For Reference

Not to be taken from this room

GALE DIRECTORY OF PUBLICATIONS AND BROADCAST MEDIA

ISSN 1048-7972

147th Edition

Published annually since 1869

GALE DIRECTORY OF PUBLICATIONS AND BROADCAST MEDIA

(Formerly *Ayer Directory of Publications*)

An annual Guide to Publications and Broadcasting Stations

Including Newspapers, Magazines, Journals, Radio Stations, Television Stations, and Cable Systems

Volume 5
International
International Indexes

Entries 41426-57122

Kristy Harper, Project Editor

GALE
CENGAGE Learning

Detroit • New York • San Francisco • New Haven, Conn • Waterville, Maine • London

GALE
CENGAGE Learning

Gale Directory of Publications and Broadcast Media, 147th Edition

Project Editor: Kristy Harper

Editorial: Kim Hunt-Lowrance, Paul Schummer

Editorial Support Services: Manny Barrido

Composition and Electronic Prepress: Gary Leach

Manufacturing: Rita Wimberley

Product Management: Michele P. LaMeau

For product information and technology assistance, contact us at **Gale Customer Support, 1-800-877-4253.** For permission to use material from this text or product, submit all requests online at **www.cengage.com/permissions.** Further permissions questions can be emailed to **permissionrequest@cengage.com**

Gale
27500 Drake Rd.
Farmington Hills, MI 48331-3535

ISBN-13: 978-1-4144-4715-5 (Set)
ISBN-10: 1-4144-4715-9 (Set)
ISBN-13: 978-1-4144-4716-2 (Volume 1)
ISBN-10: 1-4144-4716-7 (Volume 1)
ISBN-13: 978-1-4144-4717-9 (Volume 2)
ISBN-10: 1-4144-4717-5 (Volume 2)
ISBN-13: 978-1-4144-4718-6 (Volume 3)
ISBN-10: 1-4144-4718-3 (Volume 3)
ISBN-13: 978-1-4144-4719-3 (Volume 4)
ISBN-10: 1-4144-4719-1 (Volume 4)
ISBN-13: 978-1-4144-4720-9 (Volume 5)
ISBN-10: 1-4144-4720-5 (Volume 5)

ISSN 1048-7972

Printed in the United States of America
1 2 3 4 5 6 7 15 14 13 12 11

Contents

Volume 1 : Alabama - New Hampshire

Introduction ix
User's Guide xi
Abbreviations xvii
Industry Activity- New Listings and Cessations xxi
Descriptive Listings

Alabama. 1
Alaska 37
Arizona 49
Arkansas 77
California 99
Colorado 315
Connecticut 357
Delaware 397
District of Columbia 403
Florida 449
Georgia 521
Guam 579
Hawaii 581
Idaho 593
Illinois 607
Indiana 715
Iowa 763
Kansas 807
Kentucky 843
Louisiana 877
Maine 903
Maryland 917
Massachusetts 969
Michigan 1071
Minnesota 1135
Mississippi 1189
Missouri 1209
Montana 1279
Nebraska 1295
Nevada 1319
New Hampshire 1331

Volume 2 : New Jersey - Wyoming and Canada

Introduction ix
User's Guide xi

Abbreviations xvii
Industry Activity—New Listings and Cessations xxi
Descriptive Listings

New Jersey 1345
New Mexico 1427
New York 1443
North Carolina 1713
North Dakota 1765
Ohio 1779
Oklahoma 1853
Oregon 1881
Pennsylvania 1913
Puerto Rico 2033
Rhode Island 2037
South Carolina 2047
South Dakota 2069
Tennessee 2083
Texas 2119
United States Virgin Islands 2221
Utah 2223
Vermont 2235
Virginia 2245
Washington 2315
West Virginia 2353
Wisconsin 2369
Wyoming 2427

Canada

Alberta 2437
British Columbia 2463
Manitoba 2493
New Brunswick 2505
Newfoundland and Labrador 2511
Northwest Territories 2515
Nova Scotia 2517
Nunavut 2525
Ontario 2527
Prince Edward Island 2627
Quebec 2629

Saskatchewan 2653
Yukon Territory. .2663

Volume 3: Indexes

Introduction ix
User's Guide xi
Abbreviations xvii
Industry Activity-New Listings and Cessations. xxi
Broadcast and Cable Networks. 2665
News and Feature Syndicates 2673
Publishers Index 2677
Subject Indexes
   Index to Subject Terms 3077
   Agricultural Publications 3083
   Agricultural Publications (by State) 3083
   Agricultural Publications (by Subject) 3089
   Ethnic Publications 3097
   Black Publications 3097
   Foreign Language Publications 3099
   Hispanic Publications 3107
   Jewish Publications 3109
   Fraternal Publications 3111
   College Publications 3111
   Fraternal Publications 3121
   Religious Publications. 3123
   Women's Publications 3129
   Magazines 3133
   Daily Periodicals 3133
   Magazines of General Circulation 3135
   Newspapers 3193
   Daily Newspapers 3193
   Paid Community Newspapers. 3219
   Free Newspapers 3259
   Shopping Guides. 3271
   Radio Station Formats 3277
   Trade, Technical, and Professional
    Publications 3401
Newspaper Feature Editors 3571
   Names, addresses, and telephone numbers of the editors of
   features appearing in daily newspapers with circulations of
   50,000 or more. Prefaced by a list of newspapaers represented.
Master Name and Keyword Index 3575

Volume 4 : Regional Market Index

Introduction ix
User's Guide xi
Abbreviations xvii
Industry Activity—New Listings and Cessations. xxi
Regional Market Index

Newspaper Index 4029
Periodical Index 4261
Cable Index 4561
Radio Index 4569
Television Index 4653

Volume 5 : International

Introduction ix
User's Guide. xi
Abbreviations xvii
Industry Activity—New Listings and Cessations. xxi
Descriptive Listings
   Afghanistan 4681
   Albania 4683
   Algeria 4685
   Andorra 4687
   Angola 4689
   Anguilla. 4691
   Argentina 4693
   Aruba 4695
   Australia 4697
   Austria 4767
   Azerbaijan 4773
   Azores 4775
   Bahamas 4777
   Bahrain 4779
   Bangladesh 4781
   Barbados 4783
   Belarus 4785
   Belgium. 4787
   Belize 4793
   Bermuda 4795
   Bhutan 4797
   Bolivia. 4799
   Bosnia-Hercegovina 4801
   Botswana 4803
   Brazil 4805
   British Virgin Islands 4813
   Brunei Darussalam 4815
   Bulgaria. 4817
   Burkina Faso 4819
   Cambodia 4821
   Cameroon 4823
   Cayman Islands 4825
   Chile. 4827
   People's Republic of China 4829
   Colombia 4851
   Costa Rica. 4853
   Cote d'Ivoire. 4855
   Croatia 4857
   Cuba 4859
   Cyprus 4861
   Czech Republic 4863
   Denmark 4867

Dominica	4875	Morocco	5205
Dominican Republic	4877	Myanmar	5207
Ecuador	4879	Namibia	5209
Egypt	4881	Nepal	5211
El Salvador	4885	Netherlands	5215
England—see United Kingdom		Netherlands Antilles	5285
Estonia	4887	New Zealand	5287
Ethiopia	4889	Nicaragua	5303
Fiji	4891	Nigeria	5305
Finland	4893	Northern Ireland—see United Kingdom	
France	4901	Norway	5315
French West Indies	4917	Oman	5319
Georgia	4919	Pakistan	5321
Germany	4921	Panama	5331
Ghana	4963	Papua New Guinea	5333
Greece	4965	Paraguay	5335
Guatemala	4969	Peru	5337
Guyana	4971	Philippines	5339
Haiti	4973	Poland	5351
Honduras	4975	Portugal	5359
Hong Kong—See People's Republic of China		Qatar	5363
Hungary	4977	Romania	5365
Iceland	4985	Russia	5367
India	4987	Rwanda	5381
Indonesia	5043	St. Kitts and Nevis	5383
Iran	5049	St. Lucia	5385
Ireland	5053	San Marino	5387
Israel	5063	Saudi Arabia	5389
Italy	5067	Scotland—see United Kingdom	
Jamaica	5079	Senegal	5391
Japan	5081	Serbia	5393
Jordan	5131	Seychelles	5395
Kazakhstan	5133	Sierra Leone	5397
Kenya	5135	Singapore	5399
Kirgizstan	5139	Slovakia	5415
Democratic People's Republic of Korea	5141	Slovenia	5417
Republic of Korea	5143	Solomon Islands	5419
Kuwait	5151	Republic of South Africa	5421
Latvia	5155	Spain	5441
Lebanon	5157	Sri Lanka	5455
Lesotho	5163	Sudan	5461
Libyan Arab Jamahiriya	5165	Suriname	5463
Lithuania	5167	Swaziland	5465
Luxembourg	5169	Sweden	5467
Macedonia	5171	Switzerland	5475
Madagascar	5175	Syrian Arab Republic	5491
Malawi	5177	Taiwan	5493
Malaysia	5179	United Republic of Tanzania	5499
Maldives	5189	Thailand	5501
Malta	5191	Tonga	5505
Martinique	5193	Trinidad and Tobago	5507
Mauritius	5195	Tunisia	5509
Mexico	5197	Turkey	5511
Monaco	5201	Uganda	5517
Mongolia	5203	Ukraine	5519

United Arab Emirates 5521
United Kingdom 5525
Uruguay 5887
Uzbekistan 5889
Vatican City 5891
Venezuela 5893
Vietnam. 5895
West Indies 5901
Yemen 5903
Zambia 5905
Zimbabwe 5907
Publishers Index 5909
Subject Indexes
   Index to Subject Terms 6057
   Agricultural Publications 6063
   Agricultural Pubs. (by Country) 6063
   Agricultural Pubs. (by Subject) 6067
   Foreign Language Publications 6071
   Hispanic Publications 6079

Jewish Publications 6081
Fraternal Publications 6083
College Publications. 6083
Fraternal Publications 6085
Religious Publications 6087
Women's Publications 6089
Magazines 6091
Daily Periodicals 6091
Magazines of General Circulation 6093
Newspapers 6117
Daily Newspapers 6117
Paid Community Newspapers 6121
Free Newspapers 6127
Shopping Guides 6129
Trade, Technical, and Professional
   Publications 6131
Master Index 6265

The *Gale Directory of Publications and Broadcast Media* (*GDPBM*) has been the definitive media source since its inception in 1869. Formerly the *Ayer Directory of Publications*, and now in its 147th edition, *GDPBM* has grown with U.S., Canadian, and international media, and increased its scope to include the most current communication technologies. *GDPBM* now covers over 57,000 newspapers, magazines, journals, and other periodicals, as well as radio, television, and cable stations and systems. Organized to help users find facts fast, *GDPBM* covers the whole media picture—ad rates, circulation statistics, local programming, names of key personnel, and other useful, accurate information. In addition, *GDPBM* offers a geographic arrangement that provides easy access to listings. Only *GDPBM* presents print and broadcast entries in one geographic sort, then alphabetically within state, province, territory, region, or country; city; and media category (Print or Broadcast).

Highlights of this Edition

The 147th Edition of *Gale Directory of Publications and Broadcast Media* features over 1,000 new listings.

Scope and Preparation

The following categories of publications are **excluded** from the *Gale Directory of Publications and Broadcast Media*'s coverage of the U.S., Canadian, and international print and broadcast arenas:

- newsletters
- directories

Information provided in *GDPBM* is obtained primarily through research of publication and publisher websites and responses from organizations listed. Some clarification and verification of data is obtained through telephone calls. Other published sources are used to verify some information, such as the audited circulation data in publication listings.

Organizations identified as defunct are removed from the main body of entries and listed in the Master Name and Keyword Index as "Ceased." The same procedure is followed for listings that cannot be located through web research, email or subsequent attempts at telephone follow-up; these entries are listed in the Master Index as "Unable to locate." Efforts to clarify the status of such nonrespondents are ongoing.

Acknowledgments

The editors are grateful to the many media professionals who generously responded to our requests for updated information, provided additional data by telephone, email or fax, and helped in the shaping of this edition with their comments and suggestions throughout the year.

Available in Electronic Formats

Licensing. *Gale Directory of Publications and Broadcast Media* is available for licensing. The complete database is provided in a fielded format and is deliverable on such media as disk or CD-ROM. For more information, contact Gale's Business Development Group at 1-800-877-GALE, or visit our web site at http://www.gale.cengage.com/bizdev/.

Online. *Gale Directory of Publications and Broadcast Media* is accessible through Dialog online services. *GDPBM* (along with *Directories In Print*) is available as File 469 through Dialog. For more information, contact Dialog, 2250 Perimeter Park Dr., Ste. 300, Morrisville, North Carolina 27560; phone: (919)804-6400; toll-free: 800-3-DIALOG.

GDPBM is also available through InfoTrac as part of the *Gale Directory Library*. For more information, call 1-800-877-GALE.

Comments and Suggestions Welcome

If you have questions, concerns, or comments about *Gale Directory of Publications and Broadcast Media* please contact:

Project Editor
Gale Directory of Publications and Broadcast Media
Gale
27500 Drake Rd.
Farmington Hills, MI 48331-3535
Phone: (248) 699-4253
Toll-free: 800-347-GALE
Fax: (248) 699-8075
URL: http://www.gale.cengage.com

Gale Directory of Publications and Broadcast Media comprises five volumes:

- Volume 1 includes U.S. entries from Alabama to New Hampshire.

- Volume 2 encompasses U.S. listings from New Jersey to Wyoming and Canadian entries.

- Volume 3 contains U.S. and Canadian broadcast & cable networks, news & feature syndicates, and 21 indexes.

- Volume 4 contains the U.S. and Canadian regional market index.

- Volume 5 includes entries from Afghanistan to Zimbabwe and 17 indexes to International listings.

The samples and notes below offer more details on specific content and how to use the *Directory's* listings and indexes. Please note that entry information appearing in this section has been fabricated.

Sample Entries

In the fabricated samples that follow, each numbered section designates information that might appear in a *GDPBM* listing. The numbered items are explained in the descriptive paragraphs following each sample.

Sample Publication Listing

▌1▌ 222 ▪ ▌2▌ **American Computer Review**
▌3▌ Jane Doe Publishing Company, Inc.
▌4▌ 199 E. 49th St.
    PO Box 724866
    Salem, NY 10528-5555
▌5▌ Phone: (518)555-9277
▌6▌ Fax: (518)555-9288
▌7▌ Free: 800-555-5432
▌8▌ Publication E-mail: acr@jdpci.com
▌9▌ Publisher E-mail: jdpci@jdpci.com
▌10▌ Magazine for users of Super Software Plus products. ▌11▌ **Subtitle:** The Programmer's Friend. ▌12▌ **Founded:** June 1979. ▌13▌ **Freq:** Monthly (combined issue July/Aug.). ▌14▌ **Print Method:** Offset. ▌15▌ **Trim Size:** 8/12 x 11. ▌16▌ **Cols./Page:** 3. ▌17▌ **Col. Width:** 24 nonpareils. ▌18▌ **Col. Depth:** 294 agate lines. ▌19▌ **Key Personnel:** Ian Smith, Editor, phone (518)555-1201, fax (518)555-1202, ismith@jdpci.com; James Newman, Publisher; Steve Jones Jr., Advertising Mgr. ▌20▌ **ISSN:** 5555-6226. ▌21▌ **Subscription Rates:** $25; $30 Canada; $2.50 single issue. ▌22▌ **Remarks:** Color advertising not accepted. ▌23▌ **Online:** Lexis-Nexis **URL:** http://www.acrmagazine.com. ▌24▌ **Alternate Format(s):**

Braille; CD-ROM; Microform. ▌25▌ **Formerly:** Computer Software Review (Dec. 13, 1986). ▌26▌ **Feature Editors:** Ann Walker, *Consumer Affairs, Editorials,* phone (518)555-2306, fax (518)555-2307, aw@jdpci.com. ▌27▌ **Additional Contact Information: Advertising:** 123 Main St., New York, NY 10016, (201)555-1900, fax: (201)555-1908. ▌28▌ **Ad Rates:** BW: $850, PCI: $.75 ▌29▌ **Circulation:** 25,000

Description of Numbered Elements

▌1▌ **Entry Number.** Entries are numbered sequentially. Entry numbers, rather than page numbers, are used to refer to listings.

▌2▌ **Publication Title.** Publication names are listed *as they appear on the masthead or title page,* as provided by respondents.

▌3▌ **Publishing Company.** The name of the commercial publishing organization, association, or academic institution, as provided by respondents.

▌4▌ **Address.** Full mailing address information is provided wherever possible. This may include: street address; post office box; city; state or province; and ZIP or postal code. ZIP plus-four numbers are provided when known.

▌5▌ **Phone.** Phone numbers listed in this section are usually the respondent's switchboard number.

▌6▌ **Fax.** Facsimile numbers are listed when provided.

▌7▌ **Free.** Toll-free numbers are listed when provided.

▌8▌ **Publication E-mail.** Electronic mail addresses for the publication are included as provided by the listee.

▌9▌ **Publisher E-mail:** Electronic mail addresses for the publishing company are included as provided by the listee.

▌10▌ **Description.** Includes the type of publication (i.e., newspaper, magazine) as well as a brief statement of purpose, intended audience, or other relevant remarks.

▌11▌ **Subtitle.** Included as provided by the listee.

▌12▌ **Founded.** Date the periodical was first published.

▌13▌ **Frequency.** Indicates how often the publication is issued—daily, weekly, monthly, quarterly, etc. Explanatory remarks sometimes accompany this information (e.g., for weekly titles, the day of issuance; for collegiate titles, whether publication is limited to the academic year; whether certain issues are combined.)

▌14▐ Print Method. Though offset is most common, other methods are listed as provided.

▌15▐ Trim Size. Presented in inches unless otherwise noted.

▌16▐ Number of Columns Per Page. Usually one figure, but some publications list two or more, indicating a variation in style.

▌17▐ Column Width. Column sizes are given exactly as supplied, whether measured in inches, picas (6 picas to an inch), nonpareils (each 6 points, 72 points to an inch), or agate lines (14 to an inch).

▌18▐ Column Depth. Column sizes are given exactly as supplied, whether measured in inches, picas (6 picas to an inch), nonpareils (each 6 points, 72 points to an inch), or agate lines (14 to an inch).

▌19▐ Key Personnel. Presents the names and titles of contacts at each publication. May include phone, fax, and e-mail addresses if different than those for the publication and company.

▌20▐ International Standard Serial Number (ISSN). Included when provided. Occasionally, United States Publications Serial (USPS) numbers are reported rather than ISSNs.

▌21▐ Subscription Rates. Unless otherwise stated, prices shown in this section are the individual annual subscription rate. Other rates are listed when known, including multiyear rates, prices outside the United States, discount rates, library/institution rates, and single copy prices.

▌22▐ Remarks. Information listed in this section further explains the Ad Rates.

▌23▐ Online. If a publication is accessible online, that information is listed here. If the publication is available online but the details of the URL or vendor are not known, the notation "Available Online" will be listed.

▌24▐ Alternate Format(s). Lists additional mediums in which a publication may be available (other than online), including CD-ROM and microform.

▌25▐ Variant Name(s). Lists former or variant names of the publication, including the year the change took place, when known.

▌26▐ Feature Editors. Lists the names and beats of any feature editors employed by the publication.

▌27▐ Additional Contact Information. Includes mailing, advertising, news, and subscription addresses and phone numbers when different from the editorial/publisher address and phone numbers.

▌28▐ Ad Rates. Respondents may provide non-contract (open) rates in any of six categories:

GLR = general line rate

BW = one-time black & white page rate

4C = one-time four-color page rate

SAU = standard advertising unit rate

CNU = Canadian newspaper advertising unit rate

PCI = per column inch rate

Occasionally, explanatory information about other types of advertising appears in the Remarks section of the entry.

▌29▐ Circulation. Figures represent various circulation numbers; the figures are accompanied by a symbol (except for sworn and estimated figures). Following are explanations of the eight circulation classifications used by *GDPBM*, the corresponding symbols, if any, are listed at the bottom of each right hand page. All circulation figures *except* publisher's reports and estimated figures appear in boldface type.

These audit bureaus are independent, nonprofit organizations (with the exception of VAC, which is for-profit) that verify circulation rates. Interested users may contact the association for more information.

- **ABC:** Audit Bureau of Circulations, 48 W. Seegers Rd. Arlington Heights, IL 60005-3913; (224)366-6939

- **CAC:** Certified Audit of Circulations, Inc., 155 Willowbrook Blvd., Ste. 400, Wayne, NJ 07470; (973)785-3000

- **CCAB:** Canadian Circulations Audit Board, 980-90 Eglinton Ave. E, Toronto, ON Canada M4P 2Y3; (416)487-2418

- **VAC:** Verified Audit Circulation, 900 Larkspur Landing Cir. #295, Larkspur, CA 94939; (800)775-3332

- **Post Office Statement:** These figures were verified from a U.S. Post Office form.

- **Publisher's Statement:** These figures were accompanied by the signature of the editor, publisher, or other officer.

- **Sworn Statement:** These figures, which appear in **boldface** without a symbol, were accompanied by the notarized signature of the editor, publisher, or other officer of the publication.

- **Estimated Figures:** These figures, which are shown in lightface without a symbol, are the unverified report of the listee.

The footer on every odd-numbered page contains a key to circulation and entry type symbols, as well as advertising abbreviations.

Sample Broadcast Listing

▌1▐ 111 **▪2▐** WCAF-AM—1530
▌3▐ 199 E. 49th St.
PO Box 724866
Salem, NY 10528-5555
▌4▐ Phone: (518)555-9277
▌5▐ Fax: (518)555-9288
▌6▐ Free: 800-555-5432
▌7▐ E-mail: wcaf@wcaf.com
▌8▐ Format: Classical. **▌9▐ Simulcasts:** WCAF-FM. **▌10▐ Network(s):** Westwood One Radio; ABC. **▌11▐ Owner: Affici Communications, Inc., at above address. ▌12▐ Founded:** 1996. **▌13▐ Formerly:** WCAH-AM (1992). **▌14▐ Operating Hours:** Continuous; 90% local, 10% network. **▌15▐ ADI:** Elmira, NY. **▌16▐ Key Personnel:** James Smith, General Mgr., phone (518)555-1002, fax (518)555-1010, jsmith@wcaf.com; Don White, Program Dir. **▌17▐ Cities Served:** Salem, NY. **▌18▐ Postal Areas Served:** 10528; 10529. **▌19▐ Local Programs:** Who's Beethoven? Clement Goebel, Contact, (518)555-1301, fax (518)555-1320. **▌20▐ Wattage:** 5000. **▌21▐ Ad Rates:** Underwriting available. $10-15 for 30 seconds; $30-35 for 60

seconds. Combined advertising rates available with WCAF-FM. **∎22∎** **Additional Contact Information:** Mailing address: PO Box 555, Elmira, NY, 10529. **∎23∎ URL:** http://www.wcaf.com.

Description of Numbered Elements

∎1∎ Entry Number. Entries are numbered sequentially. Entry numbers (rather than page numbers) are used to refer to listings.

∎2∎ Call Letters and Frequency/Channel or **Cable Company Name.**

∎3∎ Address. Location and studio addresses appear as supplied by the respondent. If provided, alternate addresses are listed in the Additional Contact Information section of the entries (see item 22 below).

∎4∎ Phone. Telephone numbers are listed as provided.

∎5∎ Fax. Facsimile numbers are listed when provided.

∎6∎ Free. Toll-free numbers are listed when provided.

∎7∎ E-mail. Electronic mail addresses are included as provided by the listee.

∎8∎ Format. For television station entries, this subheading indicates whether the station is commercial or public. Radio station entries contain industry- defined (and, in some cases, station-defined) formats as indicated by the listee.

∎9∎ Simulcasts. Lists stations that provide simulcasting.

∎10∎ Network(s). Notes national and regional networks with which a station is affiliated. The term "independent" is used if indicated by the listee.

∎11∎ Owner. Lists the name of an individual or company, supplemented by the address and telephone number, when provided by the listee. If the address is the same as that of the station or company, the notation "at above address" is used, referring to the station or cable company address.

∎12∎ Founded. In most cases, the year the station/company began operating, regardless of changes in call letters/names and ownership.

∎13∎ Variant Name(s). For radio and television stations, former call letters and the years in which there were changes are presented as provided by the listee. Former cable company names and the years in which they were changed are also noted when available.

∎14∎ Operating Hours. Lists on-air hours and often includes percentages of network and local programming.

∎15∎ ADI (Area of Dominant Influence). The Area of Dominant Influence is a standard market region defined by the Arbitron Ratings Company for U.S. television stations. Some respondents also list radio stations as having ADIs.

∎16∎ Key Personnel. Presents the names and titles of contacts at each station or cable company.

∎17∎ Cities Served. This heading is primarily found in cable system entries and provides information on channels and the number of subscribers.

∎18∎ Postal Areas Served. This heading is primarily found in cable system entries and provides information on the postal (zip) codes served by the system.

∎19∎ Local Programs. Lists names, air times, and contact personnel of locally-produced television and radio shows.

∎20∎ Wattage. Applicable to radio stations, the wattage may differ for day and night in the case of AM stations. Occasionally a station's ERP (effective radiated power) is given in addition to, or instead of, actual licensed wattage.

∎21∎ Ad Rates. Includes rates for 10, 15, 30, and 60 seconds as provided by respondents. Some stations price advertisement spots "per unit" regardless of length; these units vary.

∎22∎ Additional Contact Information. Includes mailing, advertising, news, and studio addresses and phone numbers when different from the station, owner, or company address and phone numbers.

∎23∎ Online. If a radio station or cable company is accessible online, that information is listed here. If the station or company is available online but the details of the URL or vendor are not known, the notation "Available Online" will be listed.

Index Notes

Volumes 3 and 5 of the *Gale Directory of Publications and Broadcast Media* each feature a publishers index, referring to main section listings by entry number. Both volumes also include an index to subject terms, multiple subject indexes, and a master name and keyword index. These indexes refer to main section listings in Volumes 1 and 2 (U.S. and Canada) and Volume 5 (International) by entry number and geographic location. Volume 4 features a regional market index to all U.S. and Canadian listings, divided by publication or broadcast type. This index also refers back to main section listings in the first two volumes by entry number.

Publishers Index The Publishers Indexes in Volumes 3 (U.S. and Canada) and 5 (International) provide an alphabetical listing of the more than 18,000 publishers whose publications are listed in *GDPBM*. Entries in these indexes include publisher name, address, phone and fax numbers, and periodicals published. Multiple addresses for publishers are listed geographically by state, province, or country.

Index to Subject Terms The Index to Subject Terms is a consolidated alphabetical listing of the nearly 1,000 subject terms appearing in the Subject Indexes. Terms listed in this index are followed by page numbers in the appropriate subject index. Multiple page number citations indicate repeated uses of the terms. Additionally, "see" and "see also" references are provided.

Subject Indexes Eighteen indexes in Volume 3 (U.S. and Canada) and Fifteen indexes in Volume 5 (International) group listings by broad type or subject. These indexes have been arranged under several major categories with bleed tabs to facilitate use. Citations are presented in one of two formats:

- geographically, by states, provinces, and countries

- by subject, and within subject, geographically

Major categories are noted in the Table of Contents. Subcategories, shown as subheadings in the indexes, are listed alphabetically in the Index to Subject Terms.

Citations in the indexes refer to entry number, and for publications, provide circulation figures. (Circulation symbols are explained in footnotes on odd-numbered pages.) Additionally, the Daily Newspapers Indexes provide complete address and telephone information, and the College Publications Indexes include the names of issuing colleges and universities.

Master Name and Keyword Index The two Master Indexes provide comprehensive listings of all entries, both print and broadcast, included in Volumes 1 and 2 (U.S. and Canada) and Volume 5 (International) of *GDPBM*. Citations in these indexes are interfiled alphabetically throughout, regardless of media type.

Publication citations include the following:

- titles
- keywords within titles
- former titles
- foreign-language titles
- alternate titles

Broadcast media citations include the following:

- station call letters
- cable company names (U.S. and Canada)
- former call letters
- former cable company names (U.S. and Canada)
- radio, television, and cable company cessations

Indexing is word-by-word rather than letter-by-letter. Thus, "New York" is listed before "News." Current listings in the Index include geographic information and entry number. Former names, whether publication or broadcast, are indicated by an * and do not include a geographic designation.

Regional Market Index Volume 4 of the *Gale Directory of Publications and Broadcast Media* (*GDPBM*) features a regional market index, referring to main section entries in Volumes 1 and 2 (U.S. and Canada) by entry number. This index is divided into five sections:

- Newspaper Index
- Periodical Index
- Cable Index
- Radio Index
- Television Index

Each section is arranged geographically by region and then sorted by circulation, number of subscribing households, or Area of Dominant Influence (ADI). *[Note: Occasionally an ADI will appear under a region other than that listed. This is the result of an ADI designation which covers multiple neighboring states and will be represented multiple times.]* Newspaper and Periodical Index citations include publication title, entry number (given in parentheses immediately follow-

ing the title), publisher name, address, phone and fax numbers, publication subject, and circulation figures. Cable Index citations include cable company name, entry number (given in parentheses immediately following the title), address, phone and fax numbers, cities served and number of subscribing households. Radio and Television Index citations include station call letters, entry number (given in parentheses immediately following the title), address, phone and fax numbers, and station format.

The regions have been defined as follows:

Great Lakes States

Illinois
Indiana
Michigan
Minnesota
Ohio
Wisconsin

Great Plains States

Iowa
Kansas
Missouri
Nebraska
North Dakota
South Dakota

Middle Atlantic States

Delaware
District of Columbia
Maryland
Virginia
West Virginia

Northeastern States

Connecticut
Maine
Massachusetts
New Hampshire
New Jersey
New York
Pennsylvania
Rhode Island
Vermont

South Central States

Arkansas
Louisiana
Oklahoma
Texas
New Mexico

Southern States

Alabama
Florida
Georgia
Kentucky
Mississippi

North Carolina
Puerto Rico
South Carolina
Tennessee

Western States

Alaska
Arizona
California
Colorado
Hawaii
Idaho
Montana
Nevada
Oregon
Utah
Washington
Wyoming

Central Canadian Provinces

Ontario
Manitoba
Saskatchewan

Eastern Canadian Provinces

Newfoundland and Labrador
Prince Edward Island
Nova Scotia
New Brunswick
Quebec

Northern Canadian Provinces

Northern Territories
Yukon Territories

Western Canadian Provinces

British Columbia
Alberta

Geographic Abbreviations

U.S. State and Territory Postal Codes

AK	Alaska
AL	Alabama
AR	Arkansas
AZ	Arizona
CA	California
CO	Colorado
CT	Connecticut
DC	District of Columbia
DE	Delaware
FL	Florida
GA	Georgia
GU	Guam
HI	Hawaii
IA	Iowa
ID	Idaho
IL	Illinois
IN	Indiana
KS	Kansas
KY	Kentucky
LA	Louisiana
MA	Massachusetts
MD	Maryland
ME	Maine
MI	Michigan
MN	Minnesota
MO	Missouri
MS	Mississippi
MT	Montana
NC	North Carolina
ND	North Dakota
NE	Nebraska
NH	New Hampshire
NJ	New Jersey
NM	New Mexico
NV	Nevada
NY	New York
OH	Ohio
OK	Oklahoma
OR	Oregon
PA	Pennsylvania
PR	Puerto Rico
RI	Rhode Island
SC	South Carolina
SD	South Dakota
TN	Tennessee
TX	Texas
UT	Utah
VA	Virginia
VI	Virgin Islands
VT	Vermont
WA	Washington
WI	Wisconsin
WV	West Virginia
WY	Wyoming

Canadian Province and Territory Postal Codes

AB	Alberta
BC	British Columbia
MB	Manitoba
NB	New Brunswick
NL	Newfoundland and Labrador
NS	Nova Scotia
NT	Northwest Territories
NU	Nunavut
ON	Ontario
PE	Prince Edward Island
QC	Quebec
SK	Saskatchewan
YT	Yukon Territory

Australian State and Territory Codes

ACT	Australian Capitol Territory
NSW	New South Wales
NT	Northern Territory
QLD	Queensland
SA	South Australia
TAS	Tasmania
VIC	Victoria
WA	Western Australia

Chinese Province and Region Codes

AN	Anhui
FJ	Fujian
GS	Gansu
GD	Guangdong
GZ	Guangxi Zhuangzu
GH	Guizhou
HB	Hebei
HL	Heilongjiang
HN	Henan
HU	Hubei
HA	Hunan
JS	Jiangsu
JX	Jiangxi
JI	Jilin
LI	Liaoning
NM	Nei Monggol Zizhiqu
NH	Ningxia Huizu
QI	Qinghai
SH	Shaanxi
SD	Shandong
SX	Shanxi
SI	Sichuan
XU	Xinjiang Uygur Zizhigu
XZ	Xizang
YU	Yunnan
ZH	Zhejiang

Indian State and Territory Codes

AN	Andaman and Nicobar
AP	Andhra Pradesh
AR	Arunachal Pradesh
AS	Assam
BH	Bihar
CH	Chandigarh
DN	Dadra and Nagar Haveli
DH	Delhi
GD	Goa Daman and Diu
GJ	Gujarat
HY	Haryana
HP	Himachal Pradesh
JK	Jammu and Kashmir
KA	Karnataka
KE	Kerala
LC	Laccadive Minicoy and Amindivi
MP	Madhya Pradesh
MH	Maharashtra

MN	Manipur
MG	Meghalaya
MZ	Mizoram
MY	Mysore
NG	Nagaland
OR	Orissa
PN	Pondicherry
PJ	Punjab
RJ	Rajasthan
SK	Sikkim
TN	Tamil Nadu
TR	Tripura
UP	Uttar Pradesh
WB	West Bengal (W. Bengal)

Irish County Codes

CV	Cavan
CA	Carlow
CL	Clare
CK	Cork
DO	Donegal
DU	Dublin
GL	Galway
KR	Kerry
KL	Kildare
KK	Kilkenny
LA	Laoighis
LE	Leitrim
LI	Limerick
LO	Longford
LU	Louth
MA	Mayo
ME	Meath
MO	Monaghan
OF	Offaly
RO	Roscommon
SL	Sligo
TP	Tipperary
WA	Waterford
WE	Westmeath
WX	Wexford
WI	Wicklow

Mexican State Codes

AG	Aguascalientes
BN	Baja California Norte
BS	Baja California Sur
CM	Campeche
CP	Chiapas
CH	Chihuahua
CO	Coahuila
CL	Colima
DF	Distrito Federal
DU	Durango
GJ	Guanajuato
GU	Guerrero
HD	Hidalgo
JA	Jalisco
ME	Mexico
MI	Michoacan
MO	Morelos

NY	Nayarit
NL	Nuevo Leon
OX	Oaxaca
PU	Puebla
QT	Queretaro
QR	Quintana Roo
SP	San Luis Potosi
SN	Sinaloa
SR	Sonora
TB	Tabasco
TM	Tamaulipas
TL	Tlaxcala
VC	Veracruz
YU	Yucatan
ZA	Zacatecas

Nigerian States

AN	Anambra
BA	Bauchi
BE	Bendel
BN	Benue
BR	Borno
CR	Cross River
GO	Gongola
IM	Imo
KD	Kaduna
KN	Kano
KW	Kwara
LG	Lagos
NG	Niger
OG	Ogun
ON	Ondo
OY	Oyo
PL	Plateau
RV	Rivers
SK	Sokoto

Country Abbreviations

For England, Northern Ireland, Scotland, and Wales, please see United Kingdom (GBR).

AFG	Afghanistan
ALB	Albania
ALG	Algeria
ANG	Angola
AIA	Anguilla
ATG	Antigua-Barbuda
ARG	Argentina
AMA	Armenia
ARU	Aruba
AUS	Australia
AUT	Austria
AJN	Azerbaijan
AZO	Azores
BHS	Bahamas
BHR	Bahrain
BGD	Bangladesh
BRB	Barbados
BLR	Belarus
BEL	Belgium

BLZ	Belize
BEN	Benin
BMU	Bermuda
BTN	Bhutan
BOL	Bolivia
HBO	Bosnia-Hercegovina
BWA	Botswana
BRZ	Brazil
BRN	Brunei Darussalam
BUL	Bulgaria
BFA	Burkina Faso
BDI	Burundi
CMB	Cambodia
CMR	Cameroon
CYM	Cayman Islands
CHL	Chile
CHN	People's Republic of China
COL	Colombia
CRI	Costa Rica
COT	Cote d'Ivoire
CTA	Croatia
CUB	Cuba
CYP	Cyprus
CZE	Czech Republic
DEN	Denmark
DMA	Dominica
DOM	Dominican Republic
ECU	Ecuador
EGY	Egypt
ELS	El Salvador
EST	Estonia
ETH	Ethiopia
FAR	Faroe Islands
FIJ	Fiji
FIN	Finland
FRA	France
FGN	French Guiana
GAB	Gabon
GMB	Gambia
GRG	Georgia
GER	Germany
GHA	Ghana
GIB	Gibraltar
GRC	Greece
GTM	Guatemala
GIN	Guinea
GUY	Guyana
HTI	Haiti
HND	Honduras
HUN	Hungary
ICE	Iceland
IND	India
IDN	Indonesia
IRN	Iran
IRQ	Iraq
IRL	Ireland
ISR	Israel
ITA	Italy
JAM	Jamaica

JPN	Japan	SAU	Saudi Arabia	Ave.	Avenue
JOR	Jordan	SEN	Senegal	Bldg.	Building
KAZ	Kazakhstan	SER	Serbia	Blvd.	Boulevard
KEN	Kenya	SYC	Seychelles	boul.	boulevard
KGA	Kirgizstan	SLE	Sierra Leone	BPA	Business Publications Audit of Circulations
KOD	Korea, Democratic People's Republic of	SGP	Singapore		
		SLK	Slovakia	BTA	Best Time Available
KOR	Republic of Korea	SVA	Slovenia	BW	One-time Black & White Page Rate
KWT	Kuwait	SLM	Solomon Islands		
LAO	Lao People's Democratic Republic	SAF	Republic of South Africa	C	Central
		SPA	Spain	CAC	Certified Audit of Circulations
LAT	Latvia	SRI	Sri Lanka	CCAB	Canadian Circulations Audit Board
LBN	Lebanon	SDN	Sudan		
LES	Lesotho	SWZ	Swaziland	CEO	Chief Executive Officer
LIT	Lithuania	SWE	Sweden	Chm.	Chairman
LUX	Luxembourg	SWI	Switzerland	Chwm.	Chairwoman
MEC	Macedonia	SYR	Syrian Arab Republic	CNU	Canadian Newspaper Advertising Unit Rate
MDG	Madagascar	TWN	Taiwan		
MWI	Malawi	TDN	Tajikistan	c/o	Care of
MYS	Malaysia	TZA	United Republic of Tanzania	Col.	Column
MDV	Maldives	THA	Thailand	Coll.	College
MLI	Mali	TGO	Togo	Comm.	Committee
MAL	Malta	TGA	Tonga	Co.	Company
MTQ	Martinique	TTO	Trinidad and Tobago	COO	Chief Operating Officer
MUS	Mauritius	TUN	Tunisia	Coord.	Coordinator
MEX	Mexico	TUR	Turkey	Corp.	Corporation
MDI	Moldova	TUK	Turkmenistan	Coun.	Council
MCO	Monaco	UGA	Uganda	CP	case postale
MNG	Mongolia	URE	Ukraine	Ct.	Court
MON	Montenegro	UAE	United Arab Emirates	Dept.	Department
MOR	Morocco	GBR	United Kingdom	Dir.	Director
MOZ	Mozambique	URY	Uruguay	Div.	Division
MYA	Myanmar	UZN	Uzbekistan	Dr.	Doctor, Drive
NAM	Namibia	VAT	Vatican City	E.	East
NPL	Nepal	VEN	Venezuela	EC	East Central
NLD	Netherlands	VNM	Vietnam	ENE	East Northeast
NAT	Netherlands Antilles	BVI	British Virgin Islands	ERP	Effective Radiated Power
NCL	New Caledonia	WIN	West Indies	ESE	East Southeast
NZL	New Zealand	YEM	Yemen	Eve.	Evening
NCG	Nicaragua	ZMB	Zambia	Exec.	Executive
NER	Niger	ZWE	Zimbabwe	Expy.	Expressway
NGA	Nigeria			Fed.	Federation
NOR	Norway	**Miscellaneous Abbreviations**		Fl.	Floor
OMN	Oman	&	And	FM	Frequency Modulation
PAK	Pakistan	4C	One-Time Four Color Page Rate	FPO	Fleet Post Office
PAN	Panama			Fri.	Friday
PNG	Papua New Guinea	ABC	Audit Bureau of Circulations	Fwy.	Freeway
PAR	Paraguay	Acad.	Academy	Gen.	General
PER	Peru	Act.	Acting	GLR	General Line Rate
PHL	Philippines	Adm.	Administrative, Administration	Hd.	Head
POL	Poland	Admin.	Administrator	Hwy.	Highway
PRT	Portugal	AFB	Air Force Base	Inc.	Incorporated
QAT	Qatar	AM	Amplitude Modulation	Info.	Information
ROM	Romania	Amer.	American	Inst.	Institute
RUS	Russia	APO	Army Post Office	Intl.	International
RWA	Rwanda	Apt.	Apartment	ISSN	International Standard Serial Number
SKN	St. Kitts and Nevis	Assn.	Association		
SLC	St. Lucia	Assoc.	Associate	Jr.	Junior
SMR	San Marino	Asst.	Assistant	Libn.	Librarian
				Ln.	Lane

Ltd.	Limited	Prof.	Professor	Sun.	Sunday
Mgr.	Manager	Rd.	Road	Supt.	Superintendent
mi.	miles	RFD	Rural Free Delivery	SW	Southwest
Mktg.	Marketing	Rm.	Room	Terr.	Terrace
Mng.	Managing	ROS	Run of Schedule	Thurs.	Thursday
Mon.	Monday	RR	Rural Route	Tpke.	Turnpike
Morn.	Morning	Rte.	Route	Treas.	Treasurer
N.	North	S.	South	Tues.	Tuesday
NAS	Naval Air Station	Sat.	Saturday	Univ.	University
Natl.	National	SAU	Standard Advertising Unit Rate	USPS	United States Publications Serial
NC	North Central				
NE	Northeast	SC	South Central	VAC	Verified Audit Circulation
NNE	North Northeast	SE	Southeast	VP	Vice President
NNW	North Northwest	Sec.	Secretary	W.	West
No.	Number	Soc.	Society	WC	West Central
NW	Northwest	Sq.	Square	Wed.	Wednesday
Orgn.	Organization	Sr.	Senior	WNW	West Northwest
PCI	Per Column Inch Rate	SSE	South Southeast	WSW	West Southwest
Pkwy.	Parkway	SSW	South Southwest	x/month	Times per Month
Pl.	Place	St.	Saint, Street	x/week	Times per Week
PO	Post Office	Sta.	Station	x/year	Times per Year
Pres.	President	Ste.	Sainte, Suite		

An alphabetical listing of newly added and recently defunct media outlets. New listings precede cessations, and International citations follow those of the United States and Canada in each instance.

New Listings

United States and Canada

Acadiana Profile Magazine (Lafayette, LA)

Adelante Valle (El Centro, CA)

ADextra (Moline, IL)

Advertiser News (North Edition) (Chester, NY)

Advertiser News (South Edition) (Chester, NY)

Advertiser Times (Warren, MI)

AgAir Update (Perry, GA)

AIM Jefferson (Rockaway, NJ)

AIM Vernon (Rockaway, NJ)

AIM West Milford (Kinnelon, NJ)

AKC Family Dog (Raleigh, NC)

ALARM (Chicago, IL)

Alert (Boise, ID)

AllGreen (Westbrook, CT)

Alternatives (Boulder, CO)

America Oggi (Norwood, NJ)

American Journal of Biochemistry and Molecular Biology (New York, NY)

American Journal of Drug Discovery and Development (New York, NY)

American Journal of Food Technology (New York, NY)

American Journal of Plant Nutrition and Fertilization Technology (New York, NY)

American Spa (New York, NY)

amNew York (New York, NY)

Angeleno (Los Angeles, CA)

Angeleno Interiors (Los Angeles, CA)

Anthem Magazine (Los Angeles, CA)

AoB Plants (Cary, NC)

Arcata Eye (Arcata, CA)

Asian Journal of Animal and Veterinary Advances (New York, NY)

Asian Journal of Biochemistry (New York, NY)

Asian Journal of Earth Sciences (New York, NY)

Asian Journal of Information Manage-ment (New York, NY)

Asian Journal of Plant Pathology (New York, NY)

Asian Journal of Poultry Science (New York, NY)

The Atlantan (Atlanta, GA)

The Atlantan Brides (Atlanta, GA)

Atlanticville (Long Branch, NJ)

Auto Atlantic (Halifax, NS)

b (Baltimore, MD)

Bacteriology Journal (New York, NY)

Bartlesville Examiner-Enterprise (Bartlesville, OK)

Batavia Republican (Fairport, NY)

Beverly Hills Weekly (Beverly Hills, CA)

Bibi Magazine (New York, NY)

Bioengineered Bugs (Austin, TX)

Birding Business (Land O' Lakes, FL)

Birmingham-Bloomfield Eagle (Warren, MI)

Block Magazine (Brooklyn, NY)

Bluff Magazine (Atlanta, GA)

Boar Hunter Magazine (Baxley, GA)

Boho (Upper Montclair, NJ)

Bowhunt America (Colorado Springs, CO)

Bowie Star (Laurel, MD)

Brand X (Los Angeles, CA)

Brew Your Own (Manchester Center, VT)

Brooklyn Downtown Star (Maspeth, NY)

Camarillo Acorn (Camarillo, CA)

Canadian Immigrant (Toronto, ON)

Canadian Running (Toronto, ON)

Canine Review (Calgary, AB)

Canyon Life (Lake Forest, CA)

Canyon News (Beverly Hills, CA)

Caribbean Life (Brooklyn, NY)

Carmel Valley News (Rancho Santa Fe, CA)

CBBA-FM (Brockville, ON)

CFCF-TV (Montreal, QC)

Chapel Hill Magazine (Chapel Hill, NC)

Charlotte Creative Loafing (Charlotte, NC)

CHCH-TV (Hamilton, ON)

Chicago Social Brides (Chicago, IL)

Chimerism (Austin, TX)

China Rights Forum (New York, NY)

The Chronicle (Willimantic, CT)

CHTO-AM (Toronto, ON)

The Citizen-Coweta Edition (Fayetteville, GA)

The Citizen (Fayetteville, GA)

The Citizen of Laconia (Laconia, NH)

The Citizen-Peachtree/Tyrone (Fayetteville, GA)

CIVT-TV (Vancouver, BC)

CJCO-TV (Calgary, AB)

CJMT-TV (Toronto, ON)

Clinton-Fort Washington Gazette (Laurel, MD)

ColorLines Magazine (Oakland, CA)

Communications of the IBIMA (Norristown, PA)

Communicative & Integrative Biology (Austin, TX)

Concrete Skateboarding (Richmond, BC)

Contract Employment Weekly (Bothell, WA)

Creative Loafing Sarasota (Sarasota, FL)

Creative Loafing Tampa (Tampa, FL)

CS (Chicago Social) (Chicago, IL)

CS Interiors (Chicago, IL)

The Current of Absecon and Pleasantville (Egg Harbor Township, NJ)

The Current of Egg Harbor Township (Egg Harbor Township, NJ)

The Current of Galloway and Port Republic (Egg Harbor Township, NJ)

The Current of Mays Landing, Township of Hamilton and Egg Harbor City (Egg Harbor Township, NJ)

The Current of Northfield, Linwood and Somers Point (Egg Harbor Township, NJ)

Current Research in Cardiovascular Pharmacology (New York, NY)

Current Research in Neuroscience (New York, NY)

Current Research in Poultry Science (New York, NY)

Current Research in Tuberculosis (New York, NY)

The Daily Herald (Columbia, TN)

Dallas Brides (Dallas, TX)

Dallas Voice (Dallas, TX)

The Darke Countian (Xenia, OH)

DC (Washington, DC)

DC Velocity (North Attleboro, MA)

Del Mar Times (Del Mar, CA)

Delmarva Real Estate (Dover, DE)

Dermato-Endocrinology (Austin, TX)

Dorchester/Eastern Shore Banner (Cambridge, MD)

The Downbeach Current (Egg Harbor Township, NJ)

The Dupont Current (Washington, DC)

Durham Magazine (Durham, NC)

East Bay Classifieds (Bristol, RI)

East Brunswick Sentinel (Freehold, NJ)

The East County Observer (Bradenton, FL)

Ecologia (New York, NY)

El Especialito (Union City, NJ)

El Latino Expreso (Lorain, OH)

El Latino Expreso (Trenton, NJ)

El Mojave (Victorville, CA)

El Paracaidista (Miami Beach, FL)

El Planeta (Boston, MA)

Enlace (San Diego, CA)

The Enterprise (Lexington Park, MD) (Waldorf, MD)

Enterprising Women (Cary, NC)

The Erickson Tribune (Baltimore, MD)

European Journal of Dentistry and Medicine (New York, NY)

European Tool & Mould Making (Malibu, CA)

Examiner (Freehold, NJ)

Express (Washington, DC)

Fairport-East Rochester Post (Fairport, NY)

Fama Y Fortuna (Union City, NJ)

Farm Forum (Aberdeen, SD)

Farmington Press (Farmington, MI) (Warren, MI)

Fin de Semana Chicago (Chicago, IL)

Fin de Semana Los Angeles (Chicago, IL)

Fish Alaska Magazine (Anchorage, AK)

The Foggy Bottom Current (Washington, DC)

Forest Hills/Rego Park Times (Maspeth, NY)

Foster's Sunday Citizen (Dover, NH)

Fountain Valley View (Santa Ana, CA)

The Frankfort Station (Orland Park, IL)

Free-Time (Egg Harbor Township, NJ)

FrontDesk Chicago (Chicago, IL)

FrontDesk New York (New York, NY)

Fronteras (Columbus, OH)

Frozen and Dairy Buyer (Olathe, KS)

Gay Parent Magazine (Forest Hills, NY)

The Gazette (Fair Lawn, NJ)

Germantown News (Germantown, TN)

Get Married (Atlanta, GA)

Global Governance (Boulder, CO)

Global Outlook (Oro, ON)

GM Crops (Austin, TX)

Gold Country Times (Sutter Creek, CA)

Green Guide (Washington, DC)

Green Halifax (Halifax, NS)

Greenbelt Gazette (Laurel, MD)

Greenpoint Star & Weekly Northside News (Maspeth, NY)

Gripped Magazine (Toronto, ON)

Gut Microbes (Austin, TX)

Haute Living (Miami, FL)

Haute Living (New York, NY)

Havelock News (Havelock, NC)

Hem-Onc (Austin, TX)

The Herald (Smithfield, NC)

The Herald Weekly (Lake Norman) (Huntersville, NC)

Hesperia Star (Hesperia, CA)

Highland Community News (Highland, CA)

Hillsboro Argus Courier-Mail (Hillsboro, OR)

Hmong Today (Saint Paul, MN)

The Homer Horizon (Orland Park, IL)

Hora Hispana (New York, NY)

Houston Brides (Houston, TX)

The Hub (Long Branch, NJ)

Hyattsville-Port Towns Gazette (Laurel, MD)

IBIMA Business Review (Norristown, PA)

Imbibe Magazine (Portland, OR)

In Light Times (Las Vegas, NV)

Infinite Energy (Concord, NH)

Inked (New York, NY)

Inside Arden (Sacramento, CA)

Inside East Sacramento (Sacramento, CA)

Inside The City (Sacramento, CA)

Insight News (Minneapolis, MN)

Interiors & Sources (Cedar Rapids, IA)

International Journal of Adaptive, Resilient and Autonomic Systems (Hershey, PA)

International Journal of Adult Vocational Education and Technology (Hershey, PA)

International Journal of Advanced Pervasive and Ubiquitous Computing (Hershey, PA)

International Journal of Agent Technologies and Systems (Hershey, PA)

International Journal of Agricultural and Environmental Information Systems (Hershey, PA)

International Journal of Agricultural Research (New York, NY)

International Journal of Ambient Computing and Intelligence (Hershey, PA)

International Journal of Applied Evolutionary Computation (Hershey, PA)

International Journal of Applied Geospatial Research (Hershey, PA)

International Journal of Applied Industrial Engineering (Hershey, PA)

International Journal of Applied Logistics (Hershey, PA)

International Journal of Applied Metaheuristic Computing (Hershey, PA)

International Journal of Art, Culture and Design Technologies (Hershey, PA)

International Journal of Artificial Life Research (Hershey, PA)

International Journal of Asian Business and Information Management (Hershey, PA)

International Journal of Aviation Technology (Hershey, PA)

International Journal of Biological Chemistry (New York, NY)

International Journal of Biomaterials Research and Engineering (Hershey, PA)

International Journal of Business Intelligence Research (Hershey, PA)

International Journal of Chemoinformatics and Chemical Engineering (Hershey, PA)

International Journal of Cloud Applications and Computing (Hershey, PA)

International Journal of Computational Models and Algorithms in Medicine (Hershey, PA)

International Journal of Computer-Assisted Language Learning and Teaching (Hershey, PA)

International Journal of Computer Vision and Image Processing (Hershey, PA)

International Journal of Creative Interfaces and Computer Graphics (Hershey, PA)

International Journal of Customer Relationship Marketing and Management (Hershey, PA)

International Journal of Cyber Behavior, Psychology and Learning (Hershey, PA)

International Journal of Cyber Ethics in Education (Hershey, PA)

International Journal of Cyber Warfare & Terrorism (Hershey, PA)

International Journal of Dependable and Trustworthy Information Systems (Hershey, PA)

International Journal of Digital Crime and Forensics (Hershey, PA)

International Journal of Digital Library Systems (Hershey, PA)

International Journal of Digital Literacy and Digital Competence (Hershey, PA)

International Journal of Distributed Systems and Technologies (Hershey, PA)

International Journal of E-Health and Medical Communications (Hershey, PA)

International Journal of E-Politics (Hershey, PA)

International Journal of Embedded and Real-Time Communication Systems (Hershey, PA)

International Journal of Fuzzy System Applications (Hershey, PA)

International Journal of Game-Based Learning (Hershey, PA)

International Journal of Gaming and Computer-Mediated Simulations (Hershey, PA)

International Journal of Geotechnical Earthquake Engineering (Hershey, PA)

International Journal of Green Computing (Hershey, PA)

International Journal of Handheld Computing Research (Hershey, PA)

International Journal of Healthcare Delivery Reform Initiatives (Hershey, PA)

International Journal of Human Capital and Information Technology Professionals (Hershey, PA)

International Journal of ICT Research and Development in Africa (Hershey, PA)

International Journal of Information Communication Technologies and Human Development (Hershey, PA)

International Journal of Information Retrieval Research (Hershey, PA)

International Journal of Information System Modeling and Design. (Hershey, PA)

International Journal of Information Systems in the Service Sector (Hershey, PA)

International Journal of Information Systems and Social Change (Hershey, PA)

International Journal of Information Systems and Supply Chain Management (Hershey, PA)

International Journal of Information Technology Project Management (Hershey, PA)

International Journal of Innovation in the Digital Economy (Hershey, PA)

International Journal of Intelligent Mechatronics and Robotics (Hershey, PA)

International Journal of Interactive Communication Systems and Technologies (Hershey, PA)

International Journal of Interactive Worlds (Norristown, PA)

International Journal of Interdisciplinary Telecommunications and Networking (Hershey, PA)

International Journal of IT/Business Alignment and Governance (Hershey, PA)

International Journal of Knowledge-Based Organizations (Hershey, PA)

International Journal of Knowledge Discovery in Bioinformatics (Hershey, PA)

International Journal of Knowledge Society Research (Hershey, PA)

International Journal of Knowledge and Systems Science (Hershey, PA)

International Journal of Manufacturing Systems (New York, NY)

International Journal of Mobile Computing and Multimedia Communications (Hershey, PA)

International Journal of Mobile Human-Computer Interaction (Hershey, PA)

International Journal of Multimedia Data Engineering & Management (Hershey, PA)

International Journal of Natural Computing Research (Hershey, PA)

International Journal of Online Marketing (Hershey, PA)

International Journal of Online Pedagogy and Course Design (Hershey, PA)

International Journal of Open Source Software & Processes (Hershey, PA)

International Journal of Operations Research and Information Systems (Hershey, PA)

International Journal of Organizational and Collective Intelligence (Hershey, PA)

International Journal of People-Oriented Programming (Hershey, PA)

International Journal of Plant Breeding and Genetics (New York, NY)

International Journal of Privacy and Health Information Management (Hershey, PA)

International Journal of Public & Private Healthcare Management and Economics (Hershey, PA)

International Journal of Quality Assurance in Engineering and Technology Education (Hershey, PA)

International Journal of Secure Software Engineering (Hershey, PA)

International Journal of Service Science (Hershey, PA)

International Journal of Signs and Semiotic Systems (Hershey, PA)

International Journal of Social Ecology and Sustainable Development (Hershey, PA)

International Journal of Social and Organizational Dynamics (Hershey, PA)

International Journal of Software Science and Computational Intelligence (Hershey, PA)

International Journal of Soil Science (New York, NY)

International Journal of Space Technology Management and Innovation (Hershey, PA)

International Journal of Strategic Decision Sciences (Hershey, PA)

International Journal of Strategic Information Technology and Applications (Hershey, PA)

International Journal of Swarm Intelligence Research (Hershey, PA)

International Journal of Synthetic Emotions (Hershey, PA)

International Journal of Systems and Service-Oriented Engineering (Hershey, PA)

International Journal of Technoethics (Hershey, PA)

International Journal of Technology Diffusion (Hershey, PA)

International Journal of Technology and Educational Marketing (Hershey, PA)

International Journal of Technology in

Small and Medium Enterprises (Hershey, PA)

International Journal of Virtual Communities and Social Networking (Hershey, PA)

International Journal of Virtual and Personal Learning Environments (Hershey, PA)

International Journal of Web Services Research (Hershey, PA)

International Journal of Wireless Networks and Broadband Technologies (Hershey, PA)

Islets (Austin, TX)

It's Queens (Maspeth, NY)

Johns Creek Neighbor (Marietta, GA)

Journal of Administrative Sciences and Technology (Norristown, PA)

Journal of African Research in Business and Technology (Norristown, PA)

Journal of Business Process Oriented Software Engineering (Norristown, PA)

Journal of Cloud Computing (Norristown, PA)

Journal of E-Government Studies and Best Practices (Norristown, PA)

Journal of e-Health Management (Norristown, PA)

Journal of Electronic Banking Systems (Norristown, PA)

Journal of Enterprise Business Intelligence Systems (Norristown, PA)

Journal of Enterprise Resource Planning Studies (Norristown, PA)

Journal of European Competition Law & Practice (Cary, NC)

Journal of Financial Studies & Research (Norristown, PA)

Journal of Fisheries and Aquatic Science (New York, NY)

Journal of Human Capital (Chicago, IL)

Journal of Humanities and Information Systems (Norristown, PA)

Journal of Information Assurance & Cybersecurity (Norristown, PA)

Journal of Information Systems Knowledge and Ontologies (Norristown, PA)

Journal of Innovation and Business Best Practices (Norristown, PA)

Journal of Innovation Management in Small and Medium Enterprises (Norristown, PA)

Journal of Integrated Business Decisions (Norristown, PA)

Journal of International Dispute Settlement (Cary, NC)

Journal of Internet Social Networking

and Virtual Communities (Norristown, PA)

Journal of Interventional Gastroenterology (Austin, TX)

The Journal (Milford, DE)

Journal of Mobile Technologies, Knowledge and Society (Norristown, PA)

Journal of Molecular Cell Biology (Cary, NC)

Journal of Nature-Inspired Business Computing (Norristown, PA)

Journal of Organizational Knowledge Management (Norristown, PA)

Journal of Outsourcing and Organizational Information Management (Norristown, PA)

Journal of Pharmacology and Toxicology (New York, NY)

Journal of Plant Sciences (New York, NY)

Journal of Research in Industrial Organization (Norristown, PA)

Journal of Software Engineering (New York, NY)

Journal of Sports Management & Technology (Norristown, PA)

Journal of Supply Chain and Customer Relationship Management (Norristown, PA)

Journal of Translational Business Institution Management (Norristown, PA)

KACB-FM (College Station, TX)

KACZ-FM (Manhattan, KS)

KAGA-FM (San Angelo, TX)

KAHL-AM (San Antonio, TX)

KALH-FM (La Luz, NM)

KAWB-TV (Brainerd, MN)

KBKZ-FM (Raton, NM)

KBNM-FM(LP) (Belen, NM)

KBTE-FM (Alpharetta, GA)

KBUD-FM (Sardis, MS)

KBXT-FM (Bryan, TX)

KCHH-FM (Billings, MT)

KCKM-AM (Monahans, TX)

KCOX-AM (Jasper, TX)

KCYK-AM (Yuma, AZ)

KCYR-FM (Kerrville, TX)

KDOL-FM (Livingston, TX)

KDRP-FM (Dripping Springs, TX)

Kearny Weekly (Jersey City, NJ)

KEBG-FM (Elko, NV)

KEDU-FM (Ruidoso, NM)

KEFH-FM (Clarendon, TX)

KENM-FM (Portales, NM)

KENR-FM (Missoula, MT)

KEPS-AM (Eagle Pass, TX)

KEQP-FM (Modesto, CA)

KEQX-FM (Dublin, TX)

KERC-FM (Kermit, TX)

KESJ-AM (St. Joseph, MO)

KEXA-FM (Salinas, CA)

KFBW-FM (Portland, OR)

K15CN (Santa Ana, CA)

K15FW (Santa Aha, CA)

K51EC (Santa Ana, CA)

K56DZ (Santa Ana, CA)

K56HW (Santa Ana, CA)

K50JG (Santa Ana, CA)

K48IT (Santa Ana, CA)

K45DI (Santa Ana, CA)

K45DU (Santa Ana, CA)

K45HC (Santa Ana, CA)

K45IM (Santa Ana, CA)

K45IY (Santa Ana, CA)

K44FK (Santa Ana, CA)

K49EO (Santa Ana, CA)

K41HC (Santa Ana, CA)

K47EH (Santa Ana, CA)

K46DY (Santa Ana, CA)

K43HN (Santa Ana, CA)

K42AM (Santa Ana, CA)

K42FH (Santa Ana, CA)

K42GX (Santa Ana, CA)

K42HI (Santa Ana, CA)

K40DE (Santa Ana, CA)

K40ID (Santa Ana, CA)

K40JT (Santa Ana, CA)

KFUT-AM (Palm Springs, CA)

KFXL-TV (Kearney, NE)

KGCN-FM (Mooresville, NC)

KGHY-FM (Beaumont, TX)

KGWB-FM (Snyder, TX)

KHBC-FM (Hilo, HI)

KHMT-TV (Billings, MT)

KHNL-TV (Honolulu, HI)

KHSE-AM (Richardson, TX)

KIAH-TV (Houston, TX)

Kidney Research Journal (New York, NY)

KIJI-FM (Tamuning, GU)

KITY-FM (Llano, TX)

KJBO-TV (Wichita Falls, TX)

KJJM-TV (Dallas, TX)

KJKB-FM (Jacksboro, TX)

KJMA-FM (San Antonio, TX)

KJON-AM (Dallas, TX)

KJXK-FM (San Antonio, TX)

KKBA-FM (Corpus Christi, TX)

KKGM-AM (Dallas, TX)

KKVI-FM (Garland, TX)

KLCW-TV (Lubbock, TX)

KLCZ-FM (Lewiston, ID)

KLJY-FM (Des Peres, MO)

KLZK-FM (Lubbock, TX)

KMAX-FM (Windsor, CO)

KNBQ-FM (Seattle, WA)

K19BG (Santa Ana, CA)

K19FR (Santa Ana, CA)

KNMT-TV (Portland, OR)
KNRG-FM (Columbus, TX)
KNRX-FM (San Angelo, TX)
KNWF-FM (Saint Paul, MN)
KOCA-FM (Laramie, WY)
KOHD-TV (Bend, OR)
KPVR-FM (Moscow Mills, MO)
KPXG-TV (Portland, OR)
KQBZ-FM (Brownwood, TX)
KQCM-FM (Joshua Tree, CA)
KQTY-FM (Borger, TX)
KRCW-TV (Beaverton, OR)
KRDH-AM (Canton, TX)
KRSC-TV (Claremore, OK)
KRVF-FM (Corsicana, TX)
KRVM-AM (Eugene, OR)
KRWP-FM (Stockton, MO)
KRZI-AM (Waco, TX)
KRZS-FM (Kerrville, TX)
KSAP-FM (Port Arthur, TX)
K17ET (Santa Ana, CA)
KSGM-AM (Sainte Genevieve, MO)
KSGM-AM (Chester, IL)
KSGR-FM (Corpus Christi, TX)
K16ER (Santa Ana, CA)
KSNV-TV (Las Vegas, NV)
KSTX-FM (San Antonio, TX)
K38EE (Santa Ana, CA)
K34FH (Santa Ana, CA)
K39FW (Santa Ana, CA)
K39IN (Santa Ana, CA)
K31BW (Santa Ana, CA)
K31HO (Santa Ana, CA)
K33HZ (Santa Ana, CA)
K33IC (Santa Ana, CA)
KTMR-AM (Houston, TX)
KTRL-FM (Stephenville, TX)
KTTU-FM (Lubbock, TX)
KTTY-FM (Dallas, TX)
KTVC-TV (Grants Pass, OR)
K28EP (Santa Ana, CA)
K28IL (Santa Ana, CA)
K28JB (Santa Ana, CA)
K25DS (Santa Ana, CA)
K25IA (Santa Ana, CA)
K29GL (Santa Ana, CA)
K21FP (Santa Ana, CA)
K21HS (Santa Ana, CA)
K27FC (Santa Ana, CA)
K26CV (Santa Ana, CA)
K23GT (Santa Ana, CA)
KTWV-FM (Los Angeles, CA)
KTXI-FM (San Antonio, TX)
KUNS-TV (Seattle, WA)
KUOW-AM (Seattle, WA)
KUOW-FM (Seattle, WA)
KURK-FM (Reno, NV)
KUVA-FM (Uvalde, TX)
KVLL-FM (Lufkin, TX)
KVVL-FM (Maryville, MO)

KWBT-FM (Waco, TX)
KWHG-AM (Fallon, NV)
KWMF-AM (San Antonio, TX)
KXBT-FM (Austin, TX)
KXDX-FM (Mount Pleasant, TX)
KXLH-TV (Helena, MT)
KXXN-FM (Wichita Falls, TX)
KYEE-FM (Alamogordo, NM)
KYST-AM (Houston, TX)
KYTX-TV (Tyler, TX)
KZBI-FM (Elko, NV)
KZRB-FM (Hooks, TX)
KZTQ-FM (Reno, NV)
KZXL-FM (Lufkin, TX)
La Estrella En Casa (Fort Worth, TX)
La Frontera (Irvine, CA)
La Ganga (Watsonville, CA)
La Opinion Contigo (Longwood, FL)
La Voz (Norristown, PA)
LA Voz Nueva (Denver, CO)
Ladera Post (Lake Forest, CA)
Ladue News (Saint Louis, MO)
Lake Norman Navigator (Statesville,
NC)
Lakeville Call (Raynham, MA)
Landover-New Carrollton Gazette
(Laurel, MD)
Largo-Lanham Gazette (Laurel, MD)
Laurel Gazette (Laurel, MD)
LCN-TV (Montreal, QC)
Leader Shopper (Hutchinson, MN)
The Loganville Tribune (Monroe, GA)
The Lovely County Citizen (Eureka
Springs, AR)
mAbs (Austin, TX)
Macomb Township Chronicle (Warren,
MI)
The Manhattan Mercury (Manhattan,
KS)
Matthews-Mint Hill Weekly (Charlotte,
NC)
Meeker County Advertiser (Litchfield,
MN)
The Men's Book Chicago (Chicago, IL)
Messenger Post (Canandaigua, NY)
Metro New York (New York, NY)
Microbiology Journal (New York, NY)
Midcontinental Journal Of Archaeology
(Notre Dame, IN)
The Middle Township Gazette (Egg
Harbor Township, NJ)
Middletown-Brunswick Gazette (Fred-
erick, MD)
Milford Chronicle (Dover, DE)
Milton Neighbor (Marietta, GA)
Modern Luxury Dallas (Dallas, TX)
Modern Luxury Hawaii (Honolulu, HI)
The Mokena Messenger (Orland Park,
IL)
Moorpark Acorn (Agoura Hills, CA)

Mountain Island Weekly (Huntersville,
NC)
The New Lenox Patriot (Orland Park,
IL)
Newton Citizen (Covington, GA)
North Cobb Neighbor (Marietta, GA)
North/South Brunswick Sentinel
(Freehold, NJ)
North York Post (Toronto, ON)
Northeast Advance (Jenison, MI)
Northwest Advance (Jenison, MI)
Oak Cliff People (Dallas, TX)
Ocean City Gazette (Egg Harbor
Township, NJ)
O'Jornal (Fall River, MA)
On the Go Magazine (Pickering, ON)
The Orland Park Prairie (Orland Park,
IL)
Oxidative Medicine & Cellular Longev-
ity (Austin, TX)
Parsippany Life (Rockaway, NJ)
Peoria Independent (Dover, DE)
Philippines Today (San Bruno, CA)
The Pike County Courier (Chester,
NY)
Preston Hollow People (Dallas, TX)
Queen Creek/San Tan Valley
Independent (Apache Junction, AZ)
Queens Examiner (Maspeth, NY)
Rancho Santa Fe Review (Del Mar,
CA)
Raynham Call (Raynham, MA)
Reporte Hispano (Princeton, NJ)
Research Journal of Allergy (New
York, NY)
Research Journal of Botany (New
York, NY)
Research Journal of Business
Management (New York, NY)
Research Journal of Cardiology (New
York, NY)
Research Journal of Environmental
Sciences (New York, NY)
Research Journal of Environmental
Toxicology (New York, NY)
Research Journal of Forestry (New
York, NY)
Research Journal of Information
Technology (New York, NY)
Research Journal of Medicinal Plant
(New York, NY)
Research Journal of Microbiology
(New York, NY)
Research Journal of Parasitology
(New York, NY)
Research Journal of Physics (New
York, NY)
Research Journal of Phytochemistry
(New York, NY)

Research Journal of Radiology (New York, NY)

Research Journal of Seed Science (New York, NY)

Research Journal of Soil Biology (New York, NY)

Research Journal of Toxins (New York, NY)

Research Journal of Veterinary Sciences (New York, NY)

Riviera Interiors (Costa Mesa, CA)

Riviera Orange County (Costa Mesa, CA)

Riviera San Diego (San Diego, CA)

Rochester Post (Warren, MI)

Royal Oak Review (Warren, MI)

Rumbo (Houston, TX)

San Francisco Brides (San Francisco, CA)

Santa Cruz Valley Sun (Green Valley, AZ)

The Sarasota Observer (Long Boat Key, FL)

Secaucus Weekly (Jersey City, NJ)

Seekonk Star (Bristol, RI)

Self/Nonself (Austin, TX)

Shop Passaic & Morris (Woodland Park, NJ)

Siglo 21 (Camarillo, CA)

Simi Valley Acorn (Agoura Hills, CA)

Simply The Best Magazine (Boca Raton, FL)

The Ski Journal (Bellingham, WA)

Small GTPases (Austin, TX)

Smart Buyer (Lake Havasu City, AZ)

Solana Beach Sun (Del Mar, CA)

South Charlotte Weekly (Charlotte, NC)

South Cobb Neighbor (Marietta, GA)

Southeast Advance (Jenison, MI)

Southfield Sun (Warren, MI)

Southwest Advance (Jenison, MI)

Space Research Journal (New York, NY)

Sparta Independent (Chester, NY)

Sterling Heights Sentry (Warren, MI)

The Suburbanite (Akron, OH)

Sun City West Independent (Dover, DE)

The Sunday Review (Towanda, PA)

Super Buzz (Richmond, VA)

Surprise Independent (Dover, DE)

tbt (Saint Petersburg, FL)

Tele-Quebec (Montreal, QC)

Thousand Oaks Acorn (Agoura Hills, CA)

Times-News (Burlington, NC) (Irvine, CA)

The Tinley Junction (Orland Park, IL)

Topsail Advertiser (Surf City, NC)

Town Crier (Boardman, OH) (Youngstown, OH)

The Township Journal (Chester, NY)

Trends in Applied Sciences Research (New York, NY)

Trends in Horticultural Research (New York, NY)

Trends in Medical Research (New York, NY)

Tri-Town News (New Jersey) (Freehold, NJ)

Triathlon Magazine Canada (Toronto, ON)

Union City Reporter (Hoboken, NJ)

Union County Weekly (Charlotte, NC)

The Upper Marlboro Star (Laurel, MD)

The Upper Township Gazette (Egg Harbor Township, NJ)

The Valley Chronicle (Hemet, CA)

Valley Morning Star (Harlingen, TX)

Virulence (Austin, TX)

The Walton Sun (Santa Rosa Beach, FL)

WANK-FM (Tallahassee, FL)

Washington City Paper (Washington, DC)

Waterfront Weekly (Jersey City, NJ)

WAZC-TV (Woodstock, VA)

WAZH-TV (Woodstock, VA)

WAZT-TV (Woodstock, VA)

WAZW-TV (Woodstock, VA)

WBKT-FM (Norwich, NY)

WBLE-FM (Batesville, MS)

WBOF-FM (Fort Pierce, FL)

WCEZ-FM (Keokuk, IA)

WCXZ-AM (Harrogate, TN)

WDHI-FM (Walton, NY)

WDRT-FM (Viroqua, WI)

W18BT (Santa Ana, CA)

W18CF (Santa Ana, CA)

WEKJ-FM (Homosassa, FL)

West Bloomfield Beacon (Warren, MI)

The West Milford Messenger (Chester, NY)

West New York Reporter (Hoboken, NJ)

Westport Shorelines (Tiverton, RI)

W58CZ (Santa Ana, CA)

W59DG (Santa Ana, CA)

W51AG (Santa Ana, CA)

W51CU (Santa Ana, CA)

W51CV (Santa Ana, CA)

W51DY (Santa Ana, CA)

W57BV (Santa Ana, CA)

W56DY (Santa Ana, CA)

W52DF (Santa Ana, CA)

W50CZ (Santa Ana, CA)

W48BH (Santa Ana, CA)

W48CN (Santa Ana, CA)

W45CN (Santa Ana, CA)

W45CO (Santa Ana, CA)

W45CU (Santa Ana, CA)

W44CN (Santa Ana, CA)

W41BN (Santa Ana, CA)

W47CM (Santa Ana, CA)

W46BU (Santa Ana, CA)

W46CY (Santa Ana, CA)

W43BV-TV (Santa Ana, CA)

W43CT (Santa Ana, CA)

W42CY (Santa Ana, CA)

W14CQ (Santa Ana, CA)

WFUP-TV (Cadillac, MI)

Wheaton Gazette (Laurel, MD)

WHIJ-FM (Sarasota, FL)

WHKL-FM (Batesville, MS)

WIJD-AM (Mobile, AL)

WIJR-AM (Highland, IL)

Windsor Now (Windsor, CO)

WJDV-FM (Harrisonburg, VA)

WJHO-FM (Auburn, AL)

WJLX-AM (Jasper, AL)

WJPI-AM (Plymouth, NC)

WJQM-FM (DeForest, WI)

WKAF-FM (Brighton, MA)

WKGE-AM (Johnstown, PA)

WKZJ-FM (Columbus, GA)

WLBE-AM (Leesburg, FL)

WLGH-FM (Williamston, MI)

WLOY-AM (Wytheville, VA)

WLSN-FM (Saint Paul, MN)

WMNO-TV (Marion, OH)

WMPS-AM (Memphis, TN)

WMPY-TV (Pittsburgh, PA)

WNMN-TV (Shelburne, VT)

WNNY-TV (Burlington, VT)

WNZZ-AM (Montgomery, AL)

Woodward Talk (Warren, MI)

WPRV-AM (East Providence, RI)

WPXD-TV (Ann Arbor, MI)

WPXG-TV (Boston, MA)

WQJJ-FM (Jasper, AL)

WQNR-FM (Auburn, AL)

WRCE-AM (Elmira, NY)

WRNI-FM (Providence, RI)

W17CK (Santa Ana, CA)

W17CS (Santa Ana, CA)

W16CF (Santa Ana, CA)

W16CJ (Santa Ana, CA)

W64CN (Santa Ana, CA)

W67CO (Santa Ana, CA)

W66BV (Santa Ana, CA)

W63CW (Santa Ana, CA)

WSKX-FM (Portsmouth, NH)

WSME-AM (Jacksonville, NC)

W10BH (Santa Ana, CA)

W38BK (Santa Ana, CA)

W38CO (Santa Ana, CA)

W38CY (Santa Ana, CA)

W35CA (Santa Ana, CA)

W34CN (Santa Ana, CA)

W34CZ (Santa Ana, CA)
W34DH (Santa Ana, CA)
W39CJ (Santa Ana, CA)
W36AC (Santa Ana, CA)
W36CK (Santa Ana, CA)
W36CO (Santa Ana, CA)
W33AL (Santa Ana, CA)
W33BX (Santa Ana, CA)
W33CM (Santa Ana, CA)
W32CA (Santa Ana, CA)
W30BD (Santa Ana, CA)
W30BW (Santa Ana, CA)
W30BY (Santa Ana, CA)
WTLM-AM (Opelika, AL)
WTLX-FM (Madison, WI)
W25AD (Santa Ana, CA)
W25DR (Santa Ana, CA)
W24CK (Santa Ana, CA)
W21CI (Santa Ana, CA)
W27CQ (Santa Ana, CA)
W27CV (Santa Ana, CA)
W27CX (Santa Ana, CA)
W26BS (Santa Ana, CA)
W23AQ (Santa Ana, CA)
W22BP (Santa Ana, CA)
W22CH (Santa Ana, CA)
W22CJ (Santa Ana, CA)
W20BA (Santa Ana, CA)
W20BT (Santa Ana, CA)
W20BZ (Santa Ana, CA)
WTXK-AM (Montgomery, AL)
WTXO-FM (Anniston, AL)
WUCP LP-FM (Farragut, TN)
WUCW-TV (St. Paul, MN)
WUFX-TV (Jackson, MS)
WURV-FM (Richmond, VA)
WVBK-TV (Brattleboro, VT)
WVMD-FM (Cumberland, MD)
WVRX-FM (Washington, DC)
WVVL-FM (Enterprise, AL)
WXCX-FM (Pine City, MN)
WXIT-AM (Boone, NC)
WXXI-FM (Rochester, NY)
WZAQ-FM (Louisa, KY)
WZFT-FM (Baltimore, MD)
Ypsilanti Courier (Salino, MI)

International

Accounting Research Journal (Bradford, GBR)
African Journal of Midwifery and Women's Health (London, GBR)
Afro-Asian Journal of Finance and Accounting (Auckland, NZL)
Alborada-FM (Chillan, CHL)
AMC LOVE RADIO-FM (Tirana, ALB)
Antena Uno-FM (Santa Fe, ARG)
Antenne Kaernten-FM (Klagenfurt, AUT)
Australian Geographic Outdoor (Sydney, NW, AUS)

Australian & NZ Snowboarding (Sydney, NW, AUS)
BIG-FM (Pokhara, NPL)
The Botulinum Journal (Geneva, SWI)
Bubble Science Engineering and Technology (London, GBR)
Carolina-FM (Santiago, CHL)
COLES (Sydney, NW, AUS)
Corazon-FM (Santiago, CHL)
CR-FM (St. Poelten, AUT)
DREAM-FM (Quezon City, PHL)
Dutch Crossing (London, GBR)
DZIQ-AM (Makati City, PHL)
Early Medieval China (London, GBR)
Education Business and Society (Bradford, GBR)
Facilities-UK (Salisbury, GBR)
Free Radio Salzkammergut-FM (Bad Ischl, AUT)
GEORGE-FM (Auckland, NZL)
Geras-FM (Vilnius, LIT)
Global Business and Economics Review (Utrecht, NLD)
Hampshire (Salisbury, GBR)
The Historic Environment (London, GBR)
Indian Growth and Development Review (New Delhi, IND)
Interactive Technology and Smart Education (Bradford, GBR)
Interdisciplinary Environmental Review (Geneva, SWI)
International Journal of Accounting and Information Management (Bradford, GBR)
International Journal of Adaptive and Innovative Systems (Le Havre, FRA)
International Journal of Advanced Intelligence Paradigms (Arad, ROM)
International Journal of Advanced Mechatronic Systems (Tokyo, JPN)
International Journal of Agricultural Resources Governance and Ecology (Nathan, QL, AUS)
International Journal of Applied Cryptography (Wollongong, NW, AUS)
International Journal of Applied Decision Sciences (Geneva, SWI)
International Journal of Applied Management Science (Geneva, SWI)
International Journal of Applied Nonlinear Science (Geneva, SWI)
International Journal of Arab Culture Management and Sustainable Development (Oviedo-Asturias, SPA)
International Journal of Artificial Intelligence and Soft Computing (Kolkata, WB, IND)
International Journal of Arts and Technology (Nauplion, GRC)

International Journal of Auditing Technology (Geneva, SWI)
International Journal of Autonomous and Adaptive Communications Systems (Kozani, GRC)
International Journal of Aviation Management (Paris, FRA)
International Journal of Banking (Editorial, Bangor, GBR)
International Journal of Behavioural Accounting and Finance (Bath, GBR)
International Journal of Behavioural and Healthcare Research (Rion, GRC)
International Journal of Bio-Inspired Computation (Taiyuan, SX, CHN)
International Journal of Biomechatronics and Biomedical Robotics (Auckland, NZL)
International Journal of Biomedical Nanoscience and Nanotechnology (Geneva, SWI)
International Journal of Biometrics (Krakow, POL)
International Journal of Border Security and Immigration Policy (Geneva, SWI)
International Journal of Business Competition and Growth (Mexico City, DF, MEX)
International Journal of Business and Emerging Markets (Geneva, SWI)
International Journal of Business Excellence (Geneva, SWI)
International Journal of Business Forecasting and Marketing Intelligence (Geneva, SWI)
International Journal of Business Performance Management (London, GBR)
International Journal of Business Performance and Supply Chain Modelling (Odense, DEN)
International Journal of Cognitive Biometrics (El Sherouk City, EGY)
International Journal of Cognitive Performance Support (El Sherouk City, EGY)
International Journal of Communication Networks and Distributed Systems (Kharagpur, WB, IND)
International Journal of Complexity in Applied Science and Engineering (Geneva, SWI)
International Journal of Complexity in Leadership and Management (Singapore, SGP)
International Journal of Computational Biology and Drug Design (Geneva, SWI)
International Journal of Computational

Medicine and Healthcare (Geneva, SWI)

International Journal of Computer Aided Engineering and Technology (Darmstadt, GER)

International Journal of Computer Applications in Technology (Bristol, GBR)

International Journal of Computers in Healthcare (Adelaide, SA, AUS)

International Journal of Continuing Engineering Education and Life-Long Learning (Edinburgh, GBR)

International Journal of Corporate Governance (Geneva, SWI)

International Journal of Critical Computer-Based Systems (Naples, ITA)

International Journal of Data Analysis Techniques and Strategies (Geneva, SWI)

International Journal of Digital Culture and Electronic Tourism (Helsinki, FIN)

International Journal of Digital Enterprise Technology (Xi'an, SX, CHN)

International Journal of Economics and Accounting (London, GBR)

International Journal of Economics and Business Research (Geneva, SWI)

International Journal of Electronic Banking (Geneva, SWI)

International Journal of Electronic Democracy (London, GBR)

International Journal of Electronic Trade (Milan, ITA)

International Journal of Electronic Transport (Melbourne, VI, AUS)

International Journal of Engineering Management and Economics (Napoli, ITA)

International Journal of Engineering Systems Modelling and Simulation (Wrexham, GBR)

International Journal of Enterprise Systems Integration and Interoperability (Bari, ITA)

International Journal of Entertainment Technology and Management (Athens, GRC)

International Journal of Environment and Pollution (Geneva, SWI)

International Journal of Environment Workplace and Employment (Melbourne, VI, AUS)

International Journal of Environmental Policy and Decision Making (Geneva, SWI)

International Journal of Exergy (Geneva, SWI)

International Journal of Food Safety Nutrition and Public Health (Geneva, SWI)

International Journal of Forensic Software Engineering (Fisciano, ITA)

International Journal of Functional Informatics and Personalised Medicine (Geneva, SWI)

International Journal of Global Energy Issues (Laxenburg, AUT)

International Journal of Granular Computing Rough Sets and Intelligent Systems (Geneva, SWI)

International Journal of Healthcare Technology and Management (Enschede, NLD)

International Journal of Heavy Vehicle Systems (Geneva, SWI)

International Journal of Housing Markets and Analysis (Sydney, NW, AUS)

International Journal of Hydrology Science and Technology (Isfahan, IRN)

International Journal of Information and Decision Sciences (Geneva, SWI)

International Journal of Information Privacy Security and Integrity (Geneva, SWI)

International Journal of Information Technology Communications and Convergence (Seoul, KOR)

International Journal of Innovation and Regional Development (Thessaloniki, GRC)

International Journal of Intelligent Computing and Cybernetics (Beijing, CHN)

International Journal of Intelligent Defence Support Systems (Adelaide, SA, AUS)

International Journal of Intelligent Engineering Informatics (Beijing, CHN)

International Journal of Inventory Research (Geneva, SWI)

International Journal of Islamic and Middle Eastern Finance and Management (London, GBR)

International Journal of Knowledge-Based Development (Brisbane, QL, AUS)

International Journal of Knowledge Engineering and Data Mining (Hong Kong, CHN)

International Journal of Knowledge Engineering and Soft Data Paradigms (Tsukuba, JPN)

International Journal of Knowledge Management in Tourism and Hospitality (Sheffield, GBR)

International Journal of Lean

Enterprise Research (Groningen, NLD)

International Journal of Legal Information Design (Zurich, SWI)

International Journal of Leisure and Tourism Marketing (Geneva, SWI)

International Journal of Management and Network Economics (L'Aquila, ITA)

International Journal of Managerial and Financial Accounting (Miri, MYS)

International Journal of Managing Projects in Business (Melbourne, VI, AUS)

International Journal of Materials and Product Technology (Pfinztal, GER)

International Journal of Mechatronics and Manufacturing Systems (Geneva, SWI)

International Journal of Medical Engineering and Informatics (Geneva, SWI)

International Journal of Metaheuristics (Cardiff, GBR)

International Journal of Mining and Mineral Engineering (Geneva, SWI)

International Journal of Modelling in Operations Management (Kampar, MYS)

International Journal of Molecular Engineering (Aveiro, PRT)

International Journal of Multicriteria Decision Making (Athens, GRC)

International Journal of Multimedia Intelligence and Security (Beijing, CHN)

International Journal of Nano and Bio-materials (Geneva, SWI)

International Journal of Nanoparticles (Hefei, AN, CHN)

International Journal of Nuclear Knowledge Management (Paris, FRA)

International Journal of Ocean Systems Management (Limassol, CYP)

International Journal of Oil Gas and Coal Technology (Surra, KWT)

International Journal of Organisational Design and Engineering (Lisboa, PRT)

International Journal of Pervasive Computing and Communications (Bradford, GBR)

International Journal of Petroleum Engineering (Geneva, SWI)

International Journal of Physiotherapy and Life Physics (Siegen, GER)

International Journal of Powertrain (Geneva, SWI)

International Journal of Quality Engineering and Technology (Geneva, SWI)

International Journal of Remanufacturing (Geneva, SWI)

International Journal of Satellite Communications Policy and Management (Wuhan, CHN)

International Journal of Security and Networks (Geneva, SWI)

International Journal of Services Economics and Management (Wuhan, HU, CHN)

International Journal of Services Sciences (Geneva, SWI)

International Journal of Services Technology and Management (Tokyo, JPN)

International Journal of Shipping and Transport Logistics (Hong Kong, CHN)

International Journal of Signal and Imaging Systems Engineering (Chalkis, GRC)

International Journal of Social Computing and Cyber-Physical Systems (Geneva, SWI)

International Journal of Social and Humanistic Computing (Stockholm, SWE)

International Journal of Social Network Mining (Tirana, ALB)

International Journal of Society Systems Science (Geneva, SWI)

International Journal of Strategic Engineering Asset Management (Stavange, NOR)

International Journal of Sudan Research Policy and Sustainable Development (Wad Medani, SDN)

International Journal of Sustainable Design (Bundoora, VI, AUS)

International Journal of Sustainable Economy (Koper, SVA)

International Journal of Sustainable Manufacturing (Geneva, SWI)

International Journal of Sustainable Society (Geneva, SWI)

International Journal of Sustainable Strategic Management (Geneva, SWI)

International Journal of System Control and Information Processing (Shanghai, CHN)

International Journal of Systems Control and Communications (Dalian, CHN)

International Journal of Technology Enhanced Learning (Stockholm, SWE)

International Journal of Tourism Anthropology (Chengdu, SI, CHN)

International Journal of Transitions and Innovation Systems (Zagreb, CTA)

International Journal of Vehicle Design (Geneva, SWI)

International Journal of Vehicle Performance (Geneva, SWI)

International Journal of Web Information Systems (Bradford, GBR)

International Wood Products Journal (London, GBR)

Journal of Applied Accounting Research (Leicester, GBR)

Journal of Chinese Economic and Foreign Trade Studies (Beijing, CHN)

Journal of European Real Estate Research (County Antrim, GBR)

Journal of Financial Management of Property and Construction (Preston, GBR)

Journal of Information Communication & Ethics in Society (Bradford, GBR)

Journal of International Trade Law and Policy (Bradford, GBR)

Journal of Manual & Manipulative Therapy (London, GBR)

Journal of Paramedic Practice (London, GBR)

Journal of Place Management and Development (Manchester, GBR)

Journal of Renal Nursing (London, GBR)

Journal of Strategy and Management (Bradford, GBR)

Journal of Systems and Information Technology (Joondalup, WA, AUS)

Land Mobile (Salisbury, GBR)

Language & History (London, GBR)

Libre-FM (Viedma Rio Negro, ARG)

Life Radio-FM (Linz, AUT)

Luxury Intelligence (Monte Carlo, MCO)

Ming Studies (London, GBR)

Myer Emporium (Sydney, NW, AUS)

NET 25 (Quezon City, PHL)

NJOY Radio-FM (Lannach, AUT)

NRJ-FM (Vienna, AUT)

Pro Shop Europe (Salisbury, GBR)

Radio Arabella-FM (Vienna, AUT)

Radio DJ-FM (Tirana, ALB)

Radio FM9 (Kragujevac, SER)

Radio-Gresivaudan-FM (Crolles, FRA)

Radio Maxima-FM (Ahuachapan, ELS)

Radio Onda Libera-FM (Palestrina, ITA)

Radio Proto-FM (Nicosia, CYP)

Radio Stacioni-FM (Tirana, ALB)

Radio Vallekas-FM (Madrid, SPA)

Radio Verdon-FM (Saint-Julien-le-Montagnier, FRA)

Radio ZID Sarajevo-FM (Sarajevo, HBO)

RaW-AM (Coventry, GBR)

Recycling & Waste World (Salisbury, GBR)

RNA Radio-FM (Andorra la Vella, AND)

Social Enterprise Journal (Liverpool, GBR)

Social Responsibility Journal (Leicester, GBR)

Sorgia-FM (Belgrade, FRA)

START-FM (Vilnius, LIT)

STEREO-FM (Cairnlea, VI, AUS)

Storm-FM (Bangor, GBR)

Strategic HR Review (Bradford, GBR)

Strategic Outsourcing (Bradford, GBR)

Swindon 105.5-FM (Swindon, GBR)

T'ang Studies (London, GBR)

Tel Aviv (London, GBR)

Terrae Incognitae (London, GBR)

Tide-FM (Hamburg, GER)

Tilos Radio-FM (Budapest, HUN)

Tourism Review (Bradford, GBR)

Usus Antiquior (London, GBR)

Voice of Barbados-FM (Bridgetown, BRB)

War & Society (London, GBR)

Wiltshire Life (Salisbury, GBR)

Yass-FM (Yass, NW, AUS)

Zinc-AM (Gladstone, QL, AUS)

Zinc-FM (Maroochydore, QL, AUS)

Zinc-FM (Mackay, QL, AUS)

Zinc-FM (Cairns, QL, AUS)

Zinc-FM (The Lakes, QL, AUS)

Ziniu radijas-FM (Vilnius, LIT)

Cessations

United States and Canada

Advanced Technology for Learning (Peoria, IL)

Aware (Birmingham, AL)

Barber County Index (Medicine Lodge, KS)

Blackpowder Guns & Hunting (Birmingham, AL)

California Counties (Sacramento, CA)

Chain Leader (New York, NY)

Champs-Elysees (Nashville, TN)

Clinics in Family Practice (Philadelphia, PA)

Comparative Technology Transfer and Society (Baltimore, MD)

Contributions on Entomology International (Gainesville, FL)

Converting Magazine (Oak Brook, IL)

Cookie (New York, NY)

Denver Rocky Mountain News & Post (Denver, CO)

Discipleship Journal (Harlan, IA)

Doorways Magazine (Union City, OH)

Edwardsville Journal (St. Louis, MO)

Emergence (Philadelphia, PA)

Environmental Bioindicators (Gainesville, FL)

Essential Teacher (Alexandria, VA)

Free Lunch (Glenview, IL)
Genre (New York, NY)
Graphic Arts Monthly Magazine (Oak Brook, IL)
Hunt Club Digest (Birmingham, AL)
Infonomics (Silver Spring, MD)
Interiorscape (Clearwater, FL)
International Journal of Distributed Sensor Networks (Baton Rouge, LA)
International Journal of Geomagnetism and Aeronomy (Washington, DC)
Journal for Christian Theological Research (Saint Paul, MN)
Journal of Electronics Manufacturing (Bethlehem, PA)
Journal of Pharmaceutical Finance, Economics & Policy (Philadelphia, PA)
Journal of Whiplash & Related Disorders (Philadelphia, PA)
Journal of Atmospheric and Ocean Science (Philadelphia, PA)
Journal of Cancer Pain and Symptom Palliation (Philadelphia, PA)
Journal of Chronic Fatigue Syndrome (Philadelphia, PA)
Journal of Neuropathic Pain and Symptom Palliation (Philadelphia, PA)
Kiss Machine (Toronto, ON)
La Voz Catolica (Miami Shores, FL)
Lakeview Enterprise (Big Rapids, MI)
Law Enforcement News (New York, NY)
Leadership in Action (Hoboken, NJ)
Lectura y Vida (Newark, DE)
Lutheran Partners (Chicago, IL)
Material Handling Product News (New York, NY)
Memory Makers (Cincinnati, OH)
Mergent's Dividend Achievers (Hoboken, NJ)
Metal Producing & Processing (New York, NY)
NADA's AutoExec Magazine (McLean, VA)
New Milford Times (New Milford, CT)
New York Nights (Brooklyn, NY)
Nichi Bei Times (San Francisco, CA)
Ocean County Observer (Toms River, NJ)
Puerto Rico Sports (San Juan, PR)
Puerto Rico Travel & Tourism (San Juan, PR)
Quantum (Arlington, VA)

Restaurants & Institutions (Oak Brook, IL)
Semiconductor International (Oak Brook, IL)
Sports Illustrated for Women (New York, NY)
Tech Topics (Atlanta, GA)
The La Belle Star (La Belle, MO)
The Lemoore Advance (Hanford, CA)
The Look (Concord, ON)
The Monitor-Herald (Calhoun City, MS)
The Music Index (Sterling Heights, MI)
The National Voter (Washington, DC)
Time Style and Design (New York, NY)
Understanding Statistics (Philadelphia, PA)
Vida Actual (San Juan, PR)
Water, Air, and Soil Pollution (Guelph, ON)
Wildflower (Markham, ON)
Wireless Systems Design (New York, NY)
World Watch (Washington, DC)

International
209radio-FM (Cambridge, GBR)
Abbey-FM (Barrow, GBR)
Anales de Medicina Interna (Madrid, SPA)
Arran Voice (Brodick, GBR)
Artifact (Abingdon, GBR)
Asian Sources Gifts & Home Products (Phoenix, AZ, USA)
Australia and New Zealand Health Policy (London, GBR)
Bandolier (Oxford, GBR)
Biofilms (Cambridge, GBR)
BioMagnetic Research and Technology (London, GBR)
Card Technology Today (Kidlington, GBR)
Cattech (Dordrecht, NLD)
Cell & Chromosome (London, GBR)
China Law Review (Abingdon, GBR)
Chinese Annals of Mathematics (Shanghai, CHN)
Clinical Intensive Care (Abingdon, GBR)
Comic Bon Bon (Tokyo, JPN)
Dynamic Medicine (London, GBR)
Education for Health (Abingdon, GBR)
EMC - Dermatologie Cosmetologie (Singapore, SGP)
EMC - Endocrinologie (Singapore, SGP)

EMC - Hematologie (Singapore, SGP)
EMC - Hepatologie (Singapore, SGP)
EMC - Maladies Infectieuses (Singapore, SGP)
EMC - Medecine (Singapore, SGP)
EMC - Dentisterie (Paris, FRA)
Emergences (Abingdon, GBR)
European Clinics in Obstetrics and Gynaecology (Tokyo, JPN)
European Journal of Legal Education (Abingdon, GBR)
Far East Journal of Ocean Research (Kangnung, KOR)
Forschende Komplementarmedizin und Klassische Naturheilkunde (Freiburg, GER)
Global Slag Magazine (Surrey, GBR)
International Journal of Disaster Medicine (Abingdon, GBR)
Journal of Biomedical Discovery and Collaboration (London, GBR)
Journal of Conflict Archaeology (Leiden, NLD)
Journal of Diagnostic Radiography and Imaging (Auckland, NZL)
Learning and Teaching in the Social Sciences (Wolverhampton, GBR)
Minerals & Energy - Raw Materials Report (Lulea, SWE)
New Zealand Macguide (Auckland, NZL)
One to One (London, GBR)
Pennine-FM (Huddersfield, GBR)
Prospects (Cambridge, GBR)
Radio Hampshire-FM (Southampton, GBR)
SAGA 106.6-FM (East Midlands, GBR)
South African Journal of Chemical Engineering (Centurion, SAF)
Televisual (London, GBR)
Thalamus and Related Systems (Cambridge, GBR)
The Development Education Journal (Stoke-on-Trent, GBR)
The Journal of Financial Forecasting (London, GBR)
The Pain Clinic (London, GBR)
Time-FM (London, GBR)
Update on Cancer Therapeutics (Kidlington, GBR)
Visual Geosciences (Kingston upon Thames, GBR)

Kabul

41426 ■ ARIANA Radio-FM - 93.5
318, Darulaman St., Carte 3
Kabul, Afghanistan
Ph: 93 70 111113
Format: Information; News; Ethnic; World Beat. **Owner:**
Ariana Television Network, at above address. **Operating Hours:** Continuous. **Ad Rates:** Advertising accepted; rates available upon request. **URL:** http://www.arianatelevision.com.

41427 ■ Arman-FM - 98.1
PO Box 1045
Central Post Office
Kabul, Afghanistan
E-mail: info@arman.fm
Format: News; Talk; Top 40; World Beat. **Founded:** Apr. 2003. **Operating Hours:** Continuous. **Ad Rates:** Advertising accepted; rates available upon request. **URL:** http://www.armanfm.com; http://www.arman.fm.

Cervenake

41428 ■ Transmet-TV - 11
Rr. Ismail Qemali, No. 11
Tirana, Albania
Ph: 355 4 223911
Fax: 355 4 223911
Format: Full Service; Commercial TV. **Owner:** Radio Televizione Shqiptar, at above address. **Wattage:** 5000.
URL: http://www.rtsh.al/?fq=brenda&gj=gj1&kid=36.

Dajt

41429 ■ Transmet-TV - 57
Rr. Ismail Qemali, No. 11
Tirana, Albania
Ph: 355 4 223911
Fax: 355 4 223911
Format: Full Service; Commercial TV. **Owner:** Radio Televizione Shqiptar, at above address. **Wattage:** 5000.
URL: http://www.rtsh.al/?fq=brenda&gj=gj1&kid=36.

Delvine

41430 ■ Sopot-FM - 107 MHz
Rr. Ismail Qemali, No. 11
Tirana, Albania
Ph: 355 4 223911
Fax: 355 4 223911
Format: Full Service. **Owner:** Radio Televizione Shqiptar, at above address. **Wattage:** 1000. **URL:** http://www.rtsh.al/?fq=brenda&gj=gj1&kid=37.

Durres

41431 ■ Ishem-FM - 95.4 MHz
Rr. Ismail Qemali, No. 11
Tirana, Albania
Ph: 355 4 223911
Fax: 355 4 223911
Format: Full Service. **Owner:** Radio Televizione Shqiptar, at above address. **Wattage:** 300. **URL:** http://www.rtsh.al/?fq=brenda&gj=gj1&kid=37.

41432 ■ Transmet-TV - 25
Rr. Ismail Qemali, No. 11
Tirana, Albania
Ph: 355 4 223911
Fax: 355 4 223911
Format: Full Service; Commercial TV. **Owner:** Radio Televizione Shqiptar, at above address. **Wattage:** 1000.
URL: http://www.rtsh.al/?fq=brenda&gj=gj1&kid=36.

Elbasan

41433 ■ Petresh-FM - 95.4 MHz
Rr. Ismail Qemali, No. 11
Tirana, Albania
Ph: 355 4 223911
Fax: 355 4 223911
Format: Full Service. **Owner:** Radio Televizione Shqiptar, at above address. **Wattage:** 1000. **URL:** http://www.rtsh.al/?fq=brenda&gj=gj1&kid=37.

Gjirokaster

41434 ■ Transmet-TV - 31
Rr. Ismail Qemali, No. 11
Tirana, Albania
Ph: 355 4 223911
Fax: 355 4 223911
Format: Full Service; Commercial TV. **Owner:** Radio Televizione Shqiptar, at above address. **Wattage:** 250.
URL: http://www.rtsh.al/?fq=brenda&gj=gj1&kid=36.

Gllava

41435 ■ Transmet-TV - 9
Rr. Ismail Qemali, No. 11
Tirana, Albania
Ph: 355 4 223911
Fax: 355 4 223911
Format: Full Service; Commercial TV. **Owner:** Radio Televizione Shqiptar, at above address. **Wattage:** 2000.
URL: http://www.rtsh.al/?fq=brenda&gj=gj1&kid=36.

Ishem

41436 ■ Transmet-TV - 58
Rr. Ismail Qemali, No. 11
Tirana, Albania
Ph: 355 4 223911
Fax: 355 4 223911
Format: Full Service; Commercial TV. **Owner:** Radio Televizione Shqiptar, at above address. **Wattage:** 250.
URL: http://www.rtsh.al/?fq=brenda&gj=gj1&kid=36.

Korca

41437 ■ Transmet-TV - 54
Rr. Ismail Qemali, No. 11
Tirana, Albania
Ph: 355 4 223911
Fax: 355 4 223911
Format: Full Service; Commercial TV. **Owner:** Radio Televizione Shqiptar, at above address. **Wattage:** 100.
URL: http://www.rtsh.al/?fq=brenda&gj=gj1&kid=36.

Mide

41438 ■ Transmet-TV - 12
Rr. Ismail Qemali, No. 11
Tirana, Albania
Ph: 355 4 223911
Fax: 355 4 223911
Format: Full Service; Commercial TV. **Owner:** Radio Televizione Shqiptar, at above address. **Wattage:** 10,000. **URL:** http://www.rtsh.al/?fq=brenda&gj=gj1&kid=36.

Mile

41439 ■ Transmet-TV - 12
Rr. Ismail Qemali, No. 11
Tirana, Albania
Ph: 355 4 223911
Fax: 355 4 223911
Format: Full Service; Commercial TV. **Owner:** Radio Televizione Shqiptar, at above address. **Wattage:** 500.

URL: http://www.rtsh.al/?fq=brenda&gj=gj1&kid=36.

Peshkopi

41440 ■ Homesh-FM - 102.2 MHz
Rr. Ismail Qemali, No. 11
Tirana, Albania
Ph: 355 4 223911
Fax: 355 4 223911
Format: Full Service. **Owner:** Radio Televizione Shqiptar, at above address. **Wattage:** 300. **URL:** http://www.rtsh.al/?fq=brenda&gj=gj1&kid=37.

Petresh

41441 ■ Perserites-TV - 44
Rr. Ismail Qemali, No. 11
Tirana, Albania
Ph: 355 4 223911
Fax: 355 4 223911
Format: Full Service. **Owner:** Radio Televizione Shqiptar, at above address. **Wattage:** 150. **URL:** http://www.rtsh.al/?fq=brenda&gj=gj1&kid=36.

Pogradec

41442 ■ Cervenake-FM - 99.1 MHz
Rr. Ismail Qemali, No.11
Tirana, Albania
Ph: 355 4 223911
Fax: 355 4 223911
Format: Full Service. **Owner:** Radio Televizione Shqiptar, at above address. **Wattage:** 1000. **URL:** http://www.rtsh.al/?fq=brenda&gj=gj1&kid=37.

Puke

41443 ■ Mide-FM - 96 MHz
Rr. Ismail Qemali, No. 11
Tirana, Albania
Ph: 355 4 223911
Fax: 355 4 223911
Format: Full Service. **Owner:** Radio Televizione Shqiptar, at above address. **Wattage:** 5000. **URL:** http://www.rtsh.al/?fq=brenda&gj=gj1&kid=37.

Qafe Prush

41444 ■ Transmet-TV - 25
Rr. Ismail Qemali, No. 11
Tirana, Albania
Ph: 355 4 223911
Fax: 355 4 223911
Format: Full Service; Commercial TV. **Owner:** Radio Televizione Shqiptar, at above address. **Wattage:** 500.
URL: http://www.rtsh.al/?fq=brenda&gj=gj1&kid=36.

Sarande

41445 ■ Mile-FM - 93 MHz
Rr. Ismail Qemali, No. 11
Tirana, Albania
Ph: 355 4 223911
Fax: 355 4 223911
Format: Full Service. **Owner:** Radio Televizione Sh-

Circulation: ★ = ABC; △ = BPA; ◆ = CAC; • = CCAB; ❑ = VAC; ⊕ = PO Statement; ‡ = Publisher's Report; Boldface figures = sworn; Light figures = estimated.

qiptar, at above address. **Wattage:** 500. **URL:** http://www.rtsh.al/?fq=brenda&gj=gj1&kid=37.

Shkoder

41446 ■ Tarabosh-FM - 91 MHz
Rr. Ismail Qemali, No. 11
Tirana, Albania
Ph: 355 4 223911
Fax: 355 4 223911
Format: Full Service. **Owner:** Radio Televizione Shqiptar, at above address. **Wattage:** 500. **URL:** http://www.rtsh.al/?fq=brenda&gj=gj1&kid=37.

Sopot

41447 ■ Transmet-TV - 7
Rr. Ismail Qemali, No. 11
Tirana, Albania
Ph: 355 4 223911
Fax: 355 4 223911
Format: Full Service; Commercial TV. **Owner:** Radio Televizione Shqiptar, at above address. **Wattage:** 1000. **URL:** http://www.rtsh.al/?fq=brenda&gj=gj1&kid=36.

Tarabosh

41448 ■ Transmet-TV - 6
Rr. Ismail Qemali, No. 11
Tirana, Albania
Ph: 355 4 223911
Fax: 355 4 223911
Format: Full Service; Commercial TV. **Owner:** Radio Televizione Shqiptar, at above address. **Wattage:** 100. **URL:** http://www.rtsh.al/?fq=brenda&gj=gj1&kid=36.

Terbac

41449 ■ Transmet-TV - 7
Rr. Ismail Qemali, No. 11
Tirana, Albania
Ph: 355 4 223911
Fax: 355 4 223911
Format: Full Service; Commercial TV. **Owner:** Radio Televizione Shqiptar, at above address. **Wattage:** 150. **URL:** http://www.rtsh.al/?fq=brenda&gj=gj1&kid=36.

Tirana

41450 ■ International Journal of Social Network Mining
Inderscience Enterprises Limited
c/o Marenglen Biba, Ed.-in-Chief
University of New York, Tirana
Computer Science U.S. Department of
Rr. Komuna e Parisit
Tirana, Albania
Journal focusing on the emerging trends and industry needs associated with utilizing data mining techniques for social networking analysis. **Freq:** 4/yr. **Key Personnel:** Marenglen Biba, Editor-in-Chief, marenglenbiba@unyt.edu.al; Zbigniew W. Ras, Editor in Chief, ras@uncc.edu. **ISSN:** 1757-8485. **Subscription Rates:** EUR494 individuals print or online; EUR672 individuals print and online. **URL:** http://www.inderscience.com/browse/index.php?journalID=327.

41451 ■ AMC LOVE RADIO-FM - 90.7
BAJRRAM Curri Blvd.
European Trade Ctr., 9th Fl.
Tirana, Albania
Ph: 355 42 272670
Fax: 355 42 273289
E-mail: info@amcloveradio.net
Format: Easy Listening. **Owner:** AMC LOVE RADIO-FM, at above address. **URL:** http://www.amcloveradio.net/.

Cervenake-FM - See Pogradec

41452 ■ Dajt-FM - 99.5 MHz
Rr. Ismail Qemali, No. 11
Tirana, Albania
Ph: 355 4 223911
Fax: 355 4 223911
Format: Full Service. **Owner:** Radio Televizione Shqiptar, at above address. **Wattage:** 5000. **URL:** http://www.rtsh.al/?fq=brenda&gj=gj1&kid=37.

Homesh-FM - See Peshkopi
Ishem-FM - See Durres
Llogara-FM - See Vlore
Mide-FM - See Puke
Mile-FM - See Sarande
Perserites-TV - See Petresh
Petresh-FM - See Elbasan

41453 ■ Radio DJ-FM - 96.1
B. Curri Blvd.
ETC Business Ctr.
Tirana, Albania
Ph: 355 4 273789
Fax: 355 4 272670
E-mail: info@whatsup-radiodj.net
Format: Urban Contemporary. **Owner:** Radio DJ-FM, at above address. **URL:** http://www.whatsup-radiodj.net/.

41454 ■ Radio Stacioni-FM - 105.4
Rr. Elbasanit Nr. 38, Kati 4
Tirana, Albania
Ph: 355 4 4500694
Fax: 355 4 4500693
Format: Eclectic. **Owner:** Radio Stacioni-FM, at above address. **URL:** http://www.radiostacioni.com/.

41455 ■ Radio2-FM - 101.6
Rr. Aleksander Moisiu Nr 76/1
Ish kinostudjo Shqiperia e Re
Tirana, Albania
Ph: 355 368490
E-mail: info@plus2radio.com.al
Format: Ethnic; World Beat. **Operating Hours:** 13 hours Daily. **Ad Rates:** Advertising accepted; rates available upon request. **URL:** http://www.plus2radio.com.al.

Sopot-FM - See Delvine
Tarabosh-FM - See Shkoder
Terbac-FM - See Vlore
Transmet-TV - See Cervenake
Transmet-TV - See Dajt
Transmet-TV - See Durres
Transmet-TV - See Gjirokaster
Transmet-TV - See Gllava
Transmet-TV - See Ishem
Transmet-TV - See Korca
Transmet-TV - See Mide
Transmet-TV - See Mile
Transmet-TV - See Qafe Prush
Transmet-TV - See Sopot
Transmet-TV - See Tarabosh
Transmet-TV - See Terbac
Transmet-TV - See Zvernec
Zvernec-FM - See Vlore

Vlore

41456 ■ Llogara-FM - 88.3 MHz
Rr. Ismail Qemali, No. 11
Tirana, Albania
Ph: 355 4 223911
Fax: 355 4 223911
Format: Full Service. **Owner:** Radio Televizione Shqiptar, at above address. **Wattage:** 250. **URL:** http://www.rtsh.al/?fq=brenda&gj=gj1&kid=37.

41457 ■ Terbac-FM - 105 MHz
Rr. Ismail Qemali, No. 11
Tirana, Albania
Ph: 355 4 223911
Fax: 355 4 223911
Format: Full Service. **Owner:** Radio Televizione Shqiptar, at above address. **Wattage:** 300. **URL:** http://www.rtsh.al/?fq=brenda&gj=gj1&kid=37.

41458 ■ Zvernec-FM - 99.8 MHz
Rr. Ismail Qemali, No. 11
Tirana, Albania
Ph: 355 4 223911
Fax: 355 4 223911
Format: Full Service. **Owner:** Radio Televizione Shqiptar, at above address. **Wattage:** 3000. **URL:** http://www.rtsh.al/?fq=brenda&gj=gj1&kid=37.

Zvernec

41459 ■ Transmet-TV - 12
Rr. Ismail Qemali, No. 11
Tirana, Albania
Ph: 355 4 223911
Fax: 355 4 223911
Format: Full Service; Commercial TV. **Owner:** Radio Televizione Shqiptar, at above address. **Wattage:** 500. **URL:** http://www.rtsh.al/?fq=brenda&gj=gj1&kid=36.

Algiers

41460 ■ El Moudjahid
L'Epe-Eurl El Moudjahid
20 rue de la Liberte
Algiers, Algeria
Ph: 213 2 1737081
Fax: 213 2 1739043
Publication E-mail: elmoudja@elmoudjahid.com
Publisher E-mail: info@elmoudjahid.com
General newspaper. **Subtitle:** Edition Internet. **Freq:** Daily. **Key Personnel:** Abdelmadjid Cherbal, Publication Dir., phone 213 21 737993, cherbal@elmoudjahid.com; Djamel Kaouane, Contact, kaouane@elmoudjahid.com; Larbi Timizar, Contact, phone 213 21 736954, timizar@elmoudjahid.com. **Remarks:** Advertising accepted; rates available upon request. **URL:** http://www.elmoudjahid.com/. **Circ:** (Not Reported)

41461 ■ Liberte
37 rue Larbi Ben M'hidi
Algiers, Algeria
Ph: 213 2 1736480
Fax: 213 2 1730487
General newspaper. **Freq:** Daily. **Key Personnel:** Outoudert Abrous, Mng. Ed./Mgr. **Remarks:** Accepts advertising. **URL:** http://www.liberte-algerie.com/. **Circ:** (Not Reported)

Tlemcen

41462 ■ Radio Regionale de Tlemcen-FM - 94.7
BP 44K Les Cerisiersq
Tlemcen 13000, Algeria
Ph: 213 43 206595
Fax: 213 43 206218
Format: Information; Sports. **Owner:** La Radio Algerienne, 21, Blvd. des Martyrs, Algiers, Algeria, 213 21 483790, Fax: 213 21 230823. **Founded:** Oct. 7, 1992. **Operating Hours:** 12 hours Daily. **URL:** http://radiotelemcen.com.

41463 ■ Radio Regionale de Tlemcen-FM - 100.4
BP 44K Les Cerisiersq
Tlemcen 13000, Algeria
Ph: 213 43 206595
Fax: 213 43 206218
Format: Information; Sports. **Owner:** La Radio Algerienne, 21, Blvd. des Martyrs, Algiers, Algeria, 213 21 483790, Fax: 213 21 230823. **Founded:** Oct. 7, 1992. **Operating Hours:** 12 hours Daily. **URL:** http://radiotelemcen.com.

Circulation: ★ = ABC; △ = BPA; ◆ = CAC; • = CCAB; ❏ = VAC; ⊕ = PO Statement; ‡ = Publisher's Report; Boldface figures = sworn; Light figures = estimated.

Gale Directory of Publications & Broadcast Media/147th Ed.   **4685**

Andorra la Vella

41464 ■ RNA Radio-FM - 94.2
Biaxada del Moli 24
Andorra la Vella, Andorra
Ph: 33 376 873777
Format: Eclectic. **Owner:** Radio i Televisio d'Andorra, at
above address. **Key Personnel:** Albert Pintat, President.
URL: http://www.rtva.ad/.

Luanda

41465 ■ **Luanda Antena Comercial-FM - 95.5**
Praceta Luther King n 5
Luanda, Angola
Ph: 244 2394989
E-mail: lac@ebonet.net
Format: Contemporary Hit Radio (CHR); Ethnic. **URL:** http://www.nexus.ao/lac/.

The Valley

41466 ■ Kool-FM - 103.3
North Side
The Valley, Anguilla
Ph: (264)497-0103

Fax: (264)497-0104
E-mail: kool@koolfm103.com
Format: Ethnic; World Beat. **Ad Rates:** Advertising accepted; rates available upon request. **URL:** http://www. koolfm103.com.

Bahia Blanca

41467 ■ Radio Bahia Blanca-AM - 840
Rodriguez 55
8000 Bahia Blanca, Argentina
Ph: 54 291 4590002
Fax: 54 291 4555556
Format: Ethnic; Information; Sports. **Operating Hours:** Continuous. **Key Personnel:** Jorge Tirabasso, General Mgr., phone 54 291 4590133; Omar Groh, Gen. Coord., phone 54 291 4590170. **Ad Rates:** Advertising accepted; rates available upon request. **URL:** http://www.lu2.com.ar.

Buenos Aires

41468 ■ A & G Magazine
Argentina Oils and Fats Association
Asociacion Argentina de Grasas y Aceites
Hipolito Yrigoyen 1284
Piso 3 Depto 5
Capital Federal
Buenos Aires, Argentina
Ph: 54 11 43810555
Fax: 54 11 43810555
Publication E-mail: asaga@sitiectis.com.ar
Publisher E-mail: asaga@asaga.org.ar
Spanish language magazine covering oils and fats. **Freq:** Quarterly. **ISSN:** 0328-381X. **Subscription Rates:** 50 A individuals; 90 A two years; US$65 individuals America; US$125 two years America; US$75 other countries; US$145 other countries 2 years. **Remarks:** Advertising accepted; rates available upon request. **URL:** http://www.asaga.org.ar/. **Circ:** 1,500

41469 ■ Ameghiniana
Asociacion Paleontologica Argentina
Maipu 645 1 Piso
1006 Buenos Aires, Argentina
Ph: 54 114 3267463
Fax: 54 114 3267463
Publication E-mail: comiteeditor@apaleontologica.org.ar
Publisher E-mail: secretaria@apaleontologica.org.ar
Journal covering scientific articles on pale ontological subjects. **Founded:** 1937. **Freq:** Quarterly. **Print Method:** Offset. **Trim Size:** 8 1/4 x 11. **Cols./Page:** 3. **Col. Width:** 27 nonpareils. **Col. Depth:** 140 agate lines. **Key Personnel:** Dr. Miguel Griffin, Director. **ISSN:** 0002-7014. **Subscription Rates:** US$40 individuals; US$30 students; US$90 nonmembers. **URL:** http://www.apaleontologica.org.ar/contenido/AmeghinianaPresentacion.php.

41470 ■ Buenos Aires Herald
Buenos Aires Herald Ltd.
San Juan 141
1063 Buenos Aires, Argentina
Ph: 54 11 43491524
Fax: 54 11 43491524
Newspaper covering Argentina. **Founded:** 1876. **Freq:** Daily and Sunday. **Subscription Rates:** US$600 individuals; US$162 out of country. **Remarks:** Accepts advertising. **URL:** http://www.buenosairesherald.com. **Circ:** (Not Reported)

41471 ■ Comments on Argentine Trade
AmCham Argentina
Camara de Comercio de los Edsados Unidos en la Republica Argentina
Viamonte 1133, Piso 8
1053 Buenos Aires, Argentina
Ph: 54 114 3714500
Fax: 54 114 3718400
Publisher E-mail: amcham@amchamar.com.ar
Publication covering trade in Argentina. **Freq:** Monthly. **Key Personnel:** Daniela Martin, Editor-in-Chief. **Remarks:** Advertising accepted; rates available upon request. **URL:** http://www.amchamar.com.ar. **Circ:** (Not Reported)

41472 ■ Fotomundo
Ediciones Fotograficas Argentina S.A.
Maipu 671, 5th Fl.
Buenos Aires, Argentina
Ph: 54 432 22171
Fax: 54 432 22006
Publication E-mail: fotomundo@fotomundo.com
Publisher E-mail: fotomundo@fotomundo.com
Magazine covering photography for amateurs and professionals. **Founded:** Dec. 1966. **Freq:** Monthly. **Print Method:** Offset. **Trim Size:** 195 x 275 mm. **Key Personnel:** Robert Klein, Director. **ISSN:** 0325-7150. **URL:** http://www.fotomundo.com. **Circ:** Paid 8,000

41473 ■ Industria & Quimica
Asociacion Quimica Argentina
Sanchez de Bustamante 1749
C1425DUI Buenos Aires, Argentina
Ph: 54 11 48224886
Fax: 54 11 48224886
Publisher E-mail: aqa@aqa.org.ar
Journal containing technical articles and industry news. **Freq:** 3/yr. **ISSN:** 0368-0829. **Subscription Rates:** US$45 individuals; US$100 institutions. **Remarks:** Accepts advertising. **URL:** http://www.aqa.org.ar/iyq.htm. **Circ:** (Not Reported)

41474 ■ Integration and Trade
Institute for the Integration of Latin America and the Caribbean
Instituto para la Integracion de America Latina y el Caribe
Esmeralda 130, Pisos 16
C1035ABD Buenos Aires, Argentina
Ph: 54 11 43232350
Fax: 54 11 43232365
Publication E-mail: pubintal@iadb.org
Publisher E-mail: intal@iadb.org
Publication covering integration and trade issues in English and Spanish. **Founded:** 1965. **Freq:** Semiannual. **Trim Size:** 24 x 16.5 cm. **Key Personnel:** Richard L. Bernal, Editorial Committee; Albert Berry, Editorial Committee; Albert Fishlow, Editorial Committee. **ISSN:** 1027-5703. **Subscription Rates:** US$30 individuals revista integracn & comercion; US$30 individuals integration & trade journal. **Remarks:** Advertising not accepted. **URL:** http://www.iadb.org/intal/detalle_publicacion.asp?idioma_pub=eng&tid=4&idioma=eng&pid=367&cid=234. **Circ:** (Not Reported)

41475 ■ Journal of the Argentine Chemical Society
Asociacion Quimica Argentina
Sanchez de Bustamante 1749
C1425DUI Buenos Aires, Argentina
Ph: 54 11 48224886
Fax: 54 11 48224886
Publisher E-mail: aqa@aqa.org.ar
Journal of Asociacion Quimica Argentina. **Freq:** Semiannual. **Key Personnel:** Dr. Mario R. Feliz, Editor-in-Chief; Dr. Claudio A. Gervasi, Editorial Sec.; Prof. Cristina Anon, Assoc. Ed.; Prof. Luis Bruno Blanch, Assoc. Ed.; Prof. Carlos Brondino, Assoc. Ed. **ISSN:** 0365-0375. **URL:** http://www.aqa.org.ar/analesi.htm.

41476 ■ Journal of Argentine Dermatology
Argentinian Association of Dermatology
Asociacion Argentina de Dermatologia
Mexico 1720
1100 Buenos Aires, Argentina
Ph: 54 143 812737
English and Spanish language publication covering dermatology. **Subtitle:** Revista Argentina de Dermatologia. **Founded:** 1907. **Freq:** Quarterly. **Print Method:** Offset. **Trim Size:** 18 x 26 cm. **ISSN:** 0325-2787. **Remarks:** Advertising accepted; rates available upon request. **URL:** http://www.aad.org.ar. **Circ:** (Not Reported)

41477 ■ Journal of Latin American Hermeneutics
Instituto Universitario ISEDET
Camacua 282
1406 Buenos Aires, Argentina
Ph: 54 114 6325030
Fax: 54 114 6332825
Publication E-mail: jolah@isedet.edu.ar
Publisher E-mail: info@isedet.edu.ar
Journal covering development of Hermeneutics and biblical interpretation with focus on Latin America. **Freq:** Semiannual. **Key Personnel:** Nestor Miguez, Editor, miguez@isedet.edu.ar; Ricardo Pietrantonio, Editorial Board; Guillermo Hansen, Editorial Board. **ISSN:** 1668-2610. **URL:** http://www.isedet.edu.ar/jolah/journal.htm.

41478 ■ Plasticos
Chamber of Argentine Plastics Industries
Camara Argentina de la Industria Plastica
Jeronimo Salguero 1939/41
1425 Buenos Aires, Argentina
Ph: 54 482 19603
Fax: 54 482 65480
Publication E-mail: caip@caip.org.ar
Publisher E-mail: consultas@caip.org.ar
Spanish language publication covering plastics. **Freq:** Bimonthly. **Subscription Rates:** US$100 individuals interior of PCIA. BS. ACE and rest of the country; US$70 individuals Federal capital and GBA. **Remarks:** Advertising accepted; rates available upon request. **URL:** http://www.caip.org.ar/ing-lang/index.php?c=c_r_plasticos.php&m=2. **Circ:** 5,000

41479 ■ Revista del CIAS
Fundacion Centro de Investigacion y Accion Social
Rodriguez Pena 356, 1 Fl.
1334 4A Buenos Aires, Argentina

Circulation: ★ = ABC; △ = BPA; ◆ = CAC; • = CCAB; ❑ = VAC; ⊕ = PO Statement; ‡ = Publisher's Report; Boldface figures = sworn; Light figures = estimated.

Ph: 54 11 52297720
Publication E-mail: revista@fcias.org.ar
Publisher E-mail: administracion@fcias.org.ar
Spanish language publication covering the social sciences. **Founded:** 1957. **Freq:** Monthly. **Trim Size:** 14.5 x 21.5 cm. **Key Personnel:** Fernando E. Cervera, Director. **ISSN:** 0325-1306. **Subscription Rates:** US$70 individuals; US$15 individuals Ejemplar; US$40 individuals Estudiantes; US$10 individuals Estudiantes Ejemplar Suelto; US$120 individuals Ayuda; US$70 individuals Exterior; US$120 individuals Ejemplar Suelto en el Exterior; US$120 individuals Ayuda en el Exterior. **Remarks:** Advertising accepted; rates available upon request. **URL:** http://www.fcias.org.ar. **Circ:** (Not Reported)

41480 ■ Amadeus-FM - 103.7
Uriarte 1899 (C1414CSD)
Capital Federal
Buenos Aires, Argentina
Ph: 54 11 48338800
E-mail: amadeus@infobae.com
Format: Classical. **Operating Hours:** 18 hours Daily. **URL:** http://www.amadeus103.com.

41481 ■ Cultura Musical-FM - 100.3
Bernardo de Irigoyen 972 Subsuelo
1304 Buenos Aires, Argentina
Ph: 54 11 50319803
E-mail: amigos@culturamusical.com.ar
Format: Classical. **Operating Hours:** Continuous. **Wattage:** 25,000. **URL:** http://www.culturamusical.com.ar.

41482 ■ Flores-FM - 90.7
Avda. Nazca 881
1406 Buenos Aires, Argentina
Ph: 54 11 41305680
E-mail: info@radiofmflores.net
Format: Jazz; Contemporary Hit Radio (CHR); Ethnic. **Owner:** FM Flores, at above address. **Operating Hours:** 20.30 hours Daily. **Ad Rates:** Advertising accepted; rates available upon request. **URL:** http://www.radiofmflores.net.

41483 ■ La Isla-FM - 89.9
Torres Las Plz. J. Salguero

Ciudad Autonoma do Bs. As.
2745 Buenos Aires, Argentina
Ph: 54 11 48034434
Fax: 54 11 48076006
E-mail: fmlaisla@fmlaisla.com.ar
Format: Ethnic; World Beat. **Operating Hours:** Continuous. **Ad Rates:** Advertising accepted; rates available upon request. **URL:** http://www.fmlaisla.com.ar.

41484 ■ La Red-AM - 910
Av. Paseo Colon 505
1063 Buenos Aires, Argentina
Ph: 54 11 43380910
Fax: 54 11 43380999
Format: News; Sports. **Founded:** Nov. 19, 1929. **Operating Hours:** Continuous. **Key Personnel:** Cristina Demo, Executive of Sales, cdemo@radiolared.com.ar; Elizabeth Conigliaro, Asst. Admin., econigliaro@radiolared.com.ar; Jose Luis Villalba, Executive of Sales, jvillalba@radiolared.com.ar. **Ad Rates:** Advertising accepted; rates available upon request. **URL:** http://www.uol.com.ar/lared/web/index.htm.

41485 ■ Radio General Belgrano-AM - 840
Traful 3834
Pompeya
Buenos Aires, Argentina
Ph: 54 11 49120497
E-mail: am840generalbelgrano@hotmail.com
Format: World Beat; Ethnic. **Operating Hours:** Continuous. **Ad Rates:** Advertising accepted; rates available upon request. **URL:** http://www.am840generalbelgrano.com.

41486 ■ Universal-FM - 95.3
H.Yrigoyen 442 6to Piso
Bahia Blanca
8000 Buenos Aires, Argentina
Ph: 54 11 4559011
E-mail: noticias@fmuniversal.com
Format: Ethnic; World Beat. **Operating Hours:** Continuous. **Ad Rates:** Advertising accepted; rates available upon request. **URL:** http://www.fmuniversal.com.

Cordova

41487 ■ Espacio Apicola
Punilla 1784
5006 Cordova, Argentina
Ph: 54 351 4564337
Publisher E-mail: inform@apicultura.com.ar
Magazine covering beekeeping in Argentina. **Freq:** 5/yr. **URL:** http://www.apicultura.com.ar.

Rosario

41488 ■ Vida Rotaria
Calle Cordoba 954
Oficinas 24
S2000AWL Rosario, Argentina
Ph: 54 341 5300057
Fax: 54 341 5300058
Membership magazine of Rotary International covering current news about Rotary-related subjects. **Freq:** Monthly. **Key Personnel:** Diego F. Esmoriz, Editor. **URL:** http://www.rotary.org/languages/spanish/newsroom/regionalmags.html. **Circ:** 13,900

Santa Fe

41489 ■ Antena Uno-FM - 107.9
4 de Enero
3515 Santa Fe, Argentina
Ph: 54 342 4810366
Fax: 54 342 4810366
E-mail: aire@antena1.com.ar
Format: Public Radio. **Owner:** Antena Uno, at above address. **URL:** http://www.antena1.com.ar/.

Viedma Rio Negro

41490 ■ Libre-FM - 95.5
Guemes 781
8500 Viedma Rio Negro, Argentina
Fax: 54 2920 431999
Format: Classical; Talk. **Owner:** Libre-FM, at above address. **URL:** http://fmlibre-viedma.com.ar/.

Oranjestad

41491 ■ Eco Aruba
Rainbow Warriors International
PO Box 1154
Oranjestad, Aruba
Publication E-mail: ecoaruba@yahoo.com
Publisher E-mail: rainbowwarriorsinternational@yahoo.com
Magazine focusing on environmental conservation and sustainable development. **Founded:** 1995. **Key Personnel:** Milton Ponson, Editor-in-Chief, phone 297 5685908. **Remarks:** Accepts advertising. **URL:** http://www.ecoaruba.com/en/index.html. **Circ:** (Not Reported)

41492 ■ Cool-FM - 98.9
Caya Betico Croes 23
Oranjestad, Aruba
Ph: 297 5833100
Fax: 297 5833101
E-mail: coolaruba@gmail.com
Format: Classic Rock; Alternative/New Music/Progressive; Top 40; Contemporary Hit Radio (CHR). **Operating Hours:** 6:45 a.m.-6 a.m. Mon.-Fri.; 6 a.m.-11 p.m. **Ad Rates:** Advertising accepted; rates available upon request. **URL:** http://www.coolaruba.com.

41493 ■ Latina-FM - 92.3
Caya Betico Croes 23 Piso 1
Oranjestad, Aruba
Ph: 297 5833111
E-mail: latinaaruba@hotmail.com
Format: Ethnic; World Beat. **Operating Hours:** 18 hours Daily. **URL:** http://www.latinaaruba.com.

41494 ■ Vision-FM - 105.3
Vision Studios-Cumana 20
Oranjestad, Aruba
Ph: 297 5835656
Fax: 297 5825477
Format: Contemporary Christian; Religious. **Operating Hours:** Continuous. **URL:** http://www.visionaruba.com.

Savaneta

41495 ■ Radio Caruso Booy-FM - 102.7
Generaal Majoor de Bruinewijk No. 49
Savaneta, Aruba
Ph: 297 5847752
E-mail: radiocarusobooy@hotmail.com
Format: Ethnic; World Beat. **Operating Hours:** Continuous. **Wattage:** 300. **URL:** http://www.geocities.com/carusobooy/.

Abbotsford

41496 ■ KISS-FM - 87.6
274 Johnston St.
Abbotsford, Victoria 3067, Australia
Ph: 61 3 94171221
Fax: 61 3 94161359
E-mail: wazz@kissfm.com.au
Format: Contemporary Hit Radio (CHR). **Founded:**
2001. **Operating Hours:** Continuous. **URL:** http://www.
kissfm.com.au.

41497 ■ 3MBS-FM - 103.5
St. Euphrasia
1 St. Heliers St.
Abbotsford, Victoria 3067, Australia
Ph: 61 3 94161035
Fax: 61 3 94161036
E-mail: info@3mbs.org.au
Format: Classical; Jazz. **Operating Hours:** Continuous.
Key Personnel: Lin Bender, General Mgr., gm@3mbs.
org.au; Hermione Gilchrist, Contact; Mike Chambers,
Finance & Compliance Mgr.; Susan Batten, Educ. Off.
URL: http://www.3mbs.org.au.

Adelaide

41498 ■ Accounting Forum
University of South Australia
PO Box 2471
Adelaide, South Australia 5001, Australia
Ph: 61 883 026611
Fax: 61 883 022466
Publication for the banking, finance, and accounting
industries. **Founded:** 1975. **Freq:** Quarterly. **Key Per-
sonnel:** Prof. Glen Lehman, Editor-in-Chief, glen.
lehman@unisa.edu.au. **ISSN:** 0155-9982. **Remarks:**
Accepts advertising. **URL:** http://www.unisa.edu.au/
commerce/accounting_forum.asp. **Circ:** (Not Reported)

41499 ■ Adelaide Matters
Messenger Newspapers
31 Waymout St.
Adelaide, South Australia 5000, Australia
Lifestyle magazine. **Freq:** Monthly. **Print Method:** Heat
Set. **Trim Size:** 280 x 350 mm. **Key Personnel:** Rhian-
non Klar, Agency Account Mgr., phone 61 8 83475725,
klarr@mng.ncwsltd.com.au; Katrina Nitschke, Agency
Account Mgr., phone 61 8 83475705, nitschkek@mng.
newsltd.com.au. **Remarks:** Accepts display and classi-
fied advertising. **URL:** http://www.newsspace.com.au/
Adelaide_Matters. **Circ:** 97,418

41500 ■ The Adelaidean
Media, Marketing & Publications Unit
Office of the Vice-Chancellor
The University of Adelaide
Rm. G07, Mitchell Bldg.
Adelaide, South Australia 5005, Australia
Ph: 61 883 035174
Fax: 61 883 034838
The Adelaidean providing news about the teaching,
research and other activities of the University. **Founded:**
1992. **Freq:** Monthly February to December. **Key Per-
sonnel:** Chris Tonkin, Design; Candy Gibson, Writers;

Robyn Mills, Writers; Claire Oremland, Contributors;
Lana Guineay, Contributors; David Ellis, Editor, david.
ellis@adelaide.edu.au. **Remarks:** Accepts advertising.
URL: http://www.adelaide.edu.au/adelaidean/. **Circ:**
Combined 13,000

41501 ■ Austral Ecology
John Wiley & Sons Inc.
Wiley-Blackwell
c/o Michael Bull, Mng. Ed.
School of Biological Science
Flinders University of South Australia
PO Box 2100
Adelaide, South Australia 5001, Australia
Journal covering the field of ecological research. **Sub-
title:** A Journal of ecology in the Southern Hemisphere.
Freq: 8/yr. **Key Personnel:** Peter Clarke, Assoc. Ed.;
Ros Blanche, Assoc. Ed.; Michael Bull, Managing Edi-
tor, michael.bull@flinders.edu.au. **ISSN:** 1442-9985.
Subscription Rates: US$249 individuals print + online;
US$1,454 institutions print + online; US$1,321 institutions print or online; US$1,764 institutions, other
countries print + online; 167 other countries print + online; US$1,764 institutions, other countries print or on-
line; 1,103 institutions print + online (Australia and New
Zealand); 900 institutions print + online; EUR1,143
institutions print + online; EUR1,039 institutions print or
online. **Remarks:** Accepts advertising. **URL:** http://www.
wiley.com/bw/journal.asp?ref=1442-9985. **Former
name:** Australian Journal of Ecology. **Circ:** (Not Reported)

**41502 ■ Australasian Public Libraries and
Information Services**
Auslib Press
PO Box 622
Adelaide, South Australia 5051, Australia
Ph: 61 8 82784363
Fax: 61 8 82784000
Publisher E-mail: info@auslib.com.au
Publication covering library and information science.
Freq: Quarterly. **Key Personnel:** Alan Bundy, Editor.
ISSN: 1030-5033. **Subscription Rates:** $A 49.50
individuals; $A 45 individuals New Zealand; $A 71.50
institutions; $A 65 institutions New Zealand; $A 69.50
institutions, other countries. **Remarks:** Accepts
advertising. **URL:** http://www.auslib.com.au/periodicals.
htm. **Circ:** (Not Reported)

41503 ■ Australian Economic History Review
John Wiley & Sons Inc.
Wiley-Blackwell
c/o Dr. Martin Shanahan, Ed.
Centre for Regulation & Market Analysis
University of South Australia
North Ter.
Adelaide, South Australia 5000, Australia
Journal focusing on the historical treatment of economic,
social and business issues, particularly relating to the
countries in the Asia-Pacific region, including Australia
and New Zealand. **Subtitle:** An Asia-Pacific Journal of
Economic, Business & Social History. **Freq:** 3/yr. **Key
Personnel:** Dr. Martin Shanahan, Editor; Dr. Stephen
Morgan, Editor; Dr. John Singleton, Book Review Ed.; J.
Baten, Editorial Board; G. Boyce, Editorial Board; G.
Clark, Editorial Board. **ISSN:** 0004-8992. **Subscription**

Rates: US$265 institutions print and online; US$240
institutions print or online; EUR234 institutions print and
online; EUR213 institutions print or online; US$111 institu-
tions Australia; print or online; 185 institutions print and
online; 167 institutions print or online; US$361 institu-
tions, other countries print and online; US$328 institu-
tions, other countries print or online. **Remarks:** Accepts
advertising. **URL:** http://www.wiley.com/bw/journal.asp?
ref=0004-8992&site=1. **Circ:** (Not Reported)

41504 ■ Australian Theological Book Reviewer
Australian Theological Forum Inc.
Rm. S7, Adelaide College of Divinity
34 Lipsett Ter.
Adelaide, South Australia 5032, Australia
Ph: 61 883 542299
Fax: 61 883 542399
Online periodical covering theological and religious
literature in Australia. **Key Personnel:** Hilary Regan,
Editor; Bernadette Tobin, Contributing Ed.; Anne Grant
Henderson, Contributing Ed.; Vicky Balabanski, Editor;
Peter Lockwood, Contributing Ed.; Andrew Dutney,
Contributing Ed.; James McEvoy, Contributing Ed.;
Andrew Sloane, Contributing Ed.; Chris Mostert, Contrib-
uting Ed. **ISSN:** 1443-9220. **URL:** http://www.atf.org.au/;
http://atbr.atf.org.au/index.php?type=page&ID=1338.

41505 ■ dB Magazine
179A Hindley St.
PO Box 8260
Adelaide, South Australia 5000, Australia
Ph: 61 8 82314211
Fax: 61 8 82314393
Publisher E-mail: info@dbmagazine.com.au
Magazine for the people of Adelaide and entire South
Australia. **Freq:** Semimonthly every second Wed. **Key
Personnel:** Kate Fabbian, Advertising Mgr., phone 61 8
82314211, kate@dbmagazine.com.au; Alex Wheaton,
Editor, phone 61 8 82314218, alex@dbmagazine.com.
au; Andrew P. Street, Music, Games Ed., phone 61 8
82314212, andrew@dbmagazine.com.au; Jeremy
Wright, Webmaster. **Subscription Rates:** Free. **Re-
marks:** Advertising accepted; rates available upon
request. **URL:** http://www.dbmagazine.com.au/370/a-
about.shtml. **Circ:** (Not Reported)

**41506 ■ HOMO - Journal of Comparative Human
Biology**
Elsevier Science
c/o Maciej Henneberg, Ed.-in-Ch.
Dept. of Anatomical Sciences
University of Adelaide
Adelaide, South Australia 5005, Australia
Ph: 61 883 035479
Fax: 61 883 035998
Publisher E-mail: nlinfo-f@elsevier.com
Peer-reviewed journal dedicated to the field of biological
anthropology in relation to its population historic, onto-
genetic and ethological aspects. **Freq:** 6/yr. **Key Personnel:** Stanley J. Ulijasze, Editor, stanley.ulijaszek@
anthro.ox.ac.uk; Frank J. Ruhli, Editor, phone 41 446
355315, fax 41 446 355702, frank.ruhli@anatom.unizh.
ch; Friedrich W. Rosing, Editor, phone 49 734 4917386,
fax 49 734 4917387, friedrich.roesing@uni-ulm.de; Maciej Henneberg, Editor, maciej.henneberg@adelaide.
edu.au; Kurt W. Alt, Book Review Ed., phone 49 613

Circulation: ★ = ABC; △ = BPA; ♦ = CAC; • = CCAB; ❏ = VAC; ⊕ = PO Statement; ‡ = Publisher's Report; Boldface figures = sworn; Light figures = estimated.

Gale Directory of Publications & Broadcast Media/147th Ed. 4697

13922242, fax 49 613 13925132, altkw@mail.uni-mainz. de; Renata Henneberg, Editorial Assoc., gail.hermanis@ adelaide.edu.au. **ISSN:** 0018-442X. **Subscription Rates:** EUR189 individuals for European countries; US$193 individuals for all countries except Europe and Japan; 24,700¥ individuals; EUR670 institutions for European countries; US$754 institutions for all countries except Europe and Japan; 90,300¥ institutions; EUR141 students; 18,600¥ students; US$145 students. **URL:** http://www.elsevier.com/wps/find/journaldescription.cws_ home/701767/description.

41507 ■ Interface
Australian Theological Forum Inc.
Rm. S7, Adelaide College of Divinity
34 Lipsett Ter.
Adelaide, South Australia 5032, Australia
Ph: 61 883 542299
Fax: 61 883 542399
Official journal of the Australian Theological Forum for members. **Subtitle:** A Forum for Theology in the World. **Freq:** Semiannual. **Key Personnel:** Dr. Gordon Watson, Editor-in-Chief. **ISSN:** 1329-6264. **Subscription Rates:** $A 49.50 individuals; $A 55 institutions, other countries. **URL:** http://www.atfpress.com/index.php? type=page&ID=1370. **Circ:** 550

41508 ■ International Journal of Computers in Healthcare
Inderscience Enterprises Limited
c/o Lakhmi C. Jain, Ed.-in-Ch.
University of South Australia
Division of Information Technology, Engineering & the Environment
School of Electrical & Information Engineering, Mawson Lakes Campus
Adelaide, South Australia 5095, Australia
Peer-reviewed journal publishing original articles concerning the theory and application of the computer to biomedicine and healthcare. **Freq:** Quarterly. **Key Personnel:** Lakhmi C. Jain, Editor-in-Chief, lakhmi. jain@unisa.edu.au. **ISSN:** 1755-3199. **Subscription Rates:** EUR494 individuals print or online; EUR672 individuals print and online. **URL:** http://www. inderscience.com/browse/index.php?journalID=275.

41509 ■ International Journal for Educational Integrity
University of South Australia
PO Box 2471
Adelaide, South Australia 5001, Australia
Ph: 61 883 026611
Fax: 61 883 022466
Journal covering research in educational integrity, and the effect on pedagogy, academic standards, intercultural understanding and equity. **Freq:** Semiannual. **Key Personnel:** Helen Marsden, Editorial Board, helen. marsden@unisa.edu.au; Tracey Bretag, Editor, tracey. bretag@unisa.edu.au. **ISSN:** 1833-2595. **URL:** http:// www.ojs.unisa.edu.au/index.php/IJEI.

41510 ■ International Journal of Intelligent Defence Support Systems
Inderscience Enterprises Limited
c/o Dr. Stephen Cook, Ed.-in-Ch.
University of South Australia
Defence & Systems Institute
Mawson Lakes Campus
Adelaide, South Australia 5095, Australia.
Journal covering strategic, tactical, and operational decision making across the entire defense sector. **Freq:** 4/yr. **Key Personnel:** Dr. Stephen Cook, Editor-in-Chief, stephen.cook@unisa.edu.au; Dr. Anthony Finn, Editor-in-Chief, anthony.finn@dsto.defence.gov.au. **ISSN:** 1755-1587. **Subscription Rates:** EUR494 individuals print or online; EUR672 individuals print and online. **URL:** http://www.inderscience.com/browse/index.php? journalID=269.

41511 ■ International Journal of Narrative Therapy and Community Work
Dulwich Centre Publications Pty. Ltd.
Hutt St.
PO Box 7192
Adelaide, South Australia 5000, Australia
Ph: 61 882 233966
Fax: 61 882 324441
Publisher E-mail: dulwich@senet.com.au
Journal offering ideas for counselors, social workers, teachers, nurses, psychologists and community workers, with the latest ideas and developments in narrative therapy. **Freq:** Quarterly. **ISSN:** 1446-5019. **Subscription Rates:** $A 93 other countries; $A 77 individuals.

URL: http://www.dulwichcentre.com.au/international-journal-narrative-therapy.html.

41512 ■ Peace and Freedom
Women's International League for Peace and Freedom - Australia
Rundle Mall
PO Box 345
Adelaide, South Australia 5000, Australia
Ph: 61 8 82964357
Publisher E-mail: wilpfaustralia@wilpf.org.au
Publication covering peace. **Founded:** 1960. **Freq:** Triennial. **Print Method:** Offset. **URL:** http://www.wilpf. org.au/journal/home.htm. **Circ:** 500

41513 ■ Sustaining Regions
Australian and New Zealand Regional Science Association Inc.
c/o Prof. Andrew Beer, Ed.
School of Geography, Population & Environmental Management
Flinders University
GPO Box 2100
Adelaide, South Australia 5001, Australia
Ph: 61 8 82013522
Fax: 61 8 82013521
Publication E-mail: sustaining.regions@flinders.edu.au
Journal presenting topical articles and information on cutting edge issues affecting all Australian regions - metropolitan, remote, urban and rural. **Freq:** 3/yr. **Key Personnel:** Prof. Andrew Beer, Editor, andrew.beer@ flinders.edu.au. **Subscription Rates:** $A 66 nonmembers. **URL:** http://www.anzrsai.org/page/ publications/sustaining-regions/.

41514 ■ ENA-FM - 88.0 MHz
255 Waymouth St.
Adelaide, South Australia 5000, Australia
Ph: 61 8 82313500
E-mail: requests@radioena.com.au
Format: News; Sports. **Operating Hours:** Continuous. **URL:** http://www.radioena.com/.

41515 ■ 5AA-AM - 1395
GPO Box FIVEaa
Adelaide, South Australia 5001, Australia
Ph: 61 8 84191395
Fax: 61 8 84191462
Format: Talk; News; Information; Sports. **Operating Hours:** Continuous. **URL:** http://www.fiveaa.com.au/.

41516 ■ 5ABC-FM - 103.9
ABC Ultimo Ctr.
700 Harris St.
Ultimo, New South Wales 2007, Australia
Ph: 61 2 83331500
Fax: 61 2 83335344
Format: Classical. **Owner:** Australian Broadcasting Corp., at above address. **Key Personnel:** Graeme Bennett, Contact. **URL:** http://abc.com.au/classical/freq/ freqsa.htm.

41517 ■ 5EBI-FM - 103.1 MHz
10 Byron Pl.
Adelaide, South Australia 5000, Australia
Ph: 61 5 82117635
Fax: 61 5 82311456
Format: Ethnic; World Beat; News. **Key Personnel:** Kym Green, Station Mgr.; Henk de Weerd, Production Coord.; Cristina Descalzi, Ch. **Ad Rates:** $30 for 30 seconds. **URL:** http://www.5ebi.com.au/.

41518 ■ 5UV-AM - 101.5
228 North Ter.
Adelaide, South Australia 5000, Australia
Ph: 61 8 83035000
Fax: 61 8 83034374
E-mail: radio@adelaide.edu.au
Format: Eclectic. **Founded:** June 28, 1972. **Operating Hours:** Continuous. **Key Personnel:** Max Hicks, Sales Mgr., max.hicks@adelaide.edu.au; Deborah Welch, Station Mgr., deborah.welch@adelaide.edu.au. **Wattage:** 7000. **URL:** http://radio.adelaide.edu.au/.

41519 ■ Fresh-FM - 92.7
230 Angas St., Level 1
Adelaide, South Australia 5000, Australia
Ph: 61 8 82327927
Fax: 61 8 82240922
E-mail: admin@freshfm.com.au
Format: Urban Contemporary. **Owner:** Fresh Broadcasters Inc., at above address. **Operating Hours:**

Continuous. **Key Personnel:** Domenic Cutufia, Operations Mgr.; Michael Abela, Sales & Mktg. Mgr.; Jack Jericho, Production/Traffic Mgr. **URL:** http://www.fresh927. com.au/.

41520 ■ Radio Adelaide-FM - 101.5
228 North Ter.
Adelaide, South Australia 5000, Australia
Ph: 61 8 83035000
Fax: 61 8 83034374
E-mail: radio@adelaide.edu.au
Format: Eclectic. **Owner:** Adelaide University, The University of Adelaide, Adelaide, South Australia 5005, Australia, 61 8 83034455. **Founded:** 1972. **Former name:** Radio 5UV. **Operating Hours:** Continuous. **Key Personnel:** Deborah Welch, Station Mgr., deborah. welch@adelaide.edu.au; Max Hicks, Sales Mgr., max. hicks@adelaide.edu.au. **Wattage:** 7000. **Ad Rates:** Advertising accepted; rates available upon request. **URL:** http://www.radio.adelaide.edu.au/; http://www. adelaide.edu.au/.

41521 ■ SBS Television - 28
Locked Bag 028
Crows Nest, New South Wales 1585, Australia
Ph: 61 2 94302828
Fax: 61 2 94303047
Owner: Special Broadcasting Service, at above address. **Wattage:** 795,000 ERP. **URL:** http://www20.sbs.com.au/ transmissions/index.php?pid=2&id=437.

Airlie Beach

41522 ■ 4ABC-FM - 95.5
ABC Ultimo Ctr.
700 Harris St.
Ultimo, New South Wales 2007, Australia
Ph: 61 2 83331500
Fax: 61 2 83335344
Format: Classical. **Owner:** Australian Broadcasting Corp., at above address. **URL:** http://abc.com.au/classic/ freq/freqqld.htm.

41523 ■ SBS Television - 34
Locked Bag 028
Crows Nest, New South Wales 1585, Australia
Ph: 61 2 94302828
Fax: 61 2 94303047
Owner: Special Broadcasting Service, at above address. **Wattage:** 600 ERP. **URL:** http://www20.sbs.com.au/ transmissions/index.php?pid=2&id=187.

Aitkenvale

41524 ■ 4TCB-FM - 99.9
PO Box 332
Aitkenvale, Queensland 4814, Australia
Ph: 61 7 47251299
Fax: 61 7 47254680
E-mail: admin@livefm.com.au
Format: Contemporary Christian. **URL:** http://www. livefm.com.au/; http://www.cbonline.org.au/index.cfm? pageId=13,13,6,3293.

Albany

41525 ■ Albany Community Radio-FM - 100.9
Lotteries House 211-217 N Rd.
Albany, Western Australia 6330, Australia
Ph: 61 8 98423455
Fax: 61 8 98425850
E-mail: 1009fm@westnet.com.au
Format: Ethnic; Religious; Sports. **Owner:** Community Broadcasting Association of Australia, at above address. **Operating Hours:** Continuous. **Key Personnel:** Ken Ewers-Verge, Chm.; Hugh Cleverly, Vice Chair. **URL:** http://www.1009fm.org.au.

41526 ■ 6CRA-FM - 100.9
Lotteries House
211-217 North Rd.
Albany, Western Australia 6330, Australia
Ph: 61 8 98423455
Fax: 61 8 98425850
Format: Ethnic; Religious. **URL:** http://www.1009fm.org. au/.

Albury

41527 ■ Micronesian Journal of the Humanities and Social Sciences
Charles Sturt University
PO Box 789
Albury, New South Wales 2640, Australia
Ph: 61 2 60519849
Fax: 61 2 60519849
Publisher E-mail: kdawson@csu.edu.au
Journal dedicated to the study of human thought, behavior, and culture in Micronesia. **Freq:** Semiannual. **Key Personnel:** Samuel McPhetres, Editor; Dirk Ballendorf, Assoc. Ed.; Dirk H.R. Spennemann, Editor. **ISSN:** 1449-7336. **URL:** http://marshall.csu.edu.au/MJHSS; http://www.csu.edu.au/.

41528 ■ The River-FM - 105.7
Level 1, 540 Swift St.
Albury, New South Wales 2640, Australia
Ph: 61 2 60224600
Fax: 61 2 60224662
Format: Adult Contemporary. **Owner:** Regional Mediaworks, Level 3, 170 Pacific Hwy., Greenwich, New South Wales 2065, Australia, 61 2 84379400, Fax: 61 2 84379498. **Key Personnel:** Mike Toone, Station Mgr., mike.toone@macsc.com.au. **URL:** http://theradio.com.au/THE-RIVER-105.7-FMThe-Station.html; http://www.regionalmediaworks.com.au/region%20information.asp?region=Albur y.

41529 ■ SBS Television - 53
Locked Bag 028
Crows Nest, New South Wales 1585, Australia
Ph: 61 2 94302828
Fax: 61 2 94303047
Owner: Special Broadcasting Service, at above address. **Wattage:** 600 ERP. **URL:** http://www20.sbs.com.au/transmissions/index.php?pid=2&id=9.

Alderley

41530 ■ Albert & Logan News
Quest Community Newspapers
PO Box 104
Alderley, Queensland 4051, Australia
Ph: 61 7 33520700
Fax: 61 7 38520636
Publication E-mail: editorial@albertlogannews.com.au
Local community newspaper. **Founded:** 1877. **Freq:** Biweekly. **Key Personnel:** Ray Goodey, Editor. **Remarks:** Accepts display and classified advertising. **URL:** http://albert-and-logan.whereilive.com.au/. **Circ:** Wed. ‡73,440, Fri. ‡76,880.

41531 ■ Northside Chronicle
Quest Community Newspapers
PO Box 104
Alderley, Queensland 4051, Australia
Ph: 61 7 33520700
Fax: 61 7 33520636
Local community newspaper. **Founded:** 1985. **Freq:** Weekly (Wed.). **Key Personnel:** Andrew Dawson, Editor, phone 61 7 33520700, fax 61 7 33520640, editorial@northsiddechronicle.com.au; Belinda MacPherson, Advertising Mgr. **Remarks:** Accepts display and classified advertising. **URL:** http://www.newsspace.com.au/northside_chronicle. **Circ:** ‡62,294.

Alexandra

41532 ■ SBS Television - 68
Locked Bag 028
Crows Nest, New South Wales 1585, Australia
Ph: 61 2 94302828
Fax: 61 2 94303047
Owner: Special Broadcasting Service, at above address. **Wattage:** 20,000 ERP. **URL:** http://www20.sbs.com.au/transmissions/index.php?pid=2&id=363.

41533 ■ UG-FM - 106.9
PO Box 270
Alexandra, Victoria 3714, Australia
Ph: 61 3 57722900
Fax: 61 3 57722414
E-mail: info@ugfm.org
Format: Easy Listening; Contemporary Hit Radio (CHR). **URL:** http://ugfm.cute.com.au/.

UG-FM - See Marysville

UG-FM - See Yea

Alexandria

41534 ■ Australian Country Style
The Federal Publishing Company
170-180 Bourke Rd.
Alexandria, New South Wales 2015, Australia
Ph: 61 2 93536666
Fax: 61 2 93536699
Lifestyle magazine featuring Australia. **Subtitle:** People Homes Gardens Food Living. **Freq:** 12/yr. **Trim Size:** 220 x 276 mm. **Key Personnel:** Victoria Carey, Actg. Ed., careyv@newsmagazines.com.au; Nicole Conway, Contact, conwayn@newsmagazines.com.au. **Subscription Rates:** US$65 individuals; US$120 two years; $A 85 individuals New Zealand; $A 140 other countries New Zealand. **Remarks:** Accepts advertising. **URL:** http://www.countrystyle.com.au/index.php; http://www.fpc.com.au/page/magssite.php?pageid=18. **Ad Rates:** 4C: $A 6,600. **Circ:** ★57,780.

41535 ■ Australian Golf Digest
The Federal Publishing Company
170-180 Bourke Rd.
Alexandria, New South Wales 2015, Australia
Ph: 61 2 93536666
Fax: 61 2 93536699
Magazine for golf enthusiasts. **Freq:** Monthly. **Trim Size:** 210 x 276 mm. **Key Personnel:** Steve Keipert, Editor, keiperts@newsmagazines.com.au; Peter Curtin, Contact, curtinp@newsmagazines.com.au. **Subscription Rates:** $A 72 individuals; $A 138 two years; $A 110 individuals New Zealand; $A 225 other countries. **Remarks:** Accepts advertising. **URL:** http://www.australiangolfdigest.com.au/index.php; http://www.newsspace.com.au/australian_golf_digest; http://www.isubscribe.com.au/title_info.cfm?prodID=121. **Ad Rates:** 4C: $A 3,960. **Circ:** ★36,000.

41536 ■ Australian Good Taste
The Federal Publishing Company
170-180 Bourke Rd.
Alexandria, New South Wales 2015, Australia
Ph: 61 2 93536666
Fax: 61 2 93536699
Food and lifestyle magazine. **Freq:** Monthly. **Trim Size:** 206 x 276 mm. **Key Personnel:** Brodee Myers-Cooke, Editor. **Subscription Rates:** $A 50 individuals; $A 4.25 single issue; $A 99 two years. **Remarks:** Accepts advertising. **URL:** http://www.australiangoodtaste.com.au/; http://www.isubscribe.com.au/Magazines/Food-&-Drink/Food/Woolworths-Australian-Good-Taste.cfm. **Circ:** ★121,612.

41537 ■ Australian Parents
The Federal Publishing Company
170-180 Bourke Rd.
Alexandria, New South Wales 2015, Australia
Ph: 61 2 93536666
Fax: 61 2 93536699
Publication E-mail: parents@fpc.com.au
Parenting magazine. **Founded:** 1981. **Freq:** Bimonthly. **Trim Size:** 206 x 276 mm. **Key Personnel:** Jody Scott, Editor. **Subscription Rates:** $A 23 individuals; $A 45 two years. **Remarks:** Accepts advertising. **URL:** http://www.getprice.com.au/Australian-Parents-Magazine-Subscription-12-Month-Gpnc_440--36612044.htm; http://www.parents.com.au/. **Circ:** (Not Reported).

41538 ■ delicious.
The Federal Publishing Company
170-180 Bourke Rd.
Alexandria, New South Wales 2015, Australia
Ph: 61 2 93536666
Fax: 61 2 93536699
Food magazine. **Founded:** 2001. **Freq:** Monthly. **Trim Size:** 220 x 276 mm. **Key Personnel:** Trudi Jenkins, Editor-in-Chief. **Subscription Rates:** $A 6.95 single issue. **Remarks:** Accepts advertising. **URL:** http://www.deliciousmagazine.com.au/. **Ad Rates:** 4C: $A 11,370. **Circ:** ★134,000.

41539 ■ Fast Fours Magazine
The Federal Publishing Company
170-180 Bourke Rd.
Alexandria, New South Wales 2015, Australia
Ph: 61 2 93536666

Fax: 61 2 93536699
Publication E-mail: subs@magstore.com.au
Magazine for four-cylinder and rotary powered modified car enthusiasts. **Freq:** Monthly. **Trim Size:** 230 x 297 mm. **Key Personnel:** Tom Hall, Editor, phone 61 2 87193612, fax 61 2 97483856, thall@tasfastfours.com.au; Michael Coiro, National Advisory Mgr., phone 61 2 97413911, fax 61 2 97483596, mcoiro@expresspublications.com. **Subscription Rates:** $A 6.76 single issue; $A 59 individuals 7 issue; US$195 two years; $A 104 individuals 14 issue. **Remarks:** Accepts advertising. **URL:** http://www.fastfours.com.au. **Circ:** ★30,120.

41540 ■ Gardening Australia
The Federal Publishing Company
170-180 Bourke Rd.
Alexandria, New South Wales 2015, Australia
Ph: 61 2 93536666
Fax: 61 2 93536699
Gardening magazine. **Freq:** Monthly. **Trim Size:** 206 x 276 mm. **Key Personnel:** Frank Bardetta, Exec. Ed., bardettaf@newsmagazines.com.au; Jennifer Stackhouse, Editor, ga@newsmagazines.com.au. **Subscription Rates:** $A 5.95 single issue. **Remarks:** Accepts advertising. **URL:** http://www.gardeningaustralia.com.au/. **Circ:** ★88,606.

41541 ■ Lifestyle Pools
The Federal Publishing Company
170-180 Bourke Rd.
Alexandria, New South Wales 2015, Australia
Ph: 61 2 93536666
Fax: 61 2 93536699
Magazine featuring the latest architectural designs of pools in Australia. **Founded:** 1985. **Freq:** Semiannual. **Trim Size:** 220 x 276 mm. **Key Personnel:** Veda Dante, Editor, phone 61 409 080567, veda@vedadante.com; Carol D'Acosta, Assoc. Publisher, phone 61 2 80622077, dcostac@newsmagazines.com.au. **Remarks:** Accepts advertising. **URL:** http://www.newsspace.com.au/lifestyle_pools. **Ad Rates:** 4C: $A 2,700. **Circ:** (Not Reported).

41542 ■ Live to Ride
The Federal Publishing Company
170-180 Bourke Rd.
Alexandria, New South Wales 2015, Australia
Ph: 61 2 93536666
Fax: 61 2 93536699
Magazine for riders and lovers of Harley-Davidsons. **Founded:** 1989. **Freq:** Monthly. **Key Personnel:** Brett Cross, Contact, brett@livetoride.com.au. **Subscription Rates:** $A 69 individuals; $A 128 two years; $A 101 individuals New Zealand. **Remarks:** Accepts advertising. **URL:** http://www.livetoride.com.au/. **Ad Rates:** 4C: $A 2,350. **Circ:** ‡24,039.

41543 ■ Modern Boating
The Federal Publishing Company
170-180 Bourke Rd.
Alexandria, New South Wales 2015, Australia
Ph: 61 2 93536666
Fax: 61 2 93536699
Magazine for boating enthusiasts. **Founded:** 1965. **Freq:** 10/yr. **Trim Size:** 220 x 276 mm. **Key Personnel:** Ian Macrae, Editor. **Subscription Rates:** $A 14 individuals. **Remarks:** Accepts advertising. **URL:** http://www.modernboating.com.au/. **Ad Rates:** 4C: $A 2,100. **Circ:** ★11,131.

41544 ■ Modern Fishing
The Federal Publishing Company
170-180 Bourke Rd.
Alexandria, New South Wales 2015, Australia
Ph: 61 2 93536666
Fax: 61 2 93536699
Fishing Magazine for all amateur anglers. **Freq:** Monthly. **Trim Size:** 206 x 276 mm. **Key Personnel:** Dominic Wiseman, Advertising Mgr., wisemand@newsmagazines.com.au; Nicholas Janzen, Editor. **Subscription Rates:** US$7.95 single issue. **Remarks:** Accepts advertising. **URL:** http://www.newsspace.com.au/modern_fishing. **Circ:** ★15,556.

41545 ■ Overlander 4WD
The Federal Publishing Company
170-180 Bourke Rd.
Alexandria, New South Wales 2015, Australia

Circulation: ★ = ABC; △ = BPA; ♦ = CAC; • = CCAB; ❑ = VAC; ⊕ = PO Statement; ‡ = Publisher's Report; Boldface figures = sworn; Light figures = estimated.

Gale Directory of Publications & Broadcast Media/147th Ed.   **4699**

Ph: 61 2 93536666
Fax: 61 2 93536699
Magazine featuring 4 wheel drives. **Freq:** Monthly. **Trim Size:** 206 x 276 mm. **Key Personnel:** Drew Byrne, Advertising Mgr., byrnea@newsmagazines.com.au; Carolyn Bollaci, Contact, carolyn.bollaci@ newsdigitalmedia.com.au. **Subscription Rates:** $A 8.95 single issue. **Remarks:** Accepts advertising. **URL:** http:// www.overlander.com.au/. **Circ:** ★24,333

41546 ■ Super Food Ideas
The Federal Publishing Company
170-180 Bourke Rd.
Alexandria, New South Wales 2015, Australia
Ph: 61 2 93536666
Fax: 61 2 93536699
Food magazine. **Freq:** Monthly. **Trim Size:** 206 x 276 mm. **Key Personnel:** Nikki Roche, Advertising Mgr., rochen@newsmagazines.com.au; Rebecca Cox, Editor. **Subscription Rates:** $A 2.95 single issue. **Remarks:** Accepts advertising. **URL:** http://www.superfoodideas. com.au/; http://www.newsspace.com.au/super_food_ ideas. **Ad Rates:** 4C: $A 15,860. **Circ:** ★261,997

41547 ■ Truck Australia
The Federal Publishing Company
170-180 Bourke Rd.
Alexandria, New South Wales 2015, Australia
Ph: 61 2 93536666
Fax: 61 2 93536699
Magazine for fleet managers and trucking industry professionals. **Subtitle:** And trailer. **Freq:** Bimonthly. **Trim Size:** 206 x 276 mm. **Key Personnel:** Andrew Byrne, Advertising Mgr., byrnea@newsmagazines.com.au. **Subscription Rates:** $A 5.95 single issue. **Remarks:** Accepts advertising. **URL:** http://www.truckaustralia. com.au/. **Ad Rates:** 4C: $A 3,300. **Circ:** ★12,881

41548 ■ Truckin' Life
The Federal Publishing Company
170-180 Bourke Rd.
Alexandria, New South Wales 2015, Australia
Ph: 61 2 93536666
Fax: 61 2 93536699
Magazine featuring on trucks and trucking. **Founded:** 1976. **Freq:** Monthly. **Trim Size:** 206 x 276 mm. **Key Personnel:** Andrew Byrne, National MGAD, phone 61 2 80622656, byrnea@newsmagazines.com.au. **Subscription Rates:** US$8.50 single issue. **Remarks:** Accepts advertising. **URL:** http://www.truckinlife.com.au/; http:// www.newsspace.com.au/truckin_life. **Ad Rates:** 4C: $A 3,600. **Circ:** ★21,539

41549 ■ twowheels
The Federal Publishing Company
170-180 Bourke Rd.
Alexandria, New South Wales 2015, Australia
Ph: 61 2 93536666
Fax: 61 2 93536699
Magazine for motorcycle enthusiasts. **Freq:** Monthly. **Trim Size:** 206 x 276 mm. **Key Personnel:** Jeremy Bowdler, Editor. **Subscription Rates:** $A 8.95 single issue; US$50 individuals. **Remarks:** Accepts advertising. **URL:** http://www.twowheels.com.au/. **Ad Rates:** 4C: $A 2,645. **Circ:** ★31,453

Alice Springs

41550 ■ ABC Northern Territory-AM - 783
PO Box 1144
Alice Springs, Northern Territory 0871, Australia
Ph: 61 8 89504711
Fax: 61 8 89504799
Format: News; Talk. **Owner:** Australian Broadcasting Corporation, ABC Ultimo Ctr., 700 Harris St., Ultimo 2007, GPO Box 9994, Sydney, New South Wales 2001, Australia, 61 2 83331500, Fax 61 2 83335334. **Operating Hours:** Continuous. **Key Personnel:** Stewart Brash, Regional Program Mgr. **URL:** http://www.abc.net.au/ alicesprings/radio/.

41551 ■ 8CCC-FM - 102.1
PO Box 4185
Alice Springs, Northern Territory 0871, Australia
Ph: 61 8 89527771
Fax: 61 8 89527722
E-mail: 8ccc@netspeed.com.au
Format: Ethnic. **Founded:** Jan. 25, 1981. **Key Personnel:** Kate Lawrence, Ch.; Rebecca Gooderham, Sec. **URL:** http://www.8ccc.com.au/.

41552 ■ 8HA-AM - 900
PO Box 2106
Alice Springs, Northern Territory 0871, Australia
Ph: 61 8 89522900
Fax: 61 8 89528276
E-mail: info@8ha.com.au
Format: Full Service; Adult Contemporary. **Founded:** Mar. 2, 1971. **Key Personnel:** Phil Blackburn, Sales Mgr. **URL:** http://www.8ha.com.au/.

41553 ■ 8KIN-FM - 100.5
101 Todd St.
PO Box 2608
Alice Springs, Northern Territory 0871, Australia
Ph: 61 8 89519778
Fax: 61 8 89519717
Format: Ethnic. **URL:** http://caama.com.au/category/ music/about/.

41554 ■ Sun-FM - 96.9
PO Box 2106
Alice Springs, Northern Territory 0871, Australia
Ph: 61 8 89555969
Fax: 61 8 89528276
E-mail: info@thesun.com.au
Format: Adult Contemporary. **URL:** http://www.thesun. com.au/; http://www.regionalmediaworks.com.au/ region%20information.asp?region= Alice%20Springs.

41555 ■ Territory-FM - 98.7
Bldg. Orange 6, Level 3
Charles Darwin University
Casuarina, Northern Territory 0909, Australia
Ph: 61 8 89466266
Fax: 61 8 89451788
E-mail: frontdesk@territoryfm.com
Format: Soft Rock. **Owner:** Charles Darwin University, at above address. **URL:** http://alice.territoryfm.com/.

Annerley

41556 ■ Balance
Mental Health Association Queensland
473 Annerley Rd.
Annerley, Queensland 4103, Australia
Ph: 61 1300 729686
Fax: 61 7 31124399
Journal providing information about a wide variety of topics pertaining to mental health, including research and new advances in mental health. **Freq:** Quarterly. **Subscription Rates:** Included in membership. **URL:** http://www.brisbanemediamap.com.au/public/client/233.

Aranda

41557 ■ Environmental Toxicology
John Wiley & Sons Inc.
c/o Ian R. Falconer, Assoc. Ed.
44 Mirning Cres.
Aranda, Australian Capital Territory 2614, Australia
Publisher E-mail: info@wiley.com
Journal publishing in the areas of toxicity and toxicology of environmental pollutants in air, dust, sediment, soil and water, and natural toxins in the environment. **Freq:** Bimonthly. **Key Personnel:** Ian R. Falconer, Assoc. Ed., ian.falconer@adelaide.edu.au; Paul B. Tchounwou, Editor, phone 601979-3321, fax 601979-5853, paul.b. tchounwou@jsums.edu; R.O. Duffard, Editorial Board. **ISSN:** 1520-4081. **Subscription Rates:** US$1,166 institutions print only; US$1,250 institutions, Canada print only; US$1,292 institutions, other countries print only; US$1,409 institutions, other countries print and online; US$1,283 institutions print and online; US$1,367 institutions, Canada print and online. **Remarks:** Accepts advertising. **URL:** http://onlinelibrary.wiley.com/journal/ 10.1002/(ISSN)1522-7278. **Circ:** (Not Reported)

Armidale

41558 ■ Australian Folklore
University of New England
School of English, Communication and Theatre
Armidale
Armidale, New South Wales 2351, Australia
Ph: 61 2 67733333
Fax: 61 2 67733100
Scholarly journal covering Australian folkloric studies. **Subtitle:** An Annual Journal of Folklore Studies. **Founded:** 1987. **Freq:** Annual. **Print Method:** Docutech. **Trim Size:** 7 x 9 1/8. **Key Personnel:** Prof. John Ryan,

Editor, jryan@une.edu.au. **ISSN:** 0819-0852. **Subscription Rates:** $A 25 individuals; $A 30 institutions; $A 75 individuals 3 years; $A 85 institutions 3 years. **Remarks:** Advertising accepted; rates available upon request. **URL:** http://www.une.edu.au/ect/research.php. **Circ:** (Not Reported)

41559 ■ Boer Briefs
Boer Goat Breeders Association of Australia
c/o Agricultural Business Research Institute
University of New England
Armidale, New South Wales 2351, Australia
Ph: 61 267 735177
Fax: 61 267 721943
Magazine containing information about the Boer Goat industry. **Freq:** Quarterly. **Remarks:** Accepts advertising. **URL:** http://www.australianboergoat.com.au. **Circ:** (Not Reported)

41560 ■ The Rangeland Journal
CSIRO Publishing
c/o Dr. Wal Whalley, Ed.
The University of New England
Armidale, New South Wales 2351, Australia
Ph: 61 2 67732477
Fax: 61 2 67733283
Publisher E-mail: publishing@csiro.au
Journal focusing on research in the rangeland sciences. **Founded:** Mar. 19, 1984. **Freq:** 4/yr. **Print Method:** Offset. **Trim Size:** 11 x 13 3/4. **Cols./Page:** 4. **Col. Width:** 14 picas. **Col. Depth:** 74 picas. **Key Personnel:** Dr. Wal Whalley, Editor, rwhalley@pobox.une.edu.au; Dr. Andrew Ash, Assoc. Ed.; Dr. Brian Cooke, Assoc. Ed.; Dr. Mark Stafford-Smith, Assoc. Ed.; Neil MacLeod, Assoc. Ed. **ISSN:** 1036-9872. **Subscription Rates:** $A 465 institutions print and online (Australia and New Zealand); EUR390 institutions print and online; 300 institutions print and online; $A 580 institutions online (Australia and New Zealand); EUR310 institutions online; 240 institutions online; US$465 other countries online. **URL:** http://www.publish.csiro.au/nid/202.htm.

41561 ■ SBS Television - 30
Locked Bag 028
Crows Nest, New South Wales 1585, Australia
Ph: 61 2 94302828
Fax: 61 2 94303047
Owner: Special Broadcasting Service, at above address. **Wattage:** 120,000 ERP. **URL:** http://www20.sbs.com.au/ transmissions/index.php?pid=2&id=10.

41562 ■ TUNE-FM - 106.9
University of New England
Armidale, New South Wales 2351, Australia
Ph: 61 2 67732399
Fax: 61 2 67729195
E-mail: radio@tunefm.net
Format: Ethnic. **Owner:** UNE Students' Association, at above address. **Founded:** Apr. 27, 1970. **Operating Hours:** Continuous. **URL:** http://tunefm.net.

41563 ■ 2AD-AM - 1134
123 Rusden St.
PO Box 270
Armidale, New South Wales 2350, Australia
Ph: 61 2 67721134
Fax: 61 2 67729942
E-mail: mail@2ad.com.au
Format: News; Talk; Information. **URL:** http://www.2ad. com.au/.

Artarmon

41564 ■ Heat Magazine
Giramondo Publishing Company
PO Box 752
Artarmon, New South Wales 1570, Australia
Ph: 61 297 726350
Fax: 61 294 197934
Publication E-mail: heat@giramondopublishing.com
Publisher E-mail: books@giramondopublishing.com
Magazine covering celebrity news, gossip and fashion. Featuring movie and music reviews, and TV listings. **Founded:** July 1996. **Freq:** 3/yr. **Subscription Rates:** $A 44 individuals Australia and New Zealand; $A 52 other countries; $A 66 institutions Australia and New Zealand; $A 74 institutions, other countries. **URL:** http:// www.giramondopublishing.com/heat/index.html.

Ashford

41565 ■ SBS Television - 54
Locked Bag 028
Crows Nest, New South Wales 1585, Australia
Ph: 61 2 94302828
Fax: 61 2 94303047
Owner: Special Broadcasting Service, at above address.
Wattage: 200 ERP. **URL:** http://www20.sbs.com.au/
transmissions/index.php?pid=2&id=11.

Ashmore

Heartland-FM - See Mudgee, New South Wales

Auburn

41566 ■ ABS-FM - 93.3
24/191 Parramatta Rd.
Auburn, New South Wales 2144, Australia
Ph: 61 2 87563666
Fax: 61 2 87563633
E-mail: info@absradio.com.au
Format: Ethnic. **Founded:** Mar. 3, 2000. **Operating Hours:** Continuous. **Ad Rates:** $15-30 for 30 seconds.
URL: http://www.absradio.com.au/.

Ayr

41567 ■ SBS Television - 57
Locked Bag 028
Crows Nest, New South Wales 1585, Australia
Ph: 61 2 94302828
Fax: 61 2 94303047
Owner: Special Broadcasting Service, at above address.
Wattage: 20,000 ERP. **URL:** http://www20.sbs.com.au/
transmissions/index.php?pid=2&id=195.

Babinda

41568 ■ SBS Television - 45
Locked Bag 028
Crows Nest, New South Wales 1585, Australia
Ph: 61 2 94302828
Fax: 61 2 94303047
Owner: Special Broadcasting Service, at above address.
Wattage: 2000 ERP. **URL:** http://www20.sbs.com.au/
transmissions/index.php?pid=2&id=197.

Bairnsdale

41569 ■ SBS Television - 54
Locked Bag 028
Crows Nest, New South Wales 1585, Australia
Ph: 61 2 94302828
Fax: 61 2 94303047
Owner: Special Broadcasting Service, at above address.
Wattage: 40,000 ERP. **URL:** http://www20.sbs.com.au/
transmissions/index.php?pid=2&id=367.

Ballarat

41570 ■ SBS Television - 30
Locked Bag 028
Crows Nest, New South Wales 1585, Australia
Ph: 61 2 94302828
Fax: 61 2 94303047
Owner: Special Broadcasting Service, at above address.
Wattage: 2,000,000 ERP. **URL:** http://www20.sbs.com.
au/transmissions/index.php?pid=2&id=368.

41571 ■ 3BA-FM - 102.3
56 Lydiard St. N.
Ballarat, Victoria 3350, Australia
Ph: 61 3 53311333
Fax: 61 3 53311723
Format: Adult Contemporary; Oldies; News; Sports; Talk. **Operating Hours:** Continuous. **Wattage:** 500. **Ad Rates:** Advertising accepted; rates available upon request. **URL:** http://www.3ba.com.au.

41572 ■ Voice-FM - 99.9
15 Dawson St. S, Ste. 3 Level 1
Ballarat, Victoria 3350, Australia
Ph: 61 3 53331201
Fax: 61 3 53329540
E-mail: voicefm@ncable.net.au
Format: Public Radio; Eclectic; Information. **Owner:** Ballarat Community Radio, at above address. **Founded:** Aug. 1979. **Operating Hours:** Continuous. **Key Person-**

nel: Helen Bath, Sec./Treas., gramip@sctelco.net.au; Tony Meagher, Operations Mgr.; Tully Smith, Chm., tully. smith@hotmail.com. **Ad Rates:** Noncommercial; underwriting available. **URL:** http://www.voicefm.com.au.

Balmain

41573 ■ Jacket
c/o Australian Literary Management
2-A Booth St.
Balmain, New South Wales 2041, Australia
Online publication covering poetry and prose, and reviews, interviews, author photos, and informative articles. **Freq:** Quarterly 3-4/yr. **Key Personnel:** Pam Brown, Assoc. Ed., p.brown62@gmail.com; John Tranter, Editor. **ISSN:** 1440-4737. **Subscription Rates:** Free. **URL:** http://jacketmagazine.com/00/home.shtml.

Bankstown

41574 ■ 2MFM Muslim Community Radio-FM - 92.1
PO Box 204
Bankstown, New South Wales 1885, Australia
Ph: 61 2 97072747
Fax: 61 2 97081050
E-mail: contactus@2mfm.org
Format: Educational; Religious. **URL:** http://www.2mfm.org.

Banyo

41575 ■ Australian Ejournal of Theology
Australian Catholic University
1100 Nudgee Rd.
Banyo, Queensland 4014, Australia
Ph: 61 7 36237100
Online journal dedicated to theology within Australian Catholic University. **Founded:** Sept. 1963. **Freq:** Quarterly. **Print Method:** Offset. **Trim Size:** 6 x 9. **Cols./Page:** 1. **Col. Width:** 51 nonpareils. **Col. Depth:** 102 agate lines. **Key Personnel:** Dr. Gerard Hall, Editor, gerard.hall@acu.edu.au. **ISSN:** 1448-6326. **URL:** http://dlibrary.acu.edu.au/research/theology/ejournal/; http://www.acu.edu.au/about_acu/faculties_schools_institutes/faculties/.

Barton

41576 ■ Australian Medicine
Australian Medical Association
42 Macquarie St.
Barton, Australian Capital Territory 2600, Australia
Ph: 61 262 705400
Fax: 61 262 705499
Publisher E-mail: ama@ama.com.au
Journal of the Federal Australian Medical Association covering medicine, politics, law and ethics. **Founded:** Jan. 1988. **Freq:** Semimonthly. **Print Method:** Offset. **Trim Size:** 20 x 29 cm. **Cols./Page:** 3. **Col. Width:** 95 centimeters. **Key Personnel:** Kerry Gallagher, Sec. Gen. **Subscription Rates:** US$250 individuals; US$330 individuals; US$430 individuals. **Remarks:** Accepts advertising. **URL:** http://www.ama.com.au/node/4344. **Ad Rates:** GLR: $A 65, BW: $A 3,953, 4C: $A 3,341. **Circ:** Combined ◆26,351

41577 ■ Australian Pipeliner
Australian Pipeline Industry Association
1st Fl., 7 National Circuit
Barton, Australian Capital Territory 2600, Australia
Ph: 61 262 730677
Fax: 61 262 730588
Publisher E-mail: apia@apia.asn.au
Journal containing news about the organization, pipeline projects, new technologies, and articles by industry experts. **Founded:** 1972. **Freq:** Quarterly. **Key Personnel:** Scott Pearce, Editor; Tim Thompson, Sales Mgr.; David Marsh, Sen. Account Mgr. **Subscription Rates:** $A 77 individuals; $A 100 other countries; $A 110 individuals New Zealand, Southeast Asia. **Remarks:** Accepts advertising. **URL:** http://www.pipeliner.com.au/. **Circ:** ◆3,020

Batemans Bay

41578 ■ SBS Television - 55
Locked Bag 028

Crows Nest, New South Wales 1585, Australia
Ph: 61 2 94302828
Fax: 61 2 94303047
Owner: Special Broadcasting Service, at above address.
Wattage: 10,000 ERP. **URL:** http://www20.sbs.com.au/
transmissions/index.php?pid=2&id=12.

41579 ■ 2ABC-FM - 101.9
ABC Ultimo Ctr.
700 Harris St.
Ultimo, New South Wales 2007, Australia
Ph: 61 2 83331500
Fax: 61 2 83335344
Format: Classical. **Owner:** Australian Broadcasting Corp., at above address. **URL:** http://abc.com.au/classic/freq/freqnsw.htm.

Bathurst

41580 ■ B-ROCK-FM - 99.3
109 George St.
Bathurst, New South Wales 2795, Australia
Ph: 61 2 63317777
Fax: 61 2 63321503
Format: Classic Rock; Album-Oriented Rock (AOR); News. **Owner:** Bathurst Broadcasters Pty. Ltd., at above address. **URL:** http://www.brockfm.com.au/.

41581 ■ SBS Television - 46
Locked Bag 028
Crows Nest, New South Wales 1585, Australia
Ph: 61 2 94302828
Fax: 61 2 94303047
Owner: Special Broadcasting Service, at above address.
Wattage: 2000 ERP. **URL:** http://www20.sbs.com.au/
transmissions/index.php?pid=2&id=13.

41582 ■ 2BS-AM - 1503
109 George St.
Bathurst, New South Wales 2795, Australia
Ph: 61 2 63317777
Fax: 61 2 63321503
Format: Oldies. **Owner:** Bathurst Broadcasters Pty. Ltd., at above address. **Founded:** 1969. **Operating Hours:** Continuous weekdays; 6a.m.-12a.m. Sat.; 9a.m.-10p.m. Sun. **URL:** http://www.2bs.com.au.

41583 ■ 2MCE-FM - 94.7
Charles Sturt University
Panorama Ave.
Bathurst, New South Wales 2795, Australia
Ph: 61 2 63384790
Fax: 61 2 63384402
E-mail: 2mce@csu.edu.au
Format: Ethnic. **Founded:** May 1976. **URL:** http://www.xenware.net/2mce/?id=1457.

Baulkham Hills

41584 ■ AUUGN on the Web
AUUG Inc.
PO Box 7071
Baulkham Hills, New South Wales 2153, Australia
Ph: 61 2 88249511
Fax: 61 2 88249522
Publication E-mail: auugn@auug.org.au
Publisher E-mail: auug@auug.org.au
Publication covering information on current and future UNIX and Open Systems technologies. **Freq:** Semiannual 2/yr (February & April). **Key Personnel:** Con Zymaris, Editor. **Subscription Rates:** US$60 individuals air mail. **URL:** http://classic.auug.org.au/publications/auugn/.

41585 ■ 2CCR-FM - 90.5
PO Box 977
Baulkham Hills, New South Wales 1755, Australia
Ph: 61 2 96863888
Fax: 61 2 96395618
Format: Eclectic; Public Radio. **Operating Hours:** Continuous. **Key Personnel:** Chris Cunliffe-Jones, Chm.; Tony Jenkins, Sec.; Glenys Marcus, Treas. **URL:** http://2ccrfm.com.

Bega

41586 ■ SBS Television - 43
Locked Bag 028
Crows Nest, New South Wales 1585, Australia
Ph: 61 2 94302828

Fax: 61 2 94303047
Owner: Special Broadcasting Service, at above address.
Wattage: 10,000 ERP. **URL:** http://www20.sbs.com.au/transmissions/index.php?pid=2&id=14.

41587 ■ 2EC-AM - 765
119 Gipps St.
PO Box 471
Bega, New South Wales 2550, Australia
Ph: 61 2 64921633
Fax: 61 2 64922614
Format: Adult Contemporary. **URL:** http://2ec.com.au/.

41588 ■ 2EC-AM - 1584
119 Gipps St.
PO Box 471
Bega, New South Wales 2550, Australia
Ph: 61 2 64921633
Fax: 61 2 64922614
Format: Adult Contemporary. **URL:** http://2ec.com.au/.

41589 ■ 2EC-FM - 104.3
119 Gipps St.
Bega, New South Wales 2550, Australia
Ph: 61 2 6492 1633
Fax: 61 2 6492 2614
E-mail: powerfm@acr.net.au
Format: Contemporary Hit Radio (CHR). **Owner:** East Coast Radio Pty. Ltd., at above address. **URL:** http://www.powerfm.com.au.

Bell

41590 ■ SBS Television - 53
Locked Bag 028
Crows Nest, New South Wales 1585, Australia
Ph: 61 2 94302828
Fax: 61 2 94303047
Owner: Special Broadcasting Service, at above address.
Wattage: 10 ERP. **URL:** http://www20.sbs.com.au/transmissions/index.php?pid=2&id=203.

Bellerive

41591 ■ 7CAE-FM - 96.1 MHz
17 Alma St.
Bellerive, Tasmania 7018, Australia
E-mail: info@hobartfm.org.au
Format: Eclectic. **Owner:** Hobart FM Inc., GPO Box 1324, Hobart, Tasmania 7000, Australia, 61 3 62441900, Fax: 61 3 62448510. **URL:** http://www.hobartfm.org.au/.

Bellingen

41592 ■ 2BBB-FM - 107.3
52 Wheatley St.
Bellingen, New South Wales 2454, Australia
Ph: 61 2 66550718
Fax: 61 2 66551381
E-mail: radio@2bbb.net.au
Format: Adult Contemporary; Contemporary Hit Radio (CHR); Educational. **Operating Hours:** 16 hours Daily. **Key Personnel:** Adrian Lipscomb, Chm.; Cherie Race, Sec./Treas. **URL:** http://www.2bbb.net.au/.

Belmont

41593 ■ Rhema-FM - 96.3
Shop 15/147 Marshalltown Rd.
PO Box 886
Belmont, Victoria 3216, Australia
Ph: 61 3 52416550
Fax: 61 3 52416552
E-mail: rhema@rhemafm.org.au
Format: Contemporary Christian; Religious. **Owner:** RhemaFM Pty Ltd, at above address. **Operating Hours:** Continuous. **URL:** http://www.rhemafm.org.au/.

Bendigo

41594 ■ KLFM-FM - 96.5
PO Box 2997
Bendigo, Victoria 3554, Australia
Ph: 61 3 54441377
Fax: 61 3 54441388
E-mail: klfm@klfm.com.au
Format: Ethnic. **Founded:** 1989. **Ad Rates:** Advertising accepted; rates available upon request. **URL:** http://www.klfm.com.au.

41595 ■ 3B3 Television - 29
Locked Bag 028
Crows Nest, New South Wales 1585, Australia
Ph: 61 2 94302828
Fax: 61 2 94303047
Owner: Special Broadcasting Service, at above address.
Wattage: 2,000,000 ERP. **URL:** http://www20.sbs.com.au/transmissions/index.php?pid=2&id=370.

41596 ■ 3EON-FM - 96.5
PO Box 2997
Bendigo, Victoria 3554, Australia
Ph: 61 3 54441377
Fax: 61 3 54441388
E-mail: klfm@klfm.com.au
Format: Adult Contemporary. **Founded:** 1989. **URL:** http://www.klfm.com.au/.

Bentley

41597 ■ International Journal of Electrical Power & Energy Systems
Elsevier Science Inc.
Digital Ecosystems and Business Intelligence Institute
Curtin University of Technology
Enterprise, Unit 4, De Laeter Way
Technology Park
Bentley, Western Australia 6102, Australia
Publisher E-mail: usinfo-ehelp@elsevier.com
Peer-reviewed journal covering the theoretical developments in electrical power and energy systems and their applications. **Freq:** 10/yr. **Key Personnel:** Y. Sekine, Co-Ed.; G. Andersson, Advisory Editorial Board; N.J. Balu, Advisory Editorial Board; R. Billinton, Advisory Editorial Board; T.S. Dillon, Co-Ed., phone 61 2 95141801, fax 61 3 98945633, tharam.dillon@cbs.curtin.edu.au; P. Bornard, Advisory Editorial Board; M. Calovic, Advisory Editorial Board; J. Carpentier, Advisory Editorial Board; A. Bose, Advisory Editorial Board. **ISSN:** 0142-0615. **Subscription Rates:** EUR2,148 institutions for European countries and Iran; 285,200¥ institutions; US$2,400 institutions, other countries except Europe, Japan and Iran. **URL:** http://www.elsevier.com/wps/find/journaldescription.cws_home/30432/descriptiondescription.

Berwick

41598 ■ Berwick Leader
Leader Community Newspapers
c/o Peter Strachan, Ed.
Unit 2/11, Gloucester Ave.
Berwick, 61 3 97719900 3806, Australia
Local community newspaper. **Freq:** Weekly (Wed.). **Key Personnel:** Peter Strachan, Editor, berwick@leadernewspapers.com.au; Kristine Munroe, Sales Mgr., munroek@leadernewspapers.com.au; Karen Laumets, Sales Mgr., laumetsk@leadernewspapers.com.au. **Remarks:** Accepts advertising. **URL:** http://www.newsspace.com.au/berwick_leader. **Circ:** Wed. ‡64,566

41599 ■ Cranbourne Leader
Leader Community Newspapers
2/11 Gloucester Ave.
Berwick, Victoria 3806, Australia
Ph: 61 3 97719900
Local community newspaper. **Freq:** Weekly (Wed.). **Key Personnel:** Peter Strachan, Editor, cranbourne@leadernewspapers.com.au; Edna McMinimee, Sales Mgr., mcminimeee@leadernewspapers.com.au. **Remarks:** Accepts advertising. **URL:** http://www.newsspace.com.au/cranbourne_leader. **Circ:** Wed. ‡28,363

41600 ■ Pakenham Cardinia Leader
Leader Community Newspapers
Unit 2/11, Gloucester Ave.
Berwick, Victoria 3806, Australia
Ph: 61 3 97719900
Local community newspaper. **Key Personnel:** Peter Strachan, Editor, berwick@leadernewspapers.com.au; Karen Laumets, Sales Mgr., laumetsk@leadernewspapers.com.au. **Remarks:** Accepts advertising. **URL:** http://www.pakenhamcardinialeader.com.au/. **Circ:** (Not Reported)

Blackburn

41601 ■ Target
Tear Australia
4 Solwood Ln.

PO Box 164
Blackburn, Victoria 3130, Australia
Ph: 61 3 98777000
Fax: 61 3 98777944
Publisher E-mail: info@tear.org.au
Christian publication. **Subtitle:** Development News and Insight. **Founded:** 1973. **Freq:** Quarterly. **Print Method:** Offset. **Trim Size:** A4. **Key Personnel:** Lyn Jackson, Contact. **ISSN:** 1030-0201. **Subscription Rates:** Free. **URL:** http://www.tear.org.au/resources/target/. **Circ:** 17,000

Blackwater

41602 ■ SBS Television - 43
Locked Bag 028
Crows Nest, New South Wales 1585, Australia
Ph: 61 2 94302828
Fax: 61 2 94303047
Owner: Special Broadcasting Service, at above address.
Wattage: 20,000 ERP. **URL:** http://www20.sbs.com.au/transmissions/index.php?pid=2&id=206.

Blue Mountains

41603 ■ Blue Mountains Gazette
Rural Press Regional Publishing Proprietary Ltd.
274 Macquarie Rd.
PO Box 21
Springwood
Blue Mountains, New South Wales 2777, Australia
Ph: 61 2 47511955
Publication E-mail: editorial.bmgazette@ruralpress.com
General newspaper. **Founded:** 1963. **Key Personnel:** Michael Ticehurst, Managing Editor, phone 61 2 47511955, fax 61 2 47515556; Damian Madigan, Editor, phone 61 2 47511955, fax 61 2 47515556. **Subscription Rates:** Free. **URL:** http://bluemountains.yourguide.com.au/home.asp.

Bombala

41604 ■ Snow-FM - 91.7
28 Sharp St.
Cooma, New South Wales 2630, Australia
Ph: 61 2 64561555
Fax: 61 2 64561006
E-mail: xl@capitalradio.net.au
Format: Alternative/New Music/Progressive; Contemporary Hit Radio (CHR). **URL:** http://www.snowfm.com.au/.

Bondi Beach

41605 ■ Bondi-FM - 88.0
PO Box 7588
Bondi Beach, New South Wales 2026, Australia
Ph: 61 2 93000788
E-mail: team@bondifm.com.au
Format: Urban Contemporary. **Operating Hours:** Continuous. **URL:** http://www.bondifm.com.au/.

Bondi Junction

41606 ■ Australian T3
Derwent Howard
Level 7, 35 Grafton St.
Bondi Junction, New South Wales 2022, Australia
Ph: 61 2 83056900
Fax: 61 2 83056999
Magazine covering tomorrow's technology for today's Australian, emphasising high-quality production, editorial and photography, making technology exciting and accessible through a unique mix of cutting-edge product reviews and general lifestyle technology features. **Freq:** Monthly. **Subscription Rates:** $A 150 individuals. **URL:** http://www.isubscribe.com.au/title_info.cfm?prodid=6196&catid=26.

41607 ■ Australian Windows XP
Derwent Howard
Level 7, 35 Grafton St.
Bondi Junction, New South Wales 2022, Australia
Ph: 61 2 83056900
Fax: 61 2 83056999
Magazine cutting through the jargon of the other PC magazines to focus on the things that real people do. **Subtitle:** Australia's Official Monthly Magazine. **Freq:** Monthly. **Key Personnel:** Darren Matthews, Advertising Mgr.; Nic Healey, Contact. **Subscription Rates:** $A 120

individuals. **URL:** http://www.derwenthoward.com.au/ magazine_wxp.htm.

41608 ■ Creative Knitting
Derwent Howard
Level 7, 35 Grafton St.
Bondi Junction, New South Wales 2022, Australia
Ph: 61 2 83056900
Fax: 61 2 83056999
Publication E-mail: knitting@derwenthoward.com.au
Magazine containing new patterns and designs for the beginners and advanced knitters alike. **Freq:** Quarterly. **Key Personnel:** Bobbie Matela, Editor. **Subscription Rates:** $A 49.95 individuals. **URL:** http://www. derwenthoward.com.au/subs/creativeknitting/.

41609 ■ PlayStation 2
Derwent Howard
Level 7, 35 Grafton St.
Bondi Junction, New South Wales 2022, Australia
Ph: 61 2 83056900
Fax: 61 2 83056999
Magazine offering Australia's only playable PS2 demo DVD in every issue with a chance to try before buying. **Subtitle:** Official Magazine-Australia. **Freq:** Monthly. **Key Personnel:** Narayan Pattison, Editor. **Subscription Rates:** $A 119.95 individuals. **URL:** http://www. isubscribe.com.au/title_info.cfm?prodid=6193.

41610 ■ Urban Hitz
Derwent Howard
Level 7, 35 Grafton St.
Bondi Junction, New South Wales 2022, Australia
Ph: 61 2 83056900
Fax: 61 2 83056999
Magazine of Urban music in Australia, with interviews, news and gossip, posters, competitions, and more. **Founded:** 2003. **Freq:** Bimonthly. **Key Personnel:** Nick Cutler, Commercial Dir.; Karl Penn, Contact. **URL:** http:// www.derwenthoward.com.au/magazine_urbanhitz.htm.

Bonnie Doon

41611 ■ SBS Television - 55
Locked Bag 028
Crows Nest, New South Wales 1585, Australia
Ph: 61 2 94302828
Fax: 61 2 94303047
Owner: Special Broadcasting Service, at above address. **Wattage:** 150 ERP. **URL:** http://www20.sbs.com.au/ transmissions/index.php?pid=2&id=372.

Boonah

41612 ■ SBS Television - 54
Locked Bag 028
Crows Nest, New South Wales 1585, Australia
Ph: 61 2 94302828
Fax: 61 2 94303047
Owner: Special Broadcasting Service, at above address. **Wattage:** 80 ERP. **URL:** http://www20.sbs.com.au/ transmissions/index.php?pid=2&id=208.

Booragoon

41613 ■ Capital Community Radio-FM - 90.5
PO Box 1388
Booragoon, Western Australia 6954, Australia
Ph: 61 9 3649888
Fax: 61 9 3641155
E-mail: info@capitalcommunityradio.com
Format: Information; Public Radio; Eclectic. **Operating Hours:** Continuous. **Key Personnel:** Peter Solomon, Chm., chairman@capitalcommunityradio.com; Trevor Mosel, Contact; Alan Giles, Sec. **Ad Rates:** Underwriting available. **URL:** http://www.capitalcommunityradio. com.

Bordertown

41614 ■ 5TCB-FM - 98.5
90 DeCourcey St.
PO Box 526
Bordertown, South Australia 5268, Australia
Ph: 61 8 87522777
Fax: 61 8 87522977
E-mail: office@5tcbfm.org.au
Format: Information; Agricultural; Talk. **Operating Hours:** Continuous. **Key Personnel:** Beryl Watson,

General Mgr. **URL:** http://www.5tcbfm.org.au:

41615 ■ 5TCB-FM - 104.5
90 DeCourcey St.
PO Box 526
Bordertown, South Australia 5268, Australia
Ph: 61 8 87522777
Fax: 61 8 87522977
E-mail: office@5tcbfm.org.au
Format: Information; Agricultural; Talk. **Operating Hours:** Continuous. **Key Personnel:** Beryl Watson, General Mgr. **URL:** http://www.5tcbfm.org.au.

41616 ■ 5TCB-FM - 98.5
90 DeCourcey St.
PO Box 526
Bordertown, South Australia 5268, Australia
Ph: 61 8 87522777
Fax: 61 8 87522977
E-mail: office@5tcbfm.org.au
Format: Information; Agricultural; Talk. **Operating Hours:** Continuous. **Key Personnel:** Beryl Watson, General Mgr. **URL:** http://www.5tcbfm.org.au.

41617 ■ Flow-FM - 100.3
PO Box 407
Kapunda, South Australia 5373, Australia
Ph: 61 8 85663151
Fax: 61 8 85662729
E-mail: mail@flowfm.com.au
Format: Adult Contemporary. **URL:** http://www.flowfm. com.au/.

Boronia

41618 ■ Free Press Leader
Leader Community Newspapers
c/o Cathy Withiel, Ed.
19 Chandler Rd.
Boronia, Victoria 3155, Australia
Ph: 61 3 97622511
Local community newspaper. **Freq:** Weekly (Wed.). **Key Personnel:** Cathy Withiel, Editor, freepress@ leadernewspapers.com.au; Travis Graham, Sales Mgr., grahamt@leadernewspapers.com.au. **Remarks:** Accepts advertising. **URL:** http://free-press-leader. whereilive.com.au/. **Circ:** Wed. ‡14,887

41619 ■ Knox Leader
Leader Community Newspapers
19 Chandler Rd.
Boronia, Victoria 3155, Australia
Ph: 61 3 97622511
Local community newspaper. **Freq:** Weekly (Tues.). **Key Personnel:** Cathy Withiel, Editor, knox@ leadernewspapers.com.au; Travis Graham, Sales Mgr., grahamt@leadernewspapers.com.au. **Remarks:** Accepts advertising. **URL:** http://knox-leader.whereilive. com.au/. **Circ:** Tues. ‡62,133

Bouddi

41620 ■ SBS Television - 64
Locked Bag 028
Crows Nest, New South Wales 1585, Australia
Ph: 61 2 94302828
Fax: 61 2 94303047
Owner: Special Broadcasting Service, at above address. **Wattage:** 5100 ERP. **URL:** http://www20.sbs.com.au/ transmissions/index.php?pid=2&id=15.

Bourke

41621 ■ MAX-FM - 91.1
48 Oxley St.
Bourke, New South Wales 2840, Australia
Ph: 61 268 722333
Fax: 61 268 722810
E-mail: outback@outbackradio.com.au
Format: Full Service; Information; News. **Operating Hours:** Continuous. **URL:** http://www.outbackradio.com. au.

Bowen

41622 ■ SBS Television - 48
Locked Bag 028
Crows Nest, New South Wales 1585, Australia
Ph: 61 2 94302828

Fax: 61 2 94303047
Owner: Special Broadcasting Service, at above address. **Wattage:** 10,000 ERP. **URL:** http://www20.sbs.com.au/ transmissions/index.php?pid=2&id=210.

Bowen Hills

41623 ■ Australasian Journal of Special Education
Australian Academic Press
32 Jeays St.
Bowen Hills, Queensland 4006, Australia
Ph: 61 7 32571176
Fax: 61 7 32525908
Publisher E-mail: aap@australianacademicpress. com.au
Peer-reviewed journal covering Australian special education. **Freq:** Semiannual. **Key Personnel:** Jennifer Stephenson, Editor; David Evans, Assoc. Ed. **ISSN:** 1030-0112. **Subscription Rates:** $A 210 institutions; $A 190 institutions New Zealand; $A 230 other countries. **URL:** http://www.australianacademicpress.com.au/ Publications/Journals/ajse/.

41624 ■ The Australian Journal of Rehabilitation Counselling
Australian Academic Press Pty. Ltd.
32 Jeays St.
Bowen Hills, Queensland 4006, Australia
Ph: 61 7 32571176
Fax: 61 7 32525908
Publisher E-mail: aap@australianacademicpress. com.au
Peer-reviewed journal covering broad range of topics in the rehabilitation and disability fields. **Freq:** 2/yr. **Key Personnel:** Elias Mpofu, Editor. **ISSN:** 1323-8922. **Subscription Rates:** $A 145 individuals; $A 160 other countries. **URL:** http://www.australianacademicpress. com.au/Publications/Journals/ajrc/ajrc.htm.

41625 ■ Brain Impairment
Australian Academic Press Pty. Ltd.
32 Jeays St.
Bowen Hills, Queensland 4006, Australia
Ph: 61 7 32571176
Fax: 61 7 32525908
Publisher E-mail: aap@australianacademicpress. com.au
Peer-reviewed journal covering neurology, neuropsychology, psychiatry, clinical psychology, neuropathology, occupational therapy, physiotherapy, speech pathology and anatomy. **Founded:** 1978. **Freq:** 3/yr. **Key Personnel:** Jacinta Douglas, Editor; Robyn Tate, Editor. **ISSN:** 1443-9646. **Subscription Rates:** $A 230 individuals; $A 253 other countries. **URL:** http://www. australianacademicpress.com.au/Publications/Journals/ Brain_impairment/brainimp.htm.

41626 ■ International Journal of Disability Management Research
Australian Academic Press Pty. Ltd.
32 Jeays St.
Bowen Hills, Queensland 4006, Australia
Ph: 61 7 32571176
Fax: 61 7 32525908
Publisher E-mail: aap@australianacademicpress. com.au
Peer-reviewed journal covering disability management including prevention of injury and disability, occupational rehabilitation and employment of people with injury and disability. **Founded:** 2006. **Freq:** 2/yr. **Key Personnel:** Nicholas Buys, Editor. **ISSN:** 1833-8550. **Subscription Rates:** $A 145 individuals; $A 160 other countries. **URL:** http://www.australianacademicpress.com.au/ Publications/Journals/ijdmr/ijdmr.

41627 ■ Journal of Pacific Rim Psychology
Australian Academic Press Pty. Ltd.
32 Jeays St.
Bowen Hills, Queensland 4006, Australia
Ph: 61 7 32571176
Fax: 61 7 32525908
Publisher E-mail: aap@australianacademicpress. com.au
Peer-reviewed journal covering the human development. **Founded:** 2007. **Freq:** 2/yr. **Key Personnel:** Stuart Carr, Editor; Leo Marai, Editor. **ISSN:** 1834-4909. **Subscription Rates:** $A 145 individuals; $A 160 other countries. **URL:** http://www.australianacademicpress.

com.au/Publications/Journals/IPRC/jprp.htm

41628 ■ Journal of Smoking Cessation
Australian Academic Press Pty. Ltd.
32 Jeays St.
Bowen Hills, Queensland 4006, Australia
Ph: 61 7 32571176
Fax: 61 7 32525908
Publisher E-mail: aap@australianacademicpress.
com.au
Peer-reviewed journal covering treatment of smoking
cessation. **Founded:** 2006. **Freq:** 2/yr. **Key Personnel:**
Renee Bittoun, Editor, bittounr@med.usyd.edu.au.
ISSN: 1834-2612. **Subscription Rates:** $A 145 individu-
als; $A 160 other countries. **URL:** http://www.
australianacademicpress.com.au/Publications/Journals/
smoke_cessation/cessation.htm.

Bowral

41629 ■ SBS Television - 30
Locked Bag 028
Crows Nest, New South Wales 1585, Australia
Ph: 61 2 94302828
Fax: 61 2 94303047
Owner: Special Broadcasting Service, at above address.
Wattage: 4000 ERP. **URL:** http://www20.sbs.com.au/
transmissions/index.php?pid=2&id=16.

41630 ■ 2ST-FM - 106.7
Cor. of Bong Bong & Baynette St.
Bowral, New South Wales 2576, Australia
Fax: 61 2 44233188
E-mail: 2st@2st.com.au
Format: Sports; Talk. **Operating Hours:** Continuous.
Ad Rates: Advertising accepted; rates available upon
request. **URL:** http://www.2st.com.au.

41631 ■ 2WKT-FM - 107.1
PO Box 214
Bowral, New South Wales 2576, Australia
Ph: 61 2 48721119
Fax: 61 2 48721118
E-mail: management.hfm@exemail.com.au
Format: Ethnic. **Owner:** Highland Media Co-operative
Ltd., at above address. **Key Personnel:** Diane Ham-
mond, Ch. **URL:** http://www.highlandfm.org.au.

Box Hill

41632 ■ Fire Australia
Fire Protection Association Australia
13 Ellingworth Parade
PO Box 1049
Box Hill, Victoria 3128, Australia
Ph: 61 3 98901544
Fax: 61 3 98901577
Publication E-mail: journal@fpaa.com.au
Publisher E-mail: fpaa@fpaa.com.au
Journal including overviews of recent technological
breakthroughs in fire protection and emergency
management. **Freq:** Quarterly. **Subscription Rates:**
US$88 individuals associate; US$198 individuals. **URL:**
http://www.fpaa.com.au/information/index.php?
information=journal.

41633 ■ 3WBC-FM - 94.1
PO Box 159
Box Hill, Victoria 3128, Australia
Ph: 61 3 92854846
Fax: 61 3 92854849
E-mail: info@3wbc.org.au
Format: Ethnic. **Operating Hours:** Continuous. **Ad
Rates:** Noncommercial. **URL:** http://3wbc.org.au/.

Braidwood

41634 ■ SBS Television - 54
Locked Bag 028
Crows Nest, New South Wales 1585, Australia
Ph: 61 2 94302828
Fax: 61 2 94303047
Owner: Special Broadcasting Service, at above address.
Wattage: 480 ERP. **URL:** http://www20.sbs.com.au/
transmissions/index.php?pid=2&id=17.

Briar Hill

41635 ■ Diamond Valley Leader
Leader Community Newspapers
18 Sherbourne Rd., 1st Fl.

Briar Hill, Victoria 0000, Australia
Ph: 61 3 94321844
Local community newspaper. **Freq:** Weekly (Wed.). **Key
Personnel:** Dave Crossthwaite, Editor; Neil Honey,
Sales Mgr., diamondvalley@leadernewspapers.com.au.
Remarks: Accepts advertising. **URL:** http://diamond-
valley-leader.whereilive.com.au/. **Circ:** Wed. ‡44,693

41636 ■ Whittlesea Leader
Leader Community Newspapers
18 Sherbourne Rd., 1st Fl.
Briar Hill, Victoria 3088, Australia
Ph: 61 3 94321844
Local community newspaper. **Freq:** Weekly (Tues.). **Key
Personnel:** Sandra Olivo, Editor, whittlesea@
leadernewspapers.com.au; Karen Mulhall, Sales Mgr.,
mullhallk@leadernewspapers.com.au. **Remarks:** Accepts advertising. **URL:** http://whittlesea-leader.
whereilive.com.au/. **Circ:** Tues. ‡49,163

Bright

41637 ■ SBS Television - 29
Locked Bag 028
Crows Nest, New South Wales 1585, Australia
Ph: 61 2 94302828
Fax: 61 2 94303047
Owner: Special Broadcasting Service, at above address.
Wattage: 200 ERP. **URL:** http://www20.sbs.com.au/
transmissions/index.php?pid=2&id=374.

Brighton

41638 ■ Club Marine
Club Marine Ltd.
40 The Esplanade
Brighton, Victoria 3186, Australia
Fax: 61 386 158178
Magazine covering lifestyle and boating in Australia.
Freq: Bimonthly. **Key Personnel:** Jennifer Farrelly,
Advertising/Mktg. Mgr., jennifer.farrelly@clubmarine.
com.au; Sandra Harvey, Office Mgr., sandra.harvey@
clubmarine.com.au. **Subscription Rates:** $A 36.30
individuals to Australia; $A 42.35 individuals to New
Zealand, airmail incl; $A 60.50 other countries airmail
incl; $A 33 individuals current policy holder. **Remarks:**
Accepts advertising. **URL:** http://www.clubmarine.com.
au/. **Circ:** △78,976

Brisbane

41639 ■ Access
The University of Queensland
History Department
The University of Queensland
Brisbane, Queensland 4072, Australia
Ph: 61 733 651111
Journal covering history. **Subtitle:** History. **Founded:**
1995. **Key Personnel:** Mark Dash, Editorial Board;
Michael Barr, Editorial Board; David Cammeron, Former
members; Rebecca Craig-Smith, Former members;
Yeong-Han Cheong, Former members; Laurence Brown,
Editor. **ISSN:** 1440-8449. **Subscription Rates:** 9
individuals. **URL:** http://www.uq.edu.au/access_history/.

**41640 ■ Australian Journal of Guidance and
Counselling**
Australian Academic Press Pty. Ltd.
c/o Dr. Marilyn Campbell, Ed.
School of Learning & Professional Studies
The University of Queensland
Kelvin Grove Campus
Brisbane, Queensland 4059, Australia
Publisher E-mail: aap@australianacademicpress.
com.au
Peer-reviewed journal covering area of guidance and
counselling. **Freq:** 2/yr. **Key Personnel:** Dr. Marilyn
Campbell, Editor, ma.campbell@qut.edu.au. **ISSN:**
1037-2911. **Subscription Rates:** $A 145 institutions; $A
160 institutions, other countries; $A 55 individuals; $A
60 other countries. **Remarks:** Accepts advertising. **URL:**
http://www.australianacademicpress.com.au/
Publications/Journals/Guidance&Counselling/
guidecounsel.htm. **Circ:** (Not Reported)

41641 ■ Australian Stainless Magazine
Australian Stainless Steel Development Association
215 Adelaide St., Level 15
Brisbane, Queensland 4000, Australia
Ph: 61 7 32200722

Fax: 61 7 32200733
Publisher E-mail: assda@assda.asn.au
Magazine containing articles about stainless steel in a
variety of applications, also technical articles. **Freq:**
Quarterly. **ISSN:** 1328-1232. **Subscription Rates:**
Included in membership. **Remarks:** Accepts advertising.
URL: http://www.assda.asn.au/index.php?option=com_
content&task=view&id=52&Itemid=78. **Circ:** ‡8,000

41642 ■ Australian Studies in Journalism
The University of Queensland
School of Journalism and Communication
The University of Queensland
Brisbane, Queensland 4072, Australia
Ph: 61 733 651111
Journal covering journalism study. **Founded:** 1992.
Freq: Annual. **Print Method:** Offset & PDF. **Trim Size:**
A5. **Key Personnel:** Rod Kirkpatrick, Contact,
r.kirkpatrick@mailbox.uq.edu.au. **ISSN:** 1038-6130. **Re-
marks:** Accepts advertising. **URL:** http://www.uq.edu.
au. **Ad Rates:** BW: $A 500. **Circ:** (Not Reported)

41643 ■ Australian Women's Book Review
Hecate Press
PO Box 6099
Brisbane, Queensland 4067, Australia
Academic journal focusing on books and literature of
interest to women. **Founded:** 2000. **Freq:** Semiannual.
Key Personnel: Carole Ferrier, Editor, c.ferrier@.uq.
edu.au; Maryanne Dever, Editorial Board; Margaret
Henderson, Editorial Board; Barbara Brook, Editorial
Board; Nicole Moore, Editorial Board. **ISSN:** 1033-9434.
URL: http://emsah.uq.edu.au/; http://www.emsah.uq.
edu.au/awsr/recent/.

**41644 ■ Automotive Electrical & Air Condition-
ing News**
A.A.E.N. Proprietary Ltd.
PO Box 271
Brisbane, Queensland 4030, Australia
Ph: 61 733 566155
Fax: 61 733 566130
Publisher E-mail: office@aaen.com.au
Trade journal covering the automotive electrical and air
conditioning industry. **Founded:** 1992. **Freq:** Monthly.
Trim Size: A4. **Subscription Rates:** $A 64.90 individu-
als in Australia; $A 79 other countries. **Remarks:** Ac-
cepts advertising. **URL:** http://www.aaen.com.au. **Circ:**
3,200

41645 ■ Beanscene
Insight Publishing Pty. Ltd.
478 Kingsford Smith Dr.
PO Box 880
Brisbane, Queensland 4007, Australia
Ph: 61 7 36301388
Fax: 61 7 36301344
Publisher E-mail: admin@insightpublishing.com.au
Journal featuring coffee culture. **Freq:** Monthly. **Re-
marks:** Accepts advertising. **URL:** http://www.
insightpublishing.com.au/. **Circ:** (Not Reported)

41646 ■ CALL-EJ Online
School of Languages & Linguistics
Griffith University
Kessels Rd.
Brisbane, Queensland 4111, Australia
Online publication covering computers and language
education. **Freq:** Semiannual. **Key Personnel:** Prof.
Kazunori Nozawa, Editor, nozawa@is.ritsumei.ac.jp; Dr.
Mike Levy, Editor, michael_levy@griffith.edu.au. **ISSN:**
1442-438X. **Subscription Rates:** Free. **Remarks:**
Advertising not accepted. **URL:** http://www.tell.is.
ritsumei.ac.jp/calljonline/. **Formed by the merger of:**
CALL EJ; ON-CALL. **Circ:** (Not Reported)

41647 ■ Current Drug Delivery
Bentham Science Publishers Ltd.
c/o Istvan Toth, Ed.-in-Ch.
School of Pharmacy
University of Queensland
Brisbane, Queensland 4072, Australia
Ph: 61 733 651386
Fax: 61 733 651688
Publisher E-mail: subscriptions@bentham.org
Journal publishing peer-reviewed articles, short com-
munications, and short and in-depth reviews in the
rapidly developing field of drug delivery. **Freq:** 5/yr. **Key
Personnel:** Istvan Toth, Editor-in-Chief, i.toth@uq.edu.
au; Jay S. Trivedi, Assoc. Ed., tjs@patrinpharma.com.

ISSN: 1567-2018. **Subscription Rates:** US$1,230 individuals corporate, print; US$1,230 individuals corporate, online; US$1,480 individuals corporate, print and online; US$690 individuals academic, print; US$690 individuals academic, online; US$760 individuals academic, print and online; US$220 individuals. **Remarks:** Accepts advertising. **URL:** http://www.bentham. org/cdd/. **Circ:** (Not Reported)

41648 ■ Hecate
Hecate Press
PO Box 6099
Brisbane, Queensland 4067, Australia
Peer-reviewed journal focusing on women's issues and gender studies. **Subtitle:** A Womens' Interdiciplinary Journal. **Founded:** 1975. **Freq:** Biennial. **Key Personnel:** Carole Ferrier, PhD, Editor, c.ferrier@uq.edu.au. **ISSN:** 0311-4198. **Subscription Rates:** $A 35 individuals; $A 154 institutions. **Remarks:** Accepts advertising. **URL:** http://www.emsah.uq.edu.au/index.html?page=20194&pid=5220. **Ad Rates:** BW: $A 300. **Circ:** 1,800

41649 ■ Insight into..Healing
Insight Publishing Pty. Ltd.
478 Kingsford Smith Dr.
PO Box 880
Brisbane, Queensland 4007, Australia
Ph: 61 7 36301388
Fax: 61 7 36301344
Publisher E-mail: admin@insightpublishing.com.au
Magazine featuring topics about alternative living and thinking such as Druid, Magic, Pagan, Astrology, Feng Shui, Numerology, Organic, Psychic and more. **Freq:** Annual. **Key Personnel:** Cameron Johnston, Publisher, cam@insightpublishing.com.au. **Subscription Rates:** $A 80 individuals; $A 150 two years; $A 145 individuals New Zealand and Asia Pacific; $A 180 other countries. **Remarks:** Accepts advertising. **URL:** http://www. insightpublishing.com.au/. **Circ:** (Not Reported)

41650 ■ International Journal of Knowledge-Based Development
Inderscience Enterprises Limited
c/o Tan Yigitcanlar, Ed.-in-Chief
Queensland University of Technology
School of Urban Development
2 George St.
Brisbane, Queensland 4001, Australia
Journal covering the study on the importance of knowledge management for the business world. **Freq:** 4/yr. **Key Personnel:** Tan Yigitcanlar, Editor-in-Chief, tan. yigitcanlar@qut.edu.au. **ISSN:** 2040-4468. **Subscription Rates:** EUR494 individuals print or online; EUR672 individuals print and online. **URL:** http://www. inderscience.com/browse/index.php?journalID=354.

41651 ■ The Knowledge Tree
Australian Flexible Learning Framework
GPO Box 1326
Brisbane, Queensland 4001, Australia
Ph: 61 7 33074700
Fax: 61 7 32594371
Publisher E-mail: enquiries@flexiblelearning.net.au
E-journal providing a platform for sharing new ideas in flexible learning and leadership. **Subtitle:** An e-Journal of Learning Innovation. **Key Personnel:** Linda Smart, Editorial Team; Vlad Mezin, Editorial Team; Rowan Peter, Editorial Team; Paul Mitchell, Ed./Writer. **ISSN:** 1448-2673. **URL:** http://kt.flexiblelearning.net.au/.

41652 ■ LAWASIA Journal
LAWASIA: The Law Association for Asia and the Pacific
TC Beirne School of Law
The University of Queensland
Brisbane, Queensland 4072, Australia
Publisher E-mail: lawasia@lawasia.asn.au
Publication covering law. **Freq:** Annual. **Key Personnel:** Prof. Suri Ratnapala, Editor, s.ratnapala@law.uq.edu. au; Lisa Toohey, Editor, l.toohey@law.uq.edu.au; Dr. Jonathan Crowe, Editor, j.crowe@law.uq.edu.au. **ISSN:** 1441-3698. **URL:** http://lawasia.asn.au/lawasia-journal. htm. **Ad Rates:** BW: $A 1,350. **Circ:** 2,000

41653 ■ Twin Research and Human Genetics
Australian Academic Press Pty. Ltd.
c/o Nick Martin, Ed.
Queensland Institute of Medical Research
Royal Brisbane Hospital
Brisbane, Queensland 4029, Australia

Publisher E-mail: aap@australianacademicpress. com.au
Peer-reviewed journal covering behavioral genetics, complex diseases, endocrinology, fetal pathology, genetics, obstetrics, pediatrics, and psychiatric genetics in the field of twin studies. **Freq:** 6/yr. **Key Personnel:** Nick G. Martin, Editor. **ISSN:** 1832-4274. **Subscription Rates:** $A 445 individuals; $A 557 other countries. **Remarks:** Advertising accepted; rates available upon request. **URL:** http://www.australianacademicpress.com.au/ Publications/Journals/Twin_R/TResearch.htm. **Circ:** (Not Reported)

41654 ■ Wildlife Australia
Wildlife Preservation Society of Queensland
95 William St.
Brisbane, Queensland 4000, Australia
Ph: 61 7 32210194
Fax: 61 7 32210701
Publisher E-mail: wpsq@wildlife.org.au
Publication covering zoology and wildlife conservation. **Founded:** 1962. **Freq:** Quarterly. **Trim Size:** A4. **Key Personnel:** Ken Hill, Advertising Mgr., advertising@ wildlife.org.au. **ISSN:** 0043-5481. **Subscription Rates:** $A 42 incl. GST; US$65 out of country; $A 84 two years; $A 130 out of country. **Remarks:** Accepts advertising. **URL:** http://www.wildlife.org.au/magazine.html. **Circ:** (Not Reported)

41655 ■ ABC Brisbane-AM - 612
GPO Box 9994
Brisbane, Queensland 4001, Australia
Ph: 61 7 33775222
Fax: 61 7 33775612
Format: Ethnic; News. **Owner:** Australian Broadcasting Corporation, at above address, 61 293 335091, Fax: 61 293 332531. **Operating Hours:** Continuous. **Key Personnel:** Steve Austin, Broadcaster & Presenter; Warren Boland, Sports Commentator; Gerry Collins, Sport Broadcaster; Anne Debert, Producer; Peter Gooch, Broadcaster & Presenter; Rebecca Levingston, Producer. **URL:** http://www.abc.net.au/brisbane.

41656 ■ Brisbane Feel Good-FM - 97.3
444 Logan Rd.
Stones Cor.
Brisbane, Queensland 4151, Australia
Ph: 61 7 34214973
Fax: 61 7 33944400
E-mail: promotions@973fm.com.au
Format: Music of Your Life; Contemporary Hit Radio (CHR). **Operating Hours:** Continuous. **Ad Rates:** Advertising accepted; rates available upon request. **URL:** http://www.973fm.com.au.

41657 ■ 4BBB-FM - 105.3
GPO Box 4442
Sydney, New South Wales 2001, Australia
Format: Top 40; Country. **Owner:** Austereo Pty. Ltd., at above address. **Operating Hours:** 5a.m.-9p.m.,10p.m.-5a.m. weekdays. **Key Personnel:** Peter M. Harvie, Chm. **Ad Rates:** Advertising accepted; rates available upon request. **URL:** http://www.b105.com.au/; http:// www.austereo.com.au/.

41658 ■ 4MMM-FM - 104.5
309 N Quay
Brisbane, Queensland 4000, Australia
Ph: 61 7 33610104
Format: Classic Rock. **Owner:** Austereo Pty. Ltd., GPO Box 422, Sydney, New South Wales 2001, Australia. **URL:** http://www.triplem.com.au/brisbane; http://www. austereo.com.au/.

41659 ■ 4QR-AM - 612
15 Lissner St.
Toowong
Brisbane, Queensland 4066, Australia
Ph: 61 7 33775222
Fax: 61 7 33775612
Format: News; Talk. **Owner:** Australian Broadcasting Corporation, ABC Ultimo Ctr., 700 Harris St., Ultimo 2007, GPO Box 9994, Sydney, New South Wales 2001, Australia, 61 2 83331500, Fax: 61 2 83335344. **Founded:** Jan. 7, 1938. **Key Personnel:** Steve Austin, Contact; Terri Begley, Contact. **URL:** http://www.abc.net. au/brisbane.

Broadway

41660 ■ African Journal of Information & Communication Technology
University of Technology Sydney
PO Box 123
Broadway, New South Wales 2007, Australia
Ph: 61 2 95142000
Publisher E-mail: international@uts.edu.au
Journal on information and communication technology. **Founded:** 1971. **Freq:** Quarterly. **Print Method:** Offset. **Trim Size:** 11 x 17. **Cols./Page:** 5. **Col. Width:** 1 5/8 inches. **Col. Depth:** 76 picas. **Key Personnel:** Johnson Agbinya, Editor, johnson.agbinya@uts.edu.au; Donald Adjeroh, Editor; Amar Mukherjee, Editor, amar@cs.ucf. edu; Mieso Denko, Section Ed., denko@cis.uoguelph. ca; Aruna Seneviratne, Editor, aruna.seneviratne@nicta. com.au; Atsushi Ito, Editor; Robin M. Braun, Editor, robin.braun@uts.edu.au. **ISSN:** 1449-2679. **URL:** http:// epress.lib.uts.edu.au/ojs/index.php/ajict.

41661 ■ NOVA-FM - 96.9
Locked Bag 2009
Broadway, New South Wales 2007, Australia
Ph: 61 132410
Format: Contemporary Hit Radio (CHR); Ethnic. **Operating Hours:** Continuous. **Ad Rates:** Advertising accepted; rates available upon request. **URL:** http://www. nova969.com.au.

Broken Hill

41662 ■ SBS Television - 44
Locked Bag 028
Crows Nest, New South Wales 1585, Australia
Ph: 61 2 94302828
Fax: 61 2 94303047
Owner: Special Broadcasting Service, at above address. **Wattage:** 40,000 ERP. **URL:** http://www20.sbs.com.au/ transmissions/index.php?pid=2&id=18.

Broome

41663 ■ Goolarri-FM - 99.7
7 Blackman St.
Broome, Western Australia 6725, Australia
Ph: 61 8 9195 5333
Fax: 61 8 9195 5351
E-mail: reception@gme.com.au
Format: Ethnic. **Owner:** Goolarri Media Enterprises Pty. Ltd., at above address. **Founded:** Aug. 1991. **Operating Hours:** Continuous. **Key Personnel:** Robert Lee, Station Mgr., robert.lee@gme.com.au. **URL:** http://www. gme.com.au/radio/.

Bruthen

41664 ■ SBS Television - 50
Locked Bag 028
Crows Nest, New South Wales 1585, Australia
Ph: 61 2 94302828
Fax: 61 2 94303047
Owner: Special Broadcasting Service, at above address. **Wattage:** 200 ERP. **URL:** http://www20.sbs.com.au/ transmissions/index.php?pid=2&id=375.

Buderim

41665 ■ 4SDA-FM - 104.9
PO Box 1049
Buderim, Queensland 4556, Australia
Ph: 61 7 54501049
Fax: 61 7 54501048
E-mail: office@sunshinefm.com.au
Format: Easy Listening. **URL:** http://www.sunshinefm. com.au/.

Bunbury

41666 ■ SBS Television - 33
Locked Bag 028
Crows Nest, New South Wales 1585, Australia
Ph: 61 2 94302828
Fax: 61 2 94303047
Owner: Special Broadcasting Service, at above address. **Wattage:** 600,000 ERP. **URL:** http://www20.sbs.com.au/ transmissions/index.php?pid=2&id=519.

Circulation: ★ = ABC; △ = BPA; ♦ = CAC; • = CCAB; ❏ = VAC; ⊕ = PO Statement; ‡ = Publisher's Report; Boldface figures = sworn; Light figures = estimated.

Bundaberg

41667 ■ 4 Double B-FM - 96.3
Shop 6 Northside Plz.
90 Cavin St.
Bundaberg, Queensland 4670, Australia
Ph: 61 7 41534963
E-mail: northbridge963@yahoo.com.au
Format: Eclectic; Public Radio. **Owner:** Bundaberg
Community Broadcasting Association Inc., at above
address. **Operating Hours:** 16 hours Daily. **URL:** http://
www.geocities.com/northbridge963fm/.

Bundanoon

41668 ■ Antichthon
Australian Society for Classical Studies
3 Lorna Close
Bundanoon, New South Wales 2578, Australia
Publisher E-mail: brucemar@hinet.net.au
Internationally refereed journal of the Australian Society
for Classical Studies. **Freq:** Annual. **Key Personnel:** Dr.
Elizabeth Minchin, Editor, elizabeth.minchin@anu.edu.
au; Prof. Peter Davis, Editor, peter.davis@utas.edu.au.
ISSN: 0066-7741. **Subscription Rates:** $A 40 nonmem-
bers; $A 50 institutions; Included in membership. **URL:**
http://www.ascs.org.au/antichthon/index.html.

Bundoora

41669 ■ Australian Playwrights
Rodopi
c/o Peta Tait, Ed.
La Trobe University
Bundoora, Victoria 3086, Australia
Ph: 61 394 79171
Publisher E-mail: info@rodopi.nl
Journal covering published and unpublished Australian
drama, articles, reviews and performance reviews.
Founded: 1960. **Freq:** Monthly. **Print Method:** Offset.
Trim Size: 10 x 13 1/2. **Cols./Page:** 4. **Col. Width:** 2
5/16 inches. **Key Personnel:** Peta Tait, Editor, p.tait@
latrobe.edu.au; Ortrun Zuber-Skerritt, Founder. **ISSN:**
0921-2531. **URL:** http://www.rodopi.nl/senj.asp?SerieId=
AP.

41670 ■ Colloids and Surfaces A
Elsevier Science
c/o N. Furlong, Ed.
Research & Development, RMIT University
PO Box 71
Bundoora, Victoria 3083, Australia
Publisher E-mail: nlinfo-f@elsevier.com
Journal covering fundamental science, engineering
fundamentals, and applications of colloidal and interfacial phenomena and processes. **Subtitle:** Physico-
chemical and Engineering Aspects. **Founded:** 1980.
Freq: 60/yr. **Key Personnel:** D.C. Prieve, Editor,
dcprieve@cmu.edu; Li Junbai, Editor, phone 86 10
82614087, fax 86 10 82612629, jbli@iccas.ac.cn; D.
Langevin, Editorial Board; N. Furlong, Editor, neil.
furlong@rmit.edu.au; M. Adler, Editor, colsua@univ-mlv.
fr; G.D. Parfitt, Founding Ed. **ISSN:** 0927-7757. **Subscription Rates:** 1,035,600¥ institutions; EUR7,802
institutions for European countries & Iran; US$8,725
institutions for all countries except Europe, Japan &
Iran. **Remarks:** Accepts advertising. **URL:** http://www.
elsevier.com/wps/find/journaldescription.cws_home/
500844/description. **Circ:** (Not Reported)

**41671 ■ International Journal of Sustainable
Design**
Inderscience Enterprises Limited
c/o Prof. Aleksandar Subic, Ed.
RMIT University
School of Aerospace, Mechanical & Manufacturing
Engineering
PO Box 71
Bundoora, Victoria 3083, Australia
Journal focusing on the theoretical and practical aspects
of sustainable design. **Freq:** 4/yr. **Key Personnel:** Prof.
Aleksandar Subic, Editor, aleksandar.subic@rmit.edu.
au. **ISSN:** 1743-8284. **Subscription Rates:** EUR494
individuals print or online; EUR672 individuals print and
online. **URL:** http://www.inderscience.com/browse/index.
php?journalID=148.

Burleigh

41672 ■ Freerider MX Magazine
Morrison Media Services

Level 1, 25 Lemana Ln.
Burleigh, Queensland 4220, Australia
Ph: 61 7 55761388
Fax: 61 7 55761527
Magazine covering the broad spectrum of the motocross
world, from the elite professionals right through to the
average bush hacker. **Key Personnel:** Ben Foster, Edi-
tor, ben@freeridermx.com.au. **Subscription Rates:**
US$44.30 individuals in Australia; US$68.05 individuals
in NZ; US$83.90 two years in Australia; US$773.95
individuals in Asia Pacific; US$114.86 other countries.
Remarks: Accepts advertising. **URL:** http://www.
morrisonmedia.com.au/FRMXhome.php. **Circ:** (Not
Reported)

Burleigh Heads

41673 ■ 4CRB-FM - 89.3
PO Box 86
Burleigh Heads, Queensland 4220, Australia
Ph: 61 7 55208888
Fax: 61 7 55763802
E-mail: mail@4crb.com
Format: Eclectic; Information; News. **Operating Hours:**
Continuous. **Ad Rates:** Noncommercial; underwriting
available. **URL:** http://www.4crb.com/page3.htm.

Burnie

41674 ■ 7BU-AM - 558
31A Wilson St.
Burnie, Tasmania 7320, Australia
Ph: 61 3 64312555
Fax: 61 3 64313188
Format: Adult Contemporary. **Ad Rates:** Advertising ac-
cepted; rates available upon request. **URL:** http://
theradio.com.au/localworks.aspx?PageID=2211&
Station=HEART%20_7BU_Burnie.

Burwood (New South Wales)

**41675 ■ Australasian Emergency Nursing
Journal**
Elsevier Science Inc.
c/o R. Shaban, Ed.-in-Ch.
College of Emergency Nursing Australasia
Burwood, New South Wales 1805, Australia
Ph: 61 2 97459615
Fax: 61 2 97459619
Publisher E-mail: usinfo-ehelp@elsevier.com
Journal providing information relevant to emergency
nurses in Australia and New Zealand. **Freq:** 4/yr. **Print
Method:** Offset. **Trim Size:** 13 x 21 1/2. **Cols./Page:** 6.
Col. Width: 29 nonpareils. **Col. Depth:** 294 agate lines.
Key Personnel: M. Gerdtz, Deptuy Ed.; J. Considine,
Deputy Ed.; R. Shaban, Editor-in-Chief, editor@cena.
org.au; K. Holzhauser, Assoc. Ed.; J. Stewart, International Editorial Board; J. Ranse, Assoc. Ed. **ISSN:** 1574-
6267. **Subscription Rates:** US$277 institutions, other
countries except Europe, Japan and Iran; EUR278 institutions for European countries and Iran; 32,900¥ institutions; US$86 individuals all countries except Europe,
Japan and Iran; 10,400¥ individuals; EUR88 individuals
for European countries and Iran. **URL:** http://www.
elsevier.com/wps/find/journaldescription.cws_home/
705132/descriptiondescription.

Burwood (Victoria)

**41676 ■ The Journal of International Trade and
Economic Development**
Routledge
Taylor & Francis Group Ltd.
c/o Prof. Pasquale M. Sgro, Ed.
Deakin Business School, Deakin University
70 Elgar Rd.
Burwood, Victoria 3125, Australia
Publisher E-mail: webmaster.books@tandf.co.uk
Peer-reviewed journal for international and development
economists, economic historians, applied economists
and policy makers. **Subtitle:** An International and
Comparative Review. **Freq:** Quarterly. **Key Personnel:**
Prof. Pasquale M. Sgro, Editor, sgro@deakin.edu.au;
Prof. Bharat R. Hazari, Editor, bhazari@gmail.com; Ira
Gang, Editorial Board; Hamid Beladi, Editorial Board;
Chi-Chur Chao, Editorial Board; Giancarlo Gandolfo,
Editorial Board; Prof. David E.A. Giles, North American
Ed.; Eric W. Bond, Editorial Board; James H. Cassing,
Editorial Board; Joshua Aizenman, Editorial Board;
Susan E. Skeath, Editorial Board; Bin Xu, Editorial

Board. **ISSN:** 0963-8199. **Subscription Rates:** US$156
individuals print only; US$975 institutions online;
US$1,027 institutions print + online; 107 individuals;
588 institutions online; 619 institutions; EUR818 institutions print and online; EUR777 institutions online only;
EUR125 individuals. **Remarks:** Advertising accepted;
rates available upon request. **URL:** http://www.tandf.co.
uk/journals/routledge/09638199.html. **Circ:** (Not Reported)

Burwood East

41677 ■ Global Future
World Vision Australia
1 Vision Dr.
Burwood East, Victoria 3151, Australia
Ph: 61 392 872233
Fax: 61 392 872427
Magazine featuring debate on important development
issues. **Freq:** Quarterly. **URL:** http://www.
globalfutureonline.org/.

Burwood North

41678 ■ 2RDJ-FM - 88.1
PO Box 1088
Burwood North, New South Wales 2134, Australia
Ph: 61 2 97443284
Fax: 61 2 97441088
E-mail: info@radio2rdj.com
Format: Ethnic. **Owner:** RDJ-FM Community Radio Co-
op. Ltd., at above address. **Founded:** Nov. 5, 1983.
Operating Hours: Continuous. **URL:** http://www.
radio2rdj.com/.

Byron Bay

41679 ■ Bay-FM - 99.9
Fletcher St.
PO Box 440
Byron Bay, New South Wales 2481, Australia
Ph: 61 2 66807999
Fax: 61 2 66858399
E-mail: info@bayfm.org
Format: Ethnic; World Beat. **Owner:** BAY FM, at above
address. **Operating Hours:** Continuous. **Key Person-
nel:** Ross Elliot, President; Don Prentice, Vice President;
Des Bellamy, Treas. **URL:** http://www.bayfm.org.

41680 ■ LINC-TV - 68
PO Box 1012
Byron Bay, New South Wales 2481, Australia
Ph: 61 2 66859999
E-mail: shane@linctv.org.au
URL: http://www.linctv.org.au/.

Caboolture

41681 ■ Caboolture Shire Herald
Quest Community Newspapers
28 King St.
Caboolture, Queensland 4510, Australia
Local community newspaper. **Founded:** Aug. 1993.
Freq: Weekly (Tues.). **Key Personnel:** Nick Crockford,
Editor; Andre Grimaux, Editor, phone 61 7 54317200,
fax 61 7 54955838, editorial@caboolureherald.com.au.
Remarks: Accepts display and classified advertising.
URL: http://www.newsspace.com.au/caboolture_shire_
herald. **Circ:** ‡43,268

41682 ■ 4OUR-FM - 101.5
PO Box 418
Caboolture, Queensland 4510, Australia
E-mail: radio@1015fm.com.au
Format: Eclectic. **Founded:** June 17, 1990. **Operating
Hours:** Continuous. **Key Personnel:** Craig Hewlett,
President, craigh@1015fm.com.au. **URL:** http://www.
4our.com.au.

Cairnlea

41683 ■ Stereo-FM - 97.4
PO Box 5406
Cairnlea, Victoria 3023, Australia
Ph: 61 3 93180930
Fax: 61 3 93180866
Format: Ethnic. **Key Personnel:** Rod Boyd, General
Mgr., rod@stereo974.com; Bob Taylor, Program Mgr.,
bob@stereo974.com. **URL:** http://www.stereo974.com/.

41684 ■ STEREO-FM - 97.4
PO Box 5406
Cairnlea, Victoria 3023, Australia
Format: News; Sports; Talk; Easy Listening. **Owner:** Western Radio Broadcasters Inc., at above address. **Key Personnel:** Rod Boyd, General Mgr., rod@stereo974.com; Bob Taylor, Program Mgr., bob@stereo974.com. **URL:** http://www.stereo974.com/.

Cairns

41685 ■ International Journal for Parasitology
Elsevier Science Inc.
c/o A. Loukas, Ed.-in-Ch.
Queensland Tropical Health Alliance
James Cook University
McGregor Rd., Smithfield
Cairns, Queensland 4870, Australia
Fax: 61 3 52561396
Publisher E-mail: usinfo-ehelp@elsevier.com
Journal covers basic and applied parasitology. **Founded:** 1971. **Freq:** 14/yr. **Print Method:** Offset. **Trim Size:** 10 x 16. **Cols./Page:** 5. **Col. Width:** 1 13/16 inches. **Col. Depth:** 16 inches. **Key Personnel:** M. Meuleman, Ed. Asst.; J.P. Dalton, Specialist Ed.; B. Crabb, Specialist Ed.; I. Beveridge, Dep. Ed.; A.G. Maule, Specialist Ed.; D. Soldati, Dep. Ed. **ISSN:** 0020-7519. **Subscription Rates:** US$2,424 institutions, other countries except Europe, Japan and Iran; 288,100¥ institutions; EUR2,169 institutions for European countries and Iran. **URL:** http://www.elsevier.com/wps/find/journaldescription.cws_home/353/descriptiondescription.

41686 ■ 4CA-FM - 102.7
Level 2, Virginia House
68 Abbott St.
Cairns, Queensland 4870, Australia
Ph: 61 7 40428000
Fax: 61 7 40414699
Format: Adult Contemporary; Oldies; News. **Key Personnel:** Steve Hirst, Station Mgr., steve.hirst@primeradio.com.au; John Piva, Program Dir., john.piva@primeradio.com.au; Donny Gangemi, Promotions Mgr., donny.gangemi@primeradio.com.au. **URL:** http://www.4cafm.com.au/.

41687 ■ 4CIM-FM - 98.7
PO Box 876
Cairns, Queensland 4870, Australia
Ph: 61 7 40521155
Fax: 61 7 40521673
E-mail: admin@bbm.org.au
Format: Ethnic. **URL:** http://www.bbm.org.au/; http://www.cbonline.org.au/index.cfm?pageId=13,13,6,3267.

41688 ■ Sea-FM - 99.5
Level 2, Virginia House
68 Abbot St.
Cairns, Queensland 4870, Australia
Ph: 61 7 40500800
Fax: 61 7 40500860
Format: Adult Contemporary. **Owner:** Regional Mediaworks, Petrie House, Level 1, 80 Petrie Ter., Brisbane, Queensland 4221, Australia, 61 7 35108700, Fax: 61 7 35108799. **Key Personnel:** Campbell Stewart, Station Mgr., campbell.stewart@macsc.com.au. **URL:** http://theradio.com.au; http://www.regionalmediaworks.com.au/reglon%20information.asp?region=Cairns.

41689 ■ Zinc-FM - 102.7
Level 2, 68 Abbott St.
Cairns, Queensland 4870, Australia
Ph: 61 7 40428000
Fax: 61 7 40414699
Format: News; Classic Rock. **Owner:** Prime Radio, 17 Carnaby St., Maroochydore, Queensland 4558, Australia. **Key Personnel:** Kim O'Loughlin, Station Mgr., kim.oloughlin@primeradio.com.au; Tanya McPhee, General Sales Mgr., tanya.mcphee@primeradio.com.au; Dave Warner, Program Dir., dave.warner@primeradio.com.au. **URL:** http://www.radiozinc.com.au/cairns/.

Callaghan

41690 ■ Australian Journal of Educational & Developmental Psychology
The University of Newcastle
Callaghan Campus
University Dr.
Callaghan, New South Wales 2308, Australia

Ph: 61 2 49215000
Fax: 61 2 49214200
Publisher E-mail: enquirycentre@newcastle.edu.au
Journal covering research and reports from educational and developmental psychology. **Key Personnel:** Jennifer Archer, Editor, jennifer.archer@newcastle.edu.au; Joanne Brownlee, Assoc. Ed.; Melissa Monfries, Book Ed., melissa.monfries@newcastle.edu.au. **ISSN:** 1446-5442. **URL:** http://www.newcastle.edu.au/group/ajedp/.

41691 ■ Women and Birth
Elsevier Science Inc.
c/o Prof. Kathleen Fahy, Ed.-in-Ch.
Faculty of Health
The University of Newcastle
Newcastle
Callaghan, New South Wales, Australia
Publisher E-mail: usinfo-ehelp@elsevier.com
Journal covering all matters affecting women and birth. **Freq:** 4/yr. **Print Method:** Web offset. **Trim Size:** 8 1/2 x 11. **Cols./Page:** 3. **Col. Width:** 14 picas. **Col. Depth:** 10 inches. **Key Personnel:** Dr. Della Forster, Peer Review Panel; Dr. Lisa McKenna, Peer Review Panel; Dr. Fiona Bogossian, Peer Review Panel; Prof. Kathleen Fahy, PhD, Editor-in-Chief; Dr. Pauline Glover, Peer Review Panel; Dr. Linda Jones, Peer Review Panel; Dr. Mary Carolan, Sub-Ed.; Dr. Heather Hancock, Sub-Ed.; Dr. Jenny Gamble, Peer Review Panel. **ISSN:** 1871-5192. **Subscription Rates:** US$331 institutions, other countries except Europe, Japan and Iran; 36,800¥ institutions; EUR260 institutions for European countries and Iran; US$77 other countries except Europe, Japan and Iran; 7,800¥ individuals; EUR55 individuals for European countries and Iran. **URL:** http://www.elsevier.com/wps/find/journaldescription.cws_home/707424/descriptiondescription.

41692 ■ 2NUR-FM - 103.7
University Dr.
Callaghan, New South Wales 2308, Australia
Ph: 61 2 49215555
Fax: 61 2 49217158
E-mail: contact@2nurfm.com
Format: Eclectic. **Operating Hours:** Continuous. **Key Personnel:** Wayne Stamm, Contact, wayne@2nurfm.com. **URL:** http://www.newcastle.edu.au/services/2nur/.

Camberwell

41693 ■ Australian Journal of Career Development
Australian Council for Educational Research
19 Prospect Hill Rd.
PO Box 55
Camberwell, Victoria 3124, Australia
Ph: 61 392 775555
Fax: 61 392 775500
Australian journal covering career research. **Freq:** 3/yr. **Print Method:** Paperback, Pefect Bound. **Trim Size:** A4. **Key Personnel:** Dr. Peter McIlveen, Editor. **ISSN:** 1038-4162. **Subscription Rates:** US$94.95 individuals Australian subscribers; US$120 other countries overseas subscribers (air mail). **Remarks:** Accepts advertising. **URL:** http://www.acer.edu.au/ajcd. **Ad Rates:** BW: $A 770. **Circ:** 700

41694 ■ Australian Journal of Education
Australian Council for Educational Research
19 Prospect Hill Rd.
PO Box 55
Camberwell, Victoria 3124, Australia
Ph: 61 392 775555
Fax: 61 392 775500
Publication E-mail: aje@acer.edu.au
Scholarly journal covering contemporary educational issues and educational research. **Founded:** 1957. **Freq:** 3/yr. **Print Method:** Paperback, Perfect Bound. **Trim Size:** 176 x 250 mm. **Key Personnel:** Dr. Glenn Rowley, Editor. **ISSN:** 0004-9441. **Subscription Rates:** $A 109.95 individuals GST included; $A 174.95 institutions GST included; $A 146 individuals air mail; $A 208 institutions air mail. **Remarks:** Advertising not accepted. **URL:** http://www.acer.edu.au/press/aje. **Circ:** (Not Reported)

41695 ■ Australian Journal of Physiotherapy
Australian Physiotherapy Association
Level 1
1175 Toorak Rd.
Camberwell, Victoria 3124, Australia
Ph: 61 3 90920888

Fax: 61 3 90900899
Publisher E-mail: national.office@physiotherapy.asn.au
Journal covering physiotherapy in Australia. **Founded:** 1954. **Freq:** Quarterly. **Print Method:** Offset. **Trim Size:** 297 x 210 mm. **Key Personnel:** Dr. Paul Hodges, Editorial Board Member, p.hodges@uq.edu.au; Mark Elkins, Editorial Board Member, elkinsm@med.usyd.edu.au; Linda Denehy, PhD, Editorial Board Member, l.denehy@unimelb.edu.au; Sandra Brauer, PhD, Coord., s.brauer@uq.edu.au. **ISSN:** 0004-9514. **Remarks:** Accepts advertising. **URL:** http://physiotherapy.asn.au/index.php/quality-practice/ajp/about-ajp. **Ad Rates:** 4C: $A 1,565. **Circ:** Combined ★11,000

Campbelltown

41696 ■ Macarthur Chronicle
Cumberland Newspaper Group
Cor. Kellicar Rd. & Bolger St.
Campbelltown, New South Wales 2560, Australia
Local community newspaper. **Freq:** Weekly (Tues.). **Key Personnel:** Mandy Perrin, Editor, editor@macarthurchronicle.com.au; Belinda Dawes, Advertising Mgr., dawesb@cumberlandnewspapers.com.au. **Remarks:** Accepts display and classified advertising. **URL:** http://www.newsspace.com.au/macarthur_chronicle_. **Circ:** 76,166

Canberra (Australian Capital Territory)

41697 ■ ANU Reporter
Australian National University
Canberra, Australian Capital Territory 0200, Australia
Ph: 61 261 255111
Fax: 61 261 255931
Publication E-mail: student.information@anu.edu.au
Student newspaper. **Freq:** Quarterly. **ISSN:** 0727-386X. **Remarks:** Accepts advertising. **URL:** http://news.anu.edu.au/?cat=23. **Circ:** (Not Reported)

41698 ■ The ANZIAM Journal (The Australian & New Zealand Industrial & Applied Mathematics Journal)
The Australian Mathematical Society Inc.
Dept. of Mathematics
Australian National University
Canberra, Australian Capital Territory 0200, Australia
Ph: 61 261 258922
Fax: 61 261 258923
Publisher E-mail: office@austms.org.au
Peer-reviewed journal covering industrial and applied mathematics. **Founded:** 1975. **Freq:** Quarterly. **Key Personnel:** Andrew Bassom, Editor-in-Chief, andrew.bassom@uwa.edu.au; Graeme Hocking, Editor-in-Chief, g.hocking@murdoch.edu.au. **ISSN:** 1446-1811. **Subscription Rates:** $A 328.90 individuals online; $A 365.20 individuals print; $A 401.50 individuals print + online; $A 299 other countries online; $A 351 other countries print; $A 384 other countries print + online. **Remarks:** Advertising accepted; rates available upon request. **URL:** http://www.austms.org.au. **Formerly:** Journal of the Australian Mathematical Society - Series B - Applied Mathematics. **Circ:** Paid 450

41699 ■ Asian Studies Review
Asian Studies Association of Australia
Department of Anthropology
Research School of Pacific & Asian Studies
Australian National University
Canberra, Australian Capital Territory 0200, Australia
Publication covering Asian studies. **Freq:** Quarterly. **Key Personnel:** Peter Jackson, Editor; Kam Louie, Editorial Board; Anne Platt, Asst. Ed. **ISSN:** 1035-7823. **Subscription Rates:** US$354 individuals online only; US$393 individuals print and online. **URL:** http://asaa.asn.au/publications/asr.php; http://www.tandf.co.uk/journals/titles/10357823.asp.

41700 ■ Australian Aboriginal Studies
Aboriginal Studies Press
AIATSIS
GPO Box 553
Canberra, Australian Capital Territory 2601, Australia
Ph: 61 2 62461111
Fax: 61 2 62614285
Publisher E-mail: asp@aiatsis.gov.au
Publication covering high quality research on Australian

Circulation: ★ = ABC; △ = BPA; ◆ = CAC; • = CCAB; ❏ = VAC; ⊕ = PO Statement; ‡ = Publisher's Report; Boldface figures = sworn; Light figures = estimated.

Gale Directory of Publications & Broadcast Media/147th Ed.   4707

anthropology, archeology, and folklore. **Freq:** Semiannual. **Key Personnel:** Dr. Cressida Fforde, Editor; Rhonda Black, Director. **ISSN:** 0729-4352. **Subscription Rates:** $A 60 individuals; $A 40 students; $A 50 members of AIAtSIS; $A 130 institutions. **URL:** http://www.aiatsis.gov.au/research_program/publications/australian_aboriginal_studies.

41701 ■ Australian Journal of Construction Economics and Building
Australian Institute of Quantity Surveyors
GPO Box 1467
Canberra, Australian Capital Territory 2601, Australia
Ph: 61 2 62477433
Fax: 61 2 62489030
Publication E-mail: ajceb@aib.org.au
Publisher E-mail: contact@aiqs.com.au
Journal containing articles from academics in Australia and overseas on a range of issues including cost management for the building industry, human resource planning and management, quality control for construction projects, and risk and crisis management strategies. **Freq:** Semiannual. **ISSN:** 1445-2634. **Subscription Rates:** US$77 individuals; US$44 single issue. **URL:** http://www.aib.org.au/resources/AIB-ConstructionEconomics.htm.

41702 ■ Australian Law Management Journal
Law Council of Australia
GPO Box 1989
Canberra, Australian Capital Territory 2601, Australia
Ph: 61 2 62463788
Fax: 61 2 62480639
Publisher E-mail: mail@lawcouncil.asn.au
Australian publication covering legal practice management. **Founded:** Apr. 1988. **Freq:** Quarterly. **Trim Size:** A4. **Key Personnel:** Gerard O'Neill, Contact. **ISSN:** 0817-6515. **Remarks:** Advertising accepted; rates available upon request. **URL:** http://www.lawcouncil.asn.au. **Formerly:** Australian Legal Practice; Australian Legal Practice Management Journal. **Circ:** 700

41703 ■ Canberra Cyclist
Pedal Power ACT Inc.
GPO Box 581
Canberra, Australian Capital Territory 2601, Australia
Ph: 61 2 62487995
Fax: 61 2 62487774
Publisher E-mail: office@pedalpower.org.au
Journal of Pedal Power for members. **Freq:** Bimonthly. **Key Personnel:** Julia Widdup, Editor. **Subscription Rates:** Free to members. **Remarks:** Accepts advertising. **URL:** http://www.pedalpower.org.au. **Ad Rates:** BW: $A 150. **Circ:** 2,000

41704 ■ Communicable Diseases Intelligence
Australian Government Department of Health and Ageing
GPO Box 9848
Canberra, Australian Capital Territory 2601, Australia
Ph: 61 2 62891555
Publisher E-mail: enquiries@health.gov.au
Journal covering information about communicable diseases in Australia. **Freq:** Quarterly. **Key Personnel:** John Walker, Editor. **URL:** http://www.health.gov.au/internet/main/publishing.nsf/Content/cda-pubs-cdi-cdiintro.htm.

41705 ■ Environmental Modelling & Software
Elsevier Science Inc.
c/o A.J. Jakeman, Ed.-in-Ch.
The Fenner School of Environment & Society
The Australian National University
Bldg. 48A
Canberra, Australian Capital Territory 0200, Australia
Ph: 61 2 61254742
Fax: 61 2 61258395
Publisher E-mail: usinfo-ehelp@elsevier.com
Journal providing information on recent advances in environmental modeling and software. **Founded:** 1986. **Freq:** 12/yr. **Key Personnel:** A.J. Jakeman, Editor-in-Chief, tony.jakeman@anu.edu.au; A.E. Rizzoli, Editor, phone 41 91 6108664, fax 41 91 6108661, andrea@idsia.ch; A. Voinov, Editor, phone 802656-2985, alexey.voinov@uvm.edu; G. Guariso, Assoc. Ed.; L.M. Hilty, Editorial Board; M.J. McAleer, Editorial Board; R.J. Oglesby, Assoc. Ed.; D. Swayne, Assoc. Ed.; A.A. Jennings, Assoc. Ed.; P. Zannetti, Founding Ed. **ISSN:** 1364-8152. **Subscription Rates:** 180,400¥ institutions; US$1,360 institutions except Europe, Japan and Iran;

EUR1,516 institutions European countries & Iran. **URL:** http://www.elsevier.com/wps/find/journaldescription.cws_home/422921/descriptiondescription.

41706 ■ Flight Safety Australia
CASA
PO Box 2005
Canberra, Australian Capital Territory 2601, Australia
Ph: 61 262 131757
Fax: 61 262 171209
Publication E-mail: fsa.magazine@casa.gov.au
Professional magazine covering aviation safety in Australia. **Freq:** Bimonthly. **Key Personnel:** Margo Marchbank, Contact, phone 61 2 62171375, margo.marchbank@casa.gov.au. **ISSN:** 1325-5002. **Remarks:** Accepts advertising. **URL:** http://www.casa.gov.au/scripts/nc.dll?WCMS:STANDARD::pc=PC_91346. **Ad Rates:** 4C: $A 3,300. **Circ:** 85,000

41707 ■ IASA Journal
International Association of Sound and Audiovisual Archives
c/o Kevin Bradley, P
National Library of Australia
Canberra, Australian Capital Territory 2600, Australia
Ph: 61 2 62621636
Fax: 61 2 62621653
Publisher E-mail: kbradley@nla.gov.au
Journal covering archives. **Freq:** Semiannual. **ISSN:** 1021-562X. **Subscription Rates:** Free to members; EUR70 nonmembers. **Remarks:** Accepts advertising. **URL:** http://www.iasa-web.org. **Circ:** (Not Reported)

41708 ■ International Journal of Sports Physiology and Performance
Human Kinetics Publishers Inc.
c/o David Pyne, PhD, Ed.
Australian Institute of Sport
Dept. of Physiology
Canberra, Australian Capital Territory 2601, Australia
Ph: 61 262 141356
Fax: 61 262 141904
Publisher E-mail: info@hkusa.com
Journal covering sports physiology and related disciplines. Includes research on team sports, individual sports, performance aspects of environmental physiology, applied sports nutrition, strength and conditioning, biomedical science, and applications of sport technology. **Founded:** 1825. **Freq:** Quarterly. **Print Method:** Offset. **Cols./Page:** 6. **Col. Width:** 26 nonpareils. **Col. Depth:** 294 agate lines. **Key Personnel:** David Pyne, PhD, Editor, david.pyne@ausport.gov.au; Inigo Mujika, PhD, Assoc. Ed., inigo.mujika@usphospitales.com. **ISSN:** 1555-0265. **Subscription Rates:** US$65 individuals print; US$65 individuals electronic only; US$325 institutions electronic only; US$325 institutions print; US$49 students print; $A 49 students electronic only. **URL:** http://www.humankinetics.com/ijspp/journalabout.cfm.

41709 ■ Journal of the Australian Mathematical Society
The Australian Mathematical Society Inc.
Dept. of Mathematics
Australian National University
Canberra, Australian Capital Territory 0200, Australia
Ph: 61 261 258922
Fax: 61 261 258923
Publisher E-mail: office@austms.org.au
Journal covering pure mathematics and statistics. **Founded:** 1959. **Freq:** Bimonthly. **Key Personnel:** Michael Cowling, Editor, m.g.cowling@bham.ac.uk; L. M Batten, Assoc. Ed.; P. C. Fenton, Assoc. Ed. **ISSN:** 1446-7887. **Subscription Rates:** $A 458.70 individuals online; $A 509.30 individuals print; $A 559.90 individuals online + print; $A 417 other countries online; $A 487 other countries print; $A 533 other countries online + print. **Remarks:** Advertising accepted; rates available upon request. **URL:** http://www.austms.org.au/Publ/. **Formerly:** Journal of the Australian Mathematical Society, Series A (Pure Mathematics and Statistics). **Circ:** Paid 550

41710 ■ Motoring Directions
Australian Automobile Association
103 Northbourne Ave.
PO Box 1555
Canberra, Australian Capital Territory 2601, Australia
Ph: 61 2 62477311
Fax: 61 2 62575320
Publisher E-mail: aaa@aaa.asn.au
Publication covering automotive services. **Freq:**

Quarterly. **Key Personnel:** Mike Wilson, Editor. **ISSN:** 1323-4595. **Remarks:** Advertising not accepted. **URL:** http://www.aaa.asn.au/publications/directions.php. **Circ:** 1,800

41711 ■ Quaternary Geochronology
Elsevier Science Inc.
c/o R. Grun, Ed.-in-Ch.
The Australian National University
Research School of Earth Sciences
Earth Environment Group
Canberra, Australian Capital Territory 0200, Australia
Ph: 61 2 61253122
Fax: 61 2 61250315
Publisher E-mail: usinfo-ehelp@elsevier.com
Peer-reviewed journal focusing to the climates, landscapes, flora and fauna including the evolution and ecological impact of humans. **Founded:** 2006. **Freq:** 6/yr. **Key Personnel:** D. Kaufman, Editor, phone 928523-7192, fax 928523-9220, darrell.kaufman@nau.edu; H. Cheng, Editorial Board; A. Hogg, Editor, phone 64 7 8384278, alan.hogg@waikato.ac.nz; P. Renne, Editor, phone 510644-9200, fax 510644-9201, prenne@bgc.org; D. Richards, Editor, phone 44 117 9289828, fax 44 117 9287878, david.richards@bristol.ac.uk; R. Roberts, Editor, phone 61 2 42215319, fax 61 2 42214250, rgrob@uow.edu.au; Rainer Grun, Editor-in-Chief, rainer.grun@anu.edu.au; J. van der Plicht, Editor, phone 31 50 3634760, fax 31 50 3634738, j.van.der.plicht@phys.rug.nl. **ISSN:** 1871-1014. **Subscription Rates:** EUR465 institutions for European countries and Iran; 55,200¥ institutions; US$492 institutions, other countries except Europe, Japan and Iran; US$148 other countries except Europe, Japan and Iran; 17,000¥ individuals; EUR111 individuals for European countries and Iran. **URL:** http://www.elsevier.com/wps/find/journaldescription.cws_home/706731/descriptiondescription.

41712 ■ Royal Australian Navy News
R8-LG-042 Russell Offices
Dept. of Defence
Canberra, Australian Capital Territory 2600, Australia
Publication E-mail: navynews@defencenews.gov.au
Official newspaper of the Royal Australian Navy. **Founded:** 1958. **Freq:** Biweekly. **Print Method:** Offset. **Trim Size:** 380 x 262 mm. **Cols./Page:** 7. **Col. Width:** 36 millimeters. **Col. Depth:** 380 millimeters. **Key Personnel:** Geoff Howard, Advertising Mgr., phone 61 262 667605, geoff.howard@defencenews.gov.au; Rachel Irving, Asst. Ed.; David Kirkpatrick, Editor; Graham Davis, Asst. Ed.; Rod Horan, Director, phone 61 262 654650, rod.horan@cbr.defence.gov.au. **Subscription Rates:** US$39 individuals 23 issues, incl GST. **Remarks:** Accepts advertising. **URL:** http://www.navy.gov.au; http://www.defence.gov.au/news/navynews/editions/4803/default.htm. **Circ:** Non-paid 22,000

41713 ■ Systematic and Applied Acarology
Systematic and Applied Acarology Society
c/o Dr. Ting-Kui Qin, Treas.
Plant Biosecurity
Biosecurity Australia
Canberra, Australian Capital Territory 2601, Australia
Ph: 61 2 62723719
Fax: 61 2 6272330
Publisher E-mail: tingkui.qin@aqis.gov.au
Peer-reviewed journal including original research on mites and ticks. **Key Personnel:** Owen Seeman, Editor, owen.seeman@qm.qld.gov.au; Dr. Zhi-Qiang Zhang, Editor-in-Chief, fax 64 984 97093, zhangz@landcare.cri.nz; V. Behan-Pelletier, Editorial Board, behanpv@agr.gc.ca; Anne S. Baker, Editor, a.baker@nhm.ac.uk; Qing-hai Fan, PhD, Production Ed.; H. Dong, Editorial Board, hqdong@fudan.edu.cn; Richard G. Robbins, Editor, richard.robbins@osd.mil; Xiaoyue Hong, Managing Editor. **ISSN:** 1326-1971. **Subscription Rates:** US$45 individuals; US$88 institutions. **URL:** http://www.nhm.ac.uk/hosted_sites/acarology/saas/saa/contact.html.

41714 ■ ABC Canberra - 666 KHz
GPO Box 9994
Canberra, Australian Capital Territory 2601, Australia
Ph: 61 2 62754555
Fax: 61 2 62754601
Format: News; Talk. **Owner:** Australian Broadcasting Corporation, ABC Ultimo Ctr., 700 Harris St., Ultimo 2007, Sydney, New South Wales 2001, Australia, 61 2 83331500, Fax: 61 2 83335334. **Founded:** Jan. 1953. **Formerly:** 2CN-AM. **Operating Hours:** Continuous. **Key Personnel:** Ross Solly, Contact; Alex Sloan, Contact.

URL: http://www.abc.net.au/canberra/.

41715 ■ SBS Television - 28
Locked Bag 028
Crows Nest, New South Wales 1585, Australia
Ph: 61 2 94302828
Fax: 61 2 94303047
Owner: Special Broadcasting Service, at above address.
Wattage: 600,000 ERP. **URL:** http://www20.sbs.com.au/
transmissions/index.php?pid=2&id=1.

41716 ■ SBS Television - Weston Creek/Woden - 58
Locked Bag 028
Crows Nest, New South Wales 1585, Australia
Ph: 61 2 94302828
Fax: 61 2 94303047
Owner: Special Broadcasting Service, at above address.
Wattage: 60 ERP. **URL:** http://www20.sbs.com.au/
transmissions/index.php?pid=1&sid=1.

41717 ■ 2 Double X-FM - 98.3
PO Box 812
Canberra, Australian Capital Territory 2601, Australia
Ph: 61 2 62300100
Fax: 61 2 62485560
E-mail: info@2xxfm.org.au
Format: Public Radio; Eclectic. **Founded:** 1976. **Operating Hours:** 18 hours Daily. **Key Personnel:** Peter Finch, Station Mgr., manager@2XXfm.org.au. **Ad Rates:** Noncommercial; underwriting available. **URL:** http://www.2xxfm.org.au.

Canberra (South Australia)

41718 ■ Triple J-FM - 101.5
GPO Box 9994
Canberra, South Australia 2001, Australia
Ph: 61 130 0055536
Format: Ethnic; Heavy Metal; Alternative/New Music/Progressive. **Founded:** Jan. 19, 1975. **Operating Hours:** Continuous. **Ad Rates:** Noncommercial. **URL:** http://www.abc.net.au/triplej/.

Cannon Hill

41719 ■ 4BC-AM - 1116
77 Southgate Ave.
Cannon Hill, Queensland 4170, Australia
Ph: 61 7 39088200
Format: Talk. **Operating Hours:** Continuous. **Key Personnel:** James Johnston, Sales Dir., phone 61 7 39088232, sales@4bc.com.au. **Ad Rates:** Advertising accepted; rates available upon request. **URL:** http://www.mytalk.com.au.

41720 ■ 4BC-AM - 882
77 Southgate Ave.
Cannon Hill, Queensland 4170, Australia
Ph: 61 7 39088200
E-mail: sales@4bc.com.au
Format: Talk. **Owner:** Fairfax Media, Ltd., GPO 506, Sydney, New South Wales 2001, Australia, 61 2 92822833. **Founded:** Aug. 16, 1930. **Operating Hours:** Continuous. **Key Personnel:** James Johnston, Sales Dir., phone 61 7 39088232. **Ad Rates:** Advertising accepted; rates available upon request. **URL:** http://www.4bc.com.au/; http://www.fxj.com.au/.

Caralue Bluff

41721 ■ SBS Television - Caralue Bluff - 62
Locked Bag 028
Crows Nest, New South Wales 1585, Australia
Ph: 61 2 94302828
Fax: 61 2 94303047
Owner: Special Broadcasting Service, at above address.
Wattage: 20,000 ERP. **URL:** http://www20.sbs.com.au/
transmissions/index.php?pid=2&id=445.

Cardiff

41722 ■ Lake Macquarie News
Cumberland Newspaper Group
Cardiff Arcade, Ste. 103
286 Main Rd.
Cardiff, New South Wales 2285, Australia
Local community newspaper. **Freq:** Weekly (Thurs.). **Key Personnel:** Terry Collins, Editor; Scott Dibben, Advertising Mgr. **Remarks:** Accepts display and classi-

fied advertising. **URL:** http://www.lakemacquarienews.com.au/. **Circ:** 52,461

Carisbrook

41723 ■ Turfcraft
Rural Press Ltd.
PO Box 59
Carisbrook, Victoria, Australia
Ph: 61 3 54641382
Magazine featuring the turf industry. **Freq:** Bimonthly. **Key Personnel:** Alastair Dowie, Editor, alastair.dowie@ruralpress.com; Grant Cochrane, General Mgr., alastair.dowie@ruralpress.com; Ed Kryskow, Sales Mgr., ed.kryskow@ruralpress.com. **Subscription Rates:** $A 57.50 individuals; $A 108.24 two years. **Remarks:** Accepts advertising. **URL:** http://www.ruralpress.com/publications/detail.asp?publication_id=144. **Circ:** (Not Reported)

Carlton

41724 ■ The AUSIMM Bulletin
Australasian Institute of Mining and Metallurgy
PO Box 660
Carlton, Victoria 3053, Australia
Ph: 61 396 623166
Fax: 61 396 623662
Membership journal of the Australasian Institute of Mining and Metallurgy. **Freq:** Bimonthly. **ISSN:** 1034-6775. **Subscription Rates:** $A 176 individuals; $A 220 other countries. **Remarks:** Accepts advertising. **URL:** http://www.ausimm.com.au/content/default.aspx?ID=99. **Circ:** Combined 8,667

41725 ■ Boobook
Australasian Raptor Association
c/o Birds Australia
Green Bldg., Ste. 2-05
60 Leicester St.
Carlton, Victoria 3053, Australia
Ph: 61 3 93470757
Fax: 61 3 93479323
Publisher E-mail: secretary@ausraptor.org.au
Magazine containing important information about raptors. **Freq:** Semiannual. **Subscription Rates:** included in membership dues. **URL:** http://ausraptor.org.au/.

41726 ■ Habitat Australia
Australian Conservation Foundation
60 Leicester St., Fl. 1
Carlton, Victoria 3053, Australia
Fax: 61 3 93451166
Publication E-mail: habitat@acfonline.org.au
Publisher E-mail: acf@acfonline.org.au
Australian publication covering conservation. **Founded:** June 1973. **Freq:** Semiannual. **Key Personnel:** Don Henry, Exec. Dir., d.henry@acfonline.org.au. **ISSN:** 0310-2939. **Subscription Rates:** Free to members. **URL:** http://www.acfonline.org.au/articles/news.asp?news_id=955&c=6817. **Ad Rates:** BW: $A 1,050, 4C: $A 1,430. **Circ:** 17,000

41727 ■ Meanjin
Meanjin Company Ltd.
107 Grattan St.
Carlton, Victoria 3053, Australia
Ph: 61 39 420317
Fax: 61 39 420399
Publication covering literature and writing. **Freq:** Quarterly. **Key Personnel:** Sophie Cunningham, Editor, cusa@unimelb.edu.au; Mary Kennedy, Office Mgr., kennm@unimelb.edu.au. **ISSN:** 0815-953X. **Subscription Rates:** $A 80 individuals; $A 60 individuals concession; $A 80 institutions schools; $A 125 institutions; $A 105 individuals overseas; $A 150 institutions, other countries; $A 145 individuals two years; $A 180 individuals overseas; two years; $A 120 individuals concession. **Remarks:** Accepts advertising. **Online:** Gale. **URL:** http://www.meanjin.com.au/. **Ad Rates:** BW: $A 400. **Circ:** 2,000

41728 ■ Melbourne Journal of Politics
University of Melbourne
Department of Political Science
234 Queensberry St.
Carlton, Victoria 3053, Australia
Ph: 61 3 83449501

Publication E-mail: editors@mjp.unimelb.edu.au
Publisher E-mail: ssps-enquiries@unimelb.edu.au
Political science publication. **Freq:** Annual. **Key Personnel:** Emily Fitzgerald, Book Review Ed. **ISSN:** 0085-3224. **Subscription Rates:** $A 20 individuals plus postage. **URL:** http://www.ssps.unimelb.edu.au/research/current/mjp.

Carlton South

41729 ■ SKA-TV - 31
Trades Hall, Ste. 75
Carlton South, Victoria 3053, Australia
Ph: 61 3 96636976
Fax: 61 3 96636976
E-mail: workers@skatv.org.au
Founded: 1988. **Operating Hours:** Continuous. **Ad Rates:** Underwriting available. **URL:** http://www.skatv.org.au.

Carnarvon

41730 ■ SBS Television - 12
Locked Bag 028
Crows Nest, New South Wales 1585, Australia
Ph: 61 2 94302828
Fax: 61 2 94303047
Owner: Special Broadcasting Service, at above address.
Wattage: 5000 ERP. **URL:** http://www20.sbs.com.au/
transmissions/index.php?pid=2&id=523.

Castle Hill

41731 ■ Hills Shire Times
Cumberland Newspaper Group
3-9 Terminus St., Unit 27
Castle Hill, New South Wales 2154, Australia
Local community newspaper. **Founded:** 1952. **Freq:** Weekly (Tues.). **Key Personnel:** Therese Murray, Editor, editor@hillsshiretimes.com.au; Amanda Vass, Advertising Mgr., advertising@hillsshiretimes.com.au. **Remarks:** Accepts display and classified advertising. **URL:** http://hills-shire-times.whereilive.com.au/. **Circ:** 64,872

Casuarina

41732 ■ Territory-FM - 104.1
Bldg. 6, Orange Precinct, Level 3
Charles Darwin University
Casuarina, Northern Territory 0909, Australia
Ph: 61 8 89466266
Fax: 61 8 89451788
E-mail: frontdesk@territoryfm.com
Format: Adult Contemporary. **Owner:** Charles Darwin University, at above address. **URL:** http://www.territoryfm.com/.

Territory-FM - See Alice Springs

Ceduna

41733 ■ Flow-FM - 106.1
PO Box 407
Kapunda, South Australia 5373, Australia
Ph: 61 8 85663151
Fax: 61 8 85662729
E-mail: mail@flowfm.com.au
Format: Adult Contemporary. **URL:** http://www.flowfm.com.au/.

Cessnock

41734 ■ 2CHR-FM - 96.5
School of Arts
2 Vincent St.
PO Box 421
Cessnock, New South Wales 2325, Australia
Ph: 61 2 49911286
Fax: 61 2 49911757
E-mail: secretary@2chr.org
Format: Ethnic; Information. **Founded:** 2000. **URL:** http://www.2chr.org/.

Charlestown

41735 ■ NX-FM - 106.9
252 Pacific Hwy.
Charlestown, New South Wales 2290, Australia

Circulation: ★ = ABC; △ = BPA; ♦ = CAC; • = CCAB; ❑ = VAC; ⊕ = PO Statement; ‡ = Publisher's Report; Boldface figures = sworn; Light figures = estimated.

Ph: 61 2 49423333
Fax: 61 2 49478713
Format: Contemporary Hit Radio (CHR). **Owner:** Austereo Pty. Ltd., GPO Box 4442, Sydney, New South Wales 2001, Australia. **Key Personnel:** Peter M. Harvie, Chm. **URL:** http://www.nxfm.com.au/; http://www.austereo.com.au/.

Chatswood

41736 ■ Australian Doctor
Reed Business Information Proprietary Ltd.
Tower 2, 475 Victoria Ave.
Locked Bag 2999
Chatswood, New South Wales 2067, Australia
Ph: 61 2 94222999
Fax: 61 2 94222922
Publisher E-mail: customerservice@reedbusiness.com.au
Medical newspaper for general practitioners in Australia. **Founded:** 1985. **Freq:** Weekly. **Trim Size:** 400 mm. x 280 mm. **Cols./Page:** 5. **Col. Width:** 5 centimeters. **Col. Depth:** 37 centimeters. **Key Personnel:** Dr. Kerri Parnell, Editor-in-Chief, kerri.parnell@reedbusiness.com.au; Megan Howe, Dep. Ed., megan.howe@reedbusiness.com.au. **Subscription Rates:** US$650 individuals two years - Australia; US$660 individuals two years - New Zealand; US$670 individuals two years; US$390.01 individuals Australia; US$400 individuals New Zealand; US$410 individuals. **Remarks:** Accepts advertising. **URL:** http://www.reedbusiness.com.au/print.aspad. **Former name:** Australian Doctor Weekly. **Ad Rates:** BW: $A 4,935, 4C: $A 5,350. **Circ:** Combined 22,005

41737 ■ Australian Journal of Pharmacy
Australian Pharmaceutical Publishing Company
8 Thomas St., Level 5
Chatswood, New South Wales 2067, Australia
Ph: 61 2 81179500
Fax: 61 2 81179511
Business and professional journal for pharmacists. **Freq:** Monthly. **Trim Size:** 206 x 270 mm. **Key Personnel:** Matthew Eton, Editor, phone 61 2 81179542, matthew.eton@appco.com.au; David Weston, Publisher Dir., phone 61 2 81179590, david.weston@appco.com.au; Janet Doyle, Assoc. Ed., phone 61 2 81179544, janet.doyle@appco.com.au. **Subscription Rates:** US$96.50 individuals; US$155 two years; US$49.50 students; US$150 other countries; US$255 two years overseas; US$86 members. **Remarks:** Accepts advertising. **URL:** http://www.appco.com.au/AJP/. **Ad Rates:** 4C: $A 4,810, SAU: $A 2,180. **Circ:** ‡15,035

41738 ■ Australian and New Zealand Journal of Audiology
Australian Academic Press Pty. Ltd.
National Acoustic Laboratories
126 Greville St.
Chatswood, New South Wales 2067, Australia
Publisher E-mail: aap@australianacademicpress.com.au
Peer-reviewed journal covering field of audiology. **Freq:** 2/yr. **Key Personnel:** Teresa Ching, Editor, teresa.ching@nal.gov.au. **ISSN:** 0157-1532. **Subscription Rates:** $A 145 institutions; $A 160 institutions, other countries; $A 65 individuals; $A 86 other countries. **Remarks:** Accepts advertising. **URL:** http://www.australianacademicpress.com.au/Publications/Journals/Audiology/audiology.htm. **Circ:** (Not Reported)

41739 ■ Construction Contractor
Reed Business Information Proprietary Ltd.
Tower 2, 475 Victoria Ave.
Locked Bag 2999
Chatswood, New South Wales 2067, Australia
Ph: 61 2 94222999
Fax: 61 2 94222922
Publisher E-mail: customerservice@reedbusiness.com.au
Trade magazine covering construction. **Freq:** Monthly. **Trim Size:** 345 x 248 mm. **Key Personnel:** Kevin Gomez, Editor, phone 61 2 94222936, editor@constructioncontractor.com.au. **ISSN:** 1030-7036. **Subscription Rates:** $A 175 individuals. **Remarks:** Accepts advertising. **URL:** http://www.infolink.com.au/html/publication.htmlcc; http://www.isubscribe.com.au/title_info.cfm?prodid=6965. **Circ:** Combined 120,000

41740 ■ Manufacturers Monthly
Reed Business Information Proprietary Ltd.
Tower 2, 475 Victoria Ave.
Locked Bag 2999
Chatswood, New South Wales 2067, Australia
Ph: 61 2 94222999
Fax: 61 2 94222922
Publisher E-mail: customerservice@reedbusiness.com.au
Trade magazine covering manufacturing and technology. **Founded:** 1961. **Freq:** Monthly. **Key Personnel:** Sarah Faslon, Editor, phone 61 9422 2480, fax 61 9422 2722, sarah.faslon@aatsreedbusiness.com.au; Alan Johnson, Editor, alan.johnson@reedbusiness.com.au. **ISSN:** 0025-2530. **Subscription Rates:** $A 99 individuals; $A 109 individuals for New Zealand; $A 119 individuals; $A 189 two years; NZ$199 two years; $A 209 two years. **Remarks:** Accepts advertising. **URL:** http://www.manmonthly.com.au/; http://www.bandt.com.au/view_media.asp?mediaid=55977. **Circ:** ♦15,269

41741 ■ Natural Health & Beauty
Australian Pharmaceutical Publishing Company
8 Thomas St., Level 5
Chatswood, New South Wales 2067, Australia
Ph: 61 2 81179500
Fax: 61 2 81179511
Magazine featuring retail pharmacies, health food stores, beauty therapists, and natural therapists. **Freq:** 4/yr. **Trim Size:** 207 x 273 mm. **Key Personnel:** Janet Doyle, Editor, phone 61 2 81179554, janet.doyle@appco.com.au; David Weston, Editor, phone 61 2 81179590, david.weston@appco.com.au. **Subscription Rates:** $A 68 individuals; $A 110 two years; $A 120 other countries; $A 199 two years. **Remarks:** Accepts advertising. **URL:** http://www.nhandb.com.au; http://www.appco.com.au/index.html. **Ad Rates:** 4C: $A 3,900. **Circ:** ★11,545

41742 ■ North Shore Times
Cumberland Newspaper Group
2 Help St., Level 2
Chatswood, New South Wales 2067, Australia
Local community newspaper. **Freq:** Semiweekly (Wed. and Fri.). **Key Personnel:** Catherine Zuill, Editor, phone 61 2 94141400, editor@northshoretimes.com.au; Richard Oakley, Advertising Mgr., advertising@northshoretimes.com.au. **Remarks:** Accepts display and classified advertising. **URL:** http://www.newsspace.com.au/north_shore_times_. **Circ:** Wed. 56,944, Fri. 73,395

41743 ■ Post Script
Australian Pharmaceutical Publishing Company
8 Thomas St., Level 5
Chatswood, New South Wales 2067, Australia
Ph: 61 2 81179500
Fax: 61 2 81179511
Magazine for pharmacy assistants featuring beauty and health topics. **Freq:** 11/yr. **Trim Size:** 206 x 270 mm. **Key Personnel:** David Weston, Publisher Dir., phone 61 2 81179590, david.weston@appco.com.au; Janet Doyle, Editor, phone 61 2 81179554, janet.doyle@appco.com.au. **Subscription Rates:** $A 68 individuals; $A 120 other countries; $A 110 two years; $A 199 two years. **Remarks:** Accepts advertising. **URL:** http://www.appco.com.au/PS/. **Ad Rates:** 4C: $A 4,810. **Circ:** ★11,545

41744 ■ 2NSB-FM - 99.3
112 Victoria Ave.
PO Box 468
Chatswood, New South Wales 2057, Australia
Ph: 61 2 94196969
Fax: 61 2 94131684
Format: Eclectic; Full Service; Information; News; Public Radio. **Operating Hours:** Continuous. **Key Personnel:** John Snelson, Chm./Finance; Mark Lumley, Contact; Andrew Reynolds, Sec., andrewr@fm993.com.au. **Ad Rates:** Noncommercial. **URL:** http://www.2nsb.org.au.

Cheltenham

41745 ■ Bayside Leader
Leader Community Newspapers
2-6 Railway Rd.
Cheltenham, Victoria 3192, Australia
Ph: 61 3 92718100
Local community newspaper. **Freq:** Weekly (Tues.). **Key Personnel:** Fiona Sexton, Editor, bayside@leadernewspapers.com.au; Jenny Conyers, Sales Mgr.,

conyersj@leadernewspapers.com.au; Julie Saville, Sales Mgr., savillej@leadernewspapers.com.au. **Remarks:** Accepts advertising. **URL:** http://bayside-leader.whereilive.com.au/. **Circ:** Tues. ‡40,314

41746 ■ Dandenong Leader
Leader Community Newspapers
2-6 Railway Rd.
Cheltenham, Victoria 3192, Australia
Ph: 61 3 92718199
Local community newspaper. **Key Personnel:** Rebecca David, Editor, dandenong@leadernewspapers.com.au; Karen Laumets, Sales Mgr., laumetsk@leadernewspapers.com.au. **Remarks:** Accepts advertising. **URL:** http://www.newsspace.com.au/dandenong_leader. **Circ:** Mon. ‡43,672

41747 ■ Moorabbin Glen Eira Leader
Leader Community Newspapers
2-6 Railway Rd.
Cheltenham, Victoria 3192, Australia
Ph: 61 3 92718100
Local community newspaper. **Freq:** Weekly (Wed.). **Key Personnel:** Adrian Ballantyne, Editor, moorabbin@leadernewspapers.com.au; Karen Laumets, Sales Mgr., laumetsk@leadernewspapers.com.au. **Remarks:** Accepts advertising. **URL:** http://moorabbin-glen-eira-leader.whereilive.com.au/. **Circ:** Wed. ‡50,576

41748 ■ Moorabbin Kingston Leader
Leader Community Newspapers
2-6 Railway Rd.
Cheltenham, Victoria 3192, Australia
Ph: 61 3 92718100
Local community newspaper. **Freq:** Weekly (Wed.). **Key Personnel:** Adrian Ballantyne, Editor, moorabbin@leadernewspapers.com.au; Karen Laumets, Sales Mgr., laumetsk@leadernewspapers.com.au. **Remarks:** Accepts advertising. **URL:** http://moorabbin-kingston-leader.whereilive.com.au/. **Circ:** Wed. ‡50,576

41749 ■ Mordialloc Chelsea Leader
Leader Community Newspapers
2-6 Railway Rd.
Cheltenham, Victoria 3192, Australia
Ph: 61 3 95848400
Local community newspaper. **Freq:** Weekly (Mon.). **Key Personnel:** Dimity Barber, Editor, mordialloc.chelsea@leadernewspapers.com.au; Karen Laumets, Sales Mgr., laumetsk@leadernewspapers.com.au. **Remarks:** Accepts advertising. **URL:** http://mordialloc-chelsea-leader.whereilive.com.au/. **Circ:** Mon. ‡37,575

Chermside

41750 ■ Australian Organic Journal
Biological Farmers of Australia
PO Box 530
Chermside, Queensland 4032, Australia
Ph: 61 7 33505716
Fax: 61 7 33505996
Publisher E-mail: info@bfa.com.au
Journal containing useful information for primary industries, manufacturers, wholesalers, and retailers. **Freq:** Quarterly. **ISSN:** 1447-171X. **Subscription Rates:** $A 39 individuals; $A 10 single issue. **Remarks:** Accepts advertising. **URL:** http://www.bfa.com.au/index.asp?Sec_ID=45. **Ad Rates:** 4C: $A 550. **Circ:** Paid ‡6,000

Churchill

41751 ■ SBS Television - 52
Locked Bag 028
Crows Nest, New South Wales 1585, Australia
Ph: 61 2 94302828
Fax: 61 2 94303047
Owner: Special Broadcasting Service, at above address. **Wattage:** 500 ERP. **URL:** http://www20.sbs.com.au/transmissions/index.php?pid=2&id=378.

City East

41752 ■ NJ
Drama Australia
PO Box 15163
City East, Queensland 4002, Australia
Ph: 61 730 090664
Fax: 61 730 090668

Publisher E-mail: admin@dramaaustralia.org.au
Peer-reviewed journal of Drama Australia. **Founded:** 1976. **Freq:** Semiannual. **Key Personnel:** Prue Wales, Editor, publications@dramaaustralia.org.au; Kate Donelan, Book Review Ed., kdonelan@unimelb.edu.au. **ISSN:** 1445-2294. **Subscription Rates:** $A 100 individuals Australia; $A 125 individuals international. **URL:** http://www.dramaaustralia.org.au/publications.html.

Civic Square

41753 ■ Australian Cyclist
Bicycle Federation of Australia Inc.
PO Box 499
Civic Square, Australian Capital Territory 2608, Australia
Ph: 61 262 496761
Publication E-mail: cyclist@bicyclensw.org.au
Consumer magazine covering bicycling. **Freq:** Bimonthly. **Key Personnel:** Muriel Reddy, Editor, murielr@nuancemultimedia.com. **Remarks:** Accepts advertising. **URL:** http://www.australiancyclist.com.au/. **Circ:** (Not Reported)

Clare

41754 ■ SBS Television - 57
Locked Bag 028
Crows Nest, New South Wales 1585, Australia
Ph: 61 2 94302828
Fax: 61 2 94303047
Owner: Special Broadcasting Service, at above address. **Wattage:** 100 ERP. **URL:** http://www20.sbs.com.au/transmissions/index.php?pid=2&id=448.

Clayton

41755 ■ Alternative Law Journal
Legal Service Bulletin Co-operative Ltd.
Law Faculty
Monash University
Clayton, Victoria 3800, Australia
Ph: 61 3 95440974
Fax: 61 3 99055305
Publisher E-mail: altlj@law.monash.edu.au
Law periodical. **Founded:** 1974. **Freq:** Quarterly. **Print Method:** Offset. **Trim Size:** A4. **Key Personnel:** Melissa Castan, Editorial Board, phone 61 3 99055303; Deborah Candy, Managing Editor, phone 61 3 99053362, deb.candy@law.monash.edu.au. **ISSN:** 1037-969X. **Remarks:** Accepts advertising. **Online:** Gale. **URL:** http://www.altlj.org. **Circ:** 1,300

41756 ■ Applied GIS
Monash University ePress
Bldg. 4
Monash University
Wellington Rd.
Clayton, Victoria 3800, Australia
Fax: 61 3 99058450
Publisher E-mail: epress@lib.monash.edu.au
Peer-reviewed journal publishing articles covering specific applications of GIS, demonstrating the deployment of spatial sciences in a wide range of environmental and social science contexts. **Freq:** 3/yr. **Key Personnel:** Jim Peterson, Co-Ed., jim.peterson@arts.monash.edu.au; Prof. Ray Wyatt, Co-Ed., rgwyatt@unimelb.edu.au. **ISSN:** 1832-5505. **URL:** http://publications.epress.monash.edu/loi/ag/index.html.

41757 ■ Australian and New Zealand Journal of Criminology
Australian Academic Press Pty. Ltd.
School of Political & Social Enquiry
Monash University
Clayton, Victoria 3800, Australia
Publisher E-mail: aap@australianacademicpress.com.au
Peer-reviewed journal covering field of criminology. **Freq:** 3/yr. **Key Personnel:** Sharon Pickering, Editor, sharon.pickering@arts.monash.edu.au. **ISSN:** 0157-1532. **Subscription Rates:** $A 310 individuals; $A 326 individuals New Zealand; $A 341 other countries. **Remarks:** Accepts advertising. **URL:** http://www.australianacademicpress.com.au/Publications/Journals/Criminology/Criminology.htm. **Circ:** (Not Reported)

41758 ■ The Bible and Critical Theory
Monash University ePress

Bldg. 4
Monash University
Wellington Rd.
Clayton, Victoria 3800, Australia
Fax: 61 3 99058450
Publisher E-mail: epress@lib.monash.edu.au
Peer-reviewed journal for biblical studies, exploring the intersections between critical theory, understood in the broad sense, and biblical studies, publishing peer-reviewed articles that investigate the contributions from critical theory to biblical studies, and contributions from biblical studies to critical theory. **Freq:** 3/yr. **Key Personnel:** Julie Kelso, Managing Editor, julieanne.kelso@uq.edu.au. **ISSN:** 1832-3391. **Subscription Rates:** $A 45 individuals print; $A 29.95 individuals online only; $A 80 institutions online only. **URL:** http://publications.epress.monash.edu/loi/bc.

41759 ■ Colloquy
Centre for Comparative Literature and Cultural Studies
Bldg. 11
Monash University
Clayton, Victoria 3800, Australia
Ph: 61 399 059009
Fax: 61 399 055593
Publisher E-mail: arts-colloquy@monash.edu
Online journal publishing new works in literary and cultural studies, and related fields. **Subtitle:** Text Theory Critique. **Founded:** 1, 1994. **Freq:** Annual. **Print Method:** On-line. **Key Personnel:** Bill Ashcroft, Editorial Board; Andrew Benjamin, Editorial Board; Joy Damousi, Editorial Board; Alex Duttmann, Editorial Board; Sneja Gunew, Editorial Board; Kevin Hart, Editorial Board; Susan K. Martin, Editorial Board; Steven Muecke, Editorial Board; Paul Patton, Editorial Board; Alison Ross, Advisory Board. **ISSN:** 1325-9490. **Subscription Rates:** Free annual online. **Remarks:** Advertising not accepted. **URL:** http://colloquy.monash.edu.au/about/index.html. **Circ:** (Not Reported)

41760 ■ Division of Labour & Transaction Costs
World Scientific Publishing Company Private Ltd.
Dept. of Economics
Monash University
Clayton, Victoria 3800, Australia
Ph: 61 399 052309
Fax: 61 399 055476
Publisher E-mail: wspc@wspc.com.sg
Journal promoting classical economic thinking about network effects of division of labor and general equilibrium mechanisms that simultaneously determine interdependent benefits of specialization and number of participants in the network of division of labor (extent of the market) in a modern body of inframarginal economics. **Freq:** Semiannual. **Key Personnel:** Yew Kwang Ng, Advisory Board, kwang.ng@buseco.monash.edu.au; Cyrus C.Y. Chu, Assoc. Ed., cychu@ieas.econ.sinica.edu.tw; Dietrich Fausten, Assoc. Ed., dietrich.fausten@buseco.monash.edu.au; Lin Zhou, Assoc. Ed., lin.zhou@asu.edu. **ISSN:** 0219-8711. **Subscription Rates:** US$297 institutions and libraries; print and electronic; US$285 institutions and libraries; electronic only; US$13 individuals for postage; EUR286 institutions and libraries; electronic + print; EUR275 institutions and libraries; electronic only; EUR9 individuals for postage; S$507 individuals and libraries; electronic + print; S$487 institutions and libraries; electronic only; S$17 individuals for postage. **Remarks:** Advertising accepted; rates available upon request. **URL:** http://www.worldscinet.com/dltc/dltc.shtml. **Circ:** (Not Reported)

41761 ■ International Journal of Business Intelligence and Data Mining
Inderscience Publishers
c/o Dr. David Taniar, Ed.-in-Ch.
Clayton School of Information Technology
Monash University
Clayton, Victoria 3800, Australia
Publisher E-mail: editor@inderscience.com
Journal publishing and disseminating knowledge on an international basis in the areas of business intelligence, intelligent data analysis, and data mining. **Freq:** Quarterly. **Key Personnel:** Dr. David Taniar, Editor-in-Chief, david.taniar@infotech.monash.edu.au; Prof. Lakhmi C. Jain, Editorial Board Member; Dr. Fazel A. Famili, Editorial Board Member; Prof. Tu Bao Ho, Editorial Board Member; Prof. Michael R. Berthold, Editorial Board Member; Dr. Hillol Kargupta, Editorial Board Member. **ISSN:** 1743-8187. **Subscription Rates:**

EUR494 individuals print or online; EUR672 individuals print and online. **URL:** http://www.inderscience.com/browse/index.php?journalCODE=ijbidm.

41762 ■ International Journal of Web and Grid Services
Inderscience Publishers
c/o Dr. David Taniar, Ed.-in-Ch.
Monash University
School of Business Systems
Clayton, Victoria 3800, Australia
Publisher E-mail: editor@inderscience.com
Peer-reviewed journal proposing and fostering discussion on web and grid service technology with a focus on its application, emphasising issues of architecture, implementation, and standardisation. **Freq:** Quarterly. **Key Personnel:** Dr. David Taniar, Editor-in-Chief, david.taniar@infotech.monash.edu.au; Dr. Athman Bouguettaya, Editorial Board Member; Prof. Elizabeth Chang, Editorial Board Member. **ISSN:** 1741-1106. **Subscription Rates:** EUR494 individuals print only (surface mail); EUR534 individuals print only (airmail); EUR840 individuals online only (2-3 users); EUR672 individuals print and online. **URL:** http://www.inderscience.com/browse/index.php?journalCODE=ijwgs.

41763 ■ Mobile Information Systems
IOS Press, B.V.
c/o Dr. David Taniar, Ed.-in-Ch.
Clayton School of Information Technology
Monash University
Clayton, Victoria 3800, Australia
Ph: 61 3 99059693
Fax: 61 3 99055159
Publisher E-mail: info@iospress.nl
Journal striving to be a source for mobile information systems research and development, and to serve as an outlet for facilitating communication and networking among mobile information systems researchers, practitioners, and professionals across academics, government, industry and students. **Freq:** Quarterly. **Key Personnel:** Dr. David Taniar, Editor-in-Chief, david.taniar@infotech.monash.edu.au; Lambert Spaanenburg, Editorial Board; Han-Chieh Chao, Editorial Board; John Krogstie, Editorial Board; Albert Y. Zomaya, Editorial Board; Hong Va Leong, Editorial Board; Laurence T. Yang, Editorial Board; Dik Lun Lee, Editorial Board; Kian-Lee Tan, Editorial Board; Bala Srinivasan, Editorial Board. **ISSN:** 1574-017X. **Subscription Rates:** EUR353 institutions print and online; US$510 institutions print and online. **URL:** http://www.iospress.nl/loadtop/load.php?isbn=1574017x.

41764 ■ Monash University Law Review
Monash University
Faculty of Law
Clayton campus
Wellington Rd.
Clayton, Victoria 3800, Australia
Ph: 61 3 99026000
Fax: 61 3 99054007
Publication E-mail: law.review@law.monash.edu.au
Publisher E-mail: law.review@law.monash.edu.au
Law periodical. **Freq:** Semiannual. **Key Personnel:** Natalia Antolak-Saper, Editor; Seona March, Editor; Eleanor Mulholland, Editor. **ISSN:** 0311-3140. **Subscription Rates:** $A 60 individuals; $A 33 single issue. **Remarks:** Accepts advertising. **URL:** http://www.law.monash.edu.au/monlr/. **Circ:** (Not Reported)

Cleve

41765 ■ Eyre Peninsula Tribune
Rural Press Ltd.
37 Main St.
Cleve, South Australia 5640, Australia
Ph: 61 8 86282037
Publication E-mail: eptribune@ruralpress.com
General newspaper. **URL:** http://eyrepeninsula.yourguide.com.au.

Cleveland

41766 ■ Bayside Bulletin
Fairfax Business Media
135 Queen St.
PO Box 191
Cleveland, Queensland 4163, Australia
Ph: 61 7 38218333
Fax: 61 7 32864758

Publication E-mail: admin.bbulletin@ruralpress.com
Newspaper covering distinctive news and latest information in Redland Shire Area. **Key Personnel:** Jenny Conroy, Dep. Ed., phone 61 7 38218336, fax 61 7 32864758, mail.bbulletin@ruralpress.com; Damon Pownell, Advertising Mgr., phone 61 7 38218317, damon.pownell@ruralpress.com. **Subscription Rates:** Free. **Remarks:** Accepts advertising. **URL:** http://www.baysidebulletin.com.au/. **Circ:** (Not Reported)

41767 ■ Good Fruits & Vegetables
Rural Press Ltd.
PO Box 586
Cleveland, Queensland 4163, Australia
Ph: 61 7 38268200
Fax: 61 7 38211226
Magazine featuring the fruit and vegetable growers and industry of Australia. **Freq:** Monthly. **Key Personnel:** Brad Cooper, Editor, gfv@ruralpress.com; John Warlters, General Mgr., john.warlters@ruralpress.com; Michael Lamond, Advertising Mgr., admgr.gfv@ruralpress.com. **Subscription Rates:** $A 66 individuals; $A 118 two years; $A 5.50 single issue. **Remarks:** Accepts advertising. **URL:** http://www.ruralpress.com/publications/detail.asp?publication_id=134. **Circ:** (Not Reported)

41768 ■ Queensland Smart Farmer
Rural Press Ltd.
PO Box 586
Cleveland, Queensland 4163, Australia
Publication E-mail: qldsmartfarmer@ruralpress.com
Magazine covering the rural lifestyle of people in South East Queensland. **Freq:** Bimonthly. **Key Personnel:** Fiona Cameron, Editor. **Subscription Rates:** $A 20 individuals. **Remarks:** Accepts advertising. **URL:** http://www.ruralpress.com/publications/detail.asp?publication_id=218. **Circ:** (Not Reported)

41769 ■ The Redland Times
Fairfax Business Media
135 Queen St.
PO Box 191
Cleveland, Queensland 4163, Australia
Ph: 61 7 38218333
Publication E-mail: admin.bbulletin@ruralpress.com
Newspaper covering major local news and information to the residents of Redland Shire. **Key Personnel:** Jenny Conroy, Dep. Ed., phone 61 7 38218336, fax 61 7 32864758, mail.bbulletin@ruralpress.com; Damon Pownell, Advertising Mgr., phone 61 7 38218317. **Subscription Rates:** Free. **Remarks:** Accepts advertising. **URL:** http://www.baysidebulletin.com.au/. **Circ:** (Not Reported)

41770 ■ Bay-FM - 100.3
PO Box 1003
Cleveland, Queensland 4163, Australia
Ph: 61 7 38210022
Fax: 61 7 32869166
E-mail: bayfm@bayfm.org.au
Format: Ethnic. **Operating Hours:** Continuous. **Ad Rates:** Noncommercial; underwriting available. **URL:** http://www.bayfm.org.au.

Clifton Hill

Rete Italia-AM - See Sydney

Cloncurry

41771 ■ 4ABC-FM - 90.5
ABC Ultimo Ctr.
700 Harris St.
Ultimo, New South Wales 2007, Australia
Ph: 61 2 83331500
Fax: 61 2 83335344
Format: Classical. **Owner:** Australian Broadcasting Corp., at above address. **URL:** http://abc.com.au/classic/freq/freqqld.htm.

Cobar

41772 ■ Cobar Age
Rural Press Ltd.
27 Linsley St.
Cobar, New South Wales 2835, Australia
Ph: 61 2 68362119

Publication E-mail: mail.cobarage@ruralpress.com
General newspaper. **URL:** http://cobar.yourguide.com.au.

41773 ■ SBS Television - 12
Locked Bag 028
Crows Nest, New South Wales 1585, Australia
Ph: 61 2 94302828
Fax: 61 2 94303047
Owner: Special Broadcasting Service, at above address. **Wattage:** 80 ERP. **URL:** http://www20.sbs.com.au/transmissions/index.php?pid=2&id=21.

Cobden

41774 ■ SBS Television - 67
Locked Bag 028
Crows Nest, New South Wales 1585, Australia
Ph: 61 2 94302828
Fax: 61 2 94303047
Owner: Special Broadcasting Service, at above address. **Wattage:** 10,000 ERP. **URL:** http://www20.sbs.com.au/transmissions/index.php?pid=2&id=921.

Coffs Harbour

41775 ■ SBS Television - 69
Locked Bag 028
Crows Nest, New South Wales 1585, Australia
Ph: 61 2 94302828
Fax: 61 2 94303047
Owner: Special Broadcasting Service, at above address. **Wattage:** 300 ERP. **URL:** http://www20.sbs.com.au/transmissions/index.php?pid=2&id=22.

41776 ■ 2AIR-FM - 107.9
Jetty Village Shopping Ctr.
PO Box 2028
Coffs Harbour, New South Wales 2450, Australia
Ph: 61 2 66521071
Fax: 61 2 66528881
E-mail: office@2airfm.com.au
Format: Country; Contemporary Christian. **Owner:** Coffs Coast Community Radio, at above address. **Operating Hours:** Continuous. **URL:** http://www.2airfm.com.au/.

41777 ■ 2CHY-FM - 104.1
30 Orlando St.
Coffs Harbour, New South Wales 2450, Australia
Ph: 61 2 66511104
Format: Contemporary Hit Radio (CHR). **URL:** http://chyfm.com.au/.

Colac

41778 ■ SBS Television - 55
Locked Bag 028
Crows Nest, New South Wales 1585, Australia
Ph: 61 2 94302828
Fax: 61 2 94303047
Owner: Special Broadcasting Service, at above address. **Wattage:** 10,000 ERP. **URL:** http://www20.sbs.com.au/transmissions/index.php?pid=2&id=379.

Collie

41779 ■ Collie Mail
Rural Press Ltd.
24 Steere St.
Collie, Western Australia 6225, Australia
Ph: 61 8 97342044
Publication E-mail: editor.colliemail@ruralpress.com
General newspaper. **Key Personnel:** Raelene heston, Editor. **Remarks:** Accepts advertising. **URL:** http://collie.yourguide.com.au/home.asp. **Circ:** (Not Reported)

Collingwood

41780 ■ Animal Production Science
CSIRO Publishing
PO Box 1139
Collingwood, Victoria 3066, Australia
Ph: 61 396 627500
Fax: 61 396 627555
Publication E-mail: publishing.ajea@csiro.au
Publisher E-mail: publishing@csiro.au
Peer-reviewed journal covering research in applied agriculture. **Founded:** 1960. **Freq:** Monthly. **Key Personnel:** Wayne Bryden, Editor-in-Chief. **ISSN:** 1836-

0939. **Subscription Rates:** $A 1,680 institutions Australia & New Zealand, online only; $A 2,155 institutions Australia & New Zealand, online and print; US$1,470 institutions, other countries online only; US$1,880 institutions, other countries online and print; $A 185 individuals Australia & New Zealand, online; $A 210 individuals Australia & New Zealand, online and print; US$160 elsewhere online; US$200 elsewhere online and print. **Remarks:** Accepts advertising. **URL:** http://www.publish.csiro.au/nid/72.htm. **Formerly:** Australian Journal of Experimental Agriculture. **Ad Rates:** BW: $A 500, 4C: $A 900. **Circ:** Paid 600

41781 ■ Australasian Plant Disease Notes
CSIRO Publishing
PO Box 1139
Collingwood, Victoria 3066, Australia
Ph: 61 396 627500
Fax: 61 396 627555
Publisher E-mail: publishing@csiro.au
Journal covering wide range of scientific disciplines, including agriculture, the plant and animal sciences, and environmental management. **Founded:** 1888. **Freq:** Annual. **Print Method:** Offset. **Cols./Page:** 6. **Col. Depth:** 21 inches. **Key Personnel:** M. Glen, Sen. Ed.; Prof. D. Hanold, Editor-in-Chief. **ISSN:** 1833-928X. **URL:** http://www.publish.csiro.au/nid/208.htm.

41782 ■ Australian Journal of Chemistry
CSIRO Publishing
PO Box 1139
Collingwood, Victoria 3066, Australia
Ph: 61 396 627500
Fax: 61 396 627555
Publisher E-mail: publishing@csiro.au
Journal covering research in all branches of chemistry. **Subtitle:** An International Journal for Chemical Science. **Freq:** Monthly. **Key Personnel:** Christopher Barner-Kowollik, Assoc. Ed.; Stuart Batten, Assoc. Ed.; Paul Bernhardt, Assoc. Ed. **ISSN:** 0004-9425. **Subscription Rates:** $A 1,575 institutions Australia and New Zealand; online; $A 1,970 institutions Australia and New Zealand, print and online; EUR1,300 institutions online; EUR1,625 institutions print and online; $A 210 individuals Australia and New Zealand; online; EUR250 individuals online; 140 individuals online; 155 individuals print and online; EUR215 individuals print and online; 1,100 institutions print and online. **URL:** http://www.publish.csiro.au/nid/51.htm.

41783 ■ Australian Journal of Zoology
CSIRO Publishing
PO Box 1139
Collingwood, Victoria 3066, Australia
Ph: 61 396 627500
Fax: 61 396 627555
Publisher E-mail: publishing@csiro.au
Journal covering all branches of zoology worldwide. **Freq:** Bimonthly. **Key Personnel:** Mark Elgar, Editor-in-Chief; Phill Cassey, Editor; Peter Frappell, Editor. **ISSN:** 0004-959X. **Subscription Rates:** $A 950 institutions Australia and New Zealand; online only; $A 1,190 institutions Australia and New Zealand; online and print; $A 140 individuals Australia and New Zealand; online only; $A 160 individuals Australia and New Zealand; online and print; US$805 institutions U.S. and other countries; online; US$1,005 institutions U.S. and other countries; online and print; EUR120 individuals online; US$150 individuals U.S. and other countries; online and print. **URL:** http://www.publish.csiro.au/nid/90.htm.

41784 ■ Crop & Pasture Science
CSIRO Publishing
PO Box 1139
Collingwood, Victoria 3066, Australia
Ph: 61 396 627500
Fax: 61 396 627555
Publisher E-mail: publishing@csiro.au
Journal focusing on agricultural science including food and fiber improvement and production, plant and animal sciences, sustainable farming systems, and food quality. **Freq:** Monthly. **Key Personnel:** Prof. John Irwin, Editor-in-Chief; Chris Anderson, Publisher. **ISSN:** 0004-9409. **Subscription Rates:** $A 185 individuals online, Australia and New Zealand; $A 210 individuals print and online, Australia and New Zealand; EUR160 individuals online; EUR178 individuals print and online; EUR1,180 institutions online, Europe; EUR1,475 institutions print and online; 805 institutions online; 1,005 institutions print and online; 130 individuals print and online; 114 individuals online. **URL:** http://www.publish.csiro.au/nid/40.htm. **Formerly:** Australian Journal of Agricultural Research.

41785 ■ Earthmatters
CSIRO Publishing
PO Box 1139
Collingwood, Victoria 3066, Australia
Ph: 61 396 627500
Fax: 61 396 627555
Publication E-mail: earthmattersmailinglist@csiro.au
Publisher E-mail: publishing@csiro.au
Magazine featuring fields of minerals exploration and mining. **Freq:** 3/yr. **Key Personnel:** Bob Chamberlain, Mktg. & Communication Mgr., phone 61 73 3274469, fax 61 73 3274455, bob.chamberlain@csiro.au. **Subscription Rates:** Free. **Remarks:** Accepts advertising. **URL:** http://www.csiro.au/resources/earthmatters.html. **Circ:** (Not Reported)

41786 ■ Ecos
CSIRO Publishing
PO Box 1139
Collingwood, Victoria 3066, Australia
Ph: 61 396 627500
Fax: 61 396 627555
Publication E-mail: ecos@csiro.au
Publisher E-mail: publishing@csiro.au
Publication focusing on environmental issues & sustainability. **Subtitle:** Towards a Sustainable Future. **Founded:** 1974. **Freq:** Bimonthly. **Trim Size:** A4. **Key Personnel:** Alexandra de Blas, Editorial Advisory Committee; Mary-Lou Considine, Editor. **ISSN:** 0311-4546. **Subscription Rates:** $A 42 individuals; $A 67 institutions; $A 54 individuals schools. **Remarks:** Accepts advertising. **URL:** http://www.ecosmagazine.com/. **Circ:** Paid 7,500

41787 ■ Emu - Austral Ornithology
CSIRO Publishing
PO Box 1139
Collingwood, Victoria 3066, Australia
Ph: 61 396 627500
Fax: 61 396 627555
Publisher E-mail: publishing@csiro.au
Peer-reviewed journal covering ornithological research and reviews in the southern hemisphere and all branches of bird research, including conservation biology and applied ornithology. **Freq:** Quarterly. **Key Personnel:** Dr. Kate Buchanan, Editor, phone 61 3 52271321, kate.buchanan@deakin.edu.au; Jon Green, Assoc. Ed.; Caroline Hadley, Publisher, caroline.hadley@csiro.au. **ISSN:** 0158-4197. **Subscription Rates:** $A 465 institutions online (Australia and New Zealand); $A 600 institutions print and online (Australia and New Zealand); EUR320 institutions online; EUR410 institutions print and online; 220 institutions online; 285 institutions print and online; US$385 institutions, other countries online; US$495 institutions, other countries print and online. **URL:** http://www.publish.csiro.au/nid/96/aid/402.htm.

41788 ■ Environmental Chemistry
CSIRO Publishing
PO Box 1139
Collingwood, Victoria 3066, Australia
Ph: 61 396 627500
Fax: 61 396 627555
Publication E-mail: publishing.env@csiro.au
Publisher E-mail: publishing@csiro.au
Peer-reviewed journal addressing the fundamental chemistry behind environmental issues. **Freq:** Bimonthly. **Key Personnel:** Dr. Kevin Francesconi, Editor-in-Chief; Dr. Jenny Bennett, Publisher. **ISSN:** 1448-2517. **Subscription Rates:** $A 990 institutions online (Australia and New Zealand); EUR790 institutions online; 530 institutions online; US$950 institutions, other countries online; $A 125 individuals online; EUR120 individuals online; 85 individuals online; US$120 other countries online. **URL:** http://www.publish.csiro.au/nid/188.htm.

41789 ■ Functional Plant Biology
CSIRO Publishing
PO Box 1139
Collingwood, Victoria 3066, Australia
Ph: 61 396 627500
Fax: 61 396 627555
Publisher E-mail: publishing@csiro.au
Journal covering plant physiology. **Subtitle:** Continuing Australian Journal of Plant Physiology. **Founded:** 1974. **Freq:** Monthly. **Trim Size:** A4. **Key Personnel:** Rana Munns, Editor-in-Chief, publishing@csiro.au; Enrico Brugnoli, Editorial Board; Gerald Edwards, Editorial Board. **ISSN:** 1445-4408. **Subscription Rates:** $A

1,585 institutions online (Australia and New Zealand); $A 1,980 institutions online + print (Australia and New Zealand); EUR1,200 institutions online; EUR1,500 institutions online + print; 830 institutions online; 1,040 institutions online + print; US$1,410 institutions U.S. and other countries; online; US$1,765 institutions U.S. and other countries; online + print; US$185 individuals online (Australia and New Zealand); US$210 individuals online + print (Australia & New Zealand). **Remarks:** Advertising accepted; rates available upon request. **URL:** http://www.publish.csiro.au/nid/102.htm. **Formerly:** Australian Journal of Plant Physiology. **Circ:** (Not Reported)

41790 ■ Inside Indonesia
Indonesian Resources and Information Programme
PO Box 1326
Collingwood, Victoria 3066, Australia
Ph: 61 394 194504
Fax: 61 394 194774
Publication E-mail: admin@insideindonesia.org
Publisher E-mail: admin@insideindonesia.org
Publication covering contemporary Indonesia for scholars and travellers. **Founded:** 1983. **Freq:** Quarterly. **Key Personnel:** Gerry Van Klinken, Editor; Ron Witton, Contact. **ISSN:** 0814-1185. **Subscription Rates:** $A 1 individuals 1 copy within Australia; $A 3 individuals 1 copy Asia Pacific; $A 4 individuals 1 copy other; $A 2 individuals 2 copy within Australia; $A 4 individuals 2 copy Asia pacific; $A 6 individuals 2 copy other; $A 5 individuals postage & packaging for back issues; $A 40 individuals postage & packaging for back issues. **URL:** http://www.insideindonesia.org/.

41791 ■ Invertebrate Systematics
CSIRO Publishing
PO Box 1139
Collingwood, Victoria 3066, Australia
Ph: 61 396 627500
Fax: 61 396 627555
Publisher E-mail: publishing@csiro.au
Journal covering systematics and phylogeny of invertebrate faunas worldwide. **Freq:** Bimonthly. **Key Personnel:** Prof. Andy Austin, Editor-in-Chief, phone 61 8 83038240, fax 61 8 83034364, andy.austin@adelaide.edu.au; Bob Anderson, Editor; Shane Ahyong, Editor. **ISSN:** 1445-5226. **Subscription Rates:** $A 1,090 institutions online (Australia and New Zealand); $A 1,365 institutions print and online (Australia and New Zealand); EUR790 institutions online; EUR990 institutions print and online; 548 institutions online; 685 institutions print and online; US$950 institutions online (North America and rest of World); US$1,190 institutions print and online (North America and rest of World). **URL:** http://www.publish.csiro.au/nid/120.htm.

41792 ■ Marine & Freshwater Research
CSIRO Publishing
PO Box 1139
Collingwood, Victoria 3066, Australia
Ph: 61 396 627500
Fax: 61 396 627555
Publisher E-mail: publishing@csiro.au
Journal covering aquatic sciences. **Founded:** 1920. **Freq:** Monthly. **Print Method:** Offset. **Key Personnel:** P.I. Boon, Assoc. Ed.; J.M. Hughes, Assoc. Ed.; S. Ayvazian, Assoc. Ed. **ISSN:** 1323-1650. **Subscription Rates:** $A 1,470 institutions online (Australia and New Zealand); $A 1,840 institutions print and online (Australia and New Zealand); EUR1,175 institutions online; 810 institutions online; 1,015 institutions print and online; 1,390 institutions online (North America and rest of World); US$1,740 institutions print and online (North America and rest of World); 130 individuals print and online. **URL:** http://www.publish.csiro.au/nid/126.htm.

41793 ■ Parity
Council to Homeless Persons
2 Stanley St.
Collingwood, Victoria 3066, Australia
Ph: 61 3 94198699
Fax: 61 3 94197445
Publication E-mail: parity@chp.org.au
Publisher E-mail: admin@chp.org.au
Journal covering the whole range of issues connected with homelessness and the provision of housing and services to homeless people. **Freq:** 10/yr. **Subscription Rates:** US$90 individuals; US$45 students concession member. **URL:** http://www.chp.org.au/parity.shtml.

41794 ■ PASA
CSIRO Publishing
PO Box 1139

Collingwood, Victoria 3066, Australia
Ph: 61 396 627500
Fax: 61 396 627555
Publisher E-mail: publishing@csiro.au
Journal covering research in and astronomy and astrophysics with focus on southern hemisphere. Includes topics such as multi-wavelength observation, theoretical modelling, data processing and, particularly, southern hemisphere astronomy and astronomy with Australian instruments. **Subtitle:** Publications of the Astronomical Society of Australia. **Founded:** 1903. **Freq:** Quarterly. **Print Method:** Offset. **Cols./Page:** 6. **Col. Width:** 24 nonpareils. **Col. Depth:** 294 agate lines. **Key Personnel:** Bryan Gaensler, Chm., bgaensler@usyd.edu.au. **ISSN:** 1323-3580. **Subscription Rates:** $A 540 institutions online (Australia and New Zealand); EUR410 institutions online; 280 institutions online; US$480 elsewhere online. **URL:** http://www.publish.csiro.au/nid/138/aid/2416.htm.

41795 ■ Quarterly Essay
Black Inc.
37-39 Langridge St.
Collingwood, Victoria 3066, Australia
Ph: 61 3 94860288
Fax: 61 3 94860244
Publication E-mail: quarterlyessay@blackincbooks.com
Publisher E-mail: enquiries@blackincbooks.com
Magazine presenting contributions to political, intellectual and cultural debate. **Freq:** Quarterly. **Key Personnel:** Chris Feik, Managing Editor. **Subscription Rates:** $A 49 individuals; $A 95 two years; $A 79 other countries; $A 155 two years overseas. **URL:** http://www.quarterlyessay.com/.

41796 ■ Reproduction, Fertility and Development
CSIRO Publishing
PO Box 1139
Collingwood, Victoria 3066, Australia
Ph: 61 396 627500
Fax: 61 396 627555
Publisher E-mail: publishing@csiro.au
Journal covering vertebrate reproduction and developmental biology. Topics include assisted reproductive technologies in medicine, livestock production, wildlife conservation and pest management, covering broader aspects of embryo and fetal development and reproductive physiology, endocrinology, cell biology, genetics, and behavior. **Freq:** 9/yr. **Key Personnel:** Tony Flint, Editor; Jim Cummins, Assoc. Ed.; Alison Douglas, Assoc. Ed. **ISSN:** 1031-3613. **Subscription Rates:** $A 1,150 institutions online (Australia and New Zealand); $A 1,440 institutions print and online (Australia and New Zealand); EUR845 institutions online; EUR1,055 institutions print and online; 585 institutions online; 730 institutions print and online; US$990 other countries online; US$1,240 other countries print and online. **URL:** http://www.publish.csiro.au/nid/44.htm.

41797 ■ Wildlife Research
CSIRO Publishing
PO Box 1139
Collingwood, Victoria 3066, Australia
Ph: 61 396 627500
Fax: 61 396 627555
Publisher E-mail: publishing@csiro.au
Journal covering the ecology and management of wild animals in natural and modified habitats. **Subtitle:** Management and Conservation. **Founded:** 1965. **Freq:** 8/yr. **Print Method:** Offset/Web. **Trim Size:** 8 1/2 x 11. **Cols./Page:** 3. **Col. Width:** 27 nonpareils. **Col. Depth:** 140 agate lines. **Key Personnel:** Caroline Hadley, Publisher; Steven Belmain, Assoc. Ed.; Stan Boutin, Editor. **ISSN:** 1035-3712. **Subscription Rates:** $A 1,090 institutions online (Australia and New Zealand); $A 1,365 institutions print and online (Australia and New Zealand); EUR840 institutions online; EUR1,050 institutions print and online; 570 institutions online; 715 institutions print and online; US$990 other countries online; US$1,240 other countries print and online; $A 135 individuals online (Australia and New Zealand); $A 150 individuals print and online (Australia and New Zealand). **URL:** http://www.publish.csiro.au/nid/144.htm.

41798 ■ 3ZZZ-FM - 92.3
PO Box 1106
Collingwood, Victoria 3066, Australia
Ph: 61 3 94151928
Fax: 61 3 94151818

Circulation: ★ = ABC; △ = BPA; ◆ = CAC; • = CCAB; ❑ = VAC; ⊕ = PO Statement; ‡ = Publisher's Report; Boldface figures = sworn; Light figures = estimated.

Gale Directory of Publications & Broadcast Media/147th Ed.

4713

E-mail: admin@3zzz.com.au
Format: Public Radio; Ethnic; News. **Founded:** June 1989. **Operating Hours:** Continuous. **Ad Rates:** Noncommercial; underwriting available. **URL:** http://www.3zzz.com.au.

41799 ■ ZZZ-FM - 92.3
PO Box 1106
Collingwood, Victoria 3066, Australia
Ph: 61 3 94151928
Fax: 61 3 94151818
E-mail: admin@3zzz.com.au
Format: Public Radio; Eclectic; Ethnic. **Founded:** June 1989. **Operating Hours:** Continuous. **Ad Rates:** Underwriting available. **URL:** http://www.3zzz.com.au.

Como

41800 ■ Sonshine-FM - 98.5
End of Murray St.
Como, Western Australia 6152, Australia
Ph: 61 8 93130800
Fax: 61 8 93130801
E-mail: reception@sonshinefm.ws
Format: Contemporary Christian. **Founded:** Jan. 1988. **Operating Hours:** Continuous. **Key Personnel:** Barry Grosser, General Mgr.; Arthur Muhl, Program Mgr.; Abbey Spinelli, News Dir.; Andrew Thorn, Sales Mgr.; Chela Williams, Production Mgr. **Ad Rates:** Advertising accepted; rates available upon request. **URL:** http://www.sonshinefm.ws/.

Condell Park

41801 ■ Auburn Review Pictorial
Torch Publishing Company Pty. Ltd.
47 Allingham St.
Condell Park, New South Wales 2200, Australia
Ph: 61 2 97950000
Fax: 61 2 97950096
Publisher E-mail: torch@torchpublishing.com.au
Newspaper featuring news and events in the Auburn and Lidcombe districts. **Founded:** 1960. **Freq:** Weekly (Tues.). **Key Personnel:** Mark Kirkland, Gp. Ed.; Paul Dodds, Manager; Marsha Vescio, Gp. Sales/Mktg. Mgr. **Subscription Rates:** Free. **Remarks:** Accepts advertising. **URL:** http://www.torchpublishing.com.au/read_papers/index.html. **Circ:** 24,5469

41802 ■ Bankstown Canterbury Torch
Torch Publishing Company Pty. Ltd.
47 Allingham St.
Condell Park, New South Wales 2200, Australia
Ph: 612 9 7950000
Fax: 612 9 7950096
Publisher E-mail: torch@torchpublishing.com.au
Newspaper featuring businesses in the Bankstown and Canterbury districts. **Founded:** June 12, 1920. **Freq:** Weekly (Wed.). **Key Personnel:** Mark Kirkland, Gp. Ed.; Bernie Temple, Manager; Marsha Vescio, Gp. Sales and Mktg. Mgr. **Subscription Rates:** Free. **Remarks:** Accepts advertising. **URL:** http://www.torchpublishing.com.au/read_papers/index.html. **Circ:** 91,335

41803 ■ Cooks River Valley Times
Torch Publishing Company Pty. Ltd.
47 Allingham St.
Condell Park, New South Wales 2200, Australia
Ph: 612 9 7950000
Fax: 612 9 7950096
Publisher E-mail: torch@torchpublishing.com.au
Newspaper featuring businesses in the Earlwood and Marrickville districts. **Founded:** 1993. **Freq:** Weekly (Thurs.). **Key Personnel:** Mark Kirkland, Gp. Ed.; Toni Porter, Manager; Marsha Vescio, Gp. Sales/Mktg. Mgr. **Subscription Rates:** Free. **Remarks:** Accepts advertising. **URL:** http://www.torchpublishing.com.au/read_papers/index.html. **Circ:** 23,987

Condobolin

41804 ■ SBS Television - 56
Locked Bag 028
Crows Nest, New South Wales 1585, Australia
Ph: 61 2 94302828
Fax: 61 2 94303047
Owner: Special Broadcasting Service, at above address. **Wattage:** 200 ERP. **URL:** http://www20.sbs.com.au/transmissions/index.php?pid=2&id=23.

Coniston

41805 ■ 2LIV-FM - 94.1
39 Bridge St.
PO Box 7
Coniston, New South Wales 2500, Australia
Ph: 61 2 42288941
Fax: 61 2 42271314
Format: Contemporary Christian. **URL:** http://www.941.com.au/.

Coober Pedy

41806 ■ Flow-FM - 99.7
PO Box 407
Kapunda, South Australia 5373, Australia
Ph: 61 8 85663151
Fax: 61 8 85662729
E-mail: mail@flowfm.com.au
Format: Adult Contemporary. **URL:** http://www.flowfm.com.au/.

Coolah

41807 ■ SBS Television - 53
Locked Bag 028
Crows Nest, New South Wales 1585, Australia
Ph: 61 2 94302828
Fax: 61 2 94303047
Owner: Special Broadcasting Service, at above address. **Wattage:** 240 ERP. **URL:** http://www20.sbs.com.au/transmissions/index.php?pid=2&id=24.

Coolamon

41808 ■ 2AAA-FM - 99.1
PO Box 2019
Wagga Wagga, New South Wales 2650, Australia
Ph: 61 2 69253000
Fax: 61 2 69252300
E-mail: fm107@2aaa.net
Format: Information; Ethnic. **URL:** http://www.2aaa.net/.

Cooma

41809 ■ SBS Television - 53
Locked Bag 028
Crows Nest, New South Wales 1585, Australia
Ph: 61 2 94302828
Fax: 61 2 94303047
Owner: Special Broadcasting Service, at above address. **Wattage:** 200 ERP. **URL:** http://www20.sbs.com.au/transmissions/index.php?pid=2&id=25.

41810 ■ Snow-FM - 97.7
28 Sharp St.
Cooma, New South Wales 2630, Australia
Ph: 61 2 64561555
Fax: 61 2 64561006
E-mail: xl@capitalradio.net.au
Format: Alternative/New Music/Progressive; Contemporary Hit Radio (CHR). **Key Personnel:** Richard Wybrew, Station Mgr., wybrew@capitalradio.net.au. **URL:** http://www.snowfm.com.au/.

41811 ■ Snow-FM - 101.9
28 Sharp St.
Cooma, New South Wales 2630, Australia
Ph: 61 2 64561555
Fax: 61 2 64561006
E-mail: snow@capitalradio.net.au
Format: Alternative/New Music/Progressive; Contemporary Hit Radio (CHR). **URL:** http://www.snowfm.com.au/.

Snow-FM - See Bombala
Snow-FM - See Thredbo

41812 ■ 2XL-AM - 918
28 Sharp St.
Cooma, New South Wales 2630, Australia
Ph: 61 2 64521521
Fax: 61 2 64521006
E-mail: xl@capitalradio.net.au
Format: Talk; Full Service; Oldies. **Key Personnel:** Richard Wybrew, Station Mgr., wybrew@capitalradio.net.au. **Ad Rates:** Advertising accepted; rates available upon request. **URL:** http://www.2xl.com.au.

41813 ■ 2XL-FM - 98.7
28 Sharp St.
Cooma, New South Wales 2630, Australia

Ph: 61 2 64521521
Fax: 61 2 64521006
E-mail: xl@capitalradio.net.au
Format: News; Talk; Adult Contemporary. **Key Personnel:** Richard Wybrew, Station Mgr. **URL:** http://www.2xl.com.au/.

2XL-FM - See Thredbo

Coorparoo

41814 ■ 4MBS-FM - 103.7
384 Old Cleveland Rd.
Coorparoo, Queensland 4151, Australia
Ph: 61 7 38471717
Fax: 61 7 38472773
E-mail: info@4mbsclassicfm.com.au
Format: Classical; Jazz; News. **Founded:** Jan. 3, 1979. **Operating Hours:** Continuous. **Key Personnel:** Gary Thorpe, General Mgr., gary.thorpe@4mbsclassicfm.com.au; Maggie Findlay, Admin. Mgr.; Howard Ainsworth, Broadcasts Mgr.; Peter McCahon, Sales Mgr., peter.mccahon@4mbsclassicfm.com.au. **Ad Rates:** Advertising accepted; rates available upon request. **URL:** http://www.4mbsclassicfm.com.au/.

41815 ■ 973-FM - 97.3
PO Box 973
Coorparoo, Queensland 4151, Australia
Ph: 61 7 34214973
Fax: 61 7 33944400
E-mail: promotions@973fm.com.au
Format: Adult Contemporary; News. **Owner:** Australian Radio Network Pty. Ltd., 3 Byfield St., North Ryde, New South Wales 2113, Australia, 61 2 88999999, Fax: 61 2 88999811. **Ad Rates:** Advertising accepted; rates available upon request. **URL:** http://www.973fm.com.au/; http://www.arn.com.au/.

Cowell

41816 ■ SBS Television - 58
Locked Bag 028
Crows Nest, New South Wales 1585, Australia
Ph: 61 2 94302828
Fax: 61 2 94303047
Owner: Special Broadcasting Service, at above address. **Wattage:** 15,000 ERP. **URL:** http://www20.sbs.com.au/transmissions/index.php?pid=2&id=450.

Cowra

41817 ■ SBS Television - 45
Locked Bag 028
Crows Nest, New South Wales 1585, Australia
Ph: 61 2 94302828
Fax: 61 2 94303047
Owner: Special Broadcasting Service, at above address. **Wattage:** 60 ERP. **URL:** http://www20.sbs.com.au/transmissions/index.php?pid=2&id=26.

Cranbourne

41818 ■ 3SER Radio Casey-FM - 97.7
PO Box 977
Cranbourne, Victoria 3977, Australia
Ph: 61 3 59966977
Fax: 61 3 59966900
Format: Public Radio; Eclectic; Information; Educational. **Founded:** 1983. **Operating Hours:** 18 hours Daily. **Key Personnel:** Craig Davenport, Contact, phone 61 3 59966933, craig.davenport@3ser.org.au. **Ad Rates:** Noncommercial; underwriting available. **URL:** http://www.3ser.org.au.

Crawley

41819 ■ Australasian Journal of Victorian Studies
Australasian Victorian Studies Association
c/o Dr. Monica Anderson, Treas.
English, Communication & Cultural Studies M202
University of Western Australia
Crawley, Western Australia 6009, Australia
Publisher E-mail: monicama@iinet.net.au
Peer-reviewed journal covering Australasian Victorian studies, including archaeology, architecture, art, economics, history, sociology and related areas. **Founded:** 1995. **Freq:** Semiannual May and November. **Key Personnel:** Dr. Jock Macleod, Editor, j.macleod@griffith.

edu.au. **ISSN:** 1327-8746. **Remarks:** Advertising accepted; rates available upon request. **URL:** http://www.nla.gov.au/openpublish/index.php/AVSJ. **Formerly:** Australasian Victorian Studies Journal. **Circ:** 150

41820 ■ Outskirts
The University of Western Australia
English, Communication and Cultural Studies
Centre for Women's Studies, M202
35 Stirling Hwy.
Crawley, Western Australia 6009, Australia
Ph: 61 864 882066
Fax: 61 864 881030
Journal dealing with a wide range of feminist issues. **Subtitle:** Feminisms Along the Edge. **Freq:** Semiannual. **Key Personnel:** Alison Bartlett, Editor; Carol Bacchi, Editorial Consultant; Chilla Bulbeck, Occasional Ed.; Barbara Baird, Editorial Consultant; Margaret Allen, Occasional Ed. **ISSN:** 1445-0445. **URL:** http://www.chloe.uwa.edu.au/outskirts/.

Crows Nest

41821 ■ Burke's Backyard Magazine
Burke's Backyard
PO Box 929
Crows Nest, New South Wales 1585, Australia
Ph: 61 2 94144800
Fax: 61 2 94144801
Publication E-mail: magazine@burkesbackyard.com.au
Consumer magazine covering gardening, landscaping, outdoor living, plants and pets. **Freq:** Monthly 11 issues. **Subscription Rates:** $A 49.95 individuals; $A 89.95 two years. **URL:** http://www.burkesbackyard.com.au.

SBS Television - See Adelaide, South Australia
SBS Television - See Airlie Beach, Queensland
SBS Television - See Albury
SBS Television - See Alexandra, Victoria
SBS Television - See Armidale
SBS Television - See Ashford
SBS Television - See Ayr, Queensland
SBS Television - See Babinda, Queensland
SBS Television - See Bairnsdale, Victoria
SBS Television - See Ballarat, Victoria
SBS Television - See Batemans Bay
SBS Television - See Bathurst
SBS Television - See Bega
SBS Television - See Bell, Queensland
SBS Television - See Bendigo, Victoria
SBS Television - See Blackwater, Queensland
SBS Television - See Bonnie Doon, Victoria
SBS Television - See Boonah, Queensland
SBS Television - See Bouddi
SBS Television - See Bowen, Queensland
SBS Television - See Bowral
SBS Television - See Braidwood
SBS Television - See Bright, Victoria
SBS Television - See Broken Hill
SBS Television - See Druthen, Victoria
SBS Television - See Bunbury, Western Australia
SBS Television - See Canberra, Australian Capital Territory
SBS Television - See Carnarvon, Western Australia
SBS Television - See Churchill, Victoria
SBS Television - See Clare, South Australia
SBS Television - See Cobar
SBS Television - See Cobden, Victoria
SBS Television - See Coffs Harbour
SBS Television - See Colac, Victoria
SBS Television - See Condobolin
SBS Television - See Coolah
SBS Television - See Cooma
SBS Television - See Cowell, South Australia
SBS Television - See Cowra

SBS Television - See Eildon, Victoria
SBS Television - See Fraser, Australian Capital Territory
SBS Television - See Naracoorte, South Australia
SBS Television - See Port Lincoln, South Australia
SBS Television - See Tennant Creek, Northern Territory
SBS Television - See Toodyay, Western Australia
SBS Television - See Tuggeranong, Australian Capital Territory

41822 ■ SBS Television - Acton Road - 28
Locked Bag 028
Crows Nest, New South Wales 1585, Australia
Ph: 61 2 94302828
Fax: 61 2 94303047
Owner: Special Broadcasting Service, at above address. **Wattage:** 160 ERP. **URL:** http://www20.sbs.com.au/transmissions/index.php?pid=1&sid=1.

SBS Television - Caralue Bluff - See Caralue Bluff, South Australia

41823 ■ SBS Television - Central Tablelands - 30
Locked Bag 028
Crows Nest, New South Wales 1585, Australia
Ph: 61 2 94302828
Fax: 61 2 94303047
Owner: Special Broadcasting Service, at above address. **Wattage:** 2,000,000 ERP. **URL:** http://www20.sbs.com.au/transmissions/index.php?pid=2&id=19.

41824 ■ SBS Television - Central Western Slopes - 29
Locked Bag 028
Crows Nest, New South Wales 1585, Australia
Ph: 61 2 94302828
Fax: 61 2 94303047
Owner: Special Broadcasting Service, at above address. **Wattage:** 1,000,000 ERP. **URL:** http://www20.sbs.com.au/transmissions/index.php?pid=2&id=20.

SBS Television - Weston Creek/Woden - See Canberra, Australian Capital Territory

Croydon

41825 ■ Radio Eastern-FM - 98.1
Wyreena Community Arts Ctr.
23 Hull Rd.
PO Box 981
Croydon, Victoria 3136, Australia
Ph: 61 3 97229981
Fax: 61 3 97237305
E-mail: info@easternfm.com.au
Format: Public Radio; Eclectic; Ethnic. **Founded:** 1974. **Operating Hours:** Continuous. **Key Personnel:** Ray Lawrence, President; John Giltinan, Vice President; Rod Harris, Treas. **Ad Rates:** Underwriting available. **URL:** http://www.easternfm.com.au.

Curtin

41826 ■ Australian and New Zealand Journal of Public Health
Public Health Association of Australia
PO Box 319
Curtin, Australian Capital Territory 2605, Australia
Ph: 61 262 852373
Fax: 61 262 825438
Publisher E-mail: phaa@phaa.net.au
Peer-reviewed journal covering public health issues. **Freq:** Bimonthly. **Key Personnel:** Dr. Joanne Daly, Editor, anzjph@substitution.com.au; Prof. John Lowe, Sen. Ed.; Prof. Ross Bailie, Editorial Board; Prof. Gavin Mooney, Editorial Board. **ISSN:** 1326-0200. **Subscription Rates:** US$175 individuals America, print and online; US$294 institutions America, print and online; US$267 institutions America, online; EUR139 individuals Europe, print and online; EUR197 institutions Europe, print and online; EUR179 institutions Europe, online; 93 other countries; 303 institutions, other countries print and online; 275 institutions, other countries online. **URL:** http://www.phaa.net.au/journal.php.

Darlinghurst

41827 ■ The Chaser
Chaser Publishing Proprietary Ltd.
PO Box 293
Darlinghurst, New South Wales 1300, Australia
Ph: 61 292 804554
Fax: 61 292 804564
Satiric newspaper. **Freq:** Biweekly. **URL:** http://www.chaser.com.au.

Darwin

41828 ■ International Journal of Computational Physical Sciences
Research India Publications
c/o Prof. Jai Singh, Ed.-in-Ch.
Faculty of Technology, B-41
Charles Darwin University
Darwin, Northern Territory 0909, Australia
Publisher E-mail: info@ripublication.com
Peer-reviewed journal covering computational physical sciences. **Freq:** Semiannual. **Key Personnel:** Prof. Jai Singh, Editor-in-Chief. **URL:** http://www.ripublication.com/ijcps.htm. **Also known as:** IJCPS.

41829 ■ Mix 104.9-FM - 104.9
PO Box 1533
Darwin, Northern Territory 0801, Australia
Ph: 61 8 89411049
Format: Adult Contemporary; Oldies; Top 40. **Operating Hours:** Continuous weekdays; 6p.m.-12a.m. Sat.; 4p.m.-9p.m. Sun. **Ad Rates:** Advertising accepted; rates available upon request. **URL:** http://www.mix1049.com.au/.

41830 ■ 100-FM - 100.1
4 Peary St.
Darwin, Northern Territory 0800, Australia
Ph: 61 8 89419999
Fax: 61 8 89814299
Format: Album-Oriented Rock (AOR); Classic Rock; Top 40. **Key Personnel:** Mark Johnson, General Mgr.; Louise Poole, Program Dir.; Phil Spencer, Sales Mgr. **Ad Rates:** Advertising accepted; rates available upon request. **URL:** http://www.hot100fm.com.au/.

41831 ■ Radio Larrakia-FM - 94.5
GPO Box 4111
Darwin, Northern Territory 0810, Australia
Ph: 61 8 89482711
Fax: 61 8 89482811
E-mail: ceo@radiolarrakia.org
Format: Information; News; Ethnic. **URL:** http://www.radiolarrakia.org/.

Deakin

41832 ■ Animal Health Australia
Ste. 15, 26-28 Napier Close
Deakin, Australian Capital Territory 2600, Australia
Ph: 61 262 325522
Fax: 61 262 325511
Publication E-mail: aha@animalhealthaustralia.com.au
Publisher E-mail: aha@animalhealthaustralia.com.au
Publication covering animal health issues. **Freq:** Annual. **Key Personnel:** Dr. Ian Denney, Dir. Programs, idenney@animalhealthaustralia.com.au; Stephen Taylor, Info. & Communications Tech. Off., phone 61 262 033946; Dr. Karin Ahrling, Mgr. Animal Health Standards, kahrling@animalhealthaustralia.com.au; Dr. Mike Bond, CEO, mbond@animalhealthaustralia.com.au. **URL:** http://www.animalhealthaustralia.com.au/publications/publications_home.cfm.

41833 ■ Australian and New Zealand Property Journal
Australian Property Institute
6 Campion St.
Deakin, Australian Capital Territory 2600, Australia
Ph: 61 2 62822411
Fax: 61 2 62852194
Publication E-mail: apj@api.org.au
Publisher E-mail: national@api.org.au
Journal including research papers and court decisions affecting the property sector. **Freq:** Quarterly. **Subscription Rates:** $A 98 individuals; $A 132 other countries. **Remarks:** Accepts advertising. **URL:** http://www.propertyinstitute.com.au/index2.aspx?division=8. **Formerly:** Australian Property Journal. **Circ:** ♦ 11,270

41834 ■ Australian Pharmacist
Pharmaceutical Society of Australia
44 Thesiger Ct.

Circulation: ★ = ABC; △ = BPA; ♦ = CAC; • = CCAB; ❏ = VAC; ⊕ = PO Statement; ‡ = Publisher's Report; Boldface figures = sworn; Light figures = estimated.

Gale Directory of Publications & Broadcast Media/147th Ed.

4715

Deakin, Australian Capital Territory 2000, Australia
Ph: 61 262 834777
Fax: 61 262 852869
Publisher E-mail: psa.nat@psa.org.au
Professional journal for pharmacists in Australia. **Freq:** Monthly. **Trim Size:** 210 x 275 mm. **Cols./Page:** 3. **Key Personnel:** Grant Martin, Nat. VP; Amy Cooper, Marketing Communications Mgr.; Matthew Ryan, Mgr. Practice Prog.; Sue Lovett, Communications Coord.; James Caulfield, Journalist; Gia Karhu, Publishing Design; Helen Wallis, Publishing Support; Andrew Daniels, Managing Editor; Aaron Hall, Public Affairs Mgr. **Subscription Rates:** $A 170 individuals; $A 230 other countries; $A 16 individuals back issue; $A 26 other countries back issue. **Remarks:** Accepts advertising. **URL:** http://www.psa.org.au/site.php?id=41. **Circ:** 9,500

41835 ■ Australian Prescriber
Ste. 3, 2 Phipps Close
Deakin, Australian Capital Territory 2600, Australia
Ph: 61 2 62023100
Fax: 61 2 62826855
Publication E-mail: info@australianprescriber.com
Publisher E-mail: info@australianprescriber.com
Publication covering therapeutics for health professionals in Australia and the Asia-Pacific region. **Founded:** 1975. **Freq:** Bimonthly. **Trim Size:** A4. **Key Personnel:** Dr. J.S. Dowden, Editor; Dr. F.G. Mackinnon, Dep. Ed. **ISSN:** 0312-8008. **Remarks:** Advertising not accepted. **URL:** http://www.australianprescriber.com. **Circ:** (Not Reported)

41836 ■ inCite
Australian Library and Information Association
ALIA House, 9-11 Napier Close
Deakin, Australian Capital Territory 2600, Australia
Ph: 61 2 62158222
Fax: 61 2 62822249
Publication E-mail: incite@alia.org.au
Publisher E-mail: enquiry@alia.org.au
Trade magazine covering library and information science in Australia. **Founded:** 1980. **Freq:** Monthly. **Trim Size:** 210 x 297 mm. **Cols./Page:** 3. **Key Personnel:** Sue Hoffmann, Contact, shoffmann@hwrmedia.com.au. **ISSN:** 0158-0876. **Subscription Rates:** Free first copy (member); $A 116 members; $A 166 members overseas airmail; $A 160 nonmembers; $A 210 nonmembers overseas, surface mail. **Remarks:** Accepts advertising. **URL:** http://www.alia.org.au/incite/. **Ad Rates:** BW: $A 1,991, 4C: $A 1,990. **Circ:** Paid 8,000

41837 ■ Nutrition & Dietetics
Dietitians Association of Australia
1/8 Phipps Close
Deakin, Australian Capital Territory 2600, Australia
Ph: 61 2 61635200
Fax: 61 2 62829888
Publication E-mail: journal@daa.asn.au
Publisher E-mail: nationaloffice@daa.asn.au
Scientific journal covering food, nutrition and dietetics. **Freq:** Quarterly. **Key Personnel:** Linda Tapsell, PhD, Editor. **ISSN:** 1446-6368. **Subscription Rates:** 127 institutions UK (print and online); US$219 institutions Americas (print and online); EUR162 institutions Europe (print and online); US$250 institutions, other countries print and online; 72 individuals UK (print and online); US$129 individuals Americas (print and online); EUR108 individuals Euro zone (print and online); 72 individuals non-Euro zone (print and online); $A 171 individuals Australia/New Zealand (print and online); 72 other countries. **Remarks:** Accepts advertising. **URL:** http://www.blackwellpublishing.com/subs.asp?ref=1446-6368&site=1. **Formerly:** Australian Journal of Nutrition and Dietetics. **Ad Rates:** BW: $A 2,885. **Circ:** (Not Reported)

41838 ■ Teaching Science
Australian Science Teachers Association
Unit 7, 18 Napier Close
PO Box 334
Deakin, Australian Capital Territory 2600, Australia
Ph: 61 2 62829377
Fax: 61 2 62829477
Publisher E-mail: asta@asta.edu.au
Science-education journal including material of interest to all sectors of the science education community. **Freq:** Quarterly. **Remarks:** Accepts advertising. **URL:** http://www.asta.edu.au/resources/teachingscience. **Circ:** ‡4,000

Derby

41839 ■ 6DBY-FM - 97.9
PO Box 1210
Derby, Western Australia 6728, Australia
Ph: 61 8 91931966
Fax: 61 8 91932298
E-mail: 6dby@westnet.com.au
Format: Full Service. **URL:** http://www.6dby.com.au/.

Dickson

41840 ■ Australasian Journal of Educational Technology
c/o Prof. Catherine McLoughlin, Ed.
School of Education (ACT)
Australian Catholic University
PO Box 256
Dickson, Australian Capital Territory 2602, Australia
Ph: 61 2 62091100
Fax: 61 2 62091185
Publication E-mail: ajet-editor@ascilite.org.au
Publisher E-mail: info@ascilite.org.au
Journal covering educational technology, instructional design, educational applications of computer technologies, educational telecommunications and related areas. **Founded:** 1985. **Freq:** 3/yr. **Print Method:** Offset. **Trim Size:** A5. **Key Personnel:** Dr. Roger Atkinson, Production Ed. & Bus. Mgr., rjatkinson@bigpond.com. **ISSN:** 1449-3098. **Subscription Rates:** Free. **Remarks:** Advertising not accepted. **URL:** http://www.ascilite.org.au/ajet/about/about.html. **Former name:** Australian Journal of Educational Technology. **Circ:** Paid 700

Doonside

41841 ■ SWR-FM - 99.9
PO Box 221
Doonside, New South Wales 2767, Australia
Ph: 61 2 96760999
Fax: 61 2 98314455
E-mail: office@swrfm.org
Format: Ethnic. **Founded:** Mar. 1999. **Operating Hours:** Continuous. **URL:** http://60.242.150.120/.

Drouin

41842 ■ 3BBR-FM - 103.1
PO Box 995
Drouin, Victoria 3818, Australia
Ph: 61 56 254995
Fax: 61 56 251149
E-mail: 3bbrfm@dcsi.net.au
Format: Eclectic; Public Radio. **Ad Rates:** Underwriting available. **URL:** http://www.3bbrfm.org.au.

Dubbo

41843 ■ 2DU-AM - 1251
33-35 Carrington Ave.
PO Box 1221
Dubbo, New South Wales 2830, Australia
Ph: 61 2 68822722
Fax: 61 2 68826953
E-mail: 1251@2du.com.au
Format: Oldies; Adult Contemporary; Talk; News. **Key Personnel:** Ray Core, General Mgr.; Jon Crosby, Announcer; Bret Murray, Program Dir.; Annette Calvert, Advertising Schedules & Traffic. **Ad Rates:** Advertising accepted; rates available upon request. **URL:** http://www.2du.com.au.

East Brighton

41844 ■ Australasian Farmers' Dealers' Journal (AFDJ)
Australasian Farmers' & Dealers' Journal
Norley Australia Pty. Ltd.
22 Stradbroke Ave.
East Brighton, Victoria 3187, Australia
Ph: 61 395 927167
Publisher E-mail: afdj@bigpond.com
Journal covering the Australian farm machinery market. **Freq:** Quarterly. **Trim Size:** 210 x 275mm. **Key Personnel:** Peter Levy, Editor. **Subscription Rates:** $A 33 individuals Australia; $A 77 other countries Australia.

Remarks: Accepts advertising. **URL:** http://www.afdj.com.au/. **Ad Rates:** BW: $A 1,595, 4C: $A 2,255. **Circ:** (Not Reported)

East Brisbane

41845 ■ 4EB-FM - 98.1
140 Main St., Kangaroo Point
PO Box 7300
East Brisbane, Queensland 4169, Australia
Ph: 61 7 32408600
Fax: 61 7 32408686
E-mail: info@4eb.org.au
Format: Ethnic. **Operating Hours:** Continuous. **Key Personnel:** Peter Rehweder, Station Mgr.; Nick Dmyterko, President, president@4eb.org.au; Minas Cassimatis, Vice President. **URL:** http://www.4eb.org.au/.

East Perth

41846 ■ 96-FM - 96.1
Level 1, 169 Hay St.
East Perth, Western Australia 6004, Australia
Ph: 61 8 93239600
Fax: 61 8 93239666
Format: Adult Contemporary; News. **Owner:** Southern Cross Broadcasting (Australia) Limited, Private Bag 10, Dickson, Australian Capital Territory 2602, Australia, 61 2 62422400, Fax: 61 2 62422461. **Founded:** Aug. 8, 1980. **Key Personnel:** Declan Kelly, General Mgr., declank@96fm.com.au; Dean Ford, Production Mgr., deanf@96fm.com.au; Nick Robertson, Music Dir., nickr@96fm.com.au; Marianne Stelmach, Agency Sales Mgr., marianne@96fm.com.au. **URL:** http://www.southerncrossbroadcasting.com.au; http://www.96fm.com.au.

41847 ■ 6IX-AM - 1080
Level 1, 169 Hay St.
East Perth, Western Australia 6004, Australia
Ph: 61 8 94841080
Fax: 61 8 94211200
E-mail: ix@capitalradio.net.au
Format: Oldies; News. **Operating Hours:** Continuous. **Ad Rates:** Advertising accepted; rates available upon request. **URL:** http://www.6ix.com.au/.

41848 ■ 6PR-AM - 882
Level 1, 169 Hay St.
East Perth, Western Australia 6004, Australia
Ph: 61 8 92201400
Fax: 61 8 92201555
Format: Talk; News; Sports; Information. **Owner:** Southern Cross Broadcasting (Australia) Limited, 70 Park St., South Melbourne, Victoria, Australia, 61 3 92432100, Fax: 61 3 96825158. **Operating Hours:** Continuous weekdays; 5a.m.-12a.m. Sat.; 6a.m.-12a.m. Sun. **Key Personnel:** Declan Kelly, General Mgr., declank@6pr.com.au; John Solvander, Program Dir., johns@6pr.com.au; Gary Rendall, Promotions & Mktg. Dir., garyr@6pr.com.au; Marianne Stelmach, Natl. Sales Mgr., mariannes@96fm.com.au; Ashley Braden, Direct Sales Mgr., damiank@6pr.com.au. **URL:** http://www.6pr.com.au.

East Sydney

41849 ■ Cherrie
Evolution Publishing
Olivetti House, Level 3
140 William St.
East Sydney, New South Wales 2010, Australia
Ph: 61 2 93608934
Fax: 61 2 93609497
Magazine featuring what's hot in music, entertainment, arts, pop culture and fashion, as well as the political and social issues taking place across the world. **Freq:** Monthly. **Key Personnel:** Rachel Cook, Editor, phone 61 3 96022333. **Subscription Rates:** $A 60 individuals. **Remarks:** Accepts advertising. **URL:** http://cherrie.com.au. **Ad Rates:** BW: $A 2,160. **Circ:** Combined 19,000

41850 ■ Fellow Traveller
Evolution Publishing
Olivetti House, Level 3
140 William St.

East Sydney, New South Wales 2010, Australia
Ph: 61 2 93608934
Fax: 61 2 93609497
Magazine featuring guide of places to stay, play, dine and shop for gay and lesbian travellers. **Trim Size:** 80 x 188 mm. **Key Personnel:** Peter Walton, Publisher; Richard Watts, Online Ed., phone 61 3 96022333. **Subscription Rates:** Free. **Remarks:** Accepts advertising. **URL:** http://fellowtraveller.com.au/. **Circ:** Combined 30,000

41851 ■ Mental Health Matters
Mental Health Association New South Wales
80 William St., Level 5
East Sydney, New South Wales 2011, Australia
Fax: 61 293 396066
Publication E-mail: info@mental-health-matters.com
Publisher E-mail: info@mentalhealth.asn.au
Magazine including the latest developments in mental health prevention and disease, focusing on emotional well-being. **Freq:** Quarterly. **Subscription Rates:** included in membership dues. **URL:** http://www.mental-health-matters.com/.

41852 ■ SX News
Evolution Publishing
Olivetti House, Level 3
140 William St.
East Sydney, New South Wales 2010, Australia
Ph: 61 2 93608934
Fax: 61 2 93609497
Magazine featuring news and features, fashion, style and entertainment, music and film reviews, interviews and competitions concerning the gays and lesbian in Australia. **Freq:** Weekly. **Key Personnel:** Richard Watts, Online Ed.; Reg Domingo, Editor; Peter Walton, Publisher. **Subscription Rates:** $A 100 individuals. **Remarks:** Accepts advertising. **URL:** http://sxnews.gaynewsnetwork.com.au/. **Ad Rates:** 4C: $A 1,730. **Circ:** Combined 25,000

Echuca

41853 ■ 3GRR-FM - 104.7
PO Box 1141
Echuca, Victoria 3564, Australia
Ph: 61 3 54802085
E-mail: info@radioemfm.org.au
Format: Eclectic; Full Service. **Operating Hours:** Continuous. **URL:** http://www.radioemfm.org.au/; http://www.cbonline.org.au/index.cfm?pageId=13,11,6,3218.

Eildon

41854 ■ SBS Television - 30
Locked Bag 028
Crows Nest, New South Wales 1585, Australia
Ph: 61 2 94302828
Fax: 61 2 94303047
Owner: Special Broadcasting Service, at above address. **Wattage:** 400 ERP. **URL:** http://www20.sbs.com.au/transmissions/index.php?pid=2&id=383.

Emerald

41855 ■ 4EEE-FM - 96.3
19 Opal St.
Emerald, Queensland 4720, Australia
Ph: 61 7 49824852
Fax: 61 7 49821500
E-mail: office@4eee.com.au
Format: Country. **URL:** http://www.4eee.com.au/.

Epping

41856 ■ Northern District Times
Cumberland Newspaper Group
Carlingford Rd., Ste. 2
Epping, New South Wales 2121, Australia
Local community newspaper. **Freq:** Weekly (Wed.). **Key Personnel:** Colin Kerr, Editor, fax 61 2 90248716, editor@northerndistricttimes.com.au; Tim Costello, Advertising Mgr., advertising@northerndistricttimes.com.au. **Remarks:** Accepts display and classified advertising. **URL:** http://www.newsspace.com.au/northern_district_times_. **Circ:** 58,337

Erina

41857 ■ Star 1045-FM - 104.5
Ste. 12, Level 1
Bldg. B, Fountain Corporate
4 Ilya Ave.
PO Box 3535
Erina, New South Wales 2250, Australia
Ph: 61 2 43657000
Fax: 61 2 46357062
E-mail: enquiries@star1045.com.au
Format: Contemporary Hit Radio (CHR). **Owner:** DMG Radio Australia, Level 5, 75 Hindmarsh Sq., Adelaide, South Australia 5000, Australia, 61 8 84195000, Fax: 61 8 84195062. **Operating Hours:** Continuous. **Key Personnel:** Andy Mathers, General Mgr., generalmanager@star1045.com.au; Cassie Waters, Promotions Mgr., promotions@star1045.com.au; Steve Marsden, Chief Engineer, smarsden@dmgradio.com.au; Donna Lalor, Contact, dlalor@dmgradio.com.au; Paul Moltzen, Director, sales@star1045.com.au. **URL:** http://www.star1045.com.au/; http://www.dmgradio.com.au/site/home.aspx.

Erindale

41858 ■ Valley-FM - 89.5
PO Box 112
Erindale, South Australia 2903, Australia
Ph: 61 41 7752494
E-mail: valleyfm895@optusnet.com.au
Format: Ethnic. **Founded:** June 11, 1999. **Operating Hours:** Continuous. **Key Personnel:** Chris Moy, President. **URL:** http://www.valleyfm.com.

Eveleigh

41859 ■ Diabetic Living
Pacific Magazines
8 Central Ave.
Eveleigh, New South Wales 2015, Australia
Ph: 61 2 93942000
Health magazine. **Freq:** Bimonthly. **Trim Size:** 206 X 275 mm. **Key Personnel:** Julia Zaetta, Editor-in-Chief; Erica Goatly, Editor. **Subscription Rates:** US$34.95 individuals. **Remarks:** Accepts advertising. **URL:** http://www.meredith.com/media_portfolio/magazines.html. **Ad Rates:** 4C: $A 7,370. **Circ:** ★53,591

41860 ■ Heart Healthy Living
Pacific Magazines
8 Central Ave.
Eveleigh, New South Wales 2015, Australia
Ph: 61 2 93942000
Health magazine. **Freq:** Quarterly. **Trim Size:** 206 x 275 mm. **Key Personnel:** Samantha Brazel, Contact. **Subscription Rates:** US$19.97 individuals. **Remarks:** Accepts advertising. **URL:** http://www.hearthealthyonline.com. **Ad Rates:** 4C: $A 6,700. **Circ:** (Not Reported)

41861 ■ That's Life
Pacific Magazines
8 Central Ave.
Eveleigh, New South Wales 2015, Australia
Ph: 61 2 93942000
Lifestyle magazine. **Freq:** Weekly (Wed.). **Trim Size:** 210 x 275 mm. **Key Personnel:** Linda Smith, Editor, phone 61 2 94643413; Rose Nehme, Advertising Coord.; Scott Couper, National Advertising Mgr. **Subscription Rates:** $A 155 individuals. **Remarks:** Accepts advertising. **URL:** http://pacificmagazines.com.au/Pages/Magazines/Magazine.aspx?mid=231b77dc6abf-4a9c-8d71-9a75e7548579. **Ad Rates:** 4C: $A 12,670. **Circ:** ★274,106

41862 ■ Total Girl
Pacific Magazines
8 Central Ave.
Eveleigh, New South Wales 2015, Australia
Ph: 61 2 93942000
Magazine for girls. **Freq:** Monthly. **Trim Size:** 148 x 210 mm. **Key Personnel:** Rochelle Thompson, National Advisory Mgr.; Amanda Taylor, Editor, phone 61 2 94643152. **Subscription Rates:** $A 95 two years; $A 49.95 individuals; $A 110 two years New Zealand; $A 59.95 individuals New Zealand. **Remarks:** Accepts advertising. **URL:** http://www.totalgirl.com.au/; http://www.pacificmags.com.au/Pages/Magazines/Magazine.aspx?mid=cfe62b00-0c1d-49d7-b63e-b1dccc6581ba. **Ad Rates:** 4C: $A 4,010. **Circ:** ★51,566

41863 ■ TV Hits
Pacific Magazines
8 Central Ave.
Eveleigh, New South Wales 2015, Australia
Ph: 61 2 93942000
Entertainment Magazine for teens. **Freq:** Bimonthly. **Trim Size:** 210 x 297 mm. **Key Personnel:** Celeste Mitchell, Editor, phone 62 2 94643167; Demeter Stamell, Dep. Ed., phone 62 2 94643120; Rochelle Thompson, National Sales Mgr., phone 62 2 94642683. **Subscription Rates:** $A 34.95 12 months; $A 69.95 24 months. **Remarks:** Accepts advertising. **URL:** http://pacificmagazines.com.au/Pages/Magazines/Magazine.aspx?mid=8d118f486596-4c9d-8f0f-eb8bcd6c3dfc. **Ad Rates:** 4C: $A 5,040. **Circ:** (Not Reported)

Fairfield

41864 ■ Journal of Higher Education Policy and Management
Association for Tertiary Education Management
PO Box 251
Fairfield, Victoria 3800, Australia
Publisher E-mail: atem1@bigpond.com
Journal containing research, scholarship and practitioner papers in higher education. **Freq:** 5/yr. **Key Personnel:** Ian R. Dobson, Editor, ian.dobson@adm.monash.edu.au. **ISSN:** 1360-080X. **Subscription Rates:** US$172 individuals; US$635 institutions online only; US$640 institutions print and online. **Remarks:** Accepts advertising. **URL:** http://www.atem.org.au/activities_journal.cfm; http://www.tandf.co.uk/journals/carfax/1360080X.html. **Circ:** (Not Reported)

Farrell Flat

41865 ■ Agribusiness Connections
Agribusiness Association of Australia
PO Box 504
Farrell Flat, South Australia 5416, Australia
Ph: 61 44884 0232
Fax: 61 88127 8052
Publisher E-mail: agri@agribusiness.asn.au
Peer-reviewed journal dealing with resource management and economic issues in the food and fibre sectors. **Key Personnel:** Glenn Ronan, Editor, ronan.glenn@sagov.sa.gov.au; Bill Malcolm, Editor, b.malcolm@unimelb.edu.au. **URL:** http://www.agrifood.info/connections/index_2009.html; http://www.agrifood.info/.

Fitzroy

41866 ■ Chain Reaction
Friends of the Earth - Australia
PO Box 222
Fitzroy, Victoria 3065, Australia
Ph: 61 3 94198700
Fax: 61 3 94162081
Publication E-mail: chainreaction@foe.org.au
Publisher E-mail: cam.walker@foe.org.au
Publication covering conservation. **Subtitle:** The National Magazine of Friends of the Earth Australia. **Founded:** 1975. **Freq:** 3/yr. **ISSN:** 0312-1372. **Subscription Rates:** $A 22 individuals; $A 33 two years. **URL:** http://www.foe.org.au/resources/chain-reaction/chain-reaction/?searchterm=Chain%20reaction. **Ad Rates:** GLR: $A 120, BW: $A 480, 4C: $A 900. **Circ:** 2,500

Fitzroy North

Rete Italia-AM - See Gosford

Rete Italia-AM - See Wollongong

Five Dock

41867 ■ The Glebe
Cumberland Newspaper Group
181 First Ave.
Five Dock, New South Wales 2046, Australia
Local community newspaper. **Freq:** Weekly (Thurs.). **Key Personnel:** James Tremain, Editor, fax 61 2 90183560, editor@theglebe.com.au; Chris Flourentzou, Advertising Mgr. **Remarks:** Accepts display and classified advertising. **URL:** http://glebe.whereilive.com.au/. **Circ:** 51,698

Circulation: ★ = ABC; △ = BPA; ♦ = CAC; • = CCAB; ❑ = VAC; ⊕ = PO Statement; ‡ = Publisher's Report; Boldface figures = sworn; Light figures = estimated.

Forrestfield

41868 ■ WFOT Bulletin
World Federation of Occupational Therapists
Federation Mondiale des Ergotherapeutes
PO Box 30
Forrestfield, Western Australia 6058, Australia
Fax: 61 894 539746
Publisher E-mail: admin@wfot.org.au
Publication covering therapy. **Freq:** Semiannual in May and November. **Subscription Rates:** Included in membership. **Remarks:** Advertising not accepted. **URL:** http://www.wfot.org. **Circ:** (Not Reported)

Forster

41869 ■ Great Lakes Advocate
Rural Press Ltd.
41 Helen St.
PO Box 138
Forster, New South Wales 2428, Australia
Ph: 61 2 65546688
General newspaper. **Founded:** 1952. **Freq:** Weekly (Wed.). **Key Personnel:** Janine Watson, Editor, phone 61 2 65546688, fax 61 2 65556399, editor.gladvocate@ruralpress.com. **Remarks:** Accepts advertising. **URL:** http://forster.yourguide.com.au. **Circ:** (Not Reported)

Fortitude Valley

41870 ■ Queensland Pride
Evolution Publishing
83 Alfred St., Ste. 2
Fortitude Valley, Queensland 4066, Australia
Ph: 61 7 32160860
Magazine featuring news, entertainment, lifestyle, and community information for gays and lesbian. **Founded:** Dec. 1990. **Freq:** Monthly. **Key Personnel:** Peter Hackney, Editor. **Subscription Rates:** $A 60 individuals. **Remarks:** Accepts advertising. **URL:** http://queenslandpride.gaynewsnetwork.com.au/. **Ad Rates:** 4C: $A 1,384. **Circ:** (Not Reported)

41871 ■ 4 Triple Z-FM - 102.1
264 Barry Parade
PO Box 509
Fortitude Valley, Queensland 4006, Australia
Ph: 61 7 32521555
Fax: 61 7 32521950
E-mail: info@4zzzfm.org.au
Format: Eclectic. **Operating Hours:** Continuous. **URL:** http://www.4zzzfm.org.au/.

41872 ■ 4ZZZ-FM - 102.1
264 Barry Parade
Fortitude Valley, Queensland 4006, Australia
Ph: 61 7 32521555
Fax: 61 7 32521950
E-mail: info@4zzzfm.org.au
Format: Eclectic; Public Radio. **Operating Hours:** Continuous. **Ad Rates:** Noncommercial; underwriting available. **URL:** http://www.4zzzfm.org.au.

Frankston

41873 ■ Journal of Emergency Primary Health Care
Australian College of Ambulance Professionals
Centre for Ambulance & Paramedic Studies
Monash University
McMahons Rd.
Frankston, Victoria 3199, Australia
Ph: 61 399 044198
Fax: 61 399 044168
International e-journal to advance and promote the science and the art of prehospital care research, education, clinical practice, policy and service delivery, and to provide a forum to respond to the professional interests of the multidisciplinary emergency primary health care community. **Key Personnel:** Prof. Frank Archer, Editor; Rhona Macdonald, Managing Editor, phone 61 3 99044198, rhona.macdonald@med.monash.edu.au. **ISSN:** 1447-4999. **Subscription Rates:** Free to all readers. **Remarks:** Accepts advertising. **URL:** http://www.jephc.com/. **Circ:** (Not Reported)

Fraser

41874 ■ SBS Television - 53
Locked Bag 028

Crows Nest, New South Wales 1585, Australia
Ph: 61 2 94302828
Fax: 61 2 94303047
Owner: Special Broadcasting Service, at above address. **Wattage:** 10 ERP. **URL:** http://www20.sbs.com.au/transmissions/index.php?pid=2&id=3.

Fyshwick

41875 ■ 1WAY-FM - 91.9
PO Box 927
Fyshwick, Australian Capital Territory 2609, Australia
Ph: 61 2 62393711
Fax: 61 2 62393722
E-mail: info@1wayfm.com.au
Format: Contemporary Christian. **URL:** http://www.1wayfm.com.au/.

41876 ■ 1WAY-FM - 94.3
PO Box 927
Fyshwick, Australian Capital Territory 2609, Australia
Ph: 61 2 62393711
Fax: 61 2 62393722
E-mail: info@1wayfm.com.au
Format: Ethnic; Adult Contemporary; News. **Operating Hours:** Continuous. **Key Personnel:** Tim Malone, Station Mgr., phone 61 2 62393711, tim.malone@1wayfm.com.au. **Ad Rates:** Noncommercial; underwriting available. **URL:** http://www.1wayfm.com.au.

Garran

41877 ■ National Indigenous Times
66 Fitchett St.
Garran, Australian Capital Territory 2605, Australia
Publisher E-mail: mail@nit.com.au
Newspaper giving an in-depth look at black and white Australia, from land rights, native title and treaty to reconciliation, stolen wages and Aboriginal art. **Freq:** Biweekly. **Col. Width:** 41 millimeters. **Key Personnel:** Stephen Hagan, Editor, editor@nit.com.au. **Subscription Rates:** US$80 individuals 26 issues; US$150 individuals 52 issues. **URL:** http://www.nit.com.au/.

Geelong

41878 ■ The Australian Library Journal
Australian Library and Information Association
c/o Ann Ritchie, Ed.
PO Box 4257
Geelong, Victoria 3220, Australia
Ph: 61 401 110388
Publication E-mail: alj.editor@alia.org.au.nospam
Publisher E-mail: enquiry@alia.org.au
Journal covering library issues in Australia. **Founded:** 1951. **Freq:** Quarterly. **Key Personnel:** Ann Ritchie, Editor. **ISSN:** 0004-9670. **Subscription Rates:** Free institutional member (up to 2 copies); $A 90 members; $A 130 members overseas; airmail; $A 120 nonmembers; $A 160 nonmembers overseas; surface mail. **Remarks:** Accepts advertising. **URL:** http://alia.org.au/publishing/alj/. **Ad Rates:** BW: $A 1,200. **Circ:** (Not Reported)

41879 ■ Geelong Advertiser
The Geelong Advertiser Pty. Ltd.
PO Box 91
Geelong, Victoria 3220, Australia
Ph: 61 352 274300
General newspaper from Australia featuring the latest national, world, business, sport, entertainment and technology news. **Founded:** Nov. 21, 1840. **URL:** http://www.geelongadvertiser.com.au/index.html.

41880 ■ Rural and Remote Health
Deakin University
Faculty Of Arts
Pigdons Rd.
Geelong, Victoria 3217, Australia
Ph: 61 3 52272477
Fax: 61 3 52272001
Journal serving rural and remote communities throughout the world by providing a community forum and specific health-related information. **Key Personnel:** Prof. Paul Worley, Editor-in-Chief, paul.worley@flinders.edu.au; Chrostos Lionis, European Regional Ed.; Ian Couper, African Regional Ed. **ISSN:** 1445-6354. **URL:** http://www.rrh.org.au.

41881 ■ BAY-FM - 93.9
83 Moorabool St., Level 3
Geelong, Victoria 3220, Australia
Ph: 61 52292939
Fax: 61 52213908
E-mail: bayfm@bayfm.com.au
Format: Adult Contemporary. **URL:** http://www.bayfm.com.au/.

41882 ■ K-ROCK-FM - 95.5
PO Box 9550
Geelong, Victoria 3226, Australia
Ph: 61 3 52231955
E-mail: salesmanager@krock.com.au
Format: Album-Oriented Rock (AOR); Classic Rock; Sports. **Owner:** Geelong Broadcasters Pty Ltd., at above address. **URL:** http://www.krock,com.au/.

41883 ■ The Pulse-FM - 94.7
68-70 Lt. Ryrie St.
Geelong, Victoria 3220, Australia
Ph: 61 3 52225947
Fax: 61 3 52296504
Format: Information; News; Eclectic. **Founded:** Nov. 1984. **Operating Hours:** Continuous. **Key Personnel:** Gary Dalton, Station Mgr.; Tim Flint, Mktg. Mgr. **Ad Rates:** Noncommercial; underwriting available. **URL:** http://www.947thepulse.com.

Geeveston

41884 ■ HUON-FM - 95.3
School Rd.
Geeveston, Tasmania 7116, Australia
Ph: 61 3 62971490
Fax: 61 3 62971733
E-mail: huonfm@intas.net.au
Format: Contemporary Country; Country. **Operating Hours:** Continuous. **Ad Rates:** Advertising accepted; rates available upon request. **URL:** http://www.huonfm.com.

Geraldton

41885 ■ Soncity-FM - 97.3
227 Lester ave.
PO Box 150
Geraldton, Western Australia 6531, Australia
Ph: 61 8 99214973
Fax: 61 8 99214973
E-mail: 973fm@modnet.com.au
Format: Contemporary Christian. **Operating Hours:** Continuous. **Key Personnel:** Olaf Buma, Station Mgr.; Shane Forman, Vice-Chm.; Bill Van Ast, Sponsor Mgr. **Ad Rates:** Advertising accepted; rates available upon request. **URL:** http://973soncityfm.modnet.com.au/.

Gladesville

41886 ■ 2RRR-FM - 88.5
PO Box 644
Gladesville, New South Wales 1675, Australia
Ph: 61 2 98162988
Fax: 61 2 98171048
E-mail: office@2rrr.org.au
Format: Ethnic. **Founded:** 1976. **Operating Hours:** Continuous. **Key Personnel:** Josh Barr, Chm.; Jackie Eade, Sec. **URL:** http://2rrr.org.au.

Gladstone

41887 ■ Engineering Failure Analysis
Elsevier Science Inc.
c/o R. Clegg, Ed.-in-Ch.
Process Engineering & Light Metals Centre
Central Queensland University
Gladstone Campus, Bryan Jordan Dr.
Gladstone, Queensland 4680, Australia
Publisher E-mail: usinfo-ehelp@elsevier.com
Journal providing information on engineering failure analysis, materials parameters to problems in engineering structures, components and design. **Freq:** 8/yr. **Print Method:** Offset. **Trim Size:** 13 3/4 x 22 1/2. **Cols./Page:** 6. **Col. Width:** 13 inches. **Col. Depth:** 21 1/2 inches. **Key Personnel:** C.R.F. Azevedo, Editorial Advisory Board; R.G. Baggerly, Editorial Advisory Board; G. Clark, Editorial Advisory Board; J.H. Cleland, Editorial Advisory Board; L. Eiselstein, Editorial Advisory Board; M. Elices, Editorial Advisory Board; A.F. Grandt, Editorial Advisory

Board; M.N. James, Editorial Advisory Board; V. Infante, Assoc. Ed.; A. MacDonald, Editorial Advisory Board; D.R.H. Jones, Editor-in-Chief. **ISSN:** 1350-6307. **Subscription Rates:** 115,868¥ institutions; EUR868 institutions European countries and Iran; US$970 institutions, other countries except Europe, Japan and Iran. **URL:** http://www.elsevier.com/wps/find/journaldescription.cws_home/30190/descriptiondescription.

41888 ■ 4CC-AM - 927
65 Central Ln.
Gladstone, Queensland 4680, Australia
Ph: 61 7 49700300
Fax: 61 7 49769507
Format: Adult Contemporary; Oldies; News. **Owner:** Prime Radio (Gladstone) Pty. Ltd., PO Box 878, Dickson, Australian Capital Territory 2602, Australia. **Key Personnel:** Carly Quinn, Station Mgr., carly.quinn@primeradio.com.au; Carli Hobbs, Promotions Mgr., carli.hobbs@primeradio.com.au. **URL:** http://www.radiozinc.com.au/gladstone/.

41889 ■ Zinc-AM - 927
65 Central Ln.
PO Box 1914
Gladstone, Queensland 4680, Australia
Ph: 61 7 49700300
Fax: 61 7 49769507
Format: Classic Rock; News. **Owner:** Prime Radio, 17 Carnaby St., Maroochydore, Queensland 4558, Australia, 61 7 54751911, Fax: 61 7 54751961. **Key Personnel:** Hamish Rose, General Mgr., hamish.rose@primeradio.com.au; Joel Anderson, Promotions Mgr., joel.anderson@primeradio.com.au. **URL:** http://www.radiozinc.com.au/gladstone/.

Glen Huntly

41890 ■ 3GDR-FM - 95.7
PO Box 287
Glen Huntly, Victoria 3163, Australia
Ph: 61 3 95721466
Fax: 61 3 95721455
E-mail: mail@3gdr.asn.au
Format: Big Band/Nostalgia; Oldies. **Operating Hours:** Continuous. **Key Personnel:** Alex Hehr, Station Mgr. **URL:** http://www.3gdr.asn.au/.

Glen Iris

41891 ■ Breastfeeding Review
Australian Breastfeeding Association
PO Box 4000
Glen Iris, Victoria 3146, Australia
Ph: 61 398 850855
Fax: 61 398 850866
Publication E-mail: subscribers@breastfeeding.asn.au
Publisher E-mail: info@breastfeeding.asn.au
Publication covering breastfeeding and human lactation. **Freq:** Triennial. **Trim Size:** A4. **Key Personnel:** Kim Boyd, Contact. **ISSN:** 0729-2759. **Subscription Rates:** US$50 individuals Australian; US$56 other countries international; US$90 two years 24 month, Australian; US$102 other countries 24 month, international. **Remarks:** Advertising accepted; rates available upon request. **URL:** http://www.breastfeeding.asn.au/lrc/bfreview.html. **Circ:** (Not Reported)

41892 ■ Caulfield Glen Eira Leader
Leader Community Newspapers
1601 Malvern Rd.
Glen Iris, Victoria 3146, Australia
Ph: 61 3 99411500
Publication E-mail: theleader@leadernewspapers.com.au
Local community newspaper. **Freq:** Weekly (Tues.). **Key Personnel:** Natalie White, Editor; Jenny Conyers, Sales Mgr., conyersj@leadernewspapers.com.au. **Remarks:** Accepts advertising. **URL:** http://www.newsspace.com.au/caulfield_glen_eira_leader. **Circ:** Tues. ‡84,704

41893 ■ Port Phillip Leader
Leader Community Newspapers
1601 Malvern Rd.
Glen Iris, Victoria 3144, Australia
Local community newspaper. **Freq:** Weekly (Tues.). **Key Personnel:** Natalie White, Editor, theleader@leadernewspapers.com.au; Julie Saville, Sales Mgr., savillej@leadernewspapers.com.au. **Remarks:** Accepts advertising. **URL:** http://port-phillip-leader.whereilive.

com.au/. **Circ:** Tues. ‡84,704

41894 ■ Progress Leader
Leader Community Newspapers
1601 Malvern Rd.
Glen Iris, Victoria 3146, Australia
Ph: 61 3 99411500
Local community newspaper. **Freq:** Weekly (Tues.). **Key Personnel:** Christine Antoniou, Editor, progress@leadernewspapers.com.au; Narelle Paige, Sales Mgr., paigen@leadernewspapers.com.au. **Remarks:** Accepts advertising. **URL:** http://progress-leader.whereilive.com.au/. **Circ:** Tues. ‡70,100

41895 ■ Stonnington Leader
Leader Community Newspapers
1601 Malvern Rd.
Glen Iris, Victoria 3146, Australia
Ph: 61 3 99411500
Local community newspaper. **Freq:** Weekly (Tues.). **Key Personnel:** Ainsleight Sheridan, Editor, stonnington@leadernewspapers.com.au; Andrew Groves, Sales Mgr., grovesa@leadernewspapers.com.au. **Remarks:** Accepts advertising. **URL:** http://stonnington-leader.whereilive.com.au/. **Circ:** Tues. ‡53,310

Glen Waverley

41896 ■ National Safety
National Safety Council of Australia
Bldg. 4, Brandon Office Pk.
540 Srpingvale Rd.
Glen Waverley, Victoria 3150, Australia
Ph: 61 385 621555
Fax: 61 385 621590
Publisher E-mail: melbourne@nsca.org.au
Magazine containing up-to-date news and information on occupational health and safety. **Subscription Rates:** $A 135 individuals. **URL:** http://www.nsca.org.au/dynamic/magazine.asp.

Glenside

41897 ■ AppleSauce
South Australian Apple Users Club
PO Box 411
Glenside, South Australia 5065, Australia
Publisher E-mail: info@saauc.org.au
Official publication of the South Australian Apple Users Club Inc. **Freq:** Monthly. **Key Personnel:** Peter Carter, Editor, pcarter@acslink.net.au. **ISSN:** 1328-3057. **Remarks:** Accepts advertising. **URL:** http://www.saauc.org.au/AppleSauce/index.html. **Circ:** (Not Reported)

Gold Coast

41898 ■ Bond Law Review
Bond Law School Review Editorial Committee
Bond University
Faculty of Law
Gold Coast, Queensland 4229, Australia
Ph: 61 7 559 552008
Publication E-mail: blr@bond.edu.au
Peer-reviewed journal featuring articles, comments, and notes on the whole spectrum of legal topics and issues. **Founded:** 1989. **Freq:** Semiannual. **Key Personnel:** Prof. Denis Ong, Gen. Ed. **ISSN:** 1033-4505. **Subscription Rates:** $A 77 single issue. **Remarks:** Advertising not accepted. **URL:** http://epublications.bond.edu.au/blr/. **Circ:** (Not Reported)

41899 ■ Revenue Law Journal
Bond University
Faculty of Law
University Dr. (Off Cottesloe Dr.) Robina
BOND University 4229
Gold Coast, Queensland 4229, Australia
Ph: 61 755 9552008
Publisher E-mail: kym_hoffman@bond.edu.au
Law periodical. **Freq:** Annual. **ISSN:** 1034-7747. **Subscription Rates:** $A 90 single issue per annum. **Remarks:** Advertising not accepted. **URL:** http://epublications.bond.edu.au/rlj/. **Circ:** (Not Reported)

41900 ■ Spreadsheets in Education
Bond University
Faculty of Law
University Dr. (Off Cottesloe Dr.) Robina
BOND University 4229

Gold Coast, Queensland 4229, Australia
Ph: 61 755 9552008
Publisher E-mail: kym_hoffman@bond.edu.au
Electronic journal devoted to the publication of quality refereed articles concerned with studies of the role that spreadsheets can play in education. **Key Personnel:** Dr. Steve Sugden, Editor; Dr. Patti Cybinski, Editorial Board; Patricia Cretchley, Editorial Board; Dr. Miles Cahill, Editorial Board; Dr. John Baker, Editor; Dr. Jeff Barker, Editorial Board. **ISSN:** 1448-6156. **URL:** http://epublications.bond.edu.au/ejsie/.

Gold Coast City

41901 ■ ABC Coast-FM - 91.7
Cor. of Francis & Gold Coast Hwy.
PO Box 217
Mermaid Beach
Gold Coast City, Queensland 4218, Australia
Ph: 61 7 55952917
Fax: 61 7 55952999
Format: News; Talk. **Owner:** Australian Broadcasting Corporation, ABC Ultimo Ctr., 700 Harris St., Ultimo 2007, GPO Box 9994, Sydney, New South Wales 2001, Australia, 61 2 83331500, Fax: 61 2 83335334. **Key Personnel:** Jane Munro, Program Dir. **URL:** http://www.abc.net.au/goldcoast/.

Golden Square

41902 ■ 3BO-FM - 93.5
401-405 High St.
Golden Square, Victoria 3555, Australia
Ph: 61 3 54439300
Fax: 61 3 54413937
Format: Ethnic; World Beat. **Key Personnel:** Terry Karamaloudis, Station Mgr., phone 61 3 54439300, terry.karamaloudis@macsc.com.au. **Ad Rates:** Advertising accepted; rates available upon request. **URL:** http://www.theradio.com.au.

Goodwood

41903 ■ Australian Options
Australian Options Publishing Inc.
PO Box 431
Goodwood, South Australia 5034, Australia
Journal covering contemporary political, social, and cultural issues. **Freq:** Quarterly. **Key Personnel:** Prof. Frank Stilwell, Editorial Advisers; Peter Murphy, Editorial Advisers; Sue McCreadie, Editorial Advisers; Rob Durbridge, Editorial Advisers; Terri-Ann White, Editorial Advisers; John Wishart, Editorial Advisers; Rhonda Sharp, Editorial Advisers; Katherine Murphy, Editorial Advisers; Brian Abbie, Editorial Advisers; Dr. Roy Green, Editorial Advisers. **ISSN:** 1324-0749. **Subscription Rates:** $A 20 individuals; $A 15 individuals concession; $A 40 two years; $A 30 two years concession; $A 10 students. **Remarks:** Accepts advertising. **URL:** http://www.australian-options.org.au/index.php. **Circ:** (Not Reported)

Gosford

41904 ■ Australian Family Tree Connections
AFTC Publishing Pty Ltd.
PO Box 322
Gosford, New South Wales 2250, Australia
Ph: 61 243 292400
Fax: 61 243 292444
Publisher E-mail: subscriptions@aftc.com.au
Magazine for Australian and New Zealand family historians. **Founded:** Jan. 1993. **Freq:** Monthly. **Trim Size:** 8 x 10.75. **ISSN:** 1320-4823. **Subscription Rates:** $A 64 individuals air mail; $A 60.80 members air mail; $A 77 individuals New Zealand (air mail); $A 73.15 members air mail (New Zealand); $A 45 other countries air mail (half-year); $A 90 other countries U.S., Canada, U.K. & South Africa; $A 33 individuals air mail (half-year); $A 38.50 individuals New Zealand (half-year). **URL:** http://www.aftc.com.au. **Ad Rates:** BW: $A 280. **Circ:** (Not Reported)

41905 ■ Christine's BIG Crossword
Lovatts Publications Pty Ltd.
PO Box 999
Gosford, New South Wales 2250, Australia

Circulation: ★ = ABC; △ = BPA; ♦ = CAC; • = CCAB; ❑ = VAC; ⊕ = PO Statement; ‡ = Publisher's Report; Boldface figures = sworn; Light figures = estimated.

Gale Directory of Publications & Broadcast Media/147th Ed.

4719

Ph: 61 2 43254199

Magazine featuring classic crossword with large grids and clues that are easy to read. **Freq:** Monthly. **Key Personnel:** Christine Lovatt, Founder. **Subscription Rates:** US$32 individuals online, 6 months; US$64 individuals online; US$126 two years online; $A 6.50 single issue. **URL:** http://www.lovatts.com.au/news/products-services/magazines/view-all-titles/regular-titles/lovatts-big-crossword/.

41906 ■ Christine's Cryptic Crossword Collection
Lovatts Publications Pty Ltd.
PO Box 999
Gosford, New South Wales 2250, Australia
Ph: 61 2 43254199
Magazine featuring puzzle for cryptic lover. **Freq:** Annual. **Key Personnel:** Christine Lovatt, Founder. **Subscription Rates:** US$25 individuals; US$48 two years; NZ$32 individuals; $A 6.50 single issue. **URL:** http://www.lovatts.com.au/news/products-services/magazines/view-all-titles/regular-titles/christines-cryptic-collectio.

41907 ■ Cluewords
Lovatts Publications Pty Ltd.
PO Box 999
Gosford, New South Wales 2250, Australia
Ph: 61 2 43254199
Magazine featuring crossword with the clues built into the actual grid. **Freq:** Bimonthly. **Key Personnel:** Christine Lovatt, Founder. **Subscription Rates:** US$35 individuals online; US$69 two years online; $A 6.95 single issue. **URL:** http://www.lovatts.com.au/news/products-services/magazines/view-all-titles/regular-titles/cluewords.

41908 ■ Codecracker Starhunts
Lovatts Publications Pty Ltd.
PO Box 999
Gosford, New South Wales 2250, Australia
Ph: 61 2 43254199
Magazine featuring puzzles with an entertainment or celebrity theme. **Freq:** Quarterly. **Key Personnel:** Christine Lovatt, Founder. **Subscription Rates:** US$38 individuals; US$72 two years; $A 7.95 single issue. **URL:** http://www.lovatts.com.au/news/products-services/magazines/view-all-titles/regular-titles/codecracker-starhunts.

41909 ■ Colossus Crosswords
Lovatts Publications Pty Ltd.
PO Box 999
Gosford, New South Wales 2250, Australia
Ph: 61 2 43254199
Magazine featuring original giant crossword with varying degrees of difficulty. **Freq:** Bimonthly. **Key Personnel:** Christine Lovatt, Founder. **Subscription Rates:** US$35 individuals online; US$69 two years online; $A 6.95 single issue. **URL:** http://www.lovatts.com.au/news/products-services/magazines/view-all-titles/regular-titles/lovatts-colossus-crosswords.

41910 ■ FindaWord
Lovatts Publications Pty Ltd.
PO Box 999
Gosford, New South Wales 2250, Australia
Ph: 61 2 43254199
Magazine featuring puzzles with topics including popular entertainment, hobbies, sports and lots more. **Freq:** Bimonthly. **Key Personnel:** Christine Lovatt, Founder. **Subscription Rates:** US$20 individuals online; US$39 two years online; $A 4.50 single issue. **URL:** http://www.lovatts.com.au/news/products-services/magazines/view-all-titles/regular-titles/findaword.

41911 ■ Handy ADDoku Plus Kakuro
Lovatts Publications Pty Ltd.
PO Box 999
Gosford, New South Wales 2250, Australia
Ph: 61 2 43254199
Pocket sized puzzle magazine featuring the combination of Sudoku and Kakuro. **Freq:** Bimonthly. **Key Personnel:** Christine Lovatt, Founder. **Subscription Rates:** $A 20 individuals; $A 38 two years; $A 4.50 single issue. **Remarks:** Accepts advertising. **URL:** http://www.lovatts.com.au/news/products-services/magazines/view-all-titles/handy-titles/handy-addoku. **Circ:** (Not Reported)

41912 ■ Handy Arrowords
Lovatts Publications Pty Ltd.
PO Box 999

Gosford, New South Wales 2250, Australia
Ph: 61 2 43254199
Pocket sized magazine featuring crossword puzzles. **Freq:** Bimonthly. **Key Personnel:** Christine Lovatt, Founder. **Subscription Rates:** $A 4.50 single issue; $A 20 individuals; $A 40 two years. **Remarks:** Accepts advertising. **URL:** http://www.lovatts.com.au/news/products-services/magazines/view-all-titles/handy-titles/handy-arrowords. **Circ:** (Not Reported)

41913 ■ Handy Codecrackers
Lovatts Publications Pty Ltd.
PO Box 999
Gosford, New South Wales 2250, Australia
Ph: 61 2 43254199
Pocket sized magazine featuring more than 80 fun puzzles. **Freq:** Bimonthly. **Key Personnel:** Christine Lovatt, Founder. **Subscription Rates:** $A 4.50 single issue; $A 20 individuals; $A 40 two years. **Remarks:** Accepts advertising. **URL:** http://www.lovatts.com.au/news/products-services/magazines/view-all-titles/handy-titles/handy-codecrackers. **Circ:** (Not Reported)

41914 ■ Handy Crosswords
Lovatts Publications Pty Ltd.
PO Box 999
Gosford, New South Wales 2250, Australia
Ph: 61 2 43254199
Pocket sized magazine featuring crossword puzzles. **Freq:** Bimonthly. **Key Personnel:** Christine Lovatt, Founder. **Subscription Rates:** $A 4.50 single issue; $A 20 individuals; $A 40 two years. **Remarks:** Accepts advertising. **URL:** http://www.lovatts.com.au/news/products-services/magazines/view-all-titles/handy-titles/handy-crosswords. **Circ:** (Not Reported)

41915 ■ Handy Cryptic Crosswords
Lovatts Publications Pty Ltd.
PO Box 999
Gosford, New South Wales 2250, Australia
Ph: 61 2 43254199
Pocket sized magazine featuring cryptic crosswords. **Freq:** Bimonthly. **Key Personnel:** Christine Lovatt, Founder. **Subscription Rates:** $A 25 individuals; $A 48 two years; $A 4.50 single issue. **Remarks:** Accepts advertising. **URL:** http://www.lovatts.com.au/news/products-services/magazines/view-all-titles/handy-titles/handy-cryptics/. **Circ:** (Not Reported)

41916 ■ Handy Fill-Ins
Lovatts Publications Pty Ltd.
PO Box 999
Gosford, New South Wales 2250, Australia
Ph: 61 2 43254199
Pocket sized magazine featuring crosswords and other type of puzzles. **Freq:** Bimonthly. **Key Personnel:** Christine Lovatt, Founder. **Subscription Rates:** $A 4.50 single issue; $A 20 individuals; $A 40 two years. **Remarks:** Accepts advertising. **URL:** http://www.lovatts.com.au/news/products-services/magazines/view-all-titles/handy-titles/handy-fill-ins. **Circ:** (Not Reported)

41917 ■ Handy Wordhunt
Lovatts Publications Pty Ltd.
PO Box 999
Gosford, New South Wales 2250, Australia
Ph: 61 2 43254199
Pocket sized magazine featuring wordhunt puzzles. **Freq:** Bimonthly. **Key Personnel:** Christine Lovatt, Founder. **Subscription Rates:** $A 4.50 single issue; $A 20 individuals; $A 40 two years. **Remarks:** Accepts advertising. **URL:** http://www.lovatts.com.au/news/products-services/magazines/view-all-titles/handy-titles/handy-wordhunt. **Circ:** (Not Reported)

41918 ■ Holiday Crossword Collection
Lovatts Publications Pty Ltd.
PO Box 999
Gosford, New South Wales 2250, Australia
Ph: 61 2 43254199
Magazine for crossword and puzzle lovers. **Freq:** Quarterly. **Key Personnel:** Christine Lovatt, Founder. **Subscription Rates:** US$30 individuals online; US$59 two years online; US$9.50 single issue. **URL:** http://www.lovatts.com.au/news/products-services/magazines/view-all-titles/regular-titles/holiday-crossword-collection.

41919 ■ Large Print Crosswords
Lovatts Publications Pty Ltd.
PO Box 999
Gosford, New South Wales 2250, Australia

Ph: 61 2 43254199
Magazine featuring crosswords with special grids in a unique design. **Freq:** Quarterly. **Key Personnel:** Christine Lovatt, Founder. **Subscription Rates:** US$20 individuals; US$38 two years; $A 6.50 single issue. **URL:** http://www.lovatts.com.au/news/products-services/magazines/view-all-titles/regular-titles/large-print/.

41920 ■ MEGA!
Lovatts Publications Pty Ltd.
PO Box 999
Gosford, New South Wales 2250, Australia
Ph: 61 2 43254199
Magazine featuring crosswords. **Freq:** Bimonthly. **Key Personnel:** Christine Lovatt, Founder. **Subscription Rates:** US$35 individuals; US$65 two years; $A 6.95 single issue. **URL:** http://www.lovatts.com.au/news/products-services/magazines/view-all-titles/regular-titles/mega.

41921 ■ Puzzle Fun for Kids
Lovatts Publications Pty Ltd.
PO Box 999
Gosford, New South Wales 2250, Australia
Ph: 61 2 43254199
Magazine featuring readers' letters, jokes, and plenty of puzzles. **Freq:** Quarterly. **Key Personnel:** Christine Lovatt, Founder. **Subscription Rates:** $A 3.95 single issue; $A 15 individuals; $A 28 two years. **Remarks:** Accepts advertising. **URL:** http://www.lovatts.com.au/news/products-services/magazines/view-all-titles/handy-titles/puzzle-fun-for-kids. **Circ:** (Not Reported)

41922 ■ Super Sudoku
Lovatts Publications Pty Ltd.
PO Box 999
Gosford, New South Wales 2250, Australia
Ph: 61 2 43254199
Magazine featuring Japanese number puzzle. **Freq:** Monthly. **Key Personnel:** Christine Lovatt, Founder. **Subscription Rates:** US$25 individuals 6 months; US$49 individuals online; US$96 two years online; $A 4.95 single issue. **URL:** http://www.lovatts.com.au/news/products-services/magazines/view-all-titles/regular-titles/super-sudoku/.

41923 ■ Variety Puzzles
Lovatts Publications Pty Ltd.
PO Box 999
Gosford, New South Wales 2250, Australia
Ph: 61 2 43254199
Magazine featuring selected range of puzzles for every occasion. **Freq:** Bimonthly. **Key Personnel:** Christine Lovatt, Founder. **Subscription Rates:** $A 3.95 single issue; US$19.50 individuals online; US$39 two years online. **URL:** http://www.lovatts.com.au/news/products-services/magazines/view-all-titles/regular-titles/variety-puzzles.

41924 ■ Coast-FM - 96.3
139 Faunce St.
PO Box 19
Gosford, New South Wales 2250, Australia
Ph: 61 2 43220072
Fax: 61 2 43220075
Format: Eclectic. **Founded:** 1984. **Key Personnel:** Chayne Cleary, Prog. Convenor. **URL:** http://www.coastfm.org.au/portal/.

41925 ■ 2GO-FM - 107.7
49 Henry Parry Dr.
Gosford, New South Wales 2250, Australia
Ph: 61 2 4324 2400
Format: Adult Contemporary. **Owner:** Regional Mediaworks, Level 3, 170 Pacific Hwy., Greenwich, New South Wales 2065, Australia, 61 2 84379400, Fax: 61 2 84379498. **URL:** http://theradio.com.au/localworks.aspx?PageID=632&Station=2GO_FM_Central_Coast; http://www.regionalradioworks.com.au/region%20information.asp?region= Gosford.

Gosford (Victoria)

41926 ■ Rete Italia-AM - 801
582 Nicholson St.
Fitzroy North, Victoria 3068, Australia
Ph: 61 3 94810666
Fax: 61 3 94861412
Format: News; Sports; Talk; Ethnic. **Operating Hours:** Continuous. **Ad Rates:** Advertising accepted; rates

available upon request. **URL:** http://www.italianmedia.com.au.

Goulburn

41927 ■ Goulburn Post
Rural Press Ltd.
199 Auburn St.
PO Box 152
Goulburn, New South Wales 2580, Australia
Ph: 61 2 48273500
Publication E-mail: class.goulburnpost@ruralpress.com
General newspaper. **Key Personnel:** Gerard Walsh, Editor, editor.goulburnpost@ruralpress.com. **URL:** http://goulburn.yourguide.com.au.

41928 ■ Eagle-FM - 93.5
Union & Lagoon St.
Goulburn, New South Wales 2580, Australia
Ph: 61 2 48217777
Fax: 61 2 48212535
E-mail: eagle@capitalradio.net.au
Format: Adult Contemporary. **Key Personnel:** Steve Swadling, Station Mgr., swadling@capitalradio.net.au. **Ad Rates:** Advertising accepted; rates available upon request. **URL:** http://www.eaglefm.com.au.

41929 ■ Goulburn Community Radio-FM - 103.3
PO Box 564
Goulburn, New South Wales 2580, Australia
Ph: 61 2 48221103
E-mail: fm103.3@goulburn.net.au
Format: Eclectic; Public Radio. **Operating Hours:** Continuous. **Ad Rates:** Underwriting available. **URL:** http://site.fm103.goulburn.net.au.

41930 ■ 2JJJ-FM - 88.7
GPO Box 9994
Sydney, New South Wales 2001, Australia
Format: Alternative/New Music/Progressive; Information; News. **Operating Hours:** Continuous. **Key Personnel:** Mike McCluskey, State Dir. **URL:** http://www2b.abc.net.au/reception/frequencyfinder/asp/details.asp?transmissionid=1933&presdir=.

Grafton

41931 ■ 104.7-FM - 104.7
PO Box 276
Grafton, New South Wales 2460, Australia
Ph: 61 2 66422766
Fax: 61 2 66431309
E-mail: mynews2@1047fm.com.au
Format: Adult Contemporary. **URL:** http://www.1047fm.com.au/.

41932 ■ 2GF-AM - 1206
15 Prince St.
PO Box 276
Grafton, New South Wales 2460, Australia
Ph: 61 2 66422766
Fax: 61 2 66431309
E-mail: richie@1206am.com.au
Format: Talk; News. **URL:** http://www.1206am.com.au/.

Greenwhich

41933 ■ 2UE-AM - 954
170 Pacific Hwy.
Greenwhich, New South Wales 2065, Australia
Ph: 61 2 99309954
E-mail: sales@2ue.com.au
Format: News; Sports; Talk. **Owner:** Fairfax Media Ltd., GPO 506, Sydney, New South Wales 2001, Australia, 61 2 92822833. **Operating Hours:** Continuous. **Key Personnel:** Chris Edis, Sales Mgr., phone 61 2 99309460; Paul Bowd, Contact, phone 61 2 99309440. **Ad Rates:** Advertising accepted; rates available upon request. **URL:** http://www.fxj.com.au/; http://www.2ue.com.au/.

Grenfell

41934 ■ Grenfell Record
Rural Press Ltd.
41 Main St.
PO Box 19
Grenfell, New South Wales 2810, Australia
Ph: 61 2 63431178

Publication E-mail: mail.grenfellrecord@ruralpress.com
General newspaper. **URL:** http://grenfell.yourguide.com.au/.

Grosvenor Place

41935 ■ Resonate Journal
Australian Music Centre
PO Box N690
Grosvenor Place, New South Wales 1220, Australia
Ph: 61 2 92474677
Fax: 61 2 92412873
Publication E-mail: pubs@amcoz.com.au
Publisher E-mail: info@amcoz.com.au
Australian journal covering music. **Freq:** Semiannual. **Trim Size:** A4. **Key Personnel:** Anni Heino, Editor, a.heino@australianmusiccentre.com.au. **ISSN:** 0811-3149. **Subscription Rates:** US$7.70 individuals single copy. **URL:** http://www.amcoz.com.au/publications/journal.htm. **Former name:** Sounds Australian Journal. **Ad Rates:** BW: $A 600, 4C: $A 1,320. **Circ:** 1,700

Gungahlin

41936 ■ Mix-FM - 106.3
Bellenden St.
Gungahlin, Australian Capital Territory 2912, Australia
Ph: 61 2 62421063
Fax: 61 2 61234106
Format: Contemporary Hit Radio (CHR). **Key Personnel:** Barry Keohane, Program Dir.; Erin Miller, Music Dir.; Alison Makara, Dir. of Sales, amakara@canberrafm.com.au; Glen Kingston, Retail Sales Mgr., gkingston@mix106.com.au; Zak Davies, Promotions and Mktg. Dir., zdavies@canberrafm.com.au. **Ad Rates:** Advertising accepted; rates available upon request. **URL:** http://www.mix106.com.au.

Gympie

41937 ■ 4GY-AM - 558
21 Geordie Rd.
PO Box 42
Gympie, Queensland 4570, Australia
Ph: 61 7 54821544
Fax: 61 7 54827517
E-mail: admin@classichits.com.au
Format: Oldies. **Owner:** Broadcast Operations Group, Level Three, 8 Jones Bay Rd., Pyrmont, New South Wales 2009, Australia, 61 2 99221269, Fax: 61 2 99566680. **Founded:** Mar. 11, 1941. **Operating Hours:** Continuous. **Key Personnel:** Ben Beckinsale, Sales Mgr.; Gary Saunders, Mktg. Mgr., sales@classichits.com.au; Debbie Vink, General Mgr., debbievink@classichits.com.au. **Wattage:** 5000. **URL:** http://www.classichits.com.au/.

Halls Creek

41938 ■ Halls Creek Herald
PO Box 370
Halls Creek, Western Australia 6770, Australia
Ph: 61 891 685199
Fax: 61 891 685299
Publisher E-mail: hallscreekherald@bigpond.com
General newspaper. **Key Personnel:** Gerrard Willett, Managing Editor. **URL:** http://www.hallscreekherald.com/.

Hamilton Hill

41939 ■ Radio Fremantle-FM - 107.9
4/153 Rockingham Rd.
Hamilton Hill, Western Australia 6163, Australia
Ph: 61 8 94942100
Fax: 61 8 94942419
E-mail: admin@radiofremantle.com
Format: Eclectic. **Owner:** Radio Fremantle, at above address. **Operating Hours:** Continuous. **Ad Rates:** Underwriting available. **URL:** http://www.radiofremantle.com.

Hanwood

41940 ■ Journal of Applied Irrigation Science
Sakia.org
Farm 2538 Murray Rd.
PO Box 508

Hanwood, New South Wales 2680, Australia
Ph: 61 269 630881
Fax: 61 269 630781
Journal publishing articles relating to practical application of irrigation science. **Founded:** 1966. **Key Personnel:** Prof. Peter Wolff, Editor-in-Chief, phone 49 5542 2340, fax 49 5542 910676; Dr. Thomas M. Stein, Editor, thomas-manuel.stein@sakia.org. **ISSN:** 0049-8602. **Subscription Rates:** EUR86 individuals; EUR48 single issue. **URL:** http://www.sakia.org/cms/index.php?id=155. **Foreign language name:** Zeitschrift fur Bewasserungswirtschaft.

Hawthorn

41941 ■ The Australian Holstein Journal
Holstein Freisian Association of Australia
PO Box 489
Hawthorn, Victoria 3122, Australia
Ph: 61 3 98357600
Fax: 61 3 98357699
Publisher E-mail: enquiry@holstein.com.au
Magazine of the Holstein Freisian Association of Australia. **Freq:** Bimonthly. **ISSN:** 1328-6196. **Subscription Rates:** $A 88 individuals inc. GST; $A 120 individuals overseas. **Remarks:** Accepts advertising. **URL:** http://www.holstein.com.au. **Former name:** The Dairymen. **Ad Rates:** BW: $A 770, 4C: $A 990. **Circ:** Paid 3,000

41942 ■ Cosmos and History
Cosmos Publishing Cooperative
c/o Arran Gare
Philosophy & Cultural Inquiry
Swinburne Univ.
PO Box 218
Hawthorn, Victoria 3122, Australia
Journal on natural and social philosophy promoting new ways of thinking about physical existence, life, humanity and society etc. **Key Personnel:** Paul Ashton, Editor; Arran Gare, Editor; Claire Rafferty, Editorial Asst.; Paul Atkinson, International Editorial Board; Roberto Schiavo Lena, Editorial Asst.; Keith Ansell-Pearson, International Editorial Board. **ISSN:** 1832-9101. **URL:** http://cosmosandhistory.org/.

41943 ■ The Victoria Baptist Witness
Baptist Union of Victoria
PO Box 377
Hawthorn, Victoria 3122, Australia
Ph: 61 3 98806100
Fax: 61 3 98816123
Publication E-mail: advertisingwitness@buv.com.au
Publisher E-mail: info@buv.com.au
Newspaper covering issues for Christians. **Founded:** 1921. **Freq:** Monthly. **Print Method:** Web offset. **Cols./Page:** 6. **Col. Width:** 4 centimeters. **Col. Depth:** 37 centimeters. **Key Personnel:** Matthew J. Bevis, Editor, matthew.bevis@buv.com.au. **ISSN:** 0726-4097. **Remarks:** Accepts advertising. **URL:** http://www.buv.com.au/Ministries/Witness/WitnessAdvertising.aspx. **Ad Rates:** GLR: $A 6, BW: $A 1,050. **Circ:** Paid 14,000

Hazelbrook

41944 ■ The Australian Woodworker
Skills Publishing Proprietary Ltd.
PO Box 514
Hazelbrook, New South Wales 2779, Australia
Ph: 61 2 47592844
Fax: 61 2 47593721
Publication E-mail: aww@skillspublish.com.au
Magazine covering woodworking projects, technical information, products, show, exhibitions, book reviews, and more. **Founded:** 1985. **Freq:** Bimonthly. **Subscription Rates:** US$46.50 individuals Australia; US$59 individuals NZ, airmail; US$67.50 individuals Asia/Pacific, airmail; US$73.50 other countries airmail; US$90 two years Australia. **Remarks:** Accepts advertising. **URL:** http://www.skillspublish.com.au. **Ad Rates:** BW: $A 1,795. **Circ:** (Not Reported)

41945 ■ House & Home
Skills Publishing Proprietary Ltd.
PO Box 514
Hazelbrook, New South Wales 2779, Australia
Ph: 61 2 47592844
Fax: 61 2 47593721
Magazine covering home improvement issues for home-

Circulation: ★ = ABC; △ = BPA; ♦ = CAC; • = CCAB; ❏ = VAC; ⊕ = PO Statement; ‡ = Publisher's Report; Boldface figures = sworn; Light figures = estimated.

owners, renovators, and building contractors. **Freq:** Bimonthly. **Remarks:** Accepts advertising. **URL:** http://www.skillspublish.com.au/. **Ad Rates:** BW: $A 1,610. **Circ:** (Not Reported)

Healesville

41946 ■ Flow-FM - 106.3
PO Box 407
Kapunda, South Australia 5373, Australia
Ph: 61 8 85663151
Fax: 61 8 85662729
E-mail: mail@flowfm.com.au
Format: Adult Contemporary. **URL:** http://www.flowfm.com.au/.

41947 ■ Progress in Osteoporosis
Springer-Verlag London Ltd.
c/o Prof. Ego Seeman, Ed.
Dept. of Endocrinology
Uni of Melbourne Austin Medical Centre
Studley Rd.
Heidelberg 3084, Australia
Journal providing a summary of the most important literature published in the preceding three to four months in the field of osteoporosis. **Freq:** Quarterly. **Key Personnel:** Prof. Ego Seeman, Editor. **ISSN:** 1645-4959. **Remarks:** Advertising accepted; rates available upon request. **URL:** http://www.springeronline.com/east/journal/10210; http://www.springer.com/west/home/medicine?sgwid=4-10054-70-1153390-0. **Circ:** (Not Reported)

Heidelberg (Victoria)

41948 ■ Journal of Oral Pathology and Medicine
International Association of Oral Pathologists
Dorevitch Pathology
18 Banksia St.
Heidelberg, Victoria 3084, Australia
Ph: 61 39244 0305
Fax: 61 39244 0366
Publisher E-mail: secretary@iaop.com
Journal covering pathology. **Freq:** 10/yr. **Key Personnel:** Erik Dabelsteen, Editor-in-Chief, phone 45 353 26830, fax 45 353 26833; Ian Mackenzie, Assoc. Ed.; Stephen Porter, Assoc. Ed. **ISSN:** 0904-2512. **Subscription Rates:** US$1,132 institutions Americas (print & online); US$1,028 institutions Americas (print); US$1,028 institutions UK (online); 673 institutions UK (print & online); 611 institutions UK (print); 611 institutions UK (online); US$577 members; 344 members other countries; EUR515 members Europe. **URL:** http://www.blackwellpublishing.com/subs.asp?ref=0904-2512&site=1.

41949 ■ Inner-FM - 96.5
Warringal Ctr.
56 Burgundy St., Ste. 38
Heidelberg, Victoria 3084, Australia
Ph: 61 3 94571718
Fax: 61 3 94574674
E-mail: info@innerfm.org.au
Format: News; Eclectic; Public Radio. **Owner:** Community Broadcasting Association of Australia, Level 3, 44-54 Botany Rd., PO Box 564, Alexandria, New South Wales 2015, Australia, 61 2 93102999, Fax: 61 2 93194545. **Operating Hours:** Continuous. **Key Personnel:** Ken Petrucco, President; Paul Dellios, Vice President; Adrian Hook, Treas.; Kevin Yates, Sec. **Ad Rates:** Noncommercial; underwriting available. **URL:** http://www.innerfm.org.au.

41950 ■ 3INR-FM - 96.5
PO Box 410
Heidelberg, Victoria 3084, Australia
Ph: 61 3 94571718
Fax: 61 3 94574674
E-mail: info@innerfm.org.au
Format: Ethnic. **Key Personnel:** Ken Pentrucco, President. **Wattage:** 200 ERP. **URL:** http://www.innerfm.org.au/portal07.

Hendon Common

41951 ■ LIFE-FM - 107.9
3 Butler Dr.
Lumiere Ln.
Hendon Common, South Australia 5014, Australia
Ph: 61 8 82446800

Fax: 61 8 82446855
E-mail: email@life.on.net
Format: Religious; Information; News; Talk. **URL:** http://www.life.on.net/.

Hepburn Springs

41952 ■ Australasian Sound Archive
Australasian Sound Recordings Association
c/o Mr. Bruce Skilton
4 Swiss Mountain Ave.
Hepburn Springs, Victoria 3461, Australia
Publisher E-mail: sound@vicnet.net.au
Journal featuring papers by fellow professionals in the sound and archival industries. **Freq:** Annual. **ISSN:** 0818-5646. **Subscription Rates:** $A 50 individuals; $A 90 institutions. **URL:** http://home.vicnet.net.au/~sound/journals.htm.

Hervey Bay

41953 ■ 4WBR-FM - 105.1
PO Box 384
Hervey Bay, Queensland 4655, Australia
Ph: 61 7 41242024
Fax: 61 7 41248580
E-mail: office@rhemawidebay.com
Format: Contemporary Christian; Gospel. **Key Personnel:** Cliff Kingi, Station Mgr. **URL:** http://www.rhemawidebay.com/; http://www.cbonline.org.au/index.cfm?pageId=13,13,6,3298.

Higgins

41954 ■ Australian Model Engineering
PO Box 4721
Higgins, Australian Capital Territory 2615, Australia
Ph: 61 2 62541641
Publisher E-mail: editor@ameng.com.au
Magazine covering model engineering and model making for a general audience. **Founded:** Oct. 1987. **Freq:** Bimonthly Beginning with the January issue. **Print Method:** Offset. **Key Personnel:** David Proctor, Managing Editor, phone 61 2 62541641, fax 61 2 62541641; Mandy Proctor, Contact; Melanie Dennis, Contact, phone 61 2 62549174, fax 61 2 62549174, sales@ameng.com.au; Dave Harper, Contributing Ed., sandydave@optusnet.com.au; Gerardus Mol, Contributing Ed. **ISSN:** 0819-4734. **Subscription Rates:** US$42 individuals within Australia; $A 50 individuals New Zealand (economy airmail); $A 70 other countries economy airmail; $A 60 individuals Southern Africa & South East Asia. **Remarks:** Accepts advertising. **URL:** http://www.ameng.com.au/magazine.htm. **Ad Rates:** GLR: $A 3.85, BW: $A 290, 4C: $A 462. **Circ:** (Not Reported)

Highgate Hill

41955 ■ Pacific Waves
ICA - Australia
23 Appel St.
Highgate Hill, Queensland 4101, Australia
Magazine of ICA - Australia. **Freq:** 3/yr. **Subscription Rates:** Included in membership. **URL:** http://www.ica-australia.org/index.asp?id=108.

Hindmarsh

41956 ■ 5MBS-FM - 99.9
PO Box 57
Hindmarsh, South Australia 5000, Australia
Ph: 61 8 82326566
Fax: 61 8 82326933
E-mail: mbs@5mbs.com
Format: Jazz. **Owner:** Music Broadcasting Society of South Australia Inc., at above address. **Founded:** Feb. 1998. **Operating Hours:** Continuous. **URL:** http://www.5mbs.com.

Hobart

41957 ■ Australasian Epidemiologist
Australasian Epidemiological Association
c/o Leigh Blizzard, Pres.
Menzies Research Institute
Private Bag 23
Hobart, Tasmania 7001, Australia
Ph: 61 39 2517244

Fax: 61 39 2446017
Publisher E-mail: leigh.blizzard@utas.edu.au
Journal covering epidemiology. **Founded:** 1981. **Freq:** 3/yr. **Print Method:** Offset. **Trim Size:** 11 x 17. **Cols./Page:** 4. **Col. Width:** 2 7/16 inches. **Col. Depth:** 204 agate lines. **Key Personnel:** Sarah McNaughton, Editor; Leigh Blizzard, Scientific Ed.; Verity Cleland, Editor. **ISSN:** 1327-8835. **URL:** http://www.aea.asn.au/australasian-epidemiologist?Name=Value.

41958 ■ Freemasonry Tasmania
Grand Lodge of Tasmania
3 Sandy Bay Rd.
Hobart, Tasmania 7005, Australia
Ph: 61 3 62235814
Fax: 61 3 62238159
Publisher E-mail: gltas@aapt.net.au
Magazine containing information about freemasonry in Tasmania. **Key Personnel:** Ian Cutler, Editor, iancutler@bigond.com. **Remarks:** Accepts advertising. **URL:** http://www.freemasonrytasmania.org/busy.htmFreemasonry_Tasmania_. **Circ:** (Not Reported)

41959 ■ 107-FM - 107.3
75 Liverpool St.
Hobart, Tasmania 7000, Australia
Ph: 61 3 62311073
Fax: 61 3 62343030
Format: Easy Listening; Oldies; News; Talk. **URL:** http://theradio.com.au.

41960 ■ 7HO-FM - 101.7
334 Elizabeth St.
Hobart, Tasmania 7002, Australia
Ph: 61 3 62161017
Format: Adult Contemporary; News. **Owner:** Commercial Broadcasters Pty. Ltd., at above address. **Founded:** 1931. **Operating Hours:** 6a.m.-12a.m. Mon.-Sat.; 6a.m.-9p.m. Sun. **Ad Rates:** Advertising accepted; rates available upon request. **URL:** http://www.7hofm.com.au/.

41961 ■ 7RPH-AM - 864
136 Davey St.
Hobart, Tasmania 7000, Australia
Ph: 61 3 62241864
Fax: 61 3 62241786
E-mail: 7rph@tassie.net.au
Format: Information; News. **URL:** http://7rph.org.au/index.html.

41962 ■ 7THE-FM - 96.1
GPO Box 1324
Hobart, Tasmania 7000, Australia
Ph: 61 3 62441900
Fax: 61 3 62448510
E-mail: info@hobartfm.org.au
Format: Eclectic. **URL:** http://www.hobartfm.org.au/.

41963 ■ 7ZR-AM - 936
1-7 Liverpool St.
Hobart, Tasmania 7001, Australia
Ph: 61 3 62353333
Fax: 61 3 62353220
Format: Talk; News. **Owner:** Australian Broadcasting Corporation, ABC Ultimo Ctr., 700 Harris St., Ultimo 2007, GPO Box 9994, Sydney, New South Wales 2001, Australia, 61 2 83331500, Fax: 61 2 83335334. **Operating Hours:** Continuous. **Key Personnel:** Cath Hurley, Manager. **URL:** http://www.abc.net.au/hobart/radio/.

Holder

41964 ■ 1CMS-FM - 91.1
Grant Cammeron Ctr., Level 2A
27 Mulley St.
Holder, Australian Capital Territory 2611, Australia
Ph: 61 2 62877058
Fax: 61 2 62874348
E-mail: radio_cms@yahoo.com.au
Format: Ethnic. **Key Personnel:** Werner Albrecht, President; Guiseppe Parisi, Co-VP; Nim Osborne, Co-VP. **URL:** http://www.cmsradio.org.au/.

Hornsby

41965 ■ Hornsby & Upper North Shore Advocate
Cumberland Newspaper Group
1c Burdett St., Ste. 720, Level 7
Hornsby, New South Wales 2077, Australia

Ph: 61 2 9479 1609
Local community newspaper. **Founded:** 1919. **Freq:** Weekly (Thurs.). **Key Personnel:** Steve Graham, Editor, editor@hornsbyadvocate.com.au; Mary-Anne Beckers, Advertising Mgr., advertising@hornsbyadvocate.com.au. **Remarks:** Accepts display and classified advertising. **URL:** http://www.newsspace.com.au/hornsby_advocate_. **Circ:** 51,450

41966 ■ Triple H-FM - 100.1
PO Box 2055
Hornsby, New South Wales 1635, Australia
Ph: 61 2 94760105
E-mail: info@triplehfm.com.au
Format: Eclectic; Information; Public Radio; Talk; News. **Operating Hours:** Continuous. **Ad Rates:** Noncommercial; underwriting available. **URL:** http://www.triplehfm.com.au/.

41967 ■ 2HHH-FM - 100.1
PO Box 2055
Hornsby, New South Wales 1635, Australia
Ph: 61 2 94760105
E-mail: feedback@triplehfm.com.au
Format: Ethnic. **Owner:** Triple H FM Ltd., at above address. **Founded:** Dec. 1, 2000. **Operating Hours:** Continuous. **URL:** http://www.triplehfm.com.au/.

Horsham

41968 ■ 3HHH-FM - 96.5
24 Roberts Ave.
Horsham, Victoria 3400, Australia
Ph: 61 3 53811011
Fax: 61 3 53811155
E-mail: tripleh965fm@hotmail.com
Format: Classic Rock. **URL:** http://www.tripleh965fm.org.au.

41969 ■ 3WM-AM - 1089
2 Stawell Rd.
PO Box 606
Horsham, Victoria 3402, Australia
Ph: 61 5 3821351
Fax: 61 5 3811147
E-mail: 3wmreception@aceradio.com.au
Format: Talk; News; Oldies. **Owner:** Regional Mediaworks, Level 2, 70 Park St., South Melbourne, Victoria 3205, Australia, 61 3 99222000, Fax: 61 3 99222198. **Operating Hours:** Continuous. **Ad Rates:** Advertising accepted; rates available upon request. **URL:** http://theradio.com.au/content.aspx?PageID=6281&Station=3WM_Horsham; http://www.regionalmediaworks.com.au/region%20information.asp?region=Horsh am.

Hurstville

41970 ■ The Journal
Fairfax Community Newspapers
182 Forest Rd.
PO Box 210
Hurstville, New South Wales 2220, Australia
Ph: 61 295 983999
Fax: 61 295 983985
Community newspaper. **Subtitle:** Fairfax Community Newspapers Online. **Freq:** Weekly. **Col. Width:** 7 centimeters. **Col. Depth:** 38 centimeters. **Key Personnel:** Colin Moss, Publisher, colin.moss@fairfax.com.au; Kristina Leckenby, Sales Mgr., phone 61 3 92387682; Peter Simcock, Editor, phone 61 3 92387777, journal@fairfax.com.au. **Remarks:** Accepts advertising. **URL:** http://thejournal.yourguide.com.au/. **Circ:** (Not Reported)

Ipswich

41971 ■ River 94.9-FM - 94.9
Pine Mountain Rd., Hill St., Raymonds Hill
Ipswich, Queensland 4305, Australia
Ph: 61 7 38131000
Format: Adult Contemporary; Oldies; Top 40. **URL:** http://www.river949.com.

Jindabyne

41972 ■ Snow-FM - 94.7
Top Fl., Snowy Mountains Plz.
Jindabyne, New South Wales 2627, Australia
E-mail: xl@capitalradio.net.au
Format: Alternative/New Music/Progressive; Contempo-

rary Hit Radio (CHR). **URL:** http://www.snowfm.com.au/.

41973 ■ 2XL-FM - 96.3
Snowy Mountains Plz., Top Fl.
Jindabyne, New South Wales 2627, Australia
Ph: 61 2 64521521
Fax: 61 2 64521006
E-mail: xl@capitalradio.net.au
Format: News; Talk; Adult Contemporary. **Key Personnel:** Richard Wybrew, Station Mgr. **Ad Rates:** Advertising accepted; rates available upon request. **URL:** http://www.2xl.com.au/.

Joondalup

41974 ■ Journal of Systems and Information Technology
Emerald Group Publishing Ltd.
c/o Prof. Craig Standing, Editor
School of Management, Edith Cowan University
100 Joondalup Dr.
Joondalup, Western Australia 6027, Australia
Publisher E-mail: emerald@emeraldinsight.com
Journal focusing on providing an avenue for scholarly work that takes a systemic or holistic perspective in relation to information systems development. **Freq:** 3/yr. **Key Personnel:** Prof. Craig Standing, Editor, c.standing@ecu.edu.au; Lizzie Scott, Publisher, escott@emeraldinsight.com. **ISSN:** 1328-7265. **URL:** http://info.emeraldinsight.com/products/journals/journals.htm?id=jsit.

41975 ■ Wanneroo Times
Community Newspaper
16 Clarke Cres.
Joondalup, Western Australia 6027, Australia
Ph: 61 9 2333000
Fax: 61 9 2333001
Publication E-mail: wannerootimes@communitynews.com.au
Publisher E-mail: classifieds@communitynews.com.au
General newspaper. **Freq:** Weekly (Tues.). **URL:** http://www.communitynews.com.au/Newspapers/JoondalupWannerooTimes/tabid/64/Default.aspx.

41976 ■ Twin Cities-FM - 89.7
PO Box 3292
Joondalup, Western Australia 6919, Australia
Ph: 61 8 63042420
Fax: 61 8 63042223
E-mail: admin@twincitiesfm.com.au
Format: Eclectic; Public Radio; Information; News. **Operating Hours:** Continuous. **Ad Rates:** Underwriting available. **URL:** http://www.twincitiesfm.com.au.

Junee

41977 ■ 2AAA-FM - 97.9
PO Box 2019
Wagga Wagga, New South Wales 2650, Australia
Ph: 61 2 69253000
Fax: 61 2 69252300
E-mail: fm107@2aaa.net
Format: Ethnic; Information. **URL:** http://www.2aaa.net/.

Kadina

41978 ■ Flow-FM - 90.9
PO Box 407
Kapunda, South Australia 5373, Australia
Ph: 61 8 85663151
Fax: 61 8 85662729
E-mail: mail@flowfm.com.au
Format: Adult Contemporary. **URL:** http://www.flowfm.com.au/.

41979 ■ Gulf-FM - 89.3
Kadina Town Hall
55 Taylor St.
PO Box 390
Kadina, South Australia 5554, Australia
Ph: 61 8 88212000
Fax: 61 8 88214519
E-mail: gulffm@yp-connect.net
Format: Eclectic. **Founded:** Mar. 1998. **Operating Hours:** Continuous. **Key Personnel:** Joan Zilm, Chp.; Peter McWaters, Treas.; Lorranie Darling, Sec. **Ad Rates:** Advertising accepted; rates available upon request. **URL:** http://www.gulffm.com.au/.

Kalamunda

41980 ■ 6KCR-FM - 102.5
PO Box 916
Kalamunda, Western Australia 6926, Australia
Ph: 61 8 92930548
Fax: 61 8 92930549
E-mail: committee@kcr-fm.com
Format: Country; Jazz; Easy Listening. **Operating Hours:** Continuous. **URL:** http://www.kcr-fm.org.au/.

Kaleen

41981 ■ Andromeda Spaceways Inflight Magazine
Andromeda Spaceways
PO Box 7311
Kaleen, Australian Capital Territory 2617, Australia
Publication E-mail: asimeditor@gmail.com
Publisher E-mail: asimeditor@gmail.com
Magazine covering science fiction, fantasy, and horror anthologies. **Freq:** 6/yr. **Key Personnel:** Simon Haynes, Contact; Tehani Wessely, Editor. **Subscription Rates:** $A 49 individuals; $A 69 other countries. **Remarks:** Accepts advertising. **URL:** http://www.andromedaspaceways.com. **Circ:** (Not Reported)

Kapunda

Flow-FM - See Bordertown
Flow-FM - See Ceduna
Flow-FM - See Coober Pedy
Flow-FM - See Healesville, Victoria
Flow-FM - See Kadina
Flow-FM - See Kingscote
Flow-FM - See Penola
Flow-FM - See Pinnaroo
Flow-FM - See Roxby Downs
Flow-FM - See Streaky Bay
Flow-FM - See Tennant Creek, Northern Territory
Flow-FM - See Woomera

Katanning

41982 ■ 6WB-AM - 1071
Shop 5/121, Clive St.
Katanning, Western Australia 6317, Australia
Ph: 61 8 98212972
Fax: 61 8 98214055
Format: Adult Contemporary. **Key Personnel:** Vin Dawes, Station Mgr., phone 61 8 98814000, vdawes@radiowest.com.au. **Ad Rates:** Advertising accepted; rates available upon request. **URL:** http://theradio.com.au/localworks.aspx?PageID=2755&Station=RadioWest_Katanning.

Katoomba

41983 ■ 2BLU-FM - 89.1
PO Box 64
Katoomba, New South Wales 2780, Australia
Ph: 61 2 47829286
E-mail: info@blufm.org.au
Format: Ethnic; News; Information. **Key Personnel:** Ken Quinnell, President; Francis Dutton, Vice President. **URL:** http://www.blufm.org.au/.

Kelmscott

41984 ■ Comment News
Community Newspaper
2756 Albany Hwy., Unit 1
Kelmscott, Western Australia 6111, Australia
Ph: 61 9234 5000
Publication E-mail: commentnews@communitynews.com.au
Publisher E-mail: classifieds@communitynews.com.au
General newspaper. **Founded:** 1910. **Freq:** Weekly (Tues.). **Print Method:** Offset. **Trim Size:** 8 3/8 x 10 7/8. **Cols./Page:** 3. **Col. Width:** 2 1/4 inches. **Col. Depth:** 9 1/2 inches. **ISSN:** 0096-4859. **URL:** http://www.communitynews.com.au/OurNewspapers/CommentNews/tabid/58/Default.aspx.

Circulation: ★ = ABC; △ = BPA; ♦ = CAC; • = CCAB; ❑ = VAC; ⊕ = PO Statement; ‡ = Publisher's Report; Boldface figures = sworn; Light figures = estimated.

Kensington Gardens

41985 ■ English in Australia
Australian Association for the Teaching of English
English House
416 Magill Rd.
Kensington Gardens, South Australia 5068, Australia
Ph: 61 1800 248379
Fax: 61 8 83330394
Publisher E-mail: aate@uaate.org.au
Journal containing articles of interest to teachers of English. **Freq:** 3/yr. **Key Personnel:** Deb McPherson, Reviews Ed.; Michael Deves, Production Ed.; Dr. Karen Moni, Editor; Scott Bulfin, Reviews Ed. **Subscription Rates:** $A 77 individuals. **Remarks:** Accepts advertising. **URL:** http://www.aate.org.au/index.php?id=26. **Circ:** (Not Reported)

Kidman Park

41986 ■ Guardian Messenger
Messenger Newspapers
372 Grange Rd.
Kidman Park, South Australia 5025, Australia
Local community newspaper. **Freq:** Weekly (Wed.). **Key Personnel:** Andrew Roe, Western Sales Mgr., roea@mng.newsltd.com.au. **Remarks:** Accepts display and classified advertising. **URL:** http://www.newsspace.com.au/guardian_messenger. **Circ:** 71,025

41987 ■ Portside Messenger
Messenger Newspapers
372 Grange Rd.
Kidman Park, South Australia 5025, Australia
Local community newspaper. **Freq:** Weekly (Wed.). **Key Personnel:** Andrew Roe, Western Sales Mgr., roea@mng.newsltd.com.au. **Remarks:** Accepts display and classified advertising. **URL:** http://www.newsspace.com.au/portside_messenger. **Circ:** 32,977

Kingaroy

41988 ■ CFM-FM - 89.1
104-106 Margaret St.
Toowoomba, Queensland 4350, Australia
Ph: 61 7 46323333
Fax: 61 7 49383129
Format: Classic Rock. **Ad Rates:** Advertising accepted; rates available upon request. **URL:** http://theradio.com.au/Hitmusic.aspx?PageID=1283&Station=CFM_Darling_Downs.

Kingscote

41989 ■ Flow-FM - 95.5
PO Box 407
Kapunda, South Australia 5373, Australia
Ph: 61 8 85663151
Fax: 61 8 85662729
E-mail: mail@flowfm.com.au
Format: Adult Contemporary. **URL:** http://www.flowfm.com.au/.

Kingston (Australian Capital Territory)

41990 ■ Australian Academic & Research Libraries
Australian Library and Information Association
PO Box 6335
Kingston, Australian Capital Territory 2604, Australia
Ph: 61 2 62158222
Fax: 61 2 62822249
Publication E-mail: aarl.editor@alia.org.au
Publisher E-mail: enquiry@alia.org.au.nospam
Publication covering library and information science. **Founded:** 1970. **Freq:** Quarterly. **Trim Size:** 250 x 176 mm. **Key Personnel:** Dr. Bob Pymm, Editor. **ISSN:** 0004-8623. **Subscription Rates:** $A 81 members; $A 107 nonmembers; $A 92 members; $A 121 nonmembers; $A 107 nonmembers; $A 144 nonmembers. **URL:** http://www.alia.org.au/publishing/aarl/. **Ad Rates:** BW: $A 435. **Circ:** Paid 700

41991 ■ Australian Journal of Advanced Nursing (AJAN)
Australian Nursing Federation
Unit 3
28 Eyre St.
Kingston, Australian Capital Territory 2604, Australia

Ph: 61 2 62326533
Fax: 61 2 62326610
Publication E-mail: ajan@anf.org.au
Publisher E-mail: anfcanberra@anf.org.au
Peer-reviewed journal covering advanced nursing. **Founded:** Sept. 1983. **Freq:** Quarterly. **Key Personnel:** Joy Bickley Asher, RN, Editorial Advisory Board. **ISSN:** 1447-4328. **Subscription Rates:** US$99 members hard copy; US$77 members online; US$110 nonmembers hard copy; US$88 nonmembers online; US$297 institutions hard copy Australia; US$220 institutions online Australia; US$125 other countries hard copy; US$100 other countries online; US$355 institutions, other countries hard copy; US$252 institutions, other countries online. **Remarks:** Accepts classified advertising. **URL:** http://www.anf.org.au/html/publications_ajan.html; http://www.ajan.com.au. **Ad Rates:** BW: $A 400. **Circ:** (Not Reported)

41992 ■ Australian Nursing Journal (ANJ)
Australian Nursing Federation
Unit 3
28 Eyre St.
Kingston, Australian Capital Territory 2604, Australia
Ph: 61 2 62326533
Fax: 61 2 62326610
Publication E-mail: anj@anf.org.au
Publisher E-mail: anfcanberra@anf.org.au
Australian journal covering nursing. **Freq:** 11/yr. **Key Personnel:** Joe Korac, Advertising Mgr., joe@bbj.com.au. **Subscription Rates:** $A 33 members ANF/NSWNA/QNU; $A 66 nonmembers Australia; $A 99 institutions Australian libraries, universities, institutions; $A 130 other countries; $A 33 students. **Remarks:** Accepts advertising. **URL:** http://www.anf.org.au/html/publications_anj.html. **Circ:** ‡65,000

41993 ■ Australian Social Work
Australian Association of Social Workers
PO Box 4956
Kingston, Australian Capital Territory 2604, Australia
Ph: 61 2 62323900
Fax: 61 2 62304399
Publisher E-mail: aaswnat@aasw.asn.au
Journal addressing contemporary thinking on social work, social welfare and social policy. **Freq:** Quarterly. **ISSN:** 0312-407X. **Subscription Rates:** Included in membership. **Remarks:** Accepts advertising. **URL:** http://www.aasw.asn.au/publications/aust_socialwork/index.htm. **Circ:** 6,500

Kingston (Victoria)

41994 ■ Aphelion
Rural and Isolated Libraries Special Interest Group
Australian Library and Information Association
PO Box 6335
Kingston, Victoria 2604, Australia
Ph: 61 2 62158222
Fax: 61 2 62822249
Publication covering issues of interest to rural or isolated libraries or librarians. **ISSN:** 1036-9031. **Subscription Rates:** $A 10 individuals. **Remarks:** Accepts advertising. **URL:** http://archive.alia.org.au/sigs/rilsig/aphelion/. **Circ:** (Not Reported)

Kingswood

41995 ■ Cool Country Radio-FM - 88.0
PO Box 186
Kingswood, New South Wales 2747, Australia
Ph: 61 2 96236333
Fax: 61 2 96234567
E-mail: sales@coolcountryradio.com.au
Format: Country. **URL:** http://www.coolcountryradio.com.au.

41996 ■ 2KA-AM - 1476
PO Box 186
Kingswood, New South Wales 2747, Australia
Ph: 61 2 47316950
Fax: 61 2 47313850
E-mail: sales@coolcountryradio.com.au
Format: Country. **Operating Hours:** Continuous. **URL:** http://www.coolcountryradio.com.au/.

Kununurra

41997 ■ 6WR-AM - 693
PO Box 1336

Kununurra, Western Australia 6743, Australia
Ph: 61 8 91682214
Fax: 61 8 91691010
E-mail: radio6wr@westnet.com.au
Format: News; Information; Country. **Founded:** 1987. **Operating Hours:** Continuous. **Key Personnel:** Colin Cameron, General Mgr. **URL:** http://waringarriradio.com.au/.

The Lakes

41998 ■ Zinc-FM - 100.7
5 Martinez Ave.
The Lakes, Queensland 4812, Australia
Ph: 61 7 47294000
Fax: 61 7 47756681
Format: News; Classic Rock. **Owner:** Prime Radio, 17 Carnaby St., Maroochydore, Queensland 4558, Australia. **Key Personnel:** Bryce Nielsen, Station Mgr., bryce.nielsen@primeradio.com.au; Matt Chapman, Sales Mgr., matt.chapman@primeradio.com.au; Darren Burgess, Program Dir., darren.burgess@primeradio.com.au. **URL:** http://www.radiozinc.com.au/townsville/.

Launceston

41999 ■ LC-FM - 87.8
107-119 Paterson St.
Launceston, Tasmania 7250, Australia
Format: Educational. **Owner:** Launceston College, at above address. **Key Personnel:** Steve Tully, Contact, phone 61 3 63327774, steve.tully@education.tas.gov.au. **URL:** http://www.launc.tased.edu.au/joomla/index.php?option=com_content&task=view&id=83&Itemid=112.

Sea-FM - See Scottsdale

42000 ■ 7AD-AM - 900
109 York St.
Launceston, Tasmania 7250, Australia
Ph: 61 3 63314844
Fax: 61 3 63343322
Format: Adult Contemporary. **Ad Rates:** Advertising accepted; rates available upon request. **URL:** http://theradio.com.au/localworks.aspx?PageID=3161&Station=HEART_7AD_Devonport.

42001 ■ 7LA-AM - 1098
109 York St.
Launceston, Tasmania 7250, Australia
Ph: 61 3 63314844
Fax: 61 3 63343322
Format: Adult Contemporary. **Founded:** Dec. 13, 1930. **Ad Rates:** Advertising accepted; rates available upon request. **URL:** http://theradio.com.au/localworks.aspx?PageID=3193&Station=7LA_1098.

42002 ■ 7LTN-FM - 103.7
PO Box 1501
Launceston, Tasmania 7250, Australia
E-mail: cityparkradio@cityparkradio.com
Format: Eclectic; Talk. **URL:** http://www.cityparkradio.com/.

Laurieton

42003 ■ Camden Haven Courier
Rural Press Ltd.
57 Bold St.
PO Box 185
Laurieton, New South Wales 2443, Australia
Ph: 61 2 65598035
Publication E-mail: mail.camcourier@ruralpress.com
General newspaper. **Freq:** Weekly (Wed.). **URL:** http://laurieton.yourguide.com.au. **Circ:** Wed. ‡7,450

Leederville

42004 ■ Australian Longwall Magazine
Aspermont Limited
PO Box 78
Leederville, Western Australia 6902, Australia
Publication E-mail: editorial@longwalls.com
Publisher E-mail: contact@aspermont.com
Magazine featuring information on the longwall sector in Australia. **Freq:** 3/yr. **Trim Size:** 210 x 297 mm. **Key Personnel:** Lou Caruana, Editor, phone 61 86263 9100, fax 61 86263 9148, editorial@longwalls.com. **Remarks:**

Accepts advertising. **URL:** http://www.longwallmagazine. net/. **Circ:** 3,500

42005 ■ Australia's Mining Monthly
Aspermont Limited
PO Box 78
Leederville, Western Australia 6902, Australia
Publication E-mail: editorial@miningmonthly.com
Publisher E-mail: contact@aspermont.com
Magazine featuring mining industry in Australia. **Freq:** Monthly. **Trim Size:** 210 x 297 mm. **Key Personnel:** Noel Dyson, Editor, editorial@miningmonthly.com. **Remarks:** Accepts advertising. **URL:** http://www. miningmonthly.com/. **Circ:** ★8,268

42006 ■ Cranes and Lifting Australia
Aspermont Limited
PO Box 78
Leederville, Western Australia 6902, Australia
Publication E-mail: editorial@cranesandlifting.net
Publisher E-mail: contact@aspermont.com
Magazine covering all classes of mobile and fixed cranes, construction and workshop cranes, truck-loading cranes. **Freq:** Quarterly. **Trim Size:** 210 x 297 mm. **Key Personnel:** Chris Le Messurier, Advertising Sales Mgr., advertising@cranesandlifting.net. **Subscription Rates:** $A 59.40 individuals. **Remarks:** Accepts advertising. **URL:** http://www.cranesandlifting.net/. **Circ:** (Not Reported)

42007 ■ RESOURCESTOCKS
Aspermont Limited
PO Box 78
Leederville, Western Australia 6902, Australia
Publication E-mail: editorial.resourcestocks@ aspermont.com
Publisher E-mail: contact@aspermont.com
Journal featuring resource investment in Australia. **Freq:** 6/yr, **Trim Size:** 210 x 297 mm. **Key Personnel:** Blake Wilshaw, Editor. **Subscription Rates:** $A 138 individuals. **Remarks:** Accepts advertising. **URL:** http:// www.resourcestocks.com.au/. **Circ:** 15,000

Lidcombe

42008 ■ Journal of Intellectual & Developmental Disability
Informa Healthcare
c/o Rachel Meyes, Book Review Ed.
University of Sydney
PO Box 170
Lidcombe, New South Wales 1825, Australia
Publisher E-mail: healthcare.enquiries@informa.com
Journal covering topics on intellectual and developmental disability. **Freq:** Quarterly. **Print Method:** Offset. **Trim Size:** 8 x 10 3/4. **Cols./Page:** 3 and 2. **Col. Width:** 24 and 27 nonpareils. **Col. Depth:** 132 agate lines. **Key Personnel:** Roger J. Stancliffe, Assoc. Ed., rogerst@ med.usyd.edu.au; Susan Balandin, Editor; Helen Beange, Assoc. Ed. **ISSN:** 1366-8250. **Subscription Rates:** 380 institutions; US$690 institutions; EUR550 institutions; 765 institutions corporate; US$1,385 institutions corporate; EUR1,110 institutions corporate. **URL:** http://informahealthcare.com/jid. **Formerly:** Australia and New Zealand Journal of Developmental Disabilities.

Lightning Ridge

42009 ■ Opal-FM - 89.7
PO Box 1737
Lightning Ridge, New South Wales 2834, Australia
Ph: 61 2 68292777
Fax: 61 2 68292897
E-mail: opalfm1@bigpond.com
Format: Eclectic; Public Radio. **Founded:** Aug. 8, 1997. **Operating Hours:** Continuous. **Ad Rates:** Advertising accepted; rates available upon request. **URL:** http:// www.opalfm.com.

Lilydale

42010 ■ Lilydale & Yarra Valley Leader
Leader Community Newspapers
184 Main St.
Lilydale, Victoria 3140, Australia
Ph: 61 3 97351088
Local community newspaper. **Freq:** Weekly (Mon.). **Key Personnel:** Elaine Phelan, Editor, lilydale@ leadernewspapers.com.au; Travis Graham, Sales Mgr., grahamt@leadernewspapers.com.au. **Remarks:** Ac-

cepts advertising. **URL:** http://lilydale-yarra-valley-leader. whereilive.com.au/. **Circ:** Mon. ‡40,479

Lismore

42011 ■ Aviation Trader
PO Box 266
Lismore, New South Wales 2480, Australia
Ph: 61 2 66222133
Fax: 61 2 66222123
Publication E-mail: ads@aviationtrader.com.au
Publisher E-mail: ads@aviationtrader.com.au
Publication covering aviation goods and services. **Founded:** Oct. 1988. **Freq:** Monthly. **Print Method:** Web. **Trim Size:** 275 x 402 mm. **Key Personnel:** Aurelia Hill, Classified; Tony Shaw, Business Mgr.; Kevin Gosling, Editor and Publisher. **Subscription Rates:** US$45 individuals Australia; surface mail; US$80 individuals Asia pacific; airmail; US$112 other countries airmail. **Remarks:** Accepts advertising. **URL:** http://www. aviationtrader.com.au. **Ad Rates:** GLR: $A 9.40, BW: $A 1,640, 4C: $A 2,070. **Circ:** 16,500

Liverpool

42012 ■ Canterbury-Bankstown Express
Cumberland Newspaper Group
Reilly Ctr.
387 Hume Hwy.
Liverpool, New South Wales 2170, Australia
Local community newspaper. **Freq:** Weekly (Tues.). **Key Personnel:** Chris Zambounis, Advertising Mgr., advertising@theexpress.com.au. **Remarks:** Accepts display and classified advertising. **URL:** http://express. whereilive.com.au/. **Circ:** 74,119

42013 ■ Fairfield Advance
Cumberland Newspaper Group
Reilly Ctr.
387 Hume Hwy.
Liverpool, New South Wales 2170, Australia
Local community newspaper. **Founded:** 1946. **Freq:** Weekly (Wed.). **Key Personnel:** Melanie Darmody, Editor, editor@fairfieldadvance.com.au; Chris Zambounis, Advertising Mgr., advertising@fairfieldadvance.com.au. **Remarks:** Accepts display and classified advertising. **URL:** http://fairfield-advance.whereilive.com.au/. **Circ:** 56,116

42014 ■ Liverpool Leader
Cumberland Newspaper Group
Reilly Ctr.
387 Hume Hwy.
Liverpool, New South Wales 2170, Australia
Local community newspaper. **Freq:** Weekly (Wed.). **Key Personnel:** Melisa Mitchell, Editor, fax 61 2 87782834, editor@liverpoolleader.com.au. **Remarks:** Accepts display and classified advertising. **URL:** http://www. newsspace.com.au/liverpool_leader_. **Circ:** 58,271

42015 ■ Community Action-FM - 89.3
306 Macquarie St.
Liverpool, New South Wales 2170, Australia
Ph: 61 2 98228893
Fax: 61 2 96023232
E-mail: office@893fm.com.au
Format: Public Radio; Eclectic. **Operating Hours:** Continuous. **URL:** http://www.893fm.com.au.

42016 ■ 2GLF-FM - 89.3
306 Macquarie St.
Liverpool, New South Wales 2170, Australia
Ph: 61 2 98228893
Fax: 61 2 96023232
E-mail: office@893fm.com.au
Format: Ethnic. **URL:** http://www.893fm.com.au/.

Logan City

42017 ■ KPTK-FM - 101
8 Railway Parade
Logan City, Queensland 4114, Australia
Ph: 61 7 38088101
Fax: 61 7 38087787
Format: Contemporary Hit Radio (CHR); Information; News. **Operating Hours:** Continuous. **URL:** http://www. 101fm.asn.au.

42018 ■ Logan-FM - 101
8 Railway Parade

PO Box 2101
Logan City, Queensland 4114, Australia
Ph: 61 7 38088101
Fax: 61 7 38087787
E-mail: admin@101fm.asn.au
Format: Eclectic; Public Radio; Full Service. **Owner:** Radio Logan, Inc., at above address. **Founded:** 1984. **Operating Hours:** Continuous. **Key Personnel:** Ian Day, Junior VP, ian@101fm.asn.au; Tony Perrin, Sen. VP; David Jull, President. **Ad Rates:** Noncommercial; underwriting available. **URL:** http://www.101fm.asn.au.

42019 ■ 101-FM - 101.1
8 Railway Parade
Logan City, Queensland 4114, Australia
Ph: 61 7 38088101
Fax: 61 7 38087787
Format: Information; News; Eclectic; Public Radio. **Owner:** Radio Logan Inc., at above address. **Founded:** 1984. **Operating Hours:** Continuous. **Key Personnel:** David Jull, President; Charles Mogg, Sec. **Ad Rates:** Noncommercial; underwriting available. **URL:** http:// www.101fm.asn.au.

Logan City DC

42020 ■ 4CBL-FM - 101.1
8, Railway Parade
PO Box 2101
Logan City DC, Queensland 4114, Australia
Ph: 61 7 38088101
Fax: 61 7 38087787
E-mail: 101fmfeedback@gmail.com
Format: Eclectic. **Founded:** Nov. 18, 1988. **Operating Hours:** Continuous. **Key Personnel:** Patricia Alchin, Production Mgr.; Tony Perrin, Sen. VP. **URL:** http://www. 101fm.asn.au/.

Longford

42021 ■ Heart-FM - 95.7
PO Box 178
Longford, Tasmania 7302, Australia
Ph: 61 3 63978453
Fax: 61 3 63978264
E-mail: onair@heartfm.org
Format: Contemporary Christian; Religious. **Operating Hours:** Continuous. **URL:** http://www.heartfm.org/.

Longreach

42022 ■ 4LG-AM - 1098
102 Galah St.
PO Box 20
Longreach, Queensland 4730, Australia
Ph: 61 7 46583333
Fax: 61 7 46581627
E-mail: manager@radio4lg.com.au
Format: Oldies. **Operating Hours:** Continuous. **Key Personnel:** Laura Grant, Sales, laura@radio4lg.com. au. **Ad Rates:** Advertising accepted; rates available upon request. **URL:** http://www.radio4lg.com.au/.

Loxton

42023 ■ Riverland Christian Radio-FM - 93.9
PO Box 1680
Loxton, South Australia 5333, Australia
Ph: 61 8 85846939
Fax: 61 8 85844788
Format: Contemporary Christian; Gospel. **Owner:** Community Broadcasting Association of Australia, Level 3, 44-54 Botany Rd., Alexandria, New South Wales 2015, Australia, 61 2 93102999, Fax: 61 2 93194545. **Founded:** Dec. 11, 2005. **Operating Hours:** Continuous. **Key Personnel:** Gary Wheatcroft, General Mgr. **Ad Rates:** Noncommercial; underwriting available. **URL:** http://www.riverlandlife.org.au.

Mackay

42024 ■ Queensland Farmer
Rural Press Ltd.
PO Box 1320
Mackay, Queensland 4740, Australia
Newspaper covering lifestyle in central and northern Queensland. **Freq:** Monthly. **Key Personnel:** Ian Morgan, Editor, farmer.qcl@ruralpress.com; John Walters, General Mgr., john.warlters@ruralpress.com;

Circulation: ★ = ABC; △ = BPA; ♦ = CAC; • = CCAB; ❑ = VAC; ⊕ = PO Statement; ‡ = Publisher's Report; Boldface figures = sworn; Light figures = estimated.

Jason Ricketts, Advertising Mgr., jason.rickett@ruralpress.com. **Remarks:** Accepts advertising. **URL:** http://www.ruralpress.com/publications/detail.asp?publication_id=105. **Circ:** ‡10,000

42025 ■ 4CRM-FM - 107.5
171 Victoria St.
Mackay, Queensland 4740, Australia
Ph: 61 7 49531411
Fax: 61 7 49535649
E-mail: 4crm@4crm.com.au
Format: Eclectic; Talk. **Operating Hours:** Continuous. **Key Personnel:** Allan Berry, Station Mgr.; Ross Usher, Contact; Stan Hillard, Contact; Warren Gearside. **URL:** http://www.4crm.com.au.

42026 ■ Zinc-FM - 101.9
85 Sydney St.
PO Box 1761
Mackay, Queensland 4740, Australia
Ph: 61 7 49519800
Fax: 61 7 49535166
Format: Classic Rock; News. **Owner:** Prime Radio, 17 Carnaby St., Maroochydore, Queensland 4558, Australia. **Key Personnel:** Anthony Wight, General Mgr., anthony.wight@primeradio.com.au; Tracey Dean, Sales Mgr., tracey.dean@primeradio.com.au; Scott Linden, Program Dir., scott.linden@primeradio.com.au. **URL:** http://www.radiozinc.com.au/mackay/contact1.php.

Main Beach

42027 ■ 4CAB-FM - 107.3
Studio 23 Mariners Cove
60 Seaworld Dr.
Main Beach, Queensland 4217, Australia
Ph: 61 7 55710738
Fax: 61 7 55280134
E-mail: admin@1073.com.au
Format: Contemporary Christian. **Key Personnel:** Callum Jones, Program Mgr., callum.jones@1073.com.au. **URL:** http://www.1073.com.au/.

Maitland

42028 ■ Australasian Beekeeper
Pender Beekeeping Supplies Proprietary Ltd.
PMB 19
Maitland, New South Wales 2320, Australia
Ph: 61 2 49327999
Fax: 61 2 49325994
Publication E-mail: editor@theabk.com.au
Publisher E-mail: pendersmaitland@bigpond.com
Journal covering beekeeping. **Founded:** 1900. **Freq:** Monthly. **Key Personnel:** Des Cannon, Editor. **ISSN:** 1052-0034. **Subscription Rates:** $A 60 individuals; $A 95 out of country. **Remarks:** Accepts advertising. **URL:** http://theabk.com.au/. **Ad Rates:** GLR: $A 27.50; BW: $A 462. **Circ:** Paid 1,600

Mallacoota

42029 ■ 3MGB-FM - 96.9
PO Box 555
Mallacoota, Victoria 3892, Australia
Ph: 61 3 51580929
Fax: 61 3 51580079
E-mail: cootafm@vicnet.net.au
Format: Ethnic; World Beat. **Operating Hours:** 16 hours Daily. **Key Personnel:** Michael Drake, President; Mervyn Kimm, Vice President. **URL:** http://home.vicnet.net.au/~cootafm/.

42030 ■ 3MGB-FM - 101.7
PO Box 555
Mallacoota, Victoria 3892, Australia
Ph: 61 515 80929
Fax: 61 515 80079
E-mail: cootafm@vicnet.net.au
Format: Ethnic; World Beat. **Owner:** Community Broadcasting Association of Australia, at above address. **Operating Hours:** Continuous. **Key Personnel:** Michael Drake, President; Mervyn Kimm, Vice President. **URL:** http://home.vicnet.net.au/~cootafm/.

Mandurah

42031 ■ Coast-FM - 97.3
141-143 Mandurah Ter.
PO Box 688

Mandurah, Western Australia 6210, Australia
Ph: 61 8 95812666
Fax: 61 8 95812786
E-mail: frontdesk@973.com.au
Format: Ethnic; World Beat. **URL:** http://www.coastradio.com.au.

Manly

42032 ■ The Manly Daily
Cumberland Newspaper Group
26 Sydney Rd.
Manly, New South Wales 2095, Australia
Local community newspaper. **Founded:** 1906. **Freq:** Tue.-Sat. **Key Personnel:** Luke McIlveen, Editor, editor@manlydaily.com.au; Kerin Punton, Advertising Mgr., advertising@manlydaily.com.au. **Remarks:** Accepts display and classified advertising. **URL:** http://manly-daily.whereilive.com.au/. **Circ:** 92,590

Mansfield

42033 ■ The Jag Mag
Hughes Graphics & Design Proprietary Ltd.
PO Box 2455
Mansfield, Queensland 4152, Australia
Ph: 61 7 3349 0322
Fax: 61 7 3349 0181
Publication E-mail: info@jaguarmagazine.com
Publisher E-mail: info@jaguarmagazine.com
Consumer magazine covering Jaguars, Jaguar racing, history and related information. **Subtitle:** Jag Mag. **Founded:** 1984. **Freq:** Bimonthly. **Print Method:** Offset. **Trim Size:** 220 mm x 295 mm. **ISSN:** 1325-801X. **Subscription Rates:** US$64 individuals; $A 59.40 individuals. **Remarks:** Accepts advertising. **URL:** http://www.jaguarmagazine.com. **Formerly:** The Jaguar Magazine. **Ad Rates:** 4C: US$1,100. **Circ:** Paid 12,000

Manuka

42034 ■ ArtSound-FM - 92.7
PO Box 3573
Manuka, Australian Capital Territory 2603, Australia
Ph: 61 2 62958444
Fax: 61 2 62958499
E-mail: onair@artsound.com.au
Format: Eclectic. **Operating Hours:** Continuous. **Key Personnel:** Chris Deacon, Gen. Mgr., Engg. & Devel., cdeacon@ozemail.com.au; Richard Thwaites, President. **Wattage:** 10,000. **URL:** http://www.artsound.com.au.

Mareeba

42035 ■ KIK-FM - 88.7
Level 1, 2 Middlemiss St.
Mareeba, Queensland 4880, Australia
Ph: 61 7 40926900
Fax: 61 7 40926811
Format: Country; Contemporary Country. **Operating Hours:** Continuous. **Key Personnel:** Al Kirton, Station Mgr. **Wattage:** 2000. **URL:** http://kik-fm.com.au/.

Maroochydore

42036 ■ Hot-FM - 91.1
N.A.B Bldg.
17 Carnaby St.
Maroochydore, Queensland 4558, Australia
Ph: 61 7 54751911
Fax: 61 7 54751961
E-mail: info@primeradio.com.au
Format: Alternative/New Music/Progressive; News. **Owner:** Sunshine Coast Radio, at above address. **Operating Hours:** Continuous. **Key Personnel:** Patrick Fleming, Sales Mgr., scsales@primeradio.com.au; Deanne Johnson, Promotions Mgr., promotions@hot91.com.au. **Ad Rates:** Advertising accepted; rates available upon request. **URL:** http://www.hot91.com.au.

42037 ■ Mix-FM - 92.7
Sunshine Coast Radio Ctr.
Cor. Carnaby St. & Plz. Parade
Maroochydore, Queensland 4558, Australia
Ph: 61 7 54438444
Fax: 61 7 54437828
Format: Adult Contemporary; Sports. **Owner:** Regional Mediaworks, Petrie House, Level 1, 80 Petrie Ter., Brisbane, Queensland 4221, Australia, 61 7 35108700, Fax:

61 7 35108799. **Key Personnel:** John Williams, Station Mgr., john.williams@macsc.com.au. **URL:** http://theradio.com.au.

42038 ■ Zinc-FM - 96.1
17 Carnaby St.
PO Box 1195
Maroochydore, Queensland 4558, Australia
Ph: 61 7 54751911
Fax: 61 7 54751961
Format: News; Classic Rock. **Owner:** Prime Radio, at above address. **Key Personnel:** Steve Hirst, Station Mgr., steve.hirst@primeradio.com.au; Troy Deighton, Sales Mgr., scsales@primeradio.com.au; Jenna Black, Promotions Mgr., jenna.black@primeradio.com.au. **URL:** http://www.radiozinc.com.au/sunshine/contact1.php.

Marrickville

42039 ■ Choice
CHOICE
57 Carrington Rd.
Marrickville, New South Wales 2204, Australia
Ph: 61 295 773399
Fax: 61 295 773377
Publisher E-mail: ausconsumer@choice.com.au
Magazine featuring articles geared to helping consumers make purchases that offer the best value for price. **Founded:** 1959. **Freq:** Monthly 11/yr. **Subscription Rates:** $A 82 individuals; $A 132 institutions. **Remarks:** Accepts advertising. **URL:** http://www.choice.com.au/defaultView.aspx?id=102314& catId=100165. **Circ:** (Not Reported)

Marysville

42040 ■ UG-FM - 98.5
PO Box 270
Alexandra, Victoria 3714, Australia
Ph: 61 3 57722900
Fax: 61 3 57722414
E-mail: info@ugfm.org
Format: Easy Listening; Contemporary Hit Radio (CHR). **URL:** http://ugfm.cute.com.au/.

Mascot

42041 ■ Australian Aeronautics
Royal Aeronautical Society - Australian Div.
PO Box 573
Mascot, New South Wales 2020, Australia
Publisher E-mail: sydneybranch@raes.org.au
Australian publication covering aerospace. **Freq:** Semiannual. **Subscription Rates:** $A 20 single issue. **URL:** http://www.raes.org.au/.

McMahons Point

42042 ■ Atomic Maximum Power Computing (Australia) Magazine
Haymarket Publishing Ltd.
52 Victoria St.
McMahons Point, New South Wales 2060, Australia
Ph: 61 2 83993611
Publisher E-mail: info@haymarket.com
Magazine providing its readers with the information they need to get the most from their PCs. **Founded:** 2000. **Freq:** Monthly. **Key Personnel:** David Hollingworth, Editor. **Subscription Rates:** $A 69.95 individuals; NZ$75 individuals; $A 97 individuals Asia-Pacific; $A 113 other countries. **URL:** http://www.haymarket.com/atomic/atomic_aus_magazine/default.aspx. **Circ:** 28,555

Meekatharra

42043 ■ 6MKA-FM - 98.3
Hill St.
PO Box 259
Meekatharra, Western Australia 6642, Australia
Ph: 61 8 99811358
Fax: 61 8 99811358
E-mail: meekafm@westnet.com.au
Format: News; Country; Contemporary Hit Radio (CHR); Alternative/New Music/Progressive. **Founded:** 1995. **URL:** http://members.westnet.com.au/mka/.

Melbourne (South Australia)

42044 ■ Radio Australia-FM - 107
GPO Box 428G

Melbourne, South Australia 3001, Australia
Ph: 61 396 261500
Fax: 61 396 261899
Format: News; Talk; Information; Ethnic; Sports. **Owner:** Australian Broadcasting Corporation, GPO Box 9994, Sydney, New South Wales 2001, Australia, 61 2 83331500, Fax: 61 2 83335344. **Operating Hours:** Continuous. **URL:** http://www.radioaustralia.net.au.

Melbourne (Victoria)

42045 ■ AMTA Journal
Australian Association of Massage Therapists
85 Queen St., Level 6
Melbourne, Victoria 3000, Australia
Ph: 61 3 96913700
Fax: 61 3 96023088
Publisher E-mail: info@aamt.com.au
Journal featuring issues affecting the industry and members. **Freq:** Quarterly. **Subscription Rates:** US$66 nonmembers. **Remarks:** Accepts advertising. **URL:** http://www.aamt.com.au. **Circ:** 7,000.

42046 ■ Arena Magazine
Arena Printing and Publications Proprietary Ltd.
PO Box 18
Melbourne, Victoria 3054, Australia
Ph: 61 3 9416 0232
Fax: 61 3 9416 0684
Publication E-mail: magazine@arena.org.au
Publisher E-mail: magazine@arena.org.au
Political science publication. **Founded:** 1991. **Freq:** Bimonthly. **Print Method:** offset. **Trim Size:** 210 x 297. **Key Personnel:** Alison Caddick, Editor; Valerie Krips, Editor. **ISSN:** 1039-1010. **Subscription Rates:** $A 36 individuals includes GST & postage; $A 47 members includes GST & postage; $A 88 institutions includes GST & postage; $A 66 two years includes GST & postage. **Remarks:** Accepts advertising. **URL:** http://www.arena.org.au/. **Ad Rates:** BW: $A 250. **Circ:** 1,800.

42047 ■ Asian Review of Accounting
Victoria University
School of Accounting and Finance
PO Box 14428
Melbourne, Victoria 8001, Australia
Ph: 61 3 99194333
Fax: 61 3 99194901
Publisher E-mail: accountingandfinance@vu.edu.au
Journal covering issues in the fields of accounting, auditing, taxation, and financial management. **Freq:** Semiannual. **Key Personnel:** Dr. Jeffrey Faux, Managing Editor, jeffrey.faux@vu.edu.au. **URL:** http://www.businessandlaw.vu.edu.au/acc_fin/school_publications.asp.

42048 ■ The Australian Christian
1st Fl., 582 Heidelberg Rd.
Melbourne, Victoria 3078, Australia
Ph: 61 3 94888847
Fax: 61 3 94818543
Publication E-mail: editor@australianchristian.org.au
Magazine of the Churches of Christ in Australia covering religion for a general audience. **Founded:** 1090. **Freq:** Monthly 11/yr. **Print Method:** Offset. **Cols./Page:** 4. **Col. Width:** 10 picas. **Col. Depth:** 25 centimeters. **ISSN:** 0004-8858. **Remarks:** Accepts advertising. **URL:** http://www.australianchristian.org.au. **Ad Rates:** BW: $A 576, 4C: $A 1,153, PCI: $A 6.60. **Circ:** Paid 2,205.

42049 ■ Australian Garden History
Australian Garden History Society
Gate Lodge
100 Birdwood Ave.
Melbourne, Victoria 3004, Australia
Ph: 61 396 505043
Fax: 61 396 508470
Publisher E-mail: info@gardenhistorysociety.org.au
Journal featuring garden history primarily Australian, contains some society news. **Freq:** 5/yr. **Key Personnel:** Max Bourke, Editorial Advisory Committee; David Jones, Editorial Advisory Committee; Glen Cooke, Editorial Advisory Committee; Christine Reid, Editorial Advisory Committee, Convener. **ISSN:** 1033-3673. **Subscription Rates:** Free to all members. **Remarks:** Accepts advertising. **URL:** http://www.gardenhistorysociety.org.au. **Ad Rates:** BW: $A 550. **Circ:** (Not Reported)

42050 ■ Australian Journal of Mathematical Analysis and Applications
Austral Internet Publishing
c/o Prof. Sever S. Dragomir, Ed.-in-Ch.
PO Box 14428
Melbourne, Victoria 8001, Australia
Ph: 61 3 99194437
Fax: 61 3 96884050
Journal accepting research papers in all areas of Mathematical Analysis and its numerous applications. **Key Personnel:** Prof. Sever S. Dragomir, Editor-in-Chief, sever.dragomir@vu.edu.au; Maslina Darus, Editor; Neil S. Barnett, Editor; Dachun Yang, Editor; Jadranka Sunde, Assoc. Ed.; Edward G. Neuman, Editor; Frank Hansen, Editor; Anthony Sofo, Editor. **ISSN:** 1449-5910. **URL:** http://ajmaa.org/index.php.

42051 ■ Australian Journal of Public Administration
Institute of Public Administration, Australia
37 Little Bourke St.
Melbourne, Victoria 3000, Australia
Ph: 61 3 96532000
Fax: 61 3 96399663
Publication covering government and related issues. **Freq:** Quarterly. **Key Personnel:** John Wanna, Editor. **ISSN:** 0313-6647. **Subscription Rates:** Free to members. **Remarks:** Accepts advertising. **URL:** http://www.ipaa.org.au/; http://www.blackwellpublishing.com. **Circ:** (Not Reported)

42052 ■ Australian and New Zealand Institute of Insurance and Finance Journal
Australian and New Zealand Institute of Insurance and Finance
Level 8, 600 Bourke St.
Melbourne, Victoria 3000, Australia
Ph: 61 3 96137200
Fax: 61 3 96424166
Publisher E-mail: customerservice@theinstitute.com.au
Technical journal covering insurance and financial services issues for members and industry professionals. **Founded:** 1977. **Freq:** 5/yr. **Key Personnel:** Damian Watson, Advertising Mgr., phone 61 3 96137268, fax 61 3 96424166, dwatson@theinstitute.com.au. **ISSN:** 1443-7198. **Subscription Rates:** Included in membership. **Remarks:** Accepts advertising. **URL:** http://www.theinstitute.com.au. **Formerly:** Australian Insurance Institute Journal. **Ad Rates:** 4C: $A 4000. **Circ:** 11,379

42053 ■ Australian Tennis Magazine
Nicholson Media Group Proprietary Ltd.
1st Fl., 457 Malvern Rd.
Melbourne, Victoria 3141, Australia
Ph: 61 398 268448
Fax: 61 398 278808
Consumer magazine covering tennis across Australia and Asia Pacific. **Founded:** 1976. **Freq:** Monthly. **Trim Size:** 206 x 275 mm. **Key Personnel:** Jackie Cunningham, Advertising Mgr., jcunningham@nicholsonmedia.com; Sherryn Dove, Subscription Mgr., subscriptions@nicholsonmedia.com; Vivienne Christie, Editor, editor@tennismag.com.au. **Subscription Rates:** $A 75 individuals Australia, incl. of GST; $A 140 two years Australia, incl. of GST; $A 105 individuals Australia, 3 years; $A 105 individuals NZ/Asia Pacific; $A 130 other countries. **Remarks:** Accepts advertising. **URL:** http://www.tennismag.com.au. **Circ:** (Not Reported)

42054 ■ Australian Triathlete
Publicity Press Proprietary Ltd.
1121 High St.
Melbourne, Victoria 3143, Australia
Ph: 61 398044700
Fax: 61 398044711
Consumer magazine for triathletes. **Freq:** 9/yr. **Key Personnel:** Amy White, Editor, amy@publicitypress.com.au; Marcus Altmann, Advertising Mgr. **Subscription Rates:** US$67.50 individuals. **Remarks:** Accepts advertising. **URL:** http://www.oztri.com.au. **Circ:** 15,000

42055 ■ BRW
B.R.W. Media
Fairfax Business Media
GPO BOX 55
Melbourne, Victoria 3000, Australia
Ph: 61 3 96033888
Fax: 61 2 92821799
Publisher E-mail: brwhelp@brw.fairfax.com.au
Business publication. **Freq:** Weekly. **Key Personnel:** Sean Aylmer, Editor-in-Chief; Kevin Chinnery, Editor. **ISSN:** 0727-758X. **Subscription Rates:** $A 235 individuals. **Remarks:** Accepts advertising. **URL:** http://www.brw.com.au. **Circ:** (Not Reported)

42056 ■ Chemistry in Australia
Royal Australian Chemical Institute
c/o Prof. Helmut Hugel, Book Reviews Ed.
Dept. of Applied Chemistry
RMIT University
GPO Box 2476V
Melbourne, Victoria 3001, Australia
Ph: 61 992 52626
Fax: 61 963 91321
Publisher E-mail: member@raci.org.au
Magazine containing technical articles, information and news about chemists and the chemical industry. **Freq:** Monthly. **Key Personnel:** Robyn Taylor, Gen. Enquiries, robyn.taylor@raci.org.au; Dr. Margaret Wong, Software Review Ed., marg@freon.chem.swin.edu.au; Joanna Dettl, Advertising Mgr., phone 61 7 35116246, fax 61 7 35116427, jamdettl@bigpond.net.au; Prof. Helmut Hugel, Book Reviews Ed., helmut.hugel@rmit.edu.au; Sally Woollett, Editor, wools@westnet.com.au. **Subscription Rates:** US$170 libraries Australia (inc GST); $A 190 libraries overseas (ex GST, inc air mail delivery). **Remarks:** Accepts advertising. **URL:** http://www.raci.org.au/chemaust/index.php. **Circ:** (Not Reported)

42057 ■ Convenience World
Australians Association of Convenience Stores
8 Norris St., Surrey Hills
Coburg
Melbourne, Victoria 3127, Australia
Fax: 61 382 560143
Publisher E-mail: marketing@aacs.org.au
Magazine featuring news and information relevant to the convenience store industry. **Freq:** Monthly. **Key Personnel:** Kaan Memisoglu, Contact, kaan.memisoglu@retailmedia.com.au. **Subscription Rates:** $A 115 individuals. **Remarks:** Accepts advertising. **URL:** http://www.aacs.org.au/news/11. **Circ:** (Not Reported)

42058 ■ Electronic Journal of Structural Engineering
EJSE International Ltd.
Dept. of Civil & Environmental Engineering
University of Melbourne
Melbourne, Victoria 3052, Australia
International forum for the dissemination and discussion of leading edge research and practical applications in structural engineering. **Freq:** 3 to 6 months. **Key Personnel:** Prof. Priyan Mendis, Editor-in-Chief, pamendis@unimelb.edu.au; Prof. H. Adeli, Advisory Editorial Board, adeli.1@osu.edu; Prof. Adrian Chandler, Advisory Editorial Board, amc1@soton.ac.uk; Prof. Mark A. Bradford, Advisory Editorial Board; Prof. Nelson Lam, Dep. Ed., n.lam@civenv.unimelb.edu.au; Prof. Mir M. Ali, Advisory Editorial Board, m-ali@uiuc.edu. **ISSN:** 1443-9255. **URL:** http://www.ejse.org/.

42059 ■ Family Matters
Australian Institute of Family Studies
485 La Trobe St., Level 20
Melbourne, Victoria 3000, Australia
Ph: 61 3 92147888
Fax: 61 3 92147839
Publisher E-mail: publications@aifs.gov.au
Periodical covering family and marriage. **Freq:** Annual. **Key Personnel:** Meredith Michie, Editor. **ISSN:** 1030-2646. **Subscription Rates:** $A 66 individuals; $A 99 individuals organisations; $A 120 other countries. **URL:** http://www.aifs.gov.au/institute/pubs/fammats.html.

42060 ■ 4wdonline
Sofcom
Level 19, The Como Centre
644 Chapel St.
Melbourne, Victoria 3141, Australia
Ph: 61 3.98268300
Publication E-mail: enquiries@ebroadcast.com.au
Online magazine covering four wheel drive vehicles, events, clubs and equipment. **Subtitle:** The World's Premier 4WD Magazine Since 1995. **Subscription Rates:** US$20 individuals first month; US$10 individuals additional month. **Remarks:** Accepts advertising. **URL:**

Circulation: ★ = ABC; △ = BPA; ♦ = CAC; • = CCAB; ❏ = VAC; ⊕ = PO Statement; ‡ = Publisher's Report; Boldface figures = sworn; Light figures = estimated.

http://www.4wdonline.com/motoring.html. **Circ:** (Not Reported)

42061 ■ Global Journal of Engineering Education
UNESCO International Centre for Engineering Education
c/o Zenon J. Pudlowski, Editor-in-Chief
Monash University
Clayton
Melbourne, Victoria 3168, Australia
Publisher E-mail: uicee@eng.monash.edu.au
Journal for international engineering community. **Key Personnel:** Zenon J. Pudlowski, Editor-in-Chief. **ISSN:** 1328-3154. **Subscription Rates:** US$100 individuals membership; $A 200 institutions for multiple readership. **URL:** http://www.eng.monash.edu.au/uicee/gjee/globalj. htm.

42062 ■ Growth Factors
Taylor & Francis Ltd.
c/o Tony Burgess, Ed.-in-Ch.
Melbourne Tumour Biology Br.
Ludwig Institute for Cancer Research
Melbourne, Victoria 3050, Australia
Journal dedicated to the communication of significant basic and clinical research on the expression, structure, function and use of growth factors on cells, in animals, and in cancer treatment, publishing research papers, reviews and short communications from protein chemists, molecular biologists, physiologists, cell biologists and clinicians working on the control of cell production and differentiation. **Freq:** 6/yr. **Key Personnel:** Tony Burgess, Editor-in-Chief, tony.burgess@ludwig.edu.au; Calle Heldin, Assoc. Ed.; Yosef Yarden, Assoc. Ed. **ISSN:** 0897-7194. **Subscription Rates:** US$1,535 institutions print and online; US$1,535 institutions online only; US$1,535 individuals print and online; US$1,535 individuals online only. **Remarks:** Accepts advertising. **URL:** http://www.informaworld.com/smpp/title~content= t713642964; http://informahealthcare.com/grf. **Circ:** (Not Reported)

42063 ■ Heidelberg Leader
Leader Community Newspapers
636 St. Kilda Rd.
Melbourne, Victoria 3004, Australia
Ph: 61 3 99149000
Fax: 61 3 98758077
Local community newspaper. **Freq:** Weekly (Tues.). **Key Personnel:** Blair Corless, Editor, heidelberg@ leadernewspapers.com.au; Karen Mulhall, Sales Mgr., mulhallk@leadernewspapers.com.au. **Remarks:** Accepts advertising. **URL:** http://heidelberg-leader. whereilive.com.au/. **Circ:** Tues. ‡29,343

42064 ■ In The Black
CPA Australia
Hardie Grant Publishing
85 High St.
Prahran
Melbourne, Victoria 3181, Australia
Ph: 61 385 206444
Fax: 61 385 206422
Publisher E-mail: cpaonline@cpaaustralia.com.au
Publication for the banking, finance, and accounting industries. **Freq:** Monthly. **ISSN:** 1440-8880. **Subscription Rates:** US$116 individuals GST included; US$164 institutions GST included; US$135 other countries; US$185 other countries GST included. **Remarks:** Accepts advertising. **URL:** http://www.cpaaustralia.com.au/ cps/rde/xchg/cpa/hs.xsl/index.html. **Formerly:** Australian CPA. **Circ:** 95,000

42065 ■ International Journal of Electronic Transport
Inderscience Enterprises Limited
c/o Prof. Pieter J.A. Nagel, Assoc. Ed.
Victoria University
Institute for Logistics & Supply Chain Management
PO Box 14428
Melbourne, Victoria 8001, Australia
Journal covering the survey-based study, theoretical research, modeling, and experimental understanding of electronic enabled transport services. **Freq:** 4/yr. **Key Personnel:** Prof. Pieter J.A. Nagel, Assoc. Ed.; Dr. Maode Ma, Editor-in-Chief, emdma@ntu.edu.sg. **ISSN:** 1742-6952. **Subscription Rates:** EUR494 individuals print or online; EUR672 individuals print and online. **URL:** http://www.inderscience.com/browse/index.php? journalID=133.

42066 ■ International Journal of Environment, Workplace and Employment
Inderscience Enterprises Limited
c/o Matthew Clarke, Editorial Board
RMIT University, School of Social Science & Planning
GPO Box 2476V
Melbourne, Victoria 3001, Australia
Peer-reviewed journal covering the study on the connection between environment, workplace, and employment. **Freq:** 4/yr. **Key Personnel:** Dr. M.A. Dorgham, Editor-in-Chief, editorial@inderscience.com. **ISSN:** 1741-8437. **Subscription Rates:** EUR494 individuals print or online; EUR672 individuals print and online. **URL:** http://www.inderscience.com/browse/index. php?journalID=112.

42067 ■ International Journal of Managing Projects in Business
Emerald Group Publishing Ltd.
c/o Prof. Derek Walker, Editor
RMIT University, School of Property Construction & Project Management
GPO Box 2476V
Melbourne, Victoria 3000, Australia
Publisher E-mail: emerald@emeraldinsight.com
Journal identifying key implications for senior practitioners and managers of projects world-wide. **Freq:** 3/yr. **Key Personnel:** Prof. Derek Walker, Editor, derek. walker@rmit.edu.au; Ruth Young, Publisher, ryoung@ emeraldinsight.com. **ISSN:** 1753-8378. **URL:** http://info. emeraldinsight.com/products/journals/journals.htm?id= ijmpb.

42068 ■ Italy Down Under
Italy Down Under Pty. Ltd.
478 William St.
Melbourne, Victoria 3003, Australia
Magazine exploring the links and synergies between Italy and Australia, featuring in-depth articles covering politics and current affairs, lifestyle trends, travel and tourism, food & wine, recipes, fashion, architecture, opera, music, art, history, business, and sports. **Freq:** Quarterly. **Subscription Rates:** $A 30 individuals; $A 60 other countries airmail; $A 48 individuals airmail New Zealand; $A 55 two years. **Remarks:** Accepts advertising. **URL:** http://www.italydownunder.com.au. **Ad Rates:** BW: $A 3,950. **Circ:** (Not Reported)

42069 ■ LIJ
Law Institute of Victoria
470 Bourke St.
Melbourne, Victoria 3000, Australia
Ph: 61 396 079311
Fax: 61 396 025270
Publisher E-mail: lawinst@liv.asn.au
Professional magazine covering legal information. **Founded:** July 1927. **Freq:** Monthly 11/yr. **Key Personnel:** Greg Cooper, Advertising Mgr., phone 61 396 079496, gcooper@liv.asn.au; Mick Paskos, Managing Editor, phone 61 396 079319, mpaskos@liv.asn.au; Cam Ward, Sub-Ed., phone 61 396 079349, cward@liv. asn.au. **ISSN:** 0023-9267. **Subscription Rates:** $A 175 individuals incl. GST; domestic; $A 525 individuals online; 2 to 20 users; 1 hardcopy per issue; $A 477.25 out of country online; 2 to 20 users; plus GST; $A 840 individuals online; 21 to 100 users; incl. GST; $A 954.55 out of country online; 101 to 200 users; $A 1,050 individuals domestic; online 101-200 users; incl. GST; $A 767.65 out of country online; 21 to 100 users; incl. GST. **Remarks:** Accepts advertising. **URL:** http://www. liv.asn.au/News-and-Publications/Law-Institute-Journal. **Former name:** Law Institute Journal. **Ad Rates:** GLR: US$11.38, 4C: US$2,325. **Circ:** Combined ‡11,131

42070 ■ Local Government Focus
Eryl Morgan Publications Proprietary Ltd.
785 High St.
Melbourne, Victoria 3071, Australia
Ph: 61 394 169900
Fax: 61 394 169633
Publisher E-mail: info@lgfocus.com.au
Newspaper covering local government. **Subtitle:** Australia's National Local Government Newspaper. **Founded:** 1985. **Freq:** Monthly. **Print Method:** Web. **Trim Size:** 270 x 360 mm. **Cols./Page:** 6. **Col. Width:** 40 millimeters. **Col. Depth:** 360 millimeters. **Key Personnel:** Corinne Morgan, Contact. **ISSN:** 0819-470X. **Subscription Rates:** Free. **Remarks:** Accepts advertising. **URL:** http://www.lgfocus.com.au; http://www. loc-gov-focus.aus.net. **Ad Rates:** BW: $A 4,590, 4C: $A

4,400. **Circ:** Combined 11,800

42071 ■ Manningham Leader
Leader Community Newspapers
636 St. Kilda Rd.
Melbourne, Victoria 3004, Australia
Ph: 61 3 99149000
Fax: 61 3 98758077
Local community newspaper. **Freq:** Weekly (Wed.). **Key Personnel:** Belinda Mackowski, Editor, manningham@ leadernewspapers.com.au; Neil Honey, Sales Mgr., honeyn@leadernewspapers.com.au. **Remarks:** Accepts advertising. **URL:** http://www.newsspace.com.au/ manningham_leader_. **Circ:** Wed. ‡44,421

42072 ■ Maroondah Leader
Leader Community Newspapers
636 St. Kilda Rd.
Melbourne, Victoria 3004, Australia
Ph: 61 3 99149000
Fax: 61 3 98758077
Local community newspaper. **Freq:** Weekly (Tues.). **Key Personnel:** Bryan Allchin, Editor, phone 61 3 98758333, maroondah@leadernewspapers.com.au; Narelle Paige, Sales Mgr., paigen@leadernewspapers.com.au. **Remarks:** Accepts advertising. **URL:** http://maroondah-leader.whereilive.com.au/. **Circ:** Tues. ‡44,398

42073 ■ Melbourne Community Voice
Evolution Publishing
365 Little Collins St., Level 7, Ste. 8
Melbourne, Victoria 3000, Australia
Ph: 61 3 96022333
Magazine featuring news and features, social pages, fashion, beauty, sport, travel, automotive real estate, interviews, and reviews for gays and lesbians. **Freq:** Weekly. **Key Personnel:** Andrew Shaw, Editor; Richard Watts, Online Ed.; Peter Walton, Publisher. **Subscription Rates:** $A 100 individuals. **Remarks:** Accepts advertising. **URL:** http://mcv.gaynewsnetwork.com.au/. **Also known as:** MCV. **Ad Rates:** 4C: $A 1,730. **Circ:** Combined 20,000

42074 ■ Melbourne Leader
Leader Community Newspapers
636 St. Kilda Rd.
Melbourne, Victoria 3004, Australia
Ph: 61 3 99149000
Fax: 61 3 98758077
Local community newspaper. **Freq:** Weekly (Wed.). **Key Personnel:** Michael Gleeson, Editor, melbourne@ leadernewspapers.com.au; Karen Mulhall, Sales Mgr., mulhallk@leadernewspapers.com.au. **Remarks:** Accepts advertising. **URL:** http://melbourne-leader. whereilive.com.au/. **Circ:** Wed. ‡55,689

42075 ■ Melbourne University Law Review
The University of Melbourne
Faculty of Law
Law School
Melbourne, Victoria 3010, Australia
Ph: 61 3 83444000
Fax: 61 3 83445104
Publication E-mail: mulr@law.unimelb.edu.au
Publisher E-mail: law-mulr@unimelb.edu.au
Law periodical. **Founded:** 1957. **Freq:** 3/yr. **Key Personnel:** Rudi Kruse, Editor; Kathryn Tomasic, Editor; Christopher Tran, Editor. **ISSN:** 0025-8938. **Subscription Rates:** $A 66 single issue including postage and handling. **Remarks:** Advertising not accepted. **URL:** http://mulr.law.unimelb.edu.au/. **Circ:** (Not Reported)

42076 ■ Microbiology Australia
Australian Society for Microbiology
Ste. 23, 20 Commercial Rd.
Melbourne, Victoria 3004, Australia
Ph: 61 398 678699
Fax: 61 398 678722
Publisher E-mail: admin@theasm.com.au
Australian publication covering microbiology. **Freq:** Quarterly. **ISSN:** 1324-4272. **URL:** http://www.theasm. com.au/publications.

42077 ■ Moonee Valley Leader
Leader Community Newspapers
636 St. Kilda Rd.
Melbourne, Victoria 3004, Australia
Ph: 61 3 99149000
Fax: 61 3 98758077
Local community newspaper. **Freq:** Weekly (Mon.). **Key Personnel:** Mark Smith, Editor, mooneevalley@

leadernewspapers.com.au; Gusto Simandjuntak, Sales Mgr., simandjuntakg@leadernewspapers.com.au. **Remarks:** Accepts advertising. **URL:** http://moonee-valley-leader.whereilive.com.au/. **Circ:** Mon. ‡51,339

42078 ■ Moorabool Leader
Leader Community Newspapers
636 St. Kilda Rd.
Melbourne, Victoria 3004, Australia
Ph: 61 3 99149000
Fax: 61 3 98758077
Local community newspaper. **Freq:** Weekly (Tues.). **Key Personnel:** Andrew Jefferson, Editor, melton@leadernewspapers.com.au; Helen Meritt, Sales Mgr., merritth@leadernewspapers.com.au. **Remarks:** Accepts advertising. **URL:** http://www.newsspace.com.au/melton_leader_. **Circ:** Tues. ‡35,575

42079 ■ Moreland Leader
Leader Community Newspapers
636 St. Kilda Rd.
Melbourne, Victoria 3004, Australia
Ph: 61 3 99149000
Fax: 61 3 98758077
Local community newspaper. **Freq:** Weekly (Mon.). **Key Personnel:** Simon Craig, Editor, moreland@leadernewspapers.com.au; Gusto Simandjuntak, Sales Mgr., simandjuntakg@leadernewspapers.com.au. **Remarks:** Accepts advertising. **URL:** http://moreland-leader.whereilive.com.au/. **Circ:** Mon. ‡66,973

42080 ■ Oakleigh Monash Leader
Leader Community Newspapers
636 St. Kilda Rd.
Melbourne, Victoria 3004, Australia
Ph: 61 3 99149000
Fax: 61 3 98758077
Local community newspaper. **Freq:** Weekly (Tues.). **Key Personnel:** Allison Bannan, Editor, monash@leadernewspapers.com.au; Andrew Groves, Sales Mgr., grovesa@leadernewspapers.com.au. **Remarks:** Accepts advertising. **URL:** http://oakleigh-monash-leader.whereilive.com.au/. **Circ:** Tues. ‡70,580

42081 ■ Overland
O.L. Society Ltd.
9 David St.
Melbourne, Victoria 3001, Australia
Ph: 61 3 99149163
Fax: 61 3 96877614
Publisher E-mail: overland@vu.edu.au
Periodical focusing on history, literature, and culture. **Founded:** 1954. **Freq:** Quarterly. **Trim Size:** 185 x 248 mm. **Key Personnel:** Rjurik Davidson, Assoc. Ed.; Jeff Sparrow, Editor; Keri Glastonbury, Poetry Ed. **ISSN:** 0030-7416. **Subscription Rates:** $A 54 individuals; $A 70 institutions; $A 660 life; $A 40 individuals pensioner, concession, student; $A 96 other countries AUS. **URL:** http://web.overland.org.au/?page_id=6. **Ad Rates:** BW: US$400. **Circ:** Combined 2,000

42082 ■ Preston Leader
Leader Community Newspapers
636 St. Kilda Rd.
Melbourne, Victoria 3004, Australia
Ph: 61 3 99149000
Fax: 61 3 98758077
Local community newspaper. **Freq:** Weekly (Tues.). **Key Personnel:** Sally Fisher, Editor, phone 61 3 98758333, preston@leadernewspapers.com.au; Karen Mulhall, Sales Mgr., mulhallk@leadernewspapers.com.au. **Remarks:** Accepts advertising. **URL:** http://preston-leader.whereilive.com.au/. **Circ:** Tues. ‡38,044

42083 ■ Qualitative Research Journal
Association for Qualitative Research
Faculty of Business & Economics
Monash University
Melbourne, Victoria, Australia
Electronic journal devoted to the communication of the theory and practice of qualitative research in the human sciences. **Freq:** Semiannual. **Key Personnel:** Dr. Jan Brace Govan, jan.brace-govan@buseco.monash.edu.au. **URL:** http://www.latrobe.edu.au/aqr/index.php?option=content&task=view&id=17&Item.

42084 ■ SANE News
SANE Australia
PO Box 226
Melbourne, Victoria 3205, Australia

Ph: 61 396 825933
Fax: 61 396 825944
Publisher E-mail: info@sane.org
Newspaper featuring articles, news on research and details on innovative projects. **Freq:** Quarterly. **URL:** http://www.sane.org/information/information/sane_news.html.

42085 ■ Sexual Health
CSIRO Publishing
Melbourne Sexual Health Centre
University of Melbourne
580 Swanston St.
Melbourne, Victoria 3053, Australia
Publisher E-mail: publishing@csiro.au
Journal dedicated to improving the sexual health of women and men in developing and developed countries, featuring original and significant research on HIV/ AIDS, sexually transmissible infections, sexuality and relevant areas of reproductive health. **Freq:** Quarterly. **Key Personnel:** Prof. Christopher Fairley, Editor, cfairley@unimelb.edu.au; Prof. Roy Chan, Editor, roychan@nsc.gov.sg; Steve Wesselingh, Editorial Committee; Juliet Richters, Editorial Committee; Andrew Ball, Editorial Committee; Brian P. Mulhall, Editorial Committee. **ISSN:** 1448-5028. **Subscription Rates:** $A 475 institutions online (Australia and New Zealand); $A 595 institutions online + print (Australia and New Zealand); $A 100 individuals online (Australia and New Zealand); $A 130 individuals online + print (Australia and New Zealand); EUR88 individuals online; EUR98 individuals online + print; 65 individuals online; 80 individuals print + online; EUR405 institutions online; EUR505 institutions online + print. **URL:** http://www.publish.csiro.au/nid/164.htm.

42086 ■ Sophia
Ashgate Publishing Ltd.
Old Law Quad G08
Philosophy Department
The University of Melbourne
PO Box 4230
Melbourne, Victoria, Australia
Ph: 61 3 83444778
Publication E-mail: sophia@philosophy.unimelb.edu.au
Journal covering the philosophy of religion, metaphysical theology and ethics worldwide. **Founded:** 1962. **Freq:** Semiannual. **Key Personnel:** Purushottama Bilimoria, PhD, Editor-in-Chief; Patrick Hutchings, Editor-in-Chief; Jay L. Garfield, Editor-in-Chief. **ISSN:** 0038-1527. **URL:** http://www.philosophy.unimelb.edu.au/sophia/index.html; http://www.springer.com/socialsciences/religiousstudies/journal/11841.

42087 ■ Stamp Bulletin
Philatelic Group
Australia Post
GPO Box 1777
Melbourne, Victoria 3001, Australia
Consumer magazine covering Australian stamps. **Subscription Rates:** Free. **Remarks:** Advertising not accepted. **URL:** http://auspost.com.au/EDUCATION/teacher-stamp-bulletin.html. **Circ:** Non-paid ⊕300,000

42088 ■ Stamp Explorer
Philatelic Group
Australia Post
GPO Box 1777
Melbourne, Victoria 3001, Australia
Consumer magazine covering Australian stamps for children aged 6-13 years. **Founded:** July 1953. **Freq:** Quarterly. **Print Method:** Offset. **Trim Size:** A5. **Remarks:** Advertising not accepted. **URL:** http://www.stamps.com.au/collectors/publications/stamp-explorer. **Circ:** Non-paid ⊕300,000

42089 ■ Waverley Leader
Leader Community Newspapers
636 St. Kilda Rd.
Melbourne, Victoria 3004, Australia
Ph: 61 3 99149000
Fax: 61 3 98758077
Local community newspaper. **Freq:** Weekly (Tues.). **Key Personnel:** Allison Bannan, Editor, monash@leadernewspapers.com.au; Andrew Groves, Sales Mgr., grovesa@leadernewspapers.com.au. **Remarks:** Accepts advertising. **URL:** http://waverley-leader.whereilive.com.au/. **Circ:** Tues. ‡70,580

42090 ■ Whitehorse Leader
Leader Community Newspapers

636 St. Kilda Rd.
Melbourne, Victoria 3004, Australia
Ph: 61 3 99149000
Fax: 61 3 98758077
Local community newspaper. **Freq:** Weekly (Wed.). **Key Personnel:** Greg Gliddon, Editor, whitehorse@leadernewspapers.com.au; Neil Honey, Sales Mgr., honeyn@leadernewspapers.com.au. **Remarks:** Accepts advertising. **URL:** http://whitehorse-leader.whereilive.com.au/. **Circ:** Wed. ‡66,374

42091 ■ Joy-FM - 94.9
Level 9, 225 Bourke St.
Melbourne, Victoria 3000, Australia
Ph: 61 3 96992949
Fax: 61 3 96992646
E-mail: info@joy.org.au
Format: Ethnic. **Owner:** JOY Melbourne Incorporated, at above address. **Founded:** Dec. 1, 1993. **Key Personnel:** Stephen Duns, President. **URL:** http://joy.org.au/.

42092 ■ Joy Melbourne-FM - 94.9
Level 9, 225 Bourke St.
Melbourne, Victoria 3000, Australia
Ph: 61 3 96992949
Fax: 61 3 96992646
E-mail: onair@joy.org.au
Format: News; Sports. **Owner:** Joy Melbourne Inc., at above address. **Operating Hours:** Continuous. **Ad Rates:** Advertising accepted; rates available upon request. **URL:** http://www.joy.org.au.

42093 ■ MGV-TV - 31
501 Swanston St., Level 1
Melbourne, Victoria 3000, Australia
Ph: 61 3 96603131
Fax: 61 3 96603100
E-mail: info@c31.org.au
URL: http://www.c31.org.au/.

42094 ■ Radio Sport-AM - 927
Ground Fl.
766 Elizabeth St.
Melbourne, Victoria 3000, Australia
Ph: 61 3 93478111
Fax: 61 3 93478969
E-mail: sport927@sport927.com.au
Format: News; Sports. **Owner:** Radio Sport 927AM, at above address. **Operating Hours:** Continuous. **Ad Rates:** Advertising accepted; rates available upon request. **URL:** http://www.sport927.com.au.

42095 ■ Radio Sport-AM - 927
766 Elizabeth St., Ground Fl.
Melbourne, Victoria 3000, Australia
Ph: 61 3 93478111
Fax: 61 3 93478969
E-mail: sport927@sport927.com.au
Format: Sports. **Founded:** Mar. 1925. **Key Personnel:** Richard Fennell, Dir. of Sales, rf@sport927.com.au; Danni Kay, Mktg. Mgr./Promotions Mgr. **Ad Rates:** Advertising accepted; rates available upon request. **URL:** http://www.sport927.com.au/.

42096 ■ SYN-FM - 90.7
PO Box 12013
A'Beckett St.
Melbourne, Victoria 8006, Australia
Ph: 61 3 00254747
Fax: 61 3 99254746
Format: Ethnic. **Formed by the merger of:** 3SRA-FM (2000); 3TD (2000). **Operating Hours:** Continuous. **URL:** http://www.syn.org.au/.

42097 ■ 3PBS-FM - 106.7
47 Easey St.
Collingwood
Melbourne, Victoria 3066, Australia
Ph: 61 3 84151067
Fax: 61 3 84151831
E-mail: info@pbsfm.org.au
Format: Eclectic. **Owner:** Progressive Broadcasting Service, at above address. **Operating Hours:** Continuous. **Key Personnel:** Adrian Basso, General Mgr., adrianbasso@pbsfm.org.au; Anna Pidgeon, Product Mgr.; Courtney Clarke, Sales Mgr., courtneyclarke@pbsfm.org.au. **Wattage:** 10,000. **URL:** http://www.pbsfm.org.au.

42098 ■ 3RRR-FM - 102.7
221 Nicholson St.

Circulation: ★ = ABC; △ = BPA; ♦ = CAC; • = CCAB; ❑ = VAC; ⊕ = PO Statement; ‡ = Publisher's Report; Boldface figures = sworn; Light figures = estimated.

Gale Directory of Publications & Broadcast Media/147th Ed.

4729

PO Box 2145
Brunswick East
Melbourne, Victoria 3057, Australia
Ph: 61 3 93881027
Fax: 61 3 93889079
E-mail: 3rrr@rrr.org.au
Format: Talk; Sports; Information; Eclectic; World Beat; Alternative/New Music/Progressive. **Owner:** Triple R Broadcasters Ltd., at above address. **Founded:** 1976. **Operating Hours:** Continuous. **Key Personnel:** Dave Houchin, Station Mgr., station.manager@rrr.org.au; Mick James, Program Mgr., program.manager@rrr.org.au; Simon Winkler, Music Coord., music.coordinator@rrr.org.au. **URL:** http://www.rrr.org.au/.

42099 ■ 3WBC-FM - 94.1
PO Box 159
Melbourne, Victoria 3128, Australia
Ph: 61 3 92854846
Fax: 61 3 92854849
E-mail: info@3wbc.org.au
Format: Public Radio; Eclectic; Ethnic. **Owner:** Community Broadcasting Association of Australia, Level 3, 44-54 Botany Rd., Alexandria, New South Wales 2015, Australia, 61 2 93102999, Fax: 61 2 93194545. **Operating Hours:** Continuous. **Ad Rates:** Underwriting available. **URL:** http://www.3wbc.org.au.

42100 ■ Triple R-FM - 102.7
221 Nicholson St.
PO Box 2145
Brunswick E
Melbourne, Victoria 3057, Australia
Ph: 61 3 93881027
Fax: 61 3 93889079
E-mail: 3rrr@rrr.org.au
Format: Public Radio; Educational; News; Talk; Eclectic. **Founded:** 1976. **Key Personnel:** Dave Houchin, Station Mgr., station.manager@rrr.org.au; Mick James, Program Mgr., program.manager@rrr.org.au; Archie Cuthbertson, Contact; Brendan Palmer, Contact. **Ad Rates:** Underwriting available. **URL:** http://www.rrr.org.au.

Mentone

42101 ■ Southern-FM - 88.3
22 Balcombe Rd.
Mentone, Victoria 3194, Australia
Ph: 61 3 95830533
Fax: 61 3 95830540
E-mail: info@southernfm.org.au
Format: Ethnic. **Operating Hours:** Continuous. **Key Personnel:** Nigel Carter, Advertising Mgr., nigel.carter@southernfm.com.au. **Ad Rates:** Noncommercial. **URL:** http://www.southernfm.com.au/.

Merredin

42102 ■ 6MD-AM - 1098
1 Goerge St.
Merredin, Western Australia 6415, Australia
Ph: 61 8 90413333
Fax: 61 8 90411922
Format: Adult Contemporary. **Key Personnel:** Vin Dawes, Station Mgr., phone 61 8 98814000, vdawes@radiowest.com.au. **Ad Rates:** Advertising accepted; rates available upon request. **URL:** http://theradio.com.au/localworks.aspx?PageID=2819&Station=RadioWest_Merredin.

Merrylands

42103 ■ Buick News
Buick Club of Australia
PO Box 168
Merrylands, New South Wales 2160, Australia
Ph: 61 2 96015005
Publisher E-mail: mail@buickclub.org.au
Publication covering automobile industry. **Freq:** Monthly. **Trim Size:** A4. **Key Personnel:** Virginia Russell, Treas. **Subscription Rates:** Free to financial members. **Remarks:** Advertising accepted; rates available upon request. **URL:** http://www.buickclub.org.au/. **Circ:** 500

Midland

42104 ■ Hills Gazette
Community Newspaper

12 Old Great Northern Hwy.
Midland, Western Australia 6056, Australia
Ph: 61 9 2371900
Publication E-mail: hillsgazette@communitynews.com.au
Publisher E-mail: classifieds@communitynews.com.au
General newspaper. **Freq:** Weekly (Sat.). **URL:** http://www.communitynews.com.au/Newspapers/HillsGazetteAvonValleyGazette/tabid/63/Default.aspx.

42105 ■ Kalamunda Reporter
Community Newspaper
12 Old Great Northern Hwy.
Midland, Western Australia 6056, Australia
Ph: 61 9 2371900
Fax: 61 9 2371901
Publication E-mail: midlandkalamundareporter@communitynews.com.au
Publisher E-mail: classifieds@communitynews.com.au
General newspaper. **Freq:** Weekly (Tues.). **URL:** http://www.communitynews.com.au/OurNewspapers/MidlandKalamundaReporter/tabid/68/Default.aspx.

Mildura

42106 ■ Australian Citrus News
Citrus Australia Ltd.
PO Box 5091
Mildura, Victoria 3502, Australia
Ph: 61 350 236333
Publication E-mail: admin@australiancitrusgrowers.com
Publisher E-mail: admin@australiancitrusgrowers.com
Trade journal covering developments and marketing for the citrus industries in Australia and worldwide. **Freq:** Bimonthly. **ISSN:** 0004-8283. **Subscription Rates:** US$55 individuals per annum (6 editions) Australian; US$75 other countries per annum (6 editions) international. **Remarks:** Accepts advertising. **URL:** http://www.australiancitrusgrowers.com. **Circ:** Combined 3,000

Milperra

42107 ■ Higher Education Research and Development (HERD)
Higher Education Research and Development Society of Australasia
c/o Jennifer Ungaro, Admin. Mgr.
PO Box 27
Milperra, New South Wales 2214, Australia
Ph: 61 297 713911
Fax: 61 297 714299
Publisher E-mail: office@herdsa.org.au
International refereed journal containing articles on the theory and practice of higher and tertiary education. **Freq:** 4/yr. **Key Personnel:** Dr. Martin Davies, Editor; Prof. Ian Macdonald, Editor. **Subscription Rates:** US$20 members single copy; US$25 nonmembers single copy. **URL:** http://www.herdsa.org.au/?page_id=25.

Milton

42108 ■ Westside News
Quest Community Newspapers
10 Finchley St.
Milton, Queensland 4064, Australia
Ph: 61 7 33777777
Local community newspaper. **Founded:** 1982. **Freq:** Weekly (Wed.). **Key Personnel:** James Chalmers, Editor, fax 61 7 33777788, editorial@westsidenews.com.au; David Howarth, Advertising Mgr., howarthd@qst.newsltd.com.au. **Remarks:** Accepts display and classified advertising. **URL:** http://www.newsspace.com.au/westside_news. **Circ:** 60,423

42109 ■ Family-FM - 96.5
PO Box 965
Milton, Queensland 4064, Australia
Ph: 61 3 2175999
Fax: 61 3 2175888
E-mail: admin@96five.com
Format: Contemporary Christian; Contemporary Hit Radio (CHR). **Operating Hours:** Continuous. **Key Personnel:** Rob Cowan, CEO, rob@96five.com. **Ad Rates:** Advertising accepted; rates available upon request. **URL:** http://www.96five.com.

42110 ■ 96five-FM - 96.5
PO Box 965

Milton, Queensland 4064, Australia
Ph: 61 7 32175999
Fax: 61 7 32175888
Format: Contemporary Christian; Religious. **Owner:** 96 Five, at above address. **Operating Hours:** Continuous. **Key Personnel:** Rob Cowan, CEO. **URL:** http://www.96five.com.

Mitchell

42111 ■ 2CC-AM - 1206
52 Hoskins St., 1st Fl.
Mitchell, Australian Capital Territory 2911, Australia
Ph: 61 2 62411911
Format: Information; News; Talk. **Ad Rates:** Advertising accepted; rates available upon request. **URL:** http://www.radio2cc.com.

Mona Vale

42112 ■ Your Trading Edge
MarketSource International Pty Ltd.
PO Box 60
Mona Vale, New South Wales 2103, Australia
Ph: 61 2 99863522
Fax: 61 2 99863599
Publication E-mail: info@yte.com.au
Publisher E-mail: info@market-source.com
Magazine reporting the finance and trade industry. **Freq:** Bimonthly. **Key Personnel:** Chelsea Reid, Editor-in-Chief. **Subscription Rates:** $A 67.50 individuals Asia/Pacific; $A 77.50 other countries; $A 51.20 individuals. **Remarks:** Accepts advertising. **URL:** http://www.yte.com.au/. **Circ:** (Not Reported)

Monash

42113 ■ Communications Letters, IEEE
IEEE Communications Society
c/o J. Armstrong, Assoc. Ed.
Electrical & Computer System Engineering
Monash University
Monash, Victoria, Australia
Publisher E-mail: publications@comsoc.org
Peer-reviewed journal providing information on ensuring rapid dissemination of ideas and timely recording of developments in all fields of communications. **Freq:** 12/yr. **Key Personnel:** S.K. Wilson, Editor-in-Chief; J. Armstrong, Assoc. Ed.; C.M. Assi, Assoc. Ed. **ISSN:** 1089-7798. **URL:** http://ieeexplore.ieee.org/xpl/RecentIssue.jsp?punumber=4234; http://www.comsoc.org/pubs/jrnal/commlet.html.

Mont Albert

42114 ■ Light-FM - 89.9
673 Whitehorse Rd.
PO Box 899
Mont Albert, Victoria 3127, Australia
Ph: 61 3 98991777
Fax: 61 3 98993377
E-mail: friends@lightfm.com.au
Format: Contemporary Christian; Religious; Adult Contemporary. **Owner:** Light FM Inc., at above address. **Founded:** Dec. 1, 2002. **Operating Hours:** Continuous. **URL:** http://www.lightfm.com.au/.

Moonee Ponds

42115 ■ Farming Small Blocks
Rural Press Ltd.
10 Sydenham St.
PO Box 254
Moonee Ponds, Victoria 3039, Australia
Ph: 61 3 92870900
Fax: 61 3 93753031
Newspaper for farming landholders in Victoria. **Founded:** July 2005. **Freq:** Weekly. **Subscription Rates:** $A 27.50 individuals. **URL:** http://www.ruralpress.com/publications/detail.asp?publication_id=220.

Moranbah

42116 ■ 4R-FM - 96.9
Townsquare
PO Box 597
Moranbah, Queensland 4744, Australia
Ph: 61 7 49416811

Fax: 61 7 49419875
Format: Classic Rock; Album-Oriented Rock (AOR).
Owner: Rock FM Association Inc., at above address.
Founded: 1998. **URL:** http://rockfm.com.au/.

Mornington

42117 ■ Frankston Standard Leader
Leader Community Newspapers
c/o Natalie Kealey, Ed.
Level 1/311, Main St.
Mornington, Victoria 3931, Australia
Ph: 61 3 59953633
Local community newspaper. **Freq:** Weekly (Mon.). **Key Personnel:** Natalie Kealey, Editor; Edna McMinimee, Sales Mgr., mcminimeee@leadernewspapers.com.au. **Remarks:** Accepts advertising. **URL:** http://www.newsspace.com.au/frankston_standard_leader. **Circ:** Mon. ‡71,585

42118 ■ Mornington Peninsula Leader
Leader Community Newspapers
311 Main St., Level 1
Mornington, Victoria 3931, Australia
Ph: 61 3 59722000
Local community newspaper. **Freq:** Weekly (Tues.). **Key Personnel:** Christian Tatman, Editor, mornington@leadernewspapers.com.au; Edna McMinimee, Sales Mgr., mcminimeee@leadernewspapers.com.au. **Remarks:** Accepts advertising. **URL:** http://mornington-peninsula-leader.whereilive.com.au/. **Circ:** Tues. ‡50,495

Morphett Vale

42119 ■ Hills & Valley Messenger
Messenger Newspapers
17-19 Stanley St.
Morphett Vale, South Australia 5162, Australia
Local community newspaper. **Freq:** Weekly (Wed.). **Key Personnel:** Bill Dimou, Southern Sales Mgr., dimoub@mng.newsltd.com.au. **Remarks:** Accepts display and classified advertising. **URL:** http://www.newsspace.com.au/hills__valley_messenger. **Circ:** 19,585

42120 ■ Southern Times Messenger
Messenger Newspapers
17-19 Stanley St.
Morphett Vale, South Australia 5162, Australia
Local community newspaper. **Freq:** Weekly (Wed.). **Key Personnel:** Bill Dimou, Southern Sales Mgr., phone 61 8 83844755, dimoub@mng.newsltd.com.au. **Remarks:** Accepts display and classified advertising. **URL:** http://www.newsspace.com.au/southern_times_messenger. **Circ:** 60,540

Moruya

42121 ■ 2EAR-FM - 107.5
9 Rose St.
PO Box 86
Moruya, New South Wales 2537, Australia
Ph: 61 2 44743443
Fax: 61 2 44743500
E-mail: earfm@earfm.com
Format: Alternative/New Music/Progressive. **URL:** http://www.earfm.com/.

Morwell

42122 ■ Gippsland-FM - 104.7
PO Box 579
Morwell, Victoria 3840, Australia
Ph: 61 3 51348444
Fax: 61 3 51330555
E-mail: office@gippslandfm.org.au
Format: Eclectic; Public Radio. **Operating Hours:** Continuous. **Key Personnel:** Ken Thompson, Chm. **Ad Rates:** Underwriting available. **URL:** http://www.3gcrfm.org.au.

Mount Beauty

42123 ■ 3VKV-FM - 92.5
PO Box 331
Mount Beauty, Victoria 3699, Australia
Ph: 61 3 57544554
Fax: 61 3 57544514

E-mail: info@alpineradio.com.au
Format: Easy Listening; Oldies. **Key Personnel:** Yvonne Sutton, VP/Station Mgr. **URL:** http://www.alpineradio.com.au/.

Mount Druitt

42124 ■ Mt. Druitt - St. Marys Standard
Cumberland Newspaper Group
Gallery Level, Ste. 201
Mount Druitt, New South Wales 2770, Australia
Local community newspaper. **Founded:** 1973. **Freq:** Weekly (Wed.). **Key Personnel:** Andrew Kacimaiwai, Editor, editor@mtdruittstandard.com.au; Robert Grant, Advertising Mgr., advertising@mtdruittstandard.com.au. **Remarks:** Accepts display and classified advertising. **URL:** http://www.newsspace.com.au/mt_druitt_st_marys_standard_. **Circ:** 44,210

Mount Gambier

42125 ■ 5GTR-FM - 100.1
25 Alexander St.
PO Box 2161
Mount Gambier, South Australia 5290, Australia
Ph: 61 8 87259833
Fax: 61 8 87249153
E-mail: admin@5gtr.net
Format: Album-Oriented Rock (AOR); Country; Ethnic. **Owner:** Community Broadcasting Association of Australia, Level 3, 44-54 Botany Rd., PO Box 564, Alexandria, New South Wales 2015, Australia, 61 293 102999, Fax: 61 293 194545. **Key Personnel:** Barry Melville, General Mgr.; Cameron Woods, Communications Mgr.; Stephen McDermott, Business Mgr.; Jessie Carter, Mktg. and Sponsorship Coord.; Mia Lauze, National Training Mgr.; Wendy Coates, CB Online Content Mgr.; Brigitte Dagg, Exec. Asst. **Ad Rates:** Noncommercial; underwriting available. **URL:** http://www.5gtr.net.

42126 ■ 5MG-AM - 1476
31 Penola Rd.
Mount Gambier, South Australia 5290, Australia
Ph: 61 8 87241011
Fax: 61 8 87241099
Format: News; Talk. **Owner:** Australian Broadcasting Corporation, ABC Ultimo Ctr., 700 Harris St., Ultimo 2007, GPO Box 9994, Sydney, New South Wales 2001, Australia, 61 2 83331500, Fax: 61 2 83335344. **Key Personnel:** Alan Richardson, Regional Program Mgr. **URL:** http://www.abc.net.au/southeastsa/.

42127 ■ 5RCB-FM - 104.9
Old Railway Station Bldg.
Railway Ter.
PO Box 1465
Mount Gambier, South Australia 5290, Australia
Ph: 61 8 87239996
Fax: 61 8 87239994
E-mail: radio@rhemafmlive.com.au
Format: Contemporary Christian. **Key Personnel:** Belinda Tilley, CEO, belinda@rhemafmlive.com.au. **URL:** http://www.rhemafmlive.com.au/index.php.

42128 ■ 5SE-AM - 963
46 Commercial St. W
Mount Gambier, South Australia 5290, Australia
Ph: 61 8 87255155
Fax: 61 8 87250708
Format: Alternative/New Music/Progressive. **Key Personnel:** Michael Pearce-Raisin, Station Mgr., michael.pearceraisin@mrworks.com.au. **URL:** http://theradio.com.au.

Mount Gravatt

42129 ■ City South News
Quest Community Newspapers
1293 Logan Rd.
Mount Gravatt, Queensland 4122, Australia
Ph: 61 7 31145600
Local community newspaper. **Founded:** Feb. 1992. **Freq:** Weekly (Thurs.). **Key Personnel:** Troy Greenland, Advertising Mgr., greenlandt@qst.newsltd.com.au. **Remarks:** Accepts display and classified advertising. **URL:** http://www.newsspace.com.au/city_south_news. **Circ:** 30,398

42130 ■ South-East Advertiser
Quest Community Newspapers
1293 Logan Rd.
Mount Gravatt, Queensland 4122, Australia
Ph: 61 7 31145600
Local community newspaper. **Founded:** 1982. **Freq:** Weekly (Wed.). **Key Personnel:** Gary Shipway, Editor, phone 61 7 31145600, fax 61 7 31146522, editorial@southeastadviser.com.au. **Remarks:** Accepts display and classified advertising. **URL:** http://www.newsspace.com.au/south_east_advertiser. **Circ:** 51,802

Mount Isa

42131 ■ 4LM-AM - 666 KHz
67 West St.
Mount Isa, Queensland 4825, Australia
Ph: 61 7 47433444
Fax: 61 7 47435599
Format: Oldies; News; Talk. **Founded:** 1961. **Operating Hours:** Continuous. **Key Personnel:** Bonnie Waihi, Station Mgr., phone 61 7 47491025. **URL:** http://theradio.com.au/localworks.aspx?PageID=1763&Station=4LM_Mt_Isa.

42132 ■ Rhema-FM - 105.7
27 George St,
PO Box 1186
Mount Isa, Queensland 4825, Australia
Ph: 61 7 47437460
Format: Contemporary Christian. **URL:** http://www.rhemamountisa.com/.

Mount Macedon

42133 ■ Australian Journal of Emergency Management
Emergency Management Australia
601 Mt. Macedon Rd.
Mount Macedon, Victoria 3411, Australia
Ph: 61 3 54215100
Fax: 61 3 54215272
Publication E-mail: ajem@ema.gov.au
Publisher E-mail: aemi@ag.gov.au
Journal covering emergency management. **Founded:** 1986. **Freq:** Quarterly. **ISSN:** 1324-1540. **Subscription Rates:** $A 33; US$30 individuals GST inc; US$30 individuals GST excluding. **Remarks:** Advertising accepted; rates available upon request. **URL:** http://www.informit.com.au/product_details.asp?product=true&ContainerID=info_product_elibrary_bytitle&type=IL&id=AJEM. **Circ:** Non-paid 5,200

Mount Ommaney

42134 ■ Classic Wings
Australian Office
PO Box 625
Mount Ommaney, Queensland 4074, Australia
Ph: 61 732 790877
Fax: 61 732 790877
Publisher E-mail: admin@classicwings.com
Magazine featuring articles, photos, and industry news for classic airplane enthusiasts. **Founded:** 1994. **Freq:** Bimonthly 5/yr. **Print Method:** Sheet fed. **Trim Size:** 210 x 285 mm. **Key Personnel:** Jane Orphan, Office Mgr. New Zealand; Gill Sheather, Office Mgr. Australia; Graham Orphan, Editor, editor@classicwings.com. **ISSN:** 1172-9643. **Subscription Rates:** NZ$44 individuals New Zealand; $A 44 individuals Australia; US$39 individuals U.S.; NZ$59 other countries; NZ$84 two years New Zealand; $A 84 two years Australia; US$72 two years U.S.; NZ$109 two years rest of the world; NZ$8.50 single issue back issues; US$7 single issue back issues. **Remarks:** Accepts advertising. **URL:** http://www.classicwings.com/. **Ad Rates:** 4C: NZ$2,000. **Circ:** 13,000

Mudgee

42135 ■ Heartland-FM - 87.6
PO Box 277
Ashmore, Queensland 4214, Australia
E-mail: heartfm@bigpond.net.au
Format: Adult Contemporary. **URL:** http://www.heartlandfm.com/.

Circulation: ★ = ABC; △ = BPA; ♦ = CAC; • = CCAB; □ = VAC; ⊕ = PO Statement; ‡ = Publisher's Report; Boldface figures = sworn; Light figures = estimated.

Gale Directory of Publications & Broadcast Media/147th Ed.   4731

Murdoch

42136 ■ Chiropractic & Osteopathy
BioMed Central Ltd.
c/o Dr. Bruce F. Walker, Ed.-in-Ch.
Murdoch University
School of Chiropractic
Division of Health Sciences
Murdoch, Western Australia 6150, Australia
Ph: 61 8 93601297
Publisher E-mail: info@biomedcentral.com
Journal covering all aspects of Chiropractic and Osteopathy. **Key Personnel:** Dr. Bruce F. Walker, Editor-in-Chief, bruce.walker@murdoch.edu.au; Dr. Melainie Cameron, Assoc. Ed., phone 61 3 99194287, melainie.cameron@coca.com.au; Dr. Simon French, Assoc. Ed., simon.french@coca.com.au; Dr. Stephen M. Perle, Assoc. Ed. **ISSN:** 1746-1340. **URL:** http://www.chiroandosteo.com/. **Former name:** Australasian Chiropractic & Osteopathy.

42137 ■ Intersections
Murdoch University
School of Social Sciences and Humanities
90 South St.
Murdoch, Western Australia 6150, Australia
Ph: 61 893 602393
Fax: 61 893 606571
Journal dealing with the gender studies in the Asian region. **Subtitle:** Gender, History & Culture in the Asian Context. **Key Personnel:** John Ballard, International Advisory Board, john.ballard@anu.edu.au; Carolyn Brewer, Editor, carolyn@central.murdoch.edu.au; Barbara Andaya, International Advisory Board; Chris Berry, International Advisory Board; Niko Besnier, International Advisory Board; Tom Boellstorff, International Advisory Board; Elise Tipton, Advisory Board; Harriet Evans, Advisory Board; Subhash Chandra, International Advisory Board. **ISSN:** 1440-9151. **URL:** http://wwwsshe.murdoch.edu.au/intersections/. **Alt. Formats:** CD-ROM.

Murrayville

42138 ■ 3MBR-FM - 92.9
PO Box 139
Murrayville, Victoria 8000, Australia
Ph: 61 3 50952045
Fax: 61 3 50952346
E-mail: 3mbr@riverland.net.au
Format: Public Radio; Eclectic. **Key Personnel:** John Heintze, Station Mgr. **URL:** http://www.3mbrfm.org.au.

Naracoorte

42139 ■ SBS Television - 54
Locked Bag 028
Crows Nest, New South Wales 1585, Australia
Ph: 61 2 94302828
Fax: 61 2 94303047
Owner: Special Broadcasting Service, at above address. **Wattage:** 300 ERP. **URL:** http://www20.sbs.com.au/transmissions/index.php?pid=2&id=475.

Narrabeen

42140 ■ Radio Northern Beaches-FM - 88.7 MHz
PO Box 219
Narrabeen, New South Wales 2101, Australia
Ph: 61 2 94514887
E-mail: info2006@radionorthernbeachs.org
Format: News. **Operating Hours:** 8:45 a.m.-10:30 p.m. Mon.-Fri.; 8:45 a.m.-6 p.m. Sat.-Sun. **Ad Rates:** Underwriting available. **URL:** http://www.radionorthernbeaches.org.

42141 ■ Radio Northern Beaches-FM - 90.3
PO Box 219
Narrabeen, New South Wales 2101, Australia
Ph: 61 2 94514887
E-mail: info2006@radionorthernbeaches.org
Format: News. **Owner:** Virtual Australia, at above address. **Operating Hours:** 8:45 a.m.-10:30 p.m. Mon.-Fri.; 8:45 a.m.-6 p.m. Sat.-Sun. **Ad Rates:** Underwriting available. **URL:** http://www.radionorthernbeaches.org.

Narrabri

42142 ■ 2MAX-FM - 91.3
2 Old Newell Hwy.

Narrabri, New South Wales 2390, Australia
Ph: 61 2 67924884
Fax: 61 2 67924582
E-mail: maxfm@2maxfm.com.au
Format: Ethnic; World Beat. **Key Personnel:** Tony Parker, President; Angelia Frew, Station Mgr.; Julie Young, Treas. **URL:** http://www.2maxfm.com.au.

Nathan

42143 ■ International Journal of Agricultural Resources, Governance and Ecology
Inderscience Enterprises Limited
c/o Prof. Andrew K. Dragun, Ed.-in-Ch.
Griffith University, Australian Rivers Institute
Rm. 1.09, Environment 2 Bldg. (N13)
170 Kessels R
Nathan, Queensland 4111, Australia
Journal covering academic and research institutions and studies concerned with the complex role of agriculture in the society. **Freq:** 6/yr. **Key Personnel:** Prof. Andrew K. Dragun, Editor-in-Chief, andrew.dragun@flairwood.net; Prof. Kristin Jakobsson, Editor-in-Chief, ijweditor@flairwood.net. **ISSN:** 1462-4605. **Subscription Rates:** EUR494 individuals print or online; EUR672 individuals print and online. **URL:** http://www.inderscience.com/browse/index.php?journalID=1.

Newport

42144 ■ Hobsons Bay Leader
Leader Community Newspapers
Newport Power Sta., Douglas Pde
Newport, Victoria 3015, Australia
Ph: 61 3 93933633
Local community newspaper. **Freq:** Weekly (Tues.). **Key Personnel:** Rick Edwards, Editor, hobsonsbay@leadernewspapers.com.au; Helen Meritt, Sales Mgr., merritth@leadernewspapers.com.au. **Remarks:** Accepts advertising. **URL:** http://hobsons-bay-leader.whereilive.com.au/. **Circ:** Tues. ‡35,503

42145 ■ Maribyrnong Leader
Leader Community Newspapers
Douglas Parade
Newport, Victoria 3015, Australia
Ph: 61 3 93933633
Local community newspaper. **Freq:** Weekly (Tues.). **Key Personnel:** Rick Edwards, Editor, maribyrnong@leadernewspapers.com.au. **Remarks:** Accepts advertising. **URL:** http://maribyrnong-leader.whereilive.com.au/. **Circ:** Tues. ‡30,216

Nhulunbuy

42146 ■ Gove-FM - 106.9
Level 1, Endeavour House
Endeavour Sq.
PO Box 946
Nhulunbuy, Northern Territory 0880, Australia
Ph: 61 8 89871500
Fax: 61 8 89872144
E-mail: admin@govefm.com.au
Format: Eclectic; Public Radio. **Owner:** 8EAR Community Radio Inc., at above address. **Operating Hours:** 6 a.m to 10 p.m. Sun.-Fri.; 6 a.m.to 12 a.m. Sat. **Key Personnel:** Churyl Scheppard, Station Mgr. **Ad Rates:** Underwriting available. **URL:** http://www.govefm.com.au.

Nimbin

42147 ■ 2NIM-FM - 102.3
81 Cullen St.
PO Box 522
Nimbin, New South Wales 2480, Australia
Ph: 61 2 66890279
E-mail: nimfm@nimfm.org
Format: Eclectic; Public Radio; Religious. **URL:** http://www.nimfm.org/.

Noosa Heads

42148 ■ 4NSA-FM - 101.3
PO Box 1059
Noosa Heads, Queensland 4567, Australia
Ph: 61 7 54472233
Fax: 61 7 54553103
E-mail: admin@noosacommunityradio.org
Format: Full Service. **Founded:** 1994. **Operating**

Hours: Continuous. **URL:** http://www.noosacommunityradio.org/.

Noosaville

42149 ■ Classic Hits-FM - 107.1
PO Box 290
Noosaville, Queensland 4566, Australia
Ph: 61 7 54821544
Fax: 61 7 54827517
Format: Classic Rock; News. **Key Personnel:** Debbie Vink, General Mgr., debbievink@classichits.com.au; Ben Beckinsale, Sales and Mktg. Mgr., sales@classichits.com.au. **Ad Rates:** Advertising accepted; rates available upon request. **URL:** http://www.classichits.com.au.

42150 ■ Noosa 96.1-FM - 96.1
Noosa Dr.
PO Box 187
Noosaville, Queensland 4566, Australia
Ph: 61 7 5430 6961
Fax: 61 7 5430 6962
Format: Adult Contemporary. **URL:** http://www.heatfm.com.au/.

Normanhurst

42151 ■ The Olive Press
Australian Olive Association
The Olive Press
24 Carcoola Cres.
Normanhurst, New South Wales 2076, Australia
Journal including articles on pruning, fertilizing, irrigation, processing, marketing, and packaging. **Freq:** 3/yr. **Key Personnel:** Margaret Chidgey, Editor, phone 61 2 94893663, olivepress@australianolives.com.au. **Subscription Rates:** $A 77 individuals; $A 132 two years. **Remarks:** Accepts advertising. **URL:** http://theolivepressmagazine.com/. **Ad Rates:** BW: $A 743, 4C: $A 1,155. **Circ:** (Not Reported)

North Adelaide

42152 ■ Cruise 1323-AM - 1323
201 Tynte St.
North Adelaide, South Australia 5006, Australia
Ph: 61 8 83001000
Fax: 61 8 83001040
Format: Jazz; Oldies. **Owner:** Australian Radio Network, 3 Byfield St., North Ryde, New South Wales 2113, Australia, 61 2 88999999, Fax: 61 2 88999811. **Key Personnel:** Sally Foster, Dir. of Sales, phone 61 8 83001001, fax 61 8 83001031, sallyfoster@arn.com.au. **Ad Rates:** Advertising accepted; rates available upon request. **URL:** http://www.cruise1323.com.au/.

42153 ■ MIX 102.3-FM - 102.3
201 Tynte St.
North Adelaide, South Australia 5006, Australia
Ph: 61 8 83001000
Fax: 61 8 83001040
E-mail: community@mix1023.com.au
Format: Adult Contemporary. **Owner:** Australian Radio Network Pty. Ltd., 3 Byfield St., North Ryde, New South Wales 2113, Australia, 61 2 88999999, Fax: 61 2 88999811. **Key Personnel:** Roger Luders, Dir. of Sales, rogerluders@arn.com.au. **Ad Rates:** Advertising accepted; rates available upon request. **URL:** http://www.mix1023.com.au/; http://www.arn.com.au/.

North Hobart

42154 ■ Ultra-FM - 106.5
PO Box 95
North Hobart, Tasmania 7002, Australia
Ph: 61 3 62311065
Fax: 61 3 62348900
E-mail: admin@ultra106five.com
Format: Contemporary Hit Radio (CHR); Sports; News; Adult Contemporary. **Operating Hours:** Continuous. **Key Personnel:** Nathaniel Garvin, General Mgr., nathanielg@ultra106five.com. **URL:** http://ultra106five.com.au/results.php.

North Ipswich

42155 ■ Ipswich News
Quest Community Newspapers
Shop C6, Riverlink Shopping Centre
Cor. Pine St., The Terrace

North Ipswich, Queensland 4305, Australia
Ph: 61 7 38104600
Local community newspaper. **Founded:** July 6, 2006.
Freq: Weekly (Thurs.). **Key Personnel:** Carly Gregory, Advertising Mgr., gregoryc@qst.newsltd.com.au; Alena Wilson, Editor, phone 61 7 38104600, fax 61 7 38104610, editorial@ipswichnews.com.au. **Remarks:** Accepts display and classified advertising. **URL:** http://www.newsspace.com.au/ipswich_news. **Circ:** ‡41,178

North Melbourne

42156 ■ Animals Today
Animals Australia
37 O'Connell St.
North Melbourne, Victoria 3051, Australia
Ph: 61 3 93296333
Fax: 61 3 93296441
Publisher E-mail: enquiries@animalsaustralia.org
Publication covering philosophical and practical issues of animal protection. **Founded:** July 1993. **Freq:** Biennial. **Key Personnel:** Glenys Oogjes, Exec. Dir.; Lyn White, Communications Dir. **Subscription Rates:** Free to members. **Remarks:** Advertising accepted; rates available upon request. **URL:** http://www.animalsaustralia.org/about/animals_today_magazine.php. **Circ:** 3,000

North Nowra

42157 ■ 2ST-FM - 91.7
119 McMahons Rd.
North Nowra, New South Wales 2541, Australia
Ph: 61 2 44230055
Fax: 61 2 44233188
Format: Adult Contemporary; Easy Listening; Talk; Contemporary Country; Sports; Oldies; Information. **Ad Rates:** Advertising accepted; rates available upon request. **URL:** http://www.2st.com.au/

North Parramatta

42158 ■ Retail Pharmacy
Level 1, 410 Church St.
North Parramatta, New South Wales 2151, Australia
Ph: 61 2 98901199
Fax: 61 2 98901877
Trade magazine for pharmacists, pharmacy groups, and brokers, distributors, and manufacturers in the pharmacy industry. **Freq:** Monthly. **Print Method:** Sheetfed offset. **Trim Size:** 340 x 240mm. **Cols./Page:** 5. **Key Personnel:** Amy Looker, Editor, phone 61 2 96830117, amy.looker@retailmedia.com.au. **Subscription Rates:** US$300 individuals 12 months; 11 isssues online; $A 400 individuals 24 months; 22 issues online. **Remarks:** Accepts advertising. **URL:** http://www.retailmedia.com.au/magazine-retailpharmacy.shtml. **Ad Rates:** BW: $A 4,890. **Circ:** Controlled 7,413

North Perth

42159 ■ 6EBA-FM - 95.3 Mhz
386 Fitzgerald St.
North Perth, Western Australia 6016, Australia
E-mail: media@mrtawa.org.au
Format: Ethnic. **Owner:** Multicultural Radio & TV Association of WA Inc., at above address. **Operating Hours:** Continuous. **Key Personnel:** Helen Nikolich, Station Mgr., phone 61 8 93202351, fax 61 8 92277692, manager@6eba.com.au. **URL:** http://www.mrtawa.org.au/.

North Richmond

42160 ■ Australian Farm Journal
Rural Press Ltd.
159 Bells Line of Rd.
North Richmond, New South Wales 2754, Australia
Ph: 61 2 45704444
Fax: 61 2 45704663
Magazine covering agricultural business information. **Freq:** Monthly. **Key Personnel:** Patrick Francis, Editor, francis@ozonline.com.au; Grant Cochrane, Editor. **Subscription Rates:** $A 83.40 individuals; $A 150.12 two years; $A 6.95 single issue. **Remarks:** Accepts advertising. **URL:** http://www.farmonline.com.au/farmmags/AustralianFarmJournal/index.aspx; http://

www.ruralpress.com/publications/detail.asp?publication_id=127. **Circ:** ★4,456

42161 ■ Farm Equipment Trader
Rural Press Ltd.
159 Bells Line of Rd.
North Richmond, New South Wales 2754, Australia
Ph: 61 2 45704444
Fax: 61 2 45704663
Newspaper for farm machinery buyers and sellers. **Freq:** Monthly. **Key Personnel:** Roland Cowley, Advertising Mgr.; Garry Bird, Contact, garry.bird@ruralpress.com. **Remarks:** Accepts advertising. **URL:** http://www.ruralpress.com/publications/detail.asp?publication_id=32. **Circ:** Paid ★53,918

42162 ■ Farming Small Areas
Rural Press Ltd.
159 Bells Line of Rd.
North Richmond, New South Wales 2754, Australia
Ph: 61 2 45704444
Fax: 61 2 45704663
Publication E-mail: farmingsmallareas@ruralpress.com
Magazine for agricultural landholders. **Freq:** Bimonthly. **Key Personnel:** Kim Chapell, Editor; John Dwyer, General Mgr. **Remarks:** Accepts advertising. **URL:** http://www.ruralpress.com/publications/detail.asp?publication_id=204. **Circ:** Paid ★54,709

42163 ■ The Land
Rural Press Ltd.
159 Bells Line of Rd.
PO Box 999
North Richmond, New South Wales 2754, Australia
Publication E-mail: general.theland@ruralpress.com
Newspaper covering farming information and events in the rural areas of New South Wales. **Freq:** Weekly. **Key Personnel:** Garry Bird, Contact, garry.bird@ruralpress.com; John Dwyer, General Mgr., gm.theland@ruralpress.com; Sue Woodland, Contact. **Subscription Rates:** $A 176.30 individuals; $A 334.90 two years; $A 3.40 single issue. **Remarks:** Accepts advertising. **URL:** http://www.ruralpress.com/publications/detail.asp?publication_id=92; http://theland.farmonline.com.au/. **Circ:** ★50,492

42164 ■ NSW Agriculture Today
Rural Press Ltd.
159 Bells Line of Rd.
North Richmond, New South Wales 2754, Australia
Ph: 61 2 45704444
Fax: 61 2 45704663
Newspaper covering agriculture in New South Wales. **Freq:** Monthly. **Key Personnel:** Ron Aggs, Editor, ron.aggs@dpi.nsw.gov.au; Rhonda Johnston, Advertising Mgr., rhonda.johnston@ruralpress.com; John Dwyer, General Mgr., john.dwyer@ruralpress.com. **Subscription Rates:** Free. **URL:** http://www.ruralpress.com/publications/detail.asp?publication_id=73. **Circ:** ‡35,000

42165 ■ Queensland Country Life
Rural Press Ltd.
159 Bells Line of Rd.
North Richmond, New South Wales 2754, Australia
Ph: 61 2 45704444
Fax: 61 2 45704663
Newspaper covering agricultural events and information in Queensland. **Founded:** 1935. **Freq:** Weekly. **Key Personnel:** John Warlters, General Mgr., john.warlters@ruralpress.com; Jenny Sando, Sales Mgr., jenny.sando@ruralpress.com; Mark Phelps, Editor, editorialsec.qcl@ruralpress.com. **Subscription Rates:** $A 160 individuals; $A 286 two years; $A 3.20 single issue. **Remarks:** Accepts advertising. **URL:** http://www.ruralpress.com/publications/detail.asp?publication_id=104; http://qcl.farmonline.com.au/. **Circ:** Paid ★35,661

North Ryde

42166 ■ Australian Beading
Universal Magazines
6-8 Byfield St., Unit 5
North Ryde, New South Wales 2113, Australia
Ph: 61 2 98050399
Fax: 61 2 98050714
Publisher E-mail: mailorder@universalmagazines.com.au
Magazine for beading enthusiasts. **Freq:** Bimonthly. **Trim Size:** 230 x 278 mm. **Key Personnel:** Kelly Norton,

Editor; Kerry Walters, Advertising Mgr., phone 61 2 98870603. **Subscription Rates:** $A 45 individuals. **Remarks:** Accepts advertising. **URL:** http://www.universalmagazines.com.au/_webapp_118017/Australian_Beading. **Ad Rates:** 4C: $A 1,750. **Circ:** 30,000

42167 ■ Australian Country Collections
Universal Magazines
6-8 Byfield St., Unit 5
North Ryde, New South Wales 2113, Australia
Ph: 61 2 98050399
Fax: 61 2 98050714
Publisher E-mail: mailorder@universalmagazines.com.au
Magazine featuring home and home decors. **Freq:** Bimonthly. **Trim Size:** 230 x 278 mm. **Key Personnel:** Donna Macpherson, Editor; Angelos Tzovlas, Advertising Mgr. **Subscription Rates:** $A 30 individuals. **Remarks:** Accepts advertising. **URL:** http://www.universalmagazines.com.au/_webapp_118008/Australian_Country_Collections. **Ad Rates:** 4C: $A 2,100. **Circ:** 35,000

42168 ■ Australian Road Rider
Universal Magazines
6-8 Byfield St., Unit 5
North Ryde, New South Wales 2113, Australia
Ph: 61 2 98050399
Fax: 61 2 98050714
Publisher E-mail: mailorder@universalmagazines.com.au
Magazine focusing on motorcycles and high-performance riding. **Subtitle:** The Real Ride. **Freq:** Bimonthly. **Trim Size:** 210 x 278 mm. **Key Personnel:** Peter Thoeming, Editor; John Arens, Advertising Mgr., phone 61 2 98870331, fax 61 2 98050714, jarens@universalmagazines.com.au. **Subscription Rates:** $A 80 two years. **Remarks:** Accepts advertising. **URL:** http://www.roadrider.com.au. **Ad Rates:** BW: $A 1,370, 4C: $A 1,680. **Circ:** 27,000

42169 ■ Australian Trailrider
Universal Magazines
6-8 Byfield St., Unit 5
North Ryde, New South Wales 2113, Australia
Ph: 61 2 98050399
Fax: 61 2 98050714
Publisher E-mail: mailorder@universalmagazines.com.au
Magazine focusing on high performance motor riding. **Freq:** Bimonthly. **Trim Size:** 210 x 278 mm. **Key Personnel:** Fiona Collins, Advertising Mgr., phone 61 02 98870384; Stephen Tuff, Editor. **Subscription Rates:** $A 35 individuals. **Remarks:** Accepts advertising. **URL:** http://www.universalmagazines.com.au/_webapp_118007/Australian_Trailrider. **Circ:** (Not Reported)

42170 ■ Backyard Design Ideas
Universal Magazines
6-8 Byfield St., Unit 5
North Ryde, New South Wales 2113, Australia
Ph: 61 2 98050399
Fax: 61 2 98050714
Publisher E-mail: mailorder@universalmagazines.com.au
Magazine featuring outdoor designs and landscape. **Freq:** Bimonthly. **Trim Size:** 230 x 297 mm. **Key Personnel:** Karen Booth, Editor; Natalie Raad, Editor. **Subscription Rates:** $A 53.70 individuals; $A 99.95 two years; $A 41.70 individuals New Zealand; $A 92 individuals Asia; $A 108 other countries. **Remarks:** Accepts advertising. **URL:** http://www.universalmagazines.com.au/CustomContentRetrieve.aspx?ID=118019. **Ad Rates:** 4C: $A 3,210. **Circ:** 30,000

42171 ■ Barb's Factory Shopping Guide
Universal Magazines
6-8 Byfield St., Unit 5
North Ryde, New South Wales 2113, Australia
Ph: 61 2 98050399
Fax: 61 2 98050714
Publisher E-mail: mailorder@universalmagazines.com.au
Magazine featuring guidelines, tips and places to buy the best products and brands. **Freq:** Annual. **Trim Size:** 140 x 215 mm. **Key Personnel:** Zee Hutchison, Editor, phone 61 2 95274233, zhutchison@universalmagazines.com.au. **Remarks:** Accepts

---

Circulation: ★ = ABC; △ = BPA; ♦ = CAC; • = CCAB; ❑ = VAC; ⊕ = PO Statement; ‡ = Publisher's Report; Boldface figures = sworn; Light figures = estimated.

advertising. **URL:** http://www.universalmagazines.com.au/_webapp_168194/Barb's_Factory_Shopping_Guide. **Circ:** (Not Reported)

42172 ■ Bargain Shopper Guide to Melbourne
Universal Magazines
6-8 Byfield St., Unit 5
North Ryde, New South Wales 2113, Australia
Ph: 61 2 98050399
Fax: 61 2 98050714
Publisher E-mail: mailorder@universalmagazines.com.au
Magazine for bargain shoppers. **Freq:** Annual. **Trim Size:** 206 x 276 mm. **Key Personnel:** Beth Anderson, Editor; Zee Hutchinson, Advertising Mgr. **Remarks:** Accepts advertising. **URL:** http://www.universalmagazines.com.au/_webapp_118459/Bargain_Shoppers_-_Melbourne_2008_Edition. **Ad Rates:** BW: $A 2,000, 4C: $A 2,250. **Circ:** 35,000

42173 ■ Bathroom Yearbook
Universal Magazines
6-8 Byfield St., Unit 5
North Ryde, New South Wales 2113, Australia
Ph: 61 2 98050399
Fax: 61 2 98050714
Publisher E-mail: mailorder@universalmagazines.com.au
Magazine featuring bathroom products and designs. **Freq:** Annual. **Trim Size:** 220 x 278 mm. **Key Personnel:** Melanie Gardener, Editor, phone 61 2 98870367, mgardener@universalmagazines.com.au; Melissa Ham, Advertising Mgr., phone 61 2 98870618, mham@universalmagazines.com.au; John Oliver, Advertising Mgr., joliver@universalmagazines.com.au. **Subscription Rates:** $A 9.95 single issue. **Remarks:** Accepts advertising. **URL:** http://www.universalshop.com.au/magazine_subscriptions?cid=6226&pid=12776. **Circ:** (Not Reported)

42174 ■ BuildHOME Vic
Universal Magazines
6-8 Byfield St., Unit 5
North Ryde, New South Wales 2113, Australia
Ph: 61 2 98050399
Fax: 61 2 98050714
Publisher E-mail: mailorder@universalmagazines.com.au
Magazine featuring houses, architects and builders in Victoria. **Freq:** Semiannual. **Trim Size:** 210 x 278 mm. **Key Personnel:** Kate Telfer, Editor; Valerie Newton, Advertising Mgr., phone 61 3 98981905. **Subscription Rates:** $A 9.95 single issue. **Remarks:** Accepts advertising. **URL:** http://www.universalmagazines.com.au/_webapp_118311/BuildHOME_-_Victoria. **Ad Rates:** 4C: $A 3,325. **Circ:** (Not Reported)

42175 ■ Choosing a School for Your Child - New South Wales
Universal Magazines
6-8 Byfield St., Unit 5
North Ryde, New South Wales 2113, Australia
Ph: 61 2 98050399
Fax: 61 2 98050714
Publication E-mail: schoolchoicensw@universalmagazines.com.au
Publisher E-mail: mailorder@universalmagazines.com.au
Magazine featuring high school education issues. **Freq:** Annual. **Trim Size:** 206 x 276 mm. **Key Personnel:** Adrienne Kotz, Advertising Mgr., phone 61 2 94888661; John Oliver, Advertising Mgr., phone 61 3 96946430; Renata Gortan, Editor. **Subscription Rates:** $A 9.95 single issue. **Remarks:** Accepts advertising. **URL:** http://www.schoolchoice.com.au/schools_NSW. **Ad Rates:** BW: $A 4,295, 4C: $A 6,580. **Circ:** (Not Reported)

42176 ■ Choosing a School for Your Child - Victoria
Universal Magazines
6-8 Byfield St., Unit 5
North Ryde, New South Wales 2113, Australia
Ph: 61 2 98050399
Fax: 61 2 98050714
Publication E-mail: schoolchoicevic@universalmagazines.com.au
Publisher E-mail: mailorder@universalmagazines.com.au
Magazine featuring high school education issues. **Freq:** Annual. **Trim Size:** 206 x 276 mm. **Key Personnel:**

Beth Anderson, Editor; John Oliver, Advertising Mgr. **Subscription Rates:** $A 9.95 single issue. **Remarks:** Accepts advertising. **URL:** http://www.universalmagazines.com.au/_webapp_391101/Choosing_a_School_for_Your_Child_Victoria. **Ad Rates:** BW: $A 2,975, 4C: $A 4,590. **Circ:** (Not Reported)

42177 ■ Complete Wedding Guide Melbourne
Universal Magazines
6-8 Byfield St., Unit 5
North Ryde, New South Wales 2113, Australia
Ph: 61 2 98050399
Fax: 61 2 98050714
Publisher E-mail: mailorder@universalmagazines.com.au
Magazine featuring wedding guidelines for anyone who will marry in Melbourne. **Freq:** Biennial. **Key Personnel:** Renata Gortam, Editor; Beth Anderson, Editor; Jacqueline Parker, Advertising Mgr. **Subscription Rates:** $A 14.95 individuals. **Remarks:** Accepts advertising. **Ad Rates:** 4C: $A 2,300. **Circ:** 15,000

42178 ■ Complete Wedding Sydney
Universal Magazines
6-8 Byfield St., Unit 5
North Ryde, New South Wales 2113, Australia
Ph: 61 2 98050399
Fax: 61 2 98050714
Publisher E-mail: mailorder@universalmagazines.com.au
Magazine featuring wedding guidelines for anyone who will marry in Sydney. **Freq:** Semiannual. **Key Personnel:** Brianna Ragel, Editor; Ted Kosta, Advertising Mgr.; Beth Anderson, Editor. **Remarks:** Accepts advertising. **URL:** http://www.universalmagazines.com.au/_webapp_118013/Complete_Wedding_-_Sydney_and_Melbourne_Editions_available. **Circ:** (Not Reported)

42179 ■ Contemporary Home Design
Universal Magazines
6-8 Byfield St., Unit 5
North Ryde, New South Wales 2113, Australia
Ph: 61 2 98050399
Fax: 61 2 98050714
Publisher E-mail: mailorder@universalmagazines.com.au
Magazine featuring contemporary home designs and architecture. **Freq:** Quarterly. **Trim Size:** 230 x 286 mm. **Key Personnel:** Kate St. James, Editor; Julie Jackson, Advertising Mgr., jjackson@universalmagazines.com.au. **Subscription Rates:** $A 51 individuals New Zealand; $A 84 individuals Asia; $A 107 other countries; $A 102 two years. **Remarks:** Accepts advertising. **URL:** http://www.universalmagazines.com.au/_webapp_118005/Contemporary_Home_Design. **Circ:** (Not Reported)

42180 ■ Dirt Action
Universal Magazines
6-8 Byfield St., Unit 5
North Ryde, New South Wales 2113, Australia
Ph: 61 2 98050399
Fax: 61 2 98050714
Publisher E-mail: mailorder@universalmagazines.com.au
Magazine for Australian dirt bike fans. **Freq:** Monthly. **Trim Size:** 210 x 278 mm. **Key Personnel:** Scott Bishop, Editor; Damien Ashenhurst, Managing Editor. **Subscription Rates:** $A 80 individuals. **Remarks:** Accepts advertising. **URL:** http://www.dirtaction.com.au/. **Circ:** (Not Reported)

42181 ■ Dogs Life
Universal Magazines
6-8 Byfield St., Unit 5
North Ryde, New South Wales 2113, Australia
Ph: 61 2 98050399
Fax: 61 2 98050714
Publisher E-mail: mailorder@universalmagazines.com.au
Magazine for dog lovers and owners. **Freq:** Bimonthly. **Key Personnel:** Tim Falk, Editor, phone 61 2 98870360, fax 61 2 98870350. **Remarks:** Accepts advertising. **URL:** http://www.dogslife.com.au/. **Circ:** (Not Reported)

42182 ■ 4WD Buyers Guide
Universal Magazines
6-8 Byfield St., Unit 5
North Ryde, New South Wales 2113, Australia
Ph: 61 2 98050399
Fax: 61 2 98050714

Publisher E-mail: mailorder@universalmagazines.com.au
Magazine featuring guidelines for buyers of new and old Sport Utility Vehicles and 4 wheel drives. **Freq:** Quarterly. **Trim Size:** 210 x 278 mm. **Key Personnel:** Bill McKinnon, Editor, bill.mckinnon@bigpond.com.au; Brian Sullivan, Advertising Mgr. **Remarks:** Accepts advertising. **URL:** http://universalmagazines.com.au/CustomContentRetrieve.aspx?ID=296299. **Ad Rates:** 4C: $A 2,200. **Circ:** (Not Reported)

42183 ■ Homespun
Universal Magazines
6-8 Byfield St., Unit 5
North Ryde, New South Wales 2113, Australia
Ph: 61 2 98050399
Fax: 61 2 98050714
Publisher E-mail: mailorder@universalmagazines.com.au
Crafts and needleworks magazine. **Founded:** 1998. **Freq:** Monthly. **Print Method:** 278 x 230 mm. **Key Personnel:** Catherine Sanchez, Editor; Angelos Tzovlas, Advertising Mgr. **Subscription Rates:** $A 89.95 individuals; $A 169.95 two years; $A 78.75 individuals New Zealand; $A 197 individuals Asia; $A 231 other countries. **Remarks:** Accepts advertising. **URL:** http://www.universalmagazines.com.au/_webapp_118012/Homespun. **Ad Rates:** 4C: $A 1,350. **Circ:** (Not Reported)

42184 ■ Kit Homes
Universal Magazines
6-8 Byfield St., Unit 5
North Ryde, New South Wales 2113, Australia
Ph: 61 2 98050399
Fax: 61 2 98050714
Publisher E-mail: mailorder@universalmagazines.com.au
Magazine featuring kit home designs. **Freq:** Annual. **Trim Size:** 210 x 278 mm. **Key Personnel:** Laurie Findley, Advertising Mgr.; Tony Castor, Advertising Mgr.; Valerie Newton, Advertising Mgr. **Remarks:** Accepts advertising. **URL:** http://universalmagazines.com.au/_webapp_296304/Kit_Homes_Yearbook. **Circ:** (Not Reported)

42185 ■ Kitchen Yearbook
Universal Magazines
6-8 Byfield St., Unit 5
North Ryde, New South Wales 2113, Australia
Ph: 61 2 98050399
Fax: 61 2 98050714
Publisher E-mail: mailorder@universalmagazines.com.au
Magazine featuring kitchen designs. **Freq:** Annual. **Trim Size:** 230 x 297 mm. **Key Personnel:** Melanie Gardener, Editor, phone 61 2 98870367, mgardener@universalmagazines.com.au; Melissa Ham, Advertising Mgr., phone 61 2 98870618, mham@universalmagazines.com.au; John Oliver, Advertising Mgr., joliver@universalmagazines.com.au. **Subscription Rates:** US$9.95 single issue. **Remarks:** Accepts advertising. **URL:** http://www.magazineonline.com.au/home/kitchen_yearbook. **Circ:** (Not Reported)

42186 ■ Kitchens and Bathrooms Quarterly
Universal Magazines
6-8 Byfield St., Unit 5
North Ryde, New South Wales 2113, Australia
Ph: 61 2 98050399
Fax: 61 2 98050714
Publisher E-mail: mailorder@universalmagazines.com.au
Magazine focusing on bathroom and kitchen designs. **Freq:** Quarterly. **Trim Size:** 230 x 297 mm. **Key Personnel:** Melanie Gardener, Editor; Bev Hackett, Advertising Mgr., phone 61 2 98870363; John Oliver, Advertising Mgr., phone 61 3 96946430. **Subscription Rates:** $A 40 individuals; $A 80 two years; $A 51 individuals New Zealand; $A 135 individuals Asia; $A 174 other countries. **Remarks:** Accepts advertising. **URL:** http://www.universalmagazines.com.au/CustomContentRetrieve.aspx?ID=118015. **Circ:** (Not Reported)

42187 ■ Life Etc.
Universal Magazines
6-8 Byfield St., Unit 5
North Ryde, New South Wales 2113, Australia
Ph: 61 2 98050399
Fax: 61 2 98050714

Publisher E-mail: mailorder@universalmagazines.com.au

Lifestyle magazine for the 35+ market, that draws from ABC's television and radio programs. **Subtitle:** Real reading no gossip. **Freq:** Bimonthly. **Trim Size:** 220 x 300 mm. **Key Personnel:** Jane Southward, Editor; Margaret Graham, Advertising Mgr., phone 61 2 9887641. **Subscription Rates:** $A 32 individuals; $A 57 individuals New Zealand; $A 84 individuals Asia; $A 100 other countries; $A 50 two years. **Remarks:** Accepts advertising. **URL:** http://www.universalmagazines.com.au. **Ad Rates:** 4C: $A 6,850. **Circ:** *41,026

42188 ■ New Car Buyer
Universal Magazines
6-8 Byfield St., Unit 5
North Ryde, New South Wales 2113, Australia
Ph: 61 2 98050399
Fax: 61 2 98050714
Publisher E-mail: mailorder@universalmagazines.com.au
Magazine featuring guidelines for new car buyers. **Freq:** Quarterly. **Trim Size:** 210 x 278 mm. **Key Personnel:** Bill McKinnon, Editor; Brian Sullivan, Advertising Mgr. **Subscription Rates:** $A 8.95 single issue. **Remarks:** Accepts advertising. **URL:** http://universalmagazines.com.au/_webapp_296301/Australian_New_Car_Buyer. **Ad Rates:** 4C: $A 2,000. **Circ:** (Not Reported)

42189 ■ Outdoor Design & Living
Universal Magazines
6-8 Byfield St., Unit 5
North Ryde, New South Wales 2113, Australia
Ph: 61 2 98050399
Fax: 61 2 98050714
Publisher E-mail: mailorder@universalmagazines.com.au
Magazine contemporary residential landscape projects. **Freq:** Biennial. **Trim Size:** 230 x 297 mm. **Key Personnel:** Karen Booth, Editor; Emil Montibeler, Advertising Mgr., phone 61 2 98870310; Rachel Brus, Advertising Mgr., phone 61 2 98870619. **Subscription Rates:** $A 37.80 individuals; $A 75.60 two years; $A 111 other countries. **Remarks:** Accepts advertising. **URL:** http://www.universalmagazines.com.au/CustomContentRetrieve.aspx?ID=118313. **Circ:** (Not Reported)

42190 ■ Outdoor Design Source
Universal Magazines
Locked Bag 154
North Ryde, New South Wales 1670, Australia
Fax: 61 2 98050748
Publication E-mail: ods@universalmagazines.com.au
Publisher E-mail: mailorder@universalmagazines.com.au
Magazine featuring exterior designs. **Freq:** Quarterly. **Trim Size:** 210 x 297 mm. **Key Personnel:** Natalie Raad, Editor, phone 61 2 98870609, nraad@universalmagazines.com.au; Emil Montibeler, Publishing Mgr., phone 61 2 98870310, emontibeler@universalmagazines.com.au. **Subscription Rates:** $A 80 single issue. **Remarks:** Accepts advertising. **URL:** http://www.outdoordesign.com.au/. **Circ:** (Not Reported)

42191 ■ Outdoor Space
Universal Magazines
6-8 Byfield St., Unit 5
North Ryde, New South Wales 2113, Australia
Ph: 61 2 98050399
Fax: 61 2 98050714
Publisher E-mail: mailorder@universalmagazines.com.au
Magazine featuring landscape designs. **Freq:** Annual. **Trim Size:** 230 x 297 mm. **Key Personnel:** Jennifer Stackhouse, Editor. **Subscription Rates:** $A 9.95 single issue. **Remarks:** Accepts advertising. **URL:** http://www.universalshop.com.au/magazine_subscriptions?cid=6225&pid=15798. **Ad Rates:** 4C: $A 4,500. **Circ:** 30,000

42192 ■ Performance Buildups
Universal Magazines
6-8 Byfield St., Unit 5
North Ryde, New South Wales 2113, Australia
Ph: 61 2 98050399
Fax: 61 2 98050714
Publisher E-mail: mailorder@universalmagazines.com.au
Technical magazine featuring automotive engines and car buildups for car enthusiasts in Australia. **Freq:** Quarterly. **Trim Size:** 210 X 278 mm. **Key Personnel:** Mark Boxer, Editor-in-Chief, boxer@cunningstunts.com. **Remarks:** Accepts advertising. **URL:** http://www.magazineonline.com.au/home/performance_buildups. **Ad Rates:** 4C: $A 1,489. **Circ:** 22,000

42193 ■ Poolside
Universal Magazines
6-8 Byfield St., Unit 5
North Ryde, New South Wales 2113, Australia
Ph: 61 2 98050399
Fax: 61 2 98050714
Publisher E-mail: mailorder@universalmagazines.com.au
Magazine featuring the best pool designs and designers in Australia. **Freq:** Semiannual. **Trim Size:** 230 x 297 mm. **Key Personnel:** Vikki Mason, Editor; John Oliver, Advertising Mgr., phone 61 3 96946430. **Remarks:** Accepts advertising. **URL:** http://www.universalmagazines.com.au/_webapp_118298/Poolside. **Circ:** (Not Reported)

42194 ■ Poolside Showcase
Universal Magazines
6-8 Byfield St., Unit 5
North Ryde, New South Wales 2113, Australia
Ph: 61 2 98050399
Fax: 61 2 98050714
Publisher E-mail: mailorder@universalmagazines.com.au
Magazine featuring the best pool designs and designers in Australia. **Freq:** Semiannual. **Trim Size:** 230 x 297 mm. **Key Personnel:** Vikki Mason, Editor; John Oliver, Advertising Mgr., phone 61 3 96946430. **Subscription Rates:** $A 55 individuals. **Remarks:** Accepts advertising. **URL:** http://www.universalmagazines.com.au/_webapp_118314/Poolside_Showcase. **Circ:** 30,000

42195 ■ Quilters Companion
Universal Magazines
6-8 Byfield St., Unit 5
North Ryde, New South Wales 2113, Australia
Ph: 61 2 98050399
Fax: 61 2 98050714
Publisher E-mail: mailorder@universalmagazines.com.au
Magazine featuring patchwork and quilting. **Subtitle:** Excellence in patchwork and quilting. **Freq:** Bimonthly. **Trim Size:** 230 x 278 mm. **Key Personnel:** Clare Mooney, Editor; Rob Jordan, Advertising Mgr., phone 61 2 98870300. **Subscription Rates:** $A 60 individuals. **Remarks:** Accepts advertising. **URL:** http://www.universalmagazines.com.au/_webapp_118022/Quilters_Companion. **Ad Rates:** BW: $A 1,150. **Circ:** (Not Reported)

42196 ■ Scrapbook Creations
Universal Magazines
6-8 Byfield St., Unit 5
North Ryde, New South Wales 2113, Australia
Ph: 61 2 98050399
Fax: 61 2 98050714
Publisher E-mail: mailorder@universalmagazines.com.au
Magazine for scrap booking enthusiasts. **Freq:** Monthly. **Trim Size:** 230 x 270 mm. **Key Personnel:** Kim Taranto, Editor; Miriam Keen, Advertising Mgr. **Subscription Rates:** $A 30 individuals 6 months. **Remarks:** Accepts display and classified advertising. **URL:** http://www.universalmagazines.com.au/_webapp_118010/Scrapbook_Creations. **Ad Rates:** 4C: $A 2,500. **Circ:** (Not Reported)

42197 ■ Smart Kitchens & Bathrooms
Universal Magazines
6-8 Byfield St., Unit 5
North Ryde, New South Wales 2113, Australia
Ph: 61 2 98050399
Fax: 61 2 98050714
Publisher E-mail: mailorder@universalmagazines.com.au
Magazine featuring innovative bathroom and kitchen designs with the help of technology. **Freq:** Annual. **Trim Size:** 230 x 297 mm. **Key Personnel:** Melanie Gardener, Editor, phone 61 2 98870367, mgardener@universalmagazines.com.au; Melissa Ham, Advertising Mgr., phone 61 2 98870618, mham@universalmagazines.com.au. **Subscription Rates:** $A 9.95 single issue. **Remarks:** Accepts advertising. **URL:** http://www.magazineonline.com.au/home?p=3299. **Ad Rates:** 4C: $A 3,500. **Circ:** 25,000

42198 ■ Stone
Universal Magazines
6-8 Byfield St., Unit 5
North Ryde, New South Wales 2113, Australia
Ph: 61 2 98050399
Fax: 61 2 98050714
Publisher E-mail: mailorder@universalmagazines.com.au
Magazine featuring latest news and information on stone to home owners, architects, designers, and other industry professionals. **Freq:** Quarterly. **Trim Size:** 210 x 278 mm. **Subscription Rates:** $A 9.95 single issue. **Remarks:** Accepts advertising. **URL:** http://www.universalshop.com.au/magazine_subscriptions?cid=6224&pid=24351. **Ad Rates:** 4C: $A 2,750. **Circ:** 12,000

42199 ■ Sydney Eats
Universal Magazines
6-8 Byfield St., Unit 5
North Ryde, New South Wales 2113, Australia
Ph: 61 2 98050399
Fax: 61 2 98050714
Publisher E-mail: mailorder@universalmagazines.com.au
Magazine featuring the best food and restaurants in Sydney, Blue Mountains and Canberra. **Freq:** Annual. **Key Personnel:** John Newton; Stephanie Clifford-Smith, Editor; Margaret Sherrard, Advertising Mgr. **Subscription Rates:** $A 14.95 single issue. **Remarks:** Accepts advertising. **URL:** http://www.universalmagazines.com.au. **Circ:** (Not Reported)

42200 ■ Used Car Buyers Guide
Universal Magazines
6-8 Byfield St., Unit 5
North Ryde, New South Wales 2113, Australia
Ph: 61 2 98050399
Fax: 61 2 98050714
Publisher E-mail: mailorder@universalmagazines.com.au
Magazine featuring guidelines for buyers of used cars. **Subtitle:** Your essential guide to buying a used car. **Freq:** Quarterly. **Trim Size:** 210 x 278 mm. **Key Personnel:** Ewan Kennedy, Editor; John Arens, Advertising Mgr. **Subscription Rates:** $A 7.95 U.S. per issue. **Remarks:** Accepts advertising. **URL:** http://www.magazineonline.com.au/home/used_car_buyers_guide. **Ad Rates:** 4C: $A 2,310. **Circ:** (Not Reported)

42201 ■ WellBeing
Universal Magazines
6-8 Byfield St., Unit 5
North Ryde, New South Wales 2113, Australia
Ph: 61 2 98050399
Fax: 61 2 98050714
Publisher E-mail: mailorder@universalmagazines.com.au
Health and fitness magazine. **Freq:** Bimonthly. **Trim Size:** 220 x 300 mm. **Key Personnel:** Chelsea Hunter, Editor, cghunter@universalmagazines.com.au; Terry Robson, Editor, trobson@universalmagazines.com.au; Margaret Sherrard, Contact. **Subscription Rates:** $A 48 individuals. **Remarks:** Accepts display and classified advertising. **URL:** http://www.wellbeing.com.au/. **Ad Rates:** 4C: $A 5,050. **Circ:** (Not Reported)

42202 ■ MIX 106.5-FM - 106.5
3 Byfield St.
North Ryde, New South Wales 2113, Australia
Ph: 61 2 88999888
Fax: 61 2 88999566
E-mail: programdirector@mix1065.com.au
Format: Adult Contemporary. **Key Personnel:** Peter Colosimo, Dir. of Sales, petercolosimo@arn.com.au; Melissa Fitzgerald, Agency Sales, melissafitzgerald@arn.com.au; Kate Hurley, Contact, katehurley@mix1065.com.au. **Ad Rates:** Advertising accepted; rates available upon request. **URL:** http://www.mix1065.com.au/.

42203 ■ 96.1-FM - 96.1
Locked Bag 2110
North Ryde, New South Wales 1670, Australia
Ph: 61 2 96111961
E-mail: 961pd@arn.com.au
Format: Adult Contemporary; News. **Owner:** Australian Radio Network, 3 Byfield St., North Ryde, New South

Circulation: ★ = ABC; △ = BPA; ◆ = CAC; • = CCAB; ❑ = VAC; ⊕ = PO Statement; ‡ = Publisher's Report; Boldface figures = sworn; Light figures = estimated.

Gale Directory of Publications & Broadcast Media/147th Ed.   4735

Wales 2113, Australia, 61 2 88999999, Fax: 61 2 88999811. **Key Personnel:** Charlie Fox, Program Dir. **Ad Rates:** Advertising accepted; rates available upon request. **URL:** http://www.961.com.au/; http://www.arn.com.au.

42204 ■ 2WS-FM - 101.7
3 Byfield St.
North Ryde, New South Wales 2113, Australia
Ph: 61 2 88999888
Fax: 61 2 88999788
E-mail: sales@wsfm.com.au
Format: Oldies. **Owner:** Australian Radio Network, at above address. **Founded:** Nov. 23, 1978. **Key Personnel:** Amanda Keller, Contact, amanda@wsfm.com.au; Ron E. Sparks, Contact, rone@wsfm.com.au; Glenn Daniel, Contact, glenn@wsfm.com.au. **Ad Rates:** Advertising accepted; rates available upon request. **URL:** http://www.2ws.com.au/; http://www.arn.com.au/.

42205 ■ WSFM-FM - 101.7
3 Byfield St.
North Ryde, New South Wales 2113, Australia
Ph: 61 2 88999888
Fax: 61 2 88999788
E-mail: newsroom@wsfm.com.au
Format: Classic Rock; News. **Owner:** Australian Radio Network, at above address. **Operating Hours:** Continuous. **Key Personnel:** Anthony Fitzgerald, General Mgr.; Charlie Fox, Program Dir.; Sarah May, Promotions Mgr.; Sandy Phillips, Sales Mgr.; Glenn Daniel, News Dir. **Ad Rates:** Advertising accepted; rates available upon request. **URL:** http://www.wsfm.com.au.

North Sydney

42206 ■ Australian Banking & Finance
First Charlton Communications Proprietary Ltd.
Level 8, 122 Arthur St.
56 Berry St.
North Sydney, New South Wales 2060, Australia
Ph: 61 2 99556299
Fax: 61 2 99571512
Publisher E-mail: reception@charlton.com.au
Publication covering banking and finance issues in Australia. **Founded:** Sept. 1992. **Freq:** Bimonthly. **Trim Size:** 280 x 410 mm. **Key Personnel:** Justine Charlton, Contact. **ISSN:** 1325-1228. **Subscription Rates:** $A 170.40 individuals; US$89 individuals within Australia; US$338.30 two years overseas airmail; $A 175.50 two years within Australia. **Remarks:** Accepts advertising. **URL:** http://www.charlton.com.au; http://www.australianbankingfinance.com/. **Ad Rates:** BW: $A 6,589, 4C: $A 4,845. **Circ:** 3,850

42207 ■ Australian PC World
IDG Communications Pty. Limited - Australia
PO Box 1753
North Sydney, New South Wales 2059, Australia
Ph: 61 2 94395133
Fax: 61 2 94395512
Computer periodical. **Freq:** Monthly. **Print Method:** Web offset. **Trim Size:** 275 mm x 205 mm. **Key Personnel:** Amanda Conroy, Editorial Dir., amanda_conroy@idg.com.au; Rohan Pearce, Production Ed., rohan_pearce@idg.com.au; Elias Plastiras, Test Center Mgr., elias_plastiras@idg.com.au. **ISSN:** 0813-1384. **Subscription Rates:** $A 66 individuals includes GST, postage & handling; $A 200 other countries foreign by airmail; $A 150 for NZ/PNG by airmail. **Remarks:** Accepts advertising. **Online:** Gale. **URL:** http://www.pcworld.idg.com.au/ **Ad Rates:** BW: $A 4,380, 4C: $A 5,600. **Circ:** Paid ★50,078

42208 ■ Australian Society & Events
First Charlton Communications Proprietary Ltd.
c/o Peter Charlton, Ed.
Level 8, 122 Arthur St.
North Sydney, New South Wales 2060, Australia
Ph: 61 2 99556299
Fax: 61 2 99571512
Publisher E-mail: reception@charlton.com.au
Magazine that captures the essence of Australian society, including premieres, launches, charity events, and celebrity features, both from Australia and the international scene. **Freq:** Quarterly. **Key Personnel:** Peter Charlton, Editor, eption@charlton.com.au; Esther Cvejic, Publisher, esther@society.net.au. **Subscription Rates:** $A 35.80 individuals in Australia. **Remarks:** Ac-

cepts advertising. **URL:** http://www.charlton.com.au/ase.asp. **Circ:** 10,000

42209 ■ Australian Telecom
First Charlton Communications Proprietary Ltd.
Level 8, 122 Arthur St.
56 Berry St.
North Sydney, New South Wales 2060, Australia
Ph: 61 2 99556299
Fax: 61 2 99571512
Publisher E-mail: reception@charlton.com.au
Business magazine for people in the telecommunications/IT who need to know about the events driving their own companies and their competitors. **Freq:** Bimonthly. **Key Personnel:** Peter Charlton, Editor, phone 61 2 99556299, fax 61 2 99571512, reception@charlton.com.au. **Subscription Rates:** $A 55 individuals; $A 110 other countries. **Remarks:** Accepts advertising. **URL:** http://www.charlton.com.au/magazines/at/index.asp. **Circ:** (Not Reported)

42210 ■ Business Asia
First Charlton Communications Proprietary Ltd.
Level 8, 122 Arthur St.
56 Berry St.
North Sydney, New South Wales 2060, Australia
Ph: 61 2 99556299
Fax: 61 2 99571512
Publisher E-mail: reception@charlton.com.au
Publication covering economics. **Founded:** June 1993. **Freq:** Quarterly. **Trim Size:** 210 x 275 mm. **Key Personnel:** Randolph Ramsay, Contact; Tony May, Sales and Advertising Mgr. **ISSN:** 1320-9884. **Subscription Rates:** $A 64.90 individuals; US$140.80 institutions, other countries overseas airmail; $A 115.50 two years within Australia; US$191.40 two years overseas airmail. **Remarks:** Accepts advertising. **URL:** http://www.charlton.com.au/magazines/asia/index.asp. **Ad Rates:** BW: $A 5,830, 4C: $A 6,600. **Circ:** Combined 24,600, Paid 1,000

42211 ■ NSW Public Health Bulletin
NSW Department of Health
Locked Mail Bag 961
North Sydney, New South Wales 2059, Australia
Publication E-mail: phbulletin@doh.health.nsw.gov.au
Publisher E-mail: nswhealth@doh.health.nsw.gov.au
Bulletin covering major public health issues. **Founded:** May 1990. **Key Personnel:** Dawn Simpson, Editor. **URL:** http://www.health.nsw.gov.au/public-health/phb/phb.html.

Northbridge

42212 ■ Cockburn Gazette
Community Newspaper
120 Roe St.
Northbridge, Western Australia 6003, Australia
Ph: 61 892 132013
Fax: 61 892 371056
Publication E-mail: fremantlegazette@communitynews.com.au
Publisher E-mail: classifieds@communitynews.com.au
General newspaper. **Freq:** Weekly (Tues.). **URL:** http://www.communitynews.com.au/OurNewspapers/FremantleGazette/tabid/60/Default.aspx.

Northcote

42213 ■ Northcote Leader
Leader Community Newspapers
192 High St., 2nd Fl.
Northcote, Victoria 3070, Australia
Local community newspaper. **Freq:** Weekly (Tues.). **Key Personnel:** Sally Fisher, Editor, northcote@leadernewspapers.com.au; Karen Mulhall, Sales Mgr., mulhallk@leadernewspapers.com.au. **Remarks:** Accepts advertising. **URL:** http://northcote-leader.whereilive.com.au/. **Circ:** Tues. ‡24,072

Norwood

42214 ■ Australian Journal of Language and Literacy
Australian Literacy Educators' Association
PO Box 3203
Norwood, South Australia 5067, Australia
Ph: 61 8 83322845
Fax: 61 8 83330394
Publication E-mail: ajll@education.monash.edu.au

Publisher E-mail: alea@netspace.net.au
Education publication. **Founded:** 1978. **Freq:** 3 issues per year. **Key Personnel:** Dr. Jennifer Rennie, Managing Editor. **ISSN:** 1038-1562. **Subscription Rates:** $A 120 inst. membership plus $12 GST in Australia. **Remarks:** Accepts advertising. **URL:** http://alea.edu.au/html/publications/16/australian-journal-of-language-and-literacy. **Formerly:** Australian Journal of Reading. **Ad Rates:** BW: $A 300. **Circ:** (Not Reported)

42215 ■ East Torrens Messenger
Messenger Newspapers
94 The Parade
Norwood, South Australia 5067, Australia
Ph: 61 8 81300103
Local community newspaper. **Freq:** Weekly (Wed.). **Key Personnel:** Chris Dimitrak, Eastern Sales Mgr., phone 61 8 83100103, dimitrakc@mng.newsltd.com.au. **Remarks:** Accepts display and classified advertising. **URL:** http://www.newsspace.com.au/east_torrens_messenger. **Circ:** 33,157

42216 ■ Eastern Courier Messenger
Messenger Newspapers
94 The Parade
Norwood, South Australia 5067, Australia
Ph: 61 8 81300103
Local community newspaper. **Freq:** Weekly (Wed.). **Key Personnel:** Chris Dimitrak, Eastern Sales Mgr., dimitrakc@mng.newsltd.com.au. **Remarks:** Accepts display and classified advertising. **URL:** http://www.newsspace.com.au/eastern_courier_messenger. **Circ:** 62,673

Nubeena

42217 ■ 7TAS-FM - 97.7
PO Box 1000
Nubeena, Tasmania 7184, Australia
E-mail: info@tasmanfm.com
Format: Country; Bluegrass; News; Jazz. **URL:** http://www.tasmanfm.com/.

Nunawading

42218 ■ Australian Field Ornithology
Bird Observation & Conservation Australia
PO Box 185
Nunawading, Victoria 3131, Australia
Ph: 61 3 98775342
Fax: 61 3 98944048
Publisher E-mail: information@birdobservers.org.au
Journal covering field ornithology in Australia. **Subtitle:** Incorporating the Australian Bird Watcher. **Founded:** 1959. **Freq:** Quarterly. **Print Method:** Photo-offset. **Trim Size:** B5. **ISSN:** 1448-0107. **Subscription Rates:** $A 32 individuals; $A 40 other countries. **Remarks:** Advertising not accepted. **URL:** http://www.boca.org.au/about-boca/publications. **Former name:** The Australian Bird Watcher. **Circ:** Paid 621, Non-paid 59

Nundah

42219 ■ Australian Baking Business
The Magazine Publishing Co.
34 Station St.
PO Box 406
Nundah, Queensland 4012, Australia
Ph: 61 7 38660000
Fax: 61 7 38660066
Publisher E-mail: info@tmpc.com.au
Magazine featuring latest news, business tips, and advice written by experts in the baking industry. **Founded:** June 1996. **Freq:** Bimonthly. **Trim Size:** 210 x 297 mm. **Key Personnel:** Cassie Hansen, Editorial Coord. **Subscription Rates:** $A 55 individuals; US$95 other countries. **Remarks:** Accepts advertising. **URL:** https://www.tmpc.com.au/?main/ViewMagazine&page=ViewMagazine&magazine_id=13. **Ad Rates:** 4C: $A 1,889. **Circ:** 8,348

42220 ■ The Circuit
The Magazine Publishing Co.
34 Station St.
PO Box 406
Nundah, Queensland 4012, Australia
Ph: 61 7 38660000
Fax: 61 7 38660066
Publisher E-mail: info@tmpc.com.au
Magazine covering the electrical and electronics

industries. **Founded:** Mar. 1996. **Freq:** Monthly. **Key Personnel:** Cassie Hansen, Editorial Coord. **Subscription Rates:** $A 66 individuals; US$120 individuals overseas. **Remarks:** Accepts advertising. **URL:** https://www.tmpc.com.au/?main/ViewMagazine&page=ViewMagazine&magazine_id=1. **Circ:** 9392

42221 ■ Council Leader
The Magazine Publishing Co.
34 Station St.
PO Box 406
Nundah, Queensland 4012, Australia
Ph: 61 7 38660000
Fax: 61 7 38660066
Publisher E-mail: info@tmpc.com.au
Magazine featuring up-to-date information on local government news and relevant issues affecting councils throughout Queensland. **Founded:** 1969. **Freq:** Bimonthly. **Trim Size:** 210 X 297 mm. **Key Personnel:** Cassie Hansen, Editorial Coord. **Subscription Rates:** $A 55 individuals; US$95 other countries. **Remarks:** Accepts advertising. **URL:** https://www.tmpc.com.au/?main/ViewMagazine&page=ViewMagazine&magazine_id=3. **Ad Rates:** 4C: $A 2,156. **Circ:** 3125

42222 ■ Developers Digest
The Magazine Publishing Co.
34 Station St.
PO Box 406
Nundah, Queensland 4012, Australia
Ph: 61 7 38660000
Fax: 61 7 38660066
Publisher E-mail: info@tmpc.com.au
Magazine featuring information about the urban development industry in New South Wales. **Freq:** Bimonthly. **Trim Size:** 210 x 297 mm. **Key Personnel:** Cassie Hansen, Editorial Coord. **Subscription Rates:** $A 55 individuals; $A 95 other countries. **Remarks:** Accepts advertising. **URL:** https://www.tmpc.com.au/?main/ViewMagazine&page=ViewMagazine&magazine_id=12. **Ad Rates:** 4C: $A 1,729. **Circ:** 1750

42223 ■ Queensland Racing Magazine
The Magazine Publishing Co.
34 Station St.
PO Box 406
Nundah, Queensland 4012, Australia
Ph: 61 7 38660000
Fax: 61 7 38660066
Publisher E-mail: info@tmpc.com.au
Magazine featuring issues regarding Queensland horse racing. **Founded:** 1886. **Freq:** Monthly. **Trim Size:** 210 x 297 mm. **Key Personnel:** Cassie Hansen, Editorial Coord. **Subscription Rates:** $A 110 individuals; US$195 other countries. **Remarks:** Accepts advertising. **URL:** https://www.tmpc.com.au/?main/ViewMagazine&page=ViewMagazine&magazine_id=10. **Ad Rates:** 4C: $A 1,725. **Circ:** 4,850

Osborne Park

42224 ■ Eastern Reporter
Community Newspaper
169 Main St.
Osborne Park, Western Australia 6017, Australia
Ph: 61 9 2315200
Publication E-mail: easternsuburbsreporter@communitynews.com.au
Publisher E-mail: classifieds@communitynews.com.au
General newspaper. **Freq:** WET **URL:** http://www.communitynews.com.au/Newspapers/EasternReporter/tabid/59/Default.

42225 ■ Magic-FM - 87.8
PO Box 1487
Osborne Park, Western Australia 6916, Australia
Ph: 61 8 94840878
Fax: 61 8 93753878
E-mail: info@com.au
Format: Easy Listening; Oldies. **Operating Hours:** Continuous. **Key Personnel:** Pete Brown, Contact, petebrown@magicfm.com.au. **Ad Rates:** $5.50 for 30 seconds. **URL:** http://www.magicfm.com.au/.

Paddington

42226 ■ Eastside Radio-FM - 89.7
249A Oxford St.
PO Box 343

Paddington, New South Wales 2021, Australia
Ph: 61 2 93313000
E-mail: eastside@eastsidefm.org
Format: Information; Eclectic; Public Radio. **Founded:** 1983. **Operating Hours:** Continuous. **Key Personnel:** Tony Smythe, Station Mgr.; Phillip Fiebig, Chp. **Ad Rates:** Underwriting available. **URL:** http://www.eastsidefm.org.

Padstow

42227 ■ 2B-FM - 100.9
102 Cahors Rd.
Padstow, New South Wales 2211, Australia
Ph: 61 2 97712288
Fax: 61 2 97712288
E-mail: bfmsydney@yahoo.com.au
Format: Contemporary Hit Radio (CHR); Public Radio; Ethnic. **Founded:** 1983. **Operating Hours:** Continuous. **URL:** http://www.2bfm.com.

Paradise Point

42228 ■ Procurement Professional
BTTB Marketing Pty Ltd.
PO Box 825
Paradise Point, Queensland 4216, Australia
Ph: 61 7 55491092
Fax: 61 7 55491093
Publisher E-mail: info@bttbonline.com
Magazine for all professional purchasing practitioners in Australia. **Subtitle:** The Magazine for Purchasing and Supply. **Freq:** Bimonthly. **Trim Size:** 210 x 297 mm. **Key Personnel:** Nigel Wardropper, Publisher/Mng. Ed., nigelw@bttbonline.com. **Remarks:** Accepts advertising. **URL:** http://www.pponline.com.au/html/. **Ad Rates:** 4C: $A 2,580. **Circ:** 4,500

Parkes

42229 ■ National Library of Australia Gateways
National Library of Australia
Parkes Pl.
Parkes, Australian Capital Territory 2600, Australia
Ph: 61 2 62621111
Fax: 61 2 62571703
Publication E-mail: gateways@nla.gov.au
Trade magazine covering news about networked services in the library. **Freq:** Bimonthly. **ISSN:** 1443-0568. **Subscription Rates:** Free. **URL:** http://www.nla.gov.au/ntwkpubs/gatehome.html.

Parkside

42230 ■ Australian Educator
Australian Education Union
163 Greenhill Rd.
Parkside, South Australia 5063, Australia
Ph: 61 8 82721399
Fax: 61 8 83731254
Publisher E-mail: aeusa@aeusa.asn.au
Australian publication covering education. **Freq:** Quarterly. **ISSN:** 0728-8387. **Subscription Rates:** US$17.60 individuals Australia; US$30 elsewhere postage included. **Remarks:** Advertising accepted; rates available upon request. **URL:** http://www.aeufederal.org.au/Publications/AE/AEissues.html. **Circ:** 120,000

Parkville

42231 ■ Historical Records of Australian Science
CSIRO Publishing
c/o Prof. R.W. Home, Ed.
Dept. of History & Philosophy of Science
University of Melbourne
Parkville, Victoria 3010, Australia
Ph: 61 383 446556
Fax: 61 383 447959
Publisher E-mail: publishing@csiro.au
Journal covering biographical memoirs of deceased Fellows of the Australian Academy of Science commissioned by the Council of the Academy, and an annual bibliography of the history of Australian science. **Founded:** 1958. **Freq:** Semiannual. **Print Method:** Offset. **Cols./Page:** 6. **Col. Width:** 12 picas. **Col. Depth:** 294 agate lines. **Key Personnel:** Dr. Sara Maroske, Book Review, saramaroske@optusnet.com.au; Prof.

R.W. Home, Editor, home@unimelb.edu.au; Prof. David Craig, Editorial Committee. **ISSN:** 0727-3061. **Subscription Rates:** $A 155 institutions online (Australia and New Zealand); EUR95 institutions online; 70 institutions online; US$165 institutions online (North America and rest of world); $A 195 institutions print and online (Australia and New Zealand); EUR120 institutions print and online; 85 institutions print and online; US$210 institutions print and online (North America and rest of world). **URL:** http://www.publish.csiro.au/nid/108.htm.

42232 ■ Tissue Antigens
John Wiley & Sons Inc.
Wiley-Blackwell
Dept. of Microbiology & Immunology
University of Melbourne
Parkville, Victoria 3052, Australia
Ph: 61 3 83445709
Fax: 61 3 98885228
Publication E-mail: tissueantigens@bigpond.com
Peer-reviewed journal covering the study of genetic control of immune response, disease susceptibility and genetics, biochemistry and molecular biology of alloantigens and leukocyte differentiation. **Freq:** Monthly. **Key Personnel:** James McCluskey, Editor-in-Chief; P. Parham, Assoc. Ed.; Joe A. Trapani, Reviews Ed., joe.trapani@petermac.org; T. Sasazuki, Assoc. Ed.; D. Charron, Assoc. Ed.; S.G.E. Marsh, Assoc. Ed.; J. Trowsdale, Assoc. Ed.; R. Duquesnoy, Advisory Ed.; S. Ferrone, Advisory Ed. **ISSN:** 0001-2815. **Subscription Rates:** US$968 individuals print and online; US$867 individuals online only; US$1,325 institutions print and online; US$1,205 institutions print, online; EUR1,003 institutions print and online; EUR863 individuals print and online; EUR775 individuals online only; 790 institutions print and online; 718 institutions print, online; US$1,548 institutions, other countries print and online. **Remarks:** Advertising accepted; rates available upon request. **URL:** http://www.wiley.com/bw/journal.asp?ref=0001-2815&site=1. **Circ:** (Not Reported)

Parramatta

42233 ■ Blacktown Advocate
Cumberland Newspaper Group
142-154 Macquarie St.
Parramatta, New South Wales 2150, Australia
Ph: 61 2 96895500
Local community newspaper. **Founded:** 1945. **Freq:** Weekly (Wed.). **Key Personnel:** Simon Kent, Editor, editor@blacktownadvocate.com.au; Gisela Foote, Advertising Mgr., advertising@blacktownadvocate.com.au. **Remarks:** Accepts display and classified advertising. **URL:** http://blacktown-advocate.whereilive.com.au/. **Circ:** 51,400

42234 ■ Inner-West Weekly
Cumberland Newspaper Group
142-154 Macquarie St.
Parramatta, New South Wales 2150, Australia
Ph: 61 2 96895500
Local community newspaper. **Freq:** Weekly (Thurs.). **Key Personnel:** Robyn Ainsworth, Editor; Ben Payne, Advertising Mgr. **Remarks:** Accepts display and classified advertising. **URL:** http://www.newsspace.com.au/inner_west_weekly_. **Circ:** 52,892

42235 ■ Parramatta Advertiser
Cumberland Newspaper Group
142-154 Macquarie St.
Parramatta, New South Wales 2150, Australia
Ph: 61 2 96895500
Local community newspaper. **Freq:** Weekly (Wed.). **Key Personnel:** Rick Allen, Editor, editor@parramattaadvertiser.com.au. **Remarks:** Accepts display and classified advertising. **URL:** http://parramatta-advertiser.whereilive.com.au/. **Circ:** 82,656

42236 ■ Rotary Down Under
PO Box 779
Parramatta, New South Wales 2124, Australia
Ph: 61 296 334888
Fax: 61 298 915984
Publisher E-mail: enquiries@rotarydownunder.com.au
Membership magazine of Rotary International gives details of Rotary-related subjects and activities of Rotarians in the South West Pacific area. **Founded:** 1965. **Freq:** Monthly. **Print Method:** Offset. **Trim Size:** 276 x 205mm. **Key Personnel:** Robert J. Aitken, Editor; Mark Wallace, Assoc. Ed. **Subscription Rates:** $A 37.40 individuals. **Remarks:** Accepts advertising. **URL:** http://

Circulation: ★ = ABC; △ = BPA; ◆ = CAC; ● = CCAB; ❏ = VAC; ⊕ = PO Statement; ‡ = Publisher's Report; Boldface figures = sworn; Light figures = estimated.

Gale Directory of Publications & Broadcast Media/147th Ed. | 4737

www.rotarnet.com.au. **Ad Rates:** BW: $A 2,310, 4C: $A 3,520. **Circ:** Paid 50,000

42237 ■ Rouse Hill Times
Cumberland Newspaper Group
142-154 Macquarie St.
Parramatta, New South Wales 2150, Australia
Ph: 61 2 96895500
Local community newspaper. **Freq:** Weekly (Wed.). **Key Personnel:** David Catt, Editor, editor@rousehilltimes. com.au; Amanda Vass, Advertising Mgr., vassa@ couriernews.com.au. **Remarks:** Accepts display and classified advertising. **URL:** http://rouse-hill-times. whereilive.com.au/. **Circ:** ‡18,410

Penola

42238 ■ Flow-FM - 107.3
PO Box 407
Kapunda, South Australia 5373, Australia
Ph: 61 8 85663151
Fax: 61 8 85662729
E-mail: mail@flowfm.com.au
Format: Adult Contemporary. **URL:** http://www.flowfm. com.au/.

Penrith

42239 ■ The Australian Educational Leader
Australian Council for Educational Leaders
PO Box 1891
Penrith, New South Wales 2751, Australia
Ph: 61 2 47321201
Fax: 61 2 47321711
Publisher E-mail: admin@acel.org.au
Journal containing information on educational leadership. **Founded:** 1979. **Freq:** Quarterly. **Key Personnel:** Dubravka Vukic-Presland, Exec. Ed. **Subscription Rates:** US$66 nonmembers Australia; US$70 nonmembers rest of the world; Included in membership. **Remarks:** Accepts advertising. **URL:** http://www.acel. org.au/index.php?id=84. **Formerly:** The Practising Administrator. **Circ:** (Not Reported)

42240 ■ Penrith Press
Cumberland Newspaper Group
407-409 High St.
Penrith, New South Wales 2750, Australia
Local community newspaper. **Founded:** 1947. **Freq:** Tue. and Fri. **Key Personnel:** Brad Earl, Editor, editor@ penrithpress.com.au; Simone Cody, Advertising Mgr., codys@cumberlandnewspapers.com.au. **Remarks:** Accepts display and classified advertising. **URL:** http:// penrith-press.whereilive.com.au/. **Circ:** Tues. 54,845, Fri. 54,838

42241 ■ Television Sydney - 31
Locked Bag 1797
Penrith, New South Wales 1797, Australia
Ph: 61 2 98525000
Fax: 61 2 98525050
E-mail: email@tvs.org.au
URL: http://www.tvs.org.au/.

Perth

42242 ■ AIG Journal
Australian Institute of Geoscientists
36 Brisbane St.
Perth, Western Australia 6000, Australia
Ph: 61 894 270820
Fax: 61 894 270821
Publication E-mail: aigjournal@aig.asn.au
Publisher E-mail: aig@aig.asn.au
Peer-reviewed journal covering the field of geosciences. **Key Personnel:** Bill Shaw, President. **ISSN:** 1443-1017. **Subscription Rates:** Free online. **URL:** http://www.aig. asn.au/aigjournal.

42243 ■ Asia-Pacific Journal of Chemical Engineering
John Wiley & Sons Inc.
c/o Prof. Moses O. Tade, Ed.-in-Ch.
Dept. of Chemical Engineering
Curtin University of Technology
GPO BOX U1987
Perth, Western Australia 6845, Australia
Ph: 61 8 92667581
Fax: 61 8 92662681

Publisher E-mail: info@wiley.com
Journal covering the current engineering developments and initiatives in the Asia-Pacific region. **Freq:** 6/yr. **Key Personnel:** Prof. Moses O. Tade, Editor-in-Chief, m.o. tade@curtin.edu.au; Martyn S. Ray, Sen. Ed., m.ray@ curtin.edu; Dr. Hong Mei Yao, Editor, h.yao@curtin.edu. au. **ISSN:** 1932-2135. **URL:** http://www3.interscience. wiley.com/journal/119818575/grouphome/home.html.

42244 ■ Asia Pacific Journal of Marketing and Logistics
Emerald Group Publishing Ltd.
c/o Dr. Ian Phau, Ed.
School of Marketing
Curtin University of Technology
GPO Box U1987
Perth, Western Australia 6845, Australia
Publisher E-mail: emerald@emeraldinsight.com
Journal covering marketing and logistics in Asia Pacific. **Freq:** Quarterly. **Key Personnel:** Dr. Ian Phau, Editor, ian.phau@cbs.curtin.edu.au; Richard Whitfield, Publisher, rwhitfield@emeraldinsight.com. **ISSN:** 1355-5855. **URL:** http://info.emeraldinsight.com/products/journals/ journals.htm?id=apjml. **Also known as:** APJML.

42245 ■ Australasian Plant Pathology
CSIRO Publishing
c/o Dr. Philip O'Brien, Ed.-in-Ch.
Australasian Plant Pathology
School of Biological Sciences & Biotechnology
Murdoch University
Perth, Western Australia 6150, Australia
Ph: 61 8 93602785
Fax: 61 8 93107084
Publisher E-mail: publishing@csiro.au
Journal dedicated to plant pathology. **Founded:** 1877. **Freq:** Bimonthly. **Print Method:** Offset. **Cols./Page:** 6. **Col. Width:** 26 nonpareils. **Col. Depth:** 301 agate lines. **Key Personnel:** R. Davis, Sen. Ed.; D. Backhouse, Sen. Ed.; M. Braithwaite, Sen. Ed.; T. Burgess, Sen. Ed.; Dr. Philip O'Brien, Editor-in-Chief, obrien@murdoch.edu.au. **ISSN:** 0815-3191. **Subscription Rates:** $A 775 institutions online (Australia and New Zealand); EUR585 institutions online; $A 970 institutions print and online (Australia and New Zealand); 505 institutions print and online; 405 institutions online; US$870 institutions U.S. and other countries; print and online; US$695 institutions U.S. and other countries; online. **URL:** http://www. publish.csiro.au/nid/39.htm.

42246 ■ Australian Indigenous HealthBulletin
Australian Indigenous HealthInfoNet
Edith Cowan University
School of Indigenous Australian Studies
Kurongkurl Katitjin
2 Bradford St.
Mt. Lawley
Perth, Western Australia 6050, Australia
Ph: 61 8 93706336
Fax: 61 8 93706022
Publication E-mail: healthbulletin@ecu.edu.au
Publisher E-mail: healthinfonet@ecu.edu.au
Peer-reviewed online journal covering health aspects of indigenous people of Australia, by publishing on-going research in this area, to policy makers, service providers, researchers, students and the general community. **Founded:** June 1997. **Freq:** Quarterly. **Key Personnel:** Jane Burns, Dep. Ed.; Prof. Neil Thomson, Editor; Ineke Krom, Production Asst. **ISSN:** 1445-7253. **URL:** http:// healthbulletin.org.au/. **Formerly:** Aboriginal and Torres Strait Islander health bulletin.

42247 ■ Bellydance Oasis
Bellydance Oasis Magazine
14 Anstie Way
Perth, Western Australia 6149, Australia
Ph: 43 8 223914
Publisher E-mail: ayesha_au@yahoo.com
Magazine specializing in Middle Eastern Dance. **Freq:** Quarterly. **Key Personnel:** Alma Sarhan, Director; Kerry Stewart, Sen. Writer. **Subscription Rates:** $A 38 individuals; $A 48 out of country. **URL:** http://www. bellydanceoasis.com/.

42248 ■ Business Pulse
Chamber of Commerce and Industry of Western Australia
180 Hay St.
Perth, Western Australia 6004, Australia
Ph: 61 893 657627
Publication E-mail: advice@cciwa.com

Publisher E-mail: info@cciwa.com
Journal containing information about business, employee relations, and international trade. **Freq:** Monthly. **ISSN:** 1328-2689. **Remarks:** Accepts advertising. **URL:** http:// www.cciwa.com/Business_Pulse_news_articles. aspx238. **Circ:** (Not Reported)

42249 ■ The Clinical Biochemist Reviews
Australasian Association of Clinical Biochemists
c/o Sam Vasikaran, Ed.
Core Clinical Pathology & Biochemistry
Royal Perth Hospital
PO Box X2213
Perth, Western Australia 6001, Australia
Ph: 61 892 242453
Fax: 61 892 241789
Publisher E-mail: office@aacb.asn.au
Journal focusing on clinical biochemistry. **Founded:** 1980. **Freq:** Quarterly. **Key Personnel:** Sandy Musk, Managing Editor, phone 08 92 241186, fax 08 92 242491, sandy.musk@health.wa.gov.au; Sam Vasikaran, Editor, phone 61 8 92242453, fax 61 8 92241789, samuel.vasikaran@health.wa.gov.au; Ceri Wood, Design and Production, ceri@aacb.asn.au; Julie Newman, Assoc. Ed., julie.newman@southernhealth.org.au; Amanda Hooper, Assoc. Ed., amanda.hooper@health. wa.gov.au. **ISSN:** 0159-8090. **Subscription Rates:** $A 100 nonmembers; US$100 nonmembers international. **Remarks:** Accepts advertising. **URL:** http://old.aacb. asn.au/pubs/cbr.htm. **Ad Rates:** BW: $A 640, 4C: $A 1,320. **Circ:** (Not Reported)

42250 ■ Ecohydrology
John Wiley & Sons Inc.
c/o Prof. Keith R.J. Smettem, Ed.-in-Ch.
Centre for Ecohydrology
School of Environmental Systems Engineering
The University of Western Australia
Perth, Western Australia, Australia
Publisher E-mail: info@wiley.com
Journal covering the field of ecology and hydrology. **Freq:** Quarterly. **Key Personnel:** Prof. Keith R.J. Smettem, Editor-in-Chief, smettem@sese.uwa.edu.au; Prof. Barbara J. Bond, Assoc. Ed., barbara.bond@ oregonstate.edu; Prof. Han Dolman, Assoc. Ed., han. dolman@geo.falw.vu.nl. **ISSN:** 1936-0584. **Subscription Rates:** EUR1,696 individuals print; US$1,696 individuals print; 1,696 individuals print. **Remarks:** Accepts advertising. **URL:** http://onlinelibrary.wiley.com/ journal/10.1002/(ISSN)1936-0592. **Circ:** (Not Reported)

42251 ■ Geographical Research
John Wiley & Sons Inc.
Wiley-Blackwell
School of Social Sciences
Curtin University of Technology
GPO Box U1987
Perth, Western Australia 6845, Australia
Ph: 61 8 92667094
Fax: 61 8 92663166
Publication E-mail: ags@curtin.edu.au
Geography publication. **Freq:** Quarterly. **Key Personnel:** Phillip O'Neill, Editor; Wayne Stephenson, Editor; Clive Forster, Editor; Kevin Dunn, Editorial Advisory Board; Iain Hay, Editorial Advisory Board; Stephen Gale, Editorial Advisory Board; Kay Anderson, Editorial Advisory Board; Brian Finlayson, Editor; Hilary Winchester, Editorial Advisory Board. **ISSN:** 1745-5863. **Subscription Rates:** US$78 individuals print + online; EUR71 individuals print + online; US$56 members print + online; US$552 institutions, other countries print + online; US$501 institutions, other countries print, online; US$455 institutions print + online; US$413 institutions print, online; 56 other countries print + online. **Remarks:** Advertising accepted; rates available upon request. **URL:** http://www.wiley.com/bw/journal.asp?ref=1745- 5863&site=1. **Formerly:** Australian Geographical Studies. **Circ:** (Not Reported)

42252 ■ Curtin-FM - 100.1
PO Box U1987
Perth, Western Australia 6845, Australia
Ph: 61 8 92662121
Fax: 61 8 92662927
E-mail: radio@curtin.edu.au; studio@curtinfm.com.au
Format: News; Oldies. **Founded:** Oct. 16, 1976. **Operating Hours:** Continuous. **URL:** http://www.curtinfm. com.au/home.

42253 ■ RTR-FM - 92.1
642 Beaufort St.
Mt. Lawley

PO Box 842
Perth, Western Australia 6929, Australia
Ph: 61 8 92609200
Fax: 61 8 92609222
E-mail: rtrfm@rtrfm.com.au
Format: Information; Urban Contemporary. **Founded:** 1977. **Operating Hours:** Continuous. **Key Personnel:** Graeme Watson, General Mgr., gwatson@rtrfm.com.au. **Ad Rates:** Advertising accepted; rates available upon request. **URL:** http://www.rtrfm.com.au.

42254 ■ 6IX-FM - 105.7
PO Box 6677
Perth, Western Australia 6892, Australia
Ph: 61 8 94841080
Fax: 61 8 94211200
E-mail: ix@capitalradio.net.au
Format: Music of Your Life. **Ad Rates:** Advertising accepted; rates available upon request. **URL:** http://www.6ix.com.au.

Pialba

42255 ■ 4FCR-FM - 107.5
30 Halcro St.
Pialba, Queensland 4655, Australia
Ph: 61 7 41281079
Fax: 61 7 41940442
E-mail: fcr4@bigpond.com
Format: Easy Listening; Country. **URL:** http://www.frasercoastradio.comfypage.com/.

Pinnaroo

42256 ■ Flow-FM - 96.5
PO Box 407
Kapunda, South Australia 5373, Australia
Ph: 61 8 85663151
Fax: 61 8 85662729
E-mail: mail@flowfm.com.au
Format: Adult Contemporary. **URL:** http://www.flowfm.com.au/.

Port Adelaide

42257 ■ Weekly Times Messenger
Messenger Newspapers
1 Baynes Pl.
PO Box 197
Port Adelaide, South Australia 5015, Australia
Ph: 61 8 83475722
Local community newspaper. **Freq:** Weekly (Wed.). **Key Personnel:** Androe Roe, Western Sales Mgr., phone 61 8 82949899. **Remarks:** Accepts display and classified advertising. **URL:** http://www.newsspace.com.au/weekly_times_messenger. **Circ:** 66,079

Port Augusta

42258 ■ 5UMA-FM - 89.1
5 Jervios St.
PO Box 2192
Port Augusta, South Australia 5700, Australia
Ph: 61 8 86422422
Fax: 61 8 86425720
E-mail: info@umeewarramedia.com
Format: News; Sports. **Operating Hours:** Continuous. **Key Personnel:** Vince Coulthard, Director, vince@umeewarramedia.com. **URL:** http://www.umeewarramodia.com

Port Lincoln

42259 ■ SBS Television - 54
Locked Bag 028
Crows Nest, New South Wales 1585, Australia
Ph: 61 2 94302828
Fax: 61 2 94303047
Owner: Special Broadcasting Service, at above address. **Wattage:** 400 ERP. **URL:** http://www20.sbs.com.au/transmissions/index.php?pid=2&id=483.

Port Macquarie

42260 ■ AusSport
Australian Sports Industry Directory
PO Box 9351
Port Macquarie, New South Wales 2444, Australia
Ph: 61 265 812105

Fax: 61 265 812958
Publisher E-mail: admin@aussport.com.au
Trade magazine covering people in the Australian sports industry. **Founded:** 1994. **Freq:** Annual Latest edition 2005. **Trim Size:** 268 x 194 mm. **Cols./Page:** 3. **Key Personnel:** Randy Bable, CEO. **Subscription Rates:** $A 59 individuals includes GST; US$75 other countries. **Remarks:** Accepts advertising. **URL:** http://www.aussport.com.au/. **Ad Rates:** GLR: US$110, BW: US$2,900, 4C: US$3,265. **Circ:** 20,000

42261 ■ 2MC-FM - 100.7
19 Short St.
Port Macquarie, New South Wales 2444, Australia
Ph: 61 2 65838088
Fax: 61 2 65840406
Format: Oldies; Talk; News. **Founded:** Sept. 20, 1937. **Key Personnel:** Matt Howarth, Contact, matt.howarth@macsc.com.au. **URL:** http://www.2mcfm.com.au/; http://www.edazzle.com.au/heritage/2mc/index.htm.

Port Melbourne

42262 ■ Australian Physics
Australian Institute of Physics
61 Danks St. W
Port Melbourne, Victoria 3207, Australia
Ph: 61 3 96469515
Fax: 61 3 96456322
Publisher E-mail: aip@aip.org.au
Publication covering physics. **Freq:** Bimonthly. **Key Personnel:** John Daicopoulos, Editor-in-Chief. **ISSN:** 1036-3831. **Subscription Rates:** Included in membership. **Remarks:** Accepts advertising. **URL:** http://www.aip.org.au/content/publications. **Formerly:** Physicist. **Ad Rates:** BW: $A 1,050. **Circ:** (Not Reported)

42263 ■ B&T Weekly
Reed Business Information Proprietary Ltd.
18 Salmon St.
Port Melbourne, Victoria 3207, Australia
Ph: 61 392 457511
Fax: 61 392 457511
Publisher E-mail: customerservice@reedbusiness.com.au
Professional magazine covering advertising and marketing for executives in advertising, the media, and related professions. **Freq:** Weekly (Fri.). **Col. Depth:** 305 millimeters. **Key Personnel:** Tim Addington, Editor, phone 61 2 94228813, tim.addington@reedbusiness.com.au; Kevin Johns, Managing Editor, phone 61 2 94222051, kevin.johns@reedbusiness.com.au; David Hovenden, Publisher, david.hovenden@reedbusiness.com.au. **Subscription Rates:** US$175 individuals. **Remarks:** Accepts advertising. **URL:** http://www.bandt.com.au/. **Circ:** Combined ‡9,269

42264 ■ Houses
Architecture Media Pvt. Ltd.
Level 3, 4 Princes St.
Port Melbourne, Victoria 3207, Australia
Ph: 61 396 464760
Fax: 61 396 464918
Publisher E-mail: publisher@archmedia.com.au
Trade magazine on residential architecture. **Freq:** Bimonthly. **Trim Size:** 225 x 292 mm. **Key Personnel:** Sue Harris, Publisher, sue.harris@archmedia.com.au; Ian Close, Mng. Dir.; Cameron Bruhn, Editorial Dir., cameron.bruhn@archmedia.com.au. **Subscription Rates:** $A 68 individuals Australia & NZ; $A 116 individuals SE Asia/Pacific Island; airmail; $A 124 other countries; $A 131 two years Australia & NZ; $A 225 two years SE Asia/Pacific Island; airmail; $A 241 two years other countries. **Remarks:** Accepts advertising. **URL:** http://www.architecturemedia.com/houses/. **Circ:** (Not Reported)

42265 ■ Professional Marketing
Reed Business Information Proprietary Ltd.
18 Salmon St.
Port Melbourne, Victoria 3207, Australia
Publisher E-mail: customerservice@reedbusiness.com.au
Official journal of the Australian Marketing Institute for marketing executives. **Founded:** 1992. **Freq:** Quarterly. **Print Method:** Offset. **Trim Size:** 240 x 330 mm. **Key Personnel:** David Hovenden, Publisher; Tim Addington, Editor, phone 61 2 94228813. **Subscription Rates:** $A 24 individuals. **Remarks:** Accepts advertising. **URL:**

http://www.bandt.com.au/view_media.asp?mediaid=55334. **Circ:** (Not Reported)

Port Pirie

42266 ■ 639ABC-AM - 639
85 Grey St.
Port Pirie, South Australia 5540, Australia
Ph: 61 8 86384811
Fax: 61 8 86384899
Format: Information; News; Sports. **Owner:** Australian Broadcasting Corporation, 700 Harris St., GPO Box 9994, Ultimo, New South Wales 2007, Australia, 61 2 83331500, Fax: 61 2 83335344. **Founded:** Mar. 15, 1932. **Operating Hours:** Continuous. **Key Personnel:** Andrew Male, Regional Prog. Mgr.; Kieran Weir, Morning Show Producer. **URL:** http://www.abc.net.au.

Prospect East

42267 ■ The Australian & New Zealand Wine Industry Journal
Winetitles/Wine Publishers Proprietary Ltd.
PO Box 1006
Prospect East, South Australia 5082, Australia
Ph: 61 8 83699500
Fax: 61 8 83699501
Publisher E-mail: info@winetitles.com.au
Trade, technical, and practical journal for the wine industry covering winemaking, grape growing, finance, and marketing. **Founded:** 1986. **Freq:** Bimonthly. **Trim Size:** 210 x 297 mm. **Key Personnel:** Hartley Higgins, Publisher; Lauren Jones, Editor, lauren@winetitles.com.au; Richard Smart, Contributing Writer; Chris Colby, Contributing Writer; Jonathan Scott, Contributing Writer; Michelle Stevens, Sales & Marketing Mgr., wijsales@winetitles.com.au; David Silkstone, Contact; Tony Keys, Contributing Writer; Sonya Logan, Asst. Ed., sonya@winetitles.com.au; Elizabeth Bouzoudis, General Mgr. **ISSN:** 0819-2421. **Subscription Rates:** $A 88 individuals in Australia; $A 85 individuals in New Zealand; $A 132 elsewhere overseas; $A 165 two years in Australia; $A 160 two years in New Zealand; $A 254 two years overseas. **Remarks:** Accepts advertising. **URL:** http://www.winetitles.com.au/wij/. **Ad Rates:** 4C: $A 1,550. **Circ:** 3,000

42268 ■ Australian Viticulture
Winetitles/Wine Publishers Proprietary Ltd.
PO Box 1006
Prospect East, South Australia 5082, Australia
Ph: 61 8 83699500
Fax: 61 8 83699501
Publisher E-mail: info@winetitles.com.au
Practical vineyard management. **Subtitle:** Practical Vineyard Management. **Founded:** 1997. **Freq:** Annual. **Print Method:** Full Glass, Perfect Hand. **Trim Size:** 210 x 297 mm. **Key Personnel:** Lauren Jones, Editor, lauren@winetitles.com.au. **ISSN:** 1329-0436. **Subscription Rates:** $A 66 individuals Australia, includes GST; $A 70 individuals New Zealand; $A 100 elsewhere overseas, economy air mail; $A 121 two years Australia, includes GST; $A 130 two years New Zealand; $A 190 other countries two years. **Remarks:** Accepts advertising. **URL:** http://www.winebiz.com.au/ausvit/. **Ad Rates:** 4C: $A 1,500. **Circ:** Paid 4,000

Pyrmont

42269 ■ Appliance Retailer
The Intermedia Group
100 Harris St., Unit 39
Pyrmont, New South Wales 2009, Australia
Ph: 61 2 96602113
Fax: 61 2 96604419
Publisher E-mail: info@intermedia.com.au
Trade magazine featuring electrical appliance and electronic products. **Founded:** 1995. **Freq:** 11/yr. **Trim Size:** 185 x 270 mm. **Key Personnel:** Simon Grover, Publisher, sgrover@intermedia.com.au; Rodney Riley, General Sales Mgr., rod@intermedia.com.au. **Subscription Rates:** US$85 individuals Australia; US$136 two years Australia; US$105 individuals New Zealand; US$210 two years New Zealand; US$126 individuals Asia and other countries in the Pacific; US$252 two years Asia and other countries in the Pacific; US$155 other countries; US$310 other countries 2 years. **Remarks:** Accepts advertising. **URL:** http://www.

Circulation: ★ = ABC; △ = BPA; ♦ = CAC; • = CCAB; ❑ = VAC; ⊕ = PO Statement; ‡ = Publisher's Report; Boldface figures = sworn; Light figures = estimated.

intermedia.com.au/index.cfm?page=mag.magdesc&
mid=1&area=magazines. **Ad Rates:** BW: \$A 2,877, 4C:
\$A 4,350. **Circ:** ★7,112

**42270 ■ Australasian Dispute Resolution
Journal**
Lawbook Co.
Thomson Legal and Regulatory Ltd.
Level 5, 100 Harris St.
Pyrmont, New South Wales NSW 2009, Australia
Ph: 61 2 85877980
Fax: 61 2 85877981
Publisher E-mail: lta.service@thomson.com
Law periodical. **Freq:** Monthly. **Subscription Rates:**
US\$726 individuals. **URL:** http://www.thomsonreuters.
com.au/catalogue/shopexd.asp?id=688.

42271 ■ Australian Business Law Review
Lawbook Co.
Thomson Legal and Regulatory Ltd.
Level 5, 100 Harris St.
Pyrmont, New South Wales NSW 2009, Australia
Ph: 61 2 85877980
Fax: 61 2 85877981
Publisher E-mail: lta.service@thomson.com
Law periodical. **Freq:** Bimonthly. **Key Personnel:** Robert
Baxt, Author. **ISSN:** 0310-1053. **Subscription Rates:**
US\$1,035.62 individuals. **URL:** http://www.
thomsonreuters.com.au/catalogue/shopexd.asp?id=656.

42272 ■ Australian Giftguide
The Intermedia Group
100 Harris St., Unit 39
Pyrmont, New South Wales 2009, Australia
Ph: 61 2 96602113
Fax: 61 2 96604419
Publisher E-mail: info@intermedia.com.au
Magazine featuring ideal gifts, housewares and latest
products. **Subtitle:** For home & lifestyle retailers. **Freq:**
Quarterly. **Trim Size:** 210 x 297 mm. **Key Personnel:**
Mark Kuban, Publisher, mark@intermedia.com.au;
Marion Gerritsen, Editor, marion@intermedia.com.au.
Subscription Rates: US\$80 individuals; US\$128 two
years; US\$95 individuals New Zealand; US\$190 two
years New Zealand; US\$115 individuals Asia and other
countries in the Pacific; US\$230 two years Asia and
other countries in the Pacific; US\$135 other countries;
US\$270 other countries 2 years. **Remarks:** Accepts
advertising. **URL:** http://www.intermedia.com.au/index.
cfm?page=mag.magDesc&mid=3&area=magazines.
Circ: 9,824

42273 ■ Australian Hotelier
The Intermedia Group
100 Harris St., Unit 39
Pyrmont, New South Wales 2009, Australia
Ph: 61 2 96602113
Fax: 61 2 96604419
Publisher E-mail: info@intermedia.com.au
Magazine for hoteliers. **Freq:** 11/yr. **Trim Size:** A4. **Key
Personnel:** Simon Grover, Publisher, sgrover@
intermedia.com.au; Annette Shailer, Editor, ashailer@
intermedia.com.au; Adam Daff, Manager, adaff@
intermedia.com.au. **Subscription Rates:** US\$95
individuals Australia; \$A 152 two years Australia; \$A 115
individuals New Zealand; US\$230 two years New
Zealand; US\$132 individuals Asia and other countries in
the Pacific; US\$264 individuals Asia and other countries
in the Pacific; US\$150 other countries; US\$300 other
countries 2 years. **Remarks:** Accepts advertising. **URL:**
http://www.intermedia.com.au/index.cfm?page=mag.
magdesc&mid=35&area=magazines. **Ad Rates:** 4C: \$A
3,500. **Circ:** 6,508

42274 ■ Australian Law Journal
Lawbook Co.
Thomson Legal and Regulatory Ltd.
Level 5, 100 Harris St.
Pyrmont, New South Wales NSW 2009, Australia
Ph: 61 2 85877980
Fax: 61 2 85877981
Publisher E-mail: lta.service@thomson.com
Law periodical. **Founded:** 1927. **Freq:** Monthly. **Key
Personnel:** Justice P.W. Young, Gen. Ed. **ISSN:** 0004-
9611. **Subscription Rates:** US\$1,285 individuals. **URL:**
http://www.thomsonreuters.com.au/catalogue/shopexd.
asp?id=694.

42275 ■ bars&clubs
The Intermedia Group

100 Harris St., Unit 39
Pyrmont, New South Wales 2009, Australia
Ph: 61 2 96602113
Fax: 61 2 96604419
Publisher E-mail: info@intermedia.com.au
Magazine featuring bar, club and hotel industries in
Australia. **Subtitle:** At the forefront of bar culture. **Freq:**
Bimonthly. **Trim Size:** 277 x 230 mm. **Key Personnel:**
Simon Grover, Publisher, sgrover@intermedia.com.au;
Shane T. Williams, Managing Editor, stwilliams@
intermedia.com.au; Rebecca Harris, Editor, rharris@
intermedia.com.au. **Subscription Rates:** US\$57 indi-
viduals; US\$91.20 two years; US\$67 individuals New
Zeland; US\$134 two years New Zeland; US\$75 individuals Asia and other countries in the Pacific; US\$150 two
years Asia and other countries in the Pacific; US\$85
other countries; US\$170 other countries 2 years. **Re-
marks:** Accepts advertising. **URL:** http://www.
intermedia.com.au/index.cfm?page=mag.magdesc&
mid=37&area=magazines. **Ad Rates:** 4C: \$A 3,610.
Circ: Combined ★6,043

42276 ■ Criminal Law Journal
Lawbook Co.
Thomson Legal and Regulatory Ltd.
Level 5, 100 Harris St.
Pyrmont, New South Wales NSW 2009, Australia
Ph: 61 2 85877980
Fax: 61 2 85877981
Publisher E-mail: lta.service@thomson.com
Law periodical. **Freq:** Monthly. **Key Personnel:** Stephen
Odgers, Author; Mirko Bagaric, Author. **ISSN:** 0314-
1160. **Subscription Rates:** US\$963 individuals parts
and bound volumes. **URL:** http://www.thomson.com.au/
catalogue/shopexd.asp?id=846.

**42277 ■ Environmental and Planning Law
Journal**
Lawbook Co.
Thomson Legal and Regulatory Ltd.
Level 5, 100 Harris St.
Pyrmont, New South Wales NSW 2009, Australia
Ph: 61 2 85877980
Fax: 61 2 85877981
Publisher E-mail: lta.service@thomson.com
Law periodical. **Freq:** Bimonthly. **Key Personnel:** Gerry
Bates, Editor. **ISSN:** 0813-300X. **Subscription Rates:**
US\$751 individuals. **Online:** Gale Group. **URL:** http://
www.thomsonreuters.com.au/catalogue/shopexd.asp?
id=886&busarea=543.

42278 ■ ESTETICA Australia and New Zealand
The Intermedia Group
100 Harris St., Unit 39
Pyrmont, New South Wales 2009, Australia
Ph: 61 2 96602113
Fax: 61 2 96604419
Publisher E-mail: info@intermedia.com.au
Magazine featuring the latest international hair fashion.
Freq: 4/yr. **Trim Size:** 216 x 288 mm. **Key Personnel:**
Simon Grover, Publisher, sgrover@intermedia.com.au;
Cameron Pine, Editor, cameron@intermedia.com.au.
Subscription Rates: US\$55 individuals Australia;
US\$65 individuals New Zealand; US\$75 individuals Asia
and other countries in the Pacific; US\$85 other countries.
Remarks: Accepts advertising. **URL:** http://www.
intermedia.com.au/index.cfm?page=mag.magdesc&
mid=32&area=magazines. **Ad Rates:** 4C: \$A 2,360.
Circ: Paid ‡5,000

42279 ■ Hilton Australasia
The Intermedia Group
100 Harris St., Unit 39
Pyrmont, New South Wales 2009, Australia
Ph: 61 2 96602113
Fax: 61 2 96604419
Publisher E-mail: info@intermedia.com.au
In-room magazine in Hilton hotels. **Founded:** Feb. 2006.
Freq: 4/yr. **Trim Size:** 277 x 230 mm. **Key Personnel:**
Simon Grover, Publisher, sgrover@intermedia.com.au;
James Wilkinson, Managing Editor, jwilkinson@
intermedia.com.au. **Subscription Rates:** US\$34 indi-
viduals Australia; US\$54 two years Australia; US\$52
other countries. **Remarks:** Accepts advertising. **URL:**
https://secure.intermedia.com.au/index.cfm?page=mag.
magdesc&mid=39&area=magazines. **Ad Rates:** 4C: \$A
4,950. **Circ:** (Not Reported)

42280 ■ Hotel and Accommodation Management
The Intermedia Group

100 Harris St., Unit 39
Pyrmont, New South Wales 2009, Australia
Ph: 61 2 96602113
Fax: 61 2 96604419
Publisher E-mail: info@intermedia.com.au
Magazine featuring services of the hotel industry. **Freq:**
Bimonthly. **Trim Size:** 210 x 297 mm. **Key Personnel:**
Simon Grover, Publisher, sgrover@intermedia.com.au;
James Wilkinson, Managing Editor, jwilkinson@
intermedia.com.au; James Wells, Assoc. Publisher,
james@intermedia.com.au. **Subscription Rates:**
US\$65 individuals Australia; US\$75 two years New
Zealand; US\$85 individuals Asia and other countries in
the Pacific; US\$95 other countries. **Remarks:** Accepts
advertising. **URL:** http://www.intermedia.com.au/index.
cfm?page=mag.magdesc&mid=36&area=magazines.
Ad Rates: 4C: \$A 3,300. **Circ:** 5,578

42281 ■ Insolvency Law Journal
Lawbook Co.
Thomson Legal and Regulatory Ltd.
Level 5, 100 Harris St.
Pyrmont, New South Wales NSW 2009, Australia
Ph: 61 2 85877980
Fax: 61 2 85877981
Publisher E-mail: lta.service@thomson.com
Law periodical. **Freq:** Quarterly. **Key Personnel:** Dr.
Colin Anderson, Editor. **ISSN:** 1039-3293. **Subscription
Rates:** US\$695.52 individuals. **Online:** Gale. **URL:**
http://www.thomson.com.au/catalogue/shopexd.asp?id=
942.

42282 ■ Interior Fitout
The Intermedia Group
100 Harris St., Unit 39
Pyrmont, New South Wales 2009, Australia
Ph: 61 2 96602113
Fax: 61 2 96604419
Publisher E-mail: info@intermedia.com.au
Magazine featuring fit out industry. **Subtitle:** Educate
the market. **Founded:** 1997. **Freq:** Bimonthly. **Trim Size:**
210 x 297 mm. **Key Personnel:** Mark Kuban, Publisher,
mark@intermedia.com.au; Marion Gerritsen, Editor,
marion@intermedia.com.au; Mark Pointer, Manager,
mpointer@intermedia.com.au. **Subscription Rates:**
US\$45 individuals Australia; US\$55 individuals New
Zealand; US\$65 individuals Asia and other countries in
the Pacific; US\$80 other countries. **Remarks:** Accepts
advertising. **URL:** http://www.intermedia.com.au/index.
cfm?page=mag.magDesc&mid=9&area=magazines. **Ad
Rates:** 4C: \$A 3,350. **Circ:** ★5,466

**42283 ■ Journal of Banking and Finance Law
and Practice**
Lawbook Co.
Thomson Legal and Regulatory Ltd.
Level 5, 100 Harris St.
Pyrmont, New South Wales NSW 2009, Australia
Ph: 61 2 85877980
Fax: 61 2 85877981
Publisher E-mail: lta.service@thomson.com
Law periodical. **Freq:** Quarterly. **Key Personnel:**
Gregory Burton, Author; Robert Baxt, Author. **ISSN:**
1034-3040. **Subscription Rates:** US\$768.96
individuals. **URL:** http://www.thomson.com.au/catalogue/
shopexd.asp?id=960.

42284 ■ National Liquor News
The Intermedia Group
100 Harris St., Unit 39
Pyrmont, New South Wales 2009, Australia
Ph: 61 2 96602113
Fax: 61 2 96604419
Publisher E-mail: info@intermedia.com.au
Magazine featuring liquor and the liquor industry. **Freq:**
11/yr. **Trim Size:** 210 X 270 mm. **Key Personnel:** Si-
mon Grover, Publisher, sgrover@intermedia.com.au;
Amy Looker, Editor, alooker@intermedia.com.au; Shane
T. Williams, Manager, stwilliams@intermedia.com.au.
Subscription Rates: US\$70 individuals Australia;
US\$84 individuals New Zealand; US\$95 individuals Asia
and other countries in the Pacific; US\$105 other
countries. **Remarks:** Accepts advertising. **URL:** http://
www.intermedia.com.au/index.cfm?page=mag.
magdesc&mid=34&area=magazines. **Ad Rates:** 4C: \$A
4,490. **Circ:** ‡12,267

42285 ■ Natural Source
The Intermedia Group
100 Harris St., Unit 39

Pyrmont, New South Wales 2009, Australia
Ph: 61 2 96602113
Fax: 61 2 96604419
Publisher E-mail: info@intermedia.com.au
Magazine featuring products and services of the health-care industry. **Subtitle:** Your complete guide to Austra-lia's natural healthcare industry. **Freq:** Annual. **Key Per-sonnel:** Simon Grover, Publisher, sgrover@intermedia.com.au. **Remarks:** Accepts advertising. **URL:** http://www.intermedia.com.au/index.cfm?page=mag.magDesc&mid=20&area=magazines&guide=1. **Ad Rates:** BW: $A 1,885, 4C: $A 2,900. **Circ:** 11,600

42286 ■ The Production Book
The Intermedia Group
100 Harris St., Unit 39
Pyrmont, New South Wales 2009, Australia
Ph: 61 2 96602113
Fax: 61 2 96604419
Publication E-mail: info@productionbook.com.au
Publisher E-mail: info@intermedia.com.au
Magazine featuring film, television, advertising and multimedia industries in Australia. **Freq:** Annual. **Trim Size:** 165 x 235 mm. **Key Personnel:** Leda Kennett, Natl. Advertising Mgr., lkennett@intermedia.com.au; Nicole Sorby, Editor, nicole@intermedia.com.au. **Re-marks:** Accepts advertising. **URL:** http://www.intermedia.com.au/index.cfm?page=mag.magdesc&mid=14&area=magazines; http://www.productionbook.com.au/home.aspx. **Ad Rates:** BW: $A 2,135, 4C: $A 2,990. **Circ:** (Not Reported)

42287 ■ Professional Beauty
The Intermedia Group
100 Harris St., Unit 39
Pyrmont, New South Wales 2009, Australia
Ph: 61 2 96602113
Fax: 61 2 96604419
Publisher E-mail: info@intermedia.com.au
Business to business magazine for the Australian aesthetics industry. **Subtitle:** The bible for Australian aesthetics industry. **Freq:** 6/yr. **Trim Size:** 210 x 297 mm. **Key Personnel:** Simon Grover, Publisher, sgrover@intermedia.com.au; Sarah Bowing, Managing Editor, sarah@intermedia.com.au. **Subscription Rates:** US$80 individuals Australia; US$128 two years Australia; US$168 individuals 3 years. **Remarks:** Accepts advertising. **URL:** http://www.intermedia.com.au/index.cfm?page=mag.magdesc&mid=12&area=magazines. **Ad Rates:** 4C: $A 2,990. **Circ:** 9,000

42288 ■ Signature Cocktails
The Intermedia Group
100 Harris St., Unit 39
Pyrmont, New South Wales 2009, Australia
Ph: 61 2 96602113
Fax: 61 2 96604419
Publisher E-mail: info@intermedia.com.au
Magazine featuring cocktails. **Freq:** Annual. **Trim Size:** 135 x 165 mm. **Key Personnel:** Simon Grover, Pub-lisher, sgrover@intermedia.com.au; James Wilkinson, Managing Editor, jwilkinson@intermedia.com.au; Shane T. Williams, Manager, stwilliams@intermedia.com.au. **Subscription Rates:** US$15.95 individuals Australia; US$18.95 individuals New Zealand; US$21.95 other countries. **Remarks:** Accepts advertising. **URL:** http://www.intermedia.com.au/index.cfm?page=mag.magdesc&mid=38&area=magazines. **Circ:** (Not Reported)

42289 ■ Smoke and Mirrors
The Intermedia Group
100 Harris St., Unit 39
Pyrmont, New South Wales 2009, Australia
Ph: 61 2 96602113
Fax: 61 2 96604419
Publisher E-mail: info@intermedia.com.au
Magazine for filmmakers, make-up and special effects practitioners. **Freq:** 4/yr. **Trim Size:** 210 x 297 mm. **Key Personnel:** Mark Kuban, Publisher, mark@intermedia.com.au; Rodney Appleyard, Editor, victoria@intermedia.com.au. **Remarks:** Accepts advertising. **URL:** http://www.intermedia.com.au. **Ad Rates:** BW: $A 2,862, 4C: $A 3,300. **Circ:** ★4,483

42290 ■ Spa Australasia
The Intermedia Group
100 Harris St., Unit 39
Pyrmont, New South Wales 2009, Australia

Ph: 61 2 96602113
Fax: 61 2 96604419
Publisher E-mail: info@intermedia.com.au
Magazine featuring the best spa, resorts and hotels in Australia. **Freq:** 4/yr. **Trim Size:** A4. **Key Personnel:** Si-mon Grover, Publisher, sgrover@intermedia.com.au; Kirien Whithers, Manager, kirien@spaguru.com.au. **Sub-scription Rates:** US$90 individuals Australia; US$144 two years Australia; US$110 individuals New Zealand; US$200 two years New Zealand; US$110 individuals Asia and other countries in the Pacific; US$220 two years Asia and other countries in the Pacific; US$127 other countries; $A 254 two years other countries. **Re-marks:** Accepts advertising. **URL:** http://www.intermedia.com.au/index.cfm?page=mag.magdesc&mid=13&area=magazines. **Ad Rates:** 4C: $A 2,835. **Circ:** (Not Reported)

42291 ■ The Wanderer
The Intermedia Group
100 Harris St., Unit 39
Pyrmont, New South Wales 2009, Australia
Ph: 61 2 96602113
Fax: 61 2 96604419
Publisher E-mail: info@intermedia.com.au
Magazine for Campervan & Motorhome Club of Australia members. **Freq:** 12/yr. **Trim Size:** 210 x 297 mm. **Key Personnel:** Simon Grover, Publisher, sgrover@intermedia.com.au; David Canessa, Manager, dcanessa@intermedia.com.au. **Remarks:** Accepts advertising. **URL:** https://secure.intermedia.com.au/index.cfm?page=mag.magdesc&mid=15&area=magazines&guide=1. **Ad Rates:** 4C: $A 2,140. **Circ:** (Not Reported)

42292 ■ 2GB-AM - 873
Level 1, Bldg. C, 33-35 Saunders St.
Pyrmont, New South Wales 2009, Australia
Ph: 61 2 85700000
Fax: 61 2 85700219
Format: Talk; Sports; News; Easy Listening. **Owner:** Macquarie Radio Network, at above address. **Operat-ing Hours:** Continuous. **Ad Rates:** Advertising ac-cepted; rates available upon request. **URL:** http://2gb.com.

42293 ■ 2SM-AM - 1269
Level Three
8 Jones Bay Rd.
Pyrmont, New South Wales 2009, Australia
Ph: 61 2 96601269
Fax: 61 2 95522979
E-mail: admin@2sm.com.au
Format: Talk; Sports; Easy Listening. **Operating Hours:** Continuous. **Ad Rates:** Advertising accepted; rates available upon request. **URL:** http://www.2sm.com.au.

42294 ■ Vega-FM - 95.3
33 Saunders St.
Pyrmont, New South Wales 2009, Australia
Ph: 61 2 85697953
E-mail: contactus@vega953.com.au
Format: Contemporary Hit Radio (CHR). **Operating Hours:** Continuous. **Ad Rates:** Advertising accepted; rates available upon request. **URL:** http://www.vegafm.com.au/vega915.

Queanbeyan

42295 ■ QBN-FM - 96.7
261 Crawford St.
PO Box 984
Queanbeyan, New South Wales 2620, Australia
Ph: 61 2 62996899
Fax: 61 2 62996804
E-mail: admin@qbnfm.com.au
Format: Eclectic; Public Radio. **Operating Hours:** Continuous. **Key Personnel:** Barry Cole, Station Mgr., stationmanager@qbnfm.com.au. **Wattage:** 500. **URL:** http://www.qbnfm.com.au.

Randwick

42296 ■ Neuropsychiatric Disease and Treat-ment
International Neuropsychiatric Association
c/o Mrs. Angela Russell
Neuropsychiatric Institute
Prince of Wales Hospital

Randwick, New South Wales 2031, Australia
Ph: 61 293 823816
Fax: 61 293 823774
Publisher E-mail: angie.russell@unsw.edu.au
Journal including reports on clinical or pre-clinical stud-ies of neurological disorders. **Key Personnel:** Joseph R. Calabrese, Editorial Board; Jefddy Cummings, Edito-rial Board; Johan A. Den Boer, Editorial Board; Mike Bri-ley, Editorial Board; Giovanni Cassano, Editorial Board; Celso Arango, Editorial Board; Alan Frazer, Editorial Board; Roger Bullock, Editorial Board; Anthony David, Editorial Board; Ray Chaudhuri, Editorial Board. **ISSN:** 1176-6328. **URL:** http://www.dovepress.com/neuropsychiatric-disease-and-treatment-journal.

Raymond Terrace

42297 ■ AIE News Journal
Australian Institute of Energy
PO Box 534
Raymond Terrace, New South Wales 2324, Australia
Ph: 61 2 49649599
Fax: 61 2 49649599
Publication E-mail: editor@aie.org.au
Publisher E-mail: aie@aie.org.au
Journal covering energy. **Founded:** 1978. **Freq:** Quarterly. **Trim Size:** M4. **Key Personnel:** Joy Claridge, Contact. **Subscription Rates:** Included in membership; US$100 individuals; US$62 individuals. **Remarks:** Ac-cepts advertising. **URL:** http://aie.org.au/Content/NavigationMenu/Publications/EnergyNews/default.htm. **Circ:** Paid 1,000

Redcliffe

42298 ■ Redcliffe & Bayside Herald
Quest Community Newspapers
19 Creek St.
Redcliffe, Queensland 4020, Australia
Ph: 61 7 34808200
Local community newspaper. **Founded:** 1934. **Freq:** Weekly (Wed.). **Key Personnel:** Kylie Knight, Editor, editorial@redcliffeherald.com.au. **Remarks:** Accepts display and classified advertising. **URL:** http://www.newsspace.com.au/redcliffe_and_bayside_herald. **Circ:** 34,835

Richmond (New South Wales)

42299 ■ Hawkesbury Gazette
Rural Press Regional Publishing Proprietary Ltd.
291 Windsor St.
Richmond, New South Wales 2753, Australia
Publication E-mail: mail.hawkgazette@ruralpress.com
Community newspaper. **Founded:** 1888. **Freq:** Weekly (Wed.). **Print Method:** Offset. **Cols./Page:** 4. **Col. Width:** 6.3 centimeters. **Col. Depth:** 38 centimeters. **Key Personnel:** Paul Roberts, Managing Editor. **Re-marks:** Accepts advertising. **URL:** http://www.ruralpresssales.com.au; http://www.hawkesburygazette.com.au/. **Circ:** Paid 8,830

Richmond (Victoria)

42300 ■ ANZ Journal of Surgery
John Wiley & Sons Inc.
Wiley-Blackwell
155 Cremorne St.
Richmond, Victoria 3121, Australia
Fax: 61 3 92743391
Publication E-mail: surgery@blackwellpublishing.com
Journal focusing on clinical practice and/or research in all fields of surgery and related disciplines. **Freq:** 12/yr. **Key Personnel:** J.C. Hall, Editor-in-Chief; P.H. Chapuis, Sen. Ed.; C. Platell, Sen. Ed. **ISSN:** 1445-1433. **Sub-scription Rates:** US$295 individuals print + online; US$1,455 institutions print or online; EUR274 individuals print + online; 183 individuals print + online; US$1,601 institutions print + online; $A 949 institutions print + on-line; EUR11,140 institutions print + online; US$1,935 institutions, other countries print + online; US$1,759 institutions, other countries print or online; $A 862 institu-tions print or online. **Remarks:** Accepts advertising. **URL:** http://www.wiley.com/bw/journal.asp?ref=1445-1433&site=1. **Circ:** (Not Reported)

42301 ■ Australian Catholics
Jesuit Publications
PO Box 553

Richmond, Victoria 3121, Australia
Ph: 61 3 94219666
Fax: 61 3 94219600
Publication covering issues and news for Catholics. **Subtitle:** Faith and Living for Contemporary Catholics. **Founded:** 1993. **Freq:** 5/yr. **Trim Size:** 205 x 260 mm. **Key Personnel:** Michael McVeigh, Editor; Maggie Power, Graphic Designer; Nomeneta Schwalger, Circulation; Adam Pearson, Advertising; Paul McEvey, CEO; Andrew Hamilton, Editorial Consultant. **Subscription Rates:** US$25 individuals; US$40 two years; US$6 single issue. **Remarks:** Accepts advertising. **URL:** http://www.australiancatholics.com.au/. **Ad Rates:** BW: $A 6,000. **Circ:** 196,555

42302 ■ Australian Occupational Therapy Journal
John Wiley & Sons Inc.
Wiley-Blackwell
155 Cremorne St.
Richmond, Victoria 3122, Australia
Fax: 61 3 92743391
Publication E-mail: occupationaltherapy@blackwellpublishing.com
Journal focusing on issues relevant to occupational therapists. Official journal of OT Australia, the Australian Association of Occupational Therapists. **Freq:** Bimonthly. **Key Personnel:** Elspeth Froude, Editor; Michael Iwama, Editorial Advisory Board; Doris Pierce, Editorial Advisory Board. **ISSN:** 0045-0766. **Subscription Rates:** US$147 individuals print and online; US$410 institutions print and online; US$373 institutions print or online; 253 institutions print and online; US$333 institutions Australia; print and online; US$303 institutions Australia; print or online; $A 153 individuals print and online; EUR322 institutions print and online; EUR293 institutions print or online; US$497 institutions, other countries print and online. **Remarks:** Accepts advertising. **URL:** http://www.wiley.com/bw/journal.asp?ref=0045-0766&site=1. **Circ:** (Not Reported)

42303 ■ Journal of Gastroenterology and Hepatology
John Wiley & Sons Inc.
Wiley-Blackwell
155 Cremorne St.
Richmond, Victoria 3121, Australia
Fax: 61 3 92743391
Peer-reviewed journal dealing with gastroenterology, hepatology and endoscopy. **Freq:** Monthly. **Key Personnel:** D.K. Bhasin, Editor-in-Chief; Geoff Farrell, Editor-in-Chief; T. Chiba, Founding Ed. **ISSN:** 0815-9319. **Subscription Rates:** US$155 individuals print + online; EUR142 individuals print + online; 95 individuals print + online; US$1,511 institutions print + online; US$1,768 institutions print + online (Australia and NZ); 936 institutions print + online; US$1,834 institutions, other countries print + online; EUR1,768 institutions print + online; US$1,373 institutions print or online; US$1,606 institutions print or online (Australia and NZ). **Remarks:** Advertising accepted; rates available upon request. **URL:** http://www.wiley.com/bw/journal.asp?ref=0815-9319. **Circ:** (Not Reported)

42304 ■ Nephrology
John Wiley & Sons Inc.
Wiley-Blackwell
155 Cremorne St.
Richmond, Victoria 3121, Australia
Fax: 61 3 92743390
Publication E-mail: nephrology@blackwellpublishing.com
Journal dealing with clinical and experimental aspects of nephrology, in connection with Asian Pacific Society of Nephrology. **Freq:** 8/yr. **Key Personnel:** David C.H. Harris, Editor-in-Chief; Philip K.T. Li, Dep. Ed.; Peter G. Kerr, Dep. Ed. **ISSN:** 1320-5358. **Subscription Rates:** US$844 institutions print and online; US$767 institutions print or online; EUR662 institutions print and online; US$1,021 institutions, other countries print and online; US$928 institutions, other countries print or online; EUR602 institutions print or online; 521 institutions print and online; 473 institutions print or online. **Remarks:** Advertising accepted; rates available upon request. **URL:** http://www.wiley.com/bw/journal.asp?ref=1320-5358&site=1. **Circ:** (Not Reported)

42305 ■ GOLD 104.3-FM - 104.3
Level 2
21-31 Goodwood St.
Richmond, Victoria 3121, Australia
Ph: 61 3 94201043
Fax: 61 3 94201250

E-mail: suelapetina@arn.com.au
Format: Oldies. **Owner:** Australian Radio Network Pty. Ltd., 3 Byfield St., North Ryde, New South Wales 2113, Australia, 61 2 88999999, Fax: 61 2 88999811. **Operating Hours:** Continuous. **Key Personnel:** Michelle Walker, Dir. of Sales, michellewalker@arn.com.au. **Ad Rates:** Advertising accepted; rates available upon request. **URL:** http://www.1043fm.com.au/; http://www.arn.com.au/.

42306 ■ MIX 101.1-FM - 101.1
21-31 Goodwood St., Level 2
Richmond, Victoria 3121, Australia
Ph: 61 3 94201011
Fax: 61 3 94201155
E-mail: accessline@mix1011.com.au
Format: Adult Contemporary. **Owner:** Australian Radio Network, 3 Byfield St., North Ryde, New South Wales 2113, Australia, 61 2 88999999, Fax: 61 2 88999811. **Key Personnel:** Michelle Walker, Contact, phone 61 3 94201281, michellewalker@arn.com.au. **Ad Rates:** Advertising accepted; rates available upon request. **URL:** http://www.ttfm.com.au/; http://www.arn.com.au/.

42307 ■ Nova-FM - 100.3
Level 2, 678 Victoria St.
Richmond, Victoria 3121, Australia
Ph: 61 3 84203999
Fax: 61 3 84203862
Format: Contemporary Hit Radio (CHR); Adult Contemporary; Talk. **Owner:** DMG Radio Australia, Level 5, 75 Hindmarsh Sq., Adelaide, South Australia 5000, Australia, 61 8 84195000, Fax: 61 8 84195062. **URL:** http://www.nova100.com.au/; http://www.dmgradio.com.au/site/home.aspx.

42308 ■ NOVA-FM - 100
Level 2, 678 Victoria St.
Richmond, Victoria 3121, Australia
Ph: 61 3 84203999
Fax: 61 3 84203862
Format: Contemporary Hit Radio (CHR); Ethnic. **Owner:** DMG Radio (Australia) Pty. Ltd., Level 5, 75 Hindmarsh Sq., Adelaide, South Australia 5000, Australia. **Operating Hours:** Continuous. **Ad Rates:** Advertising accepted; rates available upon request. **URL:** http://www.nova100.com.au.

42309 ■ SEN-AM - 1116
473-479 Swan St.
Richmond, Victoria 3121, Australia
Ph: 61 3 84201116
Fax: 61 3 84201144
E-mail: enquiries@sen.com.au
Format: Sports. **Operating Hours:** Continuous. **Key Personnel:** Nick Hughes, National Direct Sales Mgr., nhughes@sen.com.au; Anthony Symth, Contact, asmyth@sen.com.au. **Ad Rates:** Advertising accepted; rates available upon request. **URL:** http://www.sen.com.au.

42310 ■ Vega-FM - 91.5
Level 2, 678 Victoria St.
Richmond, Victoria 3121, Australia
Ph: 61 3 94252915
Format: Music of Your Life; Contemporary Hit Radio (CHR). **Operating Hours:** Continuous. **Ad Rates:** Advertising accepted; rates available upon request. **URL:** http://www.vegafm.com.au/vega915.

Richmond South

42311 ■ ABR (Australian Book Review)
Australian Book Review Inc.
PO Box 2320
Richmond South, Victoria 3121, Australia
Ph: 61 394 296700
Fax: 61 394 292288
Publication E-mail: abr@vicnet.net.au
Publisher E-mail: abr@australianbookreview.com.au
Independent literary review magazine covering biography, history, fiction, poetry, children's books, art and politics. **Founded:** 1961. **Freq:** 10/yr. **Trim Size:** 210 x 270 mm. **Key Personnel:** Peter Rose, Editor, abrads@vicnet.net.au; Gail Southwell, Office Mgr., admin@australianbookreview.com.au. **ISSN:** 0155-2864. **Subscription Rates:** US$80 individuals; US$100 institutions; US$150 two years; US$190 institutions two years; US$65 students; US$120 two years concession.

Remarks: Accepts advertising. **URL:** http://home.vicnet.net.au/~abr. **Circ:** 2,000

Riverside

42312 ■ Launceston's WAY-FM - 105.3
PO Box 43
Riverside, Tasmania 7250, Australia
Ph: 61 3 63340100
Fax: 61 3 63340300
E-mail: wayadmin@wayfm.org.au
Format: Contemporary Christian; Religious. **Founded:** July 27, 1987. **Operating Hours:** 18 hours Daily. **Ad Rates:** Noncommercial; underwriting available. **URL:** http://www.wayfm.org.au.

Robina

42313 ■ Gestalt Journal of Australia and New Zealand
Gestalt Australia and New Zealand
PO Box 3728
Robina, Queensland 4230, Australia
Ph: 61 7 55809060
Publication E-mail: ozgjeditor@ganz.org.au
Publisher E-mail: contact@ganz.org.au
Journal of Gestalt Australia and New Zealand. **Freq:** Semiannual. **Key Personnel:** Richie Robertson, Editor. **Subscription Rates:** Free for members; $A 35 nonmembers per issue; $A 50 individuals per volume. **URL:** http://www.ganz.org.au/pages/mailing.html.

Rockhampton

42314 ■ Braford Annual
Australian Braford Society
122 Denham St.
PO Box 749
Rockhampton, Queensland 4700, Australia
Ph: 61 7 49275196
Fax: 1 7 49275708
Publisher E-mail: info@braford.org.au
Journal featuring yearly events and topics of interest. **Freq:** Annual. **Subscription Rates:** Free. **Remarks:** Accepts advertising. **URL:** http://www.braford.org.au/Page_About_Braford_Society.htm. **Circ:** (Not Reported)

42315 ■ Ejournalist
Central Queensland University, Division of Teaching and Learning Services
Division of Teaching and Learning Services
Bldg. 5, Bruce Hwy.
Rockhampton, Queensland 4702, Australia
Ph: 61 7 49309000
Fax: 61 7 49232100
Publisher E-mail: dtls-enquiries@cqu.edu.au
Journal covering journalism, new media, communications, graphics, websites and related issues. **Subtitle:** A Refereed Media Journal. **Founded:** May 15, 1894. **Freq:** Weekly (Thurs.). **Cols./Page:** 5. **Col. Width:** 11 picas. **Col. Depth:** 1 inches. **Key Personnel:** Prof. Alan Knight, Editor. **ISSN:** 1444-471X. **URL:** http://ejournalist.com.au/.

42316 ■ International Journal of Computational Intelligence and Applications
Imperial College Press
c/o Brijesh Verma, Ed.-in-Ch.
School of Information Technology
Central Queensland University
Bruce Hwy.
Rockhampton, Queensland 4702, Australia
Ph: 61 749 309058
Fax: 61 749 309729
Publisher E-mail: sales@wspc.co.uk
Journal dedicated to the theory and applications of computational intelligence (artificial neural networks, fuzzy systems, evolutionary computation and hybrid systems), with the main goal being to provide the scientific community and industry with a vehicle whereby ideas using two or more conventional and computational intelligence based techniques could be discussed. **Freq:** Quarterly. **Key Personnel:** Brijesh Verma, Editor-in-Chief, b.verma@cqu.edu.au; Andre De Carvalho, Editor-in-Chief, phone 55 16 2739691, fax 55 16 2739751, andre@icmc.usp.br. **ISSN:** 1469-0268. **Subscription Rates:** US$316 institutions electronic + print; EUR303 institutions electronic only. **URL:** http://www.worldscinet.com/ijcia/ijcia.shtml.

42317 ■ Studies in Learning, Evaluation, Innovation and Development
Central Queensland University, Division of Teaching and Learning Services
Division of Teaching and Learning Services
Bldg. 5, Bruce Hwy.
Rockhampton, Queensland 4702, Australia
Ph: 61 7 49309000
Fax: 61 7 49232100
Publisher E-mail: dtls-enquiries@cqu.edu.au
Peer-reviewed international journal supporting emerging scholars and the development of evidence-based practice and publishing research and scholarship about teaching and learning in formal, semi-formal and informal educational settings and sites. **Freq:** Annual. **Key Personnel:** Fons Nouwens, Editor, f.nouwens@cqu.edu.au; Patrick Alan Danaher, Editor, sleid@lists.cqu.edu.au; Geoff Danaher, Editor, g.danaher@cqu.edu.au; David Jones, Editor, d.jones@cqu.edu.au; Bobby Harreveld, Editor; Jo Luck, Editor; Jeanne McConachie, Editor. **ISSN:** 1832-2050. **URL:** http://www.sleid.cqu.edu.au/index.php.

42318 ■ 4RK-AM - 837
236 Quay St.
PO Box 911
Rockhampton, Queensland 4700, Australia
Ph: 61 7 49245111
Fax: 61 7 49245199
Format: News; Talk. **Owner:** Australian Broadcasting Corporation, ABC Ultimo Ctr., 700 Harris St., Ultimo 2007, GPO Box 9994, Sydney, New South Wales 2001, Australia, 61 2 83331500, Fax: 61 2 83335334. **Key Personnel:** Bridget Smith, Regional Content Mgr. **URL:** http://www.abc.net.au/capricornia/radio/.

Roma

42319 ■ 4RRR-FM - 101.7 MHz
42 Hawthorn St.
Roma, Queensland 4455, Australia
Ph: 61 7 46225415
Fax: 61 7 46226200
Format: Middle-of-the-Road (MOR). **Operating Hours:** Continuous. **URL:** http://www.qcba.org.au/web/4rrr.html.

Roseville

42320 ■ The Skeptic
Australian Skeptics
PO Box 268
Roseville, New South Wales 2069, Australia
Ph: 61 294 172071
Fax: 61 294 177930
Publication E-mail: editor@skeptics.com.au
Publisher E-mail: contactas3@skeptics.com.au
Publication covering phenomena. **Founded:** 1981. **Freq:** Quarterly. **Key Personnel:** Barry Williams, Contact. **ISSN:** 0726-9897. **Subscription Rates:** US$44 individuals; US$120 individuals 3 years. **Remarks:** Advertising not accepted. **URL:** http://www.skeptics.com.au/publications/magazine/. **Circ:** 3,000.

Roxby Downs

42321 ■ Flow-FM - 97.9
PO Box 407
Kapunda, South Australia 5373, Australia
Ph: 61 8 85663151
Fax: 61 8 85662729
E-mail: mail@flowfm.com.au
Format: Adult Contemporary. **URL:** http://www.flowfm.com.au/.

42322 ■ Rox-FM - 105.5
PO Box 642
Roxby Downs, South Australia 5725, Australia
Ph: 61 8 86712545
Fax: 61 8 86712934
E-mail: manager@roxfm.com.au
Format: Eclectic. **Operating Hours:** Continuous. **Key Personnel:** Kristina Meredith, Station Mgr. **URL:** http://www.roxfm.com.au/.

Rozelle

42323 ■ Beads etc
Creative Living Media
PO Box 645
Rozelle, New South Wales 2039, Australia
Ph: 61 2 95559322
Fax: 61 2 95556188
Magazine featuring beading ideas for making fabulous jewelry, garments, and bags. **Freq:** Bimonthly. **Trim Size:** 210 x 275 mm. **Key Personnel:** Deborah Segaert, Publisher/Ed.-in-Ch.; Casey Wilson, Managing Editor. **Subscription Rates:** $A 45 individuals print; $A 83.50 two years print. **Remarks:** Accepts advertising. **URL:** http://www.beadsetcmagazine.com.au/. **Ad Rates:** 4C: $A 1,221. **Circ:** (Not Reported)

42324 ■ Creative Weddings
Creative Living Media
PO Box 645
Rozelle, New South Wales 2039, Australia
Ph: 61 2 95559322
Fax: 61 2 95556188
Creative lifestyle wedding magazine. **Trim Size:** 227 x 297 mm. **Key Personnel:** Gail MacDiarmid, Editor. **Remarks:** Accepts advertising. **URL:** http://www.creativeweddings.com.au/. **Ad Rates:** 4C: $A 3,150. **Circ:** (Not Reported)

42325 ■ Down Under Quilts
Creative Living Media
PO Box 645
Rozelle, New South Wales 2039, Australia
Ph: 61 2 95559322
Fax: 61 2 95556188
Magazine for quilters of all skill levels. **Subtitle:** Australia's 1st Patchwork and Quilting Magazine. **Founded:** 1988. **Freq:** Monthly. **Trim Size:** 210 x 275 mm. **Key Personnel:** Erica Spinks, Editor; Deborah Segaert, Publisher/Ed.-in-Ch. **Subscription Rates:** $A 45 individuals print; $A 83.50 two years print. **Remarks:** Accepts advertising. **URL:** http://www.downunderquilts.com.au/. **Ad Rates:** 4C: $A 1,595. **Circ:** (Not Reported)

42326 ■ For Keeps Creative Scrapbooking
Creative Living Media
PO Box 645
Rozelle, New South Wales 2039, Australia
Ph: 61 2 95559322
Fax: 61 2 95556188
Magazine featuring scrapbooking techniques and inspiration. **Founded:** 2001. **Trim Size:** 210 x 275 mm. **Key Personnel:** Casey Wilson, Managing Editor; Deborah Segaert, Publisher/Ed.-in-Ch. **Subscription Rates:** $A 80.50 individuals; $A 150 two years. **Remarks:** Accepts advertising. **URL:** http://www.forkeepscreativescrapbooking.com.au/. **Ad Rates:** 4C: $A 1,610. **Circ:** (Not Reported)

42327 ■ i can make it myself
Creative Living Media
PO Box 645
Rozelle, New South Wales 2039, Australia
Ph: 61 2 95559322
Fax: 61 2 95556188
Craft and creative lifestyle magazine. **Key Personnel:** Fiona Murray, Editor. **Subscription Rates:** $A 9.95 single issue. **Remarks:** Accepts advertising. **URL:** http://www.icanmakeitmyself.com.au/. **Circ:** (Not Reported)

42328 ■ Parties for Kids
Creative Living Media
PO Box 645
Rozelle, New South Wales 2039, Australia
Ph: 61 2 95559322
Fax: 61 2 95556188
Magazine featuring tips and ideas on parties for kids. **Key Personnel:** Fiona Murray, Editor; Deborah Segaert, Publisher/Ed.-in-Ch. **Subscription Rates:** $A 9.95 single issue. **Remarks:** Accepts advertising. **URL:** http://partiesforkidsmagazine.com/. **Circ:** (Not Reported)

Saint Leonards

42329 ■ Acta Neuropsychiatrica
John Wiley & Sons Inc.
Wiley-Blackwell
c/o G.S. Malhi, Ed.-in-Ch.
Academic Discipline of Psychological Medicine
Northern Clinical School, University of Sydney
Bldg. 36, Royal North Shore Hospital
Saint Leonards, New South Wales 2065, Australia
Fax: 61 2 99267730
Peer-reviewed journal covering clinical, preclinical and molecular aspects of neuropsychiatric disorders. **Freq:** Bimonthly. **Key Personnel:** G.S. Malhi, Editor-in-Chief; J. Lagopoulos, Assoc. Ed.; K. Moss, Editorial Mgr., editorialoffice@actaneuropsych.com. **ISSN:** 0924-2708. **Subscription Rates:** US$428 institutions print and online; 255 institutions print and online; US$388 institutions print or online; EUR324 institutions print and online; US$500 institutions, other countries print and online; 232 institutions print, online; US$156 individuals print and online; EUR139 individuals print and online; 93 individuals print and online; US$454 institutions, other countries print or online. **Remarks:** Accepts advertising. **URL:** http://www.wiley.com/bw/journal.asp?ref=0924-2708&site=1. **Circ:** (Not Reported)

42330 ■ Australian Dental Journal
Australian Dental Association
14-16 Chandos St.
PO Box 520
Saint Leonards, New South Wales 2065, Australia
Ph: 61 299 064412
Fax: 61 299 064917
Dentistry journal. **Founded:** 1973. **Freq:** Quarterly. **Print Method:** Offset. **Trim Size:** 8 3/8 x 10 7/8. **Cols./Page:** 2 and 3. **Col. Width:** 43 and 28 nonpareils. **Col. Depth:** 130 agate lines. **Key Personnel:** Prof. Mark P. Bartold, Editor. **ISSN:** 0045-0421. **Subscription Rates:** US$333 institutions Americas (print and online); US$290 institutions Americas (online only); 179 institutions UK (print and online); 156 institutions UK (online only); EUR228 institutions Europe (print and online); EUR198 institutions Europe (online only); US$349 institutions print and online; ROW; US$304 institutions online only; ROW. **Remarks:** Advertising accepted; rates available upon request. **URL:** http://www.ada.org.au/about/publications/adj.aspx; http://www3.interscience.wiley.com/journal/118902577/home?CRETRY=1&SRETRY=0. **Circ:** Paid 10,000

42331 ■ Australian Penthouse
Horwitz Publications Proprietary Ltd.
PO Box 4455
Saint Leonards, New South Wales 1590, Australia
Magazine for men. **Freq:** Monthly. **Key Personnel:** Peter Horwitz, Publisher. **Subscription Rates:** $A 94.50 9 months, 9 issues; $A 119.40; $A 222 two years; $A 155 other countries; $A 145 New Zealand. **Remarks:** Accepts advertising. **URL:** http://www.horwitz.com.au/Australian-Penthouse.html. **Ad Rates:** BW: $A 2,870, 4C: $A 4,100. **Circ:** (Not Reported)

42332 ■ Australian Veterinary Practitioner
Australian Small Animal Veterinary Association
Unit 40, 6 Herbert St.
Saint Leonards, New South Wales 2065, Australia
Ph: 61 294 315090
Fax: 61 294 379068
Publisher E-mail: asava@ava.com.au
Journal presenting papers, case reports and other material of interest. **Freq:** Quarterly. **Subscription Rates:** Included in membership. **URL:** http://www.wsava.org/Australia1.htm; http://www.asava.com.au/.

42333 ■ Golf Australia
Horwitz Publications Proprietary Ltd.
PO Box 3355
Saint Leonards, New South Wales 1590, Australia
Magazine for Australian golfers. **Founded:** 1987. **Freq:** Monthly. **Key Personnel:** Brendan James, Editor, phone 61 2 99016142, bjames@next.com.au; David Gleeson, National Advertising Mgr., phone 61 2 99016131, dgleeson@next.com.au. **Subscription Rates:** $A 149 two years rest of world; $A 79 individuals. **Remarks:** Accepts advertising. **URL:** http://www.golfaustralia.com.au; http://www.horwitz.com.au/Golf-Australia.html. **Ad Rates:** 4C: $A 2,650. **Circ:** (Not Reported)

42334 ■ Penthouse Couples
Horwitz Publications Proprietary Ltd.
PO Box 4455
Saint Leonards, New South Wales 1590, Australia
Magazine for couples seeking to enhance their sexual fulfillment. **Key Personnel:** Ian Gerrad, Assoc. Ed. **Subscription Rates:** $A 49.50 12 months 6 issues; $A 96 24 months 12 issues; $A 70 other countries 12 months 6 issues. **Remarks:** Accepts advertising. **URL:** http://www.horwitz.com.au/Penthouse-Couples.html. **Ad Rates:** 4C: $A 600. **Circ:** (Not Reported)

42335 ■ Smart Home Ideas
Horwitz Publications Proprietary Ltd.
PO Box 5555

Circulation: ★ = ABC; △ = BPA; ♦ = CAC; • = CCAB; ❑ = VAC; ⊕ = PO Statement; ‡ = Publisher's Report; Boldface figures = sworn; Light figures = estimated.

Saint Leonards, New South Wales 1590, Australia
Magazine featuring home technology. **Freq:** Quarterly.
Key Personnel: Jim Preece, Contact, phone 61 2
99016150, jpreece@next.com.au. **Subscription Rates:**
$A 28.50; $A 66.50 other countries. **Remarks:** Accepts
advertising. **URL:** http://www.nextmedia.com.au/smart-
home-ideas/smart-home-ideas-magazine.html.   **Ad
Rates:** 4C: $A 3,000. **Circ:** (Not Reported)

42336 ■ TV Soap
Horwitz Publications Proprietary Ltd.
PO Box 5555
Saint Leonards, New South Wales 1590, Australia
Entertainment magazine for lovers of television drama,
gossip and glamour. **Subtitle:** Australia's No. 1. **Freq:**
Biweekly. **Key Personnel:** Vesna Petropoulos, Editor.
Subscription Rates: $A 42.90 6 months, 13 issues; $A
85.80 12 months 26 issues; $A 70 other countries 6
months, 13 issues; $A 140 other countries 12 months
26 issues. **Remarks:** Accepts advertising. **URL:** http://
www.tvsoap.com.au/; http://www.nextmedia.com.au/tv-
soap/tv-soap-magazine.html. **Ad Rates:** 4C: $A 3,300.
Circ: (Not Reported)

42337 ■ 2MBS-FM - 102.5
76 Chandos St.
Saint Leonards, New South Wales 2065, Australia
Ph: 61 2 94394777
Fax: 61 2 94394064
E-mail: info@2mbs.com
Format: Classical; Jazz; Folk; World Beat; Eclectic.
Founded: Feb. 1, 1975. **Operating Hours:** Continuous.
Key Personnel: Peter Bailey, Tech. Oper. Mgr., ops@
2mbs.com; Mike Smith, Station Mgr., mike.smith@2mbs.
com; Ildiko Dauda, Communications Mgr., ildiko.dauda@
2mbs.com. **Wattage:** 30,000. **URL:** http://www.2mbs.
com/.

Saint Lucia

**42338 ■ The Australian Journal of Politics and
History**
University of Queensland Press
Staff House Rd.
PO Box 6042
Saint Lucia, Queensland 4067, Australia
Ph: 61 733 657244
Fax: 61 733 657579
Publisher E-mail: uqp@wwuqp.uq.edu.au
Periodical focusing on history. **Freq:** Quarterly. **Key Per-
sonnel:** Andrew Bonnell, Editor, a.bonnell@uq.edu.au;
Ian Ward, Editor, i.ward@uq.edu.au; Paul Crook, Assoc.
Ed., ajph@uq.edu.au; Margaret Higgs, Assoc. Ed.,
ajph@uq.edu.au; Carl Ungerer, Assoc. Ed., c.ungerer@
uq.edu.au; Rae Wear, Assoc. Ed., r.wear@uq.edu.au.
ISSN: 0004-9522. **Subscription Rates:** US$87 individu-
als print & online; 61 individuals print and online; 61
individuals print and online (non euro zone); EUR77
individuals print and online; US$55 students print and
online, in the Americas; US$33 students print & online,
UK; 33 students print and online (non euro zone);
US$343 institutions online only; 217 institutions online
only; EUR276 institutions online only, (non euro zone).
Remarks: Accepts advertising on request. **URL:** http://
www.blackwellpublishing.com/submit.asp?ref=0004-
9522. **Circ:** (Not Reported)

42339 ■ Australian Literary Studies
University of Queensland Press
Staff House Rd.
PO Box 6042
Saint Lucia, Queensland 4067, Australia
Ph: 61 733 657244
Fax: 61 733 657579
Publisher E-mail: uqp@wwuqp.uq.edu.au
Publication covering literature and writing. **Founded:**
2002. **Freq:** Semiannual. **Trim Size:** 175 x 250 mm.
Key Personnel: Leigh Dale, Editor. **ISSN:** 0004-9697.
Subscription Rates: US$44 individuals; US$50 other
countries; US$82 institutions; US$90 other countries
institutional. **Remarks:** Advertising not accepted. **URL:**
http://espace.library.uq.edu.au/view/UQ:63851. **Circ:**
750

42340 ■ Journal of Australian Studies
University of Queensland Press
Staff House Rd.
PO Box 6042
Saint Lucia, Queensland 4067, Australia
Ph: 61 733 657244
Fax: 61 733 657579

Publisher E-mail: uqp@wwuqp.uq.edu.au
Peer-reviewed and cultural studies journal focusing on
Australia. **Freq:** Quarterly. **Trim Size:** 175 x 250 mm.
Key Personnel: Richard Nile, Editor; Andrea Gaynor,
Assoc. Ed.; Martin Crotty, Assoc. Ed. **ISSN:** 1444-3058.
Subscription Rates: $A 110 individuals; $A 150 institu-
tions libraries/schools; $A 60 students; $A 28 single
issue. **Remarks:** Advertising not accepted. **URL:** http://
www.api-network.com. **Circ:** 1,000

42341 ■ University of Queensland Law Journal
University of Queensland Press
Staff House Rd.
PO Box 6042
Saint Lucia, Queensland 4067, Australia
Ph: 61 733 657244
Fax: 61 733 657579
Publisher E-mail: uqp@wwuqp.uq.edu.au
Law periodical. **Founded:** 1948. **Freq:** Semiannual.
Trim Size: 175 x 250 mm. **Key Personnel:** Prof. Jim Al-
lan, Editor; Prof. Ian Dennis, International Editorial
Board; Prof. John Finnis, Editorial Board; Prof. Charles
Rickett, Editorial Board; Prof. Vaughan Lowe, Editorial
Board; Prof. Jeffrey Goldsworthy, Editorial Board; Dr. Ei-
lis Ferran, Editorial Board; Prof. Reinhard Zimmermann,
Editorial Board; Prof. Andrew Burrows, Editorial Board;
Prof. Jane Stapleton, Editorial Board. **ISSN:** 0083-4041.
Subscription Rates: $A 95 individuals; $A 155 by mail
overseas; $A 60 single issue back issues. **Remarks:**
Advertising not accepted. **Online:** Gale. **URL:** http://
www.law.uq.edu.au/uqlj/. **Circ:** (Not Reported)

42342 ■ Parrot Society of Australia News
Parrot Society of Australia
PO Box 75
Salisbury, Queensland 4107, Australia
Fax: 61 7 54331921
Publication E-mail: editor@parrotsociety.org.au
Publisher E-mail: memberships@parrotsociety.org.au
Magazine covering breeding and species-related
articles, companion parrot care and veterinary advice.
Freq: Bimonthly. **Subscription Rates:** Included in
membership. **Remarks:** Accepts advertising. **URL:** http://
www.parrotsociety.org.au/. **Circ:** (Not Reported)

Salisbury (South Australia)

42343 ■ Leader Messenger
Messenger Newspapers
25 Wiltshire St.
Salisbury, South Australia 5108, Australia
Local community newspaper. **Freq:** Weekly (Wed.). **Key
Personnel:** Matt Edwards, Northern Sales Mgr.,
edwardsm@mng.newsltd.com.au. **Remarks:** Accepts
display and classified advertising. **URL:** http://www.
newsspace.com.au/leader_messenger. **Circ:** 43,550

42344 ■ News Review Messenger
Messenger Newspapers
25 Wiltshire St.
Salisbury, South Australia 5108, Australia
Local community newspaper. **Freq:** Weekly (Wed.). **Key
Personnel:** Matt Edwards, Northern Sales Mgr.,
edwardsm@mng.newsltd.com.au. **Remarks:** Accepts
display and classified advertising. **URL:** http://www.
newsspace.com.au/news_review_messenger. **Circ:**
93,621

42345 ■ Standard Messenger
Messenger Newspapers
25 Wiltshire St.
Salisbury, South Australia 5108, Australia
Local community newspaper. **Freq:** Weekly (Wed.). **Key
Personnel:** Maria Davis, Northern Advertising Mgr.,
davism@mng.newsltd.com.au; Chris Dimitrak, Advertising Agency Sales Mgr., phone 61 8 83475715,
dimitrakc@mng.newsltd.com.au; Brenton Finch, Production Mgr., phone 61 8 83475727, finchb@mng.newsltd.
com.au. **Remarks:** Accepts display and classified
advertising. **URL:** http://messenger-news.whereilive.
com.au/. **Circ:** 35,261

42346 ■ 5PBA-FM - 89.7
PO Box 433
Salisbury, South Australia 5108, Australia
Ph: 61 8 82503735
Fax: 61 8 82817495
E-mail: pbafm@nospam.pbafm.org.au
Format: Eclectic. **Founded:** 1979. **Key Personnel:** De-
nise Guest, Exec. Off.; Steve Brown, Chm., steveb@

nospam.pbafm.org.au; Richard Walford, Treas.,
rwalford@nospam.pbafm.org.au. **URL:** http://www.
users.on.net/~pbafm2/.

42347 ■ PBA-FM - 89.7
PO Box 433
Salisbury, South Australia 5108, Australia
Ph: 61 8 82503705
Fax: 61 8 82817495
E-mail: pbafm@nospam.pbafm.org.au
Format: Eclectic; World Beat; Oldies; Jazz; Country;
Blues; Public Radio. **Founded:** Jan. 1983. **Key Person-
nel:** Denise Guest, Executive Off.; Steve Brown, Chm.,
steveb@nospam.pbafm.org.au; Richard Walford, Treas.,
rwalford@nospam.pbafm.org.au. **URL:** http://www.
users.on.net/~pbafm2/.

Sanctuary Cove

42348 ■ Jazz Radio Ltd-FM - 94.1
4H Masthead Way
PO Box 16
Sanctuary Cove, Queensland 4212, Australia
Ph: 61 7 55779999
Fax: 61 7 55779799
E-mail: info@jazzradio.com.au
Format: Jazz; News. **Owner:** Community Broadcasting
Association. of Australia, Level 3, 44-54 Botany Rd.,
Alexandria, New South Wales 2015, Australia, 61 2
93102999, Fax: 61 2 93194545. **Operating Hours:**
Continuous. **Key Personnel:** Bill Vaughan, Vice-Chm.;
Richard Barton, Director; Ray Bolwell, Director; Gary
Field, General Mgr. **Ad Rates:** Noncommercial; under-
writing available. **URL:** http://www.941fm.com.au.

Sanctuary Point

42349 ■ Bay & Basin-FM - 92.7
PO Box 30
Sanctuary Point, New South Wales 2540, Australia
Ph: 61 2 44439644
Fax: 61 2 44437040
E-mail: bbfm@shoalhaven.net.au
Format: Eclectic; Public Radio. **Operating Hours:**
Continuous. **Ad Rates:** Underwriting available. **URL:**
http://www.bbcri.com.au/index.php?page=2.

42350 ■ 2BAB-FM - 92.7
PO Box 30
Sanctuary Point, New South Wales 2540, Australia
Ph: 61 2 44439244
Fax: 61 2 44437040
E-mail: bbfm@shoalhaven.net.au
Format: Eclectic. **URL:** http://www.bbcri.com.au/index.
php?page=2.

42351 ■ New-FM - 105.3
Box 105 HRMC
Sandgate, New South Wales 2304, Australia
Ph: 61 2 49680105
Fax: 61 2 49672129
Format: Album-Oriented Rock (AOR); Classic Rock;
News; Information. **Owner:** Newcastle FM Pty. Ltd., at
above address. **Founded:** 1989. **Ad Rates:** Advertising
accepted; rates available upon request. **URL:** http://
www.newfm.com.au/.

42352 ■ 2HD-AM - 1143
173-175 Maitland Rd.
Sandgate, New South Wales 2304, Australia
Ph: 61 2 49676111
Fax: 61 2 49672129
Format: Oldies; News. **Founded:** Jan. 27, 1925. **Oper-
ating Hours:** Continuous. **Key Personnel:** Luke Grant,
Contact, luke@2hd.com.au; Brent Bultitude, Contact,
brent@2hd.com.au. **URL:** http://www.2hd.com.au.

Sandgate (Queensland)

42353 ■ Redress
Association of Women Educators
PO Box 229
Sandgate, Queensland 4017, Australia
Ph: 61 7 38693433
Fax: 61 7 38693436
Publisher E-mail: awe1@bigpond.net.au
Publication covering women. **Freq:** 3/yr. **Key Person-
nel:** Linda Oakley, Editor, lindao@optusnet.com.au.
ISSN: 1039-382X. **Subscription Rates:** Included in
membership; US$15 nonmembers back issues. **Re-**

marks: Advertising accepted; rates available upon request. **URL:** http://www.awe.asn.au/redress.php. **Circ:** (Not Reported)

Scarborough

42354 ■ Science a GoGo
PO Box 254
Scarborough, Western Australia 6019, Australia
Scientific journal. **URL:** http://www.scienceagogo.com/index.shtml.

Scottsdale

42355 ■ Sea-FM - 99.7
109 York St.
PO Box 7635
Launceston, Tasmania 7250, Australia
Ph: 61 3 63314844
Fax: 61 3 63343322
Format: Contemporary Hit Radio (CHR). **Ad Rates:** Advertising accepted; rates available upon request. **URL:** http://theradio.com.au/Hitmusic.aspx?PageID=4399&Station=SEA_99.7FM_Scottsdale.

Seddon West

42356 ■ Similia
Australian Homoeopathic Association
PO Box 104
Seddon West, Victoria 3011, Australia
Ph: 61 1300 789896
Publisher E-mail: valahavic@gmail.com
Journal containing articles about all aspects of homoeopathy and related subjects. **Freq:** Semiannual. **Key Personnel:** John Harvey, Editor. **URL:** http://www.homeopathyoz.org.

Seven Hills

42357 ■ Hope-FM - 103.2
2 Leabons Ln.
Seven Hills, New South Wales 2147, Australia
Ph: 61 2 98547000
Fax: 61 2 98314999
E-mail: mail@hope1032.com.au
Format: Contemporary Christian. **Formerly:** 2CBA-FM (Dec. 15, 2008). **Key Personnel:** John O'Donnell, Program Dir.; Derek Nelson, Promotions Mgr.; Ray Kington, Music Dir. **URL:** http://www.hope1032.com.au/.

Shepparton

42358 ■ 3SR-FM - 95.3
625 Wyndham St.
Shepparton, Victoria 3630, Australia
Ph: 61 3 58313969
Fax: 61 3 58222956
Format: Adult Contemporary; Oldies. **Owner:** Goulburn & Border Broadcasters, at above address. **Founded:** 1931. **Operating Hours:** weekdays 6a.m.-12a.m. **Key Personnel:** Leanne Hulm, Station Mgr., leanne.hulm@macsc.com.au. **URL:** http://theradio.com.au.

Silverwater

42359 ■ Australian Country Craft and Decorating
Express Publications Pty. Ltd.
Locked Bag 111
Silverwater, New South Wales 1811, Australia
Ph: 61 297 413899
Fax: 61 297 378017
Publisher E-mail: subs@magstore.com.au
Magazine delving into the beautiful world of country craft with visits into amazing country homes, fantastic projects, intriguing profiles, captivating stories and an extensive range of country and craft shopping ideas. **Key Personnel:** Marianne Roberts, Editor, mroberts@expresspublications.com.au; Sonia Spiteri-Fontana, Advertising Mgr., sspiteri@expresspublications.com.au. **Subscription Rates:** $A 39 individuals 7 issues; $A 67 individuals 13 issues; $A 1114 individuals 26 issues. **Remarks:** Accepts advertising. **URL:** http://www.accmagazine.com.au/. **Circ:** (Not Reported)

42360 ■ Australian Country Threads
Express Publications Pty. Ltd.
Locked Bag 111

Silverwater, New South Wales 1811, Australia
Ph: 61 297 413899
Fax: 61 297 378017
Publisher E-mail: subs@magstore.com.au
Guide to country-style patchwork, quilting and stitching. **Subtitle:** All you Need to Know About Country Style Stitching, Quilting and Patchwork. **Freq:** Monthly 10/yr. **Key Personnel:** Lynelle Slade, Editor, editorial@countrythreads.com.au; Danielle Tebb, Editor. **Subscription Rates:** $A 50 individuals 8 issues; $A 54 individuals 10 issues; $A 87 individuals 15 issues; $A 148 individuals 30 issues. **Remarks:** Accepts advertising. **URL:** http://www.countrythreads.com.au/. **Circ:** (Not Reported)

42361 ■ Patchwork & Stitching
Express Publications Pty. Ltd.
Locked Bag 111
Silverwater, New South Wales 1811, Australia
Ph: 61 297 413899
Fax: 61 297 378017
Publisher E-mail: subs@magstore.com.au
Magazine containing quick and easy projects, quilts, wall-hangings, stitcheries, dolls, and accessories. **Freq:** Monthly. **Key Personnel:** Robyn Ahern, Editor, editorial@pwsmagazine.com.au; Natalie Stanic, Advertising Mgr., nstanic@expresspublications.com. **Subscription Rates:** $A 44 individuals 7 issues; $A 76 individuals 13 issues; $A 128 individuals 26 issues. **Remarks:** Accepts advertising. **URL:** http://www.pwsmagazine.com.au/. **Circ:** (Not Reported)

Somerville

42362 ■ 3RPP-FM - 98.3
PO Box 602
Somerville, Victoria 3912, Australia
Ph: 61 3 59788200
Fax: 61 3 59788551
E-mail: info@3rpp.com.au
Format: Eclectic; Public Radio; Sports; Information. **Operating Hours:** Continuous. **Ad Rates:** Underwriting available. **URL:** http://3rpp.asn.au.

42363 ■ 3RPP-FM - 98.7
PO Box 602
Somerville, Victoria 3912, Australia
Ph: 61 3 59788200
Fax: 61 3 59788551
Format: Eclectic; Public Radio; Sports; Information. **Operating Hours:** Continuous. **Key Personnel:** Dr. W Peter Wright, Program Dir. **Ad Rates:** Underwriting available. **URL:** http://www.3rpp.asn.au.

South Bank

42364 ■ Australian Voice
Australian Academic Press Pty. Ltd.
PO Box 3428
South Bank, Queensland 4101, Australia
Ph: 61 7 38756231
Fax: 61 7 38756282
Publisher E-mail: aap@australianacademicpress.com.au
Peer-reviewed journal covering fields of voice science and physiology, vocal pedagogy, music literature, voice therapy and performance practice and style. **Freq:** Annual. **Key Personnel:** Adele Nisbet, Editor, a.nisbet@griffith.edu.au. **ISSN:** 1325-1317. **Subscription Rates:** $A 145 individuals; $A 160 other countries. **Remarks:** Accepts advertising. **URL:** http://www.australianacademicpress.com.au/Publications/Journals/Australian_Voice/Austvoice.htm. **Circ:** (Not Reported)

South Melbourne

42365 ■ Advocate
National Tertiary Education Union
PO Box 1323
South Melbourne, Victoria 3205, Australia
Ph: 61 392 541910
Fax: 61 392 541915
Publication E-mail: advocate@nteu.org.au
Publisher E-mail: national@nteu.org.au
Publication covering higher education. **Founded:** 1992. **Freq:** 3/yr (March, July/August, November). **Print Method:** Offset. **Trim Size:** 210 x 270 mm. **Key Personnel:** Grahame McCulloch, Publisher; Paul Clifton,

Contact; Carolyn Allport, Editor. **ISSN:** 1321-8476. **Subscription Rates:** Included in membership. **Remarks:** Advertising accepted; rates available upon request. **URL:** http://www.nteu.org.au. **Circ:** Non-paid 28,000

42366 ■ Agendas
Aged and Community Services Australia
Level 1, 36 Albert Rd.
South Melbourne, Victoria 3205, Australia
Ph: 61 3 96863460
Fax: 61 3 96863453
Publisher E-mail: info@agedcare.org.au
Magazine of Aged and Community Services Australia. **Freq:** Quarterly. **Key Personnel:** Megan Stoyles, Managing Editor, mstoyles@agedcare.org.au; Greg Mundy, CEO, gmundy@agedcare.org.au. **Subscription Rates:** $A 30 individuals. **Remarks:** Accepts advertising. **URL:** http://www.agedcare.org.au/PUBLICATIONS-&-RESOURCES/Agendas.html. **Circ:** (Not Reported)

42367 ■ Australasian Journal on Ageing
Aged and Community Services Australia
Level 1, 36 Albert Rd.
South Melbourne, Victoria 3205, Australia
Ph: 61 3 96863460
Fax: 61 3 96863453
Publisher E-mail: info@agedcare.org.au
Journal of Aged and Community Services Australia. **Founded:** 1981. **Freq:** Quarterly. **Key Personnel:** Prof. Lynne Parkinson, Editor. **Subscription Rates:** US$450 institutions print and online; US$391 institutions print; US$391 institutions online; 181 institutions print and online; EUR230 institutions print and online; 157 institutions print or online. **URL:** http://www.wiley.com/bw/journal.asp?ref=1440-6381.

42368 ■ Australian Universities Review
National Tertiary Education Union
PO Box 1323
South Melbourne, Victoria 3205, Australia
Ph: 61 392 541910
Fax: 61 392 541915
Publication E-mail: aur@nteu.org.au
Publisher E-mail: national@nteu.org.au
Journal of the National Tertiary Education Union. **Freq:** Semiannual. **Key Personnel:** Jeannie Rea, Editorial Board; Prof. Ralph Hall, Editorial Board; Dr. Ian Dobson, Editor, editor@aur.org.au. **Subscription Rates:** $A 66 individuals domestic; $A 80 other countries overseas, surface mail. **URL:** http://www.aur.org.au.

42369 ■ Curriculum and Teaching
James Nicholas Publishers, Pty. Ltd.
PO Box 5179
South Melbourne, Victoria 3205, Australia
Ph: 61 3 96905955
Fax: 61 3 96992040
Publisher E-mail: custservice@jnponline.com
Peer-reviwed Journal covering issues in curriculum theory and practice. **Founded:** 1986. **Freq:** 2/yr. **Key Personnel:** Joseph Zajda, Editor; Elliot Eisner, Consulting Ed.; Daniel Kallos, Consulting Ed. **ISSN:** 0726-416X. **Subscription Rates:** $A 484 institutions and libraries; $A 440 institutions and libraries; New Zealand; 252 institutions and libraries; Europe; US$438 institutions, other countries and libraries. **URL:** http://www.jamesnicholaspublishers.com.au/ctjrnl.htm.

42370 ■ Educational Practice and Theory
James Nicholas Publishers, Pty. Ltd.
PO Box 5179
South Melbourne, Victoria 3205, Australia
Ph: 61 3 96905955
Fax: 61 3 96992040
Publisher E-mail: custservice@jnponline.com
Peer-reviewed journal covering ideas in educational theory and practice. **Founded:** 1978. **Freq:** 2/yr. **Key Personnel:** Rea Zajda, Editor; Martin Carnoy, Consulting Ed.; Joseph Zajda, Consulting Ed. **ISSN:** 1323-577X. **Subscription Rates:** $A 440 institutions and libraries; $A 440 institutions and libraries; New Zealand; 252 institutions and libraries; Europe; US$438 institutions, other countries and libraries. **URL:** http://www.jamesnicholaspublishers.com.au/epatjrnl.htm.

42371 ■ Frontline
National Tertiary Education Union
PO Box 1323
South Melbourne, Victoria 3205, Australia
Ph: 61 392 541910

Circulation: ★ = ABC; △ = BPA; ♦ = CAC; • = CCAB; ❑ = VAC; ⊕ = PO Statement; ‡ = Publisher's Report; Boldface figures = sworn; Light figures = estimated.

Gale Directory of Publications & Broadcast Media/147th Ed.   4745

Fax: 01 392 541915
Publisher E-mail: national@nteu.org.au
Women's journal of the National Tertiary Education Union. **Freq:** Annual. **Key Personnel:** Paul Clifton, Production & Design; Carolyn Allport, Editor. **ISSN:** 1322-2945. **Subscription Rates:** Rs 260 individuals; US$40 other countries. **URL:** http://www.nteu.org.au/library/frontline/.

42372 ■ Information Technology, Education and Society
James Nicholas Publishers, Pty. Ltd.
PO Box 5179
South Melbourne, Victoria 3205, Australia
Ph: 61 3 96905955
Fax: 61 3 96992040
Publisher E-mail: custservice@jnponline.com
Peer-reviewed journal focusing on major and current issues in information technology and its relation to education and society, providing a forum for original articles from throughout the world which analyse and explore sociological and educational issues related to new and changing technologies. **Freq:** Semiannual. **Key Personnel:** Rea Zajda, Exec. Ed. **ISSN:** 1037-616X. **Subscription Rates:** $A 484 institutions; $A 440 libraries New Zealand; 252 libraries Europe; US$438 institutions, other countries. **URL:** http://www.jamesnicholaspublishers.com.au/itesjrnl.htm.

42373 ■ Journal of Postcolonial Education
James Nicholas Publishers, Pty. Ltd.
PO Box 5179
South Melbourne, Victoria 3205, Australia
Ph: 61 3 96905955
Fax: 61 3 96992040
Publisher E-mail: custservice@jnponline.com
Peer-reviewed journal focusing on postcolonial education. **Founded:** 1896. **Freq:** Semiannual. **Print Method:** Offset. **Trim Size:** 13 x 21. **Cols./Page:** 6. **Col. Width:** 2.15 inches. **Col. Depth:** 21 inches. **ISSN:** 1443-1483. **Subscription Rates:** $A 484 institutions; $A 440 institutions New Zealand; 252 institutions Europe; US$438 institutions, other countries. **URL:** http://www.jamesnicholaspublishers.com.au/jpejrnl.htm.

42374 ■ Learning and Teaching
James Nicholas Publishers, Pty. Ltd.
PO Box 5179
South Melbourne, Victoria 3205, Australia
Ph: 61 3 96905955
Fax: 61 3 96992040
Publication E-mail: editor.learnteach@jnponline.com
Publisher E-mail: custservice@jnponline.com
Peer-reviewed journal covering major models of learning and teaching. **Subtitle:** An International Journal in Classroom Pedagogy. **Freq:** 2/yr. **Key Personnel:** Nikolai Zajda, Exec. Ed.; Joseph Zajda, Sen. Consulting Ed. **ISSN:** 1832-2751. **Subscription Rates:** $A 484 institutions and libraries; $A 440 institutions and libraries; New Zealand; 252 institutions and libraries; Europe; US$438 institutions, other countries and libraries. **URL:** http://www.jamesnicholaspublishers.com.au/ltchjrnl.htm.

42375 ■ Political Crossroads
James Nicholas Publishers, Pty. Ltd.
PO Box 5179
South Melbourne, Victoria 3205, Australia
Ph: 61 3 96905955
Fax: 61 3 96992040
Publisher E-mail: custservice@jnponline.com
Peer-reviewed journal covering international social and political issues. **Freq:** 2/yr. **Key Personnel:** Joseph Zajda, Managing Editor; Marshall Goldman, Consulting Ed.; Robert Looney, Consulting Ed. **ISSN:** 1323-5761. **Subscription Rates:** $A 484 institutions and libraries; $A 440 institutions and libraries; New Zealand; 252 institutions and libraries; Europe; US$438 institutions, other countries and libraries. **URL:** http://www.jamesnicholaspublishers.com.au/pcjrnl.htm.

42376 ■ World Studies in Education
James Nicholas Publishers, Pty. Ltd.
PO Box 5179
South Melbourne, Victoria 3205, Australia
Ph: 61 3 96905955
Fax: 61 3 96992200
Publisher E-mail: custservice@jnponline.com
Peer-reviewed Journal covering global overview of significant international and comparative education research affecting educational institutions in the global

economy. **Freq:** 2/yr. **Key Personnel:** Joseph Zajda, Editor; Robert Arnove, Consulting Ed.; Mark Bray, Consulting Ed. **ISSN:** 1441-340X. **Subscription Rates:** $A 484 institutions and libraries; $A 440 institutions and libraries; New Zealand; 252 institutions and libraries; Europe; US$438 institutions, other countries and libraries. **URL:** http://www.jamesnicholaspublishers.com.au/wsejrnl.htm.

42377 ■ Magic-AM - 1278 KHz
43-49 Bank St.
South Melbourne, Victoria 3205, Australia
Ph: 61 3 92432000
Fax: 61 3 96900630
Format: Easy Listening. **Owner:** Fairfax Media, Ltd., GPO 506, Sydney, New South Wales 2001, Australia, 61 3 92822833. **Formerly:** Magic 693-AM. **Operating Hours:** Continuous. **Key Personnel:** Gary Hoffman, Station Mgr. **URL:** http://www.mytalk.com.au; http://www.fxj.com.au/.

42378 ■ 3AW-AM - 1278
43-49 Bank St.
South Melbourne, Victoria 3205, Australia
Ph: 61 3 92432000
Fax: 61 3 96900630
E-mail: sales@3aw.com.au
Format: Talk; News; Sports; Information. **Owner:** Fairfax Media, Ltd., GPO 506, Sydney, New South Wales 2001, Australia, 61 3 92822833. **Founded:** 1932. **Ad Rates:** Advertising accepted; rates available upon request. **URL:** http://www.3aw.com.au/; http://www.fxj.com.au/.

42379 ■ Triple M-FM - 105.1
257 Clarendon St.
PO Box MMM
South Melbourne, Victoria 3205, Australia
Ph: 61 3 92301051
Format: Alternative/New Music/Progressive; Sports; Contemporary Hit Radio (CHR); Eighties. **Ad Rates:** Advertising accepted; rates available upon request. **URL:** http://www.triplem.com.au/melbourne.

Southbank

42380 ■ Plastics News International
The Editors Desk Proprietary Ltd.
The Summit
163 City Rd.
Southbank, Victoria 3006, Australia
Ph: 61 3 96459887
Fax: 61 3 96459882
Publisher E-mail: publisher@plasticsnews.net
Trade magazine covering the plastics industry worldwide. **Founded:** 1958. **Freq:** 11/yr. **Print Method:** Sheetfed offset litho. **Trim Size:** 210 x 297 mm. **Key Personnel:** John F. McGough, Publisher, publisher@plasticsnews.net; Leonora Bor, Editor, editor@plasticsnews.net; Bozena Lozinska, Office Mgr., admin@plasticsnews.net. **Subscription Rates:** $A 102 individuals New Zealand; $A 95 individuals Australia; US$95 other countries. **Remarks:** Accepts advertising. **URL:** http://plasticsnews.net; http://www.plasticsnews.net. **Ad Rates:** BW: US$2,020, 4C: US$2,300. **Circ:** Paid ♦4,500, Non-paid ♦4,500

Southport

42381 ■ GOLD 92.5-FM - 92.5
2/12-14 Marine Parade
Southport, Queensland 4215, Australia
Ph: 61 7 55911925
E-mail: web.programming@goldfm.com.au
Format: Adult Contemporary; Oldies. **Founded:** Nov. 1992. **Operating Hours:** Continuous. **Key Personnel:** Steve Jorgensen, Station Mgr., phone 61 7 54568501, sjorgensen@scbnetwork.com.au. **URL:** http://theradio.com.au/localworks.aspx?PageID=344&Station=92.5_GOLDFM_Gold_Coast.

42382 ■ Hot Tomato-FM - 102.9
60 High St.
PO Box 10290
Southport, Queensland 4215, Australia
Ph: 61 7 55192000
Fax: 61 7 55192300
E-mail: contactus@1029hottomato.com.au
Format: Adult Contemporary. **Key Personnel:** Graham Miles, General Mgr., gmiles@hot-tomato.com.au; Kate

Carlyle, News Dir., kcarlyle@hot-tomato.com.au; David Crane, Chief Engineer, dcrane@hot-tomato.com.au. **URL:** http://www.1029hottomato.com.au/.

42383 ■ Sea-FM - 90.9
Level 2, Seabank Bldg.
12-14 Marine Parade
Southport, Queensland 4215, Australia
Ph: 61 7 55915000
Fax: 61 7 55916080
Format: Adult Contemporary. **Owner:** Regional Mediaworks, Petrie House, Level 1, 80 Petrie Ter., Brisbane, Queensland 4221, Australia, 61 7 35108700, Fax: 61 7 35108799. **Key Personnel:** Steve Jorgensen, Station Mgr., sjorgensen@scbnetwork.com.au. **URL:** http://theradio.com.au; http://www.regionalmediaworks.com.au/region%20information.asp?region=Gold%20Coast.

Springwood (New South Wales)

42384 ■ Logan West Leader
Quest Community Newspapers
Shop 2/28 Commercial Dr.
Springwood, New South Wales 4300, Australia
Local community newspaper. **Founded:** July 1994. **Freq:** Weekly (Wed.). **Key Personnel:** Joel Hudson, Advertising Mgr., phone 61 7 38262626, hudsonj@qst.newsltd.com.au. **Remarks:** Accepts display and classified advertising. **URL:** http://www.newsspace.com.au/logan_west_leader. **Circ:** ‡30,887

Springwood (Queensland)

42385 ■ 88-FM - 88.0
5 Bates St.
PO Box 732
Springwood, Queensland 4127, Australia
Ph: 61 7 38081200
Fax: 61 7 32902481
E-mail: info@australiatrade.com.au
Format: Information. **Ad Rates:** Advertising accepted; rates available upon request. **URL:** http://www.australiatrade.com.au.

Stafford

42386 ■ City North News
Quest Community Newspapers
Cor. Shand & Byth St.
Stafford, Queensland 4051, Australia
Local community newspaper. **Founded:** May 5, 2005. **Freq:** Weekly (Thurs.). **Key Personnel:** Grant Stockwell, Editor, phone 61 7 33520658, fax 61 7 33520601, editorial@citynorthnews.com.au; Boyd Webb, Advertising Mgr., phone 61 7 33520600, webbb@qst.newsltd.com.au. **Remarks:** Accepts display and classified advertising. **URL:** http://www.newsspace.com.au/city_north_news. **Circ:** ‡29,154

Stepney

42387 ■ Australian Mathematics Teacher (AMT)
The Australian Association of Mathematics Teachers Inc.
GPO Box 1729
Bldg. D, 80 Payneham Rd.
Stepney, South Australia 5069, Australia
Ph: 61 8 83630288
Fax: 61 8 83629288
Publisher E-mail: office@aamt.edu.au
Journal for middle school mathematics teachers. **Founded:** 1945. **Freq:** Quarterly. **Trim Size:** A4. **Key Personnel:** Judith Falle, Editor, jfalle@pobox.une.edu.au. **ISSN:** 0045-0685. **Subscription Rates:** $A 55 individuals Australia; $A 70 elsewhere. **Remarks:** Advertising accepted; rates available upon request. **URL:** http://www.aamt.edu.au/Webshop/Entire-catalogue/Australian-Mathematics-Teacher. **Circ:** Paid 3,000

42388 ■ Australian Primary Mathematics Classroom (APMC)
The Australian Association of Mathematics Teachers Inc.
GPO Box 1729
Bldg. D, 80 Payneham Rd.
Stepney, South Australia 5069, Australia
Ph: 61 8 83630288
Fax: 61 8 83629288

Publisher E-mail: office@aamt.edu.au

Journal for primary school mathematics teachers and other interested in primary mathematics education. **Founded:** 1996. **Freq:** Quarterly. **Trim Size:** A4. **Key Personnel:** Kim Beswick, Editor, kim.beswick@utas.edu.au; Tracey Muir, Editor, tracey.muir@utas.edu.au. **ISSN:** 1326-0286. **Subscription Rates:** $A 70 other countries; $A 55 individuals within Australia. **Remarks:** Advertising accepted; rates available upon request. **URL:** http://www.aamt.edu.au/Webshop/Entire-catalogue/Australian-Primary-Mathematics-Classroom. **Circ:** Paid 1,500

42389 ■ Australian Senior Mathematics Journal (ASMJ)
The Australian Association of Mathematics Teachers Inc.
GPO Box 1729
Bldg. D, 80 Payneham Rd.
Stepney, South Australia 5069, Australia
Ph: 61 8 83630288
Fax: 61 8 83629288
Publisher E-mail: office@aamt.edu.au
Journal for high school and early college mathematics teachers. **Founded:** 1987. **Freq:** Semiannual. **Trim Size:** A4. **Key Personnel:** Jill Brown, Editor, jill.brown@acu.edu.au; Gloria Stillman, Editor. **ISSN:** 0819-4564. **Subscription Rates:** $A 55 elsewhere; $A 45 individuals Australia. **Remarks:** Advertising accepted; rates available upon request. **URL:** http://www.aamt.edu.au/Webshop/Entire-catalogue/Australian-Senior-Mathematics-Journal. **Circ:** Paid 1,500

42390 ■ 5DDD-FM - 93.7
PO Box 937
Stepney, South Australia 5069, Australia
Ph: 61 8 83633937
E-mail: mail@threedradio.com
Format: Eclectic. **Founded:** 1979. **Operating Hours:** 6a.m.-3a.m. Daily. **URL:** http://www.threedradio.com/.

Stones Corner

42391 ■ 4KQ-AM - 693
444 Logan Rd.
Stones Corner, Queensland 4151, Australia
Ph: 61 7 33940693
Fax: 61 7 33944400
E-mail: 4kqpd@arn.com.au
Format: Oldies; Adult Contemporary; News. **Owner:** Australian Radio Network, 3 Byfield St., North Ryde, New South Wales 2113, Australia, 61 2 88999999, Fax: 61 2 88999811. **Key Personnel:** Laury Edwards, Contact, breakfast@4kq.com.au. **Ad Rates:** Advertising accepted; rates available upon request. **URL:** http://www.4kq.com.au/; http://www.arn.com.au.

Strathpine

42392 ■ Pine Rivers Press
Quest Community Newspapers
199 Gympie Rd.
Strathpine, Queensland 4500, Australia
Ph: 61 7 38178200
Local community newspaper. **Founded:** 1993. **Freq:** Weekly (Wed.). **Key Personnel:** Narelle De Souza, Advertising Mgr., desouzan@qst.newsltd.com.au; Nick Crockford, Editor, phone 61 7 38178200, fax 61 7 38811620, editorial@pineriverspress.com.au. **Remarks:** Accepts display and classified advertising. **URL:** http://www.newsspace.com.au/pine_rivers_press. **Circ:** 35,760

Strawberry Hills

42393 ■ ADF Health
Australasian Medical Publishing Company Ltd.
Locked Bag 3030
Strawberry Hills, New South Wales 2012, Australia
Ph: 61 2 95626666
Fax: 61 2 95626699
Publisher E-mail: medjaust@ampco.com.au
Journal featuring opinions and views about military medicine and the health. **Freq:** Semiannual. **Key Personnel:** Commander M.C. O'Connor, Asst. Ed. **ISSN:** 1443-1033. **Remarks:** Accepts advertising. **URL:** http://www.defence.gov.au/health/infocentre/journals/i-ADFHJ.htm. **Circ:** (Not Reported)

42394 ■ Australian Classic Car Monthly
Australian Classic Motoring Press 2000
PO Box 369
Strawberry Hills, New South Wales 2031, Australia
Ph: 61 293 194277
Fax: 61 293 192677
Publisher E-mail: accm@ccar.com.au
Consumer magazine covering classic automobiles. **Founded:** 1993. **Freq:** Monthly. **Subscription Rates:** US$79 individuals; US$139 two years; US$159 nonmembers 2 years; US$89 nonmembers. **Remarks:** Accepts advertising. **URL:** http://www.ccar.com.au/default.htm. **Circ:** (Not Reported)

42395 ■ Australian Health Review
Australasian Medical Publishing Company Ltd.
Locked Bag 3030
Strawberry Hills, New South Wales 2012, Australia
Ph: 61 2 95626666
Fax: 61 2 95626699
Publisher E-mail: medjaust@ampco.com.au
Journal featuring information about the health care industry. **Freq:** Quarterly. **Key Personnel:** Prof. Sandra Leggat, Editor; Andrew Wilson, Editor-in-Chief. **Subscription Rates:** $A 195 individuals print & online; $A 235 other countries print & online; 155 individuals print & online; EUR185 individuals print and online; $A 450 institutions print and online; EUR320 institutions print and online; 285 institutions print and online; $A 450 institutions print and online. **Remarks:** Accepts advertising. **URL:** http://www.aushealthreview.com.au/publications/articles/. **Circ:** (Not Reported)

42396 ■ The Medical Journal of Australia
Australasian Medical Publishing Company Ltd.
Locked Bag 3030
Strawberry Hills, New South Wales 2012, Australia
Ph: 61 2 95626666
Fax: 61 2 95626699
Publication E-mail: medjaust@ampco.com.au
Publisher E-mail: medjaust@ampco.com.au
Health publication. **Founded:** 1914. **Freq:** Biweekly. **Key Personnel:** Martin Van Der Weyden, Editor; Glenn Carter, Production Mgr. **ISSN:** 0025-729X. **Subscription Rates:** US$407 individuals print and online; US$518 other countries print and online; US$99 individuals online only. **Remarks:** Accepts classified advertising. **URL:** http://www.mja.com.au/. **Circ:** 27,459

42397 ■ FBI-FM - 94.5
PO Box 1962
Strawberry Hills, New South Wales 2012, Australia
Ph: 61 2 83322900
Fax: 61 2 83322901
E-mail: info@fbiradio.com
Format: Alternative/New Music/Progressive; Eclectic; Heavy Metal; Hip Hop; Blues. **Operating Hours:** Continuous. **Key Personnel:** James Anezis, Sales & Promotions Mgr., james@fbiradio.com; Eva Kaldor, General Mgr., evan@fbiradio.com; Meagan Loader, Sta. Dir., meagan@fbiradio.com. **URL:** http://www.fbi.org.au/.

42398 ■ Koori Radio-FM - 93.7
PO Box 966
Strawberry Hills, New South Wales 2012, Australia
Ph: 61 2 93844000
Fax: 61 2 96983990
E-mail: info@gadigal.org.au
Format: Ethnic. **Founded:** Dec. 2002. **Key Personnel:** Brad Cooke, General Mgr., brad@gadigal.org.au; Mark Ross, Production Mgr., mark@gadigal.org.au. **Wattage:** 50,000. **URL:** http://www.gadigal.org.au/.

Streaky Bay

42399 ■ Flow-FM - 99.3
PO Box 407
Kapunda, South Australia 5373, Australia
Ph: 61 8 85663151
Fax: 61 8 85662729
E-mail: mail@flowfm.com.au
Format: Adult Contemporary. **URL:** http://www.flowfm.com.au/.

Subiaco

42400 ■ Mix 94.5-FM - 94.5
450 Roberts Rd.
Subiaco, Western Australia 6008, Australia
Ph: 61 8 93820945
Fax: 61 8 93813155
Format: Adult Contemporary; Contemporary Hit Radio (CHR). **Owner:** Austereo Radio Network, GPO Box 4442, Sydney, New South Wales 2001, Australia. **Key Personnel:** Peter M. Harvie, Chm.; Michael E. Anderson, CEO; Kathryn J. Gramp, CFO/Sec. **URL:** http://www.mix.com.au/; http://www.austereo.com.au/.

42401 ■ 92.9-FM - 92.9
283 Rokeby Rd.
Subiaco, Western Australia 6008, Australia
E-mail: mail@929.com.au
Format: Top 40. **Owner:** Austereo Pty. Ltd., GPO Box 4442, Sydney, New South Wales 2001, Australia. **Key Personnel:** Peter M. Harvie, Chm. **Ad Rates:** Advertising accepted; rates available upon request. **URL:** http://www.929.com.au/; http://www.austereo.com.au/.

Sunbury

42402 ■ Macedon Ranges Leader
Leader Community Newspapers
30 Station St.
Sunbury, Victoria 3429, Australia
Ph: 61 3 97449333
Local community newspaper. **Freq:** Weekly (Tues.). **Key Personnel:** Paige Ricci, Editor, sunbury@leadernewspapers.com.au; Gusto Simandjuntak, Sales Mgr., simandjuntakg@leadernewspapers.com.au. **Remarks:** Accepts advertising. **URL:** http://macedon-ranges-leader.whereilive.com.au/. **Circ:** Tues. ‡28,456

42403 ■ Melton Leader
Leader Community Newspapers
30 Station St.
Sunbury, Victoria 3429, Australia
Ph: 61 3 97449333
Local community newspaper. **Freq:** Weekly (Tues.). **Key Personnel:** Andrew Jefferson, Editor, melton@leadernewspapers.com.au; Helen Meritt, Sales Mgr., merritth@leadernewspapers.com.au. **Remarks:** Accepts advertising. **URL:** http://www.newsspace.com.au/melton_leader_. **Circ:** Tues. ‡37,575

42404 ■ Sunbury Leader
Leader Community Newspapers
30 Station St.
Sunbury, Victoria 3429, Australia
Ph: 61 3 97449333
Local community newspaper. **Freq:** Weekly (Tues.). **Key Personnel:** Paige Picci, Editor, sunbury@leadernewspapers.com.au. **Remarks:** Accepts advertising. **URL:** http://sunbury-leader.whereilive.com.au/. **Circ:** Tues. ‡28,456

Sunshine

42405 ■ 3WRB-FM - 97.4
PO Box 217
Sunshine, Victoria 3020, Australia
Ph: 61 3 93180930
Fax: 61 3 93180866
Format: Ethnic. **Operating Hours:** Continuous. **Key Personnel:** Rod Boyd, General Mgr., rod@stereo974.com; Bob Taylor, Program Mgr., bob@stereo974.com. **URL:** http://www.stereo974.com/.

Surfers Paradise

42406 ■ Radio Metro-FM - 105.7
Tenancy C6, Level 2
Cir. on CaVIII
Surfers Paradise, Queensland 4217, Australia
Ph: 61 7 55390009
Fax: 61 7 55317826
E-mail: info@radiometro.com.au
Format: Urban Contemporary; Top 40; Blues. **URL:** http://www.radiometro.com.au/.

Surry Hills

42407 ■ AdNews
Yaffa Publishing Group
17-21 Bellevue St.
Surry Hills, New South Wales 2010, Australia
Ph: 61 292 812333
Fax: 61 292 812750
Publication E-mail: adnews@yaffa.com.au

Circulation: ★ = ABC; △ = BPA; ♦ = CAC; • = CCAB; ❑ = VAC; ⊕ = PO Statement; ‡ = Publisher's Report; Boldface figures = sworn; Light figures = estimated.

Publisher E-mail: yaffa@yaffa.com.au
Professional magazine covering marketing, media and advertising in Australia. **Freq:** Semimonthly 25/yr. **Key Personnel:** Danielle Long, Editor, phone 61 2 92138286, daniellelong@yaffa.com.au; Alison Adzievski, Advertising Mgr., phone 61 2 92138288, alisonadzievski@yaffa.com.au. **Subscription Rates:** $A 99 individuals; $A 120 individuals New Zealand; $A 135 individuals Asia; $A 180 other countries; $A 178.20 two years individual; $A 207.00 individuals 3 years; $A 100 individuals overseas. **Remarks:** Accepts advertising. **URL:** http://www.adnews.com.au. **Ad Rates:** 4C: $A 6,290. **Circ:** (Not Reported)

42408 ■ Australasian Paint & Panel
Yaffa Publishing Group
17-21 Bellevue St.
Surry Hills, New South Wales 2010, Australia
Ph: 61 292 812333
Fax: 61 292 812750
Publisher E-mail: yaffa@yaffa.com.au
Magazine featuring equipment for motor body repair. **Founded:** 1982. **Freq:** Bimonthly. **Key Personnel:** Tim Byrne, Editor, timbyrne@yaffa.com.au; Dan Lal, Advertising Production, danlal@yaffa.com.au. **Subscription Rates:** US$171.60 individuals 18 issues (Australia); US$128.70 individuals 12 issues (Australia); US$71.50 individuals Australia; US$85 individuals New Zealand; US$100 individuals Asia; US$130 other countries. **Remarks:** Accepts advertising. **URL:** http://www.yaffa.com.au/btob/app.html; http://www.paintandpanel.com.au/. **Ad Rates:** BW: $A 2,910, 4C: $A 4,170. **Circ:** ‡6,548

42409 ■ Australasian Sporting Shooter
Yaffa Publishing Group
17-21 Bellevue St.
Surry Hills, New South Wales 2010, Australia
Ph: 61 292 812333
Fax: 61 292 812750
Publisher E-mail: yaffa@yaffa.com.au
Hunting magazine featuring tips and techniques, equipment reviews, and species guides. **Founded:** 1961. **Freq:** Monthly. **Print Method:** Sheetfed offset. **Trim Size:** 8 x 10 3/4. **Cols./Page:** 2 and 3. **Col. Width:** 20 and 13 picas. **Key Personnel:** Marcus O'Dean, Editor, marcusodean@yaffa.com.au; Tony Pizzata, National Sales Mgr., tonypizzata@yaffa.com.au. **ISSN:** 0738-713X. **Subscription Rates:** US$83.60 individuals 13 issues; US$150.48 individuals 26 issues; US$200.64 individuals 36 issues; US$96 individuals New Zealand; US$110 individuals Asia; US$152 other countries. **Remarks:** Accepts advertising. **URL:** http://www.yaffa.com.au/cmag/sps.html. **Ad Rates:** BW: $A 2,580, 4C: $A 3,280. **Circ:** ★13,542

42410 ■ Australian Creative
Yaffa Publishing Group
17-21 Bellevue St.
Surry Hills, New South Wales 2010, Australia
Ph: 61 292 812333
Fax: 61 292 812750
Publisher E-mail: yaffa@yaffa.com.au
Magazine covering advertising, design, print and production. **Founded:** 1974. **Freq:** Bimonthly. **Print Method:** Web offset. **Trim Size:** 8 1/2 x 10 7/8. **Cols./Page:** 2. **Col. Width:** 17 picas. **Col. Depth:** 133 agate lines. **Key Personnel:** Larissa Meikle, Editor, larissameikle@yaffa.com.au; Anabel Gomes, Advertising Mgr., anabelgomes@yaffa.com.au; Renee Robertson, Advertising Production Mgr., reneerobertson@yaffa.com.au. **ISSN:** 0749-5056. **Subscription Rates:** US$38.50 individuals Australia; US$69.30 two years Australia; US$92.40 individuals 3 years in Australia; US$45 individuals New Zealand; US$50 individuals Asia; US$70 other countries. **Remarks:** Accepts advertising. **URL:** http://www.yaffa.com.au/btob/acr.html. **Ad Rates:** 4C: $A 3,570. **Circ:** ‡3,007

42411 ■ Australian Defence Magazine
Yaffa Publishing Group
17-21 Bellevue St.
Surry Hills, New South Wales 2010, Australia
Ph: 61 292 812333
Fax: 61 292 812750
Publisher E-mail: yaffa@yaffa.com.au
Defense business magazine covering analysis of major projects and equipment acquisitions, as well as commentary on policy and future directions for the Australian Defense Force, the New Zealand Defense Forces and regional defense issues. **Founded:** 1993. **Freq:** Monthly except December and January. **Print Method:** Web offset. **Trim Size:** 8 x 10 3/4. **Cols./Page:** 3. **Col. Width:** 2 1/4 inches. **Col. Depth:** 9 3/8 inches. **Key Personnel:** Judy Hinz, Managing Editor, phone 61 7 33486966, judyhinz@yaffa.com.au; David Jones, Advertising & Features Mgr., davidjones@yaffa.com.au. **ISSN:** 1047-0549. **Subscription Rates:** US$148.50 individuals Australia; US$350.40 individuals 3 years in Australia; US$267.30 two years Australia; US$175 individuals New Zealand; US$200 individuals Asia; US$270 other countries. **Remarks:** Accepts advertising. **URL:** http://www.yaffa.com.au/btob/adm.html; http://www.australiandefence.com.au/. **Ad Rates:** BW: $A 2,890, 4C: $A 3,450. **Circ:** ★3,985

42412 ■ Australian Flying
Yaffa Publishing Group
17-21 Bellevue St.
Surry Hills, New South Wales 2010, Australia
Ph: 61 292 812333
Fax: 61 292 812750
Publisher E-mail: yaffa@yaffa.com.au
Magazine covering flying technologies, accessories and techniques, and news. **Founded:** 1963. **Freq:** Bimonthly. **Print Method:** Offset. **Trim Size:** 8 3/8 x 10 13/16. **Cols./Page:** 3. **Col. Width:** 27 nonpareils. **Col. Depth:** 140 agate lines. **Key Personnel:** Justin Gray, Editor, justingrey@yaffa.com.au; John Cassidy, National Advertising Mgr., johncassidy@yaffa.com.au. **ISSN:** 0033-9202. **Subscription Rates:** US$40.70 individuals Australia; US$50 individuals New Zealand; US$97.68 individuals 3 years in Australia; US$73.26 two years Australia; US$55 individuals Asia; US$75 other countries. **Remarks:** Accepts advertising. **URL:** http://www.yaffa.com.au/cmag/fly.html; http://www.ausflying.com.au/. **Ad Rates:** BW: $A 2,350, 4C: $A 3,300. **Circ:** ★7,377

42413 ■ Australian Journal of Forensic Sciences
Australian Academy of Forensic Sciences
207 Albion St.
Surry Hills, New South Wales 2010, Australia
Ph: 61 2 83565868
Publisher E-mail: jim.robertson@afp.gov.au
Law periodical. **Founded:** 1968. **Freq:** Semiannual. **Key Personnel:** James Robertson, PSM, Editor. **ISSN:** 0045-0618. **Subscription Rates:** US$115 individuals; US$270 institutions online only; US$284 institutions print and online. **Remarks:** Accepts advertising. **URL:** http://www.tandf.co.uk/journals/journal.asp?issn=0045-0618&linktype=1. **Circ:** Paid 498

42414 ■ The Australian Marxist Review
Communist Party of Australia
74 Buckingham St.
Surry Hills, New South Wales 2010, Australia
Ph: 61 2 96998844
Fax: 61 2 96999833
Publisher E-mail: president@cpa.org.au
Theoretical journal of the Communist Party of Australia. **Subtitle:** Journal of the Communist Party of Australia. **Freq:** Quarterly. **Key Personnel:** Eddie Clynes, Editor, eddie@idx.com.au. **Subscription Rates:** $A 25 individuals. **URL:** http://www.cpa.org.au/amr/index.html.

42415 ■ Australian National Security Magazine
Yaffa Publishing Group
17-21 Bellevue St.
Surry Hills, New South Wales 2010, Australia
Ph: 61 292 812333
Fax: 61 292 812750
Publisher E-mail: yaffa@yaffa.com.au
Magazine dedicated to the national security industry in Australia and the government policies driving this sector. **Founded:** 2006. **Freq:** Monthly 11/yr (Dec/Jan combined). **Key Personnel:** Leigh Funston, Editor, leighfunston@yaffa.com.au; Judy Hinz, Publisher, judyhinz@yaffa.com.au. **Subscription Rates:** US$82.50 individuals for Australia; US$148.50 two years Australia; US$198 individuals 3 years for Australia; US$96 individuals for New Zealand; US$110 individuals for Asia; US$150 other countries. **Remarks:** Accepts advertising. **URL:** http://www.nationalsecuritymagazine.com.au/about.htm. **Ad Rates:** 4C: $A 2,900, SAU: $A 2,490. **Circ:** ‡3,000

42416 ■ Australian Photography
Yaffa Publishing Group
17-21 Bellevue St.
Surry Hills, New South Wales 2010, Australia
Ph: 61 292 812333
Fax: 61 292 812750
Publisher E-mail: yaffa@yaffa.com.au
Photography magazine. **Founded:** 1950. **Freq:** Monthly. **Key Personnel:** Robert Keeley, Editor, robertkeeley@yaffa.com.au; Kate Radcliffe, National Advisory Mgr., kateradcliffe@yaffa.com.au. **Subscription Rates:** US$184.80 individuals 3 years in Australia; US$138.60 two years Australia; US$77 individuals Australia; US$90 individuals New Zealand; US$105 individuals Asia; US$140 other countries. **Remarks:** Accepts advertising. **URL:** http://www.yaffa.com.au/cmag/aph.html. **Ad Rates:** BW: $A 2,380, 4C: $A 3,160. **Circ:** ★9,099

42417 ■ Australian Power Boat
Yaffa Publishing Group
17-21 Bellevue St.
Surry Hills, New South Wales 2010, Australia
Ph: 61 292 812333
Fax: 61 292 812750
Publisher E-mail: yaffa@yaffa.com.au
Boating magazine covering power cruisers, water skiers and ski boats, go-fast performance boats and associated lifestyle products. **Founded:** 1976. **Freq:** Bimonthly. **Print Method:** Offset. **Cols./Page:** 5. **Col. Width:** 26 nonpareils. **Col. Depth:** 224 agate lines. **Key Personnel:** Mick Fletoridis, Editor, mickfletoridis@yaffa.com.au; Guy Yaffa, National Advertising Mgr., guyyaffa@yaffa.com.au. **Subscription Rates:** US$38.50 individuals within Australia; US$45 individuals New Zealand; US$75 other countries; US$55 individuals Asia; US$92.40 individuals 3 years within Australia; US$69.30 individuals 2 years within Australia. **Remarks:** Accepts advertising. **URL:** http://www.yaffa.com.au/cmag/pbt.html. **Ad Rates:** BW: $A 2,190, 4C: $A 2,790. **Circ:** ‡3,000

42418 ■ Australian Sailing
Yaffa Publishing Group
17-21 Bellevue St.
Surry Hills, New South Wales 2010, Australia
Ph: 61 292 812333
Fax: 61 292 812750
Publisher E-mail: yaffa@yaffa.com.au
Sailing magazine covering instructional and practical articles. Also covers Australian yachting events and overseas races. **Founded:** 1976. **Freq:** 8/yr. **Print Method:** Offset. **Trim Size:** 11 3/8 x 17. **Cols./Page:** 5. **Col. Width:** 1 15/16 inches. **Col. Depth:** 16 inches. **Key Personnel:** Roger McMillan, Editor, rogermcmillan@yaffa.com.au; Peter Rendle, National Advisory Mgr., peterrendle@yaffa.com.au. **Subscription Rates:** US$59.40 individuals Australia; US$142.56 individuals 3 years within Australia; US$106.92 two years within Australia; US$68 individuals New Zealand; US$79 individuals Asia; US$107 other countries. **Remarks:** Accepts advertising. **URL:** http://www.yaffa.com.au/cmag/asl.html. **Ad Rates:** 4C: $A 2,560. **Circ:** ★4,416

42419 ■ Australian Yachting
Yaffa Publishing Group
17-21 Bellevue St.
Surry Hills, New South Wales 2010, Australia
Ph: 61 292 812333
Fax: 61 292 812750
Publisher E-mail: yaffa@yaffa.com.au
Magazine covering yachts over 20 feet. Also includes monohulls, multihulls, inshore and offshore racing, coastal cruising and passage making. **Founded:** 1983. **Freq:** Monthly. **Print Method:** Offset. **Trim Size:** 5 1/2 x 8 1/2. **Cols./Page:** 1. **Col. Width:** 51 nonpareils. **Col. Depth:** 93 agate lines. **Key Personnel:** Barry Henson, Editor, barryhenson@yaffa.com.au; Peter Rendle, National Advertising Mgr., peterrendle@yaffa.com.au. **ISSN:** 0043-4221. **Subscription Rates:** US$44 individuals Australia; US$55 individuals New Zealand; US$70 individuals Asia; US$90 other countries; US$79.20 two years Australia; US$105.60 individuals 3 years within Australia. **Remarks:** Accepts advertising. **URL:** http://www.yaffa.com.au/cmag/yac.html. **Ad Rates:** 4C: $A 2,560. **Circ:** ‡2,000

42420 ■ Aviation Business Magazine
Yaffa Publishing Group
17-21 Bellevue St.
Surry Hills, New South Wales 2010, Australia
Ph: 61 292 812333
Fax: 61 292 812750

Publisher E-mail: yaffa@yaffa.com.au
Magazine covering the aviation and aerospace industry in Australia and Asia Pacific region. **Founded:** 1918. **Freq:** Bimonthly. **Print Method:** Offset. **Cols./Page:** 6. **Col. Width:** 25 nonpareils. **Col. Depth:** 294 agate lines. **Key Personnel:** Doug Nancarrow, Editor, phone 61 2 92138267, dougnancarrow@yaffa.com.au. **Subscription Rates:** US$182.16 individuals 21 issues within Australia; US$136.62 individuals 14 issues within Australia; US$75.90 individuals within Australia; US$85 individuals New Zealand; US$100 individuals Asia; US$130 other countries. **Remarks:** Accepts advertising. **URL:** http://www.yaffa.com.au/btob/air.html. **Ad Rates:** BW: $A 1,480, 4C: $A 3,350. **Circ:** ★3,098

42421 ■ Bacon Busters
Yaffa Publishing Group
17-21 Bellevue St.
Surry Hills, New South Wales 2010, Australia
Ph: 61 292 812333
Fax: 61 292 812750
Publisher E-mail: yaffa@yaffa.com.au
Magazine dedicated to pig hunting. Also covers readers short stories, how-to articles, pig hunting features, technical advice, pig dog profiles and collection of pig hunting photos. **Founded:** 1995. **Freq:** Quarterly. **Print Method:** Offset. **Cols./Page:** 6. **Col. Width:** 18 nonpareils. **Col. Depth:** 294 agate lines. **Key Personnel:** Clint Magro, Editor, editor@baconbusters.com.au; Tony Pizzata, National Sales Mgr., tonypizzata@yaffa.com.au. **Subscription Rates:** US$29.70 individuals within Australia; US$71.28 individuals 3 years within Australia; US$53.46 two years within Australia; US$37 individuals New Zealand; US$42 individuals Asia; US$55 other countries. **Remarks:** Accepts advertising. **URL:** http://www.yaffa.com.au/cmag/bb.html. **Ad Rates:** 4C: US$3,120. **Circ:** ‡57,000

42422 ■ Capture
Yaffa Publishing Group
17-21 Bellevue St.
Surry Hills, New South Wales 2010, Australia
Ph: 61 292 812333
Fax: 61 292 812750
Publisher E-mail: yaffa@yaffa.com.au
Photography magazine covering marketing, training, pricing, financial and rights management issues. **Founded:** 1963. **Freq:** Bimonthly. **Print Method:** Offset. **Trim Size:** 14 x 21 3/4. **Cols./Page:** 6. **Col. Width:** 24 nonpareils. **Col. Depth:** 294 agate lines. **Key Personnel:** Marc Gafen, Editor, marcgafen@yaffa.com.au; Anabel Gomes, Advertising Mgr., anabelgomes@yaffa.com.au. **Subscription Rates:** US$38.50 individuals within Australia; US$69.30 two years within Australia; US$92.40 individuals within Australia 3 years; US$45 individuals New Zealand; US$55 individuals Asia; US$75 other countries. **Remarks:** Accepts advertising. **URL:** http://www.yaffa.com.au/btob/cph.html. **Ad Rates:** BW: $A 1,940, 4C: $A 2,580. **Circ:** ★2,826

42423 ■ Climate Control News (CCN)
Yaffa Publishing Group
17-21 Bellevue St.
Surry Hills, New South Wales 2010, Australia
Ph: 61 292 812333
Fax: 61 292 812750
Publisher E-mail: yaffa@yaffa.com.au
Magazine covering the field of HVAC/R. **Founded:** 2003. **Freq:** Monthly. **Print Method:** Web. **Trim Size:** 8 1/2 x 11. **Cols./Page:** 3. **Col. Width:** 2 5/16 inches. **Col. Depth:** 9 3/4 inches. **Key Personnel:** Phillip Ross, Editor, philross@yaffa.com.au; Nick Britton-Johnson, National Advertising Mgr., nickbrittonjohnson@yaffa.com.au. **USPS:** 097-770. **Subscription Rates:** $A 88 individuals Australia; US$211.20 individuals 3 years within Australia; US$158.40 two years Australia; US$120 individuals Asia; US$160 other countries. **Remarks:** Accepts advertising. **URL:** http://www.yaffa.com.au/btob/ccn.html. **Ad Rates:** BW: $A 2,860, 4C: $A 4,260. **Circ:** ★6,394

42424 ■ Cruising Helmsman
Yaffa Publishing Group
17-21 Bellevue St.
Surry Hills, New South Wales 2010, Australia
Ph: 61 292 812333
Fax: 61 292 812750

Publisher E-mail: yaffa@yaffa.com.au
Sailing magazine. **Founded:** 1982. **Freq:** Monthly. **Print Method:** Offset. **Cols./Page:** 6. **Col. Width:** 12 picas. **Col. Depth:** 21 inches. **Key Personnel:** Caroline Strainig, Editor, carolinestrainig@yaffa.com.au; Peter Rendle, National Advertising Mgr., peterrendle@yaffa.com.au. **USPS:** 419-700. **Subscription Rates:** US$6.95 individuals cover price; US$82.50 individuals Australian delivery; US$148.50 two years Australian delivery; US$95 individuals New Zealand delivery; US$160 other countries; US$110 individuals Asia; US$198 individuals 3 years, Australian delivery. **Remarks:** Accepts advertising. **URL:** http://www.yaffa.com.au/cmag/crh.html. **Ad Rates:** 4C: $A 3,260. **Circ:** ★7,771

42425 ■ Dance Australia
Yaffa Publishing Group
17-21 Bellevue St.
Surry Hills, New South Wales 2010, Australia
Ph: 61 292 812333
Fax: 61 292 812750
Publisher E-mail: yaffa@yaffa.com.au
Magazine devoted to dance, both as artistic expression and recreational activity. Also covers classical ballet, modern dance, entertainment dance and ballroom, with a special section for ballet schools. **Founded:** 1980. **Freq:** Bimonthly. **Print Method:** Offset. **Cols./Page:** 6. **Col. Width:** 12 picas. **Col. Depth:** 21 inches. **Key Personnel:** Karen Van Ulzen, Editor, dance@yaffa.com.au; Carol Roselli, Advertising Mgr., carolroselli@yaffa.com.au. **Subscription Rates:** US$97.68 individuals 3 years for Australia; US$73.26 two years for Australia; US$40.70 individuals for Australia; US$50 individuals for New Zealand; US$55 individuals for Asia; US$75 other countries. **Remarks:** Accepts advertising. **URL:** http://www.yaffa.com.au/cmag/dan.html. **Ad Rates:** BW: $A 2,570, 4C: $A 3,880. **Circ:** ★4,348

42426 ■ Digital Photography and Design
Yaffa Publishing Group
17-21 Bellevue St.
Surry Hills, New South Wales 2010, Australia
Ph: 61 292 812333
Fax: 61 292 812750
Publisher E-mail: yaffa@yaffa.com.au
Digital photography magazine. **Founded:** 1995. **Freq:** Bimonthly. **Print Method:** Offset. **Trim Size:** 8 1/8 x 10 7/8. **Cols./Page:** 5. **Key Personnel:** James Ostinga, Editor, jamesostinga@yaffa.com.au; Kate Radcliffe, National Advertising Mgr. **ISSN:** 0893-5238. **Subscription Rates:** US$49.50 individuals for Australian; US$60 individuals for New Zealand; US$70 individuals for Asia; US$89.10 two years for Australia; US$118.80 individuals 3 years, Australian. **Remarks:** Accepts advertising. **URL:** http://www.yaffa.com.au/cmag/dig.html. **Ad Rates:** BW: $A 2,070, 4C: $A 2,760. **Circ:** ★4,593

42427 ■ Donna Hay Magazine
83-97 Kippax St., Level 5
Surry Hills, New South Wales 2010, Australia
Ph: 61 2 92826500
Fax: 61 2 92111541
Publisher E-mail: enquiries@donnahay.com.au
Magazine containing simple but special recipe and entertaining ideas. **Subtitle:** Special Made Simple. **Freq:** Bimonthly. **Key Personnel:** Rebecca Carrick, National Advertising Mgr., phone 61 2 92826533; Sass Dickie, Advertising Mgr., phone 61 3 92921951; Melissa Fernley, NSW Advertising Mgr., phone 61 2 92826515. **Subscription Rates:** US$40 individuals. **Remarks:** Accepts advertising. **URL:** http://www.donnahay.com.au. **Circ:** ★89,192

42428 ■ Drug and Alcohol Review
Taylor & Francis Ltd.
The Langton Centre
591 S Dowling St.
Surry Hills, New South Wales 2010, Australia
Publication E-mail: dar@apsad.org.au
International meeting ground for the views, expertise and experience of all those involved in the study of treatment of alcohol, tobacco and drug problems, particularly encouraging the submission of papers which have a harm reduction perspective. **Freq:** Bimonthly. **Key Personnel:** Robin Room, Editor-in-Chief; Alison Ritter, Exec. Ed.; Robyn Richmond, Dep. Ed. **ISSN:** 0959-5236. **Subscription Rates:** US$2,417 institutions print and online; US$2,102 individuals print only; 1,345 institu-

tions print and online; $A 2,358 institutions print and online; 1,169 institutions online; US$2,102 institutions online; $A 2,050 institutions online; 375 individuals print & online; $A 762 individuals print & online. **Remarks:** Accepts advertising. **URL:** http://www.wiley.com/bw/editors.asp?ref=0959-5236&site=1. **Circ:** (Not Reported)

42429 ■ Farm Policy Journal
Australian Farm Institute Ltd.
Ste. 73, 61 Marlborough St.
Surry Hills, New South Wales 2010, Australia
Ph: 61 2 96901388
Fax: 61 2 96997270
Publisher E-mail: info@farminstitute.org.au
Journal addressing a range of policy issues that impact on agriculture. **Freq:** Quarterly. **ISSN:** 1449-2210. **Subscription Rates:** $A 250 individuals membership; $A 120 students membership; $A 120 individuals electronic copy; $A 150 individuals hard copy. **Remarks:** Accepts advertising. **URL:** http://www.farminstitute.org.au/publications/farm-policy-journal.html. **Circ:** (Not Reported)

42430 ■ Flightpath
Yaffa Publishing Group
17-21 Bellevue St.
Surry Hills, New South Wales 2010, Australia
Ph: 61 292 812333
Fax: 61 292 812750
Publisher E-mail: yaffa@yaffa.com.au
Magazine focusing on war birds, modern military aircrafts, and notable historical stories. **Founded:** 1989. **Freq:** Quarterly. **Print Method:** Offset. **Cols./Page:** 5. **Col. Width:** 2 1/16 inches. **Key Personnel:** Rob Fox, Editor, mail@robfoxphotography.com; John Cassidy, National Advisory Mgr., johncassidy@yaffa.com.au. **ISSN:** 0745-6255. **Subscription Rates:** US$33 individuals within Australia; US$79.20 individuals 3 years within Australia; US$59.40 two years within Australia; US$40 individuals New Zealand; US$50 individuals Asia; US$60 other countries. **Remarks:** Accepts advertising. **URL:** http://www.yaffa.com.au/cmag/fph.html. **Ad Rates:** BW: $A 1,720, 4C: $A 2,320. **Circ:** ‡15,500

42431 ■ Food & Drink Business
Yaffa Publishing Group
17-21 Bellevue St.
Surry Hills, New South Wales 2010, Australia
Ph: 61 292 812333
Fax: 61 292 812750
Publisher E-mail: yaffa@yaffa.com.au
Magazine covering food management news. Also covers features, new products and industry trends on food, beverage and ingredients sectors. **Founded:** 1975. **Freq:** Monthly. **Print Method:** Offset. **Trim Size:** 8 1/2 x 11. **Cols./Page:** 3 and 2. **Col. Width:** 28 and 40 nonpareils. **Col. Depth:** 140 agate lines. **Key Personnel:** Lindy Hughson, Managing Editor, lindyhughson@yaffa.com.au; Carol Ewing, National Sales Mgr. Mgr., carolewing@yaffa.com.au. **USPS:** 089-631. **Subscription Rates:** US$211.20 individuals 3 years in Australia; US$158.40 two years Australia; US$88 individuals Australia; US$105 individuals New Zealand; US$120 individuals Asia; US$160 other countries. **Remarks:** Accepts advertising. **URL:** http://www.yaffa.com.au/btob/fmn.html. **Ad Rates:** BW: $A 2,920, 4C: $A 4,030. **Circ:** ★5,294

42432 ■ FoodService News
Yaffa Publishing Group
17-21 Bellevue St.
Surry Hills, New South Wales 2010, Australia
Ph: 61 292 812333
Fax: 61 292 812750
Publisher E-mail: yaffa@yaffa.com.au
Magazine focusing on the food and beverage industry. **Founded:** 1984. **Freq:** Monthly. **Print Method:** Offset. **Trim Size:** 8 3/8 x 10 7/8. **Cols./Page:** 3. **Col. Width:** 2 1/6 inches. **Col. Depth:** 10 inches. **Key Personnel:** Anthony Huckstep, Editor, anthonyhuckstep@yaffa.com.au; Adam Cosgrove, National Advertising Mgr., adamcosgrove@yaffa.com.au; Helen Davies, Publisher, helendavies@yaffa.com.au. **ISSN:** 0043-0161. **Subscription Rates:** US$88 individuals Australia; US$211.20 individuals 3 years in Australia; US$158.40 two years Australia; US$105 individuals New Zealand; US$120 individuals Asia; US$160 other countries. **Remarks:** Accepts advertising. **URL:** http://www.yaffa.com.

Circulation: ★ = ABC; △ = BPA; ♦ = CAC; • = CCAB; ❑ = VAC; ⊕ = PO Statement; ‡ = Publisher's Report; Boldface figures = sworn; Light figures = estimated.

Gale Directory of Publications & Broadcast Media/147th Ed.

4749

au/btob/fsn.html. **Ad Rates:** BW: $A 4,550, 4C: $A 5,380. **Circ:** 12,871

42433 ■ Greetings & Gifts
Yaffa Publishing Group
17-21 Bellevue St.
Surry Hills, New South Wales 2010, Australia
Ph: 61 292 812333
Fax: 61 292 812750
Publisher E-mail: yaffa@yaffa.com.au
Magazine covering the field of gifts and greetings including industry trends and developments, product features, and supplier profiles. **Founded:** 1991. **Freq:** Bimonthly. **Print Method:** Offset. **Trim Size:** 13 x 21. **Cols./Page:** 6. **Col. Width:** 25 nonpareils. **Col. Depth:** 294 agate lines. **Key Personnel:** Alison Leader, Editor, alisonleader@yaffa.com.au; Michael Christofis, National Advertising Mgr., michaelchristofis@yaffa.com.au?. **Subscription Rates:** US$55 individuals Australia; US$132 individuals 3 years within Australia; US$99 two years Australia; US$70 individuals New Zealand; US$80 individuals Asia; US$100 other countries. **Remarks:** Accepts advertising. **URL:** http://www.yaffa.com.au/btob/gag.html. **Ad Rates:** BW: $A 1,970, 4C: $A 2,730. **Circ:** ‡5,300

42434 ■ Hospital & Agedcare
Yaffa Publishing Group
17-21 Bellevue St.
Surry Hills, New South Wales 2010, Australia
Ph: 61 292 812333
Fax: 61 292 812750
Publisher E-mail: yaffa@yaffa.com.au
Healthcare magazine covering industry issues, technical developments, product trends and government initiatives. **Founded:** 1932. **Freq:** Monthly. **Print Method:** Offset. **Trim Size:** 8 1/4 x 10 7/8. **Cols./Page:** 3. **Col. Width:** 27 nonpareils. **Col. Depth:** 140 agate lines. **Key Personnel:** Kate McDonald, Editor, hospital@yaffa.com.au; Roslyn Richards, National Advertising Mgr., roslynrichards@yaffa.com.au. **ISSN:** 0160-4317. **Subscription Rates:** US$88 individuals Australia; US$211.20 individuals 3 years (Australia); US$158.40 two years Australia; US$105 individuals New Zealand; US$120 individuals Asia; US$160 other countries. **Remarks:** Accepts advertising. **URL:** http://www.yaffa.com.au/btob/hah.html. **Formerly:** Hospital & Healthcare. **Ad Rates:** BW: $A 3,140, 4C: $A 4,310. **Circ:** 7,523

42435 ■ Marine Business
Yaffa Publishing Group
17-21 Bellevue St.
Surry Hills, New South Wales 2010, Australia
Ph: 61 292 812333
Fax: 61 292 812750
Publisher E-mail: yaffa@yaffa.com.au
Marine business magazine covering news and industry profiles in Australia. **Founded:** 1989. **Freq:** Monthly. **Print Method:** Offset. **Trim Size:** 8 1/4 x 10 7/8. **Cols./Page:** 3. **Col. Width:** 27 nonpareils. **Col. Depth:** 140 agate lines. **Key Personnel:** Scott Thomas, Editor, scottthomas@yaffa.com.au; Mike Ford, National Advertising Mgr., mikeford@yaffa.com.au. **ISSN:** 0033-6866. **Subscription Rates:** $A 88 individuals within Australia; US$158.40 two years Australia; US$211.20 individuals 3 years (Australia); US$105 individuals New Zealand; US$120 individuals Asia; US$160 other countries. **Remarks:** Accepts advertising. **URL:** http://www.yaffa.com.au/btob/min.html; http://www.marinebusiness.com.au/. **Ad Rates:** BW: $A 1,720, 4C: $A 1,990. **Circ:** 4,149

42436 ■ Nature & Health
Yaffa Publishing Group
17-21 Bellevue St.
Surry Hills, New South Wales 2010, Australia
Ph: 61 292 812333
Fax: 61 292 812750
Publisher E-mail: yaffa@yaffa.com.au
Lifestyle magazine targeting educated and responsive people who are interested in maintaining a naturally healthy lifestyle. **Founded:** 1979. **Freq:** Bimonthly. **Print Method:** Offset. **Trim Size:** 8 3/8 x 10 7/8. **Cols./Page:** 3 and 2. **Col. Width:** 13 and 20 picas. **Col. Depth:** 140 agate lines. **Key Personnel:** Pamela Allardice, Editor, pamelaallardice@yaffa.com.au; Alex Dedick, National Advertising Mgr., alexdedich@yaffa.com.au. **ISSN:** 0197-2510. **Subscription Rates:** US$48.40 individuals Australia; US$87.12 two years Australia; US$116.16 individuals 3 years (Australia); US$55 individuals New

Zealand; US$66 individuals Asia; US$88 other countries. **Remarks:** Accepts advertising. **URL:** http://www.yaffa.com.au/cmag/nah.html. **Ad Rates:** BW: $A 2,700, 4C: $A 4,310. **Circ:** ‡30,000

42437 ■ Packaging News
Yaffa Publishing Group
17-21 Bellevue St.
Surry Hills, New South Wales 2010, Australia
Ph: 61 292 812333
Fax: 61 292 812750
Publisher E-mail: yaffa@yaffa.com.au
Magazine covering information on packaging including regular columns of packaging law, marketing, environmental issues, new technology and materials handling. **Founded:** 1961. **Freq:** Monthly. **Print Method:** Offset. **Trim Size:** 7 7/8 x 10 7/8. **Cols./Page:** 3. **Col. Width:** 13 picas. **Col. Depth:** 9 1/2 inches. **Key Personnel:** Lindy Hughson, Editor, lindyhughson@yaffa.com.au. **ISSN:** 1094-0529. **Subscription Rates:** US$88 individuals Australia; US$105 individuals New Zealand; US$160 other countries; US$120 individuals Asia; US$211.20 individuals 3 years, Australia; US$158.40 two years Australia. **Remarks:** Accepts advertising. **URL:** http://www.yaffa.cqm.au/btob/pkn.html. **Ad Rates:** BW: $A 3,120, 4C: $A 4,340. **Circ:** 4,659

42438 ■ Ragtrader
Yaffa Publishing Group
17-21 Bellevue St.
Surry Hills, New South Wales 2010, Australia
Ph: 61 292 812333
Fax: 61 292 812750
Publisher E-mail: yaffa@yaffa.com.au
Fashion trade magazine for Australian industry. **Founded:** 1972. **Freq:** Fortnightly. **Key Personnel:** Assia Benmedjdoub, Editor, assia@yaffa.com.au; Sarah Shepherd, National Advisory Mgr., sarahshepherd@yaffa.com.au; Michael Christofis, Online Sales Mgr., michaelchristofis@yaffa.com.au. **Subscription Rates:** US$143 individuals Australia; US$165 individuals New Zealand; US$260 other countries; US$195 individuals Asia; US$343.20 individuals 3 years in Australia; US$257.40 two years Australia. **Remarks:** Accepts advertising. **URL:** http://www.yaffa.com.au/btob/rag.html. **Ad Rates:** BW: $A 3,750, 4C: $A 4,940. **Circ:** ‡6,000

42439 ■ Sporting Shooter
Yaffa Publishing Group
17-21 Bellevue St.
Surry Hills, New South Wales 2010, Australia
Ph: 61 292 812333
Fax: 61 292 812750
Publisher E-mail: yaffa@yaffa.com.au
Australian hunting magazine, covering tips and techniques, equipment reviews, and species guides. **Founded:** 1961. **Freq:** Monthly. **Print Method:** Offset. **Cols./Page:** 6. **Col. Width:** 21 nonpareils. **Col. Depth:** 126 agate lines. **Key Personnel:** Marcus O'Dean, Editor, marcusodean@yaffa.com.au; Tony Pizzata, National Sales Mgr., tonypizzata@yaffa.com.au. **Subscription Rates:** US$83.60 individuals Australia; US$150.48 two years Australia; US$200.64 individuals 3 years Australia; US$96 individuals New Zealand; US$110 individuals Asia; US$152 other countries. **Remarks:** Accepts advertising. **URL:** http://www.yaffa.com.au/cmag/sps.html. **Ad Rates:** BW: $A 2,580, 4C: $A 3,280. **Circ:** ‡13,542

42440 ■ Stationery News
Yaffa Publishing Group
17-21 Bellevue St.
Surry Hills, New South Wales 2010, Australia
Ph: 61 292 812333
Fax: 61 292 812750
Publisher E-mail: yaffa@yaffa.com.au
Magazine covering Australian stationery and office product reseller chain, including office product dealers, stationery and office supply wholesalers, stationery retailers, superstores and mail order houses, newsagents throughout Australia, retail chain and department store buyers, manufacturers, importers, and agents. **Founded:** 1989. **Freq:** Monthly. **Print Method:** Offset. Uses mats. **Trim Size:** 11 x 17. **Cols./Page:** 7. **Col. Width:** 185 inches. **Col. Depth:** 256 inches. **Key Personnel:** Dylan KcKinn, Editor, dylanmckinn@yaffa.com.au; Paula Firmin, National Advisory Mgr., paulafirmin@yaffa.com.au. **Subscription Rates:** US$63.80 individuals Australia; US$153.12 individuals 3 years in

Australia; US$114.84 two years Australia; US$75 individuals New Zealand; US$85 individuals Asia; US$115 other countries. **Remarks:** Accepts advertising. **URL:** http://www.yaffa.com.au/btob/stn.html. **Ad Rates:** GLR: $A 2, BW: $A 2,600, 4C: $A 3,620, PCI: $A 12. **Circ:** Paid ‡5,000

42441 ■ Toy & Hobby Retailer
Yaffa Publishing Group
17-21 Bellevue St.
Surry Hills, New South Wales 2010, Australia
Ph: 61 292 812333
Fax: 61 292 812750
Publisher E-mail: yaffa@yaffa.com.au
Toy and hobby trade magazine targeting retailers in Australia. **Founded:** 1937. **Freq:** Monthly. **Print Method:** Offset. **Trim Size:** 11 3/8 x 13 3/4. **Cols./Page:** 6. **Col. Width:** 11.6 picas. **Col. Depth:** 294 agate lines. **Key Personnel:** Stuart Loch, Editor, stuartloch@yaffa.com.au; Max Yaffa, National Advertising Mgr., maxyaffa@yaffa.com.au. **Subscription Rates:** US$88 individuals Australian delivery; US$211.20 individuals 3 years (Australian delivery); US$158.40 two years Australian delivery; US$105 individuals New Zealand delivery; US$120 individuals Asian delivery; US$160 other countries. **Remarks:** Accepts advertising. **URL:** http://www.yaffa.com.au/client/thr.html. **Ad Rates:** BW: $A 1,990, 4C: $A 2,970. **Circ:** 2,662

Sutherland

42442 ■ 2SSR-FM - 99.7
PO Box 997
Sutherland, New South Wales 1499, Australia
Ph: 61 2 95451800
Fax: 61 2 95451300
E-mail: info@2ssr.com.au
Format: Ethnic. **Founded:** 1984. **Operating Hours:** 6a.m.-7p.m. Daily. **URL:** http://www.2ssr.com.au.

Swan Hill

42443 ■ SMART-FM - 99.1
PO Box 998
Swan Hill, Victoria 3585, Australia
Ph: 61 3 50325991
Fax: 61 3 50325990
E-mail: request@smartfm.org.au
Format: Public Radio; Eclectic. **Operating Hours:** Continuous. **URL:** http://www.smartfm.org.au.

Sydney

42444 ■ Accounting, Auditing & Accountability Journal
Emerald Group Publishing Ltd.
c/o Prof. James E. Guthrie, Ed.
The University of Sydney, Faculty of Economics & Business
Economics & Business Bldg., (H69)
cor. Codrington & Rose Sts.
Sydney, New South Wales 2006, Australia
Publisher E-mail: emerald@emeraldinsight.com
Journal providing a forum for the publication of high quality manuscripts concerning the interaction between accounting/auditing and their socio-economic and political environments and is a research resource for academics working to advance current accounting theory and practice through interdisciplinary, contextual and critical inquiry. **Freq:** 6/yr. **Key Personnel:** Prof. James E. Guthrie, Editor, j.guthrie@econ.usyd.edu.au; Prof. Lee D. Parker, Editor, aaaj@unisa.edu.au; Simon Linacre, Publisher, slinacre@emeraldinsight.com; Dr. Steve Evans, Literary Ed., steve.evans@flinders.edu.au; Prof. Richard Laughlin, Assoc. Ed.; Prof. Hiroshi Okano, Exec. Editorial Board; Jesse F. Dillard, Assoc. Ed. **ISSN:** 0951-3574. **URL:** http://info.emeraldinsight.com/products/journals/journals.htm?id=aaaj.

42445 ■ Acoustics Australia
Australian Acoustical Society
School of Physics
UNSW
Sydney, New South Wales 2052, Australia
Ph: 61 2 93854954
Fax: 61 2 93856060
Publication E-mail: acousticsaustralia@acoustics.asn.au
Publisher E-mail: generalsecretary@acoustics.asn.au
Publication covering acoustics. **Founded:** 1972. **Freq:**

3/yr. **Print Method:** Offset. **Trim Size:** A4. **Key Personnel:** Joe Wolfe, Contact, j.wolfe@unsw.edu.au; Leigh Wallbank, Business Mgr., wallbank@zipworld.com.au; Marion Burgess, Contact. **ISSN:** 0814-6039. **Subscription Rates:** $A 58.08 individuals surface mail; $A 69.30 individuals overseas, airmail; $A 101.64 two years surface mail; $A 125.40 two years overseas, airmail. **Remarks:** Accepts advertising. **URL:** http://www.acoustics.asn.au/joomla/journal.html. **Ad Rates:** BW: $A 660, 4C: $A 1,200, PCI: $A 55.88. **Circ:** Paid ‡600

42446 ■ Ad Astra
National Space Society of Australia
GPO Box 7048
Sydney, New South Wales 2001, Australia
Ph: 61 291 504553
Publisher E-mail: nssa@nssa.com.au
Magazine featuring articles on all aspects of space exploration. **Freq:** Quarterly. **Subscription Rates:** $A 50 members. **URL:** http://nssa.com.au/Pages/adastra.html.

42447 ■ APC
ACP Magazines Ltd.
Level 18, 66 Goulburn St.
GPO Box 4088
Sydney, New South Wales 2000, Australia
Ph: 61 2 92889111
Fax: 61 2 92674909
Magazine covering the latest PC products, technology and software. **Founded:** May 1980. **Freq:** Monthly. **Key Personnel:** Tony Sarno, Editor, tony@apctest.com; Michael Koslowski, Publisher; Andrew Cook, Advertising Dir. **Subscription Rates:** $A 69.95 individuals; $A 139 two years. **Remarks:** Accepts advertising. **URL:** http://www.acp.com.au/apc.htm; http://apcmag.com/. **Circ:** ★28,952

42448 ■ Arabian Archaeology and Epigraphy
John Wiley & Sons Inc.
Wiley-Blackwell
c/o Prof. D.T. Potts, Ed.-in-Ch.
School of Archaeology, Classics & Ancient History
University of Sydney
Sydney, New South Wales 2006, Australia
Peer-reviewed journal focusing on studies in the archaeology, epigraphy, numismatics, and early history of Bahrain, Kuwait, Oman, Qatar, Saudi Arabia, the United Arab Emirates, and Yemen. **Freq:** Semiannual. **Key Personnel:** Prof. D.T. Potts, Editor-in-Chief; Serge Cleuziou, Editorial Board; Maurizio Tosi, Editorial Board. **ISSN:** 0905-7196. **Subscription Rates:** US$354 individuals print + online; US$788 institutions print + online; US$716 institutions print; 469 institutions print and online; 426 institutions print; 211 individuals print + online; EUR594 institutions print + online; EUR540 institutions online; US$917 institutions, other countries print + online; US$834 institutions, other countries print. **Remarks:** Accepts advertising. **URL:** http://www.wiley.com/bw/journal.asp?ref=0905-7196&site=1. **Circ:** (Not Reported)

42449 ■ Asset
Fairfax Business Media
1 Darling Island Rd., Level 1
Pyrmont
Sydney, New South Wales 2009, Australia
Publication E-mail: asset@fairfax.com.au
Magazine covering financial planning industry. **Founded:** 2000. **Freq:** Monthly. **Key Personnel:** Leng Yeow, Editor, lyeow@afr.com.au; Michael Gill, CEO/Ed.-in-Ch. **Subscription Rates:** $A 79 individuals. **URL:** http://www.assetmag.com.au/.

42450 ■ Australian
Nationwide News Proprietary Ltd.
PO Box 4245
Sydney, New South Wales 2001, Australia
Ph: 61 2 92883000
Fax: 61 2 92882250
Publisher E-mail: letters@theaustralian.com.au
Business publication. **Freq:** Daily. **Key Personnel:** Chris Mitchell, Editor-in-Chief; Paul Whittaker, Editor; Louise Evans, Managing Editor; Graham Erbacher, Sen. Dep. Ed. **Subscription Rates:** $A 361.40 individuals. **Remarks:** Accepts advertising. **Online:** Gale. **URL:** http://www.theaustralian.news.com.au/. **Ad Rates:** BW: $A 28,050. **Circ:** 131,753

42451 ■ Australian Auto Action
ACP Magazines Ltd.
54-58 Park St.
Sydney, New South Wales 2000, Australia
Ph: 61 2 92828000
Fax: 61 2 92674361
Automotive magazine covering motor, sport results, features, and reports. **Freq:** Weekly. **Trim Size:** 297 x 312 mm. **Key Personnel:** Rob Margeit, Editor. **Subscription Rates:** US$5.60 single issue. **Remarks:** Accepts advertising. **URL:** http://www.acp.com.au/auto_action.htm. **Ad Rates:** 4C: $A 2,550. **Circ:** ★12,006

42452 ■ Australian Dirt Bike Magazine
ACP Magazines Ltd.
54-58 Park St.
Sydney, New South Wales 2000, Australia
Ph: 61 2 92828000
Fax: 61 2 92674361
Magazine featuring motorcyclists and high-performance riding. **Founded:** 1975. **Freq:** Monthly. **Trim Size:** 205 x 275 mm. **Key Personnel:** Sam Maclachlan, Editor; Brian Vegh, National Sales Mgr. **Subscription Rates:** US$80.75 individuals. **Remarks:** Accepts advertising. **URL:** http://www.acp.com.au/australasian_dirt_bike.htm. **Circ:** ★26,074

42453 ■ Australian Geographic Outdoor
ACP Magazines Ltd.
54 Park St.
Sydney, New South Wales 2000, Australia
Ph: 61 2 92639813
Fax: 61 2 92639810
Magazine featuring travel guides, outdoor activities, and products while out on the Australian landscape. **Freq:** 6/yr. **Key Personnel:** Emma Bowen, Editor; Marc Connors, National Sales Mgr., phone 61 2 81149426, mconnors@acpmagazines.com.au. **Subscription Rates:** $A 42 individuals; $A 74 two years. **Remarks:** Accepts advertising. **URL:** http://www.australiangeographic.com.au/Outdoor/Index.htm; http://www.acp.com.au/outdoor_australia.htm. **Circ:** 20,000

42454 ■ Australian Gourmet Traveller
ACP Magazines Ltd.
54-58 Park St.
Sydney, New South Wales 2000, Australia
Ph: 61 2 92828000
Fax: 61 2 92674361
Food and travel magazine. **Freq:** Monthly. **Trim Size:** 225 x 297 mm. **Key Personnel:** Anthea Loucas, Editor; Matt East, Advertising Mgr. **Subscription Rates:** US$8.95 single issue. **Remarks:** Accepts advertising. **URL:** http://www.acp.com.au/australian_gourmet_traveller.htm; http://gourmettraveller.com.au/. **Ad Rates:** 4C: $A 10,598. **Circ:** ★75,107

42455 ■ Australian House & Garden
ACP Magazines Ltd.
54-58 Park St.
Sydney, New South Wales 2000, Australia
Ph: 61 2 92828000
Fax: 61 2 92674361
Magazine featuring home and garden. **Freq:** Monthly. **Trim Size:** 215 x 278 mm. **Key Personnel:** Lisa Green, Editor-in-Chief; Mathew Samuel, National Sales Mgr. **Subscription Rates:** US$6.95 single issue. **Remarks:** Accepts advertising. **URL:** http://www.acp.com.au/australian_house_garden.htm; http://www.houseandgarden.com.au/. **Ad Rates:** BW: $A 7,420, 4C: $A 12,155. **Circ:** ★105,623

42456 ■ Australian Insolvency Journal
Insolvency Practitioners Association of Australia
GPO Box 9985
Sydney, New South Wales 2001, Australia
Ph: 61 292 905700
Fax: 61 292 902820
Journal providing latest developments, rulings, news, issues affecting bankruptcy and liquidation with peer-reviewed articles and summaries of court rulings. **Freq:** Quarterly. **Remarks:** Accepts advertising. **URL:** http://www.ipaa.com.au/default.asp?menuid=160. **Circ:** (Not Reported)

42457 ■ Australian Journal of Earth Sciences
Geological Society of Australia
104 Bathurst St., Ste. 61
Sydney, New South Wales 2000, Australia
Ph: 61 2 92902194
Fax: 61 2 92902198
Publisher E-mail: info@gsa.org.au
Australian peer-reviewed journal covering geology. **Freq:** 8/yr. **Key Personnel:** A.E. Cockbain, Editor-in-Chief. **ISSN:** 0812-0099. **Subscription Rates:** 919 institutions print + online; US$1,525 institutions print + online; $A 1,197 institutions print + online; EUR1,215 institutions print + online. **URL:** http://www.tandf.co.uk/journals/TAJE; http://www.gsa.org.au/ajes/index.html.

42458 ■ Australian Journal of Jewish Studies
Australian Association of Jewish Studies
Holme Bldg., Box 233
University of Sydney
Sydney, New South Wales 2006, Australia
Ph: 61 2 93514162
Fax: 61 2 93512890
Journal containing articles about the Jewish culture. **Freq:** Semiannual. **Key Personnel:** Dr. Myer Samra, Editor. **Subscription Rates:** Included in membership. **URL:** http://www.aajs.org.au/.

42459 ■ Australian Journal of Management
Australian Graduate School of Management
University of New South Wales
Sydney, New South Wales 2052, Australia
Ph: 61 2 93851000
Publication E-mail: journal@agsm.unsw.edu.au
Journal covering management. **Founded:** 1976. **Freq:** Semiannual June and December. **Print Method:** Offset. **Key Personnel:** Robert E. Marks, Gen. Ed. **ISSN:** 1327-2020. **Subscription Rates:** $A 50 other countries; $A 45 individuals; $A 75 institutions; US$80 institutions, other countries cheques only. **Remarks:** Advertising not accepted. **URL:** http://www.agsm.edu.au; http://www.agsm.edu.au/~eajm. **Circ:** (Not Reported)

42460 ■ Australian Motorcycle News
ACP Magazines Ltd.
54-58 Park St.
Sydney, New South Wales 2000, Australia
Ph: 61 2 92828000
Fax: 61 2 92674361
Magazine for motorcycle enthusiasts. **Founded:** 1951. **Freq:** Biweekly. **Trim Size:** 206 x 275 mm. **Key Personnel:** Matthew Shields, Editor; Iain Aitken, Advertising Mgr., iaitken@acpmagazines.com.au. **Subscription Rates:** $A 7.25 single issue. **Remarks:** Accepts advertising. **URL:** http://www.acp.com.au/australian_motorcycle_news.htm. **Ad Rates:** 4C: $A 2,350. **Circ:** ★20,132

42461 ■ Australian Mountain Bike
ACP Magazines Ltd.
54-58 Park St.
Sydney, New South Wales 2000, Australia
Ph: 61 2 92828000
Fax: 61 2 92674361
Magazine for mountain bike enthusiasts. **Freq:** Bimonthly. **Trim Size:** 222 x 275 mm. **Key Personnel:** Chris Southwood, Editor; James Secher, Advertising Mgr., jsecher@motormedia.com.au. **Subscription Rates:** US$54.95 individuals. **Remarks:** Accepts advertising. **URL:** http://www.acp.com.au/australian_mountain_bike.htm. **Circ:** 20,000

42462 ■ Australian NetGuide
Australian NetGuide Proprietary Ltd.
Level 18
Civic Towers
66-68 Goulburn St.
Sydney, New South Wales 2000, Australia
Ph: 61 29288 9105
Fax: 61 29267 4909
Consumer magazine covering technology for Internet users in Australia. **Founded:** Apr. 1998. **Freq:** Monthly. **Trim Size:** A5. **Key Personnel:** Alex Zandstra, Writer/Sub-Ed.; Troy Coleman, Graphic Designer; Glenn Rees, Editor-in-Chief; Gail Lipscombe, Editor. **Subscription Rates:** $A 44.95 individuals; $A 22.50 individuals 6 months; $A 80 two years. **Remarks:** Accepts advertising. **URL:** http://www.netguide.com.au/v2/. **Ad Rates:** 4C: $A 2,671. **Circ:** ★19,134

42463 ■ Australian & NZ Snowboarding
ACP Magazines Ltd.
54-58 Park St.
Sydney, New South Wales 2000, Australia
Ph: 61 2 92828000

Fax: 61 2 92674361

Magazine covering snowboarding-related topics, interviews, products, and travel. **Freq:** 3/yr. **Key Personnel:** Chris McAlpine, Editor; Annie Clemenger, Advertising Mgr. **Subscription Rates:** $A 23.85 individuals; $A 25 individuals New Zealand; $A 32 other countries. **Remarks:** Accepts advertising. **URL:** http://www.acp.com.au/australian_nz_snowboarding.htm. **Circ:** 20,000

42464 ■ Australian PC User
ACP Magazines Ltd.
54-58 Park St.
Sydney, New South Wales 2000, Australia
Ph: 61 2 92828000
Fax: 61 2 92674361
Computer periodical. **Freq:** Monthly. **Key Personnel:** Fleur Porter, National Sales Mgr., fporter@ acpmagazines.com.au; Glenn Rees, Editor; Stephanie Fletcher, Sales Mgr., sfletcher@hwrmedia.com.au. **ISSN:** 1039-2149. **Remarks:** Accepts advertising. **URL:** http://www.acp.com.au/pc_user.htm; http://www.pcuser.com.au/. **Ad Rates:** 4C: $A 5,610. **Circ:** ★40,084

42465 ■ Australian Personal Computer
ACP Magazines Ltd.
54-58 Park St.
Sydney, New South Wales 2000, Australia
Ph: 61 2 92828000
Fax: 61 2 92674361
Publication covering computers and the office automation industry. **Freq:** Monthly. **Trim Size:** 275 x210. **Key Personnel:** Tony Sarno, Editor, tsarno@acpmagazines. com.au. **ISSN:** 0725-4415. **Remarks:** Accepts advertising. **URL:** http://www.acp.com.au/apc.htm; http://apcmag.com/. **Ad Rates:** 4C: $A 5,655. **Circ:** ★28,952

42466 ■ Australian Table
ACP Magazines Ltd.
54-58 Park St.
Sydney, New South Wales 2000, Australia
Ph: 61 2 92828000
Fax: 61 2 92674361
Food magazine for the family. **Freq:** Monthly. **Trim Size:** 210 x 275 mm. **Key Personnel:** Pat Ingram, Publisher. **Subscription Rates:** $A 3.95 single issue. **Remarks:** Accepts advertising. **URL:** http://www.acp.com.au/ Publication.aspx?id=cf0656de-50a8-4c43-a9b6-a8166674ad89&mag=Australian+Table. **Ad Rates:** 4C: $A 6,900. **Circ:** ★67,095

42467 ■ Australian Tax Forum
Taxation Institute of Australia
Level 2, 95 Pitt St.
Sydney, New South Wales 2000, Australia
Ph: 61 2 8223 0000
Fax: 61 2 8223 0077
Publisher E-mail: nsw@taxinstitute.com.au
Law periodical. **Freq:** Quarterly. **ISSN:** 0812-695X. **Subscription Rates:** $A 240 individuals print plus online; $A 265 out of country print plus online. **URL:** http://www.taxinstitute.com.au/go/publications/australian-tax-forum.

42468 ■ Australian Veterinary Journal
Australian Veterinary Association
Unit 40, 6 Herbert St.
Sydney, New South Wales 2065, Australia
Ph: 61 294 315000
Fax: 61 294 379068
Publisher E-mail: members@ava.com.au
Australian journal covering veterinary medicine. **Freq:** Monthly combined issue for Jan./Feb. **Key Personnel:** Anne Jackson, Editor; Glenn Browning, Sci. Editorial Committee. **ISSN:** 0005-0423. **Subscription Rates:** US$559 institutions print + online; US$508 institutions print only; US$508 institutions online only; 451 institutions print online (Australia); 410 institutions print only (Australia); 410 institutions online only (Australia); EUR393 institutions print and online (Europe); EUR357 institutions print only (Europe); US$607 institutions, other countries premium and online; US$551 institutions, other countries print only. **Remarks:** Accepts advertising. **URL:** http://www.ava.com.au; http://www.blackwellpublishing.com/journal.asp?ref=0005-0423& site=1. **Ad Rates:** 4C: $A 3,275. **Circ:** ‡25,000

42469 ■ The Australian Women's Weekly
ACP Magazines Ltd.
54-58 Park St.
Sydney, New South Wales 2000, Australia
Ph: 61 2 92828000

Fax: 61 2 92674361

Magazine for women. **Freq:** Monthly. **Trim Size:** 220 x 297 mm. **Key Personnel:** Helen McCabe, Editor-in-Chief; Jo Barton, National Sales Mgr. **Subscription Rates:** $A 6.80 single issue. **Remarks:** Accepts advertising. **URL:** http://www.ninemsn.com.au/; http://www.acp.com.au/the_australian_womens_weekly.htm. **Ad Rates:** 4C: $A 34,995. **Circ:** ★493,301

42470 ■ Autralian & New Zealand Skiing
ACP Magazines Ltd.
54-58 Park St.
Sydney, New South Wales 2000, Australia
Ph: 61 2 92828000
Fax: 61 2 92674361
Magazine featuring skiing. **Freq:** Annual. **Trim Size:** 225 x 300 mm. **Key Personnel:** Anne Clemenger, Advertising Mgr., clemenger@bigpond.com; Jono Brauer, Editor. **Remarks:** Accepts advertising. **URL:** http://www.acp.com.au/australian_nz_skiing.htm. **Ad Rates:** 4C: $A 2,835. **Circ:** 15,000

42471 ■ Backpacker Essentials
YHA—New South Wales
422 Kent St.
Sydney, New South Wales 2000, Australia
Ph: 02 92 611111
Fax: 02 92 611969
Publication E-mail: backpacker.essentials@yhansw.org.au
Publisher E-mail: yha@yhansw.org.au
Consumer magazine covering budget travel. **Founded:** 1997. **Freq:** 3/yr. **ISSN:** 1328-6749. **Subscription Rates:** $A 14.85 individuals; $A 29.70 two years. **URL:** http://www.backpackeressentials.com.au. **Circ:** Paid 104,000

42472 ■ Ballina Shire Advocate
APN News & Media Ltd.
100 William St., Level 4
Sydney, New South Wales 2011, Australia
Ph: 61 2 93334999
Fax: 61 2 93334900
Publisher E-mail: info@apn.com.au
Newspaper covering local issues in the Ballina community. **Freq:** Weekly (Thurs.). **Subscription Rates:** Free. **Remarks:** Accepts advertising. **URL:** http://apnap.com.au/newspapers/community/4656.html. **Circ:** ‡16,787

42473 ■ Balonne Beacon
APN News & Media Ltd.
100 William St., Level 4
Sydney, New South Wales 2011, Australia
Ph: 61 2 93334999
Fax: 61 2 93334900
Publisher E-mail: info@apn.com.au
Newspaper covering events and issues around the areas of St. George and the Balonne Shire. **Founded:** 1905. **Freq:** Weekly (Thurs.). **Subscription Rates:** $A 1 single issue. **Remarks:** Accepts advertising. **URL:** http://apnap.com.au/newspapers/community/4676.html. **Circ:** ★1,510

42474 ■ Big Rigs
APN News & Media Ltd.
100 William St., Level 4
Sydney, New South Wales 2011, Australia
Ph: 61 2 93334999
Fax: 61 2 93334900
Publisher E-mail: info@apn.com.au
Newspaper containing articles for transport workers. **Freq:** Fortnightly. **Subscription Rates:** Free. **Remarks:** Accepts advertising. **URL:** http://apnap.com.au/newspapers/special/4644.html. **Circ:** ‡24,660

42475 ■ Blackwater Herald
APN News & Media Ltd.
100 William St., Level 4
Sydney, New South Wales 2011, Australia
Ph: 61 2 93334999
Fax: 61 2 93334900
Publisher E-mail: info@apn.com.au
Newspaper covering the events in Blackwater, Bluff and surrounding areas. **Founded:** 1977. **Freq:** Weekly (Tues.). **Subscription Rates:** $A .90 single issue. **Remarks:** Accepts advertising. **URL:** http://apnap.com.au/newspapers/community/4667.html. **Circ:** ‡1,339

42476 ■ Bribie Weekly
APN News & Media Ltd.

100 William St., Level 4
Sydney, New South Wales 2011, Australia
Ph: 61 2 93334999
Fax: 61 2 93334900
Publisher E-mail: info@apn.com.au
Newspaper covering events and issues in the Bribie Island and neighboring mainland communities. **Freq:** Weekly (Fri.). **Subscription Rates:** Free. **Remarks:** Accepts advertising. **URL:** http://apnap.com.au/newspapers/community/4635.html. **Circ:** ‡11,168

42477 ■ Brisbane Times
Fairfax Media Limited
GPO 506
Sydney, New South Wales 2001, Australia
Ph: 61 2 92822833
Publisher E-mail: pmclean@fairfaxmedia.com.au
Newspaper covering local stories and news in Brisbane. **Founded:** Mar. 2007. **Key Personnel:** Conal Hanna, Managing Editor. **URL:** http://www.brisbanetimes.com.au/.

42478 ■ Buderim Chronicle
APN News & Media Ltd.
100 William St., Level 4
Sydney, New South Wales 2011, Australia
Ph: 61 2 93334999
Fax: 61 2 93334900
Publisher E-mail: info@apn.com.au
Newspaper covering local events and information in the Buderim community. **Freq:** Weekly (Fri.). **Subscription Rates:** Free. **Remarks:** Accepts advertising. **URL:** http://apnap.com.au/newspapers/community/4634.html. **Circ:** ‡18,000

42479 ■ The Bulletin with Newsweek
ACP Magazines Ltd.
54-58 Park St.
Sydney, New South Wales 2000, Australia
Ph: 61 2 92828000
Fax: 61 2 92674361
General interest publication. **Freq:** Weekly. **Key Personnel:** John Lehmann, Editor-in-Chief. **ISSN:** 1440-7485. **Remarks:** Accepts advertising. **URL:** http://www.acp.com.au/publication.aspx?id=ac279b54-772d-4b3b-9b52-58175a51aceb&mag=thebulletin. **Ad Rates:** 4C: $A 12,300. **Circ:** ★57,039

42480 ■ Bush Telegraph
APN News & Media Ltd.
100 William St., Level 4
Sydney, New South Wales 2011, Australia
Ph: 61 2 93334999
Fax: 61 2 93334900
Publisher E-mail: info@apn.com.au
Newspaper covering events and information in Warwick and surrounding districts. **Freq:** Monthly. **Remarks:** Accepts advertising. **URL:** http://apnap.com.au/newspapers/special/4651.html. **Circ:** ‡4,195

42481 ■ Byron Shire News
APN News & Media Ltd.
100 William St., Level 4
Sydney, New South Wales 2011, Australia
Ph: 61 2 93334999
Fax: 61 2 93334900
Publisher E-mail: info@apn.com.au
Newspaper covering major news, sport, events and entertainment in the Byron Shire area. **Freq:** Weekly (Thurs.). **Subscription Rates:** Free. **Remarks:** Accepts advertising. **URL:** http://apnap.com.au/newspapers/community/4658.html. **Circ:** ‡17,120

42482 ■ Caboolture News
APN News & Media Ltd.
100 William St., Level 4
Sydney, New South Wales 2011, Australia
Ph: 61 2 93334999
Fax: 61 2 93334900
Publisher E-mail: info@apn.com.au
Newspaper featuring events and information in the local area of Caboolture. **Freq:** Weekly (Wed.). **Subscription Rates:** Free. **Remarks:** Accepts advertising. **URL:** http://apnap.com.au/newspapers/community/4629.html. **Circ:** ‡33,648

42483 ■ Caloundra Weekly
APN News & Media Ltd.
100 William St., Level 4
Sydney, New South Wales 2011, Australia
Ph: 61 2 93334999

Fax: 61 2 93334900
Publisher E-mail: info@apn.com.au
Newspaper containing community news and entertainment for Caloundra residents. **Freq:** Weekly (Wed.). **Subscription Rates:** Free. **Remarks:** Accepts advertising. **URL:** http://apnap.com.au/newspapers/community/4630.html. **Circ:** ‡22,116

42484 ■ Campus Review
APN Educational Media
Level 6, 110 Walker St.
PO Box 6097
Sydney, New South Wales 2060, Australia
Ph: 61 2 99368666
Fax: 61 2 99368631
Publisher E-mail: production3@apn-ed.co.nz
Newspaper covering post-secondary education news analysis for senior academics and teachers and senior administrators in Australia. **Founded:** 1991. **Freq:** Weekly. **Subscription Rates:** $A 210 individuals online and print; $A 341 other countries online and print; $A 170 individuals online and print, for six months; $A 240 individuals online and print, New Zealand; $A 190 individuals online only; $A 420 individuals online and print (3 years); $A 315 two years online and print; $A 190 individuals print. **Remarks:** Accepts advertising. **URL:** http://www.camrev.com.au/. **Ad Rates:** BW: $A 5,933, 4C: $A 5,933. **Circ:** Combined 45,000

42485 ■ Capricorn Coast Mirror
APN News & Media Ltd.
100 William St., Level 4
Sydney, New South Wales 2011, Australia
Ph: 61 2 93334999
Fax: 61 2 93334900
Publisher E-mail: info@apn.com.au
Newspaper for Capricorn Coast and immediate hinterland region. **Freq:** Weekly (Wed.). **Subscription Rates:** Free. **Remarks:** Accepts advertising. **URL:** http://apnap.com.au/newspapers/community/4612.html. **Circ:** ‡10,843

42486 ■ Caveat
The Law Society of New South Wales
170 Phillip St.
Sydney, New South Wales 2000, Australia
Ph: 61 2 99260333
Fax: 61 2 92315809
Publisher E-mail: lawsociety@lawsocnsw.asn.au
Publication covering issues for the legal profession. **URL:** http://www.lawsociety.com.au/resources/Reports/newslettersandpublications/index.htm.

42487 ■ Central & North Burnett Times
APN News & Media Ltd.
100 William St., Level 4
Sydney, New South Wales 2011, Australia
Ph: 61 2 93334999
Fax: 61 2 93334900
Publisher E-mail: info@apn.com.au
Newspaper covering events in the area of Biggenden, Gayndah, Mundubbera, Mt. Perry, Eidsvold, Monto and surrounding rural districts. **Freq:** Weekly (Thurs.). **Subscription Rates:** $A 1 single issue. **Remarks:** Accepts advertising. **URL:** http://apnap.com.au/newspapers/community/4674.html. **Circ:** ★3,122

42488 ■ Central Queensland News
APN News & Media Ltd.
100 William St., Level 4
Sydney, New South Wales 2011, Australia
Ph: 61 2 93334999
Fax: 61 2 93334900
Publisher E-mail: info@apn.com.au
Newspaper covering events and information in the Central Highlands region. **Freq:** Semiweekly (Wed. and Fri.). **Subscription Rates:** $A 1.10 single issue. **Remarks:** Accepts advertising. **URL:** http://apnap.com.au/newspapers/community/4672.html. **Circ:** ★4,927

42489 ■ Central Telegraph
APN News & Media Ltd.
100 William St., Level 4
Sydney, New South Wales 2011, Australia
Ph: 61 2 93334999
Fax: 61 2 93334900
Publisher E-mail: info@apn.com.au
Newspaper providing local news and entertainment to Central Queensland. **Freq:** Weekly (Fri.). **Subscription**

Rates: $A 1.10 individuals. **Remarks:** Accepts advertising. **URL:** http://apnap.com.au/newspapers/community/4666.html. **Circ:** ★3,595

42490 ■ Charter
Institute of Chartered Accountants in Australia
33 Erskine St.
Sydney, New South Wales 2000, Australia
Ph: 61 2 92901344
Fax: 61 2 92621512
Publisher E-mail: service@charteredaccountants.com.au
Accounting publication. **Freq:** Monthly. **Print Method:** Web. **Trim Size:** 210 x 275 mm. **Key Personnel:** Gillian Bullock, Editor, phone 61 2 99605120, gillian@cmma.com.au; Sumit Roy, Sen. Advertising Account Mgr., sumit.roy@charteredaccountants.com.au; Geoff Kingswood, Publishing Mgr., phone 61 2 92905653, geoff.kingswood@charteredaccountants.com.au. **ISSN:** 1446-4543. **Subscription Rates:** $A 89 nonmembers incl. GST; $A 59 students also CA program candidates, inc GST; $A 129 out of country. **URL:** http://www.charteredaccountants.com.au/charter. **Formerly:** CA Charter. **Ad Rates:** BW: $A 5,800. **Circ:** ◆48,570

42491 ■ Chinchilla News and Murilla Advertiser
APN News & Media Ltd.
100 William St., Level 4
Sydney, New South Wales 2011, Australia
Ph: 61 2 93334999
Fax: 61 2 93334900
Publisher E-mail: info@apn.com.au
Newspaper covering events and entertainment in the Chinchilla region. **Freq:** Weekly (Thurs.). **Subscription Rates:** $A 1 single issue. **Remarks:** Accepts advertising. **URL:** http://apnap.com.au/newspapers/community/4669.html. **Circ:** ★3,899

42492 ■ COAST
APN News & Media Ltd.
100 William St., Level 4
Sydney, New South Wales 2011, Australia
Ph: 61 2 93334999
Fax: 61 2 93334900
Publisher E-mail: info@apn.com.au
Magazine featuring information and advice regarding areas and attractions across the Sunshine Coast region. **Freq:** Quarterly. **Subscription Rates:** Free. **URL:** http://apnap.com.au/newspapers/special/4680.html. **Circ:** ‡30,000

42493 ■ Coastal Views
APN News & Media Ltd.
100 William St., Level 4
Sydney, New South Wales 2011, Australia
Ph: 61 2 93334999
Fax: 61 2 93334900
Publisher E-mail: info@apn.com.au
Newspaper covering events and information in Clarence Valley. **Freq:** Weekly (Fri.). **Subscription Rates:** Free. **Remarks:** Accepts advertising. **URL:** http://apnap.com/newspapers/community/4662.html. **Circ:** ‡18,531

42494 ■ The Coffs Coast Advocate
APN News & Media Ltd.
100 William St., Level 4
Sydney, New South Wales 2011, Australia
Ph: 61 2 93334999
Fax: 61 2 93334900
Publisher E-mail: info@apn.com.au
Newspaper covering events and information in Coffs Harbour and surrounding districts. **Freq:** Daily and Sat. (morn.). **Subscription Rates:** $A 1 single issue Monday, Tuesday, Thursday, Friday; Free Wednesday, Saturday. **Remarks:** Accepts advertising. **URL:** http://apnap.com/newspapers/daily/4663.html. **Circ:** Paid ‡3,245, Free ‡30,666

42495 ■ COLES
ACP Magazines Ltd.
54-58 Park St.
Sydney, New South Wales 2000, Australia
Ph: 61 2 92828000
Fax: 61 2 92674361
Magazine focusing on healthy eating. **Freq:** Quarterly. **Key Personnel:** Kandy Shepherd, Editor; Gillian Cornu, Advertising Mgr., gcornu@acpmagazines.com.au. **Remarks:** Accepts advertising. **URL:** http://www.acp.au/coles.htm. **Circ:** (Not Reported)

42496 ■ Computational Linguistics
MIT Press
Centre for Language Technology, Department of Computing
Faculty of Science, Bldg. E6A, Rm. 328
Macquarie University
Sydney, New South Wales 2109, Australia
Ph: 61 298 506331
Fax: 61 298 509551
Publisher E-mail: journals-orders@mit.edu
Journal focusing exclusively on the design and analysis of natural language processing systems; providing information to university and industry linguists, computational linguists, artificial intelligence (AI) investigators, cognitive scientists, speech specialists, and philosophers on computational aspects of research on language, linguistics, and the psychology of language processing and performance. **Founded:** 1974. **Freq:** Quarterly March, June, September, December. **Key Personnel:** Robert Dale, Editor-in-Chief, robert.dale@mq.edu.au; Graeme Hirst, Book Review Ed. **ISSN:** 0891-2017. **Remarks:** Accepts advertising. **URL:** http://www.mitpressjournals.org/loi/coli. **Circ:** (Not Reported)

42497 ■ Cooloola Advertiser
APN News & Media Ltd.
100 William St., Level 4
Sydney, New South Wales 2011, Australia
Ph: 61 2 93334999
Fax: 61 2 93334900
Publisher E-mail: info@apn.com.au
Newspaper covering events and information in Gympie and the coastal townships of Tin Can Bay and Rainbow Beach. **Freq:** Weekly (Tues.). **Subscription Rates:** Free. **Remarks:** Accepts advertising. **URL:** http://apnap.com.au/newspapers/community/4625.html. **Circ:** ‡10,213

42498 ■ Cosmopolitan (Australia)
ACP Magazines Ltd.
54-58 Park St.
Sydney, New South Wales 2000, Australia
Ph: 61 2 92828000
Fax: 61 2 92674361
Consumer magazine covering lifestyle. **Freq:** Monthly. **Key Personnel:** Bronwyn McCahon, Editor; Ciara Lancaster, Sales Mgr., clancaster@hwrmedia.com.au. **Remarks:** Accepts advertising. **URL:** http://www.acp.com.au/cosmopolitan.htm; http://www.cosmopolitan.com.au/. **Ad Rates:** 4C: $A 18,950. **Circ:** ★151,213

42499 ■ The Daily Examiner
APN News & Media Ltd.
100 William St., Level 4
Sydney, New South Wales 2011, Australia
Ph: 61 2 93334999
Fax: 61 2 93334900
Publisher E-mail: info@apn.com.au
Newspaper covering New South Wales North Coast. **Freq:** Daily and Sat. (morn.). **Subscription Rates:** $A 1 single issue Monday-Friday; $A 1.10 single issue Saturday. **Remarks:** Accepts advertising. **URL:** http://apnap.com.au/newspapers/daily/4661.html. **Circ:** Mon.-Sat. ★5,670, Sat. ★6,298

42500 ■ Dalby Herald
APN News & Media Ltd.
100 William St., Level 4
Sydney, New South Wales 2011, Australia
Ph: 61 2 93334999
Fax: 61 2 93334900
Publisher E-mail: info@apn.com.au
Newspaper covering events and information in Dalby and Wambo districts. **Founded:** 1865. **Freq:** every Tuesday and Friday. **Subscription Rates:** $A 1 single issue. **Remarks:** Accepts advertising. **URL:** http://apnap.com.au/newspapers/community/4670.html. **Circ:** ★2,452

42501 ■ Descent
Society of Australian Genealogists
120 Kent St.
Sydney, New South Wales 2000, Australia
Ph: 61 292 473953
Fax: 61 292 414872
Publisher E-mail: info@sag.org.au
Journal containing articles of general genealogical and historical interest in Australia and overseas. **Freq:** Quarterly. **Subscription Rates:** Free to members. **URL:** http://www.sag.org.au/index.php?option=com_content&

Circulation: ★ = ABC; △ = BPA; ◆ = CAC; • = CCAB; ❑ = VAC; ⊕ = PO Statement; ‡ = Publisher's Report; Boldface figures = sworn; Light figures = estimated.

task~view&id~99&ItemId=144.

42502 ■ Electrical World
PO Box 5023
Sydney, New South Wales 2261, Australia
Ph: 61 2 43881186
Fax: 61 2 43886614
Publisher E-mail: desd@electricalworld.com.au
Trade magazine for electrical contractors and the power industry. **Founded:** 1000. **Freq:** Monthly. **Print Method:** Web offset. **Trim Size:** Super A4. **Key Personnel:** Desmond William Dugan, Editor, desd@electricalworld.com.au; Jenny Loasby, Contact, jennyl@electricalworld.com.au. **ISSN:** 1325-8273. **Subscription Rates:** US$88 individuals Australia; US$120 individuals Asia and Pacific regions; US$160 individuals U.K. and other overseas countries. **Remarks:** Accepts advertising. **URL:** http://www.electricalworld.com.au. **Ad Rates:** GLR: $A 2,500, BW: $A 1,800. **Circ:** Paid ‡6,749

42503 ■ Fernwood
ACP Magazines Ltd.
54-58 Park St.
Sydney, New South Wales 2000, Australia
Ph: 61 2 92828000
Fax: 61 2 92674361
Lifestyle and health magazine for women. **Subtitle:** Your Healthy Living Magazine. **Freq:** Bimonthly. **Trim Size:** 230 x 275 mm. **Key Personnel:** Donna Ogier, Editor; Sally Windrum, Advertising Mgr. **Remarks:** Accepts advertising. **URL:** http://www.acp.com.au/fernwood.htm. **Ad Rates:** 4C: $A 7,500. **Circ:** 74,250

42504 ■ FourFourTwo
Haymarket Media Pty. Ltd.
52 Victoria St.
McMahons Point
Sydney, New South Wales 2060, Australia
Ph: 61 2 83993611
Fax: 61 2 83993622
Publication E-mail: enquiries@fourfourtwo.net.au
Magazine covering football game. **Founded:** 1994. **Freq:** Monthly. **Trim Size:** 220 x 300 mm. **Key Personnel:** Trevor Treharne, Editor, phone 61 2 83997609, ttreharne@haymarketmedia.com.au; Mike Hemmingway, Sales Mgr., phone 61 2 83997603, mhemmingway@haymarketmedia.com.au. **Subscription Rates:** $A 79.95 individuals. **Remarks:** Accepts advertising. **URL:** http://au.fourfourtwo.com/magazine-currentissue.aspx; http://www.haymarketmedia.com.au/magazines.aspx. **Circ:** 100,000

42505 ■ 4x4 Australia
ACP Magazines Ltd.
54-58 Park St.
Sydney, New South Wales 2000, Australia
Ph: 61 2 92828000
Fax: 61 2 92674361
Magazine for 4x4 buyers and enthusiasts. **Subtitle:** Live the Adventure!. **Freq:** Monthly. **Trim Size:** 225 x 297 mm. **Key Personnel:** Mick Matheson, Editor; Cameron Davis, National Sales Mgr., cdavis@acpmagazines.com.au. **Subscription Rates:** $A 69.95 individuals. **Remarks:** Accepts advertising. **URL:** http://www.acp.com.au/4x4_australia.htm. **Ad Rates:** 4C: $A 2,947. **Circ:** ★18,227

42506 ■ Fraser Coast Chronicle
APN News & Media Ltd.
100 William St., Level 4
Sydney, New South Wales 2011, Australia
Ph: 61 2 93334999
Fax: 61 2 93334900
Publisher E-mail: info@apn.com.au
Newspaper covering the local news and entertainment in the Fraser Coast region. **Freq:** Mon.-Sat. **Subscription Rates:** $A 1.10 single issue Monday-Friday; $A 1.20 single issue Saturday. **Remarks:** Accepts advertising. **URL:** http://apnap.com.au/newspapers/daily/4620.html. **Circ:** Mon.-Fri. ★9,400, Sat. ★10,851

42507 ■ Gatton, Lockyer and Brisbane Valley Star
APN News & Media Ltd.
100 William St., Level 4
Sydney, New South Wales 2011, Australia
Ph: 61 2 93334999
Fax: 61 2 93334900
Publisher E-mail: info@apn.com.au
Newspaper covering the shires of Gatton, Laidley, Esk

and the western townships of the Ipswich Council area and Brisbane Valley. **Freq:** Weekly (Wed.). **Subscription Rates:** Free. **Remarks:** Accepts advertising. **URL:** http://apnap.com.au/newspapers/community/4646.html. **Circ:** ‡19,970

42508 ■ Gold Coast Mail
APN News & Media Ltd.
100 William St., Level 4
Sydney, New South Wales 2011, Australia
Ph: 61 2 93334999
Fax: 61 2 93334900
Publisher E-mail: info@apn.com.au
Newspaper covering people, events, entertainment and dining in the Gold Coast area. **Freq:** Weekly (Thurs.). **Subscription Rates:** Free. **Remarks:** Accepts advertising. **URL:** http://apnap.com.au/newspapers/community/4653.html. **Circ:** ‡28,309

42509 ■ Gourmet Traveller WINE
ACP Magazines Ltd.
54-58 Park St.
Sydney, New South Wales 2000, Australia
Ph: 61 2 92828000
Fax: 61 2 92674361
Magazine for wine lovers. **Freq:** Bimonthly. **Trim Size:** 225 x 297 mm. **Key Personnel:** Judy Sarris, Editor; Matt East, Advertising Mgr., meast@hwrmedia.com.au. **Subscription Rates:** $A 35 individuals. **Remarks:** Accepts advertising. **URL:** http://www.acp.com.au/gourmet_traveller_wine.htm; http://gourmettraveller.com.au/wine_and_drink.htm. **Ad Rates:** 4C: $A 6,230. **Circ:** ★21,948

42510 ■ Green Left Weekly
Democratic Socialist Perspective
23 Abercrombie St., Chippendale
Sydney, New South Wales 2007, Australia
Publication E-mail: subscriptions@greenleft.org.au
Publisher E-mail: dsp@dsp.org.au
Newspaper focusing on human and civil rights, global peace and environmental sustainability, democracy and equality. **Founded:** 1990. **Freq:** Weekly. **Subscription Rates:** $A 10 individuals 7 issues; $A 22 individuals 11 issues; $A 44 individuals 22 issues; $A 83 individuals 12 months; $A 154 individuals 88 issues; $A 83 by mail Asia, Oceania & New Zealand, 6 months (airmail); $A 149 by mail Asia, Oceania & New Zealand, 12 months (airmail); $A 110 by mail North & South America, Europe & the Middle East; $A 198 by mail North and South America, Europe & the Middle East. **URL:** http://www.greenleft.org.au/.

42511 ■ The Gympie Times
APN News & Media Ltd.
100 William St., Level 4
Sydney, New South Wales 2011, Australia
Ph: 61 2 93334999
Fax: 61 2 93334900
Publisher E-mail: info@apn.com.au
Newspaper covering events and information in the Gympie Gold Rush region. **Founded:** 1868. **Freq:** Daily Tue.-Sat. **Subscription Rates:** $A 1.10 single issue Tuesday-Friday; $A 1.20 single issue Saturday. **Remarks:** Accepts advertising. **URL:** http://apnap.com.au/newspapers/daily/4624.html. **Circ:** Tues.-Fri. ★5,569, Sat. ★8,569

42512 ■ Harper's Bazaar (Australia)
ACP Magazines Ltd.
54-58 Park St.
Sydney, New South Wales 2000, Australia
Ph: 61 2 92828000
Fax: 61 2 92674361
Consumer magazine covering fashion, beauty, design, and lifestyle. **Freq:** 10/yr. **Key Personnel:** Katrine Hazell, National Sales Mgr.; Edwina Mcann, Editor; Ciara Lancaster, Sales Mgr., clancaster@hwrmedia.com.au. **Remarks:** Accepts advertising. **URL:** http://www.acp.com.au/harpers_bazaar.htm; http://www.harpersbazaar.com.au/. **Circ:** Paid ★56,119

42513 ■ Hawkesbury Courier
Rural Press Regional Publishing Proprietary Ltd.
159 Bells Line of Rd.
Sydney, New South Wales 2754, Australia
Ph: 61 2 45704444
Fax: 61 2 45704663
Community newspaper. **Founded:** 1932. **Freq:** Weekly (Fri.). **Print Method:** Offset. **Cols./Page:** 4. **Col. Width:**

6.3 centimeters. **Col. Depth:** 38 centimeters. **Subscription Rates:** Free. **URL:** http://www.ruralpresssales.com.au/detail.asp?region=Hawkesbury/Blue_Mountains&paper_id=14&state=NSW. **Circ:** Non-paid 20,470

42514 ■ Hervey Bay Observer
APN News & Media Ltd.
100 William St., Level 4
Sydney, New South Wales 2011, Australia
Ph: 61 2 93334999
Fax: 61 2 93334900
Publisher E-mail: info@apn.com.au
Newspaper covering the local news and sport in Hervey Bay. **Freq:** Semiweekly (Wed. and Fri.). **Subscription Rates:** Free. **Remarks:** Accepts advertising. **URL:** http://apnap.com.au/newspapers/community/4621.html. **Circ:** ‡21,122

42515 ■ History Australia
Australian Historical Association
Macquarie University
Division of Humanities, Department of Modern History
Australian Historical Association
Morven Brown Bldg., Level 3
University of New South Wales
Sydney, New South Wales 2052, Australia
Ph: 61 2 93858355
Fax: 61 2 93851251
Publisher E-mail: theaha@unsw.edu.au
Journal on Australian history. **Founded:** 1973. **Key Personnel:** Prof. Penny Russell, Editor; Prof. Richard White, Editor. **Remarks:** Accepts advertising. **URL:** http://www.theaha.org.au/history_australia/journal.htm. **Circ:** (Not Reported)

42516 ■ Inside Cricket
ACP Magazines Ltd.
54-58 Park St.
Sydney, New South Wales 2000, Australia
Ph: 61 2 92828000
Fax: 61 2 92674361
Magazine featuring Cricket sport. **Freq:** Monthly. **Trim Size:** 210 x 275 mm. **Key Personnel:** Nick Raman, Editor; Cameron Jones, National Sales Mgr., cjones@acpmagazines.com.au. **Subscription Rates:** $A 7.60 individuals. **Remarks:** Accepts advertising. **URL:** http://www.acp.com.au/inside_cricket.htm. **Ad Rates:** 4C: $A 2,800. **Circ:** (Not Reported)

42517 ■ Inside Rugby
ACP Magazines Ltd.
54-58 Park St.
Sydney, New South Wales 2000, Australia
Ph: 61 2 92828000
Fax: 61 2 92674361
Magazine featuring rugby sport. **Subtitle:** The Australian Rugby Union Magazine. **Freq:** Monthly in Rugby season. **Trim Size:** 206 X 275 mm. **Key Personnel:** Mark Cashman, Editor; Cameron Jones, National Sales Mgr., cjones@acpmagazines.com.au. **Subscription Rates:** $A 9.95 single issue. **Remarks:** Accepts advertising. **URL:** http://www.acp.com.au/inside_rugby. **Ad Rates:** 4C: $A 2,800. **Circ:** (Not Reported)

42518 ■ International Journal of Abrasive Technology
Inderscience Publishers
c/o Prof. Jun Wang, Ed.-in-Ch.
The University of New South Wales
School of Mechanical & Manufacturing Engineering
Sydney, New South Wales 2052, Australia
Publisher E-mail: editor@inderscience.com
Peer-reviewed journal covering areas of abrasive technology. **Founded:** 2007. **Freq:** 4/yr. **Key Personnel:** Prof. Jun Wang, Editor-in-Chief, jun.wang@unsw.edu.au; Prof. Chuanzhen Huang, Assoc. Ed.; Prof. Libo Zhou, Assoc. Ed. **ISSN:** 1752-2641. **Subscription Rates:** EUR494 individuals includes surface mail, print only; EUR672 individuals print and online. **URL:** http://www.inderscience.com/browse/index.php?journalCODE=ijat.

42519 ■ International Journal of Cardiology
Mosby Inc.
c/o A.J.S. Coats, Ed.-in-Ch.
University of Sydney
Sydney, New South Wales 2006, Australia
Ph: 61 2 90369523
Fax: 61 2 90369522
Publisher E-mail: custserv.ehs@elsevier.com
Peer-reviewed journal for cardiologists. **Freq:** 24/yr. **Key**

Personnel: Prof. Anderw J.S. Coats, Editor-in-Chief, ajscoats@aol.com; C. Kawai, International Consulting Ed.; J.J. Bax, Editorial Board. **ISSN:** 0167-5273. **Subscription Rates:** US$4,060 institutions, other countries except Europe, Japan and Iran; EUR3,630 institutions for European countries and Iran; 482,000¥ institutions; EUR270 individuals for European countries and Iran; 35,500¥ individuals; $A 302 individuals for all countries except European, Japan, and Iran. **URL:** http://www.elsevier.com/wps/find/journaldescription.cws_home/506041/descriptiondescription.

42520 ■ International Journal of Housing Markets and Analysis
Emerald Group Publishing Ltd.
Faculty of Economics & Business
University of Sydney
Merewether Bldg., H04
Sydney, New South Wales 2006, Australia
Publisher E-mail: emerald@emeraldinsight.com
Journal publishing scholarly research on important development issues. **Freq:** Semiannual. **Key Personnel:** Dilip Dutta, Editor; Kelly Dutton, Publisher, kdutton@emeraldinsight.com. **ISSN:** 1446-8956. **URL:** http://info.emeraldinsight.com/products/journals/journals.htm?id=ijdi.

42521 ■ International Journal of Technology Policy and Law
Inderscience Publishers
c/o Dr. Niloufer Selvadurai, Ed.-in-Ch.
Macquarie University
Faculty of Business and Econimics
Easter Rd.
Sydney, New South Wales, Australia
Publisher E-mail: editor@inderscience.com
Peer-reviewed journal aiming to establish an effective channel of communication between policy makers, government agencies, academic and research institutions and persons concerned with the complex role of information in society. **Freq:** Quarterly. **Key Personnel:** Dr. Niloufer Selvadurai, Editor-in-Chief, niloufer.selvadurai@mq.edu.au; Dr. Thankom Gopinath Arun, Editorial Board Member; Prof. James Backhouse, Editorial Board Member. **ISSN:** 1742-4240. **Subscription Rates:** EUR494 individuals print only (surface mail); EUR840 individuals online only (2-3 users); EUR672 individuals print and online; EUR534 individuals print only (airmail). **URL:** http://www.inderscience.com/browse/index.php?journalID=121board. **Formerly:** International Journal of Information Policy and Law.

42522 ■ The Ipswich Advertiser
APN News & Media Ltd.
100 William St., Level 4
Sydney, New South Wales 2011, Australia
Ph: 61 2 93334999
Fax: 61 2 93334900
Publisher E-mail: info@apn.com.au
Newspaper covering events and issues in the city of Ipswich. **Founded:** 1978. **Freq:** Weekly (Wed.). **Subscription Rates:** Free. **Remarks:** Accepts advertising. **URL:** http://apnap.com.au/newspapers/community/4641.html. **Circ:** ‡33,753.

42523 ■ Isis Town & Country
APN News & Media Ltd.
100 William St., Level 4
Sydney, New South Wales 2011, Australia
Ph: 61 2 93334999
Fax: 61 2 93334900
Publisher E-mail: Info@apn.com.au
Newspaper covering the Childers community. **Founded:** 1982. **Freq:** Weekly (Thurs.). **Subscription Rates:** $A 1.10 single issue. **Remarks:** Accepts advertising. **URL:** http://apnap.com.au/newspapers/community/4618.html. **Circ:** ‡1,647

42524 ■ Island & Mainland News
APN News & Media Ltd.
100 William St., Level 4
Sydney, New South Wales 2011, Australia
Ph: 61 2 93334999
Fax: 61 2 93334900
Publisher E-mail: info@apn.com.au
Newspaper covering events and information on the Bribie Island and surrounding areas. **Freq:** Weekly (Wed.). **Subscription Rates:** Free. **Remarks:** Accepts advertising. **URL:** http://apnap.com.au/newspapers/community/4636.html. **Circ:** ‡11,311

42525 ■ Issues
Australian Diabetes Council
GPO Box 9824
Sydney, New South Wales 2001, Australia
Ph: 61 1300 342238
Fax: 61 296 603633
Publisher E-mail: info@australiandiabetescouncil.com
Journal investigating contemporary health and lifestyle matters related to having diabetes. **Freq:** Quarterly. **Subscription Rates:** Included in membership. **URL:** http://www.diabetesnsw.com.au/media_publications/issues.asp.

42526 ■ Journal of Australian Political Economy
Australian Political Economy Movement
University of Sydney
PO Box 76
Sydney, New South Wales 2006, Australia
Political science publication. **Freq:** Semiannual. **Key Personnel:** Frank Stilwell, Contact, frank.stilwell@sydney.edu.au; Neale Towart, Contact, n.towart@unionsnsw.org.au. **ISSN:** 0156-5826. **Subscription Rates:** $A 16 students four issues; $A 24 individuals four issues; $A 25 other countries; $A 25 institutions libraries. **URL:** http://www.jape.org/.

42527 ■ Journal of Biomimetics, Biomaterials, and Tissue Engineering
Trans Tech Publications Inc.
Biomaterials & Tissue Engineering Research Unit, AMME J07
University of Sydney
Sydney, New South Wales 2006, Australia
Publisher E-mail: info@ttp.net
Peer-reviewed Journal covering general areas of biomimetics, biomaterials, and tissue engineering. **Freq:** 4/yr. **Key Personnel:** E. Boughton, Editorial Board; S.X. Miao, Editor; H. Zreiqat, Editorial Board. **ISSN:** 1662-100X. **Subscription Rates:** EUR310 individuals print and online; EUR278 individuals print or online only. **URL:** http://www.scientific.net/JBBTE/; http://www.ttp.net/1662-100X.html.

42528 ■ Journal of Economic Dynamics and Control
Elsevier Science
c/o C. Chiarella, Ed.
University of Technology Sydney
Broadway
Sydney, New South Wales 2007, Australia
Publisher E-mail: nlinfo-f@elsevier.com
Journal focusing on computational methods in economics and finance and covering theoretical and empirical issues of economic dynamics and control. **Founded:** 1979. **Freq:** Monthly. **Key Personnel:** W.J. Den Haan, Advisory Ed.; C. Chiarella, Editor; P.N. Ireland, Editor; K.L. Judd, Advisory Ed.; C. Hommes, Editor; R.S. Pindyck, Advisory Ed. **ISSN:** 0165-1889. **Subscription Rates:** 243,700¥ institutions; EUR1,836 institutions for Europe; US$2,052 institutions, other countries; 12,600¥ individuals; EUR94 individuals for Europe; US$97 individuals other countries. **Remarks:** Accepts advertising. **URL:** http://www.elsevier.com/wps/find/journaldescription.cws_home/505547/description. **Circ:** (Not Reported)

42529 ■ Journal of Religious History
John Wiley & Sons Inc.
Wiley-Blackwell
c/o Christopher Hartney, Ed.
Studies in Religion
University of Sydney
Sydney, New South Wales 2006, Australia
Publication covering philosophy and religion. **Freq:** Quarterly. **Key Personnel:** Christopher Hartney, Editor, chris.hartney@usyd.edu.au; Carole M. Cusack, Editor, ccusack@mail.usyd.edu.au; Julie Smith, Review Ed., julie.smith@usyd.edu.au; David Hilliard, Assoc. Ed.; Lindsay Watson, Assoc. Ed.; Garry Trompf, Assoc. Ed. **ISSN:** 0022-4227. **Subscription Rates:** US$68 individuals print and online; US$475 institutions print and online; EUR417 institutions print and online; US$644 institutions, other countries print and online; 298 institutions print, online; US$432 institutions print, online; 329 institutions print and online; US$585 institutions, other countries print, online; EUR379 institutions print, online; 48 individuals print and online. **URL:** http://www.wiley.com/bw/journal.asp?ref=0022-4227&site=1.

42530 ■ The Journal of Research and Practice in Information Technology
Australian Computer Society Inc.
Queen Victoria Bldg.
PO Box Q534
Sydney, New South Wales 1230, Australia
Ph: 61 2 92993666
Fax: 61 2 92993997
Publisher E-mail: info@acs.org.au
Journal covering innovative research and practice in information technology worldwide for technology professionals and university and industry researchers. **Subtitle:** JRPIT. **Founded:** Nov. 1967. **Freq:** Quarterly. **Key Personnel:** Prof. Joan Cooper, Assoc. Ed., j.cooper@unsw.edu.au; John Hosking, Assoc. Ed., john@cs.auckland.ac.nz; Prof. Colin Fidge, Assoc. Ed., c.fidge@qut.edu.au; Prof. Hossam Elgindy, Assoc. Ed., elgindyh@cse.unsw.edu.au; Prof. Sidney Morris, Editor-in-Chief, jrpit@ballarat.edu.au. **ISSN:** 1443-458X. **Subscription Rates:** Free to members; $A 102 institutions; US$56 other countries; US$84 institutions, other countries; $A 68 individuals. **Remarks:** Accepts advertising. **URL:** http://www.acs.org.au/jrpit/. **Circ:** Combined ‡15,500

42531 ■ Journal of Science and Medicine in Sport
Elsevier Science Inc.
c/o Prof. Gregory Kolt, Ed.-in-Ch.
University of Western Sydney
School of Biomedical & Health Sciences
Sydney, New South Wales, Australia
Publisher E-mail: usinfo-ehelp@elsevier.com
Journal covering sport science and medicine related to specific applications to sport and exercise and its interaction with health. **Founded:** 1969. **Freq:** 6/yr. **Print Method:** Offset. **Trim Size:** 5 1/2 x 8 1/2. **Cols./Page:** 1. **Col. Width:** 50 nonpareils. **Col. Depth:** 100 agate lines. **Key Personnel:** Dr. Jill Cook, Editorial Board; Prof. Timothy Cable, Asst. Ed.; Dr. Kieran Fallon, Editorial Board; Prof. Gregory Kolt, Editor-in-Chief, c.finch@ballarat.edu.au; Dr. David Bishop, Asst. Ed.; Prof. Wendy Brown, Editorial Board. **ISSN:** 1440-2440. **Subscription Rates:** US$412 institutions, other countries except Europe, Japan and Iran; 44,300¥ institutions; EUR313 institutions for European countries and Iran; EUR80 individuals for European countries and Iran; 11,400¥ individuals; US$106 other countries except Europe, Japan and Iran. **URL:** http://www.elsevier.com/wps/find/journaldescription.cws_home/707423/descriptiondescription.

42532 ■ Knowledge-Based Systems
Elsevier Science Inc.
c/o Jie Lu, Ed.-in-Ch.
University of Technology
PO Box 123, Broadway
Sydney, New South Wales 2007, Australia
Publisher E-mail: usinfo-ehelp@elsevier.com
Peer-reviewed journal focusing on systems that use knowledge-based techniques. **Founded:** 1979. **Freq:** 8/yr, **Print Method:** Offset. **Trim Size:** 8 1/2 x 11. **Cols./Page:** 3. **Col. Width:** 13 picas. **Col. Depth:** 52 picas. **Key Personnel:** D. Benyon, Editorial Advisory Board; M.A. Bramer, Editorial Advisory Board; L. Candy, Editorial Advisory Board; P. Chung, Specialist Ed.; D. Diaper, Editorial Advisory Board; M. Eisenberg, Editorial Advisory Board; G. Fischer, Editorial Advisory Board; Hamido Fujita, Editor-in-Chief, issam@soft.iwate-pu.ac.jp; Jie Lu, Editor-in-Chief, jie.lu@uts.edu.au; B.R. Gaines, Editorial Advisory Board. **ISSN:** 0950-7051. **Subscription Rates:** US$1,405 institutions, other countries except Europe, Japan and Iran; EUR1,257 institutions for European countries and Iran; 166,700¥ institutions; EUR161 individuals for European countries and Iran; US$215 other countries except Europe, Japan and Iran; 24,800¥ individuals. **URL:** http://www.elsevier.com/wps/find/journaldescription.cws_home/525448/descriptiondescription.

42533 ■ The Kolan Recorder
APN News & Media Ltd.
100 William St., Level 4
Sydney, New South Wales 2011, Australia
Ph: 61 2 93334999
Fax: 61 2 93334900
Publisher E-mail: info@apn.com.au
Newspaper covering events and information in the Shire of Kolan. **Freq:** Monthly. **Subscription Rates:** Free. **Remarks:** Accepts advertising. **URL:** http://apnap.com.au/newspapers/community/4619.html. **Circ:** ‡2,400

42534 ■ Law Society Journal
The Law Society of New South Wales

170 Phillip St.
Sydney, New South Wales 2000, Australia
Ph: 61 2 99260333
Fax: 61 2 92315809
Publisher E-mail: lawsociety@lawsocnsw.asn.au
Law periodical. **Founded:** 1962. **Freq:** Monthly Except January. **Print Method:** Computer to Plate. **Trim Size:** 276 x 210 mm. **Key Personnel:** Karen Lavelle, Dep. Ed., kel@lawsocnsw.asn.au; Bob Campbell, Managing Editor, rsc@lawsocnsw.asn.au. **ISSN:** 0023-9372. **Subscription Rates:** US$195 individuals; $A 265 other countries airmail. **Remarks:** Accepts advertising. **URL:** http://www.lawsociety.com.au; http://www.lawsociety.com.au/page.asp?partid=303. **Ad Rates:** GLR: $A 16, 4C: $A 3,210. **Circ:** Paid 23,943

42535 ■ Leaping
Christian Dance Fellowship of Australia
c/o Cathy Wright, Membership Sec.
2/3A Nield Ave.
Sydney, New South Wales 2093, Australia
Publisher E-mail: admin@cdfa.org.au
Dance publication. **Freq:** 3/yr. **Key Personnel:** Alicja Harvie, National Coord. **URL:** http://www.cdfa.org.au/.

42536 ■ Limelight
Haymarket Media Pty. Ltd.
52 Victoria St.
McMahons Point
Sydney, New South Wales 2060, Australia
Ph: 61 2 83993611
Fax: 61 2 83993622
Magazine covering Australian arts and music. **Freq:** Monthly. **Trim Size:** 220 x 278 mm. **Key Personnel:** Francis Merson, Editor, fmerson@haymarketmedia.com.au. **Subscription Rates:** US$165 individuals. **Remarks:** Accepts advertising. **URL:** http://www.limelightmagazine.com.au/; http://www.haymarketmedia.com.au/magazines.aspx. **Ad Rates:** 4C: $A 4,200. **Circ:** ★11,299

42537 ■ Mackay & Sarina MidWeek
APN News & Media Ltd.
100 William St., Level 4
Sydney, New South Wales 2011, Australia
Ph: 61 2 93334999
Fax: 61 2 93334900
Publisher E-mail: info@apn.com.au
Newspaper for Mackay region. **Freq:** Weekly (Wed.). **Subscription Rates:** Free. **Remarks:** Accepts advertising. **URL:** http://apnap.com.au/newspapers/community/4607.html. **Circ:** ‡28,097

42538 ■ Macquarie Law Journal
Macquarie University
School of Law
Sydney, New South Wales 2109, Australia
Ph: 61 298 507111
Publication E-mail: publications@law.mq.edu.au
Publisher E-mail: mqinfo@mq.edu.au
Peer-reviewed journal of the Department of Law in the Division of Law at Macquarie University. **Freq:** Annual. **Key Personnel:** Dr. Shawkat Alam, Editor. **Subscription Rates:** $A 33 individuals. **URL:** http://www.law.mq.edu.au/html/MqLJ/about.htm.

42539 ■ Maritime Workers Journal
Maritime Union of Australia
Level 2, 365 Sussex St.
Sydney, New South Wales 2000, Australia
Ph: 61 2 92679134
Fax: 61 2 92613481
Publication E-mail: zoe@mua.org.au
Publisher E-mail: muano@mua.org.au
Publication covering marine. **Founded:** 1901. **Freq:** Quarterly. **Trim Size:** 205 x 275 mm. **Subscription Rates:** Free postage only to non-members; Included in membership. **Remarks:** Advertising not accepted. **URL:** http://mua.org.au/journals/. **Formerly:** Maritime Worker; Seamen's Journal; Maritime Workers' Journal. **Circ:** Non-paid ⊕10,000

42540 ■ Maroochy Weekly
APN News & Media Ltd.
100 William St., Level 4
Sydney, New South Wales 2011, Australia
Ph: 61 2 93334999
Fax: 61 2 93334900
Publisher E-mail: info@apn.com.au
Newspaper covering the latest in Maroochy Shire and the Sunshine Coast region. **Freq:** Weekly (Wed.). **Sub-**

scription Rates: Free. **Remarks:** Accepts advertising. **URL:** http://apnap.com.au/newspapers/community/4633.html. **Circ:** ‡9,865

42541 ■ The Maryborough Herald
APN News & Media Ltd.
100 William St., Level 4
Sydney, New South Wales 2011, Australia
Ph: 61 2 93334999
Fax: 61 2 93334900
Publisher E-mail: info@apn.com.au
Newspaper covering events in the city of Maryborough. **Freq:** Weekly (Wed.). **Subscription Rates:** Free. **Remarks:** Accepts advertising. **URL:** http://apnap.com.au/newspapers/community/4622.html. **Circ:** ‡11,880

42542 ■ Men's Style Australia
ACP Magazines Ltd.
54-58 Park St.
Sydney, New South Wales 2000, Australia
Ph: 61 2 92828000
Fax: 61 2 92674361
Fashion magazine for young urban men. **Freq:** Bimonthly. **Trim Size:** 235 x 297 mm. **Key Personnel:** Michael Pickering, Editor; Diana Johnson, National Advertising Mgr. **Subscription Rates:** $A 9.95 single issue. **Remarks:** Accepts advertising. **URL:** http://www.acp.com.au/mens_style_australia.htm. **Ad Rates:** 4C: $A 7,725. **Circ:** (Not Reported)

42543 ■ miceAsia.net
Business & Tourism Publishing
189 Kent St., Ste. 3
Sydney, New South Wales 2000, Australia
Ph: 61 2 82644444
Fax: 61 2 82644401
Magazine for business events industry through South East Asia. **Founded:** 2006. **Freq:** Quarterly. **Key Personnel:** Helen Batt-Rawden, Publisher/Mng. Dir., helen@btp.net.au; Brad Foster, Managing Editor, brad@btp.net.au. **Subscription Rates:** $A 60 individuals; $A 90 other countries. **Remarks:** Accepts advertising. **URL:** http://www.btp.net.au/digital-media/miceasianet.aspx. **Circ:** ‡17,548

42544 ■ mice.net
Business & Tourism Publishing
189 Kent St., Ste. 3
Sydney, New South Wales 2000, Australia
Ph: 61 2 82644444
Fax: 61 2 82644401
Magazine for the Australian business events community. **Founded:** 2000. **Freq:** Bimonthly. **Key Personnel:** Helen Batt-Rawden, Publisher/Mng. Dir., helen@btp.net.au; Brad Foster, Managing Editor, brad@btp.net.au. **Subscription Rates:** $A 60 individuals Australia, NZ and Pacific; $A 126 other countries. **Remarks:** Accepts advertising. **URL:** http://www.btp.net.au/digital-media/micenet.aspx. **Circ:** ‡14,794

42545 ■ miceNZ.net
Business & Tourism Publishing
189 Kent St., Ste. 3
Sydney, New South Wales 2000, Australia
Ph: 61 2 82644444
Fax: 61 2 82644401
Magazine for the New Zealand business events community. **Founded:** 2005. **Freq:** 3/yr. **Key Personnel:** Helen Batt-Rawden, Publisher/Mng. Dir., helen@btp.net.au; Brad Foster, Managing Editor, brad@btp.net.au. **Subscription Rates:** $A 60 individuals; $A 90 other countries. **Remarks:** Accepts advertising. **URL:** http://www.btp.net.au/digital-media/micenznet.aspx. **Circ:** ‡7,857

42546 ■ Miners MidWeek
APN News & Media Ltd.
100 William St., Level 4
Sydney, New South Wales 2011, Australia
Ph: 61 2 93334999
Fax: 61 2 93334900
Publisher E-mail: info@apn.com.au
Newspaper covering the Mackay region. **Freq:** Weekly (Wed.). **Subscription Rates:** Free. **Remarks:** Accepts advertising. **URL:** http://apnap.com.au/newspapers/community/4608.html. **Circ:** ‡5,078

42547 ■ The Morning Bulletin
APN News & Media Ltd.
100 William St., Level 4
Sydney, New South Wales 2011, Australia

Ph: 61 2 93334999
Fax: 61 2 93334900
Publisher E-mail: info@apn.com.au
Newspaper covering news and entertainment in the Rockhampton region. **Founded:** 1861. **Freq:** Mon.-Sat. **Subscription Rates:** $A 1.10 single issue Monday-Friday; $A 1.60 single issue Saturday. **Remarks:** Accepts advertising. **URL:** http://apnap.com.au/newspapers/daily/4610.html. **Circ:** Mon.-Fri. ★17,702, Sat. ★22,951

42548 ■ Mother & Baby
ACP Magazines Ltd.
54-58 Park St.
Sydney, New South Wales 2000, Australia
Ph: 61 2 92828000
Fax: 61 2 92674361
Parenting magazine. **Freq:** Bimonthly. **Key Personnel:** Abbi Rydge, National Sales Mgr., arydge@acpmagazines.com.au; Sharon Christal, Editor. **Remarks:** Accepts advertising. **URL:** http://www.acp.com.au/mother_baby.htm; http://motherandbaby.ninemsn.com.au/. **Circ:** ★134,000

42549 ■ My Perfect Wedding Planner
Studio Magazines
101-111 William St., Level 3
Sydney, New South Wales 2011, Australia
Ph: 61 2 93601422
Fax: 61 2 93609742
Magazine for future brides. **Trim Size:** 225 x 330 mm. **Key Personnel:** Kristy Meudell, Gp. Ed., kristy@studio.com.au; Thomas Boosz, Production Mgr., thomas@studio.com.au; Liz Davis, Office Mgr., liz@studio.com.au. **Subscription Rates:** $A 32 elsewhere. **Remarks:** Accepts advertising. **URL:** http://www.studiomagazines.com/mpwplanner/default.aspx. **Ad Rates:** 4C: $A 2,800. **Circ:** 30,000

42550 ■ Myer Emporium
ACP Magazines Ltd.
54-58 Park St.
Sydney, New South Wales 2000, Australia
Ph: 61 2 92828000
Fax: 61 2 92674361
Magazine focusing on the best Myer products and general fashion, beauty, and lifestyle. **Freq:** Quarterly. **Key Personnel:** Margaret Merten, Editor; Peter Harrison, Advertising Mgr. **Remarks:** Accepts advertising. **URL:** http://www.acp.com.au/myer_emporium.htm; http://www.myeremporium.com.au/. **Circ:** ★248,900

42551 ■ Nambour Weekly
APN News & Media Ltd.
100 William St., Level 4
Sydney, New South Wales 2011, Australia
Ph: 61 2 93334999
Fax: 61 2 93334900
Publisher E-mail: info@apn.com.au
Newspaper covering events in the town of Nambour, Sunshine Coast. **Founded:** 2004. **Freq:** Weekly (Wed.). **Subscription Rates:** Free. **Remarks:** Accepts advertising. **URL:** http://apnap.com.au/newspapers/community/4631.html. **Circ:** ‡10,952

42552 ■ NewsMail
APN News & Media Ltd.
100 William St., Level 4
Sydney, New South Wales 2011, Australia
Ph: 61 2 93334999
Fax: 61 2 93334900
Publisher E-mail: info@apn.com.au
Newspaper covering events in the Bundaberg area. **Founded:** 1938. **Freq:** Mon.-Sat. **Subscription Rates:** $A 1.10 single issue Monday-Friday; $A 1.50 single issue Saturday. **Remarks:** Accepts advertising. **URL:** http://apn.com.au/newspapers/daily/4616.html. **Circ:** Mon.-Fri. ★11,335, Sat. ★165,826

42553 ■ North West Country
APN News & Media Ltd.
100 William St., Level 4
Sydney, New South Wales 2011, Australia
Ph: 61 2 93334999
Fax: 61 2 93334900
Publisher E-mail: info@apn.com.au
Newspaper covering the rural North-West Queensland. **Founded:** 1987. **Freq:** Monthly. **Subscription Rates:** Free. **Remarks:** Accepts advertising. **URL:** http://apnap.com.au/newspapers/community/4665.html. **Circ:** ‡4,250

42554 ■ The North West Star
APN News & Media Ltd.
100 William St., Level 4
Sydney, New South Wales 2011, Australia
Ph: 61 2 92334999
Fax: 61 2 93334900
Publisher E-mail: info@apn.com.au
Newspaper reporting local issues and events in the Mount Isa region. **Freq:** Daily. **Subscription Rates:** $A 1.30 individuals. **Remarks:** Accepts advertising. **URL:** http://apnap.com.au/newspapers/daily/4664.html. **Circ:** ★2,936

42555 ■ Northern Downs News
APN News & Media Ltd.
100 William St., Level 4
Sydney, New South Wales 2011, Australia
Ph: 61 2 93334999
Fax: 61 2 93334900
Publisher E-mail: info@apn.com.au
Newspaper covering community issues and events in the Dalby district. **Founded:** 1950. **Freq:** Weekly (Thurs.). **Subscription Rates:** Free. **Remarks:** Accepts advertising. **URL:** http://apnap.com.au/newspapers/community/4671.html. **Circ:** ‡6,000

42556 ■ The Northern Rivers Echo
APN News & Media Ltd.
100 William St., Level 4
Sydney, New South Wales 2011, Australia
Ph: 61 2 93334999
Fax: 61 2 93334900
Publisher E-mail: info@apn.com.au
Newspaper covering events and information in Lismore, Alstonville, Wollongbar and surrounding areas. **Freq:** Weekly (Thurs.). **Subscription Rates:** Free. **Remarks:** Accepts advertising. **URL:** http://apnap.com.au/newspapers/community/4687.html. **Circ:** ‡22,980

42557 ■ Official PlayStation Magazine Australia
ACP Custom Media
54 Park St.
Sydney, New South Wales 2000, Australia
Ph: 61 292 828019
Fax: 61 292 673625
Magazine featuring new PlayStation 2 releases and news. **Freq:** Monthly. **Subscription Rates:** $A 120 individuals. **Formerly:** PlayStation 2 Official Australian Magazine.

42558 ■ PC Authority
Haymarket Media Pty. Ltd.
52 Victoria St.
McMahons Point
Sydney, New South Wales 2060, Australia
Ph: 61 2 83993611
Fax: 61 2 83993622
Magazine covering computers. **Freq:** Monthly. **Key Personnel:** Zara Baxter, Dep. Ed., zbaxter@pcauthority.com.au; William Maher, Brand Ed., wmaher@pcauthority.com.au. **Subscription Rates:** $A 79.95 individuals; $A 139.95 two years. **Remarks:** Accepts advertising. **URL:** http://www.haymarketmedia.com.au/magazines.aspx; http://www.pcauthority.com.au. **Circ:** (Not Reported)

42559 ■ Perfect Beat
Macquarie University
School of Law
Sydney, New South Wales 2109, Australia
Ph: 61 298 507111
Publisher E-mail: mqinfo@mq.edu.au
Journal publishing articles on development of new styles of popular music by indigenous peoples and their relationships (beneficial and/or problematic) with the technologies and institutions of the 20th Century media and music industries. Addresses to Australia, New Zealand, Hawaii, Papua New Guinea and the island nations of the South Pacific Forum. **Founded:** 1992. **Freq:** Semiannual Jan., and July. **Key Personnel:** Dr. Denis Crowdy, Editor, phone 61 2 98506787, denis.crowdy@mq.edu.au; Shane Homan, Review Ed.; Dr. Mark Evans, Editor, phone 61 2 98506780, fax 61 2 98506593, mark.evans@humn.mq.edu.au. **ISSN:** 1038-2909. **Subscription Rates:** US$40 individuals rest of the world; US$190 institutions print & online; US$80 individuals North America; US$75 individuals member (IASPM AU/NZ); US$181 institutions print; 90 institutions rest of the world. **URL:** http://www.dcms.mq.edu.au/perfectbeat/.

42560 ■ PESTALK
Australian Environmental Pest Managers Association
PO Box 4886
Sydney, New South Wales 2001, Australia
Ph: 61 2 92328929
Fax: 61 2 92328929
Magazine of the Australian Environmental Pest Managers Association, incorporated into the Professional Pest Manager Journal. **Freq:** Bimonthly. **URL:** http://www.aepma.com.au/.

42561 ■ Philament
University of Sydney
A20 - John Woolley Bldg.
Sydney, New South Wales 2006, Australia
Ph: 61 293 512222
Publisher E-mail: infocentre@mail.usyd.edu.au
Journal brought out by the students on cultural studies and the literary arts. **Subtitle:** An Online Journal of the Arts and Culture. **Freq:** 3/yr. **Key Personnel:** Anna Wallace, Editor; Sabina Rahman, Editor; Lachlan Montgomery, Editor; Roberta Kwan, Editor; David Adams, Editor; Shyamalika Heffernan, Editor. **ISSN:** 1449-0471. **URL:** http://www.arts.usyd.edu.au/publications/philament/about.htm.

42562 ■ The Picture Premium
ACP Magazines Ltd.
54-58 Park St.
Sydney, New South Wales 2000, Australia
Ph: 61 2 92828000
Fax: 61 2 92674361
Magazine for men. **Freq:** Monthly. **Trim Size:** 200 x 275 mm. **Key Personnel:** Boris Mihailovic, Editor; Patrick Campbell, National Sales Mgr. **Subscription Rates:** US$10.75 single issue. **Remarks:** Accepts advertising. **URL:** http://www.acp.com.au/the_picture_premium.htm. **Ad Rates:** 4C: $A 1,710. **Circ:** (Not Reported)

42563 ■ Port Curtis Post
APN News & Media Ltd.
100 William St., Level 4
Sydney, New South Wales 2011, Australia
Ph: 61 2 93334999
Fax: 61 2 93334900
Publisher E-mail: info@apn.com.au
Newspaper covering events and information in Gladstone district. **Freq:** Weekly (Mon.). **Subscription Rates:** Free. **Remarks:** Accepts advertising. **URL:** http://apnap.com.au/newspapers/community/4615.html. **Circ:** ‡14,505

42564 ■ Psychology, Public Policy, and Law
American Psychological Association
Journals Dept.
School of Psychology
University of New South Wales
Kensington
Sydney, New South Wales 2052, Australia
Publisher E-mail: journals@apa.org
Journal focusing on the links between psychology as a science and public policy and law. **Freq:** Quarterly. **Trim Size:** 7 x 10. **Key Personnel:** Jane Goodman-Delahunty, Consulting Ed.; Stanley L. Brodsky, Consulting Ed.; Roslyn M. Caldwell, Consulting Ed.; Brian H. Bornstein, Consulting Ed.; Bruce J. Winick, Legal Advisor; Connie J.A. Beck, Consulting Ed.; Neil Brewer, Consulting Ed.; Ronald Roesch, PhD, Editor; Ronald Roesch, Ed. **ISSN:** 1076-8971. **Subscription Rates:** US$55 members domestic; US$75 members surface; US$87 members air mail; US$27 students domestic; US$47 students surface; US$59 students air mail; US$89 individuals APA nonmember, domestic; US$114 nonmembers surface; US$124 nonmembers air mail; US$450 institutions domestic. **Remarks:** Accepts advertising. **URL:** http://www.apa.org/journals/law/. **Ad Rates:** BW: $A 375, 4C: $A 975. **Circ:** 2,100

42565 ■ Publications of the Astronomical Society of Australia
Astronomical Society of Australia
c/o Prof. J.W. O'Byrne
School of Physics
The University of Sydney
Sydney, New South Wales 2006, Australia
Refereed scientific journal of the Astronomical Society of Australia. **Freq:** Quarterly. **Key Personnel:** Bryan Gaensler, Editorial Board, bgaensler@usyd.edu.au.

ISSN: 1323-3580. **URL:** http://www.publish.csiro.au/nid/138.htm.

42566 ■ QT
APN News & Media Ltd.
100 William St., Level 4
Sydney, New South Wales 2011, Australia
Ph: 61 2 93334999
Fax: 61 2 93334900
Publisher E-mail: info@apn.com.au
Newspaper covering events and information for Ipswich and surrounding areas. **Subtitle:** The Queensland Times. **Freq:** Mon.-Sat. **Subscription Rates:** $A 1 single issue Monday-Friday; $A 1.50 single issue Saturday. **Remarks:** Accepts advertising. **URL:** http://apnap.com.au/newspapers/daily/4640.html. **Circ:** Mon.-Fri. ★10,792, Sat. ★13,999

42567 ■ Quadrant
Quadrant Magazine Company Inc.
PO Box 82
Sydney, New South Wales 2041, Australia
Ph: 61 2 98181155
Fax: 61 2 85804664
Publication E-mail: editor@quadrant.org.au
Publication featuring news, opinion, and commentary. **Freq:** 10/yr. **Key Personnel:** Keith Windschuttle, Editor, keithwindschuttle@quadrant.org.au; George Thomas, Dep. Ed., georgethomas@quadrant.org.au; Jean King, CEO, jeanking@quadrant.org.au. **ISSN:** 0033-5002. **Subscription Rates:** $A 75 individuals; $A 120 individuals Eastern Asia & Pacific Island; $A 90 individuals New Zealand; $A 150 other countries; $A 30 individuals online only; $A 300 individuals Quadrant Premium. **Remarks:** Accepts advertising. **Online:** Gale. **URL:** http://www.quadrant.org.au/. **Ad Rates:** BW: $A 800. **Circ:** (Not Reported)

42568 ■ The Range News
APN News & Media Ltd.
100 William St., Level 4
Sydney, New South Wales 2011, Australia
Ph: 61 2 93334999
Fax: 61 2 93334900
Publisher E-mail: info@apn.com.au
Newspaper covering local events and information in the Maleny community. **Freq:** Weekly (Thurs.). **Subscription Rates:** Free. **Remarks:** Accepts advertising. **URL:** http://apnap.com.au/newspapers/community/4638.html. **Circ:** ‡16,521

42569 ■ Real Living
ACP Magazines Ltd.
54-58 Park St.
Sydney, New South Wales 2000, Australia
Ph: 61 2 92828000
Fax: 61 2 92674361
Home and lifestyle magazine. **Freq:** Monthly. **Trim Size:** 225 x 270 mm. **Key Personnel:** Deborah Bibby, Editor; Milena Calic, National Sales Mgr. **Subscription Rates:** US$6.95 single issue. **Remarks:** Accepts advertising. **URL:** http://www.acp.com.au/real_living.htm. **Ad Rates:** 4C: $A 6,690. **Circ:** ★62,283

42570 ■ The Richmond River Express Examiner
APN News & Media Ltd.
100 William St., Level 4
Sydney, New South Wales 2011, Australia
Ph: 61 2 93334999
Fax: 61 2 93334900
Publisher E-mail: info@apn.com.au
Newspaper covering the residential and tourism area of Richmond Valley. **Freq:** Weekly (Wed.). **Subscription Rates:** Free. **Remarks:** Accepts advertising. **URL:** http://apnap.com.au/newspapers/community/4657.html. **Circ:** ‡12,468

42571 ■ The Rivertown Times
APN News & Media Ltd.
100 William St., Level 4
Sydney, New South Wales 2011, Australia
Ph: 61 2 93334999
Fax: 61 2 93334900
Publisher E-mail: info@apn.com.au
Newspaper covering local news and information in Evans Head, Woodburn, Broadwater and surrounding areas. **Freq:** Fortnightly. **Subscription Rates:** Free. **Remarks:** Accepts advertising. **URL:** http://apnap.com.au/newspapers/community/4659.html. **Circ:** ‡2,606

Circulation: ★ = ABC; △ = BPA; ◆ = CAC; • = CCAB; □ = VAC; ⊕ = PO Statement; ‡ = Publisher's Report; Boldface figures = sworn; Light figures = estimated.

42572 ■ Rockhampton and Fitzroy News
APN News & Media Ltd.
100 William St., Level 4
Sydney, New South Wales 2011, Australia
Ph: 61 2 93334999
Fax: 61 2 93334900
Publisher E-mail: info@apn.com.au
Newspaper covering events in the areas of Rockhampton and Fitzroy. **Freq:** Weekly (Wed.). **Subscription Rates:** Free. **Remarks:** Accepts advertising. **URL:** http://apnap.com.au/newspapers/community/4611.html. **Circ:** ‡24,635

42573 ■ Rural Weekly (Central Queensland edition)
APN News & Media Ltd.
100 William St., Level 4
Sydney, New South Wales 2011, Australia
Ph: 61 2 93334999
Fax: 61 2 93334900
Publisher E-mail: info@apn.com.au
Newspaper containing news for Central Queensland farmers and graziers. **Freq:** Weekly (Fri.). **Remarks:** Accepts advertising. **URL:** http://apnap.com.au/newspapers/special/4613.html. **Circ:** ‡24,937

42574 ■ Rural Weekly (North CQ edition)
APN News & Media Ltd.
100 William St., Level 4
Sydney, New South Wales 2011, Australia
Ph: 61 2 93334999
Fax: 61 2 93334900
Publisher E-mail: info@apn.com.au
Newspaper containing farming news for North Central Queensland region. **Freq:** Weekly (Thurs.). **Remarks:** Accepts advertising. **URL:** http://apnap.com.au/newspapers/special/4609.html. **Circ:** ‡15,608

42575 ■ Rural Weekly (Southern edition)
APN News & Media Ltd.
100 William St., Level 4
Sydney, New South Wales 2011, Australia
Ph: 61 2 93334999
Fax: 61 2 93334900
Publisher E-mail: info@apn.com.au
Newspaper covering Darling Downs, South Burnett, Fassifern and Logan Valley regions. **Freq:** every Thursday or Friday. **Remarks:** Accepts advertising. **URL:** http://apnap.com.au/newspapers/special/4648.html. **Circ:** ‡45,592

42576 ■ Rural Weekly (Wide Bay edition)
APN News & Media Ltd.
100 William St., Level 4
Sydney, New South Wales 2011, Australia
Ph: 61 2 93334999
Fax: 61 2 93334900
Publisher E-mail: info@apn.com.au
Newspaper covering events and information in the Wide Bay area. **Freq:** Weekly (Thurs.). **Remarks:** Accepts advertising. **URL:** http://apnap.com.au/newspapers/special/4623.html. **Circ:** ‡25,045

42577 ■ The Satellite
APN News & Media Ltd.
100 William St., Level 4
Sydney, New South Wales 2011, Australia
Ph: 61 2 93334999
Fax: 61 2 93334900
Publisher E-mail: info@apn.com.au
Newspaper covering events and issues in the Western Corridor of South-East Queensland. **Freq:** Weekly (Wed.). **Subscription Rates:** Free. **Remarks:** Accepts advertising. **URL:** http://apnap.com.au/newspapers/community/4642.html. **Circ:** ‡47,209

42578 ■ Scan
Macquarie University
School of Law
Sydney, New South Wales 2109, Australia
Ph: 61 298 507111
Publisher E-mail: mqinfo@mq.edu.au
Online journal devoted to the media arts and culture, drawing on media studies, cultural studies, media law, information and technology studies, fine arts and philosophy. **Subtitle:** Journal of Media Arts Culture. **Freq:** Quarterly. **Key Personnel:** John Sutton, Editorial Board; Jennifer Biddle, Editorial Board; Chris Chesher, Editorial Board; Tom Burvill, Editorial Board; Mitchell Dean, Editorial Board; Noel King, Editorial Board. **ISSN:** 1449-1818. **URL:** http://scan.net.au/scan/journal/index.php.

42579 ■ Slimming & Health
ACP Magazines Ltd.
54-58 Park St.
Sydney, New South Wales 2000, Australia
Ph: 61 2 92828000
Fax: 61 2 92674361
Health and fitness magazine. **Freq:** Monthly. **Trim Size:** 205 x 275 mm. **Key Personnel:** Laura Greaves, Actg. Ed. **Subscription Rates:** US$29.95 individuals 6 months; US$49.95 individuals; US$94.95 two years. **Remarks:** Accepts advertising. **URL:** http://www.acp.com.au/Publication.aspx?id=8ba3f791-e615-4579-b359-edc056962c53. **Circ:** ★33,761

42580 ■ South Burnett Times
APN News & Media Ltd.
100 William St., Level 4
Sydney, New South Wales 2011, Australia
Ph: 61 2 93334999
Fax: 61 2 93334900
Publisher E-mail: info@apn.com.au
Newspaper covering the agriculturally-diverse region of South Burnett. **Freq:** every Tuesday and Friday. **Subscription Rates:** $A 1 single issue. **Remarks:** Accepts advertising. **URL:** http://apnap.com.au/newspapers/community/4673.html. **Circ:** ★6,743

42581 ■ The Stanthorpe Border Post
APN News & Media Ltd.
100 William St., Level 4
Sydney, New South Wales 2011, Australia
Ph: 61 2 93334999
Fax: 61 2 93334900
Publisher E-mail: info@apn.com.au
Newspaper covering events and information in Stanthorpe and the Granite Belt. **Freq:** Semiweekly. **Subscription Rates:** $A 1 single issue. **Remarks:** Accepts advertising. **URL:** http://apnap.com.au/newspapers/community/4677.html. **Circ:** ★2,406

42582 ■ Studio Bambini
Studio Magazines
101-111 William St., Level 3
Sydney, New South Wales 2011, Australia
Ph: 61 2 93601422
Fax: 61 2 93609742
Fashion magazine for kids and teens. **Trim Size:** 225 x 300 mm. **Key Personnel:** Kristy Meudell, Gp. Ed., kristy@studio.com.au; Thomas Boosz, Production Mgr., thomas@studio.com.au; Liz Davis, Office Mgr., liz@studio.com.au. **Subscription Rates:** $A 20 individuals; $A 40 two years; $A 36 individuals New Zealand; $A 56 elsewhere. **Remarks:** Accepts advertising. **URL:** http://www.studiobambini.com/. **Ad Rates:** 4C: $A 4,840. **Circ:** 45,000

42583 ■ Sunshine Coast Daily
APN News & Media Ltd.
100 William St., Level 4
Sydney, New South Wales 2011, Australia
Ph: 61 2 93334999
Fax: 61 2 93334900
Publisher E-mail: info@apn.com.au
Newspaper containing lift-outs, property guide and lifestyle of Sunshine Coast. **Freq:** Weekly (Sun.). **Subscription Rates:** $A 1.40 single issue. **Remarks:** Accepts advertising. **URL:** http://apnap.com.au/newspapers/daily/4626.html. **Circ:** Mon.-Fri. ★20,259, Sat. ★30,794

42584 ■ Sunshine Coast Sunday
APN News & Media Ltd.
100 William St., Level 4
Sydney, New South Wales 2011, Australia
Ph: 61 2 93334999
Fax: 61 2 93334900
Publisher E-mail: info@apn.com.au
Newspaper reporting social events, entertainment, local opinions and sports in the Sunshine Coast. **Freq:** Sunday. **Subscription Rates:** $A 1.40 single issue. **Remarks:** Accepts advertising. **URL:** http://apnap.com.au/newspapers/daily/4627.html. **Circ:** ‡12,976

42585 ■ Surat Basin News
APN News & Media Ltd.
100 William St., Level 4
Sydney, New South Wales 2011, Australia
Ph: 61 2 93334999

Fax: 61 2 93334900
Publisher E-mail: info@apn.com.au
Newspaper covering the Surat Basin region. **Freq:** Quarterly. **Remarks:** Accepts advertising. **URL:** http://apnap.com.au/newspapers/special/4682.html. **Circ:** ‡12,500

42586 ■ The Sydney Morning Herald
Fairfax Media Limited
GPO 506
Sydney, New South Wales 2001, Australia
Ph: 61 2 92822833
Publisher E-mail: pmclean@fairfaxmedia.com.au
Newspaper covering local stories and news in Sydney. **Founded:** 1831. **Freq:** Daily. **Subscription Rates:** $A 349 individuals Monday to Sunday; 52 weeks; $A 28 individuals Monday to Sunday; direct debit every 4 weeks; $A 166 individuals weekend; 52 weeks; $A 13 individuals weekend; direct debit every 4 weeks. **Remarks:** Accepts advertising. **URL:** http://www.smh.com.au. **Circ:** (Not Reported)

42587 ■ Take 5
ACP Magazines Ltd.
54-58 Park St.
Sydney, New South Wales 2000, Australia
Ph: 61 2 92828000
Fax: 61 2 92674361
Magazine for women featuring real life stories. **Freq:** Weekly. **Trim Size:** 210 x 275 mm. **Key Personnel:** Belinda Wallis, Editor; Rohan Cubis, National Sales Mgr. **Subscription Rates:** US$2.95 single issue. **Remarks:** Accepts advertising. **URL:** http://www.acp.com.au/take_5.htm; http://www.take5mag.com.au/default.aspx. **Ad Rates:** 4C: $A 10,625. **Circ:** ★222,498

42588 ■ Toowoomba's Mail
APN News & Media Ltd.
100 William St., Level 4
Sydney, New South Wales 2011, Australia
Ph: 61 2 93334999
Fax: 61 2 93334900
Publisher E-mail: info@apn.com.au
Newspaper covering events and information in the areas of Toowoomba. **Freq:** Weekly (Thurs.). **Subscription Rates:** Free. **Remarks:** Accepts advertising. **URL:** http://apnap.com.au/newspapers/community/4647.html. **Circ:** ‡32,791

42589 ■ Tweed/Border Mail
APN News & Media Ltd.
100 William St., Level 4
Sydney, New South Wales 2011, Australia
Ph: 61 2 93334999
Fax: 61 2 93334900
Publisher E-mail: info@apn.com.au
Newspaper covering events and issues from Coolangatta to Ocean Shores. **Freq:** Weekly (Thurs.). **Subscription Rates:** Free. **Remarks:** Accepts advertising. **URL:** http://apnap.com.au/newspapers/community/4654.html. **Circ:** ‡38,754

42590 ■ Tweed Daily News
APN News & Media Ltd.
100 William St., Level 4
Sydney, New South Wales 2011, Australia
Ph: 61 2 93334999
Fax: 61 2 93334900
Publisher E-mail: info@apn.com.au
Newspaper covering events and information in the Tweed Heads community. **Founded:** 1888. **Freq:** Mon.-Sat. **Subscription Rates:** $A 1 single issue Monday-Friday; $A 1.30 single issue Saturday. **Remarks:** Accepts advertising. **URL:** http://apnap.com.au/newspapers/daily/4652.html. **Circ:** Mon.-Sat. ★4,317

42591 ■ Warwick Daily News
APN News & Media Ltd.
100 William St., Level 4
Sydney, New South Wales 2011, Australia
Ph: 61 2 93334999
Fax: 61 2 93334900
Publisher E-mail: info@apn.com.au
Newspaper covering events and information in the Darling Downs region. **Freq:** Mon.-Sat. **Subscription Rates:** $A 1.10 single issue Monday-Friday; $A 1.30 single issue Saturday. **Remarks:** Accepts advertising. **URL:** http://apnap.com.au/newspapers/daily/4649.html. **Circ:** Mon.-Sat. ★3,249, Sat. ★3,344

42592 ■ Warwick & Southern Downs Weekly
APN News & Media Ltd.
100 William St., Level 4
Sydney, New South Wales 2011, Australia
Ph: 61 2 93334999
Fax: 61 2 93334900
Publisher E-mail: info@apn.com.au
Newspaper covering Warwick, Killarney, Allora, Stanthorpe and surrounding areas. **Freq:** Weekly (Wed.). **Subscription Rates:** Free. **Remarks:** Accepts advertising. **URL:** http://apnap.com.au/newspapers/community/4650.html. **Circ:** ‡10,821

42593 ■ Whitsunday Times
APN News & Media Ltd.
100 William St., Level 4
Sydney, New South Wales 2011, Australia
Ph: 61 2 93334999
Fax: 61 2 93334900
Publisher E-mail: info@apn.com.au
Newspaper covering the local news and entertainment in Airlie Beach. **Freq:** Weekly (Thurs.). **Subscription Rates:** Free. **Remarks:** Accepts advertising. **URL:** http://apnap.com.au/newspapers/community/4606.html. **Circ:** Thurs. ‡7,431

42594 ■ ABC NewsRadio-AM - 630
GPO 9994
Sydney, New South Wales 2001, Australia
Ph: 61 2 139994
Format: News; Sports; Information. **Owner:** Australian Broadcasting Corporation, ABC Ultimo Ctr., 700 Harris St., Ultimo, New South Wales 2007, Australia, 61 2 8333 1500, Fax: 61 2 8333 5344. **Founded:** Aug. 1994. **Operating Hours:** Continuous. **Key Personnel:** Mark Scott, Mng. Dir.; David Pendleton, COO. **URL:** http://www.abc.net.au/newsradio/.

42595 ■ ABC NewsRadio-FM - 103.9
GPO Box 9994
Sydney, New South Wales 2001, Australia
Ph: 61 293 139994
Format: News. **Owner:** Australian Broadcasting Corporation, at above address. **Founded:** 1994. **URL:** http://www.abc.net.au.

42596 ■ ABC Radio National-AM - 576
GPO Box 9994
Sydney, New South Wales 2000, Australia
Ph: 61 2 83332821
Fax: 61 2 83332777
Format: Talk. **Owner:** Australian Broadcasting Corporation, 700 Harris St., Ultimo, New South Wales 2007, Australia, 61 2 83331500, Fax: 61 2 83335344. **URL:** http://www.abc.net.au/rn/.

4BBB-FM - See Brisbane, Queensland

42597 ■ MMM-FM - 104.9
Level 14, 50 Goulburn St.
Sydney, New South Wales 2000, Australia
Ph: 61 1 33353
Format: Alternative/New Music/Progressive. **Owner:** Austereo Group, Ltd., GPO Box 4442, Sydney, New South Wales, Australia. **URL:** http://www.triplem.com.au; http://www.austereo.com.au/.

42598 ■ RPH Print Radio-AM - 1224
PO Box A840
Sydney, New South Wales 1235, Australia
Ph: 61 3 98649207
E-mail: admin@rph.org.au
Format: Information; News; Sports. **Key Personnel:** Peter Luckett, Chm., phone 61 40 9064277; Ashley Morrison, Bus. Devel. Mgr., phone 61 40 9064061, bdm@rph.org.au. **URL:** http://www.rph.org.au.

42599 ■ 3FOX-FM - 101.9
GPO Box 4442
Sydney, New South Wales 2001, Australia
Format: Adult Contemporary; Contemporary Hit Radio (CHR). **Owner:** Austereo Pty. Ltd., at above address. **Key Personnel:** Peter M. Harvie, Chm. **Ad Rates:** Advertising accepted; rates available upon request. **URL:** http://fox.com.au/; http://www.austereo.com.au/.

42600 ■ 2CH-AM - 1170
Level 1, Bldg. C
33-35 Saunders St.
GPO Box 4290
Sydney, New South Wales 2001, Australia

Ph: 61 2 85700000
Fax: 61 2 85700219
Format: Easy Listening; Oldies. **Owner:** Macquarie Radio Network, at above address. **Operating Hours:** Continuous. **Ad Rates:** Advertising accepted; rates available upon request. **URL:** http://2ch.com.

42601 ■ 2DAY-FM - 104.1
50 Goulburn St., Level 15
Sydney, New South Wales 2000, Australia
Ph: 61 2 93751041
Format: Adult Contemporary. **Owner:** Austereo Pty. Ltd., GPO Box 4442, Sydney, New South Wales 2001, Australia. **Ad Rates:** Advertising accepted; rates available upon request. **URL:** http://www.2dayfm.com.au.

2JJJ-FM - See Goulburn

42602 ■ 2KY-AM - 1017
c/o Tabcorp Holdings Ltd.
PO Box 4168
Sydney, New South Wales 2001, Australia
Ph: 61 2 85711017
Fax: 61 2 92181054
Format: Sports. **Owner:** Sky Channel Pty. Ltd., 79 Frenchs Forest Rd., Frenchs Forest, New South Wales, Australia, 61 2 94528400, Fax: 61 2 94522222. **Founded:** 1925. **Operating Hours:** Continuous. **Key Personnel:** Terry Kennedy, Contact; Greg Radley, Contact; Greg Hayes, Contact. **Ad Rates:** Advertising accepted; rates available upon request. **URL:** http://www.2ky.com.au; http://www.skychannel.com.au.

42603 ■ 2MM-AM - 1665
Level 1A, 503-507 Marrickville Rd.
Dulwich Hill
Sydney, New South Wales 2203, Australia
Ph: 61 2 95646400
Fax: 61 2 95645488
E-mail: tc@2mm.com.au
Format: Ethnic; Sports. **Owner:** Mars Broadcasting Pty. Ltd., at above address. **Founded:** Sept. 1996. **Operating Hours:** Continuous. **Ad Rates:** Advertising accepted; rates available upon request. **URL:** http://www.2mm.com.au.

42604 ■ 2MM-FM - 151.925
Level 1A, 503-507 Marrickville Rd.
Dulwich Hill
Sydney, New South Wales 2203, Australia
Ph: 61 2 95646400
Fax: 61 2 95645488
E-mail: tc@2mm.com.au
Format: Ethnic; World Beat. **Operating Hours:** Continuous. **URL:** http://www.2mm.com.au.

42605 ■ 2MM-FM - 92.3
Level 1A, 503-507 Marrickville Rd.
Dulwich Hill
Sydney, New South Wales 2203, Australia
Ph: 61 2 95646400
Fax: 61 2 95645488
E-mail: tc@2mm.com.au
Format: Ethnic; World Beat. **Operating Hours:** Continuous. **URL:** http://www.2mm.com.au.

42606 ■ 2MM-FM - 99.3
Level 1A, 503-507 Marrickville Rd.
Dulwich Hill
Sydney, New South Wales 2203, Australia
Ph: 61 2 95646400
Fax: 61 2 95645488
E-mail: tc@2mm.com.au
Format: Ethnic; World Beat. **Operating Hours:** Continuous. **URL:** http://www.2mm.com.au.

42607 ■ 2MM-FM - 173.6
Level 1A, 503-507 Marrickville Rd.
Dulwich Hill
Sydney, New South Wales 2203, Australia
Ph: 61 2 95646400
Fax: 61 2 95645488
E-mail: tc@2mm.com.au
Format: Ethnic; World Beat. **Operating Hours:** Continuous. **URL:** http://www.2mm.com.au.

42608 ■ 2MMM-FM - 104.9
Level 14, 50 Goulburn St.
Sydney, New South Wales 2000, Australia
Ph: 61 2 93671000
Format: Album-Oriented Rock (AOR); Talk; Sports;

Classic Rock. **Owner:** Austereo Pty. Ltd., GPO Box 4442, Sydney, New South Wales 2001, Australia, 61 3 92301051, Fax: 61 3 95939008. **Key Personnel:** Peter M. Harvie, Chm.; Michael E. Anderson, CEO. **Ad Rates:** Advertising accepted; rates available upon request. **URL:** http://www.triplem.com.au/sydney; http://www.austereo.com.au.

Sydney (Victoria)

42609 ■ Rete Italia-AM - 1539
582 Nicholson St.
PO Box 159
Clifton Hill, Victoria 3068, Australia
Ph: 61 3 94810666
Fax: 61 3 94861412
Format: Ethnic; News; Sports; Talk. **Founded:** 1994. **Operating Hours:** Continuous. **Key Personnel:** Ivano Ercole, Station Mgr. **Ad Rates:** Advertising accepted; rates available upon request. **URL:** http://www.italianmedia.com.au.

Syndal

42610 ■ Australian Biologist
Australian Institute of Biology
PO Box 3014
Syndal, Victoria 3149, Australia
Ph: 61 3 98847405
Publisher E-mail: president@aibiol.org.au
Journal containing information about the developments in biology. **Freq:** Quarterly. **Key Personnel:** Graham Andrews, Exec. Ed., graham.andrews@interact.net.au. **Subscription Rates:** US$32 individuals non members; US$40 other countries. **URL:** http://www.aibiol.org.au/news/journal/writing.html.

Tamworth

42611 ■ Country Music Capital News
Rural Press Ltd.
2-6 Lockheed St.
PO Box 3520
Tamworth, New South Wales 2340, Australia
Ph: 61 2 67622399
Publication E-mail: capitalnews@ruralpress.com
Magazine featuring the Australian country music. **Freq:** Monthly. **Key Personnel:** Cheryl Byrnes, Contact, fax 61 2 67622350, cheryl.byrnes@ruralpress.com. **Subscription Rates:** $A 51 individuals; $A 96 two years. **Remarks:** Accepts advertising. **URL:** http://www.capitalnews.com.au/. **Circ:** (Not Reported)

42612 ■ Northern Daily Leader
92 Brisbane St.
PO Box 525
Tamworth, New South Wales 2340, Australia
Publisher E-mail: mail.ndi@ruralpress.com
General newspaper. **Freq:** Mon.-Sat. **Print Method:** Web offset. **Cols./Page:** 7. **Col. Width:** 15.5 centimeters. **Col. Depth:** 38 centimeters. **Key Personnel:** Barry McDonald, Advertising Mgr.; John Sommerlad, Managing Editor. **Remarks:** Accepts advertising. **URL:** http://www.northerndailyleader.com.au/. **Circ:** Paid 9,214

Tanunda

42613 ■ Triple B-FM - 89.1
PO Box 654
Basedow Rd.
Tanunda, South Australia 5352, Australia
Ph: 61 8 85633788
Fax: 61 8 8563078
E-mail: mail@bbbfm.com
Format: Eclectic; Information; Sports; Public Radio. **Operating Hours:** Continuous. **Ad Rates:** Noncommercial; underwriting available. **URL:** http://www.bbbfm.com.

Taree

42614 ■ 2BOB-FM - 104.7
Cor. of Macquarie & Wynter Sts.
PO Box 400
Taree, New South Wales 2430, Australia
Ph: 61 2 65526200
E-mail: admin@2bobradio.org.au
Format: Eclectic; Public Radio; Talk. **Operating Hours:**

Circulation: ★ = ABC; △ = BPA; ♦ = CAC; • = CCAB; ❏ = VAC; ⊕ = PO Statement; ‡ = Publisher's Report; Boldface figures = sworn; Light figures = estimated.

Gale Directory of Publications & Broadcast Media/147th Ed.   4759

Continuous. **Ad Rates:** Underwriting available. **URL:** http://www.2bobradio.org.au/.

42615 ■ 2RE-AM - 1557 KHz
PO Box 275
Taree, New South Wales 2430, Australia
Ph: 61 2 65510557
E-mail: sales@2re.com.au
Format: News; Talk; Sports; Oldies. **Owner:** Federation of Australian Radio Broadcasters, PO Box 299, Saint Leonards, New South Wales, Australia, Fax: 61 2 99065128. **Founded:** Feb. 21, 1953. **Operating Hours:** Continuous Mon.-Fri.; 6a.m.-12p.m. Sat.; 7a.m.-1p.m. Sun. **Ad Rates:** Advertising accepted; rates available upon request. **URL:** http://www.2re.com.au/.

Templestowe

42616 ■ FB Magazine
Elite Publishing
PO Box 800
Templestowe, Victoria 3106, Australia
Ph: 61 3 98441728
Fax: 61 3 98445300
Magazine for professionals in the furniture, furnishing, and bedding industries in Australia and New Zealand. **Freq:** 6/yr. **Trim Size:** 210 x 297 mm. **Key Personnel:** Ashley Cooper, Contact, ashley.cooper@elitepublishing. com.au. **Subscription Rates:** US$65 individuals; US$120 two years; US$170 individuals 3 years; $A 90 other countries. **Remarks:** Accepts advertising. **URL:** http://www.elitepublishing.com.au/fb/index.asp. **Formerly:** Furniture magazine; Bedding magazine. **Circ:** 8,960

42617 ■ Promotional Products Magazine
Elite Publishing
PO Box 800
Templestowe, Victoria 3106, Australia
Ph: 61 3 98441728
Fax: 61 3 98445300
Marketing featuring product marketing and advertising. **Freq:** Quarterly February, May, August and November. **Trim Size:** 210 x 297 mm. **Key Personnel:** Ashley Cooper, Contact, ashley.cooper@elitepublishing.com. au. **Remarks:** Accepts advertising. **URL:** http://www. elitepublishing.com.au/promotional/index.asp. **Circ:** Combined 6,000

42618 ■ Supplier Woodworking magazine
Elite Publishing
PO Box 800
Templestowe, Victoria 3106, Australia
Ph: 61 3 98441728
Fax: 61 3 98445300
Business magazine for manufacturers in the kitchen, furniture, joinery, shop and office fittings, cabinetmaking, timber and panel products industries in Australasia. **Freq:** Bimonthly. **Key Personnel:** Vicky Cammiade, Director, vicky.cammiade@elitepublishing.com.au. **Subscription Rates:** US$90 individuals; US$170 two years; US$245 individuals 3 years; $A 100 other countries. **Remarks:** Accepts advertising. **URL:** http://www. elitepublishing.com.au/supplier/index.asp. **Circ:** 17,000

Tennant Creek

42619 ■ Flow-FM - 100.5
PO Box 407
Kapunda, South Australia 5373, Australia
Ph: 61 8 85663151
Fax: 61 8 85662729
E-mail: mail@flowfm.com.au
Format: Adult Contemporary. **URL:** http://www.flowfm. com.au/.

42620 ■ SBS Television - 10
Locked Bag 028
Crows Nest, New South Wales 1585, Australia
Ph: 61 2 94302828
Fax: 61 2 94303047
Owner: Special Broadcasting Service, at above address. **Wattage:** 2000 ERP. **URL:** http://www20.sbs.com.au/ transmissions/index.php?pid=2&id=746.

Tenterfield

42621 ■ 2TEN-FM - 89.7
142 Manners St.
Tenterfield, New South Wales 2372, Australia

Ph: 61 2 67363444
Fax: 61 2 67362197
E-mail: info@tenfm.org.au
Format: Country; Easy Listening; Top 40; Contemporary Christian. **Key Personnel:** Rebecca Carpenter, Station Mgr.; Marion Saxby, Vice President; Peter van Schaik, President. **URL:** http://www.tenfm.org.au/.

Thredbo

42622 ■ Snow-FM - 92.9
28 Sharp St.
Cooma, New South Wales 2630, Australia
Ph: 61 2 64561555
Fax: 61 2 64561006
E-mail: xl@capitalradio.net.au
Format: Alternative/New Music/Progressive; Contemporary Hit Radio (CHR). **URL:** http://www.snowfm.com.au/.

42623 ■ 2XL-FM - 92.1
28 Sharp St.
Cooma, New South Wales 2630, Australia
Ph: 61 2 64521521
Fax: 61 2 64521006
E-mail: xl@capitalradio.net.au
Format: News; Talk; Adult Contemporary. **Key Personnel:** Richard Wybrew, Station Mgr. **Ad Rates:** Advertising accepted; rates available upon request. **URL:** http:// www.2xl.com.au/.

Toodyay

42624 ■ SBS Television - 34
Locked Bag 028
Crows Nest, New South Wales 1585, Australia
Ph: 61 2 94302828
Fax: 61 2 94303047
Owner: Special Broadcasting Service, at above address. **Wattage:** 50 ERP. **URL:** http://www20.sbs.com.au/ transmissions/index.php?pid=2&id=649.

Toowoomba

42625 ■ Australian Cotton Outlook
Rural Press Ltd.
70 Neil St.
PO Box 864
Toowoomba, Queensland 4350, Australia
Ph: 61 7 43684633
Fax: 61 7 43685491
Publication E-mail: aco.qcl@ruralpress.com
Newspaper covering the Australian cotton industry. **Freq:** Monthly. **Key Personnel:** Genevieve McCauley, Editor; Keith Hinz, Advertising Mgr., keith.hinz@ruralpress.com. **Remarks:** Accepts advertising. **URL:** http://www. ruralpress.com/publications/detail.asp?publication_id= 100. **Circ:** ‡21,150

42626 ■ Australian Journal of Organisational Behavior & Management
Human Resource Management & Employment Relations
University of Southern Queensland
West St.
Toowoomba, Queensland 4350, Australia
Ph: 61 7 46312100
Fax: 61 7 46312893
Electronic journal covering management and organizational behavior for students of the University of Southern Queensland. **Key Personnel:** Cec Pedersen, Sen. Ed. **ISSN:** 1447-574X. **URL:** http://www.usq.edu.au/ extrafiles/business/journals/HRMJournal/AJMOBHome. htm. **Former name:** Australian Journal of Management & Organisational Behaviour.

42627 ■ The Australian Mathematical Society Gazette
Australian Mathematical Publication Association Inc.
c/o Birgit Loch, Ed.
Dept. of Mathematics & Computing
University of Southern Queensland
Toowoomba, Queensland 4350, Australia
Ph: 61 7 4631 1157
Fax: 61 7 4631 5550
Publication E-mail: gazette@austms.org.au
Publisher E-mail: admin@austms.org.au
Publication covering mathematics. **Founded:** 1974. **Freq:** 5/yr (March, May, July, September, November). **Print Method:** Photo offset. **Trim Size:** 7 x 10. **Key Personnel:** Birgit Loch, Editor; Rachel Thomas, Editor;

Eileen Dallwitz, Production Ed. **ISSN:** 0311-0729. **Subscription Rates:** $A 103 individuals (GST inclusive); $A 118 individuals overseas customers; US$110 individuals overseas customers. **Remarks:** Accepts advertising. **URL:** http://www.austms.org.au; http://www.austms.org. au/Gazette. **Ad Rates:** BW: $A 380. **Circ:** 1,000

42628 ■ International Journal of Information Quality
Inderscience Publishers
c/o Dr. Latif Al-Hakim, Ed.-in-Ch.
University of Southern Queensland
School of Management & Marketing
Faculty of Business
Toowoomba, Queensland 4350, Australia
Publisher E-mail: editor@inderscience.com
Peer-reviewed journal covering implementation of information quality systems. **Founded:** 2007. **Freq:** 4/yr. **Key Personnel:** Dr. Latif Al-Hakim, Editor-in-Chief, hakim@usq.edu.au; Dr. Monica Scannapieco, Assoc. Ed.; Prof. Ganesan Shankaranayanan, Regional Ed. **ISSN:** 1751-0457. **Subscription Rates:** EUR494 individuals includes surface mail, print only; EUR672 individuals print and online. **URL:** http://www. inderscience.com/browse/index.php?journalCODE=ijiq.

42629 ■ Queensland Farmer & Grazier
Rural Press Ltd.
70 Neil St.
PO Box 864
Toowoomba, Queensland 4350, Australia
Ph: 61 7 43683222
Fax: 61 7 46382118
Newspaper covering the grain farming industry in Queensland. **Freq:** Monthly. **Key Personnel:** Graham Fuller, Editor, grafull@bigpond.net.au; Keith Hinz, Advertising Mgr., keith.hinz@ruralpress.com; John Walters, General Mgr., john.warlters@ruralpress.com. **Remarks:** Accepts advertising. **URL:** http://www. ruralpress.com/publications/detail.asp?publication_id= 106. **Circ:** ‡19,300

42630 ■ CFM-FM - 100.7
104-106 Margaret St.
Toowoomba, Queensland 4350, Australia
Ph: 61 7 46323333
Fax: 61 7 46383129
Format: Adult Contemporary. **Ad Rates:** Advertising accepted; rates available upon request. **URL:** http:// theradio.com/Hitmusic.aspx?PageID=1283&Station= CFM_Darling_Downs.

CFM-FM - See Kingaroy

42631 ■ 4GR-AM - 864
104-106 Margaret St.
Toowoomba, Queensland 4350, Australia
Ph: 61 7 46323333
Fax: 61 7 49383129
Format: Oldies. **Key Personnel:** Russ Wilson, Station Mgr., russ.wilson@macsc.com.au; Dave Harris, Contact, dave.harris@macsc.com.au. **URL:** http://theradio.com. au.

42632 ■ 4WK-AM - 1359
PO Box 403
Toowoomba, Queensland 4350, Australia
Ph: 61 7 46329999
Fax: 61 7 46391310
E-mail: news@4wk.com.au
Format: Full Service. **URL:** http://www.4wk.com.au/.

42633 ■ The Light-FM - 92.9
PO Box 3367
Village Fair
Toowoomba, Queensland 4350, Australia
Ph: 61 7 46394981
Fax: 61 7 46393077
E-mail: admin@radio929.fm
Format: Religious; Contemporary Christian; Talk. **Owner:** Toowoomba Christian Broadcasters Association Inc., at above address. **Operating Hours:** Continuous. **Key Personnel:** Ian Andersen, President; Donna Bloomfield, Admin. **Ad Rates:** Noncommercial; underwriting available. **URL:** http://www.radio929.fm.

Townsville

42634 ■ Australian Archaeology
Australian Archaeological Association
3 Queens Rd.
Railway Estate

Townsville, Queensland 4810, Australia
Journal featuring articles on archaeology. **Freq:** Semiannual. **Key Personnel:** Sean Ulm, Editor; Annie Ross, Editor. **Subscription Rates:** Included in membership; $A 120 institutions; $A 95 nonmembers. **URL:** http://www.australianarchaeologicalassociation.com.au/australian_archaeology.

42635 ■ The Electronic Journal of Australian and New Zealand History
James Cook University
School of Humanities
101 Angus
Smith Dr.
Townsville, Queensland 4811, Australia
Ph: 61 747 814111
Fax: 61 747 796371
Scholarly journal covering history in Australia and New Zealand. **Founded:** 1996. **Key Personnel:** Dr. Aviva Tuffield, Book Review Ed.; Dr. Paul Turnbull, On-Line Ed. **ISSN:** 1321-5752. **URL:** http://www.jcu.edu.au/aff/history/.

42636 ■ James Cook University Law Review
James Cook University
School of Law
101 Angus Smith Dr.
Townsville, Queensland 4811, Australia
Ph: 61 747 814111
Fax: 61 747 796371
Publication E-mail: law.review@jcu.edu.au
Publisher E-mail: enquiriestownsville@jcu.edu.au
Refereed law journal. **Freq:** Annual. **ISSN:** 1321-1072. **Subscription Rates:** $A 50 individuals; $A 55 other countries. **Remarks:** Advertising not accepted. **URL:** http://www.jcu.edu.au/law/law_review/index.htm. **Circ:** (Not Reported)

42637 ■ Journal of Rural and Tropical Public Health
James Cook University
Tourism Program
Townsville, Queensland 4811, Australia
Ph: 61 7 47814942
Fax: 61 7 47816116
Publisher E-mail: registrar@jcu.edu.au
Journal on public health with a focus on rural and tropical situations. **Freq:** Annual. **Key Personnel:** Dr. Petra Buettner, Editor-in-Chief, adrian.miller@jcu.edu.au. **ISSN:** 1832-2921. **URL:** http://www.jcu.edu.au/jrtph/index.html.

42638 ■ North Queensland Register
Rural Press Ltd.
53 Bowen Rd.
PO Box 1907
Townsville, Queensland 4810, Australia
Ph: 61 7 47593000
Fax: 61 7 47598662
Newspaper covering events and information in the rural areas of Northern Australia. **Founded:** 1891. **Freq:** Weekly (Thurs.). **Key Personnel:** John Warlters, General Mgr., john.warlters@ruralpress.com; Jim Pola, Gen. Regional Mgr., jim.pola@ruralpress.com; Jason Rickert, Advertising Mgr., jason.rickert@ruralpress.com. **Subscription Rates:** $A 76.20 individuals; $A 143.44 two years; $A 1.30 single issue. **Remarks:** Accepts advertising. **URL:** http://www.ruralpress.com/publications/detail.asp?publication_id=103. **Circ:** (Not Reported)

42639 ■ ABC North Queensland - 630 KHz
PO Box 694
Townsville, Queensland 4810, Australia
Ph: 61 7 47223011
Fax: 61 7 47223099
Format: News; Talk. **Owner:** Australian Broadcasting Corporation, ABC Ultimo Ctr., 700 Harris St., Ultimo 2007, Sydney, New South Wales 2001, Australia, 61 2 83331500, Fax: 61 2 83335344. **Formerly:** 4QN-AM. **Key Personnel:** Theresa Rockley-Hogan, Contact. **Wattage:** 50,000. **URL:** http://www.abc.net.au/northqld/.

42640 ■ 4K1G-FM - 107.1
271-279 Sturt St.
PO Box 5483
Townsville, Queensland 4810, Australia
Ph: 61 7 47725466
Fax: 61 7 47211902

E-mail: mail@4k1g.org
Format: Ethnic. **Key Personnel:** Linda Saltner, Station Mgr. **URL:** http://www.4k1g.org/.

42641 ■ 4TO-FM - 102.3
9 Martinez Ave.
Townsville, Queensland 4812, Australia
Ph: 61 7 47292111
Format: Adult Contemporary; Oldies; News; Sports. **Operating Hours:** Continuous. **Key Personnel:** David Langsford, Contact, david.langsford@macsc.com.au; Clint Corbett, Station Mgr., clint.corbett@macsc.com.au. **URL:** http://theradio.com.au.

42642 ■ 4TTT-FM - 103.9
PO Box 1033
Townsville, Queensland 4810, Australia
Ph: 61 7 47215333
Fax: 61 7 47215853
E-mail: admin@triplet.com.au
Format: Eclectic. **Operating Hours:** Continuous. **Key Personnel:** Sheena Bradshaw, Manager, stationmanager@triplet.com.au. **Wattage:** 20,000. **URL:** http://www.triplet.com.au/.

Traralgon

42643 ■ 3TR-FM - 99.5
Cor. Princes Hwy. & Coonoc Rd.
Traralgon, Victoria 3844, Australia
Ph: 61 3 51731000
Fax: 61 3 51731099
Format: Adult Contemporary; Top 40. **URL:** http://theradio.com.au/Hitmusic.aspx?PageID=6050&Station=3TR_FM_LatrobeValley_EastGippsland.

Tuggeranong

42644 ■ SBS Television - 54
Locked Bag 028
Crows Nest, New South Wales 1585, Australia
Ph: 61 2 94302828
Fax: 61 2 94303047
Owner: Special Broadcasting Service, at above address. **Wattage:** 640 ERP. **URL:** http://www20.sbs.com.au/transmissions/index.php?pid=2&id=4.

Tullamarine

42645 ■ Alfa Lotfeeding Magazine
Unit 6, 99-101 Western Ave.
Tullamarine, Victoria 3043, Australia
Technical, trade magazine covering cattle lot feeding. **Freq:** Bimonthly. **Key Personnel:** Donna Clarke, Advertising Mgr., admgr.afj@ruralpress.com; Grant Cochrane, General Mgr.; Jon Condon, Editor, phone 61 7 38268200, fax 61 7 38211226, livestockeditor.qcl@ruralpress.com. **Remarks:** Accepts advertising. **URL:** http://www.farmonline.com.au/farmmags/alfalotfeeding/index.aspx. **Circ:** Controlled 8,000

42646 ■ Australasian Flowers
Rural Press Ltd.
Unit 6, 99-101 Western Ave.
Tullamarine, Victoria 3043, Australia
Ph: 61 3 93449999
Fax: 61 3 93381044
Magazine covering the cut-flower industry in Australia. **Freq:** Quarterly. **Key Personnel:** Grant Cochrane, General Mgr.; Donna Clarke, Advertising Mgr., admgr. austhort@ruralpress.com; Brad Cooper, Editor, brad.cooper@ruralpress.com. **Subscription Rates:** $A 28 individuals; $A 50.40 two years; $A 6.95 single issue. **Remarks:** Accepts advertising. **URL:** http://www.ruralpress.com/publications/detail.asp?publication_id=125. **Circ:** Paid ‡1,009

42647 ■ Australian Dairyfarmer
Rural Press Ltd.
Unit 6, 99-101 Western Ave.
Tullamarine, Victoria 3043, Australia
Ph: 61 3 93449999
Fax: 61 3 93381044
Magazine covering the dairyfarming industry in Australia. **Freq:** Bimonthly. **Key Personnel:** Alastair Dowe, Editor, alastair.dowie@ruralpress.com; Grant Cochrane, General Mgr.; Carlene Dowie, Assoc. Ed. **Remarks:** Accepts advertising. **URL:** http://www.ruralpress.com/

publications/detail.asp?publication_id=126. **Circ:** ‡14,112

42648 ■ Australian Horticulture
Rural Press Ltd.
Unit 6, 99-101 Western Ave.
Tullamarine, Victoria 3043, Australia
Magazine featuring the horticultural industry in Australia. **Founded:** 1903. **Freq:** Monthly. **Key Personnel:** Grant Cochrane, General Mgr.; Brad Cooper, Editor, brad.cooper@ruralpress.com; Patricia Samson, Advertising Mgr., patricia.samson@ruralpress.com. **Subscription Rates:** $A 83.40 individuals; $A 150.12 two years; $A 6.95 single issue. **Remarks:** Accepts advertising. **URL:** http://www.ruralpress.com/publications/detail.asp?publication_id=128. **Circ:** *2,360

42649 ■ Australian Landcare
Rural Press Ltd.
Unit 6, 99 - 101 Western Ave.
Tullamarine, Victoria 3043, Australia
Ph: 61 3 93449999
Fax: 61 3 93381044
Magazine focusing on natural resources management. **Freq:** Quarterly. **Key Personnel:** Grant Cochrane, General Mgr.; Donna Clarke, Advertising Mgr., admgr. afj@ruralpress.com. **Subscription Rates:** $A 28.10 individuals. **Remarks:** Accepts advertising. **URL:** http://www.ruralpress.com/publications/detail.asp?publication_id=129; http://www.farmonline.com.au/farmmags/australianlandcare/index.aspx. **Circ:** ‡33,000

42650 ■ Brimbank Leader
Leader Community Newspapers
144 Melrose Dr., Level 1
Tullamarine, Victoria 3043, Australia
Ph: 61 3 83186200
Local community newspaper. **Freq:** Weekly (Tues). **Key Personnel:** Brooke Kelly, Editor, brimbank@leadernewspapers.com.au; Gusto Simandjuntak, Sales Mgr., simandjuntakg@leadernewspapers.com.au. **Remarks:** Accepts advertising. **URL:** http://brimbank-leader.whereilive.com.au/. **Circ:** Tues. ‡61,598

42651 ■ Hume Leader
Leader Community Newspapers
144 Melrose Dr., Level 1
Tullamarine, Victoria 3043, Australia
Ph: 61 3 83186200
Local community newspaper. **Freq:** Weekly (Tues). **Key Personnel:** Paige Ricci, Editor, hume@leadernewspapers.com.au; Gusto Simanjuntak, Sales Mgr., simandjuntakg@leadernewspapers.com.au. **Remarks:** Accepts advertising. **URL:** http://hume-leader.whereilive.com.au/. **Circ:** Tues. ‡42,878

42652 ■ Irrigation and Water Resources
Rural Press Ltd.
Unit 6, 99- 101 Western Ave.
Tullamarine, Victoria 3043, Australia
Ph: 61 3 93449999
Fax: 61 3 93381044
Magazine covering the developments in irrigation and water resources. **Freq:** Quarterly. **Key Personnel:** Grant Cochrane, General Mgr.; Donna Clarke, Advertising Mgr., admgr.afj@ruralpress.com. **Remarks:** Accepts advertising. **URL:** http://www.ruralpress.com/publications/detail.asp?publication_id=202. **Circ:** ‡14,500

42653 ■ Stock & Land
Rural Press Ltd.
Unit 6, 99 - 101 Western Ave.
PO Box 2544
Tullamarine, Victoria 3043, Australia
Ph: 61 3 93449999
Newspaper covering agricultural events and information in South East Australia. **Founded:** 1914. **Freq:** Weekly. **Key Personnel:** John Carson, General Mgr., john.carson@ruralpress.com; Tom Dawkins, Managing Editor. **Subscription Rates:** $A 92.82 individuals; $A 174.72 two years; $A 2.10 single issue. **Remarks:** Accepts advertising. **URL:** http://www.ruralpress.com/publications/detail.asp?publication_id=138; http://sl.farmonline.com.au/. **Circ:** Paid *10,004

Tuncurry

42654 ■ Great Lakes-FM - 101.5
16 Douglas Ave.

Circulation: ★ = ABC; △ = BPA; ♦ = CAC; • = CCAB; ❑ = VAC; ⊕ = PO Statement; ‡ = Publisher's Report; Boldface figures = sworn; Light figures = estimated.

PO Box 493
Tuncurry, New South Wales 2428, Australia
Ph: 61 2 65558433
Fax: 61 2 65556642
E-mail: info@greatlakesfm.org.au
Format: Adult Contemporary; Easy Listening. **Operating Hours:** Continuous. **Key Personnel:** Kay Holohan, Sales Mgr.; Shayne McBride, Technician. **Wattage:** 5000. **Ad Rates:** Underwriting available. **URL:** http://www.greatlakesfm.org.au.

Tweed Heads

42655 ■ Australian Birdkeeper Magazine
ABK Publications
PO Box 6288
Tweed Heads, New South Wales 2486, Australia
Ph: 61 7 55907777
Fax: 61 7 55907130
Publication E-mail: birdkeeper@birdkeeper.com.au
Publisher E-mail: birdkeeper@birdkeeper.com.au
Magazine covering popular cage/aviary birds. **Founded:** 1989. **Freq:** Bimonthly. **Trim Size:** A4. **ISSN:** 1030-8954. **Subscription Rates:** $A 69 individuals; US$95 other countries. **Remarks:** Accepts advertising. **URL:** http://www.birdkeeper.com.au/. **Circ:** 9,500

42656 ■ Radio-FM - 103.5
8 Greenway Dr.
Tweed Heads, New South Wales 2486, Australia
Ph: 61 7 55244497
Fax: 61 7 55230397
E-mail: admin@radio97.com.au
Format: Sports. **Ad Rates:** Advertising accepted; rates available upon request. **URL:** http://www.radio97.com.au.

Ultimo

5ABC-FM - See Adelaide, South Australia

42657 ■ 5ABC-FM Oak Valley - 107.3
ABC Ultimo Ctr.
700 Harris St.
Ultimo, New South Wales 2007, Australia
Ph: 61 2 83331500
Fax: 61 2 83335344
Format: Classical. **Owner:** Australian Broadcasting Corp., at above address. **URL:** http://abc.com.au/classic/freq/freqsa.htm.

4ABC-FM - See Airlie Beach, Queensland

4ABC-FM - See Cloncurry, Queensland

42658 ■ 6ABC-FM Central Agricultural - 98.9
ABC Ultimo Ctr.
700 Harris St.
Ultimo, New South Wales 2007, Australia
Ph: 61 2 83331500
Fax: 61 2 83335344
Format: Classical. **Owner:** Australian Broadcasting Corp., at above address. **URL:** http://abc.com.au/classic/freq/freqwa.htm.

2ABC-FM - See Batemans Bay

Unley

42659 ■ Agenda
Australian Graphic Design Association
PO Box 816
Unley, South Australia 5061, Australia
Ph: 11 61 84113888
Fax: 11 61 82768003
Publisher E-mail: secretariat@agda.com.au
Journal containing articles on design issues, notices and calendar of events. **Freq:** Quarterly. **URL:** http://www.agda.com.au/.

42660 ■ Pig Industry News
Rural Press Ltd.
123 Greenhill Rd.
Unley, South Australia 5061, Australia
Ph: 61 8 83725222
Magazine covering the Australian pig industry. **Freq:** Quarterly. **Key Personnel:** Joe Wallman, General Mgr. **Remarks:** Accepts advertising. **URL:** http://www.ruralpress.com/publications/detail.asp?publication_id=115. **Circ:** ‡300

42661 ■ Stock Journal
Rural Press Ltd.

123 Greenhill Rd.
Unley, South Australia 5061, Australia
Ph: 61 8 83725222
Fax: 61 8 83725288
Newspaper covering agricultural information in South Australia. **Founded:** 1904. **Freq:** Weekly. **Key Personnel:** Joe Wallman, General Mgr., gm.stockjournal@ruralpress.com; Deanna Lush, Editor, editor.stockjournal@ruralpress.com. **Subscription Rates:** $A 140.40 individuals; $A 249.60 two years; $A 3 single issue. **Remarks:** Accepts advertising. **URL:** http://www.ruralpress.com/publications/detail.asp?publication_id=118; http://sj.farmonline.com.au/. **Circ:** *15,252

Victor Harbor

42662 ■ 5EFM-FM - 89.3
18 Seaview Rd.
PO Box 591
Victor Harbor, South Australia 5211, Australia
Ph: 61 8 85525655
Fax: 61 8 85525842
E-mail: radio5efm@bigpond.com
Format: Eclectic; Public Radio. **Owner:** Community Broadcasting Association of Australia, at above address. **Operating Hours:** Continuous. **Key Personnel:** Jan Ross, Prog. Mgr.; John Mann, Station Mgr. **URL:** http://www.5efm.org.au.

42663 ■ 5EFM-FM - 94.7
18 Seaview Rd.
PO Box 591
Victor Harbor, South Australia 5211, Australia
Ph: 61 8 85525655
Fax: 61 8 85525842
E-mail: radio5efm@bigpond.com
Format: Eclectic; Public Radio. **Owner:** Encounter FM Community Broadcasters Inc, at above address. **Founded:** 1995. **Operating Hours:** Continuous. **Key Personnel:** John Mann, Station Mgr.; Maree Phillips, Program Mgr. **Ad Rates:** Underwriting available. **URL:** http://www.5efm.org.au.

42664 ■ 5GS-FM - 90.1
55 Crozier Rd.
Victor Harbor, South Australia 5211, Australia
Ph: 61 8 85527999
Fax: 61 8 85527227
E-mail: gsfm901@internode.on.net
Format: Oldies; Country; Jazz; Sports. **URL:** http://www.radio901.com.au/; http://www.cbonline.org.au/index.cfm?pageId=13,9,6,3459.

Victoria

42665 ■ International Journal of Forecasting
International Institute Of Forecasters
Department of Econometrics & Business Statistics
Monash University
Victoria 3800, Australia
Publisher E-mail: nlinfo-f@elsevier.com
Publication covering economics. **Freq:** Quarterly. **Key Personnel:** Rob J. Hyndman, Editor-in-Chief, phone 61 3 99052358, ijf@forecasters.org; Michael P. Clements, Editor, m.p.clements@warwick.ac.uk; Fred Collopy, Editor, collopy@cwru.edu; Jan G. De Gooijer, Assoc. Ed. **ISSN:** 0169-2070. **Subscription Rates:** 88,400¥ individuals Japan; US$746 other countries except Europe & Japan; $A 668 individuals European countries. **Online:** Gale. **URL:** http://www.forecasters.org/ijf/index.html.

Victoria Park

42666 ■ Farm Weekly
Rural Press Ltd.
9 Kitchener Ave.
Victoria Park, Western Australia 6100, Australia
Ph: 61 8 93615000
Newspaper covering events and information in the rural areas of Western Australia. **Freq:** Weekly. **Key Personnel:** Trevor Emery, General Mgr., gm.fw@ruralpress.com; Wendy Gould, Advertising Mgr., wendy.gould@ruralpress.com. **Subscription Rates:** $A 164.20 individuals; $A 3.40 single issue. **Remarks:** Accepts advertising. **URL:** http://www.ruralpress.com/publications/detail.asp?publication_id=154. **Circ:** *13,819

Wagga Wagga

42667 ■ Chiropractic Journal of Australia
Chiropractors' Association of Australia (National) Ltd.
c/o Dr. Rolf E. Peters, Editor
PO Box 748
Wagga Wagga, New South Wales 2650, Australia
Ph: 61 2 69224466
Fax: 61 2 69262556
Publisher E-mail: caa@caa.asn.au
Peer-reviewed journal covering chiropractic science, principles, and practice in Australia. **Freq:** Quarterly. **Key Personnel:** Dr. Rolf E. Peters, Editor, journal@caa.asn.au. **ISSN:** 1036-0913. **Subscription Rates:** $A 90 individuals Australia; $A 140 institutions in Australia; $A 115 individuals outside Australia; $A 155 institutions outside Australia. **Remarks:** Accepts advertising. **URL:** http://www.chiropractors.asn.au/. **Ad Rates:** BW: $A 715. **Circ:** 1,900

42668 ■ Daily Advertiser
Riverina Media Group
48 Trl. St.
Wagga Wagga, New South Wales 2650, Australia
Publisher E-mail: editor@dailyadvertiser.com.au
General newspaper. **Founded:** 1935. **Freq:** Daily. **Print Method:** Offset. **Trim Size:** 10 x 13. **Cols./Page:** 5. **Col. Width:** 2 inches. **Col. Depth:** 189 agate lines. **Key Personnel:** Paul McLoughlin, Editor, editor@dailyadvertiser.com.au; Peter Mahoney, Dep. Ed., pmahoney@datsailyadvertiser.com.au. **ISSN:** 0744-9798. **Subscription Rates:** US$587.60 individuals. **URL:** http://dailyadvertiser.yourguide.com.au.

42669 ■ TWO AAA-FM - 107.1
Cor. Coleman & Young St.
PO Box 2019
Wagga Wagga, New South Wales 2650, Australia
Ph: 61 2 69253000
Fax: 61 2 69252300
E-mail: fm107@2aaa.net
Format: Eclectic; Public Radio; Information. **Operating Hours:** Continuous. **Ad Rates:** Noncommercial; underwriting available. **URL:** http://www.2aaa.net.

42670 ■ 2AAA-FM - 107.9
PO Box 2019
Wagga Wagga, New South Wales 2650, Australia
Ph: 61 2 69253000
Fax: 61 2 69252300
E-mail: fm107@2aaa.net
Format: Ethnic; Information. **Founded:** June 1978. **URL:** http://www.2aaa.net/.

2AAA-FM - See Coolamon

2AAA-FM - See Junee

42671 ■ 2WLF-FM - 101.9
PO Box 751
Wagga Wagga, New South Wales 2650, Australia
Ph: 61 2 69224595
Format: Contemporary Christian. **URL:** http://www.waggaslifefm.com/.

Wahroonga

42672 ■ Electrical Solutions
Westwick-Farrow Publishing
Locked Bag 1289
Wahroonga, New South Wales 2076, Australia
Ph: 61 2 94872700
Fax: 61 2 94891265
Magazine covering electrical contracting and wholesaling markets in Australia and New Zealand. **Freq:** Bimonthly. **Trim Size:** 210 x 297 mm. **Key Personnel:** Paul Stathis, Editor, pstathis@westwick-farrow.com.au; Adrian Farrow, Publusher/CEO, afarrow@westwick-farrow.com.au; Julie Wright, Production Mgr., jwright@westwick-farrow.com.au. **Subscription Rates:** Free. **Remarks:** Accepts advertising. **URL:** http://www.westwick-farrow.com.au/mags/circulation.asp?origin=es; http://www.electricalsolutions.net.au. **Ad Rates:** BW: $A 3,902, 4C: $A 4,662. **Circ:** *7,582

42673 ■ Industrial Workwear Solutions
Westwick-Farrow Publishing
Locked Bag 1289
Wahroonga, New South Wales 2076, Australia
Ph: 61 2 94872700
Fax: 61 2 94891265
Magazine featuring industrial clothing areas. **Freq:**

Semiannual in April and October. **Trim Size:** 210 x 297 mm. **Key Personnel:** Paul Stathis, Editor, pstathis@westwick-farrow.com.au; Adrian Farrow, Publisher/CEO, afarrow@westwick-farrow.com.au; Julie Wright, Production Mgr., jwright@westwick-farrow.com.au. **Subscription Rates:** Free. **Remarks:** Accepts advertising. **URL:** http://www.westwick-farrow.com.au/mags/circulation.asp?origin=iws. **Ad Rates:** BW: $A 3,902, 4C: $A 4,560. **Circ:** 28,000

42674 ■ InMotion
Westwick-Farrow Publishing
Locked Bag 1289
Wahroonga, New South Wales 2076, Australia
Ph: 61 2 94872700
Fax: 61 2 94891265
Magazine covering fluid power, pumps and motion control industrial technology sectors in Australia and New Zealand. **Freq:** Quarterly. **Trim Size:** 210 x 297 mm. **Key Personnel:** Carolyn Jackson, Editor, cjackson@westwick-farrow.com.au; Adrian Farrow, Publisher/CEO, afarrow@westwick-farrow.com.au; Julie Wright, Production Mgr., jwright@westwick-farrow.com.au. **Subscription Rates:** Free. **Remarks:** Accepts advertising. **URL:** http://www.westwick-farrow.com.au/mags/circulation.asp?origin=inmotion. **Ad Rates:** BW: $A 3,902, 4C: $A 4,560. **Circ:** ★6,157

42675 ■ Radio Comms Asia-Pacific
Westwick-Farrow Publishing
Locked Bag 1289
Wahroonga, New South Wales 2076, Australia
Ph: 61 2 94872700
Fax: 61 2 94891265
Magazine featuring professional and commercial radio communication technology. **Freq:** Bimonthly. **Trim Size:** 210 x 297 mm. **Key Personnel:** Mike Smyth, Editor, msmyth@westwick-farrow.com.au; Adrian Farrow, Publisher/CEO, afarrow@westwick-farrow.com.au; Julie Wright, Production Mgr., jwright@westwick-farrow.com.au. **Subscription Rates:** Free. **Remarks:** Accepts advertising. **URL:** http://www.westwick-farrow.com.au/mags/circulation.asp?origin=radio; http://www.radiocomms.com.au. **Ad Rates:** BW: $A 3,902, 4C: $A 4,560. **Circ:** ★4,426

42676 ■ Safety Solutions
Westwick-Farrow Publishing
Locked Bag 1289
Wahroonga, New South Wales 2076, Australia
Ph: 61 2 94872700
Fax: 61 2 94891265
Magazine featuring safety products and services in the industrial, construction, utilities and mining sectors. **Founded:** Apr. 2003. **Freq:** Bimonthly. **Trim Size:** 210 x 297 mm. **Key Personnel:** Paul Stathis, Editor, phone 61 3 93812952, pstathis@westwick-farrow.com.au; Adrian Farrow, Publisher/CEO, afarrow@westwick-farrow.com.au; Julie Wright, Production Mgr., jwright@westwick-farrow.com.au. **Subscription Rates:** Free. **Remarks:** Accepts advertising. **URL:** http://www.westwick-farrow.com.au/mags/circulation.asp?origin=safety; http://www.safetysolutions.net.au. **Ad Rates:** BW: $A 3,902, 4C: $A 4,352. **Circ:** 7,323

42677 ■ Sustainability Matters
Westwick-Farrow Publishing
Locked Bag 1289
Wahroonga, New South Wales 2076, Australia
Ph: 61 2 94872700
Fax: 61 2 94891265
Magazine featuring waste management, resource recovery and emerging sustainability sectors. **Freq:** Bimonthly. **Trim Size:** 210 x 297 mm. **Key Personnel:** Carolyn Jackson, Editor, cjackson@westwick-farrow.com.au; Adrian Farrow, Publisher/CEO, afarrow@westwick-farrow.com.au; Julie Wright, Production Mgr., jwright@westwick-farrow.com.au. **Subscription Rates:** Free. **Remarks:** Accepts advertising. **URL:** http://www.sustainabilitymatters.net.au/; http://www.westwick-farrow.com.au/mags/circulation.asp?origin=waste. **Formerly:** Waste Streams. **Ad Rates:** BW: $A 3,902, 4C: $A 4,352. **Circ:** ★5,757

42678 ■ Voice&Data
Westwick-Farrow Publishing
Locked Bag 1289
Wahroonga, New South Wales 2076, Australia
Ph: 61 2 94872700
Fax: 61 2 94891265
Magazine for information technology and telecommunication professionals. **Freq:** Monthly. **Trim Size:** 210 x 297 mm. **Key Personnel:** Merri Mack, Editor, phone 61 2 94872700, mmack@westwick-farrow.com.au; Adrian Farrow, Publisher./CEO, afarrow@westwick-farrow.com.au; Julie Wright, Production Mgr., jwright@westwick-farrow.com.au. **Subscription Rates:** Free. **Remarks:** Accepts advertising. **URL:** http://www.westwick-farrow.com.au/mags/circulation.asp?origin=vd; http://www.voiceanddata.com.au. **Ad Rates:** BW: $A 3,902, 4C: $A 4,560. **Circ:** 7,745

42679 ■ What's New in Electronics
Westwick-Farrow Publishing
Locked Bag 1289
Wahroonga, New South Wales 2076, Australia
Ph: 61 2 94872700
Fax: 61 2 94891265
Magazine featuring the professional electronics industry in New Zealand and Australia. **Founded:** 1981. **Freq:** Monthly. **Trim Size:** 210 x 297 mm. **Key Personnel:** Mike Smyth, Editor, msmyth@westwick-farrow.com.au; Adrian Farrow, Publisher/CEO, afarrow@westwick-farrow.com.au; Julie Wright, Production Mgr., jwright@westwick-farrow.com.au. **Subscription Rates:** Free. **Remarks:** Accepts advertising. **URL:** http://www.westwick-farrow.com.au/mags/circulation.asp?origin=elec; http://www.electroline.com.au. **Ad Rates:** BW: $A 3,902, 4C: $A 4,560. **Circ:** ★7072

42680 ■ What's New in Food Technology and Manufacturing
Westwick-Farrow Publishing
Locked Bag 1289
Wahroonga, New South Wales 2076, Australia
Ph: 61 2 94872700
Fax: 61 2 94891265
Magazine featuring new products and technology developments on food industry. **Founded:** 1993. **Freq:** Bimonthly. **Trim Size:** 210 x 297 mm. **Key Personnel:** Janette Woodhouse, Ch. Ed., phone 61 2 94872700, jwoodhouse@westwick-farrow.com.au; Adrian Farrow, Publisher/CEO, afarrow@westwick-farrow.com.au; Julie Wright, Production Mgr., jwright@westwick-farrow.com.au. **Subscription Rates:** Free. **Remarks:** Accepts advertising. **URL:** http://www.westwick-farrow.com.au/mags/default.asp?origin=food; http://www.foodprocessing.com.au. **Ad Rates:** BW: $A 3,902, 4C: $A 4,560. **Circ:** ★6,892

42681 ■ What's New in LAB Technology
Westwick-Farrow Publishing
Locked Bag 1289
Wahroonga, New South Wales 2076, Australia
Ph: 61 2 94872700
Fax: 61 2 94891265
Magazine covering new products and innovative technologies to the sectors of Australian and New Zealand laboratory market. **Founded:** 1990. **Freq:** Bimonthly. **Trim Size:** 210 x 297 mm. **Key Personnel:** Janette Woodhouse, Ch. Ed., jwoodhouse@westwick-farrow.com.au; Adrian Farrow, Ch. Ed., afarrow@westwick-farrow.com.au; Julie Wright, Production Mgr., jtall@westwick-farrow.com.au. **Subscription Rates:** Free. **Remarks:** Accepts advertising. **URL:** http://www.westwick-farrow.com.au/mags/circulation.asp?origin=science; http://www.labonline.com.au. **Ad Rates:** BW: $A 3,902, 4C: $A 4,560. **Circ:** ★6,233

42682 ■ What's New in Process Technology
Westwick-Farrow Publishing
Locked Bag 1289
Wahroonga, New South Wales 2076, Australia
Ph: 61 2 94872700
Fax: 61 2 94891265
Magazine covering the latest in process control and automation technology. **Freq:** Monthly. **Trim Size:** 210 x 297 mm. **Key Personnel:** Glenn Johnson, Editor, phone 61 2 94872700, wnipt@westwick-farrow.com.au; Adrian Farrow, Publisher/CEO, afarrow@westwick-farrow.com.au; Julie Wright, Production Mgr., jwright@westwick-farrow.com.au. **Subscription Rates:** Free. **Remarks:** Accepts advertising. **URL:** http://www.westwick-farrow.com.au/mags/circulation.asp?origin=process; http://www.processonline.com.au. **Ad Rates:** BW: $A 3,902, 4C: $A 4,352. **Circ:** ★6,605

Wangaratta

42683 ■ Edge-FM - 102.1
19 Templeton St.
Wangaratta, Victoria 3677, Australia
Ph: 61 3 57221566
Format: Adult Contemporary; Oldies. **Key Personnel:** Colin Dayman, General Mgr. **Ad Rates:** Advertising accepted; rates available upon request. **URL:** http://www.edgefm.com.au/.

42684 ■ Oak-FM - 101.3
104 Murdoch Rd.
Wangaratta, Victoria 3677, Australia
Ph: 61 3 57221569
Fax: 61 3 57223443
Format: Full Service. **URL:** http://www.oakfm.com.au/home/.

Warragul

42685 ■ Warragul & Drovin Gazette
Warragul Gazette
97-103 Queen St.
PO Box 305
Warragul, Victoria 3820, Australia
Ph: 61 356 235666
Fax: 61 356 232367
Publication E-mail: editorial@warragulgazette.com.au
Publisher E-mail: admin@warragulgazette.com.au
Community newspaper. **Founded:** July 1898. **Freq:** Monthly. **Print Method:** Web offset. **Trim Size:** 26 x 38 cm. **Cols./Page:** 7. **URL:** http://www.warragulgazette.com.au/. **Circ:** Paid 10,700

Warrandyte

42686 ■ The Australian Orienteer
Orienteering Federation of Australia
c/o Mike Hubbert, Ed.
PO Box 165
Warrandyte, Victoria 3113, Australia
Publisher E-mail: orienteering@dsr.nsw.gov.au
Australian publication covering orienteering. **Freq:** Quarterly March, June, September, and December. **Key Personnel:** Dave Lotty, Director; Greg Hawthorne, Editor-in-Chief, greg.hawthorne@bigpond.com; Bob McCreddin, President. **ISSN:** 0818-6510. **Subscription Rates:** $A 40 individuals including GST; $A 49 by mail Asia Pacific, including New Zealand; $A 58 by mail rest of the world, including U.S. and Canada. **URL:** http://www.orienteering.asn.au/australianorienteer/. **Ad Rates:** 4C: $A 450. **Circ:** 2,000

Warrawong

42687 ■ Wave-FM - 96.5
Top Fl., 73 King St.
PO Box 474
Warrawong, New South Wales 2502, Australia
Ph: 61 2 42752965
Fax: 61 2 42742000
E-mail: wavefm@wavefm.com.au
Format: Adult Contemporary; News; Oldies; Easy Listening; Sports; Information. **Ad Rates:** Advertising accepted; rates available upon request. **URL:** http://www.wavefm.com.au/.

Warrnambool

42688 ■ Coast-FM - 95.3
95 Timor St.
Warrnambool, Victoria 3280, Australia
Ph: 61 3 55643888
Fax: 61 3 55643800
Format: Adult Contemporary. **Founded:** Aug. 14, 2002. **Key Personnel:** Peter Headen, General Mgr., peterh@warrnambool.aceradio.com.au; Tracey Kol, Sales Mgr., traceyk@warrnambool.aceradio.com.au; Mike Pfeiffer, Program Dir., michaelp@warrnambool.aceradio.com.au. **URL:** http://theradio.com.au.

42689 ■ 3YB-AM - 882
95 Timor St.
Warrnambool, Victoria 3280, Australia
Ph: 61 3 55643888
Fax: 61 3 55643800
Format: Adult Contemporary. **Owner:** Ace Radio Broadcasters, 18 Albert Rd., Apt. 8C, South Melbourne,

---

Circulation: ★ = ABC; △ = BPA; ◆ = CAC; • = CCAB; ⬚ = VAC; ⊕ = PO Statement; ‡ = Publisher's Report; Boldface figures = sworn; Light figures = estimated.

Victoria 3205, Australia, 61 3 96459877, Fax: 61 3 96459866. **Operating Hours:** Continuous Mon.-Fri. ,Sun.; 12a.m.-5a.m.,6a.m.-11p.m. Sat. **Key Personnel:** Peter Headen, General Mgr., peterh@warrnambool. aceradio.com.au; Tracy Kol, Sales Mgr., traceyk@ warrnambool.aceradio.com.au; Mike Pfeiffer, Program Mgr., michaelp@warrnambool.aceradio.com.au. **Ad Rates:** Advertising accepted; rates available upon request. **URL:** http://theradio.com.au/localworks.aspx? PageID=6116&Station=3YB_Warrnambool; http://www. aceradio.com.au/.

Watson

42690 ■ Australian Journal of Early Childhood
Early Childhood Australia
Knox St.
PO Box 7105
Watson, Australian Capital Territory 2602, Australia
Ph: 61 2 262421800
Fax: 61 2 262421818
Publisher E-mail: eca@earlychildhood.org.au
Australian journal covering early child issues. **Freq:** Quarterly. **Key Personnel:** Margaret Sims, Acting Ed. **ISSN:** 0312-5033. **Subscription Rates:** $A 70 individuals within Australia; $A 200 institutions; $A 220 institutions, other countries. **Remarks:** Advertising accepted; rates available upon request. **URL:** http://www. earlychildhoodaustralia.org.au/australian_journal_of_ early_childhood/about_ajec.html. **Former name:** Australian Preschool Quarterly. **Circ:** (Not Reported)

Wendouree

42691 ■ Good News Radio-FM - 103.9
3 College St.
PO Box 51
Wendouree, Victoria 3355, Australia
Ph: 61 3 53399958
Fax: 61 3 53399960
E-mail: contact@goodnewsradio.org.au
Format: Contemporary Christian; Religious. **Founded:** 1993. **Operating Hours:** Continuous. **Ad Rates:** Underwriting available. **URL:** http://www.goodnewsradio. org.au.

Werribee

42692 ■ Wyndham Leader
Leader Community Newspapers
2/51 Cherry St.
Werribee, Victoria 3030, Australia
Ph: 61 3 92269333
Local community newspaper. **Freq:** Weekly (Tues.). **Key Personnel:** Rick Edwards, Editor, wyndham@ leadernewspapers.com.au; Helen Meritt, Sales Mgr., merritth@leadernewspapers.com.au. **Remarks:** Accepts advertising. **URL:** http://wyndham-leader.whereilive.com. au/. **Circ:** Tues. ‡42,730

42693 ■ WYN-FM - 88.9
PO Box 155
Werribee, Victoria 3030, Australia
Ph: 61 921 68089
E-mail: wynfm@wynfm.org.au
Format: Public Radio; Eclectic; Information. **Founded:** 1995. **Operating Hours:** Continuous. **Ad Rates:** Noncommercial; underwriting available. **URL:** http:// www.wynfm.org.au.

West Footscray

42694 ■ Bharat Times
PO Box 6100
West Footscray, Victoria 3012, Australia
Ph: 61 3 96896406
Fax: 61 3 96896489
Publication E-mail: editor@bharattimes.com
Publisher E-mail: bharat@bharattimes.com
General newspaper. **Founded:** 1997. **Freq:** Monthly. **Print Method:** Offset. **Trim Size:** 11 1/2 x 16 3/4. **Cols./ Page:** 5. **Col. Width:** 22 nonpareils. **Col. Depth:** 210 agate lines. **ISSN:** 0026-5241. **Subscription Rates:** US$39.60 individuals. **Remarks:** Accepts advertising. **URL:** http://www.bharattimes.com/. **Circ:** (Not Reported)

West Gosford

42695 ■ Central Coast Express Advocate
Cumberland Newspaper Group
Bowen Cres., Lot 18
West Gosford, New South Wales 2250, Australia
Local community newspaper. **Freq:** Semiweekly (Wed. and Fri.). **Key Personnel:** Geoff Hawthorne, Editor, editor@expressadvocate.com.au; Scott Dibben, Advertising Mgr., advertising@expressadvocate.com.au. **Remarks:** Accepts display and classified advertising. **URL:** http://www.expressadvocate.com.au/. **Circ:** Wed. 63,103, Fri. 62,983

West Kempsey

42696 ■ TANK-FM - 103.1
PO Box 200
West Kempsey, New South Wales 2440, Australia
Ph: 61 2 65628883
Fax: 61 2 65623344
E-mail: info@tankfm.org
Format: News; Country; Oldies; Contemporary Christian; Easy Listening; Album-Oriented Rock (AOR); Eclectic. **URL:** http://www.tankfm.org/.

West Melbourne

42697 ■ Emergency Medicine Australasia
Australasian College for Emergency Medicine
34 Jeffcott St.
West Melbourne, Victoria 3003, Australia
Ph: 61 393 200444
Fax: 61 393 200400
Publisher E-mail: admin@acem.org.au
Peer-reviewed scientific journal of the Australasian College for Emergency Medicine. **Freq:** Bimonthly. **Key Personnel:** Anthony F.T. Brown, Editor-in-Chief. **ISSN:** 1441-0737. **Subscription Rates:** $A 181 individuals print + online (Australia and NZ); US$174 individuals print + online; $A 107 individuals print + online. **Remarks:** Accepts advertising. **URL:** http://www.acem.org. au/infocentre.aspx?docId=58. **Formerly:** Emergency Medicine. **Circ:** (Not Reported)

West Perth

42698 ■ Behaviour Change
Australian Association for Cognitive and Behaviour Therapy
PO Box 853
West Perth, Western Australia 6872, Australia
Publisher E-mail: sianj@graduate.uwa.edu.au
Journal containing research involving the application of cognitive behavioral principles and techniques to the assessment and treatment of various problems. **Freq:** Quarterly. **Key Personnel:** Dr. Sian Jeffery, Wa Branch Pres.; Michelle Jongenelis, Wa Branch Baseline Ed. **Subscription Rates:** Included in membership. **URL:** http://www.aacbt.org.

Westleigh

42699 ■ Australian and New Zealand Journal of Family Therapy
Australian Academic Press Pty. Ltd.
42 The Sanctuary
Sanctuary Gardens
Westleigh, New South Wales 2120, Australia
Publication E-mail: editor@anzjft.com
Publisher E-mail: aap@australianacademicpress. com.au
Peer-reviewed journal covering family therapy. **Freq:** Quarterly. **Key Personnel:** Paul Rhodes, Editor. **ISSN:** 0814-723X. **Subscription Rates:** $A 230 institutions; $A 242 institutions to New Zealand; $A 253 institutions, other countries. **URL:** http://www. australianacademicpress.com.au/Publications/Journals/ anzjft.htm.

Westminster

42700 ■ Ceramics
Ceramics: Art and Perception Proprietary Ltd.
120 Glenmore Rd.
Westminster, New South Wales 2021, Australia
Ph: 61 2 93615286
Fax: 61 2 93615402

Publisher E-mail: ceramics@ceramicart.com.au
Magazine covering ceramic art. **Subtitle:** Art and Perception. **Founded:** 1990. **Freq:** Quarterly. **Print Method:** Perfect bound. **Trim Size:** 240 x 165 mm. **Key Personnel:** Elaine O. Henry, Editor and Publisher. **ISSN:** 1035-1841. **Subscription Rates:** US$70 individuals; US$110 individuals + Ceramica Technical; US$40 individuals 2 issues. **Remarks:** Accepts advertising. **URL:** http://www.ceramicart.com.au. **Ad Rates:** BW: $A 1,050. **Circ:** 12,200

Windsor

42701 ■ 2VTR-FM - 89.9
11 Fitzgerald St.
Windsor, New South Wales 2756, Australia
Ph: 61 2 45775662
Format: Eclectic. **URL:** http://www.hawkesburyradio. com.au/.

Wodonga

42702 ■ The Weaver
La Trobe University
PO Box 821
Wodonga, Victoria 3689, Australia
Ph: 61 260 249700
Fax: 61 260 249797
Publisher E-mail: stud-admin.aw@latrobe.edu.au
Journal covering articles on emerging areas of research, theory, research practice, methodology and research tips. **Subtitle:** A Forum for New Ideas in Educational Research. **ISSN:** 1329-881X. **URL:** http://www.latrobe. edu.au/graded/weaverindex.html.

Wollongong

42703 ■ Illawarra Mercury
21 Auburn St.
PO Box 1215
Wollongong, New South Wales 2500, Australia
Ph: 61 24 2212333
Publisher E-mail: letters@illawarramercury.com.au
Daily newspaper covering personal finance, social scene, food and fashion, junior sport and entertainment. **Key Personnel:** Stuart Howie, Editor; Carol Johnstone, Dep. Ed. **URL:** http://www.illawarramercury.com.au/.

42704 ■ International Journal of Applied Cryptography
Inderscience Enterprises Limited
c/o Yi Mu, Ed.-in-Ch.
University of Wollongong
School of Information Technology & Computer Science
Faculty of Informatics
Wollongong, New South Wales 2522, Australia
Journal covering the study of cryptography. **Freq:** 4/yr. **Key Personnel:** Yi Mu, Editor-in-Chief, ymu@uow.edu. au; David Pointcheval, Editor-in-Chief, david. pointcheval@ens.fr. **ISSN:** 1753-0563. **Subscription Rates:** EUR494 individuals print or online; EUR672 individuals print and online. **URL:** http://www. inderscience.com/browse/index.php?journalID=233.

42705 ■ Journal of University Teaching and Learning Practice (JUTLP)
University of Wollongong
Northfields Ave.
Wollongong, New South Wales 2522, Australia
Ph: 61 242 213555
Publication E-mail: jutlp@uow.edu.au
Journal contributing to the knowledge pool through improvised teaching measures and learning practices in the field of higher education. Provides a forum for the teaching professionals. **Freq:** Semiannual. **Key Personnel:** Prof. Helen Carter, Sen. Ed., helen.carter@ newcastle.edu.au; Dr. Meg O'Reilly, Assoc. Ed., meg. oreilly@scu.edu.au. **ISSN:** 1449-9789. **URL:** http://ro. uow.edu.au/jutlp/.

42706 ■ Quaternary Science Reviews
Elsevier Science
c/o C.V. Murray-Wallace, Ed.-in-Ch.
University of Wollongong
School of Earth & Environmental Sciences
Wollongong, New South Wales 2522, Australia
Publisher E-mail: nlinfo-f@elsevier.com
Journal covering dating methods and focusing on new developments in the field. **Founded:** 1982. **Freq:** 28/yr. **Key Personnel:** X.P. Yang, Editor, xpyang@mail.igcas.

ac.cn; C. Hillaire-Marcel, Editor, chm@uqam.ca; C.V. Murray-Wallace, Editor-in-Chief, cwallace@uow.edu.au; C.N. Roberts, Editor, c.n.roberts@plymouth.ac.uk; R.B. Alley, Editorial Advisory Board. **ISSN:** 0277-3791. **Subscription Rates:** US$2,523 institutions for countries except Europe and Japan; 299,500¥ institutions; EUR2,256 institutions for European countries; EUR293 individuals for European countries; 39,000¥ individuals; US$329 individuals for countries except Europe and Japan. **Remarks:** Accepts advertising. **URL:** http://www.elsevier.com/wps/find/journaldescription.cws_home/636/description. **Circ:** (Not Reported)

42707 ▪ ABC Illawara-FM - 97.3
74 Kembla St., Unit 6/7
PO Box 973
Wollongong, New South Wales 2520, Australia
Ph: 61 2 42245011
Fax: 61 2 42245099
Format: Information; News; Talk; Agricultural. **Operating Hours:** Continuous. **URL:** http://www.abc.net.au/illawarra

42708 ▪ i98-FM - 98.1
Locked Bag 6198
S Coast Mail Ctr.
Wollongong, New South Wales 2521, Australia
Ph: 61 2 42234198
Fax: 61 2 42234286
E-mail: win@i98.com.au
Format: Adult Contemporary; News. **Ad Rates:** Advertising accepted; rates available upon request. **URL:** http://www.i98.com.au/.

Wollongong (Victoria)

42709 ▪ Rete Italia-AM - 1575
582 Nicholson St.
Fitzroy North, Victoria 3068, Australia
Ph: 61 3 94810666
Fax: 61 3 94861412
Format: Ethnic; News; Sports; Talk. **Operating Hours:** Continuous. **Ad Rates:** Advertising accepted; rates available upon request. **URL:** http://www.italianmedia.com.au.

Womying

42710 ▪ International Journal of Biological Sciences
Ivyspring International Publisher
PO Box 9338
Womying, New South Wales 2250, Australia
Ph: 61 243 295886
Fax: 61 243 284886
Publisher E-mail: info@ivyspring.com
Journal covering the field of biological sciences. **Freq:** Quarterly. **Key Personnel:** Chuxia Deng, PhD, Editor-in-Chief; Ellen Carpenter, Editor; James M. Mason, Editor; Shawn S. Li, Editor; Rodolfo Aramayo, Editor; Ari Elson, Editor. **ISSN:** 1449-2288. **URL:** http://www.biolsci.org/.

42711 ▪ International Journal of Medical Sciences
Ivyspring International Publisher
PO Box 9338
Womying, New South Wales 2250, Australia
Ph: 61 243 295886
Fax: 61 243 284886
Publisher E-mail: info@ivyspring.com
Journal focusing on the field of medical research,

epidemiological and public health. **Freq:** Annual. **Key Personnel:** Adrian R. Eley, Editor; Karen Downs, Editor; Dennis D. Taub, PhD, Editor-in-Chief. **ISSN:** 1449-1907. **URL:** http://www.medsci.org.

Wondai

42712 ▪ CROW-FM - 90.7
61 Haly St.
PO Box 171
Wondai, Queensland 4606, Australia
Ph: 61 7 41690700
Fax: 61 7 41690718
E-mail: info@crowfm.com.au
Format: Album-Oriented Rock (AOR). **Key Personnel:** Bob Stevenson, Sales Consultant, phone 61 7 417748580, bob@crowfm.com.au; Angie Goodchild, Sales Consultant, phone 61 7 439738332, ange@crowfm.com.au; Wayne Kratzmann, Gen. Mgr./Prog. Dir., kratzie@crowfm.com.au. **URL:** http://www.crowfm.com.au.

Woodburn

42713 ▪ Ecological Management & Restoration
John Wiley & Sons Inc.
Wiley-Blackwell
PO Box 14
Woodburn, New South Wales 2472, Australia
Fax: 61 2 66822885
Peer-reviewed journal covering the science and practice of ecosystem restoration and management. **Freq:** 3/yr. **Key Personnel:** Dr. Tein McDonald, Editor; Dr. Alaric Fisher, Editorial Board; Prof. Jann Williams, Contact; Dr. Sue Carthew, Editorial Board; Dr. Suzanne, Prober, Editorial Board; Dr. Craig Miller, Editorial Board. **ISSN:** 1442-7001. **Subscription Rates:** US$99 individuals print and online; US$384 institutions print and online; EUR302 institutions print and online; US$465 institutions, other countries print and online; US$422 institutions, other countries print or online; 238 institutions print and online; EUR93 individuals print and online; $A 82 individuals print and online; 62 other countries print and online. **Remarks:** Accepts advertising. **URL:** http://www.wiley.com/bw/journal.asp?ref=1442-7001. **Circ:** (Not Reported)

Woodend

42714 ▪ Highlands-FM - 100.7
PO Box 966
Woodend, Victoria 3442, Australia
Ph: 61 3 54272040
E-mail: thedesk@highlandsfm.org.au
Format: Ethnic; World Beat. **Key Personnel:** Ken Helmore, President, president@highlandsfm.org.au. **URL:** http://www.highlandsfm.org.au.

Woolgoolga

42715 ▪ Journal of Near Infrared Spectroscopy
IM Publications L.L.P.
c/o Graeme D. Batten, Ed.-in-Ch.
PO Box 487
Woolgoolga, New South Wales 2456, Australia
Ph: 61 266 562288
Fax: 61 266 562288
Publisher E-mail: info@impublications.co.uk
Peer-reviewed journal focusing on near infrared spectroscopy research. **Freq:** Bimonthly. **Key Personnel:** Graeme D. Batten, Editor-in-Chief, thebattens@bigpond.

com. **ISSN:** 0967-0335. **Subscription Rates:** 285 individuals in Europe (print and online); EUR410 individuals in Europe (print and online); US$520 other countries print and online; 270 individuals in Europe (online only); EUR390 individuals in Europe (online only); US$494 other countries online only. **URL:** http://www.impublications.com/nir/journal/jnirs.

Woomera

42716 ▪ Flow-FM - 101.7
PO Box 407
Kapunda, South Australia 5373, Australia
Ph: 61 8 85663151
Fax: 61 8 85662729
E-mail: mail@flowfm.com.au
Format: Adult Contemporary. **URL:** http://www.flowfm.com.au/.

Woori Yallock

42717 ▪ Yarra Valley-FM - 99.1
PO Box 991
Woori Yallock, Victoria 3139, Australia
Ph: 61 3 59615991
Fax: 61 3 59646662
E-mail: info@yarravalleyfm.com
Format: Easy Listening; Information. **Founded:** Dec. 1984. **Operating Hours:** Continuous. **Key Personnel:** Robert Jordan, Chp.; Charlene Hayes, Vice Ch.; Corleen Cooper, Sec. **Ad Rates:** Noncommercial; underwriting available. **URL:** http://www.yarravalleyfm.com.

Wynnum Central

42718 ▪ Wynnum Herald
Quest Community Newspapers
Flinders Ctr., 1st Fl.
183 Bay Ter.
Wynnum Central, Queensland 4178, Australia
Ph: 61 7 31177300
Local community newspaper. **Founded:** 1946. **Freq:** Weekly (Wed.). **Key Personnel:** Margie Maccoll, Editor, phone 61 7 31177300, fax 61 7 31177319, editor@wynnumherald.com.au; Troy Greenland, Advertising Mgr. **Remarks:** Accepts display and classified advertising. **URL:** http://www.newsspace.com.au/wynnum_herald_. **Circ:** 34,647

Yass

42719 ▪ Yass-FM - 100.3
PO Box 51
Yass, New South Wales 2582, Australia
Ph: 61 2 62265266
Fax: 61 2 62265277
E-mail: mail@yassfm.org
Format: News; Information; Folk. **Owner:** Yass Community Radio Association Inc., at above address. **URL:** http://www.yassfm.org/joomla_yassfm/index.php.

Yea

42720 ▪ UG-FM - 88.9
PO Box 270
Alexandra, Victoria 3714, Australia
Ph: 61 3 57722900
Fax: 61 3 57722414
E-mail: info@ugfm.org
Format: Easy Listening; Contemporary Hit Radio (CHR). **URL:** http://ugfm.cute.com.au/.

Altenberg

42721 ■ Biological Theory
MIT Press
Adolf Lorenz Gasse 2
A-3422 Altenberg, Austria
Publisher E-mail: journals-orders@mit.edu
Journal devoted to theoretical advances in the biological and cognitive sciences. **Subtitle:** Integrating Development, Evolution, and Cognition. **Founded:** 2005. **Freq:** Quarterly Winter, Spring, Summer, Fall. **Print Method:** Offset. **Cols./Page:** 5. **Col. Width:** 22 nonpareils. **Col. Depth:** 196 agate lines. **Key Personnel:** John Collier, Member of the Editorial Board; Andy Clark, Member of the Editorial Board; Marcello Barbieri, Member of the Editorial Board; Marion Blute, Editorial Advisory Board; Werner Callebaut, Editor-in-Chief; Michael Bradie, Member of the Editorial Board; Konstantin Anokhin, Member of the Editorial Board; Ana Barahona Echeverria, Member of the Editorial Board; Richard M. Burian, Member of the Editorial Board; Ronald A. Amundson, Member of the Editorial Board. **ISSN:** 1555-5542. **Remarks:** Accepts advertising. **URL:** http://www.mitpressjournals.org/loi/biot. **Ad Rates:** BW: 300 AS. **Circ:** Non-paid 225

Bad Ischl

42722 ■ Free Radio Salzkammergut-FM - 100.2
Lindaustrasse 28
A-4820 Bad Ischl, Austria
Ph: 43 613 225690
E-mail: office@freiesradio.at
Format: Eclectic. **Owner:** Free Association Radio Salzkammergut, at above address. **Founded:** Mar. 31, 1999. **Key Personnel:** Mario Friedwagner, Manager, mario.friedwagner@freiesradio.at. **URL:** http://www.freiesradio.at/.

Dornbirn

42723 ■ Forum Gesundheit Vorarlberg
Vorarlberger Gebietskrankenkasse
Gebietskrankenkasse
Jahngasse 4
A-6850 Dornbirn, Austria
Ph: 43 50 84551111
Fax: 43 50 84551040
Publication E-mail: forum.gesundheit@vgkk.sozvers.at
Publisher E-mail: vgkk@vgkk.at
Magazine of the District Health Insurance Fund of Vorarlberg. **Founded:** 1994. **Freq:** 5/yr. **Key Personnel:** Bernd Stracke, Contact, bernd.stracke@vgkk.sozvers.at. **Subscription Rates:** Free. **Remarks:** Accepts advertising. **URL:** http://www.vgkk.at. **Ad Rates:** 4C: EUR2,616. **Circ:** Non-paid 40,000

Graz

42724 ■ J.UCS (Journal of Universal Computer Science)
Know-Center
Inffeldgasse 21a/II
A-8010 Graz, Austria
Ph: 43 316 8739251
Fax: 43 316 8739254
Journal focusing on the field of computer science. **Founded:** 1995. **Freq:** Monthly. **Key Personnel:** Narayanan Kulathuramaiyer, Editor-in-Chief; Klaus Tochtermann, Editor-in-Chief; Hermann Maurer, Managing Editor; M. Hagiya, Editor; A. Abraham, Editor; L.C. Aiello, Editor; J. Aguilar-Ruiz, Editor; M. Ito, Editor; J. Albert, Editor. **Subscription Rates:** US$15 individuals printed special issues; EUR15 individuals printed special issues. **URL:** http://www.jucs.org/jucs_12_1.

42725 ■ Metroeconomica
John Wiley & Sons Inc.
Wiley-Blackwell
c/o Heinz D. Kurz, Mng. Ed.
University of Graz
Resowi-Zentrum F4
A-8010 Graz, Austria
Ph: 43 316 3803444
Fax: 43 316 3809520
Peer-reviewed journal focusing on wide ranging theoretical approaches to analytical economics. **Subtitle:** International Review of Economics. **Founded:** 1949. **Freq:** Quarterly. **Key Personnel:** Heinz D. Kurz, Managing Editor, heinz.kurz@kfunigraz.ac.at; Amitava Krishna Dutt, Editor; Duncan Foley, Editor; Eiji Hosoda, Editor; Marco Dardi, Editor; Reiner Franke, Editor; Adriano Birolo, Editor; Peter Skott, Editor; Neri Salvadori, Managing Editor. **ISSN:** 0026-1386. **Subscription Rates:** US$77 individuals print + online; 511 institutions print + online; 465 institutions print or online; EUR649 institutions print + online; EUR590 institutions print or online; US$858 institutions print + online; US$780 institutions print or online; US$1,001 institutions, other countries print + online; 46 other countries print + online; EUR68 individuals print + online. **Remarks:** Advertising accepted; rates available upon request. **URL:** http://www.wiley.com/bw/journal.asp?ref=0026-1386. **Circ:** (Not Reported)

Gross Enzersdorf

42726 ■ Labor Direct
Fachverlag Wien
DOK 4 NW 21-22
A-2301 Gross Enzersdorf, Austria
Ph: 43 223 94104
Fax: 43 224 97481
Publication E-mail: info@labor.at
Publisher E-mail: info@labor.at
Technical, trade journal for research laboratories. **Founded:** 1987. **Freq:** Quarterly. **Print Method:** Offset. **Trim Size:** 21 x 29.7 cm. **Cols./Page:** 2. **Col. Width:** 8.7 centimeters. **Col. Depth:** 185 millimeters. **Subscription Rates:** Free. **Remarks:** Accepts advertising. **URL:** http://www.labor.at. **Ad Rates:** BW: EUR1,453, 4C: EUR2,217. **Circ:** Non-paid 7,000

Klagenfurt

42727 ■ Antenne Kaernten-FM - 104.9
Hasnerstrasse 2
A-9020 Klagenfurt, Austria
Ph: 43 463 458880
Fax: 43 463 45888909
E-mail: servicektn@antenne.net
Format: Eclectic. **Owner:** Regional Radio GmbH & Co KG, at above address. **Key Personnel:** Micahel Fischeneder, Program Dir.; Martina Clement, Program Mgr.; Gottfried Bichler, Mng. Dir. **URL:** http://www.antenne.at/.

Krems

42728 ■ e-Beratungsjournal
E-Beratungsjournal
Ringstrabe 48
A-3500 Krems, Austria
Ph: 43 699 19201857
Publisher E-mail: redaktion@e-beratungsjournal.net
Journal covering the theory and practice of on-line consultation and computer-obtained communication. **Key Personnel:** Stefan Kuhne, Contact. **ISSN:** 1816-7632. **URL:** http://www.e-beratungsjournal.net/arch.

Lannach

42729 ■ NJOY Radio-FM - 88.2
Gallerweg 16
A-8502 Lannach, Austria
Ph: 43 313 681636
E-mail: office@njoyradio.at
Format: Information. **Owner:** Verein Basic Vocal, at above address. **Key Personnel:** Werner Strohmeier, Program Mgr., strohmeier@njoyradio.at. **URL:** http://www.njoyradio.at/.

Laxenburg

42730 ■ International Journal of Global Energy Issues
Inderscience Enterprises Limited
c/o Dr. Pallav Purohit, Assoc. Ed.
International Institute for Applied Systems Analysis
Atmospheric Pollution & Economic Development
Schlossplatz
A-2361 Laxenburg, Austria
Journal covering the study of renewable and non-renewable energy resources, energy-economic systems, energy and environment, international energy policy issues, technological innovation, and new energy sources. **Freq:** 8/yr. **Key Personnel:** Dr. Pallav Purohit, Assoc. Ed.; Dr. M.A. Dorgham, Editor-in-Chief, editorial@inderscience.com. **ISSN:** 0954-7118. **Subscription Rates:** EUR735 individuals print or online; EUR1,025 individuals print and online. **URL:** http://www.inderscience.com/browse/index.php?journalID=13.

42731 ■ Options
International Institute for Applied Systems Analysis
Institut International pour l'Analyse des Systemes Appliques
Schlossplatz 1
A-2361 Laxenburg, Austria
Ph: 43 223 68070
Fax: 43 223 671313
Publication E-mail: molina@iiasa.ac.at
Publisher E-mail: inf@iiasa.ac.at
Publication covering research. **Freq:** Quarterly. **Key Personnel:** Romeo Molina, Contact. **ISSN:** 0252-9572.

Circulation: ★ = ABC; △ = BPA; ♦ = CAC; • = CCAB; ❑ = VAC; ⊕ = PO Statement; ‡ = Publisher's Report; Boldface figures = sworn; Light figures = estimated.

URL: http://www.iiasa.ac.at/Options/index.html. Circ:
5,000

Leoben

42732 ■ **Stadt Leoben**
Erzherzog-Johann-Str 2
A-8700 Leoben, Austria
Ph: 43 384 240620
Fax: 43 384 24062320
Publisher E-mail: stadtgemeinde@leoben.at
Magazine of the local government covering city council
events, local finances and public service. **Founded:**
1970. **Print Method:** Offset. **Trim Size:** 190 x 250 mm.
Cols./Page: 4. **Col. Width:** 45 millimeters. **Col. Depth:**
250 millimeters. **URL:** http://www.leoben.at. **Circ:**
Combined ‡13,500

Lichtenberg

42733 ■ **Life Radio-FM - 100.5**
Landstrasse 12, GmbH & Co KG
A-4020 Linz, Austria
Ph: 43 732 76070
Fax: 43 732 7607333
E-mail: sekretariat@liferadio.at
Format: Eclectic. **Owner:** Life Radio-FM, at above
address. **Key Personnel:** Ulli Jelinek, Program Dir.;
Peter Pleschko, Music Ed. **URL:** http://www.liferadio.at/.

Linz

42734 ■ **Statistical Papers**
Springer Netherlands
Johannes Kepler University of Linz
Altenberger Str. 69
4040 Linz, Austria
Publisher E-mail: permissions.dordrecht@springer.com
Journal covering articles on business, economics and
finance. **Freq:** Quarterly. **Print Method:** Offset. **Trim
Size:** 13 x 22. **Cols./Page:** 6. **Col. Width:** 2 1/16 inches.
Col. Depth: 21 inches. **Key Personnel:** Gotz Trenkler,
Coord. Ed., trenkler@statistik.uni-dortmund.de; H. Bun-
ing, Editorial Board; P. De Jong, Editorial Board; Prof.
Liqun Wang, Editor, liqun_wang@umanitoba.ca; Dr.
Sylvia Fruhwirth-Schnatter, Editor, sylvia.fruehwirth-
schnatter@jku.at; M. Deistler, Editorial Board; G. Ron-
ning, Editorial Board; Dr. Walter Kramer, Editor,
walterk@statistik.uni-dortmund.de; H. Drygas, Editorial
Board. **ISSN:** 0932-5026. **Subscription Rates:** EUR627
institutions print incl. free access or e-only; EUR752.40
institutions print incl. enhanced access. **URL:** http://
www.springer.com/statistics/business/journal/362.

42735 ■ **FRO-FM - 105.0**
Kirchengasse 4
A-4040 Linz, Austria
Ph: 43 732 717277
E-mail: fro@fro.at
Format: Information; Ethnic; Eclectic. **Owner:** Freier
Rundfunk Oberosterreich GmbH, at above address. **Op-
erating Hours:** Continuous. **Ad Rates:** Advertising ac-
cepted; rates available upon request. **URL:** http://www.
fro.at.

Life Radio-FM - See Lichtenberg

Modling

42736 ■ **The British Journal of Developmental
Disabilities**
British Society for Developmental Disabilities
Weyprechtgasse 10
A-2340 Modling, Austria
Fax: 43 223 629554
Publisher E-mail: office@bjdd.org
Journal covering the mentally disabled. **Founded:** 1952.
Freq: Semiannual January and July. **Key Personnel:**
H.C. Gunzburg, PhD, Founding Ed.; Dr. B. Salmons,
Editor. **ISSN:** 0969-7950. **Subscription Rates:** 20
individuals Europe; incl. postage; EUR36 individuals incl.
postage; 24 individuals overseas; incl. airmail; EUR40
individuals overseas; incl. airmail; $A 80 individuals
overseas; incl. airmail; C$74 individuals overseas; incl.
airmail; US$54 individuals overseas; incl. airmail. **Re-
marks:** Advertising accepted; rates available upon
request. **URL:** http://www.bjdd.org/new/index.htm. **Circ:**
(Not Reported)

Mondsee

42737 ■ **European Journal of Protistology**
Elsevier Science Inc.
c/o Thomas Weisse, Ed.
Institute for Limnology of the Austrian Academy of Sciences
A-5310 Mondsee, Austria
Fax: 43 62323578
Publisher E-mail: usinfo-ehelp@elsevier.com
Journal dealing with protists, unicellular organisms
encountered in various habitats or as parasites or used
in basic research or applications. **Founded:** 1964. **Freq:**
4/yr. **Print Method:** Offset. **Trim Size:** 9 3/8 x 12 1/2.
Cols./Page: 4. **Col. Width:** 27 nonpareils. **Col. Depth:**
156 agate lines. **Key Personnel:** Thomas Weisse, Edi-
tor; H. Berger, Editorial Board; J. Pawlowski, Editorial
Board; Brian S. Leander, Editorial Board; K. Hausmann,
Assoc. Ed.; D.J. Patterson, Editorial Board; E. Aescht,
Board of Reviewers. **ISSN:** 0932-4739. **Subscription
Rates:** EUR761 institutions European countries and Iran;
104,500¥ institutions; US$846 institutions, other coun-
tries except Europe, Japan and Iran; EUR196 students
European countries and Iran; 25,600¥ students; US$846
students, other countries except Europe, Japan and
Iran; US$265 individuals except Europe, Japan and Iran;
34,100¥ individuals; EUR261 individuals European
countries and Iran. **URL:** http://www.elsevier.com/wps/
find/journaldescription.cws_home/701761/
descriptiondescription.

Reutte

42738 ■ **International Journal of Refractory Met-
als and Hard Materials**
Elsevier Science Inc.
c/o H.M. Ortner, Ed.-in-Ch.
Osterbichl 16
Breitenwang
A-6600 Reutte, Austria
Publisher E-mail: usinfo-ehelp@elsevier.com
Peer-reviewed journal covering science, technology and
application of refractory metals and hard materials. **Freq:**
6/yr. **Print Method:** Offset. **Cols./Page:** 8. **Col. Width:**
21 nonpareils. **Col. Depth:** 301 agate lines. **Key Per-
sonnel:** H.M. Ortner, Editor-in-Chief; L. Bartha, Editorial
Board; K.Y. Eun, Editorial Board; I. Smid, Assoc. Ed.; R.
German, Editorial Board; A. Shan, Assoc. Ed. for China;
P. Ettmayer, Editorial Board; S. Kang, Editorial Board;
M. Filgueira, Editorial Board. **ISSN:** 0263-4368. **Subscription Rates:** US$1,284 institutions except Europe,
Japan and Iran; EUR1,151 institutions for European
countries and Iran; 152,400¥ institutions; US$163 other
countries except Europe, Japan and Iran; 18,700¥
individuals; EUR121 individuals for European countries
and Iran. **URL:** http://www.elsevier.com/wps/find/
journaldescription.cws_home/405934/
descriptiondescription.

St. Poelten

42739 ■ **CR-FM - 94.4**
Matthias Corvinus-Strasse 15
A-3100 St. Poelten, Austria
Format: Eclectic. **Owner:** Verein Campus & City Radio
St. Polten, at above address. **URL:** http://www.
campusradio.at/.

Salzburg

42740 ■ **Geomechanics and Tunnelling**
John Wiley & Sons Inc.
Osterreichische Gesellschaft fur Geomechanik
Bayerhamerstrasse 14
5020 Salzburg, Austria
Publisher E-mail: info@wiley.com
Journal covering the field of geomechanics and
tunneling. **Freq:** 6/yr. **Key Personnel:** Prof. Georgios
Anagnostou, Contact. **ISSN:** 1865-7362. **Subscription
Rates:** 121.87 SFr institutions Switzerland and Lichtenstein (print only); EUR71 institutions Europe (print only);
55.91 institutions Europe (print only); US$117.60 institu-
tions, other countries print only. **URL:** http://onlinelibrary.
wiley.com/journal/10.1002/(ISSN)1865-7389; http://www.
oegg.at/index.php?id=8&L=2.

42741 ■ **Natur und Land**
Osterreichischer Naturschutzbund
Museumsplatz 2
A-5020 Salzburg, Austria
Ph: 43 662 642909
Fax: 43 662 6437344
Publication E-mail: natur-land@naturschutzbund.at

Publisher E-mail: bundesverband@naturschutzbund.at
Journal covering nature and the environment. **Subtitle:**
Zeitschrift des Osterreichischen Naturschutzbudes.
Founded: 1913. **Freq:** Quarterly. **Print Method:** Offset.
Trim Size: 190 x 270 cm. **Cols./Page:** 3. **Key Person-
nel:** Ingrid Hagenstein, Editor. **ISSN:** 0028-0607. **Sub-
scription Rates:** EUR18 individuals; EUR22 other
countries; EUR6 single issue double booklets. **Remarks:**
Accepts advertising. **URL:** http://www.naturschutzbund.
at. **Circ:** 12,000

Vienna

42742 ■ **ACT! The Magazine of Greenpeace
Austria**
Greenpeace Austria
Fernkorngasse 10
A-1100 Vienna, Austria
Ph: 43 154 54580
Fax: 43 154 5458098
Publisher E-mail: spenden@greenpeace.at
German language magazine covering greenpeace
Austria. **Freq:** Quarterly. **Key Personnel:** Matthias
Schickhofer, Campaign Dir., phone 54 545 8044,
matthias.schickhofer@greenpeace.at; Sonja Sagan,
Public Relation, phone 54 545 8028, sonja.sagan@
greenpeace.at. **Remarks:** Advertising not accepted.
URL: http://www.greenpeace.at/act-magazin.html. **Circ:**
(Not Reported)

42743 ■ **Amino Acids**
Springer-Verlag Tokyo
c/o Gert Lubec, Ed.-in-Ch.
Universitats Kinderklinik
Wahringer Gurtel 18-20
A-1090 Vienna, Austria
Publisher E-mail: info@springer.jp
Journal publishing contributions from all fields of amino
acid and protein research: analysis, separation, synthesis, biosynthesis, cross linking amino acids,
racemization/enantiomers, modification of amino acids
as phosphorylation, methylation, acetylation, glycosylation and nonenzymatic glycosylation, new roles for
amino acids in physiology and pathophysiology, biology,
amino acid analogues and derivatives, polyamines, radiated amino acids, peptides, stable isotopes and isotopes
of amino acids. **Freq:** 5/yr. **Key Personnel:** Gert Lubec,
Editor-in-Chief. **ISSN:** 0939-4451. **Subscription Rates:**
EUR1,766 institutions print incl. free access or e-only;
EUR2,119.20 institutions print incl. enhanced access.
Remarks: Advertising accepted; rates available upon
request. **URL:** http://www.springer.com/
springerwiennewyork/lifesciences/journal/726. **Circ:** (Not
Reported)

42744 ■ **Annals of Nutrition and Metabolism**
S. Karger Publishers Inc.
c/o Prof. Dr. I. Elmadfa, Ed.
Institute of Nutritional Sciences
University of Vienna
Althanstrasse 14
1090 Vienna, Austria
Ph: 43 142 7754901
Fax: 43 142 779549
Publisher E-mail: karger@snet.net
Scientific medical journal (English, French, and
German). **Founded:** 1959. **Freq:** 8/yr. **Print Method:**
Offset. **Trim Size:** 210 x 280 mm. **Cols./Page:** 1. **Col.
Width:** 84 nonpareils. **Col. Depth:** 141 agate lines. **Key
Personnel:** X. Lin, Editorial Board Member; F. Branca,
Editorial Board Member; P.C. Calder, Editorial Board
Member; K. Eder, Editorial Board Member; A. Kafatos,
Editorial Board Member; A. Berg, Editorial Board
Member; S. Hercberg, Editorial Board Member; N.
Houalla, Editorial Board Member; E.T. Kennedy, Edito-
rial Board Member; Prof. Dr. I. Elmadfa, Editor,
ernaehrungswissenschaften@univie.ac.at. **ISSN:** 0250-
6807. **Subscription Rates:** 3,324 SFr institutions print
and online; EUR2,374 institutions print and online;
US$3,016 institutions print and online; 3,022 SFr institu-
tions print or online; EUR2,158 institutions print or online;
US$2,740 institutions print or online. **Remarks:** Accepts
advertising. **URL:** http://content.karger.com/ProdukteDB/
produkte.asp?Aktion=JournalHome&ProduktNr=223977.
Formerly: Nutritio et Dieta (1959); Nutrition and
Metabolism. **Ad Rates:** BW: 1,630 AS. **Circ:** 1,250

42745 ■ **Applied Artificial Intelligence**
Taylor & Francis Group Journals
c/o Robert Trappl, Ed.-in-Ch.
Austrian Research Institute for Artificial Intelligence
Freyung 6/6

A-1010 Vienna, Austria
Publisher E-mail: customerservice@taylorandfrancis.com
Journal covering applied artificial intelligence. **Subtitle:** An International Journal. **Founded:** 1987. **Freq:** 10/yr. **Print Method:** Offset. **Trim Size:** 7 x 10. **Cols./Page:** 2. **Col. Width:** 42 nonpareils. **Col. Depth:** 140 agate lines. **Key Personnel:** Douglas B. Lenat, Assoc. Ed.; Rodney A. Brooks, Assoc. Ed.; Hiroaki Kitano, Assoc. Ed.; Oliviero Stock, Assoc. Ed.; Ronald S. Brachman, Assoc. Ed.; Robert Trappl, Editor-in-Chief. **ISSN:** 0883-9514. **Subscription Rates:** US$679 individuals print only; US$1,439 institutions online only; US$1,514 institutions print & online; 913 institutions print & online; EUR1,206 institutions print & online; 867 institutions online only; EUR1,146 institutions online only; 408 individuals; EUR541 individuals. **Remarks:** Accepts advertising. **URL:** http://www.tandf.co.uk/journals/titles/08839514.asp. **Circ:** Combined ‡453

42746 ■ Architektur Aktuell
Springer-Verlag
Sachsenplatz 4-6
Postfach 89
A-1201 Vienna, Austria
Ph: 43 133 024150
Fax: 43 133 0242626261
Publisher E-mail: springer@springer.at
Professional journal covering architecture. **Subtitle:** The Art of Building. **Freq:** 10/yr. **Trim Size:** 210 x 297 mm. **Key Personnel:** Gerald Albin Roedler, Editor; Matthias Boeckl, Editor-in-Chief; Anne Lacaton, Advisory Board; Dominique Boudet, Advisory Board. **ISSN:** 0570-6602. **Subscription Rates:** EUR124 institutions. **Remarks:** Accepts advertising. **URL:** http://www.springer.com/springerwiennewyork/architecture/journal/732; http://www.architektur-aktuell.at. **Ad Rates:** BW: 2,920 AS, 4C: 4,360 AS. **Circ:** 10,428

42747 ■ Austrian Economic Quarterly
Austrian Institute of Economic Research
Osterreichisches Institut fur Wirtschaftsforschung
Arsenal, Objekt 20
A-1030 Vienna, Austria
Ph: 43 179 82601
Fax: 43 179 89386
Publisher E-mail: office@wifo.ac.at
Online publication covering economics and related business issues from an Austrian perspective. **Freq:** Quarterly. **Key Personnel:** Ilse Schulz, Managing Editor, ilse.schulz@wifo.ac.at; Marianne Utiz, Managing Editor, marianne.uitz@wifo.ac.at. **ISSN:** 1605-4709. **Subscription Rates:** EUR84 individuals; EUR15 single issue. **URL:** http://www.wifo.ac.at/wwa/jsp/index.jsp?&fid=24041. **Circ:** 200

42748 ■ Auto Touring
Austrian Automobile Touring and Motorcycle Club
Osterreichischer Automobil-, Motorrad-, und Touring Club
Rechtsdienste
Schubertring 1-3
A-1010 Vienna, Austria
Ph: 43 171 1990
Fax: 43 171 9921511
Publisher E-mail: office@oeamtc.at
German language covering automotive services. **Freq:** Monthly. **Key Personnel:** Potor Pisecker, Editor-in-Chief; Helmut Eckler, Contact. **Subscription Rates:** Included in membership. **Remarks:** Advertising accepted; rates available upon request. **URL:** http://www.oeamtc.at/; http://www.autotouring.at/index.php. **Circ:** Combined 2,107,000

42749 ■ Connex
Osterreichisches Normungsinstitut
Heinestr. 38
A-1020 Vienna, Austria
Ph: 43 121 3000
Fax: 43 121 300818
Publisher E-mail: office@on-norm.at
Trade magazine covering changes in standards in Europe and worldwide. **Founded:** Jan. 1994. **Freq:** Monthly. **Print Method:** Letterpress. **Trim Size:** A3. **Key Personnel:** Dr. Johannes Stern, Editor-in-Chief, phone 43 121 300317, fax 43 121 300327, johannes.stern@on-norm.at; Regina Slameczka, Editor, phone 43 1 21300618, fax 43 1 2130032, regina.slameczka@on.norm.at. **ISSN:** 1023-9073. **Remarks:** Advertising not accepted. **URL:** http://www.on-norm.at/publish/2024.html. **Circ:** 2,100

42750 ■ Elektronik Report
Dresdner Strasse 45
A-1200 Vienna, Austria
Ph: 43 1 97000100
Fax: 43 1 970005100
Publication E-mail: kundenservice@weka.at
Publisher E-mail: kundenservice@weka.at
Trade magazine covering electronics. **Founded:** 1975. **Freq:** Monthly. **Key Personnel:** Stefan Bock, Editor, sb@weka.at. **ISSN:** 1019-410X. **URL:** http://www.industrieweb.at/elektronik/; http://www.husonmedia.com/index.php/media-search/print-item/166-elektronik-report.

42751 ■ European Journal of Cross-Cultural Competence and Management
Inderscience Enterprises Limited
c/o Frank Brueck, Exec. Ed.
Vienna University of Economics & Business Administration
Nordbergstrasse 15
A-1090 Vienna, Austria
Journal featuring issues regarding the influence of cultural differences and diversity on the management of organization of all kinds. **Freq:** Quarterly. **Key Personnel:** Frank Brueck, Exec. Ed., brueck@wu-wien.ac.at. **ISSN:** 1758-1508. **Subscription Rates:** EUR494 individuals print or online; EUR672 individuals print and online. **URL:** http://www.inderscience.com/browse/index.php?journalID=330.

42752 ■ The European Journal of Economics, Finance and Administrative Sciences
European Journals, Inc.
PO Box 1123
Vienna, Austria
Publisher E-mail: editor@eurojournals.com
Journal encompassing theoretical, empirical or policy oriented research articles, original research reports, reviews, short communication and scientific commentaries in the fields of economics and administrative sciences including both controversial and innovative ideas and detailed contributions from other directly related fields such as econometrics, economic development, trade and the environment, and political economy. **Freq:** Quarterly. **Key Personnel:** Karl V. Roberts, Editor-in-Chief. **ISSN:** 1450-2275. **Subscription Rates:** US$200 individuals. **URL:** http://www.eurojournals.com/EJEFA.htm.

42753 ■ European Journal of Scientific Research
European Journals, Inc.
PO Box 1123
Vienna, Austria
Publisher E-mail: editor@eurojournals.com
Peer-reviewed journal encompassing research articles, original research reports, reviews, short communication and scientific commentaries in the fields of applied and theoretical sciences, biology, chemistry, physics, zoology, environmental sciences, mathematics, statistics, geology, engineering, computer science, social sciences, natural and technological sciences, linguistics, medicine, industrial, and all other applied and theoretical sciences. **Freq:** Quarterly. **Key Personnel:** Karl Roberts, Editor. **ISSN:** 1450-216X. **Subscription Rates:** US$200 individuals. **URL:** http://www.eurojournals.com/EJSR.htm.

42754 ■ The European Journal of Social Sciences
European Journals, Inc.
PO Box 1123
Vienna, Austria
Publisher E-mail: editor@eurojournals.com
Peer-reviewed journal encompassing scientific articles, original research reports, reviews, short communication and scientific commentaries on cultural studies rooted in lived experience. **Freq:** Monthly. **ISSN:** 1450-2267. **Subscription Rates:** US$200 individuals. **URL:** http://www.eurojournals.com/EJSS.htm.

42755 ■ The European Journal of Technology and Advanced Engineering Research
European Journals, Inc.
PO Box 1123
Vienna, Austria
Publisher E-mail: editor@eurojournals.com
Journal encompassing scientific articles, original research reports, reviews, short communication and scientific commentaries on technology and engineering.

Freq: Quarterly. **Key Personnel:** Adrian M. Steinberg, Editor-in-Chief; Dr. Subrata Chowdhury, Editorial Advisory Board; Said Elnashaie, Editorial Advisory Board. **ISSN:** 1450-202X. **Subscription Rates:** US$99 individuals. **URL:** http://www.eurojournals.com/EJTAER.htm.

42756 ■ European Surgery
Springer Netherlands
Manometry Lab & Division of General Surgery
Department of Surgery
Vienna Medical University
Waehringer Guertel 18-20
01090 Vienna, Austria
Publisher E-mail: permissions.dordrecht@springer.com
Journal covering developments in surgical practice and research. **Subtitle:** Acta Chirurgica Austriaca. **Freq:** 6/yr. **Print Method:** Offset. **Cols./Page:** 6. **Col. Width:** 2 1/32 inches. **Col. Depth:** 294 agate lines. **Key Personnel:** H. Koch, Section Ed., phone 43 316 3854690, horst.koch@meduni-graz.at; B. Teleky, Editorial Board; J. Wallwork, Editorial Board; Hubert Hauser, Section Ed., fax 43 316 3853418, hubert.hauser@meduni-graz.at; S. Roka, Section Dir., fax 43 140 4006896, sebastian.roka@meduniwien.ac.at; L. Ch. Muller, Section Dir., fax 43 512 5042528, ludwig.mueller@uibk.ac.at; H.F. Wykypiel, Section Dir., fax 43 512 5042577, heinz.wykypiel@uibk.ac.at; F.M. Riegler, Editor-in-Chief, fax 43 140 4006898, franz.riegler@meduniwien.ac.at; B. Zupancic, Editorial Board. **ISSN:** 1682-8631. **Subscription Rates:** EUR513 institutions print incl. free access or e-only; EUR615.60 institutions print incl. enhanced access. **Remarks:** Advertising accepted; rates available upon request. **URL:** http://www.springer.com/springerwiennewyork/medicine/journal/10353. **Circ:** (Not Reported)

42757 ■ Extra Golf
Payer & Payer GesmbH
Winzerstrasse 23
A-1130 Vienna, Austria
Ph: 43 171 80246
Fax: 43 171 8024622
Publication E-mail: office@extragolf.at
Publisher E-mail: office@extragolf.at
Consumer magazine covering golf. **Subtitle:** The Magazine of the Extravagent Golfer. **Founded:** Mar. 15, 1994. **Freq:** Quarterly. **Print Method:** Offset. **Trim Size:** 788 x 290 mm. **Cols./Page:** 3. **Col. Width:** 3.15 inches. **Key Personnel:** Stephan Gurtler, Managing Editor, s.guertler@extragolf.at; Christoph Payer, Contact, christoph.payer@extragolf.at; Michel Payer, Editor-in-Chief, michel.payer@extragolf.at. **Remarks:** Accepts advertising. **URL:** http://www.extragolf.at/. **Ad Rates:** BW: EUR5,000, 4C: EUR5,800. **Circ:** Controlled 55,000

42758 ■ Fempower
WAVE Network & European Info Centre Against Violence
Bacherplatz 10-4
A-1050 Vienna, Austria
Ph: 43 154 82720
Fax: 43 154 82720
Publication E-mail: office@wave-network.org
Publisher E-mail: office@wave-network.org
Magazine featuring current information on new organizations and projects, laws and draft legislation, conferences and international topics (English and French) **Subtitle:** The Periodical of Women Against Violence Europe (WAVE). **Founded:** 2001. **Freq:** Semiannual. **Key Personnel:** Maria Pohn-Weidinger, Editor; Martina K. Steiner, Editor. **URL:** http://www.wave-network.org/start.asp?ID=16.

42759 ■ Globe Studies
Internationale Coronelli-Gesellschaft fuer Globenkunde
Dominikanerbastei 21/28
A-1010 Vienna, Austria
Ph: 43 1 5320824
Publisher E-mail: vincenzo@coronelli.org
Journal devoted to the scientific investigation and publication of questions relating to old and antique terrestrial and celestial globes, armillary spheres and planetaria. **Subtitle:** Journal of the International Coronelli Society. **URL:** http://www.coronelli.org/publikationen/globusfreund_e.html.

42760 ■ INIS Database
International Atomic Energy Agency - Austria
Agence Internationale de l'Energie Atomique

Wagramer Strasse 5
PO Box 100
A-1400 Vienna, Austria
Ph: 43 126 000
Fax: 43 126 007
Publication E-mail: inis@iaea.org
Publisher E-mail: official.mail@iaea.org
Bibliographic Database covering all the application of
nuclear science and technology. **Freq:** Semimonthly.
Key Personnel: Taghrid Atieh, inspection, t.atieh@iaea.
org. **ISSN:** 0004-7139. **Remarks:** Advertising not
accepted. **URL:** http://www.iaea.org/inisnkm/inis/basis/
subscr0.htm. **Circ:** (Not Reported)

**42761 ■ International Journal of Advanced
Robotic Systems**
Kirchengasse 43/3
A-1070 Vienna, Austria
Publication E-mail: journal@intechweb.org
Publisher E-mail: journal@intechweb.org
Journal publishing original research papers, book and
robot reviews, interviews with leading robotic experts,
presentations of robotic institutes, industrial trends and
reports. **Freq:** Quarterly. **Key Personnel:** Vedran Ko-
rdic, Editor-in-Chief; Yoseph Bar-Cohen, Assoc. Ed.;
Ronald C. Arkin, Assoc. Ed.; Kin Huat Low, Assoc. Ed.;
Thomas Braeunl, Assoc. Ed.; Pedro U. Lima, Assoc.
Ed.; Lynne E. Parker, Assoc. Ed.; Frank Lewis, Assoc.
Ed.; Munir Merdan, Editor-in-Chief; Aleksandar Lazinica,
Editor-in-Chief. **ISSN:** 1729-8806. **Subscription Rates:**
EUR380 individuals print. **URL:** http://intechweb.org/
journal.php?id=3.

42762 ■ Journal of Neural Transmission
Springer-Verlag
Sachsenplatz 4-6
Postfach 89
A-1201 Vienna, Austria
Ph: 43 133 024150
Fax: 43 133 02426261
Publisher E-mail: springer@springer.at
The journal exploring interface between basic sciences
and clinical neurology and psychiatry. The areas of inter-
est include neurochemistry, neuropharmacology, neuro-
sciences, and clinical biochemistry, neurotransmission.
Freq: Monthly. **Key Personnel:** E. Asan, Editorial Board;
Peter Riederer, Editor-in-Chief; T. Arendt, Editorial
Board; A. Apter, Editorial Board; A. Carlsson, Honorary
Ed.-in-Ch. **ISSN:** 0300-9564. **Remarks:** Advertising accepted; rates available upon request. **URL:** http://www.
springer.com/springerwiennewyork/medicine/journal/
702. **Circ:** (Not Reported)

42763 ■ Long Range Planning
Elsevier
Vienna University of Economics & Business
Nordbergstrasse 15, Unit A Fl. 6
1090 Vienna, Austria
Publication E-mail: lrp@city.ac.uk
Journal featuring strategic planning in management of
education. **Subtitle:** The International Journal of
Strategic Management. **Founded:** 1968. **Freq:** 6/yr. **Key
Personnel:** J.A. Robins, Editor-in-Chief, james.robins@
wu.ac.at. **ISSN:** 0024-6301. **Subscription Rates:**
229,600¥ institutions; EUR1,728 institutions for European
countries and Iran; US$1,934 institutions OTC; 30,900¥
individuals; EUR233 individuals for European countries
and Iran; US$261 individuals. **Remarks:** Accepts
advertising. **URL:** http://www.elsevier.com/wps/find/
journaldescription.cws_home/358/descriptiondescription.
Circ: (Not Reported)

**42764 ■ Mitteilungen Osterreiches Getranke In-
stitut**
Osterreichisches Getranke Institut
Michaelerstrasse 25
A-1180 Vienna, Austria
Ph: 43 1 47969240
Fax: 43 1 479692433
Publisher E-mail: office@oegi.at
German language publication covering beverages.
Founded: 1947. **Freq:** Periodic. **Key Personnel:** Dr.
H.-J. Schmidt, Contact, phone 43 1 47969, h.schmidt@
oegi.at. **Remarks:** Advertising accepted; rates available
upon request. **URL:** http://www.oegi.at/. **Circ:** (Not
Reported)

42765 ■ Nuclear Fusion
IOP Publishing Ltd.
PO Box 100
Wagramerstrasse 5

A-1400 Vienna, Austria
Ph: 43 126 0026195
Fax: 43 126 0029655
Publication E-mail: nf@iaea.org
Publisher E-mail: custserv@iop.org
Peer-reviewed journal covering all aspects of research
relevant to controlled thermonuclear fusion. **Freq:**
Monthly. **Key Personnel:** K. Burrel, Editorial Board; A.
Loarte, Editorial Board; G. Janeschitz, Editorial Board;
M. Kikuchi, Chm.; Y. Kamada, Editorial Board; S.V. Leb-
edev, Editorial Board; P. Thomas, Editor; M. Tabak,
Assoc. Ed.; A. Sen, Editorial Board; A. Fukuyama, Edito-
rial Board. **ISSN:** 0029-5515. **Subscription Rates:**
US$1,600 institutions for North, Central and South
America; 943 institutions, other countries. **URL:** http://
www.iop.org/ej/journal/nuclfus.

42766 ■ Progress
Austrian National Union of Students
Osterreichische Hochschulerschaft
Taubstummengasse 7-9
A-1040 Vienna, Austria
Ph: 43 131 08880
Fax: 43 131 0888036
Publication E-mail: progress@oeh.ac.at
Publisher E-mail: oeh@oeh.ac.at
German language publication covering students. **Freq:**
Monthly. **Subscription Rates:** Included in membership.
Remarks: Advertising accepted; rates available upon
request. **URL:** http://www.progress-online.at/. **Former
name:** Scope. **Circ:** (Not Reported)

42767 ■ Psychologie in Osterreich
Berufsverband Osterreichischer Psychologinnen und
Psychologen
Mollnaldplatz 4/4/39
A-1040 Vienna, Austria
Ph: 43 140 726710
Fax: 43 140 7267130
Journal of the Austrian Psychological Association cover-
ing all fields of psychology. **Founded:** 1980. **Freq:**
Quarterly. **Trim Size:** A-4. **Key Personnel:** Dr. Gerald
Kral, Editor-in-Chief. **ISSN:** 1025-1839. **Remarks:** Ac-
cepts advertising. **URL:** http://www.boep.or.at/; http://
www.boep.or.at/pio/pio2/db/suche.htm. **Circ:** Combined
⊕2,146

**42768 ■ Stichproben - Wiener Zeitschrift fur
Kritische Afrikastudien**
Institut fur Afrikanistik
Universitat zu Koln
c/o Dept. of African Studies, University of Vienna
Uni-Campus, Hof 5.1
Spitalgasse 2-4
A-1090 Vienna, Austria
Publisher E-mail: afrikanistik@uni-koeln.de
Journal covering contemporary history, social history,
politics, language and culture. **Subtitle:** Vienna Journal
of African Studies. **Founded:** 1945. **Freq:** Semiannual.
Print Method: Offset. **Cols./Page:** 8. **Col. Width:** 19
nonpareils. **Col. Depth:** 294 agate lines. **Key Person-
nel:** Birgit Englert, Editor; Elke Christiansen, Editor; Mar-
tina Ciganikova, Editor. **ISSN:** 1992-8610. **Subscription
Rates:** EUR7.25 single issue Austria; EUR9.50 single issue Europe; EUR11.25 out of country single issue;
EUR13.50 individuals Austria; EUR18 individuals Europe;
EUR22.50 out of country. **URL:** http://www.univie.ac.at/
ecco/stichproben/.

42769 ■ TermNet News
International Network for Terminology
Internationales Terminologienetz
TermNet
Zieglergasse 28
A-1070 Vienna, Austria
Ph: 43 152 4060611
Fax: 43 152 4060699
Publisher E-mail: termnet@termnet.org
Technology publication. **Freq:** Quarterly. **ISSN:** 0251-
5253. **URL:** http://linux.termnet.org.

42770 ■ TRANS
Research Institute for Austrian and International
Literature and Cultural Studies
PF 74
Vienna, Austria
Ph: 43 1 7481633
Fax: 43 1 7481615
Publisher E-mail: arlt@inst.at
Journal providing a platform for exchange of views in
the areas of literature, language, libraries and cultural

studies. **Subtitle:** Internet Journal for Cultural Studies.
Founded: 8, 1997. **Key Personnel:** Dr. Herbert Arlt,
Editor, arlt@inst.at. **Subscription Rates:** Free online.
URL: http://www.inst.at/trans/.

42771 ■ Transfer Werbeforschung & Praxis
Vienna University of Economics and Business
Administration
Augasse 2-6
A-1090 Vienna, Austria
Ph: 43 1 313364310
Fax: 43 1 31336752
Publisher E-mail: zas@wu.ac.at
Professional journal covering marketing, advertising and
market research. **Founded:** 1898. **Freq:** Quarterly.
Cols./Page: 3. **Col. Width:** 58 millimeters. **Col. Depth:**
260 millimeters. **Key Personnel:** Dr. Guenter Sch-
weiger, Contact; Barbara Koecher-Schulz, Chief
Engineer. **ISSN:** 1436-798X. **Remarks:** Accepts
advertising. **URL:** http://www.varus.com/seiten/transfer.
html. **Former name:** Werbeforschung & Praxis. **Ad
Rates:** BW: EUR1,600, 4C: EUR2,400. **Circ:** Combined
8,500

42772 ■ Transplant International
John Wiley & Sons Inc.
Wiley-Blackwell
Vienna General Hospital
Division of Transplantation
Ebene 9.D5.18
Wahringer Gurtel 18-20
A-1090 Vienna, Austria
Ph: 43 1 404006874
Fax: 43 1 404006767
Publication E-mail: transpl-int@meduniwien.ac.at
Journal serving as a forum for the exchange of scientific
information in the form of original and high-quality
papers in the field of transplantation, including clinical
and experimental studies, editorials, letters to the edi-
tors and reviews on the biology, physiology and im-
munology of transplantation of tissues and organs. **Freq:**
Monthly. **Key Personnel:** Ferdinand Muhlbacher, Editor-
in-Chief; Diego Cantarovich, Assoc. Ed.; Uwe Heemann,
Assoc. Ed.; Stefan G. Tullius, Assoc. Ed.; Per Pfeffer,
Editorial Board; Thomas Wekerle, Editor-in-Chief; Milene
Wirth Fernandez, Asst. to the Ed.; J. Langrehr, Editorial
Board; Liz Hablit, Asst. to the Ed.; Martin Meyrath, Asst.
to the Ed. **ISSN:** 0934-0874. **Subscription Rates:**
US$258 individuals print + online; EUR162 individuals
print + online; 143 other countries print + online;
US$1,581 institutions print + online; 940 institutions
print + online; EUR1,195 institutions print + online;
US$1,436 institutions print or online; EUR1,085 institu-
tions print or online; US$1,843 institutions, other
countries print + online; US$1,675 institutions, other
countries print or online. **Remarks:** Advertising accepted; rates available upon request. **URL:** http://www.
wiley.com/bw/journal.asp?ref=0934-0874&site=1. **Circ:**
(Not Reported)

42773 ■ VCO Magazin
VCO Verkehrsclub Osterreich
Braeuhausgasse 7-9
A-1050 Vienna, Austria
Ph: 43 1 8932697
Fax: 43 1 8932431
Publication E-mail: vcoe@vcoe.at
Publisher E-mail: vcoe@vcoe.at
Journal covering environmental friendly social agreeable
and economic effective transportation. **Founded:** 1988.
Freq: Bimonthly 6/yr. **Print Method:** Offset. **Trim Size:**
263 x 399 mm. **Cols./Page:** 6. **Col. Width:** 44
millimeters. **Key Personnel:** Christian Hoeller, Editor,
christian.hoeller@vcoe.at. **Remarks:** Advertising ac-
cepted; rates available upon request. **URL:** http://www.
vcoe.at. **Circ:** Paid 20,000

42774 ■ Wirschaft und Gesellschaft
AK Wien
Prinz Eugen Str. 20-22
A-1040 Vienna, Austria
Ph: 43 150 1650
Magazine covering economics, economic policy, sociol-
ogy, political science and economic history. **Founded:**
1975. **Freq:** Quarterly. **ISSN:** 0378-5130. **Subscription
Rates:** EUR33 individuals, EUR19.50 students all prices
inclusive vat; EUR10.50 single issue. **Remarks:** Advertis-
ing not accepted. **URL:** http://wien.arbeiterkammer.at/
www-397-IP-11241.html. **Circ:** Combined 900

**42775 ■ The World Journal of Biological
Psychiatry**
Informa Healthcare

c/o Dr. Siegfried Kasper, Ch. Ed.
Dept. of Psychiatry & Psychotherapy
Medical University of Vienna
Vienna, Austria
Ph: 43 1 404003568
Fax: 43 1 404003099
Publisher E-mail: healthcare.enquiries@informa.com
Journal devoted to clinical psychiatrists, educators, scientists and students interested in biological psychiatry. **Freq:** Quarterly. **Print Method:** Offset. **Cols./Page:** 6. **Col. Width:** 27 nonpareils. **Col. Depth:** 301 agate lines. **Key Personnel:** Michael Bauer, Editorial Board; Giovanni B. Cassano, Editorial Board; Carlos Roberto Hojaij, Founding Ed.; Graham Burrows, Editorial Board; Joseph Zohar, Assoc. Ed.; Hagop Akiskal, Editorial Board. **ISSN:** 1562-2975. **Subscription Rates:**

590 institutions; US$870 institutions; EUR700 institutions; 1,180 institutions; US$1,740 institutions; 1,400 AS ECM. **URL:** http://www.informaworld.com/smpp/title~db=all~content=t713721967~tab=linking.

42776 ■ NRJ-FM - 104.2
N&C Privatradiobetriebsges MBH
Glabenzgasse 11-4
A-1150 Vienna, Austria
Ph: 43 214 19104
Fax: 43 198 16099
E-mail: office@energy.at
Format: Top 40. **Owner:** Radio Energy Austria, at above address. **Key Personnel:** Mag Aline Basel, Manager, abasel@energy.at. **URL:** http://www.energy.at/.

42777 ■ Orange-FM - 94.0
Klosterneuburger Str. 1

A-1200 Vienna, Austria
Ph: 43 1 3190999
Fax: 43 1 319099914
E-mail: office@o94.at
Format: Eclectic; Ethnic. **Operating Hours:** Continuous. **Ad Rates:** Advertising accepted; rates available upon request. **URL:** http://o94.at.

42778 ■ Radio Arabella-FM - 92.9
Alser Strasse 4, Hof 1 - Altes AKH
A-1090 Vienna, Austria
Ph: 43 1 4929929
E-mail: office@radioarabella.at
Format: Contemporary Hit Radio (CHR). **Owner:** Radio Arabella-FM, at above address. **Key Personnel:** Ralph Waldhauser, Program Dir. **URL:** http://www.arabella.at/wien.

Circulation: ✶ = ABC; △ = BPA; ◆ = CAC; • = CCAB; ❑ = VAC; ⊕ = PO Statement; ‡ = Publisher's Report; Boldface figures = sworn; Light figures = estimated.

Gale Directory of Publications & Broadcast Media/147th Ed.   4771

Baku

42779 ■ The Azeri Times
44 J. Jabbarly Str.
Caspian Plz.
AZ-1065 Baku, Azerbaijan
Ph: 994 12 4367750
Fax: 994 12 4367751
Publisher E-mail: office@theazeritimes.com

Newspaper featuring latest news, information, and events. **Founded:** 1998. **Freq:** Weekly. **Subscription Rates:** 120 Rb individuals; 80 Rb individuals 6 months; 40 Rb individuals 3 months; 15 Rb individuals 1 month. **Remarks:** Accepts advertising. **URL:** http://www.theazeritimes.com/. **Circ:** 8000

42780 ■ Caspian Business News
219 Bashir Safaroglu St.
AZ1000 Baku, Azerbaijan

Ph: 99 412 4933189
Fax: 99 412 4932478
Publisher E-mail: media@cbnmail.com
Local business newspaper. **Founded:** Apr. 2000. **Freq:** Weekly. **Key Personnel:** Olga Pukhayeva, Editor; Jamil Bayramov, Editor. **Remarks:** Accepts advertising. **URL:** http://cbnextra.com/. **Circ:** Paid 4,000

Circulation: ★ = ABC; △ = BPA; ♦ = CAC; • = CCAB; ❑ = VAC; ⊕ = PO Statement; ‡ = Publisher's Report; Boldface figures = sworn; Light figures = estimated.

Sao Miguel

42781 ■ Radio Atlantida-FM - 106.3
Rua Bento Jose Morais 23-5 Sul

Ponta Delgada
Sao Miguel, 9500-772 Azores
Ph: 351 296 201910
Fax: 351 296 629856

E-mail: webmaster@radioatlantida.net
Format: Ethnic; Contemporary Hit Radio (CHR). **Ad Rates:** Advertising accepted; rates available upon request. **URL:** http://www.radioatlantida.net.

Circulation: ★ = ABC; △ = BPA; ♦ = CAC; • = CCAB; ❏ = VAC; ⊕ = PO Statement; ‡ = Publisher's Report; Boldface figures = sworn; Light figures = estimated.

Abaco

42782 ■ Abaco Journal
Marsh Harbour
PO Box AB 20642
Abaco, Bahamas
Ph: (242)367-2580
Publisher E-mail: journal@oii.net
Journal covering local issues. **Founded:** 1987. **Freq:**
Monthly. **Key Personnel:** Jack Hardy, Editor; Bill Durrell, Publisher; Betsy Bracey, Regional Ed. **Subscription Rates:** US$22 individuals; US$24 individuals
Canada; US$25 individuals U.K. & Europe. **URL:** http://
www.oii.net/journal/.

Nassau

42783 ■ Bahamas Journal of Science
Media Enterprises Ltd.

31 Shirley Park Ave.
PO Box 9240
Nassau, Bahamas
Ph: (242)325-8210
Fax: (242)325-8065
Publication E-mail: info@bahamasmedia.com
Publisher E-mail: info@bahamasmedia.com
Journal covering research and scientific issues related
to the Bahamas Islands. **Founded:** 1993. **Freq:**
Semiannual. **Print Method:** Offset. **Trim Size:** 8.5 x 11.
ISSN: 1022-2189. **Subscription Rates:** US$35
individuals. **Remarks:** Accepts advertising. **URL:** http://
www.bahamasmedia.com/. **Circ:** Paid 500

42784 ■ The Nassau Guardian
PO Box N-3011
Nassau, Bahamas
Ph: (242)302-2300
General newspaper. **Key Personnel:** Gilbert Francis,

Operations Mgr., phone 242302-2311, gilbert@
nasguard.com; Wanda Gomez, Human Resource Mgr.,
phone 242302-2310, wanda@nasguard.com; Buena E.
Wright, Advertising Mgr., phone 242302-2313, buena@
nasguard.com; Anthony Ferguson, President, phone
242302-2305, aferguson@cfal.com. **Remarks:** Accepts
advertising. **URL:** http://www.thenassauguardian.com/.
Circ: (Not Reported)

42785 ■ More-FM - 94
Carmichael Rd.
PO Box CR54245
Nassau, Bahamas
Ph: (242)361-2447
Fax: (242)361-2448
E-mail: media@more94fm.com
Format: Eclectic. **Founded:** 1995. **Operating Hours:**
Continuous. **Ad Rates:** Advertising accepted; rates
available upon request. **URL:** http://www.more94fm.com.

Circulation: ★ = ABC; △ = BPA; ◆ = CAC; • = CCAB; ❑ = VAC; ⊕ = PO Statement; ‡ = Publisher's Report; Boldface figures = sworn; Light figures = estimated.

Gale Directory of Publications & Broadcast Media/147th Ed. 4777

Manama

42786 ■ Arab World Agribusiness
Fanar Publishing WLL
Bahrain Tower, 8th Fl.
PO Box 10131
Manama, Bahrain
Ph: 973 17213900
Fax: 973 17211765
Agricultural magazine serving the Arab world. **Founded:** 1984. **Freq:** Monthly 9/yr. **Subscription Rates:** US$180 individuals Arab Agriculture included. **Remarks:** Accepts advertising. **URL:** http://www.arabworldagribusiness.com/Agribusiness/. **Ad Rates:** BW: BD 787. **Circ:** 18,715

42787 ■ Bahrain This Month (BTM)
Red House Marketing
PO Box 20461
Manama, Bahrain
Ph: 973 178 13777
Fax: 973 178 13700
Publisher E-mail: redhouse@batelco.com.bh
Magazine covering local leisure and entertainment in Bahrain. **Founded:** Sept. 1997. **Freq:** Monthly. **Trim Size:** 216 X 278 mm. **Key Personnel:** Tony Sidgwick, Asst. Ed.; Abdul C.M. Rahman, Distribution Off.; Anil Ravi Shankar, Bystander Ed.; David M. Roberston, Publishing Dir.; Bassem A. Al Khabbaz, Personnel Mgr.; Cecille Anne A. Espino, Circulation Mgr.; George F. Middleton, Publisher/Mng. Dir.; Samson Vaz, Media Admin. & Finance Mgr., samson@bahrainthismonth. com; Dr. Paul J. Balles, Editorial Consultant. **Remarks:** Accepts advertising. **URL:** http://www.bahrainthismonth.com/index.php. **Ad Rates:** BW: US$1,800, 4C: US$2,250. **Circ:** Combined 10,000

42788 ■ Gulf Construction
Al Hilal Publishing & Marketing Group
PO Box 224
Manama, Bahrain
Ph: 973 172 93131
Fax: 973 172 93400
Publication E-mail: editor@gulfconstructionworldwide.com
Publisher E-mail: adsonline@tradearabia.net
Publication providing news, features, contracts and tenders, product and technical developments, and scientific papers covering construction from architecture to landscaping, maintenance, finishing, interiors, and civil and structural work. **Founded:** 1980. **Freq:** Monthly. **Subscription Rates:** US$120 individuals; US$240 two years. **Remarks:** Accepts advertising. **URL:** http://www.gulfconstructionworldwide.com/. **Ad Rates:** BW: US$2,015, 4C: US$2,890. **Circ:** Paid 49,028

42789 ■ Gulf Daily News
Al Hilal Publishing & Marketing Group
PO Box 5300
Manama, Bahrain
Ph: 973 620222
Fax: 973 622141
Publication E-mail: gdn1@batelco.com.bh
Publisher E-mail: adsonline@tradearabia.net
Newspaper. **Subtitle:** The Voice of Bahrain. **Freq:** Daily.

Subscription Rates: US$73 individuals. **Remarks:** Accepts advertising. **URL:** http://www.gulf-daily-news.com. **Circ:** (Not Reported)

42790 ■ Gulf Industry
Al Hilal Publishing & Marketing Group
PO Box 224
Manama, Bahrain
Ph: 973 172 93131
Fax: 973 172 93400
Publisher E-mail: adsonline@tradearabia.net
Magazine for individuals with an involvement or interest in the industrial development of the Gulf region, including industrialists, factory managers, major distributors of industrial products, and government officials. **Freq:** Bimonthly. **Subscription Rates:** US$95 individuals; US$160 two years. **Remarks:** Accepts advertising. **URL:** http://www.tradearabia.com/news/gi.asp?Sn=ind. **Ad Rates:** BW: US$2,015, 4C: US$2,890. **Circ:** Paid 13,614

42791 ■ Gulf Weekly
Al Hilal Publishing & Marketing Group
PO Box 224
Manama, Bahrain
Ph: 973 172 93131
Fax: 973 172 93400
Publication E-mail: editor@gulfweekly.com
Publisher E-mail: adsonline@tradearabia.net
Newspaper. **Freq:** Weekly. **Key Personnel:** Julie Dizon, Circulation & Subscription Mgr., phone 97 329 3131, fax 97 329 3400, julie.dizon@tradearabia.net. **Remarks:** Accepts advertising. **URL:** http://www.gulfweeklyworldwide.com/cover.htm. **Ad Rates:** 4C: BD 20. **Circ:** 31,000

42792 ■ International Journal of Accounting, Auditing and Performance Evaluation
Inderscience Publishers
Prof. Prem Lal Joshi, Ed.-in-Ch.
University of Bahrain
Dept. of Accounting
PO Box 32038
Manama, Bahrain
Publisher E-mail: editor@inderscience.com
Journal publishing original scholarly papers across the whole spectrum of financial accounting, managerial accounting, accounting education, auditing, taxation, public sector accounting, capital market and accounting, accounting information systems, performance evaluation, corporate governance, ethics, and financial management. **Freq:** Quarterly. **Key Personnel:** Prof. Prem Lal Joshi, Editor-in-Chief, prem@acadjoshi.com; Prof. Robert Luther, Consulting Ed.; Prof. Alan Dunk, Consulting Ed.; Prof. Wayne G. Bremser, Consulting Ed. **ISSN:** 1740-8008. **Subscription Rates:** EUR494 individuals print or online; EUR672 individuals print and online. **URL:** http://www.inderscience.com/browse/index.php?journalCODE=ijaape.

42793 ■ Oil and Gas News
Al Hilal Publishing & Marketing Group
PO Box 224
Manama, Bahrain
Ph: 973 172 93131
Fax: 973 172 93400

Publication E-mail: hilalad@tradearabia.net
Publisher E-mail: adsonline@tradearabia.net
Journal covering news of trends, products, events and other information for senior personnel in all sectors of the petroleum industry, including oil companies, exploration, supply, marine and offshore contractors, and government agencies. **Subtitle:** The Petroleum Industry Weekly for Asia - Pacific - Middle East. **Founded:** 1983. **Freq:** Weekly. **ISSN:** 0217-6602. **Subscription Rates:** US$695 individuals; US$1,200 two years. **Remarks:** Accepts advertising. **URL:** http://www.oilandgasnewsworldwide.com/cover.asp. **Ad Rates:** BW: US$4,690, 4C: US$6,566. **Circ:** Paid 8,539

42794 ■ Travel & Tourism News Middle East
Al Hilal Publishing & Marketing Group
PO Box 224
Manama, Bahrain
Ph: 973 172 93131
Fax: 973 172 93400
Publication E-mail: editor@ttnworldwide.com
Publisher E-mail: adsonline@tradearabia.net
Newspaper for travel industry professionals, including travel and tour agents, airline and airport personnel, and government tourist offices. **Founded:** 1979. **Freq:** Monthly. **Remarks:** Accepts advertising. **URL:** http://www.ttnworldwide.com. **Ad Rates:** BW: US$3,836, 4C: US$5,371. **Circ:** Paid 6,428

42795 ■ Woman This Month
Red House Publishing Group
PO Box 20461
Manama, Bahrain
Ph: 973 17 813777
Fax: 973 17 813700
Magazine designed by women and produced specifically for women in Bahrain. **Freq:** Monthly. **Subscription Rates:** Free to Bahrain residents. **Remarks:** Accepts advertising. **URL:** http://www.womanthismonth.com/. **Circ:** (Not Reported)

42796 ■ TVMAX - 93
Bldg. 22 Old Palace Rd.
Rd. 339, Block 306
PO Box 10023
Manama, Bahrain
Ph: 973 17317317
Fax: 973 17317389
E-mail: tvmax@orbit.net
Owner: Orbit Satellite Television and Radio Network, c/o Panther Media Group, PO Box 502211, Dubai Media City, Dubai, United Arab Emirates. **URL:** http://www.orbit.net.

42797 ■ TVMAX - 92
Bldg. 22, Old Palace Rd.
Rd. 339, Block 306
PO Box 10023
Manama, Bahrain
Ph: 973 17317317
Fax: 973 17317389
E-mail: tvmax@orbit.net
Owner: Orbit Satellite Television and Radio Network, c/o Panther Media Group, PO Box 502211, Dubai Media

Circulation: ★ = ABC; △ = BPA; ♦ = CAC; • = CCAB; ❑ = VAC; ⊕ = PO Statement; ‡ = Publisher's Report; Boldface figures = sworn; Light figures = estimated.

Gale Directory of Publications & Broadcast Media/147th Ed.   4779

City, Dubai, United Arab Emirates. **URL:** http://www.
orbit.net.

42798 ■ TVMAX - 90
Bldg. 22, Old Palace Rd.

Rd. 339, Block 306
PO Box 10023
Manama, Bahrain
Ph: 973 17317317
Fax: 973 17317389

E-mail: tvmax@orbit.net
Owner: Orbit Satellite Television and Radio Network,
c/o Panther Media Group, PO Box 502211, Dubai Media
City, Dubai, United Arab Emirates. **URL:** http://www.
orbit.net.

Chittagong

42799 ■ Bangladesh Betar - Chittagong - 873 KHz
121 Kazi Nazrul Islam Ave.
Shah Bagh
Dhaka 1000, Bangladesh
Ph: 880 31 712361
Fax: 880 2 8612021
E-mail: rrc@dhaka.net
Format: News; Religious; Talk. **Owner:** Bangladesh Betar, at above address. **Founded:** Dec. 16, 1939. **Former name:** Swadhin Bangla Betar Kendra (Dec. 16, 1971). **Operating Hours:** 6 a.m.-10 a.m., 12 p.m.-11.10p.m. **Wattage:** 100,000. **URL:** http://www.betar.org.bd/.

42800 ■ Radio Foorti-FM - 98.4
Land Mark, 8th Fl.
12-14 Gulshan N C/A
Gulshan - 2
Dhaka 1212, Bangladesh
Ph: 880 2 8835747
Fax: 880 2 8835746
E-mail: info@radiofoorti.fm
Format: Oldies; Ethnic; Contemporary Hit Radio (CHR). **URL:** http://www.radiofoorti.fm/.

Comilla

42801 ■ Bangladesh Betar - Comilla - 1413 KHz
121 Kazi Nazrul Islam Ave.
Shah Bagh
Dhaka 1000, Bangladesh
Ph: 880 81 68124
Fax: 880 2 8612021
E-mail: rrc@dhaka.net
Format: News; Religious; Talk. **Owner:** Bangladesh Betar, at above address. **Founded:** Dec. 16, 1939. **Former name:** Swadhin Bangla Betar Kendra (Dec. 16, 1971). **Operating Hours:** 5 p.m.-11.10 p.m. **Wattage:** 10,000. **URL:** http://www.betar.org.bd/.

Dhaka

42802 ■ Asia-Pacific Journal of Rural Development
Centre on Integrated Rural Development for Asia and the Pacific
Chameli House
17 Topkhana Rd.
GPO Box 2883
Dhaka 1000, Bangladesh
Ph: 880 2 9558751
Fax: 880 2 9562035
Publisher E-mail: infocom@cirdap.org
Journal featuring articles dealing with agricultural economics. **Founded:** 1991. **Freq:** Semiannual. **Key Personnel:** K.A.S. Dayananda, Editor. **ISSN:** 1018-5291. **Subscription Rates:** US$20 individuals Asia-Pacific countries; Tk 300 individuals; US$35 other countries. **Remarks:** Advertising accepted; rates available upon request. **URL:** http://www.cirdap.org.sg/. **Circ:** (Not Reported)

42803 ■ Bangladesh Development Studies
Bangladesh Institute of Development Studies
Bangladesh Unnayan Gabeshona Protishthan
E-17 Agargaon
Sher-e-Bangla Nagar
GPO Box 3854
Dhaka 1207, Bangladesh
Ph: 880 281 10759
Fax: 880 281 13023
Publisher E-mail: publication@sdnbd.org
Journal featuring research articles, notes and book reviews by researchers as well as national and international scholars. **Founded:** 1973. **Freq:** Quarterly. **Key Personnel:** Quazi Shahabuddin, Chm./Dir. Gen., shahab@sdnbd.org; Omar Haider Chowdhury, Res. Dir., omar@sdnbd.org; Abu Ahmed Abdullah, Res. Dir., phone 880 281 12397, abdullah@sdnbd.org; Zaid Bakht, Res. Dir., phone 880 291 10654, zbakht@sdnbd.org. **ISSN:** 0304-095X. **Subscription Rates:** US$70 other countries foreign. **Remarks:** Accepts advertising. **URL:** http://www.bids-bd.org. **Circ:** Paid 1,500

42804 ■ Bangladesh e-Journal of Sociology
Bangladesh Sociological Society
Rm. 1054, Arts Faculty Bldg.
University of Dhaka
Dhaka 1000, Bangladesh
Publisher E-mail: bejs@bangladeshsociology.org
Journal of the Bangladesh Sociological Society (BSS), publishing research works on all areas of sociology. **Freq:** Semiannual. **Key Personnel:** Nazrul Islam, PhD, Editor, editor@bangladeshsociology.org; Aminul S. Islam, Managing Editor, mneditor@bangladeshsociology.org; Mahboob A.I. Ahmed, Book Review Ed., breditor@bangladeshsociology.org; Imdadul Haque, Assoc. Ed., konkona@bdonline.com. **ISSN:** 1819-8465. **URL:** http://www.bangladeshsociology.org.

42805 ■ Bangladesh Journal of Scientific and Industrial Research
Bangladesh National Scientific and Technical Documentation Centre
Dr. Qudrat-I-Kuda Rd.
Dhanmondi
Dhaka 1205, Bangladesh
Reports the findings of scientific and industrial research conducted in Bangladesh, India, Pakistan and Africa. **Founded:** 1966. **Freq:** Quarterly. **Key Personnel:** Dr. Mamtaz Dawlatana, Editor, bjsir07@gmail.com. **ISSN:** 0304-9809. **URL:** http://www.banglajol.info/index.php/BJSIR.

42806 ■ Bangladesh Pharmaceutical Journal
Bangladesh Pharmaceutical Society
House No. 22
Dhanmondi, Rd. No. 2
Dhaka 1205, Bangladesh
Ph: 880 2 8611370
Fax: 880 2 8613588
Publisher E-mail: bps@agni.com
Journal featuring articles related to pharmacy and pharmacology. **Founded:** 1972. **Freq:** Semiannual. **Key Personnel:** Dr. Reza-Ul Jalil, Executive Ed.; Dr. Abdul Ghani, Editor-in-Chief. **ISSN:** 0301-4606. **URL:** http://www.pharmadu.net/bps/bpsjournals.htm.

42807 ■ The Bangladesh Today
Concord Royal Ct., 4th Fl.
Plot No. 275(G), Rd. No. 27
Dhaka 1209, Bangladesh
Ph: 880 2 9118807
Fax: 880 2 9118853
Publication E-mail: editor@thebangladeshtoday.com
Publisher E-mail: contact@thebangladeshtoday.com
Newspaper. **Freq:** Daily. **Print Method:** Web Offset. **Key Personnel:** Colonel Mahmud ur Rahman Choudhury, Editor, editor@thebangladeshtoday.com. **Remarks:** Accepts advertising. **URL:** http://www.thebangladeshtoday.com/. **Ad Rates:** BW: Tk 2,200. **Circ:** (Not Reported)

42808 ■ The Daily Star
19 Karwan Bazar
Dhaka 1215, Bangladesh
Ph: 880 281 24944
Fax: 880 281 25155
Publication E-mail: editor@thedailystar.net
Publisher E-mail: editor@thedailystar.net
General newspaper. **Subtitle:** Journalism without Fear or Favor. **Founded:** Jan. 14, 1991. **Freq:** Daily. **Print Method:** Rotary offset. **Trim Size:** 23 x 33 cm. **Key Personnel:** Syed Badrul Ahsan, Contact; Abdul M. Latif Mondal, Contact; Mahfuz Anam, Contact. **Remarks:** Accepts advertising. **URL:** http://www.thedailystar.net/newDesign/index.php. **Feature Editors:** Madan Shahu, *Features*. **Circ:** 30,000

42809 ■ Equity Dialogue
Centre for Health and Population Research
68 Shaheed Tajuddin Ahmed Sharani
Mohakhali
Dhaka 1212, Bangladesh
Ph: 880 288 60523
Fax: 880 288 19133
Journal of the Centre for Health and Population Research, publishing articles concerning health issues among women and the poor. **URL:** http://www.icddrb.org/publications_index.cfm.

42810 ■ Holiday
Holiday Publication Ltd.
30, Tejgaon Industrial Area
Dhaka 1208, Bangladesh
Ph: 880 291 22950
Fax: 880 291 27927
Publisher E-mail: holiday@global-bd.net
Online community newspaper. **Founded:** Aug. 1, 1965. **Freq:** Weekly. **Print Method:** Offset (Rotary). **Subscription Rates:** Tk 540 individuals; Tk 1,500 individuals India, Nepal Bhutan & Burma; US$28 individuals; Tk 2,300 individuals others Asia; US$50 individuals U.S. & Australia; Tk 3,000 individuals Europe & Africa; US$70 individuals Europe & Africa; Tk 3,400 individuals U.S. & Australia; US$85 individuals U.S. & Australia. **Remarks:** Accepts advertising. **URL:** http://www.weeklyholiday.net/. **Ad Rates:** PCI: Tk 700. **Circ:** (Not Reported)

42811 ■ The Independent (Bangladesh)
Free Press Ltd.
32 Kazi Nazrul Islam Ave.
Karwan Bazar

Circulation: ★ = ABC; △ = BPA; ♦ = CAC; • = CCAB; ❑ = VAC; ⊕ = PO Statement; ‡ = Publisher's Report; Boldface figures = sworn; Light figures = estimated.

Dhaka 1215, Bangladesh
Ph: 880 291 29938
Fax: 880 291 27722
Publisher E-mail: editor@bol-online.com
General newspaper. **Key Personnel:** Mahbubul Alam,
Editor, editor@independent-bangladesh.com. **Remarks:**
Accepts advertising. **URL:** http://www.independent-
bangladesh.com. **Ad Rates:** BW: US$20, 4C: US$25.
Circ: (Not Reported)

42812 ■ Insurance Journal
Bangladesh Insurance Academy
53 Mohakhali Commercial Area
Dhaka 1212, Bangladesh
Ph: 880 2 9899292
Fax: 880 2 9882071
Publisher E-mail: iab@astbdmail.net
Journal covering the insurance industry in Bangladesh
with editorial content discussing current issues, markets,
and national trends. **Founded:** 1975. **Freq:** Annual. **Key
Personnel:** Elias A.K.M. Hussain, Director. **ISSN:** 1684-
0437. **Remarks:** Advertising accepted; rates available
upon request. **URL:** http://www.bia.gov.bd/publications.
html. **Circ:** Paid 300

**42813 ■ Journal of Health, Population and Nutri-
tion**
The International Centre for Diarrhoeal Disease
Research
Centre for Health and Population Research
PO Box 128
Dhaka 1000, Bangladesh
Ph: 880 2 8860523
Fax: 880 2 8823116
Publisher E-mail: info@icddrb.org
Journal dealing with the aspects of health, population
and nutrition. **Freq:** 6/yr. **Key Personnel:** Alejandro
Cravioto, Editor-in-Chief, acravioto@icddrb.org; M.
Shamsul Islam Khan, Managing Editor, msik@icddrb.
org. **Subscription Rates:** US$500 institutions developed
countries; US$250 individuals developed countries;
US$300 institutions developing countries; US$150
individuals developing countries; Tk 3,000 institutions;
Tk 2,500 individuals. **URL:** http://centre.icddrb.org/
activity/index.jsp?activityObjectID=87.

42814 ■ News from Bangladesh
Global Amitech
House No. 16, Rd. 127
Gulshan
Dhaka 1212, Bangladesh
Ph: 880 2 8827413
Fax: 880 2 9895247
Publication E-mail: nfb@citech-bd.com
Publisher E-mail: nfb@citech-bd.com
Newspaper. **Founded:** Sept. 26, 1996. **Freq:** Daily. **Key
Personnel:** Tanvir A. Chowdhury, Editor; M. Shah-
mimuzzaman, Founding Ed.; Dr. Jaffor A. Ullah, Board
of Ed. **ISSN:** 1563-9304. **Remarks:** Accepts advertising.
URL: http://www.bangladesh-web.com. **Circ:** (Not
Reported)

Bangladesh Betar - Chittagong - See Chittagong
Bangladesh Betar - Comilla - See Comilla

42815 ■ Bangladesh Betar - Dhaka A - 693 KHz
121 Kazi Nazrul Islam Ave.
Shah Bagh
Dhaka 1000, Bangladesh
Ph: 880 2 9117204
Fax: 880 2 8612021
E-mail: rrc@dhaka.net
Format: News; Religious; Talk. **Owner:** Bangladesh Be-
tar, at above address. **Founded:** Dec. 16, 1939. **Former
name:** Swadhin Bangla Betar Kendra (Dec. 16, 1971).
Operating Hours: 6 a.m.-12.10 p.m., 2.30 p.m.-11.30
p.m. **Wattage:** 1,000,000. **URL:** http://www.betar.org.
bd/.

42816 ■ Bangladesh Betar - Dhaka B - 630 KHz
121 Kazi Nazrul Islam Ave.
Shah Bagh
Dhaka 1000, Bangladesh

Ph: 880 2 9117204
Fax: 880 2 8612021
E-mail: rrc@dhaka.net
Format: News; Religious; Talk. **Owner:** Bangladesh Betar, at above address. **Founded:** Dec. 16, 1939. **Former
name:** Swadhin Bangla Betar Kendra (Dec. 16, 1971).
Operating Hours: 12 a.m.-3 a.m., 6 a.m.-7.45 a.m., 9a.
m.-11.10p.m. **Wattage:** 100,000. **URL:** http://www.betar.
org.bd/.

42817 ■ Bangladesh Betar - Dhaka C - 1170 KHz
121 Kazi Nazrul Islam Ave.
Shah Bagh
Dhaka 1000, Bangladesh
Ph: 880 2 9117204
Fax: 880 2 8612021
E-mail: rrc@dhaka.net
Format: News; Religious; Talk. **Owner:** Bangladesh Be-
tar, at above address. **Founded:** Dec. 16, 1939. **Former
name:** Swadhin Bangla Betar Kendra (Dec. 16, 1971).
Operating Hours: 3 p.m.-5 p.m. **Wattage:** 10,000. **URL:**
http://www.betar.org.bd/.

Bangladesh Betar - Khulna - See Khulna
Bangladesh Betar - Rajshahi - See Rajshahi
Bangladesh Betar - Rangamati - See Rangamati
Bangladesh Betar - Rangpur - See Rangpur
Bangladesh Betar - Sylhet - See Sylhet
Bangladesh Betar - Thakurgaon - See Thakur-
gaon

42818 ■ Radio Foorti-FM - 88.0
Land Mark, 8th Fl.
12-14 Gulshan N C/A
Gulshan - 2
Dhaka 1212, Bangladesh
Ph: 880 2 8835747
Fax: 880 2 8835746
E-mail: info@radiofoorti.fm
Format: Oldies; Ethnic; Contemporary Hit Radio (CHR).
URL: http://www.radiofoorti.fm/.

Radio Foorti-FM - See Chittagong
Radio Foorti-FM - See Sylhet

Gazipur

42819 ■ Annals of Bangladesh Agriculture
Bangabandhu Sheikh Mujibur Rahman Agricultural
University
Salna
Gazipur 1706, Bangladesh
Ph: 880 2 9205310
Fax: 880 2 9205333
Publisher E-mail: info@bsmrau.org
Journal covering all aspects of agriculture with research
articles on production, crop and pest control, and social
issues confronting agricultural area. **Founded:** 1991.
Freq: Semiannual. **ISSN:** 1025-482X. **URL:** http://www.
bsmrau.com/dept_agroforestryrs.html. **Circ:** Paid 300

Khulna

42820 ■ Bangladesh Betar - Khulna - 558 KHz
121 Kazi Nazrul Islam Ave.
Shah Bagh
Dhaka 1000, Bangladesh
Ph: 880 41 761774
Fax: 880 2 8612021
E-mail: rrc@dhaka.net
Format: News; Religious; Talk; Public Radio. **Owner:**
Bangladesh Betar, at above address. **Founded:** Dec.
16, 1939. **Former name:** Swadhin Bangla Betar Kendra
(Dec. 16, 1971). **Operating Hours:** 6 a.m. - 10 a.m., 12
p.m. -11.10p.m. **Wattage:** 100,000. **URL:** http://www.
betar.org.bd/.

Rajshahi

42821 ■ Bangladesh Betar - Rajshahi - 1080 KHz
121 Kazi Nazrul Islam Ave.
Shah Bagh

Dhaka 1000, Bangladesh
Ph: 880 721 775940
Fax: 880 2 8612021
E-mail: rrc@dhaka.net
Format: News; Religious; Talk. **Owner:** Bangladesh Be-
tar, at above address. **Founded:** Dec. 16, 1939. **Former
name:** Swadhin Bangla Betar Kendra (Dec. 16, 1971).
Operating Hours: 6 a.m.-10 a.m., 12 p.m.- 11.10 p.m.
Wattage: 10,000. **URL:** http://www.betar.org.bd/.

Rangamati

**42822 ■ Bangladesh Betar - Rangamati - 1161
KHz**
121 Kazi Nazrul Islam Ave.
Shah Bagh
Dhaka 1000, Bangladesh
Ph: 880 351 61963
Fax: 880 2 8612021
E-mail: rrc@dhaka.net
Format: News; Religious; Talk. **Owner:** Bangladesh Be-
tar, at above address. **Founded:** Dec. 16, 1939. **Former
name:** Swadhin Bangla Betar Kendra (Dec. 16, 1971).
Operating Hours: 11:30 p.m.- 4:30 p.m. **Wattage:**
10,000. **URL:** http://www.betar.org.bd/.

Rangpur

42823 ■ Bangladesh Betar - Rangpur - 1053 KHz
121 Kazi Nazrul Islam Ave.
Shah Bagh
Dhaka 1000, Bangladesh
Ph: 880 521 63205
Fax: 880 2 8612021
E-mail: rrc@dhaka.net
Format: News; Religious; Talk. **Owner:** Bangladesh Be-
tar, at above address. **Founded:** Dec. 16, 1939. **Former
name:** Swadhin Bangla Betar Kendra (Dec. 16, 1971).
Operating Hours: 6 a.m.-10 a.m., 2 p.m.-11.10 p.m.
Wattage: 20,000. **URL:** http://www.betar.org.bd/.

Sylhet

42824 ■ Bangladesh Betar - Sylhet - 963 KHz
121 Kazi Nazrul Islam Ave.
Shah Bagh
Dhaka 1000, Bangladesh
Ph: 880 821 712859
Fax: 880 2 8612021
E-mail: rrc@dhaka.net
Format: News; Religious; Talk. **Owner:** Bangladesh Be-
tar, at above address. **Founded:** Dec. 16, 1939. **Former
name:** Swadhin Bangla Betar Kendra (Dec. 16, 1971).
Operating Hours: 6 a.m.-10 a.m., 2 p.m.-11.10 p.m.
Wattage: 20,000. **URL:** http://www.betar.org.bd/.

42825 ■ Radio Foorti-FM - 89.8
Land Mark, 8th Fl.
12-14 Gulshan N C/A
Gulshan - 2
Dhaka 1212, Bangladesh
Ph: 880 2 8835747
Fax: 880 2 8835746
E-mail: info@radiofoorti.fm
Format: Oldies; Ethnic; Contemporary Hit Radio (CHR).
URL: http://www.radiofoorti.fm/.

Thakurgaon

**42826 ■ Bangladesh Betar - Thakurgaon - 999
KHz**
121 Kazi Nazrul Islam Ave.
Shah Bagh
Dhaka 1000, Bangladesh
Ph: 880 561 52037
Fax: 880 2 8612021
E-mail: rrc@dhaka.net
Format: News; Religious; Talk. **Owner:** Bangladesh Be-
tar, at above address. **Founded:** Dec. 16, 1939. **Former
name:** Swadhin Bangla Betar Kendra (Dec. 16, 1971).
Operating Hours: 3:50 p.m.-11.10 p.m. **Wattage:**
10,000. **URL:** http://www.betar.org.bd/.

Bridgetown

42827 ■ Barbados Advocate
The Advocate Company Ltd.
PO Box 230
Fontabelle
Bridgetown, Barbados
Ph: (246)467-2000
Fax: (246)434-2020
General newspaper. **Founded:** Sept. 1895. **Freq:** Daily.
Print Method: Offset. **Trim Size:** 11 x 14 7/8. **Cols./
Page:** 6. **Col. Width:** 1 5/8 inches. **Col. Depth:** 14
inches. **Key Personnel:** Sandra Clarke, Advertising
Mgr., phone 246434-2300, sclarke@barbadosadvocate.
com. **Subscription Rates:** US$938 individuals free with
super saver shipping. **Remarks:** Accepts advertising.
URL: http://www.barbadosadvocate.com/. **Circ:** (Not
Reported)

**42828 ■ The International Journal of Education
and Development using Information and Communication Technology (IJEDICT)**
The University of the West Indies
c/o Prof. Stewart Marshall, Mng. Ed.
Academic Division, Open Campus

The University of the West Indies
Cavehill Campus
Bridgetown, Barbados
Ph: (246)417-4575
Fax: (246)421-6753
Publisher E-mail: admis@sta.uwi.edu
Peer-reviewd Journal focusing on theories, best prac-
tices and policies in education or development in com-
munities throughout the world. **Freq:** Quarterly. **Key
Personnel:** Prof. Stewart Marshall, Managing Editor,
stewart.marshall@open.uwi.edu; Ed Brandon, Assoc.
Ed.; Wal Taylor, Ch. Ed.; Tony Carr, Guest Ed.; Shahram
Amiri, Editorial Board; Laura Czerniewicz, Guest Ed.;
Lone Dirckinck-Holmfeld, Guest Ed. for Special Issue on
Publisher. **ISSN:** 1814-0556. **URL:** http://ijedict.dec.uwi.
edu/index.php.

42829 ■ Gospel 97.5-FM - 97.5
River Rd.
PO Box 1267
Bridgetown, Barbados
Ph: (246)467-7355
Fax: (246)426-5377
E-mail: gospel@starcomnetwork.net
Format: Gospel. **Owner:** STARCOM Network Inc., at

above address. **URL:** http://www.gospel975.com/; http://
www.starcomnetwork.net/services/gospel.htm.

42830 ■ Hott-FM - 95.3
River Rd.
PO Box 1267
Bridgetown, Barbados
Ph: (242)430-7300
Fax: (242)426-5377
E-mail: info@hott953.com
Format: Contemporary Hit Radio (CHR); Hip Hop; Rap.
Owner: Starcom Network Inc., at above address. **Oper-
ating Hours:** Continuous. **Ad Rates:** Advertising ac-
cepted; rates available upon request. **URL:** http://www.
hott953.com.

42831 ■ Voice of Barbados-FM - 92.9
River Rd.
Bridgetown, Barbados
Ph: (246)430-7300
E-mail: info@vob929.com
Format: Full Service. **Owner:** Starcom Network Inc., at
above address. **Founded:** 1981. **Ad Rates:** Advertising
accepted; rates available upon request. **URL:** http://
www.vob929.com/.

Circulation: ★ = ABC; △ = BPA; ♦ = CAC; • = CCAB; ❑ = VAC; ⊕ = PO Statement; ‡ = Publisher's Report; Boldface figures = sworn; Light figures = estimated.

Gale Directory of Publications & Broadcast Media/147th Ed. 4783

Minsk

42832 ■ Computational Methods in Applied Mathematics
Natsiyanal'naya Akademiya Navuk Belarusi (National Academy of Sciences of Belarus)
Institute of Mathematics
11 Surganov Str.
220072 Minsk, Belarus
Ph: 375 17 2841958
Fax: 375 17 2840915
Publication E-mail: cmam@cmam.info
Publisher E-mail: nasb@presidium.bas-net.by
Journal publishing original research articles on numerical methods and their applications to science and engineering. **Freq:** Quarterly. **Key Personnel:** Prof. Peter Matus, Editor, phone 375 17 2841963, matus@im.bas-net.by. **ISSN:** 1609-4840. **Subscription Rates:** US$255 individuals print. **URL:** http://cmam.info/.

42833 ■ Vecherny Minskt
44 Skorina Ave.
220805 Minsk, Belarus
Ph: 375 172 335044
Publication E-mail: vm@nsys.by
Publisher E-mail: vm@belarus.net
General newspaper. **Founded:** Nov. 1967. **Freq:** 5/week. **Key Personnel:** Sergey Sverkunov, Editor; Nikolai Ilioushenko, Electronic Variant Ed. **Subscription Rates:** US$300 individuals Europe; US$150 individuals Europe, 6 months; US$75 individuals Europe, 3 months; US$348 other countries; US$174 other countries 6 months; US$87 other countries 3 months. **Remarks:** Accepts advertising. **URL:** http://www.belarus.net/minsk_ev/. **Circ:** Combined 100,000

42834 ■ Radius-FM - 100.9
4 Krasnaya St.
220807 Minsk, Belarus
Ph: 375 17 2843042
E-mail: radio1@tvr.by
Format: Urban Contemporary; Information. **Operating Hours:** Continuous. **Ad Rates:** Advertising accepted; rates available upon request. **URL:** http://www.radiusfm.by.

42835 ■ Radius-FM - 105.5
4 Krasnaya St.
220807 Minsk, Belarus
Ph: 375 17 2843042
E-mail: radio1@tvr.by
Format: Urban Contemporary; Information. **Ad Rates:** Advertising accepted; rates available upon request. **URL:** http://www.radiusfm.by.

42836 ■ Radius-FM - 100.5
4 Krasnaya St.
220807 Minsk, Belarus
Ph: 375 17 2843042
E-mail: radio1@tvr.by
Format: Urban Contemporary; Information. **Operating Hours:** Continuous. **Ad Rates:** Advertising accepted; rates available upon request. **URL:** http://www.radiusfm.by.

Circulation: ★ = ABC; △ = BPA; ♦ = CAC; • = CCAB; ❑ = VAC; ⊕ = PO Statement; ‡ = Publisher's Report; Boldface figures = sworn; Light figures = estimated.

Gale Directory of Publications & Broadcast Media/147th Ed. 4785

Antwerp

42837 ■ Ambiance
BMP N.V. Book & Media Publishing
Katwilgweg 2 b 3
B-2050 Antwerp, Belgium
Ph: 32 3 2103050
Fax: 32 3 2103051
Publication E-mail: info@ambiance.be
Publisher E-mail: info@bmp.be
Consumer magazine covering food, wine and traveling. **Subtitle:** Le magazine a boire, a manger et a voyager. **Founded:** 1986. **Freq:** Monthly. **Print Method:** Offset. **Trim Size:** 297 x 460 mm. **Cols./Page:** 3. **Col. Width:** 7.5 centimeters. **Key Personnel:** Theo Moormann, Director; Savina Guyo, Account Mgr.; Inge de Landtsheer, Account Exec.; Dirk De Prins, Editor. **ISSN:** 1370-0898. **Remarks:** Advertising accepted; rates available upon request. **URL:** http://www.ambiance.be/. **Former name:** Culinair Ambiance. **Circ:** Controlled 63,638

42838 ■ Clinical Neurology and Neurosurgery
Mosby Inc.
c/o Dr. Peter Paul De Deyn, Ed.-in-Ch.
Dept. of Neurology
General Hospital Middelheim
Lindendreef 1
B-2020 Antwerp, Belgium
Ph: 32 3 2803111
Fax: 32 3 2813748
Publisher E-mail: custserv.ehs@elsevier.com
Journal publishing papers and reports on the clinical aspects of neurology and neurosurgery. **Freq:** 10/yr. **Key Personnel:** Dr. Peter Paul De Deyn, Editor-in-Chief, dedeyn@skynet.be; C.S. Raine, Advisory Ed.; D.J. Brooks, Editorial Board; M.P. Barnes, Editorial Board; A.P. Aldenkamp, Editorial Board; J. Bogousslavsky, Editorial Board; T. Brandt, Editorial Board; R. Crols, Editorial Board. **ISSN:** 0303-8467. **Subscription Rates:** EUR156 individuals for European countries and Iran; US$174 other countries except Europe, Japan and Iran; 20,700¥ individuals; US$953 institutions, other countries except Europe, Japan and Iran; 113,100¥ institutions; EUR853 institutions for European countries and Iran. **URL:** http://www.elsevier.com/wps/find/journaldescription.cws_home/523832/descriptiondescription.

42839 ■ Linguistics
Mouton de Gruyter
Ctr. for Grammar, Cognition & Typology
University of Antwerp
Prinsstraat 13
2000 Antwerp, Belgium
Publication E-mail: linguistics@ua.ac.be
Publisher E-mail: info@degruyter.de
Peer-reviewed journal of languages and linguistics. **Subtitle:** An Interdisciplinary Journal of the Language Sciences. **Founded:** 1963. **Freq:** Bimonthly. **Key Personnel:** Bernard Comrie, Editorial Board; Johan van der Auwera, Editor-in-Chief; Greville Corbett, Editorial Board. **ISSN:** 0024-3949. **Subscription Rates:** EUR534 individuals print only or online only; EUR615 individuals for print & online. **Remarks:** Advertising accepted; rates available upon request. **URL:** http://www.degruyter.com/journals/linguistics/detailEn.cfm. **Circ:** (Not Reported)

42840 ■ Sparraaja
Eco N.V.
Lammekensraamveld 6 bus 52
B-2000 Antwerp, Belgium
Ph: 32 32933176
Fax: 32 32933180
In-house business magazine for SPAR retailers and employees. **Freq:** 7/year. **Key Personnel:** Paula Lauuonen, Editorial Mgr., paula.lauuonen@spar.fi. **ISSN:** 7457-0637. **Remarks:** Accepts advertising. **Circ:** Controlled 4,000

42841 ■ Studies in Educational Evaluation
Elsevier Science Inc.
c/o P. van Petegem, Ed.
Universiteit Antwerpen
Antwerp, Belgium
Publisher E-mail: usinfo-ehelp@elsevier.com
Journal covering studies in educational evaluation. **Founded:** 1974. **Freq:** 4/yr. **Print Method:** Web offset. **Trim Size:** 8 5/8 x 11 1/4. **Cols./Page:** 4. **Col. Width:** 27 nonpareils. **Col. Depth:** 156 agate lines. **Key Personnel:** M. Alkin, Assoc. Ed.; F. Dochy, Editorial Advisory Board; L. Burton, Editorial Advisory Board; Claus H. Carstensen, Assoc. Ed.; M. Segers, Editorial Advisory Board; David Nevo, Editor, dnevo@post.tau.ac.il; G. Berberoglu, Editorial Advisory Board. **ISSN:** 0191-491X. **Subscription Rates:** EUR773 institutions for European countries and Iran; US$866 institutions, other countries except Europe, Japan and Iran; 102,500¥ institutions; EUR130 individuals for European countries and Iran; US$168 other countries except Europe, Japan and Iran; 18,700¥ individuals. **URL:** http://www.elsevier.com/wps/find/journaldescription.cws_home/497/descriptiondescription.

Brussels

42842 ■ A+ Architecture/A+ Architectuur
CIAUD-ICASD
Rue Ravenstein 23
B-1000 Brussels, Belgium
Ph: 32 264 57910
Fax: 32 264 02795
Publication E-mail: redaction@a-plus.be
Publisher E-mail: secretariat@ciaud-icasd.be
Professional magazine covering architecture, urbanism, design, plastic arts and architectural practice. **Founded:** Sept. 1973. **Freq:** Bimonthly. **Key Personnel:** Audrey Contesse, Sub-Ed.; Christian Lasserre, Publisher; Stefan Devoldere, Editor. **ISSN:** 1375-5064. **Remarks:** Advertising accepted; rates available upon request. **URL:** http://www.a-plus.be. **Circ:** Combined 14,010

42843 ■ Ad!dict
Reality Bites bvba
Ad!dict Creative Lab
Barthelemylaan 20
B-1000 Brussels, Belgium
Ph: 32 228 95101
Publication E-mail: ann@addictlab.com
Publisher E-mail: info@addictlab.com
Consumer magazine covering creativity and communication for creative professionals and others. **Trim Size:** 245 x 300 mm. **URL:** http://www.addictlab.com/index.php/Home.

42844 ■ Beton
FeBe—Federation de l'Industrie du Beton
Bd du Souverain 68
B-1170 Brussels, Belgium
Ph: 32 273 58015
Fax: 32 273 47795
Publication E-mail: mail@febe.be
Publisher E-mail: mail@febe.be
Trade magazine covering precast concrete. **Key Personnel:** Eddy Dano, Director, ed@febe.be. **Remarks:** Accepts advertising. **URL:** http://www.febe.be/fr_BE/publications/list/id/7. **Circ:** (Not Reported)

42845 ■ Biomaterials
Mosby Inc.
Ave. de la Foret 103
1000 Brussels, Belgium
Publisher E-mail: custserv.ehs@elsevier.com
Peer-reviewed journal reporting on the science and application of biomaterials. **Freq:** 36/yr. **Key Personnel:** Prof. D.F. Williams, Editor-in-Chief; M. O'Donnell, Managing Editor; P. Ducheyne, Assoc. Ed. **ISSN:** 0142-9612. **Subscription Rates:** US$5,553 institutions, other countries except Europe, Japan and Iran; EUR4,965 institutions for European countries and Iran; 659,200¥ institutions. **Remarks:** Accepts advertising. **URL:** http://www.elsevier.com/wps/find/journaldescription.cws_home/30392/descriptiondescription. **Circ:** (Not Reported)

42846 ■ Cahiers de la Documentation
Association Belge de Documentation
Belgian Association for Documentation
Chaussee de Wavre 1683
B-1160 Brussels, Belgium
Ph: 32 2 6755862
Fax: 32 2 6727446
Publisher E-mail: info@abd-bvd.be
Dutch, English and French language publication covering information management. **Freq:** Quarterly. **ISSN:** 0007-9804. **URL:** http://www.abd-bvd.be.

42847 ■ Chemoecology
Springer-Verlag Tokyo
c/o Prof. Jacques M. Pasteels, Ed.-in-Ch.
Behavioural & Evolutionary Ecology
University of Brussels, CP 160/12
Ave. F. D. Roosevelt 50
B-1050 Brussels, Belgium
Ph: 32 2 6504014
Fax: 32 2 6502445
Publisher E-mail: info@springer.jp
Journal aiming to promote and stimulate the field of chemical ecology by publishing research papers that integrate ecology and chemistry in an attempt to increase understanding of the biological significance of natural products, with the scope being the evolutionary biology of chemically-mediated biotic interactions, including mechanistic approaches as well as environmental aspects. **Freq:** Quarterly. **Key Personnel:** Prof. Wittko Francke, Editor-in-Chief, chemoeco@ulb.ac.be; Prof. Jacques M. Pasteels, Editor-in-Chief; Wilhelm Boland, Assoc. Ed. **ISSN:** 0937-7409. **Subscription Rates:** EUR525 institutions print incl. free access or e-only; EUR630 institutions print incl. enhanced access. **Remarks:** Advertising accepted; rates available upon

Circulation: ★ = ABC; △ = BPA; ♦ = CAC; • = CCAB; ❏ = VAC; ⊕ = PO Statement; ‡ = Publisher's Report; Boldface figures = sworn; Light figures = estimated.

request. **URL:** http://www.springer.com/birkhauser/biosciences/journal/49. **Circ:** (Not Reported)

42848 ■ Diabetes Voice
International Diabetes Federation
Federation Internationale du Diabete
Chaussee de la Hulpe 166
B-1000 Brussels, Belgium
Ph: 32 253 85511
Fax: 32 253 85114
Publisher E-mail: info@idf.org
Publication covering diabetes and related information on developments in health policy and economics, diabetes care and management, and research worldwide (English, French and Spanish). **Subtitle:** Bulletin of the International Diabetes Federation. **Founded:** 1954. **Freq:** Quarterly plus special issues. **Key Personnel:** Helmut Henrichs, Editor-in-Chief; Tim Nolan, Editor, tim@idf.org; Oliver Jacqmain, Managing Editor. **Subscription Rates:** Free. **Remarks:** Accepts advertising. **URL:** http://www.diabetesvoice.org/en/about. **Formerly:** IDF Bulletin. **Circ:** 11,000

42849 ■ Echos AMA
Association des Maisons d'Accueil
Rue Gheude, 49
B-1070 Brussels, Belgium
Ph: 32 2 5136225
Fax: 32 2 5142300
Publisher E-mail: ama@ama.be
French language publication covering parenting. **Freq:** Quarterly. **URL:** http://www.ama.be/.

42850 ■ EE Times UK
CMP Information Ltd.
European Business Press
144 Ave. Plasky
1030 Brussels, Belgium
Publication E-mail: info@eetimes.be
Online business publication covering the electronics industry in the UK. **Founded:** 1978. **Freq:** Weekly. **Key Personnel:** Philip Ling, Editor, phone 44 1622 746580, phil.ling@eetimes.be; Jean-Pierre Joosting, Editor, jeanpierre.joosting@eetimes.be; Julien Happich, Editor-in-Chief, phone 44 33 153907865, julien.happich@eetimes.be. **Remarks:** Accepts advertising. **Online:** Gale. **URL:** http://eetimes.eu/uk. **Formerly:** Electronic Times (Jan. 2002). **Circ:** (Not Reported)

42851 ■ EPI
European Association of National Productivity Centres
Association Europeenne des Centres Nationaux de Productivite
c/o Marc de Greef, Sec. Gen.
Rue Gachard 88
B-1050 Brussels, Belgium
Ph: 32 264 34451
Fax: 32 264 34450
Publisher E-mail: ingrid.dhondt@prevent.be
Publication covering labor. **Freq:** Quarterly. **URL:** http://www.eanpc.org; http://www.eanpc.org/eanpc/epi2001.php.

42852 ■ European Accounting Review
European Accounting Association
European Institute for Advanced Studies in Management
Pl. de Brouckere Plein, 31
B-1000 Brussels, Belgium
Ph: 32 222 66660
Fax: 32 251 21929
Publisher E-mail: eaa@eiasm.be
European publication covering accounting. **Freq:** Quarterly. **Key Personnel:** Salvador Carmona, Editor. **ISSN:** 0963-8180. **Subscription Rates:** Included in membership. **URL:** http://www.eaa-online.org/r/default.asp?iId=KJIMD.

42853 ■ European Journal of Hospital Pharmacy
European Association of Hospital Pharmacists
Association Europeene des Pharmaciens des Hopitaux
rue Abbe Cuypers, 3
B-1040 Brussels, Belgium
Ph: 32 2 7416822
Fax: 32 2 7347910
Publisher E-mail: lukcism@pandora.be
European journal covering pharmacy. **Founded:** 1995. **Freq:** Bimonthly. **Key Personnel:** Prof. Stefan Muhlebach, Dep. Ed.-in-Ch.; Lasia Tang, Publisher; Prof. Graham Sewell, Editor-in-Chief. **ISSN:** 0939-9437. **Remarks:** Advertising accepted; rates available upon

request. **URL:** http://www.eahp.eu/EJHP/General. **Circ:** (Not Reported)

42854 ■ European Voice
The Economist Group
International Press Ctr.
Residence Palace
Rue de la Loi 155, Box 6
B-1040 Brussels, Belgium
Ph: 32 2 5409090
Fax: 32 2 5409070
Publication E-mail: info@europeanvoice.com
Newspaper covering European issues. **Founded:** 1995. **Freq:** Weekly (Thurs.). **Print Method:** cold set weboffset. **Trim Size:** 240 x 350 mm. **Key Personnel:** Mayssa Badr, Commercial Dir., phone 32 2 5409073, mayssabadr@economist.com. **Subscription Rates:** EUR193 individuals; EUR310 two years; EUR406 individuals 3 years. **Remarks:** Accepts advertising. **URL:** http://www.european-voice.com. **Ad Rates:** 4C: 7,750 BFr. **Circ:** △18,241

42855 ■ Federauto Magazine
Federauto
Confederation Belge du Commerce et de la Reparation Automobiles et des Secteures Connexes
avenue Jules Bordet 164
B-1140 Brussels, Belgium
Ph: 32 277 86200
Fax: 32 277 86222
Publisher E-mail: mail@federauto.be
Dutch and French language publication covering automotive. **Founded:** 1995. **Freq:** 7/yr. **Remarks:** Advertising accepted; rates available upon request. **URL:** http://www.federauto.be/page.aspx/941/. **Circ:** (Not Reported)

42856 ■ Geologica Belgica
Belgian Geological Society
c/o Eric Goemaere, Sec.
Rue Jenner 13
B-1000 Brussels, Belgium
Ph: 32 278 87622
Journal featuring earth sciences. **Freq:** Quarterly. **Key Personnel:** F. Boulvain, Editorial Board; M. Dusar, Assoc. Ed.; E. Steurbaut, Editorial Board; J.Cl. Duchesne, Executive Ed., jc.duchesne@ulg.ac.be. **ISSN:** 1379-8505. **Remarks:** Accepts advertising. **URL:** http://www.ulg.ac.be/geolsed/GB/. **Circ:** (Not Reported)

42857 ■ Greenpeace Magazine
Greenpeace Belgium
Chaussee de Haecht, 159
B-1030 Brussels, Belgium
Ph: 32 2 2740200
Fax: 32 2 2740230
Publisher E-mail: info@be.greenpeace.org
Dutch and French language magazine covering the environment. **Freq:** Quarterly. **Subscription Rates:** Included in membership. **Remarks:** Advertising not accepted. **URL:** http://www.greenpeace.org/belgium/fr/press/reports/magazine80. **Circ:** 60,000

42858 ■ Homeless in Europe
European Federation of National Organisations Working with the Homeless
Chaussee de Louvain 194
B-1210 Brussels, Belgium
Ph: 32 253 86669
Fax: 32 253 94174
Publisher E-mail: information@feantsa.org
Magazine with each issue focusing on a different aspect of homelessness in Europe. **Freq:** 3/yr. **Key Personnel:** Freek Spinnewijn, Director, freek.spinnewijn@feantsa.org. **URL:** http://www.feantsa.org/code/en/hp.asp.

42859 ■ International Journal of Research in Marketing
European Marketing Academy
Pl. de Brouckere Plein, 31
B-1000 Brussels, Belgium
Ph: 32 222 66660
Fax: 32 251 21929
Publisher E-mail: emac@eiasm.be
Marketing publication. **Freq:** 4/yr. **Key Personnel:** S. Stremersch, Policy Board; D.R. Lehmann, Policy Board; M.G. Dekimpe, Editor. **ISSN:** 0167-8116. **Subscription Rates:** EUR98 individuals for European countries and Iran; 13,000¥ individuals for Japan; US$109 other countries; EUR766 institutions for European countries and Iran; 101,700¥ institutions for Japan; US$857 other countries. **URL:** http://www.emac-online.org/r/default.

asp?iId=IHGMD; http://www.elsevier.com/wps/find/journaldescription.cws_home/505550/descriptiondescription.

42860 ■ International Review of the Armed Forces Medical Services
International Committee of Military Medicine
Comite International de Medecine Militaire
Hopital Militaire Reine Astrid
B-1120 Brussels, Belgium
Fax: 32 226 44367
Publisher E-mail: info@cimm-icmm.org
Worldwide publication covering armed forces medical services. **Founded:** 1921. **Freq:** Quarterly. **Print Method:** Offset. **ISSN:** 0035-3469. **Remarks:** Advertising accepted; rates available upon request. **URL:** http://www.cimm-icmm.org. **Circ:** (Not Reported)

42861 ■ Jeunes en Mouvement
Catholic Youth Council
Conseil de la Jeunesse Catholique
43 rue de la charite
B-1210 Brussels, Belgium
Ph: 32 223 03283
Fax: 32 223 06811
Publisher E-mail: cjc@cjc.be
French language newspaper covering youth interests. **Freq:** Quarterly. **Key Personnel:** Frederic Possemiers, Contact. **Remarks:** Advertising accepted; rates available upon request. **URL:** http://www.cjc.be/Jeunes-enmouvement.html. **Circ:** ‡25,000

42862 ■ Journal of Film Preservation
The International Federation of Film Archives
Rue Defacqz 1
B-1000 Brussels, Belgium
Ph: 32 253 83065
Fax: 32 253 44774
Publisher E-mail: info@fiafnet.org
Journal dealing with all technical and theoretical aspects of moving image archival activities. **Freq:** Semiannual. **Key Personnel:** Christian Dimitriu, Editorial Board; Robert Daudelin, Editor-in-Chief; Eileen Bowser, Editorial Board; Paolo Cherchi Usai, Editorial Board; Eric Le Roy, Editorial Board; Hisashi Okajima, Editorial Board. **ISSN:** 1609-2694. **Subscription Rates:** EUR45 individuals 4 issues; EUR30 individuals 2 issues; EUR15 individuals back issues. **URL:** http://www.fiafnet.org/uk/publications/jfp.cfm.

42863 ■ Journal of Radiotherapy and Oncology
European Society for Therapeutic Radiology and Oncology
Av. E Mounierlaan 83
B-1200 Brussels, Belgium
Ph: 32 277 59340
Fax: 32 277 95494
Publisher E-mail: info@estro.org
Professional journal covering oncology and radiotherapy. **Freq:** Monthly. **Key Personnel:** J. Overgaard, Editor-in-Chief; E. Van Der Schueren, Past Ed.; A.J. Van Der Kogel, Editor; R.P. Abratt, Editorial Board; D. Thwaites, Editor; F. MacBeth, Editorial Board; M. Baumann, Editor; H. Bartelink, Past Ed.; P. Scalliet, Editor; K.K. Ang, Editorial Board. **ISSN:** 0167-8140. **Subscription Rates:** EUR247 individuals European countries; US$394 individuals for all countries except Europe and Japan; 46,800¥ individuals; 371,000¥ institutions; US$3,126 institutions all countries except Europe and Japan; EUR2,796 institutions European countries. **URL:** http://www.estroweb.org; http://www.elsevier.com/wps/find/journaldescription.cws_home/506042/descriptiondescription.

42864 ■ Legisprudence
Hart Publishing Ltd.
c/o Luc J. Wintgens, Ed.-in-Ch.
Centre for Legislation, Regulation & Legisprudence
KU Brussels
Vrijheidslaan 17
1081 Brussels, Belgium
Ph: 32 2 4124258
Publisher E-mail: mail@hartpub.co.uk
Journal covering legislation. **Freq:** 3/yr. **Key Personnel:** Pauline Westerman, Gen. Ed., p.c.westerman@rechten.rug.nl; Luc J. Wintgens, Editor-in-Chief, phone 32 2 4124258, luc.wintgens@kubrussel.ac.be. **Subscription Rates:** 90 individuals standard, United Kingdom and Europe; 100 other countries standard; 40 individuals reduced, United Kingdom and Europe; 45 other countries reduced; 81 individuals online, standard; 36 individuals online. **Remarks:** Accepts advertising. **URL:** http://www.

hartjournals.co.uk/legisprudence/. **Circ:** (Not Reported)

42865 ■ Mathematics and Computers in Simulation
Elsevier Science
c/o Robert Beauwens, Ed.-in-Ch.
Universite Libre de Bruxelles
Av. F.D. Roosevelt 50
CP 165/84
B-1050 Brussels, Belgium
Publisher E-mail: nlinfo-f@elsevier.com
Journal providing information on recent advances in the fields of mathematics and computers, in connection with International Association for Mathematics and Computers in Simulation. **Founded:** 1959. **Freq:** 12/yr. **Key Personnel:** M.J. McAleer, Sen. Ed.; Robert Beauwens, Editor-in-Chief, rbeauwen@ulb.ac.be; Robert Vichnevetsky, Founding Ed.; A. Borghese, Editor; J. Caq, Editor; K. Gustafson, Editor. **ISSN:** 0378-4754. **Subscription Rates:** 315,700¥ institutions; EUR2,377 institutions for Europe; US$2,661 institutions, other countries. **Remarks:** Accepts advertising. **URL:** http://www.elsevier.com/wps/find/journaldescription.cws_home/505615/description. **Circ:** (Not Reported)

42866 ■ MIJARC News
International Movement of Catholic Agricultural and Rural Youth
Mouvement International de la Jeunesse Agricole et Rurale Catholique
53, Rue J. Coosemans
B-1030 Brussels, Belgium
Ph: 32 273 49211
Fax: 32 273 49225
Publisher E-mail: world@mijarc.net
Publication covering rural youth related matters in English, French, German and Spanish. **Freq:** 3/yr. **Key Personnel:** Christine Brandmeir, Sec. Gen. **Remarks:** Advertising not accepted. **URL:** http://www.mijarc.org. **Circ:** 3,000

42867 ■ Military Law and Law of War Review
International Society for Military Law and Law of War
Societe Internationale de Droit Militaire et de Droit de la Guerre
Av. de la Renaissance 30
B-1000 Brussels, Belgium
Ph: 32 273 76178
Fax: 32 273 76178
Publisher E-mail: soc-mil-law@scarlet.be
Publication covering military and war law in English, Dutch, French, German, Italian and Spanish. **Founded:** 1962. **Freq:** Annual. **ISSN:** 0556-7394. **Subscription Rates:** EUR35 members; EUR55 nonmembers. **Remarks:** Advertising not accepted. **URL:** http://www.soc-mil-law.org. **Circ:** (Not Reported)

42868 ■ New Europe
News Corporation
Ave. de Broqueville 34
B-1200 Brussels, Belgium
Ph: 32 2 5390039
Fax: 32 2 5390339
European newspaper regularly providing news from the whole European continent. **Freq:** 52/yr. **Key Personnel:** Basil A. Coronakis, Editor; Anastasia Bouyiatiotes, Publisher. **URL:** http://www.new-europe.info/new-europe/index.asp.

42869 ■ Pharmacy Today
CMPMedica
Rue du Bourdon 100
B-1180 Brussels, Belgium
Ph: 32 233 33411
Fax: 32 233 23958
Publisher E-mail: info@be.cmpmedica.com
Professional magazine covering the pharmacy field in New Zealand. **Freq:** Monthly 11/yr. **Trim Size:** A3. **Key Personnel:** Rajesh Kumar, Sen. Journalist, phone 64 9 9129258, rkumar@pharmacy-today.co.nz; Vivienne Fraser, Business Mgr., phone 64 948 84295, vfraser@pharmacy-today.co.nz; Susan Tupp, Production Coord., phone 64 948 84293, stupp@pharmacy-today.co.nz; Murray Durdle, Financial Controller, phone 64 948 84280, mdurdle@nz.cmpmedica.com; Colin Abercrombie, Mng. Dir., phone 64 948 84280, fax 64 948 96240, cabercrombie@nz.cmpmedica.com; Andrea Svendsen, Editor, phone 64 948 84269. **ISSN:** 1170-1927. **Subscription Rates:** US$72 individuals. **Remarks:** Accepts advertising. **URL:** http://www.pharmacy-today.co.nz. **Ad**

Rates: 4C: 4,052 BFr. **Circ:** (Not Reported)

42870 ■ Public Transport International
International Union Association of Public Transport
Union Internationale des Transports Publics
rue St. Marie 6
B-1080 Brussels, Belgium
Ph: 32 267 36100
Fax: 32 266 01072
Publisher E-mail: administration@uitp.com
Publication covering worldwide public transport in English, French and German. **Freq:** Bimonthly. **Key Personnel:** Catherine Furzer, Editor; Sylvie Cappaert-Blondelle, Editor-in-Chief, sylvie.cappaert@uitp.com; Hans Rat, Sec. Gen., hans.rat@uitp.com. **Subscription Rates:** EUR80 nonmembers; EUR80 other countries. **Remarks:** Accepts classified advertising. **URL:** http://www.uitp.com. **Circ:** 6,000

42871 ■ Pulp & Paper International (PPI)
RISI
326 Ave. Louise, Bte 22
B-1050 Brussels, Belgium
Ph: 32 253 60748
Fax: 32 253 75626
Publisher E-mail: info@risiinfo.com
Trade magazine covering new technologies, management issues and mill operations for the paper, pulp, paperboard industry and paper converting industries worldwide. **Founded:** 1959. **Freq:** Monthly. **Trim Size:** 297 x 210 mm. **Key Personnel:** Justin Toland, Editor. **ISSN:** 0033-409X. **Subscription Rates:** Free to qualified subscribers. **Remarks:** Accepts advertising. **URL:** http://www.risiinfo.com/risi-store/do/product/detail/pulp-paper-international.html. **Ad Rates:** BW: US$5,095, 4C: US$7,880. **Circ:** △14,180

42872 ■ Rotary Contact
Av. De L'Exposition Universelle 68
B-1083 Brussels, Belgium
Ph: 32 2 4203500
Fax: 32 2 4201110
Membership magazine of Rotary International covering current news about Rotary-related subjects in Dutch, French and German. **Founded:** 1984. **Freq:** Monthly 11/yr. **Key Personnel:** Guido Vangansewinkel, Editor. **Remarks:** Accepts advertising. **URL:** http://www.rotary.belux.org; http://www.rotary.org/en/MediaAndNews/MorePublications/RegionalMagazines/Pages/ridefault.aspx. **Circ:** 769,000

42873 ■ Via Secura
Belgian Road Safety Institute
Chaussee de Haecht 1405
B-1130 Brussels, Belgium
Ph: 32 224 41511
Fax: 32 221 64342
Trade magazine covering road safety. **Freq:** Quarterly. **Cols./Page:** 2. **Subscription Rates:** EUR7 individuals. **Remarks:** Accepts advertising. **URL:** http://www.bivv.be/main/PublicatieMateriaal/ViaSecura.shtml?language=nl. **Ad Rates:** BW: EUR400, 4C: EUR800. **Circ:** (Not Reported)

42874 ■ Watt's NEW?
Union of the Electric Industry - Eurelectric
Blvd. de l'Imperatrice 66
PO Box 2
B-1000 Brussels, Belgium
Ph: 32 251 51000
Fax: 32 251 51010
Publisher E-mail: eurelectric@eurelectric.org
Publication covering developments within the European institutions relevant to the electricity sector. English only. **Freq:** Quarterly. **Key Personnel:** Chris Boothby, Hd. of Unit. **Remarks:** Advertising not accepted. **URL:** http://www2.eurelectric.org/Content/Default.asp?. **Formerly:** MEDIA WATT. **Circ:** (Not Reported)

42875 ■ Worlds of Education
Education International
Internationle de l'Education
5, Blvd. du Roi Albert II, 8th Fl.
B-1210 Brussels, Belgium
Ph: 32 2 2240611
Fax: 32 2 2240606
Publisher E-mail: headoffice@ei-ie.org
Publication covering education. **Founded:** Dec. 2002. **Freq:** Bimonthly. **ISSN:** 1998-3433. **Subscription Rates:** Included in membership. **Remarks:** Advertising accepted; rates available upon request. **URL:** http://

www.ei-ie.org. **Alt. Formats:** Database. **Formed by the merger of:** EI Monthly Monitor; Education International. **Formerly:** The Education International Quarterly Magazine. **Circ:** 12,000

42876 ■ Youth Opinion
European Youth Forum
Forum Europeen de la Jeunesse
rue Joseph II straat 120
B-1000 Brussels, Belgium
Ph: 32 2 2306490
Fax: 32 2 2302123
Publication covering youth interests in English, French, German and Spanish. **Freq:** Quarterly. **Print Method:** Offset. **Trim Size:** A4. **Remarks:** Advertising not accepted. **URL:** http://www.youthforum.org. **Circ:** 13,000

42877 ■ Radio Contact-FM - 107
2, Ave. Jacques Georgin
B-1030 Brussels, Belgium
Ph: 32 2 3376680
Fax: 32 2 3376681
Format: Ethnic; World Beat. **Operating Hours:** 19 hours Daily. **Key Personnel:** Eric Adelbrecht, Dir. Gen.; Didier Knapen, Dir., Finance and Admin.; Michel Tourney, Dir., Programming. **Ad Rates:** Advertising accepted; rates available upon request. **URL:** http://www.radiocontact.be.

42878 ■ VRT Radio 1-FM - 94.2
Auguste Reyerslaan 52
B-1043 Brussels, Belgium
Ph: 32 274 13111
E-mail: info@radio1.be
Format: Contemporary Hit Radio (CHR). **Operating Hours:** 18 hours Daily. **Ad Rates:** Advertising accepted; rates available upon request. **URL:** http://www.radio1.be.

Diepenbeek

42879 ■ European Journal of Cancer Prevention
European Cancer Prevention Organization
Dr. Willems Instituut
Gebouw C, Universitaire Campus
B-3590 Diepenbeek, Belgium
Ph: 32 112 75734
Fax: 32 112 83677
Publisher E-mail: sabjanss@hotmail.com
European journal covering cancer prevention. **Founded:** 1993. **Freq:** Bimonthly. **Print Method:** Typest. **Key Personnel:** Magda Lewandowska, Production Ed., magda.lewandowska@wolterskluwer.com; Dr. Jaak Ph Janssens, MD, Editor; Phil Daly, Publisher. **ISSN:** 0959-8278. **Subscription Rates:** US$415 U.S.; US$1,646.10 institutions; US$438.10 other countries; US$1,755.10 institutions, other countries. **Remarks:** Advertising accepted; rates available upon request. **URL:** http://journals.lww.com/eurjcancerprev/pages/default.aspx; http://www.lww.com/product/European-Journal-Cancer-Prevention/?0959-8278. **Circ:** (Not Reported)

42880 ■ Journal of Informetrics
Elsevier Science Inc.
c/o Leo Egghe, Ed.-in-Ch.
Hasselt University
Campus Diepenbeek
Library
B-3590 Diepenbeek, Belgium
Publisher E-mail: usinfo-ehelp@elsevier.com
Journal covering fundamental quantitative aspects of information science. **Founded:** 1977. **Freq:** 4/yr. **Print Method:** Offset/Electronic. **Trim Size:** 8 1/2 x 11. **Cols./Page:** 3. **Col. Width:** 21 picas. **Col. Depth:** 55 picas. **Key Personnel:** P. Ahlgren, Editorial Board; J. Bar-Ilan, Editorial Board; K. Boyack, Editorial Board; Q. Burrell, Editorial Board; B. Cronin, Editorial Board; R.N. Kostoff, Editorial Board; W. Glanzel, Editorial Board; K. Borner, Editorial Board; Leo Egghe, Editor-in-Chief, leo.egghe@uhasselt.be. **ISSN:** 1751-1577. **Subscription Rates:** EUR409 institutions for European countries and Iran; 58,900¥ institutions; US$529 institutions, other countries except Europe, Japan and Iran; 6,400¥ individuals; EUR47 individuals for European countries and Iran; US$58 other countries except Europe, Japan and Iran. **URL:** http://www.elsevier.com/wps/find/journaldescription.cws_home/709551/descriptiondescription.

Eupen

42881 ■ Das Hitradio-FM - 100.5
Kehrweg 11
B-4700 Eupen, Belgium
Ph: 32 87 591252
Fax: 32 87 591249
E-mail: redaktion@dashitradio.de
Format: Contemporary Hit Radio (CHR). **Ad Rates:** Advertising accepted; rates available upon request. **URL:** http://www.dashitradio.de.

Gent

42882 ■ Clinica Chimica Acta
Elsevier Science
c/o J. Delanghe, Ed.-in-Ch.
Dept. of Clinical Chemistry
University Hospital Gent
De Pintelaan 185
B-9000 Gent, Belgium
Publisher E-mail: nlinfo-f@elsevier.com
Journal covering research in the field of clinical chemistry, applied molecular biology and laboratory medicine. **Subtitle:** International Journal of Clinical Chemistry and Diagnostic Laboratory Medicine. **Founded:** 1956. **Freq:** Semimonthly. **Key Personnel:** J. Delanghe, Editor-in-Chief; A.H.B. Wu, Editor-in-Chief; D. Bullock, Editorial Board. **ISSN:** 0009-8981. **Subscription Rates:** 826,500¥ institutions; EUR6,229 institutions for European countries & Iran; US$6,970 institutions for all countries except Europe, Japan & Iran; EUR385 individuals for European countries & Iran; US$516 individuals for all countries except Europe, Japan & Iran; 59,300¥ individuals. **Remarks:** Accepts advertising. **URL:** http://www.elsevier.com/wps/find/journaldescription.cws_home/506018/description. **Circ:** (Not Reported)

42883 ■ Jaarboek
Royal Academy of Dutch Language and Literature
Koninklijke Academie voor Nederlandse Taal-en Letterkunde
Koningstraat 18
B-9000 Gent, Belgium
Ph: 32 926 59340
Fax: 32 926 59349
Publisher E-mail: secretariaat@kantl.be
Dutch language publication covering Dutch culture. **Founded:** 1887. **Freq:** Annual. **ISSN:** 0770-7762. **Remarks:** Advertising not accepted. **URL:** http://www.kantl.be/. **Circ:** 300

42884 ■ Varen
Aquamedia N.V.
Vrijheidslaan 4
B-9000 Gent, Belgium
Ph: 32 921 11816
Fax: 32 921 11817
Publisher E-mail: info@varen.be
Consumer magazine covering water sports. **Subtitle:** Het Meest Gelezen Watersportmagazine van Belgie. **Founded:** 1968. **Freq:** Monthly 10/yr. **Print Method:** Offset. **Trim Size:** 210 x 297 mm. **Key Personnel:** Johan Van Loon, Contact, webmaster@varen.be; Luk Hautekiet, Contact; Rik Vyncke, Advertising Mgr., phone 32 477 302132, fax 32 937 08132, rik.vyncke@decom.be. **Subscription Rates:** EUR32 individuals; EUR60 two years. **URL:** http://www.varen.be. **Ad Rates:** BW: EUR1,165, 4C: EUR1,908. Combined 17,500

42885 ■ Verslagen en Mededelingen
Royal Academy of Dutch Language and Literature
Koninklijke Academie voor Nederlandse Taal-en Letterkunde
Koningstraat 18
B-9000 Gent, Belgium
Ph: 32 926 59340
Fax: 32 926 59349
Publisher E-mail: secretariaat@kantl.be
Dutch language publication covering Dutch culture. **Freq:** 3/yr. **Key Personnel:** Jef Mertens, Contact, redactiesecretariaat@kantl.be. **ISSN:** 0770-7762. **Subscription Rates:** EUR25 individuals; EUR12.60 single issue. **Remarks:** Advertising not accepted. **URL:** http://www.kantl.be/index.php?pag=133. **Circ:** 300

Genval

42886 ■ Health and Food
Sciences Today
rue de Rixensart 18/17
B-1332 Genval, Belgium

Ph: 32 26532158
Fax: 32 26532158
Trade magazine covering nutrition, food and health. **Founded:** 1996. **Freq:** Bimonthly. **Print Method:** Offset. **Key Personnel:** Dr. Jean Andris, Editor-in-Chief, info@healthandfood.be; Daniele Degossely, Contact. **ISSN:** 7374-626X. **Remarks:** Accepts advertising. **URL:** http://www.healthandfood.be/. **Ad Rates:** 4C: EUR3,220. **Circ:** Non-paid ⊕15,000

Ghent

42887 ■ Nephrology Dialysis Transplantation
Oxford University Press
Renal Division
University Hospital Ghent
De Pintelaan 185
9000 Ghent, Belgium
Ph: 32 9 3324402
Fax: 32 9 3324403
Publisher E-mail: webenquiry.uk@oup.com
Journal publishing original clinical and laboratory research in nephrology, dialysis and transplantation, covering all aspects of nephrology, particularly clinical nephrology, but also research relating to the basic immunology, anatomy, and physiology of the kidney. **Freq:** Monthly. **Key Personnel:** N. Lameire, Editor-in-Chief, isabel.vandorpe@ugent.be; E. Ritz, Ed. Emeriti; Jorgen Floege, Dep. Ed., juergen.floege@rwth-aachen.de; W. Bennett, Editorial Board; A. Argiles, Editorial Board; A.M. Davison, Ed. Emeriti; G. Bakris, Subject Ed.; Dr. David Wheeler, Dep. Ed., phone 44 20 78302930, fax 44 20 73178591, d.wheeler@medsch.ucl.ac.uk; T. Benzing, Editorial Board; R.W. Bilous, Editorial Board. **ISSN:** 0931-0509. **Subscription Rates:** 900 institutions corporate; print and online; 705 institutions corporate; online only; 825 institutions corporate; print only; 1,720 institutions print and online; 564 institutions online only; 660 institutions print only; 280 individuals print. **Remarks:** Advertising accepted; rates available upon request. **URL:** http://ndt.oxfordjournals.org/. **Circ:** (Not Reported)

Heverlee

42888 ■ Physica A
Elsevier Science
c/o J.O. Indekeu, Ed.
Instituut voor Theoretische Fysica
Celestijnenlaan 200
B-3001 Heverlee, Belgium
Ph: 32 163 27127
Fax: 32 163 27983
Publisher E-mail: nlinfo-f@elsevier.com
Journal covering research investigations relating to statistical mechanics and its applications. **Subtitle:** Statistical Mechanics and Its Applications. **Founded:** 1975. **Freq:** 24/yr. **Key Personnel:** Constantino Tsallis, Editor, tsallis@cbpf.br; J.O. Indekeu, Editor, joseph.indekeu@fys.kuleuven.be; H.E. Stanley, Editor, phone 617353-2617, fax 617353-3783, hes@bu.edu; Kenneth A. Dawson, Editor, kenneth@fiachra.ucd.ie; S. Abe, Advisory Editorial Board, suabe@sf6.so-net.ne.jp. **ISSN:** 0378-4371. **Subscription Rates:** EUR6,973 institutions for European countries & Iran; US$7,797 institutions for all countries except Europe, Japan & Iran; 926,600¥ institutions. **Remarks:** Advertising accepted; rates available upon request. **URL:** http://www.elsevier.com/wps/find/journaldescription.cws_home/505702/description. **Circ:** (Not Reported)

Ixelles

42889 ■ Revue Belge de Geographie
Societe Royale Belge de Geographie
CP 246 ULB Campus de la Plaine
bvd. du Triomphe
B-1050 Ixelles, Belgium
Ph: 32 2 6505079
Fax: 32 2 6505092
Publisher E-mail: srbg@ulb.ac.be
Journal covering investigations in all phases of geography of Belgium. **Founded:** 1876. **Freq:** Irregular 3-7/yr. **Key Personnel:** Christian Vandermotten, Editor. **ISSN:** 0770-0717. **URL:** http://www.srbg.be/index02.php; http://eos.wdcb.ru/icsu/navigator/html/jrn01567.htm.

Leuven

42890 ■ Acta Horticulturae
International Society for Horticultural Science
Societe Internationale de la Science Horticole
PO Box 500
B-3001 Leuven, Belgium
Ph: 32 162 29427
Fax: 32 162 29450
Publisher E-mail: info@ishs.org
Peer-reviewed publication covering botany. **Freq:** Irregular. **ISSN:** 0567-7572. **Subscription Rates:** EUR4,585 individuals. **Remarks:** Advertising accepted; rates available upon request. **URL:** http://www.ishs.org. **Circ:** (Not Reported)

42891 ■ Ancient Society
PEETERS - USA
Blijde-Inkomststraat 21
B-3000 Leuven, Belgium
Ph: 32 16 325070
Fax: 32 16 324909
Publisher E-mail: peeters@peeters-us.com
Journal covering all aspects of the society of the Greek, Hellenistic and Roman worlds, including relations with peripheral peoples and cultures. **Founded:** 1970. **Freq:** Annual. **Key Personnel:** H. Hauben, Member of the Editorial Board; P. Van Dessel, Editorial Sec.; W. Clarysse, Member of the Editorial Board; A.R. Birley, Consulting Ed.; G. Schepens, Member of the Editorial Board; L. Mooren, Member of the Editorial Board; K. Brodersen, Consulting Ed.; T. Reekmans, Hon. Ed. **ISSN:** 0066-1619. **Subscription Rates:** EUR70 individuals. **URL:** http://www.peeters-leuven.be/journoverz.asp?nr=57&number_of_volumes="0".

42892 ■ Bijdragen
PEETERS - Leuven
Bondgenotenlaan 153
B-3000 Leuven, Belgium
Ph: 32 162 35170
Fax: 32 162 28500
Publisher E-mail: peeters@peeters-leuven.be
Journal covering subjects such as philosophy and theology in northwest Europe comprising Belgium, The Netherlands, and Luxembourg. **Subtitle:** International Journal in Philosophy and Theology. **Key Personnel:** Van W. Herck, Editor; H.W.M. Rikhof, Editor. **ISSN:** 0006-2278. **URL:** http://poj.peeters-leuven.be/content.php?url=journal.php&code=bij.

42893 ■ Campuskrant
Katholieke Universiteit Leuven
Rector's Office
Oude Markt 13
B-3000 Leuven, Belgium
Ph: 32 163 24010
Fax: 32 163 24014
Publication E-mail: campuskrant@kuleuven.be
Publisher E-mail: info@kuleuven.be
University newspaper for students and alumni. **Freq:** 17/yr. **Remarks:** Accepts advertising. **URL:** http://www.kuleuven.be/ck/. **Circ:** (Not Reported)

42894 ■ Ethical Perspectives
PEETERS - Leuven
Ethical Perspectives
European Center for Ethics
Deberiotstraat 26
B-3000 Leuven, Belgium
Ph: 32 16 323796
Fax: 32 16 323788
Publication E-mail: ethical@oce.kuleuven.ac.be
Publisher E-mail: peeters@peeters-leuven.be
Journal provides a forum for exchange of ideas between fundamental and applied ethics in a global scenario. **Subtitle:** Journal of the European Ethics Network. **Key Personnel:** Prof. Bart Pattyn, Editor-in-Chief. **ISSN:** 1370-0049. **Subscription Rates:** EUR60 individuals print; EUR14 individuals pay per view online. **URL:** http://.www.ethical-perspectives.be/index.php; http://poj.peeters-leuven.be/content.php?url=journal.php&code=EP.

42895 ■ European Journal of Pediatrics
Springer Netherlands
c/o Willem Proesmans, Ed.-in-Ch.
University Hospital Gasthuisberg
Herestraat 49
03000 Leuven, Belgium
Fax: 32 16 342152

Publisher E-mail: permissions.dordrecht@springer.com Journal covering cardiology, dermatology, endocrinology, gastroenterology, intensive care medicine, medical genetics and metabolic diseases. **Freq:** Monthly. **Print Method:** Offset. **Cols./Page:** 6. **Col. Width:** 26 nonpareils. **Col. Depth:** 294 agate lines. **Key Personnel:** Michael Dillon, Editorial Board; Erik C. Bottger, Editorial Board; Willem Proesmans, Editor-in-Chief, eur-journal-pediatrics@uz.kuleuven.ac.be; Stylianos E. Antonarakis, Editorial Board; Eugen Boltshauser, Editorial Board; Beat Steinmann, Editor-in-Chief, fax 41 12 667167, eurjpediatofficezuerich@kispi.uzh.ch; Christiane De Boeck, Editorial Board; Anne Greenough, Editorial Board; Luciano Molinari, Statistical Advisor; Erik Harms, Editorial Board. **ISSN:** 0340-6199. **Subscription Rates:** EUR3,737 institutions print incl. free access or e-only; EUR4,484.40 institutions print incl. enhanced access. **Remarks:** Advertising accepted; rates available upon request. **URL:** http://www.springer.com/medicine/pediatrics/journal/431. **Circ:** (Not Reported)

42896 ■ European Review
Cambridge University Press
c/o Prof. Theo d'Haen, Ed.-in-Ch.
English Department
Leuven University
Blijde Inkomstraat 21
B-3000 Leuven, Belgium
Publisher E-mail: information@cambridge.org
Journal covering economics, history, social science, and general aspects of the sciences. **Subtitle:** Interdisciplinary Journal of the Academia Europaea. **Freq:** Quarterly. **Key Personnel:** Sir Arnold Burgen, Editorial Board, asvb@cam.ac.uk; Prof. Theo d'Haen, Editor-in-Chief, theo.dhaen@arts.kuleuven.be; Prof. Barbara Wright, Editorial Board, bwright@tcd.ie; Prof. Ivan T. Berend, Editorial Board, iberend@history.ucla.edu; Prof. Ole Petersen, Editorial Board, o.h.petersen@liverpool.ac.uk. **ISSN:** 1062-7987. **Subscription Rates:** 177 institutions online and print; US$311 institutions online and print; 156 institutions online only; US$277 institutions online only. **Remarks:** Accepts advertising. **URL:** http://journals.cambridge.org/action/displayJournal?jid=ERW. **Ad Rates:** BW: 500 BFr. **Circ:** 2,200

42897 ■ Image & Narrative
Katholieke Universiteit Leuven
Rector's Office
Oude Markt 13
B-3000 Leuven, Belgium
Ph: 32 163 24010
Fax: 32 163 24014
Publisher E-mail: info@kuleuven.be
E-magazine covering visual narratology in the broadest sense of the term. **Subtitle:** Online Magazine of the Visual Narrative. **Key Personnel:** Jan Baetens, Editor-in-Chief, jan.baetens@arts.kuleuven.be; Hilde Van Gelder, Editor-in-Chief, hilde.vangelder@arts.kuleuven.be; Anneleen Masschelein, Editor-in-Chief, anneleen.masschelein@arts.kuleuven.be; Pascal Lefevre, Editorial Board, lefevre.pascal@gmail.com; Donata Meneghelli, Editorial Board; Naomi Morgan, Editorial Board, morgann.hum@mail.uovs.ac.za; Frederick Luis Aldama, Editorial Board, aldamaf@hotmail.com; Philippe Marion, Editorial Board, marion@reci.ucl.ac.be; Michael Hein, Editorial Board, hein@uni-hamburg.de. **ISSN:** 1780-678X. **URL:** http://www.imageandnarrative.be/.

42898 ■ INTAMS review
PEETERS - USA
Faculty of Theology, K.U. Leuven
St. Michielstraat 6
B-3000 Leuven, Belgium
Publisher E-mail: peeters@peeters-us.com
Peer-reviewed journal promoting theological and cross-disciplinary reflection on marriage. **Subtitle:** Journal for the Study of Marriage and Spirituality. **Key Personnel:** Donna Orsuto, Member of the Editorial Board; Giulia Paola Di Nicola, Member of the Editorial Board; Attilio Danese, Member of the Editorial Board; David Dawson, Member of the Editorial Board; Gisbert Greshake, Member of the Editorial Board; Walter Kirchschlager, Member of the Editorial Board; Basilio Petra, Member of the Editorial Board; Enda McDonagh, Member of the Editorial Board; Klaus Demmer, Member of the Editorial Board. **ISSN:** 1370-6020. **Subscription Rates:** EUR50 individuals. **URL:** http://www.peeters-leuven.be/

journoverz.asp?nr=76&number_of_volumes="0".

42899 ■ Iranica Antiqua
PEETERS - Leuven
Bondgenotenlaan 153
B-3000 Leuven, Belgium
Ph: 32 162 35170
Fax: 32 162 28500
Publisher E-mail: peeters@peeters-leuven.be
Journal covering studies on the civilization of pre-Islamic Iran. **Founded:** 1961. **Freq:** Annual. **Key Personnel:** Prof. E. Haerinck, Editor, ernie.haerinck@ugent.be; P. Amiet, Editorial Board; M.A. Dandamayev, Editorial Board; R. Boucharlat, Editorial Board; A. Tourovets, Editorial Sec.; B. Overlaet, Editorial Sec. **ISSN:** 0021-0870. **Subscription Rates:** EUR100 individuals. **URL:** http://poj.peeters-leuven.be/content.php?url=journal&journal_code=ia.

42900 ■ Journal of Computational and Applied Mathematics
Elsevier Science
c/o M.J. Goovaerts, Ed.
Katholieke Universiteit Leuven
Centrum voor Verzekerings-wetenschap
Naamsestraat 69
B-3001 Leuven, Belgium
Ph: 32 16 323746
Fax: 32 16 323740
Publisher E-mail: nlinfo-f@elsevier.com
Journal exploring solutions from new computational techniques to scientific or engineering problems. **Founded:** 1983. **Freq:** Semimonthly. **Key Personnel:** M.J. Goovaerts, Editor, marc.goovaerts@econ.kuleuven.ac.be; T. Mitsui, Editor, tamitsui@mail.doshisha.ac.jp; M. Ng, Editor, mng@math.hkbu.edu.hk; L. Reichel, Assoc. Ed.; L. Wuytack, Editor, luc.wuytack@ua.ac.be. **ISSN:** 0377-0427. **Subscription Rates:** 645,600¥ institutions for Japan; EUR4,855 institutions; US$5,431 institutions for all countries except Europe and Japan. **Remarks:** Accepts advertising. **URL:** http://www.elsevier.com/wps/find/journaldescription.cws_home/505613/description. **Circ:** (Not Reported)

42901 ■ Microelectronic Engineering
Elsevier Science
c/o M. Van Rossum, Ed.-in-Ch.
IMEC, Kapeldreef 75
B-3001 Leuven, Belgium
Publisher E-mail: nlinfo-f@elsevier.com
Peer-reviewed journal focusing on the research in the field of integrated microelectronics. **Founded:** 1983. **Freq:** Monthly. **Key Personnel:** M. Peckerar, Editor, peckerar@eng.umd.edu; M. Van Rossum, Editor-in-Chief, vrossum@imec.be; M. Takai, Editor, takai@cqst.osaka-u.ac.jp. **ISSN:** 0167-9317. **Subscription Rates:** 391,700¥ institutions; US$3,299 institutions for all countries except Europe and Japan; EUR2,945 institutions for European countries. **Remarks:** Accepts advertising. **URL:** http://www.elsevier.com/wps/find/journaldescription.cws_home/505660/description. **Circ:** (Not Reported)

Ligny

42902 ■ Hippo News
Federation Francophone d'Equitation et d'attelage de loisir
Rue du Tienne 12
B-5140 Ligny, Belgium
Ph: 32 718 15052
Fax: 32 718 17615
Publisher E-mail: secretariat@ffe.be
Consumer magazine covering horse riding. **Founded:** 1972. **Freq:** Monthly. **Print Method:** Offset. **Trim Size:** 133 x 150 mm. **Cols./Page:** 3. **Col. Width:** 58 millimeters. **Key Personnel:** Nicole De Jamblinne, Editor, redaction@hipponews.be; Roland Heldenbergh, Editor; Laurence Englebert-Denis, Coord. **Subscription Rates:** EUR25 individuals; EUR38 individuals affiliation/license FFE. **Remarks:** Accepts advertising. **URL:** http://www.ffe.be/hipponews/. **Circ:** Paid 7,000

Maleves-Sainte-Marie-Wastines

42903 ■ Infor Marechalerie/European Farriers Journal/Der Huf
Editions DIASSE S.P.R.L.
Rue d'Opprebais 16
B-1360 Maleves-Sainte-Marie-Wastines, Belgium
Ph: 32 10 888898

Fax: 32 10 889934
Professional magazine for farriers, veterinarians and professionals in horse locomotion in Italian, English, Spanish, French and German. **Founded:** 1986. **Freq:** Bimonthly. **Print Method:** Offset. **Trim Size:** 210 x 297 mm. **ISSN:** 0774-4323. **Subscription Rates:** EUR50 individuals; US$50 other countries. **Remarks:** Accepts advertising. **URL:** http://www.farriersjournal.com/home.php?lng=IT&id=72. **Ad Rates:** BW: EUR675, 4C: EUR1,900. **Circ:** Paid 6,500

Mechelen

42904 ■ Ludus
Editions Rodopi B.V.
c/o Dr. Wim Husken, Ed.
Winketkaai 17/6
B-2800 Mechelen, Belgium
Publisher E-mail: info@rodopi.nl
Journal featuring literature in the fields of performing arts, history and theatre and drama. **Subtitle:** Medieval and Early Renaissance Theatre and Drama. **Key Personnel:** Dr. Wim Husken, Editor, wim.husken@mechelen.be. **ISSN:** 1385-0393. **URL:** http://www.rodopi.nl/senj.asp?SerieId=LUDUS.

42905 ■ Travel Magazine
Travel Productions N.V.
Hanswijkstraat 23
B-2800 Mechelen, Belgium
Ph: 32 154 50350
Fax: 32 154 50360
Publication E-mail: info@wo.be
Professional magazine covering the travel industry in Belgium and Luxembourg in Flemish and French. **Founded:** Sept. 1992. **Freq:** Monthly. **Print Method:** Magazine. **Key Personnel:** Robrecht Willaert, Editor-in-Chief, robrecht@travel-magazine.be; Michelle Van Herzeele, Advertising Mgr.; Ilse Herman, Office Mgr., yves@travel-magazine.be. **Subscription Rates:** 32 individuals. **Remarks:** Accepts advertising. **URL:** http://www.travel-magazine.be. **Ad Rates:** 4C: EUR1,365. **Circ:** Combined 7,000

Mortsel

42906 ■ Journal of Network Industries
Intersentia N.V.
Groenstraat 31
B-2640 Mortsel, Belgium
Ph: 32 368 01550
Fax: 32 365 87121
Publication E-mail: mail@intersentia.be
Publisher E-mail: mail@intersentia.be
Journal exploring the legal, economic, institutional and public policy aspects of the network industries, public utilities and services, which were once the exclusive domain of government. **Freq:** Quarterly. **Key Personnel:** Damien Geradin, Editor-in-Chief, ilse.vanderhaar@uvt.nl. **ISSN:** 1389-9597. **Subscription Rates:** EUR135 individuals. **URL:** http://www.intersentia.be/tijdschrift.asp?pid=672&pageid=0.

Oostende

42907 ■ Old Timer Dreamcar Magazine
Uitgeverij de Groeve
Postbus 728
B-8400 Oostende, Belgium
Publication E-mail: info@oldtimerdreamcar.com
Publisher E-mail: info@oldtimerdreamcar.com
Consumer magazine covering classic automobiles. **Subtitle:** Classic Cars in Belgium and Holland. **Founded:** 1985. **Freq:** 8/yr. **Print Method:** Offset Litho. **Trim Size:** A4. **Cols./Page:** 4. **Col. Width:** 45 millimeters. **Col. Depth:** 273 millimeters. **Key Personnel:** Albrecht De Groeve, Editor. **ISSN:** 0773-2465. **Remarks:** Accepts advertising. **URL:** http://www.oldtimerdreamcar.com. **Ad Rates:** BW: EUR625, 4C: EUR804. **Circ:** Paid ‡23,375

42908 ■ Zwerfauto Magazine
Uitgeverij de Groeve
Postbus 728
B-8400 Oostende, Belgium
Publication E-mail: info@zwerfauto.info
Publisher E-mail: info@oldtimerdreamcar.com
Consumer magazine covering recreational vehicles. **Subtitle:** Motorhome, Kampeerauto's, Campers. **Founded:** 1985. **Freq:** 8/yr. **Print Method:** Offset Litho. **Trim Size:** A4. **Cols./Page:** 4. **Col. Width:** 45

Circulation: ★ = ABC; △ = BPA; ◆ = CAC; • = CCAB; ❑ = VAC; ⊕ = PO Statement; ‡ = Publisher's Report; Boldface figures = sworn; Light figures = estimated.

Gale Directory of Publications & Broadcast Media/147th Ed.

4791

millimeters. Col. Depth: 270 millimeters. ISSN: 0773-2473. Remarks: Accepts advertising. URL: http://www.zwerfauto.com. Ad Rates: BW: EUR755, 4C: EUR959. Circ: Paid ‡18,825

Rekkem

42909 ■ Ons Erfdeel
Stichting Ons Erfdeel vzw
Murissonstraat 260
B-8930 Rekkem, Belgium
Ph: 32 56 411201
Fax: 32 56 414707
Publication E-mail: dirkvanassche@onserfdeel.be
Publisher E-mail: info@onserfdeel.be
Dutch language journal covering culture and society in Flanders and the Netherlands. Subtitle: Valaems - Nederlands Tweemaandelgks Cultureel Tijdschrift. Founded: 1957. Freq: Quarterly. Print Method: Offset. Key Personnel: Luc Devoldere, Ch. Ed. ISSN: 0030-2651. Subscription Rates: EUR65 individuals for Belgium; EUR67 individuals the Netherlands; EUR77 other countries; EUR17 single issue for Belgium; EUR18 single issue Netherlands; EUR20 single issue other Countries; EUR90 individuals friends. Remarks: Accepts advertising. URL: http://www.onserfdeel.be. Circ: Paid 10,000

42910 ■ Septentrion
Stichting Ons Erfdeel vzw
Murissonstraat 260
B-8930 Rekkem, Belgium
Ph: 32 56 411201
Fax: 32 56 414707
Publication E-mail: septentrion@onserfdeel.be
Publisher E-mail: info@onserfdeel.be
Journal in French covering culture and society in Flanders and the Netherlands. Subtitle: Arts, Lettres et Culture de Flandre et des Pays Bas. Founded: 1972. Freq: Quarterly. Print Method: Offset. Key Personnel: Hans Vanacker, Editorial Sec., septentrion@onserfdeel.be. ISSN: 1771-8934. Subscription Rates: EUR39 individuals for Belgium; EUR41 individuals France, Netherlands; EUR44 other countries; EUR10 single issue for Belgium; EUR11 single issue France, Netherlands; EUR12 single issue other countries. Remarks: Accepts advertising. URL: http://www.onserfdeel.be; http://www.onserfdeel.be/nl/uit_septentrion.asp. Circ: Paid 10,000

Saint-Pieters-Leeuw

42911 ■ Dedicated Systems Magazine
Dedicated Systems Experts
Bergensesteenweg 421, B12
B-1600 Saint-Pieters-Leeuw, Belgium
Ph: 32 233 11284
Professional magazine covering computer engineering for engineers. Freq: Quarterly. Key Personnel: Dr. Martin Timmerman, Editor-in-Chief. Subscription Rates: Free. Remarks: Accepts advertising. URL: http://www.dedicated-systems.com/magazine/magazine.htm. Circ: (Not Reported)

Wilsele

42912 ■ Khil'a
PEETERS - USA
Kolonel Begaultlaan 61
B-3012 Wilsele, Belgium
Ph: 32 16 228500
Fax: 32 16 235170
Publisher E-mail: peeters@peeters-us.com
Journal on archaeology in North Africa. Subtitle: Journal for Dress and Textiles of the Islamic World. Key Personnel: Fehrman J., Editor; Hanssen L., Editor; Vogelsang W., Editor. ISSN: 1781-2534. Subscription Rates: EUR60 individuals. URL: http://www.peeters-leuven.be/Journoverz.asp?nr=72&page=1&number_of_volumes=.

Wommelgem

42913 ■ Exclusief
Raymond Stuyck Consultants BVBA
Koralenhoeve 4
B-2160 Wommelgem, Belgium
Ph: 32 335 53838
Fax: 32 335 55339
Publisher E-mail: contact@exclusief.be
Consumer magazine covering lifestyle. Founded: 1977. Freq: 5/yr. Print Method: Offset. Trim Size: 207 x 296 mm. Remarks: Accepts advertising. URL: http://www.exclusief.be/. Ad Rates: BW: EUR3,200, 4C: EUR4,400. Circ: Combined 40,000

Ambergris Caye

42914 ■ The San Pedro Sun
PO Box 35
San Pedro Town
Ambergris Caye, Belize
Ph: 501 226 2070
Fax: 501 226 2905
Publisher E-mail: spsun@sanpedrosun.net
Community newspaper. **Freq:** Weekly. **Subscription Rates:** US$100 other countries; $B 100 individuals; US$60 other countries six months; $B 60 individuals six months. **URL:** http://www.sanpedrosun.net/subscription. html.

Belize City

42915 ■ The Belize Times
The Beliza Times Press Ltd.
No. 3, Queen St.
PO Box 506
Belize City, Belize
Ph: 501 224 5757
Community newspaper. **Freq:** Weekly. **Key Personnel:** Mike Rudon, Jr., Editor. **Subscription Rates:** US$52 individuals; US$100 two years individual. **Remarks:** Accepts advertising. **URL:** http://www.belizetimes.bz/. **Ad Rates:** BW: US$492. **Circ:** (Not Reported)

42916 ■ Placencia Breeze
Placencia Chapter of the Belize Tourism Industry Association
Placencia Tourism Center
10 N Park St.
Belize City, Belize
Ph: 501 5234045
Fax: 501 5233294
Publication E-mail: tourism@placencia.com
Publisher E-mail: tourism@placencia.com
Travel and tourism magazine focusing in Belize. **Freq:** Monthly. **Key Personnel:** Elysia Dial, Editor-in-Chief. **Remarks:** Accepts advertising. **URL:** http://www. placenciabreeze.com/. **Circ:** 2,500

42917 ■ Love-FM - 88.9
PO Box 1865
7145 Slaughterhouse Rd.
Belize City, Belize
Ph: 501 2032098
Fax: 501 2030529
Format: Eclectic; Talk; News; Information; Educational. **Founded:** 1992. **Operating Hours:** Continuous. **Key Personnel:** Rene Villanueva, Sr., CEO/Gen. Mgr. **Ad Rates:** Advertising accepted; rates available upon request. **URL:** http://www.lovefm.com.

42918 ■ Love-FM - 95.1
7145 Slaughterhouse Rd.
PO Box 1865
Belize City, Belize
Ph: 501 2032098
Fax: 501 2030529
Format: Eclectic; Talk; Information; News. **Operating Hours:** Continuous. **Key Personnel:** Rene Villanueva, Sr., CEO/Gen. Mgr. **Ad Rates:** Advertising accepted; rates available upon request. **URL:** http://www.lovefm. com.

San Pedro Town

42919 ■ Ambergris Today
Ambergris Today Newspaper
Pescador Dr.
Ambergris Caye
PO Box 23
San Pedro Town, Belize
Ph: 501 2263462
Fax: 501 2263483
Publication E-mail: ambergristoday@yahoo.com
Publisher E-mail: ambertoday@btl.net
Newspaper featuring information about the community and tourism in Belize. **Subscription Rates:** US$40 other countries. **Remarks:** Accepts advertising. **URL:** http:// ambergriscaye.com/ambergristoday/. **Circ:** (Not Reported)

Circulation: ＊ = ABC; △ = BPA; ◆ = CAC; • = CCAB; ❏ = VAC; ⊕ = PO Statement; ‡ = Publisher's Report; Boldface figures = sworn; Light figures = estimated.

Gale Directory of Publications & Broadcast Media/147th Ed.   4793

Hamilton

42920 ■ Bermuda Sun
Bermuda Sun Ltd.
PO Box HM 1241
Hamilton, Bermuda
Ph: 809295-3902
Fax: 809292-5597
Publisher E-mail: feedback@bermudasun.bm
Newspaper. **Founded:** 1964. **Freq:** Triennial. **Print Method:** Web offset. **Trim Size:** 15.5 x 10.25. **Key Personnel:** Don Burgess, Dep. Ed., fax 441278-1861, dburgess@bermudasun.bm; Coggie Gibbons, Reporter, phone 441278-1859, cgibbons@bermudasun.bm; James Whittaker, Reporter, phone 441278-1866, jwhittaker@bermudasun.bm; Mark Kennedy, Sub-Ed., phone 441278-1862, mkennedy@bermudasun.bm; Sirkka Huish, Sub-Ed., phone 441278-1863, shuish@bermudasun.bm; Lisa Beauchamp, General Mgr., phone 441278-1850, lbeauchamp@bermudasun.bm; Meredith Ebbin, Sen. Writer, phone 441278-1864, mebbin@bermudasun.bm; Nigel Regan, Ch. Reporter, phone 441278-1865, nregan@bermudasun.bm; Tony McWilliam, Editor-in-Chief, phone 441278-1860, tmcwilliam@bermudasun.bm; Randy French, Publisher, fax 441292-5597, rfrench@bermudasun.bm. **Remarks:** Accepts advertising. **URL:** http://bermudasun.bm/index.asp. **Ad Rates:** BW: Bm$14, PCI: Bm$15.25. **Circ:** (Not Reported)

42921 ■ Mid-Ocean News
The Bermuda Press (Holdings) Ltd.
PO Box HM1025
Hamilton, Bermuda
Ph: 441295-5881
Publication E-mail: letter@royalgazette.com
Publisher E-mail: wjszuill@royalgazette.bm
Newspaper featuring wide range of news stories, human interest features, sports, travel, and entertainment reports. **Freq:** Weekly (Fri.). **Key Personnel:** Bill Zull, Editor, wjszuill@royalgazette.bm; Davis Del Monte, Circulation Mgr., ddavis@royalgazette.bm. **Remarks:** Accepts advertising. **URL:** http://www.royalgazette.com/siftology.royalgazette/index.jsp. **Circ:** (Not Reported)

42922 ■ The Royal Gazette
The Bermuda Press (Holdings) Ltd.
PO Box HM1025
Hamilton, Bermuda
Ph: 441295-5881
Publication E-mail: letter@royalgazette.com
Publisher E-mail: wjszuill@royalgazette.bm
Newspaper featuring overseas news, sports, business, lifestyle, and opinion. **Founded:** 1828. **Freq:** Mon.-Sat. **Key Personnel:** Bill Zull, Editor, wjszuill@royalgazette.bm; Davis Del Monte, Circulation Mgr., ddavis@royalgazette.bm. **Subscription Rates:** Bm$237 individuals; Bm$119 individuals 6 months; Bm$59 individuals 3 months. **Remarks:** Accepts advertising. **URL:** http://www.royalgazette.com/siftology.royalgazette/index.jsp. **Circ:** 16,000

Circulation: ★ = ABC; △ = BPA; ◆ = CAC; ● = CCAB; ❏ = VAC; ⊕ = PO Statement; ‡ = Publisher's Report; Boldface figures = sworn; Light figures = estimated.

Gale Directory of Publications & Broadcast Media/147th Ed. 4795

Dobchula

42923 ■ Bhutan Broadcasting Service - Dobchula - 88.1 MHz
PO Box 101
Thimphu, Bhutan
Ph: 975 2 323071
Fax: 975 2 323073
E-mail: webmasterbbs@bbs.com.bt
Format: Oldies; Full Service; Educational. **Owner:** Bhutan Broadcasting Service, at above address. **Founded:** June 2000. **Operating Hours:** 7 a.m. - 12 p.m., 2 p.m - 10 p.m. Daily. **Wattage:** 50,000. **Ad Rates:** $100-200 for 15 seconds; $150-300 for 30 seconds; $250-400 for 45 seconds; $300-500 for 60 seconds. **URL:** http://www.bbs.com.bt/.

Thimphu

42924 ■ Bhutan Observer
Bhutan Observer Pvt. Ltd.
Norzin Lam
PO Box 1112
Thimphu, Bhutan
Ph: 975 2 334891
Fax: 975 2 327981
Publisher E-mail: editor@bhutanobserver.bt
Newspaper featuring news and events in Bhutan. **Founded:** June 2, 2006. **Freq:** Weekly. **Remarks:** Accepts advertising. **URL:** http://www.bhutanobserver.bt/. **Circ:** (Not Reported)

42925 ■ Journal of Bhutan Studies
The Centre for Bhutan Studies
PO Box 1111
Langjophakha
Thimphu, Bhutan
Ph: 975 2 321005
Fax: 975 2 321001
Publisher E-mail: cbs@druknet.bt
Journal covering social, cultural, and economic aspects of Bhutan. **Freq:** Semiannual. **Key Personnel:** Dasho Karma Ura, Director, dasho.k.ura@gmail.com. **URL:** http://www.bhutanstudies.org.bt.

42926 ■ Kuensel
Kuensel Corporation
PO Box 204
Thimphu, Bhutan
Ph: 975 23 21544
Fax: 975 23 22975
Publisher E-mail: circulation@kuensel.com.bt
General interest newspaper. **Founded:** 1986. **Freq:** Semiweekly (Wed. and Sat.). **Key Personnel:** Kinley Dorji, Editor-in-Chief. **ISSN:** 0259-1499. **Remarks:** Accepts advertising. **URL:** http://www.kuenselonline.com/. **Ad Rates:** BW: Ng 39,488, 4C: Ng 71,400. **Circ:** Paid 6,023

42927 ■ Bhutan Broadcasting Service - 5
PO Box 101
Thimphu, Bhutan
Ph: 975 2 323071
Fax: 975 2 323073
E-mail: webmasterbbs@bbs.com.bt
Format: News; Commercial TV. **Owner:** Bhutan Broadcasting Service, at above address. **Founded:** June 2, 1999. **Operating Hours:** 6.00 p.m. - 11.00 p.m. Daily. **Key Personnel:** Mr. Choiten Wangchuk, Dir. **Wattage:** 1000. **Ad Rates:** $350-500 for 15 seconds; $600-800 for 30 seconds; $900-1200 for 45 seconds; $1,200-1,600 for 60 seconds. **URL:** http://www.bbs.com.bt/.

42928 ■ Bhutan Broadcasting Service - 6035 KHz
PO Box 101
Thimphu, Bhutan
Ph: 975 2 323071
Fax: 975 2 323073
E-mail: webmasterbbs@bbs.com.bt
Format: Oldies; Full Service; Educational. **Owner:** Bhutan Broadcasting Service, at above address. **Founded:** 1991. **Operating Hours:** Continuous. **Key Personnel:** Choiten Wangchuk, Dir. **Wattage:** 50,000. **Ad Rates:** Advertising accepted; rates available upon request. **URL:** http://www.bbs.com.bt/.

Bhutan Broadcasting Service - Dobchula - See Dobchula

Circulation: ★ = ABC; △ = BPA; ♦ = CAC; • = CCAB; ❑ = VAC; ⊕ = PO Statement; ‡ = Publisher's Report; Boldface figures = sworn; Light figures = estimated.

Gale Directory of Publications & Broadcast Media/147th Ed.   4797

Casilla

42929 ■ Classica-FM - 107.1
Madiore No. 72
Santa Cruz de la Sierra
Casilla, Bolivia
Ph: 591 3339070
Fax: 591 3339071
E-mail: radio@classicafm.com
Format: Music of Your Life. **Operating Hours:** Continuous. **Ad Rates:** Advertising accepted; rates available upon request. **URL:** http://www.classicafm.com.

Cochabamba

42930 ■ Radio Estrelle-FM - 93.1
Sisteco Bldg.

Fl. 4, Office 3
Cochabamba, Bolivia
Ph: 591 42 4520094
Format: Information; World Beat. **Operating Hours:** Continuous. **Key Personnel:** Gonzalo Zamorano Butron, Contact, info@radioestrella.com. **URL:** http://www.radioestrella.com/fm_estrella.htm.

Oruro

42931 ■ Radio WKM-FM - 91.5
Calle Bolivar No. 934 Entre Camacho y Washington
Oruro, Bolivia
Ph: 591 2 5250290
Fax: 591 2 5250290
E-mail: wkm@wkmradio.com

Format: Ethnic; Eclectic. **Founded:** Aug. 28, 1994. **Operating Hours:** 18 hours Daily. **Key Personnel:** Victor Hugo Irahola, Exec. Dir. **Ad Rates:** Advertising accepted; rates available upon request. **URL:** http://www.wkmradio.com.

Sucre

42932 ■ Radio Loyola-AM - 1300
Calle Ayacucho N 161
Sucre, Bolivia
Ph: 591 64 42555
E-mail: loyola@radiofides.com
Format: Ethnic. **Operating Hours:** 14 hours Daily. **URL:** http://www.radioloyola.com.

Circulation: ★ = ABC; △ = BPA; ♦ = CAC; • = CCAB; ❏ = VAC; ⊕ = PO Statement; ‡ = Publisher's Report; Boldface figures = sworn; Light figures = estimated.

Gale Directory of Publications & Broadcast Media/147th Ed. 4799

Bihac

42933 ■ Radio Bihac-FM - 92.3
Krupska b.b.
Unsko Sanski Kanton
77000 Bihac, Bosnia-Hercegovina
Ph: 387 372 28089
Fax: 387 372 23770
E-mail: rtv.bi@bih.net.ba
Format: Talk; Ethnic; World Beat. **Owner:** Miro International Ptv. Ltd., Lokalradio Cottbus GmbH, D-03046 Cottbus, Germany. **URL:** http://www.rtvbihac.ba.

Bijeljina

42934 ■ Radio BN-FM - 93.4
Laze Kostica 146
Bijeljina, Bosnia-Hercegovina
Ph: 387 55 228400
E-mail: radio@rtvbn.com
Format: Information. **Operating Hours:** Continuous. **URL:** http://www.radiobn.net.

Sarajevo

42935 ■ Radio M-FM - 98.7
Fra Andela Zvizdovica 1
71000 Sarajevo, Bosnia-Hercegovina
Ph: 387 33 666822
Fax: 387 33 666628
E-mail: prviradio@radiom.net
Format: World Beat. **Operating Hours:** Continuous. **Ad Rates:** Advertising accepted; rates available upon request. **URL:** http://www.radiom.net/wcms.

42936 ■ Radio ZID Sarajevo-FM - 89.9 Mhz
Husrefa Redzica 8

71 000 Sarajevo, Bosnia-Hercegovina
Ph: 387 71 443771
Fax: 387 71 443604
E-mail: cyberzid-sa@zamir-sa.ztn.apc.org
Format: Information; Classic Rock. **Owner:** Medienhilfe, Quellenstr. 25, CH-8005 Zurich, Switzerland, 41 44 2724637, Fax: 41 44 2724682. **URL:** http://archiv. medienhilfe.ch/Projekte/BiH/Federation/Slobosna/RadioZid/Pro ject99.htm.

Tuzla

42937 ■ Radio Tuzla-AM - 774
Ulica Mirze Delibasica Br.4
75000 Tuzla, Bosnia-Hercegovina
Ph: 251 551 251440
Fax: 251 551 236666
E-mail: radiotz@inet.ba
Format: Ethnic; World Beat. **Operating Hours:** Continuous. **URL:** http://www.radiotuzla.com.

42938 ■ Radio Tuzla-FM - 103.8 MHz
Ulica Mirze Delibasica Br. 4
75000 Tuzla, Bosnia-Hercegovina
Ph: 387 251551
Fax: 387 236666
E-mail: radiotz@inet.ba
Format: Ethnic; World Beat. **Operating Hours:** Continuous. **URL:** http://www.radiotuzla.com.

42939 ■ Radio Tuzla-FM - 105.1 MHz
Ulica Mirze Delibasica Br. 4
75000 Tuzla, Bosnia-Hercegovina
Ph: 387 251551
Fax: 387 236666

E-mail: radiotz@radiotuzla.com
Format: Ethnic; World Beat. **Operating Hours:** Continuous. **URL:** http://www.radiotuzla.com.

42940 ■ Radio Tuzla-FM - 96.5 MHz
Ulica Mirze Delibasica Br.4
75000 Tuzla, Bosnia-Hercegovina
Ph: 387 251551
Fax: 387 236666
E-mail: radiotz@inet.ba
Format: Ethnic; World Beat. **Operating Hours:** Continuous. **URL:** http://www.radiotuzla.com.

Visoko

42941 ■ Radio Q-FM - 105.2
Ul. Donje Rosulje 59
71300 Visoko, Bosnia-Hercegovina
Ph: 387 32 730740
Fax: 387 32 735280
E-mail: radioq@bih.net.ba
Format: Ethnic; World Beat. **Operating Hours:** Continuous. **Ad Rates:** Advertising accepted; rates available upon request. **URL:** http://www.radioq.co.ba.

Zenica

42942 ■ BM Radio-FM - 99.3
Talica brdo 11
72000 Zenica, Bosnia-Hercegovina
Ph: 387 32 440442
Fax: 387 32 440444
E-mail: marketing@bmradio.net
Format: Ethnic; World Beat. **Ad Rates:** Advertising accepted; rates available upon request. **URL:** http://www. bmradio.net.

Gaborone

42943 ■ Botswana Journal of Technology
African Journals Online
University of Botswana
Private Bag 0061
Gaborone, Botswana
Ph: 267 3554210
Fax: 267 352309
Publisher E-mail: info@ajol.info
Peer-reviewed journal covering developments or research in the field of engineering and technology. **Freq:** Semiannual. **Key Personnel:** Joseph M. Chuma, Contact, chuma@mopipi.ub.bw; Prof. A.B. Ngowi, Contact, ngowiab@mopipi.ub.bw. **ISSN:** 1019-1593. **URL:** http://ajol.info/index.php/bjt.

42944 ■ Marang
African Journals Online
U.S. Department of of English
University of Botswana
Private Bag UB00703
Gaborone, Botswana
Ph: 267 3552978
Fax: 267 3185098
Publisher E-mail: info@ajol.info
Peer-reviewed journal covering the field of literature, language, linguistics, and theatre studies. **Subtitle:** Journal of Language and Literature. **Freq:** Annual. **Key Personnel:** Dr. Alfred J. Matiki, Editor, matiki@mopipi.ub.bw. **ISSN:** 1816-7659. **URL:** http://ajol.info/index.php/marang.

42945 ■ Mmegi/The Reporter
PO Box BR 50
Gaborone, Botswana
Ph: 267 397 4784
Fax: 267 390 5508
Publication E-mail: editor@mmegi.bw
Publisher E-mail: dikgang@mmegi.bw
Community newspaper. **Founded:** 1984. **Freq:** Daily. **Print Method:** Web. **Remarks:** Accepts advertising. **URL:** http://www.mmegi.bw. **Circ:** Paid ★16,000

42946 ■ ZJAR
SACCAR - Southern African Centre for Cooperation in Agricultural Research and Natural Resources Research and Training
PO Box 00108
Gaborone, Botswana
Ph: 267 32 8847
Fax: 267 32 8806
Publisher E-mail: bndunguru@saccar.info.bw
Scientific agricultural publication. **Freq:** Annual. **Key Personnel:** Dr. H.P.R. Tawonezvi, Editor. **Subscription Rates:** Z$20 individuals; Z$10 single issue; US$20 other countries; US$10 single issue other countries. **URL:** http://www.ibis.bw/~saccar/zjar.htm. **Circ:** 2,000

42947 ■ Gabz-FM - 96.2
Beta House, 2nd Fl.
Plot 17954
Old Lobatse Rd.
Gaborone, Botswana
Ph: 267 3170905
Fax: 267 3181443
Format: Adult Contemporary. **Owner:** GabzFM 96.2, at above address. **Operating Hours:** Continuous. **Key Personnel:** Thabiso Simmery, Sales/Mktg. Mgr. **Ad Rates:** Advertising accepted; rates available upon request. **URL:** http://www.gabzfm.com.

Bauru

42948 ■ Journal of Applied Oral Science
Faculdade De Odontologia De Bauru - USP
Servico de Biblioteca e Documentacao FO-USP
Al. Dr. Octavio Pinheiro Brisolla 9-75
17012-901 Bauru, Sao Paulo, Brazil
Publication E-mail: jaos@usp.br
Journal publishing research articles in the area of dentistry and related sciences. **Founded:** 1993. **Freq:** Bimonthly. **Key Personnel:** Carlos F. Santos, Editor-in-Chief; Ahmad S. Al-Hiyasat, Editorial Board; Dr. Ricardo Marins De Carvalho, Editorial Board. **ISSN:** 1678-7757. **Subscription Rates:** Cr$60 individuals issues published before 2006; US$60 other countries issues published before 2006; Cr$120 individuals issues published after 2006; US$100 other countries issues published after 2006; Cr$20 single issue; US$20 other countries. **URL:** http://www.scielo.br/scielo.php?pid=1678-7757&script=sci_serial. **Formerly:** Revista da Faculdade de Odontologia de Bauru.

Belo Horizonte

42949 ■ Kriterion
Federal University of Minas Gerais
Philosophy Department
Avenida Antonio Carlos
6627 Campus Pampulha
31270-301 Belo Horizonte, Mato Grosso, Brazil
Ph: 55 313 4995020
Fax: 55 313 4995060
Publication E-mail: kriterion@fafich.ufmg.br
Publisher E-mail: oficium@fafich.ufmg.br
Journal covering philosophy. **Subtitle:** Revista de Filosofia. **Founded:** 1952. **Freq:** Monthly. **Print Method:** Offset. **Trim Size:** 7 7/8 x 10 1/2. **Key Personnel:** Wolfgang Berger, Editor; Peter Brossel, Editor; Niki Pfeifer, Editor. **ISSN:** 0100-512X. **Subscription Rates:** US$15 individuals; US$30 individuals two issues. **URL:** http://www.fafich.ufmg.br.

42950 ■ Nova Economia
Universidade Federal de Minas Gerais
Av. Antonio Carlos
6627 Campus Pampulha
31270-901 Belo Horizonte, Mato Grosso, Brazil
Ph: 55 31 34095000
Publication E-mail: ne@face.ufmg.br
Journal publishing papers in all areas of economics and related fields. **Freq:** 3/yr. **Key Personnel:** Hugo E.A. da Gama Cerqueira, Editorial Committee; Ana FLavia Machado, Publisher. **ISSN:** 0103-6351. **Subscription Rates:** Free online. **URL:** http://www.face.ufmg.br/novaeconomia/eng/index.html.

42951 ■ Extra-FM - 103.9
Rua Itatiaia 117 Bonfim
31210-170 Belo Horizonte, Mato Grosso, Brazil
Ph: 55 31 21053500
Format: Ethnic; World Beat. **Operating Hours:** Continuous. **Ad Rates:** Advertising accepted; rates available upon request. **URL:** http://www.extrafm.com.br.

42952 ■ Rede Itatiaia-AM - 610
Rua Itatiaia 117 Bonfim
31210-170 Belo Horizonte, Mato Grosso, Brazil
Ph: 55 31 21053588
Fax: 55 31 21053613
Format: Talk. **Operating Hours:** Continuous. **URL:** http://www.itatiaia.com.br.

42953 ■ Rede Itatiaia-FM - 95.7
Rua Itatiaia 117
Bonfim
31210-170 Belo Horizonte, Mato Grosso, Brazil
Ph: 55 31 21053588
Fax: 55 31 21053613
Format: Talk. **Operating Hours:** Continuous. **Ad Rates:** Advertising accepted; rates available upon request. **URL:** http://www.itatiaia.com.br.

Botafogo

42954 ■ International Braz J Urol
Brazilian Society of Urology
Rua Bambina, 153
Botafogo, Rio de Janeiro, Brazil
Ph: 55 212 2464092
Fax: 55 212 2464194
Publication E-mail: brazjurol@brazjurol.com.br
Journal focusing on clinical, surgical techniques, pediatric, urological neurology, investigative urology, and urological survey covering the field of Urology. **Freq:** Bimonthly. **Key Personnel:** Dr. Francisco J.B. Sampaio, Editor. **ISSN:** 1677-5538. **URL:** http://www.brazjurol.com.br/. **Circ:** 6,000

42955 ■ Revista Brasileira de Anestesiologia
Brazilian Society of Anesthesiology
Rua Prof. Alfredo Gomes, 36
22251-080 Botafogo, Rio de Janeiro, Brazil
Ph: 55 212 5378100
Fax: 55 212 5378188
Publisher E-mail: sba2000@openlink.com.br
Journal covering anesthesiology, intensive care, pain relief and cardiopulmonary resuscitation. **Founded:** 1951. **Freq:** Semiweekly Thurs. and Mon. **Print Method:** Offset. **Cols./Page:** 6. **Col. Width:** 21 nonpareils. **Col. Depth:** 294 agate lines. **Key Personnel:** Judymara Lauzi Gozzani, Assoc. Ed.; David Ferez, Consulting Ed.; Luiz Marciano Cangiani, Assoc. Ed.; Maria Angela Tardelli, Co-Ed.; Jose Reinaldo Cerqueira Braz, Assoc. Ed.; Mario Jose da Conceicao, Editor-in-Chief. **ISSN:** 1806-907X. **Subscription Rates:** US$170 individuals. **URL:** http://www.scielo.br/revistas/rba/iaboutj.htm.

Botucatu

42956 ■ Interface
Uni Foundation and Unesp - Sao Paulo State University
Caixa Postal 592
18618-000 Botucatu, Sao Paulo, Brazil
Ph: 55 143 8153133
Fax: 55 143 8153133
Publisher E-mail: intface@fmb.unesp.br
Journal focusing on the interface of healthcare sciences and the humanities, especially communication, education and higher education. **Subtitle:** Comunicacao, Saude, Educacao. **Founded:** Aug. 1, 1997. **Freq:** Quarterly. **Print Method:** Letterpress. **Trim Size:** 7 1/2 x 10. **Cols./Page:** 3. **Key Personnel:** Antonio Pithon Cyrino, Editor; Ione Morita, Assoc. Ed.; Nildo Batista, Assoc. Ed. **ISSN:** 1414-3283. **Subscription Rates:** Cr$80 individuals; Cr$100 institutions; US$80 other countries; US$100 institutions, other countries. **URL:** http://www.scielo.br/revistas/icse/iaboutj.htm.

42957 ■ The Journal of Venomous Animals and Toxins including Tropical Diseases
The Center for the Study of Venoms and Venomous Animals
Sao Paulo State University
Rua Jose de Barros, 1780
Caixa Postal 577
Botucatu, Sao Paulo, Brazil
Ph: 55 14 38145555
Fax: 55 14 38145446
Publication E-mail: jvat@cevap.org.br
Publisher E-mail: cevap@cevap.org.br
Journal dealing with all aspects of toxins, venomous animals, their products and derivatives, and tropical diseases, in connection with Universidade Estadual Paulista (Sao Paulo State University - UNESP). **Founded:** 1995. **Freq:** Quarterly. **Key Personnel:** Benedito Barraviera, Editor-in-Chief, bbviera@jvat.org.br. **ISSN:** 1678-9199. **URL:** http://www.jvat.org.br/.

Brasilia

42958 ■ Fitopatologia Brasileira
Sociedade Brasileira de Fitopatologia
SGAS 902 Bloco B, Lote 74 - Salas 102/103
Edificio Athenas
70390-020 Brasilia, Federal District, Brazil
Ph: 55 613 2252421
Fax: 55 613 2252421
Publication E-mail: sbf-revista@ufla.br
Journal dedicated to publishing technical and scientific articles that describe original research in the area of plant pathology. **Founded:** 1924. **Freq:** 11/yr. **Print Method:** Offset. **Trim Size:** 8 1/2 x 11. **Cols./Page:** 3. **Col. Width:** 31 nonpareils. **Col. Depth:** 136 agate lines. **Key Personnel:** Ludwig H. Pfenning, Editor-in-Chief; Eduardo S G. Mizubuti, Contact; Mario Lucio V. Resende, Contact. **ISSN:** 1982-5676. **Subscription Rates:** Cr$85 individuals; US$80 individuals; Cr$100 institutions and libraries; US$100 institutions and libraries. **URL:** http://www.sbfito.com.br/fb/.

42959 ■ Radio Justica-FM - 91.1
Caixa Postal 3791
70175-900 Brasilia, Federal District, Brazil
Ph: 55 61 32173980
Format: World Beat; Ethnic; Information. **Operating Hours:** Continuous. **URL:** http://www.radiojustica.jus.br.

42960 ■ Radio Nacional-FM - 96.1
SCRN 702/3
Bloco B Edificio Radiobras
70323-900 Brasilia, Federal District, Brazil
Ph: 55 61 33274380
Format: Ethnic. **Founded:** 1977. **Operating Hours:**

Circulation: ★ = ABC; △ = BPA; ♦ = CAC; • = CCAB; ❏ = VAC; ⊕ = PO Statement; ‡ = Publisher's Report; Boldface figures = sworn; Light figures = estimated.

Continuous. **Wattage:** 20,000. **URL:** www.radiobras.gov. br/estatico/radio_nacional_fm.htm.

42961 ■ Soc. Feira-AM - 970
R. Frei Hermenegildo, 300
Capuchinhos
44050-240 Brasilia, Federal District, Brazil
Fax: 55 75 21019700
Format: Information; Ethnic; World Beat. **Founded:** 1948. **Operating Hours:** Continuous. **URL:** http://www. sociedadedefeiraam.com.br.

Campinas

42962 ■ Biota Neotropica
Centro de Referencia em Informacao Ambiental
Av Romeu Tortima, 388
Barao Geraldo
13083-791 Campinas, Sao Paulo, Brazil
Ph: 55 193 2880466
Fax: 55 193 2490960
Publisher E-mail: webmaster@cria.org.br
Journal that publishes research on the conservation and use of biodiversity in the Neotropical region. **Freq:** Semiannual. **Key Personnel:** Carlos Alfredo Joly, Editor, cjoly@obelix.unicamp.br. **ISSN:** 1676-0611. **Subscription Rates:** Free. **URL:** http://www.biotaneotropica. org.br/v3n2/en/.

42963 ■ Bragantia
Instituto Agronomico de Campinas
Avenida Barao de Itapura, 1481
13012-970 Campinas, Sao Paulo, Brazil
Ph: 55 193 2315422
Fax: 55 193 2314943
Journal devoted to agricultural sciences. **Founded:** 1981. **Freq:** Quarterly. **Print Method:** Offset. Uses mats. **Cols./Page:** 6. **Col. Width:** 12 picas. **Col. Depth:** 21 inches. **Key Personnel:** Oliveiro Guerreiro Filho, Editor-in-Chief; Carlos Pimentel, Assoc. Ed.; Celso Omoto, Assoc. Ed. **ISSN:** 0006-8705. **Subscription Rates:** Cr$100 individuals; Cr$25 single issue. **URL:** http://www. iac.sp.gov.br/Bragantia/br-comed.htm.

42964 ■ Bragantia
Instituto Agronomico de Campinas
Avenida Barao de Itapura, 1481
13012-970 Campinas, Sao Paulo, Brazil
Ph: 55 193 2315422
Fax: 55 193 2314943
Journal devoted to agricultural sciences. **Founded:** 1981. **Freq:** Quarterly. **Print Method:** Offset. Uses mats. **Cols./Page:** 6. **Col. Width:** 12 picas. **Col. Depth:** 21 inches. **Key Personnel:** Oliveiro Guerreiro Filho, Editor-in-Chief; Carlos Pimentel, Assoc. Ed.; Celso Omoto, Assoc. Ed. **ISSN:** 0006-8705. **Subscription Rates:** Cr$100 individuals; Cr$25 single issue. **URL:** http://www. iac.sp.gov.br/Bragantia/br-comed.htm.

42965 ■ Cadernos CEDES
Centro de Estudos Educacao e Sociedade, CEDES
Caixa Postal 6022 - Unicamp
13084-971 Campinas, Sao Paulo, Brazil
Publication E-mail: cadcedes@cedes.unicamp.br
Publisher E-mail: revista@cedes.unicamp.br
Journal covering the educational field. **Founded:** 1980. **Freq:** 3-6/yr. **Print Method:** Offset. **Trim Size:** 8 1/2 x 11. **Cols./Page:** 3. **Col. Width:** 12 picas. **Col. Depth:** 21 inches. **Key Personnel:** Valdir Gomes, Editor. **ISSN:** 0101-3262. **Subscription Rates:** Cr$47 individuals natural person; Cr$70 individuals legal entity; Cr$18 single issue. **URL:** http://www.cedes.unicamp.br/cad_ apresentacao.htm.

42966 ■ Cadernos Pagu
Nucleo de Estudos de Genero
Universidade Estadual de Campinas
Caixa Postal 6110
13083-970 Campinas, Sao Paulo, Brazil
Ph: 55 19 35217873
Fax: 55 19 37881704
Publication E-mail: cadpagu@unicamp.br
Journal focusing on the gender studies in Brazil. **Founded:** 1993. **Freq:** Semiannual. **Print Method:** Offset. **Trim Size:** 8 1/4 x 11. **Cols./Page:** 3. **Col. Width:** 27 nonpareils. **Col. Depth:** 140 agate lines. **Key Personnel:** Mariza Correa, Editor; Iara Beleli, Exec. Ed. **ISSN:** 0104-8333. **Subscription Rates:** US$50 individuals Brazil; US$50 individuals international; US$60 institutions Brazil; US$100 institutions international.

URL: http://www.pagu.unicamp.br/?q=node/6.

42967 ■ Ciencia e Tecnologia de Alimentos
Sociedade Brasileira de Ciencia e Tecnologia de Alimentos
Caixa Postal 271
Avenida Brazil, 2880
13001-970 Campinas, Sao Paulo, Brazil
Ph: 55 19 32415793
Fax: 55 19 32410527
Journal covering the field of food science. **Founded:** 1891. **Freq:** Triennial. **Print Method:** Offset. **Cols./ Page:** 6. **Col. Width:** 25 nonpareils. **Col. Depth:** 291 agate lines. **Key Personnel:** Suzana Caetano da Silva Lannes, Ch. Ed.; Marilde Terezinha Bordignon Luiz, Assoc. Ed. **ISSN:** 0101-2061. **Subscription Rates:** Cr$240 individuals; Cr$440 other countries; Cr$55 individuals individual issue; Cr$110 other countries individual issue. **URL:** http://www.scielo.br/revistas/cta/ iaboutj.htm.

42968 ■ Educacao & Sociedade
Centro de Estudos Educacao e Sociedade, CEDES
Caixa Postal 6022 - Unicamp
13084-971 Campinas, Sao Paulo, Brazil
Publisher E-mail: revista@cedes.unicamp.br
Journal covering academic research. **Founded:** 1948. **Freq:** Weekly (Thurs.). **Print Method:** Offset. **Cols./ Page:** 6. **Col. Width:** 2 1/16 inches. **Col. Depth:** 21 1/2 inches. **Key Personnel:** Valder Gomes, Technical Ed. **ISSN:** 0101-7330. **Subscription Rates:** Cr$14,000 individuals; Cr$11,800 individuals natural person; Cr$15,000 individuals legal entity; Cr$3,500 single issue each unit. **URL:** http://www.scielo.br/revistas/es/iaboutj. htm.

42969 ■ Journal of the Brazilian Chemical Society
Sociedade Brasileira de Quimica
Instituto de Quimica - UNICAMP
Caixa Postal 6154
13083-970 Campinas, Sao Paulo, Brazil
Ph: 55 19 37883151
Fax: 55 19 37883151
Journal on chemistry. **Freq:** Bimonthly. **Key Personnel:** Luiz Carlos Dias, Editor; Maria D. Vargas, Editor; Angelo Da Cunha Pinto, Editor; Watson Loh, Editor; Jailson B. De Andrade, Editor; Roberto M. Torresi, Editor. **ISSN:** 0103-5053. **Subscription Rates:** Cr$57 members; US$60 members abroad; Cr$150 nonmembers; US$120 other countries; Cr$150 institutions; US$180 institutions, other countries. **URL:** http://www.scielo.br/ revistas/jbchs/iaboutj.htm.

42970 ■ Kant e-Prints
Brasilian Kant Society, Campinas Section
PO Box 6133
13083-970 Campinas, Sao Paulo, Brazil
Journal of the Centre for Logic, Epistemology and the History of Science. **Key Personnel:** Zeljko Loparic, Editor, loparicz@uol.com.br. **ISSN:** 1677-1621. **URL:** http:// www.cle.unicamp.br/kant-e-prints/.

42971 ■ Opiniao Publica
University of Campinas
Center for Studies on Public Opinion
Caixa Postal 6110
13081-970 Campinas, Sao Paulo, Brazil
Ph: 55 193 5217093
Fax: 55 193 2894309
Publisher E-mail: cesop@unicamp.br
Journal covering theory and methodology in the fields of public opinion, political and social behavior, and media studies. Also includes national and international survey data on these research fields. **Founded:** 1993. **Freq:** Biennial. **Print Method:** Offset. **Trim Size:** 12 5/8 x 22. **Cols./Page:** 6. **Col. Width:** 12 picas. **Col. Depth:** 294 agate lines. **Key Personnel:** Amaury De Souza, Editor; Antonio Lavareda, Editor; Rachel Meneguello, Editor. **ISSN:** 0104-6276. **Subscription Rates:** US$8 individuals first issue in the nation; US$5 individuals second issue in the nation; US$15 other countries. **URL:** http:// www.unicamp.br/cesop/revista.htm.

Campo Grande

42972 ■ Cidade-FM - 97.9
Rua Itajai, 433
Bairro Antonio Vendas
79041-270 Campo Grande, Sao Paulo, Brazil

Ph: 67 33413030
Fax: 67 33492481
Format: Urban Contemporary; Adult Contemporary; Top 40; Ethnic. **Operating Hours:** Continuous. **Ad Rates:** Advertising accepted; rates available upon request. **URL:** http://www.cidade97.com.br.

Campo Verde

42973 ■ Cidade Bela-FM - 90.5
Av. Porto Alegre, 477
78840-000 Campo Verde, Mato Grosso do Sul, Brazil
Ph: 55 66 34193132
Format: Eclectic; Information; News. **Ad Rates:** Advertising accepted; rates available upon request. **URL:** http://www.cidadebela.fm.br.

Campos dos Goytacazes

42974 ■ Biosystems Engineering
Elsevier Science Inc.
Centro de Ciencias e Tecnologias Agropecuarias
Universidade Estadual do Norte Fluminense
Campos dos Goytacazes, Rio de Janeiro, Brazil
Publisher E-mail: usinfo-ehelp@elsevier.com
Journal covering physical sciences and engineering, developments in agriculture, food, land use and the environment. **Founded:** 1983. **Freq:** Monthly. **Print Method:** Offset. **Trim Size:** 7 x 10. **Cols./Page:** 1. **Col. Width:** 63 nonpareils. **Col. Depth:** 116 agate lines. **Key Personnel:** Prof. K. Araya, Editorial Board; Dr. P.A. Berbert, Editorial Board; Prof. W. Day, Editor-in-Chief, bill.day@silsoeresearch.org.uk; Prof. J. De Baerdemaeker, Editorial Board; Prof. E. Gasparetto, Editorial Board; Prof. R.J. Godwin, Editorial Board; Prof. J.C. Jofriet, Editorial Board; Dr. H.D. Kutzbach, Editorial Board; Dr. B.L. Maheshwari, Editorial Board; Dr. C.S. Parkin, Managing Editor. **ISSN:** 1537-5110. **Subscription Rates:** EUR1,503 institutions for European countries and Iran; 162,600¥ institutions; US$1,337 institutions, other countries except Europe, Japan and Iran. **URL:** http:// www.elsevier.com/wps/find/journaldescription.cws_ home/622795/descriptiondescription.

Carlos Barbosa

42975 ■ Estacao-FM - 89.5
Rua Humberto Acorsi, 203
Bairro Aurora
95185-000 Carlos Barbosa, Rio Grande do Sul, Brazil
Ph: 55 54 34619700
Format: Ethnic; World Beat. **Operating Hours:** Continuous. **Ad Rates:** Advertising accepted; rates available upon request. **URL:** http://www.estacaofm. com.br.

Curitiba

42976 ■ Brazilian Archives of Biology and Technology (BABT)
Tecpar
Prof. R. Algacyr Munhoz Mader, 3775 - CIC
81350-010 Curitiba, Paraiba, Brazil
Ph: 55 41 33163052
Fax: 55 41 33462872
Publication E-mail: babt@tecpar.br
Journal dealing with all aspects of biology and technology. **Freq:** Bimonthly. **Key Personnel:** Dr. Carlos Ricardo Soccol, Editor. **ISSN:** 1516-8913. **Subscription Rates:** Cr$480 individuals; US$350 other countries postage included. **URL:** http://www.scielo.br/scielo.php? script=sci_serial&pid=1516-8913&lng=en&nrm=.

42977 ■ Electronic Musicological Review
Universidade Federal do Parana
Rua XV de Novembro 1299
80060-000 Curitiba, Paraiba, Brazil
Ph: 55 413 3605002
Fax: 55 413 2642243
Publisher E-mail: gabinetereitor@ufpr.br
Peer-reviewed journal covering Brazilian music, music technology, and critical musicology. **Founded:** 1984. **Freq:** Annual. **Print Method:** Offset. **Trim Size:** 8 1/4 x 11. **Cols./Page:** 2. **Col. Width:** 38 nonpareils. **Col. Depth:** 123 agate lines. **Key Personnel:** Daniel Quaranta, Editor, danielquaranta@gmail.com; Mauricio Dottori, Editor, m.dottori@onda.com.br; Carlos Palombini, Editor, palombini@zaz.com.br. **ISSN:** 1415-9538. **URL:** http://www.rem.ufpr.br/index.html.

Feira de Santana

42978 ▪ Princesa-FM - 96.9
Rua frei Hermenegildo, 300
Capuchinhos
44100-000 Feira de Santana, Bahia, Brazil
Ph: 55 75 21019700
E-mail: princesafm@princesafm.com.br
Format: Ethnic; Contemporary Hit Radio (CHR). **Operating Hours:** Continuous. **Ad Rates:** Advertising accepted; rates available upon request. **URL:** http://www.princesafm.com.br.

Fortaleza

42979 ▪ Atlantico Sul-FM - 105.7
Av. Pontes Vieira
60130-241 Fortaleza, Ceara, Brazil
Ph: 55 85 30895269
Format: Jazz; Blues. **Operating Hours:** Continuous. **Key Personnel:** Douglas Santos, Contact, douglas@deradio.com.br; Delio Pinheiro, Exec.Dir., contatoatlanticosul@deradio.com.br. **Ad Rates:** Advertising accepted; rates available upon request. **URL:** http://www.atlanticosulfm.com.br.

42980 ▪ Calypso-FM - 106.7
Av. Almirante Tamandare, 19
Fortaleza, Ceara, Brazil
Ph: 55 85 30664000
Format: Ethnic; World Beat. **Operating Hours:** Continuous. **URL:** http://www.calypsofm.com.br.

Ilheus

42981 ▪ Gabriela-FM - 102.9
Alto da Boa Vista, 500
Ilheus, Bahia, Brazil
Ph: 55 73 36752000
Format: Reggae; Alternative/New Music/Progressive; Classic Rock; World Beat. **Operating Hours:** Continuous. **Ad Rates:** Advertising accepted; rates available upon request. **URL:** http://www.gabrielafm.com.br.

Itabuna

42982 ▪ Morena-FM - 98.7
Av. Buerarema, 819
Itabuna, Bahia, Brazil
Ph: 55 73 36131011
Fax: 55 73 36139807
Format: Classical; Jazz; Blues. **Ad Rates:** Advertising accepted; rates available upon request. **URL:** http://www.morenafm.com.

Jatai

42983 ▪ Radio Difusora de Jatai-AM - 680
Rua Jose de Carvalho Bastos, 542
Setor Centro
75800-047 Jatai, Goias, Brazil
Ph: 55 64 36311245
E-mail: contato@difusoraonline.com.br
Format: Ethnic; World Beat. **Operating Hours:** 19 hours Daily. **URL:** http://www.difusoraonline.com.br.

Jundiai

42984 ▪ Dumont-FM - 104.3
Anchieta, N 573 11 andar Centro
13201-840 Jundiai, Sao Paulo, Brazil
Ph: 55 11 45215000
Format: Ethnic; World Beat. **Owner:** Dumont FM, at above address. **URL:** http://www.dumontfm.com.br.

Limeira

42985 ▪ Estereosom-FM - 99.9
Rua Profa. Maria Ap. Martinelli Faveri, 988
Jd. Elisa Fumagalli
Limeira, Sao Paulo, Brazil
Ph: 55 19 34468585
Format: Album-Oriented Rock (AOR); Ethnic; World Beat. **Founded:** May 1979. **Ad Rates:** Advertising accepted; rates available upon request. **URL:** http://estereosom.locaweb.com.br/2006/home.aspx.

Maceio

42986 ▪ Radio-FM - 96
Mirante D. Katia Assuncao
Maceio, Alagoas, Brazil
Ph: 55 82 33113499
Format: Ethnic. **Operating Hours:** Continuous. **Ad Rates:** Advertising accepted; rates available upon request. **URL:** http://www.radio96.com.br.

Manaus

42987 ▪ Acta Amazonica
Instituto Nacional de Pesquisas da Amazonia
Av. Andre Araujo, 2936 Aleixo
69060-001 Manaus, Amazonas, Brazil
Ph: 55 92 36433377
Journal publishing original scientific contributions on Amazonia. **Key Personnel:** Ricardo A. Marenco, Editor-in-Chief. **ISSN:** 0044-5967. **Subscription Rates:** US$100 institutions; US$75 individuals. **URL:** http://www.scielo.br/revistas/aa/iaboutj.htm.

Nova Prata

42988 ▪ Caroados-FM - 103.3
Av. Placidina de Araujo, 620
95320-000 Nova Prata, Rio Grande do Sul, Brazil
Ph: 55 54 32421644
Fax: 55 54 32421644
E-mail: radio@coroadosfm.com.br
Format: Ethnic; Information; World Beat. **URL:** http://www.coroadosfm.com.br.

Pelotas

42989 ▪ Brazilian Journal of Plant Physiology
Sociedade Brasileira de Fisiologia Vegetal
Departamento de Botanica
Universidade Federal de Pelotas
96010-900 Pelotas, Rio Grande do Sul, Brazil
Ph: 55 53 32757336
Fax: 55 53 32757169
Journal publishing original research contributions related to plant physiology. **Key Personnel:** Arnoldo R. Facanha, Editor-in-Chief, arnoldo@astuenf.br. **ISSN:** 1677-0420. **Subscription Rates:** Cr$150 individuals for professionals; US$100 other countries; Cr$112.50 individuals for students. **URL:** http://www.scielo.br/scielo.php?script=sci_serial&pid=1677-0420&lng=en&nrm=.

Petropolis

42990 ▪ Computational & Applied Mathematics
Brazilian Society of Applied and Computational Mathematics
Av. Getulio Vargas 333 Quitandinha
25651-070 Petropolis, Rio de Janeiro, Brazil
Ph: 55 242 336125
Fax: 55 242 315595
Publisher E-mail: sbmac@sbmac.org.br
Journal covering research in applied computational mathematics, with interfaces in physics, engineering, chemistry, biology, operations research, statistics, social sciences and economy. **Founded:** 1958. **Freq:** Weekly (Wed.). **Print Method:** Offset. **Cols./Page:** 6. **Col. Width:** 12 nonpareils. **Col. Depth:** 290 agate lines. **Key Personnel:** Alagacone Sri Ranga, Assoc. Ed.; Domingo A. Tarzia, Editor; A. Nachbin, Editor; Felipe Ferez Pereira, Editor; Jose Mario Martinez, Editor. **ISSN:** 0101-8205. **URL:** http://www.sbmac.org.br/publi_comp.php.

Porto Alegre

42991 ▪ Journal of the Brazilian Computer Society
Sociedade Brasileira de Computacao
Av. Bento Goncalves 9500, B. Agronomia
Caixa Postal 15064
91501-970 Porto Alegre, Rio Grande do Sul, Brazil
Ph: 55 51 3166835
Fax: 55 51 3166835
Journal publishing research papers relating to all aspects of computer science. **Freq:** Quarterly. **Key Personnel:** Maria Cristina Ferreira De Oliveira, Editor-in-Chief; Tiziana Margaria, Editorial Board; Valmir C. Barbosa, Editorial Board; Mike Hinchey, Editorial Board. **ISSN:** 0104-6500. **URL:** http://www.scielo.br/scielo.php?script=sci_serial&pid=0104-6500&lng=en&nrm=.

42992 ▪ Psicologia
Psychology Graduate Course
2600 Sala 110
90035-003 Porto Alegre, Rio Grande do Sul, Brazil
Publisher E-mail: instpsico@ufrgs.br
Journal covering various aspects of psychology. **Founded:** 1933. **Freq:** 2/yr. **Print Method:** Offset. **Trim Size:** 8 1/2 x 11. **Cols./Page:** 3. **Col. Width:** 13.5 picas. **Col. Depth:** 61 picas. **Key Personnel:** Salvador Algarabel, Editor, algarabe@uv.es. **ISSN:** 0211-2159. **Subscription Rates:** EUR36 institutions; US$36 institutions. **URL:** http://www.uv.es/revispsi/.

42993 ▪ Psicologia & Sociedade
The Brazilian Association of Social Psychology
R. Ramiro Barcelos 2600 Sala 13
90035-030 Porto Alegre, Rio Grande do Sul, Brazil
Ph: 55 513 3165149
Publisher E-mail: clecimar@orion.ufrgs.br
Journal covering the theory at the interface of psychology and society. **Founded:** 1986. **Freq:** Biennial. **Print Method:** Offset. **Cols./Page:** 6. **Col. Width:** 26 nonpareils. **Col. Depth:** 294 agate lines. **Key Personnel:** Katia Maheirie, Editor; Pedrinho Guareschi, Advisory Ed.; Cleci Maraschin, Advisory Ed.; Diana Carvalho de Carvalho, Co-Ed.; Andrea V. Zanella, Co-Ed. **ISSN:** 0102-7182. **URL:** http://abrapso.org.br/siteprincipal/index.php?option=com_content&task=section&id=6&Itemid=30; http://www.scielo.br/scielo.php?script=sci_serial&pid=0102-7182&lng=en&nrm=iso. **Circ:** 1,000

Recife

42994 ▪ The Brazilian Electronic Journal of Economics (BEJE)
Universidade Federal de Pernambuco
Department of Economics
Av Prof. Moraes Rego, 1235
Recife, Pernambuco, Brazil
Journal publishing original research on economic problems. **Key Personnel:** Jose Ricardo Nogueira, Editor-in-Chief; Jose Carlos Cavalcanti, Editor-in-Chief. **ISSN:** 1516-4373. **URL:** http://www.decon.ufpe.br/econ-net/econ-net.htm.

Ribeirao Preto

42995 ▪ Brazilian Dental Journal
Dental Foundation of Ribeirao Preto
Campus Universitario - Bairro Monte Alegre
14040-010 Ribeirao Preto, Sao Paulo, Brazil
Ph: 55 16 6023952
Fax: 55 16 6023953
Publisher E-mail: forp@edu.usp.br
Journal dealing with the Brazilian Odontology research. **Key Personnel:** Jesus Djalma Pecora, Editor; Paulo Cesar Saquy, Editor; Manoel Damiao De Sousa Neto, Editor. **ISSN:** 0103-6440. **URL:** http://www.forp.usp.br/bdj/.

42996 ▪ Brazilian Journal of Medical and Biological Research
Av. Bandeirantes, 3900
14049-900 Ribeirao Preto, Sao Paulo, Brazil
Ph: 55 163 6333825
Fax: 55 163 6333825
Journal dealing with the medical and biological research. **Freq:** Monthly. **Key Personnel:** Joao Batista Calixto, Editor; Celia Carlini, Section Ed.; Luiz Juliano Neto, Section Ed.; Lewis Joel Greene, Editor; Jose Antunes Rodrigues, Editor. **ISSN:** 0100-879X **Subscription Rates:** Cr$170 members; Cr$200 nonmembers; Cr$335 institutions; US$120 other countries customer price; US$96 other countries agency price. **URL:** http://www.scielo.br/scielo.php?pid=0100-879X&script=sci_serial.

42997 ▪ Economia Aplicada
Universidade de Sao Paulo
Administracao e Contabilidade de Ribeirao Preto
Faculdade de Economia
Avenida dos Bandeirantes, 3900
14040-900 Ribeirao Preto, Sao Paulo, Brazil
Ph: 55 163 6024746
Fax: 55 163 6023884
Journal focusing on economic analysis. **Founded:** 1978. **Freq:** Monthly. **Print Method:** Offset. **Cols./Page:** 4. **Col. Width:** 30 nonpareils. **Col. Depth:** 193 agate lines. **Key Personnel:** Walter Belluzzo, Jr., Editor. **ISSN:**

1413-8050. URL: http://www.usp.br/revecap/.

42998 ■ Genetics and Molecular Biology
Sociedade Brasileira de Genetica
Rua Cap. Adelmio Norberto da Silva, 736
Alto da Boa Vista
14025-670 Ribeirao Preto, Sao Paulo, Brazil
Ph: 55 16 36218540
Fax: 55 16 33696164
Journal publishing research in genetics, evolution and related scientific disciplines. **Freq:** Quarterly. **Key Personnel:** Antonio Brito Da Cunha, Sen. Ed.; Angela M. Vianna-Morgante, Editor. **ISSN:** 1415-4757. **Subscription Rates:** Cr$500 institutions Brazil and other South American (air mail); US$216 individuals Brazil and other South American (air mail); US$300 institutions, other countries air mail; US$100 other countries air mail. **URL:** http://www.scielo.br/scielo.php?script=sci_serial&pid=1415-4757&lng=en&nrm=.

42999 ■ Genetics and Molecular Research
Fundacao de Pesquisas Cientificas de Ribeirao Preto
Av. Presidente Vargas, 2627
2 andar - Itamarati
14020-260 Ribeirao Preto, Sao Paulo, Brazil
Ph: 55 16 6201251
Fax: 55 16 6211991
Publication E-mail: gmr@funpecrp.com.br
Publisher E-mail: funpecrp@uol.com.br
Online journal publishing original, outstanding research papers in the areas of genetics, molecular biology and evolution. **Key Personnel:** Dr. Francisco A. Moura Duarte, Editor; Pedro Henrique Saldanha, Hon. Ed. **ISSN:** 1676-5680. **URL:** http://www.funpecrp.com.br/gmr2008b/index.asp.

Rio de Janeiro

43000 ■ Alea
Programa de Pos-Graduacao em Letras Neolatinas
Faculdade de Letras -UFRJ
Av. Brigadeiro Trompovsky s/n
Ilha do Fundao
Rio de Janeiro, Rio de Janeiro, Brazil
Ph: 55 2598 9798
Publisher E-mail: pgneolatinas@letras.ufrj.br
Journal providing a forum for research exchange between the Graduate Program in Romance Languages and the other Brazilian graduate programs. **Subtitle:** Estudos Neolatinos. **Key Personnel:** Edson Rosa da Silva, Editor; Marcelo Jacques de Moraes, Editor. **ISSN:** 1517-106X. **URL:** http://www.scielo.br/revistas/alea/iinstruc.htm.

43001 ■ ALEA
Instituto Nacional de Matematica Pura e Aplicada
Estrada Dona Castorina 110
22460-320 Rio de Janeiro, Rio de Janeiro, Brazil
Ph: 55 212 5295000
Fax: 55 212 5124115
Journal covering research in probability theory, stochastic processes, mathematical statistics, and their applications. **Subtitle:** Latin American Journal of Probability and Mathematical Statistics. **Founded:** 1983. **Freq:** Bimonthly. **Print Method:** Offset. **Trim Size:** 10 7/8 x 14. **Cols./Page:** 3. **Col. Width:** 12 picas. **Col. Depth:** 72 picas. **Key Personnel:** Claudio Landim, Editor; Gerard Ben Arous, Assoc. Ed.; Jean Bertoin, Assoc. Ed.; Erwin Bolthausen, Assoc. Ed.; David Brillinger, Assoc. Ed.; Pierre Collet, Assoc. Ed. **ISSN:** 1980-0436. **URL:** http://alea.impa.br/english/index.htm?language=engl.

43002 ■ ALEA
Instituto Nacional de Matematica Pura e Aplicada
Estrada Dona Castorina 110
22460-320 Rio de Janeiro, Rio de Janeiro, Brazil
Ph: 55 212 5295000
Fax: 55 212 5124115
Journal covering research in probability theory, stochastic processes, mathematical statistics, and their applications. **Subtitle:** Latin American Journal of Probability and Mathematical Statistics. **Founded:** 1983. **Freq:** Bimonthly. **Print Method:** Offset. **Trim Size:** 10 7/8 x 14. **Cols./Page:** 3. **Col. Width:** 12 picas. **Col. Depth:** 72 picas. **Key Personnel:** Claudio Landim, Editor; Gerard Ben Arous, Assoc. Ed.; Jean Bertoin, Assoc. Ed.; Erwin Bolthausen, Assoc. Ed.; David Brillinger, Assoc. Ed.; Pierre Collet, Assoc. Ed. **ISSN:** 1980-0436. **URL:** http://alea.impa.br/english/index_v7.htm.

43003 ■ Anais da Academia Brasileira de Ciencias
Academia Brasileira de Ciencias
R. Anfilofio de Carvalho, 29, 3, Rio de
20030-060 Rio de Janeiro, Rio de Janeiro, Brazil
Ph: 55 213 9078100
Fax: 55 213 9078101
Journal covering research findings in various sciences. **Founded:** 1929. **Freq:** Quarterly. **Print Method:** Offset. **Cols./Page:** 6. **Col. Width:** 26 nonpareils. **Col. Depth:** 301 agate lines. **Key Personnel:** Alexander W. A. Kellner, Editor-in-Chief. **ISSN:** 0001-3765. **Subscription Rates:** Cr$25 individuals; US$25 other countries. **URL:** http://www.scielo.br/revistas/aabc/iaboutj.htm.

43004 ■ Engenharia Sanitaria e Ambiental
Brazilian Association of Sanitary and Environmental Engineering
Av. Beira Mar, 216 - 13 Andar - Castelo
Rio de Janeiro, Rio de Janeiro, Brazil
Ph: 55 212 2103221
Fax: 55 212 2626838
Publisher E-mail: esa@abes-dn.org.br
Journal publishing original technical and scientific contributions in the field of sanitation and environment engineering as well as their interfaces. **Key Personnel:** Bela Petry, Editor; Prof. Adalberto Noyola, Editor; Jorge Arbodela Valencia, Editor. **ISSN:** 1413-4152. **URL:** http://www.scielo.br/scielo.php?script=sci_serial&pid=1413-4152&lng=en&nrm=.

43005 ■ Historia, Ciencias, Saude-Manguinhos
Fundacao Oswaldo Cruz
Av. Brasil, 4365
Manguinhos
21040-360 Rio de Janeiro, Rio de Janeiro, Brazil
Ph: 55 212 5984242
Journal dedicated to history, science and health. **Founded:** 1932. **Freq:** Quarterly. **Print Method:** Offset. **Trim Size:** 6 x 9. **Cols./Page:** 1. **Col. Width:** 52 nonpareils. **Col. Depth:** 100 agate lines. **Key Personnel:** Jaime L. Benchimol, Editor; Roberta Cardoso Cerqueira, Exec. Ed. **ISSN:** 0104-5970. **Subscription Rates:** US$70 individuals Brazil; US$100 institutions Brazil. **URL:** http://www.coc.fiocruz.br/hscience/english.htm.

43006 ■ Informativo FBCN
Brazilian Foundation for the Conservation of Nature
Fundacao Brasileira para a Conservacao da Natureza
103, Miranda Valverde St.
Botafogo
22281-020 Rio de Janeiro, Rio de Janeiro, Brazil
Ph: 55 212 5377565
Fax: 55 212 5371343
Publisher E-mail: fbcn@fbcn.org.com
Portuguese language publication covering conservation. **Freq:** Bimonthly. **Key Personnel:** Jairo Costa, President. **Subscription Rates:** Free. **Remarks:** Advertising accepted; rates available upon request. **URL:** http://www.fbcn.org.br/. **Circ:** (Not Reported)

43007 ■ International Journal of High Performance System Architecture
Inderscience Publishers
c/o Dr. Nadia Nedjah, Ed.-in-Ch.
State University of Rio de Janeiro
Rua Sao Francisco Xavier, 524
5022-D Maracana
20550-900 Rio de Janeiro, Rio de Janeiro, Brazil
Publisher E-mail: editor@inderscience.com
Peer-reviewed journal covering designs & implementation of high performance architecture. **Founded:** 2007. **Freq:** 4/yr. **Key Personnel:** Dr. Nadia Nedjah, Editor-in-Chief, nadia@eng.uerj.br. **ISSN:** 1751-6528. **Subscription Rates:** EUR494 individuals includes surface mail, print only; EUR672 individuals print and online. **URL:** http://www.inderscience.com/browse/index.php?journalCODE=ijhpsa.

43008 ■ International Journal of Innovative Computing and Applications
Inderscience Publishers
c/o Dr. Nadia Nedjah, Ed.-in-Ch.
State University of Rio de Janeiro
Rua Sao Francisco Xavier, 524
5022-D Maracana
20550-900 Rio de Janeiro, Rio de Janeiro, Brazil
Publisher E-mail: editor@inderscience.com
Peer-reviewed journal covering all new computing paradigms. **Founded:** 2007. **Freq:** 4/yr. **Key Person-**
nel: Dr. Nadia Nedjah, Editor-in-Chief, nadia@eng.uerj.br. **ISSN:** 1751-648X. **Subscription Rates:** EUR494 individuals includes surface mail, print only; EUR672 individuals print and online. **URL:** http://www.inderscience.com/browse/index.php?journalCODE=ijica.

43009 ■ International Journal of Technological Learning, Innovation & Development
Inderscience Publishers
c/o Prof. Paulo N. Figueiredo, Ed.-in-Ch.
Praia de Botafogo 190, 5th Fl., Rm. 510
22250-900 Rio de Janeiro, Rio de Janeiro, Brazil
Publisher E-mail: editor@inderscience.com
Peer-reviewed journal covering issues related to technological learning, innovation, and development. **Founded:** 2007. **Freq:** 4/yr. **Key Personnel:** Paulo N. Figueiredo, Editor-in-Chief, pnf@fgv.br; John Adeoti, Regional Ed.; Norlela Ariffin, Regional Ed. **ISSN:** 1753-1942. **Subscription Rates:** EUR494 individuals includes surface mail, print only; EUR672 individuals print and online. **URL:** http://www.inderscience.com/browse/index.php?journalCODE=ijtlid.

43010 ■ Journal of the Brazilian Society of Mechanical Sciences
ABCM
Av. Rio Branco, 124/14 Andar-Centro
20040-001 Rio de Janeiro, Rio de Janeiro, Brazil
Ph: 55 21 22210438
Fax: 55 21 25097128
Publisher E-mail: abcm@abcm.org.br
Journal on Mechanical Sciences. **Founded:** 1979. **Freq:** Quarterly. **Key Personnel:** Atila P. Silva Freire, Editor-in-Chief, atila@serv.com.ufrj.br. **ISSN:** 0100-7386. **Subscription Rates:** US$320 institutions print version; US$120 individuals print version. **URL:** http://www.scielo.br/revistas/jbsms/iaboutj.htm; http://www.abcm.org.br/.

43011 ■ Mana - Estudos de Antropologia Social
PPGAS-Museu Nacional
Graduate Program in Social Anthropology
Quinta da Boa Vista S/N - Sao Cristovao
20940-040 Rio de Janeiro, Rio de Janeiro, Brazil
Ph: 55 212 5689642
Fax: 55 212 2546695
Publisher E-mail: ppgas@alternex.com.br
Journal covering anthropology and the understanding of social and cultural reality. **Subtitle:** Studies in Social Anthropology. **Founded:** 1962. **Freq:** Semiannual. **Print Method:** Offset. **Trim Size:** 7 x 10. **Cols./Page:** 2. **Col. Width:** 21 nonpareils. **Col. Depth:** 130 agate lines. **Key Personnel:** Lygia Sigaud, Editor; Joao Pacheco de Oliveira Filho, Editor; Giralda Seyferth, Editor. **ISSN:** 0104-9313. **URL:** http://www.scielo.br/revistas/mana/iaboutj.htm; http://www.ppgasmuseu.etc.br/museu/pages/english.htmJOURNAL.

43012 ■ Memorias do Instituto Oswaldo Cruz
Instituto Oswaldo Cruz
Av. Brasil, 4365
21040-360 Rio de Janeiro, Rio de Janeiro, Brazil
Ph: 55 212 5984242
Journal covering research in the fields of parasitology, microbiology, tropical medicine as well as basic studies in immunology molecular and cell biology related to these fields. **Founded:** 1909. **Freq:** Weekly (Wed.). **Print Method:** Offset. **Cols./Page:** 6. **Col. Width:** 24 nonpareils. **Col. Depth:** 21 1/2 inches. **Key Personnel:** Dr. Ricardo Lourenco de Oliveira, Editor; Claude Pirmez, Assoc. Ed.; Claudio J. Struchiner, Editorial Board; Eloi S. Garcia, Editorial Board. **ISSN:** 0074-0276. **Subscription Rates:** US$200 institutions Brazil; US$100 individuals Brazil; US$100 institutions South America; US$50 individuals South America; US$200 institutions U.S. and Canada; US$100 individuals U.S. and Canada; US$200 institutions U.S. and Canada. **URL:** http://www.scielo.br/scielo.php?pid=0074-0276&script=sci_serial.

43013 ■ Pesquisa Veterinaria Brasileira
The Colegio Brasileiro de Patologia Animal
Embrapa-CNPAB/PSA
Km 47-Seropedica
23851-970 Rio de Janeiro, Rio de Janeiro, Brazil
Ph: 55 212 6822940
Fax: 55 212 6821081
Publisher E-mail: colegio@cbpa.org.br
Journal covering information on research in animal health. **Founded:** 1966. **Freq:** Quarterly. **Print Method:** Offset. **Trim Size:** 6 x 9. **Cols./Page:** 1. **Col. Width:** 4 1/2 inches. **Col. Depth:** 7 inches. **Key Personnel:** Clau-

dio Severo Lombardo De Barros, Assoc. Ed.; Jurgen Dobereiner, Editor; Terezinha N. Padilha Charles, Assoc. Ed.; Franklin Riet-Correa, Assoc. Ed.; Paulo Michel Roehe, Assoc. Ed.; E.H. Birgel, Advisory Board. **ISSN:** 0100-736X. **Subscription Rates:** US$16 individuals; US$32 institutions. **URL:** http://www.scielo.br/revistas/pvb/iaboutj.htm.

Salvador

43014 ■ Brazilian Journal of Infectious Diseases
The Brazilian Journal of Infectious Diseases and Contexto Publishing
Rua Alfredo Magalhaes, 04/Barra
40140-140 Salvador, Bahia, Brazil
Ph: 55 71 2642971
Fax: 55 71 2643326
Publication E-mail: bjid@bjid.com.br
Journal dealing with all aspects of infectious diseases. **Freq:** Bimonthly. **Key Personnel:** Roberto Focaccia, Assoc. Ed.; Antonio C. Pignatari, Assoc. Ed.; Helio Sader, Assoc. Ed.; Carlos Brites Alves, Assoc. Ed.; Anastacio Q. Sousa, Editor-in-Chief; Roberto Badaro, Assoc. Ed.; Andre Villela Lomar, Assoc. Ed. **ISSN:** 1413-8670. **Subscription Rates:** US$100 institutions domestic; US$120 institutions, other countries; US$60 individuals domestic; US$80 other countries; US$35 individuals domestic (special); US$55 other countries special. **URL:** http://www.scielo.br/scielo.php?script=sci_serial&pid=1413-8670&lng=en&nrm=iso.

San Antonio de Jesus

43015 ■ Andaia-FM - 104.3
Rua Tiradentes, 30
Edificio Sao Francisco, Centro 4 e 5 Andares
44570-000 San Antonio de Jesus, Bahia, Brazil
Ph: 55 75 36312924
Fax: 55 75 36312677
Format: Information; News; Ethnic; World Beat; Album-Oriented Rock (AOR). **Operating Hours:** Continuous. **Ad Rates:** Advertising accepted; rates available upon request. **URL:** http://www.andaiafm.com.br.

Santa Maria

43016 ■ Ciencia Rural
Universidade Federal de Santa Maria
Avenida Roraima No. 1000
Cidade Universitaria
Bairro Camobi
97105-900 Santa Maria, Rio Grande do Sul, Brazil
Journal devoted to the study of Agronomy, Animal Science, Veterinary Medicine, and Forestry Science. **Freq:** Bimonthly. **Key Personnel:** Rudi Weiblen, President; Carlos Alberto Ceretta, Editorial Comission; Alceu Gaspar Raiser, Editorial Comission; Ivo Wentz, Area Commitee; Adriano Brandelli, Area Commitee; Alberto Back, Area Commitee; Franklin Riet Correa, Area Commitee. **ISSN:** 0103-8478. **Subscription Rates:** US$120 other countries. **URL:** http://www.scielo.br/scielo.php?script=sci_serial&pid=0103-8478&lng=en&nrm=iso.

Sao Carlos

43017 ■ Gestao & Producao
Universidade Federal de Sao Carlos
Departamento de Engenharia de Producao
Caixa Postal 676
13565-905 Sao Carlos, Sao Paulo, Brazil
Publisher E-mail: gp@dep.ufscar.br
Journal covering research in the industrial engineering and operations management fields. **Founded:** 1890. **Freq:** April, August, and December. **Print Method:** Offset. **Trim Size:** 8 1/4 x 10 7/8. **Cols./Page:** 2. **Col. Width:** 34 nonpareils. **Col. Depth:** 126 agate lines. **Key Personnel:** Joao Amato Neto, Consulting Board; Alessandra Rachid, Consulting Board; Joao Vitor Moccellin, Consulting Board. **ISSN:** 1806-9649. **URL:** http://www.dep.ufscar.br

43018 ■ Journal of Microwaves, Optoelectronics and Electromagnetic Applications
Sociedade Brasileira de Microondas e Optoeletronica - SBMO
Campus do Instituto Maua de Tecnologia - IMT
c/o Murilo Araujo Romero, Ed.

Universidade de Sao Paulo, Escola de Engenharia de Sao Carlo
Dept. de Engenharia Eletrica
Avenida Trabalhador Sao-carlense, 400
13566-590 Sao Carlos, Sao Paulo, Brazil
Publisher E-mail: sbmo@maua.br
Journal covering latest research in the fields of Microwaves, Optoelectronics, Photonics, and Electromagnetics. **Freq:** Semiannual. **Key Personnel:** Renato Cardoso Mesquita, Editor. **ISSN:** 1516-7399. **URL:** http://www.sel.eesc.usp.br/jmo/. **Also known as:** JMO. **Formerly:** The Journal of Microwaves and Optoelectronics.

Sao Paulo

43019 ■ ABM Metalurgia e Materials
Brazilian Metallurgy and Materials Association
Associacao Brasileira de Metalurgia e Materials
Rua Antonio Comparato 218
04605-030 Sao Paulo, Sao Paulo, Brazil
Ph: 55 11 55344333
Fax: 55 11 55344330
Publication E-mail: revista@abmbrasil.com.br
Publisher E-mail: abm@abmbrasil.com.br
Portuguese and English language publication covering metallurgy. **Founded:** 1944. **Freq:** Monthly. **ISSN:** 0104-0898. **Remarks:** Accepts advertising. **URL:** http://www.abmbrasil.com.br. **Circ:** (Not Reported)

43020 ■ Acta Botanica Brasilica
Sociedade Botanica do Brasil
Caixa Postal 4005
Sao Paulo, Sao Paulo, Brazil
Ph: 55 51 33086955
Fax: 55 51 33086955
Publisher E-mail: sbb@botanica.org.br
Journal covering fundamental and applied aspects of botany. **Freq:** Quarterly. **Key Personnel:** Francisco de Assis Ribeiro dos Santos, Editor-in-Chief. **ISSN:** 0102-3306. **Subscription Rates:** Cr$160 individuals; US$70 individuals Latin America; US$80 other countries; Cr$80 students; US$35 students Latin America; US$40 students, other countries; Cr$480 institutions; US$175 institutions Latin America; US$180 institutions, other countries; Cr$105 institutions doubtful issue. **URL:** http://www.scielo.br/scielo.php?pid=0102-3306&script=sci_serial.

43021 ■ Acta Cirurgica Brasileira
Sociedade Brasileira para o Desenvolvimento da Pesquisa em Cirurgia
Al. Rio Claro, 179, 14
01332-010 Sao Paulo, Sao Paulo, Brazil
Ph: 55 113 2878814
Fax: 55 113 2878814
Publisher E-mail: sgolden@terra.com.br
Journal covering surgery and biomedical sciences. **Founded:** 1958. **Freq:** Bimonthly. **Print Method:** Offset. **Trim Size:** 8 1/4 x11. **Cols./Page:** 3. **Col. Width:** 2 1/4 inches. **Col. Depth:** 8 1/2 inches. **Key Personnel:** Alberto Schanaider, Assoc. Ed.; Lydia Masako Ferreira, Assoc. Ed.; Edna Frasson de Souza Montero, Assoc. Ed. **ISSN:** 0102-8650. **Subscription Rates:** Cr$150 individuals; Cr$75 students. **URL:** http://www.scielo.br/scielo.php?script=sci_serial&pid=0102-8650&lng=en&nrm=iso.

43022 ■ Arquivos Brasileiros de Endocrinologia & Metabologia
Brazilian Federation of Endocrinology and Metabolism Societies
Rua Botucatu, 572
Conjunto 83
04023-062 Sao Paulo, Sao Paulo, Brazil
Ph: 55 115 753011
Fax: 55 115 5499089
Journal covering endocrinology, metabolism and related sciences. **Founded:** 1947. **Freq:** Weekly (Thurs.). **Print Method:** Offset. **Cols./Page:** 6. **Col. Width:** 26 nonpareils. **Col. Depth:** 301 agate lines. **Key Personnel:** Amanda Athayde, Editor; Alfredo Halpern, Editor; Bernardo Liberman, Editor; Durval Damiani, Editor; Doris Rosenthal, Editor. **ISSN:** 0004-2730. **Subscription Rates:** Cr$90 individuals; Cr$150 individuals 2 years. **URL:** http://www.endocrino.org.br/abem/.

43023 ■ Arquivos Brasileiros de Oftalmologia
Conselho Brasileiro de Oftalmologia

Alameda Santos
1343 - 11 Andar CJ. 1110
01419-001 Sao Paulo, Sao Paulo, Brazil
Ph: 55 113 2664000
Fax: 55 113 1710953
Publication E-mail: abo@cbo.com.br
Publisher E-mail: oftalmo@cbo.com.br
Journal covering ophthalmology. **Founded:** Dec. 18, 2006. **Freq:** Weekly. **Print Method:** Offset. **Trim Size:** Tabloid. **Cols./Page:** 5. **Col. Width:** 12 nonpareils. **Col. Depth:** 145 agate lines. **Key Personnel:** Harley E.A. Bicas, Editor-in-Chief; Claudete N. Moral, Exec. Sec.; Cristina Muccioli, Assoc. Ed. **ISSN:** 0004-2749. **Subscription Rates:** US$150 individuals; US$30 single issue. **URL:** http://www.abonet.com.br/.

43024 ■ Arquivos de Neuro-Psiquiatria
Academia Brasileira de Neurologia - ABNEURO
St. Captain Cavalcanti
327 Vila Mariana
04017-000 Sao Paulo, Sao Paulo, Brazil
Ph: 55 115 0849463
Publisher E-mail: presidente@abneuro.org
Journal covering clinical and experimental researches in neurology and related areas. **Founded:** 1917. **Freq:** Bimonthly. **Print Method:** Offset. **Cols./Page:** 6. **Col. Width:** 26 nonpareils. **Col. Depth:** 301 agate lines. **Key Personnel:** Jose Antonio Livramento, Editor; Luis Dos Ramos Machado, Editor. **ISSN:** 0004-282X. **Subscription Rates:** Cr$280 individuals; US$180 other countries. **URL:** http://www.scielo.br/revistas/anp/iaboutj.htm.

43025 ■ Brazilian Journal of Chemical Engineering
Associacao Brasileira de Engenharia Quimica
Rua Libero Badaro, 152-11 andar
01008-903 Sao Paulo, Sao Paulo, Brazil
Ph: 55 113 1078747
Fax: 55 113 1044649
Publisher E-mail: abeq@abeq.org.br
Journal publishing research and innovation in the field of chemical engineering and related areas. **Freq:** Quarterly. **Key Personnel:** Reinaldo Giudici, Editor-in-Chief, phone 55 11 30912254, fax 55 11 38132380, rgiudici@usp.br; Marcelo Zaiat, Editor, phone 55 16 33738360, fax 55 16 33739550, zaiat@sc.usp.br; Beatriz Vahan Kilikian, Editor, phone 55 16 30912232, fax 55 16 30912284, kilikian@usp.br. **ISSN:** 0104-6632. **Subscription Rates:** Cr$50 individuals; Cr$100 other countries. **URL:** http://www.scielo.br/scielo.php?script=sci_serial&pid=0104-6632&lng=en&nrm=.

43026 ■ Brazilian Journal of Microbiology
Sociedade Brasileira de Microbiologia
Departamento de Microbiologia
Av. Prof. Lineu Prestes, 1374 - Sala 214
Cidade Universitaria
05508-900 Sao Paulo, Sao Paulo, Brazil
Ph: 55 113 8139647
Fax: 55 113 8139647
Publication E-mail: bjm@sbmicrobiologia.org.br
Journal on microbiology. **Freq:** Quarterly. **Key Personnel:** Dr. Bernadette D.G.M. Franco, Assoc. Ed.; Carlos Pelleschi Taborda, Assoc. Ed.; Prof. Adalberto Pessoa, Jr., Contact. **ISSN:** 1517-8382. **Subscription Rates:** Free online. **URL:** http://www.scielo.br/scielo.php?script=sci_serial&pid=1517-8382&lng=en&nrm=iso.

43027 ■ Brazilian Journal of Oral Sciences
Piracicaba Dental School - UNICAMP
Av. Limeira 901, Piracicaba
Caixa Postal 52
13414-903 Sao Paulo, Sao Paulo, Brazil
Ph: 55 19 21065200
Fax: 55 19 34210144
Publication E-mail: brjorals@fop.unicamp.br
Publisher E-mail: info@fop.unicamp.br
Journal dealing with all aspects of dentistry and related disciplines. **Freq:** Quarterly. **Key Personnel:** Dr. Jose Francisco Hofling, Editor. **ISSN:** 1677-3225. **Subscription Rates:** Cr$120 individuals for professionals; Free online; Cr$30 single issue. **URL:** http://www.fop.unicamp.br/brjorals/.

43028 ■ Brazilian Journal of Physics
Sociedade Brasileira de Fisica
Rua do Matao, travessa R, 187 - Edificio Sede
Cidade Universitaria
05508-090 Sao Paulo, Sao Paulo, Brazil

Circulation: ★ = ABC; △ = BPA; ♦ = CAC; • = CCAB; ❑ = VAC; ⊕ = PO Statement; ‡ = Publisher's Report; Boldface figures = sworn; Light figures = estimated.

Gale Directory of Publications & Broadcast Media/147th Ed.   4809

Ph: 55 11 30340429
Fax: 55 11 38146293
Journal publishing regular papers and reviews in physics. **Founded:** 1971. **Freq:** Quarterly. **Key Personnel:** Antonio Sergio Teixeira Pires, Editor; Carlos Henrique Monken, Assoc. Ed.; Helio Chachan, Assoc. Ed.; Frank P. Missell, Editorial Board; Ronald Cintra Shellard, Assoc. Ed. **ISSN:** 0103-9733. **Subscription Rates:** US$200 individuals air mail. **URL:** http://www.sbfisica.org.br/bjp/.

43029 ■ Brazilian Journal of Veterinary Research and Animal Science
Faculdade de Medicina Veterinaria e Zootecnia USP
Av. Prof. Dr. Orlando Marques de Paiva, 87
Cidade Universitaria Armando de Salles Oliveira
05508-270 Sao Paulo, Sao Paulo, Brazil
Ph: 55 11 30917636
Fax: 55 11 30313074
Publication E-mail: brazvet@edu.usp.br
Journal dealing with all aspects of veterinary medicine, zootechny and related fields. **Freq:** Bimonthly. **Key Personnel:** Masao Iwasaki, Editor-in-Chief; Maria Angelica Miglino, Sci. Ed. **ISSN:** 1413-9596. **Subscription Rates:** US$130 institutions all countries; US$10 single issue. **URL:** http://www.scielo.br/scielo.php?script=sci_serial&pid=1413-9596&lng=en&nrm=.

43030 ■ Brazilian Oral Research
Sociedade Brasileira de Pesquisa Odontologica
Av. Lineu Prestes, 2227
Cid. Universitaria
Sao Paulo, Sao Paulo, Brazil
Ph: 55 113 0917855
Fax: 55 113 0917855
Publisher E-mail: sbpqo@sbpqo.org.br
Journal publishing latest advances in the field of odontology. **Freq:** Quarterly. **Key Personnel:** Sigmar de Mello Rode, Sci. Ed.; Esther Goldenberg Birman, Honorary Ed.; Francisco Emilio Pustiglioni, Asst. Ed. **ISSN:** 1806-8324. **Subscription Rates:** Cr$70 members SBPqC; Cr$180 nonmembers; Cr$250 institutions; US$80 other countries. **URL:** http://www.scielo.br/scielo.php/script_sci_serial/pid_1806-8324/lng_en/nrm_.

43031 ■ Cadernos de Pesquisa
Fundacao Carlos Chagas
Av. Prof. Francisco Morato, 1565
05513-900 Sao Paulo, Sao Paulo, Brazil
Ph: 55 113 7233000
Fax: 55 113 7211059
Publisher E-mail: cpesquis@fcc.org.br
Journal covering studies and research in education. **Founded:** 1971. **Freq:** Quarterly June, September, December, March. **Print Method:** Offset. **Trim Size:** 6 x 9. **Cols./Page:** 1. **Col. Width:** 52 nonpareils. **Col. Depth:** 100 agate lines. **Key Personnel:** Claudia Davis, Exec. Ed.; Vera Eliana Rodrigues, Sec.; Aurea Maria Corsi, Asst. Ed.; Elba Siqueira de Sa Barretto, Editor; Albertina De Oliveira Costa, Exec. Ed. **ISSN:** 0100-1574. **Subscription Rates:** Cr$19 individuals for issues 106 to 114; Cr$22 individuals for subsequent issues. **URL:** http://www.fcc.org.br/pesquisa/publicacoes/cp/index.html.

43032 ■ Ceramica
Brazilian Ceramic Society
Av. Lineu Prestes
2242 - Cidade Universitaria
05508-900 Sao Paulo, Sao Paulo, Brazil
Ph: 55 113 8169343
Fax: 55 113 8169343
Journal covering the field of ceramic science and technology. **Founded:** 1902. **Freq:** Bimonthly. **Print Method:** Offset. **Cols./Page:** 6. **Col. Depth:** 21 inches. **Key Personnel:** R. Muccillo, Editor, rmuccill@net.ipen.br; A.E. Martinelli, Assoc. Ed.; J.A. Varela, Assoc. Ed. **ISSN:** 0366-6913. **URL:** http://www.scielo.br/revistas/ce/iaboutj.htm. **Circ:** 700

43033 ■ Ciencia e Cultura
Brazilian Association for the Advancement of Science
Sociedade Brasileira para o Progresso da Ciencia
294 - 4 andar
01222-010 Sao Paulo, Sao Paulo, Brazil
Ph: 55 11 32592766
Fax: 55 11 31061002
Publication E-mail: cienciaecultura@sbpcnet.org.br
Publisher E-mail: sbpc@sbpcnet.org.br
Portuguese and English language publication covering

science. **Freq:** Bimonthly. **Key Personnel:** Marcelo Knobel, Editor-in-Chief. **ISSN:** 0009-6725. **Remarks:** Advertising accepted; rates available upon request. **URL:** http://cienciaecultura.bvs.br/scielo.php?script=sci_serial&pid=0009-6725&lng=pt&nrm=iso. **Circ:** 1,500

43034 ■ Ciencia Hoje
Brazilian Association for the Advancement of Science
Sociedade Brasileira para o Progresso da Ciencia
294 - 4 andar
01222-010 Sao Paulo, Sao Paulo, Brazil
Ph: 55 11 32592766
Fax: 55 11 31061002
Publisher E-mail: sbpc@sbpcnet.org.br
Portuguese language publication covering science. **Founded:** July 1982. **Freq:** Monthly. **Trim Size:** 21 x 28 cm. **Key Personnel:** Alicia Ivanissevich, Editorial Exec.; Igor Waltz, Contact. **ISSN:** 0101-8515. **Subscription Rates:** US$90 individuals 11 issues. **Remarks:** Accepts advertising. **URL:** http://cienciahoje.uol.com.br/; http://www.sbpcnet.org.br/site/home/. **Circ:** Paid 13,000

43035 ■ Ciencia Hoje das Criancas
Brazilian Association for the Advancement of Science
Sociedade Brasileira para o Progresso da Ciencia
294 - 4 andar
01222-010 Sao Paulo, Sao Paulo, Brazil
Ph: 55 11 32592766
Fax: 55 11 31061002
Publisher E-mail: sbpc@sbpcnet.org.br
Portuguese language science magazine for children. **Founded:** Dec. 1986. **Freq:** Monthly. **Trim Size:** 21 x 28 cm. **ISSN:** 0103-2054. **Subscription Rates:** US$66 individuals. **Remarks:** Advertising accepted; rates available upon request. **URL:** http://www.sbpcnet.org.br/site/home/; http://cienciahoje.uol.com.br/view/418. **Circ:** Paid 194,000

43036 ■ Clinics
University of Sao Paulo
Faculdade de Medicina
Av. Dr. Eneas de Carvalho Aguiar, 255
Cerqueira Cesar
05403-000 Sao Paulo, Sao Paulo, Brazil
Ph: 55 113 0696000
Peer-reviewed journal containing articles for clinicians and researchers in the medical sciences. **Founded:** 1908. **Freq:** Monthly. **Print Method:** Offset. **Cols./Page:** 6. **Col. Width:** 25 nonpareils. **Col. Depth:** 294 agate lines. **Key Personnel:** Anuar Ibraim Mitre, Area Ed.; Kavita Kirankumar Patel-Rolim, Editorial Dir.; Mauricio Rocha e Silva, Editor. **ISSN:** 1807-5932. **Subscription Rates:** Free. **URL:** http://www.scielo.br/scielo.php?script=sci_serial&pid=1807-5932&lng=en&nrm=iso.

43037 ■ Documentacao de Estudos em Linguistica Teorica e Aplicada (DELTA)
Pontificia Universidade Catolica de Sao Paulo
Rua Monte Alegre, 984
05014-001 Sao Paulo, Sao Paulo, Brazil
Journal addressing all areas of study concerning language and speech, both theoretical and applied. **Founded:** 1985. **Freq:** Biennial. **Print Method:** Offset. **Trim Size:** 13 x 21 1/2. **Cols./Page:** 6. **Col. Width:** 2 1/16 inches. **Col. Depth:** 294 agate lines. **Key Personnel:** Leila Barbara, Editor; Kanavillil Rajagopalan, Editor. **ISSN:** 0102-4450. **Subscription Rates:** US$60 individuals; US$120 institutions; US$30 single issue; US$60 institutions single issue. **URL:** http://www.scielo.br/revistas/delta/iaboutj.htm.

43038 ■ Ecletica Quimica
UNESP - Universidade Estadual Paulista
Alameda Santos 647
01419-901 Sao Paulo, Sao Paulo, Brazil
Publisher E-mail: portal@reitoria.unesp.br
Journal covering chemistry, physics, and related areas. **Founded:** 1976. **Freq:** Quarterly. **Print Method:** Offset. **Trim Size:** 8 x 10 7/8. **Cols./Page:** 3. **Col. Width:** 27 nonpareils. **Col. Depth:** 140 agate lines. **Key Personnel:** Antonio Tallarico Adorno, Assoc. Ed., atadorno@iq.unesp.br; Antonio Eduardo Mauro, Assoc. Ed.; Assis Vicente Benedetti, Assoc. Ed. **ISSN:** 0100-4670. **Subscription Rates:** Free. **URL:** http://www.scielo.br/revistas/eq/iaboutj.htm.

43039 ■ Eletricidade Moderna
Aranda Editora Ltda.
Alameda Olga, 315
01155-900 Sao Paulo, Sao Paulo, Brazil

Ph: 55 113 8245300
Fax: 55 113 6629585
Trade magazine covering electrical engineering. **Founded:** 1972. **Freq:** Monthly. **Print Method:** Offset. **Trim Size:** 21 x 28 cm. **Key Personnel:** Jose R.A. Souza, Editor-in-Chief, jras@arandanet.com.br; Mauro Sergio Crestani, Editor, mauro@arandanet.com.br; Silvio Paulo Da Silva, Director, silvio@arandanet.com.br. **Remarks:** Accepts advertising. **URL:** http://www.arandanet.com.br/revistas/em/index.html. **Ad Rates:** BW: Cr$1,829, 4C: Cr$3,861. **Circ:** Non-paid 12,000

43040 ■ Fundicao e Servicos
Aranda Editora Ltda.
Alameda Olga, 315
01155-900 Sao Paulo, Sao Paulo, Brazil
Ph: 55 113 8245300
Fax: 55 113 6629585
Trade magazine covering the foundry industry. **Founded:** 1990. **Freq:** Monthly. **Print Method:** Offset. **Trim Size:** 21 x 28 cm. **Key Personnel:** Fernanda Nascimento, Editor, fn@arandanet.com.br; Silvio Paulo da Silva, Director, silvio@arandanet.com.br; Jose Roberto Goncalves, Editor-in-Chief, jrg@arandanet.com.br; Themistocles Rodrigues, Jr., Tech. Ed., tetraducoes@uol.com.br; Maria Carolina Garcia, Staff Writer, mcg@arandanet.com.br. **Remarks:** Accepts advertising. **URL:** http://www.arandanet.com.br/revistas/fs/index.html. **Ad Rates:** BW: Cr$1,930, 4C: Cr$2,881. **Circ:** Non-paid 8,000

43041 ■ Jornal da Ciencia Hoje
Brazilian Association for the Advancement of Science
Sociedade Brasileira para o Progresso da Ciencia
294 - 4 andar
01222-010 Sao Paulo, Sao Paulo, Brazil
Ph: 55 11 32592766
Fax: 55 11 31061002
Publication E-mail: jciencia@jornaldaciencia.org.br
Publisher E-mail: sbpc@sbpcnet.org.br
Newspaper covering science, in Portuguese. **Freq:** Monthly. **URL:** http://www.jornaldaciencia.org.br/index2.jsp.

43042 ■ Maquinas e Metals
Aranda Editora Ltda.
Alameda Olga, 315
01155-900 Sao Paulo, Sao Paulo, Brazil
Ph: 55 113 8245300
Fax: 55 113 6629585
Publication E-mail: infomm@arandanet.com.br
Trade magazine covering the machine tool industry. **Founded:** 1964. **Freq:** Monthly. **Print Method:** Offset. **Trim Size:** 21 x 28 cm. **Key Personnel:** Jose R. Goncalves, Editor-in-Chief, jrg@arandanet.com.br; Amalia Ponce, Editor, ap@arandanet.com.br; Silvio Paulo da Silva, Director, silvio@arandanet.com.br. **Subscription Rates:** US$100 individuals. **Remarks:** Accepts advertising. **URL:** http://www.arandanet.com.br/revistas/mm/index.html. **Ad Rates:** BW: Cr$1,930, 4C: Cr$3,861. **Circ:** Non-paid 15,000

43043 ■ Papeis Avulsos de Zoologia (Sao Paulo)
Sociedade Brasileira de Ciencia do Solo
c/o Hussam Zaher, Ed.-in-Ch.
Universidade de Sao Paulo, Caixa
Postal 42.494
04218-970 Sao Paulo, Sao Paulo, Brazil
Publisher E-mail: sbcs@ufv.br
Journal covering contributions in systematics, paleontology, evolutionary biology, ecology, taxonomy, anatomy, behavior, functional morphology, molecular biology, ontogeny, faunistic studies, and biogeography. **Key Personnel:** Hussam Zaher, Editor-in-Chief, editormz@usp.br; Carlos Jose Einicker Lamas, Managing Editor; Mario Cesar Cardoso de Pinna, Assoc. Ed. **ISSN:** 0031-1049. **URL:** http://www.scielo.br/scielo.php/script_sci_serial/pid_0031-1049/lng_en/nrm_iso.

43044 ■ Plastico Industrial
Aranda Editora Ltda.
Alameda Olga, 315
01155-900 Sao Paulo, Sao Paulo, Brazil
Ph: 55 113 8245300
Fax: 55 113 6629585
Trade magazine covering the plastics industry. **Founded:** 1998. **Freq:** Monthly. **Print Method:** Offset. **Trim Size:** 21 x 28 cm. **Key Personnel:** Hellen Corina de Oliveira Souza, Sen. Ed., hellen@arandanet.com.br; Silvio Paulo Da Silva, Jr., Director, silvio@arandanet.

com.br; Jose Roberto Goncalves, Editor-in-Chief, jrg@arandanet.com.br; Walkyria Dantas, Sales Mgr., wd@arandanet.com.br; Antonio Augusto Gorni, Tech. Ed., maua@gorni.eng.br; Clayton Santos Delfino, Contact, csd@arandanet.com.br. **Remarks:** Accepts advertising. **URL:** http://www.arandanet.com.br/revistas/pi/index.html. **Ad Rates:** BW: Cr$1,930, 4C: Cr$3,861. **Circ:** Non-paid 12,000

43045 ■ Psicologia USP
Instituto de Psicologia
Av. Prof. Lucio Martins Rodrigues, Trav. 4, 399 Bl. 23
Cidade Universitaria Armando de Salles Oliveira
05508-900 Sao Paulo, Sao Paulo, Brazil
Ph: 55 113 0914452
Fax: 55 113 0914462
Journal dealing with various aspects of human and biological sciences. **Freq:** Semiannual June and December. **Key Personnel:** Celso De Rui Beisiegel, Editorial Board; Franklin Leopoldo E. Silva, Editorial Board; Carolina Martuscelli Bori, Editorial Board. **ISSN:** 0103-6564. **URL:** http://www.scielo.br/revistas/pusp/iaboutj.htm.

43046 ■ Quimica Nova
Sociedade Brasileira de Quimica
Av. Prof. Lineu Prestes, 748 - Bloco 3 - Superior
Sala 371
05508-000 Sao Paulo, Sao Paulo, Brazil
Ph: 55 113 0322299
Fax: 55 113 8143602
Publisher E-mail: sbqsp@iq.usp.br
Journal covering various aspects of chemistry. **Founded:** 1866. **Freq:** Weekly (Wed.). **Print Method:** Offset. **Cols./Page:** 6. **Col. Width:** 20 nonpareils. **Col. Depth:** 301 agate lines. **Key Personnel:** Susana I. Cordoba de Torresi, Editor; Vera L. Pardini, Editor; Vitor Ferreira, Editor. **ISSN:** 1678-7064. **Subscription Rates:** US$160 institutions; US$120 individuals; Cr$245 individuals legal; Cr$118 individuals no foreign partner; Cr$35 single issue. **URL:** http://quimicanova.sbq.org.br/index.php.

43047 ■ Revista Latinoamericana de Ciencias de la Comunicacion
Latin American Association of Communications Researchers
Avenida Prof. Lucio M. Rodrigues, 443-Bloco B, Rm. 27
Cidade Universitaria
Butanta
05508-900 Sao Paulo, Sao Paulo, Brazil
Ph: 55 11 30914082
Fax: 55 11 30914224
Publisher E-mail: alaic@edu.usp.br
Journal containing scientific journal on communication studies. **Freq:** Semiannual. **Key Personnel:** Margarida M. Krohling Kunsh, Editor. **ISSN:** 1807-3026. **Subscription Rates:** US$20 individuals. **Remarks:** Accepts advertising. **URL:** http://www.alaic.net/revistas.htm. **Circ:** (Not Reported)

43048 ■ Revista Vivencia
Alcoholics Anonymous - Brazil
Junaab-Junta de Servicos Gerais de A.A. do Brasil
Av. Senador Queiros 101, 2 Andar, cj 205
PO Box 580
01060-970 Sao Paulo, Sao Paulo, Brazil
Ph: 55 11 32293611
Publisher E-mail: alcoolicosanonimos@nutec.com.br
Portuguese language publication covering substance abuse. **Freq:** Bimonthly. **Remarks:** Advertising not accepted. **URL:** http://www.alcoolicosanonimos.org.br; http://www.revistavivencia.org.br/. **Circ:** 10,000

43049 ■ RTI Redes Telecom Instalacoes
Aranda Editora Ltda.
Alameda Olga, 315
01155-900 Sao Paulo, Sao Paulo, Brazil
Ph: 55 113 8245300
Fax: 55 113 6629585
Professional magazine covering telecommunications, LAN and networking. **Founded:** 2000. **Freq:** Monthly. **Print Method:** Offset. **Trim Size:** 21 x 28 cm. **Key Personnel:** Sandra Mogami, Editor, sm@arandanet.com.br; Elcio S. Cavalcanti, Manager, elcio@arandanet.com.br. **Remarks:** Accepts advertising. **URL:** http://www.arandanet.com.br/revistas/rti/index.html. **Ad Rates:** BW: Cr$1,930, 4C: Cr$3,861. **Circ:** Non-paid 12,000

43050 ■ Sao Paulo Medical Journal
Associacao Paulista de Medicina
Unidade de Publicacoes
Av. Brigadeiro Luis Antonio 278-7 andar
278 - Bela Vista
01318-901 Sao Paulo, Sao Paulo, Brazil
Ph: 55 113 1884200
Fax: 55 113 1884255
Journal focusing on the field of clinical health science. **Freq:** Bimonthly. **Key Personnel:** Alvaro Nagib Atallah, Editor; Paulo Manuel Pego Fernandes, Editor. **ISSN:** 1516-3180. **Subscription Rates:** US$160 individuals; US$220 institutions. **URL:** http://www.scielo.br/scielo.php?script=sci_serial&pid=1516-3180&lng=en&nrm=.

43051 ■ Sao Paulo em Perspectiva
Fundacao SEADE
Av. Casper Libero, 464
01033-000 Sao Paulo, Sao Paulo, Brazil
Ph: 55 11 33135777
Fax: 55 11 21717297
Publisher E-mail: atendimento@seade.gov.br
Journal covering conjectural and structural analyses of local or international economic, social and political phenomena in several areas. **Freq:** Quarterly. **Key Personnel:** Aurilio Sergio Costa Caiado, Editor. **ISSN:** 0102-8839. **URL:** http://www.scielo.br/scielo.php?script=sci_serial&pid=0102-8839&lng=en&nrm=.

Vacaria

43052 ■ Anais da Sociedade Entomologica do Brasil
Entomological Society of Brazil
c/o Adalecio Kovaleski
Embrapa Una e Vinho
Estacao Experimental de Vacaria
Caixa Postal 1513
95200-000 Vacaria, Rio Grande do Sul, Brazil
Ph: 55 54 32321715
Publisher E-mail: adalecio@cnpuv.embrapa.br
Journal covering several specialties including entomology, bionomics, systematics, morphology, physiology, behavior, ecology, biological control, crop protection, and acarology. **Founded:** 1972. **Freq:** Weekly (Thurs.). **Print Method:** Offset. **Cols./Page:** 6. **Col. Width:** 26 nonpareils. **Col. Depth:** 294 agate lines. **Key Personnel:** Amarildo Pasini, Assoc. Ed.; Sueli Souza Martinez, Editor-in-Chief. **ISSN:** 0301-8059. **URL:** http://www.scielo.br/scielo.php?pid=0301-8059&script=sci_serial.

43053 ■ Neotropical Entomology
Entomological Society of Brazil
c/o Adalecio Kovaleski
Embrapa Una e Vinho
Estacao Experimental de Vacaria
Caixa Postal 1513
95200-000 Vacaria, Rio Grande do Sul, Brazil
Ph: 55 54 32321715
Publisher E-mail: adalecio@cnpuv.embrapa.br
Journal covering research on several specialties of entomology, including bionomics, systematics, morphology, physiology, behavior, ecology, biological control, crop protection, and acarology. **Founded:** 1969. **Freq:** Monthly. **Print Method:** Web offset. **Trim Size:** 8 x 10 7/8. **Cols./Page:** 3. **Col. Width:** 28 nonpareils. **Col. Depth:** 140 agate lines. **Key Personnel:** Sueli Souza Martinez, Exec. Ed.; Francisco Fonseca de Souza, Assoc. Ed.; Fernando Luis Consoli, Editor-in-Chief. **ISSN:** 1519-556X. **Subscription Rates:** Cr$180 individuals for the printed version; US$160 individuals abroad; Cr$180 individuals; Cr$90 students; US$65 individuals abroad. **URL:** http://www.seb.org.br/.

Vicosa

43054 ■ Agora
Sociedade Brasileira de Ciencia do Solo
Cx. Postal 231
36570 000 Vicosa, Minas Gerais, Brazil
Ph: 55 31 38992471
Publication E-mail: agora@psycho.ufrj.br
Publisher E-mail: sbcs@ufv.br
Journal covering psychoanalysis. **Subtitle:** Estudos em Teoria Psicanalitica. **Founded:** 1960. **Freq:** Triennial. **Print Method:** Offset. **Trim Size:** 8 1/2 x 11. **Cols./Page:** 3 and 2. **Col. Width:** 25 and 40 nonpareils. **Col. Depth:** 145 agate lines. **Key Personnel:** Joel Birman,

Editor; Isabel Fortes, Exec. Committee; Regina Herzog, Exec. Committee. **ISSN:** 1516-1498. **URL:** http://www.scielo.br/scielo.php?pid=1516-1498&script=sci_serial.

43055 ■ Arquivo Brasileiro de Medicina Veterinaria e Zootecnia
Sociedade Brasileira de Ciencia do Solo
Cx. Postal 231
36570 000 Vicosa, Minas Gerais, Brazil
Ph: 55 31 38992471
Publisher E-mail: sbcs@ufv.br
Journal covering scientific works on veterinary medicine, food technology and inspection and related areas. **Founded:** June 2, 1927. **Freq:** Weekly (Wed.). **Print Method:** Offset. **Cols./Page:** 6. **Col. Width:** 26 nonpareils. **Col. Depth:** 301 agate lines. **Key Personnel:** Martinho de Almeida e Silva, Editor-in-Chief; Dr. Vera Lucia Viegas de Abreu, Scientific Ed.; Hamilton C. Machado da Silva, PhD, Scientific Ed. **ISSN:** 0102-0935. **URL:** http://www.scielo.br/scielo.php?pid=0102-0935&script=sci_serial.

43056 ■ Ciencia & Saude Coletiva
Sociedade Brasileira de Ciencia do Solo
Cx. Postal 231
36570 000 Vicosa, Minas Gerais, Brazil
Ph: 55 31 38992471
Publisher E-mail: sbcs@ufv.br
Journal covering debates, analyses and results of inquiries on health. **Founded:** 1971. **Freq:** Weekly (Thurs.). **Print Method:** Offset. **Cols./Page:** 6. **Col. Width:** 25 nonpareils. **Col. Depth:** 294 agate lines. **Key Personnel:** Paulo Eduardo Mangeon Elias, Assoc. Ed.; Maria Cecilia DeSouza Minayo, Scientific Ed.; Pericles Silveira Da Costa, Asst. Ed.; Lilia Maria Dos Santos Vicentin, Exec. Ed.; Reinaldo Guimaraes, Assoc. Ed.; Everardo Duarte Nunes, Assoc. Ed.; Ligia Vieira Da Silva, Assoc. Ed.; Carlos E.S. Coimbra, Jr., Consultant Ed. **ISSN:** 1413-8123. **Subscription Rates:** US$60 individuals; US$150 institutions; US$25 single issue. **URL:** http://www.scielo.br/scielo.php?script=sci_serial&pid=1413-8123.

43057 ■ Ensaio
Sociedade Brasileira de Ciencia do Solo
Cx. Postal 231
36570 000 Vicosa, Minas Gerais, Brazil
Ph: 55 31 38992471
Publisher E-mail: sbcs@ufv.br
Journal covering educational policies based on Brazilian experiences and perspectives. **Founded:** 1971. **Freq:** Weekly (Thurs.). **Print Method:** Offset. **Cols./Page:** 6. **Col. Width:** 25 nonpareils. **Col. Depth:** 294 agate lines. **ISSN:** 0104-4036. **URL:** http://www.scielo.br/scielo.php/script_sci_serial/pid_0104-4036/lng_en/nrm_iso.

43058 ■ Entomologia y Vectores
Sociedade Brasileira de Ciencia do Solo
Cx. Postal 231
36570 000 Vicosa, Minas Gerais, Brazil
Ph: 55 31 38992471
Publisher E-mail: sbcs@ufv.br
Journal covering topics related to human and animal diseases, insect pests of cultivated plants and/or of economic interest, including related subjects such as geography and climatology applied to entomology. **Founded:** 1866. **Freq:** Quarterly March, June, September, December. **Print Method:** Offset. **Cols./Page:** 6. **Col. Width:** 11 picas. **Col. Depth:** 301 agate lines. **Key Personnel:** Maria Luiza Felippe Bauer, Assoc. Ed., mlfbauer@ioc.fiocruz.br; Jose Jurberg, Editor, jjurberg@ioc.fiocruz.br; Pedro Jurberg, Editor, jurberg@openlink.com.br; Gilberto Chaves, Editor, gc@rio.com.br. **ISSN:** 0328-0381. **Subscription Rates:** US$60 individuals; Cr$70 individuals. **URL:** http://www.scielo.br/scielo.php?script=sci_serial&pid=0328-0381.

43059 ■ Journal of Epilepsy and Clinical Neurophysiology
Sociedade Brasileira de Ciencia do Solo
Cx. Postal 231
36570 000 Vicosa, Minas Gerais, Brazil
Ph: 55 31 38992471
Publisher E-mail: sbcs@ufv.br
Journal covering clinical neurophysiology. **ISSN:** 1676-2649. **URL:** http://www.scielo.br/scielo.php?script=sci_serial&pid=1676-2649&lng=en&nrm=iso.

43060 ■ Materials Research
Sociedade Brasileira de Ciencia do Solo

Cx. Postal 231
36570 000 Vicosa, Minas Gerais, Brazil
Ph: 55 31 38992471
Publisher E-mail: sbcs@ufv.br
Journal covering reviews on materials research including materials synthesis and processing, and microstructure and properties. **Founded:** 1950. **Freq:** Weekly (Thurs.). **Print Method:** Offset. **Cols./Page:** 5. **Col. Width:** 22 nonpareils. **Col. Depth:** 196 agate lines. **Key Personnel:** Alberto Caneiro, Editorial Board; Aloisio Nelmo Klein, Editorial Board; Aldo F. Craievich, Editorial Board; Edgar Dutra Zanotto, Editor-in-Chief; Luiz Antonio Pessan, Editorial Board. **ISSN:** 1516-1439. **Subscription Rates:** US$300 institutions, other countries; US$100 other countries; Cr$100 individuals; Cr$300 institutions. **URL:** http://www.scielo.br/scielo.php?script=sci_serial&pid=1516-1439&lng=en&nrm=iso.

43061 ■ Novos Estudos Cebrap
Sociedade Brasileira de Ciencia do Solo
Cx. Postal 231
36570 000 Vicosa, Minas Gerais, Brazil
Ph: 55 31 38992471
Publisher E-mail: sbcs@ufv.br
Journal covering relevant studies and contributions in sociology, politics, anthropology and humanities. **Founded:** Oct. 1938. **Freq:** Irregular. **Print Method:** Offset. **Cols./Page:** 6. **Col. Width:** 11 1/2 inches. **Col. Depth:** 21 1/4 inches. **Key Personnel:** Joaquim Toledo, Editor. **ISSN:** 0101-3300. **Subscription Rates:** Cr$45 individuals; US$70 individuals. **URL:** http://www.scielo.br/scielo.php/script_sci_serial/pid_0101-3300/lng_en/nrm_iso.

43062 ■ Pro-Fono Revista de Atualizacao Cientifica
Sociedade Brasileira de Ciencia do Solo
Cx. Postal 231
36570 000 Vicosa, Minas Gerais, Brazil
Ph: 55 31 38992471
Publisher E-mail: sbcs@ufv.br
Journal covering the field of phonoaudiology. **Founded:**

Mar. 1983. **Freq:** Monthly. **Print Method:** Offset. **Trim Size:** 8 x 10 7/8. **Cols./Page:** 3. **Col. Width:** 26 nonpareils. **Col. Depth:** 130 agate lines. **ISSN:** 0104-5687. **URL:** http://www.profono.com.br/index.asp.

43063 ■ Radiologia Brasileira
Sociedade Brasileira de Ciencia do Solo
Cx. Postal 231
36570 000 Vicosa, Minas Gerais, Brazil
Ph: 55 31 38992471
Publisher E-mail: sbcs@ufv.br
Journal covering radiology, x-ray, nuclear medicine, ultra-sonography, computerized tomography, and magnetic resonance. **Founded:** 1956. **Freq:** 10/yr. **Print Method:** Offset. **Trim Size:** 8 x 10 7/8. **Cols./Page:** 3. **Col. Width:** 26 nonpareils. **Col. Depth:** 140 agate lines. **Key Personnel:** Giovanni Guido Cerri, Editor-in-Chief. **ISSN:** 0100-3984. **URL:** http://www.scielo.br/scielo.php/script_sci_serial/pid_0100-3984/lng_en/nrm_iso.

43064 ■ RAE eletronica
Sociedade Brasileira de Ciencia do Solo
Cx. Postal 231
36570 000 Vicosa, Minas Gerais, Brazil
Ph: 55 31 38992471
Publication E-mail: raeredacao@fgvsp.br
Publisher E-mail: sbcs@ufv.br
Journal covering management. **Founded:** 1974. **Freq:** Bimonthly. **Print Method:** Offset. **Trim Size:** 8 1/2 x 11. **Cols./Page:** 3. **Col. Width:** 27 nonpareils. **Col. Depth:** 140 agate lines. **Key Personnel:** Eduardo Diniz, Editor-in-Chief. **ISSN:** 1676-5648. **URL:** http://www.scielo.br/revistas/raeel/iaboutj.htm.

43065 ■ Rem
Sociedade Brasileira de Ciencia do Solo
Cx. Postal 231
36570 000 Vicosa, Minas Gerais, Brazil
Ph: 55 31 38992471
Publisher E-mail: sbcs@ufv.br
Journal covering engineering. **Subtitle:** Revista Escola de Minas. **Founded:** Jan. 1, 1936. **Freq:** Quarterly. **Print Method:** Offset, uses mats. **Trim Size:** 7 3/4 x 10 1/2.

Cols./Page: 3. **Col. Width:** 27 nonpareils. **Col. Depth:** 140 agate lines. **Key Personnel:** Jorio Coelho, Editor. **ISSN:** 0370-4467. **Subscription Rates:** Cr$32 individuals; US$40 other countries. **URL:** http://www.scielo.br/scielo.php?pid=0370-4467&script=sci_serial.

43066 ■ Revista Arvore
Sociedade de Investigaoes Florestais
Departamento de Engenharia Florestal
Av. P.H. Rolfs s/n - Campus UFV
36570-000 Vicosa, Minas Gerais, Brazil
Ph: 55 313 8992476
Fax: 55 313 8912166
Publisher E-mail: sif@ufv.br
Journal covering scientific value in the field of forestry and similar areas. **Founded:** 1912. **Freq:** Bimonthly. **Print Method:** Offset. Uses mats. **Cols./Page:** 6. **Col. Width:** 25 nonpareils. **Col. Depth:** 294 agate lines. **Key Personnel:** Sebastiao Venancio Martins, Managing Editor, venancio@ufv.br; Alfredo Santos Araujo Alves, Exec. Ed., r.arvore@ufv.br. **ISSN:** 0100-6762. **Subscription Rates:** Cr$75 individuals. **URL:** http://www.revistaarvore.ufv.br/arvoreweb/index.php.

Vila Olimpia

43067 ■ Arquivos Brasileiros de Cardiologia
Brazilian Society of Cardiology
Sede Sao Paulo
Av. Beira Rio 45 - 3 Andar
04548-050 Vila Olimpia, Sao Paulo, Brazil
Ph: 55 113 8496438
Publisher E-mail: funcor@cardiol.br
Journal covering articles on cardiovascular topics. **Founded:** 1948. **Freq:** Monthly. **Print Method:** Offset. **Cols./Page:** 6. **Col. Width:** 25 nonpareils. **Col. Depth:** 294 agate lines. **Key Personnel:** Luiz Felipe P. Moreira, Editor-in-Chief. **ISSN:** 0066-782X. **Subscription Rates:** US$340 individuals. **URL:** http://www.arquivosonline.com.br/.

Road Town

43068 ■ The Island Sun
Sun Enterprises (BVI) Ltd.
PO Box 21
Tortola
Road Town, British Virgin Islands
Ph: (284)494-2476
Fax: (284)494-5854
Publication E-mail: issun@candwbvi.net
Publisher E-mail: islandsun@surfbvi.com
Community newspaper. **Founded:** 1962. **Freq:** Weekly (Sat.). **Print Method:** Offset Litho. **Cols./Page:** 5. **Key Personnel:** Vernon Pickering, Editor. **Subscription**

Rates: US$55 individuals British Virgin Islands; US$85 U.S. and Canada Caribbean; US$65 individuals Virgin Islands; US$95 individuals U.K.; US$110 individuals Europe, Asia, Africa, and Australia. **Remarks:** Accepts advertising. **URL:** http://www.islandsun.com. **Ad Rates:** BW: US$300, 4C: US$795, PCI: US$8. **Circ:** Paid 3,300

Tortola

43069 ■ The British Virgin Islands Welcome Tourist Guide
Island Publishing Services Ltd.
PO Box 133
Road Town

Pasea Estate
Tortola, British Virgin Islands
Ph: (284)494-2413
Fax: (284)494-6589
Publication E-mail: jim@bviwelcome.com
Publisher E-mail: info@bviwelcome.com
Tourist guide. **Founded:** 1971. **Freq:** Bimonthly. **Print Method:** Offset litho. **Key Personnel:** Claudia Colli, Editor, fax 44 28 44946589. **Subscription Rates:** US$25; US$38 other countries. **Remarks:** Accepts advertising. **URL:** http://www.bviwelcome.com. **Ad Rates:** BW: US$1,375, 4C: US$1,875. **Circ:** Non-paid 165,000

Andulau

43070 ■ Radio Talivishen Brunei - Andulau - Pelangi - 91.0 MHz
Prime Minister's Office
Jalan Elizabeth II
Bandar Seri Begawan BS8610, Brunei Darussalam
Ph: 673 2 2243111
Format: Eclectic. **Owner:** Radio Television Brunei, at above address. **Operating Hours:** 2200-1600. **Key Personnel:** Ahmad bin Mahmud, Contact, pgahmad_pgmahmud@rtb.gov.bn. **Wattage:** 5000. **Ad Rates:** Noncommercial. **URL:** http://www.rtb.gov.bn/.

Bandar

43071 ■ RTB Pelangi-FM - 91.4
Jabatan Perdana Menteri
Bandar 8610, Brunei Darussalam
Ph: 673 2227813
Fax: 673 2223112
E-mail: pelangi914fm@rtb.gov.bn
Format: Ethnic; News; World Beat. **Owner:** Radio Televisyen Brunei, at above address. **Ad Rates:** Advertising accepted; rates available upon request. **URL:** http://www.pelangifm.com.

Bandar Seri Begawan

43072 ■ Borneo Bulletin
Brunei Press Sdn Bhd
Locked Bag No. 2
MPC Berakas
Bandar Seri Begawan 3510, Brunei Darussalam
Ph: 67 324 51468
Publication E-mail: borneobulletin2@brunet.bn
Publisher E-mail: brupress@brunet.bn
General interest English-language newspaper. **Founded:** 1953. **Freq:** Daily. **Subscription Rates:** Br$192 individuals 6 months; Br$384 individuals. **URL:** http://www.bruneipress.com.bn/links/bb_history.html. **Circ:** Mon.-Fri. 20,000, Sun. 25,000

43073 ■ The Brunei Times
3rd Fl., Wisma Haji Mohd. Taha
Jalan Gadong
Bandar Seri Begawan BE 4119, Brunei Darussalam
Ph: 673 2 428333
Fax: 673 2 428555
Publication E-mail: theeditor@bt.com.bn
Publisher E-mail: info@bt.com.bn
Newspaper featuring news and events in Brunei. **Key Personnel:** Kumushay Hudaverdi, Asst. Ch. Ed., fax 673 2 454752, kumushayhudaverdi@brunei. **Subscription Rates:** Br$172.80 individuals. **Remarks:** Accepts advertising. **URL:** http://www.bt.com.bn/en/. **Ad Rates:** BW: Br$1,780.80. **Circ:** (Not Reported)

43074 ■ Pelangi-FM - 91.4
Jabatan Perdana Menteri
Bandar Seri Begawan 8610, Brunei Darussalam
Ph: 673 2227813
Fax: 673 2223112
E-mail: pelangi914fm@rtb.gov.bn
Format: World Beat; Ethnic. **Ad Rates:** Advertising ac-
cepted; rates available upon request. **URL:** http://www.pelangifm.com.

43075 ■ Radio Talivishen Brunei - Andulau - Harmoni - 94.1 MHz
Jalan Elizabeth 11
Bandar Seri Begawan BS8610, Brunei Darussalam
Ph: 673 2243111
Format: Full Service. **Owner:** Radio Television Brunei, at above address. **Key Personnel:** Harun Al Rashid bin Moslam, Contact, harun_alrashid@rtb.gov.bn. **Wattage:** 5000. **Ad Rates:** Noncommercial. **URL:** http://www.rtb.gov.bn/.

Radio Talivishen Brunei - Andulau - Pelangi - See Andulau

Radio Talivishen Brunei - Bukit Subok - English/Chinese - See Piliphan

Radio Talivishen Brunei - Bukit Subok - Harmoni - See Harmoni

Radio Talivishen Brunei - Bukit Subok - Malay - See Bukit Subok

Radio Talivishen Brunei - Bukit Subok - Pelangi - See Pelangi

Radio Talivishen Brunei - S.Hanching - English - See South Hanching

Radio Television Brunei - See Bukit Subok

Bukit Andulau

43076 ■ Radio Television Brunei - 8
Bandar Seri Begawan
BS8610
Negara Darussalam, Brunei Darussalam
Ph: 673 22 43111
Fax: 673 22 23112
Format: Commercial TV; News; Sports; Religious. **Owner:** Radio Television Brunei, at above address. **Founded:** 1976. **Operating Hours:** 0600-2400 Daily. **Key Personnel:** Mahrub Murni, Director, phone 673 22 22852, mahrub.murni@rtb.gov.bn. **Wattage:** 20,000. **URL:** http://www.rtb.gov.bn/.

Bukit Subok

43077 ■ Radio Talivishen Brunei - Bukit Subok - Malay - 92.3 MHz
Jalan Elizabeth 11
Bandar Seri Begawan BS8610, Brunei Darussalam
Ph: 673 2243111
Format: Eclectic. **Owner:** Radio Television Brunei, at above address. **Key Personnel:** Hasnan bin Haji Suhaili, Contact, hasnan_suhaili@rtb.gov.bn. **Wattage:** 5000. **URL:** http://www.rtb.gov.bn/.

43078 ■ Radio Television Brunei - 5
Jalan Elizabeth 11
Bandar Seri Begawan BS8610, Brunei Darussalam
Ph: 673 2243111
Format: Commercial TV; News; Sports. **Owner:** Radio Television Brunei, at above address. **Founded:** 1975. **Operating Hours:** 0600-2400 Daily. **Key Personnel:** Haji Ibrahim bin Mohamad, Contact, phone 673 2223363, ibrahim_mohamad@rtb.gov.bn. **Wattage:**
10,000. **Ad Rates:** Noncommercial. **URL:** http://www.rtb.gov.bn/.

Harmoni

43079 ■ Radio Talivishen Brunei - Bukit Subok - Harmoni - 94.1 MHz
Jalan Elizabeth 11
Bandar Seri Begawan BS8610, Brunei Darussalam
Ph: 673 2243111
Format: Full Service; News. **Owner:** Radio Television Brunei, at above address. **Operating Hours:** 2200-1600. **Key Personnel:** Harun Al Rashid Moslam, Director, harun_alrashid@rtb.gov.bn. **Wattage:** 5000. **URL:** http://www.rtb.gov.bn/.

Negara

43080 ■ RTB Nasional-FM - 92.3
Bandar Seri Begawan
Negara 8610, Brunei Darussalam
Ph: 673 22 43111
E-mail: nasional923fm@rtb.gov.bn
Format: Ethnic; World Beat. **Owner:** Radio Television Brunei, at above address. **URL:** http://www.rtb.gov.bn/9.23fm/index.html.

43081 ■ RTB Nur Islam-FM - 93.3
Bandar Seri Begawan
Negara 8610, Brunei Darussalam
Ph: 673 2243111
Format: Ethnic; World Beat. **Owner:** Radio Television Brunei, at above address. **URL:** http://www.rtb.gov.bn.

Negara Darussalam

Radio Talivishen Brunei - S.Hanching - Chinese - See South Hanching

Radio Television Brunei - See Bukit Andulau

Pelangi

43082 ■ Radio Talivishen Brunei - Bukit Subok - Pelangi - 91.4 MHz
Jalan Elizabeth 11
Bandar Seri Begawan BS8610, Brunei Darussalam
Ph: 673 2243111
Format: News. **Owner:** Radio Television Brunei, at above address. **Operating Hours:** 2200-1600. **Key Personnel:** Ahmad bin Mahmud, Contact, pgahmad_pgmahmud@rtb.gov.bn. **Wattage:** 5000. **URL:** http://www.rtb.gov.bn/.

Piliphan

43083 ■ Radio Talivishen Brunei - Bukit Subok - English/Chinese - 95.9 MHz
Prime Minister's Office
Jalan Elizabeth II
Bandar Seri Begawan BS8610, Brunei Darussalam
Ph: 673 2243111
Format: News. **Owner:** Radio Television Brunei, at above address. **Operating Hours:** Continuous. **Key Personnel:** Magdalene Tan Swee Linc, Contact, magdalene_tan@rtb.gov.bn; Lai Boon Keiwe, Contact,

Circulation: ★ = ABC; △ = BPA; ♦ = CAC; • = CCAB; ❑ = VAC; ⊕ = PO Statement; ‡ = Publisher's Report; Boldface figures = sworn; Light figures = estimated.

lai_boonkeiwe@rtb.gov.bn. **Wattage:** 500. **URL:** http://www.rtb.gov.bn/.

South Hanching

43084 ■ Radio Talivishen Brunei - S.Hanching - Chinese - 711 KHz
Bandar Seri Begawan
BS8610
Negara Darussalam, Brunei Darussalam

Ph: 673 2 2243111
Fax: 673 2 2227204
E-mail: rtbipro@brunet.bn
Format: Eclectic. **Owner:** Radio Television Brunei, at above address, Fax: 673 2 2241288. **Founded:** 1957. **Wattage:** 20,000. **URL:** http://www.rtb.gov.bn.

43085 ■ Radio Talivishen Brunei - S.Hanching - English - 710 KHz
Prime Minister's Office

Jalan Elizabeth II
Bandar Seri Begawan BS8610, Brunei Darussalam
Ph: 673 2 2243111
Fax: 673 2 2224827
E-mail: rtbipro@brunet.bn
Format: Eclectic. **Owner:** Radio Television Brunei, at above address. **Founded:** 1957. **Operating Hours:** 2200-1600. **Wattage:** 20,000. **Ad Rates:** Noncommercial. **URL:** http://www.rtb.gov.bn.

Bourgas

43086 ■ Academic Open Internet Journal
Bourgas University, Technical College
1 Prof. Yakimov Blvd.
BG-8010 Bourgas, Bulgaria
Ph: 359 56 858409
Publication E-mail: aoij@btu.bg
Publisher E-mail: aoij@btu.bg
Internet science journal. **Key Personnel:** Prof. Todor Ivanov, Contact; Prof. Nikolay Ralev, Contact; Prof. Petko Barzov, Contact; Prof. Georgi Nenov, Contact; Prof. Danail Bonchev, Contact; Prof. Nechko Nechev, Contact. **ISSN:** 1311-4360. **Remarks:** Accepts advertising. **URL:** http://www.acadjournal.com. **Circ:** (Not Reported)

Ruse

43087 ■ Advanced Studies in Theoretical Physics
Hikari Ltd.
PO Box 15
BG-7005 Ruse, Bulgaria
Ph: 359 82 582277
Publisher E-mail: hikaripublishers@m-hikari.com
Peer-reviewed Journal covering all branches of theoretical physics, mathematical physics and related applied sciences. **Founded:** 2007. **Key Personnel:** M. Bellini, Editorial Board; P. Daripa, Editorial Board. **ISSN:** 1313-1311. **URL:** http://www.m-hikari.com/astp/index.html.

43088 ■ Applied Mathematical Sciences
Hikari Ltd.
PO Box 15
BG-7005 Ruse, Bulgaria
Ph: 359 82 582277
Publisher E-mail: hikaripublishers@m-hikari.com
Peer-reviewed Journal covering all areas of applied mathematical sciences. **Founded:** 2007. **Key Personnel:** E. Minchev, Managing Editor. **ISSN:** 1312-885X. **URL:** http://www.m-hikari.com/ams/index.html.

43089 ■ International Journal of Algebra
Hikari Ltd.
PO Box 15
BG-7005 Ruse, Bulgaria
Ph: 359 82 582277
Publisher E-mail: hikaripublishers@m-hikari.com
Peer-reviewed Journal covering all areas of pure and applied algebra. **Key Personnel:** Sh. S. Abhyankar, Editorial Board; T. A. Gulliver, Editorial Board; P. Ara, Editorial Board. **ISSN:** 1312-8868. **URL:** http://www.m-hikari.com/ija/index.html.

43090 ■ International Journal of Contemporary Mathematical Sciences
Hikari Ltd.
PO Box 15
BG-7005 Ruse, Bulgaria
Ph: 359 82 582277
Publisher E-mail: hikaripublishers@m-hikari.com
Journal covering all areas of pure and applied mathematical sciences. **Key Personnel:** E. Minchev, Managing Editor. **ISSN:** 1312-7586. **URL:** http://www.m-hikari.com/ijcms.html.

43091 ■ International Journal of Mathematical Analysis
Hikari Ltd.
PO Box 15
BG-7005 Ruse, Bulgaria
Ph: 359 82 582277
Publisher E-mail: hikaripublishers@m-hikari.com
Journal covering all branches of pure and applied analysis. **Founded:** 2007. **Key Personnel:** E. Minchev, Managing Editor. **ISSN:** 1312-8876. **URL:** http://www.m-hikari.com/ijma/index.html.

43092 ■ International Mathematical Forum
Hikari Ltd.
PO Box 15
BG-7005 Ruse, Bulgaria
Ph: 359 82 582277
Publisher E-mail: hikaripublishers@m-hikari.com
Peer-reviewed Journal covering all areas of pure and applied mathematics. **Key Personnel:** E. Minchev, Managing Editor. **ISSN:** 1312-7594. **URL:** http://www.m-hikari.com/imf.html.

Sofia

43093 ■ Balkan Linguistics
Bulgarian Academy of Sciences
Balgarska Akademija N.A. Naukite
1, 15 Noemvri Str.
BG-1040 Sofia, Bulgaria
Ph: 359 2 9898446
Fax: 359 2 9862523
Bulgarian language publication covering linguistics. **Founded:** 1959. **Freq:** Quarterly. **Key Personnel:** Anna Choleva, Editor-in-Chief, annach@ibl.bas.bg; Maya Vlahova, Manager, phone 359 2 9792958, mvlahova@abv.bg. **ISSN:** 0324-1653. **URL:** http://www.ibl.bas.bg/en/editions_en2.htm.

43094 ■ Bulgarian Chemical Communications
Bulgarian Academy of Sciences
Balgarska Akademija N.A. Naukite
1113 Sofia
Acad. G. Bonchev St., Bl. 103
Institute of Catalysis
1113 Sofia, Bulgaria
Publication E-mail: bioreac@bas.bg
Publication covering Bulgarian chemical communications. **Freq:** Quarterly. **Key Personnel:** A. Eliyas, Language Ed.; Prof. Venko Beschkov, Editor-in-Chief. **ISSN:** 0324-1130. **URL:** http://www.bas.bg/cgi-bin/e-cms/vis/vis.pl?s=001&p=0171&g=.

43095 ■ Bulgarian Folklore
Bulgarian Academy of Sciences
Balgarska Akademija N.A. Naukite
Acad. G. Bonchev St., Bl. 6
Institute of Folklore
1113 Sofia, Bulgaria
Publication E-mail: bulfolk@ifolk.bas.bg
Publication covering Bulgarian folklore. **Founded:** 1975. **Freq:** Quarterly. **Key Personnel:** Lyubomir Mikov, Editor-in-Chief; Prof. Mila Santova, Director. **ISSN:** 0323-9861. **URL:** http://www.bas.bg/cgi-bin/e-cms/vis/vis.pl.

43096 ■ Bulgarian Geophysical Journal
Bulgarian Academy of Sciences
Balgarska Akademija N.A. Naukite
Acad. G. Bonchev St., Bl. 3
1113 Sofia, Bulgaria
Publication E-mail: bgj@geophys.bas.bg
Bulgarian language journal covering geophysical sciences. **Freq:** Annual. **Key Personnel:** Prof. Kostadin Ganev, Editor-in-Chief; Prof. M. Kovacheva, Editor; Prof. I. Kutiev, Editor; Prof. G. Miloshev, Editor; Prof. N. Miloshev, Editor; L. Christoskov, Editor. **ISSN:** 0323-9918. **URL:** http://www.geophys.bas.bg/bgj/bgj.htm.

43097 ■ Bulgarian Musicology
Bulgarian Academy of Sciences
Balgarska Akademija N.A. Naukite
21 Krakra St.
1504 Sofia, Bulgaria
Ph: 359 2 9431901
Publication covering Bulgarian musicology. **Freq:** Quarterly. **Key Personnel:** Dimiter Hristoff, Editor-in-Chief; Agapia Balareva, Dep. Ed.-in-Ch.; Margarita Kerpitchian, Manager. **ISSN:** 0204-823X. **URL:** http://musicart.imbm.bas.bg/BM-online.html.

43098 ■ Etudes Balkaniques
Institute of Balkan Studies
1000 Sofia, 45 Moskovska St.
BG-1000 Sofia, Bulgaria
Ph: 35 929 806297
Fax: 35 929 806297
Publication E-mail: balkani@cl.bas.bg
Publisher E-mail: balkani@cl.bas.bg
Publication covering the field of Balkan studies in English, French, German, Russian, and Italian. **Founded:** 1964. **Freq:** Quarterly. **Key Personnel:** Dr. Svetlana Valkanova Todorova, Editor; Dr. Margarita Yosifova Kotseva, Editor; Dr. Agop Garabed Garabedyan, Editor-in-Chief. **ISSN:** 0324-1654. **Subscription Rates:** EUR72 individuals; EUR90 individuals U.S. & Japan. **Remarks:** Advertising not accepted. **URL:** http://www.cl.bas.bg/Balkan-Studies/default.htm. **Circ:** (Not Reported)

43099 ■ Fractional Calculus and Applied Analysis
Bulgarian Academy of Sciences
Balgarska Akademija N.A. Naukite
1, 15 Noemvri Str.
BG-1040 Sofia, Bulgaria
Ph: 359 2 9898446
Fax: 359 2 9862523
Publication E-mail: fcaa@math.bas.bg
Peer-reviewed Journal covering such topics as algebraic analysis, operational and convolutional calculi, harmonic analysis, series, orthogonal polynomials, classes of analytic functions, etc. **Freq:** Quarterly. **Key Personnel:** Dr. Virginia Kiryakova, Managing Editor, virginia@diogenes.bg; M. Caputo, Honorary Member of Editorial Board; P.L. Butzer, Honorary Member of Editorial Board. **Subscription Rates:** US$155 institutions print; US$110 individuals print; EUR70 individuals; EUR100 institutions. **URL:** http://www.diogenes.bg/fcaa/.

43100 ■ Genetics and Breeding
Bulgarian Academy of Sciences
Balgarska Akademija N.A. Naukite

Circulation: ★ = ABC; △ = BPA; ♦ = CAC; • = CCAB; ❑ = VAC; ⊕ = PO Statement; ‡ = Publisher's Report; Boldface figures = sworn; Light figures = estimated.

Gale Directory of Publications & Broadcast Media/147th Ed.　　　　4817

1, 15 Noemvri Str.
BG-1040 Sofia, Bulgaria
Ph: 359 2 9898446
Fax: 359 2 9862523
Publication E-mail: genetika@bas.bg
Journal covering different areas of theoretical and applied genetics (plant, animal, microbial) and relevant subjects. **Freq:** Quarterly. **Key Personnel:** Prof. Kostadin Gecheff, PhD, Editor-in-Chief, kgecheff@bas.bg; Prof. Aglika Edreva, Assoc. Ed. **URL:** http://ig.bas.bg/eng/index.php?p=Periodics.htm.

43101 ■ Geologica Balcanica
Bulgarian Academy of Sciences
Balgarska Akademija N.A. Naukite
1, 15 Noemvri Str.
BG-1040 Sofia, Bulgaria
Ph: 359 2 9898446
Fax: 359 2 9862523
Publication covering geology. **Founded:** 1934. **Freq:** Quarterly. **Key Personnel:** Peter Marchev, Editor-in-Chief, pmarchev@geology.bas.bg; Anna Lazarova, Sec., alazarova@geology.bas.bg; Nikolay Bonev, Editorial Board; Kristalina Stoykova, Editorial Board, stoykova@geology.bas.bg; Dr. Iskra Lakova, Editor, lakova@geology.bas.bg; Yana Tsvetanova, Editorial Board, yana_tz@clmc.bas.bg. **ISSN:** 0324-0894. **URL:** http://www.geology.bas.bg/geobal.html.

43102 ■ Journal of Bulgarian Historical Review
Bulgarian Academy of Sciences
Balgarska Akademija N.A. Naukite
52 Shipchenski prohod St., Bl. 17
Institute of History
1113 Sofia, Bulgaria
Publication covering Bulgarian history. **Founded:** 1973. **Freq:** Quarterly. **Key Personnel:** Virginia Paskaleva, Editor-in-Chief. **ISSN:** 0204-8906. **Subscription Rates:** EUR40 individuals. **URL:** http://www.bas.bg/cgi-bin/ecms/vis/vis.pl?s=001&p=0171&g=.

43103 ■ Journal of Endocrinology
Bulgarian Society of Endocrinology
Clinical Center of Endocrinology and Gerontology
Bolnitsa po Endokrinologia
6 D. Gruev Str.
BG-1303 Sofia, Bulgaria
Ph: 359 298 84933
Fax: 359 298 71553
Bulgarian and English language journal covering endocrinology. **Subtitle:** Endocrinologia. **Founded:** July 1996. **Freq:** Quarterly. **Print Method:** Offset. **Trim Size:** A4. **Key Personnel:** Prof. Dragomir Koev, Dep. Ed.; Prof. Bojan Lozanov, Editor-in-Chief. **ISSN:** 1310-8131. **URL:** http://www.medicalnet-bg.org/endocr/journal.htm. **Circ:** Paid ⊕1,500

43104 ■ Kino
Union of Bulgarian Film Makers

67 Dondukoz Blvd.
BG-1504 Sofia, Bulgaria
Ph: 359 2 9461069
Fax: 359 2 9461069
Publisher E-mail: sbfd@sbfd-bg.com
Bulgarian and English language publication covering film. **Founded:** 1946. **Freq:** Bimonthly. **ISSN:** 0864-4393. **Subscription Rates:** EUR60 individuals + packing and postage; US$79 individuals. **Remarks:** Advertising accepted; rates available upon request. **URL:** http://www.filmmakersbg.org/publications-eng.htm. **Circ:** 2,000

43105 ■ Mathematica Plus
Bulgarian Academy of Sciences
Balgarska Akademija N.A. Naukite
Institute of Mathematics & Informatics
Bulgarian Academy of Sciences
Acad. G. Bonchev Str., Block 8
BG-1113 Sofia, Bulgaria
Journal for school and university students, teachers and professional mathematicians, publishing communications and papers with original results, reviews on important domains of mathematics and informatics. **Freq:** Quarterly. **Key Personnel:** Oleg Mushkarov, Editor-in-Chief; Sava Grozdev, Editor-in-Chief; E. Kelevedzhiev, Editorial Board; G. Ganchev, Editorial Board; V. Velichkov, Editorial Board; R. Karadjova, Editorial Board. **Subscription Rates:** US$40 individuals mail expenses included. **URL:** http://www.math.bas.bg/per.html.

43106 ■ Nauka
Union of Scientists in Bulgaria
39, Madrid Blvd. Fl. 2
BG-1505 Sofia, Bulgaria
Ph: 35 929 430128
Fax: 35 929 441590
Publisher E-mail: science@usb-bg.org
Bulgarian language publication covering science. **Freq:** Bimonthly. **ISSN:** 0861-3362. **Remarks:** Advertising accepted; rates available upon request. **URL:** http://www.usb-bg.org/. **Circ:** 2,000

43107 ■ Serdica Mathematical Journal
Bulgarian Academy of Sciences
Balgarska Akademija N.A. Naukite
Institute of Mathematics & Informatics
Acad. G. Bonchev St., Bl. 8
BG-1113 Sofia, Bulgaria
Publication E-mail: serdica@math.bas.bg
Journal publishing original research papers and invited survey articles in all areas of mathematics. **Founded:** 1975. **Freq:** Quarterly. **Key Personnel:** V. Drensky, Editor-in-Chief, drensky@math.bas.bg; S. Argyros, Editor, sargyros@math.ntua.gr; S.L. Troyanski, Editor-in-Chief, troyanski@math.bas.bg; M. Domokos, Editor, domokos@renyi.hu; J. Albert, Editor, jalbert@math.ou.edu; L. Ein, Editor, ein@uic.edu. **Subscription Rates:**

EUR80 individuals. **URL:** http://www.math.bas.bg/~serdica/.

43108 ■ Sotsiologicheski Problemi
Bulgarian Sociological Association
Bul. Tzrigradsko Shosse, No. 125
Block 2, Rm. 240
BG-1113 Sofia, Bulgaria
Ph: 35 929 809892
Publisher E-mail: bsa@sociology.bas.bg
Journal covering sociology. **Freq:** Quarterly. **Key Personnel:** Koljo Koev, Editor. **ISSN:** 0324-1572. **URL:** http://www.ucm.es; http://www.isa-sociology.org/colmemb/bul.htm.

43109 ■ Jazz-FM - 104.0
3 Panayot Volov St.
BG-1504 Sofia, Bulgaria
Ph: 359 2 9430920
Fax: 359 2 9430915
E-mail: studio@jazzfmbg.com
Format: Jazz; Blues; World Beat. **Key Personnel:** Svetoslav Nikolov, Program Dir.; Roman Mihailov, Music Dir. **URL:** http://www.jazzfmbg.com/.

Stara Zagora

43110 ■ Bulgarian Journal of Veterinary Medicine (BJVM)
Trakia University
Faculty of Veterinary Medicine
Students Campus
BG-6000 Stara Zagora, Bulgaria
Ph: 359 42 673012
Publication E-mail: bjvm@uni-sz.bg
Publisher E-mail: info@uni-sz.bg
Journal reporting on basic and applied aspects of veterinary medicine and allied topics. **Freq:** Quarterly. **Key Personnel:** Lubomir Lashev, Editor; Anelia Haritova, Assoc. Ed.; Dimitrina Georgieva, Editorial Board; Johanna Fink-Gremmels, Editorial Board; Huben Hubenov, Editorial Board; Maria Andonova, Editorial Board. **ISSN:** 1311-1477. **Subscription Rates:** US$100 other countries. **URL:** http://www.uni-sz.bg/bjvm/bjvm.htm.

Varna

43111 ■ Radio Bravo-FM - 96.4
196, jk. Chayka
BG-9005 Varna, Bulgaria
Ph: 359 52 321015
E-mail: reklama@radiobravo.com
Format: Ethnic; World Beat. **Founded:** 1995. **Operating Hours:** Continuous. **Ad Rates:** Advertising accepted; rates available upon request. **URL:** http://www.radiobravo.com.

Ouagadougou

43112 ■ Savane-FM - 103.4 MHz
1676 Ave. de la Dignite, Secteur 17
Kadiogo
Ouagadougou, Burkina Faso
Ph: 226 50433743
Fax: 226 50435021
Format: Ethnic; World Beat. **Owner:** Savane Communication Tous Droits Reserves, at above address.
URL: http://www.savanefm.bf.

Circulation: ★ = ABC; △ = BPA; ♦ = CAC; • = CCAB; ❑ = VAC; ⊕ = PO Statement; ‡ = Publisher's Report; Boldface figures = sworn; Light figures = estimated.

Gale Directory of Publications & Broadcast Media/147th Ed.   **4819**

Phnom Penh

43113 ■ Phnom Penh Post
888 Bldg. F, 8th Fl.
Phnom Penh, Cambodia
Ph: 855 23 214311
Fax: 855 23 214318
Independent newspaper covering Cambodia today in English. **Freq:** Daily. **Key Personnel:** Bernie Leo, Editor-in-Chief, bernie.leo@phnompenhpost.com; Ross Dunkley, Publisher, ross.dunkley@phnompenhpost.com; Philip Bader, Managing Editor, philip.bader@phnompenhpost.com; Vong Sokheng, Dep. News Ed. **ISSN:** 1563-9673. **Subscription Rates:** US$60 individuals single-user (online edition); US$100 two years single-user (online edition); US$40 individuals 6 months (online edition); US$150 individuals print edition; US$80 individuals 6 months (print edition). **Remarks:** Accepts advertising. **URL:** http://www.phnompenhpost.com/. **Circ:** (Not Reported)

43114 ■ Beehive-FM - 105
44G St. 360, Sangkat Boeung keng kang III
Khan Chamkar morn
Phnom Penh, Cambodia
Ph: 855 23210401
Fax: 855 23210439
E-mail: sbk@online.com.kh
Format: News; Educational; Religious; Talk. **Founded:** Jan. 1, 2004. **URL:** http://www.sbk.com.kh.

43115 ■ Radio-FM - 107
No. 18, Rd. 562
Phnom Penh, Cambodia
Ph: 855 23880874
Fax: 855 23368212
E-mail: info@tv9.com.kh
Format: Ethnic; World Beat. **Operating Hours:** Continuous. **URL:** http://www.tv9.com.kh.

43116 ■ Radio FM 103 MHz - 103 MHz
No. 02, Russia Blvd.
Sangkat Monorom
Khan 7, Makara
Phnom Penh, Cambodia
Format: News; Sports. **Owner:** KCS Cambodia Co Ltd & Phnom Penh Municipality, at above address. **Founded:** Sept. 4, 1994. **Operating Hours:** Continuous. **Wattage:** 10,000. **Ad Rates:** Advertising accepted; rates available upon request. **URL:** http://www.camnet.com.kh/tv3/Radio103.htm.

43117 ■ Radio Radio-FM - 97 MHz
N 69, St. 57, Sangkat Beung Keng Kang 1
Khan Chamcarmon
Phnom Penh, Cambodia
Ph: 855 12949414
Fax: 855 23214302
E-mail: apsaratv@camnet.com.kh
Format: Information; News; Talk; Educational. **Operating Hours:** 5 a.m.-12 p.m. Daily. **Key Personnel:** Chet Sat, Dep. Exec. Dir. **Ad Rates:** Advertising accepted; rates available upon request. **URL:** http://www.apsaratv.com.kh.

43118 ■ VOA Khmer - 7155
PO Box 2306
Phnom Penh, Cambodia
Ph: 855 12515194
E-mail: khmer@voanews.com
Format: News; Information; Educational. **Operating Hours:** 1330-1430. **URL:** http://www.voanews.com/khmer.

43119 ■ VOA Khmer - 6060
PO Box 2306
Phnom Penh, Cambodia
Ph: 855 12515194
E-mail: khmer@voanews.com
Format: News; Information; Educational. **Operating Hours:** 2200-2230. **URL:** http://www.voanews.com/khmer.

43120 ■ VOA Khmer - 7130
PO Box 2306
Phnom Penh, Cambodia
Ph: 855 12515194
E-mail: khmer@voanews.com
Format: News; Information; Educational. **Operating Hours:** 2200-2230. **URL:** http://www.voanews.com/khmer.

43121 ■ VOA Khmer - 1575
PO Box 2306
Phnom Penh, Cambodia
Ph: 855 12515194
E-mail: khmer@voanews.com
Format: News; Information; Educational. **Operating Hours:** 1330-1430; 2200-2230. **URL:** http://www.voanews.com/khmer.

43122 ■ VOA Khmer - 5955
PO Box 2306
Phnom Penh, Cambodia
Ph: 855 12515194
E-mail: khmer@voanews.com
Format: News; Information; Educational. **Operating Hours:** 1330-1430. **URL:** http://www.voanews.com/khmer.

43123 ■ VOA Khmer - 15340
PO Box 2306
Phnom Penh, Cambodia
Ph: 855 12515194
E-mail: khmer@voanews.com
Format: News; Information; Educational. **Operating Hours:** 2200-2230. **URL:** http://www.voanews.com/khmer.

Circulation: ★ = ABC; △ = BPA; ♦ = CAC; • = CCAB; ❑ = VAC; ⊕ = PO Statement; ‡ = Publisher's Report; Boldface figures = sworn; Light figures = estimated.

Gale Directory of Publications & Broadcast Media/147th Ed. 4821

Buea

43124 ■ Journal of the Cameroon Academy of Sciences
African Journals Online
Biotechnology Unit
University of Buea, Box 63
SW Province
Buea, Cameroon
Publisher E-mail: info@ajol.info
Peer-reviewed journal covering all aspects of fundamental and applied research. **Freq:** 3/yr. **Key Personnel:** Prof. Vincent P.K. Titanji, Editor, titanji@aol.com. **Subscription Rates:** 20,000 Fr CFA individuals Cameroon; US$30 individuals Africa; US$40 individuals Europe/Asia; US$60 individuals America. **URL:** http://ajol.info/index.php/jcas.

Dschang

43125 ■ Cameroon Journal of Experimental Biology
African Journals Online
PO Box 377
Dschang, Cameroon
Publisher E-mail: info@ajol.info
Peer-reviewed journal covering the fields of experimental biology including biochemistry, physiology, pharmacology, toxicology, pathology, environmental biology, microbiology, parasitology, phytochemistry, food science, and agronomy. **Freq:** Semiannual. **Key Personnel:** Dr. Telesphore Benoit Nguelefack, Editor-in-Chief, fax 237 3452182, cafobios@yahoo.fr. **ISSN:** 1816-0573. **Subscription Rates:** US$20 individuals local; US$40 other

countries. **URL:** http://ajol.info/index.php/cajeb.

43126 ■ International Journal of Biological and Chemical Sciences
African Journals Online
PO Box 154
Dschang, Cameroon
Publisher E-mail: info@ajol.info
Peer-reviewed journal covering the fields of biology and chemistry. **Freq:** Quarterly. **Key Personnel:** Dr. Donatien Gatsing, Editor-in-Chief, phone 237 77 516740, fax 237 33 451102, ijbcs@yahoo.fr; Prof. Manuel Vazquez-Carrera, Assoc. Ed.; Dr. Ibrahim Hassan, Assoc. Ed. **ISSN:** 1991-8631. **Subscription Rates:** EUR40 individuals; EUR80 other countries. **URL:** http://ajol.info/index.php/ijbcs.

Ebolowa

43127 ■ RCDM-FM - 101
Centre Professionnel Don Bosco
Nko'ovos
BP 877
Ebolowa, Cameroon
Ph: 237 228 3804
E-mail: racodmvila@yahoo.fr
Format: Public Radio; Ethnic. **URL:** http://bosco.homily-service.net/rcdm/index.htm.

Yaounde

43128 ■ Cameroon Journal of Agricultural Science
African Journals Online
IRAD, Messa

Yaounde, Cameroon
Ph: 237 2233538
Fax: 237 2233538
Publisher E-mail: info@ajol.info
Peer-reviewed journal on agriculture and food science. **Freq:** Quarterly. **Key Personnel:** Dr. Jacob Mbua Ngeve, Editor-in-Chief, cjas_irad@yahoo.fr; M.O. Akoroda, International Editorial Board; R. Asiedu, International Editorial Board; O. Ndoye, International Editorial Board; J. Mbanya, Editorial Adviser; Ngah Yenika, Journal Sec.; I.L. Mbome, International Editorial Board; Rose Ekindi, Editorial Asst.; Dr. J.D. Ngou-Ngoupayou, Director; Dr. J.A. Ayuk-Takem, Director; Didier Richard, International Editorial Board; C. Nolte, International Editorial Board. **ISSN:** 1813-3320. **Subscription Rates:** 2,000 Fr CFA individuals; 4,000 Fr CFA individuals international; US$10 institutions Africa; US$20 institutions outside Africa. **URL:** http://ajol.info/index.php/cjas.

43129 ■ Clinics in Mother and Child Health
African Journals Online
PO Box 4362
Yaounde, Cameroon
Publisher E-mail: info@ajol.info
Peer-reviewed journal covering mother and child health issues. **Freq:** 3/yr. **Key Personnel:** Prof. D.O.H. Anderson, Editor-in-Chief, phone 237 2212431, fax 237 2212430, tandersondoh@yahoo.com; Dr. Chiabi Andreas, Contact, andy_chiabi@yahoo.co.uk. **ISSN:** 1812-5840. **Subscription Rates:** 10,000 Fr CFA individuals; US$500 individuals Africa; US$120 other countries. **URL:** http://ajol.info/index.php/cmch.

Circulation: ★ = ABC; △ = BPA; ◆ = CAC; • = CCAB; ❏ = VAC; ⊕ = PO Statement; ‡ = Publisher's Report; Boldface figures = sworn; Light figures = estimated.

Gale Directory of Publications & Broadcast Media/147th Ed. 4823

Buea

43124 ■ Journal of the Cameroon Academy of Sciences
African Journals Online
Biotechnology Unit
University of Buea, Box 63
SW Province
Buea, Cameroon
Publisher E-mail: info@ajol.info
Peer-reviewed journal covering all aspects of fundamental and applied research. Freq: 3/yr. Key Personnel: Prof. Vincent P.K. Titanji, Editor. titanji@aol.com. Subscription Rates: 20,000 Fr CFA individuals Cameroon, US$30 individuals Africa, US$40 individuals Europe, Asia, US$30 individuals America. URL: http://ajol.info/index.php/jcas.

Dschang

13125 ■ Cameroon Journal of Experimental Biology
African Journals Online
PO Box 377
Dschang, Cameroon
Publisher E-mail: info@ajol.info
Peer-reviewed journal covering the fields of experimental biology including biochemistry, physiology, pharmacology, toxicology, pathology, environmental biology, microbiology, parasitology, phytobanistry, food science, and agronomy. Freq: Semiannual. Key Personnel: Dr. Telesphore Benoit Nguelefack, Editor-in-Chief. fax 237 3345182. zaribio@yahoo.com. ISSN: 1816-0573. Subscription Rates: local, US$30 individuals local, US$40 other

43126 ■ International Journal of Biological and Chemical Sciences
African Journals Online
PO Box 164
Dschang, Cameroon
Publisher E-mail: info@ajol.info
Peer-reviewed journal covering the fields of biology and chemistry. Freq: Quarterly. Key Personnel: Dr. Dong-Hun Gatsing, Editor-in-Chief. phone 237 77 516 40. fax 237 33 451 02. jbos@yahoo.fr; Prof. Manuel Vazquez-Carrera, Assoc. Ed.; Dr. Ibrahim Hassan, Assoc. Ed. ISSN: 1991-8631. Subscription Rates: ... Africa, ... other countries. URL: http://ajol.info/index.php.

Ebolowa

43127 ■ RCGM-FM - 101
Centre Professionnel Don Bosco
Nko'ovos
BP 877
Ebolowa, Cameroon
Ph: 233 228 3804
E-mail: racedonvila@yahoo.fr
Format: Public Radio; Ethnic. URL: http://bosco.family.service.net/radio/index.htm

Yaounde

43128 ■ Cameroon Journal of Agricultural Science
African Journals Online
IRAD, Messa
Yaounde, Cameroon
PR 237 2223538
fax 237 2223538
Publisher E-mail: info@ajol.info
Peer-reviewed journal on agriculture and food science. Freq: Quarterly. Key Personnel: Dr. Jacob Ndoya, Editor-in-Chief. jtas_irad@yahoo.fr, M.G. Ako-roda, International Editorial Board; R. Asiedu, International Editorial Board; C.T. Ndoye, International Editorial Board; J. Mbaya, Editorial Adviser; Ngah Yanka Jaques Sap, T.; Mbome, International Editorial Board; Roca Ekpol, Editorial Adviser; Dr. J.D. Ngou Ngoupayou, Director; Dr. J.A. Ayuk-Takem, Director; Didier Bishan, International Editorial Board; C. Nolte, International Editorial Board. ISSN: 1813-3290. Subscription Rates: 2,000 Fr CFA individuals; 5,000 Fr CFA individuals International; US$70 institutions Africa; US$90 institutions outside Africa. URL: http://ajol.info/index.php/cjas.

43129 ■ Clinics in Mother and Child Health
African Journals Online
PO Box 4862
Yaounde, Cameroon
Publisher E-mail: info@ajol.info
Peer-reviewed journal covering mother and child health issues. Freq: 5/yr. Key Personnel: Prof. D.O.H Anderson, Editor-in-Chief. phone 237 221 2437, fax 237 221 2430, lamoresmoke@yahoo.com; Dr. Chiabi Andy, Contact. andy_chiabi@yahoo.co.uk. ISSN: 1812-5840. Subscription Rates: 10,000 Fr CFA individuals; US$40 individuals Africa; US$120 other countries. URL: http://ajol.info/index/php/cmch.

Grand Cayman

43130 ■ The Caymanian Compass
Cayman Free Press Ltd.
The Compass Ctr.
Shedden Rd.
PO Box 1365 GT
Grand Cayman, Cayman Islands
Ph: (345)949-5111
Fax: (345)949-7675
General newspaper. **Founded:** 1965. **Freq:** Daily. **Print Method:** Web offset. **Cols./Page:** 6. **Col. Depth:** 16 inches. **Remarks:** Accepts advertising. **URL:** http://www.caymanfreepress.com. **Ad Rates:** BW: CI$1,032, 4C: CI$1,512, PCI: CI$10.75. **Circ:** Controlled 10,500

43131 ■ C.I. Real Estate Magazine
Cayman Islands Real Estate Brokers Association
PO Box 1977
Grand Cayman, Cayman Islands
Ph: (345)949-7099
Fax: (345)949-6819
Publisher E-mail: cireba@candw.ky
Trade magazine covering real estate. **Freq:** Semiannual. **Subscription Rates:** US$40 U.S. and Canada; US$45 individuals U.K. and Europe. **Remarks:** Advertising accepted; rates available upon request. **URL:** http://www.cireba.com/. **Circ:** 13,000

Antofagasta

43132 ■ Proyecciones Journal of Mathematics
Universidad Catolica del Norte Departamento de
Matematicas
Casilla 1280
Antofagasta, Chile
Ph: 56 553 55571
Fax: 56 553 55599
Journal publishing papers on all areas of mathematics.
Also includes survey papers of quality. **Founded:** 1982.
Key Personnel: Ricardo Soto Montero, Editor, phone
56 55 355573, fax 56 55 355599, rsoto@ucn.cl; Aziz El
Kacimi, Editorial Committee International; Biswa N.
Datta, Editorial Committee International, dattab@math.
niu.edu; Carlos Conca, Editorial Committee National,
cconca@dim.uchile.cl; Graham Gladwell, Editorial Com-
mittee International, graham@gladwell.com. **ISSN:**
0716-0917. **Subscription Rates:** US$30 institutions;
US$18 individuals in Chile. **URL:** http://www.scielo.cl/
scielo.php?script=sci_serial&pid=0716-0917&lng=en&
nrm=.

Arica

43133 ■ IDESIA
Universidad de Tarapaca
Facultad de Ciencias Agronomicas
c/o Mauricio Jimenez Roco, Ed.
Facultad de Ciencias Agronomicas
Universidad de Tarapaca
Casilla
Arica 6, Chile
Ph: 56 582 05522
Fax: 56 582 20035
Publisher E-mail: edoussou@uta.cl
Journal covering farming sciences and compatible
disciplines. **Founded:** 1947. **Freq:** 3/yr. **Print Method:**
Offset. **Trim Size:** 6 x 9. **Cols./Page:** 1. **Col. Width:** 4
1/2 inches. **Col. Depth:** 7 inches. **Key Personnel:** Mau-
ricio Jimenez Roco, Editor, mjimonoz@uta.cl. **ISSN:**
0718-3429. **Subscription Rates:** 12,000 ChP individu-
als; US$8 other countries. **URL:** http://www.scielo.cl/
revistas/idesia/iinstruc.htm.

Chillan

43134 ■ Alborada-FM - 107.7
Av. Libertad
Chillan 821, Chile
Ph: 56 42 216009
Fax: 56 42 216009
Format: Public Radio. **Owner:** Alborada FM Radio, at
above address. **URL:** http://www.radioalborada.cl/.

Concepcion

43135 ■ Acta Literaria
Universidad de Concepcion
Victor Lamas 1290
Casilla 160-C
Concepcion, Chile
Ph: 56 412 204000

Fax: 56 412 227455
Literature magazine. **Founded:** 1936. **Freq:** Annual.
Print Method: Offset. **Trim Size:** 8 1/4 x 11. **Cols./
Page:** 2. **Col. Width:** 19 picas. **Col. Depth:** 54 picas.
ISSN: 0022-0337. **Subscription Rates:** US$10 individu-
als; US$17 U.S. America; US$20 individuals Europe.
URL: http://www.udec.cl/panoramaweb/index.php?
option=com_content&task=view&id=154&Itemid=122.

43136 ■ Celulosa y Papel
Pulp and Paper Technical Association
Asociacion Tecnica de la Celulosa y Papel
Janequeo 884 dep. 404
Concepcion, Chile
Ph: 56 41 2888131
Publisher E-mail: atcpchile@atcp.cl
Spanish language publication covering paper. **Freq:** 5/yr.
Subscription Rates: 110.65 ChP individuals; 22.13 ChP
individuals. **Remarks:** Advertising accepted; rates avail-
able upon request. **URL:** http://www.atcp.cl/Revista_
Tarifa.asp. **Circ:** (Not Reported)

Curico

43137 ■ Alfaomega-FM - 106.5
Avenida Alessandri 1185
Curico, Chile
Ph: 56 75 385339
Format: Ethnic; News; World Beat. **Operating Hours:**
16 hours Daily. **URL:** http://www.radioalfaomega.cl.

Iquique

43138 ■ Caribe-FM - 104.9
Tarapaca 1488
Iquique, Chile
Ph: 56 57 428825
E-mail: radio@caribefm.cl
Format: Ethnic; World Beat. **Ad Rates:** Advertising ac-
cepted; rates available upon request. **URL:** http://www.
caribefm.cl.

43139 ■ Radio Paulina-FM - 89.3
Riquelme 1032
Iquique, Chile
Ph: 56 57 391031
Fax: 56 57 391034
E-mail: info@radiopaulina.cl
Format: Information; Ethnic. **Operating Hours:** 20
hours Daily. **Ad Rates:** Advertising accepted; rates avail-
able upon request. **URL:** http://www.radiopaulina.cl.

Los Angeles

43140 ■ El Rotario de Chile
Casilla 413
Los Angeles, Chile
Ph: 56 46 43363178
Fax: 56 46 43363350
Publisher E-mail: fsocias@ctcinternet.cl
Membership magazine of Rotary International covering
current news about Rotary-related subjects in Spanish.
Founded: 1927. **Freq:** Bimonthly. **Key Personnel:**
Francisco Socias, Editor, fsocias@ctcinternet.cl. **URL:**
http://www.rotary.org/en/MediaAndNews/

MorePublications/RegionalMagazines/Pages/ridefault.
aspx. **Circ:** 5,800

Melipilla

43141 ■ Caricia-FM - 104.5
Avenida Ortuzar 935
Melipilla, Chile
Ph: 56 831 1023
Format: Ethnic; World Beat. **Wattage:** 1000. **URL:**
http://www.fmcaricia.cl.

Santiago

43142 ■ Acta Bioethica
Unidad de Bioetica de la Organizacion Panamericana
de la Salud/Organizacion Mundial de la Salud
Avenida Providencia No. 1017, Piso 7
Casilla 61-T
Santiago, Chile
Ph: 56 2 2360330
Fax: 56 2 7692377
Publisher E-mail: bioetica@chi.ops-oms.org
Journal offering pluralists perspectives on bioethical is-
sues in scientific research. **Key Personnel:** Dr.
Fernando Lolas Stepke, Director, phone 56 2 9782274,
fax 56 2 9782254, flolas@uchile.cl; Alvaro Quezada
Sepulveda, Gen. Ed., alquezad@uchile.cl. **ISSN:** 0717-
5906. **URL:** http://www.scielo.cl/revistas/abioeth/eaboutj.
htm.

43143 ■ Cuadernos de Economia
Instituto de Economia
Vicuna Mackenna, Macul
Santiago 4860, Chile
Ph: 56 235 44303
Fax: 56 255 32377
Journal covering advances in economic theory, method-
ology and applications. **Freq:** 2/yr (March and
November). **Key Personnel:** Juan Pablo Montero, Edi-
tor; Jose Miguel Sanchez, Editor; Raimundo Soto,
Editor. **Subscription Rates:** US$9 individuals Chile;
US$30 individuals Latin America; US$40 individuals U.S.
and Europe. **URL:** http://www.cuadernosdeeconomia.cl.

43144 ■ Cuadernos Mujer Salud
Latin American and Caribbean Women's Health
Network
Casilla Postal 50610
Santiago 1
Santiago, Chile
Ph: 56 2 2237077
Fax: 56 2 2231066
Publisher E-mail: secretaria@reddesalud.org
Spanish language publication covering women.
Founded: 1996. **Freq:** Annual. **Key Personnel:** Adriana
Gomez, Editor, agomez@reddesalud.org. **Subscription
Rates:** US$30 individuals. **Remarks:** Advertising not
accepted. **URL:** http://www.reddesalud.org/recursos/
rec2.php. **Circ:** (Not Reported)

**43145 ■ Journal of Technology Management &
Innovation**
JOTMI Research Group
Universidad Alberto Hurtado
Facultad de Economia y Negocios

Circulation: ★ = ABC; △ = BPA; ♦ = CAC; • = CCAB; ❑ = VAC; ⊕ = PO Statement; ‡ = Publisher's Report; Boldface figures = sworn; Light figures = estimated.

Gale Directory of Publications & Broadcast Media/147th Ed. **4827**

erasmo Escala 1905
Santiago, Chile
Ph: 56 2 8897356
Peer-reviewed journal focusing on the managerial issues and challenges brought about by the increasing pace of technological advancement. **Founded:** 1949. **Freq:** Weekly (Wed.). **Print Method:** Offset. **Cols./Page:** 5. **Col. Width:** 1 7/10 inches. **Col. Depth:** 11 1/2 inches. **Key Personnel:** Jimenez M. Alejandro, Editor-in-Chief, ljimenez@jotmi.org; Tomas Bas, Managing Editor, tomas.bas@uai.cl; Jorge Rojas, Editorial Board. **ISSN:** 0718-2724. **URL:** http://www.jotmi.org/index.php.

43146 ■ Psykhe
Pontificia Universidad Catolica de Chile
Alameda 340
Oficina 13
Santiago, Chile
Fax: 56 222 23116
Publication E-mail: psykhe@uc.cl
Journal publishing articles in various scientific and professional fields. **Founded:** 1992. **Key Personnel:** Patricio Cumsille Eltit, PhD, Editor, psykhe@uc.cl. **ISSN:** 0717-0297. **Subscription Rates:** 30 ChP students in EPUC; 40 ChP students not in EPUC; US$130 students America; US$150 students, other countries; 45 ChP individuals professionals in EPUC; 60 ChP individuals non-professionals in EPUC; US$150 individuals America; US$170 other countries; 100 ChP institutions; US$250 institutions America. **URL:** http://www.scielo.cl/revistas/psykhe/iaboutj.htm.

43147 ■ Revista Mujer Salud
Latin American and Caribbean Women's Health Network
Casilla Postal 50610
Santiago 1
Santiago, Chile
Ph: 56 2 2237077
Fax: 56 2 2231066
Publisher E-mail: secretaria@reddesalud.org
Spanish language publication covering women. **Founded:** 1990. **Freq:** Quarterly. **Key Personnel:** Adriana Gomez, Contact, publicaciones@reddesalud.org. **ISSN:** 0716-0321. **Subscription Rates:** US$70 individuals. **Remarks:** Advertising not accepted. **URL:** http://www.reddesalud.org/recursos/rec1.php. **Formerly:** Revista Redde Salud de las Mujeres Latinoamericanas y del Caribe. **Circ:** (Not Reported)

43148 ■ Revista de la SCCC
Chilean Computer Science Society
Sociedad Chilena de Ciencia de la Computacion
Blanco Encalada 2120
Casilla 2777
Santiago, Chile
English and Spanish language publication covering computer, science. **Freq:** Semiannual. **Key Personnel:** Mauricio Marin, Editor, mmarin@yahoo-inc.com. **ISSN:** 0717-4276. **Remarks:** Advertising accepted; rates available upon request. **URL:** http://www.dcc.uchile.cl/%7Emmarin/revista-sccc/sccc-web/; http://www.dcc.uchile.cl/1877/channel.html. **Circ:** (Not Reported)

43149 ■ Women's Health Collection
Latin American and Caribbean Women's Health Network
Casilla Postal 50610
Santiago 1
Santiago, Chile
Ph: 56 2 2237077
Fax: 56 2 2231066
Publisher E-mail: secretaria@reddesalud.org
Publication covering women's health. **Founded:** 1996.

Freq: Annual. **Key Personnel:** Deborah Meacham, Editor, dmeacham@reddesalud.org. **Subscription Rates:** US$30 individuals includes airmail delivery. **URL:** http://www.reddesalud.org/resourses/rec2.php.

43150 ■ Agricultura Radio-FM - 92.1
Manuel Rodriguez 15
Santiago, Chile
Ph: 56 2 3923000
Fax: 56 2 3923072
Format: Agricultural. **Operating Hours:** Continuous. **Ad Rates:** Advertising accepted; rates available upon request. **URL:** http://www.radioagricultura.cl.

43151 ■ Bio-Bio-FM - 96.9
Antonio Bellet 281
Santiago, Chile
Ph: 56 2 3919997
E-mail: biobio@laradio.cl
Format: Ethnic; World Beat. **Operating Hours:** Continuous. **URL:** http://www.radiobiobio.cl.

43152 ■ Carolina-FM - 99.3
Av. Santa Maria, piso 2. Providencia
Santiago 2670, Chile
Ph: 56 02 5717070
Fax: 56 02 5717071
Format: Album-Oriented Rock (AOR). **Owner:** Radio Carolina SA, at above address. **URL:** http://www.carolina.cl/onfire/.

43153 ■ Concierto-FM - 88.5
Eliodoro Yanez No. 1783
Santiago, Chile
Ph: 56 2 3902000
Fax: 56 2 3902047
E-mail: radio@concierto.cl
Format: Ethnic; World Beat. **URL:** http://www.concierto.cl.

43154 ■ Corazon-FM - 101.3
Av Eliodoro Yanez
Providencia
Santiago 1783, Chile
Format: Contemporary Hit Radio (CHR). **Owner:** PRISA, Gran Via 32, 28013 Madrid, Spain. **URL:** http://www.corazon.cl/.

43155 ■ Futuro-FM - 88.9
Eliodoro Yanez No. 1783
Santiago, Chile
Ph: 56 2 3902000
Fax: 56 2 3902047
E-mail: radio@futuro.cl
Format: Album-Oriented Rock (AOR); Jazz; Blues; Ethnic. **URL:** http://www.futuro.cl.

43156 ■ Horizonte-FM - 103.3
Av. Pocuro 2151
Santiago, Chile
Ph: 56 2 4105400
Fax: 56 2 4105460
Format: Ethnic; World Beat. **Owner:** Comunicaciones Horizonte, at above address. **Operating Hours:** Continuous. **Ad Rates:** Advertising accepted; rates available upon request. **URL:** http://www.horizonte.cl.

43157 ■ Imagina-FM - 88.1
Eliodoro Yanez No. 1783
Santiago, Chile
Ph: 56 2 3902000
Fax: 56 2 3812028
E-mail: radio@radioimagina.cl
Format: Ethnic; World Beat. **Operating Hours:** Continuous. **URL:** http://www.radioimagina.cl.

43158 ■ Infinita-FM - 100.1
Av. Los Leones 1285
Santiago, Chile
Ph: 56 2 7544400
Format: Adult Contemporary. **Ad Rates:** Advertising accepted; rates available upon request. **URL:** http://www.infinita.cl.

43159 ■ Radio Tierra-AM - 1300
Purisima No. 251
Recoleta
Santiago, Chile
Ph: 56 2 7377419
Format: Ethnic; World Beat. **Operating Hours:** Continuous. **Ad Rates:** Advertising accepted; rates available upon request. **URL:** http://www.radiotierra.com.

43160 ■ Rock y Pop-FM - 94.1
Eliodoro Yanez 1783
Santiago, Chile
Ph: 56 2 3812030
Fax: 56 2 3812028
E-mail: contacto@rockandpop.cl
Format: Alternative/New Music/Progressive; Contemporary Hit Radio (CHR); Heavy Metal. **Ad Rates:** Advertising accepted; rates available upon request. **URL:** http://www.rockandpop.cl.

43161 ■ Universidad de Chile Radio-FM - 102.5
Miguel Claro 509
Santiago, Chile
Ph: 56 2 9771573
E-mail: sohadht@uchile.cl
Format: Ethnic; Information; News. **Operating Hours:** Continuous. **Key Personnel:** Juan Pablo Cardenas Squella, Director, cardenas@uchile.cl. **URL:** http://www.radio.uchile.cl.

Valparaiso

43162 ■ Electronic Journal of Biotechnology
Pontificia Universidad Catolica De Valparaiso
Av. Brasil 2950
PO Box 4059
Valparaiso, Chile
International scientific electronic journal covering all areas related to biotechnology, from molecular biology and the chemistry of biological process to aquatic and earth environmental aspects, as well as computational applications, policy and ethical issues. **Freq:** 3/yr. **Key Personnel:** Graciela Munoz, Editor, edbiotec@ucv.cl. **ISSN:** 0717-3458. **Remarks:** Advertising accepted; rates available upon request. **URL:** http://www.ejbiotechnology.info/index.html. **Circ:** (Not Reported)

43163 ■ Radio Valparaiso-AM - 121
Eusebio Lillo 520 Local 12
Valparaiso, Chile
Ph: 56 32 2963793
Format: Information; Sports; Ethnic. **Owner:** Radio Valparaiso, at above address. **Operating Hours:** Continuous. **URL:** http://www.radiovalparaiso.cl.

Vina del Mar

43164 ■ UCV Radio-FM - 103.5
Agua Santa Alto 2455
Vina del Mar, Chile
Ph: 56 32 2768563
E-mail: info@ucvradio.cl
Format: Eighties; Contemporary Hit Radio (CHR). **Operating Hours:** 18 hours Daily. **Ad Rates:** Advertising accepted; rates available upon request. **URL:** http://www.ucvradio.cl.

Beijing

43165 ■ Acta Agronomica Sinica
Crop Science Society of China
12 Zhonggguancun Nan Dajie
Beijing 100081, People's Republic of China
Ph: 86 106 8918616
Fax: 86 106 8918616
Publication E-mail: xbzw@chinajournal.net.cn
Publisher E-mail: c09@cast.org.cn
Chinese and English language publication covering crop sciences. **Founded:** 1950. **Freq:** Monthly. **Key Personnel:** Xin Zhi-Yong, Editor-in-Chief, xinzhy@mail.caas.net.cn; Cheng Weihong, Editor-in-Chief, chengwh@mail.caas.net.cn. **ISSN:** 0496-3490. **Remarks:** Accepts advertising. **URL:** http://www.chinacrops.org/zwxb/en/dqml.asp. **Formerly:** Journal of Agricultural Research (1952); Academic Journal of Agriculture (1961). **Ad Rates:** BW: US$500, 4C: US$1,500. **Circ:** 12,000

43166 ■ Acta Geologica Sinica
Geological Society of China
26 Baiwanzhuang Rd.
Beijing 100037, People's Republic of China
Ph: 86 10 68999024
Fax: 86 10 68995305
Publisher E-mail: cgdzxh@yahoo.com.cn
Journal containing papers of all disciplines of geoscience. **Founded:** 1922. **Freq:** Quarterly. **ISSN:** 1000-9515. **Remarks:** Accepts advertising. **URL:** http://www.geojournals.cn/dzxben/ch/index.aspx. **Circ:** (Not Reported)

43167 ■ Acta Mathematicae Applicatae Sinica
Springer-Verlag Tokyo
Chinese Academy of Sciences
Academy of Math. & System Sciences
Beijing 100080, People's Republic of China
Publisher E-mail: info@springer.jp
Journal publishing high-quality research papers from all branches of applied mathematics, particularly welcoming those from partial differential equations, computational mathematics, applied probability, mathematical finance, statistics, dynamical systems, optimization and management science. **Freq:** Quarterly. **Key Personnel:** Tai-Ping Liu, Editor; Jia-An Yan, Editor; Mao-Cheng Cai, Assoc. Ed.; Hong Zhi An, Assoc. Ed.; Elton Hsu, Assoc. Ed.; Ji-Ye Han, Assoc. Ed.; Dao-Min Cao, Assoc. Ed.; Eckhard Platen, Assoc. Ed.; Gui-Qiang Chen, Assoc. Ed. **ISSN:** 0168-9673. **Subscription Rates:** EUR706 institutions print incl. free access or e-only; EUR847.20 institutions print incl. enhanced access. **Remarks:** Advertising accepted; rates available upon request. **URL:** http://www.springer.com/math/applications/journal/10255. **Circ:** (Not Reported)

43168 ■ Algebra Colloquium
World Scientific Publishing Company Private Ltd.
Academy of Mathematics & Systems Science
Chinese Academy of Sciences
Beijing 100190, People's Republic of China
Publisher E-mail: wspc@wspc.com.sg
Journal carrying original research articles of high level in the field of pure and applied algebra including papers from related areas, which have applications to algebra, aiming to reflect the latest developments in algebra and

promote international academic exchanges. **Founded:** 1994. **Freq:** Quarterly. **Key Personnel:** Zhexian Wan, Editor-in-Chief, wan@amss.ac.cn; Jiping Zhang, Editor-in-Chief, jzhang@pku.edu.cn; Yuen Fong, Dep. Ed.-in-Ch., fong@mail.ncku.edu.tw; Fu-An Li, Dep. Ed.-in-Ch., fal@math.ac.cn; Zhongming Tang, Managing Editor, zmtang@suda.edu.cn; Z. Arad, Editor, aradtzvi@math.biu.ac.il. **ISSN:** 1005-3867. **Subscription Rates:** US$594 institutions and libraries; electronic + print; US$570 institutions and libraries; electronic only; US$34 individuals for postage; S$970 institutions and libraries; electronic + print; S$931 institutions and libraries; electronic only; S$45 individuals for postage; EUR533 institutions and libraries; electronic + print; EUR512 institutions and libraries; electronic only; EUR23 individuals for postage. **Remarks:** Advertising accepted; rates available upon request. **URL:** http://www.worldscinet.com/ac/ac.shtml. **Circ:** (Not Reported)

43169 ■ Architectural Journal
Architectural Society of China
No. 9, Sanlihe Rd.
Beijing 100835, People's Republic of China
Ph: 86 108 8082239
Fax: 86 108 8082222
Publisher E-mail: asc@chinaasc.org
Chinese language journal covering architecture. **Freq:** Monthly. **ISSN:** 0529-1399. **Remarks:** Advertising accepted; rates available upon request. **URL:** http://www.aj.org.cn/. **Circ:** 65,000

43170 ■ Auto China
China Daily
6th Fl., B3 Tower, Ziguang Bldg.
No. 11 Huixin Dongjie
Chaoyang District
Beijing 100029, People's Republic of China
Ph: 86 10 84883300
Fax: 86 10 84883600
Periodical covering Chinese automotive industry. **Freq:** Biweekly. **Key Personnel:** Zhu Ling, Editor-in-Chief; Wang Ximin, Dep. Ed.-in-Ch.; Zhou Gengxin, Dep. Ed.-in-Ch. **URL:** http://www.chinadaily.com.cn/; http://bizchina.chinadaily.com.cn/shp_per.shtml. **Circ:** 4,000,000

43171 ■ Beijing Review
Beijing Review Publishing Co.
24 Baiwanzhuang Rd.
Beijing 100037, People's Republic of China
Ph: 86 106 8996288
Fax: 86 106 8328738
Publisher E-mail: contact@bjreview.com.cn
Periodical covering political, economic, and social developments in China today. **Subtitle:** A Magazine of Chinese News and Views. **Founded:** 1958. **Freq:** Weekly. **ISSN:** 1000-9140. **Subscription Rates:** 64 Yu individuals; 208 Yu individuals; 130 Yu individuals. **Remarks:** Advertising accepted; rates available upon request. **URL:** http://www.bjreview.com.cn/. **Circ:** ‡70,000

43172 ■ Beijing Tatler
Edipresse Asia
Bldg. No. 16, Rm. 911
China Central Pl.

89 Jian Guo Rd.
Chaoyang District
Beijing 100025, People's Republic of China
Ph: 86 10 52036778
Magazine featuring information about the business, cultural, social and sporting life of Beijing. **Freq:** Monthly. **Key Personnel:** Agatha Chan, Dir./Ch. Ed. **URL:** http://www.edipresse.com/en/par_pays/chine/magazines/beijing_tatler; http://www.bjtatler.com. **Circ:** ‡46,500

43173 ■ Beijing This Month
Asia Systems Media Corp.
Bldg. 10, Fahuasi
Tiyuguan Lu
Chongwen District
Beijing 100061, People's Republic of China
Ph: 86 10 67152382
Fax: 86 10 67152381
Publication E-mail: info@btmbeijing.com
Publisher E-mail: china@cbw.com
General interest periodical. **Freq:** Monthly. **Key Personnel:** Zhang Shirley, Dep. Ed.-in-Ch.; Ada Yuan, Sales Dir.; Wang Xuqing, Studio Dir.; Wang Lin, Bus. Devel. Dir.; Charles Dukes, Editorial Consultant; Huang Wei, Distribution Dir. **Remarks:** Accepts advertising. **URL:** http://www.btmbeijing.com. **Circ:** Free 70,000

43174 ■ British Business in China
British Chamber of Commerce in China
The British Ctr., Rm. 1001
China Life Tower
No. 16 Chaoyangmenwai Ave.
Beijing 100020, People's Republic of China
Ph: 86 108 5251111
Fax: 86 108 5251100
Publisher E-mail: information@pek.britcham.org
Publication covering British business in China. **Freq:** Bimonthly. **Subscription Rates:** Free. **Remarks:** Accepts advertising. **URL:** http://www.pek.britcham.org/. **Circ:** 2,000

43175 ■ Business Beijing
Asia Systems Media Corp.
Jian Wai SOHO, Bldg. 11, No. 2805
Chao Yang District
Beijing 100 022, People's Republic of China
Ph: 86 10 51661575
Fax: 86 10 59002947
Publisher E-mail: china@cbw.com
Chinese business magazine. **Freq:** Monthly. **Remarks:** Accepts advertising. **URL:** http://www.btmbeijing.com. **Circ:** 50,000

43176 ■ China Brief
American Chamber of Commerce - People's Republic of China
The Office Park, Tower AB, 6th Fl.
No. 10 Jintongxi Rd.
Beijing 100005, People's Republic of China
Ph: 86 10 85190800
Fax: 86 10 85190899
Publisher E-mail: amcham@amchamchina.org
Publication covering chambers of commerce. **Freq:** Monthly. **Remarks:** Advertising accepted; rates avail-

Circulation: ★ = ABC; △ = BPA; ♦ = CAC; • = CCAB; ❑ = VAC; ⊕ = PO Statement; ‡ = Publisher's Report; Boldface figures = sworn; Light figures = estimated.

Gale Directory of Publications & Broadcast Media/147th Ed. 4829

able upon request. **URL:** http://www.amchamchina.org/chinabrief. **Circ:** 2,100

43177 ■ China Business
China Business (Press) Hong Kong
103 No. 23 Bldg.
Guanying Yuan Xiqu
Xicheng District
Beijing 100035, People's Republic of China
Ph: 86 10 66561371
Fax: 86 10 66561412
Publication E-mail: xinli@chinabusiness-press.com
Publisher E-mail: songty@chinabusiness-press.com
English-language business magazine containing information involving domestic foreign trade companies, industrial-trading companies, power-enlarged enterprises, international hotels and commercial centers. **Founded:** 1993. **Freq:** 44/yr. **Key Personnel:** Li Xin, Editor-in-Chief. **Remarks:** Accepts advertising. **URL:** http://www.chinabusiness-press.com. **Circ:** (Not Reported)

43178 ■ China Daily (Hong Kong Edition)
China Daily
6th Fl., B3 Tower, Ziguang Bldg.
No. 11 Huixin Dongjie
Chaoyang District
Beijing 100029, People's Republic of China
Ph: 86 10 84883300
Fax: 86 10 84883600
Newspaper committed to helping the world know more about China and the country's integration with the international community. **Freq:** Daily. **URL:** http://www.chinadaily.com.cn/; http://www.chinadaily.com.cn/en/hk/index.html.

43179 ■ The China Nonprofit Review
Brill Academic Publishers
c/o Ming Wang, Ch. Ed.
Wushunde Bldg., Rm. 309
NGO Research Ctr., Tsinghua University
Haidan
Beijing 100084, People's Republic of China
Publication E-mail: nporeviewc@gmail.com
Publisher E-mail: marketing@brill.nl
Peer-reviewed journal covering China's non-profit organizations. **Freq:** Semiannual. **Key Personnel:** Ming Wang, Ch. Ed.; Zhihui Tong, Managing Editor. **ISSN:** 1876-5092. **Subscription Rates:** EUR50 individuals; US$68 individuals; EUR151 institutions; US$205 institutions; EUR137 institutions online only; US$186 institutions online only. **URL:** http://www.brill.nl/cnpr.

43180 ■ China Pictorial
China Pictorial Publishing House
33 Chegongzhuang W Rd.
Haidian District
Beijing 100044, People's Republic of China
Publisher E-mail: cnpictorial@gmail.com
Magazine featuring China's magnificent scenery, the life of its people, and its works of art. **Founded:** 1950. **Freq:** Monthly. **ISSN:** 0009-4420. **URL:** http://www.chinapictorial.com.cn/en/index.html. **Circ:** Paid 500,000

43181 ■ China's Foreign Trade
China Chamber of International Commerce
1 Fuxingmenwai St.
Beijing 100860, People's Republic of China
Ph: 86 10 88075716
Fax: 86 10 68030747
Publication E-mail: china@cbw.com
Periodical containing articles on Chinese economic development and specialty products, as well as information on Chinese imports and exports, and related policies and regulations. **Founded:** 1956. **Freq:** Monthly. **ISSN:** 0009-4498. **URL:** http://www.cbw.com/cft/. **Ad Rates:** BW: US$750, 4C: US$1,500. **Circ:** Paid 70,000

43182 ■ Chinese Chemical Letters
Institute of Materia Medica
Chinese Academy of Medical Sciences and Peking Union Medical College
1 Xian Nong Tan St.
Beijing 100050, People's Republic of China
Ph: 86 10 63037394
Fax: 86 10 63017757
Journal covering the entire spectrum of the discipline of chemistry. **Founded:** July 1990. **Freq:** Monthly. **Key Personnel:** Prof. Xiaoliang Wang, Editor-in-Chief. **ISSN:** 1001-8417. **URL:** http://www.imm.ac.cn/en/html/periodicals.html.

43183 ■ Chinese Journal of Applied Chemistry
Chinese Chemical Society
PO Box 2709
Beijing 100080, People's Republic of China
Ph: 86 10 62564020
Fax: 86 10 62568157
Chinese language journal covering chemistry. **Freq:** Bimonthly. **Key Personnel:** Jia-Zuan Ni, Editor. **ISSN:** 1000-0518. **Subscription Rates:** 16¥ individuals. **URL:** http://english.ciac.cas.cn/sp/200907/t20090710_22758.html.

43184 ■ Chinese Journal of Chemical Engineering
Elsevier Science Inc.
Institute of Process Engineering
Chinese Academy of Sciences
Beijing, People's Republic of China
Publisher E-mail: usinfo-ehelp@elsevier.com
Journal covering the field of chemical engineering. **Freq:** 6/yr. **Key Personnel:** Chen Jiayong, Editor-in-Chief; Yu Guocong, Editor.-in-Chief; Cen Peilin, Assoc. Ed.-in-Chief; Chen Bingzhen, Assoc. Ed.-in-Chief; Mao Zaisha, Assoc. Ed.-in-Chief; Wang Wenchuan, Assoc. Ed.-in-Chief; Xu Xi, International Advisory Board; Wang Jiading, International Advisory Board; J. Levec, International Advisory Board. **ISSN:** 1004-9541. **Subscription Rates:** US$520 institutions, other countries except Europe, Japan and Iran; EUR408 institutions for European countries and Iran; 59,300¥ institutions. **URL:** http://www.elsevier.com/wps/find/journaldescription.cws_home/707628/descrip tiondescription.

43185 ■ Chinese Journal of Plant Pathology
Chinese Society for Plant Pathology
China Agricultural University
435 Plant Protection Bldg.
Beijing 100094, People's Republic of China
Ph: 86 106 2891025
Fax: 86 106 2813785
Publisher E-mail: office@cspp.org.cn
Chinese language journal covering plant pathology. **Freq:** Bimonthly. **ISSN:** 0412-0914. **Remarks:** Advertising not accepted. **URL:** http://www.cspp.org.cn/English/index.htm. **Circ:** 1,500

43186 ■ Chinese Journal of Polymer Science
Chinese Chemical Society
PO Box 2709
Beijing 100080, People's Republic of China
Ph: 86 10 62564020
Fax: 86 10 62568157
Peer-reviewed Chinese journal covering polymer science. **Founded:** 1983. **Freq:** Bimonthly. **Key Personnel:** Fo-song Wang, Editor-in-Chief; Yong Cao, Assoc. Ed.; Shi-Kang Wu, Assoc. Ed. **ISSN:** 0256-7679. **URL:** http://www.cjps.org.

43187 ■ Chinese Medical Journal
Chinese Medical Association
c/o Wang Mouyue
42 Dongsi Xidajie
Beijing 100710, People's Republic of China
Ph: 86 10 85158321
Fax: 86 10 85158333
Publication E-mail: cmj@cma.org.cn
Publisher E-mail: cmawmy@cma.org.cn
Journal related to medicine. **Founded:** 1887. **Freq:** Semimonthly. **Key Personnel:** Ge-tu Zhaori, Ch. Ed. **ISSN:** 0366-6999. **Subscription Rates:** US$960 individuals; 1,200 Yu individuals for domestic. **URL:** http://www.cmj.org.

43188 ■ Chinese Photography
Chinese Photographers Association
61 Hongxing Huntong, Dongdan
Dongcheng District
Beijing 100005, People's Republic of China
Ph: 86 106 5252277
Publisher E-mail: cphoto@public.bta.com.cn
Chinese language publication covering photography. **Founded:** 1957. **Freq:** Monthly. **Trim Size:** 230 x 260 mm. **Key Personnel:** Wu Changyun, Editor-in-Chief; Li-ang Wenchuan, Dep. Ed.-in-Ch.; Li Bo, Dep. Ed.-in-Ch. **ISSN:** 0529-6420. **URL:** http://www.cphoto.com.cn/ss/; http://www.cpanet.com/english/about_us/department/zhongguo.htm. **Ad Rates:** GLR: US$1, PCI: US$15,000. **Circ:** Paid ⊕7,000

43189 ■ Chinese Physics Letters
IOP Publishing Ltd.

Dept. of Physics
Tsinghua University
Beijing 100084, People's Republic of China
Publication E-mail: cpl@aphy.iphy.ac.cn
Publisher E-mail: custserv@iop.org
Journal providing rapid publication of short reports and important research in all fields of physics and coverage of major advances in all aspects of physics, including the newest and most important achievements of physicists in China as well as other parts of the world. **Freq:** Monthly. **Key Personnel:** Zhu Bang-Fen, Editor; Li Xiu-Fang, Asst. to Ed.; Wu Jian-Lao, Asst. to Ed.; Huang Tao, Co-Ed.; Wang Ding-Sheng, Co-Ed.; Wu Ling-An, Co-Ed. **ISSN:** 0256-307X. **URL:** http://www.iop.org/EJ/journal/CPL.

43190 ■ Chinese Tales and Stories
Beijing Language and Culture University Press
No. 15, Xueyuan Rd.
Haidian District
Beijing 100083, People's Republic of China
Ph: 86 10 82303668
Publisher E-mail: service@blcup.net
Magazine featuring selected readings from Learning Chinese Magazine. **Founded:** Oct. 2003. **URL:** http://www.blcup.com/en/list_1.asp?id=902.

43191 ■ Communications in Theoretical Physics
IOP Publishing Ltd.
PO Box 2735
Beijing 100080, People's Republic of China
Ph: 86 10 62541813
Publication E-mail: ctp@iop.org
Publisher E-mail: custserv@iop.org
Scientific journal covering theoretical physics. **Founded:** 1982. **Freq:** Monthly. **Key Personnel:** Prof. Tso-Hsiu Ho, Editor-in-Chief; Prof. Kuang-Ta Chao, Co-Ed.; Prof. Yuan-Ben Dai, Co-Ed. **ISSN:** 0253-6102. **Subscription Rates:** US$768 institutions. **URL:** http://www.iop.org/EJ/journal/ctp.

43192 ■ Current Zoology
Institute of Zoology
Chinese Academy of Science
N Star 1 Hospital 5 Industry
W Rd., Chaong District
Beijing 100101, People's Republic of China
Ph: 86 10 64807098
Fax: 86 10 64807099
Publisher E-mail: ioz@ioz.ac.cn
Journal on zoology. **Founded:** 1935. **Freq:** Bimonthly. **Key Personnel:** Anming Meng, Editor-in-Chief; Zuwang Wang, Advisor, wangzw@panda.ioz.ac.cn. **Subscription Rates:** US$220 individuals; US$450 institutions including postage. **URL:** http://www.actazool.org/about.asp. **Formerly:** Acta Zoologica Sinica.

43193 ■ Folk Literature
Chinese Folk Literature and Art Society
10 Nongzhanguan Nanli
Nongzhanguan
Beijing 100026, People's Republic of China
Ph: 86 106 5004622
Fax: 86 106 5004622
Chinese language publication on folk literature. **Freq:** Monthly. **Remarks:** Advertising accepted; rates available upon request. **URL:** http://www.chinaculture.org/gb/en_artists/2003-09/24/content_26959.htm. **Circ:** 100,000

43194 ■ Genomics, Proteomics & Bioinformatics
Elsevier Science Inc.
Beijing Institute of Genomics
Chinese Academy of Sciences
Beijing, People's Republic of China
Publisher E-mail: usinfo-ehelp@elsevier.com
Journal covering genomics, proteomics, and bioinformatics. **Founded:** June 12, 1936. **Freq:** 4/yr. **Print Method:** Offset. **Cols./Page:** 6. **Col. Width:** 2 1/16 inches. **Col. Depth:** 294 agate lines. **Key Personnel:** Da-Cheng He, Editorial Board; Jun Yu, Editor-in-Chief, editor@genomics.org.cn; Frederick C. Leung, Editorial Board; Hwan-You Chang, Editorial Board; Run-Sheng Chen, Editorial Board; Jade Q. Clement, Editorial Board; Shu-Guang Huang, Editorial Board; Xun Gu, Editorial Board; Bai-Lin Hao, Editorial Board. **ISSN:** 1672-0229. **Subscription Rates:** 59,600¥ institutions; EUR410 institutions European countries and Iran; US$522 institutions, other countries except Europe, Japan and Iran. **URL:** http://www.elsevier.com/wps/find/

journaldescription.cws_home/707637/descriptiondescription.

43195 ■ Ham's CQ
Chinese Radio Sports Association
No. 14-A, Tiantan Dongli Zhongqu
PO Box 6106
Beijing 100061, People's Republic of China
Ph: 86 10 67050878
Fax: 86 10 67050899
Publication E-mail: ba1ham@amsat.org
Chinese language publication covering amateur radio. **Founded:** 1993. **Freq:** Quarterly. **Trim Size:** A4. **Subscription Rates:** Free to members only; US$40 nonmembers oversease. **URL:** http://www.crsa.org.cn. **Ad Rates:** BW: US$500, 4C: US$1,000. **Circ:** (Not Reported)

43196 ■ Intermetallics
Elsevier Science Inc.
c/o G. Chen, Ed.
University of Science & Technology
Beijing, People's Republic of China
Publisher E-mail: usinfo-ehelp@elsevier.com
Journal devoted to ordered chemical compounds between two or more metals and their applications. **Founded:** 1993. **Freq:** Monthly. **Print Method:** Web offset. **Trim Size:** 8 x 10 7/8. **Cols./Page:** 3. **Col. Width:** 27 nonpareils. **Col. Depth:** 140 agate lines. **Key Personnel:** G. Chen, Editor, glchen@bj.col.com.cn; Y. Mishima, Editor, mishima@materia.titech.ac.jp; V. Paidar, Editor, paidar@fzu.cz; R.W. Cahn, Founding Ed., rwc12@cam.ac.uk; I. Baker, Editorial Board; Y.A. Chang, Editorial Board; H. Clemens, Editorial Board; D.M. Dimiduk, Editorial Board; D. Banerjee, Editorial Board; S.C. Deevi, Editorial Board. **ISSN:** 0966-9795. **Subscription Rates:** EUR2,477 institutions for European countries and Iran; US$2,772 institutions, other countries except Europe, Japan and Iran; 329,100¥ institutions for Japan. **URL:** http://www.elsevier.com/wps/find/journaldescription.cws_home/423924/descriptiondescription.

43197 ■ International Journal of Intelligent Computing and Cybernetics
Emerald Group Publishing Ltd.
Beihang University
No. 37, Xueyuan Rd., Haidan District
Beijing 100 191, People's Republic of China
Publisher E-mail: emerald@emeraldinsight.com
Journal focusing on the study and understanding of the underlying principles of natural computation, and how these principles can be adopted or modified to extend and enrich computer science and engineering. **Freq:** 3/yr. **Key Personnel:** Haibin Duan, Editor-in-Chief, ijicc@buaa.edu.cn; Harry Colson, Publisher, hcolson@emeraldinsight.com. **ISSN:** 1756-378X. **URL:** http://info.emeraldinsight.com/products/journals/journals.htm?id=ijicc.

43198 ■ International Journal of Intelligent Engineering Informatics
Inderscience Enterprises Limited
c/o Dr. Lean Yu, Ed.-in-Ch.
Chinese Academy of Sciences
Academy of Mathematics & Systems Science
Beijing 100190, People's Republic of China
Journal covering the interdisciplinary research on artificial intelligence, cognitive science, knowledge engineering, information technology, and engineering management. **Freq:** 4/yr. **Key Personnel:** Dr. Lean Yu, Editor in Chief, ijieieditor@gmail.com; Prof. Nickolas S. Sapidis, Managing Editor, nsapidis@uowm.gr. **ISSN:** 1758-8715. **Subscription Rates:** EUR494 individuals print or online; EUR672 individuals print and online. **URL:** http://www.inderscience.com/browse/index.php?journalID=338.

43199 ■ International Journal of Multimedia Intelligence and Security
Inderscience Enterprises Limited
c/o Dr. Shiguo Lian, Ed.-in-Ch.
2 Science Institute South Rd.
Haidian District
Beijing 100080, People's Republic of China
Peer-reviewed journal covering the disciplines of intelligent computing, information security, biometrics, multimedia processing, communication, and applications. **Freq:** 4/yr. **Key Personnel:** Dr. Shiguo Lian, Editor-in-Chief, shiguo.lian@orange-ftgroup.com; Prof. Frank Y. Smith, Editor-in-Chief, shih@njit.edu.

ISSN: 2042-3462. **Subscription Rates:** EUR494 individuals print or online; EUR672 individuals print and online. **URL:** http://www.inderscience.com/browse/index.php?journalID=359.

43200 ■ International Journal of Sediment Research
International Research and Training Center on Erosion and Sedimentation
20 West Chegongzhuang Rd.
PO Box 366
Beijing 100044, People's Republic of China
Ph: 86 106 8413372
Fax: 86 106 8411174
Publisher E-mail: irtces@public.east.cn.net
Journal covering worldwide geology. **Freq:** Quarterly. **Key Personnel:** Prof. Wang Zhao-Yin, Editor; Prof. S.Y. Wang, Dep. Ch. Ed.; Prof. Zhou Jianjun, Dep. Ch. Ed.; C.S. Melching, Dep. Ch. Ed.; Prof. Baosheng Wu, Dep. Ch. Ed.; Prof. D. Knight, Dep. Ch. Ed.; Prof. T. Takahashi, Dep. Ch. Ed.; Prof. W.H. Graf, Dep. Ch. Ed. **ISSN:** 1001-6279. **Subscription Rates:** US$35 individuals surface mail service; US$120 members five years with surface mail service; US$96 nonmembers air mail service; US$35 members surface mail service. **Remarks:** Advertising accepted; rates available upon request. **URL:** http://www.irtces.org/old/english/irtces_web/research.htm; http://www.waser.cn/journal/journal-main.asp. **Circ:** (Not Reported)

43201 ■ International Review of Pure and Applied Physics
Serials Publications
c/o Dr. Zuntao Fu, Ed.-in-Ch.
School of Physics
Peking University
Beijing 100871, People's Republic of China
Publisher E-mail: serials@satyam.net.in
Journal covering pure and applied physics and their applications. **Freq:** Semiannual. **Key Personnel:** Dr. Zuntao Fu, Editor-in-Chief, fuzt@pku.edu.cn. **Subscription Rates:** US$200 institutions print. **URL:** http://www.serialspublications.com/journals1.asp?jid=302&jtype=1.

43202 ■ Journal of Asian Natural Products Research
Taylor & Francis Group Journals
Institute of Materia Medica
Chinese Academy of Medical Sciences
1 Xian Nong Tan St.
Beijing 100050, People's Republic of China
Publisher E-mail: customerservice@taylorandfrancis.com
Peer-reviewed journal covering chemical and pharmaceutical studies in the English language in the field of natural product research on Asian ethnic medicine. **Freq:** 12/yr. **Key Personnel:** De-Quan Yu, Editor-in-Chief, edjanpr@imm.ac.cn; Ching-Jer Chang, Regional Ed.; Shi-Shan Yu, Vice Ed.-in-Ch.; Li-Xin Dai, Vice Ed.-in-Ch.; Yao Zuchen, Editorial Board. **ISSN:** 1028-6020. **Subscription Rates:** US$593 individuals print only; US$2,007 institutions online only; US$2,230 institutions print & online; 1,719 institutions print & online; 1,547 institutions online; 488 individuals; EUR1,774 institutions print and online; EUR1,597 institutions online only; EUR472 individuals. **URL:** http://www.tandf.co.uk/journals/titles/10286020.asp.

43203 ■ Journal of Building Structure
Architectural Society of China
No. 9, Sanlihe Rd.
Beijing 100835, People's Republic of China
Ph: 86 108 8082239
Fax: 86 108 8082222
Publisher E-mail: asc@chinaasc.org
Journal covering architecture. **URL:** http://www.chinaasc.org/english/.

43204 ■ Journal of Chinese Economic and Foreign Trade Studies
Emerald Group Publishing Ltd.
c/o Prof. Zhongxiu Zhao, Editor
University of International Business & Economics
10 E Huixin St., Chaoyang District
Beijing 100 029, People's Republic of China
Publisher E-mail: emerald@emeraldinsight.com
Journal publishing both qualitative and quantitative research in all areas of Chinese business and foreign trade, technical economics, business environment, and business strategy. **Freq:** 3/yr. **Key Personnel:** Prof. Guijun Lin, Editor-in-Chief; Prof. Zhongxiu Zhao, Editor,

zhaozhx@263.net; Kelly Dutton, Publisher, kdutton@emeraldinsight.com. **ISSN:** 1754-4408. **URL:** http://info.emeraldinsight.com/products/journals/journals.htm?id=jcefts.

43205 ■ Journal of Computer Science and Technology (JCST)
Institute of Computing Technology, Chinese Academy of Sciences
No. 6 Kexueyuan South Rd.
Zhongguancun
Haidian District
PO Box 2704
Beijing 100090, People's Republic of China
Ph: 86 10 62601166
Fax: 86 10 62567724
Publication E-mail: jcst@ict.ac.cn
Publisher E-mail: xuanchuan@ict.ac.cn
Journal focusing on the fields related to computers in China. **Freq:** Bimonthly. **Key Personnel:** Prof. Jordan Ramiro, Editor, rjordan@istec.org; Ming Li, Assoc. Ed.-in-Ch.; Xiao-Dong Zhang, Exec. Ed.; Guo-Jie Li, Editor-in-Chief; Chuang Lin, Assoc. Ed.-in-Ch. **ISSN:** 1000-9000. **Remarks:** Advertising accepted; rates available upon request. **URL:** http://journal.info.unlp.edu.ar/journal/. **Circ:** (Not Reported)

43206 ■ Journal of Genetics and Genomics
Elsevier Science Inc.
Institute of Genetics & Developmental Biology
Chinese Academy of Sciences
Beijing 100101, People's Republic of China
Publisher E-mail: usinfo-ehelp@elsevier.com
Journal serving research results of genetics. **Founded:** 1974. **Freq:** Monthly. **Print Method:** Offset. Uses mats. **Trim Size:** 7 7/8 x 10 7/8. **Cols./Page:** 3. **Col. Width:** 2 1/8 inches. **Col. Depth:** 10 1/8 inches. **Key Personnel:** Liang-Biao Chen, Assoc. Ed., lbchen@genetics.ac.cn; Kang Chong, Editorial Board; Fu-Chu He, Advisory Board; Lin He, Advisory Board; Yong-Biao Xue, Editor-in-Chief, ybxue@genetics.ac.cn. **ISSN:** 1673-8527. **Subscription Rates:** EUR821 institutions for European countries and Iran; 119,300¥ institutions for Japan; US$1,043 institutions, other countries except Europe, Japan and Iran. **URL:** http://www.jgenetgenomics.org/EN/volumn/home.shtml; http://www.elsevier.com/wps/find/journaldescription.cws_home/712433/descriptiondescription. **Formerly:** Acta Genica Sinica.

43207 ■ Journal of Geographical Sciences
11 A Datun Rd.
Beijing 100101, People's Republic of China
Publication E-mail: jgs@igsnrr.ac.cn
Publisher E-mail: jgs@igsnrr.ac.cn
Professional journal covering geographical science. **Founded:** 1990. **Freq:** Quarterly. **Trim Size:** 188 x 260 mm. **Key Personnel:** Changming Liu, Assoc. Ed.-in-Ch.; Du Zheng, Editor-in-Chief. **ISSN:** 1009-637X. **Subscription Rates:** EUR573 institutions; EUR687.60 institutions print & enchanced access. **Remarks:** Accepts advertising. **URL:** http://www.springerlink.com/content/119805/. **Ad Rates:** BW: 550 Yu, 4C: 750 Yu. **Circ:** Paid ‡700

43208 ■ Journal of Molecular Structure
Chinese Chemical Society
PO Box 2709
Beijing 100080, People's Republic of China
Ph: 86 10 62564020
Fax: 86 10 62568157
Journal covering molecular structure. **Freq:** Quarterly. **Key Personnel:** Prof. Xibai Qiu, Contact, qiuxb@infoc3.icas.ac.cn. **URL:** http://www.ccs.ac.cn/web/ccsinfoen/index.htm.

43209 ■ Journal of Systems Science and Information
Research Information Ltd.
c/o Prof. Guowu Zhang, Ed.-in-Ch.
Rm. 1208/1209, Siyuan Bldg.
Northern Jiaotong University
Beijing 100044, People's Republic of China
Publisher E-mail: info@researchinformation.co.uk
Journal publishing and providing a forum for the dissemination of academic papers on systems science, and information science of interest to researchers and professionals working in systems analysis, data processing, modelling and control, and decision-making in all fields of science and engineering, where a system based approach is required. **Freq:** Quarterly. **Key Personnel:** John R. Meyer, International Editorial Board; Prof.

Guowu Zhang, Editor-in-Chief, gwzhang@center.njtu.edu.cn; Ad Bastiaansen, International Editorial Board; Edward C. Sillivan, International Editorial Board; Lei Yu, International Editorial Board; Jianping Wu, International Editorial Board. **ISSN:** 1478-9906. **Subscription Rates:** 288 individuals standard; US$576 individuals standard. **Remarks:** Advertising not accepted. **URL:** http://www.researchinformation.co.uk/jssi.php. **Circ:** (Not Reported)

43210 ■ Learning Chinese
Beijing Language and Culture University Press
No. 15, Xueyuan Rd.
Haidian District
Beijing 100083, People's Republic of China
Ph: 86 10 82303668
Publisher E-mail: service@blcup.net
Magazine featuring Chinese language. **Trim Size:** 185 x 260 mm. **Subscription Rates:** 300 Yu individuals. **URL:** http://www.blcup.com/en/list_1.asp?id=1931.

43211 ■ Life in China
Beijing Language and Culture University Press
No. 15, Xueyuan Rd.
Haidian District
Beijing 100083, People's Republic of China
Ph: 86 10 82303668
Publisher E-mail: service@blcup.net
Magazine featuring selected readings from Learning Chinese Magazine. **Founded:** Oct. 2003. **Trim Size:** 185 x 260 mm. **Subscription Rates:** 15 Yu individuals. **URL:** http://www.blcup.com/en/list_1.asp?id=900.

43212 ■ Particuology
Elsevier
c/o Mooson Kwauk, Ed.-in-Ch.
Institute of Process Engineering
Chinese Academy of Sciences
Beijing, People's Republic of China
Ph: 86 106 2554050
Journal covering papers on research, engineering, and applications in the field of particuology, including particle characterization, particle preparation, aerosol, fluidization and ultra-fine particles. **Founded:** 1905. **Freq:** Bimonthly. **Print Method:** Offset. **Trim Size:** 13 x 22 3/4. **Cols./Page:** 6. **Col. Width:** 25 nonpareils. **Col. Depth:** 129 agate lines. **Key Personnel:** Mooson Kwauk, Editor-in-Chief, mooson@home.ipe.ac.cn; Han Xu, Editor; Zhuyou Cao, Exec. Ed., phone 86 10 82629146, jcsp@home.ipe.ac.cn; Yunru Bai, Editor; Xiaoli Zhao, Editor. **ISSN:** 1674-2001. **Subscription Rates:** US$318 institutions all countries except Europe, Japan & Iran; EUR285 institutions European countries & Iran; 37,700¥ institutions. **URL:** http://www.elsevier.com/wps/find/journaldescription.editors/714856/descriptiondescription. **Formerly:** China Particuology.

43213 ■ People's Daily
People's Daily Online
Jintaixi Rd. No. 2
Chaoyang District
Beijing 100733, People's Republic of China
Ph: 86 10 65363470
Publication E-mail: info@peopledaily.com.cn
Publisher E-mail: info@peopledaily.com.cn
General online newspaper. **Founded:** June 1948. **Freq:** Daily. **Remarks:** Advertising accepted; rates available upon request. **URL:** http://english.peopledaily.com.cn/. **Circ:** 3,000,000

43214 ■ Rare Metals
No. 30
Xueyuanlu
Beijing 100083, People's Republic of China
Ph: 86 106 2333436
Fax: 86 106 2332875
Publication covering rare metals and nonferrous metals. **Founded:** 1982. **Freq:** Bimonthly. **Trim Size:** B5. **ISSN:** 1001-0521. **Remarks:** Advertising accepted; rates available upon request. **URL:** http://www.elsevier.com/wps/find/journaldescription.cws_home/708738/descriptiondescription. **Circ:** 1,000

43215 ■ Science in China Series A
Science in China Press
16, Dong-huang-cheng-gen N St.
Beijing 100717, People's Republic of China
Ph: 86 10 64016350
Journal featuring basic mathematics, applied mathematics, calculation mathematics and science engineering calculation, and statistics. **Subtitle:** Mathematics. **Freq:** Monthly. **Key Personnel:** Yang Le, Editor-in-Chief.

ISSN: 1006-9283. **Remarks:** Accepts advertising. **URL:** http://zh.scichina.com/new_web_en/Journals.asp?num=02. **Circ:** (Not Reported)

43216 ■ Science in China Series B
Science in China Press
16, Dong-huang-cheng-gen N St.
Beijing 100717, People's Republic of China
Ph: 86 10 64016350
Journal featuring theoretical chemistry, physical chemistry, organic chemistry, inorganic chemistry, polymer chemistry, biological chemistry, environmental chemistry, and chemical engineering. **Subtitle:** Chemistry. **Freq:** Bimonthly. **Key Personnel:** Li Lemin, Editor-in-Chief. **ISSN:** 1006-9291. **Remarks:** Accepts advertising. **URL:** http://zh.scichina.com/new_web_en/Journals.asp?num=04. **Circ:** (Not Reported)

43217 ■ Science in China Series C
Science in China Press
16, Dong-huang-cheng-gen N St.
Beijing 100717, People's Republic of China
Ph: 86 10 64016350
Journal featuring biology, agriculture, and medicine. **Subtitle:** Life Sciences. **Freq:** Bimonthly. **Key Personnel:** Dacheng Wang, Editor-in-Chief; Ji Yuan Li, Managing Editor. **ISSN:** 1006-9305. **Remarks:** Accepts advertising. **URL:** http://zh.scichina.com/new_web_en/Journals.asp?num=06. **Circ:** (Not Reported)

43218 ■ Science in China Series D
Science in China Press
16, Dong-huang-cheng-gen N St.
Beijing 100717, People's Republic of China
Ph: 86 10 64016350
Journal featuring geology, geochemistry, geophysics, geography, atmospheric sciences, and ocean sciences. **Subtitle:** Earth Sciences. **Freq:** Monthly. **Key Personnel:** Shu Sun, Editor-in-Chief; Jian Xue Zi, Managing Editor; Jian Jing Wei, Managing Editor. **ISSN:** 1006-9313. **Remarks:** Accepts advertising. **URL:** http://zh.scichina.com/new_web_en/Journals.asp?num=08. **Circ:** (Not Reported)

43219 ■ Science in China Series E
Science in China Press
16, Dong-huang-cheng-gen N St.
Beijing 100717, People's Republic of China
Ph: 86 10 64016350
Journal featuring mechanical engineering, engineering thermophysics, electronic engineering, architecture, astronomics, civil engineering, nuclear science and technology. **Subtitle:** Technological Sciences. **Freq:** Monthly. **Key Personnel:** Yan Luguang, Editor-in-Chief; Mei An, Managing Editor. **ISSN:** 1006-9321. **URL:** http://zh.scichina.com/new_web_en/Journals.asp?num=10.

43220 ■ Science in China Series F
Science in China Press
16, Dong-huang-cheng-gen N St.
Beijing 100717, People's Republic of China
Ph: 86 10 64016350
Journal featuring computer science and technology, control science and technology, communication and information system, electronic science and technology, and bioinformation. **Subtitle:** Information Science. **Freq:** Monthly. **Key Personnel:** Li Wei, Editor-in-Chief; Fei Song, Managing Editor. **ISSN:** 1009-2757. **URL:** http://zh.scichina.com/new_web_en/Journals.asp?num=12.

43221 ■ Science in China Series G
Science in China Press
16, Dong-huang-cheng-gen N St.
Beijing 100717, People's Republic of China
Ph: 86 10 64016350
Journal featuring basic and applied research in the fields of physics, dynamics, and astronomy. **Subtitle:** Physics, Mechanics & Astronomy. **Freq:** Monthly. **Key Personnel:** Dingsheng Wang, Editor-in-Chief; Quan E. Zhu, Managing Editor; Yan Hong Huang, Managing Editor. **ISSN:** 1672-1799. **URL:** http://zh.scichina.com/new_web_en/Journals.asp?num=14.

43222 ■ Tsinghua Science & Technology
Elsevier Science Inc.
c/o Baicheng Liu, Chm. of Editorial Committee
Tsinghua University
Beijing 100084, People's Republic of China
Publisher E-mail: usinfo-ehelp@elsevier.com
Journal covering basic theory and experimental studies in engineering fields. **Founded:** 2005. **Freq:** 6/yr. **Print**

Method: Offset. **Cols./Page:** 6. **Col. Width:** 24 nonpareils. **Col. Depth:** 295 agate lines. **Key Personnel:** Zhicheng Guan, Vice Chm. of Editorial Committee; Jialin Zhu, Vice Chm. of Editorial Committee; Song Fu, Vice Chm. of Editorial Committee; Yongjun Zhu, Vice Chm. of Editorial Committee; Cewen Nan, Vice Chm. of Editorial Committee; Wentao Du, Vice Chm. of Editorial Committee; Zhan Xu, Vice Chm. of Editorial Committee; Baicheng Liu, Chm. of Editorial Committee. **ISSN:** 1007-0214. **URL:** http://www.elsevier.com/wps/find/journaldescription.cws_home/704058/descriptiondescription.

43223 ■ Women of China
All China Women's Federation
Federation des Femmes Chinoises
15 Jia Guo Men Nei St.
Beijing 100730, People's Republic of China
Ph: 86 106 5103556
Fax: 86 106 5112107
Publisher E-mail: womenofchina@163.com
Publication covering feminism in China. **Freq:** Monthly. **Key Personnel:** Chen Zhili, President; Song Xiuyan, Vice President. **Remarks:** Accepts advertising. **URL:** http://www.womenofchina.cn/Publications/. **Circ:** 150,000

43224 ■ Wood Industry
Research Institute of the Wood Industry
Chinese Academy of Forestry
Wan Shou Shan
Beijing 100091, People's Republic of China
Ph: 86 10 62889410
Fax: 86 10 62881937
Publisher E-mail: office.mg@wood.forestry.ac.cn
Chinese and English language publication covering forest industries. **Freq:** Bimonthly Jan. March, May, July, Sept., and Nov. **Key Personnel:** Wang Kai, Editor-in-Chief. **ISSN:** 1001-8654. **Subscription Rates:** US$37 individuals Hong Kong, Macao, Taiwan; US$51 out of area. **Remarks:** Advertising accepted; rates available upon request. **URL:** http://www.forestry.ac.cn/newcaf/english/wood/mcgyy.htm. **Circ:** 5,000

43225 ■ World Journal of Gastroenterology
The WJG Press
Biomed Scientific Co. Ltd.
Rm. 903, Bldg. D, Ocean
International Ctr., No. 62
Dongsihuan Zhonglu, Chaoyang
Beijing 100025, People's Republic of China
Ph: 86 105 9080039
Fax: 86 108 5381893
Publisher E-mail: wjg@wjgnet.com
Journal covering gastroenterology, hepatology and endoscopy, with particular emphasis on clinical research and continuing education in the Asia Pacific region. **Key Personnel:** Lian-Sheng Ma, Editor-in-Chief. **URL:** http://www.wjgnet.com/1007-9327/bwcy.asp.

43226 ■ Beijing People's Broadcasting Station - 103.9 MHz
14 Jian Wai St.
Beijing 100022, People's Republic of China
Format: Information; Public Radio; News. **Founded:** Dec. 18, 1993. **Operating Hours:** Continuous. **Wattage:** 10,000. **URL:** http://www.fm1039.com.cn.

43227 ■ CCTV 8 - 8
11B, Fuxing Rd.
Media Ctr.
Beijing 100038, People's Republic of China
Ph: 86 10 88243346
E-mail: cctv-9@cctv.com
Format: Commercial TV. **Owner:** China Central Television, at above address. **Founded:** May 3, 1999. **Operating Hours:** 17 hours Daily. **URL:** http://www.cctv.com.

43228 ■ CCTV 5 - 5
11B, Fuxing Rd.
Media Ctr.
Beijing 100038, People's Republic of China
Ph: 86 10 88243346
E-mail: cctv-9@cctv.com
Format: Sports. **Owner:** China Central Television, at above address. **Founded:** Jan. 1, 1995. **Operating Hours:** 16 hours Daily. **URL:** http://www.cctv.com.

43229 ■ CCTV 4 - International - 4
11B, Fuxing Rd.
Media Ctr.

Beijing 100038, People's Republic of China
Ph: 86 10 88243346
E-mail: cctv-9@cctv.com
Format: News; Full Service. **Owner:** China Central Television, at above address. **Founded:** Oct. 1, 1992. **Operating Hours:** Continuous. **Ad Rates:** Advertising accepted; rates available upon request. **URL:** http://www.cctv.com.

43230 ■ CCTV 1 - 1
11B, Fuxing Rd.
Media Ctr.
Beijing 100038, People's Republic of China
Ph: 86 10 88243346
E-mail: cctv-9@cctv.com
Format: News; Information. **Owner:** China Central Television, at above address. **Founded:** Sept. 2, 1958. **Ad Rates:** Advertising accepted; rates available upon request. **URL:** http://www.cctv.com.

43231 ■ CCTV 7 - 7
11B, Fuxing Rd.
Media Ctr.
Beijing 100038, People's Republic of China
Ph: 86 10 88243346
E-mail: cctv-9@cctv.com
Format: Agricultural. **Owner:** China Central Television, at above address. **Founded:** Nov. 30, 1995. **Operating Hours:** 17 hours Daily. **URL:** http://www.cctv.com.

43232 ■ CCTV 6 - 6
11B, Fuxing Rd.
Media Ctr.
Beijing 100038, People's Republic of China
Ph: 86 10 88243346
E-mail: cctv-9@cctv.com
Format: Commercial TV. **Owner:** China Central Television, at above address. **Founded:** Jan. 1, 1996. **Operating Hours:** 17 hours Daily. **URL:** http://www.cctv.com.

43233 ■ CCTV 3 - 3
11B, Fuxing Rd.
Media Ctr.
Beijing 100038, People's Republic of China
Ph: 86 10 88243346
E-mail: cctv-9@cctv.com
Format: Classical. **Owner:** China Central Television, at above address. **Founded:** Nov. 30, 1995. **Operating Hours:** 19 hours Daily. **Ad Rates:** Advertising accepted; rates available upon request. **URL:** http://www.cctv.com.

43234 ■ CCTV 2 - 2
11B, Fuxing Rd.
Media Ctr.
Beijing 100038, People's Republic of China
Ph: 86 10 88243346
E-mail: cctv-9@cctv.com
Format: Full Service; Information. **Owner:** China Central Television, at above address. **Founded:** Sept. 2, 1958. **Operating Hours:** 20 hours Daily. **Ad Rates:** Advertising accepted; rates available upon request. **URL:** http://www.cctv.com.

43235 ■ China National Radio 1 - 567 KHz
2 Fuxingmenwai Dajie
Xicheng Qu
Beijing 100866, People's Republic of China
Ph: 86 10 86093114
Fax: 86 10 63909751
E-mail: cn@cnr.cn
Format: Eclectic. **Owner:** The State Administration of Radio, Film and Television, at above address. **Key Personnel:** Yang Bo, Dir. Gen. **Ad Rates:** Advertising accepted; rates available upon request. **URL:** http://www.cnr.cn.

43236 ■ China National Radio 1 - 639 KHz
2 Fuxingmenwai Dajie
Xicheng Qu
Beijing 100866, People's Republic of China
Ph: 86 10 86093114
Fax: 86 10 63909751
E-mail: cn@cnr.cn
Format: News; Information; Sports. **Owner:** The State Administration of Radio, Film and Television, at above address. **Operating Hours:** 3:58 a.m.-1:35 a.m. **Wattage:** 200,000. **URL:** http://www.cnr.cn.

43237 ■ China National Radio 1 - 540 KHz
2 Fuxingmenwai Dajie
Xicheng Qu

Beijing 100866, People's Republic of China
Ph: 86 10 86090077
Fax: 86 10 68045707
E-mail: cn@cnr.cn
Format: Eclectic. **Owner:** The State Administration of Radio, Film and Television, at above address. **Operating Hours:** 8 p.m.-5:35 p.m. (except Tues. 6 a.m.-8:55 a.m.). **Key Personnel:** Xu Guangchun, Director; Yang Bo, Director. **URL:** http://www.cnr.cn.

43238 ■ China National Radio 2 - 630 KHz
2 Fuxingmenwai Dajie
Xicheng Qu
Beijing 100866, People's Republic of China
Ph: 86 10 86093114
Fax: 86 10 63909751
E-mail: cn@cnr.cn
Format: News; Talk. **Owner:** The State Administration of Radio, Film and Television, at above address. **Operating Hours:** 4:58 a.m.-12:05 a.m. **URL:** http://www.cnr.cn.

Changchun

43239 ■ Jilin University Journal Social Sciences Edition
Jilin University
2699 Qianjin St.
Changchun 130012, Jilin, People's Republic of China
Ph: 86 431 85166885
Fax: 86 431 85166570
Publisher E-mail: advice@jlu.edu.cn
Journal covering the field of humanities and social sciences. **Founded:** 1955. **Freq:** Bimonthly. **Key Personnel:** Cui Yue-qin, Ch. Ed. **ISSN:** 0257-2834. **Subscription Rates:** 12 Yu individuals. **URL:** http://journal.jlu.edu.cn/english/index.php.

43240 ■ Journal of Jilin University Earth Science Edition
Jilin University
2699 Qianjin St.
Changchun 130012, Jilin, People's Republic of China
Ph: 86 431 85166885
Fax: 86 431 85166570
Publisher E-mail: advice@jlu.edu.cn
Journal covering the field of earth science. **Key Personnel:** Zhan Tao, President. **URL:** http://xuebao.jlu.edu.cn/dxb/EN/volumn/volumn_1135.shtml.

43241 ■ Journal of Jilin University Engineering and Technology Edition
Jilin University
2699 Qianjin St.
Changchun 130012, Jilin, People's Republic of China
Ph: 86 431 85166885
Fax: 86 431 85166570
Publisher E-mail: advice@jlu.edu.cn
Journal covering the field of engineering and technology. **Key Personnel:** Zhan Tao, President. **URL:** http://xuebao.jlu.edu.cn/gxb/EN/volumn/current.shtml.

43242 ■ Journal of Jilin University Information Science Edition
Jilin University
2699 Qianjin St.
Changchun 130012, Jilin, People's Republic of China
Ph: 86 431 85166885
Fax: 86 431 85166570
Publication E-mail: nhxb@jlu.edu.cn
Publisher E-mail: advice@jlu.edu.cn
Journal covering the field of information science. **Key Personnel:** Zhan Tao, President. **URL:** http://xuebao.jlu.edu.cn/xxb/EN/volumn/current.shtml.

43243 ■ Journal of Jilin University Medicine Edition
Jilin University
2699 Qianjin St.
Changchun 130012, Jilin, People's Republic of China
Ph: 86 431 85166885
Fax: 86 431 85166570
Publication E-mail: xuebao8586@sina.com
Publisher E-mail: advice@jlu.edu.cn
Journal covering the field of medicine. **Key Personnel:** Zhan Tao, President. **URL:** http://xuebao.jlu.edu.cn/yxb/EN/volumn/current.shtml.

43244 ■ Journal of Jilin University Science Edition
Jilin University
2699 Qianjin St.
Changchun 130012, Jilin, People's Republic of China
Ph: 86 431 85166885
Fax: 86 431 85166570
Publication E-mail: sejuj@mail.jlu.edu.cn
Publisher E-mail: advice@jlu.edu.cn
Journal covering the field of science. **Key Personnel:** Zhan Tao, President. **URL:** http://xuebao.jlu.edu.cn/lxb/EN/volumn/current.shtml.

43245 ■ Jilin Television - 19
1027 Xinmin Ave.
Changchun 130021, Jilin, People's Republic of China
Ph: 86 431 5653570
Fax: 86 431 5653860
E-mail: webmaster@jilintv.com.cn
Format: Information. **Owner:** Jilin TV, at above address. **Founded:** Oct. 1, 1959. **Key Personnel:** Shuangyi Li, Director, phone 86 431 5653736, lsy@jilintv.com.cn; Qijun Peng, Director, phone 86 431 5593789, fax 86 431 5593886, pqj@jilintv.com.cn. **Ad Rates:** Advertising accepted; rates available upon request. **URL:** http://www.jilintv.com.cn/.

Changsha

43246 ■ Transactions of Nonferrous Metals Society of China
Central South University
Central South University
Changsha 410083, Hunan, People's Republic of China
Ph: 86 731 8877114
Fax: 86 731 8877197
Publication E-mail: f-ysxb@mail.csu.edu.cn
Publisher E-mail: csuweb@mail.csu.edu.cn
Publication covering topics of interest to the Nonferrous Metals Society of China. **Founded:** Oct. 1991. **Freq:** Bimonthly. **Trim Size:** 297 x 210 mm. **Key Personnel:** Kang Yi, Chm. **ISSN:** 1003-6326. **Subscription Rates:** US$240 individuals. **Remarks:** Advertising accepted; rates available upon request. **URL:** http://www.csu.edu.cn/ysxb/ysxby.html. **Circ:** 800

43247 ■ Hunan TV 2 - 2
Hunan Golden Eagle Film
Television Culture International Convention & Exhibition Center, N 4th Fl.
Changsha 410003, Hunan, People's Republic of China
Ph: 86 731 82871680
Fax: 86 731 82871686
E-mail: media@hunantv.com
Format: Sports. **Owner:** Hunan Television Station, at above address. **URL:** http://www.hunantv.com.

Chengdu

43248 ■ International Journal of Tourism Anthropology
Inderscience Enterprises Limited
c/o Dr. Cheng Li, Ed.-in-Ch.
Sichuan University, Dept. of Tourism Culture
Tourism School
No. 29 Wangjiang Rd.
Chengdu 610064, Sichuan, People's Republic of China
Peer-reviewed journal covering the advanced theory, research and practice in the field of tourism anthropology. **Freq:** 4/yr. **Key Personnel:** Dr. Cheng Li, Editor-in-Chief, chenglibox@gmail.com. **ISSN:** 1759-0442. **Subscription Rates:** EUR494 individuals print or online; EUR672 individuals print and online. **URL:** http://www.inderscience.com/browse/index.php?journalID=343.

43249 ■ SCTV 1 - 2
No. 40, Dongsheng St.
Chengdu 610015, Sichuan, People's Republic of China
Ph: 86 28 86636065
Fax: 86 28 86641646
E-mail: webmaster@sctv.com
Format: News; Educational; Sports. **Owner:** Sichuan Television Station, at above address. **Operating Hours:** 18 hours daily. **Ad Rates:** Advertising accepted; rates available upon request. **URL:** http://www.sctv.com.cn.

43250 ■ SCTV 1 - 21
No. 40, Dongsheng St.
Chengdu 610015, Sichuan, People's Republic of China

Circulation: ★ = ABC; △ = BPA; ♦ = CAC; • = CCAB; ❑ = VAC; ⊕ = PO Statement; ‡ = Publisher's Report; Boldface figures = sworn; Light figures = estimated.

Gale Directory of Publications & Broadcast Media/147th Ed.   **4833**

Ph: 00 20 86636065
Fax: 86 28 86641646
E-mail: webmaster@sctv.com
Format: News; Educational; Sports. **Owner:** Sichuan Television Station, at above address. **Operating Hours:** 18 hours daily. **Ad Rates:** Advertising accepted; rates available upon request. **URL:** http://www.sctv.com.cn.

43251 ■ SCTV 2 - 10
No. 40, Dongsheng St.
Chengdu 610015, Sichuan, People's Republic of China
Ph: 86 28 86636065
Fax: 86 28 86641646
E-mail: webmaster@sctv.com
Format: News; Educational; Sports. **Owner:** Sichuan Television Station, at above address. **Operating Hours:** 12 pm-3 pm, 6 pm-12 am. **Ad Rates:** Advertising accepted; rates available upon request. **URL:** http://www.sctv.com.cn.

43252 ■ International Journal of Systems, Control and Communications
Inderscience Enterprises Limited
c/o Prof. Ge Guo, Ed.-in-Ch.
Dalian Maritime University
School of Information Science & Technology
Dalian 116026, People's Republic of China
Journal covering the field of systems, control, and communications engineering. **Freq:** 4/yr. **Key Personnel:** Prof. Ge Guo, Editor-in-Chief, geguo@yeah.net. **ISSN:** 1755-9340. **Subscription Rates:** EUR494 individuals print or online; EUR672 individuals print and online. **URL:** http://www.inderscience.com/browse/index.php?journalID=287.

Dalian (Liaoning)

43253 ■ Chinese Journal of Catalysis
Elsevier Science Inc.
State Key Laboratory of Catalysis
Dalian Institute of Chemical Physics
Chinese Academy of Sciences
Dalian, Liaoning, People's Republic of China
Publisher E-mail: usinfo-ehelp@elsevier.com
Journal containing reviews on heterogeneous, homogeneous, biocatalysts, photocatalysts, electrocatalysis, surface chemistry, and chemical kinetics relating to catalysis. **Founded:** 2006. **Freq:** 12/yr. **Print Method:** Offset. **Cols./Page:** 5. **Col. Width:** 10.1 inches. **Col. Depth:** 15 inches. **Key Personnel:** Yuxin Liu, Assoc. Ed.-in-Chief, lyx@dicp.ac.cn; Zi Gao, Assoc. Ed.-in-Chief, zigao@fudan.edu.cn; Yuan Kou, Assoc. Ed.-in-Chief, yuankou@pku.edu.cn; Xinhe Bao, Assoc. Ed.-in-Chief, xhbao@dicp.ac.cn; Lidun An, Board Member, aci@ytu.edu.cn; Qingling Chen, Board Member, sriptceo@mail.uninet.com.cn; Songying Chen, Board Member, songyingchen@hotmail.com; Yaoqiang Chen, Board Member, yqchen@email.scu.edu.cn; Yi Chen, Board Member, chenyi@nju.edu.cn; Liwu Lin, Editor-in-Chief, linliwu@dicp.ac.cn. **ISSN:** 1872-2067. **URL:** http://www.elsevier.com/wps/find/journaldescription.cws_home/709300/descriptiondescription.

43254 ■ Journal of Natural Gas Chemistry
Elsevier Science Inc.
c/o Xinhe Bao, Ed.-in-Ch.
Dalian Institute of Chemical Physics
Chinese Academy of Sciences
Dalian 116023, Liaoning, People's Republic of China
Publisher E-mail: usinfo-ehelp@elsevier.com
Journal covering natural gas, C1, lower hydrocarbons chemistry and hydrogen energy sources. **Founded:** 2006. **Freq:** 4/yr. **Key Personnel:** Xinhe Bao, Editor-in-Chief; A.T. Bell, Editor-in-Chief. **ISSN:** 1003-9953. **Subscription Rates:** 59,600¥ institutions; EUR410 institutions for European countries and Iran; US$522 institutions, other countries except Europe, Japan and Iran. **URL:** http://www.elsevier.com/wps/find/journaldescription.cws_home/706801/descriptiondescription.

Guangzhou

43255 ■ Guangdong Television - 3
No. 331, Huanshi Dong Lu
Guangzhou 510066, Guangdong, People's Republic of China
Ph: 86 2083313318
E-mail: gdtv@gdtv.com.cn
Owner: Guangdong TV Station, at above address. **URL:** http://www.gdtv.gov.cn.

43256 ■ Guangdong Television - 1
No. 331, Huanshi Dong Lu
Guangzhou 510066, Guangdong, People's Republic of China
Ph: 86 20 83313318
E-mail: gdtv@gdtv.com.cn
Owner: Guangdong TV Station, at above address. **URL:** http://www.gdtv.gov.cn.

43257 ■ Guangdong Television - 2
No. 331, Huanshi Dong Lu
Guangzhou 510066, Guangdong, People's Republic of China
Ph: 86 20 83313318
E-mail: gdtv@gdtv.com.cn
Owner: Guangdong TV Station, at above address. **URL:** http://www.gdtv.gov.cn.

43258 ■ International Journal of Information Science and Computer Mathematics
Pushpa Publishing House
c/o Prof. Kewen Zhao, Ed.-in-Ch.
University of Qiongzhou
Hainan 572022, People's Republic of China
Publisher E-mail: arun@pphmj.com
Peer-reviewed journal covering all aspects of information science and computer mathematics. **Freq:** Semiannual. **Key Personnel:** Prof. Kewen Zhao, Editor-in-Chief, kewen@bxemail.com. **ISSN:** 1829-4969. **Subscription Rates:** Rs 3,500 institutions print only; EUR160 institutions, other countries online only; EUR200 institutions, other countries print and online only. **URL:** http://pphmj.com/journals/ijiscm.htm.

Hainan (Guangdong)

43259 ■ International Journal of Computational and Applied Mathematics
Research India Publications
c/o Prof. Kewen Zhao, Ed.-in-Ch.
University of Qiongzhou
Department of Mathematics
Hainan 572200, Guangdong, People's Republic of China
Publisher E-mail: info@ripublication.com
Journal covering computational aspects of mathematics. **Freq:** 3/yr. **Key Personnel:** Prof. Kewen Zhao, Editor-in-Chief, kewen.zhao@yahoo.com.cn; Prof. P. Zhang, Editorial Board Members, p.zhang@wmich.edu. **ISSN:** 1819-4966. **Subscription Rates:** US$380 libraries and institution; print plus online free; US$360 libraries and institution; online only; US$140 individuals print plus online free; US$120 individuals online only; Rs 1,800 individuals. **URL:** http://www.ripublication.com/ijcam.htm.

Hangzhou

43260 ■ International Journal of Structural Engineering
Inderscience Enterprises Limited
c/o Dr. Wei-Liang Jin, Ed.-in-Ch.
A605 Anzhong Bldg.
Department of Civil Engineering, Zhejiang University
388 Yuhangtang Rd.
Hangzhou 310058, Zhejiang, People's Republic of China
Journal featuring analysis and research on structural engineering. **Freq:** Quarterly. **Key Personnel:** Dr. Wei-Liang Jin, Editor-in-Chief, jinwl@zju.edu.cn. **ISSN:** 1758-7328. **Subscription Rates:** EUR494 individuals print or online; EUR672 individuals print and online. **URL:** http://www.inderscience.com/browse/index.php?journalCODE=ijstructe.

43261 ■ Zhejiang Television - 22
111 Moganshan Rd.
Hangzhou 310005, Zhejiang, People's Republic of China
Ph: 86 571 88071234
Fax: 86 571 88903389
Format: News; Full Service. **Owner:** Zhejiang TV, at above address. **URL:** http://www.cztv.com.cn.

43262 ■ Zhejiang Television - 4
111 Moganshan Rd.
Hangzhou 310005, Zhejiang, People's Republic of China
Ph: 86 571 88071234
Fax: 86 571 88903389
Format: News; Full Service. **Owner:** Zhejiang TV, at above address. **URL:** http://www.cztv.com.cn.

Harbin

43263 ■ China Welding
China Welding Association
111 Hexing Rd.
Harbin 150080, Heilongjiang, People's Republic of China
Ph: 86 451 86340850
Fax: 86 451 86333949
Publisher E-mail: cws@public.hr.hl.cn
Chinese publication covering welding. **Freq:** Semiannual. **ISSN:** 1004-5341. **Remarks:** Advertising accepted; rates available upon request. **URL:** http://www.china-weldnet.com/English/information/CHINA%20WELDING%20Vo1.htm. **Circ:** (Not Reported)

43264 ■ Heilongjiang TV Channel 1 - 1
No. 181, Zhongshan Lu
Nangang District
Harbin 150001, Heilongjiang, People's Republic of China
Ph: 86 451 2627454
Fax: 86 451 2625497
E-mail: zbs@hljtv.com
Format: Full Service. **Owner:** Heilongjiang TV Station, at above address. **URL:** http://www.hljtv.com.

43265 ■ Heilongjiang TV Channel 2 - 2
No. 181, Zhongshan Lu
Nangang District
Harbin 150001, Heilongjiang, People's Republic of China
Ph: 86 451 2627454
Fax: 86 451 2625497
E-mail: zbs@hljtv.com
Format: Information; Sports; Full Service. **Owner:** Heilongjiang TV Station, at above address. **URL:** http://www.hljtv.com.

Hefei

43266 ■ International Journal of Nanoparticles
Inderscience Enterprises Limited
c/o Prof. Weiping Cai, Ed.-in-Ch.
Chinese Academy of Sciences
Key Lab of Materials Physics
Institute of Solid State Physics
Hefei 230031, Anhui, People's Republic of China
Journal covering chemical, physical, and biological phenomena and processes associated with nanoparticles and nanostructures. **Freq:** 4/yr. **Key Personnel:** Prof. Weiping Cai, Editor-in-Chief, wpcai@issp.ac.cn. **ISSN:** 1753-2507. **Subscription Rates:** EUR494 individuals print or online; EUR672 individuals print and online. **URL:** http://www.inderscience.com/browse/index.php?journalID=241.

Hong Kong

43267 ■ Arts of Asia
Arts of Asia Publications Ltd.
Kowloon Centre, Stes. 803-6
29-39 Ashley Rd.
Kowloon
Hong Kong, People's Republic of China
Ph: 852 23762228
Fax: 852 23763713
Publisher E-mail: info@artsofasianet.com
Magazine of Asian arts. **Founded:** 1970. **Freq:** Bimonthly. **ISSN:** 0004-4083. **Subscription Rates:** US$85 individuals. **Remarks:** Accepts advertising. **URL:** http://www.artsofasianet.com/. **Circ:** (Not Reported)

43268 ■ Artslink
Hong Kong Arts Centre
2 Harbour Rd., Wanchai
Hong Kong, People's Republic of China
Ph: 852 25820200
Periodical featuring all programs and activities presented by the Hong Kong Arts Center. **Freq:** Monthly. **Trim Size:** 180 x 210 mm. **Remarks:** Accepts advertising. **URL:** http://www.hkac.org.hk/en/publications.php. **Ad Rates:** BW: HK$6,500. **Circ:** 16,000

43269 ■ Asia Asset Management
1701, Singga Commercial Ctr.
148 Connaught Rd. W
Hong Kong, People's Republic of China
Ph: 852 25477331
Fax: 852 25489544

Publisher E-mail: enquiries@asiaasset.com
Periodical focusing on the institutional fund management industry. **Founded:** 1996. **Freq:** Monthly. **Key Personnel:** Tan Lee Hock, Editor and Publisher; David Macfarlane, Managing Editor. **ISSN:** 1029-5305. **Subscription Rates:** US$1,400 individuals; US$2,520 two years. **Remarks:** Advertising accepted; rates available upon request. **URL:** http://www.asiaasset.com/. **Circ:** (Not Reported)

43270 ■ Asia Law and Practice
Euromoney Publications (Jersey) Ltd.
5th & 17th Fl. Printing House
6 Duddell St., Central
Hong Kong, People's Republic of China
Ph: 85 225 233399
Publication E-mail: enquiries@alphk.com
Law magazine. **Freq:** Monthly. **Key Personnel:** Darren Barton, Publisher, phone 85 228 426914, fax 85 225 218900, dbarton@alphk.com; Connie Lo, Office Mgr., phone 85 228 426928, fax 85 221 149860, clo@alphk.com; Fiona Leung, Subscription Mgr., phone 85 228 426929, fax 85 221 110494, fiona.leung@euromoneyasia.com; Christopher Bisogni, Managing Editor, cbisogni@alphk.com; Gareth Fox, Hd. of Mktg., gareth.fox@euromoneyasia.com. **Subscription Rates:** US$1,856 individuals 3 year; US$1,310 two years individual; US$728 individuals. **Remarks:** Advertising accepted; rates available upon request. **URL:** http://www.alphk.com. **Circ:** (Not Reported)

43271 ■ Asia Textile & Apparel Journal
Adsale Publishing Co.
6th Fl., 321 Java Rd.
N Point
Hong Kong, People's Republic of China
Ph: 852 28118897
Fax: 852 25165119
Publication E-mail: cta.ata.edit@adsale.com.hk
Publisher E-mail: publishing@adsale.com.hk
Trade magazine on the textile and apparel industry. **Founded:** 1990. **Freq:** Bimonthly. **Key Personnel:** Naomi Lee, Editor. **Subscription Rates:** 455 Yu individuals; US$75 individuals Asia; US$85 elsewhere; 775 Yu two years; US$130 two years Asia; US$145 two years elsewhere. **Remarks:** Advertising accepted; rates available upon request. **URL:** http://www.adsale.com.hk/. **Circ:** Controlled 15,893

43272 ■ Asiamoney
Euromoney Publications PLC
Euromoney Institutional Investor (Jersey) Ltd.
27/F, 248 Queen's Rd. E
Wanchai
Hong Kong, People's Republic of China
Ph: 852 28426999
Fax: 852 21110494
Publisher E-mail: information@euromoneyplc.com
Publication for the banking, finance, and accounting industries. **Founded:** 1989. **Freq:** Monthly. **Trim Size:** 210 mm x 286 mm. **Key Personnel:** Richard Morrow, Editor, richard.morrow@asiamoney.com; Terry Rayner, Assoc. Publisher, phone 852 29128080, terry.rayner@asiamoney.com; Mee-Ling Lee, Dep. Publisher, phone 852 29128098, meeling.lee@asiamoney.com. **ISSN:** 0958-9309. **Remarks:** Accepts advertising. **URL:** http://www.asiamoney.com. **Ad Rates:** BW: 9,400 Yu, 4C: 12,550 Yu. **Circ:** (Not Reported)

43273 ■ Asian Affairs
PO Box 10086
15th Fl., Supreme Commercial Bldg.
368 King's Rd., N Point
Hong Kong, People's Republic of China
Ph: 86 852 29802240
Fax: 86 852 29802824
Publication E-mail: editor@asian-affairs.com
Publication focusing on business, economics, politics and review. **Founded:** 1997. **Freq:** Quarterly. **ISSN:** 1029-1903. **Subscription Rates:** US$75 individuals online payment (airmail). **URL:** http://www.asian-affairs.com/.

43274 ■ Asian Anthropology
Chinese University Press
Shatin Galleria, 9th Fl., Unit 1-3 & 18
18-24 Shan Mei St.
Fo Tan, Shatin
Hong Kong, People's Republic of China

Ph: 852 29465300
Fax: 852 26037355
Publisher E-mail: cup@cuhk.edu.hk
Journal covering anthropological research in Asia. **Founded:** June 2002. **Freq:** Annual. **Trim Size:** 152 x 229 mm. **Key Personnel:** Cheung Sidney Chin-hung, Editor-in-Chief, cbtan@cuhk.edu.hk; Mathews Gordon, Editor-in-Chief, cmgordon@cuhk.edu.hk. **ISSN:** 1683-478X. **Subscription Rates:** US$11.50 individuals. **URL:** http://www.chineseupress.com/asp/JournalList_en.asp?CatID=1&Lang=E&JournalID=10.

43275 ■ Asian Credit Investor
Pacific Prospect Group Ltd.
20 Fl., Admiralty Ctr., Tower 2
18 Harcourt Rd.
Hong Kong, People's Republic of China
Ph: 852 34114700
Fax: 852 34114701
Publisher E-mail: asiariskevents@incisivemedia.com
Magazine covering strategic content on the challenges and opportunities faced by Asian-based fund managers and wholesale investors. **Freq:** Quarterly. **Key Personnel:** Ben Marquand, Editor, phone 852 34114788, ben.marquand@incisivemedia.com; Harjeet Singh, Publisher, phone 852 34114838, harjeet.singh@incisivemedia.com. **URL:** http://www.pacificprospect.com/?page=publications&book_title=aci.

43276 ■ Asian Journal of English Language Teaching
Chinese University Press
Shatin Galleria, 9th Fl., Unit 1-3 & 18
18-24 Shan Mei St.
Fo Tan, Shatin
Hong Kong, People's Republic of China
Ph: 852 29465300
Fax: 852 26037355
Publisher E-mail: cup@cuhk.edu.hk
Peer-reviewed journal covering English language teaching. **Founded:** Oct. 2001. **Freq:** Annual. **Trim Size:** 152 x 229 mm. **Key Personnel:** Gwendolyn Gong, Editor, ggong@cuhk.edu.hk; Peter Yonggi Gu, Editor, peter.gu@vuw.ac.nz; Lixian Jin, Review Ed., jin@dmu.ac.uk. **ISSN:** 1026-2652. **Subscription Rates:** US$11.50 individuals. **URL:** http://www.chineseupress.com/asp/JournalList_en.asp?CatID=1&Lang=E&JournalID=7.

43277 ■ Asian Journal of Mathematics
International Press of Boston Inc.
Institute of Mathematical Sciences
Chinese University of Hong Kong
Hong Kong, People's Republic of China
Fax: 852 2603 7636
Publication E-mail: ajm@ims.cuhk.edu.hk
Publisher E-mail: ipb-info@intlpress.com
Academic journal for mathematicians. **Founded:** 1997. **Freq:** Quarterly. **Print Method:** Offset. **Trim Size:** 7 x 9. **Key Personnel:** Shing-Tung Yau, Editor-in-Chief, phone 852 2609 8038, yau@ims.cuhk.edu.hk; Raymond Chan, Editor-in-Chief; John Coates, Editor; Tony Chan, Editor; Kenji Fukaya, Editor. **ISSN:** 1093-6106. **Subscription Rates:** US$510 institutions, other countries print and online; US$311 institutions online; US$479 individuals within U.S print & online. **Remarks:** Accepts advertising. **URL:** http://www.ims.cuhk.edu.hk. **Ad Rates:** GLR: 50 Yu, BW: 250 Yu, 4C: 500 Yu. **Circ:** Combined 1,100

43278 ■ Asian Journal of Physical Education & Recreation
Dr. Stephen Hui Research Centre for Physical Recreation and Wellness
Hong Kong Baptist University
Kowloon Tong
Kowloon
Hong Kong, People's Republic of China
Ph: 852 34117400
Fax: 852 23387644
Publisher E-mail: webmaster@hkbu.edu.hk
Journal covering research or reviews in physical education, recreation, sports and fitness. **Key Personnel:** Prof. Frank Fu, Editorial Advisor; Dr. Lobo H. Louie, Editor-in-Chief; Prof. Chung Pak Kwong, Editor-in-Chief. **URL:** http://www.hkbu.edu.hk/~sosc1/shc/shc/journal.html. **Formerly:** Journal of Physical Education & Recreation.

43279 ■ Asian Journal of Surgery
Asian Surgical Association

Dept. of Surgery
University of Hong Kong Medical Center
Queen Mary Hospital
Hong Kong, People's Republic of China
Ph: 852 28554235
Fax: 852 28181186
Publisher E-mail: ajsurg@hku.hk
Asian journal covering surgery. **Founded:** 1978. **Freq:** Quarterly. **Key Personnel:** Stephen Cheng, Editor-in-Chief. **Subscription Rates:** US$300 institutions plus postage; US$120 individuals plus postage. **Remarks:** Accepts advertising. **URL:** http://www.asiansurgassoc.org/5.htm. **Circ:** Combined ‡1,350

43280 ■ Asian Venture Capital Journal
Incisive Media Limited
Admiralty Ctr., Tower Two, 20th Fl.
18 Harcourt Rd.
Hong Kong, People's Republic of China
Ph: 852 34114900
Fax: 852 34114999
Publisher E-mail: customerservices@incisivemedia.com
Journal featuring the growing venture capital, private equity and mergers and acquisitions markets. **Founded:** 1987. **Freq:** Weekly (Mon.). **Key Personnel:** Jonathon Whiteley, Mng. Dir. **Subscription Rates:** US$1,795 individuals standard; US$2,395 individuals gold; US$16,595 individuals platinum. **Remarks:** Accepts advertising. **URL:** http://www.avcj.com. **Circ:** (Not Reported)

43281 ■ The Asset
Asset Publishing & Research Ltd.
Ste. 2404, 24th Fl., Chinachem Exchange Sq.
1 Hoi Wan St.
Quarry Bay
Hong Kong, People's Republic of China
Ph: 852 25736078
Fax: 852 25737436
Publication E-mail: info@theasset.com
Finance magazine. **Founded:** 1999. **Freq:** 11/yr. **Key Personnel:** Daniel Yu, Editor-in-Chief. **Subscription Rates:** US$523 two years; US$315 individuals. **Remarks:** Accepts advertising. **URL:** http://www.theassetonline.com/. **Circ:** (Not Reported)

43282 ■ Aware
American Women's Association of Hong Kong
C-7 Monticello
48 Kennedy Rd.
Hong Kong, People's Republic of China
Ph: 852 25272961
Fax: 852 28657737
Publisher E-mail: info@awa.org.hk
Publication covering women. **Freq:** Monthly. **Remarks:** Accepts advertising. **URL:** https://www.awa.org.hk/aware.php. **Ad Rates:** BW: 5,400 Yu. **Circ:** (Not Reported)

43283 ■ bc Magazine
Carpe Diem Publications Ltd.
8th Fl., Trust Tower
68 Johnston Rd.
Wanchai
Hong Kong, People's Republic of China
Ph: 86 229 760876
Fax: 86 229 760973
Publication E-mail: hkeditorial@bcmagazine.net
Publisher E-mail: info@carpediempublications.com
Magazine covering music and popular culture in Hong Kong and around the world. **Founded:** 1994. **Freq:** Somimonthly. **Trim Size:** 280 x 204 mm. **Key Personnel:** Maggie Kuok, Mktg. Mgr.; Simon Durrant, Publisher/Ed.-in-Ch. **Remarks:** Accepts advertising. **URL:** http://www.bcmagazine.net. **Ad Rates:** 4C: 20,900 Yu. **Circ:** 30,000

43284 ■ Building Journal Hong Kong
China Trend Building Press Ltd.
Rm. 703, 9 Chong Yip St.
Kwun Tong
Kowloon
Hong Kong, People's Republic of China
Ph: 86 228 026299
Fax: 86 228 026458
Publisher E-mail: trend@building.com.hk
Journal covering building and constr... Monthly. **Trim Size:** 213 x 285 mm **Rates:** US$64 individuals Hong Kon

countries. **URL:** http://www.building.hk/bjhk.asp. **Ad Rates:** BW: HK$6,500, 4C: HK$9,500. **Circ:** (Not Reported)

43285 ■ The Bulletin
The Hong Kong General Chamber of Commerce
22nd Fl., United Ctr.
95 Queensway
Hong Kong, People's Republic of China
Ph: 85 252 99229
Fax: 85 252 79843
Publisher E-mail: chamber@chamber.org.hk
Chinese and English language publication covering business issues on HK and China. **Founded:** 1962. **Freq:** Monthly. **Trim Size:** 210 x 286 mm. **Key Personnel:** Malcolm Ainsworth, Editor; Anthony Nightingale, Chm. **Subscription Rates:** HK$360 individuals; US$85 individuals. **Remarks:** Accepts advertising. **URL:** http://www.chamber.org.hk/en/information/the-bulletin.aspx. **Ad Rates:** BW: HK$8,900, 4C: HK$13,780. **Circ:** 8,500

43286 ■ Business Strategy and the Environment
John Wiley & Sons Inc.
Corporate Environmental Governance Programme
Centre of Urban Planning & Environmental Management
University of Hong Kong
Hong Kong, People's Republic of China
Publisher E-mail: info@wiley.com
Journal seeking seeks to provide original contributions which add to the understanding of business responses to improving environmental performance. **Freq:** 8/yr. **Key Personnel:** Prof. Richard Welford, Editor-in-Chief; Dr. Maurie J. Cohen, Editorial Board; Prof. Jun Bi, Editorial Board. **ISSN:** 0964-4733. **Subscription Rates:** 217 individuals for print; US$420 other countries for print; US$1,366 institutions, other countries for print; US$1,503 institutions, other countries print and online; EUR881 institutions, other countries print; 697 institutions UK (print); EUR970 institutions, other countries print and online; 767 institutions UK (print and online). **Remarks:** Accepts advertising. **URL:** http://onlinelibrary.wiley.com/journal/10.1002/(ISSN)1099-0836. **Circ:** (Not Reported)

43287 ■ CEI Asia Pacific
Haymarket Media Limited
23/F The Centrium
60 Wyndham St. Central
Hong Kong, People's Republic of China
Ph: 852 31751900
Publisher E-mail: hr@haymarketasia.com
Magazine featuring corporate events industry. **Founded:** 2000. **Freq:** 10/yr. **Key Personnel:** Shannon Sweeney, Editor, phone 825 31751934, shannon@ceiasia.com; Richard Avery, Assoc. Publisher, phone 825 31751925, richard.avery@ceiasia.com.hk. **Subscription Rates:** Free. **URL:** http://www.haymarket.com/cei_asia_/cei_asia_chn_magazine/default.aspx; http://www.cei.asia/. **Circ:** Controlled △13,004

43288 ■ Chinese Around the World
Chinese Coordination Centre of World Evangelism
PO Box 98435
Tsimshatsui
Hong Kong, People's Republic of China
Ph: 86 852 23910411
Fax: 86 852 27894740
Publication E-mail: catw@cccowe.org
Publisher E-mail: adm@cccowe.org
Publication covering evangelism. **Founded:** 1983. **Freq:** Quarterly. **Remarks:** Advertising not accepted. **URL:** http://www.cccowe.org/eng/content_epub.php?epubId=1&issueId=8. **Circ:** 7,000

43289 ■ Ching Feng
Chinese University Press
Shatin Galleria, 9th Fl., Unit 1-3 & 18
18-24 Shan Mei St.
Fo Tan, Shatin
Hong Kong, People's Republic of China
Ph: 852 29465300
Fax: 852 26037355
Publisher E-mail: cup@cuhk.edu.hk
Journal covering Chinese religion. **Founded:** 2001. **Freq:** Semiannual. **Trim Size:** 152 x 229 mm. **Key Personnel:** Francis Ching-wah Yip, Exec. Ed. **ISSN:** 0009-4668. **Subscription Rates:** US$21.50 individuals. **URL:** http://www.chineseupress.com/asp/JournalList_en.asp?CatID=1&Lang=E&JournalID=12.

43290 ■ Choice
Consumer Council of Hong Kong
K Wah Centre, 22/F
191 Java Rd.
North Point
Hong Kong, People's Republic of China
Ph: 852 28563113
Fax: 852 28563611
Publisher E-mail: cc@consumer.org.hk
Chinese language publication covering consumers. **Freq:** Monthly. **Subscription Rates:** 99 Yu individuals incl. surface mail charge; 188 Yu two years incl. surface mail charge; 15.70 Yu single issue unit price; 215 Yu out of country (incl. air mail charge); 408 Yu out of country (incl. air mail charge) two years; 24.70 Yu single issue China, Taiwan (incl. air mail charge); 161 Yu individuals (incl. surface mail charge) China, Taiwan; 300 Yu two years (incl. surface mail charge) two year China, Taiwan; 18.90 Yu single issue (incl. surface mail charge) China, Taiwan; 161 Ptcs out of country (incl. surface mail charge) Macau. **Remarks:** Advertising not accepted. **URL:** http://www.consumer.org.hk/; http://www.consumer.org.hk/website/ws_en/choice/index.txt. **Circ:** 30,000

43291 ■ Clinical Oral Implants Research
John Wiley & Sons (Asia) Private Ltd.
c/o Niklaus P. Lang, Ed.-in-Ch.
University of Hong Kong
Faculty of Dentistry, Prince Philip Dental Hospital
34, Hospital Rd.
Hong Kong, People's Republic of China
Publisher E-mail: enquiry@wiley.com.sg
Journal focusing on scientific progress in implant dentistry and its related areas. **Freq:** Monthly. **Key Personnel:** Niklaus P. Lang, Editor-in-Chief; Tord Berglundh, Assoc. Ed.; Giovanni E. Salvi, Assoc. Ed. **ISSN:** 0905-7161. **Subscription Rates:** US$1,064 institutions print and online; US$968 institutions print; 636 institutions print and online; 577 institutions print; US$1,244 institutions, other countries print and online; US$1,130 institutions, other countries online. **Remarks:** Accepts advertising. **URL:** http://www.wiley.com/bw/journal.asp?ref=0905-7161&site=1. **Circ:** (Not Reported)

43292 ■ The Club
Cathay Pacific Airways Ltd.
The Marco Polo Club
PO Box 1024
Tsuen Wan Post Office
Hong Kong, People's Republic of China
Fax: 852 25379900
Publication E-mail: theclub@cathaypacific.com
Club offering exclusive membership and special privileges to the most valued and loyal customers. **Freq:** Weekly. **URL:** http://www.cathaypacific.com/cpa/en_intl/contactus/mpo_am.

43293 ■ Computer World Hong Kong
IDG Communications (HK) Ltd.
Ste. 601, Kah Wah Centre
191 Java Rd.
North Point
Hong Kong, People's Republic of China
Ph: 86 852 28613238
Fax: 86 852 28610953
Publisher E-mail: infohk@idg.com.hk
Magazine covering computers and computer business in Hong Kong. **Freq:** Monthly 11/yr. **Key Personnel:** Don Tennant, VP/Ed.-in-Ch.; Sumner Lemon, Contact. **Subscription Rates:** US$122 individuals within Asia; US$180 individuals outside Asia; US$230 individuals within Asia; US$12 single issue; US$18 single issue outside Asia; US$318 individuals outside Asia. **Remarks:** Accepts advertising. **URL:** http://www.computerworld.com/. **Ad Rates:** BW: HK$29,000, 4C: HK$34,000. **Circ:** (Not Reported)

43294 ■ The Correspondent
Foreign Correspondents' Club
2 Lower Albert Rd. N Block
Central
Hong Kong, People's Republic of China
Ph: 86 225 211511
Fax: 86 228 684092
Publication E-mail: fccmag@hongkongnow.com
Publisher E-mail: fcc@fcchk.org
Publication covering the press. **Freq:** Monthly. **Key Personnel:** Ernst Herb, President; Saul Lockhart, Editor,

phone 85 228 135284, fax 85 228 136394, lockhart@hkstar.com. **Remarks:** Accepts advertising. **URL:** http://www.fcchk.org/fccweb/news.html?id=F8AA6E56D8B211F092B4B73181FF091A. **Ad Rates:** BW: 8,000 Yu, 4C: 10,000 Yu. **Circ:** 1,800

43295 ■ Coutoure
Edipresse Asia
6th Fl., Guardian House
32 Oi Kwan Rd.
Hong Kong, People's Republic of China
Ph: 11 852 25477117
Fax: 11 852 28582671
Magazine on apparel & fashion. **Freq:** Semiannual. **Key Personnel:** Arne Eggers, Ch. Ed.; Roddy Yu, Director. **Subscription Rates:** US$40 individuals Asia (by airmail); 80 Yu two years Hong Kong & Macau; US$46 other countries by airmail. **URL:** http://www.couture.com.hk/. **Ad Rates:** BW: 40,000 Yu. **Circ:** 42,000

43296 ■ Digital Media
Haymarket Media Limited
23/F The Centrium
60 Wyndham St. Central
Hong Kong, People's Republic of China
Ph: 852 31751900
Publisher E-mail: hr@haymarketasia.com
Magazine featuring brand marketing on the internet and mobile platforms in Asia. **Freq:** Monthly. **Key Personnel:** David Tiltman, Managing Editor, phone 852 31751931, david.tiltman@media.com.hk; Stuart Adamson, Advertising Dir., phone 852 31751921, stuart.adamson@media.com.hk. **URL:** http://www.haymarket.com/region/china/default.aspx. **Circ:** Combined 12,000

43297 ■ East Asian Archives of Psychiatry
The Hong Kong College of Psychiatrists
Rm. 906, Hong Kong Academy of Medicine, Jockey Club Bldg.
99 Wong Chuk Hang Rd.
Aberdeen
Hong Kong, People's Republic of China
Fax: 852 28701391
Publisher E-mail: hkcpsych@hkam.org.hk
Official journal of Hong Kong College of Psychiatrists. Aims to promote Chinese psychiatric research and practice. **Founded:** 1994. **Freq:** Quarterly. **Key Personnel:** Sarah Chia, Editorial Asst.; Sam Lai, Contact. **ISSN:** 1026-2121. **Subscription Rates:** 1,000 Yu individuals; US$150 individuals. **URL:** http://www.hkjpsych.com.

43298 ■ Elite Homes
Edipresse Asia
6th Fl., Guardian House
32 Oi Kwan Rd.
Hong Kong, People's Republic of China
Ph: 11 852 25477117
Fax: 11 852 28582671
Publication E-mail: enquiry@edipresse.com.hk
Magazine featuring the luxury real estate market in Hong Kong, Asia and around the world. **Freq:** Annual. **Key Personnel:** Roddy Yu, Director; Albert Lo, Ch. Ed. **URL:** http://www.edipresse.com/en/par_pays/hong_kong/magazines/elite_homes. **Circ:** ‡16,350

43299 ■ Exporters Bulletin
The Hong Kong Exporters' Association
Star House, Rm. 825
3 Salisbury Rd.
Tsimshatsui
Kowloon
Hong Kong, People's Republic of China
Ph: 86 227 309851
Fax: 86 227 301869
Publisher E-mail: exporter@exporters.org.hk
Chinese and English language publication covering trade. **Freq:** Semiannual. **Print Method:** Offset. **Remarks:** Accepts advertising. **URL:** http://www.exporters.org.hk/Exporters_Bulletin.aspx. **Ad Rates:** BW: 530 Yu, 4C: 1,000 Yu. **Circ:** Non-paid 5,000

43300 ■ FinanceAsia
Haymarket Media Limited
23/F The Centrium
60 Wyndham St. Central
Hong Kong, People's Republic of China
Ph: 852 31751900
Publisher E-mail: hr@haymarketasia.com
Magazine featuring financial trends and investigative reports. **Founded:** 1996. **Freq:** Monthly. **Key Person-**

nel: Lara Wozniak, Editor, phone 852 21225260, lara.
wozniak@financeasia.com. **Subscription Rates:**
US$645 individuals website access; US$1,095 two
years website access; US$545 individuals print & on-
line; US$925 two years print & online; US$945 individuals print & online + website access; US$1,695 two years
print & online + website access. **Remarks:** Accepts
advertising. **URL:** http://www.haymarket.com/
financeasia/financeasia_chn_magazine/default.aspx;
http://www.financeasia.com/magazine-overview.aspx?
m=fa. **Circ:** 21,600

43301 ■ Green Alert
Conservancy Association
9/F Breakthrough Ctr.
191-197 Woosung St.
Kowloon
Hong Kong, People's Republic of China
Ph: 852 27286781
Fax: 852 27285538
Publisher E-mail: cahk@cahk.org.hk
Publication covering conservation. **Freq:** Quarterly. **Re-
marks:** Advertising accepted; rates available upon
request. **URL:** http://www.greencouncil.org/eng/
publication/headline_detail.asp?id=98. **Circ:** 1,000

43302 ■ Hinge
Hinge Marketing Ltd.
Empire Land Commerical Centre, 24th Fl.
81 Lockhart Rd.
Wanchai
Hong Kong, People's Republic of China
Publisher E-mail: hinge@hinge.hk
Architecture and design magazine. **Founded:** 1993.
Freq: Monthly. **Subscription Rates:** US$130
individuals. **Remarks:** Accepts advertising. **URL:** http://
www.hingenet.com. **Ad Rates:** BW: HK$13,800, 4C:
HK$20,000. **Circ:** (Not Reported)

43303 ■ HK Medical Journal
Hong Kong Academy of Medicine
99 Wong Chuk Hang Rd.
Aberdeen
Hong Kong, People's Republic of China
Ph: 86 852 28718888
Fax: 86 852 25055577
Publisher E-mail: hkmj@hkam.org.hk
Peer-reviewed journal covering medicine. **Founded:**
1995. **Freq:** Bimonthly. **Trim Size:** 210 x 297 mm. **Key
Personnel:** R. Kay, Editor-in-Chief; P.T. Cheung, Sen.
Ed.; K.S. Chan, Editor; K.L. Chan, Editor. **ISSN:** 1024-
2708. **Subscription Rates:** 600 Yu individuals; US$160
out of country airmail; 780 Yu individuals PRC. **Re-
marks:** Accepts advertising. **URL:** http://www.hkam.org.
hk/publications_fs.html; http://www.hkam.org.hk/; http://
www.hkmj.org/. **Ad Rates:** BW: 10,000 Yu, 4C: 13,500
Yu. **Circ:** 6,000

43304 ■ HKTDC Electronic Components & Parts
Hong Kong Trade Development Council
38th Fl., Office Tower, Convention Plz.
1 Harbour Rd.
Wanchai
Hong Kong, People's Republic of China
Ph: 852 1830668
Fax: 852 28240249
Publisher E-mail: hktdc@tdc.org.hk
Guide for electronic components and parts manufactur-
ers, traders and agents in Hong Kong. **Founded:** 1996.
Freq: Annual. **ISSN:** 1026-6712. **Remarks:** Advertising
accepted; rates available upon request. **URL:** http://info.
hktdc.com/prodmag/elecom/elecom.htm. **Formerly:**
Hong Kong Electronic Components & Parts. **Circ:** (Not
Reported)

43305 ■ HKTDC Electronics
Hong Kong Trade Development Council
38th Fl., Office Tower, Convention Plz.
1 Harbour Rd.
Wanchai
Hong Kong, People's Republic of China
Ph: 852 1830668
Fax: 852 28240249
Publisher E-mail: hktdc@tdc.org.hk
Publication focusing on innovative electronic products.
Founded: 1985. **Freq:** 4/yr. **ISSN:** 1021-8866. **Re-
marks:** Advertising accepted; rates available upon
request. **URL:** http://info.hktdc.com/prodmag/electron/

electron.htm. **Formerly:** Hong Kong Electronics. **Circ:**
Paid 50,000

43306 ■ HKTDC Enterprise
Hong Kong Trade Development Council
38th Fl., Office Tower, Convention Plz.
1 Harbour Rd.
Wanchai
Hong Kong, People's Republic of China
Ph: 852 1830668
Fax: 852 28240249
Publisher E-mail: hktdc@tdc.org.hk
Journal of gifts, toys and clothing trade. **Founded:** 1967.
Freq: Monthly. **ISSN:** 1021-5611. **Remarks:** Advertising
accepted; rates available upon request. **URL:** http://
www.tdctrade.com/prodmag/enterpri/enterpri.htm. **For-
merly:** Hong Kong Enterprise. **Circ:** Paid 150,000

**43307 ■ HKTDC Fashion - Leather Goods &
Bags**
Hong Kong Trade Development Council
38th Fl., Office Tower, Convention Plz.
1 Harbour Rd.
Wanchai
Hong Kong, People's Republic of China
Ph: 852 1830668
Fax: 852 28240249
Publisher E-mail: hktdc@tdc.org.hk
Publication providing information on leather goods and
bags. **Founded:** 1993. **Freq:** Quarterly. **Remarks:**
Advertising accepted; rates available upon request.
URL: http://info.hktdc.com/prodmag/leather/leather.htm.
Formerly: Hong Kong Leather Goods & Bags. **Circ:**
(Not Reported)

43308 ■ HKTDC Fasion - Fabrics & Accessories
Hong Kong Trade Development Council
38th Fl., Office Tower, Convention Plz.
1 Harbour Rd.
Wanchai
Hong Kong, People's Republic of China
Ph: 852 1830668
Fax: 852 28240249
Publisher E-mail: hktdc@tdc.org.hk
Publication focusing on the fashion industry with focus
on fabrics and accessories, including textiles, labels,
badges, zippers, buttons, and threads. **Founded:** 1995.
Freq: Semiannual Mar. and Sept. **Remarks:** Advertising
accepted; rates available upon request. **URL:** http://info.
hktdc.com/prodmag/fabrics/fabrics.htm. **Circ:** (Not
Reported)

43309 ■ HKTDC Fasion - Footwear
Hong Kong Trade Development Council
38th Fl., Office Tower, Convention Plz.
1 Harbour Rd.
Wanchai
Hong Kong, People's Republic of China
Ph: 852 1830668
Fax: 852 28240249
Publisher E-mail: hktdc@tdc.org.hk
Magazing focusing on the latest developments in the
footwear industry. **Founded:** 1997. **Freq:** Semiannual
Feb. & Aug. **Remarks:** Advertising accepted; rates avail-
able upon request. **URL:** http://info.hktdc.com/prodmag/
footwear/footwear.htm. **Circ:** (Not Reported)

43310 ■ HKTDC Gifts, Premium & Stationery
Hong Kong Trade Development Council
38th Fl., Office Tower, Convention Plz.
1 Harbour Rd.
Wanchai
Hong Kong, People's Republic of China
Ph: 852 1830668
Fax: 852 28240249
Publisher E-mail: hktdc@tdc.org.hk
Publication focusing on innovative gifts and creative
premiums. **Founded:** 1986. **Freq:** Quarterly. **Remarks:**
Advertising accepted; rates available upon request.
URL: http://info.hktdc.com/prodmag/gifts/gifts.htm. **For-
merly:** Hong Kong Gifts, Premiums & Stationery. **Circ:**
(Not Reported)

43311 ■ HKTDC Houseware
Hong Kong Trade Development Council
38th Fl., Office Tower, Convention Plz.
1 Harbour Rd.
Wanchai
Hong Kong, People's Republic of China
Ph: 852 1830668

Fax: 852 28240249
Publisher E-mail: hktdc@tdc.org.hk
Publication providing information on all sorts of house-
hold and hardware products. **Founded:** 1983. **Freq:**
Semiannual Apr. & Nov. **Remarks:** Advertising accepted;
rates available upon request. **URL:** http://info.hktdc.com/
prodmag/house/house.htm. **Formerly:** Hong Kong
Household. **Circ:** (Not Reported)

43312 ■ HKTDC Jewellery
Hong Kong Trade Development Council
38th Fl., Office Tower, Convention Plz.
1 Harbour Rd.
Wanchai
Hong Kong, People's Republic of China
Ph: 852 1830668
Fax: 852 28240249
Publisher E-mail: hktdc@tdc.org.hk
Magazine focusing on jewellery collection. **Founded:**
1985. **Freq:** Semiannual Mar. and Sept. **Remarks:**
Advertising accepted; rates available upon request.
URL: http://info.hktdc.com/prodmag/jewell/jewell.htm.
Formerly: Hong Kong Jewellery Collection. **Circ:** (Not
Reported)

43313 ■ HKTDC Optical
Hong Kong Trade Development Council
38th Fl., Office Tower, Convention Plz.
1 Harbour Rd.
Wanchai
Hong Kong, People's Republic of China
Ph: 852 1830668
Fax: 852 28240249
Publisher E-mail: hktdc@tdc.org.hk
Publication focusing on opticals and eyewears.
Founded: 1992. **Freq:** Annual Oct. **Remarks:** Advertis-
ing accepted; rates available upon request. **URL:** http://
info.hktdc.com/prodmag/optical/optical.htm. **Formerly:**
Hong Kong Optical. **Circ:** (Not Reported)

43314 ■ HKTDC Packaging
Hong Kong Trade Development Council
38th Fl., Office Tower, Convention Plz.
1 Harbour Rd.
Wanchai
Hong Kong, People's Republic of China
Ph: 852 1830668
Fax: 852 28240249
Publisher E-mail: hktdc@tdc.org.hk
Publication providing information on a comprehensive
range of packaging materials, machinery and services
for safe transport and appropriate presentation of any
product. **Founded:** 1996. **Freq:** Semiannual Mar. and
Sept. **Key Personnel:** Anthony Moore, Editor; Denise
Yung, Editor; Carrie Lee, Editor. **Subscription Rates:**
240 Yu individuals. **Remarks:** Advertising accepted;
rates available upon request. **URL:** http://info.hktdc.com/
prodmag/package/package.htm. **Formerly:** Hong Kong
Packaging. **Circ:** (Not Reported)

43315 ■ HKTDC Toys & Games
Hong Kong Trade Development Council
38th Fl., Office Tower, Convention Plz.
1 Harbour Rd.
Wanchai
Hong Kong, People's Republic of China
Ph: 852 1830668
Fax: 852 28240249
Publisher E-mail: hktdc@tdc.org.hk
Periodical covering innovative electronic games, tradi-
tional plush toys, and educational toys. **Founded:** 1969.
Freq: Semiannual Jan. & July. **Remarks:** Advertising
accepted; rates available upon request. **URL:** http://info.
hktdc.com/prodmag/toys/toys.htm. **Formerly:** Hong
Kong Toys. **Circ:** (Not Reported)

43316 ■ HKTDC Watch & Clock
Hong Kong Trade Development Council
38th Fl., Office Tower, Convention Plz.
1 Harbour Rd.
Wanchai
Hong Kong, People's Republic of China
Ph: 852 1830668
Fax: 852 28240249
Publisher E-mail: hktdc@tdc.org.hk
Periodical providing access to elegant yet stylish, clas-
sic yet ornate, sophisticated yet competitively-priced
timepieces produced by Hong Kong. **Founded:** 1985.
Freq: 3/yr. **Remarks:** Advertising accepted; rates avail-

able upon request. **URL:** http://info.hktdc.com/prodmag/ watch/watch.htm. **Formerly:** Hong Kong Watches and Clocks. **Circ:** (Not Reported)

43317 ■ Home Journal
Edipresse Asia
6th Fl., Guardian House
32 Oi Kwan Rd.
Hong Kong, People's Republic of China
Ph: 11 852 25477117
Fax: 11 852 28582671
Journal on interior design. **Founded:** 1980. **Freq:** Monthly. **Key Personnel:** Albert Lo, Managing Editor. **Subscription Rates:** 315 Yu individuals; US$105 individuals Asia (by surface); US$140 individuals Asia (by airmail); US$110 other countries by surface; US$170 individuals by airmail; 546 Yu two years Hong Kong & Macau; 630 Yu individuals Hong Kong & Macau (3 years). **Remarks:** Accepts advertising. **URL:** http://www. hkhomejournal.com/. **Circ:** (Not Reported)

43318 ■ Home Journal Buyer's Guide
Edipresse Asia
6th Fl., Guardian House
32 Oi Kwan Rd.
Hong Kong, People's Republic of China
Ph: 11 852 25477117
Fax: 11 852 28582671
Magazine containing directory of interiors and home products. **Freq:** Annual. **Key Personnel:** Roddy Yu, Director; Albert Lo, Ch. Ed. **URL:** http://www.edipresse. com/home-design/home-journal-buyers-guide. **Circ:** ‡36,570

43319 ■ The Hong Kong Accountant
Hong Kong Society of Accountants
Wu Chung House, 37 Fl.
213 Queen's Rd. E
Hong Kong, People's Republic of China
Ph: 862 22877228
Fax: 862 28656603
Publisher E-mail: hkicpa@hkicpa.org.hk
Hong Kong publication covering accounting, business, finance, taxation, auditing, education, innovation & technology, legal, risk management, etc. in Hong Kong, China, and international scene. **Founded:** Mar. 1988. **Freq:** Monthly. **Trim Size:** 285 x 210 mm. **Key Personnel:** John So, Editorial Coord. **ISSN:** 1029-3892. **Subscription Rates:** 840 Yu individuals. **URL:** http://www. hksa.org.hk/publications/society_journals. **Ad Rates:** BW: 17,390 Yu, 4C: 22,730 Yu. **Circ:** 35,000

43320 ■ Hong Kong Apparel
Hong Kong Trade Development Council
38th Fl., Office Tower, Convention Plz.
1 Harbour Rd.
Wanchai
Hong Kong, People's Republic of China
Ph: 852 1830668
Fax: 852 28240249
Publisher E-mail: hktdc@tdc.org.hk
Publication providing information on high-quality ready-to-wear and designer fashions and accessories. **Founded:** 1969. **Freq:** Semiannual Jan. and July. **Remarks:** Advertising accepted; rates available upon request. **URL:** http://info.hktdc.com/prodmag/apparel/ apparel.htm. **Circ:** (Not Reported)

43321 ■ Hong Kong Business
Edipresse Asia
6th Fl., Guardian House
32 Oi Kwan Rd.
Hong Kong, People's Republic of China
Ph: 11 852 25477117
Fax: 11 852 28582671
Publication E-mail: editor@hkbusiness.com.hk
Consumer magazine covering business in English. **Founded:** July 1982. **Freq:** Monthly. **Print Method:** Offset. **Trim Size:** 286 x 419 mm. **Cols./Page:** 3. **Key Personnel:** Louis Shiek, Advertisement Dir., louis. shek@edipresse.com.hk; Natalie Ho, Advertising Mgr., natalie.ho@edipresse.com.hk; Jane Chan, Advertising Mgr., jane.chan@edipresse.com.hk. **Subscription Rates:** 270 Yu individuals Hong Kong & Macau; US$75 individuals Asia (by surface); US$77 other countries by surface; US$80 individuals by airmail (Asia); US$95 other countries by airmail; 468 Yu two years Hong Kong & Macau; 540 Yu individuals Hong Kong & Macau, 3 years. **Remarks:** Accepts advertising. **URL:** http://www. hkgbusiness.com/. **Circ:** Paid 15,000

43322 ■ Hong Kong for the Business Visitor
Hong Kong Trade Development Council
38th Fl., Office Tower, Convention Plz.
1 Harbour Rd.
Wanchai
Hong Kong, People's Republic of China
Ph: 852 1830668
Fax: 852 28240249
Publisher E-mail: hktdc@tdc.org.hk
Journal of travel, tourism, business and economics. **Founded:** June 1997. **Freq:** Annual. **ISSN:** 1028-1606. **Remarks:** Advertising accepted; rates available upon request. **URL:** http://www.tdctrade.com/prodmag/visitor/ visitor.htm. **Circ:** 40,000

43323 ■ Hong Kong Design Services
Hong Kong Trade Development Council
38th Fl., Office Tower, Convention Plz.
1 Harbour Rd.
Wanchai
Hong Kong, People's Republic of China
Ph: 852 1830668
Fax: 852 28240249
Publication E-mail: hktdc@tdc.org.hk
Publisher E-mail: hktdc@tdc.org.hk
Journal of interior design and decoration. **Founded:** 1997. **Freq:** Annual. **ISSN:** 1026-6704. **URL:** http://www. tdctrade.com.

43324 ■ Hong Kong Entrepreneur
Chinese Manufacturers' Association of Hong Kong
64-66 Connaught Rd.
Hong Kong, People's Republic of China
Ph: 85 225 456166
Fax: 85 225 414541
Publisher E-mail: info@cma.org.hk
Chinese and English language publication covering manufacturing. **Freq:** Monthly. **Print Method:** Offset. **Trim Size:** 210 x 286 mm. **Subscription Rates:** 75 Yu individuals overseas by airmail; 330 Yu individuals; 561 Yu two years; 128 Yu two years overseas. **Remarks:** Accepts advertising. **URL:** http://www.cma.org.hk/hke. **Ad Rates:** BW: HK$7,500, 4C: HK$10,500. **Circ:** 4,200

43325 ■ Hong Kong Industrialist
Federation of Hong Kong Industries
Unit 415 , Hankow Ctr.
5-15 Hankow Rd.
Tsim Sha Tsui
Kowloon
Hong Kong, People's Republic of China
Ph: 86 230 21621
Fax: 86 273 60211
Publisher E-mail: fhki@fhki.org.hk
Journal covering business and economics. **Founded:** 1962. **Freq:** Monthly. **Subscription Rates:** US$400 individuals local; US$90 other countries international. **Remarks:** Accepts advertising. **URL:** http://www. industryhk.org/english/fp/fp_hki/fp_hki.php. **Circ:** Paid 7,000

43326 ■ Hong Kong Jewelry Express
Hong Kong Jewelry Manufacturers Association
Unit G, 2nd Fl., Phase 2, Kaiser Estate
51 Man Yue St.
Hunghom
Kowloon
Hong Kong, People's Republic of China
Ph: 852 27663002
Fax: 852 23623647
Publisher E-mail: enquiry@jewelry.org.hk
Chinese and English language publication covering jewelry. **Founded:** 1997. **Freq:** Quarterly every March, June, September, and November. **Subscription Rates:** 250 Yu by mail HKD; US$50 by mail other countries; 480 Yu two years HKD; US$90 two years other countries. **URL:** http://www.hkje.com/hkje/en/highlight/ hl2006d. **Ad Rates:** 4C: US$1,000. **Circ:** 7,000

43327 ■ Hong Kong Journal of Applied Linguistics
The University of Hong Kong
Centre for Applied English Studies
Pokfulam Rd.
Hong Kong, People's Republic of China
Ph: 852 28592006
Fax: 852 25473409
Publication E-mail: hkjal@hku.hk
Publisher E-mail: caes@hku.hk
Publication catering to those who use English as a

second or foreign language and have Chinese as their first language. **Founded:** Oct. 1996. **Freq:** Semiannual. **Key Personnel:** Prof. Agnes Lam, Director; Wai Lan Tsang, Editor. **ISSN:** 1028-4435. **Subscription Rates:** US$150 individuals. **URL:** http://www2.caes.hku.hk/ hkjal.

43328 ■ Hong Kong Journal of Dermatology & Venereology
Medcom Ltd.
Rm. 504-5, Cheung Tat Ctr.
18 Cheung Lee St.
Hong Kong, People's Republic of China
Ph: 86 852 25783833
Fax: 86 852 25783929
Publisher E-mail: mcl@medcom.com.hk
Magazine of dermatology. **Freq:** Monthly. **URL:** http:// www.medicine.org.hk/hksdv/journal.htm. **Formerly:** Hong Kong Dermatology and Venereology Bulletin.

43329 ■ Hong Kong Journal of Occupational Therapy
Hong Kong Occupational Therapy Association
PO Box 98241
TST Post-office
Hong Kong, People's Republic of China
Ph: 852 28051278
Publisher E-mail: mail.hkota@gmail.com
Hong Kong journal covering occupational therapy. **Freq:** Semiannual. **Key Personnel:** Kenneth N.K. Fong, PhD, Editor-in-Chief; Dr. Cecilia Li-Tsang, PhD, Assoc. Ed. **ISSN:** 1569-1861. **Subscription Rates:** US$158 individuals for European countries and Iran; 24,900¥ individuals; US$200 other countries except Europe, Japan and Iran. **Remarks:** Advertising accepted; rates available upon request. **URL:** http://www.elsevier.com/ wps/find/journaldescription.cws_home/708608/ descriptiondescription. **Circ:** (Not Reported)

43330 ■ The Hong Kong Journal of Orthopaedic Surgery
Pamela Youde Nethersole Eastern Hospital
Dept. of Orthopaedics and Traumatology
c/o The Hong Kong College of Orthopaedic Surgeons
Hong Kong Academy of Medicine, Rm. 905, 9th Fl.
Jockey Club Bldg.
99 Wong Chuk Hang Rd., Aberdeen
Hong Kong, People's Republic of China
Publisher E-mail: pyneh_enquiry@ha.org.hk
Journal that aims to serve as the communication channel for ideas and knowledge exchange in the field of orthopedic surgery among surgeons and the paramedical personnel. **Founded:** 1997. **Freq:** Semiannual. **Key Personnel:** Wing-Cheung Wu, Editor-in-Chief, hkcos@ hkcos.org.hk; James Chung-kit Cheng, Editor; Ping Chien, Editor. **ISSN:** 1028-2637. **URL:** http://hkoa.org/ hkjos/2000-1/index.htm.

43331 ■ Hong Kong Journal of Paediatrics
Medcom Ltd.
c/o Hong Kong College of Paediatricians
Rm. 801, Hong Kong Academy of Medicine Jockey Club Bldg.
99 Wong Chuk Hang Rd.
Aberdeen
Hong Kong, People's Republic of China
Ph: 852 28718871
Fax: 852 27851850
Publisher E-mail: mcl@medcom.com.hk
Official publication of the Hong Kong College of Pediatricians and Hong Kong Paediatric Society. **Founded:** 1984. **Freq:** 4/yr. **Key Personnel:** Chiu Man Chun, Member; Don M. Roberton, International Advisor; Yeung Chap Yung, Membership; Chan Chi Fung, Editor-in-Chief; David K. Stevenson, International Advisor. **ISSN:** 1013-9923. **URL:** http://www.hkjpaed.org; http://www. medicine.org.hk.

43332 ■ The Hong Kong Journal of Social Work
Hong Kong Social Workers Association Ltd.
Dept. of Social Work
Hong Kong Baptist University
Hong Kong, People's Republic of China
Publication E-mail: hkswa@hkswa.org.hk
Publisher E-mail: hkswa@hkswa.org.hk
Publication committed to the improvement of practice, extension of knowledge and promotion of communications in the broad field of social work. **Freq:** Semiannual. **Key Personnel:** Marcus Chiu, Editor-in-Chief; Sam Yu, Managing Editor; Winnie Ho, Assoc. Ed. **ISSN:** 0219-

2462. Subscription Rates: EUR102 institutions print & electronic; EUR98 institutions electronic only. **Remarks:** Accepts advertising. **URL:** http://www.worldscinet.com/hkjsw/hkjsw.shtml. **Circ:** (Not Reported)

43333 ■ Hong Kong Journal of Sociology
Chinese University Press
Shatin Galleria, 9th Fl., Unit 1-3 & 18
18-24 Shan Mei St.
Fo Tan, Shatin
Hong Kong, People's Republic of China
Ph: 852 29465300
Fax: 852 26037355
Publisher E-mail: cup@cuhk.edu.hk
Journal covering sociology. **Founded:** Nov. 2000. **Freq:** Annual. **Trim Size:** 152 x 229 mm. **Key Personnel:** Lau Siu-kai, Editor-in-Chief. **ISSN:** 1606-8610. **Subscription Rates:** US$12 individuals. **URL:** http://www.chineseupress.com/asp/JournalList_en.asp?CatID=1&Lang=E&JournalID=8.

43334 ■ The Hong Kong Journal of Sports Medicine and Sports Science
Dr. Stephen Hui Research Centre for Physical Recreation and Wellness
Hong Kong Baptist University
Kowloon Tong
Kowloon
Hong Kong, People's Republic of China
Ph: 852 34117400
Fax: 852 23387644
Publisher E-mail: webmaster@hkbu.edu.hk
Publishes articles in the field of sports medicine and sports science. **Freq:** Bimonthly. **Key Personnel:** Frank Fu, Editor-in-Chief. **ISSN:** 1728-869X. **URL:** http://www.hkbu.edu.hk/~sosc1/shc/shc/journal_old1.htmlThe%20Hong.

43335 ■ Hong Kong Law Reports & Digest
Sweet & Maxwell Asia
10 Fl. Cityplaza 3,
Taikoo Shing
Hong Kong, People's Republic of China
Ph: 852 37623227
Fax: 852 25206646
Publisher E-mail: smhk.customer.support@thomsonreuters.com
Journal of law. **Founded:** 1997. **Freq:** Biweekly. **Key Personnel:** HoYan Leung, Commissioning Ed.; Klaus Pfeifer, Managing Editor. **ISSN:** 1027-6629. **Subscription Rates:** 10,950 Yu individuals; US$1,404 individuals. **URL:** http://www.sweetandmaxwell.com.hk/.

43336 ■ Hong Kong Lawyer
The Law Society of Hong Kong
3rd Fl., Wing On House
71 Des Voeux Rd., Central
Hong Kong, People's Republic of China
Ph: 852 28460500
Fax: 852 28450387
Publisher E-mail: sg@hklawsoc.org.hk
Official journal of the Law Society of Hong Kong. **Subtitle:** The Official Journal of the Law Society of Hong Kong. **Freq:** Monthly. **Key Personnel:** Brendan Clift, Editor, phone 852 29651451, fax 852 29760840, brendan.olift@lexisnexis.com; Jennifer Luk, Sales Mgr., phone 852 29651432, fax 852 29760840, jennifer.luk@butterworths-hk.com; George Y.C. Mok, Editorial Board; Michael Philips, Editorial Board; Michael Wilkinson, Editorial Board; Anne Scully-Hill, Editorial Board; Thomas SL So, Editorial Board; Raymond Ho, Editorial Board; Bonnie S.Y. Chan, Editorial Board. **ISSN:** 1025-9554. **Remarks:** Accepts advertising. **URL:** http://www.hk-lawyer.com. **Circ:** (Not Reported)

43337 ■ The Hong Kong Manager
Hong Kong Management Association
W Haking Management Development Ctr.
14/F Fairmont House
8 Cotton Tree Dr.
Hong Kong, People's Republic of China
Ph: 852 27663303
Publication E-mail: hkmanager@hkma.org.hk
English and Chinese language publication covering management in Hong Kong. **Freq:** Quarterly. **Key Personnel:** Dr. Mike Fung, Author. **ISSN:** 0018-4594. **Remarks:** Advertising accepted; rates available upon request. **URL:** http://www.hkma.org.hk/web_info.asp?info_no=105000001&ver_type=E. **Circ:** 140,000

43338 ■ Hong Kong Medical Diary
Medcom Ltd.
Rm. 504-5, Cheung Tat Ctr.
18 Cheung Lee St.
Hong Kong, People's Republic of China
Ph: 86 852 25783833
Fax: 86 852 25783929
Publisher E-mail: mcl@medcom.com.hk
Official publication of the Federation of Medical Societies of Hong Kong. **Freq:** Monthly. **Key Personnel:** Dr. Chun-Hon Chan, Editor; Dr. Wing-Keung King, Editor-in-Chief; Chi-Fung Chan, Editor. **Remarks:** Accepts advertising. **URL:** http://www.fmshk.com.hk/hkmd/. **Circ:** 8,000

43339 ■ Hong Kong Medical Journal
Rm. 901
99 Wong Chuk Hang Rd.
Aberdeen
Hong Kong, People's Republic of China
Ph: 85 228 718822
Fax: 85 225 159061
Publisher E-mail: hkmj@hkam.org.hk
Publication of the Hong Kong Academy of Medicine (HKAM) and the Hong Kong Medical Association (HKMA). **Founded:** 1995. **Freq:** Bimonthly. **Key Personnel:** R. Kay, Editor-in-Chief; P.T. Cheung, Sen. Ed.; Its Yu, Sen. Ed.; A.K.K. Chui, Sen. Ed. **ISSN:** 1024-2708. **Subscription Rates:** 600 Yu individuals; US$160 elsewhere incl. handling fee; US$100 elsewhere PRC, incl. handling fee. **Remarks:** Accepts advertising. **URL:** http://www.hkmj.org. **Ad Rates:** BW: HK$10,000, 4C: HK$13,500. **Circ:** Paid 7,100, 7,800

43340 ■ The Hong Kong Nursing Journal
Medcom Ltd.
College of Nursing
Hyde Centre, 12th Fl.
221-226 Gloucester Rd.
Wanchai
Hong Kong, People's Republic of China
Ph: 852 25729255
Fax: 852 28386280
Publisher E-mail: mcl@medcom.com.hk
Journal focusing on improvement of the standard of clinical practice, extension of nursing knowledge and promotion of communication in the nursing profession. **URL:** http://www.fmshk.com.hk/conhk/hknj/home.htm.

43341 ■ Hong Kong Physiotherapy Journal
Hong Kong Physiotherapy Association Ltd.
PO Box 10139
General Post Office
Rm. 901, 9/F Rightful Ctr., No. 12 Tak Hing St.
Hong Kong, People's Republic of China
Ph: 852 23360172
Fax: 852 23380252
Physiotherapy journal. **Founded:** 1978. **Freq:** 3/month. **Key Personnel:** Priscillia Lam Lam, Editor-in-Chief, plamlam@hongkongpa.com.hk; Prof. Christina Hui-Chan, Editorial Board; Margaret Mak, Assoc. Ed. **ISSN:** 1013-7025. **URL:** http://www.hongkongpa.com.hk/publication/index.htm.

43342 ■ The Hong Kong Practitioner
Medcom Ltd.
The Hong Kong College of Family Physicians
7th Fl., HKAM Jockey Club Bldg.
99 Wong Chuk Hang Rd.
Hong Kong, People's Republic of China
Ph: 852 25286618
Fax: 852 26660616
Publisher E-mail: mcl@medcom.com.hk
Journal for the medical practitioners of Hong Kong. **Freq:** Quarterly. **Key Personnel:** Dr. D.V.K. Chao, Editorial Board; Dr. F.C.T. Lee, Dep. Ed.; Dr. K.K. Ng, Dep. Ed.; Dr. M.B.L. Kwong, Business Mgr.; Dr. K.K. Tse, Editorial Board Member; Dr. X. Fu, Editorial Board Member; Dr. T.K. Lam, Editorial Board Member; Dr. J. Liang, Editorial Board Member. **ISSN:** 1027-3948. **URL:** http://www.hkcfp.org.hk; http://www.hkjpaed.org/info.asp. **Circ:** 4,000

43343 ■ Hong Kong Printing
Hong Kong Trade Development Council
38th Fl., Office Tower, Convention Plz.
1 Harbour Rd.
Wanchai
Hong Kong, People's Republic of China

Ph: 852 1830668
Fax: 852 28240249
Publisher E-mail: hktdc@tdc.org.hk
Journal covering printing. **Founded:** 1997. **Freq:** Semiannual. **ISSN:** 1027-6327. **URL:** http://www.tdc.org.hk.

43344 ■ The Hong Kong Racing Journal
The Hong Kong Racing Journal Ltd.
23 Fl., Wing On Ctr., Rm. 2303-04
No. 111 Connaught Rd., Central
Hong Kong, People's Republic of China
Ph: 852 81980632
Publisher E-mail: newman@horseracing.com.hk
Publication providing HK Racing Information and Data for the Racing Enthusiast & serious and novice players alike. **Founded:** 1995. **Key Personnel:** Klein Earl, Editor, eklein@horseracing.com.hk. **URL:** http://www.horseracing.com.hk.

43345 ■ Hong Kong Surveyor
The Hong Kong Institute of Surveyors
Jardine House, Ste. 801
1 Connaught Pl.
Central
Hong Kong, People's Republic of China
Ph: 86 225 263679
Fax: 86 228 684612
Publisher E-mail: info@hkis.org.hk
Hong Kong publication covering surveying. **Freq:** Periodic. **Key Personnel:** Tang Ki-cheung, Chm.; Paul Ho, Editor; Leung Lap Ki, President. **ISSN:** 1812-3953. **URL:** http://www.hkis.org.hk/; http://www.icoste.org/Members/hkis.htm.

43346 ■ Hong Kong Tatler
Edipresse Asia
6th Fl., Guardian House
32 Oi Kwan Rd.
Hong Kong, People's Republic of China
Ph: 11 852 25477117
Fax: 11 852 28582671
Lifestyle magazine. **Freq:** Monthly. **Print Method:** Offset. **Trim Size:** 228 x 315 mm. **Key Personnel:** Sean Fitzpatrick, Editor-in-Chief; Pavan Shamdasani, Asst. Ed. **Subscription Rates:** 405 Yu individuals Hong Kong & Macau; US$165 individuals Asia (by airmail); US$115 individuals Asia (by surface); US$195 other countries by airmail; US$120 other countries by surface; 702 Yu two years Hong Kong & Macau; 810 Yu individuals 3 years (Hong Kong & Macau). **Remarks:** Advertising accepted; rates available upon request. **URL:** http://www.hktatler.com/. **Circ:** (Not Reported)

43347 ■ Human Rights Solidarity
Asian Human Rights Commission
19th Fl., Go-Up Commercial Bldg.
998 Canton Rd.
Kowloon
Hong Kong, People's Republic of China
Ph: 86 852 26986339
Fax: 86 852 26986367
Publisher E-mail: ahrc@ahrc.asia
Journal reporting human rights issues of India, China, Nepal and Philippines. **ISSN:** 1682-4148. **URL:** http://www.hrsolidarity.net/.

43348 ■ Innovative Investor
Pacific Prospect Group Ltd.
20 Fl., Admiralty Ctr., Tower 2
18 Harcourt Rd.
Hong Kong, People's Republic of China
Ph: 852 34114700
Fax: 852 34114701
Publisher E-mail: asiariskevents@incisivemedia.com
Magazine featuring structured products and alternative investments in Asia-Pacific. **Subtitle:** Maximizing Your Returns from Structured products in Asia. **Freq:** Quarterly. **Key Personnel:** Ben Marquand, Editor, phone 852 34114788, ben.marquand@incisivemedia.com; Harjeet Singh, Publisher, phone 852 34114838, harjeet.singh@incisivemedia.com. **Remarks:** Accepts advertising. **URL:** http://www.innovative-investor.com/; http://www.pacificprospect.com/?page=publications&book_title=ii. **Circ:** (Not Reported)

43349 ■ International Journal of Computer Processing of Languages
World Scientific Publishing (HK) Company Ltd.
Kowloon Central Post Office

PO Box 72482
Hong Kong, People's Republic of China
Ph: 852 27718791
Fax: 852 27718155
Publisher E-mail: hongkong@worldscientific.com.hk
Periodical covering all aspects related to the computer processing of Oriental languages. **Founded:** 1983. **Freq:** Quarterly. **Key Personnel:** Qin Lu, Editor-in-Chief, csluqin@comp.polyu.edu.hk; Key Sun Choi, Assoc. Ed., kschoi@cs.kaist.ac.kr. **ISSN:** 1793-8406. **Subscription Rates:** US$308 institutions electronic + print; US$296 institutions electronic only. **Remarks:** Accepts advertising. **URL:** http://www.worldscinet.com/; http://www.worldscinet.com/ijcpol/ijcpol.shtml. **Formerly:** International Journal of Computer Processing of Oriental Languages. **Circ:** (Not Reported)

43350 ■ International Journal of Image and Graphics
World Scientific Publishing (HK) Company Ltd.
c/o David Zhang, Editor-in-Chief
Dept. of Computing
Hong Kong Polytechnic University
Kowloon
Hong Kong, People's Republic of China
Ph: 852 27667271
Fax: 852 27740842
Publisher E-mail: hongkong@worldscientific.com.hk
Publication covering efficient and effective image and graphics technologies and systems. **Freq:** Quarterly. **Key Personnel:** David Zhang, Editor-in-Chief, csdzhang@comp.polyu.edu.hk. **ISSN:** 0219-4678. **Subscription Rates:** US$390 institutions electronic and print; US$374 institutions electronic only; EUR347 institutions electronic and print; EUR333 institutions electronic only. **Remarks:** Accepts advertising. **URL:** http://www.worldscinet.com/ijig/ijig.shtml. **Circ:** (Not Reported)

43351 ■ International Journal of Knowledge Engineering and Data Mining
Inderscience Enterprises Limited
c/o Dr. Adela S.M. Lau, Ed.-in-Ch.
Medical Informatics & Knowledge Management Specialist
The Hong Kong University of Science & Technology
Clear Water Bay, Kowloon
Hong Kong, People's Republic of China
Journal covering the theoretical and practical research development on knowledge engineering and data mining. **Freq:** 4/yr. **Key Personnel:** Dr. Adela S.M. Lau, Editor-in-Chief, adela.ijkedm@gmail.com. **ISSN:** 1755-2087. **Subscription Rates:** EUR494 individuals print or online; EUR672 individuals print and online. **URL:** http://www.inderscience.com/browse/index.php?journalID=332.

43352 ■ International Journal of Shipping and Transport Logistics
Inderscience Enterprises Limited
c/o Dr. Kee-hung Lai, Ed.
The Hong Kong Polytechnic University
U.S. Department of Logistics & Maritime Studies
Hung Hom, Kowloon
Hong Kong, People's Republic of China
Peer-reviewed journal covering all methodological aspects in the field of shipping and transport logistics. **Freq:** 4/yr. **Key Personnel:** Dr. Kee-hung Lai, Editor, lgtmlai@polyu.edu.hk; Dr. Y.H. Venus Lun, Editor, lgtvlun@polyu.edu.hk. **ISSN:** 1756-6517. **Subscription Rates:** EUR494 individuals print or online; EUR672 individuals print and online. **URL:** http://www.inderscience.com/browse/index.php?journalID=304.

43353 ■ Journal of Computational Mathematics
Global Science Press
Unit No. 1521, Level 15
Tower 1, Grand Central Plz.
138 Sha Tin Rural Committee Rd.
Shatin, N.T.
Hong Kong, People's Republic of China
Ph: 852 31051607
Fax: 852 31050207
Publisher E-mail: info@global-sci.org
Peer-reviewed journal covering computational mathematics. **Founded:** 1977. **Freq:** 6/yr. **Print Method:** Offset, Sheet Fed. **Trim Size:** 8 1/2 x 11. **Cols./Page:** 2 and 3. **Col. Width:** 27 and 42 nonpareils. **Col. Depth:** 133 agate llnes. **Key Personnel:** Shi Zhong-ci, Editor-in-Chief; Gang Bao, Managing Editor. **ISSN:** 0254-9409. **Subscription Rates:** US$600 institutions print and electronic; US$400 individuals print and electronic;

US$600 institutions electronic only; US$300 individuals electronic only. **URL:** http://www.global-sci.org/jcm/.

43354 ■ Journal of Construction Research
World Scientific Publishing Company Inc.
c/o Raymond Y.C. Tse, Ed.-in-Ch.
International City University of America
13/F Asian House
1 Hennessy Rd.
Hong Kong, People's Republic of China
Publisher E-mail: wspc@wspc.com
Peer-reviewed journal covering information on operations management and production management in the construction industry. **Founded:** 1982. **Freq:** Bimonthly. **Print Method:** Web press. **Trim Size:** 10 3/4 x 12 1/8. **Cols./Page:** 4. **Col. Width:** 14 picas. **Col. Depth:** 10 inches. **Key Personnel:** Raymond Y.C. Tse, Editor-in-Chief, rtse@icua.us; Boyd C. Paulson, Jr., Board of Consultant. **ISSN:** 1609-9451. **Subscription Rates:** US$105 institutions electronic + print; US$101 institutions electronic; EUR94 institutions electronic and print; EUR90 institutions electronic. **URL:** http://www.worldscinet.com/jcr/jcr.shtml.

43355 ■ The Journal of Dagaare Studies (JDS)
The University of Hong Kong
Department of Linguistics
Main Bldg., Rm. 126
The University of Hong Kong
Pokfulam Rd.
Hong Kong, People's Republic of China
Ph: 852 28578606
Fax: 852 25464943
Publisher E-mail: linguist@hkucc.hku.hk
Journal covering research in various areas of the Arts and Sciences having a bearing on the language, culture and society of the Dagaaba of West Africa. **Freq:** Annual. **Key Personnel:** Dr. Adams Bodomo, Editor, phone 852 28578285, fax 852 25464943, abbodomo@hku.hk. **ISSN:** 1608-0661. **Subscription Rates:** US$15 individuals inside Ghana; US$25 other countries; US$30 institutions inside Ghana; US$50 institutions, other countries. **URL:** http://www.hku.hk/linguist/staff/Bodomo/JDS/all.html.

43356 ■ Journal of Geospatial Engineering
Hong Kong Institution of Engineering Surveyors
PO Box No. 79
Tsuen Wan
Hong Kong, People's Republic of China
Publisher E-mail: secretary@hkies.org.hk
Official journal of the Hong Kong Institution of Engineering Surveyors. **Freq:** Semiannual. **Key Personnel:** Prof. Xiaoli Ding, Editor-in-Chief, phone 852 27665965, fax 852 23302994, lsxlding@polyu.edu.hk. **ISSN:** 1563-3772. **Subscription Rates:** Free to members; 350 Yu nonmembers. **URL:** http://www.hkies.org.hk/HKIES2008ee/journal_en.htm.

43357 ■ Journal of the Hong Kong College of Cardiology
Medcom Ltd.
Hong Kong College of Cardiology
Rm. 1116, 11 Fl., Bank of America Tower
12 Harcourt Rd., Central
Hong Kong, People's Republic of China
Ph: 852 28992035
Fax: 852 28992045
Publication E-mail: enquiry@hkcchk.com
Publisher E-mail: mcl@medcom.com.hk
Official publication of the Hong Kong College of Cardiology. **Founded:** 1993. **Freq:** Semiannual. **Key Personnel:** Chu-Pak Lau, Editor-in-Chief. **ISSN:** 1027-7811. **Remarks:** Accepts advertising. **URL:** http://www.hkcchk.com/journals.php. **Ad Rates:** BW: 8,000 Yu, 4C: 18,000 Yu. **Circ:** 1,000

43358 ■ Journal of the Hong Kong Geriatrics Society
Medcom Ltd.
Rm. 504-5, Cheung Tat Ctr.
18 Cheung Lee St.
Hong Kong, People's Republic of China
Ph: 86 852 25783833
Fax: 86 852 25783929
Publication E-mail: ccmlum@cuhk.edu.hk
Publisher E-mail: mcl@medcom.com.hk
Official journal of the Hong Kong Geriatrics Society. Publishes articles on geriatric medicine. **Freq:** Semiannual. **Key Personnel:** Dr. Tung-Wai Au-Yeung,

Local Editorial Board; Dr. Christopher Chor-Ming Lum, Editor-in-Chief; Dr. Stephen C. Allen, International Board of Honorary Ed. **URL:** http://hkgerisoc.org/Journal/v12200401/JHKGSv12.html. **Circ:** 1,800

43359 ■ Journal of Modern Literature in Chinese
Lingnan University
Centre for Literature and Translation
8 Castle Peak Rd., Tuen Mun, New Territories
Hong Kong, People's Republic of China
Ph: 852 26168888
Fax: 852 24638363
Journal providing a forum for discussing issues related to any aspect of modern or contemporary literature in Chinese. **Freq:** Semiannual. **Key Personnel:** Leung Ping-Kwan, Ch. Ed.; Prof. Ching-Chih Liu, Advisory Board; Christopher Lukpe, Assoc. Ed. **Subscription Rates:** 234 Yu institutions; 156 Yu individuals; US$45 institutions, other countries; US$35 other countries. **Remarks:** Accepts advertising. **URL:** http://www.ln.edu.hk/jmlc/editorial_f.html. **Circ:** (Not Reported)

43360 ■ Journal of Orthopaedic Surgery
Asia Pacific Orthopaedic Association
c/o Hong Kong Academy of Medicine Press
Rm. 901, 9th Fl., Wong Chuk Hang Rd.
Hong Kong, People's Republic of China
Ph: 85 2 28718807
Fax: 85 2 25159061
Publication E-mail: jos@josonline.org
Publisher E-mail: sec@apoa-home.org
Publication covering orthopedic surgery. **Founded:** 1962. **Freq:** 3/yr. **Key Personnel:** Dr. David Fang, Editor-in-Chief; Kenneth Cheung, Dep. Ed. **ISSN:** 1022-5563. **Subscription Rates:** 110 Yu individuals airmail. **Remarks:** Advertising accepted; rates available upon request. **URL:** http://www.josonline.org/. **Circ:** (Not Reported)

43361 ■ Journal of Psychology in Chinese Societies
The Hong Kong Psychological Society Ltd.
The Department of Psychology
University of Hong Kong
Pokfulam Rd.
Hong Kong, People's Republic of China
Ph: 852 25490364
Publisher E-mail: admin@hkps.org.hk
Chinese and English language international peer-reviewed journal aimed at promoting psychological studies of Chinese people. **Founded:** 2000. **Freq:** Semiannual. **Key Personnel:** Julian Lai, Editor; Dorcas Fok, Managing Editor. **ISSN:** 1563-3403. **Subscription Rates:** 24 Yu single issue; 40 Yu institutions. **Remarks:** Accepts advertising. **URL:** http://www.chineseupress.com/asp/JournalList_en.asp?CatID=1&Lang=E&JournalID=6. **Circ:** Paid 500

43362 ■ Journal of Translation Studies
Chinese University Press
Shatin Galleria, 9th Fl., Unit 1-3 & 18
18-24 Shan Mei St.
Fo Tan, Shatin
Hong Kong, People's Republic of China
Ph: 852 29465300
Fax: 852 26037355
Publisher E-mail: cup@cuhk.edu.hk
Journal covering translation studies and Chinese translations of literary works. **Founded:** Mar. 2000. **Freq:** Annual. **Trim Size:** 152 x 229 mm. **Key Personnel:** Lawrence K.P. Wong, Editor-in-Chief; Chan Sin-wai, Exec. Ed.; Miranda Lui, Editorial Asst. **ISSN:** 1027-7978. **Subscription Rates:** US$12 individuals. **URL:** http://www.chineseupress.com/asp/JournalList_en.asp?CatID=1&Lang=E&JournalID=4.

43363 ■ Journal of Travel & Tourism Marketing
Haworth Press Inc.
c/o Kaye S. Chon, PhD, Ed.
School of Hotel & Tourism Management
The Hong Kong Polytechnic Univ.
Hung Hom, Kowloon
Hong Kong, People's Republic of China
Publisher E-mail: getinfo@haworthpress.com
Peer-reviewed journal covering travel and tourism marketing for managers and researchers in the field. **Founded:** 1992. **Freq:** Quarterly. **Trim Size:** 6 x 8 3/8. **Key Personnel:** Kaye S. Chon, PhD, Editor, hmkchon@polyu.edu.hk. **ISSN:** 1054-8408. **Subscription Rates:** US$186 individuals online only; US$971 institutions on-

line only; 199 Yu individuals print & online; US$1,079 institutions print & online. **Remarks:** Accepts advertising. **URL:** http://www.informaworld.com/smpp/title~db=all~content=t792306980; http://www.tandf.co.uk/journals/WTTM. **Ad Rates:** BW: 315 Yu, 4C: 550 Yu. **Circ:** (Not Reported)

43364 ■ Luxe Living Kitchens & Bathrooms
Edipresse Asia
6th Fl., Guardian House
32 Oi Kwan Rd.
Hong Kong, People's Republic of China
Ph: 11 852 25477117
Fax: 11 852 28582671
Magazine featuring information on kitchen and bathroom designs. **Freq:** Annual. **Key Personnel:** Roddy Yu, Director; Albert Lo, Ch. Ed. **URL:** http://www.edipresse.com/home-design/luxe-living-kitchens-bathrooms. **Circ:** ‡25,000

43365 ■ Macau Tatler
Edipresse Asia
6th Fl., Guardian House
32 Oi Kwan Rd.
Hong Kong, People's Republic of China
Ph: 11 852 25477117
Fax: 11 852 28582671
Magazine featuring the high-society lifestyle of people in Macau. **Freq:** Quarterly. **Key Personnel:** Roddy Yu, Director; Sean Fitzpatrick, Ch. Ed. **URL:** http://www.edipresse.com/lifestyle/macau-tatler. **Circ:** ‡30,140

43366 ■ Macau Tatler Best Restaurants
Edipresse Asia
6th Fl., Guardian House
32 Oi Kwan Rd.
Hong Kong, People's Republic of China
Ph: 11 852 25477117
Fax: 11 852 28582671
Magazine featuring information on fine dining restaurants in Macau. **Freq:** Annual. **Key Personnel:** Roddy Yu, Director. **URL:** http://www.edipresse.com/en/par_pays/macao/magazines/macau_tatler_best_restaurants. **Circ:** ‡31,100

43367 ■ Malaysia Tatler
Edipresse Asia
6th Fl., Guardian House
32 Oi Kwan Rd.
Hong Kong, People's Republic of China
Ph: 11 852 25477117
Fax: 11 852 28582671
Consumer publication. **Founded:** 1989. **Freq:** Monthly. **ISSN:** 1394-7354. **Subscription Rates:** M$150 individuals; US$204 individuals South East Asia (by airmail); US$204 individuals Asia & Australia (by airmail); US$275 individuals U.K. (by airmail); US$370 U.S. airmail; US$370 other countries airmail. **URL:** http://www.malaysiatatler.com/. **Ad Rates:** BW: 8,550 Yu. **Circ:** Paid 16,400

43368 ■ Mathematical Modelling and Applied Computing
Research India Publications
c/o Dr. Wai-Ki Ching, Ed.-in-Ch.
Dept. of Mathematics
The University of Hong Kong
Pokfulam Rd.
Hong Kong, People's Republic of China
Publisher E-mail: info@ripublication.com
Journal covering engineering systems, computational engineering, computational sciences and technology, applied mathematics, mathematical methods, numerical modeling, biomedical systems, agricultural, mineral and energy resources, defense related problems, economics, business and management, environmental sciences, and model validations. **Freq:** 3/yr. **Print Method:** Offset. **Trim Size:** 13 3/4 x 21 1/2. **Cols./Page:** 6. **Col. Width:** 5 nonpareils. **Col. Depth:** 21 1/2 inches. **Key Personnel:** Andy Adamatzky, Editorial Board Member, andrew.adamatzky@uwe.ac.uk; Dr. Wai-Ki Ching, Editor-in-Chief, wching@hkusua.hku.hk; Stefania Bandini, Editorial Board Member, bandini@disco.unimib.it. **URL:** http://www.ripublication.com/mmac.htm.

43369 ■ Media
Haymarket Media Limited
23/F The Centrium
60 Wyndham St. Central
Hong Kong, People's Republic of China

Ph: 852 31751900
Publisher E-mail: hr@haymarketasia.com
Magazine featuring media and marketing industry in the Asia-Pacific Region. **Founded:** 1974. **Freq:** Fortnightly. **Key Personnel:** Atifa Hargrava, Editor, phone 852 31751933, atifa.silk@media.com.hk; Stuart Adamson, Advertising Dir., stuart.adamson@media.com.hk. **Remarks:** Accepts advertising. **URL:** http://www.haymarket.com/media/media_chn_magazine/default.aspx; http://www.brandrepublic.asia/Media/. **Circ:** Combined 12,000

43370 ■ Neuroembryology and Aging
S. Karger Publishers Inc.
The Chinese University of Hong Kong
Dept. of Anatomy
Faculty of Medicine
Shatin
Hong Kong, People's Republic of China
Ph: 852 26096895
Fax: 852 26035031
Publisher E-mail: karger@snet.net
Journal publishes original research articles and reviews dealing with biological and medical aspects of human CNS development and all kinds of disturbances occurring during ontogenesis. **Freq:** Quarterly. **Key Personnel:** N. Ulfig, Editorial Board; Y.S. Chan, Editorial Board; Wood Yee Chan, Editor-in-Chief, wy-chan@cuhk.edu.hk; David Tai-Wai Yew, Editor-in-Chief; M.A. Smith, Editorial Board; L.S. Jen, Editorial Board; D.J. Randall, Editorial Board. **ISSN:** 1661-3406. **Subscription Rates:** 862 Yu institutions print or online; EUR616 institutions print or online; US$782 institutions print or online; 948 Yu institutions print and online; EUR677 institutions print and online; US$860 institutions print and online. **Remarks:** Accepts advertising. **URL:** http://content.karger.com/ProdukteDB/produkte.asp?Aktion=JournalHome&ProduktNr=227097&ContentOnly=false. **Formerly:** Neuroembryology. **Circ:** (Not Reported)

43371 ■ Nikkei Electronics Asia
Nikkei Business Publications Asia Ltd.
Stanhope House, 17th Fl., Unit 1701A
734 King's Rd.
Quarry Bay
Hong Kong, People's Republic of China
Ph: 852 25758301
Fax: 852 25748175
Publisher E-mail: info@nikkeibp.com.hk
Magazine for engineers and managers in the electronics industry. **Freq:** Monthly. **Key Personnel:** Koji Onishi, Sales Dir., koonishi@nikkeibp.com.hk; Winco Lau, Sales Mgr., winco@nikkeibp.com.hk. **Subscription Rates:** 19,000¥ individuals. **Remarks:** Accepts advertising. **URL:** http://www.nikkeibp.com/adinfo/printmedia/pm_001002022.html. **Ad Rates:** BW: US$2,640, 4C: US$3,760. **Circ:** △28,300

43372 ■ Orient Aviation
Wilson Press HK Ltd.
Ste. 3D, Tung Shan Villa
2, Tung Shan Ter., Happy Valley
Hong Kong, People's Republic of China
Ph: 86 289 33676
Fax: 86 228 922846
Publication E-mail: orientav@netvigator.com
Publisher E-mail: cmcgee@netvigator.com
Periodical covering Asia-Pacific's commercial aviation scene. **Founded:** 1993. **Freq:** Monthly 10/yr. **Key Personnel:** Tom Ballantyne, Ch. Correspondent, tomball@ozemail.com.au; Christine McGee, Publisher/Ed.-in-Ch., cmcgee@netvigator.com; Barry Grindrod, Ch. Exec. **ISSN:** 1027-6572. **Remarks:** Accepts advertising. **URL:** http://www.orientaviation.com/. **Ad Rates:** BW: US$5,200, 4C: US$8,230. **Circ:** Paid 10,516

43373 ■ Orientations
Orientations Magazine Ltd.
815, 8th Fl., Zung Fu Industrial Bldg.
1067 King's Rd.
Quarry Bay
Hong Kong, People's Republic of China
Ph: 852 25111368
Fax: 852 25074620
Publisher E-mail: omag@netvigator.com
Publication providing information on the many and varied aspects of the arts of East Asia, the Indian Subcontinent and Southeast Asia. **Freq:** 8/yr. **Key Personnel:** Edmond Chan, Managing Editor; Elizabeth Knight, Editorial Dir.; Valerie C. Doran, Contributing Ed.; Angela Chiu, Art

Dir.; Carol Morland, Contributing Ed.; Yifawn Lee, Publisher; Bonnie Lam, Subscription Mgr.; Adrian Zecha, Consultant. **ISSN:** 0030-5448. **Subscription Rates:** US$115 individuals; EUR90 individuals; 60 individuals. **Remarks:** Accepts advertising. **URL:** http://www.orientations.com.hk/. **Ad Rates:** BW: 1,125 Yu, 4C: 1,750 Yu. **Circ:** (Not Reported)

43374 ■ Pacific Economic Review
Hong Kong Economic Association
Department of Economics & Finance
City University of Hong Kong
83 Tat Chee Ave.
Kowloon
Hong Kong, People's Republic of China
Publisher E-mail: economics@cuhk.edu.hk
Peer-reviewed journal of Hong Kong Economic Association. **Freq:** 3/yr. **Key Personnel:** Hung-Jen Wang, Editor, wangh@ntu.edu.tw; Kenneth S. Chan, Editor, kschan@cityu.edu.hk; Ke Li, Editor, kli@gsb.nihon-u.ac.jp. **ISSN:** 1361-374X. **Subscription Rates:** US$93 individuals Americas (print and online); EUR81 individuals Europe (print and online); 64 individuals rest of the world (print and online); US$641 institutions Americas (print + online); 563 institutions print + premium online (Europe); 866 institutions rest of the world (print + online); US$442 institutions UK (print + online); EUR563 institutions print + online (Europe); 489 institutions online only (Europe); US$557 institutions Americas online only. **Remarks:** Accepts advertising. **URL:** http://www.cb.cityu.edu.hk/research/per/. **Circ:** (Not Reported)

43375 ■ PC World Hong Kong
IDG Communications (HK) Ltd.
Ste. 601, Kah Wah Centre
191 Java Rd.
North Point
Hong Kong, People's Republic of China
Ph: 86 852 28613238
Fax: 86 852 28610953
Publisher E-mail: infohk@idg.com.hk
Computers magazine. **Freq:** Monthly. **Key Personnel:** Winston Raj, Editor; Harry McCracken, VP, Ed.-in-Ch. **Remarks:** Advertising accepted; rates available upon request. **URL:** http://www.pcworld.com. **Circ:** (Not Reported)

43376 ■ Profile
Communications and Public Affairs Office
The Hong Kong Polytechnic University
Hung Hom
Kowloon
Hong Kong, People's Republic of China
Ph: 852 27665100
Fax: 852 23640246
Published by the Communications and Public Affairs Office for staff and friends of The Hong Kong Polytechnic University. **Freq:** 3/yr. **Key Personnel:** Cynthia Lee, Dep. Ed., pactclee@polyu.edu.hk; Florence Chan, Editor; Aileen Wong, Managing Editor. **URL:** http://www.polyu.edu.hk/cpa/profile/. **Circ:** 13,000

43377 ■ The Prospective Accountant
Hong Kong Society of Accountants
Wu Chung House, 37 Fl.
213 Queen's Rd. E
Hong Kong, People's Republic of China
Ph: 862 22877228
Fax: 862 28656603
Publisher E-mail: hkicpa@hkicpa.org.hk
Publication covering accounting. **Freq:** Bimonthly. **Remarks:** Advertising accepted; rates available upon request. **URL:** http://www.hkicpa.org.hk/publications/student_journals/. **Circ:** (Not Reported)

43378 ■ Public Administration & Policy
Hong Kong Public Administration Association
PO Box 3350
Hong Kong, People's Republic of China
Publisher E-mail: enquire@hkpaa.org.hk
Journal covering Hong Kong and Asia-Pacific public administration. **Subtitle:** A Hong Kong and Asia-Pacific Journal. **Freq:** Semiannual. **ISSN:** 1022-0275. **Remarks:** Advertising accepted; rates available upon request. **URL:** http://www.hkpaa.org.hk/html/public.htm. **Circ:** 1,000

43379 ■ Research in International Business and Finance
Elsevier Science Inc.
c/o J.A. Batten, Assoc. Ed.

Circulation: ★ = ABC; △ = BPA; ◆ = CAC; • = CCAB; ❏ = VAC; ⊕ = PO Statement; ‡ = Publisher's Report; Boldface figures = sworn; Light figures = estimated.

Hong Kong University of Science & Technology
Kowloon
Hong Kong, People's Republic of China
Publisher E-mail: usinfo-ehelp@elsevier.com
Peer-reviewed journal featuring insights on various, economic, international business and finance topics. **Founded:** Nov. 11, 2004. **Freq:** 3/yr. **Print Method:** Offset. **Trim Size:** 6 3/4 x 10. **Cols./Page:** 1. **Col. Width:** 50 nonpareils. **Col. Depth:** 100 agate lines. **Key Personnel:** R. Aggarwal, Assoc. Ed.; T. Brailsford, Assoc. Ed.; J.S. Howe, Assoc. Ed.; S. Pynnonen, Assoc. Ed.; J.J. Choi, Assoc. Ed.; C. Kearney, Editor, colm.kearney@tcd.ie; R. Faff, Assoc. Ed.; T. Engsted, Assoc. Ed.; J.A. Batten, Assoc. Ed. **ISSN:** 0275-5319. **Subscription Rates:** US$296 institutions, other countries except Europe, Japan and Iran; EUR265 institutions for European countries and Iran; 35,300¥ institutions; 7,900¥ individuals; EUR59 individuals for European countries and Iran; US$66 other countries except Europe, Japan and Iran. **URL:** http://www.elsevier.com/wps/find/journaldescription.cws_home/699534/descriptiondescription.

43380 ■ Research Journal of Textile and Apparel
Hong Kong Institution of Textile and Apparel
63 Tai Yip St.
Kowloon Bay
Kowloon
Hong Kong, People's Republic of China
Ph: 8522263-6313
Fax: 8522758-9935
Publisher E-mail: info@hkita.org
Journal covering the Hong Kong Institution of Textile and Apparel. **Founded:** Oct. 1, 1997. **Freq:** Semiannual. **Trim Size:** 11.25 x 8.25. **Key Personnel:** Dr. Jin-lian Hu, Coord., tchujl@inet.polyu.edu.hk. **ISSN:** 1560-6074. **Subscription Rates:** US$400 members no direct application; US$100 students members; US$400 members. **Remarks:** Accepts advertising. **URL:** http://www.rjta.org; http://www.hkita.org. **Former name:** Journal of the Hong Kong Institution of Textile and Apparel. **Circ:** Paid 1,000

43381 ■ Review of Modern Literature in Chinese
Lingnan University
Centre for Literature and Translation
8 Castle Peak Rd., Tuen Mun, New Territories
Hong Kong, People's Republic of China
Ph: 852 26168888
Fax: 852 24638363
Periodical aimed at providing a review of modern Chinese literature. **Freq:** Semiannual. **Key Personnel:** George Cheng, Editor; Dr. Laurence Wong, Ch. Ed.; Katherine Chan, Asst. Ed. **URL:** http://www.ln.edu.hk/chr/publications/journals/rmlc/index_e.shtml.

43382 ■ Shop
Cathay Pacific Airways Ltd.
5/F, South Tower
Cathay Pacific City
8 Scenic Rd.
Hong Kong International Airport, Lantau
Hong Kong, People's Republic of China
Ph: 852 27471888
Fax: 852 25601411
Magazine offering duty-free items. **URL:** http://www.cathaypacific.com/dutyfree/home.html?LANG=intl.

43383 ■ Sparkle
Edipresse Asia
6th Fl., Guardian House
32 Oi Kwan Rd.
Hong Kong, People's Republic of China
Ph: 11 852 25477117
Fax: 11 852 28582671
Magazine featuring jewelry collections. **Freq:** Semiannual. **Key Personnel:** Roddy Yu, Director; Sean Li, Ch. Ed. **URL:** http://www.edipresse.com/en/par_pays/hong_kong/magazines/sparkle. **Circ:** ‡21,500

43384 ■ Time Asia
TIME Magazine
30/F Oxford House, Taikoo Pl.
979 King's Rd.
Quarry Bay
Hong Kong, People's Republic of China
Ph: 852 31283333
Fax: 852 31285043
Magazine for decision makers who value reliable, timely and authoritative news coverage. **Freq:** Weekly. **Key Personnel:** Michael Elliott, Editor; Mark Ford, Pres. & Gp. Publisher, mark_ford@timeinc.com; Andrew Butcher, Publishing Dir., andrew_butcher@timeandfortune.com. **URL:** http://www.time.com/time/magazine/asia/. **Ad Rates:** BW: US$50,180, 4C: US$77,200. **Circ:** ⋆272,363

43385 ■ Translation Quarterly
Chinese University Press
Shatin Galleria, 9th Fl., Unit 1-3 & 18
18-24 Shan Mei St.
Fo Tan, Shatin
Hong Kong, People's Republic of China
Ph: 852 29465300
Fax: 852 26037355
Publisher E-mail: cup@cuhk.edu.hk
Journal covering translation studies. **Founded:** Mar. 2005. **Freq:** Quarterly. **Trim Size:** 140 x 210 mm. **Key Personnel:** Prof. Leo Tak-hung Chan, Editor-in-Chief. **ISSN:** 1027-8559. **Subscription Rates:** US$20 individuals. **URL:** http://www.chineseupress.com/asp/JournalList_en.asp?CatID=1&Lang=E&JournalID=14.

43386 ■ WHERE Hong Kong
Miller Publishing Group L.L.C.
Asia City Publishing
301 Hollywood Centre
233 Hollywood Rd.
Hong Kong, People's Republic of China
Ph: 86 852 28505065
Fax: 86 852 25431880
Travel and tourism magazine focusing on Hong Kong, China. **Key Personnel:** Michelle Fong, Mktg. Mgr.; Tom Hilditch, Managing Editor; Steve Freeman, Publisher/Exec. Ed.; Blackie Hui, Production Mgr.; Billy Clarke, Staff Writer; Bruce Dawson, Editor; Queenie Tsang, Administration Asst. **Remarks:** Accepts advertising. **URL:** http://www.where-hongkong.com. **Circ:** (Not Reported)

43387 ■ Yuen Lin
Hong Kong Institute of Landscape Architects
Hennessy Rd. Post Office
PO Box 20561
Wanchai
Hong Kong, People's Republic of China
Ph: 85 28962833
Fax: 85 28963938
Publisher E-mail: hkilonline@gmail.com
Chinese publication covering landscaping. **Freq:** Annual. **Subscription Rates:** Free. **Remarks:** Advertising accepted; rates available upon request. **URL:** http://www.hkila.com. **Circ:** 1,000

43388 ■ FM Select-Beacon Hill - 102.4 MHz
Whampoa Garden
Hunghom
Kowloon
Hong Kong, People's Republic of China
Ph: 852 36988000
Fax: 852 21239877
E-mail: prenquiry@metroradio.com.hk
Format: News; Information. **Owner:** Metro Broadcast Corporation Limited, at above address. **Founded:** Feb. 5, 2001. **Operating Hours:** Continuous. **Wattage:** 150. **Ad Rates:** Advertising accepted; rates available upon request. **URL:** http://www.metroradio.com.hk.

43389 ■ FM Select-Castle Peak - 102.5 MHz
Basement 2, Site 6
Whampoa Garden
Hunghom
Kowloon
Hong Kong, People's Republic of China
Ph: 852 36988000
Fax: 852 21239877
E-mail: webmaster@metroradio.com.hk
Format: News; Information. **Owner:** Metro Broadcast Corporation Limited, at above address. **Founded:** Feb. 5, 2001. **Operating Hours:** Continuous. **Key Personnel:** Bianca Ma, Mng. Dir. **Wattage:** 700. **Ad Rates:** Advertising accepted; rates available upon request. **URL:** http://www.metroradio.com.hk.

43390 ■ FM Select-Cloudy Hill - 104.7 MHz
Basement 2, Site 6
Whampoa Garden
Hunghom
Kowloon
Hong Kong, People's Republic of China
Ph: 852 36988000
Fax: 852 21239877

E-mail: webmaster@metroradio.com.hk
Format: News; Information. **Owner:** Metro Broadcast Corporation Limited, at above address. **Founded:** Feb. 5, 2001. **Operating Hours:** Continuous. **Key Personnel:** Bianca Ma, Mng. Dir. **Wattage:** 500. **Ad Rates:** Advertising accepted; rates available upon request. **URL:** http://www.metroradio.com.hk.

43391 ■ FM Select-Golden Hill - 105.5 MHz
Basement 2, Site 6
Whampoa Garden
Hunghom
Kowloon
Hong Kong, People's Republic of China
Ph: 852 36988000
Fax: 852 21239877
E-mail: webmaster@metroradio.com.hk
Format: News; Information. **Owner:** Metro Broadcast Corporation Limited, at above address. **Founded:** Feb. 5, 2001. **Operating Hours:** Continuous. **Key Personnel:** Bianca Ma, Mng. Dir. **Wattage:** 100. **Ad Rates:** Advertising accepted; rates available upon request. **URL:** http://www.metroradio.com.hk.

43392 ■ FM Select-Kowloon Peak - 106.3 MHz
Whampoa Garden
Hunghom
Kowloon
Hong Kong, People's Republic of China
Ph: 852 36988000
Fax: 852 21239877
E-mail: prenquiry@metroradio.com.hk
Format: News; Information. **Owner:** Metro Broadcast Corporation Limited, at above address. **Founded:** Feb. 5, 2001. **Operating Hours:** Continuous. **Wattage:** 1000. **Ad Rates:** Advertising accepted; rates available upon request. **URL:** http://www.metroradio.com.hk.

43393 ■ FM Select-Lamma Island - 104.5 MHz
Basement 2, Site 6
Whampoa Garden
Hunghom
Kowloon
Hong Kong, People's Republic of China
Ph: 852 36988000
Fax: 852 21239877
E-mail: webmaster@metroradio.com.hk
Format: News; Information. **Owner:** Metro Broadcast Corporation Limited, at above address. **Founded:** Feb. 5, 2001. **Operating Hours:** Continuous. **Key Personnel:** Bianca Ma, Mng. Dir. **Wattage:** 500. **Ad Rates:** Advertising accepted; rates available upon request. **URL:** http://www.metroradio.com.hk.

43394 ■ FM Select-Mt. Gough - 104.0 MHz
Basement 2, Site 6
Whampoa Garden
Hunghom
Kowloon
Hong Kong, People's Republic of China
Ph: 852 36988000
Fax: 852 21239877
E-mail: webmaster@metroradio.com.hk
Format: News; Information. **Owner:** Metro Broadcast Corporation Limited, at above address. **Founded:** Feb. 5, 2001. **Operating Hours:** Continuous. **Key Personnel:** Bianca Ma, Mng. Dir. **Wattage:** 3000. **Ad Rates:** Advertising accepted; rates available upon request. **URL:** http://www.metroradio.com.hk.

43395 ■ Hit Radio-Beacon Hill - 100.5 MHz
Basement 2, Site 6
Whampoa Garden
Hunghom
Kowloon
Hong Kong, People's Republic of China
Ph: 852 36988000
Fax: 852 21239877
E-mail: webmaster@metroradio.com.hk
Format: News. **Owner:** Metro Broadcast Corporation Limited, at above address. **Founded:** Jan. 22, 2001. **Operating Hours:** Continuous. **Key Personnel:** Bianca Ma, Mng. Dir. **Wattage:** 150. **Ad Rates:** Advertising accepted; rates available upon request. **URL:** http://www.metroradio.com.hk.

43396 ■ Hit Radio-Castle Peak - 100.4 MHz
Basement 2, Site 6
Whampoa Garden
Hunghom

Kowloon
Hong Kong, People's Republic of China
Ph: 852 36988000
Fax: 852 21239877
E-mail: webmaster@metroradio.com.hk
Format: News. **Owner:** Metro Broadcast Corporation Limited, at above address. **Founded:** Jan. 22, 2001. **Operating Hours:** Continuous. **Key Personnel:** Bianca Ma, Mng. Dir. **Wattage:** 700. **Ad Rates:** Advertising accepted; rates available upon request. **URL:** http://www.metroradio.com.hk.

43397 ■ Hit Radio-Cloudy Hill - 100.0 MHz
Basement 2, Site 6
Whampoa Garden
Hunghom
Kowloon
Hong Kong, People's Republic of China
Ph: 852 36988000
Fax: 852 21239877
E-mail: webmaster@metroradio.com.hk
Format: News. **Owner:** Metro Broadcast Corporation Limited, at above address. **Founded:** Jan. 22, 2001. **Operating Hours:** Continuous. **Key Personnel:** Bianca Ma, Mng. Dir. **Wattage:** 500. **Ad Rates:** Advertising accepted; rates available upon request. **URL:** http://www.metroradio.com.hk.

43398 ■ Hit Radio-Golden Hill - 101.6 MHz
Basement 2, Site 6
Whampoa Garden
Hunghom
Kowloon
Hong Kong, People's Republic of China
Ph: 852 36988000
Fax: 852 21239877
E-mail: webmaster@metroradio.com.hk
Format: News. **Owner:** Metro Broadcast Corporation Limited, at above address. **Founded:** Jan. 22, 2001. **Operating Hours:** Continuous. **Key Personnel:** Bianca Ma, Mng. Dir. **Wattage:** 100. **Ad Rates:** Advertising accepted; rates available upon request. **URL:** http://www.metroradio.com.hk.

43399 ■ Hit Radio-Kowloon Peak - 101.8 MHz
Basement 2, Site 6
Whampoa Garden
Hunghom
Kowloon
Hong Kong, People's Republic of China
Ph: 852 36988000
Fax: 852 21239877
E-mail: webmaster@metroradio.com.hk
Format: News. **Owner:** Metro Broadcast Corporation Limited, at above address. **Founded:** Jan. 22, 2001. **Operating Hours:** Continuous. **Key Personnel:** Bianca Ma, Mng. Dir. **Wattage:** 1000. **Ad Rates:** Advertising accepted; rates available upon request. **URL:** http://www.metroradio.com.hk.

43400 ■ Hit Radio-Lamma Island - 102.1 MHz
Whampoa Garden
Hunghom
Kowloon
Hong Kong, People's Republic of China
Ph: 852 36988000
Fax: 852 21239877
E-mail: prenquiry@metroradio.com.hk
Format: Information. **Owner:** Metro Broadcast Corporation Limited, at above address. **Founded:** Jan. 22, 2001. **Operating Hours:** Continuous. **Wattage:** 500. **Ad Rates:** Advertising accepted; rates available upon request. **URL:** http://www.metroradio.com.hk.

43401 ■ Hit Radio-Mt. Gough - 99.7 MHz
Whampoa Gardens
Hunghom
Kowloon
Hong Kong, People's Republic of China
Ph: 852 21239888
Fax: 852 21239877
E-mail: prenquiry@metroradio.com.hk
Format: Full Service. **Owner:** Metro Broadcast Corporation Limited, at above address. **Founded:** Jan. 22, 2001. **Operating Hours:** Continuous. **Wattage:** 1000. **Ad Rates:** Advertising accepted; rates available upon request. **URL:** http://www.metroradio.com.hk.

43402 ■ HKCR CR1-Beacon Hill - 89.2 MHz
3 Broadcast Dr.
Kowloon
Hong Kong, People's Republic of China
Ph: 852 23365111
Fax: 852 23380021
E-mail: cs@881903.com
Format: News; Talk. **Owner:** Hong Kong Commercial Broadcasting Company Limited, at above address. **Founded:** Aug. 26, 1959. **Operating Hours:** Continuous. **Wattage:** 150. **Ad Rates:** Advertising accepted; rates available upon request. **URL:** http://www.881903.com.

43403 ■ HKCR CR1-Castle Peak - 88.6 MHz
3 Broadcast Dr.
Kowloon
Hong Kong, People's Republic of China
Ph: 852 23365111
Fax: 852 23380021
E-mail: cs@881903.com
Format: News; Talk. **Owner:** Hong Kong Commercial Broadcasting Company Limited, at above address. **Founded:** Aug. 26, 1959. **Operating Hours:** Continuous. **Wattage:** 700. **Ad Rates:** Advertising accepted; rates available upon request. **URL:** http://www.881903.com.

43404 ■ HKCR CR1-Cloudy Hill - 88.3 MHz
3 Broadcast Dr.
Kowloon
Hong Kong, People's Republic of China
Ph: 852 23365111
Fax: 852 23380021
E-mail: cs@881903.com
Format: News; Talk. **Owner:** Hong Kong Commercial Broadcasting Company Limited, at above address. **Founded:** Aug. 26, 1959. **Operating Hours:** Continuous. **Wattage:** 500. **Ad Rates:** Advertising accepted; rates available upon request. **URL:** http://www.881903.com.

43405 ■ HKCR CR1-Golden Hill - 88.9 MHz
3 Broadcast Dr.
Kowloon
Hong Kong, People's Republic of China
Ph: 852 23365111
Fax: 852 23380021
E-mail: cs@881903.com
Format: News; Talk. **Owner:** Hong Kong Commercial Broadcasting Company Ltd., at above address. **Founded:** Aug. 26, 1959. **Operating Hours:** Continuous. **Wattage:** 100. **Ad Rates:** Advertising accepted; rates available upon request. **URL:** http://www.881903.com.

43406 ■ HKCR CR1-Kowloon Peak - 89.5 MHz
3 Broadcast Dr.
Kowloon
Hong Kong, People's Republic of China
Ph: 852 23365111
Fax: 852 23380021
E-mail: cs@881903.com
Format: News; Talk. **Owner:** Hong Kong Commercial Broadcasting Company Limited, at above address. **Founded:** Aug. 26, 1959. **Operating Hours:** Continuous. **Wattage:** 1000. **Ad Rates:** Advertising accepted; rates available upon request. **URL:** http://www.881903.com.

43407 ■ HKCR CR1-Lamma Island - 89.1 MHz
3 Broadcast Dr.
Kowloon
Hong Kong, People's Republic of China
Ph: 852 23365111
Fax: 852 23380021
E-mail: cs@881903.com
Format: News; Talk. **Owner:** Hong Kong Commercial Broadcasting Company Limited, at above address. **Founded:** Aug. 26, 1959. **Operating Hours:** Continuous. **Wattage:** 500. **Ad Rates:** Advertising accepted; rates available upon request. **URL:** http://www.881903.com.

43408 ■ HKCR CR1-Mt. Gough - 88.1 MHz
3 Broadcast Dr.
Kowloon
Hong Kong, People's Republic of China
Ph: 852 23365111

Fax: 852 23380021
E-mail: cs@881903.com
Format: News; Talk. **Owner:** Hong Kong Commercial Broadcasting Company Limited, at above address. **Founded:** Aug. 26, 1959. **Operating Hours:** Continuous. **Wattage:** 3000. **Ad Rates:** Advertising accepted; rates available upon request. **URL:** http://www.881903.com.

43409 ■ HKCR CR2-Beacon Hill - 91.1 MHz
3 Broadcast Dr.
Kowloon
Hong Kong, People's Republic of China
Ph: 852 23365111
Fax: 852 23380021
E-mail: cs@881903.com
Format: News; Music of Your Life. **Owner:** Hong Kong Commercial Broadcasting Company Limited, at above address. **Founded:** Aug. 26, 1959. **Operating Hours:** Continuous. **Wattage:** 150. **Ad Rates:** Advertising accepted; rates available upon request. **URL:** http://www.881903.com.

43410 ■ HKCR CR2-Castle Peak - 91.2 MHz
3 Broadcast Dr.
Kowloon
Hong Kong, People's Republic of China
Ph: 852 23365111
Fax: 852 23380021
E-mail: cs@881903.com
Format: News; Music of Your Life. **Owner:** Hong Kong Commercial Broadcasting Company Limited, at above address. **Founded:** Aug. 26, 1959. **Operating Hours:** Continuous. **Wattage:** 700. **Ad Rates:** Advertising accepted; rates available upon request. **URL:** http://www.881903.com.

43411 ■ HKCR CR2-Cloudy Hill - 90.7 MHz
3 Broadcast Dr.
Kowloon
Hong Kong, People's Republic of China
Ph: 852 23365111
Fax: 852 23380021
E-mail: cs@881903.com
Format: News; Music of Your Life. **Owner:** Hong Kong Commercial Broadcasting Company Limited, at above address. **Founded:** Aug. 26, 1959. **Operating Hours:** Continuous. **Wattage:** 500. **Ad Rates:** Advertising accepted; rates available upon request. **URL:** http://www.881903.com.

43412 ■ HKCR CR2-Golden Hill - 90.9 MHz
3 Broadcast Dr.
Kowloon
Hong Kong, People's Republic of China
Ph: 852 23365111
Fax: 852 23380021
E-mail: cs@881903.com
Format: News; Music of Your Life. **Owner:** Hong Kong Commercial Broadcasting Company Limited, at above address. **Founded:** Aug. 26, 1959. **Operating Hours:** Continuous. **Wattage:** 100. **Ad Rates:** Advertising accepted; rates available upon request. **URL:** http://www.881903.com.

43413 ■ HKCR CR2-Kowloon Peak - 92.1 MHz
3 Broadcast Dr.
Kowloon
Hong Kong, People's Republic of China
Ph: 852 23365111
Fax: 852 23380021
F-mail: cs@881903.com
Format: News; Music of Your Life. **Owner:** Hong Kong Commercial Broadcasting Company Limited, at above address. **Founded:** Aug. 26, 1959. **Operating Hours:** Continuous. **Wattage:** 1000. **Ad Rates:** Advertising accepted; rates available upon request. **URL:** http://www.881903.com.

43414 ■ HKCR CR2-Lamma Island - 91.6 MHz
3 Broadcast Dr.
Kowloon
Hong Kong, People's Republic of China
Ph: 852 23365111
Fax: 852 23380021
E-mail: cs@881903.com
Format: News; Music of Your Life. **Owner:** Hong Kong Commercial Broadcasting Company Limited, at above address. **Founded:** Aug. 26, 1959. **Operating Hours:**

Continuous. **Wattage:** 500. **Ad Rates:** Advertising accepted; rates available upon request. **URL:** http://www.881903.com.

43415 ■ HKCR CR2-Mt.Gough - 90.3 MHz
3 Broadcast Dr.
Kowloon
Hong Kong, People's Republic of China
Ph: 852 23365111
Fax: 852 23380021
E-mail: os@881903.com
Format: News; Music of Your Life. **Owner:** Hong Kong Commercial Broadcasting Company Limited, at above address. **Founded:** Aug. 26, 1959. **Operating Hours:** Continuous. **Wattage:** 3000. **Ad Rates:** Advertising accepted; rates available upon request. **URL:** http://www.881903.com.

43416 ■ Metro Plus-Peng Chau - 1044 KHz
Whampoa Garden
Hunghom
Kowloon
Hong Kong, People's Republic of China
Ph: 852 36988000
Fax: 852 21239889
E-mail: prenquiry@metroradio.com.hk
Format: News; Information. **Owner:** Metro Broadcast Corporation Limited, at above address. **Operating Hours:** Continuous. **Wattage:** 10,000. **Ad Rates:** Advertising accepted; rates available upon request. **URL:** http://www.metroradio.com.hk.

43417 ■ RTHK Putonghua Channel - 100.9 MHz
Broadcasting House
30 Broadcast Dr.
Kowloon
Hong Kong, People's Republic of China
Ph: 852 23396300
Fax: 852 23369314
E-mail: ccu@rthk.org.hk
Format: Public Radio. **Owner:** Radio Television Hong Kong, at above address. **Operating Hours:** Continuous. **Key Personnel:** Franklin Wong Wah-kay, Dir. of Broadcasting, phone 852 23396333; Tai Keen-man, Asst. Dir. of Broadcasting (Radio), phone 852 23396323. **Wattage:** 10. **URL:** http://www.rthk.org.hk.

43418 ■ RTHK Putonghua Channel - 621 KHz
Broadcasting House
30 Broadcast Dr.
Kowloon
Hong Kong, People's Republic of China
Ph: 852 23396300
Fax: 852 23369314
E-mail: ccu@rthk.org.hk
Format: Public Radio. **Owner:** Radio Television Hong Kong, at above address. **Operating Hours:** Continuous. **Key Personnel:** Franklin Wong Wah-kay, Dir. of Broadcasting, phone 852 23396333; Tai Keen-man, Asst. Dir. of Broadcasting (Radio), phone 852 23396323. **Wattage:** 20,000. **URL:** http://www.rthk.org.hk.

43419 ■ RTHK Radio 5-Castle Peak - 106.8 MHz
Broadcasting House
30 Broadcast Dr.
Kowloon
Hong Kong, People's Republic of China
Ph: 852 23396300
Fax: 852 23369314
E-mail: ccu@rthk.org.hk
Format: Public Radio. **Owner:** Radio Television Hong Kong, at above address. **Operating Hours:** Continuous. **Key Personnel:** Franklin Wong Wah-kay, Dir. of Broadcasting, phone 852 23396333; Tai Keen-man, Asst. Dir. of Broadcasting (Radio), phone 852 23396323. **Wattage:** 10. **URL:** http://www.rthk.org.hk.

43420 ■ RTHK Radio 5-Golden Hill - 783 KHz
Broadcasting House
30 Broadcast Dr.
Kowloon
Hong Kong, People's Republic of China
Ph: 852 23396300
Fax: 852 23369314
E-mail: ccu@rthk.org.hk
Format: Public Radio. **Owner:** Radio Television Hong Kong, at above address. **Operating Hours:** Continuous. **Key Personnel:** Franklin Wong Wah-kay, Dir. of Broadcasting, phone 852 23396333; Tai Keen-man, Asst. Dir. of Broadcasting (Radio), phone 852 23396323. **Watt-

age:** 20,000. **URL:** http://www.rthk.org.hk.

43421 ■ RTHK Radio 4-Beacon Hill - 98.1 MHz
Broadcasting House
30 Broadcast Dr.
Kowloon
Hong Kong, People's Republic of China
Ph: 852 23396300
Fax: 852 23369314
E-mail: ccu@rthk.org.hk
Format: Public Radio. **Owner:** Radio Television Hong Kong, at above address. **Operating Hours:** Continuous. **Key Personnel:** Franklin Wong Wah-kay, Dir. of Broadcasting, phone 852 23396333; Tai Keen-man, Asst. Dir. of Broadcasting (Radio), phone 852 23396323. **Wattage:** 100. **URL:** http://www.rthk.org.hk.

43422 ■ RTHK Radio 4-Castle Peak - 98.7 MHZ
Broadcasting House
30 Broadcast Dr.
Kowloon
Hong Kong, People's Republic of China
Ph: 852 23396300
Fax: 852 23369314
E-mail: ccu@rthk.org.hk
Format: Public Radio. **Owner:** Radio Television Hong Kong, at above address. **Operating Hours:** Continuous. **Key Personnel:** Franklin Wong Wah-kay, Dir. of Broadcasting, phone 852 23396333; Tai Keen-man, Asst. Dir. of Broadcasting (Radio), phone 852 23396323. **Wattage:** 500. **URL:** http://www.rthk.org.hk.

43423 ■ RTHK Radio 4-Cloudy Hill - 97.8 MHz
Broadcasting House
30 Broadcast Dr.
Kowloon
Hong Kong, People's Republic of China
Ph: 852 23396300
Fax: 852 23369314
E-mail: ccu@rthk.org.hk
Format: Public Radio. **Owner:** Radio Television Hong Kong, at above address. **Operating Hours:** Continuous. **Key Personnel:** Franklin Wong Wah-kay, Dir. of Broadcasting, phone 852 23396333; Tai Keen-man, Asst. Dir. of Broadcasting (Radio), phone 852 23396323. **Wattage:** 500. **URL:** http://www.rthk.org.hk.

43424 ■ RTHK Radio 4-Golden Hill - 98.4 MHz
Broadcasting House
30 Broadcast Dr.
Kowloon
Hong Kong, People's Republic of China
Ph: 852 23396300
Fax: 852 23369314
E-mail: ccu@rthk.org.hk
Format: Public Radio. **Owner:** Radio Television Hong Kong, at above address. **Operating Hours:** Continuous. **Key Personnel:** Franklin Wong Wah-kay, Dir. of Broadcasting, phone 852 23396333; Tai Keen-man, Asst. Dir. of Broadcasting (Radio), phone 852 23396323. **Wattage:** 100. **URL:** http://www.rthk.org.hk.

43425 ■ RTHK Radio 4-Kowloon Peak - 98.9 MHz
Broadcasting House
30 Broadcast Dr.
Kowloon
Hong Kong, People's Republic of China
Ph: 852 23396300
Fax: 852 23369314
E-mail: ccu@rthk.org.hk
Format: Public Radio. **Owner:** Radio Television Hong Kong, at above address. **Operating Hours:** Continuous. **Key Personnel:** Franklin Wong Wah-kay, Dir. of Broadcasting, phone 852 23396333; Tai Keen-man, Asst. Dir. of Broadcasting (Radio), phone 852 23396323. **Wattage:** 500. **URL:** http://www.rthk.org.hk.

43426 ■ RTHK Radio 4-Lamma Island - 98.2 MHz
Broadcasting House
30 Broadcast Dr.
Kowloon
Hong Kong, People's Republic of China
Ph: 852 23396300
Fax: 852 23369314
E-mail: ccu@rthk.org.hk
Format: Public Radio. **Owner:** Radio Television Hong Kong, at above address. **Operating Hours:** Continuous. **Key Personnel:** Franklin Wong Wah-kay, Dir. of Broadcasting, phone 852 23396333; Tai Keen-man, Asst. Dir.

of Broadcasting (Radio), phone 852 23396323. **Wattage:** 300. **URL:** http://www.rthk.org.hk.

43427 ■ RTHK Radio 4-Mt. Gough - 97.6 MHz
Broadcasting House
30 Broadcast Dr.
Kowloon
Hong Kong, People's Republic of China
Ph: 852 23396300
Fax: 852 23369314
E-mail: ccu@rthk.org.hk
Format: Public Radio. **Owner:** Radio Television Hong Kong, at above address. **Operating Hours:** Continuous. **Key Personnel:** Franklin Wong Wah-kay, Dir. of Broadcasting, phone 852 23396333; Tai Keen-man, Asst. Dir. of Broadcasting (Radio), phone 852 23396323. **Wattage:** 1000. **URL:** http://www.rthk.org.hk.

43428 ■ RTHK Radio 1-Beacon Hill - 93.5 MHz
Broadcasting House
30 Broadcast Dr.
Kowloon
Hong Kong, People's Republic of China
Ph: 852 23396300
Fax: 852 23369314
E-mail: ccu@rthk.org.hk
Format: Public Radio. **Owner:** Radio Television Hong Kong, at above address. **Operating Hours:** Continuous. **Key Personnel:** Franklin Wong Wah-kay, Dir. of Broadcasting, phone 852 23396333; Tai Keen-man, Asst. Dir. of Broadcasting (Radio), phone 852 23396323. **Wattage:** 100. **URL:** http://www.rthk.org.hk.

43429 ■ RTHK Radio 1-Castle Peak - 93.4 MHz
Broadcasting House
30 Broadcast Dr.
Kowloon
Hong Kong, People's Republic of China
Ph: 852 23396300
Fax: 852 23369314
E-mail: ccu@rthk.org.hk
Format: Public Radio. **Owner:** Radio Television Hong Kong, at above address. **Operating Hours:** Continuous. **Key Personnel:** Franklin Wong Wah-kay, Dir. of Broadcasting, phone 852 23396333; Tai Keen-man, Asst. Dir. of Broadcasting (Radio), phone 852 23396323. **Wattage:** 500. **URL:** http://www.rthk.org.hk.

43430 ■ RTHK Radio 1-Cloudy Hill - 93.2 MHz
Broadcasting House
30 Broadcast Dr.
Kowloon
Hong Kong, People's Republic of China
Ph: 852 23396300
Fax: 852 23369314
E-mail: ccu@rthk.org.hk
Format: Public Radio. **Owner:** Radio Television Hong Kong, at above address. **Operating Hours:** Continuous. **Key Personnel:** Franklin Wong Wah-kay, Dir. of Broadcasting, phone 852 23396333; Tai Keen-man, Asst. Dir. of Broadcasting (Radio), phone 852 23396323. **Wattage:** 500. **URL:** http://www.rthk.org.hk.

43431 ■ RTHK Radio 1-Golden Hill - 92.9 MHz
Broadcasting House
30 Broadcast Dr.
Kowloon
Hong Kong, People's Republic of China
Ph: 852 23396300
Fax: 852 23369314
E-mail: ccu@rthk.org.hk
Format: Public Radio. **Owner:** Radio Television Hong Kong, at above address. **Operating Hours:** Continuous. **Key Personnel:** Franklin Wong Wah-kay, Dir. of Broadcasting, phone 852 23396333; Tai Keen-man, Asst. Dir. of Broadcasting (Radio), phone 852 23396323. **Wattage:** 100. **URL:** http://www.rthk.org.hk.

43432 ■ RTHK Radio 1-Kowloon Peak - 94.4 MHz
Broadcasting House
30 Broadcast Dr.
Kowloon
Hong Kong, People's Republic of China
Ph: 852 23396300
Fax: 852 23369314
E-mail: ccu@rthk.org.hk
Format: Public Radio. **Owner:** Radio Television Hong Kong, at above address. **Operating Hours:** Continuous. **Key Personnel:** Franklin Wong Wah-kay, Dir. of Broad-

casting, phone 852 23396333; Tai Keen-man, Asst. Dir. of Broadcasting (Radio), phone 852 23396323. **Wattage:** 500. **URL:** http://www.rthk.org.hk.

43433 ■ RTHK Radio 1-Lamma Island - 93.6 MHz
Broadcasting House
30 Broadcast Dr.
Kowloon
Hong Kong, People's Republic of China
Ph: 852 23396300
Fax: 852 23369314
E-mail: ccu@rthk.org.hk
Format: Public Radio. **Owner:** Radio Television Hong Kong, at above address. **Operating Hours:** Continuous. **Key Personnel:** Franklin Wong Wah-kay, Dir. of Broadcasting, phone 852 23396333; Tai Keen-man, Asst. Dir. of Broadcasting (Radio), phone 852 23396323. **Wattage:** 300. **URL:** http://www.rthk.org.hk.

43434 ■ RTHK Radio 1-Mt. Gough - 92.6 MHz
Broadcasting House
30 Broadcast Dr.
Kowloon
Hong Kong, People's Republic of China
Ph: 852 23396300
Fax: 852 23369314
E-mail: ccu@rthk.org.hk
Format: Public Radio. **Owner:** Radio Television Hong Kong, at above address. **Operating Hours:** Continuous. **Key Personnel:** Franklin Wong Wah-kay, Dir. of Broadcasting, phone 852 23396333; Tai Keen-man, Asst. Dir. of Broadcasting (Radio), phone 852 23396323. **Wattage:** 1000. **URL:** http://www.rthk.org.hk.

43435 ■ RTHK Radio 6-Peng Chau - 675 KHz
Broadcasting House
30 Broadcast Dr.
Kowloon
Hong Kong, People's Republic of China
Ph: 852 23396300
Fax: 852 23369314
E-mail: ccu@rthk.org.hk
Format: Public Radio. **Owner:** Radio Television Hong Kong, at above address. **Operating Hours:** Continuous. **Key Personnel:** Franklin Wong Wah-kay, Dir. of Broadcasting, phone 852 23396333; Tai Keen-man, Asst. Dir. of Broadcasting (Radio), phone 852 23396323. **Wattage:** 10,000. **URL:** http://www.rthk.org.hk.

43436 ■ RTHK Radio 3-Chung Hom Kok - 106.8 MHz
Broadcasting House
30 Broadcast Dr.
Kowloon
Hong Kong, People's Republic of China
Ph: 852 23396300
Fax: 852 23369314
E-mail: ccu@rthk.org.hk
Format: Public Radio. **Owner:** Radio Television Hong Kong, at above address. **Operating Hours:** Continuous. **Key Personnel:** Franklin Wong Wah-kay, Dir. of Broadcasting, phone 852 23396333; Tai Keen-man, Asst. Dir. of Broadcasting (Radio), phone 852 23396323. **Wattage:** 60. **URL:** http://www.rthk.org.hk.

43437 ■ RTHK Radio 3-Chung Hom Kok - 1584 KHz
Broadcasting House
30 Broadcast Dr.
Kowloon
Hong Kong, People's Republic of China
Ph: 852 23396300
Fax: 852 23369314
E-mail: ccu@rthk.org.hk
Format: Public Radio. **Owner:** Radio Television Hong Kong, at above address. **Operating Hours:** Continuous. **Key Personnel:** Franklin Wong Wah-kay, Dir. of Broadcasting, phone 852 23396333; Tai Keen-man, Asst. Dir. of Broadcasting (Radio), phone 852 23396323. **Wattage:** 200. **URL:** http://www.rthk.org.hk.

43438 ■ RTHK Radio 3-Golden Hill - 567 KHz
Broadcasting House
30 Broadcast Dr.
Kowloon
Hong Kong, People's Republic of China
Ph: 852 23396300
Fax: 852 23369314
E-mail: ccu@rthk.org.hk
Format: Public Radio. **Owner:** Radio Television Hong

Kong, at above address. **Operating Hours:** Continuous. **Key Personnel:** Franklin Wong Wah-kay, Dir. of Broadcasting, phone 852 23396333; Tai Keen-man, Asst. Dir. of Broadcasting (Radio), phone 852 23396323. **Wattage:** 20,000. **URL:** http://www.rthk.org.hk.

43439 ■ RTHK Radio 3-Mt. Nicholson - 97.9 MHZ
Broadcasting House
30 Broadcast Dr.
Kowloon
Hong Kong, People's Republic of China
Ph: 852 2339 6300
Fax: 852 2336 9314
E-mail: ccu@rthk.org.hk
Format: Public Radio. **Owner:** Radio Television Hong Kong, at above address, Hong Kong, People's Republic of China. **Operating Hours:** Continuous. **Key Personnel:** Franklin Wong Wah-kay, Dir. of Broadcasting, phone 852 23396333; Tai Keen-man, Assistant Dir. of Broadasting (Radio), phone 852 23396323. **Wattage:** 10. **URL:** http://www.rthk.org.hk.

43440 ■ RTHK Radio 2-Beacon Hill - 96.3 MHz
Broadcasting House
30 Broadcast Dr.
Kowloon
Hong Kong, People's Republic of China
Ph: 852 23396300
Fax: 852 23369314
E-mail: ccu@rthk.org.hk
Format: Public Radio. **Owner:** Radio Television Hong Kong, at above address. **Operating Hours:** Continuous. **Key Personnel:** Franklin Wong Wah-kay, Dir. of Broadcasting, phone 852 23396333; Tai Keen-man, Asst. Dir. of Broadcasting (Radio), phone 852 23396323. **Wattage:** 100. **URL:** http://www.rthk.org.hk.

43441 ■ RTHK Radio 2-Castle Peak - 96.4 MHz
Broadcasting House
30 Broadcast Dr.
Kowloon
Hong Kong, People's Republic of China
Ph: 852 23396300
Fax; 852 23369314
E-mail: ccu@rthk.org.hk
Format: Public Radio. **Owner:** Radio Television Hong Kong, at above address. **Operating Hours:** Continuous. **Key Personnel:** Franklin Wong Wah-kay, Dir. of Broadcasting, phone 852 23396333; Tai Keen-man, Asst. Dir. of Broadcasting (Radio), phone 852 23396323. **Wattage:** 500. **URL:** http://www.rthk.org.hk.

43442 ■ RTHK Radio 2-Cloudy Hill - 95.3 MHz
Broadcasting House
30 Broadcast Dr.
Kowloon
Hong Kong, People's Republic of China
Ph: 852 23396300
Fax: 852 23369314
E-mail: ccu@rthk.org.hk
Format: Public Radio. **Owner:** Radio Television Hong Kong, at above address. **Operating Hours:** Continuous. **Key Personnel:** Franklin Wong Wah-kay, Dir. of Broadcasting, phone 852 23396333; Tai Keen-man, Asst. Dir. of Broadcasting (Radio), phone 852 23396323. **Wattage:** 500. **URL:** http://www.rthk.org.hk.

43443 ■ RTHK Radio 2-Golden Hill - 95.6 MHz
Broadcasting House
30 Broadcast Dr.
Kowloon
Hong Kong, People's Republic of China
Ph: 852 23396300
Fax: 852 23369314
E-mail: ccu@rthk.org.hk
Format: Public Radio. **Owner:** Radio Television Hong Kong, at above address. **Operating Hours:** Continuous. **Key Personnel:** Franklin Wong Wah-kay, Dir. of Broadcasting, phone 852 23396333; Tai Keen-man, Asst. Dir. of Broadcasting (Radio), phone 852 23396323. **Wattage:** 100. **URL:** http://www.rthk.org.hk.

43444 ■ RTHK Radio 2-Kowloon Peak - 96.9 MHz
Broadcasting House
30 Broadcast Dr.
Kowloon
Hong Kong, People's Republic of China
Ph: 852 23396300
Fax: 852 23369314

E-mail: ccu@rthk.org.hk
Format: Public Radio. **Owner:** Radio Television Hong Kong, at above address. **Operating Hours:** Continuous. **Key Personnel:** Franklin Wong Wah-kay, Dir. of Broadcasting, phone 852 23396333; Tai Keen-man, Asst. Dir. of Broadcasting (Radio), phone 852 23396323. **Wattage:** 500. **URL:** http://www.rthk.org.hk.

43445 ■ RTHK Radio 2-Lamma Island - 96.0 MHz
Broadcasting House
30 Broadcast Dr.
Kowloon
Hong Kong, People's Republic of China
Ph: 852 23396300
Fax: 852 23369314
E-mail: ccu@rthk.org.hk
Format: Public Radio. **Owner:** Radio Television Hong Kong, at above address. **Operating Hours:** Continuous. **Key Personnel:** Franklin Wong Wah-kay, Dir. of Broadcasting, phone 852 23396333; Tai Keen-man, Asst. Dir. of Broadcasting (Radio), phone 852 23396323. **Wattage:** 300. **URL:** http://www.rthk.org.hk.

43446 ■ RTHK Radio 2-Mt. Gough - 94.8 MHz
Broadcasting House
30 Broadcast Dr.
Kowloon
Hong Kong, People's Republic of China
Ph: 852 23396300
Fax: 852 23369314
E-mail: ccu@rthk.org.hk
Format: Public Radio. **Owner:** Radio Television Hong Kong, at above address. **Operating Hours:** Continuous. **Key Personnel:** Franklin Wong Wah-kay, Dir. of Broadcasting, phone 852 23396333; Tai Keen-man, Asst. Dir. of Broadcasting (Radio), phone 852 23396323. **Wattage:** 1000. **URL:** http://www.rthk.org.hk.

Jinan

43447 ■ International Journal of Computational Intelligence in Bioinformatics and Systems Biology
Inderscience Enterprises Limited
c/o Dr. Yuehui Chen
School of Information Science & Engineering
Jiwei Rd. 106
Jinan 250022, Shandong, People's Republic of China
Peer-reviewed journal covering bioinformatics, systems biology, and computational intelligence. **Freq:** Quarterly. **Key Personnel:** Dr. Yuehui Chen, Editor-in-Chief, yhchen@ujn.edu.cn. **ISSN:** 1755-8034. **Subscription Rates:** EUR494 individuals print or online; EUR672 individuals print and online. **URL:** http://www.inderscience.com/browse/index.php?journalCODE=ijcibsb.

43448 ■ Shandong Television - 2
81 Jingshi Rd.
Jinan 250062, Shandong, People's Republic of China
Ph: 86 531 2951295
E-mail: webmaster@sdtv.com.cn
Owner: Shandong Television, at above address. **Operating Hours:** 17 hours daily. **URL:** http://www.sdtv.com.cn.

43449 ■ Shandong Television - 3
81 Jingshi Rd.
Jinan 250001, Shandong, People's Republic of China
Ph: 86 531 2951295
E-mail: webmaster@sdtv.com.cn
Format: Sports. **Owner:** Shandong Television, at above address. **URL:** http://www.sdtv.com.cn.

43450 ■ Shandong Television - 1
81 Jingshi Rd.
Jinan 250062, Shandong, People's Republic of China
Ph: 86 531 2951295
E-mail: webmaster@sdtv.com.cn
Format: News. **Owner:** Shandong Television, at above address. **Operating Hours:** Continuous. **URL:** http://www.sdtv.com.cn.

Kowloon

43451 ■ IEEE Transactions on Components and Packaging Technologies
The IEEE Components, Packaging and Manufacturing Technology Society
Hong Kong University of Science & Technology
Dept. of Mechanical Engineering

Clear Water Bay
Kowloon, People's Republic of China
Ph: 852 2358 7203
Fax: 852 2358 1543
Publisher E-mail: m.tickman@ieee.org
Journal describing science, engineering, technology and applications for transferring information. **Freq:** Semiannual. **Key Personnel:** S.W. Ricky Lee, Editor-in-Chief, rickylee@ust.hk; Koneru Ramakrishna, Editor-in-Chief, rama@ieee.org. **ISSN:** 1521-3331. **Subscription Rates:** US$555 nonmembers; US$12 members; US$6 members half year. **URL:** http://ieeexplore.ieee.org/xpl/RecentIssue.jsp?punumber=6144.

Luoyang

43452 ■ **China's Refractories**
Editorial Board of China's Refractories
43 Xiyuan Rd.
Luoyang 471039, People's Republic of China
Fax: 86 379 64205961
Publisher E-mail: chnr@nhcl.com.cn
Publishes important news and statistical data on the Chinese refractories market as well as technical and academic discussions. **Founded:** 1992. **Freq:** Quarterly. **Key Personnel:** Liu Jiehua, Editor-in-Chief, phone 86 379 64205961, fax 86 379 64205800, jiehua@public2.lyptt.ha.cn. **ISSN:** 1004-4493. **Subscription Rates:** US$96 individuals; US$170 two years individual. **Remarks:** Accepts advertising. **URL:** http://www.china-refract.org/cr/default.htm. **Circ:** (Not Reported)

43453 ■ **Chinese Astronomy and Astrophysics**
Elsevier Science
c/o Da-Run Xiong, Translation Ed.
Purple Mountain Observatory
Chinese Academy of Sciences
Nanjing 210008, People's Republic of China
Publisher E-mail: nlinfo-f@elsevier.com
Journal on astronomical and astrophysical sciences from China. **Founded:** 1977. **Freq:** Quarterly. **Key Personnel:** Da-Run Xiong, Translation Ed.; Shi-hui Ye, Editorial Ed.; Han Fu, Editorial Ed. **ISSN:** 0275-1062. **Subscription Rates:** EUR1,834 institutions for European countries & Iran; 243,900¥ institutions; US$2,052 institutions for all countries except Europe, Japan & Iran. **Remarks:** Accepts advertising. **URL:** http://www.elsevier.com/wps/find/journaldescription.cws_home/585/descriptiondescription. **Circ:** (Not Reported)

43454 ■ **Palaeoworld**
Elsevier Science Inc.
39 E Beijing Rd.
Nanjing 210008, People's Republic of China
Ph: 86 25 83282103
Publisher E-mail: usinfo-ehelp@elsevier.com
Peer-reviewed journal covering the studies on palaeontology and stratigraphy centered in China and the neighboring regions. **Founded:** 2006. **Freq:** Quarterly. **Print Method:** Offset. **Trim Size:** 8 1/8 x 10 7/8. **Cols./Page:** 3 and 2. **Col. Width:** 27 and 45 nonpareils. **Col. Depth:** 140 agate lines. **Key Personnel:** R.J. Aldridge, Editorial Board; L.E. Babcock, Editorial Board; P.M. Barrett, Editorial Board; S.A. Bowring, Editorial Board; X. Chen, Editorial Board; Douglas H. Erwin, Editor-in-Chief, erwind@si.edu; Jin Meng, Asst. Ed., jmeng@amnh.org; Yue Wang, Asst. Ed., yuewang@nigpas.ac.cn; Qun Yang, Editor-in-Chief, qunyang@nigpas.ac.cn; J. Aitchison, Editorial Board. **ISSN:** 1871-174X. **Subscription Rates:** US$575 institutions, other countries except Europe, Japan and Iran; 62,200¥ institutions; EUR458 institutions for European countries and Iran. **URL:** http://www.elsevier.com/wps/find/journaldescription.cws_home/706740/descriptiondescription.

43455 ■ **Pedosphere**
Elsevier Science Inc.
Soil Science Society & Institute of Soil Science
Nanjing, People's Republic of China
Publisher E-mail: usinfo-ehelp@elsevier.com
Peer-reviewed journal covering environment science, ecology, agriculture, bioscience, geoscience, forestry. **Freq:** 6/yr. **Print Method:** Offset. **Cols./Page:** 8. **Col. Width:** 19 nonpareils. **Col. Depth:** 294 agate lines. **Key Personnel:** Qi Rong Shen, Assoc. Ed.-in-Ch.; Qi-Xing Zhou, Assoc. Ed.-in-Ch.; Chu-Xia Lin, Assoc. Ed.-in-Ch.; J.M. Zhou, Editor-in-Chief; B.A. Stewart, Assoc. Ed.-in-Ch.; Zhao-Liang Zhu, Honorary Ed.-in-Ch.; R.W. Arnold, Consulting Ed.; I.M. Young, Assoc. Ed.-in-Ch.; Rong-Min Du, Assoc. Ed.-in-Ch.; D.C. Adriano, Consulting Ed. **ISSN:** 1002-0160. **Subscription Rates:** EUR377 institu-

tions for European countries and Iran; US$482 institutions, other countries except Europe, Japan and Iran; 54,700¥ institutions. **URL:** http://www.elsevier.com/wps/find/journaldescription.cws_home/707668/descriptiondescription.

Nanjing (Jiangsu)

43456 ■ **Advances in Science and Technology of Water Resources**
Hohai University
1 Xikang Rd.
Nanjing 210098, Jiangsu, People's Republic of China
Publication E-mail: jz@hhu.edu.cn
Publisher E-mail: lxsb@hhu.edu.cn
Journal containing papers on the advances and trends in water resource exploitation, utilization, and protection. **Founded:** 1981. **Freq:** Bimonthly. **Key Personnel:** Cheng Wang, Editor-in-Chief; Xiao-fang Rui, Editor-in-Chief. **ISSN:** 1006-7647. **URL:** http://kkb.hhu.edu.cn/jz/index_ejz.htm.

43457 ■ **Chemistry and Industry of Forest Products**
Institute of Chemical Industry of Forest Products, CAF
Suojin Wucun, No. 16
Nanjing 210042, Jiangsu, People's Republic of China
Ph: 86 258 5482401
Fax: 86 258 5413445
Publisher E-mail: info@forinchem.com
Professional journal covering forest industries. **Founded:** Mar. 1981. **Freq:** Quarterly. **Trim Size:** A4. **ISSN:** 0253-2417. **Remarks:** Advertising accepted; rates available upon request. **URL:** http://www.forinchem.com/eaboutus.asp. **Circ:** (Not Reported)

43458 ■ **Journal of Economics of Water Resources**
Hohai University
1 Xikang Rd.
Nanjing 210098, Jiangsu, People's Republic of China
Publication E-mail: jz@hhu.edu.cn
Publisher E-mail: lxsb@hhu.edu.cn
Journal containing issues about water resources. **Freq:** Bimonthly. **Key Personnel:** Chui-yong Zheng, Editor-in-Chief. **ISSN:** 1003-9511. **URL:** http://kkb.hhu.edu.cn/jj/index_ejj.htm.

43459 ■ **Journal of Hohai University**
Hohai University
1 Xikang Rd.
Nanjing 210098, Jiangsu, People's Republic of China
Publication E-mail: xb@hhu.edu.cn
Publisher E-mail: lxsb@hhu.edu.cn
Journal focusing on natural sciences. **Subtitle:** Natural Sciences. **Founded:** 1957. **Freq:** Bimonthly. **Key Personnel:** Cheng Wang, Editor-in-Chief; Zhong-min Yan, Editor-in-Chief. **ISSN:** 1000-1980. **URL:** http://kkb.hhu.edu.cn/xb/index_exb.htm.

43460 ■ **Water Resources Protection**
Hohai University
1 Xikang Rd.
Nanjing 210098, Jiangsu, People's Republic of China
Publication E-mail: bh@hhu.edu.cn
Publisher E-mail: lxsb@hhu.edu.cn
Journal covering the area of water resources protection. **Founded:** 1985. **Freq:** Bimonthly. **Key Personnel:** Prof. Zhen-ping Huang, Editor-in-Chief. **ISSN:** 1004-6933. **URL:** http://kkb.hhu.edu.cn/bh/index_ebh.htm.

43461 ■ **Water Science and Engineering**
Hohai University
1 Xikang Rd.
Nanjing 210098, Jiangsu, People's Republic of China
Publication E-mail: wse@hhu.edu.cn
Publisher E-mail: lxsb@hhu.edu.cn
Journal covering the academic research on water-related issues. **Founded:** 2008. **Freq:** Quarterly. **Key Personnel:** Wu Zhongru, Editor-in-Chief; Vijay P. Singh, Editor-in-Chief. **ISSN:** 1674-2370. **URL:** http://kkb.hhu.edu.cn/wse/index_wse.htm.

Shanghai

43462 ■ **Academic Journal of Shanghai Jiao Tong University Social Science Section**
Shanghai Jiao Tong University
1954 Huashan Rd.
Shanghai 200030, People's Republic of China
Ph: 86 21 62932444
Fax: 86 21 62821369

Publisher E-mail: xiaoban@mail.sjtu.edu.cn
Journal covering the field of social sciences. **Founded:** 1993. **Freq:** Semiannual. **Key Personnel:** Prof. Ye Dunping, Ch. Ed. **URL:** http://www2.sjtu.edu.cn/newweb/englishweb/teaching_re/journals/j04.htm.

43463 ■ **Beauty Home**
Shanghai Weekly Culture Media Co., Ltd.
5th Fl., 593 W Yan'an Rd.
Shanghai 200050, People's Republic of China
Ph: 86 21 61229133
Fax: 86 21 61229129
Publisher E-mail: rights@shwenyi.com
Magazine featuring Chinese lifestyle. **Founded:** 2000. **Freq:** Semimonthly. **Key Personnel:** Zhang Keping, Licensor, phone 86 21 61229133, fax 86 21 61229129. **Subscription Rates:** 9.80 Yu individuals. **URL:** http://www.wenyigroup.com.cn/ehibition/ehibition_default2.asp?pro_id=253.

43464 ■ **Calligraphy**
Shanghai Fine Arts Publishing House
593 Yan'an Rd. W
Shanghai 200050, People's Republic of China
Ph: 86 21 61229008
Fax: 86 21 61229015
Journal covering Chinese calligraphy. **Freq:** Monthly. **Key Personnel:** Xu Mingsong, Licensor, phone 86 21 61229018, fax 86 21 61229015. **Subscription Rates:** 10 Yu individuals. **URL:** http://www.wenyigroup.com.cn/ehibition/ehibition_default2.asp?pro_id=244.

43465 ■ **Calligraphy and Painting**
Shanghai Fine Arts Publishing House
593 Yan'an Rd. W
Shanghai 200050, People's Republic of China
Ph: 86 21 61229008
Fax: 86 21 61229015
Journal covering calligraphy and painting. **Founded:** 1982. **Freq:** Monthly. **Key Personnel:** Xu Mingsong, Licensor, phone 86 21 61229005, fax 86 21 61229015. **Subscription Rates:** 4.90 Yu individuals. **URL:** http://www.wenyigroup.com.cn/ehibition/ehibition_default2.asp?pro_id=241.

43466 ■ **Car & Fan**
Shanghai Scientific & Technical Publishers
71 Qinzhou Rd.
Shanghai 200235, People's Republic of China
Ph: 86 21 64089888
Fax: 86 21 64845082
Publication E-mail: cm@sstp.cn
Publisher E-mail: english-c@sstp.cn
Magazine featuring auto and motor fans, professionals and consumers. **Founded:** 2000. **Key Personnel:** Mao Wentao, President. **URL:** http://www.sstp.com.cn/english_magazine_car.php.

43467 ■ **Cell Research**
Institute of Biochemistry and Cell Biology
Shanghai Institutes for Biological Sciences
Chinese Academy of Science
319 Yue Yang Rd.
Shanghai 200031, People's Republic of China
Ph: 86 21 54920000
Fax: 86 21 54920011
Peer-reviewed journal dealing with fundamental research works in cell biology and related fields such as cell growth and differentiation, signal transduction, apoptosis, stem cells, development, immunology, neurosciences, plant cell biology, chromatin modulation, epigenetic and transcription etc. **Founded:** 1990. **Freq:** Monthly. **Key Personnel:** Pei Gang, Editor-in-Chief, gpei@sibs.ac.cn; Li Dangsheng, Dep. Ed.-in-Ch.; Chen Xiao-Ya, Editorial Board. **ISSN:** 1001-0602. **Subscription Rates:** US$864 institutions print; 600 Yu institutions print; EUR744 institutions print; 480 institutions UK/rest of world; print. **Remarks:** Advertising accepted; rates available upon request. **URL:** http://www.cell-research.com/index.asp. **Circ:** (Not Reported)

43468 ■ **Charity Matters**
Shanghai Brilliant Books
Changle Rd., Ln. 672, No. 33, Section E
Shanghai 200040, People's Republic of China
Ph: 86 21 54030490
Fax: 86 21 54045466
Publisher E-mail: rights@shwenyi.com
Magazine covering social charity activities. **Freq:** Monthly. **Key Personnel:** He Sicong, Licensor, phone 86 21 54045981, fax 86 21 54045981, rights@shwenyi.

com. **Subscription Rates:** 3.80 Yu individuals. **URL:** http://www.wenyigroup.com.cn/ehibition/ehibition_default2.asp?pro_id=263.

43469 ■ Chinese Annals of Mathematics, Series B
Springer Netherlands
c/o Ta-tsien Li, Ed.-in-Ch.
School of Mathematical Sciences
Fudan University
Shanghai 200433, People's Republic of China
Publisher E-mail: permissions.dordrecht@springer.com
Journal presenting the latest achievements in mathematical research. **Founded:** 1966. **Freq:** Bimonthly. **Print Method:** Web. **Trim Size:** 8 1/8 x 10 7/8. **Cols./Page:** 3. **Col. Width:** 27 nonpareils. **Col. Depth:** 140 agate lines. **Key Personnel:** Michael F. Atiyah, Honorary Ed.; Philippe Ciarlet, Editor; Xiaoman Chen, Editor; Guiqiang Chen, Editor; Avner Friedman, Editor; Alain Connes, Honorary Ed.; Ta-tsien Li, Editor-in-Chief; E. Weinan, Editor, weinan@math.princeton.edu; Zhihua Chen, Editor; Jiecheng Chen, Editor. **ISSN:** 0252-9599. **Subscription Rates:** EUR528 institutions print incl. free access or e-only; EUR633.60 institutions print incl. enhanced access. **URL:** http://www.springer.com/math/journal/11401.

43470 ■ Chinese Journal of Chemistry
John Wiley & Sons Inc.
Shanghai Institute of Organic Chemistry
Chinese Academy of Sciences
354 Fenglin Rd.
Shanghai 200032, People's Republic of China
Publisher E-mail: info@wiley.com
Peer-reviewed journal publishing original research results in all fields of chemistry. **Freq:** Monthly. **Key Personnel:** Ji Guozhen, Editor-in-Chief, jigz@mail.sioc.ac.cn; Ma Shengming, Dep. Assoc. Ed.-in-Ch., masm@mail.sioc.ac.cn; Fen Shouhua, Assoc. Ed.-in-Ch. **ISSN:** 1001-604X. **Subscription Rates:** EUR1,815 institutions print only; 3,032 SFr institutions print only; US$2,336 institutions print only; EUR1,997 institutions combined print with online access; 3,336 SFr institutions combined print with online access; US$2,570 institutions combined print with online access. **URL:** http://www.wiley.com/WileyCDA/WileyTitle/productCd-2434.html.

43471 ■ Comic King
Shanghai People's Fine Arts Publishing House
D Bldg., No. 33
Changle Rd., Ln. 672
Shanghai 200040, People's Republic of China
Ph: 86 21 54044520
Fax: 86 21 54032331
Publisher E-mail: mscbs@sh163.net
Magazine featuring cartoon stories. **Founded:** Aug. 1985. **Freq:** Monthly. **Key Personnel:** Le Jian, Licensor, phone 86 21 54031690, fax 86 21 54032331. **Subscription Rates:** 4.20 Yu individuals. **URL:** http://www.wenyigroup.com.cn/ehibition/ehibition_default2.asp?pro_id=280.

43472 ■ Die & Mould Technology
Shanghai Jiao Tong University
1954 Huashan Rd.
Shanghai 200030, People's Republic of China
Ph: 86 21 62932444
Fax: 86 21 62821369
Publisher E-mail: xiaoban@mail.sjtu.edu.cn
Journal featuring die and mould technology. **Founded:** 1983. **Freq:** Bimonthly. **Key Personnel:** Prof. Ruan Xueyu, Ch. Ed. **ISSN:** 1001-4934. **URL:** http://www2.sjtu.edu.cn/newweb/englishweb/teaching_re/journals/j07.htm.

43473 ■ Drive System Technique
Shanghai Jiao Tong University
1954 Huashan Rd.
Shanghai 200030, People's Republic of China
Ph: 86 21 62932444
Fax: 86 21 62821369
Publisher E-mail: xiaoban@mail.sjtu.edu.cn
Journal reporting on drive system techniques. **Founded:** 1987. **Freq:** Quarterly. **Key Personnel:** Hua Jia Shou, Ch. Ed. **ISSN:** 1006-8244. **URL:** http://www2.sjtu.edu.cn/newweb/englishweb/teaching_re/journals/j08.htm.

43474 ■ English of Science and Technology Learning
Shanghai Jiao Tong University

1954 Huashan Rd.
Shanghai 200030, People's Republic of China
Ph: 86 21 62932444
Fax: 86 21 62821369
Publisher E-mail: xiaoban@mail.sjtu.edu.cn
Journal covering the field of science and technology. **Founded:** 1980. **Freq:** Monthly. **Key Personnel:** Prof. Mao Rogui, Ch. Ed. **ISSN:** 1006-5822. **URL:** http://www2.sjtu.edu.cn/newweb/englishweb/teaching_re/journals/j12.htm.

43475 ■ Environmental Biosafety Research
EDP Sciences
U.S. Department of of Ecology & Evolutionary Biology
School of Life Sciences, Fudan University
220 Handan Rd.
Shanghai 200433, People's Republic of China
Ph: 39 422 789708
Fax: 39 422 789730
Publication E-mail: ebr@icgeb.org
Publisher E-mail: subscribers@edpsciences.org
Journal publishing peer-reviewed original research papers and review articles, as well as scientific correspondence on all types of genetically modified organisms, including plants, animals and microbes. **Freq:** Quarterly. **Key Personnel:** Bao-Rong Lu, Editor-in-Chief, mark.tepfer@icgeb.org. **ISSN:** 1635-7922. **Subscription Rates:** EUR385.94 individuals print and electronic; EUR392.29 individuals electronic; EUR328 other countries electronic; EUR419 other countries print and electronic. **URL:** http://www.ebr-journal.org/.

43476 ■ Fiction World
Shanghai Literature & Arts Publishing House
74 Shaoxing Rd.
Shanghai 200020, People's Republic of China
Ph: 86 21 64336243
Fax: 86 21 64740676
Magazine featuring Chinese literature. **Founded:** May 1981. **Freq:** Bimonthly. **Key Personnel:** Han Ying, Licensor, phone 86 21 64377833, fax 86 21 64740676. **Subscription Rates:** 10 Yu individuals. **URL:** http://www.wenyigroup.com.cn/ehibition/ehibition_default2.asp?pro_id=262.

43477 ■ International Journal of Nonlinear Modelling in Science and Engineering
Cambridge International Science Publishing
c/o Ji-Huan He, Ed.-in-Ch.
149 Yanchang Rd.
Shanghai University
PO Box 189
Shanghai 200072, People's Republic of China
Publisher E-mail: cisp@cisp-publishing.com
Journal providing a bridge between mathematics and all other aspects of sciences and engineering, with publication of reports of important fundamental research, with coverage of major advances in modelling real-life nonlinear problems and of developments with significant consequences. **Freq:** Bimonthly. **Key Personnel:** Ji-Huan He, Editor-in-Chief; Roger Grimshaw, Editorial Board; George S. Dulikravich, Editorial Board; R.M.M. Mattheij, Editorial Board; Yu Mitropolsky, Editorial Board; Ya-Pu Zhao, Editorial Board; Chiu-Yeung Chan, Editorial Board; Wing Kam Liu, Editor-in-Chief; A.K.M. Sadrul Islam, Editorial Board; Michal Kleiber, Editor; A.S. Samoilenko, Editorial Board. **ISSN:** 1472-085X. **Subscription Rates:** US$360 institutions; 240 institutions UK & Europe; US$80 individuals; 50 individuals UK and Europe. **URL:** http://www.cisp-publishing.com/ijnmse.html.

43478 ■ International Journal of Physical Sciences
Academic Journals
c/o Prof. Huisheng Peng, Ed.
Department of Macromolecular Science
Fudan University
Shanghai 200438, People's Republic of China
Publication E-mail: ijps@academicjournals.org
Publisher E-mail: service@academicjournals.org
Peer-reviewed Journal covering all areas of physics and chemistry. **Freq:** Monthly. **Key Personnel:** Prof. Huisheng Peng, Editor. **ISSN:** 1992-1950. **Remarks:** Accepts advertising. **URL:** http://www.academicjournals.org/IJPS/index.htm. **Circ:** (Not Reported)

43479 ■ International Journal of System Control and Information Processing
Inderscience Enterprises Limited

c/o Prof. Yugeng Xi, Ed.-in-Ch.
Shanghai Jiao Tong University
Dept. of Automation
800 Dongchuan Rd.
Shanghai 200240, People's Republic of China
Journal reporting on the progress and results of research in control theories and information technologies. **Freq:** 4/yr. **Key Personnel:** Prof. Yugeng Xi, Editor-in-Chief, ygxi@sjtu.edu.cn; Shaoyuan Li, Exec. Ed., syli@sjtu.edu.cn. **ISSN:** 1759-9334. **Subscription Rates:** EUR494 individuals print or online; EUR672 individuals print and online. **URL:** http://www.inderscience.com/browse/index.php?journalID=347.

43480 ■ Journal of Editorial Study
Shanghai Using the Right Word Culture Media Co., Ltd.
Jia, 384/11 Jianguo Rd. W
Shanghai 200031, People's Republic of China
Ph: 86 21 64330669
Fax: 86 21 64330669
Journal covering editorial study. **Freq:** Bimonthly. **Key Personnel:** Sun Huan, Licensor, phone 86 21 64311015, fax 86 21 64311015. **Subscription Rates:** 8 Yu individuals. **URL:** http://www.wenyigroup.com.cn/ehibition/ehibition_default2.asp?pro_id=273.

43481 ■ Journal of Noise and Vibration Control
Shanghai Jiao Tong University
1954 Huashan Rd.
Shanghai 200030, People's Republic of China
Ph: 86 21 62932444
Fax: 86 21 62821369
Publisher E-mail: xiaoban@mail.sjtu.edu.cn
Journal featuring information on noise and vibration control. **Freq:** Bimonthly. **Key Personnel:** Prof. Yan Jikuan, Ch. Ed. **ISSN:** 1006-1355. **URL:** http://www2.sjtu.edu.cn/newweb/englishweb/teaching_re/journals/j15.htm.

43482 ■ Journal of Shanghai Jiaotong University
Shanghai Jiao Tong University
1954 Huashan Rd.
Shanghai 200030, People's Republic of China
Ph: 86 21 62932444
Fax: 86 21 62821369
Publisher E-mail: xiaoban@mail.sjtu.edu.cn
Journal focusing on natural science and engineering technology. **Founded:** 1956. **Freq:** Monthly. **Key Personnel:** Prof. Sheng Zhenbang, Ch. Ed. **ISSN:** 1006-2467. **URL:** http://www2.sjtu.edu.cn/newweb/englishweb/teaching_re/journals/j02.htm.

43483 ■ Journal of Shanghai Jiaotong University Agricultural Science
Shanghai Jiao Tong University
Qixin Rd., No. 2678
Shanghai 201101, People's Republic of China
Ph: 86 21 64789728
Publisher E-mail: xiaoban@mail.sjtu.edu.cn
Journal covering the field of agricultural science. **Founded:** 1983. **Freq:** Quarterly. **Key Personnel:** Prof. Shen Weiping, Ch. Ed. **ISSN:** 1000-193X. **URL:** http://www2.sjtu.edu.cn/newweb/englishweb/teaching_re/journals/j03.htm.

43484 ■ Journal of Vibration and Shock
Shanghai Jiao Tong University
1954 Huashan Rd.
Shanghai 200030, People's Republic of China
Ph: 86 21 62932444
Fax: 86 21 62821369
Publisher E-mail: xiaoban@mail.sjtu.edu.cn
Journal covering the field of vibration engineering in China. **Founded:** 1982. **Freq:** Quarterly. **Key Personnel:** Prof. Yun Weijun, Ch. Ed. **ISSN:** 1000-3835. **URL:** http://www2.sjtu.edu.cn/newweb/englishweb/teaching_re/journals/j14.htm.

43485 ■ Laboratory Research and Exploration
Shanghai Jiao Tong University
1954 Huashan Rd.
Shanghai 200030, People's Republic of China
Ph: 86 21 62932444
Fax: 86 21 62821369
Publisher E-mail: xiaoban@mail.sjtu.edu.cn
Journal covering the fields of lab and facilities management in universities. **Founded:** 1982. **Freq:** Bimonthly. **Key Personnel:** Prof. Sheng Zhenbang, Ch. Ed. **ISSN:** 1006-7167. **URL:** http://www2.sjtu.edu.cn/newweb/

Circulation: ★ = ABC; △ = BPA; ◆ = CAC; • = CCAB; ❑ = VAC; ⊕ = PO Statement; ‡ = Publisher's Report; Boldface figures = sworn; Light figures = estimated.

Gale Directory of Publications & Broadcast Media/147th Ed.

4847

englishweb/teaching_re/journals/j09.htm.

43486 ■ Machine Design & Research
Shanghai Jiao Tong University
1954 Huashan Rd.
Shanghai 200030, People's Republic of China
Ph: 86 21 62932444
Fax: 86 21 62821369
Publisher E-mail: xiaoban@mail.sjtu.edu.cn
Journal containing issues about theory, technology and method of mechanical engineering. **Founded:** 1984. **Freq:** Quarterly. **Key Personnel:** Prof. Zhou Huijun, Ch. Ed., hjzou@sjtu.edu.cn. **ISSN:** 1006-2343. **URL:** http://www2.sjtu.edu.cn/newweb/englishweb/teaching_re/journals/j05.htm.

43487 ■ Man & Nature
Shanghai Weekly Culture Media Co., Ltd.
5th Fl., 593 W Yan'an Rd.
Shanghai 200050, People's Republic of China
Ph: 86 21 61229133
Fax: 86 21 61229129
Publisher E-mail: rights@shwenyi.com
Magazine covering nature and human culture. **Founded:** Sept. 2001. **Freq:** Monthly. **Key Personnel:** Lu Yan, Licensor, phone 86 21 61229241, fax 86 21 61229240. **Subscription Rates:** 16 Yu individuals. **URL:** http://www.wenyigroup.com.cn/ehibition/ehibition_default2.asp?pro_id=247.

43488 ■ Micro- and Nanometer Science & Technology
Shanghai Jiao Tong University
1954 Huashan Rd.
Shanghai 200030, People's Republic of China
Ph: 86 21 62932444
Fax: 86 21 62821369
Publisher E-mail: xiaoban@mail.sjtu.edu.cn
Journal covering the research area of micro-nanometer science and technology. **Key Personnel:** Prof. Qi Zhenzhon, Ch. Ed. **URL:** http://www2.sjtu.edu.cn/newweb/englishweb/teaching_re/journals/j10.htm.

43489 ■ Microcomputer Applications
Shanghai Jiao Tong University
1954 Huashan Rd.
Shanghai 200030, People's Republic of China
Ph: 86 21 62932444
Fax: 86 21 62821369
Publisher E-mail: xiaoban@mail.sjtu.edu.cn
Journal containing information for the computer industry. **Founded:** 1985. **Freq:** Bimonthly. **Key Personnel:** Prof. Wu Qidi, Ch. Ed. **ISSN:** 1007-757X. **URL:** http://www2.sjtu.edu.cn/newweb/englishweb/teaching_re/journals/j11.htm.

43490 ■ Music Lover
Shanghai Music Publishing House
74 Shaoxing Rd.
Shanghai 200020, People's Republic of China
Ph: 86 21 64376483
Fax: 86 21 64674944
Publisher E-mail: tt.smph@gmail.com
Magazine featuring classical music. **Founded:** 1979. **Freq:** Monthly. **Key Personnel:** Chu Zhengyu, Licensor, phone 86 21 64459916, fax 86 21 64459916, rights@shwenyi.com. **Subscription Rates:** 18 Yu individuals. **URL:** http://www.musiclover.com.cn; http://www.wenyigroup.com.cn/ehibition/ehibition_default2.asp?pro_id=270.

43491 ■ Nuclear Science and Techniques
Elsevier Science Inc.
c/o Zhu, De-Zhang Ed.-in-Ch.
Shanghai Institute of Applied Physics
The Chinese Academy of Sciences
Shanghai, People's Republic of China
Publisher E-mail: usinfo-ehelp@elsevier.com
Journal covering nuclear research in China. **Founded:** 1990. **Freq:** 6/yr. **Print Method:** Offset. **Trim Size:** 8 1/4 x 10 3/4. **Cols./Page:** 3 and 2. **Col. Width:** 27 and 42 nonpareils. **Col. Depth:** 137 agate lines. **Key Personnel:** Zhu De-Zhang, Editor-in-Chief; Jian-Hua He, Editorial Committee; Ya-Ming Zou, Vice Ed-in-Ch.; Jiang Da-Zhen, Vice Ed-in-Ch.; John Byrd, Editorial Committee; Wu Zi-Yu, Vice Ed-in-Ch.; Ning-Kang Huang, Editorial Committee; Zhi-Fang Chai, Editorial Committee; Kai-Rong Ye, Vice Ed-in-Ch.; Gang Huang, Editorial Committee. **ISSN:** 1001-8042. **Subscription Rates:** 61,200¥ institutions; EUR422 institutions for European countries and Iran; US$538 institutions all countries

except Europe, Japan and Iran. **URL:** http://www.elsevier.com/wps/find/journaldescription.cws_home/707823/descriptiondescription.

43492 ■ Ocean Engineering
Shanghai Jiao Tong University
1954 Huashan Rd.
Shanghai 200030, People's Republic of China
Ph: 86 21 62932444
Fax: 86 21 62821369
Publisher E-mail: xiaoban@mail.sjtu.edu.cn
Journal focusing on the subject of ocean engineering. **Freq:** Quarterly. **Key Personnel:** Prof. Dou Guoren, Ch. Ed. **ISSN:** 1005-9865. **URL:** http://www2.sjtu.edu.cn/newweb/englishweb/teaching_re/journals/j13.htm.

43493 ■ Oriental Sword
Shanghai Literature & Arts Publishing House
74 Shaoxing Rd.
Shanghai 200020, People's Republic of China
Ph: 86 21 64336243
Fax: 86 21 64740676
Magazine featuring case reports and detective stories. **Founded:** 1993. **Freq:** Monthly. **Key Personnel:** Wang Jian, Licensor, phone 86 21 64723570, fax 86 21 64723570. **Subscription Rates:** 6.50 Yu individuals. **URL:** http://www.wenyigroup.com.cn/ehibition/ehibition_default2.asp?pro_id=261.

43494 ■ Popular Medicine
Shanghai Scientific & Technical Publishers
71 Qinzhou Rd.
Shanghai 200235, People's Republic of China
Ph: 86 21 64089888
Fax: 86 21 64845082
Publication E-mail: popularmedicine@sstp.cn
Publisher E-mail: english-c@sstp.cn
Magazine featuring information on health and medicine. **Founded:** 1948. **Freq:** Bimonthly. **Key Personnel:** Mao Wentao, President. **URL:** http://www.sstp.com.cn/english_magazine_medicine.php.

43495 ■ Printing Field
Shanghai New Printing Technology Co., Ltd.
Ln. 1209, No. 60
Xinzha Rd.
Shanghai 200041, People's Republic of China
Ph: 86 21 62539220
Fax: 86 21 62553562
Publisher E-mail: snpt@printinginst.com
Magazine covering printing industry. **Founded:** 1972. **Freq:** Monthly. **Key Personnel:** Xue Xianhua, Licensor, phone 86 21 32181232, fax 86 21 32180191. **Subscription Rates:** 7 Yu individuals. **URL:** http://www.wenyigroup.com.cn/ehibition/ehibition_default2.asp?pro_id=240.

43496 ■ Radio & TV
Shanghai Scientific & Technical Publishers
71 Qinzhou Rd.
Shanghai 200235, People's Republic of China
Ph: 86 21 64089888
Fax: 86 21 64845082
Publication E-mail: rtv@citiz.net
Publisher E-mail: english-c@sstp.cn
Journal covering radio and television in China. **Founded:** 1958. **Freq:** Monthly. **Key Personnel:** Hu Dawei, President. **URL:** http://www.sstp.com.cn/english_magazine_tv.php.

43497 ■ Science Journal
Shanghai Scientific & Technical Publishers
71 Qinzhou Rd.
Shanghai 200235, People's Republic of China
Ph: 86 21 64089888
Fax: 86 21 64845082
Publication E-mail: kexue3@mail.kexuemag.com
Publisher E-mail: english-c@sstp.cn
Journal covering the modern Chinese scientific communication. **Founded:** 1915. **Freq:** Monthly. **Key Personnel:** Hu Dawei, President. **URL:** http://www.sstp.com.cn/english_magazine_science.php.

43498 ■ Scientific Pictorial
Shanghai Scientific & Technical Publishers
71 Qinzhou Rd.
Shanghai 200235, People's Republic of China
Ph: 86 21 64089888
Fax: 86 21 64845082
Publication E-mail: kxhb@sstp.cn

Publisher E-mail: english-c@sstp.cn
Magazine featuring science related articles. **Founded:** 1933. **Key Personnel:** Mao Wentao, President. **URL:** http://www.sstp.com.cn/english_magazine_pictorial.php.

43499 ■ Shanghai Pictorial
Shanghai Brilliant Books
Changle Rd., Ln. 672, No. 33, Section E
Shanghai 200040, People's Republic of China
Ph: 86 21 54030490
Fax: 86 21 54045466
Publisher E-mail: rights@shwenyi.com
Magazine covering photography. **Founded:** 1982. **Freq:** Monthly. **Key Personnel:** Zhao Songhua, Licensor, phone 86 21 54045234, fax 86 21 54045234. **Subscription Rates:** 10 Yu individuals. **URL:** http://www.wenyigroup.com.cn/ehibition/ehibition_default2.asp?pro_id=242.

43500 ■ Shanghai Residence
Shanghai Fine Arts Publishing House
593 Yan'an Rd. W
Shanghai 200050, People's Republic of China
Ph: 86 21 61229008
Fax: 86 21 61229015
Magazine featuring home decoration. **Freq:** Monthly. **Key Personnel:** Zhang Xiong, Licensor, phone 86 21 54904529, fax 86 21 54904493. **Subscription Rates:** 20 Yu individuals. **URL:** http://www.wenyigroup.com.cn/ehibition/ehibition_default2.asp?pro_id=264. **Circ:** 30,000

43501 ■ Shanghai Style
Shanghai Scientific & Technical Publishers
71 Qinzhou Rd.
Shanghai 200235, People's Republic of China
Ph: 86 21 64089888
Fax: 86 21 64845082
Publication E-mail: shfs-c@sstp.cn
Publisher E-mail: english-c@sstp.cn
Journal focusing on the fashion scene of China. **Founded:** 1986. **Freq:** Monthly. **Key Personnel:** Hu Dawei, President. **URL:** http://www.sstp.com.cn/english_magazine_style.php.

43502 ■ Shanghai Tatler
Edipresse Asia
Shanghai Office, 8th Fl.
No. 2, Ln. 139
Anshun Rd.
Shanghai 200052, People's Republic of China
Ph: 86 21 52587666
Publication E-mail: general@shtatler.com
Magazine providing exclusive information about the business, cultural, social and sporting life of Shanghai. **Freq:** Monthly. **Key Personnel:** Margaret Chua-Piano, Director; Eric Zhang, Dep. Mng. Ed. **URL:** http://www.edipresse.com/lifestyle/shanghai-tatler. **Circ:** ‡60,000

43503 ■ Shanghai Today
Today Publications Ltd.
10/F Peng Xin Apt.
811 Tian Yao Qiao Rd.
Shanghai 200030, People's Republic of China
Ph: 86 216 4825237
Fax: 86 216 4825237
Publisher E-mail: peiling@online.sh.cn
General interest magazine. **Freq:** Bimonthly. **Trim Size:** 210 x 285 mm. **Key Personnel:** J.J. Jiang, Editor; James Beardwell, Managing Editor; Fang Jun, General Mgr. **Subscription Rates:** Free to qualified subscribers. **Remarks:** Accepts advertising. **URL:** http://shanghai today.tripod.com/contact.html. **Ad Rates:** BW: US$4,900, 4C: US$7,000. **Circ:** (Not Reported)

43504 ■ Shanghai Weekly
Shanghai Weekly Culture Media Co., Ltd.
5th Fl., 593 W Yan'an Rd.
Shanghai 200050, People's Republic of China
Ph: 86 21 61229133
Fax: 86 21 61229129
Publisher E-mail: rights@shwenyi.com
Magazine featuring lifestyle in Shanghai. **Founded:** Oct. 2000. **Freq:** Weekly. **Key Personnel:** Wang Xiaolian, Licensor, phone 86 21 61229170, fax 86 21 61229200. **Subscription Rates:** 1 Yu individuals. **URL:** http://www.wenyigroup.com.cn/ehibition/ehibition_default2.asp?pro_id=255.

43505 ■ Shanghai's Best Restaurants
Edipresse Asia

Shanghai Office, 8th Fl.
No. 2, Ln. 139
Anshun Rd.
Shanghai 200052, People's Republic of China
Ph: 86 21 52587666
Magazine featuring the best restaurants in Shanghai.
Freq: Annual. **Key Personnel:** Margaret Chua-Piano, Director; Eric Zhang, Dep. Mng. Ed. **URL:** http://www.edipresse.com/food-dining/shanghais-best-restaurants. **Circ:** ‡38,000

43506 ■ Systems Engineering
Shanghai Jiao Tong University
1954 Huashan Rd.
Shanghai 200030, People's Republic of China
Ph: 86 21 62932444
Fax: 86 21 62821369
Publisher E-mail: xiaoban@mail.sjtu.edu.cn
Journal covering the field of systems engineering. **Subtitle:** Theory Methodology Applications. **Freq:** Quarterly. **Key Personnel:** Prof. Wang Huanchen, Ch. Ed. **ISSN:** 1005-2542. **URL:** http://www2.sjtu.edu.cn/newweb/englishweb/teaching_re/journals/j16.htm.

43507 ■ Theoretical and Applied Fracture Mechanics
Elsevier Science
c/o G.C. Sih, Ed.-in-Ch.
East China University of Science & Technology
130 Melong St.
Shanghai 200237, People's Republic of China
Ph: 86 216 4253500
Fax: 86 216 4253425
Publisher E-mail: nlinfo-f@elsevier.com
Journal covering original research on material damage. Materials include metal alloys, polymers, composites, rocks, ceramics, etc. **Founded:** 1984. **Freq:** Bimonthly. **Key Personnel:** G.C. Sih, Editor-in-Chief, zpg7463@yahoo.com; A. Carpinteri, Board of Ed.; C.C. Chamis, Board of Ed.; C.M. Branco, Board of Ed.; C.I. Chang, Board of Ed.; E.E. Gdoutos, Board of Ed.; K. Friedrich, Board of Ed.; E.P. Chen, Board of Ed. **ISSN:** 0167-8442. **Subscription Rates:** 187,900¥ institutions; US$1,589 institutions for all countries except Europe, Japan & Iran; EUR1,416 institutions for European countries & Iran; US$183 individuals for all countries except Europe, Japan & Iran; EUR137 individuals for European countries & Iran; 21,000¥ individuals. **Remarks:** Accepts advertising. **URL:** http://www.elsevier.com/wps/find/journaldescription.cws_home/505665/description. **Circ:** (Not Reported)

43508 ■ Travelling Scope
Shanghai Stories Culture Media Co., Ltd.
74 Shaoxing Rd.
Shanghai 200020, People's Republic of China
Ph: 86 21 64376635
Fax: 86 21 64376635
Publisher E-mail: f_weien@sohu.com
Magazine covering travel destination in different countries. **Freq:** Monthly. **Key Personnel:** Xia Qinggen, Licensor, phone 86 21 64450298, fax 86 21 64660169. **Subscription Rates:** 16 Yu individuals. **URL:** http://www.wenyigroup.com.cn/ehibition/ehibition_default2.asp?pro_id=256.

43509 ■ Using the Right Word
Shanghai Using the Right Word Culture Media Co., Ltd.
Jia, 384/11 Jianguo Rd. W
Shanghai 200031, People's Republic of China
Ph: 86 21 64330669
Fax: 86 21 64330669
Magazine covering Chinese writings. **Founded:** 1995. **Freq:** Monthly. **Key Personnel:** Wang Min, Licensor, phone 86 21 64330669, fax 86 21 64330669. **Subscription Rates:** 2 Yu individuals. **URL:** http://www.wenyigroup.com.cn/ehibition/ehibition_default2.asp?pro_id=288.

43510 ■ With
Shanghai Stories Culture Media Co., Ltd.
74 Shaoxing Rd.
Shanghai 200020, People's Republic of China
Ph: 86 21 64376635
Fax: 86 21 64376635
Publisher E-mail: f_weien@sohu.com
Magazine covering women's fashion and lifestyle. **Founded:** Dec. 18, 2002. **Freq:** Monthly. **Key Personnel:** Li Zhenyu, Licensor, phone 86 21 64372608, fax 86 21 64668742. **Subscription Rates:** 16 Yu individuals.

URL: http://www.wenyigroup.com.cn/ehibition/ehibition_default2.asp?pro_id=279.

43511 ■ World Traveller
Shanghai People's Fine Arts Publishing House
D Bldg., No. 33
Changle Rd., Ln. 672
Shanghai 200040, People's Republic of China
Ph: 86 21 54044520
Fax: 86 21 54032331
Publisher E-mail: mscbs@sh163.net
Magazine featuring travel fashion and trend. **Founded:** Oct. 2003. **Freq:** Monthly. **Key Personnel:** Le Jian, Licensor, phone 86 21 54031690, fax 86 21 54032331. **Subscription Rates:** 18 Yu individuals. **URL:** http://www.wenyigroup.com.cn/ehibition/ehibition_default2.asp?pro_id=277.

43512 ■ Yachtstyle
Edipresse Asia
8/F, No. 2, Ln. 139
Anshun Rd.
Shanghai 200052, People's Republic of China
Ph: 86 21 52587666
Fax: 86 21 62802377
Magazine featuring the local and international luxury boating and yachting. **Freq:** Semiannual. **Key Personnel:** Margaret Chua-Piano, Director. **URL:** http://www.edipresse.com/en/par_pays/chine/magazines/yachtstyle. **Circ:** ‡90,000

43513 ■ Shanghai Television - 8
651 W Nanjing Rd.
298 Weihai Rd.
Shanghai 200041, People's Republic of China
Ph: 86 21 62565899
Fax: 86 21 62678022
E-mail: adv@smg.sh.cn
Format: News. **Owner:** Shanghai Television, at above address. **Ad Rates:** Advertising accepted; rates available upon request. **URL:** http://www.stv.sh.cn.

43514 ■ Shanghai Television - 14
651 W Nanjing Rd.
298 Weihai Rd.
Shanghai 200041, People's Republic of China
Ph: 86 21 62565899
Fax: 86 21 62678022
E-mail: adv@smg.sh.cn
Format: Information. **Owner:** Shanghai Television, at above address. **Ad Rates:** Advertising accepted; rates available upon request. **URL:** http://www.stv.sh.cn.

Taiyuan

43515 ■ International Journal of Bio-Inspired Computation
Inderscience Enterprises Limited
c/o Dr. Zhihua Cui, Ed.-in-Ch.
Taiyuan University of Science & Technology
Complex System & Computational Intelligence Laboratory
Taiyuan 030024, Shanxi, People's Republic of China
Journal featuring the research results on bio-inspired computation methods and their applications. **Freq:** 6/yr. **Key Personnel:** Dr. Zhihua Cui, Editor-in-Chief, cuizhihua@gmail.com. **ISSN:** 1758-0366. **Subscription Rates:** EUR593 individuals print or online; EUR830 individuals print and online. **URL:** http://www.inderscience.com/browse/index.php?journalID=329.

43516 ■ Taiyuan Television - 26
Shanxi China Yi Fen St. 2
Taiyuan 030024, Shanxi, People's Republic of China
Ph: 86 351 5676147
Fax: 86 351 5676866
Format: Information. **Owner:** Taiyuan TV Station, at above address. **Founded:** 1996. **Ad Rates:** Advertising accepted; rates available upon request. **URL:** http://www.tytv.com.cn.

43517 ■ Taiyuan Television - 12
Shanxi China Yi Fen St. 2
Taiyuan 030024, Shanxi, People's Republic of China
Ph: 86 351 5676147
Fax: 86 351 5676866
Format: News. **Owner:** Taiyuan TV Station, at above address. **Ad Rates:** Noncommercial. **URL:** http://www.tytv.com.cn.

Tianjin

43518 ■ Tianjin People's Broadcasting Station - 567 KHz
143 Weijin Rd.
143, Weijin Lu
Heping District
Tianjin 300070, People's Republic of China
Ph: 86 22 23601782
Format: News. **Operating Hours:** Continuous (except Mon. 4:00 p.m.-9:00 p.m.). **Wattage:** 20,000. **Ad Rates:** Noncommercial. **URL:** http://www.radiotj.com.

43519 ■ Earth Science
China University of Geosciences
c/o Wang Heng Jun, Ed.-in-Ch.
China University of Geosciences
Yujiashan
Wuhan 430074, People's Republic of China
Ph: 86 278 7483606
Fax: 86 278 7483606
Publisher E-mail: cugxb@cug.edu.cn
Journal related to earth science. **Founded:** 1957. **Freq:** Bimonthly. **Key Personnel:** Wang Heng Jun, Editor-in-Chief. **ISSN:** 1000-2383. **URL:** http://www.cug.edu.cn/. **Formerly:** Journal of the China University of Geosciences.

43520 ■ International Journal of Satellite Communications Policy and Management
Inderscience Enterprises Limited
c/o Rongbu Zhu, Ed.-in-Chief
South-Central University for Nationalities
College of Computer Science
Minyuan Rd., 708
Wuhan 430074, People's Republic of China
Journal covering the study of satellite communications policy and management. **Freq:** 4/yr. **Key Personnel:** Dr. Rongbu Zhu, Editor-in-Chief, rbzhuster@gmail.com; Dr. Maode Ma, Editor, emdma@ntu.edu.sg. **ISSN:** 1742-7568. **Subscription Rates:** EUR494 individuals print or online; EUR672 individuals print and online. **URL:** http://www.inderscience.com/browse/index.php?journalID=131.

Wuhan (Hubei)

43521 ■ Earth Sciences
China University of Geosciences
No. 388 Lumo Rd.
Wuhan 430074, Hubei, People's Republic of China
Ph: 86 27 87481030
Fax: 86 27 87481030
Publisher E-mail: cugxb@cug.edu.cn
Journal covering geology and associated technology. **Freq:** Bimonthly. **Key Personnel:** Wang Hengjun, Editor-in-Chief; Zhao Pengda, President; Yin Hongfu, Vice President. **URL:** http://www.cug.edu.cn/2003/ecug/7publication/Journal.htm.

43522 ■ Gems and Gemmology
China University of Geosciences
No. 388 Lumo Rd.
Wuhan 430074, Hubei, People's Republic of China
Ph: 86 27 87481030
Fax: 86 27 87481030
Publisher E-mail: cugxb@cug.edu.cn
Magazine covering the field of jewelry in China. **Founded:** 1999. **Freq:** Quarterly. **ISSN:** 1008-214X. **URL:** http://www.cug.edu.cn/2003/ecug/7publication/CUG%20magazines3.htm.

43523 ■ International Journal of Services, Economics and Management
Inderscience Enterprises Limited
c/o Prof. Shunzhong Liu, Ed.-in-Ch.
Huazhong Normal University
School of Economics
152 Luoyu Rd.
Wuhan 430079, Hubei, People's Republic of China
Journal covering the empirical and theoretical work on services economics and management. **Freq:** 4/yr. **Key Personnel:** Prof. Shunzhong Liu, Editor-in-Chief, liushunzhong@vip.163.com. **ISSN:** 1753-0822. **Subscription Rates:** EUR494 individuals print or online; EUR672 individuals print and online. **URL:** http://www.inderscience.com/browse/index.php?journalID=236.

43524 ■ The Journal of Grey System
Research Information Ltd.
c/o Deng Julong, Ed.-in-Ch.

Dept. of Automation
Huazhong University of Science & Technology
Wuhan 430074, Hubei, People's Republic of China
Publisher E-mail: info@researchinformation.co.uk
Journal publishing original referred articles covering both
theoretical and applied aspects of the Grey System
theory and its application. **Freq:** Quarterly. **Key Personnel:** Deng Julong, Editor-in-Chief; B.M. Ayyub, Assoc.
Ed.-in-Ch.; Cheng Biao, Assoc. Ed.-in-Ch.; Zhang Jixian, Assoc. Ed.-in-Ch. **ISSN:** 0957-3720. **Subscription
Rates:** US$598 individuals print; 299 individuals. **Remarks:** Advertising not accepted. **URL:** http://www.
researchinformation.co.uk/grey.php. **Circ:** (Not Reported)

43525 ■ Safety and Environmental Engineering
China University of Geosciences
No. 388 Lumo Rd.
Wuhan 430074, Hubei, People's Republic of China
Ph: 86 27 87481030
Fax: 86 27 87481030
Publisher E-mail: cugxb@cug.edu.cn
Magazine featuring the latest scientific achievements in
the fields of safety and environment. **Founded:** 1994.
Freq: Quarterly. **ISSN:** 1671-1556. **URL:** http://www.
cug.edu.cn/2003/ecug/7publication/
CUG%20magazines2.htm.

43526 ■ Social Sciences Edition
China University of Geosciences
No. 388 Lumo Rd.
Wuhan 430074, Hubei, People's Republic of China
Ph: 86 27 87481030
Fax: 86 27 87481030
Publisher E-mail: cugxb@cug.edu.cn
Journal covering social sciences. **Founded:** Aug. 2000.
URL: http://www.cug.edu.cn/2003/ecug/7publication/
Journal.htm.

Wuxi

43527 ■ Journal of Hydrodynamics
Elsevier Science Inc.
c/o D.X. Zhu
China Ship Scientific Research Center
Wuxi, People's Republic of China
Publisher E-mail: usinfo-ehelp@elsevier.com
Journal covering research activities of hydrodynamics
related to ocean and ship engineering. **Founded:** Nov.
1972. **Freq:** 6/yr. **Print Method:** Web offset. **Trim Size:**
11 1/2 x 15. **Cols./Page:** 3. **Col. Width:** 3 1/8 inches.
Col. Depth: 13 3/4 inches. **Key Personnel:** Liandi Zhou,
Exec. Members; S.M. Fan, Exec. Member; Y.S. He,
Exec. Member; W.X. Huai, Exec. Member; D.X. Zhu,
Exec. Member; Y.C. Li, Exec. Member; S.Q. Dai, Vice
Chm.; D.M. Cai, Vice Chm. **ISSN:** 1001-6058. **Subscription Rates:** 75,100¥ institutions; EUR518 institutions for
European countries and Iran; US$656 institutions, other
countries except Europe, Japan and Iran. **URL:** http://
www.elsevier.com/wps/find/journaldescription.cws_
home/709740/descriptiondescription.

Xi'an (Shaanxi)

43528 ■ Chinese Heart Journal
Fourth Military Medical University
17 Changlexi St.
Xi'an 710032, Shaanxi, People's Republic of China
Ph: 86 29 83374315
Publisher E-mail: jiaowuchu@fmmu.edu.cn
Journal featuring heart studies and research. **Founded:**
1989. **Freq:** Bimonthly. **ISSN:** 1009-7236. **URL:** http://
en.fmmu.edu.cn/copy_1_content.jsp?urltype=news.
NewsContentUrl&wbnewsid=23759&wbtreeid=2494.

**43529 ■ Chinese Journal of Cells and Molecular
Immunology**
Fourth Military Medical University
17 Changlexi St.
Xi'an 710032, Shaanxi, People's Republic of China
Ph: 86 29 83374315
Publisher E-mail: jiaowuchu@fmmu.edu.cn
Journal of medicine, focusing on cells and molecular

immunology. **Freq:** Bimonthly. **ISSN:** 1007-8738. **URL:**
http://en.fmmu.edu.cn/lby.jsp?urltype=tree.
TreeTempUrl&wbtreeid=2494.

**43530 ■ Chinese Journal of Conservative
Dentistry**
Fourth Military Medical University
17 Changlexi St.
Xi'an 710032, Shaanxi, People's Republic of China
Ph: 86 29 83374315
Publisher E-mail: jiaowuchu@fmmu.edu.cn
Journal for advancing stomatology in China. **Founded:**
Sept. 1991. **Freq:** Bimonthly. **Key Personnel:** Ma Minge, Contact. **ISSN:** 1005-2593. **URL:** http://en.fmmu.
edu.cn/lby.jsp?urltype=tree.TreeTempUrl&wbtreeid=
2494.

43531 ■ Chinese Journal of Neuroanatomy
Fourth Military Medical University
17 Changlexi St.
Xi'an 710032, Shaanxi, People's Republic of China
Ph: 86 29 83374315
Publisher E-mail: jiaowuchu@fmmu.edu.cn
Journal on neuroscience, focusing on neuroanatomy,
including some branches of neurobiology. **Key Personnel:** Xiao-Li Ma, Managing Editor, chinjna@fmmu.edu.
cn; Yun-Qing Li, Editor-in-Chief. **ISSN:** 1001-3733. **URL:**
http://en.fmmu.edu.cn/lby.jsp?urltype=tree.
TreeTempUrl&wbtreeid=2494.

**43532 ■ International Journal of Internet
Manufacturing & Services**
Inderscience Publishers
c/o Prof. Pingyu Jiang, Ed.-in-Ch.
Xi'an Jiaotong University
CAD/CAM Institute
School of Mechanical Engineering
Xi'an 710049, Shaanxi, People's Republic of China
Publisher E-mail: editor@inderscience.com
Peer-reviewed journal covering areas of manufacturing
science & technologies, services theory and methods,
and corresponding information and knowledge management issues. **Founded:** 2007. **Freq:** 4/yr. **Key Personnel:** Prof. Pingyu Jiang, Editor-in-Chief, pjiang@mail.
xjtu.edu.cn; Prof. Shuichi Fukuda, Assoc. Ed. **ISSN:**
1751-6048. **Subscription Rates:** EUR494 individuals
includes surface mail, print only; EUR672 individuals print
and online. **URL:** http://www.inderscience.com/browse/
index.php?journalCODE=ijims.

43533 ■ Journal of Fourth Military University
Fourth Military Medical University
17 Changlexi St.
Xi'an 710032, Shaanxi, People's Republic of China
Ph: 86 29 83374315
Publication E-mail: edjfmmu@fmmu.edu.cn
Publisher E-mail: jiaowuchu@fmmu.edu.cn
Peer-reviewed journal covering advances in medical
research. **Freq:** fortnightly. **Key Personnel:** Dr. Wang
Rui, Director. **ISSN:** 1000-2790. **URL:** http://en.fmmu.
edu.cn/copy_1_content.jsp?urltype=news.
NewsContectUrl&wnnewsid=23713&wbtreeid=2494.

43534 ■ Journal of Practical Stomatology
Fourth Military Medical University
17 Changlexi St.
Xi'an 710032, Shaanxi, People's Republic of China
Ph: 86 29 83374315
Publisher E-mail: jiaowuchu@fmmu.edu.cn
Journal of medicine, focusing on practical stomatology.
Founded: Oct. 1985. **Freq:** Bimonthly. **Key Personnel:**
Prof. Zhao Yimin, Editor-in-Chief. **ISSN:** 1001-3733.
URL: http://en.fmmu.edu.cn/lby.jsp?urltype=tree.
TreeTempUrl&wbtreeid=2494.

43535 ■ Journal of Xauat (Natural Sciences)
Xi'an University of Architecture and Technology
No. 13, Yanta Rd.
Xi'an 710055, Shaanxi, People's Republic of China
Publication E-mail: jzkjdz@163.com
Publisher E-mail: intl@xauat.edu.cn
Journal covering the field of natural sciences in China.
Founded: Feb. 1957. **Key Personnel:** Hongtie Zhao,
Editor-in-Chief. **URL:** http://www.xauat.edu.cn/jdeg/jx.
html.

43536 ■ Journal of Xauat (Social Sciences)
Xi'an University of Architecture and Technology
No. 13, Yanta Rd.
Xi'an 710055, Shaanxi, People's Republic of China
Publication E-mail: jzkjds@163.com
Publisher E-mail: intl@xauat.edu.cn
Journal covering the field of social sciences in China.
Key Personnel: Anqi Zhao, Editor-in-Chief. **URL:** http://
www.xauat.edu.cn/jdeg/jx.html.

Xi'an (Shanxi)

**43537 ■ International Journal of Digital
Enterprise Technology**
Inderscience Enterprises Limited
c/o Prof. Pingyu Jiang, Ed.-in-Ch.
Xi'an Jiaotong University
CAD/CAM Institute
School of Mechanical Engineering
Xi'an 710049, Shanxi, People's Republic of China
Peer-reviewed journal covering the areas of enterprise
theory, methods, technologies, and corresponding
information and knowledge management issues. **Freq:**
4/yr. **Key Personnel:** Prof. Pingyu Jiang, Editor-in-Chief,
pjiang@mail.xjtu.edu.cn. **ISSN:** 1756-2554. **Subscription Rates:** EUR494 individuals print or online; EUR672
individuals print and online. **URL:** http://www.
inderscience.com/browse/index.php?journalID=298.

Xiangtan

43538 ■ Communications in Differential and Difference Equations
Research India Publications
c/o Prof. Yong Zhou, Ed.-in-Ch.
Department of Mathematics
Xiangtan University
Xiangtan 411105, Hunan, People's Republic of China
Publisher E-mail: info@ripublication.com
Journal covering communications in differential and difference equations. **Freq:** 3/yr (January, May and
September). **Key Personnel:** Prof. Yong Zhou, Editor-in-Chief, yzhou@xtu.edu.cn. **ISSN:** 0973-6301. **Subscription Rates:** Rs 1,400 institutions print with online
access. **URL:** http://irphouse.com/math/cdde.htm. **Also
known as:** CDDE.

43539 ■ International Journal of Computing Science and Mathematics
Inderscience Publishers
c/o Prof. Yong Zhou, Ed.-in-Ch.
Xiangtan University
School of Mathematics & Computational Science
Institute for Computational & Applied Mathematics
Xiangtan 411105, Hunan, People's Republic of China
Publisher E-mail: editor@inderscience.com
Peer-reviewed journal covering all areas of computing
science & mathematics. **Founded:** 2007. **Freq:** 4/yr.
Key Personnel: Prof. Yong Zhou, Editor-in-Chief,
yzhou@xtu.edu.cn. **ISSN:** 1752-5055. **Subscription
Rates:** EUR494 individuals includes surface mail, print
only; EUR672 individuals print and online. **URL:** http://
www.inderscience.com/browse/index.php?
journalCODE=ijcsm.

**43540 ■ International Journal of Dynamical
Systems and Differential Equations**
Inderscience Publishers
c/o Prof. Yong Zhou, Ed.-in-Ch.
Xiangtan University
School of Mathematics & Computational Science
Institute for Computational & Applied Mathematics
Xiangtan 411105, Hunan, People's Republic of China
Publisher E-mail: editor@inderscience.com
Peer-reviewed journal covering dynamical systems &
differential equations. **Founded:** 2007. **Freq:** Quarterly.
Key Personnel: Prof. Yong Zhou, Editor-in-Chief,
yzhou@xtu.edu.cn. **ISSN:** 1752-3583. **Subscription
Rates:** EUR494 individuals includes surface mail, print
only; EUR672 individuals print & online. **URL:** http://www.
inderscience.com/browse/index.php?journalCODE=
ijdsde.

Bogota

43541 ■ Acta Biologica Colombiana
Universidad Nacional de Colombia
Carrera 45, No. 26-85
Edificio Uriel Gutierrez
Bogota, Colombia
Ph: 57 131 65000
Journal covering results of basic and applied research in biology. **Founded:** 1998. **Freq:** Semiannual. **Print Method:** Sheetfed offset. **Trim Size:** 8 1/2 x 11. **Cols./Page:** 2. **Col. Width:** 3 3/8 inches. **Col. Depth:** 10 inches. **Key Personnel:** Marcela Camacho, Editor, mmcamachon@unal.edu.co; Clara Spinel, Editor, cmspinelg@unal.edu.co; Alejandro Munera, Editor, famunerag@unal.edu.co; Jorge Ossa, Editor, jeossa@quimbaya.udea.edu.co; Martha Lucia Posada, Editor, mlposada-buitrago@lbl.go. **ISSN:** 0120-548X. **Subscription Rates:** 15 CoP individuals national; US$20 other countries. **URL:** http://www.virtual.unal.edu.co/revistas/actabiol/.

43542 ■ ArtNexus
Cra 5 No. 67, 19
Bogota, Colombia
Ph: 57 1 2495514
Fax: 57 1 3129252
Publisher E-mail: customerservice@artnexus.com
Magazine featuring images and articles on Hispanic arts. **Key Personnel:** Sofia Bullrich, Contact, sofia@artnexus.com; Zulema Roca, Contact, zroca@artnexus.com. **Subscription Rates:** US$32 individuals. **URL:** http://www.artnexus.com/.

43543 ■ Biota Colombiana
Instituto de Investigacion de Recursos Biologicos Alexander von Humboldt
Cr. 13 No. 28-01
Bogota, Colombia
Ph: 57 1 2877514
Publication E-mail: biotacol@humboldt.org.co
Magazine representing an open and participative mechanism intended to develop, publish, and diffuse a taxonomic inventory of the Colombian biodiversity. **Freq:** Semiannual. **Key Personnel:** Fernando Fernandez, Editor-in-Chief. **ISSN:** 0124-5376. **Subscription Rates:** 25,000 CoP individuals in Colombia; US$25 elsewhere. **URL:** http://www.humboldt.org.co/humboldt/mostrarpagina.php?codpage=20005.

43544 ■ Caldasia
Universidad Nacional de Colombia
Carrera 45, No. 26-85
Edificio Uriel Gutierrez
Bogota, Colombia
Ph: 57 131 65000
Publication E-mail: jorangelc@unal.edu.co
Journal covering botany, zoology, ecology, related archaeology and areas, of the region of neotropical, with emphasis in Colombia. **Founded:** 1980. **Freq:** Weekly (Fri.). **Print Method:** Offset. **Cols./Page:** 4. **Col. Width:** 15 picas. **Col. Depth:** 16 inches. **Key Personnel:** Jesús Orlando Rangel, Editor, jorangelc@unal.edu.co. **ISSN:** 0366-5232. **Subscription Rates:** US$45 other countries; 350,000 CoP individuals. **URL:** http://www.unal.edu.co/icn/publicaciones/caldasia/editor.htm.

43545 ■ Revista
Colombian Academy of Exact, Physical, and Natural Sciences
Academia Colombiana de Ciencias Exactas, Fisicas y Naturales
Transversal 27 No. 39A-63
Bogota, Colombia
Ph: 57 126 80365
Fax: 57 124 43186
Publisher E-mail: accefyn@accefyn.org.co
Publication covering science. **Freq:** Annual. **Key Personnel:** Pedro Prieto, Director, revista@accefyn.org.co. **ISSN:** 0370-3908. **URL:** http://www.accefyn.org.co/PubliAcad/Periodicas/revista.htm.

43546 ■ Melodia-FM - 96.9
Derechos Reservados
Calle 45 No. 13 - 70
Bogota, Colombia
Ph: 57 1 3231500
Fax: 57 1 2884020
Format: World Beat. **Operating Hours:** Continuous. **Ad Rates:** Advertising accepted; rates available upon request. **URL:** http://www.cadenamelodia.com.

43547 ■ Radio Lider-AM - 730
Derechos Reservados calle 45, No. 13-70
Bogota, Colombia
Ph: 57 1 3231500
Fax: 57 1 2884020
Format: World Beat; Ethnic. **Operating Hours:** Continuous. **Ad Rates:** Advertising accepted; rates available upon request. **URL:** http://www.cadenamelodia.com.

43548 ■ Radio Santa Fe-AM - 1070
Calle 57 17-48
Bogota, Colombia
Ph: 57 1 3456781
Fax: 57 1 3104485
E-mail: ventas@radiosantafe.com
Format: News; Ethnic. **Operating Hours:** Continuous. **Ad Rates:** Advertising accepted; rates available upon request. **URL:** http://www.radiosantafe.com.

43549 ■ Santa Fe Stereo-AM - 1070
Calle 57 17-48
Bogota, Colombia
Ph: 57 1 3456781
Fax: 57 1 3104485
E-mail: contacto@radiosantafe.com
Format: Ethnic. **Operating Hours:** Continuous. **Ad Rates:** Advertising accepted; rates available upon request. **URL:** http://www.radiosantafe.com.

Cali

43550 ■ Colombia Rotaria
c/o Dr. Enrique Jordan, Editor
Apartado Aereo 5925
Cali, Colombia
Publisher E-mail: rotarios@norma.net
Membership magazine of Rotary International covering current news about Rotary-related subjects. **Freq:** Monthly. **Key Personnel:** Dr. Enrique Jordan-Sarria, Editor. **URL:** http://www.rotary.org/en/MediaAndNews/MorePublications/RegionalMagazines/Pages/ridefault.aspx. **Circ:** Paid 491,312

Circulation: ★ = ABC; △ = BPA; ◆ = CAC; • = CCAB; ❏ = VAC; ⊕ = PO Statement; ‡ = Publisher's Report; Boldface figures = sworn; Light figures = estimated.

Gale Directory of Publications & Broadcast Media/147th Ed.   **4851**

Ciudad Quesada

43551 ■ Radio Santa Clara-AM - 550
Apartado Postal 221-4400
Ciudad Quesada, Costa Rica
Ph: 506 4606666
Fax: 506 4606666
Format: Ethnic; World Beat. **Operating Hours:** 16 hours Daily. **URL:** http://www.radiosantaclara.org.

San Jose

43552 ■ The Tico Times
The Tico Times S.A.
PO Box 4632
San Jose 1000, Costa Rica
Ph: 506 258 1558

Fax: 506 233 6378
Publisher E-mail: info@ticotimes.net
Community newspaper. **Founded:** 1956. **Freq:** Weekly. **Print Method:** Offset. **Trim Size:** 37 x 62 cm. **Cols./Page:** 4. **Col. Width:** 6.2 centimeters. **Col. Depth:** 34 centimeters. **Key Personnel:** Abby Daniell, General Mgr., adaniell@ticotimes.net. **USPS:** 022-579. **Subscription Rates:** US$79.95 individuals print premium; US$49.95 individuals online gold; US$37.95 individuals online silver. **Remarks:** Accepts advertising. **URL:** http://www.ticotimes.net; http://www.ticotimes.net/advertise.htm. **Ad Rates:** BW: C 1,014.09, 4C: C 1,470.44. **Circ:** Combined ⊕**15,000**

43553 ■ Radio Fides-AM - 1040
PO Box 5079

San Jose 1000, Costa Rica
Ph: 506 22581415
Fax: 506 2332387
E-mail: cabinafides@hotmail.com
Format: Ethnic; Religious; News; Talk. **Founded:** July 25, 1952. **Operating Hours:** Continuous. **Ad Rates:** Advertising accepted; rates available upon request. **URL:** http://www.radiofides.co.cr.

43554 ■ Repretel Television - 11
Apdo. 2860
San Jose 1000, Costa Rica
Ph: 506 22997200
E-mail: info@repretel.com
URL: http://www.repretel.com/.

Circulation: ★ = ABC; △ = BPA; ◆ = CAC; • = CCAB; ❑ = VAC; ⊕ = PO Statement; ‡ = Publisher's Report; Boldface figures = sworn; Light figures = estimated.

Gale Directory of Publications & Broadcast Media/147th Ed. 4853

Abidjan

43555 ■ Afrique Science
African Journals Online
22 BP 1561
Abidjan, Cote d'Ivoire
Publisher E-mail: info@ajol.info
Peer-reviewed journal containing experimental, theoretical and applied results in mathematics, physics, chemistry, biology, geology, and engineering. **Subtitle:** Revue Internationale des Sciences et Technologie. **Freq:** Semiannual. **Key Personnel:** Prof. Aka Boko, Editor-in-Chief. **ISSN:** 1813-548X. **URL:** http://ajol.info/index.php/afsci.

43556 ■ Agronomie Africaine
Association Ivoirienne des Sciences Agronomiques
Agronomie Africaine
Abidjan BP 703, Cote d'Ivoire
Journal covering general agronomy, genetics and plant breeding, plant protection, storage and transformation, technologies of agricultural products, animal science, fisheries, aquaculture and environment, agricultural economics and rural sociology in Africa. **Founded:** 1946. **Freq:** 3 issues. **Print Method:** Offset. **Cols./Page:** 6. **Col. Width:** 24 nonpareils. **Col. Depth:** 298 agate lines. **Key Personnel:** Ake Severin, Contact, ake@yahoo. com. **ISSN:** 1015-2288. **Remarks:** Accepts advertising. **URL:** http://ajol.info/index.php/aga. **Circ:** (Not Reported)

43557 ■ Sciences & Nature
African Journals Online
University of Abobo-Adjame
02 BP 801
Abidjan, Cote d'Ivoire
Ph: 225 20304201
Fax: 225 20304203
Publisher E-mail: info@ajol.info
Peer-reviewed journal covering the fields of crop and animal productions and sciences. **Freq:** Semiannual. **Key Personnel:** Prof. Ehouan Etienne Ehile, Editor, eh_ehile@yahoo.fr; Prof. Zoro Bl Irie, Assoc. Ed.; Dr. Adiko Amoncho, Assoc. Ed. **ISSN:** 1812-0741. **URL:** http://ajol.info/index.php/scinat.

Circulation: ★ = ABC; △ = BPA; ◆ = CAC; • = CCAB; ❏ = VAC; ⊕ = PO Statement; ‡ = Publisher's Report; Boldface figures = sworn; Light figures = estimated.

Gale Directory of Publications & Broadcast Media/147th Ed. 4855

Hrvatski Leskovac

43558 ■ Croatian Journal of Philosophy
Kruzak D.o o.
Zastavnice 29
CT-10251 Hrvatski Leskovac, Croatia
Ph: 385 1 6590416
Fax: 385 9 8235527
Publication E-mail: kruzak@kruzak.hr
Publisher E-mail: kruzak@kruzak.hr
Journal publishing philosophical work, mainly in analytic philosophy, combining contributions from Central Europe (with a focus upon Croatia, Slovenia and Hungary) and contributions from Western Europe and US. **Freq:** Annual. **Key Personnel:** Nenad Miscevic, Editor; Dunja Jutronic, Advisory Ed.; Predrag Sustar, Managing Editor; Michael Devitt, Advisory Board; Sergio Cremaschi, Advisory Board; Elvio Baccarini, Advisory Board; Boran Bercic, Advisory Board. **URL:** http://www.kruzak.hr/?lang=en.

Split

43559 ■ Acta Adriatica
Institute of Oceanography and Fisheries
Setaliste Ivana Mestrovica 63
CT-21000 Split, Croatia
Ph: 385 214 08000
Fax: 385 213 58650
Publisher E-mail: office@izor.hr
Journal covering Croatian and foreign scientific contributions on oceanography and marine fisheries. **Founded:** 1932. **Freq:** Semiannual. **Print Method:** Offset. **Cols./Page:** 6. **Col. Width:** 12 picas. **Col. Depth:** 21 inches. **Key Personnel:** Jakov Dulcic, Editor-in-Chief; Christian Capape, Assoc. Ed. **ISSN:** 1846-0453. **URL:** http://www.izor.hr/web/guest; http://jadran.izor.hr/acta/eng/.

43560 ■ Acta Adriatica
Institute of Oceanography and Fisheries
Setaliste Ivana Mestrovica 63
CT-21000 Split, Croatia
Ph: 385 214 08000
Fax: 385 213 58650
Publisher E-mail: office@izor.hr
Journal covering Croatian and foreign scientific contributions on oceanography and marine fisheries. **Founded:** 1932. **Freq:** Semiannual. **Print Method:** Offset. **Cols./Page:** 6. **Col. Width:** 12 picas. **Col. Depth:** 21 inches. **Key Personnel:** Jasov Dulcic, Editor-in-Chief; Christian Capape, Assoc. Ed. **ISSN:** 1846-0453. **URL:** http://www.izor.hr/web/guest; http://jadran.izor.hr/acta/eng/.

Zagreb

43561 ■ Acta Clinica Croatica
Sestre milosrdnice University Hospital and Institute for Clinical Medical Research
Vinogradska cesta 29
Zagreb, Croatia
Fax: 385 1 3787111
Journal published in connection with Ministry of Science and Technology of the Republic of Croatia. **Freq:** 4/yr. **Key Personnel:** Zvonko Kusic, Editor-in-Chief; Dubravko Petrac, Editor; Miljenko Solter, Editor; Vlatko

Thaller, Editor; Milan Vrkljan, Editor. **Subscription Rates:** 600 HRK institutions; 400 HRK individuals; 200 HRK students; 800 HRK institutions, other countries; 600 HRK other countries. **URL:** http://www.acta-clinica.kbsm.hr.

43562 ■ Acta Pharmaceutica
Croatian Pharmaceutical Society
Acta Pharmaceutica, HFD, Masarykova 2
HR-10000 Zagreb, Croatia
Ph: 385 1 4872849
Fax: 385 1 4872853
Publisher E-mail: sluter@pharma.hr
Journal publishing original contributions related to pharmacy and allied sciences. **Freq:** Quarterly. **Key Personnel:** Svjetlana Luterotti, Editor-in-Chief. **ISSN:** 1330-0075. **Subscription Rates:** US$15 individuals per issue. **URL:** http://public.carnet.hr/acphee/.

43563 ■ Chemical and Biochemical Engineering Quarterly
CABEQ
PO Box 123
Berislaviceva 6
CT-10000 Zagreb, Croatia
Publication E-mail: cabeq@mapbf.pbf.hr; cabeq@pbf.hr
Publisher E-mail: cabeq@pbf.hr
Journal on chemical and biochemical engineering. **Freq:** Quarterly. **Key Personnel:** Z. Kurtanjek, Editor-in-Chief, zkurt@mapbf.pbf.hr; D. Skare, Publisher, skare@irb.hr. **ISSN:** 0352-9568. **Subscription Rates:** Free online. **URL:** http://www.pbf.hr/cabeq.

43564 ■ Croatian International Relations Review
Institute for International Relations
Institut za Medjunarodne Odnose
Ulica Ljudevita Farkasa Vukotinovica 2
PO Box 303
CT-10000 Zagreb, Croatia
Ph: 385 148 77460
Fax: 385 148 28361
Publisher E-mail: ured@irmo.hr
Croatian publication covering international relations. **Subtitle:** CIRR. **Founded:** 1995. **Freq:** Quarterly. **Key Personnel:** Dr. Mladen Stanicic, Editor-in-Chief, mladen@irmo.hr; Damir Demonja, Research Assoc., ddemonja@irmo.hr. **ISSN:** 1331-1182. **URL:** http://www.imo.hr/node/21. **Circ:** 1,000

43565 ■ Croatian Medical Journal
Madicinska Naklada
Cankarova ulica 13
10000 Zagreb, Croatia
Ph: 385 1 3779444
Fax: 385 1 3907041
Publication E-mail: cmj@mef.hr
Publisher E-mail: medicinskanaklada@medicinskanaklada.hr
Journal dealing with medicine and related research in connection with the World Association of Croatian Physicians (WACP) and Croatian Academy of Medical Sciences (CAMS). **Freq:** Bimonthly. **Key Personnel:** Ana Marusic, PhD, Editor-in-Chief; Ivan Damjanov, PhD, Editor-in-Chief; Darko Hren, Exec. Ed. **ISSN:** 0353-9504. **Subscription Rates:** EUR60 individuals; EUR40 students; EUR10 single issue; EUR100 institutions. **Re-**

marks: Accepts advertising. **URL:** http://www.cmj.hr/. **Circ:** (Not Reported)

43566 ■ Croatica Chemica Acta
Croatian Chemical Society
Horvatovac 102 A
CT-10000 Zagreb, Croatia
Ph: 385 146 06163
Fax: 385 146 06131
Publisher E-mail: ccsoc@emma.irb.hr
Journal covering all fields of chemistry including physical and theoretical chemistry, organic chemistry, biochemistry, analytical chemistry, inorganic and structural chemistry, and materials science. **Founded:** 1972. **Freq:** Quarterly. **Print Method:** Offset. **Cols./Page:** 4. **Col. Width:** 32 nonpareils. **Col. Depth:** 210 agate lines. **Key Personnel:** Prof. Nikola Kallay, Editor-in-Chief, cca@chem.pmf.hr; Ljerka Brecevic, Editor; Predrag Novak, Editor. **ISSN:** 0011-1643. **URL:** http://public.carnet.hr/ccacaa/.

43567 ■ Diskrepancija
Filozofski fakultet
Ivana Lucica 3
10000 Zagreb, Croatia
Ph: 385 1 6120000
Fax: 385 1 6156879
Publisher E-mail: diskrepancija@net.hr
Student-run journal publishing articles in social sciences and humanities. **Founded:** 2000. **Freq:** Biennial. **Key Personnel:** Valerio Bacak, Editor-in-Chief, vabacak@gmail.com. **URL:** http://www.diskrepancija.org/.

43568 ■ International Journal of Transitions and Innovation Systems
Inderscience Enterprises Limited
c/o Marina Dabic, Ed.-in-Ch.
University of Zagreb, Dept. of Managerial Economics
Faculty of Economics & Business
J. F. Kennedy Sq. 6
10000 Zagreb, Croatia
Journal focusing on the discussion in the transition role of innovation systems for the community. **Freq:** 4/yr. **Key Personnel:** Marina Dabic, Editor-in-Chief, mdabic@efzg.hr; Darko Tipuric, Assoc. Ed. **ISSN:** 1745-0071. **Subscription Rates:** EUR494 individuals print or online; EUR672 individuals print and online. **URL:** http://www.inderscience.com/browse/index.php?journalID=160.

43569 ■ Kruh i Ruze
Women's Infoteka
Varsavska 16
CT-10000 Zagreb, Croatia
Ph: 38 514 830557
Fax: 38 514 830552
Publisher E-mail: zinfo@zamir.net
Magazine providing information on women's activism, including initiatives in the areas of peace activism, lesbianism, and violence against women. **Freq:** Quarterly. **URL:** http://www.zinfo.hr/hrvatski/stranice/izdavastvo/kruhiruze/izaslibrojevi.htm.

43570 ■ Razvoj/Development
Institute for International Relations
Institut za Medjunarodne Odnose
Ulica Ljudevita Farkasa Vukotinovica 2
PO Box 303

CT-10000 Zagreb, Croatia
Ph: 385 148 77460
Fax: 385 148 28361
Publisher E-mail: ured@irmo.hr
Croatian publication covering worldwide understanding.
Freq: 3/yr. **Key Personnel:** Mladen Stanicic, Editor-in-
Chief, phone 44 385 4877462, mladen@irmo.hr. **ISSN:**
0352-4728. **URL:** http://www.imo.hr/node/229. **Circ:** 500

Camaguey

43571 ■ CMBF Radio Musical Nacional-FM - 97.5
Edificio N, Calle N, entre 23 y 21, Vedado
Havana 10400, Cuba
Ph: 53 7 8320085
E-mail: rmusical@cmbf.icrt.cu
Format: Full Service. **Key Personnel:** Eduardo Granado Castellon, Director. **URL:** http://www.cmbfradio.cu/cmbf/cmbf_radio/pro_trans_hist_cmbf/transmision.htm.

Ciego de Avila

43572 ■ CMBF Radio Musical Nacional-FM - 91.5
Edificio N, Calle N, entre 23 y 21, Vedado
Havana, Cuba
Ph: 53 7 8320085
E-mail: rmusical@cmbf.icrt.cu
Format: Full Service. **Key Personnel:** Eduardo Granado Castellon, Director. **URL:** http://www.cmbfradio.cu/cmbf/cmbf_radio/pro_trans_hist_cmbf/transmision.htm.

Cienfuegos

43573 ■ CMBF Radio Musical Nacional-FM - 92.7
Edificio N, Calle N, entre 23 y 21, Vedado
Havana, Cuba
Ph: 53 7 8320085
E-mail: rmusical@cmbf.icrt.cu
Format: Full Service. **Key Personnel:** Eduardo Granado Castellon, Director. **URL:** http://www.cmbfradio.cu/cmbf/cmbf_radio/pro_trans_hist_cmbf/transmision.htm.

Granma

43574 ■ CMBF Radio Musical Nacional-FM - 92.7
Edificio N, Calle N, entre 23 y 21, Vedado
Havana, Cuba
Ph: 53 7 8320085
E-mail: rmusical@cmbf.icrt.cu
Format: Full Service. **Key Personnel:** Eduardo Granado Castellon, Director. **URL:** http://www.cmbfradio.cu/cmbf/cmbf_radio/pro_trans_hist_cmbf/transmision.htm.

Guantanamo

43575 ■ CMBF Radio Musical Nacional-FM - 98.5
Edificio N, Calle N, entre 23 y 21, Vedado
Havana, Cuba
Ph: 53 7 8320085
E-mail: rmusical@cmbf.icrt.cu
Format: Full Service. **Key Personnel:** Eduardo Granado Castellon, Director. **URL:** http://www.cmbfradio.cu/cmbf/cmbf_radio/pro_trans_hist_cmbf/transmision.htm.

Havana

43576 ■ Cuba Foreign Trade
Chamber of Commerce of the Republic of Cuba
Calle 21, No. 661 esq. a A
Vedado Ciudad de La Habana
Havana, Cuba
Fax: 53 833 6810
Publication E-mail: public@camara.com.cu
English and Spanish language publication covering foreign trade. **Freq:** Quarterly. **ISSN:** 0864-3857. **Subscription Rates:** 5 CuP single issue. **Remarks:** Advertising accepted; rates available upon request. **URL:** http://www.camaracuba.cu. **Circ:** 3,000

43577 ■ CMBF Radio Musical Nacional-AM - 590
Edificio N, Calle N, entre 23 y 21, Vedado
Havana, Cuba
Ph: 53 7 8320085
E-mail: rmusical@cmbf.ICRT.cu
Format: Full Service. **Key Personnel:** Eduardo Granado Castellon, Director. **URL:** http://www.cmbfradio.cu/cmbf/cmbf_radio/pro_trans_hist_cmbf/transmision.htm.

43578 ■ CMBF Radio Musical Nacional-FM - 99.1
Edificio N, Calle N, entre 23 y 21, Vedado
Havana, Cuba
Ph: 53 7 8320085
E-mail: rmusical@cmbf.icrt.cu
Format: Full Service. **Key Personnel:** Eduardo Granado Castellon, Director. **URL:** http://www.cmbfradio.cu/cmbf/cmbf_radio/pro_trans_hist_cmbf/transmision.htm.

CMBF Radio Musical Nacional-FM - See Camaguey

CMBF Radio Musical Nacional-FM - See Ciego de Avila

CMBF Radio Musical Nacional-FM - See Cienfuegos

CMBF Radio Musical Nacional-FM - See Granma

CMBF Radio Musical Nacional-FM - See Guantanamo

CMBF Radio Musical Nacional-FM - See Holguin

CMBF Radio Musical Nacional-FM - See Isla de la Juventud

CMBF Radio Musical Nacional-FM - See Jacan

CMBF Radio Musical Nacional-FM - See La Cumbre

CMBF Radio Musical Nacional-FM - See Las Tunas

CMBF Radio Musical Nacional-FM - See Pinar del Rio

CMBF Radio Musical Nacional-FM - See Sancti Spiritus

CMBF Radio Musical Nacional-FM - See Santiago de Cuba

CMBF Radio Musical Nacional-FM - See Villa Clara

Holguin

43579 ■ CMBF Radio Musical Nacional-FM - 105.7
Edificio N, Calle N, entre 23 y 21, Vedado
Havana, Cuba
Ph: 53 7 8320085
E-mail: rmusical@cmbf.icrt.cu
Format: Full Service. **Key Personnel:** Eduardo Granado Castellon, Director. **URL:** http://www.cmbfradio.cu/cmbf/cmbf_radio/pro_trans_hist_cmbf/transmision.htm.

Isla de la Juventud

43580 ■ CMBF Radio Musical Nacional-FM - 96.5
Edificio N, Calle N, entre 23 y 21, Vedado
Havana, Cuba
Ph: 53 7 8320085
E-mail: rmusical@cmbf.icrt.cu
Format: Full Service. **Key Personnel:** Eduardo Granado Castellon, Director. **URL:** http://www.cmbfradio.cu/cmbf/cmbf_radio/pro_trans_hist_cmbf/transmision.htm.

Jacan

43581 ■ CMBF Radio Musical Nacional-FM - 107.9
Edificio N, Calle N, entre 23 y 21, Vedado
Havana, Cuba
Ph: 53 7 8320085
E-mail: rmusical@cmbf.icrt.cu
Format: Full Service. **Key Personnel:** Eduardo Granado Castellon, Director. **URL:** http://www.cmbfradio.cu/cmbf/cmbf_radio/pro_trans_hist_cmbf/transmision.htm.

La Cumbre

43582 ■ CMBF Radio Musical Nacional-FM - 93.7
Edificio N, Calle N, entre 23 y 21, Vedado
Havana, Cuba
Ph: 53 7 8320085
E-mail: rmusical@cmbf.icrt.cu
Format: Full Service. **Key Personnel:** Eduardo Granado Castellon, Director. **URL:** http://www.cmbfradio.cu/cmbf/cmbf_radio/pro_trans_hist_cmbf/transmision.htm.

Las Tunas

43583 ■ CMBF Radio Musical Nacional-FM - 98.3
Edificio N, Calle N, entre 23 y 21, Vedado
Havana, Cuba
Ph: 53 7 8320085
E-mail: rmusical@cmbf.icrt.cu
Format: Full Service. **Key Personnel:** Eduardo Granado Castellon, Director. **URL:** http://www.cmbfradio.cu/cmbf/cmbf_radio/pro_trans_hist_cmbf/transmision.htm.

Pinar del Rio

43584 ■ CMBF Radio Musical Nacional-FM - 98.7
Edificio N, Calle N, entre 23 y 21, Vedado
Havana, Cuba
Ph: 53 7 8320085
E-mail: rmusical@cmbf.icrt.cu
Format: Full Service. **Key Personnel:** Eduardo Granado Castellon, Director. **URL:** http://www.cmbfradio.cu/cmbf/cmbf_radio/pro_trans_hist_cmbf/transmision.htm.

Sancti Spiritus

43585 ■ CMBF Radio Musical Nacional-FM - 93.9
Edificio N, Calle N, entre 23 y 21, Vedado
Havana, Cuba
Ph: 53 7 8320085
E-mail: rmusical@cmbf.icrt.cu
Format: Full Service. **Key Personnel:** Eduardo Gra-

Circulation: ★ = ABC; △ = BPA; ♦ = CAC; • = CCAB; ❏ = VAC; ⊕ = PO Statement; ‡ = Publisher's Report; Boldface figures = sworn; Light figures = estimated.

nado Castellon, Director. **URL:** http://www.cmbfradio.cu/cmbf/cmbf_radio/pro_trans_hist_cmbf/transmision.htm.

Santiago de Cuba

43586 ■ CMBF Radio Musical Nacional-FM - 100.3
Edificio N, Calle N, entre 23 y 21, Vedado
Havana, Cuba
Ph: 53 7 8320085

E-mail: rmusical@cmbf.icrt.cu
Format: Full Service. **Key Personnel:** Eduardo Granado Castellon, Director. **URL:** http://www.cmbfradio.cu/cmbf/cmbf_radio/pro_trans_hist_cmbf/transmision.htm.

Villa Clara

43587 ■ CMBF Radio Musical Nacional-FM - 100.7
Edificio N, Calle N, entre 23 y 21, Vedado

Havana, Cuba
Ph: 53 7 8320085
E-mail: rmusical@cmbf.icrt.cu
Format: Full Service. **Key Personnel:** Eduardo Granado Castellon, Director. **URL:** http://www.cmbfradio.cu/cmbf/cmbf_radio/pro_trans_hist_cmbf/transmision.htm.

Ayia Napa

43588 ■ Radio Napa-FM - 106.3 MHz
PO Box 30582
Ayia Napa, Cyprus
Ph: 357 77 771030
E-mail: napafm@cytanet.com.cy
Format: Oldies; Music of Your Life; Alternative/New Music/Progressive. **Operating Hours:** Continuous. **Ad Rates:** Advertising accepted; rates available upon request. **URL:** http://www.radionapa.net.

Limassol

43589 ■ Earthlines
Friends of the Earth - Cyprus
PO Box 53411
Limassol 3302, Cyprus
Ph: 357 5 347042
Fax: 357 5 347043
Publisher E-mail: foecyprus@yahoo.com
Publication covering conservation, in English and Greek. **Freq:** Semiannual. **ISSN:** 1450-0450. **Remarks:** Advertising accepted; rates available upon request. **URL:** http://www.foei.org. **Circ:** (Not Reported)

43590 ■ International Journal of Ocean Systems Management
Inderscience Enterprises Limited
c/o Dr. Efstratios Georgoudis, Ed.-in-Ch.
Frederick University, Limassol Campus
18, Mariou Agathagelou Str.
Agios Georgios Havouzas
Limassol 3080, Cyprus
Journal covering the business and government management aspects of ocean systems and activities. **Freq:** 4/yr. **Key Personnel:** Dr. Efstratios Georgoudis, Editor-in-Chief, sgeorgoudis@dms.mcw.edu.cy; Angelos Menelaou, Managing Editor, am@shipoon.eu.com **ISSN:** 1752-6582. **Subscription Rates:** EUR494 individuals print or online; EUR672 individuals print and online. **URL:** http://www.inderscience.com/browse/index.php?journalID=227.

43591 ■ Choice-FM - 104.3
196 Arch. Makarios III
Ariel Cor., 1st Fl.
Office 101
Limassol 3030, Cyprus
Ph: 357 25 820820
Fax: 357 25 343435
E-mail: contact@choicefm.com.cy
Format: Contemporary Hit Radio (CHR); Music of Your Life. **Operating Hours:** Continuous. **Ad Rates:** Advertising accepted; rates available upon request. **URL:** http://www.choicefm.com.cy.

43592 ■ Coast-FM - 91.4
Themis Tower, Ste. 401
Olympion St.
Limassol 3035, Cyprus
Ph: 357 25 350914
Fax: 357 25 350916

E-mail: information@91.4coastfm.com
Format: Music of Your Life. **Ad Rates:** Advertising accepted; rates available upon request. **URL:** http://www.91.4coastfm.com.

Nicosia

43593 ■ The Cyprus Weekly
CYWEEKLY Ltd.
1 Diogenous
Engomi
PO Box 21094
Nicosia 1306, Cyprus
Ph: 357 22 744400
Fax: 357 22 668665
Publisher E-mail: cynewslive@cyprusweekly.com.cy
English language newspaper. **Founded:** Sept. 1979. **Freq:** Weekly (Fri.). **Key Personnel:** Michalis Karis, General Mgr.; Myrto Markidou, CEO; Nicos Chr Pattichis, Publisher. **Subscription Rates:** 150 individuals Greece; 200 individuals U.S./Africa; 150 individuals Europe; 200 individuals Australia. **Remarks:** Accepts advertising. **URL:** http://www.cyprusweekly.com.cy/. **Ad Rates:** BW: C 157, 4C: C 315, PCI: C 7, PCI: C 14. **Circ:** 17,000.

43594 ■ Emporoviomichaniki
Cyprus Chamber of Commerce & Industry
38, Grivas Dhigenis Ave. & 3, Deligiorgis St.
PO Box 21455
Nicosia CY-1509, Cyprus
Ph: 357 228 89800
Fax: 357 226 69048
Publisher E-mail: chamber@ccci.org.cy
Greek language newspaper covering trade. **Freq:** Monthly. **Key Personnel:** Priamos Loizides, Contact, epitiri@ccci.org.cy. **Remarks:** Advertising accepted; rates available upon request. **URL:** http://www.ccci.org.cy/public.shtm. **Circ:** 4,000

43595 ■ Financial Mirror
Financial Mirror Ltd.
PO Box 16077
Nicosia CY-2085, Cyprus
Ph: 357 22 678666
Fax: 357 22 678664
Publication E-mail: info@financialmirror.com
Publisher E-mail: info@financialmirror.com
Newspaper featuring business. **Founded:** 1993. **Freq:** Weekly. **Key Personnel:** Masis Der Parthogh, Publisher/Dir., masis@financialmirror.com. **Remarks:** Accepts advertising. **URL:** http://www.financialmirror.com/. **Ad Rates:** BW: EUR1,080. **Circ:** 4,000

43596 ■ Journal of Mediterranean Archaeology
Equinox Publishing Ltd.
c/o Prof. A. Bernard Knapp, Ed.
Cyprus American Archaeological
Research Institute
11 Andreas Demetriou
Nicosia 1066, Cyprus
Journal covering multicultural world of Mediterranean

archaeology. **Freq:** Semiannual. **Key Personnel:** John F. Cherry, Editor, john_cherry@brown.edu; Prof. A. Bernard Knapp, Editor, b.knapp@archaeology.arts.gla.ac.uk; Peter van Dommelen, Editor, p.vandommelen@archaeology.gla.ac.uk. **ISSN:** 0952-7648. **Subscription Rates:** 125 institutions, other countries print and online; US$250 institutions print and online; 40 institutions developing countries; 119 institutions, other countries print only; US$80 individuals print only; 30 students print; US$60 students print. **Remarks:** Accepts advertising. **URL:** http://www.equinoxjournals.com/ojs/index.php/JMA. **Circ:** (Not Reported)

43597 ■ POLIS
University of Cyprus
PO Box 20537
Nicosia 1678, Cyprus
Ph: 357 22 894000
Publisher E-mail: info@ucy.ac.cy
Journal featuring the Ancient Greek political thought. **Subtitle:** The Journal of the Society for Greek Political Thought. **Founded:** 1977. **Freq:** Semiannual. **Key Personnel:** Dr. Kyriakos Demetriou, Editor, k.demetriou@ucy.ac.cy. **Subscription Rates:** 26 individuals; US$52 individuals; 65 institutions; US$130 institutions. **URL:** http://www.imprint.co.uk/polis/polis.html.

43598 ■ Kiss-FM - 89
PO Box 22050
Nicosia 2018, Cyprus
Ph: 357 2 2669999
Fax: 357 2 2667989
E-mail: marketing@kissfm.com.cy
Format: Contemporary Hit Radio (CHR); Ethnic; Top 40. **Operating Hours:** Continuous. **Ad Rates:** Advertising accepted; rates available upon request. **URL:** http://www.kissfm.com.cy.

43599 ■ Radio Proto-FM - 89.3
Archangel Avo. 31
Strovolos 2057
Nicosia 21836, Cyprus
Format: News; Information; Sports; Talk. **Owner:** Radio Proto, at above address. **URL:** http://www.radioproto.com.cy/.

Pafos

43600 ■ Rock-FM - 98.5
7 Galateias Str.
Galateia Ct.
Flat 203
Pafos 8046, Cyprus
Ph: 357 26 822073
Fax: 357 26 822074
E-mail: admin@rockfm985.com
Format: Album-Oriented Rock (AOR); Classic Rock; Heavy Metal; Alternative/New Music/Progressive. **Operating Hours:** Continuous Mon.-Fri.; 8 a.m. - 7 a.m. Sat.-Sun. **Ad Rates:** Advertising accepted; rates available upon request. **URL:** http://www.rockfmcyprus.com.

Circulation: ★ = ABC; △ = BPA; ♦ = CAC; • = CCAB; ❑ = VAC; ⊕ = PO Statement; ‡ = Publisher's Report; Boldface figures = sworn; Light figures = estimated.

Gale Directory of Publications & Broadcast Media/147th Ed.

4861

Brno

43601 ■ Acta Veteriniaria Brno
University of Veterinary and Pharmaceutical Sciences
Palackeho 1-3
612 42 Brno, Czech Republic
Ph: 420 541561111
Publication E-mail: actavet@vfu.cz
Journal publishing original contributions related to the clinical studies in veterinary and biomedical sciences. **Key Personnel:** Eva Baranyiova, Editor-in-Chief. **ISSN:** 0001-7213. **URL:** http://www.vfu.cz/index.html?lang=en.

43602 ■ Archivum Mathematicum
Masarykova Universita
c/o J. Rosicky, Ed-in-Ch.
Masaryk University Faculty of Science
Kotlarska 2
CZ-611 37 Brno, Czech Republic
Publisher E-mail: info@muni.cz
Peer-reviewed journal covering research in all areas of mathematics. **Founded:** 1844. **Freq:** Monthly. **Print Method:** Uses mats. Offset. **Trim Size:** 8 1/8 x 10 7/8. **Cols./Page:** 2. **Col. Width:** 44 nonpareils. **Col. Depth:** 140 agate lines. **Key Personnel:** R. Kucera, Managing Editor, kucera@math.muni.cz; J. Rosicky, Editor-in-Chief, rosicky@math.muni.cz; O. Dosly, Editorial Board, dosly@math.muni.cz. **ISSN:** 1212-5059. **Subscription Rates:** Kcs 240 institutions; US$60 other countries; US$120 institutions, other countries. **URL:** http://www.emis.de/journals/AM/.

43603 ■ Central European Political Studies Review
International Institute of Political Science
Jostova 10
602 00 Brno, Czech Republic
Ph: 420 549 495769
Fax: 420 549 495769
Publication E-mail: iips@iips.cz
Publisher E-mail: iips@iips.cz
Journal dealing mainly on modern politics in Europe with emphasis on Central Europe. **Freq:** 3/yr. **ISSN:** 1212-7817. **URL:** http://www.cepsr.com.

Brunn

43604 ■ Differential Geometry and its Applications
Elsevier Science
c/o J. Slovak, Ed.-in-Ch.
Institute of Mathematics & Statistics
Faculty of Science, Masaryk University
Kotlarska 2
CZ-186 75 Brunn, Czech Republic
Ph: 42 5 41631251
Fax: 42 5 41210337
Publisher E-mail: nlinfo-f@elsevier.com
Peer-reviewed journal publishing articles in differential geometry and in various fields of mathematics, which use differential geometric methods and investigate geometrical structures. **Founded:** 1991. **Freq:** Bimonthly. **Key Personnel:** O. Kowalski, Editorial Board, kowalski@karlin.mff.cuni.cz; D.V. Alekseevsky, Editorial Board, d.v.alekseevsky@hull.ac.uk; R.L. Bryant, Editorial Board, bryant@math.duke.edu. **ISSN:** 0926-2245. **Subscription Rates:** US$681 institutions for all countries except Europe and Japan; 90,300¥ institutions; EUR681 institutions, other countries European countries; EUR158 individuals; US$211 individuals; 24,300¥ individuals. **Remarks:** Accepts advertising. **URL:** http://www.elsevier.com/wps/find/journaldescription.cws_home/505630/descrip tiondescription. **Circ:** (Not Reported)

Ceske Budejovice

43605 ■ Folia Parasitologica
Institute of Parasitology
Biology Centre, ASCR, v.v.i.
Branisovska 31
370 05 Ceske Budejovice, Czech Republic
Ph: 420 38 5310351
Fax: 420 38 5310388
Publication E-mail: folia@paru.cas.cz
Publisher E-mail: paru@paru.cas.cz
Journal covering various aspects of parasitology such as morphology, taxonomy, biology, biochemistry, physiology, immunology and molecular biology of parasites, and host-parasite relationships. **Founded:** 1953. **Freq:** Quarterly. **Key Personnel:** V. Bukva, Editor-in-Chief; F. Moravec, Asst. Ed.; L. Grubhoffer, Asst. Ed. **ISSN:** 0015-5683. **Subscription Rates:** EUR185 institutions print and online (Europe); EUR80 individuals print and online (Europe); EUR200 institutions, other countries; EUR95 other countries. **URL:** http://www.paru.cas.cz/folia/. **Formerly:** Czechoslovak Parasitology (1966).

43606 ■ Journal of Applied Biomedicine
University of South Bohemia
Faculty of Health and Social Studies
Jirovcova 24
370 04 Ceske Budejovice, Czech Republic
Ph: 420 387 315181
Fax: 420 387 438389
Publication E-mail: jab@zsf.jcu.cz
Peer-reviewed journal covering research in biomedicine. **Founded:** 2003. **Freq:** Quarterly. **Key Personnel:** Milos Veleminsky, Managing Editor; Josef Berger, Editor-in-Chief, berger@jcu.cz. **ISSN:** 1214-021X. **URL:** http://www.zsf.jcu.cz/jab.

Plzen

43607 ■ Ceska Radiologie
Czech Radiological Society
Ceska Radiologicka Spolecnost
c/o Prof. Jiri Ferda, MD
University Hospital, Clinic of Diagnostic Radiology
Alej Svobody 80
306 40 Plzen, Czech Republic
Ph: 42 377 103436
Fax: 42 377 103438
Publisher E-mail: ferda@fnplzen.cz
Czech and Slovak language publication covering radiology. **Founded:** 1938. **Freq:** 9/yr. **Trim Size:** A4. **ISSN:** 0069-2344. **URL:** http://www.cesradiol.cz/. **Formerly:** Ceskoslovenska Radiologie. **Ad Rates:** GLR: Kcs 30,400, BW: Kcs 34,700, 4C: Kcs 42,400. **Circ:** (Not Reported)

Prague

43608 ■ Acta Chirurgiae Plasticae
Czech Medical Association J.E. Purknye—Publishing Div.
Sokolska 31
CZ-120 26 Prague 2, Czech Republic
Ph: 420 2 24266223
Fax: 420 2 24266212
Publisher E-mail: czma@cls.cz
Journal covering field of plastic, reconstructive and aesthetic surgery, surgery of the hand, craniofacial surgery, and treatment of burns. **Freq:** 4/yr. **Trim Size:** A4. **Key Personnel:** Miroslav Tvrdek, MD, Chm. **ISSN:** 0001-5423. **Subscription Rates:** Kcs 480 individuals; EUR26.40 individuals; Kcs 120 single issue; EUR6.60 single issue. **Remarks:** Accepts advertising. **URL:** http://www.prolekare.cz/acta-chirurgiae-plasticae?utm_source=clsjep&utm_medium=clsjep-journal&utm_campaign=clsjep. **Ad Rates:** BW: Kcs 17,000, 4C: Kcs 24,000. **Circ:** (Not Reported)

43609 ■ Anaesthesiology & Intensive Critical Care Medicine
Czech Medical Association J.E. Purknye—Publishing Div.
Sokolska 31
CZ-120 26 Prague 2, Czech Republic
Ph: 420 2 24266223
Fax: 420 2 24266212
Publisher E-mail: czma@cls.cz
Scholarly journal for anesthesiologists and intensive care professionals. **Founded:** 2000. **Freq:** Bimonthly. **Print Method:** Offset. **Trim Size:** A4. **Key Personnel:** Jan Sobotka, Contact. **ISSN:** 1214-2158. **Subscription Rates:** US$98 individuals; EUR72 individuals. **Remarks:** Accepts advertising. **URL:** http://www.prolekare.cz/anesteziologie-intenzivni-medicina?utm_source=clsjep&utm_medium. **Ad Rates:** BW: Kcs 29,000, 4C: Kcs 39,500. **Circ:** Paid 1,800

43610 ■ Auto Motor a Sport (Czech)
Motor-Presse Bohemia
At Sta. 36 of Krk
140 00 Prague 4, Czech Republic
Ph: 420 2 41093410
Fax: 420 2 41721905
Consumer magazine covering automobiles for a general audience. **Founded:** 1993. **Freq:** Monthly. **Print Method:** Offset. **Cols./Page:** 4. **Key Personnel:** Renata Ben, Classifieds; Michael Kudela, Editor. **Subscription Rates:** Kcs 69 single issue. **Remarks:** Accepts advertising. **URL:** http://www.motorpresse.cz/automotorasport.asp. **Circ:** 23,500

43611 ■ Automatizace
Automatizace S.R.O.
Karlovo namesti 30
CZ-120 00 Prague 2, Czech Republic
Ph: 42 224 934513
Publication E-mail: redakce@automatizace.cz
Publisher E-mail: redakce@automatizace.cz
Trade journal covering automation and measuring technology and industrial computing. **Founded:** 1958. **Freq:** Monthly. **Print Method:** Offset. **Trim Size:** 210 x 297. **Key Personnel:** Eva Stronerova, Manager, stronerova@automatizace.cz. **ISSN:** 0005-125X. **Sub-**

scription Rates: Kcs 390 individuals; EUR50 individuals. Remarks: Accepts advertising. URL: http://www.automatizace.cz/. Ad Rates: BW: US$550, 4C: US$1,030. Circ: Combined ‡8,500

43612 ■ Ceska Revmatologie
Czech Medical Association J.E. Purknye—Publishing Div.
Sokolska 31
CZ-120 26 Prague 2, Czech Republic
Ph: 420 2 24266223
Fax: 420 2 24266212
Publisher E-mail: czma@cls.cz
Journal covering field of rheumatology. **Freq:** 4/yr. **Trim Size:** A4. **Key Personnel:** Prof. George Vencovsky, Editor. **ISSN:** 1210-7905. **Subscription Rates:** Kcs 440 individuals; EUR26.40 individuals. **Remarks:** Accepts advertising. **URL:** http://www.prolekare.cz/ceska-revmatologie?utm_source=clsjep&utm_medium=clsjep-journal&utm_campaign=clsjep. **Ad Rates:** BW: Kcs 28,000, 4C: Kcs 38,500. **Circ:** (Not Reported)

43613 ■ Cesko-Slovenska Patologie/Soudni Lekarstvi
Czech Medical Association J.E. Purknye—Publishing Div.
Sokolska 31
CZ-120 26 Prague 2, Czech Republic
Ph: 420 2 24266223
Fax: 420 2 24266212
Publisher E-mail: czma@cls.cz
Journal covering fields of forensic medicine and pathology. **Freq:** 4/yr. **Trim Size:** A4. **Key Personnel:** Prof. Ivo Steiner, Editor-in-Chief. **ISSN:** 1210-7875. **Subscription Rates:** Kcs 524 individuals; EUR19.20 individuals. **Remarks:** Accepts advertising. **URL:** http://www.prolekare.cz/cesko-slovenska-patologie. **Ad Rates:** BW: Kcs 14,000, 4C: Kcs 21,000. **Circ:** (Not Reported)

43614 ■ Ceskoslovenska Pediatrie
Czech Medical Association J.E. Purknye—Publishing Div.
Sokolska 31
CZ-120 26 Prague 2, Czech Republic
Ph: 420 2 24266223
Fax: 420 2 24266212
Publisher E-mail: czma@cls.cz
Professional medical magazine covering pediatrics. **Subtitle:** Journal of Diseases & Health Care in Childhood. **Founded:** 1945. **Freq:** Monthly. **Trim Size:** A4. **Cols./Page:** 2. **Key Personnel:** R. Kocvara, Author. **ISSN:** 0069-2328. **Remarks:** Accepts advertising. **URL:** http://www.prolekare.cz/cesko-slovenska-pediatrie?utm_source=clsjep&utm_medium=clsjep-journal&utm_campaign=clsjep. **Ad Rates:** BW: Kcs 25,000, 4C: Kcs 40,000. **Circ:** 2,500

43615 ■ Czech Business Weekly
Stanford, a.s.
Provaznicka 13
CZ-110 00 Prague, Czech Republic
Ph: 42 2 34071370
Fax: 42 2 34071877
Publication E-mail: cbw@cbw.cz
Publisher E-mail: cbw@cbw.cz
Magazine featuring business and trade in Czech Republic. **Freq:** Weekly. **Key Personnel:** Jan Chudoba, Publisher, chudoba@cbw.cz; Jana Hartvichova, Production Mgr., hartvichova@cbw.cz; Raymond Johnston, Editor-in-Chief, johnston@cbw.cz. **ISSN:** 1214-8415. **Subscription Rates:** Kcs 2300 individuals; Kcs 4300 two years; EUR160 individuals; EUR290 two years; US$290 individuals; US$550 two years. **Remarks:** Accepts advertising. **URL:** http://www.cbw.cz/. **Circ:** (Not Reported)

43616 ■ Czech Gynaecology
Czech Medical Association J.E. Purknye—Publishing Div.
Sokolska 31
CZ-120 26 Prague 2, Czech Republic
Ph: 420 2 24266223
Fax: 420 2 24266212
Publisher E-mail: czma@cls.cz
Journal covering development in gynecology in the Czech Republic and abroad. **Freq:** 6/yr. **Trim Size:** A4. **Key Personnel:** Radovan Saw, PhD, Editor-in-Chief. **ISSN:** 1210-7832. **Subscription Rates:** Kcs 660 individuals; EUR39.60 individuals. **Remarks:** Accepts advertising. **URL:** http://www.prolekare.cz/ceska-gynekologie?utm_source=clsjep&utm_medium=clsjep-journal&utm_campaign=clsjep. **Ad Rates:** BW: Kcs 30,500, 4C: Kcs 41,500. **Circ:** (Not Reported)

43617 ■ Czech Radiology
Czech Medical Association J.E. Purknye—Publishing Div.
Sokolska 31
CZ-120 26 Prague 2, Czech Republic
Ph: 420 2 24266223
Fax: 420 2 24266212
Publisher E-mail: czma@cls.cz
Journal covering diagnostic imaging, radiotherapy, nuclear medicine, and radiology. **Freq:** 6/yr. **Trim Size:** A4. **Key Personnel:** Jiri Ferda, Editor-in-Chief. **ISSN:** 1210-7883. **Subscription Rates:** Kcs 140 single issue; Kcs 560 individuals. **Remarks:** Accepts advertising. **URL:** http://www.cesradiol.cz/instruction.php. **Ad Rates:** BW: Kcs 25,000, 4C: Kcs 34,000. **Circ:** (Not Reported)

43618 ■ Czech and Slovak Neurology and Neurosurgery
Czech Medical Association J.E. Purknye—Publishing Div.
Sokolska 31
CZ-120 26 Prague 2, Czech Republic
Ph: 420 2 24266223
Fax: 420 2 24266212
Publisher E-mail: czma@cls.cz
Journal covering disciplines of neurology and neurosurgery in Czech and Slovak Republic. **Freq:** 6/yr. **Trim Size:** A4. **Key Personnel:** J. Bednarik, Editor-in-Chief. **ISSN:** 1210-7859. **Subscription Rates:** US$131 individuals; EUR96 individuals. **Remarks:** Accepts advertising. **URL:** http://www.clsjep.cz/en/nts/casop/neurologie/neurologie.asp; http://journals.indexcopernicus.com/karta.php?action=masterlist&id=366. **Ad Rates:** BW: Kcs 28,000, 4C: Kcs 39,000. **Circ:** (Not Reported)

43619 ■ Czech and Slovak Ophthalmology
Czech Medical Association J.E. Purknye—Publishing Div.
Sokolska 31
CZ-120 26 Prague 2, Czech Republic
Ph: 420 2 24266223
Fax: 420 2 24266212
Publisher E-mail: czma@cls.cz
Journal covering diagnostic methods in the field of eye diseases and their conservative and surgical treatment. **Freq:** 6/yr. **Trim Size:** B5. **Key Personnel:** Prof. Eva Wolf, PhD, Contact. **ISSN:** 1211-9059. **Subscription Rates:** Kcs 426 individuals; EUR33 individuals. **Remarks:** Accepts advertising. **URL:** http://www.prolekare.cz/ceska-slovenska-oftalmologie?utm_source=clsjep&utm_medium=clsjep-journal&utm_campaign=clsjep. **Ad Rates:** BW: Kcs 18,000, 4C: Kcs 27,000. **Circ:** (Not Reported)

43620 ■ Czech and Slovak Pharmacy
Czech Medical Association J.E. Purknye—Publishing Div.
Sokolska 31
CZ-120 26 Prague 2, Czech Republic
Ph: 420 2 24266223
Fax: 420 2 24266212
Publisher E-mail: czma@cls.cz
Journal covering field of pharmacy and allied disciplines. **Freq:** 6/yr. **Trim Size:** A4. **Key Personnel:** P. Komarek, PhD, Editor-in-Chief; Prof. Joseph Cizmarik, PhD, President. **ISSN:** 1210-7816. **Subscription Rates:** Kcs 900 individuals; EUR39.60 individuals. **Remarks:** Accepts advertising. **URL:** http://www.prolekare.cz/ceska-slovenska-farmacie?utm_source=clsjep&utm_medium=clsjep-journal&utm_campaign=clsjep. **Ad Rates:** BW: Kcs 22,000, 4C: Kcs 29,000. **Circ:** (Not Reported)

43621 ■ Czech and Slovak Psychiatry
Czech Medical Association J.E. Purknye—Publishing Div.
Sokolska 31
CZ-120 26 Prague 2, Czech Republic
Ph: 420 2 24266223
Fax: 420 2 24266212
Publisher E-mail: czma@cls.cz
Journal covering area of general and special psychiatry concerned with problems of theoretical and special psychiatry. **Freq:** 8/yr. **Trim Size:** A4. **Key Personnel:** Dr. M. Anders, Editor-in-Chief. **ISSN:** 0069-2336. **Subscription Rates:** Kcs 520 individuals. **Remarks:** Accepts advertising. **URL:** http://www.prolekare.cz/ceska-slovenska-psychiatrie?utm_source=clsjep&utm_medium=clsjep-journal&utm_campaign=clsjep. **Ad Rates:** BW: Kcs 31,000, 4C: Kcs 43,000. **Circ:** (Not Reported)

43622 ■ Czecho-Slovak Dermatology
Czech Medical Association J.E. Purknye—Publishing Div.
Sokolska 31
CZ-120 26 Prague 2, Czech Republic
Ph: 420 2 24266223
Fax: 420 2 24266212
Publisher E-mail: czma@cls.cz
Journal covering urgent dermatovenereological problems and problems of bordering disciplines. **Freq:** 6/yr. **Trim Size:** A4. **Key Personnel:** Prof. George Stork, Editor-in-Chief. **ISSN:** 0009-0514. **Subscription Rates:** Kcs 1,170 individuals; EUR42 individuals. **Remarks:** Accepts advertising. **URL:** http://www.prolekare.cz/cesko-slovenska-dermatologie?utm_source=clsjep&utm_medium=clsjep-journal&utm_campaign=clsjep. **Ad Rates:** BW: Kcs 32,000, 4C: Kcs 43,500. **Circ:** (Not Reported)

43623 ■ Divadelni Noviny
Theatre Institute
Celetna 17
CZ-110 00 Prague, Czech Republic
Ph: 42 224 809111
Fax: 42 224 809226
Publisher E-mail: info@idu.cz
Newspaper containing actual information on the Czech theatre culture, productions, personalities. **Freq:** Biweekly. **Key Personnel:** Jan Kolar, Editor-in-Chief, jan.kolar@divadlo.cz. **URL:** http://www.divadlo.cz/noviny/.

43624 ■ Epidemiology, Microbiology, Immunology
Czech Medical Association J.E. Purknye—Publishing Div.
Sokolska 31
CZ-120 26 Prague 2, Czech Republic
Ph: 420 2 24266223
Fax: 420 2 24266212
Publisher E-mail: czma@cls.cz
Journal covering epidemiological and microbiological subjects. **Freq:** 4/yr. **Trim Size:** A4. **Key Personnel:** Dr. P. Cross, Editor. **ISSN:** 1210-7913. **Subscription Rates:** Kcs 500 individuals; EUR23.60 individuals. **Remarks:** Accepts advertising. **URL:** http://www.prolekare.cz/epidemiologie?utm_source=clsjep&utm_medium=clsjepjournal&utm_campaign=clsjep. **Ad Rates:** BW: Kcs 20,000, 4C: Kcs 28,000. **Circ:** (Not Reported)

43625 ■ Internal Medicine
Czech Medical Association J.E. Purknye—Publishing Div.
Sokolska 31
CZ-120 26 Prague 2, Czech Republic
Ph: 420 2 24266223
Fax: 420 2 24266212
Publisher E-mail: czma@cls.cz
Journal covering field of internal medicine. **Freq:** 12/yr. **Trim Size:** A4. **Key Personnel:** MD. Peter Snack, Editor-in-Chief, petr.svacina@fnusa.cz. **ISSN:** 0042-773X. **Subscription Rates:** EUR55 individuals; Kcs 1,308 individuals; Kcs 109 members aged over 35 years; Kcs 1,000 members aged under 35 years. **Remarks:** Accepts advertising. **URL:** http://www.clsjep.cz/en/nts/casop/lekarstvi/lekarstvi.asp; http://www.vnitrnilekarstvi.cz/. **Circ:** (Not Reported)

43626 ■ International Journal of Speleology
International Union of Speleology
Union Internationale de Speleologie
Kalisnicka 4-6
130 00 Prague 3, Czech Republic
Ph: 42 022 0922392
Fax: 42 022 0922670
Publisher E-mail: bosak@gli.cas.cz
Worldwide journal covering speleology. **Founded:** 1964. **Freq:** Semiannual. **Key Personnel:** Jo De Waele, Editor-in-Chief, phone 39 51 2094543, fax 39 51 2094522, jo.dewaele@unibo.it. **ISSN:** 0392-6672. **Subscription Rates:** EUR22 individuals; EUR32 other countries; EUR64 institutions. **Remarks:** Advertising not accepted. **URL:** http://www.uis-speleo.org/publicat.html; http://www.ijs.speleo.it/. **Circ:** (Not Reported)

43627 ■ Journal of Czech Physicians
Czech Medical Association J.E. Purknye—Publishing Div.
Sokolska 31
CZ-120 26 Prague 2, Czech Republic
Ph: 420 2 24266223
Fax: 420 2 24266212
Publisher E-mail: czma@cls.cz
Journal covering branches of medicine. **Freq:** 12/yr.

Trim Size: A4. **Key Personnel:** Prof. Jiri Horak, Editor. **ISSN:** 0008-7335. **Subscription Rates:** Kcs 1,224 individuals; EUR59.40 individuals. **Remarks:** Accepts advertising. **URL:** http://www.clsjep.cz/en/nts/casop/lekari/lekari.asp. **Ad Rates:** BW: Kcs 24,000, 4C: Kcs 32,000. **Circ:** (Not Reported)

43628 ■ Journal Kybernetika
Czech Society for Cybernetics and Informatics
Pod Vodarenskou vezi 2
CZ-182 07 Prague 8, Czech Republic
Ph: 42 266 053901
Fax: 42 285 885789
Publisher E-mail: cski@utia.cas.cz
Czech language journal covering computer science. **Freq:** Bimonthly. **Key Personnel:** Milan Mares, Editor-in-Chief; Karel Sladky, Managing Editor; Jiri Andel, Editorial Board; Sergej Celikovsky, Editorial Board. **ISSN:** 0023-5954. **URL:** http://www.cski.cz/; http://kybernetika.utia.cas.cz/.

43629 ■ Mezinarodni Politika International Politics
Institute of International Relations - Czech Republic
Ustav Mezinarodnich Vztahu
Nerudova 3
CZ-118 50 Prague 1, Czech Republic
Ph: 42 251 108111
Fax: 42 251 108222
Publisher E-mail: info@iir.cz
Czech language publication covering worldwide politics. **Founded:** 1956. **Freq:** Monthly. **Print Method:** Typography. **Trim Size:** 20 x 27 cm. **Key Personnel:** Zdenek Zboril, Contact, zboril@iir.cz; Milena Strejckova, Exec. Ed., strejckova@iir.cz; Robert Schuster, Editor-in-Chief, schuster@iir.cz. **ISSN:** 0543-7962. **Subscription Rates:** Kcs 590 individuals; Kcs 59 single issue. **Remarks:** Advertising accepted; rates available upon request. **URL:** http://www.iir.cz/display.asp?ida=85; http://www.iir.cz. **Circ:** 3,500

43630 ■ Mezinarodni Vztahy International Relations
Institute of International Relations - Czech Republic
Ustav Mezinarodnich Vztahu
Nerudova 3
CZ-118 50 Prague 1, Czech Republic
Ph: 42 251 108111
Fax: 42 251 108222
Publisher E-mail: info@iir.cz
Czech language publication covering worldwide relations. **Founded:** 1958. **Freq:** Quarterly. **Print Method:** Typography. **Trim Size:** 17 x 24 1/2 cm. **Key Personnel:** Marie Vimerova, Exec. Ed.; Vit Benes, Editor-in-Chief. **ISSN:** 0543-7962. **Subscription Rates:** Kcs 285 individuals. **Remarks:** Accepts advertising. **URL:** http://www.iir.cz/display.asp?ida=86&idi=31. **Circ:** 7,500

43631 ■ Motorcykl (Czech)
Motor-Presse Bohemia
At Sta. 36 of Krk
140 00 Prague 4, Czech Republic
Ph: 420 2 41093410
Fax: 420 2 41721905
Consumer magazine covering motorcycle technology, history, sports, and news. **Founded:** Jan. 1991. **Freq:** Monthly. **Print Method:** Offset. **Trim Size:** 215 x 280 mm. **Cols./Page:** 4. **Col. Width:** 43 millimeters. **Key Personnel:** Richard Simeri, Editor; Renata Ben, Classifieds. **Subscription Rates:** Kcs 13.13 individuals; Kcs 74 single issue. **Remarks:** Accepts advertising. **URL:** http://www.motorpresse.cz/motocykl.asp. **Circ:** 17,000

43632 ■ Otorhinolaryngology and Phoniatrics
Czech Medical Association J.E. Purknye—Publishing Div.
Sokolska 31
CZ-120 26 Prague 2, Czech Republic
Ph: 420 2 24266223
Fax: 420 2 24266212
Publisher E-mail: czma@cls.cz
Journal covering surgical treatment of tumours of ENT organs. **Freq:** 4/yr. **Key Personnel:** H. Rauserova, Managing Editor; J. Astl, PhD, Editor-in-Chief. **ISSN:** 1210-7867. **Subscription Rates:** US$440 individuals; EUR27.20 individuals. **Remarks:** Accepts advertising. **URL:** http://www.prolekare.cz/otorinolaryngologie-foniatrie?utm_source=clsjep&utm_medium=clsjep-journal&utm_campaign=clsjep. **Ad Rates:** BW: Kcs 22,000, 4C: Kcs 29,000. **Circ:** (Not Reported)

43633 ■ Pasos
PASOS
Tesnov 3
CZ-110 00 Prague, Czech Republic
Ph: 420 222 313644
Fax: 420 222 313644
Publication E-mail: info@pasosonline.org
Publisher E-mail: info@pasos.org
Journal publishing articles on academic and management-based analysis of the diverse processes inscribed within the tourist system. Stresses on the uses of culture, the environment and territory, people, communities and spaces, and integral heritage. **Subtitle:** Journal of Tourism and Cultural Heritage. **Key Personnel:** Agustin Santana-Talavera, Director, asantana@ull.es. **ISSN:** 1695-7121. **URL:** http://www.pasosonline.org/.

43634 ■ Perspectives - The Central European Review of International Affairs
Institute of International Relations - Czech Republic
Ustav Mezinarodnich Vztahu
Nerudova 3
CZ-118 50 Prague 1, Czech Republic
Ph: 42 251 108111
Fax: 42 251 108222
Publisher E-mail: info@iir.cz
Publication covering Central European affairs. **Founded:** 1993. **Freq:** Semiannual. **Print Method:** Typography. **Trim Size:** 17 x 24 1/2 cm. **Key Personnel:** Mats Braun, Assoc. Ed., braun@iir.cz; Petr Kratochvil, Co-Ed., kratochvil@iir.cz; Vit Stritecky, Book Review Ed., stritecky@iir.cz. **ISSN:** 1210-762X. **Subscription Rates:** US$50 individuals; US$30 single issue. **Remarks:** Accepts advertising. **URL:** http://www.iir.cz/display.asp?lng=uk&ida=87&idi=32; http://www.iir.cz. **Circ:** (Not Reported)

43635 ■ Prague Daily Monitor
Monitor CE Media Services
Laubova 6
CZ-130 00 Prague 3, Czech Republic
Ph: 42 222 365216
Fax: 42 222 365271
Publisher E-mail: info@praguemonitor.com
Newspaper featuring news and events in Czec Republic. **Founded:** 2003. **Key Personnel:** Todd Benson, Contact, sales@atpraguemonitor.com. **Remarks:** Accepts advertising. **URL:** http://www.praguemonitor.com/. **Circ:** (Not Reported)

43636 ■ The Prague Post
The Prague Post S.R.O.
Stepanska 20
CZ-110 00 Prague 1, Czech Republic
Ph: 420 2 96334400
Fax: 420 2 96334450
Publisher E-mail: info@praguepost.com
English language general newspaper. **Founded:** Oct. 1991. **Freq:** Weekly. **Key Personnel:** Benjamin Cunningham, Editor-in-Chief, bcunningham@praguepost.com; Lukas Zila, Advertising Dir., lzita@praguepost.com; Bibiana Duharova, General Mgr., bduharova@praguepost.com; Benjamin Cunningham, Managing Editor, bcunningham@praguepost.com; Monroe Luther, Publisher, eagletexas@aol.com. **Subscription Rates:** Kcs 1,040 individuals 26 weeks; EUR50 individuals Europe (26 weeks); US$95 other countries 26 weeks; Kcs 1,800 individuals 52 weeks; EUR100 individuals Europe (52 weeks); US$185 other countries 52 weeks; Kcs 3,400 individuals 104 weeks; EUR190 individuals Europe (104 weeks); US$360 other countries 104 weeks. **Remarks:** Accepts advertising. **URL:** http://www.praguepost.com/. **Ad Rates:** BW: Kcs 94,900. **Circ:** Combined 50,134

43637 ■ Revizni a Posudkove Lekarstvi
Czech Medical Association J.E. Purknye—Publishing Div.
Sokolska 31
CZ-120 26 Prague 2, Czech Republic
Ph: 420 2 24266223
Fax: 420 2 24266212
Publisher E-mail: czma@cls.cz
Journal focusing on health and sickness insurance, financing and economics of the health care, methods of medical control activities, medical audit in relation to other medical disciplines, analytical and statistical analyses, problems of infosystems of health insurance companies, international comparisons, and search for optimal shape of the Czech system. **Freq:** 4/yr. **Trim Size:** A4. **Key Personnel:** MD. Jan Bohac, Editor-in-Chief. **ISSN:** 1214-3170. **Subscription Rates:** Kcs 500 individuals; EUR16.40 individuals. **Remarks:** Accepts advertising. **URL:** http://www.prolekare.cz/revizni-posudkove-lekarstvi?utm_source=clsjep&utm_medium=clsjep-journal&utm_campaign=clsjep. **Ad Rates:** BW: Kcs 22,000, 4C: Kcs 29,000. **Circ:** (Not Reported)

43638 ■ Roska
Czech Multiple Sclerosis Society
PO Box 38
CZ-120 00 Prague, Czech Republic
Ph: 42 241 728619
Fax: 42 266 712511
Magazine containing specialized information on all fields of Multiple Sclerosis. **Freq:** Quarterly. **ISSN:** 1211-4030. **Remarks:** Accepts advertising. **URL:** http://www.roska.eu/vydavatelska-cinnost/index.php. **Circ:** (Not Reported)

43639 ■ Transitions Online (TOL)
Transitions Online
Baranova 33
CZ-130 00 Prague 3, Czech Republic
Ph: 42 222 780805
Fax: 42 222 780804
Publisher E-mail: transitions@tol.org
Online publication covering politics and news in Central and Eastern Europe and the former Soviet Union. **Founded:** 1999. **Freq:** Mon.-Sat. (morn.). **Key Personnel:** Jeremy Druker, Editor-in-Chief; Tihomir Loza, Dep. Dir., tihomir.loza@virgin.net; barbara Frye, Managing Editor. **Subscription Rates:** US$48 individuals; US$29 students; US$228 libraries. **Remarks:** Accepts advertising. **URL:** http://www.tol.cz/look/TOL/home.tpl?IdLanguage=1&IdPublication=4&NrIssue=309. **Circ:** 200,000

Praha Smichov

43640 ■ Express Radio-FM - 90.3
Andel Media Centrum
Karla Englise 519/11
CS-150 00 Praha Smichov, Czech Republic
Ph: 42 2 25555903
E-mail: kacka@expresradio.cz
Format: Music of Your Life. **Operating Hours:** Continuous. **Ad Rates:** Advertising accepted; rates available upon request. **URL:** http://www.expresradio.idnes.cz.

Videnska

43641 ■ Immunology Letters
Elsevier Science Inc.
c/o V. Horejsi, Ed.-in-Ch.
Institute of Molecular Genetics
Academy of Sciences of the Czech Republic
1083 Videnska, Czech Republic
Publisher E-mail: usinfo-ehelp@elsevier.com
Journal addressing aspects of molecular and cellular immunology. **Founded:** 1979. **Freq:** 14/yr. **Print Method:** off site. **Cols./Page:** 6. **Col. Width:** 12 picas. **Col. Depth:** 21.5 inches. **Key Personnel:** L. Moretta, Exec. Board, lorenzomoretta@ospedale-gaslini.ge.it; P. Garside, Editorial Board, paul.garside@strath.ac.uk; L. Adorini, Editorial Board, luciano.adorini@bioxell.com; T. Hunig, Editorial Board, huenig@vim.uni-wuerzburg.de; A. Erdei, Editorial Board, anna.erdei@freemail.hu; H. Stockinger, Exec. Board, hannes.stockinger@univie.ac.at; A.N. Akbar, Editorial Board, a.akbar@medsch.ucl.ac.uk; P. Fisch, Editorial Board, fisch@mm11.ukl.uni-freiburg.de; N. Minato, Exec. Board, minato@imm.med.kyoto-u.ac.jp; V. Horejsi, Exec. Board, horejsi@biomed.cas.cz. **ISSN:** 0165-2478. **Subscription Rates:** EUR3,783 institutions for European countries and Iran; US$4,234 institutions, other countries except Europe, Japan and Iran; 502,300¥ institutions. **URL:** http://www.elsevier.com/wps/find/journaldescription.cws_home/506020/descriptiondescription.

Zlin

43642 ■ Folia Heyrovskyana
Vit Kabourek
Sokolska 3923
CZ-760 01 Zlin, Czech Republic
Ph: 420 577 437870

Circulation: ★ = ABC; △ = BPA; ♦ = CAC; • = CCAB; ❑ = VAC; ⊕ = PO Statement; ‡ = Publisher's Report; Boldface figures = sworn; Light figures = estimated.

Gale Directory of Publications & Broadcast Media/147th Ed.   4865

Fax: 420 577 437870
Publisher E-mail: vit@kabourek.cz
Journal covering systematic entomology worldwide.

Founded: Oct. 1992. **Print Method:** Offset. **Trim Size:** 17 X 24 cm. **Key Personnel:** Svatopluk Bily, Contact, svatopluk_bily@nm.cz. **ISSN:** 1210-4108. **Subscription**

Rates: EUR50 single issue; Kcs 500 single issue. **Remarks:** Advertising not accepted. **URL:** http://www.kabourek.cz. **Circ:** (Not Reported)

Alborg

43643 ■ Acta Psychiatrica Scandinavica
John Wiley & Sons Inc.
Wiley-Blackwell
c/o Povl Munk-Jorgensen, Ed.-in-Ch.
Unit for Psychiatric Research
Aalborg Psychiatric Hospital, Aarhus University Hospital
PO Box 210
DK-9100 Alborg, Denmark
Ph: 45 72 137220
Fax: 45 72 137235
Peer-reviewed journal focusing on clinical and experimental work in psychiatry. **Freq:** Monthly. **Key Personnel:** Povl Munk-Jorgensen, Editor-in-Chief, actapsych@rn.dk; Birgitte Christiansen, Editorial Sec.; B.N. Gangadhar, Assoc. Ed. **ISSN:** 0001-690X. **Subscription Rates:** US$1,338 institutions print and online; US$1,216 institutions print; 797 institutions print + online; EUR1,012 institutions print + online; EUR920 institutions print; 723 institutions online; US$1,560 institutions, other countries print + online; US$1,418 institutions, other countries print. **Remarks:** Accepts advertising. **URL:** http://www.wiley.com/bw/journal.asp?ref=0001-690X&site=1. **Circ:** (Not Reported)

43644 ■ Tjeck Magazine
Vesterbro 42
1. Sal th.
DK-9000 Alborg, Denmark
Ph: 45 331 84200
Publication E-mail: abonnement@tjeck.dk
Publisher E-mail: tjeck@tjeck.dk
Consumer magazine for young people aged 15-24 years. **Founded:** Sept. 1992. **Freq:** Monthly. **Print Method:** Heatset. **Cols./Page:** 3. **Col. Width:** 225 millimeters. **Col. Depth:** 298 millimeters. **Key Personnel:** Thomas Moller, Editor. **ISSN:** 1601-0043. **Subscription Rates:** 229 DKr individuals; 360 DKr; 199 DKr individuals other; 199 DKr individuals other student. **Remarks:** Accepts advertising. **URL:** http://www.tjeck.dk. **Ad Rates:** 4C: 40,000 DKr. **Circ:** Controlled 160,000

Arhus

43645 ■ Boreas
John Wiley & Sons Inc.
Wiley-Blackwell
c/o Prof. Jan A. Piotrowski, Ed.-in-Ch.
Department of Earth Sciences
University of Aarhus
C.F. Mollers Alle 1120
DK-8000 Arhus, Denmark
Ph: 45 89422555
Fax: 45 86139248
Journal publishing articles of international interest from all branches of quaternary research. **Subtitle:** An International Journal of Quaternary Research. **Founded:** 1972. **Freq:** Quarterly. **Key Personnel:** Prof. Jan A. Piotrowski, Editor-in-Chief, jan.piotrowski@geo.au.dk; Karen Luise Knudsen, Asst. Ed., karenluise.knudsen@geo.au.dk. **ISSN:** 0300-9483. **Subscription Rates:** US$387 institutions online only; US$425 institutions print + online; US$387 institutions print only; US$178 individuals print + online; US$125 institutions QRA

Society. **URL:** http://www.wiley.com/bw/journal.asp?ref=0300-9483.

43646 ■ Growth Hormone & IGF Research
Mosby Inc.
c/o J.S. Christiansen, Ed.
Dept. of Endocrinology M.
Aarhus University Hospital
DK-8000 Arhus, Denmark
Publisher E-mail: custserv.ehs@elsevier.com
Journal serving as a forum for research on the regulation of growth in humans, animals, tissues and cells. **Freq:** Bimonthly. **Key Personnel:** J.S. Christiansen, Editor; D. Clemmons, Editorial Board; J.O. Jorgensen, Assoc. Ed.; J. Frystyk, Assoc. Ed.; J. Holly, Assoc. Ed.; L. Bach, Editorial Board; C. Hoybye, Assoc. Ed.; Dr. D. Le Roith, Editor; P. Rotwein, Assoc. Ed. **ISSN:** 1096-6374. **Subscription Rates:** EUR283 individuals for European countries and Iran; EUR668 institutions for European countries and Iran; 30,400¥ individuals; 72,000¥ institutions; US$252 other countries except Europe, Japan and Iran; US$593 institutions, other countries except Europe, Japan and Iran. **URL:** http://www.elsevier.com/wps/find/journaldescription.cws_home/623041/descriptiondescription.

43647 ■ Journal of Oral Rehabilitation
John Wiley & Sons Inc.
Wiley-Blackwell
Royal Dental College
Faculty of Health Sciences
University of Aarhus
DK-8000 Arhus, Denmark
Ph: 45 894 24212
Fax: 45 894 24297
Peer-reviewed journal on dental research, covering all aspects of oral rehabilitation and applied oral physiology. **Freq:** Monthly. **Key Personnel:** J.A. De Boever, Editorial Board; Peter Svensson, Editor; J. Bader, Editorial Board; G.E. Carlsson, Editorial Board; G. Murray, Editorial Board; T. Kato, Editorial Board. **ISSN:** 0305-182X. **Subscription Rates:** US$385 individuals print and online; EUR228 individuals print and online; 311 individuals print and online (non-Euro zone); US$3,092 institutions print and online; 1,725 institutions print and online; EUR2,190 institutions print and online; US$3,716 institutions, other countries print and online; US$2,811 institutions print or online; 1,568 institutions print or online; US$3,378 institutions, other countries print or online. **Remarks:** Advertising accepted; rates available upon request. **URL:** http://www.wiley.com/bw/journal.asp?ref=0305-182x. **Circ:** (Not Reported)

43648 ■ Nordic Irish Studies
Centre for Irish Studies in Aarhus
University of Arhus
Centre for Irish Studies
Bldg. 467, Jens Chr. Skous Vej 7
DK-8000 Arhus, Denmark
Publisher E-mail: cisa@hum.au.dk
Magazine reflecting the research activities of CISA, DU-CIS and NISN and publishing articles on Irish history, politics, society, culture and literature. **Freq:** Annual. **Key Personnel:** Michael Boss, Editor, engmb@hum.au.dk; Irene Gilsenan Nordin, Editor, ign@du.se. **ISSN:** 1602-124X. **Subscription Rates:** EUR30 individuals three-year; EUR12 single issue delivery included; Free MBS. **Remarks:** Accepts advertising. **URL:** http://www.

hum.au.dk/engelsk/cisa/en/publications.html. **Circ:** (Not Reported)

43649 ■ NUMEN
International Association for the History of Religions
Association Internationale pour l'Histoire des Religions
Department of the Study of Religion
University of Aarhus
Main Bldg.
DK-8000 Arhus, Denmark
Publication covering history. **Freq:** Semiannual. **Key Personnel:** Prof. Einar Thomassen, Editor; Prof. Gustavo Benavides, Editor. **ISSN:** 0029-5973. **URL:** http://www.iahr.dk/numen.html; http://www.ingentaconnect.com/content/brill/num.

43650 ■ Radiotherapy and Oncology
Elsevier
Dept. of Experimental & Clinical Oncology
Aarhus University Hospital
DK-8000 Arhus, Denmark
Journal publishing articles of interest relating to radiation oncology. **Freq:** Monthly. **Key Personnel:** Prof. Jens Overgaard, MD, Editor-in-Chief; P. Scalliet, Editor; D. Thwaites, Editor. **ISSN:** 0167-8140. **Subscription Rates:** US$370 individuals; US$370 institutions, Canada and Mexico; EUR2,796 institutions European countries and Iran; 371,100¥ institutions; US$3,126 institutions all countries except Europe, Japan and Iran; EUR354 individuals for European countries and Iran; 46,800¥ individuals; US$394 individuals all countries except Europe, Japan and Iran. **Remarks:** Accepts advertising. **URL:** http://www.elsevier.com/wps/find/journaldescription.cws_home/506042/bibliographic; http://www.thegreenjournal.com. **Circ:** (Not Reported)

Brondby

43651 ■ Badminton
Danmarks Badminton Forbund
Idraettens Hus
Brondby Stadion 20
DK-2605 Brondby, Denmark
Ph: 45 432 62152
Fax: 45 432 62150
Publisher E-mail: dbf@badminton.dk
Danish language publication covering badminton. **Freq:** Biweekly. **Key Personnel:** Charlotte T. Malmros, Director, phone 45 432 62178, fax 45 432 62150, chma@badminton.dk. **Remarks:** Advertising accepted; rates available upon request. **URL:** http://www.badminton.dk/. **Circ:** 600

43652 ■ O-Posten
Danish Orienteering Federation
Dansk Orienterings-Forbund
Idraetten hus
Eroentby Statotion 20
DK-2605 Brondby, Denmark
Ph: 45 434 57730
Fax: 45 434 57790
Publisher E-mail: dof@do-f.dk
Danish language publication covering orienteering. **Freq:** Bimonthly. **ISSN:** 0107-4202. **Subscription Rates:** US$27 individuals. **Remarks:** Advertising accepted; rates available upon request. **URL:** http://www.cosc.iup.edu/jlwolfe/ostuff/pubs.html. **Circ:** (Not Reported)

Circulation: ★ = ABC; △ = BPA; ♦ = CAC; • = CCAB; ❑ = VAC; ⊕ = PO Statement; ‡ = Publisher's Report; Boldface figures = sworn; Light figures = estimated.

Gale Directory of Publications & Broadcast Media/147th Ed.

4867

43653 ■ Skyttebladet
Danish Shooting Union
Dansk Skytte Union
Idraettens Hus
Brondby Stadion 20
DK-2605 Brondby, Denmark
Ph: 45 432 62626
Publisher E-mail: info@skytteunion.dk
Danish language publication covering shooting. **Freq:** 8/yr. **ISSN:** 0037-6663. **Remarks:** Advertising accepted; rates available upon request. **URL:** http://www. skytteunion.dk; http://www.skytteunion.dk/db/writeable/ custompages/skyttebladet.asp. **Circ:** (Not Reported)

Copenhagen

43654 ■ Acta Archaeologica
John Wiley & Sons Inc.
Wiley-Blackwell
c/o Klavs Randsborg, Ed.-in-Ch.
Copenhagen University Amager
SAXO-instituttet, Arkaeologi
Njalsgade 80
DK-2300 Copenhagen, Denmark
Ph: 45 35324111
Fax: 45 35324105
Journal focusing on archaeology. **Founded:** 1930. **Freq:** Annual. **Key Personnel:** Klavs Randsborg, Editor-in-Chief; T. Edgren, Editorial Board; C.J. Gardberg, Editorial Board. **ISSN:** 0065-101X. **Subscription Rates:** US$168 institutions print and online (Americas); US$197 institutions, other countries print and online; US$152 institutions online (Americas); US$179 institutions, other countries print or online; EUR128 institutions print and online; 102 institutions print and online. **Remarks:** Accepts advertising. **URL:** http://www.wiley.com/bw/journal. asp?ref=0065-101X&site=1. **Circ:** (Not Reported)

43655 ■ APMIS
John Wiley & Sons Inc.
Wiley-Blackwell
Lokale 127/1
Blegdamsvej 28C
DK-2200 Copenhagen, Denmark
Ph: 45 339 36566
Fax: 45 339 38566
Publication E-mail: apmis@post2.tele.dk
Journal focusing on research in the fields of pathology, microbiology and immunology, and from related developing areas of modern biomedicine. Formerly known as Acta Pathologica, Microbiologica et Immunologica Scandinavica. **Founded:** 1924. **Freq:** Monthly. **Key Personnel:** E. Ralfkiaer, Editor-in-Chief; B. Norrild, Editor-in-Chief; Christine Moller, Asst. Ed.; L.A. Akslen, Scandinavian Board of Ed.; J. Rygaard, Editorial Consultant. **ISSN:** 0903-4641. **Subscription Rates:** EUR435 members print and online; 720 institutions print and online; 656 institutions print or online; EUR916 institutions print and online; US$487 members print and online; US$1,210 institutions print and online; US$1,100 institutions print or online; US$1,415 institutions, other countries print and online; US$1,285 institutions, other countries print or online; 290 members print and online (U.K. and non Euro zone). **Remarks:** Accepts advertising. **URL:** http://www.wiley.com/bw/journal.asp? ref=0903-4641&site=1. **Circ:** (Not Reported)

43656 ■ Bibliotek for Laeger
Danish Medical Association
Trondhjemsgade 9
DK-2100 Copenhagen, Denmark
Ph: 45 354 48500
Fax: 45 354 48503
Publisher E-mail: dadl@dadl.dk
Journal of the Danish Medial Society. **Freq:** Quarterly. **Key Personnel:** Christian Graugaard, Editor; Merete Osler, Editor; Per E. Jorgensen, Editor. **URL:** http://www. laeger.dk/portal/page/portal/LAEGERDK/LAEGER_DK/ LAEGEFAGLIGT/Bibliotek%20for%20L%C3%A6ger.

43657 ■ Boersen
A/S Forlaget Boersen
Montergade 19
1140 Copenhagen, Denmark
Ph: 99945 33320102
Fax: 99945 33122445
Publisher E-mail: redaktionen@borsen.dk
Business publication. **Freq:** Daily. **Key Personnel:** Leif Beck Fallesen, Editor-in-Chief; Bent Sorensen, Ch. Sub Ed. **Subscription Rates:** 3,195 DKr individuals private adress; EUR3,545 Individuals companies. **Remarks:** Ac-

cepts advertising. **URL:** http://borsen.dk/. **Circ:** (Not Reported)

43658 ■ Byggeforum
Danish National Association for Building
Byggesocietetet
Vimmelskaftet 47/1
DK-1161 Copenhagen, Denmark
Ph: 45 331 36637
Fax: 45 339 37890
Publisher E-mail: info@byggesoc.dk
Publication covering building industries. **Freq:** Bimonthly. **URL:** http://www.byggesocietetet.dk/; http://www. byggesocietetet.dk/byggeforum.html. **Circ:** 3,500

43659 ■ The Clinical Respiratory Journal
John Wiley & Sons Inc.
Wiley-Blackwell
Respiratory & Allergy Research Unit
Dept. of Respiratory Medicine L
Bispebjerg University Hospital
DK-2400 Copenhagen, Denmark
Ph: 45 35313569
Fax: 45 35312179
Publication E-mail: mb07@bbh.regionh.dk
Peer-reviewed journal featuring clinical research in all areas of respiratory medicine. **Freq:** Quarterly. **Key Personnel:** Vibeke Backer, Editor-in-Chief. **ISSN:** 1752-6981. **Subscription Rates:** 197 institutions UK (print and online); US$363 institutions Americas (print and online); EUR250 institutions Europe (print and online); US$385 institutions, other countries print and online; 179 institutions UK (online only); US$330 institutions Americas (online only); EUR227 institutions Europe (online only); US$330 institutions, other countries online only. **Remarks:** Accepts advertising. **URL:** http://www. wiley.com/bw/journal.asp?ref=1752-6981. **Circ:** (Not Reported)

43660 ■ Danish Medical Bulletin
Danish Medical Association
Kristianiaga 12
DK-2100 Copenhagen, Denmark
Publication E-mail: danmedbul@dadl.dk
Publisher E-mail: dadl@dadl.dk
Journal dealing with medical history, ethics, philosophy and clinical theory, in connection with Danish Medical Society. **Founded:** 1809. **Key Personnel:** Jacob Rosenberg, Editor, jacob.rosenberg@dadlnet.dk. **URL:** http:// www.danmedbul.dk/contact.html.

43661 ■ Danmarksposten
Dansk Samvirke
Kobmagergade 67, 2 sal.
DK-1150 Copenhagen K, Denmark
Ph: 45 33320913
Fax: 45 33325352
Publication E-mail: danes-worldwide@danes.dk
Publisher E-mail: danes-worldwide@danes.dk
Membership magazine for Danes living abroad. **Founded:** 1920. **Freq:** Monthly 10/yr. **Cols./Page:** 4. **Col. Width:** 45 millimeters. **ISSN:** 0011-6157. **Remarks:** Accepts advertising. **URL:** http://www.danes.dk/page. dsp?page=313. **Ad Rates:** BW: 12 DKr, 4C: 15 DKr. **Circ:** Paid 6,500

43662 ■ DANSK
Hoejbro Plads 15
DK-1200 Copenhagen K, Denmark
Ph: 45 33130444
Fax: 45 33130844
Publisher E-mail: info@danskmagazine.com
Magazine covering fashion and lifestyle trends. **Founded:** 2002. **Freq:** Quarterly. **Key Personnel:** Anders Christian Madsen, Editor. **Remarks:** Accepts advertising. **URL:** http://danskmagazine.com/. **Circ:** (Not Reported)

43663 ■ Dansk Landbrug
Vesterbrogade 4A, 4
Postboks 119
DK-1620 Copenhagen, Denmark
Ph: 45 333 94600
Fax: 45 333 94606
Publisher E-mail: dl@dansklandbrug.dk
Consumer magazine covering agriculture in Denmark. **Founded:** 1973. **Freq:** Semimonthly. **Print Method:** Offset. **Cols./Page:** 6. **Col. Width:** 40 millimeters. **Col. Depth:** 365 millimeters. **Remarks:** Accepts advertising. **URL:** http://www.dansklandbrug.dk/Forside.htm. **Circ:** Combined 116,000

43664 ■ De Farver
Federation of Danish Painting Contractors
Danske Malermestre
Postboks 1989
DK-2300 Copenhagen, Denmark
Ph: 45 32 630370
Publisher E-mail: sekretariatet@danskemalermestre.dk
Publication covering building trades. **Freq:** Quarterly. **ISSN:** 0908-9926. **Subscription Rates:** 230 individuals. **Remarks:** Advertising accepted; rates available upon request. **URL:** http://www.danskemalermestre.dk. **Circ:** 12,800

43665 ■ Djembe
Vestergade 5, 1st Fl.
DK-1456 Copenhagen K, Denmark
Ph: 45 33 918009
Publication E-mail: djembe@inform-bbs.dk
Publisher E-mail: djembe@inform-bbs.dk
Professional magazine about inspiration between cultures, covering world music, art and African, Latin American, and Asian culture in Denmark and Scandinavia. **Founded:** July 1, 1992. **Freq:** Quarterly. **Print Method:** Offset. **Trim Size:** A4. **Cols./Page:** 3. **Col. Width:** 56 millimeters. **Col. Depth:** 253 millimeters. **Key Personnel:** Mik Aidt, Editor-in-Chief. **ISSN:** 0907-3841. **Subscription Rates:** 250 DKr individuals; 320 DKr institutions; 375 DKr individuals Nordic, Europe and rest of world; US$60 individuals Nordic, Europe and rest of world; EUR50 individuals Nordic, Europe and rest of world. **Remarks:** Accepts advertising. **URL:** http:// crawfurd.dk/africa/djembe.htm. **Ad Rates:** GLR: EUR.40, BW: EUR330, 4C: EUR460. **Circ:** 1,500

43666 ■ Ecological Modelling
Elsevier Science Inc.
c/o S.E. Jorgensen
Faculty of Pharmaceutical Sciences
University of Copenhagen
Universitetsparken 2
DK-2100 Copenhagen, Denmark
Publisher E-mail: usinfo-ehelp@elsevier.com
Journal covering control of environmental pollution and management of resources. **Founded:** 1975. **Freq:** 24/yr. **Key Personnel:** R. Costanza, Editorial Advisory Board; B.D. Fath, Editor-in-Chief; W.E. Grant, Assoc. Ed.; S.N. Nielsen, Assoc. Ed.; I. Aoki, Editorial Advisory Board; S. Dzeroski, Editorial Advisory Board; T.S. Chon, Editorial Advisory Board; V. Christensen, Editorial Advisory Board; J. Devillers, Editorial Advisory Board. **ISSN:** 0304-3800. **Subscription Rates:** US$1,283 other countries except Europe, Japan and Iran; EUR1,144 individuals European countries and Iran; 151,200¥ individuals Japan; US$5,235 institutions, other countries except Europe, Japan and Iran; 621,200¥ institutions; EUR4,683 institutions European countries & Iran. **URL:** http://www.elsevier.com/wps/find/journaldescription.cws_ home/503306/descrip tiondescription.

43667 ■ ErhvervsBladet
Pilestraede 34
DK-1147 Copenhagen, Denmark
Ph: 45 337 53801
Fax: 45 337 53696
Publisher E-mail: info@erhvervsbladet.dk
Newspaper covering business. **Print Method:** Offset. **Col. Width:** 41 millimeters. **Col. Depth:** 365 millimeters. **Key Personnel:** Henning Andersen, Contact, salg@ erhvervsbladet.dk; Carsten Steno, Contact, cs@ erhvervsbladet.dk. **Remarks:** Accepts advertising. **URL:** http://www.erhvervsbladet.dk; http://www.erhvervsbladet. dk/apps/pbcs.dll/section?category=contact&type=co ntact. **Circ:** Controlled ‡105,542

43668 ■ Folkeskolen
Fagbladet Folkeskolen
Postboks 2139
Vandkunsten 12
DK-1015 Copenhagen K, Denmark
Ph: 45 336 96300
Fax: 45 336 96426
Publication E-mail: folkeskolen@dlf.org
Publisher E-mail: folkeskolen@dlf.org
Weekly magazine for teachers and online news magazine. **Founded:** 1883. **Cols./Page:** 3. **Col. Width:** 57 millimeters. **Col. Depth:** 265 millimeters. **URL:** http:// www.folkeskolen.dk. **Circ:** 84,483

43669 ■ Forfatteren
Danish Writers Association
Strandgade 6, stuen
DK-1401 Copenhagen, Denmark

Ph: 45 329 55100
Publisher E-mail: df@danskforfatterforening.dk
Danish Writer's Union magazine. **Freq:** Bimonthly 6-8/yr. **ISSN:** 0105-0753. **URL:** http://www.danskforfatterforening.dk/.

43670 ■ Forum, Tidsskrift for Kon Og Kultur
KVINFO, Danish Center for Information on Women and Gender
Christians Brygge 3
DK-1219 Copenhagen, Denmark
Ph: 45 33135088
Fax: 45 33141156
Publication E-mail: forum@kvinfo.dk
Publisher E-mail: kvinfo@kvinfo.dk
Danish and English publication covering women. **Freq:** Periodic. **Key Personnel:** Julie Breinegaard, Editor; Anita Frank Goth, Editor. **ISSN:** 1399-4549. **Remarks:** Advertising not accepted. **URL:** http://www.kvinfo.dk/side/557/english/. **Circ:** (Not Reported)

43671 ■ Geologisk Tidsskrift
Geological Society of Denmark
Geological Museum
Oster Voldgade 5-7
DK-1350 Copenhagen, Denmark
Ph: 45 353 22354
Publisher E-mail: dgfemail@gmail.com
Journal of the Geological Society of Denmark. **Subscription Rates:** 45 DKr members single volume; 72 DKr nonmembers single volume; 125 DKr members. **URL:** http://2dgf.dk/publikationer/geologisk_tidsskrift/index.html.

43672 ■ Gymnasieskolen
Danish National Union of Upper Secondary Teachers
Gymnasieskolernes Laererforening
Vesterbrogade 16
DK-1620 Copenhagen, Denmark
Ph: 45 332 90900
Fax: 45 332 90901
Publication E-mail: gymnasieskolen@gl.org
Publisher E-mail: gl@gl.org
Danish language publication covering education. **Freq:** Semimonthly. **Remarks:** Accepts advertising. **URL:** http://www.gymnasieskolen.dk. **Circ:** 15,000

43673 ■ ICES Cooperative Research Reports
International Council for the Exploration of the Sea
Conseil International pour l'Exploration de la Mer
H.C. Andersens Blvd. 44-46
DK-1553 Copenhagen V, Denmark
Ph: 45 333 86700
Fax: 45 339 34215
Publisher E-mail: info@ices.dk
Provides reports on Fishery Management, the Marine Environment, and Ecosystems. **Freq:** Periodic. **Key Personnel:** Emory Anderson, Editor, emoryanderson@comcast.net. **ISSN:** 1017-6195. **Remarks:** Advertising not accepted. **URL:** http://www.ices.dk/indexfla.asp. **Circ:** 500

43674 ■ ICES Journal of Marine Science
International Council for the Exploration of the Sea
Conseil International pour l'Exploration de la Mer
H.C. Andersens Blvd. 44-46
DK-1553 Copenhagen V, Denmark
Ph: 45 333 86700
Fax: 45 339 34215
Publisher E-mail: info@ices.dk
Journal covering marine science. **Freq:** 9/yr. **Key Personnel:** Audrey Geffen, Editor, audrey.geffen@bio.uib.no; Andrew I.L. Payne, Editor-in-Chief, andy.payne@cefas.co.uk; Pierre Pepin, Editor, pepinp@dfo-mpo.gc.ca; John Ramster, Editor, jramster@lineone.net; Verena Trenkel, Editor, verena.trenkel@ifremer.fr. **ISSN:** 1054-3139. **Subscription Rates:** 785 institutions print & online; 634 institutions online only; 719 institutions print only; 181 individuals print. **URL:** http://www.ices.dk/; http://www.oxfordjournals.org/our_journals/icesjms/about.html.

43675 ■ International Game Theory Review
World Scientific Publishing Company Private Ltd.
c/o Steffen Jorgensen, Ed.
Gammel Kongevej 31, 1.tv.
DK-1610 Copenhagen, Denmark
Fax: 45 659 30726

Publisher E-mail: wspc@wspc.com.sg
Periodical offering up-to-date insights and perspectives through original research in game theory and its applications. **Founded:** 1999. **Freq:** Quarterly. **Key Personnel:** David W.K. Yeung, Managing Editor, fax 86 852 34115585, wkyeung@hkbu.edu.hk; Steffen Jorgensen, Editor, stj@sam.sdu.dk; Leon A. Petrosjan, Editor, fax 78 123 505067, spbuoasis7@peterlink.ru. **ISSN:** 0219-1989. **Subscription Rates:** US$465 institutions and libraries; print & electronic; US$34 individuals for postage; US$446 institutions and libraries; electronic only; EUR375 institutions and libraries; print & electronic; EUR360 institutions and libraries; electronic only; EUR26 individuals for postage; S$741 institutions and libraries; print & electronic; S$711 institutions and libraries; electronic only; S$45 individuals print only. **URL:** http://www.worldscinet.com/igtr/igtr.shtml.

43676 ■ Jazz Special
Jazzbladet KS
Havnegade 41
DK-1058 Copenhagen, Denmark
Ph: 45 333 38760
Fax: 45 333 38730
Consumer magazine covering jazz worldwide. **Founded:** 1991. **Freq:** Bimonthly. **Print Method:** Offset. **Trim Size:** 219 x 280 mm. **Key Personnel:** Soren Frilis, Editor, soren@jazzspecial.dk. **ISSN:** 0906-8201. **Remarks:** Accepts advertising. **URL:** http://www.jazzspecial.dk/. **Ad Rates:** 4C: EUR800. **Circ:** Combined 10,000

43677 ■ kapital
Finansradets HUS
Amaliegade 7
DK-1256 Copenhagen, Denmark
Ph: 45 337 01000
Fax: 45 339 30260
Professional magazine for bankers and the banking industry in Denmark. **Founded:** 1990. **Freq:** Monthly. **Print Method:** Offset. **Key Personnel:** Mikael Winkler, Editor. **ISSN:** 0905-9415. **Subscription Rates:** 300 DKr individuals; 35 DKr single issue. **Remarks:** Accepts advertising. **URL:** http://www.finansraadet.dk. **Ad Rates:** BW: 12,700 DKr, 4C: 16,000 DKr. **Circ:** Paid 2,840

43678 ■ Kontakt
Danish Association for International Cooperation - Denmark
Mellemfolkeligt Samvirke
Faelledvej 12
DK-2200 Copenhagen K, Denmark
Ph: 45 773 10000
Fax: 45 773 10101
Publisher E-mail: ms@ms.dk
Danish language publication covering international issues. **Founded:** 1948. **Freq:** Bimonthly. **Remarks:** Accepts advertising. **URL:** http://www.ms.dk. **Ad Rates:** BW: US$1,300, 4C: US$1,300. **Circ:** Paid 5,000

43679 ■ Microbiological Research
Elsevier Science Inc.
Carlsberg Laboratory
Yeast Biology
Gamle Carlsberg Vej 10
Valby
DK-2500 Copenhagen, Denmark
Ph: 45 3327 5230
Fax: 45 3327 4708
Publisher E-mail: usinfo-ehelp@elsevier.com
Journal covering articles from many facets of microbiology antimicrobial drugs - biochemistry - biotechnology - environmental microbiology genetics molecular biology - molecular diagnosis - phylogeny - physiology phytopathology - systematics and taxonomy. **Founded:** 1895. **Freq:** 8/yr. **Key Personnel:** Jurgen Wendland, Editor-in-Chief, juergen.wendland@crc.dk; Antonio Di Pietro, Sen. Ed.; Ben Distel, Sen. Ed. **ISSN:** 0944-5013. **Subscription Rates:** EUR707 institutions European countries and Iran; EUR234 individuals European countries and Iran; US$234 other countries except Europe, Japan and Iran; 30,700¥ individuals; US$780 institutions, other countries except Europe, Japan and Iran; 96,500¥ institutions; EUR707 institutions for European countries and Iran. **URL:** http://www.elsevier.com/wps/find/journaldescription.cws_home/701785/descriptdescription.

43680 ■ Nuclear Instruments and Methods in Physics Research Section B
Elsevier Science
c/o H.H. Andersen, Founding Ed.
The Niels Bohr Institute

Blegdamsvej 17
DK 2100 Copenhagen, Denmark
Publisher E-mail: nlinfo-f@elsevier.com
Journal dealing with various aspects of the interaction of energetic beams with atoms, molecules and aggregate forms of matter. **Subtitle:** Beam Interactions with Materials and Atoms. **Founded:** 1984. **Freq:** 24/yr. **Key Personnel:** H.H. Andersen, Founding Ed., nimb@fys.ku.dk; Lynn E. Rehn, Editor, rehn@anl.gov; C. Trautmann, Editor, nimb@gsi.de; M.B.H. Breese, Editor, phymbhb@nus.edu.sg; I.C. Vickridge, Editor, nimb@insp.jussieu.fr; E. Alves, Advisory Editorial Board. **ISSN:** 0168-583X. **Subscription Rates:** US$12,283 institutions for all countries except Europe, Japan & Iran; EUR10,980 institutions for European countries & Iran; 1,457,900¥ institutions Japan. **Remarks:** Advertising accepted; rates available upon request. **URL:** http://www.elsevier.com/wps/find/journaldescription.cws_home/505674/description. **Circ:** (Not Reported)

43681 ■ Scandinavian Journal of Laboratory Animal Science
Scandinavian Society for Laboratory Animal Science
Dept. of Experimental Medicine
University of Copenhagen & Rigshospitalet
The Panum Institute
3 Blegdamsvej
DK-2200 Copenhagen, Denmark
Ph: 45 353 27363
Fax: 45 353 27399
Publisher E-mail: barbro.salomonsson@scandlas.org
Journal containing information and news of interest to members. **Key Personnel:** Marianne Jensen Waern, Editor, marianne.jensen-waern@kv.slu.se; Robert Murison, Editor, murison@psych.uib.no; Jann Hau, Editor-in-Chief, jhau@sund.ku.dk; Hans Jorgen Skovaard Jensen, Admin. Ed., mmhsj@mail.dk; Biborka Bereczky Veress, News Ed., biborka.bveress@bku.se; Sveinbjorn Gizurarson, Editor, sveinbj@hi.is; Axel Kornerup Hansen, Editor, akh@ifp.kvl.dk; Timo Nevalainen, Editor, timo.nevalainen@uku.fi; Aavo Lang, Editor, aavo.lang@ut.ee. **Subscription Rates:** Included in membership. **URL:** http://biomedicum.ut.ee/sjlas/news.html.

43682 ■ Scandinavian Journal of Medicine and Science in Sports
John Wiley & Sons Inc.
Wiley-Blackwell
c/o Birgitte Kjaer, Ed.-in-Ch.
Sports Medicine Research Unit
Bldg. 8, 1st Fl., Dept. of Rheumatology H
Bispebjerg Hospital, 23 Bispebjerg Bakke
DK-2400 Copenhagen, Denmark
Ph: 45 353 16089
Fax: 45 353 12733
Publication E-mail: bk01@bbh.hosp.dk
Peer-reviewed journal covering traumatologic (orthopaedic), physiologic, biomechanic, medical (including rehabilitation), sociologic, psychologic, pedagogic, historic and philosophic aspects of sport. **Freq:** Bimonthly. **Key Personnel:** Michael Kjaer, Editor-in-Chief; Jan Henriksson, Section Ed.; Erik B. Simonsen, Section Ed.; Jostein Hallen, Section Ed.; Jens Bangsbo, Editorial Board, Michael Benjamin, Editorial Board. **ISSN:** 0905-7188. **Subscription Rates:** US$74 individuals print + online; EUR67 individuals print + online; 45 individuals print + online, rest of World; US$915 institutions, other countries print + online; US$832 institutions print + online; US$715 institutions print, online; 467 institutions print and online; EUR593 institutions print and online; 424 institutions print, online; EUR539 institutions print, online. **URL:** http://www.wiley.com/bw/journal.asp?ref=0905-7188&site=1.

43683 ■ Scando-Slavica
Routledge
Taylor & Francis Group Ltd.
c/o Jens Norgard-Sorensen, Ed.-in-Ch.
University of Copenhagen
Dept. of Cross Cultural & Regional Studies
East European Division, Snorresgade 17-19
DK-2300 Copenhagen, Denmark
Publisher E-mail: webmaster.books@tandf.co.uk
Peer-reviewed journal for Slavists and Baltologists. **Freq:** Semiannual. **Key Personnel:** Barbara Lonnqvist, Editorial Board; Jens Norgard-Sorensen, Editor-in-Chief, jns@hum.ku.dk; Per Ambrosiani, Editorial Board; Krzysztof Stala, Editorial Board; Kjetil Ra Hauge, Asst. Ed., k.r.hauge@east.uio.no; Per Ambrosiani, Asst. Ed. **ISSN:** 0080-6765. **Subscription Rates:** 146 institutions

Circulation: ★ = ABC; △ = BPA; ◆ = CAC; ● = CCAB; ▢ = VAC; ⊕ = PO Statement; ‡ = Publisher's Report; Boldface figures = sworn; Light figures = estimated.

Gale Directory of Publications & Broadcast Media/147th Ed.   **4869**

online; US$246 institutions online; 154 institutions print
+ online; US$258 institutions print + online; EUR206
institutions print and online; EUR196 institutions online
only. **URL:** http://www.tandf.co.uk/journals/titles/
00806765.asp.

43684 ■ Take Off
Skandinavisk Bladforlag A/S
Kongevej 3B
DK-1610 Copenhagen V, Denmark
Ph: 45 332 38099
Fax: 45 332 37042
Publisher E-mail: info@takeoff.nu
Trade magazine covering travel in Scandinavia. **Subtitle:** Travel Trade Magazine of Scandinavia. **Founded:**
1957. **Freq:** Monthly. **Print Method:** Offset. **Trim Size:**
210 x 297. **Subscription Rates:** 625 DKr individuals
normal; 320 DKr individuals staff; 751 DKr other
countries normal. **Remarks:** Accepts advertising. **URL:**
http://www.takeoff.dk/. **Ad Rates:** BW: 12,400 DKr, 4C:
15,120 DKr. **Circ:** Paid 5,800, Combined ‡18,000

43685 ■ Ugeskrift for Laeger
Danish Medical Association
Trondhjemsgade 9
DK-2100 Copenhagen, Denmark
Ph: 45 354 48500
Fax: 45 354 48503
Publisher E-mail: dadl@dadl.dk
Journal containing articles about health and social
problems. **Freq:** Weekly. **Key Personnel:** Anne Steen-
berger, Contact; as@dadl.dk; Torben Kitaj, Editor, tki@
dadl.dk; Jacob Rosenberg, Scientific Ed. **Remarks:** Ac-
cepts advertising. **URL:** http://www.ugeskriftet.dk/portal/
page/portal/LAEGERDK/UGESKRIFT_FOR_LAEGER.
Circ: (Not Reported)

43686 ■ Radio-FM - 100
Radhuspladsen 45
DK-1550 Copenhagen, Denmark
Ph: 45 33378900
Fax: 45 33378967
E-mail: info@radio100fm.dk
Format: Ethnic; Contemporary Hit Radio (CHR). **Ad
Rates:** Advertising accepted; rates available upon
request. **URL:** http://www.radio100fm.dk.

Fredensborg

43687 ■ The School Times International
PO Box 137
DK-3480 Fredensborg, Denmark
Ph: 45 491 33394
Fax: 45 497 17755
Publisher E-mail: st@schooltimes.com
Newspaper for school children and adults who are learn-
ing English as a second language. **Founded:** 1994.
Freq: Monthly. **ISSN:** 1395-3435. **Subscription Rates:**
59 individuals; 512.50 DKr individuals. **URL:** http://www.
schooltimes.com.

Frederiksberg

**43688 ■ Acta Agriculturae Scandinavica—Sec-
tion C, Food Economics**
Taylor & Francis Group Journals
Food & Resource Economics Institute
University of Copenhagen
Rolighedsvej 25
DK-1958 Frederiksberg, Denmark
Ph: 45 35 286859
Fax: 45 35 286802
Publisher E-mail: customerservice@taylorandfrancis.
com
Journal focusing on the creation and dissemination of
new applied knowledge in the area of food economics.
Freq: Quarterly. **Key Personnel:** Mogens Lund, Editor,
mogens@foi.dk; Jorgen Dejgaard Jensen, Managing
Editor, jorgen@foi.dk. **ISSN:** 1650-7541. **Subscription
Rates:** US$103 individuals print & online; US$354
institutions online; US$393 institutions print & online.
URL: http://www.informaworld.com/smpp/title~content=
t713710315~tab=subscribe~db=all; http://www.tandf.
co.uk/journals/titles/16507541.asp.

43689 ■ Acta Crystallographica. Section E
Blackwell Munksgaard
1 Rosenorns Alle
DK-1970 Frederiksberg C, Denmark
Ph: 45 773 33333

Fax: 45 773 33377
Journal for concise reports on inorganic, metal-organic
and organic structures. **Subtitle:** Structure Reports
Online. **Key Personnel:** G. Kostorz, Editor-in-Chief, gk-
iucr@ethz.ch; R.F. Baggio, Co-Ed., baggio@cnea.gov.
ar; M. Bolte, Co-Ed., bolte@chemie.uni-frankfurt.de.
ISSN: 1600-5368. **Subscription Rates:** Free. **Remarks:**
Accepts advertising. **URL:** http://journals.iucr.org/e/
journalhomepage.html. **Circ:** (Not Reported)

43690 ■ Genes, Brain and Behavior
Blackwell Munksgaard
1 Rosenorns Alle
DK-1970 Frederiksberg C, Denmark
Ph: 45 773 33333
Fax: 45 773 33377
Peer-reviewed journal research in behavioral and neural
genetics in their broadest sense, emphasizing the
analysis of the behavioral and neural phenotypes under
consideration, the unifying theme being the genetic ap-
proach as a tool to increase understanding of these
phenotypes. **Founded:** 2002. **Freq:** Bimonthly. **Key Personnel:** Steven De Belle, Editorial Board; Wim E. Crusio, Editor-in-Chief; Joseph Takahashi, Editorial Board;
Enrico Alleva, Editorial Board; Michael F. Miles, Editorial
Board; Gene E. Robinson, Editorial Board; Maja Bucan,
Editorial Board; Alberto Ferrus, Editorial Board; Greg
Gibson, Editorial Board; Susumu Tonegawa, Editorial
Board. **ISSN:** 1601-1848. **Subscription Rates:** US$994
institutions (print and online); 467 institutions UK (print
and online); US$1,160 institutions, other countries print
and online; EUR684 institutions Europe (print and online); US$864 institutions (print only); US$1,009 institutions, other countries print only; 467 institutions UK (print
only); EUR595 institutions Europe (print only); US$864
institutions (online only); US$1,009 institutions, other
countries online only. **Remarks:** Accepts advertising.
URL: http://www.wiley.com/bw/journal.asp?ref=1601-
1848. **Circ:** (Not Reported)

43691 ■ The International Veterinary Student
International Veterinary Students' Association
Association Internationale des Etudiants Veterinaires
KVL, DSR
Dyrlaegevej 9
DK-1870 Frederiksberg, Denmark
Fax: 45 352 82152
Publisher E-mail: info@ivsa.org
Worldwide publication covering veterinary students.
Freq: Annual. **Subscription Rates:** Free. **Remarks:**
Advertising accepted; rates available upon request.
URL: http://www.ivsa.org. **Circ:** (Not Reported)

43692 ■ Magisterbladet
Nimbusparken 16
DK-2000 Frederiksberg, Denmark
Ph: 45 381 56600
Fax: 45 381 56666
Publisher E-mail: dm@dm.dk
Trade magazine covering higher education, science,
politics and working conditions for academics. **Founded:**
1918. **Freq:** Semimonthly. **Key Personnel:** Pernille
Siegumfeldt, Journalist; Janneke Abildskov, Contact;
Lisbeth Rygaard, Journalist; Thomas Bottcher,
Journalist. **ISSN:** 0903-7349. **Remarks:** Accepts
advertising. **URL:** http://www.dm.dk/NyhederOgDebat/
Magisterbladet.aspx. **Circ:** (Not Reported)

43693 ■ Oral Diseases
John Wiley & Sons Inc.
Wiley-Blackwell
Rosenorns Alle 1
DK-1970 Frederiksberg, Denmark
Publication E-mail: odiedoffice@wiley.com
Peer-reviewed journal focusing on head and neck
ailments. **Freq:** 8/yr. **Key Personnel:** Prof. Crispian
Scully, Sen. Ed., phone 44 20 79151038, fax 44 20
79151039, crispian.scully@eastman.ucl.ac.uk; Bruce J.
Baum, PhD, Sen. Ed., editor@bethesdaoralmed.com;
Lauren Patton, Assoc. Ed.; Tamer Alpagot, Editorial
Board; Hideaki Kagami, Assoc. Ed.; Jose Bagan, Assoc.
Ed.; Aaron Palmon, Assoc. Ed.; Pedro Diz Dios, Assoc.
Ed.; Salomon Amar, Assoc. Ed.; Songtao Shi, Assoc.
Ed.; Doron Aframian, Editorial Board; Oneida Arosa-
rena, Editorial Board. **ISSN:** 1354-523X. **Subscription
Rates:** US$438 individuals print + online; EUR391
individuals print + online; 261 individuals print + online;
US$1,146 institutions print + online; US$1,041 institu-
tions print, online; EUR867 institutions print + online;
EUR787 institutions print, online; US$1,336 institutions,
other countries print + online; US$1,214 institutions,

other countries print, online; 682 institutions print +
online. **Remarks:** Advertising accepted; rates available
upon request. **URL:** http://www.wiley.com/bw/journal.
asp?ref=1354-523X&site=1. **Circ:** (Not Reported)

43694 ■ Orthodontics & Craniofacial Research
Blackwell Munksgaard
1 Rosenorns Alle
DK-1970 Frederiksberg C, Denmark
Ph: 45 773 33333
Fax: 45 773 33377
A forum for the presentation and discussion of issues
pertinent to the advancement of the specialty of orth-
odontics and the evidence-based knowledge of cranio-
facial growth and development. **Freq:** Quarterly. **Key
Personnel:** Birte Melsen, Assoc. Ed.; Greg Huang,
Editorial Board; Anne Marie Kuijpers-Jagtman, Editor-in-
Chief, fax 31 243 540631, ocr.editor@gmail.com; Marc
B. Ackerman, Editorial Board; Bakr Rabie, Editorial
Board; Vittorio Cacciafesta, Editorial Board; Christos
Katsaros, Editorial Board; Christoph Bourauel, Editorial
Board. **ISSN:** 1601-6335. **Subscription Rates:** US$219
individuals The Americas (print and online); EUR195
individuals Euro zone (print and online); 131 other
countries print and online; US$209 individuals The
Americas (online only); EUR187 individuals Euro zone
(online only); 124 other countries online only; US$609
institutions The Americas (print and online); EUR462
institutions Europe (print and online); US$609 institu-
tions, other countries print and online; 363 institutions
UK (print and online). **Remarks:** Accepts advertising.
URL: http://www.wiley.com/bw/journal.asp?ref=1601-
6335. **Circ:** (Not Reported)

43695 ■ Pediatric Diabetes
Blackwell Munksgaard
1 Rosenorns Alle
DK-1970 Frederiksberg C, Denmark
Ph: 45 773 33333
Fax: 45 773 33377
Journal devoted to disseminate new knowledge relating
to the epidemiology, etiology, pathogenesis, manage-
ment, complications and prevention of diabetes in childhood and adolescence. **Freq:** 8/yr. **Key Personnel:**
Mark A. Sperling, Editor-in-Chief, masp@pitt.edu; Silva
Arslanian, Assoc. Ed.; Thomas Danne, Assoc. Ed. **ISSN:**
1399-543X. **Subscription Rates:** US$186 other coun-
tries print and online; EUR166 individuals Europe (print
and online); 112 individuals UK (print and online);
US$177 individuals online only; EUR157 individuals
Europe (online only); US$205 other countries online
only; 105 individuals UK (online only); US$900 institu-
tions (print and online); EUR680 institutions Europe (print
and online); US$1,048 institutions, other countries print
and online. **Remarks:** Accepts advertising. **URL:** http://
www.wiley.com/bw/journal.asp?ref=1399-543x. **Circ:**
(Not Reported)

43696 ■ Traffic
Blackwell Munksgaard
1 Rosenorns Alle
DK-1970 Frederiksberg C, Denmark
Ph: 45 773 33333
Fax: 45 773 33377
Journal covering the cell biology and biochemistry of in-
tracellular transport in health and disease and publish-
ing manuscripts at the forefront of this field. **Subtitle:**
The International Journal of Intracellular Transport. **Freq:**
Monthly. **Key Personnel:** Frances M. Brodsky, Review
Consultant; Mark C. P. Marsh, Editor, m.marsh@ucl.ac.
uk; Gerrit van Meer, Editor, g.vanmeer@uu.nl. **ISSN:**
1398-9219. **Subscription Rates:** 186 individuals print
and online; US$297 individuals (print and online);
EUR279 individuals Europe (print and online); 176
individuals online only; US$297 individuals (online only);
EUR263 individuals Europe (online only); 209 members
print and online; US$209 members (print and online);
EUR209 members Europe (print and online); 126 members online only. **Remarks:** Accepts advertising. **URL:**
http://www.wiley.com/bw/journal.asp?ref=1398-9219.
Circ: (Not Reported)

Glostrup

43697 ■ Aktuel Elektronik
TechMedia A/S
Neverland 35
DK-2600 Glostrup, Denmark
Ph: 45 43242628
Fax: 45 43242626
Publisher E-mail: info@techmedia.dk
Magazine featuring news and articles about the latest
technologies in electronics industry. **Freq:** 30/yr. **Key
Personnel:** Steen Drago Andersen, Editor-in-Chief, fax

45 43242670, sda@techmedia.dk. **Remarks:** Accepts advertising. **URL:** http://www.techmedia.dk/default.asp?Action=Details&Item=571. **Ad Rates:** 4C: 5,188 DKr. **Circ:** ‡6,080

43698 ■ Byggeri
Odsgard A/S
Stationsparken 25
DK-2600 Glostrup, Denmark
Ph: 45 434 32900
Fax: 45 434 31328
Publisher E-mail: odsgard@odsgard.dk
Trade journal for the active building trade in Denmark. **Freq:** 10/yr. **Print Method:** Offset. **Cols./Page:** 4. **Col. Width:** 41 millimeters. **Key Personnel:** Michael Staal, Editor, staal@odsgard.dk. **Subscription Rates:** 390 DKr individuals. **Remarks:** Accepts advertising. **URL:** http://www.odsgard.dk/default.asp?pageid=byggeri; http://www.byggeri.dk. **Ad Rates:** BW: 15,440 DKr, 4C: 3,600 DKr. **Circ:** Controlled 7,743

43699 ■ BygTek
Odsgard A/S
Stationsparken 25
DK-2600 Glostrup, Denmark
Ph: 45 434 32900
Fax: 45 434 31328
Publisher E-mail: odsgard@odsgard.dk
Trade journal for the building trade in Denmark. **Founded:** 1968. **Freq:** Monthly. **Cols./Page:** 4. **Col. Width:** 58 millimeters. **Key Personnel:** Michael Staal, Contact, staal@odsgard.dk; Steen Claesen, Contact, clasen@odsgard.dk. **Subscription Rates:** 390 DKr individuals. **Remarks:** Accepts advertising. **URL:** http://www.odsgard.dk/default.asp?pageid=bygtek. **Ad Rates:** BW: 43,100 DKr, 4C: 3,255 DKr. **Circ:** Controlled 21,146

43700 ■ BygTek Mester & Svend
Odsgard A/S
Stationsparken 25
DK-2600 Glostrup, Denmark
Ph: 45 434 32900
Fax: 45 434 31328
Publisher E-mail: odsgard@odsgard.dk
Trade journal for journeyman joiners, carpenters, and their masters. **Founded:** 1994. **Freq:** Quarterly. **Cols./Page:** 4. **Col. Width:** 58 millimeters. **Key Personnel:** Kim Anker, Contact, anker@odsgard.dk. **Remarks:** Accepts advertising. **URL:** http://www.odsgard.dk/default.asp?pageid=mesv. **Ad Rates:** BW: 29,800 DKr, 4C: 3,255 DKr. **Circ:** Controlled 26,305

43701 ■ Dansk Kemi
TechMedia A/S
Neverland 35
DK-2600 Glostrup, Denmark
Ph: 45 43242628
Fax: 45 43242626
Publisher E-mail: info@techmedia.dk
Magazine featuring information about chemistry and its development in industry and in research and education. **Key Personnel:** Katrine Meyn, Editor-in-Chief, phone 45 43242668, fax 45 43242670, km@techmedia.dk. **Remarks:** Accepts advertising. **URL:** http://www.techmedia.dk/default.asp?Action=Details&Item=571. **Ad Rates:** 4C: 3,735 DKr. **Circ:** ‡6,540

43702 ■ Elektronik & Data
Odsgard A/S
Stationsparken 25
DK-2600 Glostrup, Denmark
Ph: 45 434 32900
Fax: 45 434 31328
Publisher E-mail: odsgard@odsgard.dk
Professional journal covering electronics design and development, testing and measurement, and embedded systems for design engineers and technicians. **Freq:** 13/yr. **Trim Size:** 185 x 260 mm. **Cols./Page:** 3. **Col. Width:** 58 millimeters. **Key Personnel:** Kim Jensen, Advertising Mgr., kimjensen@odsgard.dk; Lars Kristiansen, Editor-in-Chief, phone 45 434 51063, fax 45 434 31328, elek-data@odsgard.dk. **Subscription Rates:** 390 DKr individuals Scandinavia; 450 DKr other countries. **Remarks:** Accepts advertising. **URL:** http://www.odsgard.dk/default.asp?pageid=elekdata. **Circ:** Controlled 6,388

43703 ■ Elektronik Nyt
TechMedia A/S

Neverland 35
DK-2600 Glostrup, Denmark
Ph: 45 43242628
Fax: 45 43242626
Publisher E-mail: info@techmedia.dk
Magazine featuring articles about electronics. **Freq:** Monthly. **Key Personnel:** Rolf Sylvester, Editor, phone 45 43242610, rsh@asttechmedia.dk. **Remarks:** Accepts advertising. **URL:** http://www.techmedia.dk/default.asp?Action=Details&Item=571. **Ad Rates:** 4C: 2,842 DKr. **Circ:** ‡3,391

43704 ■ Elteknik
TechMedia A/S
Neverland 35
DK-2600 Glostrup, Denmark
Ph: 45 43242628
Fax: 45 43242626
Publisher E-mail: info@techmedia.dk
Magazine featuring information on electronics, automation, and energy. **Key Personnel:** Jorgen Kindt-Ipsen, Editor-in-Chief, phone 45 43242644, jki@techmedia.dk. **Remarks:** Accepts advertising. **URL:** http://www.techmedia.dk/Default.asp?Action=Details&Item=571. **Ad Rates:** 4C: 3,727 DKr. **Circ:** ‡3,950

43705 ■ HVAC Magasinet
TechMedia A/S
Neverland 35
DK-2600 Glostrup, Denmark
Ph: 45 43242628
Fax: 45 43242626
Publisher E-mail: info@techmedia.dk
Magazine featuring information on heating, ventilation, and sanitation of buildings. **Key Personnel:** Katrine Meyn, Editor-in-Chief, phone 45 43242668, fax 45 43242670, km@techmedia.dk. **Remarks:** Accepts advertising. **URL:** http://www.techmedia.dk/Default.asp?Action=Details&Item=571. **Ad Rates:** 4C: 3,552 DKr. **Circ:** ‡350

43706 ■ IN-PAK
TechMedia A/S
Neverland 35
DK-2600 Glostrup, Denmark
Ph: 45 43242628
Fax: 45 43242626
Publisher E-mail: info@techmedia.dk
Magazine featuring information about packaging. **Key Personnel:** January Cederberg, Editor, jc@techmedia.dk. **Remarks:** Accepts advertising. **URL:** http://www.techmedia.dk/Default.asp?Action=Details&Item=571. **Ad Rates:** 4C: 3,995 DKr. **Circ:** ‡4,476

43707 ■ Installations Nyt
TechMedia A/S
Neverland 35
DK-2600 Glostrup, Denmark
Ph: 45 43242628
Fax: 45 43242626
Publisher E-mail: info@techmedia.dk
Magazine providing information to electricians, engineers, and designers about new products in installation equipment, measuring equipment, and tools and machines. **Key Personnel:** Allan Malmberg, Editor, am@techmedia.dk. **Remarks:** Accepts advertising. **URL:** http://www.techmedia.dk/Default.asp?Action=Details&Item=571. **Ad Rates:** 4C: 3,525 DKr. **Circ:** ‡3,907

43708 ■ Installations Nyt Special
TechMedia A/S
Neverland 35
DK-2600 Glostrup, Denmark
Ph: 45 43242628
Fax: 45 43242626
Publisher E-mail: info@techmedia.dk
Magazine containing specially selected articles focusing on a product news for electricians and professionals. **Key Personnel:** Rolf Sylvester-Hvid, Editor-in-Chief, phone 45 43242610, fax 45 43242670, rsh@techmedia.dk. **Remarks:** Accepts advertising. **URL:** http://www.techmedia.dk/Default.asp?Action=Details&Item=571. **Circ:** (Not Reported)

43709 ■ Levnedsmiddel Bladet
TechMedia A/S
Neverland 35
DK-2600 Glostrup, Denmark

Ph: 45 43242628
Fax: 45 43242626
Publisher E-mail: info@techmedia.dk
Magazine featuring information about tendencies and events within the food industry. **Key Personnel:** Peter Friis, Editor, pf@techmedia.dk. **Remarks:** Accepts advertising. **URL:** http://www.techmedia.dk/Default.asp?Action=Details&Item=571. **Circ:** ‡3,400

43710 ■ Maskin Aktuelt
TechMedia A/S
Neverland 35
DK-2600 Glostrup, Denmark
Ph: 45 43242628
Fax: 45 43242626
Publisher E-mail: info@techmedia.dk
Magazine providing information in the iron, metal, and engineering industries. **Freq:** Monthly. **Key Personnel:** Helle Friemann Nielsen, Editor-in-Chief, phone 45 43242637, hfn@techmedia.dk. **Remarks:** Accepts advertising. **URL:** http://www.techmedia.dk/Default.asp?Action=Details&Item=571. **Ad Rates:** 4C: 3,029 DKr. **Circ:** ‡8,200

43711 ■ Pack+Plast
TechMedia A/S
Neverland 35
DK-2600 Glostrup, Denmark
Ph: 45 43242628
Fax: 45 43242626
Publisher E-mail: info@techmedia.dk
Magazine featuring articles for the Swedish packaging market. **Freq:** 11/yr. **Key Personnel:** Borje Ahgren, Editor, phone 45 43242683, ba@techmedia.dk. **Remarks:** Accepts advertising. **URL:** http://www.techmedia.dk/Default.asp?Action=Details&Item=571. **Ad Rates:** 4C: 2,598 DKr. **Circ:** (Not Reported)

43712 ■ Plus Process
TechMedia A/S
Neverland 35
DK-2600 Glostrup, Denmark
Ph: 45 43242628
Fax: 45 43242626
Publisher E-mail: info@techmedia.dk
Journal featuring information on developments and trends in the food industry. **Key Personnel:** Klaus Hansen, Editor-in-Chief, fax 45 43242670, kh@techmedia.dk. **Remarks:** Accepts advertising. **URL:** http://www.techmedia.dk/Default.asp?Action=Details&Item=571. **Circ:** ‡5,400

43713 ■ Puff - Fagtidsskrift for Tralast og Byggemarkeder
Odsgard A/S
Stationsparken 25
DK-2600 Glostrup, Denmark
Ph: 45 434 32900
Fax: 45 434 31328
Publisher E-mail: odsgard@odsgard.dk
Trade journal for timber dealers and home improvement centers. **Freq:** 11/yr. **Print Method:** Offset. **Cols./Page:** 3. **Col. Width:** 58 millimeters. **Key Personnel:** Peter Odsgard, Editor-in-Chief, puff@odsgard.dk; Michael Staal, Contact, staal@odsgard.dk; Steen Claesen, Contact, clasen@odsgard.dk. **ISSN:** 0106-2018. **Remarks:** Accepts advertising. **URL:** http://www.odsgard.dk/default.asp?pageid=puff. **Ad Rates:** BW: 11,850 DKr, 4C: 3,435 DKr. **Circ:** Controlled ‡1,843

43714 ■ Rens & Vask samt Tekstiludlejning
TechMedia A/S
Neverland 35
DK-2600 Glostrup, Denmark
Ph: 45 43242628
Fax: 45 43242626
Publisher E-mail: info@techmedia.dk
Magazine covering the laundry and dry cleaning industry. **Key Personnel:** Jorgen Kindt-Ipsen, Editor-in-Chief, phone 45 43242644, jki@techmedia.dk. **Remarks:** Accepts advertising. **URL:** http://www.techmedia.dk/Default.asp?Action=Details&Item=571. **Ad Rates:** 4C: 1.300 DKr. **Circ:** ‡3,340

43715 ■ Scandinavian Food & Drink
TechMedia A/S
Neverland 35
DK-2600 Glostrup, Denmark
Ph: 45 43242628
Fax: 45 43242626

Circulation: ★ = ABC; △ = BPA; ◆ = CAC; • = CCAB; ❑ = VAC; ⊕ = PO Statement; ‡ = Publisher's Report; Boldface figures = sworn; Light figures = estimated.

Gale Directory of Publications & Broadcast Media/147th Ed.   **4871**

Publisher E-mail: info@techmedia.dk

Magazine featuring news which have influence on the future regarding the development, production, marketing, and distribution of foods, ingredients, machines, and equipment. **Key Personnel:** Klaus Hansen, Editor, phone 45 43242646, fax 45 43242670, kh@techmedia.dk. **Remarks:** Accepts advertising. **URL:** http://www.techmedia.dk/Default.asp?Action=Details&Item=571. **Ad Rates:** 4C: 3,432 DKr. **Circ:** ‡7,538

43716 ■ Teknisk Nyt
TechMedia A/S
Neverland 35
DK-2600 Glostrup, Denmark
Ph: 45 43242628
Fax: 45 43242626
Publisher E-mail: info@techmedia.dk
Magazine focusing on machine construction and process automation. **Key Personnel:** Helle Friemann Nielsen, Editor-in-Chief, phone 45 43242637, hfn@techmedia.dk. **Remarks:** Accepts advertising. **URL:** http://www.techmedia.dk/Default.asp?Action=Details&Item=571. **Ad Rates:** 4C: 3,753 DKr. **Circ:** ‡10,131

43717 ■ Teknisk Nyt Special Edition
TechMedia A/S
Neverland 35
DK-2600 Glostrup, Denmark
Ph: 45 43242628
Fax: 45 43242626
Publisher E-mail: info@techmedia.dk
Magazine featuring articles on mechanical and process technology. **Key Personnel:** Helle Friemann Nielsen, Editor-in-Chief, phone 45 43242637, hfn@techmedia.dk. **Remarks:** Accepts advertising. **URL:** http://www.techmedia.dk/Default.asp?Action=Details&Item=571. **Circ:** ‡10,000

43718 ■ Telekommunikation
Odsgard A/S
Stationsparken 25
DK-2600 Glostrup, Denmark
Ph: 45 434 32900
Fax: 45 434 31328
Publisher E-mail: odsgard@odsgard.dk
Professional magazine covering telecommunications. **Founded:** Oct. 1979. **Freq:** Monthly. **Cols./Page:** 3. **Col. Width:** 58 millimeters. **Col. Depth:** 260 millimeters. **Key Personnel:** Michael Staal, Contact, staal@odsgard.dk; Per Danielsen, Editor-in-Chief, danielsen@telekommunikation.dk. **Subscription Rates:** 410 DKr individuals. **Remarks:** Accepts advertising. **URL:** http://www.telekommunikation.dk; http://www.odsgard.dk/default.asp?pageid=tele. **Circ:** Controlled 6,077

43719 ■ Trae- & Mobelindustri
TechMedia A/S
Neverland 35
DK-2600 Glostrup, Denmark
Ph: 45 43242628
Fax: 45 43242626
Publisher E-mail: info@techmedia.dk
Magazine providing information on new products in woodworking industry. **Key Personnel:** Peter Friis, Editor-in-Chief, phone 45 43242616, fax 45 43242626, pf@techmedia.dk. **Remarks:** Accepts advertising. **URL:** http://www.techmedia.dk/Default.asp?Action=Details&Item=571. **Ad Rates:** BW: 3,083 DKr, 4C: 3,686 DKr. **Circ:** ‡6,315

Hellerup

43720 ■ Euroman
Euroman Publications S/A
Hellerupvej 51
DK-2900 Hellerup, Denmark
Ph: 45 394 57700
Fax: 45 394 57780
Publisher E-mail: info@euroman.dk
Consumer magazine covering lifestyle for men. **Subtitle:** AGJSR. **Founded:** 1992. **Freq:** Monthly. **Key Personnel:** Mads Lange, Editor. **Subscription Rates:** 695 individuals 12 issues. **Remarks:** Accepts advertising. **URL:** http://www.euroman.dk/. **Ad Rates:** BW: US$1,000, 4C: US$1,500. **Circ:** (Not Reported)

Herning

43721 ■ Frisorfaget
Reprohuset

Dueoddevej 14
DK-7400 Herning, Denmark
Ph: 45 97 22 48 85
Fax: 45 97 22 01 80
Publisher E-mail: info@reprohuset.dk
Professional magazine for hair salon owners in Denmark. **Freq:** Monthly. **Print Method:** Sheetfed offset. **Trim Size:** 210 x 297 mm. **ISSN:** 0901-2737. **URL:** http://www.reprohuset.dk/content/dk/frisorfaget.

43722 ■ Maskinbladet
Birk Centerpark 36
DK-7400 Herning, Denmark
Ph: 45 962 65266
Fax: 45 962 65296
Publication E-mail: mail@maskinbladet.dk
Publisher E-mail: mail@maskinbladet.dk
Trade magazine covering agriculture in Denmark. **Freq:** every 3rd Friday. **Print Method:** Offset. **Trim Size:** 258 x 360 mm. **Cols./Page:** 6. **Col. Width:** 43 millimeters. **Col. Depth:** 360 millimeters. **Key Personnel:** Ulrich Gorm Albrechtsen, Contact, uga@fbg.dk. **ISSN:** 1395-8526. **Subscription Rates:** 365 DKr individuals; 839 DKr Free to qualified subscribers to Europe; 1,077 DKr other countries. **Remarks:** Accepts advertising. **URL:** http://www.maskinbladet.dk/ukhome.html. **Circ:** 54,734

43723 ■ Textile and Clothing
Federation of Danish Textile and Clothing
Birk Centerpark 38
PO Box 507
DK-7400 Herning, Denmark
Ph: 45 971 17200
Fax: 45 971 17215
Publisher E-mail: info@textile.dk
Danish language publication covering textiles and clothing. **Freq:** 10/yr. **Remarks:** Advertising accepted; rates available upon request. **URL:** http://ec.europa.eu/enterprise/textile/index_en.htm. **Circ:** (Not Reported)

Humlebaek

43724 ■ Scandinavian Journal of Design History
Rhodos International Science and Art Publishers
Horsholmvej 17
DK-3050 Humlebaek, Denmark
Ph: 45 32543020
Fax: 45 32543022
Publisher E-mail: rhodos@rhodos.dk
Journal featuring articles on Scandinavian arts and design. **Freq:** Annual. **Key Personnel:** Mirjam Gelfer-Jorgensen, Editor. **ISSN:** 0906-3447. **Subscription Rates:** 250 DKr individuals; 21 individuals; US$31 individuals; EUR36 individuals. **URL:** http://www.rhodos.com/htmlforlag/forlagsjodh12.html.

Lyngby

43725 ■ European Journal of Mechanics - A/Solids
Elsevier Science Inc.
c/o V. Tvergaard, Ed.-in-Ch.
Danmarks Tekniske Universitet
Lyngby, Denmark
Publisher E-mail: usinfo-ehelp@elsevier.com
Journal covering physical and mathematical basis to materials engineering, technological applications includes methods of modern computational mechanics, both pure and applied research. **Founded:** Nov. 11, 1989. **Freq:** 6/yr. **Print Method:** Offset. **Cols./Page:** 5. **Col. Width:** 25 nonpareils. **Col. Depth:** 224 agate lines. **Key Personnel:** E. Van Der Giessen, Assoc. Ed.; A. Baltov, Advisory Board; S.R. Bodner, Advisory Board; Y.A.T. De Freitas, Advisory Board; V. Tvergaard, Editor-in-Chief; C. Glocker, Advisory Board; N.A. Fleck, Advisory Board; A. Corigliano, Assoc. Ed. **ISSN:** 0997-7538. **Subscription Rates:** 118,500¥ institutions; EUR891 institutions for European countries and Iran; US$1,001 institutions, other countries except Europe, Japan and Iran. **URL:** http://www.elsevier.com/wps/find/journaldescription.cws_home/600737/descriptiondescription.

Odense

43726 ■ Basic & Clinical Pharmacology & Toxicology
John Wiley & Sons Inc.
Wiley-Blackwell
University of Southern Denmark

Clinical Pharmacology
Winslowparken 19, 2nd Fl.
DK-5000 Odense, Denmark
Ph: 45 65 504237
Fax: 45 65 916089
Publication E-mail: hhorneberg@health.sdu.dk
Journal focusing on all fields of toxicology, basic and clinical pharmacology. **Freq:** 12/yr. **Key Personnel:** Kim Brosen, Editor; N. Moore, Editorial Adviser; K.E. Andersson, Editorial Adviser; H. Autrup, Editorial Adviser; S. Christensen, Editorial Adviser; Henrik Horneberg, Editorial Asst.; S. Loft, Editorial Adviser; H. Kroemer, Editorial Adviser; Tina Ludvig, Editorial Asst.; C. Garland, Editorial Adviser. **ISSN:** 1742-7835. **Subscription Rates:** US$983 institutions print and online; 585 institutions print and online; US$1,146 institutions, other countries print and online; US$893 institutions print or online; 532 institutions print or online; EUR744 institutions print and online; EUR676 institutions print or online; US$1,041 institutions, other countries print or online. **Remarks:** Accepts advertising. **URL:** http://www.wiley.com/bw/journal.asp?ref=1742-7835&site=1. **Circ:** (Not Reported)

43727 ■ International Journal of Advanced Operations Management
Inderscience Enterprises Limited
c/o Govindan Kannan, Ed.-in-Ch.
University of Southern Denmark
Department of Business & Economics
Campusvej 55
DK-5230 Odense, Denmark
Peer-reviewed journal covering research on all aspects of advanced operations management. **Freq:** Quarterly. **Key Personnel:** Govindan Kannan, Editor-in-Chief, gov@sam.sdu.dk. **ISSN:** 1758-938X. **Subscription Rates:** EUR494 individuals print or online; EUR672 individuals print and online. **URL:** http://www.inderscience.com/browse/index.php?journalID=340.

43728 ■ International Journal of Business Performance and Supply Chain Modelling
Inderscience Enterprises Limited
c/o Govindan Kannan, Ed.-in-Ch.
University of Southern Denmark
Dept. of Business & Economics
Campusvej 55
DK5230 Odense, Denmark
Peer-reviewed journal covering all aspects of supply chain modeling. **Freq:** 4/yr. **Key Personnel:** Govindan Kannan, Editor-in-Chief, gov@sam.sdu.dk. **ISSN:** 1758-9401. **Subscription Rates:** EUR494 individuals print or online; EUR672 individuals print and online. **URL:** http://www.inderscience.com/browse/index.php?journalID=341.

43729 ■ The Journal of Music and Meaning
University of Southern Denmark
Campusvej 55
DK-5230 Odense, Denmark
Ph: 45 655 01000
Fax: 45 655 01090
Publisher E-mail: sdu@sdu.dk
Journal dealing with research on music. **Freq:** Semiannual. **Key Personnel:** Cynthia M. Grund, Editor-in-Chief; Soren R. Frimodt-Moller, Managing Editor; Michael Fingerhut, Assoc. Ed.; Prof. Jens Arnspang, Assoc. Ed.; Prof. Jean-Marc Chouvel, Assoc. Ed.; David Bainbridge, PhD, Assoc. Ed. **ISSN:** 1603-7170. **URL:** http://www.musicandmeaning.net/index.php.

43730 ■ Journal of Pragmatics
Elsevier Science
c/o J.L. Mey, Ed.-in-Ch.
University of Southern Denmark
Institute of Language & Communication
DK-5230 Odense, Denmark
Publisher E-mail: nlinfo-f@elsevier.com
Peer-reviewed journal on pragmatic studies. **Subtitle:** An Interdisciplinary of Language Studies. **Founded:** 1977. **Freq:** 15/yr. **Key Personnel:** C. Caffi, Editor; E. Ogiermann, Review Ed.; J.L. Mey, Editor-in-Chief, jop@language.sdu.dk; H. Haberland, Founding Ed.; N. Norrick, Editor-in-Chief, norrick@mx.uni-saarland.de. **ISSN:** 0378-2166. **Subscription Rates:** US$245 individuals except Europe and Japan; EUR189 individuals European countries; 27,200¥ individuals; US$1,282 institutions except Europe and Japan; EUR1,146 institutions European countries; 152,100¥ institutions. **Remarks:** Accepts advertising. **URL:** http://www.elsevier.com/wps/find/journaldescription.cws_home/505593/descriptiondescription. **Circ:** (Not Reported)

43731 ■ Orbis Litterarum
John Wiley & Sons Inc.
Wiley-Blackwell
University of South Denmark
Campusvej 55
DK-5230 Odense, Denmark
Publication E-mail: orbis@litcul.sdu.dk
Peer-reviewed journal focusing on the study of European, American and related literature. **Subtitle:** International review of Literary Studies. **Freq:** Bimonthly. **Key Personnel:** Morten Nojgaard, Editor; Christian Benne, Editor; Lars Ole Sauerberg, Editor. **ISSN:** 0105-7510. **Subscription Rates:** US$651 institutions print + online; US$763 institutions, other countries print + online; US$592 institutions print, online; US$693 institutions, other countries print, online; 390 institutions print + online; 353 institutions print, online; EUR449 institutions online; EUR494 institutions print + online. **Remarks:** Accepts advertising. **URL:** http://www.wiley.com/bw/journal.asp?ref=0105-7510&site=1. **Circ:** (Not Reported)

Padborg

43732 ■ Danmarks Transport-Tidende
Dansk Transport Forlag A/S
Jernbanegade 18
DK-6330 Padborg, Denmark
Ph: 45 701 00506
Fax: 45 746 74047
Publisher E-mail: info@transinform.com
Newspaper covering all forms on transportation. **Founded:** 1978. **Freq:** Biweekly. **Cols./Page:** 6. **Col. Width:** 39 millimeters. **Col. Depth:** 360 millimeters. **Key Personnel:** Gwyn Nissen, Ch. Ed., gn@transporttidende.com. **ISSN:** 0106-0724. **Remarks:** Accepts advertising. **URL:** http://www.transporttidende.com. **Ad Rates:** GLR: 11.50 DKr, BW: 17,036 DKr, 4C: 17,036 DKr. **Circ:** Paid ◆ **4,000**

43733 ■ Trans-Inform
Dansk Transport Forlag A/S
Jernbanegade 18
DK-6330 Padborg, Denmark
Ph: 45 701 00506
Fax: 45 746 74047
Publisher E-mail: info@transinform.com
Trade magazine covering road haulage in Denmark and elsewhere. **Founded:** 1987. **Freq:** Monthly. **Cols./Page:** 4. **Col. Width:** 41 millimeters. **Col. Depth:** 265 millimeters. **Key Personnel:** Gwyn Nissen, Ch. Ed., gn@transporttidende.com. **ISSN:** 0904-6534. **Remarks:** Accepts advertising. **URL:** http://www.transinform.com. **Ad Rates:** GLR: 15.75 DKr, BW: 15,172 DKr, 4C: 15,172 DKr. **Circ:** Paid ◆ **4,000**

Roskilde

43734 ■ The Journal of Transdisciplinary Environmental Studies (TES)
Roskilde University
Department of Environment, Technology and Social Studies
Bldg. 11.2, RUC
PO Box 260
4000 Roskilde, Denmark
Ph: 45 467 42120
Fax: 45 467 43041
Publication E-mail: journal-tes@ruc.dk
Publisher E-mail: teksam@ruc.dk
Journal devoted to the study of environment in relation to planning and regulation targeting academicians and practicing professionals. **Freq:** 3/yr. **Key Personnel:** Per Christensen, Editorial Board, phone 45 963 58326, pc@i4.auc.dk; Marc Antrop, Editorial Board, phone 32 926 44705, marc.antrop@rug.ac.be; Lutz Mez, Editorial Board, phone 49 30 83855585, umwelt1@zedat.fu-berlin.de. **URL:** http://www.journal-tes.dk/.

Skive

43735 ■ ScanRef
ScanPub ApS
c/o Jens Utoft, Ed.-in-Ch.
Abakke 3
DK-7800 Skive, Denmark
Ph: 45 975 14595
Publisher E-mail: admin@scanref.dk
Trade magazine covering the refrigeration industry. **Subtitle:** Scandinavian Refrigeration Energy Food. **Founded:** 1971. **Freq:** Bimonthly. **Print Method:** Offset. **Trim Size:** A4. **Cols./Page:** 4. **Key Personnel:** Jens Utoft, Editor-in-Chief, mail@scanref.dk; Anders Hiorth, Editor, sverige@scanref.dk; Svein Erik Pedersen, Editor, svein.e.pedersen@hive.no. **ISSN:** 0284-0758. **Subscription Rates:** 450 DKr individuals Nordic countries; 675 DKr elsewhere. **Remarks:** Accepts advertising. **URL:** http://scanref.com/about.html. **Ad Rates:** BW: 16,800 DKr, 4C: 16,875 DKr. **Circ:** ‡4,650

Valby

43736 ■ Horysont (Good News)
Young Men's Christian Association and Young Women's Christian Association
Valby Langgade 19
DK-2500 Valby, Denmark
Ph: 45 36 141533
Publication E-mail: horysont@kfum-kfuk.dk
Publisher E-mail: national@kfum-kfuk.dk
Danish language publication covering the YMCA-YWCA. **Freq:** 8/yr. **Remarks:** Advertising accepted; rates available upon request. **URL:** http://www.kfum-kfuk.dk. **Circ:** (Not Reported)

43737 ■ Radio Rosa-FM - 98.9
Postbox 339
DK-2500 Valby, Denmark
Ph: 45 33 330404
E-mail: rosa@radiorosa.dk
Format: Talk; Information. **URL:** http://www.radiorosa.dk/.

Wageningen

43738 ■ International Review of Environmental and Resource Economics
Now Publishers
c/o Prof. Henk Folmer, Ed.-in-Ch.
Economics of Consumers & Households Group
Wageningen University, De Leeuwenborch, Bldg. 201
Hollandseweg 1,
DK-6706 Wageningen, Denmark
Publisher E-mail: zac.rolnik@nowpublishers.com
Journal covering environmental and resource economics. **Founded:** 1855. **Freq:** Daily. **Print Method:** Offset. **Cols./Page:** 6. **Col. Width:** 25 nonpareils. **Col. Depth:** 301 agate lines. **Key Personnel:** Prof. Tom Tietenberg, Editor-in-Chief, thtieten@colby.edu; Prof. Scott Barrett, Editor; Prof. Henk Folmer, Editor-in-Chief; Prof. Kenneth J. Arrow, Editor. **ISSN:** 1931-1465. **Subscription Rates:** EUR360 institutions print only; US$410 individuals print and electronic. **URL:** http://www.irere.net/.

Roseau

43739 ■ The Chronicle (Dominica)
The Chronicle
PO Box 1764

Roseau, Dominica
Ph: (767)448-7887
Fax: (767)448-0047
Publication E-mail: thechronicle@cwdom.dm
Publisher E-mail: thechronicle@cwdom.dm

General newspaper. **Founded:** 1996. **Freq:** Weekly (Fri.). **Print Method:** Offset. **Trim Size:** 11 x 17. **Remarks:** Accepts advertising. **URL:** http://www.news-dominica.com/new-index.cfm. **Former name**: The New Chronicle. **Circ:** 3,000

Circulation: ★ = ABC; △ = BPA; ◆ = CAC; • = CCAB; ❏ = VAC; ⊕ = PO Statement; ‡ = Publisher's Report; Boldface figures = sworn; Light figures = estimated.

Gale Directory of Publications & Broadcast Media/147th Ed. 4875

Papagayo

43740 ■ Amor-FM - 91.9
Calle 7 ma, No. 6
Papagayo, Dominican Republic
Ph: (809)550-9190
E-mail: info@amorfm91.com
Format: Ethnic; Information; Contemporary Hit Radio (CHR). **Operating Hours:** Continuous. **URL:** http://www.amorfm91.com.

Santiago

43741 ■ La Nueva-FM - 106.9
C/ Prolongacion Padres Las Casas
URB Miraflores
Calle Proyecto No. 12
Santiago, Dominican Republic
Ph: (809)971-8725
Fax: (809)582-4783
E-mail: radio@superregional.com
Format: Reggae; Ethnic; World Beat. **Owner:** La Nueva, at above address. **Key Personnel:** Marcos Rafael Cepeda, President; Miguel Brioso, Dir. Tech. **URL:** http://www.lanueva106.com.

Santo Domingo

43742 ■ Raices-FM - 102.9 MHz
Edificio Principal de las Empresas Leon Jimenes
Ave. George Washington
Santo Domingo, Dominican Republic
Ph: (809)487-1029 .
E-mail: informacion@raicesradio.org.do
Format: Ethnic; World Beat. **Founded:** Oct. 3, 2003. **Operating Hours:** Continuous. **URL:** http://www.centroleon.org.do.

Alameda

43743 ■ Colo Colo-AM - 880
Estacion Central
Alameda, Ecuador
Ph: 593 7841681
Format: Ethnic; Information; Sports; World Beat. **Oper-**

ating Hours: Continuous. **URL:** http://www. radiocolocolo.cl.

Santo Domingo

43744 ■ Radio Megaestacion-FM - 92.9
Cuadras Tras las Oficinas de Emelsad 2

Santo Domingo, Ecuador
Ph: 593 2 760475
Fax: 593 2 752128
E-mail: radiomegaestacion@hotmail.com
Format: World Beat. **Operating Hours:** Continuous.
URL: http://www.radiomegaestacion.com.

Circulation: ★ = ABC; △ = BPA; ♦ = CAC; • = CCAB; ❏ = VAC; ⊕ = PO Statement; ‡ = Publisher's Report; Boldface figures = sworn; Light figures = estimated.

Gale Directory of Publications & Broadcast Media/147th Ed. 4879

Alexandria

43745 ■ International Journal of Biotechnology & Biochemistry (IJBB)
Research India Publications
c/o Prof. Dr. Hassan Moawad Abdel Al, Ed.-in-Ch.
Nucleic Acid Research Dept.
Genetic Engineering & Biotechnology Researches Institute
PO Box 21934, New Borg El-Arab City
Alexandria 11435, Egypt
Publisher E-mail: info@ripublication.com
Journal covering the field of Biotechnology and Biochemistry. **Freq:** Quarterly. **Key Personnel:** Mohamed Morsi M. Ahmed, PhD, Assoc. Ed.; Saleh Matar, Assoc. Ed.; Prof. Dr. Hassan Moawad Abdel Al, Editor-in-Chief. **ISSN:** 0973-2691. **Subscription Rates:** US$380 institutions and library; print plus online free; US$360 institutions and library; online only; US$140 individuals print plus online free; US$120 individuals online only; Rs 2,200 individuals. **URL:** http://www.ripublication.com/ijbb.htm.

43746 ■ International Journal of Lakes and Rivers
Research India Publications
c/o Massoud A.H. Saad, PhD, Ed.-in-Ch.
University of Alexandria
Dept. of Oceanography
Faculty of Science, Moharem Bey
Alexandria 21511, Egypt
Publisher E-mail: info@ripublication.com
Journal covering information on all inland water bodies, and lotic and lentic systems. **Founded:** 1973. **Freq:** Semiannual. **Print Method:** Offset. **Trim Size:** 7 7/8 x 10 1/2. **Key Personnel:** Massoud A.H. Saad, PhD, Editor-in-Chief, saad1935@yahoo.com. **ISSN:** 0973-4570. **URL:** http://www.ripublication.com/ijlr.htm.

43747 ■ International Journal of Nanotechnology and Applications
Research India Publications
c/o Prof. Ossama M.M. El-Shazly, Ed.-in-Ch.
Alexandria University
Physics Dept., Faculty of Science
Alexandria, Egypt
Publisher E-mail: info@ripublication.com
Journal covering areas of nanotechnology. **Founded:** Mar. 2007. **Freq:** 3/yr. **Key Personnel:** Prof. Ossama M.M. El-Shazly, Editor-in-Chief, ossamashazly@gmail.com. **ISSN:** 0973-631X. **Subscription Rates:** US$380 institutions print + online; US$360 institutions online only; US$280 individuals print only; US$260 individuals online only. **URL:** http://www.ripublication.com/ijna.htm.

43748 ■ International Journal of Oceans and Oceanography (IJOO)
Research India Publications
c/o Massoud A.H. Saad, PhD, Ed.-in-Ch.
University of Alexandria
Dept. of Oceanography, Faculty of Science
Moharem Bey
Alexandria 21511, Egypt
Publisher E-mail: info@ripublication.com
Journal covering all aspects of oceans and oceanography. **Freq:** 3/yr. **Key Personnel:** Massoud A.H. Saad, PhD, Editor-in-Chief, saad@internetalex.com; Marjorie C. Aelion, Editorial Board Member; Malcolm J. Bowman, Editorial Board Member. **ISSN:** 0973-2667. **Subscription Rates:** US$320 institutions and library; print only; US$300 institutions and library; online only; US$220 individuals print only; US$200 individuals online only. **URL:** http://www.ripublication.com/ijoo.htm.

43749 ■ International Journal of Pure and Applied Physics
Research India Publications
c/o Prof. Ossama M.M. El-Shazly, Ed.-in-Ch.
Physics Dept., Faculty of Science
Alexandria University
Alexandria, Egypt
Publisher E-mail: info@ripublication.com
Journal covering pure and applied physics and its applications. **Founded:** 1973. **Freq:** Quarterly. **Print Method:** Web offset. **Trim Size:** 10 1/2 x 14 1/2. **Cols./Page:** 5. **Col. Width:** 22 nonpareils. **Col. Depth:** 186 agate lines. **Key Personnel:** I. Ahmad, Editorial Board Member; Tahir Akbas, Editorial Board Member; Prof. Ossama M.M. El-Shazly, Editor-in-Chief, elshazlyo@yahoo.com. **ISSN:** 0973-1776. **Subscription Rates:** US$380 institutions and library; print + online; US$360 institutions and library; online only; US$280 individuals print only; US$260 individuals online only; Rs 2,200 individuals. **URL:** http://www.ripublication.com/ijpap.htm.

Cairo

43750 ■ African Journal of Urology
African Journals Online
c/o Prof. Ismail Khalaf, MD, Ed.-in-Ch.
PO Box 2477
Cairo 11361, Egypt
Publisher E-mail: info@ajol.info
Peer-reviewed journal dedicated to urology. **Founded:** 1898. **Freq:** Quarterly. **Print Method:** Offset. **Cols./Page:** 6. **Col. Width:** 24 nonpareils. **Col. Depth:** 301 agate lines. **Key Personnel:** Prof. Ismail Khalaf, MD, Editor-in-Chief, ismkhalaf@yahoo.com; Prof. Mostafa Elhilali, Editorial Board; Prof. Chris Heyns, Exec. Ed.; Prof. S. Soloway, Assoc. Ed.; Prof. R. Tiguert, Assoc. Ed.; Prof. P. Paparel, Exec. Ed. **ISSN:** 1110-5704. **Subscription Rates:** US$60 individuals. **URL:** http://ajol.info/index.php/aju.

43751 ■ Afro-Arab Selections for Social Sciences
CODESRIA - Council for the Development of Social Science Research in Africa
c/o Helmi Sharawy, Ed.
Arab Research Center
8/10 Mathaf El. Manial
Cairo, Egypt
Publisher E-mail: codesria@codesria.sn
Intercultural journal featuring social sciences. **Freq:** Annual. **Key Personnel:** Helmi Sharawy, Editor, arc@ie-eg.com. **URL:** http://www.codesria.org/Links/Publications/Journals/afro_arab_selection.htm.

43752 ■ Business Today Egypt
Egypt Today
3a Rd. 199
IBA Media Bldg.
Degla, Maadi
Cairo, Egypt
Ph: 20 2 27555000
Fax: 20 2 27555050
Publication E-mail: editor@businesstodayegypt.com
Publisher E-mail: editor@egypttoday.com
Business magazine covering business in Egypt. **Key Personnel:** Elizabeth Drachman, Managing Editor. **Subscription Rates:** E 135 individuals; US$70 individuals United States, Middle East, Europe and Africa; US$120 individuals Canada, Asia and Australasia. **Remarks:** Advertising accepted; rates available upon request. **URL:** http://www.businesstodayegypt.com/. **Circ:** (Not Reported)

43753 ■ Cairo Times
14 Al Saraya Al Kubra St., Ste. 6
Garden City
Cairo, Egypt
Ph: 20 279 43396
Fax: 20 279 43396
Publisher E-mail: caitimes@cairotimes.com
Magazine covering news and business in Egypt and the Middle East. **Founded:** Mar. 1997. **Freq:** Weekly. **Print Method:** Offset. **Trim Size:** 330 x 240 mm. **Key Personnel:** Hisham Kassem, Publisher; Paul Schemm, Editor; Matthew Carrington, Dep. Ed. **Remarks:** Accepts advertising. **URL:** http://www.cairotimes.com. **Ad Rates:** 4C: US$1,300. **Circ:** Paid 5,000

43754 ■ Eastern Mediterranean Health Journal
World Health Organization - Regional Office for the Eastern Mediterranean
Abdul Razzak Al Sanhouri St.
PO Box 7608, Nasr City
Cairo 11371, Egypt
Ph: 20 2 22765000
Fax: 20 2 26702492
Publisher E-mail: webmaster@emro.who.int
English, French and Arabic language journal covering Eastern Mediterranean health subjects. **Founded:** Aug. 1995. **Freq:** Bimonthly. **Print Method:** Paper and Electronic. **Key Personnel:** Dr. Haytham M. Khayat, Editor-in-Chief; Dr. Muhammad Afzal, Exec. Dir. **ISSN:** 1687-1634. **Subscription Rates:** US$90 individuals; US$45 individuals in developing countries. **Remarks:** Advertising not accepted. **URL:** http://www.emro.who.int/emhj.htm. **Circ:** 3,500

43755 ■ Egypt Today
3a Rd. 199
IBA Media Bldg.
Degla, Maadi
Cairo, Egypt
Ph: 20 2 27555000
Fax: 20 2 27555050
Publisher E-mail: editor@egypttoday.com
Business magazine covering Egypt. **Founded:** 1979. **Freq:** Monthly. **Subscription Rates:** US$100 individuals U.S., the Middle East, Europe and Africa; US$120 individuals Canada, Asia and Australia; E 135 individuals in Egypt. **Remarks:** Accepts advertising. **URL:** http://www.egypttoday.com. **Circ:** 14,500

43756 ■ Egyptian Journal of Biochemistry and Molecular Biology
African Journals Online
Biochemistry U.S. Department of
Faculty of Medicine
Ain Shams University
Cairo, Egypt
Publisher E-mail: info@ajol.info
Peer-reviewed journal covering biochemistry and molecular biology. **Freq:** Semiannual. **Key Personnel:** Prof. Mohamed Farid El-Asmer, Editor, felasmer@hotmail.com. **ISSN:** 1687-1502. **Subscription Rates:** US$10 individuals. **URL:** http://ajol.info/index.php/ejbmb.

43757 ■ Egyptian Journal of Biomedical Sciences
African Journals Online
95 Ahmed Orabi St.
Mohandessin
Cairo 12411, Egypt
Publisher E-mail: info@ajol.info
Peer-reviewed journal containing information about biomedical research sciences. **Freq:** 3/yr. **Key Personnel:** Dr. Hossam M. Ashour, Co-Ed. in Ch., hossamking@mailcity.com; Prof. Mohamed Seif El Din Ashour, Editor-in-Chief. **ISSN:** 1110-6379. **Subscription Rates:** US$100 individuals. **URL:** http://ajol.info/index.php/ejbs2.

43758 ■ Egyptian Journal of Biotechnology
African Journals Online
95 Ahmed Orabi St.
Mohandessin
Cairo 12411, Egypt
Publisher E-mail: info@ajol.info
Peer-reviewed journal containing information about biotechnology research. **Freq:** 3/yr. **Key Personnel:** Dr. Hossam M. Ashour, Co-Ed. in Ch., hossamking@mailcity.com; Prof. Mohamed Seif El Din Ashour, Editor-in-Chief. **ISSN:** 1110-6093. **Subscription Rates:** US$100 individuals + airmail postage. **URL:** http://ajol.info/index.php/ejbiot.

43759 ■ Egyptian Journal of Computer Science
Egyptian Computer Society
Nasr City
PO Box 9009
Cairo, Egypt
Ph: 20 2 2608182
Fax: 20 2 2603880
Publisher E-mail: ecomps@ritsec3.com.eg
Arabic language journal covering computer science. **Freq:** Annual. **Remarks:** Advertising not accepted. **URL:** http://www.ifip.or.at/members/egypt.htm. **Circ:** 320

43760 ■ Egyptian Journal of Medical Laboratory Sciences
African Journals Online
Cairo Medical Syndicate Dar El-Hekma
42 Kasr El-Aini St.
Cairo, Egypt
Publisher E-mail: info@ajol.info
Peer-reviewed journal covering medical laboratory science. **Freq:** Semiannual. **Key Personnel:** Prof. Ossama Rasslan, Editor, orasslaneg@hotmail.com. **ISSN:** 1110-5593. **Subscription Rates:** US$30 individuals; US$40 institutions. **URL:** http://ajol.info/index.php/ejmls.

43761 ■ Enigma Magazine
15 Mahmoud Azmy St., off 26 July St.
2nd Fl., Zamalek
Cairo, Egypt
Ph: 20 2 7382554
Fax: 20 2 7367759
Publisher E-mail: enigma@enigma-mag.com
Magazine covering lifestyle, fashion, design, dining, technology and trends in Egypt. **Key Personnel:** Yasmine Shihata, Editor-in-Chief. **Subscription Rates:** 50 individuals; US$110 individuals. **Remarks:** Accepts advertising. **URL:** http://www.enigma-mag.com/main.htm. **Circ:** 45,000

43762 ■ International Journal of Photoenergy
Hindawi Publishing Corp.
c/o M. Sabry A. Abdel-Mottaleb, Editorial Board
Dept. of Chemistry, Faculty of Science
Ain Shams University
Cairo 11566, Egypt
Publisher E-mail: hindawi@hindawi.com
Journal dealing with the topics related to photochemistry, photophysics, photobiology and solar energy. **Founded:** 1999. **Key Personnel:** M. Sabry A. Abdel-Mottaleb, Editorial Board; D. Bahnemann, Editorial Board; Nicola Alonso-Vante, Editorial Board. **ISSN:** 1110-662X. **Subscription Rates:** US$195 individuals. **URL:** http://www.hindawi.com/journals/IJP/.

43763 ■ New Egyptian Journal of Microbiology
African Journals Online
95 Ahmed Orabi St.
Mohandessin
Cairo 12411, Egypt
Ph: 20 1 6522867
Fax: 20 2 38371549
Publisher E-mail: info@ajol.info
Peer-reviewed journal focusing on microbiological and/or immunological studies from medical or pharmaceutical perspectives. **Freq:** 3/yr. **Key Personnel:** Dr. Hossam M. Ashour, Co-Ed. in Ch., hossamking@mailcity.com; Dr. Mohamed Seif El Din Ashour, Editor-in-Chief. **ISSN:** 1687-1219. **Subscription Rates:** US$100 individuals. **URL:** http://ajol.info/index.php/nejmi.

43764 ■ Rotary Magazine
19 El Shahid Mohamed El Shibany St.
Heliopolis
Cairo 11341, Egypt
Ph: 20 22918822
Fax: 20 23924270
Publisher E-mail: hashad@link.net
Membership magazine of Rotary International covering current news about Rotary-related subjects in English, Arabic, and French. **Freq:** Quarterly. **Key Personnel:** Hussein Hashad, Editor, phone 33 20 22918822, fax 33 20 23924270, hashad@link.net. **URL:** http://www.rotary.org. **Circ:** 4,000

43765 ■ Scientific Medical Journal
African Journals Online
Cairo Medical Syndicate Dar El-Hekma
Kasr El-Aini St.
Cairo, Egypt
Publisher E-mail: info@ajol.info
Peer-reviewed journal covering all disciplines of medicine. **Subtitle:** An Official Journal of Egyptian Medical Education. **Freq:** Quarterly. **Key Personnel:** Prof. Ossama Rasslan, Editor, orasslaneg@hotmail.com. **ISSN:** 1110-5607. **Subscription Rates:** E 40 individuals; US$40 other countries. **URL:** http://ajol.info/index.php/smedj.

43766 ■ TVMAX - 93
Digital Technology Systems
Bldg. 14, Rd. 274
New Maadi
Cairo, Egypt
Ph: 20 2 5215050
Fax: 20 2 5215024
E-mail: tvmax@orbit.net
Owner: Orbit Satellite Television and Radio Network, c/o Panther Media Group, PO Box 502211, Dubai Media City, Dubai, United Arab Emirates. **URL:** http://www.orbit.net.

43767 ■ TVMAX - 92
Digital Technology Systems
Bldg. 14, Rd. 274
New Maadi
Cairo, Egypt
Ph: 20 2 5215050
Fax: 20 2 5215024
E-mail: tvmax@orbit.net
Owner: Orbit Satellite Television and Radio Network, c/o Panther Media Group, PO Box 502211, Dubai Media City, Dubai, United Arab Emirates. **URL:** http://www.orbit.net.

43768 ■ TVMAX - 91
Digital Technology Systems
Bldg. 14, Rd. 274
New Maadi
Cairo, Egypt
Ph: 20 2 5215050
Fax: 20 2 5215024
E-mail: tvmax@orbit.net
Owner: Orbit Satellite Television and Radio Network, c/o Panther Media Group, PO Box 502211, Dubai Media City, Dubai, United Arab Emirates. **URL:** http://www.orbit.net.

43769 ■ TVMAX - 90
Digital Technology Systems
Bldg. 14, Rd. 274
New Maadi
Cairo, Egypt
Ph: 20 2 5215050
Fax: 20 2 5215024
E-mail: tvmax@orbit.net
Owner: Orbit Satellite Television and Radio Network, c/o Panther Media Group, PO Box 502211, Dubai Media City, Dubai, United Arab Emirates. **URL:** http://www.orbit.net.

El Mansoura

43770 ■ International Journal of Materials Science
Research India Publications
c/o Dr. Mustafa Kamal, Ed.-in-Ch.
Mansoura University
Faculty of Science
El Mansoura, Egypt
Publisher E-mail: info@ripublication.com
Journal covering all aspects of material research. **Freq:** 4/yr. **Key Personnel:** Dr. Mustafa Kamal, Editor-in-Chief, kamal422002@yahoo.com. **ISSN:** 0973-4589. **Subscription Rates:** US$380 institutions and library; print plus online free; US$360 institutions and library; online only; US$280 individuals print plus online free; US$260 individuals online only; Rs 1,800 individuals. **URL:** http://www.ripublication.com/ijoms.htm.

El Sherouk City

43771 ■ International Journal of Cognitive Biometrics
Inderscience Enterprises Limited
c/o Dr. Kenneth Revett, Ed.
British University in Egypt, Faculty of Electronics & Computer Science
PO Box 43
El Sherouk City 11837, Egypt
Journal covering approaches to biometrics based on cognitive aspects of human behavior. **Freq:** 4/yr. **Key Personnel:** Dr. Kenneth Revett, Editor, k.revett@bue.edu.eg. **ISSN:** 2042-6461. **Subscription Rates:** EUR494 individuals print or online; EUR672 individuals print and online. **URL:** http://www.inderscience.com/browse/index.php?journalID=362.

43772 ■ International Journal of Cognitive Performance Support
Inderscience Enterprises Limited
c/o Dr. Kenneth Revett, Ed.
British University in Egypt, Faculty of Electronics & Computer Science
PO Box 43
El Sherouk City 11837, Egypt
Journal covering the research on innovative strategies in computer technology that elicits maximum interaction between man and machine. **Freq:** 4/yr. **Key Personnel:** Dr. Kenneth Revett, Editor, k.revett@bue.edu.eg. **ISSN:** 1742-7207. **Subscription Rates:** EUR494 individuals print or online; EUR672 individuals print and online. **URL:** http://www.inderscience.com/browse/index.php?journalID=126.

Ismailia

43773 ■ Egyptian Journal of Biology
African Journals Online
Zoology U.S. Department of
Faculty of Science
Suez Canal University
Ismailia, Egypt
Publisher E-mail: info@ajol.info
Peer-reviewed journal containing scientific contributions and reviews about the biological sciences. **Freq:** Annual. **Key Personnel:** Dr. Francis Gilbert, Editor, francis.gilbert@nottingham.ac.uk; Prof. Chris Barnard, Editor; Prof. Ahmed Shoukry, Editor. **ISSN:** 1110-6859. **URL:** http://ajol.info/index.php/ejb.

43774 ■ Egyptian Journal of Natural History
African Journals Online
Zoology U.S. Department of
Faculty of Science
Suez Canal University
Ismailia, Egypt
Ph: 20 64 381799
Fax: 20 64 322381
Publisher E-mail: info@ajol.info
Journal containing information about the natural history

of the Egyptian fauna and flora. **Freq:** Annual. **Key Personnel:** Prof. Ahmed Shoukry, Editor, smzalat@ccis. suez.eun.eg; Prof. Chris Barnard, Editor. **ISSN:** 1110-6867. **URL:** http://www.ajol.info/journal_index.php?jId= 195.

Circulation: ★ = ABC; △ = BPA; ◆ = CAC; • = CCAB; ❑ = VAC; ⊕ = PO Statement; ‡ = Publisher's Report; Boldface figures = sworn; Light figures = estimated.

Gale Directory of Publications & Broadcast Media/147th Ed.

4883

Ahuachapan

43775 ■ Radio Maxima-FM - 95.3
5 Residencial Villas de San Rafael Casa No. 5
Ahuachapan, El Salvador
Ph: 503 4 24133535
Format: Adult Contemporary. **Owner:** Radio Maxima, at above address. **URL:** http://www.maxima953.com/home.php.

La Libertad

43776 ■ El Camino-FM - 106.1
17 Avenida Norte poligono K, No. 26
Bosques de Santa Teresa, Ciudad Merliot
La Libertad, El Salvador
Ph: 503 22296041
E-mail: iglesia@delcamino.org.sv
Format: Religious. **URL:** http://www.delcamino.org.sv.

San Salvador

43777 ■ BMC Public Health
Asociacion Demografica Salvadorena
Edificio Profamilia
25 Av. Norte No. 583
Apartado Postal 1338
San Salvador, El Salvador
Ph: 503 22448100
Fax: 503 22448179
Publisher E-mail: info@ads.org.sv
Online journal publishing original research articles in all aspects of epidemiology and public health medicine. **Key Personnel:** Melissa Norton, Editor-in-Chief, bmcserieseditor@biomedcentral.com. **ISSN:** 1471-2458. **Remarks:** Accepts advertising. **URL:** http://www.biomedcentral.com/bmcpublichealth/. **Circ:** (Not Reported)

43778 ■ Guapa-FM - 99.7
Av. Maracaibo No. 703
Col Miramonte
San Salvador, El Salvador
Ph: 503 22 602068
Format: Ethnic; World Beat. **URL:** http://www.laguapafm.com.

Kuressaare

43779 ■ Kuresaare Pereraadio-FM - 89.4 MHz
Tallinna tn 45
EE93811 Kuressaare, Estonia
Ph: 372 45 24480
Fax: 372 45 24481
E-mail: kuressaare@pereraadio.com
Format: Contemporary Christian; Religious. **Operating Hours:** Continuous. **Key Personnel:** Valter Rooso, Contact, valterrooso@hotmail.com. **Ad Rates:** Noncommercial; underwriting available. **URL:** http://www.pereraadio.com.

43780 ■ Kuresaare Pereraadio-FM - 88.7 MHz
Tallinna tn 45
EE93811 Kuressaare, Estonia
Ph: 372 45 24480
Fax: 372 45 24481
E-mail: kuressaare@pereraadio.ee
Format: Contemporary Christian; Religious. **Operating Hours:** Continuous. **Key Personnel:** Valter Rooso, Contact, valterrooso@hotmail.com; Endel Meiusi, Contact, ekmin@comcast.net. **Ad Rates:** Noncommercial; underwriting available. **URL:** http://www.pereraadio.com.

43781 ■ Kuresaare Pereraadio-FM - 89.0 MHz
Tallinna tn. 45
EE93811 Kuressaare, Estonia
Ph: 372 45 24480
Fax: 372 45 24481
E-mail: kuressaare@pereraadio.com
Format: Contemporary Christian; Religious. **Operating Hours:** Continuous. **Key Personnel:** Valter Rooso, Contact, phone 372 52 08782, valterrooso@hotmail.com; Lea Laats, Contact, lealaats@hot.ee; Anti Toplaan, Contact, phone 372 45 95624, anti.toplaan@eelk.ee. **Ad Rates:** Noncommercial; underwriting available. **URL:** http://www.pereraadio.com.

Paide

43782 ■ Kuma Raadio-FM - 101
57 Parnu St.
72712 Paide, Estonia
Ph: 372 38 38800
Fax: 372 38 38806
E-mail: kuma@kuma.ee
Format: News; World Beat. **Owner:** Kuma Ltd., at above address. **Founded:** Sept. 1, 1993. **Operating Hours:** Continuous. **Key Personnel:** Mati Palmet, Station Mgr., phone 372 38 38807, mati@kuma.ee; Hele Parn, Advertising Ed., phone 372 38 38812, reklaam@kuma.ee; Virgo Parn, Advertising Producer, phone 372 38 38803, raadio@kuma.ee. **Ad Rates:** Advertising accepted; rates available upon request. **URL:** http://www.kuma.ee.

Tallinn

43783 ■ Estonian Literary Magazine
Estonian Institute
Suur-Karja 14
PO Box 3469
EE-10506 Tallinn, Estonia
Ph: 372 2 6314355
Fax: 372 2 6314356
Publisher E-mail: einst@einst.ee
Estonian newspaper covering literature. **Freq:** Semiannual. **Key Personnel:** Tina Randviir, Editor. **ISSN:** 1406-0345. **Subscription Rates:** Free. **URL:** http://www.estinst.ee/eng/estonian-literary-magazine-eng/. **Circ:** 2,000

43784 ■ Klassika Raadio-FM - 106.6
Kreutzwaldi 14
EE10124 Tallinn, Estonia
Ph: 372 2 6114483
Fax: 372 2 6114428
E-mail: klassika@err.ee
Format: Eclectic. **Founded:** 1995. **Operating Hours:** Continuous. **URL:** http://klassikaraadio.err.ee.

43785 ■ Radio Mania-FM - 88.8
Tartu mnt. 80 D
EE-10112 Tallinn, Estonia
Ph: 372 2 6810870
Format: Heavy Metal. **Owner:** Radio Mania, at above address. **Operating Hours:** Continuous. **Ad Rates:** Advertising accepted; rates available upon request. **URL:** http://www.mania.ee.

43786 ■ Star-FM - 96.6
Peterburi tee 81
EE11415 Tallinn, Estonia
Ph: 372 2 6220288
E-mail: info@starfm.ee
Format: Ethnic. **Operating Hours:** 14 hours Daily. **URL:** http://www.starfm.ee.

43787 ■ Tallinna Pereraadio-FM - 89.6 MHz
Endla 29
10122 Tallinn, Estonia
Ph: 372 6460212
Fax: 372 6460211
E-mail: ekm@estpak.ee
Format: Ethnic. **Operating Hours:** 18 hours Daily. **URL:** http://www.estpak.ee/~ekm/english/contacts.htm.

43788 ■ Vikerraadio-FM - 105.3
Kreutzwaldi 14
EE10124 Tallinn, Estonia
Ph: 372 2 6114318
Fax: 372 2 6114124
E-mail: viker@err.ee
Format: Ethnic; News; Information. **Key Personnel:** Riina Roomus, Editor-in-Chief, riina.roomus@err.ee; Urve Koni, Contact, urve.koni@err.ee. **URL:** http://vikerraadio.err.ee.

43789 ■ Vikerraadio-FM - 105.6
Kreutzwaldi 14
EE10124 Tallinn, Estonia
Ph: 372 2 6114318
Fax: 372 2 6114124
E-mail: viker@err.ee
Format: Ethnic; Information; News. **Key Personnel:** Riina Roomus, Editor-in-Chief, riina.roomus@err.ee; Urve Koni, Contact, urve.koni@err.ee. **URL:** http://vikerraadio.err.ee.

43790 ■ Vikerraadio-FM - 105.1
Kreutzwaldi 14
EE10124 Tallinn, Estonia
Ph: 372 2 6114318
Fax: 372 2 6114124
E-mail: viker@err.ee
Format: Ethnic; Information; News. **Founded:** Apr. 3, 1967. **Key Personnel:** Riina Roomus, Editor-in-Chief, riina.roomus@err.ee; Urve Koni, Contact. **URL:** http://vikerraadio.err.ee.

Tartu

43791 ■ Agronomy Research
Estonian University of Life Sciences
St. Kreutzwaldi 56
EE51014 Tartu, Estonia
Publisher E-mail: info@emu.ee
Journal publishing articles on issues related to modern agriculture including crop and animal science, genetics, economics, technical aspects, agriculture, and environmental relations. **Founded:** 2003. **Freq:** Biennial. **Key Personnel:** Rein Lillak, Editor-in-Chief; Rein Viiralt, Assoc. Ed.; Erkki Maeorg, Assoc. Ed.; Ao Pae, Assoc. Ed.; Avo Toomsoo, Assoc. Ed.; Endla Reintam, Assoc. Ed.; Luule Metspalu, Assoc. Ed. **ISSN:** 1406-894X. **URL:** http://www.eau.ee/.

43792 ■ Journal Eesti Arst
Easti Arsti Ou
Pepleri 32
EE51010 Tartu, Estonia
Ph: 37 274 27825
Fax: 37 274 27825
Publisher E-mail: eestiarst@eestiarst.ee
Estonian language publication covering physicians. **Founded:** 1922. **Freq:** Monthly. **Key Personnel:** Andres Soosaar, MD, Editor-in-Chief. **ISSN:** 0235-8026. **Remarks:** Advertising accepted; rates available upon request. **URL:** http://www.eestiarst.ee. **Circ:** 3,800

43793 ■ Raadio Elmar-FM - 92.2
Opetaja 9a
EE51003 Tartu, Estonia
Ph: 372 7 427520
E-mail: elmar@elmar.ee
Format: Ethnic; World Beat; Contemporary Hit Radio (CHR). **URL:** http://www.u-pop.ee/elmar.

43794 ■ Raadio Elmar-FM - 91.5
Opetaja 9A
EE51003 Tartu, Estonia
Ph: 372 7 427927
E-mail: elmar@elmar.ee
Format: Ethnic; World Beat; Contemporary Hit Radio (CHR). **Ad Rates:** Advertising accepted; rates available upon request. **URL:** http://www.u-pop.ee/elmar.

Circulation: ★ = ABC; △ = BPA; ♦ = CAC; • = CCAB; ❑ = VAC; ⊕ = PO Statement; ‡ = Publisher's Report; Boldface figures = sworn; Light figures = estimated.

Addis Ababa

43795 ■ The Addis Tribune
Tambek International
PO Box 2395
Addis Ababa, Ethiopia
Ph: 251 161 5228
Fax: 251 161 5227
Publisher E-mail: tambek@telecom.net.et
Newspaper covering news and events in Addis Ababa, Ethiopia. **Founded:** Aug. 1992. **Freq:** Weekly. **Key Personnel:** Meselech Alemu, Contact. **Subscription Rates:** US$125 individuals. **Remarks:** Accepts advertising. **URL:** http://www.addistribune.com. **Circ:** (Not Reported)

43796 ■ Bulletin of the Chemical Society of Ethiopia
African Journals Online
PO Box 32934
Addis Ababa, Ethiopia
Publication E-mail: bcse@chem.aau.edu.et
Publisher E-mail: info@ajol.info
Peer-reviewed journal covering chemical science. **Freq:** 3/yr. **Key Personnel:** Prof. B.S. Chandravanshi, Editor-in-Chief, phone 251 11 1234293, fax 251 11 1234296, cse@chem.aau.edu.et; Feleke Zewge, Assoc. Ed.; Taddese Wondimu, Assoc. Ed. **ISSN:** 1011-3924. **Subscription Rates:** E$90 individuals; E$150 institutions; US$60 other countries; US$90 institutions, other countries. **URL:** http://ajol.info/index.php/bcse.

43797 ■ Ethiopian Economic Journal of Economics
African Journals Online
PO Box 1176
Addis Ababa, Ethiopia
Publisher E-mail: info@ajol.info
Peer-reviewed journal containing information for the advancement of the Ethiopean economy. **Freq:** Semiannual. **Key Personnel:** Dr. Getnet Alemu, Contact, getneta@idr.aau.edu.et; Eyerusalem Tesfaye, Contact, library@eeaecon.org; Getnet Alemu, Editor. **ISSN:** 1993-3681. **Subscription Rates:** E$10 individuals; US$15 individuals Africa; US$18 other countries. **URL:** http://ajol.info/index.php/eje.

43798 ■ Ethiopian Journal of Biological Sciences
African Journals Online
PO Box 31819
Addis Ababa, Ethiopia
Ph: 251 11 1221299
Fax: 251 11 1552350
Publisher E-mail: info@ajol.info
Peer-reviewed journal covering biology. **Key Personnel:** Seyoum Mengistou, Editor-in-Chief, bse@bio.aau.edu.et; Zeleke Wolde Tenssay, Editor; Afework Bekele, Assoc. Ed. **ISSN:** 1819-8678. **URL:** http://ajol.info/index.php/ejbs.

43799 ■ Ethiopian Journal of Development Research
African Journals Online
Addis Ababa University
PO Box 1176
Addis Ababa, Ethiopia
Ph: 251 1 11239721
Publisher E-mail: info@ajol.info
Peer-reviewed journal covering multi-disciplinary study of development problems in Ethiopia. **Freq:** Semiannual. **Key Personnel:** Mulugeta Feseha, PhD, Editor, mulufy@idr.aau.edu.et; Berhanu Gebremichael, Managing Editor; Alula Pankhust, Assoc. Ed. **ISSN:** 0378-0813. **Subscription Rates:** E$12 individuals; E$15 institutions; US$20 other countries; US$25 institutions, other countries. **URL:** http://ajol.info/index.php/ejdr.

43800 ■ Ethiopian Journal of Health Development
African Journals Online
Tikur Abesa Hospital
PO Box 32812
Addis Ababa, Ethiopia
Ph: 251 1 513628
Fax: 251 1 517701
Publisher E-mail: info@ajol.info
Peer-reviewed journal covering all aspects of public health and medicine. **Freq:** 3/yr. **Key Personnel:** Yemane Berhane, Editor-in-Chief, editorejhd@yahoo.com. **ISSN:** 1021-6790. **URL:** http://ajol.info/index.php/ejhd.

43801 ■ Ethiopian Journal of the Social Sciences and Humanities
African Journals Online
College of Social Sciences
Addis Ababa University
PO Box 1176
Addis Ababa, Ethiopia
Ph: 251 1 239747
Publisher E-mail: info@ajol.info
Peer-reviewed journal covering the social, political, economic and cultural development in Ethiopia and the Horn of Africa. **Freq:** Semiannual. **Key Personnel:** Setargew Kenaw, Managing Editor, setargew@phil.aau.edu.et. **ISSN:** 1810-4487. **Subscription Rates:** US$15 single issue. **URL:** http://ajol.info/index.php/ejossah.

43802 ■ Journal of Ethiopian Medical Practice
African Journals Online
PO Box 8528
Addis Ababa, Ethiopia
Publisher E-mail: info@ajol.info
Peer-reviewed journal of general medical practice. **Freq:** Semiannual. **Print Method:** Offset. **Trim Size:** 8 1/4 x 10 7/8. **Cols./Page:** 2. **Col. Width:** 20.5 picas. **Col. Depth:** 56 1/2 picas. **Key Personnel:** Temesgen Mekonnen, MD, Editor-in-Chief, esgmp@telecom.net.et; Hilmineh Sinishaw, MD, Editor; Sisay Alemayehu, MD, Editor. **ISSN:** 1560-1560. **Subscription Rates:** US$15 individu-

als per copy; E$20 individuals per copy. **URL:** http://ajol.info/index.php/jemp.

43803 ■ SINET
African Journals Online
Editorial Office
PO Box 31226
Addis Ababa, Ethiopia
Publisher E-mail: info@ajol.info
Peer-reviewed journal containing articles in basic and applied sciences. **Subtitle:** Ethiopian Journal of Science. **Founded:** 1978. **Freq:** Semiannual. **Key Personnel:** Prof. Gezahegn Yirgu, Editor-in-Chief, gezahegnyirgu@yahoo.com. **ISSN:** 0379-2897. **Subscription Rates:** E$20 individuals; US$20 other countries; E$50 institutions; US$50 institutions, other countries. **URL:** http://ajol.info/index.php/sinet.

Bahir Dar

43804 ■ African Research Review
African Journals Online
Dept. of Pedagogical Science
Faculty of Education
Bahir Dar University
PO Box 79
Bahir Dar, Ethiopia
Ph: 251 911572707
Publisher E-mail: info@ajol.info
Journal covering academic issues and sustainable development in Africa. **Freq:** 3/yr. **Key Personnel:** Dr. Babajide Johnson Ojo, Editor, babaojo2002@yahoo.com. **ISSN:** 1994-9057. **Subscription Rates:** US$20 individuals; US$50 institutions. **URL:** http://www.ajol.info/journal_index.php?jid=340.

Haramaya

43805 ■ East African Journal of Sciences
African Journals Online
Haramaya University
PO Box 42
Haramaya, Ethiopia
Ph: 251 25 5530045
Fax: 251 25 5530325
Publisher E-mail: info@ajol.info
Peer-reviewed journal covering the field of agriculture, forestry, natural resources, education, natural sciences, human and animal health sciences. **Freq:** Semiannual. **Key Personnel:** Dr. Tadele Tefera, Editor-in-Chief, tadeleterfera@yahoo.com; Dr. Chemeda Fininsa, Assoc. Ed., chefigu@yahoo.com; Teshome Wolder, Contact, teshew@yahoo.com. **ISSN:** 1992-0407. **Subscription Rates:** E$50 individuals; US$25 other countries; E$100 institutions; US$50 institutions, other countries. **URL:** http://ajol.info/index.php/eajsci.

Circulation: ★ = ABC; △ = BPA; ◆ = CAC; • = CCAB; ❑ = VAC; ⊕ = PO Statement; ‡ = Publisher's Report; Boldface figures = sworn; Light figures = estimated.

Lautoka

43806 ■ Fijian Studies
Fiji Institute of Applied Studies
PO Box 7580
Lautoka, Fiji
Publisher E-mail: fias@connect.com.fj
Journal publishing scholarly articles and reviews on Fiji.
Subtitle: A Journal of Contemporary Fiji. **Freq:**
Semiannual. **Key Personnel:** Ganesh Chand, Editor;
Chandra P. Dulare, Editorial Advisory Board; Martin
Doornbos, Editorial Advisory Board; Brij V. Lal, Chp.;
Jenny Bryant-Tokalau, Editorial Advisory Board; Haroon
A. Akram-Lodhi, Editorial Advisory Board; Anirudh Singh,
Editorial Advisory Board. **Subscription Rates:** US$25
individuals within Fiji, hardcopy; US$15 students
unemployed, retired (within Fiji); $F 40 individuals Pacific
Island nations (airmail, hardcopy); $F 30 individuals
Pacific Island nations(surface mail, hardcopy); $F 50

other countries airmail, hardcopy; $F 25 other countries
electronic; US$100 institutions libraries, hardcopy (within
Fiji); $F 100 institutions, other countries hardcopy. **URL:**
http://www.fijianstudies.org/fias_fijianstudies.htm.

Suva

43807 ■ Bula-FM - 102.0
PO Box 334
Suva, Fiji
Ph: 679 3314211
Fax: 679 6665855
E-mail: bulafm@fbcl.com.fj
Format: Contemporary Hit Radio (CHR). **URL:** http://
www.radiofiji.com.fj/bula-fm/.

43808 ■ Radio Fiji Gold-FM - 100.4
PO Box 334
Suva, Fiji
Ph: 679 3304500

E-mail: rfgold@fbcl.com.fj
Format: Adult Contemporary. **URL:** http://www.radiofiji.
com.fj/fijigold/.

43809 ■ Radio Fiji One-AM - 558
PO Box 334
Suva, Fiji
Ph: 679 3302588
E-mail: rf1@fbcl.com.fj
Format: News; Information. **URL:** http://www.radiofiji.
com.fj/fiji1/.

43810 ■ Radio Mirchi-FM - 98.0
PO Box 334
Suva, Fiji
Ph: 679 3302588
Fax: 679 3301643
E-mail: 2dayfm@fbcl.com.fj
Format: Ethnic. **URL:** http://www.radiofiji.com.fj/
radiomirchi/.

Circulation: ★ = ABC; △ = BPA; ◆ = CAC; • = CCAB; ❑ = VAC; ⊕ = PO Statement; ‡ = Publisher's Report; Boldface figures = sworn; Light figures = estimated.

Gale Directory of Publications & Broadcast Media/147th Ed. 4891

Abo

43811 ■ Journal of the Economic Society of Finland
Economic Society of Finland
Ekonomiska Samfundet i Finland
Abo Akademi/ISES
Fanriksgatan 3B
FIN-20500 Abo, Finland
Ph: 358 2 2154587
Fax: 358 2 2154677
Publisher E-mail: annica.karlsson@abo.fi
Swedish language journal covering the Economic Society of Finland. **Founded:** 1913. **Freq:** 3/yr. **Key Personnel:** Malin Wikstedt, Editorial Sec. **ISSN:** 0013-3183. **Subscription Rates:** EUR25 individuals; EUR10 single issue. **Remarks:** Advertising accepted; rates available upon request. **URL:** http://www.ekonomiskasamfundet.fi/est/. **Circ:** 950

Espoo

43812 ■ Kello and Kulta
The Finnish Watchmaker Association
Opinkuja 2
FIN-02100 Espoo, Finland
Ph: 35 894 520560
Fax: 35 894 5205656
Magazine covering topics about Finnish watch and jewelry retailers, wholesalers and manufacturers. **Freq:** 8/yr. **Remarks:** Accepts advertising. **URL:** http://www.kellojakultaonline.fi. **Circ:** (Not Reported)

Hameenlinna

43813 ■ Radio Janne-FM - 101.7
Vanajantie 7 PL
FIN-13110 Hameenlinna, Finland
Ph: 358 3 644500
Fax: 358 3 6537033
Format: Ethnic; World Beat. **Operating Hours:** Continuous. **URL:** http://www.radiojanne.fi.

Helsinki

43814 ■ African Newsletter on Occupational Health and Safety
Finnish Institute of Occupational Health
Topeliuksenkatu 41 A
FIN-00250 Helsinki, Finland
Ph: 358 304 741
African newsletter on occupational health and safety. **Founded:** 1991. **Freq:** 3/yr. **Key Personnel:** Suvi Lehtinen, Editor, suvi.lehtinen@ttl.fi; Marianne Joronen, Editor, marianne.joronen@ttl.fi. **ISSN:** 0788-4877. **URL:** http://www.ttl.fi/en/publications/electronic_journals/african_newsletter/pages/default.aspx.

43815 ■ Aikuiskasvatus
KVS Foundation
Haapaniemenkatu 7-9 B, 11
FIN-00530 Helsinki, Finland
Ph: 358 207 511500
Fax: 358 207 511502
Scientific journal covering adult education. **Founded:** 1981. **Freq:** Quarterly. **Print Method:** Offset. **Cols./Page:** 3. **Col. Width:** 420 centimeters. **Col. Depth:** 215 centimeters. **Key Personnel:** Anneli Kajanto, Publication Mgr. **ISSN:** 0358-6197. **Subscription Rates:** EUR30 individuals homeland; EUR35 individuals. **Remarks:** Accepts advertising 53. **URL:** http://www.kansanvalistusseura.fi/kauppa/?action=nayta_tuotteet&tuoteryhma=5; http://www.aikuiskasvatus.fi/. **Ad Rates:** GLR: EUR53, BW: EUR269. **Circ:** Paid 2,000, Non-paid 200

43816 ■ Annales Academiae Scientiarum Fennicae Mathematica
Academia Scientiarum Fennica
c/o Prof. Olli Martio, Ed.
University of Helsinki
Dept. of Mathematics & Statistics
PO Box 68
FIN-00014 Helsinki, Finland
Publisher E-mail: mathdept@cc.helsinki.fi
Journal covering mathematics with emphasis on analysis. **Key Personnel:** Olli Martio, Editor. **ISSN:** 1239-C20X. **URL:** http://www.acadsci.fi/mathematica/.

43817 ■ Apu
A-lehdet Oy
Risto Rytin tie 33
FIN-00081 Helsinki, Finland
Ph: 358 9 75961
Fax: 358 9 75983153
Publisher E-mail: etunimi.sukunimi@a-lehdet.fi
Consumer magazine covering food, home, travel, fashion, pets and other issues for families. **Founded:** 1933. **Freq:** Weekly. **Print Method:** Engraved rotogravure. **Trim Size:** 216 x 265 mm. **Cols./Page:** 4. **Key Personnel:** Matti Saari, Editor-in-Chief; Milla Talja, Editor; Riitta Lehtimaki, Managing Editor, riitta.lehtimaki@a-lehdet.fi. **Remarks:** Accepts advertising. **URL:** http://www.apu.fi/. **Ad Rates:** 4C: EUR7,600. **Circ:** Combined 254,762

43818 ■ Arkkitehti/Finnish Architectural Review
Finnish Association of Architects
Runeberginkatu 5 A
FIN-00100 Helsinki, Finland
Ph: 35 9 584448
Fax: 35 9 58444222
Publication E-mail: safa@safa.fi
Publisher E-mail: safa@safa.fi
Professional magazine covering architecture. **Subtitle:** Finnish/English. **Founded:** 1903. **Freq:** Bimonthly 6/yr. **Trim Size:** 240 x 297 mm. **Key Personnel:** Jorma Mukala, Editor-in-Chief. **ISSN:** 0783-3660. **URL:** http://www.safa.fi. **Circ:** 4,796

43819 ■ Asian-Pacific Newsletter
Finnish Institute of Occupational Health
Topeliuksenkatu 41 A
FIN-00250 Helsinki, Finland
Ph: 358 304 741
Journal on occupational health and safety. **Founded:** Jan. 1911. **Freq:** 3/yr. **Print Method:** Offset. **Trim Size:** 6 1/3 x 9 1/4. **Cols./Page:** 1. **Col. Width:** 51 nonpareils. **Col. Depth:** 108 agate lines. **Key Personnel:** Anna-Liisa Karhula, Editor. **ISSN:** 1458-5944. **URL:** http://www.ttl.fi/internet/english/information/electronicjournals/asian-pacificnewsletter/default.htm.

43820 ■ Avotakka
A-lehdet Oy
Risto Rytin tie 33
FIN-00081 Helsinki, Finland
Ph: 358 9 75961
Fax: 358 9 75983153
Publisher E-mail: etunimi.sukunimi@a-lehdet.fi
Consumer magazine covering interior decoration in Finland. **Founded:** 1967. **Freq:** 13/yr. **Trim Size:** 230 x 273 mm. **Cols./Page:** 4. **Key Personnel:** Johanna Falck, Editor-in-Chief, johanna.falck@a-lehdet.fi. **Remarks:** Accepts advertising. **URL:** http://www.avotakka.fi/. **Ad Rates:** 4C: EUR5,750. **Circ:** Paid 81,271

43821 ■ Books from Finland
The Finnish Literature Society
PO Box 259
FIN-00171 Helsinki, Finland
Ph: 358 201 131231
Fax: 358 9 13123220
Publisher E-mail: sks@finlit.fi
Journal covering writing from and about Finland. **Founded:** 1907. **Freq:** Quarterly. **Print Method:** Offset. **Trim Size:** 170 x 250 mm. **Cols./Page:** 3. **Col. Width:** 60 millimeters. **Col. Depth:** 205 millimeters. **Key Personnel:** Soila Lehtonen, Editor-in-Chief; Hildi Hawkins, Consulting Ed.; Iris Schwanck, Editorial Board. **ISSN:** 0006-7490. **Remarks:** Accepts advertising. **URL:** http://www.finlit.fi/booksfromfinland/. **Ad Rates:** BW: EUR600. **Circ:** Combined 2,800

43822 ■ Bulletin, Classe des Sciences Mathematiques et Naturelles, Sciences mathematiques
European Mathematical Society
EMS Secretariat
Dept. of Mathematics & Statistics
PO Box 68 (Gustaf Hallstromink. 2b)
FIN-00014 Helsinki, Finland
Ph: 358 919 151503
Fax: 358 919 151400
Publisher E-mail: ems-office@helsinki.fi
Peer-reviewed mathematical journal. **Freq:** Annual. **Key Personnel:** Novi Sad B. Stankovic, Editor-in-Chief, bogoljub@uns.ns.ac.yu. **ISSN:** 0561-7332. **URL:** http://www.emis.de/journals/BSANU.

43823 ■ Chabad-Lubavitch of Finland
Chabad-Lubavitch Media Center
Ilmarinkatu 10B, Ste. 66
FIN-00100 Helsinki, Finland
Ph: 358 9 444770
Magazine featuring articles on Jewish philosophy. **URL:** http://www.lubavitch.fi/magazine/default_cdo/jewish/Magazine.htm.

43824 ■ Demi
A-lehdet Oy
Risto Rytin tie 33
FIN-00081 Helsinki, Finland
Ph: 358 9 75961
Fax: 358 9 75983153
Publication E-mail: demi@a-lehdet.fi
Publisher E-mail: etunimi.sukunimi@a-lehdet.fi
Consumer magazine covering issues for girls aged 12 to 19 years. **Founded:** 1998. **Freq:** Monthly. **Trim Size:** 230 x 273 mm. **Cols./Page:** 4. **Key Personnel:** Jenni

Circulation: ★ = ABC; △ = BPA; ♦ = CAC; • = CCAB; ❑ = VAC; ⊕ = PO Statement; ‡ = Publisher's Report; Boldface figures = sworn; Light figures = estimated.

Gale Directory of Publications & Broadcast Media/147th Ed.   4893

Lieto, Editor-in-Chief; Johanna Mikkonen, Sales Mgr. **Remarks:** Accepts advertising. **URL:** http://www.demi.fi. **Ad Rates:** 4C: EUR3,000. **Circ:** Paid 49,951

43825 ■ Eeva
A-lehdet Oy
Risto Rytin tie 33
FIN-00081 Helsinki, Finland
Ph: 358 9 75961
Fax: 358 9 75983153
Publisher E-mail: etunimi.sukunimi@a-lehdet.fi
Consumer magazine covering general issues for women. **Founded:** 1934. **Freq:** Monthly. **Print Method:** Offset. **Trim Size:** 230 x 297 mm. **Cols./Page:** 4. **Key Personnel:** Riitta Nykanen, Editor-in-Chief, riitta.nykanen@a-lehdet.fi; Riitta Castren, Managing Editor, riitta.castren@a-lehdet.fi; Pirjo Houni, Editor, pirjo.houni@a-lehdet.fi. **Remarks:** Accepts advertising. **URL:** http://www.eeva.fi/. **Ad Rates:** 4C: EUR5,285. **Circ:** Paid 96,326

43826 ■ European Journal of Pharmaceutical Sciences
Elsevier Science Inc.
Centre for Drug Research, Faculty of Pharmacy
University of Helsinki
PO Box 56
Viikinkaari 5 E
FIN-00014 Helsinki, Finland
Publisher E-mail: usinfo-ehelp@elsevier.com
Journal covering pharmaceutical sciences. **Founded:** 1993. **Freq:** 15/yr. **Print Method:** Offset. **Trim Size:** 8 3/8 x 10 7/8. **Cols./Page:** 3. **Col. Width:** 13 1/2 picas. **Col. Depth:** 54 picas. **Key Personnel:** A. Avdeef, Editorial Board; D. Brayden, Editorial Board; C. Altomare, Editorial Board; P. Artursson, Editorial Board; M.J. Alonso, Editorial Board; C.M. Caramella, Editorial Board; M. Brandl, Editorial Board; J.A. Bouwstra, Editorial Board; H. Blume, Editorial Board; O.J. Bjerrum, Editorial Board; A. Urtti, Editor-in-Chief, ejps-journal@helsinki.fi. **ISSN:** 0928-0987. **Subscription Rates:** US$1,360 institutions, other countries except Europe, Japan and Iran; EUR1,218 institutions for European countries and Iran; 161,700¥ institutions; EUR262 individuals for European countries and Iran; US$352 other countries except Europe, Japan and Iran; 40,400¥ individuals. **URL:** http://www.elsevier.com/wps/find/journaldescription.cws_home/523997/descriptiondescription.

43827 ■ Fakta
A-lehdet Oy
Risto Rytin tie 33
FIN-00081 Helsinki, Finland
Ph: 358 9 75961
Fax: 358 9 75983153
Publication E-mail: fakta@fakta.dk
Publisher E-mail: etunimi.sukunimi@a-lehdet.fi
Professional magazine covering economics and management. **Founded:** 1981. **Freq:** 11/yr. **Print Method:** Offset. **Trim Size:** 230 x 273 mm. **Cols./Page:** 4. **Key Personnel:** Timo Holtari, Editor-in-Chief; Torben Thinggaard, Contact. **Remarks:** Accepts advertising. **URL:** http://www.fakta.dk/. **Ad Rates:** 4C: EUR3,620. **Circ:** Paid 30,000

43828 ■ Finnish Music Quarterly
Pieni Roobertinkatu 16
FIN-00120 Helsinki, Finland
Ph: 358 9 68034048
Fax: 358 9 68034033
Publisher E-mail: fmq@fmq.fi
Periodical covering music in Finland. **Subtitle:** Finnish Music Quarterly. **Founded:** 1985. **Freq:** Quarterly. **Print Method:** Four Colour. **Key Personnel:** Timo Jaakola, Advertising; Anu Ahola, Editor; Juha Torvinen, Editor-in-Chief, juha.torvinen@fmq.fi. **ISSN:** 0782-1069. **Subscription Rates:** EUR30 elsewhere; EUR24 individuals (Finland and Scandinavia). **Remarks:** Accepts advertising. **URL:** http://www.fmq.fi/. **Ad Rates:** BW: FM 400. **Circ:** (Not Reported)

43829 ■ F1 Racing
A-lehdet Oy
Risto Rytin tie 33
FIN-00081 Helsinki, Finland
Ph: 358 9 75961
Fax: 358 9 75983153
Publisher E-mail: etunimi.sukunimi@a-lehdet.fi
Consumer magazine covering Formula 1 racing. **Founded:** 1994. **Freq:** Monthly. **Print Method:** Offset. **Trim Size:** 221 x 297 mm. **Cols./Page:** 4. **Subscription Rates:** 112 individuals for 51 issues per year; EUR128

individuals for 51 issues per year; US$182 individuals for 51 issues per year. **Remarks:** Accepts advertising. **URL:** http://www.autosport.com/f1racing.asp. **Ad Rates:** 4C: EUR2,860. **Circ:** Paid 18,031

43830 ■ Framework
FRAME Finnish Fund for Art Exchange
Tallberginkatu 1 C 96
FIN-00150 Helsinki, Finland
Ph: 358 40 5070809
Fax: 358 9 47800818
Publication E-mail: office@framework.fi
Publisher E-mail: office@frame-fund.fi
Magazine dedicated to contemporary art and culture. **Subtitle:** The Finnish Art Review. **Freq:** Semiannual. **Subscription Rates:** EUR15.70 individuals Finland; EUR17.80 individuals; EUR26.60 other countries; EUR10 single issue. **Remarks:** Accepts advertising. **URL:** http://www.framework.fi. **Circ:** (Not Reported)

43831 ■ Futari
Suomen Palloliitto
PL 191
FIN-00251 Helsinki, Finland
Consumer magazine covering football (soccer) in Finland. **Founded:** 1982. **Freq:** Monthly 10/yr. **Print Method:** Offset. **Trim Size:** 230 x 280 mm. **Cols./Page:** 4. **Key Personnel:** Jouko Vuorela, Contact, phone 358 9 42427330, fax 358 44 5029732, jouko.vuorela@dialogi.fi. **Remarks:** Accepts advertising. **URL:** http://www.palloliitto.fi/viestinta/futari_ja_football_magazine/. **Ad Rates:** 4C: EUR2,110. **Circ:** Paid 75,478

43832 ■ Helsingin Sanomat
Sanoma Corp.
Ludviginkatu 6-8
PO Box 1229
FIN-00101 Helsinki, Finland
Ph: 358 105 1999
Fax: 358 105 195068
Newspaper covering news and events in Scandinavia. **Founded:** 1904. **Freq:** Daily. **Key Personnel:** Antero Mukka, Managing Editor; Reetta Merilceinen, Editor-in-Chief; Kaius Niemi, Managing Editor; Janne Virkkunen, Sr. Ed.-in-Ch.; Kimmo Pietinen, Managing Editor. **Remarks:** Accepts advertising. **URL:** http://www.hs.fi/english/. **Circ:** Mon.-Sat. ‡430,785, Sun. ‡482,767

43833 ■ International Journal of Digital Culture and Electronic Tourism
Inderscience Enterprises Limited
c/o Dr. Lily Diaz-Kommonen, Assoc. Ed.
University of Art & Design Helsinki, Media Lab
135C Hammentie
SF-00560 Helsinki, Finland
Journal covering digital culture and electronic tourism. **Freq:** 4/yr. **Key Personnel:** Dr. Lily Diaz-Kommonen, Assoc. Ed.; Dr. M.A. Dorgham, Editor-in-Chief, editorial@inderscience.com. **ISSN:** 1753-5212. **Subscription Rates:** EUR494 individuals print or online; EUR672 individuals print and online. **URL:** http://www.inderscience.com/browse/index.php?journalID=247.

43834 ■ Journal of Analysis and its Applications
European Mathematical Society
EMS Secretariat
Dept. of Mathematics & Statistics
PO Box 68 (Gustaf Hallstromink. 2b)
FIN-00014 Helsinki, Finland
Ph: 358 919 151503
Fax: 358 919 151400
Publisher E-mail: ems-office@helsinki.fi
Peer-reviewed Journal featuring theoretical knowledge in the field of analysis and its applications. **Founded:** 1982. **Key Personnel:** J. Appell, Managing Editor; M. Gunther, Managing Editor; S. Luckhaus, Managing Editor. **ISSN:** 0232-2064. **Subscription Rates:** EUR190 individuals. **URL:** http://www.ems-ph.org/journals/journal.php?jrn=zaa.

43835 ■ Journal of Lie Theory
European Mathematical Society
EMS Secretariat
Dept. of Mathematics & Statistics
PO Box 68 (Gustaf Hallstromink. 2b)
FIN-00014 Helsinki, Finland
Ph: 358 919 151503
Fax: 358 919 151400
Publication E-mail: mail@heldermann.de
Publisher E-mail: ems-office@helsinki.fi
Journal focusing on research in the field of Lie algebras, Lie groups, algebraic groups, and related types of topological groups. **Founded:** 1991. **Freq:** Quarterly.

Key Personnel: K.H. Hofmann, Dep. Mng. Ed.; Karl-Hermann Neeb, Managing Editor. **ISSN:** 0949-5932. **Subscription Rates:** EUR75 single issue; EUR300 individuals. **URL:** http://www.emis.de/journals/JLT/index.html.

43836 ■ Julkaisija
RPS-yhtiot
Hietakummuntie 18
FIN-00700 Helsinki, Finland
Ph: 358 934 78070
Fax: 358 934 780710
Publication E-mail: toimitus@julkaisija.com
Publisher E-mail: toimitus@julkaisija.com
Professional magazine covering graphic communications, including publishing, printing, graphic design and web publishing and design. **Founded:** 1994. **Freq:** Bimonthly. **Print Method:** Offset. **Trim Size:** 220 x 285 mm. **Key Personnel:** Marja-Liisa Kinturi, Editor-in-Chief, marja-liisa.kinturi@julkaisija.com; Seppo Lehtonen, Sales Mgr., seppo.lehtonen@julkaisija.com. **ISSN:** 1836-519X. **Remarks:** Accepts advertising. **URL:** http://www.julkaisija.com/. **Ad Rates:** 4C: FM 2,330. **Circ:** Combined ‡2,500

43837 ■ Kampanja
Kustannus oy Kampanja
Office House, 7 krs.
Bulevardi 2-4 A
FIN-00120 Helsinki, Finland
Ph: 358 961507482
Fax: 358 96923063
Professional magazine covering marketing, advertising, communications, and marketing research. **Founded:** Dec. 1, 1992. **Freq:** Monthly. **Print Method:** Offset. **Cols./Page:** 5. **Col. Width:** 50 millimeters. **ISSN:** 1236-1054. **Remarks:** Accepts advertising. **URL:** http://www.kampanja.net/. **Circ:** Paid 7,000

43838 ■ Katso
A-lehdet Oy
Risto Rytin tie 33
FIN-00081 Helsinki, Finland
Ph: 358 9 75961
Fax: 358 9 75983153
Publisher E-mail: etunimi.sukunimi@a-lehdet.fi
Consumer magazine covering television, movies, games, technology and entertainment. **Founded:** 1960. **Freq:** Weekly. **Print Method:** Offset. **Trim Size:** 230 x 302 mm. **Cols./Page:** 4. **Key Personnel:** Heli Kettunen, Editor; Tommi Pietarinen, Contact; Ismo Lehtonen, Contact. **ISSN:** 0355-2969. **Remarks:** Accepts advertising. **URL:** http://www.telvis.fi/katso/. **Ad Rates:** 4C: EUR2,860. **Circ:** Paid 72,741

43839 ■ Kauneus ja Terveys
A-lehdet Oy
Risto Rytin tie 33
FIN-00081 Helsinki, Finland
Ph: 358 9 75961
Fax: 358 9 75983153
Publisher E-mail: etunimi.sukunimi@a-lehdet.fi
Consumer magazine covering health and fitness for women. **Founded:** 1956. **Freq:** 16/yr. **Print Method:** Offset. **Trim Size:** 230 x 273 mm. **Cols./Page:** 4. **Key Personnel:** Titta Kiuru, Editor-in-Chief, titta.kiuru@a-lehdet.fi; Sami Onkamo, Sales Mgr.; Toni Nyman, Sales Mgr., jaana.vesanen@a-lehdet.fi. **Remarks:** Accepts advertising. **URL:** http://www.kauneusjaterveys.fi/. **Ad Rates:** 4C: EUR5,600. **Circ:** Paid 73,290

43840 ■ Kauppalehti Optio
Kustannus Oy Kauppalehti
Etelaesplanadi 20
PO Box 830
FIN-00101 Helsinki, Finland
Ph: 358 950 781
Fax: 358 950 78641
Magazine reporting on business, lifestyle, and trends in Finland. **Remarks:** Accepts advertising. **URL:** http://www.kauppalehti.fi. **Circ:** ★86,577

43841 ■ Ketju
Finnish Association on Mental Retardation/Kehitysvammaliitto
Viljatie 4 A
FIN-00700 Helsinki, Finland
Ph: 358 934 8090
Fax: 358 938 53398
Publisher E-mail: kvl@kvl.fi
Professional magazine for caretakers of the mentally

handicapped. **Subtitle:** Magazine on Intellectual Disability Issues. **Print Method:** Offset. **Cols./Page:** 3. **Col. Width:** 56 millimeters. **Key Personnel:** Veli-Pekka Sinervuo, Editor-in-Chief; Anneli Puhakka, Editor; Sisko Rauhala, Editor; Kaisa Ikavalko, Editor; Eeva Gronstrand, Editor; Sirpa Palokari, Editor. **ISSN:** 0355-2918. **Remarks:** Accepts advertising. **URL:** http://www.kehitysvammaliitto.fi/julkaisut/ketju.html. **Ad Rates:** BW: FM 1,080, 4C: FM 2,240. **Circ:** Paid 3,000

43842 ■ Kuljetusyrittaja
SKAL Kustannus Oy
Nuijamiestentie 7
PO Box 38
FIN-00401 Helsinki, Finland
Ph: 358 947 8999
Fax: 358 958 78520
Publisher E-mail: skal@skal.fi
Trade magazine covering legislation, transport economy, product news and related issue of interest to the Finnish Trucking Association and its members. **Founded:** 1993. **Freq:** 10/yr. **Print Method:** Offset. **Trim Size:** 210 x 297 mm. **Cols./Page:** 4. **Col. Width:** 40 millimeters. **Col. Depth:** 270 millimeters. **Key Personnel:** Pasi Moisio, Editor-in-Chief, pasi.moisio@skal.fi. **Remarks:** Accepts advertising. **URL:** http://www.skal.fi; http://www.skal.fi/en/kuljetusyrittaja-magazine. **Former name:** Ammattiautoilija. **Ad Rates:** 4C: EUR2,950. **Circ:** Controlled 8,423

43843 ■ Landsbygdens Folk
Central Union of Swedish Speaking Agricultural Producers in Finland
Fredriksgatan 61 A 34
FIN-00100 Helsinki, Finland
Ph: 358 95 860460
Fax: 358 96 941358
Publisher E-mail: fornamn.efternamn@slc.fi
Swedish language publication covering farming in Finland. **Freq:** Weekly (Fri.). **ISSN:** 0023-8015. **Remarks:** Advertising accepted; rates available upon request. **URL:** http://www.slc.fi. **Circ:** 10,220

43844 ■ Lifelong Learning in Europe
KVS Foundation
Haapaniemenkatu 7-9 B, 11
FIN-00530 Helsinki, Finland
Ph: 358 207 511500
Fax: 358 207 511502
Journal covering education and lifelong learning in Europe. **Founded:** 1996. **Freq:** 4/yr. **Print Method:** Offset. **Cols./Page:** 4. **Col. Width:** 400 centimeters. **Col. Depth:** 240 centimeters. **Key Personnel:** Markus Palmen, Managing Editor, phone 358 207 511591. **ISSN:** 1239-6826. **Subscription Rates:** EUR45 individuals; EUR70 libraries; US$67 individuals; US$103 institutions. **Remarks:** Accepts advertising 53. **URL:** http://www.kansanvalistusseura.fi; http://www.lline.fi/. **Ad Rates:** GLR: EUR53. **Circ:** Paid 400, Non-paid 1,000

43845 ■ Liikunnan ja Urheilun Maailma
Finnish Sports Federation
Suomen Liikunta ja Urheilu
Radiokatu 20, 7th Fl.
FIN-00240 Helsinki, Finland
Ph: 358 9 348121
Fax: 358 9 34812602
Publisher E-mail: etunimi.sukunimi@slu.fi
Publication covering sports. **Founded:** 1997. **Freq:** Biweekly. **Key Personnel:** Eila Ruuskanen-Himma, Hd. Ed. **ISSN:** 1458-5936. **Remarks:** Advertising accepted; rates available upon request. **URL:** http://www.slu.fi/. **Circ:** (Not Reported)

43846 ■ Meidan Mokki
A-lehdet Oy
Risto Rytin tie 33
FIN-00081 Helsinki, Finland
Ph: 358 9 75961
Fax: 358 9 75983153
Publisher E-mail: etunimi.sukunimi@a-lehdet.fi
Consumer magazine covering travel and leisure in Finland. **Founded:** 1997. **Freq:** 8/yr. **Print Method:** Offset. **Trim Size:** 230 x 273 mm. **Cols./Page:** 4. **Key Personnel:** Soili Ukkola, Editor-in-Chief; Johanna Mikkonen, Sales Directory; Pia Lindroos, Sales Mgr. **Remarks:** Accepts advertising. **URL:** http://www.meidanmokki.fi. **Ad Rates:** 4C: EUR3,900. **Circ:** Paid 43,917

43847 ■ Meidan Talo
A-lehdet Oy
Risto Rytin tie 33
FIN-00081 Helsinki, Finland
Ph: 358 9 75961
Fax: 358 9 75983153
Publisher E-mail: etunimi.sukunimi@a-lehdet.fi
Consumer magazine covering home and garden. **Founded:** 1959. **Freq:** Monthly. **Print Method:** Offset. **Trim Size:** 230 x 273 mm. **Cols./Page:** 4. **Key Personnel:** Timo Paasky, Editor-in-Chief; Johanna Mikkonen, Sales Dir.; Salme Kantonen, Sales Mgr. **Remarks:** Accepts advertising. **URL:** http://www.meidantalo.fi/. **Ad Rates:** 4C: EUR4,400. **Circ:** Paid 61,222

43848 ■ Modin
Association of Fashion Retailers in Finland
Mannerheimintie 76 B
FIN-00250 Helsinki, Finland
Ph: 358 968 447322
Fax: 358 968 447344
Publisher E-mail: muotikaupanliitto@muotikaupanliitto.fi
Trade magazine covering fashion (textile, shoes, leather). **Founded:** May 26, 2000. **Freq:** Bimonthly. **Print Method:** Offset. **Trim Size:** 210 x 297 mm. **Cols./Page:** 3. **Col. Depth:** 250 millimeters. **ISSN:** 1457-554X. **Subscription Rates:** EUR8,000 individuals Finland; EUR7,500 individuals Finland, permanent order; EUR4,000 individuals half a year; EUR10,000 individuals EU countries; EUR11,100 other countries. **URL:** http://www.muotikaupanliitto.fi/en/modin-magazine.html. **Former name:** Teksi & Kenkalusikka. **Ad Rates:** 4C: EUR2,900. **Circ:** Paid 8,000

43849 ■ Museo
Finnish Museums Association
Suomen Museoliitto
Annankatu 16 B 50
FIN-00120 Helsinki, Finland
Ph: 358 9 58411700
Fax: 358 9 58411750
Publisher E-mail: museoliitto@museoliitto.fi
Finnish language publication covering museums. **Founded:** 1983. **Freq:** Quarterly. **Trim Size:** 27.5 x 20.5 cm. **Key Personnel:** Janne Saavalainen, Contact, janne.saavalainen@museoliitto.fi. **ISSN:** 0781-0032. **Subscription Rates:** EUR38 individuals. **Remarks:** Advertising accepted; rates available upon request. **URL:** http://www.museoliitto.fi/en.php?k=9069. **Circ:** 2,000

43850 ■ NNKY-NAKY
Young Women's Christian Association - Finland
P. Rautatiekatu 23 B
FIN-00100 Helsinki, Finland
Ph: 35 894 342290
Fax: 35 894 3422920
Publisher E-mail: nnky@ywca.fi
Finnish and Swedish language publication covering the YMCA-YWCA. **Founded:** 1896. **Freq:** Bimonthly. **ISSN:** 1238-979X. **Remarks:** Advertising accepted; rates available upon request. **URL:** http://www.ywca.fi/cgi-bin/linnea.pl?document=00010775. **Circ:** 3,500

43851 ■ Nordic Journal of Psychiatry
Taylor & Francis Ltd.
c/o Finnish Psychiatric Association
University of Helsinki
Fredrikinkatu 71 A 4
FIN-00100 Helsinki, Finland
Ph: 358 405 195247
Fax: 358 947 706611
Journal publishing original articles, review articles, special topic issues, supplements, debate columns, book reviews and a congress diary on topics such as child and adult psychiatry, psychotherapy, pharmacotherapy, social psychiatry and psychosomatic medicine. **Founded:** 1946. **Freq:** 6/yr. **Key Personnel:** Hasse Karlsson, Editor-in-Chief, hasse.karlsson@helsinki.fi; Per Hove Thomsen, Child and Adolescent Psychiatry Ed., pht@buh.aaa.dk; Veiko Vasar, National Ed., veiko.vasar@kliinikum.ee; Jyrki Korkeila, National Ed., jyrki.korkeila@utu.fi; Jonas Eberhard, National Ed., jonas.eberhard@med.lu.se. **ISSN:** 0803-9488. **Subscription Rates:** US$270 institutions print and online; US$270 individuals online only; US$270 individuals print and online; US$270 institutions online only. **Remarks:** Advertising accepted; rates available upon request. **URL:** http://www.informaworld.com/smpp/title~content=t713691698. **Circ:** (Not Reported)

43852 ■ Oberwolfach Reports
European Mathematical Society
EMS Secretariat
Dept. of Mathematics & Statistics
PO Box 68 (Gustaf Hallstromink. 2b)
FIN-00014 Helsinki, Finland
Ph: 358 919 151503
Fax: 358 919 151400
Publication E-mail: reports@mfo.de
Publisher E-mail: ems-office@helsinki.fi
Reports containing research mainly aimed at the study of the structure and inner correlations of mathematical objects and at the development of more comprehensive theories. **Freq:** Quarterly. **Key Personnel:** Gert-Martin Greuel, Editor-in-Chief. **ISSN:** 1660-8933. **Subscription Rates:** EUR220 individuals print and online. **URL:** http://www.ems-ph.org/journals/journal.php?jrn=owr.

43853 ■ Opettaja
Trade Union of Education in Finland
Opetusalan Ammattijarjesto
Rautatielaisenkatu 6
FIN-00520 Helsinki, Finland
Ph: 358 20 7489600
Fax: 358 9145821
Publisher E-mail: oaj@oaj.fi
Finnish language publication covering education. **Freq:** Weekly. **ISSN:** 0355-3965. **Remarks:** Advertising accepted; rates available upon request. **URL:** http://www.opettaja.fi/. **Circ:** 86,000

43854 ■ Paper and Timber
Finnish Paper Engineers Association
Snellmannkatu 13
PO Box 155
FIN-00171 Helsinki, Finland
Ph: 358 9 1326688
Publisher E-mail: irmelihannula@papereng.fi
Journal of the Finnish Paper Engineers Association. **Founded:** 1919. **Freq:** 8/yr. **Key Personnel:** Paavo Seppanen, Mng. Dir., paavo.seppanen@metsalehti.fi; Martti Ristimaki, Editor-in-Chief, martti.ristimaki@metsalehti.fi. **Subscription Rates:** EUR100 individuals in Finland; EUR95 individuals in Finland, standing order; EUR144 other countries; EUR139 other countries. **URL:** http://www.paperijapuu.fi/lehti. **Formerly:** Paper and Timberland. **Circ:** 4000

43855 ■ Paperi Ja Puu
Paperi ja Puu
c/o Martti Ristimaki, Ed.-in-Ch.
Metsakustannus Oy
Soidinkuja 4
FIN-00700 Helsinki, Finland
Publication E-mail: paperijapuu@metsalehti
Trade journal of the Finnish forest and allied industries. **Founded:** 1919. **Freq:** 8/yr. **Print Method:** Sheetfed offset. **Trim Size:** 210 x 297 mm. **Cols./Page:** 4. **Col. Width:** 42 millimeters. **Key Personnel:** Paavo Seppanen, Mng. Dir., phone 358 207729121, fax 358 9630365, paavo.seppanen@metsalehti.fi; Martti Ristimaki, Editor-in-Chief, phone 358 207729148, fax 358 207729139, martti.ristimaki@metsalehti.fi. **ISSN:** 0031-1243. **Subscription Rates:** EUR100 individuals for Finland; EUR144 other countries; EUR95 individuals direct debit; EUR139 individuals direct debit. **Remarks:** Accepts advertising. **URL:** http://www.paperijapuu.fi/magazine/. **Ad Rates:** BW: EUR1,900, 4C: EUR2,900. **Circ:** 4,000

43856 ■ Scientific Journal of Orienteering
International Orienteering Federation
Internationale Orientierungslauf Federation
Radiokatu 20
FIN-00093 Helsinki, Finland
Ph: 358 93 4813112
Fax: 358 93 4813113
Publisher E-mail: iof@orienteering.org
Scientific journal covering orienteering. **Freq:** Semiannual. **Key Personnel:** Andre Leumann, Editor, leumann.andre@gmx.ch. **ISSN:** 1012-0602. **URL:** http://www.orienteering.org/.

43857 ■ Soundi
A-lehdet Oy
Risto Rytin tie 33
FIN-00081 Helsinki, Finland
Ph: 358 9 75961
Fax: 358 9 75983153
Publisher E-mail: etunimi.sukunimi@a-lehdet.fi
Consumer magazine covering rock music in Finland and

worldwide. **Founded:** 1975. **Freq:** 12/yr. **Print Method:** Offset. **Trim Size:** 225 x 297 mm. **Cols./Page:** 4. **Key Personnel:** Timo Kanerva, Editor-in-Chief; Veikko Virtanen, Sales Mgr. **Remarks:** Accepts advertising. **URL:** http://www.soundi.fi/node/1333. **Ad Rates:** 4C: EUR1,792. **Circ:** Paid 25,000

43858 ■ Sulasol
Finnish Amateur Musicians' Association
Suomen Laulajain ja Soittajain Liitto
Klaneettitie 6-8
FIN-00420 Helsinki, Finland
Ph: 358 10 8200220
Fax: 358 10 8200222
Publication E-mail: lehti@sulasol.fi
Publisher E-mail: info@sulasol.fi
Finnish publication covering music. **Freq:** 5/yr. **ISSN:** 0781-7061. **Remarks:** Advertising accepted; rates available upon request. **URL:** http://www.sulasol.fi/en/magazine/. **Circ:** 1,000

43859 ■ Suomen Autolehti
Association of Automotive Technical Societies in Finland
Suomen Autoteknillinen Liitto
Koydenpunojankatu 8
FIN-00180 Helsinki, Finland
Ph: 358 96 944724
Fax: 358 96 944027
Publisher E-mail: satl@satl.fi
Finnish magazine covering automotive. **Founded:** 1933. **Freq:** 10/yr. **Print Method:** Offset. **Trim Size:** A4. **Key Personnel:** Petteri Rasanen, Editor-in-Chief, phone 358 969 44033, petteri.rasanen@suomenautolehti.fi. **ISSN:** 0355-2691. **URL:** http://www.suomenautolehti.fi/in_english.html. **Ad Rates:** BW: EUR1,400, 4C: EUR2,175. **Circ:** ‡8,473

43860 ■ Suomen Hammaslaakarilehti/Finnish Dental Journal
Finnish Dental Association
Fabianinkatu 9 B
FIN-00130 Helsinki, Finland
Ph: 358 9 6220250
Fax: 358 9 6223050
Publication E-mail: kyllikki.blomroos.etutaka@fimnet.fi
Publisher E-mail: hammaslaakariliitto@fimnet.fi
Professional magazine covering dentistry. **Founded:** Sept. 15, 1954. **Freq:** 15/yr. **Print Method:** Offset. **Trim Size:** 210 x 280 mm. **Cols./Page:** 3. **Key Personnel:** Matti Poyry, Editor-in-Chief, phone 358 9.62202539, matti.poyry@fimnet.fi; Satu Lahti, Scientific Ed.-in-Ch., phone 358 40 7012386, satu.lahti@oulu.fi; Kyllikki Blomroos, Editorial Mgr., phone 358 9 62202541, kyllikki.blomroos@fimnet.fi; Annariitta Kottonen, Editor, phone 358 9 62202552, annariitta.kottonen@fimnet.fi; Outi Hautamaki, Editor, phone 358 9 62202545, outi.hautamaki@fimnet.fi; Kaija Lirkki, Advertising Mgr., phone 358 9 62202542, fax 358 50 5431951, kaija.lirkki@fimnet.fi. **ISSN:** 0355-4090. **Subscription Rates:** FM 150. **URL:** http://www.hammaslaakariliitto.fi/hammaslaeaekaerilehti/. **Ad Rates:** BW: EUR1,260, 4C: EUR2,175. **Circ:** Combined 6,800

43861 ■ Suomen Lehdisto
Finnish Newspapers Association
PO Box 415
FIN-00121 Helsinki, Finland
Ph: 358 9 22877300
Fax: 358 9 607989
Publisher E-mail: infor@sanomalehdet.fi
Professional journal covering journalism and other issues for the media field in Finland. **Founded:** 1930. **Freq:** Monthly 10/yr. **Print Method:** Coldset. **Key Personnel:** Kaija Jappinen, Editor-in-Chief, phone 358 922 877309, kaija.jappinen@sanomalehdet.fi; Veera Malin, Sub-Ed.; Rikka Virranta, Journalist, phone 358 228 77321. **ISSN:** 0039-5587. **Subscription Rates:** EUR75 individuals. **Remarks:** Accepts advertising. **URL:** http://www.sanomalehdet.fi/index.phtml?s=170. **Ad Rates:** GLR: EUR48, BW: EUR1,650, 4C: EUR2,550. **Circ:** Combined 2,404

43862 ■ Tuulilasi
A-lehdet Oy
Risto Rytin tie 33
FIN-00081 Helsinki, Finland
Ph: 358 9 75961
Fax: 358 9 75983153
Publisher E-mail: etunimi.sukunimi@a-lehdet.fi
Consumer magazine covering automobiles. **Founded:** 1963. **Freq:** 16/yr. **Print Method:** Offset. **Trim Size:** 217

x 280 mm. **Cols./Page:** 4. **Key Personnel:** Lauri Larmela, Editor-in-Chief; Johanna Mikkonen, Sales Mgr.; Liisa Ingman, Contact. **Remarks:** Accepts advertising. **URL:** http://www.tuulilasi.fi; http://mediaguide.a-lehdet.fi/magazines/tuulilasi. **Ad Rates:** 4C: EUR6,050. **Circ:** Paid 80,071

43863 ■ Tyo Terveys Turvallisuus
Finnish Institute of Occupational Health
Topeliuksenkatu 41 A
FIN-00250 Helsinki, Finland
Ph: 358 304 741
Journal covering occupational safety and health. **Founded:** 1971. **Freq:** Monthly. **Print Method:** Offset. **Cols./Page:** 4. **Col. Width:** 49 millimeters. **Key Personnel:** Ingmar Qvist, Contact; Matti Tapiainen, Contact. **ISSN:** 0041-4816. **Remarks:** Accepts advertising. **URL:** http://www.ttl.fi/Internet/Suomi/Tiedonvalitys/TyoTerveysTurvallisuus-lehti/; http://www.ttl.fi/partner/ttt/Sivut/default.aspx. **Ad Rates:** BW: EUR3,100, 4C: EUR4,760. **Circ:** Controlled **62,933**

43864 ■ Vegaia
Vegan Society of Finland
Hameentie 48
FIN-00500 Helsinki, Finland
Ph: 358 50 3449524
Fax: 358 97 732328
Publisher E-mail: info@vegaaniliitto.fi
Finnish language publication covering vegetarianism. **Freq:** Quarterly. **ISSN:** 1237-3184. **Remarks:** Advertising accepted; rates available upon request. **URL:** http://www.vegaaniliitto.fi/. **Circ:** 400

43865 ■ Viherpiha
A-lehdet Oy
Risto Rytin tie 33
FIN-00081 Helsinki, Finland
Ph: 358 9 75961
Fax: 358 9 75983153
Publisher E-mail: etunimi.sukunimi@a-lehdet.fi
Consumer magazine covering gardening and yard. **Founded:** 1994. **Freq:** 10/yr. **Print Method:** Offset. **Trim Size:** 230 x 273 mm. **Cols./Page:** 4. **Key Personnel:** Salme Kantonen, Sales Mgr.; Johanna Mikkonen, Sales Dir.; Kiti Andrejew, Editor-in-Chief. **ISSN:** 1236-990X. **Remarks:** Accepts advertising. **URL:** http://www.viherpiha.fi/. **Ad Rates:** 4C: EUR5,150. **Circ:** Paid 99,577

43866 ■ Voi Hyvin
A-lehdet Oy
Risto Rytin tie 33
FIN-00081 Helsinki, Finland
Ph: 358 9 75961
Fax: 358 9 75983153
Publisher E-mail: etunimi.sukunimi@a-lehdet.fi
Consumer magazine covering alternative health. **Founded:** 1986. **Freq:** Bimonthly. **Print Method:** Offset. **Trim Size:** 230 x 273 mm. **Cols./Page:** 4. **Key Personnel:** Krista Launonen, Editor-in-Chief. **Remarks:** Accepts advertising. **URL:** http://www.voihyvin.fi/. **Ad Rates:** 4C: EUR3,400. **Circ:** Paid 64,246

43867 ■ KSL Lahiradio-FM - 100.3 Mhz
Kansan Sivitystyon Liitto KSL ry Hameentie 36
00530 Helsinki, Finland
Ph: 358 9 229421
Format: Information. **Key Personnel:** Tarja Muukkonen, Editor, phone 358 50 5942951, tarja.muukkonen@ksl.fi. **URL:** http://mtserver.ksl.fi/webbi/radio/?page_id=1214.

Joensuu

43868 ■ Scandinavian Journal of Statistics
John Wiley & Sons Inc.
Wiley-Blackwell
c/o Juha Alho, Ed.
Scholarship of Computing
University of Eastern Finland
PO Box 111
80101 Joensuu, Finland
Peer-reviewed journal focusing on statistics. **Freq:** Quarterly. **Key Personnel:** Martin Skold, Assoc. Ed.; Paavo Salminen, Editor; Thomas A. Severini, Assoc. Ed.; Ingrid Glad, Assoc. Ed.; Edsel A. Pena, Assoc. Ed.; Tonu Kollo, Assoc. Ed.; Zhiliang Ying, Assoc. Ed.; Gabor Lugosi, Assoc. Ed.; Juha Heikkinen, Assoc. Ed.; Juha Alho, Editor; Geurt Jongbloed, Assoc. Ed.; Rasmus Waagepetersen, Assoc. Ed. **ISSN:** 0303-6898. **Subscription Rates:** US$68 individuals print + online; EUR58 individuals print + online; 41 individuals print +

online; US$333 institutions print + online; 190 institutions print + online; 172 institutions print, online; EUR241 institutions print + online; EUR219 institutions print, online; US$390 institutions, other countries print + online; US$354 institutions, other countries print, online. **Remarks:** Advertising accepted; rates available upon request. **URL:** http://www.wiley.com/bw/journal.asp?ref=0303-6898&site=1. **Circ:** (Not Reported)

Jyvaskyla

43869 ■ Human Technology
Jyvaskylan Yliopisto, Agora Center
University of Jyvaskyla
PO Box 35
FIN-40014 Jyvaskyla, Finland
Ph: 35 814 2601211
Fax: 35 814 2601021
Publication E-mail: humantechnology@jyu.fi
Journal presenting articles that explore the issues and challenges surrounding the human role in all areas of ICT-infused societies, drawing research from multiple scientific disciplines with an eye toward how applied technology can affect human existence or how it can foster personal development and enhance research and development in industry, education, communication and other fields. **Subtitle:** An Interdisciplinary Journal on Humans in ICT Environments. **Freq:** Semiannual. **Key Personnel:** Prof. Pertti Saariluoma, Editor-in-Chief; Barbara Crawford, Managing Editor. **ISSN:** 1795-5889. **Subscription Rates:** Free. **URL:** http://www.humantechnology.jyu.fi/.

43870 ■ Keskisuomalainen
Keskisuomalainen Oyi
Aholaidantie 3
PO Box 159
FIN-40101 Jyvaskyla, Finland
Ph: 35 814 622000
Publisher E-mail: marketing@keskisuomalainen.net
General newspaper. **Founded:** July 1, 1871. **Freq:** Daily. **Print Method:** Four colour offset rotary. **Trim Size:** 405 x 525 mm. **Cols./Page:** 8. **Col. Width:** 44 millimeters. **Col. Depth:** 500 millimeters. **Key Personnel:** Pekka Mervola, Editor; Sylvi Laitinen, Mktg. Dir. **ISSN:** 0356-1402. **Subscription Rates:** EUR49 individuals 2 months. **Remarks:** Accepts advertising. **URL:** http://www.keskisuomalainen.fi/web/index.php?id=107. **Circ:** 77,865

43871 ■ ptah
The Alvar Aalto Academy
The Alvar Aalto Museum
PO Box 461
FIN-40101 Jyvaskyla, Finland
Ph: 358 14 624809
Fax: 358 14 619009
Publication covering the theory of architecture, designs, and art in English. **Freq:** Semiannual (May and Oct.). **Trim Size:** 200 x 270 mm. **Key Personnel:** Claes Caldenby, Editorial Board; Esa Laaksonen, Editor-in-Chief, phone 358 50 5557330, esa.laaksonen@alvaraalto.fi; Elina Penttinen, Editorial Asst. **ISSN:** 1239-3401. **Subscription Rates:** EUR22 individuals Finland; EUR30 out of country; EUR11 single issue. **Remarks:** Accepts advertising. **URL:** http://www.alvaraalto.fi/ptah/. **Circ:** (Not Reported)

43872 ■ Suo - Mires and Peat
Finnish Peatland Society
c/o Birgit Hyyrylainen
Turveteollisuusliitto
Vapaudenkatu 12
FIN-40100 Jyvaskyla, Finland
Ph: 35 814 3385420
Fax: 35 814 3385410
Publisher E-mail: birgit.hyyrylainen@turveliitto.fi
Journal of the Finnish Peatland Society. **Freq:** Quarterly. **Key Personnel:** Sakari Sarkkola, Editor, sakari.sarkkola@metla.fi. **Subscription Rates:** EUR35 individuals plus postage. **URL:** http://www.suoseura.fi/suo/index.html.

43873 ■ Radio Keski-Suomi-FM - 99.3
Matarankatu 6 PL 3
FIN-40101 Jyvaskyla, Finland
Ph: 358 14 4444993
Fax: 358 14 4458213
E-mail: rks@yle.fi
Format: World Beat. **Operating Hours:** Continuous. **URL:** http://ralliradio.yle.fi.

Kirkkonummi

43874 ■ The Scientific World Journal
Saflaksintie 70
02400 Kirkkonummi, Finland
Publisher E-mail: information@thescientificworld.com
Journal for scientists using IT solutions. **Founded:** 1977. **Freq:** Continuous. **Print Method:** Offset. **Cols./Page:** 6. **Col. Width:** 2 1/16 inches. **Col. Depth:** 13 inches. **ISSN:** 1537-744X. **Subscription Rates:** US$1,062 institutions; EUR958 institutions; 649 institutions; US$1,593 individuals; EUR1,437 individuals; 947 individuals. **URL:** http://www.thescientificworld.com/; http://www.thescientificworld.com/flyers/December2006Newsletter/December06Newsletter.htmlstorytwo.

43875 ■ TSW Development & Embryology
The Scientific World Journal
Saflaksintie 70
02400 Kirkkonummi, Finland
Publisher E-mail: information@thescientificworld.com
Journal covering developmental biology including developmental mechanisms, the molecular basis of pattern formation, clinical embryology and evolutionary development. **Key Personnel:** Martien A.M. Groenen, Assoc. Ed.; David Tannahill, Editor; Chris T. Amemiya, Assoc. Ed.; Robert H. Anderson, Editorial Board; Cheryll Tickle, Assoc. Ed.; Nigel A. Brown, Editorial Board; Michael K. Richardson, Editorial Board. **Subscription Rates:** US$197 institutions; EUR177 institutions; US$296 individuals regular rate; EUR266 individuals regular rate; EUR78 individuals; US$87 individuals. **URL:** http://www.thescientificworld.com/SCIENTIFICWORLDJOURNAL/main/Home.asp?menuid=52&jid=294.

43876 ■ TSW Holistic Health & Medicine
The Scientific World Journal
Saflaksintie 70
02400 Kirkkonummi, Finland
Publisher E-mail: information@thescientificworld.com
Journal covering holistic health. **Founded:** 1954. **Freq:** Continuous. **Print Method:** Offset. **Trim Size:** 8 x 10 7/8. **Cols./Page:** 3. **Col. Width:** 27 nonpareils. **Col. Depth:** 140 agate lines. **Key Personnel:** Joav Merrick, Editor, jmerrick@internet-zahav.net. **ISSN:** 1749-494X. **Subscription Rates:** US$197 institutions; EUR177 institutions; US$296 individuals regular; EUR266 individuals regular; US$87 individuals personal; EUR78 individuals personal. **URL:** http://www.thescientificworld.com/SCIENTIFICWORLDJOURNAL/main/Home.asp?ocr=1&menuid=68&jid=295.

Kuopio

43877 ■ Pathophysiology
Mosby Inc.
c/o O. Hanninen, Ed.-in-Ch.
Dept. of Physiology
University of Kuopio
PO Box 1627
70211 Kuopio, Finland
Ph: 358 17 163080
Fax: 358 17 163112
Publisher E-mail: custserv.ehs@elsevier.com
Journal publishing articles that address the etiology, development, and elimination of pathological processes. **Freq:** Monthly. **Key Personnel:** O. Hanninen, Editor-in-Chief, osmo.hanninen@uku.fi; D.N. Granger, Regional Ed., dgrange@lsuhsc.edu; O. Matsuo, Regional Ed. **ISSN:** 0929-4680. **Subscription Rates:** EUR617 institutions for European countries and Iran; US$690 institutions, other countries except Europe, Japan and Iran; 82,100¥ institutions. **URL:** http://www.elsevier.com/wps/find/journaldescription.cws_home/524214/descriptiondescription.

Kuvalehdet

43878 ■ Alibi
Otavamedia Ltd.
Maistraatinportti 1
FIN-00015 Kuvalehdet, Finland
Ph: 358 9 156665
Fax: 358 9 1566511
Documentary magazine covering the crime sector worldwide. **Freq:** Monthly. **Print Method:** Gravure. **Trim Size:** 217 x 280 mm. **Key Personnel:** Mika Lahtonen, Editor-in-Chief. **Remarks:** Advertising accepted; rates available upon request. **URL:** http://www.alibi.fi. **Circ:** Combined 37,103

43879 ■ Anna
Otavamedia Ltd.
Maistraatinportti 1
FIN-00015 Kuvalehdet, Finland
Ph: 358 9 156665
Fax: 358 9 1566511
Consumer magazine covering people, health, fashion, beauty and other issues for women. **Freq:** Weekly. **Print Method:** Offset. **Trim Size:** 230 x 297 mm. **Key Personnel:** Emma Koivula, Editor; Ilkka Seppala, President. **Remarks:** Advertising accepted; rates available upon request. **URL:** http://mediatiedot.kuvalehdet.fi/lehdet/naistenlehdet/anna/default.aspx; http://plaza.fi/ellit/muoti-ja-kauneus/anna/. **Circ:** Combined ‡148,587

43880 ■ Era
Otavamedia Ltd.
Maistraatinportti 1
FIN-00015 Kuvalehdet, Finland
Ph: 358 9 156665
Fax: 358 9 1566511
Publication E-mail: era@kuvalehdet.fi
Consumer magazine covering fishing and other outdoor sports. **Freq:** Monthly. **Print Method:** Offset. **Trim Size:** 217 x 280 mm. **Key Personnel:** Anssi Uitti, Contact; Pia Hanhikangas, Contact; Seppo Suuronen, Editor. **URL:** http://www.eralehti.fi/. **Ad Rates:** 4C: FM 2,300. **Circ:** Combined ‡52,088

43881 ■ Hymy
Otavamedia Ltd.
Maistraatinportti 1
FIN-00015 Kuvalehdet, Finland
Ph: 358 9 156665
Fax: 358 9 1566511
Consumer magazine covering entertainment, celebrity news, fashion, and related issues. **Freq:** Monthly. **Print Method:** Gravure. **Trim Size:** 217 x 297 mm. **Key Personnel:** Esko Tulusto, Editor-in-Chief; Sami Lotila, Contact, sami.lotila@otavamedia.fi; Juha-Tapio Tuomela, Contact, juha-tapio.tuomela@otavamedia.fi. **Remarks:** Advertising accepted; rates available upon request. **URL:** http://www.hymy.fi/. **Circ:** Combined ‡95,845

43882 ■ Kaksplus
Otavamedia Ltd.
Maistraatinportti 1
FIN-00015 Kuvalehdet, Finland
Ph: 358 9 156665
Fax: 358 9 1566511
Consumer magazine covering babies, pregnancy and parenting. **Freq:** Monthly. **Print Method:** Offset. **Trim Size:** 217 x 280 mm. **Remarks:** Advertising accepted; rates available upon request. **URL:** http://www.kaksplus.fi/. **Circ:** Combined ‡46,740

43883 ■ Kanava
Otavamedia Ltd.
Maistraatinportti 1
FIN-00015 Kuvalehdet, Finland
Ph: 358 9 156665
Fax: 358 9 1566511
Consumer magazine covering social, political, business and cultural issues. **Freq:** 8/yr. **Print Method:** Offset. **Trim Size:** 188 x 248 mm. **Key Personnel:** Seppo Zetterberg, Editor; Alexander Lindholm, President. **ISSN:** 0355-0303. **Remarks:** Advertising accepted; rates available upon request. **URL:** http://mediatiedot.otavamedia.fi/lehdet/erikoislehdet/kanava/default.aspx. **Circ:** Combined ‡6,056

43884 ■ Kaytannon Maamies (KM)
Otavamedia Ltd.
Maistraatinportti 1
FIN-00015 Kuvalehdet, Finland
Ph: 358 9 156665
Fax: 358 9 1566511
Professional magazine for farmers in Finland. **Freq:** 15/yr. **Print Method:** Offset. **Trim Size:** 217 x 280 mm. **Key Personnel:** Pentii Torma, Editor, pentti.torma@otavamedia.fi; Esa Mustonen, Contact, esa.mustonen@otavamedia.fi; Alexander Lindholm, President. **Remarks:** Advertising accepted; rates available upon request. **URL:** http://www.kaytannonmaamies.fi. **Circ:** Combined ‡23,791

43885 ■ Kippari
Otavamedia Ltd.

Maistraatinportti 1
FIN-00015 Kuvalehdet, Finland
Ph: 358 9 156665
Fax: 358 9 1566511
Consumer magazine covering motor boats for owners and sailors. **Freq:** 10/yr. **Print Method:** Offset. **Trim Size:** 217 x 280 mm. **Key Personnel:** Juha Virtanen, Contact; Seppo Evinsalo, Contact; Pasi Nuutinen, Contact; Vesa Leppa, Editor. **ISSN:** 0780-5373. **Remarks:** Advertising accepted; rates available upon request. **URL:** http://www.kipparilehti.fi/. **Circ:** Combined ‡16,745

43886 ■ Kodutohter
Otavamedia Ltd.
Maistraatinportti 1
FIN-00015 Kuvalehdet, Finland
Ph: 358 9 156665
Fax: 358 9 1566511
Consumer magazine covering health in Estonia. **Freq:** Monthly. **Print Method:** Offset. **Trim Size:** 215 x 280 mm. **Key Personnel:** Siiri Lelumees, Editor, siiri.lelumees@ajakirjad.ee; Ullar Ende, Contact, yllar.ende@ajakirjad.ee; Viivi Variksaar, Contact, viivi.variksaar@ajakirjad.ee; Riina Reiman-Manniste, Contact, kodutohter@ajakirjad.ee; Ingrid Luks, Contact, anu.maarand@ajakirjad.ee. **Remarks:** Advertising accepted; rates available upon request. **URL:** http://www.kodutohter.ee/. **Circ:** Combined 16,000

43887 ■ Kotiliesi
Otavamedia Ltd.
Maistraatinportti 1
FIN-00015 Kuvalehdet, Finland
Ph: 358 9 156665
Fax: 358 9 1566511
Consumer magazine covering home, food and baking, and related issues. **Freq:** Monthly. **Print Method:** Offset. **Trim Size:** 217 x 280 mm. **Key Personnel:** Leeni Peltonen, Editor-in-Chief; Alexander Lindholm, President. **ISSN:** 0023-4281. **Remarks:** Advertising accepted; rates available upon request. **URL:** http://www.kotiliesi.fi/. **Circ:** Combined ‡195,425

43888 ■ Koululainen
Otavamedia Ltd
Maistraatinportti 1
FIN-00015 Kuvalehdet, Finland
Ph: 358 9 156665
Fax: 358 9 1566511
Consumer magazine covering music, hobbies, animals, computers, games and other issues for children and young people aged 7-12 years. **Freq:** Monthly. **Print Method:** Offset. **Trim Size:** 217 x 280 mm. **Key Personnel:** Sirkku Kuusava, Editor; Marjukka Sinninen, Contact; Maikki Rantala, Contact. **Remarks:** Advertising accepted; rates available upon request. **URL:** http://www.koululainen.fi/paasivu/. **Circ:** Combined ‡44,634

43889 ■ Lemmikki
Otavamedia Ltd.
Maistraatinportti 1
FIN-00015 Kuvalehodt, Finland
Ph: 358 9 156665
Fax: 358 9 1566511
Consumer magazine covering pets for animal lovers. **Freq:** Monthly. **Print Method:** Offset. **Trim Size:** 217 x 280 mm. **Key Personnel:** Ville Kormilainen, Editor-in-Chief. **Remarks:** Advertising accepted; rates available upon request. **URL:** http://www.kuvalehdet.fi/web/guest/lemmikki. **Circ:** ‡18,152

43890 ■ Leppis
Otavamedia Ltd.
Maistraatinportti 1
FIN-00015 Kuvalehdet, Finland
Ph: 358 9 156665
Fax: 358 9 1566511
Consumer magazine for children aged 2-7 years. **Freq:** Monthly. **Print Method:** Offset. **Trim Size:** 230 x 260 mm. **Key Personnel:** Sirkku Kuusava, Editor. **Remarks:** Advertising accepted; rates available upon request. **URL:** http://www.kuvalehdet.fi/web/guest/leppis. **Circ:** Combined ‡19,992

43891 ■ Metsastys ja Kalastus
Otavamedia Ltd.
Maistraatinportti 1
FIN-00015 Kuvalehdet, Finland

Circulation: ★ = ABC; △ = BPA; ♦ = CAC; • = CCAB; ❑ = VAC; ⊕ = PO Statement; ‡ = Publisher's Report; Boldface figures = sworn; Light figures = estimated.

Gale Directory of Publications & Broadcast Media/147th Ed.   4897

Ph: 358 9 156665
Fax: 358 9 1566511
Publication E-mail: kalastus@metsastys-kalastus.com
Consumer magazine covering hunting and fishing **Freq:** 13/yr. **Print Method:** Offset. **Trim Size:** 217 x 280 mm. **Key Personnel:** Raiko Ritvanen, Editor. **Remarks:** Advertising accepted; rates available upon request. **URL:** http://www.metsastys-kalastus.com/. **Circ:** Combined ‡36,637

43892 ■ MODA
Otavamedia Ltd.
Maistraatinportti 1
FIN-00015 Kuvalehdet, Finland
Ph: 358 9 156665
Fax: 358 9 1566511
Consumer magazine covering knitting and knitwear. **Freq:** 6/yr. **Print Method:** Offset. **Trim Size:** 217 x 280 mm. **Key Personnel:** Kati Ekko, Editor-in-Chief. **Remarks:** Advertising accepted; rates available upon request. **URL:** http://plaza.fi/ellit/kasityot/. **Absorbed:** Moda Muotikaavat. **Former name:** Novita. **Circ:** Combined ‡38,256

43893 ■ Parnasso
Otavamedia Ltd.
Maistraatinportti 1
FIN-00015 Kuvalehdet, Finland
Ph: 358 9 156665
Fax: 358 9 1566511
Consumer magazine covering literature from Finnish and foreign writers, poets and essayists. **Subtitle:** Literary Magazines. **Founded:** 1951. **Freq:** 7/yr. **Print Method:** Offset. **Trim Size:** 200 x 265 mm. **Key Personnel:** Jarmo Papinniemi, Editor. **Subscription Rates:** EUR42 individuals; EUR6 single issue. **Remarks:** Advertising accepted; rates available upon request. **URL:** http://mediatiedot.otavamedia.fi/lehdet/erikoislehdet/parnasso/default.aspx. **Circ:** Combined ‡3,648

43894 ■ Seura
Otavamedia Ltd.
Maistraatinportti 1
FIN-00015 Kuvalehdet, Finland
Ph: 358 9 156665
Fax: 358 9 1566511
Consumer magazine covering lifestyle and family related issues in Finland. **Print Method:** Gravure. **Trim Size:** 217 x 280 mm. **Key Personnel:** Saija Hakoniemi, Editor-in-Chief; Marja Aalto, Contact; Eero Nokela, Contact. **Remarks:** Advertising accepted; rates available upon request. **URL:** http://mediatiedot.kuvalehdet.fi/sankari2/. **Circ:** Combined ‡211,863

43895 ■ Suomen Kuvalehti
Otavamedia Ltd.
Maistraatinportti 1
FIN-00015 Kuvalehdet, Finland
Ph: 358 9 156665
Fax: 358 9 1566511
Consumer magazine covering political and social issues. **Founded:** 1916. **Freq:** Weekly. **Print Method:** Gravure. **Trim Size:** 217 x 280 mm. **Key Personnel:** Tapani Ruokanen, Editor-in-Chief; Viola Westerberg, Contact; Jyrki Jantunen, Contact. **Remarks:** Advertising accepted; rates available upon request. **URL:** http://www.suomenkuvalehti.fi/. **Circ:** Combined ‡101,000

43896 ■ Suosikki
Otavamedia Ltd.
Maistraatinportti 1
FIN-00015 Kuvalehdet, Finland
Ph: 358 9 156665
Fax: 358 9 1566511
Consumer magazine covering music, entertainment and other issues for youth. **Freq:** Monthly. **Print Method:** Offset. **Trim Size:** 217 x 280 mm. **Key Personnel:** Ville Kormilainen, Editor-in-Chief. **Remarks:** Advertising accepted; rates available upon request. **URL:** http://suosikki.fi/; http://www.kuvalehdet.fi/web/guest/suosikki. **Circ:** ‡45,939

43897 ■ Tekniikan Maailma
Otavamedia Ltd.
Maistraatinportti 1
FIN-00015 Kuvalehdet, Finland
Ph: 358 9 156665
Fax: 358 9 1566511
Consumer magazine covering automobiles, electronics, telephones and computers. **Freq:** 20/yr. **Print Method:** Gravure. **Trim Size:** 217 x 280 mm. **Key Personnel:**

Velimatti Honkanen, Editor-in-Chief. **Remarks:** Advertising accepted; rates available upon request. **URL:** http://www.tekniikanmaailma.fi/. **Also known as:** TM. **Circ:** Combined ‡129,343

43898 ■ Tom & Jerry
Otavamedia Ltd.
Maistraatinportti 1
FIN-00015 Kuvalehdet, Finland
Ph: 358 9 156665
Fax: 358 9 1566511
Children's magazine featuring cartoons of Tom and Jerry, a cat and mouse pair of friends. **Freq:** Monthly. **Print Method:** Offset. **Trim Size:** 170 x 260 mm. **Key Personnel:** Sirkku Kuusava, Editor; Alexander Lindholm, President. **Subscription Rates:** EUR9.80 individuals. **Remarks:** Advertising accepted; rates available upon request. **URL:** http://www2.kuvalehdet.fi/verkkokauppa.jsp?cid=ve_verkkokauppa&vk_action=open&vk_product=2852621. **Circ:** Combined ‡8,559

43899 ■ TV-maailma
Otavamedia Ltd.
Maistraatinportti 1
FIN-00015 Kuvalehdet, Finland
Ph: 358 9 156665
Fax: 358 9 1566511
Consumer magazine covering television programs and entertainment news. Published with Seura and Suomen Kuvalehti as a magazine within a magazine. **Founded:** Sept. 1998. **Freq:** Weekly. **Print Method:** Gravure Printing. **Trim Size:** 205 x 270 mm. **Key Personnel:** Iina Keskinen, Reservations; Sanna Wirtavuori, Editor; Tapani Ruokanen, Editor. **ISSN:** 1456-2006. **Remarks:** Advertising accepted; rates available upon request. **URL:** http://www.lehtiapaja.fi/Otavamedia/TVmaailma/. **Circ:** Combined ‡400,000

43900 ■ Vauhdin Maailma
Otavamedia Ltd.
Maistraatinportti 1
FIN-00015 Kuvalehdet, Finland
Ph: 358 9 156665
Fax: 358 9 1566511
Consumer magazine covering motor sports in Finland. **Freq:** Monthly. **Print Method:** Offset. **Trim Size:** 217 x 280 mm. **Key Personnel:** Olli Koivusalo, Editor-in-Chief; Kikka Kuosmanen, Contact; Pia Hanhikangas, Contact; Arttu Kauranne, Contact. **Remarks:** Advertising accepted; rates available upon request. **URL:** http://www.vauhdinmaailma.fi/. **Circ:** Combined ‡33,558

43901 ■ Vene
Otavamedia Ltd.
Maistraatinportti 1
FIN-00015 Kuvalehdet, Finland
Ph: 358 9 156665
Fax: 358 9 1566511
Consumer magazine covering boats and yachting. **Freq:** 10/yr. **Print Method:** Offset. **Trim Size:** 217 x 280 mm. **Key Personnel:** Ari Inkinen, Editor; Timo Utter, Contact; Pia Hanhikangas, Contact; Kiti Westerback, Contact; Heikki Juuri-Oja, Contact; Satu Bjorn, Contact. **Remarks:** Advertising accepted; rates available upon request. **URL:** http://www.venelehti.fi/. **Circ:** Combined ‡31,702

43902 ■ Villivarsa
Otavamedia Ltd.
Maistraatinportti 1
FIN-00015 Kuvalehdet, Finland
Ph: 358 9 156665
Fax: 358 9 1566511
Consumer magazine covering horses for beginning and experienced young riders. **Freq:** Monthly. **Print Method:** Offset. **Trim Size:** 190 x 265 mm. **Key Personnel:** Villen Kormilaine, Editor. **Remarks:** Advertising accepted; rates available upon request. **URL:** http://www.kuvalehdet.fi/web/guest/villivarsa. **Circ:** Combined ‡13,538

Lahti

43903 ■ Woodworking Puuntyosto WIN
Woodpublishers Oy Ltd.
PL 211, Puistokatu 9 A
FIN-15101 Lahti, Finland
Ph: 358 373 31501
Fax: 358 373 31511
Publisher E-mail: wood@puuntyosto.com
Professional magazine for the woodworking, furniture,

and sawmill industry in Finland. Finnish with an English supplement. **Founded:** Apr. 1990. **Freq:** Monthly 10/yr. **Print Method:** Offset. **Trim Size:** 210 x 297 mm. **Cols./Page:** 4. **Col. Width:** 42 millimeters. **Key Personnel:** Tania Parviainen, Editorial Asst./Traffic Sec., tania.parviainen@elisanet.fi; Jorma Laitinen, Editor-in-Chief, jormas.laitinen@kolumbus.fi. **ISSN:** 1239-047X. **Subscription Rates:** EUR65 other countries; EUR48 individuals; EUR53 individuals Europe. **Remarks:** Accepts advertising. **URL:** http://www.puuntyosto.com/. **Former name:** Woodworking Finland. **Ad Rates:** BW: FM 1,340, 4C: FM 1,890. **Circ:** 5,000

Pori

43904 ■ Elore
Finnish Folklore Society
University of Turku
School of Cultural Production & Landscape Studies
University Consortium of Pori
Siltapuistonkatu 2
FIN-28100 Pori, Finland
Ph: 358 627 2964
Fax: 358 627 2707
Publisher E-mail: outfin@utu.fi
Hungarian language communist daily newspaper published in New York. **Founded:** Oct. 29, 1764. **Freq:** Mon.-Sun. (morn.). **Print Method:** Offset. **Trim Size:** 13 1/2 x 21 3/4. **Cols./Page:** 6. **Col. Width:** 256 nonpareils. **Col. Depth:** 301 agate lines. **Key Personnel:** Petja Aarnipuu, Ph.D., Editor-in-Chief, petja@aarnipuu.fi. **ISSN:** 1237-8593. **URL:** http://www.elore.fi/.

Rajamaki

43905 ■ Teho
TTS Institute
PO Box 5
FIN-05201 Rajamaki, Finland
Ph: 358 9 29041200
Fax: 358 9 29041285
Publisher E-mail: tts@tts.fi
Trade magazine covering agriculture, forestry and home economics. **Founded:** 1946. **Freq:** Bimonthly. **Print Method:** Offset. **Trim Size:** 194 x 270 mm. **Cols./Page:** 3. **Col. Width:** 55 millimeters. **Key Personnel:** Tarmo Luoma, Editor; Merja Sillanpaa, Contact. **ISSN:** 0355-0567. **Subscription Rates:** EUR47 nonmembers; EUR46 individuals. **Remarks:** Accepts advertising. **URL:** http://www.tts.fi. **Circ:** Paid 4,662

Savonlinna

43906 ■ SKY Journal of Linguistics
Linguistic Association of Finland
Savonlinna School of Translation Studies
PO Box 48
University of Joensuu
FIN-57101 Savonlinna, Finland
Journal containing articles, short essays and book reviews. **Freq:** Annual. **Key Personnel:** Werner Abraham, Advisory Editorial Board; Urpo Nikanne, Advisory Editorial Board; Mari Lehtinen, Editor; Kari Suomi, Advisory Editorial Board; Jussi Niemi, Advisory Editorial Board; Jaakko Hameen-Anttila, Advisory Editorial Board; Mirja Saari, Advisory Editorial Board. **Subscription Rates:** EUR17 individuals; EUR12 individuals earlier publications. **URL:** http://www.ling.helsinki.fi/sky/skyjol-en.shtml.

Tampere

43907 ■ Diabetes
Finnish Diabetes Association
Diabetes Center
Kirjoniementie 15
FIN-33680 Tampere, Finland
Ph: 35 832 860111
Fax: 35 833 600462
Publisher E-mail: diabetesliitto@diabetes.fi
Magazine containing a medical supplement, Diabetes & Physician. **Founded:** 1949. **Freq:** 10/yr. **URL:** http://www.diabetes.fi.

43908 ■ International Journal of Bioelectromagnetism
International Society for Bioelectromagnetism
Tampere University of Technology
PO Box 692
FIN-33101 Tampere, Finland
Ph: 358 40849 0020

Fax: 358 33115 2162
Journal on Bioelectromagnetism. **Key Personnel:** Jari Hyttinen, Contact, jari.hyttinen@tut.fi. **ISSN:** 1456-7857. **URL:** http://www.ijbem.org/.

Turku

43909 ■ Farma Sanomat
Farma Maaseutukeskus
Artturinkatu 2
FIN-20200 Turku, Finland
Ph: 358 10 2731500
Fax: 358 10 2337570
Publication E-mail: eila.knuutila@farma.fi
Agricultural magazine for member of FARMA. **Founded:** 1983. **Trim Size:** 188 x 260 mm. **Cols./Page:** 4. **Col. Width:** 44 millimeters. **Col. Depth:** 260 millimeters. **Key Personnel:** Raine Laakso, Contact, phone 358 2

7702438, raine.laakso@hansaprint.fi. **ISSN:** 0787-037X. **URL:** http://www.farma.fi. **Circ:** Combined 9,000

43910 ■ Progress in Industrial Ecology
Inderscience Publishers
c/o Dr. Jouni Korhonen, Ed.-in-Ch.
Faculty of Technology
Abo Akademi University
Dept. of Industrial Management, Biskopsgatan 8
FIN-20500 Turku, Finland
Publisher E-mail: editor@inderscience.com
Peer-reviewed journal contributing to international research and practice in industrial ecology for sustainable development by establishing channels of communication between academics, practitioners, business stakeholders and the government, with an interdisciplinary and international approach to the challenges of corporate social responsibility and inter-organisational environmental management. **Subtitle:** An International

Journal. **Freq:** Bimonthly. **Key Personnel:** Dr. Jouni Korhonen, Editor-in-Chief, jouni.korhonen@abo.fi; Dr. Peter A. Strachan, Editor, p.a.strachan@rgu.ac.uk; Dr. Alfred Posch, Assoc. Ed. **ISSN:** 1476-8917. **Subscription Rates:** EUR593 individuals print only (surface mail); EUR1,010 individuals online only (2-3 users); EUR643 individuals print only (airmail); EUR830 individuals print and online. **URL:** http://www.inderscience.com/browse/index.php?journalID=55.

43911 ■ Radio Robin Hood-FM - 91.5 MHZ
Itainen Rantakatu 64
FIN-20810 Turku, Finland
Ph: 358 2 2773666
E-mail: info@radiorobinhood.fi
Format: Ethnic; News. **Founded:** 1990. **Operating Hours:** Continuous. **Key Personnel:** Riita Haapakoski, Hd. Admin., phone 358 2 2773641. **URL:** http://www.radiorobinhood.fi.

Aix-en-Provence

43912 ■ International Journal of Public Sector Performance Management
Inderscience Publishers
c/o Prof. Robert Fouchet, Ed.
Universite Paul-Cezanne Aix-Marseille III
Institute of Public Management & Territorial Governance
21 rue Gaston de Saporta
F-13625 Aix-en-Provence Cedex 1, France
Publisher E-mail: editor@inderscience.com
Peer-reviewed journal covering implementation of performance management in the public sector. **Founded:** 2007. **Freq:** 4/yr. **Key Personnel:** Prof. Robert Fouchet, Editor, robert.fouchet@univ-cezanne.fr; Prof. Zeljko Sevia, Assoc. Ed. **ISSN:** 1741-1041. **Subscription Rates:** EUR494 individuals includes surface mail, print only; EUR672 individuals print and online. **URL:** http://www.inderscience.com/browse/index.php?journalCODE=ijpspm.

43913 ■ Maisons et Decors Mediterranees
Compagnie Mediterraneenne d'Edition
Europarc Pichaury C10
1330 Ave. Guillibert de la Lauziere
BP 439
F-13591 Aix-en-Provence Cedex 3, France
Ph: 33 442 371450
Fax: 33 442 242886
Publication E-mail: contact@maisonsetdecors.fr
Consumer magazine covering houses in Provence and the French Riviera. **Founded:** Jan. 1975. **Freq:** Semimonthly. **Print Method:** Offset. **Key Personnel:** A.m. Masclaux, Editor, redaction@maisonsetdecors.com. **ISSN:** 0180-4561. **Subscription Rates:** EUR20.44 individuals France. **Remarks:** Advertising accepted; rates available upon request. **URL:** http://www.info-presse.fr/fiches/maisons-decors-mediterranee_3076_gp.htm. **Circ:** Paid 100,582

Antibes

43914 ■ International Journal of Image and Video Processing (IJIVP)
Hindawi Publishing Corp.
c/o Jean-Luc Dugelay, Ed.-in-Ch.
Institut EURECOM
MultiMedia Communications Dept.
2229 Rte. des Cretes BP 193
F-06904 Antibes Cedex, France
Publisher E-mail: hindawi@hindawi.com
Journal focusing on the field of image and video processing. **Key Personnel:** Jean-Luc Dugelay, Editor-in-Chief, jean-luc.dugelay@eurecom.fr. **ISSN:** 1687-5176. **Subscription Rates:** US$295 individuals. **URL:** http://www.hindawi.com/journals/ivp/aims.html.

43915 ■ Mer & Bateaux
Boat International Group
150 rue de Goa
F-06600 Antibes, France
Ph: 33 4 97214450
Fax: 33 1 48775780
Publication E-mail: mer.et.bateaux@wanadoo.fr
Publisher E-mail: info@boatinternational.co.uk
Magazine covering French yachting market. **Freq:** Bimonthly. **Trim Size:** 223 x 275 mm. **Key Personnel:** Tony Harris, CEO; Tony Euden, Publishing Dir., tony.euden@boatinternationalmedia.com. **Remarks:** Accepts advertising. **URL:** http://www.boatinternationalmedia.com/mags/mag04.htm. **Ad Rates:** 4C: 3,850 Fr. **Circ:** 13,500

Auray

43916 ■ Voie Libre
LR Presse S.A.R.L.
12 St. of Sablen
F-56400 Auray Cedex, France
Ph: 33 297 240165
Fax: 33 297 242830
Magazine covering touristic and industrial railways in modeling and reality. **Founded:** 1997. **Freq:** Quarterly. **Print Method:** Offset. **Trim Size:** 210 x 285 mm. **Cols./Page:** 3. **Col. Width:** 59 millimeters. **Col. Depth:** 250 millimeters. **Key Personnel:** Christian Fournereau, Director. **ISSN:** 1285-5081. **Subscription Rates:** 38 individuals. **Remarks:** Accepts advertising. **URL:** http://www.locorevue.com. **Ad Rates:** BW: EUR225.62, 4C: EUR410.09. **Circ:** Combined 5,150

Avignon

43917 ■ Agronomy for Sustainable Development
EDP Sciences
INRA, Site Agroparc
F-84914 Avignon Cedex 9, France
Ph: 33 4 32722294
Fax: 33 4 32722282
Publication E-mail: agronomy@avignon.inra.fr
Publisher E-mail: subscribers@edpsciences.org
Journal covering scientific research on the interactions between cropping systems and other activities in the context of sustainable development. **Subtitle:** An International Journal in Agriculture & Environment. **Freq:** 4/yr. **Print Method:** offset. **Key Personnel:** Dr. Eric Lichtfouse, Editor-in-Chief. **ISSN:** 1774-0746. **Subscription Rates:** EUR490 individuals print and electronic, France; EUR559 individuals print and electronic, European Union; EUR596 other countries print and electronic; EUR417 other countries electronic. **Remarks:** Accepts advertising. **URL:** http://www.agronomy-journal.org/. **Ad Rates:** BW: 560 Fr, 4C: 960 Fr. **Circ:** 1,000

43918 ■ Soleil-FM - 96.3
13551 St. Martin de Crau
F-40016 Avignon Cedex, France
Ph: 33 4 90471526
Fax: 33 4 90473044
E-mail: contact@soleilfm.com
Format: Album-Oriented Rock (AOR); Contemporary Hit Radio (CHR). **Operating Hours:** Continuous. **Key Personnel:** Alain Ibanez, President; Jacqueline Etienne, Sec. **Ad Rates:** Advertising accepted; rates available upon request. **URL:** http://www.soleilfm.com.

Belgrade

43919 ■ Sorgia-FM - 91 Mhz
Ave. Paul Langevin
01200 Belgrade, France
Format: Full Service. **Owner:** Sorgia-FM, at above address. **Founded:** 1984. **Key Personnel:** Guy Catelan, President. **URL:** http://100ansderadio.free.fr/01/01-Sorgia/Sorgia.html; http://www.sorgiafm.fr/.

Bergerac

43920 ■ Bergerac-FM - 95
Bergerac 95
BP 518
F-24105 Bergerac Cedex, France
Ph: 33 5 53577622
Fax: 33 5 53631613
Format: Eclectic. **Ad Rates:** Advertising accepted; rates available upon request. **URL:** http://www.bergerac95.fr.

Bordeaux

43921 ■ Bulletin de l'ALLF
Association of French-Language Leprologists
Association des Leprologues de Lange Francaise
4 rue Jean Jacques Bel
F-33000 Bordeaux, France
Ph: 33 556 523214
Fax: 33 556 523214
Publisher E-mail: pibobin@wanadoo.fr
French language publication covering leprosy. **Freq:** Semiannual. **Subscription Rates:** Included in membership. **URL:** http://sfdermato.actu.com/allf/bulletins.html.

Boulogne

43922 ■ Werkzeug Technik
SOFETEC
66 rue Escudier
F-92100 Boulogne, France
Ph: 33 148 255030
Fax: 33 148 259054
Publication E-mail: info@werkzeug-technik.com
Technical publication covering metalworking, including cutting tools, clamping attachments, quality control and software. **Founded:** 1988. **Freq:** Bimonthly. **Print Method:** Offset. **Trim Size:** 21 x 29.7 cm. **Cols./Page:** 3. **ISSN:** 0997-6984. **Subscription Rates:** EUR46 individuals. **Remarks:** Accepts advertising. **URL:** http://www.werkzeug-technik.com/doc/qui.htm. **Circ:** Combined 8,000

Brezolles

43923 ■ Chorus
Les Editions du Verbe
LP 28
F-28270 Brezolles, France
Ph: 33 237 436660
Fax: 33 237 436271
Consumer magazine covering chanson music. **Subtitle:** Les Cahiers de la Chanson. **Founded:** Sept. 21, 1992. **Freq:** Quarterly. **Trim Size:** 190 x 270 mm. **Key Personnel:** Fred Hidalgo, Mng. Ed./Ed.-in-Ch.; Mauricette Hidalgo, Sec. Gen. of Writing. **ISSN:** 1241-7076. **Remarks:** Accepts advertising. **URL:** http://www.chorus-chanson.fr. **Ad Rates:** BW: EUR3,000. **Circ:** Paid 20,000

Circulation: * = ABC; △ = BPA; ♦ = CAC; • = CCAB; ❑ = VAC; ⊕ = PO Statement; ‡ = Publisher's Report; Boldface figures = sworn; Light figures = estimated.

Gale Directory of Publications & Broadcast Media/147th Ed.   4901

Bron

43924 ■ International Journal of Product Life-cycle Management
Inderscience Publishers
c/o Prof. Abdelaziz Bouras, Ed.-in-Ch.
PRISMa Laboratory, Lumiere Lyon II University
Technology Institute IUT Lumiere
160 Bd de l'universit
F-69676 Bron Cedex, France
Publisher E-mail: editor@inderscience.com
Peer-reviewed journal providing an authoritative source of information in the field of product lifecycle management, and is devoted to the its development, promotion and coordination of the science and practice. **Freq:** Quarterly. **Key Personnel:** Prof. Abdelaziz Bouras, Editor-in-Chief, abdelaziz.bouras@univ-lyon2.fr; Prof. Balan Gurumoorthy, Regional Ed.; Prof. Alain Bernard, Regional Ed.; Prof. Sudarsan Rachuri, Assoc. Ed. **ISSN:** 1743-5110. **Subscription Rates:** EUR494 individuals print only (surface mail); EUR672 individuals print and online; EUR840 individuals online only (2-3 users); EUR534 individuals print only (airmail). **URL:** http://www.inderscience.com/browse/index.php?journalcode=ijplm.

Cachan

43925 ■ European Journal of Mechanics - B/Fluids
Elsevier Science Inc.
Centre Mathematics & Their Applications
Higher teacher training school of Cachan
61, Avenue of President Wilson
F-94235 Cachan, France
Publisher E-mail: usinfo-ehelp@elsevier.com
Peer-reviewed journal covering all fields of fluid mechanics. **Founded:** 1997. **Freq:** 6/yr. **Key Personnel:** G.P. Galdi, Advisory Board; F.H. Busse, Advisory Board; H.H. Fernholz, Advisory Board; I.P. Castro, Advisory Board; P. Huerre, Advisory Board; T. Akylas, Advisory Board; F.T. Smith, Advisory Board; H. Aref, Advisory Board; D. Barthes-Biesel, Advisory Board; F. Dias, Editor-in-Chief, dias@cmla.ens-cachan.fr; G.J.F. van Heijst, Editor-in-Chief, g.j.f.v.heijst@tue.nl. **ISSN:** 0997-7546. **Subscription Rates:** 101,200¥ institutions; US$855 institutions, other countries except Europe, Japan and Iran; EUR762 institutions for European countries and Iran; 24,300¥ individuals; EUR158 individuals for European countries and Iran; US$211 other countries except Europe, Japan and Iran. **URL:** http://www.elsevier.com/wps/find/journaldescription.cws_home/600738/descriptiondescription.

Caen

43926 ■ Tabularia
Archaeological and Historical Research Center
Medieval
University of Caen-Low-Normandy
Esplanade of Peace
F-14032 Caen Cedex, France
Ph: 33 231 565725
Fax: 33 231 565495
Publication E-mail: crahm.tabularia@unicaen.fr
Publisher E-mail: crahm.direction@unicaen.fr
Newspaper dealing with medieval written sources of Normandy. **Subtitle:** Sources Ecrites de la Normandie Medievale. **Key Personnel:** Pierre Baudin, Editor; Elisabeth Lalou, Editorial Board; Jean-Pascal Foucher, Editorial Board; David Bates, Editorial Board; Jacques Le Maho, Editorial Board; Elisabeth M.C. Van Houts, Editorial Board; Dominique Rouet, Editorial Board. **ISSN:** 1630-7364. **Subscription Rates:** Free. **URL:** http://www.unicaen.fr/mrsh/crahm/revue/tabularia/.

Castanet-Tolosan

43927 ■ Natures Sciences Societes
EDP Sciences
INRA-SAD UPIC
BP 52627
F-31326 Castanet-Tolosan Cedex, France
Ph: 33 5 61285343
Fax: 33 5 61732077
Publication E-mail: nss@toulouse.inra.fr
Publisher E-mail: subscribers@edpsciences.org
Journal covering aspects of the relationship between man and nature, including human nature. **Freq:** 4/yr. **Print Method:** offset. **Key Personnel:** Jean-Paul Billaud, Editor-in-Chief; Daniel Terrasson, Editor-in-Chief;

Bernard Hubert, Editor-in-Chief. **ISSN:** 1240-1307. **Subscription Rates:** EUR166 institutions print and electronic (France); EUR189 institutions print and electronic (European Union); EUR204 institutions, other countries print and electronic; EUR84.74 individuals print and electronic (France); EUR93.82 individuals print and electronic (European Union); EUR103 other countries print and electronic. **Remarks:** Accepts advertising. **URL:** http://www.nss-journal.org/. **Ad Rates:** BW: 550 Fr, 4C: 950 Fr. **Circ:** 1,000

Castellane

43928 ■ Radio Verdon-FM - 91 Mhz
Les Rouvieres BP 2
83560 Saint-Julien-le-Montagnier, France
Ph: 33 4 98053000
Fax: 33 4 94800207
Format: Full Service. **Owner:** Radio Verdon, at above address. **URL:** http://www.radio-verdon.com/index.php?option=com_frontpage&Itemid=1.

Champenoux

43929 ■ Annals of Forest Science
EDP Sciences
INRA, Centre de Nancy
F-54280 Champenoux, France
Publisher E-mail: subscribers@edpsciences.org
Peer-reviewed journal covering biological and ecological bases of a sustainable forest management. **Subtitle:** A Multidisciplinary and International Journal. **Freq:** 8/yr. **Key Personnel:** Erwin Dreyer, Editor-in-Chief; David E. Hibbs, Assoc. Ed. **ISSN:** 1286-4560. **Subscription Rates:** EUR580 individuals print and electronic (without VAT); EUR641 individuals print and electronic (without VAT, European Union); EUR726 other countries print and electronic; EUR497 other countries electronic. **Remarks:** Accepts advertising. **URL:** http://www.afs-journal.org/. **Circ:** (Not Reported)

Chateau Landon

43930 ■ Maitrises
Guides et Scouts d'Europe - France
Le Relais de Poste
BP 17
F-77570 Chateau Landon, France
Ph: 33 164 455360
Fax: 33 164 294456
Publisher E-mail: agse@club-internet.fr
French language publication covering scouting. **Founded:** 1967. **Freq:** Bimonthly. **Remarks:** Advertising not accepted. **URL:** http://www.scouts-europe.org/decouvrir/revues.shtml. **Circ:** (Not Reported)

Clichy

43931 ■ Autocar Infos
SEJT
21 St. Martissot
F-92110 Clichy, France
Ph: 33 141 279737
Fax: 33 141 279730
Publisher E-mail: sejt@sejt.com
Professional magazine covering the coach and bus transportation industry. **Subtitle:** The Coach and Bus Transport Magazine. **Founded:** 1993. **Freq:** Bimonthly. **Print Method:** Offset. **Trim Size:** 21 X 29.7 cm. **Cols./Page:** 3. **Key Personnel:** Patrice de Saulieu, Director, psaulieu@routiers.com; Francois Gilbert, Editor-in-Chief, fgilbert@routiers.com; Francois Deneuter, Advertising Mgr., fdeneuter@sejt.com; Laurent de Saulieu, General Mgr., lsaulieu@routiers.com. **ISSN:** 1261-357X. **Subscription Rates:** EUR55 individuals in France. **Remarks:** Accepts advertising. **URL:** http://www.autocar-infos.com. **Ad Rates:** BW: EUR2,897, 4C: EUR3,781. **Circ:** Paid 23,000

43932 ■ Forum Chantiers
SEJT
21 St. Martissot
F-92110 Clichy, France
Ph: 33 141 279737
Fax: 33 141 279730
Publication E-mail: forum@sejt.com
Publisher E-mail: sejt@sejt.com
Professional magazine covering construction and public works. **Subtitle:** The Construction Industry Magazine. **Founded:** 1990. **Freq:** 8/yr. **Print Method:** Offset. **Trim Size:** 21 x 29.7 cm. **Cols./Page:** 3. **Key Personnel:** Patrice de Saulieu, Director; Alain Faure, Sub-Ed.; Fran-

cois Deneuter, Advertising Mgr.; Laurent de Saulieu, General Mgr.. **ISSN:** 1621-1642. **Subscription Rates:** EUR44 individuals in France. **Remarks:** Accepts advertising. **URL:** http://www.forum-chantiers.com/. **Ad Rates:** BW: EUR2,440, 4C: EUR4,344. **Circ:** Paid 15,000

43933 ■ Guide des Relais Routiers
SEJT
21 St. Martissot
F-92110 Clichy, France
Ph: 33 141 279737
Fax: 33 141 279730
Publication E-mail: lsaulieu@routiers.com
Publisher E-mail: sejt@sejt.com
Professional magazine covering restaurants. **Subtitle:** Good Restaurants Cheap and for Everybody. **Founded:** 1934. **Freq:** Annual. **Print Method:** Offset. **Trim Size:** A5. **Subscription Rates:** EUR15 individuals for the public. **Remarks:** Accepts advertising. **URL:** http://www.relais-routiers.com. **Ad Rates:** BW: EUR2,982, 4C: EUR3,529. **Circ:** Paid 50,000

43934 ■ Les Routiers
SEJT
21 St. Martissot
F-92110 Clichy, France
Ph: 33 141 279737
Fax: 33 141 279730
Publication E-mail: routiers@routiers.com
Publisher E-mail: sejt@sejt.com
Professional magazine covering regulation, vehicle test, technical innovations and other issues for truck drivers. **Subtitle:** The Road and Truck Drivers' Monthly Magazine. **Founded:** 1934. **Freq:** 11/yr. **Print Method:** Offset. **Trim Size:** 21 x 29.7 cm. **Cols./Page:** 3. **Key Personnel:** Patrice de Saulieu, Director, psaulieu@routiers.com; Francois Deneuter, Advertising Mgr., fdeneuter@sejt.com; Laurent de Saulieu, Dir. Gen., lsaulieu@routiers.com; Francois Gilbert, Sub-Ed., fgilbert@routiers.com. **ISSN:** 0243-6795. **Subscription Rates:** EUR42 individuals in France. **Remarks:** Accepts advertising. **URL:** http://www.routiers.com. **Ad Rates:** BW: EUR3,329, 4C: EUR4,369. **Circ:** Paid 45,000

43935 ■ Route Actualite/Roads News
Stepe Group Chantiers de France
202 quai de Clichy
F-92110 Clichy, France
Ph: 33 147561723
Fax: 33 147561432
Publication E-mail: contact@chantiersdefrance.com
Publisher E-mail: asurchamp@chantiersdefrance.com
Professional magazine covering highway engineering techniques and equipment, road building firms and projects, and seminar and conference proceedings in French and English. **Founded:** 1991. **Freq:** Bimonthly 8/yr. **URL:** http://www.chantiersdefrance.com/. **Circ:** Combined 8,000

43936 ■ Stations-Service Acutalites
SEJT
21 St. Martissot
F-92110 Clichy, France
Ph: 33 141 279737
Fax: 33 141 279730
Publication E-mail: ssa@sejt.com
Publisher E-mail: sejt@sejt.com
Professional magazine covering the management and development of gas stations. **Subtitle:** The Magazine for Professionals of the Service Station. **Founded:** 1990. **Freq:** Bimonthly. **Print Method:** Offset. **Trim Size:** 21 x 29.7 cm. **Cols./Page:** 3. **Key Personnel:** Patrice de Saulieu, Publication Mgr.; Laurent de Saulieu, General Mgr.; Francois Deneuter, Advertising Mgr. **ISSN:** 1249-7037. **Subscription Rates:** EUR32 individuals in France. **Remarks:** Accepts advertising. **URL:** http://www.stations-service-actualites.com. **Ad Rates:** BW: EUR1,848, 4C: EUR3,529. **Circ:** Paid 9,500

43937 ■ Transport Service
SEJT
21 St. Martissot
F-92110 Clichy, France
Ph: 33 141 279737
Fax: 33 141 279730
Publication E-mail: transportservice@sejt.com
Publisher E-mail: sejt@sejt.com
Professional magazine covering management, financial, material, and other issues for the transportation industry. **Founded:** 1997. **Freq:** Bimonthly. **Print Method:** Offset. **Trim Size:** 21 x 29.7 cm. **Cols./Page:** 3. **Key Personnel:** Francois Deneuter, Advertising Mgr., fdeneuter@

sejt.com. **ISSN:** 1282-5263. **Subscription Rates:** EUR30,000 individuals. **Remarks:** Accepts advertising. **URL:** http://www.transport-service.com.fr. **Ad Rates:** BW: EUR3,937, 4C: EUR4,802. **Circ:** Paid 30,000

43938 ■ Radio Orient-AM - 1602
98, Blvd. Victor Hugo
F-92110 Clichy, France
Ph: 33 1 41061639
Fax: 33 1 41061622
E-mail: antoineh@radioorient.com
Format: Ethnic; World Beat. **Owner:** Radio Orient, at above address. **Operating Hours:** Continuous. **Key Personnel:** Fouad Naim, Pres./Dir. Gen. **URL:** http://www.radioorient.com.

43939 ■ Radio Orient-FM - 92.7
98, Blvd. Victor Hugo
F-92110 Clichy, France
Ph: 33 1 41061639
Fax: 33 1 41061622
E-mail: antoineh@radioorient.com
Format: Ethnic; World Beat. **Owner:** Radio Orient, at above address. **Operating Hours:** Continuous. **URL:** http://www.radioorient.com.

Condom

43940 ■ Radio d'Artagnan-FM - 95.1
Ave. Peries
32110 Nogaro, France
Ph: 33 5 62690666
Fax: 33 5 62090303
E-mail: contact@radiodartagnan.com
Format: Full Service. **URL:** http://www.radiodartagnan.com/.

Crolles

43941 ■ Radio-Gresivaudan-FM - 87.8
94 rue du Brocey
38920 Crolles, France
Ph: 33 4 76089191
Format: Full Service. **Owner:** Radio-Gresivaudan, at above address. **URL:** http://www.radio-gresivaudan.org/.

Digne les Bains

43942 ■ Frequence Mistral-FM - 99.3
Les Seyes, 6 chemin des Alpilles
04000 Digne les Bains, France
Ph: 33 4 92312713
E-mail: digne@frequencemistral.net
Format: Eclectic. **URL:** http://www.frequencemistral.net/.

Dijon

43943 ■ Behavioural Processes
Elsevier Science
c/o Frank Cezilly, Ed.
Equipe Ecologie Evolutive
UMR CNRS 5561, Biogeosciences
6 Blvd. Gabriel
F-21053 Dijon, France
Publisher E-mail: nlinfo-f@elsevier.com
Journal focusing on research in animal behavior from a theoretical perspective. The study explains animal behavior, from behavioral analytic, cognitive, ethological, ecological, evolutionary, neurological and physiological points of view. **Founded:** 1977. **Freq:** 9/yr. **Key Personnel:** C.D.L. Wynne, Editor, behproc@grove.ufl.edu; Frank Cezilly, Editor, frank.cezilly@u-bourgogne.fr; S. Katz, Assoc. Ed.; R. Batsell, Editorial Board; K.G. Anderson, Assoc. Ed.; M.I. Cherry, Book Reviews Ed. **ISSN:** 0376-6357. **Subscription Rates:** 304,800¥ institutions; US$2,570 institutions for all countries except Europe, Japan & Iran; EUR2,296 institutions for European countries & Iran; EUR217 individuals for European countries & Iran; US$292 individuals for all countries except Europe, Japan & Iran; 33,600¥ individuals. **Remarks:** Accepts advertising. **URL:** http://www.elsevier.com/wps/find/journaldescription.cws_home/506046/descriptiondescription. **Circ:** (Not Reported)

43944 ■ Impact
Chambre de Commerce et d'Industrie de Dijon
Pl. Jean Bouhey
BP 17440
F-21074 Dijon Cedex, France
Ph: 33 3 80659100

Fax: 33 3 80653709
Magazine covering local economics. **Freq:** Quarterly. **Remarks:** Accepts advertising. **URL:** http://www.dijon.cci.fr/fr/applications/rechercher?sq=IMPACT. **Circ:** (Not Reported)

43945 ■ Mycorrhiza
Springer-Verlag
c/o Vivienne Gianinazzi-Pearson, Mng. Ed.
UMR 1088 INRA/CNRS 5184/U
Bourgogne Plante-Microbe-Environnement
INRA-CMSE
F-21065 Dijon Cedex, France
Ph: 33 3 80693753
Journal dedicated to research into mycorrhizas. **Freq:** 8/yr. **Key Personnel:** Vivienne Gianinazzi-Pearson, Managing Editor, gianina@dijon.inra.fr; Guido Lingua, Editorial Board; Ian A. Dickie, Editorial Board; Randy Molina, Managing Editor, molinar@onid.orst.edu; Michael F. Allen, Editorial Board; Teresa E. Pawlowska, Editorial Board. **ISSN:** 0940-6360. **Subscription Rates:** EUR1,699 institutions print incl. free access; EUR2,038.80 institutions print incl. enhanced access. **Remarks:** Advertising accepted; rates available upon request. **URL:** http://www.springer.com/lifesci/microbiology/journal/572?detailsPage=descr iption. **Circ:** (Not Reported)

Enghien-les-Bains

43946 ■ idFM - 98
46, Ave. de Ceinture
95880 Enghien-les-Bains, France
Ph: 33 1 34121222
Fax: 33 1 34129555
E-mail: idfm@fr.fm
Format: Full Service. **Operating Hours:** Continuous. **Key Personnel:** Jacques Berberides, President, phone 33 1 39642049, berberides@idfm98.fr. **URL:** http://idfm98.free.fr/index10.php.

Ferney-Voltaire

43947 ■ Focus on the Public Services
Public Services International
BP 9
F-01211 Ferney-Voltaire Cedex, France
Ph: 00 450 400404
Fax: 33 450 407320
Publisher E-mail: psi@world-psi.org
Publication covering public sector issues and trade unionism in English, French, German, Japanese, Spanish and Swedish. **Freq:** Quarterly. **Key Personnel:** Peter Waldorff, Gen. Sec. **URL:** http://www.world-psi.org. **Circ:** Free 17,000

43948 ■ International Journal of Paediatric Dentistry
International Association of Paediatric Dentistry
c/o FDI World Dental Federation
L' Avant Centre
13, chemin du Levant
F-01210 Ferney-Voltaire, France
Ph: 33 4 50426994
Fax: 33 4 50405555
Publisher E-mail: iapd@fdiworldental.org
International journal covering paediatric dentistry. **Freq:** Bimonthly. **Key Personnel:** Goran Dahllof, Editor-in-Chief; H.D. Rodd, Editor, h.d.rodd@sheffield.ac.uk; Goran Koch, Editor. **ISSN:** 0960-7439. **Subscription Rates:** US$1,512 institutions print + online, in the Americas; EUR1,041 institutions print + online, in Europe; US$1,763 institutions print + std. online, rest of world; US$1,314 institutions print, the Americas; EUR905 institutions print, in Europe; US$1,533 institutions print, rest of world; US$1,314 institutions online; EUR905 institutions online; US$1,533 institutions online; rest of world. **URL:** http://www.iapdworld.org; http://www.blackwellpublishing.com/submit.asp?ref=0960-7439.

43949 ■ Medical Student International
International Federation of Medical Students Associations
Federacion Internacional de Asociaciones de Estudiantes de Medicina
c/o WMA
Boite Postale 63
F-01212 Ferney-Voltaire Cedex 63, France
Fax: 33 450 405937
Publisher E-mail: gs@ifmsa.org
Worldwide publication covering medical students. **Key**

Personnel: Alex Guerrero, Editor-in-Chief; Raj Punjabi, Assoc. Ed. **URL:** http://www.ifmsa.org/index.php?option=com_rokdownloads&view=folder&Itemid=113&id=23:medical-student-international-(msi).

43950 ■ World Hospitals and Health Services
International Hospital Federation
Federacion Internacional de Hospitales
13 Chemin du Levant
Immeuble JB SAY
F-01210 Ferney-Voltaire, France
Ph: 33 450 426000
Fax: 33 450 426001
Publisher E-mail: info@ihf-fih.org
Publication covering developments in hospitals and health services, health services management, quality assurance, ethical issues, architecture and design, comparative analysis of health systems and strategic planning (English, French, and Spanish). **Subtitle:** The Official Journal of the International Hospital Federation. **Founded:** 1929. **Freq:** Quarterly. **Key Personnel:** Per Gunnar Svensson, PhD, Editorial Prof. **ISSN:** 0512-3135. **Subscription Rates:** US$175 nonmembers; 125 individuals for agencies with discount. **Remarks:** Accepts advertising. **URL:** http://www.ihf-fih.org/jsp/index.jsp?lnk=330. **Ad Rates:** BW: 600 Fr, 4C: 925 Fr. **Circ:** 2,500

43951 ■ World Medical Journal
World Medical Association
Association Medicale Mondiale
13 Ch. du Levant
CIB - Batiment A
F-01210 Ferney-Voltaire, France
Ph: 33 450 407575
Fax: 33 450 405937
Publisher E-mail: wma@wma.net
Worldwide journal covering medicine. **Freq:** Quarterly. **Remarks:** Advertising not accepted. **URL:** http://www.wma.net/en/30publications/20journal/index.html. **Circ:** (Not Reported)

Fontainebleau

43952 ■ Auto Retro
BP 40419
F-77309 Fontainebleau Cedex, France
Ph: 33 160 396969
Fax: 33 160 396900
Publication E-mail: autoretro@lva.fr
Publisher E-mail: autoretro@lva.fr
Consumer magazine popular automobiles and auto sport events. **Founded:** 1992. **Freq:** Weekly. **Remarks:** Accepts advertising. **URL:** http://www.auto-retro.fr/. **Circ:** (Not Reported)

43953 ■ La Vie de l'Auto
BP 40419
F-77309 Fontainebleau Cedex, France
Ph: 33 160 396969
Fax: 33 160 396900
Publication E-mail: lva@elvea.fr
Publisher E-mail: lva@lva.fr
Consumer magazine covering classic cars, including events, auctions, and sales. **Founded:** 1976. **Freq:** Weekly (Thurs.) semi-monthly in July & August. **Subscription Rates:** EUR75,000 individuals; EUR105,000 other countries; EUR142,000 two years; EUR195,000 other countries 2 years. **Remarks:** Accepts advertising. **URL:** http://www.lva.fr/. **Circ:** (Not Reported)

43954 ■ Retroviseur
BP 40419
F-77309 Fontainebleau Cedex 15, France
Ph: 33 1 60396969
Fax: 33 1 60396900
Publication E-mail: retrovis@elvea.fr
Publisher E-mail: retrovis@lva.fr
Consumer magazine covering classic cars, including events, auctions, and sales. **Founded:** 1988. **Freq:** Monthly. **Key Personnel:** A. Georges, Publication Dir.; S. Cordey, Editorial Dir.; Stephane Geffray, Editor-in-Chief. **Subscription Rates:** EUR21.90 individuals; EUR60 other countries; EUR79 two years; EUR115 two years other countries. **Remarks:** Accepts advertising. **URL:** http://www.retroviseur.fr/. **Circ:** (Not Reported)

Circulation: ★ = ABC; △ = BPA; ♦ = CAC; ● = CCAB; ❑ = VAC; ⊕ = PO Statement; ‡ = Publisher's Report; Boldface figures = sworn; Light figures = estimated.

Fontenay-aux-Roses

43955 ■ Radioprotection
EDP Sciences
BP 72
F-92263 Fontenay-aux-Roses Cedex, France
Publisher E-mail: subscribers@edpsciences.org
Journal covering aspects of radiological protection. **Freq:** 4/yr. **Key Personnel:** H. Metivier, Editor-in-Chief. **ISSN:** 0033-8451. **Subscription Rates:** EUR358.80 individuals print and electronic (including vat); EUR359 other countries print and electronic; EUR312.16 individuals electronic only; EUR261 other countries electronic only. **URL:** http://www.radioprotection.org/.

Gif-sur-Yvette

43956 ■ Journal of Physiology - Paris
Elsevier Science
c/o Yves Fregnac, Ed.-in-Ch.
Unit of Integrative & Computational Neurosciences
Institut Federatif de Neurobiologie Alfred Fessard
1 Ave. de la Terrasse
F-91198 Gif-sur-Yvette, France
Ph: 33 169 823415
Fax: 33 169 823427
Publisher E-mail: nlinfo-f@elsevier.com
Journal covering research relating to neuroscience. **Subtitle:** An International Review Journal for the Neurosciences. **Freq:** Bimonthly. **Key Personnel:** Yves Fregnac, Editor-in-Chief, yves.fregnac@iaf.cnrs-gif.fr. **ISSN:** 0928-4257. **Subscription Rates:** US$922 institutions for all countries except Europe and Japan; 109,500¥ institutions for European countries; EUR828 institutions for European countries; EUR174 individuals; US$234 individuals; 26,900¥ individuals. **Remarks:** Accepts advertising. **URL:** http://www.elsevier.com/wps/find/journaldescription.cws_home/523852/descriptiondescription. **Circ:** (Not Reported)

Gondrin

43957 ■ Crisis
International Association for Suicide Prevention
Central Administrative Office
La Barade
F-32330 Gondrin, France
Ph: 33 562 291947
Fax: 33 562 291947
Publisher E-mail: iasp1960@aol.com
Journal including life saving information for all those involved in crisis intervention and suicide prevention. **Subtitle:** The Journal of Crisis Intervention and Suicide Prevention. **Freq:** Quarterly. **Trim Size:** 210 x 277 mm. **Key Personnel:** Annette L. Beautrais, PhD, Editor-in-Chief, phone 64 3 3720408, fax 64 3 3720405, annette.beautrais@yale.edu; Diego De Leo, MD, Assoc. Ed., d.deleo@griffith.edu.au; J.F. Connolly, Editorial Board. **ISSN:** 0227-5910. **Subscription Rates:** US$132 individuals; EUR98 individuals; EUR173 institutions. **URL:** http://www.hogrefe.com/index.php?mod=journals&action=1&site=crisis.

Grenoble

43958 ■ Microelectronics Journal
Elsevier Science
c/o Bernard Courtois, Ed.-in-Ch.
TIMA/CMP
46 Ave. Felix Viallet
F-38031 Grenoble, France
Fax: 33 476 473814
Publisher E-mail: nlinfo-f@elsevier.com
Peer-reviewed journal primarily dealing with microelectronics covering Circuits and Systems and Physics and Devices. **Founded:** 1967. **Freq:** Monthly. **Key Personnel:** Bernard Courtois, Editor-in-Chief, bernard.courtois@imag.fr; Erik Jung, Editorial Board, erik.jung@izm.fraunhofer.de; J. Figueras, Editorial Board, figueras@eel.upc.es; M. Anis, Editorial Board, manis@aucegypt.edu; Prof. A. Amara, Editorial Board, amara.amara@isep.fr; E.G. Friedman, Editorial Board, friedman@ece.rochester.edu. **ISSN:** 0026-2692. **Subscription Rates:** 272,500¥ institutions; US$2,297 institutions all countries except Europe and Japan; EUR2,052 institutions for Europe. **Remarks:** Accepts advertising. **URL:** http://www.elsevier.com/wps/find/journaldescription.cws_home/405904/description. **Circ:** (Not Reported)

43959 ■ Phase Transitions
Taylor & Francis Group Journals
c/o J. Kreisel, Ed.-in-Ch.
Lab. Materiaux et Genie Physique (CNRS), MINATEC
Grenoble Institute of Technologie (INPG)
3 parvis Louis Neel
F-38016 Grenoble, France
Publisher E-mail: customerservice@taylorandfrancis.com
Peer-reviewed journal covering experimental work on many of the aspects of phase transitions in condensed matter. **Subtitle:** A Multinational Journal. **Freq:** Monthly. **Key Personnel:** J. Kreisel, Editor-in-Chief, jens.kreisel@inpg.fr; A.M. Glazer, Editorial Board; B. Noheda, Editorial Board; A. Pasturel, Editorial Board; U. Bismayer, Editorial Board; D.J. Singh, Editorial Board; E.K.H. Salje, Editorial Board; W. Kleemann, Editorial Board. **ISSN:** 0141-1594. **Subscription Rates:** 5,070 institutions print + online; 4,563 institutions online; EUR4,937 institutions print + online; US$6,201 institutions print + online; US$5,581 institutions online; EUR4,443 institutions online; 749 individuals; US$1,112 individuals; EUR885 individuals. **Remarks:** Advertising accepted; rates available upon request. **URL:** http://www.tandf.co.uk/journals/journal.asp?issn=0141-1594&linktype=1. **Circ:** (Not Reported)

Jouy-en-Josas

43960 ■ Genetics Selection Evolution
BioMed Central Ltd.
UMR Genetique et diversite animales, Bldg. 211
78352 Jouy-en-Josas Cedex, France
Publisher E-mail: info@biomedcentral.com
Peer-reviewed journal covering all facets of genetics and selection in farm and experimental animals, as well as in related species. **Freq:** 6/yr. **Print Method:** offset. **Key Personnel:** Didier Boichard, Editor-in-Chief, didier.boichard@jouy.inra.fr. **ISSN:** 0999-193X. **Subscription Rates:** EUR366 print and electronic; EUR428 print and electronic, rest of European Union; EUR445 other countries print and electronic. **Remarks:** Accepts advertising. **URL:** http://www.gse-journal.org/. **Ad Rates:** BW: 500 Fr, 4C: 900 Fr. **Circ:** 1,000

Langon

43961 ■ ARL-FM - 98.1
A.R.L
BP 156
8, Pl. des Carmes
33213 Langon Cedex, France
Ph: 33 5 56633552
Fax: 33 5 56622104
Format: Ethnic; World Beat. **Owner:** A.R.L., at above address. **Ad Rates:** Advertising accepted; rates available upon request. **URL:** http://www.arlfm.com.

43962 ■ ARL-FM - 90.0
BP 156
8, Pl. des Carmes
33213 Langon Cedex, France
Ph: 33 5 56633552
Fax: 33 5 56622104
Format: Ethnic; World Beat. **Ad Rates:** Advertising accepted; rates available upon request. **URL:** http://www.arlfm.com.

Le Havre

43963 ■ International Journal of Adaptive and Innovative Systems
Inderscience Enterprises Limited
c/o Dr. Dimitri Lefebvre, Ed.-in-Ch.
Le Havre University
Electrical Engineering & Automatic Control Research Group GREAH EA 3220
25, rue Philippe Lebon, BP 540
76058 Le Havre Cedex, France
Peer-reviewed journal covering the field of industrial activities including adaptive and innovative systems, information technologies, earth sciences, economics, engineering, and management. **Freq:** 4/yr. **Key Personnel:** Dr. Dimitri Lefebvre, Editor-in-Chief, dimitri.lefebvre@univ-lehavre.fr. **ISSN:** 1740-2107. **Subscription Rates:** EUR494 individuals print or online; EUR672 individuals print and online. **URL:** http://www.inderscience.com/browse/index.php?journalID=62.

Les Ulis

43964 ■ Apidologie
EDP Sciences
17 Ave. du Hoggar
Parc d'activites de Courtaboeuf
BP 112
F-91944 Les Ulis, France
Ph: 33 1 69187575
Fax: 33 1 69288491
Publisher E-mail: subscribers@edpsciences.org
Peer-reviewed journal covering biology of insects belonging to the superfamily Apoidea. **Subtitle:** The Leading Journal Devoted to Bee Science. **Freq:** 6/yr. **Print Method:** offset. **Key Personnel:** Anne Dufay, Managing Editor. **ISSN:** 0044-8435. **Subscription Rates:** EUR378 individuals print and electronic (without VAT, France); EUR426 individuals print and electronic (without VAT, European Union); EUR474 other countries print and electronic; EUR330 other countries electronic. **Remarks:** Accepts advertising. **URL:** http://www.apidologie.org/. **Ad Rates:** BW: 510 Fr, 4C: 950 Fr. **Circ:** 1,000

43965 ■ Hydroecologie appliquee
EDP Sciences
17 Ave. du Hoggar
Parc d'activites de Courtaboeuf
BP 112
F-91944 Les Ulis, France
Ph: 33 1 69187575
Fax: 33 1 69288491
Publisher E-mail: subscribers@edpsciences.org
Journal covering impact of man activities on the aquatic environment. **Freq:** Annual. **Key Personnel:** M. Khalanski, Editor-in-Chief; J.F. Parent, Editor-in-Chief; F. Siclet, Editor-in-Chief; L. Perotin, Managing Editor. **ISSN:** 1147-9213. **URL:** http://www.hydroecologie.org/.

43966 ■ Materiaux & Techniques
EDP Sciences
17 Ave. du Hoggar
Parc d'activites de Courtaboeuf
BP 112
F-91944 Les Ulis, France
Ph: 33 1 69187575
Fax: 33 1 69288491
Publisher E-mail: subscribers@edpsciences.org
Peer-reviewed journal covering the domain of materials. **Freq:** 6/yr. **Key Personnel:** Rene Gras, Editor-in-Chief. **ISSN:** 0032-6895. **Subscription Rates:** EUR255 individuals print and electronic (France); EUR329 individuals print and electronic (European Union); EUR329 other countries print and electronic. **URL:** http://www.mattech-journal.org/.

43967 ■ Quadrature
EDP Sciences
17 Ave. du Hoggar
Parc d'activites de Courtaboeuf
BP 112
F-91944 Les Ulis, France
Ph: 33 1 69187575
Fax: 33 1 69288491
Publisher E-mail: subscribers@edpsciences.org
Magazine of pure and applied mathematics. **Subtitle:** A magazine of pure and spicy mathematics. **Freq:** 4/yr. **Key Personnel:** Roger Mansuy, Editor-in-Chief, roger.mansuy@gmail.com; Jean-Pierre Boudine, Founder/Consulting Ed., jp.boudine@wanadoo.fr. **ISSN:** 1142-2785. **Subscription Rates:** EUR32.33 individuals for France and rest of European; EUR38 other countries; EUR59 two years for France and rest of European; EUR69 other countries. **URL:** http://www.quadrature-journal.org/.

Lyon

43968 ■ Damocles
Center for Documentation and Research of Peace and Conflicts
187 Montee de Choulans
F-69005 Lyon, France
Ph: 33 478 369303
Fax: 33 478 363683
Publisher E-mail: cdrpc@obsarm.org
Publication covering peace. **ISSN:** 0296-1199. **URL:** http://www.obsarm.org.

43969 ■ Le Rotarien
34 rue Pierre-Dupont
FR-69001 Lyon, France
Ph: 33 4 72003214
Fax: 33 4 72000507
Publisher E-mail: courjon@le-rotarien.asso.fr
Membership magazine of Rotary International covering

current news about Rotary-related subjects. **Founded:** 1952. **Freq:** Monthly. **Key Personnel:** Christophe Courjon, Editor, courjon@le-rotarien.asso.fr. **Remarks:** Accepts advertising. **URL:** http://www.rotary-francophone.org; http://www.rotary.org/en/MediaAndNews/MorePublications/RegionalMagazines/Pages/ridefault.aspx. **Circ:** Paid 40,000

43970 ■ Sericologia
International Sericultural Commission
Commission Sericicole Internationale
26 rue Bellecordiere
F-69002 Lyon, France
Ph: 33 478 504198
Fax: 33 478 860957
Publisher E-mail: info@inserco.org
English and French language publication covering sericulture. **Subtitle:** Journal of Silkworms. **Founded:** 1960. **Freq:** Quarterly. **Trim Size:** 17 x 24 cm. **ISSN:** 0250-3980. **Subscription Rates:** EUR300 individuals. **Remarks:** Advertising not accepted. **URL:** http://www.inserco.org. **Circ:** (Not Reported)

Maisons-Alfort

43971 ■ Journal of Veterinary Cardiology
Elsevier Science Inc.
National Veterinary School of Alfort
Maisons-Alfort, France
Publisher E-mail: usinfo-ehelp@elsevier.com
Journal covering retrospective studies, clinical trials, epidemiology, observational studies. **Freq:** 2/yr. **Key Personnel:** N.S. Moise, Editor-in-Chief; D.F. Hogan, Section Ed.; R. Tissier, Review Board; M.A. Oyama, Section Ed.; P.R. Fox, Section Ed.; R.F. Gilmore, Jr., Section Ed.; B. Bulmer, Section Ed.; A. Estrada, Section Ed.; V. Chetboul, Editor. **ISSN:** 1760-2734. **Subscription Rates:** US$245 institutions, other countries except Europe, Japan and Iran; 33,400¥ institutions for European countries and Iran; 16,900¥ individuals; EUR124 individuals for European countries and Iran; US$150 other countries except Europe, Japan and Iran. **URL:** http://www.elsevier.com/wps/find/journaldescription.cws_home/706413/descriptiondescription.

Manosque

43972 ■ Frequence Mistral-FM - 92.8
7 Rue Saunerie
04100 Manosque, France
Ph: 33 4 92722990
Fax: 33 4 92724662
E-mail: contact@frequencemistral.net
Format: Eclectic. **URL:** http://www.frequencemistral.net/.

Marseille

43973 ■ MAGMA
European Society for Magnetic Resonance in Medicine and Biology
c/o Patrick J. Cozzone, PhD, Ed.-in-Ch.
CRMBM-CNRS, Faculte de Medecine
27 Blvd. Jean Moulin
F-13005 Marseille, France
Fax: 33 491 256539
Publisher E-mail: office@esmrmb.org
Publication covering medical technology. **Freq:** Bimonthly. **Key Personnel:** Patrick J. Cozzone, PhD, Editor-in-Chief, magma.office@medecine.univ-mrs.fr; Rolf Gruetter, Editorial Board; Hedvig Hricak, Editorial Board; Arend Heerschap, Editorial Board; Paul A. Bottomley, Editorial Board; Georg Bongartz, MD, Co-Ed.; Isabelle Berry, MD, Co-Ed. **ISSN:** 0968-5243. **Subscription Rates:** EUR140 members; EUR112 members senior; EUR70 members student. **Remarks:** Accepts advertising. **URL:** http://www.esmrmb.org/. **Circ:** (Not Reported)

43974 ■ Radio JM-FM - 90.5
BP 340
F-13177 Marseille Cedex 20, France
Ph: 33 491 377878
Fax: 33 491 819428
E-mail: radiojm@radiojm.fr
Format: Information; Ethnic; World Beat. **Owner:** Radio JM-Le Coeur Mediterraneen, at above address. **Operating Hours:** Continuous. **URL:** http://www.radiojm.fr.

43975 ■ Radio Utopie-FM - 105.7
31 rue St. Basile

F-13001 Marseille, France
Ph: 33 4 91502626
Fax: 33 4 91845522
E-mail: utopie@chez.com
Format: Ethnic; Information. **Operating Hours:** Continuous. **URL:** http://utopie.chez.com.

Martigues

43976 ■ Radio Maritima-FM - 93.6
Av. Commandant L'herminier
BP 158
F-13694 Martigues Cedex, France
Ph: 33 4 42413600
Fax: 33 4 42413613
Format: Contemporary Hit Radio (CHR). **Owner:** Radio Maritima Martigues Communication, at above address. **Operating Hours:** Continuous. **Ad Rates:** Advertising accepted; rates available upon request. **URL:** http://www.radio-maritima.fr.

Montpellier

43977 ■ Communications and Strategies
IDATE
BP 4167
F-34092 Montpellier Cedex 5, France
Ph: 33 467 144444
Fax: 33 467 144400
Publisher E-mail: info@idate.org
Journal covering socio-economic analysis of the telecom, IT and audiovisual sectors. **Founded:** 1991. **Freq:** Quarterly. **Print Method:** Offset. **Trim Size:** 11 1/2 x 17. **Cols./Page:** 5. **Col. Width:** 10 1/2 inches. **Col. Depth:** 217 agate lines. **Key Personnel:** Edmond Baranes, Editor; James Alleman, Editorial Committee; Loretta Anania, Editorial Committee. **Subscription Rates:** EUR200 individuals online; EUR320 individuals print. **URL:** http://www.idate.org/en/Digiworld/Communications-Strategies_41_.html.

43978 ■ Infection, Genetics and Evolution
Elsevier (Singapore) Pte. Ltd.
c/o Michel Tibayrenc, Ed.-in-Ch.
UMR 2724, IRD, Centre National de la Recherche Scientifique
911 ave. agropolis
BP 64501
34394 Montpellier Cedex 5, France
Publisher E-mail: asiabkinfo@elsevier.com
Journal aiming to be the forum for developing a unified synthetic approach to the genetics of hosts, pathogens and vectors: the "Integrated Genetic Epidemiology of Infectious Diseases" (IGEID), involving evaluation of the respective impact of genetic diversity of hosts, pathogens and vectors on the transmission and severity of infectious diseases, as well as their coevolutionary interactions. **Subtitle:** Journal of Molecular Epidemiology and Evolutionary Genetics of Infectious Diseases. **Founded:** 2001. **Freq:** 8/yr. **Key Personnel:** Michel Tibayrenc, Editor-in-Chief, michel.tibayrenc@ird.fr; Francisco Ayala, Receiving Ed., fjayala@uci.edu; Thierry de Meeus, Receiving Ed., thierry.demeeus@mpl.ird.fr; David Biron, Editorial Board; Marie-Anne Shaw, Receiving Ed., genmas@leeds.ac.uk; Dominique Blanc, Editorial Board; Dominique Caugant, Editorial Board; Sansanee Chaiyaroj, Editorial Board. **ISSN:** 1567-1348. **Subscription Rates:** EUR554 institutions European countries and Iran; US$618 institutions all Countries except Europe, Japan and Iran; 73,200¥ institutions; EUR134 individuals European countries and Iran; US$178 individuals all countries except Europe, Japan and Iran; 20,500¥ individuals. **URL:** http://www.elsevier.com/wps/find/journaldescription.cws_home/621317/descriptiondescription.

43979 ■ Agora-FM - 91
BP, 11138
34008 Montpellier cedex 1, France
Ph: 33 4 67928742
Fax: 33 4 67928742
Format: Blues. **URL:** http://www.agorafm.com/.

Montrouge

43980 ■ Annales de Biologie Clinique
John Libbey Eurotext
127, Ave. de la Republique
92120 Montrouge, France
Ph: 33 1 46730660

Fax: 33 1 40840999
Publisher E-mail: contact@jle.com
Journal for clinical biologists. **Subtitle:** The link between Research, Biology and Clinical practice. **Freq:** 6/yr. **Key Personnel:** Jean-Louis Beaudeux, Editor. **ISSN:** 0003-3898. **Subscription Rates:** EUR53 single issue; EUR195 other countries online and paper; EUR165 individuals online and paper (France); EUR185 individuals online and paper (European Union and Switzerland); EUR316 institutions, other countries print; EUR280 institutions print (France); EUR304 institutions print (European Union and Switzerland). **Remarks:** Accepts advertising. **URL:** http://www.revue-abc.com/; http://www.jle.com/en/revues/bio_rech/abc/sommaire.phtml. **Circ:** (Not Reported)

43981 ■ Annales de Gerontologie
John Libbey Eurotext
127, Ave. de la Republique
92120 Montrouge, France
Ph: 33 1 46730660
Fax: 33 1 40840999
Publisher E-mail: contact@jle.com
Journal containing scientific work, literature reviews and teaching summaries in the field of gerontology and geriatrics. **Freq:** Quarterly. **Key Personnel:** Gilles Berrut, Editor. **ISSN:** 1968-0805. **Subscription Rates:** EUR45 single issue; EUR114 individuals online and paper; EUR90 individuals online and paper, France; EUR106 individuals online and paper, EU and Switzerland; EUR206 institutions print; EUR170 institutions print, France; EUR190 institutions print, EU and Switzerland. **URL:** http://www.john-libbey-eurotext.fr/en/revues/medecine/age/sommaire.md?type=text.html.

43982 ■ Bulletin du Cancer
John Libbey Eurotext
127, Ave. de la Republique
92120 Montrouge, France
Ph: 33 1 46730660
Fax: 33 1 40840999
Publisher E-mail: contact@jle.com
Journal covering the realm of cancerology. **Subtitle:** From Biology to Clinical practice: a modern approach of oncology. **Freq:** 12/yr. **Key Personnel:** Jacques-Olivier Bay, Editor-in-Chief; Gilles L'Allemain, Asst. Ed. **ISSN:** 0007-4551. **Subscription Rates:** EUR32 single issue; EUR245 individuals online + print; EUR200 individuals online + print (France); EUR230 individuals online + print (European Union and Switzerland); EUR360 institutions, other countries print; EUR310 institutions print (France); EUR340 institutions print (European Union and Switzerland). **Remarks:** Accepts advertising. **URL:** http://www.bulletinducancer.fr/; http://www.john-libbey-eurotext.fr/en/revues/medecine/bdc/sommaire.md?type=text.html. **Circ:** (Not Reported)

43983 ■ Bulletin Infirmier du Cancer
John Libbey Eurotext
127, Ave. de la Republique
92120 Montrouge, France
Ph: 33 1 46730660
Fax: 33 1 40840999
Publisher E-mail: contact@jle.com
Journal for nursing professionals. **Subtitle:** The first training journal aimed specifically at nurses working in oncology. **Freq:** Quarterly. **Key Personnel:** Veronique Laroche-Frauche, Editor-in-Chief; Gilles Cahn, Publication Dir., gilles.cahn@john-libbey-eurotext.fr; Pascale Dielenseger, Editor-in-Chief. **ISSN:** 1628-2205. **Subscription Rates:** EUR20 single issue; EUR62 other countries online; EUR42 individuals online (France); EUR54 individuals online (European Union and Switzerland); EUR82 institutions, other countries online; EUR62 institutions print (France); EUR74 institutions print (European Union and Switzerland). **Remarks:** Accepts advertising. **URL:** http://www.john-libbey-eurotext.fr/en/revues/medecine/bic/sommaire.md?type=text.html. **Circ:** (Not Reported)

43984 ■ Cahiers d'etudes et de recherches francophones/Agricultures
John Libbey Eurotext
127, Ave. de la Republique
92120 Montrouge, France
Ph: 33 1 46730660
Fax: 33 1 40840999
Publisher E-mail: contact@jle.com
Journal covering aspects of agricultural scientific research. **Subtitle:** For a fuller understanding of the farming world. **Freq:** 6/yr. **Key Personnel:** Jean-Pascal Pichot, Editor-in-Chief; Didier Picard, Editor-in-Chief. **ISSN:** 1166-7699. **Subscription Rates:** EUR38 other countries online and print; EUR78 individuals online and

print (European Union and France); EUR28 students, other countries online and print; EUR56 students online and print (European Union and France); EUR66 institutions, other countries print; EUR130 institutions print (European Union and France). **Remarks:** Accepts advertising. **URL:** http://www.john-libbey-eurotext.fr/en/revues/agro_biotech/agr/sommaire.md?type=text.html; http://www.cahiersagricultures.fr/. **Circ:** (Not Reported)

43985 ■ Cahiers d'etudes et de recherches francophones/Sante
John Libbey Eurotext
127, Ave. de la Republique
92120 Montrouge, France
Ph: 33 1 46730660
Fax: 33 1 40840999
Publisher E-mail: contact@jle.com
Journal covering tropical medicine, development, public health and epidemiology. **Subtitle:** A global approach to health and development. **Freq:** 4/yr. **Key Personnel:** Dominique Richard-Lenoble, Editor-in-Chief; Francois Chieze, Asst. Ed.; Frederic Goyet, Asst. Ed. **ISSN:** 1157-5999. **Subscription Rates:** EUR38 other countries online + print; EUR78 individuals online + print (European Union and France); EUR28 students, other countries online + print; EUR56 students online + print (European Union and France); EUR66 institutions, other countries print; EUR128 institutions print; EUR138 institutions online. **Remarks:** Accepts advertising. **URL:** http://www.john-libbey-eurotext.fr/en/revues/sante_pub/san/sommaire.md?type=text.html; http://www.cahierssante.fr/. **Circ:** (Not Reported)

43986 ■ Environnement, Risques & Sante
John Libbey Eurotext
127, Ave. de la Republique
92120 Montrouge, France
Ph: 33 1 46730660
Fax: 33 1 40840999
Publisher E-mail: contact@jle.com
Journal focusing on environment and health. **Freq:** Bimonthly. **Key Personnel:** Pierre-Andre Cabanes, Editor-in-Chief. **ISSN:** 1635-0421. **Subscription Rates:** EUR51 single issue; EUR181 other countries online and paper; EUR145 individuals online and paper; France; EUR169 individuals online and paper; Europe and Switzerland; EUR89 students, other countries online and paper; EUR85 students online and paper; France; EUR103 students online and paper; Europe and Switzerland; EUR294 institutions, other countries print; EUR270 institutions print; France; EUR306 institutions print; Europe and Switzerland. **URL:** http://www.john-libbey-eurotext.fr/en/revues/sante_pub/ers/sommaire.md?type=text.html.

43987 ■ Epilepsies
John Libbey Eurotext
127, Ave. de la Republique
92120 Montrouge, France
Ph: 33 1 46730660
Fax: 33 1 40840999
Publisher E-mail: contact@jle.com
Journal covering all subjects connected with epilepsy. **Subtitle:** Full coverage of advances in epilepsy. **Freq:** 4/yr. **Key Personnel:** Michelle Bureau, Editor-in-Chief; Alexis Arzimanoglou, Editorial Board; Michelle Bureau, Editorial Board. **ISSN:** 1149-6576. **Subscription Rates:** EUR47 single issue; EUR114 other countries print and online; EUR90 individuals print and online (France); EUR106 individuals print and online (European Union and Switzerland); EUR189 institutions, other countries print; EUR165 institutions print (France); EUR181 institutions print (European Union and Switzerland). **Remarks:** Accepts advertising. **URL:** http://www.john-libbey-eurotext.fr/en/revues/medecine/epi/sommaire.md?type=text.html; http://www.revue-epilepsies.fr/. **Circ:** (Not Reported)

43988 ■ Epileptic Disorders
John Libbey Eurotext
127, Ave. de la Republique
92120 Montrouge, France
Ph: 33 1 46730660
Fax: 33 1 40840999
Publisher E-mail: contact@jle.com
Journal covering clinical manifestations of epilepsy. **Subtitle:** The only epilepsy journal to include a DVD. **Freq:** 4/yr. **Key Personnel:** Alexis Arzimanoglou, Editor-in-Chief; Jean Aicardi, Founding Ed. **ISSN:** 1294-9361. **Subscription Rates:** EUR127 single issue; EUR340 other countries online and print; EUR286 individuals online and print (France); EUR310 individuals online and print (European Union and Switzerland); EUR500 institutions, other countries print; EUR450 institutions print (France); EUR470 institutions print (European Union and Switzerland). **Remarks:** Accepts advertising. **URL:** http://www.epilepticdisorders.com/; http://www.john-libbey-eurotext.fr/en/revues/medecine/epd/sommaire.md?type= text.html. **Circ:** (Not Reported)

43989 ■ European Cytokine Network
John Libbey Eurotext
127, Ave. de la Republique
92120 Montrouge, France
Ph: 33 1 46730660
Fax: 33 1 40840999
Publisher E-mail: contact@jle.com
Journal for physicians and cytokine specialists. **Subtitle:** The journal covering all the disciplines related to cytokines. **Freq:** 4/yr. **Key Personnel:** Didier Fradelizi, Editor-in-Chief; Jacques Bertoglio, Co-Founding Ed. **ISSN:** 1952-4005. **Subscription Rates:** EUR103 single issue; EUR218 individuals online; EUR420 institutions online. **Remarks:** Accepts advertising. **URL:** http://www.europeancytokinenetwork.com/; http://www.john-libbey-eurotext.fr/en/revues/bio_rech/ecn/sommaire.md?type=text.html. **Circ:** (Not Reported)

43990 ■ European Journal of Dermatology
John Libbey Eurotext
127, Ave. de la Republique
92120 Montrouge, France
Ph: 33 1 46730660
Fax: 33 1 40840999
Publisher E-mail: contact@jle.com
Journal covering the field of clinical dermatology and skin biology. **Freq:** Bimonthly. **Key Personnel:** Jean Thivolet, Editor; Jean-Francois Nicolas, Editor-in-Chief; Michael Hertl, Co-Ed.; Ana Gimenez-Arnau, Co-Ed.; Andrea Cavani, Co-Ed.; Jean Kanitakis, Co-Ed. **ISSN:** 1167-1122. **Subscription Rates:** EUR86 single issue; EUR296 other countries online and paper; EUR260 individuals online and paper; France; EUR284 individuals online and paper; Europe and Switzerland; EUR521 institutions, other countries print; EUR485 institutions print; France; EUR509 institutions print; Europe and Switzerland. **URL:** http://www.john-libbey-eurotext.fr/en/revues/medecine/ejd/sommaire.md?type=text.html.

43991 ■ Faire Savoir Faire
Faire Savoire Plus
46 Pl. Jules Ferry
92120 Montrouge, France
Ph: 33 1 55580606
Fax: 33 1 55580600
Publisher E-mail: fsfcontact@fairesavoirfaire.com
Professional magazine covering products, packaging, promotion, and merchandising for retailers, including supermarkets, general stores, and buying centers worldwide. **Founded:** Oct. 1990. **Freq:** Weekly. **Print Method:** Offset. **Key Personnel:** Christelle Simon, Contact, abonnement@fairesavoirfaire.com. **Remarks:** Accepts advertising. **URL:** http://www.fairesavoirfaire.com/. **Circ:** Combined 27,802

43992 ■ Hepato-Gastro
John Libbey Eurotext
127, Ave. de la Republique
92120 Montrouge, France
Ph: 33 1 46730660
Fax: 33 1 40840999
Publisher E-mail: contact@jle.com
Journal covering aspects of digestive pathology. **Subtitle:** A real reference work in gastroenterology. **Freq:** 6/yr. **Key Personnel:** Jean Paul Galmiche, Editor; Dominique Valla, Editor. **ISSN:** 1253-7020. **Subscription Rates:** EUR44 single issue; EUR176 other countries online and paper; EUR140 individuals online and paper (France); EUR164 individuals online and paper (European Union and Switzerland); EUR110 students, other countries online and paper; EUR80 students online and paper (France); EUR104 students online and paper (European Union and Switzerland); EUR271 institutions, other countries print; EUR235 institutions print (France); EUR259 institutions print (European Union and Switzerland). **Remarks:** Accepts advertising. **URL:** http://www.hepatogastro.fr/; http://www.john-libbey-eurotext.fr/en/revues/medecine/hpg/sommaire.md?type= text.html. **Circ:** (Not Reported)

43993 ■ L'Information Psychiatrique
John Libbey Eurotext
127, Ave. de la Republique
92120 Montrouge, France
Ph: 33 1 46730660
Fax: 33 1 40840999
Publisher E-mail: contact@jle.com
Journal for hospital psychiatrists. **Subtitle:** Monthly journal of hospital psychiatrists. **Freq:** 10/yr. **Key Personnel:** Thierry Tremine, Editor-in-Chief. **ISSN:** 0020-0204. **Subscription Rates:** EUR38 single issue; EUR195 other countries online and paper; EUR135 individuals online and paper (France); EUR175 individuals online and paper (European Union and Switzerland); EUR115 students, other countries online and paper; EUR85 students online and paper (France); EUR105 students online and paper (European Union and Switzerland); EUR250 institutions, other countries print; EUR190 institutions print (France); EUR230 institutions print (European Union and Switzerland). **Remarks:** Accepts advertising. **URL:** http://www.infopsy.fr/; http://www.john-libbey-eurotext.fr/en/revues/medecine/ipe/sommaire.md?type=text.html. **Circ:** (Not Reported)

43994 ■ Journal de Pharmacie Clinique
John Libbey Eurotext
127, Ave. de la Republique
92120 Montrouge, France
Ph: 33 1 46730660
Fax: 33 1 40840999
Publisher E-mail: contact@jle.com
Journal for all hospital pharmacists, researchers, and pharmaceutical industry professionals. **Subtitle:** Latest research in clinical pharmacology. **Freq:** 4/yr. **Key Personnel:** Pierre Sado, Ed.-in-Ch./Founder; Gilles Cahn, Publication Dir. **ISSN:** 0291-1981. **Subscription Rates:** EUR65 single issue; EUR154 other countries online and paper; EUR130 individuals online and paper (France); EUR146 individuals online and paper (European Union and Switzerland); EUR270 institutions, other countries print; EUR235 institutions print (France); EUR255 institutions print (European Union and Switzerland). **Remarks:** Accepts advertising. **URL:** http://www.john-libbey-eurotext.fr/en/revues/bio_rech/jpc/sommaire.md?type=text.html; http://www.revue-jpc.fr/. **Circ:** (Not Reported)

43995 ■ La Lettre de l'Internat
John Libbey Eurotext
127, Ave. de la Republique
92120 Montrouge, France
Ph: 33 1 46730660
Fax: 33 1 40840999
Publisher E-mail: contact@jle.com
Journal covering the field of medicine and biology for doctors in training. **Freq:** Quarterly. **Key Personnel:** Laurence Strompf, Editor; Olivier Mir, Editor-in-Chief. **ISSN:** 1243-7581. **Subscription Rates:** EUR38 single issue; EUR110 individuals and institution; other countries; EUR95 individuals and institution; France. **URL:** http://www.john-libbey-eurotext.fr/en/revues/sante_pub/lli/sommaire.md?typ=text.html.

43996 ■ Magnesium Research
John Libbey Eurotext
127, Ave. de la Republique
92120 Montrouge, France
Ph: 33 1 46730660
Fax: 33 1 40840999
Publisher E-mail: contact@jle.com
Journal covering the use of magnesium in biomedicine. **Subtitle:** Official organ of the international Society for the Development of Research on Magnesium. **Freq:** Quarterly. **Key Personnel:** Andrzej Mazur, Editor-in-Chief. **ISSN:** 0953-1424. **Subscription Rates:** EUR88 single issue; EUR219 other countries online and paper; EUR197 individuals online and paper (France); EUR369 institutions, other countries print; EUR329 institutions print (France, UE and Switzerland). **Remarks:** Accepts advertising. **URL:** http://www.john-libbey-eurotext.fr/en/revues/bio_rech/mrh/sommaire.md?type=text.html; http://www.magnesiumresearch.com/. **Circ:** (Not Reported)

43997 ■ Medecine therapeutique
John Libbey Eurotext
127, Ave. de la Republique
92120 Montrouge, France
Ph: 33 1 46730660
Fax: 33 1 40840999
Publisher E-mail: contact@jle.com
Internal medicine journal covering medical disciplines. **Subtitle:** From research to treatment, a leading journal of hospital medicine. **Freq:** 6/yr. **Key Personnel:** Marc Abitbol, Editor-in-Chief. **ISSN:** 1264-6520. **Subscription Rates:** EUR47 single issue; EUR158 other countries online and paper; EUR130 individuals online and paper (France); EUR150 individuals online and paper (European Union and Switzerland); EUR285 institutions, other countries print; EUR250 institutions print (France); EUR272 institutions print (European Union and Switzerland); EUR99 students, other countries online and paper; EUR75 students online and paper (France); EUR91 students online and paper (European Union & Switzerland). **Remarks:** Accepts advertising. **URL:** http://www.john-libbey-eurotext.fr/en/revues/medecine/met/sommaire.md?type=text.html; http://www.revue-mt.fr/. **Circ:** (Not Reported)

43998 ■ Medecine therapeutique cardiologie
John Libbey Eurotext
127, Ave. de la Republique

92120 Montrouge, France
Ph: 33 1 46730660
Fax: 33 1 40840999
Publisher E-mail: contact@jle.com
Journal covering all areas of cardiology. **Subtitle:** Key-link between basic research and medical practice. **Freq:** 6/yr. **Key Personnel:** Patrick Lacolley, Editor-in-Chief. **ISSN:** 1762-410X. **Remarks:** Accepts advertising. **URL:** http://www.john-libbey-eurotext.fr/en/revues/medecine/mtc/sommaire.md?type=text.html; http://www.mtcardio.fr/. **Circ:** (Not Reported)

43999 ■ Medecine therapeutique/Endocrinologie
John Libbey Eurotext
127, Ave. de la Republique
92120 Montrouge, France
Ph: 33 1 46730660
Fax: 33 1 40840999
Publisher E-mail: contact@jle.com
Journal covering information on endocrinology and metabolic disorders. **Subtitle:** A journal providing up-to-date information on endocrinology and metabolic disorders. **Freq:** 6/yr. **Key Personnel:** Didier Dewailly, Editor-in-Chief. **ISSN:** 1295-9359. **Subscription Rates:** EUR43 single issue. **Remarks:** Accepts advertising. **URL:** http://www.john-libbey-eurotext.fr/en/revues/medecine/mte/sommaire.md?type=text.html. **Circ:** (Not Reported)

44000 ■ Medecine Therapeutique/medecine de la reproduction
John Libbey Eurotext
127, Ave. de la Republique
92120 Montrouge, France
Ph: 33 1 46730660
Fax: 33 1 40840999
Publisher E-mail: contact@jle.com
Journal covering information on endocrinology and metabolic disorders. **Freq:** 6/yr. **Key Personnel:** Didier Dewailly, Editor-in-Chief. **ISSN:** 1774-640X. **Subscription Rates:** EUR47 single issue. **Remarks:** Accepts advertising. **URL:** http://www.john-libbey-eurotext.fr/en/revues/medecine/mtm/sommaire.md?type=text.html; http://www.mtmr.fr/. **Circ:** (Not Reported)

44001 ■ Medecine therapeutique/Pediatrie
John Libbey Eurotext
127, Ave. de la Republique
92120 Montrouge, France
Ph: 33 1 46730660
Fax: 33 1 40840999
Publisher E-mail: contact@jle.com
Journal covering aspects of medical practice, therapeutics, clinical biology, genetics and public health. **Subtitle:** A journal for pediatricians. **Freq:** 6/yr. **Key Personnel:** Dr. Philippe Reinert, Editor-in-Chief. **ISSN:** 1286-5494. **Subscription Rates:** EUR47 single issue; EUR166 other countries online and paper; EUR130 individuals online and paper (France); EUR154 individuals online and paper (European Union and Switzerland); EUR116 students, other countries online and paper; EUR80 students online and paper (France); EUR104 students online and paper (European Union and Switzerland); EUR286 institutions, other countries print; EUR250 institutions print (France); EUR274 institutions print (European Union and Switzerland). **Remarks:** Accepts advertising. **URL:** http://www.john-libbey-eurotext.fr/en/revues/medecine/mtp/sommaire.md?type=text.html; http://www.mtpediatrie.fr/. **Circ:** (Not Reported)

44002 ■ MT Cardio
John Libbey Eurotext
127, Ave. de la Republique
92120 Montrouge, France
Ph: 33 1 46730660
Fax: 33 1 40840999
Publisher E-mail: contact@jle.com
Journal covering the understanding cardio-vascular illnesses. **Subtitle:** Keylink between basic research and medical practice. **Freq:** 6/yr. **Key Personnel:** Ariel Cohen, Editor-in-Chief. **ISSN:** 1774-8747. **Subscription Rates:** EUR44 single issue. **Remarks:** Accepts advertising. **URL:** http://www.john-libbey-eurotext.fr/en/revues/medecine/mca/sommaire.md?type=text.html; http://www.mtcardio.fr/. **Circ:** (Not Reported)

44003 ■ Oleagineux, Corps Gras, Lipides
John Libbey Eurotext
127, Ave. de la Republique
92120 Montrouge, France
Ph: 33 1 46730660
Fax: 33 1 40840999
Publisher E-mail: contact@jle.com
Journal for the different players in the oilseeds industry.

Subtitle: A journal linking together the research community and their partners. **Freq:** 6/yr. **Key Personnel:** Jean-Claude Icart, Editor-in-Chief. **ISSN:** 1258-8210. **Remarks:** Accepts advertising. **URL:** http://www.john-libbey-eurotext.fr/en/revues/agro_biotech/ocl/sommaire.md?type=text.html; http://www.revue-ocl.fr/. **Circ:** (Not Reported)

44004 ■ Psychologie & NeuroPsychiatrie du vieillissement
John Libbey Eurotext
127, Ave. de la Republique
92120 Montrouge, France
Ph: 33 1 46730660
Fax: 33 1 40840999
Publisher E-mail: contact@jle.com
Journal for neurologists, psychiatrists, geriatricians and psychologists. **Subtitle:** Multidisciplinary journal around the ageing of the brain. **Freq:** 4/yr. **Key Personnel:** Christian Derouesne, Editor-in-Chief. **ISSN:** 1760-1703. **Subscription Rates:** EUR57 single issue; EUR144 other countries online and print; EUR120 individuals online and print (France); EUR136 individuals online and print (European Union and Switzerland); EUR99 students, other countries online and print; EUR75 students online and print (France); EUR91 students online and print (European Union and Switzerland); EUR230 institutions, other countries print; EUR200 institutions print (France); EUR220 institutions print (European Union and Switzerland). **Remarks:** Accepts advertising. **URL:** http://www.pnpv.fr/; http://www.john-libbey-eurotext.fr/en/revues/medecine/pnv/sommaire.md?type= text.html. **Circ:** (Not Reported)

44005 ■ Revue de neuropsychologie
John Libbey Eurotext
127, Ave. de la Republique
92120 Montrouge, France
Ph: 33 1 46730660
Fax: 33 1 40840999
Publisher E-mail: contact@jle.com
Journal covering all fields of neuropsychology. **Freq:** Quarterly. **Key Personnel:** Francis Eustache, Editor-in-Chief. **ISSN:** 2101-6739. **Subscription Rates:** EUR47 single issue; EUR145 other countries online and paper; EUR125 individuals online and paper; France; EUR135 individuals online and paper; Europe and Switzerland; EUR99 students, other countries online and paper; EUR75 students online and paper; France; EUR91 students online and paper; Europe and Switzerland; EUR201 institutions, other countries online and paper; EUR180 institutions print; France; EUR196 institutions print; Europe and Switzerland. **URL:** http://www.john-libbey-eurotext.fr/en/revues/medecine/nrp/sommaire.md?type=text.html.

44006 ■ Sang Thrombose Vaisseaux
John Libbey Eurotext
127, Ave. de la Republique
92120 Montrouge, France
Ph: 33 1 46730660
Fax: 33 1 40840999
Publisher E-mail: contact@jle.com
Journal covering vascular and thrombotic diseases. **Subtitle:** A major multidisciplinary journal on vascular diseases. **Freq:** 10/yr. **Key Personnel:** Bernard Levy, Editor-in-Chief. **ISSN:** 0999-7385. **Subscription Rates:** EUR190 other countries online and paper; EUR140 individuals online and paper (France); EUR180 individuals online and paper (European Union and Switzerland); EUR120 students, other countries online and paper; EUR90 students online and paper (France); EUR110 students online and paper (European Union and Switzerland); EUR285 institutions, other countries print; EUR235 institutions print (France); EUR275 institutions online and paper (European Union and Switzerland). **Remarks:** Accepts advertising. **URL:** http://www.revue-stv.com/; http://www.john-libbey-eurotext.fr/en/revues/medecine/stv/sommaire.md?type= text.html. **Circ:** (Not Reported)

44007 ■ Science et changements planetaires/ Secheresse
John Libbey Eurotext
127, Ave. de la Republique
92120 Montrouge, France
Ph: 33 1 46730660
Fax: 33 1 40840999
Publisher E-mail: contact@jle.com
Journal covering all information concerning the many areas of activity relating to drought. **Subtitle:** The sum of knowledge on desertification and combating drought. **Freq:** 4/yr. **Key Personnel:** Andre Kergreis, Editor-in-Chief. **ISSN:** 1147-7806. **Subscription Rates:** EUR33 other countries online and paper; EUR65 individuals online and paper (European Union and France); EUR22 students, other countries online and paper; EUR44

students online and paper (European Union and France); EUR55 institutions, other countries print; EUR110 institutions print (European Union and France); EUR115 institutions print and online (France). **Remarks:** Accepts advertising. **URL:** http://www.john-libbey-eurotext.fr/en/revues/agro_biotech/sec/sommaire.md?type=text.html; http://www.revue-secheresse.fr/. **Circ:** (Not Reported)

44008 ■ Virologie
John Libbey Eurotext
127, Ave. de la Republique
92120 Montrouge, France
Ph: 33 1 46730660
Fax: 33 1 40840999
Publisher E-mail: contact@jle.com
Journal covering field of virology. **Subtitle:** A Focus on all Aspects of Virology. **Freq:** 6/yr. **Key Personnel:** Henri Agut, Editor-in-Chief; Francis Barin, Editor-in-Chief; Yves Gaudin, Editor-in-Chief; Hubert Laude, Editor-in-Chief; Noel Tordo, Editor-in-Chief. **ISSN:** 1267-8694. **Subscription Rates:** EUR47 single issue; EUR166 other countries online and paper; EUR130 individuals online and paper (France); EUR154 individuals online and paper (European Union and Switzerland); EUR110 students, other countries online and paper; EUR85 students online and paper (France); EUR109 students online and paper (European Union and Switzerland); EUR281 institutions, other countries print; EUR245 institutions print (France); EUR269 institutions print (European Union and Switzerland). **Remarks:** Accepts advertising. **URL:** http://www.john-libbey-eurotext.fr/en/revues/bio_rech/vir/sommaire.md?type=text.html; http://www.revue-virologie.fr/. **Circ:** (Not Reported)

Morieres Les Avignon

44009 ■ L'Echo vegetable
L'Echo Edition
1405, route de Noves
BP 12
F-84310 Morieres Les Avignon, France
Ph: 33 490 335656
Fax: 33 490 335651
Trade magazine covering the fruit and vegetable industry from production to the market. **Founded:** 1983. **Freq:** Monthly. **Key Personnel:** Jean Harzig, Editor-in-Chief, j.harzig@vegetable.fr. **ISSN:** 1273-7011. **Subscription Rates:** EUR90 individuals; EUR110 two years individual; EUR60 individuals France; EUR80 two years individual, France. **Remarks:** Accepts advertising. **URL:** http://www.vegetable.fr. **Ad Rates:** 4C: 3,000 Fr. **Circ:** Paid 10,000

Nancy

44010 ■ Discrete Mathematics & Theoretical Computer Science
62 rue du Cardinal Mathieu
F-54000 Nancy, France
Publication E-mail: admin@dmtcs.org
Publisher E-mail: admin@dmtcs.org
Journal covering the fields of discrete mathematics and theoretical computer science. It is the only journal of the Russian Academy of Sciences devoted to discrete mathematics. **Freq:** Irregular. **Key Personnel:** Christian Krattenthaler, Editor; Jens Gustedt, Section Ed. **ISSN:** 1365-8050. **URL:** http://www.dmtcs.org/dmtcs-ojs/.

Nantes

44011 ■ Aquatic Living Resources
EDP Sciences
c/o Brigitte Milcendeau, Ed.-in-Ch.
rue de l'ile d'Yeu
BP 21105
F-44311 Nantes Cedex 3, France
Ph: 33 2 40374000
Fax: 33 2 40374001
Publisher E-mail: subscribers@edpsciences.org
Journal covering exploitation and production of all living resources in marine, brackish and freshwater environments. **Freq:** 4/yr. **Print Method:** offset. **Key Personnel:** Brigitte Milcendeau, Editor-in-Chief, bmilcend@ifremer.fr; Antonio Figueras, Assoc. Ed., pato1@iim.csic.es. **ISSN:** 0990-7440. **Subscription Rates:** EUR383 individuals print and electronic (without VAT, France); EUR396 individuals print and electronic (without VAT, European Union); EUR430 other countries print and electronic; EUR335 other countries electronic. **Remarks:** Accepts advertising. **URL:** http://www.alr-journal.org/. **Ad Rates:** BW: 550 Fr. 4C: 950 Fr. **Circ:** 1,000

Circulation: ★ = ABC; △ = BPA; ♦ = CAC; • = CCAB; ❑ = VAC; ⊕ = PO Statement; ‡ = Publisher's Report; Boldface figures = sworn; Light figures = estimated.

44012 ■ Current Gene Therapy
Bentham Science Publishers Ltd.
Inserm, Unit 643
CHU Hotel Dieu, 30 Bd Jean Monnet
44093 Nantes, France
Ph: 33 240 087410
Fax: 33 240 087411
Publication E-mail: cgt@univ-nantes.fr
Publisher E-mail: subscriptions@bentham.org
Interdisciplinary journal focused on providing current and comprehensive reviews on all aspects of gene therapy. **Subtitle:** The International Journal for In-depth Reviews on Gene Therapy. **Freq:** Bimonthly. **Key Personnel:** Ignacio Anegon, Editor-in-Chief, cgt@univ-nantes.fr; Pedro R. Lowenstein, Founding Ed.; P. Aebischer, Assoc. Ed. **ISSN:** 1566-5232. **Remarks:** Accepts advertising. **URL:** http://www.bentham.org/cgt. **Circ:** (Not Reported)

44013 ■ Electronic Communications in Probability
Institute of Mathematical Statistics
2, Rue de la Houssiniere BP 92208
F-44322 Nantes Cedex 03, France
Publisher E-mail: ims@imstat.org
Journal on probability theory. **Print Method:** Offset. **Cols./Page:** 6. **Col. Width:** 21 nonpareils. **Col. Depth:** 294 agate lines. **Key Personnel:** David J. Aldous, Assoc. Ed., aldous@stat.berkeley.edu; Marek Biskup, Assoc. Ed., biskup@math.ucla.edu; Robert C. Dalang, Assoc. Ed., robert.dalang@epfl.ch; James Allen Fill, Assoc. Ed., jimfill@jhu.edu; Franco Flandoli, Assoc. Ed., flandoli@dma.unipi.it; Jeffrey E. Steif, Assoc. Ed., steif@chalmers.se; Evarist Gine, Assoc. Ed., gine@math.uconn.edu; Brian Rider, Assoc. Ed., brian.rider@colorado.edu; Friedrich Gotze, Assoc. Ed., goetze@mathematik.uni-bielefeld.de. **ISSN:** 1083-6489. **URL:** http://www.math.washington.edu/~ejpecp/ECP/index.php.

Neuilly

44014 ■ International Herald Tribune
6 Bis, rue des Graviers
F-92521 Neuilly Cedex, France
Ph: 33 141 439361
Publication E-mail: iht@iht.com
Publisher E-mail: iht@iht.com
General interest newspaper. **Freq:** Daily. **Key Personnel:** Jean-Christophe Demarta, Advertising Dir., phone 33 1 41439381, jcdemarta@iht.com; Veronique Feldmann, Mng. Dir., phone 33 1 41439479, vfeldmann@iht.com. **Subscription Rates:** US$420 individuals. **Remarks:** Accepts advertising. **URL:** http://www.iht.com/pages/index.php. **Ad Rates:** BW: 56,795 Fr, 4C: 78,093 Fr. **Circ:** (Not Reported)

Nice

44015 ■ Gene Therapy and Regulation
World Scientific Publishing Company Private Ltd.
c/o Roger Bertolotti, Ed.-in-Ch.
CNRS, Gene Therapy & Regulation Research
Faculty of Medicine, University of Nice - Sophia Antipolis
Ave. de Valombrose
F-06107 Nice, France
Ph: 33 4 93817381
Fax: 33 4 93317253
Publisher E-mail: wspc@wspc.com.sg
Journal publishing various aspects of research on gene therapy and ancillary basic cell or molecular biology approaches including stem cell research, molecular cloning, sequencing and gene regulation. **Key Personnel:** Roger Bertolotti, Editor-in-Chief, roger.bertolotti@unice.fr; Anthony Atala, Assoc. Ed.; Connie J. Eaves, Assoc. Ed. **ISSN:** 1388-9532. **Subscription Rates:** US$360 institutions and libraries; print and electronic; US$346 institutions and libraries; electronic only; EUR303 institutions and libraries; print and electronic; EUR291 institutions and libraries; electronic only; S$553 institutions and libraries; print and electronic; S$531 institutions and libraries; electronic only. **URL:** http://www.worldscinet.com/gtr/.

44016 ■ Journal of the European Academy of Dermatology and Venereology
John Wiley & Sons Inc.
Wiley-Blackwell
c/o Maryse Clappier, Ed.

Hopital L'Archet 2, Service de Dermatologie
151 Rte., St. Antoine de Ginestiere
BP 3079
F-06202 Nice Cedex 3, France
Ph: 33 492 036119
Fax: 33 492 036532
Peer-reviewed journal covering the study of Dermatology and Venereology in relation to clinical aspects, basic sciences, and in research. **Freq:** Monthly. **Key Personnel:** Maryse Clappier, Editor, maryse.clappier@unice.fr; Prof. Jean-Paul Ortonne, Editor, ortonne@unice.fr. **ISSN:** 0926-9959. **Remarks:** Advertising accepted; rates available upon request. **URL:** http://www.wiley.com/bw/journal.asp?ref=0926-9959. **Circ:** (Not Reported)

Nogaro

44017 ■ Radio d'Artagnan-FM - 97.6
Ave. Peries
32110 Nogaro, France
Ph: 33 5 62690666
Fax: 33 5 62090303
E-mail: contact@radiodartagnan.com
Format: Full Service. **URL:** http://www.radiodartagnan.com/.

Radio d'Artagnan-FM - See Condom
Radio d'Artagnan-FM - See Viella

Orsay

44018 ■ Annales Henri Poincare
Springer-Verlag Tokyo
c/o Chantal Delongeas
Laboratoire de Physique Theorique
Batiment 210, Universite Paris Sud-XI
91405 Orsay Cedex, France
Publication E-mail: ahp@th.u-psud.fr
Publisher E-mail: info@springer.jp
Journal serving the international scientific community in theoretical and mathematical physics by collecting and publishing original research papers meeting the highest professional standards in the field with the emphasis on analytical theoretical and mathematical physics. **Freq:** 8/yr. **Key Personnel:** Vincent Rivasseau, Editor-in-Chief, rivass@th.u-psud.fr; Jean Bellissard, Section Ed., jeanbel@math.gatech.edu; Rafael D. Benguria, Section Ed., rbenguri@chopin.fis.puc.cl; Klaus Fredenhagen, Section Ed., fredenha@x4u2.desy.de; Jens Marklof, Section Ed., j.marklof@bristol.ac.uk; Viviane Baladi, Section Ed., baladi@dma.ens.fr. **ISSN:** 1424-0637. **Subscription Rates:** EUR878 institutions print incl. free access or e-only; EUR1,053.60 institutions print incl. enhanced access. **Remarks:** Advertising accepted; rates available upon request. **URL:** http://www.springer.com/birkhauser/physics/journal/23. **Circ:** (Not Reported)

44019 ■ Inventiones Mathematicae
Springer-Verlag
c/o E. Ullmo, Mng. Ed.
Universite Paris-Sud
Departement de Mathematique, Batiment 425
F-91405 Orsay Cedex, France
Fax: 33 1 69156019
Journal dealing with all aspects of mathematics. **Freq:** 3/yr. **Key Personnel:** H. Hofer, Managing Editor, inventiones.mathematicae@cims.nyu.edu; E. Frenkel, Editor, frenkel@math.berkeley.edu; E. Ullmo, Managing Editor, inventiones.mathematicae@math.u-psud.fr. **ISSN:** 0020-9910. **Subscription Rates:** EUR2,889 institutions print incl. free access; EUR2,889 institutions print incl. enhanced access. **Remarks:** Advertising accepted; rates available upon request. **URL:** http://www.springer.com/math/journal/222. **Circ:** (Not Reported)

Paris

44020 ■ Acta Astronautica
Elsevier
c/o Jean Pierre Marec, Honorary Ed.-in-Ch.
International Academy of Astronautics
BP 1268.16
F-75766 Paris Cedex 16, France
Publisher E-mail: relclient@elsevier.fr
Peer-reviewed journal publishing original articles in the fields of basic, engineering, life and social space sciences and of space technology, in connection with the International Academy of Astronautics. **Founded:** 1955. **Freq:** Semimonthly. **Key Personnel:** Rupert Gerzer, Editor-in-Chief; G. Chernyi, Publication Committee Member; M. Fust, Dep. Mng. Ed.; Jean Pierre Marec,

Honorary Ed.-in-Ch.; P. Molette, Publication Committee Member. **ISSN:** 0094-5765. **Subscription Rates:** 566,700¥ institutions; EUR4,268 institutions for European Countries; US$4,776 institutions, other countries except Europe, Japan and Iran. **Remarks:** Accepts advertising. **URL:** http://www.elsevier.com/wps/find/journaldescription.cws_home/310/descriptiondescription. **Circ:** (Not Reported)

44021 ■ L'Actualite Chimique
Societe Francais de Chimie
250, rue St. Jacques
F-75005 Paris, France
Ph: 33 140 467160
Fax: 33 140 467161
Publication E-mail: redaction@lactualitechimique.org
Publisher E-mail: sfc@sfc.fr
French language chemistry journal. **Freq:** Monthly 11/yr. **Key Personnel:** Paul Rigny, Editor-in-Chief, phone 33 1 40467164, paul.rigny@lactualitechimique.org; Severine Bleneau-Serdel, Asst. Ed., phone 33 1 40467169, bleneau@lactualitechimique.org. **Subscription Rates:** EUR110 students in France; EUR195 institutions in France; EUR130 other countries for @STD; EUR205 institutions other countries. **Remarks:** Accepts advertising. **URL:** http://www.lactualitechimique.org/. **Circ:** Paid 5,000

44022 ■ Adansonia
Museum national d'Histoire naturelle
Service des Publications Scientifiques Diffusion
57 rue Cuvier
F-75005 Paris Cedex 05, France
Ph: 33 014 0794856
Fax: 33 014 0793858
Publication E-mail: adanson@mnhn.fr
Publisher E-mail: adanson@mnhn.fr
Journal on plant biology devoted to inventory, analysis and interpretation of vascular plants biodiversity, covering topics on morphology, anatomy, biology, ecology, phylogeny, and biogeography. **Founded:** 1997. **Freq:** Semiannual. **Key Personnel:** Thierry Deroin, Editor-in-Chief. **ISSN:** 1280-8571. **Subscription Rates:** EUR40 single issue. **URL:** http://www.mnhn.fr/publication/adanson/aadanson.html.

44023 ■ Aide et Action
53 blvd. de Charonne
F-75545 Paris, France
Ph: 33 155 257000
Fax: 33 155 257029
Publisher E-mail: info@aide-et-action.org
French and English language publication covering worldwide development. **Founded:** 1981. **Freq:** Quarterly. **ISSN:** 0752-4242. **Subscription Rates:** EUR4 individuals. **Remarks:** Advertising not accepted. **URL:** http://www.aide-et-action.org/english/ewb_pages/m/magazine.php. **Formerly:** Ecoliers du Monde. **Circ:** (Not Reported)

44024 ■ Annales d'Economie et de Statistique
Institut Europlace de Finance
Palais Brongniart
Place de la Bourse
F-75002 Paris, France
Ph: 33 1 49271417
Fax: 33 1 49275628
Journal covering the fields of economic theory, econometrics and statistics. **Founded:** 1986. **Freq:** 10/yr. **Print Method:** Web Offset. **Trim Size:** 8 x 10 3/4. **Cols./Page:** 2 and 4. **Col. Width:** 21 and 27 nonpareils. **Col. Depth:** 140 agate lines. **URL:** http://www.adres.ens.fr/index-en.htmlannals.

44025 ■ Annales Francaises d'Anesthesie et de Reanimation
Elsevier
23 rue Linois
F-75724 Paris Cedex 15, France
Ph: 33 171 724646
Fax: 33 171 724664
Publisher E-mail: relclient@elsevier.fr
French language publication covering anesthesiology. **Subtitle:** Le Journal de la Societe Francaise d'Anesthesie et de Reanimation. **Founded:** 1982. **Freq:** Monthly. **Key Personnel:** J. Mantz, Editor-in-Chief; O. Paut, Contact; N. Bruder, Contact. **ISSN:** 0750-7658. **Subscription Rates:** US$178 students; EUR143 students; 19,300¥ students; EUR115 students in France; EUR331 institutions; 40,700¥ institutions; US$452 institutions. **Remarks:** Advertising accepted; rates available upon request. **URL:** http://www.elsevier.com/wps/find/journaldescription.cws_home/525540/descriptiondescription. **Circ:** Paid 5,500

44026 ■ L'Arche
FSJU
Espace Rachi 39, Rue Broca
F-75005 Paris, France
Ph: 33 421 71010
Fax: 33 421 71031
Publication E-mail: info@arche-mag.com
Publisher E-mail: info@arche-mag.com
Journal covering Jewish culture and communities.
Founded: Jan. 1, 1957. **Freq:** Monthly 11/yr. **URL:**
http://www.fsju.org/. **Circ:** Paid 20,000

44027 ■ Astronomy & Astrophysics
EDP Sciences
Observatoire de Paris
61, Ave. de l'Observatoire
F-75014 Paris, France
Ph: 33 1 43290541
Fax: 33 1 43290557
Publisher E-mail: subscribers@edpsciences.org
Journal covering aspects of astronomy and astrophysics.
Freq: Weekly. **Key Personnel:** C. Bertout, Editor-in-
Chief, aanda.paris@obspm.fr; H. Peter, Assoc. Ed.
ISSN: 0004-6361. **Subscription Rates:** EUR4,015
institutions print and electronic (France); EUR3,169.40
institutions electronic (France); EUR2,915 institutions,
other countries electronic; EUR4,015 institutions, other
countries electronic and print. **URL:** http://www.aanda.
org/.

44028 ■ Atoms for Peace
Inderscience Publishers
c/o Dr. Andre Maisseu, Ed.-in-Ch.
49 rue Lauriston
F-75116 Paris, France
Publisher E-mail: editor@inderscience.com
Peer-reviewed journal serving as an international forum
for exchange of ideas and views on the global implications of nuclear technology for economic growth,
sustainable development and international security. **Subtitle:** An International Journal. **Freq:** Quarterly. **Key Personnel:** Dr. Andre Maisseu, Editor-in-Chief, a.maisseu@
wonuc.org; Dr. Hans Blix, Honorary Advisory Board; Dr.
Rajagopala Chidambaram, Honorary Advisory Board.
ISSN: 1741-640X. **Subscription Rates:** EUR494 individuals print (surface mail); EUR672 individuals hard copy
and online; EUR840 individuals online (2-3 users). **URL:**
http://www.inderscience.com/browse/index.php?
journalCODE=afp.

44029 ■ Biology International
International Union of Biological Sciences
Union Internationale des Sciences Biologiques
Bat 442 Universite Paris-Sud 11
Orsay cedex
F-91405 Paris, France
Ph: 33 169 155027
Fax: 33 169 155747
Publisher E-mail: secretariat@iubs.org
Publication covering biology. **Freq:** Semiannual. **Key
Personnel:** Talal Younes, Dir. Emeritus. **ISSN:** 0253-
2069. **URL:** http://www.iubs.org. **Circ:** 3,000

44030 ■ Bloc Notes Publishing
Pyramyd NTCV S.A.
15 rue Turbigo
F-75002 Paris, France
Ph: 33 140 260099
Fax: 33 140 260703
Publisher E-mail: form@pyramyd.fr
Professional magazine covering computer graphics and
infographics. **Founded:** 1992. **Freq:** Monthly. **Print
Method:** Offset. **Key Personnel:** Alice Anderson, Art
Dir.; Nadia Zanoun, Advertising; Michel Chanaud,
Publisher; Patrick Morin, Editor. **ISSN:** 1240-571X. **Re-
marks:** Accepts advertising. **URL:** http://www.penrose-
press.com/idd/card.php?INDEX=MAG16986&
SUBJECT=SUB10029. **Circ:** Combined 8,000

**44031 ■ Cahiers d'Economie et Sociologie Ru-
rales**
Institut National de la Recherche Agronomique
147 rue de l'universite
F-75338 Paris Cedex 07, France
Ph: 33 142 759000
Journal covering scientific articles of economy, sociology and history devoted to agriculture, the food industries, food consumption, the rural areas and the
environment. **Founded:** 1984. **Freq:** Quarterly. **Print
Method:** Offset. **Cols./Page:** 5. **Col. Width:** 24
nonpareils. **Col. Depth:** 182 agate lines. **Subscription

Rates: EUR70 individuals France and Europe; EUR85
other countries; EUR25 single issue. **URL:** http://www.
inra.fr/esr/publications/cahiers/eng/index.phpabon.

44032 ■ Cancer Radiotherapie
Elsevier Science Inc.
Centre tumours, Hospital of Pity Salpetriere
47 Data bases of the Hospital
75651 Paris Cedex 13, France
Ph: 33 1 4217 8171
Publisher E-mail: usinfo-ehelp@elsevier.com
Journal covering cancerology, treatment of cancer by
radiotherapy. **Founded:** 1997. **Freq:** 8/yr. **Key Person-
nel:** Biete A. Sola, Editorial Board; P. Maingon, Assoc.
Ed., pmaingon@dijon.fnclcc.fr; F. Mornex, Assoc. Ed.,
francoise.mornex@chu-lyon.fr; P. Van Houtte, Assoc.
Ed.; Christine Sempe, Editor and Publisher, c.sempe@
elsevier.fr; H. Aget, Editorial Board; J.P. Bahary, Editorial
Board; C. Hennequin, Editorial Board; G.B. Biti, Editorial
Board; J. Bourhis, Editorial Board; J.J. Mazeron, Editor-
in-Chief, jean-jacques.mazeron@psl.ap-hop-paris.fr.
ISSN: 1278-3218. **URL:** http://www.elsevier.com/wps/
find/journaldescription.cws_home/522841/
descriptiondescription.

44033 ■ Combustion and Flame
Elsevier
23 rue Linois
F-75724 Paris Cedex 15, France
Ph: 33 171 724646
Fax: 33 171 724664
Publisher E-mail: relclient@elsevier.fr
Journal publishing experimental and theoretical investigations of combustion phenomena and closely allied
matters. **Freq:** Monthly. **Key Personnel:** J.A. Miller,
Assoc. Ed., jamille@sandia.gov; P. Dagaut, Editor,
phone 33 238 245466, fax 33 238 696004, dagaut@
cnrs-orleans.fr; F.N. Egolfopoulos, Editor, egolfopo@
usc.edu; P. Glarborg, Assoc. Ed., pgl@kt.dtu.dk. **ISSN:**
0010-2180. **Subscription Rates:** EUR2,026 institutions
for Europe; US$2,357 institutions for all countries except
Europe and Japan; 278,300¥ institutions. **URL:** http://
www.elsevier.com/wps/find/journaldescription.cws_
home/505736/descriptiondescription.

44034 ■ Copyright Bulletin
UNESCO
Section of Cultural Enterprise and Copyright
1 rue Miollis
F-75732 Paris Cedex 15, France
Ph: 33 1 45681000
Fax: 33 1 45671690
Publisher E-mail: bpi@unesco.org
Online publication covering copyrights and related rights
in English, Arabic, French, Russian and Spanish.
Founded: 1948. **ISSN:** 1817-4167. **Subscription
Rates:** Free. **Remarks:** Advertising not accepted. **URL:**
http://portal.unesco.org/culture/en/ev.php-URL_ID=
5130&URL_DO=DO_TOPIC&URL_SECTION=201.html.
Circ: 188

44035 ■ Current Genomics
Bentham Science Publishers Ltd.
INSERM
Unit Neuronal Cell Biiology & Pathology
Centre Paul Broca
2-ter rue d'Alesia
F-75014 Paris, France
Publisher E-mail: subscriptions@bentham.org
Journal covering all the latest and outstanding develop-
ments in genomics. **Freq:** 8/yr. **Key Personnel:** Chris-
tian Neri, Editor-in-Chief, neri@broca.inserm.fr; Olivier
Civelli, Assoc. Ed.; Robert E. Hughes, Co-Ed. **ISSN:**
1389-2029. **Subscription Rates:** US$2,820 institutions
corporate, print; US$2,820 institutions corporate, online;
US$3,380 institutions corporate, print and online;
US$1,590 institutions academic, print; US$1,590 institu-
tions academic, online; US$1,750 institutions academic,
print and online; US$360 individuals print. **Remarks:**
Accepts advertising. **URL:** http://www.bentham.com/cg.
Circ: (Not Reported)

44036 ■ Data Science Journal
International Council for Science
5 rue Auguste Vacquerie
F-75116 Paris, France
Ph: 33 145 250329
Fax: 33 142 889431
Publisher E-mail: secretariat@icsu.org
Peer-reviewed electronic journal publishing papers on

the management of data and databases in science and
technology, including descriptions of data systems, their
publication on the internet, applications and legal issues.
Key Personnel: Prof. Shuichi Iwata, Editor-in-Chief;
Prof. Niv Ahituv, Editorial Board, ahituv@post.tau.ac.il;
Prof. Liu Chuang, Editorial Board, lchuang@igsnrr.ac.
cn; Prof. Yannis Tzitzikas, Assoc. Ch. Ed., tzitzik@ics.
forth.gr; Dr. Horst Kremers, Editorial Board, office@
horst-kremers.de; Prof. Marcelle Gaune-Escard, Editorial
Board, marcelle.gaune-escard@polytech.univ-mrs.fr; Dr.
William L. Anderson, Editorial Board, band@acm.org;
Prof. Takashi Kunisawa, Assoc. Ch. Ed., kunisawa@rs.
noda.tus.ac.jp; Diane Smith, Publication Board, dsj@
codataweb.org; Dr. Daisy Selematsela, Editorial Board,
daisys@nrf.ac.za; Paul F. Uhlir, Editorial Board. **ISSN:**
1683-1470. **URL:** http://www.codata.org/dsj/index.html.

44037 ■ Diogenes
UNESCO
International Council for Philosophy and Humanistic
Studies
1 rue Miollis
Cedex 15 Paris, France
Ph: 33 145 684885
Fax: 33 140 659480
Publication E-mail: diogene@unesco.org
Publisher E-mail: cipsh@unesco.org
Journal focusing on all areas of philosophy and human-
istic studies. **Freq:** Quarterly. **Key Personnel:** Maurice
Aymard, Editor; Luca Maria Scarantino, Editor. **ISSN:**
0392-1921. **Subscription Rates:** 333 institutions print &
e-access; 300 institutions e-access; 326 institutions print
only; 44 individuals print only. **Remarks:** Accepts
advertising. **URL:** http://dio.sagepub.com/. **Circ:** (Not
Reported)

44038 ■ Disease Information
OIE
12, rue de Prony
F-75017 Paris, France
Ph: 33 1 44151888
Fax: 33 1 42670987
Publisher E-mail: oie@oie.int
Publication covering emergency notifications and animal
health follow-up reports on special epidemiological
events occurring in the territories of OIE member
countries. Keeps the international community posted on
the latest developments in the situation of animal
diseases throughout the world. **Freq:** Weekly (Thurs.).
ISSN: 1608-0610. **URL:** http://www.oie.int/eng/publicat/
en_general_information.htm.

44039 ■ Electronique International Hebdo
12 rue d'Oradour sur Glane
F-75015 Paris Cedex 15, France
Publisher E-mail: eih@groupe-tests.fr
Business publication. **Freq:** Weekly. **Key Personnel:**
Marc Laufer, Dir. of Publication; Daniel Haussmann,
Director; Patrick Boissier, Director. **ISSN:** 1157-4445.
Subscription Rates: 150 Fr individuals; 4.25 Fr single
issue. **Online:** Gale. **URL:** http://www.electronique.biz/.

44040 ■ Etapes
Pyramyd NTCV S.A.
15 rue Turbigo
F-75002 Paris, France
Ph: 33 140 260099
Fax: 33 140 260703
Publisher E-mail: form@pyramyd.fr
Professional magazine covering graphic design.
Founded: June 1994. **Freq:** Monthly. **Print Method:**
Offset. **Key Personnel:** Valerie Decroix, Editor, pmorin@
pyramyd.fr; Michel Chanaud, Publisher. **ISSN:** 1254-
7298. **Remarks:** Accepts advertising. **URL:** http://www.
pyramyd.fr/; http://www.etapes.com/magazine.
Formerly: Etapes Graphiques (Jan. 2020). **Circ:**
Combined 13,000

44041 ■ European Journal of Medical Genetics
Elsevier Science Inc.
c/o A. Verloes, Ed.-in-Ch.
Dept. of Medical Genetics, Clinical Genetic Unit
CHU Robert Debre
48 Blvd. Serurier
F-75935 Paris, France
Ph: 33 1 40035341
Fax: 33 1 40032277
Publication E-mail: ejmg.editor@gmail.com

Publisher E-mail: usinfo-ehelp@elsevier.com
Journal covering human and medical genetics of experimental models. **Founded:** 2005. **Freq:** 6/yr. **Print Method:** Web. **Cols./Page:** 6. **Col. Width:** 12 picas. **Col. Depth:** 21 inches. **Key Personnel:** G. Gillessen-Kaesbach, Assoc. Ed.; A. Rauch, Editorial Board; R. Hennekam, Assoc. Ed.; A. Verloes, Editor-in-Chief; J. Clayton-Smith, Editorial Board; K. Devriendt, Editorial Board, ejmg@uz.kuleuven.ac.be. **ISSN:** 1769-7212. **Subscription Rates:** US$655 institutions, other countries except Europe, Japan and Iran; 77,900¥ institutions; EUR587 institutions for European countries and Iran; EUR134 individuals for European countries and Iran; US$178 other countries except Europe, Japan and Iran; 20,500¥ individuals. **URL:** http://www.elsevier.com/wps/find/journaldescription.cws_home/705239/descriptiondescription.

44042 ■ **European Journal of Medicinal Chemistry**
Elsevier Science Inc.
c/o H. Galons, Ed.-in-Ch.
INSERM U648
Universite Paris Descartes
4, Ave. de l'observatoire
F-75006 Paris, France
Ph: 33 1 53739684
Fax: 33 1 53739875
Publisher E-mail: usinfo-ehelp@elsevier.com
Journal covering medicinal chemistry, organic synthesis, biological behavior, pharmacological activity. **Founded:** Nov. 11, 1987. **Freq:** Monthly. **Print Method:** Offset. **Trim Size:** 14 x 22 1/2. **Cols./Page:** 6. **Col. Width:** 26 nonpareils. **Col. Depth:** 294 agate lines. **Key Personnel:** A. Monge-Vega, Assoc. Ed., cifa@unav.es; J. Elguero, Editorial Advisory Board; F. Durant, Editorial Advisory Board; S. Goldmann, Editorial Advisory Board; F.G. De las Heras, Editorial Advisory Board; G. Folkers, Editorial Advisory Board; P.R. Andrews, Editorial Advisory Board; S. Guccione, Assoc. Ed., guccione@unict.it; O. Lafont, Hon. Ed.-in-Ch., eur.jmedchem@cep.u-psud.fr. **ISSN:** 0223-5234. **Subscription Rates:** US$1,277 institutions, other countries except Europe, Japan and Iran; EUR1,143 institutions for European countries and Iran; 151,500¥ institutions. **URL:** http://www.elsevier.com/wps/find/journaldescription.cws_home/505813/descriptiondescription.

44043 ■ **European Journal of Mineralogy**
Gebruder Borntraeger Verlagsbuchhandlung
Laboratoire de Geologie
Ecole normale Superieure
24 Rue Lhomond
F-75005 Paris, France
Publisher E-mail: mail@schweizerbart.de
Journal covering the field of mineralogy. **Freq:** Bimonthly. **Key Personnel:** Christian Chopin, Managing Editor, chopin@geologie.ens.fr. **ISSN:** 0935-1221. **URL:** http://www.borntraeger-cramer.de/j/ejm/.

44044 ■ **Europhysics News**
EDP Sciences
c/o Dr. Claude Sebenne, Ed.
Laboratoire de Mineralogie Cristallographie
Universite Pierre et Marie Curie
BP 115
F-75252 Paris Cedex 05, France
Ph: 33 1 44274510
Fax: 33 1 44274541
Publisher E-mail: subscribers@edpsciences.org
Magazine for European physics community. **Freq:** 6/yr. **Print Method:** offset. **Key Personnel:** Dr. Claude Sebenne, Editor, claude.sebenne@imcp.jussieu.fr. **ISSN:** 0531-7479. **Subscription Rates:** EUR90 institutions European Union countries; EUR108 other countries. **Remarks:** Accepts advertising. **URL:** http://www.europhysicsnews.org/. **Ad Rates:** BW: 1,900 Fr, 4C: 2,200 Fr. **Circ:** 25,000

44045 ■ **Famille Chretienne**
15-27 rue Moussorgski
F-75018 Paris Cedex 18, France
Ph: 33 153 263500
Religious magazine. **Founded:** 1978. **Freq:** Weekly. **ISSN:** 0154-6821. **Subscription Rates:** EUR84 individuals; EUR43 individuals 6 months. **Remarks:** Accepts advertising. **URL:** http://www.famillechretienne.fr/. **Circ:** (Not Reported)

44046 ■ **High Pressure Research**
Taylor & Francis Group Journals
Physique des Milieux Denses
IMPMC, CNRS UMR7590

Universite Pierre et Marie Curie
140 Rue Lournel
F-75015 Paris, France
Publisher E-mail: customerservice@taylorandfrancis.com
Peer-reviewd journal focusing on research in high pressure science and technology. **Subtitle:** An International Journal. **Freq:** Quarterly. **Key Personnel:** Stefan Klotz, Editor-in-Chief, stefan.klotz@impmc.jussieu.fr; Dr. Yanbin Wang, Regional Ed., wang@cars.uchicago.edu; Y. Akahama, Editorial Board; D. Knorr, Editorial Board; R.J. Hemley, Editorial Board; Dr. Yoshinori Katayama, Regional Ed., katayama@springs.or.jp; V.E. Fortov, Editorial Board; D.D. Klug, Editorial Board; L. Dubrovinsky, Editorial Board; J. Gonzalez, Editorial Board; K. Heremans, Editorial Board; C. Yoo, Editorial Board. **ISSN:** 0895-7959. **Subscription Rates:** US$3,294 institutions print and online only; US$3,130 institutions online only; US$627 individuals; EUR2,623 institutions print & online; EUR2,491 institutions online only; 2,435 institutions online only; 3,294 institutions print and online only; 511 individuals; EUR499 individuals. **URL:** http://www.tandf.co.uk/journals/journal.asp?issn=0895-7959&linktype=5.

44047 ■ **Higher Education Policy**
International Association of Universities
Association Internationale des Universites
Unesco House
1, rue Miollis
F-75732 Paris Cedex 15, France
Ph: 33 1 45684800
Fax: 33 1 47347605
Publisher E-mail: iau@iau-aiu.net
Publication covering colleges and universities. **Subtitle:** The Quarterly Journal of the International Association of Universities. **Freq:** Quarterly. **Key Personnel:** Jeroen Huisman, Editor, j.huisman@bath.ac.uk. **ISSN:** 0952-8733. **Subscription Rates:** 332 institutions Europe; 70 individuals Europe; US$631 U.S. institution; US$130 U.S. individual; 332 institutions, other countries; 70 other countries. **Remarks:** Advertising accepted; rates available upon request. **URL:** http://www.iau-aiu.net/scientificpub/index.html. **Circ:** (Not Reported)

44048 ■ **Historiens et Geographes**
Association des Professeurs d'Histoire et de Geographie
BP 6541
75065 Paris Cedex 2, France
Ph: 33 142 336237
Fax: 33 142 331208
Publication E-mail: a.p.h.g@wanadoo.fr
Publisher E-mail: a.p.h.g@wanadoo.fr
Professional magazine covering history, culture and geography. **Founded:** 1910. **Freq:** Quarterly. **Cols./Page:** 2. **Key Personnel:** Michele Davoust, Admin. Secretariat; Robert Marconis, Publication Dir.; Hubert Tison, Managing Editor/Ed. **ISSN:** 0000-4675. **Subscription Rates:** EUR41 individuals France; EUR51.50 other countries; EUR35 individuals France; EUR46 other countries; EUR70 institutions France; EUR78.50 institutions other countries; EUR85 individuals France , support with adhesion; EUR85 other countries support with adhesion; EUR85 individuals France, support without adhesion; EUR85 other countries support without adhesion. **Remarks:** Accepts advertising. **URL:** http://www.aphg.fr/AccueilHistoriensGeographes.htm. **Circ:** (Not Reported)

44049 ■ **International Journal of Aviation Management**
Inderscience Enterprises Limited
c/o Dr. Andreas Wald, Ed.-in-Ch.
European Business School Paris
37-39, bd Murat
75016 Paris, France
Journal covering the field of aviation management. **Freq:** 4/yr. **Key Personnel:** Dr. Andreas Wald, Editor-in-Chief, andreas.wald@ebs.edu; Prof. Jaideep Motwani, Editor-in-Chief. **ISSN:** 1755-9901. **Subscription Rates:** EUR494 individuals print or online; EUR672 individuals print and online. **URL:** http://www.inderscience.com/browse/index.php?journalCODE=ijam.

44050 ■ **International Journal of Nuclear Desalination**
Inderscience Publishers
c/o Dr. Andre Maisseu, Ed.-in-Ch.
WONUC
49 rue Lauriston
F-75116 Paris, France

Publisher E-mail: editor@inderscience.com
Peer-reviewed journal aiming to provide a highly professional and authoritative source of information in the field of nuclear desalination technology and management. **Freq:** Quarterly. **Key Personnel:** Dr. Andre Maisseu, Editor-in-Chief, a.maisseu@wonuc.org; Dr. Ibrahim Khamis, Co-Ed.-in-Ch.; Dr. Pradip K. Tewari, Assoc. Ed. **ISSN:** 1741-914X. **Subscription Rates:** EUR840 individuals online only (2-3 users); EUR494 individuals print only (surface mail); EUR534 individuals print only (airmail); EUR672 individuals online and print. **URL:** http://www.inderscience.com/browse/index.php?journalCODE=ijnd.

44051 ■ **International Journal of Nuclear Energy Science and Technology**
Inderscience Publishers
c/o Dr. Andre Maisseu, Ed.-in-Ch.
WONUC
49 rue Lauriston
F-75116 Paris, France
Publisher E-mail: editor@inderscience.com
Peer-reviewed journal providing an international medium for the communication of original research, ideas and developments in all areas of the field of nuclear energy science and technology. **Freq:** Quarterly. **Key Personnel:** Dr. Andre Maisseu, Editor-in-Chief, a.maisseu@wonuc.org. **ISSN:** 1741-6361. **Subscription Rates:** EUR494 individuals print only (surface mail); EUR840 individuals online only (2-3 users); EUR534 individuals print only (airmail); EUR672 individuals print and online. **URL:** http://www.inderscience.com/browse/index.php?journalCODE=ijnest.

44052 ■ **International Journal of Nuclear Governance, Economy and Ecology**
Inderscience Publishers
c/o Dr. Andre Maisseu, Ed.-in-Ch.
WONUC
49 rue Lauriston
F-75116 Paris, France
Publisher E-mail: editor@inderscience.com
Peer-reviewed journal proposing and fostering discussion on the evolution and governance of nuclear resources, with emphasis on the implications that policy choices have on both the welfare of humans and the ecology of the planet. **Freq:** Quarterly. **Key Personnel:** Dr. Andre Maisseu, Editor-in-Chief, a.maisseu@wonuc.org; Prof. Geoffrey Rothwell, Editorial Board Member; Prof. Geo Gatev, Editorial Board Member. **ISSN:** 1742-4186. **Subscription Rates:** EUR494 individuals print only (surface mail); EUR534 individuals print only (airmail); EUR840 individuals online only (2-3 users); EUR672 individuals print and online. **URL:** http://www.inderscience.com/browse/index.php?journalCODE=ijngee.

44053 ■ **International Journal of Nuclear Hydrogen Production and Applications**
Inderscience Publishers
c/o Prof. Andre Maisseu, Ed-in-Ch.
49, Rue Lauriston
75116 Paris, France
Publisher E-mail: editor@inderscience.com
Peer-reviewed journal covering nuclear hydrogen production and applications. **Freq:** Semiannual. **Key Personnel:** Prof. Cesare Marchetti, Editorial Board Member; Dr. Masao Hori, Editorial Board Member; Dr. Thierry Alleau, Editorial Board Member; Dr. Frano Barbir, Editorial Board Member; Dr. Hans Georg Priesmeyer, Editorial Board Member; Prof. Andre Maisseu, Editor-in-Chief, a.maisseu@wonuc.org; Prof. Rei Fernandes, Editorial Board Member; Prof. John T.S. Irvine, Editorial Board Member; Prof. Ed Lahoda, Editorial Board Member. **ISSN:** 1743-4939. **Subscription Rates:** EUR494 individuals print only (surface mail); EUR840 individuals online only (2-3 users); EUR672 individuals print and online. **URL:** http://www.inderscience.com/browse/index.php?journalID=141.

44054 ■ **International Journal of Nuclear Knowledge Management**
Inderscience Enterprises Limited
c/o Dr. Andre Maisseu, Ed.-in-Ch.
49, rue Lauriston
75116 Paris, France
Journal containing research articles, review papers, and technical notes related to the improvement of the peaceful uses of nuclear energy and the development of nuclear sciences and technologies-related knowledge. **Freq:** 4/yr. **Key Personnel:** Dr. Andre Maisseu, Editor-in-Chief, a.maisseu@wonuc.org; Dr. Xingquan Wang, Editor-in-Chief. **ISSN:** 1479-540X. **Subscription Rates:**

EUR494 individuals print or online; EUR672 individuals print and online. **URL:** http://www.inderscience.com/browse/index.php?journalID=92.

44055 ■ International Journal of Nuclear Law
Inderscience Publishers
c/o Dr. Andre Maisseu, Ed.-in-Ch.
WONUC
49 rue Lauriston
F-75116 Paris, France
Publisher E-mail: editor@inderscience.com
Peer-reviewed journal aiming to provide a forum for thoughtful analysis focusing on issues of concern to nuclear law and regulations, to arrange for and promote studies and the knowledge of legal problems related to the peaceful utilization of nuclear energy under the special aspects of the protection of man and his environment, to help promote the exchange of information and to contribute the development of legislation governing the peaceful uses of nuclear energy. **Freq:** Quarterly. **Key Personnel:** Dr. Andre Maisseu, Editor-in-Chief, a.maisseu@wonuc.org; Prof. Pierre Bringuier, Editorial Board Member; Prof. Michel Quentin, Editorial Board Member; Maria Telalian, Editorial Board Member; Dr. Pieter H.F. Bekker, Editorial Board Member; Dr. Mahdi Dajani, Editorial Board Member; Dr. Abu Mohammad Asgarkhani, Editorial Board Member; Dr. Timur Zhantikin, Editorial Board Member; Prof. Nguyen Trieu Tu, Editorial Board Member. **ISSN:** 1741-6388. **Subscription Rates:** EUR494 individuals print only (surface mail); EUR534 individuals print only (airmail); EUR840 individuals online only (2-3 users); EUR672 individuals print and online. **URL:** http://www.inderscience.com/browse/index.php?journalID=93.

44056 ■ International Journal of Refrigeration
International Institute of Refrigeration
Institut International du Froid
177, Blvd. Malesherbes
F-75017 Paris, France
Ph: 33 142 273235
Fax: 33 147 631798
English and French language worldwide journal of refrigeration. **Freq:** 8/yr. **Key Personnel:** H. Auracher, Editor-in-Chief, auracher@iet.tu-berlin.de. **ISSN:** 0140-7007. **Subscription Rates:** EUR1,419 institutions for European countries & Iran; 188,100¥ institutions; US$1,687 institutions all countries except Europe, Japan & Iran; EUR123 individuals Europe and Iran; 16,100¥ individuals; US$136 other countries. **Remarks:** Advertising accepted; rates available upon request. **URL:** http://www.iifiir.org/en/periodicals.php?rub=2; http://www.elsevier.com/wps/find/journaldescription.cws_home/30436/descriptiondescription. **Circ:** (Not Reported)

44057 ■ The International Journal of Tuberculosis and Lung Disease
International Union Against Tuberculosis and Lung Disease
68 Blvd. St. Michel
F-75006 Paris, France
Ph: 33 144 320360
Fax: 33 143 299087
Publisher E-mail: webmaster@theunion.org
Peer-reviewed international journal covering respiratory diseases. **Subtitle:** The Official Journal of the International Union Against Tuberculosis and Lung Disease. **Founded:** Jan. 1997. **Freq:** Monthly. **Trim Size:** A4. **Key Personnel:** Clare Pierard, Managing Editor; Nulda Beyers, Editor-in-Chief; Irene Roy, Technical Ed. **ISSN:** 1027-3719. **Subscription Rates:** EUR300 libraries 1 to 9 library or agency; EUR100 individuals online only. **Remarks:** Accepts advertising. **URL:** http://www.theunion.org/what-we-do/journals/ijtld; http://www.theunion.org/about-the-journal/about-the-journal.html. **Ad Rates:** BW: 1,200 Fr, 4C: 2,480 Fr. **Circ:** 2,500

44058 ■ International Journal of Uncertainty, Fuzziness and Knowledge-Based Systems
World Scientific Publishing Company Private Ltd.
c/o Bernadette Bouchon-Meunier, Ed.-in-Ch.
CNRS, Universite Paris VI
LIP6 - Pole IA
104 Ave. du President Kennedy
F-75015 Paris, France
Ph: 33 144 277003
Fax: 33 144 277000
Publisher E-mail: wspc@wspc.com.sg
Forum for research on various methodologies for the management of imprecise, vague, uncertain or incomplete information. **Founded:** 1993. **Freq:** Bimonthly. **Key Personnel:** Bernadette Bouchon-Meunier, Editor-in-Chief, bernadette.bouchon-meunier@lip6.fr; S. Moral,

Area Ed., smc@decsai.ugr.es; G. Chen, Area Ed., chengq@em.tsinghua.edu.cn; F. Klawonn, Editorial Board, f.klawonn@fh-wolfenbuettel.de; F. Esteva, Area Ed., esteva@iiia.csic.es; L. Magdalena, Area Ed., luis.magdalena@softcomputing.es; G. Mayor, Area Ed., gmayor@uib.es; D. Srinivasan, Area Ed., inuiguti@sys.es.osaka-u.ac.jp; D. Dubois, Editorial Board, dubois@irit.irit.fr. **ISSN:** 0218-4885. **Subscription Rates:** US$587 institutions and libraries; electronic + print; EUR494 institutions and libraries; electronic + print; S$948 institutions and libraries; electronic + print; US$564 institutions and libraries; electronic only; EUR474 institutions and libraries; electronic only; S$910 institutions and libraries; electronic only; US$47 individuals for postage; EUR36 individuals for postage; S$62 individuals for postage. **URL:** http://www.worldscinet.com/ijufks/ijufks.shtml.

44059 ■ International Railway Statistics
International Union of Railways
Union Internationale des Chemins de Fer
16, rue Jean Rey
F-75015 Paris, France
Ph: 33 144 492020
Fax: 33 144 492029
Publication covering worldwide railway statistics. **Freq:** Annual. **Subscription Rates:** EUR260 individuals. **URL:** http://www.uic.asso.fr.

44060 ■ International Social Science Journal
John Wiley & Sons Inc.
Wiley-Blackwell
c/o John Crowley, Ed.-in-Ch.
1 Rue Miollis
F-75732 Paris Cedex 15, France
Ph: 33 145 683828
Journal covering social sciences. **Founded:** 1949. **Freq:** Quarterly. **Key Personnel:** Jacques Carrasco, Contact; John Crowley, Editor-in-Chief, j.crowley@unesco.org; Carmel Rochet, Editorial Asst., phone 33 145 683733, c.rochet@unesco.org. **ISSN:** 0020-8701. **Subscription Rates:** US$119 individuals print + online; US$445 institutions print or online; US$490 institutions print + online; 223 institutions print + online; EUR86 individuals print + online; EUR72 members print + online; EUR283 institutions print + online; US$571 institutions, other countries print + online; US$519 institutions, other countries print or online; US$101 members print + online. **Remarks:** Accepts advertising. **URL:** http://www.wiley.com/bw/journal.asp?ref=0020-8701&site=1. **Circ:** (Not Reported)

44061 ■ Intramuros
29 rue de Meaux
F-75019 Paris, France
Ph: 33 142 039595
Fax: 33 142 039577
Publisher E-mail: info@intramuros.fr
Magazine on designing. **Founded:** 1985. **Freq:** Bimonthly. **Trim Size:** 220 x 300 mm. **Key Personnel:** Quitterie Amiel, Development and Edition, phone 33 142 039589, qamiel@intramuros.fr. **ISSN:** 1152-0969. **Remarks:** Accepts advertising. **URL:** http://www.intramuros.fr. **Ad Rates:** 4C: EUR4,900. **Circ:** Combined 25,000

44062 ■ Jeunes Agriculteurs
CNJA
14 St. Boetie
F-75382 Paris, France
Publisher E-mail: bzaoui@jeunes-agriculteurs.fr
Trade magazine covering agriculture with a focus on young farmers. **Freq:** Monthly 11/yr (July and August combined). **Print Method:** Offset. **Col. Width:** 23 millimeters. **Col. Depth:** 297 millimeters. **ISSN:** 0396-7425. **Remarks:** Accepts advertising. **URL:** http://www.magazinesubscriptionsearch.com/prd178204.php; http://www.cnja.com/. **Circ:** Paid 30,000

44063 ■ Journal Asiatique
PEETERS - Leuven
Palais de l'Institut
3, rue Mazarine
75006 Paris, France
Publication E-mail: poj@peeters-leuven.be
Publisher E-mail: peeters@peeters-leuven.be
Journal covering orientalist philology and history, humanities and the social sciences. **Founded:** 1822. **Key Personnel:** Christina Scherrer-Schaub, Managing Editor; G. Colas, Editor. **ISSN:** 0012-762X. **Subscription Rates:** EUR85 individuals. **Remarks:** Advertising accepted; rates available upon request. **URL:** http://poj.

peeters-leuven.be/content.php?url=journal.php&code=ja. **Circ:** (Not Reported)

44064 ■ Journal of the Institute of Mathematics of Jussieu
Cambridge University Press
c/o Michael Harris, Ed.-in-Ch.
Centre de Mathematiques de Jussieu
Universite Paris 7 Denis Diderot
Case Postale 7012, 2, place Jussieu
F-75251 Paris Cedex 05, France
Publisher E-mail: information@cambridge.org
Journal devoted to the study of pure mathematics including operator algebra, number theory, algebraic and Lie groups, differential and symplectic geometry, partial differential equations, Banach spaces, potential theory, mathematical physics, probability, logic, differential equations etc. The journal published in connection with the Institute of Mathematics of Jussieu. **Key Personnel:** Michael Harris, Editor-in-Chief; Peter Ozsvath, Editorial Board; J. Bourgain, Editorial Board. **ISSN:** 1474-7480. **Subscription Rates:** 228 institutions print and online; US$435 institutions print and online; 205 institutions online; US$393 institutions online. **Remarks:** Accepts advertising. **URL:** http://journals.cambridge.org/action/displayJournal?jid=JMJ. **Ad Rates:** BW: US$445. **Circ:** (Not Reported)

44065 ■ Journal of Mathematical Economics
Elsevier Science Inc.
Bernard Cornet, Ed.
University Paris I Pantheon-Sorbonne
Paris, France
Publisher E-mail: usinfo-ehelp@elsevier.com
Journal covering economic ideas using formal mathematical reasoning. **Founded:** 1974. **Freq:** 6/yr. **Print Method:** Offset. **Trim Size:** 10 x 15. **Cols./Page:** 4. **Col. Width:** 27 nonpareils. **Col. Depth:** 203 agate lines. **Key Personnel:** H. Polemarchakis, Editor; T. Hens, Editor; M. Machina, Editor; S. Zamir, Editor; K.J. Arrow, Advisory Board; R. Aumann, Advisory Board; T. Bewley, Advisory Board; A. Kajii, Editor; Bernard Cornet, Editor, cornet@univ-paris1.fr; J. Geanakoplos, Editor. **ISSN:** 0304-4068. **Subscription Rates:** US$1,964 institutions except Europe, Japan and Iran; EUR1,757 institutions for European countries and Iran; 233,200¥ institutions; EUR138 individuals for European countries and Iran; US$144 other countries except Europe, Japan and Iran; 18,500¥ individuals. **URL:** http://www.elsevier.com/wps/find/journaldescription.cws_home/505577/descriptiondescription.

44066 ■ Jukebox Magazine
Jacques Leblanc Editions
54 Rue St. Lazare
F-75009 Paris, France
Ph: 33 1 55078107
Consumer magazine covering music for collectors. **Founded:** 1984. **Freq:** Monthly 13/yr. **Print Method:** Offset. **Trim Size:** 133 x 150 mm. **Cols./Page:** 3. **Key Personnel:** Jacques Leblanc, Editor. **ISSN:** 0296-6395. **Subscription Rates:** EUR65 individuals Metropolitan France; plus one CD-Rom; EUR80 Europe; plus one CD-Rom; EUR85 Africa and DOM/TOM; airmail; EUR95 America and Asia; airmail. **Remarks:** Accepts advertising. **Available Online. URL:** http://www.jukeboxmag.com/. **Circ:** Paid 20,000

44067 ■ Karthago
PEETERS - USA
c/o M. Andre Laronade, Dir.
3, Rue Michelet
F-75006 Paris, France
Publisher E-mail: peeters@peeters-us.com
Journal on ancient civilizations of North Africa. **Subtitle:** Review of Mediterranean Archaeology. **Founded:** 1950. **Key Personnel:** N. Duval, Contact; M. Andre Laronde, Director; Ph. Bruneau, Contact; J.Ch. Balthy, Contact; F. Chamoux, Contact; Fr. Baratte, Contact; R. Turcan, Contact; J. Leclant, Contact; G.Ch. Picard, Contact; Le G. Rider, Contact. **ISSN:** 0453-3429. **URL:** http://poj.peeters-leuven.be/content.php?url=journal&journal_code=KAR.

44068 ■ Leukemia
Nature Publishing Group
c/o Dr. N. Muller-Berat Killmann, Ed.-in-Ch.
Airthm, 26 Rue Miollis
F-75015 Paris, France
Ph: 33 140 036769
Fax: 33 140 036767

Circulation: ★ = ABC; △ = BPA; ♦ = CAC; • = CCAB; ❑ = VAC; ⊕ = PO Statement; ‡ = Publisher's Report; Boldface figures = sworn; Light figures = estimated.

Gale Directory of Publications & Broadcast Media/147th Ed.   4911

Publication E-mail: leukemia@leukemianature.com
Publisher E-mail: institutions@natureny.com
Journal covering the research and treatment aspects of leukemia and allied diseases, and relevant studies on normal hemopoiesis. **Founded:** Jan., 1981. **Freq:** Bimonthly. **Print Method:** Offset. **Trim Size:** 7 7/8 x 10 3/4. **Cols./Page:** 2. **Key Personnel:** R. Ohno, Section Ed.; A. Melnick, Section Ed.; Dr. N. Muller-Berat Killmann, Editor-in-Chief, leukemia@leukemianature.com. **ISSN:** 0887-6924. **Subscription Rates:** US$937 individuals combined print and online; US$843 individuals online only. **URL:** http://www.nature.com/leu/index.html.

44069 ■ Mathematische Zeitschrift
Springer-Verlag
c/o O. Debarre, Mng. Ed.
Ecole Normale Superieure
DMA, 45, rue d Ulm
75230 Paris, France
Magazine on pure and applied mathematics. **Founded:** 1918. **Freq:** 4/yr. **Key Personnel:** T.C. Dinh, Editor, dinh@math.jussieu.fr; O. Debarre, Managing Editor, mz@dma.ens.fr; Francois Lalone, Editor, lalone@dms.umoreal.ca. **ISSN:** 0025-5874. **Subscription Rates:** EUR2,749 institutions; EUR2,749 institutions enhance access. **URL:** http://www.springer.com/math/journal/209.

44070 ■ Meat Processing Global Edition
International Meat Secretariat
6 rue de la Victoire
F-75009 Paris, France
Ph: 33 145 266897
Fax: 33 145 266898
Publisher E-mail: info@meat-ims.org
Journal of the International Meat Secretariat. **Freq:** Bimonthly. **URL:** http://www.meat-ims.org/en/publications-ims.html.

44071 ■ Mecanique & Industries
EDP Sciences
39/41 rue Louis Blanc
F-92038 Paris Cedex, France
Ph: 33 1 47176074
Fax: 33 1 47176251
Publication E-mail: secretariat@afm.asso.fr
Publisher E-mail: subscribers@edpsciences.org
Journal covering scientific and technical information in the mechanical domains in relation to industrial activities. **Founded:** 2000. **Freq:** 6/yr. **Key Personnel:** Regis Dufour, Editor-in-Chief. **ISSN:** 1296-2139. **Subscription Rates:** EUR258 individuals print and electronic (France); EUR270 individuals print and electronic (European Union); EUR305 other countries print and electronic. **URL:** http://www.mecanique-industries.org/.

44072 ■ Messages du Secours Catholique
Secours Catholique Secteur International
106, rue du Bac
F-75007 Paris Cedex 07, France
Ph: 33 145 497300
Religious publication. **Founded:** 1947. **Freq:** Monthly. **Print Method:** Offset. **Trim Size:** 22.7 x 29.7 cm. **Key Personnel:** Veronique Linares, Contact. **ISSN:** 0026-0290. **Remarks:** Advertising not accepted. **URL:** http://www.secours-catholique.org/. **Circ:** (Not Reported)

44073 ■ Option/Bio
Elsevier Science Inc.
Elsevier SAS
Paris, France
Publisher E-mail: usinfo-ehelp@elsevier.com
Journal covering clinical biology. **Founded:** Nov. 11, 1989. **Freq:** 19/yr. **Trim Size:** 6 x 9. **Cols./Page:** 1. **Col. Width:** 50 nonpareils. **Col. Depth:** 100 agate lines. **Key Personnel:** Lylia Belloul, Editor-in-Chief; B. Poggi, Editorial Board; Alain Devanlay, Gen. Sec.; C. Bohuon, Editorial Board; M. Danis, Editorial Board; C. Bertholom, Editorial Board; B. Gouget, Editorial Board; I. Collignon, Editorial Board; Philippe Brunet, Assoc. Tech. Ed.-in-Ch.; J.L. Beneytout, Editorial Board. **ISSN:** 0992-5945. **URL:** http://www.elsevier.com/wps/find/journaldescription.cws_home/505819/descriptiondescription.

44074 ■ Paris Woman Journal
34 rue de Picpus
F-75012 Paris, France
English language consumer magazine for women living in Paris. **Subtitle:** For Women Living and Networking in Paris. **Freq:** Bimonthly. **Key Personnel:** Vernita Irvin, Sen. Ed.; Brian W. Fairbanks, Entertainment Ed.; Cliff

Lee, Original Artwork Artist. **ISSN:** 1533-2055. **Subscription Rates:** Free. **Remarks:** Accepts advertising. **URL:** http://www.pariswoman.com/. **Circ:** (Not Reported)

44075 ■ Phytoma La Defense des Vegetaux
Le Carrousel
27 rue Danielle Casanova
F-75001 Paris, France
Ph: 33 1 42615142
Fax: 33 1 49279190
Publication E-mail: publicite@phytoma-ldv.com
Publisher E-mail: pmmurard@lecarrousel.fr
Agricultural magazine covering plant health and plant protection. **Freq:** Monthly. **Remarks:** Accepts advertising. **URL:** http://www.phytoma-ldv.com. **Circ:** 25,000

44076 ■ Points de Vues Initiatiques
Grande Loge de France
8, rue de puteaux
F-75017 Paris, France
Publication E-mail: pvi@gldf.org
Magazine featuring articles about freemasonry in France. **Freq:** Quarterly. **Key Personnel:** Alain Graesel, Director; Jean Erceau, Editor. **ISSN:** 0298-0983. **Subscription Rates:** EUR20 individuals.

44077 ■ Pollution Atmospherique
Association for the Prevention of Atmospheric Pollution
Association pour la Prevention de la Pollution Atmospherique
10 rue Pierre Brossolette
Le Kremlin Bicetre
F-94270 Paris, France
Ph: 33 142 111500
Fax: 33 142 111501
Publisher E-mail: contact@appa.asso.fr
English and French publication covering pollution control. **Founded:** Quarterly. **Key Personnel:** M. Rambaud, Editor-in-Chief. **ISSN:** 0032-3632. **Subscription Rates:** EUR160 individuals; EUR180 other countries. **Remarks:** Advertising accepted; rates available upon request. **URL:** http://www.appa.asso.fr/; http://www.abe.pl/html/english/detailsj.php?id=0032-3632. **Circ:** 1,500

44078 ■ Probability Theory and Related Fields
Springer-Verlag
c/o J. Bertoin, Editorial Board
Laboratoire de Probabilits et Modles Alatoires
Universite Pierre et Marie Curie
175, rue du Chevaleret
F-75013 Paris, France
Journal focusing on research in modern probability theory. **Founded:** 1962. **Freq:** Monthly. **Key Personnel:** J.F. Le Gall, Editorial Board, ptrf@dma.ens.fr; J. Bertoin, Editorial Board. **ISSN:** 0178-8051. **Subscription Rates:** EUR1,398 institutions print incl. free access; EUR1,677.60 institutions print incl. enhanced access. **Remarks:** Advertising accepted; rates available upon request. **URL:** http://www.springer.com/math/probability/journal/440. **Formerly:** Zeitschrift fr Wahrscheinlichkeitstheorie und verwandte Gebiete. **Circ:** (Not Reported)

44079 ■ Revue des Deux Mondes
Valmonde & Cie
6 rue d'Uzes
F-75081 Paris, France
Ph: 33 14233 2184
Journal covering international studies. **Founded:** Aug. 1, 1829. **Freq:** 10/yr. **Key Personnel:** Michel Crepu, Editor-in-Chief. **ISSN:** 0750-9278. **Subscription Rates:** EUR75.50 individuals; EUR53.50 students. **Remarks:** Accepts advertising. **URL:** http://www.revuedesdeuxmondes.fr/home/english.php. **Circ:** Combined 27,000

44080 ■ Revue de l'Energie
Editions Techniques et Economiques
19 rue du Banquier
F-75013 Paris, France
Ph: 33 1 55426130
Fax: 33 1 55426139
Publisher E-mail: contact-editecom@orange.fr
Business publication. **Freq:** Monthly. **ISSN:** 0303-240X. **Subscription Rates:** 199 Fr individuals; 232.79 Fr other countries. **Online:** Gale. **URL:** http://www.editecom.com/index2.php?refRevue=RE.

44081 ■ Revue de Musicologie
French Society of Musicology
Societe Francaise de Musicologie
2 rue Louvois
F-75002 Paris, France

Ph: 33 1 53798845
Music publication, in English, French and German. **Founded:** 1917. **Freq:** Semiannual. **Key Personnel:** David Fiala, Editor. **Remarks:** Advertising accepted; rates available upon request. **URL:** http://www.sfmusicologie.fr/index.php?id=64. **Circ:** (Not Reported)

44082 ■ Revue du Soignant en Sante Publique
Elsevier Science Inc.
Elsevier SAS
23 Rue Linois
75724 Paris, France
Publisher E-mail: usinfo-ehelp@elsevier.com
Journal of care and public health. **Founded:** 2004. **Freq:** 6/yr. **Key Personnel:** Jean Marie Manus, Editor-in-Chief, red-sante@elsevier.fr. **ISSN:** 1766-2389. **URL:** http://www.elsevier.com/wps/find/journaleditorialboard.cws_home/704061/edit orialboard.

44083 ■ Scientific and Technical Review
Office International des Epizooties
12 rue de Prony
F-75017 Paris, France
Ph: 33 144 151888
Fax: 33 142 670987
Publisher E-mail: oie@oie.int
Publication covering veterinary medicine in English, French and Spanish. **Founded:** 1982. **Freq:** 3/yr. **Print Method:** Professional Printer. **Trim Size:** 21 x 29.7 cm. **Key Personnel:** Bernard Vallat, Editor-in-Chief; Paul-Pierre Pastoret, Managing Editor. **ISSN:** 0253-1933. **Subscription Rates:** EUR60 individuals. **Remarks:** Advertising not accepted. **URL:** http://www.oie.int. **Formerly:** Bulletin Circulaire de L'OIE. **Circ:** 1,800

44084 ■ Statistical Inference for Stochastic Processes
Springer Netherlands
c/o Denis Bosq, Ed.-in-Ch.
Statistical Institute
University Pierre & Marie Curia
Paris, France
Publisher E-mail: permissions.dordrecht@springer.com
Journal devoted to time series analysis and the statistics of continuous time processes and dynamical systems. **Subtitle:** An International Journal devoted to Time Series Analysis and the Statistics of Continuous Time Processes and Dynamical Systems. **Founded:** 1954. **Freq:** 3/yr. **Print Method:** Offset. **Trim Size:** 1 1/4 x 16. **Cols./Page:** 5. **Col. Width:** 1 7/8 inches. **Col. Depth:** 84 agate lines. **Key Personnel:** W. Hardle, Editorial Board; M. Deistler, Editorial Board; M. Janzura, Editorial Board; Denis Bosq, Editor-in-Chief; Yury A. Kutoyants, Assoc. Ed.; R. Hopfner, Editorial Board; I.A. Ibragimov, Editorial Board; J. Chevalier, Editorial Board; Marc Hallin, Assoc. Ed.; Y. Davydov, Editorial Board. **ISSN:** 1387-0874. **Subscription Rates:** EUR397 institutions print incl. free access or e-only; EUR476.40 institutions print incl. enhanced access. **Remarks:** Advertising accepted; rates available upon request. **URL:** http://www.springer.com/math/probability/journal/11203. **Circ:** (Not Reported)

44085 ■ The Tocqueville Review/La Revue Tocqueville
University of Toronto Press-Journal Div.
La Societe Tocqueville
Laurence Duboys Fresney
69 Quai d'Orsay
F-75007 Paris, France
Publication E-mail: laurence.duboysfresney@sciences-po.fr
Publisher E-mail: journals@utpress.utoronto.ca
Scholarly journal covering political and social trends in Europe and the U.S. in English and French. **Freq:** Semiannual. **Key Personnel:** Michel Forse, Editor; Francoise Melonio, Editor; Laurence Guellec, Editor. **ISSN:** 0730-479X. **Subscription Rates:** US$45 U.S. and Canada; US$56 other countries. **Remarks:** Accepts advertising. **URL:** http://www.utpjournals.com/ttr/ttr.html. **Ad Rates:** BW: 300 Fr. **Circ:** Combined 500

44086 ■ Transfusion Clinique et Biologique
Elsevier
23 rue Linois
F-75724 Paris Cedex 15, France
Ph: 33 171 724646
Fax: 33 171 724664
Publisher E-mail: reiclient@elsevier.fr
Journal publishing transfusion activity in all its scientific and medical aspects. **Founded:** 1994. **Freq:** Bimonthly.

Key Personnel: Jean Yves Muller, Editor-in-Chief; Philippe Rouger, Editor-in-Chief; Christine Sempe, Publishing Ed.; Georges Andreu, Editorial Board; J.F. Baron, Editorial Board; Alain Beauplet, Editorial Board; John Barbara, Editorial Board; Annette Bussel, Editorial Board; Morris Blajchman, Editorial Board. **ISSN:** 1246-7820. **Subscription Rates:** EUR120 students; US$148 students; 16,100¥ students; EUR116 students in France; EUR286 institutions; US$392 institutions; 37,900¥ institutions. **URL:** http://www.elsevier.com/wps/find/journaldescription.cws_home/601020/descriptiondescription.

44087 ■ UNESCO Courier
7 Pl. de Fontenoy
F-75352 Paris 07, France
Publication E-mail: unesco.courier@unesco.org
Publisher E-mail: courier.unesco@unesco.org
Publication focusing on international relations. **Founded:** Aug. 1947. **Freq:** Monthly. **Key Personnel:** Jasmina Sopova, Editor-in-Chief, j.sopova@unesco.org; Eric Falt, Director. **ISSN:** 1993-8616. **URL:** http://portal.unesco.org/en/ev.php-URL_ID=34822&URL_DO=DO_TOPIC&URL_SECTION=201.html. **Circ:** Non-paid 40,000

44088 ■ Africa N 1-FM - 89.6
33 rue du Faubourg St. Antoine
F-75011 Paris Cedex, France
Ph: 33 1 55075801
Fax: 33 1 55079748
Format: Public Radio. **Operating Hours:** Continuous. **URL:** http://www.africa1.com.

44089 ■ Africa N 1-FM - 90.3
33 Rue du Faubourg St. Antoine
F-75011 Paris Cedex, France
Ph: 33 1 55075801
Fax: 33 1 55079748
Format: Public Radio. **Operating Hours:** Continuous. **URL:** http://www.africa1.com.

44090 ■ Africa N 1-FM - 102
33 Rue du Faubourg St. Antoine
F-75011 Paris Cedex, France
Ph: 33 1 55075801
Fax: 33 1 55079748
Format: Public Radio. **Operating Hours:** Continuous. **URL:** http://www.africa1.com.

44091 ■ Beur-FM - 106.7
BP 249
75 524 Paris Cedex 11, France
Ph: 33 8 92681067
Format: Full Service. **Key Personnel:** Maia Ket, Director, maia@beurfm.net. **URL:** http://www.beurfm.net/.

Perols

44092 ■ Lien Horticole
Hortilien - Bond Horticultural
36 Ave. Louis Pasteur
CS 40001
F-34473 Perols Cedex, France
Ph: 33 4 67504260
Fax: 33 4 67501902
Publisher E-mail: info@hortilien.com
Trade magazine covering horticulture and gardening. **Founded:** 1965. **Freq:** Weekly. **Key Personnel:** Claudine Vautier, Administration Dir., claudine@lienhorticole.fr; Francis Ginestet, Editor-in-Chief, phone 33 4 67504076, ginestet@lienhorticole.fr. **URL:** http://www.hortilien.com.

Perpignan

44093 ■ Plant Science
Elsevier Science
c/o M. Delseny, Ed.-in-Ch.
Universite de Perpignan, Physiologie et Biologie Moleculaire Vegetale URA 565, CNRS
F-66860 Perpignan Cedex, France
Publisher E-mail: nlinfo-f@elsevier.com
Peer-reviewed journal focusing on experimental plant biology. The thrust areas including genomics, proteomics, biochemistry (including enzymology), physiology, cell biology, development, genetics and molecular biology. **Founded:** 1973. **Freq:** Monthly. **Key Personnel:** G. Spangenberg, Editorial Board; M. Delseny, Editor-in-Chief, delseny@univ-perp.fr; Jonathan Gressel, Review Board, jonathan.gressel@weizmann.ac.il. **ISSN:** 0168-9452. **Subscription Rates:** EUR4,805

institutions for European Countries; US$5,378 institutions for all Countries except Europe and Japan; 638,100¥ institutions. **Remarks:** Accepts advertising. **URL:** http://www.elsevier.com/wps/find/journaldescription.cws_home/506030/description. **Circ:** (Not Reported)

Pessac

44094 ■ Radio Campus Bordeaux-FM - 88.1
Universite Michel de Montaigne Bordeaux 3
16 esplanade des Antilles
33607 Pessac Cedex, France
Ph: 33 5 57124572
Format: Full Service. **Operating Hours:** Continuous. **Key Personnel:** F. Dutheil, President. **URL:** http://www.bordeaux.radio-campus.org/accueil/actualites.aspx.

Plelan le Grand

44095 ■ Folia Primatologica
Francophone Primatological Society
Societe Francophone de Primatologie
Sta. Biologique de Paimpont
F-35380 Plelan le Grand, France
Ph: 33 299 618156
Fax: 33 299 618188
Publisher E-mail: deputte@univ-tennesl.fr
Publication covering anthropology. **Freq:** Bimonthly. **Key Personnel:** R.H. Crompton, Editor-in-Chief; J. Fischer, Editorial Board Member; J. Ganzhorn, Editorial Board Member; D.L. Gebo, Editorial Board Member; D.J. Chivers, Editorial Board Member; C. Harcourt, Editorial Asst.; A.T.C. Feistner, Editorial Board Member; G. Anzenberger, Editorial Board Member; A.F. Dixson, Editorial Board Member; E.W. Heymann, Editorial Board Member. **ISSN:** 0015-5713. **Subscription Rates:** 615 SFr individuals print; EUR455 individuals print; Germany; US$575 individuals print; 1,230 SFr institutions; EUR911 institutions; US$1,150 institutions. **Remarks:** Advertising accepted; rates available upon request. **URL:** http://content.karger.com. **Circ:** (Not Reported)

Pontcharra

44096 ■ Oxygene Radio-FM - 93
347 rue du Breda
38530 Pontcharra, France
Ph: 33 4 76976822
Fax: 33 4 76977699
E-mail: contact@oxygeneradio.fr
Format: Full Service. **URL:** http://www.oxygeneradio.fr/.

Rennes

44097 ■ Granular Matter
Springer-Verlag
c/o Daniel Bideau, Ed.
Equip with Physics of the Desord Materials
Group of Crystalline Physics
University of Rennes I
F-35042 Rennes, France
Journal covering basic research in granular media. **Freq:** 6/yr. **Key Personnel:** Stefan Luding, Managing Editor, granmat@ctw.utwente.nl; Daniel Bideau, Editor, pmhc@univ-rennes1.fr; Bernard Cambou, Editor; Robert P. Behringer, Editor-in-Chief, bob@phy.duke.edu; Hans J. Herrmann, Editor-in-Chief, hjherrmann@ethz.ch. **ISSN:** 1434-5021. **Subscription Rates:** EUR487 institutions print incl. free access; EUR584.40 institutions print incl. enhanced access. **Remarks:** Advertising accepted; rates available upon request. **URL:** http://www.springer.com/physics/mechanics/journal/10035. **Circ:** (Not Reported)

Riberac

44098 ■ The African Book Publishing Record
K.G. Saur Verlag KG
Petit Bersac
24600 Riberac, France
Ph: 33 553 905576
Fax: 33 553 905576
Publication E-mail: africanbookpublishingrecord@gmail.com
Publisher E-mail: info@degruyter.com
Journal covering new and forthcoming books published in Africa. **Founded:** 1974. **Freq:** Quarterly (April, July, Oct. and Dec.). **Trim Size:** A4. **Key Personnel:** Cecile Lomer, Editor; Woeli Dekutsey, Publisher. **ISSN:** 0306-0322. **Subscription Rates:** EUR396 individuals print or

online only; EUR456 individuals print + online; EUR109 single issue. **URL:** http://www.degruyter.de/journals/abpr/detail.cfm. **Circ:** Paid 300

Rillieux-la-Pape

44099 ■ SAR and QSAR in Environmental Research
Taylor & Francis Ltd.
c/o Dr. James Devillers, Ed.-in-Ch.
CTIS-Centtre de Traitement de l'nformation Scientifique
3 Chemin de la Graviere
F-69140 Rillieux-la-Pape, France
Peer-reviewed journal focusing on the fundamental and practical aspects of the structure-activity and structure-property relationships in the fields of environmental science, agrochemistry, toxicology, pharmacology and applied chemistry. **Freq:** 8/yr. **Key Personnel:** Dr. James DeVillers, Editor-in-Chief, j.devillers@ctis.fr; S.C. Basak, Editorial Advisory Board; R.S. Boethling, Editorial Advisory Board. **ISSN:** 1062-936X. **Subscription Rates:** 2,127 institutions print + online; 2,020 institutions online; 249 individuals print only; US$2,736 institutions print + online; US$2,599 institutions online; US$306 individuals print only; US$99 members society; EUR99 members society; EUR2,179 institutions print + online; EUR2,070 institutions online. **Remarks:** Accepts advertising. **URL:** http://www.tandf.co.uk/journals/titles/1062936x.asp. **Circ:** (Not Reported)

Rueil-Malmaison

44100 ■ La Tribune de l'Assurance
Groupe Liaison
1 Ave. Edouard Belin
F-92856 Rueil-Malmaison, France
Ph: 33 141 299999
Fax: 33 141 299513
Publication E-mail: bbensimon@groupeliaisons.fr
Professional magazine for insurance companies and brokers. **Founded:** 1996. **Freq:** Monthly. **Print Method:** Offset. **Key Personnel:** Thomas Peyronel, Contact, tpeyronel@profideo.com. **ISSN:** 1293-8566. **Remarks:** Accepts advertising. **URL:** http://www.tribune-assurance.fr/. **Circ:** Combined 15,000

Saint Cloud

44101 ■ Echappement
Groupe de Presse Michel Hommell
48-50 Blvd. Senard
F-92210 Saint Cloud, France
Magazine covering automobile racing and sports cars worldwide. **Founded:** 1968. **Freq:** Monthly. **Print Method:** Offset. **Key Personnel:** William Pac, Managing Editor; Michel Hommell, Publishing Dir. **ISSN:** 0765-1457. **Subscription Rates:** EUR4.80 single issue. **Remarks:** Accepts advertising. **URL:** http://www.echappement.com/. **Ad Rates:** 4C: EUR5,488.16. **Circ:** Paid 58,653

Saint Denis

44102 ■ L'Evolution Psychiatrique
Elsevier Science Inc.
c/o Richard Rechtmann, Ed.-in-Ch.
Institute Marcel River
The Mesnil-Saint-Denis
F-78321 Saint Denis, France
Publisher E-mail: usinfo-ehelp@elsevier.com
Journal covering protistology topics such as the structure and systematics of protists, their development, ecology, molecular biology and physiology. **Founded:** Mar. 19, 1984. **Freq:** 4/yr. **Print Method:** Offset. **Trim Size:** 11 x 13 3/4. **Cols./Page:** 4. **Col. Width:** 14 picas. **Col. Depth:** 74 picas. **Key Personnel:** Yves Thoret, President; Richard Rechtmann, Editor-in-Chief; Didier A. Chartier, Assoc. Ed.; Pierre Chenivesse, Assoc. Ed.; Manuela De Luca, Assoc. Ed.; Sophie Kecskemeti, Assoc. Ed.; Eric Marcel, Assoc. Ed.; Arnaud Martorell, Assoc. Ed.; Aurore Cartier, Editorial Sec. **ISSN:** 0014-3855. **URL:** http://www.elsevier.com/wps/find/journaldescription.cws_home/620114/descriptiondescription.

44103 ■ Global Health Promotion
International Union for Health Promotion and Education
Union Internationale de Promotion de la Sante et d'Education pour la Sante
42 Blvd. de la Liberation
93203 Saint Denis Cedex, France

Circulation: ★ = ABC; △ = BPA; ♦ = CAC; • = CCAB; ❏ = VAC; ⊕ = PO Statement; ‡ = Publisher's Report; Boldface figures = sworn; Light figures = estimated.

Gale Directory of Publications & Broadcast Media/147th Ed.

4913

Ph: 33 148 137120
Fax: 33 148 091767
Publisher E-mail: iuhpe@iuhpe.org
Publication covering health promotion and education in English, French and Spanish. **Subtitle:** International Journal of Health Promotion and Education. **Freq:** Quarterly. **Key Personnel:** Maurice B. Mittelmark, Editor-in-Chief; Martha W. Perry, Managing Editor. **ISSN:** 1025-3823. **Subscription Rates:** EUR71 individuals Europe, N America, & SW. Pacific; EUR104 institutions Europe, N America, N. & SW. Pacific; EUR37 individuals Africa, E. Mediterranean, SE Asia, Latin America; EUR42 institutions Africa, E. Mediterranean, SE Asia, Latin America. **Remarks:** Advertising accepted; rates available upon request. **URL:** http://www.iuhpe.org/?page=20&lang=en. **Formerly:** Hygie; Promotion and Education. **Circ:** (Not Reported)

Saint-Julien-le-Montagnier

44104 ■ Radio Verdon-FM - 96.5
Les Rouvieres BP 2
83560 Saint-Julien-le-Montagnier, France
Ph: 33 4 98053000
Fax: 33 4 94800207
Format: Classic Rock. **Owner:** Radio Verdon, at above address. **URL:** http://www.radio-verdon.com/index.php?option=com_frontpage&Itemid=1.

Radio Verdon-FM - See Castellane

Sisteron

44105 ■ Frequence Mistral-FM - 99.2
5 Rue Chapusie
04200 Sisteron, France
Ph: 33 4 92319520
E-mail: sisteron@frequencemistral.net
Format: Eclectic. **URL:** http://www.frequencemistral.net/.

Sophia Antipolis

44106 ■ Cardiovascular Research
European Society of Cardiology
The European Heart House
2035 Rte. des Colles
Les Templiers
F-06903 Sophia Antipolis, France
Ph: 33 492 947600
Fax: 33 492 947601
Publication covering cardiology. **Freq:** 14/yr. **Key Personnel:** Michael H. Piper, Editor-in-Chief. **ISSN:** 0008-6363. **Subscription Rates:** EUR140 members. **URL:** http://www.escardio.org/journals/cardiovascular-research/Pages/about.aspx.

44107 ■ European Heart Journal
European Society of Cardiology
The European Heart House
2035 Rte. des Colles
Les Templiers
F-06903 Sophia Antipolis, France
Ph: 33 492 947600
Fax: 33 492 947601
European journal covering cardiology. **Freq:** Semimonthly. **Key Personnel:** Thomas F. Luscher, Editor-in-Chief. **ISSN:** 0195-668X. **Subscription Rates:** 863 institutions print and online; US$1,726 institutions print and online; EUR1,295 institutions print and online; EUR140 members. **URL:** http://www.escardio.org; http://escjnls.oxfordjournals.org/.

44108 ■ Performance Evaluation
Elsevier Science
c/o Philippe Nain, Ed.-in-Ch.
INRIA Sophia-Antipolis Research Unit
B.P. 93 06902
CH-8803 Sophia Antipolis, France
Ph: 33 4 92387896
Fax: 33 4 92387858
Publisher E-mail: nlinfo-f@elsevier.com
Peer-reviewed journal providing information relative to performance aspects. Covers topics such as performance studies of computers, computer communications, telecommunications and distributed systems, resource allocation and control methods and algorithms, system reliability, modeling and analysis methods, measurement techniques and workload characterization, system architecture, design and implementation discussed from a performance viewpoint, performance evaluation applications, case studies and model validations.

Founded: 1981. **Freq:** Monthly. **Key Personnel:** Philippe Nain, Editor-in-Chief, pn-peva@lists-sop.inria.fr; M. Ajmone Marsan, International Board of Ed.; S. Balsamo, International Board of Ed.; S. Borst, International Board of Ed.; U. Ayesta, International Board of Ed.; E. Gelenbe, International Board of Ed. **ISSN:** 0166-5316. **Subscription Rates:** US$2,049 institutions for all countries except Europe, Japan & Iran; 242,800¥ institutions; EUR1,831 institutions for European countries & Iran; 32,400¥ individuals for Japan; EUR210 individuals for European countries & Iran; US$282 individuals for all countries except Europe, Japan & Iran. **Remarks:** Advertising accepted; rates available upon request. **URL:** http://www.elsevier.com/wps/find/journaldescription.cws_home/505618/descriptiondescription. **Circ:** (Not Reported)

Strasbourg

44109 ■ ALSIC (Apprentissage des Langues et Systemes d'Information et de Communication)
Universite Marc Bloch
22 Rue Descartes
F-67084 Strasbourg, France
Ph: 33 388 417300
Fax: 33 388 417354
Journal covering the disciplines of didactic, linguistic, psycholinguistics, sciences of education, linguistics-data processing, and data processing. **Subtitle:** Revue Internet francophone pour chercheurs et praticiens. **Founded:** 1935. **Freq:** Quarterly. **Print Method:** Offset. Uses mats. Trim Size: 6 x 9. **Cols./Page:** 1. **Col. Width:** 5 inches. **Col. Depth:** 7 1/2 inches. **ISSN:** 1286-4986. **URL:** http://alsic.u-strasbg.fr/.

44110 ■ Archives of Virology
International Union of Microbiological Societies
Union Internationale des Societes de Microbiologie
Institut de Biologie Moleculaire er Cellulaire de CNRS
15 Rue Descartes
F-67000 Strasbourg, France
Ph: 33 388 417022
Fax: 33 388 610680
Publisher E-mail: vanregen@ibmcu-strasbg.fr
Publication covering biology. **Freq:** Monthly. **Key Personnel:** M.H.V. Van Regenmortel, Editor-in-Chief. **ISSN:** 0304-8608. **Remarks:** Accepts advertising. **URL:** http://www.springerlink.com/home/main.mpx. **Circ:** (Not Reported)

44111 ■ Cell Adhesion & Migration
Landes Bioscience
University of Strasbourg
F-67084 Strasbourg, France
Publisher E-mail: info@landesbioscience.com
Journal covering medical and surgical handbooks useful to physicians, residents and students. **Key Personnel:** Santos Manes, Member of the Editorial Board; Derek Radisky, Member of the Editorial Board; Arthur M. Mercurio, Member of the Editorial Board; Kaoru Miyazaki, Member of the Editorial Board; Vania Braga, Member of the Editorial Board; John M. Pawelek, Member of the Editorial Board; Dominique Bagnard, PhD, Editor-in-Chief; Walter Birchmeier, Member of the Editorial Board; Nancy Boudreau, Member of the Editorial Board; Suzanne A. Eccles, Member of the Editorial Board. **ISSN:** 1933-6926. **Subscription Rates:** US$59 individuals web only; US$109 individuals web and print; US$149 other countries web and print; US$750 institutions web only; US$900 institutions web & print; US$950 institutions, other countries. **URL:** http://www.landesbioscience.com/journals/celladhesion.

44112 ■ Computational Materials Science
Elsevier Science
c/o H. Dreysse, Ed.
IPCMS-GEMME
23 rue du Loess
BP 20 Cr
F-67037 Strasbourg, France
Publisher E-mail: nlinfo-f@elsevier.com
Journal focusing on materials phenomena and computational modeling. **Founded:** 1993. **Freq:** Monthly. **Key Personnel:** S. Schmauder, Editor; H. Dreysse, Editor; W. Duan, Assoc. Ed.; J.R. Chelikowsky, Editorial Board; M. Doyama, Editorial Board; J. Hafner, Editorial Board. **ISSN:** 0927-0256. **Subscription Rates:** US$1,962 institutions for all countries except Europe, Japan & Iran; 231,800¥ institutions; EUR1,746 institutions for European countries & Iran. **Remarks:** Accepts advertising. **URL:** http://www.elsevier.com/wps/find/

journaldescription.cws_home/523412/descriptiondescription. **Circ:** (Not Reported)

44113 ■ News d'Ill
University Centre of Journalism Teaching
Centre Universitaire d'Enseignement du Journalisme
11, rue du Marechal Juin
F-67043 Strasbourg Cedex, France
Ph: 33 68 858300
Fax: 33 68 858574
Publisher E-mail: scola@cuej.unistra.fr
French language publication covering communications. **Freq:** Quarterly. **Key Personnel:** Alain Chanel, Publication Dir., redactions@cuej.u-strasbg.fr. **ISSN:** 0996-9624. **URL:** http://cuej.u-strasbg.fr/.

44114 ■ World Journal of Microbiology and Biotechnology
International Union of Microbiological Societies
Union Internationale des Societes de Microbiologie
Institut de Biologie Moleculaire er Cellulaire de CNRS
15 Rue Descartes
F-67000 Strasbourg, France
Ph: 33 388 417022
Fax: 33 388 610680
Publisher E-mail: vanregen@ibmcu-strasbg.fr
Worldwide journal covering biology. **Freq:** Bimonthly. **Key Personnel:** Peter J. Large, Editor-in-Chief, p.j.large@hull.ac.uk; C. Ratledge, Editorial Consultant. **Remarks:** Accepts advertising. **URL:** http://www.springerlink.com/content/h366741552xh4567/. **Circ:** (Not Reported)

Talence

44115 ■ Polycyclic Aromatic Compounds
Taylor & Francis Group Journals
c/o Philippe Garrigues, Ed.-in-Ch.
Institut des Science Moleculaires (ISM)
Batiment A12, Universite de Bordeaux 1, 351
Cours de la Liberation
F-33405 Talence, France
Ph: 33 540 006283
Publisher E-mail: customerservice@taylorandfrancis.com
Journal dealing with all aspects of research related to polycyclic aromatic compounds (PAC). **Freq:** 5/yr. **Key Personnel:** Philippe Garrigues, Editor-in-Chief, p.garrigues@lptc.u-bordeaux1.fr; Stephen A. Wise, Topical Ed., phone 301975-3112, fax 301977-0685, stephen.wise@nist.gov; Curt M. White, Topical Ed., curt.white@netl.doe.gov; Maximilian Zander, Founding Ed.; Douglas A. Lane, Topical Ed., phone 416739-4859, fax 416739-5916, douglas.lane@ec.gc.ca; Victor Snieckus, Topical Ed., phone 613533-2239, fax 613533-2837, snieckus@chem.queensu.ca; Steve Myers, Topical Ed., phone 502852-0928, fax 502852-7868, sr.myers@louisville.edu; A.T. Balaban, Topical Ed., phone 409741-4313, fax 409740-4787, balabana@arctic.tamug.tamu.edu. **ISSN:** 1040-6638. **Subscription Rates:** 3,703 institutions print + online; US$4,668 institutions print + online; 3,518 institutions online; US$4,434 institutions online; EUR3,716 institutions print + online; EUR3,530 institutions online; 1,188 individuals; US$1,972 individuals; EUR1,570 individuals. **Remarks:** Advertising accepted; rates available upon request. **URL:** http://www.tandf.co.uk/journals/journal.asp?issn=1040-6638& linktype=5. **Circ:** (Not Reported)

Tarbes

44116 ■ Engineering Applications of Artificial Intelligence
Elsevier Science Inc.
ENIT-LGP
Ave. d'Azereix
BP 1629
F-65016 Tarbes, France
Publication E-mail: eaai@neuf.fr
Publisher E-mail: usinfo-ehelp@elsevier.com
Journal describing the practical application of artificial intelligence methods in all branches of engineering. **Founded:** 1991. **Freq:** 8/yr. **Print Method:** Offset. **Cols./Page:** 6. **Col. Width:** 2 1/6 inches. **Col. Depth:** 301 agate lines. **Key Personnel:** Dr. R.A. Vingerhoeds, Consulting Ed.; Prof. B. Grabot, Editor-in-Chief, bernard.grabot@enit.fr; Prof. P. Perner, Board of Ed.; Prof. R. Unland, Dep. Ed.-in-Ch.; Prof. E. Brown, Board of Ed.; Prof. C. Chan, Board of Ed.; Dr. C.W. Chan, Board of Ed.; H. Adeli, Assoc. Ed.; A. Alessandri, Assoc. Ed.

ISSN: 0952-1976. **Subscription Rates:** 12,800¥ individuals; US$107 other countries except Europe, Japan and Iran; EUR97 individuals European countries and Iran; US$1,632 institutions, other countries except Europe, Japan and Iran; EUR1,458 institutions European countries & Iran; 195,500¥ institutions. **URL:** http://www. elsevier.com/wps/find/journaldescription.cws_home/975/ descriptiondescription.

Terrasson Lavilledieu

44117 ■ Radio Vallee Vezere-FM - 104.4 MHz
4 rue Rastignac
F-24120 Terrasson Lavilledieu, France
Ph: 33 5 53500250
Fax: 33 5 53503896
Format: Ethnic; World Beat; Sports. **Operating Hours:** Continuous. **URL:** http://www.radiovalleevezere.com.

Toulouse

44118 ■ Annales de Physique
EDP Sciences
c/o E. Suraud, Ed.-in-Ch.
Laboratoire de Physique Quantique
Universite Paul Sabatier
118, Rte. de Narbonne
F-31062 Toulouse Cedex, France
Publisher E-mail: subscribers@edpsciences.org
Journal covering all aspects of physics. **Freq:** Bimonthly. **Key Personnel:** E. Suraud, Editor-in-Chief, eric. suraud@irsamc.ups-tlse.fr; Catherine Boisson, Editorial Board, catherine.boisson@obspm.fr. **ISSN:** 0003-4169. **Subscription Rates:** EUR455 individuals print and electronic (without VAT); EUR390 individuals electronic (without VAT); EUR480 other countries print and electronic; EUR390 other countries electronic. **URL:** http:// www.annphys.org/.

44119 ■ Asymptotic Analysis
IOS Press, B.V.
c/o Alain Bensoussan, Ed.-in-Ch.
18 Ave. Edouard Belin
F-31401 Toulouse Cedex 9, France
Ph: 33 5 61282316
Publisher E-mail: info@iospress.nl
Journal aiming to publish original mathematical results in the asymptotic theory of problems affected by the presence of small or large parameters, and to give specific indications of their possible applications to different fields of natural sciences. **Freq:** 20/yr. **Key Personnel:** Alain Bensoussan, Editor-in-Chief, aa. delabarre@gmail.com; S. Kamin, Editorial Board; A. Ambrosetti, Editorial Board; J. Frehse, Editorial Board; H.D. Alber, Editorial Board; C. Bardos, Editorial Board; A. Friedman, Editorial Board; L.S. Frank, Founding Ed.; C.D. Levermore, Editorial Board; Y. Sibuya, Editorial Board. **ISSN:** 0921-7134. **Subscription Rates:** EUR1,620 institutions print and online; US$2,275 institutions print and online. **URL:** http://www.iospress.nl/ loadtop/load.php?isbn=09217134.

44120 ■ Fuzzy Sets and Systems
Elsevier Science
c/o D. Dubois, Ed.-in-Ch.
Institut de Recherche en Informatique de Toulouse
Universite Paul Sabatier
118 rte. de Narbonne
F-31062 Toulouse Cedex 9, France
Publisher E-mail: nlinfo-f@elsevier.com
Peer-reviewed journal in Information Science and Engineering in connection with International Fuzzy Systems Association (IFSA), featuring international advancement of the theory and application of fuzzy sets and systems. **Subtitle:** An International Journal in Information Science and Engineering. **Founded:** 1978.

Freq: Semimonthly. **Key Personnel:** B. De Baets, Editor-in-Chief, bernard.debaets@ugent.be; D. Dubois, Editor-in-Chief, didier.dubois@irit.fr; M. Sugeno, Advisory Ed., michio.sugeno@softcomputing.es. **ISSN:** 0165-0114. **Subscription Rates:** 656,400¥ institutions; US$5,537 institutions for all countries except Europe and Japan; EUR4,949 institutions for European countries. **Remarks:** Accepts advertising. **URL:** http://www. elsevier.com/wps/find/journaldescription.cws_home/ 505545/descrip tion. **Circ:** (Not Reported)

Valenciennes

44121 ■ Pour nos Jardins
40 Rte. d'Aulnoy
F-59300 Valenciennes, France
Ph: 33 3 27463750
Fax: 33 3 27290812
Publisher E-mail: contacts@jardiniersdefrance.com
Consumer magazine covering gardening. **Freq:** Monthly. **ISSN:** 1273-5892. **Remarks:** Accepts advertising. **URL:** http://www.jardiniersdefrance.com/fr/pnj/numero.asp. **Circ:** (Not Reported)

Vandoeuvre-les-Nancy

44122 ■ Process Biochemistry
Elsevier Science Inc.
c/o J. Boudrant, Ed.-in-Ch.
Laboratory of Chemical Engineering Sciences
2 Aveue de la Foret de Haye
BP 172
F-54505 Vandoeuvre-les-Nancy, France
Publisher E-mail: usinfo-ehelp@elsevier.com
Journal devoted to bioactive molecules or elements, and living organisms. **Founded:** 1991. **Freq:** 12/yr. **Print Method:** Offset. **Cols./Page:** 4. **Col. Width:** 29 nonpareils. **Col. Depth:** 224 agate lines. **Key Personnel:** H.J. Cha, Editorial Board; A. Durand, Editorial Board; D. Cantero, Editorial Board; R. Borja, Editorial Board; F. Chen, Editorial Board; E. Doyle, Editorial Board; Z.X. Deng, Editorial Board; J. Chen, Editorial Board; J. Boudrant, Editor-in-Chief, joseph.boudrant@ ensaia.inpl-nancy.fr; Z. Aksu, Editorial Board; J.J. Zhong, Editor-in-Chief, jjzhong@sjtu.edu.cn. **ISSN:** 1359-5113. **Subscription Rates:** 249,300¥ institutions; US$2,101 institutions, other countries except Europe, Japan and Iran; EUR1,879 institutions for European countries and Iran; 54,900¥ individuals; US$478 other countries except Europe, Japan and Iran; EUR356 individuals for European countries and Iran. **URL:** http://www.elsevier. com/wps/find/journaldescription.cws_home/422857/ descriptiondescription.

Viella

44123 ■ Radio d'Artagnan-FM - 104
Ave. Peries
32110 Nogaro, France
Ph: 33 5 62690666
Fax: 33 5 62090303
E-mail: contact@radiodartagnan.com
Format: Full Service. **URL:** http://www.radiodartagnan. com/.

Villefranche-sur-Mer

44124 ■ Aquatic Microbial Ecology
Inter-Research Science Center
Observatoire Oceanographie de Villefranche
Station Zoologique, B.P. 28
F-06230 Villefranche-sur-Mer, France
Ph: 33 4 93763821
Fax: 33 4 93763834
Publisher E-mail: ir@int-res.com

Journal covering all aspects of aquatic microbial dynamics. **Key Personnel:** Fereidoun Rassoulzadegan, Editor-in-Chief, rassoul@obs-vlfr.fr; Paul A. del Giorgio, Editor-in-Chief, del_giorgio.paul@uqam.ca; Gunnar Bratbak, Editor, gunnar.bratbak@bio.uib.no. **ISSN:** 0948-3055. **Subscription Rates:** EUR796 individuals online; EUR816 individuals Germany, print and online; EUR842 other countries print and online. **URL:** http:// www.int-res.com/journals/ame/ame-home/.

Villejuif

44125 ■ Sciences Sociales et Sante
John Libbey Eurotext
7, rue Guy Moquet
F-94801 Villejuif, France
Publisher E-mail: contact@jle.com
Journal covering major health issues. **Subtitle:** A multidisciplinary forum on Public Health. **Freq:** Quarterly. **Key Personnel:** Doris Bonnet, Editor-in-Chief; Sebastien Darbon, Editor-in-Chief. **ISSN:** 0294-0337. **Subscription Rates:** EUR50 single issue; EUR124 other countries online and paper; EUR100 individuals online and paper (France); EUR116 individuals online and paper (European Union and Switzerland); EUR94 students, other countries online and paper; EUR70 students online and paper (France); EUR86 students online and paper (European Union and Switzerland); EUR204 institutions, other countries print; EUR180 institutions print (France); EUR196 institutions print (European Union and Switzerland). **Remarks:** Accepts advertising. **URL:** http:// www.john-libbey-eurotext.fr/en/revues/sante_pub/sss/ sommaire.md?type=text.html; http://www.revue-sss.fr/. **Circ:** (Not Reported)

Villeurbanne

44126 ■ Mathematical Modelling of Natural Phenomena
Research India Publications
c/o V. Volpert, Ed.-in-Ch.
Institute of Mathematics
University Lyon 1
F-69622 Villeurbanne, France
Fax: 33 472 448053
Publisher E-mail: info@ripublication.com
Journal covering mathematical modeling in biology, medicine, chemistry, physics, and other areas. **Founded:** 1919. **Freq:** Bimonthly. **Key Personnel:** V. Volpert, Editor-in-Chief, volpert@math.univ-lyon1.fr; A. Golovin, Assoc. Ed.; S. Petrovskii, Assoc. Ed. **ISSN:** 0973-5348. **Subscription Rates:** US$360 libraries and institution; online only; US$280 individuals online only; US$300 individuals print plus online free; US$390 libraries and institution; print plus online free. **URL:** http:// www.ripublication.com/mmnp.htm.

Villiers-Saint-Frederic

44127 ■ International Journal of Electric and Hybrid Vehicles
Inderscience Publishers
c/o Benoit Maisseu, Ed.
Renault IDVU, VSF PMB 1 00
42 Rt. de Boyres
F-78640 Villiers-Saint-Frederic, France
Publisher E-mail: editor@inderscience.com
Peer-reviewed journal covering field of electric and hybrid automotive systems. **Founded:** 2007. **Freq:** 4/yr. **Key Personnel:** Benoit Maisseu, Editor, benoit. maisseu@renault.com; Prof. C.C. Chan, Regional Ed.; Prof. Shigeyuki Minami, Regional Ed. **ISSN:** 1751-4088. **Subscription Rates:** EUR494 individuals includes surface mail, print only; EUR672 individuals print and online. **URL:** http://www.inderscience.com/browse/index. php?journalCODE=ijehv.

Circulation: ★ = ABC; △ = BPA; ◆ = CAC; • = CCAB; ❑ = VAC; ⊕ = PO Statement; ‡ = Publisher's Report; Boldface figures = sworn; Light figures = estimated.

Gale Directory of Publications & Broadcast Media/147th Ed.

4915

Saint Barthelemy

44128 ■ Radio Saint Barth-FM - 103.7 MHz
BP 1113
Saint Barthelemy, French West Indies
Ph: 590 277474

Fax: 590 277410
E-mail: radiostbarth@wanadoo.fr
Format: Ethnic; News; World Beat. **Operating Hours:** Continuous. **URL:** http://www.radiostbarth.com/.

44129 ■ Radio Saint Barth-FM - 98.7 MHz
BP 1113

Saint Barthelemy, French West Indies
Ph: 590 277474
Fax: 590 277410
E-mail: radiostbarth@wanadoo.fr
Format: Ethnic; News; World Beat. **Operating Hours:** Continuous. **URL:** http://www.radiostbarth.com/.

Circulation: ★ = ABC; △ = BPA; ◆ = CAC; • = CCAB; ❏ = VAC; ⊕ = PO Statement; ‡ = Publisher's Report; Boldface figures = sworn; Light figures = estimated.

Tbilisi

44130 ■ Annals of Biomedical Research and Education
Tbilisi State Medical University
33 Vazha-Pshavela Ave.
0177 Tbilisi, Georgia
Ph: 7 995 32391879
Fax: 7 995 32392284
Publication E-mail: abre@tsmu.edu
Publisher E-mail: iad@tsmu.edu
Journal covering biomedical research and education. **Key Personnel:** R. Khetsuriani, Editor-in-Chief; N. Tatishvili, Assoc. Ed.; V. Kipiani, Assoc. Ed.; N. Manjavidze, Sec. **ISSN:** 1512-0929. **URL:** http://abre.tsmu.edu/journal.htm.

44131 ■ Computer Science and Telecommunications
Georgian Internet Academy
17a, Chavchavadze Ave.
380028 Tbilisi, Georgia
Ph: 79 953 2913198
Publisher E-mail: info@internet-academy.org.ge
Journal publishing articles containing new scientific results in the field of theoretical and applied problems in computer science and telecommunications. **Key Personnel:** Tinatin Davitashvili, Editorial Board; Hamlet Meladze, Editor-in-Chief. **ISSN:** 1512-1232. **URL:** http://gesj.internet-academy.org.ge/en/title_en.php?b_sec=&section_l=comp.

44132 ■ Education Sciences & Psychology
Georgian Internet Academy
17a, Chavchavadze Ave.
380028 Tbilisi, Georgia
Ph: 79 953 2913198
Publication E-mail: journal@internet-academy.org.ge
Publisher E-mail: info@internet-academy.org.ge
Journal publishing articles containing new scientific results in the areas of education sciences and psychology. **Key Personnel:** Alexander Velijanashvili, Exec. Sec.; Nina Karbelashvili, Editor-in-Chief. **ISSN:** 1512-1801. **URL:** http://gesj.internet-academy.org.ge/.

44133 ■ Georgian Mathematical Journal
Walter de Gruyter Inc.
c/o I. Kiguradze, Ed.-in-Ch.
A. Razmadze Mathematical Institute
Aleksidze Str. 1
0193 Tbilisi, Georgia
Publisher E-mail: info@degruyterny.com
Peer-reviewed Journal containing research articles in pure and applied mathematics. **Founded:** 1994. **Freq:** Quarterly. **Key Personnel:** I. Kiguradze, Managing Editor; T. Shervashidze, Exec. Ed. **ISSN:** 1072-947X. **Subscription Rates:** EUR299 individuals print or online; EUR344 individuals print + online; EUR83 single issue print only. **URL:** http://www.degruyter.com/journals/gmj/detailEn.cfm.

44134 ■ Journal of Biological Physics and Chemistry
Association of Modern Scientific Investigation
Mosashvili 1/15
380062 Tbilisi, Georgia
Ph: 995 32 225993
Publisher E-mail: tata16@gmx.net
Journal publishing both experimental and theoretical work characterizing biological processes in terms of mathematical relations between the physical variables specifying the state of a living organism and its environment. **Freq:** Semiannual. **Key Personnel:** Dr. Jeremy J. Ramsden, Editor-in-Chief, j.ramsden@unibas.ch; Prof. David Mikelandze, Dep. Ed., d.mikelandze@mymail.ge. **ISSN:** 1512-0856. **URL:** http://www.amsi.ge/jbpc/index.html.

44135 ■ Journal of Pharmaceutical and Biomedical Analysis
Elsevier Science
c/o Bezhan Chankvetadze, Ed.
Tbilisi State University
Molecular Recognition & Separation Science Laboratory
School of Chemistry
380028 Tbilisi, Georgia
Publisher E-mail: nlinfo-f@elsevier.com
Journal covering research on pharmaceutical and biomedical analysis. **Founded:** 1983. **Freq:** 15/yr. **Key Personnel:** Sandor Gorog, Editor, phone 36 126 05604, fax 36 143 16281, o.gorog@richter.hu; Sergio Pinzauti, Editor, phone 39 554 573718, fax 39 554 573779, pinz@unifi.it; Ruin Moaddel, Editor, phone 410558-8294, moaddel@comcast.net; Jun Haginaka, Editor, phone 81 798 459949, fax 81 798 412792, jpba@mukogawa-u.ac.jp; Bezhan Chankvetadze, Editor, jpba_bezhan@yahoo.com. **ISSN:** 0731-7085. **Subscription Rates:** 482,500¥ institutions; US$4,067 institutions except Europe and Japan; EUR3,634 institutions European countries. **Remarks:** Accepts advertising. **URL:** http://www.elsevier.com/wps/find/journaldescription.cws_home/525434/descrip tiondescription. **Circ:** (Not Reported)

Circulation: ★ = ABC; △ = BPA; ◆ = CAC; • = CCAB; � = VAC; ⊕ = PO Statement; ‡ = Publisher's Report; Boldface figures = sworn; Light figures = estimated.

Gale Directory of Publications & Broadcast Media/147th Ed. 4919

Aachen

44136 ■ Colloid and Polymer Science
Springer-Verlag Tokyo
Institut fur Physikalische Chemie
RWTH Aachen
Landoltweg 2
D-52056 Aachen, Germany
Ph: 49 241 8094760
Fax: 49 241 8092327
Publisher E-mail: info@springer.jp
Journal devoted to colloid and polymer science and its interdisciplinary interactions. **Freq:** 18/yr. **Key Personnel:** F. Kremer, Editor, phone 49 341 9732550, fax 49 341 9732599, kremer@physik.uni-leipzig.de; W. Richtering, Editor, cps@pc.rwth-aachen.de; K.L. Ngai, Regional Ed., fax 202767-0546, ngai@estd.nrl.navy.mil; M. Antonietti, Editorial Board; V.P. Shibaev, Regional Ed., lcp@genebee.msu.su; M. Ballauff, Editorial Board; D. Exerowa, Editorial Board; Hiroyuki Ohshima, Regional Ed., ohshima@rs.noda.tus.ac.jp; Jinfeng Dong, Regional Ed., jfdong@whu.edu.cn; Prof. Andrew I. Lyon, Regional Ed., lyon@chemistry.gatech.edu. **ISSN:** 0303-402X. **Subscription Rates:** EUR4,139 institutions print incl. free access or e-only; EUR4,966.80 institutions print incl. enhanced access. **Remarks:** Advertising accepted; rates available upon request. **URL:** http://www.springer.com/chemistry/polymer/journal/396. **Circ:** (Not Reported)

44137 ■ Gb - Das Magazin fur Zierpflanzenbau
Haymarket Media GmbH & Co. KG
c/o Dr. Heinrich Dressler
Martin-Luther-Strasse 3-5
D-52062 Aachen, Germany
Ph: 49 241 4095611
Fax: 49 241 4095619
Publisher E-mail: info@haymarket.de
Magazine covering topics such as marketing, cultivation, technology, pest management, and business administration. **Freq:** Monthly. **Key Personnel:** Dr. Heinrich Dressler, Contact. **Remarks:** Accepts advertising. **URL:** http://gaertnerboerse.de/. **Ad Rates:** BW: EUR2,469.76, 4C: EUR1,218. **Circ:** 2,846

Alfeld

44138 ■ Deutsche Briefmarken Zeitung/Sammler Express (DBZ/SE)
Schaper Philatelie-Verlag GmbH
Postfach 1642
D-31046 Alfeld, Germany
Ph: 49 5181 80090
Fax: 49 5181 800933
Publisher E-mail: info@d-b-z.de
Consumer magazine covering stamp collecting. **Founded:** 1925. **Freq:** Semimonthly. **Print Method:** Offset. **Trim Size:** 205 x 286 mm. **ISSN:** 1438-2830. **Remarks:** Accepts advertising. **URL:** http://www.d-b-z.de/. **Ad Rates:** BW: EUR1,227, 4C: EUR2,043. **Circ:** Combined 41,000

Aschaffenburg

44139 ■ Schrot & Korn
Bio Verlag Gmbh
Magnolienweg 23
D-63741 Aschaffenburg, Germany
Ph: 49 6021 44890
Fax: 49 6021 4489499
Publisher E-mail: info@bioverlag.de
Consumer publication covering natural food. **Subtitle:** Das Naturkostmagazin. **Founded:** Sept. 1, 1985. **Freq:** Monthly. **Print Method:** Offset. **Trim Size:** 210 x 280 mm. **Subscription Rates:** Free. **URL:** http://www.schrotundkorn.de/index.html. **Circ:** Non-paid 411,689

Augsburg

44140 ■ IFSCC Magazine
International Federation of Societies of Cosmetic Chemists
Beethovenstr. 16
D-86150 Augsburg, Germany
Publication E-mail: ifscc.mag@sofw.com
Publisher E-mail: enquiries@ifscc.org
Publication covering cosmetology. **Freq:** Quarterly. **Subscription Rates:** EUR218 individuals including shipping; EUR223 individuals including airmail. **Remarks:** Accepts advertising. **URL:** http://www.ifscc.org/pubs.htm. **Circ:** (Not Reported)

44141 ■ Paneuropa Deutschland
Paneuropa-Union Deutschland e.V.
Paneuropa-Verlag GmbH
Hafnerberg 2
D-86152 Augsburg, Germany
Ph: 49 821 5024221
Fax: 49 821 5024283
Publication E-mail: paneuropa-verlag@suv.de
Publisher E-mail: paneuropa-union@t-online.de
German language publication covering international cooperation. **Freq:** Quarterly. **Key Personnel:** Bernd Posselt, President; Dr. Dirk Hermann, Ch. Ed.; Ursula Schleicher, Vice President; Prof. Alfred Gomolka, Vice President. **ISSN:** 0932-7592 **Subscription Rates:** EUR12 individuals. **Remarks:** Advertising accepted; rates available upon request. **URL:** http://de.paneuropa.org/index.php/pan/publikationen/die_themen. **Circ:** (Not Reported)

44142 ■ Progress in Solid State Chemistry
Elsevier Science
c/o A. Reller, Ed.
Solid State Chemistry
University of Augsburg
D-86135 Augsburg, Germany
Publisher E-mail: nlinfo-f@elsevier.com
Journal presenting a chemical view of the solid state by offering latest reviews by experts in the area. Emphasizes on relating physical properties and structural chemistry. **Founded:** 1964. **Freq:** Quarterly. **Key Personnel:** A. Reller, Editor, armin.reller@physik.uni-augsburg.de; M. Subramanian, Editor, mas.subramanian@oregonstate.edu; P. D. Battle, Editorial Advisory Board. **ISSN:** 0079-6786. **Subscription Rates:** EUR109 individuals for European Countries; US$126 individuals for all Countries except Europe and Japan; 14,700¥ individuals; US$1,165 institutions for all Countries except Europe and Japan; 138,200¥ institutions; EUR1,044 institutions for European Countries. **URL:** http://www.elsevier.com/wps/find/journaldescription.cws_home/417/description.

44143 ■ Radio Fantasy-FM - 93.4
Ludwig St. 1
D-86150 Augsburg, Germany
Ph: 49 821 5077100
Fax: 49 821 5077555
Format: Ethnic; Contemporary Hit Radio (CHR). **Ad Rates:** Advertising accepted; rates available upon request. **URL:** http://www.fantasy.de.

Bad Harzburg

44144 ■ Steel Grips
GRIPS media GmbH
Eichendorffstr. 64
D-38667 Bad Harzburg, Germany
Ph: 49 532 254575
Fax: 49 532 254574
Publisher E-mail: grips@t-online.de
English language publication covering steelmaking and processing, plantbuilding, R& D. **Subtitle:** Journal of Steel and Related Materials. **Founded:** 2003. **Freq:** Bimonthly. **Key Personnel:** Kerstin Garbracht, Editor-in-Chief, editor@steel-grips.com; Clemens Garbracht, Publisher, c.garbracht@gripsmedia.info. **ISSN:** 1866-8453. **Subscription Rates:** EUR24,700 individuals; EUR23,085 individuals; EUR23,085 individuals; EUR4,500 single issue; EUR4,206 single issue; EUR4,500 single issue; EUR4,206 single issue. **Remarks:** Advertising accepted; rates available upon request. **URL:** http://www.steel-grips.com. **Formerly:** stehl and eisen. **Circ:** 5,000

Bamberg

44145 ■ European Sociological Review
Oxford University Press
c/o Dr. Hans-Peter Blossfeld, Ed.
Fakultat Sozial und Wirtschaftswissenschaften
Otto-Friedrich-Universitat Bamberg
Lichtenhaidestr. 11
D-96045 Bamberg, Germany
Ph: 49 95 18632595
Fax: 49 95 18632597
Publisher E-mail: webenquiry.uk@oup.com
Social science journal in the area of empirical, quantitative and comparative studies, containing articles in all fields of sociology ranging in length from short research notes up to major reports. **Freq:** 6/yr. **Key Personnel:** Dr. Hans-Peter Blossfeld, Editor; Michelle Jackson, Assoc. Ed.; Luis Garrido Medina, Editorial Board; Hiroshi Ishida, Editorial Board; Richard Breen, Editorial Board; Merike Darmody, Assoc. Ed.; Josef Bruderl, Editorial Board; Louis-Andre Vallet, Assoc. Ed.; Robert Erikson, Editorial Board. **ISSN:** 0266-7215. **Subscription Rates:** 353 institutions print and online; US$706 institutions print and online; EUR530 institutions print and online; 323 institutions print; US$646 institutions print; EUR485 institutions print; 77 institutions developing Countries - print only; US$154 institutions developing Countries - print only; EUR116 institutions developing Countries - print only; 69 individuals print only, single issue. **Remarks:** Advertising accepted; rates available upon request. **URL:** http://esr.oupjournals.org/. **Circ:** (Not Reported)

44146 ■ Journal of the European Society of Women in Theological Research
PEETERS - USA
c/o Dr. Sabine Bieberstein, Ed.
Obere Brucke 2
D-96047 Bamberg, Germany
Publisher E-mail: peeters@peeters-us.com
Journal on theological research. **Key Personnel:** Dr. Sabine Bieberstein, Editor; Anne Claire Mulder, Editor; Magda Misset Van De Weg, Editor; Angela Berlis, Editor; Charlotte Methuen, Editor. **ISSN:** 1783-2454. **Subscription Rates:** EUR35 individuals. **URL:** http://www.peeters-leuven.be/journoverz.asp?nr=70&number_of_volumes="0".

Bayreuth

44147 ■ Physics and Chemistry of Minerals
Springer-Verlag
c/o Catherine A. McCammon, Ed.
Bayerisches Geoinstitut
Universitat Bayreuth
D-95440 Bayreuth, Germany
Fax: 49 921 553769
Journal dealing with physical or chemical studies on minerals or solids related to minerals. **Freq:** 10/yr. **Key Personnel:** Catherine A. McCammon, Editor, catherine.mccammon@uni-bayreuth.de; M. Matsui, Editor, m.matsui@sci.u-hyogo.ac.jp; M. Rieder, Editor, milan.rieder@jhu.edu; K.D. Becker, Advisory Board; G. Calas, Advisory Board; J.A. Tyburczy, Advisory Board; L.V. Bershov, Advisory Board; J.D. Bass, Advisory Board; M. Akaogi, Advisory Board. **ISSN:** 0342-1791. **Subscription Rates:** EUR2,424 institutions print incl. free access; EUR2,908.80 institutions print incl. enhanced access. **Remarks:** Advertising accepted; rates available upon request. **URL:** http://www.springer.com/earthsciences/mineralogy/journal/269. **Circ:** (Not Reported)

Berlin

44148 ■ Advances in Calculus of Variations
Walter de Gruyter GmbH & Co. KG
Genthiner Strasse 13
D-10785 Berlin, Germany
Ph: 49 302 60050
Fax: 49 302 6005251
Publisher E-mail: info@degruyter.com
Journal focusing on the calculus of variation and its related applications. **Freq:** Quarterly. **Trim Size:** 170 x 240 mm. **Key Personnel:** Frank Duzaar, Managing Editor, duzaar@mi.uni-erlangen.de; Nicola Fusco, Managing Editor, n.fusco@mi.unina.it. **ISSN:** 1864-8258. **Subscription Rates:** EUR324 individuals print or online; EUR373 individuals print + online; EUR89 single issue. **Remarks:** Accepts advertising. **URL:** http://www.degruyter.de/journals/acv/detailEn.cfm. **Ad Rates:** BW: DM 300. **Circ:** ‡200

44149 ■ Anglia
Walter de Gruyter GmbH & Co. KG
Genthiner Strasse 13
D-10785 Berlin, Germany
Ph: 49 302 60050
Fax: 49 302 6005251
Publisher E-mail: info@degruyter.com
Journal focusing on English philology. **Founded:** 1878. **Freq:** 3/yr. **Print Method:** Web Offset. **Trim Size:** 110 x 180 mm. **Key Personnel:** Stephan Kohl, Editor; Lucia KoRnexl, Editor; Hans Sauer, Editor. **ISSN:** 0340-5222. **Subscription Rates:** EUR216 individuals print + online; EUR188 individuals print or online only; EUR69 single issue. **Remarks:** Accepts advertising. **URL:** http://www.degruyter.de/journals/anglia/detailEn.cfm. **Ad Rates:** BW: DM 550. **Circ:** ‡540

44150 ■ Antike und Abendland
Walter de Gruyter GmbH & Co. KG
Genthiner Strasse 13
D-10785 Berlin, Germany
Ph: 49 302 60050
Fax: 49 302 6005251
Publisher E-mail: info@degruyter.com
Journal covering topics of classical studies, ancient history, Germanic studies, romance studies and English studies. **Freq:** Annual. **Print Method:** Offset. **Trim Size:** 188 x 125 mm. **Key Personnel:** Dr. Christoph Riedweg, Editor; Dr. Wilhelm Kuhlmann, Editor; Dr. Helmut Krasser, Editor; Dr. Wolfgang Schuller, Editor; Dr. Rainer Stillers, Editor. **ISSN:** 0003-5696. **Remarks:** Accepts advertising. **URL:** http://www.degruyter.de/journals/antike/detailEn.cfm. **Ad Rates:** BW: DM 550. **Circ:** ‡450

44151 ■ Anwaltsblatt
Deutscher Anwaltverlag GmbH
Suffering Rd., 11 Office Brussels
D-10179 Berlin, Germany
Ph: 49 307 261520
Fax: 49 307 26152
Publisher E-mail: anwaltsblatt@anwaltverein.de
Professional magazine covering law. **Founded:** 1950. **Key Personnel:** Dr. Peter Hamacher, Editor; Udo Henke, Editor; Dr. Nicolas Luehrig, Editor. **ISSN:** 0171-7227. **URL:** http://www.anwaltverein.de/leistungen/anwaltsblatt. **Circ:** Combined 113,000

44152 ■ Arbitrium
Walter de Gruyter GmbH & Co. KG
Genthiner Strasse 13
D-10785 Berlin, Germany
Ph: 49 302 60050
Fax: 49 302 6005251
Publisher E-mail: info@degruyter.com
Journal focusing on German literature studies. **Founded:** 1983. **Freq:** 3/yr. **Print Method:** Web Offset. **Key Personnel:** Wolfgang Harms, Editor; Peter Strohschneider, Editor; Friedrich Vollhardt, Editor. **ISSN:** 0723-2977. **Subscription Rates:** EUR124 individuals print + online; EUR108 individuals print or online only; EUR40 single issue. **Remarks:** Accepts advertising. **URL:** http://www.degruyter.de/journals/arbitrium/detailEn.cfm. **Ad Rates:** BW: DM 500. **Circ:** ‡460

44153 ■ arcadia
Walter de Gruyter GmbH & Co. KG
Genthiner Strasse 13
D-10785 Berlin, Germany
Ph: 49 302 60050
Fax: 49 302 6005251
Publisher E-mail: info@degruyter.com
Journal focusing on the comparative studies of literature and liberal arts. **Freq:** Semiannual. **Trim Size:** 171 x 245 mm. **Key Personnel:** Dr. Vivian Liska, Editor; Dr. John Neubauer, Editor; Dr. Jurgen Wertheimer, Editor. **ISSN:** 0003-7982. **Subscription Rates:** EUR180 individuals print + online; EUR156 individuals print or online only; EUR86 single issue. **Remarks:** Accepts advertising. **URL:** http://www.degruyter.de/journals/arcadia/detailEn.cfm. **Ad Rates:** BW: DM 600. **Circ:** ‡500

44154 ■ Archiv fur Geschichte der Philosophie
Walter de Gruyter GmbH & Co. KG
Genthiner Strasse 13
D-10785 Berlin, Germany
Ph: 49 302 60050
Fax: 49 302 6005251
Publisher E-mail: info@degruyter.com
Journal describing epochs of the history of western philosophy, from antiquity up to the 20th century. **Freq:** 3/yr. **Key Personnel:** Prof. Christia Mercer, Editor; Simon Weber, Editor, agph@uni-bonn.de; Dr. Christoph Horn, Managing Editor; Dr. Wolfgang Bartuschat, Managing Editor. **ISSN:** 0003-9101. **Subscription Rates:** EUR188 individuals print or online only; EUR216 individuals print and online; EUR69 single issue. **URL:** http://www.degruyter.de/journals/agp/detailEn.cfm?sel=he. **Circ:** 650

44155 ■ Archiv fur Papyrusforschung
Walter de Gruyter GmbH & Co. KG
Genthiner Strasse 13
D-10785 Berlin, Germany
Ph: 49 302 60050
Fax: 49 302 6005251
Publisher E-mail: info@degruyter.com
Journal focusing on papyrus studies. **Founded:** 1901. **Freq:** Semiannual. **Print Method:** Web Offset. **Key Personnel:** Jean-luc Fournet, Editor; Dr. Barbel Kramer, Editor; Dr. Luppe Wolfgang, Editor. **ISSN:** 0066-6459. **Subscription Rates:** EUR240 institutions print + online; EUR209 institutions print or online; EUR115 single issue. **Remarks:** Accepts advertising. **URL:** http://www.degruyter.de/journals/apf/detailEn.cfm. **Ad Rates:** BW: DM 300. **Circ:** ‡300

44156 ■ Archives of Animal Nutrition
Taylor & Francis Group Journals
Freie Universitat Berlin
Institut fur Tierernahrung
FB Veterinarmedizin
Brummerstrasse 34
D-14195 Berlin, Germany
Publisher E-mail: customerservice@taylorandfrancis.com
Journal covering the biochemical and physiological basis of animal nutrition. **Freq:** Bimonthly. **Key Personnel:** Ortwin Simon, Editor-in-Chief, osimon@zedat.fu-berlin.de; Annette Simon, Editorial Off.; Knud Erik Bach-Knudsen, Editorial Board. **ISSN:** 1745-039X. **Subscription Rates:** US$460 individuals print only; US$2,318 institutions online only; 2,441 institutions print & online. **URL:** http://www.informaworld.com/smpp/title~content=t713453455~db=all.

44157 ■ Aschkenas
Walter de Gruyter GmbH & Co. KG
Genthiner Strasse 13
D-10785 Berlin, Germany
Ph: 49 302 60050
Fax: 49 302 6005251
Publisher E-mail: info@degruyter.com
Journal focusing on the history and culture of Ashkenazi Jews. **Freq:** Semiannual. **Key Personnel:** Hans Otto Horch, Editor; Robert Jutte, Editor; Markus J. Wenninger, Editor. **ISSN:** 1016-4987. **Subscription Rates:** EUR124 individuals print + online; EUR108 individuals print or online; EUR59 single issue. **Remarks:** Accepts advertising. **URL:** http://www.degruyter.de/journals/aschk/detailEn.cfm?sel=be. **Ad Rates:** BW: DM 450. **Circ:** ‡320

44158 ■ ballettanz
Friedrich Berlin Publishing Group
Knesebeckstr. 59-61
D-10719 Berlin, Germany
Ph: 49 30 25449520
Fax: 49 30 25449524
Publication E-mail: redaktion@ballet-tanz.de
Magazine covering dance and ballet in Europe. **Subtitle:** Europe's Leading Dance Magazine. **Founded:** 1994. **Freq:** Monthly (double issue Aug./Sep. and a yearbook). **Trim Size:** 240 x 300 mm. **Key Personnel:** Arnd Wesemann, Editor; Heike Drisch, Contact, ads@ballet-tanz.de; Hartmut Regitz, Editor; Sofie Goblirsch, Editorial Staff. **Subscription Rates:** EUR119 individuals within Europe; EUR82 students; EUR9.50 single issue; EUR14 individuals double issue. **Remarks:** Accepts advertising. **URL:** http://www.ballet-tanz.de/. **Ad Rates:** BW: EUR1,800, 4C: EUR2,500. **Circ:** 12,000

44159 ■ Beitrage zur Geschichte der deutschen Sprache und Literatur
Walter de Gruyter GmbH & Co. KG
Genthiner Strasse 13
D-10785 Berlin, Germany
Ph: 49 302 60050
Fax: 49 302 6005251
Publisher E-mail: info@degruyter.com
Journal featuring the German language and literature. **Founded:** 1874. **Freq:** 3/yr. **Print Method:** Web Offset. **Key Personnel:** Ulrike Demske, Editor; Klaus Grubmuller, Editor; Jan-Dirk Muller, Editor. **ISSN:** 0005-8076. **Subscription Rates:** EUR163 individuals print + online; EUR142 individuals print or online only; EUR52 single issue. **Remarks:** Accepts advertising. **URL:** http://www.degruyter.de/journals/pbb/detailEn.cfm. **Ad Rates:** BW: DM 550. **Circ:** ‡540

44160 ■ Biological Chemistry
Walter de Gruyter GmbH & Co. KG
Genthiner Strasse 13
D-10785 Berlin, Germany
Ph: 49 302 60050
Fax: 49 302 6005251
Publisher E-mail: info@degruyter.com
Journal covering articles on the developments in the molecular life sciences. **Freq:** Monthly. **Trim Size:** 21 x 29.7 cm. **Key Personnel:** H. Sies, Editor-in-Chief; K. Sandhoff, Exec. Ed.; A. Wittinghofer, Exec. Ed.; W. Baumeister, Editorial Board; B. Bukau, Editorial Board; F.U. Hartl, Exec. Ed. **ISSN:** 1431-6730. **Subscription Rates:** EUR1,364 institutions print or online only; EUR1,569 institutions print + online; EUR289 individuals print + online; EUR125 single issue. **URL:** http://www.degruyter.de/journals/bc/detailEn.cfm.

44161 ■ Biomedizinische Technik
Walter de Gruyter GmbH & Co. KG
Genthiner Strasse 13
D-10785 Berlin, Germany
Ph: 49 302 60050
Fax: 49 302 6005251
Publisher E-mail: info@degruyter.com
Peer-reviewed journal covering the field of biomedical technology and information technology. **Freq:** Bimonthly. **Trim Size:** 21 x 29.7 cm. **Key Personnel:** Gerhard M. Artmann, Editorial Board; Ulrich Boenick, Editorial Board; Olaf Dossel, Editor-in-Chief; Hermann Gilly, Assoc. Ed.; Steffen Leonhardt, Assoc. Ed; Thomas

Stieglitz, Assoc. Ed.; Bernhard Clasbrummel, Editorial Board; Peter Boesiger, Assoc. Ed.; Jens Haueisen, Assoc. Ed. **ISSN:** 0013-5585. **Subscription Rates:** EUR85 single issue; EUR462 individuals print or online only; EUR532 individuals print and online. **URL:** http://www.degruyter.de/journals/bmt/detailEn.cfm.

44162 ■ Botanica Marina
Walter de Gruyter GmbH & Co. KG
Genthiner Strasse 13
D-10785 Berlin, Germany
Ph: 49 302 60050
Fax: 49 302 6005251
Publisher E-mail: info@degruyter.com
Peer-reviewed journal covering all aspects of marine botany. **Freq:** Bimonthly. **Trim Size:** 21 x 29.7 cm. **Key Personnel:** Anthony R.O. Chapman, Editor-in-Chief, achapman@dal.ca; Ruth Falshaw, Assoc. Ed.; Susana Enriquez, Assoc. Ed. **ISSN:** 0006-8055. **Subscription Rates:** EUR1,289 institutions print or online; EUR1,483 institutions print + online; EUR184 individuals print + online. **URL:** http://www.degruyter.de/journals/bm/detailEn.cfm.

44163 ■ Bundesgesundheitsblatt - Gesundheitsforschung - Gesundheitsschutz
Springer Netherlands
Robert-Koch-Institut - Redaktion Bundesgesundheitsblatt
Nordufer 20
13353 Berlin, Germany
Publisher E-mail: permissions.dordrecht@springer.com
Journal covering health protection questions. **Freq:** Monthly. **Key Personnel:** Dr. Heidemarie Rohdewohld, Contact, rohdewohldh@rki.de. **ISSN:** 1436-9990. **Subscription Rates:** EUR126.17 institutions print incl. free access or e-only; EUR151.40 institutions print incl. enhanced access. **Remarks:** Advertising accepted; rates available upon request. **URL:** http://www.springer.com/medicine/journal/103. **Circ:** (Not Reported)

44164 ■ Byzantinische Zeitschrift
Walter de Gruyter GmbH & Co. KG
Genthiner Strasse 13
D-10785 Berlin, Germany
Ph: 49 302 60050
Fax: 49 302 6005251
Publisher E-mail: info@degruyter.com
Journal containing the studies of literature, history and art history of Byzantine. **Freq:** Semiannual. **Key Personnel:** Albrecht Berger, Editor. **ISSN:** 0007-7704. **Subscription Rates:** EUR319 institutions print + online; EUR277 institutions print or online only; EUR152 single issue. **Remarks:** Accepts advertising. **URL:** http://www.degruyter.de/journals/bz/detailEn.cfm?sel=ai. **Ad Rates:** BW: DM 300. **Circ:** ‡650

44165 ■ Clinical Chemistry and Laboratory Medicine
Walter de Gruyter GmbH & Co. KG
Genthiner Strasse 13
D-10785 Berlin, Germany
Ph: 49 302 60050
Fax: 49 302 6005251
Publisher E-mail: info@degruyter.com
Journal covering latest developments in the clinical laboratory sciences. **Freq:** Monthly. **Key Personnel:** Mario Plebani, Editor-in-Chief; Giuseppe Lippi, Editor; Philippe Gillery, Editor. **ISSN:** 1434-6621. **Subscription Rates:** EUR1,520 institutions print + online; EUR1,322 institutions print or online only; EUR277 individuals print and online. **URL:** http://www.degruyter.de/journals/cclm/detailEn.cfm.

44166 ■ Communication and Medicine
Mouton de Gruyter
Genthiner Strasse 13
D-10785 Berlin, Germany
Ph: 49 30 260050
Fax: 49 30 26005251
Publisher E-mail: info@degruyter.de
Peer-reviewed journal consolidating different traditions of discourse and communication research in its commitment to an understanding of psychosocial, cultural and ethical aspects of healthcare in contemporary societies. **Subtitle:** An Interdisciplinary Journal of Healthcare, Ethics and Society. **Freq:** Annual. **Key Personnel:** Srikant Sarangi, Editor, commed@cardiff.ac.uk. **ISSN:** 1612-1783. **URL:** http://www.degruyter.com/journals/commed/detailEn.cfm.

44167 ■ Corpus Linguistics and Linguistic Theory
Mouton de Gruyter
Genthiner Strasse 13
D-10785 Berlin, Germany
Ph: 49 30 260050
Fax: 49 30 26005251
Publisher E-mail: info@degruyter.de
Peer-reviewed journal publishing original corpus-based research focusing on theoretically relevant issues in all core areas of linguistic research (phonology, morphology, syntax, semantics, pragmatics), or other recognized topic areas. **Freq:** Annual. **Key Personnel:** Anatol Stefanowitsch, Outgoing Ed.-in-Ch.; Stefan Th. Gries, Editor-in-Chief, stgries@linguistics.ucsb.edu. **ISSN:** 1613-7027. **Subscription Rates:** EUR185 individuals print or online; EUR213 individuals print + online; EUR102 single issue print only. **URL:** http://www.degruyter.com/journals/cllt/detailEn.cfm.

44168 ■ Crystal Research and Technology
John Wiley & Sons Inc.
c/o Dr. Wolfgang Neuman, Ed.-in-Ch.
Institut fur Physik - Kristallographie
Humboldt-Universitat-zu Berlin
Newtonstr. 15
D-12489 Berlin, Germany
Ph: 49 30 20937761
Fax: 49 30 20937760
Publisher E-mail: info@wiley.com
Journal focusing on research in the field of crystallography. **Freq:** Monthly. **Key Personnel:** Dr. Wolfgang Neuman, Editor-in-Chief, wolfgang.neuman@physik.hu-berlin.de; Dr..Peter Gornert, Editorial Board; Dr. Klaus W. Benz, Consulting Ed., klaus-werner.benz@fmf.uni-freiburg.de; H. Kleessen, Managing Editor; Dr. Roberto Fornari, Editorial Board; Dr. Peter Paufler, Editorial Board. **ISSN:** 0232-1300. **Subscription Rates:** EUR291 individuals print; 434 SFr individuals Switzerland and Lichtenstein (print); US$399 other countries print; EUR2,320 institutions print; 3,973 SFr institutions Switzerland and Lichtenstein (print); US$3,241 institutions, other countries print. **URL:** http://onlinelibrary.wiley.com/journal/10.1002/(ISSN)1521-4079.

44169 ■ Das Neue China
Gesellschaft fur Deutsch-Chinesische Freundschaft Berlin e.v.
German-Chinese Friendship Association
Innsbrucker Strasse 3
D-10825 Berlin, Germany
Ph: 49 308 545744
Fax: 49 308 547629
Publisher E-mail: gdcf-berlin@t-online.de
German language publication covering intercultural affairs. **Subtitle:** Magazine for China and East Asia. **Founded:** 1973. **Freq:** Quarterly. **Key Personnel:** Dagmar Yu-Dembski, Contact, yu-dembski@dnc-online.de. **ISSN:** 0172-4878. **Subscription Rates:** EUR16 individuals; EUR4 single issue. **Remarks:** Advertising accepted; rates available upon request. **URL:** http://www.dnc-online.de. **Circ:** 2,000

44170 ■ Der Steuezahler
Bund der Steuezahler
Franzosische Str 9-12
10117 Berlin, Germany
Ph: 49 30 2593960
Fax: 49 30 25939625
Publisher E-mail: info@steuerzahler.de
Membership magazine covering tax and financial issues. **Founded:** Jan. 1950. **Freq:** Monthly. **URL:** http://www.steuerzahler.de/.

44171 ■ Deutsche Entomologische Zeitschrift
John Wiley & Sons Inc.
c/o Dr. Manfred Asche, Mng. Ed.
Museum fur Naturkunde der Humboldt-Universitat zu Berlin
Invalidenstr. 43
D-10115 Berlin, Germany
Ph: 49 30 20938519
Fax: 49 30 20938565
Publisher E-mail: info@wiley.com
Peer-reviewed journal focusing on systematic entomology. **Freq:** Semiannual. **Key Personnel:** Dr. Hannelore Hoch, Editor-in-Chief; Dr. Manfred Asche, Managing Editor, manfred.asche@museum.hu-berlin.de; Dr. Holger H. Dathe, Editorial Board. **ISSN:** 1435-1951. **Subscription Rates:** EUR478 institutions print

only; 826 SFr institutions print only; US$559 institutions, other countries print only; EUR314 institutions print with online access; 909 SFr institutions print with online access; US$616 institutions, other countries print with online access; 285 institutions print only; 5,527 institutions print with online access. **URL:** http://www3.interscience.wiley.com/cgi-bin/jhome/110425999.

44172 ■ Deutsche Zeitschrift fur Wirtschafts- und Insolvenzrecht
Walter de Gruyter GmbH & Co. KG
Genthiner Strasse 13
D-10785 Berlin, Germany
Ph: 49 302 60050
Fax: 49 302 6005251
Publisher E-mail: info@degruyter.com
Journal covering European insolvency law. **Key Personnel:** Rainer Funke, Editor; Reinfrid Fischer, Editor; Wilhelm Bichlmeier, Editor; Dr. Hermann Wilfried Bayer, Editor; Dr. Hartmut Oetker, Editor; Dr. Stefan Smid, Editor. **ISSN:** 1439-1589. **Subscription Rates:** EUR251 individuals print or online; EUR120 students print and online; EUR132 students; EUR23 single issue. **URL:** http://www.degruyter.com/rs/280_1822_ENU_h.htm.

44173 ■ European Biotechnology Science & Industry News
Biocom AG
Stralsunder Str. 58-59
D-13355 Berlin, Germany
Ph: 49 30 2649210
Fax: 49 30 26492111
Publisher E-mail: service@biocom.de
Journal constituting timely news from science and industry, background reports on new EU legislation, current debates and financing initiatives from Brussels, as well as market analyses and previews on upcoming technology trends. **Freq:** Bimonthly. **Key Personnel:** Dr. Patrick Dieckhoff, Contact. **ISSN:** 1618-8276. **Subscription Rates:** EUR100 individuals; EUR50 students. **URL:** http://www.biocom.de/. **Circ:** 15,000

44174 ■ European Company and Financial Law Review
De Gruyter Rechtswissenschaften Verlags GmbH
Genthiner Strasse 13
D-10785 Berlin, Germany
Ph: 49 302 60050
Fax: 49 302 6005251
Publisher E-mail: wdg-info@degruyter.de
Journal focusing on all areas of European company law and the financing of companies and business entities. **Freq:** Quarterly. **Key Personnel:** Dr. Heribert Hirte, Managing Editor, heribert.hirte@jura.uni-hamburg.de; Dr. Wulf Goette, Editor; Dr. Gerd Krieger, Editor; Dr. Holger Fleischer, Managing Editor; Dr. Hans-Joachim Priester, Editor; Dr. Peter H.C. Hommelhoff, Editor; Dr. Hanno Merkt, Managing Editor. **ISSN:** 1613-2548. **Subscription Rates:** EUR308 individuals print or online; EUR355 individuals print and online; EUR228 individuals print; EUR248 individuals print and online; EUR85 single issue. **URL:** http://www.degruyter.com/journals/ecfr/detailEn.cfm.

44175 ■ European Photography
PO Box 08 02 27
D-10002 Berlin, Germany
International art magazine for contemporary photography and new media. **Founded:** Jan. 1, 1980. **Freq:** Biennial. **Trim Size:** 240 x 300 mm. **Key Personnel:** Andreas Mueller-Pohle, Editor and Publisher. **ISSN:** 0172-7028. **Subscription Rates:** EUR64 two years; EUR80 other countries two years; outside Europe; EUR16 single issue plus 7.50 for handling and postage. **URL:** http://www.european-photography.de/pavillon/pav_ep.shtml.

44176 ■ European Review of Contract Law
De Gruyter Rechtswissenschaften Verlags GmbH
Genthiner Strasse 13
D-10785 Berlin, Germany
Ph: 49 302 60050
Fax: 49 302 6005251
Publisher E-mail: wdg-info@degruyter.de
Journal covering such diverse areas of the law as sales, standard contract terms, distribution chains, marketing practices, research and development agreements, contract law copyright aspects, financial and investment services contracts, insurance contracts and e-commerce, also non-discrimination within and outside labor law and more generally important aspects of labor contracts and other symbiotic contracts. **Freq:** Quarterly. **Key Personnel:** Dr. Stefan Grundmann, Managing Editor. **ISSN:** 1614-9920. **Subscription Rates:** EUR260

Circulation: ★ = ABC; △ = BPA; ♦ = CAC; • = CCAB; ❑ = VAC; ⊕ = PO Statement; ‡ = Publisher's Report; Boldface figures = sworn; Light figures = estimated.

Gale Directory of Publications & Broadcast Media/147th Ed.   **4923**

individuals print or online; EUR299 individuals print and online; EUR72 single issue. **URL:** http://www.degruyter.com/journals/ercl/detailEn.cfm.

44177 ■ European State Aid Law Quarterly
Lexxion Verlagsgesellschaft mbH
Guntzelstr. 63
10717 Berlin, Germany
Ph: 49 30 8145060
Fax: 49 30 81450622
Publisher E-mail: info@lexxion.de
Journal focusing entirely on European State aid law, covering all current issues in this field and concentrating particularly on the decision-makers' views to be presented in articles and comments. **Freq:** Quarterly. **Key Personnel:** Peter Schutterle, Editorial Board; Christian Koenig, Editorial Board; Andreas Bartosch, Editorial Board; Adinda Sinnaeve, Editorial Board; Vernon E. Vig, Editorial Board; Leigh Hancher, Editorial Board. **ISSN:** 1619-5272. **Subscription Rates:** EUR472.94 individuals vat is included; postage and handling are included; EUR118.24 single issue vat is included; postage and handling are included. **URL:** http://www.lexxion.eu/estal.

44178 ■ Fabula
Walter de Gruyter GmbH & Co. KG
Genthiner Strasse 13
D-10785 Berlin, Germany
Ph: 49 302 60050
Fax: 49 302 6005251
Publisher E-mail: info@degruyter.com
Journal featuring interrelationship between oral and literary traditions. **Freq:** Semiannual. **Key Personnel:** Dr. Rolf Wilhelm Brednich, Editor, rbredni@gwdg.de; Christine Shojaei Kawan, Editor, ckawan@gwdg.de. **ISSN:** 0014-6242. **Subscription Rates:** EUR146 institutions print or online only; EUR168 institutions print + online; EUR80 single issue. **URL:** http://www.degruyter.de/journals/fabula/detailEn.cfm. **Circ:** 450

44179 ■ Feddes Repertorium
John Wiley & Sons Inc.
Institut fur Biologie, Spezielle Botanik und Arboretum
Humboldt-Universitat zu Berlin
Spathstr. 80-81
D-12437 Berlin, Germany
Ph: 49 30 6366941
Fax: 49 30 6369446
Publisher E-mail: info@wiley.com
Journal focusing on botanical taxonomy and geobotany. **Freq:** 8/yr. **Key Personnel:** Dr. Gunther Natho, Editor; Dr. Thomas Stutzel, Co-Ed. **ISSN:** 0014-8962. **Subscription Rates:** US$1,402 institutions, other countries for print; 1,830 SFr institutions for print; EUR1,114 institutions for print; EUR1,258 institutions combined print with online access; 2,013 SFr institutions combined print with online access; US$1,543 institutions, other countries combined print with online access. **URL:** http://onlinelibrary.wiley.com/journal/10.1002/(ISSN)1522-239Xb.

44180 ■ Flieger Revue
Moller Buch und Zeitschriften Verlag KG
Oraniendamm 48
D-13469 Berlin, Germany
Ph: 49 30 419090
Fax: 49 30 41909599
Publication E-mail: redaktion@fliegerrevue.de
Magazine covering aviation and space. **Subtitle:** Magazin fur Luft und Raumfahrt. **Founded:** 1952. **Freq:** Monthly. **Print Method:** Offset. **Trim Size:** 270 x 097 mm. **Key Personnel:** Detlef Billig, Editor-in-Chief, extra@fliegerrevue.de; Kai Lange, Advertising Mgr., k.lange@fliegerrevue.de; Lutz Buchmann, Editor-in-Chief, l.buchmann@fliegerrevue.de. **ISSN:** 0941-889X. **Subscription Rates:** EUR44 individuals. **URL:** http://www.fliegerrevue.de/. **Ad Rates:** BW: EUR3,010, 4C: EUR4,360. **Circ:** Paid 25,485

44181 ■ Folia Linguistica
Walter de Gruyter GmbH & Co. KG
Genthiner Strasse 13
D-10785 Berlin, Germany
Ph: 49 302 60050
Fax: 49 302 6005251
Publisher E-mail: info@degruyter.com
Peer-reviewed journal covering indexing and abstracting services. **Freq:** Semiannual. **Key Personnel:** Dr. Hans Henrich Hock, Editor, hhhock@uiuc.edu; Dr. Teresa Fanego, Editor, teresa.fanego@usc.es; Christopher Beedham, Editorial Board. **ISSN:** 0165-4004. **Subscription Rates:** EUR264 institutions print or online only; EUR304 institutions print and online; EUR97 single issue.

URL: http://www.degruyter.de/journals/follin/detailEn.cfm.

44182 ■ Forum Mathematicum
Walter de Gruyter GmbH & Co. KG
Genthiner Strasse 13
D-10785 Berlin, Germany
Ph: 49 302 60050
Fax: 49 302 6005251
Publisher E-mail: info@degruyter.com
Journal covering topics on general mathematics, applied mathematics and mathematical physics. **Freq:** Bimonthly. **Print Method:** Offset. **Key Personnel:** Andrew Ranicki, Editor, aar@maths.ed.ac.uk; Frank Duzaar, Editor, duzaar@mi.uni-erlangen.de; Michel Fliess, Editor, michel.fliess@polytechnique.fr; Joram Lindenstrauss, Editor, joram@math.huji.ac.il; Giovanni Gallavotti, Editor, giovanni.gallavotti@roma1.infn.it; Karl-Hermann Neeb, Editor, neeb@mathematik.tu-darmstadt.de; Manfred Droste, Editor, droste@informatik.uni-leipzig.de; Josselin Garnier, Editor, garnier@cict.fr; Frederick R. Cohen, Editor, cohf@math.rochester.edu. **ISSN:** 0933-7741. **Subscription Rates:** EUR649 institutions print or online only; EUR746 institutions print and online; EUR119 single issue. **URL:** http://www.degruyter.de/journals/forum/detailEn.cfm. **Circ:** 300

44183 ■ Forum Qualitative Sozialforschung
Institut fuer Klinische Psychologie und Gemeindepsychologie
Freie Universitat
Habelschwerdter Allee 45
D-14195 Berlin, Germany
Ph: 49 308 3855753
Fax: 49 308 3851233
Peer-reviewed journal promoting discussion and cooperation among qualitative researchers from different countries and social science disciplines. **Founded:** 1999. **Freq:** 3/yr. **Key Personnel:** Dr. Katja Mruck, Editor, katja.mruck@fu-berlin.de. **ISSN:** 1438-5627. **URL:** http://www.qualitative-research.net/index.php/fqs/index.

44184 ■ Fossil Record
John Wiley & Sons Inc.
c/o Martin Aberhan, Ed.-in-Ch.
Museum fur Naturkunde,
Leibniz Institute for Research on Evolution & Biodiversity
Humboldt University Berlin, Invalidenstr. 43
10115 Berlin, Germany
Ph: 49 30 20938578
Fax: 49 30 20938868
Publisher E-mail: info@wiley.com
Journal covering the field of palaeontology. **Founded:** 1998. **Freq:** 3/yr. **Key Personnel:** Martin Aberhan, Editor-in-Chief, martin.aberhan@museum.hu-berlin.de; Dieter Korn, Managing Editor, dieter.korn@museum.hu-berlin.de; Christian Klug, Co-Ed. **ISSN:** 1435-1943. **Subscription Rates:** EUR351 institutions Europe (print and online); 533 SFr institutions Switzerland and Lichtenstein (print and online); US$470 Institutions, other countries print and online; 240 institutions Europe (print and online); EUR319 institutions Europe (print only); 484 SFr institutions Switzerland and Lichtenstein (print only); US$427 institutions, other countries print only; 218 institutions Europe (print only). **Remarks:** Accepts advertising. **URL:** http://onlinelibrary.wiley.com/journal/10.1002/(ISSN)1860-1014. **Circ:** (Not Reported)

44185 ■ Fruhmittelalterliche Studien
Walter de Gruyter GmbH & Co. KG
Genthiner Strasse 13
D-10785 Berlin, Germany
Ph: 49 302 60050
Fax: 49 302 6005251
Publisher E-mail: info@degruyter.com
Journal covering medieavalistic studies. **Key Personnel:** Dr. Hagen Keller, Editor; Dr. Gerd Althoff; Dr. Christel Meier-Staubach, Editor. **ISSN:** 0071-9706. **URL:** http://www.degruyter.de/journals/fmst/detailEn.cfm.

44186 ■ Germanistik
Walter de Gruyter GmbH & Co. KG
Genthiner Strasse 13
D-10785 Berlin, Germany
Ph: 49 302 60050
Fax: 49 302 6005251
Publisher E-mail: info@degruyter.com
Journal covering the study of German language and literature. **Freq:** Semiannual. **Print Method:** Web Offset. **Key Personnel:** Wilfried Barner, Editor; Ulla Fix, Editor; Jurgen Fohrmann, Editor. **ISSN:** 0016-8912. **Subscription Rates:** EUR217 individuals print + online; EUR189

individuals print or online only; EUR104 single issue. **Remarks:** Accepts advertising. **URL:** http://www.degruyter.de/journals/germ/detailEn.cfm. **Ad Rates:** BW: DM 850. **Circ:** 1,300

44187 ■ Golem
Emdener Str. 33
D-10551 Berlin, Germany
Ph: 49 176 51003202
Fax: 49 30 39731371
Magazine featuring the Jewish philosophical, theological, sociological, literary and poetic perspectives. **Subtitle:** Europaisch-Judisches Magazin. **Key Personnel:** Toby Axelrod, Editor; Hartmut Bomhoff, Editor; Norma Drimmer, Editor. **Subscription Rates:** EUR5 individuals. **URL:** http://www.golem-journal.de/.

44188 ■ Groove
Kopenicker Str. 178/179
D-10997 Berlin, Germany
Ph: 49 30 44312020
Fax: 49 30 2807098
Consumer magazine covering electronic music and club culture. **Key Personnel:** Heiko Hoffmann, Editor-in-Chief, phone 30 44 312020, heiko@groove.de. **Subscription Rates:** EUR26 individuals plus CDR; EUR46 individuals Europe. **URL:** http://www.groove.de.

44189 ■ Holzforschung
Walter de Gruyter GmbH & Co. KG
Genthiner Strasse 13
D-10785 Berlin, Germany
Ph: 49 302 60050
Fax: 49 302 6005251
Publisher E-mail: info@degruyter.com
Journal covering on the latest research in the field of biology, chemistry, physics and technology of wood and wood components. **Subtitle:** International Journal of the Biology, Chemistry, Physics, and Technology of Wood. **Freq:** Bimonthly. **Print Method:** Web offset. **Trim Size:** 21 X 29.7 cm. **Key Personnel:** Oskar Faix, Editor-in-Chief; C. Heitner, Advisory Board; B. Holmbom, Advisory Board. **ISSN:** 0018-3830. **Subscription Rates:** EUR1,437 institutions libraries, print or online only; EUR1,653 institutions libraries, print + online; EUR268 individuals print + online. **URL:** http://www.degruyter.de/journals/holz/detailEn.cfm. **Ad Rates:** BW: DM 500. **Circ:** 400

44190 ■ Iberoromania
Walter de Gruyter GmbH & Co. KG
Genthiner Strasse 13
D-10785 Berlin, Germany
Ph: 49 302 60050
Fax: 49 302 6005251
Publisher E-mail: info@degruyter.com
Journal providing articles about the Ibero-Romance languages and literature of Europe and America. **Freq:** Semiannual. **Print Method:** Web Offset. **Key Personnel:** Dietrich Briesemeister, Editor; Rolf Eberenz, Editor; Dieter Ingenschay, Editor. **ISSN:** 0019-0993. **Subscription Rates:** EUR95 individuals print + online; EUR83 individuals print or online only; EUR46 single issue. **Remarks:** Accepts advertising. **URL:** http://www.degruyter.de/journals/ibero/detailEn.cfm. **Circ:** (Not Reported)

44191 ■ Innovative Food Science and Emerging Technologies
Elsevier (Singapore) Pte. Ltd.
c/o Dietrich Knorr, Ed.
Dept. of Food Technology & Food Process Engineering
Berlin University of Technology
Konigin-Luise-Str. 22
D-14195 Berlin, Germany
Fax: 49 308 327663
Publisher E-mail: asiabkinfo@elsevier.com
Official scientific journal of the European Federation of Food Science and Technology, examining the latest developments and innovations that are contributing to the improvement of quality, safety and nutritional value of traditional foods. **Freq:** Quarterly. **Key Personnel:** Dietrich Knorr, Editor, dietrich.knorr@tu-berlin.de; Marc Hendrickx, Editor, marc.hendrickx@biw.kuleuven.ac.be; K. Autio, Editorial Board; S. Brul, Editorial Board; M. Cole, Editorial Board; P.J. Fryer, Editorial Board. **ISSN:** 1466-8564. **Subscription Rates:** US$692 institutions for all countries except Europe, Japan and Iran; 82,200¥ institutions; EUR619 institutions European countries and Iran; US$133 individuals for all countries except Europe, Japan and Iran; 15,600¥ individuals; EUR119 individuals European countries and Iran. **URL:** http://www.elsevier.com/wps/find/journaldescription.cws_home/620381/descriptiondescription.

44192 ■ International Journal of Colorectal Disease
Springer-Verlag Tokyo
c/o H.J. Buhr, Ed.-in-Ch.
Chirurgische Klinik I, Campus Benjamin Franklin
Universitatsmedizin Berlin
Hindenburgdamm 30, Charite
D-12200 Berlin, Germany
Publisher E-mail: info@springer.jp
Journal publishing papers and original research articles which deal with the physiology and pathophysiology of diseases involving the entire gastrointestinal tract, also publishing reviews and coverage of controversial issues from rapidly developing areas in gastroenterology and gastrointestinal surgery. **Freq:** Monthly. **Key Personnel:** H.J. Buhr, Editor-in-Chief; H.G. Hotz, Asst. to the Ed.; Z. Cohen, Editor. **ISSN:** 0179-1958. **Subscription Rates:** EUR2,024 institutions print incl. free access or e-only; EUR2,428.80 institutions print incl. enhanced access. **Remarks:** Advertising accepted; rates available upon request. **URL:** http://www.springer.com/medicine/surgery/journal/384. **Circ:** (Not Reported)

44193 ■ International Journal of Innovation in Education
Inderscience Enterprises Limited
c/o Prof. Heike Wiesner, Ed.
Harriet Taylor Mill Institute
Berlin School of Economics
Badensche Str. 50-51
D-10825 Berlin, Germany
Journal focusing on educational innovation. **Freq:** Quarterly. **Key Personnel:** Prof. Heike Wiesner, Editor, wiesner@hwr.berlin.de; Dr. Sabine Zauchner, Editor, sabine.zauchner@donau-uni.ac.at. **ISSN:** 1755-151X. **Subscription Rates:** EUR494 individuals print or online; EUR672 individuals print and online. **URL:** http://www.inderscience.com/browse/index.php?journalCODE=ijiie.

44194 ■ International Journal of Practical Theology
Walter de Gruyter GmbH & Co. KG
Humboldt University to Berlin
Theological Faculty
Unter den Linden 6
D-10099 Berlin, Germany
Publisher E-mail: info@degruyter.com
Journal serving constructive theory of ecclesiastical and religious practice in society. **Freq:** Semiannual. **Key Personnel:** Maureen Junker-Kenny, Editor; Robert Schreiter, Editor; Friedrich Schweitzer, Editor; Christian Grethlein, Editor; Duncan Forrester, Editor; Joon Kwan Un, Editor; Bonnie J. Miller-McLemore, Editor; Richard R. Osmer, Editor; Norbert Mette, Editor; Jaco Dreyer, Editor. **ISSN:** 1430-6921. **Subscription Rates:** EUR125 individuals print or online only; EUR144 individuals print and online; EUR69 single issue. **URL:** http://www.degruyter.de/journals/ijpt/detailEn.cfm.

44195 ■ International Journal of the Sociology of Language
Walter de Gruyter GmbH & Co. KG
Genthiner Strasse 13
D-10785 Berlin, Germany
Ph: 49 302 60050
Fax: 49 302 6005251
Publisher E-mail: info@degruyter.com
Peer-reviewed journal contributing towards study of language use in social behavior. **Freq:** Bimonthly. **Key Personnel:** Florian Coulmas, Editor, coulmas@dijtokyo.org; Joshua A. Fishman, Editor, joshuaafishman@aol.com. **ISSN:** 0165-2516. **Subscription Rates:** EUR409 institutions print or online only; EUR471 institutions print and online; EUR98 individuals; EUR75 single issue. **URL:** http://www.degruyter.de/journals/ijsl/detailEn.cfm.

44196 ■ International Review of Applied Linguistics in Language Teaching
Walter de Gruyter GmbH & Co. KG
Genthiner Strasse 13
D-10785 Berlin, Germany
Ph: 49 302 60050
Fax: 49 302 6005251
Publisher E-mail: info@degruyter.com
Peer-reviewed journal covering all topics on naturalistic and instructed language learning. **Freq:** Quarterly. **Key Personnel:** Leah Roberts, Editor, leah.roberts@mpi.nl; Peter Jordens, Editor; Eric Kellerman, Editor. **ISSN:** 0019-042X. **Subscription Rates:** EUR249 institutions print or online only; EUR287 institutions print and online; EUR69 single issue. **URL:** http://www.degruyter.de/journals/iral/detailEn.cfm.

44197 ■ Internationales Archiv fur Sozialgeschichte der deutschen Literatur
Walter de Gruyter GmbH & Co. KG
Genthiner Strasse 13
D-10785 Berlin, Germany
Ph: 49 302 60050
Fax: 49 302 6005251
Publisher E-mail: info@degruyter.com
Journal focusing on the study of German literature. **Freq:** Semiannual. **Key Personnel:** Norbert Bachleitner, Editor; Christian Begemann, Editor; Walter Erhart, Editor. **ISSN:** 0340-4528. **Subscription Rates:** EUR124 individuals print + online; EUR108 individuals print or online only; EUR59 single issue. **Remarks:** Accepts advertising. **URL:** http://www.degruyter.de/journals/iasl/detailEn.cfm. **Circ:** (Not Reported)

44198 ■ Internationales Jahrbuch des Deutschen Idealismus
Walter de Gruyter GmbH & Co. KG
Genthiner Strasse 13
D-10785 Berlin, Germany
Ph: 49 302 60050
Fax: 49 302 6005251
Publisher E-mail: info@degruyter.com
Journal covering topics in literary theory. **Freq:** Annual. **Print Method:** Offset. **Trim Size:** 155 x 230 mm. **Key Personnel:** Karl P. Ameriks, Editor; Jurgen Stolzenberg, Editor; Fred Rush, Editor. **ISSN:** 1613-0472. **Remarks:** Accepts advertising. **URL:** http://www.degruyter.de/journals/ijbdi/detailEn.cfm. **Ad Rates:** BW: DM 550. **Circ:** ‡350

44199 ■ Jahrbuch fur Wissenschaft und Ethik
Walter de Gruyter GmbH & Co. KG
Genthiner Strasse 13
D-10785 Berlin, Germany
Ph: 49 302 60050
Fax: 49 302 6005251
Publisher E-mail: info@degruyter.com
Journal covering ethical questions arising from modern developments in science and technology. **Founded:** Nov. 11, 1996. **Print Method:** Web offset. **Trim Size:** 15.5 x 23 cm. **Cols./Page:** 8. **Col. Width:** 11 inches. **Col. Depth:** 21 inches. **Key Personnel:** Ludger Honnefelder, Contact; Dieter Sturman, Contact. **ISSN:** 1430-9017. **URL:** http://www.degruytor.do/oont/glob/neutralMbw.cfm?rc=16035.

44200 ■ Journal of African Languages and Linguistics
Walter de Gruyter GmbH & Co. KG
Genthiner Strasse 13
D-10785 Berlin, Germany
Ph: 49 302 60050
Fax: 49 302 6005251
Publisher E-mail: info@degruyter.com
Peer-reviewed journal covering African language studies, synchronic, diachronic and theoretical data oriented. **Founded:** 1979. **Freq:** Semiannual. **Print Method:** Offset. **Trim Size:** 11 1/2 x 16 3/4. **Cols./Page:** 5. **Col. Width:** 22 nonpareils. **Col. Depth:** 210 agate lines. **Key Personnel:** Felix K. Ameka, Editor, f.k.ameka@let.leidenuniv.nl; Azeh Amha, Editor, a.amha@lct.lcidenuniv.nl; Maarten Kossmann, Review Ed. **ISSN:** 0167-6164. **Subscription Rates:** EUR195 institutions print or online only; EUR225 institutions print + online; EUR42 individuals print only. **URL:** http://www.degruyter.de/journals/jall/detailEn.cfm.

44201 ■ Journal of Ancient Christianity
Walter de Gruyter GmbH & Co. KG
Genthiner Strasse 13
D-10785 Berlin, Germany
Ph: 49 302 60050
Fax: 49 302 6005251
Publisher E-mail: info@degruyter.com
Peer-reviewed journal publishing articles on ancient Christianity. **Freq:** Semiannual. **Print Method:** Web offset. **Key Personnel:** Prof. Hanns Christof Brennecke, Editor; Dr. Christoph Markschies, Editor; Prof. Volker Henning Drecoll, Editor. **ISSN:** 0949-9571. **Subscription Rates:** EUR177 individuals print or online only; EUR204 individuals print and online; EUR65 single issue. **Remarks:** Accepts advertising. **URL:** http://www.degruyter.de/journals/zac/detailEn.cfm. **Ad Rates:** BW: DM 200. **Circ:** 400

44202 ■ Journal of Applied Crystallography
International Union of Crystallography
Union Internationale de Cristallographie
c/o A. R. Kaysser-Pyzalla, Ed.
Wissenschaftliche Geschaftsfuhrung
Glienicker Strasse 100
D-14109 Berlin, Germany
Publisher E-mail: execsec@iucr.org
Journal publishing articles on applications of crystallographic techniques and the related apparatus and computer software. **Freq:** Bimonthly. **Key Personnel:** S.E. Ealick, Co-Ed., see3@cornell.edu; P.F. Fewster, Co-Ed., paul.fewster@panalytical.com; G. Kostorz, Co-Ed., gk-iucr@ethz.ch; K.A. Kantardjieff, Co-Ed., kkantardjieff@fullerton.edu; D. Chateigner, Co-Ed., daniel.chateigner@ensicaen.fr; A.J. Allen, Co-Ed., andrew.allen@nist.gov; J.R. Helliwell, Co-Ed., john.helliwell@manchester.ac.uk; E. Dodson, Co-Ed., e.dodson@ysbl.york.ac.uk; S. Ciccariello, Co-Ed., ciccariello@pd.infn.it; W.I.F. David, Co-Ed., bill.david@rl.ac.uk; A. R. Kaysser-Pyzalla, Editor, ahke.pyzalla@helmholtz-berlin.de. **ISSN:** 0021-8898. **Subscription Rates:** US$228 individuals print and online; US$206 individuals online only; US$834 institutions print and online; US$758 institutions online only; EUR204 individuals print and online; 136 other countries print and online; DM 167; 124 other countries online; EUR204 individuals online; 401 institutions online (ROW). **URL:** http://journals.iucr.org/j/journalhomepage.html.

44203 ■ Journal of Applied Geodesy
Walter de Gruyter GmbH & Co. KG
Genthiner Strasse 13
D-10785 Berlin, Germany
Ph: 49 302 60050
Fax: 49 302 6005251
Publisher E-mail: info@degruyter.com
Peer-reviewed journal covering application of geodesy to engineering and other natural sciences. **Freq:** Quarterly. **Print Method:** Offset. **Cols./Page:** 6. **Col. Width:** 24 nonpareils. **Col. Depth:** 301 agate lines. **Key Personnel:** Naser El-Sheimy, Editorial Board; Cheinway Hwang, Editorial Board; Gunther Retscher, Editorial Sec.; Alan Dodson, Editorial Board; Fritz K. Brunner, Editorial Board; Linlin Ge, Editorial Board; Hansjorg Kutterer, Editorial Board; Wolfgang Niemeier, Editorial Board. **ISSN:** 1862-9016. **Subscription Rates:** EUR121 single issue; EUR439 individuals print or online only; EUR505 individuals print + online. **URL:** http://www.degruyter.de/journals/jag/detailEn.cfm.

44204 ■ Journal of Cerebral Blood Flow and Metabolism
Nature Publishing Group
c/o Ulrich Dirnagl, Ed.-in-Ch.
Center for Stroke Research Berlin
Charite University Medicine
Campus Mitte
D-10098 Berlin, Germany
Publisher E-mail: institutions@natureny.com
Journal featuring timely, peer-reviewed contributions highlighting experimental, theoretical, and clinical aspects of brain circulation and metabolism. **Founded:** 1981. **Freq:** Monthly. **Print Method:** Sheetfed Offset. **Trim Size:** 8 1/4 x 11. **Key Personnel:** Jean-Claude Baron, Editorial Board; Roger P. Simon, Editorial Board; Nabil J. Alkayed, Editorial Board; Ulrich Dirnagl, MD, Editor-in-Chief, ulrich.dirnagl@charite.de. **ISSN:** 0271-678X. **Subscription Rates:** US$1,199 institutions online only; US$540 individuals combined print and online; EUR507 individuals combined print and online; 86,100¥ individuals combined print and online; US$490 individuals online only; EUR457 individuals online only; 77,900¥ individuals online only; 294 individuals online only. **Remarks:** Accepts advertising. **URL:** http://www.nature.com/jcbfm/about.html. **Circ:** 1,151

44205 ■ Journal of International Biotechnology Law
De Gruyter Rechtswissenschaften Verlags GmbH
Genthiner Strasse 13
D-10785 Berlin, Germany
Ph: 49 302 60050
Fax: 49 302 6005251
Publisher E-mail: wdg-info@degruyter.de
Journal dealing with the legal implications of the latest developments in the sphere of biotechnology and genetic engineering. **Freq:** Bimonthly. **Key Personnel:** Tade M. Spranger, Editor-in-Chief, tade.spranger@jibl.com; Holger Menk, Managing Editor, holger.menk@jibl.com; Christian Kopetzki, Editorial Board; George J. Annas, Editorial Board; Sven J.R. Bostyn, Editorial Board; Robert P. George, Editorial Board. **ISSN:** 1612-6068.

Subscription Rates: EUR429 individuals print or online; EUR493 individuals print and online. URL: http://www.degruyter.de/journals/jibl/detailEn.cfm.

44206 ■ Journal of Literary Theory
Walter de Gruyter GmbH & Co. KG
Genthiner Strasse 13
D-10785 Berlin, Germany
Ph: 49 302 60050
Fax: 49 302 6005251
Publisher E-mail: info@degruyter.com
Journal covering variety of trends in literary theory. **Freq:** Semiannual. **Print Method:** Offset. **Trim Size:** 8 1/4 x 11. **Cols./Page:** 3. **Col. Width:** 27 nonpareils. **Col. Depth:** 140 agate lines. **Key Personnel:** Gerhard Lauer, Editor; Fotis Jannidis, Editor; Simone Winko, Editor. **ISSN:** 1862-5290. **Subscription Rates:** EUR114 individuals print or online only; EUR132 individuals print and online; EUR63 single issue. **URL:** http://www.degruyter.de/journals/jlt/detailEn.cfm.

44207 ■ Journal of Mathematical Cryptology
Walter de Gruyter GmbH & Co. KG
Genthiner Strasse 13
D-10785 Berlin, Germany
Ph: 49 302 60050
Fax: 49 302 6005251
Publisher E-mail: info@degruyter.com
Journal covering algebra, algebraic geometry, coding theory, combinatorics, number theory, probability and stochastic processes. **Freq:** Quarterly. **Print Method:** Offset. **Key Personnel:** Rainer Steinwandt, Managing Editor; Mike Burmester, Editorial Board; Simon Blackburn, Editorial Board; Ernie Brickell, Editorial Board; Gerhard Frey, Editorial Board; Otokar Grosek, Editorial Board; Spyros Magliveras, Managing Editor; Ed Dawson, Editorial Board; Tran Van Trung, Managing Editor. **ISSN:** 1862-2976. **Subscription Rates:** EUR335 individuals print or online only; EUR385 individuals print + online; EUR92 single issue. **URL:** http://www.degruyter.de/journals/jmc/detailEn.cfm. **Circ:** 170

44208 ■ Journal of Non-Equilibrium Thermodynamics
Walter de Gruyter GmbH & Co. KG
Genthiner Strasse 13
D-10785 Berlin, Germany
Ph: 49 302 60050
Fax: 49 302 6005251
Publisher E-mail: info@degruyter.com
Journal integrating science, engineering and related natural systems through exchanging information on non-equilibrium phenomena in science and explaining fuzzy models of non-equilibrium phenomena. **Freq:** Quarterly. **Trim Size:** 17 x 24 cm. **Key Personnel:** E.E. Michaelides, Editor; J.U. Keller, Editor-in-Chief; W. Muschik, Editor; B. Ahlborn, Honorary Board; B. Andresen, Editorial Advisory Board; Bejan A. Durham, Editorial Advisory Board. **ISSN:** 0340-0204. **Subscription Rates:** EUR1,037 individuals print + online only; EUR902 individuals print and online; EUR248 single issue. **URL:** http://www.degruyter.de/journals/jnet/detailEn.cfm. **Ad Rates:** BW: DM 250. **Circ:** 200

44209 ■ Journal of Perinatal Medicine
Walter de Gruyter GmbH & Co. KG
Genthiner Strasse 13
D-10785 Berlin, Germany
Ph: 49 302 60050
Fax: 49 302 6005251
Publisher E-mail: info@degruyter.com
Journal covering research in perinatal medicine. **Freq:** Bimonthly. **Trim Size:** 21 x 28 cm. **Key Personnel:** B.K. Young, Editorial Board; F.C. Battaglia, Editorial Board; Joachim W. Dudenhausen, Editor-in-Chief; E.Z. Saling, Founding Ed. **ISSN:** 0300-5577. **Subscription Rates:** EUR587 institutions print or online only; EUR675 institutions print + online; EUR273 individuals print + online. **URL:** http://www.degruyter.de/journals/jpm/detailEn.cfm.

44210 ■ Journal of Vascular Research
European Society for Microcirculation
Dept. of Physiology
Freie Universitat Berlin
Arnimallee 22
D-14195 Berlin, Germany
Ph: 49 308 4451632
Fax: 49 308 4451634
Publisher E-mail: esmmail@charite.de
Journal covering vascular research. **Freq:** Bimonthly. **Key Personnel:** U. Pohl, Editor; G.A. Meininger, Editor. **ISSN:** 1018-1172. **Subscription Rates:** US$1,693 institutions print only; US$1,863 institutions print and

online; EUR1,342 institutions. **URL:** http://content.karger.com/ProdukteDB/produkte.asp?Aktion=JournalHome&ProduktNr=224160.

44211 ■ Kant-Studien
Walter de Gruyter GmbH & Co. KG
Genthiner Strasse 13
D-10785 Berlin, Germany
Ph: 49 302 60050
Fax: 49 302 6005251
Publisher E-mail: info@degruyter.com
Journal covering documentation section, containing current state of research. **Freq:** Quarterly. **Key Personnel:** Dr. Thomas M. Seebohm, Editor; Dr. Manfred Baum, Editor; Dr. Bernd Dorflinger, Editor. **ISSN:** 0022-8877. **Subscription Rates:** EUR170 individuals print or online only; EUR196 institutions print + online; EUR47 single issue. **URL:** http://www.degruyter.de/journals/ks/detailEn.cfm. **Circ:** 1000

44212 ■ Kritikon Litterarum
Walter de Gruyter GmbH & Co. KG
Genthiner Strasse 13
D-10785 Berlin, Germany
Ph: 49 302 60050
Fax: 49 302 6005251
Publisher E-mail: info@degruyter.com
Journal covering international literary and cultural studies. **Freq:** Semiannual. **Print Method:** Web Offset. **Key Personnel:** Alain Niderst, Editor; Gerhard Giesemann, Editor; Manfred Putz, Editor. **ISSN:** 0340-9767. **Subscription Rates:** EUR216 individuals print and online; EUR188 individuals print or online only; EUR103 single issue. **URL:** http://www.degruyter.de/journals/kritikon/detailEn.cfm. **Circ:** 150

44213 ■ LaboratoriumsMedizin
Walter de Gruyter GmbH & Co. KG
Genthiner Strasse 13
D-10785 Berlin, Germany
Ph: 49 302 60050
Fax: 49 302 6005251
Publisher E-mail: info@degruyter.com
Peer-reviewed journal covering reports on the developments of various disciplines of laboratory medicine. **Founded:** 1958. **Freq:** Bimonthly. **Print Method:** Web offset. **Trim Size:** 11 1/4 x 17 1/4. **Cols./Page:** 6. **Col. Width:** 1 5/8 inches. **Col. Depth:** 16 inches. **Key Personnel:** Dr. F. Deisenhammer, Editor; Dr. C.T. Nebe, Editor; Dr. P. Luppa, Editor; Dr. H. Renz, Editor; Dr. Henri Wallaschofski, Editor; Dr. K.P. Kohse, Editor; Dr. G. Rothe, Editor; Dr. R. Junker, Editor; Dr. M. Klouche, Editor. **ISSN:** 0342-3026. **Subscription Rates:** EUR385 individuals print or online only; EUR443 individuals print and online; EUR71 single issue. **URL:** http://www.degruyter.de/journals/labmed/detailEn.cfm.

44214 ■ Landschaftsarchitekten
Bund Deutscher Landschaftsarchitekten
Bundesgeschaeftstelle
Koepenicker St. 48/49
D-10179 Berlin, Germany
Ph: 49 302 787150
Fax: 49 302 7871555
Publisher E-mail: info@bdla.de
German language publication covering architecture. **Founded:** 1991. **Freq:** Quarterly. **ISSN:** 0949-2305. **URL:** http://www.bdla.de. **Ad Rates:** GLR: EUR40, BW: EUR2, 4C: EUR8. **Circ:** 2,500

44215 ■ Language and Cognition
Walter de Gruyter GmbH & Co. KG
Genthiner Strasse 13
D-10785 Berlin, Germany
Ph: 49 302 60050
Fax: 49 302 6005251
Publisher E-mail: info@degruyter.com
Peer-reviewed journal featuring the interaction between language and cognition. **Subtitle:** An Interdisciplinary Journal of Language and Cognitive Science. **Freq:** Semiannual. **Print Method:** Web Offset. **Key Personnel:** Daniel Casasanto, Editor; Seana Coulson, Editor; Vyvyan Evans, Editor. **ISSN:** 1866-9808. **Subscription Rates:** EUR205 individuals print + online; EUR178 individuals print or online only; EUR98 single issue. **URL:** http://www.degruyter.de/journals/langcog/detailEn.cfm. **Circ:** 700

44216 ■ Laser & Photonics Reviews
Wiley-VCH Verlag GmbH
Rotherstr. 21
D-10245 Berlin, Germany
Ph: 49 30 47031321
Fax: 49 30 47031399

Publication E-mail: laser@wiley-vch.de
Publisher E-mail: info@wiley-vch.de
Journal covering research on laser physics and photonics. **Freq:** Bimonthly. **Key Personnel:** Guido W. Fuchs, PhD, Editor-in-Chief; Regina Hagen, Proj. Ed.; Sonja Hoffman, Contact. **ISSN:** 1863-8880. **Subscription Rates:** US$2,520 institutions print only; US$2,772 institutions print & e-access; EUR1,803 institutions print only; EUR1,984 institutions print & e-access. **URL:** http://www.wiley-vch.de/publish/en/journals/newJournals/2414/?sID=0365b90e5912fab435f9c1771c711215.

44217 ■ Laser Technik Journal
John Wiley & Sons Inc.
c/o Francisco Velasco, Ed.
Rotherstrasse 21
D-10245 Berlin, Germany
Publisher E-mail: info@wiley.com
Journal covering the study of laser techniques. **Freq:** 6/yr. **Key Personnel:** Francisco Velasco, Editor; Dr. Andreas Thoss, Publisher, laserjournal@wiley-vch.de. **ISSN:** 1613-7728. **Remarks:** Accepts advertising. **URL:** http://www3.interscience.wiley.com/journal/114099272/home. **Circ:** (Not Reported)

44218 ■ Lebende Sprachen
Walter de Gruyter GmbH & Co. KG
Genthiner Strasse 13
D-10785 Berlin, Germany
Ph: 49 302 60050
Fax: 49 302 6005251
Publisher E-mail: info@degruyter.com
Journal focusing on languages and culture. **Freq:** Quarterly. **Key Personnel:** Eter A. Schmitt, Editor; Reinhold Werner, Editor. **ISSN:** 0023-9909. **Subscription Rates:** EUR90 individuals print + online; EUR78 individuals print or online only; EUR21 single issue. **URL:** http://www.degruyter.de/journals/les/detailEn.cfm.

44219 ■ Libri
Walter de Gruyter GmbH & Co. KG
Genthiner Strasse 13
D-10785 Berlin, Germany
Ph: 49 302 60050
Fax: 49 302 6005251
Publisher E-mail: info@degruyter.com
Journal highlighting the functions of libraries and information services. **Freq:** Quarterly. **Print Method:** Web Offset. **Key Personnel:** Nancy R. John, Editor, nrj@uic.edu; Ian M. Johnson, i.m.johnson@rgu.ac.uk; Svend Larsen, Editor, sl@statsbiblioteket.dk. **ISSN:** 0024-2667. **Subscription Rates:** EUR272 individuals print or online; EUR313 individuals print + online; EUR75 single issue. **Remarks:** Accepts advertising. **URL:** http://www.degruyter.de/journals/libri/detailEn.cfm. **Ad Rates:** BW: DM 550, 4C: DM 1,000. **Circ:** 2,900

44220 ■ Mammalia
Walter de Gruyter GmbH & Co. KG
Genthiner Strasse 13
D-10785 Berlin, Germany
Ph: 49 302 60050
Fax: 49 302 6005251
Publisher E-mail: info@degruyter.com
Peer-reviewed Journal focusing on the inventory, analysis and interpretation of mammalian diversity. **Freq:** Quarterly. **Key Personnel:** Christiane Denys, Editor-in-Chief; Stephane Aulagnier, Assoc. Ed.; Francois Catzeflis, Assoc. Ed. **ISSN:** 0025-1461. **Subscription Rates:** EUR86 individuals print and online; EUR252 institutions print and online; EUR219 institutions print or online only. **URL:** http://www.degruyter.de/journals/mammalia/detailEn.cfm.

44221 ■ Microform & Imaging Review
Walter de Gruyter GmbH & Co. KG
Genthiner Strasse 13
D-10785 Berlin, Germany
Ph: 49 302 60050
Fax: 49 302 6005251
Publisher E-mail: info@degruyter.com
Journal providing reports on projects and technical developments in document conservation in libraries and archives. **Freq:** Quarterly. **Print Method:** Web Offset. **Key Personnel:** Ken Middleton, Editor-in-Chief; Barbara Fischer, Managing Editor. **ISSN:** 0949-5770. **Subscription Rates:** EUR277 individuals print + online; EUR240 individuals print or online only; EUR66 single issue. **Remarks:** Accepts advertising. **URL:** http://www.degruyter.de/journals/mir/detailEn.cfm?sel=pi. **Ad Rates:** BW: DM 550, 4C: DM 1,000. **Circ:** 2000

44222 ■ Microsystem Technologies
Springer-Verlag

c/o B. Michel, Ed.-in-Ch.
Head of MicroMaterials Center Berlin
Fraunhofer IZM
Volmerstrasse 9 B
D-12489 Berlin, Germany
Peer-reviewed journal covering the electromechanical, materials science, design, and manufacturing issues of Micro- and Nanosystems Information Storage and Processing Systems and their components. **Freq:** 12/yr. **Key Personnel:** B. Bhushan, Editor-in-Chief; B. Michel, Editor-in-Chief; W.A. Challener, Editorial Board; G.G. Adams, Editorial Board; R.A. De Callafon, Editorial Board; T. Gessner, Editorial Board. **ISSN:** 0946-7076. **Subscription Rates:** EUR1,907 institutions; EUR2,288.40 institutions enhanced access. **URL:** http://www.springer.com/engineering/electronics/journal/542.

44223 ■ Naharaim
Walter de Gruyter GmbH & Co. KG
Genthiner Strasse 13
D-10785 Berlin, Germany
Ph: 49 302 60050
Fax: 49 302 6005251
Publisher E-mail: info@degruyter.com
Peer-reviewed journal covering topics in literary theory. **Freq:** Semiannual. **Key Personnel:** Ashraf Noor, Editor; Aleida Assmann, Editor; Gabriel Motzkin, Editor. **ISSN:** 1862-9148. **Subscription Rates:** EUR103 individuals print or online only; EUR118 individuals print and online; EUR57 single issue. **URL:** http://www.degruyter.de/journals/naharaim/detailEn.cfm.

44224 ■ Neue Zeitschrift fur Systematische Theologie und Religionsphilosophie
Walter de Gruyter GmbH & Co. KG
Genthiner Strasse 13
D-10785 Berlin, Germany
Ph: 49 302 60050
Fax: 49 302 6005251
Publisher E-mail: info@degruyter.com
Journal focusing on breadth of responsible thought in the controversial issue of contemporary theology. **Freq:** Quarterly. **Print Method:** Offset. **Trim Size:** 7 3/8 x 9 1/4. **Cols./Page:** 3. **Col. Width:** 12 picas. **Col. Depth:** 46.5 picas. **Key Personnel:** Dr. Luco J. Van Den Brom, Editor, l.j.van.den.brom@theol.rug.nl; Dr. Svend Andersen, Editor, andersen@teologi.aau.dk; Dr. Walter Sparn, Editor, wrsparn@theologie.uni-erlangen.de; Dr. Oswald Bayer, Editor, oswald.bayer@uni-tuebingen.de; Christoph Schwobel, Editor, phone 49 7071 2972066, fax 49 7071 295029, christoph.schwoebel@uni-tuebingen.de. **ISSN:** 0028-3517. **Subscription Rates:** EUR177 individuals print or online only; EUR204 institutions print + online; EUR60 students; EUR49 single issue. **URL:** http://www.degruyter.de/journals/nzsth/detailEn.cfm. **Circ:** 250

44225 ■ Neuroforum
German Neuroscience Society
c/o Meino Alexandra Gibson, Sec.
Max Delbruck Center for Moleculare Medizin
Robert Roessle Str. 10
D-13122 Berlin, Germany
Ph: 49 30 94063133
Fax: 49 30 94063819
Publisher E-mail: gibson@mdc-berlin.de
Journal containing review articles, book reviews, historical and methodological articles, information on grants programs, prizes and more. **Freq:** Quarterly. **Key Personnel:** Wolfgang H. Oertel, Editorial Board; Herbert Zimmermann, Editorial Board; Niels Birbaumer, Editorial Board; Dr. Helmut Kettenmann, Editor-in-Chief. **ISSN:** 0947-0875. **Subscription Rates:** Free for members. **Remarks:** Accepts advertising. **URL:** http://nwg.glia.mdc-berlin.de. **Circ:** (Not Reported)

44226 ■ PIK
Walter de Gruyter GmbH & Co. KG
Genthiner Strasse 13
D-10785 Berlin, Germany
Ph: 49 302 60050
Fax: 49 302 6005251
Publisher E-mail: info@degruyter.com
Journal featuring super computers, parallel computers and high-output-workstations. **Freq:** Quarterly. **Print Method:** Web Offset. **Key Personnel:** Otto Spaniol, Editor. **ISSN:** 0930-5157. **Subscription Rates:** EUR277 individuals print + online; EUR240 individuals print or online only; EUR66 single issue. **Remarks:** Accepts advertising. **URL:** http://www.degruyter.de/journals/pik/detailEn.cfm. **Ad Rates:** BW: DM 550, 4C: DM 1,000. **Circ:** ‡3,200

44227 ■ Praehistorische Zeitschrift
Walter de Gruyter GmbH & Co. KG
Genthiner Strasse 13
D-10785 Berlin, Germany
Ph: 49 302 60050
Fax: 49 302 6005251
Publisher E-mail: info@degruyter.com
Journal focusing on the field of prehistoric archaeology. **Founded:** 1926. **Freq:** Semiannual. **Print Method:** Web Offset. **Key Personnel:** Francois Bertemes, Editor; Wolfram Schier, Editor; Karl-Heinz Willroth, Editor. **ISSN:** 0079-4848. **Subscription Rates:** EUR216 individuals print + online; EUR188 individuals print or online only; EUR103 single issue. **Remarks:** Accepts advertising. **URL:** http://www.degruyter.de/journals/pz/detailEn.cfm. **Ad Rates:** BW: DM 550. **Circ:** 500

44228 ■ Report Psychologie
Deutscher Psychologen Verlag GmbH
Am Kollnischen Park 2
D-10179 Berlin, Germany
Ph: 49 30 209166410
Fax: 49 30 209166413
Publisher E-mail: verlag@psychologenverlag.de
Professional journal covering psychology. **Founded:** 1974. **Freq:** 10/yr. **Print Method:** Offset. **Cols./Page:** 4. **Col. Width:** 47 millimeters. **Col. Depth:** 259 millimeters. **ISSN:** 0344-9602. **Subscription Rates:** EUR54 individuals; EUR72 other countries Ausland; EUR37.80 single issue student/unemployed. **URL:** http://www.psychologenverlag.de/product_info.php/info/p166_Report-Psychologie-10-2010.html. **Ad Rates:** BW: EUR1,300. **Circ:** 13,000

44229 ■ Romanistisches Jahrbuch
Walter de Gruyter GmbH & Co. KG
Genthiner Strasse 13
D-10785 Berlin, Germany
Ph: 49 302 60050
Fax: 49 302 6005251
Publisher E-mail: info@degruyter.com
Journal providing information on romance languages, literature and art history at German and Austrian universities. **Freq:** Annual. **Print Method:** Web Offset. **Trim Size:** 118 x 182 mm. **Key Personnel:** Andreas Kablitz, Editor; Bernhard Konig, Editor; Margot Kruse, Editor. **ISSN:** 0080-3898. **Remarks:** Accepts advertising. **URL:** http://www.degruyter.de/journals/romjb/detailEn.cfm. **Ad Rates:** BW: DM 550. **Circ:** 300

44230 ■ Semiotica
Walter de Gruyter GmbH & Co. KG
Genthiner Strasse 13
D-10785 Berlin, Germany
Ph: 49 302 60050
Fax: 49 302 6005251
Publisher E-mail: info@degruyter.com
Peer-reviewed journal focusing on semiotic studies, reviews of selected literature in this field, and occasional guest editorials and reports. **Freq:** Quarterly. **Print Method:** Offset. **Trim Size:** 8 1/2 x 11. **Cols./Page:** 3. **Key Personnel:** Marcel Danesi, Editor-in-Chief, marcel.danesi@utoronto.ca; Paul Perron, Assoc. Ed., p.perron@utoronto.ca. **ISSN:** 0037-1998. **Subscription Rates:** EUR699 individuals print or online only; EUR799 individuals print and online; EUR154 single issue. **Remarks:** Accepts advertising. **URL:** http://www.degruyter.de/journals/semiotica/detailEn.cfm. **Circ:** (Not Reported)

44231 ■ Text & Talk
Walter de Gruyter GmbH & Co. KG
Genthiner Strasse 13
D-10785 Berlin, Germany
Ph: 49 302 60050
Fax: 49 302 6005251
Publisher E-mail: info@degruyter.com
Peer-reviewed journal focusing on methodology. **Founded:** 1981. **Freq:** Bimonthly. **Print Method:** Offset. **Trim Size:** 14.8 X 22.5 cm. **Cols./Page:** 3. **Col. Width:** 26 nonpareils. **Col. Depth:** 96 agate lines. **Key Personnel:** Prof. Srikant Sarangi, Editor, textandtalk@cardiff.ac.uk. **ISSN:** 1860-7330. **Subscription Rates:** EUR414 institutions print or online only; EUR477 institutions print + online; EUR78 individuals print only; US$105 members print only; EUR78 members print only. **Remarks:** Accepts advertising. **URL:** http://www.degruyter.de/journals/text/detailEn.cfm. **Circ:** (Not Reported)

44232 ■ Theoretical Linguistics
Walter de Gruyter GmbH & Co. KG
Genthiner Strasse 13
Institut fur deutsche Sprache und Linguistik
Humboldt-University Berlin

Unter den Linden 6
D-10099 Berlin, Germany
Publisher E-mail: info@degruyter.com
Peer-reviewed journal covering articles on general linguistic interest, reactions, comments and reflections on it. **Freq:** 3/yr. **Print Method:** Offset. **Cols./Page:** 6. **Col. Width:** 26 nonpareils. **Col. Depth:** 301 agate lines. **Key Personnel:** Thomas Becker, Assoc. Ed.; Edit Doron, Assoc. Ed.; Wolfgang Sternefeld, Assoc. Ed.; Hans Uszkoreit, Assoc. Ed.; Katalin E. Kiss, Assoc. Ed.; Stephen M. Wechsler, Assoc. Ed.; Martin Haspelmath, Assoc. Ed.; Bart Geurts, Assoc. Ed.; Scott Myers, Assoc. Ed. **ISSN:** 0301-4428. **Subscription Rates:** EUR177 individuals print or online only; EUR204 individuals print and online; EUR65 single issue. **URL:** http://www.degruyter.de/journals/theolin/detailEn.cfm.

44233 ■ Trends in Classics
Walter de Gruyter GmbH & Co. KG
Genthiner Strasse 13
D-10785 Berlin, Germany
Ph: 49 302 60050
Fax: 49 302 6005251
Publisher E-mail: info@degruyter.com
Journal focusing on the study of Greek and Latin texts. **Freq:** Semiannual. **Key Personnel:** Franco Montanari, Editor; Antonios Rengakos, Editor. **ISSN:** 1866-7473. **Subscription Rates:** EUR147 institutions print and online; EUR128 institutions print or online only; EUR70 single issue. **Remarks:** Accepts advertising. **URL:** http://www.degruyter.de/journals/tic/detailEn.cfm. **Ad Rates:** BW: DM 200. **Circ:** 250

44234 ■ VBI-Nachrichten
Association of Consulting Engineers of Germany
Verband Beratender Ingenieure
Budapester Strasse 31
D-10787 Berlin, Germany
Ph: 49 30 260620
Fax: 49 30 26062100
Publication E-mail: versand@vbi.de
Publisher E-mail: vbi@vbi.de
German language publication covering engineering. **Freq:** Monthly. **Key Personnel:** Volker Zappe, Editor, phone 49 30 26062240, zappe@vbi.de. **URL:** http://www.vbi.de/service/vbi-nachrichten.html.

44235 ■ VdK Zeitung
Sozialverband VdK Deutschland
In den Mistergarten 4
D-10117 Berlin, Germany
Ph: 49 30 726290400
Fax: 49 30 726290499
Publication E-mail: presse@vdk.de
Publisher E-mail: presse@vdk.de
German language publication covering the disabled. **Freq:** Monthly. **Print Method:** Newspaper. **Trim Size:** 280 x 428 mm. **Remarks:** Accepts advertising. **URL:** http://www.vdk.de. **Circ:** Paid 1,121,210

44236 ■ Verhandlungen der Gesellschaft fur Okologie
Ecological Society of Germany, Austria and Switzerland
Gesellschaft fur Okologie
c/o TU Berlin, Institute of Ecology
Rothenburgstrasse 12
D-12165 Berlin, Germany
Ph: 49 30 31471396
Fax: 49 30 31471355
Publisher E-mail: info@gfoe.org
Online German language publication covering ecology. **Founded:** 1971. **Freq:** Annual. **Remarks:** Advertising accepted; rates available upon request. **URL:** http://www.gfoe.org/en/gfoe-publications.html. **Circ:** (Not Reported)

44237 ■ ZAAC - Zeitschrift fur anorganische und allgemeine Chemie
John Wiley & Sons Inc.
c/o Dr. Christian Limberg, Ed.
Humboldt University
Brook-Taylor-Strasse 2
D-12489 Berlin, Germany
Ph: 49 30 20937382
Fax: 49 30 20936966
Publisher E-mail: info@wiley.com
International scientific journal publishing original papers on new research results from all areas of inorganic chemistry, solid state chemistry, and co-ordination chemistry. **Freq:** 15/yr. **Key Personnel:** Dr. Martin Jan-

Circulation: ★ = ABC; △ = BPA; ♦ = CAC; • = CCAB; ❑ = VAC; ⊕ = PO Statement; ‡ = Publisher's Report; Boldface figures = sworn; Light figures = estimated.

Gale Directory of Publications & Broadcast Media/147th Ed.   **4927**

sen, Editor, phone 49 1168 91500, fax 49 1168 91502, zaac@fkf.mpg.de; Dr. Thomas M. Klapotke, Editor, zaac@cup.uni-muenchen.de; Dr. Christian Limberg, Editor, christian.limberg@chemie.hu-berlin.de. **ISSN:** 0044-2313. **Subscription Rates:** US$3,451 institutions for USA and Canada print and online; EUR1,761 institutions print and online; 2,770 institutions print and online; US$4,210 institutions rest of the world; 4,210 SFr institutions print and online; US$833 individuals print only for USA and Canada; EUR833 individuals; 601 individuals; 857 SFr individuals. **URL:** http://www3.interscience. wiley.com/cgi-bin/jhome/10005159.

44238 ■ Zeitschrift des Deutschen Vereins fur Kunstwissenschaft
Society for the Study of German Art
Geschaftsstelle Berlin
Jebensstrasse 2
D-10623 Berlin, Germany
Ph: 49 3 3139932
Fax: 49 3 75632108
Publisher E-mail: dvfk@aol.com
Journal containing papers on German art. **Freq:** Semiannual. **ISSN:** 0044-2135. **URL:** http://dvfk-berlin. de/.

44239 ■ Zeitschrift fur Orient-Archaologie
Walter de Gruyter GmbH & Co. KG
Genthiner Strasse 13
D-10785 Berlin, Germany
Ph: 49 302 60050
Fax: 49 302 6005251
Publisher E-mail: info@degruyter.com
Journal covering the study in the field of archeology in Levant, Mesopotamia and the Arabian Peninsular. **Founded:** 2008. **Freq:** Annual. **Key Personnel:** Ricardo Eichmann, Editor; Margarete van Ess, Editor. **ISSN:** 1868-9078. **URL:** http://www.degruyter.de/cont/fb/at/ atMbwEn.cfm?rc=36959.

44240 ■ Zeitschrift fur romanische Philologie
Walter de Gruyter GmbH & Co. KG
Genthiner Strasse 13
D-10785 Berlin, Germany
Ph: 49 302 60050
Fax: 49 302 6005251
Publisher E-mail: info@degruyter.com
Journal covering Romance literature up to the Renaissance. **Founded:** 1877. **Freq:** Quarterly. **Print Method:** Web Offset. **Key Personnel:** Gunther Holtus, Editor. **ISSN:** 0049-8661. **Subscription Rates:** EUR263 individuals print + online; EUR229 individuals print or online only; EUR63 single issue. **Remarks:** Accepts advertising. **URL:** http://www.degruyter.de/journals/zrp/ detailEn.cfm. **Ad Rates:** BW: DM 550. **Circ:** 520

44241 ■ Zeitschrift fur Rezensionen zur germanistischen Sprachwissenschaft
Walter de Gruyter GmbH & Co. KG
Genthiner Strasse 13
D-10785 Berlin, Germany
Ph: 49 302 60050
Fax: 49 302 6005251
Publisher E-mail: info@degruyter.com
Journal focusing on the German linguistic studies. **Freq:** Semiannual. **Print Method:** Web Offset. **Key Personnel:** Christa Durscheid, Editor; Michael Elmentaler, Editor; Alexander Lasch, Editor. **ISSN:** 1867-1691. **Subscription Rates:** EUR113 individuals print + online; EUR98 individuals print or online only; EUR54 single issue. **Remarks:** Accepts advertising. **URL:** http://www. degruyter.de/journals/zrs/detailEn.cfm. **Circ:** 200

44242 ■ Berliner Rundfunk-FM - 91.4
Grunewaldstrasse 3
D-12165 Berlin, Germany
Ph: 49 30 20191400
Fax: 49 30 20191200
E-mail: info@berliner-rundfunk.de
Format: Ethnic; World Beat. **Operating Hours:** Continuous. **Key Personnel:** Detlef Noormann, Mng. Dir./Prog. Dir., detlef.noormann@berliner-rundfunk.de. **URL:** http://www.berliner-rundfunk.de.

44243 ■ InfoRadioBerl.-Brand.-FM - 93.1
Masurenallee 8-14
D-14057 Berlin, Germany
Ph: 49 30 979930
Fax: 49 30 9799319
E-mail: info@inforadio.de
Format: Ethnic; World Beat. **URL:** http://www.inforadio. de.

Biebergemund

44244 ■ Entomologia Generalis
Gebruder Borntraeger Verlagsbuchhandlung
c/o Dr. August Wilhelm Steffan, Ed.-in-Ch.
Am Bergborn 1
D-63599 Biebergemund, Germany
Ph: 49 6050 912910
Publisher E-mail: mail@schweizerbart.de
Journal covering all fields of research on insects and other terrestrial arthropods. **Subtitle:** Journal of General and Applied Entomology. **Freq:** Quarterly. **Key Personnel:** Dr. August Wilhelm Steffan, Editor-in-Chief, wilhelm. steffan@t-online.de. **ISSN:** 0171-8177. **URL:** http://www. borntraeger-cramer.de/j/entomologia-generalis/.

Bielefeld

44245 ■ Documenta Mathematica
Universitat Bielefeld
Fakultat fur Mathematik
Postfach 100131
D-33501 Bielefeld, Germany
Ph: 49 521 10600
Fax: 49 521 1065844
Publisher E-mail: post@uni-bielefeld.de
Scientific journal covering general mathematics. **Founded:** 1996. **Freq:** Monthly. **Print Method:** Offset. **Trim Size:** 8 1/4 x 11. **Cols./Page:** 2. **Col. Width:** 46 nonpareils. **Col. Depth:** 126 agate lines. **Key Personnel:** Alfred K. Loius, Managing Editor, louis@num.uni-sb.de; Ulf Rehmann, Managing Editor, rehmann@math. uni-bielefeld.de; Peter Schneider, Managing Editor, pschnei@math.uni-muenster.de. **ISSN:** 1431-0635. **URL:** http://www.math.uiuc.edu/documenta/.

44246 ■ HIDEAWAYS
Klocke Publishing Company
Hoefeweg 40
D-33619 Bielefeld, Germany
Ph: 49 5 2191111
Fax: 49 5 2191112
Publisher E-mail: info@klocke-publishing-company.com
Travel magazine. **Subtitle:** Luxury travel for premium consumer. **Founded:** 1996. **Print Method:** Sheetfed offset. **Trim Size:** 210 x 297 mm. **Key Personnel:** Thomas Klocke, Editor; Wolfgang Pohl, Advertising Mgr. **Subscription Rates:** EUR30 individuals. **Remarks:** Accepts advertising. **URL:** http://www.hideaways.de/heft-13/e-index.htm; http://www.klocke-verlag.de/welcome/ go_media.php?lang=en&p=e_media_hideaways_rates. **Circ:** 60,000

44247 ■ Sun & Wind Energy
BVA Bielefelder Verlag GmbH & Co. KG
Niederwall 53
D-33602 Bielefeld, Germany
Ph: 49 521 595514
Fax: 49 521 595518
Publisher E-mail: kontakt@bva-bielefeld.de
Magazine featuring information on renewable energy. **Freq:** Monthly. **Key Personnel:** Dr. Bernhard von Schubert, Publisher; Dr. Volker Buddensiek, Editor; Ralf Ossenbrink, Editor. **Remarks:** Accepts advertising. **URL:** http://www.sunwindenergy.com/swe/. **Circ:** (Not Reported)

44248 ■ YACHTING & STYLE
Klocke Publishing Company
Hoefeweg 40
D-33619 Bielefeld, Germany
Ph: 49 5 2191111
Fax: 49 5 2191112
Publisher E-mail: info@klocke-publishing-company.com
Lifestyle magazine featuring concentrating on luxurious motor and sailing yachts. **Subtitle:** Maritime Flair at its Most Stylish. **Freq:** 3/yr. **Print Method:** Sheetfed offset. **Trim Size:** 210 x 297 mm. **Key Personnel:** Bernd Teichgraber, Editor. **Subscription Rates:** EUR24 individuals. **Remarks:** Accepts advertising. **URL:** http:// www.yachting-and-style.de/index.php. **Ad Rates:** BW: DM 5,800, 4C: DM 8,500. **Circ:** 60,000

44249 ■ Hertz-FM - 87.9
Universitatsstrasse 25
D-33615 Bielefeld, Germany
Ph: 49 521 9114511
Fax: 49 521 9114545
E-mail: info@radiohertz.de
Format: Ethnic; World Beat; Public Radio. **Operating Hours:** Continuous. **Ad Rates:** Noncommercial. **URL:** http://www.radiohertz.de.

Bochum

44250 ■ International Journal of Hygiene and Environmental Health
Elsevier Science Inc.
c/o Michael Wilhelm, Ed.-in-Ch.
Universitatsstrasse 150
D-44801 Bochum, Germany
Publisher E-mail: usinfo-ehelp@elsevier.com
Peer-reviewd journal covering the research in the areas of hygiene, toxicology, environmental and occupational health. **Founded:** 1883. **Freq:** 6/yr. **Key Personnel:** Undine A. Nash, Editor, thofern@gmx.net; Konrad Botzenhart, Editorial Board; Silvio De Flora, Editorial Board; Daniel L. Costa, Editorial Board; Marianne Borneff Lipp, Editorial Board; Michael Wilhelm, Editor-in-Chief, wilhelm@hygiene.rub.de; Jurgen Angerer, Editor, angerer@asumed.med.uni-erlangen.de; Stefano Bonassi, Editorial Board; Hermann M. Bolt, Editorial Board; William W. Au, PhD, Editor, william.au@utmb.edu. **ISSN:** 1438-4639. **Subscription Rates:** EUR701 institutions for European countries and Iran; 95,500¥ institutions; US$767 institutions, other countries except Europe, Japan and Iran; EUR688 institutions for Germany, Austria and Switzerland; EUR297 individuals for European countries and Iran; 38,900¥ individuals; US$291 individuals except Europe, Japan and Iran; EUR223 students for European countries and Iran; 29,200¥ students; EUR218 students for European countries and Iran. **URL:** http://www.elsevier.com/wps/find/ journaldescription.cws_home/701771/ descriptiondescription.

44251 ■ Regulatory Peptides
Elsevier Science Inc.
Dept. of Medicine I
Ruhr-University Bochum
St. Josef Hospital
Gudrunstr 56
44797 Bochum, Germany
Ph: 49 234 5092311
Fax: 49 234 5092309
Publisher E-mail: usinfo-ehelp@elsevier.com
Journal provides interdisciplinary studies on the physiology and pathology of peptides of the gut, endocrine and nervous systems which regulate cell or tissue function. **Founded:** 1981. **Freq:** 21/yr. **Print Method:** Offset. **Trim Size:** 5 1/2 x 8 1/2. **Cols./Page:** 1. **Col. Width:** 50 nonpareils. **Col. Depth:** 100 agate lines. **Key Personnel:** J. Meier, Assoc. Ed.; W.E. Schmidt, Editor-in-Chief, wolfgang.e.schmidt@ruhr-uni-bochum.de; T. Chiba, Editorial Board; J. Fahrenkrug, Editorial Board; G.H. Greeley, Editorial Board; W.G. Forssmann, Editorial Board; D. Podolsky, Editorial Board; G.J. Dockray, Editorial Board. **ISSN:** 0167-0115. **Subscription Rates:** EUR3,566 institutions for European countries and Iran; US$3,988 institutions, other countries except Europe, Japan and Iran; 473,100¥ institutions; EUR167 individuals for European countries and Iran; US$225 other countries except Europe, Japan and Iran; 25,900¥ individuals. **URL:** http://www.elsevier.com/wps/find/ journaldescription.cws_home/506031/ descriptiondescription.

44252 ■ Respiratory Physiology & Neurobiology
Elsevier Science Inc.
c/o P. Scheid, Ed.
Institut fur Physiologie
Ruhr-Universitat Bochum
Universitatsstrasse 150
D-44780 Bochum, Germany
Ph: 49 234 3229100
Fax: 49 234 3214191
Publisher E-mail: usinfo-ehelp@elsevier.com
Journal devoted to the field of respiration. **Founded:** 1966. **Freq:** 15/yr. **Print Method:** Offset. **Cols./Page:** 6. **Col. Width:** 2 1/16 inches. **Col. Depth:** 21 1/2 inches. **Key Personnel:** A. Jones, Editorial Board; L. Kubin, Editorial Board; P. Kumar, Editorial Board; J.C. Leiter, Editorial Board; T.E. Dick, Editorial Board; J.P. Mortola, Editorial Board; P. Scheid, Editor, editor@rpnb.org. **ISSN:** 1569-9048. **Subscription Rates:** EUR141 individuals for European countries and Iran; US$158 other countries except Europe, Japan and Iran; 18,600¥ individuals; US$2,951 institutions, other countries except Europe, Japan and Iran; 350,400¥ institutions; EUR2,639 institutions for European countries and Iran. **URL:** http:// www.elsevier.com/wps/find/journaldescription.cws_ home/622727/descriptiondescription.

Bonn

44253 ■ **Behorden Spiegel**
ProPress Publishing Group Ltd.
Am Buschhof 8
D-53227 Bonn, Germany
Newspaper covering information technology, telecommunications, and other technical features for public administrators. There is a national edition as well as regional editions for Berlin and Bonn. **Subtitle:** Independent Journal of Civil Service. **Founded:** Apr. 1985. **Freq:** Monthly. **Print Method:** Offset. **Trim Size:** 285 x 430 mm. **ISSN:** 1437-8337. **Subscription Rates:** EUR1 single issue. **Remarks:** Accepts advertising. **URL:** http://www.behoerdenspiegel.de. **Ad Rates:** BW: EUR7,353, 4C: EUR10,137. **Circ:** 104,000

44254 ■ **Die Bundeswehr**
Deutscher Bundeswehr-Verband e.V.
Sudstrasse 123
D-53175 Bonn, Germany
Ph: 49 228 38230
Fax: 49 228 3823220
Publisher E-mail: service@dbwv.de
Member magazine of the German Federal Armed Forces Association. **Founded:** Dec. 1956. **Freq:** Monthly. **Cols./ Page:** 4. **Key Personnel:** Yann Bombeke, Contact; Frank Henning, Contact. **ISSN:** 0007-5949. **Remarks:** Accepts advertising. **URL:** http://www.dbwv.de/dbwv/interd.nsf/d/starta. **Circ:** (Not Reported)

44255 ■ **Ecology and Farming**
International Federation of Organic Agriculture Movements
Charles-de-Gaulle-St. 5
D-53113 Bonn, Germany
Ph: 49 228 9265010
Fax: 49 228 9265099
Publisher E-mail: headoffice@ifoam.org
Publication covering organic farming. **Founded:** 1976. **Freq:** 3/yr. **ISSN:** 1016-5061. **Subscription Rates:** EUR25 two years e-Magazine. **Remarks:** Advertising accepted; rates available upon request. **URL:** http://www.ifoam.org/. **Circ:** 2,000

44256 ■ **Europa Cantat Magazine**
Europa Cantat - European Federation of Young Choirs
Europaische Foderation Junger Choro
c/o Haus del Kultur
Weberstr. 59a
D-53113 Bonn, Germany
Ph: 49 228 9125663
Fax: 49 228 9125658
Publisher E-mail: info@europacantat.org
European magazine covering music in English, French and German. **Founded:** 1993. **Freq:** Quarterly. **Key Personnel:** Nuria Tura, Editor; Kjetil Aaman, Editorial Board; Sonja Greiner, Editorial Board; Montserrat Gual, Editorial Board; Jean Smeets, Editorial Board; Jeroen Schrijner, Editorial Board. **ISSN:** 1022-0755. **Remarks:** Advertising accepted; rates available upon request. **URL:** http://www.europacantat.org/publications-press/ec-magazine/. **Circ:** (Not Reported)

44257 ■ **European Journal of Development Research**
European Association of Development Research and Training Institutes
Association Europeenne des Instituts Recherche et de Formation en
Matiere de Development
Kaiser-Friedrich-Strasse 11
53113 Bonn, Germany
Ph: 49 228 2618101
Fax: 49 228 2618103
Publisher E-mail: postmaster@eadi.org
European journal covering development research. **Freq:** 4/yr. **Key Personnel:** Rajneesh Narula, Editor-in-Chief. **ISSN:** 0957-8811. **Subscription Rates:** EUR65 members print only; EUR250 institutions print only. **Remarks:** Advertising not accepted. **URL:** http://www.eadi.org/index.php?id=293. **Circ:** (Not Reported)

44258 ■ **European Review of Agricultural Economics**
Oxford University Press
c/o Thomas Heckelei, Ed.
Department for Food & Resource Economics
University of Bonn
Nussallee 21
D-53115 Bonn, Germany

Ph: 49 228 732332
Fax: 49 228 734693
Publisher E-mail: webenquiry.uk@oup.com
Journal covering research in the field of agricultural economics in the European community. **Freq:** 4/yr. **Key Personnel:** Christoph Weiss, Editor, cweiss@wu.ac.at; Thomas Heckelei, Editor, thomas.heckelei@ilr.uni-bonn. de; Paolo Sckokai, Editor, phone 39 523 599290, fax 39 523 599282, paolo.sckokai@unicatt.it. **ISSN:** 0165-1587. **Subscription Rates:** 383 institutions corporate; print and online; 319 institutions corporate; online only; 351 institutions corporate; print only; 306 institutions print and online; 255 institutions online only; 281 institutions print only; 64 individuals print; 48 members print. **URL:** http://erae.oxfordjournals.org/.

44259 ■ **Fairkehr**
Fairkehr Verlags GmbH
Niebuhrstr. 16b
D-53113 Bonn, Germany
Ph: 49 228 9858545
Publisher E-mail: editorial@fairkehr.de
Member magazine covering tourism. **Freq:** Bimonthly. **Key Personnel:** Michael Adler, Contact. **Subscription Rates:** EUR23 individuals. **Remarks:** Accepts advertising. **URL:** http://www.fairkehr.de/magframeset. html. **Circ:** ‡65,000

44260 ■ **Flug Revue**
Motor-Presse Verlag GmbH & Company KG
Ubierstrasse 83
53173 Bonn, Germany
Ph: 49 228 9565100
Publication E-mail: redaktion@flugrevue.de
Publisher E-mail: redaktion@flugrevue.de
Professional magazine covering aviation issues, including military aircraft, technology, space, airlines, airports and economy. **Founded:** 1956. **Freq:** Monthly. **Print Method:** Offset. **Trim Size:** 8 3/8 x 10 15/16. **Cols./ Page:** 4. **Col. Width:** 1 11/16 inches. **Key Personnel:** Dr. Friedrich Wehrle, Contact. **ISSN:** 0015-4547. **Remarks:** Accepts advertising. **URL:** http://www.flugrevue. de/en/home.6651.htm. **Circ:** Combined 50,000

44261 ■ **Frau und Politik**
Frauen-Union der Christian Demokratischen Union Deutschlands
Konrad-Adenauer-Haus
Friedrich-Ebert-Alle 73-75
D-53113 Bonn, Germany
Ph: 49 228 544315
Fax: 49 228 544586
Publication E-mail: info@frauundpolitik.ch
German language publication covering women and politics. **Freq:** Bimonthly. **URL:** http://www.frauundpolitik. ch/.

44262 ■ **german research**
John Wiley & Sons Inc.
Deutsche Forschungsgemeinschaft
Press & Public Relations Division
Kennedyallee 40
D-53175 Bonn, Germany
Ph: 49 2 288851
Fax: 49 2 288852180
Publisher E-mail: info@wiley.com
Journal covering arts, humanities, and many fields of natural science. **Freq:** 3/yr. **Key Personnel:** Dr. Rembert Unterstell, Publishing Exec. Ed.; Marco Finetti, Editor-in-Chief. **ISSN:** 0172-1526. **Subscription Rates:** EUR64 individuals print only, rest of Europe; 133 Eg individuals print only, Switzerland and Liechtenstein; US$69 other countries print only; EUR71 individuals combined print with online access; 146 Eg individuals combined print with online access; US$76 other countries combined print with online access. **URL:** http://onlinelibrary.wiley.com/journal/10.1002/(ISSN)1522-2322.

44263 ■ **Informatik Spektrum**
German Informatics Society
Gesellschaft fur Informatik
Ahrstrasse 45
D-53175 Bonn, Germany
Ph: 49 228 302145
Fax: 49 228 302167
Publisher E-mail: gs@gi-ev.de
German language publication covering computer science. **Founded:** 1977. **Freq:** Bimonthly. **Key Personnel:** Prof. G. Dueck, Contact, dueck@de.ibm.com; Hermann Engesser, Contact; Prof. H.C. Mayr, Contact,

heinrich@ifit.uni-klu.ac.at; Prof. Arndt Bode, Contact; K. Dittrich, Contact, dittrich@ifi.unizh.ch; Prof. P. Dadam, Contact, dadam@informatik.uni-ulm.de; Prof. F. Mattern, Contact, mattern@inf.ethz.ch; Prof. W. Brauer, Contact, brauer@informatik.tu-muenchen.de. **ISSN:** 0170-6012. **Subscription Rates:** 534 institutions. **Remarks:** Advertising accepted; rates available upon request. **URL:** http://www.springerlink.com. **Circ:** 24,000

44264 ■ **Journal of Population Economics**
Springer-Verlag
c/o Zahra Siddique
Schaumburg-Lippe-Str. 5-9
D-53113 Bonn, Germany
Journal dealing with topics, focusing on the relationship between economic and demographic problems. **Freq:** 4/yr. **Key Personnel:** Klaus F. Zimmermann, Editor-in-Chief, zimmermann@iza.org; Deborah Cobb-Clark, Editor, fax 61 2 61250187, dcclark@coombs.anu.edu.au; Daniel S. Hamermesh, Assoc. Ed.; Christian Dustmann, Editor, fax 44 20 79162775, c.dustmann@ucl.ac.uk; Alessandro Cigno, Editor, fax 39 55 472102, cigno@ unifi.it; Heather Antecol, Assoc. Ed. **ISSN:** 0933-1433. **Subscription Rates:** EUR960 institutions print incl. free access; EUR1,081.20 institutions print incl. enhanced access. **Remarks:** Advertising accepted; rates available upon request. **URL:** http://www.springer.com/economics/population/journal/148. **Circ:** (Not Reported)

44265 ■ **Kultur Politik**
Bundesverband Bildender Kuenstlerinnen und Kuenstler
Weberstr. 61
Anzeigenabteilung
D-53113 Bonn, Germany
Ph: 49 228 216107
Fax: 49 228 96699690
Publisher E-mail: bbkbundesverband@aol.com
German language publication covering artists. **Freq:** Quarterly. **ISSN:** 0941-4657. **Remarks:** Accepts advertising. **URL:** http://www.bbk-bundesverband.de/. **Circ:** (Not Reported)

44266 ■ **MILITARY TECHNOLOGY**
Monch Publishing Group
Heilsbachstrasse 26
W-53123 Bonn, Germany
Ph: 49 228 64830
Fax: 49 228 6483109
Publisher E-mail: info@moench-group.com
Magazine covering aspects of modern military defense technology, requirements, procurements and programs. **Founded:** 1977. **Freq:** Monthly. **Trim Size:** 210 x 285 mm. **Key Personnel:** Dr. Dennis-Peter Merklinghaus, Editor-in-Chief, phone 49 228 6483118, fax 49 228 6483109, dennis.merklinghaus@moench-group.com; Stephen Barnard, Publisher, phone 49 228 6483136, fax 49 228 6483109, stephen.barnard@moench-group. com; Stephen Elliott, Managing Editor, phone 49 228 6483120, fax 49 228 6483109, stephen.elliott@moench-group.com. **ISSN:** 0722-3226. **Subscription Rates:** EUR130 individuals; EUR13.50 single issue; US$190 individuals; US$20 single issue. **Remarks:** Accepts advertising. **URL:** http://www.moench-group.com/military-technology.php. **Circ:** 25,000

44267 ■ **Nato's Nations and Partners for Peace**
Monch Publishing Group
Heilsbachstrasse 26
W-53123 Bonn, Germany
Ph: 49 228 64830
Fax: 49 228 6483109
Publisher E-mail: info@moench-group.com
Journal featuring information about the military operations and administration around the world. **Founded:** 1955. **Freq:** Quarterly. **Trim Size:** 210 x 285 mm. **Key Personnel:** Manfred Sadlowski, Editor and Publisher, phone 49 228 64830, fax 49 228 6483109, manfred. sadlowski@moench-group.com; Harald Kujat, Chm.; Dennis-Peter Merklinghaus, Managing Editor, phone 49 228 6483118, fax 49 228 6483109, dennis. merklinghaus@moench-group.com. **Subscription Rates:** EUR75 individuals; EUR25 single issue; US$110 individuals; US$39 single issue. **Remarks:** Accepts advertising. **URL:** http://www.moench-group.com/natos-nations.php. **Circ:** 22,000

44268 ■ **Naval Forces**
Monch Publishing Group
Heilsbachstrasse 26
W-53123 Bonn, Germany

Circulation: ★ = ABC; △ = BPA; ♦ = CAC; • = CCAB; ❑ = VAC; ⊕ = PO Statement; ‡ = Publisher's Report; Boldface figures = sworn; Light figures = estimated.

Ph: 49 228 64830

Fax: 49 228 6483109

Publisher E-mail: info@moench-group.com

Journal featuring modern defense at sea. **Subtitle:** International Forum for Maritime Power. **Founded:** 1980. **Freq:** Bimonthly. **Trim Size:** 210 x 285 mm. **Key Personnel:** Wolfgang Legien, Editor-in-Chief, phone 49 228 6483113, fax 49 228 6483109, legien@moench-group.com; Jan Wiedemann, Publisher, phone 49 228 6483128, fax 49 228 6483109, wiedemann@moench-group.com; Hartmut Manseck, Mktg. Mgr., phone 49 228 6483139, fax 49 228 6483109, manseck@moench-group.com. **Subscription Rates:** EUR85 individuals; EUR15 single issue; US$125 individuals; US$22.50 single issue. **Remarks:** Accepts advertising. **URL:** http://www.moench-group.com/naval-forces.php. **Circ:** 16,000

44269 ■ Plant Signaling & Behavior
Landes Bioscience
Institute of Cellular & Molecular Botany
University of Bonn
Bonn, Germany
Publisher E-mail: info@landesbioscience.com
Journal covering topics on molecules and organelles, tissues and organs, signal perception and transduction and signaling complexes (signalosomes). **Key Personnel:** Thomas Paul Jahn, Assoc. Ed., tpj@kvl.dk; Axel Mithoefer, Editorial Board, amithoefer@ice.mpg.de; Frantisek Baluska, Editor-in-Chief, unb15e@uni-bonn.de; Gwyneth Ingram, Assoc. Ed., gwyneth.ingram@ed.ac.uk; Jean Vidal, Editor, vidal@ibp.u-psud.fr; Pierre Abad, Editorial Board, abad@antibes.inra.fr; Stefano Mancuso, Editor-in-Chief, stefano.mancuso@unifi.it; Harald Keller, Editorial Board, keller@antibes.inra.fr; Dieter Volkmann, Editor-in-Chief, unb110@uni-bonn.de; Tony Trewavas, Editor-in-Chief, trewavas@ed.ac.uk. **ISSN:** 1559-2316. **Subscription Rates:** US$200 U.S. and Canada web and print; US$369 other countries web and print; US$1,900 institutions Usa and Canada, web and print; US$2,020 institutions, other countries web and print. **URL:** http://www.landesbioscience.com/journals/psb/.

44270 ■ Safety & Security International
Monch Publishing Group
Heilsbachstrasse 26
W-53123 Bonn, Germany
Ph: 49 228 64830
Fax: 49 228 6483109
Publisher E-mail: info@moench-group.com
Magazine designed for safety and security sector. **Key Personnel:** David Braun Lacerda, Editor, phone 49 228 6483117, fax 49 157 73747147, david.braun-lacerda@gmx.de; Christian Lauterer, Co-Publisher, fax 49 228 6483109, c.lauterer@moench-group.com. **Remarks:** Accepts advertising. **URL:** http://www.moench-group.com/safety-and-security.php. **Circ:** (Not Reported)

44271 ■ TECNOLOGIA MILITAR
Monch Publishing Group
Heilsbachstrasse 26
W-53123 Bonn, Germany
Ph: 49 228 64830
Fax: 49 228 6483109
Publisher E-mail: info@moench-group.com
Journal featuring information on economic, political and operational status of defense and security industry in Latin America and the Iberian Peninsula. **Founded:** 1978. **Freq:** Quarterly. **Key Personnel:** Franz Thiele, Editor-in-Chief, phone 49 228 64830, fax 49 228 6483109, franz.thiele@moench-group.com; Christian Lautererl, Co-Pub., phone 49 228 6483117, fax 49 228 6483109, c.lauterer@moench-group.com. **Subscription Rates:** US$35 individuals; EUR25 individuals; EUR10 single issue. **Remarks:** Accepts advertising. **URL:** http://www.moench-group.com/tecnologia-militar.php. **Circ:** 10,000

44272 ■ WEHRTECHNIK
Monch Publishing Group
Heilsbachstrasse 26
W-53123 Bonn, Germany
Ph: 49 228 64830
Fax: 49 228 6483109
Publisher E-mail: info@moench-group.com
Magazine featuring the latest information on military defense equipment. **Founded:** 1968. **Freq:** Quarterly. **Key Personnel:** Volker Schwichtenberg, Publisher, phone 49 228 6483116, fax 49 228 6483109, volker.schwichtenberg@moench-group.com; Christian Laut-

erer, Co-Publisher, phone 49 228 6483117, fax 49 228 6483109, christian.lauterer@moench-group.com; Rudolf K. Schiwon, Editor, phone 49 228 64830, fax 49 228 6483109, rolf.schiwon@moench-group.com. **ISSN:** 0722-8880. **Subscription Rates:** EUR12.50 single issue. **Remarks:** Accepts advertising. **URL:** http://www.moench-group.com/wehrtechnik.php. **Circ:** 12,000

44273 ■ Zeitschrift fur die Neutestamentliche Wissenschaft
Walter de Gruyter GmbH & Co. KG
Evangelisch-Theologisches Seminar der Universitat Bonn
Am Hof 1
D-53113 Bonn, Germany
Publisher E-mail: info@degruyter.com
Journal covering the exegesis of the new testament and knowledge of the early church. **Founded:** Mar. 1954. **Freq:** Semiannual. **Print Method:** Offset. **Trim Size:** 6 x 9. **Cols./Page:** 1. **Col. Width:** 66 nonpareils. **Col. Depth:** 119 agate lines. **Key Personnel:** Dr. Michael Wolter, Editor. **ISSN:** 0044-2615. **Subscription Rates:** EUR146 individuals print or online only; EUR168 individuals print + online; EUR80 students print only. **URL:** http://www.degruyter.de/journals/znw/detailEn.cfm. **Circ:** 1,050

Braunschweig

44274 ■ CLEAN
Wiley-VCH Verlag GmbH
c/o Prof. Dr. Mufit Bahadir, Ed.-in-Ch.
Braunschweig University of Technology
Institute of Ecological Chemistry & Waste Analysis
Hagenring 30
D-38106 Braunschweig, Germany
Publication E-mail: clean@wiley-vch.de
Publisher E-mail: info@wiley-vch.de
Peer-reviewed Journal covering all aspects of sustainability and environmental safety. **Subtitle:** Soil, Air, Water. **Freq:** Monthly. **Key Personnel:** Prof. Mufit Bahadir, Editor-in-Chief; Nicola Senesi, Editor; Robert Kreugzig, Editor. **ISSN:** 1863-0650. **Subscription Rates:** EUR972 institutions print only; EUR1,070 institutions print & e-access; EUR972 institutions e-access; US$1,198 institutions print only; US$1,318 institutions print & e-access; US$1,198 institutions e-access. **Remarks:** Accepts advertising. **URL:** http://www.wiley-vch.de/publish/en/journals/newJournals/2047/?sID=d64c3865af8b0a90bfb40b69ce27b257. **Circ:** (Not Reported)

44275 ■ Deutsche Baumschule
Haymarket Media GmbH & Co. KG
Frankfurter Str., 3d (ARTmax)
D-38122 Braunschweig, Germany
Ph: 49 531 380040
Fax: 49 531 3800425
Publisher E-mail: info@haymarket.de
Magazine for Germany's nursery owners and plant suppliers. **Founded:** 1949. **Freq:** Monthly. **Key Personnel:** Sabine Muller, Contact, red.dt.baumschule@haymarket.de. **URL:** http://www.haymarket.com/deutsche_baumschule/deutsche_baumschule_ger_magazine/default.aspx; http://www.deutschebaumschule.de/.

44276 ■ Friedhofs Kultur
Haymarket Media GmbH & Co. KG
Frankfurter Str., 3d (ARTmax)
D-38122 Braunschweig, Germany
Ph: 49 531 380040
Fax: 49 531 3800425
Publisher E-mail: info@haymarket.de
Magazine featuring information regarding funeral gardening, weeding techniques, machinery or cemetery administration. **Key Personnel:** Evelin Scheibe, Editor, phone 49 531 3800413, fax 49 531 3800440, red.friedhofskultur@haymarket.de. **URL:** http://www.haymarket.com/friedhofskultur/friedhofskultur_ger_magazine/default.aspx; http://www.friedhofskultur.de/.

44277 ■ Gestalten & Verkaufen
Haymarket Media GmbH & Co. KG
Frankfurter Str., 3d (ARTmax)
D-38122 Braunschweig, Germany
Ph: 49 531 380040
Fax: 49 531 3800425
Publisher E-mail: info@haymarket.de
Magazine for florists and garden retailers. **Freq:** Monthly. **Key Personnel:** Christine Meyn, Editor-in-Chief, phone 49 30 2789430, fax 49 30 27894313, christine.meyn@

haymarket.de. **URL:** http://www.haymarket.com/gestalten_and_verkaufen/gandv__gestalten_and_verkaufen_ger_magazine/default.aspx; http://www.gundv.de/.

44278 ■ Molecular Informatics
Wiley-VCH Verlag GmbH
c/o Dr. Knut Baumann, Ed.
Technical University Braunschweig
Institute of Pharmaceutical Chemistry
Beethovenstr. 55
D-38106 Braunschweig, Germany
Ph: 49 531 3912751
Fax: 49 531 3912799
Publisher E-mail: info@wiley-vch.de
Peer-reviewed journal covering molecular modelling, computer graphics and other computer-assisted methods in the design and development of biologically active compounds as applied to medicinal, agricultural and environmental chemistry. **Freq:** Monthly. **Key Personnel:** Dr. Knut Baumann, Editor, k.baumann@tu-braunschweig.de; Dr. Gisbert Schneider, Editor, phone 41 44 6337327, gisbert.schneider@chemie.uni-frankfurt.de; Prof. Gerhard Ecker, Editor, phone 43 42 7755110, fax 43 42 779551, gerhard.f.ecker@univie.ac.at. **ISSN:** 1868-1743. **Subscription Rates:** EUR1,696 institutions print; 1,100 institutions print, rest of world; 2,583 SFr institutions; US$2,155 institutions print. **URL:** http://www3.interscience.wiley.com/journal/104557877/home. **Formerly:** QSAR & Combinatorial Science.

44279 ■ TASPO
Haymarket Media GmbH & Co. KG
Frankfurter Str., 3d (ARTmax)
D-38122 Braunschweig, Germany
Ph: 49 531 380040
Fax: 49 531 3800425
Publisher E-mail: info@haymarket.de
Newspaper focusing on horticulture business. **Key Personnel:** Iris Anger, Editor-in-Chief, phone 49 531 3800411, fax 49 531 3800440, iris.anger@haymarket.de. **URL:** http://www.haymarket.com/taspo/taspo_ger_magazine/default.aspx; http://www.taspo.de/.

Bremen

44280 ■ Archive of Applied Mechanics
Springer-Verlag Tokyo
c/o Reinhold Kienzler, Ed.-in-Ch.
Universitat Bremen, IW3
PO Box 330440
D-28334 Bremen, Germany
Publisher E-mail: info@springer.jp
Journal disseminating the results of scientific research in the fields of solid mechanics, fluid mechanics, structural mechanics, dynamics and control, including related disciplines, in a form useful to engineering practice. **Freq:** Monthly. **Key Personnel:** Reinhold Kienzler, Editor-in-Chief, aam_eic@mechanik.uni-bremen.de; W. Becker, Editorial Board; D. Marghitu, Editorial Board; N. Aksel, Editorial Board; D. Gross, Editorial Board; Frank Jablonski, Managing Editor, aam@mechanik.uni-bremen.de; L. Gaul, Editorial Board. **ISSN:** 0939-1533. **Subscription Rates:** EUR2,300 institutions print incl. free access or e-only; EUR2,760 institutions print incl. enhanced access. **Remarks:** Advertising accepted; rates available upon request. **URL:** http://www.springer.com/new%26forthcomingtitles%28default%29/journal/419. **Circ:** (Not Reported)

44281 ■ Modell Fan
Carl Ed. Schuenemann KG
Zweite Schlachtpforte 7
D-28195 Bremen, Germany
Ph: 49 421 369030
Fax: 49 421 3690339
Publisher E-mail: kontakt@schuenemann-verlag.de
Consumer magazine covering models for hobbyists. **Founded:** 1974. **Freq:** Monthly. **ISSN:** 1341-5104. **Subscription Rates:** EUR15 individuals. **Remarks:** Accepts advertising. **URL:** http://www.schuenemann-verlag.de/kontakt.php; http://www.modell-fan.de. **Ad Rates:** GLR: EUR1.26, BW: EUR1,355, 4C: EUR2,135. **Circ:** 12,152

44282 ■ Umwelt-Medizin-Gesellschaft
UMG Verlag GmbH
Frielenger Str. 31
D-28215 Bremen, Germany
Ph: 49 421 3649714
Fax: 49 421 4984252
Publisher E-mail: info@umg-verlag.de
German language publication covering physicians.

Founded: 1988. Freq: Quarterly. ISSN: 1437-2606. Subscription Rates: EUR33. Remarks: Advertising accepted; rates available upon request. URL: http://www.umwelt-medizin-gesellschaft.de. Circ: 4,000

44283 ■ Bremen Eins-FM - 87.85
Diepenau 10
D-28195 Bremen, Germany
Ph: 49 421 24642112
Fax: 49 421 24642198
E-mail: bremeneins@radiobremen.de
Format: Sports; Ethnic. Operating Hours: 20 hours Daily. URL: http://www.radiobremen.de/bremeneins.

44284 ■ Bremen Eins-FM - 92.75
Diepenau 10
D-28195 Bremen, Germany
Ph: 49 421 24642112
Fax: 49 421 24642198
E-mail: bremeneins@radiobremen.de
Format: Sports; Ethnic. Operating Hours: 20 hours Daily. URL: http://www.radiobremen.de/bremeneins.

44285 ■ Bremen Eins-FM - 93.8
Diepenau 10
D-28195 Bremen, Germany
Ph: 49 421 24642112
Fax: 49 421 24642198
E-mail: bremeneins@radiobremen.de
Format: Sports; Ethnic. URL: http://www.radiobremen.de/bremeneins.

44286 ■ Bremen Eins-FM - 89.3
Diepenau 10
D-28195 Bremen, Germany
Ph: 49 421 24642112
Fax: 49 421 24642198
E-mail: bremeneins@radiobremen.de
Format: Sports; Ethnic. Operating Hours: 20 hours Daily. URL: http://www.radiobremen.de/bremeneins.

44287 ■ Energy Bremen-FM - 89.8
Erste Schlachtpforte 1
D-28195 Bremen, Germany
Ph: 49 180 5022600
Fax: 49 421 3356677
E-mail: radio@energy-bremen.de
Format: Contemporary Hit Radio (CHR). Operating Hours: Continuous. Ad Rates: Advertising accepted; rates available upon request. URL: http://www.energy.de/bremen/index.html.

Buxtehude

44288 ■ Reise & Preise
Hauptstr. 14
D-21614 Buxtehude, Germany
Ph: 49 416 171690
Fax: 49 416 1716915
Publication E-mail: redaktion@reise-preise.de
Publisher E-mail: verlag@reise-preise.de
Consumer magazine covering travel and tourism worldwide. Subtitle: Flightplanners Magazin. Founded: 1987. Freq: Quarterly. Print Method: Content: Rotary offset- cover; sheet offset. Trim Size: 210 x 297 mm. Key Personnel: Oliver Kuhn, Contact. ISSN: 0932-4186. Subscription Rates: EUR17 individuals; EUR22 other countries; EUR35 by mail air mail. Remarks: Accepts advertising. URL: http://www.reise-preise.de. Circ: Combined 125,000

Cologne

44289 ■ Brains, Minds and Media
Di PP - NRW
Julicher Strasse 6
D-50674 Cologne, Germany
Ph: 49 221 400750
Fax: 49 221 40075180
Publication E-mail: editors@brains-minds-media.org
Publisher E-mail: dipp@hbz-nrw.de
Journal publishing brief papers and supplementary materials (optional) on media in neural and cognitive science. Key Personnel: Martin Egelhaaf, Editor-in-Chief; Robert Cannon, Editorial Board Member; Johannes Zanker, Editorial Board Member; Stephen Grossberg, Editorial Board Member; Ralf Hofacker, Editorial Staff; Jeff Yoshimi, Editorial Board Member; Soren Lorenz, Editorial Coord. ISSN: 1861-1680. URL: http://www.brains-minds-media.org.

44290 ■ Ceramic Forum International
German Ceramic Society
Deutsche Keramische Gesellschaft
Am Grott 7
D-51147 Cologne, Germany
Ph: 49 220 396648
Fax: 49 220 369301
Publisher E-mail: blum@dkg.de
Publication covering worldwide ceramics in English and German. Freq: Monthly. Key Personnel: Karin Scharrer, Editorial Contact, phone 49 7221 502241, fax 49 7221 502222, scharrer@cfi.de. ISSN: 0173-9913. Subscription Rates: EUR126.50 individuals + shipment fees; EUR17 single issue; EUR132.70 other countries + shipment fees. Remarks: Advertising accepted; rates available upon request. URL: http://www.cfi.de. Circ: (Not Reported)

44291 ■ Christliche Frau
Union of German Catholic Women
Katholischer Deutscher Frauenbund
Kaesenstrasse 18
D-50677 Cologne, Germany
Ph: 49 2 21860920
Fax: 49 2 218609279
Publisher E-mail: bundesverband@frauenbund.de
German language publication covering women and Catholicism. Freq: 11/yr. Remarks: Accepts advertising. URL: http://www.frauenbund.de/. Circ: (Not Reported)

44292 ■ Drug Testing and Analysis
John Wiley & Sons Inc.
c/o Prof. Mario Thevis, Ed.-in-Ch.
German Sport University Cologne
Institute of Biochemistry
Am Sportpark Mungersdorf 6
50933 Cologne, Germany
Publisher E-mail: info@wiley.com
Journal exploring the analytical techniques used to determine controlled and potentially controversial compounds. Founded: Jan. 2009. Freq: Monthly. Key Personnel: Prof. Mario Thevis, Editor-in-Chief, m.thevis@biochem.dshs-koeln.de; Dr. Tiia Kuuranne, Assoc. Ed., tiia.kuuranne@yhtyneetlaboratoriot.fi; Dr. Ray Kazlauskas, Assoc. Ed., ray.kazlauskas@measurement.gov.au. ISSN: 1942-7603. Remarks: Accepts advertising. URL: http://onlinelibrary.wiley.com/journal/10.1002/(ISSN)1942-7611. Circ: (Not Reported)

44293 ■ E-Learning and Education
Di PP - NRW
Julicher Strasse 6
D-50674 Cologne, Germany
Ph: 49 221 400750
Fax: 49 221 40075180
Publication E-mail: eleed@campussource.de
Publisher E-mail: dipp@hbz-nrw.de
Journal offering a platform for new scientific research results from the widespread area of all e-Learning aspects. Key Personnel: Bernd Kramer, Editor-in-Chief; Martin Roos, Book Review Ed.; Manfred Postel, Proj. Report Ed.; Jens Krinke, Editor-in-Chief; Michael Klebl, Editorial Board; Rob Koper, Editorial Board. ISSN: 1860-7470. URL: http://eleed.campussource.de.

44294 ■ Frankfurter Afrikanistische Blatter
Rudiger Koppe Verlag
Wendelinstrasse 73-75
D-50933 Cologne, Germany
Ph: 49 221 4911236
Fax: 49 221 4994336
Publisher E-mail: info@koeppe.de
Journal focusing on tone system in African languages. Freq: Annual. Key Personnel: Rose-Juliet Anyanwu, Editor. ISSN: 0937-3039. URL: http://www.koeppe.de/katalog/katalog_reihe.php?lan=en&Sigle=SZ275.

44295 ■ German Risk and Insurance Review
Di PP - NRW
Universitat zu Koln
Seminar fur ABWL, Risikomanagement und Versicherungsleh
Kerpener St. 30
D-50937 Cologne, Germany
Ph: 49 221 4702439
Publisher E-mail: dipp@hbz-nrw.de
Electronic journal for risk management and insurance, also covering related subjects such as social insurance, actuarial science, risk theory and insurance law. Key Personnel: Frau Andrea Koranda, Contact. ISSN: 1860-

5400. URL: http://www.risk-insurance.de/index_html?set_language=en&cl=en.

44296 ■ Journal of Virtual Reality and Broadcasting
Di PP - NRW
Julicher Strasse 6
D-50674 Cologne, Germany
Ph: 49 221 400750
Fax: 49 221 40075180
Publisher E-mail: dipp@hbz-nrw.de
Online journal covering topics related to the fields of virtual reality, interface techniques, computer graphics and interactive broadcasting. Key Personnel: Jens Herder, Editor-in-Chief; Michael Uwe Mobius, Publishing Supvr. ISSN: 1860-2037. URL: http://www.jvrb.org.

44297 ■ Kadmos
Walter de Gruyter GmbH & Co. KG
University Koln
Institut far Altertumskunde
Albertus-Magnus-Platz
D-50931 Cologne, Germany
Publisher E-mail: info@degruyter.com
Journal publishing papers and communications relating to pre-Greek and early Greek epigraphy. Founded: 1973. Freq: Semiannual. Print Method: Web offset. Trim Size: 11 x 14. Cols./Page: 3. Col. Width: 26 nonpareils. Col. Depth: 140 agate lines. Key Personnel: Dr. W. Blumel, Editor, wolfgang.bluemel@uni-koeln.de. ISSN: 0022-7498. Subscription Rates: EUR159 individuals print or online only; EUR183 individuals print and online. URL: http://www.degruyter.de/journals/kadmos/detailEn.cfm. Circ: 330

44298 ■ Language@internet
Di PP - NRW
Julicher Strasse 6
D-50674 Cologne, Germany
Ph: 49 221 400750
Fax: 49 221 40075180
Publisher E-mail: dipp@hbz-nrw.de
Online journal focusing research on the pivotal role of language under the new medial conditions of use and interacting with the various societal domains, with the center of interest being linguistic concerns, including sociolinguistic, discourse analytic, and pragmatic perspectives, and including the conditions, functions and constraints of the societal domains like law, economy or medicine. Key Personnel: Dieter Stein, Founding Ed.; Jannis Androutsopoulos, Editorial Board; Naomi Baron, Editorial Board; David Crystal, Editorial Board; Susan C. Herring, Editor-in-Chief. ISSN: 1860-2029. URL: http://www.dipp.nrw.de/journals/languageatinternet; http://www.languageatinternet.de.

44299 ■ Law in Africa
Rudiger Koppe Verlag
Wendelinstrasse 73-75
D-50933 Cologne, Germany
Ph: 49 221 4911236
Fax: 49 221 4994336
Publisher E-mail: info@koeppe.de
Journal of the African Law Association. Freq: Semiannual. Key Personnel: O.V.C. Okene, Contact. ISSN: 1435-0963. URL: http://www.koeppe.de/katalog_reihe.php?lan=en&Sigle=RA996.

44300 ■ Protist
Elsevier Science Inc.
c/o Michael Melkonian, Ed.-in-Ch.
Universitat zu Koln
Botanisches Institut
Cologne, Germany
Ph: 49 2214702475
Fax: 49 2214705181
Publisher E-mail: usinfo-ehelp@elsevier.com
Journal covering molecular, cell and developmental biology, biochemistry, systematics and phylogeny, and ecology of protists. Freq: 4/yr. Print Method: Offset. Trim Size: 12 1/2 x 22 1/2. Cols./Page: 6. Col. Depth: 21 inches. Key Personnel: B.S.C. Leadbeater, Editorial Board; Sandra L. Baldauf, Editorial Board; K. Gull, Editorial Board; G.C. Clark, Editorial Board; S. Purton, Editorial Board; B.J. Finlay, Editorial Board; J.O. Corliss, Editorial Board; Michael Melkonian, Editor-in-Chief, michael.melkonian@uni-koeln.de; Linda Sperling, Editorial Board; E. Meyer, Editorial Board. ISSN: 1434-4610. Subscription Rates: US$311 students, other countries except Europe, Japan and Iran; EUR920 institutions

Circulation: ★ = ABC; △ = BPA; ◆ = CAC; • = CCAB; ❑ = VAC; ⊕ = PO Statement; ‡ = Publisher's Report; Boldface figures = sworn; Light figures = estimated.

Gale Directory of Publications & Broadcast Media/147th Ed.   4931

European countries and Iran; US$989 institutions, other countries except Europe, Japan and Iran; 122,600¥ institutions; EUR312 individuals for European countries and Iran; US$311 other countries except Europe, Japan and Iran; 40,800¥ individuals; EUR234 students European countries and Iran; 40,800¥ students. **URL:** http://www.elsevier.com/wps/find/journaldescription.cws_home/701796/descriptiondescription.

44301 ■ RT eJournal
Di PP - NRW
Julicher Strasse 6
D-50674 Cologne, Germany
Ph: 49 221 400750
Fax: 49 221 40075180
Publication E-mail: redaktion@rtejournal.de
Publisher E-mail: dipp@hbz-nrw.de
Electronic magazine publishing articles from the field of generative or additive manufacturing - also known as Rapid Technology. **Subtitle:** Forum fuer Rapid Technolgie. **Key Personnel:** Dr. Andreas Gebhardt, Editor. **ISSN:** 1614-0923. **URL:** http://www.rtejournal.de/index_html?set_language=en&cl=en.

44302 ■ Social Work and Society
Di PP - NRW
Julicher Strasse 6
D-50674 Cologne, Germany
Ph: 49 221 400750
Fax: 49 221 40075180
Publisher E-mail: dipp@hbz-nrw.de
Journal dedicated to critical analysis of the relationship between social work, social policy, the state and economic forces. **Key Personnel:** Yueh-Ching Chou, Editor; Chris Clark, Editor; Lena Dominelli, Editor. **ISSN:** 1613-8953. **URL:** http://www.socwork.net.

44303 ■ Sprache und Geschichte in Afrika
Rudiger Koppe Verlag
Wendelinstrasse 73-75
D-50933 Cologne, Germany
Ph: 49 221 4911236
Fax: 49 221 4994336
Publisher E-mail: info@koeppe.de
Journal focusing on language change in Africa. **Freq:** Irregular. **Key Personnel:** Wilhelm J.G. Mohlig, Editor. **ISSN:** 0170-5946. **URL:** http://www.koeppe.de/katalog/katalog_reihe.php?lan=en&Sigle=SV706.

44304 ■ Yearbook of African Law
Rudiger Koppe Verlag
Wendelinstrasse 73-75
D-50933 Cologne, Germany
Ph: 49 221 4911236
Fax: 49 221 4994336
Publisher E-mail: info@koeppe.de
Journal focusing on African Law. **Freq:** Annual. **Key Personnel:** Kurt Madlener, Editor. **ISSN:** 0722-2181. **URL:** http://www.koeppe.de/katalog/katalog_reihe.php?lan=en&Sigle=YR997.

44305 ■ Domradio-FM - 96.75
Domkloster 3
D-50667 Cologne, Germany
Ph: 49 221 258860
Fax: 49 221 2588633
E-mail: info@domradio.de
Format: Ethnic; World Beat. **Operating Hours:** 16 hours Daily. **URL:** http://www.domradio.com.

44306 ■ Domradio-FM - 93.95
Domkloster 3
D-50667 Cologne, Germany
Ph: 49 221 258860
Fax: 49 221 2588633
E-mail: info@domradio.de
Format: Ethnic; World Beat. **URL:** http://www.domradio.com.

Darmstadt

44307 ■ GIT Sicherheit Management
GIT Sicherheit + Management
Postfach 11 05 64
D-64420 Darmstadt, Germany
Ph: 49 61 5180910
Fax: 49 61 518090146
Publisher E-mail: info@gitverlag.com
Trade magazine covering safety and security for management in industry and public service. **Freq:** 10/yr. **Key Personnel:** Steffen Ebert, Editor, steffen.ebert@wiley.com; Dr. Heiko Baumgartner, Contact, heiko.

baumgartner@wiley.com; Dr. Katina Leondaris, Contact, katina.leondaris@wiley.com; Regina Berg-Jauerning, Contact, regina.berg-jauernig@wiley.com. **Remarks:** Accepts advertising. **URL:** http://www.gitverlag.com/en/print/2/32/index.html. **Circ:** ‡28,281

44308 ■ Hospital Post
GIT Verlag GmbH
KG, Rosslerstrasse 90
D-64293 Darmstadt, Germany
Ph: 49 615 180900
Fax: 49 615 18090146
Publisher E-mail: info@gitverlag.com
Journal for hospital in-patient care in Europe, aimed at management in the European healthcare business. **Freq:** Bimonthly. **Key Personnel:** Christiane Rothermel, Editor, christiane.rothermel@wiley.com. **ISSN:** 1611-1524. **Subscription Rates:** EUR70 individuals; EUR14 single issue; EUR35 students. **URL:** http://www.gitverlag.com/. **Circ:** ‡43,000

44309 ■ International Journal of Computer Aided Engineering and Technology
Inderscience Enterprises Limited
c/o Dr. Yan Luo, Ed.-in-Ch.
Technology University of Darmstadt
64289 Darmstadt, Germany
Journal reporting research and applications which highlight the opportunities and limitations of computer aided engineering and technology in today's lifecycle-oriented, knowledge-based era of production. **Freq:** 4/yr. **Key Personnel:** Dr. Yan Luo, Editor-in-Chief, ijcaet@gmail.com. **ISSN:** 1757-2657. **Subscription Rates:** EUR494 individuals print or online; EUR672 individuals print and online. **URL:** http://www.inderscience.com/browse/index.php?journalID=313.

44310 ■ International Journal on Digital Libraries
Springer-Verlag
c/o Erich J. Neuhold, Ed.-in-Ch.
Fraunhofer IPSI, Dolivostr. 15
D-64293 Darmstadt, Germany
Ph: 49 615 1869802
Journal on digital libraries focusing on advancing the theory and practice of acquisition, definition, organization, management, and dissemination of digital information via global networking. **Freq:** Quarterly. **Key Personnel:** Erich J. Neuhold, Editor-in-Chief, neuhold@ipsi.fhg.de; Nabil R. Adam, Exec. Ed.-in-Ch., phone 973353-5239, fax 973353-5003, adam@adam.rutgers.edu; Richard Furuta, Editor-in-Chief, phone 979845-3839, furuta@cs.tamu.edu; Maristella Agosti, Editorial Board; Hsinchun Chen, Editorial Board; Vijay Atluri, Editorial Board. **ISSN:** 1432-5012. **Subscription Rates:** EUR325 institutions print incl. free access; EUR390 institutions print incl. enhanced access. **Remarks:** Advertising accepted; rates available upon request. **URL:** http://www.dljournal.org/; http://www.springer.com/computer/databasemanagement%26informationret rieval/journal/799. **Circ:** (Not Reported)

44311 ■ Optik
Elsevier Science Inc.
c/o Theo Tschudi, Ed.
Institute of Applied Physics
Darmstadt University of Technology
Darmstadt, Germany
Ph: 49 6151 162022
Fax: 49 6151 164123
Publisher E-mail: usinfo-ehelp@elsevier.com
Journal devoted to light and electron optics. **Founded:** 1946. **Freq:** 18/yr. **Print Method:** Letterpress. **Cols./Page:** 6. **Col. Width:** 12 3/4 picas. **Col. Depth:** 301 agate lines. **Key Personnel:** Hartmut Bartelt, Board; Michael J. Damzen, Board; Francois Flory, Board; Min Gu, Board; Theo Tschudi, Editor, theo.tschudi@physik.tu-darmstadt.de; John Caulfield, Board; Antoinette Raess-Tschudi, Secretariat of the Ed., ant.tschudi@bluewin.ch; Eusebio Bernabeu, Editorial Board; Ari T. Friberg, Editorial Board; Siegfried Boseck, Editorial Board. **ISSN:** 0030-4026. **Subscription Rates:** EUR2,533 institutions European countries and Iran; US$2,676 institutions, other countries except Europe, Japan and Iran; 336,000¥ institutions. **URL:** http://www.elsevier.com/wps/find/journaldescription.cws_home/701788/descriptiondescription.

44312 ■ Screening
GIT Verlag GmbH
KG, Rosslerstrasse 90
D-64293 Darmstadt, Germany
Ph: 49 615 180900

Fax: 49 615 18090146
Publisher E-mail: info@gitverlag.com
Journal focusing on new trends and developments in drug discovery, covering all aspects of research, as well as strategies of pharmaceutical companies and start-up companies. **Subtitle:** Trends in Drug Discovery. **Freq:** Quarterly. **Key Personnel:** Dr. Martin Friedrich, Editor. **Subscription Rates:** EUR49 individuals; EUR14 single issue; EUR24.50 students. **URL:** http://www.gitverlag.com/. **Circ:** ‡12,000

Detmold

44313 ■ Extratour
German Youth Hostel Association
Deutsches Jugendherbergswerk
Bismarck Rte. 8
D-32756 Detmold, Germany
Ph: 49 523 174010
Fax: 49 523 1740149
Publication E-mail: extratour@djh.de
Publisher E-mail: service@djh.org
Publication covering travel. **Founded:** 1920. **Freq:** Bimonthly. **Key Personnel:** Klaus Erfmann, Contact. **Remarks:** Advertising accepted; rates available upon request. **URL:** http://www.jugendherberge.de; http://www.extratouronline.de. **Formerly:** Jugendherberge. **Circ:** 900,000

Dortmund

44314 ■ Accreditation and Quality Assurance
Springer-Verlag Tokyo
c/o Ernst-Heiner Korte, Ed.-in-Ch./Mng. Ed.
ISAS - Institute for Analytical Sciences
Bunsen-Kirchhoff-Str. 11
D-44139 Dortmund, Germany
Ph: 49 231 97100345
Fax: 49 231 97100346
Publisher E-mail: info@springer.jp
Journal publishing scientific and technical contributions, short communications, discussion and position papers as well as other information on all aspects relevant to quality and reliability in chemical measurement, focusing on the following topics: accreditation, certification, ISO/IEC 17025, ISO 9001:2000, GLP/GMP, quality assurance, traceability, measurement uncertainty, validation, calibration, proficiency testing, reference materials, definitions and quantities and units. **Freq:** Monthly. **Key Personnel:** P. De Bievre, Editor-in-Chief, paul.de.bievre@skynet.be; Ernst-Heiner Korte, Ed.-in-Ch./Mng. Ed., editor@acqual.de; A. Alink, Intercontinental Editorial Board; L. Besley, Intercontinental Editorial Board; A. Fajgelj, Intercontinental Editorial Board; I. Kuselman, Intercontinental Editorial Board; M. Milton, Intercontinental Editorial Board; G. Price, Intercontinental Editorial Board. **ISSN:** 0949-1775. **Subscription Rates:** EUR445 institutions print incl. free access or e-only; EUR534 institutions print incl. enhanced access. **Remarks:** Advertising accepted; rates available upon request. **URL:** http://www.springer.com/chemistry/analytical/journal/769. **Circ:** (Not Reported)

44315 ■ Chemical Engineering and Processing
Elsevier Science Inc.
Dept. of Biochemical & Chemical Engineering
Technische Universitat Dortmund
Bldg. G2, Office 6.19, Emil-Figge-Strasse 70
D-44227 Dortmund, Germany
Publisher E-mail: usinfo-ehelp@elsevier.com
Journal focused on practicing engineers in industry and academia. **Subtitle:** Process Intensification. **Founded:** 1984. **Freq:** Monthly. **Trim Size:** 8 1/8 x 10 3/4. **Cols./Page:** 3. **Col. Width:** 27 nonpareils. **Col. Depth:** 120 agate lines. **Key Personnel:** J. Chen, Editorial Advisory Board; G. Wild, Editor, cep@ensic.inpl-nancy.fr; A. Gorak, Editor, gorak.cep@ct.uni-dortmund.de; G. Akay, Editorial Advisory Board; D. Trent, Editorial Advisory Board; K. Sundmacher, Editorial Advisory Board; F. Larachi, Editorial Advisory Board; E. Drioli, Editorial Advisory Board; A. Stankiewicz, Editor, a.stankiewicz@3me.tudelft.nl. **ISSN:** 0255-2701. **Subscription Rates:** 319,700¥ institutions; US$2,696 institutions, other countries except Europe, Japan and Iran; EUR2,408 institutions for European countries and Iran; EUR175 individuals for European countries and Iran; US$235 other countries except Europe, Japan and Iran; 27,100¥ individuals. **URL:** http://www.elsevier.com/wps/find/journaldescription.cws_home/504081/descriptiondescription.

44316 ■ International Journal on Software Tools for Technology Transfer (STTT)
Springer-Verlag
c/o Bernhard Steffen, Ed.-in-Ch.
Fachbereich Informatik
Universitat Dortmund
Otto-Hahn-Str. 14
D-44221 Dortmund, Germany
Publication E-mail: sttt@cs.uni-dortmund.de
Journal covering all aspects of tools that aid in the development of computer systems. **Freq:** 6/yr. **Key Personnel:** Matthew Dwyer, Editorial Board, dwyer@cse.unl.edu; Bernhard Steffen, Editor-in-Chief, steffen@cs.uni-dortmund.de; Tiziana Margaria, Coord. Ed., tiziana.margaria@cs.uni-potsdam.de; Ed Brinksma, Editorial Board; Stefania Gnesi, Editorial Board; Hubert Garavel, Editorial Board; Susanne Graf, Editorial Board; Kurt Jensen, Editorial Board. **ISSN:** 1433-2779. **Subscription Rates:** EUR447 institutions print incl. free access; EUR536.40 institutions print incl. enhanced access. **Remarks:** Advertising accepted; rates available upon request. **URL:** http://www.springer.com/computer/programming/journal/10009. **Circ:** (Not Reported)

44317 ■ Korrespondenzblatt
Sozialdienst Katholischer Frauen
Agnes-Neuhaus-Str. 5
D-44135 Dortmund, Germany
Ph: 49 231 5570260
Fax: 49 231 55702660
Publisher E-mail: info@skl-zentrale.de
German language publication covering the social work of a Catholic organization of women. **Founded:** 1917. **Freq:** Biennial. **Key Personnel:** Jachmann Willmer, Contact, jachmann-willmer@skf-zentrale.de. **Remarks:** Advertising accepted; rates available upon request. **URL:** http://www.skf-zentrale.de/html/korrespondenzblatt.html. **Circ:** 750

Dreieich

44318 ■ Made in Germany—International Edition
Made in Germany Publication GmbH
Siemensstrasse 18
D-63303 Dreieich, Germany
Ph: 49 010 0900597
Fax: 49 610 334175
Publication E-mail: info@made-in-germany-web.de
Publisher E-mail: info@made-in-germany-web.de
Professional magazine covering technology for the business community worldwide. **Subtitle:** Technology, Products, and Services. **Founded:** 1983. **Freq:** Bimonthly. **Print Method:** Offset. **Trim Size:** 200 x 266 mm. **Cols./Page:** 3. **Key Personnel:** Willoughby Ann Walshe, Editorial Coord.; Armin H. Loescher, Mng. Dir./Publishing Coord.; Nadja Starkloff, Editorial Asst. **ISSN:** 0179-6291. **Subscription Rates:** EUR51 individuals plus 25 airmail postage; EUR10 single issue plus 4 airmail postage. **Remarks:** Accepts advertising. **URL:** http://www.made-in-germany-web.de/. **Ad Rates:** BW: EUR5,215, 4C: EUR9,387. **Circ:** Combined ‡110,000

Dresden

44319 ■ AEU - International Journal of Electronics and Communications
Elsevier Science Inc.
c/o Dr. Ralf Lehnert, Ed.-in-Ch.
Dept. of Electrical Engineering & Information Techniques
Chair for Telecommunications
Technische Universitat Dresden
D-01062 Dresden, Germany
Ph: 49 351 46333942
Fax: 49 351 46337163
Publisher E-mail: usinfo-ehelp@elsevier.com
Journal focused on electronics and communications. **Founded:** 1947. **Freq:** 12/yr. **Print Method:** Offset. **Trim Size:** 7 1/8 x 10. **Cols./Page:** 5. **Col. Width:** 22 nonpareils. **Col. Depth:** 210 agate lines. **Key Personnel:** Ricardo Depine, Editorial Board; Andreas Herkersdorf, Editorial Board; Tetsuo Nishi, Editorial Board; Wolfgang Schwarz, Editorial Board; Prof. Ralf Lehnert, Editor-in-Chief, aeue@ifn.et.tu-dresden.de. **ISSN:** 1434-8411. **Subscription Rates:** EUR430 individuals European countries and Iran; EUR1,312 institutions European countries and Iran; US$1,440 institutions, other countries except Europe, Japan and Iran; 179,000¥ institutions; 56,200¥ individuals; US$516 other countries except Europe, Japan and Iran. **URL:** http://www.elsevier.com/

wps/find/journaldescription.cws_home/701750/descriptiondescription.

Duisburg

44320 ■ Mechanism and Machine Theory
Elsevier Science
c/o Andres Kecskemethy, Ed.-in-Ch.
Lehrstuhl fur Mechanik
Gerhard Mercator Universitat Duisburg
Lotharstrasse 1
D-47057 Duisburg, Germany
Publisher E-mail: nlinfo-f@elsevier.com
Journal dealing with mechanism and machine science. **Founded:** 1966. **Freq:** Monthly. **Key Personnel:** Andres Kecskemethy, Editor-in-Chief, a.kecskemethy@uni-duisburg.de; J. Angeles, Editorial Advisory Board; T. Huang, Editorial Advisory Board. **ISSN:** 0094-114X. **Subscription Rates:** 421,200¥ institutions; EUR3,174 institutions for Europe; US$3,548 institutions, other countries for all countries except Europe and Japan; US$139 individuals for all countries except Europe and Japan; 16,200¥ individuals; EUR123 individuals for European Countries. **Remarks:** Accepts advertising. **URL:** http://www.elsevier.com/wps/find/journaldescription.cws_home/303/description. **Circ:** (Not Reported)

Dusseldorf

44321 ■ Behavioural Brain Research
Elsevier Science
c/o J.P. Huston, Ed.-in-Ch.
Institute of Physiological Psychology
University of Dusseldorf
Universitatsstrasse 1
D-40225 Dusseldorf, Germany
Ph: 49 211 8114296
Fax: 49 211 8112024
Publisher E-mail: nlinfo-f@elsevier.com
Journal publishing articles in the area of behavioral neuroscience. **Founded:** 1980. **Freq:** 20/yr. **Key Personnel:** T.E. Robinson, Editor-in-Chief; J.P. Huston, Editor-in-Chief, bbr@uni-duesseldorf.de; J.P. Aggleton, Editorial Board. **ISSN:** 0166-4328. **Subscription Rates:** US$6,934 institutions for all countries except Europe, Japan & Iran; 823,600¥ institutions; EUR6,934 institutions for European countries & Iran. **Remarks:** Accepts advertising. **URL:** http://www.elsevier.com/wps/find/journaldescription.cws_home/506045/descriptiondescription. **Circ:** (Not Reported)

44322 ■ Constructions
University of Dusseldorf
Universitatsstr. 1
D-40225 Dusseldorf, Germany
Ph: 49 211 8100
Publisher E-mail: webmaster@uni-duesseldorf.de
Peer-reviewed journal covering linguistic research concerned with the structure, use, function, and development in language and linguistics. **Founded:** 1906. **Freq:** Irregular. **Print Method:** Offset. **Trim Size:** 8 1/8 x 10 7/8. **Cols./Page:** 3. **Col. Width:** 26 nonpareils. **Col. Depth:** 136 agate lines. **Key Personnel:** Alexander Bergs, Editor; Anette Rosenbach, Editor. **ISSN:** 0024-3078. **URL:** http://www.constructions-online.de/.

44323 ■ Der Praktiker
DVS-Verlag GmbH
Aachener Strasse 172
D-40223 Dusseldorf, Germany
Ph: 49 2 1115910
Fax: 49 2 11159150
Publisher E-mail: media@dvs-hg.de
German language publication covering welding. **Freq:** Monthly. **Key Personnel:** Carolin Hesse, Contact, carolin.hesse@dvs-hg.de; Dietmar Rippegather, Editor, dietmar.rippegather@dvs-hg.de; Christian Bothur, Editor, christian.bothur@dvs-hg.de. **ISSN:** 0554-9965. **Remarks:** Advertising accepted; rates available upon request. **URL:** http://www.derpraktiker.de/. **Circ:** 17,000

44324 ■ European Physical Journal E. Soft Matter
Springer-VDI-Verlag
VDI-Platz 1
D-14197 Dusseldorf, Germany
Ph: 49 211 61030
Fax: 49 211 6103300
Publisher E-mail: leserservice@technikwissen.de
Journal about physical soft matter. **Key Personnel:** Georg Maret, External Advisor; Richard A.L. Jones,

Editor-in-Chief; Hans Herrmann, Editor; James A. Forrest, Editor; Erwin Frey, Editor; Mark W. Matsen, Editor. **ISSN:** 1292-8941. **URL:** http://www.springerlink.com/content/104404/.

44325 ■ Gefahrstoffe-Reinhaltung der Luft
Springer-VDI-Verlag
VDI-Platz 1
D-14197 Dusseldorf, Germany
Ph: 49 211 61030
Fax: 49 211 6103300
Publisher E-mail: leserservice@technikwissen.de
German language publication covering pollution control. **Subtitle:** Air Quality Control. **Freq:** 9/yr. **Trim Size:** A4. **ISSN:** 0949-8036. **Subscription Rates:** EUR284 individuals. **Remarks:** Advertising accepted; rates available upon request. **URL:** http://www.technikwissen.de/gest/. **Circ:** 2,000

44326 ■ German Medical Science
Arbeitsgemeinschaft der Wissenschaftlichen Medizinischen Fachgesellschaften
Ubierstr. 20
D-40223 Dusseldorf, Germany
Ph: 49 211 312828
Fax: 49 211 316819
Publication E-mail: info@egms.de
Publisher E-mail: awmf@awmf.org
E-journal offering open access to all scientists from the field of medicine to publish their research results online. **Key Personnel:** Dr. Hans Reinauer, Contact. **ISSN:** 1612-3174. **URL:** http://www.egms.de/dynamic/en/index.htm.

44327 ■ Juristische Rundschau (JR)
Walter de Gruyter GmbH & Co. KG
Lehrstuhl fur Burgerliches Recht und Zivilprozebrecht
Universitatsstr. 1
D-40225 Dusseldorf, Germany
Publisher E-mail: info@degruyter.com
Journal covering articles on right development in teachings and jurisdiction. **Print Method:** Offset. **Cols./Page:** 8. **Col. Width:** 1 7/8 inches. **Col. Depth:** 21 inches. **Key Personnel:** Dr. Dirk Olzen, Editor, carmen.prazeus@uni-duesseldorf.de; Gerhard Schafer, Editor, gerh.schaefer@googlemail.com. **ISSN:** 0022-6920. **Subscription Rates:** EUR293 individuals print order online; EUR337 individuals print plus online; EUR27 single issue print only. **URL:** http://www.degruyter.de/journals/jr/detailEn.cfm.

44328 ■ Literaturschau Stahl + Eisen
Steel Institute VDEh
Sohnstr. 65
D-40237 Dusseldorf, Germany
Publication covering the metal trade. **Founded:** 1969. **Freq:** Monthly. **Key Personnel:** Gerd Krause, Editor-in-Chief, phone 49 211 6707570, fax 49 211 3707436, gerd.krause@stahleisen.de. **ISSN:** 0933-8934. **Remarks:** Accepts advertising. **URL:** http://www.stahleisen.de/html/home.php?. **Formerly:** Zeitschriften- und Bucherschau Stahl und Eisen. **Ad Rates:** BW: DM 2,213, 4C: DM 3,011. **Circ:** (Not Reported)

44329 ■ MPT International
Steel Institute VDEh
PO Box 10 51 64
D-40042 Dusseldorf, Germany
Publication E-mail: mpt@stahleisen.de
Trade publication covering metals. **Founded:** 1978. **Freq:** Bimonthly. **Key Personnel:** Arnt Hannewald, Editor-in-Chief, phone 49 211 6707568, fax 49 211 6707388, arnt.hannewald@stahleisen.de; Marie-Luise Kliem, Asst. Ed., phone 49 211 6707572, fax 49 211 6707388, marie-luise.kliem@stahleisen.de; Sigrid Klinge, Advertising Mgr., phone 49 211 6707552, fax 49 211 6707517, sigrid.klinge@stahleisen.de. **ISSN:** 0935-7254. **Subscription Rates:** EUR154 individuals incl. 7% vat; EUR31 single issue. **Remarks:** Accepts advertising. **URL:** http://www.stahleisen.de/html/home.php?language=english&page=zeitschriften&title=mpt_english. **Ad Rates:** BW: EUR3,190, 4C: EUR3,988. **Circ:** 10,232

44330 ■ Parasitology Research
Springer-Verlag GmbH & Company KG
c/o H. Mehlhorn, Ed.-in-Ch.
Heinrich-Heine-Universitat, Institut fur Zoomorphologie Zellbiologie und Parasitologie
Universitatsstrasse 1 (Geb. 26.03.00.70)
D-40225 Dusseldorf, Germany

Circulation: ★ = ABC; △ = BPA; ◆ = CAC; • = CCAB; ❑ = VAC; ⊕ = PO Statement; ‡ = Publisher's Report; Boldface figures = sworn; Light figures = estimated.

Gale Directory of Publications & Broadcast Media/147th Ed.   4933

Publisher E-mail: webmaster@springer.com
International journal on parasitology including general, biological, medical and veterinary parasitology; protozoology, helminthology, entomology; morphology (incl. pathomorphology, ultrastructure); biochemistry, physiology (incl. pathophysiology); parasite-host-relationships (incl. immunology, host specificity); life history, ecology, epidermiology; and diagnosis, chemotherapy and control of parasitic diseases. **Freq:** Bimonthly. **Key Personnel:** H. Melhorn, Editor-in-Chief, mehlhorn@uni-duesseldorf.de; B. Chobotar, Editor, chob@andrews.edu; D.D. Despommier, Editorial Board; R. Lucius, Editorial Board; B. Loos-Frank, Editorial Board. **ISSN:** 0932-0113. **Subscription Rates:** EUR5,403 institutions print incl. free access or e-only; EUR6,483.60 institutions enhanced access. **Remarks:** Advertising accepted; rates available upon request. **URL:** http://www.springer.com/biomed/medicalmicrobiology/journal/436. **Circ:** (Not Reported)

44331 ■ Progress in Computational Fluid Dynamics
Inderscience Publishers
c/o Dr. A.C. Benim, Exec. Ed.
Dept. of Mechanical & Process Engineering
Dusseldorf University of Applied Sciences
Josef-Gockeln-Str. 9
D-40474 Dusseldorf, Germany
Publisher E-mail: editor@inderscience.com
Peer-reviewed journal aiming to disseminate information relating to development and refinement of mathematical and numerical models, software tools and their innovative applications in the area of computational fluid dynamics. **Subtitle:** An International Journal. **Freq:** 8/yr. **Key Personnel:** Dr. A.C. Benim, Exec. Ed., alicemal.benim@fh-duesseldorf.de; Dr. K. Abe, Editorial Board Member; Dr. M. Amato, Editorial Board Member; Dr. T.J. Chung, American Ed.; Prof. A.J. Baker, Editorial Board Member; Gerhard Muller, European Ed. **ISSN:** 1468-4349. **Subscription Rates:** EUR1,240 individuals online only (2-3 users); EUR735 individuals print only (surface mail); EUR795 individuals print only (airmail); EUR1,025 individuals print and online. **URL:** http://www.inderscience.com/browse/index.php?journalID=23board.

44332 ■ Psycho-Social-Medicine
Arbeitsgemeinschaft der Wissenschaftlichen Medizinischen Fachgesellschaften
Ubierstr. 20
D-40223 Dusseldorf, Germany
Ph: 49 211 312828
Fax: 49 211 316819
Publication E-mail: info@egms.de
Publisher E-mail: awmf@awmf.org
E-journal publishing articles from the whole area of psychosocial research in medicine. **Key Personnel:** Dr. Jorn von Wietersheim, Editor-in-Chief. **ISSN:** 1860-5214. **URL:** http://www.egms.de/en/journals/psm/index.shtml.

44333 ■ Schmalenbach Business Review
Verlagsgruppe Handelsblatt GmbH
Kasernenstr. 67
D-40213 Dusseldorf, Germany
Ph: 49 211 8870
Fax: 49 211 8872980
Publisher E-mail: info@vhb.de
Journal covering research in the field of accounting, finance, taxation, marketing and neo-institutionalism. **Freq:** Quarterly January, April, July, October. **Key Personnel:** Clemens Borsig, Editor; Wolfgang Ballwieser, Editor; Karen Gedenk, Editor. **Subscription Rates:** US$135 institutions; US$31.30 students; US$67 individuals; 65 institutions; 32 individuals; 15.10 students; EUR91 institutions; EUR45 individuals; EUR21 students. **Remarks:** Advertising accepted; rates available upon request. **URL:** http://www.fachverlag.de/sbr/aims.html. **Circ:** (Not Reported)

44334 ■ Schweissen & Schneiden
DVS-Verlag GmbH
Aachener Strasse 172
D-40223 Dusseldorf, Germany
Ph: 49 2 1115910
Fax: 49 2 11159150
Publisher E-mail: media@dvs-hg.de
German language publication covering welding. **Freq:** Monthly. **Key Personnel:** Carolin Hesse, Contact; Dietmar Rippegather, Editor, dietmar.rippegather@dvs-hg.de. **ISSN:** 0036-7184. **Remarks:** Advertising accepted; rates available upon request. **URL:** http://www.schweissenuschneiden.de/; http://www.dvs-media.eu/index.php?idcat=65. **Circ:** 14,000

44335 ■ VDI Nachrichten
VDI Verlag
VDI-Platz 1
D-40468 Dusseldorf, Germany
Ph: 49 211 61880
Fax: 49 211 6188112
Publisher E-mail: info@vdi-nachrichten.com
Community newspaper covering technology, economy, and local news. **Freq:** Weekly. **Cols./Page:** 6. **Key Personnel:** Frau Somnitz, Contact, phone 49 211 6188441, fax 49 211 6188209, isomnitz@vdi-nachrichten.com. **ISSN:** 0042-1758. **Subscription Rates:** EUR120 individuals incl. postage. **URL:** http://www.vdi-nachrichten.com/.

Edewecht

44336 ■ Rettungsdienst
Stumpf & Kossendey
Postfach 1361
D-26183 Edewecht, Germany
Ph: 49 440 591810
Fax: 49 440 5918133
Publication E-mail: rettungsdienst@skverlag.de
Publisher E-mail: service@skverlag.de
Professional journal covering emergency medicine. **Founded:** 1978. **Freq:** Monthly. **Key Personnel:** Edda Wieker, Contact, wieker@skverlag.de. **ISSN:** 0178-2525. **Remarks:** Accepts advertising. **URL:** http://www.skverlag.de. **Circ:** Paid 22,500

Erfurt

44337 ■ Landeswelle-FM - 99.7
Mehringstrasse 5
D-99086 Erfurt, Germany
Ph: 49 180 5222150
Fax: 49 180 5222180
E-mail: kontakt@landeswelle.de
Format: Ethnic; World Beat. **Ad Rates:** Advertising accepted; rates available upon request. **URL:** http://www.landeswelle.de.

Erlangen

44338 ■ GAMM - Mitteilungen
John Wiley & Sons Inc.
c/o Dr. Paul Steinmann, Ed.
Friedrich-Alexander Universitat Erlangen-Nurnberg
Lehrstuhl fur Technische Mechanik
Egerlandstrasse 5
D-91058 Erlangen, Germany
Ph: 49 9131 8528501
Fax: 49 9131 8528503
Publisher E-mail: info@wiley.com
Journal focusing on applied mathematics. **Freq:** 5/yr. **Key Personnel:** Dr. Paul Steinmann, Editor, steinmann@ltm.uni-erlangen.de; G. Bohme, Advisory Board; R. Ansorge, Advisory Board. **ISSN:** 0936-7195. **Subscription Rates:** EUR90 institutions print only; 180 SFr institutions print only (Switzerland and Lichtenstein); US$113 institutions, other countries print only; EUR99 institutions print and online; 198 SFr institutions print and online (Switzerland and Lichtenstein); US$125 institutions, other countries print and online. **URL:** http://onlinelibrary.wiley.com/journal/10.1002/(ISSN)1522-2608.

44339 ■ International Archives of Occupational and Environmental Health
Springer-Verlag
Department & Out-Patient Clinic for Occupational Social & Environmental Medicine
University of Erlangen-Nuremberg
Schillerstrasse 25-29
D-91054 Erlangen, Germany
Ph: 49 9131 8522312
Fax: 49 9131 8522317
Journal focusing on occupational and environmental health. **Freq:** 8/yr. **Key Personnel:** H. Drexler, Editor-in-Chief, hans.drexler@rzmail.uni-erlangen.de; M.S. Morgan, Editor, mmorgan@u.washington.edu; K.H. Schaller, Assoc. Ed., iaoeh.khschaller@rzmail.uni-erlangen.de; D. Llson, Editor, lison@toxi.ucl.ac.be; M. Ikeda, Editor, ikeda@kyotokojohokenkai.or.jp; S. Langard, Editor, sverre.langard@rikshospitalet.no; A. Zober, Editor, andreas.zober@basf.com. **ISSN:** 0340-0131. **Subscription Rates:** EUR3,186 institutions print incl. free access; EUR3,823.20 institutions print incl. enhanced access. **URL:** http://www.springer.com/medicine/internal/journal/420.

44340 ■ Journal of Molecular Modeling
Springer-Verlag GmbH & Company KG
c/o Tim Clark, Ed.-in-Ch.
Computer-Chemie-Centrum
University Erlangen-Nurnberg
Nagelsbachstrasse 25
D-91052 Erlangen, Germany
Fax: 49 913 18526565
Publisher E-mail: webmaster@springer.com
Journal focusing on Life Science Modeling, Materials Modeling and Computational Chemistry. **Key Personnel:** Tim Clark, Editor-in-Chief, jmolmod@chemie.uni-erlangen.de; James J.P Stewart, Editorial Board; Manfred J. Sippl, Editorial Board; Johann Gasteiger, Editorial Board; Rod E. Hubbard, Editorial Board; Peter A. Politzer, Sen. Ed., ppolitzer@uno.edu; Jean L. Rivail, Editorial Board; Jurgen Brickmann, Editorial Board; Gerald M Maggiora, Editorial Board; Frank Blaney, Editorial Board. **ISSN:** 1610-2940. **Remarks:** Advertising accepted; rates available upon request. **URL:** http://www.springer.com/chemistry/journal/894; http://www.springer.com/west/home/biomed?sgwid=4-124-70-1116860-0. **Circ:** (Not Reported)

44341 ■ SIAM Journal on Scientific Computing
Society for Industrial & Applied Mathematics
c/o Ulrich Rude, Ed.-in-Ch.
Lehrstuhl fuer Simulation
Universitat Erlanger-Nuernberg
Cauestr. 6
D-91058 Erlangen, Germany
Publication E-mail: epsupport@siam.org
Publisher E-mail: service@siam.org
Journal containing research articles on solving scientific problems through the use of computers. **Founded:** 1980. **Freq:** Bimonthly. **Print Method:** Offset. **Trim Size:** 6 3/4 x 10. **Cols./Page:** 1. **Col. Width:** 31 picas. **Col. Depth:** 50 picas. **Key Personnel:** Ulrich Rude, Editor-in-Chief, ruede@informatik.uni-erlangen.de. **ISSN:** 1064-8275. **Subscription Rates:** US$111 individuals; US$117 other countries; US$85 individuals electronic only; US$782 institutions domestic; US$912 institutions, other countries; US$742.90 institutions electronic only. **Remarks:** Accepts advertising. **URL:** http://www.siam.org/journals/sisc.php; http://epubs.siam.org. **Formerly:** SIAM Journal on Scientific and Statistical Computing. **Ad Rates:** BW: DM 400. **Circ:** (Not Reported)

44342 ■ Strahlentherapie und Onkologie
Springer Netherlands
c/o Dr. R. Sauer, Ed.-in-Ch.
Universitats-Strahlenklinik
Universitatsstrasse 27
D-91054 Erlangen, Germany
Ph: 49 9131 8533405
Fax: 49 9131 8534060
Publisher E-mail: permissions.dordrecht@springer.com
Peer-reviewed journal focusing on radio oncology, radiation biology and radiation physics. **Founded:** 1912. **Freq:** Monthly. **Key Personnel:** Prof. R. Sauer, Editor-in-Chief, rolf.sauer@uk-erlangen.de; Dr. N. Willich, Editor; Dr. P. Lukas, Editor; Dr. Th. Herrmann, Editor; Dr. A. Mayer, Editor; Dr. J. Hammer, Editor; Dr. H.-P. Rodemann, Editor; Dr. P. Kneschaurek, Editor; Dr. R. Fietkau, Editor. **ISSN:** 0179-7158. **Subscription Rates:** EUR466.36 institutions print incl. free access or e-only; EUR559.63 institutions print incl. enhanced access. **Remarks:** Advertising accepted; rates available upon request. **URL:** http://www.springer.com/medicine/radiology/journal/66. **Circ:** (Not Reported)

44343 ■ Zeitschrift fur die Alttestamentliche Wissenschaft
Walter de Gruyter GmbH & Co. KG
Kochstr. 6
D-91054 Erlangen, Germany
Publisher E-mail: info@degruyter.com
Journal focusing on the field of research in the old testament and early Judaism. **Founded:** 1963. **Freq:** Quarterly. **Print Method:** Offset. **Cols./Page:** 5. **Col. Width:** 24 nonpareils. **Col. Depth:** 224 agate lines. **Key Personnel:** Dr. Ernst Joachim Waschke, Editor, waschke@theologie.uni-halle.de; Dr. Jurgen Van Oorschot, Editor, juergen.v.oorschot@theologie.uni-erlangen.de; Dr. Sebastian Gratz, Editor, graetz@uni-mainz.de; Prof. Jan Christian Gertz, Editor, zaw@wts.uni-heidelberg.de. **ISSN:** 0044-2526. **Subscription Rates:** EUR251 individuals print or online only; EUR289 individuals print + online; EUR82 students; EUR69 single

issue. **URL:** http://www.degruyter.de/journals/zaw/detailEn.cfm. **Circ:** 1,200

44344 ■ Zeitschrift fur Antikes Christentum
Walter de Gruyter GmbH & Co. KG
University of Erlangen Nuernberg
Institut for Historical Theology
Kochstrasse 6
D-91054 Erlangen, Germany
Publisher-E-mail: info@degruyter.com
Journal covering articles on scholars of church history, history of religion, and classical antiquity. **Subtitle:** Journal of Ancient Christianity. **Freq:** Semiannual. **Key Personnel:** Dr. H.Ch. Brennecke, Contact; Dr. Volker Henning Drecoll, Contact; Dr. Ch. Markschies, Contact; Volker Drecoll, Editor. **ISSN:** 0949-9571. **Subscription Rates:** EUR177 individuals print only or online only; EUR204 individuals print + online; EUR65 single issue. **URL:** http://www.degruyter.de/journals/zac/detailEn.cfm. **Circ:** 400

Eschborn

44345 ■ Gate Technology and Development
German Appropriate Technology Exchange
Deutsches Zentrum fur Entwicklungstechnologien
Postfach 5180
D-65726 Eschborn, Germany
Ph: 49 619 6790
Fax: 49 619 679115
Publisher E-mail: info@gtz.de
Publication covering technology and development. **Freq:** Quarterly. **ISSN:** 0723-2225. **Remarks:** Advertising accepted; rates available upon request. **URL:** http://www.gtz.de. **Circ:** (Not Reported)

Essen

44346 ■ Das Mechanische Musikinstrument
Gesellschaft fur Selbstspielende Musikinstrumente
Emmastr. 56
D-45130 Essen, Germany
Ph: 49 201 784927
Fax: 49 201 7266240
Publisher E-mail: president@musica-mechanica.dc
German language publication covering music. **Freq:** PER. **ISSN:** 0721-6092. **Subscription Rates:** Free to members; EUR60 individuals to Libraries & Institutions; EUR22.50 single issue including postage. **Remarks:** Advertising accepted; rates available upon request. **URL:** http://www.musica-mechanica.de. **Circ:** (Not Reported)

44347 ■ Radio Essen-FM - 102.2
Lindenallee 6
D-45127 Essen, Germany
Ph: 49 201 224499
Fax: 49 201 2458522
E-mail: info@102.2radioessen.de
Format: Contemporary Hit Radio (CHR). **Owner:** Radio Essen, at above address. **Ad Rates:** Advertising accepted; rates available upon request. **URL:** http://www.102.2radioessen.de.

Ettlingen

44348 ■ Aquaristik
Postfach 250
D-76256 Ettlingen, Germany
Ph: 49 724 3575105
Fax: 49 724 3575100
Consumer magazine covering fish. **Subtitle:** Aktuelle Subwasserpraxis. **Founded:** 1993. **Freq:** Bimonthly. **Print Method:** Offset. **Trim Size:** 270 x 237 mm. **Key Personnel:** Angelika Muller, Contact, a.mueller@daehne.de; Friedrich Bitter, Contact, phone 49 593 791531, fax 49 593 791532, fbitter@daehne.de. **ISSN:** 0947-6520. **Subscription Rates:** EUR28.80 individuals; EUR31 other countries. **URL:** http://www.aquaristik-online.de. **Circ:** Controlled 26,364

44349 ■ DIY
Daehne Verlag GmbH
PO Box 100 250
D-76256 Ettlingen, Germany
Ph: 49 724 35750
Fax: 49 724 3575200
Publisher E-mail: info@daehne.de
Trade journal covering the do-it-yourself market in Europe. **Subtitle:** Branchenmagazine Fuer Deu Do-It-Yourself-Handel. **Founded:** 1989. **Freq:** 11/yr. **Trim**

Size: A4. **Key Personnel:** Dr. Joachim Bengelsdorf, Editorial Staff, phone 49 575 208, j.bengelsdorf@daehne.de; Rainer Strand, Managing Editor, phone 49 575 207, r.stmad@daehne.de; Hans-Ludwig Ziegler, Editorial Staff, phone 49 575 203, h.ziegler@daehne.de; Ulrich Haspel, Editorial Staff, phone 49 575 204, u.haspel@daehne.de. **ISSN:** 0837-5406. **Subscription Rates:** EUR123 individuals 11 issues; EUR128 other countries. **Remarks:** Accepts advertising. **URL:** http://www.diyonline.de. **Ad Rates:** BW: EUR2,790, 4C: EUR5,130. **Circ:** Combined 9,231

44350 ■ Pet in Europe
Daehne Verlag GmbH
PO Box 100 250
D-76256 Ettlingen, Germany
Ph: 49 724 35750
Fax: 49 724 3575200
Publisher E-mail: info@daehne.de
Magazine offering expert information on the international pet trade and on suppliers and service-providers in the pet sector. **Freq:** Bimonthly. **Key Personnel:** Ralf Majer-Abele, Managing Editor, r.majer-abele@daehne.de; Philipp Gardemin, Contact, p.gardemin@daehne.de. **Subscription Rates:** EUR46 individuals in Germany; EUR48 individuals other Countries; EUR24 individuals overseas airmail. **URL:** http://www.daehne.com/db/produkte/produkte_e.asp?art=10&s=e&b=pet.

Euskirchen

44351 ■ Tourenfahrer/Motorrad Reisen
Reiner H. Nitschke Verlags-GmbH
Eifelring 28
D-53879 Euskirchen, Germany
Ph: 49 2251650460
Fax: 49 22516504699
Publication E-mail: tourenfahrer@nitschke-verlag.de
Consumer magazine covering travel, accessories, products and reports for motocyclists. **Founded:** 1981. **Freq:** Monthly. **Print Method:** rollen-offset/ctp. **Trim Size:** 210 x 280mm. **Cols./Page:** 4. **Col. Width:** 43 centimeters. **Col. Depth:** 248 millimeters. **Key Personnel:** Reiner H. Nitchke, Editor; Linda Lattemann, Contact. **ISSN:** 0933-4440. **Subscription Rates:** EUR51 individuals; EUR66 out of country; EUR5 single issue. **Remarks:** Accepts advertising. **URL:** http://www.tourenfahrer.de. **Circ:** Paid ‡65,170

Feldkirchen

44352 ■ Journal of Coptic Studies
PEETERS - USA
c/o Prof. Dr. K. Schussler, Ed.
Olbergring 23
D-83620 Feldkirchen, Germany
Ph: 49 8063 7219
Fax: 49 8063 5600
Publisher E-mail: peeters@peeters-us.com
Journal focusing on literature, history, art, archeology, and related subjects, during pre-modern era focusing on Coptic language only. **Freq:** Annual. **Key Personnel:** Dr. Karlheinz Schussler, Editor. **ISSN:** 1016-5584. **Remarks:** Advertising accepted; rates available upon request. **URL:** http://poj.peeters-leuven.be/content.php?url=journal&journal_code=JCS. **Circ:** (Not Reported)

Fellbach

44353 ■ Restaurator
Walter de Gruyter GmbH & Co. KG
c/o Dr. Irene Bruckle, Ed.
Staatliche Akademie der Bildenden Kunste Stuttgart
Hohenstrasse 16
D-70736 Fellbach, Germany
Publication E-mail: restauratorjournal-gb@web.de
Publisher E-mail: info@degruyter.com
Journal covering the conservation of library and archive materials. **Freq:** Quarterly. **Print Method:** Web Offset. **Key Personnel:** Dr. Irene Bruckle, Editor. **ISSN:** 0034-5806. **Subscription Rates:** EUR324 individuals print + online; EUR281 individuals print or online only; EUR77 single issue. **Remarks:** Accepts advertising. **URL:** http://www.degruyter.de/journals/restaur/detailEn.cfm. **Ad Rates:** BW: DM 550, 4C: DM 1,000. **Circ:** ‡3,500

Flensburg

44354 ■ ECMI Journal on Ethnopolitics and Minority Issues in Europe
European Centre for Minority Issues

Schiffbrucke 12
D-24939 Flensburg, Germany
Ph: 49 4 61141490
Fax: 49 4 611414919
Publisher E-mail: info@ecmi.de
Multi-disciplinary journal addressing minority issues across a broad range of studies, such as ethnopolitics, democratization, conflict management, good governance, participation, minority issues and minority rights. **Key Personnel:** Timofey Agarin, Editor-in-Chief; Will Kymlicka, International Editorial Board; Lauri Hannikainen, International Editorial Board; Francois Grin, International Editorial Board; Rainer Hofmann, International Editorial Board; Richard Caplan, International Editorial Board; Marie-Janine Calic, International Editorial Board; Jennifer Jackson Preece, International Editorial Board; Donald Horowitz, International Editorial Board; Gudmundur Alfredsson, International Editorial Board. **ISSN:** 1617-5247. **URL:** http://www.ecmi.de/jemie/index.html.

44355 ■ International Journal of Globalisation and Small Business
Inderscience Publishers
c/o Dr. Susanne Royer, Ed.
University of Flensburg
International Institute of Management
Munketoft 3
D-24937 Flensburg, Germany
Publisher E-mail: editor@inderscience.com
Peer-reviewed journal aiming to develop, promote and coordinate the research and practice in globalisation and small business management, to help professionals working in the field, small business owners, business educators and policy makers to contribute or disseminate information and to learn from each other's work. **Freq:** Quarterly. **Key Personnel:** Dr. Susanne Royer, Editor, royer@uni-flensburg.de; Prof. Helmut M. Dietl, Editorial Board Member; Prof. Rod McNaughton, Editorial Board Member; Prof. Lars Bengtsson, Editorial Board Member; Prof. Marion Festing, Editorial Board Member; Dr. Britta Boyd, Editorial Board Member; Prof. Kerry Brown, Editorial Board Member; Dr. Denise Fletcher, Editorial Board Member; Dr. Rajesh K. Pillania, Editorial Board Member. **ISSN:** 1479-3059. **Subscription Rates:** EUR494 individuals print only (surface mail); EUR840 individuals online only (2-3 users); EUR534 individuals print only (airmail); EUR672 individuals print and online. **URL:** http://www.inderscience.com/browse/index.php?journalCODE=ijgsb.

Frankfurt

44356 ■ Agrifuture
German Agricultural Society
Deutsche Landwirtschafts-Gesellschaft
Eschborner Landstrasse 122
D-60489 Frankfurt, Germany
Ph: 49 69 247880
Fax: 49 69 24788110
Publisher E-mail: info@dlg.org
English and French language publication covering agricultural development. **Subtitle:** The Magazine for the European Business Feruier. **Founded:** Jan. 1998. **Freq:** Quarterly. **Key Personnel:** Thomas Preusse, Editor-in-Chief; Reinhard Geissel, Managing Editor. **Subscription Rates:** Free. **Remarks:** Accepts advertising. **URL:** http://www.agrifuture.com. **Circ:** 20,000

44357 ■ Allgemeine Fleischer Zeitung
Deutscher Fleischer-Verband
Kennedyallee 53
D-60596 Frankfurt, Germany
Ph: 49 696 33020
Fax: 49 696 3302150
Publisher E-mail: info@fleischerhandwerk.de
German language publication covering the meat industry. **Freq:** Weekly. **Key Personnel:** Gerd Abeln, Contact, gerd.abeln@fleischwirtschaft.de. **Remarks:** Accepts advertising. **URL:** http://www.fleischerhandwerk.de. **Ad Rates:** BW: DM 7,187, 4C: DM 12,577. **Circ:** (Not Reported)

44358 ■ Archiv der Pharmazie
John Wiley & Sons Inc.
c/o Dr. Holger Stark, Ed.-in-Ch.
Institut fur Pharmazeutische Chemie Biozentrum
Marie-Curie-Strasse 9
60439 Frankfurt, Germany

Ph: 49 69 79829302
Fax: 49 69 79829258
Publisher E-mail: info@wiley.com
Journal covering all fields of pharmaceutical and medicinal chemistry. **Freq:** Monthly. **Key Personnel:** Dr. Holger Stark, Editor-in-Chief, h.stark@pharmchem.uni-frankfurt.de; Dr. Andreas Link, Sen. Ed. **ISSN:** 0365-6233. **Subscription Rates:** EUR1,407 institutions Europe (print only); 922 institutions Europe (print only); 2,256 SFr institutions Switzerland (print only); US$1,806 institutions, other countries print only; EUR1,548 institutions Europe (print and online); 1,015 institutions Europe (print and online); 2,482 SFr institutions Switzerland (print and online); US$1,987 institutions, other countries print and online. **URL:** http://onlinelibrary.wiley.com/journal/10.1002/(ISSN)1521-4184.

44359 ■ DLG-Mitteilungen
German Agricultural Society
Deutsche Landwirtschafts-Gesellschaft
Eschborner Landstrasse 122
D-60489 Frankfurt, Germany
Ph: 49 69 247880
Fax: 49 69 24788110
Publication E-mail: dlg-mitteilungen@dlg.org
Publisher E-mail: info@dlg.org
German language publication covering agricultural development. **Freq:** Monthly. **Key Personnel:** Thomas Preusse, Contact, t.preusse@dlg.org; Friedrich Rathing, Contact, b.stange@dlg.org; Dr. Christian Bickert, Contact, c.bickert@dlg.org; Annegret Munscher, Contact, a.muenscher@dlg.org; Lisa Langbehn, Contact, dlg-mitteilungen@dlg.org; Bianca Stange, Contact, b.stange@dlg.org. **ISSN:** 0341-0412. **Remarks:** Advertising accepted; rates available upon request. **URL:** http://www.dlg-mitteilungen.de. **Circ:** 12,000

44360 ■ Frankfurter Allgemeine
Frankfurter Allgemeine Zeitung GmbH
Hellerhofstr. 2-4
D-60327 Frankfurt, Germany
Publisher E-mail: vertrieb@faz.de
Business publication. **Founded:** Nov. 1949. **Freq:** Daily. **ISSN:** 0174-4909. **Online:** Gale. **URL:** http://www.faz.net/s/homepage.html.

44361 ■ Herzschrittmachertherapie & Elektrophysiologie
Springer Netherlands
J. W Goethe University Clinic
Medical Clinic III - Cardiology
Theodor-Stern-Kai 7
60590 Frankfurt, Germany
Publisher E-mail: permissions.dordrecht@springer.com
Journal on modern operation techniques and experimental methods in cardiac pacemaker therapy & electrical physiology. **Subtitle:** German Journal of Cardiac Pacing and Electrophysiology. **Freq:** Quarterly. **Print Method:** Offset. **Cols./Page:** 6. **Col. Width:** 26 nonpareils. **Col. Depth:** 21 1/2 inches. **Key Personnel:** Dr. Carsten W. Israel, Editor, cwisrael@em.uni-frankfurt.de; Prof. Helmut U. Klein, Sen. Ed. **ISSN:** 0938-7412. **Subscription Rates:** EUR345 institutions print incl. free access or e-only; EUR414 institutions print incl. enhanced access. **Remarks:** Advertising accepted; rates available upon request. **URL:** http://www.springer.com/steinkopff/kardiologie/journal/399. **Circ:** (Not Reported)

44362 ■ Literaturnachrichten
Society for the Promotion of African, Asian, and Latin American Literature
PO Box 10 01 16
D-60001 Frankfurt, Germany
Ph: 49 69 2102143
Fax: 49 69 2102227
Publication E-mail: litprom@book-fair.com
Publisher E-mail: litprom@book-fair.com
German language publication covering literature from Africa, Asia, and Latin America. **Subtitle:** Africa-Asia-Latin America. **Founded:** 1983. **Freq:** Quarterly in Mar, Jun, Oct, Dec. **Print Method:** Offset. **Trim Size:** 749 x 230 mm. **ISSN:** 0935-7807. **URL:** http://www.litprom.de/literaturnachrichten.html. **Ad Rates:** BW: EUR400, 4C: EUR500. **Circ:** 3,500

44363 ■ WWF Journal
World Wide Fund for Nature - Germany
Umweltstiftung WWF - Deutschland
Rebstocker StraBe 55
D-60326 Frankfurt, Germany
Ph: 49 697 91440
Fax: 49 696 17221

Publisher E-mail: info@wwf.de
Journal covering world wildlife conservation, in German. **Freq:** Quarterly. **Subscription Rates:** for members. **URL:** http://www.wwf.de/.

Frankfurt am Main

44364 ■ Beilstein Journal of Organic Chemistry
Beilstein - Institut zur Foerderung der Chemischen Wissenschaften
Trakehner Strasse 7-9
D-60487 Frankfurt am Main, Germany
Ph: 49 69 7167320
Fax: 49 69 71673219
Publication E-mail: bjoc@manchester.ac.uk
Publisher E-mail: info@beilstein-institut.de
Journal covering organic chemistry in its broadest sense, including: organic synthesis, organic reactions, natural products chemistry, supramolecular chemistry and chemical biology. **Key Personnel:** Jonathan Clayden, Editor-in-Chief; Prof. Benjamin List, Advisory Board; Prof. Jack E. Baldwin, Advisory Board; Prof. Alexandre Alexakis, Advisory Board; Prof. Michael Goebel, Advisory Board; Prof. Kelly Chibale, Advisory Board; Prof. Roald Hoffmann, Advisory Board. **Subscription Rates:** Free online. **URL:** http://bjoc.beilstein-journals.org.

44365 ■ Deutscher Fachuerlag GmbH
Lebensmittel Zeitung DIREKT
Mainzer Landstr. 251
D-60326 Frankfurt am Main, Germany
Fax: 49 69 7595 01
Publisher E-mail: info@dfv.de
Trade magazine for the food and food retailing industry. **Founded:** Jan. 1998. **Freq:** Monthly 11/yr. **Cols./Page:** 5. **Col. Width:** 38 millimeters. **Col. Depth:** 300 millimeters. **Key Personnel:** Uwe Rosmanith, Editor-in-Chief; Peter Russ, Contact; Michael Schellenberger, Management Board; Dr. Rolf Grisebach, Management Board; Peter Esser, Executive Board; Florian Fischer, Executive Board; Peter Kley, Management Board; Markus Gotta, Executive Board; Joerg Hintz, Mng. Dir. **ISSN:** 1435-3423. **Remarks:** Accepts advertising. **URL:** http://www.dfv-fachbuch.de/. **Former name:** Spar Aktuell; Der Neue Weg; Lebensmittel Zeitung DIREKT. **Ad Rates:** BW: EUR3,600, 4C: EUR3,600. **Circ:** 89,208

44366 ■ Journal of African Archaeology
Africa Magna Verlag
J. W Goethe-University
60323 Frankfurt am Main, Germany
Publication E-mail: info@african-archaeology.de
Journal publishing papers focusing on aspects of African archaeology and related disciplines. **Freq:** Semiannual. **Key Personnel:** Peter Breunig, Editor, breunig@em.uni-frankfurt.de; Sonja Magnavita, Editor. **ISSN:** 1612-1651. **Subscription Rates:** EUR130 institutions single print only (all continents); EUR65 institutions single print only (Africa); EUR480 institutions single print and online; EUR95 individuals print and online; EUR430 libraries print & online. **URL:** http://www.african-archaeology.de.

44367 ■ Olympisches Feuer
National Olympic Committee for Germany
Nationales Olympisches Komitee fur Deutschland
Otto-Fleck-Schneise 12
D-60528 Frankfurt am Main, Germany
Ph: 49 69 67000
Fax: 49 69 674906
Publisher E-mail: office@dosb.de
Publication covering the Olympic Games. **Founded:** 1886. **Freq:** Bimonthly. **URL:** http://www.dosb.de/de/olympia/olympisches-feuer/noc/no_cache/?sword_list%5B0%5D=olympisches&sword_list%5B1%5D=feuer.

44368 ■ Pro Familia Magazin
Pro Familia: Deutsche Gesellschaft fur Familienplanung,
Stresemannallee 3
D-60596 Frankfurt am Main, Germany
Ph: 49 69 639002
Fax: 49 69 639852
Publication E-mail: magazin@profamilia.de
Publisher E-mail: info@profamilia.de
German language magazine covering family planning. **Freq:** Quarterly. **Key Personnel:** Regine Wlassitschau, Contact, phone 49 69 639002, presse@profamilia.de. **ISSN:** 0175-2960. **Subscription Rates:** EUR19.50 individuals; EUR21.50 out of country; EUR5.10 single issue. **Remarks:** Advertising accepted; rates available

upon request. **URL:** http://www.profamilia.de. **Circ:** 7,000

44369 ■ Selbstpsychologie
Brandes und Apsel Verlag GmbH
Scheidswaldstr. 22
D-60385 Frankfurt am Main, Germany
Publisher E-mail: info@brandes-apsel-verlag.de
Journal discussing and developing the theoretical foundations and clinical practice of psychoanalytic self psychology. **Subtitle:** Europaeische Zeitschrift fuer Psychoanalytische Therapie und Forschung. **Freq:** Quarterly. **ISSN:** 1615-343X. **URL:** http://www.brandes-apsel-verlag.de/cgibib/germinal_shop.exe/showtemplate?page=brap_texte.html&texte_id=1&caller=brap.

Freiburg

44370 ■ Language and Computers
Editions Rodopi B.V.
c/o Christian Mair, Ed.
English Dept.
Albert-Ludwigs-Universitat Freiburg
Kollegiengebaude IV
D-79085 Freiburg, Germany
Publisher E-mail: info@rodopi.nl
Journal focusing on language and computers. **Subtitle:** Studies in Practical Linguistics. **Key Personnel:** Christian Mair, Editor, christian.mair@anglistik.uni-freiburg.de; Charles F. Meyer, Editor, meyer@cs.umb.edu. **ISSN:** 0921-5034. **URL:** http://www.rodopi.nl/senj.asp?SerieId=LC.

44371 ■ Mind and Matter
Imprint Academic
Institut fur Grenzgebiete der Psychologie und Psychohyg
Wilhelmstr. 3a
D-79098 Freiburg, Germany
Ph: 49 761 2072118
Fax: 49 761 2072191
Publisher E-mail: keith@imprint.co.uk
Journal aimed at a readership interested in all aspects of mind-matter research from the perspectives of sciences and the humanities, devoted to the publication of empirical, theoretical, and conceptual research and the discussion of its results. **Subtitle:** An International Interdisciplinary Journal of Mind-Matter Research. **Freq:** Semiannual. **Key Personnel:** Harald Atmanspacher, Editor-in-Chief, editor@mindmatter.de. **ISSN:** 1611-8812. **Subscription Rates:** 26 individuals includes mailing; 65 institutions includes mailing; US$14 individuals airmail extra per volume; US$130 institutions includes mailing; US$52 individuals includes mailing; 7 individuals airmail extra per volume. **URL:** http://www.mindmatter.de/.

44372 ■ Renewable Energy Focus
International Solar Energy Society
Villa Tannheim
Wiesentalstrasse 50
D-79115 Freiburg, Germany
Ph: 49 761 459060
Fax: 49 761 4590699
Publisher E-mail: hq@ises.org
Publication covering solar energy. **Freq:** Bimonthly. **Key Personnel:** David Hopwood, Editor, d.hopwood@elsevier.com. **Remarks:** Accepts advertising. **URL:** http://www.ises.org/; http://www.renewableenergyfocus.com/. **Formerly:** SunWorld (June 2000); Refocus. **Circ:** 86,140

44373 ■ Solar Energy Journal
International Solar Energy Society
Villa Tannheim
Wiesentalstrasse 50
D-79115 Freiburg, Germany
Ph: 49 761 459060
Fax: 49 761 4590699
Publisher E-mail: hq@ises.org
Journal covering solar energy. **Freq:** Monthly. **Key Personnel:** Dr. D. Yogi Goswami, Editor-in-Chief. **ISSN:** 0038-092X. **Subscription Rates:** EUR52 members paper version; EUR45 members electronic version. **URL:** http://www.ises.org; http://www.ises.org/shortcut.nsf/to/sej.

44374 ■ Viszeralmedizin
S. Karger Publishers Inc.
c/o Dr. Sven Riestenpatt

PO Box 79095
79095 Freiburg, Germany
Ph: 49 761 4520722
Fax: 49 761 4520714
Publisher E-mail: karger@snet.net
Medical journal in English and German. **Subtitle:** Gastrointestinal Medicine and Surgery. **Freq:** Quarterly. **Trim Size:** 210 x 297 mm. **Key Personnel:** Ernst Klar, Editor-in-Chief; Joachim Mossner, Editor-in-Chief; Pierre-Alain Clavien, Editorial Board; Markus M. Lerch, Assoc. Ed.; Hans-Peter Bruch, Editorial Board; Andrea Frilling, Editorial Board; Jacob R. Izbicki, Assoc. Ed.; Reinhard Bittner, Sen. Ed. **ISSN:** 1662-6664. **Subscription Rates:** US$267 institutions print or online; EUR197 institutions print or online; 286 SFr institutions print or online; US$329 institutions print and online; EUR243 institutions print and online; 352 SFr institutions print and online. **Remarks:** Accepts advertising. **URL:** http://content.karger.com/ProdukteDB/produkte.asp?Aktion=JournalHome&ProduktNr=223970. **Foreign language name:** Surgical Gastroenterologie. **Formerly:** Chirurgische Gastroenterologie. **Circ:** Combined 4,000

Freising

44375 ■ Systematic and Applied Microbiology
Elsevier Science Inc.
c/o Karl-Heinz Schleifer, Exec. Ed.
Lehrstuhl fur Mikrobiologie der TU Munchen
Am Hochanger 4
D-85350 Freising, Germany
Ph: 49 8161 715441
Fax: 49 8161 715475
Publisher E-mail: usinfo-ehelp@elsevier.com
Journal dealing with various aspects of microbial diversity and systematics of prokaryotes. **Founded:** 1980. **Freq:** 8/yr. **Key Personnel:** Otto Kandler, Editor; Karl-Heinz Schleifer, Exec. Ed., schleife@mikro.biologie.tu-muenchen.de; Ralf Conrad, Editor; Chris Rodgers, Language Ed., phone 34 977 744660; Ramon Rossello-Mora, Exec. Ed., phone 34 971 611826, fax 34 971 611761, rossello-mora@uib.es; Michael Blaut, Editor; Brian Austin, Editor; Jean Paul Euzeby, Editor; Rudolf Amann, Exec. Ed., phone 49 2028930, fax 49 2028580, ramann@mpi-bremen.de; Milton Costa, Editor. **ISSN:** 0723-2020. **Subscription Rates:** EUR1,133 institutions European countries and Iran; US$1,248 institutions, other countries except Europe, Japan and Iran; 165,800¥ institutions; EUR410 students European countries and Iran; EUR546 institutions European countries and Iran; US$547 other countries except Europe, Japan and Iran; 71,400¥ individuals. **URL:** http://www.elsevier.com/wps/find/journaldescription.cws_home/701801/descrip tiondescription.

Friedland

44376 ■ Indogermanische Forschungen
Walter de Gruyter GmbH & Co. KG
Schladeberg 20
D-37133 Friedland, Germany
Publisher E-mail: info@degruyter.com
Journal featuring areas of historical-comparative linguistics, historical linguistics, typology and characteristics of the languages of the Indogermanic family language. **Freq:** Annual. **Trim Size:** 230 x 155 mm. **Key Personnel:** Prof. Wolfgang P Schmid, Editor; Eckhard Eggers, Editor. **ISSN:** 0019-7262. **Remarks:** Accepts advertising. **URL:** http://www.degruyter.de/journals/igf/detailEn.cfm. **Ad Rates:** BW: DM 600. **Circ:** 350

Garching

44377 ■ Bioprocess and Biosystems Engineering
Springer-Verlag GmbH & Company KG
c/o Dirk Weuster-Botz, Ed.-in-Ch.
Lehrstuhl fur Bioverfahrenstechnik
Boltzmannstr. 15
D-85748 Garching, Germany
Publisher E-mail: webmaster@springer.com
Peer-reviewed journal focusing on the multidisciplinary approaches for integrative bioprocess design. **Freq:** 9/yr. **Key Personnel:** Dirk Weuster-Botz, Editor-in-Chief, bpbse@lrz.tum.de; Sang Yup Lee, Assoc. Ed., leesy@kaist.ac.kr; Gunnar Liden, Assoc. Ed., gunnar.liden@chemeng.lth.se; John A. Morgan, Assoc. Ed., jamorgan@ecn.purdue.edu; Hiroshi Shimizu, Assoc. Ed., shimizu@bio.eng.osaka-u.ac.jp; Jian-Jiang Zhong, Assoc. Ed., jjzhong@sjtu.edu.cn. **ISSN:** 1615-7591.

Subscription Rates: EUR1,935 institutions; EUR2,322 institutions enhanced access. **Remarks:** Advertising accepted; rates available upon request. **URL:** http://www.springer.com/chemistry/biotech/journal/449. **Circ:** (Not Reported)

44378 ■ Chemical Physics
Elsevier Science Inc.
c/o W. Domcke, Ed.
Technische Universitat Munchen
Garching, Germany
Publisher E-mail: usinfo-ehelp@elsevier.com
Journal covering the fields of spectroscopy and molecular structure, interacting systems, relaxation phenomena, fundamental problems in molecular reactivity. **Founded:** 1973. **Freq:** 36/yr. **Print Method:** Offset. **Cols./Page:** 5. **Col. Width:** 24 nonpareils. **Col. Depth:** 196 agate lines. **Key Personnel:** R.M. Hochstrasser, Editor, fax 215898-0590, hochstra@sas.upenn.edu; W. Domcke, Editor, chemphys@ch.tum.de; H.P. Trommsdorff, Advisory Editorial Board, chemphys@ujf-grenoble.fr; G.L. Hofacker, Special Ed., hofacker@ch.tum.de; P. Alivisatos, Advisory Editorial Board; P. Anfinrud, Advisory Editorial Board; W. Zinth, Advisory Editorial Board; P.F. Barbara, Advisory Editorial Board; R. Bini, Advisory Editorial Board; L.D. Barron, Advisory Editorial Board. **ISSN:** 0301-0104. **Subscription Rates:** EUR8,723 institutions for European countries and Iran; US$9,757 institutions, other countries except Europe, Japan and Iran; 1,157,900¥ institutions. **URL:** http://www.elsevier.com/wps/find/journaldescription.cws_home/505699/descriptiondescription.

44379 ■ physica status solidi (a)
John Wiley & Sons Inc.
c/o Martin Stutzmann, Ed.-in-Ch.
Walter-Schottky-Institute
Technische Universitat Muenchen
Am Coulombwall
D-85748 Garching, Germany
Fax: 49 89 28912737
Publisher E-mail: info@wiley.com
Journal focusing on the field of solid state physics. **Subtitle:** Applications and Materials Science. **Freq:** Monthly. **Key Personnel:** Martin Stutzmann, Editor-in-Chief, stutz@wsi.tum.de; Shuit Tong Lee, Editorial Board; Martin S. Brandt, Regional Ed., mbrandt@physik.tu-muenchen.de. **ISSN:** 0031-8965. **Subscription Rates:** EUR6,410 institutions for print; 10,147 SFr institutions for print; US$8,346 institutions, other countries print only; EUR14,102 institutions print with online access; 22,323 SFr institutions print with online; US$18,361 institutions, other countries print with online access. **URL:** http://onlinelibrary.wiley.com/journal/10.1002/(ISSN)1862-6319.

44380 ■ physica status solidi (b)
John Wiley & Sons Inc.
Walter-Schottky-Institut
Technische Universitat Muenchen
Am Coulombwall
D-85748 Garching, Germany
Fax: 49 892 8912737
Publisher E-mail: info@wiley.com
Journal focusing on the field of solid state physics. **Freq:** Monthly. **Key Personnel:** Martin Stutzmann, Editor-in-Chief, stutz@wsi.tum.de; John I.B. Wilson, Editorial Board, Michael S. Shur, Regional Ed., shurm@rpi.edu; Pablo Ordejon, Regional Ed., ordejon@icmab.es; Martin S. Brandt, Regional Ed., mbrandt@physik.tu-muenchen.de; Shuit-Tong Lee, Regional Ed., st.lee@cityu.edu.hk; Stefan Hildebrandt, Managing Editor; Marilia J. Caldas, Regional Ed. **ISSN:** 0370-1972. **Subscription Rates:** EUR6,410 institutions for print only; 10,147 SFr institutions for print only; US$8,346 institutions, other countries for print only; EUR14,102 institutions combined print with online access; 122,323 SFr institutions combined print with online access; US$18,361 institutions, other countries combined print with online access. **URL:** http://onlinelibrary.wiley.com/journal/10.1002/(ISSN)1521-3951/homepage/edbd.html.

44381 ■ physica status solidi (c)
John Wiley & Sons Inc.
Walter-Schottky-Institut
Technische Universitat Muenchen
Am Coulombwall
85748 Garching, Germany
Fax: 49 89 28912737
Publisher E-mail: info@wiley.com
Journal focusing on the field of solid state physics. **Freq:** Monthly. **Key Personnel:** Martin Stutzmann, Editor-in-Chief, stutz@wsi.tum.de; Martin S. Brandt, Regional

Ed., mbrandt@physik.tu-muenchen.de; Shuit-Tong Lee, Editorial Board. **ISSN:** 1610-1634. **Subscription Rates:** US$428 individuals for print; US$5,348 institutions for print; US$5,883 institutions for print and online. **URL:** http://onlinelibrary.wiley.com/journal/10.1002/(ISSN)1610-1642.

Garmisch-Partenkirchen

44382 ■ Radio Oberland-FM - 97.5
Marienplatz 17
Postfach 1752
D-82467 Garmisch-Partenkirchen, Germany
Ph: 49 882 193020
Fax: 49 882 1930230
E-mail: redaktion@radio-oberland.de
Format: Sports; Ethnic. **Operating Hours:** Continuous. **Ad Rates:** Advertising accepted; rates available upon request. **URL:** http://www.radio-oberland.de.

Giessen

44383 ■ Andrologia
John Wiley & Sons Inc.
Wiley-Blackwell
c/o Dr. Wolf-Bernhard Schill, Ed.-in-Ch.
Zentrum fur Dermatologie und Adrologie
Gaffkystrasse 14
D-35385 Giessen, Germany
Ph: 49 641 9943200
Fax: 49 641 9943209
Journal focusing on the current clinical, morphological, biochemical, and experimental status of organic male infertility and sexual disorders in men. Official publication of the Deutsche Gesellschaft fur Andrologie. **Freq:** Bimonthly. **Key Personnel:** Dr. Uwe Paasch, Editor-in-Chief, uwe.paasch@medizin.uni-leipzig.de; Dr. Wolf-Bernhard Schill, Editor-in-Chief, wolf-bernhard.schill@derma.med.uni-giessen.de; G. Aumuller, Editor. **ISSN:** 0303-4569. **Subscription Rates:** US$501 individuals print + online; US$328 members print + online; US$819 institutions print + online; US$744 institutions print or online; US$868 institutions, other countries print or online; EUR406 individuals print + online (Euro zone); 174 members print + online (U.K. and Euro zone); EUR547 institutions print or online; US$954 institutions, other countries print + online; 474 institutions print + online. **Remarks:** Accepts advertising. **URL:** http://www.wiley.com/bw/journal.asp?ref=0303-4569&site=1. **Circ:** (Not Reported)

44384 ■ Cardiovascular Research
Mosby Inc.
Physiologisches Institute, Medical Faculty
Justus-Leibig-Universitat
Aulweg 129
D-35392 Giessen, Germany
Ph: 49 641 9947242
Fax: 49 641 9947209
Publisher E-mail: custserv.ehs@elsevier.com
Journal publishing basic and clinical research in cardiovascular physiology and pathophysiology. **Founded:** 1995. **Freq:** 14/yr. **Key Personnel:** Hans Michael Piper, Editor-in-Chief; David Garcia Dorado, Co-Ed.; Gerhild Euler, Assoc. Ed.; Heinrich Sauer, Assoc. Ed.; Thomas Noll, Assoc. Ed.; Marisol Ruiz-Meana, Assoc. Ed. **ISSN:** 0008-6363. **Subscription Rates:** 281 individuals print; US$562 individuals print; EUR422 individuals print; 892 institutions print and online; US$1,784 institutions print and online; EUR1,338 institutions print and online; 691 institutions online; US$1,382 institutions online; EUR1,037 institutions print; 817 institutions print. **URL:** http://cardiovascres.oxfordjournals.org/.

44385 ■ Cross/Cultures
Rodopi
c/o Dr. Gordon Collier, Ed.
Dept. of English & American Studies
Justus Liebig University
Otto-Behaghel-Strasse 10
D-35394 Giessen, Germany
Fax: 49 641 9930089
Publisher E-mail: info@rodopi.nl
Journal covering post-colonial English literature. **Subtitle:** Readings in the Post/Colonial Literatures in English. **Founded:** 1980. **Freq:** Quarterly. **Print Method:** Offset. **Trim Size:** 8 3/8 x 10 7/8. **Cols./Page:** 3. **Col. Width:** 13.5 picas. **Col. Depth:** 54 picas. **Key Personnel:** Hena Maes-Jelinek, Editor, hmaes@ulg.ac.

Circulation: ★ = ABC; △ = BPA; ♦ = CAC; • = CCAB; ❑ = VAC; ⊕ = PO Statement; ‡ = Publisher's Report; Boldface figures = sworn; Light figures = estimated.

Gale Directory of Publications & Broadcast Media/147th Ed.

4937

be; Dr. Gordon Collier, Editor, gordon.r.collier@anglistik. uni-giessen.de; Geoffrey Davis, Editor, davis@anglistik1. rwth-aachen.de. **ISSN:** 0924-1426. **URL:** http://www. rodopi.nl/senj.asp?SerieId=CC.

44386 ■ International Journal of Systematic and Evolutionary Microbiology

Society for General Microbiology
c/o Peter Kampfer, Ed.-in-Ch.
Institut fur Angewandte Mikrobiologie
Justus-Liebig-Universitat Giessen
Heinrich-Buff-Ring 26-32
D-35392 Giessen, Germany
Fax: 49 641 9937359
Publication E-mail: ijsem@sgm.ac.uk

Professional journal covering bacterial systematics and evolution. **Founded:** 1951. **Freq:** Bimonthly. **Trim Size:** 275 x 210 mm. **Cols./Page:** 2. **Col. Width:** 84 millimeters. **Col. Depth:** 235 millimeters. **Key Personnel:** Peter Kampfer, Editor-in-Chief, peter.kaempfer@ umwelt.uni-giessen.de; Richard J. Birtles, Assoc. Ed., fax 44 15 17946005, richard.birtles@liv.ac.uk; Hans-Jurgen Busse, Assoc. Ed., fax 43 125 0772190, hans-juergen.busse@vu-wien.ac.at; Jongsik Chun, Assoc. Ed., fax 82 288 84911, jchun@snu.ac.kr; David P. Labeda, Assoc. Ed., labeda_ijsem@mchsi.com; John Bowman, Assoc. Ed., fax 61 362 262642, john.bowman@ utas.edu.au; Jean-Francois Bernardet, Assoc. Ed., fax 33 134 652591, jean-francois.bernardet@jouy.inra.fr; Christian Hertel, Assoc. Ed., fax 49 5431 183114, c.hertel@dil-ev.de. **ISSN:** 1466-5026. **Subscription Rates:** 640 individuals print & online (U.K.); 610 individuals online only (U.K.); US$1,055 U.S., Canada, and Mexico print & online; US$1,020 U.S., Canada, and Mexico online only. **Remarks:** Accepts advertising. **URL:** http://ijs.sgmjournals.org. **Former name:** International Journal of Systematic Bacteriology. **Ad Rates:** BW: DM 495, 4C: DM 945. **Circ:** Combined 925

44387 ■ Journal of Individual Differences

Hogrefe & Huber Publishers
c/o Juergen Hennig, PhD, Ed.-in-Ch.
Dept. of Psychology & Sport Sciences
University of Giessen
Otto-Behaghel-Str. 10
D-35394 Giessen, Germany
Ph: 49 641 9926150
Fax: 49 641 9926159
Publisher E-mail: customerservice@hogrefe-publishing. com

Journal covering differences between humans and animals with respect to their behavior, emotion, cognition, and developmental aspects. **Freq:** Quarterly. **Print Method:** Offset litho. **Trim Size:** 8 1/4 x 11. **Key Personnel:** Thomas Rammsayer, Assoc. Ed.; Burkhard Brocke, Assoc. Ed.; Aljoscha Neubauer, Assoc. Ed.; Sam Gosling, Assoc. Ed.; Philip J. Corr, Assoc. Ed.; Juergen Hennig, PhD, Editor-in-Chief, juergen.hennig@psychol. uni-giessen.de. **ISSN:** 1614-0001. **Subscription Rates:** US$204 institutions; EUR149 institutions; US$125 individuals; EUR89 individuals; US$68 single issue; EUR49 single issue. **Remarks:** Accepts advertising. **URL:** http://www.hogrefe.com/index.php?mod=journals&action=1&site=jid. **Ad Rates:** BW: DM 530. **Circ:** 400

44388 ■ Neurogenetics

Springer-Verlag
c/o Ulrich Muller, Ed.
Institut fur Humangenetik
der Justus-Liebig-Universitat
Schlangenzahl 14
D-35392 Giessen, Germany
Fax: 49 641 9941609

Journal focusing mainly on Neurogenetic disorders. **Freq:** 4/yr. **Key Personnel:** Ulrich Muller, Editor, ulrich. mueller@humangenetik.med.uni-giessen.de; James R. Lupski, Editor, jlupski@bcm.tmc.edu; Manuel B. Graeber, Editor, fax 44 20 88467794, m.graeber@imperial. ac.uk; Robert Brown, Editorial Board; John Collinge, Editorial Board; Alexis Brice, Editorial Board; Xandra O. Breakefield, Editorial Board; Jacqueline S. De Belleroche, Editorial Board; John Crabbe, Editorial Board. **ISSN:** 1364-6745. **Subscription Rates:** EUR633 institutions print incl. free access; EUR759.60 institutions print incl. enhanced access. **Remarks:** Advertising accepted; rates available upon request. **URL:** http://www.springer. com/biomed/neuroscience/journal/10048. **Circ:** (Not Reported)

Gottingen

44389 ■ Advances in Geosciences

Copernicus GmbH
Bahnhofsallee 1e
D-37081 Gottingen, Germany
Ph: 49 551 900339
Fax: 49 551 900339
Publisher E-mail: info@copernicus.org
Peer-reviewed journal for publication of collections of short, self-contained communications in the Earth, planetary and solar system sciences. **Key Personnel:** Nadine Deisel, Contact. **ISSN:** 1680-7340. **URL:** http://www.advances-in-geosciences.net/.

44390 ■ Advances in Radio Science

Copernicus GmbH
Bahnhofsallee 1e
D-37081 Gottingen, Germany
Ph: 49 551 900339
Fax: 49 551 900339
Publisher E-mail: info@copernicus.org
Peer-reviewed journal covering the field of radio science and engineering. **Key Personnel:** Karl-Jorg Langenberg, Managing Editor, phone 49 561 8046368, fax 49 561 8046489, langenberg@uni-kassel.de; Ulrich Stumper, Editor, phone 49 531 5922220, fax 49 531 5922205, ulrich.stumper@ptb.de; Madhu Chandra, Editor, phone 49 371 5313168, fax 49 371 5313216, madhu.chandra@infotech.tu-chemnitz.de; Matthias Forster, Editor, phone 49 89 300003525, fax 49 89 300003569, mfo@mpe.mpg.de; Frank Sabath, Editor, phone 49 5192 136606, franksabath@bwb.org; Gottfried Mann, Editor, phone 49 331 7499292, fax 49 331 7499352, gmann@aip.de. **ISSN:** 1684-9965. **URL:** http://www.copernicus.org/URSI/ars/ars.html.

44391 ■ Allergy and Clinical Immunology International

Hogrefe & Huber Publishers
c/o Dr. Christine Hogrefe, Mng. Ed.
Hogrefe & Huber Publishers
Rohnsweg 25
D-37085 Gottingen, Germany
Ph: 49 551 496090
Fax: 49 551 496098
Publisher E-mail: customerservice@hogrefe-publishing. com
Journal covering allergy and immunology and is also aimed at primary care physicians, rheumatologists, internists, and pediatricians. **Freq:** Bimonthly. **Trim Size:** 210 x 297 mm. **Key Personnel:** Dr. Christine Hogrefe, Managing Editor, christinehogrefe@hogrefe.com. **ISSN:** 0838-1925. **Subscription Rates:** 149 institutions; 92 individuals; 58 members; US$162 institutions; US$99 individuals; US$63 members. **Remarks:** Accepts advertising. **URL:** http://www.acii.net/aimsscop.html. **Ad Rates:** BW: DM 2,690, 4C: DM 3,990. **Circ:** (Not Reported)

■ Astrophysics and Space Sciences Transactions

Copernicus GmbH
Bahnhofsallee 1e
D-37081 Gottingen, Germany
Ph: 49 551 900339
Fax: 49 551 900339
Publisher E-mail: info@copernicus.org
Peer-reviewed journal covering all fields of astrophysics and space sciences and related technology. **Freq:** 2/yr. **Key Personnel:** Klaus Scherer, Exec. Ed., phone 49 5556 9955023, kls@tp4.rub.de; Horst Fichtner, Exec. Ed. **ISSN:** 1810-6528. **URL:** http://www.astrophysics-and-space-sciences-transactions.net/index.html.

44393 ■ Basic and Applied Ecology

Ecological Society of Germany, Austria and Switzerland
Gesellschaft fur Okologie
c/o Teja Tscarntke, Ed.-in-Ch.
Agroecology, University of Gottingen
Waldweg 26
D-37073 Gottingen, Germany
Ph: 49 551 399209
Fax: 49 551 398806
Publisher E-mail: info@gfoe.org
Publication covering ecology. **Founded:** 2000. **Freq:** 6/yr. **Key Personnel:** Teja Tscharntke, Editor-in-Chief, ttschar@gwdg.de; Klaus Hovemeyer, Managing Editor, mschaef@gwdg.de. **ISSN:** 1439-1791. **Subscription Rates:** EUR551 institutions Germany, Austria, Switzer-

land, Liechtenstein; EUR206 individuals Germany, Austria, Switzerland, Liechtenstein; EUR583 institutions; EUR206 individuals; 79,700¥ institutions; 26,900¥ individuals; US$650 institutions, other countries; US$207 other countries; EUR83 single issue Germany, Austria, Switzerland, Liechtenstein; 12,000¥ single issue. **URL:** http://www.elsevier.de/baae; http://www. gfoe.org/gfoe-publications/basic-and-applied-ecology. html?L=1.

44394 ■ Biogeosciences Discussions

Copernicus GmbH
Bahnhofsallee 1e
D-37081 Gottingen, Germany
Ph: 49 551 900339
Fax: 49 551 900339
Publisher E-mail: info@copernicus.org
International scientific journal dedicated to the publication and discussion of research articles, short communications and review papers on all aspects of the interactions between the biological, chemical and physical processes in terrestrial or extraterrestrial life with the geosphere, hydrosphere and atmosphere. **Key Personnel:** Albrecht Neftel, Editor-in-Chief, phone 41 1 3777504, fax 41 1 3777201, gattuso@obs-vlfr.fr; Jurgen Kesselmeier, Editor-in-Chief, phone 49 6131 305492, fax 49 6131 305487, jks@mpch-mainz.mpg.de. **ISSN:** 1810-6277. **URL:** http://www.biogeosciences-discuss. net/papers_in_open_discussion.html.

44395 ■ Diversities

UNESCO
Section of Cultural Enterprise and Copyright
Max Planck Institute for the Study of Religious & Ethnic Diversity
U.S. Department of of Socio-Cultural Diversity
PO Box 2833
D-37081 Gottingen, Germany
Ph: 49 551 4956114
Publisher E-mail: bpi@unesco.org
Journal dealing with social science research in the fields of migration, multiculturalism, and minority rights. **Key Personnel:** Matthias Koenig, Board member, matthias. koenig@sowi.uni-goettingen.de; Gabriele Alex, Editor. **ISSN:** 2079-6595. **URL:** http://portal.unesco.org/shs/en/ ev.php-URL_ID=2547&URL_DO=DO_TOPIC&URL_ SECTION=201.html. **Formerly:** International Journal on Multicultural Societies (IJMS).

44396 ■ Ethik in der Medizin

Academy for Ethics in Medicine
Akademie fur Ethik in der Medizin
Humboldtallee 36
D-37073 Gottingen, Germany
Ph: 49 551 399680
Publisher E-mail: info@aem-online.de
German language publication covering medical ethics. **Freq:** Quarterly. **Key Personnel:** Susanne Raphael, Contact. **ISSN:** 0935-7335. **Remarks:** Advertising accepted; rates available upon request. **URL:** http://www. idem.uni-goettingen.de/. **Circ:** (Not Reported)

44397 ■ European Journal of Anaesthesiology

Cambridge University Press
c/o Prof. Thomas Crozier, Ed.-in-Ch.
Georg-August Universitat
Robert-Koch-Strasse 40
37075 Gottingen, Germany
Publisher E-mail: customer_service@cup.org
Journal to promote advances in microscopy. **Key Personnel:** Prof. Thomas Crozier, Editor-in-Chief, tcrozie@ gwdg.de; Prof. Jean-Pierre Haberer, Editor, jean-pierre. haberer@htd.ap-hop-paris.fr; Prof. Martin Tramer, Editor, martin.tramer@hcuge.ch. **ISSN:** 0265-0215. **Subscription Rates:** 884 institutions print and online; US$1,680 institutions print and online; EUR1,320 institutions print and online; 772 institutions online only; US$1,467 institutions online only; EUR1,150 institutions online only; 176 individuals print and online; US$335 individuals print and online; EUR262 individuals print and online. **Remarks:** Accepts display advertising. **URL:** http://journals. cambridge.org/action/displayJournal?jid=EJA. **Ad Rates:** BW: 850, 4C: 1,210. **Circ:** 8,600

44398 ■ Forest Policy and Economics

Elsevier Science
c/o M. Krott, Ed.-in-Ch.
Institute for Forest Policy & Nature Conservation
Georg-August-University of Gottingen
D-37077 Gottingen, Germany
Publisher E-mail: nlinfo-f@elsevier.com
International journal featuring various policy issues including economics and planning, relating to the forest

and forest industries sector in connection with European Forest Institute. **Founded:** 2000. **Freq:** 8/yr. **Key Personnel:** M. Krott, Editor-in-Chief, mkrott@gwdg.de; M. Ahmad, Editorial Advisory Board; B. Arts, Editorial Advisory Board. **ISSN:** 1389-9341. **Subscription Rates:** EUR497 institutions for European countries; US$560 institutions for all countries except Europe and Japan; 66,100¥ institutions; US$296 individuals for all countries except Europe and Japan; EUR221 individuals for European countries; 34,000¥ individuals. **Remarks:** Accepts advertising. **URL:** http://www.elsevier.com/wps/find/journaldescription.cws_home/620157/descriptiondescription. **Circ:** (Not Reported)

44399 ■ In Silico Biology
IOS Press, B.V.
c/o Dr. E. Wingender, Ed.-in-Ch.
Dept. of Bioinformatics
University of Gottingen
Goldschmidtstrasse 1
D-37077 Gottingen, Germany
Ph: 49 551 3914911
Fax: 49 551 3914914
Publisher E-mail: info@iospress.nl
Peer-reviewed journal focusing in the application of theoretical/ mathematical/computational tools onto biological systems rather than to describe new algorithms, promoting the development of a more integrated view of living systems. **Freq:** Bimonthly. **Key Personnel:** Dr. E. Wingender, Editor-in-Chief, e.wingender@med.uni-goettingen.de; J.W. Fickett, Editorial Board; P. Bucher, Editorial Board; T. Gaasterland, Editorial Board; P. Bork, Editorial Board. **ISSN:** 1386-6338. **Subscription Rates:** EUR487 individuals print and online; US$682 individuals print and online. **URL:** http://www.iospress.nl/loadtop/load.php?isbn=13866338.

44400 ■ Ocean Science
Copernicus GmbH
Bahnhofsallee 1e
D-37081 Gottingen, Germany
Ph: 49 551 900339
Fax: 49 551 900339
Publisher E-mail: info@copernicus.org
Peer-reviewed journal covering all aspects of ocean science, experimental, theoretical and laboratory. **Key Personnel:** Sabine Arnault, Topic Ed., phone 33 1 44274971, fax 33 1 44277159, sa@locean-ipsl.upmc.fr; John A. Johnson, Exec. Ed., phone 44 1603 593710, fax 44 1603 593868, j.johnson@uea.ac.uk; William Jenkins, Exec. Ed., wjenkins@whoi.edu. **ISSN:** 1812-0784. **Subscription Rates:** EUR293 individuals print; EUR81 single issue print only; EUR132 members print; EUR36 single issue print (member); EUR40 other countries air mail. **URL:** http://www.ocean-science.net/index.html.

44401 ■ Ocean Science Discussions
Copernicus GmbH
Bahnhofsallee 1e
D-37081 Gottingen, Germany
Ph: 49 551 900339
Fax: 49 551 900339
Publisher E-mail: info@copernicus.org
International scientific journal dedicated to the publication and discussion of research articles, short communications and review papers on all aspects of ocean science, experimental, theoretical and laboratory. **Key Personnel:** David Webb, Ch. Exec. Ed., phone 44 23 80596199, fax 44 23 80596204, david.webb@noc.soton.ac.uk; John Johnson, Exec. Ed., phone 44 1603 592598, fax 44 1603 593868, j.johnson@uea.ac.uk; Bernard Barnier, Topic Ed., phone 33 4 76825066, fax 33 4 76825271, bernard.barnier@hmg.inpg.fr; Jack Barth, Topic Ed., barth@coas.oregonstate.edu; Sabine Arnault, Topic Ed., phone 33 1 44274971, sa@lodyc.jussieu.fr. **ISSN:** 1812-0806. **Subscription Rates:** EUR293 individuals print; EUR81 single issue print; EUR132 individuals print; EUR36 single issue print; EUR40 individuals air mail (outside Europe). **URL:** http://www.ocean-sci-discuss.net/volumes_and_issues.html.

44402 ■ Social Geography
Copernicus GmbH
Bahnhofsallee 1e
D-37081 Gottingen, Germany
Ph: 49 551 900339
Fax: 49 551 900339
Publisher E-mail: info@copernicus.org
Journal providing a forum for contributions that combine a strong theoretical orientation with praxis-related matters of concern, focusing on the interrelation of society, practice and space and its implications for every day-

life, social and environmental policy or economic practice. **Key Personnel:** Anthony Giddens, Editor-in-Chief, social.geography@uni-jena.de; Antje Schlottmann, Exec. Ed., phone 49 6979 822980, fax 49 6979 823548, schlottm@em.uni-frankfurt.de; Benno Werlen, Editor-in-Chief; Matthew Hannah, Editor-in-Chief, phone 44 1970 622782, mch@aber.ac.uk; Dana Sprunk, Exec. Ed., phone 49 3641 948904, fax 49 3641 948842. **ISSN:** 1729-4274. **Subscription Rates:** EUR200 individuals print; EUR122 single issue print only. **URL:** http://www.soc-geogr.net/volumes_and_issues.html.

Grasbrunn

44403 ■ natur+kosmos
Konradin Publishing Group
Bretonischer Ring 13
D-85630 Grasbrunn, Germany
Ph: 49 89 45616220
Fax: 49 89 45616300
Publisher E-mail: info@konradin.de
Lifestyle magazine featuring conservation of resources. **Freq:** Monthly. **Key Personnel:** Ilona Jerger, Editor, redaktion@natur.de; Jacqueline Lindner, Contact, phone 49 89 45616145, fax 49 89 45616300, jacqueline.lindner@konradin.de. **Subscription Rates:** EUR63 individuals for students; EUR47.40 individuals upon certification; EUR72 individuals for international; EUR5.90 individuals. **Remarks:** Accepts advertising. **URL:** http://www.natur.de/scripts/basics/natur/news/basics.prg; http://www.konradin.de/konradin/en/zeitschriften/232726.html?rubid=277744. **Ad Rates:** BW: EUR5,000, 4C: EUR7,500. **Circ:** 84,278

Greifswald

44404 ■ Journal of Solid State Electrochemistry
Springer-Verlag
c/o Fritz Scholz, Ed.-in-Ch.
Universitat Greifswald
Institut fur Biochemie
Felix-Hausdorff-Str. 4
D-17487 Greifswald, Germany
Journal dedicated to all aspects of solid-state chemistry and solid-state physics in electrochemistry. **Freq:** Monthly. **Key Personnel:** Fritz Scholz, Editor-in-Chief, fscholz@uni-greifswald.de; Michael Hermes, Managing Editor, jossec@michael-hermes.com. **ISSN:** 1432-8488. **Subscription Rates:** EUR846 institutions print incl. free access; EUR1,015.20 institutions print incl. enhanced access. **Remarks:** Advertising accepted; rates available upon request. **URL:** http://www.springer.com/chemistry/physical/journal/10008. **Circ:** (Not Reported)

44405 ■ MLQ - Mathematical Logic Quarterly
John Wiley & Sons Inc.
Greifswald Institut fu Mathematik und Informatik
Ernst-Moritz-Arndt-Universitat
Friedrich-Ludwig-Jahn-Str. 15a
D-17487 Greifswald, Germany
Publisher E-mail: info@wiley.com
Journal publishing original contributions on mathematical logic and foundations of mathematics and related areas, such as general logic, model theory, recursion theory, set theory, proof theory and constructive mathematics, algebraic logic, nonstandard models, and logical aspects of theoretical computer science. **Freq:** Bimonthly. **Key Personnel:** Armin Hemmerling, Managing Editor, mlq@uni-greifswald.de; John T. Baldwin, Editor; Klaus Ambos-Spies, Editor; Ulrich Kohlenbach, Editor; Douglas S. Bridges, Editor; Marat M. Arslanov, Editor; Carl G. Jockusch, Editor; Alexander Kechris, Editor; Gunter Asser, Editor. **ISSN:** 0942-5616. **Subscription Rates:** EUR838 institutions print only, rest of Europe; 1,326 SFr institutions print only, Switzerland and Liechtenstein; US$1,030 institutions, other countries print only. **URL:** http://www3.interscience.wiley.com/journal/60500242/home.

Gutersloh

44406 ■ ZI-Ziegelindustrie International
Federal National Association of the German Brick Industry
Bundesverband der Deutschen Ziegelindustrie
Avenwedder Str. 55
D-33331 Gutersloh, Germany
Publisher E-mail: info@ziegel.de
German language publication covering the building industry. **Freq:** 10/yr. **Key Personnel:** Ingo Wanders, Hd. of advertising, phone 49 5241 8041973, ingo.

wanders@bauverlag.de; Anett Fischer, Contact, phone 49 5241 8089264, anett.fischer@bauverlag.de. **Subscription Rates:** EUR224.40 individuals Germany; EUR250.80 other countries; EUR147 students. **Remarks:** Accepts advertising. **URL:** http://www.zi-online.info. **Circ:** (Not Reported)

Halle

44407 ■ Flora
Elsevier Science Inc.
c/o Eckehart J. Jager, Ed.
Institut fur Geobotanik und Botanischer Garten
Neuwerk 21
D-06108 Halle, Germany
Publisher E-mail: usinfo-ehelp@elsevier.com
Journal covering distribution of morphology and function of ecology of plants. **Subtitle:** Morphology, Distribution, Functional Ecology of Plants. **Founded:** Jan. 1955. **Freq:** 12/yr. **Print Method:** Offset. **Trim Size:** 8 x 10 7/8. **Cols./Page:** 3. **Col. Width:** 13 picas. **Col. Depth:** 140 agate lines. **Key Personnel:** Rainer Losch, Editor, phone 49 211 8114878, fax 49 211 8113335, loesch@uni-duesseldorf.de; Eckehart J. Jager, Editor; Andres Bresinsky, Editorial Board; Helge Bruelheide, Editorial Board; Otto L. Lange, Editor; Christian Brochmann, Editorial Board; Ulrich Deil, Editorial Board; Hermann Heilmeier, Editorial Board; Reinhard Bornkamm, Editorial Board; Maria Soledad Jimenez, Editorial Board. **ISSN:** 0367-2530. **Subscription Rates:** 136,000¥ institutions; US$1,076 institutions, other countries except Europe and Japan; EUR999 institutions for European countries and Iran; EUR313 individuals for European countries and Iran; US$271 other countries except Europe and Japan; 35,400¥ individuals. **URL:** http://www.elsevier.com/wps/find/journaldescription.cws_home/701764/descriptiondescription.

44408 ■ RTL-FM - 89
Stadtcenter Rolltreppe
Grobe Ulrichstra0e 60 D
D-06108 Halle, Germany
Ph: 49 180 5777890
E-mail: service@89.0rtl.de
Format: Contemporary Hit Radio (CHR). **Key Personnel:** Tim Grunert, Program Mgr. **Ad Rates:** Advertising accepted; rates available upon request. **URL:** http://www.89.0rtl.de.

Hamburg

44409 ■ AngelWoche
AngelWoche/Deutsche Sportfischer Zeitung
Troplowitzstrasse 5
D-22529 Hamburg, Germany
Ph: 49 40 38906131
Fax: 49 40 38906307
Newspaper covering fishing. **Subtitle:** Deutsche Sportfischer Zeitung. **Founded:** Apr. 1984. **Freq:** Semimonthly. **Print Method:** Offset. **Key Personnel:** Rolf Schwarzer, Editor-in-Chief. **Remarks:** Accepts advertising. **URL:** http://www.angelwoche.de/. **Circ:** Paid 80,000

44410 ■ Auto Bild
Axel Springer Verlag
Axel-Springer-Platz 1
D-20350 Hamburg, Germany
Ph: 49 40 34700
Publisher E-mail: information@axelspringer.de
Consumer magazine covering automobiles. **Founded:** 1986. **Freq:** Weekly. **Print Method:** Rotagravure-Cover. **Key Personnel:** Dr. Hans Hamer, Mng. Publisher; Peter Felske, Editor-in-Chief. **Subscription Rates:** EUR1 individuals. **Remarks:** Accepts advertising. **URL:** http://www.autobild.de. **Ad Rates:** BW: EUR22,100, 4C: EUR32,200. **Circ:** Paid 700,244

44411 ■ BILD der FRAU
Axel Springer Verlag
Axel-Springer-Platz 1
D-20350 Hamburg, Germany
Ph: 49 40 34700
Publisher E-mail: information@axelspringer.de
Entertainment magazine for women. **Founded:** 1983. **Freq:** Weekly. **Key Personnel:** Sandra Immoor, Editor-in-Chief. **Subscription Rates:** EUR.42 single issue. **Remarks:** Accepts advertising. **URL:** http://www.bilddderfrau.de/. **Circ:** ‡1,274,182

44412 ■ Climate of the Past
Copernicus GmbH

Circulation: ★ = ABC; △ = BPA; ◆ = CAC; • = CCAB; ❑ = VAC; ⊕ = PO Statement; ‡ = Publisher's Report; Boldface figures = sworn; Light figures = estimated.

Gale Directory of Publications & Broadcast Media/147th Ed.   4939

c/o Martin Claussen, Co-Ed.-in-Ch.
Max Planck Institute for Meteorology
Bundesstr. 53
D-20146 Hamburg, Germany
Ph: 49 40 41173225
Fax: 49 40 41173350
Publisher E-mail: info@copernicus.org
Peer-reviewed journal covering study of the climate history of the Earth. **Key Personnel:** Denis-Didier Rousseau, Co-Ed.-in-Ch., phone 33 1 44322724, fax 33 1 44322727, denis.rousseau@lmd.ens.fr; Luc Beaufort, Editor, phone 33 442 971571, fax 33 442 9715; beaufort@cerege.fr; Gerald Ganssen, Co-Ed.-in-Ch., phone 31 20 5987369, fax 31 20 5989941, gerald.ganssen@falw.vu.nl; Martin Claussen, Co-Ed.-in-Ch., martin.claussen@zmaw.de; Eric W. Wolff, Co-Ed.-in-Ch., phone 44 1223 221491, fax 44 1223 221279, ewwo@bas.ac.uk. **ISSN:** 1814-9324. **Subscription Rates:** EUR224 members print; EUR498 individuals print only; EUR91 single issue print; EUR41 members single print; Free online access; EUR80 other countries air mail. **URL:** http://www.climate-of-the-past.net.

44413 ■ Der Islam
Walter de Gruyter GmbH & Co. KG
Edmund-Siemers-Allee 1 - Flugel Ost
D-20146 Hamburg, Germany
Publication E-mail: der_islam@uni-hamburg.de
Publisher E-mail: info@degruyter.com
Journal featuring the history and culture of Islamic world. **Founded:** 1910. **Freq:** Semiannual. **Print Method:** Web Offset. **Key Personnel:** Lawrence I. Conrad, Editor. **ISSN:** 0021-1818. **Subscription Rates:** EUR206 individuals print + online; EUR180 individuals print or online only; EUR99 single issue. **Remarks:** Accepts advertising. **URL:** http://www.degruyter.com/journals/islam/detailEn.cfm. **Ad Rates:** BW: DM 550. **Circ:** 500

44414 ■ European Addiction Research
S. Karger Publishers Inc.
c/o Dr. Christian Haasen, Ed.
Klinik fur Psychiatrie
Martinistrasse 52
D-20246 Hamburg, Germany
Fax: 49 404 28032999
Publication E-mail: ear@uke.uni-hamburg.de
Publisher E-mail: karger@snet.net
Journal covering addiction research. **Founded:** 1995. **Freq:** Quarterly. **Trim Size:** 210 x 280 mm. **Key Personnel:** W. Van Den Brink, Editor; A. Kastelic, Editorial Board Member; L. San, Editorial Board Member; J. Schwab, Editorial Sec.; G. Fischer, Editorial Board Member; M. Gossop, Editorial Board Member; A. Kokkevi, Editorial Board Member; J. Rehm, Editorial Board Member. **ISSN:** 1022-6877. **Subscription Rates:** 1,078 SFr institutions print or online; EUR770 institutions print or online; US$978 institutions print or online; 1,186 SFr institutions print and online; EUR847 institutions print and online; US$1,076 institutions print and online. **Remarks:** Accepts advertising. **URL:** http://content.karger.com/ProdukteDB/produkte.asp?Aktion=JournalHome&ProduktNr=224233. **Ad Rates:** BW: DM 1,600. **Circ:** Combined 900

44415 ■ Flieger Magazin
Jahr Top Special Verlag
Troplowitzstrasse 5
D-22529 Hamburg, Germany
Ph: 49 403 89060
Fax: 49 403 8906300
Publication E-mail: redaktion@fliegermagazin.de
Professional magazine covering aviation for pilots in German speaking European countries. **Founded:** 1978. **Freq:** Monthly. **Print Method:** Offset. **Trim Size:** 215 x 280. **Key Personnel:** Thomas Borchert, Editor-in-Chief, phone 49 403 8906520, thomas.borchert@fliegermagazin.de. **ISSN:** 0170-5504. **Subscription Rates:** EUR54 individuals. **URL:** http://www.fliegermagazin.de/. **Ad Rates:** BW: EUR3,540, 4C: EUR6,192, PCI: EUR1.69. **Circ:** Paid 25,305

44416 ■ FRAU von HEUTE
Axel Springer Verlag
Brieffach 7940
20350 Hamburg, Germany
Publisher E-mail: information@axelspringer.de
Entertainment magazine for women. **Founded:** 2003. **Freq:** Weekly. **Key Personnel:** Christian Personn, Editor-in-Chief. **Subscription Rates:** EUR44.20 individuals. **Remarks:** Accepts advertising. **URL:** http://www.frauvonheute.de/. **Circ:** ‡349,348

44417 ■ Groups — Complexity — Cryptology
Walter de Gruyter Inc.
c/o Gerhard Rosenberger, Mng. Ed.
Department Mathematik
Universitat Hamburg
Bundesstr. 55
20146 Hamburg, Germany
Publisher E-mail: info@degruyterny.com
Peer-reviewed Journal containing articles in the areas of combinatorial and computational group theory, complexity theory, and cryptology. **Founded:** 2009. **Freq:** Semiannual. **Key Personnel:** Gerhard Rosenberger, Managing Editor; Vladimir Shpilrain, Managing Editor. **ISSN:** 1867-1144. **Subscription Rates:** EUR154 individuals print or online; EUR178 individuals print + online; EUR85 single issue. **URL:** http://www.degruyter.com/journals/gcc/detailEn.cfm.

44418 ■ HORZU
Axel Springer Verlag
Axel-Springer-Platz 1
D-20350 Hamburg, Germany
Ph: 49 40 34700
Publisher E-mail: information@axelspringer.de
Magazine featuring television and radio program. **Founded:** 1946. **Freq:** Weekly. **Key Personnel:** Dr. Thomas Garms, Editor-in-Chief. **Subscription Rates:** EUR17.54 individuals within Europe; EUR226.72 individuals outside. **Remarks:** Accepts advertising. **URL:** http://www.hoerzu.de/. **Circ:** ‡1,538,346

44419 ■ International Journal of Information Security
Springer Netherlands
c/o Dieter Gollmann, Mng. Ed.
TU Hamburg-Harburg
FB 4-14
21071 Hamburg, Germany
Publisher E-mail: permissions.dordrecht@springer.com
Journal on research in information security. **Founded:** 1964. **Freq:** 6/yr. **Print Method:** Offset. **Trim Size:** 11 1/2 x 17 1/2. **Cols./Page:** 5. **Col. Width:** 2 inches. **Col. Depth:** 16 inches. **Key Personnel:** Eiji Okamoto, Editor-in-Chief, okamoto@risk.tsukuba.ac.jp; Miguel Soriano, Editorial Board; Mike Burmester, Editorial Board; Heiko Mantel, Editorial Board; Edward Dawson, Editorial Board; Elisa Bertino, Editorial Board; Masahiro Mambo, Editorial Sec., meadows@itd.nrl.navy.mil; Ryoichi Sasaki, Editorial Board; Phil Porras, Editorial Board; Moti Yung, Editorial Board; Dieter Gollmann, Managing Editor, diego@tuhh.de; Javier Lopez, Editor-in-Chief, jlm@lcc.uma.es. **ISSN:** 1615-5262. **Subscription Rates:** EUR494 institutions print incl. free access or e-only; EUR592.80 institutions print incl. enhanced access. **URL:** http://www.springer.com/computer/securityandcryptology/journal/10207.

44420 ■ Merian
Jahreszeiten Verlag GmbH
Possmoorweg 2
D-22301 Hamburg, Germany
Ph: 49 402 7170
Fax: 49 402 7172056
Publisher E-mail: jahreszeitenverlag@jalag.de
Consumer magazine covering local culture and travel. **Subtitle:** The Pleasure of Travelling. **Founded:** July 1948. **Freq:** Monthly. **Print Method:** Rotary offset. **Key Personnel:** Andreas Hallaschka, Editor-in-Chief. **Subscription Rates:** EUR7.95 single issue. **Remarks:** Advertising accepted; rates available upon request. **URL:** http://www.jalag.de/89.0.html. **Circ:** Paid ◆88,953

44421 ■ Oil World Monthly
ISTA Mielke GmbH
Langenberg 25
D-21077 Hamburg, Germany
Ph: 49 407 610500
Publication E-mail: contact@oilworld.biz
Publisher E-mail: info@oilworld.biz
Publication offering insight into the future of oils & fats, oilseeds, oilmeals and grains as well as livestock and aquaculture products and the interdependencies between the five sectors and the 50 commodities. **Freq:** Monthly. **Key Personnel:** Thomas Mielke, Ed./Dir., thomas.mielke@oilworld.biz. **URL:** http://www.oilworld.biz/app.php?ista=8de817d02592f9a4be1b1f8020a2fad8.

44422 ■ Petra
Jahreszeiten Verlag GmbH
Possmoorweg 2
D-22301 Hamburg, Germany

Ph: 49 402 7170
Fax: 49 402 7172056
Publisher E-mail: jahreszeitenverlag@jalag.de
Consumer magazine covering fashion, beauty and lifestyle for women. **Subtitle:** DAS Mode & Trend Magazine. **Founded:** 1964. **Freq:** Monthly. **Trim Size:** 210 x 280 mm. **Remarks:** Accepts advertising. **URL:** http://www.woche.de/17.0.html. **Ad Rates:** BW: DM 22,500. **Circ:** Paid ‡295,102

44423 ■ Plan Post
Plan International Deutschland e.V.
Bramfelder Str. 70
D-22305 Hamburg, Germany
Ph: 49 406 11400
Fax: 49 406 1140140
Publisher E-mail: info@plan-deutschland.de
German language publication covering child welfare. **Founded:** 1989. **Freq:** Quarterly. **Print Method:** Offset. **Key Personnel:** Ute Kretschmann, Pressestelle. **Subscription Rates:** Free for foster parents. **Remarks:** Accepts advertising. **URL:** http://www.plan-deutschland.de/aktuelles/plan-post/?no_cache=1. **Circ:** Non-paid 176,000

44424 ■ Theoretical and Applied Climatology
Springer-Verlag New York Inc.
c/o H. Grassl, Mng. Ed.
Max Planck Institute for Meteorology
Bundesstrabe 55
D-20146 Hamburg, Germany
Fax: 49 40 41173 350
Publisher E-mail: service-ny@springer.com
Journal covering climate modeling, climatic changes and climate forecasting, meteorology, geophysics and bioclimatology. **Key Personnel:** H. Grassl, Managing Editor, barbara.zinecker@zmaw.de. **ISSN:** 0177-798X. **Remarks:** Advertising accepted; rates available upon request. **URL:** http://www.springer.com/springerwiennewyork/geosciences/journal/704. **Circ:** (Not Reported)

44425 ■ ZuhauseWohnen
Jahreszeiten Verlag GmbH
Possmoorweg 2
D-22301 Hamburg, Germany
Ph: 49 402 7170
Fax: 49 402 7172056
Publisher E-mail: jahreszeitenverlag@jalag.de
Consumer magazine covering home, garden, and lifestyle. **Founded:** Feb. 1967. **Freq:** Monthly. **Print Method:** Offset. **Trim Size:** 213 x 280 mm. **Key Personnel:** Regine Kuhlei, Editor-in-Chief; Oliver Voss, Director; Achim Fransman, Advertising Dir. **ISSN:** 0941-1070. **Subscription Rates:** EUR3.20 single issue. **Remarks:** Accepts advertising. **URL:** http://www.jalag.de/89.0.html. **Ad Rates:** BW: EUR12,300, 4C: EUR18,910. **Circ:** Combined 132,845

44426 ■ NDR-FM - 90.3
Rothenbaumchaussee 132-134
D-20149 Hamburg, Germany
Ph: 49 40 41560
Fax: 49 40 447602
E-mail: info@ndr.de
Format: Ethnic; World Beat. **Operating Hours:** Continuous. **Ad Rates:** Advertising accepted; rates available upon request. **URL:** http://www.ndr903.de.

44427 ■ Rock n Pop Radio-FM - 106.8
Rodingsmarkt 29
D-20459 Hamburg, Germany
Ph: 49 40 3709070
Fax: 49 40 37090760
Format: Classic Rock; Contemporary Hit Radio (CHR). **Ad Rates:** Advertising accepted; rates available upon request. **URL:** http://www.106acht.de.

44428 ■ Tide-FM - 96.0
Kunst-und Mediencampus Hamburg
Finkenau 35
22081 Hamburg, Germany
Ph: 49 40 32599030
Fax: 49 40 325990319
Format: Adult Contemporary. **Owner:** TIDE GmbH, at above address. **URL:** http://www.tidenet.de/.

Hannover

44429 ■ Annals of Hematology
Springer-Verlag Tokyo

c/o A. Ganser, Ed.-in-Ch.
Medizinische Hochschule Hannover
Carl-Neuberg-Strasse 1
D-30625 Hannover, Germany
Fax: 49 511 5328041
Publisher E-mail: info@springer.jp
Journal covering the whole spectrum of clinical and experimental hematology, hemostaseology, blood transfusion, and related aspects of medical oncology, including the diagnosis and treatment of leukemias, lymphatic neoplasias and solid tumors as well as transplantation of hematopoietic stem cells; also general aspects of oncology, molecular biology and immunology as pertinent to problems of human blood disease. **Freq:** Monthly. **Key Personnel:** A. Ganser, Editor-in-Chief, ganser.arnold@mh-hannover.de; B. Barlogie, Section Ed.; E. Montserrat, Section Ed. **ISSN:** 0939-5555. **Subscription Rates:** EUR2,159 institutions print incl. free access or e-only; EUR2,590.80 institutions print incl. enhanced access. **Remarks:** Advertising accepted; rates available upon request. **URL:** http://www.springer.com/medicine/internal/journal/277. **Circ:** (Not Reported)

44430 ■ c't magazine
Heise Zeitschriften Verlag GmbH & Co. KG
Helstorfer Str. 7
D-30625 Hannover, Germany
Ph: 49 511 53520
Fax: 49 511 5352129
Publication E-mail: ct@ct.de
Publisher E-mail: post@heise.de
Trade magazine covering computers focusing on personal computers, Macintosh and Linux. **Subtitle:** Magazin fuer Computer Technik. **Founded:** Dec. 1983. **Freq:** Semimonthly. **Print Method:** Offset Rotary Printing. **Trim Size:** 297 x 210 mm. **Key Personnel:** Detlef Grell, Editor-in-Chief; Christian Persson, Editor-in-Chief; Christian Heise, Publisher. **ISSN:** 0724-8679. **Remarks:** Accepts advertising. **URL:** http://www.heise.de/ct/. **Ad Rates:** BW: EUR9,400, 4C: EUR11,900. **Circ:** Paid 379,350, Paid 233,521

44431 ■ Experimental and Toxicologic Pathology
Elsevier Science Inc.
Cultex-Laboratories GmbH
Hannover Medical Pk.
Feodor-Lynen-Strasse 21
30625 Hannover, Germany
Fax: 49 511 563586
Publisher E-mail: usinfo-ehelp@elsevier.com
Journal covering experimental research on disease processes and toxicology including cell biological investigations. **Founded:** 1967. **Freq:** Bimonthly. **Print Method:** Letterpress and offset. **Trim Size:** 210 x 280 mm. **Cols./Page:** 3. **Col. Width:** 27 nonpareils. **Col. Depth:** 140 agate lines. **Key Personnel:** Kunio Doi, Editorial Board; Ulrich Deschl, Exec. Ed., ulrich.deschl@bc.boehringer-ingelheim.com; Daniel Costa, Editorial Board; Wilfried Bartsch, Editorial Board; Michaela Aufderheide, Editorial Board; Daniel Dietrich, Editorial Board; Gary A. Boorman, Editorial Board; Clemens Dasenbrock, Editorial Board; Ulrich Mohr, Exec. Ed., u.mohr@cultex-laboratories.com. **ISSN:** 0940-2993. **Subscription Rates:** EUR1,031 institutions for European countries and Iran; 140,100¥ institutions; US$1,130 institutions, other countries except Europe, Japan and Iran. **URL:** http://www.elsevier.com/wps/find/journaldescription.cws_home/701762/descriptiondescription.

44432 ■ Forschungsberichte aus Technik und Naturwissenschaften
John Wiley & Sons Inc.
Technische Informationsbiliothek (TIB)
Welfgarten B 1
D-30167 Hannover, Germany
Ph: 49 511 7622268
Fax: 49 511 715936
Publisher E-mail: info@wiley.com
Bilingual journal focusing on science and technology. **Freq:** Quarterly. **ISSN:** 0343-5520. **URL:** http://www.wiley.com/WileyCDA/WileyTitle/productCd-2054.html.

44433 ■ iX
Heise Zeitschriften Verlag GmbH & Co. KG
Helstorfer Str. 7
D-30625 Hannover, Germany
Ph: 49 511 53520
Fax: 49 511 5352129

Publisher E-mail: post@heise.de
Trade magazine for information technology professionals. **Subtitle:** Magazin fur Professionelle Informationstechnik. **Founded:** 1988. **Freq:** Monthly. **Key Personnel:** Michael Hanke, Advertising Mgr., michael.hanke@heise.de; Oliver Kuhn, International Account Mgr., oliver.kuehn@heise.de; Colin Smith, Contact, colin@osp-uk.com; Leslie Hallanan, Contact, leslie@avanimedia.com. **ISSN:** 0935-9680. **Subscription Rates:** EUR6 single issue. **Remarks:** Accepts advertising. **URL:** http://www.heise.de/ix/. **Circ:** (Not Reported)

44434 ■ Musicae Scientiae
European Society for the Cognitive Sciences of Music
c/o Reinhard Kopiez, Pres.
Hochschule fur Musik und Theater
Emmichplatz 1
30175 Hannover, Germany
Ph: 49 511 3100608
Fax: 49 511 3100600
Publisher E-mail: kopiez@hmt-hannover.de
Journal presenting papers in sciences of music. **Founded:** 1997. **Freq:** Semiannual plus special issues. **Key Personnel:** Mario Baroni, Advisory Board; Prof. Jukka Louhivuori, Editor. **ISSN:** 1029-8649. **Subscription Rates:** Included in membership. **Remarks:** Accepts advertising. **URL:** http://www.escom.org/page2/page2.html. **Circ:** (Not Reported)

44435 ■ Studia Leibnitiana
International Gottfried Wilhelm Leibniz Society
Gottfried-Wilhelm-Leibniz-Gesellschaft
Niedersaechsische Landesbibliothek
Waterloostrasse 8
D-30169 Hannover, Germany
Ph: 49 511 1267331
Fax: 49 511 1267202
Publisher E-mail: info@leibnizgesellschaft.de
Publication covering philosophy in English, French and German. **Subtitle:** Zeitschrift fur Geschichte deu Philosophie und deu Wissenschuften. **Founded:** 1969. **Freq:** Semiannual. **Key Personnel:** Juergen Herbst, Editor; Sven Erdner, Editor. **ISSN:** 0039-3185. **Subscription Rates:** EUR97.60 individuals. **Remarks:** Advertising not accepted. **URL:** http://www.steiner-verlag.de/Studia/. **Circ:** (Not Reported)

44436 ■ Telepolis
Heise Zeitschriften Verlag GmbH & Co. KG
Helstorfer Str. 7
D-30625 Hannover, Germany
Ph: 49 511 53520
Fax: 49 511 5352129
Publisher E-mail: post@heise.de
Consumer magazine covering Internet culture. **Subtitle:** Magazin der Netzkultur. **Key Personnel:** Florian Rotzer, Contact; Peter Muhlbauer, Contact; Michaela Simon, Contact. **URL:** http://www.heise.de/tp/.

Heidelberg

44437 ■ Analytical and Bioanalytical Chemistry
Springer-Verlag GmbH & Company KG
Tiergartenstr. 17
D-69121 Heidelberg, Germany
Ph: 49 622 14870
Fax: 49 622 13454229
Publisher E-mail: webmaster@springer.com
International journal dealing with all aspects of the analytical and bioanalytical sciences, covering all fields of pure and applied analytical chemistry and bioanalysis, including topics at their interfaces with the life and health sciences, the engineering and materials sciences, environmental science, the earth sciences. **Freq:** 8/yr. **Key Personnel:** Sylvia Daunert, Editor, phone 305243-4005, fax 305243-4005, sdaunert@med.miami.edu; Christina E. Dyllick, Managing Editor, abc@springer.com; Kiyokatsu Jinno, Editor, jinno@chrom.tutms.tut.ac.jp; Klaus G. Heumann, Editor, heumann@uni-mainz.de; Philippe Garrigues, Editor, p.garrigues@ism.u-bordeaux1.fr; Stephen A. Wise, Editor, stephen.wise@nist.gov. **ISSN:** 1618-2642. **Subscription Rates:** EUR5,649 institutions; EUR6,778.80 institutions enhanced access. **Remarks:** Advertising accepted; rates available upon request. **URL:** http://www.springer.com/chemistry/analytical/journal/216. **Circ:** (Not Reported)

44438 ■ Animal Cognition
Springer-Verlag GmbH & Company KG

c/o Tatiana Czeschlik, Ed.-in-Ch.
Muehltalstrasse 2
D-69121 Heidelberg, Germany
Fax: 49 6221 418315
Publisher E-mail: webmaster@springer.com
Interdisciplinary journal publishing current research from various backgrounds and disciplines (ethology, behavioral ecology, animal behavior and learning, cognitive sciences, comparative psychology and evolutionary psychology) on all aspects of animal (and human) cognition in an evolutionary framework. **Freq:** Bimonthly. **Key Personnel:** Tatiana Czeschlik, Editor-in-Chief, animal.cognition@t-online.de; Ken Cheng, Editorial Board, ken@galliform.bhs.mq.edu.au; Luc-Alain Giraldeau, Editorial Board, giraldeau.luc-alain@uqam.ca; Irene M. Pepperberg, Editorial Board, impepper@media.mit.edu; Jacqueline Emmerton, Editorial Board, jemmert@psych.purdue.edu; Winand H. Dittrich, Editorial Board, winand.dittrich@kgu.de; Nathan J. Emery, Editorial Board, n.j.emery@qmul.ac.uk; Vincent Janik, Editorial Board, vj@st-and.ac.uk; Richard Byrne, Editorial Board, rwb@st-and.ac.uk. **ISSN:** 1435-9448. **Subscription Rates:** EUR463 institutions; EUR555.60 institutions enhanced access. **Remarks:** Advertising accepted; rates available upon request. **URL:** http://www.springer.com/lifesci/behavioural/journal/10071. **Circ:** (Not Reported)

44439 ■ Annals of Software Engineering
Springer-Verlag
Tiergartenstrasse 17
D-69121 Heidelberg, Germany
Ph: 49 6221 4878808
Peer-reviewed journal covering all aspects of software engineering. **Freq:** Annual. **Key Personnel:** Osman Balci, Editor-in-Chief; William H. Farr, Editorial Board; Mare-Claude Gaudel, Editorial Board. **ISSN:** 1022-7091. **Subscription Rates:** US$477 institutions. **Remarks:** Accepts advertising. **URL:** http://springerlink.metapress.com/content/101741/; http://www.springer.com/computer/programming/journal/10480. **Circ:** (Not Reported)

44440 ■ Applied Physics A
Springer-Verlag GmbH & Company KG
Tiergartenstr. 17
D-69121 Heidelberg, Germany
Ph: 49 622 14870
Fax: 49 622 13454229
Publisher E-mail: webmaster@springer.com
International journal for the rapid publication of experimental and theoretical investigations in applied research, focusing on nanostructured materials and their applications. **Subtitle:** Materials Science & Processing. **Freq:** Quarterly. **Key Personnel:** M. Stuke, Editor-in-Chief, fax 49 551 2011330; Y. Horikoshi, Board of Ed.; S. Bauer, Board of Ed.; C. Fotakis, Board of Ed.; D.H.A. Blank, Board of Ed.; S. Gorb, Board of Ed. **ISSN:** 0947-8396. **Subscription Rates:** EUR4,943 institutions; EUR5,931.60 institutions enhanced access. **Remarks:** Advertising accepted; rates available upon request. **URL:** http://www.springer.com/materials/journal/339. **Circ:** (Not Reported)

44441 ■ Basic Research in Cardiology
Springer-Verlag GmbH & Company KG
Tiergartenstr. 17
D-69121 Heidelberg, Germany
Ph: 49 622 14870
Fax: 49 622 13454229
Publisher E-mail: webmaster@springer.com
International journal for cardiovascular research, including molecular and cellular biology, biochemistry, biophysics, pharmacology, physiology and pathology and clinical cardiology. **Freq:** Bimonthly. **Key Personnel:** Dr. Gerd Heusch, Editor, phone 49 201 7234480, fax 49 201 7234481; H. Katus, Consulting Ed.; J. Bauersachs, Editorial Board; M. Bohm, Consulting Ed.; D. Baumgart, Editorial Board; C. Bode, Editorial Board; M. Avkiran, Editorial Board; J.M. Canty, Editorial Board. **ISSN:** 0300-8428. **Subscription Rates:** EUR1,702 institutions; EUR2,042.40 institutions enhanced access. **Remarks:** Advertising accepted; rates available upon request. **URL:** http://www.springer.com/steinkopf/kardiologie/journal/395. **Circ:** (Not Reported)

44442 ■ Behavioral Ecology and Sociobiology
Springer-Verlag Tokyo
Behavioral Ecology & Sociobiology
Muehltalstrasse 9
D-69121 Heidelberg, Germany
Fax: 49 622 1418315

Publication E-mail: behav.ecol.sociobiol@t-online.de
Publisher E-mail: info@springer.jp
Journal publishing reviews and original contributions dealing with quantitative empirical and theoretical studies in the analysis of animal behavior on the level of the individual, population and community. **Freq:** Monthly. **Key Personnel:** Tatiana Czeschlik, Editor-in-Chief; Vincent Janik, Assoc. Ed.; Gareth Jones, Assoc. Ed.; Susan C. Alberts, Assoc. Ed.; Jens Krause, Assoc. Ed.; William Cooper, Assoc. Ed. **ISSN:** 0340-5443. **Subscription Rates:** EUR4,139 institutions print incl. free access or e-only; EUR4,966.80 institutions print incl. enhanced access. **Remarks:** Advertising accepted; rates available upon request. **URL:** http://www.springer.com/lifesci/behavioural/journal/265. **Circ:** (Not Reported)

44443 ■ Biological Cybernetics
Springer-Verlag GmbH & Company KG
Tiergartenstr. 17
D-69121 Heidelberg, Germany
Ph: 49 622 14870
Fax: 49 622 13454229
Publisher E-mail: webmaster@springer.com
Interdisciplinary journal for the experimental, theoretical and application-oriented aspects of information processing in organisms, including sensory, motor, cognitive, and ecological phenomena, covering topics such as: experimental studies of biological systems including quantitative modeling; computational, technical, or theoretical studies with relevance for understanding biological information processing; and artificial implementation of biological information processing and self-organizing principles. **Freq:** Bimonthly. **Key Personnel:** John Rinzel, Co-Ed.-in-Ch., phone 212998-3308, fax 212995-4011, rinzel@cns.nyu.edu; Leo J. Van Hemmen, Editor-in-Chief, phone 49 89 28912362, fax 49 89 28914656, bc@tum.de; Horace Barlow, Editor; Neil Burgess, Editor; Walter Senn, Co-Ed.-in-Ch., phone 41 31 6318721, fax 41 31 6314611, wsenn@cns.unibe.ch; Ad Aertsen, Editor; Paul C. Bressloff, Editor; Catherine E. Carr, Editor; Philip H. Brownell, Editor; Anthony N. Burkitt, Editor. **ISSN:** 0340-1200. **Subscription Rates:** EUR4,358 institutions; EUR5,229.60 institutions enhanced access. **Remarks:** Advertising accepted; rates available upon request. **URL:** http://www.springer.com/biomed/neuroscience/journal/422. **Circ:** (Not Reported)

44444 ■ Cell and Tissue Research
Springer-Verlag GmbH & Company KG
Tiergartenstr. 17
D-69121 Heidelberg, Germany
Ph: 49 622 14870
Fax: 49 622 13454229
Publisher E-mail: webmaster@springer.com
Peer-reviewed journal publishing regular articles and reviews in the areas of molecular, cell, and supracellular biology. **Freq:** 3/yr. **Key Personnel:** K. Unsicker, Managing Editor, ku39@anat.uni-freiburg.de; T. Pihlajaniemi, Section Ed., taina.pihlajaniemi@oulu.fi; M. Furutani-Seiki, Section Ed., mfs22@bath.ac.uk; W.W. Franke, Section Ed., w.franke@dkfz-heidelberg.de; A. Oksche, Section Ed., andreas.oksche@anatomie.med.uni-giessen.de; H.W. Korf, Section Ed., korf@em.uni-frankfurt.de. **ISSN:** 0302-766X. **Subscription Rates:** EUR7,083 institutions; EUR8,499.60 institutions enhanced access. **Remarks:** Advertising accepted; rates available upon request. **URL:** http://www.springer.com/biomed/humangenetics/journal/441. **Circ:** (Not Reported)

44445 ■ Chinese-German Journal of Clinical Oncology
Springer-Verlag GmbH & Company KG
Tiergartenstr. 17
D-69121 Heidelberg, Germany
Ph: 49 622 14870
Fax: 49 622 13454229
Publisher E-mail: webmaster@springer.com
International professional academic journal on oncology. **Freq:** Monthly. **Key Personnel:** Wu Mengchao, Editor-in-Chief; Anmin Chen, Editor-in-Chief; A.D. Ho, Editor-in-Chief. **ISSN:** 1610-1979. **Subscription Rates:** EUR525 institutions; EUR630 institutions enhanced access. **Remarks:** Advertising accepted; rates available upon request. **URL:** http://www.springer.com/medicine/oncology/journal/10330. **Circ:** (Not Reported)

44446 ■ Climate Dynamics
Springer-Verlag
Tiergartenstrasse 17
D-69121 Heidelberg, Germany
Ph: 49 6221 4878808
International journal featuring research on all aspects of

the dynamics of the global climate system. Covers paleoclimatic, diagnostic, analytical, and numerical modeling research on the structure and behavior of the atmosphere; oceans, cryosphere, biomass and land surface as interacting components of the dynamics of global climate; physical and biogeochemical processes governing climate and climate change; and climate dynamics on particular scales of space and time. **Subtitle:** Observational, Theoretical and Computational Research on the Climate System. **Founded:** 1986. **Freq:** 8/yr. **Trim Size:** A4 Short. **Key Personnel:** A. Berger, Editorial Board; Dr. J.C. Duplessy, Exec. Ed., jean-claude.duplessy@lsce.cnrs-gif.fr; Prof. E.K. Schneider, Exec. Ed., clidyn@cola.iges.org. **ISSN:** 0930-7575. **Subscription Rates:** EUR3,921 institutions; EUR4,705.20 institutions enhanced access. **Remarks:** Accepts advertising. **URL:** http://www.springerlink.com/content/100405/. **Circ:** (Not Reported)

44447 ■ Clinical Oral Investigations
Springer-Verlag GmbH & Company KG
Tiergartenstr. 17
D-69121 Heidelberg, Germany
Ph: 49 622 14870
Fax: 49 622 13454229
Publisher E-mail: webmaster@springer.com
International and multidisciplinary forum for publications from all fields of oral medicine, including maxillofacial and oral surgery, prosthetics and restorative dentistry, operative dentistry, endodontics, periodontology, orthodontics, dental materials science, clinical trials, epidemiology, pedodontics, oral implant, preventive dentistry, oral pathology, oral basic sciences. **Founded:** 1997. **Freq:** Quarterly. **Key Personnel:** G. Schmalz, Editor-in-Chief; D. Van Steenberghe, Founding Ed.; M. Goldberg, Founding Ed.; W. Raab, Editorial Board; W. Gernet, Assoc. Ed.; C. Lindqvist, Assoc. Ed.; R.G. Caffesse, Editorial Board; S. Bayne, Assoc. Ed.; D. Arenholt-Bindslev, Editorial Board; M. Kern, Editorial Board. **ISSN:** 1432-6981. **Subscription Rates:** EUR370 institutions; EUR444 institutions enhanced access. **Remarks:** Advertising accepted; rates available upon request. **URL:** http://www.springer.com/medicine/journal/784. **Circ:** (Not Reported)

44448 ■ Cluster Computing
Springer-Verlag
Tiergartenstrasse 17
D-69121 Heidelberg, Germany
Ph: 49 6221 4878808
Scientific journal covering computing. **Subtitle:** The Journal of Networks, Software Tools and Applications. **Freq:** 4/yr. **Key Personnel:** Salim Hariri, Editor-in-Chief; C.S. Raghavendra, Ed.-in-Ch. for Special Issues; Valerie Taylor, Editorial Board; Mark Baker, Editorial Board; Ioana Banicescu, Editorial Board; Franck Cappello, Editorial Board; Dongyan Xu, Editorial Board; Jeffrey J Ivans, Editorial Board; Manish Parashar, Editorial Board. **ISSN:** 1386-7857. **Subscription Rates:** EUR509 institutions; EUR610.80 institutions enhanced access. **Remarks:** Accepts advertising. **URL:** http://www.springerlink.com/content/101766/; http://www.springer.com/computer/communications/journal/10586. **Circ:** (Not Reported)

44449 ■ Computational Geosciences
Springer-Verlag
Tiergartenstrasse 17
D-69121 Heidelberg, Germany
Ph: 49 6221 4878808
Scientific, multidisciplinary journal covering computational geosciences. **Freq:** 4/yr. **Key Personnel:** Jan Dirk Jansen, Editor-in-Chief; Mary F. Wheeler, Editor-in-Chief; Clint Dawson, Editor-in-Chief. **ISSN:** 1420-0597. **Subscription Rates:** EUR496 institutions; EUR595.20 institutions enhanced access. **Remarks:** Accepts advertising. **URL:** http://www.springerlink.com/content/101744/; http://www.springer.com/math/journal/10596?detailsPage=description. **Circ:** (Not Reported)

44450 ■ Computational Management Science
Springer-Verlag GmbH & Company KG
Tiergartenstr. 17
D-69121 Heidelberg, Germany
Ph: 49 622 14870
Fax: 49 622 13454229
Publisher E-mail: webmaster@springer.com
International journal focusing on all computational aspects of management science, providing a publishing outlet for novel research results, and occasional surveys, in computational methods, models and empirical analysis for decision making in economics, finance, manage-

ment, and related aspects of engineering. **Freq:** Quarterly. **Key Personnel:** Berc Rustem, Editor-in-Chief, phone 44 20 75948345, fax 44 20 75818024, br@doc.ic.ac.uk; Sergei Butenko, Assoc. Ed.; Erol Gelenbe, Assoc. Ed.; Hans Amman, Editor-in-Chief, h.m. amman@uu.nl; Istvan Maros, Assoc. Ed.; Michael C. Bartholomew-Biggs, Assoc. Ed.; Mark Broadie, Assoc. Ed.; Janos Mayer, Assoc. Ed.; Endre Boros, Assoc. Ed.; Panos Pardalos, Editor-in-Chief, phone 352392-9011, fax 352392-3537, pardalos@cao.ise.ufl.edu. **ISSN:** 1619-697X. **Subscription Rates:** EUR323 institutions; EUR387.60 institutions enhanced access. **Remarks:** Advertising accepted; rates available upon request. **URL:** http://www.springer.com/business/operationsresearch/journal/10287. **Circ:** (Not Reported)

44451 ■ Coral Reefs
Springer-Verlag GmbH & Company KG
Tiergartenstr. 17
D-69121 Heidelberg, Germany
Ph: 49 622 14870
Fax: 49 622 13454229
Publisher E-mail: webmaster@springer.com
Peer-reviewed journal containing analytical and theoretical papers on both modern and ancient reefs, encouraging the search for generalizations about reef structure and dynamics and reflecting the growing awareness among reef workers of the importance of experimentation, modeling, quantification and applied science in reef studies. **Freq:** Quarterly. **Key Personnel:** Dr. Richard E. Dodge, Editorial Board; Dr. Howard R. Lasker, Editorial Board; Dr. Hugh Sweatman, Biology Ed., h.sweatan@aims.gov.au; Prof. Rolf P.M. Bak, Editor-in-Chief, coralreefjournal@nioz.com; Dr. Bernhard Riegl, Geology Ed., phone 954262-3671, fax 954262-3648, rieglb@nova.edu; Dr. Andrew Baird, Biology Ed., andrew.baird@jcu.edu.au; Dr. Marlin Atkinson, Editorial Board; Dr. Peter J. Edmunds, Editorial Board. **ISSN:** 0722-4028. **Subscription Rates:** EUR1,131 institutions; EUR1,357.20 institutions enhanced access. **Remarks:** Advertising accepted; rates available upon request. **URL:** http://www.springer.com/lifesci/ecology/journal/338. **Circ:** (Not Reported)

44452 ■ Diabetologia
Springer-Verlag
Tiergartenstrasse 17
D-69121 Heidelberg, Germany
Ph: 49 6221 4878808
Journal publishing research papers in the field of diabetes. **Subtitle:** Clinical and Experimental Diabetes and Metabolism. **Freq:** 12/yr. **Key Personnel:** Judy Naylor, Managing Editor; Edwin Gale, Editor-in-Chief; Angelika Bierhaus, Assoc. Ed. **ISSN:** 0012-186X. **Subscription Rates:** EUR1,989 institutions print incl. free access; EUR2,386.80 institutions print incl. enhanced access. **URL:** http://www.springer.com/medicine/internal/journal/125.

44453 ■ Environmental Earth Sciences
Springer-Verlag GmbH & Company KG
Tiergartenstr. 17
D-69121 Heidelberg, Germany
Ph: 49 622 14870
Fax: 49 622 13454229
Publisher E-mail: webmaster@springer.com
International, multidisciplinary journal concerned with all aspects of interactions between humans, ecosystems and the earth. **Freq:** 8/yr. **Key Personnel:** James W. LaMoreaux, Editor-in-Chief, jlamoreaux@pela.com; Ann McCarley, Asst. Ed.; Andreas Dahmke, Editorial Board; Robert C. Ahlert, Editorial Board; Emilio Custodio, Editorial Board; Paolo Bono, Editorial Board; Thomas E. Bruner, Editorial Board; Sean T. Brennan, Editorial Board; Yuan Daoxian, Editorial Board. **ISSN:** 0943-0105. **Remarks:** Advertising accepted; rates available upon request. **URL:** http://www.springer.com/earthsciences/geology/journal/254. **Formerly:** Environmental Geology. **Circ:** (Not Reported)

44454 ■ Environmental Modeling & Assessment
Springer-Verlag
Tiergartenstrasse 17
D-69121 Heidelberg, Germany
Ph: 49 6221 4878808
Peer-reviewed journal covering environmental modeling and regulations. **Freq:** 4/yr. **Key Personnel:** Jerzy A. Filar, Editor-in-Chief; G.J. Olsder, Advisory Ed.; C. Carraro, Editorial Board; N.K. Neerchal, Editorial Board; Y. Parlange, Advisory Ed.; J.B. Krawczyk, Editorial Board; A. Mynett, Editorial Board; M-L. Wu, Editorial Board; J. Taylor, Editorial Board; R. Ulanowicz, Advisory Ed. **ISSN:**

1420-2026. **Remarks:** Accepts advertising. **URL:** http://www.springer.com/environment/journal/10666. **Circ:** (Not Reported)

44455 ■ European Archives of Otorhinolaryngology
Springer-Verlag
Tiergartenstrasse 17
D-69121 Heidelberg, Germany
Ph: 49 6221 4878808
European archives covering otorhinolaryngology and head & neck. **Subtitle:** and Head & Neck. **Founded:** 1864. **Freq:** Monthly. **Key Personnel:** Jochen A. Werner, Managing Editor; Prof. Jan Olofsson, Managing Editor; P. Ambrosch, Editorial Board; H. Hellquist, Editorial Board; A. Ferlito, Editorial Board; K. Herrmann, Editorial Board. **ISSN:** 0937-4477. **Subscription Rates:** EUR3,575 institutions; EUR4,290 institutions enhanced access. **Remarks:** Advertising accepted; rates available upon request. **URL:** http://www.springer.com/medicine/otorhinolaryngology/journal/405. **Circ:** (Not Reported)

44456 ■ European Spine Journal
Springer-Verlag
Tiergartenstrasse 17
D-69121 Heidelberg, Germany
Ph: 49 6221 4878808
Journal focusing on spine surgery and all related disciplines, including functional and surgical anatomy of the spine, biomechanics and pathophysiology, diagnostic procedures, and neurology, in connection with the Spine Society of Europe. **Freq:** 12/yr. **Key Personnel:** F. Pellise-Urquiza, Dep. Ed.; M. Aebi, Editor-in-Chief; K. Abumi, Advisory Board; M. Szpalski, Dep. Ed.; E. Acaroglu, Advisory Board; C. Bolger, Advisory Board; N. Boos, Advisory Board; R. Gunzburg, Asst. to the Ed.in-Ch.; V. Arlet, Deputy Ed.; F.B. Christensen, Editorial Board. **ISSN:** 0940-6719. **Subscription Rates:** EUR2,001 institutions print incl. free access; EUR2,401.20 institutions print incl. enhanced access. **URL:** http://www.springer.com/medicine/orthopedics/journal/586.

44457 ■ FEBS Letters
Elsevier Science Inc.
The University of Heidelberg
Biochemistry Centre (BZH)
Im Neuenheimer Feld 328
D-69120 Heidelberg, Germany
Publication E-mail: febs.letters@bzh.uni-heidelberg.de
Publisher E-mail: usinfo-ehelp@elsevier.com
Peer-reviewed journal covering biochemistry. **Founded:** 1968. **Freq:** 24/yr. **Key Personnel:** Felix Wieland, Managing Editor, felix.wieland@bzh.uni-heidelberg.de; Patricia McCabe, Editorial Mgr., patricia.mccabe@bzh.uni-heidelberg.de; Daniela Ruffell, Asst. Ed., daniela.ruffell@bzh.uni-heidelberg.de; Jesus Avila, Editor, javila@cbm.uam.es; Robert Barouki, Editor, robert.barouki@biomedicale.univ-paris5.fr; Peter Brzezinski, Editor, peterb@dbb.su.se; Michael R. Bubb, Editor, bubbmr@medicine.ufl.edu; Giovanni Cesareni, Editor, cesareni@uniroma2.it; Richard Cogdell, Editor, r.cogdell@bio.gla.ac.uk; Quan Chen, Editor, chenquan@nankai.edu.cn. **ISSN:** 0014-5793. **Subscription Rates:** US$6,385 institutions; other countries except Europe, Japan and Iran; 814,700¥ institutions; EUR5,707 institutions for European countries and Iran; US$919 other countries except Europe, Japan and Iran; EUR726 institutions for European countries and Iran; 105,700¥ institutions. **URL:** http://www.elsevier.com/wps/find/journaldescription.cws_home/506085/descriptiondescription; http://www.febsletters.org/.

44458 ■ Health Care Management Science
Springer-Verlag
Tiergartenstrasse 17
D-69121 Heidelberg, Germany
Ph: 49 6221 4878808
Scientific, interdisciplinary journal covering health care services and management. **Freq:** 4/yr. **Key Personnel:** Yasar A. Ozcan, Editor-in-Chief; Ann van Ackere, Editorial Board; Pedro Pita Barros, Editorial Board. **ISSN:** 1386-9620. **Subscription Rates:** EUR538 institutions; EUR645.60 institutions enhanced access. **Remarks:** Accepts advertising. **URL:** http://www.springerlink.com/content/101767/; http://www.springer.com/business/operationsresearch/journal/10729. **Circ:** (Not Reported)

44459 ■ Hernia
Springer-Verlag
Tiergartenstrasse 17
D-69121 Heidelberg, Germany
Ph: 49 6221 4878808
Journal devoted to studies on various types of hernias such as groin hernias, internal hernias, hernias of the abdominal wall (anterior and postero-lateral aspects), the diaphragm and the perineum. **Subtitle:** The World Journal of Hernia and Abdominal Wall Surgery. **Founded:** 1997. **Freq:** 6/yr. **Key Personnel:** V. Schumpelick, Editor-in-Chief; R.J. Fitzgibbons, Editor-in-Chief; A. Kingsnorth, Assoc. Ed.; R. Bendavid, Assoc. Ed. **ISSN:** 1265-4906. **Subscription Rates:** EUR630 institutions print incl. free access; EUR756 institutions print incl. enhanced access. **Remarks:** Advertising accepted; rates available upon request. **URL:** http://www.springer.com/medicine/surgery/journal/10029. **Circ:** (Not Reported)

44460 ■ Histochemistry and Cell Biology
Springer-Verlag
Tiergartenstrasse 17
D-69121 Heidelberg, Germany
Ph: 49 6221 4878808
Journal focusing on molecular histology and cell biology with research inputs in the areas of localization and identification of molecular components, metabolic activities and cell biological aspects of cells and tissues. **Freq:** 6/yr. **Key Personnel:** D. Drenckhahn, Editor-in-Chief; J. Roth, Editor-in-Chief. **ISSN:** 0948-6143. **Subscription Rates:** EUR4,450 institutions print incl. free access; EUR5,340 institutions print incl. enhanced access. **Remarks:** Advertising accepted; rates available upon request. **URL:** http://www.springer.com/medicine/anatomie/journal/418. **Circ:** (Not Reported)

44461 ■ Innovations in Systems and Software Engineering
Springer-Verlag
Tiergartenstrasse 17
D-69121 Heidelberg, Germany
Ph: 49 6221 4878808
Peer-reviewed journal publishing advanced issues related to Systems Engineering, Systems Integration, Software Engineering, Software Development and other related areas that are specifically of interest to NASA. **Subtitle:** A NASA journal. **Freq:** 4/yr. **Key Personnel:** Michael G. Hinchey, Editor-in-Chief, mike.hinchey@lero.ie; Ben Benokraitis, Editorial Board; Sten F. Andler, Editorial Board; Shawn A. Bohner, Editor-in-Chief, sbohner@vt.edu; Jonathan P. Bowen, Assoc. Ed.-in-Ch.; Colin J. Neill, Assoc. Ed.-in Ch.; Ricky W. Butler, Editorial Board; Helen Gill, Editorial Board. **ISSN:** 1614-5046. **Subscription Rates:** EUR420 institutions; EUR504 institutions enhanced access. **URL:** http://www.springer.com/computer/programming/journal/11334.

44462 ■ International Journal of Legal Medicine
Springer-Verlag
Tiergartenstrasse 17
D-69121 Heidelberg, Germany
Ph: 49 6221 4878808
Journal focusing on developments in research in the area of forensic medicine. **Freq:** Bimonthly. **Key Personnel:** B. Budowle, Editor; A. Busuttil, Editor; W. Eisenmenger, Editor; P. Forster, Editor; S.D. Ferrara, Editor; H. Pfeiffer, Editor-in-Chief, pfeiffh@uni-muenster.de. **ISSN:** 0937-9827. **Subscription Rates:** EUR1,699 institutions print incl. free access; EUR2,038.80 institutions print incl. enhanced access. **Remarks:** Advertising accepted; rates available upon request. **URL:** http://www.springer.com/medicine/forensic/journal/414. **Circ:** (Not Reported)

44463 ■ Journal fur Betriebswirtschaft
Springer-Verlag
Tiergartenstrasse 17
D-69121 Heidelberg, Germany
Ph: 49 6221 4878808
Journal focusing on marketing and management. **Freq:** 3/yr. **Key Personnel:** Dr. Nikolaus Franke, Editor, nikolaus.franke@wu-wien.ac.at; Dr. Gerhard Speckbacher, Editor, gerhard.speckbacher@wu-wien.ac.at. **ISSN:** 0344-9327. **Subscription Rates:** EUR246 institutions print incl. free access; EUR295.20 institutions print incl. enhanced access. **Remarks:** Advertising accepted; rates available upon request. **URL:** http://www.springer.com/business%26management/journal/11301. **Circ:** (Not Reported)

44464 ■ Journal of Geodesy
Springer-Verlag
Tiergartenstrasse 17
D-69121 Heidelberg, Germany
Ph: 49 6221 4878808
Peer-reviewed journal covering the field of geoscience.
Freq: Monthly. **Key Personnel:** P. Clarke, Editor, peter.clarke@ncl.ac.uk; A. Dermanis, Editor, dermanis@topo.auth.gr; Y.Q. Chen, Editor, lsyqchen@polyu.edu.hk; P. Willis, Editor, pascal.willis@ign.fr; P. Ditmar, Editor, dermanis@topo.auth.gr; Dr. Roland A.P. Klees, Editor-in-Chief, r.klees@tudelft.nl. **ISSN:** 0949-7714. **Subscription Rates:** EUR1,460 institutions; EUR1,752 institutions enhanced access. **Remarks:** Advertising accepted; rates available upon request. **URL:** http://www.springer.com/earthsciences/geophysics/journal/190. **Circ:** (Not Reported)

44465 ■ Journal of Mathematical Biology
Springer-Verlag
Tiergartenstrasse 17
D-69121 Heidelberg, Germany
Ph: 49 6221 4878808
Journal on mathematical biology. **Freq:** Bimonthly. **Key Personnel:** M. Gyllenberg, Editor-in-Chief; S.A. Levin, Honorary Ed.; A. Hastings, Editorial Board; K.P. Hadeler, Honorary Ed.; M. Lewis, Editor-in-Chief. **ISSN:** 0303-6812. **Subscription Rates:** EUR1,368 institutions print incl. free access; EUR1,641.60 institutions print incl. enhanced access. **Remarks:** Advertising accepted; rates available upon request. **URL:** http://www.springer.com/mathematics/mathematicalbiology/journal/285. **Circ:** (Not Reported)

44466 ■ Mathematische Annalen
Springer-Verlag
Tiergartenstrasse 17
D-69121 Heidelberg, Germany
Ph: 49 6221 4878808
Journal covering a wide spectrum of modern mathematics. **Founded:** 1868. **Freq:** 4/yr. **Key Personnel:** Y. Giga, Editor, labgiga@ms.u-tokyo.ac.jp; N. Hitchin, Managing Editor, hitchin@maths.ox.ac.uk; W.B. Johnson, Editor, johnson@math.tamu.edu; H. Koch, Editor, koch@math.uni-bonn.de; N. Mok, Editor, nmok@hkucc.hku.hk. **ISSN:** 0025-5831. **Subscription Rates:** EUR2,799 institutions print incl. free access; EUR2,799 institutions print incl. enahanced access. **URL:** http://www.springer.com/math/journal/208.

44467 ■ Mineralium Deposita
Springer-Verlag
Tiergartenstrasse 17
D-69121 Heidelberg, Germany
Ph: 49 6221 4878808
Peer-reviewed journal focusing on economic geology, including nonmetallic mineral deposits, experimental and applied geochemistry, with emphasis on mineral deposits. **Freq:** 8/yr. **Key Personnel:** Bernd Lehmann, Editor, fax 49 5323 722511, lehmann@min.tu-clausthal.de; Patrick J. Williams, Editor, fax 61 7 47814020, patrick.williams@jcu.edu.au; Fernando Barra, Editorial Board. **ISSN:** 0026-4598. **Subscription Rates:** EUR1,718 institutions; EUR2,061.60 institutions enhanced access. **Remarks:** Advertising accepted; rates available upon request. **URL:** http://www.springer.com/earthsciences/geology/journal/126?detailsPage=description. **Circ:** (Not Reported)

44468 ■ Multimedia Systems
Springer-Verlag
Tiergartenstrasse 17
D-69121 Heidelberg, Germany
Ph: 49 6221 4878808
Professional journal covering emerging technologies, including digital video and audio. **Freq:** Bimonthly. **Key Personnel:** Cormac J. Sreenan, Editorial Board Member, phone 353 21 4903629, fax 353 21 4274390, cjs@cs.ucc.ie; Michael Zink, Editorial Board Member, zink@cs.umass.edu; Prashant Shenoy, Editorial Board Member, shenoy@cs.umass.edu; Ralf Steinmetz, Editorial Board Member; Thomas Plagemann, Editor-in-Chief, phone 47 22 852743, fax 47 22 852401, plageman@ifi.uio.no. **ISSN:** 0942-4962. **Subscription Rates:** EUR66.95 individuals. **URL:** http://www.springer.com/computer/informationsystems/journal/530.

44469 ■ Neuroradiology
Springer-Verlag
Tiergartenstrasse 17
D-69121 Heidelberg, Germany
Ph: 49 6221 4878808
Journal dealing with neuroradiological diagnosis and treatment, in connection with European Society of Neuroradiology and the Japanese Neuroradiological Society. **Freq:** 12/yr. **Key Personnel:** J.V. Byrne, Editor-in-Chief. **ISSN:** 0028-3940. **Subscription Rates:** EUR1,580 institutions print incl. free access; EUR1,896 institutions print incl. enhanced access. **Remarks:** Advertising ac-

Circulation: ★ = ABC; △ = BPA; ◆ = CAC; ● = CCAB; ❑ = VAC; ⊕ = PO Statement; ‡ = Publisher's Report; Boldface figures = sworn; Light figures = estimated.

Gale Directory of Publications & Broadcast Media/147th Ed.
4943

cepted; rates available upon request. **URL:** http://www.springer.com/medicine/radiology/journal/234. **Circ:** (Not Reported)

44470 ■ Oecologia
Springer-Verlag
Tiergartenstrasse 17
D-69121 Heidelberg, Germany
Ph: 49 6221 4878808
Journal focusing on ecological research. **Freq:** 4/yr. **Key Personnel:** Roland Brandl, Editor-in-Chief, oecologi@staff.uni-marburg.de; Russell K. Monson, Editor-in-Chief, russell.monson@colorado.edu; Christian Korner, Editor-in-Chief, grossk@kbs.msu.edu. **ISSN:** 0029-8549. **Subscription Rates:** EUR5,375 institutions print incl. free access; EUR6,450 institutions print incl. enhanced access. **URL:** http://www.springer.com/lifesci/ecology/journal/442.

44471 ■ Pediatric Surgery International
Springer-Verlag
Tiergartenstrasse 17
D-69121 Heidelberg, Germany
Ph: 49 6221 4878808
Journal publishing latest information from the entire spectrum of pediatric surgery. Covers clinical and experimental surgery, and related fields. **Freq:** Monthly. **Key Personnel:** P. Puri, Editor; M.E. Hollwarth, Editor. **ISSN:** 0179-0358. **Subscription Rates:** EUR1,932 institutions print incl. free access; EUR2,318.40 institutions print incl. enhanced access. **Remarks:** Advertising accepted; rates available upon request. **URL:** http://www.springer.com/medicine/surgery/book/978-3-540-40738-6. **Circ:** (Not Reported)

44472 ■ Pflugers Archiv
Springer-Verlag
Tiergartenstrasse 17
D-69121 Heidelberg, Germany
Ph: 49 6221 4878808
Journal publishing results of original research in the field of pathophysiological or methodological sciences which can be used for further investigation of physiological mechanisms. **Subtitle:** European Journal of Physiology. **Freq:** Monthly. **Key Personnel:** H. Murer, Emeriti Ed.; Bernd Nilius, Editor-in-Chief; Rene Bindels, Exec. Ed. **ISSN:** 0031-6768. **Subscription Rates:** EUR5,616 institutions print incl. free access; EUR6,739.20 institutions print incl. enhanced access. **Remarks:** Advertising accepted; rates available upon request. **URL:** http://www.springer.com/biomed/humanphysiology/journal/424. **Circ:** (Not Reported)

44473 ■ Plant Cell Reports
Springer-Verlag
Tiergartenstrasse 17
D-69121 Heidelberg, Germany
Ph: 49 6221 4878808
Journal covering all aspects of research in plant genetics, molecular biology and biotechnology. **Freq:** Monthly. **Key Personnel:** Gunther Hahne, Editor-in-Chief, plantcellreports@ghahne.fastmail.fm; Michael E. Horn, Editor-in-Chief, vonbekx@aol.com; Arie Altman, Editor, altman@agri.huji.ac.il; Federica Brandizzi, Editor, brandizz@msu.edu; Wendy Harwood, Editor, wendy.harwood@bbsrc.ac.uk; Mark C. Jordan, Editor, mcjordan@agr.gc.ca; Hiroyasu Ebinuma, Editor; Huw Jones, Editor, huw.jones@bbsrc.ac.uk; Lise Jouanin, Editor, jouanin@versailles.inra.fr. **ISSN:** 0721-7714. **Subscription Rates:** EUR2,168 institutions print incl. free access; EUR2,601.60 institutions print incl. enhanced access. **Remarks:** Advertising accepted; rates available upon request. **URL:** http://www.springer.com/lifesci/cellbiology/journal/299. **Circ:** (Not Reported)

44474 ■ Review of Economic Design
Springer-Verlag
Tiergartenstrasse 17
D-69121 Heidelberg, Germany
Ph: 49 6221 4878808
Journal consisting of creative art and science of inventing, analyzing and testing economic, social and political institutions and mechanisms aimed at achieving individual objectives and social goals. **Freq:** 4/yr. **Key Personnel:** Atila Abdulkadiroglu, Editor-in-Chief, atila.abdulkadiroglu@duke.edu; Matthew O. Jackson, Assoc. Ed.; S. Reiter, Assoc. Ed.; A. Alkan, Assoc. Ed.; G. Demange, Assoc. Ed.; Tarik Kara, Asst. Ed.; Murat R. Sertel, Founding Ed.-in-Ch.; T. Saijo, Assoc. Ed.; M. Yildiz, Assoc. Ed. **ISSN:** 1434-4742. **Subscription Rates:** EUR284 institutions print incl. free access; EUR340.80 institutions print incl. enhanced access. **Remarks:** Advertising accepted; rates available upon request.

URL: http://www.springer.com/economics/journal/10058. **Circ:** (Not Reported)

44475 ■ Rheumatology International
Springer-Verlag GmbH & Company KG
Tiergartenstr. 17
D-69121 Heidelberg, Germany
Ph: 49 622 14870
Fax: 49 622 13454229
Publisher E-mail: webmaster@springer.com
Independent journal reflecting world-wide progress in the research, diagnosis and treatment of the various rheumatic diseases. **Freq:** Monthly. **Key Personnel:** Prof. Ernst M. Lemmel, Editor-in-Chief; J. Grifka, Advisory Board; R.N. Maini, Advisory Board. **ISSN:** 0172-8172. **Subscription Rates:** EUR2,000 institutions; EUR2,400 institutions enhanced access. **Remarks:** Advertising accepted; rates available upon request. **URL:** http://www.springer.com/medicine/rheumatology/journal/296. **Circ:** (Not Reported)

44476 ■ Teaching Business Ethics
Springer-Verlag
Tiergartenstrasse 17
D-69121 Heidelberg, Germany
Ph: 49 6221 4878808
Journal dealing with scholars who were mainly interested in teaching. **Founded:** 1997. **Freq:** 7/yr. **Key Personnel:** Alex C. Michalos, Editor-in-Chief; Deborah C. Poff, Editor. **ISSN:** 1382-6891. **Subscription Rates:** EUR268 institutions print incl. free access; EUR2,841 institutions print incl. enhanced access. **Remarks:** Advertising accepted; rates available upon request. **URL:** http://www.springer.com/philosophy/ethics/journal/11234. **Circ:** (Not Reported)

44477 ■ Telecommunication Systems
Springer-Verlag
Tiergartenstrasse 17
D-69121 Heidelberg, Germany
Ph: 49 6221 4878808
Scientific journal covering the modeling, analysis, design and management of telecommunication systems. **Freq:** 4/yr. **Key Personnel:** Bezalel Gavish, Editor-in-Chief; Kemal Altinkemer, Editorial Board; Michael Bartolacci, Editorial Board. **ISSN:** 1018-4864. **Subscription Rates:** EUR1,624 institutions; EUR1,948.80 institutions enhanced access. **Remarks:** Accepts advertising. **URL:** http://www.springerlink.com/content/101753/; http://www.springer.com/business/businessinformationsystems/journal/11235. **Circ:** (Not Reported)

44478 ■ Theoretical and Applied Genetics
Springer-Verlag
Tiergartenstrasse 17
D-69121 Heidelberg, Germany
Ph: 49 6221 4878808
Journal covering original research on plant genomics, plant genetics, and plant biotechnology. **Subtitle:** International Journal of Plant Breeding Research. **Founded:** 1929. **Freq:** 8/yr. **Key Personnel:** Eva Bauer, Managing Editor; Albrecht E. Melchinger, Editor-in-Chief; Jochen C. Reif, Managing Editor; Alain Charcosset, Editorial Board; Bernd Friebe, Editorial Board; Martin Bohn, Editorial Board; Fred Van Eeuwijk, Editorial Board; Jorge Dubcovsky, Editorial Board; Heiko C. Becker, Editorial Board. **ISSN:** 0040-5752. **Subscription Rates:** EUR6,426 institutions print incl. free access; EUR7,711 institutions print incl. enhanced access. **Remarks:** Advertising accepted; rates available upon request. **URL:** http://www.springer.com/new%26forthcomingtitles%28default%29/journal/122. **Formerly:** Der Zchter. **Circ:** (Not Reported)

44479 ■ Tribology Letters
Springer-Verlag
Tiergartenstrasse 17
D-69121 Heidelberg, Germany
Ph: 49 6221 4878808
Scientific journal covering the science of Tribology and its applications. **Freq:** 3/yr. **Key Personnel:** Wilfred T. Tysoe, Editor-in-Chief; Nicholas D. Spencer, Editor-in-Chief; Gabor A. Somorjai, Consulting Ed. **ISSN:** 1023-8883. **Subscription Rates:** EUR1,302 institutions; EUR1,562.40 institutions enhanced access. **Remarks:** Accepts advertising. **URL:** http://springerlink.metapress.com/content/101775/; http://www.springer.com/materials/surfacesinterfaces/journal/11249?detailsPage=description. **Circ:** (Not Reported)

44480 ■ Zeitschrift fur Unternehmens- und Gesellschaftsrecht (ZGR)
Walter de Gruyter GmbH & Co. KG
Friedrich-Ebert-Platz 2
D-69117 Heidelberg, Germany

Publisher E-mail: info@degruyter.com
Journal covering humanities, medicine, the sciences and law. **Founded:** Dec. 1980. **Freq:** Bimonthly. **Print Method:** Offset. **Trim Size:** 11 1/4 x 15 1/4. **Cols./Page:** 4. **Col. Width:** 14 picas. **Col. Depth:** 168 agate lines. **Key Personnel:** Dr. Peter Hommelhoff, Editor, peter.hommelhoff@urz.uni-heidelberg.de; Dr. Wulf Goette, Editor; Dr. Hans Joachim Priester, Editor; Dr. Holger Fleischer, Editor; Dr. Heribert Hirte, Editor; Dr. Gerd Krieger, Editor; Klaus J. Hopt, Editor. **ISSN:** 0340-2479. **Subscription Rates:** EUR335 individuals print or online; EUR385 individuals print plus online; EUR198 students; EUR75 single issue. **URL:** http://www.degruyter.de/journals/zgr/detailEn.cfm.

Helgoland

44481 ■ Helgoland Marine Research
Springer-Verlag
c/o Heinz-Dieter Franke, Ed.-in-Ch.
Alfred Wegener Institute for Polar & Marine Research
Biologische Anstalt Helgoland
PO Box 180
D-27483 Helgoland, Germany
Ph: 49 472 5819346
Fax: 49 472 5819369
Journal covering research on biology of marine and brackish water organisms. **Freq:** 4/yr. **Key Personnel:** Heinz-Dieter Franke, Editor-in-Chief, hfranke@awi-bremerhaven.de. **ISSN:** 1438-387X. **Subscription Rates:** EUR207 institutions print incl. free access; EUR248.40 institutions print incl. enhanced access. **URL:** http://www.springer.com/lifesci/ecology/journal/10152.

Heppenheim

44482 ■ From the Martin Buber House
International Council of Christians and Jews
Internationaler Rat der Christen und Juden
Martin Buber House
Postfach 1129
D-64629 Heppenheim, Germany
Ph: 49 625 26896810
Fax: 49 625 268331
Publisher E-mail: info@iccj-buberhouse.de
Ecumenical publication. **Freq:** Periodic. **Remarks:** Advertising not accepted. **URL:** http://www.iccj.org/. **Circ:** (Not Reported)

Herford

44483 ■ CodeBreakers Journal (CBJ)
CodeBreakers Journal
Lange Strasse 31
32051 Herford, Germany
Ph: 49 5221 6913324
Publisher E-mail: info@codebreakers-journal.com
Journal primarily concerned with all aspects of software security, through research works on computational methods with an eye on security aspects. The major areas of thrust including Secure Software Engineering, IT-Security, IT-Anti-Security, Virus-Research, Software-Protection and Reverse Code Engineering, and Cryptanalysis and all other features of security analysis. **Key Personnel:** Dr. Thorsten Schneider, Chief Editor/Publisher; Eduardo Labir, Editor. **ISSN:** 1864-7049. **URL:** http://www.codebreakers-journal.com.

Herten

44484 ■ VW Scene International
TV Trend Verlag GmbH
Hertener Mark 7
D-45699 Herten, Germany
Ph: 49 2366 808248
Fax: 49 2366 808248
Publication E-mail: info@vest-netz.de
Consumer magazine covering Volkswagen automobiles worldwide. **Founded:** 1989. **Freq:** Monthly. **Print Method:** Offset. **Trim Size:** 210 x 285 mm. **Cols./Page:** 3. **Col. Width:** 55 millimeters. **Key Personnel:** Thomas Ebeling, Editor-in-Chief. **ISSN:** 0942-3257. **Subscription Rates:** EUR4 single issue. **Remarks:** Accepts advertising. **URL:** http://vw-scene.de/. **Circ:** (Not Reported)

Heusenstamm

44485 ■ Allgemeine Papier-Rundschau
Keppler Verlag GmbH

Postfach 1353
D-63131 Heusenstamm, Germany
Ph: 49 6104 6060
Fax: 49 6104 606121
Publisher E-mail: info@kepplermediengruppe.de
Business publication. **Freq:** Weekly. **Key Personnel:** Gerhard W. Brucker, Editor-in-Chief. **ISSN:** 0002-5917. **Subscription Rates:** DM 190 individuals; DM 220 other countries. **Remarks:** Accepts advertising. **URL:** http://www.a-p-r.de/. **Ad Rates:** BW: DM 2,275, 4C: DM 3,655. **Circ:** (Not Reported)

Homburg

44486 ▪ Clinical Research in Cardiology
Springer Netherlands
Klinik fur Innere Medizin III, Kardiologie
Angiologie und Internistische Intensivmedizin
Kirrberger Strasse
66421 Homburg, Germany
Publisher E-mail: permissions.dordrecht@springer.com
Peer-reviewed journal covering clinical cardiovascular research. **Founded:** 1980. **Freq:** 12/yr. **Print Method:** Offset. **Trim Size:** 8 1/4 x 10 3/4. **Cols./Page:** 3. **Col. Width:** 13 3/5 picas. **Col. Depth:** 136 agate lines. **Key Personnel:** G. Baumann, Editorial Board; J.P. Bassand, Editorial Board; E. Erdmann, Editorial Board; S. Anker, Editorial Board; P. Brugada, Editorial Board; R. Erbel, Editorial Board; C. Bode, Editorial Board; A. Coats, Editorial Board; S. Erdine, Editorial Board; Prof. Th. Eschenhagen, Consulting Ed.; Prof. H.C.G. Heusch, Consulting Ed.; Prof. Michael Bohm, Ch. Ed. **ISSN:** 1861-0684. **Subscription Rates:** EUR960 institutions print incl. free access or e-only; EUR1,152 institutions print incl. enhanced access. **Remarks:** Advertising accepted; rates available upon request. **URL:** http://www.springer.com/steinkopff/kardiologie/journal/392. **Circ:** (Not Reported)

Jena

44487 ▪ Chemie der Erde / Geochemistry
Elsevier Science
c/o Klaus Heide, Ed.-in-Ch.
Elsevier GmbH, Office Jena
Lobdergraben 14a
D-07743 Jena, Germany
Ph: 49 364 1948600
Fax: 49 364 1948602
Publisher E-mail: nlinfo-f@elsevier.com
Journal dealing with topics relating to geochemistry discussing chemical problems in the geosciences, geo-ecology and environmental sciences. **Subtitle:** Interdisciplinary Journal for Chemical Problems of the Geosciences and Geoecology. **Freq:** Quarterly. **Key Personnel:** Klaus Heide, Editor-in-Chief, ckh@rz.uni-jena.de; Charles A. Geiger, Assoc. Ed.; Georg Buchel, Assoc. Ed.; Udo Haack, Assoc. Ed.; Hans W. Hubberten, Assoc. Ed.; Klaus Keil, Assoc. Ed.; Burha Sadiklar, Assoc. Ed.; Patrick O'Brien, Assoc. Ed.; Brian Horsfield, Assoc. Ed. **ISSN:** 0009-2819. **Subscription Rates:** 18,400¥ individuals; EUR141 individuals for European countries & Iran; US$144 individuals for all countries except Europe, Japan & Iran; US$569 institutions for all countries except Europe, Japan & Iran; EUR503 institutions for European countries & Iran; 68,500¥ institutions. **Remarks:** Accepts advertising. **URL:** http://www.elsevier.com/wps/find/journaldescription.cws_home/701755/description. **Circ:** (Not Reported)

44488 ▪ European Psychologist
American Psychological Association
Journals Dept.
c/o Rainer K. Silbereisen, PhD, Ed.-in-Ch.
Dept. of Dev. Psychology & Center for Applied Dev. Science
University of Jena
Am Steiger 3/1
D-07743 Jena, Germany
Ph: 49 3641 945201
Fax: 49 3641 945202
Publisher E-mail: journals@apa.org
English language journal of applied and research psychology throughout Europe, publishing reviews of specific fields and original papers of seminal importance. **Freq:** Quarterly. **Key Personnel:** Rainer K. Silbereisen, PhD, Editor-in-Chief, rainer.silbereisen@uni-jena.de. **ISSN:** 1016-9040. **Subscription Rates:** EUR52 individuals; EUR109 institutions library; US$57 individuals; US$120 institutions; EUR36.50 single issue; US$48

single issue. **URL:** http://www.apa.org/journals/epp/.

44489 ▪ Journal of Basic Microbiology
John Wiley & Sons Inc.
Ursula May
Kunitz
Vor dem Obertore 7
D-07751 Jena, Germany
Ph: 49 3641 448384
Fax: 49 3641 528396
Publication E-mail: mayursula@hotmail.com
Publisher E-mail: info@wiley.com
Journal focusing on general aspects of microbial physiology, biochemistry, cytology, genetics, ecology, taxonomy, virology and biotechnology. **Freq:** Bimonthly. **Key Personnel:** Dr. Erika Kothe, Editor-in-Chief; Horst Malke, Honorary Ed.; Ahmet Asan, Advisory Board. **ISSN:** 0233-111X. **Subscription Rates:** EUR1,146 institutions print or online; 1,839 SFr institutions print or online, Switzerland and Lichtenstein; US$1,443 institutions, other countries print or online; US$241 individuals print, rest of Europe; 350 SFr individuals print, Switzerland and Lichtenstein; US$274 other countries print; 736 institutions print or online, rest of Europe; EUR1,318 institutions print and online (rest of Europe); US$1,660 institutions, other countries print and online; 2,115 SFr institutions print and online (Switzerland and Lichtenstein). **URL:** http://onlinelibrary.wiley.com/journal/10.1002/(ISSN)1521-4028.

44490 ▪ Journal of Cancer Research and Clinical Oncology
Springer-Verlag
c/o Klaus Hoffken, Ed.-in-Ch.
Klinikum der Friedrich-Schiller-Universitat
Klinik und Poliklinik fur Innere Medizin II
D-07740 Jena, Germany
Journal publishing important and latest papers in the areas of experimental and clinical oncology. **Freq:** 12/yr. **Key Personnel:** Klaus Hoffken, Editor-in-Chief; Herbert G. Sayer, Managing Editor; H.E. Gabbert, Vice Ed.-in-Ch. **ISSN:** 0171-5216. **Subscription Rates:** EUR3,470 institutions print incl. free access; EUR4,164 institutions print incl. enhanced access. **Remarks:** Advertising accepted; rates available upon request. **URL:** http://www.springer.com/medicine/oncology/journal/432. **Circ:** (Not Reported)

44491 ▪ Theory in Biosciences
Springer Netherlands
Friedrich Schiller University of Jena
Ernst-Haeckel-Haus, Berggasse 7
D-07743 Jena, Germany
Ph: 49 364 1949500
Fax: 49 364 1949502
Publisher E-mail: permissions.dordrecht@springer.com
Journal dealing with the concepts of theoretical biology. **Founded:** 1881. **Freq:** Quarterly. **Trim Size:** 170 mm x 240 mm. **Key Personnel:** Peter F. Stadler, Editor-in-Chief, phone 49 341 9716690, fax 49 341 9716679, peter.stadler@bioinf.uni-leipzig.de; Jurgen Jost, Editor-in-Chief, phone 49 341 9959552, fax 49 341 9959555, jjost@mis.mpg.de; Olaf Breidbach, Editor-in-Chief, olaf.breidbach@uni-jena.de; Michael Weingarten, Editorial Board; Wolfgang Banzhaf, Editorial Board; Anton Markos, Editorial Board. **ISSN:** 1431-7613. **Subscription Rates:** EUR381 institutions print including free access or e-only; EUR457.20 institutions print including enhanced access. **URL:** http://www.springer.com/lifesci/journal/12064. **Formerly:** Biologisches Zentralblatt.

Karlsruhe

44492 ▪ COSSMA
Health and Beauty Business Media GmbH & Co. KG
Karl-Friedrich-Strasse 14-18
D-76133 Karlsruhe, Germany
Ph: 49 721 1650
Publisher E-mail: info@health-and-beauty.com
Magazine with news from the cosmetic industry. **Key Personnel:** Jurgen Volpp, Mng. Dir., phone 49 721 165833; Hendrik van der Vliet, Publishing Dir., phone 49 721 165304, hendrik.vandervliet@health-and-beauty.com. **Remarks:** Accepts advertising. **URL:** http://www.cossma.com/home.html?lang=en. **Circ:** (Not Reported)

44493 ▪ International Journal of Modern Physics B
World Scientific Publishing Company Private Ltd.
c/o W. Schommers, Ed.-in-Ch.
Forschungszentrum Karlsruhe
Institute for Scientific Computing
D-76021 Karlsruhe, Germany

Ph: 49 724 7822432
Publisher E-mail: wspc@wspc.com.sg
Periodical covering the most important aspects as well as the latest developments in condensed matter, statistical, applied physics and high TC superconductivity. **Founded:** 1987. **Freq:** 32/yr. **Key Personnel:** M. Di Ventra, Contact; Wang Yu Peng, Editor-in-Chief, yupeng@aphy.iphy.ac.cn; W. Schommers, Editor-in-Chief, wolfram.schommers@iwr.fzk.de. **ISSN:** 0217-9792. **Subscription Rates:** US$4,897 institutions and libraries; electronic + print; EUR4,095 institutions and libraries; electronic + print; S$7,867 institutions and libraries; electronic + print; US$4,701 institutions and libraries; electronic only; EUR3,931 institutions and libraries; electronic only; S$7,552 institutions and libraries; electronic only; US$125 individuals add postage; EUR98 individuals add postage; S$166 individuals add postate. **URL:** http://www.worldscinet.com/ijmpb/ijmpb.shtml. **Circ:** Paid 300

44494 ▪ Neues Jahrbuch fur Mineralogie Abhandlungen
Gebruder Borntraeger Verlagsbuchhandlung
c/o Heinz-Gunter Stosch, Ch. Ed.
Karlsruher Institut fur Technologie
Institut fur Angewandte Geowissenschaften
Mineralogie und Petrologie, Adenauerring 20b, Geb. 50.40
D-76131 Karlsruhe, Germany
Publisher E-mail: mail@schweizerbart.de
Journal covering the field of mineralogy. **Founded:** 1807. **Freq:** 2-3/yr. **Key Personnel:** Heinz-Gunter Stosch, Ch. Ed., stosch@img.uka.de; Gene C. Ulmer, Ch. Ed., gulmer@temple.edu. **ISSN:** 0077-7757. **URL:** http://www.borntraeger-cramer.de/j/n-jb-min/.

44495 ▪ Protoplasma
Springer-Verlag
c/o Peter Nick, Ed.-in-Ch.
University Karlsruhe
D-76128 Karlsruhe, Germany
Publisher E-mail: springer@springer.at
Journal covering structural and macromolecular cell biology of protists, fungi, plants, and animals, as well as prokaryotes. **Subtitle:** An International Journal of Cell Biology. **Freq:** Quarterly. **Key Personnel:** K. Harter, Editor; Peter Nick, Editor-in-Chief; A.R. Hardnam, Editor; B. Kost, Editor; R. Stick, Editor; H.H. Kassemeyer, Contact; M. Heinlein, Editorial Board; F.W. Heinlein, Editorial Board. **ISSN:** 0033-183X. **Remarks:** Advertising accepted; rates available upon request. **URL:** http://www.springer.com/springerwiennewyork/lifesciences/journal/709. **Circ:** (Not Reported)

44496 ▪ Die neue Welle-FM - 101.8
Albert-Nestler-Strasse 26
D-76131 Karlsruhe, Germany
Ph: 49 721 20160
Fax: 49 721 2016111
E-mail: info@meine-neue-welle.de
Format: Ethnic; World Beat. **URL:** http://www.meine-neue-welle.de.

Kassel

44497 ▪ Heat and Mass Transfer
Springer-Verlag
c/o Prof. A. Luke, Ed.-in-Ch.
Universitat Kassel
Institut fur Thermodynamik
Kurt-Wolters-Strasse 3
D-34109 Kassel, Germany
Journal devoted to new developments with regard to basic research in the field of heat and mass transfer phenomena, as well as related material properties and their measurements. **Freq:** 12/yr. **Key Personnel:** Prof. D. Mewes, Honorary Ed.; Prof. F. Mayinger, Honorary Ed.; Prof. A. Luke, Editor-in-Chief. **ISSN:** 0947-7411. **Subscription Rates:** EUR3,073 institutions print incl. free access; EUR3,687.60 institutions print incl. enhanced access. **Remarks:** Advertising accepted; rates available upon request. **URL:** http://www.springer.com/engineering/mechanicaleng/journal/231. **Formerly:** Warme-und Stoffubertragung. **Circ:** (Not Reported)

44498 ▪ Journal of Agriculture and Rural Development in the Tropics and Subtropics
Kassel University Press GmbH
Diagonale 10
D-34127 Kassel, Germany
Ph: 49 561 8042159

Circulation: ★ = ABC; △ = BPA; ♦ = CAC; • = CCAB; ❑ = VAC; ⊕ = PO Statement; ‡ = Publisher's Report; Boldface figures = sworn; Light figures = estimated.

Gale Directory of Publications & Broadcast Media/147th Ed.   4945

Fax: 49 561 8043429
Publisher E-mail: geschaeftsfuehrung@upress.uni-kassel.de
Journal of the Centre for International Rural Development. **ISSN:** 1612-9830. **URL:** http://www.uni-kassel.de/agrar/trop/default.php?language=de&cPath=9; http://www.uni-kassel.de/upress/publi/abstract.php?0041-3186_003.

44499 ■ Zeitschrift fur germanistische Linguistik
Walter de Gruyter GmbH & Co. KG
Lehrstuhl fur Germanistische Sprachwissenschaft
Fachbereich 09
Germanistik, University Kassel
D-34109 Kassel, Germany
Publisher E-mail: info@degruyter.com
Journal focusing on the standard language. **Freq:** 3/yr. **Print Method:** Offset. **Cols./Page:** 4. **Col. Width:** 21 3/5 nonpareils. **Col. Depth:** 10 inches. **Key Personnel:** Dr. Angelika Linke, Editor, alinke@ds.unizh.ch; Dr. Helmuth Feilke, Editor, helmuth.feilke@germanistik.uni-giessen.de; Dr. Vilmos Agel, Editor, agel@uni-kassel.de. **ISSN:** 0301-3294. **Subscription Rates:** EUR177 individuals print or online only; EUR204 individuals print and online; EUR32 students print only; EUR65 single issue. **URL:** http://www.degruyter.de/journals/zgl/detailEn.cfm. **Circ:** 700

Katlenburg-Lindau

44500 ■ Living Reviews in Solar Physics
Max-Planck-Institut for Solar System Research
Max-Planck-Str. 2
D-37191 Katlenburg-Lindau, Germany
Ph: 49 555 69790
Fax: 49 555 6979240
Publication E-mail: info@solarphysics.livingreviews.org
Fully electronic, peer-reviewed journal, publishing reviews of research in all areas of solar and heliospheric physics. **Freq:** Annual. **Key Personnel:** Sami Solanki, Editor-in-Chief. **ISSN:** 1614-4961. **URL:** http://solarphysics.livingreviews.org/.

44501 ■ Natural Hazards and Earth System Sciences (NHESS)
Copernicus Gesellschaft
Max-Planck-Str. 13
D-37191 Katlenburg-Lindau, Germany
Ph: 49 5556 995550
Fax: 49 5556 9955570
Publisher E-mail: info@copernicus.org
Journal publishing original research related to natural hazards, in connection with European Geosciences Union (EGU). **Freq:** 12/yr. **Key Personnel:** Guzzetti Fausto, Managing Editor, f.guzzetti@irpi.cnr.it; Ana Barros, Editor, barros@duke.edu. **ISSN:** 1561-8633. **Subscription Rates:** EUR1,263 individuals print; EUR116 individuals single issue (print only); EUR568 members print; EUR52 members single issue print only. **URL:** http://www.nat-hazards-earth-syst-sci.net/volumes_and_issues.html.

Kiel

44502 ■ International Journal of Wine Business Research (IJWBR)
Emerald Group Publishing Ltd.
c/o Prof. Ulrich R. Orth, Ed.
Agribusiness & Food Marketing
Christian-Albrechts-Universitat Kiel
Wilhelm-Seelig-Platz 6/7
D-24098 Kiel, Germany
Publisher E-mail: emerald@emeraldinsight.com
Journal dedicated to the academic field of wine business, particularly management and marketing. Includes applications of marketing principles to wine and spirit products, the place of viticulture in local economies, especially its relationship with tourism, case studies on wine brands, ethical issues in marketing of alcoholic beverages, structure of brand ownership, and marketing through retail outlets, hotel and catering outlets. **Founded:** 1883. **Freq:** Daily Mon. through Sat. **Print Method:** Offset. **Trim Size:** 13 x 21. **Cols./Page:** 6. **Col. Width:** 25 nonpareils. **Col. Depth:** 300 agate lines. **Key Personnel:** Martyn Lawrence, Publisher, mlawrence@emeraldinsight.com; Prof. Ulrich R. Orth, Editor, ijwbr@ae.uni-kiel.de. **ISSN:** 1751-1062. **URL:** http://info.emeraldinsight.com/products/journals/journals.htm?id=ijwbr.

44503 ■ Journal of Cranio-Maxillofacial Surgery
Mosby Inc.
Fur Mund-Kiefer & Plastische Geischtschirurgie
Universitatsklinikum Schleswig-Holstein - Campus Kiel
Arnold-Hellerstr. 16
24105 Kiel, Germany
Ph: 49 431 5972820
Fax: 49 431 5974084
Publisher E-mail: custserv.ehs@elsevier.com
Journal publishing articles covering all aspects of surgery of the head, face and jaw. **Freq:** 8/yr. **Key Personnel:** S. Becker, Asst. Ed., karston.gundlach@med.uni-rostock.de; H.F. Sailer, Section Ed.; B. Gattinger, Section Ed.; M.E. Foster, Asst. Ed., mef100@argonet.uk; F.W. Neukam, Section Ed.; J. Wiltfang, Editor-in-Chief, wiltfang@mkg.uni-kiel.de. **ISSN:** 1010-5182. **Subscription Rates:** US$277 individuals; US$700 institutions; US$172 individuals trainee/resident; 31,900¥ individuals; 76,300¥ institutions; 18,500¥ individuals trainee/resident; EUR297 individuals; EUR745 institutions; EUR172 individuals trainee/resident. **Remarks:** Accepts advertising. **URL:** http://www.elsevier.com/wps/find/journaldescription.cws_home/623049/descriptiondescription. **Circ:** (Not Reported)

44504 ■ Mammalian Biology
Elsevier Science Inc.
c/o Frank E. Zachos, Mng. Ed.
Christian-Albrechts-Universitat Kiel
Zoologisches Institut
D-24118 Kiel, Germany
Ph: 49 431 8804529
Fax: 49 431 8801389
Publisher E-mail: usinfo-ehelp@elsevier.com
Journal devoted to the publication of research on mammal. **Founded:** 1955. **Freq:** 6/yr. **Print Method:** Offset. **Trim Size:** 5 1/2 x 8 1/2. **Cols./Page:** 1. **Col. Width:** 50 nonpareils. **Col. Depth:** 100 agate lines. **Key Personnel:** Frank E. Zachos, Managing Editor, fzachos@zoologie.uni-kiel.de; Marco Apollonio, Subject Ed., phone 39 79 228667, fax 39 79 228665, marcoapo@uniss.it; Heiko Rodel, Subject Ed., klaus.hacklaender@boku.ac.at; Thomas M. Kaiser, Subject Ed., phone 49 40 428387653, fax 49 40 428383937, thomas.kaiser@uni-hamburg.de; Marcelo R. Sanchez-Villagra, Subject Ed., phone 41 44 6342342, fax 49 44 6344923, m.sanchez@pim.unizh.ch. **ISSN:** 1616-5047. **Subscription Rates:** EUR101 students European countries and Iran; 72,200¥ institutions; US$588 institutions, other countries except Europe, Japan and Iran; EUR530 institutions for European countries and Iran. **URL:** http://www.elsevier.com/wps/find/journaldescription.cws_home/701782/descriptiondescription.

44505 ■ Marine Biology
Springer-Verlag
c/o Ulrich Sommer, Ed.-in-Ch.
IFM-GEOMAR Kiel
D-24105 Kiel, Germany
International journal devoted to plankton research with reference to biology, physiology, biochemistry and genetics of planktons both under laboratory and in the ocean. **Subtitle:** International Journal on Life in Oceans and Coastal Waters. **Freq:** 7/yr. **Key Personnel:** Maria Byrne, Assoc. Ed., mbyrne@anatomy.usyd.edu.au; Ulrike Berninger, Assoc. Ed., ulrike.berninger@sbg.ac.at; Judith P. Grassle, Assoc. Ed., jgrassle@imcs.rutgers.edu; Ulrich Sommer, Editor-in-Chief, ir@int-res.com; Kedong Yin, Editor, k.yin@griffith.edu.au; Dr. Sven Uthicke, Assoc. Ed., s.uthicke@aims.gov.au; Michael Kuhl, Assoc. Ed., mkuhl@bi.ku.dk; Rebecca Lewson, Assoc. Ed., rlewson@sunstreoke.sdu.edu; Myron Pech, Assoc. Ed., myron.peck@uni-hamburg.de. **ISSN:** 0025-3162. **Subscription Rates:** EUR5,542 institutions; EUR6,650.40 institutions enhanced access. **URL:** http://www.springer.com/lifesci/ecology/journal/227.

44506 ■ Meer & Yachten
Boat International Group
Edimer, Flensburger Str. 87
D-24106 Kiel, Germany
Ph: 49 431 336883
Fax: 49 431 331485
Publication E-mail: my@boatinternational.co.uk
Publisher E-mail: info@boatinternational.co.uk
Magazine covering luxury yacht for German speaking readers. **Founded:** 1991. **Freq:** Bimonthly. **Trim Size:** 223 x 275 mm. **Key Personnel:** Tony Harris, CEO; Tony Euden, Publishing Dir., tony.euden@boatinternationalmedia.com. **Remarks:** Accepts

advertising. **URL:** http://www.boatinternationalmedia.com/mags/mag05.htm. **Ad Rates:** 4C: DM 3,850. **Circ:** 15,025

44507 ■ Polar Biology
Springer-Verlag
Institute for Polar Ecology
Wischhofstrasse 1-3, Gebaude 12
D-24148 Kiel, Germany
Journal bringing about an interaction between polar ecosystems and polar life forms, oceanography and climatology in the context of polar life. **Freq:** Monthly. **Key Personnel:** Luca Bargelloni, Editor; Michael A. Castellini, Editor; Gotthilf Hempel, Founding Ed.; Irmtraut Hempel, Founding Ed.; Steven L. Chown, Editor; Rolf Gradinger, Editor. **ISSN:** 0722-4060. **Subscription Rates:** EUR2,906 institutions print incl. free access; EUR3,487.20 institutions print incl. enhanced access. **Remarks:** Advertising accepted; rates available upon request. **URL:** http://www.springer.com/lifesci/ecology/journal/300. **Circ:** (Not Reported)

44508 ■ Review of World Economics
Springer-Verlag
Kiel Institute for World Economy
Dusternbrooker Weg 120
D-24100 Kiel, Germany
Fax: 49 431 8814526
Publication covering economics. **Founded:** 1913. **Freq:** Quarterly. **Key Personnel:** Harmen Lehment, Managing Editor, harmen.lehment@ifw-kiel.de; Dennis Snower, Editor; David Helpman, International Advisory Board. **ISSN:** 1610-2878. **Subscription Rates:** EUR212 institutions; EUR254.40 institutions enhanced access. **URL:** http://www.springerlink.com/content/112760/; http://www.springer.com/economics/internationaleconomics/journal/10290. **Formerly:** Weltwirtschaftliches Archiv (Jan. 2003).

Kissing

44509 ■ Elektronik
WEKA Fachzeitschriften Verlag GmbH
Gruber Strasse 46A
D-85586 Kissing, Germany
Ph: 49 812 1950
Publisher E-mail: info@elektroniknet.de
Trade magazine covering electronics for industrial users and design engineers. **Founded:** 1952. **Freq:** Semimonthly plus 8 special issues (Elektronik Wireless/Elektronik Automotive). **Print Method:** Offset. **Trim Size:** A4. **ISSN:** 0013-5658. **Remarks:** Accepts advertising. **URL:** http://www.elektroniknet.de/. **Ad Rates:** BW: EUR4,595, 4C: EUR6,850. **Circ:** Controlled 30,000

Kleve

44510 ■ Antenne Niederrhein-FM - 87.65
Stechbahn 2-8
D-47533 Kleve, Germany
Ph: 49 2821 722710
Fax: 49 2821 722799
E-mail: redaktion@antenneniederrhein.de
Format: Contemporary Hit Radio (CHR). **Ad Rates:** Advertising accepted; rates available upon request. **URL:** http://www.antenneniederrhein.de/start.html.

Koblenz

44511 ■ Antenne Koblenz-FM - 98.0
Friedrich-Ebert-Ring 54
D-56068 Koblenz, Germany
Ph: 49 261 988200
Fax: 49 261 9882050
E-mail: info@antenne-koblenz.de
Format: Ethnic; World Beat. **Operating Hours:** Continuous. **URL:** http://www.akoblenz.de.

Konstanz

44512 ■ European Union Politics
Sage Publications Inc.
Department of Politics & Management
University of Konstanz
PO Box D86
D-78457 Konstanz, Germany
Publisher E-mail: info@sagepub.com
Peer-reviewed journal focusing on all aspects of the processes of government, politics and policy in the European Union. **Freq:** Quarterly. **Key Personnel:** Gerald Schneider, Exec. Ed.; Christian Rauh, Managing

Editor; Sonja Schaudt, Managing Editor. **ISSN:** 1465-1165. **Subscription Rates:** US$787 institutions print & e-access; US$708 institutions e-access; US$771 institutions print only; US$83 individuals print only; US$212 institutions single, print; US$27 single issue print. **Remarks:** Accepts advertising. **URL:** http://www.sagepub.com/journalsProdDesc.nav?prodId=Journal200928; http://eup.sagepub.com/. **Circ:** (Not Reported)

44513 ■ Hochzeit
Terra Verlag GmbH
Neuhauser Strasse 21
D-78464 Konstanz, Germany
Ph: 49 75 3181220
Fax: 49 75 31812299
Publication E-mail: info@hochzeit-magazin.de
Consumer bridal magazine. **Founded:** 1966. **Freq:** Bimonthly. **Print Method:** Offset. **Trim Size:** 266 X 300 (WxH). **Key Personnel:** Marina Litterscheidt, Editor-in-Chief, phone 49 753 1812231, litterscheidt@hochzeit-magazin.de; Ingrid Dreisbach, Contact, phone 49 753 1812232, dreisbach@hochzeit-magazin.de. **Subscription Rates:** DM 40 individuals incl. of vat; DM 73 out of country Switzerland. **Remarks:** Accepts advertising. **URL:** http://www.hochzeit-magazin.de; http://www.terraverlag.de/magazine/hz/hz.html. **Ad Rates:** 4C: EUR6,280. **Circ:** Combined 84,400

44514 ■ Linguistic Typology
Walter de Gruyter GmbH & Co. KG
Sprachwissenschaft
University Konstanz
D-78457 Konstanz, Germany
Publisher E-mail: info@degruyter.com
Peer-reviewed journal focusing on the empirical dimensions of the typological enterprise. **Founded:** 1994. **Freq:** 3/yr. **Print Method:** Offset. Accepts mats. **Trim Size:** 11 1/4 x 17 1/4. **Cols./Page:** 6. **Col. Width:** 1 5/8 inches. **Col. Depth:** 16 inches. **Key Personnel:** Frans Plank, Editor-in-Chief, frans.plank@uni-konstanz.de; Larry M. Hyman, Assoc. Ed.; Marianne Mithun, Assoc. Ed. **ISSN:** 1430-0532. **Subscription Rates:** EUR194 individuals print or online only; EUR223 individuals print and online; EUR71 single issue; EUR43 students; EUR66 members. **URL:** http://www.degruyter.de/journals/lintyp/detailEn.cfm.

Kumhausen

44515 ■ AgrarMEGA
SPIEGLHOF media GmbH
Grammelkam 3
D-84036 Kumhausen, Germany
Ph: 49 8743 303570
Fax: 49 8743 967654
Publication E-mail: info@agrar-net.com
Publisher E-mail: info@spieglhof-media.de
Magazine providing information on agriculture. **URL:** http://www.agrar-net.com/mega/.

Landsberg

44516 ■ Journal of Soils and Sediments
Ecomed Verlagsgesellschaft AG & Co. KG
Unternehmensbereich ecomed Medizin
Justus von Liebig-Str. 1
D-86899 Landsberg, Germany
Ph: 49 622 8191125
Fax: 49 622 8191125
Publisher E-mail: info@ecomed.de
Journal entirely devoted to soils and sediments, not only with contaminated, but also with intact and disturbed soils and sediments. **Subtitle:** Protection, Risk Assessment and Remediation. **Freq:** Bimonthly. **Key Personnel:** Prof. Ulrich Forstner, Editor-in-Chief, u.foerstner@tu-harburg.de; Wim Salomons, Editor-in-Chief, wim.salomons@home.nl; Zhihong Xu, Editor-in-Chief, zhihong.xu@griffith.edu.au. **ISSN:** 1439-0108. **Subscription Rates:** EUR382 institutions print incl. free online access; EUR458 institutions print incl. enhanced online access. **Remarks:** Accepts advertising. **URL:** http://www.springer.com/environment/soilscience/journal/11368. **Circ:** (Not Reported)

Leinfelden-Echterdingen

44517 ■ bild der wissenschaft
Konradin Publishing Group
Ernst-Mey-Strasse 8
70771 Leinfelden-Echterdingen, Germany
Ph: 49 711 75940
Fax: 49 711 7594390
Publisher E-mail: info@konradin.de
Magazine featuring scientific and technical innovations. **Freq:** Monthly. **Key Personnel:** Wolfgang Hess, Editor-in-Chief, phone 49 711 7594301, fax 49 711 7595835, wissenschaft@konradin.de; Julia Raudenbusch, Contact, phone 49 711 7594468, fax 49 711 5186400, julia.raudenbusch@konradin.de. **Subscription Rates:** EUR77.40 individuals per year; EUR63 individuals for student. **Remarks:** Accepts advertising. **URL:** http://www.wissenschaft.de/wissenschaft/home.html; http://www.konradin.de/konradin/en/zeitschriften/232728.html?rubid=277744. **Circ:** 105,059

44518 ■ DAMALS
Konradin Publishing Group
Ernst-Mey-Strasse 8
70771 Leinfelden-Echterdingen, Germany
Ph: 49 711 75940
Fax: 49 711 7594390
Publisher E-mail: info@konradin.de
Magazine featuring history, art and culture, politics and social questions. **Freq:** Monthly. **Key Personnel:** Dr. Marlene Hiller, Editor, phone 49 711 7594418, fax 49 711 75945836, damals@konradin.de. **Subscription Rates:** EUR88.80 individuals currently Inland; EUR97.20 individuals International. **Remarks:** Accepts advertising. **URL:** http://www.damals.de/sixcms/detail.php?template_id=3058; http://www.konradin.de/konradin/en/zeitschriften/232727.html?rubid=277744. **Circ:** 32,799

44519 ■ DER AUGENOPTIKER
Konradin Publishing Group
Ernst-Mey-Strasse 8
70771 Leinfelden-Echterdingen, Germany
Ph: 49 711 75940
Fax: 49 711 7594390
Publisher E-mail: info@konradin.de
Magazine featuring fashion, trends, marketing and communications in eye care. **Freq:** Monthly. **Key Personnel:** Theo Mahr, Editor, phone 49 711 7594240, fax 49 711 7594397, ao.anzeigen@konradin.de. **Remarks:** Accepts advertising. **URL:** http://www.ao-online.de/ao/live/start/1.html; http://www.konradin.de/konradin/en/zeitschriften/232729.html?rubid=232643. **Ad Rates:** BW: EUR2,885, 4C: EUR4,445. **Circ:** 9,836

44520 ■ Der Deutsche Tabakbau
Konradin Publishing Group
Ernst-Mey-Strasse 8
70771 Leinfelden-Echterdingen, Germany
Ph: 49 711 75940
Fax: 49 711 7594390
Publisher E-mail: info@konradin.de
Magazine for tobacco growers, agricultural organizations, the tobacco industry and the unprocessed tobacco trade. **Freq:** BIM. **Key Personnel:** Herbert Steins, Contact. **Remarks:** Accepts advertising. **URL:** http://www.konradin.de/konradin/en/zeitschriften/275224.html?rubid=273657. **Circ:** 3,000

44521 ■ die Kontaktlinse
Konradin Publishing Group
Ernst-Mey-Strasse 8
70771 Leinfelden-Echterdingen, Germany
Ph: 49 711 75940
Fax: 49 711 7594390
Publisher E-mail: info@konradin.de
Magazine for contact lens adjustment. **Freq:** 10/yr. **Key Personnel:** Wolfgang Cagnolati, Editor-in-Chief, phone 49 711 7594295, fax 49 711 7594397, kl.redaktion@konradin.de; Hilmar Bussacker, Editor, phone 49 711 7594295, fax 49 711 7594397; Susanne Kramer-Bartsch, Editor, kl.redaktion@konradin.de. **Subscription Rates:** EUR170 individuals per order. **Remarks:** Accepts advertising. **URL:** http://www.kon-online.de/kl/live/start/1.html; http://www.konradin.de/konradin/en/zeitschriften/233052.html?rubid=232643. **Ad Rates:** BW: EUR1,725, 4C: EUR2,895. **Circ:** 2,569

44522 ■ Elektro Automation
Konradin Verlag Robert Kohlhammer GmbH
Ernst-Mey-Str.8
D-70771 Leinfelden-Echterdingen, Germany
Ph: 49 711 75940
Fax: 49 711 7594390
Publisher E-mail: info@konradin.de
Professional journal covering technical information, products, systems, and services for engineers in the applied electronics, automation, machine building, and electrical industry. **Founded:** 1950. **Freq:** Monthly. **Print Method:** Offset. **Trim Size:** 210 x 297 mm. **Key Personnel:** Stefan Ziegler, Editor, phone 49 711 7594417, fax 49 711 7594221, ea.redaktion@konradin.de; Andreas Hugel, Sales & Mktg. Mgr., phone 49 711 7594472, fax 49 711 7594399, ea.anzeigen@konradin.de. **Remarks:** Accepts advertising. **URL:** http://www.ea-online.de/ea/live/start/1.html; http://www.konradin.de/konradin/en/zeitschriften/233120.html?rubid=232646. **Circ:** Combined ‡21,617

44523 ■ EPP Europe
Konradin Verlag Robert Kohlhammer GmbH
Ernst-Mey-Str.8
D-70771 Leinfelden-Echterdingen, Germany
Ph: 49 711 75940
Fax: 49 711 7594390
Publication E-mail: epp.anzeigen@konradin.de
Publisher E-mail: info@konradin.de
Trade magazine covering electronics manufacturing in Europe. In English with summaries in German, French and Italian. **Subtitle:** Electronic Production and Test. **Freq:** 5/yr. **Key Personnel:** Andreas Hugel, Sales Dir., phone 49 711 7594472, andreas.hugel@konradin.de; Volker Tisken, Editor-in-Chief, phone 49 711 7594254, fax 49 711 7594221, volker.tisken@konradin.de; Sabine Schweizer, Editorial Asst., phone 49 711 7594255, fax 49 711 7594221, sabine.schweizer@konradin.de. **ISSN:** 0172-6250. **Subscription Rates:** EUR100.80 individuals Germany; EUR101.50 other countries; EUR7.40 single issue. **Remarks:** Accepts advertising. **URL:** http://www.epp-online.de/epp/live/start/1.html; http://www.konradin.de. **Circ:** Combined ‡20,040

44524 ■ ErgoMed
Konradin Publishing Group
Ernst-Mey-Strasse 8
70771 Leinfelden-Echterdingen, Germany
Ph: 49 711 75940
Fax: 49 711 7594390
Publisher E-mail: info@konradin.de
Magazine featuring fields of ergonomics, hygiene at work and environmental medicine. **Freq:** 6/yr. **Key Personnel:** Dr. Dirk-Matthias Rose, Editor, d.rose@ias-stiftung.de; Bernd Wilfing, Contact, phone 49 6221 644622, fax 49 6221 644640, bernd.wilfing@haefner-verlag.de; Anne Fahlke, Contact, phone 49 6221 644615, fax 49 6221 644640, anne.fahlke@konradin.de. **Remarks:** Accepts advertising. **URL:** http://www.ergo-med.de/em/live/start/1.html; http://www.konradin.de/konradin/en/zeitschriften/279517.html?rubid=277748. **Ad Rates:** BW: EUR720, 4C: EUR1,044. **Circ:** 2,800

44525 ■ Lackiererblatt
Konradin Publishing Group
Ernst-Mey-Strasse 8
70771 Leinfelden-Echterdingen, Germany
Ph: 49 711 75940
Fax: 49 711 7594390
Publisher E-mail: info@konradin.de
Magazine featuring automobile painting industry. **Founded:** 1992. **Freq:** Annual. **Key Personnel:** Michael Rehm, Editor-in-Chief, phone 49 711 7594532, fax 49 711 7594532, michael.rehm@konradin.de; Edith Gocz, Editorial Asst., phone 49 711 7594298, fax 49 711 7594397, edith.gocz@konradin.de; Carola Gayda, Advertising Mgr., phone 49 711 7594432, fax 49 711 7594432, carola.gayda@konradin.de. **Subscription Rates:** EUR67.90 individuals per order; EUR37.10 individuals per student. **Remarks:** Accepts advertising. **URL:** http://www.lackiererblatt.de/; http://www.konradin.de/konradin/en/zeitschriften/233069.html?rubid=232644. **Ad Rates:** BW: EUR2,460, 4C: EUR3,900. **Circ:** 5,904

44526 ■ Malerblatt
Konradin Publishing Group
Ernst-Mey-Strasse 8
70771 Leinfelden-Echterdingen, Germany
Ph: 49 711 75940
Fax: 49 711 7594390
Publisher E-mail: info@konradin.de
Magazine covering painting, plastering, dry work and interior decorating trades. **Freq:** Monthly. **Key Personnel:** Ulrich Schweizer, Editor-in-Chief, phone 49 711 7594496, fax 49 711 7594397, ulrich.schweizer@konradin.de; Ursula Kramer, Contact, phone 49 711 7594497, fax 49 711 7594397, ursula.kraemer@konradin.de. **Subscription Rates:** EUR111.60 individuals per year; EUR62.40 individuals for student per year. **Remarks:** Accepts advertising. **URL:** http://www.malerblatt.de; http://www.konradin.de/konradin/en/

Circulation: ★ = ABC; △ = BPA; ◆ = CAC; ● = CCAB; ❑ = VAC; ⊕ = PO Statement; ‡ = Publisher's Report; Boldface figures = sworn; Light figures = estimated.

Gale Directory of Publications & Broadcast Media/147th Ed.   4947

zeitschriften/233066.html?rubid=232644. **Ad Rates:** BW: EUR4,896, 4C: EUR7,356. **Circ:** 23,096

44527 ■ Metamorphose
Konradin Publishing Group
Ernst-Mey-Strasse 8
70771 Leinfelden-Echterdingen, Germany
Ph: 49 711 75940
Fax: 49 711 7594390
Publisher E-mail: info@konradin.de
Architectural trade magazine featuring rebuilding, renovation and the preservation of historic monuments. **Freq:** 6/yr. **Key Personnel:** Christian Weather, Editor, phone 49 711 6554144, cs@schoenwetterjournalismus. de; Simon Boehm, Editor, phone 49 8225 3078831, info@architektur-dokumentation.de; Tanya Feil, Editor, phone 49 711 12895292, mail@tanjafeil.de. **Subscription Rates:** EUR13.30 individuals per order; EUR111.60 individuals per year; EUR41 students per year. **Remarks:** Accepts advertising. **URL:** http://www5.meta-mag.de/ meta/home/detail.html; http://www.konradin.de/konradin/ en/zeitschriften/278442.html?rubid=232644. **Ad Rates:** BW: EUR3,750, 4C: EUR5,610. **Circ:** 11,916

44528 ■ Quality Engineering
Konradin Verlag Robert Kohlhammer GmbH
Ernst-Mey-Str.8
D-70771 Leinfelden-Echterdingen, Germany
Ph: 49 711 75940
Fax: 49 711 7594390
Publisher E-mail: info@konradin.de
Professional magazine for quality managers in industry. **Founded:** 1982. **Freq:** 10/yr. **Key Personnel:** Werner Gotz, Contact, phone 49 711 7594451, fax 49 711 75941451, qe.redaktion@konradin.de. **Remarks:** Accepts advertising. **URL:** http://www.qe-online.de/qe/live/ start/1.html; http://www.konradin.de/konradin/en/ zeitschriften/233121.html?rubid=232646. **Circ:** Controlled 25,000

44529 ■ Sicherheitsbeauftragter
Konradin Publishing Group
Ernst-Mey-Strasse 8
70771 Leinfelden-Echterdingen, Germany
Ph: 49 711 75940
Fax: 49 711 7594390
Publisher E-mail: info@konradin.de
Trade magazine covering safety at work. **Freq:** 10/yr. **Key Personnel:** David Wiechmann, Editor-in-Chief, phone 49 6221 644619, david.wiechmann@haefner-verlag.de; Weigand Naumann, Editor, phone 49 6221 644617, weigand.naumann@haefner-verlag.de. **Subscription Rates:** EUR36.30 individuals print/online + premium. **Remarks:** Accepts advertising. **URL:** http:// www.sicherheitsbeauftragter.de/sib/live/start/1.html; http://www.konradin.de/konradin/en/zeitschriften/ 279513.html?rubid=277748. **Ad Rates:** BW: EUR2,060, 4C: EUR2,987. **Circ:** 14,092

44530 ■ Sicherheitsingenieur
Konradin Publishing Group
Ernst-Mey-Strasse 8
70771 Leinfelden-Echterdingen, Germany
Ph: 49 711 75940
Fax: 49 711 7594390
Publisher E-mail: info@konradin.de
Trade magazine covering safety at work. **Freq:** 12/yr. **Key Personnel:** Dr. Christiane Eichhorn, Editor, phone 49 6221 644634, fax 49 6221 644640, christiane. eichhorn@konradin.de; Verena Manek, Editor, phone 49 6221 644625, fax 49 6221 644640, verena.manek @konradin.de; Weigand Naumann, Editor-in-Chief, phone 49 6221 644617, fax 49 6221 644640, weigand. naumann@haefner-verlag.de. **Remarks:** Accepts advertising. **URL:** http://www.si-magazin.de/si/live/start/ 1.html; http://www.konradin.de/konradin/en/zeitschriften/ 279511.html?rubid=277748. **Ad Rates:** BW: EUR1,100, 4C: EUR1,595. **Circ:** 5,020

Lemgo

44531 ■ Contributions to Algebra and Geometry
Heldermann Verlag
Langer Graben 17
D-32657 Lemgo, Germany
Ph: 49 526 110226
Fax: 49 526 115264
Publisher E-mail: mail@heldermann.de
Journal covering areas of algebra, geometry, algebraic geometry and related fields. **Founded:** 1971. **Freq:** Semiannual. **Key Personnel:** H. Martini, Managing Editor; G. Stroth, Managing Editor; J. Stuckrad, Managing

Editor. **ISSN:** 0138-4821. **Subscription Rates:** EUR140 individuals per volume including surface mail shipment. **URL:** http://www.heldermann.de/BAG/bagcover.htm.

44532 ■ Journal of Convex Analysis
Heldermann Verlag
Langer Graben 17
D-32657 Lemgo, Germany
Ph: 49 526 110226
Fax: 49 526 115264
Publisher E-mail: mail@heldermann.de
Journal covering field of convex analysis. **Founded:** 1994. **Freq:** 4/yr. **Key Personnel:** G. Buttazzo, Managing Editor; L. Thibault, Managing Editor; R.J-B. Wets, Contact. **ISSN:** 0944-6532. **Subscription Rates:** EUR280 individuals per volume including surface mail shipment. **URL:** http://www.heldermann.de/JCA/ jcacover.htm.

44533 ■ Journal for Geometry and Graphics
Heldermann Verlag
Langer Graben 17
D-32657 Lemgo, Germany
Ph: 49 526 110226
Fax: 49 526 115264
Publisher E-mail: mail@heldermann.de
Peer-reviewed journal focusing on field of graphics and graphics-related geometry. **Founded:** 1997. **Freq:** Semiannual. **Key Personnel:** R.E. Barr, Managing Editor; H. Stachel, Managing Editor; M. Kato, Managing Editor. **ISSN:** 1433-8157. **Subscription Rates:** EUR100 individuals including surface mail shipment. **URL:** http:// www.heldermann.de/JGG/jggcover.htm.

Lengerich

44534 ■ Transplantationsmedizin
Pabst Science Publishers
Eichengrund 28
D-49525 Lengerich, Germany
Journal publishing in the fields of transplant medicine and related research. **Key Personnel:** Wolfgang Pabst, MA, Editor, wp@pabst-publishers.com. **ISSN:** 0946-9648. **URL:** http://www.transplantation.de.

Lubeck

44535 ■ Berichte zur Wissenschaftsgeschichte
John Wiley & Sons Inc.
c/o Dr. Cornelius Borck, Ed.-in-Ch.
Institut fur Medizin und Wissenschaftsgeschichte
Universitat zu Lubeck
Konigstrasse 42
D-23552 Lubeck, Germany
Ph: 49 451 70799812
Fax: 49 451 70799899
Publisher E-mail: info@wiley.com
German-language chemistry journal. **Freq:** Quarterly. **Key Personnel:** Dr. Cornelius Borck, Editor-in-Chief, borck@imgwf.uni-luebeck.de; Dr. Burghard Weiss, Editor, phone 49 451 70799816, weiss@imgwf.uni-luebeck. de; Carina S. Kniep, Publisher, stm-journals@wiley-vch. de. **ISSN:** 0170-6233. **Subscription Rates:** EUR261 institutions print (rest of Europe); 403 SFr institutions print (Switzerland and Lichtenstein); US$267 institutions, other countries print. **URL:** http://as.wiley.com/ WileyCDA/WileyTitle/productCd-2031.html; http://www3. interscience.wiley.com/cgi-bin/jhome/60500215.

Magdeburg

44536 ■ Restorative Neurology and Neuroscience
IOS Press, B.V.
c/o Bernhard A. Sabel, PhD, Ed.-in-Ch.
Institute of Medical Psychology, Medical School
University of Magdeburg
Leipzigerstrasse 44
D-39120 Magdeburg, Germany
Ph: 49 391 6721800
Fax: 49 391 6721803
Publisher E-mail: info@iospress.nl
Journal publishing papers relating the plasticity and response of the nervous system to accidental of experimental injuries or interventions, transplantation, neurodegenerative disorders, and experimental strategies to improve regeneration or functional recovery. **Freq:** Bimonthly. **Key Personnel:** Bernhard A. Sabel, PhD, Editor-in-Chief, rnn@med.ovgu.de; B. Kolb, PhD, Editorial Board; J. Breshnahan, PhD, Editorial Board; D. Hovda, PhD, Editorial Board; D. Stein, PhD, Founding Ed.; W. Freed, Editorial Board; T. Schallert, PhD, Edito-

rial Board; J. Ramirez, PhD, Editorial Board; Donald G. Stein, PhD, Founding Ed. **ISSN:** 0922-6028. **Subscription Rates:** EUR1,032 institutions print and online; US$1,467 institutions print and online. **URL:** http://www. iospress.nl/loadtop/load.php?isbn=09226028.

44537 ■ MDR 1 - Radio Sachsen-Anhalt-FM - 92.3
Stadtpark Str. 8
D-39114 Magdeburg, Germany
Ph: 49 391 5392289
Format: News; Sports. **Key Personnel:** Dr. Winfried Bettecken, Contact, sachsen-anhalt-hoerfunkleitung@ mdr.de. **URL:** http://www.mdr.de.

Mainz

44538 ■ Biogeosciences
Copernicus GmbH
c/o Jurgen Kesselmeier, Ed.-in-Ch.
Max Planck Institute for Chemistry, Biogeochemistry
Joh.-J.-Becher Weg 27
55128 Mainz, Germany
Publisher E-mail: info@copernicus.org
Peer-reviewed journal containing research articles, short communications and review papers on all aspects of the interactions between the biological, chemical and physical processes in terrestrial or extraterrestrial life with the geosphere, hydrosphere and atmosphere. **Key Personnel:** Albrecht Neftel, Editor-in-Chief, phone 41 1 3777504, fax 41 1 3777201, albrecht.neftel@art.admin. ch. **ISSN:** 1726-4170. **Subscription Rates:** EUR137 single issue print; EUR1,496 individuals print only; EUR673 members print; EUR62 members print only; EUR137 other countries. **URL:** http://www.biogeosciences.net.

44539 ■ Das Orchester
Schott Musik International
Weihergarten 5
D-55116 Mainz, Germany
Ph: 49 613 12460
Fax: 49 613 1246211
Publication E-mail: zeitschriften.leserservice@schott-music.de
Publisher E-mail: info@schott-music.de
Professional magazine covering music and employment for orchestral musicians worldwide. **Subtitle:** Zeitschrift fur Orchesterkultur und Rundfunk-Chorwesen. **Founded:** 1953. **Freq:** 11/yr. **Print Method:** Offset. **Trim Size:** 210 x 297 mm. **ISSN:** 0030-4468. **Subscription Rates:** EUR78 individuals Germany; EUR68 students Germany; EUR97 individuals; EUR87 students. **Remarks:** Accepts advertising. **URL:** http://www.schott-music.com/ shop/journals/das_orchester/; http://www.dasorchester. de/. **Ad Rates:** BW: DM 1,685, 4C: DM 2,435. **Circ:** Paid 20,000

44540 ■ International Poster Journal of Dentistry and Oral Medicine
Quintessenz Verlags-GmbH
Prof. Knut A. Grotz
Direktor der Klinik fur Mund-Kiefer-Gesichtschirurgie der HSK Dr. Horst Schmidt Klinik Wiesbaden
Lehrauftrag University-Klinik Mainz
D-55131 Mainz, Germany
Ph: 49 613 1177334
Fax: 49 613 1176602
Publisher E-mail: info@quintessenz.de
Journal focusing on the field of dentistry and oral medicine, published in connection with German Society of Dento-Maxillo-Facial Sciences. **Founded:** Mar. 1999. **Freq:** Quarterly. **Key Personnel:** Prof. Knut A. Grotz, Editor-in-Chief, groetz@uni-mainz.de; Joachim Liebers, Product Mgr.; Norbert Schulz, Editor. **ISSN:** 1612-7749. **URL:** http://ipj.quintessenz.de/.

44541 ■ Journal of Structural Geology
Elsevier Science
c/o C.W. Passchier, Ed.-in-Ch.
Dept. of Geology, University of Mainz
D-55099 Mainz, Germany
Ph: 49 613 13923217
Fax: 49 613 13923863
Publisher E-mail: nlinfo-f@elsevier.com
Journal on structural geology and tectonics. **Freq:** Monthly. **Key Personnel:** C.W. Passchier, Editor-in-Chief, editor@mail-jsg.org; D.A. Ferrill, Editorial Advisory Board; J. Hippertt, Editor, phone 55 313 5591600, fax 55 313 5591606, jhippertt@terra.com.br; R. Holdsworth, Editor, phone 44 19 13342299, fax 44 19 13342301, r.e. holdsworth@durham.ac.uk; W.M. Dunne, Editor, wdunne@utk.edu; T.G. Blenkinsop, Editor, phone 61

747 814318, fax 61 747 251501, thomas.blenkinsop@jcu.edu.au. **ISSN:** 0191-8141. **Subscription Rates:** 29,300¥ individuals; EUR220 individuals for Europe; US$246 individuals other countries; 247,200¥ institutions; EUR1,863 institutions for Europe; US$2,082 institutions, other countries. **Remarks:** Accepts advertising. **URL:** http://www.elsevier.com/wps/find/journaldescription.cws_home/539/description ndescription. **Circ:** (Not Reported)

44542 ■ Medical Microbiology and Immunology
Springer-Verlag Tokyo
Institute for Medical Microbiology
University of Mainz
Obere Zahlbacher Strasse 67
Hochhaus am Augustusplatz
D-55101 Mainz, Germany
Publisher E-mail: info@springer.jp
Journal publishing articles on all aspects of the inter-relationship between infectious agents and their hosts, such as aspects of microbial and viral pathogenesis and the immunological host response to infections and other fields of microbiology, including mycology and parasitology. **Freq:** Quarterly. **Key Personnel:** S. Bhakdi, Editor-in-Chief, sbhakdi@mail.uni-mainz.de; H.W. Doerr, Editor-in-Chief, h.w.doerr@em.uni-frankfurt.de; S. Ackermann, Editorial Board. **ISSN:** 0300-8584. **Subscription Rates:** EUR1,662 institutions print incl. free access or e-only; EUR1,994.40 institutions print incl. enhanced access. **Remarks:** Advertising accepted; rates available upon request. **URL:** http://www.springer.com/biomed/medicalmicrobiology/journal/430. **Circ:** (Not Reported)

44543 ■ Micron
Elsevier Science
c/o J.R. Harris, Ed.
Institute of Zoology
Muller Weg 6
University of Mainz
D-55099 Mainz, Germany
Publisher E-mail: nlinfo-f@elsevier.com
Peer-reviewed journal covering design, application, practice or theory of microscopy and microanalysis. Reports on optical and electron beam systems with regard to computer image processing and other image analytical methodologies. **Founded:** 1969. **Freq:** 8/yr. **Key Personnel:** J.R. Harris, Editor; D.J.H. Cockayne, Editor; R.F. Egerton, Editor; D. Bhella, Editorial Board; G. Botton, Editorial Board; N.D. Browning, Editorial Board. **ISSN:** 0968-4328. **Subscription Rates:** 229,400¥ institutions for Japan; EUR1,729 institutions for Europe; US$1,932 institutions all countries except Europe and Japan; EUR159 individuals; US$213 individuals; 24,600¥ individuals. **Remarks:** Accepts advertising. **URL:** http://www.elsevier.com/wps/find/journaldescription.cws_home/475/description. **Circ:** (Not Reported)

44544 ■ Polymer Bulletin
Springer-Verlag
c/o Prof. Klaus Mullen, Ed.
Max-Planck-Institut fr Polymerforschung
Ackermannweg 10
D-55021 Mainz, Germany
Journal focusing on polymer science, including chemistry, physical chemistry, physics and material science. **Freq:** Bimonthly. **Key Personnel:** Prof. Yoshiki Chujo, Editor; Prof. R. Faust, Editorial Board; Dr. Markus Klapper, Managing Editor. **ISSN:** 0170-0839. **Subscription Rates:** EUR2,298 institutions print incl. free access; EUR2,757.60 institutions print incl. enhanced access. **Remarks:** Advertising accepted; rates available upon request. **URL:** http://www.springer.com/chemistry/polymer/journal/289. **Circ:** (Not Reported)

44545 ■ Swahili - Forum
Johannes Gutenberg Universitaet Mainz
Institut fuer Ethnologie und Afrikastudien
Forum Universitatis 6
D 55099 Mainz, Germany
Ph: 49 6131 3922798
Fax: 49 6131 3923730
Publisher E-mail: ifeaspage@uni-mainz.de
Journal inviting scholars and writers to submit papers on all aspects of Swahili language, culture and society, as well as book reviews pertaining to these topics, which will be published in Swahili, English, French and German. **Freq:** Annual. **Key Personnel:** Rose-Marie Beck, Editor, r.m.beck@em.uni-frankfurt.de; Lutz Diegner, Editor, lutzdiegner@web.de; Thomas Geider, Editor,

thgeider@arcor.de. **ISSN:** 1614-2373. **URL:** http://www.ifeas.uni-mainz.de/SwaFo/.

44546 ■ Tobacco Journal International
Verlagsgruppe Rhein Main
Erich-Dombrowski-Strasse 2
D-55127 Mainz, Germany
Ph: 49 613 1484950
Fax: 49 613 1484933
Trade journal for the tobacco industry worldwide. **Founded:** 1963. **Freq:** Bimonthly. **Print Method:** Offset. **Subscription Rates:** EUR128.40 other countries airmail; EUR123.90 individuals airmail; EUR108.29 individuals surface mail; EUR114.30 other countries surface mail. **Remarks:** Accepts advertising. **URL:** http://www.tobaccojournal.com. **Ad Rates:** BW: US$2,540, 4C: US$4,088. **Circ:** 6,000

Mannheim

44547 ■ Addiction Biology
John Wiley & Sons Inc.
Wiley-Blackwell
c/o Rainer Spanagel, Ed.-in-Ch.
Central Institute of Mental Health (CIMH)
University of Heidelberg
D-68159 Mannheim, Germany
Journal aiming at advancing understanding regarding aspects on the action of drugs of abuse and addictive processes with papers being accepted whose content is geared towards behavioral, molecular, genetic, biochemical, neuro-biological and pharmacological fields of animal experimentation and clinical research. **Freq:** Quarterly. **Key Personnel:** Rainer Spanagel, Editor-in-Chief; Markus Heilig, Editor. **ISSN:** 1355-6215. **Subscription Rates:** 588 institutions print or online; 646 institutions print + online; 269 individuals print + online; US$971 institutions print or online; US$1,069 institutions print + online; US$971 individuals print + online; EUR747 institutions print or online; EUR820 institutions print + online; EUR747 individuals print + online. **URL:** http://www.wiley.com/bw/journal.asp?ref=1355-6215&site=1.

Marburg

44548 ■ Journal of Comparative Physiology B
Springer-Verlag
c/o Gerhard Heldmaier, Ed.-in-Ch.
Zoologisches Institut
Universitat Marburg
Karl-von-Frisch-Strasse
D-35043 Marburg, Germany
Fax: 49 642 12828937
Peer-reviewed journal focusing on all aspects of physiology including metabolism and enzymology, metabolic regulation, respiration and gas transport, physiology of body fluids, circulation, temperature relations, endocrine regulation and muscular physiology. **Freq:** 8/yr. **Key Personnel:** Gerhard Heldmaier, Editor-in-Chief, heldmaier@staff.uni-marburg.de; Rochelle Buffenstein, Advisory Board; Denis Andrade, Advisory Board; Wolfgang Clauss, Advisory Board; Hannah V. Carey, Editorial Board, careyh@vetmed.wisc.edu; Gregory A. Ahearn, Advisory Board; Pat J. Butler, Advisory Board; Don Bradshaw, Advisory Board; Ian D. Hume, Editorial Board, ianhume@bio.usyd.edu.au; Manfred K. Grieshaber, Advisory Board. **ISSN:** 0174-1578. **Subscription Rates:** EUR2,751 institutions; EUR3,301.20 institutions enhanced access. **Remarks:** Advertising accepted; rates available upon request. **URL:** http://www.springer.com/lifesci/biochemistry/journal/360. **Circ:** (Not Reported)

Munich

44549 ■ Anatomia, Histologia, Embryologia
John Wiley & Sons Inc.
Wiley-Blackwell
c/o Dr. Fred Sinowatz, Ed.-in-Ch.
Institut fur Tieranatomie II der Universitat Munchen
Anatomia Histologia Embryologia
Veterinastrabe 13
D-80539 Munich, Germany
Ph: 49 89 21802563
Journal focusing on anatomical investigations involving human, veterinary and zoological studies. Journal of the World Association of Veterinary Anatomists. **Freq:** Bimonthly. **Key Personnel:** Dr. Fred Sinowatz, Editor-in-Chief, ahe-editor@wiley.com; Suzanne Albrecht, Journal Publishing Mgr., suzanne.albrecht@ber.

blackwellpublishing.com; B. Vollmerhaus, Editorial Board; W.M. Amselgruber, Editorial Board; M. Delverdier, Editorial Board; P. Simoens, Editorial Board. **ISSN:** 0340-2096. **Subscription Rates:** US$362 individuals print and online; EUR293 individuals print and online (Euro zone); 196 individuals print and online (U.K. and non Euro zone); 216 other countries print and online; US$1,895 institutions print and online; EUR1,302 institutions print and online; 1,026 institutions print and online; US$2,210 institutions, other countries print and online; US$191 members print and online. **Remarks:** Accepts advertising. **URL:** http://www.wiley.com/bw/journal.asp?ref=0340-2096&site=1. **Circ:** (Not Reported)

44550 ■ Architecture, Technology, Culture (ATC)
Rodopi
c/o Klaus Benesch, Ed.
Dept. of English/American Studies
University of Munich
Schellingstrasse 3
D-80799 Munich, Germany
Fax: 49 89 21805423
Publisher E-mail: info@rodopi.nl
Journal covering the theory, history, and politics of technology. **Founded:** 1970. **Freq:** Quarterly. **Print Method:** Offset. **Trim Size:** 10 1/4 x 13 3/8. **Cols./Page:** 3 and 5. **Col. Width:** 16.5 and 10 picas. **Col. Depth:** 70 picas. **Key Personnel:** Miles Orvell, Editor; David E. Nye, Editor; Jeffrey L. Meikle, Editor; Klaus Benesch, Editor, klaus.benesch@lrz.uni-muenchen.de. **ISSN:** 1871-0115. **URL:** http://www.rodopi.nl/senj.asp?SerieId=ATC.

44551 ■ Bayerisches Arzteblatt
Bayerische Landesarztekammer
Muhlbaurstr. 16
D-81677 Munich, Germany
Ph: 49 89 41470
Fax: 49 89 4147280
Publisher E-mail: blaek@blaek.de
Professional, medical magazine of The Bavarian Medical Chamber. **Freq:** Monthly. **Cols./Page:** 3. **Key Personnel:** Dagmar Nedbal, Editor; Dr. H. Hellmut Koch, Publisher. **ISSN:** 0005-7126. **Subscription Rates:** DM 3 single issue; DM 36 individuals. **Remarks:** Accepts advertising. **URL:** http://www.blaek.de. **Circ:** (Not Reported)

44552 ■ Business Traveller
BRT Reise Publishing GmbH
Schulstr. 34
D-80634 Munich, Germany
Ph: 49 891 679971
Fax: 49 891 679937
Consumer magazine covering business travel. **Freq:** Bimonthly. **Print Method:** Offset. **Trim Size:** 206 x 275 mm. **Cols./Page:** 3. **Key Personnel:** Marc Tuegel, Editor-in-Chief, tuegel@businesstraveller.de. **Remarks:** Accepts advertising. **URL:** http://www.businesstraveller.de/de,03e9,03eb; wirueberuns.html. **Circ:** Paid 260,000

44553 ■ Catena
Elsevier Science
c/o K. Auerswald, Editorial Board
Technische Universitat Munchen
Dept. of Grassland Science
Am Hochanger 2
D-85350 Munich, Germany
Publisher E-mail: nlinfo-f@elsevier.com
Multidisciplinary journal of soil science, hydrology and geomorphology with emphasis on geoecology and landscape evolution. **Subtitle:** An Interdisciplinary Journal of Soil Science - Hydrology - Geomorphology focusing on Geoecology and Landscape Evolution. **Founded:** 1993. **Freq:** Monthly. **Key Personnel:** K. Auerswald, Editorial Board; O. Slaymaker, Editor, olav@geog.ubc.ca; H.A. Viles, Editorial Board; M.J. Singer, Editor, mjsinger@ucdavis.edu; H. Rohdenburg, Founding Ed.; A.P.J. de Roo, Editor, ad.de-roo@jrc.ec.europa.eu; P. Ashmore, Editorial Board; G. Benito, Editorial Board. **ISSN:** 0341-8162. **Subscription Rates:** 219,500¥ institutions; US$1,851 institutions for all countries except Europe, Japan & Iran; EUR1,656 institutions for European countries & Iran. **Remarks:** Accepts advertising. **URL:** http://www.elsevier.com/wps/find/journaldescription.cws_home/524609/descriptiondescription. **Circ:** (Not Reported)

44554 ■ CESifo Forum
Ifo Institute for Economic Research
Poschingerstr. 5

Circulation: ★ = ABC; △ = BPA; ◆ = CAC; • = CCAB; ❑ = VAC; ⊕ = PO Statement; ‡ = Publisher's Report; Boldface figures = sworn; Light figures = estimated.

Gale Directory of Publications & Broadcast Media/147th Ed. **4949**

D-81679 Munich, Germany
Ph: 49 899 2240
Fax: 49 899 85369
Publisher E-mail: ifo@ifo.de
Journal covering economics with an European perspective. **Freq:** Quarterly. **Key Personnel:** Chang Woon Nam, Editor. **ISSN:** 1615-245X. **Subscription Rates:** EUR50 individuals; EUR12.50 single issue. **URL:** http://www.cesifo-group.de/portal/page/portal/ifoHome/b-publ/b2journal.

44555 ■ Computern im Handwerk
C.V. Computern-Verlags GmbH
Beethovenplatz 2
D-80336 Munich, Germany
Ph: 49 895 446560
Fax: 49 895 31327
Publication E-mail: anzeigen@cv-verlag.de
Publisher E-mail: info@cv-verlag.de
Professional magazine covering computer and telecommunications technology in business. **Founded:** 1984. **Freq:** Monthly 10/yr. **Print Method:** Offset. **Trim Size:** 210 x 280 mm. **Key Personnel:** Heide Tschinkel-Neureuther, Advertising Mgr.; Horst Neureuther, Editor and Publisher. **Subscription Rates:** Cd 29 individuals + 7% vat; DM 3 single issue + 7% vat. **Remarks:** Accepts advertising. **URL:** http://www.handwerke.de. **Ad Rates:** BW: DM 7,644, 4C: DM 9,876. **Circ:** Combined ‡72,351

44556 ■ DECO
Winkler Medien Verlag GmbH
Nymphenburger Strasse 1
D-80335 Munich, Germany
Ph: 49 89 2900110
Fax: 49 89 29001199
Publication E-mail: deco@intime-services.de
Publisher E-mail: info@winkler-online.de
Consumer magazine covering interior design, including fabrics, furniture, wallpaper, carpet, and accessories. **Subtitle:** Home. **Founded:** 1979. **Freq:** Bimonthly. **Print Method:** Offset. **Trim Size:** 210 x 297 mm. **Key Personnel:** Gaby Reckstat, Editor-in-Chief, phone 49 89 29001144; Sabine Kochan, Contact, phone 49 89 482468; Karin Masi, Contact, phone 39 026 596997; Anne Gelpke, Contact, phone 49 89 29001189; Steffi Baerwald, Editorship, phone 49 89 29001166; Julia Maier, Editorship, phone 49 89 29001188; Michaela Rellier, Contact, phone 49 89 29001177; Friederike Sauter, Editor, phone 49 89 29001189; Klaus Winkler, Contact, klaus.winkler@winkler-online.de. **Remarks:** Accepts advertising. **URL:** http://www.winkler-online.de/magazine/deco-eng.php. **Formerly:** DECO- Wohnen mit Textilien/ DECO- Stoffe & Interieurs. **Ad Rates:** BW: EUR4,250, 4C: EUR6,800. **Circ:** Paid 68,000

44557 ■ Die Pirsch
Deutscher Landwirtschaftsverlag GmbH
Lothstrasse 29
D-80797 Munich, Germany
Ph: 49 89 127051
Fax: 49 89 12705335
Publication E-mail: pirschredaktion@dlv.de
Publisher E-mail: dlv.muenchen@dlv.de
Consumer magazine covering hunting in West Germany. **Founded:** 1948. **Freq:** Semimonthly. **Print Method:** Offset. **Trim Size:** 210 x 297 mm. **Cols./Page:** 4. **Col. Width:** 45 millimeters. **Col. Depth:** 270 millimeters. **Key Personnel:** Frau Christa Kiermeier, Contact; Stefanie Stadler, Contact. **ISSN:** 1437-4420. **Remarks:** Accepts advertising. **URL:** http://www.pirsch.de. **Ad Rates:** BW: EUR2,786, 4C: EUR5,227. **Circ:** Combined 48,244

44558 ■ DLZ Agrarmagazin
Deutscher Landwirtschaftsverlag GmbH
Lothstrasse 29
D-80797 Munich, Germany
Ph: 49 89 127051
Fax: 49 89 12705335
Publication E-mail: reddlz@dlv.de
Publisher E-mail: dlv.muenchen@dlv.de
Agricultural magazine for management, production, and technical positions. **Founded:** 1949. **Freq:** Monthly. **Key Personnel:** Detlef Steinert, Editor-in-Chief, detlef.steinert@dlv.de; Wilfried Imkampe, Contact, wilfried.imkampe@dlv.de; Josef Koch, Contact, josef.koch@dlv.de. **Subscription Rates:** EUR63 individuals inland; EUR78.80 individuals Austria; 137.70 SFr individuals Switzerland; EUR89 other countries. **Remarks:** Accepts advertising. **URL:** http://www.dlz-agrarmagazin.de/. **Circ:** Paid 71,000

44559 ■ Economics and Human Biology
Elsevier (Singapore) Pte. Ltd.
Dept. of Economics
Ludwig-Maximilians-Universitat Munchen
Ludwigstrasse 33/IV
D-80539 Munich, Germany
Ph: 49 89 21803169
Fax: 49 89 339233
Publisher E-mail: asiabkinfo@elsevier.com
Journal devoted to the exploration of the effect of socioeconomic processes on human beings as biological organisms. **Founded:** 2003. **Freq:** Quarterly. **Key Personnel:** John Komlos, Editor, john.komlos@gmx.de; S.A. Carson, Editorial Asst.; R. Fogel, Editorial Board; J. Behrman, Editorial Board; J. Cawley, Editor; A. Bhargava, Editorial Board; D. Bishai, Editorial Board; T.J. Cole, Editorial Board; H. Alderman, Editorial Board; C.M. Becker, Editorial Board. **ISSN:** 1570-677X. **Subscription Rates:** US$72 individuals all countries except Europe, Japan and Iran; EUR66 individuals European countries and Iran; 8,700¥ individuals; 62,000¥ institutions; US$520 institutions all countries except Europe, Japan and Iran; EUR465 institutions European countries and Iran. **URL:** http://www.elsevier.com/wps/find/journaldescription.cws_home/622964/description.

44560 ■ European Journal of Cell Biology
Elsevier Science Inc.
c/o Manfred Schliwa, Ed.
Adolf-Butenandt-Institut
Zellbiologie
Schillerstr. 42
D-80336 Munich, Germany
Ph: 49 89 218075883
Fax: 49 89 218075882
Publisher E-mail: usinfo-ehelp@elsevier.com
Journal covering experimental cell investigation, reviews, original articles and short communications on the structure, function and macromolecular organization of cells and cell components. **Founded:** 1969. **Freq:** 12/yr. **Key Personnel:** Manfred Schliwa, Editor, phone 49 89 218075883, fax 49 89 218075882, schliwa@bio.med.uni-muenchen.de; M. Blasco, Editorial Board; Dagmar Gebauer, Managing Editor, phone 49 6131 372064, fax 49 6131 5539577, d.gebauer@elsevier.com; Sabine Werner, Editor, phone 41 1 6333941, fax 41 1 6331174, sabine.werner@cell.biol.ethz.ch; Reinhard Jahn, Editorial Board; M. Aepfelbacher, Editorial Board; Hans Bloemendal, Hon. Ed., h.bloemendal@ncmls.kun.nl; K. Brix, Editorial Board; R. Benavente, Editorial Board; P. Boukamp, Editorial Board. **ISSN:** 0171-9335. **Subscription Rates:** US$2,164 institutions, other countries except Europe, Japan and Iran; 265,900¥ institutions; EUR1,960 institutions for European countries and Iran; EUR323 students European countries and Iran; US$436 other countries except Europe, Japan and Iran; 56,400¥ individuals; EUR431 individuals for European countries and Iran; 42,300¥ students; US$327 students, other countries except Europe, Japan and Iran. **URL:** http://www.elsevier.com/wps/find/journaldescription.cws_home/701760/descriptiondescription.

44561 ■ Fortschritte der Physik/Progress of Physics
John Wiley & Sons Inc.
c/o Dr. Dieter Lust, Ed.
Max-Planck-Inst. f. Physik (Werner-Heisenberg-Institut)
Foehringer Ring 6
D-80805 Munich, Germany
Ph: 49 89 32354282
Fax: 49 89 32354304
Publisher E-mail: info@wiley.com
Journal focusing on the theoretical and experimental study of the fundamental constituents of matter and their interactions. **Freq:** 12/yr. **Key Personnel:** Dr. Dieter Lust, Editor, luest@mppmu.mpg.de; Dr. Hans-Jog Otto, Assoc. Ed., otto@physik.hu-berlin.de; Wolfgang Schleich, Co-Ed., wolfgang.schleich@uni-ulm.de. **ISSN:** 0015-8208. **Subscription Rates:** EUR291 individuals print only; 459 SFr individuals Switzerland and Lichtenstein (print only); US$380 other countries print only; EUR2,647 institutions print only; 4,645 SFr institutions Switzerland and Lichtenstein (print only); US$3,654 institutions, other countries print only. **URL:** http://www3.interscience.wiley.com/cgi-bin/jhome/5007072.

44562 ■ Fraunhofer (English)
Fraunhofer-Gesellschaft zur Forderung der Angewandten Forschung
Hansastrasse 27c
D-80686 Munich, Germany

Ph: 49 89 12050
Fax: 49 89 12057531
English language magazine covering research, technology, and innovation. **Freq:** Semiannual. **ISSN:** 1615-7028. **Subscription Rates:** Free to qualified subscribers. **URL:** http://www.fraunhofer.de.

44563 ■ Fraunhofer Magazin
Fraunhofer-Gesellschaft zur Forderung der Angewandten Forschung
Hansastrasse 27c
D-80686 Munich, Germany
Ph: 49 89 12050
Fax: 49 89 12057531
Publication E-mail: presse@zv.fraunhofer.de
German language publication covering research. **Founded:** 1989. **Freq:** Semiannual. **Print Method:** Offset. **Key Personnel:** Franz Miller, Editor-in-Chief, phone 49 89 12051301, fax 49 89 12057513. **ISSN:** 1615-7028. **Remarks:** Advertising accepted; rates available upon request. **URL:** http://www.fraunhofer.de/fhg/EN/publications/magazin/index.jsp. **Circ:** (Not Reported)

44564 ■ International Journal of Pattern Recognition and Artificial Intelligence
World Scientific Publishing Company Private Ltd.
Dept. of Computer Science
University of Munster
Einsteinstrasse 62
D-48149 Munich, Germany
Publisher E-mail: wspc@wspc.com.sg
Journal for researchers in industry and academia, publishing both applications and theory-oriented articles on new developments in the fields of pattern recognition and artificial intelligence. **Freq:** 8/yr. **Key Personnel:** P.S.P. Wang, Editor-in-Chief, pwang@ccs.neu.edu; X. Jiang, Editor-in-Chief, xjiang@math.uni-muenster.de; J.K. Aggarwal, Assoc. Ed. **ISSN:** 0218-0014. **Subscription Rates:** US$1,248 institutions and libraries; electronic + print; EUR1,117 institutions and libraries; electronic + print; S$2,030 institutions and libraries; electronic + print; US$1,198 institutions and libraries; electronic only; EUR1,072 institutions and libraries; electronic only; S$1,949 institutions and libraries; electronic only; US$50 individuals print only; EUR34 individuals print only; S$67 individuals print only. **Remarks:** Advertising accepted; rates available upon request. **URL:** http://www.worldscinet.com/ijprai/ijprai.shtml. **Circ:** (Not Reported)

44565 ■ International Tax and Public Finance
International Institute of Public Finance
Institut International de Finances Publiques
PO Box 86 04 46
D-81631 Munich, Germany
Ph: 49 899 2241281
Fax: 49 899 077952281
Publisher E-mail: hebele@iipf.org
Worldwide publication covering economics. **Freq:** Quarterly. **Key Personnel:** D. Dharmapala, Editor-in-Chief; E. Janeba, Editor-in-Chief; Ruud A. De Mooij, Policy Watch Ed.; Alan Auerbach, Assoc. Ed.; Timothy Besley, Assoc. Ed.; David E. Wildasin, Assoc. Ed.; Robin Boadway, Assoc. Ed.; Ronald B. Davies, Policy Watch Ed.; Lans Bovenberg, Assoc. Ed.; Deborah Swenson, Assoc. Ed. **ISSN:** 0927-5940. **URL:** http://www.iipf.net; http://www.springer.com/east/home/generic/search/results?SGWID=5-40109-7035680940-0.

44566 ■ Journal of Neurology
Springer-Verlag New York Inc.
University of Munich
Clinical Ctr. Grosshadern
Neurological hospital
Marchioninistrasse 15
D-81377 Munich, Germany
Ph: 49 89 70952570
Fax: 49 89 70958883
Publisher E-mail: service-ny@springer.com
Peer-reviewed journal of the European Neurological Society. **Key Personnel:** Prof. Gerard Said, Joint Ch. Ed., grrdsd@gmail.com; Dr. M. Strupp, Asst. Ed., mstrupp@brain.nefo.med.uni-muenchen.de; F. Fazekas, Editorial Board; Prof. T. Brandt, Joint Ch. Ed.; M. Dieterich, Editorial Board; Dr. W. Poewe, Review Ed.; G. Frisoni, Editorial Board. **ISSN:** 0340-5354. **URL:** http://www.springer.com/steinkopff/neurologie/journal/415.

44567 ■ Journal of Psychiatric Research
Mosby Inc.
Max-Planck-Institute of Psychiatry
Kraepelinstrasse 10

D-80804 Munich, Germany
Publisher E-mail: custserv.ehs@elsevier.com
Journal for psychiatrists. **Freq:** 12/yr. **Key Personnel:**
Florian Holsboer, Editor-in-Chief; Alan F. Schatzberg,
Editor-in-Chief; M. Ising, Asst. Ed. **ISSN:** 0022-3956.
Subscription Rates: 312,900¥ institutions; EUR2,357
institutions for European countries and Iran; US$2,636
institutions, other countries except Europe, Japan and
Iran. **URL:** http://www.elsevier.com/wps/find/
journaldescription.cws_home/241/descriptiondescription.

44568 ■ Kunst Chronik
Fachverlag Hans Carl GmbH
c/o Zentralinstitut fur Kunstgeschichte
Meiserstr. 10
D-80333 Munich, Germany
Ph: 49 911 9528520
Fax: 49 911 952858120
Publisher E-mail: info@hanscarl.com
Journal covering the European history of art. **Freq:**
Monthly. **Print Method:** Offset. **Trim Size:** 168 x 240
mm. **Key Personnel:** Dr. Peter Diemer, Editor. **ISSN:**
0023-5474. **Subscription Rates:** EUR65.90 individuals
inland; EUR40.90 students; EUR134.90 other countries.
Remarks: Accepts advertising. **URL:** http://www.
hanscarl.com/deutsch/fachzeitschriften/fachzeit_
kunstchronik.html. **Ad Rates:** BW: EUR402. **Circ:** 2,869

44569 ■ LSV aktuell
Land -und forstwirtschaftliche Berufsgenossenschaft
Franken und Oberbayern
Neumarkter Strasse 35
D-81673 Munich, Germany
Ph: 49 89 45480382
Fax: 49 89 436639813
Publication E-mail: presse@fob.lsv.de
Publisher E-mail: presse@fob.lsv.de
Trade magazine covering safety and other news and
information for insured members. **Subtitle:** The Agricul-
tural Technical Periodical. **Founded:** 1960. **Freq:**
Quarterly. **Trim Size:** 210 x 297 mm. **Cols./Page:** 3.
Col. Depth: 265 millimeters. **Subscription Rates:** Free
to qualified subscribers. **Remarks:** Accepts advertising.
URL: http://www.lsv.de/fob/; http://www.lsv-aktuell.de.
Formerly: Sicherheit fur Haus & Hof. **Ad Rates:** 4C:
EUR2,096. **Circ:** (Not Reported)

44570 ■ MADCHEN
Axel Springer Verlag
Loonrodstr. 52
80636 Munich, Germany
Ph: 49 89 697490
Fax: 49 89 69749430
Publication E-mail: info@asmm.de
Publisher E-mail: information@axelspringer.de
Fashion and beauty magazine for women. **Founded:**
1976. **Freq:** every fortnightly. **Key Personnel:** Nina
Maurischat, Editor-in-Chief; Christian Medweth,
Publisher. **Subscription Rates:** EUR1.70 single issue;
EUR44.20 individuals. **Remarks:** Accepts advertising.
URL: http://www.maedchen.de/. **Circ:** ‡158,029

44571 ■ Metal Hammer
Axel Springer Verlag
Leonrodstrasse 52
80636 Munich, Germany
Ph: 49 89 697490
Fax: 49 89 14038
Publisher E-mail: information@axelspringer.de
Magazine for hard music fan. **Founded:** 1984. **Freq:**
Monthly. **Key Personnel:** Thorsten Zhan, Editor-in-
Chief, thorsten@metal-hammer.de; Petra Schurer,
Contact, petra@metal-hammer.de; Tobias Gerber,
Editor. **Subscription Rates:** EUR4.60 single issue. **Re-
marks:** Accepts advertising. **URL:** http://www.metal-
hammer.de/Home.html. **Circ:** ‡42,996

44572 ■ Munich Found
Transnet Internet Services GmbH
Lilienstr. 3-5
D-81669 Munich, Germany
Ph: 49 894 8903350
Fax: 49 894 8903355
Publisher E-mail: registry@trans.net
Consumer magazine covering local arts, entertainment,
food and more. Features an events calendar. **Founded:**
1989. **Freq:** Monthly 10/yr. **Key Personnel:** Angela
Wilson, Editor and Publisher. **Subscription Rates:**
EUR30 individuals; EUR40 individuals Europe;
EUR60 individuals U.S.; US$45 individuals Germany;
US$50 individuals Europe; US$70 individuals U.S. **URL:**
http://www.munichfound.com/. **Circ:** 10,000

44573 ■ MUSIKEXPRESS
Axel Springer Verlag
Leonrodstr. 52
80636 Munich, Germany
Ph: 49 89 697490
Fax: 49 89 69749430
Publication E-mail: info@asmm.de
Publisher E-mail: information@axelspringer.de
Music magazine featuring aspects of the pop-culture
lifestyle. **Founded:** 1983. **Freq:** Monthly. **Key Person-
nel:** Christian Stolberg, Editor-in-Chief; Sassan Nias-
seri, Online Ed.; Josef Winker, Editor. **Subscription
Rates:** EUR4.49 single issue. **Remarks:** Accepts
advertising. **URL:** http://www.musikexpress.de/Home.
html. **Circ:** ‡52,398

44574 ■ Mycoses
John Wiley & Sons Inc.
Wiley-Blackwell
c/o Dr. Hans Christian Korting, Ed.-in-Ch.
Ludwig-Maximilians-Universitat
Dermatologische Klinik und Poliklinik
Frauenlobstrasse 9-11
D-80337 Munich, Germany
Ph: 49 89 51476203
Fax: 49 89 51606204
Peer-reviewed journal covering original contributions on
the pathogenesis, therapy, diagnosis, prophylaxis, and
epidemiology of fungal infectious diseases in humans
and animals, and on the biology of pathogenic fungi.
Subtitle: Diagnosis, Therapy and Prophylaxis of Fungal
Diseases. **Freq:** Bimonthly. **Key Personnel:** Dr. Hans
Christian Korting, Editor-in-Chief, mycoses.muenchen@
t-online.de; Dr. Martin Schaller, Dep. Ed., martin.
schaller@med.uni-tuebingen.de; Dr. Andreas Groll, Dep.
Ed., grollan@mednet.uni-muenster.de. **ISSN:** 0933-
7407. **Subscription Rates:** US$367 individuals print
and online; EUR298 individuals print and online; 198
individuals for non-Euro zone (print and online); 219
other countries print and online; US$837 institutions
print and online; EUR603 institutions print and online;
US$977 institutions, other countries print and online;
US$761 institutions print or online; EUR547 institutions
print or online; 431 institutions print or online. **Remarks:**
Advertising accepted; rates available upon request.
URL: http://www.wiley.com/bw/journal.asp?ref=0933-
7407. **Circ:** (Not Reported)

44575 ■ Natur & Heilen
Verlag Natur & Heilen
Nikolaistr. 5
D-80802 Munich, Germany
Ph: 49 89 38015910
Fax: 49 89 38015916
Publisher E-mail: info@naturundheilen.com
Consumer magazine covering natural healing and
health. **Subtitle:** Die Monatszeitschrift fur gesundes
Leben. **Founded:** 1924. **Freq:** Monthly. **Print Method:**
Offset. **Trim Size:** 3. **Cols./Page:** 40. **Col. Width:** MMS
inches. **Key Personnel:** Hansjorg Volkhardt, Editor;
Anne Devillard, Ch. Ed.; Irene Stolze, Editorial. **ISSN:**
0932-3503. **Subscription Rates:** EUR47.40 individuals
annual; EUR3.80 single issue. **Remarks:** Accepts
advertising. **URL:** http://www.naturundheilen.info/. **Ad
Rates:** BW: EUR2,000, 4C: EUR3,380. **Circ:** Paid 55,590

**44576 ■ Official Journal of the European Patent
Office**
European Patent Office
Europaisches Patentamt
Erhardtstrasse 27
D-80469 Munich, Germany
Ph: 49 89 23990
Publication E-mail: official-journal@epo.org
Journal covering the European patent office in English,
French and German. **Founded:** 1978. **Freq:** Monthly.
ISSN: 0170-9291. **Subscription Rates:** EUR84 individu-
als; EUR46 individuals within Europe; EUR76 individuals
outside Europe. **Remarks:** Accepts advertising. **URL:**
http://www.epo.org/patents/law/legal-texts/journal.html.
Ad Rates: BW: EUR700. **Circ:** Paid ‡2,200, Non-paid
‡2,100

44577 ■ Organisms Diversity & Evolution
Elsevier (Singapore) Pte. Ltd.
Zoologische Staatssammlung Munchen
Munchhausenstrasse 21
D-81247 Munich, Germany
Ph: 49 898 107104
Fax: 49 898 107300
Publisher E-mail: asiabkinfo@elsevier.com
Journal devoted to the understanding of organismal

diversity, of interest to biologists (botanists, mycologists,
protistologists, zoologists), paleontologists, systematists
& taxonomists. **Freq:** 5/yr. **Key Personnel:** Gerhard
Haszprunar, Editor-in-Chief, haszi@zsm.mwn.de; Klaus
Klass, Editor-in-Chief, klaus.klass@snsd.smwk.sachsen.
de; Joachim W. Kadereit, Editor-in-Chief, kadereit@uni-
mainz.de. **ISSN:** 1439-6092. **URL:** http://www.elsevier.
com/wps/find/journaldescription.cws_home/701789/
descrip tiondescription.

44578 ■ POPCORN
Axel Springer Verlag
Leonrodstr. 52
80636 Munich, Germany
Ph: 49 89 697490
Fax: 49 89 69749430
Publication E-mail: info@asmm.de
Publisher E-mail: information@axelspringer.de
Entertainment magazine for teenagers. **Founded:** 1977.
Freq: Monthly. **Key Personnel:** Norbert Lalla, Editor.
Subscription Rates: EUR2.10 single issue. **Remarks:**
Accepts advertising. **URL:** http://www.popcorn-mag.de/.
Circ: ‡188,349

**44579 ■ Radiation and Environmental Biophys-
ics**
Springer-Verlag
c/o Anna A. Friedl, Ed.-in-Ch.
Ludwig-Maximilians University
Radiobiological Institute
Schillerstrasse 42
D-80336 Munich, Germany
Journal focusing on radiation research and biophysics.
Founded: 1963. **Freq:** 4/yr. **Key Personnel:** Werner
Ruhm, Editor-in-Chief, radiatenvironbiophys@lrz.uni-
muenchen.de; Anna A. Friedl, Editor-in-Chief; David J.
Brenner, Assoc. Ed. **ISSN:** 0301-634X. **Subscription
Rates:** EUR1,861 institutions print incl. free access;
EUR2,233.20 institutions print incl. enhanced access.
Remarks: Advertising accepted; rates available upon
request. **URL:** http://www.springer.com/physics/
biophysics/journal/411. **Circ:** (Not Reported)

44580 ■ Rinderzucht/Fleckvieh
Deutscher Landwirtschaftsverlag GmbH
Lothstrasse 29
D-80797 Munich, Germany
Ph: 49 89 127061
Fax: 49 89 12705335
Publisher E-mail: dlv.muenchen@dlv.de
Trade magazine covering cattle breeding. **Subtitle:**
Zucht, Management & Market. **Founded:** June 1994.
Freq: Quarterly. **Key Personnel:** Johannes Urban,
Editor-in-Chief. **ISSN:** 0948-7247. **Subscription Rates:**
EUR24 individuals for Germany; EUR31.30 individuals
Austria; 48.20 SFr individuals for Switzerland. **URL:**
http://www.rinderzucht-fleckvieh.de.

44581 ■ SG Susswarenhandel
Sweets Global Network e.V.
Grillparzerstr. 38
D-81675 Munich, Germany
Ph: 49 89 4706093
Fax: 49 89 4703783
Publisher E-mail: info@sg-network.org
Publication covering food. **Freq:** Monthly. **Key Person-
nel:** Hans Strohmaier, Editor; Susanne Hansen, Sub-
scription Svcs.; Susanne Peters, Advertisements. **Sub-
scription Rates:** EUR55 other countries; EUR30
individuals in Germany, plus taxes. **Remarks:** Accepts
advertising. **URL:** http://www.sg-network.org. **Ad Rates:**
BW: DM 1,800, 4C: DM 2,780. **Circ:** 6,500

44582 ■ STARFLASH
Axel Springer Verlag
Leonrodstr. 52
80636 Munich, Germany
Ph: 49 89 697490
Fax: 49 89 69749430
Publication E-mail: redaktion@starflash.de
Publisher E-mail: information@axelspringer.de
Entertainment magazine for young women. **Founded:**
2002. **Freq:** Monthly. **Key Personnel:** Norbert Lalla,
Editor-in-Chief; Christian Medweth, Publisher; Carol
Schuhler, Editor. **Subscription Rates:** EUR26.40
individuals. **Remarks:** Accepts advertising. **URL:** http://
www.starflash.de/Home.html. **Circ:** ‡69,073

44583 ■ Televizion
Internationales Zentralinstitut fur das Jugend-und Bil-
dungsfernsehen
Rundfunkplatz 1
D-80335 Munich, Germany

Circulation: ★ = ABC; △ = BPA; ◆ = CAC; • = CCAB; ❑ = VAC; ⊕ = PO Statement; ‡ = Publisher's Report; Boldface figures = sworn; Light figures = estimated.

Ph: 49 895 9002991
Fax: 49 895 9002379
Publisher E-mail: izi@brnet.de
Journal publishing current program formats and current issues relating to children, youth and educational television. **Freq:** Annual. **Key Personnel:** Dr. Maya Gotz, Contact, maya.goetz@brnet.de. **ISSN:** 0943-4755. **URL:** http://www.br-online.de/jugend/izi/deutsch/publikation/television/televizion.htm; http://www.br-online.de/jugend/izi/deutsch/publikation/publikationen.htm.

44584 ■ Tour Das Rennrad-Magazin
Delius Klasing Verlag GmbH
Steinerstr. 15 Haus D
D-81369 Munich, Germany
Ph: 49 897 296030
Fax: 49 897 2960333
Publication E-mail: redaktion@tour-magazin.de
Publisher E-mail: info@delius-klasing.de
Consumer journal covering bicycle racing and news. **Subtitle:** Das Rennrad-Magazin. **Founded:** 1977. **Freq:** Monthly. **Key Personnel:** Uwe Geissler, Publisher; Thomas Musch, Editor. **Remarks:** Accepts advertising. **URL:** http://www.tour-magazin.de. **Circ:** Controlled 85,000

44585 ■ Unsere Jagd
Deutscher Landwirtschaftsverlag GmbH
Lothstrasse 29
D-80797 Munich, Germany
Ph: 49 89 127051
Fax: 49 89 12705335
Publication E-mail: info@jagderleben.de
Publisher E-mail: dlv.muenchen@dlv.de
Consumer magazine covering hunting in East Germany. **Founded:** 1950. **Freq:** Monthly. **Trim Size:** 210 x 297 mm. **Cols./Page:** 4. **Col. Width:** 45 millimeters. **Col. Depth:** 270 millimeters. **Subscription Rates:** EUR46.90 individuals; EUR53 individuals OTC; EUR81.55 individuals Switzerland. **Remarks:** Accepts advertising. **URL:** http://www.jagderleben.de/uj/heftvorschau. **Ad Rates:** BW: EUR2,786, 4C: EUR5,227. **Circ:** Combined ‡42,781

44586 ■ W & V Werben & Verkaufen
Hultschiner Strasse 8
81677 Munich, Germany
Ph: 49 89 21837999
Publisher E-mail: webmaster@wuv.de
Trade magazine covering advertising, marketing, media and sales. **Founded:** 1963. **Freq:** Weekly. **Print Method:** Offset. **Trim Size:** 230 x 300 mm. **Cols./Page:** 4. **Key Personnel:** Dr. Jochen Kalka, Editor-in-Chief, phone 49 89 21837026, jkalka@efv.de; Dr. Karl Ulrich, CEO. **ISSN:** 0042-9538. **Remarks:** Accepts advertising. **URL:** http://www.wuv.de/. **Circ:** Controlled 33,885

44587 ■ Wood Science and Technology
Springer Publishing Co.
Holzforschung Munchen
Technische University Munchen
Winzererstr. 45
D-80797 Munich, Germany
Ph: 49 89 21806475
Fax: 49 89 21806487
Publisher E-mail: cs@springerpub.com
Journal covering the entire field of wood and pulp. **Key Personnel:** D.S. Argyropoulos, Editorial Board; N.G. Lewis, Editorial Board; P. Hoffmeyer, Editorial Board; F.A. Kamke, Editorial Board; B. Butterfield, Editorial Board; S. Chow, Editorial Board; B. Holmbom, Editorial Board; R. Evans, Editorial Board; R. Patt, Editorial Board; K. Takabe, Editorial Board; Gerd Wegener, Editor-in-Chief; J.R. Barnett, Co-Ed.-in-Ch. **ISSN:** 0043-7719. **URL:** http://www.springer.com/lifesciences/forestry/journal/226.

44588 ■ YAM!
Axel Springer Verlag
Leonrodstr. 52
80636 Munich, Germany
Publisher E-mail: information@axelspringer.de
Magazine for young Germans. **Founded:** 2000. **Freq:** Monthly. **Key Personnel:** Carol Schuhler, Editor; Sabrins Doschek, Online Ed. **Subscription Rates:** EUR1.30 single issue. **Remarks:** Accepts advertising. **URL:** http://www.yam.de/. **Circ:** ‡106,915

44589 ■ Zeitschrift fur Assyriologie und Vorderasiatische Archaologie
Walter de Gruyter GmbH & Co. KG
Fakultat fur Kulturwissenschaften

Institut fur Assyriologie und Hethitologie der University Munich
Geschw. Scholl-Platz
D-80539 Munich, Germany
Publisher E-mail: info@degruyter.com
Journal covering articles on ancient eastern philology, religious, legal, economic and social history, together with middle eastern archaeology and art history. **Freq:** Semiannual. **Print Method:** Offset. **Cols./Page:** 6. **Col. Width:** 11 1/2 picas. **Col. Depth:** 21 1/2 inches. **Key Personnel:** Dr. Walther Sallaberger, Editor, wasa@assyr.fak12.uni-muenchen.de. **ISSN:** 0084-5299. **Subscription Rates:** EUR198 individuals print or online only; EUR228 individuals print + online; EUR109 single issue. **URL:** http://www.degruyter.de/journals/za/detailEn.cfm. **Circ:** 500

44590 ■ Bayern 4 Klassik-FM - 103.2
Rundfunkplatz 1
D-80335 Munich, Germany
Ph: 49 89 59004646
Fax: 49 89 59004171
E-mail: info@br-klassik.de
Format: Jazz; World Beat; Classical. **URL:** http://www.br-online.de.

44591 ■ B5 Aktuell-FM - 90
Rundfunkplatz 1
D-80300 Munich, Germany
Fax: 49 89 59002395
E-mail: b5aktuell@br-online.de
Format: Ethnic; News. **URL:** http://www.br-online.de.

44592 ■ B5 Aktuell-FM - 87.8
Rundfunkplatz 1
D-80300 Munich, Germany
Fax: 49 89 59002395
E-mail: b5aktuell@br-online.de
Format: News; Sports. **Operating Hours:** Continuous. **URL:** http://www.br-online.de.

44593 ■ Charivari-FM - 95.5
Paul-Heyse-Str. 2-4
D-80336 Munich, Germany
Ph: 49 89 5447100
Fax: 49 89 5380940
E-mail: radio@charivari.de
Format: Ethnic; Contemporary Hit Radio (CHR). **Operating Hours:** Continuous. **Ad Rates:** Advertising accepted; rates available upon request. **URL:** http://www.charivari.de.

Munster

44594 ■ Acta Neuropathologica
Springer-Verlag Tokyo
c/o Werner Paulus, Ed.-in-Ch.
Institute of Neuropathology
University Hospital Muenster
Domagkstrasse 19
D-48149 Munster, Germany
Ph: 49 251 8356967
Fax: 49 251 8356971
Publisher E-mail: info@springer.jp
Journal publishing manuscripts dealing with disease mechanisms, general, experimental, comparative, and molecular pathology of the nervous tissue, with special interest in interdisciplinary studies on abnormalities in structure, genetics, function, basic molecular mechanisms and on the pathogenesis of neurological disorders. **Freq:** Bimonthly. **Key Personnel:** K.A. Jellinger, Former Ed.-in-Ch.; Werner Paulus, Editor-in-Chief, werner.paulus@uni-muenster.de; C. Duyckaerts, Editorial Board; H. Lassmann, Editorial Board; J.E. Galvin, Editorial Board. **ISSN:** 0001-6322. **Subscription Rates:** EUR6,179 institutions print incl. free access; EUR7,414.80 institutions print incl. enhanced access. **Remarks:** Advertising accepted; rates available upon request. **URL:** http://www.springer.com/medicine/pathology/journal/401. **Circ:** (Not Reported)

44595 ■ Applied Microbiology and Biotechnology
Springer-Verlag Tokyo
Institut fur Molekulare Mikrobiologie und Biotechnologie
Westfalische Wilhelms-Universitat Munster
Corrensstrasse 3
D-48149 Munster, Germany
Ph: 49 251 8339821
Fax: 49 251 8338388

Publisher E-mail: info@springer.jp
Journal publishing papers on the following aspects of applied microbiology and biotechnology: biotechnological products and process engineering, biotechnologically relevant enzymes and proteins, applied genetics and molecular biotechnology, genomics and proteomics, applied microbial and cell physiology and environmental biotechnology. **Freq:** Bimonthly. **Key Personnel:** Alexander Steinbuchel, Editor-in-Chief, amb@uni-muenster.de; Akira Kimura, Assoc. Ed., phone 81 75 3446414, fax 81 75 3446420, akimura@hera.eonet.ne.jp; George N. Bennett, Editor; Arnold L. Demain, Assoc. Ed., phone 973408-3937, fax 973408-3504, ademain@drew.edu; Uwe T. Bornscheuer, Editor; Gerhard H. Braus, Editor; Claudia Schmidt-Dannert, Assoc. Ed., phone 612625-5782, fax 612625-5780, schmi232@umn.edu; Gerrit Eggink, Editor; Axel A. Brakhage, Editor; John D. Coates, Editor. **ISSN:** 0175-7598. **Subscription Rates:** EUR6,553 institutions print incl. free access or e-only; EUR7,863.60 institutions print incl. enhanced access. **Remarks:** Advertising accepted; rates available upon request. **URL:** http://www.springer.com/chemistry/biotech/journal/253. **Circ:** (Not Reported)

44596 ■ Archive for Mathematical Logic
Springer-Verlag Tokyo
Institut fur Mathematische Logik und Grundlagenforschung
Universitat Munster
Einsteinstrasse 62
D-48149 Munster, Germany
Publication E-mail: rds@uni-muenster.de
Publisher E-mail: info@springer.jp
Journal publishing research papers and occasionally surveys or expositions on mathematical logic, also welcoming contributions from other related areas, such as theoretical computer science or philosophy, as long as the methods of mathematical logic play a significant role. **Freq:** 8/yr. **Key Personnel:** W. Pohlers, Editor; A. Pillay, Editor; R. Schindler, Editor. **ISSN:** 0933-5846. **Subscription Rates:** EUR1,087 institutions print incl. free access or e-only; EUR1,304.40 institutions print incl. enhanced access. **Remarks:** Advertising accepted; rates available upon request. **URL:** http://www.springer.com/math/journal/153. **Circ:** (Not Reported)

44597 ■ Best Practice & Research Clinical Anesthesiology
Elsevier Science
c/o Prof. Hugo Van Aken, Ed.-in-Ch.
Klinik fur Anasthesiologie
Universitat Munster
Albert Schweitzer St. 33
D-48129 Munster, Germany
Publisher E-mail: nlinfo-f@elsevier.com
Journal providing complete report on current issues related to clinical practice and anesthesiology. **Freq:** Quarterly. **Key Personnel:** Prof. Hugo Van Aken, Editor-in-Chief, hva@anit.uni-muenster.de; A. Aitkenhead, Editorial Board; D.C.H Cheng, Editorial Board; A.W. Gelb, Editorial Board; H. Kehlet, Editorial Board; I. Acalovschi, Editorial Board; S. Gelman, Editorial Board; J. Andres, Editorial Board; M.E. Durieux, Editorial Board; D. Spahn, Editorial Board; K. Shingu, Editorial Board; S. Schug, Editorial Board. **ISSN:** 1521-6896. **Subscription Rates:** US$257 individuals for all countries except Europe, Japan & Iran; EUR289 individuals for European countries & Iran; 31,200¥ individuals; US$408 institutions for all countries except Europe, Japan & Iran; 49,500¥ institutions; EUR460 institutions for European countries & Iran. **Remarks:** Accepts advertising. **URL:** http://www.elsevier.com/wps/find/journaldescription.cws_home/623000/description. **Circ:** (Not Reported)

44598 ■ Information Systems and E-Business Management (ISeB)
Springer-Verlag
c/o Jorg Becker, Ed.-in-Ch.
University of Muenster
Dept. of Information Systems
Leonardo Campus 3
D-48149 Munster, Germany
Journal reporting advances in information systems management and e-business for both academics and industry specialists. **Freq:** Quarterly. **Key Personnel:** Jorg Becker, Editor-in-Chief, becker@wi.uni-muenster.de; Michael J. Shaw, Editor-in-Chief, mjshaw@cba.uiuc.edu; A. Whinston, Advisory Board; I. Benbasat, Advisory Board; R.D. Galliers, Advisory Board. **ISSN:** 1617-9846. **Subscription Rates:** EUR351.60 institutions print incl. free access; EUR293 institutions print incl. enhanced access. **URL:** http://www.springer.com/

business%26management/businessinformation systems/journal/10257.

44599 ■ Journal of Business Chemistry (JoBC)
Institut fur betriebswirtschaftliches Management
Leonardo-Campus 1
D-48149 Munster, Germany
Ph: 49 251 8331810
Fax: 49 251 8331818
Publisher E-mail: mail@wirtschaftschemie.de
Journal publishing latest developments in the field of business chemistry. Covers developments in management and strategies for the chemical industry. **Founded:** May 2004. **Freq:** 3/yr. **Key Personnel:** Jens Leker, Editor-in-Chief; Irina Kli10utch, Exec. Ed., ik@businesschemistry.org; Clive-Steven Curran, Editor, csc@businesschemistry.org. **ISSN:** 1613-9615. **Subscription Rates:** EUR30 individuals; EUR60 institutions. **URL:** http://www.businesschemistry.org/.

44600 ■ Journal fur die reine und angewandte Mathematik
Walter de Gruyter GmbH & Co. KG
Mathematisches Institut
Universitat Munster
Einsteinstrabe 62
D-48149 Munster, Germany
Publisher E-mail: info@degruyter.com
Journal covering mathematics periodicals. **Freq:** Monthly. **Print Method:** Offset. **Cols./Page:** 6. **Col. Width:** 2 1/16 inches. **Col. Depth:** 21.5 picas. **Key Personnel:** Dr. Rainer Weissauer, Managing Editor, phone 49 6221 545692, fax 49 6221 548312, weissauer.crelle@mathi.uni-heidelberg.de; Paul Vojta, Editor, vojta@math.berkeley.edu; Marc Levine, Editor, marc@neu.edu; Joachim Cuntz, Editor, cuntz@math.uni-muenster.de. **ISSN:** 0075-4102. **Subscription Rates:** EUR2,449 individuals print or online only; EUR2,874 individuals print and online; EUR229 single issue. **URL:** http://www.degruyter.de/journals/crelle/detailEn.cfm. **Circ:** 750

44601 ■ Review of Palaeobotany and Palynology
Elsevier Science
c/o H. Kerp, Ed.-in-Ch.
Westfalische Wilhelms-Universitat
Forschungsstelle fur Palaobotanik
Hindenburgplatz 57
D-48143 Munster, Germany
Ph: 49 251 8323966
Fax: 49 251 8323966
Publisher E-mail: nlinfo-f@elsevier.com
International journal covering all fields of paleobotany and palynology dealing with all groups, ranging from marine palynomorphs to higher land plants. It publishes articles in which paleobotany and palynology are applied for solving fundamental geological and biological problems. **Founded:** 1967. **Freq:** 20/yr. **Key Personnel:** H. Kerp, Editor-in-Chief, kerp@uni-muenster.de; H. Visscher, Editorial Board; T.N. Taylor, Book Review Ed. **ISSN:** 0034-6667. **Subscription Rates:** US$2,924 institutions for all countries except Europe and Japan; EUR2,616 institutions for European countries; 347,200¥ institutions; EUR183 individuals for European countries; 24,100¥ individuals; US$207 individuals for all countries except Europe and Japan. **Remarks:** Accepts advertising. **URL:** http://www.elsevier.com/wps/find/journaldescription.cws_home/503359/descriptiondescription. **Circ:** (Not Reported)

Nuremberg

44602 ■ Berge
Olympia-Verlag GmbH
Badstr. 4-6
D-90402 Nuremberg, Germany
Ph: 49 911 2160
Publisher E-mail: info@olympia-verlag.de
Consumer magazine covering mountain climbing and outdoor recreation worldwide. **Founded:** 1983. **Freq:** Bimonthly. **Cols./Page:** 3. **ISSN:** 0947-5958. **Subscription Rates:** US$365 individuals; US$690 single issue. **Remarks:** Accepts advertising. **URL:** http://www.alpin.de/home; http://www.berge.de. **Circ:** Paid 32,000

44603 ■ Brauwelt Chinese
Fachverlag Hans Carl GmbH
Andernacher St. 33a
D-90411 Nuremberg, Germany
Ph: 49 911 95250

Fax: 49 911 9528581
Publisher E-mail: info@hanscarl.com
Journal covering the beer and brewing industry in Chinese. **Freq:** 3/yr. **Trim Size:** 210 x 297 mm. **Key Personnel:** Dr. Karl-Ullrich Heyse, Publisher, phone 49 911 952850, fax 49 911 952858160, info@hanscarl.com; Dr. Lydia Winkelmann, Editor-in-Chief, phone 49 911 9528558. **Subscription Rates:** EUR65.90 individuals by land; EUR86.90 individuals inland; EUR95.90 other countries by land; EUR106.90 other countries by air; EUR109.90 other countries by sal; EUR135.90 other countries by air; EUR62.90 students; EUR22.90 single issue. **URL:** http://www.hanscarl.com/deutsch/fachzeitschriften/fachzeit_brauweltchinesisch.html; http://www.brauweltinternational.com. **Ad Rates:** BW: EUR3,353, 4C: EUR4,769. **Circ:** Combined ‡4,221

44604 ■ Brauwelt Deutsch
Fachverlag Hans Carl GmbH
Andernacher St. 33a
D-90411 Nuremberg, Germany
Ph: 49 911 95250
Fax: 49 911 9528581
Publisher E-mail: info@hanscarl.com
Trade magazine covering sales issues and technical, technological and economic developments for the brewing industry and producers of non-alcoholic beverages. **Subtitle:** Special Journal Covering the Brewing and Beverage Industries - World-wide. **Freq:** 36/yr. **Trim Size:** 210 x 297 mm. **Subscription Rates:** EUR169.85 individuals inland; EUR137.90 individuals Ausland; EUR34.90 students. **Remarks:** Accepts advertising. **URL:** http://www.hanscarl.com/englisch/entrance_index.html. **Ad Rates:** BW: EUR3,626, 4C: EUR5,063. **Circ:** Paid ‡5,543

44605 ■ Brauwelt en Espanol
Fachverlag Hans Carl GmbH
Andernacher St. 33a
D-90411 Nuremberg, Germany
Ph: 49 911 95250
Fax: 49 911 9528581
Publisher E-mail: info@hanscarl.com
Spanish language trade magazine covering the brewing and beverage market in Latin America and worldwide. **Freq:** 4/yr. **Trim Size:** 210 x 297 mm. **Key Personnel:** Michael Schmitt, Managing Editor, phone 49 911 9528562, fax 49 911 952858120, m.schmitt@hanscarl.com. **URL:** http://www.hanscarl.com/englisch/entrance_index.html. **Ad Rates:** BW: EUR2,507, 4C: EUR3,923. **Circ:** (Not Reported)

44606 ■ Brauwelt International
Fachverlag Hans Carl GmbH
Andernacher St. 33a
D-90411 Nuremberg, Germany
Ph: 49 911 95250
Fax: 49 911 9528581
Publisher E-mail: info@hanscarl.com
Trade journal covering brewing and the beverage industry worldwide. **Freq:** Bimonthly. **Trim Size:** 210 x 297 mm. **Key Personnel:** Michael Schmitt, Contact, phone 49 911 9528562, fax 49 911 952858120, m.schmitt@hanscarl.com. **URL:** http://www.brauweltinternational.com/; http://www.hanscarl.com/englisch/entrance_index.html. **Ad Rates:** BW: EUR3,237, 4C: EUR4,977. **Circ:** (Not Reported)

44607 ■ Brauwelt in Russian
Fachverlag Hans Carl GmbH
Andernacher St. 33a
D-90411 Nuremberg, Germany
Ph: 49 911 95250
Fax: 49 911 9528581
Publisher E-mail: info@hanscarl.com
Russian language trade magazine covering the brewing and beverage industry in Russian speaking countries and worldwide. **Freq:** 4/yr. **Trim Size:** 210 x 297 mm. **Key Personnel:** Michael Schmitt, Managing Editor, phone 49 911 9528562, fax 49 911 952858120, m.schmitt@hanscarl.com. **URL:** http://www.hanscarl.com/englisch/entrance_index.html. **Ad Rates:** BW: EUR3,353, 4C: EUR4,769. **Circ:** (Not Reported)

44608 ■ dedica
Dr. Harnisch International Publications
Blumenstrasse 15
D-90402 Nuremberg, Germany
Ph: 49 911 20180
Fax: 49 911 2018100
Publication E-mail: dedica@harnisch.com

Publisher E-mail: info@harnisch.com
Journal covering business gifts, incentives, and promotions. **Freq:** 4/yr. **Key Personnel:** Yvonne Weiss, Editor, phone 49 911 2018245, fax 49 911 2018100, yvonne.weiss@harnisch.com; Dr. Claus-Jorg Harnisch, Managing Editor, phone 49 911 2018103, jharnisch@harnisch.com. **Subscription Rates:** EUR34 individuals. **Remarks:** Accepts advertising. **URL:** http://www.dedica.de/. **Circ:** 19,993

44609 ■ Der Weihenstephaner
Fachverlag Hans Carl GmbH
Andernacher St. 33a
D-90411 Nuremberg, Germany
Ph: 49 911 95250
Fax: 49 911 9528581
Publisher E-mail: info@hanscarl.com
Publication of former students at the Department of Brewing and Faculty for Brewing Science of the Technical University Munich-Weihenstephan. **Freq:** Quarterly. **Trim Size:** 210 x 297 mm. **Key Personnel:** Dr. E. Geiger, Contact. **Subscription Rates:** EUR53.90 institutions. **Remarks:** Accepts advertising. **URL:** http://www.hanscarl.com/englisch/entrance_index.html. **Ad Rates:** BW: EUR1,822, 4C: EUR2,955. **Circ:** (Not Reported)

44610 ■ Element + BAU
Dr. Harnisch International Publications
Blumenstrasse 15
D-90402 Nuremberg, Germany
Ph: 49 911 20180
Fax: 49 911 2018100
Publication E-mail: eb@harnisch.com
Publisher E-mail: info@harnisch.com
Magazine covering all aspects of building and construction. **Freq:** 6/yr. **Key Personnel:** Armin Konig, Editor-in-Chief; Benno Keller, Publisher, keller@harnisch.com; Claus-Jorg Harnisch, Publisher. **Remarks:** Accepts advertising. **URL:** http://www.harnisch.com/ebau/. **Circ:** 6,800

44611 ■ Food Marketing & Technology
Dr. Harnisch International Publications
Blumenstrasse 15
D-90402 Nuremberg, Germany
Ph: 49 911 20180
Fax: 40 011 2018100
Publication E-mail: fmt@harnisch.com
Publisher E-mail: info@harnisch.com
Journal covering new marketing strategies and trends, equipment and processing methods, innovative technologies, raw materials and additives, packaging systems and other important topics of selling and purchasing marketing. **Freq:** 6/yr. **Print Method:** offset. **Key Personnel:** Ian Healey, Editor-in-Chief, phone 49 911 2018215, fax 49 911 2018100, healey@harnisch.com. **Subscription Rates:** EUR80 individuals; EUR98 individuals surface mail; EUR114 individuals airmail. **Remarks:** Accepts advertising. **URL:** http://www.harnisch.com/fmt/index.php. **Ad Rates:** BW: DM 3,990, 4C: DM 5,340. **Circ:** 18,500

44612 ■ Food Technologie
Dr. Harnisch International Publications
Blumenstrasse 15
D-90402 Nuremberg, Germany
Ph: 49 911 20180
Fax: 49 911 2018100
Publication E-mail: ftm@harnisch.com
Publisher E-mail: info@harnisch.com
Journal covering food ingredients, processing technology, measuring, weighing, and packaging. **Freq:** 5/yr. **Print Method:** offset. **Key Personnel:** Sebastian Martinek, Editor-in-Chief, phone 49 911 2018235, fax 49 911 2018100, martinek@harnisch.com; Benno Keller, Publisher, phone 49 911 2018200, benno.keller@harnisch.com. **Subscription Rates:** EUR60 individuals; EUR65 other countries. **Remarks:** Accepts advertising. **URL:** http://www.harnisch.com/fmtg/. **Ad Rates:** BW: DM 3,570, 4C: DM 4,920. **Circ:** 11,668

44613 ■ Getranke! Technologie & Marketing
Dr. Harnisch International Publications
Blumenstrasse 15
D-90402 Nuremberg, Germany
Ph: 49 911 20180
Fax: 49 911 2018100
Publication E-mail: gtm@harnisch.com
Publisher E-mail: info@harnisch.com
Journal covering new products and technologies in the beverage industry. **Freq:** 6/yr. **Print Method:** offset. **Key**

Personnel: Benno Keller, Publisher, phone 49 911 2018200, fax 49 911 2018100, keller@harnisch.com; Ian Healey, Contact, phone 49 911 2018215, healey@harnisch.com. **Subscription Rates:** EUR58 individuals; EUR63 other countries. **Remarks:** Accepts advertising. **URL:** http://www.harnisch.com/gtm/index.php. **Ad Rates:** BW: DM 3,515, 4C: DM 4,865. **Circ:** 8,905

44614 ■ Getrankemarkt
Fachverlag Hans Carl GmbH
Andernacher St. 33a
D-90411 Nuremberg, Germany
Ph: 49 911 95250
Fax: 49 911 9528581
Publisher E-mail: info@hanscarl.com
Trade journal for marketing and sales in the beverage industry and gastronomy. **Freq:** Bimonthly. **Key Personnel:** Michael Schmitt, Managing Editor, phone 49 911 9528562, fax 49 911 952858120, m.schmitt@hanscarl.com. **Remarks:** Accepts advertising. **URL:** http://www.hanscarl.com/englisch/entrance_index.html. **Ad Rates:** BW: EUR4,276, 4C: EUR5,764. **Circ:** 16,833

44615 ■ Industrie Diamanten Rundschau
Dr. Harnisch International Publications
Blumenstrasse 15
D-90402 Nuremberg, Germany
Ph: 49 911 20180
Fax: 49 911 2018100
Publication E-mail: idr@harnisch.com
Publisher E-mail: info@harnisch.com
Magazine featuring developments in the world of industrial diamond and cubic boron nitride (CBN). **Freq:** 4/yr. **Print Method:** offset. **Key Personnel:** Dr. Claus-Jorg Harnisch, Publisher, phone 49 911 2018103, fax 49 911 2018100, jharnisch@harnisch.com; Benno Keller, Publisher, keller@harnisch.com. **Subscription Rates:** EUR15 single issue; DM 48 individuals. **Remarks:** Accepts advertising. **URL:** http://www.harnisch.com/idr/. **Circ:** 6,800

44616 ■ Monatsschrift fur Brauwissenschaft
Fachverlag Hans Carl GmbH
Andernacher St. 33a
D-90411 Nuremberg, Germany
Ph: 49 911 95250
Fax: 49 911 9528581
Publisher E-mail: info@hanscarl.com
Online scientific publication of the Faculty of Brewing, Food Technology and Dairy Industry of the Technical University Munich-Weihenstephan, the Testing and Teaching Institute for Brewing in Berlin, and the Scientific Station for Breweries, Munich. **Freq:** 6/yr. **Key Personnel:** Dr. Lydia Winkelmann, Editor-in-Chief, phone 49 911 9528558. **Remarks:** Advertising accepted; rates available upon request. **URL:** http://www.brauwissenschaft.de/. **Circ:** (Not Reported)

44617 ■ Wellness Foods Europe
Dr. Harnisch International Publications
Blumenstrasse 15
D-90402 Nuremberg, Germany
Ph: 49 911 20180
Fax: 49 911 2018100
Publication E-mail: wfe@harnisch.com
Publisher E-mail: info@harnisch.com
Journal covering health ingredients, nutraceutical foods and beverages. **Freq:** 3/yr. **Print Method:** offset. **Key Personnel:** Silke Watkins, Editor-in-Chief, phone 49 911 2018115, fax 49 911 2018100, wfe@harnisch.com. **Subscription Rates:** EUR36 individuals; EUR51 other countries surface mail; EUR63 other countries airmail. **Remarks:** Accepts advertising. **URL:** http://www.harnisch.com/well/. **Circ:** 6,011

44618 ■ WOODWORKING INTERNATIONAL
Dr. Harnisch International Publications
Blumenstrasse 15
D-90402 Nuremberg, Germany
Ph: 49 911 20180
Fax: 49 911 2018100
Publication E-mail: win@harnisch.com
Publisher E-mail: info@harnisch.com
Magazine covering aspects of woodworking. **Freq:** 4/yr. **Print Method:** offset. **Key Personnel:** Benno Keller, Publisher, phone 49 911 2018200, fax 49 911 2018100, keller@harnisch.com; Dr. Gunther Harnisch, President, phone 49 911 2018210, jharnisch@harnisch.com. **Subscription Rates:** EUR62 individuals; EUR96 other countries including postage; EUR117 other countries airmail. **Remarks:** Accepts advertising. **URL:** http://www.harnisch.com/win/. **Circ:** 12,000

44619 ■ Charivari-FM - 98.6
Senefelderstrasse 7
D-90409 Nuremberg, Germany
Ph: 49 911 51910
Fax: 49 911 5191121
E-mail: info@funkhaus.de
Format: Ethnic; Contemporary Hit Radio (CHR). **Owner:** Funkhaus Nurnberg, at above address. **Operating Hours:** Continuous. **Key Personnel:** Alexander Koller, Mng. Dir.; Stefan Fejfar, Contact; Johannes Scherbaum, Contact. **Ad Rates:** Advertising accepted; rates available upon request. **URL:** http://www.charivari986.de.

44620 ■ Hit Radio N1-FM - 92.9 MHz
Senefelderstrasse 7
D-90409 Nuremberg, Germany
Ph: 49 911 51910
Fax: 49 911 5191100
E-mail: info@hitradion1.de
Format: Ethnic; World Beat. **URL:** http://www.hitradion1.de.

Offenburg

44621 ■ Hitradio Ohr-FM - 90.5
Private Rundfunkgesellschaft Ortenau KG
Haupt Str. 83a
D-77652 Offenburg, Germany
Ph: 49 781 5043000
E-mail: info@hitradio-ohr.de
Format: World Beat; Ethnic. **Operating Hours:** Continuous. **Key Personnel:** Manuel Kempf, Contact; Markus Knoll, Contact. **Ad Rates:** Advertising accepted; rates available upon request. **URL:** http://www.radio-ohr.de.

44622 ■ Hitradio Ohr-FM - 101.6
Haupt Str. 83a
D-77652 Offenburg, Germany
Ph: 49 781 5043000
E-mail: info@hitradio-ohr.de
Format: Ethnic; World Beat. **Key Personnel:** Manuel Kempf, Contact. **URL:** http://www.radio-ohr.de.

Oldenburg

44623 ■ Chemkon - Chemie konkret, Forum fuer Unterricht und Didaktik
John Wiley & Sons Inc.
Carl von Ossietzky Universitat Oldenburg
Postfach 2053
D-26111 Oldenburg, Germany
Ph: 49 441 7983833
Fax: 49 441 7983691
Publication E-mail: chemkon@uni-oldenburg.de
Publisher E-mail: info@wiley.com
German-language chemistry journal. **Freq:** Quarterly. **Key Personnel:** Walter Jansen, Editor; Bolko Flintjer, Editor; Alfred Flint, Editor. **ISSN:** 0944-5846. **Subscription Rates:** EUR78 individuals print only; 166 SFr individuals print only; US$107 other countries print only; EUR77 institutions print only; 167 SFr institutions print only; US$107 institutions, other countries print only; US$107 institutions online only; 55 institutions online only; EUR77 institutions online only; 167 SFr institutions online only. **Remarks:** Accepts advertising. **URL:** http://as.wiley.com/WileyCDA/WileyTitle/productCd-2106.html; http://www3.interscience.wiley.com/journal/60500243/home. **Circ:** (Not Reported)

44624 ■ EARSeL eProceedings
European Association of Remote Sensing Laboratories
c/o Rainer Reuter, Ed.-in-Ch.
University of Oldenburg
Institute of Physics
D-26111 Oldenburg, Germany
Publisher E-mail: earsel@meteo.fr
Journal devoted to scientific publications in all fields of Earth observation and remote sensing, such as: land use and land cover, geology, forestry, ice and snow, atmosphere, ocean and coastal zones, urban areas; developing countries, new methods: hyperspectral, active/passive, 3-D, data fusion, time-series analysis, and environmental risks and hazards. **Key Personnel:** Rainer Reuter, Editor-in-Chief, rainer.reuter@eproceedings.org; Zbigniew Bochenek, Editor, zbigniew.bochenek@eproceedings.org; Matthias Braun, Editor, matthias.braun@eproceedings.org. **ISSN:** 1729-3782. **URL:** http://www.eproceedings.org/.

Oldendorf

44625 ■ Aquatic Biology
Inter-Research Science Center
Nordbunte 23 (3, 5, 28, 30)
D-21385 Oldendorf, Germany
Ph: 49 413 27127
Fax: 49 413 28883
Publisher E-mail: ir@int-res.com
Journal covering research on all aspects of the biology of organisms living in marine and fresh waters. **Founded:** 2007. **Key Personnel:** Dr. Otto Kinne, Editor-in-Chief, kinne@int-res.com; Hans Heinrich Janssen, Assoc. Ed.-in-Ch., hans.janssen@int-res.com; Matthias Seaman, Assoc. Ed.-in-Ch., matthias@int-res.com. **ISSN:** 1864-7782. **Subscription Rates:** EUR597 individuals; EUR632 other countries; EUR612 individuals Germany. **URL:** http://www.int-res.com/journals/ab/ab-home/.

44626 ■ Diseases of Aquatic Organisms
Inter-Research Science Center
Nordbunte 23 (3, 5, 28, 30)
D-21385 Oldendorf, Germany
Ph: 49 413 27127
Fax: 49 413 28883
Publisher E-mail: ir@int-res.com
Journal covering all aspects of disease phenomena in aquatic organisms. **Key Personnel:** John Austin, Managing Editor, john@int-res.com; Alex D. Hyatt, Editor-in-Chief, alex.hyatt@csiro.au; Sven Klimpel, Editor-in-Chief, sven.klimpel@uni-duesseldorf.de. **ISSN:** 0177-5103. **Subscription Rates:** EUR895 individuals online; EUR1,020 individuals Germany, print and online; EUR1,053 other countries print and online; EUR199 individuals per volume. **URL:** http://www.int-res.com/journals/dao/dao-home/.

44627 ■ Endangered Species Research
Inter-Research Science Center
Nordbunte 23 (3, 5, 28, 30)
D-21385 Oldendorf, Germany
Ph: 49 413 27127
Fax: 49 413 28883
Publisher E-mail: ir@int-res.com
Journal covering research on all species and habitats of conservation concern. **Key Personnel:** Otto Kinne, Founding Ed., kinne@int-res.com; Dr. Brendan J. Godley, Editor-in-Chief, b.j.godley@exeter.ac.uk; Penny Kuhn, Managing Editor, pkuhn@accesswave.ca. **ISSN:** 1863-5407. **Subscription Rates:** EUR612 individuals Germany, print and online; EUR632 other countries print and online; EUR199 individuals per volume; EUR597 individuals. **URL:** http://www.int-res.com/journals/esr/esr-home/.

44628 ■ Ethics in Science and Environmental Politics
Inter-Research
Nordbunte 23
D-21385 Oldendorf, Germany
Ph: 49 413 27127
Fax: 49 413 28883
Publisher E-mail: ir@int-res.com
Journal providing a global stage for presenting, discussing and developing the new ethical constructs of eco-ethics and econ-ethics, their bearing on science and politics, and their significance for the future development of nature and humanity. **Key Personnel:** Prof. Mike Archer, Editor, m.archer@unsw.edu.au; Dr. Guy Lanza, Editor, Dr. Virginia Burkett, Editor, virginia_burkett@usgs.gov; Prof. Sam Berry, Editor, rjberry@ucl.ac.uk; Dr. Stephanie Suhr-Sliester, Editor-in-Chief, steffi@int-res.com; Penny Kuhn, Managing Editor, pkuhn@accesswave.ca. **ISSN:** 1611-8014. **Subscription Rates:** EUR195 individuals; EUR80 single issue; EUR205 other countries air mail; EUR200 individuals for Germany. **URL:** http://www.int-res.com/journals/esep/.

44629 ■ Marine Ecology Progress Series (MEPS)
Inter-Research
c/o Otto Kinne, Ed.-in-Ch.
International Ecology Institute
Eco-Ethics International Union
Nordbunte 23
D-21385 Oldendorf, Germany
Publisher E-mail: ir@int-res.com
Journal covering marine ecology including microbiology, botany, zoology, ecosystem research, biological oceanography, ecological aspects of fisheries and aquaculture, pollution, conservation, and resource management. **Key Personnel:** Otto Kinne, Editor-in-Chief, phone 49

41 327127, fax 49 41 328883, kinne@int-res.com; Hans Heinrich Janssen, Asst. Ed.-in-Ch., hans.janssen@int-res.com; Matthias Seaman, Asst. Ed.-in-Ch., matthias@int-res.com. **ISSN:** 0171-8630. **Subscription Rates:** EUR4,680 individuals print & online version; EUR4,200 individuals online only; EUR216 elsewhere; EUR72 individuals for Germany; EUR195 individuals per volume. **URL:** http://www.int-res.com/journals/meps/meps-home/.

Osnabruck

44630 ■ Journal of Zoological Systematics and Evolutionary Research
John Wiley & Sons Inc.
Wiley-Blackwell
c/o Prof. Wilfried Westheide, Ed.-in-Ch.
University Osnabruck
Fachbereich Biologie/Chemie
AG Spezielle Zoologie, Barbarastr. 11
D-49069 Osnabruck, Germany
Peer-reviewed journal covering the field of zoology, and evolutionary biology. **Freq:** Quarterly. **Key Personnel:** Prof. Martin Fischer, Editor, martin.fischer@uni-jena.de; Prof. Wilfried Westheide, Editor-in-Chief, wilfried.westheide@biologie.uni-osnabrueck.de; Prof. Diether Sperlich, Editor, diether.sperlich@uni-tuebingen.de; Prof. Alessandro Minelli, Editor, alessandro.minelli@unipd.it; Dr. Lutz Bachmann, Editorial Board, bachmann@ulrik.uio.no; Dr. Walter Bock, Editorial Board, wb4@columbia.edu. **ISSN:** 0947-5745. **Subscription Rates:** US$213 individuals print and online; EUR197 individuals print and online; 132 individuals print and online; 768 institutions print and online; US$1,291 institutions print and online; 768 institutions print, online; EUR976 institutions print and online; US$1,652 institutions, other countries print and online; EUR887 institutions print, online; US$1,173 institutions print, online. **Remarks:** Advertising accepted; rates available upon request. **URL:** http://www.wiley.com/bw/journal.asp?ref=0947-5745&site=1. **Circ:** (Not Reported)

Ostfildern

44631 ■ Advanced Synthesis & Catalysis
John Wiley & Sons Inc.
Otto-Schuster-Str. 20
D-73760 Ostfildern, Germany
Ph: 49 711 1205603
Fax: 49 711 1205604
Publication E-mail: asc@wiley-vch.de
Publisher E-mail: info@wiley.com
Journal focusing on organic and organometallic chemistry. **Freq:** 18/yr. **Print Method:** Offset. **Trim Size:** 210 x 280 mm. **Key Personnel:** Joe P. Richmond, Editor; Thomas R. Baker, Academic Advisory Board; Kunisuke Izawa, Industrial Advisory Board. **ISSN:** 1615-4150. **Subscription Rates:** EUR2,393 institutions print or online (rest of Europe); 3,583 SFr institutions print or online(Switzerland and Liechtenstein); US$2,794 institutions, other countries print or online. **Remarks:** Accepts advertising. **URL:** http://onlinelibrary.wiley.com/journal/10.1002/(ISSN)1615-4169. **Ad Rates:** 4C: EUR1,110. **Circ:** 1,000

Paderborn

44632 ■ Particle and Particle Systems Characterization.
John Wiley & Sons Inc.
c/o Prof. Hans-Joachim Schmid, Ed.-in-Ch.
Universitt Paderborn
Pohlweg 55
33098 Paderborn, Germany
Ph: 49 5251 602404
Fax: 49 5251 603207
Publisher E-mail: info@wiley.com
Peer-reviewed journal focusing on the field of particle sizing and characterization. **Freq:** Bimonthly. **Key Personnel:** D.W. Fuerstenau, Advisory Board; Prof. Hans-Joachim Schmid, Editor-in-Chief, hans-joachim.schmid@upb.de; J.A. Dodds, Advisory Board; F. Ebert, Advisory Board; Dr. Reg Davies, Honorary Ed.; Dr. Sotiris E. Pratsinis, Editorial Board, pratsinis@ptl.mavt.ethz.ch; Prof. Hans-Joachim Schmid, Managing Editor, hans-joachim.schmid@upb.de; M.M. Figueiredo, Advisory Board; H. Fissan, Advisory Board; L.G. Austin, Advisory Board; Prof. Richard Williams, Editorial Board, phone 44 113 2332801, fax 44 113 2332781, r.a.williams@leeds.ac.uk. **ISSN:** 0934-0866. **Subscription Rates:** EUR615 individuals print only; 889 SFr individuals Switzerland and Lichtenstein (print only); US$701 other countries print; EUR1,465 institutions Europe (print only); 2,530 SFr institutions Switzerland and Lichtenstein (print only); US$1,946 institutions, other countries print. **URL:** http://www3.interscience.wiley.com/journal/5008440/home.

Pfinztal

44633 ■ International Journal of Materials and Product Technology
Inderscience Enterprises Limited
c/o Dr. Ing. Peter Eyerer, Assoc. Ed.
Fraunhofer Institut fur Chemische Technologie
Joseph-von-Fraunhofer-Strasse 7
76327 Pfinztal, Germany
Peer-reviewed journal covering all aspects of technologies related to materials. **Freq:** 12/yr. **Key Personnel:** Dr. Ing. Peter Eyerer, Assoc. Ed.; Dr. M.A. Dorgham, Editor-in-Chief, editorial@inderscience.com. **ISSN:** 0268-1900. **Subscription Rates:** EUR1,025 individuals print or online; EUR1,434 individuals print and online. **URL:** http://www.inderscience.com/browse/index.php?journalID=20.

Poing

44634 ■ Computer Reseller News
CMP-WEKA Verlag GmbH & Company KG
Gruber Str. 46 A
D-85586 Poing, Germany
Ph: 49 812 1951512
Fax: 49 812 1951597
Publisher E-mail: info@cmp-weka.de
Professional magazine covering computer reseller news. **Subtitle:** The Magazine for Resellers, VAR's and System Houses. **Founded:** Mar. 1995. **Freq:** Weekly. **Print Method:** Offset. **Trim Size:** 280 x 381 mm. **Cols./Page:** 3. **Col. Width:** 58 millimeters. **Key Personnel:** Samba Schulte, Dep. Ed.-in-Ch.; Martin Fryba, Editor-in-Chief; Markus Reuter, Editor-in-Chief. **Remarks:** Accepts advertising. **URL:** http://www.crn.de/; http://www.crn.de/cms/1.0.html. **Circ:** Controlled 33,136

44635 ■ Datacom
CMP-WEKA Verlag GmbH & Company KG
Gruber Str. 46 A
D-85586 Poing, Germany
Ph: 49 812 1951512
Fax. 49 812 1951597
Publication E-mail: info@datacom-magazin.de
Publisher E-mail: info@cmp-weka.de
Professional magazine for management in data- and tele-communications. **Subtitle:** Management Magazine for Data- and Tele-Communication. **Founded:** 1984. **Freq:** Monthly. **Print Method:** Offset. **Trim Size:** 182 x 268 mm. **Cols./Page:** 3. **ISSN:** 0176-3288. **Remarks:** Advertising accepted; rates available upon request. **URL:** http://www.datacom-magazin.de. **Circ:** Combined 11,014

44636 ■ Information Week
CMP-WEKA Verlag GmbH & Company KG
Gruber Str. 46 A
D-85586 Poing, Germany
Ph: 49 812 1951512
Fax. 49 812 1951597
Publisher E-mail: info@cmp-weka.de
Professional magazine covering information technology in business. **Freq:** Monthly. **Print Method:** Offset. **Trim Size:** 230 x 300 mm. **Cols./Page:** 3. **Col. Width:** 58 millimeters. **Key Personnel:** Markus Bereszewski, Editor-in-Chief. **Remarks:** Accepts advertising. **URL:** http://www.informationweek.de. **Circ:** Combined 75,253

44637 ■ Network Computing
CMP-WEKA Verlag GmbH & Company KG
Gruber Str. 46 A
D-85586 Poing, Germany
Ph: 49 812 1951512
Fax: 49 812 1951597
Publisher E-mail: info@cmp-weka.de
Professional magazine covering product, service and technology news for network professionals. **Subtitle:** For IT by IT. **Founded:** Mar. 1998. **Freq:** Semimonthly. **Print Method:** Offset. **Trim Size:** 230 x 300 mm. **Cols./Page:** 3. **Col. Width:** 58 millimeters. **Key Personnel:** Ralf Ladner, Editor-in-Chief; Bernd Reder, Online Ed.; Mike Fratto, Editor, mfratto@techweb.com. **Remarks:** Accepts advertising. **URL:** http://www.networkcomputing.de. **Circ:** Combined 52,181

Potsdam

44638 ■ Astronomische Nachrichten
John Wiley & Sons Inc.
Astrophysikalisches Institut Potsdam
Sternwarte Babelsberg
An der Sternwarte 16
D-14482 Potsdam, Germany
Ph: 49 33 17499232
Fax: 49 33 17499200
Publisher E-mail: info@wiley.com
Journal focusing on astronomy and astrophysics. **Freq:** 10/yr. **Key Personnel:** K.G. Strassmeier, Editor-in-Chief, kstrassmeier@aip.de; G. Hasinger, Editor, ghasinger@aip.de; H.W. Yorke, Editor, yorke@lear.jpl.nasa.gov. **ISSN:** 0004-6337. **Subscription Rates:** EUR1,358 institutions for print; 2,377 SFr institutions for print, Switzerland and Lichtenstein; US$1,684 institutions, other countries for print; rest of World; EUR338 individuals for print; 471 SFr individuals for print; Switzerland and Lichtenstein; US$399 other countries for print; rest of World. **URL:** http://www3.interscience.wiley.com/journal/60500255/home.

44639 ■ Biophysical Reviews and Letters
World Scientific Publishing Company Private Ltd.
Max Planck Institute of Colloids & Interfaces
Research Campus Golm
D-14424 Potsdam, Germany
Publisher E-mail: wspc@wspc.com.sg
International peer-reviewed journal publishing original research papers, review articles and brief communications in the field of experimental and theoretical Biophysics, covering the whole area of Bionanosciences, including Biomolecules, Biocolloids (membranes, filaments, and minerals), Bioenergetics (molecular motors, growing filaments), Biofunctional, Bioinspired and Biomimetic Materials, as well as physical aspects of Structural and Molecular Cell Biology, Computational Biophysics, Bioinformatics, and fundamental issues related to the Life Sciences. **Freq:** Quarterly. **Key Personnel:** Reinhard Lipowsky, Managing Editor, reinhard.lipowsky@mpikg.mpg.de; P.C. Huang, Managing Editor, pchuang@jhsph.edu; Francoise Brochard-Wyart, Assoc. Ed.; Zongchao Jia, Managing Editor, jia@post.queensu.ca; Daiwen Yang, Assoc. Ed. **ISSN:** 1793-0480. **Subscription Rates:** US$445 institutions and libraries; electronic + print; US$427 institutions and libraries; electronic only; US$34 individuals for postage; S$721 institutions and libraries; electronic + print; S$692 institutions and libraries; electronic only; S$45 individuals for postage; US$45 institutions and libraries; electronic + print; EUR335 institutions and libraries; electronic only; EUR26 individuals for postage. **Remarks:** Advertising accepted; rates available upon request. **URL:** http://www.worldscinet.com/brl/brl.shtml. **Circ:** (Not Reported)

44640 ■ Journal of Carbohydrate Chemistry
Taylor & Francis Group Journals
c/o Peter H. Seeberger, Ed.
Max-Planck-Institute of Colloids & Interfaces
Dept. of Biomolecular Systems
Am Muhlenberg 1
144763 Potsdam, Germany
Publisher E-mail: customerservice@taylorandfrancis.com
Journal serves as an international forum for research advances involving the chemistry and biology of carbohydrates. **Freq:** 9/yr. **Key Personnel:** Peter H. Seeberger, Editor; Joachim Thiem, Regional Ed.; Robert M. Giuliano, Regional Ed.; Hans Peter Wessel, Regional Ed.; Laurence A. Mulard, Regional Ed.; C. Auge, Editorial Board. **ISSN:** 0732-8303. **Subscription Rates:** US$485 individuals; US$2,442 institutions print and online; US$2,319 institutions online; 293 individuals; 1,474 institutions print + online; 1,400 institutions online; EUR1,944 institutions print and online; EUR1,846 institutions online only; EUR386 individuals. **URL:** http://www.tandf.co.uk/journals/titles/07328303.asp.

Ratingen

44641 ■ Deutsche Briefmarken Revue
PSBN Verlags GmbH
Eisenhuttenstr. 4
40882 Ratingen, Germany
Ph: 49 21022046830
Fax: 49 2102895825
Publisher E-mail: info@deutsche-briefmarken-revue.de
Consumer magazine covering philately in Germany. **Founded:** 1950. **Freq:** Monthly. **Print Method:** Offset.

Circulation: ★ = ABC; △ = BPA; ♦ = CAC; • = CCAB; ❑ = VAC; ⊕ = PQ Statement; ‡ = Publisher's Report; Boldface figures = sworn; Light figures = estimated.

Gale Directory of Publications & Broadcast Media/147th Ed.

4955

Trim Size: 210 x 280 mm. **Subscription Rates:** EUR42 individuals. **URL:** http://www.deutsche-briefmarken-revue.de. **Ad Rates:** BW: EUR750, 4C: EUR1,400. **Circ:** Combined 30,000

Regensburg

44642 ■ Armenisch-Deutsche Korrespondenz
Deutsch-Armenische Gesellschaft
Pruefeninger Str. 55
D-93049 Regensburg, Germany
Ph: 49 941 27768
Fax: 49 941 21221
Publisher E-mail: post@dag-online.de
German and Armenian language publication covering intercultural affairs. **Founded:** 1973. **Freq:** Quarterly. **ISSN:** 0936-9325. **Subscription Rates:** EUR650 single issue; EUR2,050 individuals; EUR26 institutions; Included in membership. **Remarks:** Advertising accepted; rates available upon request. **URL:** http://www.deutsch-armenische-gesellschaft.de; http://www.german-armenian-society.de/. **Circ:** 680

44643 ■ Economic Systems
Elsevier Science Inc.
Dept. of Economics
Osteuropa-Institut Regensburg
Landshuter Strasse 4
D-93047 Regensburg, Germany
Ph: 49 941 9435412
Fax: 49 941 9435427
Publisher E-mail: usinfo-ehelp@elsevier.com
Peer-reviewed journal for the analysis of market and non-market solutions to allocation and distribution problems as well as attempts at and proposals for their reform. **Founded:** 2001. **Freq:** 4/yr. **Print Method:** Offset. **Cols./Page:** 6. **Col. Width:** 24 nonpareils. **Col. Depth:** 294 agate lines. **Key Personnel:** C. Bowman, Editorial Board; A.M. Kutan, American Ed., akutan@siue.edu; J. Fidrmuc, Editorial Board; H.J. Wagener, Editorial Board; P. Harms, Editorial Board; R. Frensch, Managing Editor, frensch@osteuropa-institut.de; R. Heaney, Editorial Board; W. Kohler, Editorial Board; E. Kocenda, Editorial Board; I. Korhonen, Editorial Board. **ISSN:** 0939-3625. **Subscription Rates:** EUR58 individuals for European countries and Iran; 8,500¥ individuals; US$415 institutions, other countries except Europe, Japan and Iran; US$77 other countries except Europe, Japan and Iran; EUR371 institutions for European countries and Iran; 49,200¥ institutions. **URL:** http://www.elsevier.com/wps/find/journaldescription.cws_home/621171/descriptiondescription.

44644 ■ Mathematische Nachrichten
John Wiley & Sons Inc.
c/o Dr. R. Mennicken, Ed.-in-Ch.
NWF I-Mathematics
University of Regensburg
Universitatsstr. 31
D-93053 Regensburg, Germany
Publisher E-mail: info@wiley.com
Journal focusing on applied mathematics and related mathematical subjects. **Freq:** 12/yr. **Key Personnel:** Dr. R. Mennicken, Editor-in-Chief, math.nachr@googlemail.com; A. Bottcher, Advisory Board; F. Klopp, Editor; J. Bruning, Advisory Board; F. Finster, Editor; R. Schilling, Editor; F. Gesztesy, Editor; K. Hulek, Editor. **ISSN:** 0025-584X. **Subscription Rates:** EUR4,628 institutions print only; 7,517 SFr institutions print only, Switzerland and Liechtenstein; US$6,006 institutions, other countries print only; EUR450 individuals print only; 668 SFr individuals print only, Switzerland and Liechtenstein; US$558 other countries print only. **URL:** http://onlinelibrary.wiley.com/journal/10.1002/(ISSN)1522-2616.

Rossdorf

44645 ■ Skeptiker
Society for the Scientific Investigation of Para-Science
Gesellschaft zur Wissenschaftlichen Untersuchung von Parawissenschaften
Arheilger Weg 11
D-64380 Rossdorf, Germany
Ph: 49 6154 695021
Fax: 49 6154 695022
German language publication criticizing psendoscientific phenomena. **Subtitle:** Journal for Science and Critical Thinking. **Founded:** 1987. **Freq:** Quarterly. **Trim Size:** A4. **Key Personnel:** Inge Huesgen, Editor. **ISSN:** 0936-9244. **Remarks:** Advertising accepted; rates available upon request. **URL:** http://www.gwup.org; http://www.

gwup.org/zeitschrift. **Circ:** 3,000

Rostock

44646 ■ Catalysis Communications
Elsevier (Singapore) Pte. Ltd.
c/o A. Bruckner, Ed.
Leibniz-Institut fur Katalyse
e.V. an der Universitat Rostock
Albert-Einstein-Str. 29a
D-18059 Rostock, Germany
Ph: 49 30 63924301
Fax: 49 39 63924454
Publisher E-mail: asiabkinfo@elsevier.com
Journal aiming to provide rapid publication of important short papers across the broad spectrum of catalytic research covering homogeneous, heterogeneous and enzymatic catalysis. **Founded:** 2000. **Freq:** 15/yr. **Key Personnel:** A. Bruckner, Editor; A.A. Adesina, Editorial Board; C. Bolm, Editorial Board; James G. Goodwin, Jr., Editor-in-Chief, james.goodwin@ces.clemson.edu; A. Adesina, Editorial Board; R. Gomez, Editorial Board; J. Caro, Editorial Board; V.R. Choudhary, Editorial Board; V. Guliants, Editorial Board. **ISSN:** 1566-7367. **Subscription Rates:** US$934 institutions all countries except Europe, Japan and Iran; 111,300¥ institutions; EUR838 institutions European countries and Iran; EUR265 individuals European countries and Iran; US$355 individuals all countries except Europe, Japan and Iran; 40,700¥ individuals. **URL:** http://www.elsevier.com/wps/find/journaldescription.cws_home/621120/descriptiondescription.

44647 ■ Demographic Research
Max-Planck-Gesellschaft (Max Planck Society)
Max Planck Institute for Demographic Research
Konrad-Zuse-Strasse 1
D-18057 Rostock, Germany
Ph: 49 381 20810
Fax: 49 381 2081280
Publisher E-mail: post@gv.mpg.de
Journal publishing articles on demography. **Founded:** July 1999. **Freq:** Semiannual. **Key Personnel:** Nico Keilman, Editor; Joshua R. Goldstein, Publisher; John B. Casterline, Assoc. Ed. **ISSN:** 1435-9871. **URL:** http://www.demographic-research.org/.

44648 ■ Journal of Marine Systems
Elsevier Science
c/o W. Fennel, Ed.-n-Ch.
Institut fur Ostseeforschung Warnemunde
Seestrasse 15
D-18119 Rostock, Germany
Ph: 49 381 5197110
Fax: 49 381 5197114
Publisher E-mail: nlinfo-f@elsevier.com
Journal for oceanographers and marine geologists. **Founded:** 1990. **Freq:** 20/yr. **Key Personnel:** W. Fennel, Editor-in-Chief, wolfgang.fennel@io-warnemuende.de; E. Hofmann, Editor-in-Chief, hofmann@ccpo.odu.edu. **ISSN:** 0924-7963. **Subscription Rates:** US$3,149 institutions for all countries except Europe and Japan; EUR2,813 institutions, other countries for European countries; 373,800¥ institutions; EUR262 individuals; US$352 individuals; 40,400¥ individuals. **Remarks:** Accepts advertising. **URL:** http://www.elsevier.com/wps/find/journaldescription.cws_home/503344/description. **Circ:** (Not Reported)

44649 ■ Lohro-FM - 90.2
Margaretenstrasse 43
D-18057 Rostock, Germany
Ph: 49 381 6666577
Fax: 49 381 6665799
E-mail: info@lohro.de
Format: Public Radio; Eclectic. **Operating Hours:** Continuous. **URL:** http://www.lohro.de.

Saale

44650 ■ ZAMM - Zeitschrift fur Angewandte Mathematik und Mechanik
John Wiley & Sons Inc.
c/o Dr. Beate Platzer
Martin-Luther-Universitat
Halle-Wittenberg
Fachbereich Ingenieurwissenschaften
D-06099 Saale, Germany
Ph: 49 34 55528438
Fax: 49 34 55527361
Publication E-mail: zamm@iw.uni-halle.de

Publisher E-mail: info@wiley.com
Journal focusing on applied mathematics. **Freq:** Monthly. **Key Personnel:** Dr. E. Kreuzer, Editorial Board; Dr. R. Mennicken, Honorary Editorial Board; A. Mielke, Editorial Board; Dr. Holm Altenbach, Ed.-in-Ch./Mng. Ed.; Prof. Stefan Odenbach, Editor-in-Chief; Dr. Christian Wieners, Editor-in-Chief. **ISSN:** 0044-2267. **Subscription Rates:** US$2,392 institutions, other countries for print; EUR1,685 institutions Europe (print); 1,220 institutions Europe (print); 2,965 SFr institutions Switzerland and Lichtenstein (print). **URL:** http://onlinelibrary.wiley.com/journal/10.1002/(ISSN)1521-4001.

Saarbrucken

44651 ■ Archiv der Mathematik
Springer-Verlag Tokyo
Field 6.1 Mathematics
University of Saarland
Post Box 15 11 50
D-66041 Saarbrucken, Germany
Publisher E-mail: info@springer.jp
Journal publishing short, high-quality research papers in every area of mathematics which are not overly technical in nature and addressed to a broad readership. **Freq:** Bimonthly. **Key Personnel:** Ernst-Ulrich Gekeler, Managing Editor, gekeler@math.uni-sb.de; Gabriele Nebe, Editor, nebe@math.rwth-aachen.de; Erwin Bolthausen, Editor, eb@amath.unizh.ch; Philippe Michel, Editor, philippe.michel@epfl.ch; Bernd Kawohl, Editor, kawohl@mi.uni-koeln.de; Thomas Bartsch, Editor, thomas.bartsch@math.uni-giessen.de; Wolfgang Arendt, Editor, wolfgang.arendt@uni-ulm.de; Derek Holt, Editor, dfh@maths.warwick.ac.uk. **ISSN:** 0003-889X. **Subscription Rates:** EUR918 institutions print incl. free access or e-only; EUR1,101.60 institutions print incl. enhanced access. **Remarks:** Advertising accepted; rates available upon request. **URL:** http://www.springer.com/birkhauser/mathematics/journal/13. **Circ:** (Not Reported)

44652 ■ Progress in Materials Science
Elsevier Science
c/o E. Arzt, Ed.
Leibniz Industry for New Materials
& Professor for New Materials
Saarland University, Campus D2 2
D-66123 Saarbrucken, Germany
Publisher E-mail: nlinfo-f@elsevier.com
Journal covering latest developments in the science of materials and their utilization in engineering. **Founded:** 1949. **Freq:** 8/yr. **Key Personnel:** B. Cantor, Editor, vc@york.ac.uk; E. Arzt, Editor, progress@inm-gmbh.de; S. Suresh, Editor, ssuresh@mit.edu. **ISSN:** 0079-6425. **Subscription Rates:** US$2,204 institutions for all countries except Europe and Japan; 261,500¥ institutions; EUR1,969 institutions European countries. **URL:** http://www.elsevier.com/wps/find/journaldescription.cws_home/414/description.

44653 ■ Classic Rock Radio-FM - 100.6
Richard-Wagner-Str. 58-60
D-66111 Saarbrucken, Germany
Ph: 49 681 372522
Fax: 49 681 372522
E-mail: hotline@salue.de
Format: Classic Rock. **Owner:** Euro Radio Saar Gmbh, at above address. **Operating Hours:** Continuous. **Key Personnel:** Sascha Thiel, Mng. Dir., sascha.thiel@salue.de; Gary Sahner, Prog. Coord., gary.sahner@salue.de; Uwe Loll, Program Dir., uwe.loll@salue.de. **URL:** http://www.classicrock-radio.de.

Saint Augustin

44654 ■ Journal of Systems Architecture
European Association for Microprocessing and Microprogramming
PO Box 2043
D-53743 Saint Augustin, Germany
Ph: 49 224 19326633
Fax: 49 224 19326746
Publication E-mail: jsa@elet.polimi.it
Publisher E-mail: euromicro@t-online.de
Journal of the European Association for Microprocessing and Microprogramming. **URL:** http://www.euromicro.org/Publications.html.

Seewiesen

44655 ■ Arthropod Structure & Development

Elsevier Science Inc.
c/o R.A. Steinbrecht, Coord. Ed.
Max-Planck Institut fur Verhaltensphysiologie
D-82319 Seewiesen, Germany
Publisher E-mail: usinfo-ehelp@elsevier.com
Peer-reviewed journal providing information on micro- and neuroanatomy, development, biomechanics, organogenesis of the arthropoda. **Founded:** 1972. **Freq:** 6/yr. **Print Method:** Web press. **Trim Size:** 7 1/8 x 10. **Cols./Page:** 3. **Col. Depth:** 10 inches. **Key Personnel:** R.A. Steinbrecht, Coord. Ed., asd@orn.mpg.de; N.J. Strausfeld, Coord. Ed., flybrain@neurobio.arizona.edu; J. Billen, Section Ed., johan.billen@bio.kuleuven.ac.be; S.N. Gorb, Section Ed., s.gorb@mf.mpg.de; B. Beltz, Section Ed., bbeltz@wellesley.edu; W. Rossler, Section Ed., roessler@biozentrum.uni-wuerzburg.de; G. Pass, Section Ed., guenther.pass@univie.ac.at; J.A.T. Dow, Section Ed., j.a.t.dow@bio.gla.ac.uk; M. Grbic, Section Ed., mgrbic@uwo.ca. **ISSN:** 1467-8039. **Subscription Rates:** 191,300¥ institutions; US$1,613 institutions, other countries except Europe, Japan and Iran; EUR1,442 institutions for European countries and Iran; US$147 other countries except Europe, Japan and Iran; 16,900¥ individuals; EUR110 individuals for European countries and Iran. **URL:** http://www.elsevier.com/wps/find/journaldescription.cws_home/356/descriptiondescription.

Siegen

44656 ■ International Journal of Physiotherapy and Life Physics

Inderscience Enterprises Limited
c/o Dr. Changlin Zhang, Ed.-in-Ch.
Siegen University
U.S. Department of Music & Music Education
Hochstrasse 57
D-57076 Siegen, Germany
Journal covering various natural medicines and therapies, such as acupuncture, music therapy, infrared therapy, soft-laser therapy, electric pulse therapy, sauna therapy, foot-bath therapy, massage, meditation, psychotherapy, hand-touching therapy, and pray therapy. **Freq:** 4/yr. **Key Personnel:** Dr. Changlin Zhang, Editor-in-Chief, zhang.biophysik@musik.uni-siegen.de. **ISSN:** 2040-4549. **Subscription Rates:** EUR494 individuals print or online; EUR672 individuals print and online. **URL:** http://www.inderscience.com/browse/index.php?journalID=355.

Stechlin

44657 ■ Limnologica

Elsevier Science Inc.
Leibniz-Institut fur Gewasserokologie und Binnenfischerei
Abteilung Limnologie Geschichteter Seen
Alte Fischerhutte 2
D-16775 Stechlin, Germany
Ph: 49 33 0826990
Fax: 49 33 08269917
Publisher E-mail: usinfo-ehelp@elsevier.com
Journal covering ecology and hydrobiology of inland waters and adjacent biotopes. **Founded:** 1962. **Freq:** 4/yr. **Key Personnel:** Rainer Koschel, Managing Editor, rko@igb-berlin.de; Irmgard Blindow, Advisory Board; Ingemar Ahlgren, Advisory Board; Jurgen Benndorf, Editorial Board, juergen.benndorf@tu-dresden.de; Walter Geller, Editorial Board, walter.geller@ufz.de; Edit Tesch, Editorial Asst., tesch@igb-berlin.de; Daniel Hering, Editorial Board, daniel.hering@uni-due.de; Tom Berman, Advisory Board; Gunnel Ahlgren, Advisory Board. **ISSN:** 0075-9511. **Subscription Rates:** US$566 institutions, other countries except Europe, Japan and Iran; 67,900¥ institutions; EUR497 institutions for European countries and Iran; US$135 other countries except Europe, Japan and Iran; 17,700¥ individuals; EUR137 individuals for European countries and Iran. **URL:** http://www.elsevier.com/wps/find/journaldescription.cws_home/701781/descrip tiondescription.

Straubing

44658 ■ International Journal of Antimicrobial Agents

International Society of Chemotherapy
c/o Kurt G. Naber, Pres.
Department of Urology
Hospital St. Elisabeth
St. Elisabeth 23
D-94315 Straubing, Germany
Ph: 49 9421 7101700
Fax: 49 9421 710270
Publisher E-mail: kurt@nabers.de
Worldwide journal covering chemotherapy. **Subtitle:** Official Journal of the International Society of Chemotherapy. **Founded:** 1991. **Freq:** Monthly. **Key Personnel:** Alasdair Geddes, Editor-in-Chief. **ISSN:** 0924-8579. **Subscription Rates:** 240,400¥ institutions; US$2,024 institutions for all countries except Europe and Japan; EUR1,811 institutions for European countries. **Remarks:** Advertising accepted; rates available upon request. **URL:** http://www.ischemo.org/05_3_Journal.htm; http://www.elsevier.com/wps/find/journaldescription.cws_home/505521/descriptiondescription. **Circ:** (Not Reported)

Stuttgart

44659 ■ Advances in Bryology

Gebruder Borntraeger Verlagsbuchhandlung
Johannesstr. 3A
D-70176 Stuttgart, Germany
Ph: 49 711 351456
Fax: 49 711 351456
Publisher E-mail: mail@schweizerbart.de
Journal covering all aspects of research involving bryophytes. **Key Personnel:** Royce E. Longton, Editor. **URL:** http://www.borntraeger-cramer.de/j/advances-in-bryology/.

44660 ■ Aerokurier

Motor-Presse Verlag GmbH & Company KG
Leuschnerstr. 1
D-70174 Stuttgart, Germany
Ph: 49 711 18201
Fax: 49 711 18217779
Publication E-mail: aerokurier@compuserve.com
Publisher E-mail: redaktion@flugrevue.de
Trade magazine covering civil aviation worldwide, including general aviation, business aviation, helicopters, sport aviation, gliding, and related fields. **Founded:** 1957. **Freq:** Monthly. **Key Personnel:** Gerhard Marzinzik, Editor-in-Chief; Volker K. Thomalla, Editor-in-Chief; Dr. Bernd Gaubatz, Editor; Renate Strecker, Editor; Martin Schulz, Editor; Gabriele Beinert, Office Management; Patrick Holland-Moritz, Editor. **Subscription Rates:** EUR4.50 single issue; EUR11.50 individuals. **Remarks:** Accepts advertising. **URL:** http://www.aerokurier.rotor.com/. **Circ:** (Not Reported)

44661 ■ Aquatic Insects

Taylor & Francis Group Journals
Staatliches Museum fur Naturkunde
Rosenstein 1
D-70191 Stuttgart, Germany
Publisher E-mail: customerservice@taylorandfrancis.com
Peer-reviewed journal publishing original research on both the systematics and the ecology of aquatic insects. **Subtitle:** International Journal of Freshwater Entomology. **Freq:** Quarterly. **Key Personnel:** Dr. Arnold H. Staniczek, Editor, staniczek.smns@naturkundemuseum-bw.de; M. Brancucci, Editorial Board; H. Malicky, Editorial Board; P.S. Cranston, Editorial Board; J.E. Brittain, Editorial Board; G.W. Courtney, Editorial Board. **ISSN:** 0165-0424. **Subscription Rates:** US$413 individuals print; US$777 institutions for print and online; US$738 institutions online. **URL:** http://www.informaworld.com/smpp/title~content=t713817864.

44662 ■ Bibliotheca Mycologica

Gebruder Borntraeger Verlagsbuchhandlung
Johannesstr. 3A
D-70176 Stuttgart, Germany
Ph: 49 711 351456
Fax: 49 711 351456
Publisher E-mail: mail@schweizerbart.de
Journal covering the studies of fungi. **Key Personnel:** I. Melo, Editor; J. Cardoso, Editor; M.T. Telleria, Editor. **ISSN:** 0067-8066. **URL:** http://www.borntraeger-cramer.de/j/bibliotheca-mycologica/.

44663 ■ Bibliotheca Phycologica

Gebruder Borntraeger Verlagsbuchhandlung
Johannesstr. 3A
D-70176 Stuttgart, Germany
Ph: 49 711 351456
Fax: 49 711 351456
Publisher E-mail: mail@schweizerbart.de
Journal covering the studies of algae. **Key Personnel:** Ludwig Kies, Editor, l.kies@botanik.uni-hamburg.de; Reinhard Schnetter, Editor, reinhard.schnetter@bot1.bio.uni-giessen.de. **ISSN:** 0067-8112. **URL:** http://www.borntraeger-cramer.de/j/bibliotheca-phycologica/.

44664 ■ Contributions to Sedimentary Geology

Gebruder Borntraeger Verlagsbuchhandlung
Johannesstr. 3A
D-70176 Stuttgart, Germany
Ph: 49 711 351456
Fax: 49 711 351456
Publisher E-mail: mail@schweizerbart.de
Journal covering the field of sedimentary geology. **Freq:** Semiannual. **ISSN:** 1436-3542. **URL:** http://www.borntraeger-cramer.de/j/contributions-to-sedimentary-geology/.

44665 ■ Diatom Research

Gebruder Borntraeger Verlagsbuchhandlung
Johannesstr. 3A
D-70176 Stuttgart, Germany
Ph: 49 711 351456
Fax: 49 711 351456
Publisher E-mail: mail@schweizerbart.de
Journal focusing on diatom research and studies. **Freq:** Annual. **ISSN:** 0269-249X. **URL:** http://www.borntraeger-cramer.de/j/diatom-research/.

44666 ■ Eiszeitalter und Gegenwart Quaternary Science Journal

Gebruder Borntraeger Verlagsbuchhandlung
Johannesstr. 3A
D-70176 Stuttgart, Germany
Ph: 49 711 351456
Fax: 49 711 351456
Publisher E-mail: mail@schweizerbart.de
Journal covering all fields of quaternary research. **Freq:** Quarterly. **Key Personnel:** Holger Freund, Editor, holger.freund@icbm.terramare.de. **ISSN:** 0424-7116. **URL:** http://www.schweizerbart.de/j/eiszeitalter-und-gegenwart/.

44667 ■ European Journal of Pediatric Surgery

Georg Thieme Verlag Stuttgart
Rudigerstr. 14
Postfach 30 11 20
D-70469 Stuttgart, Germany
Ph: 49 711 89310
Fax: 49 711 8931298
Publisher E-mail: kundenservice@thieme.de
English and German language publication covering spinal injury. **Freq:** Bimonthly. **Key Personnel:** I. Fattorini, Assoc. Ed.; R.J. Fitzgerald, Assoc. Ed.; J.A. Tovar, Assoc. Ed.; Y. Aigrain, Assoc. Ed.; R. Domini, Assoc. Ed.; A.M. Rokitansky, Assoc. Ed.; B.M. Ure, Editor-in-Chief; A. De Backer, Assoc. Ed. **ISSN:** 0939-7248. **Subscription Rates:** EUR398 institutions print only; EUR258 individuals print & online; EUR206 individuals special introductory rate. **URL:** http://www.thieme.de/fz/ejps/.

44668 ■ Fundamental and Applied Limnology

Gebruder Borntraeger Verlagsbuchhandlung
Johannesstr. 3A
D-70176 Stuttgart, Germany
Ph: 49 711 351456
Fax: 49 711 351456
Publication E-mail: fal@awi.de
Publisher E-mail: mail@schweizerbart.de
Journal covering freshwater research. **Freq:** Monthly. **Key Personnel:** Maarten Boersma, Ch. Ed. **URL:** http://www.borntraeger-cramer.de/j/fal/.

44669 ■ Meteorologische Zeitschrift

Gebruder Borntraeger Verlagsbuchhandlung
Johannesstr. 3A
D-70176 Stuttgart, Germany
Ph: 49 711 351456
Fax: 49 711 351456
Publication E-mail: editorial-office@metzet.de
Publisher E-mail: mail@schweizerbart.de
Journal covering all fields of meteorology. **Founded:** 1866. **Freq:** 6/yr. **Key Personnel:** Marion Schnee, Editor. **ISSN:** 0941-2948. **URL:** http://www.metzet.de/.

44670 ■ Methods of Information in Medicine

Schattauer Publishers
Hoelderlinstr. 3
D-70174 Stuttgart, Germany

Circulation: ★ = ABC; △ = BPA; ♦ = CAC; • = CCAB; ❑ = VAC; ⊕ = PO Statement; ‡ = Publisher's Report; Boldface figures = sworn; Light figures = estimated.

Gale Directory of Publications & Broadcast Media/147th Ed.   **4957**

Ph: 49 711 229870
Fax: 49 711 2298750
Publisher E-mail: info@schattauer.de
Scientific medical journal covering medical informatics and statistics. **Founded:** 1962. **Freq:** Bimonthly. **Trim Size:** 220 x 290 mm. **Key Personnel:** J.H. Van Bemmel, Sen. Ed.; R. Haux, Editor-in-Chief; I. Hoffmann, Editorial Asst.; D. Aronsky, Assoc. Ed.; T.Y. Leong, Assoc. Ed. **ISSN:** 0026-1270. **Subscription Rates:** EUR549 institutions; EUR228 individuals; EUR90 students; EUR72 single issue. **URL:** http://www.schattauer.de/en/magazine/subject-areas/journals-a-z/methods.html. **Ad Rates:** BW: EUR965, 4C: EUR1,955. **Circ:** Paid 800

44671 ■ Nervenheilkunde
Schattauer Publishers
Hoelderlinstr. 3
D-70174 Stuttgart, Germany
Ph: 49 711 229870
Fax: 49 711 2298750
Publisher E-mail: info@schattauer.de
Scientific medical journal covering neurology and psychiatry. **Subtitle:** Nerve Medicine. **Founded:** 1982. **Freq:** Monthly. **Trim Size:** 210 x 280 mm. **Key Personnel:** Dr. Anja Borchers, Editor, phone 49 7 112298771, fax 49 7 112298765, anja.borchers@schattauer.de. **ISSN:** 0722-1541. **Subscription Rates:** EUR264 institutions; EUR160 individuals; EUR80 students; EUR28 single issue. **Remarks:** Accepts advertising. **URL:** http://www.schattauer.de/en/magazine/subject-areas/journals-a-z/nervenheilkunde.html. **Ad Rates:** BW: EUR3,780, 4C: EUR5,210. **Circ:** Paid 32,500

44672 ■ Neues Jahrbuch fur Geologie und Palaontologie
Gebruder Borntraeger Verlagsbuchhandlung
c/o Dr. Gunter Schweigert
Staatliches Museum fur Naturkunde
Rosenstein 1
D-70191 Stuttgart, Germany
Fax: 49 711 8936100
Publisher E-mail: mail@schweizerbart.de
Journal covering all fields of geology. **Founded:** 1807. **Freq:** Monthly. **Key Personnel:** Dr. Martin Langer, Editor, martin.langer@uni-bonn.de. **ISSN:** 0077-7749. **URL:** http://www.borntraeger-cramer.de/j/n-jb-geol-pal/.

44673 ■ Nova Hedwigia
Gebruder Borntraeger Verlagsbuchhandlung
Johannesstr. 3A
D-70176 Stuttgart, Germany
Ph: 49 711 351456
Fax: 49 711 351456
Publisher E-mail: mail@schweizerbart.de
Journal containing articles in taxonomy, morphology, ultrastructure and ecology of all groups of cryptogamic plants. **Freq:** Semiannual. **Key Personnel:** W. Frey, Ch. Ed., wfrey@gmx.de. **ISSN:** 0029-5035. **URL:** http://www.borntraeger-cramer.de/j/nova-hedwigia/.

44674 ■ Nuclear Engineering and Design
Elsevier Science
c/o G. Lohnert, Editorial Advisory Board
Institut fur Kernenergetik und Energiesysteme
University Stuttgart
Pfaffenwaldring 31
D-70550 Stuttgart, Germany
Fax: 49 711 6852010
Publisher E-mail: nlinfo-f@elsevier.com
Peer-reviewed journal covering various subjects related to engineering, design, safety and construction of nuclear fission reactors in connection with European Nuclear Society and International Association for Structural Mechanics in Reactor Technology. **Subtitle:** An International Journal devoted to all aspects of Nuclear Fission Energy. **Founded:** 1965. **Freq:** 12/yr. **Key Personnel:** Y.A. Hassan, Editor-in-Chief, fax 979845-6443, hassan@ne.tamu.edu; G. Lohnert, Editorial Advisory Board; J. Chao, Editor, drjasonchao@unitednuclear.net; K. Kudo, Editorial Advisory Board; V. Asmolov, Editorial Advisory Board; G. Berthoud, Editorial Advisory Board; B. Bishop, Editorial Advisory Board; R. Gueldner, Editorial Advisory Board. **ISSN:** 0029-5493. **Subscription Rates:** EUR6,650 institutions for European countries & Iran; 882,100¥ institutions; US$7,476 institutions for all countries except Europe, Japan & Iran. **Remarks:** Advertising accepted; rates available upon request. **URL:** http://www.elsevier.com/wps/find/journaldescription.cws_home/505661/description. **Circ:** (Not Reported)

44675 ■ Nuklearmedizin
Schattauer Publishers

Hoelderlinstr. 3
D-70174 Stuttgart, Germany
Ph: 49 711 229870
Fax: 49 711 2298750
Publisher E-mail: info@schattauer.de
Scientific medical journal covering nuclear medicine. **Subtitle:** Nuclear Medicine, Molecular Imaging and Therapy. **Founded:** 1961. **Freq:** Bimonthly. **Print Method:** Offset. **Trim Size:** 210 x 280 mm. **Key Personnel:** Dr. Barbara Tshisuaka, Editor-in-Chief, barbara.tshisuaka@schattauer.de. **ISSN:** 0029-5566. **Subscription Rates:** EUR465 institutions; EUR231 individuals; EUR48 members; EUR75 students. **Remarks:** Accepts advertising. **URL:** http://www.schattauer.de/en/magazine/subject-areas/journals-a-z/nuklearmedizin-nuclearmedicine.html. **Ad Rates:** BW: EUR1,290, 4C: EUR2,305. **Circ:** Paid 3,100

44676 ■ Phytocoenologia
Gebruder Borntraeger Verlagsbuchhandlung
Johannesstr. 3A
D-70176 Stuttgart, Germany
Ph: 49 711 351456
Fax: 49 711 351456
Publisher E-mail: mail@schweizerbart.de
Journal covering all aspects of phytosociology. **Subtitle:** International Journal of Vegetation Ecology. **Founded:** 1973. **Freq:** Quarterly. **Key Personnel:** Ulrich Deil, Editor-in-Chief, ulrich.deil@biologie.uni-freiburg.de; Dr. M.G. Barbour, Ch. Ed. **ISSN:** 0340-269X. **URL:** http://www.borntraeger-cramer.de/j/phytocoenologia/.

44677 ■ Plinius
Gebruder Borntraeger Verlagsbuchhandlung
Johannesstr. 3A
D-70176 Stuttgart, Germany
Ph: 49 711 351456
Fax: 49 711 351456
Publisher E-mail: mail@schweizerbart.de
Journal covering the field of mineralogy and petrology. **Subtitle:** Italian Supplement to European Journal of Mineralogy. **Freq:** Semiannual. **Key Personnel:** Marco Pasero, Editor. **URL:** http://www.schweizerbart.de/publications/detail/artno/147080935/Plinius-Volume--35.

44678 ■ Senckenbergiana biologica
Gebruder Borntraeger Verlagsbuchhandlung
Johannesstr. 3A
D-70176 Stuttgart, Germany
Ph: 49 711 351456
Fax: 49 711 351456
Publisher E-mail: mail@schweizerbart.de
Journal covering the field of zoology and botany. **Freq:** Semiannual. **Trim Size:** A4. **ISSN:** 0037-2102. **URL:** http://www.borntraeger-cramer.de/j/senckenbergiana-biologica/.

44679 ■ Solid State Ionics
Elsevier Science Inc.
Max-Planck-Institut fur Festkorperforschung
Heisenbergstrasse 1
D-70569 Stuttgart, Germany
Ph: 49 711 6891720
Fax: 49 711 6891722
Publisher E-mail: usinfo-ehelp@elsevier.com
Journal devoted to physics, chemistry and materials science of diffusion, mass transport, and reactivity of solids. **Founded:** 1980. **Freq:** 40/yr. **Print Method:** Offset. **Cols./Page:** 6. **Col. Width:** 22 nonpareils. **Col. Depth:** 298 agate lines. **Key Personnel:** J. Maier, Editor, ssi@fkf.mpg.de; A.N. Cormack, Editor, cormack@alfred.edu; R. Merkle, Editorial Asst.; K. Funke, Editor, k.funke@uni-muenster.de; J. Kilner, Editor, phone 44 20 75946733, fax 44 20 75946736, j.kilner@imperial.ac.uk; K. Eguchi, Editor, fax 81 75 3832520, eguchi@scl.kyoto-u.ac.jp; M.S. Whittingham, Founding Ed.; M. Blesa, Assoc. Editorial Board; T. Norby, Editor, phone 47 22840654, fax 47 22840651, truls.norby@kjemi.uio.no. **ISSN:** 0167-2738. **Subscription Rates:** US$109 other countries except Europe, Japan and Iran; 13,800¥ individuals; EUR99 individuals for European countries and Iran; EUR5,167 institutions for European countries and Iran; 686,900¥ institutions; US$5,809 institutions, other countries except Europe, Japan and Iran. **URL:** http://www.elsevier.com/wps/find/journaldescription.cws_home/505677/descriptiondescription.

44680 ■ Sonntag Aktuell
Postfach 10 44 62
70039 Stuttgart, Germany
Ph: 49 7205 3501
Fax: 49 7205 3509

Publisher E-mail: redaktion@soak.zgs.de
General newspaper. **Founded:** 1979. **Freq:** Weekly (Sun.). **Print Method:** Offset. **Cols./Page:** 7. **Col. Width:** 45 millimeters. **Col. Depth:** 492 millimeters. **Key Personnel:** Andreas Braun, Editor-in-Chief; Dr. Richard Rebmann, Contact; Roland Weber, Contact. **Remarks:** Accepts advertising. **URL:** http://www.sonntag-aktuell.de/. **Circ:** Paid 506,884

44681 ■ Synfacts
Georg Thieme Verlag Stuttgart
Rudigerstr. 14
Postfach 30 11 20
D-70469 Stuttgart, Germany
Ph: 49 711 89310
Fax: 49 711 8931298
Publisher E-mail: kundenservice@thieme.de
Journal providing an overview of the most interesting current trends in synthetic chemistry and will keep the synthetic chemist at the forefront of all important developments. **Subtitle:** Highlights in Current Synthetic Organic Chemistry. **Freq:** Monthly. **Key Personnel:** Dr. Susanne Haak, Managing Editor, phone 49 711 8931786, susanne.haak@thieme.de; Dr. Selena Boothroyd, Sci. Ed., selena.boothroyd@thieme.de; Helene Deufel, Production Ed., phone 49 711 8931929, helene.deufel@thieme.de. **ISSN:** 1861-1958. **Subscription Rates:** US$999 individuals faculty, The Americas; EUR999 other countries faculty; US$1,089 institutions The Americas; EUR899 institutions, other countries; US$369 individuals The Americas; EUR299 other countries; US$99 students; EUR99 students rest of the world. **URL:** http://www.thieme-chemistry.com/products/journals/synfacts.html.

44682 ■ Synthesis-Stuttgart
Georg Thieme Verlag
PO Box 301120
D-70451 Stuttgart, Germany
Ph: 49 711 89310
Fax: 49 711 8931410
Publisher E-mail: custsomerservice@thieme.de
Peer-reviewed journal covering all fields of organic chemistry, including organometallic, organoheteroatom, medicinal, biological, and photochemistry, but also related disciplines. **Founded:** 1920. **Freq:** Semimonthly 24 times in 2007. **Print Method:** Offset. **Cols./Page:** 6. **Col. Width:** 26 nonpareils. **Col. Depth:** 280 agate lines. **Key Personnel:** D. Enders, Editor-in-Chief, enders@rwth-aachen.de; T. Fukuyama, Regional Ed., synth@mol.f.u-tokyo.ac.jp; M. Lautens, Regional Ed., mtan@chem.utoronto.ca; T. Bach, Regional Ed., synthesis@ch.tum.de. **ISSN:** 0039-7881. **Subscription Rates:** US$2,876 institutions print + online; US$2,244 institutions print; US$575 individuals; US$134 single issue; $A 2,351 institutions, other countries print + online; $A 1,769 institutions, other countries print; $A 408 other countries; $A 93 other countries. **URL:** http://www.thieme-connect.com/ejournals/toc/synthesis.

44683 ■ Thrombosis and Haemostasis
Schattauer Publishers
Hoelderlinstr. 3
D-70174 Stuttgart, Germany
Ph: 49 711 229870
Fax: 49 711 2298750
Publisher E-mail: info@schattauer.de
Scientific, medical journal covering thrombosis and hemostasis. **Subtitle:** International Journal for Vascular Biology and Medicine. **Founded:** 1957. **Freq:** Monthly. **Print Method:** Offset. **Trim Size:** 210 x 280 mm. **Key Personnel:** Klaus T. Preissner, PhD, Editorial Board; Dr. Elinor Switzer, Managing Editor, elinor.switzer@schattauer.de; Dr. Gregory Y.H. Lip, Editor-in-Chief, g.y.h.lip@bham.ac.uk. **ISSN:** 0340-6245. **Subscription Rates:** EUR879 institutions print and online; US$1,230.60 institutions print and online; EUR228 students; US$319.20 students; EUR74 single issue; US$103.60 single issue; EUR396 individuals; US$554.40 individuals. **Remarks:** Accepts advertising. **URL:** http://www.schattauer.de/en/magazine/subject-areas/journals-a-z/thrombosis-and-haemostasis.html. **Former name:** Thrombosis et Diathesis haemorrhagica. **Ad Rates:** BW: EUR1,725, 4C: EUR2,980. **Circ:** Paid 3,180

44684 ■ V.C.O.T.
Schattauer Publishers
Hoelderlinstr. 3
D-70174 Stuttgart, Germany
Ph: 49 711 229870
Fax: 49 711 2298750

Publisher E-mail: info@schattauer.de
Scientific medical journal covering orthopedics and traumatology in veterinary medicine. **Subtitle:** Veterinary and Comparative Orthopaedics and Traumatology. **Founded:** 1988. **Freq:** Quarterly. **Trim Size:** 220 x 290 mm. **Key Personnel:** Kenneth A. Johnson, PhD, Editor-in-Chief, kenneth.johnson@usyd.edu.au; G. Sumner-Smith, Emeritus Ed.-in-Ch.; C.E. Eger, Assoc. Ed. **ISSN:** 0932-0814. **Subscription Rates:** EUR418 institutions; EUR198 individuals; EUR84 students; EUR84 members; EUR72 single issue. **URL:** http://www.schattauer.de/en/magazine/subject-areas/journals-a-z/vcot.html. **Ad Rates:** BW: EUR950, 4C: EUR1,565. **Circ:** Paid 1,800

44685 ■ Zeitschrift der Deutschen Geologischen Gesellschaft
Gebruder Borntraeger Verlagsbuchhandlung
Johannesstr. 3A
D-70176 Stuttgart, Germany
Ph: 49 711 351456
Fax: 49 711 351456
Publisher E-mail: mail@schweizerbart.de
Peer-reviewed journal covering fields of geology, hydrogeology, paleontology, tectonics, and sedimentology. **Freq:** Annual. **Key Personnel:** Andreas Hoppe, Editor-in-Chief. **ISSN:** 0012-0189. **URL:** http://www.borntraeger-cramer.de/j/zdgg-alt/E-zdgg.html.

44686 ■ Zeitschrift fur Geomorphologie
Gebruder Borntraeger Verlagsbuchhandlung
Johannesstr. 3A
D-70176 Stuttgart, Germany
Ph: 49 711 351456
Fax: 49 711 351456
Publisher E-mail: mail@schweizerbart.de
Peer-reviewed journal covering all fields of geomorphology. **Freq:** Quarterly. **Key Personnel:** Karlheinz Pfeffer, Ch. Ed., prof.pfeffer@online.de. **ISSN:** 0372-8854. **URL:** http://www.borntraeger-cramer.de/j/zeitschrift-fuer-geomorphologie/.

44687 ■ Zeitschrift fur Sprachwissenschaft
Walter de Gruyter GmbH & Co. KG
Institut fur Linguistik/Germanistik
Universitat Stuttgart
Keplerstr. 17
D-70174 Stuttgart, Germany
Publisher E-mail: info@degruyter.com
Promotes linguistic research with contributions from all fields and trends of modern linguistics. **Founded:** 1960. **Freq:** Semiannual. **Print Method:** Offset. **Trim Size:** 6 7/8 x 10. **Cols./Page:** 2. **Col. Width:** 32 nonpareils. **Col. Depth:** 112 agate lines. **Key Personnel:** Elisabeth Stark, Editor, estark@zedat.fu-berlin.de; Jochen Geilfub-Wolfgang, Editor. **ISSN:** 0721-9067. **Subscription Rates:** EUR108 institutions print or online only; EUR124 institutions print + online; EUR59 single issue. **URL:** http://www.degruyter.de/journals/zs/detailEn.cfm. **Circ:** ‡1,400

44688 ■ Big-FM - 87.8
Kronenstrasse 24
Im Zeppelin Carre
D-70173 Stuttgart, Germany
Ph: 49 711 284200
Fax: 49 711 28420490
E-mail: community@big-fm.de
Format: Contemporary Hit Radio (CHR); Album-Oriented Rock (AOR). **Operating Hours:** Continuous. **Ad Rates:** Advertising accepted; rates available upon request. **URL:** http://www.mybigfm.de.

44689 ■ Big-FM - 92.6
Kronenstrasse 24
D-70173 Stuttgart, Germany
Ph: 49 711 28420
Fax: 49 711 28420
E-mail: info@big-fm.de
Format: Contemporary Hit Radio (CHR); News; Sports. **Ad Rates:** Advertising accepted; rates available upon request. **URL:** http://www.bigfm-saarland.de.

44690 ■ DIE NEUE-FM - 107.7
Konigstrasse 2
D-70173 Stuttgart, Germany
Ph: 49 711 1635511
Fax: 49 711 1626161
E-mail: info@dieneue1077.de
Format: Contemporary Hit Radio (CHR); Album-Oriented Rock (AOR). **URL:** http://www.dieneue1077.de.

44691 ■ HoRadS-FM - 99.2 MHz
c/o Hochschule der Medien Stuttgart
Wolframstrasse 32
D-70191 Stuttgart, Germany
Ph: 49 711 89232620
Fax: 49 711 25706311
Format: Eclectic; Public Radio. **Operating Hours:** Continuous. **Ad Rates:** Noncommercial. **URL:** http://www.horads.de.

Tubingen

44692 ■ Journal of Institutional & Theoretical Economics
Mohr Siebeck
Postfach 2040
72010 Tubingen, Germany
Publisher E-mail: info@mohr.de
Publication covering economics. **Freq:** Quarterly. **Key Personnel:** Dr. Georg Siebeck, Publisher, siebeck@mohr.de; Elmar Wolfstetter, Editor. **ISSN:** 0932-4569. **Subscription Rates:** DM 174 individuals including electronic access; DM 294 institutions including IP-controlled electronic access. **URL:** http://www.mohr.de/en/journals/economics/journal-of-institutional-and-theoretical-economics-jite/journal.html.

44693 ■ Progress in Particle and Nuclear Physics
Elsevier Science
c/o Amand Faessler, Ed.-in-Ch.
Institute of Theoretical Physics
University of Tubingen
Auf der Morgenstelle 14
D-72076 Tubingen, Germany
Ph: 49 707 1297637
Fax: 49 707 1296400
Publisher E-mail: nlinfo-f@elsevier.com
Journal covering latest developments in the field of nuclear and particle physics. Includes topics such as the application of nuclear physics in the medical and archaeological fields, nucleo-genesis and related matters. **Founded:** 1977. **Freq:** Quarterly. **Key Personnel:** Amand Faessler, Editor-in-Chief, amand.faessler@uni-tuebingen.de; Kees De Jager, Editorial Board, kees@jlab.org; S. Brodsky, Editorial Board, sjbth@slac.stanford.edu. **ISSN:** 0146-6410. **Subscription Rates:** EUR1,806 institutions European countries; 240,000¥ institutions; US$2,022 institutions for all countries except Europe and Japan; 33,700¥ individuals; EUR218 individuals; US$293 individuals. **Remarks:** Accepts advertising. **URL:** http://www.elsevier.com/wps/find/journaldescription.cws_home/419/description. **Circ:** (Not Reported)

44694 ■ Zeitschrift fur die gesamte Strafrechtswissenschaft
Walter de Gruyter GmbH & Co. KG
Eberhard-Karls-University Tubingen
Lehrstuhl fur Europaisches Strafrecht und Strafprozessrecht
Wilhelmstr. 7
D-72074 Tubingen, Germany
Publisher E-mail: info@degruyter.com
Journal covering information on criminal law and criminology. **Print Method:** Offset. **Trim Size:** 10 1/2 x 16. **Cols./Page:** 5. **Col. Width:** 2 inches. **Col. Depth:** 16 inches. **Key Personnel:** Dr. Barbara Huber, Contact; Prof. Albin Eser, Contact; Dr. Joachim Vogel, Contact. **ISSN:** 0084-5310. **Subscription Rates:** EUR178 students print + online; EUR349 individuals print or online only; EUR401 individuals print + online. **URL:** http://www.degruyter.de/journals/zstw/detailEn.cfm.

Tutzing

44695 ■ BIO—Gesundheit fur Korper Geist und Seele
Bio-Ritter GmbH
Montashauserstr. 8
D-82327 Tutzing, Germany
Publication E-mail: biomagazin@aol.com
Trade journal covering health and natural healing. **Founded:** 1980. **Freq:** Bimonthly. **Key Personnel:** Monica Ritter, Managing Editor. **Subscription Rates:** EUR24.90 individuals; EUR28.80 other countries. **Remarks:** Accepts advertising. **URL:** http://www.biomagazin.de/. **Circ:** (Not Reported)

Ulm

44696 ■ Klassik Uhren
Ebner Verlag
Karlstr. 41
D-89073 Ulm, Germany
Ph: 49 731 152002
Fax: 49 731 1520171
Publication E-mail: klassik-uhren@ebnerverlag.de
Trade magazine covering clocks and timepieces. **Subtitle:** Journal Fuer Sammler Klassischer Zeitmesser. **Founded:** 1978. **Freq:** Bimonthly. **Print Method:** Offset. **Trim Size:** 21 x 28. **Key Personnel:** Christian Pfeiffer-Belli, Editor-in-Chief. **ISSN:** 0894-5845. **Subscription Rates:** DM 132 individuals; DM 27 single issue. **URL:** http://www.ebnerverlag.de/. **Circ:** 7,339

Unterfoehring

44697 ■ TELE-satellite International Magazine
TELE-Satellite Medien GmbH
PO Box 1234
D-85766 Unterfoehring, Germany
Trade magazine covering equipment test reports of new satellite products, including receivers, LNB and dishes, internet-via-satellite, satellite telephone, worldwide. **Freq:** Bimonthly. **Trim Size:** 210 x 297 mm. **Key Personnel:** Alexander Wiese, Mng. Ed./CEO. **ISSN:** 0931-4733. **Subscription Rates:** EUR58 individuals. **Remarks:** Accepts advertising. **URL:** http://www.tele-satellite.com/. **Alt. Formats:** CD-ROM. **Circ:** ‡148,430

Vaterstetten

44698 ■ E-Commerce Magazin
WIN verlags
Johann-Sebastian-Bach-Str. 5
D-85591 Vaterstetten, Germany
Ph: 49 810 63500
Fax: 49 810 6350190
Trade magazine covering Internet technology applications for business. **Founded:** 1998. **Freq:** 7/yr. **Print Method:** Roll offset, staple binding. **Trim Size:** 210 x 297 mm. **Cols./Page:** 8. **Key Personnel:** Dunja Koelwel, Editor-in-Chief, dk@win-verlag.de; Hans J. Grohmann, Publisher. **ISSN:** 1436-8021. **Subscription Rates:** EUR58 individuals Germany; EUR60 individuals abroad. **Remarks:** Accepts advertising. **URL:** http://www.e-commerce-magazin.de. **Ad Rates:** BW: EUR4,550, 4C: EUR7,410. **Circ:** ‡14,675

Villingen-Schwenningen

44699 ■ Modell
Neckar-Verlag GmbH
Klosterring 1
D-78050 Villingen-Schwenningen, Germany
Ph: 49 772 189870
Fax: 49 772 1898750
Publisher E-mail: service@neckar-verlag.de
Trade magazine covering rc-modell-airplanes. **Subtitle:** Fachzeitschrift fur der funkgesteuerten Modellflug. **Founded:** 1958. **Freq:** Monthly. **Print Method:** Offset. **Trim Size:** 185 x 265 mm. **Key Personnel:** Goetz Rudiger, Editor, goetz@neckar-verlag.de. **ISSN:** 0540-5203. **Subscription Rates:** EUR62 individuals; EUR9.10 single issue with DVD; EUR4.20 single issue. **Remarks:** Accepts advertising. **URL:** http://www.neckar-verlag.de/. **Ad Rates:** BW: EUR1,074, 4C: EUR1,611, CNU: EUR16, PCI: EUR84. **Circ:** Combined 33,500

Weimar

44700 ■ Antenne Thuringen-FM - 107.2
Belvederer Allee 25
D-99425 Weimar, Germany
Ph: 49 36 43552552
Fax: 49 36 43552444
E-mail: kontakt@antennethueringen.de
Format: Contemporary Hit Radio (CHR). **Owner:** Antenne Thuringen GmbH & Co., at above address. **Ad Rates:** Advertising accepted; rates available upon request. **URL:** http://www.antennethueringen.de.

Weinheim

44701 ■ BioEssays
John Wiley & Sons Inc.
Boschstrasse 12
69469 Weinheim, Germany

Circulation: ★ = ABC; △ = BPA; ◆ = CAC; • = CCAB; ▢ = VAC; ⊕ = PO Statement; ‡ = Publisher's Report; Boldface figures = sworn; Light figures = estimated.

Ph: 49 6201 606354
Fax: 49 6201 606525
Publisher E-mail: info@wiley.com
Journal publishing news, reviews and commentaries in contemporary biology that have a molecular, genetic, cellular, or physiological dimension. **Freq:** Monthly. **Key Personnel:** Andrew Moore, Editor-in-Chief; John Mattick, Editorial Board; Andreas Wagner, Editorial Board; Graham E. Budd, Editorial Board; Ralf J. Sommer, Editorial Board; Marilyn B. Renfree, Editorial Board; William F. Martin, Editorial Board; Lawrence J. Marsh, Editorial Board. **ISSN:** 0265-9247. **Subscription Rates:** US$181 individuals print only; US$1,709 institutions print and online; US$1,877 institutions, Canada print and online; US$1,553 institutions print only; US$1,721 institutions, Canada print only; US$1,805 institutions, other countries print only; US$1,961 institutions, other countries print and online. **Remarks:** Accepts advertising. **URL:** http://onlinelibrary.wiley.com/journal/10.1002/(ISSN)1521-1878. **Circ:** (Not Reported)

44702 ■ Chemie Ingenieur Technik
Wiley-VCH Verlag GmbH
Boschstrasse 12
D-69469 Weinheim, Germany
Ph: 49 620 1606520
Fax: 49 620 1606525
Publisher E-mail: info@wiley-vch.de
Magazine forming a medium of exchange for verfahrensingenieure, technical chemists, apparatus farmer and biotechnologist. **Freq:** Monthly. **Key Personnel:** Prisca Henheik, Assoc. Ed.; Barbara Bock, Editor; Vera Koster, Assoc. Ed. **ISSN:** 0009-286X. **Subscription Rates:** EUR220 individuals students, print only; EUR1,940 institutions print, Europe; EUR2,134 institutions print & e-access, Europe; EUR1,940 institutions e-access, Europe; US$2,554 institutions e-access only, outside Europe; US$2,554 institutions print only, outside Europe; US$2,810 institutions print & e-access, outside Europe. **Remarks:** Advertising accepted; rates available upon request. **URL:** http://www.wiley-vch.de/publish/en/journals/alphabeticIndex/2004/?sID=k8nukestaqaqfigbincv4fskc7. **Circ:** (Not Reported)

44703 ■ Chemistry
Wiley-VCH Verlag GmbH
PO Box 101161
D-69451 Weinheim, Germany
Ph: 49 620 16060
Fax: 49 620 1606328
Publication E-mail: chemasianj@wiley-vch.de
Publisher E-mail: info@wiley-vch.de
Peer-reviewed Journal covering all aspects of chemistry. **Subtitle:** An Asian Journal. **Freq:** Monthly. **Key Personnel:** Andrew Kelly, Asst. Ed.; Brian Johnson, Editor; Sean Mathai, Assoc. Ed. **ISSN:** 1861-4728. **Remarks:** Accepts advertising. **URL:** http://www.wiley-vch.de/publish/en/journals/newJournals/2451/?sID=. **Circ:** (Not Reported)

44704 ■ ChemMedChem
John Wiley & Sons Ltd.
Postfach 101161
D-69451 Weinheim, Germany
Ph: 49 6201 606142
Fax: 49 6201 606331
Publication E-mail: chemmedchem@wiley-vch.de
Publisher E-mail: cs-journals@wiley.co.uk
Journal covering integrating research works from chemistry, biology and medicine. The areas of interest ranging from drug design and discovery to drug development and delivery, from molecular modeling to combinatorial chemistry, from target validation to lead generation and ADMET studies etc. **Freq:** Monthly. **Key Personnel:** Natalia Ortuzar, Dep. Ed.; Peter Golitz, Editor. **ISSN:** 1860-7179. **Subscription Rates:** EUR138 individuals print only; US$4,811 institutions, other countries print only; US$154 other countries print only; EUR3,736 institutions print only. **Remarks:** Accepts advertising. **URL:** http://www3.interscience.wiley.com/cgi-bin/jabout/110485305/2452_info.html. **Circ:** (Not Reported)

44705 ■ ChemSusChem
Wiley-VCH Verlag GmbH
PO Box 101161
D-69451 Weinheim, Germany
Ph: 49 620 16060
Fax: 49 620 1606328
Publication E-mail: chemsuschem@wiley-vch.de
Publisher E-mail: info@wiley-vch.de
Journal covering research at the interface of chemistry and sustainability. **Freq:** Monthly. **Key Personnel:** Peter

Golitz, Editor; Guido Kemeling, Dep. Ed. **ISSN:** 1864-5631. **Remarks:** Accepts advertising. **URL:** http://www.wiley-vch.de/publish/en/journals/newJournals/2476/?sID=4a66c72210bd89fd39031d5a2bbfc14b. **Circ:** (Not Reported)

44706 ■ Journal of Biophotonics
Wiley-VCH Verlag GmbH
PO Box 101161
D-69451 Weinheim, Germany
Ph: 49 620 16060
Fax: 49 620 1606328
Publisher E-mail: info@wiley-vch.de
Journal covering research on the interaction between light and biological material. **Freq:** Bimonthly. **Key Personnel:** Andreas Thoss, PhD, Publisher, jbp@wiley-vch.de; Jurgen Popp, Editor-in-Chief, juergen.popp@uni-jena.de. **ISSN:** 1864-063X. **Remarks:** Accepts advertising. **URL:** http://www.wiley-vch.de/publish/en/journals/newJournals/2475/?sID=cf52baad5d3c6970a273b87e4bfc985f. **Circ:** (Not Reported)

44707 ■ Lipid Technology
Wiley-VCH Verlag GmbH
PO Box 101161
D-69451 Weinheim, Germany
Ph: 49 620 16060
Fax: 49 620 1606328
Publication E-mail: lipid-technology@wiley-vch.de
Publisher E-mail: info@wiley-vch.de
Journal covering lipids and biodiesel. **Freq:** Monthly. **Key Personnel:** Frank D. Gunstone, Editor. **ISSN:** 0956-666X. **Subscription Rates:** US$1,020 institutions print only; US$1,123 institutions print & e-access; US$1,020 institutions e-access; EUR810 institutions print only; EUR892 institutions print & e-access; EUR810 institutions e-access. **Remarks:** Accepts advertising. **URL:** http://www.wiley-vch.de/publish/en/journals/newJournals/2472/?sID=0df44b52cz783b0573fe503b1c599ee17. **Circ:** (Not Reported)

44708 ■ Starch/Staerke
John Wiley & Sons Inc.
Boschstrasse 12
D-69469 Weinheim, Germany
Publisher E-mail: info@wiley.com
Journal focusing on carbohydrates such as cellulose, starch, and sugars produced by photosynthesis, and examining the new technology necessary to exploit these resources. **Freq:** Monthly. **Key Personnel:** James N. Bemiller, Advisory Board; Qunyu Gao, Advisory Board; Richard F. Tester, Editor; Emmerich Berghofer, Advisory Board; Felix Escher, Advisory Board; Ann-Charlotte Eliasson, Advisory Board; Peter J. Reilly, Editorial Board; Petra Mischnick, Editorial Board; Wolfgang Bergthaller, Editorial Board. **ISSN:** 0038-9056. **Subscription Rates:** EUR1,488 institutions print or online; 2,391 SFr institutions print or online (Switzerland and Liechtenstein); US$1,894 institutions, other countries print or online. **Remarks:** Accepts advertising. **URL:** http://onlinelibrary.wiley.com/journal/10.1002/(ISSN)1521-379X. **Circ:** (Not Reported)

Wetzlar

44709 ■ ERF 1-AM - 1539
Evangeliums-Rundfunk Deutschland e.V.
Berliner Ring 62
D-35573 Wetzlar, Germany
Ph: 49 6441 9570
Fax: 49 6441 957180
E-mail: info@erf.de
Format: Contemporary Christian; Religious. **Operating Hours:** 19 hours Daily. **Ad Rates:** Advertising accepted; rates available upon request. **URL:** http://www.erf.de.

Wiesbaden

44710 ■ Anatolian Archaeological Studies
Harrassowitz Verlag
Kreuzberger Ring 7b-d
D-65205 Wiesbaden, Germany
Ph: 49 611 5300
Fax: 49 611 530
Publisher E-mail: verlag@harrassowitz.de
Journal of archaeology. **Freq:** Annual. **ISSN:** 1345-7829. **URL:** http://www.harrassowitz-verlag.de.

44711 ■ Central Asiatic Journal
Harrassowitz Verlag

Kreuzberger Ring 7b-d
D-65205 Wiesbaden, Germany
Ph: 49 611 5300
Fax: 49 611 530
Publisher E-mail: verlag@harrassowitz.de
Journal covering languages, literature, history and archaeology of Central Asia. **Freq:** Semiannual. **Key Personnel:** Stary Giovanni, Editor. **URL:** http://www.harrassowitz-verlag.de.

44712 ■ Dialog
German Direct Marketing Association
Hasengartenstr. 14
65189 Wiesbaden, Germany
Ph: 49 611 977930
Fax: 49 611 9779399
Publisher E-mail: info@ddv.de
Magazine of the German Direct Marketing Association. **URL:** http://www.ddv.de.

Wilhelmshaven

44713 ■ Geo-Marine Letters
Springer-Verlag
c/o Burg W. Flemming, Ed.-in-Ch.
Senckenberg Institute
Marine Science Division
Suedstrand 40
D-26382 Wilhelmshaven, Germany
Peer-reviewed journal publishing brief original studies and reviews dealing with processes, products and techniques in marine geology, geophysics, and geochemistry. **Freq:** 6/yr. **Key Personnel:** Burg W. Flemming, Editor-in-Chief; Gavin Birch, Editorial Board; Monique T. Delafontaine, Assoc. Ed.; Paul Aharon, Editorial Board; Karin Andreassen, Editorial Board; Brian D. Bornhold, Editorial Board. **ISSN:** 0276-0460. **Subscription Rates:** EUR1,053 institutions; EUR1,263.60 institutions enhanced access. **Remarks:** Advertising accepted; rates available upon request. **URL:** http://www.springer.com/earthsciences/geology/journal/367. **Circ:** (Not Reported)

Witten

44714 ■ TeensMag
Bundes-Verlag GmbH
Bodenborn 43
D-58452 Witten, Germany
Ph: 49 230 2930930
Fax: 49 230 293093689
Publication E-mail: info@teensmag.net
Publisher E-mail: info@bundes-verlag.de
Christian, consumer magazine covering trends, music, and religion for teenagers. **Subtitle:** Trends, Glaube, Action, Tiefgang. **Founded:** 1985. **Freq:** Bimonthly. **Cols./Page:** 4. **Col. Width:** 44 millimeters. **Key Personnel:** Frieder Trommer, Contact. **Subscription Rates:** EUR17.40 individuals. **URL:** http://www.teensmag.net. **Formerly:** Teens. **Ad Rates:** BW: EUR967, 4C: EUR1,227. **Circ:** Combined 20,000

Wuppertal

44715 ■ International Economics and Economic Policy
Springer Netherlands
c/o Dr. Paul J.J. Welfens, Mng. Ed.
European Institute for International Economic Relations
University of Wuppertal
Gaussstr. 20
42119 Wuppertal, Germany
Publisher E-mail: permissions.dordrecht@springer.com
Journal devoted to economic policy. **Founded:** 1998. **Freq:** Quarterly. **Print Method:** Web offset. **Trim Size:** 8 3/8 x 10 7/8. **Cols./Page:** 2 and 3. **Key Personnel:** Dr. Paul J.J. Welfens, Managing Editor, welfens@uni-wuppertal.de; Stefan C. Collignon, Editorial Board; Patrick Artus, Editorial Board; Matthew B. Canzoneri, Editorial Board; John T. Addison, Editorial Board; Lucas Bretschger, Editorial Board; Alain Chappert, Editorial Board; Dr. Jurgen Wolters, Managing Editor, wolters@wiwiss.fu-berlin.de; Dr. Holger C. Wolf, Managing Editor, wolfhc@georgetown.edu; Pierre-Richard Agenor, Editorial Board. **ISSN:** 1612-4804. **Subscription Rates:** EUR359 institutions print incl. free access or e-only; EUR430.80 institutions print incl. enhanced access. **URL:** http://www.springer.com/economics/internationaleconomics/journal/10368.

Wurzburg

44716 ■ Advances in Geometry
Walter de Gruyter GmbH & Co. KG
c/o Theo Grundhofer, Mng. Ed.
Mathematisches Institut
Universitat Wurzburg
Am Hubland
D-97074 Wurzburg, Germany
Publisher E-mail: info@degruyter.com
Scholarly journal reporting advances in Geometry. **Freq:**
Quarterly. **Print Method:** Offset. **Trim Size:** 24 x 17 cm.
Key Personnel: Karl Strambach, Managing Editor,
advgeom@mi.uni-erlangen.de; Eiichi Bannai, Editor,
bannai@math.kyushu-u.ac.jp; Frank Duzaar, Editor,
duzaar@mi.uni-erlangen.de; Graziano Gentili, Editor,
gentili@unifi.it. **ISSN:** 1615-715X. **Subscription Rates:**
EUR377 individuals print only or online only; EUR434
individuals print + online; EUR104 single issue. **Remarks:** Accepts advertising. **URL:** http://www.degruyter.
de/journals/advgeom/detailEn.cfm. **Circ:** (Not Reported)

44717 ■ CHIP
Vogel Verlag und Druck GmbH & Company KG
Max-Planck-Str. 7/9
D-97082 Wurzburg, Germany
Ph: 49 931 4180
Fax: 49 931 4182100
Publisher E-mail: info@vogel.de
Magazine covering new developments in the computer
and communications field. **Subtitle:** Computer &
Communications. **Founded:** 1978. **Freq:** Monthly. **Print
Method:** Offset. **Trim Size:** 210 x 297 mm. **Key Personnel:** Thomas Pyczak, Editor-in-Chief; Gabriele
Guoitzsch, Sales Mgr.; Christian Riedel, Editor-in-Chief.
Subscription Rates: EUR25 individuals. **Remarks:** Accepts advertising. **URL:** http://www.chip.de/cxo/b2b_
artikelunterseite_10794988.html. **Circ:** Controlled
345,780

**44718 ■ Computational Methods and Function
Theory**
Heldermann Verlag
c/o Prof. Dr. Stephan Ruscheweyh, Mng. Ed.
Mathematisches Institut
Universitat Wurzburg
Wurzburg, Germany
Publisher E-mail: mail@heldermann.de
Peer-reviewed mathematics journal publishing original
research papers in complex analysis, and on applications or computational methods related to complex
analysis. **Founded:** 2001. **Freq:** Semiannual. **Key Personnel:** Prof. Dr. Stephan Ruscheweyh, Managing
Editor. **ISSN:** 1617-9447. **Subscription Rates:** EUR220
individuals including surface mail shipment. **URL:** http://
www.heldermann.de/CMF/cmfcover.htm.

44719 ■ Cytogenetic and Genome Research
S. Karger Publishers Inc.
c/o Michael Schmid, Ed.-in-Ch.
Biozentrum, Am Hubland
Dept. of Human Genetics
D-97074 Wurzburg, Germany
Ph: 49 931 8884077
Fax: 49 931 8884058
Publisher E-mail: karger@snet.net
Journal covering animal cytogenetics, including molecular, clinical and comparative cytogenetics. **Founded:**
1962. **Freq:** 16/yr. **Print Method:** Offset. **Trim Size:** 7
7/8 x 10 3/4. **Cols./Page:** 3. **Col. Width:** 26 nonpareils.
Col. Depth: 140 agate lines. **Key Personnel:** Martina
Guttenbach, Managing Editor, guttenbach@biozentrum.
uni-wuerzburg.de; Claus Steinlein, Editorial Admin.,
claus.steinlein@biozentrum.uni-wuerzburg.de; Michael
Schmid, Editor-in-Chief, m.schmid@biozentrum.uni-
wuerzburg.de; Judith A. Hartz, Managing Editor, hartz@
centric.net; Mechthild Buche, Managing Editor, bueche@
aiozentrum.uni-wuerzburg.de. **ISSN:** 1424-8581.
Subscription Rates: EUR3,740 institutions print or online; US$4,752 institutions print or online; 5,236 SFr
institutions print or online; 5,760 SFr institutions print
and online; EUR4,116 institutions print and online;
US$5,228 institutions print and online. **URL:** http://
content.karger.com/ProdukteDB/produkte.asp?Aktion=
JournalHome&ProduktNr=224037.

44720 ■ Economic Quality Control
Walter de Gruyter Inc.
c/o Elart von Collani, Mng. Ed.
Volkswirtschaftliches Institut
University of Wurzburg
Sanderring 2
97070 Wurzburg, Germany
Publisher E-mail: info@degruyterny.com
Peer-reviewed Journal covering economic control and
maintenance policies for production and inventory. **Subtitle:** International Journal for Quality and Reliability.
Founded: 1986. **Freq:** 2/yr. **Key Personnel:** Elart von
Collani, Managing Editor, collani@mathematik.uni-
wuerzburg.de. **ISSN:** 0940-5151. **Subscription Rates:**
EUR92 individuals print or online; EUR106 individuals
print + online; EUR51 single issue print only. **URL:** http://
www.degruyter.com/journals/eqc/detailEn.cfm.

44721 ■ Knowledge Organization
Ergon Verlag
Keesburgstr. 11
D-97074 Wurzburg, Germany
Ph: 49 931 280084
Fax: 49 931 282872
Publisher E-mail: service@ergon-verlag.de
Publication covering information management.
Founded: 1973. **Freq:** Quarterly. **Key Personnel:**
Richard P. Smiraglia, Editor-in-Chief, richard.smiraglia@
liu.edu; Joseph T. Tennis, Book Review Ed., reviews@
isko.org. **ISSN:** 0943-7444. **Subscription Rates:**
EUR115 individuals. **URL:** http://www.isko.org/ko.html.

**44722 ■ MM Industrial Magazine Western
Europe**
Vogel Verlag und Druck GmbH & Company KG
Max-Planck-Str. 7/9
D-97082 Wurzburg, Germany
Ph: 49 931 4180
Fax: 49 931 4182100
Publication E-mail: info@vogel.de
Publisher E-mail: info@vogel.de
Technical, business magazine for Europe in English.
Founded: 1984. **Freq:** Quarterly. **Print Method:** Offset.
Cols./Page: 4. **Col. Width:** 46 millimeters. **Col. Depth:**
270 millimeters. **Remarks:** Accepts advertising. **URL:**
http://www.maschinenmarkt.vogel.de. **Ad Rates:** BW:
DM 8,550. **Circ:** Controlled 20,000

44723 ■ MM Maschinenmarkt
Vogel Verlag und Druck GmbH & Company KG
Max-Planck-Str. 7/9
D-97082 Wurzburg, Germany
Ph: 49 931 4180
Fax: 49 931 4182100
Publisher E-mail: info@vogel.de
Professional magazine covering sector-related engineering and business information. **Subtitle:** The Industrial
Magazine. **Founded:** 1894. **Freq:** Weekly. **Print
Method:** Offset. **Trim Size:** 216 x 303 mm. **Cols./Page:**
4. **Col. Width:** 46 millimeters. **Col. Depth:** 270
millimeters. **Key Personnel:** Ken Fouhy, Editor-in-Chief,
ken.fouhy@vogel.de; Bernhard Kuttkat, Dep. Ed.-in-Ch.,
phone 49 9314182415, bernhard.kuttkat@vogel.de; Dietmar Kuhn, Editor, phone 49 931418 2449, dietmar.
kuhn@vogel.de. **ISSN:** 0341-5775. **Subscription
Rates:** EUR270 individuals by surface mail. **Remarks:**
Accepts advertising. **URL:** http://www.maschinenmarkt.
vogel.de. **Ad Rates:** BW: DM 5,976, 4C: DM 7,177. **Circ:**
Combined 44,200

44724 ■ Process
Vogel Verlag und Druck GmbH & Company KG
Max-Planck-Str. 7/9
D-97082 Wurzburg, Germany
Ph: 49 931 4180
Fax: 49 931 4182100
Publisher E-mail: info@vogel.de
Professional magazine for engineers and technicians in
the chemical, pharmaceutical, and process engineering
industries. **Subtitle:** Magazine for Chemical and Pharmaceutical Technology. **Founded:** 1995. **Freq:** Monthly.
Print Method: Offset. **Trim Size:** 210 x 297 mm. **Key
Personnel:** Reiner Ottinger, Contact, reiner.oettinger@
vogel.de; Gerd Kielburger, Publisher, gerd.kielburger@
vogel.de; Marion Henig, Contact, marion.henig@vogel.
de. **ISSN:** 0946-2856. **Remarks:** Accepts advertising.
URL: http://www.process.vogel.de/. **Ad Rates:** BW:
EUR4,829, 4C: EUR6,099. **Circ:** Combined ‡28,041

Accra

44725 ■ Bongo News
Ghana Wildlife Society
PO Box 13252
Accra, Ghana
Publisher E-mail: ghanawild@4u.com.gh
Journal containing information on the current environmental issues. **Subscription Rates:** Free for members. **URL:** http://www.ghanawildlifesociety.org/about_gws/publications.html.

44726 ■ Ghana Medical Journal
African Journals Online
PO Box 1596
Accra, Ghana
Ph: 233 21 670510
Fax: 233 21 670511
Publisher E-mail: info@ajol.info
Peer-reviewed journal covering articles on general medical practice and medical sciences. **Founded:** 1952. **Freq:** Quarterly. **Print Method:** Offset. **Trim Size:** 8 1/8 x 10 7/8. **Cols./Page:** 3. **Col. Width:** 34 nonpareils. **Col. Depth:** 210 agate lines. **Key Personnel:** Prof. David Ofori-Adjei, Editor in Chief, phone 233 21 665457, gmj@dslghana.com; Linda Osei Konadu, Managing Editor; Mercy M. Newman, Editor. **ISSN:** 0855-0328. **Subscription Rates:** Cd 200,000 individuals; US$50 individuals. **URL:** http://ajol.info/index.php/gmj; http://www.ghanamedassn.org/Journal/html/journal.html.

44727 ■ The Ghanaian Chronicle
General Porfolio Ltd.
Private Mail Bag
Accra, Ghana
Ph: 233 21 222319
Fax: 233 21 232608
Publication E-mail: chronicl@africaonline.com.gh
Newspaper featuring news and events. **Key Personnel:** Emmanuel Akli, Editor; R.G. Coomson, General Mgr. **ISSN:** 0855-1677. **Remarks:** Accepts advertising. **URL:** http://www.ghanaian-chronicle.com/. **Circ:** (Not Reported)

44728 ■ Institute of African Studies
African Journals Online
PO Box 73
Legon
Accra, Ghana
Publication E-mail: iaspubs@ug.edu.gh
Publisher E-mail: info@ajol.info
Peer-reviewed journal covering the field humanities and social sciences in Africa. **Subtitle:** Research Review. **Freq:** Semiannual. **Key Personnel:** Prof. M.E. Kropp Dakubu, Editor-in-Chief, medakubu@ug.edu.gh. **ISSN:** 0855-4412. **Subscription Rates:** US$35 individuals. **URL:** http://ajol.info/index.php/iasrr.

44729 ■ NKO Magazine
Ghana Wildlife Society
PO Box 13252
Accra, Ghana
Publisher E-mail: ghanawild@4u.com.gh
Magazine of the Ghana Wildlife Society. **Subscription Rates:** Free for members. **URL:** http://www.ghanawildlifesociety.org/about_gws/publications.html.

44730 ■ West African Journal of Applied Ecology
African Journals Online
U.S. Department of of Soil Science
Box LG 245
Legon
Accra, Ghana
Publisher E-mail: info@ajol.info
Peer-reviewed journal covering the field of ecology, agriculture, and water pollution. **Freq:** Semiannual. **Key Personnel:** Dr. M.K. Abekoe, Contact, k_abekoe@ug.edu.gh; Prof. S.K.A. Danso, Editor-in-Chief, phone 233 21 512533, ecolab@ug.edu.gh. **ISSN:** 0855-4307. **Subscription Rates:** Free. **URL:** http://ajol.info/index.php/wajae.

44731 ■ Citi-FM - 97.3
Tettey Loop, No. 11
Adabraka
PO Box 30211
Accra, Ghana
Ph: 233 21 226013
Fax: 233 21 226183
E-mail: info@citifmonline.com
Format: Full Service. **Operating Hours:** Continuous. **Key Personnel:** Samuel Attah-Mensah, Mng. Dir.; Fred Chidi, News Ed.; Jessica Saforo, Program Mgr.; Nii Armah Dagadu, Bus. Devel. Mgr.; Innocent Eddah, Station Engr. **Wattage:** 5000. **Ad Rates:** Advertising accepted; rates available upon request. **URL:** http://www.citifmonline.com.

44732 ■ Joy-FM - 99.7
PO Box 17202
Accra, Ghana
Ph: 233 21 226151
Fax: 233 21 233697
E-mail: info@myjoyonline.com
Format: News; Sports; Information; Ethnic; World Beat. **Key Personnel:** Patrick Ayivor, Online Bus. Mgr.; Isaac Yeboah, Online Ed.; Stephen Agyei Jantuah, Operations Mgr. **Ad Rates:** Advertising accepted; rates available upon request. **URL:** http://news.myjoyonline.com/.

44733 ■ Peace-FM - 104.3
PO Box 17470
Achimota, Mile 7 Jct.
Accra, Ghana
Ph: 233 21 406677
Fax: 233 21 406531
Format: News; Information. **Ad Rates:** Advertising accepted; rates available upon request. **URL:** http://www.peacefmonline.com.

Kumasi

44734 ■ Agricultural and Food Science Journal of Ghana
Crops Research Institute
PO Box 3785
Kumasi, Ghana
Ph: 233 51 60396
Publisher E-mail: cridirector@cropsresearch.org
Journal covering agriculture and food science. **Founded:** 1888. **Freq:** Annual. **Print Method:** Offset. **Trim Size:** 13 7/8 x 22 1/2. **Cols./Page:** 6. **Col. Width:** 1 3/4 inches. **Col. Depth:** 21 1/2 inches. **Key Personnel:** Dr. H.K. Dapaah, Tech. Ed.; Dr. G.K.S. Aflakpui, Editor-in-Chief, gksaflakpui@cropsresearch.org; K. Obeng, Editor. **ISSN:** 0855-5591. **Subscription Rates:** Cd 120 individuals; US$45 other countries. **URL:** http://ajol.info/index.php/afsjg.

44735 ■ Ghana Journal of Forestry
African Journals Online
Forestry Research Institute
University PO Box 63
Kumasi, Ghana
Ph: 233 51 60123
Fax: 233 51 60121
Publisher E-mail: info@ajol.info
Peer-reviewed journal covering forest science and related disciplines. **Freq:** Semiannual. **Key Personnel:** Dr. A.A. Oteng-Amoako, Editor-in-Chief, oamoako@forig.org; Dr. Daniel Ofori, Editor; Naomi Appiah, Contact, nappiah@forig.org. **ISSN:** 0855-1707. **Subscription Rates:** US$20 single issue; US$35 individuals; US$55 institutions. **URL:** http://ajol.info/index.php/gjf.

Legon

44736 ■ Ghana Journal of Science
Ghana Science Association
PO Box 7
Legon, Ghana
Ph: 233 302 937886
Publisher E-mail: gsa@ug.edu.gh
Journal of the Ghana Science Association. **ISSN:** 0855-1448. **Subscription Rates:** US$15 individuals overseas; 10 individuals overseas. **URL:** http://www.ajol.info/journal_index.php?jid=86&ab=gjs.

44737 ■ Journal of the Ghana Science Association
Ghana Science Association
PO Box 7
Legon, Ghana
Ph: 233 302 937886
Publisher E-mail: gsa@ug.edu.gh
Peer-reviewed journal including refereed articles from papers read at the biennial conferences. **Freq:** Semiannual. **Key Personnel:** Prof. Aboagye Menyeh, Editor-in-Chief. **Subscription Rates:** Cd 18 individuals; Cd 30 institutions; US$75 other countries air mail; US$200 institutions, other countries air mail. **URL:** http://www.ajol.info/journal_index.php?jid=94&tran=0&ab=0; http://www.ghanascience.org/index.php?p=about-us.

Navrongo

44738 ■ Ghana Journal of Development Studies
African Journals Online
Ctr. for Research & Graduate Studies
University for Development Studies
PO Box 24
Navrongo, Ghana
Ph: 233 742 22449
Fax: 233 742 22449

Circulation: ★ = ABC; △ = BPA; ♦ = CAC; • = CCAB; □ = VAC; ⊕ = PO Statement; ‡ = Publisher's Report; Boldface figures = sworn; Light figures = estimated.

Gale Directory of Publications & Broadcast Media/147th Ed.

4963

Publisher E-mail: info@ajol.info
Peer-reviewed journal covering works on development policy, programming, and projects. **Freq:** Semiannual. **Key Personnel:** Dr. Agnes Atia Apusigah, Editor-in-Chief, awingura2008@yahoo.com. **ISSN:** 0855-6768. **Subscription Rates:** Cd 30,000 individuals; US$25 individuals. **URL:** http://ajol.info/index.php/gjds.

Tamale

44739 ■ Ghana Library Journal
African Journals Online
University for Development Studies
PO Box TL 1652
Tamale, Ghana
Ph: 233 24 4201511
Publisher E-mail: info@ajol.info
Peer-reviewed journal covering the subject of librarianship in Ghana. **Freq:** Annual. **Key Personnel:** I.K. Antwi,

Editor-in-Chief, ikantwi1993@yahoo.com; HR Asamoah-Hassan, Contact, maadwoa2000@yahoo.com. **ISSN:** 0855-3033. **Subscription Rates:** US$20 individuals. **URL:** http://ajol.info/index.php/glj.

Winneba

44740 ■ African Journal of Educational Studies in Mathematics and Sciences
African Journals Online
University College of Education of Winneba
PO Box 25
Winneba, Ghana
Ph: 233 24 4323186
Fax: 233 432 22361
Publisher E-mail: info@ajol.info
Peer-reviewed journal containing information about the fields of mathematics, science education, and related disciplines. **Freq:** Annual. **Key Personnel:** Prof. Jophus

Anamuah-Mensah, Editor-in-Chief, jam@uew.edu.gh; Dr. K.D. Mereku, Contact, dkmereku@uew.edu.gh. **ISSN:** 0855-501X. **URL:** http://ajol.info/index.php/ajesms.

44741 ■ Mathematics Connection
African Journals Online
U.S. Department of of Mathematics Education
University College of Education of Winneba
PO Box 25
Winneba, Ghana
Publisher E-mail: info@ajol.info
Peer-reviewed journal covering mathematics education in Ghana. **Freq:** Annual. **Key Personnel:** Dr. Kofi Mereku, Exec. Ed., dkmereku@uew.edu.gh; S.A. Gyimah, Managing Editor; Adwoah Nkrumah, Contact, mamaadwoa2004@yahoo.com. **ISSN:** 0855-4706. **Subscription Rates:** Cd 45,000 individuals. **URL:** http://ajol.info/index.php/mc.

Athens

44742 ■ EKISTICS
Athens Center of Ekistics
24 Strat. Syndesmou St.
GR-106 73 Athens, Greece
Ph: 30 2103623216
Fax: 30 2103629337
Publisher E-mail: ekistics@otonet.gr
Publication for the architecture and design industries. **Subtitle:** The Science of Human Settlements. **Founded:** 1955. **Freq:** Bimonthly. **Key Personnel:** P. Psomopoulos, Editor. **ISSN:** 0013-2942. **Subscription Rates:** US$150 individuals; US$120 individuals for WSE members. **Remarks:** Advertising not accepted. **URL:** http://www.ekistics.org. **Circ:** (Not Reported)

44743 ■ Global Nest
Global NEST
University of the Aegean
Voulgaroktonou st. 30
GR-114 72 Athens, Greece
Ph: 30 210 6492450
Fax: 30 210 6492499
Publisher E-mail: secretary@gnest.org
International Journal covering all aspects of environmental sciences. **Key Personnel:** Prof. Themistocles Lekkas, Editor-in-Chief; Dr. Dionysis Assimacopoulos, Exec. Ed.; V. Kotroni, Thematic Ed.; J. Davis, Thematic Ed.; H. Flocas, Thematic Ed.; T. Albanis, Thematic Ed.; E. Baltas, Thematic Ed.; D. Diakoulaki, Thematic Ed.; M. Aloupi, Thematic Ed.; A. Aivasidis, Thematic Ed. **ISSN:** 1790-7632. **Subscription Rates:** EUR100 individuals. **URL:** http://www.gnest.org/Journal/journal.htm.

44744 ■ Hellenic Orthodontic Review
Greek Orthodontic Society
95-97 Mavromichali St.
GR-114 72 Athens, Greece
Ph: 30 210 3615432
Fax: 30 210 3615432
Publisher E-mail: info@grortho.gr
Journal covering orthodontics. **Founded:** 1920. **Freq:** Semiannual. **Print Method:** Offset. **Trim Size:** 8 1/4 x 10 3/4. **Cols./Page:** 3. **Col. Width:** 13.5 picas. **Col. Depth:** 60 picas. **Key Personnel:** Moschos A. Papadopoulos, Editor, mikepap@dent.auth.gr; H.P. Bantleon, International Editorial Board; S.E. Bishara, International Editorial Board; L. Bondemark, International Editorial Board; C.J. Burstone, International Editorial Board; G. Farronato, International Editorial Board. **ISSN:** 1108-1279. **Subscription Rates:** 60 Dr institutions; 30 Dr individuals. **URL:** http://www.grortho.gr/hor/.

44745 ■ Hellenic Radiology Journal
Hellenic Radiological Society
P. Kyriakou 21
GR-115 21 Athens, Greece
Ph: 30 164 51489
Publisher E-mail: info@helrad.org
Journal covering all technical and clinical aspects of diagnostic imaging and intervention. **Freq:** Quarterly. **URL:** http://www.helrad.org/whoweare/whoweare.htm.

44746 ■ International Journal of Electronic Governance
Inderscience Publishers
c/o Prof. Panagiotis Georgiadis, Ed.-in-Ch.
University of Athens
E-Government Laboratory, TYPA bldg.
Panepistimiopolis Ilission
GR-15784 Athens, Greece
Publisher E-mail: editor@inderscience.com
Peer-reviewed journal covering areas of electronic governance. **Founded:** 2007. **Freq:** 4/yr. **Key Personnel:** Prof. Panagiotis Georgiadis, Editor-in-Chief, georgiad@di.uoa.gr; Prof. Dimitris Gouscos, Exec. Ed., gouscos@media.uoa.gr. **ISSN:** 1742-7509. **Subscription Rates:** EUR494 individuals includes surface mail, print only; EUR672 individuals print and online. **URL:** http://www.inderscience.com/browse/index.php?journalCODE=ijeg.

44747 ■ International Journal of Entertainment Technology and Management
Inderscience Enterprises Limited
c/o Efstathia-Maria Pitsa, Mng. Ed.
Athens University of Economics & Business
Dept. of Management Science & Technology
76, Patission Str.
104 34 Athens, Greece
Journal covering the research and application domain of entertainment technology and management. **Freq:** 4/yr. **Key Personnel:** Efstathia-Maria Pitsa, Managing Editor, efstathia_p@yahoo.gr; Dr. Hugo Liu, Editor-in-Chief, hugo@media.mit.edu; Prof. Don Marinelli, Editor-in-Chief, dm2l@andrew.cmu.edu. **ISSN:** 1475-8954. **Subscription Rates:** EUR494 individuals print or online; EUR672 individuals print and online. **URL:** http://www.inderscience.com/browse/index.php?journalID=73.

44748 ■ International Journal of Knowledge and Learning
Inderscience Publishers
ELTRUN, The E-Business Research Center
Athens University of Economics & Business
GR-104 34 Athens, Greece
Publisher E-mail: editor@inderscience.com
Peer-reviewed journal fostering multidisciplinary discussion and research on knowledge-intensive approaches to learning management and learning processes at the individual, organisational and national levels, emphasizing knowledge representation issues, social and organisational elements, and architectural and design issues of learning management systems. **Freq:** 4/yr. **Key Personnel:** Dr. Christian Guetl, Assoc. Ed.; Amit P. Sheth, Editorial Board Advisor; Martin Dzbor, Editorial Board Member; Konstantina N. Zefkili, Managing Editor, k.zefkili@ucl.ac.uk; Prof. Ernesto Damiani, Editor-in-Chief, damiani@dti.unimi.it; Dr. Andrew L.S. Goh, Book Ed. **ISSN:** 1741-1009. **Subscription Rates:** EUR494 individuals print only (surface mail); EUR840 individuals online only (2-3 users); EUR672 individuals print only (airmail). **URL:** http://www.inderscience.com/browse/index.php?journalCODE=ijkl.

44749 ■ International Journal of Multicriteria Decision Making
Inderscience Enterprises Limited
c/o John Psarras, Ed.-in-Ch.
National Technical University of Athens
Dept. of Electrical & Computer Engineering
9 Heroon Polytechneiou Str.
15780 Athens, Greece
Journal covering all aspects of multicriteria decision making, including theoretical studies, empirical investigations, comparisons, and real-world applications. **Freq:** 4/yr. **Key Personnel:** John Psarras, Editor-in-Chief, john@epu.ntua.gr; Constantin Zopounidis, Editor-in-Chief, kostas@dpem.tuc.gr. **ISSN:** 2040-106X. **Subscription Rates:** EUR494 individuals print or online; EUR672 individuals print and online. **URL:** http://www.inderscience.com/browse/index.php?journalID=350.

44750 ■ Journal of Cross-Cultural Psychology
International Association for Cross-Cultural Psychology
University of Athens
Dept. of Psychology
11 Herodou Attikou St.
GR-10674 Athens, Greece
Ph: 30 210 7241194
Fax: 30 210 7277534
Publisher E-mail: dgeorgas@psych.uoa.gr
Journal covering cross-cultural psychology. **Freq:** Bimonthly. **Key Personnel:** David Matsumoto, Editor, dm@sfsu.edu; Walter J. Lonner, Founding & Special Issues Ed., walt.lonner@wwu.edu. **ISSN:** 0022-0221. **URL:** http://www.ac.wwu.edu/; http://www.iaccp.org/drupal/node/8.

44751 ■ Journal of Southeast European and Black Sea Studies
Hellenic Foundation for European and Foreign Policy
Vas. Sofias 49
GR-10676 Athens, Greece
Ph: 30 210 7257110
Fax: 30 210 7257114
Publisher E-mail: eliamep@eliamep.gr
Journal containing information about politics, regional issues, security and cooperation. **Freq:** Quarterly. **Key Personnel:** Thanos Veremis, Editor; Theodore Couloumbis, Editor; Fiona Hill, Assoc. Ed.; Shireen Hunter, Editor; Susan Woodward, Editor; Franz-Lothar Altmann, Editor. **ISSN:** 1468-3857. **Subscription Rates:** US$498 institutions print + online; US$473 institutions online; US$131 individuals; 300 institutions print + online; 285 institutions online; 84 individuals; EUR396 institutions print + online; EUR376 institutions online; EUR104 individuals. **Remarks:** Accepts advertising. **URL:** http://www.eliamep.gr/en/publications/. **Circ:** (Not Reported)

44752 ■ Naftiliaki
Diorama Publishers Ltd.
132 Syngrou Ave.
Kallithea
GR-176 71 Athens, Greece
Ph: 30 210 9214205
Fax: 30 210 9214675
Publisher E-mail: amaroid@otenet.gr
Trade magazine covering the shipping industry in Greece. **Subtitle:** The Greek Shipping Review. **Founded:** 1957. **Freq:** Semiannual May and November. **Print Method:** Offset. **Trim Size:** A4. **Remarks:** Accepts advertising. **URL:** http://www.diorama.gr/. **Ad Rates:** BW: EUR2,240, 4C: EUR3,055. **Circ:** Paid 4,000

44753 ■ NY-LONDON Shows
Passerella Network S.A.

72-74 Aspasias St.
Cholargos
GR-155 61 Athens, Greece
Ph: 30 210 6548344
Fax: 30 210 6537149
Publisher E-mail: info@eu-moda.com
Magazine featuring all major collections in New York and London. **Freq:** 2/yr. **Subscription Rates:** EUR40 individuals single copy; US$46 individuals single copy; EUR46 other countries single copy; EUR69 individuals Europe; US$87 individuals; EUR89 other countries; EUR130 individuals Europe, 4 issues; US$166 individuals 4 issues; EUR173 other countries 4 issues; EUR190 individuals 6 issues. **Remarks:** Accepts advertising. **URL:** http://www.inpasserella.com/index.cfm. **Circ:** (Not Reported)

44754 ■ Paris Catwalks
Passerella Network S.A.
72-74 Aspasias St.
Cholargos
GR-155 61 Athens, Greece
Ph: 30 210 6548344
Fax: 30 210 6537149
Publisher E-mail: info@eu-moda.com
Magazine featuring all major collections in Paris, Rome. **Freq:** 2/yr. **Subscription Rates:** EUR40 individuals single copy; US$46 individuals single copy; EUR46 other countries single copy; EUR69 individuals Europe; US$87 individuals; EUR89 other countries; EUR130 individuals Europe, 4 issues; US$166 individuals 4 issues; EUR173 other countries 4 issues; EUR190 individuals 6 issues. **Remarks:** Accepts advertising. **URL:** http://www.inpasserella.com/index.cfm. **Circ:** (Not Reported)

44755 ■ Passerella di Donna
Passerella Network S.A.
72-74 Aspasias St.
Cholargos
GR-155 61 Athens, Greece
Ph: 30 210 6548344
Fax: 30 210 6537149
Publisher E-mail: info@eu-moda.com
Magazine featuring all major collections in Milan, Italy. **Freq:** 2/yr. **Subscription Rates:** EUR40 individuals single copy; US$46 individuals single copy; EUR46 other countries single copy; EUR69 individuals Europe; US$87 individuals; EUR89 other countries; EUR130 individuals Europe, 4 issues; US$166 individuals 4 issues; EUR173 other countries 4 issues; EUR190 individuals 6 issues. **Remarks:** Accepts advertising. **URL:** http://www.inpasserella.com/index.cfm. **Circ:** (Not Reported)

44756 ■ Stomatologia
Stomatological Society of Greece
17 Kallirroes St.
GR-117 43 Athens, Greece
Ph: 30 210 9214325
Fax: 30 210 9214204
Publication E-mail: stomsoc@otenet.gr
Publisher E-mail: stomsoc@otenet.gr
Greek language publication covering dentistry. **Freq:** Quarterly. **ISSN:** 0039-1700. **Subscription Rates:** US$80. **Remarks:** Advertising accepted; rates available upon request. **URL:** http://www.mednet.gr/stomsoc/journal-en.htm. **Circ:** 2,000

44757 ■ Trofima kai Pota
110 Sigrou Ave.
GR-117 41 Athens, Greece
Ph: 30 210 9240748
Fax: 30 210 9242650
Publication E-mail: info@triaina.com
Publisher E-mail: info@triaina.com
Trade magazine covering the food and beverage industry in Greece, Cyprus and abroad. **Founded:** 1976. **Freq:** 11/yr. **Print Method:** Offset. **Trim Size:** 220 x 285 mm. **Cols./Page:** 4. **Col. Width:** 4.1 millimeters. **Col. Depth:** 18.5 millimeters. **Key Personnel:** Nikos Korovilas, Publisher. **ISSN:** 1106-3718. **Subscription Rates:** EUR130 individuals; EUR50 students; EUR70 institutions; EUR150 other countries; EUR100 individuals Cyprus. **Remarks:** Accepts advertising. **URL:** http://www.triaina.com. **Ad Rates:** BW: EUR1,500, 4C: EUR2,060. **Circ:** 3,809

Chalkis

44758 ■ International Journal of Signal and Imaging Systems Engineering
Inderscience Enterprises Limited
c/o Prof. Dimitrios A. Karras, Ed.-in-Chief
Chalkis Institute of Technology
U.S. Department of Automation

34400 Psachana Evoias
Chalkis, Greece
Journal covering the theoretical, experimental and applied aspects of the engineering design of signal and imaging systems. **Freq:** 4/yr. **Key Personnel:** Prof. George Constantine Giakos, Editor-in-Chief, giakos@uakron.edu; Prof. Dimitrios A. Karras, Editor-in-Chief, dakarras@ieee.org. **ISSN:** 1748-0698. **Subscription Rates:** EUR494 individuals print or online; EUR672 individuals print and online. **URL:** http://www.inderscience.com/browse/index.php?journalID=185.

Crete

44759 ■ Transportation Research Part C
Elsevier Science
c/o M. Papageorgiou, Ed.-in-Ch.
Technical University of Crete
GR-731 00 Crete, Greece
Publisher E-mail: nlinfo-f@elsevier.com
Peer-reviewed journal covering planning, design, operation, control, management, maintenance and rehabilitation of transportation systems, services and components. **Subtitle:** Emerging Technologies - An International Journal. **Founded:** 1993. **Freq:** Bimonthly. **Key Personnel:** M. Papageorgiou, Editor-in-Chief, markos@dssl.tuc.gr; T.G. Crainic, Assoc. Ed.; H.S. Mahmassani, Assoc. Ed.; P. Varaiya, Assoc. Ed.; Y. Wang, Book Review Ed. **ISSN:** 0968-090X. **Subscription Rates:** EUR189 individuals for European countries & Iran; US$245 individuals for all countries except Europe, Japan & Iran; 27,400¥ individuals; EUR1,143 institutions for European countries & Iran; 1,279¥ institutions for all countries except Europe, Japan & Iran; US$152,000 institutions for Japan. **Remarks:** Accepts advertising. **URL:** http://www.elsevier.com/wps/find/journaldescription.cws_home/130/description. **Circ:** (Not Reported)

Kapandriti

44760 ■ Anticancer Research
International Institute of Anticancer Research
1st km Kapandritiou-Kalamou Rd.
PO Box 22
GR-190 14 Kapandriti, Greece
Ph: 30 229 5053389
Fax: 30 229 5052945
Publisher E-mail: iiar@iiar-anticancer.org
Journal dedicated to cancer research and treatment. **Founded:** 1963. **Freq:** Weekly (Thurs.). **Print Method:** Offset. **Cols./Page:** 5. **Col. Width:** 1 7/8 inches. **Col. Depth:** 14 inches. **Key Personnel:** B.B. Aggarwal, Editorial Board. **ISSN:** 0250-7005. **Subscription Rates:** EUR1,650 institutions online; EUR1,670 institutions print; EUR1,700 institutions print & online; EUR780 individuals online; EUR800 individuals print; EUR830 individuals print & online; EUR148 single issue. **URL:** http://www.iiar-anticancer.org/main.php?id=2.

Kozani

44761 ■ International Journal of Autonomous and Adaptive Communications Systems
Inderscience Enterprises Limited
WCOF Prof. Athanasios Vasilakos, Ed.-in-Ch.
University of Western Macedonia
Dept. of Computer & Telecommunications Engineering
GR 50100 Kozani, Greece
Journal covering the foundational, engineering, and technological aspects of communications systems exhibiting emergent and adaptive behavior. **Freq:** 4/yr. **Key Personnel:** Prof. Athanasios Vasilakos, Editor-in-Chief, vasilako@ath.forthnet.gr; Dr. Jen-Yeu Chen, Managing Editor, jenyeu@mail.ndhu.edu.tw. **ISSN:** 1754-8632. **Subscription Rates:** EUR494 individuals print or online; EUR672 individuals print and online. **URL:** http://www.inderscience.com/browse/index.php?journalID=263.

Nauplion

44762 ■ International Journal of Arts and Technology
Inderscience Enterprises Limited
c/o Prof. Athanasios Vasilakos, Ed.-in-Ch.
Dept. of Theatre Studies
University of Peloponnese
V.Konstantinou & Terzaki
21100 Nauplion, Greece
Journal focusing on the multi-disciplinary emerging area of computational art. **Freq:** 4/yr. **Key Personnel:** Prof.

Athanasios Vasilakos, Editor-in-Chief, vasilako@ath.forthnet.gr; Dr. Magy Seif El-Nasr, Managing Editor, magy@sfu.ca. **ISSN:** 1754-8853. **Subscription Rates:** EUR494 individuals print or online; EUR672 individuals print and online. **URL:** http://www.inderscience.com/browse/index.php?journalID=264.

Nikea

44763 ■ ICUs and Nursing Web Journal
Tzavella 121
GR-184 50 Nikea, Greece
Ph: 30 104 902095
E-publication encompassing the practice, research and policy roles of RNs worldwide. **Freq:** Quarterly. **Key Personnel:** Kalofissudis Ioannis, Ed./Mng. Ed.; Sharon L. Van Sell, Assoc. Ed., svansell@twu.edu; Jo Ann Walton, Consulting Ed., jo.walton@aut.ac.nz; Teresa Moreno Casbas, Consulting Ed.; Jean Watson, Assoc. Ed.; Arlene J. Lowenstein, PhD, Assoc. Ed.; Stafylaraki Anastasia, Consulting Ed.; Melanie Ann Jasper, Consulting Ed., melanie.jasper@port.ac.uk; Binioris Spiros, PhD, Consulting Ed.; Lois H. Neuman, PhD, Assoc. Ed. **ISSN:** 1108-7366. **Subscription Rates:** US$20 individuals; US$30 institutions; EUR20 other countries; EUR30 institutions, other countries. **Remarks:** Accepts advertising. **URL:** http://www.nursing.gr/. **Circ:** (Not Reported)

Patras

44764 ■ International Journal of Decision Sciences, Risk and Management
Inderscience Enterprises Limited
c/o Dr. Athanassios Mihiotis, Ed.-in-Ch.
School of Social Science
Hellenic Open University
57-59 Bouboulinas Str.
GR-262 22 Patras, Greece
Peer-reviewed journal focusing on decision making and management. **Freq:** Quarterly. **Key Personnel:** Dr. Athanassios Mihiotis, Editor-in-Chief, mihiotis@eap.gr. **ISSN:** 1753-7169. **Subscription Rates:** EUR494 individuals print or online; EUR672 individuals print and online. **URL:** http://www.inderscience.com/browse/index.php?journalCODE=ijdsrm.

44765 ■ International Journal of Tourism Policy
Inderscience Publishers
c/o Prof. George Agiomirgianakis, Ed.-in-Ch.
Hellenic Open University
Scholarship of Social Science
57-59 Bouboulinas St.
GR-26222 Patras, Greece
Publisher E-mail: editor@inderscience.com
Peer-reviewed journal covering international tourism development. **Founded:** 2007. **Freq:** 4/yr. **Key Personnel:** Prof. George Agiomirgianakis, Editor-in-Chief, gmagios@eap.gr; Dr. Konstantinos Andriotis, Editor-in-Chief, k.andriotis@cut.ac.cy; Dr. Christof Pforr, Book Review Ed. **ISSN:** 1750-4090. **Subscription Rates:** EUR494 individuals includes surface mail, print only; EUR672 individuals print and online. **URL:** http://www.inderscience.com/browse/index.php?journalCODE=ijtp.

44766 ■ Theoretical Computer Science
European Association for Theoretical Computer Science
c/o Ioannis Chatzigiannakis, Sec.
Research and Academy Computer Technology
International
1 N Kazantzaki St.
University of Patras Campus
26500 Patras, Greece
Publisher E-mail: secretary@eatcs.org
Publication covering computer science. **Founded:** 1975. **Freq:** 52/yr. **Key Personnel:** Prof. Don Sannella, Editor-in-Chief, dts@inf.ed.ac.uk; A. Apostolico, Editorial Board, axa@cc.gatech.edu; Ding-Zhu Du, Editorial Board, dzd@cs.umn.edu; F. Cucker, Editorial Board, macucker@sobolev.cityu.edu.hk; Prof. M. Nivat, Founding Ed., maurice.nivat@liafa.jussieu.fr; Prof. Giorgio Ausiello, Editor-in-Chief, ausiello@dis.uniroma1.it; X. Deng, Editorial Board, xiaotie.deng@cityu.edu.hk; O. Watanabe, Editorial Board, watanabe@is.titech.ac.jp; M. Crochemore, Editorial Board, maxime.crochemore@univ-mlv.fr. **ISSN:** 0304-3975. **Subscription Rates:** EUR6,335 institutions European countries; 840,800¥ institutions; US$7,089 institutions for all countries except Europe and Japan; US$26 students; 3,700¥ students; EUR20 students. **URL:** http://www.eatcs.org/; http://www.elsevier.com/wps/find/journaldescription.cws_home/

505625/descriptiondescription.

Piraeus

44767 ■ International Journal of Applied Systemic Studies
Inderscience Publishers
c/o Prof. Nikitas Assimakopoulos, Ed.-in-Ch.
University of Piraeus
Department of Informatics
80, Karaoli & Dimitriou Str.
GR-185 34 Piraeus, Greece
Publisher E-mail: editor@inderscience.com
Peer-reviewed journal covering applications of systemic methodologies & studies. **Founded:** 2007. **Freq:** 4/yr. **Key Personnel:** Prof. Nikitas Assimakopoulos, Editor-in-Chief, assinik@unipi.gr; Prof. Markus Schwaninger, Honorary Ed.; Dr. Ambjorn Naeve, Honorary Ed.; Dr. Nikolaos Georgopoulos, Asst. Ed.; Ioannis Theocharopoulos, Asst. Ed. **ISSN:** 1751-0589. **Subscription Rates:** EUR494 individuals includes surface mail, print only; EUR672 individuals print and online. **URL:** http://www.inderscience.com/browse/index.php?journalCODE=ijass.

44768 ■ International Journal of Economic Research
Serials Publications
c/o Nicholas Apergis, Ed.-in-Ch.
Dept. of Finance & Banking Management
University of Piraeus
80 Karaoili & Dimitriou Str
GR-185 34 Piraeus, Greece
Publisher E-mail: serials@satyam.net.in
Journal covering economics, econometrics and economic history. **Founded:** Apr. 8, 1971. **Freq:** Semiannual. **Print Method:** Offset. **Trim Size:** 8 x 10 7/8. **Cols./Page:** 5. **Key Personnel:** Panayotis Alexakis, Managing Editor; Parantap Basu, Managing Editor; Dionysios Chionis, Managing Editor; Nicholas Apergis, Editor-in-Chief, napergis@unipi.gr. **ISSN:** 0972-9380. **Subscription Rates:** US$125 institutions print. **URL:** http://www.serialspublications.com/journals1.asp?jid=178&jtype=1.

44769 ■ Journal of Applied Systems Studies
Cambridge International Science Publishing
c/o Nikitas A. Assimakopoulos, Ed.-in-Ch.
Department of Informatics
University of Piraeus
80 Karaoli & Dimitriou St.
GR-185 34 Piraeus, Greece
Fax: 30 1 32104142328
Publisher E-mail: cisp@cisp-publishing.com
Journal covering the development of methodologies based on the laws and rules of various sciences. **Founded:** Mar. 2000. **Freq:** 6/yr. **Key Personnel:** Nikitas A. Assimakopoulos, Editor-in-Chief, assinik@unipi.gr; Russell L. Ackoff, International Advisory Board; Bela H. Banathy, International Advisory Board. **ISSN:** 1466-7738. **Subscription Rates:** US$250 institutions; US$150 individuals; US$50 members. **URL:** http://www.unipi.gr/jass/.

Rion

44770 ■ International Journal of Behavioural and Healthcare Research
Inderscience Enterprises Limited
c/o Chistos Manolopoulos, Assoc. Ed.
University of Patra
Research Academic Computer Technology Institute
Bldg. D. Maritsas, N. Kazantzakis St.
Rion, Greece
Peer-reviewed journal featuring experimental and theoretical papers that deal with behavioral and healthcare concerns. **Freq:** 4/yr. **Key Personnel:** Chistos Manolopoulos, Assoc. Ed.; Demetri Kantarelis, Editor, dkan@besiweb.com. **ISSN:** 1755-3539. **Subscription Rates:** EUR494 individuals print or online; EUR672 individuals print and online. **URL:** http://www.inderscience.com/browse/index.php?journalID=274.

Thessaloniki

44771 ■ European Journal
European Centre for the Development of Vocational Training - Cedefop
PO Box 22427
GR-551 02 Thessaloniki, Greece
Ph: 30 231 0490111
Fax: 30 231 0490049
Publisher E-mail: info@cedefop.europa.eu
European journal covering vocational training in English (ISSN: 0378-5068), French (ISSN: 3078-5092), German (ISSN: 0378-5106), Portuguese (ISSN: 0874-145X) and Spanish (ISSN: 0258-7483). **Subtitle:** Vocational Training. **Founded:** Mar. 1994. **Freq:** 3/yr. **Trim Size:** A4. **Key Personnel:** Martin Mulder, Chm. **ISSN:** 0378-5068. **Remarks:** Advertising not accepted. **URL:** http://www.cedefop.europa.eu/EN/publications/6009.aspx. **Circ:** (Not Reported)

44772 ■ Hellenic Journal of Psychology
Psychological Society of Northern Greece
School of Psychology
Aristotle University of Thessaloniki
GR-541 24 Thessaloniki, Greece
Publisher E-mail: efklides@psy.auth.gr
Journal containing articles in Psychology. **Freq:** 3/yr. **ISSN:** 1790-1391. **URL:** http://www.pseve.org/journal.asp.

44773 ■ International Journal of Innovation and Regional Development
Inderscience Enterprises Limited
c/o Prof. Panayiotis H. Ketikidis, Ed.-in-Ch.
University of Sheffield
Dept. of Computer Science, Information Services
13 Tsimiski St.
54624 Thessaloniki, Greece
Journal covering the discussion on regional dimensions of innovation and development in the fields of business, manufacturing, and service. **Freq:** 4/yr. **Key Personnel:** Prof. Panayiotis H. Ketikidis, Editor-in-Chief, ijird@seerc.org; Dr. Elias G. Carayannis, Assoc. Ed. **ISSN:** 1753-0660. **Subscription Rates:** EUR494 individuals print or online; EUR672 individuals print and online. **URL:** http://www.inderscience.com/browse/index.php?journalID=234.

44774 ■ Journal of Agricultural and Food Economics
Serials Publications
c/o Prof. Konstantinos Mattas, Ed.
Dept. of Agricultural Economics
Aristotle University of Thessaloniki
PO Box 225
GR-541 24 Thessaloniki, Greece
Publisher E-mail: serials@satyam.net.in
Journal covering agriculture and food economics. **Freq:** Semiannual. **Key Personnel:** Murray McGregor, Editorial Board; Charles Machethe, Editorial Board; Mohammad Jabbar, Editorial Board; Agapi Somwaru, Editorial Board; Prof. Konstantinos Mattas, Editor. **ISSN:** 0973-5100. **Subscription Rates:** US$125 institutions print. **URL:** http://www.serialspublications.com/journals1.asp?jid=304&jtype=1.

44775 ■ Journal of Biological Research
Aristotle University of Thessaloniki
School of Biology
GR-541 24 Thessaloniki, Greece
Journal featuring articles on such topics as morphology, anatomy, cytology, genetics, molecular biology, development & differentiation, and more. **Freq:** Semiannual. **Key Personnel:** Dr. A.M. Bosabalidis, Editor-in-Chief, artbos@bio.auth.gr; Dr. A. Staikou, Co-Ed., astaikou@bio.auth.gr; Dr. S.P. Sgardelis, Co-Ed., sgardeli@bio.auth.gr; Dr. T.J. Abatzopoulos, Co-Ed., abatzop@bio.auth.gr. **URL:** http://www.jbr.gr/.

Xanthi

44776 ■ Strain
John Wiley & Sons Inc.
Wiley-Blackwell
c/o Prof. Emmanuel E. Gdoutos, Ed.
Scholarship of Engineering
Democritus University of Thrace
L69 3GH Xanthi, Greece
Ph: 30 25410 79651
Fax: 30 25410 79652
Journal of the British Society for Strain Measurement. **Subtitle:** International Journal for Strain Management. **Founded:** 1960. **Freq:** Bimonthly. **Trim Size:** A4. **Cols./Page:** 2. **Key Personnel:** Dr. Bob Mines, Editorial Council; Isaac Daniel, Board Member; Fabrice Pierron, Editorial Council; David Nowell, Board Member; Josef Eberhardsteiner, Editorial Council; Leslie Banks-Sills, Board Member; Janice Barton, Editorial Council; Prof. Emmanuel E. Gdoutos, Editor, egdoutos@civil.duth.gr; Augusto Ajovalasit, Board Member; Phil Withers, Board Member. **ISSN:** 0039-2103. **Subscription Rates:** US$642 institutions print + online; US$583 institutions print or online; 346 institutions print + online; 314 institutions print or online; EUR439 institutions print + online; EUR399 institutions print or online; US$749 institutions, other countries print + online; US$680 institutions, other countries print or online. **Remarks:** Accepts advertising. **URL:** http://www.wiley.com/bw/journal.asp?ref=0039-2103&site=1. **Circ:** Non-paid 650

Circulation: ★ = ABC; △ = BPA; ◆ = CAC; • = CCAB; ❑ = VAC; ⊕ = PO Statement; ‡ = Publisher's Report; Boldface figures = sworn; Light figures = estimated.

Gale Directory of Publications & Broadcast Media/147th Ed.   **4967**

Alta Verapaz

44777 ■ Emisoras Unidas-FM - 91.1
4 calle 6-84, zona 13
Guatemala City, Guatemala
Ph: 502 2 4405139
Format: News; Information. **Owner:** Grupo Emisoras Unidas, at above address. **Key Personnel:** Felipe Valenzuela, Dir. Gen. **URL:** http://radio.emisorasunidas.com/frecuencias.php.

Baja Verapaz

44778 ■ Emisoras Unidas-FM - 94.3
4 calle 6-84, zona 13
Guatemala City, Guatemala
Ph: 502 2 4405139
Format: News; Information. **Owner:** Grupo Emisoras Unidas, at above address. **Key Personnel:** Felipe Valenzuela, Dir. Gen. **URL:** http://radio.emisorasunidas.com/frecuencias.php.

Chichicastenango

44779 ■ Emisoras Unidas-FM - 90.3
4 calle 6-84, zona 13
Guatemala City, Guatemala
Ph: 502 2 4405139
Format: News; Information. **Owner:** Grupo Emisoras Unidas, at above address. **Key Personnel:** Felipe Valenzuela, Dir. Gen. **URL:** http://radio.emisorasunidas.com/frecuencias.php.

Chimaltenango

44780 ■ Emisoras Unidas-FM - 91.1
4 calle 6-84, zona 13
Guatemala City, Guatemala
Ph: 502 2 4405139
Format: News; Information. **Owner:** Grupo Emisoras Unidas, at above address. **Key Personnel:** Felipe Valenzuela, Dir. Gen. **URL:** http://radio.emisorasunidas.com/frecuencias.php.

Chiquimula

44781 ■ Emisoras Unidas-FM - 89.9
4 calle 6-84, zona 13
Guatemala City, Guatemala
Ph: 502 2 4405139
Format: News; Information. **Owner:** Grupo Emisoras Unidas, at above address. **Key Personnel:** Felipe Valenzuela, Dir. Gen. **URL:** http://radio.emisorasunidas.com/frecuencias.php.

Coatepeque

44782 ■ Emisoras Unidas-FM - 98.7
4 calle 6-84, zona 13
Guatemala City, Guatemala
Ph: 502 2 4405139
Format: News; Information. **Owner:** Grupo Emisoras Unidas, at above address. **Key Personnel:** Felipe Valenzuela, Dir. Gen. **URL:** http://radio.emisorasunidas.com/frecuencias.php.

El Peten

44783 ■ Emisoras Unidas-FM - 98.9
4 calle 6-84, zona 13
Guatemala City, Guatemala
Ph: 502 2 4405139
Format: News; Information. **Owner:** Grupo Emisoras Unidas, at above address. **Key Personnel:** Felipe Valenzuela, Dir. Gen. **URL:** http://radio.emisorasunidas.com/frecuencias.php.

Escuintla

44784 ■ Emisoras Unidas-FM - 91.9
4 calle 6-84, zona 13
Guatemala City, Guatemala
Ph: 502 2 4405139
Format: News; Information. **Owner:** Grupo Emisoras Unidas, at above address. **Key Personnel:** Felipe Valenzuela, Dir. Gen. **URL:** http://radio.emisorasunidas.com/frecuencias.php.

Guatemala City

44785 ■ International Journal for Equity in Health
International Society for Equity in Health
5ta. Calle 20-15 zona 11
Colonia Mirador 1
01011 Guatemala City, Guatemala
Ph: 502 2472 8530
Fax: 502 2475 2974
Publisher E-mail: wflores@worldwidedialup.net
Journal featuring articles about the differences in health across population and population groups through economic, geographical, demographical, and social conditions. **Key Personnel:** Lars-Olov Bygren, Sen. Ed.; Gerald Bloom, Sen. Ed.; Barbara Starfield, Editor-in-Chief; Leiyu Shi, Dep. Ed.; Lars Borgquist, Sen. Ed. **URL:** http://www.iseqh.org/journal_en.htm.

44786 ■ Clasica-FM - 106.5
6a. Av. 0-60 Zona 4
Torre Profesional I
Oficina 903, Centro Comercial Z. 4
Guatemala City, Guatemala
Ph: 34 2 4112030
Fax: 34 2 4112005
Format: Ethnic; World Beat. **URL:** http://www.rcn.com.gt.

Emisoras Unidas-AM - See Retalhuleu

44787 ■ Emisoras Unidas-FM - 89.7
4 calle 6-84, zona 13
Guatemala City, Guatemala
Ph: 502 2 4405139
Format: News; Information. **Owner:** Grupo Emisoras Unidas, at above address. **Key Personnel:** Felipe Valenzuela, Dir. Gen. **URL:** http://radio.emisorasunidas.com/frecuencias.php.

Emisoras Unidas-FM - See Alta Verapaz

Emisoras Unidas-FM - See Baja Verapaz

Emisoras Unidas-FM - See Chichicastenango

Emisoras Unidas-FM - See Chimaltenango

Emisoras Unidas-FM - See Chiquimula

Emisoras Unidas-FM - See Coatepeque

Emisoras Unidas-FM - See El Peten

Emisoras Unidas-FM - See Escuintla

Emisoras Unidas-FM - See Huehuetenango

Emisoras Unidas-FM - See Occidente

Emisoras Unidas-FM - See Quiche

Emisoras Unidas-FM - See Retalhuleu

Emisoras Unidas-FM - See San Marcos

Emisoras Unidas-FM - See Santa Rosa

Emisoras Unidas-FM - See Suchitepequez

Emisoras Unidas-FM - See Zacapa

44788 ■ Radio Cultural TGN-FM - 100.5
4a Avenida 30-09, Zona 3
Apartado Postal 601
01901 Guatemala City, Guatemala
Ph: 502 24721745
Fax: 502 24400260
Format: Ethnic; World Beat. **Operating Hours:** Continuous. **URL:** http://radiocultural.net.

44789 ■ Shock-FM - 105.3
4 Calle 23-03, Zona 14
01014 Guatemala City, Guatemala
Ph: 502 23670767
Format: Album-Oriented Rock (AOR); Ethnic; World Beat. **URL:** http://www.shock.fm.

Huehuetenango

44790 ■ Emisoras Unidas-FM - 104.1
4 calle 6-84, zona 13
Guatemala City, Guatemala
Ph: 502 2 4405139
Format: News; Information. **Owner:** Grupo Emisoras Unidas, at above address. **Key Personnel:** Felipe Valenzuela, Dir. Gen. **URL:** http://radio.emisorasunidas.com/frecuencias.php.

Occidente

44791 ■ Emisoras Unidas-FM - 104.3
4 calle 6-84, zona 13
Guatemala City, Guatemala
Ph: 502 2 4405139
Format: News; Information. **Owner:** Grupo Emisoras Unidas, at above address. **Key Personnel:** Felipe Valenzuela, Dir. Gen. **URL:** http://radio.emisorasunidas.com/frecuencias.php.

Quiche

44792 ■ Emisoras Unidas-FM - 90.3
4 calle 6-84, zona 13
Guatemala City, Guatemala
Ph: 502 2 4405139
Format: News; Information. **Owner:** Grupo Emisoras Unidas, at above address. **Key Personnel:** Felipe Valenzuela, Dir. Gen. **URL:** http://radio.emisorasunidas.com/frecuencias.php.

Retalhuleu

44793 ■ Emisoras Unidas-AM - 1130

4 calle 6-84, zona 13
Guatemala City, Guatemala
Ph: 502 2 4405139
Format: News; Information. **Owner:** Grupo Emisoras Unidas, at above address. **Key Personnel:** Felipe Valenzuela, Dir. Gen. **URL:** http://radio.emisorasunidas.com/frecuencias.php.

44794 ■ Emisoras Unidas-FM - 103.1
4 calle 6-84, zona 13
Guatemala City, Guatemala
Ph: 502 2 4405139
Format: News; Information. **Owner:** Grupo Emisoras Unidas, at above address. **Key Personnel:** Felipe Valenzuela, Dir. Gen. **URL:** http://radio.emisorasunidas.com/frecuencias.php.

San Marcos

44795 ■ Emisoras Unidas-FM - 104.3
4 calle 6-84, zona 13

Guatemala City, Guatemala
Ph: 502 2 4405139
Format: News; Information. **Owner:** Grupo Emisoras Unidas, at above address. **Key Personnel:** Felipe Valenzuela, Dir. Gen. **URL:** http://radio.emisorasunidas.com/frecuencias.php.

Santa Rosa

44796 ■ Emisoras Unidas-FM - 89.9
4 calle 6-84, zona 13
Guatemala City, Guatemala
Ph: 502 2 4405139
Format: News; Information. **Owner:** Grupo Emisoras Unidas, at above address. **Key Personnel:** Felipe Valenzuela, Dir. Gen. **URL:** http://radio.emisorasunidas.com/frecuencias.php.

Suchitepequez

44797 ■ Emisoras Unidas-FM - 92.3

4 calle 6-84, zona 13
Guatemala City, Guatemala
Ph: 502 2 4405139
Format: News; Information. **Owner:** Grupo Emisoras Unidas, at above address. **Key Personnel:** Felipe Valenzuela, Dir. Gen. **URL:** http://radio.emisorasunidas.com/frecuencias.php.

Zacapa

44798 ■ Emisoras Unidas-FM - 89.9
4 calle 6-84, zona 13
Guatemala City, Guatemala
Ph: 502 2 4405139
Format: News; Information. **Owner:** Grupo Emisoras Unidas, at above address. **Key Personnel:** Felipe Valenzuela, Dir. Gen. **URL:** http://radio.emisorasunidas.com/frecuencias.php.

Georgetown

44799 ■ CARICOM Perspective
Caribbean Community
PO Box 10827
Georgetown, Guyana
Ph: 592 22 20001
Fax: 592 22 20171
Publisher E-mail: info@caricom.org
Publication covering economic integration. **Freq:** Annual.
ISSN: 0254-962X. **Remarks:** Advertising not accepted.
URL: http://www.caricom.org/. **Circ:** 3,000

44800 ■ Dayclean
Working People's Alliance
Walter Rodney House
80 Croal St.
Stabroek
Georgetown, Guyana
Ph: 592 2 53679
Fax: 592 2 53679
Newspaper covering political parties. **Freq:** Monthly.
Remarks: Advertising accepted; rates available upon request. **URL:** http://www.guyanacaribbeanpolitics.com/wpa/wpa.html. **Circ:** 5,000

44801 ■ Thunder
People's Progressive Party
41 Robb St.
Georgetown, Guyana
Ph: 592 272095
Fax: 592 272096
Publisher E-mail: ppp@guyana.net.gy
Publication covering political parties. **Freq:** Quarterly.
Key Personnel: Janet Jagan, Editor. **URL:** http://www.ppp-civic.org.

Port-au-Prince

44802 ■ Radio Galaxie-FM - 104.5
17, rue Pavee
Port-au-Prince, Haiti
Ph: 509 2239941
E-mail: galaxie@radiogalaxiehaiti.com
Format: Ethnic; Information; Sports; World Beat. **URL:**
http://www.radiogalaxiehaiti.com.

Circulation: ★ = ABC; △ = BPA; ♦ = CAC; • = CCAB; ❏ = VAC; ⊕ = PO Statement; ‡ = Publisher's Report; Boldface figures = sworn; Light figures = estimated.

Gale Directory of Publications & Broadcast Media/147th Ed. 4973

Tegucigalpa

44803 ■ **Honduras This Week**
Colonia Payaqui
frente al Instituto San Miguel, casa No. 3644
Tegucigalpa, Honduras
Ph: 504 239 0285

Fax: 504 232 2300
English language independent community newspaper.
Subtitle: Your Central American Weekly Review.
Founded: Sept. 1988. **Freq:** Weekly (Sat.). **Key Personnel:** Nicole Marrder, Web Ed.; Stanley Marrder, Webmaster. **Subscription Rates:** 350 Lp individuals Honduras; US$81 individuals Central America, South America, Panama, Belize; US$81 U.S., Canada, and Mexico; US$91 individuals Europe; US$95 individuals Asia & Africa. **Remarks:** Accepts advertising. **URL:** http://www.hondurasthisweek.com. **Ad Rates:** BW: 451 Lp, 4C: 17,600 Lp. **Circ:** 6,000

Circulation: ★ = ABC; △ = BPA; ◆ = CAC; • = CCAB; ❑ = VAC; ⊕ = PO Statement; ‡ = Publisher's Report; Boldface figures = sworn; Light figures = estimated.

Budapest

44804 ■ Across Languages and Cultures
Akademiai Kiado Rt.
Prielle Kornelia u. 19/D
PO Box 245
H-1117 Budapest, Hungary
Ph: 36 146 48282
Fax: 36 146 48251
Publisher E-mail: info@akkrt.hu
Journal publishing articles and reviews on all sub-disciplines of translation and interpreting studies. **Subtitle:** A Multidisciplinary Journal for Translation and Interpreting Studies. **Founded:** 1999. **Freq:** Semiannual. **Trim Size:** 17 x 25 cm. **Key Personnel:** Karoly Krisztina, Managing Editor, karolyk@ludens.elte.hu; Klaudy Kinga, Editor-in-Chief, kklaudy@ludens.elte.hu; Heltai Pal, Consulting Ed., heltai@gtk.gau.hu. **ISSN:** 1585-1923. **Subscription Rates:** EUR148 individuals online; US$205 individuals online; EUR170 individuals print and online; US$238 individuals print and online. **URL:** http://akkrt.hu/2/journals/products/linguistics/across_languages_and_cultures_eng.

44805 ■ Acta Alimentaria
Akademiai Kiado Rt.
Prielle Kornelia u. 19/D
PO Box 245
H-1117 Budapest, Hungary
Ph: 36 146 48282
Fax: 36 146 48251
Publisher E-mail: info@akkrt.hu
Journal covering food science. **Subtitle:** An International Journal of Food Science. **Founded:** 1972. **Freq:** Quarterly. **Print Method:** Offset. **Cols./Page:** 6. **Col. Width:** 25 nonpareils. **Col. Depth:** 301 agate lines. **Key Personnel:** P. Raspor, Co-Ed.; Jozsef Farkas, Editor-in-Chief; W.H. Holzapfel, Co-Ed. **ISSN:** 0139-3006. **Subscription Rates:** EUR317 individuals online; US$438 individuals online; EUR364 individuals print and online; US$508 individuals print and online. **URL:** http://akkrt.hu/9/journals/products/agricultural_sciences/acta_alimentaria_eng.

44806 ■ Acta Antiqua Academiae Scientiarum Hungaricae
Akademiai Kiado Rt.
Prielle Kornelia u. 19/D
PO Box 245
H-1117 Budapest, Hungary
Ph: 36 146 48282
Fax: 36 146 48251
Publisher E-mail: info@akkrt.hu
Journal covering ancient studies including history, literature, philology and material culture of the ancient east and classical antiquity. **Founded:** 1951. **Freq:** 4/yr. **Print Method:** Offset. **Trim Size:** 17 x 25 cm. **Cols./Page:** 6. **Col. Width:** 26 nonpareils. **Col. Depth:** 301 agate lines. **Key Personnel:** Edit Krahling, Managing Editor; Prof. Miklos Maroth, Editor-in-Chief. **ISSN:** 0044-5975. **Subscription Rates:** EUR257 individuals online; US$354 individuals online, valid only in North America (Canada, U.S.); EUR296 individuals print and online; US$412 individuals print and online. **URL:** http://akkrt.hu/10/journals/products/classical_studies/acta_antiqua_academiae_scientiarum_hungaricae_eng.

44807 ■ Acta Archaeologica Academiae Scientiarum Hungaricae
Akademiai Kiado Rt.
Prielle Kornelia u. 19/D
PO Box 245
H-1117 Budapest, Hungary
Ph: 36 146 48282
Fax: 36 146 48251
Publisher E-mail: info@akkrt.hu
Journal devoted to the results achieved by Hungarian archaeologists. **Founded:** 1951. **Freq:** Semiannual. **Print Method:** Offset. **Trim Size:** 21 x 29 cm. **Cols./Page:** 6. **Col. Width:** 26 nonpareils. **Col. Depth:** 301 agate lines. **Key Personnel:** Solti Judit, Editor, solti@archeo.mta.hu; Gabler Denes, Editor-in-Chief, gabler@archeo.mta.hu. **ISSN:** 0001-5210. **Subscription Rates:** EUR296 individuals online; US$411 individuals online; EUR340 individuals print and online; US$476 individuals print and online. **URL:** http://akkrt.hu/11/journals/products/archaeology/acta_archaeologica_academiae_scientiarum_hungaricae_eng.

44808 ■ Acta Biologica Hungarica
Akademiai Kiado Rt.
Prielle Kornelia u. 19/D
PO Box 245
H-1117 Budapest, Hungary
Ph: 36 146 48282
Fax: 36 146 48251
Publisher E-mail: info@akkrt.hu
Journal covering experimental biology. Also covers cytology, morphology, embryology, genetics, endocrinology, radiation biology, cellular level of biological regulation, ethnology and environmental biology with emphasis on toxicology. **Founded:** 1950. **Freq:** 4/yr. **Print Method:** Offset. **Cols./Page:** 6. **Col. Width:** 2 1/16 inches. **Col. Depth:** 21 1/2 inches. **Key Personnel:** Karoly Elekes, Editor, elekes@tres.blki.hu. **ISSN:** 0236-5383. **Subscription Rates:** EUR372 individuals online; US$512 individuals online; EUR428 individuals print and online; US$596 individuals print and online. **URL:** http://akkrt.hu/12/journals/products/biology/acta_biologica_hungarica_eng.

44809 ■ Acta Geodaetica et Geophysica Hungarica
Akademiai Kiado Rt.
Prielle Kornelia u. 19/D
PO Box 245
H-1117 Budapest, Hungary
Ph: 36 146 48282
Fax: 36 146 48251
Publisher E-mail: info@akkrt.hu
Journal covering the fields of geodesy and geophysics including aeronomy and space physics, geomathematics, seismology, solid earth physics and history. **Founded:** 1966. **Freq:** 4/yr. **Print Method:** Offset. **Trim Size:** 14 x 22 1/2. **Cols./Page:** 6. **Col. Width:** 2 1/16 inches. **Col. Depth:** 21 1/2 inches. **Key Personnel:** Jozsef Zavoti, Editor-in-Chief, zavoti@ggki.hu; Viktor Wesztergom, Editor, wv@ggki.hu. **ISSN:** 1217-8977. **Subscription Rates:** EUR358 individuals online; US$498 U.S. and Canada online; EUR412 individuals print and online; US$580 individuals print and online. **URL:** http://akkrt.hu/16/journals/products/earth_sciences/acta_geodaetica_et_geophysica_hungarica_eng.

44810 ■ Acta Geologica Hungarica
Akademiai Kiado Rt.
Prielle Kornelia u. 19/D
PO Box 245
H-1117 Budapest, Hungary
Ph: 36 146 48282
Fax: 36 146 48251
Publisher E-mail: info@akkrt.hu
Journal covering geological topics. **Founded:** Oct. 1, 1880. **Freq:** 4/yr. **Print Method:** Offset. **Trim Size:** 13 x 21 1/2. **Cols./Page:** 6. **Col. Width:** 2 1/16 inches. **Col. Depth:** 21 1/2 inches. **Key Personnel:** Agnes Krivan-Horvath, Editor, krivan@iris.geobio.elte.hu; Gabor Schmiedl, Editor, schmiedl@iris.geobio.elte.hu; Janos Haas, Editor-in-Chief, haas@ludens.elte.hu. **ISSN:** 1788-2281. **Subscription Rates:** EUR240 individuals; US$300 other countries valid only in North America (Canada, U.S.). **URL:** http://www.akkrt.hu/main.php?folderID=1589&articleID=3895&ctag=articlelist&iid=1.

44811 ■ Acta Historiae Artium
Akademiai Kiado Rt.
Prielle Kornelia u. 10/D
PO Box 245
H-1117 Budapest, Hungary
Ph: 36 146 48282
Fax: 36 146 48251
Publisher E-mail: info@akkrt.hu
Journal covering the history of art. **Founded:** 1953. **Freq:** Annual. **Print Method:** Offset. **Trim Size:** 21 x 29 cm. **Cols./Page:** 6. **Col. Width:** 25 nonpareils. **Col. Depth:** 301 agate lines. **Key Personnel:** Erno Marosi, Editor-in-Chief. **ISSN:** 0001-5830. **Subscription Rates:** EUR279 individuals; US$389 individuals. **URL:** http://akkrt.hu/17/journals/products/art_history/acta_historiae_artium_eng.

44812 ■ Acta Juridica Hungarica
Akademiai Kiado Rt.
Prielle Kornelia u. 19/D
PO Box 245
H-1117 Budapest, Hungary
Ph: 36 146 48282
Fax: 36 146 48251
Publisher E-mail: info@akkrt.hu
Journal covering the impact of communist and democratic socio-legal experiences, globalization, international criminal law, and tort liability. **Subtitle:** Hungarian Journal of Legal Studies. **Freq:** 4/yr. **Trim Size:** 17 x 25 cm. **Key Personnel:** Vanda Lamm, Editor-in-Chief, lamm@jog.mta.hu. **ISSN:** 1216-2574. **Subscription Rates:** EUR264 individuals online; US$365 U.S. and Canada online; EUR304 individuals print and online; US$424 individuals print and online. **URL:** http://akkrt.hu/18/journals/products/law/acta_juridica_hungarica_eng.

44813 ■ Acta Linguistica Hungarica
Akademiai Kiado Rt.
Benczur utca 33
H-1068 Budapest, Hungary
Ph: 36 1 3510413
Fax: 36 1 3229297
Publisher E-mail: info@akkrt.hu
Journal covering theoretical issues concerning Hungarian and other Finno-Ugric languages. **Freq:** 4/yr. **Trim Size:** 17 x 25 cm. **Key Personnel:** Ferenc Kiefer, Edi-

Circulation: ★ = ABC; △ = BPA; ♦ = CAC; • = CCAB; ❏ = VAC; ⊕ = PO Statement; ‡ = Publisher's Report; Boldface figures = sworn; Light figures = estimated.

Gale Directory of Publications & Broadcast Media/147th Ed.

4977

tor, kiefer@nytud.hu; Peter Siptar, Assoc. Ed.; Katalin E. Kiss, Editor. **ISSN:** 1216-8076. **Subscription Rates:** EUR292 individuals online only; US$402 U.S. and Canada online; EUR336 individuals print + online; US$468 individuals print + online. **URL:** http://akkrt.hu/19/journals/products/linguistics/acta_linguistica_hungarica_eng.

44814 ■ Acta Microbiologica et Immunologica Hungarica
Akademiai Kiado Rt.
PO Box 370
H-1445 Budapest, Hungary
Ph: 36 1 2102930
Fax: 36 1 2102959
Publication E-mail: actamih@net.sote.hu
Publisher E-mail: info@akkrt.hu
Journal covering medical and veterinary bacteriology, virology, parasitology, immunology, epidemiology, agricultural and industrial microbiology, molecular biology, and biotechnology. **Founded:** 1954. **Freq:** 4/yr. **Print Method:** Letterpress and offset. **Trim Size:** 8 1/2 x 11. **Cols./Page:** 3. **Col. Width:** 30 nonpareils. **Col. Depth:** 126 agate lines. **Key Personnel:** Zsuzsanna Banos, Editor; Karoly Nagy, Editor-in-Chief. **ISSN:** 1217-8950. **Subscription Rates:** EUR327 individuals online; US$453 individuals online; EUR376 individuals print and online; US$528 individuals print and online. **URL:** http://akkrt.hu/21/journals/products/medicine/acta_microbiologica_et_immunologica_hungarica_eng.

44815 ■ Acta Oeconomica
Akademiai Kiado Rt.
Prielle Kornelia u. 19/D
PO Box 245
H-1117 Budapest, Hungary
Ph: 36 146 48282
Fax: 36 146 48251
Publisher E-mail: info@akkrt.hu
Journal covering Eastern European and Hungarian economics. Also covers international economics, European integration, labor economics, industrial organization, finance, and business economics. **Subtitle:** Periodical of the Hungarian Academy of Sciences. **Founded:** 1966. **Freq:** 4/yr. **Print Method:** Offset. **Trim Size:** 17 x 25 cm. **Cols./Page:** 4. **Col. Width:** 2 1/4 inches. **Col. Depth:** 15 inches. **Key Personnel:** Adam Torok, Editor-in-Chief, torokadam@yahoo.com; Judit Vanyai, Editor, vanyai@econ.core.hu. **ISSN:** 0001-6373. **Subscription Rates:** EUR292 individuals online; US$402 individuals online; EUR336 individuals print and online; US$468 individuals print and online. **URL:** http://akkrt.hu/22/journals/products/economics/acta_oeconomica_eng.

44816 ■ Acta Orientalia Academiae Scientiarum Hungaricae
Akademiai Kiado Rt.
Prielle Kornelia u. 19/D
PO Box 245
H-1117 Budapest, Hungary
Ph: 36 146 48282
Fax: 36 146 48251
Publisher E-mail: info@akkrt.hu
Journal covering oriental studies, including Turkish, Mongolian, Manchurian, Chinese, Tibetan, Indian, Iranian and Semitic philology, literature, and history. **Founded:** Mar. 23, 1950. **Freq:** 4/yr. **Print Method:** Offset. **Trim Size:** 17 x 25 cm. **Cols./Page:** 6. **Col. Width:** 12 picas. **Col. Depth:** 21 inches. **Key Personnel:** Istvan Vasary, Editor-in-Chief, vasaryi@gmail.com. **ISSN:** 0001-6446. **Subscription Rates:** EUR282 individuals online; US$386 individuals online; EUR324 individuals print and online; US$456 individuals print and online. **URL:** http://akkrt.hu/23/journals/products/oriental_studies/acta_orientalia_academiae_scientiarum_hungaricae_eng.

44817 ■ Acta Physiologica Hungarica
Akademiai Kiado Rt.
c/o Dr. Jeno Bartha, Mng. Ed.
Institute of Human Physiology, Semmelweis University
Ulloi UT 78/A
Tuzolto u. 37-47
H-1094 Budapest, Hungary
Fax: 36 1 2667480
Publisher E-mail: info@akkrt.hu
Journal covering physiological and pathophysiological science and medicine. **Founded:** 1887. **Freq:** 4/yr. **Print Method:** Offset. **Trim Size:** B5. **Cols./Page:** 6. **Col. Width:** 12 inches. **Col. Depth:** 21 inches. **Key Personnel:** Emil Monos, Editor-in-Chief, monos@elet2.sote.hu; Akos Koller, Co-Ed., koller.akos@net.sote.hu; Laszlo

Lenard, Co-Ed., laszlo.lenard@aok.pte.hu. **ISSN:** 0231-424X. **Subscription Rates:** EUR296 individuals online; US$408 individuals online, valid only in North America (Canada, U.S.); EUR340 individuals print and online; US$476 individuals print and online. **URL:** http://akkrt.hu/24/journals/products/medicine/acta_physiologica_hungarica_eng.

44818 ■ Acta Phytopathologica et Entomologica Hungarica
Akademiai Kiado Rt.
PO Box 102
H-1525 Budapest, Hungary
Ph: 36 1 4877533
Fax: 36 1 4877555
Publication E-mail: acta@nki.hu
Publisher E-mail: info@akkrt.hu
Journal covering infectious diseases of plants, damages caused by insects, and basic aspects of chemical and biological protection. Also covers topics on resistance against plant diseases and physiological, biochemical and molecular questions of plant resistance and susceptibility. **Founded:** 1966. **Freq:** one volume of four issues. **Print Method:** Offset. **Trim Size:** 11.625 x 21.25. **Cols./Page:** 6. **Key Personnel:** Zoltan Kiraly, Editor-in-Chief, zkir@nki.hu. **ISSN:** 0238-1249. **Subscription Rates:** EUR285 individuals online; US$396 individuals online; EUR328 individuals print and online; US$458 individuals print and online. **URL:** http://akkrt.hu/25/journals/products/biology/acta_phytopathologica_et_entomologica_hungarica_eng.

44819 ■ Acta Veterinaria Hungarica
Akademiai Kiado Rt.
c/o Janos Meszaros, Ed.-in-Ch.
Veterinary Medical Research Institute
Hungarian Academy of Sciences
PO Box 18
H-1581 Budapest, Hungary
Ph: 36 1 4674078
Fax: 36 1 2521069
Publisher E-mail: info@akkrt.hu
Journal covering animal physiology, biochemistry, morphology, nutrition and reproduction, veterinary microbiology, immunology, parasitology, pharmacology, clinical veterinary medicine, pathogenesis, diagnosis and control of infectious, parasitic and metabolic diseases of animals. **Founded:** 1951. **Freq:** 4/yr. **Print Method:** Offset. **Trim Size:** 14 x 22 3/4. **Cols./Page:** 6. **Col. Width:** 12 picas. **Col. Depth:** 21 1/2 inches. **Key Personnel:** Janos Meszaros, Editor-in-Chief, meszaros@vmri.hu; Tibor Gaal, Editorial Advisory Board; Andras Szekely, Managing Editor, szekely.a@mail.datanet.hu. **ISSN:** 0236-6290. **Subscription Rates:** EUR306 individuals online; US$424 other countries online, valid only in North America (Canada, U.S.); EUR352 individuals print and online; US$496 individuals print and online. **URL:** http://akkrt.hu/6/journals/products/veterinary/acta_veterinaria_hungarica_eng.

44820 ■ Acta Zoologica Academiae Scientiarum Hungaricae
Hungarian Natural History Museum and Hungarian Academy of Sciences
Ludovika ter 2-6
H-1083 Budapest, Hungary
Ph: 36 1 2101085
Fax: 36 1 2101075
Journal covering the fields of animal taxonomy and systematic, zoogeography, animal ecology, population biology, biodiversity studies and nature conservation problems. **Founded:** Feb. 1, 1994. **Freq:** Quarterly other issues in May, August and November. **Print Method:** Offset. Uses mats. **Cols./Page:** 6. **Col. Width:** 10 picas. **Col. Depth:** 16 inches. **Key Personnel:** Gabor Bakonyi, Editor-in-Chief; S. Mahunka, Editor; L. Papp, Editorial Adviser; J. Voros, Managing Editor; C. Csuzdi, Managing Editor. **USPS:** 618-380. **Subscription Rates:** US$90 individuals. **URL:** http://actazool.nhmus.hu/.

44821 ■ Agrokemia es Talajtan
Akademiai Kiado Rt.
Prielle Kornelia u. 19/D
PO Box 245
H-1117 Budapest, Hungary
Ph: 36 146 48282
Fax: 36 146 48251
Publisher E-mail: info@akkrt.hu
Journal covering agronomy and soil science including plant nutrition, fertilizers, manure, soil tillage, soil biotechnology and ecophysiology, irrigation and drainage, landscape formation and environmental management in

rural regions. **Subtitle:** Agrochemistry and Soil Science. **Founded:** 1968. **Freq:** 4/yr. **Print Method:** Offset. Accepts mats. **Trim Size:** 17 x 24 cm. **Cols./Page:** 6. **Col. Width:** 25 nonpareils. **Col. Depth:** 301 agate lines. **Key Personnel:** Gyorgy Varallyay, Editor-in-Chief; Attila Anton, Editorial Board; Istvan Buzas, Editorial Board. **ISSN:** 0002-1873. **Subscription Rates:** EUR83 individuals online; US$114 individuals online, valid only in North America (Canada, U.S.); EUR98 individuals print and online; US$134 individuals print and online. **URL:** http://akkrt.hu/26/journals/products/agricultural_sciences/agrokemia_es_talajtan_agrochemistry_and_soil_science_eng.

44822 ■ Antik Tanulmanyok
Akademiai Kiado Rt.
Prielle Kornelia u. 19/D
PO Box 245
H-1117 Budapest, Hungary
Ph: 36 146 48282
Fax: 36 146 48251
Publisher E-mail: info@akkrt.hu
Journal covering studies on literature, language, history, and material culture of Ancient Greece and Rome. **Freq:** 2/yr. **Trim Size:** 17 x 25 cm. **Key Personnel:** Tibor Szepessy, Editor-in-Chief; Laszlo Horvath, Editor. **ISSN:** 0003-567X. **Subscription Rates:** EUR56 individuals online only; US$78 U.S. and Canada online only; EUR66 individuals print + online; US$90 individuals print + online. **URL:** http://akkrt.hu/29/journals/products/classical_studies/antik_tanulmanyok_studies_on_antiquity_eng.

44823 ■ Archaeologiai Ertesito
Akademiai Kiado Rt.
Hungarian National Museum
PO Box 364
H-1370 Budapest, Hungary
Ph: 36 1 3382122
Publisher E-mail: info@akkrt.hu
Journal covering field of archaeology. **Founded:** 1868. **Freq:** 2/yr. **Trim Size:** 20 x 29 cm. **Key Personnel:** Tibor Kovacs, Editor-in-Chief, kovacs.tibor@hnm.hu; Eva Garam, Assoc. Ed. **ISSN:** 0003-8032. **Subscription Rates:** EUR74 individuals online only; US$104 U.S. and Canada online only; US$87 individuals print + online; US$122 individuals print + online. **URL:** http://akkrt.hu/30/journals/products/archaeology/archaeologiai_ertesito_archaeological_bulletin_eng.

44824 ■ Atrium
Sanoma Budapest Kiadoi Rt.
Montevideo utca 9
H-1037 Budapest, Hungary
Ph: 36 1 4371100
Fax: 36 1 4372303
Publisher E-mail: eszter.kovacs@sanomabp.hu
Magazine featuring architectural design. **Freq:** Bimonthly. **Print Method:** Offset. **Trim Size:** 220 x 300 mm. **Key Personnel:** Csato Edina, Coord., phone 36 1 4373906, fax 36 1 4371180, e.csato@sanomabp.hu. **Subscription Rates:** 780 Ft individuals. **Remarks:** Accepts advertising. **URL:** http://www.sanomabp.hu/sajtohirdetes/index.php?action=termek&site=33. **Circ:** 15,000

44825 ■ Baratok Kozt Magazin
Sanoma Budapest Kiadoi Rt.
Montevideo utca 9
H-1037 Budapest, Hungary
Ph: 36 1 4371100
Fax: 36 1 4372303
Publication E-mail: bkmagazin@sanomabp.hu
Publisher E-mail: eszter.kovacs@sanomabp.hu
Magazine featuring information about celebrities, behind-the-scenes stories, and issues in connection with the popular TV series. **Freq:** Quarterly. **Print Method:** Offset. **Trim Size:** 210 x 285 mm. **Key Personnel:** Csato Edina, Coord. **Subscription Rates:** 215 Ft individuals. **Remarks:** Accepts advertising. **URL:** http://www.sanomabp.hu/sajtohirdetes/index.php?action=termek&site=21. **Circ:** 60,000

44826 ■ Central European Political Science Review
Magyar Tudomanyos Akademia, Szazadveg Politikai Iskola
Benczur 33
H-1068 Budapest, Hungary
Publisher E-mail: szaboi@mtapti.hu
Publication containing up-to-date information on the place and role that the Central European region has in an integrated Europe, in the field of politics, economics,

culture and structure. **Founded:** 2000. **Freq:** Quarterly. **Key Personnel:** Janos Simon, Editor, cepsr@mtapti.hu; Samuel Barnes, International Advisory Committee; Zora Butorova, International Advisory Committee. **URL:** http://www.ucm.es/info/cpuno/aecpa/asoc/avisos/117.htm.

44827 ■ Community Ecology
Akademiai Kiado Rt.
Prielle Kornelia u. 19/D
PO Box 245
H-1117 Budapest, Hungary
Ph: 36 146 48282
Fax: 36 146 48251
Publisher E-mail: info@akkrt.hu
Journal creating a common global forum for community ecologists. **Subtitle:** An Interdisciplinary Journal Reporting Progress in Community and Population Studies. **Founded:** 2000. **Freq:** Semiannual. **Trim Size:** 20 x 27 1/2 cm. **Key Personnel:** Janos Podani, Editor-in-Chief, podani@ludens.elte.hu; Laszlo Orloci, Hon. Ed.-in-Ch. **ISSN:** 1585-8553. **Subscription Rates:** US$294 individuals online; EUR210 individuals online; EUR242 individuals print and online; US$340 individuals print and online. **URL:** http://akkrt.hu/33/journals/products/biology/community_ecology_eng.

44828 ■ Epites - Epiteszettudomany
Akademiai Kiado Rt.
Department of History of Architecture & of Monuments
Budapest University of Technology & Economics
Muegyetem rkp. 3, Bldg. K II. 60
H-1521 Budapest, Hungary
Ph: 36 1 4631330
Fax: 36 1 4631638
Publisher E-mail: info@akkrt.hu
Journal covering the fields of architectonics and architecture. **Freq:** 4/yr. **Trim Size:** 17 x 24 cm. **Key Personnel:** Janos Szabo, Editor-in-Chief, szabo@ep-mech.me.bme.hu; Ferenc Vamossy, Editor. **ISSN:** 0013-9661. **Subscription Rates:** EUR77 individuals online only; US$102 U.S. and Canada online only; EUR90 individuals print + online; US$126 U.S. and Canada print + online. **URL:** http://akkrt.hu/34/journals/products/engineering_sciences/epites_epiteszettudomany_architectonics_and_architecture_eng.

44829 ■ Fakanal
Sanoma Budapest Kiadoi Rt.
Montevideo utca 9
H-1037 Budapest, Hungary
Ph: 36 1 4371100
Fax: 36 1 4372303
Publisher E-mail: eszter.kovacs@sanomabp.hu
Magazine covering gastronomy. **Freq:** 10/yr. **Print Method:** Offset. **Trim Size:** 175 x 255 mm. **Key Personnel:** Kantor Anita, Coord. **Subscription Rates:** 229 Ft individuals. **Remarks:** Accepts advertising. **URL:** http://www.nlcafe.hu/gasztro/. **Circ:** Paid ‡25,162

44830 ■ Fakanal Recepttar
Sanoma Budapest Kiadoi Rt.
Montevideo utca 9
H-1037 Budapest, Hungary
Ph: 36 1 4371100
Fax: 36 1 4372303
Publisher E-mail: eszter.kovacs@sanomabp.hu
Magazine featuring recipes. **Freq:** Semiannual. **Print Method:** Offset. **Trim Size:** 148 x 210 mm. **Key Personnel:** Krisztina Wilhelm, Coord., phone 36 1 4373912, fax 36 1 4371180, a.kantor@sanomabp.hu. **Subscription Rates:** 440 Ft individuals. **Remarks:** Accepts advertising. **URL:** http://www.sanomacentrum.hu/; http://receptek.wyw.hu/detail.php?id=49. **Circ:** 26,425

44831 ■ Figyelo
Sanoma Budapest Kiadoi Rt.
Montevideo utca 9
H-1037 Budapest, Hungary
Ph: 36 1 4371100
Fax: 36 1 4372303
Publication E-mail: fn@sanomabp.hu
Publisher E-mail: eszter.kovacs@sanomabp.hu
Magazine featuring news, analyses, forecasts, and background information about the economy. **Freq:** Weekly (Thurs.). **Print Method:** Offset. **Trim Size:** 200 x 267 mm. **Key Personnel:** Ms. Wilhelm Krisztina, Coord., phone 36 1 4373905, fax 36 1 4371180. **Remarks:** Accepts advertising. **URL:** 437-1180. **Circ:** Paid 11,522

44832 ■ Figyelo TOP 200
Sanoma Budapest Kiadoi Rt.
Montevideo utca 9
H-1037 Budapest, Hungary
Ph: 36 1 4371100
Fax: 36 1 4372303
Publisher E-mail: eszter.kovacs@sanomabp.hu
Magazine featuring information about the biggest companies in Hungary. **Freq:** Annual. **Print Method:** Offset. **Trim Size:** 205 x 285 mm. **Key Personnel:** Ms. Wilhelm Krisztina, Coord., phone 36 1 4373905, fax 36 1 4371180. **Remarks:** Accepts advertising. **URL:** http://www.sanomabp.hu/sajtohirdetes/index.php?action=termek&site=29. **Circ:** Paid 10,000

44833 ■ Figyelo Trend
Sanoma Budapest Kiadoi Rt.
Montevideo utca 9
H-1037 Budapest, Hungary
Ph: 36 1 4371100
Fax: 36 1 4372303
Publisher E-mail: eszter.kovacs@sanomabp.hu
Magazine featuring in-depth analysis of a given economic sector or area. **Freq:** Quarterly. **Print Method:** Offset. **Trim Size:** 200 x 267 mm. **Key Personnel:** Ms. Wilhelm Krisztina, Coord., phone 36 1 4373905, fax 36 1 4371180, k.wilhelm@sanomabp.hu. **Remarks:** Accepts advertising. **URL:** http://www.sanomabp.hu/sajtohirdetes/index.php?action=termek&site=30. **Circ:** ‡15,000

44834 ■ Fules
Sanoma Budapest Kiadoi Rt.
Montevideo utca 9
H-1037 Budapest, Hungary
Ph: 36 1 4371100
Fax: 36 1 4372303
Publication E-mail: fules@sanomabp.hu
Publisher E-mail: eszter.kovacs@sanomabp.hu
Puzzle magazine featuring games, entertainment, and quizzes. **Freq:** Weekly (Tues.). **Print Method:** Offset. **Trim Size:** 165 x 236 mm. **Key Personnel:** Ms. Rakosi Gabriella, Coord., phone 36 1 4373635, fax 36 1 4371180, g.rakosi@sanomabp.hu. **Remarks:** Accepts advertising. **URL:** http://www.sanomabp.hu/sajtohirdetes/index.php?action=termek&site=6. **Circ:** Paid ‡68,605

44835 ■ Hungarian Medical Journal
Akademiai Kiado Rt.
Prielle Kornelia u. 19/D
PO Box 245
H-1117 Budapest, Hungary
Ph: 36 146 48282
Fax: 36 146 48251
Publisher E-mail: info@akkrt.hu
Journal covering fields of experimental and clinical medicine. **Founded:** 2006. **Freq:** 4/yr. **Key Personnel:** Mihaly Szegedy-Maszak, Editor-in-Chief; Thomas Cooper, Editor. **ISSN:** 1788-6139. **Subscription Rates:** EUR220 individuals print & online; US$308 U.S. and Canada print & online. **URL:** http://akkrt.hu/35/journals/products/linguistics/hungarian_studies_ong.

44836 ■ The Hungarian Quarterly
8 Naphegy Ter.
H-1016 Budapest, Hungary
Ph: 36 148 80024
Fax: 36 148 80023
Publisher E-mail: quarterly@mail.datanet.hu
English language journal covering arts and society worldwide. **Freq:** Quarterly. **Key Personnel:** Kati Konczol, Editorial Sec.; Rudolf Fischer, Language Ed.; Peter Doherty, Language Ed.; Miklos Vajda, Ed. Emeritus; Zsofia Zachar, Editor. **ISSN:** 0028-5390. **Subscription Rates:** US$70 individuals; US$125 two years; US$100 institutions; US$184 institutions 2 years; EUR50 individuals; EUR90 two years; EUR75 institutions; EUR130 institutions 2 years. **Remarks:** Accepts advertising. **URL:** http://www.hungarianquarterly.com. **Ad Rates:** BW: US$300, 4C: US$400. **Circ:** (Not Reported)

44837 ■ Hungarian Studies
Akademiai Kiado Rt.
Prielle Kornelia u. 19/D
PO Box 245
H-1117 Budapest, Hungary
Ph: 36 146 48282
Fax: 36 146 48251

Publisher E-mail: info@akkrt.hu
Journal covering interdisciplinary research dealing with the Hungarian people. Topics include history, language and literature, fiction, cultural history, ethnological research and geography. **Founded:** Jan. 1985. **Freq:** Semiannual. **Print Method:** Offset. **Trim Size:** 17 x 25 cm. **Cols./Page:** 3. **Col. Width:** 27 nonpareils. **Col. Depth:** 133 agate lines. **Key Personnel:** Andrea Seidler, Editor; Thomas Cooper, Editor; Mihaly Szegedy-Maszak, Editor-in-Chief; Jozsef Jankovics, Editor. **ISSN:** 0236-6568. **Subscription Rates:** EUR191 individuals online; US$265 individuals online; EUR220 individuals print and online; US$308 individuals print and online. **URL:** http://akkrt.hu/35/journals/products/linguistics/hungarian_studies_eng.

44838 ■ International Sports Magazine
International Sport Press Association
Association Internationale de la Presse Sportive
AIPS Headquarters
H-1054 Budapest, Hungary
Ph: 36 1 3112689
Fax: 36 1 3533807
Publisher E-mail: aips@mail.matav.hu
Magazine covering worldwide sports in English, French and Spanish. **Freq:** Annual. **Remarks:** Advertising accepted; rates available upon request. **URL:** http://www.vol.net.mt/org/aips_mediasport/brief.htm. **Circ:** 9,000

44839 ■ IWF Handbook
International Weightlifting Federation
Istvanmezei ut 1-3
H-1146 Budapest, Hungary
Ph: 36 135 30530
Fax: 36 135 30199
Trade publication covering weightlifting in Arabic, English, French and Spanish. **Freq:** Quadrennial. **Subscription Rates:** US$15 individuals includes postage, in Europe; US$18 individuals includes postage, outside Europe. **Remarks:** Advertising not accepted. **URL:** http://www.iwf.net/. **Formerly:** Constitution and Technical Rules. **Circ:** (Not Reported)

44840 ■ Journal Applied Ecology and Environmental Research
Corvinus University of Budapest
Fovam ter 8
H 1093 Budapest, Hungary
Fax: 36 1 4825000
Publication E-mail: aeer@uni-corvinus.hu
Publisher E-mail: intoffice@uni-corvinus.hu
Journal containing papers and case studies on applied ecology and environmental research. **Key Personnel:** Levente Hufnagel, PhD, Editor-in-Chief. **ISSN:** 1589-1623. **URL:** http://www.ecology.kee.hu/.

44841 ■ Journal of Evolutionary Psychology
Akademiai Kiado Rt.
Prielle Kornelia u. 19/D
PO Box 245
H-1117 Budapest, Hungary
Ph: 36 146 48282
Fax: 36 146 48251
Publisher E-mail: info@akkrt.hu
Journal publishing theoretical and empirical studies from the intersection of two rapidly developing research fields, cultural psychology and evolutionary psychology. **Founded:** 2002. **Freq:** Quarterly. **Trim Size:** 17 x 25 cm. **Key Personnel:** Tom Dickins, Editor-in-Chief, jep@uel.ac.uk; Bereczkei Tamas, Editor, btamas@btk.pte.hu; Daniel Nettle, Editor, daniel.nettle@ncl.ac.uk; David Lawson, Book Review Ed., d.lawson@ucl.ac.uk. **ISSN:** 1589-5254. **Subscription Rates:** US$246 individuals online; EUR177 individuals online; EUR204 individuals print and online; US$288 individuals print and online. **URL:** http://akkrt.hu/41/journals/products/psychology/journal_of_evolutionary _psychology_eng. **Formerly:** Journal of Cultural and Evolutionary Psychology.

44842 ■ Journal of Planar Chromatography
Akademiai Kiado Rt.
Prielle Kornelia u. 19/D
PO Box 245
H-1117 Budapest, Hungary
Ph: 36 146 48282
Fax: 36 146 48251
Publisher E-mail: info@akkrt.hu
Journal covering all fields of planar chromatography. **Freq:** 6/yr. **Key Personnel:** B. Spangenberg, Editor-in-Chief. **ISSN:** 0933-4173. **Subscription Rates:** EUR376 individuals online only; US$516 U.S. and Canada online

only; EUR432 individuals print + online; US$600 U.S. and Canada print + online. **URL:** http://akkrt.hu/38/ journals/products/chemistry/jpc_journal_of_planar _chromatography_modern_tlc.

44843 ■ Kismama
Sanoma Budapest Kiadoi Rt.
Montevideo utca 9
H-1037 Budapest, Hungary
Ph: 36 1 4371100
Fax: 36 1 4372303
Publication E-mail: kismama@sanomabp.hu
Publisher E-mail: eszter.kovacs@sanomabp.hu
Magazine covering parenthood. **Freq:** Monthly. **Print Method:** Offset. **Trim Size:** 213 x 280 mm. **Key Personnel:** Wilhelm Krisztina, Coord., phone 36 1 4373905, fax 36 1 4371180. **Remarks:** Accepts advertising. **URL:** http://www.sanomabp.hu/sajtohirdetes/index.php? action=termek&site=31. **Circ:** Paid 19,535

44844 ■ Kismama Mintaszam
Sanoma Budapest Kiadoi Rt.
Montevideo utca 9
H-1037 Budapest, Hungary
Ph: 36 1 4371100
Fax: 36 1 4372303
Publisher E-mail: eszter.kovacs@sanomabp.hu
Magazine featuring child parenting. **Freq:** Annual. **Print Method:** Offset. **Trim Size:** 213 x 280 mm. **Key Personnel:** Csato Edina, Coord., phone 36 1 4373906, fax 36 1 4371180, e.csato@sanomabp.hu. **Subscription Rates:** Free. **Remarks:** Accepts advertising. **URL:** http://www.sanomabp.hu/sajtohirdetes/index.php?action= termek&site=23. **Circ:** Free 130,000

44845 ■ Kismama 9 Honap
Sanoma Budapest Kiadoi Rt.
Montevideo utca 9
H-1037 Budapest, Hungary
Ph: 36 1 4371100
Fax: 36 1 4372303
Publisher E-mail: eszter.kovacs@sanomabp.hu
Magazine featuring series of topics like pregnancy, birth, and taking care of the babies. **Freq:** Annual. **Trim Size:** 200 x 265 mm. **Key Personnel:** Ms. Wilhelm Krisztina, Coord., k.wilhelm@sanomabp.hu. **Remarks:** Accepts advertising. **URL:** http://www.sanomabp.hu/ sajtohirdetes/index.php?action=termek&site=9. **Circ:** Paid 30,970

44846 ■ Magyar Pszichologiai Szemle
Akademiai Kiado Rt.
Center for Cognitive Science
Budapest University of Tecnology & Economics
Muegyetem rkp. 9.
H-1111 Budapest, Hungary
Ph: 36 1 4631072
Publisher E-mail: info@akkrt.hu
Journal covering research findings of Hungarian psychologists. **Subtitle:** Hungarian Psychological Review. **Founded:** 1974. **Freq:** Annual. **Print Method:** Offset. **Trim Size:** 17 x 25 cm. **Key Personnel:** Csaba Pleh, Editor-in-Chief, pleh@cogsci.bme.hu. **ISSN:** 0025-0279. **Subscription Rates:** EUR88 individuals online; US$120 individuals online, valid only in North America (Canada, U.S.); EUR104 individuals print and online; US$140 individuals print and online. **URL:** http://akkrt. hu/45/journals/products/psychology/magyar_ pszichologiai_szemle_hungarian_psychological_review.

44847 ■ Magyar Sebeszet
Akademiai Kiado Rt.
Prielle Kornelia u. 19/D
PO Box 245
H-1117 Budapest, Hungary
Ph: 36 146 48282
Fax: 36 146 48251
Publisher E-mail: info@akkrt.hu
Journal covering Hungarian surgical contributions. **Subtitle:** Journal of the Hungarian Surgical Society. **Founded:** 1947. **Freq:** Bimonthly. **Key Personnel:** Attila Olah, Editor-in-Chief. **ISSN:** 0025-0295. **Subscription Rates:** EUR168 individuals online only; US$270 U.S. and Canada online only; EUR198 individuals print + online; US$270 U.S. and Canada print + online. **URL:** http://akkrt.hu/46/journals/products/medicine/magyar_ sebeszet_hungarian_journal_of_surgery.

44848 ■ Market!ng&Media
Sanoma Budapest Kiadoi Rt.
Montevideo utca 9
H-1037 Budapest, Hungary
Ph: 36 1 4371100

Fax: 36 1 4372303
Publisher E-mail: eszter.kovacs@sanomabp.hu
Magazine covering marketing, media, and advertisements. **Freq:** Semimonthly. **Print Method:** Offset. **Trim Size:** 215 x 276 mm. **Key Personnel:** Ms. Bosanszki Piroska, Corrd., phone 36 1 4373905, fax 36 1 4371180, p.bosanszki@sanomabp.hu. **Remarks:** Accepts advertising. **URL:** http://www.sanomabp.hu/ sajtohirdetes/index.php?action=termek&site=19. **Circ:** Combined ‡1,520

44849 ■ Maxima Special
Sanoma Budapest Kiadoi Rt.
Montevideo utca 9
H-1037 Budapest, Hungary
Ph: 36 1 4371100
Fax: 36 1 4372303
Publication E-mail: maxima@sanomabp.hu
Publisher E-mail: eszter.kovacs@sanomabp.hu
Magazine featuring topics that is currently in the focus of young women's interest. **Freq:** Semiannual. **Print Method:** Offset. **Trim Size:** 190 x 250 mm. **Key Personnel:** Ms. Rakosi Gabriella, Coord., phone 36 1 4373635, fax 36 1 4371180. **Remarks:** Accepts advertising. **URL:** http://www.sanomabp.hu/sajtohirdetes/index.php? action=termek&site=14. **Circ:** Paid 44,183

44850 ■ Meglepetes
Sanoma Budapest Kiadoi Rt.
Montevideo utca 9
H-1037 Budapest, Hungary
Ph: 36 1 4371100
Fax: 36 1 4372303
Publication E-mail: meglepetes@sanomabp.hu
Publisher E-mail: eszter.kovacs@sanomabp.hu
Magazine featuring women's interests. **Freq:** Weekly (Thurs.). **Print Method:** Offset. **Trim Size:** 205 x 280 mm. **Key Personnel:** Ms. Selmeczi Andrea, Coord., phone 36 1 4373639, fax 36 1 4371180, a.selmeczi@ sanomabp.hu. **Remarks:** Accepts advertising. **URL:** http://www.sanomabp.hu/sajtohirdetes/index.php? action=termek&site=18. **Circ:** Paid 94,838

44851 ■ Meglepetes Raadas
Sanoma Budapest Kiadoi Rt.
Montevideo utca 9
H-1037 Budapest, Hungary
Ph: 36 1 4371100
Fax: 36 1 4372303
Publisher E-mail: eszter.kovacs@sanomabp.hu
Magazine covering gastronomy. **Freq:** Semiannual. **Print Method:** Offset. **Trim Size:** 205 x 280 mm. **Key Personnel:** Selmeczi Andrea, Coord., phone 36 1 4373639, fax 36 1 4371180, a.selmeczi@sanomabp.hu. **Remarks:** Accepts advertising. **URL:** http://www. sanomabp.hu/sajtohirdetes/index.php?action=termek& site=11. **Circ:** Paid 65,900

44852 ■ Mentalhigiene es Pszichoszomatika
Akademiai Kiado Rt.
c/o Dr. Barna Konkoly Thege, Ed.-in-Ch.
Institute of Behavioral Sciences
Semmelweis University
Nagyvarad ter 4
H-1089 Budapest, Hungary
Ph: 36 1 2102930
Fax: 36 1 2102955
Publisher E-mail: info@akkrt.hu
Journal covering theoretical and practical issues related to mental health promotion. **Freq:** 4/yr. **Trim Size:** 16.5 x 24 cm. **Key Personnel:** Maria Kopp, Editor-in-Chief, kopmar@net.sote.hu; Dr. Barna Konkoly Thege, Editor. **ISSN:** 1419-8126. **Subscription Rates:** EUR51 individuals online; US$68 U.S. and Canada online; EUR60 individuals print and online; US$80 U.S. and Canada print and online. **URL:** http://akkrt.hu/9/journals/.

44853 ■ Muveszettorteneti Ertesito
Akademiai Kiado Rt.
Prielle Kornelia u. 19/D
PO Box 245
H-1117 Budapest, Hungary
Ph: 36 146 48282
Fax: 36 146 48251
Publisher E-mail: info@akkrt.hu
Journal covering research on the world and Hungarian history of arts from the Middle Ages up to now. **Founded:** 1952. **Freq:** 2/yr. **Key Personnel:** Anna Javor, Editor-in-Chief, javor.anna@mng.hu; Arpad Miko, Editor. **ISSN:** 0027-5247. **Subscription Rates:** EUR84 individuals online; US$118 U.S. and Canada online. **URL:** http://akkrt.

hu/43/journals/products/art_history/muveszettorteneti_ ertesito_bulletin_of_history_of_arts.

44854 ■ Nanopages
Akademiai Kiado Rt.
Prielle Kornelia u. 19/D
PO Box 245
H-1117 Budapest, Hungary
Ph: 36 146 48282
Fax: 36 146 48251
Publisher E-mail: info@akkrt.hu
Journal devoted to research in nanotechnology. **Subtitle:** An Interdisciplinary Journal of Nano Science and Technology. **Founded:** 2005. **Freq:** Quarterly. **Print Method:** Offset. **Trim Size:** B5. **Cols./Page:** 6. **Col. Width:** 24 nonpareils. **Col. Depth:** 294 agate lines. **Key Personnel:** Zoltan Konya, Editor; Akos Kukovecz, Editor; Imre Kiricsi, Editor-in-Chief; Tibor Braun, Consulting Ed. **ISSN:** 1787-4033. **Subscription Rates:** EUR100 individuals; US$140 individuals valid only in North America (Canada, U.S.). **URL:** http://akkrt.hu/50/ journals/products/physics/nanopages_eng.

44855 ■ National Geographic Kids
Sanoma Budapest Kiadoi Rt.
Montevideo utca 9
H-1037 Budapest, Hungary
Ph: 36 1 4371100
Fax: 36 1 4372303
Publication E-mail: info@ngkids.hu
Publisher E-mail: eszter.kovacs@sanomabp.hu
Magazine featuring interesting things, inventions, and amazing stories from the world of animals. **Freq:** 10/yr. **Print Method:** Offset. **Key Personnel:** Ms. Selmeczi Andrea, Coord., phone 36 1 4373639, fax 36 1 4371180. **Remarks:** Accepts advertising. **URL:** http://www. sanomabp.hu/sajtohirdetes/index.php?action=termek& site=36. **Circ:** Paid ‡41,873

44856 ■ National Geographic Special
Sanoma Budapest Kiadoi Rt.
Montevideo utca 9
H-1037 Budapest, Hungary
Ph: 36 1 4371100
Fax: 36 1 4372303
Publication E-mail: ng@sanomabp.hu
Publisher E-mail: eszter.kovacs@sanomabp.hu
Magazine featuring interesting stories and photographs. **Freq:** 4/yr. **Print Method:** Offset. **Trim Size:** 229 x 276 mm. **Key Personnel:** Selmeczi Andrea, Coord., phone 36 1 4373639, fax 36 1 4371180, a.selmeczi@ sanomabp.hu. **Remarks:** Accepts advertising. **URL:** http://www.sanomabp.hu/sajtohirdetes/index.php? action=termek&site=46. **Circ:** ‡16,000

44857 ■ Nok Lapja
Sanoma Budapest Kiadoi Rt.
Montevideo utca 9
H-1037 Budapest, Hungary
Ph: 36 1 4371100
Fax: 36 1 4372303
Publisher E-mail: eszter.kovacs@sanomabp.hu
Magazine featuring women's interests. **Freq:** Weekly (Wed.). **Print Method:** Offset. **Trim Size:** 220 x 300 mm. **Key Personnel:** Mitrovics Aniko, Coord., phone 36 1 4373637, fax 36 1 4371180, a.mitrovics@sanomabp. hu. **Remarks:** Accepts advertising. **URL:** http://www. sanomabp.hu/sajtohirdetes/index.php?action=termek& site=3. **Circ:** Paid 253,749

44858 ■ Nok Lapja Egeszseg
Sanoma Budapest Kiadoi Rt.
Montevideo utca 9
H-1037 Budapest, Hungary
Ph: 36 1 4371100
Fax: 36 1 4372303
Publication E-mail: egeszseg@sanomabp.hu
Publisher E-mail: eszter.kovacs@sanomabp.hu
Magazine featuring health-related topics. **Founded:** Apr. 2007. **Freq:** Monthly. **Trim Size:** 205 x 275 mm. **Key Personnel:** Kantor Anita, Coord., phone 36 1 4373912, fax 36 1 4371180, a.kantor@sanomabp.hu. **Remarks:** Accepts advertising. **URL:** http://www.sanomabp.hu/ sajtohirdetes/index.php?action=termek&site=58. **Circ:** Paid 27,439

44859 ■ Nok Lapja Eskuvo
Sanoma Budapest Kiadoi Rt.
Montevideo utca 9
H-1037 Budapest, Hungary
Ph: 36 1 4371100

Fax: 36 1 4372303
Publisher E-mail: eszter.kovacs@sanomabp.hu
Magazine featuring wedding. **Freq:** Annual. **Print Method:** Offset. **Trim Size:** 215 x 280 mm. **Key Personnel:** Szabo Patricia, Contact. **Remarks:** Accepts advertising. **URL:** http://www.sanomabp.hu/nok_lapja_eskuvo/4953/?fid=392. **Circ:** ‡28,000

44860 ■ Nok Lapja Evszakok
Sanoma Budapest Kiadoi Rt.
Montevideo utca 9
H-1037 Budapest, Hungary
Ph: 36 1 4371100
Fax: 36 1 4372303
Publisher E-mail: eszter.kovacs@sanomabp.hu
Magazine featuring women's interests. **Freq:** 10/yr. **Print Method:** Offset. **Trim Size:** 210 x 270 mm. **Key Personnel:** Kantor Anita, Coord., phone 36 1 4373912, fax 36 1 4371180, a.kantor@sanomabp.hu. **Remarks:** Accepts advertising. **URL:** http://www.sanomabp.hu/sajtohirdetes/index.php?action=termek&site=37. **Circ:** Paid 22,300

44861 ■ Nok Lapja Konyha
Sanoma Budapest Kiadoi Rt.
Montevideo utca 9
H-1037 Budapest, Hungary
Ph: 36 1 4371100
Fax: 36 1 4372303
Publisher E-mail: eszter.kovacs@sanomabp.hu
Magazine covering gastronomy. **Freq:** 10/yr. **Trim Size:** 220 x 277 mm. **Key Personnel:** Csaki Szilvia, Coord., sz.csaki@sanomabp.hu. **Remarks:** Accepts advertising. **URL:** http://www.sanomabp.hu/sajtohirdetes/index.php?action=termek&site=10. **Circ:** Paid 37,893

44862 ■ Orvosi Hetilap
Akademiai Kiado Rt.
Prielle Kornelia u. 19/D
PO Box 245
H-1117 Budapest, Hungary
Ph: 36 146 48282
Fax: 36 146 48251
Publisher E-mail: info@akrt.hu
Journal covering fields of experimental and clinical medicine. **Subtitle:** Scientific Journal of the Lajos Markusovszky Foundation. **Founded:** 1857. **Freq:** Weekly. **Key Personnel:** Karoly Racz, Editor-in-Chief. **ISSN:** 0030-6002. **Subscription Rates:** EUR604 individuals online only; US$834 U.S. and Canada online only; EUR710 individuals print + online; US$982 U.S. and Canada print + online. **URL:** http://akkrt.hu/53/journals/products/medicine/orvosi_hetilap_hungarian_medical_journal.

44863 ■ Otthon
Sanoma Budapest Kiadoi Rt.
Montevideo utca 9
H-1037 Budapest, Hungary
Ph: 36 1 4371100
Fax: 36 1 4372303
Publication E-mail: otthon@sanomabp.hu
Publisher E-mail: eszter.kovacs@sanomabp.hu
Magazine covering lifestyle and interior design. **Freq:** Monthly. **Print Method:** Offset. **Trim Size:** 215 x 300 mm. **Key Personnel:** Ms. Selmeczi Andrea, Coord., phone 36 1 4373639, fax 36 1 4371180, a.selmeczi@sanomabp.hu. **Remarks:** Accepts advertising. **URL:** http://www.sanomabp.hu/sajtohirdetes/index.php?action=termek&site=38. **Circ:** Paid 41,066

44864 ■ Pollack Periodica
Akademiai Kiado Rt.
Prielle Kornelia u. 19/D
PO Box 245
H-1117 Budapest, Hungary
Ph: 36 146 48282
Fax: 36 146 48251
Publisher E-mail: info@akrt.hu
Journal covering aspects of systems and structures of engineering and information sciences. **Subtitle:** An International Journal for Engineering and Information Sciences. **Founded:** 2006. **Freq:** 3/yr. **Key Personnel:** Amalia Ivanyi, Editor-in-Chief, aivanyi@morpehus.pte.hu; Miklos Ivanyi, Editor-in-Chief. **ISSN:** 1788-1994. **Subscription Rates:** EUR198 individuals online only; US$273 U.S. and Canada online only; EUR228 individuals print + online; US$318 U.S. and Canada print + online. **URL:** http://akkrt.hu/55/journals/products/engineering_sciences/pollack_periodica_eng.

44865 ■ Praktika
Sanoma Budapest Kiadoi Rt.
Montevideo utca 9
H-1037 Budapest, Hungary
Ph: 36 1 4371100
Fax: 36 1 4372303
Publication E-mail: praktika@iqpress.hu
Publisher E-mail: eszter.kovacs@sanomabp.hu
Magazine featuring women's interests. **Freq:** Monthly. **Print Method:** Offset. **Trim Size:** 200 x 265 mm. **Key Personnel:** Selmeczi Andrea, Coord., phone 36 1 4373639, fax 36 1 4371180, a.selmeczi@sanomabp.hu. **Remarks:** Accepts advertising. **URL:** http://www.praktika.hu/. **Circ:** Paid 40,067

44866 ■ Progress in Agricultural Engineering Sciences
Akademiai Kiado Rt.
Prielle Kornelia u. 19/D
PO Box 245
H-1117 Budapest, Hungary
Ph: 36 146 48282
Fax: 36 146 48251
Publisher E-mail: info@akrt.hu
Journal publishing original papers, review papers and preliminary communications in the field of agricultural, environmental and process engineering. **Founded:** 2004. **Freq:** Annual. **Trim Size:** 17 x 25 cm. **Key Personnel:** Andras Fekete, Editor-in-Chief, andras.fekete@uni-corvinus.hu; Peter Szendro, President. **ISSN:** 1786-335X. **Subscription Rates:** EUR73 individuals online; US$101 individuals online; EUR84 individuals print and online; US$118 individuals print and online. **URL:** http://akkrt.hu/56/journals/products/engineering_sciences/progress_in_agricultural_engineering_sciences_eng.

44867 ■ Review of Sociology of the Hungarian Sociological Association
Akademiai Kiado Rt.
Corvinus University of Budapest
H-1093 Budapest, Hungary
Publisher E-mail: info@akrt.hu
Journal covering sociological thought and research with emphasis on Hungarian society. **Founded:** 1828. **Freq:** Annual one volume of two issues. **Print Method:** Offset. **Trim Size:** 17 x 25 cm. **Cols./Page:** 6. **Col. Width:** 2 1/16 inches. **Col. Depth:** 21 inches. **Key Personnel:** Lengyel Gyorgy, Editor-in-Chief, gyorgy.lengyel@uni-corvinus; Gyorgy Ferge, Editorial Board; Cseh Szombathy, Editorial Board; Laszlo Csepeli, Editorial Board; Angelusz Robert, Editorial Board; Bela Janky, Assoc. Ed. **ISSN:** 1417-8648. **URL:** http://www.akkrt.hu/main.php?folderID=1617&articleID=3917&ctag=articlelist&iid=1.

44868 ■ RTV Musormagazin
Sanoma Budapest Kiadoi Rt.
Montevideo utca 9
H-1037 Budapest, Hungary
Ph: 36 1 4371100
Fax: 36 1 4372303
Publication E-mail: szrtv@sanomabp.hu
Publisher E-mail: eszter.kovacs@sanomabp.hu
Magazine featuring radio and television schedule. **Freq:** Weekly (Fri.). **Print Method:** Cold-set. **Trim Size:** 205 x 270 mm. **Key Personnel:** Hamori Ivan, Contact, phone 36 1 4371515, fax 36 1 4371499. **Remarks:** Accepts advertising. **URL:** http://www.sanomabp.hu/termekek/ketheti_rtv_musormagazin/4959/?fid=392. **Circ:** Paid ‡74,540

44869 ■ Scientometrics
Akademiai Kiado Rt.
Prielle Kornelia u. 19/D
PO Box 245
H-1117 Budapest, Hungary
Ph: 36 146 48282
Fax: 36 146 48251
Publisher E-mail: info@akrt.hu
Journal covering scientometrics. **Subtitle:** An International Journal for all Quantitative Aspects of the Science of Science, Communication in Science and Science Policy. **Founded:** 1978. **Freq:** four volumes of 12 issues. **Print Method:** Offset. **Trim Size:** 17 x 25 cm. **Cols./Page:** 2. **Col. Width:** 17 picas. **Col. Depth:** 48 picas. **Key Personnel:** Andras Schubert, Editor; J.P. Courtial, Editorial Board; A.T. Balaban, Editorial Board; Wolfgang Glanzel, Co-Ed.; Braun Tibor, Editor-in-Chief; P. Vinkler, Editorial Board. **ISSN:** 0138-9130. **URL:** http://akkrt.hu/

59/journals/products/other_sciences/scientometrics_eng.

44870 ■ Society and Economy
Akademiai Kiado Rt.
Prielle Kornelia u. 19/D
PO Box 245
H-1117 Budapest, Hungary
Ph: 36 146 48282
Fax: 36 146 48251
Publisher E-mail: info@akrt.hu
Journal covering the field of social science. **Subtitle:** Journal of the Corvinus University of Budapest. **Founded:** 1979. **Freq:** 2/yr. **Print Method:** Offset. **Trim Size:** B5. **Cols./Page:** 3. **Col. Width:** 28 nonpareils. **Col. Depth:** 133 agate lines. **Key Personnel:** Trautmann Laszlo, Editor-in-Chief. **ISSN:** 1588-9726. **Subscription Rates:** EUR144 individuals online only; US$199 other countries valid only in North America (Canada, U.S.); EUR166 individuals print and online; US$232 individuals print and online. **URL:** http://akkrt.hu/60/journals/products/economics/society_and_economy_eng.

44871 ■ Southeast European Politics
Albanian Political Science Association
Department of Political Science, Central European University
Nador U. 9
H-1051 Budapest, Hungary
Publisher E-mail: alpsa@alpsa.org
Journal published jointly with Central European University and the Independent Macedonian Political Science Association. **Key Personnel:** Florian Bieber, Editor; Tome Sandevski, Book Reviews Ed.; Maria Spirova, Assoc. Ed.; Zidas Daskalovski, Editor; Altin Ilirjani, Editor. **ISSN:** 1586-9733. **URL:** http://www.seep.ceu.hu/.

44872 ■ Southeast European Politics Online
Central European University
Nador u. 9
1051 Budapest, Hungary
Ph: 36 1 3273000
Publisher E-mail: public@ceu.hu
Journal devoted to political science, international relations, contemporary history and other areas of academic research focusing on Southeastern Europe or pertaining to the region. **Freq:** 3/yr. **Key Personnel:** Altin Ilirjani, Editor; Zidas Daskalovski, Editor; Florian Bieber, Editor. **ISSN:** 1586-9733. **URL:** http://www.seep.ceu.hu.

44873 ■ Story Special
Sanoma Budapest Kiadoi Rt.
Montevideo utca 9
H-1037 Budapest, Hungary
Ph: 36 1 4371100
Fax: 36 1 4372303
Publisher E-mail: eszter.kovacs@sanomabp.hu
Magazine featuring events in the life of the popular personalities in Hungary. **Freq:** Semiannual. **Print Method:** Offset. **Trim Size:** 210 x 285 mm. **Key Personnel:** Ms. Kantor Anita, phone 36 1 4373912, fax 36 1 4371180, a.kantor@sanomabp.hu. **Remarks:** Accepts advertising. **URL:** http://www.sanomabp.hu/sajtohirdetes/index.php?action=termek&site=43. **Circ:** Paid 110,116

44874 ■ Structural and Multidisciplinary Optimization
Springer Netherlands
Dept. of Structural Mechanics
Budapest University of Technology & Economics
Muegyetem rkpt. 3, Kmf. 35
1521 Budapest, Hungary
Ph: 36 26 362592
Fax: 36 1 4631099
Publisher E-mail: permissions.dordrecht@springer.com
Journal covering topics on optimally designing structures and multidisciplinary optimization techniques. **Freq:** Bimonthly. **Key Personnel:** R. Haftka, Co-Ed., haftka@ufl.edu; V.V. Toropov, Co-Ed., v.v.toropov@leeds.ac.uk; George I.N. Rozvany, Editor, smo.rozvany@t-online.hu. **ISSN:** 1615-147X. **Subscription Rates:** EUR2822 institutions print incl. free access or e-only; EUR3386.40 institutions print incl. enhanced access. **URL:** http://www.springer.com/engineering/journal/158.

44875 ■ Studia Musicologica Academiae Scientiarum Hungaricae
Akademiai Kiado Rt.
PO Box 28

Circulation: ★ = ABC; △ = BPA; ♦ = CAC; • = CCAB; ❑ = VAC; ⊕ = PO Statement; ‡ = Publisher's Report; Boldface figures = sworn; Light figures = estimated.

Gale Directory of Publications & Broadcast Media/147th Ed.   **4981**

H-1250 Budapest, Hungary
Ph: 36 1 375282
Publication E-mail: studia@zti.hu
Publisher E-mail: info@akkrt.hu
Journal covering musicology. **Founded:** 1961. **Freq:** one volume of four issues. **Print Method:** Offset. **Trim Size:** 8 1/2 x 11. **Cols./Page:** 3. **Col. Width:** 28 nonpareils. **Col. Depth:** 140 agate lines. **Key Personnel:** Laszlo Somfai, Editor-in-Chief. **ISSN:** 1788-6244. **Subscription Rates:** EUR282 individuals online only; US$386 U.S. and Canada online only; EUR324 individuals print and online; US$456 U.S. and Canada print and online. **URL:** http://akkrt.hu/61/journals/products/musicology/studia_musicologica_eng.

44876 ■ Studia Scientiarum Mathematicarum Hungarica
Akademiai Kiado Rt.
Prielle Kornelia u. 19/D
PO Box 245
H-1117 Budapest, Hungary
Ph: 36 146 48282
Fax: 36 146 48251
Publisher E-mail: info@akkrt.hu
Journal covering mathematics, including algebra, combinatorics, differential equations, functional analysis, geometry, numerical methods, probability and mathematical statistics, and statistical physics. **Founded:** 1966. **Freq:** Quarterly. **Print Method:** Offset. **Trim Size:** 8 1/2 x 11. **Cols./Page:** 3. **Col. Width:** 26 nonpareils. **Col. Depth:** 126 agate lines. **Key Personnel:** Gabor Sagi, Managing Editor, sagi@renyi.hu; Peter Pal Palfy, Editor-in-Chief, ppp@renyi.hu; Istvan Juhasz, Dep. Ed.-in-Ch., juhasz@renyi.hu. **ISSN:** 0081-6906. **Subscription Rates:** EUR344 individuals online; US$479 individuals online; EUR396 individuals print and online; US$556 individuals print and online. **URL:** http://akkrt.hu/62/journals/products/mathematics/studia_scientiarum_mathematicarum_hungarica_eng.

44877 ■ Szines RTV
Sanoma Budapest Kiadoi Rt.
Montevideo utca 9
H-1037 Budapest, Hungary
Ph: 36 1 4371100
Fax: 36 1 4372303
Publication E-mail: szrtv@sanomabp.hu
Publisher E-mail: eszter.kovacs@sanomabp.hu
Magazine featuring information about programs in television. **Freq:** Weekly (Sat.). **Print Method:** Offset. **Trim Size:** 200 x 285 mm. **Key Personnel:** Ispan Judit, Coord., phone 36 1 4373638, fax 36 1 4371180, j.ispan@sanomabp.hu. **Remarks:** Accepts advertising. **URL:** http://www.sanomabp.hu/sajtohirdetes/index.php?action=termek&site=1. **Circ:** Paid 211,125

44878 ■ Tajfutas
Magyar Tajekozodasi Futo Szovestseg
Dozsa Gyorgy ut 1-3
H-1143 Budapest, Hungary
Ph: 36 1 2215878
Fax: 36 1 2514602
Publisher E-mail: tajfuto@mtfsz.hu
Hungarian language publication covering orienteering. **Freq:** 8/yr. **Key Personnel:** Viktor Hites, Editor; Istvan Hajdu, President. **ISSN:** 0133-4697. **Subscription Rates:** 1,600 Ft. **Remarks:** Advertising accepted; rates available upon request. **URL:** http://www.mtfsz.hu. **Circ:** (Not Reported)

44879 ■ Tarsadalom es Gazdasag (Society and Economy)
Akademiai Kiado Rt.
Prielle Kornelia u. 19/D
PO Box 245
H-1117 Budapest, Hungary
Ph: 36 146 48282
Fax: 36 146 48251
Publisher E-mail: info@akkrt.hu
Journal covering theoretical and applied economics, economic policy, international economics, political and legal sciences, sociology and business studies. **Subtitle:** Journal of the Corvinus University of Budapest. **Founded:** 1979. **Freq:** Semiannual. **Trim Size:** 8 1/4 x 10 3/4. **Cols./Page:** 3. **Col. Width:** 33 nonpareils. **Col. Depth:** 154 agate lines. **Key Personnel:** Polyanszky T. Zoltan, Editor, potozapa@uni-corvinus.hu; Temesi Jozsef, Editor-in-Chief, jozsef.temesi@uni-corvinus; Attila Agh, Editorial Board. **ISSN:** 1588-9734. **Subscription Rates:** EUR58 individuals; US$76 individuals. **URL:**

http://www.akkrt.hu/main.php?folderID=1603&articleID=3924&ctag=articlelist&iid=1.

44880 ■ Tarsadalomkutatas
Akademiai Kiado Rt.
Prielle Kornelia u. 19/D
PO Box 245
H-1117 Budapest, Hungary
Ph: 36 146 48282
Fax: 36 146 48251
Publisher E-mail: info@akkrt.hu
Journal covering field of social science. **Founded:** 1983. **Freq:** 4/yr. **Trim Size:** 17 x 25 cm. **Key Personnel:** Kalman Kulcsar, Editor-in-Chief, nageli@mtapti.hu; Vera Gathy, Editor, gat9586@helka.iif.hu; Tamas Rozgonyi, Editor, ajtai@socio.mta.hu. **ISSN:** 0231-2522. **Subscription Rates:** EUR71 individuals online only; US$100 U.S. and Canada online only; EUR84 individuals print + online; US$116 U.S. and Canada print + online. **URL:** http://akkrt.hu/64/journals/products/sociology/tarsadalomkutatas_social_science_research.

44881 ■ UZLET & SIKER
Sanoma Budapest Kiadoi Rt.
Montevideo utca 9
H-1037 Budapest, Hungary
Ph: 36 1 4371100
Fax: 36 1 4372303
Publisher E-mail: eszter.kovacs@sanomabp.hu
Magazine featuring practical information, analysis, and advice for small and middle-sized enterprises. **Freq:** 10/yr. **Print Method:** Offset. **Trim Size:** 200 x 267 mm. **Key Personnel:** Torok Marta, Coord., phone 36 1 4371218, fax 36 1 4371180, m.torok@sanomabp.hu. **Subscription Rates:** 350 Ft individuals. **Remarks:** Accepts advertising. **URL:** http://www.fn.hu/vallalkozas/20080701/uzlet_siker_minositett_vallalkozas_palyazat/. **Circ:** ‡20,346

44882 ■ WHERE Budapest
Miller Publishing Group L.L.C.
Wesselenyi utca 4
III.16
H-1077 Budapest, Hungary
Travel and tourism magazine focusing on Budapest, Hungary. **Founded:** 1936. **Key Personnel:** Bianca Otero, Editor-in-Chief. **Remarks:** Accepts advertising. **URL:** http://www.wherebudapest.hu/. **Circ:** (Not Reported)

44883 ■ World Weightlifting
International Weightlifting Federation
Istvanmezei ut 1-3
H-1146 Budapest, Hungary
Ph: 36 135 30530
Fax: 36 135 30199
Publication covering worldwide weightlifting in English and Spanish. **Freq:** Quarterly. **Subscription Rates:** US$40 individuals Europe; US$50 individuals outside Europe. **Remarks:** Advertising accepted; rates available upon request. **URL:** http://www.iwf.net. **Circ:** (Not Reported)

44884 ■ Katolikus Radio-AM - 1341 kHz
PO Box 879
H-1385 Budapest, Hungary
Ph: 36 1 2553366
Fax: 36 1 2553399
E-mail: info@katradio.hu
Format: Religious. **Operating Hours:** Continuous. **URL:** http://www.katolikusradio.hu.

44885 ■ Tilos Radio-FM - 90.3
Ulloi ut 32. (Maria u. 54.)
H-1085 Budapest, Hungary
Ph: 36 1 4768491
Fax: 36 1 4768492
E-mail: radio@tilos.hu
Format: Public Radio. **Owner:** Tilos Kulturalis Alapitvany, at above address. **URL:** http://tilos.hu/.

Debrecen

44886 ■ Aequationes Mathematicae
Springer-Verlag Tokyo
Universitat de Debrecen
Institute of Mathematics
Pf. 12
4010 Debrecen, Hungary
Publication E-mail: aeqmath@unideb.hu
Publisher E-mail: info@springer.jp
International journal of pure and applied mathematics,

emphasizing functional equations, dynamical systems, iteration theory and combinatorics. **Freq:** 3/yr. **Key Personnel:** Ludwig Reich, Honorary Ed.; Hans Havlicek, Editor; Morris W. Hirsch, Editor; Walter Benz, Editor; Branko Grunbaum, Editor; Jens Schwaiger, Assoc. Mng. Ed., jens.schwaiger@uni-graz.at; Attila Gilanyi, Managing Editor, gilanyi@math.klte.hu; Gian-Luigi Forti, Editor; Claudi Alsina, Editor; Bruce Ebanks, Editor. **ISSN:** 0001-9054. **Subscription Rates:** EUR1,018 institutions; EUR1,221.60 institutions enhanced access. **Remarks:** Advertising accepted; rates available upon request. **URL:** http://www.springer.com/birkhauser/mathematics/journal/10. **Circ:** (Not Reported)

44887 ■ Archives of Gerontology and Geriatrics
Mosby Inc.
c/o I. Zs-Nagy, Ed.-in-Ch.
University Medical School
H-4012 Debrecen, Hungary
Publisher E-mail: custserv.ehs@elsevier.com
Journal publishing papers in experimental gerontology and clinical and social geriatrics. **Freq:** Bimonthly. **Key Personnel:** S. Hoyer, Editorial Board; I. Zs-Nagy, Editor-in-Chief; R. Asplund, Editorial Board; A. Ahmed, Editorial Board; L.K. Chen, Editorial Board; V.V. Bezrukov, Editorial Board; C. Bertoni-Freddari, Editorial Board; T. Fulop, Editorial Board; M. Fioravant, Editorial Board. **ISSN:** 0167-4943. **Subscription Rates:** US$151 individuals. **URL:** http://journals.elsevierhealth.com/periodicals/agg.

44888 ■ Gerontology and Geriatrics
Elsevier Science Inc.
University Medical School
04012 Debrecen, Hungary
Publisher E-mail: usinfo-ehelp@elsevier.com
Journal dealing with the basic mechanisms of aging at molecular, cellular, tissue or organ levels. **Founded:** 1965. **Freq:** 6/yr. **Print Method:** Offset. **Cols./Page:** 5. **Col. Width:** 12 1/16 inches. **Col. Depth:** 13 inches. **Key Personnel:** I. Zs-Nagy, Editor-in-Chief; S. Hoyer, Member of the Editorial Board; R. Asplund, Member of the Editorial Board; G. Bako, Member of the Editorial Board; Y. Arai, Member of the Editorial Board; A. Ahmed, Member of the Editorial Board; C. Bertoni Freddari, Member of the Editorial Board. **ISSN:** 0167-4943. **Subscription Rates:** EUR2,193 institutions; 291,300¥ institutions; US$2,455 institutions, other countries except Europe and Japan; US$161 individuals except Europe and Japan; EUR145 individuals; 19,200¥ individuals. **URL:** http://www.elsevier.com/wps/find/journaldescription.cws_home/506044/descriptiondescription.

Egyetem

44889 ■ Verbum
Akademiai Kiado Rt.
c/o Adam Aniko, Ed.-in-Ch.
Piliscsaba-Klotilidliget, U. 1
H-2087 Egyetem, Hungary
Ph: 36 263 75375
Publisher E-mail: info@akkrt.hu
Journal covering music, video, multimedia and web-based development. **Founded:** 1948. **Freq:** Semiannual. **Print Method:** Offset. **Trim Size:** 15.5 x 23.5 cm. **Cols./Page:** 3. **Col. Width:** 2 1/4 inches. **Col. Depth:** 10 inches. **Key Personnel:** Adam Aniko, Editor-in-Chief, adama@btk.ppke.hu; Paul Richard Blum, Editorial Board; Eva Martonyi, Editorial Board. **ISSN:** 1585-079X. **Subscription Rates:** EUR122 individuals; US$152 individuals. **URL:** http://www.akkrt.hu/main.php?folderID=1613&articleID=3919&ctag=articlelist&iid=1.

Martonvasar

44890 ■ Acta Agronomica Hungarica
Akademiai Kiado Rt.
c/o Zoltan Bedo, Ed.-in-Ch.
Brunszvik u. 2
H-2462 Martonvasar, Hungary
Ph: 36 22 569509
Publisher E-mail: info@akkrt.hu
Journal covering applied and basic research in plant genetics, plant breeding, plant cultivation, plant physiology, plant biochemistry, plant ecology, foraging culture, and history of agriculture. **Subtitle:** An International Multidisciplinary Journal in Agricultural Science. **Founded:** 1950. **Freq:** 4/yr. **Trim Size:** 17 x 25 cm. **Key Personnel:** Zoltan Bedo, Editor-in-Chief, bedoz@mail.mgki.hu; Emil Paldi, Editor, paldie@mail.mgki.hu. **ISSN:** 0238-

0161. **Subscription Rates:** EUR320 individuals online; US$446 individuals online; EUR368 individuals print and online; US$516 individuals print and online. **URL:** http://akkrt.hu/1/journals/products/agricultural_sciences/acta_agronomica _hungarica_eng.

Miskolc-Egyetemvaros

44891 ■ Journal of Computational and Applied Mechanics
Miskolci Egyetem
University of Miskolc
H-3515 Miskolc-Egyetemvaros, Hungary
Ph: 36 465 65111
Journal publishing research papers on theoretical and applied mechanics, special emphasis given to articles on computational mechanics, continuum mechanics (mechanics of solid bodies, fluid mechanics), heat and mass transfer, dynamics and biomechanics. **Freq:** Annual. **Key Personnel:** Prof. Istvan Paczelt, Editor-in-Chief, mechpacz@uni-miskolc.hu; Laszlo Baranyi, Editorial Board; Wolfram Frank, Editorial Board; Ulrich Gabbert, Editorial Board; Edgar Bertoti, Editorial Board. **ISSN:** 1586-2070. **URL:** http://mab.mta.hu/~szeidl/.

Nyiregyhaza

44892 ■ Acta Mathematica Academiae Paedagogicae Nyiregyhaziensis
College of Nyiregyhaza
Institute of Mathematics & Computer Science
PO Box 166
H-4401 Nyiregyhaza, Hungary
Peer-reviewed journal covering mathematics. **Founded:** 1965. **Freq:** Annual. **Print Method:** Offset. **Trim Size:** 11 x 17. **Cols./Page:** 7. **Col. Width:** 16 nonpareils. **Col. Depth:** 224 agate lines. **Key Personnel:** G. Gat, Editor-in-Chief, gatgy@nyf.hu; Z. Kovacs, Editor-in-Chief, kovacsz@nyf.hu; V. Bovdi, Editor, amapn@yf.hu. **ISSN:** 1786-0091. **URL:** http://www.emis.de/journals/AMAPN/index.html.

Pecs

44893 ■ Acta Botanica Hungarica
Akademiai Kiado Rt.
c/o Attila Borhidi, Ed.-in-Ch.
Department of Botany
University of Pecs
Ifjusag utja 6
H-7624 Pecs, Hungary
Publisher E-mail: info@akkrt.hu
Journal covering plant anatomy and histology, cryptogam and phanerogam taxonomy, molecular phylogeny, plant geography, plant sociology, vegetation science, tropical botany, ethnobotany, paleobotany, and palynology. **Founded:** 1954. **Freq:** 4/yr. **Key Personnel:** Attila Borhidi, Editor-in-Chief, borhidi@ttk.pte.hu; Laszlo Lokos, Managing Editor, lokos@bot.nhmus.hu; Laszlo Pergovits, Managing Editor, perego@zool.nhmus.hu. **ISSN:** 0236-6495. **Subscription Rates:** EUR306 individuals online only; US$424 U.S. and Canada online only; EUR352 individuals print + online; US$496 individuals print + online. **URL:** http://akkrt.hu/13/journals/products/botany/acta_botanica_hungarica_eng.

Szeged

44894 ■ Acta Ethnographica Hungarica
Akademiai Kiado Rt.
Department of Ethology & Cultural Anthropology
University of Szeged
Egyetem U. 2.
H-6722 Szeged, Hungary
Publisher E-mail: info@akkrt.hu
Journal covering scientific advances in the field of ethnography, folklore, and cultural and social anthropology. **Subtitle:** An International Journal of Ethnography. **Founded:** July 1980. **Freq:** Semiannual. **Print Method:** Offset. **Trim Size:** 17 x 25 cm. **Cols./Page:** 6. **Col. Width:** 2 1/8 inches. **Col. Depth:** 21 1/2 inches. **Key Personnel:** Barna Gabor, Editor; Simon Andras, Review Ed.; Mod Laszlo, Review Ed. **ISSN:** 1216-9803. **Subscription Rates:** EUR285 individuals online; US$398 individuals online; EUR328 individuals print and online; US$460 individuals print and online. **URL:** http://akkrt.hu/15/journals/products/ethnography/acta_ethnographica_hungarica_eng.

Szekszard

44895 ■ Alisca Radio-FM - 94.3
Szent Laszlo u. 19.
7100 Szekszard, Hungary
Ph: 36 74 410191
Format: Information. **Operating Hours:** 18 hours Daily. **URL:** http://www.alisca.hu.

Circulation: ★ = ABC; △ = BPA; ◆ = CAC; ● = CCAB; ❑ = VAC; ⊕ = PO Statement; ‡ = Publisher's Report; Boldface figures = sworn; Light figures = estimated.

Reykjavik

44896 ■ Acta Ophthalmologica
John Wiley & Sons Inc.
Wiley-Blackwell
c/o Prof. Einar Stefansson, Ed.-in-Ch.
University of Iceland, National University Hospital
Dept. of Ophthalmology
IS-101 Reykjavik, Iceland
Ph: 354 543 7217
Fax: 354 543 4831
Peer-reviewed journal focusing on ophthalmology. **Freq:** 8/yr. **Key Personnel:** Prof. Einar Stefansson, Editor-in-Chief; Tero Kivela, Board of Dir.; Jan Ulrik Prause, Board of Dir.; Anna Midelfart, Board of Dir.; Thomas Olsen, Board of Dir.; Stefan Seregard, Board of Dir.; Gunnar Hovding, Board of Dir.; Pinar Aydin, Board of Dir.; Fridbert Jonasson, Board of Dir.; Hannu Uusitalo, Board of Dir.; Bryndis Thordardottir, Editorial Mgr., phone 354 897 9752; Erling Haaskjold, Editorial Board. **ISSN:** 1755-375X. **Subscription Rates:** US$526 institutions print + online; US$478 institutions print; US$225 individuals print + online; US$560 institutions, other countries print + online; 225 individuals print + online; EUR400 institutions print + online; US$560 institutions, other countries online; EUR478 institutions print; EUR339 individuals print + online. **Remarks:** Accepts advertising. **URL:** http://www.wiley.com/bw/journal.asp?ref=1755-375X&site=1. **Formerly:** Acta Ophthalmologica Scandinavica. **Circ:** (Not Reported)

44897 ■ Atlantica
Iceland Review
Borgartuni 23-105
IS-105 Reykjavik, Iceland
Ph: 354 512 7575
Fax: 354 561 8646
Publication E-mail: atlantica@heimur.is
Publisher E-mail: icelandreview@icelandreview.com
In-flight magazine for Icelandair in English. **Freq:** Bimonthly. **URL:** http://icelandreview.com.

44898 ■ Bokasafnid
Icelandic Library and Information Science Association
Lagmuli 7
IS-108 Reykjavik, Iceland
Ph: 35 455 37290
Fax: 35 458 89239
Publisher E-mail: upplysing@bokis.is
Professional journal covering library and information science. **Freq:** Annual. **ISSN:** 1670-0066. **Subscription Rates:** Included in membership. **Remarks:** Accepts advertising. **URL:** http://www.bokasafnid.is/. **Circ:** (Not Reported)

44899 ■ Chemistry and Physics of Lipids
Elsevier Science
c/o G.G. Haraldsson, Assoc. Ed.
Science Institute, University of Iceland
Dunhaga 3
IS-107 Reykjavik, Iceland
Publisher E-mail: nlinfo-f@elsevier.com
Peer-reviewed journal devoted to chemical and physical aspects of lipids in relation molecular biology. **Founded:** 1967. **Freq:** 8/yr. **Key Personnel:** G.G. Haraldsson, Assoc. Ed., gghar@raunvis.hi.is; R.N. McElhaney, Editor-in-Chief, rmcelhan@ualberta.ca; Y. Barenholz, Editorial Advisory Board; R. Bartucci, Editorial Advisory Board; R. Bittman, Editorial Advisory Board; J.M. Boggs, Editorial Advisory Board. **ISSN:** 0009-3084. **Subscription Rates:** US$3,696 institutions for all countries except Europe, Japan & Iran; EUR3,303 institutions for European countries & Iran; 439,000¥ institutions Japan; 32,400¥ individuals; EUR210 individuals for European countries & Iran; US$282 individuals for all countries except Europe, Japan & Iran. **Remarks:** Accepts advertising. **URL:** http://www.elsevier.com/wps/find/journaldescription.cws_home/506036/description. **Circ:** (Not Reported)

44900 ■ European Journal of International Management
Inderscience Publishers
c/o Vlad Vaiman, Exec. Ed.
Reykjavik University
School of Business
Ofanleiti 2
103 Reykjavik, Iceland
Publisher E-mail: editor@inderscience.com
Peer-reviewed journal covering issues in international management theory & practice. **Founded:** 2007. **Freq:** 4/yr. **Key Personnel:** Vlad Vaiman, Exec. Ed., editors@ejim-global.org; Gerhard Apfelthaler, Assoc. Ed.; Nigel Holden, Assoc. Ed. **ISSN:** 1751-6757. **Subscription Rates:** EUR593 individuals includes surface mail, print only; EUR830 individuals print and online. **URL:** http://www.inderscience.com/browse/index.php?journalCODE=ejim.

44901 ■ Iceland Review
Borgartuni 23-105
IS-105 Reykjavik, Iceland
Ph: 354 512 7575
Fax: 354 561 8646
Publisher E-mail: icelandreview@icelandreview.com
English language magazine covering nature, culture and travel in Iceland. **Founded:** 1963. **Freq:** Quarterly. **Key Personnel:** Bjarni Brynjolfsson, Editor, bjarni@icelandreview.com. **Subscription Rates:** US$39.50

individuals; 26 individuals; EUR36 individuals. **URL:** http://icelandreview.com/.

44902 ■ Rotary Norden
Oy Haakan Nordqvist Consulting Ab
c/o Markus Orn Antonsson
Vesturgata 36A
ICE-101 Reykjavik, Iceland
Ph: 354 545 1400
Publisher E-mail: markusoa@simnet.is
Membership magazine of Rotary International covering current news about Rotary-related subjects in Danish, Finnish, Norwegian, and Swedish. **Freq:** Monthly 8/yr. **Print Method:** Rotation offset. **Key Personnel:** Per O. Dantoft, Editor-in-Chief, rotary@mail.dk; Ottar Julsrud, Editor, julsrud@online.no; Borje Alstrom, Editor, phone 46 60 170340, fax 46 63 34014, alstrom@mh.se. **Remarks:** Accepts advertising. **URL:** http://www.rotary.org/en/mediaandnews/morepublications/regionalmagazines/pages/ridefault.aspx. **Ad Rates:** BW: 1,600 IKr. **Circ:** 69,000

44903 ■ Scandinavian Journal of History
Routledge
Taylor & Francis Group Ltd.
c/o Gudmundur Halfdanarson, Ed.-in-Ch.
Dept. of History, University of Iceland
Arnagardur, Sudurgata
IS-101 Reykjavik, Iceland
Publisher E-mail: webmaster.books@tandf.co.uk
Journal covering Scandinavian history and surveying themes in recent Scandinavian historical research. **Freq:** Quarterly. **Key Personnel:** Marjaana Niemi, Editor, marjaana.niemi@uta.fi; Poul Villaume, Editor, villaume@hum.ku.dk; Gudmundur Halfdanarson, Editor-in-Chief, ghalfd@hi.is. **ISSN:** 0346-8755. **Subscription Rates:** 193 institutions print + online; US$321 institutions print + online; 183 institutions online; US$304 institutions online; 96 individuals; US$160 individuals; EUR254 institutions print and online; EUR241 institutions online only; EUR128 individuals. **URL:** http://www.tandf.co.uk/journals/titles/03468755.asp.

Torshavn

44904 ■ Ras 2-FM - 102.5
Vagsbotnur
PO Box 76
FO-100 Torshavn, Iceland
Ph: 354 298409999
Fax: 354 298409990
E-mail: ras2@ras2.fo
Format: Ethnic; World Beat. **Operating Hours:** Continuous. **URL:** http://www.ras2.fo.

Circulation: ★ = ABC; △ = BPA; ◆ = CAC; •= CCAB; ▢ = VAC; ⊕ = PO Statement; ‡ = Publisher's Report; Boldface figures = sworn; Light figures = estimated.

Gale Directory of Publications & Broadcast Media/147th Ed. 4985

Adilabad

44905 ■ All India Radio Adilabad - 1485 KHz
Akashvani Bhavan
Sansad Marg
New Delhi 110 001, Delhi, India
Ph: 91 11 23421006
Fax: 91 11 23421956
E-mail: adilabad@air.org.in
Format: Eclectic. **Owner:** Prasar Bharati, at above address. **Founded:** 1986. **Key Personnel:** M.C. Aggarwal, Engr.-in-Ch., phone 91 11 23421058, fax 91 11 23421006, einc@air.org.in; Mohan Singh, Ch. Engr., Proj., phone 91 11 23421184. **Wattage:** 1000. **Ad Rates:** $80-150 for 10 seconds; $120-225 for 15 seconds; $240-450 for 30 seconds; $480-900 for 60 seconds. **URL:** http://www.allindiaradio.org.

Agartala

44906 ■ All India Radio Agartala - 1269 KHz
Palace Compound
N Gate
Agartala 799 001, Tripura, India
Ph: 91 381 2324225
E-mail: airagar@rediffmail.com
Format: Eclectic. **Owner:** Prasar Bharati, Akashvani Bhavan, Sansad Marg, New Delhi 110 001, Delhi, India, 91 11 23421006, Fax: 91 11 23421956. **Founded:** 1967. **Key Personnel:** M.C. Aggarwal, Engr.-in-Ch., phone 91 11 23421058, fax 91 11 23421006, einc@air.org.in. **Wattage:** 20,000. **Ad Rates:** $150-300 for 10 seconds; $225-450 for 15 seconds; $450-900 for 30 seconds; $900-1,800 for 60 seconds. **URL:** http://www.allindiaradio.org.

Agra

44907 ■ All India Radio Agra - 1530 KHz
Vibhav Nagar
Agra 282 001, Uttar Pradesh, India
Ph: 91 562 2332297
E-mail: agra@air.org.in
Format: Eclectic. **Owner:** Prasar Bharati, Akashvani Bhavan, Sansad Marg, New Delhi 110 001, Delhi, India, 91 11 23421006, Fax: 91 11 23421956. **Founded:** 1989. **Key Personnel:** M.C. Aggarwal, Engr.-in-Ch., phone 91 11 23421058, fax 91 11 23421006, einc@air.org.in. **Wattage:** 20,000. **Ad Rates:** $180-400 for 10 seconds; $270-600 for 15 seconds; $540-1,200 for 30 seconds; $1,080-2,400 for 60 seconds. **URL:** http://www.allindiaradio.org.

Ahmedabad

44908 ■ Divya Bhaskar
280, Sarkhej-Gandhinagar Hwy.
Near YMCA Club
Ahmedabad 380 015, Gujarat, India
Ph: 91 793 9888850
Publisher E-mail: contact@imd.co.in
General newspaper. **URL:** http://www.divyabhaskar.co.in/.

44909 ■ Sandesh
Sandesh Bhavan, Lad Society Rd., Vastrapur
Ahmedabad 380 054, Gujarat, India
Ph: 91 794 0004000
Fax: 91 794 0004242
Publisher E-mail: sandesh@sandesh.com
General newspaper. **Key Personnel:** Puneet Singhvi, Contact, phone 91 981 1202579, fax 91 124 4008604, international.adsales@indiatimes.co.in. **Subscription Rates:** Rs 3,800 individuals Ahmedabad; Rs 575 individuals Wednesday supplement; Rs 575 individuals Sunday supplement; Rs 1,150 individuals Wednesday & Sunday; US$40 individuals. **Remarks:** Accepts advertising. **URL:** http://www.sandesh.com. **Circ:** (Not Reported)

44910 ■ Texincon
National Information Centre for Textile and Allied Subjects
c/o ATIRA
PO Box Ambawadi Vistar
Ahmedabad 380 015, Gujarat, India
Ph: 91 79 26307921
Fax: 91 79 26304677
Periodical dedicated to polymers and textiles. **Freq:** Quarterly. **Key Personnel:** Hina Shah, Contact, atiraad1@sancharnet.in. **ISSN:** 0970-5686. **Subscription Rates:** US$50 other countries. **Remarks:** Accepts advertising. **URL:** http://www.atira-rnd-tex.org/fac_nictas_des.htm. **Circ:** Paid 1,000

44911 ■ Textile Association (India) Journal
Textile Association
Dinesh Hall
Ashram Rd.
Ahmedabad 380 009, Gujarat, India
Ph: 91 79 26582123
Fax: 91 79 26586311
Publisher E-mail: taiahd1@dataone.in
Publication of textile technology. **Freq:** Bimonthly. **Key Personnel:** Prof. M. D. Teli, Editor. **ISSN:** 0368-4636. **Subscription Rates:** US$75 other countries. **Remarks:** Accepts advertising. **URL:** http://www.taindia.com. **Ad Rates:** BW: Rs 3,000. **Circ:** Paid 10,000

44912 ■ All India Radio Ahmedabad - 846 KHz
Navarangpura HO
PO Box 4005
Ahmedabad 380 009, Gujarat, India
Ph: 91 79 27541539
E-mail: airahmad1@sancharnet.in
Format: Eclectic. **Owner:** Prasar Bharati, Akashvani Bhavan, Sansad Marg, New Delhi 110 001, Delhi, India, 91 11 23421006, Fax: 91 11 23421956. **Founded:** 1949. **Key Personnel:** M.C. Aggarwal, Engr.-in-Ch., phone 91 11 23421058, fax 91 11 23421006, einc@air.org.in. **Wattage:** 200,000. **Ad Rates:** $200-550 for 10 seconds; $300-825 for 15 seconds; $600-1,650 for 30 seconds; $1,200-3,300 for 60 seconds. **URL:** http://www.allindiaradio.org.

Ahmednagar

44913 ■ All India Radio Ahmednagar - 100.1 KHz
Akashvani Bhavan

Sansad Marg
New Delhi 110 001, Delhi, India
Ph: 91 11 23421006
Fax: 91 11 23421956
E-mail: naresh2_anr@sancharnet.in
Format: Eclectic. **Owner:** Prasar Bharati, at above address. **Founded:** 1991. **Key Personnel:** M.C. Aggarwal, Engr.-in-Ch., phone 91 11 23421058, fax 91 11 23421006, einc@air.org.in. **Wattage:** 6000. **Ad Rates:** $80-150 for 10 seconds; $120-225 for 15 seconds; $240-450 for 30 seconds; $480-900 for 60 seconds. **URL:** http://www.allindiaradio.org.

Ahwa

44914 ■ All India Radio Ahwa (Dangs) - 1485 KHz
Akashvani Bhavan
Sansad Marg
New Delhi 110 001, Delhi, India
Ph: 91 11 23421006
Fax: 91 11 23421956
E-mail: airahwa@sancharnet.in
Format: Eclectic. **Owner:** Prasar Bharati, at above address. **Founded:** 1994. **Key Personnel:** M.C. Aggarwal, Engr.-in-Ch., phone 91 11 23421058, fax 91 11 23421006, einc@air.org.in; Mohan Singh, Ch. Engr., Proj., phone 91 11 23421184. **Wattage:** 1000. **Ad Rates:** $80-150 for 10 seconds; $120-225 for 15 seconds; $240-450 for 30 seconds; $480-900 for 60 seconds. **URL:** http://www.allindiaradio.org.

Aizawl

44915 ■ All India Radio Aizawl - 540 KHz
Radio Tila
Tuikhuahtlang
Aizawl 796 001, Mizoram, India
Ph: 91 389 2322114
E-mail: airzawl@sancharnet.in
Format: Eclectic. **Owner:** Prasar Bharati, Akashvani Bhavan, Sansad Marg, New Delhi 110 001, Delhi, India, 91 11 23421006, Fax: 91 11 23421956. **Founded:** 1966. **Key Personnel:** M.C. Aggarwal, Engr.-in-Ch., phone 91 11 23421058, fax 91 11 23421006, einc@air.org.in. **Wattage:** 20,000. **Ad Rates:** $100-200 for 10 seconds; $150-300 for 15 seconds; $300-600 for 30 seconds; $600-1,200 for 60 seconds. **URL:** http://www.allindiaradio.org.

Akola

44916 ■ All India Radio Akola - 102.4 KHz
Civil Lines
Akola 444 001, Maharashtra, India
Ph: 91 724 2457064
E-mail: akl_airakola@sancharnet.in
Format: Eclectic. **Owner:** Prasar Bharati, Akashvani Bhavan, Sansad Marg, New Delhi 110 001, Delhi, India, 91 11 23421006, Fax: 91 11 23421956. **Founded:** 1992. **Key Personnel:** M.C. Aggarwal, Engr.-in-Ch., phone 91 11 23421058, fax 91 11 23421006, einc@air.org.in. **Wattage:** 6000. **Ad Rates:** $80-150 for 10 seconds; $120-225 for 15 seconds; $240-450 for 30 seconds;

Circulation: ★ = ABC; △ = BPA; ♦ = CAC; • = CCAB; ❑ = VAC; ⊕ = PO Statement; ‡ = Publisher's Report; Boldface figures = sworn; Light figures = estimated.

Gale Directory of Publications & Broadcast Media/147th Ed.   4987

$480-900 for 60 seconds. **URL:** http://www.allindiaradio. org.

Aligarh

44917 ■ Aligarh Journal of English Studies
Aligarh Muslim University
Dept. of Political Science
Aligarh 202 002, Uttar Pradesh, India
Journal on literary criticism and collections. **Freq:** Semiannual. **ISSN:** 0258-0365. **Subscription Rates:** US$15 individuals. **URL:** http://www.printsjournals.com/ orderform?journalid=PI-002780. **Circ:** Paid 350

44918 ■ MAAS Journal of Islamic Science
Muslim Association for the Advancement of Science
Darul Fikr.
The Main Rd., Iqra Colony
New Sir Sayyed Nagar
Aligarh 202 002, Uttar Pradesh, India
Ph: 91 571 3290443
Publisher E-mail: maas147@rediffmail.com
Periodical on Islam. **Founded:** 1985. **Freq:** Semiannual. **Key Personnel:** M. Riaz Kirmani, Editor, maas@ndb. vsnl.net.in. **ISSN:** 0970-1672. **Subscription Rates:** Rs 300 individuals; Rs 1,000 institutions. **Remarks:** Accepts advertising. **URL:** http://www.maasindia.org; http:// www.journalofislamicscience.com/. **Circ:** Paid 1,000

Allahabad

44919 ■ Advances and Applications in Discrete Mathematics
Pushpa Publishing House
Vijaya Niwas
198 Mumfordganj
Allahabad 211002, Uttar Pradesh, India
Publisher E-mail: arun@pphmj.com
Peer-reviewed journal covering theory and applications of different parts of discrete mathematics. **Freq:** Quarterly. **Key Personnel:** Prof. K.K. Azad, Managing Editor, kkazad@pphmj.com. **ISSN:** 0974-1658. **Subscription Rates:** EUR205 institutions, other countries online; EUR250 institutions, other countries print and online; Rs 3,500 institutions print. **URL:** http://www.pphmj. com/journals/aadm.htm.

44920 ■ Advances and Applications in Statistics
Pushpa Publishing House
Vijaya Niwas
198 Mumfordganj
Allahabad 211002, Uttar Pradesh, India
Publisher E-mail: arun@pphmj.com
Peer-reviewed journal covering theoretical and applied statistics. **Freq:** Bimonthly. **Key Personnel:** Prof. K.K. Azad, Managing Editor, kkazad@pphmj.com. **ISSN:** 0972-3617. **Subscription Rates:** EUR475 institutions, other countries online; EUR595 institutions, other countries print and online; Rs 9,000 institutions print. **URL:** http://www.pphmj.com/journals/adas.htm.

44921 ■ Advances in Computer Science and Engineering
Pushpa Publishing House
Vijaya Niwas
198 Mumfordganj
Allahabad 211002, Uttar Pradesh, India
Publisher E-mail: arun@pphmj.com
Peer-reviewed journal covering aspects of computer science and engineering. **Freq:** 3/yr (March, July and November). **Key Personnel:** Prof. K.K. Azad, Managing Editor, kkazad@pphmj.com. **ISSN:** 0973-6999. **Subscription Rates:** EUR240 institutions, other countries online; EUR298 institutions, other countries print and online; Rs 4,000 institutions print. **URL:** http://www.pphmj. com/journals/acse.htm.

44922 ■ Advances in Differential Equations and Control Processes
Pushpa Publishing House
Vijaya Niwas
198 Mumfordganj
Allahabad 211002, Uttar Pradesh, India
Publisher E-mail: arun@pphmj.com
Peer-reviewed journal covering theory and applications of differential equations and control processes. **Freq:** Quarterly. **Key Personnel:** Prof. K.K. Azad, Managing Editor, kkazad@pphmj.com. **Subscription Rates:** EUR205 institutions, other countries online; EUR250 institutions, other countries print and online; Rs 3,500 institutions print. **URL:** http://www.pphmj.com/journals/ adecp.htm.

44923 ■ Advances in Fuzzy Sets and Systems
Pushpa Publishing House
Vijaya Niwas
198 Mumfordganj
Allahabad 211002, Uttar Pradesh, India
Publisher E-mail: arun@pphmj.com
Peer-reviewed Journal covering all fields of fuzzy sets and systems. **Freq:** 3/yr (February, June and October). **Key Personnel:** Prof. K.K. Azad, Managing Editor, kkazad@pphmj.com. **ISSN:** 0973-421X. **Subscription Rates:** EUR270 institutions, other countries online; EUR330 institutions, other countries print and online; Rs 5,000 institutions print. **URL:** http://www.pphmj.com/journals/afss.htm.

44924 ■ Current Development in Theory and Applications of Wavelets
Pushpa Publishing House
Vijaya Niwas
198 Mumfordganj
Allahabad 211002, Uttar Pradesh, India
Publisher E-mail: arun@pphmj.com
Peer-reviewed journal covering theory and applications of wavelet analysis, Gabor analysis, and general time-frequency analysis. **Freq:** 3/yr (April, August and December). **Key Personnel:** Prof. K.K. Azad, Managing Editor, kkazad@pphmj.com. **ISSN:** 0973-5607. **Subscription Rates:** EUR175 institutions, other countries online; EUR220 institutions, other countries print and online; Rs 3,000 institutions print. **URL:** http://www.pphmj.com/journals/cdtaw.htm.

44925 ■ Far East Journal of Applied Mathematics
Pushpa Publishing House
Vijaya Niwas
198 Mumfordganj
Allahabad 211002, Uttar Pradesh, India
Publisher E-mail: arun@pphmj.com
Peer-reviewed journal covering the field of applied mathematics. **Founded:** 1997. **Freq:** Monthly. **Key Personnel:** Prof. K.K. Azad, Principal Ed., kkazad@pphmj. com; Mohammedi R. Abdel-Aziz, Editorial Board; Tungyang Chen, Editorial Board; Mohammad Hosseini Aliabadi, Editorial Board. **ISSN:** 0972-0960. **Subscription Rates:** EUR690 other countries online; EUR845 individuals print and online; Rs 12,000 institutions print. **Remarks:** Accepts advertising. **URL:** http://www.pphmj.com/journals/fjam.htm. **Circ:** (Not Reported)

44926 ■ Far East Journal of Dynamical Systems
Pushpa Publishing House
Vijaya Niwas
198 Mumfordganj
Allahabad 211002, Uttar Pradesh, India
Publisher E-mail: arun@pphmj.com
Peer-reviewed journal containing research papers in dynamical systems. **Founded:** 1997. **Freq:** 3/yr. **Key Personnel:** K.K. Azad, Managing Editor, kkazad@ pphmj.com; N.P. Bhatia, Editorial Board; Florin N. Diacu, Editorial Board. **ISSN:** 0972-1118. **Subscription Rates:** EUR330 institutions print and online; EUR270 institutions online; Rs 5,000 institutions print. **URL:** http://www. pphmj.com/journals/fjds.htm.

44927 ■ Far East Journal of Electronics and Communications
Pushpa Publishing House
Vijaya Niwas
198 Mumfordganj
Allahabad 211002, Uttar Pradesh, India
Publisher E-mail: arun@pphmj.com
Peer-reviewed journal covering aspect of electronics and communications. **Freq:** 3/yr (April, August and December). **Key Personnel:** Prof. K.K. Azad, Managing Editor, kkazad@pphmj.com. **ISSN:** 0973-7006. **Subscription Rates:** EUR240 institutions, other countries online; EUR298 institutions, other countries print and online; Rs 4,000 institutions print. **URL:** http://www.pphmj.com/journals/fjec.htm.

44928 ■ Far East Journal of Experimental and Theoretical Artificial Intelligence
Pushpa Publishing House
Vijaya Niwas
198 Mumfordganj
Allahabad 211002, Uttar Pradesh, India
Publisher E-mail: arun@pphmj.com
Peer-reviewed journal covering areas of artificial intelligence. **Freq:** 4/yr (February, May, August and November). **Key Personnel:** Prof. K.K. Azad, Managing Editor, kkazad@pphmj.com; Prof. Shun-Feng Su, Editor-in-Chief, su@orion.ee.ntust.edu.tw. **ISSN:** 0974-3261.

Subscription Rates: EUR205 institutions, other countries online; EUR250 institutions, other countries print and online; Rs 3,500 institutions print. **URL:** http://www.pphmj. com/journals/fejetai.htm.

44929 ■ Far East Journal of Mathematical Education
Pushpa Publishing House
Vijaya Niwas
198 Mumfordganj
Allahabad 211002, Uttar Pradesh, India
Publisher E-mail: arun@pphmj.com
Peer-reviewed journal covering aspects of mathematical education at all levels-preschool through adult. **Freq:** Semiannual. **Key Personnel:** Prof. K.K. Azad, Managing Editor, kkazad@pphmj.com. **ISSN:** 0973-5631. **Subscription Rates:** EUR175 institutions, other countries online; EUR220 institutions, other countries print and online; Rs 3,000 institutions print. **URL:** http://www.pphmj.com/journals/fjme.htm.

44930 ■ Far East Journal of Mathematical Sciences
Pushpa Publishing House
Vijaya Niwas
198 Mumfordganj
Allahabad 211002, Uttar Pradesh, India
Publisher E-mail: arun@pphmj.com
Peer-reviewed journal covering the mathematical sciences. **Founded:** 1993. **Freq:** Monthly. **Key Personnel:** Prof. K.K. Azad, Editor, kkazad@pphmj.com; Campanino Massimo, Editorial Board; Antonio Carbone, Editorial Board. **ISSN:** 0971-4332. **Subscription Rates:** EUR690 institutions, other countries online; EUR845 institutions print and online; Rs 12,000 institutions print. **Remarks:** Accepts advertising. **URL:** http://www.pphmj. com/journals/fjms.htm. **Circ:** (Not Reported)

44931 ■ Indian Journal of Economics
University of Allahabad
PO Box 2005
Allahabad 211002, Uttar Pradesh, India
Ph: 91 0532460846
Fax: 91 0532609857
Publication E-mail: info@indianjournalofeconomics.com
Publication on business and economics. **Founded:** Jan. 1916. **Freq:** Quarterly. **Key Personnel:** Prof. P. N. Mehrotra, Managing Editor. **ISSN:** 0019-5170. **Subscription Rates:** Rs 450 individuals; Rs 1,150 institutions. **Remarks:** Advertising not accepted. **URL:** http://www. indianjournalofeconomics.com/about.htm. **Circ:** 500

44932 ■ International Journal of Functional Analysis, Operator Theory and Applications
Pushpa Publishing House
Vijaya Niwas
198 Mumfordganj
Allahabad 211002, Uttar Pradesh, India
Publisher E-mail: arun@pphmj.com
Peer-reviewed journal covering all aspects of functional analysis and operator theory. **Freq:** Semiannual. **Key Personnel:** Prof. K.K. Azad, Editor-in-Chief, kkazad@ pphmj.com. **Subscription Rates:** Rs 3,500 institutions print only; EUR160 institutions, other countries online only; EUR200 institutions, other countries print and online. **URL:** http://pphmj.com/journals/ijaota.htm.

44933 ■ International Journal of Numerical Methods and Applications
Pushpa Publishing House
Vijaya Niwas
198 Mumfordganj
Allahabad 211002, Uttar Pradesh, India
Publisher E-mail: arun@pphmj.com
Peer-reviewed journal covering all aspects in the area of numerical methods. **Freq:** Semiannual. **Key Personnel:** Prof. K.K. Azad, Editor-in-Chief, kkazad@pphmj.com. **Subscription Rates:** Rs 5,000 institutions print only; EUR240 institutions, other countries online only; EUR298 institutions, other countries print and online. **URL:** http:// pphmj.com/journals/IJNMA.htm.

44934 ■ Journal of the Interdisciplinary Crossroads
Spectrum Press
c/o Umesh C. Chattopadhyaya, Ed.
Department of Ancient History, Culture & Archaeology
University of Allahabad
Allahabad, Uttar Pradesh, India
Publisher E-mail: subscription@spectrumpress.net
Peer-reviewed journal providing a platform for all cultures with a holistic perspective in a global scenario and a better understanding of mankind. **Freq:** 3/yr. **Trim Size:** 160 x 240 mm. **Key Personnel:** Umesh C. Chat-

topadhyaya, Editor; Indrani Chattopadhyaya, Managing Editor; Patrick A. Heelan, Editorial Advisory Board; Anthony Judge, Editorial Advisory Board; Nico Stehr, Guest Ed.; Ranjan Ghosh, Assoc. Ed.; Frank R. Ankersmit, Editorial Advisory Board; Richard Kearney, Editorial Advisory Board; Antonio T. De Nicolas, Editorial Advisory Board; Sorin Antohi, Editorial Advisory Board. **ISSN:** 0972-9801. **Subscription Rates:** Rs 1,400 institutions for India; Rs 650 individuals for India; Rs 400 students for India; Rs 500 single issue institution; Rs 250 single issue individual; Rs 150 single issue student. **URL:** http://www.jic.in/index.htm.

44935 ■ JP Journal of Algebra, Number Theory and Applications
Pushpa Publishing House
Vijaya Niwas
198 Mumfordganj
Allahabad 211002, Uttar Pradesh, India
Publisher E-mail: arun@pphmj.com
Peer-reviewed journal covering aspects of Algebra, number theory and their applications. **Freq:** Bimonthly. **Key Personnel:** Prof. K.K. Azad, Managing Editor, kkazad@pphmj.com. **ISSN:** 0972-5555. **Subscription Rates:** EUR330 institutions, other countries online; EUR410 institutions, other countries print and online; Rs 7,000 institutions print. **URL:** http://www.pphmj.com/journals/jpanta.htm.

44936 ■ JP Journal of Biostatistics
Pushpa Publishing House
Vijaya Niwas
198 Mumfordganj
Allahabad 211002, Uttar Pradesh, India
Publisher E-mail: arun@pphmj.com
Peer-reviewed journal covering theory and applications of biostatistics. **Freq:** 3/yr (February, June and October). **Key Personnel:** Prof. K.K. Azad, Managing Editor, kkazad@pphmj.com. **ISSN:** 0973-5143. **Subscription Rates:** EUR175 institutions, other countries online; EUR220 institutions, other countries print and online; Rs 3,000 institutions print. **URL:** http://www.pphmj.com/journals/jpb.htm.

44937 ■ JP Journal of Fixed Point Theory and Applications
Pushpa Publishing House
Vijaya Niwas
198 Mumfordganj
Allahabad 211002, Uttar Pradesh, India
Publisher E-mail: arun@pphmj.com
Peer-reviewed journal covering new developments in fixed point theory. **Freq:** 3/yr (April, August and December). **Key Personnel:** Prof. K.K. Azad, Managing Editor, kkazad@pphmj.com. **ISSN:** 0973-4228. **Subscription Rates:** EUR175 institutions, other countries online; EUR220 institutions, other countries print and online; Rs 3,000 institutions print. **URL:** http://www.pphmj.com/journals/jpfpta.htm.

44938 ■ JP Journal of Heat and Mass Transfer
Pushpa Publishing House
Vijaya Niwas
198 Mumfordganj
Allahabad 211002, Uttar Pradesh, India
Publisher E-mail: arun@pphmj.com
Peer-reviewed journal covering aspects of heat and mass transfer. **Freq:** 3/yr (February, June and October). **Key Personnel:** Prof. K.K. Azad, Managing Editor, kkazad@pphmj.com. **ISSN:** 0973-5763. **Subscription Rates:** EUR175 institutions, other countries online; EUR220 institutions, other countries print and online; Rs 3,000 institutions print. **URL:** http://www.pphmj.com/journals/jphmt.htm.

44939 ■ JP Journal of Solids and Structures
Pushpa Publishing House
Vijaya Niwas
198 Mumfordganj
Allahabad 211002, Uttar Pradesh, India
Publisher E-mail: arun@pphmj.com
Peer-reviewed journal covering aspects of mechanics of solids and structures. **Freq:** 3/yr (March, July and November). **Key Personnel:** Prof. K.K. Azad, Managing Editor, kkazad@pphmj.com; Prof. Misbahul M. Amin, Editor-in-Chief, pphmj.solids@gmail.com. **ISSN:** 0973-5615. **Subscription Rates:** EUR175 institutions, other countries online; EUR220 institutions, other countries print and online; Rs 3,000 institutions print. **URL:** http://www.pphmj.com/journals/jpss.htm.

44940 ■ All India Radio Allahabad - 100.3 MHz
Z-9, Dayanand Marg

Allahabad 211 001, Uttar Pradesh, India
Ph: 91 532 2622530
E-mail: airalld@sancharnet.in
Format: Eclectic. **Owner:** Prasar Bharati, Akashvani Bhavan, Sansad Marg, New Delhi 110 001, Delhi, India, 91 11 23421006, Fax: 91 11 23421956. **Founded:** 1949. **Operating Hours:** 0025-1200, 1245-1730. **Key Personnel:** M.C. Aggarwal, Engr.-in-Ch., phone 91 11 23421058, fax 91 11 23421006, einc@air.org.in. **Wattage:** 10,000. **Ad Rates:** $150-300 for 10 seconds; $225-450 for 15 seconds; $450-900 for 30 seconds; $900-1,800 for 60 seconds. **URL:** http://www.allindiaradio.org.

Almora

44941 ■ All India Radio Almora - 999 KHz
Akashvani Bhavan
Sansad Marg
New Delhi 110 001, Delhi, India
Ph: 91 11 23421006
Fax: 91 11 23421956
E-mail: amair@nde.vsnl.net.in
Format: Eclectic. **Owner:** Prasar Bharati, at above address. **Founded:** 1986. **Key Personnel:** M.C. Aggarwal, Engr.-in-Ch., phone 91 11 23421058, fax 91 11 23421006, einc@air.org.in; Mohan Singh, Ch. Engr., Proj., phone 91 11 23421184. **Wattage:** 1000. **Ad Rates:** $100-200 for 10 seconds; $150-300 for 15 seconds; $300-600 for 30 seconds; $600-1,200 for 60 seconds. **URL:** http://www.allindiaradio.org.

Alwar

44942 ■ All India Radio Alwar - 103.1 MHz
Scheme No. 6
Mangal Vihar
Alwar 301 001, Rajasthan, India
Ph: 91 144 2700955
E-mail: airalwar@sancharnet.in
Format: Eclectic. **Owner:** Prasar Bharati, Akashvani Bhavan, Sansad Marg, New Delhi 110 001, Delhi, India, 91 11 23421006, Fax: 91 11 23421956. **Founded:** 1991. **Key Personnel:** M.C. Aggarwal, Engr.-in-Ch., phone 91 11 23421058, fax 91 11 23421006, einc@air.org.in. **Wattage:** 6000. **Ad Rates:** $80-150 for 10 seconds; $120-225 for 15 seconds; $240-450 for 30 seconds; $480-900 for 60 seconds. **URL:** http://www.allindiaradio.org.

Ambikapur

44943 ■ All India Radio Ambikapur - 1260 KHz
Kumar Pl.
PO Box 27
Ambikapur 497 001, Surguja District, India
Ph: 91 774 230600
E-mail: airamb@sancharnet.in
Format: Eclectic. **Owner:** Prasar Bharati, Akashvani Bhavan, Sansad Marg, New Delhi 110 001, Delhi, India, 91 11 23421006, Fax: 91 11 23421956. **Founded:** 1976. **Key Personnel:** M.C. Aggarwal, Engr.-in-Ch., phone 91 11 23421058, fax 91 11 23421006, einc@air.org.in. **Wattage:** 20,000. **Ad Rates:** $100-200 for 10 seconds; $150-300 for 15 seconds; $300-600 for 30 seconds; $600-1,200 for 60 seconds. **URL:** http://www.allindiaradio.org.

Anantpur

44944 ■ All India Radio Anantpur - 101.7 MHz
Near Collectorate
Anantpur 515 001, Andhra Pradesh, India
Ph: 91 8554 232933
E-mail: airatp@sancharnet.in
Format: Eclectic. **Owner:** Prasar Bharati, Akashvani Bhavan, Sansad Marg, New Delhi 110 001, Delhi, India, 91 11 23421006, Fax: 91 11 23421956. **Founded:** 1991. **Key Personnel:** M.C. Aggarwal, Engr.-in-Ch., phone 91 11 23421058, fax 91 11 23421006, einc@air.org.in. **Wattage:** 6000. **Ad Rates:** $80-150 for 10 seconds; $120-225 for 15 seconds; $240-450 for 30 seconds; $480-900 for 60 seconds. **URL:** http://www.allindiaradio.org.

Aurangabad

44945 ■ All India Radio Aurangabad - 1521 KHz
Jalna Rd.

Aurangabad 431 005, Maharashtra, India
Ph: 91 240 2331001
E-mail: airagbd@rediffmail.com
Format: Eclectic. **Owner:** Prasar Bharati, Akashvani Bhavan, Sansad Marg, New Delhi 110 001, Delhi, India, 91 11 23421006, Fax: 91 11 23421956. **Founded:** 1976. **Key Personnel:** M.C. Aggarwal, Engr.-in-Ch., phone 91 11 23421058, fax 91 11 23421006, einc@air.org.in. **Wattage:** 1000. **Ad Rates:** $150-300 for 10 seconds; $225-450 for 15 seconds; $450-900 for 30 seconds; $900-1,800 for 60 seconds. **URL:** http://www.allindiaradio.org.

Balaghat

44946 ■ All India Radio Balaghat - 101.3 KHz
Akashvani Bhavan
Sansad Marg
New Delhi 110 001, Delhi, India
Ph: 91 11 23421006
Fax: 91 11 23421956
E-mail: airbgt@sancharnet.in
Format: Eclectic. **Owner:** Prasar Bharati, at above address. **Founded:** 1992. **Key Personnel:** M.C. Aggarwal, Engr.-in-Ch., phone 91 11 23421058, fax 91 11 23421006, einc@air.org.in. **Wattage:** 6000. **Ad Rates:** $80-150 for 10 seconds; $120-225 for 15 seconds; $240-450 for 30 seconds; $480-900 for 60 seconds. **URL:** http://www.allindiaradio.org.

Balasore

44947 ■ International Journal of Educational Administration
Research India Publications
c/o Brajamohan Otta, Assoc. Ed.
Distance & Continuing Education
F. M. University, Vyasa Vihar
Balasore 756019, Orissa, India
Publisher E-mail: info@ripublication.com
Journal covering nature of educational administration, organizational theory, educational leadership and present day practices. **Subtitle:** Challenges and Prospects. **Freq:** 4/yr. **Key Personnel:** Brajamohan Otta, Assoc. Ed. **URL:** http://www.ripublication.com/ijea.htm.

Bangalore

44948 ■ Amruth
Foundation for Revitalization of Local Health
74/2 Jarakbhande Kaval
Attur Post, Via. Yelehanka
Bangalore 560 064, Karnataka, India
Ph: 91 808 568000
Fax: 91 808 567926
Publisher E-mail: info@frlht.org.in
Traditional healthcare magazine. **Freq:** Bimonthly. **Key Personnel:** Amita Kaushal, Asst. Ed. **Subscription Rates:** Rs 240 individuals; US$30 other countries; Rs 400 institutions. **URL:** http://www.heritageamruth.com/. **Ad Rates:** BW: Rs 200, 4C: Rs 400. **Circ:** Paid ⊕5,000

44949 ■ Asia Pacific Disability Rehabilitation Journal
Shree Ramana Maharishi Academy for the Blind
J-124, Ushas Apt.
16th Main, 4th Block
Jayanagar
Bangalore 560 011, Karnataka, India
Ph: 91 80 26633762
Fax: 91 80 26633762
Publisher E-mail: mail@srmab.org.in
Journal on social service focusing on disability and rehabilitation, particulary community based rehabilitation. **Founded:** Jan. 1990. **Freq:** Semiannual January & July. **Key Personnel:** Dr. Maya Thomas, Editor, thomasmaya@hotmail.com. **Subscription Rates:** Free on request. **URL:** http://www.dinf.ne.jp/doc/english/asia/resource/apdrj/apdrj.html. **Circ:** Paid 2,000

44950 ■ The Asian Age
Asian Age (South) Ltd.
68 Lavelle Rd.
Bangalore 560 001, Karnataka, India
Ph: 91 80 2270830
Fax: 91 80 2273561
General newspaper. **Founded:** 1997. **Freq:** Daily. **Print**

Circulation: ★ = ABC; △ = BPA; ◆ = CAC; • = CCAB; ❏ = VAC; ⊕ = PO Statement; ‡ = Publisher's Report; Boldface figures = sworn; Light figures = estimated.

Method: Offset - Newsline 30. **Key Personnel:** Shekhar Bhatia, Editor; M.J. Akbar, Ed.-in-Ch./Mng. Dir. **Subscription Rates:** Rs 1.50 single issue. **Remarks:** Accepts advertising. **URL:** http://www.asianage.com/. **Circ:** Paid 28,870

44951 ■ Bulletin of Materials Science
Indian Academy of Sciences
C.V. Raman Ave.
PO Box 8005
Sadashivanagar
Bangalore 560 080, Karnataka, India
Ph: 91 802 3612546
Fax: 91 802 3616094
Publication E-mail: matersci@ias.ernet.in
Publisher E-mail: office@ias.ernet.in
Illustrated technical journal. **Founded:** 1979. **Freq:** Bimonthly. **Print Method:** Offset. **Trim Size:** 21 x 28 cm. **Key Personnel:** S.B. Krupanidhi, Editor; A.H. Chokshi, Editorial Committee; H.L. Bhat, Editorial Committee; D.C. Agrawal, Editorial Committee; G.U. Kulkarni, Editorial Committee; Murali Sastry, Editorial Committee; D. Bahadur, Editorial Committee; S. Basu, Editorial Committee; S.K. Bhaumik, Editorial Committee; H.S. Maiti, Editorial Committee. **ISSN:** 0250-4707. **Subscription Rates:** Rs 400 institutions RSA; Rs 500 two years. **Remarks:** Advertising not accepted. **URL:** http://www.ias.ac.in/matersci/. **Circ:** 2,228

44952 ■ Current Colorectal Cancer Reports
Current Science Association
C.V. Raman Ave.
PO Box 8001
Bangalore 560 080, Karnataka, India
Ph: 91 802 3612310
Fax: 91 802 3616094
Publisher E-mail: currsci@ias.ernet.in
Journal that covers information on colon cancer and how to treat it with bio medications naturally. **Freq:** Quarterly. **Key Personnel:** Jaffer A. Ajani, Editor-in-Chief; Robert Bresalier, Editorial Board Member; Charles Blanke, Editorial Board Member. **ISSN:** 1556-3790. **Subscription Rates:** US$95 individuals print & online; US$81 students residents, print & online; US$95 individuals online only; US$95 individuals print only; US$314 institutions academic, print only; US$628 institutions corporate, print only. **URL:** http://www.current-reports.com/home_journal.cfm?JournalID=CL.

44953 ■ Current Heart Failure Reports
Current Science Association
C.V. Raman Ave.
PO Box 8001
Bangalore 560 080, Karnataka, India
Ph: 91 802 3612310
Fax: 91 802 3616094
Publisher E-mail: currsci@ias.ernet.in
Journal that covers information on heart attacks and how to prevent them by using bio medications naturally. **Freq:** Quarterly. **Key Personnel:** Gerd Hasenfuss, MD, Assoc. Ed.; Jay N. Cohn, MD, Editorial Board Member; Wilson S. Colucci, Editor-in-Chief; Kirkwood F. Adams, Jr., Editorial Board Member; Gary S. Francis, Editorial Board Member; Marvin A. Konstam, Editorial Board Member. **ISSN:** 1546-9530. **Subscription Rates:** US$151 individuals; US$76 individuals; US$105 individuals; US$302 institutions; US$604 institutions. **URL:** http://www.current-reports.com/home_journal.cfm?JournalID=HF.

44954 ■ Current Hematology Reports
Current Science Association
C.V. Raman Ave.
PO Box 8001
Bangalore 560 080, Karnataka, India
Ph: 91 802 3612310
Fax: 91 802 3616094
Publication E-mail: info_phl@currentmedicinegroup.com
Publisher E-mail: currsci@ias.ernet.in
Journal that covers information on blood diseases and how to treat or prevent them using bio medications naturally. **Freq:** Bimonthly. **Key Personnel:** Steven R. Deitcher, Editor; Dieter Hoelzer, Assoc. Ed.; James N. George, Editor. **ISSN:** 1540-3408. **URL:** http://www.current-reports.com/home_journal.cfm?journalid=he.

44955 ■ Current Hepatitis Reports
Current Science Association
C.V. Raman Ave.
PO Box 8001

Bangalore 560 080, Karnataka, India
Ph: 91 802 3612310
Fax: 91 802 3616094
Publisher E-mail: currsci@ias.ernet.in
Journal that covers information on hepatitis A and B and treatments and preventing using bio medications naturally. **Key Personnel:** Bruce R. Bacon, Editor-in-Chief; Rajender K. Reddy, Editor-in-Chief; Jean-Michel Pawlotsky, Assoc. Ed. **ISSN:** 1540-3416. **Subscription Rates:** US$95 individuals; US$76 students; US$302 institutions academic; US$604 institutions corporate. **URL:** http://www.current-reports.com/home_journal.cfm?JournalID=HP.

44956 ■ Current Science
Current Science Association
C.V. Raman Ave.
PO Box 8001
Bangalore 560 080, Karnataka, India
Ph: 91 802 3612310
Fax: 91 802 3616094
Publisher E-mail: currsci@ias.ernet.in
Illustrated scientific journal. **Founded:** 1932. **Freq:** fortnightly. **Print Method:** Offset. **Trim Size:** 21 x 28 cm. **Key Personnel:** P. Balaram, Editor; K.S. Gandhi, Assoc. Ed.; N.V. Joshi, Assoc. Ed. **ISSN:** 0011-3891. **Subscription Rates:** Rs 3,000 institutions government departments, universities; Rs 5,000 institutions commercial establishment, Business houses; Rs 1,000 institutions school and colleges; Rs 1,000 two years; Rs 1,600 individuals 3 years; Rs 2,700 individuals 5 years; US$100 individuals air mail; US$300 institutions, other countries; US$15 single issue. **Remarks:** Accepts advertising. **URL:** http://www.ias.ac.in/. **Ad Rates:** BW: US$10,000. **Circ:** 5,500

44957 ■ Deccan Herald
The Printers (Mysore) Ltd.
75 Mahatma Gandhi Rd.
PO Box 5331
Bangalore 560 001, Karnataka, India
Ph: 91 80 25880000
Fax: 91 80 25880523
General newspaper. **Founded:** 1948. **Freq:** Daily. **Key Personnel:** Anand Rama Goud, Advertising Mgr., anandramagoud@deccanherald.co.in; Bob P. Seshadri, Website Advertisement, bobseshadri@deccanherald.co.in; Badri Narayan, Advertising Mgr., ngbadri@deccanherald.co.in; D.B. Dutta, Vice President, db.dutta@deccanherald.co.in. **ISSN:** 0971-717X. **Subscription Rates:** Rs 17,185 other countries by airmail; Rs 3,094 other countries Sunday edition by airmail; Rs 1,415 individuals; Rs 272 individuals Sunday edition; Rs 194 individuals Wednesday edition; Rs 194 individuals Friday edition; Rs 3,042 individuals Wednesday edition by airmail; Rs 3,042 individuals Friday edition by airmail; Rs 6,580 other countries sea mail; Rs 1,014 other countries Sunday edition by sea mail. **Remarks:** Advertising accepted; rates available upon request. **URL:** http://www.deccanherald.com/. **Circ:** Paid ★147,538

44958 ■ The Economic Times
Bennet, Coleman & Company Ltd.
No. 17, Du Parc Trinity, 9th Fl.
M.G. Rd.
Bangalore 560 001, Karnataka, India
Financial news daily. **Founded:** 1985. **Freq:** Daily. **Key Personnel:** Harsha Dandapani, Contact. **Subscription Rates:** Rs 2 Mon.-Fri.; Rs 7 Sun. **Remarks:** Accepts advertising. **URL:** http://www.economictimes.com. **Circ:** Paid 24,489

44959 ■ Indian Institute of Science Journal
Indian Institute of Science
The Registrar
Bangalore 560 012, Karnataka, India
Ph: 91 802 3600757
Fax: 91 802 3600683
Publisher E-mail: regr@admin.iisc.ernet.in
Scientific journal. **Founded:** 1914. **Freq:** Quarterly. **Key Personnel:** Vasant Natarajan, Member, vasant@physics.iisc.ernet.in; T.N. Guru Row, Editor, ssctng@sscu.iisc.ernet.in; M.S. Shaila, Member, shaila@mcbl.iisc.ernet.in; Debasish Ghose, Member, dghose@aero.iisc.ernet.in; Debasis Sengupta, Member, dsen@caos.iisc.ernet.in; G.K. Ananthasuresh, Member, suresh@mecheng.iisc.ernet.in; Sundarrajan Asokan, Member, sasokan@isu.iisc.ernet.in; S. Venkadesan, Exec. Ed.,

venky@library.iisc.ernet.in. **ISSN:** 0019-4964. **Subscription Rates:** Rs 1,200 individuals; Rs 300 single issue; US$400 individuals overseas; US$100 single issue overseas. **Remarks:** Accepts advertising. **URL:** http://journal.library.iisc.ernet.in/. **Circ:** Paid 500

44960 ■ Indian Institute of World Culture Bulletin
Indian Institute of World Culture
No. 6, B.P. Wadia Rd.
Basavanagudi
Bangalore 560 004, Karnataka, India
Ph: 91 80 6678581
Educational magazine. **Founded:** 1981. **Freq:** Monthly. **ISSN:** 0251-1630. **URL:** http://www.ultindia.org.

44961 ■ Indian Journal of Aerospace Medicine
Indian Society of Aerospace Medicine
Indian Air Force
Vimanapura
Bangalore 560 017, Karnataka, India
Ph: 91 802 5224131
Publication E-mail: iamiaf@vsnl.net
Publisher E-mail: admin@isam-india.org
Publication on aerospace medicine. **Founded:** 1954. **Freq:** Semiannual. **Key Personnel:** J.K. Gupta, President; C.K. Ranjan, Editorial Advisory Board; S. Chowdhary, Editorial Advisory Board; Pankaj Tyagi, Ed. **ISSN:** 0970-6666. **Subscription Rates:** Rs 400 individuals; US$45 other countries; Rs 200 single issue; US$25 single issue other countries. **URL:** http://www.medind.nic.in/iab/iabm.shtml.

44962 ■ Indian Silk
Central Silk Board
CSB Complex
B.T.M. Layout, Madivala
Hosur Rd.
Bangalore 560 068, Karnataka, India
Ph: 91 80 26282699
Fax: 91 80 26681511
Publication E-mail: indsilk@silkboard.org
Publisher E-mail: csb@silkboard.org
Magazine focusing on silk and textile. **Freq:** Monthly. **Key Personnel:** M. Sathiyavathy, Editor-in-Chief; M.N. Ramesha, Editor. **ISSN:** 0536-695X. **Subscription Rates:** Rs 360 individuals; US$30 individuals Bangladesh, Bhutan, Nepal, Pakistan; US$65 other countries. **Remarks:** Accepts advertising. **URL:** http://www.indiansilk.kar.nic.in/indian_silk.html. **Formerly:** Silk in India. **Circ:** (Not Reported)

44963 ■ International Journal of Aerospace Innovations
Multi-Science Publishing Company Ltd.
c/o Dr. G. Jagadeesh, Ed.-in-Ch.
Dept. of Aerospace Engineering
Indian Institute of Science
Bangalore 560 012, Karnataka, India
Publisher E-mail: info@multi-science.co.uk
Journal covering the latest technological developments in aerospace engineering. **Freq:** Quarterly. **Key Personnel:** Dr. G. Jagadeesh, Editor-in-Chief, jagadeeshgopalan@gmail.com. **ISSN:** 1757-2258. **Subscription Rates:** 267 individuals print and online; 245 individuals print only; 233 individuals online only. **Remarks:** Accepts advertising. **URL:** http://www.multi-science.co.uk/ijai.htm. **Circ:** (Not Reported)

44964 ■ International Journal of Yoga
Medknow Publications Pvt Ltd.
Swami Vivekananda Yoga Anusandhana Samsthana
No. 19, Eknath Bhavan, Gavipuram Cir.
KG Nagar
Bangalore 560019, Karnataka, India
Peer-reviewed journal covering Yoga therapy. **Founded:** 1978. **Freq:** Quarterly. **Print Method:** Offset. **Trim Size:** 7 x 10. **Cols./Page:** 1. **Col. Width:** 63 nonpareils. **Col. Depth:** 124 agate lines. **Key Personnel:** Prof. Nagendra H.R., Editor-in-Chief; Prof. Swamy NVC, Editor; Dr. Srinivasan TM, Exec. Ed. **ISSN:** 0973-6131. **Subscription Rates:** Rs 1,500 individuals; Rs 1,500 institutions; US$150 other countries; US$200 institutions, other countries; Rs 1,200 individuals online; Rs 1,800 individuals print and online. **Remarks:** Accepts advertising. **URL:** http://www.ijoy.org.in/. **Circ:** (Not Reported)

44965 ■ Journal of Astrophysics and Astronomy
Indian Academy of Sciences
C.V. Raman Ave.
PO Box 8005

Sadashivanagar
Bangalore 560 080, Karnataka, India
Ph: 91 802 3612546
Fax: 91 802 3616094
Publication E-mail: jaa@ias.ernet.in
Publisher E-mail: office@ias.ernet.in
Scientific journal focusing on astronomy. **Founded:** 1980. **Freq:** Quarterly. **Print Method:** Offset. **Trim Size:** 7 x 9 1/2. **Key Personnel:** Rajaram Nityananda, Assoc. Ed.; Chanda J. Jog, Editor-in-Chief. **ISSN:** 0250-6335. **Subscription Rates:** Rs 300 institutions India; Rs 400 two years individual. **URL:** http://www.ias.ac.in/jaa/index.html. **Circ:** Paid 800

44966 ■ Journal of Biosciences
Indian Academy of Sciences
C.V. Raman Ave.
PO Box 8005
Sadashivanagar
Bangalore 560 080, Karnataka, India
Ph: 91 802 3612546
Fax: 91 802 3616094
Publication E-mail: jbiosci@ias.ernet.in
Publisher E-mail: office@ias.ernet.in
Scientific journal focusing on biology. **Founded:** 1979. **Freq:** Quarterly. **Key Personnel:** Durgadas P Kasbekar, Editor; Ashima Anand, Editorial Board, ashima_anand@hotmail.com; Rustom Antia, Editorial Board, rantia@emory.edu. **ISSN:** 0250-5991. **Subscription Rates:** Rs 500 two years individual; Rs 400 institutions. **URL:** http://www.ias.ac.in/jbiosci/index.html. **Circ:** Paid 2,100

44967 ■ Journal of Chemical Sciences
Indian Academy of Sciences
C.V. Raman Ave.
PO Box 8005
Sadashivanagar
Bangalore 560 080, Karnataka, India
Ph: 91 802 3612546
Fax: 91 802 3616094
Publisher E-mail: office@ias.ernet.in
Peer-reviewed Journal covering all areas of chemical sciences. **Freq:** Bimonthly. **Key Personnel:** S.S. Krishnamurthy, Editor; Uday Maitra, Assoc. Ed.; Sujit Roy, Editorial Board; Smaresh Bhattacharyya, Editorial Board; C.N.R. Rao, Editorial Board; Charusita Chakravarty, Editorial Board. **ISSN:** 0253-4134. **Subscription Rates:** Rs 400 institutions; Rs 500 two years. **URL:** http://www.ias.ac.in/chemsci/index.html.

44968 ■ Journal of Cutaneous and Aesthetic Surgery
Medknow Publications Pvt Ltd.
c/o Venkat Charmalaya-Ctr. for Advanced Dermatology
3437, 1st G cross, 7th main
Subbanna Garden
Vijay Nagar
Bangalore 560040, Karnataka, India
Publication E-mail: editor@jcasonline.org
Peer-reviewed journal covering aesthetic and skin surgery. **Freq:** Quarterly. **Key Personnel:** Venkatram Mysore, Editor-in-Chief; Somesh Gupta, Assoc. Ed.; Munish Paul, Dep. Ed. **ISSN:** 0378-6326. **Subscription Rates:** Rs 1,000 individuals print; Rs 2,000 institutions print; US$100 individuals print; US$200 institutions print; Rs 800 individuals online; Rs 1,600 institutions online; US$80 individuals online; US$160 institutions online; Rs 1,200 individuals print and online; US$240 institutions print and online. **Remarks:** Accepts advertising. **URL:** http://www.jcasonline.com. **Circ:** (Not Reported)

44969 ■ Journal of Dharma
c/o Augustine Thottakara, Ed.
Dharmaram Vidya Kshetram
Centre for the Study of World Religions
Dharmaram College
Bangalore 560 029, Karnataka, India
Publisher E-mail: saju@chackalackal.com
Publication on world religions. **Subtitle:** An International Quarterly of World Religions. **Founded:** 1975. **Freq:** Quarterly. **Print Method:** Offset. **Trim Size:** 24 x 15.5 cm. **Key Personnel:** Augustine Thottakara, Editor, thotaka@bgl.vsnl.net.in; J.G. Arapura, Assoc. Ed.; Thomas Aykara, Assoc. Ed.; J.B. Chethimattam, Assoc. Ed.; Thomas Kadankavil, Assoc. Ed.; Thomas Kalam, Assoc. Ed.; Antony Kalliath, Assoc. Ed.; Cherian Menacherry, Assoc. Ed.; G.C. Nayak, Assoc. Ed.; David Scott, Assoc. Ed. **ISSN:** 0253-7222. **Subscription**

Rates: Rs 120; Rs 325; Rs 30 individuals India; Rs 80 individuals three years; US$200 individuals foreign (air mail), three years; Rs 500 individuals foreign (air mail), three years. **Remarks:** Advertising not accepted. **URL:** http://www.journalofdharma.com/. **Circ:** Paid 1,800

44970 ■ Journal of Earth System Science
Indian Academy of Sciences
C.V. Raman Ave.
PO Box 8005
Sadashivanagar
Bangalore 560 080, Karnataka, India
Ph: 91 802 3612546
Fax: 91 802 3616094
Publication E-mail: jessc@ias.ernet.in
Publisher E-mail: office@ias.ernet.in
Interdisciplinary journal publishing high-quality research, including new data, ideas, and conceptual advances in Earth System Science in its broadest sense, covering the solid earth, the atmosphere, the hydrosphere, and the biosphere; addressing related aspects of planetary and space sciences. **Freq:** Quarterly. **Key Personnel:** S.R. Shetye, Editor-in-Chief; G.S. Bhat, Editorial Board; P. Dewangan, Assoc. Ed. **ISSN:** 0253-2143. **Subscription Rates:** Rs 400 institutions; Rs 500 individuals two years. **URL:** http://www.ias.ac.in/jessci/index_body.html.

44971 ■ Journal of Genetics
Indian Academy of Sciences
C.V. Raman Ave.
PO Box 8005
Sadashivanagar
Bangalore 560 080, Karnataka, India
Ph: 91 802 3612546
Fax: 91 802 3616094
Publication E-mail: jgenet@ias.ernet.in
Publisher E-mail: office@ias.ernet.in
Science journal on genetics featuring charts and illustrations. **Founded:** 1985. **Freq:** 3/yr. **Print Method:** Offset. **Trim Size:** 210 x 280 mm. **Key Personnel:** Amitabh Joshi, Editor-in-Chief; Kunal Ray, Assoc. Ed.; Partha P. Majumder, Assoc. Ed. **ISSN:** 0022-1333. **Subscription Rates:** Rs 300 libraries; Rs 400 two years personal. **Remarks:** Advertising not accepted. **URL:** http://www.ias.ac.in/jgenet. **Circ:** Paid 1000

44972 ■ Journal of the Geological Society of India
Geological Society of India
No. 63, 12th Cross
Basappa Layout
Gavipuram
Bangalore 560 019, Karnataka, India
Ph: 91 80 26522943
Fax: 91 80 26613352
Publisher E-mail: gsocind@gmail.com
Periodical on geology. **Founded:** 1959. **Freq:** Monthly. **Print Method:** Offset. **Trim Size:** 28 x 21 cm. **Key Personnel:** B. Mahabaleswar, Editor. **ISSN:** 0016-7622. **Remarks:** Advertising not accepted. **URL:** http://www.geosocindia.org/JournalInformation.aspx; http://www.springer.com/earthsciencesandgeography/geology/journal/12594. **Circ:** Paid 2,000

44973 ■ Journal of Human Reproductive Sciences
Medknow Publications Pvt Ltd.
Bangalore Assisted Conception Ctr.
6/7 Kumara Krupa Rd.
High Grounds
Bangalore 560 001, Karnataka, India
Publication E-mail: editor@jhrsonline.org
Peer-reviewed journal focusing on human reproductive sciences. **Founded:** Jan. 2008. **Freq:** Quarterly. **Key Personnel:** Kamini A. Rao, Editor-in-Chief; Madjuri Patil, Asst. Ed.; Gamal Serour, Assoc. Ed. **ISSN:** 0974-1208. **Subscription Rates:** Rs 1,200 individuals print only; Rs 1,500 institutions print only; US$150 other countries print only; US$150 institutions, other countries print only; Rs 1,500 individuals print and online; Rs 1,800 institutions print and online; US$180 other countries print and online; US$180 institutions, other countries print and online; Rs 1,000 individuals online; Rs 1,200 institutions online. **Remarks:** Accepts advertising. **URL:** http://www.jhrsonline.org. **Circ:** (Not Reported)

44974 ■ Journal of Indian Prosthodontic Society
Medknow Publications Pvt Ltd.

c/o Ravindra C. Savadi, Ed.
296/D 5th block, 9th main, 38th cross
Jayanagar
Bangalore 560011, Karnataka, India
Peer-reviewed journal containing case reports, scientific studies, literature reviews and tips for the prosthodontic community. **Freq:** Bimonthly. **Key Personnel:** Dr. Ravindra C. Savadi, Editor, editor@jprosthodont.com. **ISSN:** 0972-4052. **Subscription Rates:** Rs 3,000 individuals India; Rs 4,000 institutions India; US$150 other countries; US$300 institutions, other countries. **URL:** http://www.jprosthodont.com.

44975 ■ Journal of Natural Remedies
Natural Remedies Private Ltd.
Plot No.5B Veerasandra Indl. Area
19 K.M. Stone, Hosur Rd.
Bangalore 560 100, Karnataka, India
Ph: 91 804 1859999
Fax: 91 804 0209817
Publication E-mail: jnr@naturalremedy.com
Publisher E-mail: info@naturalremedy.com
Journal publishing research work in the area of phytopharmacology and clinical reports of herbal drugs, also printing articles on phytochemistry, quality control and agronomy of medicinal plants, with special emphasis given to research work related to bioactivity-directed fractionation of plant extracts leading to novel bioactive molecules. **Subtitle:** Dedicated to Medicinal Plant Research. **Freq:** Semiannual. **Key Personnel:** A. Amit, Editor; D. Prashanth, Assoc. Ed. **Subscription Rates:** Rs 500 individuals; US$50 other countries. **URL:** http://www.jnronline.com/; http://www.naturalremedy.com/jnr-journal-of-natural-remedies.htm.

44976 ■ Journal of Young Pharmacists
Medknow Publications Pvt Ltd.
c/o Dr. Mueen Ahmed, Ed.-in-Ch.
H.Q.: Al-Ameen College of Pharmacy
Near Lalbagh Main Gate
Hosur Rd.
Bangalore 560 027, Karnataka, India
Publication E-mail: editor@jyoungpharm.in
Peer-reviewed journal of the InPharm Association. **Freq:** Quarterly. **Key Personnel:** Dr. Mueen Ahmed, Editor-in-Chief; Dr. Everlado Attard, Assoc. Ed.; Dr. Ambrose Furey, Assoc. Ed. **ISSN:** 0975-1483. **Subscription Rates:** Rs 2,000 individuals print only; Rs 2,000 institutions print only; US$350 other countries print only; US$350 institutions, other countries print only; Rs 2,400 individuals print and online; Rs 2,400 institutions print and online; US$420 other countries print and online; US$420 institutions, other countries print and online; Rs 1,600 individuals online; Rs 1,600 institutions online. **Remarks:** Accepts advertising. **URL:** http://www.jyoungpharm.in. **Circ:** (Not Reported)

44977 ■ Karnataka Medical Journal
Indian Medical Association, Karnataka State Branch
IMA House
Alur Venkata Rao Rd.
Bangalore 560 018, Karnataka, India
Medical journal of Karnataka. **Founded:** 1939. **Freq:** Quarterly. **Key Personnel:** Dr. R. Jyothiswaroop, Editor. **ISSN:** 0377-9378. **Subscription Rates:** Rs 75 individuals; Rs 100 institutions. **Remarks:** Accepts advertising. **URL:** http://www.medindia.net/doctors/journals/indian/indian_journals.asp?stype=alpha&jid=68. **Circ:** Paid 5,000

44978 ■ The New Indian Express
Express Publications (Madurai) Ltd.
Express Bldg.
1 Queens Rd.
Bangalore 560 001, Karnataka, India
General newspaper. **Founded:** 1932. **Freq:** Daily. **Key Personnel:** G. Ulaganathan, Editor. **Subscription Rates:** Rs 2 single issue; Rs 4 individuals Sunday edition. **Remarks:** Accepts advertising. **URL:** http://www.expressbuzz.com/edition/default.aspx. **Circ:** (Not Reported)

44979 ■ NTI Bulletin
National Tuberculosis Institute—India
No. 8 Bellary Rd.
Bangalore 560 003, Karnataka, India
Ph: 91 80 3441192
Fax: 91 80 3440952
Publication E-mail: ntiindia@blr.vsnl.net.in

Circulation: ★ = ABC; △ = BPA; ♦ = CAC; • = CCAB; ❑ = VAC; ⊕ = PO Statement; ‡ = Publisher's Report; Boldface figures = sworn; Light figures = estimated.

Gale Directory of Publications & Broadcast Media/147th Ed.   4991

Publisher E-mail: ntiindia@blr.vsnl.net.in
Medical journal on research in tuberculosis and other respiratory diseases. **Founded:** 1963. **Freq:** Semiannual. **Key Personnel:** Dr. V.K. Chadha, Co-Ed.; Sudha S. Murthy, Publication Sec.; V.K. Challu, Member; K.P. Unnikrishnan, Ch. Statistical Off.; N. Srikantaramu, Statistical Asst.; Sanjay Singh, Field Investigator; S.R. Kusuma, Lab Techn.; Dr. Prahlad Kumar, Editor. **ISSN:** 0047-9136. **URL:** http://medind.nic.in/nac/nacm.shtml. **Circ:** 1,000

44980 ■ Pharmacognosy @MAG
Medknow Publications Pvt Ltd.
c/o Prof. BG Shivananda, Ed.-in-Ch.
Al-Ameen College of Pharmacy
Near Lalbagh Main Gate
Hosur Rd.
Bangalore 560 027, Karnataka, India
@MAG publishing medicinal plant research and development. **Freq:** Quarterly. **Key Personnel:** B.G. Shivananda, Editor-in-Chief, editor@phcog.com; Dr. Mueen Ahmed, Managing Editor, mueen.ahmed@phcog.net; Dr. Arun Kumar, Editor. **ISSN:** 0973-1296. **Subscription Rates:** Rs 2,000 individuals print only; Rs 2,000 institutions print only; US$350 other countries print only; US$350 institutions, other countries print only; Rs 2,400 individuals print and online; Rs 2,400 institutions print and online; US$420 other countries print and online; US$420 institutions, other countries print and online; Rs 1,600 individuals online; US$280 other countries online. **Remarks:** Accepts advertising. **URL:** http://www.phcog.com/aboutus.asp. **Circ:** (Not Reported)

44981 ■ Pramana - Journal of Physics
Indian Academy of Sciences
C.V. Raman Ave.
PO Box 8005
Sadashivanagar
Bangalore 560 080, Karnataka, India
Ph: 91 802 3612546
Fax: 91 802 3616094
Publication E-mail: pramana@ias.ernet.in
Publisher E-mail: office@ias.ernet.in
Peer-reviewed Journal covering current research in physics. **Freq:** Monthly. **Key Personnel:** Rohini M. Godbole, Editor, rohini@cts.iisc.ernet.in; Ramesh C. Budhani, Member, rcb@iitk.ac.in; N. V. Madhusudana, Assoc. Ed., nvmadhu@rri.res.in; Amit Roy, Member, gs.roy@iuac.res.in; Rajiv V. Gavai, Member, gavai@tifr.res.in; S. Phatak, Member, phatak@iopb.res.in. **ISSN:** 0304-4289. **Subscription Rates:** Rs 750 institutions; Rs 700 individuals. **URL:** http://www.ias.ac.in/pramana/index.htm.

44982 ■ Proceedings of the Indian Academy of Sciences
Indian Academy of Sciences
C.V. Raman Ave.
PO Box 8005
Sadashivanagar
Bangalore 560 080, Karnataka, India
Ph: 91 802 3612546
Fax: 91 802 3616094
Publisher E-mail: office@ias.ernet.in
Peer-reviewed Journal covering current research in Mathematics. **Freq:** Quarterly. **Key Personnel:** Gadadhar Misra, Editor; C.S. Seshadri, Editorial Board; A. Sitaram, Editorial Board; S.S. Abhyankar, Editorial Board; K.B. Athreya, Editorial Board; B. Bagchi, Editorial Board; B.V. Rao, Editorial Board; R. Sridharan, Editorial Board; Kapil H. Paranjape, Assoc. Ed.; S.G. Dani, Editorial Board. **ISSN:** 0253-4142. **Subscription Rates:** Rs 300 institutions for India; Rs 400 individuals for India. **URL:** http://www.ias.ac.in/mathsci/.

44983 ■ Profound (The Dialog Corporation) - Mathematical Sciences
Indian Academy of Sciences
C.V. Raman Ave.
PO Box 8005
Sadashivanagar
Bangalore 560 080, Karnataka, India
Ph: 91 802 3612546
Fax: 91 802 3616094
Publication E-mail: mathsci@ias.ernet.in
Publisher E-mail: office@ias.ernet.in
Journal publishing refereed papers covering current research in mathematics. **Founded:** 1934. **Freq:** Quarterly. **Key Personnel:** Gadadhar Misra, Editor; B.

Bagchi, Editorial Board; S.G. Dani, Editorial Board; Kapil H Paranjape, Assoc. Ed.; K.B. Athreya, Editorial Board; S.S. Abhyankar, Editorial Board. **ISSN:** 0253-4142. **Subscription Rates:** Rs 250 institutions; Rs 175 individuals. **URL:** http://www.ias.ac.in/mathsci/index.html.

44984 ■ Quarterly Journal of the Mythic Society
Mythic Society
Nrupatunga Rd.
Bangalore 560 001, Karnataka, India
Ph: 91 80 2215034
Publication focusing on social research. **Founded:** 1909. **Freq:** Quarterly. **Print Method:** DTP. **Key Personnel:** S.U. Kamath, Editor. **ISSN:** 0047-8555. **Remarks:** Advertising not accepted. **URL:** http://www.children-of-bangalore.com/mythics.htm. **Circ:** Paid 340

44985 ■ Resonance
Indian Academy of Sciences
C.V. Raman Ave.
PO Box 8005
Sadashivanagar
Bangalore 560 080, Karnataka, India
Ph: 91 802 3612546
Fax: 91 802 3616094
Publication E-mail: resonance@ias.ernet.in
Publisher E-mail: office@ias.ernet.in
Peer-reviewed Journal on science education. **Subtitle:** Journal of Science Education. **Founded:** 1996. **Freq:** Monthly. **Key Personnel:** N. Mukunda, Council of Ed.; M.K. Chandrashekaran, Council of Ed.; S. Mahadevan, Ch. Ed. **ISSN:** 0971-8044. **Subscription Rates:** Rs 400 institutions; Rs 900 two years institution; Rs 1,300 institutions 36 issues; Rs 2,000 institutions 60 issues; Rs 110 individuals 60 issues; US$100 institutions, other countries; Rs 400 two years; Rs 650 individuals 36 issues. **URL:** http://www.ias.ac.in/resonance/about_us.htm. **Circ:** Paid 8,000

44986 ■ Sadhana
Indian Academy of Sciences
C.V. Raman Ave.
PO Box 8005
Sadashivanagar
Bangalore 560 080, Karnataka, India
Ph: 91 802 3612546
Fax: 91 802 3616094
Publication E-mail: sadhana@ias.ernet.in
Publisher E-mail: office@ias.ernet.in
Publication focusing on engineering science. **Subtitle:** Academy Profound (The Dialog Corporation) in Engineering Sciences. **Founded:** 1978. **Freq:** Bimonthly. **Print Method:** Photo Offset. **Trim Size:** 9 1/2 x 7. **Key Personnel:** G.V. Anand, Assoc. Ed.; R.N. Iyengar, Editor; V.H. Arakerl, Editorial Board. **ISSN:** 0256-2499. **Subscription Rates:** Rs 400 institutions; Rs 500 two years. **Remarks:** Advertising not accepted. **URL:** http://www.ias.ac.in/sadhana/index.html. **Circ:** Paid 850

44987 ■ Sanjevani
Karnataka News Pulications Pvt. Ltd.
11/2, Queens Rd.
Bangalore 560 052, Karnataka, India
General newspaper. **URL:** http://www.sanjevani.com/.

44988 ■ Systematic Reviews in Pharmacy
Medknow Publications Pvt Ltd.
c/o Dr. Mueen Ahmed KK, Ed.-in-Ch.
H.Q.: Al-Ameen College of Pharmacy
Near Lalbagh Main Gate
Hosur Rd.
Bangalore 560 027, Karnataka, India
Peer-reviewed journal on pharmaceutical research and development. **Freq:** Semiannual. **Key Personnel:** Dr. Mueen Ahmed, KK, Editor-in-Chief, editor@sysrevpharm.org; Dr. Everlado Attard, Assoc. Ed.; Dr. Ambrose Furey, Assoc. Ed. **Subscription Rates:** Rs 3,500 individuals print; US$500 institutions print; Rs 2,188 single issue print; US$312 single issue print; Rs 2,800 individuals online; US$400 institutions online; Rs 4,200 individuals print and online; US$600 institutions print and online. **Remarks:** Accepts advertising. **URL:** http://www.sysrevpharm.org. **Circ:** (Not Reported)

44989 ■ All India Radio Bangalore - 612 KHz
Raj Bhavan Rd.
Bangalore 560 013, Karnataka, India
Ph: 91 80 22268151
E-mail: airnu@bgl.vsnl.net.in
Format: Eclectic. **Owner:** Prasar Bharati, Akashvani

Bhavan, Sansad Marg, New Delhi 110 001, Delhi, India, 91 11 23421006, Fax: 91 11 23421956. **Founded:** 1955. **Key Personnel:** M.C. Aggarwal, Engr.-in-Ch., phone 91 11 23421058, fax 91 11 23421006, einc@air.org.in. **Wattage:** 200,000. **Ad Rates:** $200-550 for 10 seconds; $300-825 for 15 seconds; $600-1,650 for 30 seconds; $1,200-3,300 for 60 seconds. **URL:** http://www.allindiaradio.org.

Banswara

44990 ■ All India Radio Banswara - 101.3 MHz
Akashvani Bhavan
Sansad Marg
New Delhi 110 001, Delhi, India
Ph: 91 11 23421006
Fax: 91 11 23421956
E-mail: airbsw_jp1@sancharnet.in
Format: Eclectic. **Owner:** Prasar Bharati, at above address. **Founded:** 1991. **Key Personnel:** M.C. Aggarwal, Engr.-in-Ch., phone 91 11 23421058, fax 91 11 23421006, einc@air.org.in; Mohan Singh, Ch. Engr., Proj., phone 91 11 23421184. **Wattage:** 6000. **Ad Rates:** $80-150 for 10 seconds; $120-225 for 15 seconds; $240-450 for 30 seconds; $480-900 for 60 seconds. **URL:** http://www.allindiaradio.org.

Bareilly

44991 ■ All India Radio Bareilly - 100.4 MHz
Lal Phatak
Badaun Rd.
PO Box 15
Bareilly 243 001, Uttar Pradesh, India
Ph: 91 581 2517220
E-mail: airbly@nde.vsnl.net.in
Format: Eclectic. **Owner:** Prasar Bharati, Akashvani Bhavan, Sansad Marg, New Delhi 110 001, Delhi, India, 91 11 23421006, Fax: 91 11 23421956. **Founded:** 1993. **Key Personnel:** M.C. Aggarwal, Engr.-in-Ch., phone 91 11 23421058, fax 91 11 23421006, einc@air.org.in. **Wattage:** 6000. **Ad Rates:** $100-200 for 10 seconds; $150-300 for 15 seconds; $300-600 for 30 seconds; $600-1,800 for 60 seconds. **URL:** http://www.allindiaradio.org.

Baripada

44992 ■ All India Radio Baripada - 1485 KHz
Akashvani Bhavan
Sansad Marg
New Delhi 110 001, Delhi, India
Ph: 91 11 23421006
Fax: 91 11 23421956
E-mail: baripada@air.org.in
Format: Eclectic. **Owner:** Prasar Bharati, at above address. **Founded:** 1991. **Key Personnel:** M.C. Aggarwal, Engr.-in-Ch., phone 91 11 23421058, fax 91 11 23421006, einc@air.org.in. **Wattage:** 1000. **Ad Rates:** $80-150 for 10 seconds; $120-225 for 15 seconds; $240-450 for 30 seconds; $480-900 for 60 seconds. **URL:** http://www.allindiaradio.org.

Barmer

44993 ■ All India Radio Barmer - 1458 KHz
Laxmi Nagar
Barmer 344 001, Rajasthan, India
Ph: 91 2982 220361
E-mail: airbmr@sancharnet.in
Format: Eclectic. **Owner:** Prasar Bharati, Akashvani Bhavan, Sansad Marg, New Delhi 110 001, Delhi, India, 91 11 23421006, Fax: 91 11 23421956. **Founded:** 1992. **Key Personnel:** M.C. Aggarwal, Engr.-in-Ch., phone 91 11 23421058, fax 91 11 23421006, einc@air.org.in. **Wattage:** 20,000. **Ad Rates:** $80-150 for 10 seconds; $120-225 for 15 seconds; $240-450 for 30 seconds; $480-900 for 60 seconds. **URL:** http://www.allindiaradio.org.

Bathinda

44994 ■ All India Radio Bhatinda - 101.1 MHz
Akashvani Bhavan
Sansad Marg
New Delhi 110 001, Delhi, India
Ph: 91 11 23421006
Fax: 91 11 23421956

E-mail: airbti@sancharnet.in
Format: Eclectic. **Owner:** Prasar Bharati, at above address. **Founded:** 1991. **Key Personnel:** M.C. Aggarwal, Engr.-in-Ch., phone 91 11 23421058, fax 91 11 23421006, einc@air.org.in. **Wattage:** 6000. **Ad Rates:** $80-150 for 10 seconds; $120-225 for 15 seconds; $240-450 for 30 seconds; $480-900 for 60 seconds. **URL:** http://www.allindiaradio.org.

Beed

44995 ■ All India Radio Beed - 102.9 KHz
Khandeshwari Rd.
Beed 431 122, Maharashtra, India
Ph: 91 2442 222905
E-mail: airbeed@bom6.vsnl.net.in
Format: Eclectic. **Owner:** Prasar Bharati, Akashvani Bhavan, Sansad Marg, New Delhi 110 001, Delhi, India, 91 11 23421006, Fax: 91 11 23421956. **Founded:** 1990. **Key Personnel:** M.C. Aggarwal, Engr.-in-Ch., phone 91 11 23421058, fax 91 11 23421006, einc@air.org.in. **Wattage:** 6000. **Ad Rates:** $80-150 for 10 seconds; $120-225 for 15 seconds; $240-450 for 30 seconds; $480-900 for 60 seconds. **URL:** http://www.allindiaradio.org.

Belgaum (Karnataka)

44996 ■ Journal of Indian Academy of Oral Medicine and Radiology
Medknow Publications Pvt Ltd.
c/o Dr. Arvind Shetti, Ed.-in-Ch.
Shiva Basava Sadan, 1386/2A plot No. 14
Jadhav Nagar
Belgaum 590 010, Karnataka, India
Peer-reviewed journal of the Indian Academy of Oral Medicine and Radiology. **Freq:** Quarterly. **Key Personnel:** Dr. Arvind Shetti, Editor-in-Chief. **ISSN:** 0972-1363. **Subscription Rates:** Rs 2,500 individuals print only; Rs 2,500 institutions print only; US$450 other countries print only; US$450 institutions, other countries print only; Rs 3,000 individuals print and online; Rs 3,000 institutions print and online; US$540 other countries print and online; US$540 institutions, other countries print and online. **Remarks:** Accepts advertising. **URL:** http://www.jiaomr.org. **Circ:** (Not Reported)

Belgaum (Maharashtra)

44997 ■ Tarun Bharat
Tarun Bharat Daily Pvt. Ltd.
3524, Narvekar Galli
Belgaum 590 002, Maharashtra, India
Ph: 91 831 2404333
Fax: 91 831 2428603
General newspaper. **URL:** http://www.tarunbharat.com/INDEX.ASP.

Belonia

44998 ■ All India Radio Belonia - 103.7 MHz
Akashvani Bhavan
Sansad Marg
New Delhi 110 001, Delhi, India
Ph: 91 11 23421006
Fax: 91 11 23421956
E-mail: airbelon@sancharnet.in
Format: Eclectic. **Owner:** Prasar Bharati, at above address. **Founded:** 1992. **Key Personnel:** M.C. Aggarwal, Engr.-in-Ch., phone 91 11 23421058, fax 91 11 23421006, einc@air.org.in; Mohan Singh, Ch. Engr., Proj., phone 91 11 23421184. **Wattage:** 6000. **Ad Rates:** $80-150 for 10 seconds; $120-225 for 15 seconds; $240-450 for 30 seconds; $480-900 for 60 seconds. **URL:** http://www.allindiaradio.org.

Berhampur

44999 ■ All India Radio Berhampur - 100.6 MHz
Akashvani Bhavan
Sansad Marg
New Delhi 110 001, Delhi, India
Ph: 91 11 23421006
Fax: 91 11 23421956
E-mail: airbmr@sancharnet.in
Format: Eclectic. **Owner:** Prasar Bharati, at above address. **Founded:** 1993. **Key Personnel:** M.C. Aggarwal, Engr.-in-Ch., phone 91 11 23421058, fax 91 11 23421006, einc@air.org.in; Mohan Singh, Ch. Engr., Proj., phone 91 11 23421184. **Wattage:** 6000. **Ad Rates:** $80-150 for 10 seconds; $120-225 for 15 seconds; $240-450 for 30 seconds; $480-900 for 60 seconds. **URL:** http://www.allindiaradio.org.

Betul

45000 ■ All India Radio Betul - 103.1 KHz
Akashvani Bhavan
Sansad Marg
New Delhi 110 001, Delhi, India
Ph: 91 11 23421006
Fax: 91 11 23421956
E-mail: airbetul@sancharnet.in
Format: Eclectic. **Owner:** Prasar Bharati, at above address. **Founded:** 1991. **Key Personnel:** M.C. Aggarwal, Engr.-in-Ch., phone 91 11 23421058, fax 91 11 23421006, einc@air.org.in. **Wattage:** 6000. **Ad Rates:** $80-150 for 10 seconds; $120-225 for 15 seconds; $240-450 for 30 seconds; $480-900 for 60 seconds. **URL:** http://www.allindiaradio.org.

Bhadrawati

45001 ■ All India Radio Bhadrawati - 675 KHz
J. P. S. Colony
Paper Tower
Bhadrawati 577 302, Karnataka, India
Ph: 91 8282 2670228
E-mail: taranga@sancharnet.in
Format: Eclectic. **Owner:** Prasar Bharati, Akashvani Bhavan, Sansad Marg, New Delhi 110 001, Delhi, India, 91 11 23421006, Fax: 91 11 23421956. **Founded:** 1965. **Key Personnel:** M.C. Aggarwal, Engr.-in-Ch., phone 91 11 23421058, fax 91 11 23421006, einc@air.org.in. **Wattage:** 20,000. **Ad Rates:** $100-200 for 10 seconds; $150-300 for 15 seconds; $300-600 for 30 seconds; $600-1,200 for 60 seconds. **URL:** http://www.allindiaradio.org.

Bhagalpur

45002 ■ All India Radio Bhagalpur - 1458 KHz
Adampur
Bhagalpur 812 001, Bihar, India
Ph: 91 641 2400952
E-mail: seairbgp@dte.vsnl.net.in
Format: Eclectic. **Owner:** Prasar Bharati, Akashvani Bhavan, Sansad Marg, New Delhi 110 001, Delhi, India, 91 11 23421006, Fax: 91 11 23421956. **Founded:** 1967. **Key Personnel:** M.C. Aggarwal, Engr.-in-Ch., phone 91 11 23421058, fax 91 11 23421006, einc@air.org.in. **Wattage:** 20,000. **Ad Rates:** $100-200 for 10 seconds; $150-300 for 15 seconds; $300-600 for 30 seconds; $600-1,200 for 60 seconds. **URL:** http://www.allindiaradio.org.

Bhatkal

45003 ■ Sahil Daily
Bhatkal Media Publishing Society
SahilOnline, First Fl., Jamaat Complex
Next to KSRTC Bus Stand
Bhatkal 581 320, Karnataka, India
Ph: 91 838 5320768
Fax: 91 838 5223252
Publisher E-mail: info@sahilonline.org
General newspaper. **Founded:** 1973. **Freq:** Daily. **Print Method:** Offset. **Cols./Page:** 6. **Col. Width:** 21 1/2 inches. **Col. Depth:** 301 agate lines. **Key Personnel:** Aynaz Sattar, Editor; Naushad Kasimji, Legal Advisor; Inayatullah Gawai, Managing Editor; Fauzan Patel, Supporting Ed. **URL:** http://www.sahilonline.org/english/.

Bhawanipatna

45004 ■ All India Radio Bhawanipatna - 1206 KHz
Nektiguda
Bhawanipatna 766 001, Kalahandi district, India
Ph: 91 6670 230911
E-mail: airbpn21@sancharnet.in
Format: Eclectic. **Owner:** Prasar Bharati, Akashvani Bhavan, Sansad Marg, New Delhi 110 001, Delhi, India, 91 11 23421006, Fax: 91 11 23421956. **Founded:** 1993. **Key Personnel:** M.C. Aggarwal, Engr.-in-Ch., phone 91 11 23421058, fax 91 11 23421006, einc@air.org.in.

Wattage: 200,000. **Ad Rates:** $80-150 for 10 seconds; $120-225 for 15 seconds; $240-450 for 30 seconds; $480-900 for 60 seconds. **URL:** http://www.allindiaradio.org.

Bhopal

45005 ■ The Annals of Medical Entomology
S Z Husainy
101/22 Shivaji Nagar
Bhopal 462001, Madhya Pradesh, India
Publisher E-mail: anmedent@sancharnet.in
Medical science publication. **Founded:** 1992. **Freq:** Semiannual. **Key Personnel:** Zakir Husain Husainy, PhD, Ch. Ed., anmedent@sancharnet.in; Mohammad Ali Husainy, Editor. **ISSN:** 0971-135X. **Subscription Rates:** Rs 100 individuals; US$10 other countries plus air charges; Rs 50 single issue plus postage; US$5 other countries single copy, plus air charges. **Remarks:** Accepts advertising. **URL:** http://www.anmedent.com/. **Circ:** Paid 3,500

45006 ■ Dainik Bhaskar
6, Dwarka Sadan, Press Complex
Bhopal 462 011, Madhya Pradesh, India
Ph: 91 755 3988884
Fax: 91 755 270466
General newspaper. **Remarks:** Accepts advertising. **URL:** http://www.bhaskar.com/. **Circ:** (Not Reported)

45007 ■ Ultra Scientist of Physical Sciences
PO Box 93, GPO
Bhopal 462 001, Madhya Pradesh, India
Ph: 91 755 2533437
Publisher E-mail: chiefeditor@ultrascientists.org
Publication dedicated to the physical sciences. **Founded:** 1989. **Freq:** Semiannual. **Key Personnel:** A. H. Ansari, Editor-in-Chief. **ISSN:** 0970-9150. **Subscription Rates:** Rs 300 individuals; Rs 900 institutions; US$30 other countries; US$75 institutions, other countries. **Remarks:** Accepts advertising. **URL:** http://www.ultrascientist.org/JUSPS/index.htm. **Ad Rates:** BW: Rs 1,000. **Circ:** (Not Reported)

45008 ■ All India Radio Bhopal - 1593 KHz
Shyamla Hills
Bhopal 462 002, Madhya Pradesh, India
Ph: 91 755 2661160
E-mail: airbpl@sancharnet.in
Format: Eclectic. **Owner:** Prasar Bharati, Akashvani Bhavan, Sansad Marg, New Delhi 110 001, Delhi, India, 91 11 23421006, Fax: 91 11 23421956. **Founded:** 1956. **Key Personnel:** M.C. Aggarwal, Engr.-in-Ch., phone 91 11 23421058, fax 91 11 23421006, einc@air.org.in. **Wattage:** 10,000. **Ad Rates:** $180-400 for 10 seconds; $270-600 for 15 seconds; $540-1,200 for 30 seconds; $1,080-2,400 for 60 seconds. **URL:** http://www.allindiaradio.org.

Bhubaneswar (Orissa)

45009 ■ Dharitri
B - 26, Industrial Estate
PO Box 144
Bhubaneswar 751 010, Orissa, India
Ph: 91 674 2580348
Fax: 91 674 2586854
Publication E-mail: advt@dharitri.com
General newspaper. **URL:** http://www.dharitri.com.

45010 ■ International Journal of Computational Vision and Robotics
Inderscience Enterprises Limited
c/o Prof. Srikanta Patnaik, Ed.-in-Ch.
Interscience Institute of Management & Technology
P.O.: Kantabada
Bhubaneswar 752 024, Orissa, India
Peer-reviewed journal covering field of machine vision, robotics, cognition, and perception. **Freq:** Quarterly. **Key Personnel:** Srikanta Patnaik, Editor-in-Chief, patnaik_srikanta@yahoo.co.in. **ISSN:** 1752-9131. **Subscription Rates:** EUR494 individuals print or online; EUR672 individuals print and online. **URL:** http://www.inderscience.com/browse/index.php?journalCODE=ijcvr.

45011 ■ International Journal of Power and Energy Conversion
Inderscience Enterprises Limited
c/o Prof. P.K. Dash, Ed.-in-Ch.
Silicon Institute of Technology

Circulation: ★ = ABC; △ = BPA; ◆ = CAC; • = CCAB; ❑ = VAC; ⊕ = PO Statement; ‡ = Publisher's Report; Boldface figures = sworn; Light figures = estimated.

Chandrasekharpur Patia
Bhubaneswar 751 024, Orissa, India
Journal covering the field of power generation, transmission, and distribution. **Freq:** Quarterly. **Key Personnel:** Prof. P.K. Dash, Editor-in-Chief, pkdash.india@gmail.com; Dr. B.K. Panigrahi, Editor-in-Chief, bijayaketan.panigrahi@gmail.com. **ISSN:** 1757-1154. **Subscription Rates:** EUR494 individuals print or online; EUR672 individuals print and online. **URL:** http://www.inderscience.com/browse/index.php?journalCODE=ijpec.

45012 ■ The New Indian Express
Express Publications (Madurai) Ltd.
25-A Janpath Rd., Unit III
Bhubaneswar 751 001, Orissa, India
General newspaper. **Founded:** 1932. **Freq:** Daily. **Key Personnel:** P.S. Sundaram, Editor. **Remarks:** Accepts advertising. **URL:** http://www.epmltd.com/FirstFrame-nw.htm. **Circ:** (Not Reported)

45013 ■ Sambad
Eastern Media Limited
B-27, Industrial Estate, Rasulgarh
Bhubaneswar 751 010, Orissa, India
Ph: 91 674 2585351
Fax: 91 674 2588517
Publisher E-mail: sambadadvt@easternmedia.in
General newspaper. **Founded:** Oct. 4, 1984. **Remarks:** Accepts advertising. **URL:** http://www.orissasambad.com/. **Circ:** (Not Reported)

Bhubaneswar (West Bengal)

45014 ■ Pragativadi
178/B, Mancheswar Industrial Estate
Bhubaneswar 751 010, West Bengal, India
Ph: 91 674 2588297
Fax: 91 674 2582709
Publisher E-mail: pragativadi@pragativadi.com
General newspaper. **Freq:** Daily. **Key Personnel:** Samahit Bal, Exec. Ed. **Remarks:** Accepts advertising. **URL:** http://www.pragativadi.com/. **Circ:** ★200,921

Bhuj

45015 ■ All India Radio Bhuj - 1314 KHz
PO Box 01
Bhuj 370 001, Kachchh district, India
Ph: 91 2832 250852
E-mail: airbhujad1@sancharnet.in
Format: Eclectic. **Owner:** Prasar Bharati, Akashvani Bhavan, Sansad Marg, New Delhi 110 001, Delhi, India, 91 11 23421006, Fax: 91 11 23421956. **Founded:** 1965. **Key Personnel:** M.C. Aggarwal, Engr.-in-Ch., phone 91 11 23421058, fax 91 11 23421006, einc@air.org.in. **Wattage:** 10,000. **Ad Rates:** $100-200 for 10 seconds; $150-300 for 15 seconds; $300-600 for 30 seconds; $600-1,200 for 60 seconds. **URL:** http://www.allindiaradio.org.

Bijapur

45016 ■ All India Radio Bijapur - 101.8 MHz
Akashvani Bhavan
Sansad Marg
New Delhi 110 001, Delhi, India
Ph: 91 11 23421006
Fax: 91 11 23421956
E-mail: airbjp@sancharnet.in
Format: Eclectic. **Owner:** Prasar Bharati, at above address. **Founded:** 1997. **Key Personnel:** M.C. Aggarwal, Engr.-in-Ch., phone 91 11 23421058, fax 91 11 23421006, einc@air.org.in. **Wattage:** 6000. **Ad Rates:** $80-150 for 10 seconds; $120-225 for 15 seconds; $240-450 for 30 seconds; $480-900 for 60 seconds. **URL:** http://www.allindiaradio.org.

Bikaner

45017 ■ Journal of Camel Practice and Research
Camel Publishing House
67 Gandhi Nagar W
Near Lalgarh Palace
Bikaner 334 001, Rajasthan, India
Ph: 91 151 2521282
Fax: 91 151 2204100
Publisher E-mail: tkedjcpr@datainfosys.net
Scientific journal providing information on camels.

Founded: 1994. **Freq:** Semiannual. **Print Method:** Offset. **Trim Size:** 20.5 x 27.5 cm. **Key Personnel:** Dr. T.K. Gahlot, Editor, tkcamelvet@yahoo.com. **ISSN:** 0971-6777. **Subscription Rates:** Rs 1,000 individuals. **Remarks:** Accepts advertising. **URL:** http://www.camelsandcamelids.com/. **Ad Rates:** BW: US$300, 4C: US$800. **Circ:** Paid 750

45018 ■ All India Radio Bikaner - 1395 KHz
Akashvani Bhavan
Sansad Marg
New Delhi 110 001, Delhi, India
Ph: 91 11 23421006
Fax: 91 11 23421956
E-mail: airbkn@sancharnet.in
Format: Eclectic. **Owner:** Prasar Bharati, at above address. **Founded:** 1963. **Key Personnel:** M.C. Aggarwal, Engr.-in-Ch., phone 91 11 23421058, fax 91 11 23421006, einc@air.org.in; Mohan Singh, Ch. Engr., Proj., phone 91 11 23421184. **Wattage:** 20,000. **Ad Rates:** $100-200 for 10 seconds; $150-300 for 15 seconds; $300-600 for 30 seconds; $600-1,200 for 60 seconds. **URL:** http://www.allindiaradio.org.

Bilaspur

45019 ■ All India Radio Bilaspur - 103.2 KHz
Nutan Colony
PO Box 49
Bilaspur 495 001, Madhya Pradesh, India
Ph: 91 7752 254700
E-mail: airbilas@sancharnet.in
Format: Eclectic. **Owner:** Prasar Bharati, Akashvani Bhavan, Sansad Marg, New Delhi 110 001, Delhi, India, 91 11 23421006, Fax: 91 11 23421956. **Founded:** 1991. **Key Personnel:** M.C. Aggarwal, Engr.-in-Ch., phone 91 11 23421058, fax 91 11 23421006, einc@air.org.in. **Wattage:** 6000. **Ad Rates:** $80-150 for 10 seconds; $120-225 for 15 seconds; $240-450 for 30 seconds; $480-900 for 60 seconds. **URL:** http://www.allindiaradio.org.

Bolangir

45020 ■ All India Radio Bolangir - 101.9 MHz
Palach Line
Bolangir 767 001, Orissa, India
Ph: 91 6652 232280
E-mail: airbgr@sancharnet.in
Format: Full Service; Eclectic. **Owner:** Prasar Bharati, Akashvani Bhavan, Sansad Marg, New Delhi 110 001, Delhi, India, 91 11 23421006, Fax: 91 11 23421956. **Founded:** 1993. **Key Personnel:** M.C. Aggarwal, Engr.-in-Ch., phone 91 11 23421058, fax 91 11 23421006, einc@air.org.in. **Wattage:** 3000. **Ad Rates:** $80-150 for 10 seconds; $120-225 for 15 seconds; $240-450 for 30 seconds; $480-900 for 60 seconds. **URL:** http://www.allindiaradio.org.

Calcutta

45021 ■ Indian Journal of Physics, Part A
Indian Association for the Cultivation of Science
c/o J.K. Bhattacharjee, Ed.-in-Ch.
Dept. of Theoretical Physics
Indian Association for the Cultivation of Science
Jadavpur
Calcutta 700 032, West Bengal, India
Publication E-mail: ijp@iacs.res.in
Publication on physics. **Founded:** 1926. **Freq:** Monthly. **Print Method:** Offset. **Key Personnel:** Dr. K.K. Datta, Assoc. Ed.; J.K. Bhattacharjee, Editor-in-Chief; S.M. Bhattacharjee, Editor; R.K. Moitra, Editor; S.P. Bhattacharyya, Editor; P.K. Mukherjee, Editor; Indrani Bose, Editor; D.S. Ray, Editor; Bikas K. Chakrabarti, Editor; Arnab Rai Choudhuri, Editor. **ISSN:** 0973-1458. **Subscription Rates:** Rs 1,500 individuals including postage; US$500 other countries including air freight; US$50 single issue including air freight; Rs 150 single issue including postage. **Remarks:** Advertising not accepted. **URL:** http://www.iacs.res.in/ijp/. **Circ:** Combined ‡800

Calicut

45022 ■ Rheedea
Indian Association for Angiosperm Taxonomy
c/o University of Calicut
Dept. of Botany

Calicut 673 635, Kerala, India
Science magazine focusing on angiosperm taxonomy. **Founded:** 1991. **Freq:** Semiannual June & December. **Print Method:** Offset. **Key Personnel:** K.S. Manilal, Ch. Ed.; S.R. Yadav, Exec. Ed.; D. Narasimhan, Editor; M.K. Janarthanam, Editor; D.K. Singh, Editorial Board. **ISSN:** 0971-2313. **Subscription Rates:** Rs 500 individuals India; US$40 individuals rest of the world; Rs 1,000 institutions India; US$50 institutions rest of the world. **URL:** http://www.iaat.org.in/rheedea.html; http://www.iaat.org.in. **Circ:** Paid 500

45023 ■ Indian Journal of Nephrology
Indian Society of Nephrology
Postgraduate Institute of Medical Education & Research
Chandigarh 160 012, India
Ph: 91 172 2756733
Fax: 91 172 2744401
Publication E-mail: ijcm@iapsm.org
Publisher E-mail: vjha@pginephro.org
Journal covering advances in pediatric nephrology and management of common problems including nephrotic syndrome, urinary tract infections, tubular disorders, hypertension, malformations and renal failure. **Key Personnel:** V. Sakhuja, Editor; K.K. Malhotra, Editorial Board; A. Gupta, Contact; S.K. Agarwal, Assoc. Ed.; R.K. Sharma, Emeritus Ed. **URL:** http://medind.nic.in/iav/iavm.shtml.

Chandigarh (Chandigarh)

45024 ■ Indian Journal of Community Medicine
Indian Association of Preventive & Social Medicine
Postgraduate Institute of Medical Education & Research
Chandigarh 160 012, Chandigarh, India
Ph: 91 172 2744993
Fax: 91 172 2744993
Publisher E-mail: ijcm@iapsm.org
Journal for education of the medical community. **Founded:** 1960. **Freq:** 9/yr. **Print Method:** Offset. **Trim Size:** 8 1/8 x 10 7/8. **Cols./Page:** 3. **Col. Width:** 27 nonpareils. **Col. Depth:** 140 agate lines. **Key Personnel:** Arun K. Aggarwal, Managing Editor; Dr. Rajesh Kumar, Editor-in-Chief; Dr. Amarjeet Singh, Editor. **ISSN:** 0970-0218. **URL:** http://medind.nic.in/iaj/iajaj.shtml.

45025 ■ The Tribune
The Tribune Trust
The Tribune House
Sector 29-C
Chandigarh 160 030, Chandigarh, India
Ph: 91 172 2655066
Fax: 91 172 2651293
General interest newspaper. **Founded:** 1881. **Freq:** Daily. **Key Personnel:** Raj Chengappa, Ed.-in-Ch./Publisher, editorinchief@tribuneindia.com. **Subscription Rates:** Rs 8,220 other countries; Rs 768 individuals. **Remarks:** Accepts classified advertising. **URL:** http://www.tribuneindia.com. **Circ:** Paid 203,900

45026 ■ All India Radio Chandigarh - 103.1 MHz
Sector 34D
Chandigarh 160 022, Chandigarh, India
Ph: 91 172 2606125
E-mail: airchd@sify.com
Format: Eclectic. **Owner:** Prasar Bharati, Akashvani Bhavan, Sansad Marg, New Delhi 110 001, Delhi, India, 91 11 23421006, Fax: 91 11 23421956. **Founded:** 1997. **Operating Hours:** 0025-1200; 1245-1730. **Key Personnel:** M.C. Aggarwal, Engr.-in-Ch., phone 91 11 23421058, fax 91 11 23421006, einc@air.org.in. **Wattage:** 3000. **Ad Rates:** $90-140 for 10 seconds; $135-210 for 15 seconds; $270-420 for 30 seconds; $540-840 for 60 seconds. **URL:** http://www.allindiaradio.org.

Chandrapur

45027 ■ All India Radio Chandrapur - 103.0 KHz
Civil Lines
Chandrapur 442 401, Maharashtra, India
Ph: 91 172 254655
E-mail: airchan_cha@sancharnet.in
Format: Eclectic. **Owner:** Prasar Bharati, Akashvani Bhavan, Sansad Marg, New Delhi 110 001, Delhi, India, 91 11 23421006, Fax: 91 11 23421956. **Key Personnel:** M.C. Aggarwal, Engr.-in-Ch., phone 91 11 23421058, fax 91 11 23421006, einc@air.org.in. **Wattage:** 6000. **Ad Rates:** $80-150 for 10 seconds;

$120-225 for 15 seconds; $240-450 for 30 seconds; $480-900 for 60 seconds. **URL:** http://www.allindiaradio.org.

45028 ■ Journal of Forensic Dental Sciences
Medknow Publications Pvt Ltd.
c/o Dr. B. Sivapathasundharam, Ed-in-Ch.
Department of Oral & Maxillofacial Pathology
Meenakshi Ammal Dental College & Hospital
Chennai 600 095, India
Ph: 91 44 23782566
Peer-reviewed journal of the Indian Association of Forensic Odontology. **Freq:** Semiannual. **Key Personnel:** Dr. B. Sivapathasundharam, Editor-in-Chief, drsivapatham@yahoo.co.in; Dr. S. Balagopal, Exec. Ed.; Dr. G. Sriram, Assoc. Ed. **ISSN:** 0974-2948. **Subscription Rates:** Rs 1,200 individuals print only; Rs 1,500 institutions print only; US$120 other countries print only; US$150 institutions, other countries print only; Rs 1,000 individuals print and online; Rs 1,200 institutions print and online; US$95 other countries print and online; US$120 institutions, other countries print and online. **Remarks:** Accepts advertising. **URL:** http://www.jfds.org. **Circ:** (Not Reported)

Chennai (Tamil Nadu)

45029 ■ Chess Mate
Anand Aaron
No. 12, 6th Main Rd.
Kasthuribai Nagar
Adyar
Chennai 600 020, Tamil Nadu, India
Ph: 91 44 24450587
Publication E-mail: aaronchessacademy@yahoo.com
Publisher E-mail: aaronchessacademy@yahoo.com
Periodical on chess, sports and recreation. **Founded:** 1983. **Freq:** Monthly. **Key Personnel:** Manuel Aaron, Editor. **ISSN:** 0970-9142. **Subscription Rates:** Rs 25 single issue; Rs 120 individuals six months; Rs 420 two years; Rs 600 individuals for three years; Rs 240 individuals. **Remarks:** Accepts advertising. **URL:** http://www.chess-mate.com. **Circ:** 3,000

45030 ■ Daily Thanthi
86, E.V.K. Sampath Rd.
Vepary
Chennai 600 007, Tamil Nadu, India
Ph: 91 442 6618661
Fax: 91 442 6618797
Publisher E-mail: managerms@dt.co.in
General newspaper. **Founded:** 1942. **Subscription Rates:** Rs 1,488 individuals inside country; Rs 13,312 other countries foreign. **URL:** http://www.dailythanthi.com. **Circ:** ★113,404

45031 ■ The Economic Times
Bennet, Coleman & Company Ltd.
Times House
126/127 Chamiers Rd.
Nandanam
Chennai 600 034, Tamil Nadu, India
Financial news daily. **Founded:** 1994. **Freq:** Daily. **Remarks:** Accepts advertising. **URL:** http://economictimes.indiatimes.com/?. **Circ:** Paid 26,592

45032 ■ Frontline
Kasturi & Sons Ltd.
859-860 Anna Salai
Chennai 600 002, Tamil Nadu, India
Ph: 91 442 8413344
Fax: 91 442 8415325
Publication E-mail: frontline@thehindu.co.in
Publisher E-mail: bleditor@thehindu.co.in
Magazine covering political and other issues. **Founded:** 1984. **Freq:** Biweekly. **ISSN:** 0970-1710. **Subscription Rates:** Rs 200 individuals half yearly; Rs 650 two years; Rs 350 individuals; Rs 3600 other countries by air mail. **Remarks:** Accepts advertising. **URL:** http://www.flonnet.com/; http://www.hinduonnet.com/fline/. **Circ:** Paid 62,348

45033 ■ Hindu Business Line
Kasturi & Sons Ltd.
859-860 Anna Salai
Chennai 600 002, Tamil Nadu, India
Ph: 91 442 8413344
Fax: 91 442 8415325
Publication E-mail: bleditor@thehindu.co.in

Publisher E-mail: bleditor@thehindu.co.in
Newspaper covering business, economics, banks and banking. **Founded:** 1994. **Freq:** Daily. **Key Personnel:** N. Ram, Editor. **ISSN:** 0971-7528. **Subscription Rates:** Rs 1,444 individuals all days; Rs 1,697 individuals by post; Rs 208 individuals any specific day; Rs 244 individuals by post. **Remarks:** Accepts advertising. **URL:** http://www.thehindubusinessline.com. **Circ:** Paid 24,823

45034 ■ Hindu Index
Kasturi & Sons Ltd.
859-860 Anna Salai
Chennai 600 002, Tamil Nadu, India
Ph: 91 442 8413344
Fax: 91 442 8415325
Publisher E-mail: bleditor@thehindu.co.in
Periodical containing bibliographies and indexes. **Freq:** Monthly. **Subscription Rates:** Rs 100 single issue; Rs 1,500 individuals; Rs 2,500 individuals. **URL:** http://www.hindu.com/thehindu/subsrate.htm.

45035 ■ Hindu International Edition
Kasturi & Sons Ltd.
859-860 Anna Salai
Chennai 600 002, Tamil Nadu, India
Ph: 91 442 8413344
Fax: 91 442 8415325
Publisher E-mail: bleditor@thehindu.co.in
Periodical related to social science. **Founded:** 1974. **Freq:** Weekly. **Key Personnel:** N. Ravi, Editor. **ISSN:** 0257-5310. **Subscription Rates:** Rs 600 out of country for Bangladesh, Bhutan & Nepal; US$46 other countries. **Remarks:** Accepts advertising. **URL:** http://www.thehindubusinessline.com/2000/01/coinfo/thie00.htm. **Circ:** Paid 5,000

45036 ■ The Hindu Weekly
Kasturi & Sons Ltd.
859-860 Anna Salai
Chennai 600 002, Tamil Nadu, India
Ph: 91 442 8413344
Fax: 91 442 8415325
Publisher E-mail: bleditor@thehindu.co.in
Newspaper. **Founded:** 1878. **Freq:** Weekly. **Key Personnel:** N. Ravi, Editor. **Subscription Rates:** Rs 3.50 single issue. **Remarks:** Accepts advertising. **URL:** http://www.thehindu.com/th125/stories/2003091300820400.htm. **Circ:** (Not Reported)

45037 ■ Income Tax Reports
Company Law Institute of India Private Ltd.
2 Vaithyaram St.
T. Nagar
Chennai 600 017, Tamil Nadu, India
Ph: 91 44 24350752
Fax: 91 44 24322015
Publisher E-mail: info@taxlawsonline.com
Journal covering income tax law, wealth tax, gift tax and estate duty. **Founded:** 1933. **Freq:** Weekly. **Print Method:** Offset. **Trim Size:** 6.5 x 9.75. **ISSN:** 0019-3453. **Subscription Rates:** Rs 4,120 individuals for Indian customers; Rs 5,490 individuals for overseas customers. **Remarks:** Advertising not accepted. **URL:** http://www.taxlawsonline.com/estore/default.asp. **Formerly:** ITR. **Circ:** Paid 16,500

45038 ■ Indian Leather
120 Vepery High Rd.
Periamet
Chennai 600 003, Tamil Nadu, India
Ph: 91 44 25386566
Fax: 91 44 28343685
Publication E-mail: info@indianleatherdigest.com
Publisher E-mail: indianleather@vsnl.net
Trade periodical focusing on the leather industry. **Subtitle:** Digest of Leather News. **Founded:** 1967. **Freq:** Monthly Offset. **Print Method:** Offset. **Trim Size:** 22 x 14 cm. **Key Personnel:** S. Ranganathan, Editor and Publisher; S. Dhinakaran, Assoc. Ed. **ISSN:** 0019-574X. **Subscription Rates:** Rs 400 individuals; US$100 other countries; Rs 1,000 individuals for three years; US$280 individuals for 3 years, U.S. **Remarks:** Accepts advertising. **URL:** http://www.indianleatherdigest.com/. **Ad Rates:** BW: US$250, 4C: US$400. **Circ:** Paid 1,500

45039 ■ Indiavarta
Express Gardens, II Main Rd.
Ambatur Industrial Estate
Chennai 600 058, Tamil Nadu, India

Ph: 91 442 3457655
Fax: 91 44 23457619
Publisher E-mail: shopping@indiavarta.com
General newspaper. **URL:** http://www.indiavarta.com/StoreFront/default.aspx.

45040 ■ Indo - US Business
Indo-American Chamber of Commerce
8-A, Bishop Wallers Ave., W Mylapore
Chennai 600 004, Tamil Nadu, India
Fax: 91 44 4998391
Publisher E-mail: ho@iaccindia.com
Journal focusing on Indo-US business. **Founded:** 1970. **Freq:** Monthly. **Key Personnel:** V. Rangaraj, Editor; R. Veeramani, Editor/President. **Subscription Rates:** Rs 500 individuals. **URL:** http://www.iaccindia.com/pub1.htm. **Circ:** Paid 1,800

45041 ■ Industrial Economist
S. Viswanathan
S-15, Industrial Estate, Guindy
Chennai 600 032, Tamil Nadu, India
Ph: 91 442 342248
Fax: 91 442 349382
Industrial journal. **Founded:** 1968. **Freq:** Biweekly. **Key Personnel:** S. Viswanathan, Editor and Publisher, viswanathan.ie@gmail.com. **ISSN:** 0019-8188. **Subscription Rates:** US$200 individuals. **Remarks:** Accepts advertising. **URL:** http://www.industrialeconomist.com/. **Ad Rates:** BW: Rs 25,000, BW: Rs 15,000, 4C: Rs 40,000, 4C: Rs 20,000. **Circ:** Paid 25,000

45042 ■ International Journal of Spray and Combustion Dynamics
Multi-Science Publishing Company Ltd.
c/o Dr. R.I. Sujith, Ed.-in-Ch.
Dept. of Aerospace Engineering
IIT Madras
Chennai 600 036, Tamil Nadu, India
Publication E-mail: ijscd@iitm.ac.in
Publisher E-mail: info@multi-science.co.uk
Journal covering research on spray and combustion dynamics. **Freq:** Quarterly. **Key Personnel:** Dr. R.I. Sujith, Editor-in-Chief. **ISSN:** 1756-8277. **Subscription Rates:** 267 individuals print and online; 245 individuals print only; 223 individuals online only. **URL:** http://www.multi-science.co.uk/ijscd.htm.

45043 ■ International Journal of Trichology
Medknow Publications Pvt Ltd.
P.H. Rd., No. 853
Kilpauk
Chennai 600 010, Tamil Nadu, India
Peer-reviewed journal of the Hair Research Society of India. **Freq:** 3/yr. **Key Personnel:** Patrick Yesudian, Editor-in-Chief; Desmond J. Tobin, Exec. Ed.; Murugusundram Sundaram, Exec. Ed. **ISSN:** 0974-7753. **Subscription Rates:** Rs 1,000 individuals print only; Rs 1,500 institutions print only; US$100 other countries print only; US$200 institutions, other countries print only; Rs 1,200 individuals print and online; Rs 1,800 institutions print and online; US$120 other countries print and online; US$240 institutions, other countries print and online; Rs 800 individuals online; US$160 institutions online. **Remarks:** Accepts advertising. **URL:** http://www.ijtrichology.com. **Circ:** (Not Reported)

45044 ■ Jantar Mantar
Tamil Nadu Science Forum
Balaji Sampath, C2 Ratna Apts.
AH 250, Shanti Colony, Annanagar
Chennai 600 040, Tamil Nadu, India
Ph: 91 446 213638
Magazine focusing on the mysteries of nature and on the intricacies of man made structures. **Founded:** 1992. **Freq:** Bimonthly. **Print Method:** Offset. **Trim Size:** 10 13/16 x 14. **Cols./Page:** 5. **Col. Width:** 24 nonpareils. **Col. Depth:** 192.5 agate lines. **Key Personnel:** Dr. P.B. Sunil Kumar, Editor; C.S. Venkateswaran, Publisher. **Subscription Rates:** Rs 90 individuals; Rs 180 two years individual. **URL:** http://www.ashanet.org/projects/project-view.php?p=338.

45045 ■ Journal of Conservative Dentistry
Medknow Publications Pvt Ltd.
c/o Dr. Velayutham GopiKrishna, Ed.-in-Ch.
Department of Conservative Dentistry
Meenakshi Ammal Dental College
Maduravoyal
Chennai 600 095, Tamil Nadu, India

Circulation: ★ = ABC; △ = BPA; ♦ = CAC; • = CCAB; □ = VAC; ⊕ = PO Statement; ‡ = Publisher's Report; Boldface figures = sworn; Light figures = estimated.

Gale Directory of Publications & Broadcast Media/147th Ed.

4995

Publication E-mail: editor@jcd.org.in
Peer-reviewed journal covering conservative dentistry. **Freq:** Quarterly. **Key Personnel:** Dr. Velayutham GopiKrishna, Editor-in-Chief; Dr. Krithika Datta, Assoc. Ed.; Dr. Nandini Suresh, Assoc. Ed. **ISSN:** 0972-0707. **Subscription Rates:** Rs 3,000 individuals print only; Rs 3,000 institutions print only; US$150 other countries print only; US$150 institutions, other countries print only; Rs 3,600 individuals print and online; Rs 3,600 institutions print and online; US$180 other countries print and online; US$180 institutions, other countries print and online; Rs 2,400 individuals online; US$120 institutions online. **Remarks:** Accepts advertising. **URL:** http://www.jcd.org.in. **Circ:** (Not Reported)

45046 ■ Journal of Digital Information Management
Digital Information Research Foundation
New No. 11, Ramanujam St.
T. Nagar
Chennai 600 017, Tamil Nadu, India
Ph: 91 44 24340861
Publisher E-mail: info@dirf.org
Journal covering digital information processing, digital content management, digital world structuring, digital libraries, metadata, information management and other related fields. **Freq:** Quarterly. **Key Personnel:** Daisy Jacobs, Editor, daisy.jacobs@up.ac.za; Pit Pichappan, Editor, pichappan@dirf.org. **ISSN:** 0972-7272. **Subscription Rates:** US$260 institutions online only; US$190 individuals online only; EUR210 institutions online only; EUR160 individuals online only; US$340 institutions print and online; EUR300 institutions print and online; US$240 individuals print and online; EUR200 individuals print and online. **URL:** http://www.dirf.org/jdim/.

45047 ■ Journal of Energy, Heat and Mass Transfer
Regional Centre for Energy, Heat and Mass Transfer for Asia and the Pacific
IIT Madras, Campus
Chennai 600 036, Tamil Nadu, India
Ph: 91 442 2574932
Fax: 91 442 2570094
Publisher E-mail: arbijhmt@iitm.ac.in
Technological journal focusing on the developments in the fields of energy, heat and mass transfer. **Founded:** 1978. **Freq:** Quarterly. **Key Personnel:** A.R. Balakrishnan, Editor, arbijhmt@iitm.ac.in; N.K. Anand, Editor, nkanand@mengr.tamu.edu. **ISSN:** 0970-9991. **Subscription Rates:** Rs 600 individuals India; US$100 other countries including airmail postage; US$80 other countries Pakistan, Bangladesh & Sri Lanka. **URL:** http://www.che.iitm.ac.in/~arbala/JEHMT.html. **Circ:** Paid 200

45048 ■ Journal of Indian Society of Periodontology
Medknow Publications Pvt Ltd.
S Ave., H 11 A
Kamaraj Nagar
Thiruvanmiyur
Chennai 600041, Tamil Nadu, India
Peer-reviewed journal covering periodontics. **Freq:** Quarterly. **Key Personnel:** Dhandapani Arunachalam, Editor; Ashish Nichani, Asst. Ed.; Neha Gupta, Managing Editor. **ISSN:** 0972-124X. **URL:** http://www.jisponline.com.

45049 ■ Journal of Oral and Maxillofacial Pathology
Medknow Publications Pvt Ltd.
c/o Dr. Elizabeth Joshua, Ed.
Department of Oral & Maxillofacial Pathology
Ragas Dental College & Hospital
E Coast Rd., 2/102
Chennai 600 119, Tamil Nadu, India
Peer-reviewed journal of the Indian Association of Oral and Maxillofacial Pathologists. **Freq:** Semiannual. **Key Personnel:** Dr. Elizabeth Joshua, Editor, drqej@yahoo.co.in; T. Rooban, Assoc. Ed.; KM Vidya, Assoc. Ed. **ISSN:** 0973-029X. **Subscription Rates:** Rs 1,000 individuals print only; Rs 1,500 institutions print only; US$100 other countries print only; US$150 institutions, other countries print only; Rs 1,200 individuals print and online; Rs 1,800 institutions print and online; US$120 other countries print and online; US$180 institutions, other countries print and online. **Remarks:** Accepts advertising. **URL:** http://www.jomfp.in. **Circ:** (Not Reported)

45050 ■ Journal of Oriental Research
The Kuppuswami Sastri Research Institute
84 Thiru Vi Ka Rd.
Mylapore
Chennai 600 004, Tamil Nadu, India
Ph: 91 442 4985320
Fax: 91 442 4985320
Periodical on Oriental studies. **Founded:** 1927. **Freq:** Irregular. **Key Personnel:** S.S. Janaki, Editor. **ISSN:** 0022-3301. **Subscription Rates:** US$25 individuals. **URL:** http://snsvo4.seekandsource.com/tksri/vopage1.html. **Circ:** Paid 500

45051 ■ Krishnamurti Foundation Bulletin
Krishnamurti Foundation
Vasanta Vihar
124 Greenways Rd.
RA Puram
Chennai 600 028, Tamil Nadu, India
Ph: 91 24937803
Publisher E-mail: publications@kfionline.org
Religion bulletin. **Founded:** 1970. **Freq:** 3/yr. **Print Method:** Offset. **Trim Size:** 8.5 x 5.5. **ISSN:** 0047-3693. **Subscription Rates:** Rs 75 individuals; US$5 other countries. **Remarks:** Advertising not accepted. **URL:** http://www.kfionline.org/publications/periodicals.asp. **Circ:** Paid 1,300

45052 ■ Leather News India
Council for Leather Exports
CMDA Tower-II, 3rd Fl.
Gandhi Irwin Bridge Rd., Egmore
Chennai 600 008, Tamil Nadu, India
Ph: 91 44 28594367
Fax: 91 44 28594363
Publisher E-mail: cle@vsnl.com
Leather industry trade publication. **Founded:** 1984. **Freq:** Monthly. **ISSN:** 0023-9828. **Subscription Rates:** Rs 100 single issue; US$1000 individuals; US$60 individuals. **Remarks:** Accepts advertising. **URL:** http://www.leatherindia.org. **Circ:** Paid 3,000

45053 ■ The New Indian Express
Express Publications (Madurai) Ltd.
Express Gardens
29 2nd Rd.
Ambattur Industrial Estate
Chennai 600 058, Tamil Nadu, India
General newspaper. **Founded:** 1932. **Freq:** Daily. **Remarks:** Accepts advertising. **URL:** http://www.expressbuzz.com/edition/default.aspx. **Circ:** Paid 324,165

45054 ■ News Today
News Today Printers & Publishers Private Ltd.
15 Vellala St.
Kodambakkam
Chennai 600 024, Tamil Nadu, India
General evening newspaper. **Founded:** 1982. **Freq:** Daily (eve.). **Print Method:** Offset. **Key Personnel:** T.R. Jawahar, Contact, trjawahar@vsnl.net. **Remarks:** Accepts advertising. **URL:** http://www.newstodaynet.com. **Ad Rates:** GLR: Rs 200, BW: Rs 84,800, 4C: Rs 69,600, PCI: Rs 400. **Circ:** Paid 39,050

45055 ■ Review of Development and Change
Madras Institute of Development Studies
79 Second Main Rd.
Gandhi Nagar
Adyar
Chennai 600 020, Tamil Nadu, India
Ph: 91 442 4412589
Fax: 91 442 4910872
Publisher E-mail: office@mids.ac.in
General magazine on social sciences. **Founded:** 1996. **Freq:** Semiannual. **Trim Size:** A4. **Key Personnel:** R. Maria Saleth, Editor; A.R. Venkatachalapathy, Editorial Committee; Ajit Menon, Editorial Committee; Barbara Harris, Editorial Advisory Board; Chandan Mukherjee, Editorial Advisory Board. **ISSN:** 0012-155X. **Subscription Rates:** Rs 100 individuals India & other SAARC countries; Rs 150 institutions India & other SAARC countries; US$25 individuals foreign, by airmail; 20 individuals foreign, by airmail; US$50 institutions foreign, by airmail; 40 institutions foreign, by airmail. **Remarks:** Advertising not accepted. **URL:** http://www.mids.ac.in/rdc.htm; http://www.mids.ac.in/; http://www.blackwellpublishing.com/subs.asp?ref=0012-155x&site=1. **Circ:** Paid 300

45056 ■ Rotary News/Rotary Samachar
3rd Fl., Dugar Towers
34 Marshalls Rd.
Egmore
Chennai 600 008, Tamil Nadu, India
Ph: 91 444 2145666
Fax: 91 442 8528818
Publisher E-mail: rotarynews@rosaonline.org
Membership magazine of Rotary International covering current news about Rotary-related subjects in English and Hindi. **Founded:** July 1952. **Freq:** Monthly. **Key Personnel:** T.K. Balakrishnan, Editor, rotarynews@rosaonline.org. **Subscription Rates:** Rs 360 members; Rs 180 members half year. **URL:** http://www.rotary.org/en/MediaAndNews/MorePublications/RegionalMagazines/Pages/ridefault.aspx; http://www.rosaonline.org/ROSA/. **Ad Rates:** BW: Rs 8,000. **Circ:** Paid ⊕75,000

45057 ■ The Sportstar
Kasturi & Sons Ltd.
859-860 Anna Salai
Chennai 600 002, Tamil Nadu, India
Ph: 91 442 8413344
Fax: 91 442 8415325
Publication E-mail: sssub@thehindu.co.in
Publisher E-mail: bleditor@thehindu.co.in
General interest periodical. **Founded:** 1978. **Freq:** Weekly. **ISSN:** 0971-359X. **Subscription Rates:** Rs 350 individuals by post; Rs 4,000 individuals by airmail overseas; Rs 25 single issue. **Remarks:** Accepts advertising. **URL:** http://www.sportstaronnet.com. **Circ:** Paid 98,230

45058 ■ Sruti
PS Narayanan
10 (Old No. 14) First St.
Kasturi Ranga Rd.
Chennai 600 018, Tamil Nadu, India
Ph: 91 44 28128070
Fax: 91 44 28111902
Publication E-mail: sruti.magazine@gmail.com
Publisher E-mail: sruti@eth.net
Periodical on music and dance. **Subtitle:** India's Premier Music and Dance Magazine. **Founded:** 1983. **Freq:** Monthly. **Key Personnel:** V. Ramnarayan, Editor. **ISSN:** 0970-7816. **Subscription Rates:** Rs 540 individuals; Rs 2,110 other countries. **Remarks:** Accepts advertising. **URL:** http://www.sruti.com/. **Circ:** (Not Reported)

45059 ■ Theosophist
The Theosophical Publishing House
The Theosophical Society
Adyar
Chennai 600 020, Tamil Nadu, India
Ph: 91 44 24912474
Publication E-mail: intl.hq@ts-adyar.org
Publisher E-mail: intl.hq@ts-adyar.org
Publication on theosophy, philosophy and religion. **Founded:** 1879. **Freq:** Monthly. **Print Method:** Offset. **Trim Size:** 18 x 24 cm. **Key Personnel:** Radha Burnier, President. **ISSN:** 0972-1851. **Subscription Rates:** Rs 60 individuals; US$12 other countries; Rs 700 institutions; US$150 institutions, other countries. **Remarks:** Accepts advertising. **URL:** http://ts-adyar.org/magazines.html. **Circ:** Paid 3,000

45060 ■ The Vedanta Kesari
Sri Ramakrishna Math
31 Ramakrishna Math Rd.
Mylapore
Chennai 600 004, Tamil Nadu, India
Ph: 91 44 24621110
Fax: 91 44 24934589
Publication E-mail: srkmath@vsnl.com
Publisher E-mail: srkmath@vsnl.com
Periodical covering culture and spirituality. **Subtitle:** The Lion of Vedanta. **Founded:** 1914. **Freq:** Monthly. **Print Method:** Offset. **Trim Size:** 18.3 x 24.1 cm. **Key Personnel:** Swami Gautamananda, Editor, srkmath@vsnl.com. **ISSN:** 0042-2983. **Subscription Rates:** Rs 100 individuals; Rs 1,500 other countries. **Remarks:** Accepts advertising. **URL:** http://www.sriramakrishnamath.org/. **Ad Rates:** BW: Rs 3,000, 4C: Rs 3,500. **Circ:** Paid 95,000

45061 ■ Vivekananda Kendra Patrika
Vivekananda Kendra Prakashan Trust
5 Singarachari St.
Triplicane

Chennai 600 005, Tamil Nadu, India
Ph: 91 442 8440042
Fax: 91 442 8442960
Publisher E-mail: vkpt@vkendra.org
Magazine containing items of cultural and philosophical interest. **Founded:** 1972. **Freq:** Semiannual. **Print Method:** Offset. **ISSN:** 0970-9053. **Remarks:** Accepts advertising. **URL:** http://www.vkendra.org/periodicals. **Ad Rates:** GLR: Rs 5,000, BW: Rs 7,000, 4C: Rs 15,000. **Circ:** Paid 2,000

45062 ■ Yuva Bharati
Vivekananda Kendra Prakashan Trust
5 Singarachari St.
Triplicane
Chennai 600 005, Tamil Nadu, India
Ph: 91 442 8440042
Fax: 91 442 8442960
Publisher E-mail: vkpt@vkendra.org
Publication geared toward the youth market. **Subtitle:** Voice of Youth. **Founded:** 1973. **Freq:** Monthly. **Print Method:** Offset. **Trim Size:** A5. **ISSN:** 0302-6981. **Remarks:** Accepts advertising. **URL:** http://www.vkendra.org/periodicals. **Ad Rates:** GLR: Rs 250, BW: Rs 1,250, 4C: Rs 4,500. **Circ:** Paid 6,400

45063 ■ All India Radio Chennai 'A' - 720 KHz
7, Kamarajar Salai
Mylapore
Chennai 600 004, Tamil Nadu, India
Ph: 91 44 24984060
E-mail: airchennai@vsnl.com
Format: Full Service; Eclectic. **Owner:** Prasar Bharati, Akashvani Bhavan, Sansad Marg, New Delhi 110 001, Delhi, India, 91 11 23421006, Fax: 91 11 23421956. **Founded:** 1938. **Key Personnel:** M.C. Aggarwal, Engr.-in-Ch., phone 91 11 23421058, fax 91 11 23421006, einc@air.org.in. **Wattage:** 200,000. **Ad Rates:** $200-550 for 10 seconds; $300-825 for 15 seconds; $600-1,650 for 30 seconds; $1,200-3,300 for 60 seconds. **URL:** http://www.allindiaradio.org.

45064 ■ All India Radio Chennai 'B' - 1017 KHz
7, Kamarajar Salai
Mylapore
Chennai 600 004, Tamil Nadu, India
Ph: 91 44 24984060
E-mail: airchennai@vsnl.com
Format: Full Service; Eclectic. **Owner:** Prasar Bharati, Akashvani Bhavan, Sansad Marg, New Delhi 110 001, Delhi, India, 91 11 23421006, Fax: 91 11 23421956. **Key Personnel:** M.C. Aggarwal, Engr.-in-Ch., phone 91 11 23421058, fax 91 11 23421006, einc@air.org.in. **Wattage:** 20,000. **Ad Rates:** $200-550 for 10 seconds; $300-825 for 15 seconds; $600-1,650 for 30 seconds; $1,200-3,300 for 60 seconds. **URL:** http://www.allindiaradio.org.

Chhatarpur

45065 ■ All India Radio Chhattarpur - 675 KHz
PO Box 1
Chhatarpur 471 001, Madhya Pradesh, India
Ph: 91 7682 244587
E-mail: airchip@sancharnet.in
Format: Eclectic. **Owner:** Prasar Bharati, Akashvani Bhavan, Sansad Marg, New Delhi 110 001, Delhi, India, 91 11 23421006, Fax: 91 11 23421956. **Founded:** 1976. **Key Personnel:** M.C. Aggarwal, Engr.-in-Ch., phone 91 11 23421058, fax 91 11 23421006, einc@air.org.in. **Wattage:** 20,000. **Ad Rates:** $150-300 for 10 seconds; $225-450 for 15 seconds; $450-900 for 30 seconds; $900-1,800 for 60 seconds. **URL:** http://www.allindiaradio.org.

Chindwara

45066 ■ All India Radio Chindwara - 102.2 KHz
PO Box 34
Chindwara 480 001, Madhya Pradesh, India
Ph: 91 7162 244350
E-mail: airchhin@sancharnet.in
Format: Eclectic. **Owner:** Prasar Bharati, Akashvani Bhavan, Sansad Marg, New Delhi 110 001, Delhi, India, 91 11 23421006, Fax: 91 11 23421956. **Founded:** 1992. **Key Personnel:** M.C. Aggarwal, Engr.-in-Ch., phone 91 11 23421058, fax 91 11 23421006, einc@air.org.in. **Wattage:** 6000. **Ad Rates:** $80-150 for 10 seconds; $120-225 for 15 seconds; $240-450 for 30 seconds;

$480-900 for 60 seconds. **URL:** http://www.allindiaradio.org.

Chitradurga

45067 ■ All India Radio Chitradurga - 102.6 MHz
PO Box 72
Chitradurga 577 501, Karnataka, India
Ph: 91 8198223281
E-mail: stnengr@sancharnet.in
Format: Eclectic. **Owner:** Prasar Bharati, Akashvani Bhavan, Sansad Marg, New Delhi 110 001, Delhi, India, 91 11 23421006, Fax: 91 11 23421956. **Founded:** 1991. **Key Personnel:** M.C. Aggarwal, Engr.-in-Ch., phone 91 11 23421058, fax 91 11 23421006, einc@air.org.in. **Wattage:** 6000. **Ad Rates:** $80-150 for 10 seconds; $120-225 for 15 seconds; $240-450 for 30 seconds; $480-900 for 60 seconds. **URL:** http://www.allindiaradio.org.

Chittorgarh

45068 ■ All India Radio Chittorgarh - 102.9 MHz
Sector 4
Gandhi Nagar
Chittorgarh 312 001, Rajasthan, India
Ph: 91 1472 244764
E-mail: airchrrj@sancharnet.in
Format: Eclectic. **Owner:** Prasar Bharati, Akashvani Bhavan, Sansad Marg, New Delhi 110 001, Delhi, India, 91 11 23421006, Fax: 91 11 23421956. **Founded:** 1991. **Key Personnel:** M.C. Aggarwal, Engr.-in-Ch., phone 91 11 23421058, fax 91 11 23421006, einc@air.org.in. **Wattage:** 6000. **Ad Rates:** $80-150 for 10 seconds; $120-225 for 15 seconds; $240-450 for 30 seconds; $480-900 for 60 seconds. **URL:** http://www.allindiaradio.org.

Churu

45069 ■ All India Radio Churu - 100.7 MHz
Akashvani Bhavan
Sansad Marg
New Delhi 110 001, Delhi, India
Ph: 91 11 23421006
Fax: 91 11 23421956
E-mail: airchuru@yahoo.com
Format: Eclectic. **Owner:** Prasar Bharati, at above address. **Founded:** 1992. **Key Personnel:** M.C. Aggarwal, Engr.-in-Ch., phone 91 11 23421058, fax 91 11 23421006, einc@air.org.in; Mohan Singh, Ch. Engr., Proj., phone 91 11 23421184. **Wattage:** 6000. **Ad Rates:** $80-150 for 10 seconds; $120-225 for 15 seconds; $240-450 for 30 seconds; $480-900 for 60 seconds. **URL:** http://www.allindiaradio.org.

Cochin

45070 ■ Cashew Bulletin
Cashew Export Promotion Council of India
Chittoor Rd.
PO Box 1709
Cochin 682 016, Kerala, India
Ph: 91 484 2376459
Fax: 91 484 2377973
Publisher E-mail: cashew@vsnl.com
Journal on the food industry. **Founded:** 1964. **Freq:** Monthly. **ISSN:** 0008-7300. **Subscription Rates:** Rs 100 individuals; US$35 other countries; Rs 10 single issue. **Remarks:** Accepts advertising. **URL:** http://www.cashewindia.org/php/cepcContents.php?CatID=10. **Ad Rates:** BW: Rs 1,000. **Circ:** 700

45071 ■ Central Marine Fisheries Research Institute Bulletin
Central Marine Fisheries Research Institute
PO Box 1603
Ernakulam N P.O.
Cochin 682 018, Kerala, India
Ph: 91 484 2394867
Fax: 91 484 2394909
Publisher E-mail: mdcmfri@md2.vsnl.net.in
Periodical focusing on the fisheries industry. **Founded:** 1968. **Freq:** Irregular. **Key Personnel:** Dr. G. Syda Rao, Director. **ISSN:** 0972-236X. **Remarks:** Advertising not accepted. **URL:** http://www.cmfri.com. **Circ:** (Not Reported)

45072 ■ Central Marine Fisheries Research Institute Special Publication
Central Marine Fisheries Research Institute
PO Box 1603
Ernakulam N P.O.
Cochin 682 018, Kerala, India
Ph: 91 484 2394867
Fax: 91 484 2394909
Publisher E-mail: mdcmfri@md2.vsnl.net.in
Journal focusing on the fisheries industry. **Founded:** 1977. **Freq:** Irregular. **Key Personnel:** Dr. G. Syda Rao, Director. **ISSN:** 0972-2351. **Remarks:** Advertising not accepted. **URL:** http://www.cmfri.com. **Circ:** (Not Reported)

45073 ■ Fishery Technology
Society of Fisheries Technologists (India)
Matsyapuri PO
Cochin 682 029, Kerala, India
Ph: 91 484 2666845
Fax: 91 484 2668212
Publisher E-mail: info@fishtech.org
Bulletin on technology, fisheries and aquaculture. **Founded:** 1964. **Freq:** Semiannual. **Key Personnel:** Nirmala Thampuran, Editor; George Ninan, Asst. Ed.; P.T. Lakshmanan, Editorial Board; M.P. Remesan, Editorial Board; K. Gopakumar, Editorial Consultant; P.V. Dehadrai, Editorial Consultant; S.N. Dwivedi, Editorial Consultant; Gajendra Singh, Editorial Consultant; Trevor Platt, Editorial Consultant; John M. Ryder, Editorial Consultant. **ISSN:** 0015-3001. **Subscription Rates:** Rs 150 individuals includes postage. **Remarks:** Advertising not accepted. **URL:** http://www.fishtech.org/html/ftechjournal/index.htm. **Circ:** Paid 750

45074 ■ Indian Cashew Journal
Cashew Export Promotion Council of India
Chittoor Rd.
PO Box 1709
Cochin 682 016, Kerala, India
Ph: 91 484 2376459
Fax: 91 484 2377973
Publisher E-mail: cashew@vsnl.com
Magazine on food technology. **Freq:** Quarterly. **ISSN:** 0019-4484. **Subscription Rates:** Rs 50 single issue; Rs 150 individuals; US$30 individuals outside India. **Remarks:** Accepts advertising. **URL:** http://www.cashewindia.org/php/cepcContents.php?CatID=10. **Ad Rates:** BW: Rs 2,500. **Circ:** Paid 2,000

45075 ■ Indian Journal of Fisheries
Central Marine Fisheries Research Institute
PO Box 1603
Ernakulam N P.O.
Cochin 682 018, Kerala, India
Ph: 91 484 2394867
Fax: 91 484 2394909
Publisher E-mail: mdcmfri@md2.vsnl.net.in
Publication on fisheries and aquaculture. **Founded:** 1954. **Freq:** Quarterly. **Key Personnel:** Dr. G. Syda Rao, Director. **ISSN:** 0970-6011. **URL:** http://www.cmfri.com/html/cmfriJF01.html. **Circ:** 500

45076 ■ Spices India
Ministry of Commerce
Spices Board
Sugandha Bhavan
Palarivattom P.O.
Cochin 682 025, Kerala, India
Ph: 91 484 2333610
Fax: 91 484 2331429
Publisher E-mail: spicesboard@vsnl.com
Publication on Indian spices. Contains informative articles on cultivation methods, post-harvest technology, research and development. **Freq:** Monthly. **Key Personnel:** Sreekantan P.S. Thampi, Ch. Ed.; S. Kannan, Editorial Advisory Committee; S. Palanichamy, Editor; Krishnan V.K. Nair, Publisher. **ISSN:** 0970-5805. **Subscription Rates:** Rs 50 individuals. **Remarks:** Accepts advertising. **URL:** http://www.indianspices.com. **Circ:** Paid 3,000

Coimbatore

45077 ■ Ancient Science of Life
The Ayurvedic Trust
The Arya Vaidya Pharmacy (Coimbatore) Ltd.
326 Perumal Koil St.
Ramanathapuram

Circulation: ★ = ABC; △ = BPA; ♦ = CAC; • = CCAB; ❏ = VAC; ⊕ = PO Statement; ‡ = Publisher's Report; Boldface figures = sworn; Light figures = estimated.

Gale Directory of Publications & Broadcast Media/147th Ed.   4997

Coimbatore 641 045, Tamil Nadu, India
Ph: 91 422 2315412
Fax: 91 422 2314953
Publisher E-mail: ayurveda@vsnl.com
Journal covering research papers on Ayurveda, Yoga, medicinal plants and other allied subjects. **Freq:** Quarterly. **ISSN:** 0257-7941. **Remarks:** Accepts advertising. **URL:** http://www.avpayurveda.com/index.php?option=com_docman&task=cat_view&gid=71&Itemid=174. **Circ:** Paid 2,000

45078 ▪ All India Radio Coimbatore - 999 KHz
Akashvani Bhavan
Sansad Marg
New Delhi 110 001, Delhi, India
Ph: 91 11 23421006
Fax: 91 11 23421956
E-mail: aircbe@md5.vsnl.net.in
Format: Eclectic. **Owner:** Prasar Bharati, at above address. **Founded:** 1966. **Key Personnel:** M.C. Aggarwal, Engr.-in-Ch., phone 91 11 23421058, fax 91 11 23421006, einc@air.org.in; Mohan Singh, Ch: Engr., Proj., phone 91 11 23421184. **Wattage:** 20,000. **Ad Rates:** $180-400 for 10 seconds; $270-600 for 15 seconds; $540-1,200 for 30 seconds; $1,080-2,400 for 60 seconds. **URL:** http://www.allindiaradio.org.

Cuddapah

45079 ▪ All India Radio Cuddapah - 900 KHz
RTC Bus Stand Rd.
Opposite to R&B Guest
Cuddapah 516 001, Andhra Pradesh, India
Ph: 91 8562 244310
E-mail: airkdp@sancharnet.in
Format: Eclectic. **Owner:** Prasar Bharati, Akashvani Bhavan, Sansad Marg, New Delhi 110 001, Delhi, India, 91 11 23421006, Fax: 91 11 23421956. **Founded:** 1963. **Key Personnel:** M.C. Aggarwal, Engr.-in-Ch., phone 91 11 23421058, fax 91 11 23421006, einc@air.org.in. **Wattage:** 100,000. **Ad Rates:** $180-400 for 10 seconds; $270-600 for 15 seconds; $540-1,200 for 30 seconds; $1,080-2,400 for 60 seconds. **URL:** http://www.allindiaradio.org.

Cuttack

45080 ▪ Chandrabhaga
Tinkonia Bagicha
Cuttack 753 001, Orissa, India
Magazine of Indian poetry and prose. **Subtitle:** A Selection of Indian Writing. **Founded:** 2000. **Freq:** Semiannual. **Print Method:** Offset. **Trim Size:** 237 x 160 mm. **Key Personnel:** Jayanta Mahapatra, Editor; Rabindra K. Swain, Managing Editor. **Subscription Rates:** Rs 250 individuals; US$25 elsewhere; Rs 400 institutions; Rs 150 single issue institution. **Remarks:** Accepts advertising. **URL:** http://www.chandrabhaga.cjb.net. **Formerly:** Chandrabhaga: A Magazine of World Writing. **Ad Rates:** BW: Rs 5,000, 4C: Rs 15,000. **Circ:** Paid ‡300

45081 ▪ Hepatitis B Annual
Medknow Publications Pvt Ltd.
Department of Gastroenterology
S.C.B. Medical College
Mangalabag
Cuttack 753007, Orissa, India
Journal covering different aspects of Hepatitis B viral infection including epidemiology, prevention and disease control, and management of the infection. **Founded:** 1935. **Freq:** Annual. **Print Method:** Offset. **Cols./Page:** 6. **Col. Width:** 22 nonpareils. **Col. Depth:** 301 agate lines. **Key Personnel:** S.P. Singh, Editor; Y.K. Chawla, Editor; Niranhan Rout, Assoc. Ed. **ISSN:** 0972-9747. **Subscription Rates:** Rs 500 individuals; Rs 500 institutions; US$120 individuals; US$120 individuals. **URL:** http://www.hepatitisbannual.org/.

45082 ▪ All India Radio Cuttack - 972 KHz
Akashvani Bhavan
Sansad Marg
New Delhi 110 001, Delhi, India
Ph: 91 11 23421006
Fax: 91 11 23421956
E-mail: ctk_cbsctc@sancharnet.in
Format: Eclectic; Full Service. **Owner:** Prasar Bharati, at above address. **Founded:** 1948. **Key Personnel:** M.C. Aggarwal, Engr.-in-Ch., phone 91 11 23421058,

fax 91 11 23421006, einc@air.org.in; Mohan Singh, Ch. Engr. Proj., phone 91 11 23421184. **Wattage:** 300,000. **Ad Rates:** $180-400 for 10 seconds; $270-600 for 15 seconds; $540-1,200 for 30 seconds; $1,080-2,400 for 60 seconds. **URL:** http://www.allindiaradio.org.

Daltonganj

45083 ▪ All India Radio Daltonganj - 103.0 MHz
Akashvani Bhavan
Sansad Marg
New Delhi 110 001, Delhi, India
Ph: 91 11 23421006
Fax: 91 11 23421956
E-mail: airlive@air.org.in
Format: Eclectic; Full Service. **Owner:** Prasar Bharati, at above address. **Founded:** 1963. **Key Personnel:** M.C. Aggarwal, Engr.-in-Ch., phone 91 11 23421058, fax 91 11 23421006, einc@air.org.in; Mohan Singh, Ch. Engr. (Proj.), phone 91 11 23421184. **Wattage:** 6000. **Ad Rates:** $80-150 for 10 seconds; $120-225 for 15 seconds; $240-450 for 30 seconds; $480-900 for 60 seconds. **URL:** http://www.allindiaradio.org.

Daman

45084 ▪ All India Radio Daman - 102.3 KHz
Opposite Varkunt Mota Fliya
Daman 396 210, Goa Daman and Diu, India
Ph: 91 2638 252966
E-mail: val_air_daman@sancharnet.in
Format: Eclectic. **Owner:** Prasar Bharati, Akashvani Bhavan, Sansad Marg, New Delhi 110 001, Delhi, India, 91 11 23421006, Fax: 91 11 23421956. **Founded:** 1995. **Key Personnel:** M.C. Aggarwal, Engr.-in-Ch., phone 91 11 23421058, fax 91 11 23421006, einc@air.org.in. **Wattage:** 3000. **Ad Rates:** $80-150 for 10 seconds; $120-225 for 15 seconds; $240-450 for 30 seconds; $480-900 for 60 seconds. **URL:** http://www.allindiaradio.org.

Darbhanga

45085 ▪ All India Radio Darbhanga - 1296 KHz
Akashvani Bhavan
Sansad Marg
New Delhi 110 001, Delhi, India
Ph: 91 11 23421006
Fax: 91 11 23421956
E-mail: airdbg@sify.com
Format: Eclectic. **Owner:** Prasar Bharati, at above address. **Founded:** 1976. **Key Personnel:** M.C. Aggarwal, Engr.-in-Ch., phone 91 11 23421058, fax 91 11 23421006, einc@air.org.in; Mohan Singh, Ch. Engr., Proj., phone 91 11 23421184. **Wattage:** 10,000. **Ad Rates:** $100-200 for 10 seconds; $150-300 for 15 seconds; $300-600 for 30 seconds; $600-1,200 for 60 seconds. **URL:** http://www.allindiaradio.org.

Davangere

45086 ▪ Indian Society of Pedodontics and Preventive Dentistry Journal
Indian Society of Pedodontics and Preventive Dentistry
c/o Prof. V.V. Subba Reddy, Ed.-in-Ch.
College of Dental Sciences
Pavilion Rd.
Davangere 577 004, Karnataka, India
Medical journal focusing on dentistry. **Subtitle:** Journal of Indian Society of Pedodontics and Preventive Dentistry. **Founded:** 1983. **Freq:** Quarterly. **Print Method:** Offset. **Trim Size:** 8 1/2 x 11 1/2. **Key Personnel:** Prof. Amrit Tewari, Patron; Prof. H.S. Chawla, Ed./Advisor; Prof. V.V. Subba Reddy, Editor-in-Chief; Prof. Sobha Tandon, Editorial Board; Prof. Navneet Grewal, Editorial Board; Prof. A.R. Prabhakar, Editorial Board; Prof. S.G. Damle, Editorial Board. **ISSN:** 0970-4388. **Subscription Rates:** Rs 1,400 individuals; Rs 2,000 institutions; US$100 individuals; US$180 institutions. **Remarks:** Accepts advertising. **URL:** http://www.jisppd.com/subscribe.asp. **Ad Rates:** BW: US$200, 4C: US$300. **Circ:** Combined 1,500

Delhi

45087 ▪ The Anthropologist
Kamla-Raj Enterprises
2273 Gali Bari Paharwali
Chawri Bazar

PO Box 1120
Delhi 110 006, Delhi, India
Ph: 91 124 3284126
Fax: 91 124 4361193
Publisher E-mail: kre@vsnl.com
Peer-reviewed journal of contemporary and applied studies of man. **Subtitle:** International Journal of Contemporary and Applied Studies of Man. **Founded:** 1999. **Freq:** 4/yr. **Trim Size:** 180 x 240 mm. **Key Personnel:** Dr. A.K. Kalla, Contact, phone 91 11 27666614, akkalla@rediffmail.com; Dr. J.R. Gaur, Contact, fsl_hp@yahoo.com. **ISSN:** 0972-0073. **Subscription Rates:** US$150 institutions; US$40 single issue institute; US$100 individuals; US$35 single issue individual. **Remarks:** Accepts advertising. **URL:** http://www.krepublishers.com/. **Ad Rates:** GLR: US$150, BW: US$250, 4C: US$350. **Circ:** Paid 250

45088 ▪ Ave
Vidyajyoti College of Theology
4-A, Raj Niwas Marg
Delhi 110054, Delhi, India
Ph: 91 11 23943556
Publisher E-mail: principalvj@gmail.com
Journal featuring daily reflections based on the liturgical cycle. **Founded:** 1938. **Freq:** Monthly. **Key Personnel:** C. Pragasan, SJ, Ch. Ed. **URL:** http://vidyajyoti.in/?page_id=74.

45089 ▪ Dairy India Yearbook
P R Gupta
A-25 Priyadarshini Vihar
Delhi 110 092, Delhi, India
Ph: 91 112 2543326
Fax: 91 112 2543039
Publication E-mail: yearbook@nda.vsnl.net.in
Publisher E-mail: yearbook@nda.vsnl.net.in
Periodical providing trade, technical and economic information on dairy industry. **Founded:** 1983. **Key Personnel:** P.R. Gupta, Publisher, phone 91 122 543326, fax 91 122 543039. **ISSN:** 0970-9932. **Subscription Rates:** US$295 individuals plus air postage & handling. **URL:** http://www.indiadairy.com/book_dairy_india.html. **Circ:** Paid 2,500

45090 ▪ Defence Science Journal
Defence Scientific Information & Documentation Centre
Defence Research & Development Organisation (DRDO)
Ministry of Defence, Metcalfe House
Delhi 110 054, Delhi, India
Ph: 91 122 3902482
Publisher E-mail: dirdesidoc@vsnl.net
Scientific journal on military. **Founded:** 1949. **Freq:** Quarterly. **Trim Size:** A4. **Key Personnel:** Dr. Al Moorthy, Editor-in-Chief; Shashi Tyagi, Editor; Alka Bansal, Editor. **ISSN:** 0011-748X. **Subscription Rates:** Rs 500 institutions libraries/Govt.depts/; 18 institutions, other countries libraries/Govt.depts/; US$40 institutions, other countries libraries/Govt.depts/; Rs 100 individuals; 10 other countries; US$24 other countries; Rs 150 single issue; 5 single issue; US$12 single issue. **Remarks:** Advertising not accepted. **URL:** http://www.drdo.com/pub/dsj/dsjhome.htm. **Circ:** 600

45091 ▪ Demography India
Hindustan Publishing Corp.
c/o Office of the Managing Editor
Institute of Economic Growth
Delhi University Enclave
Delhi 110 007, Delhi, India
Ph: 91 112 7667101
Fax: 91 112 7257410
Publisher E-mail: hpcpd@hpc.cc
Periodical on demography. **Founded:** 1972. **Freq:** Semiannual. **Key Personnel:** S.N Dwivedi, Editor; N. Audinarayana, Editor; R.P. Tyagi, Managing Editor. **ISSN:** 0970-454X. **Subscription Rates:** Rs 500 individuals; US$60 individuals. **URL:** http://www.iasp.ac.in/. **Circ:** 950

45092 ▪ DESIDOC Bulletin of Information Technology
Defence Scientific Information & Documentation Centre
Defence Research & Development Organisation (DRDO)
Ministry of Defence, Metcalfe House
Delhi 110 054, Delhi, India
Ph: 91 122 3902482
Publication E-mail: dirdesidoc@vsnl.net

Publisher E-mail: dirdesidoc@vsnl.net
Journal on information technology. **Founded:** 1980. **Freq:** Bimonthly. **ISSN:** 0971-4383. **Subscription Rates:** Rs 150 individuals; Rs 450 institutions; US$24 other countries; US$40 institutions, other countries. **URL:** http://publications.drdo.gov.in/ojs/index.php/djlit. **Circ:** Paid 700

45093 ■ IAMR Report
Institute of Applied Manpower Research
A-7, Narela Institutional Area
Delhi 110 040, Delhi, India
Ph: 91 11 27787214
Fax: 91 11 27783467
Contains reports on business and economics, as well as labor and industrial relations. **Freq:** Irregular. **URL:** http://www.iamrindia.gov.in/iamrReports.htm.

45094 ■ IAMR Working Paper
Institute of Applied Manpower Research
A-7, Narela Institutional Area
Delhi 110 040, Delhi, India
Ph: 91 11 27787214
Fax: 91 11 27783467
Contains working papers on topics related to business and economics, as well as labor and industrial relations. **Founded:** 1963. **Freq:** Irregular. **URL:** http://www.iamrindia.gov.in/workingPaper.htm.

45095 ■ Indian Chemical Engineer
Indian Institute of Chemical Engineers
c/o Dr. Anil Kunar Saroha, Ed.
Dept. of Chemical Engineering
Indian Institute of Technology
Delhi 110 016, Delhi, India
Publication E-mail: ice.journal@yahoo.com
Publisher E-mail: iichehq@vsnl.com
Scientific journal on chemical and biochemical engineering. **Founded:** 1959. **Freq:** Quarterly. **Key Personnel:** Dr. Anil Kunar Saroha, Editor, phone 91 33 24146670. **ISSN:** 0019-4506. **Subscription Rates:** Rs 500 individuals; US$150 other countries. **Remarks:** Accepts advertising. **URL:** http://www.iiche.org.in/; http://www.informaworld.com/smpp/title~db=all~content=t908483045. **Ad Rates:** BW: Rs 4,500, 4C: Rs 10,000. **Circ:** Paid 5,000

45096 ■ Indian Journal of Allergy Asthma and Immunology
Indian College of Allergy Asthma and Immunology
c/o Prof. S.N. Gaur, Ed.
Dept. of Respiratory Virology
V.P. Chest Institute University of Delhi
Delhi 110 007, Delhi, India
Peer-reviewed journal covering allergy, asthma, rhinitis, urticaria, hypersensitivity pneumonitis and other associated respiratory diseases & laboratory aspects of clinical immunology. **Founded:** 1955. **Freq:** Semiannual. **Print Method:** Letterpress. **Cols./Page:** 6. **Col. Width:** 12.75 picas. **Col. Depth:** 301 agate lines. **Key Personnel:** Prof. N.K. Ganguli, Editorial Board; Dr. Rajendra Prasad, Editorial Board; Prof. Sunirmal Chanda, Editorial Board; Prof. M. Fahim, Editorial Board; Prof. S.K. Katiyar, Editorial Board; Dr. S.V. Gangal, Editorial Board; Prof. S.N. Gaur, Editor; Prof. N.K. Jain, Editorial Board; Prof. M.K. Agarwal, Editorial Board; Prof. V.K. Jain, Editorial Board. **ISSN:** 0972-6691. **Subscription Rates:** Rs 250 institutions; US$60 institutions. **URL:** http://medind.nic.in/iac/iacaj.shtml.

45097 ■ Indian Journal of Otolaryngology and Head and Neck Surgery
Association of Otolaryngologists of India
397 Jagriti Enclave
Delhi 110 092, Delhi, India
Publisher E-mail: rkk3000@gmail.com
Publication on otolaryngology and head and neck surgery. **Freq:** Quarterly. **Key Personnel:** P.S.N. Murphy, Chm.; G.C. Sahoo, Editorial Board; B. Viswanatha, Editorial Board; Dr. D. Dwarakanatha Reddy, Editor. **ISSN:** 0019-5421. **URL:** http://www.entindia.net/2008/12/indian-journal-of-otolaryngology-and.html; http://www.springer.com/medicine/otorhinolaryngology/journal/12070. **Circ:** 3,500

45098 ■ Indian Labour Journal
Government of India Department of Periodicals
Civil Lines
Delhi 110 054, Delhi, India

Ph: 91 112 517409
Government periodical on labor and industrial relations. **Founded:** 1960. **Freq:** Monthly. **ISSN:** 0019-5723. **Subscription Rates:** Rs 70 individuals. **Remarks:** Accepts advertising. **URL:** http://labourbureau.nic.in/LPpub6.htm. **Circ:** Paid 1,250

45099 ■ International Journal of Human Genetics
Kamla-Raj Enterprises
PO Box 1120
Delhi 110 006, Delhi, India
Ph: 91 11 23284126
Fax: 91 12 44361193
Publisher E-mail: kre@vsnl.com
Journal designed for prompt publication of original and significant articles on all aspects of Human Genetics (Anthropogenetics, Biochemical Genetics, Biometry, Clinical Genetics, Cytogenetics, Genetic Epidemiology, Genetic Testing, Evolution and Population Genetics, Immunogenetics, Molecular Genetics). **Freq:** Quarterly. **Key Personnel:** Dr. S.M.S. Chahal, Editorial Board, smschahal@rediffmail.com; Dr. Max P. Baur, Editorial Board, max.baur@meb.uni-bonn.de; Dr. Sarita Agarwal, Editorial Board, sarita@sgpgi.ac.in. **ISSN:** 0972-3757. **Subscription Rates:** US$100 institutions; Rs 4,000 institutions corporate bodies; US$40 single issue institution; Rs 1,200 single issue institution; US$100 individuals; Rs 3,000 individuals; US$35 single issue individual; Rs 1,000 single issue individual. **URL:** http://www.krepublishers.com/02-Journals/IJHG/IJHG-00-0-000-000-2001-Web/IJHG-00-0-000-000-2001-1-Cover.htm.

45100 ■ Journal of Human Ecology
Kamla-Raj Enterprises
2273 Gali Bari Paharwali
Chawri Bazar
PO Box 1120
Delhi 110 006, Delhi, India
Ph: 91 112 3284126
Fax: 91 124 4361193
Publisher E-mail: kre@vsnl.com
Periodical focusing on human ecology. Serves as a forum for social and life scientists and health professionals. **Subtitle:** International, Interdisciplinary Journal of Man - Environment Relationship. **Founded:** 1990. **Freq:** 12/yr. **Trim Size:** 180 x 240 mm. **Key Personnel:** Dr. J. Mahanta, Director, icmrrcdi@hub.nic.in; M.K. Bhasin, Contact. **ISSN:** 0970-9274. **Subscription Rates:** US$400 institutions; Rs 12,000 institutions; US$40 single issue institution; Rs 1,200 single issue institution; US$350 individuals; Rs 10,000 individuals India; US$33 single issue individual. **Remarks:** Accepts advertising. **URL:** http://www.krepublishers.com. **Ad Rates:** GLR: US$150, BW: US$250, 4C: US$350. **Circ:** Paid 500

45101 ■ Journal of Social Sciences (Delhi)
Kamla-Raj Enterprises
2273 Gali Bari Paharwali
Chawri Bazar
PO Box 1120
Delhi 110 006, Delhi, India
Ph: 91 112 3284126
Fax: 91 124 4361193
Publisher E-mail: kre@vsnl.com
Journal reporting original research, theoretical articles and brief communications in social sciences. Raises issues across disciplinary boundaries facilitating exchange of views. Intends to serve as a forum of social scientist especially for those who share common interest in understanding of various problems related to contemporary society. **Subtitle:** Interdisciplinary Reflection of Contemporary Society. **Founded:** 1997. **Freq:** Monthly. **Trim Size:** 180 x 240 mm. **Key Personnel:** Dr. Ferran Casas, Director, fcasas@tsaligues.udg.es; Dr. D.K. Behera, Editorial Board, deepakbehera@hotmail.com; Dr. Oyaziwo O. Aluede, Editorial Board, oyaziwoaluede@yahoo.com; Dr. B.V. Babu, Editorial Board, babubontha@gmail.com; Dr. M.K. Bhasin, Editorial Board, kre@vsnl.com; Dr. Veena Bhasin, Editorial Board, kre@vsnl.com; Dr. Motilal Dash, Editorial Board, dash@bits-pilani.ac.in. **ISSN:** 0971-8923. **Subscription Rates:** US$400 institutions; Rs 1,200 institutions; US$40 single issue institution; Rs 1,200 single issue institution; US$350 individuals; Rs 1,000 individuals; US$35 single issue individual; Rs 1,000 single issue individual. **Remarks:** Accepts advertising. **URL:** http://www.

krepublishers.com. **Ad Rates:** GLR: US$150, BW: US$250, 4C: US$350. **Circ:** Paid 300

45102 ■ Journal of Vector Borne Diseases
Malaria Research Centre
Indian Council of Medical Research
22 Sham Nath Marg
Delhi 110 054, Delhi, India
Ph: 91 112 3981690
Fax: 91 112 3946150
Publication E-mail: editor.jvbd@mrcindia.org
Publisher E-mail: director@mrcindia.org
Peer-reviewed journal covering vector borne diseases and ways to control them. **Subtitle:** JVBD. **Freq:** Quarterly. **Print Method:** Offset. **Trim Size:** 8 1/2 x 11. **Key Personnel:** Dr. Jane M. Carlton, Editorial Board; Dr. S. Pattanayak, Editorial Board; Prof. M.K.K. Pillai, Editorial Board; Dr. Pascal Ringwald, Editorial Board; Dr. V.K. Dua, Editor; Dr. P.K. Mittal, Editorial Committee; U. Sreehari, Asst. Ed. **ISSN:** 0972-9062. **Subscription Rates:** US$150 individuals; US$40 other countries. **Remarks:** Advertising not accepted. **URL:** http://www.mrcindia.org/journal. **Formerly:** Indian Journal of Malariology (2003). **Circ:** 300

45103 ■ Manpower Journal
Institute of Applied Manpower Research
A-7, Narela Institutional Area
Delhi 110 040, Delhi, India
Ph: 91 11 27787214
Fax: 91 11 27783467
Peer-reviewed magazine focusing on manpower issues. **Founded:** 1965. **Freq:** Quarterly. **ISSN:** 0542-5808. **URL:** http://www.iamrindia.gov.in/_manpowerJournal.htm. **Circ:** Paid 500

45104 ■ Studies of Tribes and Tribals
Kamla-Raj Enterprises
PO Box 1120
Delhi 110 006, Delhi, India
Ph: 91 11 23284126
Fax: 91 12 44361193
Publication E-mail: kre@vsnl.com
Publisher E-mail: kre@vsnl.com
Journal serving as a forum of socio-cultural and life scientists and health professionals, especially those who share common interests in understanding human beings especially aboriginals, backwards and minorities. **Freq:** Semiannual. **Key Personnel:** Dr. Veena Bhasin, Editor, phone 91 124 4361430, kre.@airmail.in; Dr. Shyngle K. Balogun, Editorial Board, shyngle61@yahoo.com; Dr. Adeyinka Abideen Aderinto, Editorial Board, aderinto@yahoo.com; Dr. M.K. Bhasin, Editorial Board; Dr. F.C. de Beer, Editorial Board, dbeerc@unisa.ac.za; Dr. Bibhash Dhar, Editorial Board, bibhash@sancharnet.in; Dr. Robert J. Gregory, Editorial Board, bobbygreg@gmail.com; Dr. L. Hens, Editorial Board, sgillot@meko.vub.ac.be. **ISSN:** 0972-639X. **Subscription Rates:** US$75 institutions; Rs 2,000 individuals; US$40 institutions; Rs 1,200 institutions; US$60 single issue institution; Rs 1,500 single issue institution; US$35 single issue individual; Rs 1,000 single issue individual. **URL:** http://www.krepublishers.com/KRE-New-J/index.html.

45105 ■ Tattvaviveka
Vidyajyoti College of Theology
4-A, Raj Niwas Marg
Delhi 110054, Delhi, India
Ph: 91 11 23943556
Publisher E-mail: principalvj@gmail.com
Journal featuring theological articles revolving around a theme of current interest. **Freq:** Annual. **Key Personnel:** S. Keni Philomin Raj, Ch. Ed.; Anima Tirkey, SAP, Assoc. Ed. **URL:** http://vidyajyoti.in/?page_id=78.

45106 ■ Technology Focus
Defence Scientific Information & Documentation Centre
Defence Research & Development Organisation (DRDO)
Ministry of Defence, Metcalfe House
Delhi 110 054, Delhi, India
Ph: 91 122 3902482
Publisher E-mail: dirdesidoc@vsnl.net
Periodical dedicated to defense technology. **Founded:** 1992. **Freq:** Bimonthly. **Print Method:** Offset. **Trim Size:** 15.5 x 10.9. **Key Personnel:** Dr. Mohinder Singh, Editorial Committee; Ashok Kumar, Editor; Vinod Kumari, Editor. **ISSN:** 0971-4413. **Subscription Rates:** Free. **Remarks:** Advertising not accepted. **URL:** http://www.

Circulation: ★ = ABC; △ = BPA; ♦ = CAC; ● = CCAB; ❑ = VAC; ⊕ = PO Statement; ‡ = Publisher's Report; Boldface figures = sworn; Light figures = estimated.

Gale Directory of Publications & Broadcast Media/147th Ed.

4999

drdo.org/pub/techfocus/welcome3.htm. **Circ:** Controlled 3,000

45107 ■ Tibetan Review
c/o Tibetan SOS Hostel
Sector 14 Ext., Rohini
Delhi 110 085, Delhi, India
Ph: 91 11 27860828
Fax: 91 11 27569702
Publication E-mail: tibrev@vsnl.com
Publisher E-mail: tibrev@vsnl.com
Tibetan history, politics and administration publication. **Founded:** Jan. 1968. **Freq:** Monthly. **ISSN:** 0040-6708. **Subscription Rates:** Rs 8 single issue; Rs 90 individuals; Rs 60 students; Rs 240 individuals Nepal & Bhutan; Rs 160 students Nepal & Bhutan; Rs 950 other countries; US$25 other countries; EUR25 other countries; 15 other countries. **URL:** http://www.tibetanreview.net/. **Circ:** Paid 4,500

45108 ■ Vachan Sudha
Vidyajyoti College of Theology
4-A, Raj Niwas Marg
Delhi 110054, Delhi, India
Ph: 91 11 23943556
Publisher E-mail: principalvj@gmail.com
Journal featuring daily reflections based on the liturgical cycle. **Freq:** Monthly. **Key Personnel:** Vijay Minj, SJ, Coord. **URL:** http://vidyajyoti.in/?page_id=76.

45109 ■ Vidyajyoti Journal of Theological Reflection
Vidyajyoti College of Theology
4-A, Raj Niwas Marg
Delhi 110054, Delhi, India
Ph: 91 11 23943556
Publication E-mail: vjtrdelhi@gmail.com; vjtrdelhi@bol.net.in
Publisher E-mail: principalvj@gmail.com
Journal covering areas of Christian theology and service, inter-religious dialogue, Indian theology, social concerns, and trends significant for religion in the modern times. **Founded:** 1938. **Freq:** Monthly. **Key Personnel:** S. Arokiasamy, Editor; T.K. John, Asst. Ed. **URL:** http://vidyajyoti.in/?page_id=71.

Dharamsala

45110 ■ DOLMA
Tibetan Women's Association
Bhagsunath Rd.
PO McLeod Ganj
Dharamsala 176219, Himachal Pradesh, India
Ph: 91 1892 221527
Fax: 91 1892 221528
Publisher E-mail: twa@tibetanwomen.org
Tibetan and English language publication covering feminism. **Freq:** Annual. **URL:** http://www.tibetanwomen.org/publications/dolma/.

45111 ■ Rangzen
Tibetan Youth Congress
PO McLeod Ganj
Dharamsala 176 219, Himachal Pradesh, India
Ph: 91 1892 21554
Fax: 91 1892 21849
Publisher E-mail: tyc4rangzen@yahoo.com
English and Tibetan language publication covering youth. **Freq:** Quarterly. **Remarks:** Advertising accepted; rates available upon request. **URL:** http://www.tibetanyouthcongress.org/publication.html. **Circ:** (Not Reported)

45112 ■ Tibet Journal
Library of Tibetan Works & Archives
Gangchen Kyishong
Dharamsala 176 215, Himachal Pradesh, India
Ph: 91 1892 22467
Fax: 91 1892 23723
Publisher E-mail: ltwa@ndf.vsnl.net.in
Tibetan history and culture publication. **Subtitle:** A Publication of Tibetan Studies. **Founded:** 1975. **Freq:** Quarterly. **Print Method:** Offset. **Trim Size:** 9 x 6.4. **Key Personnel:** Tashi Tsering, Editorial Board; Gyatsho Tshering, Editor-in-Chief. **ISSN:** 0970-5368. **Subscription Rates:** Rs 125 individuals; US$30 other countries airmail; Rs 35 single issue; US$7.50 other countries single copy air mail; US$25 other countries sea mail. **Remarks:** Accepts advertising. **Online:** EBSCO. **URL:** http://www.tibet.com/. **Circ:** Paid 1,000

45113 ■ All India Radio Dharamsala - 103.4 MHz
Civil Lines
Dharamsala 176 213, Himachal Pradesh, India
Ph: 91 1892 223293
E-mail: dsh_airdsl@sancharnet.in
Format: Eclectic. **Owner:** Prasar Bharati, Akashvani Bhavan, Sansad Marg, New Delhi 110 001, Delhi, India, 91 11 23421006, Fax: 91 11 23421956. **Founded:** 1994. **Key Personnel:** M.C. Aggarwal, Engr.-in-Ch., phone 91 11 23421058, fax 91 11 23421006, einc@air.org.in. **Wattage:** 10,000. **Ad Rates:** $80-150 for 10 seconds; $120-225 for 15 seconds; $240-450 for 30 seconds; $480-900 for 60 seconds. **URL:** http://www.allindiaradio.org.

Dharwad

45114 ■ All India Radio Dharwad - 765 KHz
Akashvani Bhavan
Sansad Marg
New Delhi 110 001, Delhi, India
Ph: 91 11 23421006
Fax: 91 11 23421956
E-mail: airdwd@sancharnet.in
Format: Eclectic. **Owner:** Prasar Bharati, at above address. **Founded:** 1950. **Key Personnel:** M.C. Aggarwal, Engr.-in-Ch., phone 91 11 23421058, fax 91 11 23421006, einc@air.org.in; Mohan Singh, Ch. Engr., Proj., phone 91 11 23421184. **Wattage:** 200,000. **Ad Rates:** $150-300 for 10 seconds; $225-450 for 15 seconds; $450-900 for 30 seconds; $900-1,800 for 60 seconds. **URL:** http://www.allindiaradio.org.

Dhule

45115 ■ All India Radio Dhule - 100.5 MHz
Akashvani Bhavan
Sansad Marg
New Delhi 110 001, Delhi, India
Ph: 91 11 23421006
Fax: 91 11 23421956
E-mail: airdia@sancharnet.in
Format: Eclectic. **Owner:** Prasar Bharati, at above address. **Founded:** 1994. **Key Personnel:** M.C. Aggarwal, Engr.-in-Ch., phone 91 11 23421058, fax 91 11 23421006, einc@air.org.in. **Wattage:** 6000. **Ad Rates:** $80-150 for 10 seconds; $120-225 for 15 seconds; $240-450 for 30 seconds; $480-900 for 60 seconds. **URL:** http://www.allindiaradio.org.

Dibrugarh

45116 ■ All India Radio Dibrugarh - 567 KHz
Malakhubasa
Dibrugarh 786 001, Assam, India
Ph: 91 373 2324425
E-mail: airdbr@sancharnet.in
Format: Eclectic. **Owner:** Prasar Bharati, Akashvani Bhavan, Sansad Marg, New Delhi 110 001, Delhi, India, 91 11 23421006, Fax: 91 11 23421956. **Founded:** 1969. **Key Personnel:** M.C. Aggarwal, Engr.-in-Ch., phone 91 11 23421058, fax 91 11 23421459, einc@air.org.in. **Wattage:** 300,000. **Ad Rates:** $150-300 for 10 seconds; $225-450 for 15 seconds; $450-900 for 30 seconds; $900-1,800 for 60 seconds. **URL:** http://www.allindiaradio.org.

Diphu

45117 ■ All India Radio Diphu - 1584 kHz
Akashvani Bhavan
Sansad Marg
New Delhi 110 001, Delhi, India
Ph: 91 11 23421006
Fax: 91 11 23421956
Format: Eclectic; Full Service. **Owner:** Prasar Bharati, at above address. **Founded:** 1996. **Key Personnel:** M.C. Aggarwal, Engr.-in-Ch., phone 91 11 23421058, fax 91 11 23421006, einc@air.org.in; Mohan Singh, Ch. Engr. Proj., phone 91 11 23421184. **Wattage:** 1000. **Ad Rates:** $80-150 for 10 seconds; $120-225 for 15 seconds; $240-450 for 30 seconds; $480-900 for 60 seconds. **URL:** http://www.allindiaradio.org.

Faizabad

45118 ■ All India Radio Faizabad - 101.9 MHz
Begumganj Garahiya
Faizabad 224 001, Uttar Pradesh, India

Ph: 91 5278 261498
E-mail: airfzd@sancharnet.in
Format: Eclectic. **Owner:** Prasar Bharati, Akashvani Bhavan, Sansad Marg, New Delhi 110 001, Delhi, India, 91 11 23421006, Fax: 91 11 23421956. **Founded:** 1993. **Key Personnel:** M.C. Aggarwal, Engr.-in-Ch., phone 91 11 23421058, fax 91 11 23421006, einc@air.org.in. **Wattage:** 6000. **Ad Rates:** $80-150 for 10 seconds; $120-225 for 15 seconds; $240-450 for 30 seconds; $480-900 for 60 seconds. **URL:** http://www.allindiaradio.org.

Gangtok

45119 ■ All India Radio Gangtok - 1404 KHz
Old M.L.A. Hostel
Gangtok 737 101, Sikkim, India
Ph: 91 3592 202600
E-mail: airgtk@sancharnet.in
Format: Eclectic. **Owner:** Prasar Bharati, Akashvani Bhavan, Sansad Marg, New Delhi 110 001, Delhi, India, 91 11 23421006, Fax: 91 11 23421956. **Founded:** 1996. **Key Personnel:** M.C. Aggarwal, Engr.-in-Ch., phone 91 11 23421058, fax 91 11 23421006, einc@air.org.in. **Wattage:** 20,000. **Ad Rates:** $100-200 for 10 seconds; $150-300 for 15 seconds; $300-600 for 30 seconds; $600-1,200 for 60 seconds. **URL:** http://www.allindiaradio.org.

Garhwal

45120 ■ Divine Life
Divine Life Society
PO Shivananda Nagar
Tehri-Garhwal
Garhwal 249 192, Uttar Pradesh, India
Ph: 91 135 2430040
Fax: 91 135 2442046
Publisher E-mail: generalsecretary@sivanandaonline.org
Periodical covering religion; focuses on Hinduism. **Founded:** 1970. **Freq:** Monthly. **Key Personnel:** Swami Krishnananda, Editor, phone 91 135 430040. **ISSN:** 0012-4206. **URL:** http://sivanandaonline.org/memberarea/form.asp; http://sivanandaonline.org/html/magazine/e-magazine.shtm.

Ghaziabad

45121 ■ Asian Journal of Chemistry
11-100 Rajendra Nagar
Sector 3, Sahibabad
Ghaziabad 201 005, Uttar Pradesh, India
Ph: 91 120 4102551
Publisher E-mail: ajchem@rediffmail.com
Scientific journal covering chemistry. **Founded:** Jan. 1989. **Freq:** Quarterly. **ISSN:** 0970-7077. **Subscription Rates:** Rs 4000 print or online; Rs 6000 print and online. **Remarks:** Advertising accepted; rates available upon request. **URL:** http://www.asianjournalofchemistry.co.in. **Circ:** Paid 700

Godhra

45122 ■ All India Radio Godhra - 102.2 KHz
Akashvani Bhavan
Sansad Marg
New Delhi 110 001, Delhi, India
Ph: 91 11 23421006
Fax: 91 11 23421956
E-mail: airgdh@sancharnet.in
Format: Eclectic. **Owner:** Prasar Bharati, at above address. **Founded:** 1991. **Key Personnel:** M.C. Aggarwal, Engr.-in-Ch., phone 91 11 23421058, fax 91 11 23421006, einc@air.org.in. **Wattage:** 6000. **Ad Rates:** $80-150 for 10 seconds; $120-225 for 15 seconds; $240-450 for 30 seconds; $480-900 for 60 seconds. **URL:** http://www.allindiaradio.org.

Gorakhpur

45123 ■ All India Radio Gorakhpur - 909 KHz
Town Hall
Gorakhpur 273 001, Uttar Pradesh, India
Ph: 91 551 2334604
E-mail: seairgkp@sancharnet.in
Format: Eclectic. **Owner:** Prasar Bharati, Akashvani Bhavan, Sansad Marg, New Delhi 110 001, Delhi, India, 91 11 23421006, Fax: 91 11 23421956. **Founded:** 1972.

Key Personnel: M.C. Aggarwal, Engr.-in-Ch., phone 91 11 23421058, fax 91 11 23421006, einc@air.org.in. **Wattage:** 100,000. **Ad Rates:** $180-400 for 10 seconds; $270-600 for 15 seconds; $540-1,200 for 30 seconds; $1,080-2,400 for 60 seconds. **URL:** http://www. allindiaradio.org.

Gulbarga

45124 ■ All India Radio Gulbarga - 1107 KHz
Municipal Garden
Gulbarga 585 103, Karnataka, India
Ph: 91 8472 2421143
E-mail: airglb@vsnl.com
Format: Eclectic. **Owner:** Prasar Bharati, Akashvani Bhavan, Sansad Marg, New Delhi 110 001, Delhi, India, 91 11 23421006, Fax: 91 11 23421956. **Founded:** 1966. **Key Personnel:** M.C. Aggarwal, Engr.-in-Ch., phone 91 11 23421058, fax 91 11 23421006, einc@air.org.in. **Wattage:** 20,000. **Ad Rates:** $100-200 for 10 seconds; $150-300 for 15 seconds; $300-600 for 30 seconds; $600-1,200 for 60 seconds. **URL:** http://www. allindiaradio.org.

Guna

45125 ■ All India Radio Guna - 102.3 KHz
Akashvani Bhavan
Sansad Marg
New Delhi 110 001, Delhi, India
Ph: 91 11 23421006
Fax: 91 11 23421956
E-mail: seairguna@sancharnet.in
Format: Eclectic. **Owner:** Prasar Bharati, at above address. **Founded:** 1993. **Key Personnel:** M.C. Aggarwal, Engr.-in-Ch., phone 91 11 23421058, fax 91 11 23421006, einc@air.org.in; Mohan Singh, Ch. Engr. Proj., phone 91 11 23421184. **Wattage:** 6000. **Ad Rates:** $80-150 for 10 seconds; $120-225 for 15 seconds; $240-450 for 30 seconds; $480-900 for 60 seconds. **URL:** http://www.allindiaradio.org.

Gurgaon

45126 ■ Dataquest
Cyber Media India Ltd.
B-35, Sector 32, Institutional
Gurgaon 122001, Haryana, India
Ph: 91 124 4031234
Fax: 91 124 2380694
Publisher E-mail: info@pubserv.com
Periodical on computers with a database management focus. **Founded:** 1982. **Freq:** Monthly. **Trim Size:** 26.60 x 19.6. **Key Personnel:** Pravir Ganguly, Editor. **ISSN:** 0970-034X. **Subscription Rates:** Rs 420 individuals; US$50 other countries Bangladesh/Bhutan/Myanmar/Nepal/Pakistan/Sri Lanka; US$75 other countries. **Remarks:** Accepts advertising. **URL:** http://www.dqindia.com/. **Ad Rates:** BW: Rs 200. **Circ:** 40,000

45127 ■ The Times of India
Times Internet Ltd.
I World Tower
DLF City Phas V (Opp DLF Golf Course)
Gurgaon 122 002, Haryana, India
General newspaper. **Founded:** Apr. 1, 1919. **Freq:** Daily. **Print Method:** Offset. **Trim Size:** 8 1/2 x 11. **Cols./Page:** 2. **Col. Width:** 44 nonpareils. **Col. Depth:** 140 agate lines. **Key Personnel:** Upen Rai, Dir., Sales; Sanjive Sethi, Dir., Telecom; Dinesh Wadhawan, Mng. Dir. & CEO; Vinay Kumar, Dir., Corporate Strategy; Mohit Hira, Dir., Mktg.; Rajesh Kalra, Ch. Ed. **ISSN:** 0011-5401. **URL:** http://timesofindia.indiatimes.com/.

45128 ■ Vision
Management Development Institute
Mehrauli Rd.
Sukhrali
Gurgaon 122 007, Haryana, India
Ph: 91 124 4560000
Fax: 91 124 4560456
Publication on business perspectives. **Freq:** Quarterly. **Key Personnel:** Joshua Abor, Editorial Board; Debi S. Saini, Editor. **ISSN:** 0970-6623. **Subscription Rates:** Rs 600 individuals; US$50 other countries. **URL:** http://www.mdi.ac.in/intellect_capital/vision.asp?id=3. **Circ:** Paid 500

Guwahati

45129 ■ Assam Tribune
Assam Tribune Private Ltd.
Tribune Bldg.
Guwahati 718 003, Assam, India
Publisher E-mail: edit.tribune@gmail.com
General newspaper. **Founded:** 1938. **Freq:** Daily. **URL:** http://www.assamtribune.com. **Circ:** Paid 94,196

45130 ■ International Journal of Ultra Wideband Communications and Systems
Inderscience Enterprises Limited
c/o Dr. R.S. Kshetrimayum, Ed.-in-Ch.
Electronics & Communications Engineering Department
Indian Institute of Technology Guwahati
Guwahati 781 039, Assam, India
Peer-reviewed journal covering ultra wideband communications and systems. **Freq:** Quarterly. **Key Personnel:** Dr. R.S. Kshetrimayum, Editor-in-Chief, krs@iitg.ernet.in. **ISSN:** 1758-728X. **Subscription Rates:** EUR494 individuals print or online; EUR672 individuals print and online. **URL:** http://www.inderscience.com/browse/index.php?journalCODE=ijuwbcs.

45131 ■ All India Radio Guwahati - 729 KHz
Chandmari
Guwahati 781 003, Assam, India
Ph: 91 361 2660357
E-mail: airgau@sancharnet.in
Format: Eclectic. **Owner:** Prasar Bharati, Akashvani Bhavan, Sansad Marg, New Delhi 110 001, Delhi, India, 91 11 23421006, Fax: 91 11 23421956. **Founded:** 1948. **Key Personnel:** M.C. Aggarwal, Engr.-in-Ch., phone 91 11 23421058, fax 91 11 23421459, einc@air.org.in. **Wattage:** 100,000. **Ad Rates:** $180-400 for 10 seconds; $270-600 for 15 seconds; $540-1,200 for 30 seconds; $1,080-2,400 for 60 seconds. **URL:** http://www. allindiaradio.org.

Gwalior

45132 ■ All India Radio Gwalior - 1386 KHz
Gandhi Rd.
Gwalior 474 002, Madhya Pradesh, India
Ph: 91 751 2341700
E-mail: seairgwl1@sancharnet.in
Format: Eclectic. **Owner:** Prasar Bharati, Akashvani Bhavan, Sansad Marg, New Delhi 110 001, Delhi, India, 91 11 23421006, Fax: 91 11 23421956. **Founded:** 1964. **Key Personnel:** M.C. Aggarwal, Engr.-in-Ch., phone 91 11 23421058, fax 91 11 23421006, einc@air.org.in. **Wattage:** 20,000. **Ad Rates:** $150-300 for 10 seconds; $225-450 for 15 seconds; $450-900 for 30 seconds; $900-1,800 for 60 seconds. **URL:** http://www. allindiaradio.org.

Haflong

45133 ■ All India Radio Haflong - 100.2 MHz
Dima Hasao
Haflong 788 819, Assam, India
Ph: 91 3673 236682
Fax: 91 3673 236688
E-mail: info@airhaflong.org
Format: Eclectic; Full Service. **Owner:** Prasar Bharati, Akashvani Bhavan, Sansad Marg, New Delhi 110 001, Delhi, India, 91 11 23421058, Fax: 91 11 23421956. **Founded:** 1992. **Key Personnel:** M.C. Aggarwal, Engr.-in-Ch., phone 91 11 23421058, fax 91 11 23421006, einc@air.org.in; Mohan Singh, Ch. Engr. Proj., phone 91 11 23421184. **Wattage:** 6000. **Ad Rates:** $80-150 for 10 seconds; $120-225 for 15 seconds; $240-450 for 30 seconds; $480-900 for 60 seconds. **URL:** http://airhaflong.org/haflong.html.

Hamirpur

45134 ■ All India Radio Hamirpur - 101.8 MHz
Akashvani Bhavan
Sansad Marg
New Delhi 110 001, Delhi, India
Ph: 91 11 23421006
Fax: 91 11 23421956
Format: Eclectic; Full Service. **Owner:** Prasar Bharati, at above address. **Founded:** 1994. **Key Personnel:** M.C. Aggarwal, Engr.-in-Ch., phone 91 11 23421058, fax 91 11 23421006, einc@air.org.in; Mohan Singh, Ch. Engr. Proj., phone 91 11 23421184. **Wattage:** 6000. **Ad**

Rates: $80-150 for 10 seconds; $120-225 for 15 seconds; $240-450 for 30 seconds; $480-900 for 60 seconds. **URL:** http://www.allindiaradio.org.

Hassan

45135 ■ All India Radio Hassan - 102.2 MHz
Salagame Rd.
PO Box 22
Hassan 573 201, Karnataka, India
Ph: 91 8172 246321
E-mail: air_hsn@yahoo.co.in
Format: Eclectic. **Owner:** Prasar Bharati, Akashvani Bhavan, Sansad Marg, New Delhi 110 001, Delhi, India, 91 11 23421006, Fax: 91 11 23421956. **Founded:** 1991. **Key Personnel:** M.C. Aggarwal, Engr.-in-Ch., phone 91 11 23421058, fax 91 11 23421006, einc@air.org.in. **Wattage:** 6000. **Ad Rates:** $80-150 for 10 seconds; $120-225 for 15 seconds; $240-450 for 30 seconds; $480-900 for 60 seconds. **URL:** http://www.allindiaradio. org.

Hisar

45136 ■ Research on Crops
Gaurav Society of Agricultural Research Information Centre
Systematic Printers, Near Video Market, Udayapuria St.
Mohalla Udayapuria
Udayapuria St.
Hisar 125 001, Haryana, India
Ph: 91 16 62230467
Publisher E-mail: mdgsaric@yahoo.com
Journal for the dissemination of latest research (both basic and applied) on all type of crop plants grown throughout the world. **Subtitle:** An International Journal. **Freq:** Bimonthly. **Key Personnel:** Dr. Ved Pal Singh, Editor-in-Chief, aricindia@hotmail.com. **ISSN:** 0972-3226. **Subscription Rates:** Rs 1,000 institutions; US$300 institutions, other countries. **URL:** http://www.cropresearch.org/index2.html.

Hospet

45137 ■ All India Radio Hospet - 100.5 MHz
Akashvani Bhavan
Sansad Marg
New Delhi 110 001, Delhi, India
Ph: 91 11 23421006
Fax: 91 11 23421956
E-mail: airfmhpt@sancharnet.in
Format: Eclectic. **Owner:** Prasar Bharati, at above address. **Founded:** 1992. **Key Personnel:** M.C. Aggarwal, Engr.-in-Ch., phone 91 11 23421058, fax 91 11 23421006, einc@air.org.in. **Wattage:** 10,000. **Ad Rates:** $80-150 for 10 seconds; $120-225 for 15 seconds; $240-450 for 30 seconds; $480-900 for 60 seconds. **URL:** http://www.allindiaradio.org.

Howrah

45138 ■ Journal of Technology
Bengal Engineering and Science University
PO Botanic Garden
Howrah 711 103, West Bengal, India
Ph: 91 33 26684561
Fax: 91 33 26682916
Science and technology periodical. **Founded:** 1956. **Freq:** Semiannual 2/yr. **Print Method:** DTP. **Trim Size:** 24.5 x 18 cm. **ISSN:** 0047-2824. **Subscription Rates:** US$8 individuals print; US$4 individuals electronic. **Remarks:** Advertising not accepted. **URL:** http://www.becs.ac.in/. **Circ:** Paid 250

Hyderabad

45139 ■ FAPCCI Review
Federation of Andhra Pradesh Chambers of Commerce and Industry
11-6-841
PO Box 14, Red Hills
Hyderabad 500 004, Andhra Pradesh, India
Ph: 91 40 23395515
Fax: 91 40 23395525
Publisher E-mail: info@fapcci.org
Periodical focusing on trade, commerce, and industry. **Freq:** Weekly. **Key Personnel:** Sri Suraj Prasad Agarwal, President; Sri K.Harish Chandra Prasad, Sen. VP.

Circulation: ★ = ABC; △ = BPA; ◆ = CAC; • = CCAB; ❑ = VAC; ⊕ = PO Statement; ‡ = Publisher's Report; Boldface figures = sworn; Light figures = estimated.

Gale Directory of Publications & Broadcast Media/147th Ed.   5001

Subscription Rates: Free for members. URL: http://www.periodicals.ru/import/good.phtml?id=386159.

45140 ■ The Icfai Journal of Accounting Research
ICFAI University Press
Plot. 6-3-354/1, Stellar Sphinx
Rd. 1, Banjara Hills
Panjagutta
Hyderabad 500 082, Andhra Pradesh, India
Ph: 91 40 23430449
Fax: 91 40 23430447
Publisher E-mail: info@iupindia.org
Journal featuring research reports in the field of accounting. Freq: Quarterly. Key Personnel: E.N. Murthy, Editor; G.R.K. Murty, Managing Editor. Subscription Rates: Rs 625 individuals; Rs 1,650 individuals 3 years. URL: http://www.iupindia.in/.

45141 ■ The Icfai Journal of Alternative Dispute Resolution
ICFAI University Press
Plot. 6-3-354/1, Stellar Sphinx
Rd. 1, Banjara Hills
Panjagutta
Hyderabad 500 082, Andhra Pradesh, India
Ph: 91 40 23430449
Fax: 91 40 23430447
Publisher E-mail: info@iupindia.org
Journal focusing on arbitration, conciliation, mediation, negotiation, and settlement of disputes. Freq: Quarterly. Subscription Rates: Rs 625 individuals. URL: http://www.iupindia.org/ijadr.asp.

45142 ■ The Icfai Journal of Audit Practice
ICFAI University Press
Plot. 6-3-354/1, Stellar Sphinx
Rd. 1, Banjara Hills
Panjagutta
Hyderabad 500 082, Andhra Pradesh, India
Ph: 91 40 23430449
Fax: 91 40 23430447
Publisher E-mail: info@iupindia.org
Journal featuring information about auditing for accountants, finance professionals, and auditors. Freq: Quarterly. Key Personnel: E.N. Murthy, Editor; G.R.K. Murty, Managing Editor. Subscription Rates: Rs 625 individuals; Rs 1,650 individuals three years. URL: http://www.iupindia.org/ijap.asp.

45143 ■ The Icfai Journal of Bank Management
ICFAI University Press
Plot. 6-3-354/1, Stellar Sphinx
Rd. 1, Banjara Hills
Panjagutta
Hyderabad 500 082, Andhra Pradesh, India
Ph: 91 40 23430449
Fax: 91 40 23430447
Publisher E-mail: info@iupindia.org
Journal focusing on the areas of risk management, forex markets, retail banking, HRD & leadership, banking, supervision, convergence of financial services, and e-banking. Freq: Quarterly. Key Personnel: G.R.K. Murty, Managing Editor; E.N. Murthy, Editor. Subscription Rates: Rs 625 individuals; Rs 1,650 individuals three years. URL: http://www.iupindia.org/ijbm.asp.

45144 ■ The Icfai Journal of Behavioral Finance
ICFAI University Press
Plot. 6-3-354/1, Stellar Sphinx
Rd. 1, Banjara Hills
Panjagutta
Hyderabad 500 082, Andhra Pradesh, India
Ph: 91 40 23430449
Fax: 91 40 23430447
Publisher E-mail: info@iupindia.org
Journal focusing on behavioral economics, behavior of markets, behavioral aspects influencing investment decisions of managers and behavioral aspects in corporate finance decision. Freq: Quarterly. Subscription Rates: Rs 625 individuals; Rs 1,650 individuals three years. URL: http://www.iupindia.org/Behavioral_Finance.asp.

45145 ■ The Icfai Journal of Corporate and Securities Law
ICFAI University Press
Plot. 6-3-354/1, Stellar Sphinx
Rd. 1, Banjara Hills
Panjagutta
Hyderabad 500 082, Andhra Pradesh, India
Ph: 91 40 23430449

Fax: 91 40 23430447
Publisher E-mail: info@iupindia.org
Journal focusing on capital markets, mutual funds, corporate governance trading and regulatory authorities. Freq: Quarterly. Subscription Rates: Rs 625 individuals; Rs 1,650 individuals three years. URL: http://www.iupindia.org/ijcsl.asp.

45146 ■ The Icfai Journal of Cyber Law
ICFAI University Press
Plot. 6-3-354/1, Stellar Sphinx
Rd. 1, Banjara Hills
Panjagutta
Hyderabad 500 082, Andhra Pradesh, India
Ph: 91 40 23430449
Fax: 91 40 23430447
Publisher E-mail: info@iupindia.org
Journal focusing on internet, information technology, and international cyber law. Freq: Quarterly. Subscription Rates: US$32 individuals; Rs 1,650 individuals three years. URL: http://www.iupindia.org/ijcl.asp.

45147 ■ The Icfai Journal of Derivatives Markets
ICFAI University Press
Plot. 6-3-354/1, Stellar Sphinx
Rd. 1, Banjara Hills
Panjagutta
Hyderabad 500 082, Andhra Pradesh, India
Ph: 91 40 23430449
Fax: 91 40 23430447
Publisher E-mail: info@iupindia.org
Peer-reviewed journal featuring articles dealing with derivative valuation and risk management. Freq: Quarterly. Subscription Rates: Rs 625 individuals; Rs 1,650 individuals 3 years. URL: http://www.iupindia.org/ijdm.asp.

45148 ■ The Icfai Journal of Employment Law
ICFAI University Press
Plot. 6-3-354/1, Stellar Sphinx
Rd. 1, Banjara Hills
Panjagutta
Hyderabad 500 082, Andhra Pradesh, India
Ph: 91 40 23430449
Fax: 91 40 23430447
Publisher E-mail: info@iupindia.org
Journal focusing on problems in employment, employer-employee relations, social security, labor welfare legislation, health, safety and welfare of workers. Freq: Quarterly. Subscription Rates: Rs 625 individuals; Rs 1,650 individuals 3 years. URL: http://www.iupindia.org/ijeml.asp.

45149 ■ The Icfai Journal of Entrepreneurship Development
ICFAI University Press
Plot. 6-3-354/1, Stellar Sphinx
Rd. 1, Banjara Hills
Panjagutta
Hyderabad 500 082, Andhra Pradesh, India
Ph: 91 40 23430449
Fax: 91 40 23430447
Publisher E-mail: info@iupindia.org
Journal focusing on entrepreneurship mindset, entrepreneurship opportunity, motivation, and case studies. Freq: Quarterly. Subscription Rates: Rs 625 individuals; Rs 1,650 individuals three years. URL: http://www.iupindia.in/Entrepreneurship_Development.asp.

45150 ■ The Icfai Journal of Environmental Economics
ICFAI University Press
Plot. 6-3-354/1, Stellar Sphinx
Rd. 1, Banjara Hills
Panjagutta
Hyderabad 500 082, Andhra Pradesh, India
Ph: 91 40 23430449
Fax: 91 40 23430447
Publisher E-mail: info@iupindia.org
Journal featuring issues pertaining to valuation of ecosystem benefits from environmental improvements, environmental planning, role of government and non-governmental organizations and also the various innovations related to environment. Freq: Quarterly. Key Personnel: E.N. Murthy, Editor; G.R.K. Murty, Managing Editor. Subscription Rates: Rs 625 individuals; Rs 1,650 individuals 3 years. URL: http://www.iupindia.org/ijee.asp.

45151 ■ The Icfai Journal of Financial Economics
ICFAI University Press
Plot. 6-3-354/1, Stellar Sphinx
Rd. 1, Banjara Hills
Panjagutta
Hyderabad 500 082, Andhra Pradesh, India
Ph: 91 40 23430449
Fax: 91 40 23430447
Publisher E-mail: info@iupindia.org
Journal focusing on the issue of economics, finance, statistics, and econometrics. Freq: Quarterly. Subscription Rates: Rs 625 individuals; Rs 1,650 individuals three years. URL: http://www.iupindia.in/Financial_Economics.asp.

45152 ■ The Icfai Journal of Financial Risk Management
ICFAI University Press
Plot. 6-3-354/1, Stellar Sphinx
Rd. 1, Banjara Hills
Panjagutta
Hyderabad 500 082, Andhra Pradesh, India
Ph: 91 40 23430449
Fax: 91 40 23430447
Publisher E-mail: info@iupindia.org
Journal focusing on identifying financial risk, risk management models, accounting for derivatives, risk-hedging techniques, and asset liability management. Freq: Quarterly. Key Personnel: E.N. Murthy, Editor; G.R.K Murty, Managing Editor. Subscription Rates: Rs 625 individuals; Rs 1,650 individuals three years. URL: http://www.iupindia.in/FinancialRisk_Management.asp.

45153 ■ The Icfai Journal of Governance and Public Policy
ICFAI University Press
Plot. 6-3-354/1, Stellar Sphinx
Rd. 1, Banjara Hills
Panjagutta
Hyderabad 500 082, Andhra Pradesh, India
Ph: 91 40 23430449
Fax: 91 40 23430447
Publisher E-mail: info@iupindia.org
Journal focusing on critical evaluation of public policies and governance at the national, state, and local levels. Freq: Quarterly. Key Personnel: E.N. Murthy, Editor; G.R.K. Murty, Managing Editor. Subscription Rates: Rs 625 individuals; Rs 1,650 individuals three years. URL: http://www.iupindia.in/Governanceand_PublicPolicy.asp.

45154 ■ The Icfai Journal of Healthcare Law
ICFAI University Press
Plot. 6-3-354/1, Stellar Sphinx
Rd. 1, Banjara Hills
Panjagutta
Hyderabad 500 082, Andhra Pradesh, India
Ph: 91 40 23430449
Fax: 91 40 23430447
Publisher E-mail: info@iupindia.org
Journal focusing on legal principles relating to medico-legal, socio-legal, medical-malpractice, tort-claims, malpractice-insurance, drug-safety and efficacy issues, and ethical values with health science. Freq: Quarterly. ISSN: 0972-785X. Subscription Rates: Rs 625 individuals; Rs 1,650 individuals three years. URL: http://www.iupindia.org/ijhl.asp.

45155 ■ The Icfai Journal of History and Culture
ICFAI University Press
Plot. 6-3-354/1, Stellar Sphinx
Rd. 1, Banjara Hills
Panjagutta
Hyderabad 500 082, Andhra Pradesh, India
Ph: 91 40 23430449
Fax: 91 40 23430449
Publisher E-mail: info@iupindia.org
Journal focusing on the historical developments from the ancient past to the contemporary times. Freq: Quarterly. Key Personnel: E.N. Murthy, Editor; G.R.K. Murty, Managing Editor. Subscription Rates: Rs 625 individuals; Rs 1,650 individuals three years. URL: http://www.iupindia.in/History_Culture.asp.

45156 ■ The Icfai Journal of International Business Law
ICFAI University Press
Plot. 6-3-354/1, Stellar Sphinx
Rd. 1, Banjara Hills

Panjagutta
Hyderabad 500 082, Andhra Pradesh, India
Ph: 91 40 23430449
Fax: 91 40 23430447
Publisher E-mail: info@iupindia.org
Journal focusing on international trade agreements and financial law. **Freq:** Quarterly. **Subscription Rates:** Rs 625 individuals; Rs 1,650 individuals 3 years. **URL:** http://www.iupindia.org/ijibl.asp.

45157 ■ The Icfai Journal of Knowledge Management
ICFAI University Press
Plot. 6-3-354/1, Stellar Sphinx
Rd. 1, Banjara Hills
Panjagutta
Hyderabad 500 082, Andhra Pradesh, India
Ph: 91 40 23430449
Fax: 91 40 23430447
Publisher E-mail: info@iupindia.org
Journal focusing on product knowledge, services knowledge, process knowledge, customer knowledge, and knowledge assets. **Freq:** Bimonthly. **Subscription Rates:** Rs 625 individuals. **URL:** http://www.iupindia.in/Knowledge_Management.asp.

45158 ■ The Icfai Journal of Life Sciences
ICFAI University Press
Plot. 6-3-354/1, Stellar Sphinx
Rd. 1, Banjara Hills
Panjagutta
Hyderabad 500 082, Andhra Pradesh, India
Ph: 91 40 23430449
Fax: 91 40 23430447
Publisher E-mail: info@iupindia.org
Journal focusing on botany, zoology, evolutionary biology, microbiology, and biochemistry. **Freq:** Quarterly. **Subscription Rates:** Rs 625 individuals; Rs 1,650 individuals three years. **URL:** http://www.iupindia.in/Life_Sciences.asp.

45159 ■ The Icfai Journal of Managerial Economics
ICFAI University Press
Plot. 6-3-354/1, Stellar Sphinx
Rd. 1, Banjara Hills
Panjagutta
Hyderabad 500 082, Andhra Pradesh, India
Ph: 91 40 23430449
Fax: 91 40 23430447
Publisher E-mail: info@iupindia.org
Journal focusing on managerial decision-making from all functional areas of economics. **Freq:** Quarterly. **Subscription Rates:** Rs 625 individuals; Rs 1,650 individuals three years. **URL:** http://www.iupindia.in/Managerial_Economics.asp.

45160 ■ The Icfai Journal of Mergers & Acquisitions
ICFAI University Press
Plot. 6-3-354/1, Stellar Sphinx
Rd. 1, Banjara Hills
Panjagutta
Hyderabad 500 082, Andhra Pradesh, India
Ph: 91 40 23430449
Fax: 91 40 23430447
Publisher E-mail: info@iupindia.org
Journal focusing on mergers and acquisitions, pre-merger issues, post-merger issues, cross-border mergers, and regulatory aspects. **Freq:** Quarterly. **Subscription Rates:** Rs 625 individuals; Rs 1,650 individuals 3 years. **URL:** http://www.iupindia.org/.

45161 ■ The Icfai Journal of Monetary Economics
ICFAI University Press
Plot. 6-3-354/1, Stellar Sphinx
Rd. 1, Banjara Hills
Panjagutta
Hyderabad 500 082, Andhra Pradesh, India
Ph: 91 40 23430449
Fax: 91 40 23430447
Publisher E-mail: info@iupindia.org
Journal focusing on monetary policies and issues. **Freq:** Quarterly. **Key Personnel:** E.N. Murthy, Editor; G.R.K. Murty, Managing Editor. **Subscription Rates:** Rs 625 individuals; Rs 1,650 individuals three years. **URL:** http://www.iupindia.in/Monetary_Economics.asp.

45162 ■ The Icfai Journal of Operations Management
ICFAI University Press
Plot. 6-3-354/1, Stellar Sphinx
Rd. 1, Banjara Hills
Panjagutta
Hyderabad 500 082, Andhra Pradesh, India
Ph: 91 40 23430449
Fax: 91 40 23430447
Publisher E-mail: info@iupindia.org
Journal focusing on inventory control, supply chain management, enterprise resource planning, total quality management, business process re-engineering, logistics management, and flexible manufacturing systems. **Freq:** Quarterly. **Subscription Rates:** Rs 625 individuals; Rs 1,650 individuals three years. **URL:** http://www.iupindia.in/Operations_Management.asp.

45163 ■ The Icfai Journal of Organizational Behavior
ICFAI University Press
Plot. 6-3-354/1, Stellar Sphinx
Rd. 1, Banjara Hills
Panjagutta
Hyderabad 500 082, Andhra Pradesh, India
Ph: 91 40 23430449
Fax: 91 40 23430447
Publisher E-mail: info@iupindia.org
Journal focusing on organization design, job, performance, motivation and satisfaction, work-life balance, group dynamics, and leadership. **Freq:** Quarterly. **Key Personnel:** E.N. Murthy, Editor; G.R.K. Murty, Managing Editor. **Subscription Rates:** Rs 625 individuals; Rs 1,650 individuals three years. **URL:** http://www.iupindia.in/Organizational_Behavior.asp.

45164 ■ The Icfai Journal of Public Finance
ICFAI University Press
Plot. 6-3-354/1, Stellar Sphinx
Rd. 1, Banjara Hills
Panjagutta
Hyderabad 500 082, Andhra Pradesh, India
Ph: 91 40 23430449
Fax: 91 40 23430447
Publisher E-mail: info@iupindia.org
Journal focusing on fiscal policy, economic stabilization, and tax reforms. **Freq:** Quarterly. **Key Personnel:** E.N. Murthy, Editor; G.R.K. Murty, Managing Editor. **Subscription Rates:** Rs 625 individuals; Rs 1,650 individuals three years. **URL:** http://www.iupindia.in/Public_Finance.asp.

45165 ■ The Icfai Journal of Risk & Insurance
ICFAI University Press
Plot. 6-3-354/1, Stellar Sphinx
Rd. 1, Banjara Hills
Panjagutta
Hyderabad 500 082, Andhra Pradesh, India
Ph: 91 40 23430449
Fax: 91 40 23430447
Publisher E-mail: info@iupindia.org
Journal focusing on the advancement of knowledge in risk management approaches, tools, practices, and hedging techniques. **Freq:** Quarterly. **Subscription Rates:** Rs 625 individuals; Rs 1,650 individuals three years. **URL:** http://www.iupindia.in/Risk_Insurance.asp.

45166 ■ The Icfai Journal of Science & Technology
ICFAI University Press
Plot. 6-3-354/1, Stellar Sphinx
Rd. 1, Banjara Hills
Panjagutta
Hyderabad 500 082, Andhra Pradesh, India
Ph: 91 40 23430449
Fax: 91 40 23430447
Publisher E-mail: info@iupindia.org
Journal focusing on science, engineering, technology, education and their applications. **Freq:** Quarterly. **Key Personnel:** E.N. Murthy, Editor; G.R.K. Murty, Managing Editor. **Subscription Rates:** Rs 625 individuals; Rs 1,650 individuals three years. **URL:** http://www.iupindia.in/Science_Technology.asp.

45167 ■ The Icfai Journal of Services Marketing
ICFAI University Press
Plot. 6-3-354/1, Stellar Sphinx
Rd. 1, Banjara Hills
Panjagutta

Hyderabad 500 082, Andhra Pradesh, India
Ph: 91 40 23430449
Fax: 91 40 23430447
Publisher E-mail: info@iupindia.org
Journal featuring latest research, concepts, and managerial implications in the service sector covering financial services, educational services, travel and hospitality services, consultancy services, and many others. **Freq:** Quarterly. **Subscription Rates:** Rs 625 individuals; Rs 1,650 individuals 3 years. **URL:** http://www.iupindia.org/.

45168 ■ The Icfai Journal of Soft Skills
ICFAI University Press
Plot. 6-3-354/1, Stellar Sphinx
Rd. 1, Banjara Hills
Panjagutta
Hyderabad 500 082, Andhra Pradesh, India
Ph: 91 40 23430449
Fax: 91 40 23430447
Publisher E-mail: info@iupindia.org
Journal featuring issues pertaining to soft skills and communication. **Freq:** Quarterly. **Key Personnel:** E.N. Murthy, Editor; G.R.K. Murty, Managing Editor. **Subscription Rates:** Rs 625 individuals; Rs 1,650 individuals three years. **URL:** http://www.iupindia.in/Soft_Skills.asp.

45169 ■ The Icfai Journal of Urban Policy
ICFAI University Press
Plot. 6-3-354/1, Stellar Sphinx
Rd. 1, Banjara Hills
Panjagutta
Hyderabad 500 082, Andhra Pradesh, India
Ph: 91 40 23430449
Fax: 91 40 23430447
Publisher E-mail: info@iupindia.org
Journal featuring the coherent and intelligent debate on managing urban growth and efficient development. **Freq:** Quarterly. **Key Personnel:** E.N. Murthy, Editor; G.R.K. Murty, Managing Editor. **Subscription Rates:** Rs 625 individuals; Rs 1,650 individuals 3 years. **URL:** http://www.iupindia.org/ijup.asp.

45170 ■ Icfai Reader
ICFAI University Press
Plot. 6-3-354/1, Stellar Sphinx
Rd. 1, Banjara Hills
Panjagutta
Hyderabad 500 082, Andhra Pradesh, India
Ph: 91 40 23430449
Fax: 91 40 23430447
Publisher E-mail: info@iupindia.org
Magazine featuring issues in finance. **Freq:** Monthly. **Subscription Rates:** Rs 625 individuals. **URL:** http://www.iupindia.org/icfai_reader.asp.

45171 ■ Indian Academy of Geoscience Journal
Indian Academy of Geoscience
Osmania University
Hyderabad 500 007, Andhra Pradesh, India
Scientific journal on earth sciences. **Founded:** 1958. **Freq:** Semiannual. **ISSN:** 0379-5160. **Remarks:** Accepts advertising. **URL:** http://www.periodicals.ru/import/good.phtml?id=429584. **Former name:** Journal of the Indian Geoscience Academy. **Circ:** Paid ★300

45172 ■ Indian Journal of Pharmacology
Indian Pharmacological Society
Food & Drug Toxicology Research Centre
National Institute of Nutrition
Tarnaka
Hyderabad 500 007, Andhra Pradesh, India
Ph: 91 40 27008921
Publication on pharmacology. **Freq:** Bimonthly (February, April, June, august, October and December). **Key Personnel:** R.K. Dikshit, Chief Ed.; Arunabha Ray, Editorial Board. **ISSN:** 0253-7613. **Subscription Rates:** Rs 3,500 individuals; US$250 other countries; Rs 3,500 institutions; US$250 other countries institutions. **Remarks:** Accepts advertising. **URL:** http://medind.nic.in/ibi/ibim.shtml; http://www.ijp-online.com/. **Circ:** 2,000

45173 ■ Insurance Chronicle
ICFAI University Press
Plot. 6-3-354/1, Stellar Sphinx
Rd. 1, Banjara Hills
Panjagutta
Hyderabad 500 082, Andhra Pradesh, India
Ph: 91 40 23430449

Fax: 91 40 23430447
Publisher E-mail: info@iupindia.org
Magazine featuring insurance business environment.
Freq: Monthly. **Subscription Rates:** Rs 625 individuals.
URL: http://www.iupindia.in/.

45174 ■ Journal of the Henry Martyn Institute
Henry Martyn Institute
International Center for Research, Interfaith Realations
and Recociliation
PO Box 153
Hyderabad, Andhra Pradesh, India
Ph: 91 402 4014258
Fax: 91 402 4014231
Publisher E-mail: hmipublications@gmail.com
Publication on the Islamic religion. **Founded:** 1930.
Freq: Semiannual. **Key Personnel:** Edwin A. Schick,
Contact; Robert Schick, Contact. **ISSN:** 0970-4698.
Subscription Rates: Rs 175 individuals Indian subcon-
tinent; Rs 300 two years Indian subcontinent; Rs 500
individuals Indian subcontinent; Rs 200 institutions
Indian subcontinent; Rs 350 two years Indian subcontinent; Rs 550 institutions Indian subcontinent; US$20
institutions, other countries via surface mail; US$25
institutions via surface mail; US$45 institutions 2 years,
via surface mail; US$65 institutions 3 years, via surface
mail. **Remarks:** Accepts advertising. **URL:** http://www.
hmiindia.com/journal_henry.html. **Formerly:** Henry Martyn Institute of Islamic Studies Bulletin. **Circ:** Paid 370

45175 ■ Journal of Research—ANGRAU
Acharya N G Ranga Agricultural University
Rajendranagar
Hyderabad 500 030, Andhra Pradesh, India
Publisher E-mail: angrau@ap.nic.in
Periodical covering issues in agriculture research. **Freq:**
Quarterly. **Key Personnel:** Dr. Shaik Mohammad, Edi-
tor; Dr. P. Gidda Reddy, Managing Editor. **Subscription
Rates:** Rs 250 individuals; Rs 1,000 institutions. **URL:**
http://www.angrau.net/
Journal%20of%20ResearchANGRAU.htm.

45176 ■ Journal of Rural Development
Ministry of Rural Development
National Institute of Rural Development
Rajendranagar
Hyderabad 500 030, Andhra Pradesh, India
Ph: 91 402 4008526
Fax: 91 402 4015277
Social science journal focusing on rural development.
Founded: 1967. **Freq:** Quarterly. **Key Personnel:** V.S.
Sampath, Ed./Chm.; C. Subba Rao, Production; Dr. S.
Rajakutty, Managing Editor. **ISSN:** 0970-3357. **Sub-
scription Rates:** Rs 200 individuals plus (regd. post
charges); Rs 500 institutions plus (regd. post charges);
US$50 other countries; 40 other countries; Rs 3,500
individuals life membership; Rs 1,200 institutions
membership. **URL:** http://www.nird.org.in/
Journal%20of%20Rural%20Development.html. **Circ:**
Paid 1,000

45177 ■ The New Indian Express
Express Publications (Madurai) Ltd.
Lower Tank Bund Rd.
Domalguda
Hyderabad 500 029, Andhra Pradesh, India
General newspaper. **Founded:** 1932. **Freq:** Daily. **Re-
marks:** Accepts advertising. **URL:** http://www.
expressbuzz.com/edition/default.aspx. **Circ:** (Not
Reported)

45178 ■ Nutrition
National Institute of Nutrition
Indian Council of Medical Research
Jamai-Osmania
Hyderabad 500 007, Andhra Pradesh, India
Ph: 91 40 27008921
Fax: 91 40 27019074
Publisher E-mail: nin@ap.nic.in
Magazine on food and nutrition. **Founded:** 1966. **Freq:**
Quarterly. **ISSN:** 0550-404X. **Subscription Rates:** Rs 8
individuals. **URL:** http://www.ninindia.org/; http://www.
ninindia.org/periodicals.htm. **Circ:** Paid 4,000

45179 ■ Porfolio Organizer
ICFAI University Press
Plot. 6-3-354/1, Stellar Sphinx
Rd. 1, Banjara Hills
Panjagutta
Hyderabad 500 082, Andhra Pradesh, India

Ph: 91 40 23430449
Fax: 91 40 23430447
Publisher E-mail: info@iupindia.org
Magazine featuring investment and portfolio
management. **Freq:** Monthly. **Subscription Rates:** Rs
625 individuals; Rs 1,650 individuals 3 years. **URL:**
http://www.iupindia.in/.

45180 ■ Professional Banker
ICFAI University Press
Plot. 6-3-354/1, Stellar Sphinx
Rd. 1, Banjara Hills
Panjagutta
Hyderabad 500 082, Andhra Pradesh, India
Ph: 91 40 23430449
Fax: 91 40 23430447
Publisher E-mail: info@iupindia.org
Magazine featuring banking statistics and banking news.
Freq: Monthly. **Subscription Rates:** Rs 940 individuals;
Rs 2,475 individuals 3 years. **URL:** http://www.iupindia.
in.

45181 ■ Projects & Profits
ICFAI University Press
Plot. 6-3-354/1, Stellar Sphinx
Rd. 1, Banjara Hills
Panjagutta
Hyderabad 500 082, Andhra Pradesh, India
Ph: 91 40 23430449
Fax: 91 40 23430447
Publisher E-mail: info@iupindia.org
Magazine featuring cutting edge knowledge pertaining
to project management. **Freq:** Monthly. **Subscription
Rates:** Rs 625 individuals; Rs 1,650 individuals 3 years.
URL: http://www.iupindia.in.

45182 ■ The Siasat Daily
Jawaharlal Nehru Rd.
Hyderabad 500 001, Andhra Pradesh, India
Ph: 91 402 4744180
Fax: 91 402 4603188
Publisher E-mail: contact@siasat.com
General newspaper. **Founded:** 1962. **Freq:** 16/yr. **Trim
Size:** 8 1/2 x 11. **ISSN:** 0021-9517. **URL:** http://www.
siasat.com/.

45183 ■ The Square and Compasses
Grand Lodge of India
c/o Vishwanathan Ganesan, Sub-Ed.
B-106 Shantishikara Apt.
Raj Bhavan Rd.
Somajiguda
Hyderabad 500 082, Andhra Pradesh, India
Ph: 91 40 23398267
Fax: 91 40 23390980
Publisher E-mail: glindia@nde.vsnl.net.in
Journal featuring Masonic literature. **Key Personnel:**
Vishwanathan Ganesan, Sub.-Ed., primetrust@satyam.
net.in. **URL:** http://www.masonindia.org/sqcomps.html.

45184 ■ Treasury Management
Association of Certified Treasury Managers
52 Nagarjuna Hills
Hyderabad 500 082, Andhra Pradesh, India
Ph: 91 402 343536874
Fax: 91 402 3352521
Publication E-mail: info@actmindia.org
Publisher E-mail: info@actmindia.org
Magazine containing case studies for treasury and risk
management professionals. **Freq:** Monthly. **URL:** http://
www.actmindia.org/.

45185 ■ All India Radio Hyderabad 'A' - 738 KHz
Rocklands
Saifabad
Hyderabad 500 004, Andhra Pradesh, India
Ph: 91 40 23230043
E-mail: hyderabad@air.org.in
Format: Eclectic. **Owner:** Prasar Bharati, Akashvani
Bhavan, Sansad Marg, New Delhi 110 001, Delhi, India,
91 11 23421006, Fax: 91 11 23421956. **Founded:** 1935.
Key Personnel: M.C. Aggarwal, Engr.-in-Ch., phone 91
11 23421058, fax 91 11 23421006, einc@air.org.in.
Wattage: 200,000. **Ad Rates:** $200-550 for 10 seconds;
$300-825 for 15 seconds; $600-1,650 for 30 seconds;
$1,200-3,300 for 60 seconds. **URL:** http://www.
allindiaradio.org.

**45186 ■ All India Radio Hyderabad 'B' - 1377
KHz**
Rocklands

Saifabad
Hyderabad 500 004, Andhra Pradesh, India
Ph: 91 40 23230043
E-mail: airhyd@hd2.vsnl.net.in
Format: Eclectic; Full Service. **Owner:** Prasar Bharati,
Akashvani Bhavan, Sansad Marg, New Delhi 110 001,
Delhi, India, 91 11 23421006, Fax: 91 11 23421956.
Key Personnel: M.C. Aggarwal, Engr.-in-Ch., phone 91
11 23421058, fax 91 11 23421006, einc@air.org.in; Mo-
han Singh, Ch. Engr. (Proj.), phone 91 11 23421184.
Wattage: 20,000. **Ad Rates:** $200-550 for 10 seconds;
$300-825 for 15 seconds; $600-1,650 for 30 seconds;
$1,200-3,300 for 60 seconds. **URL:** http://www.
allindiaradio.org.

Imphal

45187 ■ All India Radio Imphal - 882 KHz
Palace Compound
Imphal 795 001, Manipur, India
Ph: 91 385 2220248
E-mail: airimphal@sancharnet.in
Format: Eclectic. **Owner:** Prasar Bharati, Akashvani
Bhavan, Sansad Marg, New Delhi 110 001, Delhi, India,
91 11 23421006, Fax: 91 11 23421956. **Founded:** 1963.
Key Personnel: M.C. Aggarwal, Engr.-in-Ch., phone 91
11 23421058, fax 91 11 23421006, einc@air.org.in.
Wattage: 300,000. **Ad Rates:** $100-200 for 10 seconds;
$150-300 for 15 seconds; $300-600 for 30 seconds;
$600-1,200 for 60 seconds. **URL:** http://www.
allindiaradio.org.

Indore

45188 ■ Naidunia
Naidunia News & Networks Pvt. Ltd.
60/1, Babu Labhchand Chhajlani Marg
Indore 452 009, Madhya Pradesh, India
Ph: 91 731 2763111-14
Fax: 91 731 2763118-120
Publisher E-mail: response@naidunia.com
General newspaper. **Founded:** June 5, 1947. **Freq:**
4/wk -Mon.-Thurs. **Print Method:** Offset. **Trim Size:** 10
1/4 x 16. **Cols./Page:** 6. **Col. Width:** 1 1/2 inches. **Key
Personnel:** Alok Mehta, Ch. Ed., alok.mehta@naidunia.
com. **Subscription Rates:** Rs 3 individuals. **URL:** http://
epaper.naidunia.com/.

45189 ■ All India Radio Indore - 648 KHz
Malwa House
Indore 452 001, Madhya Pradesh, India
Ph: 91 731 2701828
E-mail: airindore@sancharnet.in
Format: Eclectic. **Owner:** Prasar Bharati, Akashvani
Bhavan, Sansad Marg, New Delhi 110 001, Delhi, India,
91 11 23421006, Fax: 91 11 23421956. **Founded:** 1955.
Key Personnel: M.C. Aggarwal, Engr.-in-Ch., phone 91
11 23421058, fax 91 11 23421006, einc@air.org.in.
Wattage: 200,000. **Ad Rates:** $180-400 for 10 seconds;
$270-600 for 15 seconds; $540-1,200 for 30 seconds;
$1,080-2,400 for 60 seconds. **URL:** http://www.
allindiaradio.org.

Itanagar

45190 ■ All India Radio Itanagar - 675 KHz
'C' Sector
PO Box 174
Itanagar 791 111, Arunachal Pradesh, India
Ph: 91 360 2212883
E-mail: itanagar@air.org.in
Format: Eclectic. **Owner:** Prasar Bharati, Akashvani
Bhavan, Sansad Marg, New Delhi 110 001, Delhi, India,
91 11 23421006, Fax: 91 11 23421956. **Founded:** 1986.
Key Personnel: M.C. Aggarwal, Engr.-in-Ch., phone 91
11 23421058, fax 91 11 23421459, einc@air.org.in.
Wattage: 100,000. **Ad Rates:** $100-200 for 10 seconds;
$150-300 for 15 seconds; $300-600 for 30 seconds;
$600-1,200 for 60 seconds. **URL:** http://www.
allindiaradio.org.

Jabalpur

45191 ■ All India Radio Jabalpur - 801 KHz
373 Napier Town
Jabalpur 482 001, Madhya Pradesh, India
Ph: 91 761 2667342
E-mail: sgeavjbp@sancharnet.in
Format: Eclectic. **Owner:** Prasar Bharati, Akashvani

Bhavan, Sansad Marg, New Delhi 110 001, Delhi, India, 91 11 23421006, Fax: 91 11 23421956. **Founded:** 1964. **Key Personnel:** M.C. Aggarwal, Engr.-in-Ch., phone 91 11 23421058, fax 91 11 23421006, einc@air.org.in; Mohan Singh, Ch. Engr., Proj., phone 91 11 23421184. **Wattage:** 200,000. **Ad Rates:** $180-400 for 10 seconds; $270-600 for 15 seconds; $540-1,200 for 30 seconds; $1,080-2,400 for 60 seconds. **URL:** http://www.allindiaradio.org.

Jagdalpur

45192 ■ All India Radio Jagdalpur - 756 KHz
PO Box 61
Jagdalpur 494 001, Madhya Pradesh, India
Ph: 91 778 2222300
E-mail: airjdp@sancharnet.in
Format: Eclectic. **Owner:** Prasar Bharati, Akashvani Bhavan, Sansad Marg, New Delhi 110 001, Delhi, India, 91 11 23421006, Fax: 91 11 23421956. **Founded:** 1977. **Key Personnel:** M.C. Aggarwal, Engr.-in-Ch., phone 91 11 23421058, fax 91 11 23421006, einc@air.org.in; Mohan Singh, Ch. Engr., Proj., phone 91 11 23421184. **Wattage:** 100,000. **Ad Rates:** $100-200 for 10 seconds; $150-300 for 15 seconds; $300-600 for 30 seconds; $600-1,200 for 60 seconds. **URL:** http://www.allindiaradio.org.

Jaipur

45193 ■ Diamond World
International Journal House
A-95 Journal House
Janta Colony
Jaipur 302 004, Rajasthan, India
Ph: 91 141 2614398
Fax: 91 141 2602973
Publication E-mail: gemjournal@satyam.net.in
Publisher E-mail: diaworld@sancharnet.in
Periodical covering jewelry. Contains illustrations. **Founded:** 1973. **Freq:** Biweekly. **Print Method:** Offset. **Trim Size:** 22.8 x 17.75 cm. **Key Personnel:** Alok Kala, Editor. **ISSN:** 0970-7727. **Subscription Rates:** Rs 2,500 individuals 3 years; Rs 1,000 individuals; US$100 other countries airmail; US$250 other countries 3 years. **Remarks:** Accepts advertising. **URL:** http://www.diamondworld.net/publication-Default.aspx?vid=1. **Ad Rates:** BW: US$1,000, 4C: US$1,500. **Circ:** 8,000

45194 ■ Gem & Jewellery Yearbook
International Journal House
A-95 Journal House
Janta Colony
Jaipur 302 004, Rajasthan, India
Ph: 91 141 2614398
Fax: 91 141 2602973
Publication E-mail: gemjournal@satyam.net.in
Publisher E-mail: diaworld@sancharnet.in
Publication on antique jewelleries and collectibles. **Founded:** 1974. **Freq:** Annual. **Print Method:** Offset. **Trim Size:** 14.25 x 22 cm. **Cols./Page:** 4. **Subscription Rates:** Rs 1,000 individuals; US$50 by mail. **Remarks:** Accepts advertising. **URL:** http://www.diamondworld.net/publication-Default.aspx?vid=7. **Ad Rates:** BW: US$500, 4C: US$1,000. **Circ:** Paid 4,500

45195 ■ Indian Journal of Clinical Biochemistry
Association of Clinical Biochemists of India
c/o Dr. Praveen Sharma, Ed.-in-Ch.
Dept. of Biochemistry
SMS Medical College & Hospital
Jaipur 302 004, Rajasthan, India
Ph: 91 141 2722562
Fax: 91 141 2552537
Journal covering research in the field of clinical biochemistry, bioinformatics, pathology, microbiology, molecular biology, cellular biology, and genetics. **Founded:** 1985. **Freq:** Semiannual. **Print Method:** Offset. **Trim Size:** 11 1/2 x 14. **Cols./Page:** 4. **Col. Width:** 24 nonpareils. **Col. Depth:** 171 agate lines. **Key Personnel:** Dr. Praveen Sharma, Editor-in-Chief, praveensharma55@gmail.com. **URL:** http://medind.nic.in/iaf/iafaj.shtml.

45196 ■ Indian Journal of Sexually Transmitted Diseases
Indian Association for the Study of Sexually Transmitted Diseases
11/34, Shri Girdhar Hospital & Research Ctr.
Girdhar Marg
Malviya Nagar
Jaipur 302 017, Rajasthan, India
Journal dedicated to sexually transmitted diseases. **Key Personnel:** Abhishek Sharma, MD, Contact; Yogesh Marfatia, Editor-in-Chief; Puneet Bhargava, Assoc. Ed. **URL:** http://medind.nic.in/; http://medind.nic.in/ibo/iboct.shtml.

45197 ■ Journal of Gem Industry
Gem & Jewellery Information Centre
A-95 Journal House
Janta Colony
Jaipur 302 004, Rajasthan, India
Ph: 91 141 2614398
Fax: 91 141 2602973
Publication E-mail: gemjournal@satyam.net.in
Publisher E-mail: diaworld@sancharnet.in
Periodical covering the jewelry and gem industry. **Founded:** 1963. **Freq:** Bimonthly. **Print Method:** Offset. **Trim Size:** 22.8 x 17.75 cm. **ISSN:** 0022-1244. **Subscription Rates:** Rs 525 individuals; Rs 1,425 individuals 3 years; Rs 2,225 individuals 5 years; US$60 other countries airmail; US$35 other countries seamail. **Remarks:** Accepts advertising. **URL:** http://www.gemjournal.com/html/book5.htm. **Ad Rates:** BW: US$1,100, 4C: US$1,600. **Circ:** 8,750

45198 ■ Lung India
Medknow Publications Pvt Ltd.
c/o Virendra Singh, Ed.
SMS Medical College & Hospital
Jawahar Lal Nehru Marg.
Jaipur 302004, Rajasthan, India
Peer-reviewed journal of the Indian Chest Society. **Founded:** Aug. 15, 1982. **Freq:** Quarterly. **Key Personnel:** Dr. Virendra Singh, Editor; Dr. N.K. Jain, Assoc. Ed.; Dr. J.C. Suri, Assoc. Ed. **ISSN:** 0970-2113. **Subscription Rates:** Rs 1,000 individuals print only; Rs 2,000 institutions print only; US$100 other countries print only; US$250 institutions, other countries print only; Rs 1,200 individuals print and online; Rs 1,200 institutions print and online; US$120 other countries print and online; US$300 institutions, other countries print and online; Rs 800 individuals online; Rs 1,600 institutions online. **Remarks:** Accepts advertising. **URL:** http://www.lungindia.com. **Circ:** (Not Reported)

45199 ■ Statistical Abstract of Rajasthan
Directorate of Economics and Statistics, Rajasthan
Tilak Marg
C-Scheme
Jaipur, Rajasthan, India
Fax: 91 2229756
Publication featuring statistics pertaining to Rajasthan State. **Founded:** 1958. **Freq:** Annual. **ISSN:** 0081-4717. **Subscription Rates:** Rs 142 individuals. **URL:** http://statistics.rajasthan.gov.in/publication.asp?sch=1.

45200 ■ All India Radio Jaipur - 1476 KHz
5 Pk. House
Mirza Ismail Rd.
Jaipur 302 001, Rajasthan, India
Ph: 91 141 2363196
E-mail: airjpr@datainfosys.net
Format: Eclectic. **Owner:** Prasar Bharati, Akashvani Bhavan, Sansad Marg, New Delhi 110 001, Delhi, India, 91 11 23421006, Fax: 91 11 23421956. **Founded:** 1955. **Operating Hours:** 0025-1200, 1245-1730. **Key Personnel:** M.C. Aggarwal, Engr.-in-Ch., phone 91 11 23421058, fax 91 11 23421006, einc@air.org.in. **Wattage:** 1000. **Ad Rates:** $180-400 for 10 seconds; $270-600 for 15 seconds; $540-1,200 for 30 seconds; $1,080-2,400 for 60 seconds. **URL:** http://www.allindiaradio.org.

Jaisalmer

45201 ■ All India Radio Jaisalmer - 101.8 MHz
Akashvani Bhawan
Vyas Colony
Jaisalmer 345 001, Rajasthan, India
Ph: 91 2992 251632
E-mail: seairjsm@sancharnet.in
Format: Eclectic. **Owner:** Prasar Bharati, Akashvani Bhavan, Sansad Marg, New Delhi 110 001, Delhi, India, 91 11 23421006, Fax: 91 11 23421956. **Founded:** 1994. **Key Personnel:** M.C. Aggarwal, Engr.-in-Ch., phone 91 11 23421058, fax 91 11 23421006, einc@air.org.in. **Wattage:** 10,000. **Ad Rates:** $80-150 for 10 seconds; $120-225 for 15 seconds; $240-450 for 30 seconds;

$480-900 for 60 seconds. **URL:** http://www.allindiaradio.org.

Jalandhar

45202 ■ All India Radio Jalandhar 'A' - 873 KHz
Akashvani Bhavan
Sansad Marg
New Delhi 110 001, Delhi, India
Ph: 91 11 23421006
Fax: 91 11 23421956
E-mail: airjal@jla.vsnl.net.in
Format: Eclectic; Full Service. **Owner:** Prasar Bharati, at above address. **Founded:** 1949. **Key Personnel:** M.C. Aggarwal, Engr.-in-Ch., phone 91 11 23421058, fax 91 11 23421006, einc@air.org.in; Mohan Singh, Ch. Engr. Proj., phone 91 11 23421184. **Wattage:** 300,000. **Ad Rates:** $180-400 for 10 seconds; $270-600 for 15 seconds; $540-1,200 for 30 seconds; $1,080-2,400 for 60 seconds. **URL:** http://www.allindiaradio.org.

Jalgaon

45203 ■ All India Radio Jalgaon - 963 KHz
Jilha Peth
PO Box 52
Jalgaon 425 001, Maharashtra, India
Ph: 91 257 2225196
E-mail: airjal_jal@sancharnet.in
Format: Eclectic. **Owner:** Prasar Bharati, Akashvani Bhavan, Sansad Marg, New Delhi 110 001, Delhi, India, 91 11 23421006, Fax: 91 11 23421956. **Founded:** 1976. **Key Personnel:** M.C. Aggarwal, Engr.-in-Ch., phone 91 11 23421058, fax 91 11 23421006, einc@air.org.in. **Wattage:** 20,000. **Ad Rates:** $150-300 for 10 seconds; $225-450 for 15 seconds; $450-900 for 30 seconds; $900-1,800 for 60 seconds. **URL:** http://www.allindiaradio.org.

Jammu

45204 ■ Daily Excelsior
S.D. Rohmetra
Excelsior House
Janipura
Jammu 180 007, Jammu and Kashmir, India
Ph: 91 191 2537901
Fax: 91 191 2537831
Publication E-mail: editor@dailyexcelsior.com
Publisher E-mail: editor@dailyexcelsior.com
Regional newspaper of Jammu. **Founded:** 1965. **Freq:** Daily. **Key Personnel:** S.D. Rohmetra, Publisher & Owner, phone 91 191 2537055, fax 91 191 2537831. **Subscription Rates:** Rs 900 individuals. **Remarks:** Accepts advertising. **URL:** http://www.dailyexcelsior.com/. **Ad Rates:** GLR: Rs 3, BW: Rs 120, 4C: Rs 240, PCI: Rs 15. **Circ:** Paid 135,700

45205 ■ Kashmir Times
Kashmir Times Publications
Residency Rd.
Jammu 180 001, Jammu and Kashmir, India
Ph: 91 19 15247937
Fax: 91 19 12542028
Publisher E-mail: vbhasin@sancharnet.in
General newspaper of Kashmir. **Founded:** 1954. **Freq:** Daily. **Print Method:** Offset. **Trim Size:** 53 x 41 cm. **Key Personnel:** Prabodh Jamwal, Editor, phone 91 0191543676, fax 91 0191542028; Anuradha Bhasin Jamwal, Exec. Ed.; Ved Bhasin, Chm. **Subscription Rates:** US$300 individuals airmail; US$150 individuals surface mail. **Remarks:** Accepts advertising. **URL:** http://www.kashmirtimes.com. **Ad Rates:** GLR: Rs 350, BW: Rs 148,400, 4C: Rs 800, PCI: Rs 3,001. **Circ:** Paid 160,000

45206 ■ All India Radio Jammu - 990 KHz
Radio Kashmir
Palace Rd.
Jammu 180 001, Jammu and Kashmir, India
Ph: 91 191 2543408
E-mail: airjammu2002@yahoo.co.uk
Format: Eclectic. **Owner:** Prasar Bharati, Akashvani Bhavan, Sansad Marg, New Delhi 110 001, Delhi, India, 91 11 23421006, Fax: 91 11 23421956. **Founded:** 1947. **Key Personnel:** M.C. Aggarwal, Engr.-in-Ch., phone 91 11 23421058, fax 91 11 23421006, einc@air.org.in. **Wattage:** 300,000. **Ad Rates:** $150-300 for 10 seconds;

Circulation: ★ = ABC; △ = BPA; ♦ = CAC; • = CCAB; ❑ = VAC; ⊕ = PO Statement; ‡ = Publisher's Report; Boldface figures = sworn; Light figures = estimated.

$225-450 for 15 seconds; $450-900 for 30 seconds; $900-1,800 for 60 seconds. **URL:** http://www.allindiaradio.org.

Jamshedpur

45207 ■ Management and Labour Studies
XLRI
Circuit House Area E
Jamshedpur 831 001, Bihar, India
Ph: 91 657 3983333
Fax: 91 657 2227814
Publisher E-mail: xlwebmaster@xlri.ac.in
Publication focusing on labor and industrial relations. **Founded:** 1975. **Freq:** Quarterly. **Key Personnel:** A.C. Jesurajan, Editor, jesuraj@xlri.ac.in. **ISSN:** 0258-042X. **Subscription Rates:** Rs 300 individuals; US$30 other countries; 20 other countries; Rs 550 two years; US$50 two years overseas; 30 two years overseas. **Remarks:** Accepts advertising. **URL:** http://www.xlri.ac.in/scripts/mls.php. **Circ:** Paid 1,500

Jamshedpur (Delhi)

45208 ■ All India Radio Jamshedpur - 1584 KHz
Akashvani Bhavan
Sansad Marg
New Delhi 110 001, Delhi, India
Ph: 91 11 23421006
Fax: 91 11 23421956
E-mail: jsr_airjsr@sancharnet.in
Format: Eclectic. **Owner:** Prasar Bharati, at above address. **Founded:** 1990. **Key Personnel:** M.C. Aggarwal, Engr.-in-Ch., phone 91 11 23421058, fax 91 11 23421006, einc@air.org.in; Mohan Singh, Ch. Engr., Proj., phone 91 11 23421184. **Wattage:** 1000. **Ad Rates:** $100-200 for 10 seconds; $150-300 for 15 seconds; $300-600 for 30 seconds; $600-1,200 for 60 seconds. **URL:** http://www.allindiaradio.org.

Jeypore

45209 ■ All India Radio Jeypore - 1467 KHz
Akashvani Bhavan
Sansad Marg
New Delhi 110 001, Delhi, India
Ph: 91 11 23421006
Fax: 91 11 23421956
E-mail: airjeyp@sancharnet.in
Format: Eclectic. **Owner:** Prasar Bharati, at above address. **Founded:** 1964. **Key Personnel:** M.C. Aggarwal, Engr.-in-Ch., phone 91 11 23421058, fax 91 11 23421006, einc@air.org.in; Mohan Singh, Ch. Engr., Proj., phone 91 11 23421184. **Wattage:** 100,000. **Ad Rates:** $100-200 for 10 seconds; $150-300 for 15 seconds; $300-600 for 30 seconds; $600-1,200 for 60 seconds. **URL:** http://www.allindiaradio.org.

Jhalawar

45210 ■ All India Radio Jhalawar - 103.2 MHz
Jungle Rd.
Jhalawar 326 001, Rajasthan, India
Ph: 91 7432 232642
E-mail: airjhlr@rediffmail.com
Format: Eclectic. **Owner:** Prasar Bharati, Akashvani Bhavan, Sansad Marg, New Delhi 110 001, Delhi, India, 91 11 23421006, Fax: 91 11 23421956. **Founded:** 1993. **Key Personnel:** M.C. Aggarwal, Engr.-in-Ch., phone 91 11 23421058, fax 91 11 23421006, einc@air.org.in. **Wattage:** 6000. **Ad Rates:** $80-150 for 10 seconds; $120-225 for 15 seconds; $240-450 for 30 seconds; $480-900 for 60 seconds. **URL:** http://www.allindiaradio.org.

Jhansi

45211 ■ All India Radio Jhansi - 103.0 MHz
Kanpur Rd.
Jhansi 284 128, Uttar Pradesh, India
Ph: 91 517 2320457
Format: Eclectic. **Owner:** Prasar Bharati, Akashvani Bhavan, Sansad Marg, New Delhi 110 001, Delhi, India, 91 11 23421006, Fax: 91 11 23421956. **Founded:** 1993. **Key Personnel:** M.C. Aggarwal, Engr.-in-Ch., phone 91 11 23421058, fax 91 11 23421006, einc@air.org.in. **Wattage:** 6000. **Ad Rates:** $80-150 for 10 seconds; $120-225 for 15 seconds; $240-450 for 30 seconds;

$480-900 for 60 seconds. **URL:** http://www.allindiaradio.org.

Jodhpur

45212 ■ Advances in Horticulture and Forestry
Indian Periodical
5 New Pali Rd.
PO Box 33
Jodhpur 342001, Rajasthan, India
Ph: 91 291 2433323
Fax: 91 291 2512580
Publisher E-mail: info@indianperiodical.in
Journal covering horticulture and forestry. **Key Personnel:** R.K. Khetarpal, Editor-in-Chief; Arun Lal, Exec. Ed.; H.N. Gour, Exec. Ed. **ISSN:** 0971-0507. **URL:** http://www.indianperiodical.in/ip/journalview.aspx?jrnl=ahf&jrnltitle=AdvancesinHorticultureandForestry.

45213 ■ Advances in Plant Physiology
Indian Periodical
5 New Pali Rd.
PO Box 33
Jodhpur 342001, Rajasthan, India
Ph: 91 291 2433323
Fax: 91 291 2512580
Publisher E-mail: info@indianperiodical.in
Journal covering the advances in plant physiology. **Key Personnel:** A. Hemantaranjan, Editor-in-Chief; Dr. Anjali Bharti, Exec. Ed. **ISSN:** 0972-9917. **URL:** http://www.indianperiodical.in/ip/journalview.aspx?jrnl=app&jrnltitle=AdvancesinPlantPhysiology.

45214 ■ Annals of Arid Zone
Scientific Publishers - India
5-A New Pali Rd.
PO Box 91
Jodhpur 342 001, Rajasthan, India
Ph: 91 291 2433323
Fax: 91 291 2624154
Publisher E-mail: info@scientificpub.com
Periodical on earth science, agriculture and animal husbandry. **Freq:** Quarterly. **ISSN:** 0570-1791. **Subscription Rates:** US$200 institutions. **Remarks:** Accepts advertising. **URL:** http://www.scientificpub.com. **Circ:** Paid 800

45215 ■ Annual Review of Plant Pathology
Indian Periodical
5 New Pali Rd.
PO Box 33
Jodhpur 342001, Rajasthan, India
Ph: 91 291 2433323
Fax: 91 291 2512580
Publisher E-mail: info@indianperiodical.in
Journal covering plant pathology. **Founded:** Oct. 2002. **Freq:** Annual. **Key Personnel:** R.K. Khetarpal, Editor-in-Chief; H.N. Gour, Exec. Ed.; S.D. Purohit, Exec. Ed. **ISSN:** 0972-9712. **URL:** http://www.indianperiodical.in/ip/journalview.aspx?jrnl=arpp&jrnltitle=AnnualReviewofPlantPathology.

45216 ■ Bulletin of Pure and Applied Mathematics
Indian Periodical
c/o P.K. Banerji, Ed.-in-Ch.
Dept. of Mathematics
Faculty of Science
J.N.V. University
Jodhpur 342 005, Rajasthan, India
Publisher E-mail: info@indianperiodical.in
Journal covering research in pure and applied mathematics. **Key Personnel:** P.K. Banerji, Editor-in-Chief, banerjipk@yahoo.com. **ISSN:** 0973-5933. **URL:** http://www.indianperiodical.in/ip/journalview.aspx?jrnl=bpam&jrnltitle=BulletinofPureandAppliedMathematics.

45217 ■ Current Tax Reporter
K. Kumar
34 Heavy Industrial Area
Jodhpur 342 003, Rajasthan, India
Ph: 91 291 2745452
Fax: 91 291 2745470
Publication E-mail: info@currenttaxreporter.com
Publisher E-mail: info@currenttaxreporter.com
Journal on public finance. **Founded:** 1972. **Freq:** Weekly. **ISSN:** 0971-0043. **URL:** http://www.currenttaxreporter.com. **Circ:** 10,000

45218 ■ The Indian Anaesthetists' Forum
A 54/3 Arvind Nagar

Golf Link Rd.
Jodhpur 342 011, Rajasthan, India
Journal reporting issues related to anesthesiology, critical care and pain management. **Key Personnel:** Dr. R.S. Sharma, President; Dr. Pradeep Bhatia, Editor; Dr. K.L. Tulsiani, Forum Pres.; Dr. Surendra Bhutra, Overseas Member; Dr. Prafull Kachawaha, Sec. **ISSN:** 0973-0311. **URL:** http://www.theiaforum.org/.

45219 ■ Indian Journal of Applied Entomology
Indian Periodical
5 New Pali Rd.
PO Box 33
Jodhpur 342001, Rajasthan, India
Ph: 91 291 2433323
Fax: 91 291 2512580
Publisher E-mail: info@indianperiodical.in
Journal covering applied entomology. **Key Personnel:** Dr. R.C. Saxena, Editor-in-Chief; Dr. R. Swaminathan, Exec. Ed.; Dr. N.K. Bajpai, Exec. Ed. **ISSN:** 0970-9509. **URL:** http://www.indianperiodical.in/ip/journalview.aspx?jrnl=ijae&jrnltitle=IndianJournalofAppliedEntomology.

45220 ■ Indian Journal of Biochemistry and Biophysics
Scientific Publishers - India
5-A New Pali Rd.
PO Box 91
Jodhpur 342 001, Rajasthan, India
Ph: 91 291 2433323
Fax: 91 291 2624154
Publisher E-mail: info@scientificpub.com
Scientific journal regarding biochemistry. **Founded:** 1964. **Freq:** Bimonthly. **Key Personnel:** S.C. Sharma, Editor, scs@niscair.res.in; R.S. Jayasomu, Assoc. Ed. **ISSN:** 0301-1208. **Subscription Rates:** US$330 individuals (including air mail charges); US$65 single issue (including air mail charges); Rs 1,900 individuals; Rs 380 single issue. **URL:** http://www.niscair.res.in/sciencecommunication/researchjournals/rejour/ijbb/ijbb0.asp. **Circ:** 1,000

45221 ■ Indian Journal of Chemical Technology
Scientific Publishers - India
5-A New Pali Rd.
PO Box 91
Jodhpur 342 001, Rajasthan, India
Ph: 91 291 2433323
Fax: 91 291 2624154
Publication E-mail: ijct@niscair.res.in
Publisher E-mail: info@scientificpub.com
Scientific publication of academic interest on chemical technology. **Freq:** Bimonthly. **Key Personnel:** Dr. R S Beniwal, Ed.-in-Charge, rsb@niscair.res.in; Manju Srivastava, Asst. Ed. **ISSN:** 0971-457X. **Subscription Rates:** Rs 1,600 individuals; US$300 individuals (including air mail charges); Rs 320 single issue; US$60 single issue (including air mail charges). **URL:** http://www.niscair.res.in/sciencecommunication/researchjournals/rejour/ijct/ijct0.asp. **Circ:** 1,200

45222 ■ Indian Journal of Engineering and Materials Sciences
Scientific Publishers - India
5-A New Pali Rd.
PO Box 91
Jodhpur 342 001, Rajasthan, India
Ph: 91 291 2433323
Fax: 91 291 2624154
Publication E-mail: ijems@niscair.res.in
Publisher E-mail: info@scientificpub.com
Publication covering engineering and medical sciences. **Founded:** 1994. **Freq:** Bimonthly. **Key Personnel:** Dr. R.S. Beniwal, Editor, rsb@niscair.res.in. **ISSN:** 0971-4588. **Subscription Rates:** US$300 institutions; Rs 1,600 institutions; Rs 320 single issue; US$60 single issue. **URL:** http://www.niscair.res.in/ScienceCommunication/ResearchJournals/rejour/ijems/ijems0.asp.

45223 ■ Indian Journal of Experimental Biology
Scientific Publishers - India
5-A New Pali Rd.
PO Box 91
Jodhpur 342 001, Rajasthan, India
Ph: 91 291 2433323
Fax: 91 291 2624154
Publication E-mail: ijeb@niscair.res.in
Publisher E-mail: info@scientificpub.com
Publication on experimental biology. **Founded:** 1963.

Freq: Monthly. **Key Personnel:** Rajiv Mathur, Editor, rmathur@niscair.res.in; Dr. M.K. Singhal, Assoc. Ed., mks@niscair.res.in; G. Chandrasekar, Asst. Ed., gcs@niscair.res.in. **ISSN:** 0019-5189. **Subscription Rates:** US$660 individuals; Rs 2,850 individuals; Rs 285 single issue; US$66 single issue. **URL:** http://www.niscair.res.in/ScienceCommunication/ResearchJournals/rejour/ijeb/ijeb0.asp. **Circ:** 1,200

45224 ■ Indian Journal of Pure & Applied Physics
Scientific Publishers - India
5-A New Pali Rd.
PO Box 91
Jodhpur 342 001, Rajasthan, India
Ph: 91 291 2433323
Fax: 91 291 2624154
Publisher E-mail: info@scientificpub.com
Publication on pure and applied physics. **Founded:** 1963. **Freq:** Monthly. **Key Personnel:** Prof. S.K. Joshi, Editorial Board; Poonam Bhatt, Editor, poonam@niscair.res.in; Prabha Gupta, Assoc. Ed., prabha@niscair.res.in. **ISSN:** 0019-5596. **Subscription Rates:** US$55 single issue (including air mail charges); Rs 320 single issue; Rs 3,200 individuals; US$550 individuals (including air mail charges). **URL:** http://www.niscair.res.in/sciencecommunication/researchjournals/rejour/ijpap/ijpap0.asp. **Circ:** 1,200

45225 ■ Journal of Arid Legumes
Indian Periodical
5 New Pali Rd.
PO Box 33
Jodhpur 342001, Rajasthan, India
Ph: 91 291 2433323
Fax: 91 291 2512580
Publisher E-mail: info@indianperiodical.in
Journal covering legume crops. **Key Personnel:** A. Henry, Editor-in-Chief; D. Kumar, Exec. Ed.; J.V. Singh Hisar, Exec. Ed. **ISSN:** 0973-0907. **URL:** http://www.indianperiodical.in/ip/journalview.aspx?jrnl=jal&jrnltitle=JournalofAridLegumes.

45226 ■ Journal of Economic and Taxonomic Botany
Scientific Publishers
New Pali Rd.
PO Box 91
Jodhpur 342 001, Rajasthan, India
Ph: 91 291 2433323
Fax: 91 291 2512580
Publisher E-mail: info@scientificpub.com
Science magazine focusing on botany. **Founded:** 1976. **Freq:** Quarterly. **Key Personnel:** V. Singh, Editor-in-Chief; M.M. Bhandari, Exec. Ed.; Pawan Kumar, Mng. Dir. **ISSN:** 2050-9768. **Subscription Rates:** Rs 240 individuals; US$240 institutions, other countries. **URL:** http://www.scientificpub.com.

45227 ■ Journal of Phytopharmacotherapy and Natural Products
Indian Periodical
5 New Pali Rd.
PO Box 33
Jodhpur 342001, Rajasthan, India
Ph: 91 291 2433323
Fax: 91 291 2512580
Publisher E-mail: info@indianperiodical.in
Journal covering medicinal plants and natural products. **Freq:** Quarterly. **Key Personnel:** Amritpal Singh Saroya, Editor-in-Chief; V.S. Mathur, Exec. Ed.; Narendra Singh, Exec. Ed. **ISSN:** 0973-5941. **URL:** http://www.indianperiodical.in/ip/journalview.aspx?jrnl=jpnp&jrnltitle.

45228 ■ Phytomorphology
Scientific Publishers - India
5-A New Pali Rd.
PO Box 91
Jodhpur 342 001, Rajasthan, India
Ph: 91 291 2433323
Fax: 91 291 2624154
Publication E-mail: phytomorphology@myrealbox.com
Publisher E-mail: info@scientificpub.com
Scientific publication on botany. **Founded:** 1950. **Freq:** Quarterly. **Key Personnel:** N.S. Rangaswami, Editor. **ISSN:** 0031-9449. **Subscription Rates:** Rs 500 institutions; 85 institutions; US$120 institutions; Rs 250 individuals; 36 other countries; US$65 other countries. **Remarks:** Advertising not accepted. **URL:** http://

phytomorphology.tripod.com/. **Circ:** Paid 1,200

45229 ■ Reserve Bank of India Bulletin
Scientific Publishers - India
5-A New Pali Rd.
PO Box 91
Jodhpur 342 001, Rajasthan, India
Ph: 91 291 2433323
Fax: 91 291 2624154
Publisher E-mail: info@scientificpub.com
Bulletin on banks and banking finance by Reserve Bank of India. **Founded:** 1947. **Freq:** Monthly. **Key Personnel:** A.M. Pedgaonkar, Editorial Committee; Balwant Singh, Editorial Committee; Janak Raj, Editorial Committee; Gunjeet Kaur, Editor; Brajamohan Misra, Editorial Committee. **ISSN:** 0034-5512. **Remarks:** Accepts advertising. **URL:** http://www.rbi.org.in/scripts/BS_ViewBulletin.aspx. **Circ:** Paid 5,300

45230 ■ All India Radio Jodhpur - 102.1 MHz
Paoata 'C' Rd.
PO Box 607
Jodhpur 342 006, Rajasthan, India
Ph: 91 291 2544141
E-mail: airjodh_jp1@sancharnet.in
Format: Eclectic. **Owner:** Prasar Bharati, Akashvani Bhavan, Sansad Marg, New Delhi 110 001, Delhi, India, 91 11 23421006, Fax: 91 11 23421956. **Founded:** 1965. **Operating Hours:** 0025-1200, 1245-1730. **Key Personnel:** M.C. Aggarwal, Engr.-in-Ch., phone 91 11 23421058, fax 91 11 23421006, einc@air.org.in. **Wattage:** 6000. **Ad Rates:** $150-300 for 10 seconds; $225-450 for 15 seconds; $450-900 for 30 seconds; $900-1,800 for 60 seconds. **URL:** http://www.allindiaradio.org.

Joranda

45231 ■ All India Radio Joranda - 1485 KHz
Akashvani Bhavan
Sansad Marg
New Delhi 110 001, Delhi, India
Ph: 91 11 23421006
Fax: 91 11 23421956
Format: Eclectic; Full Service. **Owner:** Prasar Bharati, at above address. **Founded:** 1995. **Key Personnel:** M.C. Aggarwal, Engr.-in-Ch., phone 91 11 23421058, fax 91 11 23421006, einc@air.org.in; Mohan Singh, Ch. Engr. Proj., phone 91 11 23421184. **Wattage:** 1000. **Ad Rates:** $80-150 for 10 seconds; $120-225 for 15 seconds; $240-450 for 30 seconds; $480-900 for 60 seconds. **URL:** http://www.allindiaradio.org.

Jorhat

45232 ■ All India Radio Jorhat - 103.4 MHz
Akashvani Bhavan
Sansad Marg
New Delhi 110 001, Delhi, India
Ph: 91 11 23421006
Fax: 91 11 23421956
E-mail: edairjorhat@rediffmail.com
Format: Eclectic. **Owner:** Prasar Bharati, at above address. **Founded:** 1991. **Key Personnel:** M.C. Aggarwal, Engr.-in-Ch., phone 91 11 23421058, fax 91 11 23421006, einc@air.org.in. **Wattage:** 10,000. **Ad Rates:** $80-150 for 10 seconds; $120-225 for 15 seconds; $240-450 for 30 seconds; $480-900 for 60 seconds. **URL:** http://www.allindiaradio.org.

Jowai

45233 ■ All India Radio Jowai - 101.1 MHz
Akashvani Bhavan
Sansad Marg
New Delhi 110 001, Delhi, India
Ph: 91 11 23421006
Fax: 91 11 23421956
E-mail: jowai@air.org.in
Format: Eclectic. **Owner:** Prasar Bharati, at above address. **Founded:** 1995. **Key Personnel:** M.C. Aggarwal, Engr.-in-Ch., phone 91 11 23421058, fax 91 11 23421006, einc@air.org.in. **Wattage:** 6000. **Ad Rates:** $80-150 for 10 seconds; $120-225 for 15 seconds; $240-450 for 30 seconds; $480-900 for 60 seconds. **URL:** http://www.allindiaradio.org.

Kailashahar

45234 ■ All India Radio Kailashahar - 103.2 MHz
Akashvani Bhavan
Sansad Marg
New Delhi 110 001, Delhi, India
Ph: 91 11 23421006
Fax: 91 11 23421956
E-mail: airkailash@sancharnet.in
Format: Eclectic. **Owner:** Prasar Bharati, at above address. **Founded:** 1992. **Key Personnel:** M.C. Aggarwal, Engr.-in-Ch., phone 91 11 23421058, fax 91 11 23421006, einc@air.org.in. **Wattage:** 3000. **Ad Rates:** $80-150 for 10 seconds; $120-225 for 15 seconds; $240-450 for 30 seconds; $480-900 for 60 seconds. **URL:** http://www.allindiaradio.org.

Kannur

45235 ■ All India Radio Cannanore - 101.5 MHz
Akashvani Bhavan
Sansad Marg
New Delhi 110 001, Delhi, India
Ph: 91 11 23421006
Fax: 91 11 23421956
E-mail: cnn_aircnr@sancharnet.in
Format: Eclectic. **Owner:** Prasar Bharati, at above address. **Founded:** 1991. **Key Personnel:** M.C. Aggarwal, Engr.-in-Ch., phone 91 11 23421058, fax 91 11 23421006, einc@air.org.in; Mohan Singh, Ch. Engr., Proj., phone 91 11 23421184. **Wattage:** 6000. **Ad Rates:** $100-200 for 10 seconds; $150-300 for 15 seconds; $300-600 for 30 seconds; $600-1,200 for 60 seconds. **URL:** http://www.allindiaradio.org.

Kanpur

45236 ■ International Journal of Tomography and Statistics
Indian Society for Development and Environment Research
c/o R.K.S. Rathore, Ed.-in-Ch.
Dept. of Mathematics
Indian Institute of Technology
Kanpur 208016, Uttar Pradesh, India
Publisher E-mail: ceser_isder@yahoo.co.in
Journal covering the latest research and developments in computerized tomography and statistics. **Freq:** 3/yr. **Key Personnel:** R.K.S Rathore, Editor-in-Chief; Tanuja Srivastava, Exec. Ed., tanujfma@yahoo.com; Xue-Cheng Tai, Editor. **ISSN:** 0972-9976. **Subscription Rates:** EUR550 individuals print; EUR700 institutions print; EUR500 individuals online; EUR1,000 institutions print and online; US$475 institutions online only; US$675 institutions print only; US$975 institutions print. **URL:** http://www.ceser.res.in/ijts.html.

45237 ■ All India Radio Kanpur - 1449 KHz
Akashvani Bhavan
Sansad Marg
New Delhi 110 001, Delhi, India
Ph: 91 11 23421006
Fax: 91 11 23421956
E-mail: airkanpur@vsnl.net
Format: Eclectic. **Owner:** Prasar Bharati, at above address. **Founded:** 1963. **Operating Hours:** 0025-1200, 1245-1730. **Key Personnel:** M.C. Aggarwal, Engr.-in-Ch., phone 91 11 23421058, fax 91 11 23421006, einc@air.org.in. **Wattage:** 1000. **Ad Rates:** $180-280 for 10 seconds; $270-420 for 15 seconds; $540-840 for 30 seconds; $1,080-1,680 for 60 seconds. **URL:** http://www.allindiaradio.org.

Karaikal

45238 ■ All India Radio Karaikal - 100.3 MHz
Radio Ave.
Nehru Nagar
Karaikal 609 605, Pondicherry, India
Ph: 91 4368 222288
E-mail: airatkkl@vsnl.net
Format: Eclectic. **Owner:** Prasar Bharati, Akashvani Bhavan, Sansad Marg, New Delhi 110 001, Delhi, India, 91 11 23421006, Fax: 91 11 23421956. **Founded:** 1995. **Key Personnel:** M.C. Aggarwal, Engr.-in-Ch., phone 91 11 23421058, fax 91 11 23421006, einc@air.org.in. **Wattage:** 6000. **Ad Rates:** $80-150 for 10 seconds; $120-225 for 15 seconds; $240-450 for 30 seconds;

$480-900 for 60 seconds. **URL:** http://www.allindiaradio.org.

Karaikudi

45239 ■ Current Titles in Electrochemistry
Society for Advancement of Electrochemical Science and Technology
CECRI Campus
Karaikudi 630 006, Maharashtra, India
Ph: 91 456 5224198
Fax: 91 456 5227713
Publisher E-mail: saestkkd@yahoo.com
Scientific journal covering chemistry. Features an index. **Founded:** 1969. **Freq:** Monthly. **Print Method:** Offset. **Key Personnel:** Dr. M. Jayachandran, Editor. **ISSN:** 0300-4376. **Remarks:** Advertising accepted; rates available upon request. **URL:** http://www.saest.com/publications.htm. **Circ:** Combined 900

Kargil

45240 ■ All India Radio Kargil 'B' - 1584 KHz
Akashvani Bhavan
Sansad Marg
New Delhi 110 001, Delhi, India
Ph: 91 11 23421006
Fax: 91 11 23421956
E-mail: airlive@air.org.in
Format: Eclectic; Full Service. **Owner:** Prasar Bharati, at above address. **Founded:** 1997. **Key Personnel:** M.C. Aggarwal, Engr.-in-Ch., phone 91 11 23421058, fax 91 11 23421006, einc@air.org.in; Mohan Singh, Ch. Engr. (Proj.), phone 91 11 23421184. **Wattage:** 1000. **Ad Rates:** $80-150 for 10 seconds; $120-225 for 15 seconds; $240-450 for 30 seconds; $480-900 for 60 seconds. **URL:** http://www.allindiaradio.org.

Kariavattom

45241 ■ Entomon
Association for Advancement of Entomology
c/o Dept. of Zoology
University of Kerala
Trivandrum
Kariavattom 695 581, Kerala, India
Scientific journal on entomology. **Founded:** 1976. **Freq:** Quarterly. **Print Method:** DTP-offset. **Key Personnel:** K.H. Hoffmann, Editorial Board; Tanaka Seiji, Editorial Board; C.C. Abraham, Editorial Board; N. Mohandas, Editorial Board; Gupta Aparna Dutta, Editorial Board; R. Gadagkar, Editorial Board; T.C. Narendran, Editorial Board; O.P. Dubey, Editorial Board; K.S.S. Nair, Editorial Board. **ISSN:** 0377-9335. **Subscription Rates:** Rs 2000 institutions; Rs 300 individuals; US$250 institutions (air mail); US$100 individuals (air mail). **Remarks:** Accepts advertising. **URL:** http://entomon-aae.org/. **Circ:** Paid 400

Karwar

45242 ■ All India Radio Karwar - 102.3 MHz
Akashvani Bhavan
Sansad Marg
New Delhi 110 001, Delhi, India
Ph: 91 11 23421006
Fax: 91 11 23421956
E-mail: kwrair@sancharnet.in
Format: Eclectic. **Owner:** Prasar Bharati, at above address. **Founded:** 1994. **Key Personnel:** M.C. Aggarwal, Engr.-in-Ch., phone 91 11 23421058, fax 91 11 23421006, einc@air.org.in; Mohan Singh, Ch. Engr., Proj., phone 91 11 23421184. **Wattage:** 3000. **Ad Rates:** $80-150 for 10 seconds; $120-225 for 15 seconds; $240-450 for 30 seconds; $480-900 for 60 seconds. **URL:** http://www.allindiaradio.org.

Kathua

45243 ■ All India Radio Kathua - 102.2 MHz
Akashvani Bhavan
Sansad Marg
New Delhi 110 001, Delhi, India
Ph: 91 11 23421006
Fax: 91 11 23421956
E-mail: airkathua@sancharnet.in
Format: Eclectic. **Owner:** Prasar Bharati, at above address. **Founded:** 1991. **Key Personnel:** M.C. Aggarwal, Engr.-in-Ch., phone 91 11 23421058, fax 91 11

23421006, einc@air.org.in. **Wattage:** 10,000. **Ad Rates:** $80-150 for 10 seconds; $120-225 for 15 seconds; $240-450 for 30 seconds; $480-900 for 60 seconds. **URL:** http://www.allindiaradio.org.

Keonjhar

45244 ■ All India Radio Keonjhar - 1584 KHz
Akashvani Bhavan
Sansad Marg
New Delhi 110 001, Delhi, India
Ph: 91 11 23421006
Fax: 91 11 23421956
E-mail: kjr_airkjr@sancharnet.in
Format: Eclectic. **Owner:** Prasar Bharati, at above address. **Founded:** 1988. **Key Personnel:** M.C. Aggarwal, Engr.-in-Ch., phone 91 11 23421058, fax 91 11 23421006, einc@air.org.in. **Wattage:** 1000. **Ad Rates:** $80-150 for 10 seconds; $120-225 for 15 seconds; $240-450 for 30 seconds; $480-900 for 60 seconds. **URL:** http://www.allindiaradio.org.

Khandwa

45245 ■ All India Radio Khandwa - 101.2 KHz
Akashvani Bhavan
Sansad Marg
New Delhi 110 001, Delhi, India
Ph: 91 11 23421006
Fax: 91 11 23421956
E-mail: seairknw@sancharnet.in
Format: Eclectic. **Owner:** Prasar Bharati, at above address. **Founded:** 1990. **Key Personnel:** M.C. Aggarwal, Engr.-in-Ch., phone 91 11 23421058, fax 91 11 23421006, einc@air.org.in. **Wattage:** 6000. **Ad Rates:** $80-150 for 10 seconds; $120-225 for 15 seconds; $240-450 for 30 seconds; $480-900 for 60 seconds. **URL:** http://www.allindiaradio.org.

Kharagpur

45246 ■ International Journal of Communication Networks and Distributed Systems
Inderscience Enterprises Limited
c/o Dr. Sudip Misra, Ed.-in-Ch.
Indian Institute of Technology
School of Information Technology
Kharagpur 721302, West Bengal, India
Journal covering the areas of communication networks and distributed systems. **Freq:** 8/yr. **Key Personnel:** Dr. Sudip Misra, Editor-in-Chief, smisra.editor@gmail.com. **ISSN:** 1754-3916. **Subscription Rates:** EUR735 individuals print or online; EUR1,025 individuals print and online. **URL:** http://www.inderscience.com/browse/index.php?journalID=261.

45247 ■ International Journal of Industrial Electronics and Drives
Inderscience Enterprises Limited
c/o Dr. Chandan Chakraborty, Ed.-in-Ch.
Department of Electrical Engineering
Indian Institute of Technology Kharagpur
Kharagpur 721 302, West Bengal, India
Peer-reviewed journal focusing on industrial electronics, industrial drives, and power converter. **Freq:** Quarterly. **Key Personnel:** Dr. Chandan Chakraborty, Editor-in-Chief, eic.ijied@gmail.com. **ISSN:** 1757-3874. **Subscription Rates:** EUR494 individuals print or online; EUR672 individuals print and online. **URL:** http://www.inderscience.com/browse/index.php?journalCODE=ijied.

45248 ■ International Journal of Information and Coding Theory
Inderscience Enterprises Limited
c/o Dr. Sudip Misra, Ed.-in-Ch.
School of Information Technology
Indian Institute of Technology
Kharagpur 721 302, West Bengal, India
Journal covering information and coding theory applications. **Freq:** Quarterly. **Key Personnel:** Dr. Sudip Misra, Editor-in-Chief, smisra.editor@gmail.com. **ISSN:** 1753-7703. **Subscription Rates:** EUR494 individuals print or online; EUR672 individuals print and online. **URL:** http://www.inderscience.com/browse/index.php?journalCODE=ijicot.

Kochi

45249 ■ Deshabhimani
Chintha Printing and Publishing Co. (P) Ltd.
Kerala State Committee
Kochi 695 001, Kerala, India

Ph: 91 484 2530739
Fax: 91 484 2530006
Publisher E-mail: feedback@deshabhimani.com
General newspaper. **Freq:** Daily. **Key Personnel:** V.V. Dakshinamoorthy, Ch. Ed. **URL:** http://www.deshabhimani.com/.

45250 ■ Indian Coconut Journal
Coconut Development Board
PO Box 1021
Kera Bhavan
Kochi 682 011, Kerala, India
Ph: 91 484 2376265
Fax: 91 484 2377902
Publication E-mail: enk_cdrkochi@sancharnet.in
Publisher E-mail: cdbkochi@dataone.in
Scientific journal focusing on agriculture and animal husbandry. **Freq:** Monthly. **ISSN:** 0367-7281. **Subscription Rates:** Rs 60 individuals; Rs 200 other countries; Rs 1,600 individuals lifetime. **URL:** http://www.coconutboard.nic.in/publi.htm. **Circ:** Paid 2,000

45251 ■ Madhyamam
PO Box 2014, Pulleppady
Kochi 682 018, Kerala, India
Publisher E-mail: contact@madhyamamonline.com
General newspaper. **Founded:** 1987. **Freq:** Daily (morn.). **Print Method:** Offset. **Cols./Page:** 6. **Col. Width:** 18 nonpareils. **Col. Depth:** 301 agate lines. **URL:** http://www.madhyamam.com/.

45252 ■ The New Indian Express
Express Publications (Madurai) Ltd.
Express House
Kaloor
Kochi 682 017, Kerala, India
Daily Newspaper. **Founded:** 1932. **Freq:** Daily. **Print Method:** Offset. **Trim Size:** 546 x 350 mm. **Remarks:** Accepts advertising. **URL:** http://www.expressbuzz.com/edition/default.aspx. **Ad Rates:** GLR: Rs 500, BW: Rs 95, 4C: Rs 245. **Circ:** Paid 67,134

45253 ■ QPMPA Journal of Medical Sciences
Qualified Private Medical Practitioners Association
Vallamattan Estate
Ravipuram
M.G. Rd.
Kochi 682015, Kerala, India
Ph: 91 484 2383287
Publisher E-mail: mail@qpmpa.org
Physicians journal covering medical science. **Freq:** Monthly. **Key Personnel:** Dr. Joseph Stephen, Mng. Dir.; Dr. Kishore K. Kumar, Contact, kumarkishore@satyam.net.in. **Subscription Rates:** Rs 500 individuals; Rs 50 single issue. **URL:** http://qpmpa.org/html/journal_of_medical_science.htm.

45254 ■ All India Radio Cochin - 102.3 MHz
Akashvani Bhavan
Sansad Marg
New Delhi 110 001, Delhi, India
Ph: 91 11 23421006
Fax: 91 11 23421956
E-mail: airkochi@vsnl.com
Format: Eclectic; Full Service. **Owner:** Prasar Bharati, at above address. **Founded:** 1989. **Key Personnel:** M.C. Aggarwal, Engr.-in-Ch., phone 91 11 23421058, fax 91 11 23421006, einc@air.org.in; Mohan Singh, Ch. Engr. (Proj.), phone 91 11 23421184. **Wattage:** 6000. **Ad Rates:** $150-300 for 10 seconds; $225-450 for 15 seconds; $450-900 for 30 seconds; $900-1,800 for 60 seconds. **URL:** http://www.allindiaradio.org.

Kohima

45255 ■ All India Radio Kohima - 639 KHz
PO Box 42
Kohima 797 001, Nagaland, India
Ph: 91 370 2242899
E-mail: airkohima@rediffmail.com
Format: Eclectic. **Owner:** Prasar Bharati, Akashvani Bhavan, Sansad Marg, New Delhi 110 001, Delhi, India, 91 11 23421006, Fax: 91 11 23421956. **Founded:** 1963. **Key Personnel:** M.C. Aggarwal, Engr.-in-Ch., phone 91 11 23421058, fax 91 11 23421006, einc@air.org.in. **Wattage:** 100,000. **Ad Rates:** $100-200 for 10 seconds; $150-300 for 15 seconds; $300-600 for 30 seconds; $600-1,200 for 60 seconds. **URL:** http://www.allindiaradio.org.

Kolhapur

45256 ■ Pudhari
Pudhari Bhavan, 2318 C, Bhausingji Rd.
Kolhapur 416 002, Maharashtra, India
Ph: 91 231 2543111
Fax: 91 231 2543124
Publisher E-mail: kolhapur@pudhari.in
General newspaper. **URL:** http://epaper.pudhari.com/
epapermain.aspx.

45257 ■ All India Radio Kolhapur - 102.7 KHz
Sardar Colony
Tarabai Pk.
Kolhapur 416 003, Maharashtra, India
Ph: 91 231 2652704
E-mail: airkolhapur@gmail.com
Format: Eclectic. **Owner:** Prasar Bharati, Akashvani
Bhavan, Sansad Marg, New Delhi 110 001, Delhi, India,
91 11 23421006, Fax: 91 11 23421956. **Founded:** 1992.
Key Personnel: M.C. Aggarwal, Engr.-in-Ch., phone 91
11 23421058, fax 91 11 23421006, einc@air.org.in.
Wattage: 6000. **Ad Rates:** $100-200 for 10 seconds;
$150-300 for 15 seconds; $300-600 for 30 seconds;
$600-1,200 for 60 seconds. **URL:** http://www.
allindiaradio.org.

Kolkata (Gujarat)

45258 ■ Asian Journal of Transfusion Science
Medknow Publications Pvt Ltd.
TATA Medical Ctr.
14 Main Arterial Rd.
New Town
Kolkata 700156, Gujarat, India
Ph: 91 33 22810175
Fax: 91 33 22811199
Online journal covering educational articles for the medi-
cal community. **Founded:** 1919. **Freq:** Weekly (Fri.).
Print Method: Offset. **Trim Size:** 11 x 17. **Cols./Page:**
5. **Col. Width:** 10.8 nonpareils. **Col. Depth:** 96 agate
lines. **Key Personnel:** Dr. N. Choudhury, Editor; Dr. Priti
Desai, Sub-Ed.; Dr. Ripal Shah, Asst. Ed. **ISSN:** 0973-
6247. **Subscription Rates:** Rs 1,200 individuals print;
Rs 1,000 individuals online; Rs 1,500 individuals print
and online. **Remarks:** Accepts advertising. **URL:** http://
www.ajts.org/. **Circ:** (Not Reported)

Kolkata (West Bengal)

45259 ■ The Asian Age
Asian Age (Eastern) India Publishers Ltd.
7th Fl., Kankaria Estate
6, Little Russell St.
Kolkata 700 071, West Bengal, India
Ph: 91 33 22890676
Fax: 91 33 22890686
General newspaper. **Founded:** 1994. **Freq:** Daily. **Key
Personnel:** M. J. Akbar, Ed.-in-Ch./Mng. Dir., mjakbar@
asianage.com. **Remarks:** Accepts advertising. **URL:**
http://www.asianage.com. **Circ:** (Not Reported)

**45260 ■ Bulletin of the Ramakrishna Mission
Institute of Culture**
Ramakrishna Mission Institute of Culture
Gol Pk.
Kolkata 700 029, West Bengal, India
Ph: 91 33 24641303
Fax: 91 33 24661235
Publisher E-mail: rmic@vsnl.com
Publication focusing on education and culture. **Founded:**
Jan. 1950. **Freq:** Monthly. **Print Method:** Offset. **Trim
Size:** 29.75 x 19.75. **ISSN:** 0971-2755. **Remarks:** Ac-
cepts advertising. **URL:** http://www.sriramakrishna.org/
bulletin.php. **Circ:** Paid 4,200

45261 ■ Business World
ABP Pvt. Limited Publication
6 Prafulla Sarkar St.
Kolkata 700 001, West Bengal, India
Ph: 91 33 22345374
Fax: 91 33 22253241
Journal on business and economics. **Founded:** 1987.
Freq: Weekly 52/yr. **Key Personnel:** Prosenjit Datta,
Editor. **ISSN:** 0970-8197. **Remarks:** Accepts advertising.
URL: http://www.businessworld.in/. **Circ:** 37,204

45262 ■ Calcutta Statistical Association Bulletin
Calcutta Statistical Association

Calcutta University
New Science Bldg.
35 B.C. Rd.
Kolkata 700 019, West Bengal, India
Statistics journal. **Founded:** 1947. **Freq:** Quarterly.
ISSN: 0008-0683. **Subscription Rates:** Rs 400 individuals inclusive of postage; US$80 other countries inclusive
of postage. **Remarks:** Accepts advertising. **URL:** http://
www.calcuttastatisticalassociation.org. **Circ:** 350

45263 ■ Decision
Indian Institute of Management
Publication Division Institute of Management
D.H. Rd.
Joka
PO Box 16757
Kolkata 700 104, West Bengal, India
Ph: 91 33 24678300
Fax: 91 33 24678307
Publisher E-mail: publication@iimcal.ac.in
Management oriented periodical. **Founded:** 1974. **Freq:**
Semiannual. **Key Personnel:** Rohit Varman, Editor;
Manish Thakur, Book Review Ed.; Biswatosh Saha,
Editorial Board Member; Sanjit Singh, Editorial Board
Member; Raveendra Chittoor, Editorial Board Member.
ISSN: 0304-0941. **Subscription Rates:** Rs 500 individu-
als; US$100 other countries foreign air mail; Rs 2000
institutions; Rs 400 individuals hand delivery; US$100
single issue for institutions; Rs 500 single issue individuals; Rs 400 single issue hand delivery to individuals; Rs
2000 single issue for institutions. **Remarks:** Accepts
advertising. **URL:** http://www.iimcal.ac.in/research/
decision/. **Circ:** 300

45264 ■ The Economic Times
Bennet, Coleman & Company Ltd.
Times of India
105/7A, S.N. Banerjee Rd.
Kolkata 700 084, West Bengal, India
Financial news daily. **Founded:** 1976. **Freq:** Daily. **Key
Personnel:** Mr. Avijit Dasgupta, Contact. **Remarks:** Ac-
cepts advertising. **URL:** http://economictimes.indiatimes.
com/?. **Circ:** Paid 43,228

45265 ■ Energy for Sustainable Development
Princeton University
Princeton Environmental Institute
International Energy Initiative
164/6 Prince Anwar Shah Rd.
Kolkata 700 045, West Bengal, India
Ph: 91 33 242288645
Publisher E-mail: sribasb@gmail.com
Journal acting as a link between developed and developing nations in the matter of energy goals, policies, and
issues particularly in developing countries and also
endorsing South-South interactions to tackle these
issues. **Freq:** Quarterly. **Key Personnel:** Gautam S.
Dutt, Editor; Rangan Banerjee, Assoc. Ed.; S.C. Bhattacharya, Assoc. Ed. **ISSN:** 0973-0826. **Subscription
Rates:** US$436 institutions, other countries; EUR347
institutions European countries, Iran; 50,900¥ institutions Japan. **Remarks:** Advertising accepted; rates
available upon request. **URL:** http://www.elsevier.com/
wps/find/journaldescription.cws_home/717028/
descriptiondescription; http://www.ieiglobal.org/
membership.html. **Circ:** (Not Reported)

45266 ■ Ganashtaki
74A Acharya Jagadish Chandra Bose Rd.
Kolkata 700 016, West Bengal, India
General newspaper. **URL:** http://www.ganashakti.com.

45267 ■ Geological Survey of India News
Geological Survey of India
27 Jawaharlal Nehru Rd.
Kolkata 700 016, West Bengal, India
Ph: 91 33 22861676
Fax: 91 33 22861656
Periodical on geology. **Founded:** 1970. **Freq:** Monthly.
ISSN: 0378-4029. **Remarks:** Accepts advertising. **URL:**
http://www.gsi.gov.in/news.htm. **Circ:** 2,500

45268 ■ Horticultural Journal
Agri-Horticultural Society of India
1 Alipore Rd.
Kolkata 700 027, West Bengal, India
Ph: 91 33 24791713
Fax: 91 33 24793580
Publisher E-mail: ahsi@vsnl.net
Journal covering aspects of horticulture. **Freq:** Annual.
ISSN: 0971-1872. **Remarks:** Accepts advertising. **URL:**

http://www.agrihorticultureindia.com/publication.html.
Circ: (Not Reported)

45269 ■ IASLIC Bulletin
Indian Association of Special Libraries and Information
Centres
P-291 CIT Scheme No. 6M
Kankurgachi
Kolkata 700 054, West Bengal, India
Ph: 91 33 23629651
Publisher E-mail: iaslic@vsnl.net
Library and information sciences bulletin with book
reviews and indexes. **Founded:** 1956. **Freq:** Quarterly.
Key Personnel: Dr. Arjun Dasgupta, Honorary Ed.; Ms.
Sangita Pal, Honorary Asst. Ed.; Dr. A.R.D. Prasad,
Member; Prof. Juran Krishna Sarkhel, Member,
jksharkhel@hotmail.com; Prof. Pijushkanti Panigrahi,
Honorary Assoc. Ed. **ISSN:** 0018-8441. **Subscription
Rates:** Rs 1,500 individuals; US$120 other countries.
Remarks: Accepts advertising. **URL:** http://www.
iaslic1955.org.in/bulletin.htm. **Circ:** Paid 1,600

45270 ■ IIM Metal News
Indian Institute of Metals
Metals House, Plot 13/4
Block AQ, Sector V, Salt Lake City
Kolkata 700091, West Bengal, India
Ph: 91 33 23675004
Fax: 91 33 23675335
Publisher E-mail: iiomcal@dataone.in
Journal of the Indian Institute of Metals. **Founded:** 1979.
Freq: Quarterly. **ISSN:** 0972-0480. **Subscription Rates:**
Free to members; Rs 900 nonmembers; Rs 2,400
nonmembers 3 years; Rs 1,200 institutions; Rs 3,000
institutions 3 years. **URL:** http://www.iim-india.net/page.
php?id=52.

45271 ■ Indian Heart Journal
The Cardiological Society of India
P-60 C.I.T Rd.
Scheme VII-M
Kankurgachi
Kolkata 700 054, West Bengal, India
Ph: 91 33 23557837
Fax: 91 33 23556308
Publisher E-mail: csi@cal2.vsnl.net.in
Peer-reviewed journal covering the field of cardiovascu-
lar diseases and medical sciences. **Freq:** Bimonthly.
Key Personnel: H.K. Chopra, Honorary Ed.,
drhkchopra@yahoo.com; Dr. Rakesh Gupta, Assoc. Ed.
ISSN: 0019-4832. **URL:** http://indianheartjournal.com/.
Circ: Paid 1,500

45272 ■ Indian Institute of Metals Transactions
Indian Institute of Metals
Metals House, Plot 13/4
Block AQ, Sector V, Salt Lake City
Kolkata 700091, West Bengal, India
Ph: 91 33 23675004
Fax: 91 33 23675335
Publisher E-mail: iiomcal@dataone.in
Academic publication on metallurgy featuring book
reviews and charts. **Founded:** 1948. **Freq:** Bimonthly.
Trim Size: 283 x 210 mm. **Key Personnel:** Dr. Bhanu
K. Sankara Rao, Editor-in-Chief, fax 91 411 4280301,
bhanu@igcar.ernet.In; Dr. S.N. Ojha, Editor, fax 91 542
2369478, ojha_bhu@yahoo.co.in; Prof. Vibhuti N. Misra,
Editor, fax 91 674 2581160, vnmisra@rrlbhu.res.in.
ISSN: 0972-2815. **Subscription Rates:** Rs 300 mem-
bers; Rs 800 members 3 years; Rs 6,000 institutions;
Rs 2,500 nonmembers; US$400 other countries. **Re-
marks:** Accepts advertising. **URL:** http://www.igcar.
ernet.in/transiim/; http://www.iim-india.net/page.php?id=
61. **Circ:** Paid 4,000

45273 ■ Indian Museum Bulletin
S.K. Chakraborti
Indian Museum
27 Jawaharlal Nehru Rd.
Kolkata 700 016, West Bengal, India
Ph: 91 332 495699
Fax: 91 332 495696
Journal on Indian museums. **Founded:** 1966. **Freq:**
Annual. **ISSN:** 0019-5987. **URL:** http://www.
indianmuseumkolkata.org/. **Circ:** Paid 500

45274 ■ Indian National Bibliography
Central Reference Library
Government of India
Ministry of Culture

Kolkata, West Bengal, India
Ph: 91 33 24791721
Fax: 91 33 24791722
Publisher E-mail: crlinb@cal3.vsnl.net.in
Bibliography of Indian periodicals. **Founded:** 1957.
Freq: Monthly plus annual volume. **Key Personnel:**
Iqbal Ahmad, Asst. Ed.; D. Subramanian, Asst. Ed.; K.K.
Deka, Asst. Ed.; P.K. Upadhyay, Asst. Ed.; K.K. Sarma,
Asst. Ed.; Tapan Banerjee, Asst. Ed.; S.K. Gupta, Asst.
Ed.; K. Madhavan, Asst. Ed.; H. Chandrasekhariah,
Asst. Ed.; Dulalchandra Shee, Asst. Ed. **ISSN:** 0019-
6002. **URL:** http://www.crlindia.gov.in/indian.htm. **Circ:**
Paid 500

45275 ■ Indian Welding Journal
Indian Institute of Welding
3A, Doctor U.N. Brahmachari St.
Kolkata 700 017, West Bengal, India
Ph: 91 33 22813208
Fax: 91 33 22401350
Publisher E-mail: indianwelding@vsnl.net
Technological journal focusing on metallurgy. **Founded:**
1968. **Freq:** Quarterly. **Key Personnel:** A. K. Mitra,
Editor. **ISSN:** 0046-9092. **Subscription Rates:** Rs 80.
Remarks: Accepts advertising. **URL:** http://www.iiwindia.
com. **Ad Rates:** BW: Rs 3,000, 4C: Rs 8,000. **Circ:**
Paid 5,000

**45276 ■ Institution of Engineers (India)
Aerospace Engineering Division Journal**
The Institution of Engineers
8 Gokhale Rd.
Kolkata 700 020, West Bengal, India
Ph: 91 332 2238230
Technological journal focusing on aerospace
engineering. **Founded:** 1978. **Freq:** Semiannual. **Print
Method:** Offset. **Key Personnel:** Shri S.R. Vijayamo-
hankumar, Contact. **ISSN:** 0257-3423. **Remarks:** Ac-
cepts advertising. **URL:** http://www.ieindia.org/tech/as.
htm. **Ad Rates:** BW: Rs 3,000. **Circ:** Paid 4,000

**45277 ■ Institution of Engineers (India)
Agricultural Engineering Division Journal**
The Institution of Engineers
8 Gokhale Rd.
Kolkata 700 020, West Bengal, India
Ph: 91 332 2238230
Technological journal focusing on agricultural
engineering. **Founded:** 1983. **Freq:** Semiannual. **Print
Method:** Offset. **Key Personnel:** Dr. Shri D.V. Nagab-
hushan, Chm. **ISSN:** 0257-3431. **Remarks:** Accepts
advertising. **URL:** http://www.ieindia.org/tech/ag.htm. **Ad
Rates:** BW: Rs 3,000. **Circ:** Paid 4,000

**45278 ■ Institution of Engineers (India)
Architectural Engineering Division Journal**
The Institution of Engineers
8 Gokhale Rd.
Kolkata 700 020, West Bengal, India
Ph: 91 332 2238230
Technological journal focusing on architectural
engineering. **Founded:** 1984. **Freq:** Semiannual. **Print
Method:** Offset. **Key Personnel:** Shri P.K. Maity, Chm.
ISSN: 0257-344X. **Remarks:** Accepts advertising. **URL:**
http://www.ieindia.org/publish/ar/ar.htm. **Ad Rates:** BW:
Rs 4,500. **Circ:** Paid 5,000

**45279 ■ Institution of Engineers (India) Chemi-
cal Engineering Division Journal**
The Institution of Engineers
8 Gokhale Rd.
Kolkata 700 020, West Bengal, India
Ph: 91 332 2238230
Technological journal focusing on chemical engineering.
Founded: 1920. **Freq:** Semiannual. **Print Method:**
Offset. **Key Personnel:** Shri N.B. Vasoya, Chm. **ISSN:**
0020-3351. **Remarks:** Accepts advertising. **URL:** http://
www.ieindia.org/publish/ch/ch.htm. **Ad Rates:** BW: Rs
4,500. **Circ:** Paid 5,000

**45280 ■ Institution of Engineers (India) Civil
Engineering Division Journal**
The Institution of Engineers
8 Gokhale Rd.
Kolkata 700 020, West Bengal, India
Ph: 91 332 2238230
Technological journal focusing on civil engineering.
Founded: 1920. **Freq:** Quarterly. **Print Method:** Offset.
Key Personnel: Shri Jagdish Mohan, Chm. **ISSN:** 0373-
1995. **Remarks:** Accepts advertising. **URL:** http://www.

ieindia.org/publish/cv/vol84cv.htm. **Ad Rates:** BW: Rs
8,000. **Circ:** Paid 30,000

**45281 ■ The Institution of Engineers (India)
Computer Engineering Division Journal**
The Institution of Engineers
8 Gokhale Rd.
Kolkata 700 020, West Bengal, India
Ph: 91 332 2238230
Technological journal focusing on computer engineering.
Founded: 1984. **Freq:** Semiannual. **Print Method:**
Offset. **Key Personnel:** Brig. S.V.S. Chowdhry, Chm.
ISSN: 0971-0469. **Remarks:** Accepts advertising. **URL:**
http://www.ieindia.org/tech/cp.htm. **Ad Rates:** BW: Rs
4,500. **Circ:** Paid 5,000

**45282 ■ The Institution of Engineers (India)
Electrical Engineering Division Journal**
The Institution of Engineers
8 Gokhale Rd.
Kolkata 700 020, West Bengal, India
Ph: 91 332 2238230
Technological journal focusing on electrical engineering.
Founded: 1920. **Freq:** Quarterly. **Print Method:** Offset.
Key Personnel: Shri V.L. Malhotra, Chm. **ISSN:** 0020-
3386. **Remarks:** Accepts advertising. **URL:** http://www.
ieindia.org/tech/el.htm. **Ad Rates:** BW: Rs 7,000. **Circ:**
Paid 17,000

**45283 ■ Institution of Engineers (India) Electron-
ics and Telecommunication Engineering Division Journal**
The Institution of Engineers
8 Gokhale Rd.
Kolkata 700 020, West Bengal, India
Ph: 91 332 2238230
Technological journal focusing on electronics and
telecommunication engineering. **Founded:** 1920. **Freq:**
Semiannual. **Print Method:** Offset. **Key Personnel:** Shri
S.C. Rudra, Chm. **ISSN:** 0251-1096. **Remarks:** Accepts
advertising. **URL:** http://www.ieindia.org/publish/et/et.
htm. **Ad Rates:** BW: Rs 6,000. **Circ:** Paid 10,000

**45284 ■ Institution of Engineers (India)
Environmental Engineering Division Journal**
The Institution of Engineers
8 Gokhale Rd.
Kolkata 700 020, West Bengal, India
Ph: 91 332 2238230
Academic journal covering environmental engineering.
Freq: Semiannual. **Print Method:** Offset. **Trim Size:**
A4. **Key Personnel:** Dr. L.K. Bisoyi, Ch., ieioscbb@sify.
com. **Remarks:** Accepts advertising. **URL:** http://www.
ieindia.org/tech/en.htm. **Ad Rates:** BW: Rs 6,000. **Circ:**
Paid ‡8,000

**45285 ■ Institution of Engineers (India) Hindi
Journal**
The Institution of Engineers
8 Gokhale Rd.
Kolkata 700 020, West Bengal, India
Ph: 91 332 2238230
Journal for engineers. **Freq:** Semiannual. **Print Method:**
Offset. **Trim Size:** A4. **Remarks:** Accepts advertising.
URL: http://www.ieindia.org. **Ad Rates:** BW: Rs 4,500.
Circ: Paid ‡5,000

**45286 ■ The Institution of Engineers (India)
Inter-disciplinary Panels Journal**
The Institution of Engineers
8 Gokhale Rd.
Kolkata 700 020, West Bengal, India
Ph: 91 332 2238230
Technological journal focusing on inter-disciplinary
panels. **Founded:** 1920. **Freq:** Semiannual. **Print
Method:** Offset. **ISSN:** 0251-1118. **Remarks:** Accepts
advertising. **URL:** http://www.ieindia.org/publish/id/id.
htm. **Ad Rates:** BW: Rs 6,000. **Circ:** Paid 12,000

**45287 ■ Institution of Engineers (India) Marine
Engineering Division Journal**
The Institution of Engineers
8 Gokhale Rd.
Kolkata 700 020, West Bengal, India
Ph: 91 332 2238230
Academic journal covering marine engineering. **Freq:**
Semiannual. **Print Method:** Offset. **Trim Size:** A4. **Re-
marks:** Accepts advertising. **URL:** http://www.ieindia.
org/publish/mr/mr.htm. **Ad Rates:** BW: Rs 3,000. **Circ:**
Paid ‡4,000

**45288 ■ The Institution of Engineers (India)
Mechanical Engineering Division Journal**
The Institution of Engineers
8 Gokhale .Rd.
Kolkata 700 020, West Bengal, India
Ph: 91 332 2238230
Technological journal focusing on mechanical
engineering. **Founded:** 1920. **Freq:** Quarterly. **Print
Method:** Offset. **Key Personnel:** Shri T.M. Gunaraja,
Chm. **ISSN:** 0020-3408. **Remarks:** Accepts advertising.
URL: http://www.ieindia.org/publish/mc/mc.htm. **Ad
Rates:** BW: Rs 7,000. **Circ:** Paid 20,000

**45289 ■ The Institution of Engineers (India)
Metallurgical and Materials Engineering Division
Journal**
The Institution of Engineers
8 Gokhale Rd.
Kolkata 700 020, West Bengal, India
Ph: 91 332 2238230
Technological journal focusing on metallurgy and materi-
als engineering. **Founded:** 1983. **Freq:** Semiannual.
Print Method: Offset. **Key Personnel:** Dr. N.R. Ban-
dyopadhyay, Chm. **ISSN:** 0257-4411. **Remarks:** Accepts
advertising. **URL:** http://www.ieindia.org/publish/mm/
mm.htm. **Ad Rates:** BW: Rs 3,000. **Circ:** Paid 4,000

**45290 ■ Institution of Engineers (India) Mining
Engineering Division Journal**
The Institution of Engineers
8 Gokhale Rd.
Kolkata 700 020, West Bengal, India
Ph: 91 332 2238230
Technological journal focusing on mining engineering.
Founded: 1920. **Freq:** Semiannual. **Print Method:**
Offset. **Key Personnel:** Shri Chandra Mohan, Chm.
ISSN: 0257-442X. **Remarks:** Accepts advertising. **URL:**
http://www.ieindia.org/publish/mn/mn.htm. **Ad Rates:**
BW: Rs 3,000. **Circ:** Paid 4,000

**45291 ■ Institution of Engineers (India) Produc-
tion Engineering Division Journal**
The Institution of Engineers
8 Gokhale Rd.
Kolkata 700 020, West Bengal, India
Ph: 91 332 2238230
Technological journal focusing on production
engineering. **Founded:** 1984. **Freq:** Semiannual. **Print
Method:** Offset. **Key Personnel:** Shri V.K. Joshi, Chm.
ISSN: 0257-6708. **Remarks:** Accepts advertising. **URL:**
http://www.ieindia.org/publish/pr/pr.htm. **Ad Rates:** BW:
Rs 4,500. **Circ:** Paid 5,000

**45292 ■ Institution of Engineers (India) Techni-
cians' Journal**
The Institution of Engineers
8 Gokhale Rd.
Kolkata 700 020, West Bengal, India
Ph: 91 332 2238230
Engineering journal. **Freq:** Semiannual. **Print Method:**
Offset. **Trim Size:** A4. **Remarks:** Accepts advertising.
URL: http://www.ieindia.org. **Ad Rates:** BW: Rs 25,000.
Circ: Paid ‡260,000

**45293 ■ Institution of Engineers (India) Tech-
norama**
The Institution of Engineers
8 Gokhale Rd.
Kolkata 700 020, West Bengal, India
Ph: 91 332 2238230
Engineering journal. **Founded:** 1992. **Freq:** 2/yr. **Print
Method:** Offset. **Trim Size:** 19 x 27 cm. **ISSN:** 0971-
3344. **Remarks:** Accepts advertising. **URL:** http://www.
ieindia.org. **Ad Rates:** 4C: Rs 30,000. **Circ:** Paid 90,000

**45294 ■ Institution of Engineers (India) Textile
Engineering Division Journal**
The Institution of Engineers
8 Gokhale Rd.
Kolkata 700 020, West Bengal, India
Ph: 91 332 2238230
Technological journal focusing on textile engineering.
Founded: 1978. **Freq:** Semiannual. **Key Personnel:**
Shri G. Sreekantha, Contact. **ISSN:** 0257-4438. **Re-
marks:** Accepts advertising. **URL:** http://www.ieindia.
org/tech/tx.htm. **Ad Rates:** BW: Rs 3,000. **Circ:** Paid
4,000

**45295 ■ International Journal of Artificial Intel-
ligence and Soft Computing**
Inderscience Enterprises Limited
c/o Prof. Amit Konar, Ed.-in-Ch.

Jadavpur University
Artificial Intelligence Laboratory
Dept. of Electronics & Tele-Communication Engineering
Kolkata, West Bengal, India
Journal covering the theoretical and applied research on artificial intelligence and soft computing. **Freq:** 4/yr. **Key Personnel:** Prof. Amit Konar, Editor-in-Chief, amitkonar_inderscience@yahoo.com. **ISSN:** 1755-4950. **Subscription Rates:** EUR494 individuals print or online; EUR672 individuals print and online. **URL:** http://www.inderscience.com/browse/index.php?journalID=280.

45296 ■ Journal of the Indian Medical Association (JIMA)
Indian Medical Association
IMA House
53 Creek Row
Kolkata 700 014, West Bengal, India
Ph: 91 332 2378092
Fax: 91 332 2366437
Publication E-mail: jima@vsnl.com
Publisher E-mail: inmedici@vsnl.com
Medical journal with details of other medical journals of India and abroad. **Founded:** 1930. **Freq:** Monthly. **Subscription Rates:** Rs 1,500 individuals; Rs US$82 other countries; Rs 150 single issue; US$7 single issue foreign countries. **Remarks:** Accepts advertising. **URL:** http://www.ima-india.org/IMA_publications.html. **Circ:** (Not Reported)

45297 ■ Journal of Optics
Optical Society of India
92 Acharya Prafulla Chandra Rd.
Kolkata 700 009, West Bengal, India
Ph: 91 33 23522411
Fax: 91 33 23522411
Publisher E-mail: osiindia@rediffmail.com
Science magazine focusing on optics in India. **Founded:** 1972. **Freq:** Quarterly. **Key Personnel:** Prof. M. De, Chm.; Prof. A. Basuray, Editor. **ISSN:** 0972-8821. **Subscription Rates:** Rs 2,500 institutions inland; US$250 institutions, other countries; Rs 200 individuals inland; US$20 other countries; Rs 50 individuals single copy, inland; US$5 individuals single copy, foreign; Rs 750 institutions single copy, inland; US$75 institutions, other countries single copy. **Remarks:** Accepts advertising. **URL:** http://www.osiindia.org/journal.php. **Ad Rates:** BW: Rs 5,000. **Circ:** Paid 600

45298 ■ The Management Accountant
Institute of Cost and Works Accountants of India
12 Sudder St.
Kolkata 700 016, West Bengal, India
Ph: 91 33 22441031
Fax: 91 33 22440993
Publisher E-mail: ceo@icwai.org
Accounts publication. **Founded:** 1955. **Freq:** Monthly. **Key Personnel:** Shri Kunal Banerjee, President; Shri A.S Durga Prasad, Vice President; Singh Jaikant, Director; S.R. Bhargave, Member. **ISSN:** 0025-1674. **Subscription Rates:** Rs 300 individuals; Rs 50 students; Rs 100 students paid by a demand draft. **Remarks:** Accepts advertising. **URL:** http://www.icwai.org/icwai/institute-manag-acct.asp. **Ad Rates:** BW: Rs 12,000; BW: Rs 1,200. **Circ:** Paid 25,000

45299 ■ Nano Science and Nano Technology
Trade Science Inc.
c/o Alokmay Datta, Editorial Board
Saha Institute of Nuclear Physics
1/AF Bidhannagar
Kolkata 700064, West Bengal, India
Publisher E-mail: help@tsijournals.com
Journal covering research in the fundamental theory, practice and application of analytical and bioanalytical science including miniaturization of analytical systems, bioanalyses, chromatography, mass spectrometry, electrophoresis, electrochemist, sampling and sample handling, and atomic and molecular spectroscopy. **Subtitle:** An Indian Journal. **Founded:** 1984. **Freq:** 2/yr. **Print Method:** Offset. **Trim Size:** 7 1/4 x 9 1/4. **Cols./Page:** 3. **Col. Width:** 2 1/4 inches. **Col. Depth:** 9 3/8 inches. **Key Personnel:** Alokmay Datta, Editorial Board. **ISSN:** 0974-7494. **Subscription Rates:** Rs 1,200 individuals; US$120 other countries. **URL:** http://www.tsijournals.com/nsnt/.

45300 ■ Opsearch
Operational Research Society of India

39, Mahanirvan Rd.
Kolkata 700029, West Bengal, India
Magazine on business management. **Founded:** 1964. **Freq:** Quarterly March, June, September and December. **Key Personnel:** Prof. Bani K. Sinha, Chm.; Prof. A.K. Verma, Editor-in-Chief; Prof. Dinesh U. Kumar, Assoc. Ed. **ISSN:** 0030-3887. **Subscription Rates:** Rs 1,200 individuals India; US$90 other countries; Rs 2,300 individuals India, 2 years; US$170 other countries 2 years; Rs 3,200 individuals India, 3 years; US$240 other countries 3 years. **Remarks:** Accepts advertising. **URL:** http://www.orsi.in/index.php?action=publication. **Circ:** Paid 2,000

45301 ■ Personnel Today
National Institute of Personnel Management
3 Fl., Tower Block 1582
Rajdanga Main Rd.
Kolkata 700 107, West Bengal, India
Ph: 91 33 24417253
Fax: 91 33 24417256
Publisher E-mail: nipm@cal2.vsnl.net.in
Magazine dealing with human resources, labor and personnel management. **Founded:** 1949. **Freq:** Quarterly. **ISSN:** 0970-8405. **Remarks:** Accepts advertising. **URL:** http://www.nipm.in/publication.php. **Circ:** Paid 6,000

45302 ■ Rally
All India Catholic University Federation
St. Xavier's College
30 Mother Teresa Sarani
Kolkata 700 016, West Bengal, India
Community magazine on Roman Catholics. **Founded:** 1973. **Freq:** Monthly. **ISSN:** 0048-668X. **URL:** http://www.goethals.org/aicuf.htm. **Circ:** Paid 1,500

45303 ■ Sankhya
Indian Statistical Institute
203, B.T. Rd.
Kolkata 700108, West Bengal, India
Fax: 91 33 25776035
Publication E-mail: sankhya_a@isical.ac.in
Publisher E-mail: postmaster@isibang.ac.in
Journal publishing research articles in the broad areas of applied statistics, mathematical statistics and probability. **Subtitle:** The Indian Journal of Statistics. **Freq:** Bimonthly. **Key Personnel:** Pranab K. Sen, Editor-in-Chief. **URL:** http://www.isical.ac.in/sankhya.php.

45304 ■ Seagull Theatre Quarterly
Seagull Foundation for the Arts
26 Circus Ave.
Kolkata 700 019, West Bengal, India
Ph: 91 33 22873636
Publication E-mail: stq@seagullindia.com
Publisher E-mail: stq@seagullindia.com
Performing arts magazine. **Founded:** 1994. **Print Method:** Offset. **Trim Size:** 300 x 200 mm. **Subscription Rates:** Rs 50 individuals back issues; Rs 100 individuals double issues; US$2.50 single issue. **URL:** http://www.seagullindia.com/stq/homealt.html.

45305 ■ The Statesman
The Statesman Ltd.
Statesman House
4 Chowringhee Sq.
Kolkata 700 001, West Bengal, India
Ph: 91 33 22127070
Fax: 91 33 22126181
Publication E-mail: thestatesman@vsnl.net
Publisher E-mail: thestatesman@vsnl.com
General newspaper. **Founded:** 1875. **Freq:** Daily. **Print Method:** Web Offset. **Key Personnel:** Ravindra Kumar, Ed./Managing Dir. **Remarks:** Accepts advertising. **URL:** http://www.thestatesman.org/. **Ad Rates:** BW: Rs 1,050, BW: Rs 1,260, 4C: Rs 1,775, 4C: Rs 2,150. **Circ:** Paid 180,000, Sun. 230,000

45306 ■ The Telegraph
ABP Pvt. Ltd.
6 Prafulla Sarkar St.
Kolkata 700 001, West Bengal, India
Ph: 91 33 22345374
Fax: 91 33 22253243
Publication E-mail: ttedit@abpmail.com
Publisher E-mail: ttedit@abpmail.com
General interest newspaper. **Founded:** July 7, 1982.

Freq: Daily. **Key Personnel:** Nisha Malik, Contact, nisha.malik@abp.in. **Remarks:** Accepts advertising. **URL:** http://www.telegraphindia.com. **Circ:** Paid 247,497

45307 ■ Udbodhan
Ramakrishna Math
1 Udbodhan Ln.
Kolkata 700 003, West Bengal, India
Ph: 91 33 25542248
Publication E-mail: info@udbodhan.org
Publisher E-mail: info@udbodhan.org
Periodical covering religion and theology. **Founded:** 1899. **Freq:** Monthly. **Trim Size:** 185 x 240 cm. **ISSN:** 0971-4316. **Subscription Rates:** Rs 3000 individuals life subscription for India only; Rs 80 individuals living in India, Nepal, and Bhutan; Rs 600 individuals Bangladesh; Rs 1,200 other countries by airmail; Rs 600 other countries by seamail. **Remarks:** Accepts advertising. **URL:** http://www.udbodhan.org/mag.htm. **Ad Rates:** GLR: Rs 125, BW: Rs 5,000. **Circ:** Paid 55,000, Non-paid 1,000

45308 ■ Aamar-FM - 106.2
Calcutta FM Broadcast Ctr., 4th Fl.
2/3/1, Southern Ave.
Kolkata 700 026, West Bengal, India
Ph: 91 33 24657706
Format: Oldies; Ethnic; World Beat. **Owner:** HITZ FM Radio India Pvt Ltd., at above address. **Operating Hours:** Continuous. **Key Personnel:** Sanjay Ahmed, Contact; Suvendu Majumder, Contact. **Ad Rates:** Advertising accepted; rates available upon request. **URL:** http://www.aamar106fm.com.

45309 ■ All India Radio Calcutta 'A' - 657 KHz
Eden Garden
Kolkata 700 001, West Bengal, India
Ph: 91 33 22485336
E-mail: aircal@cal.vsnl.net.in
Format: Eclectic; Full Service. **Owner:** Prasar Bharati, Akashvani Bhavan, Sansad Marg, New Delhi 110 001, Delhi, India, 91 11 23421006, Fax: 91 11 23421956. **Founded:** 1927. **Key Personnel:** M.C. Aggarwal, Engr.-in-Ch., phone 91 11 23421058, fax 91 11 23421006, einc@air.org.in; Mohan Singh, Ch. Engr. (Proj.), phone 91 11 23421184. **Wattage:** 200,000. **Ad Rates:** $200-550 for 10 seconds; $300-825 for 15 seconds; $600-1,650 for 30 seconds; $1,200-3,300 for 60 seconds. **URL:** http://www.allindiaradio.org.

45310 ■ All India Radio Calcutta 'B' - 1008 KHz
Eden Garden
Kolkata 700 001, West Bengal, India
Ph: 91 33 22485336
E-mail: aircbs@cal3.vsnl.net.in
Format: Eclectic; Full Service. **Owner:** Prasar Bharati, Akashvani Bhavan, Sansad Marg, New Delhi 110 001, Delhi, India, 91 11 23421006, Fax: 91 11 23421956. **Key Personnel:** M.C. Aggarwal, Engr.-in-Ch., phone 91 11 23421058, fax 91 11 23421006, einc@air.org.in; Mohan Singh, Ch. Engr. (Proj.), phone 91 11 23421184. **Wattage:** 100,000. **Ad Rates:** $200-550 for 10 seconds; $300-825 for 15 seconds; $600-1,650 for 30 seconds; $1,200-3,300 for 60 seconds. **URL:** http://www.allindiaradio.org.

Kota

45311 ■ 1st Industrial Magazine
1st Industrial Magazine Online
E-3, Industrial Estate
Kota 321 006, Rajasthan, India
Ph: 91 744 360835
Fax: 91 744 450276
Online magazine covering technology and industry for businessmen, technical professionals, engineers, and industrial dealers. **Founded:** Jan. 1, 2000. **Print Method:** Offset. **Key Personnel:** Ashish Raj, Contact, webmaster@4eit.com. **Remarks:** Accepts advertising. **URL:** http://www.industrialmag.com/. **Circ:** (Not Reported)

45312 ■ All India Radio Kota - 1413 KHz
Jhalawar Rd.
Kota 324 001, Rajasthan, India
Ph: 91 744 2322443
E-mail: airkota@sancharnet.in
Format: Eclectic. **Owner:** Prasar Bharati, Akashvani Bhavan, Sansad Marg, New Delhi 110 001, Delhi, India,

91 11 23421006, Fax: 91 11 23421956. **Founded:** 1987. **Key Personnel:** M.C. Aggarwal, Engr.-in-Ch., phone 91 11 23421058, fax 91 11 23421006, einc@air.org.in. **Wattage:** 1000. **Ad Rates:** $150-300 for 10 seconds; $225-450 for 15 seconds; $450-900 for 30 seconds; $900-1,800 for 60 seconds. **URL:** http://www.allindiaradio.org.

Kothagudem

45313 ■ All India Radio Kothagudem - 100.1 MHz
Akashvani Bhavan
Sansad Marg
New Delhi 110 001, Delhi, India
Ph: 91 11 23421006
Fax: 91 11 23421956
E-mail: airkgm2004@yahoo.com
Format: Full Service; Eclectic. **Owner:** Prasar Bharati, at above address. **Founded:** 1989. **Key Personnel:** M.C. Aggarwal, Engr.-in-Ch., phone 91 11 23421058, fax 91 11 23421006, einc@air.org.in. **Wattage:** 6000. **Ad Rates:** $80-150 for 10 seconds; $120-225 for 15 seconds; $240-450 for 30 seconds; $480-900 for 60 seconds. URL: http://www.allindiaradio.org.

Kottayam

45314 ■ Deepika
Rashtra Deepika Ltd.
PO Box 7
Kottayam 686 001, Kerala, India
Ph: 91 481 2566706
Fax: 91 481 2567947
General newspaper. **Key Personnel:** Dr. Francis Cleetus, Chm.; Fr. Alexander Palicada, Editor. **URL:** http://www.deepika.com/.

45315 ■ Malayala Manorama
Manoramaonline
Malayala Manorama
PO Box 26
Kottayam 686 001, Kerala, India
Ph: 91 481 2563646
Fax: 91 481 2565398
Publisher E-mail: customersupport@mm.co.in
General newspaper. **Freq:** Daily. **URL:** http://www.manoramaonline.com. **Circ:** ‡1,700,192

Kurnool

45316 ■ All India Radio Kurnool - 102.4 MHz
Bellary Rd.
Kurnool 518 003, Andhra Pradesh, India
Ph: 91 8518 259386
E-mail: airknl@rediffmail.com
Format: Eclectic. **Owner:** Prasar Bharati, Akashvani Bhavan, Sansad Marg, New Delhi 110 001, Delhi, India, 91 11 23421006, Fax: 91 11 23421956. **Founded:** 1992. **Key Personnel:** M.C. Aggarwal, Engr.-in-Ch., phone 91 11 23421058, fax 91 11 23421006, einc@air.org.in. **Wattage:** 6000. **Ad Rates:** $80-150 for 10 seconds; $120-225 for 15 seconds; $240-450 for 30 seconds; $480-900 for 60 seconds. **URL:** http://www.allindiaradio.org.

Kurseong

45317 ■ All India Radio Kurseong - 1440 KHz
Akashvani Bhavan
Sansad Marg
New Delhi 110 001, Delhi, India
Ph: 91 11 23421006
Fax: 91 11 23421956
E-mail: airkurseong@justmailz.com
Format: Eclectic. **Owner:** Prasar Bharati, at above address. **Founded:** 1962. **Key Personnel:** M.C. Aggarwal, Engr.-in-Ch., phone 91 11 23421058, fax 91 11 23421006, einc@air.org.in; Mohan Singh, Ch. Engr., Proj., phone 91 11 23421184. **Wattage:** 1000. **Ad Rates:** $100-200 for 10 seconds; $150-300 for 15 seconds; $300-600 for 30 seconds; $600-1,200 for 60 seconds. **URL:** http://www.allindiaradio.org.

Kurukshetra

45318 ■ All India Radio Kurukshetra - 101.4 MHz
Akashvani Bhavan
Sansad Marg

New Delhi 110 001, Delhi, India
Ph: 91 11 23421006
Fax: 91 11 23421956
E-mail: airkkr@rediffmail.com
Format: Eclectic. **Owner:** Prasar Bharati, at above address. **Founded:** 1991. **Key Personnel:** M.C. Aggarwal, Engr.-in-Ch., phone 91 11 23421058, fax 91 11 23421006, einc@air.org.in. **Wattage:** 6000. **Ad Rates:** $80-150 for 10 seconds; $120-225 for 15 seconds; $240-450 for 30 seconds; $480-900 for 60 seconds. **URL:** http://www.allindiaradio.org.

Leh

45319 ■ All India Radio Leh - 1053 KHz
Akashvani Bhavan
Sansad Marg
New Delhi 110 001, Delhi, India
Ph: 91 11 23421006
Fax: 91 11 23421956
E-mail: seairladakh2002@yahoo.co.in
Format: Eclectic. **Owner:** Prasar Bharati, at above address. **Founded:** 1971. **Key Personnel:** M.C. Aggarwal, Engr.-in-Ch., phone 91 11 23421058, fax 91 11 23421006, einc@air.org.in; Mohan Singh, Ch. Engr., Proj., phone 91 11 23421184. **Wattage:** 20,000. **Ad Rates:** $100-200 for 10 seconds; $150-300 for 15 seconds; $300-600 for 30 seconds; $600-1,200 for 60 seconds. **URL:** http://www.allindiaradio.org.

Lucknow

45320 ■ Abstracts of Current Literature in Toxicology
Indian Institute of Toxicology Research
Mahatma Gandhi Marg
PO Box 80
Lucknow 226 001, Uttar Pradesh, India
Ph: 91 522 2621856
Fax: 91 522 2628227
Publisher E-mail: director@itrcindia.org
Contains abstracts on environmental science and toxicology. **Founded:** 1988. **Freq:** Quarterly. **Print Method:** Computer: CDS-ISIS software. **Trim Size:** 28 x 20.5 cm. **ISSN:** 0970-440X. **URL:** http://www.iitrindia.org/IJournal.html.

45321 ■ Current Central Legislation
Eastern Book Co.
34 Lalbagh
Lucknow 226 001, Uttar Pradesh, India
Ph: 91 522 4033601
Fax: 91 522 2624328
Publisher E-mail: sales@ebc-india.com
Law periodical. **Founded:** 1975. **Freq:** Monthly. **Key Personnel:** P.L. Malik, Editor; K.K. Malik, Editor. **ISSN:** 0253-6579. **Subscription Rates:** Rs 850 individuals book post; Rs 1,054 individuals reg. post. **Remarks:** Accepts advertising. **URL:** http://webstore.ebc-india.com/product_info.php?cpath=5002_260&products_id=7010&oscsid=d4b1023bc157f6eb5fd64bd0beb4eaee. **Circ:** 2,500

45322 ■ Indian Journal of Psychological Medicine
Indian Journal of Psychiatry
B-8, Sector A
Mahanagar
Lucknow 226 006, Uttar Pradesh, India
Publication focusing on the topic of neuroscience. **Freq:** Semiannual. **Key Personnel:** Dr. M.S. Reddy, Editor. **ISSN:** 0253-7176. **Subscription Rates:** Rs 1,200 individuals print only; Rs 1,200 institutions print only; US$100 individuals overseas; US$100 institutions print only. **Remarks:** Accepts advertising. **URL:** http://www.ijpm.info/aboutus.asp. **Circ:** (Not Reported)

45323 ■ Journal of Environmental Biology
Triveni Enterprises
1/206 Vikas Nagar
Lucknow 226 022, Uttar Pradesh, India
Ph: 91 522 2769181
Fax: 91 522 2769018
Publication E-mail: j_environ_biol@yahoo.com
Publisher E-mail: rcdalela@sancharnet.in
Scientific research journal focusing on research in the fields of environmental sciences and toxicology. **Founded:** 1980. **Freq:** Quarterly. **Print Method:** Offset. **Trim Size:** 27 x 21 cm. **Key Personnel:** Dr. Muhammad

Iqbal, Res. Ed., iqbalg5@yahoo.co.in; Dr. Balakrishna P. Murthy, Res. Ed., fippat@giasmd01.vsnl.net.in; Dr. William J. Rea, Res. Ed., wjr@ehcd.com; Dr. T.K. Ghosh, Res. Ed., ghoshtk2@rediffmail.com; Dr. S.V.S. Rana, Res. Ed., sureshvs_rana@yahoo.com; Dr. M.S. Mithyantha, Res. Ed., msmithyantha@rallis.co.in; Dr. S.J.S. Flora, Res. Ed., sjsflora@hotmail.com; Dr. Madhoolika Agarwal, Res. Ed., madhoo@banaras.ernet.in; Dr. Anubha Kaushik, Consulting Ed., aks_10@yahoo.com; Dr. R.C. Dalela, Editor-in-Chief, rcdale@sancharnet.in. **ISSN:** 0254-8704. **Subscription Rates:** Rs 2,000 institutions; US$300 institutions other countries; Rs 1,500 individuals; US$250 other countries. **Remarks:** Accepts advertising. **URL:** http://www.jeb.co.in/. **Ad Rates:** BW: US$600, 4C: US$800. **Circ:** 50,000

45324 ■ Lucknow Law Times
Eastern Book Co.
34 Lalbagh
Lucknow 226 001, Uttar Pradesh, India
Ph: 91 522 4033601
Fax: 91 522 2624328
Publisher E-mail: sales@ebc-india.com
Law journal. **Founded:** 1960. **Freq:** Monthly. **Key Personnel:** P.L. Malik, Editor; K.K. Malik, Editor. **ISSN:** 0459-9756. **Subscription Rates:** Rs 880 individuals book post; Rs 1,084 individuals regd. post. **Remarks:** Accepts advertising. **URL:** http://webstore.ebc-india.com/product_info.php?products_id=7011. **Circ:** 3,000

45325 ■ Palaeobotanist
Birbal Sahni Institute of Palaeobotany
53 University Rd.
Lucknow 226 007, Uttar Pradesh, India
Ph: 91 522 2740008
Fax: 91 522 2740485
Publisher E-mail: director@bsip.res.in
Science magazine focusing on botany. **Founded:** 1952. **Freq:** 3/yr. **Key Personnel:** Dr. Naresh Chandra Mehrotra, PhD, Director. **ISSN:** 0031-0174. **Subscription Rates:** Rs 900; US$90 other countries. **URL:** http://www.bsip.res.in/paleobotanists.htm. **Circ:** Paid 400

45326 ■ Supreme Court Cases
Eastern Book Co.
34 Lalbagh
Lucknow 226 001, Uttar Pradesh, India
Ph: 91 522 4033601
Fax: 91 522 2624328
Publisher E-mail: sales@ebc-india.com
Publication of law cases. **Founded:** 1969. **Freq:** Weekly. **Key Personnel:** Surendra Malik, Editor; P.L. Malik, Editor; Sumeet Malik, Assoc. Ed. **ISSN:** 0039-5951. **Subscription Rates:** Rs 5,950 individuals book post; Rs 6,698 individuals reg. post; Rs 7,000 individuals bound. **Remarks:** Accepts advertising. **URL:** http://www.ebc-india.com; http://webstore.ebc-india.com/product_info.php?cpath=5002_267&products_id=7007. **Circ:** Paid 10,000

45327 ■ Supreme Court Cases (Criminal)
Eastern Book Co.
34 Lalbagh
Lucknow 226 001, Uttar Pradesh, India
Ph: 91 522 4033601
Fax: 91 522 2624328
Publisher E-mail: sales@ebc-india.com
Publication of criminal law cases. **Freq:** Monthly. **Key Personnel:** P.L. Malik, Editor; Surendra Malik, Editor. **ISSN:** 0253-6544. **Subscription Rates:** Rs 1,475 individuals book post; Rs 1,679 individuals regular post. **Remarks:** Accepts advertising. **URL:** http://www.ebc-india.com; http://webstore.ebc-india.com/product_info.php?cpath=5002_268&products_id=7008&oscsid=dce68993e5036794f344a5a8d26e7085. **Circ:** Paid 3,000

45328 ■ Supreme Court Cases (Labour and Services)
Eastern Book Co.
34 Lalbagh
Lucknow 226 001, Uttar Pradesh, India
Ph: 91 522 4033601
Fax: 91 522 2624328
Publisher E-mail: sales@ebc-india.com
Publication of civil law cases. **Freq:** Monthly. **Key Personnel:** P.L. Malik, Editor; Surendra Malik, Editor; K.K. Venugopal, Editorial Board; F.S. Nariman, Editorial Board; Soli J. Sorabjee, Editorial Board; Sunil Gupta, Editorial Board; Kapil Sibal, Editorial Board. **ISSN:** 0253-

6552. **Subscription Rates:** Rs 1,175 individuals book post; Rs 1,379 individuals regd. post. **Remarks:** Accepts advertising. **URL:** http://webstore.ebc-india.com/product_info.php?cPath=5002_269&products_id=7009&osCsid=37a93eda0eeaf904a3d75e29c8feed61. **Circ:** Paid 2,200

45329 ■ Tourism Recreation Research
Centre for Tourism Research and Development
A-965/6 Indira Nagar
Lucknow 226 016, Uttar Pradesh, India
Ph: 91 522 2310144
Fax: 91 522 2340313
Publication E-mail: tejvirsingh@hotmail.com
Publisher E-mail: tejvirsingh@hotmail.com
Periodical dedicated to tourism research. **Founded:** 1976. **Freq:** 3/yr (April - August - December). **Print Method:** Offset. **Key Personnel:** Tej Vir Singh, Editor-in-Chief, tvsingh@sancharnet.in; Shalini Singh, Exec. Ed. **ISSN:** 0250-8281. **Subscription Rates:** US$300 institutions print + online; US$250 institutions print or online; US$105 single issue print + online; US$85 single issue printed or online. **Remarks:** Accepts advertising. **URL:** http://www.trrworld.org. **Ad Rates:** BW: US$100, 4C: US$400. **Circ:** Paid 2,000

45330 ■ All India Radio Lucknow - 747 KHz
18, Vidhan Sabha Marg
Lucknow 226 001, Uttar Pradesh, India
Ph: 91 522 2237470
E-mail: airlko@sancharnet.in
Format: Eclectic. **Owner:** Prasar Bharati, Akashvani Bhavan, Sansad Marg, New Delhi 110 001, Delhi, India, 91 11 23421006, Fax: 91 11 23421956. **Founded:** 1938. **Key Personnel:** M.C. Aggarwal, Engr.-in-Ch., phone 91 11 23421058, fax 91 11 23421006, einc@air.org.in. **Wattage:** 300,000. **Ad Rates:** $200-550 for 10 seconds; $300-825 for 15 seconds; $600-1,650 for 30 seconds; $1,200-3,300 for 60 seconds. **URL:** http://www.allindiaradio.org.

Ludhiana

45331 ■ Indian Journal of Urology
Urological Society of India
c/o Dr. Kim Mammmen
Christian Medical Colorado & Hospital
Sathya Gardens, Saligramam
Ludhiana 141008, Punjab, India
Ph: 91 161 5026999
Fax: 91 161 5010909
Publisher E-mail: kjmammen@gmail.com
Journal dedicated to urology. **Founded:** 1985. **Freq:** Quarterly. **Print Method:** Offset. **Trim Size:** 6 x 9. **Cols./Page:** 1. **Col. Width:** 60 nonpareils. **Col. Depth:** 108 agate lines. **Key Personnel:** Dr. Nitin S. Kekre, Editor; Dr. Santosh Kumar, Asst. Ed.; Dr. Rajeev Kumar, Asst. Ed. **ISSN:** 0970-1591. **Subscription Rates:** Rs 1,800 individuals; Rs 2,400 institutions; US$150 individuals; US$250 institutions. **URL:** http://www.indianjurol.com/.

Lunglei

45332 ■ All India Radio Lunglei - 101.9 MHz
Akashvani Bhavan
Sansad Marg
New Delhi 110 001, Delhi, India
Ph: 91 11 23421006
Fax: 91 11 23421956
E-mail: airlunglei@sancharnet.in
Format: Eclectic. **Owner:** Prasar Bharati, at above address. **Founded:** 1995. **Key Personnel:** M.C. Aggarwal, Engr.-in-Ch., phone 91 11 23421058, fax 91 11 23421006, einc@air.org.in; Mohan Singh, Ch. Engr., Proj., phone 91 11 23421184. **Wattage:** 6000. **Ad Rates:** $80-150 for 10 seconds; $120-225 for 15 seconds; $240-450 for 30 seconds; $480-900 for 60 seconds. **URL:** http://www.allindiaradio.org.

Madikeri

45333 ■ All India Radio Mercara - 103.1 MHz
Akashvani Bhavan
Sansad Marg
New Delhi 110 001, Delhi, India
Ph: 91 11 23421006
Fax: 91 11 23421956

E-mail: airfm_mdk@vsnl.com
Format: Eclectic. **Owner:** Prasar Bharati, at above address. **Founded:** 1993. **Key Personnel:** M.C. Aggarwal, Engr.-in-Ch., phone 91 11 23421058, fax 91 11 23421006, einc@air.org.in; Mohan Singh, Ch. Engr., Proj., phone 91 11 23421184. **Wattage:** 6000. **Ad Rates:** $80-150 for 10 seconds; $120-225 for 15 seconds; $240-450 for 30 seconds; $480-900 for 60 seconds. **URL:** http://www.allindiaradio.org.

Madras

45334 ■ Indian Veterinary Journal
V.D. Padmanaban
Indian Veterinary Association
New No. 11 , Old No. 7, Chamiers Rd.
Nandanam
Madras 600 035, Tamil Nadu, India
Ph: 91 444 351006
Fax: 91 444 338894
Publisher E-mail: ivj@md3.vsnl.net.in
Journal focusing on veterinary science. **Founded:** 1924. **Freq:** Monthly. **Print Method:** Offset. **Trim Size:** 2.4 x 18.2 cm. **Key Personnel:** Dr. S.R. Pattabiraman, Editor; Dr. P.S. Krishnamurthi, Editor; Dr. D. Selvarajan, Editor; Dr. M. Ommurugan, Editor. **ISSN:** 0019-6479. **Subscription Rates:** Rs 500 institutions Government & public; Rs 350 individuals veterinary professional; Rs 400 individuals non veterinary professional; Rs 250 individuals student and retired veterinarian; US$160 institutions; Rs 3,500 members. **Remarks:** Accepts advertising. **URL:** http://www.indvetjournal.com. **Ad Rates:** BW: Rs 2,500. **Circ:** Paid 8,000

45335 ■ Institute of Asian Studies Journal
G. John Samuel
Institute of Asian Studies
Sholinganallur
Madras 600 119, Tamil Nadu, India
Ph: 91 442 4502212
Publisher E-mail: ias@xlweb.com
Periodical focusing on Asian culture and literature. **Founded:** 1983. **Freq:** Semiannual. **Key Personnel:** J.B. Santiago, Assoc. Ed.; Sharina Appanna, Assoc. Ed.; Dr. P. Thiagarajan, Editor. **ISSN:** 0970-2814. **Subscription Rates:** US$180 institutions print and online bundle.; US$171 institutions online only. **Remarks:** Accepts advertising. **URL:** http://www.xlweb.com/heritage/asian/. **Circ:** Paid 500

Madurai

45336 ■ Dinamalar
T.V.R. House
Dinamalar Ave.
Madurai 625 016, Tamil Nadu, India
Ph: 91 452 2380903
Fax: 91 452 2380907
Publisher E-mail: dmrmdu@dinamalar.in
General newspaper. **Remarks:** Accepts advertising. **URL:** http://www.dinamalar.com/. **Circ:** (Not Reported)

45337 ■ All India Radio Madurai - 1269 KHz
Lady Doak College Rd.
Chokkikulum
PO Box 49
Madurai 625 002, Tamil Nadu, India
Ph: 91 452 2531366
E-mail: airmadurai@vsnl.com
Format: Eclectic. **Owner:** Prasar Bharati, Akashvani Bhavan, Sansad Marg, New Delhi 110 001, Delhi, India, 91 11 23421006, Fax: 91 11 23421956. **Founded:** 1987. **Key Personnel:** M.C. Aggarwal, Engr.-in-Ch., phone 91 11 23421058, fax 91 11 23421006, einc@air.org.in. **Wattage:** 20,000. **Ad Rates:** $150-300 for 10 seconds; $225-450 for 15 seconds; $450-900 for 30 seconds; $900-1,800 for 60 seconds. **URL:** http://www.allindiaradio.org.

Mandsaur

45338 ■ Asian Journal of Pharmaceutics
Medknow Publications Pvt Ltd.
BRNSS Contract Research Ctr.
Mhow-Neemuch Rd.
Post Box No. 6
Mandsaur 458 001, Madhya Pradesh, India
Ph: 91 7422 255734

Fax: 91 7422 255504
Publication E-mail: editor@asiapharmaceutics.info
Peer-reviewed journal covering pharmaceutics. **Freq:** Quarterly. **Key Personnel:** Amit Talesara, Assoc. Ed. **ISSN:** 0973-8398. **Subscription Rates:** Rs 1,000 individuals print only; Rs 2,000 institutions print only; US$100 other countries print only; US$200 institutions, other countries print only; Rs 1,200 individuals print and online; Rs 2,400 institutions print and online; US$120 other countries print and online; US$240 institutions, other countries print and online; Rs 800 individuals online; Rs 1,600 institutions online. **Remarks:** Accepts advertising. **URL:** http://www.asiapharmaceutics.info. **Circ:** (Not Reported)

45339 ■ International Journal of Green Pharmacy
Medknow Publications Pvt Ltd.
c/o B. R. Nahata College of Pharmacy-SIRO
Mhow-Neemuch Rd.
P. B. No. 6
Mandsaur 458 001, Madhya Pradesh, India
Ph: 91 7422 255734
Fax: 91 7422 255504
Peer-reviewed journal covering green pharmacy. **Freq:** Quarterly. **Key Personnel:** Dr. V. B. Gupta, Editor-in-Chief; Emmanuel Toppo, Assoc. Ed. **ISSN:** 0973-8258. **Subscription Rates:** Rs 1,500 individuals print only; Rs 2,500 institutions print only; US$100 other countries print only; US$200 institutions, other countries print only; Rs 1,800 individuals print and online; Rs 3,000 institutions print and online; US$120 other countries print and online; US$240 institutions, other countries print and online; Rs 1,200 individuals online; US$600 institutions online. **Remarks:** Accepts advertising. **URL:** http://www.greenpharmacy.info. **Circ:** (Not Reported)

Mangalore

45340 ■ All India Radio Mangalore - 100.3 MHz
Kadri Hills
Mangalore 575 004, Karnataka, India
Ph: 91 824 2211383
E-mail: airmnglr@sancharnet.in
Format: Eclectic. **Owner:** Prasar Bharati, Akashvani Bhavan, Sansad Marg, New Delhi 110 001, Delhi, India, 91 11 23421006, Fax: 91 11 23421956. **Founded:** 1976. **Key Personnel:** M.C. Aggarwal, Engr.-in-Ch., phone 91 11 23421058, fax 91 11 23421006, einc@air.org.in. **Wattage:** 10,000. **Ad Rates:** $150-300 for 10 seconds; $225-450 for 15 seconds; $450-900 for 30 seconds; $900-1,800 for 60 seconds. **URL:** http://www.allindiaradio.org.

Markapur

45341 ■ All India Radio Markapur - 101.5 MHz
Prakasam Dist.
Markapur 523 316, Andhra Pradesh, India
Ph: 91 8596 222067
E-mail: markapuram@air.org.in
Format: Eclectic. **Owner:** Prasar Bharati, Akashvani Bhavan, Sansad Marg, New Delhi 110 001, Delhi, India, 91 11 23421006, Fax: 91 11 23421956. **Founded:** 1993. **Key Personnel:** M.C. Aggarwal, Engr.-in-Ch., phone 91 11 23421058, fax 91 11 23421006, einc@air.org.in. **Wattage:** 6000. **Ad Rates:** $80-150 for 10 seconds; $120-225 for 15 seconds; $240-450 for 30 seconds; $480-900 for 60 seconds. **URL:** http://www.allindiaradio.org.

Mathura

45342 ■ All India Radio Mathura - 1584 KHz
Varindavan Rd.
P O Gytri
Tapobhumi
Mathura 281 003, Uttar Pradesh, India
Ph: 91 565 2530144
E-mail: air-mtr@indiatimes.com
Format: Eclectic. **Owner:** Prasar Bharati, Akashvani Bhavan, Sansad Marg, New Delhi 110 001, Delhi, India, 91 11 23421006, Fax: 91 11 23421956. **Founded:** 1967. **Key Personnel:** M.C. Aggarwal, Engr.-in-Ch., phone 91 11 23421058, fax 91 11 23421006, einc@air.org.in. **Wattage:** 1000. **Ad Rates:** $100-200 for 10 seconds; $150-300 for 15 seconds; $300-600 for 30 seconds;

Circulation: ∗ = ABC; △ = BPA; ♦ = CAC; • = CCAB; ❑ = VAC; ⊕ = PO Statement; ‡ = Publisher's Report; Boldface figures = sworn; Light figures = estimated.

Gale Directory of Publications & Broadcast Media/147th Ed.

5013

$600-1,200 for 60 seconds. **URL:** http://www.
allindiaradio.org.

Meerut

**45343 ■ Cardiovascular & Hematological Agents
in Medicinal Chemistry**
Bentham Science Publishers Ltd.
Department of Pharmaceutical Technology
Meerut Institute of Engineering & Technology
Meerut 250 005, Uttar Pradesh, India
Ph: 91 121 2439019
Fax: 91 121 2439058
Publisher E-mail: subscriptions@bentham.org
Journal covering all the latest and outstanding develop-
ments in medicinal chemistry and rational drug design
for the discovery of new cardiovascular & hematological
agents. **Freq:** Quarterly. **Key Personnel:** Dr. S.P. Gupta,
Editor-in-Chief, spgbits@gmail.com; G.A. Head, Edito-
rial Board; S.P. Bottari, Editorial Board; R.K. Andrews,
Editorial Board; Y. Higashi, Editorial Board; P.K. Bhatna-
gar, Editorial Board; J.W.N. Akkerman, Regional Ed.; S.
Chackalamannil, Editorial Board; J. Gutkowska, Editorial
Board. **ISSN:** 1871-5257. **Subscription Rates:**
US$1,400 institutions corporate, print; US$1,400 institutions corporate, online; US$1,680 institutions corporate,
print and online; US$780 institutions academic, print;
US$780 institutions academic, online; US$180 individu-
als; US$860 individuals academic, print and online. **Re-
marks:** Accepts advertising. **URL:** http://www.bentham.
org/cmccha/. **Formerly:** Current Medicinal Chemistry.
Cardiovascular & Hematological Agents. **Circ:** (Not
Reported)

45344 ■ Current Enzyme Inhibition
Bentham Science Publishers Ltd.
c/o Satya P. Gupta, Ed.-in-Ch.
Meerut Institute of Engineering & Technology
Meerut, Uttar Pradesh, India
Publisher E-mail: subscriptions@bentham.org
Journal focusing on recent advances in enzyme inhibition studies, mainly with regard to inhibitory processes
of enzymes, recognition of active sites, and the discovery
of agonists and antagonists, leading to the design and
development of new drugs of significant therapeutic
value. **Freq:** Quarterly. **Key Personnel:** Satya P. Gupta,
Editor-in-Chief; James M. Briggs, Editor; Peter M. Fischer, Editor; T. Takahashi, Editorial Advisory Board.
ISSN: 1573-4080. **Remarks:** Advertising accepted; rates
available upon request. **URL:** http://www.bentham.org/
cei/index.htm. **Circ:** (Not Reported)

45345 ■ Indian Journal of Political Science
Indian Political Science Association
c/o Sanjeev Kumar Sharma, Ed.
Chaudhary Charan Singh University
Meerut 250 005, Uttar Pradesh, India
Ph: 91 121 2768234
Fax: 91 121 2768234
Publication on political science. **Founded:** 1939. **Freq:**
Quarterly. **Print Method:** Off-set printing. **Key Personnel:** Sanjeev Kumar Sharma, Editor, ijpseditor@yahoo.
co.in. **ISSN:** 0019-5510. **Subscription Rates:** Rs 150
members; Rs 50 members single; Rs 400 members
three years; Rs 100 individuals single; Rs 300 individuals; Rs 800 individuals three years; Rs 150 institutions
single; Rs 600 institutions; US$20 other countries single;
US$60 members other countries. **URL:** http://www.ijps.
net/. **Circ:** 500

Mohindergarh

45346 ■ Crop Research
Agricultural Research Information Centre
c/o Dr. Ved Pal Singh, Ed.-in-Ch.
Krishi Vigyan Kendra
Mohindergarh 123 029, Haryana, India
Scientific journal focusing on agriculture and animal
husbandry. **Founded:** 1988. **Freq:** 3/yr. **Key Personnel:** Dr. Ved Pal Singh, Editor-in-Chief, aricindia@
hotmail.com; Dr. Everaldo Attard, Assoc. Ed., pwesche@
mail.udlap.mx. **ISSN:** 0970-4884. **Subscription Rates:**
Rs 3,000 institutions; US$300 institutions, other
countries. **URL:** http://www.cropresearch.org. **Circ:**
2,000

Mokokchung

**45347 ■ All India Radio Mokokchung - 100.9
MHz**
Akashvani Bhavan
Sansad Marg
New Delhi 110 001, Delhi, India
Ph: 91 11 23421006
Fax: 91 11 23421956
E-mail: airlive@air.org.in
Format: Eclectic; Full Service. **Owner:** Prasar Bharati,
at above address. **Founded:** 1996. **Key Personnel:**
M.C. Aggarwal, Engr.-in-Ch., phone 91 11 23421058,
fax 91 11 23421006, einc@air.org.in; Mohan Singh, Ch.
Engr. (Proj.), phone 91 11 23421184. **Wattage:** 6000.
Ad Rates: $80-150 for 10 seconds; $120-225 for 15
seconds; $240-450 for 30 seconds; $480-900 for 60
seconds. **URL:** http://www.allindiaradio.org.

Mount Abu

45348 ■ All India Radio Mount Abu - 103.5 MHz
Akashvani Bhavan
Sansad Marg
New Delhi 110 001, Delhi, India
Ph: 91 11 23421006
Fax: 91 11 23421956
E-mail: airmtabu@sancharnet.in
Format: Eclectic. **Owner:** Prasar Bharati, at above
address. **Founded:** 1997. **Key Personnel:** M.C. Aggar-
wal, Engr.-in-Ch., phone 91 11 23421058, fax 91 11
23421006, einc@air.org.in; Mohan Singh, Ch. Engr.,
Proj., phone 91 11 23421184. **Wattage:** 6000. **Ad Rates:**
$180-400 for 10 seconds; $270-600 for 15 seconds;
$540-1,200 for 30 seconds; $1,080-2,400 for 60
seconds. **URL:** http://www.allindiaradio.org.

Mumbai

45349 ■ Accommodation Times
Anmol Bldg., Gr. Fl.
1st Ln.
7th Rd.
Santacruz E
Mumbai 400 055, Maharashtra, India
Ph: 91 226 114221
Publisher E-mail: info@accommodationtimes.com
Magazine Accommodation Times covering reports,
interprets and informs about new housing projects
industrial galas, business premises construction technology, housing finance, stamp duty, rent acts, and a host
of other related subjects. **Founded:** 1986. **Freq:**
Bimonthly. **Subscription Rates:** Rs 240 individuals. **Remarks:** Accepts advertising. **URL:** http://www.
accommodationtimes.com/AT/Index.asp. **Circ:** Paid
19,254

45350 ■ Annals of Pediatric Cardiology
Medknow Publications Pvt Ltd.
Glenmark Cardiac Ctr.
10 Nandadeep
Dr. Ambedkar Rd., 209 D
Matunga
Mumbai 400 019, Maharashtra, India
Publication E-mail: editor@annalspc.com
Peer-reviewed journal covering pediatric cardiology.
Freq: Semiannual. **Key Personnel:** Bharat Dalvi, Edi-
tor; R. Krishna Kumar, Editor; BRJ Kannan, Assoc. Ed.;
Robin Pinto, Assoc. Ed.; Sachin Talwar, Assoc. Ed.; Balu
Vaidyanathan, Assoc. Ed. **ISSN:** 0974-2069. **Subscrip-
tion Rates:** Rs 1,000 individuals print only; Rs 1,000
institutions print only; US$100 other countries print only;
US$100 institutions, other countries print only; Rs 800
individuals online; US$80 individuals online; Rs 800
institutions online; US$80 institutions online. **Remarks:**
Accepts advertising. **URL:** http://www.annalspc.com.
Circ: (Not Reported)

45351 ■ Apparel
Clothing Manufacturers' Association of India
902 Mahalaxmi Chambers
22 Bhulabhai Desai Rd.
Mumbai 400 026, Maharashtra, India
Ph: 91 22 23538245
Fax: 91 22 23515908
Publisher E-mail: cmai@vsnl.com
Journal on textile industries and fabrics. **Founded:** 1967.
Freq: Monthly. **Key Personnel:** Premal Udani, Presi-
dent; Rajesh Bhagat, Publisher. **Subscription Rates:**

Rs 1,200 individuals RSA; US$120 other countries; Rs
2,400 two years RSA; US$240 two years other countries.
Remarks: Accepts advertising. **URL:** http://www.
apparelreview.com. **Circ:** Paid 10,000

45352 ■ The Asian Age
145, Mathuradas Mills Compound
Near Sai Mandir, N.M. Joshi Marg
Lower Parel
Mumbai 400 013, Maharashtra, India
Ph: 91 22 24955825
Fax: 91 22 24965847
General newspaper. **Founded:** 1994. **Freq:** Daily. **Key
Personnel:** M.J. Akbar, Ed.-in-Ch./Mng. Dir. **Remarks:**
Accepts advertising. **URL:** http://www.asianage.com/.
Circ: 40,436

45353 ■ Auto Monitor
Infomedia 18 Ltd.
A Wing, Rugby House
J.K. Sawant Marg, Dadar
Mumbai 400 028, Maharashtra, India
Ph: 91 22 30245000
Fax: 91 22 30034499
Publisher E-mail: ho@infomedia18.in
Magazine featuring motoring and auto industry. **Subtitle:**
India's No.1 Magazine for Automotive News, Views &
Analysis. **Freq:** Bimonthly. **Key Personnel:** Avijit Bhat-
tacharya, Contact, avijit.bhattacharya@infomediaindia.
com. **Subscription Rates:** Rs 770 individuals; Rs 7,500
other countries. **Remarks:** Accepts advertising. **URL:**
http://www.automonitor.co.in; http://www.Infomedia18.in/
template.php?id=136. **Circ:** (Not Reported)

45354 ■ AV Max
Infomedia 18 Ltd.
A Wing, Rugby House
J.K. Sawant Marg, Dadar
Mumbai 400 028, Maharashtra, India
Ph: 91 22 30245000
Fax: 91 22 30034499
Publisher E-mail: ho@infomedia18.in
Audio-video magazine for music enthusiasts. **Freq:**
Monthly. **Key Personnel:** Ms. Ruby Roy, Contact, ruby.
roy@infomedia18.in. **Subscription Rates:** Rs 599
individuals; Rs 1,699 individuals 3 years; Rs 3,750 other
countries. **Remarks:** Accepts advertising. **URL:** http://
www.infomedia18.in/template.php?id=147. **Circ:** (Not
Reported)

45355 ■ Better Interiors
Infomedia 18 Ltd.
A Wing, Rugby House
J.K. Sawant Marg, Dadar
Mumbai 400 028, Maharashtra, India
Ph: 91 22 30245000
Fax: 91 22 30034499
Publisher E-mail: ho@infomedia18.in
Magazine featuring interior designing. **Freq:** Monthly.
Key Personnel: Chitra Pandit, Contact, chitra.pandit@
infomedia18.in. **Subscription Rates:** Rs 799 individu-
als; Rs 2,250 individuals 3 years; Rs 3,750 other
countries. **Remarks:** Accepts advertising. **URL:** http://
www.betterinteriors.in/; http://www.infomedia18.in/
template.php?id=148. **Circ:** (Not Reported)

45356 ■ Better Photography
Infomedia 18 Ltd.
A Wing, Rugby House
J.K. Sawant Marg, Dadar
Mumbai 400 028, Maharashtra, India
Ph: 91 22 30245000
Fax: 91 22 30034499
Publisher E-mail: ho@infomedia18.in
Magazine featuring the art and science of photography.
Freq: Monthly. **Key Personnel:** Ms. Ruby Roy, Contact,
ruby.roy@infomedia18.in. **Subscription Rates:** Rs 999
individuals; Rs 3,750 other countries. **Remarks:** Ac-
cepts advertising. **URL:** http://www.betterphotography.
in/; http://www.infomedia18.in/template.php?id=146.
Circ: (Not Reported)

45357 ■ Bombay Chartered Accountant Journal
Bombay Chartered Accountants' Society
Jolly Bhavan 2
7, New Marine Lines
Churchgate
Mumbai 400 020, Maharashtra, India
Ph: 91 22 61377600
Fax: 91 22 61377666

Publication E-mail: journal@bcasonline.org
Publisher E-mail: bca@bcasonline.org
Periodical on accounting, auditing, and taxation.
Founded: 1968. **Freq:** Monthly. **Print Method:** Offset.
Trim Size: 28 x 21 cm. **Remarks:** Accepts advertising.
URL: http://www.bcasonline.org. **Ad Rates:** BW: Rs
4,000, 4C: Rs 8,000. **Circ:** Paid 12,100

45358 ■ Bombay Hospital Journal
Bombay Hospital Institute of Medical Sciences
4th Fl., Medical Research Center Ext. Bldg.
12 Marine Lines
Mumbai 400 020, Maharashtra, India
Ph: 91 222 2067676
Fax: 92 222 2080871
Journal on hospitals. **Founded:** 1959. **Freq:** Quarterly.
Trim Size: 24 x 18 cm. **Key Personnel:** Dr. O.P. Kapoor,
Editor, webmaster@indiaspace.com. **ISSN:** 0524-0182.
Subscription Rates: Rs 200 individuals inclusive of
calendar of events; Rs 200 other countries inclusive of
calendar of events. **Remarks:** Accepts advertising. **URL:**
http://www.bhj.org/. **Ad Rates:** BW: Rs 10,000, 4C: Rs
16,000. **Circ:** Paid 5,000

45359 ■ Chemical Engineering World
Jasubhai Media Private Ltd.
Taj Bldg., 4th Fl.
210 Dr. D.N. Rd.
Fort
Mumbai 400 001, Maharashtra, India
Ph: 91 22 40373636
Fax: 91 22 40373635
Publisher E-mail: godfrey_lobo@jasubhai.com
Illustrated technical journal. **Founded:** 1966. **Freq:**
Monthly. **ISSN:** 0009-2517. **Subscription Rates:** Rs
1,000 individuals; Rs 1,920 two years. **Remarks:** Accepts advertising. **URL:** http://www.cewindia.com. **Ad
Rates:** BW: US$800, 4C: US$1,000. **Circ:** 44,000

45360 ■ Chemical News
Indian Chemical Manufacturers Association
Bombay Regional Office
Sir Vithaldas Chambers
16 Mumbai Samachar Marg
Mumbai 400 001, Maharashtra, India
Ph: 91 222 2048043
Fax: 91 222 2048057
Publisher E-mail: icmawro@icmaindia.com
Scientific journal covering technology and chemical and
biochemical concerns. **Founded:** 1956. **Freq:** Monthly.
ISSN: 0009-2576. **Subscription Rates:** Rs 1,000
individuals; US$150 other countries. **Remarks:** Accepts
advertising. **URL:** http://www.icmaindia.com/pub/asp/
ChemIndNews.asp. **Formerly:** Chemical Industry News.
Ad Rates: BW: Rs 2,000, 4C: Rs 3,500. **Circ:** 3,000

45361 ■ Chemical Weekly
Sevak Publications
602, 6th Fl., B-Wing, Godrej Coliseum
Off Eastern Express Hwy.
K.J. Somaiya Hospital Rd.
Sio E
Mumbai 400 022, Maharashtra, India
Ph: 91 22 24044477
Fax: 91 22 24044450
Publisher E-mail: editorial@chemicalweekly.com
Chemical industry publication. **Founded:** 1957. **Freq:**
Weekly (Tues.). **Print Method:** Offset. **Trim Size:** 26 x
20 cm. **Key Personnel:** Vijay Raghavan, Partner, vijay@
chemicalweekly.com; P. Ramachandran, Pres., Bus.
Devel., ram@chemicalweekly.com; Dr. R. Rajagopal,
Consulting Ed., rraj@chemicalweekly.com; R. Sarangan, Partner; Ravi Raghavan, Editor, ravi@
chemicalweekly.com. **ISSN:** 0045-6500. **Subscription
Rates:** Rs 1,200 individuals; US$300 other countries.
Remarks: Accepts advertising. **URL:** http://www.
chemicalweekly.com/; http://www.chemicalweekly.com/
publ/sub_details.php. **Ad Rates:** BW: US$7,000, 4C:
US$15,000. **Circ:** 87,000

45362 ■ Chip
Infomedia 18 Ltd.
A Wing, Rugby House
J.K. Sawant Marg, Dadar
Mumbai 400 028, Maharashtra, India
Ph: 91 22 30245000
Fax: 91 22 30034499
Publisher E-mail: ho@infomedia18.in
Magazine featuring computer technology. **Freq:** Monthly.

Key Personnel: Jamshed Avari, Dep. Ed.; Sunder
Thiyagarajan, General Mgr. **Subscription Rates:** Rs
1,900 individuals; Rs 3,750 other countries. **Remarks:**
Accepts advertising. **URL:** http://www.chip-india.com/.
Circ: 110,000

45363 ■ Chitraleka
22, Andheri Ind.Est., Off Veera Desai Rd.
Andheri W
Mumbai 400 053, Maharashtra, India
Ph: 91 225 6921692
Fax: 91 222 6730858
Publisher E-mail: mumbai@chitralekha.com
Newspaper focusing on the professional development,
education, and training of young dancers. **Freq:** Weekly.
Subscription Rates: Rs 900 individuals Gujarati; Rs
575 individuals Marathi. **Remarks:** Accepts advertising.
URL: http://www.chitralekha.com/. **Circ:** (Not Reported)

45364 ■ Computer Society of India Journal
Computer Society of India
122 TV Industrial Estate
S.K. Ahire Marg, Worli
Worli
Mumbai 400 030, Maharashtra, India
Ph: 91 22 24943422
Fax: 91 22 24950543
Publisher E-mail: csi@bom2.vsnl.net.in
Periodical focusing on the computer industry. **Founded:**
1970. **Freq:** Quarterly. **ISSN:** 0045-7892. **Remarks:** Accepts advertising. **URL:** http://www.csi-india.org/. **Ad
Rates:** BW: Rs 9,000. **Circ:** Paid 3,000

45365 ■ CSI Adhyayan
Computer Society of India
122 TV Industrial Estate
S.K. Ahire Marg, Worli
Worli
Mumbai 400 030, Maharashtra, India
Ph: 91 22 24943422
Fax: 91 22 24950543
Publisher E-mail: csi@bom2.vsnl.net.in
Magazine containing information of interest to computer
science and information technology students. **Freq:**
Quarterly. **Key Personnel:** Dr. M.L. Goyal, Contact.
URL: http://www.ifip.or.at/members/india.htm.

45366 ■ CSI Communications
Computer Society of India
122 TV Industrial Estate
S.K. Ahire Marg, Worli
Worli
Mumbai 400 030, Maharashtra, India
Ph: 91 22 24943422
Fax: 91 22 24950543
Publisher E-mail: csi@bom2.vsnl.net.in
Journal of the Computer Society of India. **Founded:**
1965. **Freq:** Monthly. **Key Personnel:** Prof. P. Thrimuthy,
President. **ISSN:** 0970-647X. **URL:** http://www.csi-india.
org/web/csi.

45367 ■ Digit
Jasubhai Media Private Ltd.
Taj Bldg., 4th Fl.
210 Dr. D.N. Rd
Fort
Mumbai 400 001, Maharashtra, India
Ph: 91 22 40373636
Fax: 91 22 40373635
Publisher E-mail: godfrey_lobo@jasubhai.com
Online magazine covering information about information
technology products, computing, internet, hardware and
software. **Founded:** 1977. **Freq:** Monthly. **Print Method:**
Web Offset. **Trim Size:** 11 1/2 x 17. **Cols./Page:** 7. **Col.
Width:** 1 5/16 inches. **Col. Depth:** 16 inches. **Subscription Rates:** Rs 4,320 individuals three years; Rs 3,060
two years; Rs 1,600 individuals. **URL:** http://www.
thinkdigit.com/.

45368 ■ The Economic Times
Bennet, Coleman & Company Ltd.
Times of India Bldg.
Dr. D.N. Road
Mumbai 400 001, Maharashtra, India
Financial news daily. **Founded:** 1961. **Freq:** Daily. **Key
Personnel:** Gautam Shelar, Contact, gautam.shelar@
indiatimes.co.in. **ISSN:** 0972-0685. **Remarks:** Accepts
advertising. **URL:** http://economictimes.indiatimes.
com/?. **Circ:** Paid 108,302

45369 ■ Electrical & Electronics
Infomedia 18 Ltd.
A Wing, Rugby House
J.K. Sawant Marg, Dadar
Mumbai 400 028, Maharashtra, India
Ph: 91 22 30245000
Fax: 91 22 30034499
Publisher E-mail: ho@infomedia18.in
Magazine featuring Indian and international electrical
and electronics industries. **Freq:** Dimonthly. **Key Personnel:** Sudhanva Jategaonkar, Contact. **Subscription
Rates:** Rs 480 individuals; Rs 999 individuals 3 years;
Rs 1,875 other countries. **Remarks:** Accepts advertising.
URL: http://www.infomediaindia.com/template.php?id=
137. **Circ:** (Not Reported)

45370 ■ Feed Trends
Compound Livestock Feed Manufacturers' Association
of India
111 Mittal Chamber, 11th Fl.
Nariman Pt.
Mumbai 400 021, Maharashtra, India
Ph: 91 222 2026103
Fax: 91 222 2880128
Publisher E-mail: clafma@bom4.vsnl.net.in
Publication covering feed trends. **Freq:** Bimonthly. **Subscription Rates:** Free. **Remarks:** Advertising accepted;
rates available upon request. **URL:** http://www.
clfmaofindia.org/publication.aspx. **Circ:** 1,000

45371 ■ Health
Magna Publishing Company Ltd.
Magna House
100/E Old Prabhadevi Rd.
Prabhadevi
Mumbai 400 025, Maharashtra, India
Ph: 91 224 362270
Fax: 91 224 306523
Publisher E-mail: magnapub@vsnl.com
Periodical on health and nutrition information. **Founded:**
1989. **Freq:** Monthly. **Subscription Rates:** Rs 510
individuals; Rs 960 two years; Rs 1,600 other countries.
Remarks: Accepts advertising. **URL:** http://www.
magnamags.com/index.php?templateName=health.
Formerly: Health & Nutrition. **Circ:** Paid 102,214

45372 ■ IEEMA Journal
Indian Electrical and Electronics Manufacturers' Association
501 Kakad Chambers
132 Dr. Annie Besant Rd.
Worli
Mumbai 400 018, Maharashtra, India
Ph: 91 222 4930532
Fax: 91 222 4932705
Publisher E-mail: mumbai@ieema.org
Journal covering electronics. **Founded:** June 1981.
Freq: Monthly. **Trim Size:** 210 mm. x 297 mm. **Key
Personnel:** Sunil More, Dir. Gen. **ISSN:** 0970-2946.
Subscription Rates: Rs 300 individuals; Rs 550 two
years; Rs 750 individuals 36 (3 years). **Remarks:** Accepts advertising. **URL:** http://www.ieema.org/ieema_
journal.aspx. **Ad Rates:** BW: Rs 18,000. **Circ:** 10,000

45373 ■ India Today
Living Media India Ltd.
Trade Ctr.
2nd Fl.Kamla City,
S.B. Marg Lower Parel (W)
Mumbai 400 013, Maharashtra, India
Ph: 91 22 24983355
Publisher E-mail: malcolm.mistry@intoday.com
General news periodical. **Founded:** 1975. **Freq:** Weekly.
ISSN: 0019-4239. **Subscription Rates:** Rs 1,950
individuals 26 issues. **Remarks:** Accepts advertising.
URL: http://indiatoday.digitaltoday.in. **Circ:** Paid 932,079

45374 ■ India Today Plus
Living Media India Ltd.
Trade Ctr.
2nd Fl.Kamla City,
S.B. Marg Lower Parel (W)
Mumbai 400 013, Maharashtra, India
Ph: 91 22 24983355
Publication E-mail: myitpp@intoday.com
Publisher E-mail: malcolm.mistry@intoday.com
Consumer publication offering an international canvas
on exotic holidays, wines, cigars, luxury cruises, golf
and tennis. **Subtitle:** Guide to Good Living. **Founded:**

Circulation: ★ = ABC; △ = BPA; ◆ = CAC; • = CCAB; ❑ = VAC; ⊕ = PO Statement; ‡ = Publisher's Report; Boldface figures = sworn; Light figures = estimated.

1996. **Freq:** Monthly. **Subscription Rates:** Rs 1,200 individuals; Rs 2,400 two years; Rs 3,600 individuals 3 years. **Remarks:** Accepts advertising. **URL:** http://www.india-today.com/. **Circ:** Paid 89,000

45375 ■ Indian Cement Review
Wadhera Publications
General Assurance Bldg., 1st Fl.
232 D.N. Rd.
Mumbai 400 001, Maharashtra, India
Publisher E-mail: info@wadherapublications.com
Magazine focusing on business, production and operations management in the cement industry. **Founded:** Sept. 1985. **Freq:** Monthly. **Print Method:** Offset. **ISSN:** 0970-6119. **Subscription Rates:** Rs 500 individuals; US$150 individuals; Rs 50 single issue. **Remarks:** Accepts advertising. **URL:** http://www.wadherapublications.com/profile.htm. **Ad Rates:** BW: Rs 3,000, 4C: Rs 5,250. **Circ:** Paid 4,000

45376 ■ Indian Construction
Builders' Association of India
G-1/G-20 7th Fl.
Commerce Ctr.
J. Dadajee Rd.
Tardeo
Mumbai 400034, Maharashtra, India
Ph: 91 222 3514802
Fax: 91 222 3520507
Publisher E-mail: bai@vsnl.com
Construction industry's professional periodical. **Freq:** Monthly. **Key Personnel:** D.L. Desai, Chm.; Raj Pal Arora, Contact. **ISSN:** 0971-1244. **Subscription Rates:** Rs 500 individuals. **Remarks:** Accepts advertising. **URL:** http://www.bainet.org. **Ad Rates:** BW: Rs 15,000, 4C: Rs 25,000. **Circ:** Paid 7,000

45377 ■ Indian Drugs
Indian Drug Manufacturers Association
102-B Poonan Chambers
Dr. A.B. Rd.
Worli
Mumbai 400 018, Maharashtra, India
Ph: 91 22 24944624
Fax: 91 22 24950723
Publication E-mail: ppr@idmaindia.com
Publisher E-mail: idma1@idmaindia.com
Scientific journal on pharmacology. **Freq:** Monthly. **ISSN:** 0019-462X. **Subscription Rates:** Rs 1,000 individuals. **Remarks:** Accepts advertising. **URL:** http://www.idma-assn.org/publications.html. **Circ:** Paid 6,000

45378 ■ Indian Journal of Cancer
Indian Cancer Society
Lady Ratan Tata Medical and Research Centre
M. Karve Rd., Cooperage
Mumbai 400 021, Maharashtra, India
Ph: 91 22 22029941
Fax: 91 22 22872745
Publisher E-mail: info@indiancancersociety.org
Scientific publication on oncology. **Founded:** 1963. **Freq:** Quarterly. **Key Personnel:** Purvish M. Parikh, Editor-in-Chief. **ISSN:** 0019-509X. **Subscription Rates:** Rs 240 individuals post free; US$35 other countries seamail (plus postage 10). **URL:** http://www.indiancancersociety.org/activities-ics/ij-cancer.htm; http://www.indianjcancer.com/. **Ad Rates:** BW: Rs 900. **Circ:** 1,600

45379 ■ Indian Journal of Critical Care Medicine
Indian Society of Critical Care Medicine
Prayag Hospital
Bldg. No.3 Office No.12, 5th Fl.
Navjivan Premises Co-op Society Ltd.
Dr. D. Bhadkamkar Rd.
Mumbai 400 008, Maharashtra, India
Ph: 91 22 65268504
Fax: 91 22 23054843
Publisher E-mail: isccm1@vsnl.net
Journal dealing with research, education and dissemination of knowledge in the fields of critical and emergency medicine. **Founded:** 1997. **Freq:** Quarterly. **Print Method:** Sheetfed Offset. **Trim Size:** 8 1/2 x 11. **Key Personnel:** Dr. Sandhya Talekar, Ch. Ed.; Vijaylaxmi Kamat, Asst. Ed.; Arvind Bhome, National Executive Committee; R.K. Mani; National Executive Committee; Praveen Khilnani, National Executive Committee; K. Chugh, Members of Editorial Board; Shirish Prayag, Executive Ed.; J.V. Divatia, Asst. Ed. **ISSN:** 0972-5229. **Subscription Rates:** Rs 1,200 individuals; Rs 1,800

institutions; US$150 individuals overseas; US$150 institutions overseas. **Remarks:** Accepts advertising. **URL:** http://www.ijccm.org/. **Circ:** (Not Reported)

45380 ■ Indian Journal of Gastroenterology
Indian Society of Gastroenterology
23 Bombay Mutual Ter.
534 Sandhurst Bridge
Mumbai 400 007, Maharashtra, India
Ph: 91 22 23613333
Fax: 91 22 24175626
Publication E-mail: ijg@indianjgastroastro.com
Publisher E-mail: ijg@indianjgastroastro.com
Publication on gasteroenterology. **Founded:** Apr. 1982. **Freq:** Continuous 3/yr. **Print Method:** Color offset. **Trim Size:** 26.7 x 21.5 cm. **Key Personnel:** Dr. Shobna Bhatia, Editor; Philip Abraham, Ed. Emeritus. **ISSN:** 0254-8860. **Subscription Rates:** Rs 400 individuals personal; Rs 1,000 institutions; US$50 other countries; US$100 institutions, other countries. **Remarks:** Accepts advertising. **URL:** http://www.indianjgastro.com/. **Ad Rates:** BW: Rs 2,500, 4C: Rs 7,500. **Circ:** 1,200

45381 ■ Indian Journal of Human Genetics
Medknow Publications Pvt Ltd.
Institute of Immunohaematology
KEM Hospital, NMS Bldg., 13th Fl.
Mumbai 400012, Maharashtra, India
Journal covering human genetics. **Freq:** Quarterly. **Key Personnel:** K. Gosh, Editor. **ISSN:** 0971-6866. **Subscription Rates:** US$100 other countries; US$150 institutions, other countries; Rs 1,500 individuals; Rs 1,500 institutions. **Remarks:** Accepts advertising. **URL:** http://www.ijhg.com/; http://www.medknow.com/journals.asp. **Circ:** (Not Reported)

45382 ■ Indian Journal of Medical and Paediatric Oncology
Medknow Publications Pvt Ltd.
c/o Dr. Sudeep Gupta, Ed.-in-Ch.
Tata Memorial Hospital, Rm 15
Parel
Mumbai 400 012, Maharashtra, India
Publication E-mail: editor@ijmpo.org
Peer-reviewed journal covering pediatric and medical oncology. **Freq:** Quarterly. **Key Personnel:** Sudeep Gupta, Editor-in-Chief; Kumar Prabhash, Editor; Brijesh Arora, Editor; Gauri S. Bhattacharya, Editor; Satya Dattatreya, Editor; Bhawna Sirohi, Editor. **ISSN:** 0971-5851. **Subscription Rates:** Rs 1,000 individuals print only; Rs 1,000 institutions print only; US$150 other countries print only; US$150 institutions, other countries print only; Rs 1,200 individuals print and online; Rs 1,200 institutions print and online; US$180 other countries print and online; US$180 institutions, other countries print and online; Rs 800 institutions online; US$120 individuals online. **Remarks:** Accepts advertising. **URL:** http://www.ijmpo.org. **Circ:** (Not Reported)

45383 ■ Indian Journal of Medical Sciences
Indian Journal of Medical Sciences Trust
A-109, Kanara Business Center
Off Link Rd., Ghatkopar (E)
Kurla W
Mumbai 400 075, Maharashtra, India
Ph: 91 22 66491818
Fax: 91 22 66491817
Publisher E-mail: ijms@medknow.com
Publication on medical science. **Founded:** 1948. **Freq:** Monthly. **Key Personnel:** Dr. D.K. Sahu, Editor, editor@indianjmedsci.org. **ISSN:** 0019-5359. **Subscription Rates:** Rs 1,200 individuals. **Remarks:** Accepts advertising. **URL:** http://www.indianjmedsci.org. **Circ:** 3,000

45384 ■ Indian Journal of Nuclear Medicine
Society of Nuclear Medicine, India
c/o Radiation Medicine Ctr., B.A.R.C.
T.M.C. Annexe
Parel
Mumbai 400 012, Maharashtra, India
Ph: 91 022 24149428
Fax: 91 022 24157098
Publication E-mail: ijnm@tendercare.com
Publisher E-mail: malhotraarun@gmail.com
Journal covering the fields of nuclear medicine, radiopharmaceutical chemistry, radiation biology, instrumentation physics and related fields including thyroidology. **Freq:** Quarterly. **Key Personnel:** R. Kashyap, Editor-in-

Chief; M K Chopra, Treas. **URL:** http://medind.nic.in/iaw/iawm.shtml.

45385 ■ Indian Journal of Ophthalmology
All India Ophthalmological Society
P.D. Hinduja National Hospital & Medical Research Centre
Veer Savarkar Marg
Mahim
Mumbai 400 016, Maharashtra, India
Publisher E-mail: :rajvardhanazad@hotmail.com
Publication concerning Ophthalmology. **Freq:** Quarterly. **Key Personnel:** Barun Kumar Nayak, Editor, editor@ijo.in. **ISSN:** 0301-4738. **Subscription Rates:** Rs 2,000 individuals; Rs 3,000 institutions; US$180 individuals; US$300 institutions. **Remarks:** Accepts advertising. **URL:** http://www.aios.org/journal.htm. **Ad Rates:** BW: Rs 7,000, 4C: Rs 13,000. **Circ:** (Not Reported)

45386 ■ Indian Journal of Pharmaceutical Sciences
The Indian Pharmaceutical Association
Kalina
Santacruz (E)
Mumbai 400 098, Maharashtra, India
Ph: 91 222 6671072
Fax: 91 222 6670744
Publisher E-mail: ipacentre@ipapharma.org
Publication covering the field of pharmacology. **Freq:** Bimonthly. **Key Personnel:** Dr. Krishna Iyer, Asst. Ed.; T.B. Nair, Exec. Sec.; Dr. Chhanda Kapadia, Editorial Asst.; Dr. Rao V.S.V. Vadlamudi, Editor; Dr. D.D. Hegde, Editorial Asst.; Dr. Hema Nair, Editorial Asst. **ISSN:** 0250-474X. **Subscription Rates:** Rs 2,500 individuals; Rs 2,500 institutions; US$100 other countries; US$200 institutions, other countries. **URL:** http://www.ijpsonline.com/aboutus.asp.

45387 ■ Indian Journal of Plastic Surgery
Association of Plastic Surgeons of India
4th Fl., 770 Vimal Smruti
Ghantl Rd., Parsi Colony
Dadar
Mumbai 400 014, Maharashtra, India
Ph: 91 222 4143308
Publisher E-mail: singhkarun@hotmail.com
Publication on plastic surgery. **Freq:** Semiannual. **Print Method:** Sheetfed offset. **Trim Size:** 8 1/2 x 11. **Key Personnel:** Prof. Mukund Jagannath, Advisory board; Prof. Ramesh Sharma, Advisory board; Ajoy Singh, Advisory board; David Elliot, International Advisory Board; C. Thomas, International Advisory Board; Philip K.T. Chen, International Advisory Board; Prof. Sasanka S. Chatterjee, Advisory Board; Dr. Mukund Thatte, Editor, editor@ijps.org. **ISSN:** 0970-0358. **Subscription Rates:** Rs 1,200 individuals India; Rs 2,000 institutions India; US$100 individuals overseas (U.S.); US$200 institutions overseas (U.S.). **Remarks:** Accepts advertising. **URL:** http://www.ijps.org/. **Circ:** 35,000

45388 ■ Indian Journal of Social Work
Partha N. Mukherji
Tata Institute of Social Sciences
Sion-Trombay Rd.
PO Box 8313
Mumbai 400 088, Maharashtra, India
Ph: 91 22 25563289
Fax: 91 22 25562912
Journal focusing on the study of social work. **Founded:** 1940. **Freq:** Quarterly January, April, July, and October. **Key Personnel:** S. Parasuraman, Editor. **ISSN:** 0019-5634. **Subscription Rates:** Rs 250 individuals India; Rs 600 institutions India; US$25 individuals South Asia; US$40 institutions South Asia; US$55 individuals SE Asia, Middle East, Africa, South America; US$70 institutions SE Asia, Middle East, Africa, South America; US$65 individuals North America/Europe/Australia/New Zealand; US$120 institutions North America/Europe/Australia/New Zealand. **Remarks:** Accepts advertising. **URL:** http://www.tiss.edu/ijsw.htm. **Circ:** 1,200

45389 ■ Indian Shipping
Indian National Shipowners' Association
22 Maker Tower-F, 2nd Fl.
Cuffe Parade
Mumbai 400 005, Maharashtra, India
Ph: 91 22 22182103
Fax: 91 22 22182104
Publisher E-mail: webmaster@insa.org.in
Trade periodical focusing on the Indian shipping industry.

Founded: 1949. **Freq:** Monthly. **Key Personnel:** S. Hajara, President, phone 91 22 22026666, fax 91 22 22022933, s.hajara@sci.co.in; Yudhishthir D. Khatau, Contact, phone 91 22 56350207, fax 91 22 56350271, ydk@varunship.com; A.R. Ramakrishnan, Contact, phone 91 22 66601100, fax 91 22 24954312, arramakrishnan@essar.com; Anil Devli, Contact, phone 91 22 66220100, fax 91 22 22836805, devli@shreyas.co.in; Atul J. Agarwal, Vice President, phone 91 22 66373333, fax 91 22 66373344, atul@mercator.in; K.M. Sheth, Contact, phone 91 22 24985331, fax 91 22 24921200, k_sheth@greatship.com; R.L. Pai, Contact, phone 91 22 22716135, fax 91 22 22716137, r_l_pai@ril.com; R. Srinivasan, Contact, phone 91 44 28241431, fax 91 44 28266976, srinivasan@wam.co.in. **ISSN:** 0970-4299. **Subscription Rates:** Rs 625 individuals annual subscription. **Remarks:** Accepts advertising. **URL:** http://www.insa.org.in. **Circ:** Paid 1,000

45390 ■ India's Stamp Journal
Empire of India Philatelic Society
EIPS, S.A. Vijaykar & Company
1008 Raheja Center
10th Fl., Nariman Point
Mumbai 400 021, Maharashtra, India
Journal covering philately. **Founded:** 1939. **Freq:** Irregular. **Key Personnel:** Vispi S. Dastur, Editor. **ISSN:** 0019-6851. **Subscription Rates:** Rs 100 individuals; US$12 other countries airmail. **URL:** http://www.stampsofindia.com/infobase/a602.htm.

45391 ■ Insurance Institute of India Journal
Insurance Institute of India
Universal Insurance Bldg., 6th Fl.
Sir Pherozshah Mehta Rd.
Mumbai 400 001, Maharashtra, India
Ph: 91 22 22872923
Fax: 91 22 22873491
Publisher E-mail: iiiexams@vsnl.net
Periodical focusing on insurance education, training and research. **Founded:** 1975. **Freq:** Semiannual. **Key Personnel:** V.H.P. Pinto, Editor. **URL:** http://www.insuranceinstituteofindia.com/. **Circ:** Paid 15,000

45392 ■ International Journal for Ayurveda Research
Medknow Publications Pvt Ltd.
B-9, Kanara Business Center
Off Link Rd., Ghatkopar E
Mumbai 400075, Maharashtra, India
Ph: 91 22 56491818
Fax: 91 22 56491817
Peer-reviewed journal covering ayurveda research. **Freq:** 3/yr. **Key Personnel:** Dr. U. M. Thatte, Ch. Ed.; Dr. N B Brindavanam, Assoc. Ed.; Prof. K. K. Bhutani, Assoc. Ed.; Dr. Ram Manohar, Assoc. Ed.; Dr. Tanuja Nesari, Exec. Ed.; Dr. Supriya Bhalerao, Exec. Ed. **ISSN:** 0974-7788. **Subscription Rates:** Rs 600 individuals print only; Rs 1,200 institutions print only; US$60 other countries print only; US$120 institutions, other countries print only. **URL:** http://www.ijaronline.com.

45393 ■ International Journal of Diabetes in Developing Countries
Medknow Publications Pvt Ltd.
c/o Prof. H.B. Chandalia, Ed.
Diabetes Endocrine Nutrition Management & Research Ctr.
103-104 Lady Ratan Tata Medical Ctr., M. Karve Rd.
Mumbai 400 021, Maharashtra, India
Ph: 91 22 22871613
Fax: 91 22 22840255
Journal targets clinicians, research workers, paramedical personnel, nutritionists and health care personnel working in the field of diabetes. **Founded:** 1980. **Freq:** Quarterly. **Print Method:** Offset. **Trim Size:** 8 1/2 x 11. **Cols./Page:** 3. **Col. Width:** 2 1/4 inches. **Col. Depth:** 14 inches. **Key Personnel:** Prof. H.B. Chandalia, Editor. **ISSN:** 0973-3930. **Subscription Rates:** Rs 1,000 individuals; Rs 1,500 institutions; US$100 other countries; US$100 institutions, other countries. **URL:** http://www.ijddc.com.

45394 ■ International Journal of Emerging and Multidisciplinary Fluid Science
Multi-Science Publishing Company Ltd.
c/o S.D. Sharma, Ed.-in-Ch.
Dept. of Aerospace Engineering
Indian Institute of Technology
Mumbai 400 076, Maharashtra, India
Publisher E-mail: info@multi-science.co.uk
Journal covering research on fluid sciences. **Freq:** Quarterly. **Key Personnel:** Dr. S.D. Sharma, Editor-in-Chief, sds@aero.iitb.ac.in. **ISSN:** 1756-8315. **Subscription Rates:** 267 individuals print and online; 245 individuals print only; 223 individuals online only. **URL:** http://www.multi-science.co.uk/ijemfs.htm.

45395 ■ Journal of Association of Physicians of India
Association of Physicians of India
Turf Estate, No. 6 & 7, Ground Fl.
Opposite Shakti Mills Compound
Dr. E. Moses Rd.
Mumbai 400 011, Maharashtra, India
Ph: 91 222 4912218
Fax: 91 222 4920263
Journal intended for practicing physicians. publishes articles in the field of internal medicine, in connection with Association of Physicians of India. **Freq:** Monthly. **Key Personnel:** Dr. Shashank R. Joshi, Emeritus Ed.; Falguni Parikh, Assoc. Ed.; V.R. Joshi, Emeritus Ed.; Surendra Daga, Assoc. Ed.; N.P. Singh, Asst. Ed.; A.R. Chogle, Assoc. Ed.; G. Narsimulu, Asst. Ed.; Aspi R. Billimoria, Assoc. Ed.; Dr. Siddharth N. Shah, Editor and Publisher; Shyam Sunder, Asst. Ed. **Subscription Rates:** Rs 6,000 individuals; US$300 individuals. **URL:** http://www.japi.org/. **Circ:** 200,000

45396 ■ Journal of Cancer Research and Therapeutics
Medknow Publications Pvt Ltd.
B-9, Kanara Business Center
Off Link Rd., Ghatkopar E
Mumbai 400075, Maharashtra, India
Ph: 91 22 56491818
Fax: 91 22 56491817
Journal dedicated to basic and clinical sciences in oncology, including radiation oncology. **Freq:** Quarterly. **Key Personnel:** Dr. Nagraj G. Huilgol, Editor-in-Chief. **ISSN:** 0973-1482. **Subscription Rates:** Rs 1,500 individuals; Rs 2,000 institutions; US$100 other countries; US$250 institutions, other countries. **Remarks:** Accepts advertising. **URL:** http://www.cancerjournal.net. **Circ:** (Not Reported)

45397 ■ Journal of Craniovertebral Junction and Spine
Medknow Publications Pvt Ltd.
B-9, Kanara Business Center
Off Link Rd., Ghatkopar E
Mumbai 400075, Maharashtra, India
Ph: 91 22 56491818
Fax: 91 22 56491817
Publication E-mail: editor@jcvjs.com
Peer-reviewed journal covering craniovertebral junction and spine. **Freq:** Semiannual. **Key Personnel:** Atul Goel, Editor-in-Chief; Kuniyoshi Abumi, Editor; Ed Benzel, Editor. **ISSN:** 0974-8237. **Subscription Rates:** Rs 1,000 individuals print only; Rs 1,200 institutions print only; US$100 other countries print only; US$150 institutions, other countries print only. **Remarks:** Accepts advertising. **URL:** http://www.jcvjs.com. **Circ:** (Not Reported)

45398 ■ Journal of Dental Implants
Medknow Publications Pvt Ltd.
B-9, Kanara Business Center
Off Link Rd., Ghatkopar E
Mumbai 400075, Maharashtra, India
Ph: 91 22 56491818
Fax: 91 22 56491817
Peer-reviewed journal of the Indian Society of Oral Implantologists. **Founded:** Jan. 2009. **Freq:** Quarterly. **Key Personnel:** Savio Lourenco, Editor. **ISSN:** 0974-6781. **Subscription Rates:** Rs 1,000 individuals print; Rs 1,500 institutions print; Rs 800 individuals online; Rs 1,200 institutions online; Rs 1,200 individuals print and online; Rs 1,800 institutions print and online. **Remarks:** Accepts advertising. **URL:** http://www.jdionline.org. **Circ:** (Not Reported)

45399 ■ Journal of Family Welfare
Family Planning Association of India
Bajaj Bhavan
Nariman Point
Mumbai 400 021, Maharashtra, India
Ph: 91 22 22029080
Fax: 91 22 40863201
Publication E-mail: fpai@giasbm01.vsnl.net.in
Publisher E-mail: fpai@fpaindia.org
Medical journal focusing on reproductive medicine and technology. **Founded:** 1954. **Freq:** Semiannual. **Key Personnel:** Avabai B. Wadia, Advisory Board. **ISSN:** 0022-1074. **URL:** http://medind.nic.in/jah/jahaj.shtml. **Circ:** Paid 1,500

45400 ■ Journal of Financial Management and Analysis
Om Sai Ram Centre for Financial Management Research
15 Prakash Co-operative Housing Society
Relief Rd.
Santacruz W
Mumbai 400 054, Maharashtra, India
Refereed journal covering financial management theory application to practice using new concepts and methodologies and case studies to aid prudent policy formulation. **Founded:** 1988. **Freq:** Semiannual. **Print Method:** Computerised Publishing (D.T.P.). **Trim Size:** A4. **Key Personnel:** M.R.K. Swamy, Editor. **ISSN:** 0970-4205. **Remarks:** Advertising accepted; rates available upon request. **URL:** http://isidev.nic.in/jrnls/j59.html. **Circ:** Paid 3,000

45401 ■ Journal of Gynecological Endoscopy and Surgery
Medknow Publications Pvt Ltd.
c/o Dr. Prakash Trivedi
National Institute of Endoscopic & Laser Foundation
Tilak Rd.
Ghatkopar E
Mumbai 400 077, Maharashtra, India
Publication E-mail: editor@gynecendoscopy.org
Peer-reviewed journal covering clinical and bioengineering aspects of obstetric and gynecological endoscopy. **Freq:** Semiannual. **Key Personnel:** Dr. Hrishikesh D. Pai, Editor; Dr. Rakesh Sinha, Dep. Ed.; Dr. P.K. Shah, Assoc. Ed. **ISSN:** 0974-1216. **Subscription Rates:** Rs 1,000 individuals print only; Rs 1,000 institutions print only; US$150 other countries print only; US$150 institutions, other countries print only; Rs 1,200 individuals print and online; Rs 1,200 institutions print and online; US$180 other countries print and online; US$180 institutions, other countries print and online. **Remarks:** Accepts advertising. **URL:** http://www.gynecendoscopy.org. **Circ:** (Not Reported)

45402 ■ Journal of Medical Physics
Medknow Publications Pvt Ltd.
c/o Dr. A.S. Pradhan, Ed.-in-Ch.
CT & CRS Bldg., Bhabha Atomic Research Ctr.
Radiological Physics & Advisory Division
Anushaktinagar
Mumbai 400 094, Maharashtra, India
Publication E-mail: editor@jmp.org.in
Peer-reviewed journal of the Association of Medical Physicists of India. **Freq:** Quarterly. **Key Personnel:** Dr. A.S. Pradhan, Editor-in-Chief; Dr. A. Shanta, Assoc. Ed.; Dr. S.D. Sharman, Assoc. Ed. **ISSN:** 0971-6203. **Subscription Rates:** Rs 600 individuals print only; Rs 1,200 institutions print only; US$120 other countries print only; US$120 institutions, other countries print only; Rs 800 individuals print and online; Rs 1,500 institutions print and online; US$145 other countries print and online; US$145 institutions, other countries print and online. **Remarks:** Accepts advertising. **URL:** http://www.jmp.org.in. **Circ:** (Not Reported)

45403 ■ Journal of Minimal Access Surgery (JMAS)
Indian Association of Gastrointestinal Endosurgeons
Journal of Minimal Access Surgery
Rm. 2103, Dept. of Minimal Access Surgery
P. D. Hinduja National Hospital
Veer Savarkar Marg, Mahim
Mumbai 400 016, Maharashtra, India
Publisher E-mail: rjact@gmail.com
Peer-reviewed journal covering the topics of laparoscopic and thoracoscopic surgery laparoscopic urology and gastrointestinal endoscopy with particular emphasis on Minimal Access Surgery. **Founded:** 2005. **Freq:** Quarterly. **Key Personnel:** Prof. Tehemton E. Udwadia, Editor-in-Chief; D.S. Bhandarkar, Editor; R. Ardhanari, Editor; A.N. Dalvi, Editorial Board; P.K. Chowbey, Editor; J.S. Kulkarni, Editorial Board. **ISSN:** 0972-9941. **Subscription Rates:** Rs 1,200 individuals print only; Rs

---

Circulation: ★ = ABC; △ = BPA; ◆ = CAC; • = CCAB; ❑ = VAC; ⊕ = PO Statement; ‡ = Publisher's Report; Boldface figures = sworn; Light figures = estimated.

2,000 institutions print only; US$120 other countries print only; US$200 institutions, other countries print only; Rs 1,500 individuals print and online; Rs 2,400 institutions print and online; US$145 other countries print and online; US$240 institutions, other countries print and online. **URL:** http://www.journalofmas.com/.

45404 ■ The Journal of Obstetrics and Gynaecology of India
Federation of Obstetric & Gynaecological Societies of India
Gr Fl., Model Residency Tower
605, Baburao Jagtap Rd.
Jacob Cir.
Mahalaxmi E
Mumbai 400 001, Maharashtra, India
Ph: 91 22 23021648
Fax: 91 22 23021383
Publisher E-mail: fogsi@bom7.vsnl.net.in
Medical journal focusing on obstetrics and gynecology in India. **Founded:** 1950. **Freq:** Bimonthly. **Print Method:** Offset. **Trim Size:** 8-1/2 x 11. **Key Personnel:** Mahendra N. Parikh, Ed. Emeritus; C.N. Purandare, Assoc. Ed.; Adi E. Dastur, Editor; V.N. Purandare, Ed. Emeritus; R.D. Pandit, Ed. Emeritus. **ISSN:** 0022-3190. **Remarks:** Accepts advertising. **URL:** http://www.fogsi.org/fogsi_journal.html; http://journalseek.net/cgi-bin/journalseek/journalsearch.cgi?field=issn&que ry=0022-3190. **Alt. Formats:** CD-ROM. **Circ:** Paid 18,200

45405 ■ Journal of Postgraduate Medicine
Seth G.S. Medical College and K.E.M. Hospital
Acharya Donde Marg
Parel
Mumbai 400 012, Maharashtra, India
Ph: 91 22 24136051
Fax: 91 22 24143435
Medical journal on postgraduate medicine featuring charts and illustrations. **Founded:** 1955. **Freq:** Quarterly. **Print Method:** Offset. **Trim Size:** 8 1/2 x 11. **Key Personnel:** Sandeep Bavdekar, Editor; D. Muzumdar, Assoc. Ed.; Nithya Gogtay, Assoc. Ed.; Sanjay Mehta, Editorial Board Member; Sunil Pandya, Journal Ombudsman; D.K. Sahu, Managing Editor; Thomas B. Ferguson, Advisory Board; Nobuo Hashimoto, Advisory Board; Atul Goel, Editorial Board Member. **ISSN:** 0022-3859. **Subscription Rates:** Rs 1,000 individuals print only; Rs 1,500 institutions print only; US$100 individuals print only; US$150 institutions print only; Rs 1,200 individuals print and online; Rs 1,800 institutions print and online; US$120 other countries print and online; US$180 institutions, other countries print and online. **Remarks:** Accepts advertising. **URL:** http://www.jpgmonline.com. **Alt. Formats:** CD-ROM. **Ad Rates:** BW: Rs 5,000, 4C: Rs 10,000. **Circ:** 2,000

45406 ■ Kalnirnay
Sumangal Press Private Ltd.
G-8
Cross Rd. A
MIDC
Andheri (E)
Mumbai 400 093, Maharashtra, India
Ph: 91 22 28234745
Publication of a unique blend of almanac, magazine, recipe book and a visual source of day-to-day information. **Founded:** 1973. **Subscription Rates:** Rs 6 single issue; US$6 single issue American edition. **URL:** http://www.kalnirnay.com/. **Circ:** 8,000,000

45407 ■ Keemat
Consumer Guidance Society of India
Block 'J' Mahapalika Marg
Mumbai 400 001, Maharashtra, India
Ph: 91 22 621612
Fax: 91 22 659715
Publisher E-mail: cgsibom@mtnl.net.in
Publication focusing on consumer education and protection. **Founded:** 1972. **Freq:** Monthly. **Key Personnel:** Dr. S. G. Bhat, Editor. **URL:** http://www.cgsiindia.org. **Circ:** Paid 2,000

45408 ■ Man-Made Textiles in India
Synthetic and Art Silk Mills' Research Association
Sasmira Marg
Worli
Mumbai 400 030, Maharashtra, India
Ph: 91 22 24935351
Fax: 91 22 24930225

Publisher E-mail: sasmira@vsnl.com
Publication on textiles/technical textiles, and polymers in India. **Founded:** 1958. **Freq:** Monthly. **Print Method:** Offset. **Trim Size:** 28 x 21.5 cm. **Key Personnel:** Mihir R. Mehta, Vice President; Maganlal H. Doshi, President; Sunil S. Mehta, Council Member; S.H. Bachkaniwala, Council Member; D.V. Radia, Council Member; V.I. Bachkaniwala, Council Member; N.D. Shah, Council Member; Y.K. Kusumgar, Council Member. **ISSN:** 0377-7537. **Subscription Rates:** Rs 600 individuals; US$100 other countries; Rs 300 students. **Remarks:** Accepts advertising. **URL:** http://www.sasmira.org/publication.htm; http://www.sasmira.org/downloads.htm. **Ad Rates:** BW: Rs 2,500, 4C: Rs 5,000. **Circ:** Paid 1,500

45409 ■ Marg
Marg Publications
Army & Navy Bldg., 3rd Fl.
148 Mahatma Gandhi Rd.
Mumbai 400 001, Maharashtra, India
Ph: 91 22 22842520
Fax: 91 22 22047102
Publisher E-mail: margpub@tata.com
Art magazine. **Subtitle:** A Magazine of the Arts. **Founded:** Oct. 1946. **Freq:** Quarterly. **Trim Size:** 9 1/2 x 12 3/4. **Key Personnel:** Mulk Raj Anand, Editor. **ISSN:** 0972-1444. **Subscription Rates:** Rs 950 individuals; US$74 other countries. **Remarks:** Accepts advertising. **URL:** http://www.marg-art.org/magazines.asp. **Circ:** Paid 1,500

45410 ■ Medical Law Cases for Doctors
Medknow Publications Pvt Ltd.
Institute of Medicine & Law
Kalpak Estate, 6A/201
S.M. Rd.
Antop Hill
Mumbai 400 037, Maharashtra, India
Ph: 99 22 20426263
Fax: 99 22 24017910
Publication E-mail: editor@mlcd.in
Journal featuring medical law case reports for Indian doctors. **Freq:** Monthly. **ISSN:** 0974-1234. **Subscription Rates:** Rs 1,650 individuals ordinary post; Rs 1,890 individuals registered post. **URL:** http://www.mlcd.in.

45411 ■ Mens Sana Monographs
Medknow Publications Pvt Ltd.
14, Shiva Kripa, Trimurty Rd.
Nahur, Mulund W
Mumbai 400080, Maharashtra, India
Ph: 91 22 25682740
Fax: 91 22 25690505
Peer-reviewed journal covering psychiatric, biomedical, psychological and philosophical consequences of social disorders. **Freq:** Bimonthly. **Key Personnel:** Ajai R. Singh, MD, Editor; Shakuntala A. Singh, PhD, Dep. Ed. **ISSN:** 0973-1229. **Subscription Rates:** Rs 750 individuals two years; US$100 other countries two years; Rs 900 institutions two years; US$150 institutions, other countries two years; Rs 600 individuals retired teacher/researcher, two years; US$70 individuals retired teacher/researcher, international; Rs 600 students two years; US$70 students, other countries two years; Rs 35,000 individuals patron, two years; US$3,500 individuals patron, two years, international. **URL:** http://www.msmonographs.org/.

45412 ■ Mid-Day
Mid Day Publications Ltd.
64 Sitaram Mills Compound
N.M. Joshi Marg, Lower Parel
Lower Parel (E)
Mumbai 400 011, Maharashtra, India
Ph: 91 22 23017171
General newspaper. **Founded:** 1979. **Freq:** Mon.-Sat. **Key Personnel:** Shishir Joshi, Ch. Ed. **Remarks:** Accepts advertising. **URL:** http://www.middaymultimedia.com/news-media.asp. **Circ:** Paid 122,630

45413 ■ Middle East African Journal of Ophthalmology
Medknow Publications Pvt Ltd.
B-9, Kanara Business Center
Off Link Rd., Ghatkopar E
Mumbai 400075, Maharashtra, India
Ph: 91 22 56491818
Fax: 91 22 56491817
Peer-reviewed journal of the Middle East African Council of Ophthalmology. **Founded:** 1993. **Freq:** Quarterly.

Key Personnel: Deepak P. Edward, MD, Editor-in-Chief; Ahmed M. Abu El-Asrar, Assoc. Ed.; Alexander Bialasiewicz, Assoc. Ed. **ISSN:** 0974-9233. **Subscription Rates:** Rs 1,000 individuals print only; Rs 2,000 institutions print only; US$100 other countries print only; US$250 institutions, other countries print only; Rs 800 individuals online; Rs 1,600 institutions online; Rs 1,200 individuals print and online; Rs 2,400 institutions print and online. **URL:** http://www.meajo.org.

45414 ■ Modern Food Processing
Infomedia 18 Ltd.
A Wing, Rugby House
J.K. Sawant Marg, Dadar
Mumbai 400 028, Maharashtra, India
Ph: 91 22 30245000
Fax: 91 22 30034499
Publisher E-mail: ho@infomedia18.in
Magazine featuring Indian and international food processing industry. **Freq:** Bimonthly. **Key Personnel:** Sudhanva Jategaonkar, Contact. **Subscription Rates:** Rs 799 individuals; Rs 1,200 two years; Rs 3,750 other countries. **Remarks:** Accepts advertising. **URL:** http://eshop.infomedia18.in/productdetails.php?id=19. **Circ:** (Not Reported)

45415 ■ Modern Machine Tools
Infomedia 18 Ltd.
A Wing, Rugby House
J.K. Sawant Marg, Dadar
Mumbai 400 028, Maharashtra, India
Ph: 91 22 30245000
Fax: 91 22 30034499
Publisher E-mail: ho@infomedia18.in
Magazine featuring machine tools and ancillary industries. **Freq:** Monthly. **Key Personnel:** Sudhanva Jategaonkar, Contact, phone 91 22 24232849, sudhanva@infomediaindia.com. **Subscription Rates:** Rs 799 individuals; Rs 3,750 other countries. **Remarks:** Accepts advertising. **URL:** http://www.infomedia18.in/template.php?id=134. **Circ:** (Not Reported)

45416 ■ Modern Medicare
Infomedia 18 Ltd.
A Wing, Rugby House
J.K. Sawant Marg, Dadar
Mumbai 400 028, Maharashtra, India
Ph: 91 22 30245000
Fax: 91 22 30034499
Publisher E-mail: ho@infomedia18.in
Magazine featuring medical and healthcare industry. **Freq:** Monthly. **Key Personnel:** Sudhanva Jategaonkar, Contact, phone 91 22 40302323, fax 91 22 24302707, sudhanva@infomediaindia.com. **Subscription Rates:** Rs 799 individuals; Rs 1,999 individuals 3 years; Rs 3,750 other countries. **Remarks:** Accepts advertising. **URL:** http://www.infomedia18.in/template.php?id=133; http://www.modernmedicare.in/. **Circ:** (Not Reported)

45417 ■ Modern Packaging & Design
Infomedia 18 Ltd.
A Wing, Rugby House
J.K. Sawant Marg, Dadar
Mumbai 400 028, Maharashtra, India
Ph: 91 22 30245000
Fax: 91 22 30034499
Publisher E-mail: ho@infomedia18.in
Magazine featuring packaging applications and design improvement. **Freq:** Bimonthly. **Key Personnel:** Sudhanva Jategaonkar, Contact. **Subscription Rates:** Rs 401 individuals; Rs 1,875 other countries. **Remarks:** Accepts advertising. **URL:** http://eshop.infomedia18.in/productdetails.php?id=18. **Circ:** (Not Reported)

45418 ■ Modern Pharmaceuticals
Infomedia 18 Ltd.
A Wing, Rugby House
J.K. Sawant Marg, Dadar
Mumbai 400 028, Maharashtra, India
Ph: 91 22 30245000
Fax: 91 22 30034499
Publisher E-mail: ho@infomedia18.in
Magazine featuring Indian and international pharmaceutical industry. **Freq:** Bimonthly. **Key Personnel:** Daara Patel, Sec.-Gen. **Subscription Rates:** Rs 799 individuals; Rs 3,750 other countries; Rs 1,999 individuals 3 years. **Remarks:** Accepts advertising. **URL:** http://www.modernpharma.in. **Circ:** (Not Reported)

45419 ■ Modern Plastics & Polymers
Infomedia 18 Ltd.
A Wing, Rugby House
J.K. Sawant Marg, Dadar
Mumbai 400 028, Maharashtra, India
Ph: 91 22 30245000
Fax: 91 22 30034499
Publisher E-mail: ho@infomedia18.in
Magazine featuring Indian and international plastics and polymers industry. **Freq:** Bimonthly. **Key Personnel:** Vijay Merchant, Editorial Advisory Board; A.E. Ladhabhoy, Editorial Advisory Board; Dr. Sushil K. Verma, Editorial Advisory Board. **Subscription Rates:** Rs 799 individuals; Rs 3,750 other countries; Rs 1,999 individuals 3 years. **Remarks:** Accepts advertising. **URL:** http://www.modernplasticsandpolymers.in/. **Circ:** (Not Reported)

45420 ■ Modern Textiles
Infomedia 18 Ltd.
A Wing, Rugby House
J.K. Sawant Marg, Dadar
Mumbai 400 028, Maharashtra, India
Ph: 91 22 30245000
Fax: 91 22 30034499
Publisher E-mail: ho@infomedia18.in
Magazine featuring textile and machinery industries. **Freq:** Bimonthly. **Key Personnel:** Sudhanva Jategaonkar, Contact. **Subscription Rates:** Rs 600 individuals; Rs 1,200 two years. **Remarks:** Accepts advertising. **URL:** http://www.infomediaindia.com/template.php?id=141. **Circ:** (Not Reported)

45421 ■ Nuclear India
Department of Atomic Energy
Anushakti Bhavan
Chatrapathi Shivaji Maharaj Marg
Mumbai 400 001, Maharashtra, India
Ph: 91 222 2029328
Fax: 91 222 2048476
Magazine on nuclear technology. **Founded:** 1962. **Freq:** Monthly. **ISSN:** 9929-5523. **URL:** http://www.dae.gov.in/. **Circ:** 5,000

45422 ■ Offshore World (OW)
Jasubhai Media Private Ltd.
Taj Bldg., 4th Fl.
210 Dr. D.N. Rd.
Fort
Mumbai 400 001, Maharashtra, India
Ph: 91 22 40373636
Fax: 91 22 40373635
Publisher E-mail: godfrey_lobo@jasubhai.com
Magazine featuring various facets of the hydrocarbon and allied industries including oil and gas exploration, production, and transportation. **Key Personnel:** Jasu Shah, Publisher; Mittravinda Ranjan, Editor, mittra_ranjan@jasubhai.com. **URL:** http://www.oswindia.com/.

45423 ■ Oman Journal of Ophthalmology
Medknow Publications Pvt Ltd.
B-9, Kanara Business Center
Off Link Rd., Ghatkopar E
Mumbai 400075, Maharashtra, India
Ph: 91 22 56491818
Fax: 91 22 56491817
Peer-reviewed journal of the Oman Ophthalmic Society. **Freq:** 3/yr. **Key Personnel:** Dr. Abdullatif Al Raisi, Ch. Ed. **ISSN:** 0974-620X. **Remarks:** Accepts advertising. **URL:** http://ojoonline.org. **Circ:** (Not Reported)

45424 ■ Opportunities Today
Opportunities Today Publication Pvt. Ltd.
Radio Bhuvan
3/35 Kamal Mansion
Arthur Bunder Rd.
Near Radio Club, Colaba
Mumbai 400 005, Maharashtra, India
Ph: 91 222 2853081
Fax: 91 222 2875269
Publisher E-mail: rbcs@vsnl.com
General interest consumer magazine. **Founded:** Sept. 1971. **Freq:** Monthly. **Print Method:** Offset. **Key Personnel:** Sunita Motwani-Makhija, Director; Subhash Motwani, Director. **Remarks:** Advertising accepted; rates available upon request. **URL:** http://www.rbcsgroup.com. **Circ:** 15,000

45425 ■ Overdrive
Infomedia 18 Ltd.

A Wing, Rugby House
J.K. Sawant Marg, Dadar
Mumbai 400 028, Maharashtra, India
Ph: 91 22 30245000
Fax: 91 22 30034499
Publisher E-mail: ho@infomedia18.in
Magazine featuring automobiles. **Freq:** Monthly. **Key Personnel:** Ms. Ruby Roy, Contact. **Subscription Rates:** Rs 799 individuals; Rs 3,750 other countries. **Remarks:** Accepts advertising. **URL:** http://www.overdrive.in/; http://www.infomedia18.in/template.php?id=143. **Circ:** (Not Reported)

45426 ■ Packaging India
Indian Institute of Packaging
E-2, MIDC Area
Andheri E
Mumbai 400 093, Maharashtra, India
Ph: 91 228 219803
Publication E-mail: infoiip@iip-in.com
Publisher E-mail: iip@bom4.vsnl.net.in
Publication on packaging and the packaging industry. **Founded:** 1968. **Freq:** Bimonthly. **Print Method:** Offset. **Trim Size:** 24 x 18 cm. **Key Personnel:** Bhushan Surpur, Asst. dir.; Rajiv Dhar, Director. **ISSN:** 0030-9125. **Subscription Rates:** Rs 750 individuals India; US$150 individuals overseas. **Remarks:** Accepts advertising. **URL:** http://www.iip-in.com/InfoPeriodical.htm. **Formerly:** Packaging India. **Ad Rates:** BW: US$11, 4C: US$500. **Circ:** Paid 2,500

45427 ■ Parsiana
Parsiana Publications Private Ltd.
K.K. (Navsari) Chambers, Ground Fl.
39B Amrit Keshav Nayak Rd., Fort
Mumbai 400 001, Maharashtra, India
Ph: 91 22 078104
Fax: 91 22 075572
Publisher E-mail: info@parsiana.com
Community magazine focusing on the development and achievements of Zoroastrians in all fields of endeavour. **Subtitle:** The International Zoroastrian Link Medium. **Founded:** Nov. 1964. **Freq:** Semimonthly. **Print Method:** Offset. **Trim Size:** 19.8 x 27.5 cm. **Key Personnel:** Jehangir R. Patel, Editor. **ISSN:** 0971-3786. **Subscription Rates:** Rs 600 individuals India; Rs 3,250 other countries airmail; Rs 2,000 other countries sea mail; Rs 1,150 two years India; Rs 6,400 other countries two years, airmail; Rs 3,900 other countries two years, sea mail; Rs 1,700 individuals India, 3 years; Rs 9,600 other countries 3 years, airmail; Rs 5,800 other countries 3 years, sea mail. **Remarks:** Accepts advertising. **URL:** http://parsiana.com. **Ad Rates:** BW: Rs 5,000, 4C: Rs 14,450. **Circ:** Paid 3,352

45428 ■ Pharma Bio World
Jasubhai Media Private Ltd.
Taj Bldg., 4th Fl.
210 Dr. D.N. Rd.
Fort
Mumbai 400 001, Maharashtra, India
Ph: 91 22 40373636
Fax: 91 22 40373635
Publisher E-mail: godfrey_lobo@jasubhai.com
Magazine covering the pharmaceutical and biotechnology fields. **Founded:** 1960. **Freq:** Monthly. **Print Method:** Offset. **Cols./Page:** 6. **Col. Width:** 24 nonpareils. **Col. Depth:** 294 agate lines. **Key Personnel:** Thomas Antony, Editor, thomas_antony@jasubhai.com. **USPS:** 906-620. **Subscription Rates:** Rs 1,000 individuals; Rs 1,920 two years. **Remarks:** Accepts advertising. **URL:** http://www.jasubhai.com/print.php?op=PharPBW; http://www.pharmabioworld.com. **Ad Rates:** BW: EUR700, 4C: EUR900. **Circ:** (Not Reported)

45429 ■ Pharma Times
The Indian Pharmaceutical Association
Kalina
Santacruz (E)
Mumbai 400 098, Maharashtra, India
Ph: 91 222 6671072
Fax: 91 222 6670744
Publisher E-mail: ipacentre@ipapharma.org
Pharmacology magazine. **Founded:** 1969. **Freq:** Monthly. **Key Personnel:** Kaushik Desai, Advisory Board; Dr. Alka Mukne, Editor. **ISSN:** 0031-6849. **Subscription Rates:** Rs 150 single issue; Rs 1,500 individuals inland; Rs 4,000 individuals 3 years; Rs 6,000

individuals 5 years; US$15 other countries single copy; US$150 other countries. **Remarks:** Accepts advertising. **URL:** http://www.ipapharma.org/aboutPT.aspx. **Circ:** Paid 6,500

45430 ■ Pharmacognosy Research
Medknow Publications Pvt Ltd.
B-9, Kanara Business Center
Off Link Rd., Ghatkopar E
Mumbai 400075, Maharashtra, India
Ph: 91 22 56491818
Fax: 91 22 56491817
Peer-reviewed journal focusing on the research of natural medicine. **Freq:** Bimonthly. **Key Personnel:** Mueen Ahmed, Managing Editor, mueen.ahmed@phcog.net. **ISSN:** 0974-8490. **URL:** http://www.phcogmag.com/about-pharmacognosy-research.

45431 ■ Photo Imaging
Infomedia 18 Ltd.
A Wing, Rugby House
J.K. Sawant Marg, Dadar
Mumbai 400 028, Maharashtra, India
Ph: 91 22 30245000
Fax: 91 22 30034499
Publisher E-mail: ho@infomedia18.in
Magazine featuring photography related industries. **Freq:** Monthly. **Key Personnel:** Rajeev Pathria, Contact. **Subscription Rates:** Rs 290 individuals; Rs 755 individuals 3 years; Rs 3,750 other countries. **Remarks:** Accepts advertising. **URL:** http://www.infomediaindia.com/template.php?id=135. **Circ:** (Not Reported)

45432 ■ Process & Plant Engineering
Shanvik Publications Private Ltd.
Sterling Centre
Basement
Subhash Nagar
Opp. Cardinal Gracious High School, Bandra E
Mumbai 400 051, Maharashtra, India
Ph: 91 222 6550022
Fax: 91 222 6550088
Publisher E-mail: ksk_shanvik@yahoo.com
Publication on process and plant engineering. **Founded:** 1983. **Freq:** Quarterly. **Print Method:** Offset. **Trim Size:** 28 x 21.5 cm. **Col. Width:** 8.5 centimeters. **Key Personnel:** Suresh Kadam, Ch. Ed. & Mng. Dir.; Satish Kadam, Assoc. Ed. & Dir. **ISSN:** 0970-1729. **Subscription Rates:** Rs 500 individuals India; US$100 individuals overseas; Rs 1,200 individuals India, 3 years; US$250 individuals overseas, 3 years; Rs 2,000 individuals India, 5 years; US$400 individuals overseas, 5 years. **Remarks:** Accepts advertising. **URL:** http://www.shanviks.com. **Ad Rates:** BW: Rs 1,000, 4C: Rs 1,900. **Circ:** Paid 16,000

45433 ■ PVRI Review
Medknow Publications Pvt Ltd.
B-9, Kanara Business Center
Off Link Rd., Ghatkopar E
Mumbai 400075, Maharashtra, India
Ph: 91 22 56491818
Fax: 91 22 56491817
Peer-reviewed journal of the Pulmonary Vascular Research Institute. **Freq:** Quarterly. **Key Personnel:** Dr. S. Harikrishnan, Editor; Ghazwan Butrous, Exec. Ed., Ioana Preston, Exec. Ed. **ISSN:** 0974-6013. **Subscription Rates:** Rs 1,000 individuals print only; Rs 2,000 institutions print only; US$100 other countries print only; US$200 institutions, other countries print only. **Remarks:** Accepts advertising. **URL:** http://www.pvrireview.org. **Circ:** (Not Reported)

45434 ■ Reserve Bank of India Bulletin—Weekly Statistical Supplement
Reserve Bank of India—Department of Economic Analysis & Policy/Division of Reports Reviews & Publications
Fort
Mumbai 400 001, Maharashtra, India
Bulletin on banks and banking finance by Reserve Bank Of India. **Founded:** 1949. **Freq:** Weekly. **Subscription Rates:** Rs 50 individuals; US$17 other countries. **URL:** http://www.rbi.org.in/. **Circ:** Paid 1,400

45435 ■ Reserve Bank of India Occasional Papers
Reserve Bank of India—Department of Economic Analysis & Policy/Division of Reports Reviews & Publications

Circulation: ★ = ABC; △ = BPA; ◆ = CAC; • = CCAB; ❑ = VAC; ⊕ = PO Statement; ‡ = Publisher's Report; Boldface figures are sworn; Light figures are estimated.

Gale Directory of Publications & Broadcast Media/147th Ed. 5019

Fort
Mumbai 400 001, Maharashtra, India
Papers on banks and banking finance by Reserve Bank Of India. **Founded:** 1980. **Freq:** Quarterly. **Subscription Rates:** Rs 80 individuals inclusive of postage; US$45 other countries inclusive of registered air mail charges. **Remarks:** Accepts advertising. **URL:** http://www.rbi.org.in/scripts/QuarterlyPublications.aspx?head=Occasional%20Papers. **Circ:** Paid 1,000

45436 ■ Saudi Journal of Anaesthesia
Medknow Publications Pvt Ltd.
B-9, Kanara Business Center
Off Link Rd., Ghatkopar E
Mumbai 400075, Maharashtra, India
Ph: 91 22 56491818
Fax: 91 22 56491817
Peer-reviewed journal of the Saudi Anaesthetic Association. **Freq:** 3/yr. **Key Personnel:** Abdulhamid Al-Saeed, Editor-in-Chief; Abdelazeem El-Dawlatly, Assoc. Ed.; Jamal Alhashemi, Assoc. Ed. **ISSN:** 1658-354X. **Subscription Rates:** Rs 2,000 individuals print only; Rs 2,000 institutions print only; US$150 other countries print only; US$150 institutions, other countries print only; Rs 1,600 individuals online; US$120 other countries online; Rs 2,400 individuals print and online; US$180 other countries print and online. **Remarks:** Accepts advertising. **URL:** http://www.saudija.org. **Circ:** (Not Reported)

45437 ■ Screen World
Screen World Publication
H/9 171, Snehankoor Soc.
New M.H.L.B.T. Rd.
Borivali
Mumbai 4000 092, Maharashtra, India
Ph: 91 22 28692244
Publication E-mail: screenworld@hotmail.com
Publisher E-mail: swpub@bom3.vsnl.net.in
Publication focusing on the television, motion picture, audio, video and broadcast industries. **Founded:** 1987. **Freq:** Monthly and annual issue. **Print Method:** Offset. **Trim Size:** A4. **Key Personnel:** Rajendra Ojha, Editor, phone 91 2228692244. **ISSN:** 0971-2305. **Subscription Rates:** Rs 1500 individuals. **Remarks:** Accepts advertising. **URL:** http://www.screenworldindia.com. **Formerly:** Screen World Publication. **Ad Rates:** BW: Rs 8,000, 4C: Rs 1,500. **Circ:** 2,500

45438 ■ SEA Monthly News Circular
Solvent Extractors' Association of India
142 Jolly Maker Chambers No. 2, 14th Fl.
225 Nariman Point
Mumbai 400 021, Maharashtra, India
Ph: 91 222 2021475
Fax: 91 222 2021692
Publisher E-mail: solvent@vsnl.com
Publication covering the vegetable oilseed, oil, oil meals and compound feeds industry and trade in India. **Freq:** Monthly. **Print Method:** Offset. **Subscription Rates:** Included in membership. **URL:** http://www.seaofindia.com. **Ad Rates:** BW: US$100, 4C: US$1,000. **Circ:** 1,500

45439 ■ SKOAR
Jasubhai Media Private Ltd.
Taj Bldg., 4th Fl.
210 Dr. D.N. Rd.
Fort
Mumbai 400 001, Maharashtra, India
Ph: 91 22 40373636
Fax: 91 22 40373635
Publication E-mail: skrybe@9dot9.in
Publisher E-mail: godfrey_lobo@jasubhai.com
Magazine covering computer and video games. Also features hardware reviews, workshops, and views of people involved in the Indian and international gaming industry. **URL:** http://www.skoar.com/.

45440 ■ Soaps, Detergents & Toiletries Review
Wadhera Publications
General Assurance Bldg., 1st Fl.
232 D.N. Rd.
Mumbai 400 001, Maharashtra, India
Publisher E-mail: info@wadherapublications.com
Features reviews on cosmetics, soaps and toiletries. **Founded:** Jan. 1969. **Freq:** Monthly. **Cols./Page:** 2 and 3. **ISSN:** 0379-5608. **Subscription Rates:** Rs 500 individuals; US$150 other countries; Rs 50 single issue. **Remarks:** Accepts advertising. **URL:** http://www.

wadherapublications.com/profile.htm. **Ad Rates:** BW: Rs 3,000, 4C: Rs 5,250. **Circ:** Paid 4,000

45441 ■ Society
Magna Publishing Company Ltd.
Magna House
100/E Old Prabhadevi Rd.
Prabhadevi
Mumbai 400 025, Maharashtra, India
Ph: 91 224 362270
Fax: 91 224 306523
Publisher E-mail: magnapub@vsnl.com
General interest periodical. **Founded:** 1979. **Freq:** Monthly. **Subscription Rates:** Rs 1,800 other countries; Rs 960 two years; Rs 510 individuals; Rs 1,350 individuals 3 years. **Remarks:** Accepts advertising. **URL:** http://www.magnamags.com/index.php?templateName=society. **Circ:** Paid 85,093

45442 ■ Stardust
Magna Publishing Company Ltd.
Magna House
100/E Old Prabhadevi Rd.
Prabhadevi
Mumbai 400 025, Maharashtra, India
Ph: 91 224 362270
Fax: 91 224 306523
Publisher E-mail: magnapub@vsnl.com
Magazine on film stars and movies. **Founded:** 1971. **Freq:** Monthly. **Subscription Rates:** Rs 510 individuals; Rs 960 two years; Rs 1,800 other countries; Rs 1,350 individuals 3 years. **Remarks:** Accepts advertising. **URL:** http://www.magnamags.com/index.php?templateName=stardust. **Circ:** Paid 308,170

45443 ■ Studio Systems
6/C-5, Sangeeta Apts.
Ground Fl., Juhu Rd.
Santacruz (W)
Mumbai 400 049, Maharashtra, India
Ph: 91 22 26609147
Publisher E-mail: broadcast@studio-system.com
Trade magazine covering the audio, video and broadcasting industries. **Founded:** 1986. **Freq:** Bimonthly. **Print Method:** Offset. **Trim Size:** 21 x 28 cm. **Key Personnel:** Anil Chopra, Editor and Publisher, chopra@studio-systems.com. **Subscription Rates:** Rs 500 individuals; Rs 1000 two years; US$36 out of country by airmail; US$72 out of country two years, by airmail. **Remarks:** Accepts advertising. **URL:** http://www.studio-systems.com/. **Formerly:** Playback & Fast Forward. **Ad Rates:** BW: Rs 29,250. **Circ:** Paid 12,500

45444 ■ Sunday Mid-Day
Mid Day Publications Ltd.
64 Sitaram Mills Compound
N.M. Joshi Marg, Lower Parel
Lower Parel (E)
Mumbai 400 011, Maharashtra, India
Ph: 91 22 23017171
General interest periodical. **Founded:** 1980. **Freq:** Weekly. **Key Personnel:** Alpana Lath, Editor; Clayton Murzello, Sports Ed. **Remarks:** Advertising accepted; rates available upon request. **URL:** http://www.mid-day.com/. **Circ:** Paid 117,449

45445 ■ Surabhi
Cinema Vision India
501, Adarsh Nagar
M.H.B. Colony
New Link Rd.
Jogeshwari (W)
Mumbai 400 102, Maharashtra, India
Ph: 91 22 6320739
Fax: 91 22 6366642
Publication E-mail: contact@indiasurabhi.com
Publisher E-mail: cvi@indiasurabhi.com
Magazine covering fascinating facets of Indian culture. **URL:** http://www.indiasurabhi.com/index.html.

45446 ■ Taxation Law Reports
All India Reporter Pvt.Ltd.
Edows House, 1st Fl.
Nagindas Master Rd.
Fort
Mumbai 400 023, Maharashtra, India
Finance, economics and taxation law reports. **Freq:** Bimonthly. **Remarks:** Accepts advertising. **URL:** http://allindiareporter.in/taxation.php. **Circ:** Paid 1,500

45447 ■ The Theosophical Movement
Theosophy Company (India) Private Ltd.
40 New Marine Lines
Mumbai 400 020, Maharashtra, India
Publication covering topics in theosophy. **Subtitle:** A Magazine Devoted to The Living of the Higher Life. **Founded:** 1930. **Freq:** Monthly. **Print Method:** Offset Process. **Trim Size:** 22 1/2 cm x 15 cm. **ISSN:** 0040-5884. **Subscription Rates:** Rs 30 individuals; US$12 other countries. **URL:** http://www.teosofia.com/TTM.html. **Formerly:** The Theosophical Movement. **Circ:** Paid 380, Non-paid 380

45448 ■ Tomorrow's Technology Today
Infomedia 18 Ltd.
A Wing, Rugby House
J.K. Sawant Marg, Dadar
Mumbai 400 028, Maharashtra, India
Ph: 91 22 30245000
Fax: 91 22 30034499
Publisher E-mail: ho@infomedia18.in
Magazine covering technology and technological equipment, including phones, laptops, televisions, camcorders, and more. **Subtitle:** The World's No.1 Gadget Magazine. **Founded:** Dec. 2006. **Freq:** Monthly. **Key Personnel:** Ruby Roy, Contact. **Subscription Rates:** Rs 799 individuals; Rs 3,750 other countries. **Remarks:** Accepts advertising. **URL:** http://www.t3india.com/; http://www.infomedia18.in/template.php?id=215. **Circ:** (Not Reported)

45449 ■ Vivek
Centre for Development of Advanced Computing
8th Fl. Air India Bldg.
Nariman Point
Mumbai 400 021, Maharashtra, India
Ph: 91 22 22024641
Fax: 91 22 22049573
Publication E-mail: vivek@saathi.ncst.ernet.in
Publication on computers and artificial intelligence. **Freq:** Quarterly January, April, July and October. **Key Personnel:** S. Ramani, Editor; K.S.R. Anjaneyulu, Associate Ed.; M. Sasikumar, Associate Ed. **ISSN:** 0970-8618. **Subscription Rates:** Rs 100 individuals; US$20 other countries; Rs 125 individuals regd. post; US$40 institutions, other countries regd. post. **URL:** http://www.cdac.in. **Circ:** Paid 400

45450 ■ Yoga and Total Health
The Yoga Institute
Shri Yogendra Marg
Prabhat Colony
Santa Cruz E
Mumbai 400 055, Maharashtra, India
Ph: 91 22 26110506
Publisher E-mail: yogainstitute@gmail.com
Publication on yoga and health. **Founded:** 1933. **Freq:** Monthly. **Key Personnel:** Dr. Jayadeva Yogendra, Editor. **ISSN:** 0970-1737. **Subscription Rates:** Rs 150 individuals India; US$25 other countries airmail. **Remarks:** Accepts advertising. **URL:** http://www.theyogainstitute.org/. **Formerly:** The Journal of the Institute. **Circ:** Paid 2,000

45451 ■ Young Scientists Journal
Medknow Publications Pvt Ltd.
B-9, Kanara Business Center
Off Link Rd., Ghatkopar E
Mumbai 400075, Maharashtra, India
Ph: 91 22 56491818
Fax: 91 22 56491817
Peer-reviewed journal covering science and technology studies for young people. **Freq:** Quarterly. **Key Personnel:** Jonathan Rodgers, Team Ldr., jonathan.rogers@ysjournal.com; Pamela Barraza Flores, Editor-in-Chief, pamela.barrazaflores@ysjournal.com. **ISSN:** 0974-6102. **URL:** http://www.butrousfoundation.com/ysjournal.

45452 ■ All India Radio Mumbai 'A' - 1044 KHz
Broadcasting House
Backbay Reclamation
Mumbai 400 020, Maharashtra, India
Ph: 91 22 22029362
E-mail: sdairmumbai@vsnl.net
Format: Eclectic; Full Service. **Owner:** Prasar Bharati, PO Box 500, New Delhi 110 001, Delhi, India, 91 11 23421006, Fax: 91 11 23421956. **Founded:** 1927. **Key Personnel:** M.C. Aggarwal, Engr.-in-Ch., phone 91 11 23421058, fax 91 11 23421006, einc@air.org.in; Mohan Singh, Ch. Engr. Proj., phone 91 11 23421184. **Watt-**

age: 100,000. **Ad Rates:** $200-550 for 10 seconds; $300-825 for 15 seconds; $600-1,650 for 30 seconds; $1,200-3,300 for 60 seconds. **URL:** http://www.allindiaradio.org.

45453 ■ All India Radio Mumbai 'B' - 558 KHz
Broadcasting House
Backbay Reclamation
Mumbai 400 020, Maharashtra, India
Ph: 91 22 22029362
E-mail: sdairmumbai@vsnl.net
Format: Eclectic; Full Service. **Owner:** Prasar Bharati, Akashvani Bhavan, Sansad Marg, New Delhi 110 001, Delhi, India, 91 11 23421006, Fax: 91 11 23421956. **Key Personnel:** M.C. Aggarwal, Engr.-in-Ch., phone 91 11 23421058, fax 91 11 23421006, einc@air.org.in; Mohan Singh, Ch. Engr. Proj., phone 91 11 23421184. **Wattage:** 100,000. **Ad Rates:** $200-550 for 10 seconds; $300-825 for 15 seconds; $600-1,650 for 30 seconds; $1,200-3,300 for 60 seconds. **URL:** http://www.allindiaradio.org.

45454 ■ Radio One-FM - 94.3
I-18 Everest Chambers
10th Fl., Office No. 18
156-D, J. Dadajee Rd.
Tardeo
Mumbai 400034, Maharashtra, India
Ph: 91 22 66105700
Fax: 91 22 66105701
E-mail: radioone@mid-day.com
Format: Ethnic; World Beat. **Operating Hours:** Continuous. **Ad Rates:** $1,000-4,000 for 10 seconds. **URL:** http://www.radioone.in/.

Murshidabad

45455 ■ All India Radio Murshidabad - 102.2 MHz
Akashvani Bhavan
Sansad Marg
New Delhi 110 001, Delhi, India
Ph: 91 11 23421006
Fax: 91 11 23421956
E-mail: airmsd@sancharnet.in
Format: Eclectic. **Owner:** Prasar Bharati, at above address. **Founded:** 1990. **Key Personnel:** M.C. Aggarwal, Engr.-in-Ch., phone 91 11 23421058, fax 91 11 23421006, einc@air.org.in. **Wattage:** 6000. **Ad Rates:** $80-150 for 10 seconds; $120-225 for 15 seconds; $240-450 for 30 seconds; $480-900 for 60 seconds. **URL:** http://www.allindiaradio.org.

45456 ■ Star of Mysore
15-C, Industrial 'A' Layout
Academy Newspapers Pvt. Ltd.
Mysore 570 015, India
Ph: 91 821 2496520
Publisher E-mail: voice@starofmysore.com
General newspaper. **Key Personnel:** K.B. Ganapathy, Editor. **URL:** http://www.starofmysore.com/main.asp?type=editor.

Mysore (Karnataka)

45457 ■ Indian Journal of Sericulture
Central Sericultural Research & Training Institute
Srirampuram
Mysore 570 008, Karnataka, India
Ph: 91 821 480314
Fax: 91 821 480845
Publisher E-mail: rkdatta@csrti.ernet.in
Government periodical covering topics related to sericulture research. **Founded:** 1962. **Freq:** Semiannual. **Print Method:** Offset. **Key Personnel:** R.K. Datta, Editor. **ISSN:** 0445-7722. **Remarks:** Advertising not accepted. **URL:** http://www.mylibnet.org/csrti.htmlpub; http://www.mylibnet.org/. **Circ:** Paid 700

45458 ■ Journal of Indian Folkloristics
Jawaharlal Handoo
Central Institute of Indian Languages
Manasagangothri, Hunsur Rd.
Manasagangotri
Mysore 570 006, Karnataka, India
Ph: 91 821 2345000
Fax: 91 821 2515032
Publisher E-mail: udaya@ciil.stpmy.soft.net
Journal focusing on Indian folklore. **Founded:** 1978.

Freq: Semiannual. **Remarks:** Accepts advertising. **URL:** http://www.ciil.org/. **Circ:** Paid 1,100

45459 ■ Samachar
MysoreSamachar
Samachar Bldg. No. 49, 1st Fl.
Devaraj Urs Rd.
Mysore 570 001, Karnataka, India
Ph: 91 821 2423574
Publisher E-mail: samachar@mysoresamachar.com
General newspaper. **Key Personnel:** Gouri Satya, Editor, gourisatya@mysoresamachar.com. **Remarks:** Accepts advertising. **URL:** http://www.mysoresamachar.com/. **Circ:** (Not Reported)

45460 ■ All India Radio Mysore - 100.6 MHz
Akashvani Bhavan
Sansad Marg
New Delhi 110 001, Delhi, India
Ph: 91 11 23421006
Fax: 91 11 23421956
E-mail: airmys@blr.vsnl.net.in
Format: Eclectic. **Owner:** Prasar Bharati, at above address. **Founded:** 1935. **Key Personnel:** M.C. Aggarwal, Engr.-in-Ch., phone 91 11 23421058, fax 91 11 23421006, einc@air.org.in; Mohan Singh, Ch. Engr., Proj., phone 91 11 23421184. **Wattage:** 10,000. **Ad Rates:** $150-300 for 10 seconds; $225-450 for 15 seconds; $450-900 for 30 seconds; $900-1,800 for 60 seconds. **URL:** http://www.allindiaradio.org.

Nagaon

45461 ■ All India Radio Nowgong - 102.7 MHz
Akashvani Bhavan
Sansad Marg
New Delhi 110 001, Delhi, India
Ph: 91 11 23421006
Fax: 91 11 23421956
Format: Eclectic; Full Service. **Owner:** Prasar Bharati, at above address. **Founded:** 1994. **Key Personnel:** M.C. Aggarwal, Engr.-in-Ch., phone 91 11 23421058, fax 91 11 23421459, einc@air.org.in. **Wattage:** 6000. **Ad Rates:** $80-150 for 10 seconds; $120-225 for 15 seconds; $240-450 for 30 seconds; $480-900 for 60 seconds. **URL:** http://www.allindiaradio.org.

Nagaur

45462 ■ All India Radio Nagaur - 103.7 MHz
Bansi Rd.
Nagaur 341 001, Rajasthan, India
Ph: 91 1582 240847
E-mail: airngr@datainfosys.net
Format: Eclectic. **Owner:** Prasar Bharati, Akashvani Bhavan, Sansad Marg, New Delhi 110 001, Delhi, India, 91 11 23421006, Fax: 91 11 23421956. **Founded:** 1991. **Key Personnel:** M.C. Aggarwal, Engr.-in-Ch., phone 91 11 23421058, fax 91 11 23421006, einc@air.org.in. **Wattage:** 6000. **Ad Rates:** $80-150 for 10 seconds; $120-225 for 15 seconds; $240-450 for 30 seconds; $480-900 for 60 seconds. **URL:** http://www.allindiaradio.org.

Nagercoil

45463 ■ All India Radio Nagercoil - 101.0 MHz
Konam
Nagercoil 629 004, Tamil Nadu, India
Ph: 91 4652 260242
E-mail: airncoil@sancharnet.in
Format: Eclectic. **Owner:** Prasar Bharati, Akashvani Bhavan, Sansad Marg, New Delhi 110 001, Delhi, India, 91 11 23421006, Fax: 91 11 23421956. **Founded:** 1984. **Key Personnel:** M.C. Aggarwal, Engr.-in-Ch., phone 91 11 23421058, fax 91 11 23421006, einc@air.org.in. **Wattage:** 10,000. **Ad Rates:** $80-150 for 10 seconds; $120-225 for 15 seconds; $240-450 for 30 seconds; $480-900 for 60 seconds. **URL:** http://www.allindiaradio.org.

Nagpur

45464 ■ All India Reporter
All India Reporter Pvt.Ltd.
Congress Nagar
Nagpur 440 012, Maharashtra, India
Ph: 91 712 2526991

Fax: 91 712 2526283
Law periodical. **Freq:** Monthly. **Trim Size:** 14 x 21 cm. **ISSN:** 0002-5593. **Remarks:** Accepts advertising. **URL:** http://allindiareporter.in/index.php. **Ad Rates:** BW: Rs 9,000. **Circ:** Paid 43,000

45465 ■ Criminal Law Journal
All India Reporter Pvt.Ltd.
Congress Nagar
Nagpur 440 012, Maharashtra, India
Ph: 91 712 2526991
Fax: 91 712 2526283
Journal on criminal law. **Founded:** 1904. **Freq:** Monthly. **Trim Size:** 14 x 21 cm. **ISSN:** 0011-1325. **Remarks:** Accepts advertising. **URL:** http://allindiareporter.in/. **Ad Rates:** BW: Rs 9,000. **Circ:** 16,800

45466 ■ Indian Literature in Environmental Engineering
National Environmental Engineering Research Institute
Nehru Marg
Nagpur 440 020, Maharashtra, India
Ph: 91 712 2249885
Fax: 91 712 2249900
Publisher E-mail: director@neeri.res.in
Contains bibliographic reviews of Indian literature in the field of environmental engineering. **Subtitle:** A Bibliographic Review. **Founded:** 1971. **Freq:** Annual. **Key Personnel:** Dr. Sukumar Devotta, Director. **Subscription Rates:** Rs 80; US$5 other countries. **URL:** http://www.neeri.res.in/project_details.php?PID=275&DIV=12.

45467 ■ Indian Minerals Year Book
Indian Bureau of Mines
Bureau of Mines
Indian Indira Bhavan
Civil Lines
Nagpur 440 002, Maharashtra, India
Publisher E-mail: cgibm@ibm.mah.nic.in
Periodical focusing on the Indian mineral industry. **Founded:** 1959. **Freq:** Annual. **Key Personnel:** A.K. Singh, Sen. Ed. **ISSN:** 0445-7897. **Subscription Rates:** Rs 2,600 individuals; US$160.33 other countries; EUR79.16 other countries. **URL:** http://ibm.nic.in/. **Formerly:** Indian Minerals Year Book.

45468 ■ Journal of Environmental Science and Engineering
National Environmental Engineering Research Institute
Nehru Marg
Nagpur 440 020, Maharashtra, India
Ph: 91 712 2249885
Fax: 91 712 2249900
Publication E-mail: jese@neeri.res.in
Publisher E-mail: director@neeri.res.in
Periodical dedicated to environmental health. **Freq:** Quarterly. **Key Personnel:** Dr. S.R. Wate, Editor-in-Chief; Arindam Ghosh, Editor. **ISSN:** 0367-827X. **Subscription Rates:** Rs 150 individuals; US$40 other countries; Rs 600 institutions; US$200 institutions, other countries. **URL:** http://www.neeri.res.in/jese.html. **Formerly:** Indian Journal of Environmental Health. **Circ:** 1,200

45469 ■ Labour and Industrial Cases
All India Reporter Pvt.Ltd.
Congress Nagar
Nagpur 440 012, Maharashtra, India
Ph: 91 712 2526991
Fax: 91 712 2526283
Publication of labor and industrial cases. **Founded:** 1968. **Freq:** Monthly. **Trim Size:** 14 x 21 cm. **Subscription Rates:** US$276 individuals; US$150 individuals airmail. **Remarks:** Accepts advertising. **URL:** http://allindiareporter.in/labour.php. **Ad Rates:** BW: Rs 9,000. **Circ:** Paid 4,000

45470 ■ All India Radio Nagpur - 100.6 MHz
Civil Lines
Nagpur 440 001, Maharashtra, India
Ph: 91 712 2533833
E-mail: airngp@nagpur.dot.net.in
Format: Eclectic. **Owner:** Prasar Bharati, Akashvani Bhavan, Sansad Marg, New Delhi 110 001, Delhi, India, 91 11 23421006, Fax: 91 11 23421956. **Founded:** 1948. **Operating Hours:** 0025-1200, 1245-1730. **Key Personnel:** M.C. Aggarwal, Engr.-in-Ch., phone 91 11 23421058, fax 91 11 23421006, einc@air.org.in. **Wattage:** 6000. **Ad Rates:** $180-400 for 10 seconds; $270-600 for 15 seconds; $540-1,200 for 30 seconds; $1,080-

Circulation: ★ = ABC; △ = BPA; ♦ = CAC; • = CCAB; ❑ = VAC; ⊕ = PO Statement; ‡ = Publisher's Report; Boldface figures = sworn; Light figures = estimated.

Gale Directory of Publications & Broadcast Media/147th Ed.   5021

2,400 for 60 seconds. **URL:** http://www.allindiaradio.org.

Najibabad

45471 ■ All India Radio Najibabad - 954 KHz
Kotwali Rd.
Najibabad 246 763, Uttar Pradesh, India
Ph: 91 1341 230098
E-mail: najibabad@aair.org.in
Format: Eclectic. **Owner:** Prasar Bharati, Akashvani Bhavan, Sansad Marg, New Delhi 110 001, Delhi, India, 91 11 23421006, Fax: 91 11 23421956. **Founded:** 1978. **Key Personnel:** M.C. Aggarwal, Engr.-in-Ch., phone 91 11 23421058, fax 91 11 23421006, einc@air.org.in. **Wattage:** 100,000. **Ad Rates:** $150-300 for 10 seconds; $225-450 for 15 seconds; $450-900 for 30 seconds; $900-1,800 for 60 seconds. **URL:** http://www.allindiaradio.org.

Nanded

45472 ■ All India Radio Nanded - 101.1 MHz
Vasrani
Nanded 431 603, Maharashtra, India
Ph: 91 2462 226623
E-mail: airnanded@vsnl.com
Format: Eclectic. **Owner:** Prasar Bharati, Akashvani Bhavan, Sansad Marg, New Delhi 110 001, Delhi, India, 91 11 23421006, Fax: 91 11 23421956. **Founded:** 1991. **Key Personnel:** M.C. Aggarwal, Engr.-in-Ch., phone 91 11 23421058, fax 91 11 23421006, einc@air.org.in. **Wattage:** 6000. **Ad Rates:** $80-150 for 10 seconds; $120-225 for 15 seconds; $240-450 for 30 seconds; $480-900 for 60 seconds. **URL:** http://www.allindiaradio.org.

Nasik

45473 ■ Abhivyakti and Expressions
Abhivyakti Media for Development
31-A, Survey No. 8, Kalyani Nagar
Anandvali Shiwar, Gangapur Rd.
Nasik 422 005, Maharashtra, India
Ph: 91 253 346128
Publisher E-mail: amdnsk@vsnl.com
English and Marathi language publication covering developmental education. **Freq:** Quarterly. **URL:** http://www.abhivyakti.org.in. **Circ:** 1,000

45474 ■ All India Radio Nasik - 101.4 KHz
Gangapur Rd.
Nasik 422 005, Maharashtra, India
Ph: 91 253 2342774
E-mail: airnsk_nsk@sancharnet.in
Format: Eclectic. **Owner:** Prasar Bharati, Akashvani Bhavan, Sansad Marg, New Delhi 110 001, Delhi, India, 91 11 23421006, Fax: 91 11 23421956. **Founded:** 1994. **Key Personnel:** M.C. Aggarwal, Engr.-in-Ch., phone 91 11 23421058, fax 91 11 23421006, einc@air.org.in; Mohan Singh, Ch. Engr., Proj., phone 91 11 23421184. **Wattage:** 6000. **Ad Rates:** $80-150 for 10 seconds; $120-225 for 15 seconds; $240-450 for 30 seconds; $480-900 for 60 seconds. **URL:** http://www.allindiaradio.org.

45475 ■ Indian Growth and Development Review
Emerald Group Publishing Ltd.
Indian Statistical Industry, Delhi Ctr.
7 SJS Sansanwal Marg
New Delhi 1100116, India
Publisher E-mail: emerald@emeraldinsight.com
Journal publishing high quality peer reviewed articles on economic growth and development. **Freq:** Annual. **Key Personnel:** Prof. Satya P. Das, Editor, igdr@isid.ac.in; Kelly Dutton, Publisher, kdutton@emeraldinsight.com. **ISSN:** 1753-8254. **URL:** http://info.emeraldinsight.com/products/journals/journals.htm?id=igdr.

New Delhi (Delhi)

45476 ■ Abhigyan
Foundation for Organisational Research and Education
Adhitam Kendra
B-18 Qutab Institutional Area
New Delhi 110 016, Delhi, India
Ph: 91 11 41242424
Fax: 91 11 26964229
Publisher E-mail: mareena@fsm.ac.in
Social science periodical. **Subtitle:** Asia's Leading

Journal on Management & Organizations. **Founded:** 1983. **Freq:** Quarterly Latest edition July-September 2009. **ISSN:** 0970-2385. **Remarks:** Accepts advertising. **URL:** http://www.fsm.ac.in/pub_abhigyan.html. **Ad Rates:** BW: Rs 6,000. **Circ:** Paid 500

45477 ■ Advances in Dynamical Systems and Applications
Research India Publications
D1/71, Top Fl., Rohini Sec-16
New Delhi 110 089, Delhi, India
Ph: 91 11 65394240
Fax: 91 11 27297815
Publisher E-mail: info@ripublication.com
Journal covering differential and dynamic equations and their applications. **Founded:** 1981. **Freq:** Semiannual. **Print Method:** Web press. **Trim Size:** 7 1/8 x 10. **Cols./Page:** 5. **Col. Width:** 24 nonpareils. **Col. Depth:** 186 agate lines. **Key Personnel:** Haydar Akca, Editorial Board; Dr. Martin Bohner, Editor-in-Chief; R.P. Agarwal, Editorial Board. **ISSN:** 0973-5321. **Subscription Rates:** US$280 institutions and library; print plus online free; US$260 institutions and library; online only; US$180 individuals print plus online free; US$140 individuals online only; Rs 1,800 individuals. **URL:** http://www.ripublication.com/adsa.htm.

45478 ■ Africa Quarterly
Indian Council for Cultural Relations
Azad Bhavan
Indraprastha Estate
New Delhi 110 002, Delhi, India
Ph: 91 11 23379309
Fax: 91 11 23378639
Publication E-mail: pdpub@iccrindia.org
Publisher E-mail: webmaster@iccrindia.net
Political journal on Africa. **Freq:** Quarterly. **ISSN:** 0001-9828. **URL:** http://www.iccrindia.net/publications.html. **Circ:** Paid 1,900

45479 ■ Afro-Asian Journal of Rural Development
Afro-Asian Rural Development Organization
2, State Guest Houses Complex
Chanakyapuri
New Delhi 100 021, Delhi, India
Ph: 91 11 24100475
Fax: 91 11 24672045
Publisher E-mail: aardohq@nde.vsnl.net.in
English language publication covering agriculture and rural development issues in AFro-Asian countries. **Founded:** Aug. 1966. **Freq:** Biennial. **Print Method:** Offset. **Key Personnel:** Dr. Bahar Munip, Editor. **ISSN:** 0972-3021. **Subscription Rates:** Rs 500 individuals; US$40 other countries air mail. **Remarks:** Advertising not accepted. **URL:** http://www.aardo.org/. **Circ:** Combined 400

45480 ■ Aim
Evangelical Fellowship of India
805/92 Deepali Bldg.
Nehru Pl.
New Delhi 110 019, Delhi, India
Ph: 91 11 26431133
Fax: 91 11 26285350
Publisher E-mail: mail@efionline.org
Periodical on religion. **Freq:** Monthly. **Key Personnel:** Solomon R. John, Managing Editor. **Subscription Rates:** Rs 100 individuals. **Remarks:** Accepts advertising. **URL:** http://www.efionline.org. **Ad Rates:** BW: Rs 1,200. **Circ:** Combined 3,300

45481 ■ AIOE Labour News
All India Organisation of Employers
Federation House
Tansen Marg
New Delhi 110 001, Delhi, India
Ph: 91 112 3738770
Fax: 91 112 3320714
Publisher E-mail: info@councilofindianemployers.com
Periodical on labor and industrial relations. **Freq:** Monthly. **Key Personnel:** R. C. Pande, Editor. **ISSN:** 0001-1630. **Subscription Rates:** Rs 1395; US$30 other countries. **Remarks:** Accepts advertising. **URL:** http://www.ioe-emp.org/en/members-regions/index.html?tx_gsifeuserlist_pi1%5BshowUid%5D=65. **Circ:** Paid 1,000

45482 ■ Algebraic Hyperstructures and Applications
Taru Publications
G-159, Pushkar Enclave

Pashchim Vihar
New Delhi 110 063, Delhi, India
Ph: 91 114 2331159
Fax: 91 114 2321126
Publisher E-mail: info@tarupublications.com
Journal covering fractal dimensions including Box-counting and Hausdorff dimensions. **Key Personnel:** Prof. R. Migliorato, Editor, renato.migliorato@unime.it; Prof. P. Corsini, Editor, corsini@dimi.uniud.it; Prof. Mario Gionfriddo, Editor, gionfriddo@dmi.unict.it; Prof. Bal Kishan Dass, Editor, bkdass@tarupublications.com. **Subscription Rates:** Rs 1,200 individuals within India; US$60 out of country outside India. **URL:** http://www.tarupublications.com/books/aha/aha.htm.

45483 ■ Annals of Cardiac Anaesthesia
Indian Association of Cardiovascular Thoracic Anaesthesiologists
624, Academic Block
GB Pant Hospital
New Delhi 110 002, Delhi, India
Ph: 91 112 3232877
Publisher E-mail: ancard@hotmail.com
Journal dedicated to cardiac anesthesia. **Founded:** 1923. **Freq:** Biennial. **Print Method:** Offset. **Trim Size:** 13 x 21 1/2. **Cols./Page:** 6. **Key Personnel:** Dr. Deepak K. Tempe, Ch. Ed.; Dr. A.S. Tomar, Editor; Dr. Pragati Ganjoo, Editor. **ISSN:** 0971-9784. **URL:** http://medind.nic.in/aad/aadm.shtml.

45484 ■ Artha Suchi
National Council of Applied Economic Research
Parisila Bhawan
11 Indraprastha Estate
New Delhi 110 002, Delhi, India
Ph: 91 11 23379861
Fax: 91 11 23370164
Publisher E-mail: infor@ncaer.org
Bibliographic indexed abstracts of articles on business and economics. **Freq:** Quarterly. **Key Personnel:** N.J. Sebastian, Editor. **ISSN:** 0970-8162. **Subscription Rates:** 300 individuals; US$80 other countries. **URL:** http://www.ncaer.org/journals.html. **Circ:** Paid 120

45485 ■ Asia Pacific Tech Monitor
Asian and Pacific Centre for Transfer of Technology
C-2 Qutab Institutional Area
PO Box 4575
New Delhi 110 016, Delhi, India
Ph: 91 11 26966509
Fax: 91 11 26856274
Publisher E-mail: postmaster@apctt.org
Periodical on technology, business, economics and environmental science. **Freq:** Bimonthly. **ISSN:** 0256-9957. **Remarks:** Accepts advertising. **URL:** http://www.techmonitor.net/. **Ad Rates:** BW: Rs 7,500, 4C: Rs 10,000. **Circ:** Paid 2,000

45486 ■ The Asian Age
S 7, Green Pk. Main Market
New Delhi 110 016, Delhi, India
Ph: 91 11 2653001
Fax: 91 11 26530027
General newspaper. **Founded:** 1994. **Freq:** Daily. **Key Personnel:** M.J. Akbar, Ed.-in-Ch./Mng. Dir. **Remarks:** Accepts advertising. **URL:** http://www.asianage.com/. **Circ:** 6,722

45487 ■ Asso Cham Bulletin
Associated Chambers of Commerce and Industry of India
Corporate Office, 1, Community Ctr. Zamrudpur
Kailash Colony
New Delhi 110 048, Delhi, India
Ph: 91 11 46550555
Fax: 91 11 46536481
Publisher E-mail: assocham@nic.in
Commerce periodical. **Freq:** Monthly. **Key Personnel:** T. S. Sampat Kumar, Editor. **Subscription Rates:** Rs 1,500 individuals. **Remarks:** Accepts advertising. **URL:** http://www.assocham.org/publications/per.php. **Ad Rates:** BW: Rs 4,000, 4C: Rs 6,000. **Circ:** Paid 9,000

45488 ■ Asso Cham News & Views
Associated Chambers of Commerce and Industry of India
Corporate Office, 1, Community Ctr. Zamrudpur
Kailash Colony
New Delhi 110 048, Delhi, India
Ph: 91 11 46550555
Fax: 91 11 46536481

Publisher E-mail: assocham@nic.in
Commerce periodical. **Freq:** Weekly. **Subscription Rates:** Rs 2,000 individuals. **Remarks:** Accepts advertising. **URL:** http://www.assocham.org/publications/per.php. **Ad Rates:** BW: Rs 2,000, 4C: Rs 3,000. **Circ:** Paid 1,500

45489 ■ Biology Today
MTG Learning Media (P) Ltd.
406, Taj Apt., Ring Rd.
Near Safdarjung Hospital
New Delhi 110 029, Delhi, India
Ph: 91 11 46686000
Fax: 91 26 191601
Publisher E-mail: info@mtg.in
Biology publication covering study material for exams in India. **Freq:** Monthly. **Subscription Rates:** Rs 1,470 individuals; Rs 2,695 two years. **URL:** http://www.pcmbtoday.com/mtgpp/biology/sep2007.php.

45490 ■ Business Today
Living Media India Ltd.
c/o Chaitanya Kalbag, Ed.
Videocon Tower, 5th Fl.
E-1 Jhandewalan Ext.
New Delhi 110 055, Delhi, India
Publisher E-mail: malcolm.mistry@intoday.com
Periodical covering business news. **Founded:** 1992. **Freq:** Biweekly. **Key Personnel:** Chaitanya Kalbag, Editor, ashish.bagga@intoday.com; Ashish Bagga, CEO, ashish.bagga@intoday.com. **Subscription Rates:** Rs 370 individuals. **Remarks:** Accepts advertising. **URL:** http://businesstoday.digitaltoday.in. **Circ:** Paid 127,378

45491 ■ Champak (English)
Delhi Press Patra Prakashan Ltd.
E-3 Jhandewala Estate
New Delhi 110 055, Delhi, India
Ph: 91 112 3529557
Fax: 91 112 3625020
Children's magazine (English). **Founded:** 1975. **Freq:** Fortnightly. **ISSN:** 0971-1651. **Subscription Rates:** Rs 300 individuals print only; Rs 1,435 other countries print only; Rs 15 single issue. **Remarks:** Advertising accepted; rates available upon request. **URL:** http://www.womansera.com/shop/cheng.aspx?cat=. **Circ:** Paid 34,185

45492 ■ Champak (Gujarati)
Delhi Press Patra Prakashan Ltd.
E-3 Jhandewala Estate
New Delhi 110 055, Delhi, India
Ph: 91 112 3529557
Fax: 91 112 3625020
Children's magazine (Gujarati). **Founded:** 1972. **Freq:** Biweekly. **Subscription Rates:** Rs 10 single issue print copy; Rs 225 individuals print copy; Rs 1,230 other countries print copy. **Remarks:** Advertising accepted; rates available upon request. **URL:** http://www.womansera.com/shop/chguj.aspx?cat=. **Circ:** Paid 10,000

45493 ■ Champak (Hindi)
Delhi Press Patra Prakashan Ltd.
E-3 Jhandewala Estate
New Delhi 110 055, Delhi, India
Ph: 91 112 3529557
Fax: 91 112 3625020
Children's magazine (Hindi). **Founded:** 1968. **Freq:** Biweekly. **Subscription Rates:** Rs 300 individuals print copy; Rs 1,435 other countries; Rs 15 single issue. **Remarks:** Advertising accepted; rates available upon request. **URL:** http://www.womansera.com/shop/chhid.aspx?cat=. **Circ:** Paid 71,705

45494 ■ Champak (Kannada)
Delhi Press Patra Prakashan Ltd.
E-3 Jhandewala Estate
New Delhi 110 055, Delhi, India
Ph: 91 112 3529557
Fax: 91 112 3625020
Children's magazine (Kannada). **Founded:** 1992. **Freq:** Monthly. **Subscription Rates:** Rs 10 single issue print copy; Rs 1,230 other countries print copy; Rs 225 individuals print copy. **Remarks:** Advertising accepted; rates available upon request. **URL:** http://www.womansera.com/shop/chkan.aspx?cat=. **Circ:** Paid 10,000

45495 ■ Champak (Marathi)
Delhi Press Patra Prakashan Ltd.
E-3 Jhandewala Estate
New Delhi 110 055, Delhi, India
Ph: 91 112 3529557
Fax: 91 112 3625020
Children's magazine (Marathi). **Founded:** 1971. **Freq:** Biweekly. **Subscription Rates:** Rs 10 single issue print copy; Rs 1,230 other countries print copy; Rs 225 individuals print copy. **Remarks:** Advertising accepted; rates available upon request. **URL:** http://www.womansera.com; http://www.womansera.com/shop/chmrt.aspx?cat=. **Circ:** Paid 17,000

45496 ■ Chemistry Today
MTG Learning Media (P) Ltd.
406, Taj Apt., Ring Rd.
Near Safdarjung Hospital
New Delhi 110 029, Delhi, India
Ph: 91 11 46686000
Fax: 91 26 191601
Publisher E-mail: info@mtg.in
Chemistry publication featuring study material for IIT-JEE exams in India. **Freq:** Monthly. **Subscription Rates:** Rs 1,470 individuals; Rs 2,695 two years. **URL:** http://www.pcmbtoday.com/mtgpp/chem/sep2007.php.

45497 ■ Computers Today
Living Media India Ltd.
201 Competent House
F-14, Connaught Pl.
New Delhi 110 001, Delhi, India
Publication E-mail: ctoday@india-today.com
Publisher E-mail: malcolm.mistry@intoday.com
Periodical covering the infotech sector. **Subtitle:** India's Widely Read Infotech Magazine. **Founded:** 1985. **Freq:** Biweekly. **Trim Size:** 27.5 x 20 cm. **ISSN:** 0970-0129. **Remarks:** Accepts advertising. **URL:** http://indiatoday.intoday.in/site/. **Circ:** Paid 49,134

45498 ■ Contributions to Himalayan Geology
Hindustan Publishing Corp.
4805 Bharat Ram Rd.
24 Darya Ganj
New Delhi 110 002, Delhi, India
Ph: 91 113 254401
Fax: 91 116 193511
Publisher E-mail: hpcpd@hpc.cc
Periodical covering the earth sciences and geology, with a focus on the Himalayas. **Founded:** 1979. **Freq:** Irregular. **ISSN:** 0970-5325. **URL:** http://www.thebookservice.com/home.htm.

45499 ■ Contributions to Indian Sociology
Sage Publications India Private Ltd.
B-1/I-1 Mohan Cooperative Industrial Area
Mathura Rd.
New Delhi 110 044, Delhi, India
Ph: 91 11 40539222
Fax: 91 11 40539234
Publisher E-mail: info@sagepub.in
Journal presenting different theoretical approaches of studying society in India. **Founded:** 1957. **Freq:** 3/yr. **Key Personnel:** Amita Baviskar, Editor; Veena Narogal, Review Ed.; Nandini Sundar, Editor. **ISSN:** 0069-9667. **Subscription Rates:** US$374 institutions combined (print & e-access); US$40 single issue; US$337 institutions e-access; US$374 institutions backfile lease, e-access; US$917 institutions backfile purchase, e-access; US$367 institutions print only; US$93 individuals print only; US$135 institutions single print. **Remarks:** Accepts advertising. **URL:** http://www.sagepub.com/journalsProdDesc.nav?prodId=Journal200929. **Circ:** 900

45500 ■ Cooperator
National Cooperative Union of India
3 Siri Institutional Area
August Kranti Marg
New Delhi 110 016, Delhi, India
Ph: 91 11 26861472
Fax: 91 11 26863248
Publisher E-mail: ncuidel@ndb.vsnl.net.in
Journal on economics. **Founded:** 1963. **Freq:** Monthly. **ISSN:** 0010-8464. **Subscription Rates:** Rs 300 individuals; US$50 other countries; Rs 30 single issue. **Remarks:** Accepts advertising. **URL:** http://www.ncui.net/. **Ad Rates:** BW: Rs 5,000. **Circ:** 2,700

45501 ■ Cosmopolitan (India)
Living Media India Ltd.
c/o Payal Puri, Ed.
Videocon Tower, 5th Fl.
E-1 Jhandewalan Ext.
New Delhi 110 055, Delhi, India
Publisher E-mail: malcolm.mistry@intoday.com
Periodical providing information for working women. **Founded:** 1996. **Freq:** Monthly. **Subscription Rates:** Rs 900 individuals; Rs 1,560 two years. **Remarks:** Accepts advertising. **URL:** http://cosmo.intoday.in/cosmopolitan/index.jsp. **Circ:** Paid ★78,000

45502 ■ Current Consumer Cases
International Law Book Co.
1562 Church Rd.
Kashmere Gate
New Delhi 110 006, Delhi, India
Ph: 91 11 3867810
Fax: 91 11 23864769
Publisher E-mail: ilbco@vsnl.com
Law periodical covering consumer cases. **Founded:** 1994. **Freq:** Monthly. **Subscription Rates:** Rs 1,500 individuals. **URL:** http://www.supremecourtcaselaw.com/CCC.htm.

45503 ■ Down To Earth
Society for Environmental Communications
41, Tughlakabad Institutional Area
New Delhi 110062, Delhi, India
Ph: 91 11 29955124
Fax: 91 11 29955879
Publisher E-mail: editor@downtoearth.org.in
Magazine highlighting environmental threats in India and the world. **Founded:** May 1992. **Freq:** Biweekly. **Key Personnel:** Sunita Narain, Editor. **Subscription Rates:** Rs 360 individuals print only; US$48 individuals print only; Rs 315 individuals online only; US$7 individuals online only; Rs 660 two years print only; US$77 two years print only; Rs 585 two years online only; US$13 two years online only. **Remarks:** Accepts advertising. **URL:** http://www.downtoearth.org.in/default.htm. **Circ:** (Not Reported)

45504 ■ Drugs Cases
International Law Book Co.
1562 Church Rd.
Kashmere Gate
New Delhi 110 006, Delhi, India
Ph: 91 11 3867810
Fax: 91 11 23864769
Publisher E-mail: ilbco@vsnl.com
Periodical covering legal, medical, and pharmacological issues. **Freq:** Monthly. **Subscription Rates:** Rs 10,800 individuals; US$960 other countries. **URL:** http://www.supremecourtcaselaw.com/DC_Full_Set.htm.

45505 ■ The Economic Times
Bennet, Coleman & Company Ltd.
Times House
7 Bahadurshah Zafar Marg
New Delhi 400 002, Delhi, India
Ph: 91 11 23302000
Financial news daily. **Founded:** 1990. **Freq:** Mon.-Sat. **Subscription Rates:** Rs 2 Mon. Fri.; Rs 6 Sat. **Remarks:** Accepts advertising. **URL:** http://economictimes.indiatimes.com/. **Circ:** Paid 19,804, Combined 400,000

45506 ■ Electronics For You
EFY Enterprises Private Ltd.
D-87/1
Okhla Industrial Area Phase-I
New Delhi 110 020, Delhi, India
Ph: 91 11 26810601
Fax: 91 11 26817563
Publisher E-mail: info@efyindia.com
Periodical covering the electronics field. **Founded:** Jan. 1969. **Freq:** Monthly. **Key Personnel:** Mr. Ramesh Chopra, CEO, efy@vsnl.com. **ISSN:** 0013-516X. **Subscription Rates:** Rs 650 individuals 12 copies, 1 year; Rs 1,945 individuals 36 copies, 3 years; Rs 3,240 individuals 60 copies, 6 years. **Remarks:** Accepts advertising. **URL:** http://www.electronicsforu.com/electronicsforu/default.asp. **Circ:** Paid 47,151

45507 ■ Employment News
Ministry of Information & Broadcasting
Assistant Business Manager
Employment News

Circulation: ★ = ABC; △ = BPA; ◆ = CAC; • = CCAB; ❑ = VAC; ⊕ = PO Statement; ‡ = Publisher's Report; Boldface figures = sworn; Light figures = estimated.

Gale Directory of Publications & Broadcast Media/147th Ed.

5023

E Block IV
R.K. Puram
New Delhi 110 066, Delhi, India
Publication E-mail: editor_rc@yahoo.co.in
Publisher E-mail: jsp.inb@nic.in
Government publication on business, economics and Careers. **Founded:** 1976. **Freq:** Weekly. **Key Personnel:** Suryakant Sharma, Business Mgr. **Subscription Rates:** Rs 350 individuals. **URL:** http://www.employmentnews.gov.in/. **Circ:** Paid 426,000

45508 ■ Endontology
Indian Endodontic Society
C-44, Gulmohan Pk.
New Delhi 110 049, Delhi, India
Ph: 91 22 23082714
Fax: 91 22 25243223
Publisher E-mail: bangaks@vsnl.com
Journal aiming at improving the standard of endodontic research, teaching and clinical practice in India, dedicated to the continuing professional development in the speciality of endodontics. **Subtitle:** Journal of Indian Endodontic Society. **Freq:** Semiannual. **Key Personnel:** Dr. B. Sureshchandra, Editor. **Subscription Rates:** Rs 300 individuals; US$25 other countries; Rs 500 institutions; US$50 institutions, other countries. **URL:** http://medind.nic.in/eaa/eaam.shtml.

45509 ■ Energy Management
National Productivity Council
Utpadakta Bhawan, 5-6 Institutional Area
Lodhi Rd.
New Delhi 110 003, Delhi, India
Ph: 91 112 4690331
Fax: 91 112 4615002
Publisher E-mail: info@npcindia.org
Management oriented periodical on the energy industry. **Founded:** 1977. **Freq:** Quarterly. **ISSN:** 0970-289X. **URL:** http://www.npcindia.org/Energy_Management.htm. **Circ:** Paid 1,500

45510 ■ Epigraphia Indica
Archaeological Society of India
B-17, Qutab Institutional Area
New Delhi 110 016, Delhi, India
Ph: 91 11 26523728
Fax: 91 11 26960654
Archaeology periodical. **Founded:** 1888. **Freq:** Irregular. **Key Personnel:** K. G. Krishnan, Editor, asi@del3.vsnl.net.in. **ISSN:** 0013-9564. **Subscription Rates:** Rs 64. **URL:** http://asi.nic.in/asi_publ_epigraphical_indica.asp. **Circ:** Paid 740

45511 ■ Facts for You
EFY Enterprises Private Ltd.
D-87/1
Okhla Industrial Area Phase-I
New Delhi 110 020, Delhi, India
Ph: 91 11 26810601
Fax: 91 11 26817563
Publisher E-mail: info@efyindia.com
Periodical covering business and economics. **Founded:** 1979. **Freq:** Monthly. **ISSN:** 0970-2652. **Subscription Rates:** Rs 1,200 individuals; Rs 2,330 individuals 3 years; Rs 3,290 individuals 5 years. **Remarks:** Accepts advertising. **URL:** http://www.ffymag.com/index.asp?id=18. **Ad Rates:** BW: Rs 14,000; 4C: Rs 20,000. **Circ:** Paid 5,000

45512 ■ FAI Abstract Service
Fertiliser Association of India
10 Shaheed Jit Singh Marg
New Delhi 110 067, Delhi, India
Ph: 91 11 26567144
Fax: 91 11 26960052
Publisher E-mail: general@faidelhi.org
Science digest covering the areas of agriculture and animal husbandry. **Founded:** 1962. **Freq:** Monthly. **Print Method:** Offset. **Trim Size:** 24 x 18.5 cm. **ISSN:** 0014-5564. **Subscription Rates:** Rs 10 single issue; Rs 100 individuals. **URL:** http://www.faidelhi.org/content.htm. **Circ:** Paid 2,200

45513 ■ Fertiliser Association of India's Fertiliser Statistics
Fertiliser Association of India
10 Shaheed Jit Singh Marg
New Delhi 110 067, Delhi, India
Ph: 91 11 26567144
Fax: 91 11 26960052

Publisher E-mail: general@faidelhi.org
Periodical covering technology in agriculture and animal husbandry; contains statistics on fertilizer and agriculture. **Founded:** 1956. **Freq:** Annual. **Print Method:** Offset. **Trim Size:** 20 x 15 cm. **ISSN:** 0971-0787. **Subscription Rates:** Rs 1,000 nonmembers hard copy or CD; Rs 800 members hard copy or CD; US$85 other countries hard copy or CD; US$110 individuals hard copy or CD. **Remarks:** Accepts advertising. **URL:** http://www.faidelhi.org/content.htm. **Ad Rates:** BW: US$200, 4C: US$300, PCI: US$600. **Circ:** 2,000

45514 ■ Fertiliser Marketing News
Fertiliser Association of India
10 Shaheed Jit Singh Marg
New Delhi 110 067, Delhi, India
Ph: 91 11 26567144
Fax: 91 11 26960052
Publisher E-mail: general@faidelhi.org
Periodical on the marketing of fertilizers. **Founded:** 1970. **Freq:** Monthly. **Print Method:** Offset. **Trim Size:** 24 x 18.5 cm. **ISSN:** 0257-8034. **Subscription Rates:** Rs 20 single issue; Rs 200 individuals; US$35 other countries including postage by airmail. **Remarks:** Accepts advertising. **URL:** http://www.faidelhi.org/content.htm. **Ad Rates:** 4C: US$2,600. **Circ:** Paid 3,000

45515 ■ Finance India
Indian Institute of Finance
Ashok Vihar
PO Box 8486
New Delhi 110 052, Delhi, India
Ph: 91 11 27136257
Fax: 91 11 27454128
Publication E-mail: aa@iif.edu
Publisher E-mail: aa@iif.edu
Academic/scholarly publication covering Business, economics, banking and accounting. **Founded:** 1987. **Freq:** Quarterly. **Print Method:** Offset. **Trim Size:** 8 x 4 1/2. **Key Personnel:** Prof. Aman Agarwal, Assoc. Ed.; Prof. J.D. Agarwal, Ch. Ed. **ISSN:** 0970-3772. **Subscription Rates:** Rs 1,500 individuals; Rs 1,800 institutions; US$100 other countries U.S./Euro; US$120 institutions, other countries U.S./Euro; US$50 single issue back issue. **Remarks:** Accepts advertising. **URL:** http://www.financeindia.org/fi.htm. **Ad Rates:** BW: Rs 10,000. **Circ:** Paid 1,200

45516 ■ The Financial Express
Indian Express Newspapers (Bombay) Ltd.
9&10, Bhadur Shah Zafar Marg
Express Bldg.
New Delhi 110002, Delhi, India
Ph: 91 11 23702618
Fax: 91 11 23702141
Publisher E-mail: editor@expressindia.com
Financial newspaper. **Founded:** 1961. **Freq:** Daily. **ISSN:** 0015-2005. **Subscription Rates:** Rs 4 Mon.-Sat.; Rs 8 Sun. **Remarks:** Accepts advertising. **Online:** Gale. **URL:** http://www.financialexpress.com/. **Circ:** Paid 11,991

45517 ■ Folklore Research Journal
Hindustan Publishing Corp.
4805 Bharat Ram Rd.
24 Darya Ganj
New Delhi 110 002, Delhi, India
Ph: 91 113 254401
Fax: 91 116 193511
Publisher E-mail: hpcpd@hpc.cc
Scholarly publication covering social science; focuses on folklore and mythology research. **Founded:** 1995. **Freq:** Triennial. **Key Personnel:** Moira Smith, Editor; Danille Elise Christensen, Managing Editor. **ISSN:** 0737-7037. **URL:** http://inscribe.iupress.org/loi/jfr.

45518 ■ Gas News
All India Industrial Gases Manufacturers Association
66 Masjid Moth, 2nd Fl.
Near Uday Pk.
New Delhi 110 049, Delhi, India
Ph: 91 11 26251688
Fax: 91 11 26255732
Publisher E-mail: aiigma@vsnl.com
Publication covering gases. **Freq:** Bimonthly. **Subscription Rates:** Rs 500 individuals. **Remarks:** Advertising accepted; rates available upon request. **URL:** http://www.aiigma.org. **Circ:** (Not Reported)

45519 ■ Gender, Technology & Development
Sage Publications India Private Ltd.
B-1/I-1 Mohan Cooperative Industrial Area
Mathura Rd.
New Delhi 110 044, Delhi, India
Ph: 91 11 40539222
Fax: 91 11 40539234
Publisher E-mail: info@sagepub.com
An international, refereed journal exploring the linkages between changing gender relations and technological development. **Founded:** 1997. **Freq:** 3/yr. **Print Method:** Offset. **Key Personnel:** Cecilia Ng, Editor; Nirmala Banerjee, Advisory Board; Thanh-Dam Truong, Advisory Board; Bernadette Resurreccion, Editor; Kyoko Kusakabe, Editor; Mari Osawa, Advisory Board; Mary Ann Pama, Editorial Asst.; Donna Haraway, Advisory Board. **ISSN:** 0971-8524. **Subscription Rates:** US$335 institutions combined, print & e-access; US$35 single issue print only; US$302 institutions e-access; US$336 institutions all online; US$302 institutions backfile purchase, e-access; US$328 institutions print only; US$81 individuals print only; US$120 single issue institution. **Remarks:** Accepts advertising. **URL:** http://www.sagepub.com/journalsProdDesc.nav?prodId=Journal200816. **Ad Rates:** BW: Rs 100. **Circ:** 400

45520 ■ Global Review of Business and Economic Research
Serials Publications
4830-24 Ansari Rd.
Darya Ganj
New Delhi 110 002, Delhi, India
Ph: 91 11 23245225
Fax: 91 11 23272135
Publisher E-mail: serials@satyam.net.in
Peer-reviewed journal covering advanced concepts, initial treatments and fundamental research in fields of business and economics. **Freq:** Semiannual. **Key Personnel:** Dr. Mazhar M. Islam, Editor, mazhar.islam@famu.edu; Shawkat Hammoudeh, Assoc. Ed.; Jeffrey B. Nugent, Assoc. Ed. **ISSN:** 0973-127X. **Subscription Rates:** US$125 institutions print. **URL:** http://www.serialspublications.com/journals1.asp?jid=199&jtype=1.

45521 ■ Good Housekeeping
Living Media India Pvt. Ltd.
Videocon Tower, 13th Fl.
E-1, Jhandewalan Ext.
New Delhi 110 055, Delhi, India
Ph: 91 112 3684848
Fax: 91 112 3684841
Publisher E-mail: wecare@intoday.com
Magazine of interest to women. **Freq:** Monthly. **Subscription Rates:** Rs 1,170 two years; Rs 675 individuals. **URL:** http://subscriptions.digitaltoday.in/subscriptions/goodhousekeeping/goodhouse.html.

45522 ■ Health and Population
National Institute of Health and Family Welfare
Baba Gang Nath Marg
Munirka
New Delhi 110 067, Delhi, India
Ph: 91 11 26165959
Fax: 91 11 26101623
Publisher E-mail: info.nihfw@nic.in
Medical periodical on reproductive medicine and technology. **Subtitle:** Perspectives and Issues. **Founded:** 1972. **Freq:** Quarterly. **Key Personnel:** Prof. T. Mathiyazhagan, Editor; Prof. K. Kalaivani, Editor-in-Chief; B.C. Patro, Asst. Ed.; Prof. M. Bhattacharya, Contact; Dr. S. Menon, Contact; Dr. Gita Bamezai, Contact; Salek Chand, Contact. **ISSN:** 0253-6803. **Subscription Rates:** Rs 500 individuals life membership; Rs 100 individuals; Rs 25 individuals single copy; US$100 other countries foreign (including air mail postage). **Remarks:** Accepts advertising. **URL:** http://www.nihfw.org/Publications/Journal/Journal.html. **Circ:** Paid 1,000

45523 ■ Highway Research Record
Indian Roads Congress
Jamnagar House
Shahjahan Rd.
New Delhi 110 011, Delhi, India
Ph: 91 112 6716778
Fax: 91 112 6183669
Publisher E-mail: secretary@irc.org.in
General trade publication on civil engineering, transportation and the automobile industry. **Founded:** 1974.

Freq: Annual. **ISSN:** 0970-2598. **URL:** http://www.irc.org.in. **Circ:** Paid 8,500

45524 ■ The Hindu
Kasturi & Sons Ltd.
210 2nd Fl.
Ansal Bhavan
16 Kasturba Gandhi Marg
New Delhi 110 001, Delhi, India
Publisher E-mail: bleditor@thehindu.co.in
General newspaper. **Founded:** 1878. **Freq:** Daily. **Subscription Rates:** Rs 463 individuals half yearly, through news agent; Rs 594 individuals half yearly, by post; Rs 929 individuals through news agent; Rs 1,192 individuals by post. **Remarks:** Accepts advertising. **URL:** http://www.hindu.com. **Circ:** 1,180,000

45525 ■ ICMR Bulletin
Indian Council of Medical Research
Division of Publication & Information
V. Ramalingaswami Bhawan
Ansari Nagar
New Delhi 110 029, Delhi, India
Ph: 91 112 6588895
Fax: 91 112 6588662
Publisher E-mail: icmrhqds@sansad.nic.in
Medical science bulletin providing medical research articles, seminar and training program calendars. **Freq:** Monthly. **Key Personnel:** Dr. K. Satyanarayana, Editor; Dr. V.M. Katoch, Director. **ISSN:** 0377-4910. **URL:** http://www.icmr.nic.in/bulletin.htm. **Circ:** Paid 7,500

45526 ■ ICSSR Journal of Abstracts and Reviews
Indian Council of Social Science Research
J.N.U. Institutional Area
Aruna Asaf Ali Marg
New Delhi 110 067, Delhi, India
Ph: 91 11 26179849
Fax: 91 11 26179836
Publisher E-mail: info@icssr.org
Publication of abstracts of articles from Indian political science periodicals. **Subtitle:** Political Science. **Freq:** Semiannual. **Key Personnel:** S.K. Chaubey, Editor, info@icssr.org. **ISSN:** 0250-9660. **Remarks:** Accepts advertising. **URL:** http://www.icssr.org/rsp_main.htm. **Formerly:** ICSSR Journal of Abstracts and Reviews. **Circ:** Paid 550

45527 ■ ICSSR Journal of Abstracts and Reviews
Indian Council of Social Science Research
J.N.U. Institutional Area
Aruna Asaf Ali Marg
New Delhi 110 067, Delhi, India
Ph: 91 11 26179849
Fax: 91 11 26179836
Publisher E-mail: info@icssr.org
Journal of selected book reviews on sociology and social anthropology including criminology. **Subtitle:** Sociology and Social Anthropology. **Freq:** Semiannual. **Key Personnel:** Karuna Ahmed, Editor. **ISSN:** 0302-7546. **Subscription Rates:** Rs 30 single issue; Rs 50 institutions. **URL:** http://www.icssr.org/rsp_main.htm. **Formerly:** ICSSR Journal of Abstracts and Reviews. **Circ:** Paid 450

45528 ■ ICSSR Journal of Abstracts and Reviews
Indian Council of Social Science Research
J.N.U. Institutional Area
Aruna Asaf Ali Marg
New Delhi 110 067, Delhi, India
Ph: 91 11 26179849
Fax: 91 11 26179836
Publisher E-mail: info@icssr.org
Publication of abstracts of articles on Indian business, economics and statistics periodicals. **Subtitle:** Economics. **Freq:** Semiannual. **Key Personnel:** A.K. Singh, Editor, info@icssr.org. **ISSN:** 0250-9695. **Remarks:** Accepts advertising. **URL:** http://www.icssr.org/rsp_main.htm. **Formerly:** ICSSR Journal of Abstracts and Reviews. **Circ:** Paid 550

45529 ■ ICSSR Journal of Abstracts and Reviews
Indian Council of Social Science Research
J.N.U. Institutional Area
Aruna Asaf Ali Marg
New Delhi 110 067, Delhi, India
Ph: 91 11 26179849

Fax: 91 11 26179836
Publisher E-mail: info@icssr.org
Publication of abstracts of research articles on geography published in Indian journals. **Subtitle:** Geography. **Freq:** Semiannual. **Key Personnel:** Dr. Arun P. Bali, Managing Editor, icssredcell@hotmail.com; Prof. T.N. Madan, Editor-in-Chief. **ISSN:** 0250-9687. **Remarks:** Accepts advertising. **URL:** http://www.icssr.org/journals.htm. **Formerly:** ICSSR Journal of Abstracts and Reviews. **Circ:** Paid 550

45530 ■ IETE Journal of Education
Institution of Electronics and Telecommunication Engineers
2 Institutional Area
Lodi Rd.
New Delhi 110 003, Delhi, India
Ph: 91 11 43538800
Fax: 91 11 24649429
Publisher E-mail: ietend@giasdl01.vsnl.net.in
Educational magazine. **Freq:** Quarterly. **Trim Size:** 11 x 8. **Key Personnel:** Ranjan Bose, Editor-in-Chief; Jayanta Basak, Editor, bjayanta@in.ibm.com. **ISSN:** 0970-1664. **Subscription Rates:** Rs 250 individuals; US$35 other countries. **Remarks:** Accepts advertising. **URL:** http://je.ietejournals.org/. **Ad Rates:** BW: Rs 8,000. **Circ:** Paid 25,000

45531 ■ IETE Journal of Research
Institution of Electronics and Telecommunication Engineers
2 Institutional Area
Lodi Rd.
New Delhi 110 003, Delhi, India
Ph: 91 11 43538800
Fax: 91 11 24649429
Publisher E-mail: ietend@giasdl01.vsnl.net.in
Technological and telecommunication magazine. **Founded:** 2001. **Freq:** Bimonthly. **Trim Size:** 11 x 8. **Key Personnel:** Prof. Shiban Kishen Koul, Editor-in-Chief, eicjr@ietejournals.org; Arun Kumar, Editor. **ISSN:** 0377-2063. **Subscription Rates:** Rs 150 individuals; US$140 individuals. **URL:** http://jr.ietejournals.org/. **Circ:** Paid 2,000

45532 ■ IETE Technical Review
Institution of Electronics and Telecommunication Engineers
2 Institutional Area
Lodi Rd.
New Delhi 110 003, Delhi, India
Ph: 91 11 43538800
Fax: 91 11 24649429
Publisher E-mail: ietend@giasdl01.vsnl.net.in
Technological and telecommunication magazine. **Freq:** Bimonthly. **Trim Size:** 11 x 8. **Key Personnel:** M. Jagadesh Kumar, Editor-in-Chief, eictr@ietejournals.org; Navakant Bhat, Editor. **ISSN:** 0256-4602. **Subscription Rates:** Rs 750 individuals; US$140 other countries plus air surcharge. **Remarks:** Accepts advertising. **URL:** http://tr.ietejournals.org/. **Ad Rates:** BW: Rs 8,000. **Circ:** Paid 8,000

45533 ■ India Central Statistical Organization Monthly Abstract of Statistics
Central Statistical Organization—India
Sardar Patel Bhavan
Sansad Marg
New Delhi 110 001, Delhi, India
Ph: 91 233 89604
Fax: 91 233 86384
Government publication on statistics with charts and book reviews. **Freq:** Monthly. **ISSN:** 0019-4174. **Subscription Rates:** Rs 648; US$233.28 other countries. **URL:** http://mospi.nic.in/mospi_cso_rept_pubn.htm. **Circ:** Paid 650

45534 ■ India Central Statistical Organization Statistical Abstract
Central Statistical Organization—India
Sardar Patel Bhavan
Sansad Marg
New Delhi 110 001, Delhi, India
Ph: 91 233 89604
Fax: 91 233 86384
Government publication containing statistics with abstracts and indexes. **Founded:** 1951. **Freq:** Annual. **ISSN:** 0073-6155. **URL:** http://mospi.nic.in/mospi_cso_rept_pubn.htm.

45535 ■ India Perspectives
Ministry of External Affairs—India
Rm. 152, A Wing
Shastri Bhavan
New Delhi 110 001, Delhi, India
Ph: 91 112 3389471
Fax: 91 112 3384319
Publisher E-mail: jsxp@mea.gov.in
Magazine focusing on social science. **Founded:** 1988. **Freq:** Monthly. **Key Personnel:** Bharat Bhushan, Editor. **ISSN:** 0970-5074. **URL:** http://meaindia.nic.in/.

45536 ■ Indian Cooperative Review
National Cooperative Union of India
3 Siri Institutional Area
August Kranti Marg
New Delhi 110 016, Delhi, India
Ph: 91 11 26861472
Fax: 91 11 26863248
Publisher E-mail: ncuidel@ndb.vsnl.net.in
Research Journal on Indian co-operatives. **Founded:** 1963. **Freq:** Quarterly. **ISSN:** 0019-4581. **Subscription Rates:** Rs 240 individuals. **Remarks:** Accepts advertising. **URL:** http://www.ncui.net/. **Ad Rates:** BW: Rs 5,000. **Circ:** Paid 1,000

45537 ■ Indian Dairyman
Indian Dairy Association
IDA House
Sector IV
R.K. Puram
New Delhi 110 022, Delhi, India
Ph: 91 116 170781
Fax: 91 116 174719
Publication E-mail: ida@nde.vsnl.net.in
Publisher E-mail: ida@nde.vsnl.net.in
Scientific journal focusing on dairying and animal husbandry. **Founded:** 1949. **Freq:** Monthly. **Print Method:** Offset. **Trim Size:** 28 x 21.5 cm. **Key Personnel:** Mr. Sushil Soni, Editor. **ISSN:** 0019-4603. **Remarks:** Accepts advertising. **URL:** http://www.indairyasso.org. **Ad Rates:** BW: Rs 3,450, 4C: Rs 6,900. **Circ:** Paid 2,000

45538 ■ Indian Defence Review
Lancer Publishers & Distributors
K-32A (F.F) Green Park Main
New Delhi 110 016, Delhi, India
Ph: 91 11 6867339
Fax: 91 11 6862077
Scientific journal on military. **Subtitle:** India's Best Known Military Publication. **Founded:** 1986. **Freq:** Quarterly. **Key Personnel:** Bharat Verma, Editor. **ISSN:** 0970-2512. **Subscription Rates:** Rs 1,000 individuals; US$80 other countries. **Remarks:** Accepts advertising. **URL:** http://www.bharat-rakshak.com/; http://www.lancerpublishers.com/idr.shtml. **Circ:** Paid 4,000

45539 ■ Indian Development Review
Serials Publications
4830-24 Ansari Rd.
Darya Ganj
New Delhi 110 002, Delhi, India
Ph: 91 11 23245225
Fax: 91 11 23272135
Publisher E-mail: serials@satyam.net.in
Journal covering healthcare, education, power, and water supply in India. **Subtitle:** An International Journal of Development Economics. **Freq:** Semiannual. **Key Personnel:** V.B. Jugale, PhD, Editor-in-Chief. **ISSN:** 0972-9437. **Subscription Rates:** US$125 institutions print. **URL:** http://www.serialspublications.com/journals1.asp?jid=200&jtype=1.

45540 ■ Indian Economic and Social History Review
Sage Publications India Private Ltd.
B-1/I-1 Mohan Cooperative Industrial Area
Mathura Rd.
New Delhi 110 044, Delhi, India
Ph: 91 11 40539222
Fax: 91 11 40539234
Publisher E-mail: info@sagepub.in
Journal devoted to the study of the social and economic history of India, and South Asia more generally. **Freq:** Quarterly. **Key Personnel:** Ashutosh Kumar, Editorial Asst.; K.N. Raj, Editorial Advisor; G. Balachandran, Editorial Board; Aparna Basu, Editorial Advisor; Sunil Kumar, Editor; Pankaj Kumar Jha, Editorial Asst. **ISSN:**

Circulation: ★ = ABC; △ = BPA; ◆ = CAC; • = CCAB; ❑ = VAC; ⊕ = PO Statement; ‡ = Publisher's Report; Boldface figures = sworn; Light figures = estimated.

Gale Directory of Publications & Broadcast Media/147th Ed.   **5025**

0019-4646. Subscription Rates: US$453 institutions combined (print & e-access); US$408 institutions e-access; US$444 institutions print only; US$117 individuals print only; US$453 institutions all online content; US$1,214 other countries backfile all online; US$122 single issue print only; US$38 individuals print only. **Remarks:** Accepts advertising. **URL:** http://www.sagepub.com/journalsProdDesc.nav?prodId=Journal201284. **Circ:** Paid 900

45541 ■ Indian Educational Review
National Council of Educational Research and Training
Sri Aurbindo Marg
New Delhi 110 016, Delhi, India
Ph: 91 112 6560620
Fax: 91 112 6868419
Publisher E-mail: proncert@yahoo.co.in
Journal of opinion and research in the field of education. **Freq:** Semiannual. **Key Personnel:** A.K. Singh, Editor. **ISSN:** 0872-561X. **Subscription Rates:** Rs 50 single issue; US$2 single issue; 1 single issue; Rs 100 individuals; US$4 individuals; 2 individuals. **URL:** http://www.ncert.nic.in/html/journals.htm. **Circ:** Paid 1,000

45542 ■ Indian Export Bulletin
India Trade Promotion Organisation
Pragati Bhavan, Pragati Maidan
New Delhi 110 001, Delhi, India
Ph: 91 11 23371540
Fax: 91 11 23371492
Publisher E-mail: itpo@vsnl.com
Magazine on business and economics. **Freq:** Weekly. **Subscription Rates:** Rs 25 single issue. **Remarks:** Accepts advertising. **URL:** http://www.tradeportalofindia.com/contentmgmt/Desktops2.asp?compid=itpo&itemcode=l001. **Circ:** Paid 5,000

45543 ■ The Indian Express
Indian Express Newspapers (Bombay) Ltd.
9&10, Bhadur Shah Zafar Marg
Express Bldg.
New Delhi 110002, Delhi, India
Ph: 91 11 23702618
Fax: 91 11 23702141
Publisher E-mail: editor@expressindia.com
General newspaper. **Founded:** 1977. **Freq:** Daily. **Key Personnel:** Shekhar Gupta, Editor-in-Chief. **Remarks:** Accepts advertising. **URL:** http://www.indianexpress.com/. **Circ:** Paid 76,857

45544 ■ Indian Farming
Indian Council of Agricultural Research
Krishi Anusandhan Bhaven
Dr. Rajendra Prasad Rd.
New Delhi 110 114, Delhi, India
Ph: 91 112 5843657
Publisher E-mail: bmicar@icar.org.in
Scientific journal focusing on agriculture and animal husbandry. **Founded:** 1950. **Freq:** Monthly. **Print Method:** Offset, Trim Size: 22 x 28 cm. **Key Personnel:** V.K. Bharti, Ch. Production Off.; Kuldeep Sharma, Editor. **ISSN:** 0019-4786. **Subscription Rates:** Rs 250 individuals; US$65 individuals; Rs 25 single issue; US$10 single issue. **Remarks:** Accepts advertising. **URL:** http://www.icar.org.in/en/node/217. **Circ:** Paid 51,200

45545 ■ Indian Highways
Indian Roads Congress
Jamnagar House
Shahjahan Rd.
New Delhi 110 011, Delhi, India
Ph: 91 112 6716778
Fax: 91 112 6183669
Publisher E-mail: secretary@irc.org.in
Scientific journal on civil engineering. **Freq:** Monthly. **ISSN:** 0376-7256. **Subscription Rates:** US$42.65 individuals. **Remarks:** Accepts advertising. **URL:** http://www.irc.org.in. **Ad Rates:** BW: Rs 4,500, 4C: Rs 14,000. **Circ:** Paid 6,500

45546 ■ Indian Horticulture
Indian Council of Agricultural Research
Krishi Anusandhan Bhaven
Dr. Rajendra Prasad Rd.
New Delhi 110 114, Delhi, India
Ph: 91 112 5843657
Publisher E-mail: bmicar@icar.org.in
Magazine on gardening. **Freq:** Bimonthly. **ISSN:** 0019-4875. **Subscription Rates:** Rs 125 individuals; US$35

individuals; Rs 25 single issue. **URL:** http://www.icar.org.in/en/node/217. **Circ:** Paid 12,000

45547 ■ Indian Journal of Agricultural Engineering
Indian Council of Agricultural Research
Krishi Anusandhan Bhaven
Dr. Rajendra Prasad Rd.
New Delhi 110 114, Delhi, India
Ph: 91 112 5843657
Publisher E-mail: bmicar@icar.org.in
Publication on agricultural engineering. **Freq:** Quarterly. **ISSN:** 0971-2356. **URL:** http://www.icar.org.in/en/node/208. **Circ:** 4,000

45548 ■ Indian Journal of Agricultural Sciences
Indian Council of Agricultural Research
Krishi Anusandhan Bhaven
Dr. Rajendra Prasad Rd.
New Delhi 110 114, Delhi, India
Ph: 91 112 5843657
Publisher E-mail: bmicar@icar.org.in
Scientific publication on agricultural sciences. **Freq:** Monthly. **Key Personnel:** Kuldeep Sharma, Editor; Sh B. Majumder, Incharge; V.K. Bharti, Ch. Production Off.; Dr. R.P. Sharma, Editor; Sh Hansraj, Info. System Off.; S.K. Joshi, Business Mgr. **ISSN:** 0019-5022. **Subscription Rates:** Rs 500 individuals; US$125 single issue; Rs 1,500 institutions. **URL:** http://www.icar.org.in/node/208. **Circ:** 2,000

45549 ■ Indian Journal of Animal Sciences
Indian Council of Agricultural Research
Krishi Anusandhan Bhaven
Dr. Rajendra Prasad Rd.
New Delhi 110 114, Delhi, India
Ph: 91 112 5843657
Publisher E-mail: bmicar@icar.org.in
Publication on veterinary medicine. **Freq:** Monthly. **Key Personnel:** Kuldeep Sharma, Editor; V.K. Bharti, Ch. Production Off.; Dr. R.P. Sharma, Editor. **ISSN:** 0367-8318. **Subscription Rates:** Rs 500 individuals; Rs 125 single issue; US$1,500 institutions. **URL:** http://www.icar.org.in/node/208. **Circ:** 2,000

45550 ■ The Indian Journal of Crop Science
Satish Serial Publishing House
115, Express Tower
Commercial Complex
Azadpur
New Delhi 110033, Delhi, India
Ph: 91 11 27672852
Fax: 91 11 27672046
Publisher E-mail: info@satishserial.com
Journal focusing on new developments in crop science and their applications. **Key Personnel:** S.P. Singh, Editor-in-Chief; L.K. Gangwar, Assoc. Ed. **ISSN:** 0973-4880. **Subscription Rates:** Rs 2,250 individuals print with online; US$150 other countries print with online; Rs 1,500 institutions print with online; US$100 institutions print with online. **Remarks:** Accepts advertising. **URL:** http://www.satishserial.com/index.php?p=issn0973-4880. **Circ:** (Not Reported)

45551 ■ Indian Journal of Dairy Science
Indian Dairy Association
IDA House
Sector IV
R.K. Puram
New Delhi 110 022, Delhi, India
Ph: 91 116 170781
Fax: 91 116 174719
Publication E-mail: ida@nde.vsnl.net.in
Publisher E-mail: ida@nde.vsnl.net.in
Publication on the field of dairy science. **Founded:** 1948. **Freq:** Bimonthly. **Print Method:** Offset. **Trim Size:** 28 x 21.5 cm. **Key Personnel:** Dr. N.R. Bhasin, Chm.; Dr. Bhupinder Singh, Exec. Ed. **ISSN:** 0019-5146. **Subscription Rates:** Rs 400 individuals; US$20 out of country. **Remarks:** Accepts advertising. **URL:** http://www.indairyasso.org/. **Ad Rates:** BW: Rs 1,500, CNU: Rs 750, PCI: Rs 3,500. **Circ:** (Not Reported)

45552 ■ Indian Journal of Economics & Business
Serials Publications
4830-24 Ansari Rd.
Darya Ganj
New Delhi 110 002, Delhi, India
Ph: 91 11 23245225
Fax: 91 11 23272135

Publisher E-mail: serials@satyam.net.in
Journal covering economics and business. **Founded:** Feb. 1949. **Freq:** Semiannual. **Print Method:** Offset. **Trim Size:** 10 1/4 x 14. **Cols./Page:** 5. **Col. Width:** 21 nonpareils. **Col. Depth:** 217 agate lines. **Key Personnel:** Prof. Kishore G. Kulkarni, PhD, Editor; Prof. Bansi Sawhney, PhD, Editor; S.K. Jha, Managing Editor. **ISSN:** 0972-5784. **Subscription Rates:** US$50 institutions print. **URL:** http://www.serialspublications.com/journals1.asp?jid=201&jtype=1.

45553 ■ Indian Journal of Fibre & Textile Research
National Institute of Science and Information Resources
Council of Scientific and Industrial Research
Anusandhan Bhawan
2 Rafi Marg
New Delhi 110001, Delhi, India
Ph: 91 11 23710340
Fax: 91 11 23320932
Publication E-mail: ijftr@niscair.res.in
Publisher E-mail: itweb@csir.res.in
Publication covering textile and polymers research. **Founded:** Mar. 1976. **Freq:** Quarterly. **Key Personnel:** Neelu Srivastav, Editor. **ISSN:** 0971-0426. **Subscription Rates:** US$240 individuals; Rs 1,000 individuals; Rs 340 single issue; US$80 single issue. **Remarks:** Accepts advertising. **URL:** http://www.niscair.res.in/sciencecommunication/researchjournals/rejour/ijftr/ijftr0.asp. **Formerly:** Indian Journal of Textile Research (1989). **Circ:** Combined ‡300

45554 ■ Indian Journal of Gender Studies
Sage Publications India Private Ltd.
B-1/I-1 Mohan Cooperative Industrial Area
Mathura Rd.
New Delhi 110 044, Delhi, India
Ph: 91 11 40539222
Fax: 91 11 40539234
Publisher E-mail: info@sagepub.in
Publication focusing on gender studies. **Freq:** 3/yr. **Key Personnel:** Malavika Karlekar, Editor; Leela Kasturi, Editor; Bina Agarwal, Editorial Advisory Board. **ISSN:** 0971-5215. **Subscription Rates:** US$328 institutions combined; US$295 institutions e-access; US$321 institutions print only; US$85 individuals print only; US$295 institutions backfile purchase, e-access; US$37 single issue; US$328 individuals all online content. **Remarks:** Accepts advertising. **URL:** http://www.sagepub.com/journalsProdDesc.nav?prodId=Journal200917. **Circ:** (Not Reported)

45555 ■ Indian Journal of History of Science
Indian National Science Academy
Bahadur Shah Zafar Marg
New Delhi 110 002, Delhi, India
Ph: 91 11 23221931
Fax: 91 11 23235648
Publisher E-mail: insa@giasdl01.vsnl.net.in
Publication on the history of science and technology. **Freq:** Quarterly. **ISSN:** 0019-5235. **URL:** http://www.insa.ac.in/html/journals.asp. **Circ:** 380

45556 ■ Indian Journal of Human Rights and Justice
Serials Publications
4830-24 Ansari Rd.
Darya Ganj
New Delhi 110 002, Delhi, India
Ph: 91 11 23245225
Fax: 91 11 23272135
Publisher E-mail: serials@satyam.net.in
Journal covering human rights and dignity. **Freq:** Semiannual. **Key Personnel:** Dr. Subhash Chandra Singh, Ch. Ed. **ISSN:** 0973-3418. **Subscription Rates:** US$150 institutions print. **URL:** http://www.serialspublications.com/journals1.asp?jid=394&jtype=1.

45557 ■ Indian Journal of Human Rights and the Law
Serials Publications
4830-24 Ansari Rd.
Darya Ganj
New Delhi 110 002, Delhi, India
Ph: 91 11 23245225
Fax: 91 11 23272135
Publisher E-mail: serials@satyam.net.in
Journal covering general human rights including international women's human rights. **Founded:** 1888. **Freq:** Semiannual. **Print Method:** Offset. **Trim Size:** 13 1/4 x

21. Cols./Page: 8. Col. Width: 1 1/2 inches. Col. Depth: 21 inches. Key Personnel: Neera Bharihoke, Editor, neera_bh@hotmail.com. ISSN: 0973-0818. Subscription Rates: US$80 institutions print. URL: http://www.serialspublications.com/journals1.asp?jid=392&jtype=1.

45558 ■ Indian Journal of Marine Sciences
National Institute of Science and Information Resources
Council of Scientific and Industrial Research
Anusandhan Bhawan
2 Rafi Marg
New Delhi 110001, Delhi, India
Ph: 91 11 23710340
Fax: 91 11 23320932
Publication E-mail: ijms@niscair.res.in
Publisher E-mail: itweb@csir.res.in
Publication covering marine sciences. Founded: 1972. Freq: Quarterly. Key Personnel: Dr. J. Sundaresan, Editor; Dr. V.P. Dimri, Editorial Board; Prof. B.N. Goswami, Editorial Board, goswami@tropmet.res.in; Dr. M. Mohan Joseph, Editorial Board; Dr. K.S. Krishna, Editorial Board, krishna@nio.org; Prof. Peter S. Liss, Editorial Board. ISSN: 0379-5136. Subscription Rates: Rs 1,000 individuals; US$240 individuals; Rs 340 single issue; US$80 single issue. URL: http://www.niscair.res.in/sciencecommunication/researchjournals/rejour/ijms/ijms0.asp.

45559 ■ Indian Journal of Marketing
Associated Management Consultants (P) Ltd.
Y-21 Hauz Khas
New Delhi 110 016, Delhi, India
Ph: 91 11 42654857
Publication on marketing. Freq: Monthly. Key Personnel: S. Gilani, Editor; Priyanka Gilani, Managing Editor. ISSN: 0019-5316. Subscription Rates: Rs 1,200 individuals; US$125 other countries. Remarks: Accepts advertising. URL: http://www.indianjournalofmarketing.com/. Circ: Paid 2,500

45560 ■ Indian Journal of Mathematics and Mathematical Sciences
Serials Publications
4830-24 Ansari Rd.
Darya Ganj
New Delhi 110 002, Delhi, India
Ph: 91 11 23245225
Fax: 91 11 23272135
Publisher E-mail: serials@satyam.net.in
Journal covering current research in mathematics. Freq: Semiannual. Key Personnel: A. Solairaju, Editor-in-Chief, solairama@yahoo.co.in. ISSN: 0973-3329. Subscription Rates: US$125 institutions print. URL: http://www.serialspublications.com/journals1.asp?jid=411&jtype=1.

45561 ■ Indian Journal of Medical Research
Indian Council of Medical Research
Division of Publication & Information
V. Ramalingaswami Bhawan
Ansari Nagar
New Delhi 110 029, Delhi, India
Ph: 91 112 6508805
Fax: 91 112 6588662
Publisher E-mail: icmrhqds@sansad.nic.in
Medical publication with original communications on a specific topic of biomedical research. Founded: 1913. Freq: Monthly. Print Method: Offset. Trim Size: 8 1/2 x 11. Key Personnel: Dr. Anju Sharma, Assoc. Ed.; K. Satyanarayana, Editor; Dr. N.C. Jain, Assoc. Ed.; Dr. S.S. Agarwal, Contact; Dr. M.K. Bhan, Contact. ISSN: 0971-5916. URL: http://www.icmr.nic.in/ijmr/ijmr.htm. Circ: Paid 700

45562 ■ Indian Journal of Microbiology
Association of Microbiologists of India
c/o R.C. Kuhad
Division of Microbiology
University of Delhi, South Campus
Benito Juarez Rd.
New Delhi 110 012, Delhi, India
Ph: 91 112 68885270
Publisher E-mail: kuhad@gmail.com
Journal covering all areas of microbiology. Freq: Quarterly. Key Personnel: Rup Lal, Editor-in-Chief, ijmami@gmail.com; Pantnagar R. Goel, Editor. ISSN: 0046-8991. Subscription Rates: EUR26 individuals; EUR286 institutions print; EUR26 individuals; EUR238 institutions print + online. Remarks: Accepts

advertising. URL: http://www.springer.com/lifesci/microbiology/journal/12088. Circ: (Not Reported)

45563 ■ Indian Journal of Palliative Care
Medknow Publications Pvt Ltd.
c/o Dr. Sushma Bhatnagar, Ed.
Institute Rotary Cancer Hospital, Rm. 242
All India Institute of Medical Sciences
New Delhi 110029, Delhi, India
Peer-reviewed journal dealing with scientific content from clinical and basic sciences, in connection with Indian Association of Palliative Care. Freq: Semiannual. Print Method: Sheetfed Offset. Trim Size: 6.5 x 8. Key Personnel: Dr. Reena George, Editorial Board; Dr. Sushma Bhatnagar, Editor, editor@jpalliativecare.com. ISSN: 0973-1075. Subscription Rates: Rs 1,000 individuals; Rs 1,200 institutions; Rs 30 other countries; Rs 60 institutions, other countries; Rs 800 individuals online; Rs 1,000 institutions online; Rs 1,200 individuals print and online; Rs 1,500 institutions print and online. Remarks: Accepts advertising. URL: http://www.jpalliativecare.com/. Circ: (Not Reported)

45564 ■ Indian Journal of Pediatrics
125, 2nd Fl.
Gautam Nagar
PO Box 3875
New Delhi 110 049, Delhi, India
Ph: 91 112 6568098
Fax: 91 112 6857587
Publication E-mail: ijp@vsnl.net
Publisher E-mail: ijp.journal.vsnl.net@vsnl.net
Publication on pediatrics. Founded: Jan. 1, 2000. Freq: Monthly. Print Method: Offset. Trim Size: 23 x 16 cm. Key Personnel: A. Chaudhuri, Ed. Emeritus; A. Kumar, Editor; M.K. Bhan, Editor; V. Kalra, Editor; D.K. Mitra, Editor; N.K. Arora, Editor; P.S.N. Menon, Editor; Dr. I.C. Verma, Editor-in-Chief. ISSN: 0019-5456. Subscription Rates: Rs 1,400 individuals; Rs 3,500 institutions; US$300 individuals; US$400 institutions other countries. Remarks: Accepts advertising. URL: http://medind.nic.in/icb/icbm.shtml. Former name: Indian Journal of Pediatrics. Ad Rates: BW: Rs 100, 4C: Rs 400. Circ: 20,000

45565 ■ Indian Journal of Pure and Applied Mathematics
Indian National Science Academy
Bahadur Shah Zafar Marg
New Delhi 110 002, Delhi, India
Ph: 91 11 23221931
Fax: 91 11 23235648
Publisher E-mail: insa@giasdl01.vsnl.net.in
Publication covering the realms of pure and applied mathematics. Freq: Bimonthly. Key Personnel: Ajit Iqbal Singh, Assoc. Ed.; V. Kannan, Editor; I.B.S. Passi, Editorial Board; H.G. Dales, Editorial Board; R. Balasubramanian, Advisory Board; Phoolan Prasad, Editorial Board; V.D. Sharma, Editorial Board; Prakasa Rao, Editorial Board. ISSN: 0019-5588. URL: http://www.insa.ac.in/html/journals.aspMathematics.

45566 ■ Indian Journal of Radio & Space Physics
National Institute of Science and Information Resources
Council of Scientific and Industrial Research
Anusandhan Bhawan
2 Rafi Marg
New Delhi 110001, Delhi, India
Ph: 91 11 23710340
Fax: 91 11 23320932
Publication E-mail: ijrsp@niscair.res.in
Publisher E-mail: itweb@csir.res.in
Publication covering radio and space physics. Founded: 1972. Freq: Bimonthly. Print Method: Offset. Key Personnel: Kamlesh Arora, Editor, kamlesh@niscair.res.in; Prof. Archana Bhattacharyya, Editorial Board; Prof. Madhu Chandra, Editorial Board. ISSN: 0367-8393. Subscription Rates: Rs 1,000 individuals; US$240 other countries includes first class mail; Rs 200 single issue; US$48 other countries includes first class mail. Remarks: Advertising accepted; rates available upon request. URL: http://www.niscair.res.in/sciencecommunication/researchjournals/rejour/ijrsp/ijrsp0.asp. Circ: (Not Reported)

45567 ■ Indian Journal of Technical Education
Indian Society for Technical Education
Shaheed Jeet Singh Marg

Near Katwaria Sarai
Opp. Sanskrit Vidyapeeth
New Delhi 110 016, Delhi, India
Ph: 91 11 26963431
Fax: 91 11 26852421
Publication E-mail: istedhq@vsnl.net
Publisher E-mail: istedhq@vsnl.net
Peer-reviewed academic journal focusing on technical education. Founded: 1971. Freq: Quarterly. ISSN: 0971-3034. Subscription Rates: Rs 500 individuals ISTE members; Rs 800 individuals 1 year; Rs 600 institutions members of ISTE for 3 years; Rs 800 institutions non-member, 1 year; Rs 1,000 individuals industry/govt./dept., 1 year. Remarks: Accepts advertising. URL: http://www.isteonline.in. Ad Rates: BW: Rs 20,000. Circ: Paid 12,000

45568 ■ Indian Journal of Transport Management
Association of State Road Transport Undertakings
Plot No.4-A, PSP Block
Pocket-14, Sector-8
New Delhi 110 075, Delhi, India
Ph: 91 11 26499784
Fax: 91 11 43294242
Publisher E-mail: asrtu@del2.vsnl.net.in
Journal focusing on transportation management. Founded: 1966. Freq: Quarterly. Print Method: Offset. Trim Size: 240 x 180 mm. Key Personnel: J.K. Bahuguna, Editor. ISSN: 0972-5695. Remarks: Accepts advertising. URL: http://www.indiaenvironmentportal.org.in/taxonomy/term/9342?page=1. Ad Rates: BW: Rs 6,000, 4C: Rs 8,400. Circ: 2,000

45569 ■ Indian Journal of Tuberculosis
Tuberculosis Association of India
3 Red Cross Rd.
New Delhi 110 001, Delhi, India
Ph: 91 11 23715217
Fax: 91 11 23711303
Publisher E-mail: info@tbassnindia.org
Medical journal focusing on tuberculosis. Founded: 1953. Freq: Quarterly. Key Personnel: Lalit Kant, Editor; V.K. Arora, Editor; M.M. Singh, Editor; L.S. Chauhan, Assoc. Ed.; D. Banerjee, Member; D. Raghunath, Member; R.K. Srivastava, Editor-in-Chief. ISSN: 0019-5707. Subscription Rates: Rs 800 individuals; US$30 out of country SAARC countries; US$35 out of country Eastern countries; US$40 other countries; Rs 200 single issue. Remarks: Accepts advertising. URL: http://tbassnindia.org/IndianJournalofTB.html. Circ: Paid 1,500

45570 ■ Indian Literary Index
Sahitya Akademi
Rabindra Bhavan
35 Ferozeshah Rd.
New Delhi 110 001, Delhi, India
Ph: 91 112 3386626
Fax: 91 112 3382428
Publisher E-mail: secy@sahitya-akademi.org
Contains documentation covering literary news. Subtitle: Documentation List of Creative and Critical Writings and Literary News. Founded: 1988. Freq: Bimonthly. Subscription Rates: Rs 50 individuals. URL: http://www.sahitya-akademi.gov.in/.

45571 ■ Indian Media Studies Journal
Satish Serial Publishing House
115, Express Tower
Commercial Complex
Azadpur
New Delhi 110033, Delhi, India
Ph: 91 11 27672852
Fax: 91 11 27672046
Publisher E-mail: info@satishserial.com
Journal covering field of various mass communication. Freq: Semiannual. Key Personnel: Dr. Anil K. Rai'Ankit, Editor-in-Chief. ISSN: 0972-9348. Subscription Rates: Rs 1800 individuals print with online; US$135 other countries print with online; Rs 1200 individuals print or online only; US$90 individuals print or online only. Remarks: Accepts advertising. URL: http://www.satishserial.com/index.php?p=issn0972-9348. Circ: (Not Reported)

45572 ■ Indian Mountaineer
Indian Mountaineering Foundation
6 Benito Juarez Rd.

Circulation: ★ = ABC; △ = BPA; ♦ = CAC; • = CCAB; ❏ = VAC; ⊕ = PO Statement; ‡ = Publisher's Report; Boldface figures = sworn; Light figures = estimated.

Gale Directory of Publications & Broadcast Media/147th Ed.

5027

New Delhi 110 021, Delhi, India
Ph: 91 112 4111211
Fax: 91 112 4113412
Publisher E-mail: indmount@bol.net.in
Periodical focusing on mountaineering in India. **Founded:** 1978. **Freq:** Annual. **Key Personnel:** Akhil Bakshi, Editor. **ISSN:** 0971-426X. **Subscription Rates:** Rs 1,000 individuals India/Nepal; Rs 2,000 individuals club/ association, India/Nepal; US$500 other countries; Rs 100 single issue; US$15 single issue. **Remarks:** Accepts advertising. **URL:** http://www.indmount.org/publications.html. **Circ:** Paid 2,000

45573 ■ Indian National Science Academy Biographical Memoirs of Fellows
Indian National Science Academy
Bahadur Shah Zafar Marg
New Delhi 110 002, Delhi, India
Ph: 91 11 23221931
Fax: 91 11 23235648
Publisher E-mail: insa@giasdl01.vsnl.net.in
Periodical containing biographies of Fellows of the Indian National Science Academy. **Founded:** 1966. **Freq:** Irregular. **ISSN:** 0547-7557. **Subscription Rates:** Rs 300 individuals; US$60 individuals. **URL:** http://www.insa-india.org/publicat.htm.

45574 ■ Indian National Science Academy Year Book
Indian National Science Academy
Bahadur Shah Zafar Marg
New Delhi 110 002, Delhi, India
Ph: 91 11 23221931
Fax: 91 11 23235648
Publisher E-mail: insa@giasdl01.vsnl.net.in
Scientific journal. **Founded:** 1960. **Freq:** Annual. **ISSN:** 0073-6619. **URL:** http://www.insa.ac.in/html/journals.asp. **Circ:** Paid 1,000

45575 ■ Indian Pediatrics
Indian Academy of Pediatrics
115/4 Ground Fl.
Gautam nagar
New Delhi 110 049, Delhi, India
Ph: 91 11 26961468
Publication E-mail: jiap@nic.in
Publisher E-mail: centraloffice@iapindia.org
Medical journal focusing on pediatrics. **Founded:** 1964. **Freq:** Monthly. **Print Method:** Offset. **Key Personnel:** Piyush Gupta, Editor-in-Chief; Varinder Singh, Assoc. Ed. **ISSN:** 0019-6061. **Subscription Rates:** US$470 institutions, other countries libraries; US$400 other countries; Rs 6,500 institutions libraries; Rs 8,500 out of country Nepal & Bangladesh. **Remarks:** Accepts advertising. **URL:** http://www.indianpediatrics.net. **Ad Rates:** BW: Rs 12,000, 4C: Rs 16,000. **Circ:** Paid 17,500

45576 ■ Indian Roads Congress Highway Research Bulletin
Indian Roads Congress
Jamnagar House
Shahjahan Rd.
New Delhi 110 011, Delhi, India
Ph: 91 112 6716778
Fax: 91 112 6183669
Publisher E-mail: secretary@irc.org.in
Periodical covering road transportation in India. **Freq:** Semiannual. **ISSN:** 0376-4788. **Subscription Rates:** Rs 40 individuals; Free to members. **Remarks:** Accepts advertising. **URL:** http://www.irc.org.in. **Circ:** Paid 8,500

45577 ■ Indian Social Science Review
Sage Periodicals India Private Ltd.
PO Box 4215
New Delhi 110 048, Delhi, India
Ph: 91 11 6419884
Fax: 91 11 6472426
Multidisciplinary journal focusing on social and political science. **Founded:** 1999. **Freq:** Semiannual. **Key Personnel:** T. N. Madan, Editor. **ISSN:** 0972-0731. **URL:** http://www.icssr.org/journals.htm.

45578 ■ Indian Sugar
Indian Sugar Mills Association
C Block, 2nd Fl.
Ansal Plz., August Kranti Marg, Andrews Ganj
New Delhi 110 049, Delhi, India
Ph: 91 11 26262294
Fax: 91 11 26263231

Publisher E-mail: isma@indiansugar.com
Journal focusing on the Indian sugar industry. **Subtitle:** Complete Sugar Journal. **Founded:** 1950. **Freq:** Monthly. **ISSN:** 0019-6428. **Subscription Rates:** Rs 300 individuals. **Remarks:** Accepts advertising. **URL:** http://www.indiansugar.com. **Circ:** Paid 1,100

45579 ■ Institute of Town Planners, India Journal
Institute of Town Planners, India
4-A Ring Rd.
I.P. Estate
New Delhi 110 002, Delhi, India
Ph: 91 112 3702455
Fax: 91 112 3702453
Publisher E-mail: itpidel@nda.vsnl.net.in
Journal covering city planning and urban development. **Founded:** 1955. **Freq:** Semiannual. **Key Personnel:** Dr. Ashok Kumar, Sec.; Shri S.S. Mathur, Sec. Gen. **ISSN:** 0537-9679. **Remarks:** Accepts advertising. **URL:** http://www.itpindia.org/publication.htm; http://itpi.org.in/. **Circ:** (Not Reported)

45580 ■ International Journal of Applied Business and Economic Research
Serials Publications
4830-24 Ansari Rd.
Darya Ganj
New Delhi 110 002, Delhi, India
Ph: 91 11 23245225
Fax: 91 11 23272135
Publisher E-mail: serials@satyam.net.in
Online journal covering applied business and economic research. **Founded:** 1963. **Freq:** Semiannual. **Print Method:** Offset. **Cols./Page:** 6. **Col. Width:** 21 nonpareils. **Col. Depth:** 231 agate lines. **Key Personnel:** Prof. Mokhtar M. Metwally, Editor; Sadrudin Ahmad, Editorial Board; Thomas Bradtke, Editorial Board. **ISSN:** 0972-7302. **Subscription Rates:** Rs 2,000 institutions print. **URL:** http://www.serialspublications.com/journals1.asp?jid=220&jtype=1.

45581 ■ International Journal for Computational Vision and Biomechanics
Serials Publications
4830-24 Ansari Rd.
Darya Ganj
New Delhi 110 002, Delhi, India
Ph: 91 11 23245225
Fax: 91 11 23272135
Publisher E-mail: serials@satyam.net.in
Journal covering computational vision and biomechanics. **Freq:** Semiannual. **Key Personnel:** Joao Manuel R.S. Tavares, Editor; R.M. Natal Jorge, Editor. **ISSN:** 0973-6778. **Subscription Rates:** US$250 institutions print. **URL:** http://www.serialspublications.com/journals1.asp?jid=374&jtype=1.

45582 ■ International Journal of Engineering Studies
Research India Publications
c/o Dr. Bijaya Kumar Panigrahi, Ed.-in-Ch.
Department of Electrical Engineering
Indian Institute of Technology
Hauz Khas
New Delhi, Delhi, India
Publisher E-mail: info@ripublication.com
Peer-reviewed journal covering engineering studies. **Freq:** 4/yr. **Key Personnel:** Dr. Bijaya Kumar Panigrahi, Editor-in-Chief, bkpanigrahi@ee.iitd.ac.in; Prof. N.P. Mahalik, Editor, nmahalik@att.net. **ISSN:** 0975-6469. **Subscription Rates:** US$780 institutions and library; print plus online free; US$760 institutions and library; online only; US$240 individuals print plus online free; US$220 individuals online only; Rs 4,800 individuals. **URL:** http://www.ripublication.com/ijes.htm. **Also known as:** IJES.

45583 ■ International Journal of Environment and Development
Serials Publications
4830-24 Ansari Rd.
Darya Ganj
New Delhi 110 002, Delhi, India
Ph: 91 11 23245225
Fax: 91 11 23272135
Publisher E-mail: serials@satyam.net.in
Journal covering ecological studies, and environmental policies, legislation, and impact assessment. **Founded:** Feb. 1959. **Freq:** Semiannual. **Print Method:** Offset. **Trim Size:** 8 x 10 7/8. **Cols./Page:** 3. **Col. Width:** 26

nonpareils. **Col. Depth:** 140 agate lines. **Key Personnel:** Dr. Falendra K. Sudan, Editor; Vijay Kumar, Managing Editor. **ISSN:** 0973-3574. **Subscription Rates:** US$125 institutions print. **URL:** http://www.serialspublications.com/journals1.asp?jid=423&jtype=1.

45584 ■ International Journal of Scientific Computing
Serials Publications
4830-24 Ansari Rd.
Darya Ganj
New Delhi 110 002, Delhi, India
Ph: 91 11 23245225
Fax: 91 11 23272135
Publisher E-mail: serials@satyam.net.in
Journal covering numerical methods and techniques for scientific computation. **Freq:** Semiannual. **Key Personnel:** P.S. Rama Chandra Rao, Editor-in-Chief, patibanda20@yahoo.co.in. **ISSN:** 0973-578X. **Subscription Rates:** US$250 institutions print. **URL:** http://www.serialspublications.com/journals1.asp?jid=375&jtype=1.

45585 ■ International Journal of Sociology of the Family
M D Periodicals Private Ltd.
11 Darya Ganj
New Delhi 110 002, Delhi, India
Ph: 91 11 3268645
Fax: 91 11 3275542
Journal covering the study of social problems. **Founded:** 1971. **Freq:** Semiannual. **Key Personnel:** Man Singh Das, Founding and Consulting Ed., mandas25@hotmail.com; Barbara Hanson, Editor-in-Chief, phone 416736-2100, fax 416650-3876, irjs@yorku.ca. **ISSN:** 0020-7667. **Subscription Rates:** Rs 400; US$70 other countries. **Remarks:** Accepts advertising. **URL:** http://www.yorku.ca/irjs. **Circ:** Paid 1,200

45586 ■ International Journal of Statistics and Systems
Research India Publications
D1/71, Top Fl., Rohini Sec-16
New Delhi 110 089, Delhi, India
Ph: 91 11 65394240
Fax: 91 11 27297815
Publisher E-mail: info@ripublication.com
Journal covering statistics and management systems. **Founded:** 1957. **Freq:** Semiannual. **Print Method:** Offset. **Cols./Page:** 3. **Col. Width:** 27 nonpareils. **Col. Depth:** 140 agate lines. **Key Personnel:** Emad-Eldin A.A. Aly, Assoc. Ed.; Miguel A. Arcones, Editorial Board Member; Hossein Arsham, Assoc. Ed.; Sunil K. Mathur, Assoc. Ed.; Ibrahim A. Ahmad, Editorial Board Member. **ISSN:** 0973-2675. **Subscription Rates:** US$320 institutions print and online; US$220 individuals print only; US$300 institutions online only; US$200 individuals online only. **URL:** http://www.ripublication.com/ijss.htm.

45587 ■ International Journal of Theoretical and Applied Computer Sciences (IJTACS)
GBS Publishers & Distributors
4866/24, Ground Fl.
Ansari Rd.
Darya Ganj
New Delhi 110 002, Delhi, India
Ph: 91 11 23264904
Fax: 91 11 27893171
Publisher E-mail: info@gbspublisher.com
Journal covering computational science, scientific computing, and applied science and engineering. **Founded:** 1870. **Freq:** Semiannual. **Print Method:** Offset. **Cols./Page:** 8. **Col. Width:** 18 nonpareils. **Col. Depth:** 294 agate lines. **Key Personnel:** Prof. P.V.S Srinivas, Editor-in-Chief. **Subscription Rates:** US$80 individuals; US$120 institutions. **URL:** http://www.gbspublisher.com/ijtacs.htm.

45588 ■ International Review of Fuzzy Mathematics
Serials Publications
4830-24 Ansari Rd.
Darya Ganj
New Delhi 110 002, Delhi, India
Ph: 91 11 23245225
Fax: 91 11 23272135
Publisher E-mail: serials@satyam.net.in
Journal covering theory and applications of fuzzy sets and systems. **Founded:** 1980. **Freq:** Semiannual. **Print Method:** Offset. **Trim Size:** 11 1/2 x 13 1/2. **Cols./Page:**

4. **Col. Width:** 2 3/8 inches. **Col. Depth:** 12 1/2 inches. **Key Personnel:** Wieslaw A. Dudek, Managing Editor; Prof. Jianming Zhan, Editor-in-Chief, zhanjianming@hotmail.com; Prof. Eun Hwan Roh, Editor-in-Chief, ehroh@cue.ac.kr; Hee Sik Kim, Managing Editor. **ISSN:** 0973-4392. **Subscription Rates:** US$100 institutions print. **URL:** http://www.serialspublications.com/journals1.asp?jid=300&jtype=1.

45589 ■ International Review of Pure and Applied Chemistry
Serials Publications
4830-24 Ansari Rd.
Darya Ganj
New Delhi 110 002, Delhi, India
Ph: 91 11 23245225
Fax: 91 11 23272135
Publisher E-mail: serials@satyam.net.in
Journal covering pure and applied chemistry. **Freq:** Semiannual. **Key Personnel:** Mehmet Yaman, Editor-in-Chief, myaman@firat.edu.tr; Gokce Kaya, Assoc. Ed. **ISSN:** 0973-3876. **Subscription Rates:** US$200 institutions print. **URL:** http://www.serialspublications.com/journals1.asp?jid=425&jtype=1.

45590 ■ Invention Intelligence
National Research Development Corporation
20-22 Zamroodpur Community Ctr.
Kailash Colony Ext.
New Delhi 110 048, Delhi, India
Ph: 91 11 29240410
Fax: 91 11 29230506
Publisher E-mail: write2@nrdc.in
Scientific journal focusing on technology transfer, research and development, and IPR. **Founded:** 1965. **Freq:** Bimonthly. **Print Method:** Offset. **Trim Size:** 27 x 19cm. **Key Personnel:** Chander Mohan, Manager, phone 91 29248010, chandermohan@nrdc.in. **ISSN:** 0970-0056. **Subscription Rates:** Rs 150 individuals; Rs 280 two years; US$60 other countries by airmail. **Remarks:** Accepts advertising. **URL:** http://www.nrdcindia.com/pub.htmlntelligence. **Ad Rates:** BW: Rs 3,500, 4C: Rs 4,500. **Circ:** Paid 3,000

45591 ■ Irrigation and Drainage
The International Commission on Irrigation and Drainage
48 Nyaya Marg
Chanakyapuri
New Delhi 110 021, Delhi, India
Ph: 91 112 6116837
Fax: 91 112 6115962
Publisher E-mail: icid@icid.org
Trade bulletin with articles on irrigation, drainage, river training and flood control. **Founded:** June 24, 1950. **Freq:** 5/yr. **ISSN:** 1531-0353. **Subscription Rates:** US$468 individuals full print and electronic; US$425 individuals full print or online only; US$320 individuals. **Remarks:** Accepts advertising. **URL:** http://www.icid.org/wiley_journal.html. **Formerly:** ICID Journal. **Circ:** Paid 2,900

45592 ■ Islam and the Modern Age
Zakir Husain Institute of Islamic Studies
Jamia Millia Islamia
Jamia Nagar
New Delhi 110 025, Delhi, India
Ph: 91 112 6981717
Fax: 91 112 6980229
Community magazine. **Founded:** 1970. **Freq:** Quarterly. **Key Personnel:** Prof. Akhtarul Wasey, Editor. **ISSN:** 0021-1826. **Subscription Rates:** Rs 20; US$20 other countries. **Remarks:** Accepts advertising. **URL:** http://www.jmi.nic.in/Journals/ima.htm. **Circ:** Paid 1,000

45593 ■ Journal of Bio-Inspired Computation Research
Research India Publications
D1/71, Top Fl., Rohini Sec-16
New Delhi 110 089, Delhi, India
Ph: 91 11 65394240
Fax: 91 11 27297815
Publisher E-mail: info@ripublication.com
Journal covering research in bio-inspired computation. **URL:** http://www.ripublication.com/jbicr.htm. **Also known as:** JBICR.

45594 ■ Journal of Cytology
Medknow Publications Pvt Ltd.
c/o V.S. Nijhawan, Ed.in-Ch.
621/25 Defence Officers Enclave
SP Marg
New Delhi 110 021, Delhi, India
Peer-reviewed journal of the Indian Academy of Cytologists. **Freq:** Quarterly. **Key Personnel:** V.S. Nijhawan, Editor-in-Chief, editor@jcytol.org; Prabal Deb, Assoc. Ed.; Rohit Tewari, Asst. Ed. **ISSN:** 0970-9371. **Subscription Rates:** Rs 2,000 individuals print only; Rs 2,000 institutions print only; US$125 other countries print only; US$200 institutions, other countries print only; Rs 2,400 individuals print and online; Rs 2,400 institutions print and online; US$150 other countries print and online; US$240 institutions, other countries print and online; US$100 individuals online; Rs 1,600 institutions online. **Remarks:** Accepts advertising. **URL:** http://www.jcytol.org. **Circ:** (Not Reported)

45595 ■ Journal of Discrete Mathematical Sciences and Cryptography
Taru Publications
G-159, Pushkar Enclave
Pashchim Vihar
New Delhi 110 063, Delhi, India
Ph: 91 114 2331159
Fax: 91 114 2321126
Publisher E-mail: info@tarupublications.com
Journal focusing on mathematical science and cryptography. **Founded:** 1998. **Freq:** Bimonthly. **Print Method:** Offset. **Trim Size:** 7 X 9.5. **Key Personnel:** Prof. B.D. Acharya, Advisory Ed., acharyad@alpha.nic.in; Prof. K.K. Dewan, Advisory Ed., kkdewan123@yahoo.co.in; Prof. Bal Kishan Dass, Editor-in-Chief, dassbk@rediffmail.com; Prof. Klaus Denecke, Assoc. Ed., kdenecke@rz.uni-potsdam.de; Prof. Michele Elia, Assoc. Ed., eliamike@tin.it; Prof. T. Berger, Assoc. Ed., berger@ece.cornell.edu; Prof. S. Innamorati, Assoc. Ed., innamora@ing.univaq.it; Prof. A. Poli, Assoc. Ed., poli@cict.fr; Prof. Berhard Ruf, Assoc. Ed., ruf@mat.unimi.it. **ISSN:** 0972-0529. **Subscription Rates:** Rs 3,000 individuals print; Rs 3,000 individuals online; Rs 4,000 individuals print + online; US$400 other countries print; US$350 other countries online; US$400 other countries print + online. **Remarks:** Advertising not accepted. **URL:** http://www.tarupublications.com/journals/jdmsc/jdmsc.htm. **Circ:** Paid 240

45596 ■ Journal of Educational Planning and Administration
National Institute of Educational Planning and Administration
17-B Sri Aurobindo Marg
New Delhi 110 016, Delhi, India
Ph: 91 112 6863562
Fax: 91 112 6853041
Publisher E-mail: nuepa@nuepa.org
Academic publication on education and administration issues. **Founded:** 1987. **Freq:** Quarterly. **Print Method:** Offset. **Trim Size:** 7 1/4 x 9 1/2. **Key Personnel:** Jandhyala B.G. Tilak, Editor, phone 91 112 6962120, fax 91 112 6865180, jepa@niepa.org. **ISSN:** 0971-3859. **Subscription Rates:** Rs 150 individuals brought out every January, April, July and October; Rs 350 institutions brought out every January, April, July and October; US$60 individuals brought out every January, April, July and October; US$85 institutions brought out every January, April, July and October. **Remarks:** Accepts advertising. **URL:** http://www.nuepa.org/Pub_Jepa.html. **Ad Rates:** BW: Rs 2,000. **Circ:** Paid 700

45597 ■ The Journal of Entrepreneurship
Sage Publications India Private Ltd.
B-1/I-1 Mohan Cooperative Industrial Area
Mathura Rd.
New Delhi 110 044, Delhi, India
Ph: 91 11 40539222
Fax: 91 11 40539234
Publisher E-mail: info@sagepub.in
Periodical on business and economics. **Founded:** 1992. **Freq:** Semiannual. **Key Personnel:** Sasi Misra, Editor; Hrishikes Bhattacharya, Editorial Board; Ashok Madnani, Editorial Office; M. Akbar, Editorial Board; Y.K. Alagh, Advisory Board; Padmini Swaminathan, Editorial Board; Dinesh N Awasthi, Editorial Board; Mario Rutten, Advisory Board; Rodrigo Varela, Advisory Board. **ISSN:** 0971-3557. **Subscription Rates:** US$314 institutions combined, print & e-access; US$52 single issue; US$283 institutions e-access; US$314 individuals all online content; US$283 institutions backfile purchase, e-access; US$308 institutions print only; US$80 individuals print only; US$169 institutions single, print. **Remarks:** Accepts advertising. **URL:** http://www.sagepub.com/journalsProdDesc.nav?prodId=Journal200956. **Circ:** Paid 500

45598 ■ Journal of Human Values
Sage Publications India Private Ltd.
B-1/I-1 Mohan Cooperative Industrial Area
Mathura Rd.
New Delhi 110 044, Delhi, India
Ph: 91 11 40539222
Fax: 91 11 40539234
Publisher E-mail: info@sagepub.in
Philosophical magazine on human values in the business environment. **Founded:** 1995. **Freq:** Semiannual April, October. **Key Personnel:** SK Chakraborty, Founder/Ed.; Samir Ranjan Chatterjee, Editorial Board; P. Bhattacharya, Editorial Board; Kenneth Goodpaster, Editorial Board; Prof. C Panduranga Bhatta, Editor; Peter Pruzan, Editorial Advisory Board. **ISSN:** 0971-6858. **Subscription Rates:** US$310 institutions combined, print & e-access; US$279 institutions e-access; US$310 individuals all online content; US$279 institutions backfile purchase, e-access; US$304 institutions print only; US$81 individuals print only; US$53 single issue. **Remarks:** Accepts advertising. **URL:** http://www.sagepub.com/journalsProdDesc.nav?prodId=Journal200829. **Circ:** Paid 600

45599 ■ Journal, Indian Academy of Clinical Medicine
Indian Academy of Clinical Medicine
A-Block
CGO Complex
Lodhi Rd.
New Delhi 110 003, Delhi, India
Ph: 91 243 56446
Fax: 91 435 9445
Official journal of the Indian Academy of Clinical Medicine. **Key Personnel:** B.B. Rewari, Editor; Alladi Mohan, Sec.; Pushpa Yadav, Member; B. Gupta, Member; Vijay Achari, Advisiory Board; D.G. Jain, Assoc. Ed.; Rita Sood, Member. **URL:** http://medind.nic.in/jac/jacm.shtml.

45600 ■ Journal of Indian Association for Child and Adolescent Mental Health
Indian Association for Child and Adolescent Mental Health
Dept. of Psychiatry
All India Institute of Medical Sciences
New Delhi 110 029, Delhi, India
Publication E-mail: editor@jiacam.org
Official journal of the Indian Association for Child and Adolescent Mental Health, accepting original articles, review articles, case reports, conference announcements, summary of trials, letters to the editor and conference reports. **Key Personnel:** Dr. Indira Sharma, Vice President; Dr. Beena Johnson, Executive Ed.; Pratap Sharan, Editor. **ISSN:** 0973-1342. **URL:** http://www.jiacam.org.

45601 ■ Journal of Indian Association of Pediatric Surgeons
Indian Association of Pediatric Surgeons
Dept. of Pediatric Surgery
All India Institute of Medical Sciences
Ansari Nagar
New Delhi 110 029, Delhi, India
Ph: 91 112 6594297
Fax: 91 112 6588663
Publisher E-mail: publishing@medknow.com
Journal covering pediatric surgical topics. **Founded:** 1995. **Freq:** Quarterly. **Print Method:** Offset. **Cols./Page:** 4. **Col. Width:** 28 nonpareils. **Col. Depth:** 140 agate lines. **Key Personnel:** Dr. Subir K. Chatterjee, Emeritus Editor; B. Mukhopadhyay, Editor; Dr. K.L.N. Rao, Editor-in-Chief. **ISSN:** 0971-9261. **Subscription Rates:** Rs 2,000 individuals; Rs 3,000 institutions; US$100 individuals; US$300 institutions; Rs 80 other countries; US$240 other countries institution. **URL:** http://www.jiaps.com/aboutus.asp.

45602 ■ Journal of Indian Education
National Council of Educational Research and Training
Sri Aurbindo Marg
New Delhi 110 016, Delhi, India
Ph: 91 112 6560620

Circulation: ★ = ABC; △ = BPA; ♦ = CAC; • = CCAB; ❑ = VAC; ⊕ = PO Statement; ‡ = Publisher's Report; Boldface figures = sworn; Light figures = estimated.

Fax: 91 112 6868419
Publication E-mail: crc@giasdl01.vsnl.net.in
Publisher E-mail: proncert@yahoo.co.in
Journal of Indian education teaching methods.
Founded: 1975. **Freq:** Quarterly. **ISSN:** 0377-0435.
Subscription Rates: Rs 45 single issue; US$2 single
issue; 1 single issue; Rs 180 individuals; US$8 individu-
als; 4 individuals. **URL:** http://www.ncert.nic.in/html/
journals.htm. **Circ:** Paid 1,200

45603 ■ Journal of Indian Law Institute
Indian Law Institute
Bhagwandas Rd.
New Delhi 110 001, Delhi, India
Ph: 91 11 23387526
Fax: 91 11 23782140
Publisher E-mail: ili@ilidelhi.org
Journal covering law. **Founded:** 1958. **Freq:** Quarterly.
Key Personnel: Prof. D.S. Sengar, Editor; Prof. S. Si-
vakumar, Editor. **ISSN:** 0019-5731. **Subscription Rates:**
Rs 700 individuals. **URL:** http://www.ilidelhi.org/
publication.htm.

45604 ■ Journal of Indian Roads Congress
Indian Roads Congress
Jamnagar House
Shahjahan Rd.
New Delhi 110 011, Delhi, India
Ph: 91 112 6716778
Fax: 91 112 6183669
Publisher E-mail: secretary@irc.org.in
Periodical on the Indian road transportation and traffic
industry and all related issues with the highways.
Founded: 1934. **Freq:** Quarterly. **Print Method:** Offset.
ISSN: 0258-0500. **Subscription Rates:** Rs 200
individuals. **Remarks:** Advertising not accepted. **URL:**
http://www.irc.org.in. **Circ:** Paid 8,500

**45605 ■ Journal of the Indian Society of Soil
Science**
Indian Society of Soil Science
Indian Agricultural Research Institute
Division of Soil Science & Agricultural Chemistry
Dev Prakash Shastri Marg, Pusa
New Delhi 110 012, Delhi, India
Ph: 91 11 25841991
Fax: 91 11 25841529
Publisher E-mail: isss.secretary@gmail.com
Scientific journal focusing on soil science. **Founded:**
1953. **Freq:** Quarterly in March, June, Sept., and Dec.
Trim Size: 245 x 185 mm. **Key Personnel:** Dr. P.D.
Sharma, Vice President, parshotamsharma@yahoo.co.
in; Dr. J.C. Katyal, President, jc_katyal@rediffmail.com.
ISSN: 0019-638X. **Subscription Rates:** Rs 1,500
individuals; US$160 other countries. **Remarks:** Advertis-
ing not accepted. **URL:** http://www.isss-india.org/journal.
html. **Circ:** Paid 2,500

**45606 ■ Journal of Information & Optimization
Sciences**
Taru Publications
G-159, Pushkar Enclave
Pashchim Vihar
New Delhi 110 063, Delhi, India
Ph: 91 114 2331159
Fax: 91 114 2321126
Publisher E-mail: info@tarupublications.com
Periodical on information and optimization sciences.
Founded: 1980. **Freq:** Bimonthly January, March, May,
July, September and November. **Print Method:** Offset.
Trim Size: 7 x 9.5. **Key Personnel:** Prof. Bal Kishan
Dass, Ch. Ed., dassbk@rediffmail.com; Prof. P.K. Kapur,
Advisory Ed., pkkapur@himalaya.du.ac.in; Prof. Hideki
Imai, Advisory Ed., imai@iis.u-tokyo.ac.jp. **ISSN:** 0252-
2667. **Subscription Rates:** Rs 3,000 individuals print;
Rs 3,000 individuals online; Rs 4,000 individuals print +
online; US$400 out of country print; US$350 out of
country online; US$400 out of country print + online.
Remarks: Advertising not accepted. **URL:** http://www.
tarupublications.com/journals/jios/jios.htm; http://www.
tarupublications.com. **Circ:** Paid 480

**45607 ■ Journal of Intellectual Property Law &
Practice**
Oxford University Press
YMCA Library Bldg.
1st Fl.
Jai Singh Rd.
PO Box 43
New Delhi 110 001, Delhi, India

Ph: 91 11 43600300
Fax: 91 11 23360897
Publisher E-mail: admin.in@oup.com
Journal covering the full range of substantive IP topics,
practice-related matters such as litigation, enforcement,
drafting and transactions, plus relevant aspects of
related subjects such as competition and world trade
law. **Freq:** Monthly. **Key Personnel:** Prof. Jeremy Phillips, Editor. **ISSN:** 1747-1532. **Subscription Rates:** 395
institutions print and online; 356 institutions online only;
375 institutions print only. **URL:** http://jiplp.
oxfordjournals.org/.

**45608 ■ Journal of Interdisciplinary Mathemat-
ics**
Taru Publications
G-159, Pushkar Enclave
Pashchim Vihar
New Delhi 110 063, Delhi, India
Ph: 91 114 2331159
Fax: 91 114 2321126
Publisher E-mail: info@tarupublications.com
Peer-reviewed journal covering mathematics. **Founded:**
1998. **Freq:** Bimonthly. **Print Method:** Offset. **Trim Size:**
7 x 9.5. **Key Personnel:** Prof. P.K. Jain, Editorial Board,
pawanujain@vsnl.net; Prof. Bal Kishan Dass, Editor-in-
Chief, dassbk@rediffmail.com; Prof. Q. Mushtaq, Edito-
rial Board, qmushtaq@apollo.net; Prof. F. Eugeni, Edito-
rial Board, eugenif@tin.it; Prof. Michael J. Ryan, Assoc.
Ed., m.j.ryan@hull.ac.uk; Prof. Carlos A. Coelho, Assoc.
Ed., coelho@math.isa.ult.pt; Prof. Francesco Altomare,
Assoc. Ed., altomare@dm.uniba.it; Prof. Hossein Arsham, Assoc. Ed., harsham@ubalt.edu; Prof. A. Cam-
bini, Assoc. Ed., acambini@ec.unipi.it. **ISSN:** 0972-
0502. **Subscription Rates:** Rs 3,000 individuals print;
Rs 3,000 individuals online; Rs 4,000 individuals print +
online; US$400 out of country print; US$350 out of
country online; US$400 out of country print + online.
Remarks: Advertising not accepted. **URL:** http://www.
tarupublications.com/journals/jim/jim.htm. **Circ:** Paid 240

**45609 ■ Journal of International Economic
Review**
Serials Publications
4830-24 Ansari Rd.
Darya Ganj
New Delhi 110 002, Delhi, India
Ph: 91 11 23245225
Fax: 91 11 23272135
Publisher E-mail: serials@satyam.net.in
Journal covering quantitative economics including
econometrics, macroeconomics, theory, and applied
economics. **Freq:** Semiannual. **Key Personnel:** Prof.
Muzafar Shah Habibullah, Editor-in-Chief. **ISSN:** 0975-
2080. **Subscription Rates:** US$75 institutions print.
URL: http://www.serialspublications.com/journals1.asp?
jid=385&jtype=1.

45610 ■ Journal of Islamic History
Pharos Media & Publishing (P) Ltd.
D-84 Abul Fazl Enclave-I
Jamia Nagar
New Delhi 110 025, Delhi, India
Ph: 91 11 26947483
Fax: 91 11 26945825
Publisher E-mail: info@pharosmedia.com
Islamic history journal. **Founded:** 1995. **Freq:** Quarterly.
Key Personnel: Dr. Zafarul-Islam Khan, Editor; Prof.
Abd al-Halim Awis, Editorial Board; Dr. Mazin Motab-
baqani, Editorial Board. **Subscription Rates:** Rs 200
individuals in India and Bangladesh; Rs 400 institutions
in India and Bangladesh; Rs 100 students in India and
Bangladesh; US$10 other countries in Pakistan; US$5
students individuals in Pakistan; US$20 institutions in
Pakistan; US$30 other countries by airmail; US$15
students by airmail; US$60 institutions by airmail. **Re-
marks:** Accepts advertising. **URL:** http://www.
pharosmedia.com/islamic.htm. **Circ:** Paid 2,000

45611 ■ Journal of Islamic Law Review
Serials Publications
4830-24 Ansari Rd.
Darya Ganj
New Delhi 110 002, Delhi, India
Ph: 91 11 23245225
Fax: 91 11 23272135
Publisher E-mail: serials@satyam.net.in
Peer-reviewed journal dedicated to classical and modern
Islamic law in Muslim and non-Muslim countries. **Freq:**

Semiannual. **Key Personnel:** Prof. Abdul Haseeb Ansari, Contact, ahaseeb@iiu.edu.my. **ISSN:** 0973-2918.
Subscription Rates: Rs 2,000 institutions print. **URL:**
http://www.serialspublications.com/journals1.asp?jid=
393&jtype=1.

45612 ■ Journal of Laboratory Physicians
Medknow Publications Pvt Ltd.
c/o Dr. Sarman Singh, Ed.-in-Ch.
All India Institute of Medical Sciences
PO Box 4938
New Delhi 110 029, Delhi, India
Peer-reviewed journal covering laboratory medicine.
Founded: Jan. 2009. **Freq:** Semiannual. **Key Personnel:** Dr. Sarman Singh, Editor-in-Chief; Dr. Purva
Mathur, Asst. Ed., purvamathur@yahoo.co.in; Dr. Arul-
selvi Subramanian, Asst. Ed. **ISSN:** 0974-2727. **Subscription Rates:** Rs 1,000 individuals print only; Rs
1,500 institutions print only; US$100 other countries
print only; US$150 institutions, other countries print only;
Rs 1,200 individuals print and online; Rs 1,800 institutions print and online; US$120 other countries print and
online; US$180 institutions, other countries print and on-
line; Rs 800 individuals online; Rs 1,200 institutions
online. **Remarks:** Accepts advertising. **URL:** http://www.
jlponline.org. **Circ:** (Not Reported)

**45613 ■ Journal of Mathematical Analysis and
Approximation Theory**
Serials Publications
4830-24 Ansari Rd.
Darya Ganj
New Delhi 110 002, Delhi, India
Ph: 91 11 23245225
Fax: 91 11 23272135
Publisher E-mail: serials@satyam.net.in
Journal covering mathematical analysis and approxima-
tion theory. **Freq:** Semiannual. **ISSN:** 0973-5119. **Sub-
scription Rates:** US$250 institutions print. **URL:** http://
www.serialspublications.com/journals1.asp?jid=415&
jtype=1.

45614 ■ Journal of Objective Studies
Institute of Objective Studies
PO Box 9725
162-Joga Bai Ext.
Jamia Nagar
New Delhi 110 025, Delhi, India
Ph: 91 11 26981187
Fax: 91 11 26981104
Publisher E-mail: ios1@vsnl.com
Journal specializing in the study of changing problems
of the relationship between Religion and Law. **Founded:**
1992. **Freq:** Semiannual. **Key Personnel:** Prof. M. Ish-
tiaq, Managing Editor; Dr. Ishtiyaque Danish, Editor;
Prof. Z.M. Khan, Editor-in-Chief. **ISSN:** 0971-3220. **Sub-
scription Rates:** Rs 75 students; Rs 125 individuals for
India; Rs 200 institutions for India; Rs 100 students other
SAARC countries; Rs 150 individuals other SAARC
countries; Rs 250 institutions other SAARC countries;
US$25 other countries students; US$30 other countries
for individuals; US$40 institutions, other countries. **Re-
marks:** Accepts advertising. **URL:** http://www.iosworld.
org/jj2000.htm; http://www.iosworld.org/journalpage3.
htm. **Circ:** (Not Reported)

45615 ■ Journal of Pediatric Neurosciences
Medknow Publications Pvt Ltd.
c/o Dr. V.P. Singh
C5/12, 1st Fl.
Safdarjung Development Area
New Delhi 110016, Delhi, India
Journal covering pediatric neuroscience. **Founded:**
1952. **Freq:** Semiannual. **Print Method:** Offset. **Trim
Size:** 8.5 x 11. **Cols./Page:** 5. **Col. Width:** 2 1/16
inches. **Col. Depth:** 13 1/4 inches. **Key Personnel:**
Sanjay Behari, Editorial Board; Suresh Sankhla, Editor;
Uday Andar, Editorial Board. **ISSN:** 1817-1745. **Sub-
scription Rates:** Rs 1,000 individuals; US$100 other
countries; US$100 institutions, other countries; Rs 1,000
institutions. **Remarks:** Accepts advertising. **URL:** http://
www.pediatricneurosciences.com/. **Circ:** (Not Reported)

**45616 ■ Journal of Plant Biochemistry and Bio-
technology**
Society for Plant Biochemistry and Biotechnology
Division of Biochemistry
Indian Agricultural Research Institute
New Delhi 110 012, Delhi, India
Publication on plant biochemistry and biotechnology.

Founded: 1992. **Freq:** Semiannual. **Print Method:** Offset. **Key Personnel:** Dr. T.R. Sharma, Ch. Ed., sharmatr@nrcpb.org; S.R. Bhat, Editorial Board. **ISSN:** 0971-7811. **Subscription Rates:** EUR190 individuals; US$245 individuals. **Remarks:** Advertising not accepted. **URL:** http://www.iospress.nl/loadtop/load.php?isbn=09717811. **Circ:** Paid 750

45617 ■ Journal of Scientific and Industrial Research
National Institute of Science Communication and Information Resources
Dr. K S Krishnan Marg
Pusa Campus
New Delhi 110 012, Delhi, India
Ph: 91 11 25841647
Fax: 91 11 25847062
Publisher E-mail: webmaster@niscair.res.in
Journal focusing on science and technology, industry and management. **Founded:** 1942. **Freq:** Monthly. **Print Method:** Offset. **Trim Size:** A-4. **Key Personnel:** Dr. P.D. Tyagi, Editor; Dr. J.B. Gandhi, Assoc. Ed.; Dr. Sanjay Sengupta, Assoc. Ed. **ISSN:** 0022-4456. **Subscription Rates:** Rs 2,250 individuals; US$540 other countries. **URL:** http://niscair.res.in/sciencecommunication/ResearchJournals/rejour/Jsir/jsir0.asp. **Ad Rates:** BW: US$500; 4C: US$875. **Circ:** Paid 1100

45618 ■ Journal of Social Anthropology
Serials Publications
4830-24 Ansari Rd.
Darya Ganj
New Delhi 110 002, Delhi, India
Ph: 91 11 23245225
Fax: 91 11 23272135
Publisher E-mail: serials@satyam.net.in
Journal covering social anthropology. **Founded:** 1917. **Freq:** Semiannual. **Print Method:** Offset. **Cols./Page:** 6. **Col. Width:** 26 nonpareils. **Col. Depth:** 294 agate lines. **Key Personnel:** Dr. N.K. Das, Editor, nkdas49@gmail.com; Dr. Nilakantha Panigrahi, Assoc. Ed.; Dr. Lidia Julianna Guzy, Assoc. Ed. **ISSN:** 0973-3582. **Subscription Rates:** US$150 institutions print. **URL:** http://www.serialspublications.com/journals1.asp?jid=407&jtype=1.

45619 ■ Journal of Social and Economic Policy
Serials Publications
4830-24 Ansari Rd.
Darya Ganj
New Delhi 110 002, Delhi, India
Ph: 91 11 23245225
Fax: 91 11 23272135
Publisher E-mail: serials@satyam.net.in
Peer-reviewed journal covering social and economic issues. **Freq:** Semiannual. **Key Personnel:** Prof. N. Narayana, Ch. Ed., jsep.editor@gmail.com; S.K. Jha, Managing Editor, serials@satyam.net.in. **ISSN:** 0973-3426. **Subscription Rates:** Rs 2,000 institutions print. **URL:** http://www.serialspublications.com/journals1.asp?jid=383&jtype=1.

45620 ■ Journal of Statistics and Management Systems
Taru Publications
G-159, Pushkar Enclave
Pashchim Vihar
New Delhi 110 063, Delhi, India
Ph: 91 114 2331159
Fax: 91 114 2321126
Publisher E-mail: info@tarupublications.com
Journal focusing on statistics and management systems. **Founded:** 1998. **Freq:** Bimonthly. **Print Method:** Offset. **Trim Size:** 7 x 9.5. **Key Personnel:** Prof. Bal Kishan Dass, Editor-in-Chief, dassbk@rediffmail.com; Prof. P.R. Parthasarathy, Editorial Board, prp@iitm.ac.in; Prof. M. Kurano, Assoc. Ed., kurano@math.e.chibau.ac.jp; Prof. K.K. Aggarwal, Editorial Board, aggarwal_krishna@hotmail.com; Prof. S.N. Gupta, Editorial Board, sngupta@uncg.edu; Prof. A. Sapounakis, Assoc. Ed., arissap@unipi.gr; Prof. C.A. Botsaris, Assoc. Ed., botsaris@otenet.gr; Prof. K.L. Mak, Assoc. Ed., makkl@hkucc.hku.hk; Prof. Andrew Rosalsky, Assoc. Ed., rosalsky@stat.ufl.edu; Prof. Masoom M. Ali, Assoc. Ed., mali@bsu.edu. **ISSN:** 0972-0510. **Subscription Rates:** Rs 3,000 individuals print; US$400 out of country print; Rs 3,000 individuals online; US$350 out of country online; Rs 4,000 individuals print + online; US$400 out of

country print + online. **Remarks:** Advertising not accepted. **URL:** http://www.tarupublications.com/journals/jsms/jsms.htm. **Circ:** Paid 240

45621 ■ Labour and Industrial Law Reporter
International Law Book Co.
1562 Church Rd.
Kashmere Gate
New Delhi 110 006, Delhi, India
Ph: 91 11 3867810
Fax: 91 11 23864769
Publisher E-mail: ilbco@vsnl.com
Publication covering industrial law and labor topics. **Founded:** 1975. **Freq:** Monthly. **Subscription Rates:** US$1,050 individuals full set; Rs 14,310 individuals full set. **URL:** http://www.supremecourtcaselaw.com/lilr_full_set.htm.

45622 ■ Manushi
Manushi Trust
C1 - 202, Lajpat Nagar
New Delhi 110 024, Delhi, India
Publisher E-mail: editor@manushi-india.org
Journal on women and society. **Founded:** 1979. **Freq:** Bimonthly. **Key Personnel:** Madhu Purnima Kishwar, Founder/Ed. **ISSN:** 0257-7305. **Subscription Rates:** Rs 150 individuals; Rs 180 institutions; Rs 350 individuals Sri Lanka, Pakistan, Bangladesh, Nepal; Rs 450 institutions; $A 30 out of country; C$30 out of country; EUR15 out of country; US$25 out of country; US$15 out of country; US$36 out of country. **Remarks:** Advertising not accepted. **URL:** http://www.manushi-india.org/manushi-trust.htm. **Circ:** Paid 10,000

45623 ■ Margin
National Council of Applied Economic Research
Parisila Bhawan
11 Indraprastha Estate
New Delhi 110 002, Delhi, India
Ph: 91 11 23379861
Fax: 91 11 23370164
Publisher E-mail: infor@ncaer.org
Publication on business and economics. **Founded:** 1968. **Freq:** Quarterly. **Key Personnel:** Suman Berry, Editor-in-Chief; Anuradha Bhasin, Managing Editor. **ISSN:** 0973-8010. **Subscription Rates:** Rs 1,600 institutions; Rs 825 individuals. **URL:** http://www.ncaer.org/journals.html. **Circ:** Paid 600

45624 ■ Mass Media in India
Ministry of Information & Broadcasting
Smt. Stuti Narain Kacker
Rm. No. 552, A-Wing, Shastri Bhawan
New Delhi 110 001, Delhi, India
Ph: 91 112 3384453
Publisher E-mail: jsp.inb@nic.in
Government publication covering mass communications. **Founded:** 1978. **Freq:** Annual. **URL:** http://www.experiencefestival.com/mass_media_in_india.

45625 ■ Mathematics Today
MTG Learning Media (P) Ltd.
406, Taj Apt., Ring Rd.
Near Safdarjung Hospital
New Delhi 110 029, Delhi, India
Ph: 91 11 46686000
Fax: 91 26 191601
Publisher E-mail: info@mtg.in
Publication focusing on mathematics. **Freq:** Monthly. **Subscription Rates:** Rs 1,470 individuals; Rs 2,695 two years. **Remarks:** Accepts advertising. **URL:** http://www.pcmbtoday.com/mtgpp/maths/sep2007.php. **Ad Rates:** BW: Rs 1,200, 4C: Rs 3,000. **Circ:** Paid 50,000

45626 ■ Medicinal and Aromatic Plants Abstracts
National Institute of Science Communication
Council of Scientific and Industrial Research
Dr. K.S. Krishnan Marg Pusa Campus
New Delhi 110 012, Delhi, India
Ph: 91 11 25841647
Fax: 91 11 25847062
Publisher E-mail: webmaster@niscair.res.in
Publication featuring information about world publications on medicinal and aromatic plants. **Founded:** 1979. **Freq:** Bimonthly. **Print Method:** Offset. **Key Personnel:** Mr. S.D. Panwar, Editor, sdp@niscair.res.in; Dr. Darshan Sharma, Assoc. Ed., darshan@niscair.res.in; Mr. Rahul Kamble, Assoc. Ed., rahul@niscair.res.in. **ISSN:** 0250-4367. **Subscription Rates:** Rs 2,250 individuals

airmail; US$600 other countries airmail; Rs 450 single issue; US$120 single issue other countries. **URL:** http://www.niscair.res.in; http://www.niscair.res.in/sciencecommunication/abstractingjournals/mapaintro.asp. **Circ:** Paid 550

45627 ■ Municipalities and Corporation Cases
International Law Book Co.
1562 Church Rd.
Kashmere Gate
New Delhi 110 006, Delhi, India
Ph: 91 11 3867810
Fax: 91 11 23864769
Publisher E-mail: ilbco@vsnl.com
Contains court cases dealing with municipalities and corporations. **Founded:** 1973. **Freq:** Monthly. **ISSN:** 0377-757X. **Subscription Rates:** Rs 700 individuals; Rs 18,000 individuals full set; US$1600 individuals full set. **URL:** http://www.supremecourtcaselaw.com/MCC.htm.

45628 ■ Muslim & Arab Perspectives
Pharos Media & Publishing (P) Ltd.
D-84 Abul Fazl Enclave-I
Jamia Nagar
New Delhi 110 025, Delhi, India
Ph: 91 11 26947483
Fax: 91 11 26945825
Publisher E-mail: info@pharosmedia.com
Publication focusing on ethnic studies of Muslims and Arabs. **Founded:** 1993. **Freq:** Quarterly. **Key Personnel:** Zafarul-Islam Khan, Editor. **ISSN:** 0971-4367. **Subscription Rates:** Rs 250 individuals Nepal; EUR25 individuals; Rs 500 institutions; EUR50 institutions. **Remarks:** Accepts advertising. **URL:** http://www.pharosmedia.com/map.htm; http://www.pharosmedia.com/journals.htm. **Circ:** Paid 3,000

45629 ■ The National Medical Journal of India
All India Institute of Medical Sciences
Ansari Nagar
New Delhi 110 029, Delhi, India
Ph: 91 11 26588500
Fax: 91 11 26588663
Publication E-mail: nmji@aiims.aiims.ac.in
Journal covering the medical sciences. **Founded:** 1988. **Freq:** Bimonthly. **Print Method:** Offset. **Trim Size:** 210 x 280 mm. **Key Personnel:** P. Sahni, Editor; S. Nundy, Emeritus Ed.; K.S. Reddy, Editorial Board; S.S. Agarwal, Editorial Board; R.Y. Calne, Editorial Board; S. Chandrasekar, Editorial Board; John Black, Editorial Board. **ISSN:** 0970-258X. **Subscription Rates:** Rs 600 individuals; Rs 1100 two years; US$85 out of country; US$150 two years overseas. **Remarks:** Accepts advertising. **URL:** http://www.nmji.in/. **Ad Rates:** BW: US$150, 4C: US$120. **Circ:** Combined ‡2,500

45630 ■ Neurology India
Neurological Society of India
c/o Dr. B.S. Sharma
Dept. of Neurosurgery
Neurosciences Centre, All India Institute of Medical Sciences
New Delhi 110 029, Delhi, India
Ph: 91 11 26593291
Publisher E-mail: droharmabs@yahoo.com
Medical journal focusing on neurology. **Founded:** 1952. **Freq:** Quarterly. **Key Personnel:** Dr. J.M.K. Murthy, Editor, jmkmurthy@sify.com; Dr. V.K. Khosla, President, khoslavk@gmail.com. **ISSN:** 0028-3886. **Subscription Rates:** Rs 1,500 individuals; Rs 2,500 institutions; US$120 other countries; US$2,000 institutions, other countries; postage and handling extra. **Remarks:** Accepts advertising. **URL:** http://www.neurosocietyindia.com/NeurologyIndia.aspx; http://www.neurologyindia.com/. **Circ:** Paid 1,600

45631 ■ The Nursing Journal of India
Trained Nurses Association of India
Florence Nightingale Ln.
L-17 Green Pk.
New Delhi 110 016, Delhi, India
Ph: 91 112 6566665
Fax: 91 112 6858304
Publisher E-mail: tnai_2003@yahoo.com
Journal on nursing. **Founded:** 1910. **Freq:** Monthly. **ISSN:** 0029-6503. **Subscription Rates:** Rs 1,100 individuals non TNAI members, plus postage; US$165 other countries non TNAI members, plus postage. **Remarks:** Accepts advertising. **URL:** http://tnaionline.org/

Circulation: ★ = ABC; △ = BPA; ♦ = CAC; • = CCAB; □ = VAC; ⊕ = PO Statement; ‡ = Publisher's Report; Boldface figures = sworn; Light figures = estimated.

thenursing.htm. **Circ:** Paid 6,000

45632 ■ Organiser
Bharath Prakashan (Delhi) Ltd.
Sanskriti Bhawan
D.B. Gupta Rd.
New Delhi 110 055, Delhi, India
Ph: 91 112 3626977
Fax: 91 112 3516635
Publication E-mail: editor@organiserweekly.com
Publisher E-mail: editor@organiserweekly.com
General news magazine. **Founded:** 1947. **Freq:** Weekly.
Key Personnel: R. Balashankar, Editor. **ISSN:** 0030-5014. **Subscription Rates:** Rs 325 individuals; Rs 625 individuals 2 years; Rs 1,500 individuals 5 years; Rs 2,500 by mail foreign (by air). **Remarks:** Accepts advertising. **URL:** http://www.organiser.org/dynamic/modules.php?name=Content&pa=showpage&pid=279.
Ad Rates: BW: Rs 47,500. **Circ:** Paid 8,632

45633 ■ Outlook
C. Raveendra
The Outlook Group
AB-10, Safdarjung Enclave
New Delhi 110 029, Delhi, India
Ph: 91 112 6191421
Fax: 91 112 6191420
Publisher E-mail: outlook@outlookindia.com
General news magazine. **Founded:** Oct. 1995. **Freq:** Weekly. **Key Personnel:** Vinod Mehta, Editor-in-Chief; Bishwadeep Moitra, Exec. Ed.; Sunit Arora, Bus. Ed.; Nandini Mehta, Managing Editor; Ajaz Ashraf, Foreign Ed.; Ajith Pillai, Sen. Ed.; Anjali Puri, Sen. Ed.; Smita Gupta, Political Ed.; Sunil Menon, Sen. Ed.; Sheela Reddy, Books Ed. **Subscription Rates:** US$75 other countries 26 issues; US$53 individuals Bhutan/Bangladesh/Nepal, 51 issues; Rs 3,300 other countries 26 issues; Rs 2,400 individuals Bhutan/Bangladesh/Nepal, 51 issues. **Remarks:** Accepts advertising. **URL:** http://www.outlookindia.com/. **Circ:** Paid 178,276

45634 ■ Overseas Business Contacts
Associated Chambers of Commerce and Industry of India
Corporate Office, 1, Community Ctr. Zamrudpur
Kailash Colony
New Delhi 110 048, Delhi, India
Ph: 91 11 46550555
Fax: 91 11 46536481
Publisher E-mail: assocham@nic.in
Magazine on international business and business contacts. **Freq:** Biweekly. **Subscription Rates:** Rs 2,000 individuals. **Remarks:** Accepts advertising. **URL:** http://www.assocham.org/publications/per.php. **Ad Rates:** BW: Rs 6,000, 4C: Rs 8,000. **Circ:** Paid 4,000

45635 ■ The Pharma Review
KONGPOSH Publications Pvt. Ltd.
ICS House, 2nd Fl., C-19
Commercial Complex
New Delhi 110 016, Delhi, India
Ph: 91 11 26855839
Fax: 91 11 26855876
Publisher E-mail: info@kppub.com
Magazine focusing on the pharmaceutical industry. **Freq:** Bimonthly. **Subscription Rates:** Rs 500 individuals; US$125 other countries. **Remarks:** Accepts advertising. **URL:** http://www.kppub.com/pharma_review.htm. **Circ:** (Not Reported)

45636 ■ Physics For You
MTG Learning Media (P) Ltd.
406, Taj Apt., Ring Rd.
Near Safdarjung Hospital
New Delhi 110 029, Delhi, India
Ph: 91 11 46686000
Fax: 91 26 191601
Publisher E-mail: info@mtg.in
Physics publication featuring study material for exams in India. **Freq:** Monthly. **Subscription Rates:** Rs 1,470 individuals; Rs 2,695 two years. **URL:** http://www.pcmbtoday.com; http://www.pcmbtoday.com/mtgpp/physics/sep2007.php.

45637 ■ Prevention of Food Adulteration Cases
International Law Book Co.
1562 Church Rd.
Kashmere Gate
New Delhi 110 006, Delhi, India
Ph: 91 11 3867810

Fax: 91 11 23864769
Publisher E-mail: ilbco@vsnl.com
Law journal dealing with law on the prevention of food adulteration. **Founded:** 1972. **Freq:** Monthly. **Subscription Rates:** Rs 450 individuals; US$30 individuals; Rs 33,750 individuals full set; US$2,250 individuals full set. **URL:** http://www.supremecourtcaselaw.com/FAC.htm.

45638 ■ Productivity
National Productivity Council
Utpadakta Bhawan, 5-6 Institutional Area
Lodhi Rd.
New Delhi 110 003, Delhi, India
Ph: 91 112 4690331
Fax: 91 112 4615002
Publisher E-mail: info@npcindia.org
Publication on production management. **Founded:** 1959. **Freq:** Quarterly. **Key Personnel:** K.P. Sunny, Editor. **ISSN:** 0032-9924. **Subscription Rates:** Rs 1,200 individuals inland; Rs 300 single issue; US$100 other countries foreign; US$25 single issue other countries; US$50 individuals SAARC; US$15 single issue SAARC individual. **Remarks:** Accepts advertising. **URL:** http://www.npcindia.org/period.htmproductivity. **Circ:** Paid 3,000

45639 ■ Productivity News
National Productivity Council
Utpadakta Bhawan, 5-6 Institutional Area
Lodhi Rd.
New Delhi 110 003, Delhi, India
Ph: 91 112 4690331
Fax: 91 112 4615002
Publisher E-mail: info@npcindia.org
Publication on production management. **Founded:** 1963. **Freq:** Bimonthly. **Trim Size:** 21 1/2 x 22 cm. **ISSN:** 0970-5597. **Subscription Rates:** Rs 300 individuals; US$30 other countries. **Remarks:** Accepts advertising. **URL:** http://www.npcindia.org/period.htmproductivity. **Ad Rates:** BW: Rs 5,500, 4C: Rs 1,450. **Circ:** Paid 2,500

45640 ■ Psychology and Developing Societies
Sage Publications India Private Ltd.
B-1/I-1 Mohan Cooperative Industrial Area
Mathura Rd.
New Delhi 110 044, Delhi, India
Ph: 91 11 40539222
Fax: 91 11 40539234
Publisher E-mail: info@sagepub.in
Research journal on psychiatry and psychology. **Founded:** 1989. **Freq:** Semiannual. **Key Personnel:** Ajit K. Dalal, Editor; Dharma Bhawuk, Consulting Ed.; Henry S.R. Kao, Editorial Board; Ramadhar Singh, Editorial Board; Anand Paranjpe, Editorial Board; Janak Pandey, Editorial Board; John W. Berry, Editorial Board; Purnima Singh, Assoc. Ed.; Namita Pande, Assoc. Ed.; Rashmi Kumar, Assoc. Ed. **ISSN:** 0971-3336. **Subscription Rates:** US$326 institutions print & e-access; US$60 single issue; US$293 institutions e-access; US$326 institutions e-access plus backfile (all online content); US$293 institutions backfile purchase, e-access; US$319 institutions print only; US$93 individuals print only; US$175 institutions single, print. **Remarks:** Accepts advertising. **URL:** http://www.sagepub.com/journalsProdDesc.nav?prodId=Journal200945. **Circ:** Paid 500

45641 ■ Recent Advances in Pediatrics
Jaypee Brothers Medical Publishers Private Ltd.
4838/24 Ansari Rd.
Daryaganj
PO Box 7193
New Delhi 110 002, Delhi, India
Ph: 91 11 23272143
Fax: 91 11 23276490
Publisher E-mail: jaypee@jaypeebrothers.com
Medical journal focusing on pediatrics. **Freq:** Irregular. **Key Personnel:** Suraj Gupte, Editor. **Subscription Rates:** Rs 20 individuals. **URL:** http://www.jaypeebrothers.com/pgDetails.aspx?cat=s&book_id=81-8061-723-8.

45642 ■ Recent Researches in Geology
Hindustan Publishing Corp.
4805 Bharat Ram Rd.
24 Darya Ganj
New Delhi 110 002, Delhi, India
Ph: 91 113 254401
Fax: 91 116 193511

Publisher E-mail: hpcpd@hpc.cc
Publication focusing on geology research. **Founded:** 1973. **Freq:** Irregular. **Key Personnel:** K.L Rai, Editor; Gurdeep Singh, Editor. **ISSN:** 0970-9606. **Subscription Rates:** US$53 individuals. **URL:** http://www.vedamsbooks.com/no11351.htm.

45643 ■ Religion and Law Review
Institute of Objective Studies
PO Box 9725
162-Joga Bai Ext.
Jamia Nagar
New Delhi 110 025, Delhi, India
Ph: 91 11 26981187
Fax: 91 11 26981104
Publisher E-mail: ios1@vsnl.com
Community magazine on Religion and Law. **Founded:** 1992. **Freq:** Semiannual. **Key Personnel:** Prof. Tahir Mahamood, Founder Ed.; Dr. Christian W. Troll, Contact; Qazi Mujahid-Ul-Islam, Contact. **ISSN:** 0971-3212. **Subscription Rates:** Rs 100 individuals; Rs 150 institutions; US$10 other countries SAARC Countries; US$15 institutions SAARC Countries; US$25 other countries; US$40 institutions, other countries. **Remarks:** Accepts advertising. **URL:** http://www.iosworld.org/rlr0.htm. **Circ:** (Not Reported)

45644 ■ Resources, Energy and Development
Tata Energy Research Institute
Darbari Seth Block
IHC Complex, Lodhi Rd.
Lodhi Rd.
New Delhi 110 003, Delhi, India
Ph: 91 112 4682100
Fax: 91 112 4682144
Publisher E-mail: mailbox@teri.res.in
Journal of energy and power resources. **Freq:** Semiannual. **ISSN:** 0973-0516. **Subscription Rates:** EUR135 individuals; US$162 individuals. **Remarks:** Accepts advertising. **URL:** http://www.iospress.nl/loadtop/load.php?isbn=09730516. **Formed by the merger of:** Journal of Environmental Studies and Policy; Pacific and Asian Journal on Energy. **Circ:** Paid 1,800

45645 ■ Review of Applied Economics
Serials Publications
4830-24 Ansari Rd.
Darya Ganj
New Delhi 110 002, Delhi, India
Ph: 91 11 23245225
Fax: 91 11 23272135
Publisher E-mail: serials@satyam.net.in
Journal devoted to the practical applications of economic ideas. **Freq:** Semiannual. **Key Personnel:** Christopher Gan, Editor; Minsoo Lee, Assoc. Ed. **ISSN:** 0973-1687. **Subscription Rates:** US$95 institutions print. **URL:** http://www.serialspublications.com/journals1.asp?jid=384&jtype=1.

45646 ■ Roshni
All India Women's Conference
Sarojini House
6 Bhagwan Dass Rd.
New Delhi 110 001, Delhi, India
Ph: 91 112 3389680
Fax: 91 112 3384092
Publisher E-mail: info@aiwc.org
Publication on women and their problems. **Founded:** 1940. **Freq:** Quarterly. **Key Personnel:** Dr. Manorama Bawa, President; Shivani Mehta, Vice President. **URL:** http://www.aiwc.org/publications.htm. **Circ:** Paid 500

45647 ■ School Science
National Council of Educational Research and Training
Sri Aurbindo Marg
New Delhi 110 016, Delhi, India
Ph: 91 112 6560620
Fax: 91 112 6868419
Publisher E-mail: proncert@yahoo.co.in
Journal on science and education for secondary schools published by National Council of Educational Research and Training. **Founded:** 1962. **Freq:** Quarterly. **Key Personnel:** R. Joshi, Contact. **ISSN:** 0036-679X. **Subscription Rates:** Rs 55 single issue; US$2 single issue; 1 single issue; Rs 220 individuals; US$8 individuals; 4 individuals. **Remarks:** Accepts advertising. **URL:** http://www.ncert.nic.in/html/journals.htm. **Circ:** Paid 1,000

45648 ■ Science, Technology & Society
Sage Publications India Private Ltd.
B-1/I-1 Mohan Cooperative Industrial Area

Mathura Rd.
New Delhi 110 044, Delhi, India
Ph: 91 11 40539222
Fax: 91 11 40539234
Publisher E-mail: info@sagepub.in
General science magazine. **Subtitle:** An International Journal Devoted to the Developing World. **Founded:** 1996. **Freq:** Semiannual March and September. **Print Method:** Offset. **Key Personnel:** V.V. Krishna, Editor; Roland Waast, Editor. **ISSN:** 0971-7218. **Subscription Rates:** US$344 institutions all online content; US$310 institutions backfile purchase, e-access; US$337 institutions print only; US$88 individuals print only; US$124 institutions single; US$38 single issue; US$310 institutions e-access; US$344 institutions combined (print & e-access). **Remarks:** Accepts advertising. **URL:** http://www.sagepub.com/journalsProdDesc.nav?prodId=Journal200804. **Ad Rates:** BW: Rs 100. **Circ:** Paid 500

45649 ■ Screen
Indian Express Newspapers (Bombay) Private Ltd.
9&10 Bhadur Shah Zafar Marg
Express Bldg., ITO
New Delhi 110 002, Delhi, India
Ph: 91 11 23702618
Fax: 91 11 23702141
Publisher E-mail: editor@expressindia.com
English publication focusing on Indian and international films. **Founded:** 1950. **Freq:** Weekly. **Key Personnel:** Bhawana Somaaya, Editor. **ISSN:** 0036-9551. **Remarks:** Accepts advertising. **URL:** http://www.screenindia.com/; http://www.expressindia.com/screen. **Circ:** Paid 28,700

45650 ■ SESI Journal
Tata Energy Research Institute
Darbari Seth Block
IHC Complex, Lodhi Rd.
Lodhi Rd.
New Delhi 110 003, Delhi, India
Ph: 91 112 4682100
Fax: 91 112 4682144
Publisher E-mail: mailbox@teri.res.in
Publication focusing on solar and other renewable energy sources. **Founded:** 1987. **Freq:** Semiannual. **ISSN:** 0970-2466. **Subscription Rates:** US$150 individuals; US$24 other countries. **Remarks:** Accepts advertising. **URL:** http://www.sesi.in/sesijournal.asp. **Formerly:** SESI Journal. **Circ:** Paid 2,000

45651 ■ Social Welfare
Central Social Welfare Board
Samaj Kalyan Bhawan
B-12, Qutab Institutional Area
New Delhi 110 016, Delhi, India
Ph: 91 112 6960059
Political science publication. **Freq:** Monthly. **Key Personnel:** Poonam Sharma, Editor; Anju Srivastava, Editor; Manjit Singh, Asst. Ed.; Neelam Bhardwaj, Joint Dir.; Rimjhim Prasad, Exec. Dir.; Rajani Patil, Chp. **ISSN:** 0037-8038. **Subscription Rates:** Rs 10 single issue for life; Rs 100 individuals social welfare or Samaj Kalyan; 160 IKr individuals social welfare & Samaj Kalyan; US$14 other countries Bangladesh, Sri Lanka, Nepal, Bhutan & Pakistan; US$40 out of country international; Rs 1,000 individuals life membership social welfare or Samaj Kalyan; Rs 1,600 individuals combined life membership for social welfare. **URL:** http://cswb.gov.in/index1.asp?linkid=236&langid=1. **Circ:** Paid 3,000

45652 ■ South Asian Survey
Sage Publications India Private Ltd.
B-1/I-1 Mohan Cooperative Industrial Area
Mathura Rd.
New Delhi 110 044, Delhi, India
Ph: 91 11 40539222
Fax: 91 11 40539234
Publisher E-mail: info@sagepub.in
Publication covering Asian history. Serves as a forum to share fresh thinking and to debate matters of national and regional concern to the countries of South Asia. **Freq:** Semiannual March and September. **Key Personnel:** Varun Sahni, Editor; I.P. Khosla, Editor-in-Chief. **ISSN:** 0971-5231. **Subscription Rates:** US$314 institutions all online content; US$283 institutions backfile purchase, e-access; US$308 institutions print only; US$89 institutions print only; US$169 individuals single, print; US$58 single issue; US$314 institutions combined (print & e-access); US$283 institutions e-access. **Re-**

marks: Accepts advertising. **Online:** Sage Publications Ltd. **URL:** http://www.sagepub.com/journalsProdDesc.nav?prodId=Journal200973. **Circ:** Paid 500

45653 ■ Standards India
Bureau of Indian Standards
Manak Bhavan
9 Bahadur Shah Zafar Marg
New Delhi 110 002, Delhi, India
Ph: 91 112 3230131
Fax: 91 112 3234062
Publication E-mail: pub@bis.org.in
Publisher E-mail: info@bis.org.in
Publication on metrology and standards. **Freq:** Monthly. **Print Method:** Offset. **Key Personnel:** Kala Variar, Editor, phone 91 112 3237995, fax 91 112 3231105. **ISSN:** 0970-2628. **Subscription Rates:** Rs 700 individuals; Rs 350 individuals. **Remarks:** Advertising not accepted. **URL:** http://www.bis.org.in/other/ad-india.htm. **Circ:** Paid 4,000

45654 ■ Statistical Pocket Book
Central Statistical Organization—India
Sardar Patel Bhavan
Sansad Marg
New Delhi 110 001, Delhi, India
Ph: 91 233 89604
Fax: 91 233 86384
Periodical featuring Indian statistical data. **Subtitle:** India. **Founded:** 1956. **Freq:** Annual. **ISSN:** 0081-5012. **URL:** http://mospi.nic.in/mospi_cso_rept_pubn.htm; http://mospi.nic.in/stat_act_t9.htm.

45655 ■ Strategic Analysis
Institute for Defence Studies and Analyses
1, Development Enclave, (near USI)
Rau Tula Ram Marg
New Delhi 110 010, Delhi, India
Ph: 91 11 26717983
Fax: 91 11 26154191
Publisher E-mail: idsa@vsnl.com
Journal containing research papers, short communications and commentaries contributed by Institute for Defence Studies and Analyses research faculty and external scholars. **Founded:** 1977. **Freq:** Bimonthly. **Print Method:** Offset. **Trim Size:** 7.2 x 9.6. **Key Personnel:** Narendra Sisodia, Editor. **ISSN:** 0970-0161. **Subscription Rates:** US$619 institutions print + online; US$557 institutions online only; US$94 individuals; 316 institutions print and online; 284 institutions online only; 59 individuals; EUR494 institutions print and online; EUR445 institutions online only; EUR94 individuals. **Remarks:** Advertising not accepted. **URL:** http://www.idsa.in/strategicanalysis. **Circ:** Paid 2,200

45656 ■ Strategic Digest
Institute for Defence Studies and Analyses
1, Development Enclave, (near USI)
Rau Tula Ram Marg
New Delhi 110 010, Delhi, India
Ph: 91 11 26717983
Fax: 91 11 26154191
Publisher E-mail: idsa@vsnl.com
Journal containing digest of current literature. **Founded:** Jan. 1971. **Freq:** Monthly. **Print Method:** Offset. **Trim Size:** 7.2 x 9.6. **ISSN:** 0970-017X. **Subscription Rates:** Rs 550 individuals; Rs 50 single issue. **Remarks:** Advertising not accepted. **URL:** http://www.idsa.in. **Circ:** Paid 2,200

45657 ■ Studies in History (New Delhi)
Sage Publications India Private Ltd.
B-1/I-1 Mohan Cooperative Industrial Area
Mathura Rd.
New Delhi 110 044, Delhi, India
Ph: 91 11 40539222
Fax: 91 11 40539234
Publisher E-mail: info@sagepub.in
Journal examining regional problems and pays attention to some of the neglected periods of India's past. Reflects the considerable expansion and diversification that has occurred in historical research in India in recent years. **Freq:** Semiannual. **Key Personnel:** Yogesh Sharma, Editorial Advisory Board; Najaf Haider, Editor. **ISSN:** 0257-6430. **Subscription Rates:** US$328 institutions print and online; US$295 institutions online only; US$321 institutions print only; US$89 individuals print only. **Remarks:** Accepts advertising. **URL:** http://www.sagepub.com/journalsProdDesc.nav?prodId=Journal200953. **Circ:** Paid 500

45658 ■ TerraGreen
The Energy and Resources Institute
Darbari Seth Block
IHC Complex, Lodhi Rd.
New Delhi 110 003, Delhi, India
Ph: 91 11 24682100
Fax: 91 11 24682144
Publisher E-mail: mailbox@teri.res.in
Magazine dealing with environment, energy, and sustainable development news from India. **Freq:** Monthly. **Key Personnel:** Dr. R.K. Pachauri, Editor-in-Chief; Leena Srivastava, Editorial Board; R.K. Batra, Editorial Board; Roshni Sengupta, Editorial Coord.; Rajiv Seth, Editorial Board; Anupama Jauhry, Managing Editor. **Subscription Rates:** Rs 400 individuals; US$102 individuals; Rs 750 two years; US$192 two years; Rs 1,000 individuals 3 years (free online); US$252 individuals 3 years (free online). **URL:** http://terragreen.teriin.org/.

45659 ■ TIDEE—Teri Information Digest on Energy and Environment
Tata Energy Research Institute
Darbari Seth Block
IHC Complex, Lodhi Rd.
Lodhi Rd.
New Delhi 110 003, Delhi, India
Ph: 91 112 4682100
Fax: 91 112 4682144
Publisher E-mail: mailbox@teri.res.in
Information digest on power and energy resources. **Founded:** 1991. **Freq:** Quarterly. **ISSN:** 0972-6721. **Subscription Rates:** EUR1,400 individuals print; US$2,100 individuals print and online. **Remarks:** Accepts advertising. **URL:** http://www.iospress.nl/loadtop/load.php?isbn=09726721. **Formerly:** TIDE—Teri Information Digest on Energy. **Circ:** Paid 2,200

45660 ■ The Upper India Motorist
Automobile Association of Upper India
C-8 Qutab Institutional Area
Behind of Qutab Hotel
New Delhi 110 016, Delhi, India
Ph: 91 11 26965397
Fax: 91 11 26866302
Publisher E-mail: aauindia@airtelmail.in
Publication on automotive and transportation. **Founded:** 1954. **Freq:** Monthly. **Key Personnel:** T. K. Malhotra, President, aauindia@de13.vsnl.net.in; R.K. Anand, Vice President. **ISSN:** 0500-6813. **Subscription Rates:** Included in membership. **Remarks:** Accepts advertising. **URL:** http://www.aaui.org/publications.htm. **Circ:** Combined 20,000

45661 ■ USI Journal
United Service Institution of India
Rao Tula Ram Marg (Opp. Signal Enclave)
PO Box 8
Vasant Vihar PO
New Delhi 110 057, Delhi, India
Ph: 91 11 26146755
Fax: 91 11 26149773
Publisher E-mail: sudhir1@ndf.vsnl.net.in
Periodical covering defense and national security (English). **Founded:** 1871. **Freq:** Quarterly. **Print Method:** Offset. **Key Personnel:** P.J.S. Sandhu, Dep. Dir. & Ed., dde@usiofindia.org. **ISSN:** 0041-770X. **Subscription Rates:** Rs 500 individuals; Rs 1,000 two years; 40 other countries; US$65 other countries; Rs 1,500 individuals 3 years. **Remarks:** Accepts advertising. **URL:** http://www.usiofindia.org/Publications/Journal/. **Ad Rates:** BW: Rs 2,500, PCI: Rs 80. **Circ:** Paid 9,500

45662 ■ VATIS Update Biotechnology
Asian and Pacific Centre for Transfer of Technology
C-2 Qutab Institutional Area
PO Box 4575
New Delhi 110 016, Delhi, India
Ph: 91 11 26966509
Fax: 91 11 26856274
Publisher E-mail: postmaster@apctt.org
Periodical focusing on biotechnology information. **Founded:** 1993. **Freq:** Bimonthly. **Print Method:** Offset. **Trim Size:** 28 x 21.5 cm. **ISSN:** 0971-5657. **Subscription Rates:** Rs 1,000 individuals; US$100 other countries. **Remarks:** Accepts advertising. **URL:** http://www.techmonitor.net/tm/index.php?title=Welcome_to_

Techmonitor.net. **Ad Rates:** BW: US$3,750, 4C: US$5,000. **Circ:** 700

45663 ▪ VATIS Update Food Processing
Asian and Pacific Centre for Transfer of Technology
C-2 Qutab Institutional Area
PO Box 4575
New Delhi 110 016, Delhi, India
Ph: 91 11 26966509
Fax: 91 11 26856274
Publisher E-mail: postmaster@apctt.org
Publication featuring information on value added technology. **Founded:** 1993. **Freq:** Bimonthly. **Print Method:** Offset. **Trim Size:** 28 x 21.5 cm. **Key Personnel:** Nanjundappa Srinivasan, Editor; Dr. Satyabrata Sahu, Editor. **ISSN:** 0971-5622. **Remarks:** Accepts advertising. **URL:** http://www.techmonitor.net/tm/index.php?title=VATIS_Update_Food_Processing_. **Ad Rates:** BW: US$3,750, 4C: US$5,000. **Circ:** 500

45664 ▪ VATIS Update Non-Conventional Energy
Asian and Pacific Centre for Transfer of Technology
C-2 Qutab Institutional Area
PO Box 4575
New Delhi 110 016, Delhi, India
Ph: 91 11 26966509
Fax: 91 11 26856274
Publisher E-mail: postmaster@apctt.org
Publication featuring information on value added technology of non conventional energy. **Founded:** 1993. **Freq:** Bimonthly. **Print Method:** Offset. **Trim Size:** 28 x 21.5 cm. **Key Personnel:** Dr. K. Ramanathan, Editor; Nanjundappa Srinivasan, Editor; Dr. Satyabrata Sahu, Editor. **ISSN:** 0971-5630. **Remarks:** Accepts advertising. **URL:** http://www.techmonitor.net/tm/index.php?title=VATIS_Update_Non-conventional_Energy_._Jul-Aug_2010. **Ad Rates:** BW: US$3,750, 4C: US$5,000. **Circ:** 700

45665 ▪ VATIS Update Ozone Layer Protection
Asian and Pacific Centre for Transfer of Technology
C-2 Qutab Institutional Area
PO Box 4575
New Delhi 110 016, Delhi, India
Ph: 91 11 26966509
Fax: 91 11 26856274
Publisher E-mail: postmaster@apctt.org
Publication featuring information on value added technology of environment protection. **Founded:** 1993. **Freq:** Bimonthly. **Print Method:** Offset. **Trim Size:** 28 x 27.5 cm. **Key Personnel:** Nanjundappa Srinivasan, Editorial Board; Sushma Choudhary, Editorial Board; Dr. Sachidananda Satapathy, Editorial Board; Dr. Satyabrata Sahu, Editorial Board; R. Chandramohan, Editorial Board; Usha Chandrashekar, Editorial Board. **ISSN:** 0971-5657. **Remarks:** Accepts advertising. **URL:** http://www.techmonitor.net/tm/index.php?title=VATIS_Update_Ozone_Layer_Protection_._May-Jun_2010. **Ad Rates:** BW: US$3,750, 4C: US$5,000. **Circ:** 2,300

45666 ▪ VATIS Update Waste Management
Asian and Pacific Centre for Transfer of Technology
C-2 Qutab Institutional Area
PO Box 4575
New Delhi 110 016, Delhi, India
Ph: 91 11 26966509
Fax: 91 11 26856274
Publisher E-mail: postmaster@apctt.org
Publication featuring information on value added technology of waste management. **Founded:** 1994. **Freq:** Bimonthly. **Print Method:** Offset. **Trim Size:** 28 x 21.5 cm. **Key Personnel:** Nanjundappa Srinivasan, Editorial Board; Dr. D.B. Boralkar, Editorial Board. **ISSN:** 0971-5665. **Remarks:** Accepts advertising. **URL:** http://www.techmonitor.net/techmon/07jan_feb/was/was_home.htm. **Ad Rates:** BW: US$3,750, 4C: US$5,000. **Circ:** 500

45667 ▪ Vayu Mandal
Indian Meteorological Society
601, Satellite Bldg.
India Meteorological Department
Lodi Rd.
New Delhi 110 003, Delhi, India
Ph: 91 11 24620701
Fax: 91 11 24699216
Publisher E-mail: sdatti@yahoo.com
Journal on environment and meteorology. **Freq:** Quarterly. **Key Personnel:** S. K. Dash, Contact; R.C. Bhatia, President, phone 91 11 24611842, rc_bhatia@

hotmail.com. **ISSN:** 0970-1397. **Subscription Rates:** Rs 50 members; US$10 other countries; Rs 1000 institutions. **Remarks:** Accepts advertising. **URL:** http://www.ncmrwf.gov.in/ims/. **Circ:** Paid 1,000

45668 ▪ Woman's Era
Delhi Press Patra Prakashan Ltd.
E-3 Jhandewala Estate
New Delhi 110 055, Delhi, India
Ph: 91 112 3529557
Fax: 91 112 3625020
Women's magazine (English). **Founded:** 1973. **Freq:** Biweekly. **Subscription Rates:** Rs 30 single issue print; Rs 135 single issue print; Rs 315 individuals pdf copy (six months); Rs 450 individuals pdf copy; Rs 45 individuals pdf copy; Rs 650 individuals print copy; US$70 other countries print copy; US$35 other countries print copy (six months). **Remarks:** Advertising accepted; rates available upon request. **URL:** http://www.womansera.com/shop/we.aspx. **Circ:** Paid 79,428

45669 ▪ Working Class
Centre of Indian Trade Unions
B.T. Ranadive Bhawan
13-A, Rouse Ave.
New Delhi 110 002, Delhi, India
Ph: 91 11 23221288
Fax: 91 11 23221284
Publisher E-mail: citu@bol.net.in
Bulletin of working class and labor. **Freq:** Monthly. **Key Personnel:** M.K. Pandhe, Editor. **ISSN:** 0377-6611. **Remarks:** Accepts advertising. **URL:** http://www.citucentre.org/monthly_journals/working_class.php. **Circ:** Paid 6,500

45670 ▪ Yojana
Ministry of Information & Broadcasting
Smt. Stuti Narain Kacker
Rm. No. 552, A-Wing, Shastri Bhawan
New Delhi 110 001, Delhi, India
Ph: 91 112 3384453
Publisher E-mail: jsp.inb@nic.in
Government publication on planning. **Freq:** Monthly. **ISSN:** 0044-0515. **Subscription Rates:** Rs 7 single issue; Rs 70 individuals; Rs 135 two years; Rs 190 individuals 3 years. **Remarks:** Accepts advertising. **URL:** http://publicationsdivision.nic.in/Journals/Yojana-Eng.htm. **Circ:** Paid 150,000

45671 ▪ Youth Hosteller
Youth Hostels Association of India
5 Nyaya Marg
Chanakyapuri
New Delhi 110 021, Delhi, India
Ph: 91 112 6110250
Fax: 91 112 6113469
Publisher E-mail: info@yhainda.org
English and Hindi publication covering youth hostelling in India and abroad plus allied topics. **Freq:** 3/yr. **Print Method:** Offset. **Trim Size:** A4. **Subscription Rates:** Rs 30 members. **Remarks:** Advertising not accepted. **URL:** http://www34.brinkster.com/vizagbusiness/pages/YHAI/services.htm. **Circ:** 45,000

45672 ▪ AIR-FM - 106.4
Akashvani Bhavan, Rm. No. 204
Sansad Marg
PO Box 500
New Delhi 110 001, Delhi, India
Ph: 91 11 23421062
Fax: 91 11 23421062
E-mail: airlive@air.org.in
Format: Educational; Information. **Key Personnel:** Shri Brijeshwar Singh, Dir. Gen., phone 91 11 23421300, fax 91 11 23421956; Shri K.M. Paul, Engr. in Ch., phone 91 11 23421058, fax 91 11 23421459; Sh G.C Rai, Ch. Engr. (STI(T)), phone 91 11 27216128, fax 91 11 27216128, delhi.stit@air.org.in. **Ad Rates:** Advertising accepted; rates available upon request. **URL:** http://www.allindiaradio.org.

All India Radio Adilabad - See Adilabad, Andhra Pradesh

All India Radio Ahmednagar - See Ahmednagar, Maharashtra

All India Radio Ahwa (Dangs) - See Ahwa, Gujarat

All India Radio Almora - See Almora

All India Radio Balaghat - See Balaghat, Karnataka

All India Radio Banswara - See Banswara, Rajasthan

All India Radio Baripada - See Baripada, Orissa

All India Radio Belonia - See Belonia, Tripura

All India Radio Berhampur - See Berhampur, Orissa

All India Radio Betul - See Betul, Madhya Pradesh

All India Radio Bhatinda - See Bathinda, Punjab

All India Radio Bijapur - See Bijapur, Karnataka

All India Radio Bikaner - See Bikaner, Rajasthan

All India Radio Cannanore - See Kannur, Kerala

All India Radio Churu - See Churu, Rajasthan

All India Radio Cochin - See Kochi, Kerala

All India Radio Coimbatore - See Coimbatore, Tamil Nadu

All India Radio Cuttack - See Cuttack, Orissa

All India Radio Daltonganj - See Daltonganj

All India Radio Darbhanga - See Darbhanga, Bihar

45673 ▪ All India Radio Delhi 'A' - 819 KHz
Akashvani Bhavan
Sansad Marg
New Delhi 110 001, Delhi, India
Ph: 91 11 23421006
Fax: 91 11 23421956
Format: Eclectic; Full Service. **Owner:** Prasar Bharati, at above address. **Founded:** 1936. **Key Personnel:** M.C. Aggarwal, Engr.-in-Ch., phone 91 11 23421058, fax 91 11 23421006, einc@air.org.in; Mohan Singh, Ch. Engr. Proj., phone 91 11 23421184. **Wattage:** 200,000. **Ad Rates:** $200-550 for 10 seconds; $300-825 for 15 seconds; $600-1,650 for 30 seconds; $1,200-3,300 for 60 seconds. **URL:** http://www.allindiaradio.org

45674 ▪ All India Radio Delhi 'B' - 666 KHz
Akashvani Bhavan
Sansad Marg
New Delhi 110 001, Delhi, India
Ph: 91 11 23421006
Fax: 91 11 23421956
E-mail: akjain@air.org.in
Format: Eclectic; Full Service. **Owner:** Prasar Bharati, at above address. **Founded:** 1936. **Key Personnel:** M.C. Aggarwal, Engr.-in-Ch., phone 91 11 23421058, fax 91 11 23421006, einc@air.org.in; Mohan Singh, Ch. Engr. Proj., phone 91 11 23421184. **Wattage:** 100,000. **Ad Rates:** $200-550 for 10 seconds; $300-825 for 15 seconds; $600-1,650 for 30 seconds; $1,200-3,300 for 60 seconds. **URL:** http://www.allindiaradio.org.

All India Radio Dharwad - See Dharwad, Karnataka

All India Radio Dhule - See Dhule, Maharashtra

All India Radio Diphu - See Diphu, Assam

All India Radio Godhra - See Godhra, Gujarat

All India Radio Guna - See Guna, Madhya Pradesh

All India Radio Hamirpur - See Hamirpur, Himachal Pradesh

45675 ▪ All India Radio Hazaribagh - 102.1 MHz
Akashvani Bhavan
Sansad Marg
New Delhi 110 001, Delhi, India
Ph: 91 11 23421006
Fax: 91 11 23421956
Format: Eclectic; Full Service. **Owner:** Prasar Bharati, at above address. **Founded:** 1992. **Key Personnel:** M.C. Aggarwal, Engr.-in-Ch., phone 91 11 23421058, fax 91 11 23421006, einc@air.org.in; Mohan Singh, Ch. Engr. Proj., phone 91 11 23421184. **Wattage:** 3000. **Ad Rates:** $80-150 for 10 seconds; $120-225 for 15 seconds; $240-450 for 30 seconds; $480-900 for 60 seconds. **URL:** http://www.allindiaradio.org.

All India Radio Hospet - See Hospet, Karnataka

All India Radio Jalandhar 'A' - See Jalandhar, Punjab

All India Radio Jamshedpur - See Jamshedpur

All India Radio Jeypore - See Jeypore, Orissa

All India Radio Joranda - See Joranda, Orissa

All India Radio Jorhat - See Jorhat, Assam

All India Radio Jowai - See Jowai, Meghalaya

All India Radio Kailashahar - See Kailashahar, Tripura

All India Radio Kanpur - See Kanpur, Uttar Pradesh

All India Radio Kargil 'B' - See Kargil, Jammu and Kashmir

All India Radio Karwar - See Karwar, Karnataka

All India Radio Kathua - See Kathua, Jammu and Kashmir

All India Radio Keonjhar - See Keonjhar, Orissa

All India Radio Khandwa - See Khandwa, Madhya Pradesh

All India Radio Kothagudem - See Kothagudem, Andhra Pradesh

All India Radio Kurseong - See Kurseong, West Bengal

All India Radio Kurukshetra - See Kurukshetra, Haryana

All India Radio Leh - See Leh, Jammu and Kashmir

All India Radio Lunglei - See Lunglei, Mizoram

All India Radio Mercara - See Madikeri, Karnataka

All India Radio Mokokchung - See Mokokchung, Nagaland

All India Radio Mount Abu - See Mount Abu, Rajasthan

All India Radio Murshidabad - See Murshidabad, West Bengal

All India Radio Mysore - See Mysore, Karnataka

All India Radio Nizamabad - See Nizamabad, Andhra Pradesh

All India Radio Nowgong - See Nagaon, Assam

All India Radio Obra - See Obra, Rajasthan

All India Radio Ootacamund - See Ootacamund, Tamil Nadu

All India Radio Pasighat - See Pasighat, Arunachal Pradesh

All India Radio Pauri - See Pauri

All India Radio Poonch - See Poonch, Jammu and Kashmir

All India Radio Puri - See Puri, Orissa

All India Radio Purnia - See Purnia, Bihar

All India Radio Rohtak - See Rohtak, Haryana

All India Radio Sagar - See Sagar, Madhya Pradesh

All India Radio Sasaram - See Sasaram, Bihar

All India Radio Satara - See Satara, Maharashtra

All India Radio Sawaimadhopur - See Sawaimadhopur, Rajasthan

All India Radio Shillong - See Shillong, Meghalaya

All India Radio Siliguri - See Siliguri, West Bengal

All India Radio Solapur - See Solapur, Maharashtra

All India Radio Suratgarh - See Suratgarh, Rajasthan

All India Radio Tawang - See Tawang, Arunachal Pradesh

All India Radio Tirupati - See Tirupati, Andhra Pradesh

All India Radio Udaipur - See Udaipur, Rajasthan

All India Radio Warangal - See Warangal, Andhra Pradesh

Nizamabad

45676 ■ All India Radio Nizamabad - 103.2 MHz
Akashvani Bhavan
Sansad Marg
New Delhi 110 001, Delhi, India
Ph: 91 11 23421006
Fax: 91 11 23421956
E-mail: air_nzb@yahoo.com
Format: Eclectic. **Owner:** Prasar Bharati, at above address. **Founded:** 1990. **Key Personnel:** M.C. Aggarwal, Engr.-in-Ch., phone 91 11 23421058, fax 91 11 23421006, einc@air.org.in; Mohan Singh, Ch. Engr.,

Proj., phone 91 11 23421184. **Wattage:** 6000. **Ad Rates:** $80-150 for 10 seconds; $120-225 for 15 seconds; $240-450 for 30 seconds; $480-900 for 60 seconds. **URL:** http://www.allindiaradio.org.

Obra

45677 ■ All India Radio Obra - 102.7 MHz
Akashvani Bhavan
Sansad Marg
New Delhi 110 001, Delhi, India
Ph: 91 11 23421006
Fax: 91 11 23421956
E-mail: airobra@satyam.net.in
Format: Eclectic. **Owner:** Prasar Bharati, at above address. **Founded:** 1993. **Key Personnel:** M.C. Aggarwal, Engr.-in-Ch., phone 91 11 23421058, fax 91 11 23421006, einc@air.org.in; Mohan Singh, Ch. Engr., Proj., phone 91 11 23421184. **Wattage:** 6000. **Ad Rates:** $80-150 for 10 seconds; $120-225 for 15 seconds; $240-450 for 30 seconds; $480-900 for 60 seconds. **URL:** http://www.allindiaradio.org.

Ootacamund

45678 ■ All India Radio Ootacamund - 1602 KHz
Akashvani Bhavan
Sansad Marg
New Delhi 110 001, Delhi, India
Ph: 91 11 23421006
Fax: 91 11 23421956
E-mail: airooty@sancharnet.in
Format: Eclectic; Full Service. **Owner:** Prasar Bharati, at above address. **Founded:** 1994. **Key Personnel:** M.C. Aggarwal, Engr.-in-Ch., phone 91 11 23421058, fax 91 11 23421006, einc@air.org.in; Mohan Singh, Ch. Engr. (Proj.), phone 91 11 23421184. **Wattage:** 1000. **Ad Rates:** $80-150 for 10 seconds; $120-225 for 15 seconds; $240-450 for 30 seconds; $480-900 for 60 seconds. **URL:** http://www.allindiaradio.org.

Osmanabad

45679 ■ All India Radio Osmanabad - 101.3 KHz
Tambri Vibhag
Osmanabad 413 501, Maharashtra, India
Ph: 91 247 2226060
E-mail: osd_airosm@sancharnet.in
Format: Eclectic. **Owner:** Prasar Bharati, Akashvani Bhavan, Sansad Marg, New Delhi 110 001, Delhi, India, 91 11 23421006, Fax: 91 11 23421956. **Founded:** 1996. **Key Personnel:** M.C. Aggarwal, Engr.-in-Ch., phone 91 11 23421058, fax 91 11 23421006, einc@air.org.in. **Wattage:** 3000. **Ad Rates:** $80-150 for 10 seconds; $120-225 for 15 seconds; $240-450 for 30 seconds; $480-900 for 60 seconds. **URL:** http://www.allindiaradio.org.

Palakkad

45680 ■ Mathrubhumi
Dr. A R Menon Rd.
K.P.Kesavamenon Rd.
Palakkad 678 001, Kerala, India
Ph: 91 491 2504446
Fax: 91 491 2521600
Publisher E-mail: mbipkd@mpp.co.in
General newspaper. **Founded:** Mar. 18, 1923. **Freq:** 7/yr. **Print Method:** Web. **Trim Size:** 11 1/2 x 17. **Cols./Page:** 4. **Col. Width:** 14 picas. **Col. Depth:** 16 inches. **ISSN:** 0192-009X. **Remarks:** Accepts advertising. **URL:** http://www.mathrubhumi.com. **Circ:** (Not Reported)

Panaji

45681 ■ The Navhind Times
Navhind Papers & Publication Ltd.
Navhind Bhavan
Panaji 403 001, Goa Daman and Diu, India
Publication E-mail: navhind@navhindtimes.com
General newspaper. **Founded:** 1963. **Freq:** Daily. **Print Method:** Web offset. **Key Personnel:** Arun Sinha, Editor, phone 91 832 6651120, editor@navhindtimes.com; Pramod Revankar, General Mgr., phone 91 832 6651104. **Subscription Rates:** Rs 2.50 single issue; Rs 3 Sunday edition. **URL:** http://www.navhindtimes.com/. **Ad Rates:** GLR: Rs 300, BW: Rs 74,000, 4C: Rs 1,480,000. **Circ:** Paid 33,287

45682 ■ All India Radio Panaji - 1287 KHz

PO Box 220
Altinho
Panaji 403 001, Goa Daman and Diu, India
Ph: 91 832 2225546
E-mail: airpanji@goatelecom.com
Format: Eclectic. **Owner:** Prasar Bharati, Akashvani Bhavan, Sansad Marg, New Delhi 110 001, Delhi, India, 91 11 23421006, Fax: 91 11 23421956. **Founded:** 1962. **Key Personnel:** M.C. Aggarwal, Engr.-in-Ch., phone 91 11 23421058, fax 91 11 23421006, einc@air.org.In. **Wattage:** 100,000. **Ad Rates:** $100-200 for 10 seconds; $150-300 for 15 seconds; $300-600 for 30 seconds; $600-1,200 for 60 seconds. **URL:** http://www.allindiaradio.org.

Parbhani

45683 ■ All India Radio Parbhani - 1305 KHz
Jamkar Colony
Parbhani 431 401, Maharashtra, India
Ph: 91 2452 221428
E-mail: airprb@rediffmail.com
Format: Eclectic. **Owner:** Prasar Bharati, Akashvani Bhavan, Sansad Marg, New Delhi 110 001, Delhi, India, 91 11 23421006, Fax: 91 11 23421956. **Founded:** 1998. **Key Personnel:** M.C. Aggarwal, Engr.-in-Ch., phone 91 11 23421058, fax 91 11 23421006, einc@air.org.in. **Wattage:** 20,000. **Ad Rates:** $100-200 for 10 seconds; $150-300 for 15 seconds; $300-600 for 30 seconds; $600-1,200 for 60 seconds. **URL:** http://www.allindiaradio.org.

Pasighat

45684 ■ All India Radio Pasighat - 1062 KHz
Akashvani Bhavan
Sansad Marg
New Delhi 110 001, Delhi, India
Ph: 91 11 23421006
Fax: 91 11 23421956
E-mail: passighat@air.org.in
Format: Eclectic; Full Service. **Owner:** Prasar Bharati, at above address. **Founded:** 1966. **Key Personnel:** Kijir Mindo, Program Dir., phone 91 11 2222262; M.C. Aggarwal, Engr.-in-Ch., phone 91 11 23421058, fax 91 11 23421459, einc@air.org.in. **Wattage:** 10,000. **Ad Rates:** $100-200 for 10 seconds; $150-300 for 15 seconds; $300-600 for 30 seconds; $600-1,200 for 60 seconds. **URL:** http://www.allindiaradio.org.

Patiala

45685 ■ Journal of Indian Academy of Forensic Medicine
Indian Academy of Forensic Medicine
SCO-3, Chowk Dukhniwaran Sahib, Sirhind Rd.
Shaheed-E-Azam Press
Patiala 147 005, Punjab, India
Ph: 91 175 2357981
Journal covering forensic medicine and allied fields. **Founded:** 1912. **Freq:** Quarterly. **Print Method:** Offset. **Trim Size:** 11 1/8 x 13 5/8. **Cols./Page:** 6. **Col. Width:** 24 nonpareils. **Col. Depth:** 298 agate lines. **Key Personnel:** Dr. H.K. Gorea, Editor in-Chief, phone 91 175 2357981, gorea_r@yahoo.com; Dr. A.S. Thind, Joint Ed. **URL:** http://medind.nic.in/jal/jalm.shtml.

45686 ■ Panjab Past and Present
Punjabi University
Punjabi University
Patiala 147 002, Punjab, India
Ph: 91 175 3046366
Publisher E-mail: ucc@pbi.ac.in
Periodical covering the history and culture of Punjab. **Founded:** 1967. **Freq:** Semiannual. **Key Personnel:** Param Bakhshish Singh, Contact. **ISSN:** 0031-0786. **Subscription Rates:** Rs 100 individuals; Rs 50 single issue. **Remarks:** Accepts advertising. **URL:** http://www.punjabiuniversity.ac.in. **Circ:** Paid 500

45687 ■ All India Radio Patiala - 100.2 MHz
Phase-I
Urban Estate
Patiala 147 002, Punjab, India
Ph: 91 175 2282779
E-mail: airptl@sancharnet.in
Format: Eclectic. **Owner:** Prasar Bharati, Akashvani Bhavan, Sansad Marg, New Delhi 110 001, Delhi, India,

91 11 23421006, Fax: 91 11 23421956. **Founded:** 1992. **Key Personnel:** M.C. Aggarwal, Engr.-in-Ch., phone 91 11 23421058, fax 91 11 23421006, einc@air.org.in. **Wattage:** 6000. **Ad Rates:** $80-150 for 10 seconds; $120-225 for 15 seconds; $240-450 for 30 seconds; $480-900 for 60 seconds. **URL:** http://www.allindiaradio.org.

Patna

45688 ■ All India Radio Patna 'A' - 621 KHz
Chajju Bagh
Fraser Rd.
Patna 800 001, Bihar, India
Ph: 91 612 2224367
E-mail: airpatna@dte.vsnl.net.in
Format: Full Service; Eclectic. **Owner:** Prasar Bharati, Akashvani Bhavan, Sansad Marg, New Delhi 110 001, Delhi, India, 91 11 23421006, Fax: 91 11 23421956. **Founded:** 1948. **Key Personnel:** M.C. Aggarwal, Engr.-in-Ch., phone 91 11 23421058, fax 91 11 23421006, einc@air.org.in. **Wattage:** 100,000. **Ad Rates:** $180-400 for 10 seconds; $270-600 for 15 seconds; $540-1,200 for 30 seconds; $1,080-2,400 for 60 seconds. **URL:** http://www.allindiaradio.org.

Pauri

45689 ■ All India Radio Pauri - 1602 KHz
Akashvani Bhavan
Sansad Marg
New Delhi 110 001, Delhi, India
Ph: 91 11 23421006
Fax: 91 11 23421956
Format: Eclectic. **Owner:** Prasar Bharati, at above address. **Founded:** 1996. **Key Personnel:** M.C. Aggarwal, Engr.-in-Ch., phone 91 11 23421058, fax 91 11 23421006, einc@air.org.in; Mohan Singh, Ch. Engr., Proj., phone 91 11 23421184. **Wattage:** 1000. **Ad Rates:** $80-150 for 10 seconds; $120-225 for 15 seconds; $240-450 for 30 seconds; $480-900 for 60 seconds. **URL:** http://www.allindiaradio.org.

Pondicherry

45690 ■ The Advent
Sri Aurobindo Ashram Trust
123 S.V. Patel Salai
Pondicherry 605 001, Pondicherry, India
Ph: 91 413 2233656
Fax: 91 413 2223328
Publisher E-mail: mail@sabda.in
Illustrated journal on Hinduism and philosophy. **Founded:** 1944. **Freq:** Quarterly. **Print Method:** Offset Printing-Photographic Process. **Trim Size:** 6 1/2 x 9 1/2. **Subscription Rates:** Rs 50 individuals; US$25 other countries. **Remarks:** Accepts advertising. **URL:** http://www.sabda.in/catalog/booksearch.php?category_key=X. **Ad Rates:** BW: Rs 1,000. **Circ:** Paid 1,000

45691 ■ The Bulletin of Sri Aurobindo International Centre of Education
Sri Aurobindo Ashram Trust
123 S.V. Patel Salai
Pondicherry 605 001, Pondicherry, India
Ph: 91 413 2233656
Fax: 91 413 2223328
Publisher E-mail: mail@sabda.in
Bulletin on education and culture. **Founded:** 1949. **Freq:** Quarterly. **Trim Size:** 9.75 x 7.25. **ISSN:** 0970-7417. **Subscription Rates:** Rs 120 individuals English-French-Hindi edition; US$29 other countries by air (English-French-Hindi edition); US$17 other countries by sea (English-French-Hindi edition). **Remarks:** Accepts advertising. **URL:** http://www.sabda.in/catalog/booksearch.php?category_key=X. **Ad Rates:** BW: Rs 1,500. **Circ:** Paid 800

45692 ■ Indian Journal of Medical Microbiology
Indian Association of Medical Microbiologists
A-3 No. 38 Rue Labourdonnaise
Pondicherry 605 001, Pondicherry, India
Ph: 91 423 2227422
Fax: 91 413 2223052
Publication E-mail: ijmm@lvpei.org
Publisher E-mail: rkanungo1@gmail.com
Publication covering immunology. **Freq:** Quarterly January, April, July, and October. **Key Personnel:** V. Lakshmi, Assoc. Ed.; Dr. Reba Kanungo, Editor. **ISSN:**

0255-0857. **Subscription Rates:** Rs 3,000 individuals; Rs 3,000 institutions; US$300 individuals overseas; US$300 institutions overseas. **Remarks:** Accepts advertising. **URL:** http://www.ijmm.org. **Circ:** (Not Reported)

45693 ■ Mother India
Sri Aurobindo Ashram Trust
123 S.V. Patel Salai
Pondicherry 605 001, Pondicherry, India
Ph: 91 413 2233656
Fax: 91 413 2223328
Publisher E-mail: mail@sabda.in
General review of culture containing articles, essays, poems and reminiscences by various disciples. **Founded:** 1949. **Freq:** Monthly. **ISSN:** 0027-1543. **Subscription Rates:** Rs 200 individuals; US$70 other countries by air; US$35 other countries by sea. **Remarks:** Accepts advertising. **URL:** http://www.sabda.in/catalog/booksearch.php?category_key=X. **Circ:** Paid 1,050

Poonch

45694 ■ All India Radio Poonch - 100.7 MHz
Akashvani Bhavan
Sansad Marg
New Delhi 110 001, Delhi, India
Ph: 91 11 23421006
Fax: 91 11 23421956
E-mail: airlive@air.org.in
Format: Eclectic; Full Service. **Owner:** Prasar Bharati, at above address. **Founded:** 1994. **Key Personnel:** M.C. Aggarwal, Engr.-in-Ch., phone 91 11 23421058, fax 91 11 23421006, einc@air.org.in; Mohan Singh, Ch. Engr. (Proj.), phone 91 11 23421184. **Wattage:** 6000. **Ad Rates:** $80-150 for 10 seconds; $120-225 for 15 seconds; $240-450 for 30 seconds; $480-900 for 60 seconds. **URL:** http://www.allindiaradio.org.

Port Blair

45695 ■ All India Radio Port Blair (A&N Islands) - 684 KHz
Haddo Post
Port Blair 744 102, Andaman and Nicobar Islands, India
Ph: 91 3192 230260
E-mail: airpb@dte.vsnl.net.in
Format: Eclectic. **Owner:** Prasar Bharati, Akashvani Bhavan, Sansad Marg, New Delhi 110 001, Delhi, India, 91 11 23421006, Fax: 91 11 23421956. **Founded:** 1963. **Key Personnel:** M.C. Aggarwal, Engr.-in-Ch., phone 91 11 23421058, fax 91 11 23421006, einc@air.org.in. **Wattage:** 20,000. **Ad Rates:** $100-200 for 10 seconds; $150-300 for 15 seconds; $300-600 for 30 seconds; $600-1,200 for 60 seconds. **URL:** http://www.allindiaradio.org.

Pune

45696 ■ C-DAC Connect
Centre for Development of Advanced Computing
Pune University
Ganeshkhind
Pune 411 007, Maharashtra, India
Ph: 91 20 25704100
Fax: 91 20 25694004
Magazine providing a platform for exchange of ideas among its members within and outside the organization. **Freq:** Quarterly. **Key Personnel:** R.K. Arora, Exec. Dir.; Anahita Rane, Editor. **URL:** http://www.cdac.in/html/connect/connidx.asp.

45697 ■ Medical Journal Armed Forces India
Armed Forces Medical Services
c/o Armed Forces Medical College
Pune 411 040, Maharashtra, India
Ph: 91 20 32927071
Fax: 91 20 26813065
Publisher E-mail: mjafipune@yahoo.co.in
Medical journal of interest to armed forces. **Founded:** 1945. **Freq:** Quarterly. **Key Personnel:** Lt. Col. Sukhmeet Minhas, Tech. Ed.; Col. Atul Kotwal, Editor-in-Chief. **ISSN:** 0377-1237. **Subscription Rates:** Rs 300 individuals; Rs 500 institutions; Rs 1,500 individuals life time. **Remarks:** Accepts advertising. **URL:** http://medind.nic.in/maa/maam.shtml. **Ad Rates:** BW: Rs 5,000, 4C: Rs 10,000. **Circ:** Paid 5,000

45698 ■ Mira
Sadhu Vaswani Mission
10 Sadhu Vaswani Path
Pune 411 001, Maharashtra, India
Ph: 91 20 40064447
Fax: 91 20 26127474
Publisher E-mail: dadajpvaswani@sadhuvaswani.org
Journal focusing on Indian culture. **Founded:** 1933. **Freq:** Monthly. **Key Personnel:** Gangaram Sajandas, Editor. **ISSN:** 0026-5780. **Subscription Rates:** Rs 100 individuals; US$20 other countries. **URL:** http://www.sadhuvaswani.org/svm/books.html.

45699 ■ Prajnan (Pune)
National Institute of Bank Management
NIBM Post Office
Kondhwe Khurd
Pune 411 048, Maharashtra, India
Ph: 91 20 26833080
Fax: 91 20 26834478
Journal covering banking and banking management with a special feature on software reviews. **Subtitle:** Journal of Social and Management Services. **Founded:** 1972. **Freq:** Quarterly. **Key Personnel:** Dr. Rajaram Dasgupta, Editor. **ISSN:** 0970-8448. **Subscription Rates:** Rs 200 individuals; Rs 375 two years. **Remarks:** Accepts advertising. **URL:** http://nibmindia.org/index.aspx?idp=31&idc=62. **Circ:** (Not Reported)

45700 ■ Sakal
Sakal Paper Limited
595, Budhwar Peth
Pune 411 002, Maharashtra, India
Ph: 91 20 24405500
General newspaper. **URL:** http://72.78.249.125/esakal/index.htm.

45701 ■ All India Radio Pune - 101.0 MHz
Shivaji Nagar
Pune 411 005, Maharashtra, India
Ph: 91 20 25536352
E-mail: airpune@vsnl.com
Format: Eclectic. **Owner:** Prasar Bharati, Akashvani Bhavan, Sansad Marg, New Delhi 110 001, Delhi, India, 91 11 23421006, Fax: 91 11 23421956. **Founded:** 1953. **Operating Hours:** 0025-1200, 1245-1730. **Key Personnel:** M.C. Aggarwal, Engr.-in-Ch., phone 91 11 23421058, fax 91 11 23421006, einc@air.org.in. **Wattage:** 6000. **Ad Rates:** $180-400 for 10 seconds; $270-600 for 15 seconds; $540-1,200 for 30 seconds; $1,080-2,400 for 60 seconds. **URL:** http://www.allindiaradio.org.

Puri

45702 ■ All India Radio Puri - 103.4 MHz
Akashvani Bhavan
Sansad Marg
New Delhi 110 001, Delhi, India
Ph: 91 11 23421006
Fax: 91 11 23421956
E-mail: airpuri@sancharnet.in
Format: Eclectic. **Owner:** Prasar Bharati, at above address. **Founded:** 1995. **Key Personnel:** M.C. Aggarwal, Engr.-in-Ch., phone 91 11 23421058, fax 91 11 23421006, einc@air.org.in. **Wattage:** 3000. **Ad Rates:** $80-150 for 10 seconds; $120-225 for 15 seconds; $240-450 for 30 seconds; $480-900 for 60 seconds. **URL:** http://www.allindiaradio.org.

Purnia

45703 ■ All India Radio Purnia - 102.3 MHz
Akashvani Bhavan
Sansad Marg
New Delhi 110 001, Delhi, India
Ph: 91 11 23421006
Fax: 91 11 23421956
Format: Eclectic. **Owner:** Prasar Bharati, at above address. **Founded:** 1992. **Key Personnel:** M.C. Aggarwal, Engr.-in-Ch., phone 91 11 23421058, fax 91 11 23421006, einc@air.org.in; Mohan Singh, Ch. Engr., Proj., phone 91 11 23421184. **Wattage:** 6000. **Ad Rates:** $80-150 for 10 seconds; $120-225 for 15 seconds; $240-450 for 30 seconds; $480-900 for 60 seconds. **URL:** http://www.allindiaradio.org.

Raigarh

45704 ■ All India Radio Raigarh - 100.7 KHz
Chote Attarmude

PO Box 21
Raigarh 496 001, Madhya Pradesh, India
Ph: 91 7762 222187
E-mail: seair_rih@sancharnet.in
Format: Eclectic. **Owner:** Prasar Bharati, Akashvani Bhavan, Sansad Marg, New Delhi 110 001, Delhi, India, 91 11 23421006, Fax: 91 11 23421956. **Founded:** 1992. **Key Personnel:** M.C. Aggarwal, Engr.-in-Ch., phone 91 11 23421058, fax 91 11 23421006, einc@air.org.in. **Wattage:** 6000. **Ad Rates:** $80-150 for 10 seconds; $120-225 for 15 seconds; $240-450 for 30 seconds; $480-900 for 60 seconds. **URL:** http://www.allindiaradio.org.

Raipur

45705 ■ All India Radio Raipur - 981 KHz
Kamal Nehru Marg
Civil Lines
Raipur 492 001, Madhya Pradesh, India
Ph: 91 771 2423009
E-mail: airrypur@sancharnet.in
Format: Eclectic. **Owner:** Prasar Bharati, Akashvani Bhavan, Sansad Marg, New Delhi 110 001, Delhi, India, 91 11 23421006, Fax: 91 11 23421956. **Founded:** 1963. **Key Personnel:** M.C. Aggarwal, Engr.-in-Ch., phone 91 11 23421058, fax 91 11 23421006, einc@air.org.in; Mohan Singh, Ch. Engr., Proj., phone 91 11 23421184. **Wattage:** 100,000. **Ad Rates:** $180-400 for 10 seconds; $270-600 for 15 seconds; $540-1,200 for 30 seconds; $1,080-2,400 for 60 seconds. **URL:** http://www.allindiaradio.org.

Rajkot

45706 ■ Biochemistry
Trade Science Inc.
126, Prasheel Pk.
SanjayRaj Farm House
Nr. Saurashtra University
Rajkot 360 005, Gujarat, India
Fax: 91 281 3042233
Publisher E-mail: help@tsijournals.com
Peer-reviewed journal covering research articles related to chemistry and biology. **Subtitle:** An Indian Journal. **Freq:** 3/yr. **Key Personnel:** Akira Hirao, Editorial Board; A.R. Kulkarni, Editorial Board; A.M. Tamburro, Editorial Board; Ali Tuncel, Editorial Board; Cristina Nativi, Editorial Board; Chang-Sik Ha, Editorial Board. **ISSN:** 0974-7427. **Subscription Rates:** Rs 1,800 individuals; US$180 other countries. **URL:** http://www.tsijournals.com/bcaij/.

45707 ■ Biotechnology
Trade Science Inc.
126, Prasheel Pk.
SanjayRaj Farm House
Nr. Saurashtra University
Rajkot 360 005, Gujarat, India
Fax: 91 281 3042233
Publisher E-mail: help@tsijournals.com
Peer-reviewed journal covering research on all phases of biotechnology. **Subtitle:** An Indian Journal. **Founded:** 1931. **Freq:** 4/yr. **Print Method:** Offset. **Trim Size:** 10 x 16. **Cols./Page:** 5. **Col. Width:** 1.80 inches. **Col. Depth:** 16 inches. **ISSN:** 0974-7435. **Subscription Rates:** Rs 2,400 individuals; US$240 other countries. **URL:** http://www.tsijournals.com/btaij/.

45708 ■ Chemical Technology
Trade Science Inc.
126, Prasheel Pk.
SanjayRaj Farm House
Nr. Saurashtra University
Rajkot 360 005, Gujarat, India
Fax: 91 281 3042233
Publisher E-mail: help@tsijournals.com
Peer-reviewed journal covering field of chemical engineering and technology. **Subtitle:** An Indian Journal. **Freq:** 2/yr. **ISSN:** 0974-7443. **Subscription Rates:** Rs 1,200 individuals; US$120 other countries. **URL:** http://www.tsijournals.com/ctaij/.

45709 ■ Materials Science
Trade Science Inc.
126, Prasheel Pk.
SanjayRaj Farm House
Nr. Saurashtra University

Rajkot 360 005, Gujarat, India
Fax: 91 281 3042233
Publisher E-mail: help@tsijournals.com
Peer-reviewed journal covering fundamental research at the interface of chemistry, chemical engineering, and material science. **Subtitle:** An Indian Journal. **Founded:** 1967. **Freq:** 4/yr. **Print Method:** Offset. **Trim Size:** 8 1/2 x 11. **Cols./Page:** 2. **Col. Width:** 19 picas. **Col. Depth:** 53 picas. **Key Personnel:** Xavier F. Perrin, Editorial Board; B. Viswanathan, Editorial Board; Durga P. Ojha, Editorial Board; Birinchi Kumar Das, Editorial Board; Weibor Tsai, Editorial Board; Oscar L. Malta, Editorial Board. **ISSN:** 0974-7486. **Subscription Rates:** Rs 2,400 individuals; US$240 institutions, other countries. **URL:** http://www.tsijournals.com/msaij/.

45710 ■ All India Radio Rajkot - 810 KHz
Opposite Race Course
Sitaram Pandit Marg
Rajkot 360 001, Gujarat, India
Ph: 91 281 2441013
E-mail: airajkot@sancharnet.in
Format: Eclectic. **Owner:** Prasar Bharati, Akashvani Bhavan, Sansad Marg, New Delhi 110 001, Delhi, India, 91 11 23421006, Fax: 91 11 23421956. **Founded:** 1955. **Key Personnel:** M.C. Aggarwal, Engr.-in-Ch., phone 91 11 23421058, fax 91 11 23421006, einc@air.org.in. **Wattage:** 300,000. **Ad Rates:** $180-400 for 10 seconds; $270-600 for 15 seconds; $540-1,200 for 30 seconds; $1,080-2,400 for 60 seconds. **URL:** http://www.allindiaradio.org.

Rampur

45711 ■ All India Radio Rampur - 891 KHz
PO Box 17
Rampur 244 901, Uttar Pradesh, India
Ph: 91 595 2325209
E-mail: airrmp09@sancharnet.in
Format: Eclectic. **Owner:** Prasar Bharati, Akashvani Bhavan, Sansad Marg, New Delhi 110 001, Delhi, India, 91 11 23421006, Fax: 91 11 23421956. **Founded:** 1965. **Key Personnel:** M.C. Aggarwal, Engr.-in-Ch., phone 91 11 23421058, fax 91 11 23421006, einc@air.org.in. **Wattage:** 20,000. **Ad Rates:** $150-300 for 10 seconds; $225-450 for 15 seconds; $450-900 for 30 seconds; $900-1,800 for 60 seconds. **URL:** http://www.allindiaradio.org.

Ranchi

45712 ■ Ranchi Express
55 Baralal St.
Ranchi 834 001, Bihar, India
Ph: 91 651 2206320
Fax: 91 651 2206213
General newspaper. **Founded:** Aug. 1963. **Freq:** Daily. **Print Method:** Web offset. **Trim Size:** 35 x 53 cm. **Cols./Page:** 8. **Col. Width:** 3.8 centimeters. **Key Personnel:** Ajay Maroo, Editor-in-Chief. **Subscription Rates:** Rs 900 individuals; Rs 450 individuals half yearly; Rs 225 individuals quarterly. **Remarks:** Accepts advertising. **URL:** http://www.ranchixpress.com/. **Circ:** Controlled 45,000

45713 ■ All India Radio Ranchi - 549 KHz
6 Ratu Rd.
Ranchi 843 001, Bihar, India
Ph: 91 651 2283315
E-mail: seairran@yahoo.co.in
Format: Eclectic. **Owner:** Prasar Bharati, Akashvani Bhavan, Sansad Marg, New Delhi 110 001, Delhi, India, 91 11 23421006, Fax: 91 11 23421956. **Founded:** 1957. **Key Personnel:** M.C. Aggarwal, Engr.-in-Ch., phone 91 11 23421058, fax 91 11 23421006, einc@air.org.in; Gautam Sengupta, Program Dir. **Wattage:** 100,000. **Ad Rates:** $150-300 for 10 seconds; $225-450 for 15 seconds; $450-900 for 30 seconds; $900-1,800 for 60 seconds. **URL:** http://www.allindiaradio.org.

Ratnagiri

45714 ■ All India Radio Ratnagiri - 1143 KHz
Thiba Palace Rd.
Ratnagiri 415 612, Maharashtra, India
Ph: 91 2352 222166
E-mail: air_rtn@sancharnet.in
Format: Eclectic. **Owner:** Prasar Bharati, Akashvani

Bhavan, Sansad Marg, New Delhi 110 001, Delhi, India, 91.11 23421006, Fax: 91 11 23421956. **Founded:** 1977. **Key Personnel:** M.C. Aggarwal, Engr.-in-Ch., phone 91 11 23421058, fax 91 11 23421006, einc@air.org.in. **Wattage:** 20,000. **Ad Rates:** $100-200 for 10 seconds; $150-300 for 15 seconds; $300-600 for 30 seconds; $600-1,200 for 60 seconds. **URL:** http://www.allindiaradio.org.

Rewa

45715 ■ All India Radio Rewa - 1179 KHz
6 Civil Lines
Rewa 486 001, Madhya Pradesh, India
Ph: 91 7662 256398
E-mail: airrewa@indiatimes.com
Format: Eclectic. **Owner:** Prasar Bharati, Akashvani Bhavan, Sansad Marg, New Delhi 110 001, Delhi, India, 91 11 23421006, Fax: 91 11 23421956. **Founded:** 1977. **Key Personnel:** M.C. Aggarwal, Engr.-in-Ch., phone 91 11 23421058, fax 91 11 23421006, einc@air.org.in. **Wattage:** 20,000. **Ad Rates:** $150-300 for 10 seconds; $225-450 for 15 seconds; $450-900 for 30 seconds; $900-1,800 for 60 seconds. **URL:** http://www.allindiaradio.org.

Rohtak

45716 ■ All India Radio Rohtak - 1143 KHz
Akashvani Bhavan
Sansad Marg
New Delhi 110 001, Delhi, India
Ph: 91 11 23421006
Fax: 91 11 23421956
E-mail: airrtk@nde.vsnl.net.in
Format: Eclectic. **Owner:** Prasar Bharati, at above address. **Founded:** 1976. **Key Personnel:** M.C. Aggarwal, Engr.-in-Ch., phone 91 11 23421058, fax 91 11 23421006, einc@air.org.in. **Wattage:** 20,000. **Ad Rates:** $180-400 for 10 seconds; $270-600 for 15 seconds; $540-1,200 for 30 seconds; $1,080-2,400 for 60 seconds. **URL:** http://www.allindiaradio.org.

Roorkee

45717 ■ Analytical Chemistry
Trade Science Inc.
c/o A.N. Garg
Chemistry Dept.
Indian Institute of Technology
Roorkee 247 667, Uttar Pradesh, India
Publisher E-mail: help@tsijournals.com
Peer-reviewed journal covering analytical and bioanalytical science. **Subtitle:** An Indian Journal. **Founded:** 1887. **Freq:** 4/yr. **Print Method:** Letterpress. **Trim Size:** 13 x 21 1/2. **Cols./Page:** 6. **Col. Width:** 24 nonpareils. **Col. Depth:** 301 agate lines. **Key Personnel:** Hector Goicoechea, Editorial Board; Hosny Ibrahim, Editorial Board; I.N. Papadoyannis, Editorial Board; Dimitrios Gavril, Editorial Board; H.S. Joshi, Editorial Board; Hong-Wen Gao, Editorial Board; Jean-Francois Gal, Editorial Board. **USPS:** 479-780. **Subscription Rates:** Rs 2,400 individuals; US$240 other countries. **URL:** http://www.tsijournals.com/acaij/.

45718 ■ International Journal of Ecology and Development
Indian Society for Development and Environment Research
PO Box 113
Roorkee 247-667, Uttar Pradesh, India
Publisher E-mail: ceser_isder@yahoo.co.in
Journal featuring the latest research and developments in ecology and development. **Freq:** 3/yr. **Key Personnel:** Dr. Tanuja Srivastava, Editor-in-Chief, eic.ijed@yahoo.com; Dr. Kaushal K. Srivastava, Editor-in-Chief. **ISSN:** 0972-9984. **Subscription Rates:** EUR550 individuals print; EUR775 institutions print; EUR500 institutions online; EUR1,000 institutions print and online; US$475 institutions online only; US$675 institutions print only; US$975 institutions print & online. **URL:** http://www.ceser.res.in/ijed.html.

45719 ■ International Journal of Mathematics and Statistics (IJMS)
Indian Society for Development and Environment Research
PO Box 113
Roorkee 247-667, Uttar Pradesh, India

Publisher E-mail: ceser_isder@yahoo.co.in

Journal focusing on the latest developments in the area of mathematics and statistics. **Freq:** Semiannual. **Key Personnel:** Tanuja Srivastava, Editor-in-Chief; Delfim F.M. Torres, Editor-in-Chief; Joao Pedro Cruz, Exec. Ed. **ISSN:** 0973-8347. **Subscription Rates:** EUR700 individuals print; US$1,100 institutions print only; US$1,600 institutions print & online; EUR1,000 institutions print only for Europe; EUR1,500 institutions print & online; US$990 institutions print only for SAARC countries & Africa only; EUR1,490 institutions print & online. **URL:** http://www.ceser.res.in/ijms.html.

Rourkela

45720 ■ All India Radio Rourkela - 102.6 MHz
Jhirpani
Rourkela 769 042, Orissa, India
Ph: 91 661 2475624
E-mail: airrkl@dte.vsnl.net.in
Format: Eclectic. **Owner:** Prasar Bharati, Akashvani Bhavan, Sansad Marg, New Delhi 110 001, Delhi, India, 91 11 23421006, Fax: 91 11 23421956. **Founded:** 1995. **Key Personnel:** M.C. Aggarwal, Engr.-in-Ch., phone 91 11 23421058, fax 91 11 23421006, einc@air.org.in. **Wattage:** 6000. **Ad Rates:** $80-150 for 10 seconds; $120-225 for 15 seconds; $240-450 for 30 seconds; $480-900 for 60 seconds. **URL:** http://www.allindiaradio.org.

Sagar

45721 ■ All India Radio Sagar - 102.6 KHz
Akashvani Bhavan
Sansad Marg
New Delhi 110 001, Delhi, India
Ph: 91 11 23421006
Fax: 91 11 23421956
E-mail: airsagar@mail.com
Format: Eclectic. **Owner:** Prasar Bharati, at above address. **Founded:** 1993. **Key Personnel:** M.C. Aggarwal, Engr.-in-Ch., phone 91 11 23421058, fax 91 11 23421006, einc@air.org.in. **Wattage:** 5000. **Ad Rates:** $80-150 for 10 seconds; $120-225 for 15 seconds; $240-450 for 30 seconds; $480-900 for 60 seconds. **URL:** http://www.allindiaradio.org.

Sambalpur

45722 ■ All India Radio Sambalpur - 945 KHz
Kuchery Rd.
PO Box 3
Sambalpur 768 001, Orissa, India
Ph: 91 663 2521054
E-mail: airsbp@dataone.in
Format: Eclectic. **Owner:** Prasar Bharati, Akashvani Bhavan, Sansad Marg, New Delhi 110 001, Delhi, India, 91 11 23421006, Fax: 91 11 23421956. **Founded:** 1963. **Key Personnel:** M.C. Aggarwal, Engr.-in-Ch., phone 91 11 23421058, fax 91 11 23421006, einc@air.org.in; Mohan Singh, Ch. Engr., Proj., phone 91 11 23421184. **Wattage:** 100,000. **Ad Rates:** $150-300 for 10 seconds; $225-450 for 15 seconds; $450-900 for 30 seconds; $900-1,800 for 60 seconds. **URL:** http://www.allindiaradio.org.

Sangli

45723 ■ All India Radio Sangli - 1251 KHz
Kolhapur Rd.
Sangli 416 416, Maharashtra, India
Ph: 91 233 2332883
E-mail: san_airsng@sancharnet.in
Format: Eclectic. **Owner:** Prasar Bharati, Akashvani Bhavan, Sansad Marg, New Delhi 110 001, Delhi, India, 91 11 23421006, Fax: 91 11 23421956. **Founded:** 1963. **Key Personnel:** M.C. Aggarwal, Engr.-in-Ch., phone 91 11 23421058, fax 91 11 23421006, einc@air.org.in. **Wattage:** 20,000. **Ad Rates:** $150-300 for 10 seconds; $225-450 for 15 seconds; $450-900 for 30 seconds; $900-1,800 for 60 seconds. **URL:** http://www.allindiaradio.org.

Sasaram

45724 ■ All India Radio Sasaram - 103.4 MHz
Akashvani Bhavan
Sansad Marg
New Delhi 110 001, Delhi, India
Ph: 91 11 23421006

Fax: 91 11 23421956
E-mail: airssr@sancharnet.in
Format: Eclectic. **Owner:** Prasar Bharati, at above address. **Founded:** 1991. **Key Personnel:** M.C. Aggarwal, Engr.-in-Ch., phone 91 11 23421058, fax 91 11 23421006, einc@air.org.in. **Wattage:** 6000. **Ad Rates:** $80-150 for 10 seconds; $120-225 for 15 seconds; $240-450 for 30 seconds; $480-900 for 60 seconds. **URL:** http://www.allindiaradio.org.

Satara

45725 ■ All India Radio Satara - 103.1 KHz
Akashvani Bhavan
Sansad Marg
New Delhi 110 001, Delhi, India
Ph: 91 11 23421006
Fax: 91 11 23421956
E-mail: str_airsat@sancharnet.in
Format: Eclectic. **Owner:** Prasar Bharati, at above address. **Founded:** 1992. **Key Personnel:** M.C. Aggarwal, Engr.-in-Ch., phone 91 11 23421058, fax 91 11 23421006, einc@air.org.in. **Wattage:** 6000. **Ad Rates:** $80-150 for 10 seconds; $120-225 for 15 seconds; $240-450 for 30 seconds; $480-900 for 60 seconds. **URL:** http://www.allindiaradio.org.

Sawaimadhopur

45726 ■ All India Radio Sawaimadhopur - 101.5 MHz
Akashvani Bhavan
Sansad Marg
New Delhi 110 001, Delhi, India
Ph: 91 11 23421006
Fax: 91 11 23421956
E-mail: airswm@sancharnet.in
Format: Eclectic. **Owner:** Prasar Bharati, at above address. **Founded:** 1992. **Key Personnel:** M.C. Aggarwal, Engr.-in-Ch., phone 91 11 23421058, fax 91 11 23421006, einc@air.org.in; Mohan Singh, Ch. Engr., Proj., phone 91 11 23421184. **Wattage:** 6000. **Ad Rates:** $80-150 for 10 seconds; $120-225 for 15 seconds; $240-450 for 30 seconds; $480-900 for 60 seconds. **URL:** http://www.allindiaradio.org.

Shahdol

45727 ■ All India Radio Shahdol - 102.0 KHz
Pali Rd.
Shahdol 484 001, Madhya Pradesh, India
Ph: 91 7652 245170
E-mail: seairsdl@sancharnet.in
Format: Eclectic. **Owner:** Prasar Bharati, Akashvani Bhavan, Sansad Marg, New Delhi 110 001, Delhi, India, 91 11 23421006, Fax: 91 11 23421956. **Founded:** 1992. **Key Personnel:** M.C. Aggarwal, Engr.-in-Ch., phone 91 11 23421006, fax 91 11 23421006, einc@air.org.in. **Wattage:** 6000. **Ad Rates:** $80-150 for 10 seconds; $120-225 for 15 seconds; $240-450 for 30 seconds; $480-900 for 60 seconds. **URL:** http://www.allindiaradio.org.

Shillong (Assam)

45728 ■ International Journal of Jurisprudence and Philosophy of Law
Serials Publications
c/o Dr. Jagat Pal, Ed.-in-Ch.
Dept. of Philosophy
North Eastern Hill University
Shillong 793 022, Assam, India
Publisher E-mail: serials@satyam.net.in
Journal covering philosophy of law and general jurisprudence. Topics include the nature of law, law and morality, justice, rightness and natural law, law and reason, artificial intelligence and law, legal obligation, rights validity and the legitimacy of law, rules and acts, legal reasoning, interpretation, deontic logic and expert systems in law. **Freq:** Semiannual. **Key Personnel:** Dr. B.P. Dwivedi, Editorial Board; Prof. Asha Mukharjee, Editorial Board; Dr. Jyoti J. Mozika, Editorial Board; Prof. Binod Kumar Agarwala, Editorial Board; Dr. L.N. Lenka, Editorial Board; Dr. Jagat Pal, Editor-in-Chief, jagat_pal1949@rediffmail.com. **ISSN:** 0973-676X. **Subscription Rates:** US$100 institutions print. **URL:** http://www.serialspublications.com/journals1.asp?jid=395&jtype=1.

Shillong (Meghalaya)

45729 ■ The Shillong Times
Manas Chaudhuri
Rilbong
Shillong 793 004, Meghalaya, India
Ph: 91 364 2223488
Fax: 91 364 2229488
Publisher E-mail: letters@theshillongtimes.com
General newspaper. **Founded:** 1945. **Freq:** Daily. **Key Personnel:** Patricia Mukhim, Editor. **Subscription Rates:** Rs 2 single issue. **Remarks:** Accepts advertising. **URL:** http://www.theshillongtimes.com/. **Circ:** Paid 28,245

45730 ■ All India Radio Shillong - 864 KHz
Akashvani Bhavan
Sansad Marg
New Delhi 110 001, Delhi, India
Ph: 91 11 23421006
Fax: 91 11 23421956
E-mail: airshil@sancharnet.in
Format: Eclectic. **Owner:** Prasar Bharati, at above address. **Founded:** 1966. **Key Personnel:** M.C. Aggarwal, Engr.-in-Ch., phone 91 11 23421058, fax 91 11 23421006, einc@air.org.in; Mohan Singh, Ch. Engr., Proj., phone 91 11 23421184. **Wattage:** 10,000. **Ad Rates:** $150-300 for 10 seconds; $225-450 for 15 seconds; $450-900 for 30 seconds; $900-1,800 for 60 seconds. **URL:** http://www.allindiaradio.org.

Shimla

45731 ■ Studies in Humanities and Social Sciences
Indian Institute of Advanced Study
Rashtrapati Nivas
Shimla 171 005, Himachal Pradesh, India
Ph: 91 177 2831275
Fax: 91 177 2831389
Publication E-mail: proiias@gmail.com
Publisher E-mail: director@iias.org
Social science periodical. **Founded:** 1994. **Freq:** Semiannual. **Print Method:** Offset. **Trim Size:** 6 x 9.5. **Key Personnel:** Prof. V.C. Srivastava, Director. **ISSN:** 0972-1401. **URL:** http://www.iias.org/periodicals.html. **Circ:** Paid 1,000

45732 ■ All India Radio Shimla - 774 KHz
Choura Maidan
Shimla 171 004, Himachal Pradesh, India
Ph: 91 177 2652350
E-mail: airshimla@yahoo.com
Format: Eclectic. **Owner:** Prasar Bharati, Akashvani Bhavan, Sansad Marg, New Delhi 110 001, Delhi, India, 91 11 23421006, Fax: 91 11 23421956. **Founded:** 1955. **Key Personnel:** M.C. Aggarwal, Engr.-in-Ch., phone 91 11 23421058, fax 91 11 23421006, einc@air.org.in. **Wattage:** 100,000. **Ad Rates:** $100-200 for 10 seconds; $150-300 for 15 seconds; $300-600 for 30 seconds; $600-1,200 for 60 seconds. **URL:** http://www.allindiaradio.org.

Shivpuri

45733 ■ All India Radio Shivpuri - 100.2 KHz
Physical College
Shivpuri 473 551, Madhya Pradesh, India
Ph: 91 7492 221071
E-mail: airshivpuri@sancharnet.in
Format: Eclectic. **Owner:** Prasar Bharati, Akashvani Bhavan, Sansad Marg, New Delhi 110 001, Delhi, India, 91 11 23421006, Fax: 91 11 23421956. **Founded:** 1991. **Key Personnel:** M.C. Aggarwal, Engr.-in-Ch., phone 91 11 23421058, fax 91 11 23421006, einc@air.org.in. **Wattage:** 6000. **Ad Rates:** $150-300 for 10 seconds; $225-450 for 15 seconds; $450-900 for 30 seconds; $900-1,800 for 60 seconds. **URL:** http://www.allindiaradio.org.

Silchar

45734 ■ All India Radio Silchar - 828 KHz
Silchar
Silchar 788 001, Assam, India
Ph: 91 3842 263865
E-mail: airsil@dte.vsnl.net.in
Format: Eclectic. **Owner:** Prasar Bharati, Akashvani Bhavan, Sansad Marg, New Delhi 110 001, Delhi, India, 91 11 23421006, Fax: 91 11 23421956. **Founded:** 1967.

Key Personnel: M.C. Aggarwal, Engr.-in-Ch., phone 91 11 23421058, fax 91 11 23421006, einc@air.org.in; Mohan Singh, Ch. Engr., Proj., phone 91 11 23421184. Wattage: 10,000. Ad Rates: $100-200 for 10 seconds; $150-300 for 15 seconds; $300-600 for 30 seconds; $600-1,200 for 60 seconds. URL: http://www.allindiaradio.org.

Siliguri

45735 ■ All India Radio Siliguri - 711 KHz
Akashvani Bhavan
Sansad Marg
New Delhi 110 001, Delhi, India
Ph: 91 11 23421006
Fax: 91 11 23421956
E-mail: airsil@dte.vsnl.net.in
Format: Eclectic. Owner: Prasar Bharati, at above address. Founded: 1963. Key Personnel: M.C. Aggarwal, Engr.-in-Ch., phone 91 11 23421058, fax 91 11 23421006, einc@air.org.in; Mohan Singh, Ch. Engr., Proj., phone 91 11 23421184. Wattage: 200,000. Ad Rates: $150-300 for 10 seconds; $225-450 for 15 seconds; $450-900 for 30 seconds; $900-1,800 for 60 seconds. URL: http://www.allindiaradio.org.

Solapur

45736 ■ All India Radio Solapur - 1602 kHz
Akashvani Bhavan
Sansad Marg
New Delhi 110 001, Delhi, India
Ph: 91 11 23421006
Fax: 91 11 23421956
E-mail: spr_airsolr@sancharnet.in
Format: Full Service; Eclectic. Owner: Prasar Bharati, at above address. Founded: 1986. Key Personnel: M.C. Aggarwal, Engr.-in-Ch., phone 91 11 23421058, fax 91 11 23421006, einc@air.org.in. Wattage: 1000. Ad Rates: $80-150 for 10 seconds; $120-225 for 15 seconds; $240-450 for 30 seconds; $480-900 for 60 seconds. URL: http://www.allindiaradio.org.

Srinagar

45737 ■ Greater Kashmir
Fayaz Ahmad Kaloo
6 Pratap Pk.
Residency Rd.
Srinagar 190 001, Jammu and Kashmir, India
Ph: 91 192 474339
Fax: 91 192 477782
Publication E-mail: editor@greaterkashmir.com
Publisher E-mail: editor@greaterkashmir.com
Regional newspaper of Kashmir. Founded: 1993. Freq: Daily. Print Method: Web Offset fast 200. Trim Size: 38.5 x 50 cm. Key Personnel: Fayaz Ahmad Kaloo, Editor. Remarks: Accepts advertising. URL: http://www.greaterkashmir.com. Ad Rates: GLR: Rs 250, BW: Rs 950, 4C: Rs 1,550, PCI: Rs 220. Circ: Paid 70,820

45738 ■ Jammu and Kashmir Law Reporter
High Court of Jammu and Kashmir
Srinagar 190 001, Jammu and Kashmir, India
Law journal. Founded: 1970. Freq: Monthly. Key Personnel: Mufti Salah-Ud-Din Arshad, Editor. Subscription Rates: Rs 30. URL: http://www.jkhighcourt.nic.in/. Circ: Paid 475

45739 ■ Kashmir Observer
Haza Complex
Residency Rd.
Kashmir
Srinagar 190 001, Jammu and Kashmir, India
Publication E-mail: editor@kashmirobserver.net
Publisher E-mail: advt@kashmirobserver.net
Newspaper focusing on news from the Kashmir region and the South Asian subcontinent. Freq: Daily (morn.). Trim Size: 41 x 53 cm. Key Personnel: Shahid Ansari, Online Ed., haiderey@gmail.com; Sajjad Haider, Pub./Ed.-in-Ch., sajjad.ko@gmail.com. Remarks: Accepts advertising. URL: http://www.kashmirobserver.com/. Circ: (Not Reported)

45740 ■ All India Radio Srinagar - 1116 KHz
Radio Kashmir
Srinagar 190 001, Jammu and Kashmir, India
Ph: 91 194 2452191

E-mail: srinagar@air.org.in
Format: Eclectic. Owner: Prasar Bharati, Akashvani Bhavan, Sansad Marg, New Delhi 110 001, Delhi, India, 91 11 23421006, Fax: 91 11 23421956. Founded: 1948. Key Personnel: M.C. Aggarwal, Engr.-in-Ch., phone 91 11 23421058, fax 91 11 23421006, einc@air.org.in. Wattage: 200,000. Ad Rates: $150-300 for 10 seconds; $225-450 for 15 seconds; $450-900 for 30 seconds; $900-1,800 for 60 seconds. URL: http://www.allindiaradio.org.

Surat

45741 ■ All India Radio Surat - 101.1 MHz
Bhatar Rd.
Surat 395 001, Gujarat, India
Ph: 91 261 2234450
E-mail: airsurat_ad1@sancharnet.in
Format: Eclectic. Owner: Prasar Bharati, Akashvani Bhavan, Sansad Marg, New Delhi 110 001, Delhi, India, 91 11 23421006, Fax: 91 11 23421956. Founded: 1992. Key Personnel: M.C. Aggarwal, Engr.-in-Ch., phone 91 11 23421058, fax 91 11 23421006, einc@air.org.in. Wattage: 6000. Ad Rates: $150-300 for 10 seconds; $225-450 for 15 seconds; $450-900 for 30 seconds; $900-1,800 for 60 seconds. URL: http://www.allindiaradio.org.

Suratgarh

45742 ■ All India Radio Suratgarh - 918 KHz
Akashvani Bhavan
Sansad Marg
New Delhi 110 001, Delhi, India
Ph: 91 11 23421006
Fax: 91 11 23421956
E-mail: airsuratgarh@yahoo.com
Format: Eclectic. Owner: Prasar Bharati, at above address. Founded: 1981. Key Personnel: M.C. Aggarwal, Engr.-in-Ch., phone 91 11 23421058, fax 91 11 23421006, einc@air.org.in; Mohan Singh, Ch. Engr., Proj., phone 91 11 23421184. Wattage: 300,000. Ad Rates: $150-300 for 10 seconds; $225-450 for 15 seconds; $450-900 for 30 seconds; $900-1,800 for 60 seconds. URL: http://www.allindiaradio.org.

Tawang

45743 ■ All India Radio Tawang - 1521 KHz
Akashvani Bhavan
Sansad Marg
New Delhi 110 001, Delhi, India
Ph: 91 11 23421006
Fax: 91 11 23421956
E-mail: air_tawang@yahoo.com
Format: Eclectic. Owner: Prasar Bharati, at above address. Founded: 1977. Key Personnel: L.C. Deka, Program Dir., phone 91 11 23222230; M.C. Aggarwal, Engr.-in-Ch., phone 91 11 23421058, fax 91 11 23421459, einc@air.org.in. Wattage: 10,000. Ad Rates: $80-150 for 10 seconds; $120-225 for 15 seconds; $240-450 for 30 seconds; $480-900 for 60 seconds. URL: http://www.allindiaradio.org.

Tezu

45744 ■ All India Radio Tezu - 1332 KHz
Lohit Dist.
Tezu 792 001, Arunachal Pradesh, India
Ph: 91 3804 222240
E-mail: airtezu@sancharnet.in
Format: Eclectic. Owner: Prasar Bharati, Akashvani Bhavan, Sansad Marg, New Delhi 110 001, Delhi, India, 91 11 23421006, Fax: 91 11 23421956. Founded: 1967. Key Personnel: M.C. Aggarwal, Engr.-in-Ch., phone 91 11 23421058, fax 91 11 23421459, einc@air.org.in. Wattage: 10,000. Ad Rates: $80-150 for 10 seconds; $120-225 for 15 seconds; $240-450 for 30 seconds; $480-900 for 60 seconds. URL: http://www.allindiaradio.org.

Thane

45745 ■ Indian Concrete Journal (ICJ)
Associated Cement Companies Ltd.
Research & Consultancy Directorate
ACC Thane Complex
Lal Bahadur Shastri Marg

Near Teen Haath Naka
Thane 400 604, Maharashtra, India
Ph: 91 222 5823631
Fax: 91 222 5837378
Publication E-mail: info@icjonline.com
Publisher E-mail: info@icjonline.com
Scientific Journal featuring construction and the construction trades. Founded: Aug. 1960. Freq: Monthly. Print Method: Offset. Trim Size: 8 1/2 x 11. ISSN: 0019-4565. Subscription Rates: US$100 individuals; US$190 individuals 2 years; US$275 individuals 3 years; Rs 750 individuals, 2 years. Remarks: Accepts advertising. URL: http://www.icjonline.com/. Ad Rates: BW: US$550, 4C: US$900. Circ: Paid 3,000

45746 ■ Indian Journal of Occupational and Environmental Medicine
Medknow Publications Pvt Ltd.
Siemens Ltd., Kalwa Works
Thane-Belapur Rd.
Thane 400601, Maharashtra, India
Ph: 91 22 27600111
Fax: 91 22 27623730
Peer-reviewed journal covering information on occupational and environmental medicine. Freq: Quarterly. Key Personnel: Dr. G.K. Kulkani, Editor, ganesh.kulkarni@siemens.com; Dr. S. Kartikeyan, Assoc. Ed. ISSN: 0973-2284. Subscription Rates: Rs 1,000 individuals; Rs 1,200 institutions; US$100 other countries; US$120 institutions, other countries; Rs 800 individuals online; US$80 other countries online; Rs 1,200 individuals print and online; Rs 1,500 institutions print and online. Remarks: Accepts advertising. URL: http://www.ijoem.com. Circ: (Not Reported)

Thanjavur

45747 ■ International Journal of Computing and Applications
Serials Publications
c/o Dr. M. Thiyagarajan, Ed.-in-Ch.
School of Humanities & Sciences
SASTRA Deemed University
Thirumalaisamudram
Thanjavur 613 402, Tamil Nadu, India
Publisher E-mail: serials@satyam.net.in
Journal covering contemporary computers and their applications. Freq: Semiannual. Key Personnel: Dr. R.S. Ramasamy, Editorial Board; Dr. Rm. Somasundaram, Editorial Board; Dr. L. Ganesan, Editorial Board; Dr. M. Thiyagarajan, Editor-in-Chief, m_thiyagarajan@yahoo.com; Dr. A.M.S. Ramasamy, Editorial Board. ISSN: 0973-5704. Subscription Rates: US$150 institutions print. URL: http://www.serialspublications.com/journals1.asp?jid=238&jtype=1.

Thiruvananthapuram

45748 ■ Loyola Journal of Social Sciences
Loyola College of Social Sciences
Sreekariyam PO
Thiruvananthapuram 695 017, Kerala, India
Ph: 91 471 2591018
Fax: 91 471 2591760
Publisher E-mail: lcsstvm@asianetindia.com
Social sciences publication focusing on research in sociology, social psychology, anthropology and related fields. Founded: 1987. Freq: Semiannual. Key Personnel: M.K. George, Ch. Ed.; R. Sooryamurthy, Editor. ISSN: 0971-4960. Subscription Rates: Rs 150 institutions; Rs 275 institutions two years; Rs 120 individuals; Rs 225 two years; Rs 100 students; Rs 200 students two years; Rs 1,500 individuals lifetime; US$25 institutions, other countries; US$45 institutions, other countries two years; US$250 other countries lifetime. Remarks: Accepts advertising. URL: http://www.loyolacollegekerala.edu.in/Publications.htm. Ad Rates: BW: Rs 5,000. Circ: Paid 300

45749 ■ Trends in Biomaterials & Artificial Organs
Society for Biomaterials and Artificial Organs
Division of Biosurface Technology
Biomedical Technology Wing
Sree Chitra Tirunal Institute for Medical Sciences & Technology
Poojapura

Thiruvananthapuram 695 012, Kerala, India
Ph: 91 471 2520214
Fax: 91 471 2341814
Journal covering progress in the area of biomaterials and artificial organs. **Freq:** Semiannual. **Key Personnel:** Chandra P. Sharma, Editor, sharmacp@mail. sctimat.ac.in; R.E. Baier, Assoc. Ed. **ISSN:** 0971-1198. **Subscription Rates:** Free to members; Rs 3,250 institutions. **URL:** http://www.angelfire.com/space2/ trends/index.html; http://www.sbaoi.org/society_journal. htm.

Thrissur

45750 ■ Journal of Tropical Agriculture
Kerala Agricultural University
c/o B.M. Kumar, Ed.
College of Forestry, KAU PO
Kerala Agricultural University
Thrissur 680 656, Kerala, India
Ph: 91 487 2370050
Fax: 91 487 2371040
Peer-reviewed journal focusing on tropical agriculture. **Founded:** 1962. **Freq:** Semiannual. **Print Method:** Offset. **Trim Size:** 1/4 crown. **Key Personnel:** B.M. Kumar, Editor, bmkumar.kau@gmail.com. **ISSN:** 0971-636X. **Subscription Rates:** Rs 300 individuals print; US$75 other countries print. **Remarks:** Advertising not accepted. **URL:** http://www.kau.edu; http://www.jtropag. in/index.php/ojs. **Circ:** Paid 500

Tiruchirapalli

45751 ■ Swamy Botanical Club Journal
Swamy Botanical Club
c/o Dr. K.V. Krishnamurthy
Dept. of Plant Sciences
Bharathidasan University
Tiruchirapalli 620 024, Tamil Nadu, India
Ph: 91 431 2407048
Fax: 91 431 2407032
Publication on botany. **Founded:** 1982. **Print Method:** DTP. **Trim Size:** 11 x 8.5. **ISSN:** 0256-9493. **Subscription Rates:** Rs 1824 individuals; Rs 3648 institutions. **Remarks:** Accepts advertising. **URL:** http://www.bdu.ac. in. **Formerly:** SBCI News Letter. **Circ:** Paid 250

45752 ■ All India Radio Tiruchirapalli - 936 KHz
28-3 Promende Rd.
PO Box 54
Tiruchirapalli 620 001, Tamil Nadu, India
Ph: 91 431 2410127
E-mail: try_airtry@sancharnet.in
Format: Eclectic. **Owner:** Prasar Bharati, Akashvani Bhavan, Sansad Marg, New Delhi 110 001, Delhi, India, 91 11 23421006, Fax: 91 11 23421956. **Founded:** 1939. **Key Personnel:** M.C. Aggarwal, Engr.-in-Ch., phone 91 11 23421058, fax 91 11 23421006, einc@air.org.in; Mohan Singh, Ch. Engr., Proj., phone 91 11 23421184. **Wattage:** 100,000. **Ad Rates:** $180-400 for 10 seconds; $270-600 for 15 seconds; $540-1,200 for 30 seconds; $1,080-2,400 for 60 seconds. **URL:** http://www. allindiaradio.org.

Tirunelveli

45753 ■ International Journal of Criminal Justice Sciences (IJCJS)
Department of Criminology and Criminal Justice
Manonmaniam Sundaranar University
Abishekapatti
Tirunelveli 627 012, Tamil Nadu, India
Publisher E-mail: cjfindia@gmail.com
Peer-reviewed journal covering issues in criminology, criminal justice, and victimology. **Freq:** Semiannual. **Key Personnel:** Madhava P. Soma Sundaram, International Editorial Advisory; K. Jaishankar, Editor-in-Chief; Mili M. Krishnan, Editorial Asst.; T. Lakshmi Narayana, Editorial Asst.; Mahfuzul I. Khondaker, Assoc. Ed. **ISSN:** 0973-5089. **URL:** http://www.ijcjs.co.nr/.

45754 ■ All India Radio Tirunelveli - 1197 KHz
Sarojini Pk.
Tirunelveli 627 002, Tamil Nadu, India
Ph: 91 462 2561139
E-mail: airtvl@md5.vsnl.net.in
Format: Eclectic. **Owner:** Prasar Bharati, Akashvani Bhavan, Sansad Marg, New Delhi 110 001, Delhi, India, 91 11 23421006, Fax: 91 11 23421956. **Founded:** 1963.

Key Personnel: M.C. Aggarwal, Engr.-in-Ch., phone 91 11 23421058, fax 91 11 23421006, einc@air.org.in. **Wattage:** 20,000. **Ad Rates:** $150-300 for 10 seconds; $225-450 for 15 seconds; $450-900 for 30 seconds; $900-1,800 for 60 seconds. **URL:** http://www. allindiaradio.org.

Tirupati (Andhra Pradesh)

45755 ■ All India Radio Tirupati - 103.2 MHz
Akashvani Bhavan
Sansad Marg
New Delhi 110 001, Delhi, India
Ph: 91 11 23421006
Fax: 91 11 23421956
E-mail: airtpty@yahoo.com
Format: Eclectic. **Owner:** Prasar Bharati, at above address. **Founded:** 1991. **Key Personnel:** M.C. Aggarwal, Engr.-in-Ch., phone 91 11 23421058, fax 91 11 23421006, einc@air.org.in. **Wattage:** 10,000. **Ad Rates:** $80-150 for 10 seconds; $120-225 for 15 seconds; $240-450 for 30 seconds; $480-900 for 60 seconds. **URL:** http://www.allindiaradio.org.

Tirupati (Karnataka)

45756 ■ Environmental Science
Trade Science Inc.
c/o P. Chiranjeevi, Editorial Board
Dept. of Chemistry
S.V. University
Tirupati 517 502, Karnataka, India
Publisher E-mail: help@tsijournals.com
Peer-reviewed journal covering research articles in inorganic chemistry. **Subtitle:** An Indian Journal. **Founded:** 1948. **Freq:** 6/yr. **Print Method:** Offset. **Cols./Page:** 8. **Col. Width:** 23 nonpareils. **Col. Depth:** 280 agate lines. **Key Personnel:** P. Chiranjeevi, Editorial Board; Shushi Chen, Editorial Board; Mehmet A. Oturan, Editorial Board. **ISSN:** 0974-7451. **Subscription Rates:** US$360 other countries; Rs 3,600 individuals. **URL:** http://www.tsijournals.com/esaij/.

Trivandrum

45757 ■ Annals of Indian Academy of Neurology
Medknow Publications Pvt Ltd.
Dept. of Neurology, Rm. 1409
Trivandrum 695011, Kerala, India
Ph: 91 471 2524468
Fax: 91 471 2524468
Magazine covering information on neuroscience. **Subtitle:** Official Journal of Indian Academy of Neurology. **Freq:** Quarterly. **Key Personnel:** Dr. Sanjeev V. Thomas, Editor; Satish Khadikar, Assoc. Ed.; Bhuma Vengamma, Assoc. Ed. **ISSN:** 0972-2327. **Subscription Rates:** Rs 1,500 individuals print; US$150 institutions print; Rs 1,200 individuals online; US$120 other countries online. **Remarks:** Accepts advertising. **URL:** http:// www.annalsofian.org/. **Circ:** (Not Reported)

45758 ■ Calicut Medical Journal
Calicut Medical College Calicut Medical College P.O
PO Thiruvanathapuram
Trivandrum, Kerala, India
Publisher E-mail: vathom@hotmail.com
Journal focusing on medical issues having an impact on the quality of health care. **Key Personnel:** Dr. P.V. Ramachandran, Founding Ch. Ed.; Dr. Johnson Francis, Assoc. Ed., francisj@calicutmedicalcollege.ac.in; Dr. Varghese Thomas, Editor-in-Chief, drvt@sancharnet.in; Dr. Vinod Scaria, Exec. Ed., vinodscaria@yahoo.co.in; Annie Varghese, Managing Editor. **Subscription Rates:** Free for online. **URL:** http://calicutmedicaljournal.org.

45759 ■ Journal of Orthopaedics
Calicut Medical College Calicut Medical College P.O
PO Thiruvanathapuram
Trivandrum, Kerala, India
Publisher E-mail: vathom@hotmail.com
Online journal on the perspectives in tropical orthopaedics. **Key Personnel:** Dr. P. Gopinathan, Ch. Ed. **ISSN:** 0972-978X. **URL:** http://www.jortho.org/index. html.

Tura

45760 ■ All India Radio Tura - 1233 KHz
Dakopgiri

Tura 794 001, Meghalaya, India
Ph: 91 3651 232935
E-mail: airtura@sancharnet.in
Format: Eclectic. **Owner:** Prasar Bharati, Akashvani Bhavan, Sansad Marg, New Delhi 110 001, Delhi, India, 91 11 23421006, Fax: 91 11 23421956. **Founded:** 1984. **Key Personnel:** M.C. Aggarwal, Engr.-in-Ch., phone 91 11 23421058, fax 91 11 23421006, einc@air.org.in. **Wattage:** 20,000. **Ad Rates:** $100-200 for 10 seconds; $150-300 for 15 seconds; $300-600 for 30 seconds; $600-1,200 for 60 seconds. **URL:** http://www. allindiaradio.org.

Tuticorin

45761 ■ All India Radio Tuticorin - 1053 KHz
Millerpuram
Palayamkottai Rd.
Tuticorin 628 008, Tamil Nadu, India
Ph: 91 461 2310027
E-mail: airttn@md4.vsnl.net.in
Format: Eclectic. **Owner:** Prasar Bharati, Akashvani Bhavan, Sansad Marg, New Delhi 110 001, Delhi, India, 91 11 23421006, Fax: 91 11 23421956. **Founded:** 1994. **Key Personnel:** M.C. Aggarwal, Engr.-in-Ch., phone 91 11 23421058, fax 91 11 23421006, einc@air.org.in. **Wattage:** 200,000. **Ad Rates:** $100-200 for 10 seconds; $150-300 for 15 seconds; $300-600 for 30 seconds; $600-1,200 for 60 seconds. **URL:** http://www. allindiaradio.org.

Udaipur

45762 ■ All India Radio Udaipur - 1125 KHz
Akashvani Bhavan
Sansad Marg
New Delhi 110 001, Delhi, India
Ph: 91 11 23421006
Fax: 91 11 23421956
E-mail: airudpur@sancharnet.in
Format: Eclectic. **Owner:** Prasar Bharati, at above address. **Founded:** 1967. **Key Personnel:** M.C. Aggarwal, Engr.-in-Ch., phone 91 11 23421058, fax 91 11 23421006, einc@air.org.in; Mohan Singh, Ch. Engr., Proj., phone 91 11 23421184. **Wattage:** 10,000. **Ad Rates:** $150-300 for 10 seconds; $225-450 for 15 seconds; $450-900 for 30 seconds; $900-1,800 for 60 seconds. **URL:** http://www.allindiaradio.org.

Udupi

45763 ■ Indian Journal of Occupational Therapy
All India Occupational Therapists' Association
Dept. of Occupational Therapy
Manipal College of Allied Sciences
Udupi 576 104, Karnataka, India
Ph: 91 820 2574136
Fax: 91 820 2571915
Publisher E-mail: shovansaha@yahoo.com
Publication on occupational therapy. **Freq:** 3/yr (April, August, and December). **Key Personnel:** Dr. M.S. Warhade, Editor, madanwarhade@gmail.com; Dr. Sofia Azad, Assoc. Ed., sofiaazad2000@yahoo.co.in; Dr. Anuradha Pai, Editorial Board; Dr. Anwar Ali Dhamani, Editorial Board. **ISSN:** 0445-7706. **Subscription Rates:** Rs 100 individuals; US$10 individuals overseas; Rs 5,000 members life; US$400 members life overseas; Rs 700 students one time. **URL:** http://medind.nic.in/iba/ ibam.shtml. **Circ:** 750

Vadodara

45764 ■ Navnirman
Gujarat Engineering Research Institute
Race Course
Vadodara 390 007, Gujarat, India
Publisher E-mail: geribrd@rediffmail.com
Publication featuring charts and illustrated maps on construction. **Founded:** 1960. **Freq:** Bimonthly. **ISSN:** 0028-162X. **URL:** http://www.gerionline.org/. **Circ:** Paid 250

Varanasi

45765 ■ Indian Journal of Preventive and Social Medicine
Banaras Hindu University
Institute of Medical Sciences
Department of Preventive and Social Medicine

A-Block, CGO Complex, Lodhi Rd.
Varanasi 110 003, Uttar Pradesh, India
Publication covering preventive medicine, public health, and safety. **Founded:** 1973. **Freq:** Quarterly. **Key Personnel:** S.C. Mohapatra, Ch. Ed.; Ratan K. Srivastava, Managing Editor; C.P. Mishra, Editor. **ISSN:** 0301-1216. **Remarks:** Accepts advertising. **URL:** http://medind.nic.in/ibl/iblm.shtml. **Circ:** (Not Reported)

45766 ■ All India Radio Varanasi - 1242 KHz
Mahamoor Ganj
Varanasi 221 010, Uttar Pradesh, India
Ph: 91 542 2220497
E-mail: airvaranasi@satyam.net.in
Format: Eclectic. **Owner:** Prasar Bharati, Akashvani Bhavan, Sansad Marg, New Delhi 110 001, Delhi, India, 91 11 23421006, Fax: 91 11 23421956. **Founded:** 1962. **Key Personnel:** M.C. Aggarwal, Engr.-in-Ch., phone 91 11 23421058, fax 91 11 23421006, einc@air.org.in. **Wattage:** 100,000. **Ad Rates:** $180-400 for 10 seconds; $270-600 for 15 seconds; $540-1,200 for 30 seconds; $1,080-2,400 for 60 seconds. **URL:** http://www.allindiaradio.org.

Vijayawada

45767 ■ All India Radio Vijayawada - 837 KHz
Punnammathota
Vijayawada 520 010, Andhra Pradesh, India
Ph: 91 866 2476212
E-mail: vjwairvza@sancharnet.in
Format: Eclectic. **Owner:** Prasar Bharati, Akashvani Bhavan, Sansad Marg, New Delhi 110 001, Delhi, India, 91 11 23421006, Fax: 91 11 23421956. **Founded:** 1948. **Key Personnel:** M.C. Aggarwal, Engr.-in-Ch., phone 91 11 23421058, fax 91 11 23421459, einc@air.org.in. **Wattage:** 100,000. **Ad Rates:** $180-400 for 10 seconds;

$270-600 for 15 seconds; $540-1,200 for 30 seconds; $1,080-2,400 for 60 seconds. **URL:** http://www.allindiaradio.org.

Visakhapatnam

45768 ■ All India Radio Vishakhapatnam - 927 KHz
Siripuram Jn
Visakhapatnam 530 003, Andhra Pradesh, India
Ph: 91 891 2565550
E-mail: airvisakhapatnam@nettlinx.com
Format: Eclectic. **Owner:** Prasar Bharati, Akashvani Bhavan, Sansad Marg, New Delhi 110 001, Delhi, India, 91 11 23421006, Fax: 91 11 23421956. **Founded:** 1963. **Key Personnel:** M.C. Aggarwal, Engr.-in-Ch., phone 91 11 23421058, fax 91 11 23421459, einc@air.org.in. **Wattage:** 100,000. **Ad Rates:** $180-400 for 10 seconds; $270-600 for 15 seconds; $540-1,200 for 30 seconds; $1,080-2,400 for 60 seconds. **URL:** http://www.allindiaradio.org.

Warangal

45769 ■ All India Radio Warangal - 103.5 MHz
Akashvani Bhavan
Sansad Marg
New Delhi 110 001, Delhi, India
Ph: 91 11 23421006
Fax: 91 11 23421956
E-mail: airwgl@yahoo.com
Format: Eclectic. **Owner:** Prasar Bharati, at above address. **Founded:** 1990. **Key Personnel:** M.C. Aggarwal, Engr.-in-Ch., phone 91 11 23421058, fax 91 11 23421006, einc@air.org.in. **Wattage:** 10,000. **Ad Rates:** $80-150 for 10 seconds; $120-225 for 15 seconds; $240-450 for 30 seconds; $480-900 for 60 seconds.

URL: http://www.allindiaradio.org.

Wardha

45770 ■ Journal of Neurosciences in Rural Practice
Medknow Publications Pvt Ltd.
c/o Dr. Amit Agrawal, Ed.-in-Ch.
Department of Neurosurgery
Datta Meghe Institute of Medical Sciences
Sawangi (Meghe)
Wardha 442 004, Maharashtra, India
Publication E-mail: editor@ruralneuropractice.com
Peer-reviewed journal covering rural healthcare practices on neurosciences. **Freq:** Bimonthly. **Key Personnel:** Dr. Amit Agrawal, Editor-in-Chief; Arvind Bhake, Exec. Ed.; Rafael Cincu, Exec. Ed. **Subscription Rates:** Rs 100 individuals print; Rs 2,000 institutions print; US$100 other countries print; US$200 institutions, other countries print. **URL:** http://www.ruralneuropractice.com.

Yavatmal

45771 ■ All India Radio Yavatmal - 102.7 KHz
Godani Rd.
Yavatmal 445 001, Maharashtra, India
Ph: 91 7232 245582
E-mail: airyml_yml@sancharnet.in
Format: Eclectic. **Owner:** Prasar Bharati, Akashvani Bhavan, Sansad Marg, New Delhi 110 001, Delhi, India, 91 11 23421006, Fax: 91 11 23421956. **Founded:** 1992. **Key Personnel:** M.C. Aggarwal, Engr.-in-Ch., phone 91 11 23421058, fax 91 11 23421006, einc@air.org.in. **Wattage:** 6000. **Ad Rates:** $80-150 for 10 seconds; $120-225 for 15 seconds; $240-450 for 30 seconds; $480-900 for 60 seconds. **URL:** http://www.allindiaradio.org.

Circulation: ★ = ABC; △ = BPA; ♦ = CAC; • = CCAB; ❏ = VAC; ⊕ = PO Statement; ‡ = Publisher's Report; Boldface figures = sworn; Light figures = estimated.

Gale Directory of Publications & Broadcast Media/147th Ed.   5041

Ambarawa

45772 ■ Radio Swara Palagan Sehati (SPS) - 648 KHz
Jl. Jend. Sudirman, No. 17-A
50614 Semarang, Indonesia
Ph: 62 298 591354
Fax: 62 298 591355
E-mail: radioprssni@radioprssni.com
Format: Eclectic. **Owner:** Federation of Indonesian National Commercial Broadcasters, Pengurus Pusat, Jalan Raya Pondok Gede 96, 13810 Jakarta, Indonesia, 62 21 8414311, 62 21 8414312, Fax: 62 21 8414314. **Key Personnel:** Bagus Atma Negara, Contact. **Ad Rates:** Noncommercial. **URL:** http://www.radioprssni.com/prssninew/profildetail.asp?id=457.

Bali

45773 ■ Hard Rock Radio-FM - 87.8
PT Radio Baturiti Menaraswara
Pertokoan Teras Bali, No. 4
Jl. By Pass Ngurah Rai Tuban, Kuta
Bali, Indonesia
Ph: 62 361 759478
Fax: 62 361 768088
Format: Eclectic. **Ad Rates:** Advertising accepted; rates available upon request. **URL:** http://www.hardrockfm.com.

Bandung

45774 ■ Delta-FM - 94.4
Mal Paris van Java FF 01 B
Jl. Sukajadi, No. 137-139
40162 Bandung, Indonesia
Ph: 62 22 82063808
Fax: 62 22 82063809
Format: Ethnic; News. **Owner:** Delta FM Radio, at above address. **Operating Hours:** 18 hours Daily. **URL:** http://ww2.deltafm.net.

45775 ■ Delta-FM - 94.4
Mal Paris van Java FF 01 B
Jl. Sukajadi No. 137-139
40162 Bandung, Indonesia
Ph: 62 22 82063808
Format: Ethnic. **Owner:** Delta FM Radio, at above address. **Operating Hours:** 18 hours Daily. **URL:** http://www.deltafmjakarta.com.

45776 ■ MGT-FM - 101.1 MHz
Jalan Buah Batu, No. 8
40262 Bandung, Indonesia
Ph: 62 22 7311205
Fax: 62 22 7300397
E-mail: mgtradio@gmail.com
Format: Ethnic. **Ad Rates:** Advertising accepted; rates available upon request. **URL:** http://www.mgtradio.com.

45777 ■ Prambors Bandung-FM - 98.4
Jl. Sukajadi No. 137-139
40162 Bandung, Indonesia
Ph: 62 22 82063812
Fax: 62 22 82063809

E-mail: bandung@pramborsfm.com
Format: Ethnic; World Beat. **URL:** http://www.pramborsfm.com.

45778 ■ Radio Leidya Swara Utama, Bandung - 828 KHz
Jalan Babakan Tarogong No. 216 B
40254 Bandung, Indonesia
Ph: 62 22 5225786
Fax: 62 22 5225787
Format: Eclectic. **Owner:** Persatuan Radio Siaran Swasta Nasional Indonesia, Jl. Sukamaju, No. 37, 40161 Bandung, Indonesia, 62 22 2038362, 62 22 2032844, Fax: 62 22 2039550. **Key Personnel:** Leidyawati Effendi, Contact. **Wattage:** 250. **URL:** http://www.prssnijabar.or.id; http://www.bandung.go.id/?fa=berita.detail&id=1199.

45779 ■ Radio Paksi, Bandung - 1152 KHz
Jl. Jend. A. Yani, Blk. 96 Kota
Bandung, Indonesia
Ph: 62 22 7272850
Format: Eclectic. **Owner:** Federation of Indonesian National Commercial Broadcasters, Pengurus Pusat, Jalan Raya Pondok Gede 96, 13810 Jakarta, Indonesia, 62 21 8414311, 62 21 8414312, Fax: 62 21 8414314. **URL:** http://www.prssnijabar.or.id.

Banjar

45780 ■ Radio Cempaka Angkasa, Ciamis - 792 KHz
Jl. Pamarican No. 28
46321 Banjar, Indonesia
Ph: 62 265 741539
Fax: 62 265 741539
E-mail: radioprssni@radioprssni.com
Format: Eclectic. **Owner:** Federation of Indonesian National Commercial Broadcasters, Pengurus Pusat, Jalan Raya Pondok Gede 96, 13810 Jakarta, Indonesia. **Key Personnel:** Dr. H. Gandjar Suwargani, Chm. URI: http://www.radioprssni.com.

Banjarmasin

45781 ■ Radio Kharismanada Rasisonia (La Fozsy), Banjarmasin - 738 KHz
Jalan K.S. Tubun, Rt 10
Komplek Pertokoan Hi
70243 Banjarmasin, Indonesia
Ph: 62 511 3267772
Fax: 62 511 3263836
E-mail: radioprssni@radioprssni.com
Format: Eclectic. **Owner:** Federation of Indonesian National Commercial Broadcasters, Pengurus Pusat, Jalan Raya Pondok Gede 96, 13810 Jakarta, Indonesia, 62 21 8414311, Fax: 62 21 8414314. **Key Personnel:** Alex Rusli, Contact. **Wattage:** 250. **URL:** http://www.radioprssni.com/prssninew/profildetail.asp?id=676.

Banjarnegara

45782 ■ Radio Suara Selomanik (RSS), Banjarnegara - 918 KHz
Pengurus Pusat
Jalan Raya Pondok Gede 96

13810 Jakarta, Indonesia
Ph: 62 21 8414311
Fax: 62 21 8414314
E-mail: radioprssni@radioprssni.com
Format: Eclectic. **Key Personnel:** Dr. H. Gandjar Suwargani, Chm.; Ulfatun Subandi, Contact. **Ad Rates:** Noncommercial. **URL:** http://www.radioprssni.com.

Bekasi

45783 ■ Radio Purnayudha, Bekasi - 1044 KHz
Jl. Delta Silicon Blok AE No. 56 A Lippo Cikarang
17530 Bekasi, Indonesia
Ph: 62 21 8908724
Fax: 62 21 8973872
Format: Eclectic. **Owner:** Persatuan Radio Siaran Swasta Nasional Indonesia, Jl. Sukamaju No. 37, 40161 Bandung, Indonesia, 62 22 2038362, 62 22 2032844, Fax: 62 22 2039550. **Wattage:** 250. **Ad Rates:** Advertising accepted; rates available upon request. **URL:** http://www.prssnijabar.or.id.

Blora

45784 ■ Radio Duta Suara Garuda Sakti, Blora - 1242 KHz
Jl. Raya Jepon No. 140-B
58261 Blora, Indonesia
Ph: 62 296 531755
Fax: 62 296 532239
E-mail: radioprssni@radioprssni.com
Format: Eclectic. **Owner:** Federation of Indonesian National Commercial Broadcasters, Pengurus Pusat, Jalan Raya Pondok Gede 96, 13810 Jakarta, Indonesia, 62 21 8414311, 62 21 8414312, Fax: 62 21 8414314. **Key Personnel:** Dr. H. Gandjar Suwargani, Chm.; Paul Budianto, BA, Contact. **URL:** http://www.radioprssni.com/prssninew/profildetail.asp?id=426.

Bogor

45785 ■ Radio Republik Indonesia, Bogor - 1242 KHz
Jalan Pangrango, No. 34
16161 Bogor, Indonesia
Ph: 62 251 315484
Format: Eclectic. **Owner:** Radio Republik Indonesia, Jl. Medan Merdeka, 10110 Jakarta, Indonesia. **Wattage:** 1000. **URL:** http://www.rribogor.info/index.html.

Buleleng

45786 ■ Radio Cakra Swara Perkasa, Singaraja - 1044 KHz
Jl. WR Supratman No. 35
81116 Buleleng, Indonesia
Ph: 62 362 32777
Fax: 62 362 31771
E-mail: radioprssni@radioprssni.com
Format: Eclectic. **Owner:** Federation of Indonesian National Commercial Broadcasters, Pengurus Pusat, Jalan Raya Pondok Gede 96, 13810 Jakarta, Indonesia, 62 21 8414311, 62 21 8414312, Fax: 62 21 8414314. **Key Personnel:** Dr. H. Gandjar Suwargani, Chm. **Wattage:** 250. **Ad Rates:** Noncommercial. **URL:** http://www.

Circulation: ★ = ABC; △ = BPA; ◆ = CAC; ● = CCAB; ❑ = VAC; ⊕ = PO Statement; ‡ = Publisher's Report; Boldface figures = sworn; Light figures = estimated.

Gale Directory of Publications & Broadcast Media/147th Ed.

5043

radioprssni.com/prssninew/profildetail.asp?id=662.

Cilacap

Radio Gagah Sehat Berbobot (Gasebo), Majenang - See Majenang

45787 ■ Radio Wijaya Adikusuma, Cilacap - 102.6
Jalan Dr. Cipto No. 18
53231 Cilacap, Indonesia
Ph: 62 282 541694
E-mail: wijayafm_cilacap@yahoo.com
Format: Eclectic. **Owner:** Federation of Indonesian National Commercial Broadcasters, Pengurus Pusat, Jalan Raya Pondok Gede 96, 13810 Jakarta, Indonesia, 62 218 414311, Fax: 62 218 414314. **Key Personnel:** Djudju Setyaningsih, Contact. **Ad Rates:** Advertising accepted; rates available upon request. **URL:** http://www.radioprssni.com/prssninew/profildetail.asp?id=402.

Denpasar

45788 ■ Radio Swara Yudha, Denpasar - 828 KHz
Jl. Gunung Catur II Blok E/6
80117 Denpasar, Indonesia
Ph: 62 361 425177
Fax: 62 361 425177
E-mail: radioprssni@radioprssni.com
Format: Eclectic. **Owner:** Federation of Indonesian National Commercial Broadcasters, Pengurus Pusat, Jalan Raya Pondok Gede 96, 13810 Jakarta, Indonesia, 62 21 8414311, 62 21 8414312, Fax: 62 21 8414314. **Key Personnel:** I Gusti Ngurah Ananda Dimitri, Contact. **Wattage:** 250. **Ad Rates:** Noncommercial. **URL:** http://www.radioprssni.com/prssninew/profildetail.asp?id=633.

Depok

45789 ■ Radio Swara Pakusarakan Pratita, Sawangan - 684 KHz
Jl. Bojongsari Raya, No. 17
16516 Depok, Indonesia
Ph: 62 251 611005
E-mail: radioprssni@radioprssni.com
Format: Eclectic. **Owner:** Federation of Indonesian National Commercial Broadcasters, Pengurus Pusat, Jalan Raya Pondok Gede 96, 13810 Jakarta, Indonesia, 62 21 8414311, 62 21 8414312, Fax: 62 21 8414314. **Key Personnel:** Yusli Susanto, Contact. **Ad Rates:** Advertising accepted; rates available upon request. **URL:** http://www.radioprssni.com/prssninew/profildetail.asp?id=314.

East Java

45790 ■ Radio Swara Fiskaramatama - 936 KHz
Jalan Veteran 6-8
68211 East Java, Indonesia
Ph: 62 332 421423
Fax: 62 332 421423
E-mail: radioprssni@radioprssni.com
Owner: Federation of Indonesian National Commercial Broadcasters, Pengurus Pusat, Jalan Raya Pondok Gede 96, 13810 Jakarta, Indonesia, 62 2184 14311, Fax: 62 2184 14314. **Former name:** Radio Suara Fiskarama, Bondowoso. **Key Personnel:** H. Gandjar Suwargani, Chm.; Djudjur Setiawan Arief, Contact. **Ad Rates:** Noncommercial. **URL:** http://www.radioprssni.com.

Garut

45791 ■ Radio Nusantara Bharata Citra (NBC), Garut - 882 KHz
Jalan Pembangunan 254
44151 Garut, Indonesia
Ph: 62 262 233600
E-mail: info@prssnijabar.or.id
Format: Eclectic. **Owner:** Persatuan Radio Siaran Swasta Nasional Indonesia, Jl. Sukamaju, No. 37, 40161 Bandung, Indonesia, 62 22 2038362, 62 22 2032844, Fax: 62 22 2039550. **Wattage:** 300. **URL:** http://www.prssnijabar.or.id.

Gorontalo

45792 ■ Radio Swara Gorontalo Permai, Gorontalo - 684 KHz
Jalan Raya Pondok Gede 96
13810 Jakarta, Indonesia
Ph: 62 218 414311
Fax: 62 218 414314
E-mail: radioprssni@radioprssni.com
Owner: Federation of Indonesian National Commercial Broadcasters, at above address. **Key Personnel:** Shidki Wahab, Contact. **Ad Rates:** Noncommercial. **URL:** http://www.radioprssni.com/prssninew/profildetail.asp?id=788.

Jakarta

45793 ■ BOLA SportsLine
Jl. Palmerah Barath, No. 33-37
10270 Jakarta, Indonesia
Ph: 62-21 53677835
Fax: 62 21 5301952
Publisher E-mail: redaksi@bolanews.com
Newspaper covering sports. **Key Personnel:** Ian Situmorang, Dir./Gen. Mgr.; Eko Widodo, Exec. Ed. **ISSN:** 0852-6729. **URL:** http://www.bolanews.com.

45794 ■ Cocoinfo International
Asian & Pacific Coconut Community
3rd Fl., Lina Bldg.
Jl. H.R. Rasuna Said Kav.B7
Kuningan
12920 Jakarta, Indonesia
Ph: 62 21 5221712
Fax: 62 21 5221714
Publisher E-mail: apcc@indo.net.id
Non-technical publication helping in the promotion, processing and marketing of coconut products. **Freq:** Semiannual. **Subscription Rates:** US$25 individuals Asia & Pacific; US$30 other countries USA. **URL:** http://www.apccsec.org/pjcoinfo.htm.

45795 ■ Cord
Asian & Pacific Coconut Community
3rd Fl., Lina Bldg.
Jl. H.R. Rasuna Said Kav.B7
Kuningan
12920 Jakarta, Indonesia
Ph: 62 21 5221712
Fax: 62 21 5221714
Publisher E-mail: apcc@indo.net.id
Journal featuring articles on coconut research and development. **Freq:** Semiannual. **Subscription Rates:** US$25 individuals U.S. & elsewhere; US$20 individuals Asia & Pacific. **URL:** http://www.apccsec.org/serials.php.

45796 ■ Economics and Finance in Indonesia
University of Indonesia
Institute for Economic and Social Research
Jalan Raya Salemba 4
10430 Jakarta, Indonesia
Ph: 62 217 78880139
Publication E-mail: surjadi@lpem-feui.org
Business and economics journal. **Founded:** 1948. **Freq:** Quarterly. **URL:** http://www.lpem.org/petunjuk.html. **Circ:** 4,000

45797 ■ Gatra
Gatra.com
Gedung Gatra
Jl. Kalibata Timur IV, No. 15
12740 Jakarta, Indonesia
Ph: 62 21 7973535
Fax: 62 21 79196941
Publisher E-mail: gatracom@gatra.com
News magazine of Indonesia. **Founded:** 1995. **Freq:** Weekly. **Remarks:** Advertising accepted; rates available upon request. **URL:** http://www.gatra.com/2005-05-05/kontak.php. **Circ:** (Not Reported)

45798 ■ Gizi Indonesia
Akedemi Gizi
Jl. Hang Jebat III/F3
Kebayoran Baru
PO Box 8 KBB
Jakarta, Indonesia
Publication E-mail: jgi0609@yahoo.co.id
Journal covering nutrition and dietics. **Freq:** Quarterly. **Key Personnel:** Eman Sumarna, Editor. **ISSN:** 0436-0265. **Subscription Rates:** 1,200 Rp. **Remarks:** Advertising accepted; rates available upon request. **URL:** http://www.gizi.net/jurnal-gizi/index.shtml. **Circ:** (Not Reported)

45799 ■ Indonesian Commercial Newsletter
P.T. Data Consult Inc.
Maya Indah Bldg.
Jalan Kramat Raya, No. 5-L
10450 Jakarta, Indonesia
Ph: 62 21 3904711
Fax: 62 21 3901877
Publisher E-mail: info@datacon.co.id
Business publication. **Founded:** 1978. **Freq:** Biweekly. **Key Personnel:** D. Ganjar Sidik, Editor-in-Chief; Agustina R. Effendy, Sen. Ed.; Giri Buana, Managing Editor. **ISSN:** 0853-2086. **Subscription Rates:** 4,000,000 Rp individuals hardcopy; 2,400,000 Rp individuals hardcopy, 6 months; 3,600,000 Rp individuals e-mail; English/Indonesian; 2,000,000 Rp individuals e-mail English/Indonesian, 6 months; 5,900,000 Rp individuals hardcopy + e-mail; 3,500,000 Rp individuals hardcopy + e-mail, 6 months; US$550 other countries hardcopy, Asian countries & Australia; US$600 other countries hardcopy, Europe, Canada & USA; US$450 other countries e-mail; 800 Rp other countries hardcopy + e-mail. **URL:** http://www.datacon.co.id/ICN.html.

45800 ■ Indonesian Quarterly
Centre for Strategic and International Studies
Jakarta Post Bldg., 3rd Fl.
Jl. Palmerah Barat 142-243
10270 Jakarta, Indonesia
Ph: 62 21 53654601
Fax: 62 21 53654607
Political science journal. **Founded:** 1972. **Freq:** Quarterly. **ISSN:** 0304-2170. **Subscription Rates:** US$160,000 individuals Indonesia; US$125 individuals Asia, Pacific, Australia; US$155 individuals Europe, Africa; US$190 individuals U.S., Canada, Central America; US$220 individuals South America, others; Rs 50,000 single issue Indonesia. **Remarks:** Advertising accepted; rates available upon request. **URL:** http://www.csis.or.id/publications_journal_title.asp?id=1&tab=0. **Circ:** Paid 3,000

45801 ■ The Jakarta Post
PT Bina Media Tenggara
Jl. Palmerah Selatan 15
10270 Jakarta, Indonesia
Ph: 62 215 300476
Fax: 62 215 350050
Publication E-mail: editorial@thejakartapost.com
Publisher E-mail: editorial@thejakartapost.com
English language general newspaper. **Founded:** Apr. 25, 1983. **Freq:** Daily (morn.). **Key Personnel:** Jusuf Wanandi, Director; Sabam Siagian, Dir./Sen. Ed.; Vincent Lingga, Sen. Ed.; Wayan Sadia, Editorial Staff; Endy M. Bayuni, Editor-in-Chief; Riyadi Suparno, Managing Editor; Harry Bhaskara, Sen. Ed. **Subscription Rates:** 66,000 Rp individuals per month for Indonesia area; 279,000 Rp individuals per quarterly for Indonesia; 4,000 Rp single issue. **Remarks:** Accepts advertising. **URL:** http://www.thejakartapost.com/about. **Circ:** 30,552

45802 ■ Tempo Interactive
PT. Tempo Inti Media
Kebayoran Center Blok A11 - A15
Jl. Kebayoran Baru
Mayestik
12440 Jakarta, Indonesia
Ph: 62 21 7255625
Fax: 62 21 7255645
Publication E-mail: interaktif@tempo.co.id
Publisher E-mail: iklannews@tempo.co.id
General interest online periodical. **Founded:** 1996. **Freq:** Daily. **Remarks:** Advertising accepted; rates available upon request. **URL:** http://www.tempointeractive.com. **Circ:** (Not Reported)

45803 ■ Delta-FM - 99.1
Ratu Plz., Office Tower, 19th Fl.
Jl. Jend. Sudirman kav. 9
10270 Jakarta, Indonesia
Ph: 62 21 72784033
Fax: 62 21 7237616
E-mail: program@deltafm.net
Format: Ethnic; News. **Owner:** Delta FM Radio, at above address. **Operating Hours:** 18 hours Daily. **URL:** http://ww2.deltafm.net.

45804 ■ Hard Rock Radio-FM - 87.6
PT Radio Antar Nusa Djaja
Gedung Sarinah, 8th Fl.
Jl. MH. Thamrin 11
10350 Jakarta, Indonesia
Ph: 62 21 3146556
Fax: 62 21 3144772
Format: Eclectic. **Ad Rates:** Advertising accepted; rates available upon request. **URL:** http://www.hardrockfm.com.

45805 ■ Lite-FM - 105.8
Menara BTN lt. 19
Jl. Gajah Mada No. 1, Harmoni
10130 Jakarta, Indonesia
Ph: 62 21 6332703
Fax: 62 21 6342707
Format: World Beat; Ethnic. **Formerly:** Ramako-FM (June 2, 2008). **Operating Hours:** Continuous. **Ad Rates:** Advertising accepted; rates available upon request. **URL:** http://www.litefmjakarta.com/.

45806 ■ Prambors Jakarta-FM - 102.2
Ratu Plz. Office Tower Lt. 20
Jl. Jend. Sudirman kav 9
10270 Jakarta, Indonesia
Ph: 62 21 7223313
Fax: 62 21 7223350
E-mail: info@pramborsfm.com
Format: Ethnic; World Beat. **Key Personnel:** Niken Puspitawangi, Program Dir. **Ad Rates:** Noncommercial. **URL:** http://www.pramborsfm.com.

45807 ■ Radio Leonardus Buana Suara, Salatiga - 774 KHz
Pengurus Pusat
Jalan Raya Pondok Gede 96
13810 Jakarta, Indonesia
Ph: 62 218 414311
Fax: 62 218 414314
E-mail: radioprssni@radioprssni.com
Owner: Federation of Indonesian National Commercial Broadcasters, at above address. **Key Personnel:** H.Gandjar Suwargani, Chm. **Wattage:** 200. **URL:** http://www.radioprssni.com.

45808 ■ Radio Pelangi Nusantara, Jakarta - 882 KHz
Komplek Taman
Mini Indonesia Indah
Pandok, Gede
Jakarta, Indonesia
E-mail: radioprssni@radioprssni.com
Format: Eclectic. **Owner:** Federation of Indonesian National Commercial Broadcasters, Pengurus Pusat, Jalan Raya Pondok Gede 96, 13810 Jakarta, Indonesia, 62 218 414311, Fax: 62 218 414314. **Key Personnel:** H. Gandjar Suwargani, Chm. **Ad Rates:** Advertising accepted; rates available upon request. **URL:** http://www.radioprssni.com.

45809 ■ Radio Puspa Dwi Swara Cipta (P2SC), Jakarta - 936 KHz
Jalan Dakota V/1
15223 Jakarta, Indonesia
Ph: 62 21 4256034
Fax: 62 21 4254006
E-mail: radioprssni@radioprssni.com
Format: Eclectic. **Owner:** Federation of Indonesian National Commercial Broadcasters, Pengurus Pusat, Jalan Raya Pondok Gede 96, 13810 Jakarta, Indonesia, 62 21 8414311, 62 21 8414312, Fax: 62 21 8414314. **Key Personnel:** Dr. H. Gandjar Suwargani, Chm.; Soetardjo Koentojo, Contact. **Wattage:** 250. **URL:** http://www.radioprssni.com.

45810 ■ Radio Rina Bestari, Rantepao - 738 KHz
Pengurus Pusat
Jalan Raya Pondok Gede 96
13810 Jakarta, Indonesia
Ph: 62 184 14311
Fax: 62 184 14314
E-mail: radioprssni@radioprssni.com
Owner: Federation of Indonesian National Commercial Broadcasters, at above address. **Key Personnel:** H. Gandjar Suwargani, Chm. **Ad Rates:** Noncommercial. **URL:** http://www.radioprssni.com.

45811 ■ Radio S.B.S., Purbalingga - 828 KHz
Pengurus Pusat
Jalan Raya Pondok Gede 96
13810 Jakarta, Indonesia
Ph: 62 218 414311
Fax: 62 218 414314
E-mail: radioprssni@radioprssni.com
Owner: Federation of Indonesian National Commercial Broadcasters, at above address. **Key Personnel:** H.Gandjar Suwargani, Chm. **Ad Rates:** Noncommercial. **URL:** http://www.radioprssni.com.

45812 ■ Radio Suara Maung Sakti, Banjarnegara - 810 KHz
Pengurus Pusat
Jalan Raya Pondok Gede 96
13810 Jakarta, Indonesia
Ph: 62 218 414311
Fax: 62 218 414314
E-mail: radioprssni@radioprssni.com
Owner: Federation of Indonesian National Commercial Broadcasters, at above address. **Key Personnel:** H. Gandjar Suwargani, Chm. **URL:** http://www.radioprssni.com.

Radio Suara Selomanik (RSS), Banjarnegara - See Banjarnegara

Radio Swara Gorontalo Permai, Gorontalo - See Gorontalo

45813 ■ Radio Swara Graha Jelita, Surakarta - 792 KHz
Pengurus Pusat
Jalan Raya Pondok Gede 96
13810 Jakarta, Indonesia
Ph: 62 218 414311
Fax: 62 218 414314
E-mail: radioprssni@radioprssni.com
Owner: Federation of Indonesian National Commercial Broadcasters, at above address. **Key Personnel:** H.Gandjar Suwargani, Chm. **Ad Rates:** Noncommercial. **URL:** http://www.radioprssni.com.

45814 ■ Radio Swara Melati Gramedia, Mempawah - 738 KHz
Pengurus Pusat
Jalan Raya Pondok Gede 96
13810 Jakarta, Indonesia
Ph: 62 218 414311
Fax: 62 218 414314
E-mail: radioprssni@radioprssni.com
Owner: Federation of Indonesian National Commercial Broadcasters, at above address. **Key Personnel:** H.Gandjar Suwargani, Chm. **URL:** http://www.radioprssni.com.

45815 ■ Radio Warastra Bewara Swara, Palembang - 810 KHz
Pengurus Pusat
Jalan Raya Pondok Gede 96
13810 Jakarta, Indonesia
Ph: 62 218 414311
Fax: 62 218 414314
E-mail: radioprssni@radioprssni.com
Owner: Federation of Indonesian National Commercial Broadcasters, at above address. **Key Personnel:** H Gandjar Suwargani, Chm. **Wattage:** 250. **Ad Rates:** Noncommercial. **URL:** http://www.radioprssni.com.

Jambi

45816 ■ Radio Batanghari Permai (BHP), Jambi - 648 KHz
Jalan Gajah Mada No. 8
Kampung Tengah
36621 Jambi, Indonesia
Ph: 62 741 583309
E-mail: radiobhp@telkom.net
Format: Eclectic. **Owner:** Federation of Indonesian National Commercial Broadcasters, Pengurus Pusat, Jalan Raya Pondok Gede 96, 13810 Jakarta, Indonesia, 62 218 414311, Fax: 62 218 414314. **URL:** http://www.radioprssni.com/prssninew/profildetail.asp?id=813.

Kandangan

45817 ■ Radio Purnama Nada, Kandangan - 684 KHz
Jalan Pahlawan, No. 33
71211 Kandangan, Indonesia
Ph: 62 517 21435

Fax: 62 517 21439
Format: Eclectic. **Owner:** Federation of Indonesian National Commercial Broadcasters, Pengurus Pusat, Jalan Raya Pondok Gede 96, 13810 Jakarta, Indonesia, 62 218 414311, Fax: 62 218 414314. **Key Personnel:** H. Akhmad Syarkawi, Contact. **URL:** http://www.radioprssni.com/prssninew/profildetail.asp?id=683.

Karawang

45818 ■ Radio Histori Gita Jaya, Karawang - 1206 KHz
Jalan K.H.A. Dahlan 1
41311 Karawang, Indonesia
Ph: 62 267 403432
Fax: 62 267 403432
Format: Eclectic. **Owner:** Federation of Indonesian National Commercial Broadcasters, Pengurus Pusat PRSSNI, Jalan Raya Pondok Gede 96, 13810 Jakarta, Indonesia, Fax: 62 21 8414314. **Key Personnel:** Ruddy Heryanto, Director. **URL:** http://www.radioprssni.com/Anggota/jabar/swarahistori.htm.

45819 ■ Radio Swadaya Cempaka 23, Karawang - 1602 KHz
Jalan Cempaka, No. 5
41314 Karawang, Indonesia
Ph: 62 267 402224
Format: Eclectic. **Owner:** Persatuan Radio Siaran Swasta Nasional Indonesia, Jl. Sukamaju, No. 37, 40161 Bandung, Indonesia, 62 22 2038362, 62 22 2032844, Fax: 62 22 2039550. **Key Personnel:** Iwan Suhendra, Contact. **Wattage:** 250. **URL:** http://www.prssnijabar.or.id.

Kebumen

45820 ■ Radio Diantara Vita Kharisma (DVK), Kebumen - 558 KHz
Jalan Kutoarjo 60
54312 Kebumen, Indonesia
Ph: 62 287 381444
Fax: 62 287 381617
E-mail: radioprssni@radioprssni.com
Format: Eclectic. **Owner:** Federation of Indonesian National Commercial Broadcasters, Pengurus Pusat, Jalan Raya Pondok Gede 96, Jakarta 13810, Indonesia, 62 21 8414311, 62 21 8414312, Fax: 62 21 8414314. **Key Personnel:** Ny. Hj. Artaty Kamal, Contact. **Ad Rates:** Advertising accepted; rates available upon request. **URL:** http://www.radioprssni.com/prssninew/profildetail.asp?id=414.

Klaten

45821 ■ Radio Roro Djonggrang B.S., Prambanan - 648 KHz
Jalan Pemukti Baru
No. 9, Tlogo Prambanan
57454 Klaten, Indonesia
Ph: 62 274 497322
Fax: 02 274 496913
E-mail: rdbs_prambanan@yahoo.com
Format: Eclectic. **Owner:** Federation of Indonesian National Commercial Broadcasters, Pengurus Pusat, Jalan Raya Pondok Gede 96, 13810 Jakarta, Indonesia, 62 218 414311, Fax: 62 218 414314. **Key Personnel:** Sarwadhi Hazar, Contact. **Ad Rates:** Noncommercial. **URL:** http://www.radioprssni.com/prssninew/profildetail.asp?id=422.

Kuningan

45822 ■ Radio Ewangga, Kuningan - 954 KHz
Jl. Raya Ciawigebang No. 94
Kapandayan Ciawigebang
45511 Kuningan, Indonesia
Ph: 62 232 871133
Fax: 62 232 871133
E-mail: ewangga@lycos.com
Format: Eclectic. **Owner:** Persatuan Radio Siaran Swasta Nasional Indonesia, Jl. Sukamaju 37, 40161 Bandung, Indonesia, 62 22 2038362, 62 22 2032844, Fax: 62 22 2039550. **Key Personnel:** Aga Adi Nugraha, Contact. **Ad Rates:** Noncommercial. **URL:** http://www.prssnijabar.or.id.

Circulation: ★ = ABC; △ = BPA; ◆ = CAC; • = CCAB; ❑ = VAC; ⊕ = PO Statement; ‡ = Publisher's Report; Boldface figures = sworn; Light figures = estimated.

Kupang

45823 ■ Radio Balistik, Kupang - 918 KHz
Jalan Nusa Indah, No. 21 B
85117 Kupang, Indonesia
Ph: 62 380 833220
Fax: 62 380 824011
E-mail: balistikgroup.kp@telkom.net
Format: Eclectic. **Owner:** Federation of Indonesian National Commercial Broadcasters, Pengurus Pusat, Jalan Raya Pondok Gede 96, 13810 Jakarta, Indonesia, 62 21 8414311, 62 21 8414312, Fax: 62 21 8414314. **Key Personnel:** Ronny Jhons Arnoldus, Contact. **Ad Rates:** Noncommercial. **URL:** http://www.radioprssni.com/prssninew/profildetail.asp?id=700.

Kuta

45824 ■ Bali & Beyond Magazine
PT Bumi Dian Kusuma
Jl. Bypass Ngurah Rai 120C
Lt. 2
80361 Kuta, Indonesia
Ph: 62 361 752764
Fax: 62 361 762096
Publication E-mail: mag@baliandbeyond.co.id
Publisher E-mail: mag@baliandbeyond.co.id
Online tourism magazine. **Subtitle:** The Best Tourism Magazine On-line in Bali. **Freq:** Monthly. **Key Personnel:** Nyoman Ari Gunadi, Managing Editor, eric@baliandbeyond.co.id; Goestamar Ardibarata, Deputy Gen. Mgr. **Subscription Rates:** Rs 120,000 individuals; US$130 individuals Asia, Australia, Africa; US$150 individuals Europe, America. **Remarks:** Advertising accepted; rates available upon request. **URL:** http://www.baliandbeyond.co.id/about.html. **Circ:** 20,000

Lampung Timur

45825 ■ Radio Suryagita Paramarta (SGP), Labuhan Maringgai - 855 KHz
Jalan Raya Panjang Sribawono 576
Lampung Timur, Indonesia
Ph: 62 725 660704
E-mail: radioprssni@radioprssni.com
Format: Eclectic. **Owner:** Federation of Indonesian National Commercial Broadcasters, Pengurus Pusat, Jalan Raya Pondok Gede 96, 13810 Jakarta, Indonesia, 62 21 8414311, 62 21 8414312, Fax: 62 21 8414314. **Ad Rates:** Noncommercial. **URL:** http://www.radioprssni.com/prssninew/profildetail.asp?id=185.

Langkat

Radio Suara Langkat Tanjung Persada, Tanjungpura - See Tanjungpura

Majalengka

45826 ■ Radio Indraswara Cakrawalanada, Majalengka - 810 KHz
Jalan Pramuka, No. 10
45418 Majalengka, Indonesia
Ph: 62 233 281320
E-mail: indraswara@plasa.com
Format: Eclectic. **Owner:** Persatuan Radio Siaran Swasta Nasional Indonesia, Jl. Sukamaju, No. 37, 40161 Bandung, Indonesia, 62 22 2038362, 62 22 2032844, Fax: 62 22 2039550. **Key Personnel:** Yusuf Abdullatief, Contact. **URL:** http://www.prssnijabar.or.id.

Majenang

45827 ■ Radio Gagah Sehat Berbobot (Gasebo), Majenang - 720 KHz
Jalan Diponegoro 18
Majenang
53257 Cilacap, Indonesia
Ph: 62 282 621334
E-mail: radioprssni@radioprssni.com
Format: Eclectic. **Owner:** Federation of Indonesian National Commercial Broadcasters, Pengurus Pusat, Jalan Raya Pondok Gede 96, 13810 Jakarta, Indonesia, 62 21 8414311, Fax: 62 21 8414314. **Key Personnel:** Sugeng Priyadi, Contact. **Ad Rates:** Noncommercial. **URL:** http://www.radioprssni.com/prssninew/profildetail.asp?id=404.

Makassar

45828 ■ Prambors Makassar-FM - 105.1
Jl. D.R. Ratulangi No. 35
Makassar, Indonesia
Ph: 62 411 834703
Fax: 62 411 834701
E-mail: pramborsmakassar@yahoo.com
Format: Ethnic; World Beat. **Key Personnel:** Munafri Arifudin, Station Mgr.; Yessi Rizky Mulya, Program Dir. **Ad Rates:** Noncommercial. **URL:** http://www.pramborsfm.com.

Malang

45829 ■ Radio Republik Indonesia, Malang - 891 KHz
Jalan Candi Panggung No. 58
Mojolangu
65142 Malang, Indonesia
Ph: 62 341 404504
Fax: 62 341 481522
Format: Eclectic. **Owner:** Radio Republik Indonesia, Jl. Medan Merdeka Barat, No. 4-5, 10110 Jakarta, Indonesia. **Wattage:** 10,000. **URL:** http://www.rri-online.com/; http://www.rri-malang.com/.

45830 ■ Radio Republik Indonesia, Malang - 105.1 MHz
Jalan Candi Panggung No. 58
Mojolangu
65142 Malang, Indonesia
Ph: 62 341 404504
Fax: 62 341 481522
Format: Eclectic. **Owner:** Radio Republik Indonesia, Jl. Medan Merdeka Barat, No. 4-5, 10110 Jakarta, Indonesia. **URL:** http://www.rri-online.com/; http://www.rri-malang.com/.

45831 ■ Radio Tritara Yaksa (TT-77), Malang - 828 KHz
Jalan Dr. Sutomo No. 26
65111 Malang, Indonesia
Ph: 62 341 327950
Format: Eclectic. **Owner:** Federation of Indonesian National Commercial Broadcasters, Pengurus Pusat, Jalan Raya Pondok Gede 96, 13810 Jakarta, Indonesia, 62 21 8414311, 62 21 8414312, Fax: 62 21 8414314. **URL:** http://www.radiojatim.or.id/?mod=profil_radio_anggota&id=60&t=TT77.

Manado

45832 ■ Delta-FM - 99.3
Jl. Mesjid Istiqlal, No. 6
95121 Manado, Indonesia
Ph: 62 431 859995
Fax: 62 431 856184
Format: Ethnic; News. **Operating Hours:** 18 hours Daily. **URL:** http://ww2.deltafm.net.

Mataram

45833 ■ Radio Suta Remaja, Mataram - 1062 KHz
Jl. RA. Kartini 49
83121 Mataram, Indonesia
Ph: 62 370 633029
Fax: 62 370 633029
E-mail: radioprssni@radioprssni.com
Format: Eclectic. **Owner:** Federation of Indonesian National Commercial Broadcasters, Pengurus Pusat, Jalan Raya Pondok Gede 96, 13810 Jakarta, Indonesia, 62 21 8414311, 62 21 8414312, Fax: 62 21 8414314. **Key Personnel:** Dr. H. Gandjar Suwargani, Chm. **Wattage:** 250. **Ad Rates:** Advertising accepted; rates available upon request. **URL:** http://www.radioprssni.com/prssninew/profildetail.asp?id=691.

Medan

45834 ■ Delta-FM - 105.8
Mandiri Bldg., Lt. 3
Jl. Imam Bonjol, No. 16-D
20112 Medan, Indonesia
Ph: 62 61 4534682
Fax: 62 61 4534686
Format: Ethnic; News. **Operating Hours:** 18 hours Daily. **URL:** http://ww2.deltafm.net.

45835 ■ Prambors Medan-FM - 97.5
Mandiri Bldg., Lt.3
Jl. Imam Bonjol No. 16-D
20112 Medan, Indonesia
Ph: 62 61 77820975
Fax: 62 61 8218144
E-mail: medan@pramborsfm.com
Format: Ethnic; World Beat. **Key Personnel:** Boy Henry, Jr., General Mgr.; Muhammad Iqbal, Program Dir. **Ad Rates:** Noncommercial. **URL:** http://www.pramborsfm.com.

45836 ■ Radio Republik Indonesia, Medan - 88.8 MHz
Jalan Jenderal Gatot Subroto, No. 214
20123 Medan, Indonesia
Ph: 62 61 8463116
Format: Eclectic. **Owner:** Radio Republik Indonesia, Jl. Medan Merdeka Barat, No. 4-5, 10110 Jakarta, Indonesia. **Key Personnel:** Dr. H. Gandjar Suwargani, Chm. **Ad Rates:** Noncommercial. **URL:** http://www.rrimedan.net/.

45837 ■ Radio Republik Indonesia, Medan - 801 KHz
Jalan Jenderal Gatot Subroto, No. 214
20123 Medan, Indonesia
Ph: 62 61 8463116
Format: Eclectic. **Owner:** Radio Republik Indonesia, Jl. Medan Merdeka Barat, No. 4-5, 10110 Jakarta, Indonesia. **Key Personnel:** Dr. H. Gandjar Suwargani, Chm. **Wattage:** 1000. **Ad Rates:** Advertising accepted; rates available upon request. **URL:** http://www.rrimedan.net/.

Negara

45838 ■ Radio Dhirgantara, Negara - 918 KHz
Jalan Udayana 45
82213 Negara, Indonesia
Ph: 62 365 41249
Fax: 62 365 41356
E-mail: radioprssni@radioprssni.com
Format: Eclectic. **Owner:** Federation of Indonesian National Commercial Broadcasters, Pengurus Pusat, Jalan Raya Pondok Gede 96, 13810 Jakarta, Indonesia, 62 218 414311, Fax: 62 218 414314. **Key Personnel:** H. Gandjar Suwargani, Chm. **Ad Rates:** Noncommercial. **URL:** http://www.radioprssni.com.

Ogan Komering Ulu

45839 ■ Radio Suaramitra Bayu Buana, Belitang - 720 KHz
Jalan Kapasan, No. 112
32382 Ogan Komering Ulu, Indonesia
Ph: 62 735 450584
Fax: 62 735 450158
E-mail: rsmbb_belitang@yahoo.com
Owner: Federation of Indonesian National Commercial Broadcasters, Pengurus Pusat, Jalan Raya Pondok Gede 96, 13810 Jakarta, Indonesia, 62 218 414311, Fax: 62 218 414314. **Key Personnel:** A. Marindharto, Contact. **Ad Rates:** Noncommercial. **URL:** http://www.radioprssni.com/prssninew/profildetail.asp?id=138.

Palembang

45840 ■ Radio Garuda Kenten Jaya, Palembang - 954 KHz
Jalan Dr. M. Isa 38, 8 Ilir
30114 Palembang, Indonesia
Ph: 62 711 710176
Fax: 62 711 351755
E-mail: radioprssni@radioprssni.com
Format: Eclectic. **Owner:** Federation of Indonesian National Commercial Broadcasters, Pengurus Pusat, Jalan Raya Pondok Gede 96, 13810 Jakarta, Indonesia, 62 218 414311, Fax: 62 218 414314. **Key Personnel:** H. Gandjar Suwargani, Chm.; Ahmad Fauzi Syahtri, Contact. **Wattage:** 150. **URL:** http://www.radioprssni.com.

45841 ■ Radio Gema Mutiara, Palembang - 1062 KHz
Gedung Utama Lantai 5 Universitas PGRI
Jl. Jend. A. Yani Lrg. Gotong, Royong 9/10
Palembang, Indonesia
Ph: 62 711 7940778

E-mail: radioprssni@radioprssni.com
Format: Eclectic. **Owner:** Federation of Indonesian National Commercial Broadcasters, Pengurus Pusat, Jalan Raya Pondok Gede 96, 13810 Jakarta, Indonesia, 62 21 8414311, 62 21 8414312, 62 21 8414314. **Key Personnel:** Dr. H. Gandjar Suwargani, Chm. **Wattage:** 250. **Ad Rates:** Noncommercial. **URL:** http://www.radioprssni.com/prssninew/profildetail.asp?id=169.

Pamekasan

45842 ■ Radio Suara Pamekasan Indah, Pamekasan - 738 KHz
Jalan Trunojoyo, No. 22
69313 Pamekasan, Indonesia
Ph: 62 324 323131
E-mail: radioprssni@radioprssni.com
Owner: Federation of Indonesian National Commercial Broadcasters, Pengurus Pusat, Jalan Raya Pondok Gede 96, 13810 Jakarta, Indonesia, 62 218 414311, Fax: 62 218 414314. **Key Personnel:** H. Suharto, Contact. **Ad Rates:** Noncommercial. **URL:** http://www.radioprssni.com/prssninew/profildetail.asp?id=572.

Pandeglang

45843 ■ Radio Swara Angkasa Megah, Pandeglang - 558 KHz
Jalan Raya Serang, Km. 2
42200 Pandeglang, Indonesia
Ph: 62 253 201260
E-mail: radioprssni@radioprssni.com
Format: Eclectic. **Owner:** Federation of Indonesian National Commercial Broadcasters, Pengurus Pusat, Jalan Raya Pondok Gede 96, 13810 Jakarta, Indonesia, 62 21 8414311, 62 21 8414312, Fax: 62 21 8414314. **Key Personnel:** Dra. Hj. Euis Nuryati, Contact. **URL:** http://www.radioprssni.com/prssninew/profildetail.asp?id=372.

Pangandaran

45844 ■ Radio Duta Angkasa, Pangandaran - 1044 KHz
Jl. Raya Timur No. 316
Ciamis
46396 Pangandaran, Indonesia
Ph: 62 265 630606
Fax: 62 265 630606
E-mail: info@prssnijabar.or.id
Format: Eclectic. **Owner:** Persatuan Radio Siaran Swasta Nasional Indonesia, Jl. Sukamaju No. 37, 40161 Bandung, Indonesia, 62 22 2038362, 62 22 2032844, Fax: 62 22 2039550. **URL:** http://www.prssnijabar.or.id.

Pekalongan

45845 ■ Radio Santo Bernardus D.S., Pekalongan - 648 KHz
Jalan Barito No. 4
51116 Pekalongan, Indonesia
Ph: 62 285 424747
Fax: 62 285 422747
E-mail: radioprssni@radioprssni.com
Format: Eclectic. **Owner:** Federation of Indonesian National Commercial Broadcasters, Pengurus Pusat, Jalan Raya Pondok Gede 96, 13810 Jakarta, Indonesia, 62 21 8414311, 62 21 8414312, 62 21 8414314. **Key Personnel:** Heru Santoso, Contact. **URL:** http://www.radioprssni.com/prssninew/profildetail.asp?id=440.

Pemalang

45846 ■ Radio Gita Swara Alfina, Pemalang - 720 KHz
Jalan Brigjen Katamso No. 1
52311 Pemalang, Indonesia
Ph: 62 284 321692
Fax: 62 284 322533
E-mail: radioprssni@radioprssni.com
Format: Eclectic. **Owner:** Federation of Indonesian National Commercial Broadcasters, Pengurus Pusat, Jalan Raya Pondok Gede 96, 13810 Jakarta, Indonesia, 62 21 8414311, Fax: 62 21 8414314. **Key Personnel:** Yusuf Sulaeman, Contact. **URL:** http://www.radioprssni.com/prssninew/profildetail.asp?id=447.

Purwokerto

45847 ■ Radio Republik Indonesia, Purwokerto - 756 KHz
Jalan Jendral Sudirman, No. 427
53116 Purwokerto, Indonesia
Ph: 62 281 635222
Fax: 62 281 636222
Format: Eclectic. **Owner:** Radio Republik Indonesia, Jl. Medan Merdeka Barat, No. 4-5, 10110 Jakarta, Indonesia. **Wattage:** 2000/10,000. **URL:** http://rri-sejatnet.net/purwokerto/.

Salatiga

45848 ■ Radio Swara Zenith Angkasa, Salatiga - 702 KHz
Jalan Osa Maliki, No. 29
50721 Salatiga, Indonesia
Ph: 62 298 321390
Fax: 62 298 322181
E-mail: zenithslg@bmp.net.id
Owner: Federation of Indonesian National Commercial Broadcasters, Pengurus Pusat, Jalan Raya Pondok Gede 96, 13810 Jakarta, Indonesia, 62 218 414311, Fax: 62 218 414314. **Key Personnel:** Sigit Yuniarso, Contact. **Ad Rates:** Noncommercial. **URL:** http://www.radioprssni.com/prssninew/profildetail.asp?id=826.

Sanggau

45849 ■ Radio Aries Sanggau Perkasa, Sanggau - 900 KHz
Sudirman No. 43 D
78512 Sanggau, Indonesia
Ph: 62 564 23093
E-mail: radioprssni@radioprssni.com
Owner: Federation of Indonesian National Commercial Broadcasters, Pengurus Pusat, Jalan Raya Pondok Gede 96, 13810 Jakarta, Indonesia, 62 218 414311, Fax: 62 218 414314. **Key Personnel:** H. Gandjar Suwargani, Chm.; Harsono Taib, Contact. **Ad Rates:** Noncommercial. **URL:** http://www.radioprssni.com.

Semarang

45850 ■ Prambors Semarang-FM - 102
Jl. Erlangga Raya, No. 58
50241 Semarang, Indonesia
Ph: 62 24 8310307
Fax: 62 24 3574869
E-mail: semarang@pramborsfm.com
Format: Ethnic; World Beat. **Key Personnel:** Sapto Adhi Nugroho, General Mgr.; Diaz Aditya, Program Dir. **Ad Rates:** Noncommercial. **URL:** http://www.pramborsfm.com.

45851 ■ Radio Lusiana Namberwan, Semarang - 720 KHz
Jalan Raung, No. 7
50232 Semarang, Indonesia
Ph: 62 24 8319407
E-mail: radioprssni@radioprssni.com
Format: Eclectic. **Owner:** Federation of Indonesian National Commercial Broadcasters, Pengurus Pusat, Jalan Raya Pondok Gede 96, 13810 Jakarta, Indonesia, 62 21 8414311, 62 21 8414312, Fax: 62 21 8414314. **Key Personnel:** Noto Soebronto, Contact. **Wattage:** 250. **Ad Rates:** Advertising accepted; rates available upon request. **URL:** http://www.radioprssni.com/prssninew/profildetail.asp?id=470.

45852 ■ Radio Pasopati Andalan, Semarang - 936 KHz
Jalan Satria Selatan
50171 Semarang, Indonesia
Ph: 62 247 614426
E-mail: radioprssni@radioprssni.com
Owner: Federation of Indonesian National Commercial Broadcasters, Pengurus Pusat, Jalan Raya Pondok Gede 96, 13810 Jakarta, Indonesia, 62 218 414311, Fax: 62 218 414314. **Key Personnel:** H. Gandjar Suwargani, Chm. **Ad Rates:** Noncommercial. **URL:** http://www.radioprssni.com.

45853 ■ Radio Republik Indonesia, Semarang - 801 KHz
Jln. Jend. A. Yani, No. 144-146
50136 Semarang, Indonesia
Ph: 62 24 8316330
Format: Eclectic. **Owner:** Radio Republik Indonesia, Jl. Medan Merdeka Barat, No. 4-5, 10110 Jakarta, Indonesia. **Wattage:** 10,000. **URL:** http://rri-sejateng.net/semarang/.

Radio Swara Palagan Sehati (SPS) - See Ambarawa

Seminyak

45854 ■ The Beat
PT Kubu Dua Media
Jl. Petitenget 12A
Kerobokan
Bali
Seminyak, Indonesia
Ph: 62 7463751
Fax: 62 8475458
Publisher E-mail: info@beatmag.com
Entertainment magazine. **Subtitle:** Bali & Jakarta's Free Entertainment Gig Guide. **Freq:** Biweekly. **Key Personnel:** Agatha Chloe Salmun, Director, agatha@beatmag.com. **Subscription Rates:** Rs 200,000 individuals; 100,000 Rp individuals 6 months. **URL:** http://www.beatmag.com/bali/228/index.html.

Sidenreng Rappang

45855 ■ Radio Bambapuang, Pangkajene - 882 KHz
Jl. Andi Nohong, No. 1 Pangkajene
91611 Sidenreng Rappang, Indonesia
Ph: 62 421 91383
E-mail: radioprssni@radioprssni.com
Owner: Federation of Indonesian National Commercial Broadcasters, Pengurus Pusat, Jalan Raya Pondok Gede 96, 13810 Jakarta, Indonesia, 62 21 8414311, Fax: 62 21 8414314. **Wattage:** 500. **Ad Rates:** Advertising accepted; rates available upon request. **URL:** http://www.radioprssni.com; http://radiosulsel.com/index.php?option=com_content&view=article&id=73&Item id=47.

Solo Baru

45856 ■ Prambors Solo-FM - 99.2
Jl. Raya Solo Permai HH-34
57552 Solo Baru, Indonesia
Ph: 62 271 626690
Fax: 62 271 626041
E-mail: solo@pramborsfm.com
Format: Ethnic; World Beat. **Owner:** Prambors FM Indonesia, at above address. **Key Personnel:** Sapto Adhi Nugroho, General Mgr. **Ad Rates:** Noncommercial. **URL:** http://www.pramborsfm.com.

Sukabumi

45857 ■ Radio Bestari, Sukabumi - 648 KHz
Pengurus Cabang Sukabumi
Jl. Otto Iskandarinata, No. 144
43143 Sukabumi, Indonesia
Ph: 62 266 226946
Fax: 62 266 224218
Format: Eclectic. **Owner:** Federation of Indonesian National Commercial Broadcasters, Pengurus Pusat, Jalan Raya Pondok Gede 96, 13810 Jakarta, Indonesia, 62 218 414311, Fax: 62 218 414314. **Key Personnel:** Dedeh R. Kartawijaya, Contact. **URL:** http://www.radioprssni.com/.

Sukoharjo

45858 ■ Radio Pancabayu Madugondo (Suara RPM), Sukoharjo - 819 KHz
Jl. Madegondo 15
57552 Sukoharjo, Indonesia
Ph: 62 272 621689
Fax: 62 272 621689
E-mail: radioprssni@radioprssni.com
Owner: Federation of Indonesian National Commercial Broadcasters, Pengurus Pusat, Jalan Raya Pondok Gede 96, 13810 Jakarta, Indonesia, 62 218 414311, Fax: 62 218 414314. **Key Personnel:** H. Gandjar Suwargani, Chm. **Ad Rates:** Noncommercial. **URL:** http://www.radioprssni.com.

Circulation: ★ = ABC; △ = BPA; ♦ = CAC; • = CCAB; ❑ = VAC; ⊕ = PO Statement; ‡ = Publisher's Report; Boldface figures = sworn; Light figures = estimated.

Surabaya

45859 ■ Delta-FM - 96.8
Hotel Garden Palace Lt.7 & Lt. 1
Jl. Yos Sudarso, No.11
60271 Surabaya, Indonesia
Ph: 62 31 5316646
Fax: 62 31 5327077
Format: Ethnic. **Owner:** Delta FM Radio, at above address. **Founded:** 1967. **Operating Hours:** 18 hours Daily. **URL:** http://ww2.deltafm.net.

45860 ■ Hard Rock-FM - 89.7
Graha Pena 12th Fl., Ste. 1201
Jl. Ahmad Yani 88
60234 Surabaya, Indonesia
Ph: 62 31 8250088
Fax: 62 31 8250072
E-mail: surabaya@hardrockfm.com
Format: Eclectic. **Owner:** Hard Rock FM, Gedung Sarinah 8th Fl., Jl. MH. Thamrin 11, 10350 Jakarta, Indonesia, 62 21 3908471, Fax: 62 21 3908473. **Operating Hours:** Continuous. **Ad Rates:** Advertising accepted; rates available upon request. **URL:** http://www.hardrockfm.com/.

45861 ■ Prambors Surabaya-FM - 89.3
Hotel Garden Palace, Ground Fl., Lt. 8
Jl. Yos Sudarso, No. 11
Surabaya, Indonesia
Ph: 62 31 5320126
Fax: 62 31 5327077
E-mail: prambors_sby@yahoo.com
Format: Ethnic; World Beat. **Owner:** Prambors FM Indonesia, at above address. **Key Personnel:** Gusto Adrianus, General Mgr.; Nurwendy Alditya Putra, Program Dir. **Ad Rates:** Noncommercial. **URL:** http://www.pramborsfm.com.

45862 ■ Radio DJ-FM - 94.8
Jl. Citandui 14
60264 Surabaya, Indonesia
Ph: 62 31 5613002
Fax: 62 31 5683749
E-mail: contact@djfm.co.id
Format: Contemporary Hit Radio (CHR). **Operating Hours:** Continuous. **URL:** http://www.djfm.co.id.

45863 ■ Radio Menara III, Surabaya - 864 KHz
Jalan Simolawang 1/96
60144 Surabaya, Indonesia
Ph: 62 31 3769693
E-mail: menara3@plasa.com
Format: Eclectic. **Owner:** Federation of Indonesian National Commercial Broadcasters, Pengurus Pusat, Jalan Raya Pondok Gede 96, 13810 Jakarta, Indonesia, 62 21 8414311, 62 21 8414312, Fax: 62 21 8414314. **Ad Rates:** Noncommercial. **URL:** http://www.radioprssni.com/prssninew/profildetail.asp?id=594.

45864 ■ Radio Miniwati Pesona Indah, Surabaya - 846 KHz
Jl. Darmahusada Indah Barat II/21
60285 Surabaya, Indonesia
Ph: 62 31 5945344
Fax: 62 31 5922751
E-mail: radioprssni@radioprssni.com
Format: Eclectic. **Owner:** Federation of Indonesian National Commercial Broadcasters, Pengurus Pusat, Jalan Raya Pondok Gede 96, 13810 Jakarta, Indonesia, 62 21 8414311, 62 21 8414312, Fax: 62 21 8414314. **Key Personnel:** Harryanto Karnadi, Contact. **URL:** http://www.radioprssni.com/prssninew/profildetail.asp?id=593.

45865 ■ Radio Republik Indonesia, Surabaya - 585 KHz
Jalan Pemuda 82-90
60271 Surabaya, Indonesia
Ph: 62 31 5342091
Fax: 62 31 5341327
Format: Eclectic. **Owner:** Radio Republik Indonesia, Jl. Medan Merdeka Barat, No. 4-5, 10110 Jakarta, Indonesia. **Wattage:** 50,000. **URL:** http://pro4.rrisby.net/.

45866 ■ Radio Sonara-FM - 98
Jl. Raya Darmo Permai Utara, No. 74-80
60226 Surabaya, Indonesia
Ph: 62 31 7321496

Fax: 62 31 7327101
E-mail: marketing@sonorasurabaya.co.id
Format: Ethnic; World Beat; Information; Sports; News. **Owner:** Kompleks Permata Hijau, at above address. **Operating Hours:** Continuous. **URL:** http://www.sonorasurabaya.co.id.

Surakarta

45867 ■ Radio Konservatori, Surakarta - 738 KHz
Jalan H. Agus Salim, No. 22
57147 Surakarta, Indonesia
Ph: 62 271 781777
Fax: 62 271 714685
Format: Eclectic. **Owner:** Federation of Indonesian National Commercial Broadcasters, Pengurus Pusat, Jalan Raya Pondok Gede 96, 13810 Jakarta, Indonesia, 62 21 8414311, Fax: 62 21 8414314. **Key Personnel:** S. Djarot Soediroprono, Contact. **Ad Rates:** Noncommercial. **URL:** http://www.radioprssni.com/prssninew/profildetail.asp?id=483.

45868 ■ Radio Ramakusala, Surakarta - 666 KHz
Jalan Purworejo VI/10
Mangkubumen Banjarsari
57139 Surakarta, Indonesia
Ph: 62 271 718758
Fax: 62 271 719770
E-mail: radiorama@plasa.com
Format: Eclectic. **Owner:** Federation of Indonesian National Commercial Broadcasters, Pengurus Pusat, Jalan Raya Pondok Gede 96, 13810 Jakarta, Indonesia, 62 218 414311, Fax: 62 218 414314. **Key Personnel:** R. Budi Santoso, BA, Contact. **Wattage:** 250. **URL:** http://www.radioprssni.com/prssninew/profildetail.asp?id=484.

45869 ■ Radio Republik Indonesia, Surakarta - 1053 KHz
Jln. Abdul Rahman Saleh, No. 51
PO Box 240
57133 Surakarta, Indonesia
Ph: 62 271 639230
Fax: 62 271 668200
E-mail: divppuska@rri-online.com
Format: Eclectic. **Owner:** Radio Republik Indonesia, Jl. Medan Merdeka Barat, No. 4-5, 10110 Jakarta, Indonesia. **Wattage:** 1000. **URL:** http://www.rri-online.com/; http://www.rri.co.id.

Tangerang

45870 ■ Physics Journal of the Indonesian Physical Society
Pusat Penelitian Fisika LIPI
Kompleks PUSPIPTEK Serpong
15310 Tangerang, Indonesia
Ph: 62 217 560570
Fax: 62 217 560554
Peer-reviewed journal devoted to physics, in connection with the Indonesian Physical Society. **Founded:** 1992. **Freq:** 3/yr. **Key Personnel:** Masno Ginting, Editor; Mitra Djamal, Editor; Suhk Kun Oh, Editor. **ISSN:** 1410-8860. **URL:** http://pj.hfi.fisika.net/; http://www.jurnal.lipi.go.id/situs/pjhfi/.

45871 ■ Radio Bharata Bhaktinusa, Tangerang - 738 KHz
Jl. Meriah, No. 3
12270 Tangerang, Indonesia
Ph: 62 21 78361338
E-mail: radioprssni@radioprssni.com
Format: Eclectic. **Owner:** Federation of Indonesian National Commercial Broadcasters, Pengurus Pusat, Jalan Raya Pondok Gede 96, 13810 Jakarta, Indonesia, 62 21 8414311, 62 21 8414312, Fax: 62 21 8414314. **Key Personnel:** Tienneke Herawati, Contact. **URL:** http://www.radioprssni.com/prssninew/profildetail.asp?id=379.

Tanjungbalai

45872 ■ Radio Suara Tanjung Berjaya, Tanjungbalai - 810 KHz
Jl. Mt. Haryono No. 64
21311 Tanjungbalai, Indonesia
Ph: 62 622 92786

E-mail: radioprssni@radioprssni.com
Owner: Federation of Indonesian National Commercial Broadcasters, Pengurus Pusat, Jalan Raya Pondok Gede 96, 13810 Jakarta, Indonesia, 62 218 414311, Fax: 62 218 414314. **Key Personnel:** H. Gandjar Suwargani, Chm. **Ad Rates:** Noncommercial. **URL:** http://www.radioprssni.com.

Tanjungpura

45873 ■ Radio Suara Langkat Tanjung Persada, Tanjungpura - 1206 KHz
Jl. Pemuda Gg.Singa Dua No. 29-A
20850 Langkat, Indonesia
Ph: 62 61 4575755
Fax: 62 61 4562000
E-mail: radioprssni@radioprssni.com
Format: Eclectic. **Owner:** Federation of Indonesian National Commercial Broadcasters, Pengurus Pusat, Jalan Raya Pondok Gede 96, 13810 Jakarta, Indonesia, 62 21 8414311, 62 21 8414312, Fax: 62 21 8414314. **Key Personnel:** Dr. H. Gandjar Suwargani, Chm.; T. Fadel Bakri Zahrat, Contact. **URL:** http://www.radioprssni.com/prssninew/profildetail.asp?id=046.

Tasikmalaya

45874 ■ Radio Buana Jaya, Tasikmalaya - 1224 KHz
Jalan Raya Sukamantri 107
Ciawi
Tasikmalaya, Indonesia
E-mail: radioprssni@radioprssni.com; ppjkt@indosat.net.id
Format: Eclectic. **Owner:** Federation of Indonesian National Commercial Broadcasters, Pengurus Pusat PRSSNI, Jalan Raya Pondok Gede 96, 13810 Jakarta, Indonesia, 62 21 8414311, 62 21 8414312, Fax: 62 21 8414314. **Key Personnel:** Drs. H. Gandjar Suwargani, Chm.; Ida Aida, Contact. **Wattage:** 250. **URL:** http://www.radioprssni.com.

Tegal

45875 ■ Radio Raka, Tegal - 1044 KHz
Jalan Tentara Pelajar, No. 52
52122 Tegal, Indonesia
Ph: 62 283 355353
E-mail: raka.net@plasa.com
Format: Eclectic. **Owner:** Federation of Indonesian National Commercial Broadcasters, Pengurus Pusat, Jalan Raya Pondok Gede 96, 13810 Jakarta, Indonesia, Fax: 62 218 414314. **Key Personnel:** Eka Hardiyanto, Contact. **Wattage:** 250. **Ad Rates:** Noncommercial. **URL:** http://www.radioprssni.com/Anggota/jateng/raka.htm.

45876 ■ Radio Suara Tegal Agung Raya (Star), Tegal - 846 KHz
Jalan Raya Kramat, Km. 7
52181 Tegal, Indonesia
Ph: 62 283 357492
Fax: 62 283 353457
Format: Eclectic. **Owner:** Federation of Indonesian National Commercial Broadcasters, Pengurus Pusat, Jalan Raya Pondok Gede 96, 13810 Jakarta, Indonesia, 62 21 8414311, 62 21 8414313, Fax: 62 21 8414314. **Ad Rates:** Noncommercial. **URL:** http://www.radioprssni.com/prssninew/profildetail.asp?id=493.

Wonosobo

45877 ■ Radio Purnamasidi, Wonosobo - 720 KHz
Jalan Dieng 1A
56311 Wonosobo, Indonesia
Ph: 62 286 321336
Fax: 62 286 323098
E-mail: purnamasidi_wsb@yahoo.com
Format: Eclectic. **Owner:** Federation of Indonesian National Commercial Broadcasters, Pengurus Pusat, Jalan Raya Pondok Gede 96, 13810 Jakarta, Indonesia, 62 21 8414311, 62 21 8414312, Fax: 62 21 8414314. **Key Personnel:** Ahmad Fauzi, Contact. **URL:** http://www.radioprssni.com/prssninew/profildetail.asp?id=504.

Isfahan

45878 ■ International Journal of Hydrology Science and Technology
Inderscience Enterprises Limited
c/o Dr. Saeid Eslamian, Ed.-in-Ch.
Isfahan University of Technology
Dept. of Water Engineering
Isfahan 84156, Iran
Journal covering research and practical studies on hydrological science, technology, water resources, and related topics including water, air, and soil pollution and hazardous waste issues. **Freq:** 4/yr. **Key Personnel:** Dr. Saeid Eslamian, Editor-in-Chief, ijh.res@gmail.com. **ISSN:** 2042-7808. **Subscription Rates:** EUR494 individuals print or online; EUR672 individuals print and online. **URL:** http://www.inderscience.com/browse/index.php?journalID=364.

45879 ■ Journal of Research in Medical Sciences
Isfahan University of Medical Sciences
PO Box 81745-319
Isfahan 81745, Iran
Publisher E-mail: webmaster@mui.ac.ir
Peer-reviewed journal publishing original contributions in the field of clinical medicine. **Freq:** Bimonthly. **Key Personnel:** Mohsen Janghorbani, Editor; Ashraf Aminorroaya, Editor; Selman A. Ali, Editorial Board; Mahin Hashemipour, Editor; Leila Azadbakht, Assoc. Ed.; Mehdi Nematbakhsh, Chm. **ISSN:** 1735-1995. **URL:** http://journals.mui.ac.ir/jrms/.

Kashan

45880 ■ International Journal of Pure & Applied Mathematical Sciences (IJPAMS)
GBS Publishers & Distributors
c/o Prof. A.R. Ashrafi, Ed -in-Ch.
Dept. of Mathematics
University of Kashan
Kashan 51167, Iran
Publisher E-mail: info@gbspublisher.com
Peer-reviewed journal covering pure mathematics and its applications. **Founded:** 1941. **Freq:** Semiannual. **Print Method:** Offset. **Cols./Page:** 6. **Col. Width:** 26 nonpareils. **Col. Depth:** 301 agate lines. **Key Personnel:** A.R. Ashrafi, Editor-in-Chief, ashrafi@kashanu.ac.ir; G. Barsegian, Assoc. Ed.; Feng Qi, Assoc. Ed. **ISSN:** 0972-9828. **Subscription Rates:** US$80 individuals; US$120 institutions library; US$180 individuals print and electronic. **URL:** http://www.gbspublisher.com/ijpams.htm.

Kerman

45881 ■ Global Journal of Mathematics and Mathematical Sciences (GJMMS)
GBS Publishers & Distributors
c/o M.R. Molaei, Editorial Board
Dept. of Mathematics
University of Kerman
PO Box 76135-133
Kerman 96130, Iran
Publisher E-mail: info@gbspublisher.com
Peer-reviewed journal covering theoretical and applied mathematical sciences. **Founded:** 1980. **Freq:** Quarterly. **Print Method:** Offset. **Trim Size:** 10 x 15. **Cols./Page:** 4. **Col. Width:** 27 nonpareils. **Col. Depth:** 203 agate lines. **Key Personnel:** M.R. Molaei, Editorial Board, molaei_mreza@yahoo.com; A.R. Ashrafi, Assoc. Ed.; Feng Qi, Assoc. Ed. **ISSN:** 0972-9836. **URL:** http://www.gbspublisher.com/gjmms.htm.

45882 ■ Journal of Dynamical Systems and Geometric Theories
IOS Press Inc.
c/o M.R. Molaei, Ed.-in-Ch.
Dept. of Mathematics
University of Kerman
PO Box 76135-133
Kerman 96130, Iran
Publisher E-mail: sales@iospress.com
Journal covering dynamical systems and geometry, the interactions between these two subjects and their relationships with the other branches of knowledge. **Founded:** 2002. **Freq:** Semiannual. **Print Method:** Offset. **Trim Size:** 8 x 10 3/4. **Cols./Page:** 3. **Col. Width:** 28 nonpareils. **Col. Depth:** 140 agate lines. **Key Personnel:** M. Abukhaled, Editorial Board; G.L. Naber, Editorial Board; V. Kostov, Editorial Board; B.S. Attili, Editorial Board; M.R. Molaei, Editor-in-Chief, mrmolaei@mail.uk.ac.ir; R.M. Santilli, Editorial Board. **ISSN:** 1726-037X. **Subscription Rates:** EUR145 individuals; US$180 individuals. **URL:** http://www.iospress.nl/loadtop/load.php?isbn=1726037x.

Shiraz

45883 ■ Iranian Journal of Medical Sciences
Shiraz University of Medical Sciences
PO Box 71348-1878
Shiraz 71934, Iran
Ph: 98 71 12122454
Fax: 98 71 12351865
Publication E-mail: ijms@sums.ac.ir
Publisher E-mail: nashr@sums.ac.ir
Publishes original clinical and research experiences of physicians on prevalent diseases in the region and relevant medical problems. **Founded:** 1970. **Freq:** Quarterly. **Key Personnel:** Behrooz Astaneh, MD, Acting Ed.; Z. Barzin, Exec. Ed. **ISSN:** 0253-0716. **URL:** http://ijms.sums.ac.ir/site/default.aspx. **Circ:** Paid 3,000

45884 ■ Iranian Journal of Science and Technology
Shiraz University
School of Engineering
Zand Ave.
Shiraz, Iran
Ph: 98 711 6286531
Fax: 98 711 2337852
Publication E-mail: ijst71@shirazu.ac.ir
Publishes theoretical, fundamental and experimental research papers from the engineering disciplines and all areas of basic science. **Founded:** 1971. **Freq:** Quarterly. **Key Personnel:** Prof. Mahmood Yaghoubi, Editor-in-Chief, phone 98 711 6474614, fax 98 711 6474614. **ISSN:** 0360-1307. **Subscription Rates:** US$200 institutions; 180,000 RI institutions; US$100 individuals; 40,000 RI individuals; US$25 single issue; 30,000 RI single issue. **Remarks:** Advertising accepted; rates available upon request. **URL:** http://www.shirazu.ac.ir/en/index.php?page_id=113. **Circ:** Paid 1,000

Tehran

45885 ■ Acta Medica Iranica
Tehran University of Medical Sciences Faculty of Medicine
PO Box 14155-6447
Tehran 1417613151, Iran
Ph: 98 21 88953001
Fax: 98 21 66404377
Publication E-mail: acta@sina.tums.ac.ir
Publisher E-mail: jafarian@tums.ac.ir
International journal which publishes original research papers, case reports, review articles and letters to the editor. **Founded:** 1960. **Freq:** Bimonthly. **Key Personnel:** A. R. Dehpour, PhD, Editor-in-Chief; Z. Hussain-Khan, MD, Assoc. Ed.; S. Ejtemaei-Mehr, Assoc. Ed. **ISSN:** 0044-6025. **Subscription Rates:** 40,000 RI individuals; US$40 other countries. **URL:** http://medicine.tums.ac.ir; http://journals.tums.ac.ir/index.aspx?org_id=59&culture_var=en. **Circ:** Paid 2,000

45886 ■ Advances in Aerospace and Applications
Research India Publications
c/o Dr. M. Taeibi-Rahni, Ed.-in-Ch.
Sharif University of Technology
Aerospace Engineering Department
Tehran, Iran
Publisher E-mail: info@ripublication.com
Journal covering the research in aerospace and their application. **Freq:** 3/yr. **Key Personnel:** Dr. M. Taeibi-Rahni, Editor-in-Chief. **URL:** http://www.ripublication.com/aasa.htm.

45887 ■ Applied Entomology and Phytopathology
Agricultural Biotechnology Research Institute of Iran
c/o Plant Pests & Diseases Research Institute
Chamran Park Way
Tabnak Ave., No. 1-2
PO Box 1454
Tehran, Iran
Publisher E-mail: dorri@abrii.ac.ir
Journal featuring entomology and phytopathology. **Freq:** Annual. **ISSN:** 1026-5007. **URL:** http://www.abrii.ac.ir/en/news/journals.html.

45888 ■ DARU
Research Institute of Nuclear Medicine
Tehran University of Medical Sciences
PO Box 14155-6559
Tehran, Iran
Ph: 98 216 491070
Fax: 98 216 419537
Publication E-mail: daru@sina.tums.ac.ir
Publisher E-mail: office@sina.tums.ac.ir
Journal covering research in pharmaceutical sciences especially pharmaceutical and biomedical analyses, chemistry & medicinal chemistry, medical biotechnology, pharmaceutics, pharmacognosy & natural products, toxicology & pharmacology, clinical pharmacy & phar-

Circulation: ★ = ABC; △ = BPA; ◆ = CAC; • = CCAB; ❏ = VAC; ⊕ = PO Statement; ‡ = Publisher's Report; Boldface figures = sworn; Light figures = estimated.

Gale Directory of Publications & Broadcast Media/147th Ed. 5049

macotherapy, quality control of foods and drugs, social aspects of pharmacy, and drug design. **Founded:** 1950. **Freq:** Quarterly. **Print Method:** Offset. Uses mats. **Trim Size:** 8 1/8 x 10 7/8. **Cols./Page:** 3. **Col. Width:** 12 3/5 picas. **Col. Depth:** 55 picas. **Key Personnel:** Abbas Shafiee, Chm.; Ali Khalaj, Editor-in-Chief; Mohammad Abdollahi, Assoc. Ed. **ISSN:** 1560-8115. **URL:** http://journals.tums.ac.ir/index.aspx?org_id=59&culture_var=en.

45889 ■ Hepatitis Monthly
Tehran Hepatitis Center
PO Box 14155-3651
Tehran, Iran
Ph: 98 218 967923
Fax: 98 218 958048
Journal covering liver diseases with special attention to hepatitis. **Founded:** 1971. **Freq:** Quarterly. **Print Method:** Offset. **Trim Size:** 6 7/8 x 9 15/16. **Cols./Page:** 2. **Col. Width:** 34 nonpareils. **Col. Depth:** 116 agate lines. **Key Personnel:** Kamran BagheriLankarani, Chm.; Seyed-Moayed Alavian, Founder/Ed.-in-Ch.; Mohammad Hossein Somi, Assoc. Ed. **ISSN:** 1735-143X. **Subscription Rates:** US$70 other countries; US$80 institutions, other countries; 400,000 RI individuals; 500,000 RI institutions. **URL:** http://hepmon.com/.

45890 ■ International Journal of Engineering
Materials and Energy Research Center
PO Box 14155-4777
Tehran 15169, Iran
Ph: 98 21 88771626
Fax: 98 21 88773352
Publication E-mail: office@ije.ir
Publisher E-mail: info@merc.ac.ir
Provides a forum for publication of significant engineering advancements and developments in chemical, civil, computer and interdisciplinary areas of engineering. **Founded:** 1988. **Freq:** Quarterly. **Key Personnel:** S.K. Sadrnezhaad, Editor-in-Chief, sadrnezh@sharif.edu; J. Rashed-Mohassel, Assoc. Ed. **ISSN:** 1025-2495. **Subscription Rates:** 250,000 RI individuals; EUR180 individuals Japan, Oceania & North/Central America; EUR160 individuals other countries; 500,000 RI institutions; EUR230 institutions Japan, Oceania & North/Central America; EUR212 institutions, other countries. **Remarks:** Advertising accepted; rates available upon request. **URL:** http://www.ije.ir/. **Circ:** (Not Reported)

45891 ■ Iran
British Institute of Persian Studies
1553 Dr. Ali Shariati Ave.
Qolhak
Tehran 19396, Iran
Ph: 98 21 2601937
Fax: 98 21 2604901
Publisher E-mail: bips@parsonline.net
Peer-reviewed journal covering the field of Persian studies. **Subtitle:** Journal of the British Institute of Persian Studies. **Founded:** 1961. **Freq:** Annual. **Key Personnel:** Prof. C.E. Bosworth, Editor; Dr. Cameron A. Petrie, Editor; Prof. Vanessa Martin, Editor. **ISSN:** 0578-6967. **Subscription Rates:** 36 individuals incl. postage. **URL:** http://www.bips.ac.uk/journal/.

45892 ■ Iran Exports & Imports
Iran Exports Publication Co. Ltd.
No. 44, Golpar Alley
20th St., Khaled Slamboli Ave.
Tehran, Iran
Ph: 98 21 22200646
Fax: 98 21 22200632
Publication E-mail: info@iranexportsmagazine.com
Publisher E-mail: info@iranexportsmagazine.com
Journal covering the production of goods and services, exports and imports, and Iranian economic issues, with the intent of promoting trade between Iran and other countries. **Founded:** 1987. **Freq:** Bimonthly. **Key Personnel:** Seyed Alireza Kazemi Doulabi, Exec. Dir.; Ahmad Nikfarjam, Editor-in-Chief. **ISSN:** 1016-8885. **Subscription Rates:** EUR40 individuals Asia, Middle East; EUR50 individuals USA, Africa, Australia; EUR45 individuals Europe; 320,000 RI individuals. **Remarks:** Advertising accepted; rates available upon request. **URL:** http://www.iranexportsmagazine.com/. **Circ:** Paid 5,000

45893 ■ Iran News
PO Box 15875-8551
Tehran, Iran
Ph: 98 21 44253450
Fax: 98 21 44253478

Publisher E-mail: info@irannewsdaily.com
Newspaper. **Founded:** 1994. **Freq:** Daily. **Key Personnel:** Payman Jalali, Mng. Dir. **ISSN:** 1024-6053. **Remarks:** Accepts advertising. **URL:** http://www.irannewsdaily.com. **Circ:** (Not Reported)

45894 ■ Iran Weekly Press Digest
2 Hessar Faraj Alley
Golabdareh St.
Darband Ave.
Tehran 19736, Iran
Ph: 98 212 733291
Fax: 98 212 708364
Publication E-mail: editor@iranwpd.com
Publisher E-mail: editor@iranwpd.com
Publication covering political, social and economic affairs in Iran. **Founded:** Dec. 1987. **Freq:** Weekly. **ISSN:** 1564-2054. **Subscription Rates:** US$400 individuals online only. **Remarks:** Accepts advertising. **URL:** http://www.iranwpd.com/. **Circ:** (Not Reported)

45895 ■ Iranian Biomedical Journal
Pasteur Institute of Iran
Pasteur Ave.
Tehran 1316943551, Iran
Ph: 98 216 6492596
Fax: 98 216 6492596
Publication E-mail: ibj@institute.pasteur.ac.ir
Publisher E-mail: ibj@pasteur.ac.ir
Journal dealing with all aspects of biomedical sciences. **Freq:** Quarterly. **Key Personnel:** Mohsen Abolhassani, Editor; Mitra Saffari, Exec. Mgr. **ISSN:** 1028-852X. **Subscription Rates:** US$20 students; US$50 individuals; US$100 institutions. **URL:** http://ibj.pasteur.ac.ir/.

45896 ■ Iranian Economic Review
University of Tehran
Faculty of Economics
Kargar Shomali Ave.
PO Box 14155-6445
Tehran 14114, Iran
Ph: 98 21 88634001
Fax: 98 21 88632472
Journal featuring articles pertaining to economics. **Founded:** 1994. **Freq:** Semiannual. **Key Personnel:** Drucilla Ekwurzel, Assoc. Ed. **ISSN:** 1026-6542. **URL:** http://journals.ut.ac.ir/page/journal-main-page.html?jourld=51.

45897 ■ Iranian Journal of Allergy, Asthma and Immunology
Immunology, Asthma & Allergy Research Institute
Children's Medical Center
No. 62 Dr. Gharib St., Keshavarz Blvd.
PO Box 14185-863
Tehran 14194, Iran
Ph: 98 216 6935855
Fax: 98 216 6428995
Publisher E-mail: iaari@hbi.ir
Journal focusing on basic and clinical research taking place in the field of immunology. **Freq:** Quarterly. **Key Personnel:** Mostafa Moin, Chm.; Mohammad Bagher Eslami, PhD, Editor-in-Chief; Mohammad Hossein Nicknam, Dep. Ed. **ISSN:** 1735-1502. **URL:** http://www.iaari.hbi.ir/journal/.

45898 ■ Iranian Journal of Biotechnology (IJB)
NIGEB - National Research Center for Genetic Engineering and Biotechnology
Pajoohesh Blvd. Tehran -Karaj Hwy., 15th km.
Tehran, Iran
Ph: 98 214 4580301
Fax: 98 214 4580396
Publication E-mail: ijb@nigeb.ac.ir
Journal focusing on the field of Genetic engineering and Biotechnology. **Freq:** Quarterly. **Key Personnel:** Allameh Abdolamir, Managing Editor, allameha@modares.ac.ir; Abbas Lotfi, Editor-in-Chief, lotfi-ab@nigeb.ac.ir. **URL:** http://ijb.nigeb.ac.ir/index.php/ijb.

45899 ■ Iranian Journal of Chemistry and Chemical Engineering
R&M Afzal
PO Box 14155-4364
Tehran, Iran
Ph: 98 21 6497572
Publication E-mail: ijjccejournal@gmail.com
Publisher E-mail: ijcce@jdcord.jd.ac.ir
Journal featuring original research articles, reviews and short communications on all areas of pure and applied chemistry and chemical engineering. **Founded:** 1981.

Freq: Semiannual. **Key Personnel:** Dr. Jafar Towfighi Darian, Contact. **ISSN:** 1021-9986. **Subscription Rates:** EUR150 individuals Europe, Asia and Africa; EUR200 individuals Americas, Japan & Australia; EUR200 institutions Europe, Asia and Africa; EUR250 institutions Americas, Japan and Australia. **URL:** http://www.ijcce.ac.ir/IJCCE/index.htm. **Circ:** Controlled 2,000

45900 ■ Iranian Journal of Electrical and Computer Engineering
Jahad Daneshgahi
PO Box 16765-1899
Tehran, Iran
Ph: 98 21 7453382
Fax: 98 21 7453106
Publication E-mail: info@ijece.org
Publisher E-mail: info@ijece.org
Features papers that discuss new theoretical developments and techniques in the field of electrical or computer engineering and their application to real world problems. **Founded:** 2002. **Freq:** Semiannual. **Key Personnel:** Sadegh H.R. Mohammadi, Editor-in-Chief. **ISSN:** 1682-0053. **Subscription Rates:** US$15 students; US$25 students two years; US$25 individuals; US$40 individuals two years; US$50 institutions; US$85 institutions two years. **Remarks:** Advertising accepted; rates available upon request. **URL:** http://www.ijece.org/. **Circ:** (Not Reported)

45901 ■ Iranian Journal of Endocrinology and Metabolism
Endocrine Research Center
24 Parvaneh St.
Tehran 19395, Iran
Ph: 98 212 2432500
Fax: 98 212 2416264
Publisher E-mail: info@endocrine.ac.ir
Journal publishing information on endocrinology and on better management of patients with endocrine disorders. **Freq:** Quarterly. **Key Personnel:** A. Bahrami, Editorial Board; K. Adeli, Editorial Board; H. Gharib, Editorial Board; M. Amini, Editorial Board; H. Assadian, Editorial Board. **ISSN:** 1726-9148. **Subscription Rates:** US$85 individuals Asia, India and Africa; US$170 individuals Asia, India and Africa; US$110 individuals Western Europe, U.S. and Australia; US$220 institutions western Europe, U.S. and Australia. **URL:** http://ijem.org.ir/index.php?slc_lang=en&sid=1; http://erc.ac.ir/.

45902 ■ Iranian Journal of Environmental Health Science & Engineering
Tehran University of Medical Sciences
Department of International Relations
PO Box 14155-6559
Tehran, Iran
Ph: 98 216 491070
Fax: 98 216 419537
Publisher E-mail: office@sina.tums.ac.ir
Peer-reviewed journal covering research on all aspects of environmental health science, engineering and management. **Freq:** Quarterly. **Key Personnel:** S. Nasseri, Editor-in-Chief; A. Mesdaghinia, Chm.; B. Bina, Editorial Board; J. Nouri, Editorial Board; M.L Bouguerra, Editorial Board; R. Nabizadeh, Assoc. Ed.; F. Izadpanah, Executive Mgr. **ISSN:** 1735-1979. **URL:** http://journals.tums.ac.ir/description.aspx?org_id=59&culture_var=en&journal_id=13&issue_id=1711&segment=en.

45903 ■ Iranian Journal of Fisheries Science
Iranian Fisheries Research Organization
PO Box 14155-6116
Tehran, Iran
Ph: 98 21 66919133
Fax: 98 21 66420731
Publisher E-mail: info@ifro.ir
Journal featuring articles pertaining to fisheries sciences. **Founded:** 1999. **Freq:** Semiannual. **Key Personnel:** Issa Sharifpour, PhD, Editor-in-Chief; Shokoofeh Shamsi, PhD, Co-Ed. **ISSN:** 1562-2916. **Subscription Rates:** US$73 individuals. **Remarks:** Advertising accepted; rates available upon request. **URL:** http://en.ifro.ir/portal.aspx?tabid=220. **Circ:** (Not Reported)

45904 ■ Iranian Journal of Nuclear Medicine
Research Institute of Nuclear Medicine
Shariati Hospital
North Kargar Ave.
Tehran 14114, Iran
Ph: 98 21 88633333
Fax: 98 21 88026905
Publication E-mail: irjnm@tums.ac.ir

Publisher E-mail: office@sina.tums.ac.ir
Journal featuring articles pertaining to nuclear medicine. **Founded:** 1993. **Freq:** Semiannual. **Key Personnel:** Mohsen Saghari, Chm./Ed. **ISSN:** 1691-2824. **Subscription Rates:** US$60 institutions elsewhere; US$30 individuals elsewhere. **URL:** http://journals.tums.ac.ir/index.aspx?org_id=59&culture_var=en.

45905 ■ Iranian Journal of Pediatrics
Tehran University of Medical Sciences Faculty of Medicine
PO Box 14155-6447
Tehran 1417613151, Iran
Ph: 98 21 88953001
Fax: 98 21 66404377
Publication E-mail: ijp@tums.ac.ir
Publisher E-mail: jafarian@tums.ac.ir
Peer-reviewed journal dealing with Pediatrics. **Founded:** 1985. **Freq:** Quarterly. **Key Personnel:** Gholam-Reza Walizadeh, MD, Editor-in-Chief; Vahid Ziaee, MD, Assoc. Ed. **ISSN:** 1018-4406. **URL:** http://journals.tums.ac.ir/index.aspx?org_id=59&culture_var=en.

45906 ■ Iranian Journal of Pharmaceutical Research
School of Pharmacy
Shaheed Beheshti University of Medical Sciences and Health Services
Vali-e Asr St.
PO Box 14155-6153
Tehran, Iran
Ph: 98 218 8873703
Fax: 98 218 8873703
Publication E-mail: info@ijpr-online.com
Peer-reviewed Journal covering all aspects on Pharmaceutical Research. **Freq:** Quarterly. **Key Personnel:** Seyed Alireza Mortazavi, Editor-in-Chief; Reza Aboofazeli, Editorial Board; Alireza Foroumadi, Editorial Board; Jamshid Salamzadeh, Exec. Committee; Farzad Kobarfard, Editorial Board; Hossein Vatanpour, Editorial Board; Nasrin Moazami, Editorial Board; Faraz Mojab, Assoc. Ed.; Alireza Shafaati, Editorial Board. **ISSN:** 1735-0328. **URL:** http://www.ijpr-online.com/.

45907 ■ Iranian Journal of Pharmacology and Therapeutics
Iran University of Medical Sciences, Razi Institute for Drug Research
PO Box 14155-6183
Tehran, Iran
Ph: 98 21 88052977
Fax: 98 21 88052977
Publication E-mail: ijpt@iums.ac.ir
Publisher E-mail: masmah99@iums.ac.ir
Journal publishing regular research papers, reviews, mini-reviews and case reports which deal with all aspects of experimental and clinical pharmacology. **Freq:** Semiannual. **Key Personnel:** Prof. Massoud Mahmoudian, Editor-in-Chief, masmah99@iums.ac.ir; Soltan Ahmed Ebrahimi, Managing Editor, ebrahimi@

iums.ac.ir; Armin Madadkar Sobhani, Exec. Dir./Tech. Ed., ams@iums.ac.ir. **ISSN:** 1735-2657. **URL:** http://ijpt.iums.ac.ir/index.php/ijpt.

45908 ■ Iranian Journal of Public Health
Iranian Public Health Association
c/o Dr. Bijan Sadrizadeh, Pres.
Ministry of Health & Medical Education
14th Fl., Simaye Iran St., Phase 5
Sharak Gharb
Tehran, Iran
Ph: 98 21 88364369
Fax: 98 21 88364111
Publication E-mail: ijph@tums.ac.ir
Publisher E-mail: sadrizadehb@mohme.gov.ir
Journal featuring articles pertaining to public health and safety. **Founded:** 1971. **Freq:** Quarterly. **Key Personnel:** Prof. Dariush D. Farhud, PhD, Editor-in-Chief. **ISSN:** 0304-4556. **Subscription Rates:** 60,000 RI individuals; US$50 other countries. **URL:** http://journals.tums.ac.ir/description.aspx?org_id=59&culture_var=en&journal_id=5&issue_id=1437&segment=en. **Circ:** Paid 2,000

45909 ■ Iranian Journal of Radiology
Tehran University of Medical Sciences Faculty of Medicine
Medical Imaging Ctr.
Imam Khomeini Hospital
Tehran, Iran
Ph: 98 21 66581579
Fax: 98 21 66581578
Publication E-mail: info@ijr.ir
Publisher E-mail: jafarian@tums.ac.ir
Journal on radiology. **Freq:** Quarterly. **Key Personnel:** Karim Vessal, MD, Ed.-in-Ch./Founder; A. Shakouri Rad, MD, Managing Editor; K. Firouznia, MD, Co-Ed.-in-Ch. **ISSN:** 1735-1065. **Subscription Rates:** 120,000 RI individuals; US$50 other countries; 150,000 RI institutions; US$60 institutions, other countries. **URL:** http://journals.tums.ac.ir/description.aspx?org_id=59&culture_var=en&journal_id=6&issue_id=1424&segment=en.

45910 ■ Iranian Polymer Journal
Iran Polymer Institute
PO Box 14965-115
Tehran, Iran
Ph: 98 21 4580000
Fax: 98 21 4580021
Publication E-mail: info@ippi.ac.ir
Publisher E-mail: info@ippi.ac.ir
Journal featuring articles pertaining to polymer science and technology. **Founded:** 1992. **Freq:** Monthly. **Key Personnel:** A. Rahimi, PhD, Editor, a.rahimi@ippi.ac.ir; H. Mivehchi, Editor, h.mivehchi@ippi.ac.ir; H. Mirzadeh, PhD, Editor-in-Chief, h.mirzadeh@ippi.ac.ir. **ISSN:** 1735-5265. **Subscription Rates:** 120,000 RI students; 180,000 RI individuals; 240,000 RI institutions; EUR259 students Asia, Africa, Europe; EUR330 individuals Asia, Africa, Europe; EUR379 institutions Asia, Africa, Europe; EUR333 students USA, Far East, Australia; EUR337 individuals USA, Far East, Australia; EUR444 institutions

USA, Far East, Australia. **URL:** http://journal.ippi.ac.ir/. **Circ:** Paid 3,000

45911 ■ Mahjubah
Islamic Thought Foundation
No. 766, Valiy-e Asr St.
PO Box 14155-3899
Tehran 14158, Iran
Ph: 98 21 8897663
Fax: 98 21 8902725
Publisher E-mail: info@itf.org.ir
Islamic family magazine. **Freq:** Monthly. **ISSN:** 1019-0767. **Subscription Rates:** US$40 individuals Asian countries; EUR45 individuals European countries. **URL:** http://www.mahjubah.com/mahjubah_home.aspx. **Circ:** Paid 30,000

45912 ■ Message of Thaqalayn
Ahl al-Bayt ('a) World Assembly
PO Box 15815-1956
Tehran, Iran
Ph: 98 21 890226
Journal containing articles and studies on Ahlul Beiyt's affairs. **Freq:** Quarterly. **URL:** http://www.al-islam.org/mot/.

45913 ■ Scientia Iranica
Sharif University of Technology
PO Box 11365-8639
Tehran, Iran
Ph: 98 21 66022727
Fax: 98 21 66005310
Publication E-mail: scientia@sharif.edu
Publisher E-mail: info@sharif.ir
Journal covering computer engineering, mathematics, mechanical engineering, earthquake engineering, chemistry, civil engineering, chemical and petroleum engineering, transportation engineering, science, and fuzzy logic engineering. **Founded:** 1991. **Freq:** Quarterly. **Key Personnel:** Abolhassan Vafai, Editor-in-Chief, vafai@sharif.edu; M.K. Agarwal, Advisory Editorial Board; R. Abbaschian, Advisory Editorial Board; R. Ansorge, Advisory Editorial Board; C.S. Desai, Advisory Editorial Board; H. Adeli, Advisory Editorial Board. **ISSN:** 1026-3098. **Subscription Rates:** 110,000 RI institutions; 90,000 RI individuals; US$330 institutions, other countries; US$240 individuals. **URL:** http://www.scientiairanica.com/. **Circ:** Paid 5,000

45914 ■ Tehran Times
No. 18 Bimeh Ln.
Nejatollahi St.
PO Box 14155-4843
Tehran, Iran
Ph: 98 21 88800295
Fax: 98 21 88808214
Publisher E-mail: info@tehrantimes.com
Newspaper. **Founded:** 1979. **Freq:** Daily. **Key Personnel:** Parviz Esmaeili, Mng. Dir., phone 98 21 88800789, fax 98 21 88800788, esmaeili@tehrantimes.com. **ISSN:** 0795-5820. **Remarks:** Accepts advertising. **URL:** http://www.tehrantimes.com. **Circ:** (Not Reported)

Circulation: ★ = ABC; △ = BPA; ◆ = CAC; ● = CCAB; ❑ = VAC; ⊕ = PO Statement; ‡ = Publisher's Report; Boldface figures = sworn; Light figures = estimated.

Gale Directory of Publications & Broadcast Media/147th Ed.   5051

Abbeyfeale

45915 ■ West Limerick 102-FM - 101.4
Enterprise Centre
Sheehans Rd.
Newcastle West, Limerick, Ireland
Ph: 353 69 66200
E-mail: contact@westlimerick102.ie
Format: Full Service. **Operating Hours:** 7 a.m.-1 a.m. Daily. **URL:** http://www.westlimerickradio.ie/ws/listen-live.

Athlone

45916 ■ Midlands 103-FM - 95.4
Tindle House
Axis Business Pk.
Tullamore, Offaly, Ireland
Ph: 353 57 9351333
Fax: 353 57 9352444
Format: Full Service. **Key Personnel:** Albert Fitzgerald, Mng. Dir., albert@midlandsradio.fm; William Faulkner, Station Mgr., will@midlandsradio.fm. **Ad Rates:** Advertising accepted; rates available upon request. **URL:** http://www.midlandsradio.fm/default.aspx.

Ballsbridge

45917 ■ 104-FM - 104.4
Hume House
Pembroke Rd.
Ballsbridge 4, Dublin, Ireland
Ph: 353 1 6689401
Format: Top 40; Adult Contemporary; Hip Hop; Blues; Urban Contemporary; Full Service. **Operating Hours:** Continuous **Key Personnel:** Margaret Nelson, CEO; Dave Kelly, Program Dir.; Pat Gill, Production Dir. **Ad Rates:** Advertising accepted; rates available upon request. **URL:** http://www.fm104.ie/.

Bantry

45918 ■ 4FM - 94.8
5th Fl., Latin Hall
Golden Ln.
Dublin 8, Dublin, Ireland
Ph: 353 1 4255400
Fax: 353 1 4255444
E-mail: info@4fm.ie
Format: Eclectic. **URL:** http://www.4fm.ie/.

Bishopstown

45919 ■ Red-FM - 104.5
University Technological Ctr., Unit 1
Curraheen Rd.
Bishopstown, Cork, Ireland
Ph: 353 21 4865500
E-mail: info@redfm.ie
Format: Top 40; Sports; Folk. **Founded:** Jan. 16, 2002. **Operating Hours:** Continuous. **Key Personnel:** Louise Leahy, Promotions Mgr.; Grainne Murane, Sales Mgr., phone 333 21 4865505. **Ad Rates:** $32-62.40 for 20 seconds; $40-78 for 30 seconds; $48-93.60 for 40

seconds; $80-156 for 60 seconds. **URL:** http://www.redfm.ie/.

Blackrock

45920 ■ Hotel & Catering Review
Jemma Publications
Grattan House
Temple Rd.
Blackrock, Dublin, Ireland
Ph: 353 1 7642700
Fax: 353 1 7642750
Publisher E-mail: sales@jemma.ie
Magazine featuring hotel, restaurant, food service, and catering market. **Subtitle:** Ireland's premier magazine for the hospitality and catering industry. **Founded:** 1974. **Freq:** Monthly. **Trim Size:** 210 x 297 mm. **Key Personnel:** Sarah Grennan, Editor, phone 353 1 7642704; Hilary O'Shaughnessy, Commercial Mgr., phone 353 1 7642717. **Subscription Rates:** EUR74 individuals Ireland; EUR99.79 individuals United Kingdom; EUR116.42 individuals Europe; EUR153.19 other countries. **Remarks:** Accepts advertising. **URL:** http://www.hotelandcateringreview.ie/. **Circ:** (Not Reported)

45921 ■ Irish Hardware
Jemma Publications
Grattan House
Temple Rd.
Blackrock, Dublin, Ireland
Ph: 353 1 7642700
Fax: 353 1 7642750
Publisher E-mail: sales@jemma.ie
Magazine for hardware, builders merchant, housewares and gardening sectors in Ireland. **Founded:** 1939. **Freq:** Monthly. **Key Personnel:** Martin Foran, Editor, phone 353 1 7642702; Dermot Casey, Commercial Mgr., phone 353 1 7642700. **Subscription Rates:** EUR74 individuals Ireland; EUR99.79 individuals United Kingdom; EUR116.42 individuals Europe; EUR153.19 other countries. **Remarks:** Accepts advertising. **URL:** http://www.irishhardware.sitestogo.biz/. **Ad Rates:** 4C: IR 2,200. **Circ:** ★1,664

45922 ■ Irish Printer
Jemma Publications
Grattan House
Temple Rd.
Blackrock, Dublin, Ireland
Ph: 353 1 7642700
Fax: 353 1 7642750
Publisher E-mail: sales@jemma.ie
Magazine featuring the Irish printing and graphic arts industry. **Founded:** 1974. **Freq:** Monthly. **Trim Size:** 210 x 297 mm. **Key Personnel:** Maev Martin, Editor, phone 353 1 7642706. **Subscription Rates:** EUR74 individuals Ireland; EUR99.79 individuals United Kingdom; EUR116.42 individuals Europe; EUR153.19 other countries. **Remarks:** Accepts advertising. **URL:** http://www.irishprinter.sitestogo.biz/. **Ad Rates:** 4C: IR2,200. **Circ:** (Not Reported)

45923 ■ Licensing World
Jemma Publications
Grattan House
Temple Rd.
Blackrock, Dublin, Ireland
Ph: 353 1 7642700

Fax: 353 1 7642750
Publisher E-mail: sales@jemma.ie
Magazine for the pub, nightclub and off license sectors in Ireland. **Founded:** 1942. **Freq:** Monthly. **Trim Size:** 210 x 297 mm. **Key Personnel:** Nigel Tynan, Editor, phone 353 1 7642700, fax 353 1 7642750; Nicola Hickey, Circulation Mgr., phone 353 1 7642727. **Subscription Rates:** EUR74 individuals Ireland; EUR99.79 individuals United Kingdom; EUR116.42 individuals Europe; EUR153.19 other countries. **Remarks:** Accepts advertising. **URL:** http://www.licensingworld.sitestogo. biz/. **Ad Rates:** 4C: IR2,800. **Circ:** (Not Reported)

Bray

45924 ■ Dublin's Country-FM - 106.8
Radio Ctr.
Killarney Rd.
Bray, Wicklow, Ireland
Ph: 353 1 2724770
Fax: 353 1 2724753
E-mail: mail@countrymix.ie
Format: Country. **Operating Hours:** Continuous. **URL:** http://countrymix.ie.

Buncrana

45925 ■ Inish Times Newspaper
Inish Times
42 Upper Main St.
Buncrana, Donegal, Ireland
Publisher E-mail: info@inishtimes.com
Newspaper covering news, sports, and events in the Inishowen Peninsula. **Subtitle:** Inishowen's Own Local Newspaper. **Founded:** July 15, 1999. **Freq:** Weekly (Wed.). **Key Personnel:** Simon McGeady, Reporter; Donald Campbell, Production Mgr.; Liam Porter, Editor; Mary Faulkner, Advertising Mgr.; Kevin Callaghan, Managing Editor. **Remarks:** Accepts advertising. **URL:** http://inishtimes.com/. **Circ:** Paid ‡6,000

Carndonagh

45926 ■ Inishowen Community Radio-FM - 105
Pound St. Carndonagh
Inishowen
Carndonagh, Donegal, Ireland
Ph: 353 74 9329105
Fax: 353 46 9023718
E-mail: studio@icrfm.ie
Format: Eclectic; Public Radio. **Owner:** Inishowen Community Radio, at above address. **Operating Hours:** 13 hours Daily. **Ad Rates:** Advertising accepted; rates available upon request. **URL:** http://www.icrfm.ie.

Carrigaline

45927 ■ 4FM - 97.4
5th Fl., Latin Hall
Golden Ln.
Dublin 8, Dublin, Ireland
Ph: 353 1 4255400
Fax: 353 1 4255444
E-mail: info@4fm.ie
Format: Eclectic. **URL:** http://www.4fm.ie/.

Circulation: ★ = ABC; △ = BPA; ♦ = CAC; • = CCAB; ❑ = VAC; ⊕ = PO Statement; ‡ = Publisher's Report; Boldface figures = sworn; Light figures = estimated.

Castlebar

45928 ■ Connaught Telegraph
Connaught Telegraph Ltd.
Cavendish Ln.
Castlebar, Mayo, Ireland
Ph: 353 94 9021711
Fax: 353 94 9024007
Independent family-run newspaper. **Subtitle:** Be Just and Fear Not. **Founded:** 1828. **Freq:** Weekly (Wed.). **Remarks:** Accepts advertising. **URL:** http://www.con-telegraph.ie/. **Circ:** 75,000

45929 ■ CRC-FM - 102.9 fm
Market Sq.
Castlebar, Mayo, Ireland
Ph: 353 9425555
E-mail: studio@crcfm.ie
Format: Ethnic. **Founded:** June 30, 1995. **Operating Hours:** 8:00 a.m.-9:30 p.m. Daily. **Key Personnel:** Pat Staton, Station Mgr. **URL:** http://www.crcfm.ie/.

Cavan

45930 ■ The Anglo-Celt
Sta. House
Cavan, Cavan, Ireland
Ph: 353 49 4331100
Community newspaper. **Founded:** 1846. **Freq:** Weekly (Wed.). **Print Method:** Web offset. **Trim Size:** 16 x 21 cm. **Cols./Page:** 9. **Key Personnel:** Barbara Fortune, Advertising Mgr., phone 353 49 4379708, barbaraf@anglocelt.net; Tom Carron, Deputy Ed. **Remarks:** Accepts advertising. **URL:** http://www.anglocelt.ie/. **Ad Rates:** BW: IR4,458, 4C: IR5,638. **Circ:** ‡16,600

Claremorris

45931 ■ Fleet Transport
JJDS Publications
D'Alton St.
Fairview
Claremorris 3, Mayo, Ireland
Ph: 353 94 9372819
Fax: 353 94 9373571
Publication E-mail: info@fleet.ie
Publisher E-mail: enquiries@fleet.ie
Trade magazine covering trucking and transportation in Ireland. **Founded:** 1987. **Freq:** Monthly. **Trim Size:** 297mm x 210mm. **Key Personnel:** Jarlath Sweeney, Editor, editor@fleet.ie; Orla Sweeney, Administration Mgr.; Mary Morrissey, Advertising Mgr. **ISSN:** 1393-4856. **Subscription Rates:** EUR65 individuals Ireland; EUR85 individuals UK & Europe; EUR120 elsewhere worldwide. **URL:** http://www.fleet.ie. **Formerly:** Fleet Management Magazine. **Circ:** Combined 6,200

Clarenbridge

45932 ■ CORKnow
Golden Egg Productions
Harris House
Tuam Rd.
Clarenbridge, Galway, Ireland
Ph: 353 91 384350
Fax: 353 91 384351
Lifestyle magazine featuring fashion in Cork. **Freq:** Monthly. **Trim Size:** 217 x 300 mm. **Key Personnel:** Katy Harrington, Editor, editor@corknow.ie; Patricia Mc-Crossan, Mng. Dir.; Jo Lavelle, Dep. Ed. **Subscription Rates:** EUR92 individuals USA; EUR44 individuals Ireland; EUR55 individuals to United Kingdom; EUR72 individuals to European Union. **Remarks:** Accepts advertising. **URL:** http://www.corknow.ie/. **Ad Rates:** 4C: IR1,450. **Circ:** (Not Reported)

45933 ■ GALWAYnow
Golden Egg Productions
Harris House
Tuam Rd.
Clarenbridge, Galway, Ireland
Ph: 353 91 384350
Fax: 353 91 384351
Lifestyle magazine featuring fashion in Galway. **Freq:** 10/yr. **Trim Size:** 217 x 300 mm. **Key Personnel:** Sinead Ni Neachtain, Editor; Patricia McCrossan, Mng. Dir.; Jo Lavelle, Dep. Ed. **Subscription Rates:** EUR44 individuals; EUR55 individuals to United Kingdom; EUR72 individuals to European Union; EUR92 U.S. **Remarks:** Accepts advertising. **URL:** http://www.galwaynow.com/advertise.php. **Ad Rates:** 4C: IR1,450. **Circ:** (Not Reported)

Clifden

45934 ■ 4FM - 104.2
5th Fl., Latin Hall
Golden Ln.
Dublin 8, Dublin, Ireland
Ph: 353 1 4255400
Fax: 353 1 4255444
E-mail: info@4fm.ie
Format: Eclectic. **URL:** http://www.4fm.ie/.

Clonmel

45935 ■ Tipp-FM - 95.3
Premier Broadcast Ctr., Unit 4A
Gurtnafleur Business Pk.
Clonmel, Tipperary, Ireland
Ph: 353 5225299
Fax: 353 5225447
E-mail: reception@tippfm.com
Format: Eclectic; Ethnic; News; Sports. **Operating Hours:** Continuous. **Ad Rates:** Advertising accepted; rates available upon request. **URL:** http://www.tippfm.com.

Cork

45936 ■ Clays and Clay Minerals
The Clay Minerals Society
c/o Kevin Murphy, Mng. Ed.
Inchafune
Dunmanway
Cork, Cork, Ireland
Ph: 353 21 2345401
Fax: 353 21 2345419
Publisher E-mail: cms@clays.org
Journal focusing on the developments in the field of clay materials. **Freq:** Bimonthly. **Key Personnel:** Joseph W. Stucki, Editor-in-Chief, jstucki@illinois.edu; Kevin Murphy, Managing Editor, kmurphy@iol.ie; Peter Komadel, Assoc. Ed.; Richard K. Brown, Assoc. Ed.; Sabine Petit, Assoc. Ed.; Lynda Williams, Assoc. Ed. **ISSN:** 0009-8604. **Subscription Rates:** US$350 institutions; US$390 institutions, other countries. **URL:** http://ccm.geoscienceworld.org/.

45937 ■ Irish Examiner
City Quarter
Lapps Quay
Cork, Cork, Ireland
Ph: 353 214 72722
Newspaper covering news and events in Ireland and throughout the world. **Subscription Rates:** EUR2.27 individuals Ireland; EUR4.35 individuals England; EUR4.35 individuals Europe; EUR5.60 individuals rest of the world. **Remarks:** Accepts advertising. **URL:** http://www.irishexaminer.com. **Circ:** (Not Reported)

45938 ■ Literacy
John Wiley & Sons Inc.
Wiley-Blackwell
c/o Kathy Hall, Ed.
University College Cork
Dept. of Education
Cork, Cork, Ireland
Peer-reviewed journal covering the study and development of literacy. **Freq:** 3/yr. **Key Personnel:** Kathy Hall, Editor, k.hall@ucc.ie; Sue Ellis, Reviews Ed., sue.ellis@strath.ac.uk. **ISSN:** 1741-4350. **Subscription Rates:** 71 other countries print and online; US$132 individuals Americas (print and online); EUR107 individuals Euro zone (print and online); 223 institutions UK (print and online); US$424 institutions Americas (print and online); EUR282 institutions Europe (print and online), US$494 institutions, other countries print and online; 202 institutions UK (print or online only); US$385 institutions Americas (print or online only); EUR256 institutions Europe (print or online only). **Remarks:** Accepts advertising. **URL:** http://www.wiley.com/bw/journal.asp?ref=1741-4350. **Circ:** (Not Reported)

45939 ■ Cork Campus Radio-FM - 98.3
University College Cork
Cork, Cork, Ireland
Ph: 353 21 4902170
E-mail: radio@ucc.ie
Format: Eclectic. **Founded:** July 31, 1995. **Operating Hours:** 8 a.m.-5.30 p.m. Mon.-Fri. **Key Personnel:** Catriona Chambers, Contact; Kieran Hurley, Station Producer, kieran.hurley@ucc.ie. **URL:** http://www.ucc.ie/ccr/.

45940 ■ 4FM - 94.8
5th Fl., Latin Hall
Golden Ln.
Dublin 8, Dublin, Ireland
Ph: 353 1 4255400
Fax: 353 1 4255444
E-mail: info@4fm.ie
Format: Eclectic. **URL:** http://www.4fm.ie/.

Drogheda

45941 ■ LM-FM - 95.8
Rathmullan Rd.
PO Box 958
Drogheda, Louth, Ireland
Ph: 353 41 9832000
Fax: 353 41 9832957
E-mail: info@lmfm.ie
Format: Full Service; Contemporary Hit Radio (CHR). **URL:** http://www.lmfm.ie/.

Dublin

45942 ■ Accountancy Ireland
Chartered Accountants House
47-49 Pearse St.
Dublin IRL-4, Dublin, Ireland
Ph: 353 163 77200
Fax: 353 166 80842
Publication E-mail: editor@accountancyireland.ie
Publisher E-mail: ca@icai.ie
Professional journal covering accounting, auditing, tax information, information technology and general business issues for chartered accountants in Ireland. **Subtitle:** Journal for Chartered Accountants in Ireland. **Founded:** 1969. **Freq:** Bimonthly. **Print Method:** Sheet-fed offset. **Trim Size:** 210 x 297 mm. **Key Personnel:** Daisy Downes, Author. **ISSN:** 0001-4699. **Subscription Rates:** EUR41.41 individuals Europe; EUR87.23 elsewhere; EUR74.01 individuals 2 years; 35.34 individuals; 63.16 individuals 2 years; EUR87.23 individuals; EUR167.40 individuals 2 years; 74 individuals; 142 individuals 2 years. **URL:** http://www.accountancyireland.ie/. **Ad Rates:** BW: EUR2,585, 4C: EUR2,520. **Circ:** Controlled ★26,475

45943 ■ Adult Learner
National Association of Adult Education
Aos-Oideachas Naisiunta Tri Aontu Saorlach
2nd Fl., 83-87 Main St.
Ranelagh
Dublin IRL-6, Dublin, Ireland
Ph: 353 1 4068220
Fax: 353 1 4068227
Publisher E-mail: mail@aontas.com
Irish and English language journal covering adult education. **Founded:** 1986. **Freq:** Annual. **Key Personnel:** Jacinta Cuthbert, Hd., Organisational Development, jcuthbert@aontas.com; Marian Duffy, President. **ISSN:** 0790-8040. **URL:** http://www.aontas.com/pubsandlinks/publications.htmltheadultlearner. **Circ:** 500

45944 ■ An Leabharlann
Library Association of Ireland
Cumann Leabharan N.A. h Eireann
53 Upper Mount St.
Dublin IRL-2, Dublin, Ireland
Publisher E-mail: honsec@libraryassociation.ie
Publication covering libraries. **Freq:** Quarterly. **Key Personnel:** Marjory Sliney, Editor; Marian Keyes, Production Mgr. **ISSN:** 0023-9542. **Subscription Rates:** Free for members. **URL:** http://www.libraryassociation.ie; http://www.anleabharlann.ie/. **Ad Rates:** BW: IR600. **Circ:** (Not Reported)

45945 ■ An Phoblacht
An Phoblacht/Republican News
58 Parnell Sq.
Dublin IRL-1, Dublin, Ireland
Ph: 353 187 33611
Fax: 353 187 33074
Publisher E-mail: aprn@irlnet.com
Political newspaper. **Freq:** Weekly. **Key Personnel:** Martin Spain, Editor; Christy Finnegan, Editor, aprn32@iol.ie. **Subscription Rates:** EUR65 individuals Ireland; 75 individuals England, Scotland, and Wales; EUR110 by mail Europe; EUR110 individuals airmail; Europe; EUR113 individuals U.S.; EUR120 individuals Canada; EUR125 individuals Australia; EUR130 elsewhere. **Remarks:** Advertising accepted; rates available upon request. **URL:** http://aprnonline.com/. **Circ:** 18,000

45946 ■ Astronomy and Space Magazine
Astronomy Ireland
PO Box 2888
Dublin IRL-5, Dublin, Ireland
Ph: 353 1 8470777
Fax: 353 1 8470771
Publisher E-mail: sec@astronomy.ie
Magazine covering astronomy and space. **Founded:** 1990. **Freq:** Monthly. **Key Personnel:** David Moore, Editor. **ISSN:** 0791-8062. **Subscription Rates:** EUR75 individuals European; EUR48 individuals full; EUR40 students; EUR75 other countries. **URL:** http://www.astronomy.ie/magazine.html. **Ad Rates:** 4C: EUR295. **Circ:** 9,000

45947 ■ Auto Ireland
Harmonia
Rosemount House
Dundrum Rd.
Dundrum
Dublin 16, Dublin, Ireland
Ph: 353 1 2405300
Magazine covering motorsports. **Freq:** Annual. **Remarks:** Accepts advertising. **URL:** http://www.harmonia.ie//26. **Circ:** (Not Reported)

45948 ■ Business Ireland
Ashville Media Group
Longboat Quay
57-59 Sir John Rogerson's Quay
Dublin 2, Dublin, Ireland
Ph: 353 1 4322200
Fax: 353 1 6727100
Publisher E-mail: info@ashville.com
Magazine featuring business in Ireland. **Founded:** 2003. **Freq:** 5/yr. **URL:** http://www.ashville.com/case_studies/business.htm. **Circ:** 2,500

45949 ■ C-4
16 Glencairn Ave.
Leopardstown
Dublin IRL-18, Dublin, Ireland
Magazine featuring articles, letters, and opinion out of Dublin. **Freq:** Monthly 10/yr. **Subscription Rates:** US$209 individuals; US$199 individuals; US$197 individuals; US$119 individuals. **URL:** http://theophobia.tripod.com/.

45950 ■ CancerWise
Eireann Healthcare Publications
122 Lower Baggot St.
Dublin IRL-2, Dublin, Ireland
Ph: 353 147 53300
Fax: 353 166 24927
Publisher E-mail: cgoodey@eireannpublications.ie
Journal featuring the developments in cancer care. **Freq:** Quarterly. **Trim Size:** 204 x 288 mm. **Key Personnel:** Sinead Jeffrey, Editor, sjeffrey@eireannpublications.ie; Cliodna O'Hanlon, Advertising Mgr., cohanlon@eireannpublications.ie; Caoimhe Tierney, Operations Dir., ctierney@eireannpublications.ie. **Subscription Rates:** EUR57 individuals. **Remarks:** Accepts advertising. **URL:** http://www.canoorwise.ie/ **Ad Rates:** 4C: IR1,520. **Circ:** 3,159

45951 ■ Confetti
Dyflin Media Ltd.
Cunningham House, 1st Fl.
130 Francis St.
Dublin, Dublin, Ireland
Ph: 353 1 4167900
Fax: 353 1 4167901
Publisher E-mail: info@dyflin.ie
Magazine featuring wedding needs for Irish brides. **Subtitle:** A Bride's Best Friend. **Freq:** Quarterly. **Key Personnel:** Ciara Elliott, Editor, ciara@confetti.ie. **Subscription Rates:** EUR6 single issue; EUR30 individuals for Ireland 4 issues; EUR46 individuals to United Kingdom; EUR70 individuals for USA and Europe. **Remarks:** Accepts advertising. **URL:** http://www.confetti.ie/; http://www.dyflin.ie/m_confetti.htm. **Ad Rates:** 4C: IR2,000. **Circ:** ★17,000

45952 ■ Consumer Choice
Consumers' Association of Ireland
43-44 Chelmsford Rd.
Dublin 6, Dublin, Ireland
Ph: 35 314 978600
Fax: 35 314 978601
Publisher E-mail: cai@consumerassociation.ie
Magazine showing how products compare in value, performance and reliability. **Freq:** Monthly. **Key Person-**
nel: Dorothy Gallagher, Exec. Member; James Doorley, Chp.; Michael Kilcoyne, Vice Chp.; Ann Woods, Honorary Sec.; Frank Dawe, Exec. Member. **Subscription Rates:** 211 individuals package; 190 individuals. **URL:** http://www.consumerassociation.ie/index.php?option=com_content&view=article&id=26&Itemid=15.

45953 ■ DiabetesWise
Eireann Healthcare Publications
122 Lower Baggot St.
Dublin IRL-2, Dublin, Ireland
Ph: 353 147 53300
Fax: 353 166 24927
Publisher E-mail: cgoodey@eireannpublications.ie
Journal for health professionals with an interest in diabetes care. **Freq:** Quarterly. **Trim Size:** 204 x 288 mm. **Key Personnel:** Katie Moten, Editor, kmoten@eireannpublications.ie; Cliodna O'Hanlon, Advertising Mgr., cohanlon@eireannpublications.ie; Caoimhe Tierney, Operations Dir., ctierney@eireannpublications.ie. **Subscription Rates:** EUR57 individuals. **Remarks:** Accepts advertising. **URL:** http://www.eireannpublications.ie/index.php?site_pid=14&page_pid=4. **Ad Rates:** 4C: IR 2,125. **Circ:** 4,227

45954 ■ Eigse
National University Of Ireland
49 Merrion Sq.
Dublin 2, Dublin, Ireland
Ph: 353 1 4392424
Fax: 353 1 4392466
Publisher E-mail: registrar@nui.ie
Journal covering research in the field of Irish language and literature. **Subtitle:** A Journal of Irish Studies. **Founded:** 1939. **Freq:** Annual. **Key Personnel:** Prof. Padraig A. Breatnach, Editor. **ISSN:** 0013-2608. **Subscription Rates:** EUR20 individuals. **URL:** http://www.nui.ie/eigse/; http://www.nui.ie/publications/eigse.asp.

45955 ■ Employment Law Review
FirstLaw Ltd.
Top Fl.
Merchants Ct.
Merchants Quay
Dublin IRL-8, Dublin, Ireland
Ph: 353 1 6790370
Fax: 353 1 6790057
Publisher E-mail: sales@firstlaw.ie
Guide to 2004 employment law for employment practitioners. **Freq:** 6/yr. **Key Personnel:** John Eardly, Editor. **ISSN:** 9044-8028. **Subscription Rates:** EUR345 individuals. **URL:** http://www.firstlaw.ie.

45956 ■ Film Ireland
Filmbase
Curved Street Bldg.
Temple Bar
Dublin 2, Dublin, Ireland
Ph: 353 1 6796716
Fax: 353 1 6796717
Publisher E-mail: info@filmbase.ie
Magazine featuring exchange of ideas and news on film making and cinema. **Freq:** Bimonthly. **Key Personnel:** Niamh Creely, Editor; Ross Whitaker, Commissioning Ed.; Gordon Gaffney, Advertising/Sales. **Subscription Rates:** EUR35 individuals; EUR95 individuals corporate; EUR45 individuals United Kingdom; EUR110 individuals United Kingdom; corporate; EUR70 other countries; EUR140 other countries corporate. **Remarks:** Accepts advertising. **URL:** http://www.filmireland.net/. **Circ:** (Not Reported)

45957 ■ Finance Dublin
Fintel Publications Ltd.
6 The Mall, Beacon Ct.
Sandyford
Dublin IRL-18, Dublin, Ireland
Ph: 353 129 30565
Fax: 353 129 30560
Publication E-mail: editorial@financedublin.com; subs@financedublin.com; mb@financedublin.com
Publisher E-mail: editorial@fintel.org
Professional magazine covering financial services and corporate finance. **Founded:** 1987. **Freq:** Monthly. **Trim Size:** A3. **Key Personnel:** Valerie Hannigan, Contact, phone 353 312 930566, vh@fintel.org; Martina Bermingham, Contact, mb@fintel.org. **Subscription Rates:** EUR675.32 individuals Republic of Ireland; 420 individuals; EUR595 individuals; US$775 other countries. **Remarks:** Accepts advertising. **URL:** http://www.financedublin.com/. **Ad Rates:** BW: IR2,200. **Circ:** Combined ★5,000

45958 ■ FireCall
Ashville Media Group
Longboat Quay
57-59 Sir John Rogerson's Quay
Dublin 2, Dublin, Ireland
Ph: 353 1 4322200
Fax: 353 1 6727100
Publisher E-mail: info@ashville.com
Journal covering firefighting. **Founded:** 1971. **Freq:** Quarterly. **Remarks:** Accepts advertising. **URL:** http://www.ashville.com/advertise/emergency-publications/firecall/. **Circ:** 1,500

45959 ■ Food Ireland
Tara Publishing Company Ltd.
Poolbeg House
1-2 Poolbeg St.
Dublin 2, Dublin, Ireland
Ph: 353 124 13000
Fax: 353 124 13020
Publication E-mail: foodireland@tarapublishingco.com
Trade magazine covering the food, dairy and processing industry in Ireland. **Founded:** 1980. **Freq:** Annual. **Key Personnel:** Kathleen Belton, Contact, kathleenbelton@tarapublishingco.com. **ISSN:** 0124-3250. **Subscription Rates:** EUR35 individuals. **Remarks:** Accepts advertising. **URL:** http://www.tarapublishingco.com; http://www.retailnews.ie/. **Circ:** Combined 2,000

45960 ■ Food & Wine Magazine
Harmonia
Rosemount House
Dundrum Rd.
Dundrum
Dublin 16, Dublin, Ireland
Ph: 353 1 2405300
Magazine covering food, drink, home entertaining, dining out and travel. **Freq:** 10/yr. **Key Personnel:** Ross Golden Bannon, Editor, ross@harmonia.ie. **Subscription Rates:** EUR39.90 individuals; 27.93 individuals. **Remarks:** Accepts classified advertising. **URL:** http://www.harmonia.ie//6. **Circ:** ★7,429

45961 ■ French Politics
Palgrave Macmillan
Law & Government Group
Business School
Dublin City University
Dublin 9, Dublin, Ireland
Publication E-mail: french-politics@dcu.ie
Publisher E-mail: booksellers@palgrave.com
Peer-reviewed journal focusing on the lifetime work and contributions to political science. **Freq:** 4/yr. **Key Personnel:** Andrew Appleton, Editor; Robert Elgie, Editor; Pepper D. Culpepper, Book Review Ed. **ISSN:** 1476-3419. **Subscription Rates:** 436 institutions, other countries print; US$797 institutions print; 61 other countries print and online; US$113 individuals print and online. **URL:** http://www.palgrave-journals.com/fp/index.html.

45962 ■ Gazette
Law Society of Ireland
Blackhall Pl.
Dublin 7, Dublin, Ireland
Ph: 35 316 724800
Fax: 35 316 724801
Publication E-mail: gazette@lawsociety.ie
Publisher E-mail: general@lawsociety.ie
Publication covering law. **Freq:** Periodic. **Key Personnel:** Mark McDermott, Editor, phone 353 1 6724828, fax 353 1 6724877. **Subscription Rates:** EUR57 individuals. **URL:** http://www.lawsociety.ie/gazette/. **Circ:** 12,000

45963 ■ HeartWise
Eireann Healthcare Publications
122 Lower Baggot St.
Dublin IRL-2, Dublin, Ireland
Ph: 353 147 53300
Fax: 353 166 24927
Publisher E-mail: cgoodey@eireannpublications.ie
Journal featuring updates and changes in cardiology. **Subtitle:** The official journal of the Irish Heart Foundation. **Freq:** Quarterly. **Trim Size:** 204 x 288 mm. **Key Personnel:** Katie Moten, Editor, kmoten@eireannpublications.ie; Cliodna O'Hanlon, Advertising Mgr., cohanlon@eireannpublications.ie; Caoimhe Tierney, Operations Dir., ctierney@eireannpublications.ie. **Subscription Rates:** EUR57 individuals. **Remarks:** Accepts advertising. **URL:** http://www.eireannpublications.

Circulation: ★ = ABC; △ = BPA; ♦ = CAC; • = CCAB; ❑ = VAC; ⊕ = PO Statement; ‡ = Publisher's Report; Boldface figures = sworn; Light figures = estimated.

ie/index.php?site_pid=14&page_pid=4HEARTWISE. **Ad Rates:** 4C: IR2,125. **Circ:** 3,185

45964 ■ Historical Biology
Taylor & Francis Group Journals
Scholarship of Biology & Environmental Science
Science Ctr.
University College of Dublin
Belfield
Dublin, Dublin, Ireland
Publisher E-mail: customerservice@taylorandfrancis.com
Journal focusing on evolutionary trends within animal and plant groups having both living and fossil representatives. **Subtitle:** An International Journal of Paleobiology. **Freq:** 4/yr. **Key Personnel:** Gareth Dyke, Editor-in-Chief, gareth.dyke@ucd.ie; Dr. Matthew A. Wills, Assoc. Ed.; Prof. R.D.K. Thomas, Assoc. Ed.; Dr. Mark Norell, Assoc. Ed.; Dr. Daniel Miller, Assoc. Ed.; Dr. Nick Fraser, Assoc. Ed. **ISSN:** 0891-2963. **Subscription Rates:** US$1,059 institutions print + online; US$1,006 institutions online; EUR844 institutions print + online; EUR801 institutions online; 808 institutions print + online; 768 institutions online; 151 individuals; US$184 individuals; EUR147 individuals. **URL:** http://www.tandf.co.uk/journals/titles/08912963.asp.

45965 ■ IBEC Economic Trends
Irish Business and Employers' Confederation
Confederation House
84-86 Lower Baggot St.
Dublin IRL-2, Dublin, Ireland
Ph: 353 16 051500
Fax: 353 16 381500
Publisher E-mail: info@ibec.ie
Trade publication covering economic trends. **Freq:** Monthly. **Key Personnel:** David Croughan, Ch. Economist, david.croughan@ibec.ie. **Remarks:** Advertising not accepted. **URL:** http://www.ibec.ie. **Circ:** (Not Reported)

45966 ■ In Touch
35 Parnell Sq.
Dublin IRL-1, Dublin, Ireland
Ph: 353 1 8047700
Fax: 353 1 8722462
Publication E-mail: editor@into.ie
Publisher E-mail: info@into.ie
Trade magazine covering trade union news for professional educators. **Founded:** 1997. **Freq:** Monthly 11/yr. **Print Method:** Web and print. **Trim Size:** A4. **Key Personnel:** John Carr, Editor; Tom O'Sullivan, Editor; Lori Kealy, Asst. Ed.; Mary Bird Smyth, Contact. **ISSN:** 1393-4813. **URL:** http://www.into.ie/. **Circ:** Combined 27,100

45967 ■ International Journal for Quality in Health Care
International Society for Quality in Health Care
2 Parnell Sq. E
Dublin 3002, Dublin, Ireland
Ph: 353 1 8717049
Fax: 353 1 8783845
Publisher E-mail: info@isqua.org
Peer-reviewed journal covering topics related to quality and safety in health care. **Founded:** 1972. **Freq:** Semiweekly (Wed. and Sun.). **Print Method:** Offset. **Trim Size:** 11 1/2 x 16. **Cols./Page:** 5. **Col. Width:** 11.7 picas. **Col. Depth:** 210 agate lines. **Key Personnel:** Eric Scheneider, Editor-in-Chief; Ezequiel Garcia Elorio, Dep. Ed. **ISSN:** 1353-4505. **Subscription Rates:** 599 institutions print & online; 459 institutions online only; 549 institutions print only; 749 institutions corporate, print and online; 574 institutions corporate, online; 686 institutions corporate, print; 95 individuals personal. **URL:** http://intqhc.oxfordjournals.org/.

45968 ■ International Review of Entrepreneurship
Senate Hall Academic Publishing
PO Box 8261
Shankill
Dublin, Dublin, Ireland
Publisher E-mail: info@senatehall.com
Peer-reviewed journal covering teaching, strategies, lecture, and research on entrepreneurship. **Key Personnel:** Andrew Burke, Editor; Marilyn Kourilsky, Editor; David Audretsch, Editor. **Subscription Rates:** US$465 institutions U.S. and rest of the world, library; US$180 individuals U.S. and rest of the world, print and online; EUR330 institutions Europe, library; EUR160 individuals

Europe, print and online; 290 institutions Great Britain, library; 115 individuals Great Britain, print and online. **URL:** http://www.senatehall.com/entrepreneurship?phpMyAdmin=z1KTe0qLPc6ABagn-uIsTF2Z3Gf. **Formerly:** International Journal of Entrepreneurship Education (Sept. 2020).

45969 ■ Ireland at Your Leisure
Ashville Media Group
Longboat Quay
57-59 Sir John Rogerson's Quay
Dublin 2, Dublin, Ireland
Ph: 353 1 4322200
Fax: 353 1 6727100
Publisher E-mail: info@ashville.com
Magazine featuring the different destination in Ireland. **URL:** http://www.ashville.com/case_studies/avis.htm. **Circ:** ★41,000

45970 ■ Irish Architectural and Decorative Studies
Irish Georgian Society
74 Merrion Sq.
Dublin IRL-2, Dublin, Ireland
Ph: 353 1 6767053
Fax: 353 1 6620290
Publisher E-mail: info@igs.ie
Publication covering Irish architecture and decoration. **Freq:** Annual. **Remarks:** Advertising not accepted. **URL:** http://www.igs.ie. **Circ:** (Not Reported)

45971 ■ Irish Archives
Irish Society for Archives
UCD Archives, University College Dublin
James Joyce Library
Belfield
Dublin 4, Dublin, Ireland
Ph: 35 317 167555
Fax: 35 317 161146
Publisher E-mail: archives@ucd.ie
Publication covering Irish archives. **Freq:** Annual. **Key Personnel:** Elizabeth McEvoy, Editor, emcevoy@nationalarchives.ie; Kate Manning, Website Ed., kate.manning@ucd.ie; Dr. Susan Hood, Editor, susan.hood@rcbdub.or; Dr. Raymond Refausse, Chp., raymond.refausse@rcbdub.org; Andrew Whiteside, Hon. Sec., isar@eircom.net. **URL:** http://www.ucd.ie/archives/isa/isa-journal.html.

45972 ■ Irish Chemical News
Institute of Chemistry of Ireland
Instituid Ceimice N.A. hEireann
Cardiff Ln.
PO Box 9322
Dublin 2, Dublin, Ireland
Publisher E-mail: info@instituteofchemistry.org
Irish publication covering chemistry. **Freq:** Semiannual. **URL:** http://www.chemistryireland.org/html/ichemnews.html.

45973 ■ Irish Folk Music Studies
Folk Music Society of Ireland
Cumann Cheol Tire Eireann
c/o The Irish Traditional Music Archive
63 Merrion Sq.
Dublin IRL-2, Dublin, Ireland
Ph: 35 316 619699
Fax: 35 316 624585
Publisher E-mail: sales@itma.ie
Publication covering Irish folk music studies, in English and Gaelic. **Freq:** Periodic. **Key Personnel:** Nicholas Carolan, Editor; Therese Smith, Editor; Hugh Shields, Editor. **ISSN:** 0332-298X. **Subscription Rates:** 7.50 individuals; US$11.50 individuals. **URL:** http://homepage.eircom.net; http://homepage.eircom.net/~shields/fmsi/

45974 ■ Irish Geography
Geographical Society of Ireland
Cumann Tireolaiochta N.A. hEireann
Geography Dept.
National University of Ireland
Belfield
Dublin IRL-4, Dublin, Ireland
Ph: 35 317 167777
Premier peer-reviewed journal covering Irish geography. **Freq:** 3/yr. **Key Personnel:** Dr. Padraig Carmody, Editor, carmodyp@tcd.ie. **Subscription Rates:** 133 institutions print + online; US$266 institutions print + online; EUR212 institutions print + online. **URL:** http://www.ucd.ie/gsi/publications.htm.

45975 ■ Irish Journal of Education
St. Patrick's College
Educational Research Centre
Dublin IRL-9, Dublin, Ireland
Ph: 353 1 8373789
Fax: 353 1 8378997
Publisher E-mail: info@erc.ie
Journal covering all aspects of education, including philosophy, history, sociology, and comparative education, for teachers at all levels and interested others. **Founded:** 1967. **Freq:** Irregular. **Trim Size:** 6 x 9. **Key Personnel:** Dr. Thomas Kellaghan, Editor. **ISSN:** 0021-1257. **Subscription Rates:** EUR10 individuals Europe; US$20 other countries. **Remarks:** Advertising not accepted. **URL:** http://www.erc.ie/?s=9. **Circ:** Paid 500

45976 ■ The Irish Journal of French Studies
Association des Etudes Francaises et Francophones d'Irlande
Dept. of French
Trinity College Dublin
Dublin 2, Dublin, Ireland
Journal welcoming articles on any aspect of research in the area of French and Francophone culture and society. **Freq:** Annual. **Key Personnel:** Johnnie Gratton, Gen. Ed., grattonj@tcd.ie. **ISSN:** 0954-1500. **URL:** http://www.adeffi.ie/cahiers.html.

45977 ■ Irish Journal of Medical Science
Royal Academy of Medicine in Ireland
Frederick House, 4th Fl.
19 S Frederick St.
Dublin 2, Dublin, Ireland
Ph: 353 1 6334820
Fax: 353 1 6334918
Publication E-mail: journal@rami.ie
Publisher E-mail: secretary@rami.ie
Medical journal. **Founded:** Nov. 11, 1832. **Freq:** Quarterly. **Trim Size:** 288 x 204 mm. **Key Personnel:** John Daly, Editorial Consultant; Brian Sheppard, Editor; Conor Shields, Info. Systems Consultant; Helen Moore, Managing Editor, helenmoore@rcpi.ie; Alan Kelly, Statistical Consultant; T.N. Walsh, Editor; David Bouchier-Hayes, Editor-in-Chief. **ISSN:** 0021-1265. **Remarks:** Advertising accepted; rates available upon request. **URL:** http://www.ijms.ie. **Circ:** (Not Reported)

45978 ■ Irish Journal of Psychological Medicine
MedMedia Group
25 Adelaide St.
Dun Laoghaire
Dublin, Dublin, Ireland
Ph: 35 312 803967
Fax: 35 312 807076
Journal focusing on original Irish psychiatric and psychological research. **Freq:** Quarterly March, June, September and December. **Key Personnel:** Andrea McAdam, Admin., andrea@medmedia.ie; Leon Ellison, Gp. Advertising Mgr., phone 353 128 03967, fax 353 128 07076, leon@medmedia.ie. **Subscription Rates:** EUR170 individuals for European countries; EUR170 individuals for rest of the world. **URL:** http://www.ijpm.org/.

45979 ■ Irish Kitchens and Bathrooms
Dyflin Media Ltd.
Cunningham House, 1st Fl.
130 Francis St.
Dublin, Dublin, Ireland
Ph: 353 1 4167900
Fax: 353 1 4167901
Publisher E-mail: info@dyflin.ie
Magazine featuring bathroom and kitchen designs. **Subtitle:** The Essential House and Home Guide. **Freq:** Annual. **Key Personnel:** Karen Hesse, Editor, editor@houseandhome.ie. **Subscription Rates:** EUR5.95 single issue. **Remarks:** Accepts advertising. **URL:** http://www.dyflin.ie/m_irish_kitchen_and_bathrooms.htm. **Ad Rates:** 4C: IR2,850. **Circ:** 25,000

45980 ■ Irish Medical Journal
c/o Dr. John Murphy, Ed.
10 Fitzwilliam Pl.
Dublin IRL-2, Dublin, Ireland
Professional magazine covering medicine in Ireland. **Founded:** 1867. **Freq:** 10/yr. **Key Personnel:** Lorna Duffy, Asst. Ed.; L. Daly, Editorial Advisory Board Member; M. Patton, Editorial Board Member; D. Powell, Editorial Advisory Board Member; B. Day, Editorial Board Member; C. O'Herlihy, Editorial Advisory Board Member; Dr. John Murphy, Editor. **ISSN:** 0332-3102. **Subscription Rates:** EUR225 individuals Ireland, U.K.; EUR360

other countries. **Remarks:** Accepts advertising. **URL:** http://www.imj.ie. **Ad Rates:** BW: IR825, 4C: IR1,206. **Circ:** Paid 8,800.

45981 ■ Irish Mountain Log
Mountaineering Council of Ireland
Sport HQ
13 Joyce Way
Parkwest Business Pk.
Dublin IRL-12, Dublin, Ireland
Ph: 35 316 251115
Fax: 35 316 251116
Publisher E-mail: mci@eircom.net
Official publication of the Mountaineering Council of Ireland. **Freq:** Quarterly. **Key Personnel:** Patrick O'Sullivan, Editor, phone 353 1 8378166, iml-editor@ mountaineering.ie. **Remarks:** Accepts advertising. **URL:** http://www.mountaineering.ie/membersandservices/ viewdetails.asp?ID=5. **Circ:** 9,500.

45982 ■ Irish Pharmachem Industry Buyers' Guide
Tara Publishing Company Ltd.
Poolbeg House
1-2 Poolbeg St.
Dublin 2, Dublin, Ireland
Ph: 353 124 13000
Fax: 353 124 13020
Trade magazine covering the pharmaceutical and chemical processing and manufacturing industries. **Founded:** 1998. **Freq:** 10/yr. **Trim Size:** 210 X 297 mm. **Key Personnel:** Kathleen Belton, Contact, kathleenbelton@tarapublishingco.com. **Subscription Rates:** EUR35 individuals. **Remarks:** Accepts advertising. **URL:** http://www.irishpharmachem.com/ default.aspx. **Ad Rates:** 4C: IR3,295. **Circ:** Combined 2,124.

45983 ■ Irish Pharmacist
GreenCross Publishing
Lower Ground Fl.
5 Harrington St.
Dublin 8, Dublin, Ireland
Ph: 353 147 89770
Fax: 353 147 89764
Journal for pharmacists in Ireland. **Freq:** 11/yr. **Key Personnel:** Maura Henderson, Contact; Graham Cooke, Contact. **Subscription Rates:** EUR85 individuals. **Remarks:** Accepts advertising. **URL:** http://www. greencrosspublishing.ie/publication.aspx?contentid=4. **Ad Rates:** 4C: IR1,250. **Circ:** 2,089.

45984 ■ Irish Psychiatrist
Eireann Healthcare Publications
122 Lower Baggot St.
Dublin IRL-2, Dublin, Ireland
Ph: 353 147 53300
Fax: 353 166 24927
Publisher E-mail: cgoodey@eireannpublications.ie
Official journal of the Irish Psychiatric Society, catering to all Irish doctors with an interest in psychiatry. **Subtitle:** The Official Journal of the Irish Psychiatrist Association. **Freq:** Bimonthly. **Trim Size:** 204 X 288 mm. **Key Personnel:** Caoimhe Tierney, Operations Dir., ctierney@ eireannpublications.ie; Dr. Brian O'Shea, Medical Ed.; Amanda O'Keeffe, Advertising Mgr., aokeefe@ eireannpublications.ie; Cora Mannion, Editor, cmannion@eireannpublications.ie. **Subscription Rates:** EUR75 individuals. **Remarks:** Accepts advertising. **URL:** http://www.irishpsychiatrist.ie/index.php?site_pid=3& page_pid=1. **Ad Rates:** 4C: IR1,685. **Circ:** 3,322.

45985 ■ Irish Studies in International Affairs
Royal Irish Academy
19 Dawson St.
Dublin 2, Dublin, Ireland
Ph: 353 1 6762570
Fax: 353 1 6762346
Publisher E-mail: webmaster@ria.ie
Irish publication covering arts and sciences. **Founded:** 1977. **Freq:** Annual. **Key Personnel:** Dr. John Doyle, Editor. **ISSN:** 0332-1460. **Subscription Rates:** EUR35 individuals print and online; EUR106 institutions print and online; EUR20 students print and online; EUR95 institutions online only. **Remarks:** Advertising not accepted. **URL:** http://www.ria.ie/publications/journals/irish-studies-in-international-affairs.aspx. **Circ:** (Not Reported)

45986 ■ Irish Sword
Military History Society of Ireland
Newman House
86 St. Stephen's Green

Dublin 2, Dublin, Ireland
Publication covering military history. **Founded:** 1949. **Freq:** Semiannual. **Key Personnel:** Pat Kirby, Joint Honorary Member Sec., patandpatkirby@eircom.net. **ISSN:** 0021-1389. **Subscription Rates:** EUR425 individuals international commission. **Remarks:** Advertising not accepted. **URL:** http://www.mhsi.ie/thesword.htm. **Circ:** 900

45987 ■ Irish Tatler
Harmonia
Rosemount House
Dundrum Rd.
Dundrum
Dublin 16, Dublin, Ireland
Ph: 353 1 2405300
Magazine covering fashion for women. **Founded:** 1890. **Freq:** 11/yr. **Key Personnel:** Elaine Prendeville, Editor, eprendeville@harmonia.ie; Niamh Carwood, Sales Mgr., ncarwood@harmonia.ie. **Subscription Rates:** EUR22 individuals; 15.40 individuals. **Remarks:** Accepts advertising. **URL:** http://www.harmonia.ie//7. **Circ:** ★26,427.

45988 ■ Irish Times
The Irish Times
24-28 Tara St.
Dublin 2, Dublin, Ireland
Ph: 353 1 6758000
Fax: 353 1 6758035
Publisher E-mail: services@irishtimes.com
Newspaper offering coverage and analysis of politics, finance, foreign news, sports, and the arts. **Founded:** Mar. 29, 1859. **Freq:** Daily Monday to Saturday. **Remarks:** Accepts advertising. **URL:** http://www.irishtimes. com/. **Circ:** 116,061.

45989 ■ It's All About Living
Ashville Media Group
Longboat Quay
57-59 Sir John Rogerson's Quay
Dublin 2, Dublin, Ireland
Ph: 353 1 4322200
Fax: 353 1 6727100
Publisher E-mail: info@ashville.com
Magazine covering health management and Vhi Healthcare products. **Freq:** Quarterly. **URL:** http://www. ashville.com/case_studies/vhi.htm.

45990 ■ Journal of Strategic Management Education
Senate Hall Academic Publishing
PO Box 8261
Shankill
Dublin, Dublin, Ireland
Publisher E-mail: info@senatehall.com
Journal covering the teaching of strategic management. **Key Personnel:** Annabelle Gawer, Editor-in-Chief; Arnoldo Hax, Editorial Board. **ISSN:** 1649-3877. **Subscription Rates:** US$465 institutions, other countries U.S., print and online, library; EUR395 institutions Europe, print and online, library; 295 institutions Great Britain, print and online, library; US$195 individuals U.S. & rest of the world, print & online; EUR160 individuals Europe, print & online; 115 individuals Great Britain, print & online. **URL:** http://www.senatehall.com/strategic-management? phpMyAdmin=z1KTe0qLPc6ABagn-uIsTF2Z3Gf.

45991 ■ Maternity & Infant
Ashville Media Group
Longboat Quay
57-59 Sir John Rogerson's Quay
Dublin 2, Dublin, Ireland
Ph: 353 1 4322200
Fax: 353 1 6727100
Publication E-mail: editorial@infant.ie
Publisher E-mail: info@ashville.com
Magazine containing information for Irish parents having children from 6 months to 6 years old. **Freq:** Bimonthly. **Key Personnel:** Emily Manning, Editor. **Subscription Rates:** EUR28 individuals. **Remarks:** Accepts advertising. **URL:** http://www.maternityandinfant.ie. **Circ:** 15,000

45992 ■ Motoring Life
48 N Great Georges St.
Dublin IRL-1, Dublin, Ireland
Ph: 353 187 80444
Fax: 353 187 87740
Publication E-mail: info@motoringlife.ie
Publisher E-mail: info@motoringlife.ie
Consumer magazine covering automobiles. **Freq:**

Bimonthly. **Key Personnel:** Jim Glennon, Production, production@motoringlife.ie; George Courtney, Advertising, advertising@motoringlife.ie; Ian Adcock, Contributor; Nick Hall, Contributor; Genaloine Herbert, Editor, gherbert@motoringlife.ie. **Subscription Rates:** EUR18.50 individuals 7 issues, including postage (Ireland). **Remarks:** Accepts advertising. **URL:** http:// www.motoringlife.ie/subs.htm; http://www.motoringlife. ie/. **Circ:** (Not Reported)

45993 ■ OsteoWise
Eireann Healthcare Publications
122 Lower Baggot St.
Dublin IRL-2, Dublin, Ireland
Ph: 353 147 53300
Fax: 353 166 24927
Publisher E-mail: cgoodey@eireannpublications.ie
Journal featuring developments on bone disease. **Freq:** Quarterly. **Trim Size:** 204 x 288 mm. **Key Personnel:** Sinead Jeffrey, Editor, sjeffrey@eireannpublications.ie; Cliodna O'Hanlon, Advertising Mgr., cohanlon@ eireannpublications.ie; Caoimhe Tierney, Operations Dir., ctierney@eireannpublications.ie. **Subscription Rates:** EUR57 individuals. **Remarks:** Accepts advertising. **URL:** http://www.eireannpublications.ie/ index.php?site_pid=14&page_pid=4OSTEOWISE. **Circ:** 2,921

45994 ■ Pioneer
Pioneer Total Abstinence Association
27 Upper Sherrard St.
Dublin IRL-1, Dublin, Ireland
Ph: 35 318 749464
Fax: 35 318 748485
Publisher E-mail: enquiries@pioneertotal.ie
Magazine containing information on religion, general topics and youth. **Freq:** Monthly. **Subscription Rates:** EUR28.50 single issue Ireland; EUR38 single issue U.K.; EUR45 single issue other countries and United States of America. **Remarks:** Accepts advertising. **URL:** http:// www.pioneerassociation.ie/pioneer-magazine. **Circ:** (Not Reported)

45995 ■ Prudence
Dyflin Media Ltd.
Cunningham House, 1st Fl.
130 Francis St.
Dublin, Dublin, Ireland
Ph: 353 1 4167900
Fax: 353 1 4167901
Publisher E-mail: info@dyflin.ie
Magazine for women. **Subtitle:** A-List Lifestyle At Realist Prices. **Founded:** Oct. 2004. **Freq:** Bimonthly. **Key Personnel:** Annete O'Meara, Editor, annette@prudence. ie. **Subscription Rates:** EUR2.95 single issue; EUR15 individuals Ireland; EUR27 two years Ireland; EUR52.50 individuals to United Kingdom & Europe. **Remarks:** Accepts advertising. **URL:** http://www.prudence.ie/; http:// www.dyflin.ie/m_prudence.htm. **Ad Rates:** 4C: IR5,000. **Circ:** ★11,035

45996 ■ Quaternary International
International Union for Quaternary Research
Union Internationale pour l'Etude du Quarternaire
Dept. of Geography, Museum Bldg.
Trinity College
Dublin 2, Dublin, Ireland
Ph: 353 1 6081213
Publisher E-mail: pcoxon@tcd.ie
Worldwide journal covering geology. **Subtitle:** The Journal of the International Union for Quaternary Research. **Freq:** 36/yr. **Key Personnel:** Norm R. Catto, Editor-in-Chief, phone 709737-8413, fax 709737-3119, ncatto@morgan.ucs.mun.ca. **ISSN:** 1040-6182. **Subscription Rates:** 13,400¥ individuals; US$115 individuals except Europe, Japan and Iran; EUR102 individuals for European countries and Iran; 148,500¥ institutions; EUR1,125 institutions for European countries and Iran; US$1,254 institutions except Europe, Japan and Iran. **URL:** http://www.inqua.tcd.ie/publications_quaternary_ international.html.

45997 ■ Reach
Irish Association of Teachers in Special Education
Drumconda Education Ctr.
Drumconda
Dublin 9, Dublin, Ireland
Publication E-mail: reacheditor@iatse.ie
Publisher E-mail: info@iatse.ie
Journal of the Irish Association of Teachers in Special Education. **Founded:** 6, 1987. **Freq:** Semiannual. **Subscription Rates:** EUR25 individuals Ireland and UK; EUR43 two years Ireland and UK; EUR30 other countries;

Circulation: ★ = ABC; △ = BPA; ◆ = CAC; • = CCAB; ❑ = VAC; ⊕ = PO Statement; ‡ = Publisher's Report; Boldface figures = sworn; Light figures = estimated.

Gale Directory of Publications & Broadcast Media/147th Ed.   5057

EUR52 two years rest of world; EUR36 individuals USA and world; EUR65 two years USA and world. **URL:** http://www.iatse.ie/Reach.aspx.

45998 ■ Show Times
Association of Irish Musical Societies
25 Harcourt Lodge
Goldenbridge
Dublin 8, Dublin, Ireland
Publisher E-mail: admin@aims.ie
Publication covering musical show. **Freq:** 9/yr. **Key Personnel:** Winston Johnston, President, phone 44 2891 463153; Tina O'Kelly, Editor, phone 353 87 6023025; Fiona Shirran, Seminar Admin., phone 353 87 2058095, fiona@aims.ie. **Subscription Rates:** EUR30 individuals. **Remarks:** Advertising accepted; rates available upon request. **URL:** http://www.aims.ie/services_showtimes.asp. **Circ:** (Not Reported)

45999 ■ U Magazine
Harmonia
Rosemount House
Dundrum Rd.
Dundrum
Dublin 16, Dublin, Ireland
Ph: 353 1 2405300
Magazine covering fashion, beauty news, celebrity interviews and any topics that cater women's interest. **Freq:** Biweekly. **Key Personnel:** Amy Kiernan, Sales Mgr., akiernan@harmonia.ie; Jennifer Stevens, Editor, jstevens@harmonia.ie. **Subscription Rates:** EUR1.50 single issue; IR1.20 single issue; EUR37.50 individuals; 26.25 individuals. **Remarks:** Accepts advertising. **URL:** http://www.harmonia.ie//20. **Circ:** ★34,103

46000 ■ Dublin's Q102-FM - 102.2
Macken House
39-40 Upper Mayor St.
Dublin 1, Dublin, Ireland
Ph: 353 1 8506500
Fax: 353 1 8506555
E-mail: info@q102.ie
Format: Adult Contemporary. **URL:** http://www.q102.ie/index.asp.

46001 ■ 4FM - 94.9
5th Fl., Latin Hall
Golden Ln.
Dublin 8, Dublin, Ireland
Ph: 353 1 4255400
Fax: 353 1 4255444
E-mail: info@4fm.ie
Format: Eclectic. **Ad Rates:** $2380-5425 for 30 seconds. **URL:** http://www.4fm.ie/.

4FM - See Bantry, Cork

4FM - See Carrigaline, Cork

4FM - See Clifden, Galway

4FM - See Cork, Cork

4FM - See Fermoy, Cork

4FM - See Galway, Galway

4FM - See Limerick, Limerick

4FM - See Macroom, Cork

4FM - See Naas, Kildare

4FM - See Youghal, Cork

46002 ■ Near-FM - 90.3
Northside Civic Ctr.
Bunratty Rd.
Dublin 17, Dublin, Ireland
Ph: 353 1 8671190
Fax: 353 1 8486111
Format: Ethnic. **Operating Hours:** Continuous. **Key Personnel:** Sally Galiana, Station Mgr.; Vincent Teeling, Chp. **URL:** http://www.near.ie.

46003 ■ NewsTalk 106-FM - 106
Marconi House
Digges Ln.
Dublin 2, Dublin, Ireland
Ph: 353 1 6445100
Fax: 353 1 6445101
E-mail: info@newstalk.ie
Format: News; Talk. **Operating Hours:** 6:30 a.m.-12 a.m. Daily. **Key Personnel:** Garrett Harte, Editor, garrett@newstalk.ie; John Keogh, News Dir., johnkeogh@newstalk.ie; Cera Ward, Sales Dir., cward@newstalk.ie; Michael Markey, Mktg. Dir., mjmarkey@newstalk.ie. **Ad Rates:** $65-250 for 30 seconds. **URL:** http://www.newstalk106.ie/.

46004 ■ Q102-FM - 102.2
Macken House
39-40 Upper Mayor St.
Dublin 1, Dublin, Ireland
Ph: 353 1 8506500
Fax: 353 1 8506555
E-mail: info@q102.ie
Format: Adult Contemporary. **URL:** http://www.q102.ie.

46005 ■ SPIN-FM - 103.8
The Malthouse
Grand Canal Quay
Dublin 2, Dublin, Ireland
Ph: 353 1 6564600
Fax: 353 1 8550711
Format: Talk; Ethnic; Contemporary Hit Radio (CHR). **Operating Hours:** Continuous. **Key Personnel:** Mark O'Sullivan, Sales Mgr., ruairi.conroy@98fm-spin1038.ie. **URL:** http://spin1038.com.

46006 ■ Today-FM - 102
Marconi House
Digges Ln.
Dublin 2, Dublin, Ireland
Ph: 353 1 850715100
Format: Top 40; Sports; Contemporary Hit Radio (CHR). **Operating Hours:** Continuous. **Key Personnel:** Lars Humborg, Traffic Mgr., phone 353 1 8049098, lhumborg@todayfm.com; Ray McKeon, Sales Dir., phone 353 1 8049025, rmckeon@todayfm.com; Maria McKenzie, Advertising Sales Mgr., phone 353 1 8049078, mmckenzie@todayfm.com; Grainne Moynihan, Sr. Account Mgr. Agency Sales, phone 353 1 8049095, gmoynihan@todayfm.com; Emma Keegan, Contact, phone 353 1 8049036, ekeegan@todayfm.com. **Ad Rates:** Advertising accepted; rates available upon request. **URL:** http://www.todayfm.com.

Dun Laoghaire

46007 ■ Afloat
Irish Marine Press
2 Lower Glenageary Rd.
Dun Laoghaire, Dublin, Ireland
Ph: 353 01 2846161
Fax: 353 01 2846192
Magazine covering news, equipment and latest trends in boating and sailing. **Subtitle:** Ireland's Sailing and Motorboating magazine. **Freq:** 10/yr. **Subscription Rates:** EUR50 individuals; EUR99 other countries. **URL:** http://www.afloat.ie/.

Dundrum

46008 ■ FINS
Mac Communications
Taney Hall
Eglinton Terr.
Dundrum 14, Dublin, Ireland
Ph: 353 1 2960000
Fax: 353 1 2960383
Publisher E-mail: info@maccom.ie
Magazine featuring surfing, windsurfing and kitesurfing. **Freq:** Quarterly. **Trim Size:** A4. **Key Personnel:** Tony Lynch, Editor, tony@finsmag.com. **Subscription Rates:** EUR25 individuals Ireland/Northern Ireland; EUR35 other countries; 25 individuals U.K.; 20 individuals Ireland/Northern Ireland. **Remarks:** Accepts advertising. **URL:** http://maccommunications.ie/publications/fins.htm; http://www.finsmag.com/. **Circ:** Combined 10,000

46009 ■ Irish Medical News
Mac Communications
Taney Hall
Eglinton Terr.
Dundrum 14, Dublin, Ireland
Ph: 353 1 2960000
Fax: 353 1 2960383
Publication E-mail: imn@maccommunications.ie
Publisher E-mail: info@maccom.ie
Magazine featuring news and opinion about clinical issues. **Freq:** Weekly (Mon.). **Trim Size:** 273 x 395 mm. **Key Personnel:** Pricilla Lynch, Editor; Carol Manweiler, Publisher, cmanweiler@communications.ie. **Subscription Rates:** Free doctors in all specialties throughout Ireland; EUR199 individuals; EUR230 individuals; EUR299 individuals rest of the world. **Remarks:** Accepts advertising. **URL:** http://www.irishmedicalnews.ie/. **Ad Rates:** BW: EUR1180, 4C: EUR1733. **Circ:** ★6,750

46010 ■ Living It
Mac Communications

Taney Hall
Eglinton Terr.
Dundrum 14, Dublin, Ireland
Ph: 353 1 2960000
Fax: 353 1 2960383
Publisher E-mail: info@maccom.ie
Magazine for 50 years old and up readers in Ireland. **Freq:** Bimonthly. **Trim Size:** 206 x 276 mm. **Key Personnel:** Colin McGarrigle, Editor, colin@maccom.ie. **Subscription Rates:** EUR18 individuals. **Remarks:** Accepts advertising. **URL:** http://maccommunications.ie/publications/livingit.htm. **Ad Rates:** 4C: EUR2,100. **Circ:** 10,000

46011 ■ Visitor
Mac Communications
Taney Hall
Eglinton Terr.
Dundrum 14, Dublin, Ireland
Ph: 353 1 2960000
Fax: 353 1 2960383
Publisher E-mail: info@maccom.ie
Magazine for travellers and holidaymakers in Ireland. **Freq:** Annual. **Trim Size:** A4. **Key Personnel:** Colin McGarrigle, Editor, colin@maccom.ie. **Remarks:** Accepts advertising. **URL:** http://maccommunications.ie/publications/visitor.htm. **Ad Rates:** 4C: EUR6,250. **Circ:** ★200,000

Ennis

46012 ■ Clare-FM - 102.9
Abbeyfield Ctr.
Francis St.
Ennis, Clare, Ireland
Ph: 353 65 6828888
Fax: 353 65 6823366
Format: News; Sports; Talk; Adult Contemporary; Top 40. **Operating Hours:** Continuous. **Key Personnel:** Michael Ryan, Sales Mgr., mryan@clare.fm; Muireann McMahon, Acctg. Mgr., mmcmahon@clare.fm. **Ad Rates:** $15-24 for 15 seconds; $19-29 for 20 seconds; $23-39 for 30 seconds; $28-50 for 40 seconds; $39-69 for 60 seconds. **URL:** http://www.clarefm.ie.

Clare-FM - See Ennistymon

Clare-FM - See Maghera

Clare FM2 - See Killaloe

Ennistymon

46013 ■ Clare-FM - 95.2
Abbeyfield Ctr.
Francis St.
Ennis, Clare, Ireland
Format: Full Service; Ethnic. **URL:** http://www.clarefm.ie.

Fermoy

46014 ■ 4FM - 95.2
5th Fl., Latin Hall
Golden Ln.
Dublin 8, Dublin, Ireland
Ph: 353 1 4255400
Fax: 353 1 4255444
E-mail: info@4fm.ie
Format: Eclectic. **URL:** http://www.4fm.ie/.

Gaillimhe

46015 ■ Foinse
An Cheathru Rua
Gaillimhe, Galway, Ireland
Ph: 353 91 595520
Fax: 353 91 595524
Publisher E-mail: nuacht@foinse.ie
National newspaper. **Founded:** 1996. **Freq:** Weekly. **Key Personnel:** Sean Tadhg Gairbhi, Editor, seant@foinse.ie; Sean Clancy, Contact, seanc@foinse.ie. **Subscription Rates:** EUR57 individuals Ireland; EUR74 individuals Europe; EUR159 individuals rest of the world; US$190 individuals rest of the world. **URL:** http://www.foinse.ie/baile.php.

Galway

46016 ■ Australian Journal of Irish Studies
Centre for Irish Studies
National University of Ireland
Galway, University Rd.

Galway 6150, Galway, Ireland
Ph: 353 91 492051
Fax: 353 91 524411
Journal embracing research on the Irish in Australia and
New Zealand as well as Irish Studies in the more
traditional sense of Irish history, language, literature and
other cultural forms. **Key Personnel:** Bob Reece, Editor.
URL: http://wwwsoc.murdoch.edu.au/cfis/ajis.html.

46017 ■ City Tribune
Connacht Tribune Ltd.
15 Market St.
Galway, Galway, Ireland
Ph: 353 915 36222
Fax: 353 915 67970
Publisher E-mail: news@ctribune.ie
Newspaper serving Galway City. **Founded:** 1909. **Freq:**
Weekly (Fri.). **Print Method:** Lithographic. **Trim Size:**
412 x 578 mm. **Key Personnel:** Michael Glynn, Editor,
phone 44 353 91536222, mglynn@ctribune.ie. **Sub-
scription Rates:** EUR90 individuals 26 weeks, Ireland;
EUR148 individuals 26 weeks, UK; EUR168 individuals 26
weeks, USA; EUR169 individuals 52 weeks, Ireland;
EUR286 individuals 52 weeks, USA. **Remarks:** Accepts advertising. **URL:** http://
www.galwaynews.ie/galwaycitytribune. **Ad Rates:** GLR:
EUR2.55, BW: EUR3,840, 4C: EUR5,760, PCI: EUR8. **Circ:**
29,970

46018 ■ Connacht Sentinel
Connacht Tribune Ltd.
15 Market St.
Galway, Galway, Ireland
Ph: 353 915 36222
Fax: 353 915 67970
Publisher E-mail: news@ctribune.ie
Tabloid serving Galway City. **Founded:** May 22, 1909.
Freq: Weekly (Tues.). **Print Method:** Lithographic. **Trim
Size:** 289 x 412 mm. **Key Personnel:** Brendan Carroll,
Editor, phone 44 353 91536231, brendan.carroll@
ctribune.ie. **Subscription Rates:** EUR78 individuals
Ireland; EUR104 individuals Great Britain & Europe;
EUR104 other countries U.S. & Worldwide; EUR44
individuals Ireland; EUR57 individuals Great Britain &
Europe; EUR57 individuals U.S. & Worldwide. **Remarks:**
Accepts advertising. **URL:** http://www.galwaynews.ie/
connachtsentinel. **Ad Rates:** GLR: EUR61, BW:
EUR6,570, 4C: EUR11,120, PCI: EUR2.50. **Circ:** 8,480

46019 ■ Connacht Tribune
Connacht Tribune Ltd.
15 Market St.
Galway, Galway, Ireland
Ph: 353 915 36222
Fax: 353 915 67970
Publisher E-mail: news@ctribune.ie
Newspaper serving Galway City and surrounding county.
Founded: 1909. **Freq:** Weekly (Thurs.). **Print Method:**
Lithographic. **Trim Size:** 412 x 578 mm. **Key Person-
nel:** David Hickey, Ch. Exec. Off., phone 44 353
91536213, david.hickey@ctribune.ie; Dave O'Connell,
Editor, phone 44 353 91536224, dave.oconnell@
ctribune.ie. **Subscription Rates:** EUR169 individuals
Ireland; EUR286 individuals Great Britain & Europe;
EUR325 individuals U.S. & Worldwide; EUR90 individuals
Ireland; EUR148 individuals Great Britain & Europe;
EUR168 individuals U.S. & Worldwide. **URL:** http://www.
galwaynews.ie/connachttribune. **Ad Rates:** GLR: EUR2.
55, BW: EUR5,225, 4C: EUR6,375, PCI: EUR12. **Circ:**
★26,457

46020 ■ 4FM - 104.9
5th Fl., Latin Hall
Golden Ln.
Dublin 8, Dublin, Ireland
Ph: 353 1 4255400
Fax: 353 1 4255444
E-mail: info@4fm.ie
Format: Eclectic. **URL:** http://www.4fm.ie/.

46021 ■ Galway Bay-FM - 95.8
Sandy Rd.
Galway, Galway, Ireland
Ph: 353 9 1770077
Fax: 353 9 1752689
Format: Adult Contemporary; Oldies; Full Service;
Urban Contemporary. **Operating Hours:** 7a.m.-10p.m.
weekdays; 8a.m.-1a.m. Sat.; 8a.m.-12a.m. Sun. **Key
Personnel:** Keith Finnegan, CEO, keith@galwaybayfm.
ie. **Ad Rates:** $9-50 for 30 seconds. **URL:** http://www.
galwaybayfm.ie

Grand Canal Quay

46022 ■ Dublin-FM - 98.0
Level 3, South Block
The Malt House
Grand Canal Quay 2, Dublin, Ireland
Ph: 353 1 4398800
Fax: 353 1 4398899
E-mail: news@dublins98.ie
Format: World Beat; Ethnic. **Operating Hours:**
Continuous. **Wattage:** 5000. **URL:** http://dublins98.ie.

Greystone

46023 ■ Easy Food
Zahra Publishing
1st Fl.
Barker House
Church Rd.
Greystone, Wicklow, Ireland
Ph: 353 1 2557566
Publisher E-mail: gmiltiadou@zahrapublishing.com
Magazine featuring cooking tips, budget recipes, easy
meal ideas and nutrition information. **Freq:** Monthly.
Trim Size: 206 x 276 mm. **Key Personnel:** Ciara Mc-
Donnell, Editor, editoreasyfood@zahrapublishing.com;
Gina Miltiadou, Publisher, gmiltiadou@zahrapublishing.
com; John Mullins, Advertising Dir., jmullins@
zahrapublishing.com. **Subscription Rates:** EUR30
individuals. **Remarks:** Accepts advertising. **URL:** http://
www.easyfood.ie/. **Ad Rates:** 4C: EUR3,250. **Circ:**
★27,599

46024 ■ Easyhealth
Zahra Publishing
1st Fl.
Barker House
Church Rd.
Greystone, Wicklow, Ireland
Ph: 353 1 2557566
Publisher E-mail: gmiltiadou@zahrapublishing.com
Magazine featuring food that provides everyday solu-
tions to better health and well-being for the whole family.
Founded: 2006. **Freq:** Quarterly. **Trim Size:** 215 x 276
mm. **Key Personnel:** Emma Parkin, Editor,
editoreasyhealth@zahrapublishing.com; Gina Miltiadou,
Publisher, gmiltiadou@zahrapublishing.com; John Mul-
lins, Advertising Dir., jmullins@zahrapublishing.com.
Subscription Rates: EUR13 individuals; 12 individuals.
Remarks: Accepts advertising. **URL:** http://www.
easyhealth.ie/. **Ad Rates:** 4C: EUR3,250. **Circ:** (Not
Reported)

Kilcar

46025 ■ Marine Times Newspaper
Marine Media Ltd.
Ballymoon Industrial Estate
Kilcar, Donegal, Ireland
Ph: 353 749 738836
Fax: 353 749 738841
Publication E-mail: marinetimes@eircom.net
Newspaper covering the fishing and aquaculture indus-
tries in Ireland. **Freq:** Monthly. **Cols./Page:** 6. **Col.
Width:** 4.25 centimeters. **Col. Depth:** 30 centimeters.
Key Personnel: Ann Murray, Advertising; Mark McCar-
thy, Editor. **Subscription Rates:** EUR40 individuals
republic/Northern Ireland; EUR55 individuals Scotland,
England & Wales; EUR70 individuals Europe; EUR15
individuals digital; EUR1.50 single issue digital. **Remarks:**
Accepts advertising. **URL:** http://www.marinetimes.ie.
Circ: 6,250

Kilkenny

46026 ■ KCLR 96-FM - 96
The Broadcast Centre
Carlow Rd.
Kilkenny, Kilkenny, Ireland
Ph: 353 1890 909696
Fax: 353 56 7796299
E-mail: info@kclr96fm.com
Format: Full Service. **URL:** http://www.kclr96fm.com/.

Killaloe

46027 ■ Clare FM2 - 96.6
Abbeyfield Ctr.
Francis St.
Ennis, Clare, Ireland

E-mail: info@clarefm.ie
Format: Full Service; Ethnic. **URL:** http://www.clarefm.
ie.

Kiltegan

46028 ■ Africa
Saint Patrick's Missionary Society
St. Patrick's
Kiltegan, Wicklow, Ireland
Ph: 35 359 6473600
Fax: 35 359 6473622
Publication E-mail: africa@spms.org
Publisher E-mail: spsoff@iol.ie
Catholic publication. **Subtitle:** St. Patrick's Missions.
Founded: 1938. **Freq:** Monthly except February, August
and October. **Print Method:** Lithographic. **Trim Size:**
281 x 211 mm. **Key Personnel:** Fr. John Carroll, Editor;
Fr. Martin Smith, Editor. **Subscription Rates:** EUR12
individuals Ireland; US$10 individuals; 10 individuals
Scotland, England. **Remarks:** Advertising not accepted.
URL: http://www.spms.org/stpatricksmissionarysociety/
Main/AfricaMagazine.htm. **Circ:** 130,000

Limerick

46029 ■ Limerick Leader
Limerick Leader Ltd.
54 O'Connell St.
Limerick, Limerick, Ireland
Ph: 353 61 214500
Publisher E-mail: letters@limerickleader.ie
Newspaper covering news, sports, and events in
Limerick County and the North Munster area. **Founded:**
Aug. 9, 1889. **Freq:** Sat. and Sun. Mon. and Wed.
Subscription Rates: EUR78 individuals; EUR189.80
individuals Ireland, Northern Ireland; EUR306.80 individu-
als in U.K. mainland; EUR306.80 individuals in continental
Europe; EUR332.80 U.S. and other countries. **Remarks:**
Accepts advertising. **URL:** http://www.limerick-leader.ie.
Circ: (Not Reported)

46030 ■ Limerick Post
Limerick Post Newspaper
The Red Church
Henry St.
Limerick, Limerick, Ireland
Ph: 353 614 13322
Fax: 353 614 17684
Publication E-mail: info@limerickpost.ie
Community newspaper. **Founded:** May 1986. **Freq:**
Weekly. **Print Method:** Web offset. **Cols./Page:** 8. **Col.
Depth:** 400 millimeters. **ISSN:** 1393-8150. **Subscrip-
tion Rates:** Free. **Remarks:** Accepts advertising. **URL:**
http://www.limerickpost.ie. **Ad Rates:** GLR: EUR6.50,
BW: EUR2,475, 4C: EUR2,268, PCI: EUR33.50. **Circ:**
★50,000

46031 ■ 4FM - 104.2
5th Fl., Latin Hall
Golden Ln.
Dublin 8, Dublin, Ireland
Ph: 353 1 4255400
Fax: 353 1 4255444
E-mail: info@4fm.ie
Format: Eclectic. **URL:** http://www.4fm.ie/.

46032 ■ Live 95-FM - 95
Radio House
Dock Rd.
Limerick, Limerick, Ireland
Ph: 353 61 461900
Fax: 353 61 461995
Format: Adult Contemporary; Easy Listening; Sports;
News; Classical; Folk. **Owner:** UTV, Ormeau Rd., Bel-
fast BT7 1EB, United Kingdom. **Operating Hours:** 12
a.m.-8 p.m. weekdays; Continuous Sat.-Sun. **Ad Rates:**
Advertising accepted; rates available upon request.
URL: http://95fm.u.tv/.

46033 ■ Lyric-FM - 96
Cornmarket Sq.
Limerick, Limerick, Ireland
Ph: 353 61 207300
Fax: 353 61 207390
E-mail: lyric@rte.ie
Format: Classical; Jazz. **Owner:** RTE, Donnybrook,
Dublin, Dublin, Ireland, 353 1 2083111, Fax: 353 1
2083080. **Operating Hours:** Continuous. **Ad Rates:**
$25-75 for 10 seconds; $35-105 for 15 seconds; $40-
120 for 20 seconds; $50-150 for 30 seconds; $66.50-

Circulation: ★ = ABC; △ = BPA; ♦ = CAC; ✦ = CCAB; □ = VAC; ⊕ = PO Statement; ‡ = Publisher's Report; Boldface figures = sworn; Light figures = estimated.

Gale Directory of Publications & Broadcast Media/147th Ed.   **5059**

199.50 for 40 seconds; $75-225 for 45 seconds; $83.50-250.50 for 50 seconds; $100-300 for 60 seconds. **URL:** http://www.rte.ie/lyricfm/.

Longford

46034 ■ Longford Leader
Longford Leader Ltd.
Leader House
Dublin Rd.
Longford, Longford, Ireland
Ph: 353 434 5241
Community newspaper. **Founded:** 1897. **Freq:** Weekly. **Key Personnel:** Sheila Reilly, Editor, sheila.reilly@longford-leader.ie. **Remarks:** Accepts advertising. **URL:** http://www.longford-leader.ie/. **Ad Rates:** BW: IR2,750, 4C: IR3,163. **Circ:** Paid 13,550

46035 ■ Shannonside-FM - 104.1
MasterTech Business Pk., Unit 1E
Athlone Rd.
Longford, Longford, Ireland
Ph: 353 43 3347777
Fax: 353 43 3349384
E-mail: info@shannonside.ie
Format: Full Service. **Operating Hours:** Continuous. **Key Personnel:** Joao Soares, General Mgr., joao@shannonside.ie; Eithne Kelly, Prog. Coord., eithne@shannonside.ie. **URL:** http://www.shannonside.ie.

Macroom

46036 ■ 4FM - 97.4
5th Fl., Latin Hall
Golden Ln.
Dublin 8, Dublin, Ireland
Ph: 353 1 4255400
Fax: 353 1 4255444
E-mail: info@4fm.ie
Format: Eclectic. **URL:** http://www.4fm.ie/.

Maghera

46037 ■ Clare-FM - 96.4
Abbeyfield Ctr.
Francis St.
Ennis, Clare, Ireland
Format: Full Service; Ethnic. **URL:** http://www.clarefm.ie.

Maynooth

46038 ■ Irish Journal of American Studies
Irish Association for American Studies
School of English, Media & Theatre Studies
National University of Ireland
Maynooth, Kildare, Ireland
Publisher E-mail: jon.mitchell@nuim.ie
Irish publication covering American studies. **Freq:** Annual. **Key Personnel:** Philip Coleman, Editor, editor@ijasonline.com. **ISSN:** 1351-3818. **Remarks:** Advertising accepted; rates available upon request. **URL:** http://www.ijasonline.com/; http://www.americanstudiesinireland.materdei.ie/pages/irish-journal-of-american-studies.php. **Circ:** 100

Monaghan

46039 ■ Shannonside Northern Sound-FM - 94.8
Thomas Ash St.
Cavan & Millton Business Pk.
Monaghan, Monaghan, Ireland
Ph: 353 4772666
Fax: 353 4784447
E-mail: info@northernsound.ie
Format: Full Service; Adult Contemporary. **Operating Hours:** Continuous. **Key Personnel:** Joao Soares, General Mgr., joao@shannonside.ie; Eithne Kelly, Prog. Coord., eithne@shannonside.ie; John Lynch, Sports Ed., johnlynch@shannonside.ie. **URL:** http://www.northernsound.ie.

Monkstown

46040 ■ Treoir
Traditional Irish Music, Singing and Dancing Society
Comhaltas Ceoltoiri Eireann
32 Belgrave Sq.
Monkstown, Dublin, Ireland
Ph: 353 12 800295
Fax: 353 12 803759
Publisher E-mail: eolas@comhaltas.ie
English and Irish language publication covering music, song and dance. **Freq:** Quarterly. **ISSN:** 0790-004X. **Subscription Rates:** EUR12 individuals Ireland and Europe; US$20 individuals U.S. & Canada; 9 individuals Britain; US$20 individuals Australia & New Zealand. **Remarks:** Advertising accepted; rates available upon request. **URL:** http://comhaltas.ie/music/treoir/. **Circ:** 15,000

Mullingar

46041 ■ Midlands 103-FM - 96.5
Harbour Place Shopping Ctr.
Mullingar, Westmeath, Ireland
Ph: 353 44 9344666
Fax: 353 44 9344022
Format: Full Service. **Key Personnel:** Albert Fitzgerald, Mng. Dir., albert@midlandsradio.fm; William Faulkner, Station Mgr., will@midlandsradio.fm. **Ad Rates:** Advertising accepted; rates available upon request. **URL:** http://www.midlandsradio.fm/default.aspx.

Naas

46042 ■ Irish Family History Journal
Irish Family History Society
PO Box 36
Naas, Kildare, Ireland
Publisher E-mail: ifhs@eircom.net
Journal containing stories of family history research. **Freq:** Annual. **Key Personnel:** Margaret Purcell, Contact; Rex G. Meyer, Contact; James Gribbon Meyer, Contact; James Kinsella, Contact; Anne Gabrielle Murton, Contact; Patricia Moorhead, Contact. **Subscription Rates:** Free to members. **URL:** http://homepage.eircom.net/~ifhs/IFHSpub.htm.

46043 ■ 4FM - 94.6
5th Fl., Latin Hall
Golden Ln.
Dublin 8, Dublin, Ireland
Ph: 353 1 4255400
Fax: 353 1 4255444
E-mail: info@4fm.ie
Format: Eclectic. **URL:** http://www.4fm.ie/.

Navan

46044 ■ Columban Mission
Missionary Society of Saint Columban
St. Columban's
Dalgan Pk.
Navan, Meath, Ireland
Ph: 35 346 9021525
Catholic publication. **Freq:** 8/yr. **Key Personnel:** Fr. Arturo Aguilar, Publisher; Sr. Jeanne Jansen, Editor; Kate Kenny, Managing Editor. **ISSN:** 0095-4438. **Subscription Rates:** US$10 individuals. **Remarks:** Advertising not accepted. **URL:** http://www.columban.org/content/view/34/36/. **Circ:** 500,000

46045 ■ The Far East
Missionary Society of Saint Columban
St. Columban's
Dalgan Pk.
Navan, Meath, Ireland
Ph: 35 346 9021525
Catholic publication. **Founded:** 1918. **Freq:** 8/yr. **Print Method:** Web offset. **Trim Size:** A4. **Key Personnel:** Fr. Cyril Lovett, Editor. **Subscription Rates:** EUR15 by mail; EUR10 individuals promoter. **Remarks:** Advertising not accepted. **URL:** http://www.columban.com/femajn_may_june_07.html. **Circ:** 135,000

46046 ■ Meath Chronicle
Meath Chronicle Group of Publications
Market Sq.
Navan, Meath, Ireland
Ph: 353 46 9079600
Publication E-mail: info@meath-chronicle.ie
Community newspaper. **Founded:** 1897. **Freq:** Weekly. **Print Method:** Web offset. **Cols./Page:** 8. **Col. Width:** 39 millimeters. **Col. Depth:** 540 millimeters. **Key Personnel:** Ken Davis, Editor, ken@meathchronicle.ie. **Remarks:** Accepts advertising. **URL:** http://www.meathchronicle.ie/. **Circ:** Paid 16,010

Nenagh

46047 ■ Nenagh Guardian
13 Summerhill
Nenagh, Tipperary, Ireland
Ph: 353 673 1214
Fax: 353 673 3401
Publication E-mail: editorial@nenaghguardian.ie
Publisher E-mail: info@nenaghguardian.ie
Community newspaper. **Founded:** 1838. **Freq:** Weekly (Wed.) Saturday evening. **Print Method:** Web offset. **Cols./Page:** 9. **Col. Width:** 1 5/8 inches. **Col. Depth:** 21 inches. **Key Personnel:** Garry Cotter, Editor. **Subscription Rates:** EUR33.80 individuals Ireland, 3 months; EUR67.60 individuals Ireland, 6 months; EUR135.20 individuals Ireland; EUR52 individuals Great Britain & rest of the world, 3 months; EUR104 individuals Great Britain & rest of the world, 6 months; EUR208 individuals Great Britain & rest of the world. **Remarks:** Accepts advertising. **URL:** http://www.nenaghguardian.ie/. **Ad Rates:** BW: EUR2,560. **Circ:** Paid *8,347

Newcastle West

46048 ■ West Limerick 102-FM - 102.2
Enterprise Centre
Sheehans Rd.
Newcastle West, Limerick, Ireland
Ph: 353 69 66200
E-mail: contact@westlimerick102.ie
Format: Full Service. **Operating Hours:** 7 a.m.-1 a.m. Daily. **URL:** http://www.westlimerickradio.ie/ws/listen-live.

West Limerick 102-FM - See Abbeyfeale

46049 ■ West Limerick 102-FM (Shannon Estuary Area) - 101.6
Enterprise Centre
Sheehans Rd.
Newcastle West, Limerick, Ireland
Ph: 353 69 66200
E-mail: contact@westlimerick102.ie
Format: Full Service. **Operating Hours:** 7 a.m.-1 a.m. Daily. **URL:** http://www.westlimerickradio.ie/ws/listen-live.

Newhall

46050 ■ KFM-FM - 97.3
M7 Business Pk.
Newhall, Kildare, Ireland
Ph: 353 45 898999
Fax: 353 45 898993
E-mail: info@kfmradio.com
Format: Eclectic; Information; News. **Operating Hours:** Continuous. **Key Personnel:** Robbie Dunbar, Manager; Trevor Hull, Sales Mgr., trevor@kfmradio.com; Donna Fenlon, Contact; Sarah Donnelly, Contact, traffic@kfmradio.com; Ciara Plunkett, Editor, ciara@kfmradio.com; Killian Whelan, Editor. **URL:** http://www.kfmradio.com.

46051 ■ KFM-FM - 97.6
Kfm Broadcast Ctr.
Newhall, Kildare, Ireland
Ph: 353 45 898999
Fax: 353 45 898993
E-mail: info@kfmradio.com
Format: Eclectic; Information; News. **Operating Hours:** Continuous. **Key Personnel:** Trevor Hull, Sales Mgr., trevor@kfmradio.com; Robbie Dunbar, Manager; Donna Fenlon, Contact; Sarah Donnelly, Contact, traffic@kfmradio.com; Ciara Plunkett, Editor, ciara@kfmradio.com; Killian Whelan, Editor. **URL:** http://www.kfmradio.com.

North Wall

46052 ■ 104-FM - 104
Macken House
Mayor St. Upper
North Wall 4, Dublin, Ireland
Ph: 353 1 5006623
Fax: 353 1 8461975
Format: Alternative/New Music/Progressive; Contemporary Hit Radio (CHR); News; Sports. **Operating Hours:** Continuous. **Key Personnel:** Helen Cruise, Sales Mgr.; Niamh Darcy, Traffic Mgr. **URL:** http://www.fm104.ie.

Patrick's Place

46053 ■ 96-FM - 96.4
Broadcasting House
Patrick's Place, Cork, Ireland
Ph: 353 21 4551596
Fax: 353 21 4551500
E-mail: info@96fm.ie
Format: Adult Contemporary. **Owner:** UTV, Ormeau Rd., Belfast BT7 1EB, United Kingdom, 353 2083111, Fax: 353 2083080. **Operating Hours:** Continuous. **Key Personnel:** Joy Hennebry, Gp. Sales Mgr.; Louise Jesson, National Sales Dir.; Kieran McGeary, Program Dir. **Ad Rates:** Advertising accepted; rates available upon request. **URL:** http://www.96fm.ie/.

Sandyford

46054 ■ Bike Buyers Guide
Page7 Media
Arena House
Arena Rd.
Sandyford 18, Dublin, Ireland
Ph: 353 1 2405528
Publisher E-mail: info@page7media.ie
Magazine featuring the latest road test, news, racing reviews and events. **Freq:** Monthly. **URL:** http://www.page7media.ie; http://www.cbg.ie/subs/magazine.asp?ID=4.

46055 ■ Farm & Plant Buyers Guide
Page7 Media
Arena House
Arena Rd.
Sandyford 18, Dublin, Ireland
Ph: 353 1 2405528
Publisher E-mail: info@page7media.ie
Magazine featuring new and second hand farm and plant machinery available in Ireland. **Freq:** Biweekly. **URL:** http://www.page7media.ie.

46056 ■ Modified Motors
Page7 Media
Arena House
Arena Rd.
Sandyford 18, Dublin, Ireland
Ph: 353 1 2405528
Publisher E-mail: info@page7media.ie
Magazine featuring Ireland's hottest Modified cars, test drives, reader profiles and product reviews. **Freq:** Monthly. **URL:** http://www.page7media.ie; http://www.cbg.ie/subs/magazine.asp?ID=5.

46057 ■ The Stock Market
Page7 Media
Arena House
Arena Rd.
Sandyford 18, Dublin, Ireland
Ph: 353 1 2405528
Publisher E-mail: info@page7media.ie
Magazine featuring the important facts and figures that Irish investors need to know concerning all stocks in Ireland. **Freq:** Quarterly. **URL:** http://www.page7media.ie.

46058 ■ Used Car Price Guide
Page7 Media
Arena House
Arena Rd.
Sandyford 18, Dublin, Ireland
Ph: 353 1 2405528
Publisher E-mail: info@page7media.ie
Magazine featuring the list of used car prices in Ireland. **Freq:** Monthly. **URL:** http://www.page7media.ie.

Tipperary

46059 ■ Tipperary Mid West Community Radio - 104.8
St. Michael St.
Tipperary, Tipperary, Ireland
Ph: 353 62 52555
Fax: 353 62 52671
Format: Full Service. **Key Personnel:** Anne Power, Station Mgr.; Michael Maguire, Chm. **Ad Rates:** $12 for 20 seconds; $10 for 30 seconds. **URL:** http://www.tippmidwestradio.com/website/index.asp.

Tralee

46060 ■ Kerry's Eye
22 Ashe St.
Tralee, Kerry, Ireland
Ph: 353 667 149200
Publisher E-mail: news@kerryseye.com
Newspaper. **Founded:** 1974. **Key Personnel:** Brendan Kennelly, Advertising Dir., advertising@kerryseye.com. **Subscription Rates:** EUR125 individuals Ireland; EUR160 individuals in U.K.; EUR275 individuals in U.S. by airmail; EUR175 individuals Europe; EUR65 individuals Ireland 6 months; EUR80 individuals in U.K. 6 months; EUR140 individuals in U.S. by airmail 6 months; EUR90 individuals Europe 6 months. **Remarks:** Accepts advertising. **URL:** http://www.kerryseye.com. **Circ:** (Not Reported)

46061 ■ Radio Kerry-FM - 96.2
Maine St.
Tralee, Kerry, Ireland
Ph: 353 66 7123666
E-mail: info@radiokerry.ie
Format: Talk; Full Service; Classical; Folk. **Founded:** 1990. **Operating Hours:** Continuous. **Key Personnel:** Melanie O'Sullivan, Sales/Mktg. Mgr.; Fiona Stack, General Mgr.; Paul Byrne, Ch. Executive. **Ad Rates:** $17.60-30.80 for 15 seconds; $20.90-37.40 for 20 seconds; $27.50-48.40 for 30 seconds; $36.30-68.20 for 40 seconds; $47.30-86.90 for 60 seconds. **URL:** http://www.radiokerry.ie/.

Tullamore

Midlands 103-FM - See Athlone, Westmeath

Waterford

46062 ■ Munster Express
37 The Quay
Waterford, Waterford, Ireland
Ph: 353 51 872141
Publisher E-mail: news@munster-express.ie
Newspaper covering Waterford City and County, South Kilkenny, Carric-on-Suir, South Tipperary, New Ross, and South Wexford. **Founded:** 1859. **Freq:** Semiweekly. **Key Personnel:** Liz McGough, Advertising Mgr.; Patrick Blewitt, Advertising Rep.; Rebecca Hunt, Advertising Rep.; Chris Walsh, Accounts Mgr.; John O'Connor, News Ed. **Subscription Rates:** EUR136.80 individuals Ireland & Northern Ireland; EUR278.40 individuals England, Scotland & Wales; EUR170.40 individuals Northern Ireland; EUR278.40 other countries rest of world. **Remarks:** Accepts advertising. **URL:** http://www.munster-express.ie. **Ad Rates:** BW: 4,116. **Circ:** 100,000

46063 ■ Waterford News & Star
25 Michael St.
Waterford, Waterford, Ireland
Ph: 353 518 74951
Fax: 353 518 55281
Publication E-mail: editor@waterford-news.ie
Publisher E-mail: sales@waterford-news.com
Newspaper serving Waterford, Ireland. **Freq:** Weekly (Fri.). **Key Personnel:** Mark Feane, Contact. **Remarks:** Accepts advertising. **URL:** http://www.waterford-news.com. **Circ:** (Not Reported)

46064 ■ WLR-FM - 97.5
Broadcast Ctr.
Waterford, Waterford, Ireland
Ph: 353 51 872248
Fax: 353 51 846148
E-mail: reception@wlrfm.com
Format: Easy Listening; Folk; Eclectic; Full Service; Oldies; Talk. **Operating Hours:** Continuous. **Key Personnel:** Pat Maher, Station Engr., patm@wlrfm.com; Wayne Brown, Production Engr., wayne@wlrfm.com; Roddy Cleere, Production Asst., roddy@wlrfm.com. **Ad Rates:** Advertising accepted; rates available upon request. **URL:** http://wlrfm.com/.

Waterford City

46065 ■ Waterford Today
36 Mayor's Walk
Waterford City, Waterford, Ireland
Ph: 353 51 854135
Fax: 353 51 854140
Publisher E-mail: info@waterford-today.ie
Newspaper serving Waterford City. **Freq:** Weekly. **Key Personnel:** Michael O'Connor, Sales Exec., michael@ waterford-today.ie; Danielle McCormack, Sales Exec., danielle@waterford-today.ie; Paddy Gallagher, Editor, editor@waterford-today.ie. **Remarks:** Accepts advertising. **URL:** http://www.waterford-today.ie/. **Ad Rates:** BW: IR1,900, BW: IR1,900. **Circ:** 27,000

46066 ■ Beat-FM - 102
The Broadcast Centre
Ardkeen
Waterford City, Waterford, Ireland
Ph: 353 51849102
Fax: 353 51849103
E-mail: studio@beat102103.com
Format: Music of Your Life. **Operating Hours:** Continuous. **Key Personnel:** Gabrielle Cummins, CEO/Prog. Controller, gabrielle.cummins@beat102103.com; Catriona Whelan, Hd. of Sales, catriona.whelan@beat102103.com. **URL:** http://www.beat102103.com.

46067 ■ Beat-FM - 103
The Broadcast Centre
Ardkeen
Waterford City, Waterford, Ireland
Ph: 353 51849102
Fax: 353 51849103
E-mail: studio@beat102103.com
Format: Music of Your Life. **Operating Hours:** Continuous. **Key Personnel:** Gabrielle Cummins, CEO/Prog. Controller, gabrielle.cummins@beat102103.com; Catriona Whelan, Hd. of Sales, catriona.whelan@beat102103.com; Jenny McCarthy, Account Devel. Exec., jenny.mccarthy@beat102103.com. **URL:** http://www.beat102103.com.

46068 ■ WLR-FM - 95.1
The Broadcast Centre
F.29 The Plaza
Dungarvan Shopping Centre
Waterford City, Waterford, Ireland
Ph: 353 5843951
Fax: 353 5845822
E-mail: reception@wlrfm.com
Format: News; Sports; Eclectic. **Operating Hours:** Continuous. **Key Personnel:** Des Whelan, Mng. Dir., des@wlrfm.com; Tim Hassett, Sales Mgr., tim@wlrfm.com; Audrey Hennessey, Contact; Susan O'Mahony, Contact; Jennifer Codd, Contact, jennifer@wlrfm.com. **Ad Rates:** Advertising accepted; rates available upon request. **URL:** http://www.wlrfm.com.

Westport

46069 ■ The Mayo News
The Fairgreen
Westport, Mayo, Ireland
Ph: 353 98 25311
Fax: 353 98 26108
Publisher E-mail: info@mayonews.ie
Newspaper with particular reference to farming, commercial, industrial, tourism, sporting and cultural advancement . **Subtitle:** The Voice of Community. **Founded:** 1982. **Freq:** Weekly. **Key Personnel:** Sean Staunton, Editor. **Subscription Rates:** EUR185 individuals Ireland; EUR290 individuals U.K. and Europe; EUR340 individuals U.S. **Remarks:** Accepts advertising. **URL:** http://www.mayonews.ie/. **Ad Rates:** BW: 2,376, 4C: 2,970. **Circ:** (Not Reported)

Wexford

46070 ■ South East Radio-FM - 95.6
Custom House Quay
Wexford, Wexford, Ireland
Ph: 353 53 9145200
Fax: 353 53 9145295
E-mail: info@southeastradio.ie
Format: Adult Contemporary; Folk; Oldies; News; Information. **Operating Hours:** Continuous Mon.-Fri.; 7 a.m.-1:30 a.m Sat.; 8 a.m.-1:30 a.m Sun. **Key Personnel:** Eamonn Buttle, Managing Dir., ebuttle@ southeastradio.ie; Marion Barry, Sales Mgr., mbarry@ southeastradio.ie. **Ad Rates:** $11-21 for 10 seconds; $14.30-27.30 for 15 seconds; $17.60-33.60 for 20 seconds; $22-42 for 30 seconds; $28.60-54.60 for 40 seconds; $30.80-58.80 for 45 seconds; $35.20-67.20 for 50 seconds; $39.60-75.60 for 60 seconds. **URL:** http://www.southeastradio.ie/.

Circulation: ★ = ABC; △ = BPA; ◆ = CAC; ● = CCAB; ❑ = VAC; ⊕ = PO Statement; ‡ = Publisher's Report; Boldface figures = sworn; Light figures = estimated.

Youghal

46071 ■ Community Radio Youghal-FM - 104
League of the Cross
Catherine St.
Youghal, Cork, Ireland
Ph: 353 2491199
Fax: 353 2491199
E-mail: info@youghalradio.com
Format: Full Service; Classical; Ethnic; Sports; Easy
Listening. **Operating Hours:** 12 p.m.-10 p.m. Mon.,Tue.
& Thu.; 12 noon-9 p.m. Tue., & Fri. **URL:** http://www.
youghalradio.com.

46072 ■ CRY-FM - 104
Catherine St.
Youghal, Cork, Ireland
Ph: 353 2491199
Format: Classical; Ethnic; Full Service; Sports. **Owner:**
Youghal Communications Ltd., at above address. **Oper-
ating Hours:** 12 noon-8 p.m. Mon. & Wed.; 12 noon-9

p.m. Tue., Thu., & Fri. **URL:** http://www.youghalradio.
com.

46073 ■ 4FM - 97.2
5th Fl., Latin Hall
Golden Ln.
Dublin 8, Dublin, Ireland
Ph: 353 1 4255400
Fax: 353 1 4255444
E-mail: info@4fm.ie
Format: Eclectic. **URL:** http://www.4fm.ie/.

Beer-Sheva

46074 ■ Complex Analysis and Operator Theory
Springer Netherlands
Ben-Gurion University of the Negev
Beer-Sheva, Israel
Publisher E-mail: permissions.dordrecht@springer.com
Journal covering system theory, harmonic analysis, probability, statistics, learning theory, and other related fields. **Founded:** 1971. **Freq:** Quarterly. **Print Method:** Offset. **Trim Size:** 8 1/2 x 11. **Cols./Page:** 2. **Col. Width:** 42 nonpareils. **Col. Depth:** 140 agate lines. **Key Personnel:** Alain Berlinet, Editorial Board; Turgay H. Kaptanoglu, Editorial Board; Harry Dym, Editorial Board; Joseph Ball, Editorial Board; Laurent Baratchart, Editorial Board; Hari Bercovici, Editorial Board; Aad Dijksma, Editorial Board; Aurelian Gheondea, Editorial Board; Daniel Alpay, Editor-in-Chief, dany@math.bgu.ac.il; Simeon Reich, Editorial Board; Olof Staffans, Editorial Board. **ISSN:** 1661-8254. **Subscription Rates:** EUR262 institutions print incl. free access or e-only; EUR314.40 institutions print incl. enhanced access. **URL:** http://www.springer.com/birkhauser/mathematics/journal/11785.

East Jerusalem

46075 ■ Palestine Report
Jerusalem Media and Communication Center
PO Box 25047
Khalil El Sakakeeni St.
IL-97300 East Jerusalem, Israel
Ph: 972 2 5838266
Fax: 972 2 5836837
Publication E-mail: palreport@palestinereport.org
Publisher E-mail: jmcc@jmcc.org
Newspaper. **Freq:** Weekly. **Key Personnel:** Omar Karmi, Managing Editor, omar@palestinereport.org; Joharah Baker, Editor-in-Chief, joharah@jmcc.org. **URL:** http://www.palestinereport.ps/article.php?article=171.

Haifa

46076 ■ International Journal of Multiphase Flow
Elsevier Science
c/o G. Hetsroni, Founding Ed.
Israel Institute of Technology
Dept. of Mechanical Engineering
Technion
IL-32000 Haifa, Israel
Publisher E-mail: nlinfo-f@elsevier.com
Journal focusing on fluid mechanics and rheological studies. **Founded:** 1974. **Freq:** 10/yr. **Key Personnel:** G. Hetsroni, Founding Ed.; J. Magnaudet, Assoc. Ed., phone 33 561 285991, magnau@imft.fr; A. Prosperetti, Editor-in-Chief, phone 410516-8534, prosperetti@jhu.edu; S. Balachandar, Assoc. Ed., fax 352392-7303, bala1s@ufl.edu; J. Kim, Assoc. Ed., kimjh@eng.umd.edu. **ISSN:** 0301-9322. **Subscription Rates:** US$136 individuals except Europe and Japan; 16,100¥ individuals; EUR123 individuals European countries; US$3,250 institutions except Europe and Japan; EUR2,907 institutions European countries; 385,700¥ institutions. **Remarks:** Accepts advertising. **URL:** http://www.elsevier.com/wps/find/journaldescription.cws_home/234/

descriptiondescription. **Circ:** (Not Reported)

46077 ■ Khulyot
University of Haifa
Mount Carmel
IL-31905 Haifa, Israel
Ph: 972 4 8240111
Publisher E-mail: webmaster@univ.haifa.ac.il
Journal covering Yiddish literature and its connection to Hebrew literature. **Subtitle:** Journal of Yiddish Research. **Founded:** 1993. **Freq:** Annual. **Key Personnel:** Shalom Luria, Editor; Haya Bar-Yitzchak, Editor. **Subscription Rates:** 60 IS individuals; US$15 other countries; US$28 institutions, other countries. **URL:** http://yiddish.haifa.ac.il/khulyot/kindex.html.

46078 ■ Mechanical Systems and Signal Processing
Elsevier Science
c/o Simon G. Braun, Ed.
Technion-Israel Institute of Technology
Faculty of Mechanical Engineering
IL-32000 Haifa, Israel
Publisher E-mail: nlinfo-f@elsevier.com
Peer-reviewed journal providing a forum for discussion on recent advances in mechanical, aeronautical and civil engineering, published in connection with the Society for Experimental Mechanics. **Founded:** 1987. **Freq:** 8/yr. **Key Personnel:** Simon G. Braun, Editor, braun@tx.technion.ac.il; Martin Trethewey, Assoc. Tech. Ed., mwt2@psu.edu; Nicolo Bachschmid, Editorial Board, nicolo.bachschmid@polimi.it. **ISSN:** 0888-3270. **Subscription Rates:** 58,800¥ individuals; EUR544 individuals for European countries; US$486 institutions for all countries except Europe and Japan; US$1,491 institutions for all countries except Europe and Japan; EUR1,668 institutions for European countries; 180,300¥ institutions. **Remarks:** Accepts advertising. **URL:** http://www.elsevier.com/wps/find/journaldescription.cws_home/622912/description. **Circ:** (Not Reported)

46079 ■ Reviews in Analytical Chemistry
Freund Publishing House Ltd.
Department of Chemistry
Israel Institute of Technology
IL-32000 Haifa, Israel
Ph: 972 4 8292579
Fax: 972 4 8292579
Publisher E-mail: h_freund@netvision.net.il
Journal covering branches modern analytical chemistry. **Founded:** 1982. **Freq:** 4/yr. **Print Method:** 6 1/4 x 9 1/2. **Key Personnel:** Prof. Israel Schechter, Editor-in-Chief, israel@techunix.technion.ac.il. **ISSN:** 0793-0135. **Subscription Rates:** US$350 institutions. **Remarks:** Accepts advertising. **URL:** http://www.freundpublishing.com/JOURNALS/chemistry_and_chemical_engineering. **Ad Rates:** BW: 500 IS, 4C: 2,400 IS. **Circ:** (Not Reported)

Jerusalem

46080 ■ Azure
The Shalem Center
13 Yehoshua Bin-Nun St.
93102 Jerusalem, Israel
Ph: 972 2 560 5555

Publisher E-mail: inquiries@shalem.org.il
Journal covering various aspects of Israeli and Jewish thought, society, and politics, as well as research on Jewish history and philosophy (English and Hebrew). **Subtitle:** Ideas for the Jewish Nation. **Founded:** 1996. **Freq:** Quarterly. **Key Personnel:** Assaf Sagiv, Editor-in-Chief; Lorena Avraham, Managing Editor. **Subscription Rates:** US$40 individuals print; US$19.95 individuals online; US$75 two years print; US$34.95 two years online. **Remarks:** Accepts advertising. **URL:** http://www.azure.org.il. **Ad Rates:** BW: 400 IS. **Circ:** (Not Reported)

46081 ■ B'Or Ha'Torah
Association of Jewish Religious Professionals from the Former Soviet Union
PO Box 5749
6 David Yellin St.
Jerusalem, Israel
Ph: 97 226 427521
Fax: 97 226 427521
Publisher E-mail: info@borhatorah.org
Peer-reviewed English language publication covering Jewish culture. **Subtitle:** Science, The Arts & Modern Life in the Light of the Torah. **Founded:** 1982. **Freq:** Annual. **Print Method:** Offset. **Trim Size:** 17 x 24 cm. **Key Personnel:** Prof. Herman Branover, Editor-in-Chief; Ilana Attia, Managing Editor. **ISSN:** 0333-6298. **Subscription Rates:** US$19 single issue. **URL:** http://www.borhatorah.org. **Circ:** 5,000

46082 ■ Hamodia (Israel)
Agudath Israel World Organization
Organisation Mondiale Agudath Israel
5 Yehudah Hamacabi St.
PO Box 1306
IL-91002 Jerusalem, Israel
Ph: 972 2 538 9255
Fax: 972 2 500 3384
Publisher E-mail: media@hamodia.co.uk
Hebrew language newspaper for the Jewish community. **Freq:** Weekly. **Subscription Rates:** 70 individuals; 125 other countries. **URL:** http://www.hamodia.co.uk.

46083 ■ International Journal of Adolescent Medicine and Health
Freund Publishing House Ltd.
Box 1260
IL-91012 Jerusalem, Israel
Ph: 972 2 6708192
Fax: 972 2 6703657
Publisher E-mail: h_freund@netvision.net.il
Peer-reviewed journal covering all aspects of adolescence. **Freq:** 4/yr. **Key Personnel:** Prof. Joav Merrick, MD, Editor-in-Chief, jmerrick@internet-zahav.net; Emanuel Chigier, Founding Ed.; Myrna Kohen, Production Ed. **ISSN:** 0334-0139. **Subscription Rates:** US$330 individuals. **URL:** http://www.freundpublishing.com/JOURNALS/medicine_and_medical_sciences.htm.

46084 ■ International Journal on Disability and Human Development
Freund Publishing House Ltd.
Box 1260
IL-91012 Jerusalem, Israel
Ph: 972 2 6708192
Fax: 972 2 6703657

Publisher E-mail: h_freund@netvision.net.il
Peer-reviewed journal covering areas of ability, disability and human development. **Freq:** 4/yr. **Key Personnel:** Prof. Joav Merrick, MD, Editor-in-Chief, jmerrick@ internet-zahav.net; Eli Carmeli, PhD, Editorial Board; Mohammed Morad, Editorial Board. **ISSN:** 1565-012X. **Subscription Rates:** US$299 individuals. **URL:** http:// www.freundpublishing.com/JOURNALS/medicine_and_ medical_sciences.htm.

46085 ■ Israel Exploration Journal
Israel Exploration Society
PO Box 7041
IL-91070 Jerusalem, Israel
Ph: 972 262 57991
Fax: 972 262 47772
Publisher E-mail: ies@vms.huji.ac.il
Scholarly journal covering the archaeology, history, and geography of Israel. **Founded:** 1950. **Freq:** Semiannual. **Key Personnel:** M. Tadmor, Editor; S. Ahituv, Editor; Tsipi Kuper-Blau, Production Ed. **ISSN:** 0021-2059. **Subscription Rates:** US$60 individuals. **Remarks:** Advertising not accepted. **URL:** http://israelexplorationsociety. huji.ac.il/. **Circ:** Paid 2,000

46086 ■ Jerusalem Magazine
Price Communications, Inc.
PO Box 23498
91234 Jerusalem, Israel
Ph: 972 2 5862031
Fax: 972 2 5863019
Publisher E-mail: pricecoma@gmail.com
Magazine featuring articles about Jerusalem. **URL:** http://www.jerusalemmagazine.com/.

46087 ■ Journal of Basic & Clinical Physiology & Pharmacology
Freund Publishing House Ltd.
Department of Physiology
Hadassah Medical School
Hebrew University
IL-91010 Jerusalem, Israel
Publisher E-mail: h_freund@netvision.net.il
Journal covering physiological and pharmacological sciences. **Freq:** Quarterly. **Key Personnel:** Prof. Michal Horowitz, Editor; Dr. V. Buchner, Asst. Ed. **ISSN:** 0334-1534. **Subscription Rates:** US$360 individuals. **URL:** http://www.freundpublishing.com/JOURNALS/medicine_ and_medical_sciences.htm.

46088 ■ Journal of Biopharmaceutics and Biotechnology
American Scientific Publishers
c/o Prof. Abraham J. Domb, PhD, Ed.-in-Ch.
Dept. of Medicinal Chemistry, School of Pharmacy
Faculty of Medicine, The Hebrew University of Jerusalem
PO Box 12065
IL-91120 Jerusalem, Israel
Ph: 972 2 6757573
Publisher E-mail: order@aspbs.com
Journal covering all aspects of pharmaceutics, biotechnology, and medicine. **Key Personnel:** Prof. Abraham J. Domb, PhD, Editor-in-Chief, adomb@md.huji.ac.il. **Subscription Rates:** US$300 individuals; US$350 other countries personal; US$580 institutions; US$595 institutions, other countries. **Remarks:** Accepts advertising. **URL:** http://www.aspbs.com/jbb/. **Circ:** (Not Reported)

46089 ■ Menorah
Keren Hayesod
48 king George St.
PO Box 7583
91074 Jerusalem, Israel
Ph: 972 2 6701811
Fax: 972 2 6701925
Publication E-mail: redaktion@menorah-sweden.com
Publisher E-mail: info@kh-uia.org.il
Magazine covering Israel, including politics, history, tourism, business, technology, science, medicine, and culture. **Founded:** 1970. **Print Method:** Offset. **Trim Size:** A4. **Cols./Page:** 3. **Key Personnel:** Ms Noodle, Editor-in-Chief; Regina Rodau, Publisher. **URL:** http:// www.menorah-sweden.com. **Circ:** Combined 13,600

Raanana

46090 ■ Israel Journal of Veterinary Medicine
Israel Veterinary Medical Association
PO Box 22

IL-43100 Raanana, Israel
Ph: 97 297 419929
Fax: 97 297 431778
Publisher E-mail: ivma@zahav.net.il
Journal focusing on clinical veterinary medicine, veterinary science, zoonoses and comparative medicine. **Freq:** Quarterly. **Key Personnel:** Zeev Trainin, Editor; T. Waner, Co-Ed. **ISSN:** 0334-9152. **URL:** http://www. isrvma.org/TextPage.aspx?ID=14.

Ramat Aviv

46091 ■ Reviews in Chemical Engineering
Freund Publishing House Ltd.
Department of Fluid Mechanics & Heat Transfer
Faculty of Engineering
Tel Aviv University
Ramat Aviv, Israel
Ph: 972 3 6408127
Fax: 972 3 6407334
Publisher E-mail: h_freund@netvision.net.il
Journal covering chemical engineering and applied chemistry. **Freq:** 6/yr. **Key Personnel:** N. Brauner, Editor, brauner@eng.tau.ac.il; Dan Luss, Editor, dluss@uh. edu. **ISSN:** 0167-8299. **Subscription Rates:** US$410 individuals. **URL:** http://www.freundpublishing.com/ JOURNALS/chemistry_and_chemical_engineering.

Ramat Gan

46092 ■ Common Knowledge
Duke University Press
Bar-Ilan University
Faculty of Humanities
52900 Ramat Gan, Israel
Ph: 972 3 5317740
Fax: 972 3 5347601
Publication E-mail: comknow@mail.biu.ac.il
Publisher E-mail: orders@dukepress.edu
Periodical including essays on the humanities, intellectual history, the arts, and social sciences. **Freq:** 3/yr. **Key Personnel:** Jeffrey M. Perl, Editor; Aden Bar-Tura, Managing Editor. **ISSN:** 0961-754X. **Subscription Rates:** 27 IS individuals print and online; US$108 institutions online; US$122 institutions print and online; US$111 institutions print. **Remarks:** Accepts advertising. **URL:** http://www.dukeupress.edu/ck/. **Ad Rates:** BW: 300 IS. **Circ:** 400

46093 ■ European Journal of Political Economy
Elsevier Science Inc.
Dept. of Economics
Bar-Ilan University
IL-52900 Ramat Gan, Israel
Ph: 972 3 531 8345
Fax: 972 3 535 3180
Publisher E-mail: usinfo-ehelp@elsevier.com
Journal serving theoretical and empirical research on economic phenomena. **Founded:** 1980. **Freq:** 4/yr. **Print Method:** Offset. **Trim Size:** 10 3/8 x 13. **Cols./Page:** 5. **Col. Width:** 1 13/16 inches. **Col. Depth:** 01762680 inches. **Key Personnel:** J. De Haan, Editor, j.de.haan@ eco.rug.nl; H.W. Ursprung, Editor, phone 49 7531 882332, fax 49 7531 883130, heinrich.ursprung@uni-konstanz.de; A.L. Hillman, Editor, phone 972 3 5318345, fax 972 3 5353180, hillman@mail.biu.ac.il; F. Breyer, Editorial Board; T. Besley, Editorial Board; J. Buchanan, Editorial Board; R. Congleton, Editorial Board; T. Aidt, Editorial Board. **ISSN:** 0176-2680. **Subscription Rates:** US$951 institutions, other countries except Europe, Japan and Iran; EUR851 institutions for European countries and Iran; 112,800¥ institutions; US$81 other countries except Europe, Japan and Iran; 10,900¥ individuals; EUR84 individuals for European countries and Iran. **URL:** http://www.elsevier.com/wps/find/ journaldescription.cws_home/505544/ descriptiondescription.

46094 ■ Israel Medical Association Journal (IMAJ)
Israel Medical Association
2 Twin Towers, 11th Fl., 35 Jabotinsky St.
PO Box 3604
IL-52136 Ramat Gan, Israel
Ph: 97 236 100418
Fax: 97 237 519673
Publisher E-mail: tguvot@ima.org.il
Journal focusing on all aspects of medical sciences and medicine in Israel. **Founded:** 1999. **Freq:** Monthly. **Key Personnel:** Yehuda Shoenfeld, MD, Editor-in-Chief;

Joshua Shemer, MD, Assoc. Ed.; Gad Keren, MD, Assoc. Ed. **Subscription Rates:** US$220 nonmembers. **URL:** http://www.ima.org.il/imaj/.

46095 ■ Jewish Studies, an Internet Journal
Bar-Ilan University
Faculty of Jewish Studies
IL-59200 Ramat Gan, Israel
Ph: 972 3 5318111
Publication E-mail: jsij@mail.biu.ac.il
Publisher E-mail: spokesman.office@mail.biu.ac.il
Peer-reviewed electronic journal dealing with all fields of Jewish studies. **Freq:** Semiannual. **Key Personnel:** James L. Kugel, Editor-in-Chief; Hanan Eshel, Editorial Board; Albert Baumgarten, Editorial Board; Shamma Friedman, Editorial Board; Leib Moscovitz, Managing Editor; Yosef Rivlin, Assoc. Ed.; Jay Harris, Editorial Board; Israel Knohl, Editorial Board. **ISSN:** 1565-7388. **URL:** http://www.biu.ac.il/js/JSIJ/.

46096 ■ Journal of the Israel Heart Society
Israel Heart Society
1 Twin Towers, 5th Fl., Rm. 509
33 Jabotinsky
IL-52511 Ramat Gan, Israel
Ph: 97 236 122577
Fax: 97 236 122588
Publisher E-mail: ihs@israel-heart.org.il
Journal including review articles and abstracts. **Key Personnel:** Chaim Lotan, Pres. Elect; Gad Keren, President; Doron Zahger, Sec. Gen. **URL:** http://www. israel-heart.org.il/.

Tel Aviv

46097 ■ Corrosion Reviews
Freund Publishing House Ltd.
Biomaterials & Corrosion Laboratory
Department of Solid Mechanics, Materials & Systems
Tel Aviv University
IL-69978 Tel Aviv, Israel
Publisher E-mail: h_freund@netvision.net.il
Journal covering corrosion science and engineering. **Freq:** 6/yr. **Key Personnel:** Dr. Noam Eliaz, Editor-in-Chief, neliaz@eng.tau.ac.il; Prof. Ron Latanision, Editor-in-Chief, rlatanision@exponent.com; D.S. Cohen, Production Ed., freund6@netvision.net.il. **ISSN:** 0048-7538. **Subscription Rates:** US$410 individuals. **URL:** http://www.freundpublishing.com/Corrosion_Reviews/ CorrPrev.html.

46098 ■ Drug Metabolism and Drug Interactions
Freund Publishing House Ltd.
PO Box 35010
61350 Tel Aviv, Israel
Ph: 972 3 5628540
Fax: 972 3 5628538
Publisher E-mail: h_freund@netvision.net.il
Journal covering mechanisms on drug metabolism and drug interaction. **Freq:** 4/yr. **Key Personnel:** H.E. Freund, Editor. **ISSN:** 0334-2190. **Subscription Rates:** US$360 individuals. **URL:** http://www.freundpublishing. com/JOURNALS/medicine_and_medical_sciences.htm.

46099 ■ ERETZ
Eretz Hatzvi Ltd.
5 Ma'avar Yabok St.
IL-67440 Tel Aviv, Israel
Ph: 97 236 912211
Fax: 97 236 091890
Publisher E-mail: oksana@eretz.com
Publication covering geography in Israel. **Subtitle:** The Magazine of Israel. **Founded:** 1985. **Freq:** Bimonthly. **Key Personnel:** Yadin Roman, Ed. in Ch./ Publisher, yadin@eretz.com; Talia Volkovitcher, Mng. Dir., talia. eretz@gmail.com. **Subscription Rates:** US$79 individuals; US$145 two years. **Remarks:** Accepts advertising. **URL:** http://www.eretz.com/. **Circ:** 50,000

46100 ■ Geometric and Functional Analysis (GAFA)
Birkhauser Publishing Ltd.
Miriam Hercberg
School of Mathematical Sciences
Tel Aviv University
IL-69978 Tel Aviv, Israel
Publisher E-mail: stromberger@birkhauser.ch
Journal covering various topics in geometry and analysis. **Founded:** 1991. **Key Personnel:** M. Gromov, Editor; P. Sarnak, Editor; V. Milman, Managing Editor; S.

Donaldson, Editor. **ISSN:** 1016-443X. **URL:** http://www.springer.com/birkhauser/mathematics/journal/39.

46101 ■ Ha'aretz
IHT Ha'aretz
21 Schocken St.
IL-61001 Tel Aviv, Israel
Ph: 972 3 5121205
Fax: 927 3 6810012
Publisher E-mail: feedback@haaretz.co.il
General newspaper. **Freq:** Daily except Saturday. **Key Personnel:** Eran Gez, Production Dir., erang@haaretz.co.il; Amos Schocken, Publisher, aschocken@haaretz.co.il; Dov Alfon, Editor, editor@haaretz.co.il; Shlomi Barzel, Sports Ed., shlomiba@haaretz.co.il. **Subscription Rates:** US$276 individuals in Israel; US$195 individuals in North America; US$132 individuals in Europe; US$192 individuals in Africa & Asia; US$240 individuals in Australia, South America & far East. **Remarks:** Accepts advertising. **URL:** http://www.haaretz.com/; http://www.haaretz.co.il. **Circ:** Combined 75,000, Free 95,000

46102 ■ Heterocyclic Communications
Freund Publishing House Ltd.
PO Box 35010
61350 Tel Aviv, Israel
Ph: 972 3 5628540
Fax: 972 3 5628538
Publisher E-mail: h_freund@netvision.net.il
Journal covering heterocyclic communications. **Subtitle:** An International Journal in Heterocyclic Chemistry. **Freq:** 6/yr. **Key Personnel:** Prof. R.R. Gupta, Editor. **ISSN:** 0793-0283. **Subscription Rates:** US$380 individuals. **URL:** http://www.freundpublishing.com/Heterocyclic_Communications/heteroinstr.htm.

46103 ■ History & Memory
Indiana University Press
School of History
Tel Aviv University
Ramat Aviv
IL-69978 Tel Aviv, Israel
Publication E-mail: shimrat@post.tau.ac.il
Publisher E-mail: iupress@indiana.edu
Scholarly journal covering historical consciousness. **Subtitle:** Studies in Representation of the Past. **Freq:** Semiannual. **Print Method:** offset. **Trim Size:** 6 x 9. **Key Personnel:** Gadi Algazi, Sen. Ed.; Philippa Shimrat, Managing Editor; Guy Beiner, Editorial Board. **ISSN:** 0935-560X. **Subscription Rates:** 30 IS individuals; 52 IS institutions; 15.50 IS single issue; 26 IS single issue institutions. **Remarks:** Accepts advertising. **URL:** http://muse.jhu.edu/journals/history_and_memory/. **Ad Rates:** BW: 275 IS. **Circ:** 650

46104 ■ International Journal of Nonlinear Sciences and Numerical Simulation
Freund Publishing House Ltd.
PO Box 35010
61350 Tel Aviv, Israel
Ph: 972 3 5628540
Fax: 972 3 5628538
Publisher E-mail: h_freund@netvision.net.il
Journal covering fields of nonlinear sciences and numerical simulation. **Freq:** 12/yr. **Key Personnel:** Ji-Huan He, Editor-in-Chief; M.S. El Naschie, Co-Ed.; Guang Meng, Co-Ed. **ISSN:** 1565-1339. **Subscription Rates:** US$549 individuals. **URL:** http://www.freundpublishing.com/International_Journal_Nonlinear_Sciences_Numerical%20Simulation/Math.htm; http://www.ijnsns.com.

46105 ■ International Journal of Turbo and Jet Engines
Freund Publishing House Ltd.
PO Box 35010
61350 Tel Aviv, Israel
Ph: 972 3 5628540
Fax: 972 3 5628538
Publisher E-mail: h_freund@netvision.net.il
Journal covering the field of turbo and jet engines. **Freq:** 4/yr. **Key Personnel:** Dr. Benjamin Gal-Or, Editor-in-Chief; Dr. Valery Sherbaum, Dep. Dir.; I. Glicksman, Prod. Ed., imgn8@netvision.net.il. **ISSN:** 0334-0082. **Subscription Rates:** US$399 individuals. **URL:** http://www.freundpublishing.com/JOURNALS/materials_science_and_engineering.htm.

46106 ■ Isokinetics and Exercise Science
IOS Press, B.V.
Dept. of Physical Therapy
Sackler Faculty of Medicine
Tel Aviv University
Ramat Aviv
IL-69978 Tel Aviv, Israel
Ph: 972 3 6409019
Fax: 972 3 6409223
Publisher E-mail: info@iospress.nl
International journal devoted to the study of theoretical and applied aspects of human muscle performance, publishing studies associated with the methodology of muscle performance especially with respect to the issues of reproducibility and validity of testing, description of normal and pathological mechanical parameters which are derivable from muscle testing and uses in basic research topics such as motor learning paradigms and electromyography. **Freq:** Quarterly. **Key Personnel:** Prof. Zeevi Dvir, Editor-in-Chief, zdvir@post.tau.ac.il; M. Bobbert, Editorial Board; R.W. Bohannon, Editorial Board; V. Baltzopoulos, Editorial Board; F. Mayer, Editorial Board; F. Noyes, Editorial Board. **ISSN:** 0959-3020. **Subscription Rates:** EUR448 individuals print and online; US$630 individuals print and online. **URL:** http://www.iospress.nl/loadtop/load.php?isbn=09593020.

46107 ■ Journal of Children and Media
Routledge
Taylor & Francis Group Ltd.
Tel Aviv University
Tel Aviv, Israel
Publisher E-mail: webmaster.books@tandf.co.uk
Peer-reviewed journal focusing on the study of the effects of media in the lives of children. **Freq:** 4/yr. **Key Personnel:** Dafna Lemish, Editor; Daniel Anderson, Editorial Board; Stephen Aufenanger, Editorial Board. **ISSN:** 1748-2798. **Subscription Rates:** 272 institutions print + online; 258 institutions online; 64 individuals; US$450 institutions print + online; US$427 institutions online; US$106 individuals; EUR360 institutions print and online; EUR342 institutions online only; EUR85 individuals. **URL:** http://www.tandf.co.uk/journals/titles/17482798.asp.

46108 ■ Journal of the Mechanical Behavior of Materials
Freund Publishing House Ltd.
PO Box 35010
61350 Tel Aviv, Israel
Ph: 972 3 5628540
Fax: 972 3 5628538
Publisher E-mail: h_freund@netvision.net.il
Journal covering all modern engineering materials. **Freq:** 6/yr. **Key Personnel:** Prof. K. Kishimoto, Editor; Prof. Elias C. Aifantis, Editor; J. De Hosson, Editor. **ISSN:** 0334-8938. **Subscription Rates:** US$380 individuals. **URL:** http://www.freundpublishing.com/JOURNALS/materials_science_and_engineering.htm.

46109 ■ Justice
International Association of Jewish Lawyers and Jurists
10 Daniel Frish St.
IL-64731 Tel Aviv, Israel
Ph: 97 236 910070
Fax: 97 236 953855
Publisher E-mail: info@intjewishlawyers.org
Publication covering law. **Founded:** 1969. **Freq:** Quarterly. **ISSN:** 0793-176X. **Subscription Rates:** US$50 individuals including postage. **Remarks:** Advertising accepted; rates available upon request. **URL:** http://www.intjewishlawyers.org/main/index.php?option=com_content&view=article&id=49&Itemid=57. **Circ:** 8,100

46110 ■ Main Group Metal Chemistry
Freund Publishing House Ltd.
PO Box 35010
61350 Tel Aviv, Israel
Ph: 972 3 5628540
Fax: 972 3 5628538
Publisher E-mail: h_freund@netvision.net.il
Journal covering fields of main group metal and semi-metal chemistry. **Founded:** 1977. **Freq:** 6/yr. **Print Method:** 6 1/4 x 9 1/2. **Key Personnel:** Dr. M. Zangen, Editor-in-Chief; I. Glicksman, Production Ed., imgn8@netvision.net.il. **ISSN:** 0792-1241. **Subscription Rates:** US$380 individuals. **Remarks:** Accepts advertising.

URL: http://www.freundpublishing.com/JOURNALS/chemistry_and_chemical_engineering. **Ad Rates:** BW: 800 IS, 4C: 1,500 IS. **Circ:** (Not Reported)

46111 ■ Reviews in Inorganic Chemistry
Freund Publishing House Ltd.
PO Box 35010
61350 Tel Aviv, Israel
Ph: 972 3 5628540
Fax: 972 3 5628538
Publisher E-mail: h_freund@netvision.net.il
Journal covering developments in the various fields of inorganic and organometallic compounds. **Freq:** 6/yr. **Key Personnel:** Dr. M. Zangen, Editor; I. Glicksman, Production Ed., imgn8@netvision.net.il. **ISSN:** 0193-4929. **Subscription Rates:** US$385 individuals. **Remarks:** Accepts advertising. **URL:** http://www.freundpublishing.com/JOURNALS/chemistry_and_chemical_engineering.htm. **Circ:** (Not Reported)

46112 ■ Science and Engineering of Composite Materials
Freund Publishing House Ltd.
PO Box 35010
61350 Tel Aviv, Israel
Ph: 972 3 5628540
Fax: 972 3 5628538
Publisher E-mail: h_freund@netvision.net.il
Journal covering all aspects related to the structure and performance under simulated and actual service conditions of composites. **Freq:** Quarterly. **Key Personnel:** Omri Rand, Editorial Board; Prof. Soung V. Hoa, Editor-in-Chief, hoasuon@alcor.concordia.ca; M. Zako, Editor; R. Pyrz, Editor. **ISSN:** 0334-181X. **Subscription Rates:** US$360 individuals. **URL:** http://www.freundpublishing.com/JOURNALS/materials_science_and_engineering.htm.

46113 ■ Targima
Israel Translators' Association
Agudat Hametargmim Beyisrael
PO Box 16173
IL-61161 Tel Aviv, Israel
Hebrew language publication covering translation. **Freq:** Biennial. **Remarks:** Advertising not accepted. **URL:** http://www.ita.org.il/. **Circ:** 450

46114 ■ Theoretical Inquiries in Law
Berkeley Electronic Press
c/o Daphne Barak-Erez, Ed.-in-Ch.
Tel Aviv University
Tel Aviv, Israel
Publication E-mail: info@bepress.com
Publisher E-mail: info@bepress.com
Peer-reviewed journal providing multi-disciplinary analysis of law, in connection with the Cegla Center for Interdisciplinary Research of the Law. **Freq:** 2/yr (Jan. and Jul.). **Key Personnel:** Daphne Barak-Erez, Editor-in-Chief; Michael Birhnack, Editor; Ehud Kamar, Editor; Yoram Margalioth, Editor; Yuval Shany, Editor. **ISSN:** 1565-3404. **Subscription Rates:** US$150 institutions academic; US$450 institutions corporate. **URL:** http://www.bepress.com/til.

Wingate

46115 ■ European Review of Aging and Physical Activity
Springer Netherlands
The Zinman College
42902 Wingate, Israel
Publisher E-mail: permissions.dordrecht@springer.com
Journal devoted to physical activity and aging in the biomedical and behavioral sciences. **Founded:** 1974. **Freq:** Semiannual. **Print Method:** Offset. **Trim Size:** 13 x 21 1/2. **Cols./Page:** 6. **Col. Width:** 19 nonpareils. **Col. Depth:** 210 agate lines. **Key Personnel:** Wildor Hollmann, Editorial Board; Greg Gass, Editorial Board; Wojtek Chodzko-Zajko, Editorial Board; Rolf Ehrsam, Editorial Board; Eino Heikkinen, Editorial Board; Ursula Lehr, Editorial Board; Uri Goldbourt, Editorial Board; Ehud Goldhamer, Editorial Board; Neil Alexander, Editorial Board; Alberto Duarte, Editorial Board; Michael Sagiv, Editor-in-Chief, sagiv@macam.ac.il. **ISSN:** 1813-7253. **Subscription Rates:** EUR251 institutions print incl. free access or e-only; EUR301.20 institutions print incl. enhanced access. **URL:** http://www.springer.com/medicine/family/journal/11556.

Circulation: ★ = ABC; △ = BPA; ♦ = CAC; • = CCAB; ❑ = VAC; ⊕ = PO Statement; ‡ = Publisher's Report; Boldface figures = sworn; Light figures = estimated.

Alessandria

46116 ■ Artifara
Edizioni dell' Orso
Via Urbano Rattazzi n. 47
I-15100 Alessandria, Italy
Ph: 39 131 252349
Fax: 39 131 257567
Publisher E-mail: direzione.commerciale@ediorso.it
Magazine of the language and literature of the Iberian and Latin American people. **Subtitle:** Revista de Lenguas y Literaturas Ibericas y Latinoamericanas. **Key Personnel:** Fernando Martinez De Carnero, Editorial Dir.; Aldo Ruffinatto, Director. **ISSN:** 1594-378X. **Subscription Rates:** EUR30 individuals; EUR50 individuals. **URL:** http://www.artifara.com.

Ancona

46117 ■ Chemistry and Ecology
Taylor & Francis Group Journals
Institute of Marine Science
University of Ancona
Via Brecce Bianche
I-60131 Ancona, Italy
Publisher E-mail: customerservice@taylorandfrancis.com
Peer-reviewed journal focusing on the relationship between chemistry and ecological processes. **Freq:** Bimonthly. **Key Personnel:** W. Baumeister, Editor; C.H. Chung, Editor; K. Takatsu, Editor; E. Carafoli, Editor; M. Muramatsu, Editor; S. Orrenius, Editor. **ISSN:** 0275-7540. **Subscription Rates:** 2,049 institutions print + online; 1,947 institutions online; US$2,661 institutions print + online; US$2,527 institutions online; EUR2,119 institutions print + online; EUR2,013 institutions online. **URL:** http://www.tandf.co.uk/journals/journal.asp?issn=0275-7540& linktype=5.

46118 ■ International Journal of Computational Intelligence Studies
Inderscience Enterprises Limited
c/o Prof. Claudio Turchetti, Ed.-in-Ch.
Department of Biomedical Engineering, Electronics & Telecommunications, Universita Politecnica delle Marche
Via Brecce Bianche, 12
I-60131 Ancona, Italy
Journal featuring articles on experiments, theories, and applications of computational intelligence. **Freq:** Quarterly. **Key Personnel:** Prof. Claudio Turchetti, Editor-in-Chief, c.turchetti@univpm.it. **ISSN:** 1755-4977. **Subscription Rates:** EUR494 individuals print or online; EUR672 individuals print and online. **URL:** http://www.inderscience.com/browse/index.php?journalCODE=ijcistudies.

L'Aquila

46119 ■ International Journal of Management and Network Economics
Inderscience Enterprises Limited
c/o Prof. Massimo Gastaldi, Ed.-in-Ch.
University of L'Aquila
U.S. Department of Electrical & Information Engineering
Poggio di Roio

67040 L'Aquila, Italy
Journal covering the study of network industries. **Freq:** 4/yr. **Key Personnel:** Prof. Massimo Gastaldi, Editor-in-Chief, gastaldi@ing.univaq.it; Prof. Nathan Levialdi, Editor-in-Chief, levialdi@disp.uniroma2.it. **ISSN:** 1754-2316. **Subscription Rates:** EUR494 individuals print or online; EUR672 individuals print and online. **URL:** http://www.inderscience.com/browse/index.php?journalID=259.

Arcavacata di Rende

46120 ■ International Journal of Artificial Organs
Wichtig Editore Srl
Department of Chemical & Materials Engineering
University of Calabria
I-87030 Arcavacata di Rende, Italy
Peer-reviewed Journal covering field of artificial organs. **Freq:** Monthly. **Trim Size:** 8 1/4 x 11. **Key Personnel:** Gerardo Catapano, Editor-in-Chief, catapano@unical.it; Michela Zucchetti, Managing Editor, michela.zucchetti@wichtig.it; George Dunea, Coord. Ed., geodunea@aol.com. **ISSN:** 1724-6040. **Subscription Rates:** EUR486 individuals Europe; EUR580 individuals rest of the world; EUR368 individuals online only; EUR786 institutions Europe; EUR880 institutions, other countries; EUR580 institutions online only; EUR357 individuals residents - Europe; EUR451 individuals residents - rest of the world. **Remarks:** Accepts advertising. **URL:** http://www.artificial-organs.com/public/ijao/default.aspx. **Circ:** 3,000

Bari

46121 ■ Endocrine, Metabolic & Immune Disorders - Drug Targets
Bentham Science Publishers Ltd.
c/o Emilio Jirillo, Ed.-in-Ch.
Universita degli Studi di Bari
Piazza Giulio Cesare-Policlinico
Bari, Italy
Publisher E-mail: subscriptions@bentham.org
Journal devoted to timely reviews of experimental and clinical studies in the field of endocrine, metabolic, and immune disorders. **Freq:** Quarterly. **Key Personnel:** Emilio Jirillo, Editor-in-Chief; Michael J. Quon, Editor-in-Chief; S.L. Berga, Assoc. Ed. **ISSN:** 1871-5303. **Subscription Rates:** US$1,310 institutions corporate, print; US$1,310 institutions corporate, online; US$1,570 institutions corporate, print and online; US$730 individuals academic, print; US$730 individuals academic, online; US$800 individuals academic, print and online; US$180 individuals print. **Remarks:** Accepts advertising. **URL:** http://www.bentham.org/cdtiemd. **Formerly:** Current Drug Targets. Immune, Endocrine & Metabolic Disorders. **Circ:** (Not Reported)

46122 ■ International Journal of Enterprise Systems Integration and Interoperability
Inderscience Enterprises Limited
c/o Prof. Michele Dassisti, Ed.-in-Ch.
Dipartimento di Ingegneria Meccanica e Gestionale
Politecnico di Bari
Viale Japigia 182
70126 Bari, Italy
Journal covering the study of interoperability, with

emphasis on the implications that both software and organizational strategies have for human welfare. **Freq:** 4/yr. **Key Personnel:** Prof. Michele Dassisti, Editor-in-Chief, m.dassisti@poliba.it. **ISSN:** 1745-3143. **Subscription Rates:** EUR494 individuals print or online; EUR672 individuals print and online. **URL:** http://www.inderscience.com/browse/index.php?journalID=163.

Bergamo

46123 ■ Rotary
c/o Pernice Editori s.r.l.
Via. Verdi 1
IT-24121 Bergamo, Italy
Ph: 39 35 241227
Fax: 39 35 4220153
Membership magazine of Rotary International covering current news about Rotary-related subjects. **Founded:** 1924. **Freq:** Monthly. **Key Personnel:** Andrea Pernice, Editor, andrea.pernice@perniceeditori.it. **URL:** http://www.rotary.org/en/MediaAndNews/MorePublications/RegionalMagazines/Pages/ridefault.aspx. **Circ:** 491,312

Bisceglie

46124 ■ Mosaico di Pace
Pax Christi - Italy
Segreteria Nazionale
Via Petronelli 6
I-70052 Bisceglie, BA, Italy
Ph: 39 80 3953507
Fax: 39 80 3953450
Publication E-mail: info@mosaicodipace.it
Publisher E-mail: info@paxchristi.jt
Italian language publication covering peace. **Subtitle:** Rivista Mensile Promossa Da Pax Christi. **Founded:** 1990. **Freq:** Monthly. **Key Personnel:** Alex Zanotelli, Director. **Remarks:** Advertising accepted; rates available upon request. **URL:** http://www.paxchristi.it. **Circ:** (Not Reported)

Bologna

46125 ■ Bollettino di Storia delle Scienze Matematiche
Italian Mathematical Union
Unione Matematica Italiana
Piazza di Porta San Donato, 5
I-40126 Bologna, Italy
Ph: 39 51 243190
Fax: 39 51 4214169
Publisher E-mail: umi@dm.unibo.it
Publication covering mathematics in English, French Italian and Latin. **Freq:** 3/yr. **Key Personnel:** Franco Brezzi, Editor-in-Chief. **ISSN:** 1972-6724. **Subscription Rates:** EUR115 individuals Italy; EUR165 other countries. **Remarks:** Advertising not accepted. **URL:** http://umi.dm.unibo.it/italiano/Editoria/Editoria.html. **Circ:** (Not Reported)

46126 ■ 4OR
Springer-Verlag New York Inc.
c/o Silvano Martello, Ed.-in-Ch.
DEIS University di Bologna
Viale Risorgimento 2
I-40136 Bologna, Italy

Circulation: ★ = ABC; △ = BPA; ♦ = CAC; • = CCAB; ▢ = VAC; ⊕ = PO Statement; ‡ = Publisher's Report; Boldface figures = sworn; Light figures = estimated.

Gale Directory of Publications & Broadcast Media/147th Ed.

5067

Ph: 39 51 2093022
Publisher E-mail: service-ny@springer.com
Journal covering theory and applications of operations research. **Subtitle:** A Quarterly Journal of Operations Research. **Founded:** 1966. **Freq:** Quarterly. **Print Method:** Offset. **Trim Size:** 6 x 9. **Cols./Page:** 1. **Col. Width:** 4 1/2 inches. **Col. Depth:** 7 inches. **Key Personnel:** Philippe Baptiste, Editor-in-Chief, philippe.baptiste@polytechnique.fr; Gianni Di Pillo, Editorial Board; Thierry Marchant, Editor-in-Chief, thierry.marchant@ugent.be; Silvano Martello, Editor-in-Chief. **ISSN:** 1619-4500. **URL:** http://www.springer.com/business/operationsresearch/journal/10288.

46127 ■ Il Nuovo Club
Editrice Il Campo
Via. Amendola 11
I-40121 Bologna, Italy
Ph: 39 512 55544
Fax: 39 512 55360
Trade magazine covering fitness and sports facilities management. **Subtitle:** Attualita e Management el Circoli Sportivi e Delle Palestre. **Founded:** 1989. **Freq:** Bimonthly. **Trim Size:** 23 x 31.5 cm. **Key Personnel:** Federico Maestrami, Director; Claudia Gamberini, Web Mgr. **Subscription Rates:** EUR39 individuals Italy; EUR78 individuals Europe; EUR90 other countries. **Remarks:** Accepts advertising. **URL:** http://www.fitnesstrend.com/pubblicazione/Notizie/Pubblicazioni/RIVISTE/ILNUOVOCLUBmagazine.html. **Ad Rates:** 4C: EUR1,653. **Circ:** Controlled 10,000

46128 ■ Piscine Oggi
Editrice Il Campo
Via. Amendola 11
I-40121 Bologna, Italy
Ph: 39 512 55544
Fax: 39 512 55360
Trade magazine for swimming pool, water parks, spas and facilities management and private customers. **Founded:** 1973. **Freq:** Quarterly. **Trim Size:** 21 x 29.5 cm. **Key Personnel:** Federico Maestrami, Director. **Subscription Rates:** EUR7 single issue. **Remarks:** Accepts advertising. **URL:** http://www.piscineoggi.it/. **Ad Rates:** 4C: EUR1,807.60. **Circ:** Controlled 15,000

Bussolengo

46129 ■ La Razza Bruna
Association Nazionale Razza Bruna
Localita Ferlina 204
I-37012 Bussolengo, VR, Italy
Ph: 39 456 760111
Fax: 39 457 156655
Publisher E-mail: anarb@anarb.it
Trade magazine of the Italian Brown Cattle Breeders Association covering technical and economic articles in Italian with English and German summaries. **Freq:** Bimonthly. **Subscription Rates:** EUR20 individuals; EUR28 out of country. **Remarks:** Accepts advertising. **URL:** http://www.anarb.it/. **Ad Rates:** BW: EUR67,140; 4C: EUR111,040. **Circ:** 10,000

Carimate

46130 ■ Doctor Os
Ariesdue S.R.L.
Via. Airoldi 11
I-22060 Carimate, CO, Italy
Ph: 39 31 792135
Fax: 39 31 790743
Scientific, Italian language journal covering dentistry. **Subtitle:** Monthly Publication on Dental Updating. **Founded:** Jan. 1990. **Freq:** 9/yr. **Print Method:** Offset. **Trim Size:** 21 x 28 cm. **Cols./Page:** 3. **ISSN:** 1120-7140. **Subscription Rates:** EUR50 individuals Italy; EUR180 other countries Asia and America; EUR150 other countries. **Remarks:** Accepts advertising. **URL:** http://www.ariesdue.it. **Ad Rates:** BW: EUR1,520, 4C: EUR2,115. **Circ:** 15,000

46131 ■ Journal of Osseointegration
Ariesdue S.R.L.
Via. Airoldi 11
I-22060 Carimate, CO, Italy
Ph: 39 31 792135
Fax: 39 31 790743
English and Italian language journal covering oral implantology for dental professionals in Europe. **Founded:** 1999. **Freq:** 3/yr. **Print Method:** Offset. **Trim Size:** 21 x 28 cm. **Cols./Page:** 3. **ISSN:** 1123-2318. **Subscription Rates:** EUR40 individuals in Italy; EUR60 other countries

in European; EUR90 other countries in Asia, America. **Remarks:** Accepts advertising. **URL:** http://www.ariesdue.it/. **Formerly:** Italian Journal of Oral Implantology. **Ad Rates:** BW: EUR1,250, 4C: EUR1,790. **Circ:** Controlled ‡9,000

Carros

46132 ■ Frequence K-FM - 103.4 MHz
4 Blvd. de la Colle Belle
I-06510 Carros, Italy
Ph: 39 4 93290015
Fax: 39 4 93087096
Format: Jazz; News; Classic Rock; Sports; Heavy Metal. **Founded:** 1988. **Operating Hours:** Continuous. **Ad Rates:** Advertising accepted; rates available upon request. **URL:** http://www.frequencek.com.

Chiavari

46133 ■ Rivista Italiana Difesa
Monch Publishing Group
Martiri della Liberazione, 79/3
I-16043 Chiavari, Italy
Ph: 39 185 308606
Fax: 39 185 309063
Publication E-mail: rid@rid.it
Publisher E-mail: info@moench-group.com
Magazine featuring information and analysis on defense issues at the international level. **Founded:** 1982. **Freq:** Monthly. **Trim Size:** 210 x 297 mm. **Key Personnel:** Franco Lazzari, Contact, lazzari@moench-group.com; Stephen Orr, Mktg. Mgr., phone 49 228 6483105, fax 49 228 6483109, stephen.orr@moench-group.com. **Subscription Rates:** EUR44 individuals; EUR82 two years; EUR85 individuals to Europe; EUR110 other countries 12 copies; EUR160 two years to Europe. **Remarks:** Accepts advertising. **URL:** http://www.rid.it/; http://www.moench-group.com/rivista-italiana.php. **Circ:** 30,000

Cinisello Balsamo

46134 ■ RMO—Rivista di Meccanica Oggi
VNU Business Publications Italia
Via. Gorki 69
I-20092 Cinisello Balsamo, MI, Italy
Ph: 39 556 60341
Fax: 39 556 6034238
Trade magazine covering machining, metal working, welding, machine shop equipment and related topics. **Subtitle:** Rivista di Meccanica Oggi. **Freq:** Monthly. **Print Method:** Web offset. **Key Personnel:** Richard Halpenny, Gen. Exec. Mgr. **ISSN:** 1127-6010. **Subscription Rates:** EUR49.50 other countries. **Remarks:** Accepts advertising. **URL:** http://www.vnu.it/rmo/. **Circ:** Combined ‡14,000

46135 ■ Sicurezza
Gruppo Editoriale JCE S.R.L.
Via. Patecchio
I-20141 Cinisello Balsamo, MI, Italy
Ph: 39 257 316011
Fax: 39 257 316291
Trade magazine covering fire and security. **Freq:** Monthly. **Key Personnel:** Massimo Cassani, Editor-in-Chief. **Remarks:** Accepts advertising. **URL:** http://www.fieramilanotech.it/?id=MjQ0LTM1MjUtMzUyMC1FTkcg. **Circ:** (Not Reported)

Cremona

46136 ■ Ippologia
SCIVAC
Via. Trecchi 20
I-26100 Cremona, Italy
Ph: 39 372 460440
Fax: 39 372 457091
Publication E-mail: info@sive.it
Publisher E-mail: info@scivac.it
Scientific journal covering equine veterinary science. **Founded:** 1990. **Freq:** Quarterly. **Trim Size:** 21 x 29.7. **Key Personnel:** Francesca Chiari, Sec., phone 39 372 403507, francesca.chiari@evsrl.it. **ISSN:** 1120-5776. **Remarks:** Accepts advertising. **URL:** http://cms.sive.it/gDocument.aspx?id=821. **Circ:** (Not Reported)

Faenza

46137 ■ Giornale del Marmo—International Stone Magazine
Gruppo Editoriale Faenza Editrice S.p.A.

Via Granarolo 175/3
I-48018 Faenza, RA, Italy
Ph: 39 546 673781
Fax: 39 546 660440
Publication E-mail: info@faenza.com
Publisher E-mail: info.faenza@businessmedia24.com
Trade magazine covering the stone industry. **Founded:** 1964. **Freq:** Bimonthly. **Print Method:** Offset. **Trim Size:** 21 x 29.7 cm. **ISSN:** 1123-8259. **Subscription Rates:** EUR700 single issue. **Remarks:** Accepts advertising. **URL:** http://www.faenza.com/rivisteonlinedx.asp?id=426&flagk=1. **Ad Rates:** BW: 1,170 Lr, 4C: 1,350 Lr. **Circ:** Combined 7,000

Ferrara

46138 ■ Circuits and Systems II
IEEE Circuits and Systems Society
c/o ENDIF, University of Ferrara
Via Saragat
44100 Ferrara, Italy
Ph: 39 0532 974997
Fax: 39 0532 974870
Publisher E-mail: cas-info@ieee.org
Journal focusing on video systems architecture, video quality assessment, and other video-technology related topics. **Subtitle:** Express Briefs. **Freq:** 12/yr. **Key Personnel:** Yong Lian, Editor-in-Chief, tcas2eic@nus.edu.sg; Albert Wang, Assoc. Ed., aw@ee.ucr.edu; Antonio Liscidini, Assoc. Ed., antonio.liscidini@unipv.it. **ISSN:** 1549-7747. **URL:** http://tcas2.polito.it/.

Fiorentino

46139 ■ Aestimum
Firenze University Press
Facolta di Agraria di Firenze
P.le delle Cascine, 18
50144 Fiorentino, Italy
Publisher E-mail: info@fupress.com
Journal focusing on territorial economy, environmental and ecological topics and researches on both theoretical and applied level. **Freq:** Biennial. **Key Personnel:** Prof. Paolo Gajo, Editor-in-Chief. **ISSN:** 1592-6117. **Subscription Rates:** Free in electronic format; EUR50 individuals. **URL:** http://www.fupress.com/rivista.asp?ID=3.

Fisciano

46140 ■ International Journal of Forensic Software Engineering
Inderscience Enterprises Limited
c/o Dr. Pierluigi Ritrovato, Ed.-in-Ch.
Centro di Ricerca in Matematica Pura ed Applicata
Via Ponte don Melillo
84084 Fisciano, Italy
Journal covering all aspects related to software engineering for robust and faults/defects tolerant systems and services design and implementation. **Freq:** 4/yr. **Key Personnel:** Dr. Pierluigi Ritrovato, Editor-in-Chief, ritrovato@crmpa.unisa.it. **ISSN:** 1743-5099. **Subscription Rates:** EUR494 individuals print or online; EUR672 individuals print and online. **URL:** http://www.inderscience.com/browse/index.php?journalID=137.

Florence

46141 ■ Annali di Storia di Firenze
Firenze University Press
Borgo Albizi 28
50122 Florence, Italy
Ph: 39 552 743051
Fax: 39 552 743058
Publisher E-mail: info@fupress.com
Journal covering tests, arguments, documents and bibliography analysis on the history of Florence. **Key Personnel:** Prof. Marcello Verga, Director, marcello.verga@unifi.it; Prof. Andrea Zorzi, Director, zorzi@unifi.it; Prof. Anna Benvenuti, Contact; Prof. Bruna Bocchini, Contact; Prof. Carlo Corsini, Contact; Prof. Enrica Blacks, Contact. **ISSN:** 1827-6946. **URL:** http://www.dssg.unifi.it/SDF/annalidistoriadifirenze.htm.

46142 ■ Cromohs
Firenze University Press
Borgo Albizi 28
50122 Florence, Italy
Ph: 39 552 743051
Fax: 39 552 743058

Publisher E-mail: info@fupress.com
Journal dealing with studies and research relating to modern historical culture. **Founded:** 1995. **Freq:** Annual. **Key Personnel:** Guido Abbattista, Editor, gabbattista@units.it; Rolando Minuti, Editor, rolando. minuti@unifi.it. **ISSN:** 1123-7023. **Subscription Rates:** Free. **URL:** http://www.cromohs.unifi.it/eng/index.html.

46143 ■ European Journal of International Law
Oxford University Press
c/o Anny Bremner, Mng. Ed.
European University Institute
Via Boccaccio 121
I-50133 Florence, Italy
Ph: 39 55 4685555
Fax: 39 55 4685517
Publisher E-mail: webenquiry.uk@oup.com
Journal dealing with issues of international law, providing a forum for the exploration of the conceptual and theoretical dimensions of international law as well as for up-to-date analysis of topical issues. **Freq:** 4/yr. **Key Personnel:** Anny Bremner, Managing Editor, anny. bremner@iue.it; Philip Alston, Honorary Editorial Board; Pierre-Marie Dupuy, Honorary Editorial Board; Joseph Weiler, Editor-in-Chief; Bruno Simma, Editorial Board; Antonio Cassese, Honorary Editorial Board. **ISSN:** 0938-5428. **Subscription Rates:** 226 institutions corporate; print and online; 188 institutions corporate; online only; 207 institutions corporate; print only; 180 institutions print and online; 150 institutions online only; 165 institutions print only; 49 individuals print; 39 students print; 39 members print. **Remarks:** Advertising accepted; rates available upon request. **URL:** http://ejil.oxfordjournals. org. **Circ:** (Not Reported)

46144 ■ Global Bioethics
Firenze University Press
Borgo Albizi 28
50122 Florence, Italy
Ph: 39 552 743051
Fax: 39 552 743058
Publisher E-mail: info@fupress.com
Journal covering bioethics. **Founded:** 1978. **Freq:** Annual. **Print Method:** Offset. **Trim Size:** 6 x 9. **Key Personnel:** A.B. Chiarelli, Editor; A. Autiero, Advisory Board; E.P. Odum, Advisory Board. **ISSN:** 0131-5289. **URL:** http://www.fupress.com/ricercacatalogo.asp.

46145 ■ Nuncius
Publishing House Leo S. Olschki
Istituto e Museo di Storia della Scienza
Piazza Giudici 1
I-50122 Florence, Italy
Ph: 39 552 65311
Fax: 39 552 653130
Publisher E-mail: celso@olschki.it
Magazine covering science and aimed at science historians. **Subtitle:** Annali di Storia della Scienza. **Founded:** Jan. 27, 1986. **Freq:** Semiannual. **Trim Size:** 17 x 24 cm. **Key Personnel:** Ferdinando Abbri, Editorial Board; Mara Miniati, Editorial Board; Marco Beretta, Editor; Paolo Brenni, Editorial Board; Pietro Corsi, Editorial Board; Giovanni Di Pasquale, Editorial Board; Gianna Gheri, Editorial Asst.; Marta Stefani, Managing Editor; Claudio Pogliano, Editorial Board; Paolo Galluzzi, Director. **ISSN:** 0394-7394. **Subscription Rates:** EUR60 individuals Italy; EUR71 individuals online edition; EUR55 individuals online edition only; EUR82 other countries. **Remarks:** Accepts advertising. **URL:** http://www.olschki.it/riviste/nuncius.htm. **Ad Rates:** BW: EUR800. **Circ:** (Not Reported)

Frascati

46146 ■ The European Physical Journal A-Hadrons and Nuclei
Springer-Verlag
c/o Enzo de Sanctis, Ed.-in-Ch.
Istituto Nazionale di Fisica Nucleare
Laboratori Nazionali di Frascati
Via E Fermi, 40
00044 Frascati, Italy
Scientific journal dealing with all aspects of the structure of hadrons and nuclei. **Freq:** 3/yr. **Key Personnel:** B.R. Fulton, Editor, brf2@york.ac.uk; Haiyan Gao, Editor, gao@tunl.duke.edu; P. Braun-Munzinger, Editor, p.braun-munzinger@gsi.de; Enzo De Sanctis, Editor-in-Chief, enzo.decanctis@lnf.infn.it; Nicola Bianchi, Editor, nicola.bianchi@lnf.infn.it; S. Kubono, Editor, kubono@

cns.s.u-tokyo.ac.jp. **ISSN:** 1434-6001. **Subscription Rates:** US$3,300 institutions; US$3,960 institutions enhanced access. **URL:** http://www.springer.com/physics/elementary/journal/10050.

Frosinone

46147 ■ Radio Onda Libera-FM - 97.1
Via Santa Maria, 30/40
00036 Palestrina, Italy
Ph: 39 6 9535787
Fax: 39 6 9537203
Format: News. **Owner:** Radio Onda Libera, at above address. **Founded:** 1977. **Key Personnel:** Paolo Filippi, Director. **URL:** http://lnx.ondalibera.it/2006/index.php?option=com_content&task=view&id=16 &Itemid=44.

Genoa

46148 ■ Epistemologia
Tilgher-Genova
Via Assarotti 31/15
16122 Genoa, Italy
Ph: 39 10 8391140
Fax: 39 10 870653
Publisher E-mail: tilgher@tilgher.it
Journal covering the philosophy of science. **Subtitle:** An Italian Journal for the Philosophy of Science. **Freq:** Semiannual. **Key Personnel:** Evandro Agazzi, Editor. **ISSN:** 0392-9760. **Subscription Rates:** EUR50 individuals print only; EUR68 individuals print only (Europe); EUR76 other countries print only; EUR72 individuals print and online; EUR90 individuals print and online (Europe); EUR98 other countries print and online; EUR44 individuals online only. **URL:** http://www.tilgher.it/(qjho3sqvub5ahq45s5p4j3mk)/index.aspx?lang=eng&tpr=1.

46149 ■ Giornale di Metafisica
Tilgher-Genova
Via Assarotti 31/15
16122 Genoa, Italy
Ph: 39 10 8391140
Fax: 39 10 870653
Publisher E-mail: tilgher@tilgher.it
Journal focusing on speculative philosophy. **Founded:** 1946. **Freq:** 3/yr. **Key Personnel:** Giuseppe Nicolaci, Director. **ISSN:** 0017-0372. **Subscription Rates:** EUR62 individuals print only; EUR85 individuals print only (Europe); EUR97 other countries print only; EUR89 individuals print and online; EUR112 individuals print and online (Europe); EUR124 other countries print and online; EUR54 individuals online only. **URL:** http://www.tilgher.it/(qjho3sqvub5ahq45s5p4j3mk)/index.aspx?lang=eng&tpr=2.

46150 ■ International Journal of Shape Modeling
World Scientific Publishing Company Private Ltd.
c/o B. Falcidieno, Ed.-in-Ch.
Institute for Applied Mathematics & Information Technology National Research Council
Via De Marini 6
I-16149 Genoa, Italy
Ph: 39 106 475667
Fax: 39 106 475660
Publisher E-mail: wspc@wspc.com.sg
Journal of computer graphics. **Founded:** 1994. **Freq:** Semiannual. **Key Personnel:** B. Falcidieno, Editor-in-Chief, falcidieno@ima.ge.cnr.it; A.T. Fomenko, Assoc. Ed.; T.L. Kunii, Assoc. Ed. **ISSN:** 0218-6543. **Subscription Rates:** US$222 institutions and libraries; electronic and print; EUR192 institutions and libraries; electronic and print; S$350 institutions and libraries; electronic and print; US$213 institutions and libraries; electronic only; EUR184 institutions and libraries; electronic only; S$336 institutions and libraries; electronic only; US$13 individuals for postage; EUR9 individuals for postage; S$17 individuals for postage. **URL:** http://www.worldscinet.com/ijsm/ijsm.shtml.

46151 ■ Journal of the Pancreas
ES Burioni Ricerche Bibliografiche
Corso Firenze 41/2
I-16136 Genoa, Italy
Ph: 39 108 605500
Fax: 39 108 605530
Publisher E-mail: info@burioni.it
Electronic journal focusing on the entire spectrum of the pancreatic gland aspects: normal function, etiology, epidemiology, prevention, genetics, pathophisiology, diagnosis, surgical and medical management of pancre-

atic diseases including cancer, inflammatory diseases, diabetes mellitus, cystic fibrosis and other congenital disorders. **Freq:** Bimonthly. **Key Personnel:** Rafaelle Pezzilli, Editor-in-Chief, raffaele.pezzilli@aosp.bo.it. **ISSN:** 1590-8577. **Remarks:** Accepts advertising. **URL:** http://www.joplink.net. **Circ:** (Not Reported)

46152 ■ Nuova Corrente
Tilgher-Genova
Via Assarotti 31/15
16122 Genoa, Italy
Ph: 39 10 8391140
Fax: 39 10 870653
Publisher E-mail: tilgher@tilgher.it
Journal covering literary and philosophical topics. **Founded:** 1954. **Freq:** Semiannual. **Key Personnel:** Stefano Verdino, Editor-in-Chief. **ISSN:** 0029-6155. **Subscription Rates:** EUR50 individuals print only; EUR68 individuals print only (Europe); EUR76 other countries print only; EUR72 individuals print and online; EUR90 individuals print and online (Europe); EUR98 other countries print and online; EUR44 individuals online only. **URL:** http://www.tilgher.it/(qjho3sqvub5ahq45s5p4j3mk)/index.aspx?lang=eng&tpr=3.

46153 ■ Rivista di Biologia
Tilgher-Genova
Via Assarotti 31/15
16122 Genoa, Italy
Ph: 39 10 8391140
Fax: 39 10 870653
Publisher E-mail: tilgher@tilgher.it
Journal covering the field of Theoretical Biology. **Founded:** 1919. **Freq:** 3/yr. **Key Personnel:** Silvano Traverso, Editor-in-Chief, silvano.traverso@tilgher.it. **ISSN:** 0035-6050. **Subscription Rates:** EUR62 individuals print only; EUR85 individuals print only (Europe); EUR97 other countries print only; EUR89 individuals print and online; EUR112 individuals print and online (Europe); EUR124 other countries print and online; EUR54 individuals online only. **URL:** http://www.tilgher.it/(qjho3sqvub5ahq45s5p4j3mk)/index.aspx?lang=eng&tpr=4.

46154 ■ Textus
Tilgher-Genova
Via Assarotti 31/15
16122 Genoa, Italy
Ph: 39 10 8391140
Fax: 39 10 870653
Publisher E-mail: tilgher@tilgher.it
Journal featuring the literature, culture and language of English-speaking countries. **Founded:** 1988. **Freq:** 3/yr. **Key Personnel:** Carlo Maria Bajetta, Editor. **ISSN:** 1824-3967. **Subscription Rates:** EUR62 individuals print only; EUR85 individuals print only (Europe); EUR97 other countries print only; EUR89 individuals print and online; EUR112 individuals print and online (Europe); EUR124 other countries print and online; EUR54 individuals online only. **URL:** http://www.tilgher.it/(qjho3sqvub5ahq45s5p4j3mk)/index.aspx?lang=eng&tpr=5.

Grugliasco

46155 ■ International Journal of Food Microbiology
Elsevier Science B.V.
c/o L. Cocolin, Ed.-in-Ch.
DIVAPRA, Faculty of Agriculture
University of Turin
Via Leonardo da Vinci 44
10095 Grugliasco, Italy
Journal covering food microbiology. An official journal of the International Union of Microbiological Societies (IUMS) and the International Committee on Food Microbiology and Hygiene (ICFMH). **Founded:** 1984. **Freq:** Semimonthly. **Key Personnel:** C.O. Gill, Editor; L. Cocolin, Editor-in-Chief, lscocolin.ijfm@unito.it; N.P. Skovgaard, Book Review Editor. **ISSN:** 0168-1605. **Subscription Rates:** US$242 other countries all countries except Europe, Japan and Iran; 28,100¥ individuals; EUR215 individuals European countries and Iran; EUR4,159 institutions European countries and Iran; 552,100¥ institutions; US$4,650 institutions, other countries. **Remarks:** Accepts advertising. **URL:** http://www.elsevier.com/wps/find/journaldescription.cws_home/505514/descriptiondescription. **Circ:** 450

Ischia Porto

46156 ■ Marine Ecology
John Wiley & Sons Inc.

Circulation: ★ = ABC; △ = BPA; ◆ = CAC; • = CCAB; ❏ = VAC; ⊕ = PO Statement; ‡ = Publisher's Report; Boldface figures = sworn; Light figures = estimated.

Gale Directory of Publications & Broadcast Media/147th Ed.

5069

Wiley-Blackwell
c/o Maria Cristina Gambi, Ed.
Stazione Zoologica, Anton Dohrn
Laboratorio di Ecologia del Benthos
I-80077 Ischia Porto, Italy
Journal publishing original contributions related to the
structure and dynamics of marine benthic and pelagic
ecosystems. **Subtitle:** An Evolutionary Perspective.
Freq: Quarterly. **Key Personnel:** James P. Barry, Edito-
rial Board; Maria Cristina Gambi, Editor, gambimc@szn.
it; Lisa Levin, Editor, llevin@ucsd.edu; Maurizio Ribera
D'Alcala, Assoc. Ed., maurizio@szn.it; Craig M. Young,
Assoc. Ed., cmyoung@uoregon.edu; Francesco Paolo
Patti, Editorial Board; Fabio Badalamenti, Editorial
Board; Michael Stachowitsch, Book Review Ed.,
stachow5@univie.ac.at; Carlo Nike Bianchi, Editorial
Board; Rosanna Messina, Editorial Asst.; John Costello,
Editorial Board; Marta Estrada, Editorial Board. **ISSN:**
0173-9565. **Subscription Rates:** US$228 individuals
print + online; EUR213 individuals print + online; 141
individuals print + online (non Euro zone); US$1,099
institutions print + online; EUR828 institutions print + online; 652 institutions print + online; US$1,407 institu-
tions, other countries print + online; 652 institutions
print + online; US$998 institutions print or online;
EUR753 institutions print or online. **URL:** http://www.
wiley.com/bw/journal.asp?ref=0173-9565&site=1. **Formerly:** Pubblicazioni della Stazione Zoologica di Napoli.

Messina

46157 ■ International Journal of Economic Policy in Emerging Economies
Inderscience Publishers
c/o Dr. Bruno S. Sergi, Ed.
University of Messina
Via T. Cannizzaro, 278
I-98122 Messina, Italy
Publisher E-mail: editor@inderscience.com
Peer-reviewed journal covering all areas of economic
policy. **Founded:** 2007. **Freq:** 4/yr. **Key Personnel:** Dr.
Bruno S. Sergi, Editor, bsergi@unime.it. **ISSN:** 1752-
0452. **Subscription Rates:** EUR494 individuals includes
surface mail, print only; EUR672 individuals print & online.
URL: http://www.inderscience.com/browse/index.php?
journalCODE=ijepee.

46158 ■ International Journal of Monetary Economics & Finance
Inderscience Publishers
c/o Dr. Bruno S. Sergi, Ed.
University of Messina
Faculty of Political Science
Via T. Cannizzaro, 278
I-98122 Messina, Italy
Publisher E-mail: editor@inderscience.com
Peer-reviewed journal covering international monetary
economics and finance. **Founded:** 2007. **Freq:** 4/yr.
Key Personnel: Dr. Bruno S. Sergi, Editor, bsergi@
unime.it; Dr. Moorad Choudhry, Managing Editor,
mooradc@hotmail.com; Prof. Roman Matousek, Managing Editor, r.matousek@londonmet.ac.uk. **ISSN:** 1752-
0479. **Subscription Rates:** EUR494 individuals includes
surface mail, print only; EUR672 individuals print and
online. **URL:** http://www.inderscience.com/browse/index.
php?journalCODE=ijmef.

46159 ■ International Journal of Trade and Global Markets
Inderscience Publishers
c/o Dr. Bruno S. Sergi, Ed.
University of Messina
Faculty of Political Science
Via T. Cannizzaro, 278
I-98122 Messina, Italy
Publisher E-mail: editor@inderscience.com
Peer-reviewed journal covering international trade &
economic growth. **Founded:** 2007. **Freq:** 4/yr. **Key Per-
sonnel:** Dr. Bruno S. Sergi, Editor, bsergi@unime.it;
Prof. Roman Matousek, Regional Ed.; Prof. Abel Ade-
kola, Regional Ed. **ISSN:** 1742-7541. **Subscription
Rates:** EUR494 individuals surface mail, print only;
EUR672 individuals print and online. **URL:** http://www.
inderscience.com/browse/index.php?journalCODE=
ijtgm.

Milan

46160 ■ Aggiornamento Medico
Kurtis Editrice
via Luigi Zoja, 30
20153 Milan, Italy

Ph: 39 2 48202740
Fax: 39 2 48201219
Publication E-mail: agm@kurtis.it
Publisher E-mail: info@kurtis.it
Journal covering medical sciences and practice.
Founded: Jan. 1982. **Freq:** 10/yr. **Key Personnel:** Can-
zio Fuse, CEO. **ISSN:** 0392-3002. **Subscription Rates:**
EUR35 individuals print and online; EUR50 institutions
print and online. **URL:** http://www.kurtis.it/agm/en/. **Circ:**
40,683

46161 ■ Aging Clinical and Experimental Research
Kurtis Editrice
via Luigi Zoja, 30
20153 Milan, Italy
Ph: 39 2 48202740
Fax: 39 2 48201219
Publication E-mail: aging@kurtis.it
Publisher E-mail: info@kurtis.it
Journal covering field of gerontology and geriatrics. **Sub-
title:** Official journal of the Italian Society of Gerontology
and Geriatrics. **Freq:** Bimonthly. **Key Personnel:** Gaet-
ano Crepaldi, Editor-in-Chief; N. Marchionni, Assoc. Ed.
ISSN: 1594-0667. **Subscription Rates:** EUR80 individu-
als print and online; EUR210 institutions print and online;
EUR50 individuals online. **URL:** http://www.kurtis.it/aging/
en/.

46162 ■ Agro Food
Teknoscienze S.R.L.
Via. Brianza 22
I-20127 Milan, Italy
Ph: 39 2 26809375
Fax: 39 2 2847226
Publication E-mail: subscription@teknoscienze.com
Publisher E-mail: info@teknoscienze.com
Publication covering agricultural technology. **Founded:**
1990. **Trim Size:** 210 x 297 mm. **Key Personnel:** Si-
vana Maini, Exec. Ed., silvana@teknoscienze.com;
Carla Scesa, Editor-in-Chief, info@teknoscienze.com.
Subscription Rates: EUR105 individuals Italy, print edi-
tion; EUR145 other countries print edition; EUR100 other
countries online edition. **Remarks:** Accepts advertising.
URL: http://www.teknoscienze.com/storico_testate.asp?
tipologia=AGRO. **Ad Rates:** BW: EUR2,050, 4C:
EUR2,800. **Circ:** Combined 7,000

46163 ■ Annali dell'Istituto Superiore di Sanita
Kurtis Editrice
via Luigi Zoja, 30
20153 Milan, Italy
Ph: 39 2 48202740
Fax: 39 2 48201219
Publisher E-mail: info@kurtis.it
Journal covering various fields of public health.
Founded: 1938. **Freq:** Quarterly. **Key Personnel:** En-
rico Alleva, Editor-in-Chief; Enrico Garaci, Editor. **ISSN:**
0021-2571. **Subscription Rates:** EUR57 individuals;
EUR67 other countries. **URL:** http://www.kurtis.it/annali/
en/comitato.cfm.

46164 ■ CDA
Reed Business Information S.p.a.
Viale G. Richard 1/A
I-20143 Milan, Italy
Ph: 39 281 8301
Fax: 39 281 830406
Trade magazine covering heating and cooling. **Subtitle:**
Condizionamento Dell'Aria. **Founded:** 1956. **Freq:**
Monthly 11/yr. **Print Method:** Offset. **Trim Size:** A4.
Subscription Rates: EUR78 individuals; EUR117
individuals. **Remarks:** Accepts advertising. **URL:** http://
www.reedbusiness.it. **Ad Rates:** 4C: EUR2,180. **Circ:**
Controlled ★3,800

46165 ■ Chimica Oggi (Chemistry Today)
Teknoscienze S.R.L.
Via. Brianza 22
I-20127 Milan, Italy
Ph: 39 2 26809375
Fax: 39 2 2847226
Publication E-mail: subscription@teknoscienze.com
Publisher E-mail: info@teknoscienze.com
Publication covering chemicals and pharmaceuticals.
Founded: 1983. **Trim Size:** 210 x 297 mm. **Key Person-
nel:** Ian Grayson, Editorial Board; Luciano Caglioti,
Editorial Board; Quirinius B. Broxterman, Editorial Board.
Subscription Rates: EUR110 individuals in Italy, print
edition; EUR190 other countries print edition; EUR100
other countries online edition. **Remarks:** Accepts
advertising. **URL:** http://www.teknoscienze.com/testata.
asp?id_testata=89. **Ad Rates:** BW: 2,450 Lr, 4C: 3,200
Lr. **Circ:** Combined 8,000

46166 ■ Eating and Weight Disorders
Kurtis Editrice
via Luigi Zoja, 30
20153 Milan, Italy
Ph: 39 2 48202740
Fax: 39 2 48201219
Publisher E-mail: info@kurtis.it
Journal covering eating disorders and obesity. **Subtitle:**
Studies on Anorexia, Bulimia and Obesity. **Founded:**
1996. **Freq:** Quarterly. **Key Personnel:** Massimo Cuz-
zolaro, MD, Editor-in-Chief, massimo.cuzzolaro@
fastwebnet.it; Ottavio Bosello, Exec. Ed.; Saverio Cinti,
Exec. Ed. **ISSN:** 1124-4909. **Subscription Rates:** EUR60
individuals print and online; EUR120 institutions print and
online. **URL:** http://www.kurtis.it/ewd/en/.

46167 ■ L'Endocrinologo
Kurtis Editrice
via Luigi Zoja, 30
20153 Milan, Italy
Ph: 39 2 48202740
Fax: 39 2 48201219
Publication E-mail: l_endocrinologo@kurtis.it
Publisher E-mail: info@kurtis.it
Journal covering information on endocrinology and
metabolism disorders. **Subtitle:** Official Journal of the
Italian Society of Endocrinology. **Freq:** Bimonthly. **Key
Personnel:** Aldo Pinchera, Editorial Board; Canzio
Fuze, Director. **ISSN:** 1590-170X. **Subscription Rates:**
EUR90 individuals print and online; EUR150 institutions
print and online; EUR40 individuals online. **URL:** http://
www.kurtis.it/endocrinologo/en/.

46168 ■ European Journal of Internal Medicine
Elsevier Science Inc.
c/o Prof. P.M. Mannucci, Ed.-in-Ch.
Angelo Bianchi Bonomi Hemophilia & Thrombosis Cen-
tre
Dept. of Internal Medicine
Via Pace 9
I-20122 Milan, Italy
Fax: 39 2 50320723
Publisher E-mail: usinfo-ehelp@elsevier.com
Journal for promoting the science and practice of internal
medicine in Europe. **Founded:** 1990. **Freq:** 6/yr. **Print
Method:** Offset. **Trim Size:** 12 1/2 x 22 3/4. **Cols./Page:**
6. **Col. Width:** 11.2 picas. **Col. Depth:** 294 agate lines.
Key Personnel: I. Duris, Editorial Board; Prof. P.M.
Mannucci, Editor-in-Chief; Dr. A. Jotkowitz, Assoc. Ed.;
P.R.J. Falger, Editorial Board; Prof. S. Vanderschueren,
Assoc. Ed.; B. Fantin, Editorial Board; Dr. J. Kellet,
Assoc. Ed.; J.L. Dupond, Editorial Board; J. Mustonen,
Editorial Board; J.W.F. Elte, Editorial Board. **ISSN:** 0953-
6205. **Subscription Rates:** EUR395 institutions for
European countries and Iran; 49,600¥ institutions;
US$442 institutions, other countries except Europe,
Japan and Iran; 6,200¥ individuals; EUR51 individuals
for European countries and Iran; US$59 other countries
except Europe, Japan and Iran. **URL:** http://www.
elsevier.com/wps/find/journaldescription.cws_home/
620034/descriptiondescription; http://www.ejinme.com/.
Circ: 1,439

46169 ■ European Journal of Ophthalmology
Wichtig Editore Srl
Via Friuli 72
20135 Milan, Italy
Ph: 39 255 195443
Fax: 39 255 195971
Publication E-mail: ejo@brancato.net
Peer-reviewed Journal for ophthalmologists and visual
science specialists. **Founded:** 1991. **Freq:** 6/yr. **Key
Personnel:** Prof. Rosario Brancato, Editor-in-Chief,
ejo@brancato.net; Francesco Bandello, Assoc. Ed.
ISSN: 1120-6721. **Subscription Rates:** EUR155 individuals Europe; EUR210 individuals rest of the world; EUR80
individuals online; EUR290 institutions Europe; EUR345
institutions, other countries; EUR210 institutions online
only; EUR70 individuals residents - Europe; EUR85
individuals residents - rest of the world. **Remarks:** Accepts advertising. **URL:** http://www.eur-j-ophthalmol.
com/public/ejo/default.aspx. **Circ:** (Not Reported)

46170 ■ European Transactions on Telecom-munications
John Wiley & Sons Inc.
c/o Prof. Achille Pattavina, Ed.-in-Ch.
Politecnico di Milano
Dip. di Elletronica e Informazione
Via Ponzio 34/5
I-20133 Milan, Italy
Publication E-mail: ett@cefriel.it

Publisher E-mail: info@wiley.com

Journal concentrating on the various applications of telecommunications including communication networks, communication theory, information theory, mobile networks, optical communications, cryptography/security, signal processing, transmission systems, and wireless communications. **Freq:** 8/yr. **Key Personnel:** Prof. Achille Pattavina, Editor-in-Chief; Prof. Markus Fiedler, Editor; Prof. Maurice Bellanger, Editor; Prof. U. Killat, Advisory Board; R. Raheli, Advisory Board; R. Mathar, Advisory Board; Prof. Geng-Sheng Kuo, Editor; Dr. Basilio Catania, Editor; Prof. John M. Senior, Editor. **ISSN:** 1124-318X. **Subscription Rates:** US$435 other countries print only; US$579 institutions, other countries print or online; US$638 institutions, other countries print and online. **URL:** http://onlinelibrary.wiley.com/journal/10.1002/(ISSN)1541-8251.

46171 ■ Focus on Italy
British Chamber of Commerce for Italy
Via Dante 12
I-20121 Milan, Italy
Ph: 39 287 7798
Fax: 39 286 461885
Publisher E-mail: bcci@britchamitaly.com
English language publication covering the activities of the British chamber of commerce for Italy. **Freq:** Annual. **Key Personnel:** Maria Rosa Allegra, Business Development/Commercial Services; Susan Boyle, English Language Consultancy Service. **Subscription Rates:** Included in membership. **Remarks:** Accepts advertising. **URL:** http://www.britchamitaly.com/about-focus-on-italy/focus-on-italy. **Circ:** (Not Reported)

46172 ■ Foto-Notiziario
Mediaspazio S.R.L.
Via. M. Melloni 17
I-20129 Milan, Italy
Publication E-mail: redazione@fotonotiziario.it
Publisher E-mail: abbonamento@fotonotiziario.it
Trade magazine covering photography for professionals. **Subtitle:** Il Portale Della Fotografia. **Founded:** 1946. **Freq:** Weekly. **Print Method:** Offset. **Trim Size:** 230 x 320 mm. **Cols./Page:** 3 and 4. **Key Personnel:** Gisella Scattolin, Publication Dir., g.scattolin@fotonotiziario.it. **URL:** http://www.fotonotiziario.it. **Ad Rates:** 4C: EUR2,200. **Circ:** 12,500

46173 ■ Il Cardiologo
Kurtis Editrice
via Luigi Zoja, 30
20153 Milan, Italy
Ph: 39 2 48202740
Fax: 39 2 48201219
Publication E-mail: il_cardiologo@kurtis.it
Publisher E-mail: info@kurtis.it
Journal for cardiologist. **Freq:** Quarterly. **Key Personnel:** A. L'Abbate, Editor-in-Chief; Canzio Fuse, Director. **ISSN:** 1592-842X. **Subscription Rates:** EUR50 individuals print and online; EUR130 institutions print and online; EUR50 individuals online. **URL:** http://www.kurtis.it/cardiologo/en/.

46174 ■ Il Ginecologo
Kurtis Editrice
via Luigi Zoja, 30
20153 Milan, Italy
Ph: 39 2 48202740
Fax: 39 2 48201219
Publication E-mail: il_ginecologo@kurtis.it
Publisher E-mail: info@kurtis.it
Journal covering obstetrics and gynecology. **Freq:** Quarterly. **Key Personnel:** Felice Petraglia, Editor-in-Chief; Caterina Bocchi, Contact. **ISSN:** 1827-7152. **Subscription Rates:** EUR70 individuals print and online; EUR130 institutions print and online; EUR30 individuals online. **URL:** http://www.kurtis.it/ginecologo/en/.

46175 ■ Industrial and Corporate Change
Oxford University Press
c/o Franco Malerba, Ed.
Universita Bacconi
Via Roentgen, 1
I-20136 Milan, Italy
Ph: 39 2 58365473
Fax: 39 2 58363399
Publisher E-mail: webenquiry.uk@oup.com
Journal presenting and interpreting the evidence on corporate and industrial change, drawing from an interdisciplinary set of approaches and theories from

economics, sociology of organization, organization theory, political science, and social psychology and covering the following topics: the internal structures of firms; the history of technologies; the evolution of industries; the nature of competition; the decision rules and strategies; the relationship between firms' characteristics and the institutional environment; the sociology of management and of the workforce; the performance of industries over time; the labor process and the organization of production; the relationship between, and boundaries of, organizations and markets; the nature of the learningprocess underlying technological and organizational change. **Freq:** 6/yr. **Key Personnel:** Glenn R. Carroll, Editor, carroll_glenn@gsb.stanford.edu; J. Chytry, Managing Editor, chytry@haas.berkeley.edu; David Teece, Editor, teece@haas.berkeley.edu. **ISSN:** 0960-6491. **Subscription Rates:** 569 institutions corporate; print and online; 474 institutions corporate; online only; 521 institutions corporate; print only; 455 institutions print and online; 379 institutions online only; 417 institutions print only; 73 individuals print; 53 members print. **Remarks:** Advertising accepted; rates available upon request. **URL:** http://icc.oupjournals.org/. **Circ:** (Not Reported)

46176 ■ International Journal of Biological Markers
Wichtig Editore Srl
Via Friuli 72
20135 Milan, Italy
Ph: 39 255 195443
Fax: 39 255 195971
Journal covering basic and applied research in the field of tumor markers. **Freq:** Quarterly. **Trim Size:** 8 1/4 x 11. **Key Personnel:** Massimo Gion, Editor-in-Chief, cnabo@provincia.venezia.it; Maria Grazia Daidone, Co-Ed., daidone@istitutotumori.mi.it; Robin Leake, Editor. **ISSN:** 1724-6008. **Subscription Rates:** EUR234 individuals Europe; EUR271 individuals rest of the world; EUR180 individuals online only; EUR378 institutions Europe; EUR415 institutions, other countries; EUR280 institutions online only; EUR164 individuals residents (Europe); EUR201 individuals residents (rest of the world); EUR97 individuals residents (online only). **Remarks:** Accepts advertising. **URL:** http://www.biological-markers.com/public/jbm/default.aspx. **Circ:** 1,500

46177 ■ International Journal of Electronic Trade
Inderscience Enterprises Limited
c/o Ernesto Damiani, Ed.-in-Ch.
University of Milan
Dept. of Information Technology
Via Bramante 65
Milan, Italy
Journal focusing on the discussion and research on the new generation of electronic commerce and electronic trade for businesses, consumers, governments and society, in local and global contexts. **Freq:** 4/yr. **Key Personnel:** Ernesto Damiani, Editor-in-Chief, ijkl-info@unimi.it; Christian Huemer, Exec. Ed., huemer@big.tuwien.ac.at. **ISSN:** 1742-7525. **Subscription Rates:** EUR494 individuals print or online; EUR672 individuals print and online. **URL:** http://www.inderscience.com/browse/index.php?journalID=129.

46178 ■ Ipertensione
Kurtis Editrice
via Luigi Zoja, 30
20153 Milan, Italy
Ph: 39 2 48202740
Fax: 39 2 48201219
Publication E-mail: ipertensione@kurtis.it
Publisher E-mail: info@kurtis.it
Journal covering field of arterial hypertension. **Subtitle:** e Prevenzione Cardiovascolare. **Freq:** Quarterly. **Key Personnel:** E. Agabiti Rosei, Editor-in-Chief; Canzio Fuze, Director. **ISSN:** 1122-8601. **Subscription Rates:** EUR65 individuals print and online; EUR105 institutions print and online; EUR40 individuals online. **URL:** http://www.kurtis.it/ipertensione/en/.

46179 ■ Italian Food Machines
Zeus International S.R.L.
Viale Lunigiana, 14
I-20125 Milan, Italy
Ph: 39 2 67100605
Fax: 39 2 67100621
Publisher E-mail: info@editricezeus.com
Trade magazine covering the food industry in Eastern Europe, Russia and China in Russian and English.

Founded: 1989. **Freq:** 4/yr. **Print Method:** Offset. **Trim Size:** 21 x 28.7. **Key Personnel:** Sonia Bennati, Editorial Mgr., bennati@editricezeus.com; Enrico Maffizzoni, Editor, direzione@editricezeus.com. **Subscription Rates:** EUR55 individuals Europe; US$70 other countries. **URL:** http://www.editricezeus.com/industria3alimentare.html; http://www.itfoodonline.com. **Ad Rates:** BW: EUR1,100, 4C: EUR1,350. **Circ:** 4,000

46180 ■ Italian Magazine Food Processing
Zeus International S.R.L.
Viale Lunigiana, 14
I-20125 Milan, Italy
Ph: 39 2 67100605
Fax: 39 2 67100621
Publication E-mail: redazione@editricezeus.com
Publisher E-mail: info@editricezeus.com
Technical magazine for the food and beverage industry in English, German, French and Spanish. **Founded:** 1989. **Freq:** Bimonthly. **Print Method:** Offset. **Trim Size:** 21 x 28.7 cm. **Key Personnel:** Sonia Bennati, Editorial Mgr., bennati@editricezeus.com; Enrico Maffizzoni, Editor, direzione@editricezeus.com. **Subscription Rates:** US$104 other countries; 90 Lr individuals Europe. **URL:** http://www.editricezeus.com/industria2alimentare.html. **Ad Rates:** BW: EUR1,035, 4C: EUR1,350. **Circ:** 5,500

46181 ■ Journal of Applied Biomaterials & Biomechanics
Wichtig Editore Srl
Via Friuli 72
20135 Milan, Italy
Ph: 39 255 195443
Fax: 39 255 195971
Journal covering clinical and laboratory research in the field of Biomaterial Sciences. **Freq:** 3/yr. **Trim Size:** 8 1/4 x 11. **Key Personnel:** Alberto Cigada, Editor-in-Chief; Luigi Nicolais, Editor-in-Chief; Luigi Ambrosio, Assoc. Ed.; Mario Barbosa, Assoc. Ed.; Dirk Grijpma, Assoc. Ed.; Antonio Merolli, Assoc. Ed.; James Kirkpatrick, Editor-in-Chief; Paolo Tranquilli Leali, Editor-in-Chief; Riccardo Pietrabissa, Assoc. Ed.; Livio Quagliarella, Assoc. Ed. **ISSN:** 1724-6024. **Subscription Rates:** EUR193 individuals within Europe; EUR225 other countries; EUR130 individuals online only; EUR318 institutions within Europe; EUR350 institutions, other countries; EUR250 institutions online only. **Remarks:** Advertising accepted; rates available upon request. **URL:** http://www.jabb.biz/public/jabb/default.aspx. **Circ:** (Not Reported)

46182 ■ Journal of Endocrinological Investigation
Kurtis Editrice
via Luigi Zoja, 30
20153 Milan, Italy
Ph: 39 2 48202740
Fax: 39 2 48201219
Publication E-mail: jei@kurtis.it
Publisher E-mail: info@kurtis.it
Journal covering clinical and experimental studies in endocrinology and related fields. **Founded:** 1978. **Freq:** 11/yr. **Key Personnel:** E. Ghigo, Sen. Advisory Council; F. Buzi, Advisory Council; P. de Feo, Assoc. Ed. **ISSN:** 0391-4097. **Subscription Rates:** EUR180 individuals print and online; EUR350 institutions print and online; EUR140 individuals online. **URL:** http://www.jendocrinolinvest.it/jei/en/index.cfm.

46183 ■ Journal of Mental Health Policy and Economics
I.C.M.P.E.
Via Daniele Crespi, 7
I-20123 Milan, Italy
Ph: 39 2 58106901
Fax: 39 2 58106901
Publisher E-mail: info@icmpe.org
Peer-reviewed journal devoted to the application of health and economic research, and policy analysis in the area of mental health to the benefit of people with mental and addictive disorders. **Founded:** 1998. **Freq:** Quarterly. **Key Personnel:** Willard G. Manning, Editor; Massimo Moscarelli, Editor. **ISSN:** 1091-4358. **Subscription Rates:** EUR280 individuals; EUR520 institutions. **URL:** http://www.icmpe.org/test1/journal/journal.htm.

46184 ■ The Journal of Vascular Access
Wichtig Editore Srl
Nephrology & Dialysis Dept.
Ospedale San Paolo
Via A. Di Rudini 8
I-20142 Milan, Italy

Circulation: ★ = ABC; △ = BPA; ♦ = CAC; • = CCAB; □ = VAC; ⊕ = PO Statement; ‡ = Publisher's Report; Boldface figures = sworn; Light figures = estimated.

Gale Directory of Publications & Broadcast Media/147th Ed.   5071

Ph: 39 2 81844371
Fax: 39 2 89129989
Peer-reviewed journal containing clinical and laboratory investigations in the field of vascular access. **Freq:** Quarterly. **Trim Size:** 8 1/4 x 11. **Key Personnel:** Diego Brancaccio, Honorary Ed.; Maurizio Gallieni, Coord. Ed. **ISSN:** 1724-6032. **Subscription Rates:** EUR180 individuals Europe; EUR212 other countries; EUR120 individuals online only; EUR258 institutions Europe; EUR290 institutions, other countries; EUR170 institutions online only; EUR135 individuals residents-Europe; EUR167 individuals residents-rest of the world; 80 Lr individuals residents-online only. **URL:** http://www.vascular-access. info/public/jva/default.aspx. **Ad Rates:** BW: EUR1,050. **Circ:** (Not Reported)

46185 ■ La Rivista della Scuola
Girgenti Editore S.R.L.
Casella Postale 10016
I-20100 Milan, Italy
Fax: 39 266 983333
Publisher E-mail: redazione@girgenti.it
Consumer magazine covering education. **Founded:** 1979. **Freq:** Semimonthly 23/yr. **ISSN:** 1121-0761. **Subscription Rates:** EUR38 individuals; EUR74 two years. **Remarks:** Accepts advertising. **URL:** http://www.girgenti. it. **Ad Rates:** BW: EUR2,940, 4C: EUR4,410. **Circ:** (Not Reported)

46186 ■ M&D/Musica e Dischi
Musica e Dischi
Via De Amicis 47
I-20123 Milan, Italy
Ph: 39 02 89402837
Fax: 39 02 8323843
Publication E-mail: info@musicaedischi.it
Publisher E-mail: info@musicaedischi.it
Trade magazine covering music for music dealers. **Founded:** 1945. **Print Method:** Offset. **Trim Size:** 210 x 297 mm. **Cols./Page:** 4. **Key Personnel:** Mario De Luigi, Editor. **URL:** http://www.musicaedischi.it.

46187 ■ Mani Tese
Piazza Gambara 7/9
I-20146 Milan, Italy
Ph: 39 240 75165
Fax: 39 240 46890
Publication E-mail: ufficiostampa@manitese.it
Publisher E-mail: manitese@manitese.it
Italian language publication covering worldwide development. **Freq:** Monthly. **Remarks:** Advertising not accepted. **URL:** http://www.manitese.it/index.php? mensilemanitese. **Circ:** 36,000

46188 ■ Obesity and Metabolism
Kurtis Editrice
via Luigi Zoja, 30
20153 Milan, Italy
Ph: 39 2 48202740
Fax: 39 2 48201219
Publication E-mail: obesity@kurtis.it
Publisher E-mail: info@kurtis.it
Journal covering obesity and metabolic disorders. **Freq:** Quarterly. **Key Personnel:** Felipe Casanueva, MD, Editor-in-Chief, obesityandmetabolism@usc.es; Canzio Fuze, CEO; Ottavio Bosello, Assoc. Ed. **ISSN:** 1825-3865. **Subscription Rates:** EUR70 individuals print and online; EUR130 institutions print and online; EUR50 individuals online. **URL:** http://www.kurtis.it/obesity/en/.

46189 ■ Office Automation
Soiel International S.R.L.
Via. Martiri Oscuri 3
I-20125 Milan, Italy
Ph: 39 2 26148855
Fax: 39 2 26149333
Publication E-mail: office.automation@soiel.it
Publisher E-mail: soiel@soiel.it
Trade magazine covering data processing, networking, telecommunications and systems for the office for professionals. **Founded:** 1980. **Freq:** Monthly. **Print Method:** Offset. **Trim Size:** 210 x 297 mm. **Key Personnel:** Grazia Gargiulo, Director. **ISSN:** 1120-0138. **Remarks:** Accepts advertising. **URL:** http://www.soiel.it/ testate/office_auto/sommario.htm. **Circ:** 17,000

46190 ■ Officelayout
Soiel International S.R.L.
Via. Martiri Oscuri 3
I-20125 Milan, Italy
Ph: 39 2 26148855
Fax: 39 2 26149333
Publisher E-mail: soiel@soiel.it
Trade magazine covering the design, organization and furnishing of office spaces. **Founded:** 1984. **Freq:** Bimonthly. **Print Method:** Offset. **Trim. Size:** 233 x 297 mm. **Key Personnel:** Grazia Gargiulo, Director, office. layout@soiel.it. **ISSN:** 1120-012X. **Remarks:** Accepts advertising. **URL:** http://www.soiel.it/testate/office_lay/ sommario.htm. **Ad Rates:** 4C: 3,800 Lr. **Circ:** 20,000

46191 ■ Prima Comunicazione
Editoriale Genesis S.R.L.
via Vincenzo Monti 15
I-20123 Milan, Italy
Ph: 39 2 4819 4401
Fax: 39 2 4800 2708
Publisher E-mail: prima@primaonline.it
Trade magazine covering the media industry, including print, television, advertising and Internet. **Founded:** 1973. **Trim Size:** 205 x 285 mm. **Cols./Page:** 3. **Col. Width:** 56 millimeters. **Col. Depth:** 250 millimeters. **Key Personnel:** Umberto Brunetti, Contact; Alessandra Ravetta, Contact. **Subscription Rates:** EUR94 individuals Italy; EUR155 other countries; EUR212 individuals extra continent. **Remarks:** Accepts advertising. **URL:** http://www.primaonline.it/. **Circ:** Paid ‡15,000

46192 ■ Rassegna Alimentare
Zeus International S.R.L.
Viale Lunigiana, 14
I-20125 Milan, Italy
Ph: 39 2 67100605
Fax: 39 2 67100621
Publisher E-mail: info@editricezeus.com
Trade magazine covering technical and other issues for the food industry in Italy. **Founded:** 1981. **Freq:** Bimonthly. **Print Method:** Offset. **Trim Size:** 21 x 29.7 cm. **Key Personnel:** Sonia Bennati, Editorial Mgr., bennati@editricezeus.com; Enrico Maffizzoni, Editor, direzione@editricezeus.com. **Subscription Rates:** US$104 individuals outside Europe; EUR90 single issue. **URL:** http://www.editricezeus.com/industria1alimentare. html. **Ad Rates:** BW: EUR1,035, 4C: EUR1,350. **Circ:** 6,000

46193 ■ Rodeo
Superstudio 13
Via Forcella 13
I-20144 Milan, Italy
Ph: 39 2 89405560
Fax: 39 2 80420126
Publisher E-mail: info@rodeomagazine.net
Magazine providing guide to fashion, design, art, cinema, literature, music and photography. **Founded:** 2003. **Freq:** Monthly. **Key Personnel:** Marcelo Burlon, Editor-in-Chief, marcelo@rodeomagazine.net; Simona Varchi, Publisher, simona@rodeomagazine.net. **Remarks:** Accepts advertising. **URL:** http://www. rodeomagazine.it/news. **Circ:** (Not Reported)

46194 ■ Sipario
CAMA
Via Rosales, 3
I-20124 Milan, Italy
Ph: 39 265 3270
Fax: 39 229 060005
Publisher E-mail: direzione@sipario.it
Consumer magazine covering theater, opera, and cinema. **Founded:** 1945. **Freq:** Monthly. **Print Method:** Offset. **Cols./Page:** 3. **Key Personnel:** Mattia Giorgetti, Coord.; Mario Giorgetti, Editor-in-Chief. **ISSN:** 1123-458X. **Remarks:** Accepts advertising. **URL:** http://www. sipario.it/. **Circ:** Combined 16,000

46195 ■ Sole 24ore
Editrice Il Sole
Via Monte Rosa 91
I-20149 Milan, Italy
Publisher E-mail: gruppo24ore@ilsole24ore.com
Business publication. **Freq:** Daily. **ISSN:** 0391-786X. **Online:** Gale. **URL:** http://www.ilsole24ore.com/.

46196 ■ Stampi
Italian Association of Precision Moulds, Dies and Tooling Manufacturers
viale Fulvio Testi 128
I-20092 Milan, Italy
Ph: 39 226 255392
Fax: 39 226 255214
Publisher E-mail: info@ucisap.it
Magazine containing discussions on the problems faced by the sector, as well as information relevant to the industry. **Freq:** Monthly. **Subscription Rates:** Free to all members. **Remarks:** Accepts advertising. **URL:** http:// www.ucisap.it/en/pubblicazioni/pubblicazioni.html. **Circ:** (Not Reported)

46197 ■ Theriogenology
Mosby Inc.
c/o F. Gandolfi, PhD, Co-Ed.-in-Ch.
Instituto di Anatomia
degli Animali
Domestici
I-20133 Milan, Italy
Publisher E-mail: custserv.ehs@elsevier.com
Journal for researchers, clinicians, and industry professionals involved in animal reproduction biology. **Founded:** 1995. **Freq:** 18/yr. **Key Personnel:** F. Gandolfi, PhD, Co-Ed.-in-Ch.; J. Kastelic, PhD, Co-Ed.-in-Ch. **ISSN:** 0093-691X. **Subscription Rates:** US$1,877 institutions; US$459 individuals; US$2,134 institutions, other countries; US$527 other countries. **Remarks:** Accepts advertising. **URL:** http://www.elsevier.com/wps/ find/journaldescription.cws_home/525024/ descriptiondescription. **Circ:** (Not Reported)

46198 ■ Urodinamica
Kurtis Editrice
via Luigi Zoja, 30
20153 Milan, Italy
Ph: 39 2 48202740
Fax: 39 2 48201219
Publisher E-mail: info@kurtis.it
Journal covering urodynamics and related fields. **Subtitle:** Neurourology, Continence and Pelvic Floor. **Freq:** Quarterly. **Key Personnel:** Walter Artibani, Editor-in-Chief; Antonio Cucchi, Exec. Ed.; Roberto Carone, Editor. **ISSN:** 1120-5989. **Subscription Rates:** EUR70 individuals print and online; EUR120 institutions print and online; EUR40 individuals online. **URL:** http://www.kurtis. it/urodinamica/en/.

Modena

46199 ■ Invertebrate Survival Journal (ISJ)
Universita degli Studi di Modena e Reggio Emilia
Via Universita 4
I-41100 Modena, Italy
Ph: 39 52 2522604
Journal dealing with the basic defense mechanisms in invertebrates. **Key Personnel:** Enzo Ottaviani, Editor-in-Chief; Eguileor M. De, Editorial Board; D. Malagoli, Executive Ed.; A. Beschin, Editorial Board; S. Sacchi, Asst. Ed.; K.P. Chen, Editorial Board; L. Ballarin, Editorial Board; A.M. Fallon, Editorial Board; Martinez J.I. Ramos, Editorial Board. **ISSN:** 1824-307X. **URL:** http:// www.isj.unimo.it/.

Naples

46200 ■ International Journal of Critical Computer-Based Systems
Inderscience Enterprises Limited
c/o Dr. Francesco Flammini, Ed.-in-Ch.
University of Naples Federico II
Dept. of Computer & Systems Engineering
Via Claudio 21
80125 Naples, Italy
Journal covering all the topics related to the engineering of computer-based systems employed in mission and safety critical applications. **Freq:** 4/yr. **Key Personnel:** Dr. Francesco Flammini, Editor-in-Chief, frflammi@ unina.it; Prof. Valeria Vittorini, Assoc. Ed. **ISSN:** 1757-8779. **Subscription Rates:** EUR494 individuals print or online; EUR672 individuals print and online. **URL:** http:// www.inderscience.com/browse/index.php?journalID= 325.

46201 ■ Journal of Geochemical Exploration
Elsevier Science
c/o B. De Vivo, Ed.-in-Ch.
Universita di Napoli Federico II
Dipartimento di Scienze della Terra
Via Mezzocannone 8
I-80134 Naples, Italy
Publisher E-mail: nlinfo-f@elsevier.com
Journal publishing all aspects of geochemistry of the environment. **Founded:** 1972. **Freq:** Monthly. **Key Personnel:** B. De Vivo, Editor-in-Chief, bdevivo@unina.it; J. Hoogewerff, Assoc. Ed.; R.A. Ayuso, Assoc. Ed. **ISSN:** 0375-6742. **Subscription Rates:** EUR240 individuals European countries; US$269 individuals all countries except Europe and Japan; 31,700¥ individuals; US$1,863 institutions all countries except Europe and

Japan; 221,300¥ institutions; EUR1,665 institutions European countries. **Remarks:** Accepts advertising. **URL:** http://www.elsevier.com/wps/find/journaldescription.cws_home/503342/descriptiondescription. **Circ:** (Not Reported)

46202 ■ Nutrition, Metabolism, & Cardiovascular Diseases
Mosby Inc.
Dept. Clinical & Experimental Medicine
Federico II University
Via S Pansini 5
I-80131 Naples, Italy
Publisher E-mail: custserv.ehs@elsevier.com
Journal serving as a forum designed to focus on the powerful interplay between nutritional and metabolic alterations, and cardiovascular disorders. **Freq:** 12/yr. **Key Personnel:** Prof. Paolo Rubba, Editor-in-Chief, scalaros@unina.it; F. Brighenti, Assoc. Ed.; F. Dotta, Assoc. Ed. **ISSN:** 0930-4753. **Subscription Rates:** EUR180 individuals for European countries and Iran; US$228 other countries except Europe, Japan and Iran; 24,100¥ individuals; US$774 institutions, other countries except Europe, Japan and Iran; EUR599 institutions for European countries and Iran; 81,100¥ institutions. **Remarks:** Accepts advertising. **URL:** http://www.nmcd-journal.com; http://www.elsevier.com/wps/find/journaldescription.cws_home/704955/description. **Circ:** (Not Reported)

46203 ■ Web Journal on Cultural Patrimony
University of Naples
c/o Presidenza
Facolta di Studi Arabo-Islamici e del Mediterraneo
L'Orientale
via Nuova Marina n. 59
80133 Naples, Italy
Ph: 39 0816909303
Fax: 39 0816909396
Publisher E-mail: international@unina.it
Peer-reviewed academic Journal focusing on protection, conservation, valorization and study of international material as well as immaterial, cultural patrimony. **Key Personnel:** Fabio Maniscalco, Director, maniscalco_fabio@libero.it. **ISSN:** 1827-8868. **URL:** http://www.webjournal.unior.it/.

Napoli

46204 ■ International Journal of Engineering Management and Economics
Inderscience Enterprises Limited
c/o Prof. Corrado lo Storto, Ed.-in-Ch.
University of Naples Federico II
Dept. of Economics & Engineering Management
School of Engineering, Piazzale V. Tecchio n. 80
80125 Napoli, Italy
Journal covering the field of engineering management and engineering economics. **Freq:** 4/yr. **Key Personnel:** Prof. Corrado lo Storto, Editor-in-Chief, corrado.lostorto@unina.it. **ISSN:** 1756-5154. **Subscription Rates:** EUR494 individuals print or online; EUR672 individuals print and online. **URL:** http://www.inderscience.com/browse/index.php?journalID=299.

Padua

46205 ■ Inorganic Chemistry Communications
Elsevier Science
c/o U. Belluco, Ed.
PO Box 976
I-35100 Padua, Italy
Publisher E-mail: nlinfo-f@elsevier.com
Journal dealing with the areas of inorganic, organometallic and supramolecular chemistry. **Founded:** 1998. **Freq:** Monthly. **Key Personnel:** T.E. Bitterwolf, Editor, bitterte@uidaho.edu; U. Belluco, Editor, icaub@tin.it; C.-Y. Su, Editor, cesscy@mail.sysu.edu.cn. **ISSN:** 1387-7003. **Subscription Rates:** 22,100¥ individuals; EUR166 individuals European countries; US$187 individuals all countries except Europe and Japan; 105,600¥ institutions; EUR796 institutions European countries; US$8,896 institutions all countries except Europe and Japan. **Remarks:** Accepts advertising. **URL:** http://www.elsevier.com/wps/find/journaldescription.cws_home/600912/description. **Circ:** (Not Reported)

46206 ■ Italia Turistica
Italia Turistica S.A.S.
Via. G. Fiocco, 9
I-35124 Padua, Italy
Ph: 39 498 011180
Fax: 39 498 011182

Publisher E-mail: info@italiaturistica.net
Consumer magazine covering Italy in Italian, English and German for travelers and tourists. **Freq:** Bimonthly Feb, Apr, Jun, Aug, Oct, Dec. **Print Method:** Roto offset. **Subscription Rates:** 31 Lr individuals Italy; 62 Lr individuals abroad. **Remarks:** Accepts advertising. **URL:** http://www.italiaturistica.net; http://www.fromitaly.it/italiaturistica. **Circ:** Combined 150,000

Palermo

46207 ■ Annals of Burns and Fire Disasters
Mediterranean Council for Burns and Fire Disasters
Via C. Lazzaro
90127 Palermo, Italy
Ph: 39 916 663631
Fax: 39 915 96404
Publisher E-mail: mbcpa@medbc.com
Journal covering common themes, analogies, and contrasts in the fields of prevention, treatment and functional recovery from burns and fire disasters. **Founded:** 1911. **Freq:** Quarterly. **Print Method:** Offset. **Trim Size:** 8 1/4 x 11. **Cols./Page:** 3. **Key Personnel:** M. Masellis, MD, Editor; S.W.A. Gunn, MD, Editor. **ISSN:** 1592-9566. **Subscription Rates:** US$10 members; US$15 nonmembers. **URL:** http://www.medbc.com/annals/.

46208 ■ Sikania
Casa Editrice Krea S.R.L.
Piazza Don Bosco 6
I-90143 Palermo, Italy
Ph: 39 91 543506
Fax: 39 91 6373378
Publication E-mail: info@sikania.it
Publisher E-mail: info@sikania.it
Consumer magazine covering tourism, culture and traditions of Sicily. **Founded:** 1984. **Freq:** Monthly. **Print Method:** Offset. **Key Personnel:** Hanne Carstensen, Contact; Maria Cristina Castellucci, Contact. **ISSN:** 1123-7058. **Subscription Rates:** EUR30 nonmembers; EUR93 elsewhere non-members; EUR55 members; EUR135 elsewhere for members. **Remarks:** Accepts advertising. **URL:** http://www.sikania.it/sitokrea/en_krea.html. **Ad Rates:** BW: EUR1,050, 4C: EUR1,550. **Circ:** Paid 10,000

Palestrina

Radio Onda Libera-FM - See Frosinone
Radio Onda Libera-FM - See Rome

Pavia

46209 ■ Haematologica/The Hematology Journal
European Hematology Association
Giuseppe Belli 4
I-27100 Pavia, Italy
Ph: 39 382 27129
Fax: 39 382 394705
Publisher E-mail: info@ehaweb.org
Journal containing the results from basic and clinical research in hematology. **Key Personnel:** Mario Cazzola, Editor-in-Chief; Clara Camaschella, Assoc. Ed.; Elias Campo, Assoc. Ed. **ISSN:** 0390-6078. **Subscription Rates:** EUR400 institutions; EUR150 individuals; EUR75 individuals online only. **URL:** http://www.haematologica-thj.org/. **Formed by the merger of:** Haematologica (2005); The Hematology Journal.

46210 ■ Numerische Mathematik
Springer-Verlag
c/o Franco Brezzi, Ed.-in-Ch.
Istituto di Analisi Numerica - C.N.R.
Via Ferrata 1
I-27100 Pavia, Italy
Fax: 39 382 548300
Journal publishing articles on latest developments in Numerical Analysis. **Freq:** 4/yr. **Key Personnel:** Franco Brezzi, Editor-in-Chief, brezzi@imati.cnr.it; Tony F. Chan, Editor-in-Chief, fax 310206-6673, tonyc@college.ucla.edu; Michael Griebel, Editor-in-Chief, fax 49 228 737864, nm@iam.uni-bonn.de. **ISSN:** 0029-599X. **Subscription Rates:** EUR2,368 institutions print incl. free access; EUR2,841.60 institutions print incl. enhanced access. **Remarks:** Advertising accepted; rates available upon request. **URL:** http://www.springer.com/mathematics/numericalandcomputationalmathematics/journal/211. **Circ:** (Not Reported)

46211 ■ Structural Control and Health Monitoring
John Wiley & Sons Inc.
Dipartimento di Meccanica Strutturale
Universita di Pavia
Ferrata 1
I-27100 Pavia, Italy
Publisher E-mail: info@wiley.com
Journal focusing on the field of structural control and all aspects of structural control theory and technology. **Freq:** 8/yr. **Key Personnel:** Lucia Faravelli, Editor-in-Chief; Y. Suzuki, Advisory Board; Tsu-Teh Soong, Honorary Ed.; W.J. Staszewski, Advisory Board; G. Chen, Advisory Board; F. Casciati, Advisory Board; C. Boller, Advisory Board. **ISSN:** 1545-2255. **Subscription Rates:** US$416 other countries print only; US$554 institutions, other countries print only; EUR358 institutions print only; 282 institutions print only; EUR394 institutions print and online; 311 institutions print and online; US$610 institutions, other countries print and online. **URL:** http://as.wiley.com/WileyCDA/WileyTitle/productCd-STC.html. **Formerly:** Journal of Structural Control and Health Monitoring.

Peschiera Borromeo

46212 ■ Agri Parts
Koster Publishing S.p.A.
Via. della Liberazione, 1
I-20068 Peschiera Borromeo, MI, Italy
Ph: 39 255 305067
Fax: 39 255 305068
Publication E-mail: koster@kotser.it
Publisher E-mail: koster@koster.it
Trade magazine covering parts for agricultural machinery and equipment. **Subtitle:** Il Giornale Del Rivenditore Agricolo. **Founded:** 2000. **Freq:** Bimonthly. **Print Method:** Offset. **Trim Size:** 285 mm x 367 mm. **Cols./Page:** 3. **Subscription Rates:** EUR35 individuals Italy; EUR60 other countries. **URL:** http://www.koster.it/agriparts/index.asp. **Ad Rates:** BW: EUR900, 4C: EUR1,260. **Circ:** 10,000

46213 ■ Bellauto
Koster Publishing S.p.A.
Via. della Liberazione, 1
I-20068 Peschiera Borromeo, MI, Italy
Ph: 39 255 305067
Fax: 39 255 305068
Publisher E-mail: koster@koster.it
Professional magazine covering automobile repair. **Founded:** 1998. **Freq:** 9/yr. **Print Method:** Offset. **Trim Size:** 210 mm x 275 mm. **Cols./Page:** 3. **Subscription Rates:** EUR50 individuals. **URL:** http://www.koster.it/bellauto/index.asp. **Ad Rates:** 4C: EUR1,460. **Circ:** Combined 12,400

46214 ■ Euro Electric News
Koster Publishing S.p.A.
Via. della Liberazione, 1
I-20068 Peschiera Borromeo, MI, Italy
Ph: 39 255 305067
Fax: 39 255 305068
Publisher E-mail: koster@koster.it
Trade magazine covering economics, finance and technical issues for the electrotechnical sector. **Founded:** 1998. **Freq:** 18/yr. **Print Method:** Offset. **Trim Size:** 210 x 275 mm. **Cols./Page:** 3. **Subscription Rates:** EUR150 individuals; EUR180 individuals. **Remarks:** Accepts advertising. **URL:** http://www.koster.it/Euroelectric/index.asp. **Ad Rates:** BW: EUR3,000. **Circ:** Paid 15,000

46215 ■ Il Giornale dei Veicoli Commerciali
Koster Publishing S.p.A.
Via. della Liberazione, 1
I-20068 Peschiera Borromeo, MI, Italy
Ph: 39 255 305067
Fax: 39 255 305068
Publisher E-mail: koster@koster.it
Trade magazine covering light truck production, equipment, accessories, maintenance and sales. **Founded:** 1999. **Freq:** Bimonthly. **Print Method:** Offset. **Trim Size:** 245 x 340 mm. **Subscription Rates:** EUR35 individuals; EUR50 other countries. **Remarks:** Advertising accepted; rates available upon request. **URL:** http://www.koster.it/veicolicommerciali/index.asp. **Circ:** Paid 20,000

46216 ■ Il Gommone e la Nautica per Tutti
Koster Publishing S.p.A.
Via. della Liberazione, 1
I-20068 Peschiera Borromeo, MI, Italy

Circulation: ★ = ABC; △ = BPA; ◆ = CAC; • = CCAB; ❏ = VAC; ⊕ = PO Statement; ‡ = Publisher's Report; Boldface figures = sworn; Light figures = estimated.

Gale Directory of Publications & Broadcast Media/147th Ed.   5073

Ph: 39 255 305067
Fax: 39 255 305068
Publisher E-mail: koster@koster.it
Consumer magazine covering boating and tourism.
Founded: 1976. **Freq:** Monthly. **Print Method:** Offset.
Trim Size: 210 x 275 mm. **Cols./Page:** 3. **Subscription Rates:** EUR90 individuals. **Remarks:** Accepts advertising. **URL:** http://www.ilgommone.net/. **Ad Rates:** BW: EUR1,530, 4C: EUR2,400. **Circ:** Combined 31,000

Pinerolo

46217 ■ Ingredienti Alimentari
Chiriotti Editori SpA
Viale Rimembranza, 60
10064 Pinerolo, Italy
Ph: 39 121 393127
Fax: 39 121 794480
Publisher E-mail: info@chiriottieditori.it
Magazine dealing with the world of food ingredients: raw materials, semifinished products, additives, flavours, food colours, sweeteners, improving agents and all the products used in food processing and optimization. **Subtitle:** Aromi Additivi Semilavorati. **Freq:** Bimonthly. **Key Personnel:** Giuseppe Chiriotti, Director. **Subscription Rates:** EUR40 individuals; EUR95 other countries airmail; US$115 other countries; EUR65 individuals Europe. **URL:** http://chiriotti.it/index.php?option=com_content&view=article&id=13&Itemid=17&lang=en.

Pisa

46218 ■ Bollettino Telematico di Filosofia Politica
Universita di Pisa
Dipartimento di Scienze della Politica
Via Serafini, 3
56126 Pisa, Italy
Ph: 39 502 212412
Fax: 39 502 212400
Publisher E-mail: bfp@sp.unipi.it
Journal covering review articles, bibliographies, book reviews, and teaching resources about political philosophy, both from an historical and contemporary perspective. **Key Personnel:** Maria Chiara Pievatolo, Contact. **ISSN:** 1591-4305. **URL:** http://bfp.sp.unipi.it/hj05b/.

Rocca di Papa

46219 ■ New Humanity
Focolare Movement
Via. di Frascati 306
I-00040 Rocca di Papa, Italy
Ph: 39 694 7989
Fax: 39 694 749320
Publisher E-mail: sif@focolare.org
Italian language publication covering Catholicism. **Subtitle:** Cultural Bimonthly Review. **Founded:** 1979. **Freq:** Bimonthly. **URL:** http://www.focolare.org; http://www.new-humanity.org/uk/_about.htm. **Circ:** 5,000

Rome

46220 ■ Aeronautica & Difesa
Edizioni Monografie S.R.L.
Casella Postale 2118
I-00100 Rome, Italy
Ph: 39 651 80534
Fax: 39 651 00013
Publication E-mail: aerodife@tin.it
Professional magazine covering aeronautics and defense. **Founded:** 1987. **Freq:** Monthly. **Print Method:** Roto offset. **Trim Size:** 21 x 29.7 cm. **Cols./Page:** 3. **ISSN:** 0394-820X. **Remarks:** Accepts advertising. **URL:** http://www.aeroflight.co.uk/mags/italy/itymag05.htm. **Circ:** (Not Reported)

46221 ■ Apiacta
International Federation of Beekeepers' Associations
Federation Internationale des Associations d'Apiculture
Corso Vittorio Emanuele 101
I-00186 Rome, Italy
Ph: 39 668 52286
Fax: 39 668 52287
Publisher E-mail: apimondia@mclink.it
Publication covering apiculture in English, French, German and Spanish. **Freq:** Quarterly. **Key Personnel:** Dr. Wyatt A. Mangum, Editor-in-Chief, wmangum@umw.edu. **ISSN:** 0003-6455. **Subscription Rates:** US$28

individuals; US$4 individuals. **Remarks:** Advertising accepted; rates available upon request. **URL:** http://www.beekeeping.com/apimondia/index_us.htm. **Circ:** 250

46222 ■ Attualita Italia-Australia
Associazione Italia-Australia
Via Lombardia 14
I-00187 Rome, Italy
Ph: 39 6 916508992
Fax: 39 6 233201031
Publication E-mail: info@australiaitalia.it
Publisher E-mail: info@australiaitalia.it
Publication covering Australian culture, art and business trade with Italy. **Founded:** 1986. **Freq:** Bimonthly. **Print Method:** Offset. **Cols./Page:** 2. **Remarks:** Accepts advertising. **URL:** http://www.australiaitalia.it/. **Ad Rates:** 4C: US$500. **Circ:** Non-paid 6,000

46223 ■ Carmel in the World
Carmelite Third Order
Tiers Ordre Carmelitaine
Via. Giovanni Lanza, 138
I-00184 Rome, Italy
Ph: 39 64620181
Fax: 39 646201847
English and Italian language Catholic publication. **Freq:** 3/yr. **ISSN:** 0394-7742. **Subscription Rates:** US$13 individuals; EUR10 individuals; 7 individuals. **Remarks:** Advertising not accepted. **URL:** http://carmelites.org/carmelintheworld/. **Circ:** (Not Reported)

46224 ■ Club 3
Periodici San Paolo
Via. Alessandro Severo 58
I-00145 Rome, Italy
Ph: 39 065 978600
Fax: 39 065 978660
Publication E-mail: club3@stpauls.it
Christian magazine for senior citizens. **Freq:** Monthly. **Key Personnel:** Manuel Gandin, Editor; Giuseppe Altamore, Managing Editor, giuseppe.altamore@stpauls.it. **Remarks:** Accepts advertising. **URL:** http://www.vivereinarmonia.it/. **Circ:** (Not Reported)

46225 ■ Cognitive Processing
Springer-Verlag GmbH & Company KG
ECONA
University of Rome La Sapienza
Via dei Marsi, 78
I-00185 Rome, Italy
Publication E-mail: cp.iqcs@tin.it
Publisher E-mail: webmaster@springer.com
Peer-reviewed journal covering the multidisciplinary field of cognitive science. **Freq:** Quarterly. **Key Personnel:** Marta Olivetti Belardinelli, Ch. Ed.; Thomas Hunefeldt, Managing Editor; Tito F. Arecchi, Assoc. Ed.; Ned Block, Assoc. Ed.; Bruno Laeng, Assoc. Ed.; Henrik Hautop, Assoc. Ed. **ISSN:** 1612-4782. **Subscription Rates:** EUR282 institutions; EUR338.40 institutions enhanced access. **Remarks:** Advertising accepted; rates available upon request. **URL:** http://www.springer.com/biomed/neuroscience/journal/10339. **Circ:** (Not Reported)

46226 ■ Development
Society for International Development - Italy
Societe Internationale pour le Developpement
Via. Panisperna 207
I-00184 Rome, Italy
Ph: 39 648 72172
Fax: 39 648 72170
Publication covering worldwide development. **Founded:** 1957. **Freq:** Quarterly March, June, September, December. **Key Personnel:** Wendy Harcourt, Editor. **ISSN:** 1011-6370. **Subscription Rates:** 31 individuals in Europe; US$52 individuals; 31 individuals elsewhere; 305 institutions in Europe; US$508 institutions; 305 institutions elsewhere. **Remarks:** Advertising accepted; rates available upon request. **URL:** http://www.sidint.org/. **Circ:** 3,000

46227 ■ Diabetes/Metabolism Research and Reviews
John Wiley & Sons Inc.
Universita Campus Bio-Medico
Via Alvaro del Portillo 21
I-00128 Rome, Italy
Ph: 39 62 225419160
Fax: 39 62 22541456
Publication E-mail: diabetes@wiley.co.uk
Publisher E-mail: info@wiley.com
Journal focusing on diabetes and related areas of metabolism. **Freq:** 8/yr. **Key Personnel:** Jesse Roth,

Editor-in-Chief; Ann Danoff, Co-Ed.; Bernhard O. Boehm, Co-Ed. **ISSN:** 1520-7552. **Subscription Rates:** US$210 other countries for print; 121 individuals for print; US$895 institutions, other countries for print; EUR578 institutions print; 457 institutions print (UK). **Remarks:** Accepts advertising. **URL:** http://www3.interscience.wiley.com/journal/10009394/home. **Circ:** (Not Reported)

46228 ■ Experimental Brain Research
Springer-Verlag
c/o F. Lacquaniti, Ed.-in-Ch.
Dept. of Neuroscience, Human Physiology Section
University of Rome Tor Vergata & Scientific Institute
Santa Lucia
Via Ardeatina 306
I-00179 Rome, Italy
Ph: 39 6 51501477
Journal publishing on various aspects of experimental research of the central and peripheral nervous system relevant to cerebral functions. **Founded:** 1966. **Freq:** 4/yr. **Key Personnel:** F. Lacquaniti, Editor, fax 39 6 51501477, lacquaniti@caspur.it; C. Marzi, Editor, carloalberto.marzi@univr.it; M.A. Goodale, Editor, mgoodale@uwo.ca. **ISSN:** 0014-4819. **Subscription Rates:** EUR9,357 institutions print incl. free access; EUR11,228.40 institutions print incl. enhanced access. **Remarks:** Advertising accepted; rates available upon request. **URL:** http://www.springer.com/biomed/neuroscience/journal/221. **Circ:** (Not Reported)

46229 ■ Famiglia Cristiana
Periodici San Paolo
Via. Alessandro Severo 58
I-00145 Rome, Italy
Ph: 39 065 978600
Fax: 39 065 978660
Publication E-mail: famigliacristiana@stpauls.it
Christian family magazine. **Subtitle:** Weekly Magazine of Current News, Information and Culture. **Founded:** 1931. **Freq:** Weekly. **Key Personnel:** Don Antonio Sciortino, Editor-in-Chief, direzionefc@stpauls.it; M. Fulvio Donadei, Advertising Mgr., fax 39 48072360, fulvio.donadei@stpauls.it. **Remarks:** Accepts advertising. **URL:** http://www.famigliacristiana.it. **Circ:** 966,671

46230 ■ Geneflow
Bioversity International
Via dei Tre Denari, 472a
Maccarese
I-00057 Rome, Italy
Ph: 39 06 61181
Fax: 39 06 61181
Publisher E-mail: bioversity@cgiar.org
Publication covering botany. **Freq:** Annual. **URL:** http://www.bioversityinternational.org/index.php?id=19&user_bioversitypublications_pi1%5BshowUid%5D=3378.

46231 ■ Genes & Nutrition
Springer Netherlands
c/o Giuditta Perozzi, Ed.
National Research Institute on Food & Nutrition
Via Ardeatina 546
I-00178 Rome, Italy
Publication E-mail: genes_and_nutrition@inran.it
Publisher E-mail: permissions.dordrecht@springer.com
Journal covering research on genetics and nutrition relationship. **Freq:** Quarterly. **Key Personnel:** Giuditta Perozzi, Editor; Fabio Virgili, Editor; Pascale Anderle, Editorial Board. **ISSN:** 1555-8932. **Subscription Rates:** EUR489 institutions print including free access or e-only; EUR586.80 institutions print including enhanced access. **URL:** http://www.springer.com/biomed/humangenetics/journal/12263.

46232 ■ High Blood Pressure & Cardiovascular Prevention
Adis International Ltd.
c/o Prof. Massimo Volpe, Md, Ed.-in-Ch.
2nd Faculty of Medicine, University of Rome, La Sapienza
Via di Grottarossa
I-00189 Rome, Italy
Medical journal devoted to the field of hypertension and prevention of cardiovascular disease, with continuous reviews on the management of hypertension and cardiovascular disease. **Freq:** Quarterly. **Key Personnel:** Prof. Massimo Volpe, MD, Editor-in-Chief, journalhbp@adis.co.nz; F. Cosentino, Dep. Ed.; S. Rubattu, Dep. Ed. **ISSN:** 1220-9879. **Subscription Rates:** US$105 individuals online only; US$125 individuals print

& online. **URL:** http://adisonline.com/highbloodpressure/Pages/default.aspx.

46233 ▪ Il Fiasco
DeAgostini Professionale S.p.A.
Mazzini Tree-Lined Ave., 25
I-00195 Rome, Italy
Ph: 39 632 17538
Fax: 39 632 17808
Publisher E-mail: mc9423@mclink.it
Professional magazine covering tax law for consultants offices, entrepreneurs, executives and tax law experts. **Founded:** 1977. **Freq:** Weekly. **ISSN:** 1124-9307. **Remarks:** Accepts advertising. **URL:** http://sistemailfisco.leggiditalia.it/. **Circ:** (Not Reported)

46234 ▪ International Journal of Environment and Health
Inderscience Publishers
c/o Prof. Marcelo Enrique Conti, Ed.-in-Ch.
Universita di Roma La Sapienza
Dipartimento per le Tecnologie, le Risorse e lo Sviluppo
Via Del Castro Laurenziano 9
I-00161 Rome, Italy
Publisher E-mail: editor@inderscience.com
Journal publishing original and review articles focusing on the different aspects of environmentally-related health problems, covering both theoretical modelling and applied research: analytical monitoring of biological, chemical and physical contaminants; applied clinical studies; ecotoxicology and biomonitoring; environmental biosensors and biomarkers; ecosystem protection and management; environmental restoration and recovery; environmentally related diseases/pathologies; regulatory aspects and legislation; bioethical issues. **Freq:** Quarterly. **Key Personnel:** Prof. Marcelo Enrique Conti, Editor-in-Chief, marcelo.conti@uniroma1.it; Prof. Hanns Moshammer, Editorial Board Member; Prof. Mauro Mecozzi, Editorial Board Member; Dr. Irene Calesini, Editorial Board Member; Prof. Franco Mazzei, Assoc. Ed.; Prof. Otmaro Enrique Roses, Assoc. Ed.; Prof. Luigi Campanella, Editorial Board Member; Dr. Mauro Mecozzi, Editorial Board Member. **ISSN:** 1743-4955. **Subscription Rates:** EUR494 individuals print or online; EUR672 individuals print and online. **URL:** http://www.inderscience.com/browse/index.php?journalCODE=ijenvh.

46235 ▪ International Journal of Technology and Globalisation
Inderscience Publishers
c/o Prof. Daniele Archibugi, Co-Ed.
Italian National Research Council
Institute for Studies on Scientific Research
Via dei Taurini, 19
I-00185 Rome, Italy
Publisher E-mail: editor@inderscience.com
Peer-reviewed journal providing a refereed and authoritative source of analysis on the interactions between technological innovation and globalisation, serving as an international forum for exchange of ideas and views on the global implications of technology for economic growth, sustainable development and international security. **Subtitle:** Economy, Sustainability and Security. **Freq:** Quarterly. **Key Personnel:** Prof. Daniele Archibugi, Co-Ed., daniele.archibugi@cnr.it; Dr. Caroline Wagner, Regional Ed.; Prof. Calestous Juma, Co-Ed., calestous_juma@harvard.edu; Dr. Patarapong Intarakumnerd, Regional Ed.; Prof. Banji Oyelaran-Oyeyinka, Regional Ed.; Dr. Peilei Fan, Assoc. Ed. **ISSN:** 1476-5667. **Subscription Rates:** EUR494 individuals hard copy only (surface mail); EUR672 individuals hard copy and online; EUR534 individuals hard copy only (airmail); EUR840 individuals online only (2-3 users). **URL:** http://www.inderscience.com/browse/index.php?journalCODE=ijtg.

46236 ▪ Jesus
Periodici San Paolo
Via. Alessandro Severo 58
I-00145 Rome, Italy
Ph: 39 065 978600
Fax: 39 065 978660
Publication E-mail: jesus@stpauls.it
Consumer magazine covering religion. **Founded:** 1978. **Freq:** Monthly. **Trim Size:** 21 x 28 cm. **Key Personnel:** Vincenzo Marras, Editor-in-Chief, fax 39 480 72486, vincenzo.marras@stpaul.it. **Remarks:** Accepts advertising. **URL:** http://www.sanpaolo.org/jesus. **Circ:** 68,173

46237 ▪ La Clessidra
Sothis Editrice S.R.L.
Via. Pietro Maestri 3
I-00191 Rome, Italy
Ph: 39 6 3296563
Fax: 39 6 3295624
Publisher F-mail: sothis@sothis.net
Trade magazine covering the watch industry. **Subtitle:** Since 1945. **Founded:** 1945. **Freq:** Bimonthly. **Trim Size:** 175 x 250 mm. **Key Personnel:** Mara Cella, Editorial Coord., mara.cella@sothis.net; Simone Bruni, Director; Fabrizio Rinversi, Editor-in-Chief, fabrizio.rinversi@sothis.net. **Subscription Rates:** EUR26 individuals; EUR70 individuals air mail; EUR60 by mail in Asia, Africa & U.S.; by airmail; EUR110 individuals Asia, Africa & U.S.; by courier. **Remarks:** Accepts advertising. **URL:** http://www.sothis.net/sothis/riviste2.asp?clessidra/introduzione. **Circ:** Combined 25,000

46238 ▪ Medicina e Morale
Universita Cattolica Del Sacro Cuore
Largo F. Vito 1
I-00168 Rome, Italy
Ph: 39 6 30151
Publication E-mail: amministrazionemedmor@rm.unicatt.it
Publisher E-mail: rettorato@rm.unicatt.it
Scientific journal covering bioethics. **Founded:** 1951. **Freq:** Bimonthly. **Key Personnel:** Angelo Fiori, Director; Elio Sgreccia, Director. **Subscription Rates:** EUR63 individuals Europe (print only); EUR69 other countries print only; EUR48 institutions book store (print only); EUR53 other countries book store (print only); EUR45 individuals online only; EUR80 individuals Europe (online and print); EUR90 other countries online and print; EUR16 single issue; EUR45 other countries online only. **URL:** http://www.rm.unicatt.it/cdb/.

46239 ▪ L'Orologio
Editore Argo S.R.L.
Circonvaliazione Nomentana 212/214
I-00162 Rome, Italy
Ph: 39 6 8606129
Fax: 39 6 8606324
Publication E-mail: argo@argoeditore.net
Publisher E-mail: argo@argoeditore.net
Consumer magazine covering issues for watch enthusiasts and collectors. **Subtitle:** La Macchina Del Tempo. **Founded:** 1992. **Freq:** Monthly. **Print Method:** Roto-offset. **Trim Size:** 210 x 270 mm. **Key Personnel:** Renato Giussani, Director. **Remarks:** Accepts advertising. **URL:** http://www.argoeditore.net. **Circ:** (Not Reported)

46240 ▪ Progressio
World Christian Life Community
Borgo Santo Spirito, 4
I-00195 Rome, Italy
Ph: 39 668 977792
Fax: 39 668 977220
Publisher E-mail: exsec@cvx-clc.net
Publication covering Catholicism in English, French and Spanish. **Freq:** Semiannual. **ISSN:** 0033-0728. **Subscription Rates:** US$24 individuals North America; C$30 individuals North America; US$19 individuals South America, Asia, Africa; $A 35 individuals; EUR23 individuals. **Remarks:** Advertising not accepted. **URL:** http://www.cvx-clc.net/l-en/progressio.html. **Circ:** (Not Reported)

46241 ▪ Shalom
Comunita Ebraica di Roma
Lungotevere Cenci (Tempio)
I-00186 Rome, Italy
Ph: 39 6 6840061
Fax: 39 6 68400684
Publisher E-mail: shalom.mensile@libero.it
Consumer magazine covering news, culture and politics for a Jewish audience. **Founded:** 1952. **Key Personnel:** Giacomo Kahn, Director; Simone Tedeschi, Contact. **URL:** http://www.shalom.it/. **Circ:** Combined 10,000

46242 ▪ Statistical Methods and Applications
Springer Netherlands
University The Sapienza di Roma
Dept. Statistica, Probabilita e Statistiche Applicate
P.le A. Moro, 5
I-00100 Rome, Italy
Publisher E-mail: permissions.dordrecht@springer.com
Journal covering biological, demographic, economic, health, physical, social and other scientific domains. **Subtitle:** Journal of the Italian Statistical Society.

Founded: 1976. **Freq:** Quarterly. **Print Method:** Offset. **Trim Size:** 8 1/4 x 11. **Cols./Page:** 3. **Col. Width:** 27 nonpareils. **Col. Depth:** 140 agate lines. **Key Personnel:** Andrea Cerioli, Co-Ed.; Lucio Barabesi, Editorial Board; Roberto Baragona, Editorial Board; Francesco Battaglia, Editor; Francesco Bartolucci, Editorial Board; Cinzia Carota, Editorial Board. **ISSN:** 1618-2510. **Subscription Rates:** EUR335 institutions print incl. free access or e-only; EUR402 institutions print incl. enhanced access. **URL:** http://www.springer.com/statistics/journal/10260.

46243 ▪ Travelling Interline International
Interline International Club
Via Nazionale, 204
I-00184 Rome, Italy
Ph: 39 6 4871721
Fax: 39 6 4871618
Publisher E-mail: info@interlinegroup.it
Trade magazine covering tourism and culture. **Founded:** Sept. 1992. **Freq:** Monthly. **Print Method:** Offset. **Cols./Page:** 4. **Col. Width:** 5 centimeters. **Col. Depth:** 31 centimeters. **Key Personnel:** Liliana Comande, Editor, l.comande@travellinginterline.it; Marco Comande, Publisher, m.comande@travellinginterline.it. **Remarks:** Accepts advertising. **URL:** http://travelling.travelsearch.it/. **Circ:** Combined 20,000

46244 ▪ Tuttoscuola
Editoriale Tuttoscuola SRL
Via. Della Scrofa 39
00186 Rome, Italy
Ph: 39 6 68307851
Fax: 39 6 68802728
Publication E-mail: tuttoscuola@tuttoscuola.com
Publisher E-mail: tuttoscuola@tuttoscuola.com
Consumer magazine covering educational and school policy, tutoring, foreign education systems, teachers and other issues in Italy. **Founded:** 1975. **Freq:** Monthly. **Print Method:** Offset. **Cols./Page:** 3. **ISSN:** 0391-7967. **URL:** http://www.tuttoscuola.com. **Circ:** Paid ‡45,000

46245 ▪ WHERE Rome
Miller Publishing Group L.L.C.
172 via Ostiense
I-00154 Rome, Italy
Ph: 39 6 5781615
Fax: 39 6 5781755
Travel and tourism magazine focusing on Rome, Italy. **Key Personnel:** Federico Schiaffino, Editor; Angela M. Di Pietro, Mng. Dir. **Remarks:** Accepts advertising. **URL:** http://www.whererome.it/. **Circ:** (Not Reported)

46246 ▪ Radio Onda Libera-FM - 99 Mhz
Via Santa Maria, 30/40
00036 Palestrina, Italy
Ph: 39 6 9535787
Fax: 39 6 9537203
E-mail: ondalibera@ondalibera.it
Format: News. **Owner:** Radio Onda Libera, at above address. **Founded:** 1977. **Key Personnel:** Paolo Filippi, Director. **URL:** http://www.ondalibera.it/.

Rozzano

46247 ▪ Autopro
Editoriale Domus S.p.A.
Via. Gianni Mazzocchi 1/3
I-20089 Rozzano, MI, Italy
Publisher E-mail: editorialedomus@edidomus.it
Trade magazine covering technical appraisals and related information for car workshops, garages, garage mechanics, car accessory retailers and car dealers. **Founded:** 1998. **Freq:** Bimonthly. **Print Method:** Roto offset. **Trim Size:** 20.4 x 27 cm. **Key Personnel:** Mauro Tedeschini, Managing Editor. **Remarks:** Accepts advertising. **URL:** http://www.edidomus.it/Ed/menuverticale/autopro.cfm?lingua=_eng. **Ad Rates:** 4C: EUR2,100. **Circ:** 27,000

46248 ▪ Domus
Editoriale Domus S.p.A.
Via. Gianni Mazzocchi 1/3
I-20089 Rozzano, MI, Italy
Publisher E-mail: editorialedomus@edidomus.it
Professional magazine covering architecture, urban planning, furnishing, art and design. **Founded:** 1928. **Freq:** Monthly. **Trim Size:** 24.5 x 32.5 cm. **Key Personnel:** Giovanna Mazzocchi Bordone, Publisher; Alessandro Mendini, Editor-in-Chief. **Subscription Rates:**

EUR189 individuals Europe, Mediterranean; EUR199 individuals Africa, America, Asia; EUR209 individuals Oceania. **Remarks:** Accepts advertising. **URL:** http://www.domusweb.it/domus2k6/index.cfm?lingua=_eng. **Circ:** Combined 51,000

46249 ■ Domus Kit
Editoriale Domus S.p.A.
Via. Gianni Mazzocchi 1/3
I-20089 Rozzano, MI, Italy
Publisher E-mail: editorialedomus@edidomus.it
Consumer magazine and kit covering cardboard architectural model building of world monuments, including the Tower of Pisa, Tower Bridge and Basilica of St. Mark's. **Founded:** 1983. **Freq:** Triennial. **Key Personnel:** Giovanna Mazzocchi Bordone, Publisher. **URL:** http://www.domuskits.com/. **Circ:** Combined 15,000

46250 ■ Il Cucchiaio D'Argento
Editoriale Domus S.p.A.
Via. Gianni Mazzocchi 1/3
I-20089 Rozzano, MI, Italy
Publisher E-mail: editorialedomus@edidomus.it
Consumer magazine covering cooking, recipes, wine, and menus. **Founded:** 1950. **URL:** http://www.cucchiaio.it/cucina/avvio.cfm.

46251 ■ Meridiani
Editoriale Domus S.p.A.
Via. Gianni Mazzocchi 1/3
I-20089 Rozzano, MI, Italy
Publisher E-mail: editorialedomus@edidomus.it
Consumer magazine covering travel and tourism. **Founded:** 1988. **Freq:** Monthly. **Trim Size:** 19.2 x 27 cm. **Key Personnel:** Remo Guerrini, Editor. **Remarks:** Accepts advertising. **URL:** http://www.edidomus.it/ed/menuverticale/meridiani.cfm?lingua=_eng. **Circ:** ‡31,066

46252 ■ Quattroruote
Editoriale Domus S.p.A.
Via. Gianni Mazzocchi 1/3
I-20089 Rozzano, MI, Italy
Publisher E-mail: editorialedomus@edidomus.it
Consumer magazine covering automobiles. **Founded:** 1956. **Print Method:** Rotogravure. **Trim Size:** 204 x 270 mm. **Cols./Page:** 4. **Key Personnel:** Charles Cavill, Editor-in-Chief. **Remarks:** Accepts advertising. **URL:** http://www.quattroruote.it. **Circ:** ‡464,393

46253 ■ Ruoteclassiche
Editoriale Domus S.p.A.
Via. Gianni Mazzocchi 1/3
I-20089 Rozzano, MI, Italy
Publisher E-mail: editorialedomus@edidomus.it
Consumer magazine covering automobile history, engineering and classic automobiles. **Founded:** 1987. **Freq:** Monthly. **Trim Size:** 22 x 28.7 cm. **Key Personnel:** Raffaele Laurenzi, Editor. **Remarks:** Accepts advertising. **URL:** http://www.edidomus.it/Ed/menuverticale/ruoteclassiche.cfm?lingua=_eng. **Circ:** 50,600

46254 ■ Tuttotrasporti
Editoriale Domus S.p.A.
Via. Gianni Mazzocchi 1/3
I-20089 Rozzano, MI, Italy
Publisher E-mail: editorialedomus@edidomus.it
Trade magazine covering automobile and truck road tests, new products, surveys and used vehicles for fleer managers and others. **Founded:** 1978. **Freq:** Monthly. **Print Method:** Roto Offset. **Trim Size:** 20.5 x 27 cm. **Key Personnel:** Marcello Minerbi, Managing Editor. **Remarks:** Accepts advertising. **URL:** http://www.edidomus.it/Ed/menuverticale/tuttotrasporti.cfm?lingua=_eng; http://www.quattroruote.it/trasporti. **Ad Rates:** 4C: 7,200 Lr. **Circ:** 22,127

46255 ■ Tuttoturismo
Editoriale Domus S.p.A.
Via. Gianni Mazzocchi 1/3
I-20089 Rozzano, MI, Italy
Publisher E-mail: editorialedomus@edidomus.it
Consumer magazine covering travel and tourism. **Founded:** Dec. 1977. **Freq:** Monthly. **Trim Size:** 23 x 28.5 cm. **Key Personnel:** Nicoletta Salvatori, Editor. **Remarks:** Accepts advertising. **URL:** http://www.edidomus.it/ed/menuverticale/tuttoturismo.cfm. **Circ:** Combined ‡41,623

46256 ■ Vendo & Compro
Editoriale Domus S.p.A.

Via. Gianni Mazzocchi 1/3
I-20089 Rozzano, MI, Italy
Publisher E-mail: editorialedomus@edidomus.it
Consumer magazine covering used cars in Italy. **Founded:** 1997. **Freq:** Monthly. **Print Method:** Roto Offset. **Trim Size:** 20.7 x 28.5 cm. **Key Personnel:** Mauro Tedeschini, Editor, direttore@vendoecompro.it. **Remarks:** Accepts advertising. **URL:** http://www.edidomus.it/ed/menuverticale/quattroruote.cfm?vis=4&lingua=_eng. **Ad Rates:** 4C: EUR7,200. **Circ:** Combined 125,000

46257 ■ Volare
Editoriale Domus S.p.A.
Via. Gianni Mazzocchi 1/3
I-20089 Rozzano, MI, Italy
Publisher E-mail: editorialedomus@edidomus.it
Magazine covering all aspects of civil, commercial and military aviation, including flying schools and aeronautical sports. **Founded:** 1998. **Freq:** Monthly. **Trim Size:** 22 x 28.7 cm. **Key Personnel:** Giuseppe Braga, Managing Editor; Giovanna Mazzocchi Bordone, Publisher. **Remarks:** Accepts advertising. **URL:** http://www.edidomus.it/Ed/menuverticale/volare.cfm?lingua=_eng. **Circ:** 17,618

Siena

46258 ■ Clinical Hemorheology and Microcirculation
IOS Press, B.V.
c/o S. Forconi, Ed.-in-Ch.
Siena Toronto Ctre.
University of Siena
Banchi di Sotto 81
I-53100 Siena, Italy
Ph: 39 577 232456
Publisher E-mail: info@iospress.nl
Peer-reviewed international scientific journal serving as an aid to understanding the flow properties of blood and the relationship to normal and abnormal physiology. **Freq:** Monthly. **Key Personnel:** S. Forconi, Editor-in-Chief, forconi@unisi.it; G. Ambrosio, Editorial Board; F. Jung, Editor-in-Chief, jai-wunpark@t-online.de; A.L. Copley, Founding Ed.; J.F. Stoltz, Editor-in-Chief, phone 33 383 683452, patrick.menu@medecine.uhp-nancy.fr; H.J. Meiselman, Editorial Board; C. Allegra, Editorial Board; H.H. Lipowski, Editorial Board; S. Witte, Founding Ed.; H. Niimi, Editor-in-Chief, phone 81 668 727485, sekij@ri.ncvc.go.jp. **ISSN:** 1386-0291. **Subscription Rates:** EUR1,314 individuals print and online; US$1,790 institutions print and online. **URL:** http://www.iospress.nl/loadtop/load.php?isbn=13860291.

46259 ■ Tissue & Cell
Mosby Inc.
c/o R. Dallai, Ed.
Dept. of Evolutionary Biology
University of Siena
Via A. Moro 2
I-53100 Siena, Italy
Publisher E-mail: custserv.ehs@elsevier.com
Journal publishing original research in the organization of cells, their components and extracellular products at all levels. **Freq:** Bimonthly. **Key Personnel:** R. Dallai, Editor; W.J. Dougherty, Editorial Board; M.C. Holley, Editorial Board; G.C. Godman, Editorial Board; D.S. Smith, Founding Ed.; D. Herbert, Editorial Board; J. Auber, Editorial Board; R.A. Hess, Editorial Board; N.J. Lane, Editorial Board; H. Chemes, Editorial Board; M. Mazzini, Editorial Board; J. Ryerse, Editorial Board. **ISSN:** 0040-8166. **Subscription Rates:** EUR1,273 institutions for European countries and Iran; 137,600¥ institutions; US$1,131 institutions, other countries except Europe, Japan and Iran. **Remarks:** Accepts advertising. **URL:** http://www.elsevier.com/wps/find/journaldescription.cws_home/623075/descriptiondescription. **Circ:** (Not Reported)

Trento

46260 ■ ACAV Informa
Associazione Centro Aiuti Volontari Cooperazione Sviluppo Terzo Mondo
Via Sighele, 3
I-38100 Trento, Italy
Ph: 39 461 935893
Fax: 39 461 935893
Publisher E-mail: acav@acavtn.it
Italian language publication covering agricultural development. **Freq:** Monthly. **Remarks:** Advertising not

accepted. **URL:** http://www.acavtn.it/. **Circ:** (Not Reported)

46261 ■ Applied Ontology
IOS Press, B.V.
National Research Council
Institute for Cognitive Sciences & Technologies
Laboratory for Applied Ontology
Via alla Cascata, 56/C
I-38100 Trento, Italy
Ph: 39 461 314871
Publisher E-mail: info@iospress.nl
Journal focusing on information content in its broadest sense, including two broad kinds of content-based research activities: ontological analysis and conceptual modeling. **Freq:** Quarterly. **Key Personnel:** Mark A. Musen, Editor-in-Chief, phone 650725-3390, musen@stanford.edu; Nicola Guarino, Editor-in-Chief, guarino@loa-cnr.it; Natasha Noy, Editorial Board; Anthony Cohn, Editorial Board; Hans Akkermans, Editorial Board; John A. Bateman, Editorial Board; Chris Menzel, Editorial Board; Olivier Bodenreider, Editorial Board; Barry Smith, Editorial Board. **ISSN:** 1570-5838. **Subscription Rates:** EUR463 institutions print and online; US$640 institutions print and online. **URL:** http://www.iospress.nl/loadtop/load.php?isbn=15705838; http://www.applied-ontology.org/.

46262 ■ International Journal of Agent-Oriented Software Engineering
Inderscience Publishers
c/o Paolo Giorgini, Ed.
University of Trento
Department of Information & Communication Technology
Via Sommarive, 14
I-38050 Trento, Italy
Publisher E-mail: editor@inderscience.com
Peer-reviewed journal covering software engineering aspects of the use of agent technology for the development of IT systems. **Founded:** 2007. **Freq:** 4/yr. **Key Personnel:** Paolo Giorgini, Editor, paolo.giorgini@unitn.it; Brian Henderson-Sellers, Editor, brian@it.uts.edu.au; Marie-Pierre Gleizes, Assoc. Ed.; Jorg Muller, Assoc. Ed.; James Odell, Assoc. Ed.; Lin Padgham, Assoc. Ed. **ISSN:** 1746-1375. **Subscription Rates:** EUR494 individuals includes surface mail, print only; EUR672 individuals print and online. **URL:** http://www.inderscience.com/browse/index.php?journalCODE=ijaose.

Trezzano Sul Naviglio

46263 ■ Foto Shoe 15 International
Editoriale di Foto Shoe S.R.L.
Via. Leonardo da Vinci 43
I-20090 Trezzano Sul Naviglio, Italy
Ph: 39 02 4459091
Fax: 39 02 48402959
Publisher E-mail: central@fotoshoe.com
Trade magazine covering the shoe and leather goods components and materials industry. **Founded:** 1973. **Freq:** Bimonthly. **Key Personnel:** Lorenzo Raggi, Editor, raggi@fotoshoe.com. **Subscription Rates:** EUR215 individuals by airmail; US$275 individuals extra-Europe air-mail; by airmail; US$310 individuals extra-Europe registered; by airmail. **Remarks:** Accepts advertising. **URL:** http://www.fotoshoe.com. **Circ:** Combined 8,000

46264 ■ Foto Shoe 30
Editoriale di Foto Shoe S.R.L.
Via. Leonardo da Vinci 43
I-20090 Trezzano Sul Naviglio, Italy
Ph: 39 02 4459091
Fax: 39 02 48402959
Publisher E-mail: central@fotoshoe.com
Trade magazine covering the shoe and leather goods industry. **Founded:** 1969. **Freq:** 8/yr. **Cols./Page:** 4. **Key Personnel:** Lorenzo Raggi, Editor, raggi@fotoshoe.com. **Subscription Rates:** EUR260 individuals Europe; air-mail; US$340 individuals extra-Europe; air-mail; US$385 individuals extra-Europe registered; air-mail. **Remarks:** Accepts advertising. **URL:** http://www.fotoshoe.com. **Circ:** Combined 8,000

Trieste

46265 ■ Journal of Geometry and Physics
Elsevier Science
SISSA/ISAS
International School for Advanced Studies
Via Beirut 4
I-34014 Trieste, Italy

Publisher E-mail: nlinfo-f@elsevier.com
Journal on mathematical physics. **Founded:** 1988. **Freq:** Monthly. **Key Personnel:** U. Bruzzo, Exec. Ed., jgpub@sissa.it; M. Cahen, Editorial Board; A. Trautman, Editorial Board; V.I. Arnold, Editorial Board; S. Benenti, Editorial Board; M. Francaviglia, Editorial Board. **ISSN:** 0393-0440. **Subscription Rates:** US$1,896 institutions all countries except Europe and Japan; EUR1,693 institutions European countries; 225,000¥ institutions. **Remarks:** Accepts advertising. **URL:** http://www.elsevier. com/wps/find/journaldescription.cws_home/523339/descriptiondescription. **Circ:** (Not Reported)

46266 ■ PoS (Proceedings of Science)
SISSA/ISAS
Via Bonomea, 265
34136 Trieste, Italy
Ph: 39 40 3787111
Fax: 39 40 3787249
Publisher E-mail: protocollo@pec.sissa.it
Journal dealing with conference publishing requirements. **Key Personnel:** Amos Breskin, Exec. Editorial Committee; Marc Henneaux, Exec. Editorial Committee; Viatcheslav Mukhanov, Exec. Editorial Committee. **ISSN:** 1824-8039. **Subscription Rates:** Free. **URL:** http://pos. sissa.it/POSwhat.html.

46267 ■ Transactions on Control Systems Technology
IEEE Control Systems Society
c/o Thomas Parisini, Ed.-in-Chief
Dept. of Electrical, Electronic & Computer Engineering
University of Trieste
34127 Trieste, Italy
Publisher E-mail: member.services@ieee.org
Magazine on technological advances in the design, realization, and operation of control systems. **Founded:** 1977. **Freq:** Bimonthly. **Print Method:** Irregular. **Cols./Page:** 2. **Col. Width:** 26 nonpareils. **Col. Depth:** 94 agate lines. **Key Personnel:** Dr. Ian J. Fialho, Assoc. Ed., ian.j.fialho@boeing.com; Dr. Christian Bohn, Assoc. Ed., bohn@atsiei.tu-clausthal.de; Maria Letizia Corradini, Assoc. Ed., letizia.corradini@unicam.it; Dr. GuoXiao Guo, Assoc. Ed., guoxiao.guo@wdc.com. **ISSN:** 1063-6536. **URL:** http://www.ieeecss.org/publications/control-systems-technology.html.

Turin

46268 ■ Acta Vulnologica
Edizioni Minerva Medica
C. So Bramante 83-85
I-10126 Turin, Italy
Ph: 39 116 78282
Fax: 39 116 74502
Publisher E-mail: minervamedica@minervamedica.it
Journal on the pathophysiology and clinical medicine of chronic cutaneous ulcers. **Subtitle:** Organo Ufficiale dell'Associazione Italiana Ulcere Cutanee. **Freq:** Quarterly. **Key Personnel:** L.M. Chinni, Editor-in-Chief. **ISSN:** 1721-2596. **Subscription Rates:** EUR90 individuals print and online; 85 Lr individuals print.

46269 ■ Auto & Design
Corso Francia 54
I-10143 Turin, Italy
Fax: 39 114 88120
Trade magazine covering automobile and industrial design, new trends, concept cars, and related subjects. **Founded:** 1979. **Freq:** Bimonthly. **Print Method:** Offset. **Trim Size:** 220 x 290 mm. **Cols./Page:** 4. **Col. Width:** 5 centimeters. **Key Personnel:** Eros Sogno, Art Dir.; Fulvio Cinti, Editor, fulvio.cinti@autodesignmagazine.com; Silvia Baruffaldi, Managing Editor, silvia.baruffaldi@autodesignmagazine.com. **ISSN:** 0393-8387. **Subscription Rates:** EUR1,800 out of country plus air mail Europe; EUR2,300 out of country air mail Africa; EUR2,200 out of country air mail Mediterranean Basin; EUR4,200 individuals air mail America; EUR4,200 out of country air mail Asia; EUR6,000 out of country airmail Oceania. **Remarks:** Accepts advertising. **URL:** http://www. autodesignmagazine.com. **Circ:** Paid 12,000

46270 ■ Contrast Media & Molecular Imaging
John Wiley & Sons Inc.
c/o Silvio Aime, Ed.-in-Ch.
Dept. of Chemistry
University of Torino
Via P Giuria 7
I-10125 Turin, Italy

Publisher E-mail: info@wiley.com
Journal covering the areas of contrast media and molecular imaging. **Freq:** Bimonthly. **Key Personnel:** Silvio Aime, Editor-in-Chief, silvio.aime@unito.it; Robert N. Muller, Editor-in-Chief, robert.muller@umh.ac.be; Michal Neeman, Assoc. Ed., michal.neeman@weizmann.ac.ll. **ISSN:** 1555-4309 **Remarks:** Accepts advertising. **URL:** http://onlinelibrary.wiley.com/journal/10.1002/(ISSN)1555-4317. **Circ:** (Not Reported)

46271 ■ Economics of Innovation and New Technology
Taylor & Francis Group Journals
c/o Cristiano Antonelli, Mng. Ed.
Fondazione Giovanni Agnelli
Via Giacosa 38
I-10125 Turin, Italy
Publisher E-mail: customerservice@taylorandfrancis. com
Peer-reviewed journal covering theoretical and empirical analysis of innovation and new technology, bridging the contributions of economic theory and empirical economics in this field. **Freq:** 8/yr. **Key Personnel:** Cristiano Antonelli, Managing Editor, agnellifoundation@fga.it; Paul Stoneman, Co-Ed.; Bo Carlsson, Editorial Board; Stanley M. Besen, Editorial Board, smb@crai.com; Dominique Foray, Assoc. Ed.; Nick Crafts, Editorial Board; Robin Cowan, Editorial Board; Paul A. David, Co-Ed.; Rebecca Henderson, Assoc. Ed.; Bronwyn Hall, Assoc. Ed. **ISSN:** 1043-8599. **Subscription Rates:** 1,019 institutions print + online; US$1,314 institutions print + online; 917 institutions online; US$1,183 institutions online; 187 individuals; US$226 individuals; EUR180 individuals; EUR941 institutions online; EUR1,046 institutions print + online. **Remarks:** Advertising accepted; rates available upon request. **URL:** http://www.tandf.co. uk/journals/titles/10438599.asp. **Circ:** (Not Reported)

46272 ■ Impegno
Young Women's Christian Association - Italy
Unione Cristiana Delle Giovani
Via San Secondo 70
I-10128 Turin, Italy
Ph: 39 11 5683369
Fax: 39 11 5131427
Publisher E-mail: segreteria@ywca-ucdg.it
Italian language publication covering the YWCA. **Founded:** 1900. **Freq:** Quarterly. **Remarks:** Advertising not accepted. **URL:** http://www.ywca-ucdg.it/seconda. html. **Circ:** 500

46273 ■ Mathematical Models and Methods in Applied Sciences
World Scientific Publishing Company Private Ltd.
c/o Nicola Bellomo, Ed.
Dipartimento di Matematica
Politecnico di Torino
Corso Duca degli Abruzzi, 24
I-10129 Turin, Italy
Fax: 39 011 5647599
Publisher E-mail: wspc@wspc.com.sg
Periodical providing a medium of exchange for scientists engaged in applied sciences. **Founded:** 1991. **Freq:** Monthly. **Key Personnel:** Nicola Bellomo, Editor, nicola. bellomo@polito.it; D.N. Arnold, Assoc. Ed.; J. Soler, Assoc. Ed.; J. Xu, Assoc. Ed.; E. Zuazua, Assoc. Ed.; M. Pulvirenti, Assoc. Ed. **ISSN:** 0218-2025. **Subscription Rates:** US$1,609 institutions and libraries; electronic + print; US$1,545 institutions and libraries; electronic only; US$56 individuals for postage; EUR44 individuals for postage; EUR1,360 institutions and libraries; electronic + print; EUR1,306 institutions and libraries; electronic only; EUR75 individuals for postage; S$2,506 institutions and libraries; electronic only; S$2,610 institutions and libraries; electronic + print. **URL:** http://www.worldscinet.com/m3as/m3as.shtml.

46274 ■ Rock Mechanics and Rock Engineering
Springer-Verlag
c/o G. Barla, Ed.
Dipartimento di Ingeneria Strutturale
Politecnico di Torino
Corso Duca degli Abruzzi 24
I-10129 Turin, Italy
Fax: 39 11 5644899
Publisher E-mail: springer@springer.at
Journal publishing the experimental and theoretical aspects of rock mechanics, including laboratory and field testing, methods of computation and field observation of structural behavior. **Freq:** 5/yr. **Key Personnel:**

M. Bonini, Asst. Ed., fax 39 11 5644899, rm_re@polito. it; G. Barla, Editor, rm_re@polito.it; N. Barton, Editorial Board; K. Kovari, Co-Ed., fax 41 1 6331097, kovari@igt. baug.ethz.ch; O. Aydan, Editorial Board; T.B. Celestino, Editorial Board; C. Dowding, Editorial Board; G. Anagnostou, Editorial Board; H.H. Einstein, Co-Ed., fax 617253-6044, einstein@mit.edu; C. Carranza Torres, Editorial Board. **ISSN:** 0723-2632. **Remarks:** Advertising accepted; rates available upon request. **URL:** http:// www.springer.com/springerwiennewyork/geosciences/journal/603. **Circ:** (Not Reported)

46275 ■ TTG Italia
TTG Italia S.p.A.
Via Nota 6
I-10122 Turin, TO, Italy
Ph: 39 11 4366300
Fax: 39 11 4366500
Publication E-mail: redazione@ttgitalia.com
Publisher E-mail: ttgitalia@ttgitalia.com
Trade magazine covering travel and tourism for professionals in Italy. **Subtitle:** Travel Trade Gazette. **Founded:** 1973. **Freq:** 2/week. **Print Method:** Web offset. **Trim Size:** 410 x 285mm. **Key Personnel:** Reno Vangelista, Editor-in-Chief, vangelista@ttgitalia.com; Barbara Rebora, Advertising Mgr., rebora@ttgitalia.com. **Subscription Rates:** US$200 individuals. **Remarks:** Accepts advertising. **URL:** http://www.ttgitalia.com/pagine/index.aspx. **Ad Rates:** 4C: EUR2,770. **Circ:** 9,000

Udine

46276 ■ Advances in Fuzzy Mathematics
Research India Publications
c/o Piergiulio Corsini, Ed.-in-Ch.
University of Udine
Via delle Scienze 206
I-33100 Udine, Italy
Publisher E-mail: info@ripublication.com
Journal devoted to fuzzy sets and systems and their applications. **Founded:** 1904. **Freq:** Semiannual. **Print Method:** Offset. **Trim Size:** 12 x 16. **Cols./Page:** 5. **Col. Width:** 23 nonpareils. **Col. Depth:** 224 agate lines. **Key Personnel:** G.A. Anastassiou, Editorial Board Member; Yuh-Wen Chen, Editorial Board Member; Piergiulio Corsini, Editor-in-Chief, corsini@dimi.uniud.it; R.A. Borzooei, Editorial Board Member; Rafik Aliev, Editor; Ismat Beg, Editorial Board Member. **ISSN:** 0973-533X. **Subscription Rates:** US$280 institutions and library; print plus free online; US$260 institutions and library; online only; US$180 individuals print plus free online; US$160 individuals online only; Rs 1,800 individuals. **URL:** http://www.ripublication.com/afm.htm.

Varese

46277 ■ Musica
Zecchini Editore
Via. Tonale 60
I-21100 Varese, Italy
Ph: 39 332 331041
Fax: 39 332 331013
Publication E-mail: info@rivistamusica.com
Publisher E-mail: info@zecchini.com
Magazine covering classical music. **Subtitle:** Italy's Leading Classical Music Magazine since 1977. **Founded:** May 1977. **Freq:** Monthly. **Print Method:** Offset. **Trim Size:** 210 x 297 mm. **Cols./Page:** 4. **Col. Width:** 185 millimeters. **Col. Depth:** 252 millimeters. **ISSN:** 0392-5544. **Subscription Rates:** EUR59 individuals Italy; EUR90 other countries; EUR89 individuals anniversary supporter, only for Italy, 7 cd gift; EUR149 individuals anniversary supporter, only for Italy, 15 cd gift; EUR215 individuals anniversary supporter, only for Italy, 30 cd gift; EUR105 two years Italy; EUR170 two years foreign. **Remarks:** Accepts advertising. **URL:** http://www.rivistamusica.com; http://www.zecchini.com/riviste.php. **Circ:** (Not Reported)

Vernasca

46278 ■ Flortecnica
Ace International
Via. Mocomero 26
I-29010 Vernasca, PC, Italy
Ph: 39 991 0719
Fax: 39 991 0719
Publisher E-mail: info@flortecnica.it
Trade magazine covering ornamental horticulture for

Circulation: ★ = ABC; △ = BPA; ◆ = CAC; • = CCAB; ❑ = VAC; ⊕ = PO Statement; ‡ = Publisher's Report; Boldface figures = sworn; Light figures = estimated.

Gale Directory of Publications & Broadcast Media/147th Ed.   5077

professionals in Italy. **Subtitle:** l'informazione nel Florovivaismo/the Information in Horticulture. **Founded:** 1977. **Freq:** Monthly. **Print Method:** Offset Litho. **Trim Size:** 210 x 280 mm. **Cols./Page:** 3. **Col. Width:** 5.7 centimeters. **Col. Depth:** 25.7 centimeters. **Key Personnel:** Arturo Croci, Managing Editor; Aldo Colombo, Collaborator. **ISSN:** 1122-7958. **Subscription Rates:** US$150 by mail; US$40 by mail surface mail. **Remarks:** Accepts advertising. **URL:** http://www.flortecnica.net; http://www.flortecnica.org. **Ad Rates:** BW: EUR483, 4C: EUR866. **Circ:** Controlled 6,800

46279 ■ Flortecnica Data e Fiori
Ace International
Via. Mocomero 26
I-29010 Vernasca, PC, Italy
Ph: 39 991 0719
Fax: 39 991 0719
Publication E-mail: info@flortecnica.it
Publisher E-mail: info@flortecnica.it
Professional magazine for garden centers and florists.

Founded: 1979. **Freq:** Quarterly. **Print Method:** Offset Litho. **Trim Size:** 210 x 280 mm. **Cols./Page:** 3. **Col. Width:** 5.7 centimeters. **Col. Depth:** 25.7 centimeters. **ISSN:** 1122-7966. **Subscription Rates:** EUR50 individuals costs; EUR85 by mail; EUR60 individuals only for abroad; US$150 by mail; EUR30 individuals; US$40 by mail. **Remarks:** Accepts advertising. **URL:** http://www.flortec.it. **Formerly:** Data e Fiori. **Circ:** Controlled 6,800

Verona

46280 ■ L'Informatore Agrario
Edizione L'Informatore Agrario S.p.A.
Via. Bencivenga/Biondani 16
I-37133 Verona, VR, Italy
Ph: 39 458 057511
Fax: 39 455 97510
Publisher E-mail: info@informatoreagrario.it
Professional magazine covering agriculture. **Founded:** 1945. **Freq:** Weekly. **Print Method:** Roto offset. **Cols./Page:** 3. **Col. Width:** 58 millimeters. **Key Personnel:**

Rossana Rizzotti, Circulation Mgr., phone 39 458009480, fax 39 458012980, abbonamenti@informatoreagrario.it; Giovanni Rizzotti, Editor, g.rizzotti@informatoreagrario.it. **ISSN:** 0020-0689. **Remarks:** Accepts advertising. **URL:** http://www.informatoreagrario.it. **Circ:** Combined 35,211

46281 ■ Vita in Campagna
Edizione L'Informatore Agrario S.p.A.
Via. Bencivenga/Biondani 16
I-37133 Verona, VR, Italy
Ph: 39 458 057511
Fax: 39 455 97510
Publisher E-mail: info@informatoreagrario.it
Magazine covering practical agriculture for part-time farmers, gardeners, and others. **Founded:** 1983. **Freq:** Monthly. **Print Method:** Roto offset. **Cols./Page:** 3. **Col. Width:** 58 millimeters. **Key Personnel:** Giorgio Vincenzi, Director. **ISSN:** 1120-3005. **Remarks:** Accepts advertising. **URL:** http://www.informatoreagrario.it/. **Circ:** Combined 74,211

Kingston

46282 ■ The Children's Own
The Gleaner Company Ltd.
7 N St.
PO Box 40
Kingston, Jamaica
Ph: (876)922-3400
Fax: (809)922-6223
Free: (888)453-2637
Publisher E-mail: feedback@jamaica-gleaner.com
Newspaper covering education and creative learning for children. **URL:** http://www.jamaica-gleaner.com/gleaner/about/newspapers.html.

46283 ■ Destination Jamaica
Jamaica Hotel and Tourist Association
2 Ardenne Rd.
St. Ann
Kingston, Jamaica
Ph: (876)920-3482
Fax: (876)929-1054
Publisher E-mail: info@jhta.org
Publication covering hospitality industries. **Freq:** Annual. **Key Personnel:** Ned Wong, Dir. and Mgr. **Remarks:** Advertising accepted; rates available upon request. **URL:** http://www.jhta.org/publications.htm. **Circ:** (Not Reported)

46284 ■ The Farmer
Jamaica Agricultural Society
67 Church St.
PO Box 609
Kingston, Jamaica
Ph: (809)922-6102
Fax: (809)922-6103
Publisher E-mail: jas@jamaica-focus.com
Magazine featuring agricultural topics focusing on Jamaica and the Caribbean Area. **Freq:** Quarterly. **URL:** http://www.jasjm.org/p/Farmer.htm.

46285 ■ The Gleaner
The Gleaner Company Ltd.
7 N St.
PO Box 40
Kingston, Jamaica
Ph: (876)922-3400
Fax: (809)922-6223
Free: (888)453-2637
Publisher E-mail: feedback@jamaica-gleaner.com
General newspaper. **Founded:** 1834. **Freq:** Mon.-Sat. **Subscription Rates:** US$38.25 individuals; 23.91

individuals; US$38.25 other countries. **Remarks:** Accepts advertising. **URL:** http://www.jamaica-gleaner.com/. **Circ:** (Not Reported)

46286 ■ Jamaica Journal of Science and Technology
Scientific Research Council
Hope Gardens
PO Box 350
Kingston 06, Jamaica
Ph: (876)927-1771
Fax: (876)927-1990
Publisher E-mail: prinfo@src-jamaica.org
Jamaican journal covering science and technology. **Founded:** Apr. 1990. **Freq:** Annual. **Trim Size:** letter. **Key Personnel:** Prof. Mervyn Curtis, Contact; Dr. Elaine Fisher, Contact; Robert Lancashire, Editorial Board; Dr. Monty Patrick Jones, Exec. Sec.; Dr. Audia Barnett, Exec. Dir.; Dr. Wayne McLaughlin, Contact; Prof. Tara Dasgupta, Editor-in-Chief; Trevor Jackson, Contact; Prof. Bert Fraser-Reid, Contact. **ISSN:** 1016-2054. **Subscription Rates:** US$25 institutions; US$20 individuals; US$5 individuals postage and handling. **Remarks:** Advertising accepted; rates available upon request. **URL:** http://www.src-jamaica.org/; http://www.src-jamaica.org/publications/jjst.htm. **Formerly:** Journal of the Scientific Research Council of Jamaica. **Circ:** (Not Reported)

46287 ■ The Jamaica Observer
The Jamaica Observer Ltd.
40-42 1/2 Beechwood Ave.
Kingston 5, Jamaica
Ph: (809)920-8136
Fax: (876)968-2025
Publication E-mail: editorial@jamaicaobserver.com
Publisher E-mail: editorial@jamaicaobserver.com
General newspaper. **Founded:** Mar. 5, 1992. **Freq:** Daily. **URL:** http://www.jamaicaobserver.com.

46288 ■ The Star
The Gleaner Company Ltd.
7 N St.
PO Box 40
Kingston, Jamaica
Ph: (876)922-3400
Fax: (809)922-6223
Free: (888)453-2637
Publisher E-mail: feedback@jamaica-gleaner.com
Community newspaper. **Remarks:** Accepts advertising. **URL:** http://www.jamaica-star.com/thestar/20101007/. **Circ:** (Not Reported)

46289 ■ The Sunday Gleaner
The Gleaner Company Ltd.
7 N St.
PO Box 40
Kingston, Jamaica
Ph: (876)922-3400
Fax: (809)922-6223
Free: (888)453-2637
Publisher E-mail: feedback@jamaica-gleaner.com
Newspaper covering local news and entertainment. **Founded:** 1939. **Freq:** Daily. **Remarks:** Accepts advertising. **URL:** http://jamaica-gleaner.com/. **Circ:** (Not Reported)

46290 ■ Track and Pools
The Gleaner Company Ltd.
7 N St.
PO Box 40
Kingston, Jamaica
Ph: (876)922-3400
Fax: (809)922-6223
Free: (888)453-2637
Publisher E-mail: feedback@jamaica-gleaner.com
Newspaper covering racing. **URL:** http://www.jamaica-gleaner.com/gleaner/about/newspapers.html.

46291 ■ The War Cry
Salvation Army - Caribbean Territory
3 Waterloo Rd.
PO Box 378
Kingston 10, Jamaica
Ph: (876)929-6190
Fax: (876)929-7960
Publication covering criminal justice. **Freq:** Biweekly. **URL:** http://www.salvationarmycarib.org/www_car.nsf/vw-sublinks/87273925AC40703F05256DF8005321A9?openDocument. **Circ:** 300,000

46292 ■ The Weekend Star
The Gleaner Company Ltd.
7 N St.
PO Box 40
Kingston, Jamaica
Ph: (876)922-3400
Fax: (809)922-6223
Free: (888)453-2637
Publisher E-mail: feedback@jamaica-gleaner.com
Newspaper covering local music, dance, theater and social culture. **Founded:** 1951. **Freq:** Weekly. **Remarks:** Accepts advertising. **URL:** http://jamaica-gleaner.com/. **Circ:** (Not Reported)

Circulation: ★ = ABC; △ = BPA; ♦ = CAC; • = CCAB; ❑ = VAC; ⊕ = PO Statement; ‡ = Publisher's Report; Boldface figures = sworn; Light figures = estimated.

Abashiri

46293 ■ JOQM - 1449 KHz
Nishi 5, Chuo 2-chome
Kita 1
Sapporo 060-8501, Japan
Ph: 81 11 2325800
E-mail: info@hbc.co.jp
Format: Eclectic. **Owner:** Hokkaido Broadcasting Co., Ltd. (HBC), at above address. **Operating Hours:** Continuous. **Key Personnel:** Takashi Watanabe, President. **Wattage:** 5000. **URL:** http://www.hbc.co.jp/.

46294 ■ JOVX - 909 KHz
1-1, Nishi 8-chome
Kita 1-jo, Chuo-ku
Sapporo 060-8705, Japan
Ph: 81 11 2411181
Format: Eclectic. **Owner:** The Sapporo Television Broadc., Co., Ltd., at above address. **Operating Hours:** Continuous. **Wattage:** 5000. **URL:** http://www.stv.ne.jp/.

Akita

46295 ■ JOBI-TV - 37
2-14, Yabase-Honcho 3-chome
Akita 010-8668, Japan
Ph: 81 18 8666121
Owner: Akita Television Co., Ltd. (AKT), at above address. **Founded:** 1969. **Wattage:** 10,000. **URL:** http://www.akt.co.jp/.

46296 ■ JOPU - 82.8 MHz
7-10, Yabase-Honcho 3-chome
Akita 010-0973, Japan
Ph: 81 18 8241155
Format: Eclectic. **Owner:** Akita FM Broadcasting System (ABS), at above address. **Founded:** 1985. **Operating Hours:** 0500-0400. **Wattage:** 3000. **Ad Rates:** Advertising accepted; rates available upon request. **URL:** http://www.fm-akita.co.jp/.

46297 ■ JOTR - 936 KHz
9-42, Sanno 7-chome
Akita 010-8611, Japan
Ph: 81 188 248533
Format: Eclectic. **Owner:** Akita Broadcasting System (ABS), at above address. **Founded:** Nov. 1, 1953. **Operating Hours:** Continuous. **Wattage:** 5000. **URL:** http://www.akita-abs.co.jp/.

46298 ■ JOUB - 774 KHz
2-2-1 Jinnan
Shibuya-ku
Tokyo 150-8001, Japan
Ph: 81 3 34651111
Fax: 81 3 34698110
E-mail: nhkworld@nhk.jp
Format: Educational. **Owner:** Nippon Hoso Kyokai (NHK), at above address. **Operating Hours:** 2030-1640 (2030-1500, Sun. & Mon.). **Key Personnel:** Shigeo Fukuchi, President. **Wattage:** 500,000. **URL:** http://www.nhk.or.jp.

46299 ■ JOUK - 86.7 MHz
2-2-1 Jinnan
Shibuya-ku
Tokyo 150-8001, Japan
Ph: 81 3 34651111
Fax: 81 3 34698110
Format: News. **Owner:** Nippon Hoso Kyokai (NHK), at above address. **Operating Hours:** Continuous. **Key Personnel:** Shigehiro Komaru, Chm. **Wattage:** 3000. **URL:** http://www.nhk.or.jp.

46300 ■ JOUK - 1503 KHz
2-2-1 Jinnan
Shibuya-ku
Tokyo 150-8001, Japan
Ph: 81 3 34651111
Fax: 81 3 34698110
E-mail: nhkworld@nhk.jp
Format: News. **Owner:** Nippon Hoso Kyokai (NHK), at above address. **Operating Hours:** Continuous. **Key Personnel:** Shigeo Fukuchi, President; Hidemi Hyuga, Exec. Dir. Gen. **Wattage:** 10,000. **Ad Rates:** Noncommercial. **URL:** http://www.nhk.or.jp.

46301 ■ JOXX-TV - 31
233-209, Okawabata
Kawashiri-machi
Akita 010-0941, Japan
Ph: 81 18 8665111
Fax: 81 18 8665115
Owner: Akita Asahi Broadcasting Co., Ltd. (AAB), at above address. **Founded:** 1992. **Wattage:** 10,000. **URL:** http://www.aab-tv.co.jp/.

Amagasaki

46302 ■ Daruma Magazine
Daruma Publishing
c/o Takeguchi Momoko
Mukonoso Higashi 1-12-5
Amagasaki 661-0032, Japan
Ph: 81 664 365874
Fax: 81 004 301002
Publisher E-mail: momoko@gao.ne.jp
Magazine covering Japanese art and antiques in English. **Founded:** 1994. **Freq:** Quarterly. **ISSN:** 0952-1765. **Subscription Rates:** 1,500¥ individuals outside Japan; US$15 individuals; 1,200¥ individuals. **URL:** http://www.darumamagazine.com/.

Aomori

46303 ■ JOAH-TV - 34
125-1 Shibata
Arakawa
Aomori 030-0181, Japan
Ph: 81 177 62 1111
Fax: 81 177 39 1199
Owner: Asahi Broadcasting Aomori Co., Ltd. (ABA), 1 Jusannich-machi, Hachinohe 031-0042, Japan, 81 178 47 2111, Fax: 81 178 22 1338. **Founded:** 1991. **Wattage:** 10,000. **URL:** http://www.aba-net.com/.

46304 ■ JOAI-TV - 38
4-8, Matsumori 1-chome
Aomori 030-8686, Japan
Ph: 81 17 7412233
Owner: Aomori Television Co., Ltd. (ATV), at above

address. **Founded:** 1969. **Wattage:** 10,000. **URL:** http://www.atv.co.jp/.

JOGO - See Hachinohe

46305 ■ JOGR - 1233 KHz
260-8677 Matsumori
Aomori 030-0965, Japan
Ph: 81 17 7431234
Format: Eclectic. **Owner:** Aomori Broadcasting Corporation (RAB), at above address. **Founded:** 1953. **Operating Hours:** Continuous. **Wattage:** 5000. **Ad Rates:** Advertising accepted; rates available upon request. **URL:** http://www.rab.co.jp/.

46306 ■ JOGR-TV - 1
8-1, Matsumori 1-chome
Aomori 030-0965, Japan
Ph: 81 177 431234
Owner: Aomori Broadcasting Corporation (RAB), at above address. **Founded:** 1959. **Wattage:** 5000. **URL:** http://www.rab.co.jp/.

46307 ■ JOTC - 1521 KHz
2-2-1 Jinnan
Shibuya-ku
Tokyo 150-8001, Japan
Ph: 81 3 34651111
Fax: 81 3 34698110
E-mail: nhkworld@nhk.jp
Format: Educational. **Owner:** Nippon Hoso Kyokai (NHK), at above address. **Operating Hours:** 2030-1640 (2030-1500, Sun. & Mon.). **Key Personnel:** Shigeo Fukuchi, President. **Wattage:** 1000. **URL:** http://www.nhk.or.jp.

46308 ■ JOTG - 86.0 MHz
2-2-1 Jinnan
Shibuya-ku
Tokyo 150-8001, Japan
Ph: 81 3 34651111
Fax: 81 3 34698110
Format: News. **Owner:** Nippon Hoso Kyokai (NHK), at above address. **Operating Hours:** Continuous. **Key Personnel:** Hidemi Hyuga, Exec. Dir. Gen. **Wattage:** 3000. **URL:** http://www.nhk.or.jp.

46309 ■ JOTG - 963 KHz
2-2-1 Jinnan
Shibuya-ku
Tokyo 150-8001, Japan
Ph: 81 3 34651111
Fax: 81 3 34811350
E-mail: nhkworld@nhk.jp
Format: News. **Owner:** Nippon Hoso Kyokai (NHK), at above address. **Operating Hours:** Continuous. **Key Personnel:** Shigeo Fukuchi, President; Hidemi Hyuga, Exec. Dir. Gen. **Wattage:** 5000. **Ad Rates:** Noncommercial. **URL:** http://www.nhk.or.jp.

46310 ■ JOWU - 80.0 MHz
7-19, Tsutsumi-machi 1-chome
Aomori 030-0812, Japan
Ph: 81 17 7351181
Fax: 81 17 7351186
Format: Eclectic. **Owner:** Aomori FM Broadcasting Corporation (RAB), at above address. **Founded:** Mar.

Circulation: ★ = ABC; △ = BPA; ♦ = CAC; • = CCAB; ❏ = VAC; ⊕ = PO Statement; ‡ = Publisher's Report; Boldface figures = sworn; Light figures = estimated.

20, 1987. **Operating Hours:** Continuous. **Key Personnel:** Huzimoto Kiyoe, President. **Wattage:** 1000. **Ad Rates:** Advertising accepted; rates available upon request. **URL:** http://www.afb.co.jp.

Asahikawa

46311 ■ JOCC - 1602 KHz
2-2-1 Jinnan
Shibuya-ku
Tokyo 150-8001, Japan
Ph: 81 3 34651111
Fax: 81 3 34698110
E-mail: nhkworld@nhk.jp
Format: Educational. **Owner:** Nippon Hoso Kyokai (NHK), at above address. **Operating Hours:** 2030-1640 (2030-1500, Sun. & Mon.). **Key Personnel:** Shigehiro Komaru, Chm.; Shigeo Fukuchi, President. **Wattage:** 1000. **Ad Rates:** Noncommercial. **URL:** http://www.nhk. or.jp.

46312 ■ JOCG - 621 KHz
2-2-1 Jinnan
Shibuya-ku
Tokyo 150-8001, Japan
Ph: 81 3 34651111
Fax: 81 3 34811350
E-mail: nhkworld@nhk.jp
Format: News. **Owner:** Nippon Hoso Kyokai (NHK), at above address. **Operating Hours:** Continuous. **Key Personnel:** Shigeo Fukuchi, President; Hidemi Hyuga, Exec. Dir. Gen. **Wattage:** 3000. **URL:** http://www.nhk.or. jp.

46313 ■ JOWL - 1197 KHz
1-1, Nishi 8-chome
Kita 1-jo, Chuo-ku
Sapporo 060-8705, Japan
Ph: 81 11 2411181
E-mail: radio@stv.ne.jp
Format: Eclectic. **Owner:** The Sapporo Television Broadcasting Co., Ltd., at above address. **Operating Hours:** Continuous. **Wattage:** 3000. **URL:** http://www. stv.ne.jp/.

Asanuno

46314 ■ JOEE-TV Asanuno - 50
21-3, Moto-machi
Naka-ku
Hiroshima 730-8504, Japan
Ph: 81 82 2221155
E-mail: tv@rcc.net
Owner: Chugoku Broadcasting Co., Ltd. (RCC), at above address. **Founded:** 1959. **Wattage:** 100. **URL:** http://www.rcc.co.jp.

Chiba

46315 ■ Behaviormetrika
The Behaviormetric Society of Japan
The Institute of Statistical Mathematics
c/o Associate Professor Kenichi Kikuchi
2-2-1 Miyama, Funabashi
Chiba 274-8510, Japan
Ph: 81 47 4721182
Fax: 81 47 4721241
Publisher E-mail: kikuchi@is.sci.toho-u.ac.jp
Journal focusing on theory, methodology and application pertaining to behaviorometrics. **Freq:** Semiannual. **Key Personnel:** Kohei Adachi, Ch. Ed.; Tatsuo Otsu, Editor-in-Chief; Akinori Okada, Gen. Ed. **URL:** http://wwwsoc. nii.ac.jp/bsj/journal/behaviormetrika_e.html.

46316 ■ The Bulletin of Tokyo Dental College
Tokyo Dental College Society
Tokyo Dental College
1-2-2 Masago, Mihama-ku
Chiba 261-8502, Japan
Bulletin focusing on all aspects of dentistry. **Key Personnel:** Katsuji Okuda, Contact; Yuzuru Kaneko, Editor-in-Chief; Masaki Shimono, Editor. **ISSN:** 0040-8891. **URL:** http://www.tdc.ac.jp/bulletinoftdc/.

46317 ■ DNA Research
Oxford University Press
c/o Michio Oishi, Ed.-in-Ch.
Kazusa DNA Research Institute
2-6-7 Kazusa-kamatari
Kisarazu

Chiba 292-0818, Japan
Ph: 81 438 523944
Fax: 81 438 523911
Publisher E-mail: webenquiry.uk@oup.com
Peer-reviewed journal containing articles on structures and function of genes and genomes published in connection with Kazusa DNA Research Institute. **Founded:** 1994. **Freq:** 6/yr. **Key Personnel:** Mituru Takanami, Honorary Ed.-in-Ch., m.takanami@nifty.ne.jp; Masahiro Sugiura, Editor, phone 81 528 726021, fax 81 528 726021, sugiura@nsc.nagoya-cu.ac.jp; Michio Oishi, Editor-in-Chief, dnar-eic@kazusa.or.jp; Satoshi Tabata, Editor, tabata@kazusa.or.jp; Shoji Tsuji, Editor, tsuji@m. u-tokyo.ac.jp; Masahiro Yano, Editor, myaho@nias.affrc. go.jp. **ISSN:** 1340-2838. **Subscription Rates:** 187 institutions print only; US$374 institutions print only; EUR281 institutions print only. **URL:** http://dnaresearch. oxfordjournals.org/.

46318 ■ IEICE Transactions on Fundamentals of Electronics, Communications and Computer Sciences
Oxford University Press
c/o Hirosuke Yamamoto, Ed.-in-Ch.
Graduate School of Frontier Sciences
University of Tokyo
1-5-1 Kashiwanoha, Kashiwa-shi
Chiba 277-8561, Japan
Fax: 81 4 71363936
Journal covering topics relating to science and technology of electronics, information and communication. **Freq:** Monthly. **Key Personnel:** Hirosuke Yamamoto, Editor-in-Chief, hirosuke@ieice.org. **ISSN:** 0916-8508. **URL:** http://www.ieice.org.

46319 ■ Journal of Yamashina Institute for Ornithology
Yamashina Institute for Ornithology
115 Konoyama
Abiko-shi
Chiba 270-1145, Japan
Ph: 81 4 71821101
Fax: 81 4 71821106
Publisher E-mail: bird@yamashina.or.jp
Journal of ornithology. **Founded:** 1952. **Freq:** Semiannual. **ISSN:** 0044-0183. **URL:** http://www. yamashina.or.jp/hp/english/publications.html. **Circ:** Paid 700

46320 ■ Mycoscience
Springer-Verlag Tokyo
c/o Takashi Yaguchi, Ed.-in-Ch.
Medical Mycology Research Center
Chiba University
1-8-1 Inohana, Chuou-ku, Chiba
Chiba 260-8673, Japan
Ph: 81 48 2262790
Fax: 81 48 2262486
Publisher E-mail: info@springer.jp
Journal publishing original research articles and reviews on various aspects of fungi including yeasts and other organisms that traditionally have been studied by mycologists with research covering systematics (taxonomy by traditional methods and systematics by molecular methods), evolution, phylogeny, morphology, ecology, physiology, biochemistry, genetics, and molecular biology, to such agricultural, medical, and industrial applications as pathology (human, animal, and plant); pharmaceuticals, food processing, and other biotechnologies. **Freq:** Bimonthly. **Key Personnel:** Takashi Yaguchi, Editor-in-Chief, t-yaguchi@faculty. chiba; Tadanori Aimi, Editor, taimi@muses.tottori-u.ac.jp; Norihide Amano, Editor, norihide_amano@suntory.co.jp. **ISSN:** 1340-3540. **Subscription Rates:** EUR234 institutions print incl. free access or e-only; EUR280.80 institutions print incl. enhanced access. **Remarks:** Advertising accepted; rates available upon request. **URL:** http:// www.springer.com/lifesci/microbiology/journal/10267. **Circ:** (Not Reported)

46321 ■ JOCL-TV - 46
1-25, Miyako-cho 1-chome
Chuo-ku
Chiba 260-0001, Japan
Ph: 81 43 2313111
Owner: Chiba Television Broadcasting Corporation (CTC), at above address. **Founded:** 1971. **Wattage:** 5000. **URL:** http://www.chiba-tv.com/.

46322 ■ JOGV - 78.0 MHz
WBG St. 6 Maribuuesuto 27F

2-chome, Mihama-ku
Chiba 261-7127, Japan
Ph: 81 43 3517878
Format: Eclectic. **Owner:** FM Sound Chiba Co., Ltd. (BaY-FM), at above address. **Founded:** 1989. **Operating Hours:** Continuous (off the air Sun. 1920-2000). **Wattage:** 5000. **Ad Rates:** Advertising accepted; rates available upon request. **URL:** http://www.bayfm.co.jp/.

46323 ■ JOMP - 80.7 MHz
2-2-1 Jinnan
Shibuya-ku
Tokyo 150-8001, Japan
Ph: 81 3 34651111
Fax: 81 3 34698110
Format: News. **Owner:** Nippon Hoso Kyokai (NHK), at above address. **Operating Hours:** Continuous. **Key Personnel:** Hidemi Hyuga, Exec. Dir. Gen. **Wattage:** 5000. **URL:** http://www.nhk.or.jp.

JOUD - See Maebashi

JOUD - See Tokyo

Chiyoda

46324 ■ JOEE-TV Chiyoda - 59
21-3, Moto-machi
Naka-ku
Hiroshima 730-8504, Japan
Ph: 81 82 2221155
E-mail: tv@rcc.net
Owner: Chugoku Broadcasting Co., Ltd. (RCC), at above address. **Founded:** 1959. **Wattage:** 100. **URL:** http://www.rcc.co.jp.

Daimon

46325 ■ JOEE-TV Daimon - 59
21-3, Moto-machi
Naka-ku
Hiroshima 730-8504, Japan
Ph: 81 82 2221155
E-mail: tv@rcc.net
Owner: Chugoku Broadcasting Co., Ltd. (RCC), at above address. **Founded:** 1959. **Wattage:** 10. **Ad Rates:** Noncommercial. **URL:** http://www.1350.jp/.

Daiwa

46326 ■ JOEE-TV Daiwa - 55
21-3, Moto-machi
Naka-ku
Hiroshima 730-8504, Japan
Ph: 81 82 8221155
E-mail: tv@rcc.net
Owner: Chugoku Broadcasting Co., Ltd. (RCC), at above address. **Founded:** 1959. **Wattage:** 1. **Ad Rates:** Noncommercial. **URL:** http://www.1350.jp/.

Enbetsu

46327 ■ Hokkaido Hoso - 864 KHz
2, Nishi 5-chome
Kita 1-jo, Chuo-ku
Sapporo 060-8501, Japan
Ph: 81 11 2325800
Fax: 81 11 2323120
E-mail: info@hbc.co.jp
Format: Eclectic. **Owner:** Hokkaido Broadcasting Co., Ltd. (HBC), at above address. **Founded:** 1951. **Operating Hours:** Continuous. **Key Personnel:** Osamu Naganuma, President. **Wattage:** 1000. **URL:** http://www. hbc.co.jp/.

Esashi

46328 ■ JOFM - 1269 KHz
Nishi 5, Chuo 2-chome
Kita 1
Sapporo 060-8501, Japan
Ph: 81 11 2325800
E-mail: info@hbc.co.jp
Format: Eclectic. **Owner:** Hokkaido Broadcasting Co., Ltd. (HBC), at above address. **Operating Hours:** Continuous. **Key Personnel:** Takashi Watanabe, President. **Wattage:** 1000. **URL:** http://www.hbc.co.jp/.

46329 ■ Sapporo TV Hoso - 882 KHz
1-1, Nishi 8
Kita 1, Chuo

Sapporo 060-8705, Japan
Ph: 81 11 2411181
E-mail: radio@stv.jp
Format: Eclectic. **Owner:** The Sapporo Television Broadcasting Co., Ltd., at above address. **Founded:** 1962. **Operating Hours:** Continuous. **Wattage:** 1000. **URL:** http://www.stv.ne.jp/.

Fuchu

46330 ■ JOEE-TV Fuchu - 59
21-3, Moto-machi
Naka-ku
Hiroshima 730-8504, Japan
Ph: 81 82 2221155
E-mail: rcc@rcc.net
Owner: Chugoku Broadcasting Co., Ltd. (RCC), at above address. **Founded:** 1959. **Wattage:** 100. **URL:** http://www.rcc.co.jp.

Fukue

46331 ■ Nagasaki Hoso - 1431 KHz
1-35, Uwamachi
Nagasaki 850-8650, Japan
Ph: 81 824 31111
Fax: 81 958 245501
E-mail: mb-info@nbc-nagasaki.co.jp
Format: Eclectic. **Owner:** Nagasaki Broadcasting Co., Ltd. (NBC), at above address. **Operating Hours:** Continuous. **Wattage:** 1000. **Ad Rates:** Noncommercial. **URL:** http://www.nbc-nagasaki.co.jp.

Fukui

46332 ■ Journal of Chemical Software
Chemical Software Society of Japan
Dept. of Chemistry & Biology Engineering
Fukui National College of Technology
Geshi-cho, Sabae
Fukui 916-0064, Japan
Ph: 81 778 621111
Fax: 81 778 621108
Publisher E-mail: tadayosi@fukui-nct.ac.jp
Journal covering chemistry. **Founded:** 1992. **Freq:** Quarterly. **Key Personnel:** Haruo Hosoya, Contact; Takayuki Hoshi, Contact; Mitsuhiro Hirai, Contact. **ISSN:** 0918-0761. **URL:** http://www.sccj.net/CSSJ/jcs/content.html.

46333 ■ Weed Biology and Management
John Wiley & Sons Inc.
Wiley-Blackwell
c/o Dr. Toshihito Yoshioka, Ed.-in-Ch.
Fukui Prefectural University
4-1-1, Matsuoka-Kenjojima
Fukui 910-1195, Japan
Journal covering all aspects of weed science. **Freq:** Quarterly. **Key Personnel:** Dr. Tohru Tominaga, Editor; Toshihito Yoshioka, Editor-in-Chief, wbmeditor@wssj.jp. **ISSN:** 1444-6162. **Subscription Rates:** 139 other countries print and online; US$226 individuals Americas (print and online); EUR208 individuals Euro zone (print and online); US$497 institutions Americas (print and online); 308 institutions UK (print and online); EUR392 institutions Europe (print and online); US$604 institutions, other countries print and online; 280 institutions UK (print or online only); US$452 institutions Americas (print or online only); EUR356 institutions Europe (print or online only). **Remarks:** Accepts advertising. **URL:** http://www.wiley.com/bw/journal.asp?ref=1444-6162. **Circ:** (Not Reported)

46334 ■ JOFC - 1521 KHz
2-2-1 Jinnan
Shibuya-ku
Tokyo 150-8001, Japan
Ph: 81 3 34651111
Fax: 81 3 34698110
E-mail: nhkworld@nhk.jp
Format: Educational. **Owner:** Nippon Hoso Kyokai (NHK), at above address. **Operating Hours:** 2030-1640 (2030-1500, Sun. & Mon.). **Key Personnel:** Shigeo Fukuchi, President. **Wattage:** 1000. **Ad Rates:** Noncommercial. **URL:** http://www.nhk.or.jp.

46335 ■ JOFG - 83.4 MHz
2-2-1 Jinnan
Shibuya-ku
Tokyo 150-8001, Japan

Ph: 81 3 34651111
Fax: 81 3 34698110
Format: News. **Owner:** Nippon Hoso Kyokai (NHK), at above address. **Operating Hours:** Continuous. **Key Personnel:** Hidemi Hyuga, Exec. Dir. Gen. **Wattage:** 1000. **Ad Rates:** Advertising accepted; rates available upon request. **URL:** http://www.nhk.or.jp.

46336 ■ JOFG - 927 KHz
2-2-1 Jinnan
Shibuya-ku
Tokyo 150-8001, Japan
Ph: 81 3 34651111
Fax: 81 3 34811350
E-mail: nhkworld@nhk.jp
Format: News. **Owner:** Nippon Hoso Kyokai (NHK), at above address. **Operating Hours:** Continuous. **Key Personnel:** Shigeo Fukuchi, President; Hidemi Hyuga, Exec. Dir. Gen. **Wattage:** 5000. **URL:** http://www.nhk.or.jp.

46337 ■ JOFI-TV - 39
3-410, Toiya-cho
Fukui 918-8688, Japan
Ph: 81 776 21 2233
Fax: 81 776 21 6727
Owner: Fukui Television Broadcasting Corporation (FTB), at above address. **Founded:** 1969. **Wattage:** 10,000. **URL:** http://www.fukui-tv.co.jp/.

46338 ■ JOLU - 76.1 MHz
1-1, Miyuki 1-chome
Fukui 910-8553, Japan
Ph: 81 776 212100
Fax: 81 776 212101
Format: Eclectic. **Owner:** Fukui FM Broadcasting Co., Ltd., at above address. **Founded:** 1984. **Operating Hours:** 0500-0400. **Wattage:** 1000. **URL:** http://www.fmfukui.jp/.

46339 ■ JOPR - 864 KHz
37-1-1, Owada-cho
Fukui 910-8588, Japan
Ph: 81 776 571000
Format: Eclectic. **Owner:** Fukui Broadcasting Co., Ltd. (FBC), at above address. **Founded:** 1952. **Operating Hours:** Continuous. **Wattage:** 5000. **URL:** http://www.fbc.jp/.

Fukuoka

46340 ■ Caving Journal
Speleological Society of Japan
c/o Kitakyushu Museum of Natural History & Human History
2-4-1 Higashida, Yahatahigashi-ku
Kitakyushyu
Fukuoka 805-0071, Japan
Publisher E-mail: info@speleology.jp
Periodical covering Japanese caves and caving. **Freq:** 3/yr. **URL:** http://www.speleology.jp/en/tcj/tcj_2e.html.

46341 ■ Fukuoka Now
Fukuoka Now Ltd.
3F Abundant Bldg.
1-5-11 Akasaka
Chuo-ku
Fukuoka 810-0042, Japan
Ph: 81 927 622505
Fax: 81 927 622509
Publisher E-mail: info@fukuoka-now.com
General interest online magazine. **Founded:** Dec. 25, 1998. **Freq:** Monthly. **Key Personnel:** Emiko Szasz, Manager; Nick Szasz, CEO/Publisher; Alex Deacon, Editor. **Subscription Rates:** Free. **URL:** http://www.fukuoka-now.com.

46342 ■ The Gaijin Gleaner
2084-22 Ooaza Masue
Nijou-Machi
Itoshima-gun
Fukuoka 819-16, Japan
Ph: 81 923 292041
Fax: 81 923 292041
Publication E-mail: gleaner@gol.com
General interest magazine. **Founded:** June 1994. **Freq:** Monthly. **Key Personnel:** Nikolas May, Editor; William Fish, Consulting Ed.; Yinka Selly, Letters Ed. **Subscription Rates:** 1,800¥ individuals; 150¥ single issue. **Remarks:** Accepts advertising. **URL:** http://kyushu.com/

gleaner/about.shtml. **Ad Rates:** BW: 3,500¥. **Circ:** Paid 1,600

46343 ■ International Journal of Biotronics
Kyushu University
Biotron Institute
Kyushu University 12
6-10-1 Hakozaki
Higashi-ku, Fukuoka-shi
Fukuoka 812-8581, Japan
Ph: 81 926 423066
Fax: 81 926 423069
Publication E-mail: btronics@agr.kyushu-u.ac.jp
Publisher E-mail: seikan@agr.kyushu-u.ac.jp
International journal of Biotronic covering environmental control and environmental biology. **Subtitle:** Environment Control and Environmental Biology. **Founded:** 1972. **Freq:** Annual. **Trim Size:** B5. **Key Personnel:** Jiro Chikushi, Editor-in-Chief; P.T. Austin, Editor; M. Aydin, Editor; P.R. Berliner, Editor; H. Nonami, Editor; D.C. Tremmel, Editor; S.A. Prior, Editor; G. Holroyd, Editor; T.W. Tibbitts, Editor; K.T. Ingram, Assoc. Ed. **ISSN:** 1348-4478. **Remarks:** Advertising not accepted. **URL:** http://133.5.207.201/bio/yochis/institute/etronics.html. **Formerly:** Biotronics. **Circ:** Free 1,000

46344 ■ Journal of the Speleological Society of Japan
Speleological Society of Japan
c/o Kitakyushu Museum of Natural History & Human History
2-4-1 Higashida, Yahatahigashi-ku
Kitakyushyu
Fukuoka 805-0071, Japan
Publisher E-mail: info@speleology.jp
Earth sciences journal. **Founded:** 1976. **Freq:** Annual. **Key Personnel:** Syun-ichi Ueno, Chm. **ISSN:** 0386-233X. **URL:** http://www.speleology.jp/publish/journal_2e.html. **Circ:** Paid 250

46345 ■ Legal Medicine
Mosby Inc.
c/o N. Ikeda, Ed.-in-Ch.
Dept. of Forensic Pathology & Science
Kyushu University
Higashi-ku
Fukuoka 812-8582, Japan
Ph: 81 92 6426121
Fax: 81 92 6426126
Publisher E-mail: custserv.ehs@elsevier.com
Journal providing an international forum for the publication of original articles, reviews and correspondence on subjects that cover practical and theoretical areas of interest relating to the wide range of legal medicine. **Freq:** 6/yr. **Key Personnel:** H. Takizawa, Emeritus Ed.-in-Ch.; B. Budowle, Editor; W. Keil, Editor; H. Maeda, Editor; A. Takatsu, Emeritus Ed.-in-Ch.; W. Eisenmenger, Editor; A. Carracedo, Editor; M. Yoshino, Editor; N. Ikeda, Editor-in-Chief, n-ikeda@forensic.med.kyushu-u.ac.jp; A. Ishii, Editor; T. Kondo, Editor. **ISSN:** 1344-6223. **Subscription Rates:** EUR344 institutions for European countries and Iran; US$386 institutions, other countries except Europe, Japan and Iran; 46,000¥ institutions. **URL:** http://www.legalmedicinejournal.com/; http://www.elsevier.com/wps/find/journaldescription.cws_home/621254/descrip tiondescription.

46346 ■ JODU - 80.7 MHz
Watanabe-dori
Minami Bldg.
Chuo-ku
Fukuoka 810-8575, Japan
Ph: 81 92 5330807
Fax: 81 92 5330801
Format: Eclectic. **Owner:** Fukuoka FM Broadcasting Co., Ltd. (Beat Station), at above address. **Founded:** 1970. **Operating Hours:** Continuous. **Wattage:** 3000. **Ad Rates:** Advertising accepted; rates available upon request. **URL:** http://fmfukuoka.co.jp/.

46347 ■ JODU-FM - 76.1 MHz
Kiyokawa, Chuo-ku
Minami Bldg.
Fukuoka 542-0071, Japan
Ph: 81 92 5330807
Fax: 81 92 5330801
Format: Eclectic. **Owner:** FM Inter-Wave Inc. (Inter FM), at above address. **Founded:** 1996. **Wattage:** 10,000. **Ad Rates:** Noncommercial. **URL:** http://fmfukuoka.co.jp/company/main.html.

Circulation: ★ = ABC; △ = BPA; ◆ = CAC; • = CCAB; ❑ = VAC; ⊕ = PO Statement; ‡ = Publisher's Report; Boldface figures = sworn; Light figures = estimated.

JOFO - See Kitakyushu

46348 ■ JOFR - 1278 KHz
3-8, Momochihama 2-chome
Sawara-ku
Fukuoka 814-8585, Japan
Ph: 81 92 8526666
Format: Eclectic. **Owner:** RKB Mainichi Broadcasting Corporation (RKB), at above address. **Founded:** 1951. **Operating Hours:** Continuous. **Wattage:** 50,000. **URL:** http://www.rkb.ne.jp/.

46349 ■ JOFW - 76.1 MHz
NTT-T Bldg., 7th Fl.
2-5-35 Tenjin
Chuo-ku
Fukuoka 810-8565, Japan
Ph: 81 92 7520761
Fax: 81 92 7157610
E-mail: 761@lovefm.co.jp
Format: Eclectic. **Owner:** Kyushu International FM Inc. (Love FM 761), at above address. **Founded:** 1997. **Operating Hours:** Continuous. **Wattage:** 1000. **Ad Rates:** Advertising accepted; rates available upon request. **URL:** http://lovefm.co.jp.

46350 ■ JOIF - 1413 KHz
1-1, Nagahama 1-chome
Chuo-ku
Fukuoka 810-8571, Japan
Ph: 81 92 7211234
Format: Eclectic. **Owner:** Kyushu Asahi Broadcasting Corporation (KBC), at above address. **Founded:** 1954. **Operating Hours:** Continuous. **Key Personnel:** Minoru Gonduo, President. **Wattage:** 50,000. **URL:** http://www.kbc.co.jp/.

46351 ■ JOIL - 720 KHz
1-1, Nagahama 1-chome
Chuo-ku
Fukuoka 810-8571, Japan
Ph: 81 92 7525127
Owner: Kyushu Asahi Broadcasting Co., Ltd., at above address. **Operating Hours:** Continuous. **Wattage:** 1000. **URL:** http://www.kbc.co.jp/.

46352 ■ JOLK - 612 KHz
2-2-1 Jinnan
Shibuya-ku
Tokyo 150-8001, Japan
Ph: 81 3 34651111
Fax: 81 3 34811350
E-mail: nhkworld@nhk.jp
Format: News. **Owner:** Nippon Hoso Kyokai (NHK), at above address. **Operating Hours:** Continuous. **Key Personnel:** Shigehiro Komaru, Chm.; Shigeo Fukuchi, President; Hidemi Hyuga, Exec. Dir. Gen. **Wattage:** 100,000. **URL:** http://www.nhk.or.jp.

46353 ■ JOLK - 84.8 MHz
2-2-1 Jinnan
Shibuya-ku
Tokyo 150-8001, Japan
Ph: 81 3 34651111
Fax: 81 3 34698110
Format: News. **Owner:** Nippon Hoso Kyokai (NHK), at above address. **Operating Hours:** Continuous. **Wattage:** 3000. **Ad Rates:** Noncommercial. **URL:** http://www.nhk.or.jp.

46354 ■ JORV - 78.7 MHz
9-11, Furusenba-machi
Kokurakita-ku
Kitakyushu 802-8570, Japan
Format: Eclectic. **Owner:** FM Kyusyu Co., Ltd. (Cross FM), at above address. **Founded:** 1993. **Operating Hours:** Continuous. **Wattage:** 3000. **Ad Rates:** Advertising accepted; rates available upon request. **URL:** http://www.crossfm.co.jp/index.html.

Fukushima

46355 ■ New Cicada
New Cicada Press
40-11 Kubo
Date-gun
Hobara-machi
Fukushima 960-0602, Japan
Journal of literature. **Subtitle:** Haiku and Short Poetry Magazine. **Founded:** 1984. **Key Personnel:** Tadao

Okazaki, Editor. **ISSN:** 0911-6567. **Subscription Rates:** 800¥ single issue.

46356 ■ JOFD - 1602 KHz
2-2-1 Jinnan
Shibuya-ku
Tokyo 150-8001, Japan
Ph: 81 3 34651111
Fax: 81 3 34698110
E-mail: nhkworld@nhk.jp
Format: Educational. **Owner:** Nippon Hoso Kyokai (NHK), at above address. **Operating Hours:** 2030-1640 (2030-1500, Sun. & Mon.). **Key Personnel:** Shigeo Fukuchi, President. **Wattage:** 1000. **Ad Rates:** Noncommercial. **URL:** http://www.nhk.or.jp.

46357 ■ JOFP - 85.3 MHz
2-2-1 Jinnan
Shibuya-ku
Tokyo 150-8001, Japan
Ph: 81 3 34651111
Fax: 81 3 34698110
Format: News. **Owner:** Nippon Hoso Kyokai (NHK), at above address. **Operating Hours:** Continuous. **Key Personnel:** Hidemi Hyuga, Exec. Dir. Gen. **Wattage:** 1000. **Ad Rates:** Advertising accepted; rates available upon request. **URL:** http://www.nhk.or.jp.

46358 ■ JOFP - 1323 KHz
2-2-1 Jinnan
Shibuya-ku
Tokyo 150-8001, Japan
Ph: 81 3 34651111
Fax: 81 3 34811350
E-mail: nhkworld@nhk.jp
Format: News. **Owner:** Nippon Hoso Kyokai (NHK), at above address. **Operating Hours:** Continuous. **Key Personnel:** Shigeo Fukuchi, President; Hidemi Hyuga, Exec. Dir. Gen. **Wattage:** 1000. **Ad Rates:** Noncommercial. **URL:** http://www.nhk.or.jp.

46359 ■ JOKI-TV - 31
1-1, Nishi-Chuo
Fukushima 960-8531, Japan
Ph: 81 24 5315111
Fax: 81 24 5355233
E-mail: tuf@tuf.co.jp
Owner: TV-U Fukushima,Inc. (TUF), at above address. **Founded:** 1983. **Wattage:** 30,000. **URL:** http://www.tuf.co.jp.

46360 ■ JOPX-TV - 11
2-5, Oyama cho
Fukushima 960-8508, Japan
Ph: 81 24 5368000
E-mail: hensei@fukushima-tv.co.jp
Owner: Fukushima Telecasting Co., Ltd. (FTV), at above address. **Founded:** 1963. **Wattage:** 3000. **URL:** http://www.fukushima-tv.co.jp/.

46361 ■ JOTV - 81.8 MHz
4-4, Koriyama
Fukushima 960-8013, Japan
Ph: 81 24 9919000
Fax: 81 24 9919100
Format: Eclectic. **Owner:** FM Fukushima, Inc., at above address. **Operating Hours:** Continuous. **Wattage:** 1000. **Ad Rates:** Advertising accepted; rates available upon request. **URL:** http://www.fmf.co.jp/.

46362 ■ JOTV-FM - 81.8 MHz
4-4, Koriyama
Fukushima 960-8031, Japan
Ph: 81 24 5229000
Fax: 81 24 5229100
Format: Eclectic. **Owner:** FM Fukushima, Inc., at above address. **Founded:** 1995. **Wattage:** 1000. **URL:** http://www.fmf.co.jp/pc-index.html.

JOWO - See Koriyama

46363 ■ JOWR - 1458 KHz
3-17, Otamachi
Fukushima 960-8655, Japan
Ph: 81 24 5314321
Fax: 81 24 5314329
Format: Eclectic. **Owner:** Radio Fukushima Broadcasting Co., Ltd. (RFC). **Founded:** 1953. **Operating Hours:** Continuous. **Wattage:** 1000. **URL:** http://www.rfc.jp.

Fukuyama

46364 ■ JOEE-TV Fukuyama - 7
21-3, Moto-machi
Naka-ku
Hiroshima 730-8504, Japan
Ph: 81 82 2221155
E-mail: rcc@rcc.net
Owner: Chugoku Broadcasting Co., Ltd. (RCC), at above address. **Founded:** 1959. **Wattage:** 100. **URL:** http://www.rcc.co.jp.

Geihokuitamura

46365 ■ JOEE-TV Geihokuitamura - 47
21-3, Moto-machi
Naka-ku
Hiroshima 730-8504, Japan
Ph: 81 82 2221155
E-mail: tv@rcc.net
Owner: Chugoku Broadcasting Co., Ltd. (RCC), at above address. **Founded:** 1959. **Wattage:** 3. **URL:** http://www.rcc.co.jp.

Geihokuyahata

46366 ■ JOEE-TV Geihokuyahata - 39
21-3, Moto-machi
Naka-ku
Hiroshima 730-8504, Japan
Ph: 81 82 2221155
E-mail: tv@rcc.net
Owner: Chugoku Broadcasting Co., Ltd. (RCC), at above address. **Founded:** 1959. **Wattage:** 10,000. **Ad Rates:** Advertising accepted; rates available upon request. **URL:** http://www.rcc.co.jp.

Gifu

46367 ■ JOOP - 83.6 MHz
2-2-1 Jinnan
Shibuya-ku
Tokyo 150-8001, Japan
Ph: 81 3 34651111
Fax: 81 3 34698110
Format: News. **Owner:** Nippon Hoso Kyokai (NHK), at above address. **Operating Hours:** Continuous. **Key Personnel:** Hidemi Hyuga, Exec. Dir. Gen. **Wattage:** 1000. **Ad Rates:** Noncommercial. **URL:** http://www.nhk.or.jp.

46368 ■ JOXV - 80.0 MHz
35 St. 10-302 Ono, 4-chome
Ogaki
Gifu 503-8580, Japan
Ph: 81 584 830180
Fax: 81 584 830189
E-mail: info@radio-80.com
Format: Eclectic. **Owner:** Gifu FM Broadcast Company Ltd (Radio 80), at above address. **Founded:** 2001. **Operating Hours:** Continuous. **Wattage:** 1000. **URL:** http://www.radio-80.com/.

46369 ■ JOZF - 1431 KHz
8, Imako-machi
Gifu 500-8588, Japan
Ph: 81 58 2641181
Format: Eclectic. **Owner:** Gifu Broadcasting System (GBS), at above address. **Founded:** 1962. **Operating Hours:** Continuous (off the air Mon. 1600 -2000). **Key Personnel:** Mikio Sugiyama, CEO/Chm. **Wattage:** 5000. **URL:** http://www.zf-web.com.

Hachinohe

46370 ■ JOGO - 1485 KHz
Matsumori
Aomori 030-0965, Japan
Ph: 81 17 7431234
Format: Eclectic. **Owner:** Aomori Broadcasting Corp., at above address. **Operating Hours:** Continuous. **Wattage:** 1000. **URL:** http://www.rab.co.jp/.

Hagi

46371 ■ JOPL - 1485 KHz
Shunan Pk. District
Yamaguchi 745-8686, Japan
Ph: 81 834 321111

Fax: 81 834 320046
Format: Eclectic. **Owner:** Yamaguchi Broadcasting, Co., Ltd., at above address. **Operating Hours:** Continuous. **Wattage:** 1000. **URL:** http://4ch.kry.co.jp.

Hakodate

46372 ■ Plankton and Benthos Research
Plankton Society of Japan
c/o Mar. Biodiversity Lab.
3-1-1 Minatomachi
Hokkaido
Hakodate 041-8611, Japan
Ph: 81 138 405543
Fax: 81 138 405542
Publisher E-mail: plankton@fish.hokudai.ac.jp
Journal covering biology. **Freq:** Semiannual. **Key Personnel:** Yoshinari Endo, Editor; Dr. Susumu Ohtsuka, Editor-in-Chief, fax 81 846 230038, ohtsuka@hiroshima-u.ac.jp. **ISSN:** 1343-0874. **Subscription Rates:** 12,000¥. **URL:** http://www.plankton.jp/PBE/. **Formerly:** Plankton Biology and Ecology. **Circ:** Paid 700

46373 ■ JOVK - 675 KHz
2-2-1 Jinnan
Shibuya-ku
Tokyo 150-8001, Japan
Ph: 81 3 34651111
Fax: 81 3 34811350
E-mail: nhkworld@nhk.jp
Format: News. **Owner:** Nippon Hoso Kyokai (NHK), at above address. **Operating Hours:** Continuous. **Key Personnel:** Shigeo Fukuchi, President; Hidemi Hyuga, Exec. Dir. Gen. **Wattage:** 5000. **URL:** http://www.nhk.or.jp.

Hamamatsu

46374 ■ JODC - 1521 KHz
2-2-1 Jinnan
Shibuya-ku
Tokyo 150-8001, Japan
Ph: 81 3 34651111
Fax: 81 3 34811350
E-mail: nhkworld@nhk.jp
Format: Educational. **Owner:** Nippon Hoso Kyokai (NHK), at above address. **Operating Hours:** 2030-1640 (2030-1500, Sun. & Mon.). **Key Personnel:** Shigeo Fukuchi, President; Hidemi Hyuga, Exec. Dir. Gen. **Wattage:** 1000. **Ad Rates:** Noncommercial. **URL:** http://www.nhk.or.jp.

JOKU - See Shizuoka

Hikone

46375 ■ JP Journal of Geometry and Topology
Pushpa Publishing House
Section of Mathematics
School of Engineering
University of Shiga Prefecture
Hikone 522-8533, Japan
Publisher E-mail: arun@pphmj.com
Peer-reviewed journal covering aspects of geometry and topology and their applications. **Freq:** 3/yr (March, July and November). **Key Personnel:** Prof. Yasuo Matsushita, Editor-in-Chief, matsushita.y@usp.ac.jp; Prof. K.K. Azad, Managing Editor. **ISSN:** 0972-415X. **Subscription Rates:** EUR175 institutions, other countries online; EUR220 institutions, other countries print and online; Rs 3,000 institutions print. **URL:** http://www.pphmj.com/journals/jpgt.htm.

46376 ■ JOBW - 1215 KHz
Karasuma, Kamigyo-ku
Kyoto 602-8588, Japan
Format: Eclectic. **Owner:** Kyoto Broadc.System Co., Ltd., at above address. **Operating Hours:** Continuous. **Wattage:** 1000. **URL:** http://www.kbs-kyoto.co.jp/.

46377 ■ JOQP - 945 KHz
2-2-1 Jinnan
Shibuya-ku
Tokyo 150-8001, Japan
Ph: 81 3 34651111
Fax: 81 3 34811350
E-mail: nhkworld@nhk.jp
Format: News. **Owner:** Nippon Hoso Kyokai (NHK), at above address. **Operating Hours:** Continuous. **Key Personnel:** Shigeo Fukuchi, President; Hidemi Hyuga,

Exec. Dir. Gen. **Wattage:** 1000. **Ad Rates:** Noncommercial. **URL:** http://www.nhk.or.jp.

Himeji

46378 ■ International Journal of Reasoning-based Intelligent Systems
Inderscience Enterprises Limited
c/o Kazumi Nakamatsu, Ed.-in-Ch.
School of Human Science & Environment
University of Hyogo
1-1-12, Shinzaike-honcho, Hyogo
Himeji 670-0092, Japan
Journal covering the field of reasoning-based intelligent systems. **Freq:** Quarterly. **Key Personnel:** Kazumi Nakamatsu, Editor-in-Chief, nakamatu@shse.u-hyogo.ac.jp. **ISSN:** 1755-0556. **Subscription Rates:** EUR494 individuals print or online; EUR672 individuals print and online. **URL:** http://www.inderscience.com/browse/index.php?journalCODE=ijris.

Hiroshima

46379 ■ Hiroshima Journal of Mathematics Education
Hiroshima University
Dept. of Mathematics Education
1-1-1 Kagamiyama
Higashi-Hiroshima
Hiroshima 739-8524, Japan
Ph: 81 824 246810
Fax: 81 824 227076
Publication devoted to the publication of research papers in the field of mathematics education. **Founded:** 1993. **Freq:** Annual. **Key Personnel:** Mutsumi Amasaki, Editor; Mitsunori Imaoka, Editor; Hideki Iwasaki, Editor. **ISSN:** 0919-1720. **URL:** http://home.hiroshima-u.ac.jp/matedu/journal/journal.html.

46380 ■ Hiroshima Mathematical Journal
Hiroshima University
Faculty of Science
1-3-1 Kagamiyama
Higashi-Hiroshima
Hiroshima 739-8526, Japan
Ph: 81 82 4247350
Fax: 81 82 4240710
Publisher E-mail: jimu@math.sci.hiroshima-u.ac.jp
Publishes original papers in pure and applied mathematics. **Founded:** 1971. **Freq:** 3/yr. **Key Personnel:** Masafumi Yoshino, Editor; Yoshio Agaoka, Editor; Kunimochi Sakamoto, Managing Editor; Ryo Kobayashi, Editor; Seiichi Kamada, Editor. **ISSN:** 0018-2079. **URL:** http://www.math.sci.hiroshima-u.ac.jp; http://www.math.sci.hiroshima-u.ac.jp/hmj/. **Circ:** 400

46381 ■ Journal of Radiation Research
Japan Radiation Research Society
c/o N Nakamura, Ed.-in-Ch.
c/o Genetics Dept.
Radiation Effects Research Foundation
5-2 Hijiyama Pk., Minami-ku
Hiroshima 732-0815, Japan
Ph: 81 822 613139
Fax: 81 822 637279
Publication E-mail: jrr@wwwsoc.nii.ac.jp
Publishes original articles in the field of radiation research, including studies in radiation physics, chemistry, biology, radioecology and medicine. **Founded:** 1960. **Freq:** Quarterly. **Key Personnel:** N. Nakamura, Editor-in-Chief. **ISSN:** 0449-3060. **Remarks:** Advertising accepted; rates available upon request. **URL:** http://wwwsoc.nii.ac.jp/jrr/index-e.html. **Circ:** Paid 1,500

46382 ■ Oral Radiology
Japanese Society for Oral and Maxillofacial Radiology
c/o Keiji Tanimoto, Ed.-in-Ch.
Department of Oral & Maxillofacial Radiology
Graduate School of Biomedical Sciences, Hiroshima University
1-2-3, Kasumi, Minami-ku
Hiroshima 734-8553, Japan
Ph: 81 82 2575690
Fax: 81 82 2575692
Journal of dentistry. **Founded:** 1985. **Freq:** Semiannual. **Key Personnel:** Keiji Tanimoto, Editor-in-Chief, kg@hiroshima-u.ac.jp. **ISSN:** 0911-6028. **Remarks:** Advertising accepted; rates available upon request. **URL:** http://

wwwsoc.nii.ac.jp/jsomr/eoralradiology.html. **Circ:** (Not Reported)

JOEE-TV Asanuno - See Asanuno

JOEE-TV Chiyoda - See Chiyoda

JOEE-TV Daimon - See Daimon

JOEE-TV Daiwa - See Daiwa

JOEE-TV Fuchu - See Fuchu

JOEE-TV Fukuyama - See Fukuyama

JOEE-TV Geihokuitamura - See Geihokuitamura

JOEE-TV Geihokuyahata - See Geihokuyahata

JOEE-TV Hiroshimanishiyamamoto - See Hiroshimanishiyamamoto

JOEE-TV Hiroshimayagi - See Hiroshimayagi

JOEE-TV Hiwa - See Hiwa

JOEE-TV Innoshima - See Innoshima

JOEE-TV Itsukaichi - See Itsukaichi

JOEE-TV Kabe - See Kabe

JOEE-TV Kake - See Kake

JOEE-TV Kimita - See Kimita

JOEE-TV Kitamidori - See Kitamidori

JOEE-TV Koi - See Koi

JOEE-TV Kuchiwa - See Kuchiwa

JOEE-TV Kui - See Kui

JOEE-TV Kure - See Kure

JOEE-TV Kurekotsubo - See Kurekotsubo

JOEE-TV Kurose - See Kurose

JOEE-TV Kyowa - See Kyowa

JOEE-TV Mihara - See Mihara

JOEE-TV Mihara-nakanomachi - See Mihara-nakanomachi

JOEE-TV Minamimidori - See Minamimidori

JOEE-TV Mirasaka - See Mirasaka

JOEE-TV Mitsugi - See Mitsugi

JOEE-TV Miyoshi - See Miyoshi

JOEE-TV Mukaihara - See Mukaihara

JOEE-TV Onomichi - See Onomichi

JOEE-TV Ooasa - See Ooasa

JOEE-TV Oogaki - See Oogaki

JOEE-TV Ootake - See Ootake

JOEE-TV Saeki - See Saeki

JOEE-TV Saijyo - See Saijyo

JOEE-TV Saijyo - See Saijyo

JOEE-TV Sakugi - See Sakugi

JOEE-TV Seno - See Seno

JOEE-TV Senotateishi - See Senotateishi

JOEE-TV Serakozan - See Serakozan

JOEE-TV Shinichitsunekanemaru - See Shinichitsunekanemaru

JOEE-TV Shiraki - See Shiraki

JOEE-TV Shiwa - See Shiwa

JOEE-TV Shobara - See Shobara

JOEE-TV Takamiya - See Takamiya

JOEE-TV Takano - See Takano

JOEE-TV Takehara - See Takehara

JOEE-TV Takeharakita - See Takeharakita

JOEE-TV Togouchi - See Togouchi

JOEE-TV Tojyo - See Tojyo

JOEE-TV Tojyochidori - See Tojyochidori

JOEE-TV Tomo - See Tomo

JOEE-TV Toyama - See Toyama

JOEE-TV Yachiyo - See Yachiyo

JOEE-TV Yasuura - See Yasuura

JOEE-TV Yoshida - See Yoshida

JOEE-TV Yuki - See Yuki

46383 ■ JOER - 1350 KHz
21-3, Naka-ku
Hiroshima 730-8504, Japan
Ph: 81 82 2221155
E-mail: radio@rcc.net
Format: Eclectic. **Owner:** Chugoku Broadcasting Co.,

Circulation: ★ = ABC; △ = BPA; ◆ = CAC; • = CCAB; ❏ = VAC; ⊕ = PO Statement; ‡ = Publisher's Report; Boldface figures = sworn; Light figures = estimated.

Ltd. (RCC), at above address. **Founded:** 1959. **Operating Hours:** Continuous. **Wattage:** 20,000. **URL:** http://www.1350.jp/.

46384 ■ JOER-TV - 4
21-3, Naka-ku
Hiroshima 730-8504, Japan
Ph: 81 82 2221155
E-mail: rcc@rcc.net
Owner: Chugoku Broadcasting Co., Ltd. (RCC), at above address. **Founded:** 1959. **Wattage:** 10,000. **URL:** http://www.rcc.co.jp.

46385 ■ JOFK - 1071 KHz
2-2-1 Jinnan
Shibuya-ku
Tokyo 150-8001, Japan
Ph: 81 3 34651111
Fax: 81 3 34811350
E-mail: nhkworld@nhk.jp
Format: News. **Owner:** Nippon Hoso Kyokai (NHK), at above address. **Operating Hours:** Continuous. **Key Personnel:** Shigeo Fukuchi, President; Hidemi Hyuga, Exec. Dir. Gen. **Wattage:** 20,000. **URL:** http://www.nhk.or.jp.

46386 ■ JOFK - 88.3 MHz
2-2-1 Jinnan
Shibuya-ku
Tokyo 150-8001, Japan
Ph: 81 3 34651111
Fax: 81 3 34811350
Format: News. **Owner:** Nippon Hoso Kyokai (NHK), at above address. **Operating Hours:** Continuous. **Wattage:** 1000. **URL:** http://www.nhk.or.jp.

46387 ■ JOGM-TV - 35
19-2, Hakushimakita
Naka-ku
Hiroshima 730-8552, Japan
Ph: 81 82 2113811
Fax: 81 82 2235509
E-mail: opinion@home-tv.co.jp
Owner: Hiroshima Home Television Co., Ltd. (HOME), at above address. **Founded:** 1970. **Wattage:** 30,000. **URL:** http://www.home-tv.co.jp/.

46388 ■ JOGU - 78.2 MHz
8-2, Minamimachi 1-chome
Minami-ku
Hiroshima 734-8511, Japan
Ph: 81 82 2512200
Fax: 81 82 2556633
E-mail: jogu@hiroshima-fm.co.jp
Format: Eclectic. **Owner:** Hiroshima FM Broadcasting Co., Ltd., at above address. **Founded:** 1982. **Operating Hours:** Continuous. **Wattage:** 1000. **Ad Rates:** Advertising accepted; rates available upon request. **URL:** http://www.hiroshima-fm.co.jp/.

Hiroshimanishiyamamoto

46389 ■ JOEE-TV Hiroshimanishiyamamoto - 55
21-3, Moto-machi
Naka-ku
Hiroshima 730-8504, Japan
Ph: 81 82 2221155
E-mail: tv@rcc.net
Owner: Chugoku Broadcasting Co., Ltd. (RCC), at above address. **Founded:** 1959. **URL:** http://www.1350.jp/.

Hiroshimayagi

46390 ■ JOEE-TV Hiroshimayagi - 32
21-3, Moto-machi
Naka-ku
Hiroshima 730-8504, Japan
Ph: 81 82 2221155
E-mail: tv@rcc.net
Owner: Chugoku Broadcasting Co., Ltd. (RCC), at above address. **Founded:** 1959. **Wattage:** 1. **URL:** http://www.rcc.co.jp.

Hiwa

46391 ■ JOEE-TV Hiwa - 53
21-3, Moto-machi
Naka-ku
Hiroshima 730-8504, Japan
Ph: 81 82 2221155

E-mail: tv@rcc.net
Owner: Chugoku Broadcasting Co., Ltd. (RCC), at above address. **Founded:** 1959. **Wattage:** 1. **URL:** http://www.1350.jp/.

Hokadate

46392 ■ JOHO - 900 KHz
Nishi 5, Chuo 2-chome
Kita 1
Sapporo 060-8501, Japan
Ph: 81 11 2325800
Format: Eclectic. **Owner:** Hokkaido Broadcasting Co., Ltd. (HBC), at above address. **Operating Hours:** Continuous. **Key Personnel:** Takashi Watanabe, President. **Wattage:** 5000. **URL:** http://www.hbc.co.jp/.

Ibaraki

46393 ■ Journal of Japanese Association of Hydrological Sciences
Japanese Association of Hydrological Science
c/o Geologican Survey of Japan
AIST
Tsukuba-shi
Ibaraki 305-8567, Japan
Ph: 81 298613693
Fax: 81 298613684
Publisher E-mail: jahs@ps.sakura,ne.jp
Earth sciences journal. **Founded:** 1967. **Freq:** Quarterly. **ISSN:** 0914-3009. **Subscription Rates:** 8,000¥. **URL:** http://wwwsoc.nii.ac.jp/jahs/English/eng-index.htm. **Formerly:** Hydrology.

46394 ■ Sago Communication
Tsukuba Sago Fund
Institute of Applied Biochemistry
791-27 Inaoka
Tsukuba-shi
Ibaraki 305-0071, Japan
Ph: 81 298380152
Fax: 81 298380152
Journal covering botany. **Founded:** 1990. **Freq:** 3/yr. **Key Personnel:** Shigeru Hisajima, Editor. **ISSN:** 0917-6470. **Circ:** Free 650

46395 ■ Tsukuba Journal of Mathematics
University of Tsukuba
Institute of Mathematics
Tsukuba-shi
Tennoudai 1-1-1
Ibaraki 305-8571, Japan
Ph: 81 29 8534235
Fax: 81 29 8536201
Publisher E-mail: webmaster@math.tsukuba.ac.jp
Mathematics journal. **Founded:** 1977. **Freq:** Semiannual. **Key Personnel:** Jun Morita, Editorial Committee; Yuji Kasahara, Editorial Committee; Tatsuo Kimura, Editorial Committee; Takao Yamaguchi, Chm.; Hiroshi Isozaki, Editorial Committee; Hisao Kato, Editorial Committee. **ISSN:** 0387-4982. **URL:** http://www.math.tsukuba.ac.jp/.

Ikeda

46396 ■ Shikoku Hoso - 1269 KHz
5-2, Nakatokushima-cho 2-chome
Tokushima 770-8573, Japan
Fax: 08 862 31269
Format: Eclectic. **Owner:** Shikoku Broadcasting Co., Ltd. (JRT), at above address. **Founded:** 1952. **Operating Hours:** Continuous. **Key Personnel:** Kondo Mayor, President. **Wattage:** 1000. **Ad Rates:** Noncommercial. **URL:** http://www.jrt.co.jp.

Innoshima

46397 ■ JOEE-TV Innoshima - 50
21-3, Moto-machi
Naka-ku
Hiroshima 730-8504, Japan
Ph: 81 82 2221155
E-mail: tv@rcc.net
Owner: Chugoku Broadcasting Co., Ltd. (RCC), at above address. **Founded:** 1959. **Wattage:** 10. **Ad Rates:** Noncommercial. **URL:** http://www.rcc.co.jp.

Itsukaichi

46398 ■ JOEE-TV Itsukaichi - 60
21-3, Moto-machi
Naka-ku
Hiroshima 730-8504, Japan
Ph: 81 82 2221155
E-mail: tv@rcc.net
Owner: Chugoku Broadcasting Co., Ltd. (RCC), at above address. **Founded:** 1959. **Wattage:** 10. **URL:** http://www.rcc.co.jp.

Iwakuni

46399 ■ JOPN - 918 KHz
Shunan Pk. District
Yamaguchi 745-8686, Japan
Ph: 81 834 321111
Fax: 81 834 320046
Format: Eclectic. **Owner:** Yamaguchi Broadc., Co., Ltd., at above address. **Operating Hours:** Continuous. **Wattage:** 1000. **URL:** http://www.kry.co.jp/.

Izumo

46400 ■ San'in Hoso - 1431 KHz
1-71, Nishi-Fukubara 1-chome
Yonago 683-8670, Japan
Ph: 81 859 332111
Format: Eclectic. **Owner:** Broadc. System of San-in, at above address. **Operating Hours:** Continuous. **Wattage:** 1000. **Ad Rates:** Advertising accepted; rates available upon request. **URL:** http://bss.jp/.

Joetsu

46401 ■ JODO - 1530 KHz
3-18, Kawagishi-cho
Niigata 951-8655, Japan
Ph: 81 25 2674111
Fax: 81 25 2663584
E-mail: info@bsn-niigata.co.jp
Format: Eclectic. **Owner:** Broad. System of Niigata, Inc, at above address. **Operating Hours:** Continuous. **Wattage:** 1000. **URL:** http://www.ohbsn.com/top.asp.

Kabe

46402 ■ JOEE-TV Kabe - 49
21-3, Moto-machi
Naka-ku
Hiroshima 730-8504, Japan
Ph: 81 82 2221155
E-mail: tv@rcc.net
Owner: Chugoku Broadcasting Co., Ltd. (RCC), at above address. **Founded:** 1959. **Wattage:** 10,000. **Ad Rates:** Noncommercial. **URL:** http://www.rcc.co.jp.

Kagoshima

46403 ■ Diseases of the Esophagus
International Society for Diseases of the Esophagus
Kokusai Shokudo Shikkan Kaigi
Department of Surgical Oncology and Digestive Surgery
Kagoshima University
8-35-1, Sakuragaoka
Kagoshima 890-8520, Japan
Ph: 9 9275 5361
Fax: 9 9265 7426
Publisher E-mail: isde2010@convention.co.jp
Publication covering diseases of the esophagus. **Founded:** 1979. **Freq:** Bimonthly. **Trim Size:** A4. **Key Personnel:** Kenneth Wang, Editor-in-Chief; Claude Deschamps, Editor-in-Chief; Brenda Levos-Beale, Managing Editor. **ISSN:** 1120-8694. **Subscription Rates:** US$897 institutions print + premium online/the Americas; 552 institutions print + premium online/Europe + VAT; 552 institutions, other countries print/premium online; US$815 institutions print + std. online/the Americas; 501 institutions print + std. online/Europe + VAT; 501 institutions print + std. online/elsewhere; US$775 institutions online only; 476 institutions, other countries online only. **Remarks:** Accepts advertising. **URL:** http://www.isde.net. **Circ:** (Not Reported)

46404 ■ Hepatology Research
Mosby Inc.
c/o Hirohito Tsubouchi,Ed.-in-Ch.
35-1 Sakuragaoka, Kagoshima-shi

Kagoshima 890-8520, Japan
Ph: 81 99 2755323
Fax: 81 99 3643504
Publisher E-mail: custserv.ehs@elsevier.com
Journal publishing basic and clinical research in the field of hepatology. **Freq:** Monthly. **Key Personnel:** Hirohito Tsubouchi, Editor-in-Chief, htsubo@m2.kufm. kagoshima-u.ac.jp. **ISSN:** 1386-6346. **URL:** http://www3. interscience.wiley.com/journal/118507311/home.

46405 ■ South Pacific Studies
Kagoshima University Research Center for the Pacific Islands
1-21-24 Korimoto
Kagoshima 890-8580, Japan
Ph: 81 992 857394
Fax: 81 992 856197
Publisher E-mail: shimaken@cpi.kagoshima-u.ac.jp
Science journal. **Founded:** 1980. **Freq:** Semiannual. **Key Personnel:** Oki Kimihiko, Editor-in-Chief; Kobari Toru, Editorial Board. **ISSN:** 0916-0752. **URL:** http://cpi. kagoshima-u.ac.jp/publications/southpacificstudies/sps/ sps00/southpacificstudies.html. **Formerly:** Memoirs of the Kagoshima University Research Center for the South Pacific. **Circ:** Controlled 700

46406 ■ JOCF - 1107 KHz
5-25, Korai-cho
Kagoshima 890-8570, Japan
Ph: 81 99 2547111
Format: Eclectic. **Owner:** Minaminihon Broadcasting Co., Ltd. (MBC), at above address. **Founded:** 1953. **Operating Hours:** Continuous. **Wattage:** 20,000. **URL:** http://www.mbc.co.jp/.

46407 ■ JOHC - 1386 KHz
2-2-1 Jinnan
Shibuya-ku
Tokyo 150-8001, Japan
Ph: 81 3 34651111
Fax: 81 3 34698110
E-mail: nhkworld@nhk.jp
Format: Educational. **Owner:** Nippon Hoso Kyokai (NHK), at above address. **Operating Hours:** 2030-1640 (2030-1500, Sun. & Mon.). **Key Personnel:** Shigeo Fukuchi, President. **Wattage:** 10,000. **URL:** http://www. nhk.or.jp.

46408 ■ JOHG - 85.6 MHz
2-2-1 Jinnan
Shibuya-ku
Tokyo 150-8001, Japan
Ph: 81 3 34651111
Fax: 81 3 34698110
Format: News. **Owner:** Nippon Hoso Kyokai (NHK), at above address. **Operating Hours:** Continuous. **Key Personnel:** Hidemi Hyuga, Exec. Dir. Gen. **Wattage:** 1000. **Ad Rates:** Advertising accepted; rates available upon request. **URL:** http://www.nhk.or.jp.

46409 ■ JOHG - 576 KHz
2-2-1 Jinnan
Shibuya-ku
Tokyo 150-8001, Japan
Ph: 81 3 34651111
Fax: 81 3 34811350
E-mail: nhkworld@nhk.jp
Format: News. **Owner:** Nippon Hoso Kyokai (NHK), at above address. **Operating Hours:** Continuous. **Key Personnel:** Shigeo Fukuchi, President; Hidemi Hyuga, Exec. Dir. Gen. **Wattage:** 10,000. **URL:** http://www.nhk. or.jp.

46410 ■ JOOV - 79.8 MHz
1-38, Higashisengoku-cho
Kagoshima 892-8579, Japan
Ph: 81 99 2391133
Fax: 81 99 2391120
Format: Eclectic. **Owner:** FM Kagoshima Co., Ltd., at above address. **Founded:** 1992. **Operating Hours:** Continuous. **Wattage:** 1000. **Ad Rates:** Advertising accepted; rates available upon request. **URL:** http://www. myufm.co.jp/index2.html.

Kake

46411 ■ JOEE-TV Kake - 5
21-3, Moto-machi
Naka-ku
Hiroshima 730-8504, Japan

Ph: 81 82 2221155
E-mail: rcc@rcc.net
Owner: Chugoku Broadcasting Co., Ltd. (RCC), at above address. **Founded:** 1959. **Wattage:** 1. **URL:** http://www.rcc.co.jp.

Kanagawa

46412 ■ Biological Sciences in Space
Japanese Society for Biological Sciences in Space
c/o Institute of Space & Astronautical Science /JAXA
Yoshino-dai
Sagamihara
Kanagawa 229-8510, Japan
Ph: 81 42 7598230
Fax: 81 42 7598449
Publisher E-mail: jsbss@surc.isas.jaxa.jp
Journal covering biology. **Founded:** 1987. **Freq:** Quarterly. **Key Personnel:** Kenichi Ijiri, Editor-in-Chief; Yoriko Atomi, Editor; Shoji A. Baba, Editor. **ISSN:** 0914-9201. **URL:** http://www.jsbss.jp/journal/index.html. **Circ:** Paid 500

Kanazawa

46413 ■ JOHV - 80.5 MHz
45, Ishikawa-cho 2-chome
Kanazawa 920-8605, Japan
Ph: 81 76 2628050
Fax: 81 76 2628058
Format: Soft Rock; Classic Rock. **Owner:** FM Ishikawa Broadcasting Co., Ltd, at above address. **Founded:** 1990. **Operating Hours:** 0400-0300. **Wattage:** 1000. **Ad Rates:** Advertising accepted; rates available upon request. **URL:** http://www.fmishikawa.co.jp/.

46414 ■ JOIH-TV - 37
Chi 18, Kannondo-cho
Kanazawa 920-0388, Japan
Ph: 81 76 2672141
Owner: Ishikawa Television Broadcasting Corporation (ITC), at above address. **Founded:** Mar. 7, 1969. **Wattage:** 10,000. **URL:** http://www.ishikawa-tv.com/.

46415 ■ JOJB - 1386 KHz
2-2-1 Jinnan
Shibuya-ku
Tokyo 150-8001, Japan
Ph: 81 3 34651111
Fax: 81 3 34698110
E-mail: nhkworld@nhk.jp
Format: Educational. **Owner:** Nippon Hoso Kyokai (NHK), at above address. **Operating Hours:** 2030-1640 (2030-1500, Sun. & Mon.). **Key Personnel:** Shigehiro Komaru, Chm.; Shigeo Fukuchi, President. **Wattage:** 10,000. **URL:** http://www.nhk.or.jp.

46416 ■ JOJK - 82.2 MHz
2-2-1 Jinnan
Shibuya-ku
Tokyo 150-8001, Japan
Ph: 81 3 34651111
Fax: 81 3 34698110
Format: News. **Owner:** Nippon Hoso Kyokai (NHK), at above address. **Operating Hours:** Continuous. **Key Personnel:** Hidemi Hyuga, Exec. Dir. Gen. **Wattage:** 1000. **Ad Rates:** Noncommercial. **URL:** http://www.nhk. or.jp.

46417 ■ JOJK - 1224 KHz
2-2-1 Jinnan
Shibuya-ku
Tokyo 150-8001, Japan
Ph: 81 3 34651111
Fax: 81 3 34811350
E-mail: nhkworld@nhk.jp
Format: News. **Owner:** Nippon Hoso Kyokai (NHK), at above address. **Operating Hours:** Continuous. **Key Personnel:** Shigeo Fukuchi, President; Hidemi Hyuga, Exec. Dir. Gen. **Wattage:** 10,000. **Ad Rates:** Noncommercial. **URL:** http://www.nhk.or.jp.

46418 ■ JOMR - 1107 KHz
2-1, Honda-machi 3-chome
Kanazawa 920-8560, Japan
Ph: 81 76 2628111
Fax: 81 76 2238851
E-mail: mro@mro.co.jp
Format: Eclectic. **Owner:** Hokuriku Broadcasting Co., Ltd. (MRO). **Founded:** 1952. **Operat-**

ing Hours: Continuous. **Wattage:** 5000. **URL:** http://www.mro.co.jp/.

46419 ■ JOWX-TV - 33
Kobu 2-136
Kanazawa 920-0386, Japan
Ph: 81 76 2403344
E-mail: office@tvkanazawa.co.jp
Owner: Television Kanazawa Co., Ltd. (KTK), at above address. **Founded:** 1990. **Wattage:** 10,000. **URL:** http://www.tvkanazawa.co.jp/.

46420 ■ JOWY-TV - 25
1-32-2, Matsushima
Kanazawa 920-0393, Japan
Ph: 81 76 2698800
Fax: 81 76 2698811
Owner: Hokuriku Asahi Broadcasting Co., Ltd. (HAB), at above address. **Founded:** 1991. **Key Personnel:** Akira Huruta Sakai, President. **Wattage:** 10,000. **URL:** http://www.hab.co.jp/.

Kawasaki

46421 ■ Industrial Health
National Institute of Industrial Health
6-21-1, Nagao
Tama-ku
Kawasaki 214-8585, Japan
Ph: 81 44 8656111
Fax: 81 44 8656116
Occupational health journal. **Founded:** 1963. **Freq:** Quarterly. **Key Personnel:** Shunichi Araki, Editor-in-Chief; Shin-ichi Sawada, Managing Editor; Masaya Takahashi, Managing Editor. **ISSN:** 0019-8366. **URL:** http://www.jniosh.go.jp/old/niih/jp/index.html. **Circ:** 1,100

46422 ■ Journal of Science of Labour
Institute for Science of Labour
2-8-14 Sugao
Miyamae-ku
Kawasaki 216-8501, Japan
Ph: 81 44 9772121
Fax: 81 44 9777504
Occupational health journal. **Founded:** 1924. **Freq:** Monthly. **ISSN:** 0022-443X. **Remarks:** Advertising accepted; rates available upon request. **URL:** http://www. isl.or.jp/isl-e2002revised.htmlpublication. **Circ:** Paid 2,500

Kimita

46423 ■ JOEE-TV Kimita - 55
21-3, Moto-machi
Naka-ku
Hiroshima 730-8504, Japan
Ph: 81 82 2221155
E-mail: tv@rcc.net
Owner: Chugoku Broadcasting Co., Ltd. (RCC), at above address. **Founded:** 1959. **Wattage:** 1. **URL:** http://www.rcc.co.jp.

Kitakyushu

46424 ■ JOFO - 1197 KHz
3-8, Momochihama 2-chome
Sawara-ku
Fukuoka 814-8585, Japan
Ph: 81 92 8526666
Fax: 81 92 8526673
Format: Eclectic. **Owner:** RKB Mainichi Broadcasting Corporation (RKB), at above address. **Founded:** 1951. **Operating Hours:** Continuous. **Wattage:** 1000. **URL:** http://www.rkb.ne.jp/.

JORV - See Fukuoka

46425 ■ JOSB - 1602 KHz
2-2-1 Jinnan
Shibuya-ku
Tokyo 150-8001, Japan
Ph: 81 3 34651111
Fax: 81 3 34698110
E-mail: nhkworld@nhk.jp
Format: Educational. **Owner:** Nippon Hoso Kyokai (NHK), at above address. **Operating Hours:** 2030-1640 (2030-1500, Sun. & Mon.). **Key Personnel:** Shigehiro Komaru, Chm.; Shigeo Fukuchi, President. **Wattage:** 1000. **URL:** http://www.nhk.or.jp.

Circulation: ★ = ABC; △ = BPA; ◆ = CAC; • = CCAB; ❏ = VAC; ⊕ = PO Statement; ‡ = Publisher's Report; Boldface figures = sworn; Light figures = estimated.

46426 ■ JOSK - 540 KHz
2-2-1 Jinnan
Shibuya-ku
Tokyo 150-8001, Japan
Ph: 81 3 34651111
Fax: 81 3 34811350
E-mail: nhkworld@nhk.jp
Format: News. **Owner:** Nippon Hoso Kyokai (NHK), at above address. **Operating Hours:** Continuous. **Key Personnel:** Shigeo Fukuchi, President; Hidemi Hyuga, Exec. Dir. Gen. **Wattage:** 1000. **URL:** http://www.nhk.or.jp.

Kitami

46427 ■ JOKD - 702 KHz
2-2-1 Jinnan
Shibuya-ku
Tokyo 150-8001, Japan
Ph: 81 3 34651111
Fax: 81 3 34698110
E-mail: nhkworld@nhk.jp
Format: Educational. **Owner:** Nippon Hoso Kyokai (NHK), at above address. **Operating Hours:** 2030-1640 (2030-1500, Sun. & Mon.). **Key Personnel:** Shigeo Fukuchi, President. **Wattage:** 10,000. **Ad Rates:** Noncommercial. **URL:** http://www.nhk.or.jp.

46428 ■ JOKP - 1188 KHz
2-2-1 Jinnan
Shibuya-ku
Tokyo 150-8001, Japan
Ph: 81 3 34651111
Fax: 81 3 34811350
E-mail: nhkworld@nhk.jp
Format: News. **Owner:** Nippon Hoso Kyokai (NHK), at above address. **Operating Hours:** Continuous. **Key Personnel:** Shigeo Fukuchi, President; Hidemi Hyuga, Exec. Dir. Gen. **Wattage:** 10,000. **URL:** http://www.nhk.or.jp.

Kitamidori

46429 ■ JOEE-TV Kitamidori - 5
21-3, Moto-machi
Naka-ku
Hiroshima 730-8504, Japan
Ph: 81 82 2221155
E-mail: tv@rcc.net
Owner: Chugoku Broadcasting Co., Ltd. (RCC), at above address. **Founded:** 1959. **Wattage:** 1. **URL:** http://www.rcc.co.jp.

Kobe

46430 ■ Funkcialaj Ekvacioj, Serio Internacia
Mathematical Society of Japan
Division of Functional Equations
c/o Faculty of Science
Kobe Univ.
Kobe 657-8501, Japan
Mathematics journal. **Founded:** 1949. **Freq:** 3/yr. **Key Personnel:** Shu Nakamura, Editorial Board; Hitoshi Ishii, Editorial Board; Nguyen Van Minh, Editorial Board; Masatoshi Noumi, Editorial Board; Masaaki Yoshida, Editorial Board; Yoshio Tsutsumi, Editorial Board; Kazuo Okamoto, Editorial Board; Izumi Takagi, Editorial Board. **ISSN:** 0532-8721. **Subscription Rates:** US$240 individuals. **URL:** http://www.math.kobe-u.ac.jp/~fe/.

46431 ■ Kansai Time Out
402 Shinko Bldg.
8 Kaigan-dori
Chuo-ku
Kobe 650-0024, Japan
Ph: 81 783 937033
Fax: 81 783 937039
Publication E-mail: ktoedit@kto.co.jp
English language news magazine. **Freq:** Monthly. **Subscription Rates:** 3,000¥ individuals; 5,700¥ two years; 5,000¥ other countries; 9,500¥ two years overseas. **Remarks:** Accepts advertising. **URL:** http://www.japanfile.com/modules/news/; http://www.kto.co.jp/. **Circ:** (Not Reported)

46432 ■ Kobe Journal of Mathematics
Tsurukabuto 1-2-1
Nada
Kobe 657-8501, Japan
Publisher E-mail: nakanisi@math.s.kobe-u.ac.jp
Mathematics journal. **Founded:** 1984. **Freq:** Semiannual. **Key Personnel:** Yasutaka Nakanishi, Managing Editor, nakanisi@math.s.kobe-u.ac.jp; Yasunari Higuchi, Editorial Commitee; Takahisa Miyama, Editorial Commitee. **ISSN:** 0289-9051. **URL:** http://www.math.kobe-u.ac.jp/jmsj/kjm.

46433 ■ Kobe Journal of Medical Sciences
Kobe University
School of Medicine
7-5-1 Kusunoki-cho
Chuo-ku
Kobe 650-0017, Japan
Publication E-mail: journal@med.kobe-u.ac.jp
Medical science journal. **Founded:** 1951. **Freq:** Bimonthly. **Key Personnel:** Hozuka Akita, Editor; Atsu Aiba, Editor; Takayoshi Kuno, Editor; Shun-ichi Nakamura, Editor-in-Chief. **ISSN:** 1883-0498. **URL:** http://www.med.kobe-u.ac.jp/journal/. **Circ:** Paid 650

46434 ■ Kobe University Economic Review
Kobe University Graduate School of Economics
2-1 Rokkodai-cho
Nada-ku
Kobe 657-8501, Japan
Ph: 81 78 8811212
Journal covering economics. **Founded:** 1955. **Freq:** Annual. **Key Personnel:** Kazuhiro Ohtani, Author. **ISSN:** 0454-1111. **URL:** http://www.econ.kobe-u.ac.jp/www-old/english/publication/er.html. **Circ:** 650

46435 ■ JOIV - 89.9 MHz
5-4, Hatoba-cho
Chuo-ku
Kobe 650-8589, Japan
Ph: 81 78 3220899
Fax: 81 78 3221008
E-mail: info@kiss-fm.co.jp
Format: Eclectic. **Owner:** Hyogo FM Radio Broadcasting Co., Ltd. (Kiss-FM Kobe), at above address. **Founded:** 1990. **Operating Hours:** Continuous. **Wattage:** 1000. **Ad Rates:** Advertising accepted; rates available upon request. **URL:** http://www.kiss-fm.co.jp/.

Kochi

46436 ■ Phycological Research
John Wiley & Sons Inc.
Wiley-Blackwell
c/o Ichiro Mine, Ed.-in-Ch.
Graduate School of Kuroshio Science
Kochi University
2-5-1 Akebono-cho
Kochi 780-8520, Japan
Journal encouraging exchange of information on research phycology in terms of phylogenetics and taxonomy, ecology and population biology, morphology, cellular and molecular biology, physiology and biochemistry, genetics, photobiology, biotechnology, and fisheries. The journal published in connection with the Japanese Society of Phycology. **Freq:** Quarterly. **Key Personnel:** Ichiro Mine, Editor-in-Chief, mine@cc.kochi-u.ac.jp; John M. Archibald, Assoc. Ed.; Olivier De Clerck, Assoc. Ed.; Daisuke Honda, Assoc. Ed.; Mona Hoppenrath, Assoc. Ed. **ISSN:** 1322-0829. **Subscription Rates:** US$763 institutions print and online; US$922 institutions, other countries print and online; US$226 individuals print and online; 139 other countries print and online; US$693 institutions print or online; US$838 institutions, other countries print or online; EUR598 institutions print and online; EUR543 institutions print or online; 428 institutions print and online. **Remarks:** Advertising accepted; rates available upon request. **URL:** http://www.wiley.com/bw/journal.asp?ref=1322-0829&site=1. **Circ:** (Not Reported)

46437 ■ JOLV - 81.6 MHz
Falconer No. 5 No. 1
cho 2-chome
Kochi 780-8532, Japan
Ph: 81 888 721100
Fax: 81 888 728787
Format: Eclectic. **Owner:** FM Kochi Broadcasting Co., Ltd. (KFM), at above address. **Founded:** 1992. **Operating Hours:** Continuous. **Wattage:** 500. **Ad Rates:** Advertising accepted; rates available upon request. **URL:** http://www.fmkochi.com/index.html.

46438 ■ JORB - 1152 KHz
2-2-1 Jinnan

Shibuya-ku
Tokyo 150-8001, Japan
Ph: 81 3 34651111
Fax: 81 3 34811350
E-mail: nhkworld@nhk.jp
Format: Educational. **Owner:** Nippon Hoso Kyokai (NHK), at above address. **Operating Hours:** 2030-1640 (2030-1500, Sun. & Mon.). **Key Personnel:** Shigehiro Komaru, Chm.; Shigeo Fukuchi, President. **Wattage:** 10,000. **URL:** http://www.nhk.or.jp.

46439 ■ JORK - 990 KHz
2-2-1 Jinnan
Shibuya-ku
Tokyo 150-8001, Japan
Ph: 81 3 34651111
Fax: 81 3 34811350
E-mail: nhkworld@nhk.jp
Format: News. **Owner:** Nippon Hoso Kyokai (NHK), at above address. **Operating Hours:** Continuous. **Key Personnel:** Shigeo Fukuchi, President; Hidema Hyuga, Exec. Dir. Gen. **Wattage:** 10,000. **URL:** http://www.nhk.or.jp.

46440 ■ JOZR - 900 KHz
2-15, Hon-machi 3-chome
Kochi 780-8550, Japan
Ph: 81 888 222111
Format: Eclectic. **Owner:** Kochi Broadcasting Co., Ltd. (RKC), at above address. **Founded:** 1953. **Operating Hours:** Continuous. **Wattage:** 5000. **URL:** http://www.rkc-kochi.co.jp/.

Kofu

46441 ■ JOCV - 83.0 MHz
Aria Kawada-machi, 105
Kofu 400-8550, Japan
Ph: 81 55 2281100
Fax: 81 55 2286669
Format: Eclectic. **Owner:** FM Fuji Co., Ltd. (FMF), at above address. **Founded:** 1988. **Operating Hours:** 2000-1800 on weekdays; 2000-1600 on Sun. **Wattage:** 1000. **Ad Rates:** Advertising accepted; rates available upon request. **URL:** http://www.fmfuji.co.jp.

46442 ■ JOJF - 765 KHz
6-10, Kitaguchi 2-chome
Kofu 400-8525, Japan
Ph: 81 552 313000
Fax: 81 552 313043
E-mail: ybs@ybs.ne.jp
Format: Eclectic. **Owner:** Yamanashi Broadcasting System (YBS), at above address. **Founded:** 1954. **Operating Hours:** Continuous. **Wattage:** 5000. **URL:** http://www.ybs.ne.jp.

46443 ■ JOKC - 1602 KHz
2-2-1 Jinnan
Shibuya-ku
Tokyo 150-8001, Japan
Ph: 81 3 34651111
Fax: 81 3 34698110
E-mail: nhkworld@nhk.jp
Format: Educational. **Owner:** Nippon Hoso Kyokai (NHK), at above address. **Operating Hours:** 2030-1640 (2030-1500, Sun. & Mon.). **Key Personnel:** Shigeo Fukuchi, President. **Wattage:** 1000. **Ad Rates:** Noncommercial. **URL:** http://www.nhk.or.jp.

46444 ■ JOKG - 85.6 MHz
2-2-1 Jinnan
Shibuya-ku
Tokyo 150-8001, Japan
Ph: 81 3 34651111
Fax: 81 3 34698110
Format: News. **Owner:** Nippon Hoso Kyokai (NHK), at above address. **Operating Hours:** Continuous. **Key Personnel:** Hidemi Hyuga, Exec. Dir. Gen. **Wattage:** 1000. **Ad Rates:** Noncommercial. **URL:** http://www.nhk.or.jp.

46445 ■ JOKG - 927 KHz
2-2-1 Jinnan
Shibuya-ku
Tokyo 150-8001, Japan
Ph: 81 3 34651111
Fax: 81 3 34811350
E-mail: nhkworld@nhk.jp
Format: News. **Owner:** Nippon Hoso Kyokai (NHK), at above address. **Operating Hours:** Continuous. **Key**

Personnel: Shigeo Fukuchi, President; Hidemi Hyuga, Exec. Dir. Gen. **Wattage:** 5000. **URL:** http://www.nhk.or.jp.

Koi

46446 ■ JOEE-TV Koi - 40
21-3, Moto-machi
Naka-ku
Hiroshima 730-8504, Japan
Ph: 81 82 2221155
E-mail: tv@rcc.net
Owner: Chugoku Broadcasting Co., Ltd. (RCC), at above address. **Founded:** 1959. **Wattage:** 10. **Ad Rates:** Noncommercial. **URL:** http://www.1350.jp/.

Koriyama

46447 ■ Journal of Acarological Society of Japan
Acarological Society of Japan
c/o Gen-ichi Kuriki, PhD, Sec.
Dept. of Biology
Ohu University
Tomita 31-1
Koriyama 963-8611, Japan
Fax: 81 24 9337372
Journal of entomology. **Founded:** 1974. **Freq:** Semiannual. **Key Personnel:** Norihide Hinomoto, Managing Editor; Teruki Kadosaka, Editor-in-Chief. **ISSN:** 0918-1067. **Subscription Rates:** 5,000¥. **Remarks:** Advertising accepted; rates available upon request. **URL:** http://acari.ac.affrc.go.jp. **Circ:** Paid 350

46448 ■ JOJI-TV - 35
3-6, Kuwano 4-chome
Koriyama 963-8535, Japan
Ph: 81 24 9331111
Owner: Fukushima Broadcasting Co., Ltd. (KFB), at above address. **Founded:** 1981. **Wattage:** 30,000. **URL:** http://www.kfb.co.jp/.

46449 ■ JOVI-TV - 33
13-23, Ikenodai
Koriyama 963-8533, Japan
Ph: 81 24 9233300
Owner: Fukushima Central Television Co., Ltd. (FCT), at above address. **Founded:** 1970. **Wattage:** 30,000. **URL:** http://www.fct.co.jp/.

46450 ■ JOWO - 1098 KHz
13-17, Otamachi
Fukushima 960-8655, Japan
Ph: 81 24 5314321
Fax: 81 24 5314329
Format: Eclectic. **Owner:** R.Fukushima Broadc. Co., Ltd., at above address. **Founded:** 1953. **Operating Hours:** Continuous. **Wattage:** 5000. **URL:** http://www.rfc.co.jp/.

Kuchiwa

46451 ■ JOEE-TV Kuchiwa - 34
21-3, Moto-machi
Naka-ku
Hiroshima 730-8504, Japan
Ph: 81 82 2221155
E-mail: tv@rcc.net
Owner: Chugoku Broadcasting Co., Ltd. (RCC), at above address. **Founded:** 1959. **Wattage:** 3. **URL:** http://www.rcc.co.jp.

Kui

46452 ■ JOEE-TV Kui - 55
21-3, Moto-machi
Naka-ku
Hiroshima 730-8504, Japan
Ph: 81 82 2221155
E-mail: tv@rcc.net
Owner: Chugoku Broadcasting Co., Ltd. (RCC), at above address. **Founded:** 1959. **Wattage:** 1. **URL:** http://www.rcc.co.jp.

Kumamoto

46453 ■ Kumamoto Journal of Mathematics
Kumamoto University
Faculty of Science
39-1 Kurokami 2-chome
Kumamoto 860-8555, Japan
Ph: 81 963 442111
Mathematics journal. **Freq:** Annual. **Key Personnel:** Mikio Furushima, Editor; Susumu Tanabe, Editor-in-Chief, kjm@sci.kumamoto-u.ac.jp; Yuji Hamana, Editor. **ISSN:** 0914-675X. **URL:** http://www.sci.kumamoto-u.ac.jp/~haraoka/journal.html.

46454 ■ JOBF - 1197 KHz
30, Yamasaki-cho
Kumamoto 860-8611, Japan
Ph: 81 96 3285511
Format: Eclectic. **Owner:** Kumamoto Broadcasting Co., Ltd. (RKK), at above address. **Founded:** 1953. **Operating Hours:** Continuous. **Wattage:** 10,000. **URL:** http://www.rkk.co.jp/.

46455 ■ JOGB - 873 KHz
2-2-1 Jinnan
Shibuya-ku
Tokyo 150-8001, Japan
Ph: 81 3 34651111
Fax: 81 3 34698110
E-mail: nhkworld@nhk.jp
Format: Educational. **Owner:** Nippon Hoso Kyokai (NHK), at above address. **Operating Hours:** 2030-1640 (2030-1500, Sun. & Mon.). **Key Personnel:** Shigeo Fukuchi, President. **Wattage:** 500,000. **Ad Rates:** Advertising accepted; rates available upon request. **URL:** http://www.nhk.or.jp.

46456 ■ JOGK - 756 KHz
2-2-1 Jinnan
Shibuya-ku
Tokyo 150-8001, Japan
Ph: 81 3 34651111
Fax: 81 3 34811350
E-mail: nhkworld@nhk.jp
Format: News. **Owner:** Nippon Hoso Kyokai (NHK), at above address. **Operating Hours:** Continuous. **Key Personnel:** Shigeo Fukuchi, President; Hidemi Hyuga, Exec. Dir. Gen. **Wattage:** 10,000. **Ad Rates:** Advertising accepted; rates available upon request. **URL:** http://www.nhk.or.jp.

46457 ■ JOGK - 85.4 MHz
2-2-1 Jinnan
Shibuya-ku
Tokyo 150-8001, Japan
Ph: 81 3 34651111
Fax: 81 3 34698110
Format: News. **Owner:** Nippon Hoso Kyokai (NHK), at above address. **Operating Hours:** Continuous. **Key Personnel:** Hidemi Hyuga, Exec. Dir. Gen. **Wattage:** 1000. **Ad Rates:** Noncommercial. **URL:** http://www.nhk.or.jp.

Kure

46458 ■ JOEE-TV Kure - 9
21-3, Moto-machi
Naka-ku
Hiroshima 730-8504, Japan
Ph: 81 82 2221155
E-mail: rcc@rcc.net
Owner: Chugoku Broadcasting Co., Ltd. (RCC), at above address. **Founded:** 1959. **Wattage:** 74. **Ad Rates:** Noncommercial. **URL:** http://www.rcc.co.jp.

Kurekotsubo

46459 ■ JOEE-TV Kurekotsubo - 56
21-3, Moto-machi
Naka-ku
Hiroshima 730-8504, Japan
Ph: 81 82 2221155
E-mail: tv@rcc.net
Owner: Chugoku Broadcasting Co., Ltd. (RCC), at above address. **Founded:** 1959. **Wattage:** 100. **Ad Rates:** Noncommercial. **URL:** http://www.rcc.co.jp.

Kurose

46460 ■ JOEE-TV Kurose - 60
21-3, Moto-machi
Naka-ku
Hiroshima 730-8504, Japan
Ph: 81 82 2221155

E-mail: tv@rcc.net
Owner: Chugoku Broadcasting Co., Ltd. (RCC), at above address. **Founded:** 1959. **Wattage:** 10,000. **URL:** http://www.rcc.co.jp.

Kushiro

46461 ■ JOPC - 1152 KHz
2-2-1 Jinnan
Shibuya-ku
Tokyo 150-8001, Japan
Ph: 81 3 34651111
Fax: 81 3 34698110
E-mail: nhkworld@nhk.jp
Format: Educational. **Owner:** Nippon Hoso Kyokai (NHK), at above address. **Operating Hours:** 2030-1640 (2030-1500, Sun. & Mon.). **Key Personnel:** Shigeo Fukuchi, President. **Wattage:** 10,000. **Ad Rates:** Noncommercial. **URL:** http://www.nhk.or.jp.

46462 ■ JOPG - 585 KHz
2-2-1 Jinnan
Shibuya-ku
Tokyo 150-8001, Japan
Ph: 81 3 34651111
Fax: 81 3 34811350
E-mail: nhkworld@nhk.jp
Format: News. **Owner:** Nippon Hoso Kyokai (NHK), at above address. **Operating Hours:** Continuous. **Key Personnel:** Shigeo Fukuchi, President; Hidemi Hyuga, Exec. Dir. Gen. **Wattage:** 10,000. **URL:** http://www.nhk.or.jp.

46463 ■ JOQL - 1404 KHz
Nishi 5, Chuo 2-chome
Kita 1
Sapporo 060-8501, Japan
Ph: 81 11 2325800
E-mail: info@hbc.co.jp
Format: Eclectic. **Owner:** Hokkaido Broadcasting Co., Ltd. (HBC), at above address. **Operating Hours:** Continuous. **Key Personnel:** Takashi Watanabe, President. **Wattage:** 5000. **URL:** http://www.hbc.co.jp/.

46464 ■ JOWS - 882 KHz
1-1, Nishi 8
Kita 1, Chuo
Sapporo 060-8705, Japan
Ph: 81 11 2411181
E-mail: radio@stv.jp
Format: Eclectic. **Owner:** The Sapporo Television Broadcasting Co., Ltd., at above address. **Founded:** 1962. **Operating Hours:** Continuous. **Wattage:** 3000. **URL:** http://www.stv.ne.jp/.

Kyoto

46465 ■ Acta Histochemica et Cytochemica
Japan Society of Histochemistry and Cytochemistry
c/o Nakanishi Printing Co., Ltd.
Shimotachiuri-Ogawa
Kamikyo-ku
Kyoto 602-8048, Japan
Ph: 81 75 4153661
Fax: 81 75 4153662
Publisher E-mail: jshc@nacos.com
Journal covering biology. **Founded:** 1960. **Freq:** Bimonthly. **Key Personnel:** Koji Takehiko, Editor-in-Chief, phone 81 95 8197025, fax 81 95 8197028, tkoji@nagasaki-u.ac.jp. **ISSN:** 0044-5991. **Remarks:** Advertising accepted; rates available upon request. **URL:** http://www.jstage.jst.go.jp/browse/ahc/_vols. **Circ:** Paid 1,800

46466 ■ Advanced Powder Technology
Elsevier Science
The Society of Powder Technology
No. 5 Kyoto Bldg., 181 Kitamachi
Karasuma-dori, Rokujo-agaru
Shimogyo-ku
Kyoto 600-8176, Japan
Publication E-mail: aptj@nifty.com
Publisher E-mail: nlinfo-f@elsevier.com
Journal publishing original research papers on powder engineering and technology in connection with the Society of Powder Technology. **Subtitle:** International Journal of Science & Technology of Powder & Particulate Materials. **Freq:** 6/yr. **Key Personnel:** Y. Mori, Editor-in-Chief; K. Gotoh, Honorary Ed. in Ch.; K. Morikawa, Founding Ed.; H. Fudouzi, Editorial Board; George V.

Franks, Exec. Ed.; H. Ichikawa, Editorial Board; Y. Endo, Editorial Board; Hee Dong Jang, Exec. Ed. **ISSN:** 0921-8831. **Subscription Rates:** EUR1,066 institutions European countries and Iran; US$1,355 institutions for all countries except Europe, Japan and Iran; 178,300¥ institutions. **URL:** http://www.elsevier.com/wps/find/journaldescription.cws_home/717712/description.

46467 ■ Breeding Science
Japanese Society of Breeding
c/o Administrative Office of Japanese Society of Breeding
Nakanishi Printing Co., Ltd.
Shimotachiuri Ogawa-higashi
Kamikyo-ku
Kyoto 602-8048, Japan
Ph: 81 754 153661
Fax: 81 754 153662
Publisher E-mail: jsb@nacos.com
Journal covering agriculture. **Founded:** 1951. **Freq:** Quarterly. **Key Personnel:** Kazutoshi Okuno, Editorial Board; Darshan S. Brar, Editorial Board; Jun Abe, Editorial Board; Hiroshi Kato, Editorial Board; Masashi Hirai, Editorial Board; Michael J. Bonman, Editorial Board; Takuji Sasaki, Editor-in-Chief; Andris Kleinhofs, Editorial Board. **Remarks:** Advertising accepted; rates available upon request. **URL:** http://www.nacos.com/jsb/e/index_e.html. **Circ:** Paid 2,000

46468 ■ Chemistry Letters
Chemical Society of Japan
c/o Tamejiro Hiyama, Ed.-in-Ch.
Kyoto University, Dept. of Material Chemistry
Graduate School of Engineering
Katsura, Saikyo-Ku
Kyoto 615-8510, Japan
Publisher E-mail: info@chemistry.or.jp
Journal featuring research results on all aspects of science at the interface of chemistry and biology and on advances in drug design and development. **Founded:** 1894. **Freq:** Monthly. **Print Method:** Offset. **Trim Size:** 13 x 21. **Cols./Page:** 6. **Col. Width:** 26 nonpareils. **Col. Depth:** 294 agate lines. **Key Personnel:** Tamejiro Hiyama, Editor-in-Chief; Takashi Kato, Sen. Assoc. Ed., kato@chiral.t.u-tokyo.ac.jp. **Subscription Rates:** 7,200¥ individuals; 45,600¥ individuals corporate; US$92 individuals via surface mail (other areas); US$830 individuals corporate (other areas). **URL:** http://www.csj.jp/journals/chem-lett/index.html. **Circ:** ‡43,200

46469 ■ Clinical Pediatric Endocrinology
Japanese Society for Pediatric Endocrinology
Academic Sq.
2-348-302 Ryogae-cho
Kyoto 612-8082, Japan
Ph: 81 75 4688772
Fax: 81 75 4688773
Publisher E-mail: jspe@ac-square.com.jp
Journal of pediatric endocrinology. **Founded:** 1989. **Freq:** Quarterly. **Key Personnel:** Yukihiro Hasegawa, MD, Editor-in-Chief. **ISSN:** 0918-5739. **Subscription Rates:** 5,000¥ individuals. **Remarks:** Advertising accepted; rates available upon request. **URL:** http://jspe.umin.jp/e_index.htm. **Circ:** (Not Reported)

46470 ■ Current Herpetology
Herpetological Society of Japan
Dept. of Zoology
Graduate School of Science
Kyoto University
Kitashirakawa-Oiwakecho Sakyo-ku
Kyoto 606-8502, Japan
Publisher E-mail: tom@zoo.zool.kyoto-u.ac.jp
Journal of zoology. **Founded:** 1964. **Freq:** Semiannual. **Key Personnel:** Dr. Tsutomu Hikida, Contact, tom@zoo.zool.kyoto-u.ac.jp; Yukihiro Kohmatsu, Contact. **ISSN:** 1345-5834. **URL:** http://zoo.zool.kyoto-u.ac.jp/herp/CurrHerp/index.html.

46471 ■ Doshisha American Studies
Doshisha University Center for American Studies
Graduate School of American Studies
Doshisha University
Kyoto 602-8580, Japan
Ph: 81 752 513931
Fax: 81 752 513091
Publication E-mail: ji-amekn@mail.doshisha.ac.jp
Publisher E-mail: ji-amekn@mail.doshisha.ac.jp
History journal. **Founded:** 1963. **Freq:** Annual. **ISSN:** 0420-0918. **URL:** http://www.america-kenkyusho.jp/

english/index4.html. **Circ:** Paid 750

46472 ■ International Journal of Hematology
Japanese Society of Hematology
Kinki Invention Ctr.
14 Yoshida Kawahara-cho
Sakyo-ku
Kyoto 606-8305, Japan
Ph: 81 757 522844
Fax: 81 757 522842
Publisher E-mail: info@jshem.or.jp
Publishes articles in fields of clinical and experimental hematology. **Founded:** 1938. **Freq:** 8/yr. **Key Personnel:** Toshio Suda, Editor-in-Chief; Charles Abrams, International Editorial Board; Daniel Catovsky, International Editorial Board; Richard Champlin, International Editorial Board. **ISSN:** 0925-5710. **Remarks:** Advertising accepted; rates available upon request. **URL:** http://www.jshem.or.jp/en/journal/ijh.html. **Circ:** Paid 5,000

46473 ■ Japanese Circulation Journal
Japanese Circulation Society
8th Fl., Cube Oike Bldg.
599 Bano-cho Karasuma Aneyakoji
Nakagyo-ku
Kyoto 604-8172, Japan
Ph: 81 752 575830
Fax: 81 752 131675
Publisher E-mail: admin@j-circ.or.jp
Medical science journal. **Founded:** 1935. **Freq:** Annual. **Key Personnel:** Dr. Masunori Matsuzaki, MD, Editor-in-Chief. **ISSN:** 0047-1828. **Remarks:** Advertising accepted; rates available upon request. **URL:** http://www.j-circ.or.jp/english/circulation_journal/circulation_journal.html. **Circ:** Paid 19,000

46474 ■ Japanese Journal of Radiological Technology
Japan Society of Radiological Technology
View-Fort Gojokarasuma
167 Higashikazariya-cho, Shinmachi-higashiiru
Gojodori, Shimogyo-ku
Kyoto 600-8107, Japan
Ph: 81 753 548989
Fax: 81 753 522556
Publisher E-mail: office@jsrt.or.jp
Journal featuring subjects on therapeutic radiological technology and radiological technology studies. **Freq:** Monthly. **ISSN:** 0369-4305. **URL:** http://www.jsrt.or.jp/web_data/english.html.

46475 ■ Japanese Religions
National Christian Council of Japan
Center for the Study of Japanese Religions
Karasuma-Shimotachiuri
Kamikyo-ku
Kyoto 602-8011, Japan
Ph: 81 75 4321945
Publisher E-mail: studycen@mbox.kyoto-inet.or.jp
Journal covering religion. **Founded:** 1959. **Freq:** Semiannual January and July. **Key Personnel:** Martin Repp, Editor. **ISSN:** 0448-8954. **Subscription Rates:** 4,000¥ individuals; US$36 other countries; 5,000¥ institutions; US$44 institutions, other countries. **URL:** http://www.japanese-religions.jp/publications. **Circ:** Paid 500

46476 ■ Journal of General Plant Pathology
Springer-Verlag Tokyo
Laboratory of Plant Pathology
Kyoto University
Kyoto 606-8502, Japan
Publisher E-mail: info@springer.jp
Journal welcoming all manuscripts dealing with plant diseases or their control, including pathogen characterization, identification of pathogens, disease physiology and biochemistry, molecular biology, morphology and ultrastructure, genetics, disease transmission, ecology and epidemiology, chemical and biological control, disease assessment, and other topics relevant to plant pathological disorders. **Freq:** Bimonthly. **Key Personnel:** Tetsuro Okuno, Editor-in-Chief, phone 81 75 7536131, fax 81 75 7536131, okuno@kais.kyoto-u.ac.jp; Kazuya Akimitsu, Assoc. Ed.; Jozsef Burgyan, Assoc. Ed.; Sheng Yang He, Assoc. Ed.; Yasufumi Hikichi, Assoc. Ed.; Masayasu Kato, Assoc. Ed.; Kook-Hyung Kim, Assoc. Ed.; Yasuyuki Kubo, Assoc. Ed.; Steven A. Lommel, Assoc. Ed.; Shigetou Namba, Assoc. Ed.; Tatsuya Nagata, Assoc. Ed. **ISSN:** 1345-2630. **Subscription Rates:** EUR389 institutions print incl. free access or

e-only; EUR466.80 institutions print incl. enhanced access. **Remarks:** Advertising accepted; rates available upon request. **URL:** http://www.springer.com/lifesci/plantsciences/journal/10327. **Circ:** (Not Reported)

46477 ■ Journal of Pesticide Science
Pesticide Science Society of Japan
Division of Applied Life Sciences
Graduate School of Agriculture
Kyoto Univ.
Kyoto 606-8502, Japan
Ph: 81 75 7536123
Fax: 81 75 7536123
Publication E-mail: jsps@kais.kyoto-u.ac.jp
Publisher E-mail: nouyaku@mocha.ocn.ne.jp
Publishes original scientific papers in English or Japanese which deal with pesticides in a broad sense. **Founded:** 1992. **Freq:** Quarterly. **Key Personnel:** Prof. Hisashi Miyagawa, Contact. **ISSN:** 0916-9962. **Subscription Rates:** US$40 individuals. **URL:** http://wwwsoc.nii.ac.jp/pssj2/eng/journal/index.html. **Circ:** Paid 2,000

46478 ■ Journal of Pharmacological Sciences
Japanese Pharmacological Society
Kahtohya Bldg.
Gokomachi-Ebisugawa
Nakagyo-ku
Kyoto 604-0982, Japan
Ph: 81 752 524484
Fax: 81 752 524618
Publication E-mail: journal@pharmacol.or.jp
Pharmacy journal. **Founded:** 1951. **Freq:** Quarterly. **Key Personnel:** Susumu Okabe, PhD, Editor-in-Chief; Keitaro Hashimoto, PhD, President. **ISSN:** 0021-5198. **Subscription Rates:** 277¥; US$277 other countries. **URL:** http://plaza.umin.ac.jp/JPS1927/jjp/. **Formerly:** The Japanese Journal of Pharmacology. **Circ:** Paid 2,400

46479 ■ Kyoto Journal
Heian Bunka Center
35 Minamigoshomachi
Okazaki
Sakyo-ku
Kyoto 606-8334, Japan
Ph: 81 757 611433
Fax: 81 757 511196
Publication E-mail: feedback@kyotojournal.org
Publisher E-mail: kyotojo@mbox.kyoto-net.or.jp
Journal of oriental studies. **Founded:** 1987. **Freq:** Quarterly. **Key Personnel:** John Einarsen, Founding Ed./Art Dir.; Ken Rodgers, Managing Editor. **ISSN:** 0913-5200. **Subscription Rates:** US$50 individuals Asia; US$80 two years; 4,200¥ individuals; 8,000¥ two years; US$50 elsewhere; US$85 elsewhere two years; 1,500¥ single issue; US$15 single issue; US$32 individuals; US$59 two years. **Remarks:** Advertising accepted; rates available upon request. **URL:** http://www.kyotojournal.org/. **Circ:** Paid 3,000

46480 ■ Kyoto Review of Southeast Asia
Kyoto University
Graduate School of Science
Yoshida-Honmachi
Sakyo-Ku
Kyoto 606-8501, Japan
Ph: 81 757 537531
Publisher E-mail: kyomu@office.sci
Journal promoting exchange among the intellectual communities of Southeast Asia, bringing news of important publications, debates, and ideas into region-wide circulation through lively and accessible writing. **URL:** http://kyotoreview.cseas.kyoto-u.ac.jp/issue/issue5/index.html.

46481 ■ The Kyoto Shimbun News
The Kyoto Shimbun Newspaper Company Ltd.
Karasuma Ebisugawa-agaru
Nakagyo-ku
Kyoto 604-8577, Japan
Ph: 81 752 415277
Fax: 81 752 221956
Publication E-mail: kpdesk@mb.kyoto-np.co.jp
Publisher E-mail: kpdesk@mb.kyoto-np.co.jp
General newspaper. **Freq:** Daily. **URL:** http://www.kyoto-np.co.jp/kp/english/index.html.

46482 ■ Mathematics Applied in Science and Technology
Research India Publications
c/o Masami Ito, Ed.-in-Ch.

Faculty of Science, Sangyo University
Kita-Ku
Kamigamo
Kyoto 603-8555, Japan
Publisher E-mail: info@ripublication.com
Journal covering mathematics and applications in sciences such as pure and applied mathematics, theoretical computer science, mathematical physics, theoretical mechanics, probability and mathematical statistics, chemistry, biology, psychology, sociology and economics, and applications of mathematics to the engineering sciences. **Founded:** 1927. **Freq:** 3/yr. **Print Method:** Offset. **Trim Size:** 17 x 25 cm. **Cols./Page:** 1. **Col. Width:** 55 nonpareils. **Col. Depth:** 105 agate lines. **Key Personnel:** G.A. Anastassiou, Editorial Board Member; S.I. Bakhtiyarov, Editorial Board Member; Nicola Bellomo, Editorial Board Member; Shigeru Aoki, Editorial Board Member; Masami Ito, Editor-in-Chief, ito@ksuvx0. kyoto-su.ac.jp; G.A. Afrouzi, Editorial Board Member; Ioannis K. Argyros, Editorial Board Member; Doren Levy, Editorial Board Member; Oscar Ibarra, Editorial Board Member. **ISSN:** 0973-6344. **Subscription Rates:** US$180 libraries and institution; print plus online free; US$160 libraries and institution; online only; US$140 individuals print plus online free; US$120 individuals online only. **URL:** http://www.ripublication.com/mast.htm.

46483 ■ Progress of Theoretical Physics
Yukawa Institute for Theoretical Physics
Kitashirakawa Oiwake-Cho
Kyoto 606-8502, Japan
Ph: 81 75 7537000
Fax: 81 75 7537020
Publication E-mail: ptp@yukawa.kyoto-u.ac.jp
Physics journal. **Founded:** 1946. **Freq:** Monthly. **Key Personnel:** Taichiro Kugo, Hd. Ed.; Sinya Aoki, Editor. **ISSN:** 0033-068X. **Subscription Rates:** 88,200¥ institutions surface mail; 37,200¥ individuals surface mail; 51,200¥ individuals airmail; 102,200¥ institutions airmail. **URL:** http://www2.yukawa.kyoto-u.ac.jp/ ~ptpwww/.

46484 ■ Progress of Theoretical Physics - Supplement
Yukawa Institute for Theoretical Physics
Kitashirakawa Oiwake-Cho
Kyoto 606-8502, Japan
Ph: 81 75 7537000
Fax: 81 75 7537020
Physics journal. **Founded:** 1955. **Freq:** Quarterly. **ISSN:** 0375-9687. **Subscription Rates:** 3,045¥ members; 4,620¥ nonmembers; 7,400¥ other countries. **URL:** http://www2.yukawa.kyoto-u.ac.jp/~ptpwww/link-supplement.html.

46485 ■ Psychologia
Psychologia Society
Dept. of Cognitive Psychology in Education
Graduate School of Education
Kyoto University
Kyoto 606-8501, Japan
Fax: 81 757 533049
Publisher E-mail: psysoc@educ.kyoto-u.ac.jp
Publishes symposia, general surveys, reviews, brief reports, notes and discussions, as well as representative original works in very broad fields of psychology. **Founded:** 1957. **Freq:** Quarterly. **Key Personnel:** Noboru Sakano, President; Sakiko Yoshikawa, Editor; Shoji Itakura, Editorial Board; Takashi Kusumi, Assoc. Ed.; Raymond W. Gibbs, Jr., Editorial Board; Kazuo Fujita, Editorial Board; Stephen A. Dewhurst, Editorial Board; Kaori Karasawa, Editorial Board; Yutaka Kano, Editorial Board; Med Hafsi, Editorial Board; Makiko Naka, Editorial Board. **ISSN:** 0033-2852. **Subscription Rates:** 8,000¥ individuals; 12,000¥ institutions library. **Remarks:** Advertising accepted; rates available upon request. **URL:** http://www.educ.kyoto-u.ac.jp/cogpsy/ psychologia/. **Circ:** Paid 900

46486 ■ Publications of Seto Marine Biological Laboratory
Kyoto University
Graduate School of Science
Yoshida-Honmachi
Sakyo-Ku
Kyoto 606-8501, Japan
Ph: 81 757 537531

Publisher E-mail: kyomu@office.sci
Journal covering biology. **Founded:** 1949. **Freq:** Annual. **Key Personnel:** Yoshihisa Shirayama, Editor. **ISSN:** 0037-2870. **URL:** http://www.kyoto-u.ac.jp; http://www. seto.kyoto-u.ac.jp/publications_e.htm. **Circ:** 460

JOBO - See Maizuru
46487 ■ JOBR - 1143 KHz
Kamichojamachi
Karasumadori
Kamigyo-ku
Kyoto 602-8588, Japan
Ph: 81 75 4312160
Format: Eclectic. **Owner:** Kyoto Broadcasting System Co., Ltd. (KBS), at above address. **Founded:** 1951. **Operating Hours:** Continuous. **Key Personnel:** Yamazaki Hiro, Mng. Dir. **Wattage:** 20,000. **URL:** http:// www.kbs-kyoto.co.jp/.

46488 ■ JOBR-TV - 34
Kamichojamachi
Karasumadori
Kamigyo-ku
Kyoto 602-8588, Japan
Ph: 81 75 4312160
Fax: 81 75 4310700
Owner: Kyoto Broadcasting System Co., Ltd. (KBS), at above address. **Founded:** 1969. **Wattage:** 10,000. **URL:** http://www.kbs-kyoto.co.jp/.

JOBW - See Hikone
46489 ■ JOKV - 89.4 MHz
8th Fl., Cocon Karusama
620 Ward St.
Shimogyo
Kyoto 600-8566, Japan
Ph: 81 75 3440894
Fax: 81 75 3441894
Format: Eclectic. **Owner:** FM Kyoto, Inc., at above address. **Founded:** 1991. **Operating Hours:** Continuous. **Wattage:** 3000. **Ad Rates:** Noncommercial. **URL:** http://fm-kyoto.jp.

46490 ■ JOOK - 621 KHz
2-2-1 Jinnan
Shibuya-ku
Tokyo 150-8001, Japan
Ph: 81 3 34651111
Fax: 81 3 34811350
E-mail: nhkworld@nhk.jp
Format: News. **Owner:** Nippon Hoso Kyokai (NHK), at above address. **Operating Hours:** Continuous. **Key Personnel:** Shigeo Fukuchi, President; Hidemi Hyuga, Exec. Dir. Gen. **Wattage:** 1000. **URL:** http://www.nhk.or. jp.

46491 ■ JOOK - 82.8 MHz
2-2-1 Jinnan
Shibuya-ku
Tokyo 150-8001, Japan
Ph: 81 3 34651111
Fax: 81 3 34698110
Format: News. **Owner:** Nippon Hoso Kyokai (NHK), at above address. **Operating Hours:** Continuous. **Key Personnel:** Hidemi Hyuga, Exec. Dir. Gen. **Wattage:** 1000. **URL:** http://www.nhk.or.jp.

Kyowa

46492 ■ JOEE-TV Kyowa - 55
21-3, Moto-machi
Naka-ku
Hiroshima 730-8504, Japan
Ph: 81 82 2221155
E-mail: tv@rcc.net
Owner: Chugoku Broadcasting Co., Ltd. (RCC), at above address. **Founded:** 1959. **Wattage:** 3. **URL:** http://www.1350.jp/.

Maebashi

46493 ■ JOML-TV - 48
38-2, Kamikoide-machi 3-chome
Maebashi 371-8548, Japan
Ph: 81 27 2190001
Owner: Gunma Television Co., Ltd. (GTV), at above address. **Founded:** 1971. **Wattage:** 1000. **URL:** http:// www.gtv.co.jp/.

46494 ■ JORU - 86.3 MHz
1-4-8, Wakamiyacho
Maebashi 371-8533, Japan
Ph: 81 27 2348000
Format: Eclectic. **Owner:** Gunma FM Broadcasting Co., Ltd. (FMG), at above address. **Founded:** 1985. **Operating Hours:** Continuous. **Wattage:** 1000. **Ad Rates:** Advertising accepted; rates available upon request. **URL:** http://www.fmgunma.com.

46495 ■ JOTP - 81.6 MHz
2-2-1 Jinnan
Shibuya-ku
Tokyo 150-8001, Japan
Ph: 81 3 34651111
Fax: 81 3 34698110
Format: News. **Owner:** Nippon Hoso Kyokai (NHK), at above address. **Operating Hours:** Continuous. **Key Personnel:** Hidemi Hyuga, Exec. Dir. Gen. **Wattage:** 1000. **URL:** http://www.nhk.or.jp.

46496 ■ JOUD - 78.8 MHz
2-11, Wakaba
Mihama-ku
Chiba 261-8586, Japan
Ph: 81 43 2765111
Fax: 81 43 2972781
Format: Eclectic. **Owner:** University Broadcasting Station, at above address. **Operating Hours:** 2100-1500. **Wattage:** 1000. **URL:** http://www.u-air.ac.jp/.

Maizuru

46497 ■ JOBO - 1215 KHz
Karasuma, Kamigyo-ku
Kyoto 602-8588, Japan
Format: Eclectic. **Owner:** Kyoto Broadcasting System Co., Ltd., at above address. **Operating Hours:** Continuous. **Wattage:** 2000. **URL:** http://www.kbs-kyoto. co.jp/.

Marugame

46498 ■ Nishi Nippon Hoso - 1449 KHz
8-15, Marunouchi
Takamatsu 760-8575, Japan
Ph: 81 878 267333
Format: Eclectic. **Owner:** Nishinippon Broadcasting Co., Ltd., at above address. **Operating Hours:** Continuous. **Key Personnel:** Kunio Yoshioka, President. **Wattage:** 1000. **Ad Rates:** Noncommercial. **URL:** http:// www.rnc.co.jp/.

Matsue

46499 ■ JOMI-TV - 34
721, Nishikawazu-cho
Matsue 690-8666, Japan
Ph: 81 852233434
Fax: 81 852223973
Owner: San-In Chuo Television Broadcasting Co., Ltd. (TSK), at above address. **Founded:** 1970. **Wattage:** 10,000. **URL:** http://www.tsk-tv.com/index_main.html.

46500 ■ JOTB - 1593 KHz
2-2-1 Jinnan
Shibuya-ku
Tokyo 150-8001, Japan
Ph: 81 3 34651111
Fax: 81 3 34698110
E-mail: nhkworld@nhk.jp
Format: Educational. **Owner:** Nippon Hoso Kyokai (NHK), at above address. **Operating Hours:** 2030-1640 (2030-1500, Sun. & Mon.). **Key Personnel:** Shigeo Fukuchi, President. **Wattage:** 10,000. **URL:** http://www. nhk.or.jp.

46501 ■ JOTK - 1296 KHz
2-2-1 Jinnan
Shibuya-ku
Tokyo 150-8001, Japan
Ph: 81 3 34651111
Fax: 81 3 34811350
E-mail: nhkworld@nhk.jp
Format: News. **Owner:** Nippon Hoso Kyokai (NHK), at above address. **Operating Hours:** Continuous. **Key Personnel:** Shigeo Fukuchi, President; Hidemi Hyuga, Exec. Dir. Gen. **Wattage:** 10,000. **URL:** http://www.nhk. or.jp.

Circulation: ★ = ABC; △ = BPA; ♦ = CAC; • = CCAB; ❑ = VAC; ⊕ = PO Statement; ‡ = Publisher's Report; Boldface figures = sworn; Light figures = estimated.

Gale Directory of Publications & Broadcast Media/147th Ed.   5091

46502 ■ JOVU - 77.4 MHz
Central Bldg. 383, Tono-machi
Matsue 690-8508, Japan
Ph: 81 852 275111
Fax: 81 852 279883
Format: Eclectic. **Owner:** San-In FM Broadcasting Co.,
Ltd. (FSK), at above address. **Founded:** 1986. **Operating Hours:** Continuous. **Wattage:** 500. **Ad Rates:**
Advertising accepted; rates available upon request.
URL: http://www.fm-sanin.co.jp/.

Matsumoto

46503 ■ JONI-TV - 30
4-18, Marunouchi
Matsumoto 390-8611, Japan
Ph: 81 263 362002
Owner: Television Shinshu Broadcasting Co., Ltd.
(TSB), 1-1-1 Wakasato, Nagano 380-8555, Japan.
Founded: 1980. **Wattage:** 10,000. **URL:** http://www.tsb.
co.jp/.

46504 ■ JOSO - 864 KHz
Question Imperial Palace Town 1200
Nagano 380-8521, Japan
Ph: 81 26 2370500
Format: Eclectic. **Owner:** Shin-Etsu Broadcasting Co.,
Ltd. (SBC), at above address. **Founded:** 1997. **Operating Hours:** Continuous. **Wattage:** 1000. **URL:** http://
sbc21.co.jp/.

JOZU - See Nagano

Matsuyama

46505 ■ JOAF - 1116 KHz
1-1-1, Hon-cho
Matsuyama 790-8510, Japan
Ph: 81 89 9153333
Fax: 81 89 9152370
Format: Eclectic. **Owner:** Nankai Broadcasting Co.,
Ltd.(RNB), at above address. **Founded:** 1953. **Operating Hours:** Continuous. **Wattage:** 5000. **URL:** http://
www.rnb.co.jp/.

JOAL - See Niihama

JOAM - See Uwajima

46506 ■ JOEU - 79.7 MHz
10-7, Takehara-cho 1-chome
Matsuyama 790-8565, Japan
Ph: 81 89 9451111
Fax: 81 89 9451179
Format: Eclectic. **Owner:** FM Ehime Broadcasting Co.,
at above address. **Founded:** 1982. **Operating Hours:**
Continuous. **Wattage:** 1000. **Ad Rates:** Advertising accepted; rates available upon request. **URL:** http://www.
joeufm.co.jp/.

46507 ■ JOZK - 963 KHz
2-2-1 Jinnan
Shibuya-ku
Tokyo 790-8501, Japan
Ph: 81 3 34651111
Fax: 81 3 34811350
E-mail: nhkworld@nhk.jp
Format: News. **Owner:** Nippon Hoso Kyokai (NHK), at
above address. **Operating Hours:** Continuous. **Key
Personnel:** Shigeo Fukuchi, President; Hidemi Hyuga,
Exec. Dir. Gen. **Wattage:** 5000. **Ad Rates:** Advertising
accepted; rates available upon request. **URL:** http://
www.nhk.or.jp.

46508 ■ JOZK - 87.7 MHz
2-2-1 Jinnan
Shibuya-ku
Tokyo 150-8001, Japan
Ph: 81 3 34651111
Fax: 81 3 34811350
Format: News. **Owner:** Nippon Hoso Kyokai (NHK), at
above address. **Operating Hours:** Continuous. **Wattage:** 1000. **Ad Rates:** Noncommercial. **URL:** http://www.
nhk.or.jp.

Mihara

46509 ■ JOEE-TV Mihara - 49
21-3, Moto-machi
Naka-ku
Hiroshima 730-8504, Japan
Ph: 81 82 2221155

E-mail: rcc@rcc.net
Owner: Chugoku Broadcasting Co., Ltd. (RCC), at
above address. **Founded:** 1959. **Wattage:** 10. **URL:**
http://www.rcc.co.jp.

Mihara-nakanomachi

46510 ■ JOEE-TV Mihara-nakanomachi - 57
21-3, Moto-machi
Naka-ku
Hiroshima 730-8504, Japan
Ph: 81 82 2221155
E-mail: tv@rcc.net
Owner: Chugoku Broadcasting Co., Ltd. (RCC), at
above address. **Founded:** 1959. **Wattage:** 3. **URL:**
http://www.1350.jp/.

Minamimidori

46511 ■ JOEE-TV Minamimidori - 5
21-3, Moto-machi
Naka-ku
Hiroshima 730-8504, Japan
Ph: 81 82 2221155
E-mail: tv@rcc.net
Owner: Chugoku Broadcasting Co., Ltd. (RCC), at
above address. **Founded:** 1959. **Wattage:** 1. **Ad Rates:**
Noncommercial. **URL:** http://www.rcc.co.jp.

Mirasaka

46512 ■ JOEE-TV Mirasaka - 46
21-3, Moto-machi
Naka-ku
Hiroshima 730-8504, Japan
Ph: 81 82 2221155
E-mail: tv@rcc.net
Owner: Chugoku Broadcasting Co., Ltd. (RCC), at
above address. **Founded:** 1959. **Wattage:** 3. **Ad Rates:**
Noncommercial. **URL:** http://www.rcc.co.jp.

Mito

46513 ■ Entomological Science
Entomological Society of Japan
National History Laboratory
Faculty of Science
Ibaraki Univ.
Mito 310-8512, Japan
Ph: 81 292 288377
Fax: 81 292 288403
Publisher E-mail: es@mcs.ibaraki.ac.jp
Journal of entomology. **Founded:** 1998. **Freq:** Quarterly
March, June, September and December. **Key Personnel:** Jun-Ichi Kojima, Editorial Board; Hideharu Numata,
Editor-in-Chief. **ISSN:** 1343-8786. **Subscription Rates:**
124 individuals print + online; US$200 individuals print
+ online; EUR185 individuals print + online; 409 institutions print + online; US$409 institutions print + online;
EUR520 institutions print + online. **URL:** http://wwwsoc.
nii.ac.jp/entsocj/e/e-home.htm.

46514 ■ JOEP - 83.2 MHz
2-2-1 Jinnan
Shibuya-ku
Tokyo 150-8001, Japan
Ph: 81 3 34651111
Fax: 81 3 34698110
Format: News. **Owner:** Nippon Hoso Kyokai (NHK), at
above address. **Operating Hours:** Continuous. **Key
Personnel:** Hidemi Hyuga, Exec. Dir. Gen. **Wattage:**
1000. **Ad Rates:** Noncommercial. **URL:** http://www.nhk.
or.jp.

46515 ■ JOYF - 1197 KHz
2084 Senba-cho
Mito 310-8505, Japan
Ph: 81 29 2442121
Fax: 81 29 2438955
Format: Eclectic. **Owner:** Ibaraki Broadcasting System
(IBS), at above address. **Founded:** 1963. **Operating
Hours:** 2045-2000; Sat. 2100-1930; Sun. 2045-1430.
Wattage: 5000. **URL:** http://www.ibs-radio.com.

Mitsugi

46516 ■ JOEE-TV Mitsugi - 56
21-3, Moto-machi
Naka-ku
Hiroshima 730-8504, Japan

Ph: 81 82 2221155
E-mail: tv@rcc.net
Owner: Chugoku Broadcasting Co., Ltd. (RCC), at
above address. **Founded:** 1959. **Wattage:** 3. **Ad Rates:**
Noncommercial. **URL:** http://www.1350.jp/.

Miyagi

**46517 ■ Research and Practice in Forensic
Medicine**
Tohoku University
School of Medicine
2-1 Seiryo-machi
Aoba-ku
Sendai-shi
Miyagi 980-8575, Japan
Publisher E-mail: med-kyom@bureau.tohoku.ac.jp
Journal of forensic medicine. **Founded:** 1954. **Freq:**
Annual. **Key Personnel:** Kaoru Sagisaka, Editor. **ISSN:**
0289-0755. **Subscription Rates:** 4,000¥. **Circ:** Paid
1,000

Miyazaki

46518 ■ Grassland Science
Japanese Society of Grassland Science
c/o Faculty of Agriculture
University of Miyazaki
Gakuen-kibanadai-Nishi-1-1
Miyazaki 889-2192, Japan
Publisher E-mail: sgakkai@naro.affrc.go.jp
Publishes original contributions in the field of grassland
science and technology. **Founded:** 1955. **Freq:**
Quarterly. **Key Personnel:** Makoto Kobayashi, Managing Editor; Keith Betteridge, Editorial Board; Suguru
Saiga, President; Masahito Hirata, Vice President; David
Chapman, Editorial Board; Bryan Kindiger, Editorial
Board; Hitoshi Nakagawa, Editorial Board. **ISSN:** 1744-
6961. **Subscription Rates:** US$451 institutions the
Americas, print & online; EUR295 institutions Europe,
print & online; 232 institutions print & online; US$392
institutions print or online. **Remarks:** Accepts classified
advertising. **URL:** http://www.wiley.com/bw/journal.asp?
ref=1744-6961&site=1. **Circ:** Paid 1,400

46519 ■ Journal of Japan Glaucoma Society
Nihon Ryokunaisho
Miyazaki Ika Daigaku Gankagaku Kyoshitsu
5200 Kihara
Miyazaki-gun
Kiyotake-cho
Miyazaki 889-1601, Japan
Medical science journal. **Founded:** 1990. **Freq:** Annual.
ISSN: 0917-4338. **URL:** http://www.ryokunaisho.jp/
english/activites.html.

46520 ■ JOMC - 1467 KHz
2-2-1 Jinnan
Shibuya-ku
Tokyo 150-8001, Japan
Ph: 81 3 34651111
Fax: 81 3 34698110
E-mail: nhkworld@nhk.jp
Format: Educational. **Owner:** Nippon Hoso Kyokai
(NHK), at above address. **Operating Hours:** 2030-1640
(2030-1500, Sun. & Mon.). **Key Personnel:** Shigeo
Fukuchi, President. **Wattage:** 1000. **URL:** http://www.
nhk.or.jp.

46521 ■ JOMG - 540 KHz
2-2-1 Jinnan
Shibuya-ku
Tokyo 150-8001, Japan
Ph: 81 3 34651111
Fax: 81 3 34698110
E-mail: nhkworld@nhk.jp
Format: News. **Owner:** Nippon Hoso Kyokai (NHK), at
above address. **Operating Hours:** Continuous. **Key
Personnel:** Shigeo Fukuchi, President. **Wattage:** 5000.
URL: http://www.nhk.or.jp.

46522 ■ JOMU - 83.2 MHz
2-78, Gion
Miyazaki 880-8583, Japan
Ph: 81 985 223344
Format: Eclectic. **Owner:** Miyazaki FM Broadcasting
Co., Ltd., at above address. **Founded:** 1984. **Operating
Hours:** Continuous. **Wattage:** 1000. **Ad Rates:** Advertising accepted; rates available upon request. **URL:** http://
www.joyfm.co.jp/.

46523 ■ JONF - 936 KHz
6-7, Nishi 4-chome
Tachibana-dori
Miyazaki 880-8639, Japan
Ph: 81 985 253111
Fax: 81 985 260310
E-mail: mrtwebm@mrt-miyazaki.co.jp
Format: Eclectic. **Owner:** Miyazaki Broadcasting Co., Ltd. (MRT), at above address. **Founded:** 1954. **Operating Hours:** Continuous. **Wattage:** 5000. **URL:** http://www.mrt-miyazaki.co.jp/.

Miyoshi

46524 ■ JOEE-TV Miyoshi - 9
21-3, Moto-machi
Naka-ku
Hiroshima 730-8504, Japan
Ph: 81 82 2221155
E-mail: rcc@rcc.net
Owner: Chugoku Broadcasting Co., Ltd. (RCC), at above address. **Founded:** 1959. **Wattage:** 75. **Ad Rates:** Noncommercial. **URL:** http://www.rcc.co.jp.

Morioka

46525 ■ JODF - 684 KHz
6-1, Shike-cho
Morioka 020-8566, Japan
Ph: 81 19 6233111
Fax: 81 19 6544806
E-mail: wide@ibc.co.jp
Format: Eclectic. **Owner:** Iwate Broadcasting Co., Ltd. (IBC), at above address. **Founded:** 1953. **Operating Hours:** Continuous. **Wattage:** 5000. **URL:** http://www.ibc.co.jp/.

46526 ■ JODF-TV - 6
6-1, Shike-cho
Morioka 020-8566, Japan
Ph: 81 19 6233111
Owner: Iwate Broadcasting Co., Ltd. (IBC), at above address. **Founded:** 1959. **Key Personnel:** Masaki Abe, President. **Wattage:** 3000. **URL:** http://www.ibc.co.jp/.

46527 ■ JOII-TV - 35
2-10, Uchimaru
Morioka 020-0023, Japan
Ph: 81 19 6241166
Owner: Television Iwate Corporation (TVI), at above address. **Founded:** 1969. **Key Personnel:** Takao Abe, Exec. Dir. **Wattage:** 10,000. **URL:** http://www.tvi.jp/.

46528 ■ JOIY-TV - 31
6-5, Moriokaeki-Nishidori 2-chome
Morioka 020-0045, Japan
Ph: 81 19 6292525
Owner: Iwate Asahi TelevisionCo., Ltd.(IAT), at above address. **Founded:** 1996. **Wattage:** 10,000. **URL:** http://www.iat.co.jp/.

JOLO - See Ofunato

46529 ■ JOQC - 1386 KHz
2-2-1 Jinnan
Shibuya-ku
Tokyo 150-8001, Japan
Ph: 81 3 34651111
Fax: 81 3 34698110
E-mail: nhkworld@nhk.jp
Format: Educational. **Owner:** Nippon Hoso Kyokai (NHK), at above address. **Operating Hours:** 2030-1640 (2030-1500, Sun. & Mon.). **Key Personnel:** Shigeo Fukuchi, President. **Wattage:** 10,000. **URL:** http://www.nhk.or.jp.

46530 ■ JOQG - 531 KHz
2-2-1, Jinnan
Shibuya-ku
Tokyo 150-8001, Japan
Ph: 81 3 34651111
Fax: 81 3 34698110
E-mail: nhkworld@nhk.jp
Format: News. **Owner:** Nippon Hoso Kyokai (NHK), at above address. **Operating Hours:** Continuous. **Key Personnel:** Shigehiro Komaru, Chm.; Shigeo Fukuchi, President. **Wattage:** 10,000. **URL:** http://www.nhk.or.jp.

46531 ■ JOQU - 76.1 MHz
2-10 Cir.
Morioka 020-8512, Japan

Ph: 81 19 6255511
Fax: 81 19 6255519
Format: Eclectic. **Owner:** Iwate FM Broadcastomg Co., Ltd. (IBC), at above address. **Founded:** Oct. 1, 1985. **Operating Hours:** 0500-0400. **Wattage:** 1000. **Ad Rates:** Advertising accepted; rates available upon request. **URL:** http://www.fmii.co.jp/.

46532 ■ JOYH-TV - 33
89 Aza St.
Motomiya
Morioka 020-0866, Japan
Ph: 81 19 6563300
Owner: Iwate Menkoi Television Co., Ltd. (MIT), at above address. **Founded:** 1991. **Wattage:** 10,000. **URL:** http://www.menkoi-tv.co.jp/.

Mukaihara

46533 ■ JOEE-TV Mukaihara - 48
21-3, Moto-machi
Naka-ku
Hiroshima 730-8504, Japan
Ph: 81 82 2221155
E-mail: tv@rcc.net
Owner: Chugoku Broadcasting Co., Ltd. (RCC), at above address. **Founded:** 1959. **Wattage:** 3. **Ad Rates:** Noncommercial. **URL:** http://www.1350.jp/.

Muroran

46534 ■ JOIQ - 945 KHz
2-2-1 Jinnan
Shibuya-ku
Tokyo 150-8001, Japan
Ph: 81 3 34651111
Fax: 81 3 34811350
E-mail: nhkworld@nhk.jp
Format: News. **Owner:** Nippon Hoso Kyokai (NHK), at above address. **Operating Hours:** Continuous. **Key Personnel:** Shigeo Fukuchi, President; Hidemi Hyuga, Exec. Dir. Gen. **Wattage:** 3000. **URL:** http://www.nhk.or.jp.

46535 ■ JOIZ - 1125 KHz
2-2-1 Jinnan
Shibuya-ku
Tokyo 150-8001, Japan
Ph: 81 3 34651111
Fax: 81 3 34698110
E-mail: nhkworld@nhk.jp
Format: Educational. **Owner:** Nippon Hoso Kyokai (NHK), at above address. **Operating Hours:** 2030-1640 (2030-1500, Sun. & Mon.). **Key Personnel:** Shigeo Fukuchi, President. **Wattage:** 1000. **Ad Rates:** Noncommercial. **URL:** http://www.nhk.or.jp.

46536 ■ Sapporo TV Hoso - 1440 KHz
1-1, Nishi 8-chome
Kita 1-jo, Chuo-ku
Sapporo 060-8705, Japan
Ph: 81 11 2411181
E-mail: radio@stv.jp
Format: Eclectic. **Owner:** The Sapporo Television Broadcasting Co., Ltd., at above address. **Founded:** 1962. **Operating Hours:** Continuous. **Wattage:** 3000. **URL:** http://www.stv.ne.jp/.

Nagano

46537 ■ New Entomologist
Entomological Society of Shinshu
Shinshu Daigaku Nogakubu Oyo
Konchugaku Kyoshitsu
8304 Kamiina-gun
Nagano 399-4598, Japan
Ph: 81 265 771100
Fax: 81 265 771400
Publisher E-mail: insect2@gipmc.shinshu-u.ac.jp
Journal of entomology. **Founded:** 1951. **Freq:** Semiannual. **Key Personnel:** Hiroshi Nakamura, Editor-in-Chief; Shizuo Fujitama, Editor; Shigehiro Furihata, Editor. **ISSN:** 0028-4955. **URL:** http://www12.plala.or.jp/NewEntomologist/hiromusi_009.htm.

46538 ■ JOGH-TV - 20
989-1, Kurita
Nagano 380-8550, Japan
Ph: 81 262231000

Fax: 81 262231030
Owner: Asahi Broadcasting Nagano Co., Ltd. (ABN), at above address. **Founded:** 1991. **Key Personnel:** Kikuti Seiiti, President. **Wattage:** 10,000. **URL:** http://www.abn-tv.co.jp/.

46539 ■ JOLH-TV - 38
131-7, Okada-machi
Nagano 380-8633, Japan
Ph: 81 26 2273000
Owner: Nagano Broadcasting Systems, Inc. (NBS), at above address. **Founded:** 1969. **Wattage:** 10,000. **URL:** http://www.nbs-tv.co.jp/.

46540 ■ JONB - 1467 KHz
2-2-1 Jinnan
Shibuya-ku
Tokyo 150-8001, Japan
Ph: 81 3 34651111
Fax: 81 3 34698110
E-mail: nhkworld@nhk.jp
Format: Educational. **Owner:** Nippon Hoso Kyokai (NHK), at above address. **Operating Hours:** 2030-1640 (2030-1500, Sun. & Mon.). **Key Personnel:** Shigeo Fukuchi, President. **Wattage:** 1000. **URL:** http://www.nhk.or.jp.

46541 ■ JONK - 819 KHz
2-2-1 Jinnan
Shibuya-ku
Tokyo 150-8001, Japan
Ph: 81 3 34651111
Fax: 81 3 34811350
E-mail: nhkworld@nhk.jp
Format: News. **Owner:** Nippon Hoso Kyokai (NHK), at above address. **Operating Hours:** Continuous. **Key Personnel:** Shigeo Fukuchi, President; Hidema Hyuga, Exec. Dir. Gen. **Wattage:** 5000. **Ad Rates:** Noncommercial. **URL:** http://www.nhk.or.jp.

JOSO - See Matsumoto

46542 ■ JOSR - 1098 KHz
Question Imperial Palace Town 1200
Nagano 381-8521, Japan
Ph: 81 26 2370500
Format: Eclectic. **Owner:** Shin-Etsu Broadcasting Co., Ltd. (SBC), at above address. **Founded:** 1952. **Operating Hours:** Continuous. **Wattage:** 5000. **URL:** http://sbc21.co.jp/.

46543 ■ JOSR-TV - 11
1200 Imperial Palace Town
Nagano 381-8521, Japan
Ph: 81 26 2370500
Owner: Shin-Etsu Broadcasting Co., Ltd. (SBC), at above address. **Founded:** 1958. **Wattage:** 1000. **URL:** http://sbc21.co.jp/.

46544 ■ JOZU - 79.7 MHz
1-13-5, Honjo
Matsumoto 390-8520, Japan
Ph: 81 263 334400
Format: Eclectic. **Owner:** Nagano FM Broadcasting Co., Ltd, at above address. **Founded:** 1988. **Operating Hours:** 0500-0400. **Key Personnel:** Tatsuo Kitayama, President. **Wattage:** 1000. **Ad Rates:** Advertising accepted; rates available upon request. **URL:** http://www.fmnagano.co.jp/.

Nagasaki

46545 ■ Acta Medica Nagasakiensia
Nagasaki University
School of Medicine
Sakamoto 1-12-4
Nagasaki-shi
Nagasaki 852-8523, Japan
Ph: 81 95 8497000
Fax: 81 95 8497166
Publication E-mail: contact_amn@ml.nagasaki-u.ac.jp
Medical science journal. **Founded:** 1939. **Freq:** Irregular. **Key Personnel:** Masataka Uetani, Editor-in-Chief, uetani@nagasaki-u.ac.jp; Tadaomi Aikawa, Editor; Kazbek N. Apsalikov, Editor. **ISSN:** 0001-6055. **URL:** http://www.med.nagasaki.u.ac.jp/amn/. **Circ:** 350

46546 ■ Sensors and Actuators B
Elsevier Science Inc.
c/o Prof. Y. Shimizu, Ed.
Dept. of Materials Science & Engineering

Nagasaki University
1-14 Bunkyo-machi
Nagasaki 852-8521, Japan
Ph: 81 95 8192643
Fax: 81 95 8192644
Publisher E-mail: usinfo-ehelp@elsevier.com
Journal devoted to research and development of chemical transducers. **Subtitle:** Chemical. **Founded:** 1990. **Freq:** 16/yr. **Key Personnel:** E. Katz, Editorial Board; Prof. E. Bakker, Editor, bakker.eric@gmail.com; Prof. Y. Shimizu, Editor; Prof. R. Narayanaswamy, Editor, phone 44 161 3064891, fax 44 161 30649111, ramaier. narayanaswamy@manchester.ac.uk; Y. Baba, Editorial Board; T. Laurell, Editorial Board; U. Weimar, Editorial Board; J. Wang, Editorial Board; Prof. M. Koudelka-Hep, Editorial Board; V. Lantto, Editorial Board. **ISSN:** 0925-4005. **Subscription Rates:** US$5,204 institutions, other countries except Europe, Japan and Iran; 618,000¥ institutions; EUR4,651 institutions for European countries and Iran. **URL:** http://www.elsevier.com/wps/find/ journaldescription.cws_home/504104/ descriptiondescription.

46547 ■ JOAC - 1377 KHz
2-2-1 Jinnan
Shibuya-ku
Tokyo 150-8001, Japan
Ph: 81 3 34651111
Fax: 81 3 34698110
E-mail: nhkworld@nhk.jp
Format: Educational. **Owner:** Nippon Hoso Kyokai (NHK), at above address. **Operating Hours:** 2030-1640 (2030-1500, Sun. & Mon.). **Key Personnel:** Shigeo Fukuchi, President. **Wattage:** 1000. **Ad Rates:** Noncommercial. **URL:** http://www.nhk.or.jp.

46548 ■ JOAG - 684 KHz
2-2-1 Jinnan
Shibuya-ku
Tokyo 150-8001, Japan
Ph: 81 3 34651111
Fax: 81 3 34811350
E-mail: nhkworld@nhk.jp
Format: News. **Owner:** Nippon Hoso Kyokai (NHK), at above address. **Operating Hours:** Continuous. **Key Personnel:** Shigeo Fukuchi, President; Hidemi Hyuga, Exec. Dir. Gen. **Wattage:** 5000. **Ad Rates:** Noncommercial. **URL:** http://www.nhk.or.jp.

46549 ■ JOHU - 79.5 MHz
5-5, Cho Eiiti
Nagasaki 850-8550, Japan
Ph: 81 95 8282020
Fax: 81 95 8266105
Format: Eclectic. **Owner:** FM Nagasaki Co., Ltd. (FMN), at above address. **Founded:** 1982. **Operating Hours:** Continuous. **Wattage:** 1000. **Ad Rates:** Advertising accepted; rates available upon request. **URL:** http://www. .fmnagasaki.co.jp/outline/.

JOMF - See Sasebo

JOUO - See Saga

46550 ■ JOUR - 1233 KHz
1-35, Uwamati
Nagasaki 850-8650, Japan
Ph: 81 95 8243111
Format: Eclectic. **Owner:** Nagasaki Broadcasting Co., Ltd. (NBC), at above address. **Founded:** 1953. **Operating Hours:** Continuous. **Wattage:** 5000. **URL:** http:// www.nbc-nagasaki.co.jp.

Nagasaki Hoso - See Fukue

Nagoya

46551 ■ Asian Ethnology
Asian Folklore Studies
Nanzan University
18, Yamazato-cho
Showa-ku
Nagoya 466-8673, Japan
Ph: 81 52 8323111
Fax: 81 52 8336157
Publisher E-mail: nuai@ic.nanzan-u.ac.jp
Publication covering anthropology, folklore, and religion. **Founded:** 1942. **Freq:** Semiannual. **Key Personnel:** Scott Schnell, Editor; Benjamin Dorman, Editor. **ISSN:** 1882-6865. **Subscription Rates:** US$35 individuals; EUR25 individuals; US$50 institutions; EUR35 institutions; 3,500¥ individuals; 5,000¥ institutions. **Remarks:** Advertising not accepted. **URL:** http://www.nanzan-u.ac.

jp/SHUBUNKEN/publications/afs/afsMain.htm. **Formerly:** Asian Folklore Studies. **Circ:** Paid 450

46552 ■ Coastal Engineering Journal
World Scientific Publishing Company Private Ltd.
c/o Norimi Mizutani, Ed.-in-Ch.
Dept. of Civil Engineering
Nagoya University
Furo-cho, Chikusa-ku
Nagoya 464-8603, Japan
Publisher E-mail: wspc@wspc.com.sg
Peer-reviewed journal focusing on fields of coastal, harbor and offshore engineering. **Founded:** 1958. **Freq:** Quarterly. **Key Personnel:** Yoshimi Goda, Honorary Ed., goda@ecoh.co.jp; Ron Cox, Editor; Hitoshi Gotoh, Editor; Ioan Nistor, Editor; Norimi Mizutani, Editor-in-Chief, mizutani@civil.nagoya-u.ac.jp. **ISSN:** 0578-5634. **Subscription Rates:** US$629 institutions and libraries; print & electronic; US$39 individuals for postage; US$604 institutions and libraries; electronic only; EUR509 institutions and libraries; print & electronic; EUR523 institutions and libraries; electronic only; EUR31 individuals for postage; S$1,121 institutions and libraries; print & electronic; S$1,076 institutions and libraries; electronic only; S$52 individuals for postage. **URL:** http://www.worldscinet. com/cej/cej.shtml.

46553 ■ Japanese Journal of Religious Studies
Nanzan Institute for Religion and Culture
Nanzan University
18 Yamazato-cho
Showa-ku
Nagoya 466-8673, Japan
Ph: 81 52 8323111
Fax: 81 52 8336157
Publisher E-mail: nirc@ic.nanzan-u.ac.jp
Academic journal covering religious studies related to Japan. **Founded:** 1974. **Freq:** Semiannual. **Trim Size:** 23.4 cm. x 16.1 cm. **Key Personnel:** Benjamin Dorman, Editor; Akaike Noriaki, Advisory Board; Hayashi Makoto, Advisory Board; Paul L. Swanson, Editor. **ISSN:** 0304-1042. **Subscription Rates:** US$35 other countries; US$50 institutions, other countries; EUR25 individuals Europe; 3,500¥ individuals; 5,000¥ institutions; EUR35 institutions Europe. **Remarks:** Advertising not accepted. **URL:** http://www.nanzan-u.ac.jp/SHUBUNKEN/contact/ contact.htm. **Alt. Formats:** CD-ROM. **Formerly:** Contemporary Religions in Japan. **Circ:** Combined 510

46554 ■ Journal of Plasma and Fusion Research
Japan Society of Plasma Science and Nuclear Fusion Research
3-1-1-4F, Uchiyama
Chikusa-ku
Nagoya 464-0073, Japan
Ph: 81 527 353185
Fax: 81 527 353485
Journal of nuclear physics. **Founded:** 1958. **Freq:** Annual. **Key Personnel:** Kozo Yamazaki, Editor-in-Chief. **ISSN:** 0918-7928. **URL:** http://www.jspf.or.jp/PFR.

46555 ■ Journal of Smooth Muscle Research
Japanese Society of Smooth Muscle Research
c/o Hikaru Suzuki, Ch. Ed.
Dept. of Physiology
Nagoya City University Medical School
Mizuho-ku
Nagoya 467-8601, Japan
Ph: 81 667 212332
Fax: 81 667 301394
Medical science journal. **Founded:** 1965. **Freq:** 6/yr. **Key Personnel:** Hikaru Suzuki, Ch. Ed.; Michio Hongo, Press.Ed. **ISSN:** 0916-8737. **Remarks:** Advertising accepted; rates available upon request. **URL:** http:// wwwsoc.nii.ac.jp/jsmr/jsmr1/jsmr1.html. **Circ:** 950

46556 ■ Nagoya Mathematical Journal
Nagoya University
Graduate School of Mathematics
Furo-cho, Chikusa-ku
Nagoya 464-8601, Japan
Ph: 81 52 7895111
Publisher E-mail: nuinfo@post.jimu.nagoya-u.ac.jp
Mathematics journal. **Founded:** 1950. **Freq:** Quarterly. **Key Personnel:** Akihiko Gyoja, Managing Editor; Fred B. Weissler, Editor; Ken-ichi Yoshida, Editor; Shigefumi Mori, Assoc. Ed.; Shigeru Mukai, Assoc. Ed.; Jerry L. Bona, Assoc. Ed.; Etienne Ghys, Editor; Shin Nayatani, Editor; Akio Tamagawa, Assoc. Ed. **ISSN:** 0027-7630. **Remarks:** Advertising accepted; rates available upon request. **URL:** http://www.math.nagoya-u.ac.jp/en/ journal/index.html. **Circ:** Controlled 1,150

46557 ■ Nanzan Review of American Studies
Nanzan University
18 Yamazato-cho
Showa-ku
Nagoya-shi
Nagoya 466-8673, Japan
Ph: 81 52 8323111
Fax: 81 52 8336985
Publisher E-mail: n-somu@nanzan-u.ac.jp
History journal. **Founded:** 1979. **Freq:** Annual. **ISSN:** 0288-3872. **URL:** http://www.nanzan-u.ac.jp/AMERICA/ english/kanko.html.

46558 ■ Radiation Safety Management
Japanese Society of Radiation Safety Management
Radiation Sciences Division, Radioisotope Research Center
Nagoya University
Furo-cho Chikusa-ku
Nagoya 464-8602, Japan
Ph: 81 527 892569
Fax: 81 527 895048
Publication E-mail: maekoshi@met.nagoya-u.ac.jp
Official journal of the Japanese Society of Radiation Safety Management. **Freq:** Annual. **Key Personnel:** Takayoshi Yamamoto, PhD, Editor-in-Chief; Keiji Oda, PhD, Editorial Board Member; Yasuhito Isozumi, PhD, Editorial Board Member; Susumu Osaki, PhD, Editorial Board Member; Kazuyoshi Masumoto, PhD, Editorial Board Member. **ISSN:** 1347-1511. **URL:** http://www.nv-med.com/journals/jrsm_en/.

46559 ■ Regional Development Dialogue
United Nations Centre for Regional Development
1-47-1 Nagono
Nakamura-ku
Nagoya 450-0001, Japan
Ph: 81 52 5619377
Fax: 81 52 5619375
Publication E-mail: rds@uncrd.or.jp
Publisher E-mail: rep@uncrd.or.jp
Journal covering current regional development issues. **Subtitle:** An International Journal Focusing on Third World. **Founded:** 1980. **Freq:** Semiannual spring and autumn. **Key Personnel:** Kazunobu Onogawa, Director. **ISSN:** 0250-6505. **Subscription Rates:** US$40 individuals developed countries; US$30 individuals developing countries. **Remarks:** Advertising accepted; rates available upon request. **URL:** http://www.uncrd.or.jp/pub/rdd. htm. **Circ:** Paid 1,000

46560 ■ JOAR - 1053 KHz
1-2-8, Sakae Shin
Naka-ku
Nagoya 460-8405, Japan
Ph: 81 52 2418111
Format: Eclectic. **Owner:** Chubu-Nippon Broadcasting Co., Ltd. (CBC), at above address. **Founded:** 1951. **Operating Hours:** Continuous. **Wattage:** 50,000. **URL:** http://www.hicbc.com/.

46561 ■ JOAR-TV - 5
1-2-8, Sakae Shin
Naka-ku
Nagoya 460-8405, Japan
Ph: 81 52 2418111
Owner: Chubu-Nippon Broadcasting Co., Ltd. (CBC), at above address. **Founded:** 1956. **Wattage:** 10,000. **URL:** http://www.hicbc.com/.

46562 ■ JOCH-TV - 35
154, Takamine-cho
Showa-ku
Nagoya 466-8635, Japan
Ph: 81 52 8323111
Owner: Chukyo Television Broadcasting Co., Ltd. (CTV), at above address. **Founded:** Mar. 1, 1969. **Key Personnel:** Norimitsu Shiyouzi, President. **Wattage:** 30,000. **URL:** http://www.ctv.co.jp/indexmenu.html.

46563 ■ JOCI-TV - 25
4-8, Osu 2-chome
Naka-ku
Nagoya 460-8325, Japan
Ph: 81 52 2030250
Fax: 81 52 2019259
Owner: Aichi Television Broadcasting Co., Ltd. (TVA), at above address. **Founded:** 1983. **Wattage:** 10,000. **URL:** http://www.tv-aichi.co.jp.

46564 ■ JOCK - 729 KHz
2-2-1 Jinnan
Shibuya-ku
Tokyo 150-8001, Japan
Ph: 81 3 34651111
Fax: 81 3 34811350
E-mail: nhkworld@nhk.jp
Format: News. **Owner:** Nippon Hoso Kyokai (NHK), at above address. **Operating Hours:** Continuous. **Key Personnel:** Shigeo Fukuchi, President; Hidemi Hyuga, Exec. Dir. Gen. **Wattage:** 50,000. **Ad Rates:** Noncommercial. **URL:** http://www.nhk.or.jp.

46565 ■ JOCU - 80.7 MHz
15-18, Naka 2-chome
Chiyoda-ku
Nagoya 460-8388, Japan
Ph: 81 52 2635141
Format: Eclectic. **Owner:** Efuemu Corp., at above address. **Founded:** 1969. **Operating Hours:** Continuous. **Wattage:** 10,000. **Ad Rates:** Advertising accepted; rates available upon request. **URL:** http://www.fma.co.jp/.

46566 ■ JOFX-TV - 1
14-27, Sakura Azuma 1-chome
Higashi-ku
Nagoya 461-8501, Japan
Ph: 81 52 951 2511
Owner: Tokai Television Broadcasting Co., Ltd. (THK), at above address. **Founded:** 1958. **Wattage:** 10,000. **URL:** http://www.tokai-tv.com/menu.html.

46567 ■ JOQV - 77.8 MHz
3-20-17, Marunouchi
Nagoya 460-8578, Japan
Ph: 81 52 9720778
Fax: 81 52 9730307
Format: Eclectic. **Owner:** FM Nagoya Inc. (ZIP-FM), at above address. **Founded:** 1993. **Operating Hours:** Continuous. **Wattage:** 10,000. **Ad Rates:** Advertising accepted; rates available upon request. **URL:** http://zip-fm.co.jp/.

46568 ■ JOSF - 1332 KHz
1-14-27, Higashisakura
Higashi-ku
Nagoya 461-8503, Japan
Ph: 81 52 9512525
Format: Eclectic. **Owner:** Tokai Radio Broadcasting Co., Ltd., at above address. **Founded:** 1960. **Operating Hours:** Continuous. **Wattage:** 50,000. **Ad Rates:** Advertising accepted; rates available upon request. **URL:** http://www.tokairadio.co.jp/.

Naha

46569 ■ JOIU - 87.3 MHz
40, Kowan, Urasoe
Okinawa 901-2525, Japan
Ph: 81 98 8772361
Fax: 81 98 8761601
Format: Eclectic. **Owner:** FM Okinawa Broadcasting Corporation, at above address. **Founded:** Sept. 1, 1984. **Operating Hours:** Continuous. **Wattage:** 1000. **Ad Rates:** Advertising accepted; rates available upon request. **URL:** http://www.fmokinawa.co.jp/.

46570 ■ JORR - 738 KHz
3-1, Kumoji 2-chome
Naha 900-8711, Japan
Ph: 81 988 672151
E-mail: info@rbc-ryukyu.co.jp
Format: Eclectic. **Owner:** Ryukyu Broadcasting Corporation (RBC), at above address. **Founded:** 1954. **Operating Hours:** Continuous. **Wattage:** 10,000. **URL:** http://www.rbc-ryukyu.co.jp/.

46571 ■ JOXR - 864 KHz
1-4-8, Nishi
Naha 900-8604, Japan
Ph: 81 98 8692211
Format: Eclectic. **Owner:** Radio Okinawa Corporation (ROK), at above address. **Founded:** 1960. **Operating Hours:** 1950-1800 (2000 - 1800, Fri. & Sat.; 2000 - 1630 Sun.). **Key Personnel:** Kunio Tottori, President. **Wattage:** 10,000. **URL:** http://www.rokinawa.co.jp/.

Nayoro

46572 ■ JOTL - 1494 KHz
Nishi 5, Chuo 2-chome
Kita 1
Sapporo 060-8501, Japan
Ph: 81 11 2325800
E-mail: info@hbc.co.jp
Format: Eclectic. **Owner:** Hokkaido Broadcasting Co., Ltd. (HBC), at above address. **Operating Hours:** Continuous. **Key Personnel:** Takashi Watanabe, President. **Wattage:** 1000. **URL:** http://www.hbc.co.jp/.

Niigata

46573 ■ Nihonkai Mathematical Journal
Niigata University
Sado Marine Biological Station
Dept. of Mathematics
Faculty of Science
Niigata 950-2181, Japan
Ph: 81 252 627000
Fax: 81 252 626539
Publisher E-mail: info-nu@adm.niigata-u.ac.jp
Publishes original contributions to all disciplines in mathematics. **Founded:** 1964. **Freq:** Semiannual. **Key Personnel:** Osamu Hatori, Editor, nmj@math.sc.niigata-u.ac.jp; Nobuhiro Innami, Editor; Tamaki Tanaka, Editor-in-Chief. **URL:** http://mathweb.sc.niigata-u.ac.jp/nmj/index.html.

FM Radio Niigata - See Yahiko

JODO - See Joetsu

46574 ■ JODR - 1116 KHz
3-18, Kawagishi-cho
Chuo-ku
Niigata 951-8655, Japan
Ph: 81 25 2674111
Format: Eclectic. **Owner:** Broadcasting System of Niigata, Inc. (BSN), at above address. **Founded:** 1952. **Operating Hours:** Continuous. **Wattage:** 5000. **URL:** http://www.ohbsn.com.

46575 ■ JODR-TV - 5
3-18, Kawagishi-cho
Niigata 951-8655, Japan
Ph: 81 25 2674111
Fax: 81 25 2663584
Owner: Broadcasting System of Niigata, Inc. (BSN), at above address. **Founded:** 1958. **Wattage:** 5000. **URL:** http://www.ohbsn.com/top.asp.

46576 ■ JONH-TV - 35
2-3-1, Yachiyo Chou Ku
Niigata 950-8572, Japan
Ph: 81 25 2458181
Fax: 81 25 2498839
Owner: Niigata Sogo Television Co., Ltd. (NST), at above address. **Founded:** 1968. **Wattage:** 30,000. **URL:** http://www.nsttv.com/.

46577 ■ JOPI-TV - 29
1-11, Shinko-cho
Chuo-ko
Niigata 950-8555, Japan
E-mail: mail@teny.co.jp
Owner: Television Niigata Network Co., Ltd.(TeNY), at above address. **Founded:** 1981. **Wattage:** 30,000. **URL:** http://www.teny.co.jp/.

46578 ■ JOQB - 1593 KHz
2-2-1 Jinnan
Shibuya-ku
Tokyo 150-8001, Japan
Ph: 81 3 34651111
Fax: 81 3 34698110
E-mail: nhkworld@nhk.jp
Format: Educational. **Owner:** Nippon Hoso Kyokai (NHK), at above address. **Operating Hours:** 2030-1640 (2030-1500, Sun. & Mon.). **Key Personnel:** Shigeo Fukuchi, President. **Wattage:** 10,000. **URL:** http://www.nhk.or.jp.

46579 ■ JOQK - 82.3 MHz
2-2-1 Jinnan
Shibuya-ku
Tokyo 150-8001, Japan
Ph: 81 3 34651111
Fax: 81 3 34698110
Format: News. **Owner:** Nippon Hoso Kyokai (NHK), at above address. **Operating Hours:** Continuous. **Key Personnel:** Hidemi Hyuga, Exec. Dir. Gen. **Wattage:** 1000. **Ad Rates:** Advertising accepted; rates available upon request. **URL:** http://www.nhk.or.jp.

46580 ■ JOQK - 837 KHz
2-2-1 Jinnan
Shibuya-ku
Tokyo 150-8001, Japan
Ph: 81 3 34651111
Fax: 81 3 34811350
E-mail: nhkworld@nhk.jp
Format: News. **Owner:** Nippon Hoso Kyokai (NHK), at above address. **Operating Hours:** Continuous. **Key Personnel:** Shigeo Fukuchi, President; Hidemi Hyuga, Exec. Dir. Gen. **Wattage:** 10,000. **URL:** http://www.nhk.or.jp.

46581 ■ JOUX-TV - 21
6-2230-19, Bruno-cho
Chuo-ko
Niigata 951-8521, Japan
Ph: 81 25 2230021
Owner: The Niigata Television Network 21, Inc. (NT-21), at above address. **Founded:** 1983. **Key Personnel:** Tomoo Ball, President. **Wattage:** 30,000. **URL:** http://uxtv.jp/.

JOWV - See Yahiko

46582 ■ JOXU - 77.5 MHz
4-3-5, W Chuo Ku
Niigata, Japan
Ph: 81 25 2462311
Format: Eclectic. **Owner:** FM Radio Niigata Co., Ltd. (FRN), at above address. **Founded:** 1987. **Operating Hours:** 0400-0300. **Key Personnel:** Masumura Tsutomu, President. **Wattage:** 1000. **Ad Rates:** Advertising accepted; rates available upon request. **URL:** http://www.fmniigata.com/.

Niihama

46583 ■ JOAL - 1116 KHz
1-1-1, Hon-cho
Matsuyama 790-8510, Japan
Ph: 81 89 9153333
Fax: 81 89 9152370
Format: Eclectic. **Owner:** Nankai Broadcasting Co., Ltd.(RNB), at above address. **Founded:** 1953. **Operating Hours:** Continuous. **Wattage:** 1000. **URL:** http://www.rnb.co.jp/.

Obihiro

46584 ■ JOHW - 1269 KHz
Nishi 5, Chuo 2-chome
Kita 1
Sapporo 060-8501, Japan
Ph: 81 11 2325800
E-mail: info@hbc.co.jp
Format: Eclectic. **Owner:** Hokkaido Broadcasting Co., Ltd. (HBC), at above address. **Operating Hours:** Continuous. **Key Personnel:** Takashi Watanabe, President. **Wattage:** 5000. **URL:** http://www.hbc.co.jp/.

46585 ■ JOOC - 1125 KHz
2-2-1 Jinnan
Shibuya-ku
Tokyo 150-8001, Japan
Ph: 81 3 34651111
Fax: 81 3 34698110
E-mail: nhkworld@nhk.jp
Format: Educational. **Owner:** Nippon Hoso Kyokai (NHK), at above address. **Operating Hours:** 2030-1640 (2030-1500, Sun. & Mon.). **Key Personnel:** Shigeo Fukuchi, President. **Wattage:** 1000. **URL:** http://www.nhk.or.jp.

46586 ■ JOOG - 603 KHz
2-2-1 Jinnan
Shibuya-ku
Tokyo 150-8001, Japan
Ph: 81 3 34651111
Fax: 81 3 34811350
E-mail: nhkworld@nhk.jp
Format: News. **Owner:** Nippon Hoso Kyokai (NHK), at above address. **Operating Hours:** Continuous. **Key Personnel:** Shigeo Fukuchi, President; Hidemi Hyuga,

---

Circulation: ★ =ABC; △ = BPA; ◆ = CAC; • = CCAB; ❑ = VAC; ⊕ = PO Statement; ‡ = Publisher's Report; Boldface figures = sworn; Light figures = estimated.

Gale Directory of Publications & Broadcast Media/147th Ed.   **5095**

Exec. Dir. General. **Wattage:** 5000. **URL:** http://www. nhk.or.jp.

46587 ■ JOWM - 1071 KHz
1-1, Nishi 8-chome
Kita 1-jo, Chuo-ku
Sapporo 060-8705, Japan
Ph: 81 11 2411181
E-mail: radio@stv.jp
Format: Eclectic. **Owner:** The Sapporo Television Broadcasting Co., Ltd., at above address. **Operating Hours:** Continuous. **Wattage:** 5000. **Ad Rates:** Noncommercial. **URL:** http://www.stv.ne.jp/.

Ofunato

46588 ■ JOLO - 684 KHz
6-1, Shike-cho
Morioka 020-8566, Japan
Ph: 81 196 233111
Fax: 81 196 544806
Owner: Iwate Broadcasting Co., Ltd. (IBC), at above address. **Founded:** 1951. **Operating Hours:** Continuous. **Key Personnel:** Masaki Abe, President; Keiji Kawashima, Mng. Dir. **Wattage:** 1000. **URL:** http:// www.ibc.co.jp/.

Ohtsu

46589 ■ JOBL-TV - 30
16-1, Tsurunosato
Ohtsu 520-8585, Japan
Owner: Biwalo Broadcasting Co., Ltd.(BBC), at above address. **Founded:** 1972. **Wattage:** 1000. **URL:** http:// www.bbc-tv.co.jp/.

Oita

46590 ■ Artificial Life and Robotics
Springer-Verlag Tokyo
Dept. of Electrical & Electronic Engineering
Nippon Bunri University
1727 Oaza Ichiki
Oita 870-0397, Japan
Publisher E-mail: info@springer.jp
Journal of computers. **Founded:** 1997. **Freq:** Quarterly. **Key Personnel:** Masanori Sugisaka, Editor-in-Chief; Kazuyuki Aihara, Dep. Ed.; Mark A. Bedau, Editorial Board; Thomas S. Ray, Assoc. Ed.; Joshua Epstein, Assoc. Ed.; John L. Casti, Assoc. Ed.; Hidenori Kimura, Assoc. Ed.; Keigo Watanabe, Dep. Ed. **ISSN:** 1433-5298. **Subscription Rates:** EUR481 institutions print incl. free access; EUR577.20 institutions print incl. enhanced access. **Remarks:** Accepts advertising. **URL:** http://www.springer.com/computer/artificial/journal/10015. **Circ:** (Not Reported)

46591 ■ JOGF - 1098 KHz
1-1, Imazuru 3-chome
Oita 870-8620, Japan
Ph: 81 97 5581111
E-mail: obs@e-obs.com
Format: Eclectic. **Owner:** Oita Broadcasting System (OBS), at above address. **Founded:** 1953. **Operating Hours:** Continuous. **Wattage:** 5000. **URL:** http://www.e-obs.com/.

46592 ■ JOID - 1467 KHz
2-2-1 Jinnan
Shibuya-ku
Tokyo 150-8001, Japan
Ph: 81 3 34651111
Fax: 81 3 34698110
E-mail: nhkworld@nhk.jp
Format: Educational. **Owner:** Nippon Hoso Kyokai (NHK), at above address. **Operating Hours:** 2030-1640 (2030-1500, Sun. & Mon.). **Key Personnel:** Shigehiro Komaru, Chm.; Shigeo Fukuchi, President. **Wattage:** 1000. **URL:** http://www.nhk.or.jp.

46593 ■ JOIP - 88.9 MHz
2-2-1 Jinnan
Shibuya-ku
Tokyo 150-8001, Japan
Ph: 81 3 34651111
Fax: 81 3 34698110
Format: News. **Owner:** Nippon Hoso Kyokai (NHK), at above address. **Operating Hours:** Continuous. **Key Personnel:** Hidemi Hyuga, Exec. Dir. Gen. **Wattage:** 1000. **Ad Rates:** Advertising accepted; rates available upon request. **URL:** http://www.nhk.or.jp.

46594 ■ JOIP - 639 KHz
2-2-1 Jinnan
Shibuya-ku
Tokyo 150-8001, Japan
Ph: 81 3 34651111
Fax: 81 3 34811350
E-mail: nhkworld@nhk.jp
Format: News. **Owner:** Nippon Hoso Kyokai (NHK), at above address. **Operating Hours:** Continuous. **Key Personnel:** Shigeo Fukuchi, President; Hidemi Hyuga, Exec. Dir. Gen. **Wattage:** 5000. **URL:** http://www.nhk.or.jp.

46595 ■ JOJV - 88.0 MHz
17-19, Higashikasuga-machi
Oita 870-8558, Japan
Ph: 81 97 5348888
Fax: 81 97 5380788
Format: Eclectic. **Owner:** FM Oita Broadcasting Co., Ltd., at above address. **Founded:** 1990. **Operating Hours:** Continuous. **Wattage:** 1000. **Ad Rates:** Advertising accepted; rates available upon request. **URL:** http:// www.fmoita.co.jp/.

Okayama

46596 ■ Acta Medica Okayama
Okayama University
School of Medicine
2-5-1 Shikata-cho
Shikata-cho
Okayama 700-8558, Japan
Ph: 81 862 357057
Fax: 81 862 357059
Publication E-mail: actamed@cc.okayama-u.ac.jp
Medical science journal. **Founded:** 1928. **Freq:** Bimonthly. **Print Method:** Offset. **Trim Size:** 212 x 274 mm. **Key Personnel:** Tadaatsu Akagi, MD, Editor-in-Chief. **ISSN:** 0386-300X. **Remarks:** Advertising not accepted. **URL:** http://www.okayama-u.ac.jp/user/med/acta//acta_home.html. **Circ:** Controlled 580

46597 ■ Journal of Japanese Society of Autologous Blood Transfusion
Nihon Jikoketsu Yuketsu Kenkyukai
Kawasaki Ika Daigaku Masuika
577 Matsushima
Kurashiki-shi
Okayama 701-0114, Japan
Medical science journal. **Founded:** 1989. **Freq:** Semiannual. **Key Personnel:** Takeshi Fuji, Editor. **ISSN:** 0915-0188. **Subscription Rates:** 5,000¥.

46598 ■ Journal of Oral Tissue Engineering
Japanese Association of Regenerative Dentistry
5-1, 2-Chome
Shikata-Cho
Okayama 700-8525, Japan
Ph: 81 86 2356672
Fax: 81 86 2356674
Publication E-mail: imai@cc.osaka-dent.ac.jp
Publisher E-mail: shunjii@md.okayama-u.ac.jp
Journal of the Japanese Association of Regenerative Dentistry. **Founded:** 2003. **Freq:** 5/yr. **ISSN:** 1348-9623. **Subscription Rates:** Free MBR. **URL:** http://wwwsoc.nii.ac.jp/jard/indexa-e.html.

46599 ■ Mathematical Journal of Okayama University
Okayama University
Faculty of Science
Faculty of Science
Dept. of Mathematics
Okayama University
Okayama 700-8530, Japan
Mathematics journal. **Founded:** 1952. **Freq:** Semiannual. **Key Personnel:** Kazuhisa Shimakawa, Editorial Board; Hideo Tamura, Editorial Board; Hiroaki Nakamura, Managing Editor. **ISSN:** 0030-1566. **URL:** http://www.math.okayama-u.ac.jp/mjou/index.html.

46600 ■ JOKB - 1386 KHz
2-2-1 Jinnan
Shibuya-ku
Tokyo 150-8001, Japan
Ph: 81 3 34651111
Fax: 81 3 34698110
E-mail: nhkworld@nhk.jp
Format: Educational. **Owner:** Nippon Hoso Kyokai (NHK), at above address. **Operating Hours:** 2030-1640

(2030-1500, Sun. & Mon.). **Key Personnel:** Shigehiro Komaru, Chm.; Shigeo Fukuchi, President. **Wattage:** 5000. **URL:** http://www.nhk.or.jp.

46601 ■ JOKK - 88.7 MHz
2-2-1 Jinnan
Shibuya-ku
Tokyo 150-8001, Japan
Ph: 81 3 34651111
Fax: 81 3 34698110
Format: News. **Owner:** Nippon Hoso Kyokai (NHK), at above address. **Operating Hours:** Continuous. **Key Personnel:** Hidemi Hyuga, Exec. Dir. Gen. **Wattage:** 1000. **URL:** http://www.nhk.or.jp.

46602 ■ JOKK - 603 KHz
2-2-1 Jinnan
Shibuya-ku
Tokyo 150-8001, Japan
Ph: 81 3 34651111
Fax: 81 3 34811350
E-mail: nhkworld@nhk.jp
Format: News. **Owner:** Nippon Hoso Kyokai (NHK), at above address. **Operating Hours:** Continuous. **Key Personnel:** Shigeo Fukuchi, President; Hidemi Hyuga, Exec. Dir. Gen. **Wattage:** 5000. **URL:** http://www.nhk.or.jp.

46603 ■ JOVV - 76.8 MHz
1-8-45, Kita-ku
Okayama 700-0821, Japan
Ph: 81 86 2267680
Fax: 81 86 2267681
Format: Eclectic. **Owner:** Okayama FM Broadc., Co., Ltd., at above address. **Founded:** Apr. 14, 1998. **Operating Hours:** Continuous. **Wattage:** 1000. **Ad Rates:** Advertising accepted; rates available upon request. **URL:** http://www.fm-okayama.co.jp/.

46604 ■ JOYR - 1494 KHz
1-3, Marunouchi 2-chome
Okayama 700-8580, Japan
Format: Eclectic. **Owner:** Sanyo Broadcasting Co., Ltd. (RSK), at above address. **Founded:** 1953. **Operating Hours:** Continuous. **Wattage:** 10,000. **URL:** http://www.rsk.co.jp/company/index.html.

46605 ■ JOYR-TV - 11
1-3, Marunouchi 2-chome
Okayama 700-8580, Japan
Ph: 81 862 2255741
Owner: Sanyo Broadcasting Co., Ltd. (RSK), at above address. **Founded:** 1958. **Wattage:** 10,000. **URL:** http:// www.rsk.co.jp/.

Okinawa

46606 ■ JOAD - 1125 KHz
2-2-1 Jinnan
Shibuya-ku
Tokyo 150-8001, Japan
Ph: 81 3 34651111
Fax: 81 3 34698110
E-mail: nhkworld@nhk.jp
Format: Educational. **Owner:** Nippon Hoso Kyokai (NHK), at above address. **Operating Hours:** 2030-1640 (2030-1500, Sun. & Mon.). **Key Personnel:** Shigeo Fukuchi, President. **Wattage:** 10,000. **Ad Rates:** Noncommercial. **URL:** http://www.nhk.or.jp.

46607 ■ JOAP - 549 KHz
2-2-1 Jinnan
Shibuya-ku
Tokyo 150-8001, Japan
Ph: 81 3 34651111
Fax: 81 3 34698110
E-mail: nhkworld@nhk.jp
Format: News. **Owner:** Nippon Hoso Kyokai (NHK), at above address. **Operating Hours:** Continuous. **Key Personnel:** Shigeo Fukuchi, President. **Wattage:** 10,000. **Ad Rates:** Noncommercial. **URL:** http://www.nhk.or.jp.

46608 ■ JOAP - 88.1 MHz
2-2-1 Jinnan
Shibuya-ku
Tokyo 150-8001, Japan
Ph: 81 3 34651111
Fax: 81 3 34811350
Format: News. **Owner:** Nippon Hoso Kyokai (NHK), at above address. **Operating Hours:** Continuous. **Key**

Personnel: Hidemi Hyuga, Exec. Dir. Gen. **Wattage:** 1000. **Ad Rates:** Noncommercial. **URL:** http://www.nhk.or.jp.

JOIU - See Naha

Onomichi

46609 ■ JOEE-TV Kurahashi - 40
21-3, Moto-machi
Naka-ku
Onomichi 730-8504, Japan
Ph: 81 82 2221155
E-mail: tv@rcc.net
Owner: Chugoku Broadcasting Co., Ltd. (RCC), at above address. **Founded:** 1959. **Wattage:** 10. **Ad Rates:** Noncommercial. **URL:** http://www.1350.jp/.

46610 ■ JOEE-TV Onomichi - 10
21-3, Moto-machi
Naka-ku
Hiroshima 730-8504, Japan
Ph: 81 82 2221155
E-mail: rcc@rcc.net
Owner: Chugoku Broadcasting Co., Ltd. (RCC), at above address. **Founded:** 1959. **Wattage:** 1000. **URL:** http://www.rcc.co.jp.

Ooasa

46611 ■ JOEE-TV Ooasa - 46
21-3, Moto-machi
Naka-ku
Hiroshima 730-8504, Japan
Ph: 81 82 2221155
E-mail: tv@rcc.net
Owner: Chugoku Broadcasting Co., Ltd. (RCC), at above address. **Founded:** 1959. **Wattage:** 10. **Ad Rates:** Noncommercial. **URL:** http://www.1350.jp/.

Oogaki

46612 ■ JOEE-TV Oogaki - 49
21-3, Moto-machi
Naka-ku
Hiroshima 730-8504, Japan
Ph: 81 82 2221155
E-mail: rcc@rcc.net
Owner: Chugoku Broadcasting Co., Ltd. (RCC), at above address. **Founded:** 1959. **Wattage:** 100. **URL:** http://www.rcc.co.jp.

Ootake

46613 ■ JOEE-TV Ootake - 57
21-3, Moto-machi
Naka-ku
Hiroshima 730-8504, Japan
Ph: 81 82 2221155
E-mail: tv@rcc.net
Owner: Chugoku Broadcasting Co., Ltd. (RCC), at above address. **Founded:** 1959. **Wattage:** 10. **Ad Rates:** Noncommercial. **URL:** http://www.1350.jp/.

Osaka

46614 ■ Advances in Applied Mathematical Analysis
Research India Publications
c/o Prof. Shigeyoshi Owa, Ed.-in-Ch.
Kinki University
Dept. of Mathematics
School of Science & Engineering
Osaka 577-8502, Japan
Publisher E-mail: info@ripublication.com
Journal covering advances in mathematical analysis and its applications. Topics include classical mathematical analysis, functional analysis, numerical analysis, probability, statistics, and combinatorics. **Freq:** Semiannual. **Key Personnel:** Prof. Shigeyoshi Owa, Editor-in-Chief, owa@math.kindai.ac.jp; Yasar Polatoglu, Co-Ed., y.polatoglu@iku.edu.tr; Jay M. Jahangiri, Co-Ed., jjahangi@kent.edu. **ISSN:** 0973-5313. **Subscription Rates:** US$280 institutions and library; print plus online free; US$180 individuals print plus online free; US$160 individuals online only; US$260 institutions and library; online only; Rs 1,800 individuals. **URL:** http://www.ripublication.com/aama.htm.

46615 ■ Applied Surface Science
Elsevier Science Inc.
Institute of Scientific & Industrial Research
Osaka University
8-1 Mihogaoka
Ibarikai
Osaka 567-0047, Japan
Fax: 81 6 68798454
Publisher E-mail: usinfo-eholp@elsevier.com
Journal covering physics and chemistry of surfaces and interfaces. **Founded:** 1978. **Freq:** 24/yr. **Print Method:** Offset. **Trim Size:** 7 7/8 x 10 1/2. **Key Personnel:** D.E. Aspnes, Advisory Editorial Board; M. Balkanski, Advisory Editorial Board; J.C. Bean, Advisory Editorial Board; S. Chambers, Advisory Editorial Board; B.N. Dev, Advisory Editorial Board; M. Henzler, Advisory Editorial Board; S. Hofmann, Advisory Editorial Board; F.H.P.M. Habraken, Editor, f.h.p.m.habraken@phys.uu.nl; H. Kobayashi, Editor, ass@sanken.osaka-u.ac.jp; R.R.L. Opila, Editor, opila@udel.edu; H. Rudolph, Editor, h.rudolph@phys.uu.nl. **ISSN:** 0169-4332. **Subscription Rates:** US$8,665 institutions, other countries except Europe, Japan and Iran; 1,027,800¥ institutions; EUR7,744 institutions European countries and Iran. **URL:** http://www.elsevier.com/wps/find/journaldescription.cws_home/505669/descriptiondescription.

46616 ■ BioFactors
IOS Press, B.V.
c/o E. Niki, Ed.-in-Ch.
Human Stress Signal Research Center
Ikeda
Osaka 563-8577, Japan
Ph: 81 72 7519991
Fax: 81 72 7519964
Publisher E-mail: info@iospress.nl
International journal aiming to identify and increase the understanding of the precise biochemical effects and roles of the large number of trace substances that are required by living organisms, including vitamins and trace elements, as well as growth factors and regulatory substances made by cells themselves. **Freq:** Monthly. **Key Personnel:** J. Terao, Editor-in-Chief, terao@nutr.med.tokushima-u.ac.jp; E. Niki, Editor-in-Chief, etsuo-niki@aist.go.jp; T.C. Stadtman, Founding Ed. **ISSN:** 0951-6433. **Subscription Rates:** EUR1,098 individuals print and online; US$1,429 individuals print and online; EUR220 individuals online; US$260 individuals online. **URL:** http://www.iospress.nl/loadtop/load.php?isbn=09516433.

46617 ■ Genes & Genetic Systems
Genetics Society of Japan
c/o Takashi Gojobori, Pres.
National Institute of Genetics
Osaka University, Suita
Osaka 565-0871, Japan
Ph: 81 668 798317
Fax: 81 668 798320
Publication E-mail: tgojobor@genes.nig.ac.jp
Publisher E-mail: japgenet@lab.nig.ac.jp
Journal of genetics. **Founded:** 1921. **Freq:** Bimonthly. **Key Personnel:** Sadao Ishiwa, Advisory Board; Hideo Shinagawa, Advisory Board; Takashi Endo, Editor-in-Chief, phone 81 757 536137, fax 81 757 536486, ggsiden@kais.kyoto-u.ac.jp. **ISSN:** 1341-7568. **Remarks:** Advertising accepted; rates available upon request. **URL:** http://wwwsoc.nii.ac.jp/gsj3/GGS.html. **Circ:** Paid 2,000

46618 ■ Japanese Journal of Environment, Entomology and Zoology
Japanese Society of Environmental Entomology and Zoology
Seiyu Bldg.
12-19 Nishi-Hon-Machi 1-chome
Nishi-ku
Osaka 550-0005, Japan
Journal of entomology. **Founded:** 1989. **Freq:** Quarterly. **ISSN:** 0915-4698.

46619 ■ Journal of Approximation Theory and Applications
Serials Publications
c/o Shigeyoshi Owa, Ed.-in-Ch.
Department of Mathematics
School of Science & Engineering
Kinki University, Higashi-Osaka
Osaka 577-8502, Japan

Publisher E-mail: serials@satyam.net.in
Journal devoted to advances in pure and applied approximation theory and related areas. Areas include classical, abstract and constructive approximation, degree of approximation, fourier expansions, interpolation of operators, interpolation and quadratures, and multivariate approximation. **Founded:** 1979. **Freq:** Semiannual. **Print Method:** Offset. **Cols./Page:** 6. **Col. Width:** 18 nonpareils. **Col. Depth:** 189 agate lines. **Key Personnel:** Nak Eun Cho, Editorial Board; Maslina Darus, Editorial Board; Jay M. Jahangiri, Editorial Board; Ozlem H. Guney, Editorial Board; Keiko Fujita, Editorial Board; Shigeyoshi Owa, Editor-in-Chief, owa@math.kindai.ac.jp. **ISSN:** 0973-287X. **Subscription Rates:** US$80 institutions print. **URL:** http://www.serialspublications.com/journals1.asp?jid=308&jtype=1.

46620 ■ Journal of Bioscience and Bioengineering
Society for Biotechnology, Japan
c/o Faculty of Engineering
Osaka University
2-1 Yamada-Oka
Suita-shi
Osaka 565-0871, Japan
Ph: 81 6 68762731
Fax: 81 6 68792034
Publisher E-mail: info@sbj.or.jp
Publication devoted to the advancement and dissemination of knowledge concerning fermentation technology, biochemical engineering, food technology and microbiology. **Founded:** 1923. **Freq:** Bimonthly. **Key Personnel:** Hisao Ohtake, Editor-in-Chief, hohtake@bio.eng.osaka-u.ac.jp; Masahiro Kino-oka, Assoc. Ed. **ISSN:** 1389-1723. **Subscription Rates:** US$1,702 institutions, other countries; EUR1,521 institutions Europe, Japan, Iran. **Remarks:** Accepts advertising. **URL:** http://www.elsevier.com/wps/find/journaldescription.cws_home/505516/descriptiondescription; http://www.jbb.sfbj.org/. **Circ:** (Not Reported)

46621 ■ Journal of Japanese Society of Computational Statistics
Japanese Society of Computational Statistics
c/o Toshimitsu Hamasaki, Ed.
Dept. of Biomedical Statistics
Osaka University, Graduate School of Medicine
2-2 Yamadaoka
Osaka 565-0871, Japan
Publication E-mail: jjscs@medstat.med.osaka-u.ac.jp
Publisher E-mail: office@jscs.or.jp
Publishes scientific papers that address any aspect of the discipline of computational statistics. **Founded:** 1988. **Freq:** Annual. **Key Personnel:** Yoshimichi Ochi, Assoc. Ed.; Yoshiharu Sato, Assoc. Ed.; Harry M. Cullings, Assoc. Ed.; Atsuhiro Hayashi, Assoc. Ed.; Yoshisada Shibata, Assoc. Ed.; Shingo Shirahata, Assoc. Ed.; Toshimitsu Hamasaki, Editor; Sadanori Konishi, Assoc. Ed.; Koji Kanefuji, Assoc. Ed. **ISSN:** 0915-2350. **URL:** http://www.jscs.or.jp/oubun/indexE.html. **Circ:** Paid 400

46622 ■ Journal of Kansai Society of Naval Architects
Kansai Society of Naval Architects
c/o Graduate School of Engineering, Osaka University
2-1 Yamada-oka
Suita
Osaka 565-0871, Japan
Publisher E-mail: office@ksnaj.or.jp
Journal of transportation. **Founded:** 1912. **Freq:** Semiannual March, September. **ISSN:** 1346-7727. **URL:** http://www.jstage.jst.go.jp/browse/jksna/-char/en/.

46623 ■ Journal of Nuclear and Radiochemical Sciences
Japan Society of Nuclear and Radiochemical Sciences
c/o Prof. Seiichi Shibata, Sec.
Research Reactor Institute
Kyoto University
2 Asahiro-nishi, Kumatori-cho, Sennan-gun
Osaka 590-0494, Japan
Fax: 81 72 4512632
Publisher E-mail: jnrs.office2008@radiochem.org
Journal including topics related with all aspects of nuclear and radiochemistry and related fields. **Key Personnel:** Takaumi Kimura, Editor-in-Chief; Yoshitaka Ohkubo, Assoc. Ed.; Seiya Nagao, Assoc. Ed. **Subscrip-**

tion Rates: Included in membership. URL: http://www. radiochem.org/publ-e.html.

46624 ■ Journal of Periodontal Research
John Wiley & Sons Inc.
Wiley-Blackwell
c/o Shinya Murakami, Ed.
Osaka University, Graduate School of Dentistry
U.S. Department of of Periodontology, Division of Oral Biology & Disease Control
1-8 Yamadaoka, Suita
Osaka 565-0871, Japan
Peer-reviewed journal focusing on clinical and basic investigations relating to periodontology. **Freq:** Bimonthly. **Key Personnel:** Jorgen Slots, Editor; Prof. Isao Ishikawa, Ed. Emeritus; Mark Bartold, Assoc. Ed. **ISSN:** 0022-3484. **Subscription Rates:** US$995 institutions print and online; US$904 institutions print or online; 592 institutions print and online; 538 institutions print or online; EUR752 institutions print or online; EUR683 institutions print or online; US$1,160 institutions, other countries print and online; US$1,054 institutions, other countries print or online. **Remarks:** Advertising accepted; rates available upon request. **URL:** http://www. wiley.com/bw/journal.asp?ref=0022-3484. **Circ:** (Not Reported)

46625 ■ Journal of Textile Engineering
Textile Machinery Society of Japan
8-4 Utsubo Honmachi 1 chome
Nishi-ku
Osaka 550-0004, Japan
Ph: 81 6 64434691
Fax: 81 6 64434694
Publisher E-mail: i-love-tmsj@nifty.com
Journal of textile engineering. **Freq:** Bimonthly. **Key Personnel:** Mitsuo Matsudaira, Editor-in-Chief. **ISSN:** 1346-8235. **Subscription Rates:** 9,720¥ individuals surface mail; Free to members. **URL:** http://wwwsoc.nii. ac.jp/tmsj/japan/index-e.html.

46626 ■ Mathematica Japonica
Japanese Association of Mathematical Sciences
Shin Sakai-Higashi Bldg.
2-1-18 Minami Hanadaguchi-cho
Sakai
Osaka 590-0075, Japan
Ph: 81 722 221850
Fax: 81 722 227987
Publication E-mail: pbls@jams.or.jp
Publishes original papers in mathematical sciences submitted from all over the world. **Founded:** 1948. **Freq:** Semiannual 2 volumes of 3 issues in each per year. **Key Personnel:** Kiyoshi Iseki, Board of Mng. Ed. **ISSN:** 0025-5513. **Subscription Rates:** US$360 individuals. **URL:** http://www.jams.or.jp/notice/mj/mj.html. **Circ:** Paid 950

46627 ■ Osaka Journal of Mathematics
Osaka University
Graduate School of Science
1-1 Machikaneyama-cho
Toyonaka-shi
Osaka 560-0043, Japan
Fax: 81 668 505288
Publisher E-mail: rigakudaigakuin@ns.jim.osaka-u.ac.jp
Publication devoted entirely to the publication of original works in mathematics and related fields. **Founded:** 1964. **Freq:** Quarterly. **Key Personnel:** A. Fujiki, Editor; E. Date, Assoc. Ed.; T. Kanenobu, Assoc. Ed.; N. Hayashi, Assoc. Ed.; T. Hibi, Assoc. Ed.; M. Furusawa, Assoc. Ed.; S. Doi, Assoc. Ed.; S. Aida, Assoc. Ed.; Y. Imayoshi, Assoc. Ed. **ISSN:** 0030-6126. **URL:** http:// www.math.sci.osaka-u.ac.jp/ojm/.

46628 ■ Questions and Answers in General Topology
Symposium of General Topology
Uzumasa Higashiga-oka
13-2 Neyagawa-shi
Osaka 572-0841, Japan
Publication devoted primarily to rapid publication of questions and answers that arise from research in general topology and related areas. **Founded:** 1983. **Freq:** Semiannual. **Key Personnel:** Yasunao Hattori, Managing Editor, hattori@riko.shimane-u.ac.jp; K. Yokoi, Editor. **ISSN:** 0918-4732. **Subscription Rates:** 6,000¥. **Remarks:** Advertising not accepted. **URL:** http://qagt. za.org/. **Circ:** Paid 200

46629 ■ Viva Origino
Society for the Study of the Origin and Evolution of Life

Dept. of Applied Chemistry
Graduate School of Engineering
Osaka Prefecture University
Sakai, Gakuen-cho 1-1
Osaka 599-8531, Japan
Publisher E-mail: ashimada@kankyo.envr.tsukuba.ac.jp
Journal covering biology. **Founded:** 1971. **Freq:** Quarterly. **Key Personnel:** Dr. Kunio Kawamura, Editor-in-Chief; Dr. Noriko Fujii, PhD, Sec. **ISSN:** 0910-4003. **URL:** http://www.origin-life.gr.jp; http://www.origin-life.gr. jp/EN-vo.html.

46630 ■ JOAW - 76.5 MHz
3F, Osaka World Trade Center Bldg.
1-14-16, Osaka Nankoukita
Suminoe-ku
Osaka 559-8522, Japan
Ph: 81 66 15 7650
Format: Ethnic. **Owner:** Kansai Intermedia Corporation (FM Co ECOELO), at above address. **Founded:** 1995. **Operating Hours:** Continuous. (off the air Sun. 1700-2130). **Wattage:** 10,000. **Ad Rates:** Advertising accepted; rates available upon request. **URL:** http://www. cocolo.co.jp/.

46631 ■ JOBK - 666 KHz
2-2-1 Jinnan
Shibuya-ku
Tokyo 150-8001, Japan
Ph: 81 3 34651111
Fax: 81 3 34811350
E-mail: nhkworld@nhk.jp
Format: News. **Owner:** Nippon Hoso Kyokai (NHK), at above address. **Operating Hours:** Continuous. **Key Personnel:** Shigeo Fukuchi, President; Hidemi Hyuga, Exec. Dir. Gen. **Wattage:** 100,000. **Ad Rates:** Advertising accepted; rates available upon request. **URL:** http:// www.nhk.or.jp.

46632 ■ JOBK - 88.1 MHz
2-2-1 Jinnan
Shibuya-ku
Tokyo 150-8001, Japan
Ph: 81 3 34651111
Fax: 81 3 34811350
Format: News. **Owner:** Nippon Hoso Kyokai (NHK), at above address. **Operating Hours:** Continuous. **Key Personnel:** Hidemi Hyuga, Exec. Dir. Gen. **Wattage:** 10,000. **URL:** http://www.nhk.or.jp.

46633 ■ JOFV - 80.2 MHz
Kita 2-6
Tenjinbashi 2-chome
Kita-ku
Osaka 530-8580, Japan
Ph: 81 66 3548025
Format: Eclectic. **Owner:** FM 802 Co., Ltd., at above address. **Founded:** 1989. **Operating Hours:** Continuous. **Key Personnel:** Tetsuro Kawakami, Director; Toshiyuki Arai, Director. **Wattage:** 10,000. **Ad Rates:** Advertising accepted; rates available upon request. **URL:** http://funky802.com.

46634 ■ JONR - 1008 KHz
1-1-30 Fukushima
Fukushima-ku
Osaka 553-8503, Japan
Ph: 81 66 4585321
Owner: Asahi Broadcasting Corporation (ABC), at above address. **Founded:** Mar. 15, 1951. **Operating Hours:** Continuous. **Key Personnel:** Katsunobu Watanabe, President. **Wattage:** 50,000. **URL:** http://www. asahi.co.jp/.

46635 ■ JOOR-TV - 4
17-1, Chayamachi
Kita-ku
Osaka 530-8304, Japan
Ph: 81 6 63757504
Fax: 81 6 63593503
Format: Sports; Talk. **Owner:** Mainichi Broadcasting System, Inc. (MBS), at above address. **Founded:** 1959. **Key Personnel:** Kazutomo Kawauchi, President; Fumio Tanaka, Exec. Mng. Dir. **Wattage:** 10,000. **URL:** http:// www.mbs.jp/.

46636 ■ Osaka - 3374 KHz
4-1-20 Otemae
Chuo-ku
Osaka 540-8501, Japan

E-mail: nhkworld@nhk.jp
Format: Educational. **Owner:** Nippon Hoso Kyokai (NHK), 2-2-1 Jinnan, Shibuya-ku, Tokyo 150-8001, Japan, 81 3 34651111, Fax: 81 3 34698110. **Operating Hours:** 0800-1300. **Key Personnel:** Shigeo Fukuchi, President; Hidemi Hyuga, Exec. Dir. Gen. **Wattage:** 300. **URL:** http://www.nhk.or.jp.

Otsu

46637 ■ JOQP - 84.0 MHz
2-2-1, Jinnan
Shibuya-ku
Tokyo 150-8001, Japan
Ph: 81 3 34651111
Fax: 81 3 34698110
Format: Eclectic. **Owner:** Nippon Hoso Kyokai (NHK), at above address. **Operating Hours:** Continuous. **Wattage:** 1000. **Ad Rates:** Advertising accepted; rates available upon request. **URL:** http://www.nhk.or.jp.

46638 ■ JOUV - 77.0 MHz
19-10, Nishinosho
Otsu 520-0818, Japan
Ph: 81 75 5270814
Fax: 81 75 5270836
E-mail: fmshiga@e-radio.co.jp
Format: Eclectic. **Owner:** FM Shiga Co., Ltd. (E-Radio), at above address. **Founded:** 1997. **Operating Hours:** Continuous. **Wattage:** 1000. **Ad Rates:** Advertising accepted; rates available upon request. **URL:** http://www. e-radio.co.jp/.

Saeki

46639 ■ JOEE-TV Saeki - 55
21-3, Moto-machi
Naka-ku
Hiroshima 730-8504, Japan
Ph: 81 82 2221155
E-mail: tv@rcc.net
Owner: Chugoku Broadcasting Co., Ltd. (RCC), at above address. **Founded:** 1959. **Wattage:** 10. **URL:** http://www.1350.jp/.

Saga

46640 ■ JONV - 77.9 MHz
286-5, Sagansukueabiru
Saga 840-0023, Japan
Ph: 81 952 257790
Fax: 81 952 297200
Format: Eclectic. **Owner:** FM Saga Co., Ltd., at above address. **Founded:** 1992. **Operating Hours:** Continuous. **Wattage:** 500. **Ad Rates:** Advertising accepted; rates available upon request. **URL:** http://www. fmsaga.co.jp/.

46641 ■ JOSP - 963 KHz
2-2-1 Jinnan
Shibuya-ku
Tokyo 150-8001, Japan
Ph: 81 3 34651111
Fax: 81 3 34811350
E-mail: nhkworld@nhk.jp
Format: News. **Owner:** Nippon Hoso Kyokai (NHK), at above address. **Operating Hours:** Continuous. **Key Personnel:** Shigeo Fukuchi, President; Hidemi Hyuga, Exec. Dir. Gen. **Wattage:** 1000. **Ad Rates:** Noncommercial. **URL:** http://www.nhk.or.jp.

46642 ■ JOUO - 1458 KHz
1-35, Uwamachi
Nagasaki 850-8650, Japan
Ph: 81 958 243111
Fax: 81 958 245501
E-mail: mb-info@nbc-nagasaki.co.jp
Format: Eclectic. **Owner:** Nagasaki Broadcasting Co., Ltd. (NBC), at above address. **Founded:** 1952. **Operating Hours:** Continuous. **Wattage:** 1000. **URL:** http:// www.nbc-nagasaki.co.jp.

Sagamihara

46643 ■ Aikido Journal
KK Aiki News
14-17-103 Matsugae-cho
Kanagawa
Sagamihara 228-0813, Japan

Ph: 81 427 482423

Sports magazine. **Founded:** 1974. **Freq:** Bimonthly. **Key Personnel:** Stanley Pranin, Contact. **ISSN:** 1340-5624. **Subscription Rates:** US$29.75 individuals online; US$54.75 two years online. **Remarks:** Advertising accepted; rates available upon request. **URL:** http://www.aikidojournal.com/blog/. **Circ:** Paid 12,000

Saijyo

46644 ■ JOEE-TV Saijyo - 10
21-3, Moto-machi
Naka-ku
Hiroshima 730-8504, Japan
Ph: 81 82 2221155
E-mail: rcc@rcc.net
Owner: Chugoku Broadcasting Co., Ltd. (RCC), at above address. **Founded:** 1959. **Wattage:** 10,000. **URL:** http://www.rcc.co.jp.

46645 ■ JOEE-TV Saijyo - 9
21-3, Moto-machi
Naka-ku
Hiroshima 730-8504, Japan
Ph: 81 82 2221155
E-mail: rcc@rcc.net
Owner: Chugoku Broadcasting Co., Ltd. (RCC), at above address. **Founded:** 1959. **Wattage:** 3. **Ad Rates:** Noncommercial. **URL:** http://www.rcc.co.jp.

Saitama

46646 ■ JODV - 79.5 MHz
Nishiki-cho
Omiya Ward
Saitama 330-8579, Japan
Format: Eclectic. **Owner:** Nack5 Co., Ltd, at above address. **Founded:** 1988. **Operating Hours:** Continuous. **Wattage:** 5000. **Ad Rates:** Advertising accepted; rates available upon request. **URL:** http://www.nack5.co.jp/.

Sakugi

46647 ■ JOEE-TV Sakugi - 46
21-3, Moto-machi
Naka-ku
Hiroshima, Japan
Ph: 81 82 2221155
E-mail: tv@rcc.net
Owner: Chugoku Broadcasting Co., Ltd. (RCC), at above address. **Founded:** 1959. **Wattage:** 3. **Ad Rates:** Noncommercial. **URL:** http://www.1350.jp/.

Sakyo-ku

46648 ■ Fluid Dynamics Research
Elsevier Science Inc.
c/o S. Kida, Ed.-in-Ch.
Dept. of Mechanical Engineering & Science
Graduate School of Engineering
Kyoto University
Sakyo-ku 606-8501, Japan
Publisher E-mail: usinfo-ehelp@elsevier.com
Peer-reviewed journal serving theoretical, numerical and experimental studies that contribute to fundamental understanding and/or application of fluid. **Founded:** 1986. **Freq:** Monthly. **Print Method:** Offset. **Cols./Page:** 5. **Col. Width:** 2 1/16 inches. **Col. Depth:** 13 1/4 inches. **Key Personnel:** Y. Fukumoto, Assoc. Ed.; T. Kajishima, Assoc. Ed.; H.J. Sung, Regional Ed., hjsung@kaist.ac.kr; Z. Warhaft, Regional Ed., zw16@cornell.edu; K. Ishii, Assoc. Ed.; M. Yamada, Assoc. Ed.; K. Suga, Assoc. Ed.; Y. Tsuji, Assoc. Ed.; Y. Hayashi, Assoc. Ed.; A. Sasoh, Assoc. Ed.; S. Kida, Editor-in-Chief, kida@mech.kyoto-u.ac.jp. **ISSN:** 0169-5983. **Subscription Rates:** US$1,114 institutions, other countries except Europe and Japan; EUR996 institutions; 132,400¥ institutions. **URL:** http://www.elsevier.com/wps/find/journaldescription.cws_home/505708/descriptiondescription.

Sapporo

46649 ■ Hand Surgery
World Scientific Publishing Company Private Ltd.
c/o A Minami, Ed.-in-Ch.
Dept. of Orthopaedic Surgery
Hokkaido University Graduate School of Medicine

Kita 15, Nishi 7
Sapporo 060-8638, Japan
Ph: 81 11 7173532
Fax: 81 11 7065933
Publisher E-mail: wspc@wspc.com.sg
Periodical covering injury and diseases of the hand and upper limb and related research. **Founded:** 1996. **Freq:** 3/yr. **Key Personnel:** A. Minami, Editor-in-Chief; M. Beppu, Co-Ed., phone 81 449 778111, fax 81 449 779683, beppu917@yg8.so-net.ne.jp; M.A. Tonkin, Co-Ed., phone 61 299 267778, fax 61 299 267774, mtonkin@surgery.usyd.edu.au; S. Coleman, Editorial Board; G. Balakrishnan, Editorial Board; F. Kanaya, Editorial Board. **ISSN:** 0218-8104. **Subscription Rates:** US$315 institutions and libraries; print & electronic; US$19 individuals for postage; US$302 institutions and libraries; electronic only; EUR254 institutions and libraries; print & electronic; EUR244 institutions and libraries; electronic only; EUR15 individuals for postage; S$504 institutions and libraries; print & electronic; S$484 institutions and libraries; electronic only; S$25 individuals for postage. **URL:** http://www.worldscinet.com/hs/hs.shtml.

46650 ■ Hokkaido Mathematical Journal
Hokkaido University
Department of Mathematics
Faculty of Science
kita 10
Nishi 8
Kita-ku
Sapporo 060-0810, Japan
Fax: 81 11 7561244
Publishes significant research articles in all areas of mathematics. **Founded:** 1972. **Freq:** Quarterly. **Key Personnel:** Asao Arai, Editor-in-Chief; Hiroaki Terao, Editor; Prof. Tohru Ozawa, Editorial Board; Tomoyuki Yoshida, Editor; Prof. Charles M. Elliott, Editorial Board; Keizo Yamaguchi, Editor; Goo Ishikawa, Editor; Michiko Yuri, Editor; Asao Arai, Editor-in-Chief. **ISSN:** 0385-4035. **URL:** http://coe.math.sci.hokudai.ac.jp/literature/hmj/index.html.en. **Circ:** Paid 720

46651 ■ Japanese Journal of Veterinary Research
Hokkaido University Faculty of Veterinary Medicine
Kita 18
Nishi 9
Kita-ku
Sapporo 060-0818, Japan
Fax: 81 117 065190
Journal of veterinary science. **Founded:** 1954. **Freq:** Quarterly. **Key Personnel:** Prof. Toshiyuki Takahashi, Editor-in-Chief. **ISSN:** 0047-1917. **URL:** http://eprints.lib.hokudai.ac.jp/dspace/handle/2115/865. **Circ:** 650

46652 ■ Xene
Xene Inc.
Oji Fudosan Sapporo Bldg.
1st Fl., Minami 1 Nishi 11
Chuo-ku
Hokkaido
Sapporo 060-0061, Japan
Ph: 81 11 2720757
Fax: 81 11 2720758
Publisher E-mail: info@xene.net
General interest magazine. **Freq:** Bimonthly. **Trim Size:** A4. **Key Personnel:** Lynn Onozuka, Editor-in-Chief; Carey Paterson, English Ed.; Hiiro Mujin, Publisher; Mariko Hirano, Editorial Mgr. **Subscription Rates:** 1,800¥ individuals 1 to 2 copies; 2,000¥ individuals for 3 to 50 copies; 6,000¥ out of area for 3 to 5 copies; 2,500¥ individuals for 51 to 99 copies; 7,000¥ individuals in Japan/for 51 to 99 copies; Free for 100 & more number of copies. **Remarks:** Advertising accepted; rates available upon request. **URL:** http://www.xene.net/english/index.htm. **Circ:** 30,000

Hokkaido Hoso - See Enbetsu
46653 ■ JOBM-TV - 27
1-5, Nishi 14-chome
kita 1-jo
Chuo-ku
Sapporo 060-8527, Japan
Ph: 81 11 2145200
Fax: 81 11 2713599
Owner: Hokkaido Cultural Broadcasting Co., Ltd. (UHB), at above address. **Founded:** 1972. **Wattage:** 30,000. **URL:** http://www.uhb.co.jp/uhb.html.

JOFM - See Esashi

46654 ■ JOFU - 80.4 MHz
Sapporo Clock Tower
Central kita Sapporo Nishi 2-chome Bldg. 14F
Sapporo 060-8532, Japan
Ph: 81 11 2410804
Fax: 81 11 2516305
Format: Eclectic. **Owner:** FM Hokkaido Broadcasting Co., Ltd. (AIR-G'), at above address. **Founded:** 1982. **Operating Hours:** 0500-0400. **Key Personnel:** Sato Mitsuaki, President. **Wattage:** 5000. **Ad Rates:** Advertising accepted; rates available upon request. **URL:** http://www.air-g.co.jp/.

46655 ■ JOHH-TV - 35
10-17, Higashi 4-jo 13-chome
Toyohira-ku
Sapporo 062-8501, Japan
Ph: 81 11 8214411
Owner: Hokkaido Television Broadcasting Ltd.(HTB), at above address. **Founded:** 1968. **Wattage:** 30,000. **URL:** http://www.htb.co.jp/.

46656 ■ JOHI-TV - 17
12-4, Odori-Higashi 6-chome
Chuo-ku
Sapporo 060-8517, Japan
Ph: 81 11 2321117
Owner: Television Hokkaido Broadcasting Co., Ltd. (TVH), at above address. **Founded:** 1989. **Wattage:** 30,000. **URL:** http://www.tv-hokkaido.co.jp/.

JOHO - See Hokadate

46657 ■ JOHR - 1287 KHz
2, Nishi 5-Chome
Kita 1-jo
Chuo-ku
Sapporo 060-8501, Japan
Ph: 81 11 2325800
E-mail: info@hbc.co.jp
Format: Eclectic. **Owner:** Hokkaido Broadcasting Co., Ltd. (HBC), at above address. **Founded:** 1952. **Operating Hours:** Continuous. **Key Personnel:** Osamu Naganuma, President. **Wattage:** 50,000. **URL:** http://www.hbc.co.jp.

46658 ■ JOHR-TV - 1
Nishi 5, Chuo 2-chome
kita 1
Sapporo 060-8501, Japan
Ph: 81 11 2325800
E-mail: info@hbc.co.jp
Owner: Hokkaido Broadcasting Co., Ltd. (HBC), at above address. **Founded:** 1957. **Key Personnel:** Takashi Watanabe, President. **Wattage:** 10,000. **URL:** http://www.hbc.co.jp.

JOHW - See Obihiro

46659 ■ JOKX-TV - 5
1-1, Nishi 8-chome
Kita 1-jo, Chuo-ku
Sapporo 060-8705, Japan
Ph: 81 11 2411181
E-mail: tv@stv.ne.jp
Format: News; Full Service; Sports. **Owner:** The Sapporo Television Broadcasting Co., Ltd. (STV), at above address. **Founded:** 1959. **Wattage:** 10,000. **URL:** http://www.stv.ne.jp/.

46660 ■ JOPV - 82.5 MHz
Nishi Bldg. 4 new 7-chome
Hokkaido
Kita-ku
Sapporo 060-8557, Japan
Ph: 81 11 7078250
Fax: 81 11 7078311
Format: Eclectic. **Owner:** FM North Wave Co., Ltd. (North Wave), at above address. **Founded:** 1993. **Operating Hours:** Continuous. **Wattage:** 5000. **Ad Rates:** Advertising accepted; rates available upon request. **URL:** http://825.fm/northwave/.

JOQL - See Kushiro
JOQM - See Abashiri
JOTL - See Nayoro
JOTS - See Wakkanai
JOVX - See Abashiri

46661 ■ JOWF - 1440 KHz
1-1, Nishi 8-chome

Circulation: ★ = ABC; △ = BPA; ♦ = CAC; • = CCAB; ❑ = VAC; ⊕ = PO Statement; ‡ = Publisher's Report; Boldface figures = sworn; Light figures = estimated.

Kita 1-jo
Chuo-ku
Sapporo 060-8705, Japan
Ph: 81 11 2411181
E-mail: radio@stv.ne.jp
Format: Eclectic. **Owner:** The Sapporo Television Broadcasting Co., Ltd. (STV), at above address. **Founded:** 1962. **Operating Hours:** Continuous. **Wattage:** 50,000. **URL:** http://www.stv.ne.jp/.

JOWL - See Asahikawa

JOWM - See Obihiro

46662 ■ JOWN - 639 KHz
1-1, Nishi 8-chome
Kita 1-jo, Chuo-ku
Sapporo 060-8705, Japan
Ph: 81 11 2411181
Fax: 81 11 2027290
E-mail: radio@stv.ne.jp
Format: Eclectic. **Owner:** The Sapporo Television Broadcasting, Ltd., at above address. **Operating Hours:** Continuous. **Wattage:** 5000. **URL:** http://www.stv.ne.jp/.

JOWS - See Kushiro

Sapporo TV Hoso - See Esashi

Sapporo TV Hoso - See Muroran

Sapporo TV Hoso - See Tomakomai

Sasebo

46663 ■ JOMF - 1098 KHz
1-35, Uwamachi
Nagasaki 850-8650, Japan
Ph: 81 958 243111
Fax: 81 958 245501
E-mail: mb-info@nbc-nagasaki.co.jp
Format: Eclectic. **Owner:** Nagasaki Broadcasting Co., Ltd. (NBC), at above address. **Operating Hours:** Continuous. **Wattage:** 1000. **URL:** http://www.nbc-nagasaki.co.jp.

Sendai

46664 ■ Bio-Medical Materials and Engineering
IOS Press, B.V.
c/o Toshimitsu Yokobori, Jr., Ed.-in-Ch.
Department of Nano Mechanics
Graduate School of Engineering
Tohoku University, Aobayama 01, Aobaku
Sendai 980-8579, Japan
Ph: 81 22 7956894
Fax: 81 22 7956894
Publisher E-mail: info@iospress.nl
Peer-reviewed interdisciplinary journal publishing original research papers, review articles and brief notes on materials and engineering for biological and medical systems. **Freq:** Bimonthly. **Key Personnel:** Toshimitsu Yokobori, Jr., Editor-in-Chief, yokobori@md.mech.tohoku.ac.jp; W. Bonfield, Honorary Ed.; E.Y.S. Chao, Honorary Ed.; J.B. Park, Exec. Ed. **ISSN:** 0959-2989. **Subscription Rates:** EUR907 individuals regular; US$1,282 individuals regular. **URL:** http://www.iospress.nl/loadtop/load.php?isbn=09592989.

46665 ■ Ecological Research
Springer-Verlag Tokyo
c/o Masakado Kawata, Ed.-in-Ch.
Tohoku University
Aoba 6-3
Aramaki, Aoba-ku
Sendai 980-8578, Japan
Publisher E-mail: info@springer.jp
Journal publishing original research papers, reviews, technical reports, and notes and comments covering all aspects of ecology and ecological sciences. **Founded:** 1986. **Freq:** Bimonthly. **Key Personnel:** Masakado Kawata, Editor-in-Chief; Min Cao, Board of Ed.; Tohru Nakashizuka, Assoc. Ed.-in-Ch.; Jotaro Urabe, Assoc. Ed.-in-Ch.; Barry W. Brook, Board of Ed.; Michael Boots, Board of Ed. **ISSN:** 0912-3814. **Subscription Rates:** EUR650 institutions print incl. free access or e-only; EUR780 institutions print incl. enhanced access. **Remarks:** Advertising accepted; rates available upon request. **URL:** http://www.springer.com/lifesci/ecology/journal/11284. **Circ:** (Not Reported)

46666 ■ High Temperature Materials and Processes
Freund Publishing House Ltd.
Tohoku University

Sendai, Japan
Publisher E-mail: h_freund@netvision.net.il
Journal covering field of high temperature materials and processes. **Freq:** 6/yr. **Key Personnel:** Prof. Y. Waseda, Editor-in-Chief; Prof. T. Goswami, Assoc. Ed.; Prof. W.G. Davenport, Assoc. Ed. **ISSN:** 0334-6455. **Subscription Rates:** US$410 individuals. **URL:** http://www.freundpublishing.com/JOURNALS/materials_science_and_engineering.htm.

46667 ■ International Journal of Applied Electromagnetics and Mechanics
IOS Press, B.V.
Advanced Systems Evaluation Laboratory
Institute of Fluid Science
Tohoku University
Katahira 2-1-1, Aoba-ku
Sendai 980-8577, Japan
Ph: 81 222 175248
Fax: 81 222 175248
Publisher E-mail: info@iospress.nl
Journal contributing to intersciences by coupling applied electromagnetics, mechanics and materials and stimulating the further development of current technology in industry, covering subjects such as: physics and mechanics of electromagnetic materials and devices; computational electromagnetic in materials and devices; and applications of electromagnetic fields and forces. **Freq:** MON. **Key Personnel:** Sadik Dost, Editorial Board; T. Takagi, Editor-in-Chief, ijaem@wert.ifs.tohoku.ac.jp; Seiji Chonan, Editorial Board; R. Albanese, Editorial Board; Satish S. Upda, Regional Ed., upda@egr.msu.edu; Joel Pouget, Editorial Board. **ISSN:** 1383-5416. **Subscription Rates:** EUR1,084 institutions print and online; US$1,540 institutions print and online. **URL:** http://www.iospress.nl/loadtop/load.php?isbn=13835416.

46668 ■ Pharmacometrics
Japanese Society of Pharmacometrics
2-11-12 Ichibancho
Sendai 980-0811, Japan
Ph: 81 22 2673810
Fax: 81 22 2220515
Pharmacy journal. **Founded:** 1967. **Freq:** Monthly. **Key Personnel:** Hikaru Ozawa, Editor. **ISSN:** 0300-8533. **Subscription Rates:** 10,000¥. **Remarks:** Advertising accepted; rates available upon request. **Circ:** Paid 1,200

46669 ■ Tohoku Journal of Experimental Medicine
Tohoku University Medical Press
2-1 Seiryo-machi
Aoba-ku
Miyagi
Sendai 980-8575, Japan
Fax: 81 22 7178185
Publisher E-mail: office@journal.med.tohoku.ac.jp
Journal of experimental medicine. **Founded:** 1920. **Freq:** Monthly. **Key Personnel:** S. Shibahara, Editor-in-Chief, phone 81 22 7178113, fax 81 22 7178118, shibahar@mail.tains.tohoku.ac.jp; N. Osumi, Editorial Board; A.G. Coran, Editorial Board; Y. Oka, Editorial Board; J. Alam, Editorial Board; W. Hida, Editorial Board. **ISSN:** 0040-8727. **Subscription Rates:** US$388 out of country; 33,000¥ institutions. **URL:** http://journal.med.tohoku.ac.jp. **Circ:** Paid 800

46670 ■ Tohoku Mathematical Journal
Tohoku University
Mathematical Institute
Aramaki aza Aoba
6-3 Aoba-ku
Miyagi
Sendai 980-8578, Japan
Fax: 81 22 7956400
Publisher E-mail: tmj@math.tohoku.ac.jp
Mathematics journal. **Founded:** 1911. **Freq:** Quarterly. **Key Personnel:** Masayoshi Takeda, Editor; Akihiko Yukie, Editor; Izumi Takagi, Editor; Masanori Isida, Managing Editor; Seiki Nishikawa, Editor. **ISSN:** 0040-8735. **URL:** http://www.math.tohoku.ac.jp/tmj/index.html. **Circ:** Paid 1,000

46671 ■ Tohoku Psychologica Folia
Tohoku University
Faculty of Arts and Letters
Kawauchi
Aoba-ku
Miyagi
Sendai 980-8576, Japan

Ph: 81 22 7956048
Fax: 81 22 7953703
Journal of psychology. **Founded:** 1933. **Freq:** Annual. **Key Personnel:** Jiro Gyoba, Editorial Board; Ken-ichi Ohbuchi, Editor-in-Chief; Toru Hariu, Editorial Board. **ISSN:** 0040-8743. **URL:** http://www.sal.tohoku.ac.jp/psychology/folia/folia.htm. **Circ:** 525

46672 ■ JOEM-TV - 32
9-1, Futabagaoka 2-chome
Aoba-ku
Sendai 981-8511, Japan
Ph: 81 22 2768111
Fax: 81 22 2768115
Owner: Higashi Nippon Broadcasting Co., Ltd. (KHB), at above address. **Founded:** 1975. **Wattage:** 30,000. **URL:** http://www.khb-tv.co.jp/.

46673 ■ JOHK - 82.5 MHz
2-2-1 Jinnan
Shibuya-ku
Tokyo 150-8001, Japan
Ph: 81 3 34651111
Fax: 81 3 34698110
Format: News. **Owner:** Nippon Hoso Kyokai (NHK), at above address. **Operating Hours:** Continuous. **Wattage:** 5000. **URL:** http://www.nhk.or.jp.

46674 ■ JOHK - 891 KHz
2-2-1 Jinnan
Shibuya-ku
Tokyo 150-8001, Japan
Ph: 81 3 34651111
Fax: 81 3 34811350
E-mail: nhkworld@nhk.jp
Format: News. **Owner:** Nippon Hoso Kyokai (NHK), at above address. **Operating Hours:** Continuous. **Key Personnel:** Shigeo Fukuchi, President; Hidemi Hyuga, Exec. Dir. Gen. **Wattage:** 20,000. **Ad Rates:** Advertising accepted; rates available upon request. **URL:** http://www.nhk.or.jp.

46675 ■ JOIR - 1260 KHz
26-1, Taihaku
Sendai 982-0831, Japan
Ph: 81 22 2291111
E-mail: info@tbc-sendai.co.jp
Format: Eclectic. **Owner:** Tohoku Broadcasting Co., Ltd. (TBC), at above address. **Founded:** 1952. **Operating Hours:** Continuous. **Wattage:** 20,000. **URL:** http://www.tbc-sendai.co.jp/.

46676 ■ JOJU - 77.1 MHz
10-28, Honcho 2-chome
Aoba-ku
Sendai 980-8420, Japan
Ph: 81 22 2657711
Fax: 81 22 2610567
E-mail: datefm@datefm.co.jp
Format: News. **Owner:** Sendai FM Broadcasting, Inc. (FMS), at above address. **Founded:** Dec. 1, 1982. **Operating Hours:** 0500-0400. **Wattage:** 5000. **Ad Rates:** Advertising accepted; rates available upon request. **URL:** http://www.datefm.co.jp.

46677 ■ JOMM-TV - 34
5-33, Hinode-cho 1-chome
Miyagino-ku
Sendai 983-8611, Japan
Ph: 81 22 2363411
Owner: Miyagi Television Broadcasting Co., Ltd. (MMT), at above address. **Founded:** 1970. **Wattage:** 30,000. **URL:** http://www.mmt-tv.co.jp/.

46678 ■ JOOX-TV - 12
5-8-33, Kamisugi
Aoba-ku
Sendai 980-0011, Japan
Ph: 81 22 2671213
Owner: Sendai Television Broadcasting Corporation (OX), at above address. **Founded:** 1962. **Wattage:** 10,000. **URL:** http://www.ox-tv.co.jp/.

Seno

46679 ■ JOEE-TV Seno - 57
21-3, Moto-machi
Naka-ku
Hiroshima 730-8504, Japan
Ph: 81 82 2221155

E-mail: tv@rcc.net
Owner: Chugoku Broadcasting Co., Ltd. (RCC), at above address. **Founded:** 1959. **Wattage:** 1. **URL:** http://www.1350.jp/.

Senotateishi

46680 ■ JOEE-TV Senotateishi - 58
21-3, Moto-machi
Naka-ku
Hiroshima 730-8504, Japan
Ph: 81 82 2221155
E-mail: tv@rcc.net
Owner: Chugoku Broadcasting Co., Ltd. (RCC), at above address. **Founded:** 1959. **URL:** http://www.1350.jp/.

Serakozan

46681 ■ JOEE-TV Serakozan - 57
21-3, Moto-machi
Naka-ku
Hiroshima 730-8504, Japan
Ph: 81 82 2221155
E-mail: rcc@rcc.net
Owner: Chugoku Broadcasting Co., Ltd. (RCC), at above address. **Founded:** 1959. **Wattage:** 10,000. **URL:** http://www.rcc.co.jp.

Shiga

46682 ■ Japanese Journal of Rheumatism and Joint Surgery
Nihon Ryumachi Kansetsu Geka Gakkai
Shiga Ika Daigaku Seikei Gekagaku Kyoshitsu
Seta Tsukiwacho
Otsu-shi
Shiga, Japan
Medical science journal. **Founded:** 1982. **Freq:** Quarterly. **ISSN:** 0287-3214.

Shimane

46683 ■ Congenital Anomalies
John Wiley & Sons (Asia) Private Ltd.
c/o Prof. Hiroki Otani, Ed.-in-Ch.
Department of Developmental Biology
Faculty of Medicine
Shimane University
Shimane 693-8501, Japan
Ph: 81 853 202102
Fax: 81 853 202100
Publisher E-mail: enquiry@wiley.com.sg
Journal focusing on the etiology, mechanisms and prevention of abnormal development, including structural and functional birth defects, pregnancy loss, and reproductive disabilities. Official English journal of the Japanese Teratology Society. **Freq:** Quarterly. **Key Personnel:** Prof. Hiroki Otani, Editor-in-Chief, anatomy1@med.shimane-u.ac.jp; Nigel A. Brown, Editorial Board. **ISSN:** 0914-3505. **Subscription Rates:** US$562 institutions print and online; US$510 institutions print; 346 institutions print and online; 314 institutions print; EUR439 institutions print and online; EUR439 institutions print and online, US$679 institutions, other countries print and online; US$616 institutions, other countries online. **Remarks:** Accepts advertising. **URL:** http://www.wiley.com/bw/journal.asp?ref=0914-3505&site=1. **Circ:** (Not Reported)

Shimonoseki

46684 ■ JOPM - 918 KHz
Shunan Pk. District
Yamaguchi 745-8686, Japan
Ph: 81 834 321111
Fax: 81 834 320046
Format: Eclectic. **Owner:** Yamaguchi Broadc., Co., Ltd., at above address. **Operating Hours:** Continuous. **Wattage:** 1000. **URL:** http://www.kry.co.jp/.

Shinichitsunekanemaru

46685 ■ JOEE-TV Shinichitsunekanemaru - 43
21-3, Moto-machi
Naka-ku
Hiroshima 730-8504, Japan
Ph: 81 82 2221155

E-mail: tv@rcc.net
Owner: Chugoku Broadcasting Co., Ltd. (RCC), at above address. **Founded:** 1959. **Wattage:** 3. **Ad Rates:** Noncommercial. **URL:** http://www.rcc.co.jp.

Shiraki

46686 ■ JOEE-TV Shiraki - 57
21-3, Moto-machi
Naka ku
Hiroshima 730-8504, Japan
Ph: 81 82 2221155
E-mail: tv@rcc.net
Owner: Chugoku Broadcasting Co., Ltd. (RCC), at above address. **Founded:** 1959. **Wattage:** 10. **URL:** http://www.1350.jp/.

Shiwa

46687 ■ JOEE-TV Shiwa - 48
21-3, Moto-machi
Naka-ku
Hiroshima 730-8504, Japan
Ph: 81 82 2221155
E-mail: tv@rcc.net
Owner: Chugoku Broadcasting Co., Ltd. (RCC), at above address. **Founded:** 1959. **Wattage:** 10,000. **Ad Rates:** Advertising accepted; rates available upon request. **URL:** http://www.rcc.co.jp.

Shizuoka

46688 ■ Journal of Faculty of Marine Science and Technology of Tokai University
Tokai University
Faculty of Marine Science and Technology
20-1 Ori-Do 3-chome
ShimizuOrido
Shizuoka 424-8610, Japan
Ph: 81 543340472
Fax: 81 243357109
Journal of oceanography. **Founded:** 1966. **Freq:** Semiannual. **ISSN:** 0375-3271.

46689 ■ JOKU - 79.2 MHz
133-24, Tokiwa-cho
Hamamatsu 430-8575, Japan
Ph: 81 53 4571152
Format: Eclectic. **Owner:** Shizuoka FM Broadcasting Co., Ltd, at above address. **Founded:** 1983. **Operating Hours:** Continuous. **Wattage:** 1000. **Ad Rates:** Advertising accepted; rates available upon request. **URL:** http://www.k-mix.co.jp/.

46690 ■ JOPB - 639 KHz
2-2-1 Jinnan
Shibuya-ku
Tokyo 150-8001, Japan
Ph: 81 3 34651111
Fax: 81 3 34698110
E-mail: nhkworld@nhk.jp
Format: Educational. **Owner:** Nippon Hoso Kyokai (NHK), at above address. **Operating Hours:** 2030-1640 (2030-1500, Sun. & Mon.). **Key Personnel:** Shigeo Fukuchi, President. **Wattage:** 10,000. **URL:** http://www.nhk.or.jp.

46691 ■ JOPK - 882 KHz
2-2-1 Jinnan
Shibuya-ku
Tokyo 150-8001, Japan
Ph: 81 3 34651111
Fax: 81 3 34811350
E-mail: nhkworld@nhk.jp
Format: News. **Owner:** Nippon Hoso Kyokai (NHK), at above address. **Operating Hours:** Continuous. **Key Personnel:** Shigeo Fukuchi, President; Hidemi Hyuga, Exec. Dir. Gen. **Wattage:** 10,000. **Ad Rates:** Noncommercial. **URL:** http://www.nhk.or.jp.

46692 ■ JOPK - 88.8 MHz
2-2-1 Jinnan
Shibuya-ku
Tokyo 150-8001, Japan
Ph: 81 3 34651111
Fax: 81 3 34698110
Format: News. **Owner:** Nippon Hoso Kyokai (NHK), at above address. **Operating Hours:** Continuous. **Key Personnel:** Hidemi Hyuga, Exec. Dir. Gen. **Wattage:**

1000. **URL:** http://www.nhk.or.jp.

46693 ■ JOQH-TV - 35
18-65, Kurihara
Shizuoka 422-8525, Japan
Ph: 81 54 2616111
Owner: Shizuoka Telecasting Co., Ltd. (SUT), at above address. **Founded:** 1968. **Wattage:** 10,000. **URL:** http://www.sut-tv.com/.

46694 ■ JOSI-TV - 33
15, Azuma-cho
Shizuoka 420-8567, Japan
Ph: 81 54 2513300
Owner: Shizuoka Asahi Television Co., Ltd. (SATV), at above address. **Founded:** 1978. **Wattage:** 10,000. **URL:** http://www.satv.co.jp/.

46695 ■ JOSX-TV - 31
563, Nakahara
Shizuoka 422-8560, Japan
Ph: 81 54 2838111
Fax: 81 54 2838127
E-mail: message@tv-sdt.co.jp
Owner: Shizuoka Daiichi Television Corporation (SDT), at above address. **Founded:** 1979. **Wattage:** 10,000. **URL:** http://www.tv-sdt.co.jp/top.html.

46696 ■ JOVR - 1404 KHz
1-1, Toro 3-chome
Suruga-ku
Shizuoka 420-8033, Japan
Ph: 81 54 2848900
Fax: 81 54 2848994
Format: Eclectic. **Owner:** Shizuoka Broadcasting System (SBS), at above address. **Founded:** 1952. **Operating Hours:** Continuous. **Wattage:** 10,000. **URL:** http://www.digisbs.com.

Shobara

46697 ■ JOEE-TV Shobara - 43
21-3, Moto-machi
Naka-ku
Hiroshima 730-8504, Japan
Ph: 81 82 2221155
E-mail: tv@rcc.net
Owner: Chugoku Broadcasting Co., Ltd. (RCC), at above address. **Founded:** 1959. **Wattage:** 10. **URL:** http://www.1350.jp/.

Shunan

46698 ■ JOPF-TV - 11
Park District
Shunan 745-8686, Japan
Ph: 81 834 321111
Fax: 81 834 320046
Owner: Yamaguchi Broadcasting Co., Ltd. (KRY), at above address. **Founded:** 1956. **Wattage:** 1000. **URL:** http://www.kry.co.jp/.

Takamatsu

46699 ■ JOHD - 1035 KHz
2-2-1 Jinnan
Shibuya-ku
Tokyo 150-8001, Japan
Ph: 81 3 34651111
Fax: 81 3 34698110
E-mail: nhkworld@nhk.jp
Format: Educational. **Owner:** Nippon Hoso Kyokai (NHK), at above address. **Operating Hours:** 2030-1640 (2030-1500, Sun. & Mon.). **Key Personnel:** Shigetaka Komori, Chm.; Shigeo Fukuchi, President. **Wattage:** 1000. **URL:** http://www.nhk.or.jp.

46700 ■ JOHP - 86.0 MHz
2-2-1 Jinnan
Shibuya-ku
Tokyo 150-8001, Japan
Ph: 81 3 34651111
Fax: 81 3 34698110
Format: News. **Owner:** Nippon Hoso Kyokai (NHK), at above address. **Operating Hours:** Continuous. **Key Personnel:** Hidemi Hyuga, Exec. Dir. Gen. **Wattage:** 1000. **URL:** http://www.nhk.or.jp.

46701 ■ JOHP - 1368 KHz
2-2-1 Jinnan
Shibuya-ku

Circulation: ★ = ABC; △ = BPA; ◆ = OAC; • = CCAB; ❏ = VAC; ⊕ = PO Statement; ‡ = Publisher's Report; Boldface figures = sworn; Light figures = estimated.

Gale Directory of Publications & Broadcast Media/147th Ed.

5101

Tokyo 150-8001, Japan
Ph: 81 3 34651111
Fax: 81 3 34698110
E-mail: nhkworld@nhk.jp
Format: News. **Owner:** Nippon Hoso Kyokai (NHK), at above address. **Operating Hours:** Continuous. **Key Personnel:** Shigeo Fukuchi, President; Hidemi Hyuga, Exec. Dir. Gen. **Wattage:** 5000. **URL:** http://www.nhk.or.jp.

46702 ■ JOKF - 1449 KHz
8-15, Marunouchi
Takamatsu 760-8575, Japan
Ph: 81 87 8267333
Format: Eclectic. **Owner:** Nishi-Nippon Broadcasting Co., Ltd. (RNC), at above address. **Founded:** Oct. 1, 1953. **Operating Hours:** Continuous (off the air Sun. 1630-2030.). **Wattage:** 5000. **URL:** http://www.rnc.co.jp/.

46703 ■ JOYU - 78.6 MHz
4-23, Seebio-cho 1-chome
Takamatsu 760-8584, Japan
Ph: 81 87 8391111
Fax: 81 87 8377855
Format: Eclectic. **Owner:** FM Kagawa Broadcasting Co., Ltd., at above address. **Founded:** 1988. **Operating Hours:** Continuous. **Wattage:** 1000. **Ad Rates:** $10,000-13,000 for 10 seconds; $13,000-16,000 for 15 seconds; $16,000-20,000 for 20 seconds; $20,000-25,000 for 30 seconds. **URL:** http://www.fmkagawa.co.jp/.

Nishi Nippon Hoso - See Marugame

Takamiya

46704 ■ JOEE-TV Takamiya - 47
21-3, Moto-machi
Naka-ku
Hiroshima 730-8504, Japan
Ph: 81 82 2221155
E-mail: tv@rcc.net
Owner: Chugoku Broadcasting Co., Ltd. (RCC), at above address. **Founded:** 1959. **Wattage:** 3. **URL:** http://www.rcc.co.jp.

Takano

46705 ■ JOEE-TV Takano - 46
21-3, Moto-machi
Naka-ku
Hiroshima 730-8504, Japan
Ph: 81 82 2221155
E-mail: tv@rcc.net
Owner: Chugoku Broadcasting Co., Ltd. (RCC), at above address. **Founded:** 1959. **Wattage:** 10,000. **Ad Rates:** Noncommercial. **URL:** http://www.rcc.co.jp.

Takaoka

46706 ■ JOJH-TV - 32
Marunouchi 1, No. 40
Takaoka 933-0057, Japan
Owner: Tulip- TV Inc.(TUT), at above address. **Founded:** 1990. **Wattage:** 10,000. **URL:** http://www.tulip-tv.co.jp/.

Takehara

46707 ■ JOEE-TV Takehara - 59
21-3, Moto-machi
Naka-ku
Hiroshima 730-8504, Japan
Ph: 81 82 2221155
E-mail: rcc@rcc.net
Owner: Chugoku Broadcasting Co., Ltd. (RCC), at above address. **Founded:** 1959. **Wattage:** 100. **URL:** http://www.rcc.co.jp.

Takeharakita

46708 ■ JOEE-TV Takeharakita - 44
21-3, Moto-machi
Naka-ku
Hiroshima 730-8504, Japan
Ph: 81 82 2221155
E-mail: tv@rcc.net
Owner: Chugoku Broadcasting Co., Ltd. (RCC), at above address. **Founded:** 1959. **Wattage:** 3. **URL:** http://www.1350.jp/.

Tattori

46709 ■ JOHL - 1431 KHz
1-71, Nishi-Fukubara 1-chome
Yonago 683-8670, Japan
Ph: 81 859 332111
Format: Eclectic. **Owner:** Broadc. System of San-in, at above address. **Operating Hours:** Continuous. **Wattage:** 1000. **Ad Rates:** Noncommercial. **URL:** http://bss.jp/.

Tochigi

46710 ■ Journal of Equine Science
Japanese Society of Equine Science
Equine Research Institute 321-4 Tokami-cho
Utsunomiya-Shi
Tochigi 320-0856, Japan
Publisher E-mail: jes@center.equinst.go.jp
Journal covering the equine veterinary field. **Founded:** 1963. **Freq:** 10/yr. **Print Method:** Offset. **Trim Size:** 9 x 10 7/8. **Cols./Page:** 3. **ISSN:** 1340-3516. **URL:** http://www.jstage.jst.go.jp/browse/jes/-char/en.

Togouchi

46711 ■ JOEE-TV Togouchi - 55
21-3, Moto-machi
Naka-ku
Hiroshima 730-8504, Japan
Ph: 81 82 2221155
E-mail: tv@rcc.net
Owner: Chugoku Broadcasting Co., Ltd. (RCC), at above address. **Founded:** 1959. **Wattage:** 3. **URL:** http://www.1350.jp/.

Tojyo

46712 ■ JOEE-TV Tojyo - 10
21-3, Moto-machi
Naka-ku
Hiroshima 730-8504, Japan
Ph: 81 82 2221155
E-mail: tv@rcc.net
Owner: Chugoku Broadcasting Co., Ltd. (RCC), at above address. **Founded:** 1959. **Wattage:** 3. **Ad Rates:** Noncommercial. **URL:** http://www.rcc.co.jp.

Tojyochidori

46713 ■ JOEE-TV Tojyochidori - 36
21-3, Moto-machi
Naka-ku
Hiroshima 730-8504, Japan
Ph: 81 82 2221155
E-mail: tv@rcc.net
Owner: Chugoku Broadcasting Co., Ltd. (RCC), at above address. **Founded:** 1959. **Wattage:** 1. **URL:** http://www.rcc.co.jp.

Tokushima

46714 ■ Journal of Mathematics
University of Tokushima
Faculty of Integrated Arts and Sciences
2-1 Minamijosanjima-cho
Tokushima 770-8506, Japan
Ph: 81 88 6567103
Mathematics journal. **Founded:** 1967. **Freq:** Annual. **Key Personnel:** Toru Ishihara, Contact. **ISSN:** 1346-7387. **URL:** http://www-math.ias.tokushima-u.ac.jp/journal/mat.html.

46715 ■ Journal of Medical Investigation
Tokushima University
Faculty of Medicine
3-18-15, Kuramoto-cho
Tokushima 770-8503, Japan
Ph: 81 88 6337104
Fax: 81 88 6337115
Publisher E-mail: jmi@basic.med.tokushima-u.ac.jp
Journal of experimental medicine. **Founded:** 1954. **Freq:** Semiannual. **Key Personnel:** Toshio Doi, Assoc. Ed.; Saburo Sone, Editorial Board; Hiroshi Sei, Editor-in-Chief. **ISSN:** 1343-1420. **URL:** http://medical.med.tokushima-u.ac.jp/jmi/.

46716 ■ Social Science Research of University of Tokushima
University of Tokushima

Faculty of Integrated Arts and Sciences
2-1 Minamijosanjima-cho
Tokushima 770-8506, Japan
Ph: 81 88 6567103
Social science journal. **Founded:** 1988. **Freq:** Annual. **Key Personnel:** Tatsuya Deguchi, Contact. **URL:** http://www.ias.tokushima-u.ac.jp/bulletin/soc.html.

46717 ■ JOJR - 1269 KHz
5-2, Nakatokushima-cho 2-chome
Tokushima 770-8573, Japan
Ph: 81 886 557510
Fax: 81 886 241201
E-mail: eco-6@jrt.jp
Format: Eclectic. **Owner:** Shikoku Broadcasting Co., Ltd. (JRT), at above address. **Founded:** 1952. **Operating Hours:** Continuous. **Key Personnel:** Kondo Mayor, President. **Wattage:** 5000. **URL:** http://www.jrt.co.jp.

46718 ■ JOMV - 80.7 MHz
1-6, Saiwai-cho
Tokushima 770-8567, Japan
Ph: 81 88 6562111
Fax: 81 88 6243515
Format: Information; Public Radio. **Owner:** FM Tokushima Broadcasting Co., at above address. **Founded:** 1992. **Operating Hours:** Continuous. **Wattage:** 1000. **Ad Rates:** Advertising accepted; rates available upon request. **URL:** http://www.fm-tokushima.co.jp/.

46719 ■ JOXK - 945 KHz
2-2-1 Jinnan
Shibuya-ku
Tokyo 150-8001, Japan
Ph: 81 3 34651111
Fax: 81 3 34811350
E-mail: nhkworld@nhk.jp
Format: News. **Owner:** Nippon Hoso Kyokai (NHK), at above address. **Operating Hours:** Continuous. **Key Personnel:** Shigeo Fukuchi, President; Hidemi Hyuga, Exec. Dir. Gen. **Wattage:** 5000. **URL:** http://www.nhk.or.jp.

46720 ■ JOXK - 83.4 MHz
2-2-1 Jinnan
Shibuya-ku
Tokyo 150-8001, Japan
Ph: 81 3 34651111
Fax: 81 3 34698110
Format: News. **Owner:** Nippon Hoso Kyokai (NHK), at above address. **Operating Hours:** Continuous. **Key Personnel:** Hidemi Hyuga, Exec. Dir. Gen. **Wattage:** 1000. **URL:** http://www.nhk.or.jp.

Shikoku Hoso - See Ikeda

Tokyo

46721 ■ Acta Asiatica
Institute of Eastern Culture
The Toho Gakkai
2-4-1 Nishi Kanda
Chiyoda-ku
Tokyo 101-0065, Japan
Ph: 81 332 627221
Fax: 81 332 627227
Publication E-mail: iec@tohogakkai.com
Publisher E-mail: iec@tohogakkai.com
Journal on oriental studies. **Subtitle:** Bulletin of the Institute of Eastern Culture. **Founded:** 1961. **Freq:** Semiannual. **ISSN:** 0567-7254. **Subscription Rates:** 4,200¥ individuals. **URL:** http://www.tohogakkai.com. **Circ:** Paid 1,000

46722 ■ Acta Diabetologica
Springer-Verlag Tokyo
No. 2, Funato Bldg.
1-11-11 Kudan-kita
Chiyoda-ku
Tokyo 102-0073, Japan
Ph: 81 368 317000
Fax: 81 368 317001
Publisher E-mail: info@springer.jp
Journal publishing reports of experimental and clinical research on diabetes mellitus and related metabolic diseases. **Freq:** Quarterly. **Key Personnel:** G. Pozza, Editor-in-Chief; R. Bonadonna, Assoc. Ed.; M. Federici, Managing Editor. **ISSN:** 0940-5429. **Subscription Rates:** EUR541 institutions print incl. free access or e-only; EUR649.20 institutions print incl. enhanced

access. **Remarks:** Advertising accepted; rates available upon request. **URL:** http://www.springer.com/medicine/internal/journal/592. **Circ:** (Not Reported)

46723 ■ Acta Endoscopica
Springer-Verlag Tokyo
No. 2, Funato Bldg.
1-11-11 Kudan-kita
Chiyoda-ku
Tokyo 102-0073, Japan
Ph: 81 368 317000
Fax: 81 368 317001
Publisher E-mail: info@springer.jp
Journal for gastroenterologists, gynecologists, e.n.t., pneumologists, urologists, anatomopathologists, surgeons, echographists, radiologists, veterinarians and all physicians interested by endoscopy, publishing original articles concerning endoscopy in its medical and surgical applications; experimental studies of endoscopic instrumentations; and bibliographical analysis. **Freq:** Bimonthly. **Key Personnel:** D. Heresbach, Editor-in-Chief; G. Lesur, Editor-in-Chief. **ISSN:** 0240-642X. **Subscription Rates:** EUR254 institutions print incl. free access or e-only; EUR304.80 institutions print incl. enhanced access. **Remarks:** Advertising accepted; rates available upon request. **URL:** http://www.springer.com/medicine/internal/journal/10190. **Circ:** (Not Reported)

46724 ■ Acta Mathematica Sinica
Springer-Verlag Tokyo
No. 2, Funato Bldg.
1-11-11 Kudan-kita
Chiyoda-ku
Tokyo 102-0073, Japan
Ph: 81 368 317000
Fax: 81 368 317001
Publisher E-mail: info@springer.jp
Journal publishing significant research papers from all branches of pure and applied mathematics, providing authoritative reviews of current developments in mathematical research. **Freq:** Monthly. **Key Personnel:** Zhi-Ming Ma, Managing Editor; Liqun Zhang, Managing Editor; Gang Tian, Editor; Fanghua Lin, Editor. **ISSN:** 1439-8516. **Subscription Rates:** EUR977 institutions print incl. free access or e-only; EUR1,172.40 institutions print incl. enhanced access. **Remarks:** Advertising accepted; rates available upon request. **URL:** http://www.springer.com/math/journal/10114. **Circ:** (Not Reported)

46725 ■ Acta Mechanica
Springer-Verlag Tokyo
No. 2, Funato Bldg.
1-11-11 Kudan-kita
Chiyoda-ku
Tokyo 102-0073, Japan
Ph: 81 368 317000
Fax: 81 368 317001
Publisher E-mail: info@springer.jp
Journal in the field of theoretical and applied mechanics, covering elasticity, plasticity, vibrations, rigid body dynamics, hydrodynamics, and gasdynamics with special attention to recently developed areas such as non-Newtonian fluid dynamics, micro/nano mechanics, smart materials and structures, and issues at the interface of mechanics and materials. **Founded:** 1965. **Freq:** Quarterly. **Key Personnel:** N. Aksel, Editorial Board; H. Irschik, Editorial Board; A. Soldati, Editorial Board. **ISSN:** 0001-5970. **Subscription Rates:** EUR4,915 institutions print incl. free access or e-only; EUR5,898 institutions print incl. enhanced access. **Remarks:** Advertising accepted; rates available upon request. **URL:** http://www.springer.com/springerwiennewyork/engineering/journal/707. **Circ:** (Not Reported)

46726 ■ Acta Mechanica Sinica
Springer-Verlag Tokyo
No. 2, Funato Bldg.
1-11-11 Kudan-kita
Chiyoda-ku
Tokyo 102-0073, Japan
Ph: 81 368 317000
Fax: 81 368 317001
Publisher E-mail: info@springer.jp
Journal aiming to report recent developments in mechanics and other related fields of research, covering all disciplines in the field of theoretical and applied mechanics, including not only the classical subdivisions such as solid and fluid mechanics, but also the recently emerging areas such as biomechanics and nanomechanics, exploring analytical, computational and experimental

progresses in all areas of mechanics. **Founded:** 1985. **Freq:** Bimonthly. **Key Personnel:** Gengdong Cheng, Editor-in-Chief, chenggd@dlut.edu.cn; Huajian Gao, Editor-in-Chief, huajian_gao@brown.edu; Wei Shyy, Editor-in-Chief, weishyy@umich.edu. **ISSN:** 0567-7718. **Subscription Rates:** EUR751 institutions print incl. free access or e-only; EUR901.20 institutions print incl. enhanced access. **Remarks:** Advertising accepted; rates available upon request. **URL:** http://www.springer.com/new%26forthcomingtitles%28default%29/journal/10409. **Circ:** (Not Reported)

46727 ■ Actinomycetologica
Society for Actinomycetes, Japan
c/o Kitasato Institute for Life Sciences
Kitasato University
5-9-1 Shirokane
Minato-ku
Tokyo 108-8641, Japan
Ph: 81 3 57916133
Fax: 81 3 57916133
Publisher E-mail: actinomycetologica@lisci.kitasato-u.ac.jp
Journal of microbiology. **Founded:** 1962. **Freq:** Semiannual. **Key Personnel:** Miyadoh Shinji, Editorial Board; Hiroyuki Osada, Editorial Board; Fumio Kato, Editorial Board; Kozo Ochi, Editorial Board; Haruo Ikeda, Editorial Board; Michael Goodfellow, Editorial Board; Masaaki Kizuka, Editorial Board; Tamotsu Furumai, Editorial Board; Michihiko Kobayashi, Editorial Board. **ISSN:** 0914-5818. **URL:** http://www.nih.go.jp/saj/journal.

46728 ■ Adaptation
Oxford University Press
4-5-10-8F Shiba, Minato-ku
Tokyo 108-8386, Japan
Ph: 81 3 54445858
Fax: 81 3 34542929
Peer-reviewed Journal covering literary and film studies. **Freq:** Semiannual. **Key Personnel:** Deborah Cartmell, Editor; Imelda Whelehan, Editor; Timothy Corrigan, Editor. **ISSN:** 1755-0637. **Subscription Rates:** US$256 institutions print & online; US$214 institutions online only; US$236 institutions print only; US$100 individuals; EUR192 institutions print & online; EUR161 institutions online only; EUR177 institutions print only; EUR75 individuals; 118 institutions print only; 50 individuals. **Remarks:** Accepts advertising. **URL:** http://adaptation.oxfordjournals.org/. **Circ:** (Not Reported)

46729 ■ Afternoon
Kodansha Ltd.
2-12-21 Otowa
Bunkyo-ku
Tokyo 112-8001, Japan
Ph: 81 3 3946 6201
Fax: 81 3 3944 9915
Comic magazine featuring manga for fans under 30 years old. **Freq:** Monthly. **Key Personnel:** Sawako Noma, President. **URL:** http://www.kodansha.co.jp/english/manga/magazines.html.

46730 ■ Afternoon Season Zokan
Kodansha Ltd.
2-12-21 Otowa
Bunkyo-ku
Tokyo 112-8001, Japan
Ph: 81 3 3940 0201
Fax: 81 3 3944 9915
Entertainment comic magazine for teenage boys. **Freq:** Bimonthly. **Key Personnel:** Sawako Noma, President. **URL:** http://www.animenewsnetwork.com/encyclopedia/company.php?id=3517.

46731 ■ Algebra Universalis
Springer-Verlag Tokyo
No. 2, Funato Bldg.
1-11-11 Kudan-kita
Chiyoda-ku
Tokyo 102-0073, Japan
Ph: 81 368 317000
Fax: 81 368 317001
Publisher E-mail: info@springer.jp
Journal welcoming papers from the areas of universal algebra and lattice theory, as well as papers inspired by or having applications to these areas. **Freq:** Quarterly. **Key Personnel:** George Gratzer, Editor-in-Chief, gratzer@ms.umanitoba.ca; P. Dehornoy, Editorial Board, dehornoy@math.unicaen.fr; J. Berman, Editorial Board; R.W. Quackenbush, Exec. Ed., qbush@cc.umanitoba.ca; J.G. Raftery, Editorial Board, raftery@ukzn.ac.za;

C.R. Platt, Exec. Ed., platt@cc.umanitoba.ca; R. Willard, Editorial Board, rdwillar@math.uwaterloo.ca. **ISSN:** 0002-5240. **Subscription Rates:** EUR1,222 institutions print incl. free access or e-only; EUR1,466.40 institutions print incl. enhanced access. **Remarks:** Advertising accepted; rates available upon request. **URL:** http://www.springer.com/birkhauser/mathematics/journal/12. **Circ:** (Not Reported)

46732 ■ Allergology International
John Wiley & Sons Inc.
Wiley-Blackwell
Japanese Society of Allergology
MY Bldg., 4th Fl.
1-13-3, Ueno, Taito-ku
Tokyo 110-0005, Japan
Publication E-mail: info@jsaweb.jp
Official English language journal of the Japanese Society of Allergology, publishing peer-reviewed articles of scientific excellence in human and experimental allergology, and related fields of research. **Freq:** Quarterly. **Key Personnel:** Jean Bousquet, Editorial Board; Stephen J. Galli, Editorial Board; Xaver Baur Hamburg, Editorial Board; Kenji Nakanishi Hyogo, Editorial Board; Tak H. Lee, Editorial Board; Hirohisa Saito, Editor-in-Chief. **ISSN:** 1323-8930. **Remarks:** Accepts advertising. **URL:** http://ai.jsaweb.jp/index.html. **Circ:** (Not Reported)

46733 ■ American Literary History
Oxford University Press
4-5-10-8F Shiba, Minato-ku
Tokyo 108-8386, Japan
Ph: 81 3 54445858
Fax: 81 3 34542929
Journal covering the history of American literature. **Founded:** 1997. **Freq:** 4/yr. **Print Method:** Offset. **Trim Size:** 8 1/2 x 11. **Cols./Page:** 3. **Col. Width:** 43.5 nonpareils. **Key Personnel:** Prof. Gordon Hutner, Editor, hutner@express.cites.uiuc.edu; Mary Unger, Managing Editor; Michael Simeone, Asst. Ed. **ISSN:** 0896-7148. **Subscription Rates:** 175 institutions print and online; US$262 institutions print and online; EUR262 institutions print and online; 72 institutions school (print and online); US$108 institutions school (print and online); EUR108 institutions school (print and online); 50 individuals; US$75 individuals; EUR75 individuals; 28 students. **URL:** http://alh.oxfordjournals.org/.

46734 ■ Analytical Sciences
Japan Society for Analytical Chemistry
Gotanda Sanhaitsu
26-2 Nishigotanda
Shinagawa-ku
Tokyo 141-0031, Japan
Ph: 81 3 34903351
Fax: 81 3 34903572
Publisher E-mail: analytsci@jsac.or.jp
Journal publishing papers on all aspects of the theory and practice of analytical sciences, including fundamental and applied, inorganic and organic, wet chemical and instrumental methods. **Subtitle:** An International Journal. **Founded:** 1985. **Freq:** Monthly. **Key Personnel:** T. Imasaka, Editor. **ISSN:** 0910-6340. **Subscription Rates:** US$120 other countries incl. surface mail; US$240 institutions, other countries; US$70 individuals airmail. **URL:** http://www.jsac.or.jp/cgi-bin/analsci/page/about.html. **Circ:** Paid 3,600

46735 ■ Animal Science Journal
Japanese Society of Animal Science
201 Nagatani Corporas
Ikenohata 2-9-4
Taito-ku
Tokyo 110-0008, Japan
Ph: 81 3 38288409
Fax: 81 3 38287649
Publisher E-mail: tikusan@blue.ocn.ne.jp
Journal covering agriculture. **Founded:** 1985. **Freq:** Bimonthly. **Key Personnel:** Kunihiko Naito, Editor-in-Chief; Naomi Kashiwazaki, Exec. Ed. **ISSN:** 1344-3941. **Subscription Rates:** US$483 individuals print + online; US$895 institutions print + online; US$814 institutions print or online; 299 individuals print + online; 554 institutions print + online; 503 institutions print or online; EUR447 individuals print + online; EUR703 institutions print + online; EUR639 institutions print or online; US$1,085 institutions, other countries print + online. **Remarks:** Accepts advertising. **URL:** http://wwwsoc.nii.ac.jp/jszs/index-e.html; http://www.wiley.com/bw/journal.asp?ref=1344-3941; http://wwwsoc.nii.ac.jp/jszs/contents/conte.html. **Circ:** Paid 3,000

Circulation: ★ = ABC; △ = BPA; ◆ = CAC; • = CCAB; ❑ = VAC; ⊕ = PO Statement; ‡ = Publisher's Report; Boldface figures = sworn; Light figures = estimated.

46736 ■ Annali di Matematica Pura ed Applicata
Springer-Verlag Tokyo
No. 2, Funato Bldg.
1-11-11 Kudan-kita
Chiyoda-ku
Tokyo 102-0073, Japan
Ph: 81 368 317000
Fax: 81 368 317001
Publisher E-mail: info@springer.jp
Journal publishing articles on any subject of pure and applied mathematics, authored by scientists of all nationalities. **Freq:** Quarterly. **Key Personnel:** Giorgio Talenti, Editor-in-Chief; Vincenzo Ancona, Editor; John M. Ball, Editor. **ISSN:** 0373-3114. **Subscription Rates:** EUR345 institutions print incl. free access or e-only; EUR414 institutions print incl. enhanced access. **Remarks:** Advertising accepted; rates available upon request. **URL:** http://www.springer.com/math/journal/10231. **Circ:** (Not Reported)

46737 ■ Annals of Combinatorics
Springer-Verlag Tokyo
No. 2, Funato Bldg.
1-11-11 Kudan-kita
Chiyoda-ku
Tokyo 102-0073, Japan
Ph: 81 368 317000
Fax: 81 368 317001
Publisher E-mail: info@springer.jp
Journal publishing contributions to combinatorial mathematics in all its respects, including problems and theories that have arisen, or will arise, in applications to computer science, biology, statistics, probability, physics and chemistry, as well as over work of a combinatorial nature in representation theory, number theory topology, algebraic geometry and the theory of special functions. **Freq:** Quarterly. **Key Personnel:** William Y. Chen, Managing Editor, chen@nankai.edu.cn; George E. Andrews, Managing Editor, andrews@math.psu.edu; Peter Paule, Managing Editor, peter.paule@risc.uni-linz.ac.at. **ISSN:** 0218-0006. **Subscription Rates:** EUR546 institutions print incl. free access or e-only; EUR655.20 institutions print incl. enhanced access. **Remarks:** Advertising accepted; rates available upon request. **URL:** http://www.springer.com/birkhauser/mathematics/journal/26. **Circ:** (Not Reported)

46738 ■ Annals of Finance
Springer-Verlag Tokyo
No. 2, Funato Bldg.
1-11-11 Kudan-kita
Chiyoda-ku
Tokyo 102-0073, Japan
Ph: 81 368 317000
Fax: 81 368 317001
Publisher E-mail: info@springer.jp
Journal providing an outlet for original research in all areas of finance and its applications to other disciplines having a clear and substantive link to the general theme of finance, such as accounting and finance, asset pricing, banking and finance, capital markets and finance, computational finance, corporate finance, derivatives, dynamical and chaotic systems in finance, economics and finance, empirical finance, experimental finance, finance and the theory of the firm, financial econometrics, financial institutions, mathematical finance, money and finance, portfolio analysis, regulation, stochastic analysis and finance, stock market analysis, systemic risk and financial stability. **Freq:** Quarterly. **Key Personnel:** Charalambos D. Aliprantis, Editor; C. Mayer, Co-Ed.; S. Bhattacharya, Co-Ed.; F. Allen, Advisory Board; L. Hansen, Co-Ed.; R.C. Merton, Advisory Board; G. Constantinides, Co-Ed.; R.J. Shiller, Co-Ed. **ISSN:** 1614-2446. **Subscription Rates:** EUR314 institutions print incl. free access or e-only; EUR376.80 institutions print incl. enhanced access. **Remarks:** Advertising accepted; rates available upon request. **URL:** http://www.springer.com/business/finance/journal/10436. **Circ:** (Not Reported)

46739 ■ Annals of Nuclear Medicine
Japanese Society of Nuclear Medicine
2-28-45 Honkomagome
Bunkyo-ku
Tokyo 113-0021, Japan
Ph: 81 339 470976
Fax: 81 339 472535
Medical science journal. **Founded:** 1987. **Freq:** 8/yr. **Key Personnel:** Tomio Inoue, Director; Tamaki Nagara, Author. **ISSN:** 0914-7187. **URL:** http://www.jsnm.org/english/publications/20070406-0.

46740 ■ Annals of Regional Science
Springer-Verlag Tokyo
No. 2, Funato Bldg.
1-11-11 Kudan-kita
Chiyoda-ku
Tokyo 102-0073, Japan
Ph: 81 368 317000
Fax: 81 368 317001
Publisher E-mail: info@springer.jp
Journal promoting high quality scholarship on the important theoretical and empirical issues in regional science, publishing papers which make a new or substantial contribution to the body of knowledge in which the spatial dimension plays a fundamental role, such as regional economics, resource management, location theory, urban and regional planning, transportation and communication, human geography, population distribution and environmental quality. **Freq:** 3/yr. **Key Personnel:** T.J. Kim, Assoc. Ed.; Borje Johansson, Editor, phone 46 36 156439, fax 46 36 121832, jobo@jibs.hj.se; Laurie Schintler, Book Review Ed., lschintl@gmu.edu; I. Gordon, Assoc. Ed.; D.B. Audretsch, Assoc. Ed.; Roger R. Stough, Editor, rstough@gmu.edu. **ISSN:** 0570-1864. **Subscription Rates:** EUR790 institutions print incl. free access or e-only; EUR948 institutions print incl. enhanced access. **Remarks:** Advertising accepted; rates available upon request. **URL:** http://www.springer.com/economics/regionalscience/journal/168. **Circ:** (Not Reported)

46741 ■ Annals of Thoracic and Cardiovascular Surgery
Medical Tribune Inc.
2-1 Nibancho
Chiyoda-ku
Tokyo 102-0084, Japan
Ph: 81 3 32397217
Fax: 81 3 32399375
Medical science journal. **Founded:** 1995. **Freq:** Bimonthly. **Trim Size:** A4. **Key Personnel:** Yukiyasu Sezai, Editor-in-Chief; Harubumi Kato, Editor; Shiaki Kawada, Editor. **ISSN:** 1341-1098. **Remarks:** Accepts advertising. **URL:** http://www.atcs.jp/. **Circ:** (Not Reported)

46742 ■ Antarctic Record
National Institute of Polar Research
10-3 Midoricho
Tachikawa
Tokyo 190-8518, Japan
Ph: 81 42 5120608
Fax: 81 42 5283146
Journal of geography. **Founded:** 1957. **Freq:** 3/yr. **ISSN:** 0085-7289. **URL:** http://www.nipr.ac.jp/english/index.html. **Circ:** 1,000

46743 ■ Anthropological Science
Business Center for Academic Societies Japan
Gakkai Ctr. C21
5-16-9 Honkomagome
Bunkyo-Ku
Tokyo 113-8622, Japan
Ph: 81 358 145800
Fax: 81 358 145823
Journal covering anthropology. **Founded:** 1993. **Freq:** Quarterly. **Key Personnel:** Gen Suwa, Editor-in-Chief, phone 81 584 12836, fax 81 584 18451, as@um.u-tokyo.ac.jp; Hisao Baba, Editorial Board; K. Adachi, Editorial Board; Rebecca Cann, Assoc. Ed.; Peter Brown, Assoc. Ed.; M.T. Douglas, Editorial Board. **ISSN:** 0918-7960. **Subscription Rates:** 8,000¥ members regular; 5,000¥ students; 12,000¥ institutions. **Remarks:** Advertising accepted; rates available upon request. **URL:** http://www.nacos.com/asn/as.html. **Circ:** Paid 1,300

46744 ■ Apparel Production News
New Japan Sewing Machine News Ltd.
2nd Fl., Kosumo Bldg.
8-5 Sugamo 1-chome
Toshima-ku
Tokyo 170-0002, Japan
Ph: 81 3 39422574
Fax: 81 3 39421827
Journal covering apparels. **Founded:** 1987. **Freq:** Monthly. **Key Personnel:** Makoto Nakajima, Editor. **ISSN:** 0914-7594. **Subscription Rates:** 9,600¥. **Remarks:** Advertising accepted; rates available upon request. **Circ:** Paid 9,000

46745 ■ Applicable Algebra in Engineering, Communication and Computing
Springer-Verlag Tokyo
No. 2, Funato Bldg.
1-11-11 Kudan-kita
Chiyoda-ku
Tokyo 102-0073, Japan
Ph: 81 368 317000
Fax: 81 368 317001
Publisher E-mail: info@springer.jp
Journal publishing mathematically rigorous, original research papers reporting on algebraic methods and techniques relevant to all domains concerned with computers, intelligent systems and communications, including, but not limited to, vision, robotics, system design, fault tolerance and dependability of systems, VLSI technology, signal processing, signal theory, coding, error control techniques, cryptography, protocol specification, networks, software engineering, arithmetics, algorithms, complexity, computer algebra, programming languages, logic and functional programming, algebraic specification, term rewriting systems, theorem proving, graphics, modeling, knowledge engineering, expert systems, and artificial intelligence methodology. **Freq:** Bimonthly. **Key Personnel:** Jacques Calmet, Editor-in-Chief, phone 49 721 6084208, fax 49 721 6086116, calmet@ira.uka.de; Paul Camion, Editorial Board; John Cannon, Editorial Board; Teo Mora, Mng. Board, theomora@disi.unige.it. **ISSN:** 0938-1279. **Subscription Rates:** EUR610 institutions print incl. free access or e-only; EUR732 institutions print incl. enhanced access. **Remarks:** Advertising accepted; rates available upon request. **URL:** http://www.springer.com/computer/mathematics/journal/200. **Circ:** (Not Reported)

46746 ■ Applied Entomology and Zoology
Japanese Society of Applied Entomology and Zoology
c/o Japan Plant Protection Association
1-43-11 Komagome
Toshima-ku
Tokyo 170-8484, Japan
Fax: 81 298 386077
Journal covering biology. **Founded:** 1966. **Freq:** Quarterly. **Key Personnel:** Toshiharu Akino, Editor; Masahiro Osakabe, Editor; Yoshihiro Yamada, Editor. **ISSN:** 0003-6862. **Remarks:** Advertising accepted; rates available upon request. **URL:** http://odokon.org/en/aez.php. **Circ:** Paid 1,900

46747 ■ Applied Magnetic Resonance
Springer-Verlag Tokyo
No. 2, Funato Bldg.
1-11-11 Kudan-kita
Chiyoda-ku
Tokyo 102-0073, Japan
Ph: 81 368 317000
Fax: 81 368 317001
Publisher E-mail: info@springer.jp
Journal providing an international forum for the application of magnetic resonance in physics, chemistry, biology, medicine, geochemistry, ecology, engineering, and related fields. **Freq:** Quarterly. **Key Personnel:** K.M. Salikhov, Editor-in-Chief, fax 81 784 32765075, salikhov@kfti.knc.com; S.A. Dzuba, Editorial Board; A.N. Garroway, Editorial Board; K.P. Mishra, Advisory Board; S. Yamauchi, Editorial Board. **ISSN:** 0937-9347. **Subscription Rates:** EUR1,829 institutions print incl. free access or e-only; EUR2,194.80 institutions print incl. enhanced access. **Remarks:** Advertising accepted; rates available upon request. **URL:** http://www.springer.com/springerwiennewyork/physics/journal/723. **Circ:** (Not Reported)

46748 ■ Archive for History of Exact Sciences
Springer-Verlag Tokyo
No. 2, Funato Bldg.
1-11-11 Kudan-kita
Chiyoda-ku
Tokyo 102-0073, Japan
Ph: 81 368 317000
Fax: 81 368 317001
Publisher E-mail: info@springer.jp
Journal aiming to give rapid and full publication to writings of exceptional depth, scope, and permanence, covering mathematics and natural philosophy and experiment in the physical sciences. **Freq:** Bimonthly. **Key Personnel:** J.L. Berggren, Editorial Board, len_berggren@sfu.ca; J.J. Gray, Editor-in-Chief, j.j.gray@open.ac.uk. **ISSN:** 0003-9519. **Subscription Rates:** EUR1,071 institutions print incl. free access or e-only; EUR1,285.20 institutions print incl. enhanced access.

Remarks: Advertising accepted; rates available upon request. **URL:** http://www.springer.com/math/journal/407. **Circ:** (Not Reported)

46749 ■ Archives of Dermatological Research
Springer-Verlag Tokyo
No. 2, Funato Bldg.
1-11-11 Kudan-kita
Chiyoda-ku
Tokyo 102-0073, Japan
Ph: 81 368 317000
Fax: 81 368 317001
Publisher E-mail: info@springer.jp
Journal publishing original contributions in the field of experimental dermatology, including papers on biochemistry, morphology and immunology of the skin. **Freq:** 10/yr. **Key Personnel:** U. Mrowietz, Editor-in-Chief, umrowietz@dermatology.uni-kiel.de; J.T. Elder, Overseas Ed., jelder@umich.edu; Eun-So Lee, Overseas Ed., emorita@med.shimane-u.ac.jp. **ISSN:** 0340-3696. **Subscription Rates:** EUR1,581 institutions print incl. free access or e-only; EUR1,897.20 institutions print incl. enhanced access. **Remarks:** Advertising accepted; rates available upon request. **URL:** http://www.springer.com/medicine/dermatology/journal/403. **Circ:** (Not Reported)

46750 ■ Archives of Microbiology
Springer-Verlag Tokyo
No. 2, Funato Bldg.
1-11-11 Kudan-kita
Chiyoda-ku
Tokyo 102-0073, Japan
Ph: 81 368 317000
Fax: 81 368 317001
Publisher E-mail: info@springer.jp
Journal publishing papers on all areas of basic research in microbiology, particularly biochemical, molecular genetic, physiological, and/or physical investigations into microbial cells and their interactions with their environments, including their eukaryotic hosts. **Freq:** Bimonthly. **Key Personnel:** Erko Stackebrandt, Editor-in-Chief; Mary M. Allen, Editor; Pierre Beguin, Editor; Andreas Brune, Editor; Axel A. Brakhage, Editor; Timothy Donohue, Editor. **ISSN:** 0302-8933. **Subscription Rates:** EUR3,841 institutions print incl. free access or e-only; EUR4,609.20 institutions print incl. enhanced access. **Remarks:** Advertising accepted; rates available upon request. **URL:** http://www.springer.com/lifesci/microbiology/journal/203. **Circ:** (Not Reported)

46751 ■ Archives of Orthopaedic and Trauma Surgery
Springer-Verlag Tokyo
No. 2, Funato Bldg.
1-11-11 Kudan-kita
Chiyoda-ku
Tokyo 102-0073, Japan
Ph: 81 368 317000
Fax: 81 368 317001
Publisher E-mail: info@springer.jp
Journal for physicians in clinical practice and research in the extensive field of orthopedics and traumatology, publishing papers that deal with diseases and injuries of the musculoskeletal system from all fields and aspects of medicine. **Freq:** Monthly. **Key Personnel:** M. Blauth, Editor-in-Chief; J. Goldhahn, Editor-in-Chief. **ISSN:** 0936-8051. **Subscription Rates:** EUR3,021 institutions print incl. free access or e-only; EUR3,625.20 institutions print incl. enhanced access. **Remarks:** Advertising accepted; rates available upon request. **URL:** http://www.springer.com/medicine/orthopedics/journal/402. **Circ:** (Not Reported)

46752 ■ Archives of Toxicology
Springer-Verlag Tokyo
No. 2, Funato Bldg.
1-11-11 Kudan-kita
Chiyoda-ku
Tokyo 102-0073, Japan
Ph: 81 368 317000
Fax: 81 368 317001
Publisher E-mail: info@springer.jp
Journal providing up-to-date information on the latest advances in toxicology with particular emphasis on studies relating to defined effects of chemicals and mechanisms of toxicity, including toxic activities at the molecular level, in humans and experimental animals. **Freq:** Monthly. **Key Personnel:** J.G. Hengstler, Editor-in-Chief, archtox@ifado.de; E. Corsini, Advisory Ed.; M. Arand, Assoc. Ed. **ISSN:** 0340-5761. **Subscription Rates:** EUR3,375 institutions print incl. free access or e-only;

EUR4,050 institutions print incl. enhanced access. **Remarks:** Advertising accepted; rates available upon request. **URL:** http://www.springer.com/biomed/pharmaceuticalscience/journal/204. **Circ:** (Not Reported)

46753 ■ Asia Electronics Industry
Dempa Publications Inc.
1-11-15 Higashi Gotanda
Shinagawa-Ku
Tokyo 141-8715, Japan
Ph: 81 334 456111
Fax: 81 334 447515
Journal of electrical engineering. **Founded:** 1996. **Freq:** Monthly. **Subscription Rates:** Free to qualified readers in Asian region; US$150 individuals Asian & Pacific region; US$260 two years. **Remarks:** Advertising accepted; rates available upon request. **URL:** http://aei.dempa.net; http://aei.dempa.net/paidsub/index.html. **Circ:** 51,000

46754 ■ Asia Pacific Review
Taylor & Francis Group Journals
Institute for International Policy Studies
Tokyo, Japan
Publisher E-mail: customerservice@taylorandfrancis.com
Journal focusing on Asian business topics. **Freq:** Semiannual. **Key Personnel:** Terri Nii, Editor; Yoshio Okawara, Editorial Board; Ryukichi Imai, Editorial Board; Prof. Taizo Yakushiji, Editorial Dir.; Masahiko Aoki, International Advisory Board. **ISSN:** 1343-9006. **Subscription Rates:** 193 institutions print and online; 183 institutions online; 53 individuals; US$322 institutions print and online; US$305 institutions online; US$83 individuals; EUR257 institutions print and online; EUR244 institutions online only; EUR66 individuals. **URL:** http://www.tandf.co.uk/journals/titles/13439006.asp. **Circ:** (Not Reported)

46755 ■ Asian-Pacific Book Development
Asia-Pacific Cultural Centre for Unesco
6 Fukuro-Machi
Shinjuku-ku
Tokyo 162-8484, Japan
Ph: 81 332 694435
Fax: 81 332 694510
Publisher E-mail: general@accu.or.jp
Journal of publishing and trade. **Founded:** 1989. **Freq:** Quarterly. **Key Personnel:** Muneharu Kusaba, Editor-in-Chief. **ISSN:** 0916-7838. **URL:** http://www.accu.or.jp/. **Circ:** Paid 2,500

46756 ■ Astronomy and Astrophysics Review
Springer-Verlag Tokyo
No. 2, Funato Bldg.
1-11-11 Kudan-kita
Chiyoda-ku
Tokyo 102-0073, Japan
Ph: 81 368 317000
Fax: 81 368 317001
Publisher E-mail: info@springer.jp
Journal encompassing all areas of astronomy and astrophysics, including subjects bordering on other fields such as developments in atomic, molecular or particle physics directly relevant to astronomy, as well as cosmic ray physics, studies in the solar systems and computational procedures with specific astronomic applications. **Freq:** Quarterly. **Key Personnel:** Thierry J.L. Courvoisier, Editor-in-Chief, thierry.courvoisier@obs.unige.ch; Martin C.E. Huber, Editor; Jean Surdej, Editor; Raffaela Morganti, Editor; Michael Perryman, Editor; Andreas Quirrenbach, Editor. **ISSN:** 0935-4956. **Subscription Rates:** EUR401 institutions print incl. free access or e-only; EUR481.20 institutions print incl. enhanced access. **Remarks:** Advertising accepted; rates available upon request. **URL:** http://www.springer.com/astronomy/astrophysics/journal/159. **Circ:** (Not Reported)

46757 ■ Atoms in Japan
Japan Atomic Industrial Forum
Dai-ichi Chojiya Bldg. 5th Fl.
1-2-13, Shiba-daimon
Minato-ku
Tokyo 105-8605, Japan
Ph: 81 3 57770750
Fax: 81 3 57770760
Journal of nuclear energy. **Founded:** 1957. **Freq:** Monthly. **Key Personnel:** Kazuhisa Mori, Editor-in-Chief; Nobuo Ishizuka, Editor; Toshimasa Mizukami, Editor. **ISSN:** 0403-9319. **Subscription Rates:** 58,000¥

individuals; US$350 other countries. **URL:** http://www.jaif.or.jp.

46758 ■ Axis
Axis Inc.
5-17-1 Roppongi
Minato-ku
Tokyo 106-0032, Japan
Ph: 81 3 35872781
Magazine covering interior decoration and design. **Subtitle:** World Design Journal. **Founded:** 1947. **Freq:** Bimonthly. **URL:** http://www.axisinc.co.jp.

46759 ■ Be Love
Kodansha Ltd.
2-12-21 Otowa
Bunkyo-ku
Tokyo 112-8001, Japan
Ph: 81 3 3946 6201
Fax: 81 3 3944 9915
Comic magazine featuring drama and romance for mature women. **Freq:** Semimonthly. **Key Personnel:** Sawako Noma, President. **URL:** http://www.kodansha.co.jp/english/manga/magazines.html.

46760 ■ Be Love Parfait
Kodansha Ltd.
2-12-21 Otowa
Bunkyo-ku
Tokyo 112-8001, Japan
Ph: 81 3 3946 6201
Fax: 81 3 3944 9915
Comic magazine featuring stories about married couples and tackles the problems that can occur between wives and mothers-in-law, whether or not they are living under the same roof. **Freq:** Monthly. **Key Personnel:** Sawako Noma, President. **URL:** http://www.kodansha.co.jp/english/manga/magazines.html.

46761 ■ Bessatsu Friend
Kodansha Ltd.
2-12-21 Otowa
Bunkyo-ku
Tokyo 112-8001, Japan
Ph: 81 3 3946 6201
Fax: 81 3 3944 9915
Comic magazine for teenage girls featuring love stories about modern, upbeat, and cheerful highschoolers. **Freq:** Monthly. **Key Personnel:** Sawako Noma, President. **URL:** http://www.kodansha.co.jp/english/manga/magazines.html.

46762 ■ Big Comic Original
Shogakukan Inc.
2-3-1, Hitotsubashi
Chiyoda-ku
Tokyo 101-8001, Japan
Entertainment comic magazine. **Founded:** Feb. 18, 1974. **Freq:** Bimonthly. **Key Personnel:** Masahiro Oga, President. **Subscription Rates:** 260¥ individuals. **URL:** http://big-3.jp/.

46763 ■ Big Comic Spirits
Shogakukan Inc.
2-3-1, Hitotsubashi
Chiyoda-ku
Tokyo 101-8001, Japan
Entertainment comic magazine. **Founded:** Oct. 14, 1980. **Freq:** Weekly (Mon.). **Key Personnel:** Masahiro Oga, President. **Subscription Rates:** 260¥ individuals. **URL:** http://www.shogakukan.co.jp/english/.

46764 ■ Biological & Pharmaceutical Bulletin
Pharmaceutical Society of Japan
The Pharmaceutical Society of Japan
2-12-15, Shibuya
Shibuya-ku
Tokyo 150-0002, Japan
Ph: 81 334 063325
Fax: 81 334 981835
Publication E-mail: ronb@pharm.or.jp
Publisher E-mail: doi@pharm.or.jp
Journal covering a wide spectrum of subjects in chemistry such as physical and inorganic chemistry, organic chemistry, natural products chemistry, medicinal chemistry, analytical chemistry, pharmacognosy, and physical pharmacy. **Founded:** 1993. **Key Personnel:** Susumu Kobayashi, Editor-in-Chief; Hidetoshi Arakawa, Editor; Isao Fujii, Editor; Yoshiyasu Fukuyama, Editor; Shinji Funayama, Editor. **ISSN:** 0918-6158. **Subscription**

Circulation: ★ = ABC; △ = BPA; ◆ = CAC; ● = CCAB; ❏ = VAC; ⊕ = PO Statement; ‡ = Publisher's Report; Boldface figures = sworn; Light figures = estimated.

Gale Directory of Publications & Broadcast Media/147th Ed.   5105

Rates: US$125 members surface mail; US$80 members air mail postage. **URL:** http://cpb.pharm.or.jp/; http://bpb.pharm.or.jp/.

46765 ■ Biology and Fertility of Soils
Springer-Verlag Tokyo
No. 2, Funato Bldg.
1-11-11 Kudan-kita
Chiyoda-ku
Tokyo 102-0073, Japan
Ph: 81 368 317000
Fax: 81 368 317001
Publisher E-mail: info@springer.jp
Journal publishing original papers, reviews and short communications on all fundamental and applied aspects of biology (microflora and microfauna) and fertility (productivity) of soils. **Freq:** 8/yr. **Key Personnel:** Paolo Nannipieri, Editor-in-Chief, fax 39 55 333273, paolo.nannipieri@unifi.it; Johannes C.G. Ottow, Founding Ed.; Giacomo Pietramellara, Editorial Mgr., pietra1@unifi.it; Kazuyuki Inubushi, Regional Ed., inubushi@faculty.chiba-u.jp; Jagdish K. Ladha, Regional Ed., j.k.ladha@cgiar.org. **ISSN:** 0178-2762. **Subscription Rates:** EUR1,878 institutions print incl. free access or e-only; EUR2,253.60 institutions print incl. enhanced access. **Remarks:** Advertising accepted; rates available upon request. **URL:** http://www.springer.com/lifesci/agriculture/journal/374. **Circ:** (Not Reported)

46766 ■ Biomechanics and Modeling in Mechanobiology
Springer-Verlag Tokyo
No. 2, Funato Bldg.
1-11-11 Kudan-kita
Chiyoda-ku
Tokyo 102-0073, Japan
Ph: 81 368 317000
Fax: 81 368 317001
Publisher E-mail: info@springer.jp
Journal promoting basic and applied research that integrates the expanding knowledge-bases in the allied fields of biomechanics and mechanobiology using approaches that are experimental, theoretical, or computational, addressing phenomena at the nano, micro, or macro levels. **Freq:** 6/yr. **Key Personnel:** Gerhard A. Holzapfel, Editor-in-Chief, holzapfel@tugraz.at; Jay D. Humphrey, Editor-in-Chief, jhumphrey@tamu.edu; Peter J. Hunter, Editorial Board, p.hunter@auckland.ac.nz; Timothy J. Pedley, Editorial Board, t.j.pedley@damtp.cam.ac.uk; Stephen C. Cowin, Editorial Board, scowin@earthlink.net; Thomas J.R. Hughes, Editorial Board, hughes@ices.utexas.edu; Gerard A. Ateshian, Editorial Board, ateshian@columbia.edu; Kozaburo Hayashi, Editorial Board, khayashi@bme.ous.ac.jp; Roger D. Kamm, Editorial Board, rdkamm@mit.edu. **ISSN:** 1617-7959. **Subscription Rates:** EUR540 institutions print incl. free access or e-only; EUR648 institutions print incl. enhanced access. **Remarks:** Advertising accepted; rates available upon request. **URL:** http://www.springer.com/new%26forthcomingtitles%28default%29/journal/10237. **Circ:** (Not Reported)

46767 ■ Bioscience, Biotechnology, and Biochemistry
Japan Society for Bioscience, Biotechnology and Agrochemistry
Gakkai Ctr. Bldg.
2-4-16 Yayoi
Bunkyo-ku
Tokyo 113-0032, Japan
Ph: 81 3 38118789
Fax: 81 3 38151920
Publication E-mail: henshu@jsbba.or.jp
Publisher E-mail: imudaihyo@jsbba.or.jp
Journal covering biology. **Founded:** 1992. **Freq:** Monthly. **ISSN:** 0916-8451. **Remarks:** Advertising accepted; rates available upon request. **URL:** http://www.jsbba.or.jp/e/e_03/bbb_e.html. **Circ:** Paid 3,600

46768 ■ Brain Tumor Pathology
Springer-Verlag Tokyo
No. 2, Funato Bldg.
1-11-11 Kudan-kita
Chiyoda-ku
Tokyo 102-0073, Japan
Ph: 81 368 317000
Fax: 81 368 317001
Publisher E-mail: info@springer.jp
Medical science journal. **Founded:** 1983. **Freq:** Semiannual. **Key Personnel:** Kintomo Takakura, Honorary Ed.; Yoichi Nakazato, Editor-in-Chief; Hayato Ikota,

Managing Editor; Takanori Hirose, Editorial Board; Takamasa Kayama, Editorial Board; Soichiro Shibui, Editorial Board; Junichi Kuratsu, Editorial Board; Toru Iwaki, Assoc. Ed.; Toshihiko Wakabayashi, Editorial Board; Teiji Tominaga, Editorial Board; Toshiki Yoshimine, Editorial Board; Masato Abe, Editorial Board. **ISSN:** 1433-7398. **Subscription Rates:** EUR148 institutions print incl. free access or e-only; EUR177.60 institutions enhanced access. **Remarks:** Accepts advertising. **URL:** http://www.springer.com/medicine/oncology/journal/10014. **Circ:** (Not Reported)

46769 ■ Bulletin of the Chemical Society of Japan
Chemical Society of Japan
1-5 Kanda-Surugadai
Chiyoda-Ku
Tokyo 101-8307, Japan
Ph: 81 332 926161
Fax: 81 332 926318
Publisher E-mail: info@chemistry.or.jp
Journal devoted to research in theoretical and physical chemistry, analytical and inorganic chemistry, organic and biological chemistry, and applied and materials chemistry. **Freq:** Monthly. **Key Personnel:** Kohei Tamao, Editor-in-Chief; Akira Harada, Sen. Assoc. Ed.; Tatsuo Arai, Assoc. Ed. **ISSN:** 0009-2673. **Subscription Rates:** 10,200¥ individuals; 72,000¥ individuals corporate; US$143 other countries; US$1,200 other countries. **Remarks:** Accepts advertising. **URL:** http://www.csj.jp/csj-en/journals/bcsj.html. **Circ:** ‡37,200

46770 ■ Bulletin of Engineering Geology and the Environment
Springer-Verlag Tokyo
No. 2, Funato Bldg.
1-11-11 Kudan-kita
Chiyoda-ku
Tokyo 102-0073, Japan
Ph: 81 368 317000
Fax: 81 368 317001
Publisher E-mail: info@springer.jp
Journal promoting and encouraging the advancement of engineering geology through technological activities and research; improving teaching and training in engineering geology; and collecting, evaluating and disseminating the results of engineering geological activities on a world wide basis. **Freq:** Quarterly. **Key Personnel:** Brian A. Hawkins, Editor-in-Chief, phone 44 117 9251880, fax 44 117 9273994, brian_hawkins@btconnect.com; Dr. Fred Baynes, President, fredb@iinet.net.au; M. Trott, Asst. to the Ed.-in-Ch.; R. Cojean, Co-Ed., cojean@cgi.ensmp.fr; H. Chen, Editorial Board, hchen@ntu.edu.tw; Jean-Louis Durville, Editorial Board, jean-louis durville@equipement.gouv.fr. **ISSN:** 1435-9529. **Subscription Rates:** EUR580 institutions print incl. free access or e-only; EUR636 institutions print incl. enhanced access. **Remarks:** Advertising accepted; rates available upon request. **URL:** http://www.springer.com/earthsciences/journal/10064. **Circ:** (Not Reported)

46771 ■ Bulletin of Volcanology
Springer-Verlag Tokyo
No. 2, Funato Bldg.
1-11-11 Kudan-kita
Chiyoda-ku
Tokyo 102-0073, Japan
Ph: 81 368 317000
Fax: 81 368 317001
Publication E-mail: bulvolc@eps.mcgill.ca
Publisher E-mail: info@springer.jp
Journal publishing papers on volcanoes, their products, their eruptive behavior, and their hazards. **Freq:** 8/yr. **Key Personnel:** James DL. White, Exec. Dir., bull.volc@otago.ac.nz; M.A. Clynne, Assoc. Ed., mclynne@usgs.gov. **ISSN:** 0258-8900. **Subscription Rates:** EUR1,635 institutions print or online; EUR1,962 institutions print & enhanced access. **Remarks:** Advertising accepted; rates available upon request. **URL:** http://www.springer.com/earthsciencesandgeography/geology/journal/445. **Circ:** (Not Reported)

46772 ■ Calcolo
Springer-Verlag Tokyo
No. 2, Funato Bldg.
1-11-11 Kudan-kita
Chiyoda-ku
Tokyo 102-0073, Japan
Ph: 81 368 317000
Fax: 81 368 317001
Publisher E-mail: info@springer.jp
Journal publishing original contributions on numerical

analysis and its applications, and on the theory of computation. **Freq:** Quarterly. **Key Personnel:** Bruno Codenotti, Managing Editor; Dario Bini, Editor; Sebastiano Seatzu, Editor. **ISSN:** 0008-0624. **Subscription Rates:** EUR166 institutions print incl. free access or e-only; EUR199.20 institutions print incl. enhanced access. **Remarks:** Advertising accepted; rates available upon request. **URL:** http://www.springer.com/math/cse/journal/10092. **Circ:** (Not Reported)

46773 ■ Calculus of Variations and Partial Differential Equation
Springer-Verlag Tokyo
No. 2, Funato Bldg.
1-11-11 Kudan-kita
Chiyoda-ku
Tokyo 102-0073, Japan
Ph: 81 368 317000
Fax: 81 368 317001
Publisher E-mail: info@springer.jp
Journal publishing many of the important top-quality contributions to the field of calculus and the closely related areas of differential geometry and mathematical physics, stressing the interactions between analysts, geometers, and physicists. **Freq:** Quarterly. **Key Personnel:** Gerhard Huisken, Managing Editor, gerhard.huisken@aei.mpg.de; L. Ambrosio, Managing Editor, luigi@ambrosio.sns.it; S.Y.A. Chang, Editorial Board, chang@math.princeton.edu; L.C. Evans, Editorial Board, evans@math.berkeley.edu; H. Brezis, Editorial Board, brezis@ann.jussieu.fr; A. Malchiodi, Managing Editor, malchiod@sissa.it; Y. Giga, Editorial Board, jourgiga@ms.u-tokyo.ac.jp; J.M. Ball, Editorial Board, ball@maths.ox.ac.uk. **ISSN:** 0944-2669. **Subscription Rates:** EUR878 institutions print incl. free access or e-only; EUR1,053.60 institutions print incl. enhanced access. **Remarks:** Advertising accepted; rates available upon request. **URL:** http://www.springer.com/math/analysis/journal/526. **Circ:** (Not Reported)

46774 ■ Calorimetry and Thermal Analysis
Japan Society of Calorimetry and Thermal Analysis
Miyazawa Bldg. 601
1-6-7 Iwamoto-chyo
Chiyoda-ku
Tokyo 101-0032, Japan
Fax: 81 3 58217439
Publisher E-mail: netsu@mbd.nifty.com
Publishes the original papers, short notes, review articles, lectures, commentary and other various information for calorimetry and thermal analysis and its related fields. **Founded:** 1974. **Freq:** Quarterly. **ISSN:** 0386-2615. **URL:** http://wwwsoc.nii.ac.jp/jscta/e/society_4.html.

46775 ■ Cambridge Journal of Regions, Economy & Society
Oxford University Press
4-5-10-8F Shiba, Minato-ku
Tokyo 108-8386, Japan
Ph: 81 3 54445858
Fax: 81 3 34542929
Journal covering research on changes and developments in regions, economy and society. **Freq:** 3/yr. **Key Personnel:** Susan Christopherson, Editorial Board. **ISSN:** 1752-1378. **Subscription Rates:** 66 institutions; US$132 institutions; EUR99 institutions; 13 individuals; US$27 individuals; EUR20 individuals; EUR83 individuals corporate subscribers; US$165 individuals corporate subscribers; EUR124 individuals corporate subscribers. **Remarks:** Accepts advertising. **URL:** http://cjres.oxfordjournals.org/. **Circ:** (Not Reported)

46776 ■ CanCam
Shogakukan Inc.
2-3-1, Hitotsubashi
Chiyoda-ku
Tokyo 101-8001, Japan
Fashion magazine for women. **Founded:** Oct. 23, 1981. **Freq:** Monthly. **Key Personnel:** Masahiro Oga, President. **Subscription Rates:** 600¥ individuals. **URL:** http://cancam.tv/index.html.

46777 ■ Cancer Chemotherapy and Pharmacology
Springer-Verlag Tokyo
No. 2, Funato Bldg.
1-11-11 Kudan-kita
Chiyoda-ku
Tokyo 102-0073, Japan
Ph: 81 368 317000
Fax: 81 368 317001

Publisher E-mail: info@springer.jp

Journal addressing a wide range of pharmacologic and oncologic concerns on both experimental and clinical levels with the primary focus on new anticancer agents, their experimental screening, preclinical toxicology and pharmacology, single and combined drug administration modalities, and clinical phase I, II and III trials. **Freq:** Bimonthly. **Key Personnel:** D.R. Newell, Editor-in-Chief, phone 44 191 2228057, fax 44 191 2227556, herbie. newell@ncl.ac.uk; M.J. Egorin, Editor-in-Chief, phone 412623-3252, fax 412623-1212, egorinmj@msx.upmc. edu. **ISSN:** 0344-5704. **Subscription Rates:** EUR4,540 institutions print incl. free access or e-only; EUR5,448 institutions print incl. enhanced access. **Remarks:** Advertising accepted; rates available upon request. **URL:** http://www.springer.com/biomed/cancer/journal/ 280. **Circ:** (Not Reported)

46778 ■ Cancer Immunology, Immunotherapy
Springer-Verlag Tokyo
No. 2, Funato Bldg.
1-11-11 Kudan-kita
Chiyoda-ku
Tokyo 102-0073, Japan
Ph: 81 368 317000
Fax: 81 368 317001
Publisher E-mail: info@springer.jp
Journal for tumor immunologists, clinical oncologists, virologists, and medical microbiologists involved in the development of methods of treatment and therapies for cancer patientsm, providing a forum for the most recent experimental and clinical advances in tumor immunology. **Freq:** Monthly. **Key Personnel:** G. Pawelec, Editor-in-Chief, cii.pawelec@t-online.de; Enrico Mihich, Editor-in-Chief, enrico.mihich@roswellpark.org; A. Anichini, Editorial Board. **ISSN:** 0340-7004. **Subscription Rates:** EUR4,150 institutions print incl. free access or e-only; EUR4,980 institutions print incl. enhanced access. **Remarks:** Advertising accepted; rates available upon request. **URL:** http://www.springer.com/biomed/cancer/ journal/262. **Circ:** (Not Reported)

46779 ■ Capital Markets Law Journal
Oxford University Press
4-5-10-8F Shiba, Minato-ku
Tokyo 108-8386, Japan
Ph: 81 3 54445858
Fax: 81 3 34542929
Peer-reviewed Journal covering on aspects related to capital markets including debt, derivatives, equity, high yield products, securitization, and repackaging. **Founded:** 1978. **Freq:** Monthly. **Print Method:** Offset. Uses mats. **Cols./Page:** 3. **Col. Width:** 28 nonpareils. **Col. Depth:** 135 agate lines. **Key Personnel:** Jeffrey Golden, Gen. Ed.; Lachlan Burn, Gen. Ed. **ISSN:** 1750-7219. **Subscription Rates:** 525 institutions print and online; US$1,050 institutions print and online; EUR788 institutions print and online; 127 individuals; US$254 individuals; EUR191 individuals; 40 single issue; US$79 single issue; EUR60 single issue. **URL:** http://cmlj. oxfordjournals.org/.

46780 ■ Cellular and Molecular Life Sciences
Springer-Verlag Tokyo
No. 2, Funato Bldg.
1-11-11 Kudan-kita
Chiyoda-ku
Tokyo 102-0073, Japan
Ph: 81 368 317000
Fax: 81 368 317001
Publisher E-mail: info@springer.jp
Peer-reviewed journal covering all aspects of biological and biomedical research, focusing on molecular and cellular aspects of biomedicine, cell biology, immunology, molecular genetics, neuroscience, biochemistry, pharmacology and physiology related to pharmacology. **Freq:** Biweekly. **Key Personnel:** Klaus Eichmann, Editor-in-Chief; F. Hucho, Editorial Board; Johannes Korn, Managing Editor. **ISSN:** 1420-682X. **Subscription Rates:** EUR3,406 institutions; EUR4,087.20 institutions enhanced access. **Remarks:** Advertising accepted; rates available upon request. **URL:** http://www.springer. com/birkhauser/biosciences/journal/18. **Circ:** (Not Reported)

46781 ■ Central European Journal of Operations Research
Springer-Verlag Tokyo
No. 2, Funato Bldg.
1-11-11 Kudan-kita
Chiyoda-ku
Tokyo 102-0073, Japan

Ph: 81 368 317000
Fax: 81 368 317001
Publisher E-mail: info@springer.jp
Journal focusing on topics such as: finance and banking, measuring productivity and efficiency in the public sector, environmental and energy issues, computational tools for strategic decision support, production management and logistics and planning and scheduling. **Freq:** Quarterly. **Key Personnel:** Ulrike Leopold-Wildburger, Editor-in-Chief, ulrlke.leopold@uni-graz.at; Georg Pflug, Editor-in-Chief, georg.pflug@univie.ac.at; Rudolf Vetschera, Editor-in-Chief, rudolf.vetschera@univie.ac. at. **ISSN:** 1435-246X. **Subscription Rates:** EUR314 institutions print incl. free access or e-only; EUR376.80 institutions print incl. enhanced access. **Remarks:** Advertising accepted; rates available upon request. **URL:** http://www.springer.com/business/ operationsresearch/journal/10100. **Circ:** (Not Reported)

46782 ■ Chem-Bio Informatics Journal
Chem-Bio Informatics Society
Iida Bldg., Rm. 301
4-3-16, Yoga
Setagaya-ku
Tokyo 158-0097, Japan
Ph: 81 3 54915423
Fax: 81 3 54915462
Publisher E-mail: cbitaff@cbi-society.org
Journal of the Chem-Bio Informatics Society. **Freq:** Quarterly. **Key Personnel:** Yoshiro Nakata, Exec. Ed.; Masafumi Yohda, Editor-in-Chief. **ISSN:** 1347-6297. **URL:** http://www.cbi.or.jp/cbi/englishindex.html.

46783 ■ Chemical & Pharmaceutical Bulletin
Pharmaceutical Society of Japan
12-15 Shibuya 2-chome
Shibuya-Ku
Tokyo 150-0002, Japan
Fax: 81 334 981835
Publisher E-mail: doi@pharm.or.jp
Journal covering all areas of the pharmaceutical sciences and chemistry. **Freq:** Monthly. **Key Personnel:** Hideaki Otsuka, Editor; Hidetoshi Arakawa, Editor; Mukund P. Sibi, Editor; Hisao Nakai, Editor; Yukinobu Ikeya, Editor; Hiroshi Kogen, Editor; Henli B. Kagan, Editor; Susumu Kobayashi, Editor-in-Chief; Shigeru Itai, Editor; Toshimasa Ishida, Editor. **ISSN:** 0009-2363. **Subscription Rates:** US$125 individuals surface mail; US$80 individuals additional air mail postage. **URL:** http://cpb.pharm.or.jp/.

46784 ■ Child's Nervous System
Springer-Verlag Tokyo
No. 2, Funato Bldg.
1-11-11 Kudan-kita
Chiyoda-ku
Tokyo 102-0073, Japan
Ph: 81 368 317000
Fax: 81 368 317001
Publisher E-mail: info@springer.jp
Journal encompassing all aspects of the pediatric neurosciences: development and growth, degenerative disorders, hereditary diseases, neurology, neurosurgery, neurooncology, neurophysiology, and trauma. **Freq:** Monthly. **Key Personnel:** C.D. Rocco, Editor; R. Abbott, Assoc. Ed.; N. Akalan, Assoc. Ed. **ISSN:** 0256-7040. **Subscription Rates:** EUR2,843 institutions print incl. free access or e-only; EUR3,411.60 institutions print incl. enhanced access. **Remarks:** Advertising accepted; rates available upon request. **URL:** http://www.springer. com/medicine/surgery/journal/381. **Circ:** (Not Reported)

46785 ■ Chromatographia
Springer-Verlag Tokyo
No. 2, Funato Bldg.
1-11-11 Kudan-kita
Chiyoda-ku
Tokyo 102-0073, Japan
Ph: 81 368 317000
Fax: 81 368 317001
Publisher E-mail: info@springer.jp
Journal promoting the rapid communication of new techniques and developments in the field of analytical chemistry. **Founded:** 1968. **Freq:** Monthly. **Key Personnel:** T.A. Berger, Editor, tabergersfc@aol.com; H. Lingeman, Editor, h.lingeman@few.vu.nl; G. Massolini, Editor, g.massolini@unipv.it. **ISSN:** 0009-5893. **Subscription Rates:** EUR1,989.72 institutions print incl. free access or e-only; EUR2,387.66 institutions print incl. enhanced access. **Remarks:** Advertising accepted; rates available upon request. **URL:** http://www.springer.com/chemistry/

analytical/journal/10337. **Circ:** (Not Reported)

46786 ■ ClassNK Magazine
Nippon Kaiji Kyokai
4-7 Kioi-cho
Chiyoda-ku
Tokyo 102-8567, Japan
Ph: 81 332 301201
Fax: 81 352 262012
Publisher E-mail: bnd@classnk.or.jp
Magazine covering marine industries. **Freq:** Annual. **Key Personnel:** Kenji Ogawa, Chm. and Pres. **URL:** http:// www.classnk.or.jp/hp/publications/pub_top.asp.

46787 ■ Clean Technologies and Environmental Policy
Springer-Verlag Tokyo
No. 2, Funato Bldg.
1-11-11 Kudan-kita
Chiyoda-ku
Tokyo 102-0073, Japan
Ph: 81 368 317000
Fax: 81 368 317001
Publisher E-mail: info@springer.jp
Journal with two major thrusts: clean technologies and environmental policy, creating an international forum for discussing the science and engineering of technologies, and mathematical and computer-based methods and models for designing, analyzing, and measuring cleanliness of products and processes. **Freq:** Bimonthly. **Key Personnel:** Subhas K. Sikdar, Editor-in-Chief, sikdar. subhas@epa.gov; Ravi Jain, Editor-in-Chief, rjain@uop. edu; Masaki Hosomi, Assoc. Ed., hosomi@cc.tuat.ac.jp; Adisa Azapagic, Editorial Board, adisa.azapagic@ manchester.ac.uk; Earl Beaver, Editorial Board, erbeav@aol.com; Eric Beckman, Editorial Board, eric@ engr.pitts.edu; Asher Brenner, Editorial Board, brenner@ bgu.ac.il; Anil Dikshit, Editorial Board, akd_iit@yaoo.co. in; John Glaser, News Ed., glaser.john@epa.gov. **ISSN:** 1618-954X. **Subscription Rates:** EUR442 institutions print incl. free access or e-only; EUR530.40 institutions print incl. enhanced access. **Remarks:** Advertising accepted; rates available upon request. **URL:** http://www. springer.com/environment/sustainabledevelopment/ journal/10098. **Circ:** (Not Reported)

46788 ■ Clinical Autonomic Research
Springer-Verlag Tokyo
No. 2, Funato Bldg.
1-11-11 Kudan-kita
Chiyoda-ku
Tokyo 102-0073, Japan
Ph: 81 368 317000
Fax: 81 368 317001
Publisher E-mail: info@springer.jp
Journal aiming to draw together and disseminate research work from various disciplines and specialties dealing with clinical problems resulting from autonomic dysfunction, including cardiovascular system, neurology, diabetes, endocrinology, urology, pain disorders, ophthalmology, gastroenterology, toxicology and clinical pharmacology, skin infectious diseases, renal disease. **Freq:** Bimonthly. **Key Personnel:** Horacio Kaufmann, Editor-in-Chief; Christopher J. Mathias, Editor-in-Chief; Jose Martinez, Managing Editor; I. Biaggioni, Editorial Board; M. Chapleau, Editorial Board; M.J. Aminoff, Editorial Board; F. Axelrod, Editorial Board; K. Abe, Editorial Board; G. Burnstock, Editorial Board. **ISSN:** 0959-9851. **Subscription Rates:** EUR1,409 institutions print incl. free access or e-only; EUR1,690.80 institutions print incl. enhanced access. **Remarks:** Advertising accepted; rates available upon request. **URL:** http://www. springer.com/steinkopff/neurologie/journal/10286. **Circ:** (Not Reported)

46789 ■ Clinical and Experimental Nephrology
Springer-Verlag Tokyo
No. 2, Funato Bldg.
1-11-11 Kudan-kita
Chiyoda-ku
Tokyo 102-0073, Japan
Ph: 81 368 317000
Fax: 81 368 317001
Publisher E-mail: info@springer.jp
Peer-reviewed journal covering the study of nephrology. **Founded:** 1997. **Freq:** Quarterly. **Key Personnel:** Tatsuo Sakai, Co-Ed.-in-Ch.; Kenjiro Kimura, Editor-in-Chief; Hirofumi Makino, Consulting Ed.; Eiji Kusano, Consulting Ed.; Tsuyoshi Watanabe, Consulting Ed.; Kota Takahashi, Consulting Ed. **ISSN:** 1342-1751. **Subscription Rates:** US$234 institutions print incl. free ac-

Circulation: ★ = ABC; △ = BPA; ♦ = CAC; • = CCAB; ❏ = VAC; ⊕ = PO Statement; ‡ = Publisher's Report; Boldface figures = sworn; Light figures = estimated.

Gale Directory of Publications & Broadcast Media/147th Ed.   5107

cess or e-only; US$280.80 institutions enhanced access. **Remarks:** Accepts advertising. **URL:** http://www. springer.com/medicine/nephrology/journal/10157. **Circ:** (Not Reported)

46790 ■ Computational Complexity
Springer-Verlag Tokyo
No. 2, Funato Bldg.
1-11-11 Kudan-kita
Chiyoda-ku
Tokyo 102-0073, Japan
Ph: 81 368 317000
Fax: 81 368 317001
Publisher E-mail: info@springer.jp
Journal presenting research in computational complexity which is a subject at the interface between mathematics and theoretical computer science, with a clear mathematical profile and strictly mathematical format. **Founded:** 1991. **Freq:** Quarterly. **Key Personnel:** Joachim Von Zur Gathen, Editor-in-Chief, gathen@bit. uni-bonn.de; Peter Burgisser, Assoc. Ed., pbuerg@upb. de; Sanjeev Arora, Assoc. Ed., arora@cs.princeton.edu. **ISSN:** 1016-3328. **Subscription Rates:** EUR488 institutions print incl. free access or e-only; EUR585.60 institutions print incl. enhanced access. **Remarks:** Advertising accepted; rates available upon request. **URL:** http:// www.springer.com/birkhauser/computerscience/journal/ 37. **Circ:** (Not Reported)

46791 ■ Computational Mechanics
Springer-Verlag Tokyo
No. 2, Funato Bldg.
1-11-11 Kudan-kita
Chiyoda-ku
Tokyo 102-0073, Japan
Ph: 81 368 317000
Fax: 81 368 317001
Publisher E-mail: info@springer.jp
Journal reporting original research of scholarly value and of reasonable permanence in those areas of computational mechanics which involve and enrich the rational application of mechanics, mathematics, and numerical methods in the practice of modern engineering. **Freq:** Bimonthly. **Key Personnel:** Peter Wriggers, Editor-in-Chief, wriggers@ibnm.uni-hannover. de; C. Felippa, Advisory Board; M. Bonnet, Advisory Board; F. Brezzi, Advisory Board; D.E. Beskos, Editor, d.e.beskos@upatras.gr; K.J. Bathe, Advisory Board; D. Peric, Advisory Board; T. Belytschko, Advisory Board; W.K. Liu, Editor, w-liu@northwestern.edu; O. Allix, Advisory Board. **ISSN:** 0178-7675. **Subscription Rates:** EUR3,459 institutions print incl. free access or e-only; EUR4,150.80 institutions print incl. enhanced access. **Remarks:** Advertising accepted; rates available upon request. **URL:** http://www.springer.com/ new%26forthcomingtitles%28default%29/journal/466. **Circ:** (Not Reported)

46792 ■ Computational Statistics
Springer-Verlag Tokyo
No. 2, Funato Bldg.
1-11-11 Kudan-kita
Chiyoda-ku
Tokyo 102-0073, Japan
Ph: 81 368 317000
Fax: 81 368 317001
Publisher E-mail: info@springer.jp
Journal providing a forum for computer scientists, mathematicians, and statisticians in a variety of fields of statistics such as biometrics, econometrics, data analysis, graphics, simulation, algorithms, knowledge based systems, and Bayesian computing, promoting the publication of applications and methodological research in the field of Computational Statistics. **Freq:** Quarterly. **Key Personnel:** W.K. Fung, Assoc. Ed.; M.C. Minnotte, Assoc. Ed.; J. Antoch, Assoc. Ed.; S. Bengio, Assoc. Ed.; Jurgen Symanzik, Editor, symanzik@math.usu.edu; C. Agostinelli, Assoc. Ed.; L. Bauwens, Assoc. Ed.; Friedrich Leisch, Editor-in-Chief, cost@stat.uni-muenchen.de; Esposito V. Vinzi, Assoc. Ed.; Yuichi Mori, Editor, mori@soci.ous.ac.jp. **ISSN:** 0943-4062. **Subscription Rates:** EUR622 institutions print incl. free access or e-only; EUR746.40 institutions print incl. enhanced access. **Remarks:** Advertising accepted; rates available upon request. **URL:** http://www.springer.com/ statistics/journal/180. **Circ:** (Not Reported)

46793 ■ Computing Japan
Japan Incorporated Communications K.K.
Minami-Aoyama 1st Bldg., 10th Fl.
7-8-1 Minami Aoyama, Minato-Ku
Tokyo 107-0062, Japan

Ph: 81 334 992099
Fax: 81 334 993109
Publication E-mail: cjmaster@cjmag.co.jp
Publisher E-mail: info@japaninc.com
Online journal of computers. **Founded:** 1999. **Freq:** Monthly. **Key Personnel:** Daniel Scuka, Managing Editor, daniel@cjmag.co.jp; Terrie Lloyd, Publisher, terrie@ cjmag.co.jp; Robert Jamison, Assoc. Publisher, robert@ cjmag.co.jp. **Remarks:** Accepts advertising. **URL:** http:// www.japaninc.com/cpj/index.html. **Ad Rates:** BW: 385,000¥, 4C: 550,000¥. **Circ:** (Not Reported)

46794 ■ Computing and Visualization in Science
Springer-Verlag Tokyo
No. 2, Funato Bldg.
1-11-11 Kudan-kita
Chiyoda-ku
Tokyo 102-0073, Japan
Ph: 81 368 317000
Fax: 81 368 317001
Publisher E-mail: info@springer.jp
Journal for scientists eager to cooperate in solving scientific and technological challenges, devoted to computational sciences. **Freq:** 8/yr. **Key Personnel:** Gabriel Wittum, Managing Editor; Peter Deuflhard, Editorial Board, deuflhard@zib.de; Rainer Helmig, Editorial Board, rainer.helmig@iws.uni-stuttgart.de; Randolph E. Bank, Editorial Board, rbank@ucsd.edu; Miloslav Feistauer, Editorial Board, feist@ms.mff.cuni.cz. **ISSN:** 1432-9360. **Subscription Rates:** EUR597 institutions print incl. free access or e-only; EUR716.40 institutions print incl. enhanced access. **Remarks:** Advertising accepted; rates available upon request. **URL:** http://www. springer.com/math/cse/journal/791. **Circ:** (Not Reported)

46795 ■ Concrete Library International
Japan Society of Civil Engineers
Yotsuya 1-Chome
Shinjuku-Ku
Tokyo 160-0004, Japan
Ph: 81 3 33553452
Fax: 81 3 53592769
Journal covering civil engineering. **Founded:** 1983. **Freq:** Semiannual. **Key Personnel:** Tetsuo Harada, Chm. **ISSN:** 0913-4913. **Subscription Rates:** US$80 individuals. **URL:** http://www.jsce.or.jp/publication/e/ book/c_l_i.html.

46796 ■ Continuum Mechanics and Thermodynamics
Springer-Verlag Tokyo
No. 2, Funato Bldg.
1-11-11 Kudan-kita
Chiyoda-ku
Tokyo 102-0073, Japan
Ph: 81 368 317000
Fax: 81 368 317001
Publisher E-mail: info@springer.jp
Journal providing a forum for presenting new ideas in continuum and quasi-continuum modeling of systems with a large number of degrees of freedom and sufficient complexity to require thermodynamic closure with major emphasis placed on papers attempting to bridge the gap between discrete and continuum approaches as well as micro- and macro-scales, by means of homogenization, statistical averaging and other mathematical tools aimed at the judicial elimination of small time and length scales. **Freq:** 8/yr. **Key Personnel:** L. Truskinovsky, Editor-in-Chief, trusk@lms.polytechnique.fr; Stefan Seelecke, Editor-in-Chief, stefan_seelecke@ncsu.edu; S. Conti, Editor, conti@math.uni-duisburg.de; R. Abeyaratne, Editor, rohan@mit.edu; V. Berdichevsky, Editor, vberd@eng.wayne.edu; Wolfgang Mueller, Managing Editor, mcmt@mech2.pi.tu-berlin.de; L.C. Evans, Editor, evans@math.berkeley.edu; R.E. Caflisch, Editor, caflisch@math.ucla.edu; K. Hutter, Founding Ed. **ISSN:** 0935-1175. **Subscription Rates:** EUR1,358 institutions print incl. free access or e-only; EUR1,629.60 institutions print incl. enhanced access. **Remarks:** Advertising accepted; rates available upon request. **URL:** http://www. springer.com/new%26forthcomingtitles%28default%29/ journal/161. **Circ:** (Not Reported)

46797 ■ Contributions to Mineralogy and Petrology
Springer-Verlag Tokyo
No. 2, Funato Bldg.
1-11-11 Kudan-kita
Chiyoda-ku
Tokyo 102-0073, Japan
Ph: 81 368 317000

Fax: 81 368 317001
Publisher E-mail: info@springer.jp
Journal publishing contributions to geochemistry (including isotope geology), the petrology and genesis of igneous, metamorphic and sedimentary rocks, experimental petrology and mineralogy and distribution and significance of elements and their isotopes in the rocks. **Freq:** Bimonthly. **Key Personnel:** J. Hoefs, Exec. Ed., phone 49 5 51393986, fax 49 5 51393982, jhoefs@gwdg.de; T.L. Grove, Exec. Ed., phone 617253-2878, fax 617253-7102, tlgrove@mit.edu; Christian Ballhaus, Editorial Board, phone 49 228 732933, ballhaus@uni-bonn.de; Jonathan Blundy, Editorial Board, phone 44 11 79545447, jon.blundy@bris.ac.uk; Hans Keppler, Editorial Board, fax 49 92 1553769, hans.keppler@uni-bayreuth.de; G. Moore, Editorial Board, gordon.moore@ asu.edu. **ISSN:** 0010-7999. **Subscription Rates:** EUR4,109 institutions print incl. free access or e-only; EUR4,930.80 institutions print incl. enhanced access. **Remarks:** Advertising accepted; rates available upon request. **URL:** http://www.springer.com/earthsciences/ geology/journal/410. **Circ:** (Not Reported)

46798 ■ Cytologia
c/o Japan Mendel Society
Toshin Bldg.
Hongo 2-27-2
Bunkyo-ku
Tokyo 113-0033, Japan
Fax: 81 3 38145352
Publisher E-mail: mendel-cytologia@ib.k.u-tokyo.ac.jp
Journal covering biology. **Subtitle:** International Journal of Cytogenetics and Cell Biology. **Founded:** 1929. **Freq:** Quarterly. **Trim Size:** B5. **Key Personnel:** Shigeyuki Kawano, Editor-in-Chief; Hideo Hirokawa, Assoc. Ed.; Momoki Hirai, Editor; Toshiyuki Nagata, Managing Editor; Kiichi Fukui, Assoc. Ed; Sachihiro Matsunaga, Editorial Advisory Board; Masahiro Hizume, Editor; Haruki Hashimoto, Editorial Advisory Board; Nobuko Ohmido, Editorial Advisory Board. **ISSN:** 0011-4545. **Subscription Rates:** 25,000¥ individuals; 6,500¥ single issue. **Remarks:** Advertising accepted; rates available upon request. **URL:** http://square.umin.ac.jp/mendel/ CYTOLOGIA.htm. **Circ:** Paid 1,000

46799 ■ Daily Yomiuri
The Yomiuri Shimbun
1-7-1 Otemachi
Chiyoda-Ku
Tokyo 100-8055, Japan
General newspaper (English). **Freq:** Daily. **Subscription Rates:** 2,650¥ individuals per month. **Remarks:** Accepts advertising. **URL:** http://www.yomiuri.co.jp/dy/. **Ad Rates:** BW: 2,268,000¥. **Circ:** 75,540

46800 ■ Decisions in Economics and Finance
Springer-Verlag Tokyo
No. 2, Funato Bldg.
1-11-11 Kudan-kita
Chiyoda-ku
Tokyo 102-0073, Japan
Ph: 81 368 317000
Fax: 81 368 317001
Publisher E-mail: info@springer.jp
The official publication of the Association for Mathematics. **Freq:** Semiannual. **Key Personnel:** M. Li Calzi, Assoc. Ed.; S. Holzer, Ed./Mng. Dir., holzer@ units.it; P. Siconolfi, Assoc. Ed.; P. Bank, Assoc. Ed.; E. Pitacco, Assoc. Ed.; T. Zariphopoulou, Assoc. Ed. **ISSN:** 1593-8883. **Subscription Rates:** EUR169 institutions; EUR202.80 institutions enhanced access. **Remarks:** Advertising accepted; rates available upon request. **URL:** http://www.springer.com/economics/ economictheory/journal/10203. **Circ:** (Not Reported)

46801 ■ Dessert
Kodansha Ltd.
2-12-21 Otowa
Bunkyo-ku
Tokyo 112-8001, Japan
Ph: 81 3 3946 6201
Fax: 81 3 3944 9915
Comic magazine for teenage girls featuring stories with handsome boys and fabulous love stories. **Freq:** Monthly. **Key Personnel:** Sawako Noma, President. **URL:** http://www.kodansha.co.jp/english/manga/ magazines.html.

46802 ■ Development Genes and Evolution
Springer-Verlag Tokyo
No. 2, Funato Bldg.

1-11-11 Kudan-kita
Chiyoda-ku
Tokyo 102-0073, Japan
Ph: 81 368 317000
Fax: 81 368 317001
Publisher E-mail: info@springer.jp
Journal publishing reports on all major aspects of development biology with a special emphasis on topics that deal with evolutionary questions. **Freq:** Monthly. **Key Personnel:** Volker Hartenstein, Editor-in-Chief, phone 310206-7523, fax 310206-3987, volkerh@mcdb. ucla.edu; Siegfried Roth, Communicating Ed.; Claude Desplan, Communicating Ed.; Matthias Hammerschmidt, Communicating Ed.; Thomas Hollemann, Communicating Ed.; Mark Q. Martindale, Communicating Ed.; Ralf J. Sommer, Reviews Ed., phone 49 707 1601371, fax 49 707 1601498, ralf.sommer@tuebingen.mpg.de. **ISSN:** 0949-944X. **Subscription Rates:** EUR1,142 institutions print incl. free access or e-only; EUR1,370.40 institutions print incl. enhanced access. **Remarks:** Advertising accepted; rates available upon request. **URL:** http://www. springer.com/lifesci/developmentalbiology/journal/427. **Circ:** (Not Reported)

46803 ■ Earth Planets and Space
Center for Academic Publications Japan
2-4-16 Yayoi
Bunkyo-Ku
Tokyo 113-0032, Japan
Ph: 81 3 38175821
Publisher E-mail: office_contact@capj.or.jp
Earth sciences journal. **Founded:** 1997. **Freq:** Monthly. **Key Personnel:** Kiyoshi Yomogida, Editor-in-Chief, eps-ed@belinda.sci.hokudai.ac.jp; Shamita Das, Editor; Benjamin Fong Chao, Editor; Bernard Chouet, Editor; Peter L. Dyson, Editor; Alan G. Jones, Editor. **ISSN:** 1880-5981. **Subscription Rates:** US$630 institutions online version and CD; US$550 institutions hard copy; US$1,180 institutions online service, hard copy and CD; US$60 individuals online service only. **Remarks:** Advertising accepted; rates available upon request. **URL:** http://www.terrapub.co.jp/journals/EPS/index.html. **Circ:** Paid 800

46804 ■ The East
The East Publications Inc.
Mamiana Arc Bldg., 1F
2-1 Higashi-Azabu 3
Minato-ku
Tokyo 106-0044, Japan
Ph: 81 332243751
Fax: 81 332243754
Publication E-mail: psyenji@theeast.co.jp
English language magazine covering Japanese culture for others. **Founded:** 1964. **Subscription Rates:** 4,800¥ Japan; US$38 other countries; 8,800¥ two years Japan; US$70 two years other countries. **Remarks:** Advertising accepted; rates available upon request. **URL:** http://www.theeast.co.jp. **Circ:** (Not Reported)

46805 ■ Eat
Cornucopia K.K.
8F Mita Hillside Bldg.
4-1-9, Mita
Minato-ku
Tokyo 108-0073, Japan
Ph: 81 354 846680
Fax: 81 354 846683
Magazine providing original solutions for companies from a diverse range of industries. **Freq:** 16/yr. **Key Personnel:** Ayako Chujo, President. **URL:** http:// eatcreative.jp/.

46806 ■ Economics of Governance
Springer-Verlag Tokyo
No. 2, Funato Bldg.
1-11-11 Kudan-kita
Chiyoda-ku
Tokyo 102-0073, Japan
Ph: 81 368 317000
Fax: 81 368 317001
Publisher E-mail: info@springer.jp
Journal fostering research on governance at many levels: corporations, non-profit organizations, local government, federal government, customs unions, international organizations. **Freq:** 4/yr. **Key Personnel:** Amihai Glazer, Editor, aglazer@uci.edu; Joan Esteban, Board of Assoc. Ed.; Sam Bucovetsky, Board of Assoc. Ed.; Roger Noll, Board of Assoc. Ed.; Robert Dur, Editor,

dur@few.eur.nl; Wolfgang Buchholz, Board of Assoc. Ed.; Kai A. Konrad, Board of Assoc. Ed., kkonrad@ medea.wz-berlin.de; Mark Gradstein, Board of Assoc. Ed.; James Robinson, Board of Assoc. Ed. **ISSN:** 1435-6104. **Subscription Rates:** EUR252 institutions print incl. free access or e-only; EUR302.40 institutions print incl. enhanced access. **Remarks:** Advertising accepted; rates available upon request. **URL:** http://www.springer. com/economics/journal/10101. **Circ:** (Not Reported)

46807 ■ Ecosystems
Springer-Verlag Tokyo
No. 2, Funato Bldg.
1-11-11 Kudan-kita
Chiyoda-ku
Tokyo 102-0073, Japan
Ph: 81 368 317000
Fax: 81 368 317001
Publisher E-mail: info@springer.jp
Journal whose research bridges fundamental ecology and environmental ecology and environmental problem-solving, and spans boundaries of scale, discipline and perspective. **Freq:** 8/yr. **Key Personnel:** Monica G. Turner, Editor-in-Chief; David Schindler, Advisory Board; Pamela Matson, Advisory Board; Suzann McClenahan, Managing Editor, ecosys@zoology.wisc.edu; Gene E. Likens, Advisory Board; Walter V. Reid, Advisory Board; John A. Wiens, Advisory Board; Simon Levin, Advisory Board; Harold A. Mooney, Advisory Board. **ISSN:** 1432-9840. **Subscription Rates:** EUR727 institutions print incl. free access or e-only; EUR872.40 institutions print incl. enhanced access. **Remarks:** Advertising accepted; rates available upon request. **URL:** http://www.springer. com/lifesci/ecology/journal/10021?detailsPage= editorialBoard. **Circ:** (Not Reported)

46808 ■ Electrical Engineering
Springer-Verlag Tokyo
No. 2, Funato Bldg.
1-11-11 Kudan-kita
Chiyoda-ku
Tokyo 102-0073, Japan
Ph: 81 368 317000
Fax: 81 368 317001
Publisher E-mail: info@springer.jp
Journal publishing original papers in the extensive field of electrical and electronic engineering, accepting contributions which are fundamental for the development of electrical engineering and its applications, including overlaps to physics. **Freq:** Bimonthly. **Key Personnel:** Dr. Armin Schnettler, Editor-in-Chief, schnettler@rwth-aachen.de; Bernhard Schowe-von der Brelie, Managing Editor. **ISSN:** 0948-7921. **Subscription Rates:** EUR1,273 institutions print incl. free access or e-only; EUR1,527.60 institutions print incl. enhanced access. **Remarks:** Advertising accepted; rates available upon request. **URL:** http://www.springer.com/ engineering/electronics/journal/202. **Circ:** (Not Reported)

46809 ■ Emergency Radiology
Springer-Verlag Tokyo
No. 2, Funato Bldg.
1-11-11 Kudan-kita
Chiyoda-ku
Tokyo 102-0073, Japan
Ph: 81 368 317000
Fax: 81 368 317001
Publisher E-mail: info@springer.jp
Journal advancing and improving the radiological aspects of emergency care; establishing emergency radiology as an area of special interest in the field of diagnostic imaging; improving methods of education in emergency radiology; providing, through formal meetings, a mechanism for presentation of scientific papers on various aspects of emergency radiology and continuing education; promoting research in emergency radiology by clinical and basic science investigators, including residents and other trainees; and acting as the resource body on emergency radiology for those interested in emergency patient care. **Freq:** Bimonthly. **Key Personnel:** Stephen R. Baker, MD, Emeritus Ed.; John H. Harris, Jr., Emeritus Ed.; Ronald J. Zagoria, MD, Editor-in-Chief, rzagoria@wfubmc.edu; Mariano Scaglione, Editorial Board; Digna R. Kool, Editorial Board; Theodore E. Keats, Emeritus Ed. **ISSN:** 1070-3004. **Subscription Rates:** EUR474 institutions print incl. free access or e-only; EUR568.80 institutions print incl. enhanced access. **Remarks:** Advertising accepted; rates available upon request. **URL:** http://www.springer.

com/medicine/radiology/journal/10140. **Circ:** (Not Reported)

46810 ■ Engineering with Computers
Springer-Verlag Tokyo
No. 2, Funato Bldg.
1-11-11 Kudan-kita
Chiyoda-ku
Tokyo 102-0073, Japan
Ph: 81 368 317000
Fax: 81 368 317001
Publisher E-mail: info@springer.jp
International journal for simulation-based engineering, publishing original papers and authoritative state-of-the-art reviews on the technologies supporting simulation-based engineering, and examples of operational simulation-based engineering systems. **Freq:** Quarterly. **Key Personnel:** Prof. Mark S. Shephard, Editor, phone 518276-6795, fax 518276-4886, shephard@scorec.rpi. edu; Charbel Farhat, Editorial Board; Klaus J. Bathe, Editorial Board; Robert H. Dodds, Editorial Board; Peter M. Finnigan, Editorial Board; Roland W. Lewis, Editorial Board; Graham F Carey, Editorial Board; Ted D. Blacker, Editorial Board; E.J. Haug, Editorial Board. **ISSN:** 0177-0667. **Subscription Rates:** EUR783 institutions; EUR939.60 institutions enhanced access. **Remarks:** Advertising accepted; rates available upon request. **URL:** http://www.springer.com/computer/ informationsystems/journal/366. **Circ:** (Not Reported)

46811 ■ Environmental Chemistry Letters
Springer-Verlag Tokyo
No. 2, Funato Bldg.
1-11-11 Kudan-kita
Chiyoda-ku
Tokyo 102-0073, Japan
Ph: 81 368 317000
Fax: 81 368 317001
Publisher E-mail: info@springer.jp
Journal publishing four-page articles of significance in geology, chemistry, physics and biology. **Freq:** Quarterly. **Key Personnel:** Jan Schwarzbauer, Managing Editor, schwarzbauer@lek.rwth-aachen.de; Eric Lichtfouse, Editor, eric.lichtfouse@dijon.inra.fr; Josef Caslavsky, Assoc. Ed., caslavsky@fch.vutbr.cz; Michele Aresta, Assoc. Ed., aresta@metea.uniba.it; Angela Dibenedetto, Assoc. Ed., a.dibenedetto@chimica.uniba.it; Didier Robert, Managing Editor, drobert@univ-metz.fr; Montserrat Filella, Assoc. Ed., montserrat.filella@cabe.unige. ch. **ISSN:** 1610-3653. **Subscription Rates:** EUR265 institutions print incl. free access or e-only; EUR318 institutions print incl. enhanced access. **Remarks:** Advertising accepted; rates available upon request. **URL:** http://www.springer.com/environment/ environmentalchemistry/journal/10311. **Circ:** (Not Reported)

46812 ■ Environmental Economics and Policy Studies
Springer-Verlag Tokyo
No. 2, Funato Bldg.
1-11-11 Kudan-kita
Chiyoda-ku
Tokyo 102-0073, Japan
Ph: 81 368 317000
Fax: 81 368 317001
Publisher E-mail: info@springer.jp
Journal of environmental studies. **Founded:** 1998. **Freq:** Quarterly. **Key Personnel:** T. Awaji, Managing Editor; E. Hosoda, Editor-in-Chief; T. Murota, Managing Editor; K. Ueta, Managing Editor; H. Imura, Assoc. Ed.; M. Munasinghe, Assoc. Ed. **ISSN:** 1432-847X. **Subscription Rates:** EUR224 institutions print incl. free access; EUR268 institutions print incl. enhanced access. **Remarks:** Accepts advertising. **URL:** http://www.springer.com/ economics/environmental/journal/10018. **Circ:** (Not Reported)

46813 ■ Environmental Mutagen Research
Japanese Environmental Mutagen Society
c/o Oral Health Association of Japan
Konagome TS Bldg., 4th Fl.
1-43-9 Komagome
Toshima-ku
Tokyo 170-0003, Japan
Journal of genetics. **Founded:** 1978. **Freq:** 3/yr. **Key Personnel:** Keiji Wakabayashi, President. **ISSN:** 0910-0865. **URL:** http://www.jstage.jst.go.jp/browse/jems.

46814 ■ Esophagus
Springer-Verlag Tokyo
No. 2, Funato Bldg.

Circulation: ★ = ABC; △ = BPA; ♦ = CAC; • = CCAB; ❏ = VAC; ⊕ = PO Statement; ‡ = Publisher's Report; Boldface figures = sworn; Light figures = estimated.

Gale Directory of Publications & Broadcast Media/147th Ed.

5109

1-11-11 Kudan-kita
Chiyoda-ku
Tokyo 102-0073, Japan
Ph: 81 368 317000
Fax: 81 368 317001
Publisher E-mail: info@springer.jp
Peer-reviewed journal covering the study on the field of benign and malignant diseases of the esophagus. **Freq:** Quarterly. **Key Personnel:** Nobutoshi Ando, Editor-in-Chief; Hisanori Ariga, Assoc. Ed.; Masato Hareyama, Editorial Board; Hiromasa Fujita, Assoc. Ed.; Yoshihiko Maehara, Assoc. Ed.; Atsushi Ohtsu, Assoc. Ed. **ISSN:** 1612-9059. **Subscription Rates:** US$253 institutions print incl. free access or e-only; US$303.60 institutions enhanced access. **Remarks:** Advertising accepted; rates available upon request. **URL:** http://www.springer.com/medicine/internal/journal/10388. **Circ:** (Not Reported)

46815 ■ European Archives of Psychiatry and Clinical Neuroscience
Springer-Verlag Tokyo
No. 2, Funato Bldg.
1-11-11 Kudan-kita
Chiyoda-ku
Tokyo 102-0073, Japan
Ph: 81 368 317000
Fax: 81 368 317001
Publisher E-mail: info@springer.jp
Journal dealing with all aspects of psychiatry and related clinical neuroscience, including clinical psychiatry, psychopathology, epidemiology as well as brain imaging, neuropathological, neurophysiological, neurochemical and moleculargenetic studies of psychiatric disorders. **Freq:** 8/yr. **Key Personnel:** Dr. W.F. Gattaz, Managing Editor, phone 55 11 30696962, fax 55 11 30629029, gattaz@usp.br; Dr. J.F.W. Deakin, Managing Editor, phone 44 161 2757427, fax 44 161 2757429, bdeakin@fs1.scg.man.ac.uk; Dr. H.J. Moller, Editor-in-Chief, christine.hauer@med.uni-muenchen.de; Dr. H.C.H. Hafner, Editor, hhaefner@as200.zi-mannheim.de. **ISSN:** 0940-1334. **Subscription Rates:** EUR1,876 institutions print incl. free access or e-only; EUR2,251.20 institutions print incl. enhanced access. **Remarks:** Advertising accepted; rates available upon request. **URL:** http://www.springer.com/steinkopff/psychiatrie/journal/406. **Circ:** (Not Reported)

46816 ■ European Food Research and Technology
Springer-Verlag Tokyo
No. 2, Funato Bldg.
1-11-11 Kudan-kita
Chiyoda-ku
Tokyo 102-0073, Japan
Ph: 81 368 317000
Fax: 81 368 317001
Publisher E-mail: info@springer.jp
Journal publishing research papers and review articles on fundamental and applied food research with the mission being the fast publication of high quality papers on front-line research, newest techniques and on developing trends in the following sections: chemistry and biochemistry, technology and molecular biotechnology, nutritional chemistry and toxicology, analytical and sensory methodologies and food physics. **Freq:** Bimonthly. **Key Personnel:** T. Henle, Editor-in-Chief; T. Hoffman, Editor-in-Chief; E. Anklam, Editorial Board; W. Baltes, Editorial Board; P.S. Belton, Editorial Board; R. Einspanier, Editorial Board; T. Haertle, Editorial Board; R. Amado, Editorial Board; R.J. Fritsch, Editorial Board; A. Arnoldi, Editorial Board; M. Kovac, Editorial Board; S. Saguy, Editorial Board. **ISSN:** 1438-2377. **Subscription Rates:** EUR2,384 institutions print incl. free online or e-access only; EUR2,860.80 institutions print incl. enhanced access. **Remarks:** Advertising accepted; rates available upon request. **URL:** http://www.springer.com/lifesci/foodscience/journal/217. **Circ:** (Not Reported)

46817 ■ European Journal of Applied Physiology
Springer-Verlag Tokyo
No. 2, Funato Bldg.
1-11-11 Kudan-kita
Chiyoda-ku
Tokyo 102-0073, Japan
Ph: 81 368 317000
Fax: 81 368 317001
Publisher E-mail: info@springer.jp
Journal publishing original research utilising a wide

range of techniques and approaches which can contribute to our understanding of the function of the intact healthy human body under a variety of environmental and exercise conditions, such as those experienced in occupational, sporting, recreational and daily activities throughout the human life-span from childhood to old age. **Freq:** Bimonthly. **Key Personnel:** Susan A. Ward, Editor-in-Chief, ejap@dsl.pipex.com; A. De Haan, Editor; D. Linnarsson, Review Ed.; R.H. Morton, Statistical Consultant; R. Bottinelli, Editor. **ISSN:** 1439-6319. **Subscription Rates:** EUR5,380 institutions print incl. free access or e-Only; EUR6,456 institutions print incl. enhanced access. **Remarks:** Advertising accepted; rates available upon request. **URL:** http://www.springer.com/biomed/humanphysiology/journal/421. **Circ:** (Not Reported)

46818 ■ Evening
Kodansha Ltd.
2-12-21 Otowa
Bunkyo-ku
Tokyo 112-8001, Japan
Ph: 81 3 3946 6201
Fax: 81 3 3944 9915
Manga magazine for readers between 25 to 35 years old. **Freq:** Monthly. **Key Personnel:** Sawako Noma, President. **URL:** http://www.kodansha.co.jp/english/manga/magazines.html.

46819 ■ Experimental Animals
Japanese Association for Laboratory Animal Science
Akamon Royal Hts., Rm. 1103
5-29-12 Hongo
Bunkyo-ku
Tokyo 113-0033, Japan
Ph: 81 338 148276
Fax: 81 338 143990
Publisher E-mail: jdk06323@nifty.ne.jp
Journal of experimental medicine. **Founded:** 1952. **Freq:** Quarterly January, April, July and October. **Key Personnel:** Hiromichi Yoneda, Editor-in-Chief; Ja-June Jang, Editor; Lianfeng Zhang, Editor. **ISSN:** 1341-1357. **Remarks:** Advertising accepted; rates available upon request. **URL:** http://wwwsoc.nii.ac.jp/jalas/english/en_journal.html. **Circ:** Paid 2,300

46820 ■ Extremophiles
Springer-Verlag Tokyo
No. 2, Funato Bldg.
1-11-11 Kudan-kita
Chiyoda-ku
Tokyo 102-0073, Japan
Ph: 81 368 317000
Fax: 81 368 317001
Publisher E-mail: info@springer.jp
Journal covering biotechnology. **Subtitle:** Life Under Extreme Conditions. **Founded:** 1997. **Freq:** Bimonthly. **Key Personnel:** Koki Horikoshi, Founding Ed.; Helena Santos, Reviews Ed.; Arnold Driessen, Managing Editor; Tadashi Matsunaga, Managing Editor; Tohru Kobayashi, Editorial Board; Li Huang, Managing Editor; Frank Robb, Managing Editor; Garo Antranikian, Editor-in-Chief; Michael Adams, Editorial Board. **ISSN:** 1431-0651. **Subscription Rates:** EUR668 institutions print incl. free access; EUR801.60 institutions print incl. enhanced access. **Remarks:** Accepts advertising. **URL:** http://www.springer.com/lifesci/microbiology/journal/792. **Circ:** (Not Reported)

46821 ■ Fashion Color
Japan Fashion Color Association
Nihon Ryukoshoku Kyokai
Fukushima Bldg. 6F
1-5-3, Nihonbashi-Muromachi
Chuo-ku
Tokyo 103-0022, Japan
Ph: 81 3 32421680
Fax: 81 3 32421686
Publisher E-mail: jafca@japanfashion.or.jp
Japanese language publication covering fashion. **Freq:** Quarterly. **URL:** http://www.jafca.org/.

46822 ■ Ferrum
Iron and Steel Institute of Japan
Niikura Bldg., 2nd Fl.
2 Kanda, Tsukasacho, 2-chome
Chiyoda-Ku
Tokyo 101-0048, Japan
Ph: 81 3 52097011
Fax: 81 3 32571110
Publication from the Iron and Steel Institute of Japan. **Subtitle:** Bulletin of the Iron and Steel Institute of Japan.

Founded: Jan. 1, 1996. **Freq:** Monthly. **Trim Size:** A4. **ISSN:** 1134-1688. **Subscription Rates:** 4,000¥ single issue; 54,000¥ individuals. **URL:** http://www.isij.or.jp; http://www.isij.or.jp/E_Katsudo/E_Kaiho/e_index.htm. **Ad Rates:** BW: 150,000¥, 4C: 350,000¥. **Circ:** Combined 10,000

46823 ■ Financial Times Japan
Financial Times (Japan) Ltd.
Yamato Seimei Bldg. 21F
1-1-7 Uchisaiwaicho
Chiyoda-ku
Tokyo 100-0011, Japan
Ph: 81 335 811422
Fax: 81 335 811423
Publisher E-mail: circulation.fttokyo@ft.com
General newspaper. **Founded:** 1990. **Freq:** Daily. **Remarks:** Advertising accepted; rates available upon request. **URL:** http://www.ftasia.net. **Circ:** Paid 7,000

46824 ■ Fish Pathology
Japanese Society of Fish Pathology
c/o Laboratory Genetics & Biochemistry
Tokyo University of Fisheries
4-5-7 Konan
Minato
Tokyo 108-8477, Japan
Fish Pathology. **Founded:** 1966. **Freq:** Quarterly. **Key Personnel:** M. Sano, Managing Editor; T. Nakai, Editor-in-Chief. **ISSN:** 0388-788X. **Subscription Rates:** 6,000¥. **Remarks:** Advertising accepted; rates available upon request. **URL:** http://www.fish-pathology.com/english.html. **Circ:** Paid 1,000

46825 ■ Fisheries Science
John Wiley & Sons (Asia) Private Ltd.
c/o Tokyo University of Marine Science & Technology
KLonan 4-5-7
Minato
Tokyo 108-8477, Japan
Publisher E-mail: enquiry@wiley.com.sg
Journal focusing on fishing science and technology, fisheries resources, Aquaculture, oceanography, ecology, physiology, pathology, nutrition, marine biotechnology, biological and organic chemistry, and Food Chemistry and technology. Official journal of the Japanese Society of Fisheries Science. **Freq:** Bimonthly. **Key Personnel:** Takayuki Katagiri, Managing Editor; Shuichi Kitada, Sen. Ed.; Shigeki Matsunaga, Sen. Ed.; Ikuo Hirono, Editor; Daisuke Fujita, Editor; Seinen Chow, Editor; Toshio Takeuchi, Editor-in-Chief; Makoto Endo, Editor; Takashi Matsuishi, Editor. **ISSN:** 0919-9268. **Subscription Rates:** EUR209 individuals print and online; 468 institutions print and premium online; 425 institutions print and standard online; 404 institutions premium online only. **Remarks:** Accepts advertising. **URL:** http://www.wiley.com/bw/journal.asp?ref=0919-9268&site=1. **Circ:** (Not Reported)

46826 ■ Food Science and Technology Research
Business Center for Academic Societies
Gakkai Center C21
5-16-9 Honkomagome
Bunkyo-ku
Tokyo 113-8622, Japan
Ph: 81 3 58145800
Fax: 81 3 58145823
Journal of food and food industry. **Founded:** 1995. **Freq:** Quarterly. **Key Personnel:** M. Nakajima, Editor; M. Murata, Editor. **ISSN:** 1344-6606. **Subscription Rates:** US$751 institutions CHF; US$556 institutions Germany; US$702 institutions U.S.A. **Remarks:** Accepts advertising. **URL:** http://content.karger.com/ProdukteDB/produkte.asp?Aktion=JournalHome&ProduktNr=227093. **Circ:** (Not Reported)

46827 ■ Forestry Technology
Japan Forest Technology Association
Nippon Ringyo Gijutsu Kyokai
7 Rokuban-cho
Chiyoda-ku
Tokyo 102-0085, Japan
Ph: 81 3 32615281
Fax: 81 3 32615393
Japanese language publication covering forestry. **Freq:** Monthly. **Remarks:** Advertising accepted; rates available upon request. **URL:** http://www.jafta.or.jp/. **Circ:** (Not Reported)

46828 ■ Gastric Cancer
Springer-Verlag Tokyo
No. 2, Funato Bldg.
1-11-11 Kudan-kita
Chiyoda-ku
Tokyo 102-0073, Japan
Ph: 81 368 317000
Fax: 81 368 317001
Publisher E-mail: info@springer.jp
Peer-reviewed journal containing significant studies related to stomach neoplasms. **Founded:** 1999. **Freq:** Quarterly. **Key Personnel:** Yuko Kitagawa, Editor-in-Chief; Oichiro Kobori, Ed. Emeritus; Yoshiro Saikawa, Managing Editor; Murray F. Brennan, Consulting Ed.; Haruo Sugano, Consulting Ed.; Toshio Takahashi, Consulting Ed.; Keiichi Maruyama, Consulting Ed.; Jaffer A. Ajani, Editorial Board Member; Keiichi Maruyama, Consulting Ed.; Anthony T.R. Axon, Editorial Board Member; Toshiro Konishi, Editorial Board Member; Eugenio Santoro, Editorial Board Member. **ISSN:** 1436-3291. **Subscription Rates:** EUR253 institutions print incl. free access or e-only; EUR303.60 institutions enhanced access. **Remarks:** Accepts advertising. **URL:** http://www.springer.com/medicine/oncology/journal/10120. **Circ:** (Not Reported)

46829 ■ Gekkan Shonen Magazine
Kodansha Ltd.
2-12-21 Otowa
Bunkyo-ku
Tokyo 112-8001, Japan
Ph: 81 3 3946 6201
Fax: 81 3 3944 9915
Magazine for boys aged 9 years and above featuring stories about sports, fishing, martial arts, history, and school life. **Freq:** Monthly. **Key Personnel:** Sawako Noma, President. **URL:** http://www.kodansha.co.jp/english/manga/magazines.html.

46830 ■ Geochemical Journal
Business Center for Academic Societies Japan
c/o Prof. Y. Sano, Exec. Ed.
Ocean Research Institute
University of Tokyo
Tokyo, Japan
Earth sciences journal. **Founded:** 1966. **Freq:** Bimonthly. **Key Personnel:** Prof. Y. Sano, Exec. Ed., gj@ori.u-tokyo.ac.jp; H. Amakawa, Assoc. Ed., amakawah@ori.u-tokyo.ac.jp; D. Fortin, Assoc. Ed., dfortin@uottawa.ca. **ISSN:** 0016-7002. **Subscription Rates:** 25,000¥ individuals. **Remarks:** Advertising accepted; rates available upon request. **URL:** http://www.terrapub.co.jp/journals/GJ/index.html. **Circ:** Paid 1,300

46831 ■ Graphs and Combinatorics
Springer-Verlag Tokyo
No. 2, Funato Bldg.
1-11-11 Kudan-kita
Chiyoda-ku
Tokyo 102-0073, Japan
Ph: 81 368 317000
Fax: 81 368 317001
Publisher E-mail: info@springer.jp
International journal focusing on research concerning all aspects of combinatorial mathematics. **Founded:** 1985. **Freq:** Bimonthly. **Key Personnel:** J. Pach, Editor; Mikio Kano, Editor-in-Chief; E. Bannai, Editor; D. Avis, Editor; H.J. Broersma, Editor; H. Enomoto, Consulting Ed.; Katsuhiro Ota, Co-Mng. Ed.; N. Alon, Editor; V. Chvatal, Consulting Ed.; B. Bollobas, Consulting Ed.; Akira Saito, Managing Editor; X. Li, Editor. **ISSN:** 0911-0119. **Subscription Rates:** EUR488 institutions print incl. free access or e-only; EUR585.60 institutions enhanced access. **Remarks:** Accepts advertising. **URL:** http://www.springer.com/math/numbers/journal/373. **Circ:** (Not Reported)

46832 ■ Heart and Vessels
Springer-Verlag Tokyo
The Heart Institute of Japan, Tokyo Women's Medical University
8-1 Kawada-Cho, Shinjuku-ku
Tokyo 162-8666, Japan
Publisher E-mail: info@springer.jp
Medical science journal. **Founded:** 1985. **Freq:** Semiannual. **Key Personnel:** Nobuhisa Hagiwara, Editor-in-Chief; Yoichi Goto, Editor; Masayasu Hiraoka, Editor; Joseph E. Bavaria, Editorial Board; Motoaki Sugawara, Editor; Hiroyuki Tsutsui, Editor; Kazuyuki Shimada, Editor; Hiroyuki Yamagishi, Editor; Shinichi Taka-

moto, Editor; Makoto Nakazawa, Editorial Board; Masayasu Hiraoka, Editor; Hiromi Kurosawa, Editor. **ISSN:** 0910-8327. **Subscription Rates:** EUR375 institutions print incl. free access or e-only; EUR450 institutions enhanced access. **Remarks:** Accepts advertising. **URL:** http://www.springer.com/medicine/internal/journal/380. **Ad Rates:** BW: 70,000¥. **Circ:** Paid 1,000

46833 ■ Hiragana Times
3F Ebisawa Bldg., 5-10-10 Shinjuku
Shinjuku-Ku
Tokyo 160-0065, Japan
Ph: 81 3 33418989
Fax: 81 3 33418987
Publication E-mail: info@hiraganatimes.com
Publisher E-mail: info@hiraganatimes.com
Japanese and English language magazine covering issues in Japan and culture. **Founded:** Nov. 11, 1986. **Freq:** Monthly. **Key Personnel:** Hasegawa Katsuyuki, Editor-in-Chief. **Subscription Rates:** 6,000¥ individuals; 10,000¥ out of country; 8,400¥ individuals + audio version; 14,000¥ two years + audio version; 12,400¥ other countries + audio version; 22,000¥ other countries + audio version (2 years); 18,000¥ two years overseas. **URL:** http://www.hiraganatimes.com/.

46834 ■ Hitachi Cable Review
Hitachi Cable Company Ltd.
4-14-1 Sotokanda
Chiyoda-ku
Tokyo 101-8971, Japan
Journal of electrical engineering. **Founded:** 1982. **Freq:** Annual August. **ISSN:** 0914-899X. **URL:** http://www.hitachi-cable.co.jp.

46835 ■ Hypertension Research
Japanese Society of Hypertension Center for Academic Societies Osaka
3-28-8 Hongo, Bunkyo-ku
Tokyo 113-0033, Japan
Ph: 81 3 68019786
Fax: 81 3 68019787
Publisher E-mail: office@jpnsh.org
Medical science journal. **Founded:** 1978. **Freq:** Semiannual. **ISSN:** 0916-9636. **Remarks:** Advertising accepted; rates available upon request. **URL:** http://www.jpnsh.org/; http://www.jstage.jst.go.jp/. **Circ:** (Not Reported)

46836 ■ Ichthyological Research
Springer-Verlag Tokyo
No. 2, Funato Bldg.
1-11-11 Kudan-kita
Chiyoda-ku
Tokyo 102-0073, Japan
Ph: 81 368 317000
Fax: 81 368 317001
Publisher E-mail: info@springer.jp
Journal publishing research papers on original work, either descriptive or experimental, that advances the understanding of the diversity of fishes. **Founded:** 1950. **Freq:** Quarterly. **Key Personnel:** Edward O. Murdy, Editor; Gento Shinohara, Editor, s-gento@kahaku.go.jp; Kunio Sasaki, Editor-in-Chief; Akihisa Iwata, Editor. **ISSN:** 1341-8998. **Subscription Rates:** EUR328 institutions print incl. free access; EUR393.60 Institutions print incl. enhanced access. **Remarks:** Accepts advertising. **URL:** http://www.springer.com/lifesci/zoology/journal/10228. **Circ:** Paid 700

46837 ■ Idea
Seibundo Shinkosha Publishing Company Ltd.
Seibundo Shinkosha Co., Ltd.
IPB Bldg., 5th Fl.
3-3-11 Hongo, Bunkyoku
Tokyo 113-0033, Japan
Ph: 81 3 58057763
Fax: 81 3 58057766
Publication E-mail: info@idea-mag.com
International graphic design magazine. **Founded:** 1953. **Freq:** Bimonthly. **ISSN:** 0019-1299. **Remarks:** Advertising accepted; rates available upon request. **URL:** http://www.idea-mag.com. **Circ:** Paid 32,000

46838 ■ IEICE Electronics Express
Institute of Electronics, Information and Communication Engineers
Kikai-Shinko-Kaikan Bldg.
5-8, Shibakoen 3 chome
Minato-ku
Tokyo 105-0011, Japan

Ph: 81 334 336691
Fax: 81 334 336659
Journal covering the entire field of advanced electronics. **Freq:** Semimonthly. **Key Personnel:** Prof. Kohroh Kobayashi, Editor-in-Chief. **ISSN:** 1349-2543. **URL:** http://www.elex.ieice.org/.

46839 ■ IEICE Transactions on Communications
Institute of Electronics, Information and Communication Engineers
Kikai-Shinko-Kaikan Bldg., Annex 3F
5-22 Shibakoen 3 chome
Minato-Ku
Tokyo 105-0011, Japan
Ph: 81 334 336692
Fax: 81 334 336616
Publication covering information management. **Freq:** Monthly. **Key Personnel:** Hiroyuki Arai, Editor-in-Chief, fax 81 45 3381157, arai@ynu.ac.jp; Shu Namiki, Editor, fax 81 29 8615640, shu.namiki@aist.go.jp; Makoto Taromaru, Editor, phone 81 77 4951508, taromaru@atr.jp. **ISSN:** 0916-8516. **Remarks:** Advertising accepted; rates available upon request. **URL:** http://ietcom.oxfordjournals.org/. **Circ:** 2,600

46840 ■ IEICE Transactions on Electronics
Institute of Electronics, Information and Communication Engineers
Kikai-Shinko-Kaikan Bldg., Annex 3F
5-22 Shibakoen 3 chome
Minato-Ku
Tokyo 105-0011, Japan
Ph: 81 334 336692
Fax: 81 334 336616
Publication covering information management. **Freq:** Monthly. **Key Personnel:** Hidetoshi Onedera, Editor-in-Chief, fax 81 75 7535343, onodera@i.kyoto-u.ac.jp; Toshiro Hiramoto, Editor, fax 81 3 54526265, hiramoto@nano.iis.u-tokyo.ac.jp; Yoshiaki Nakano, Editor, fax 81 3 54525151, nakano@rcast.u-tokyo.ac.jp. **ISSN:** 0916-8524. **URL:** http://www.jstage.jst.go.jp/browse/transele/_vols.

46841 ■ IEICE Transactions on Information and Systems
Institute of Electronics, Information and Communication Engineers
Kikai-Shinko-Kaikan Bldg., Annex 3F
5-22 Shibakoen 3 chome
Minato-Ku
Tokyo 105-0011, Japan
Ph: 81 334 336692
Fax: 81 334 336616
Publication covering information management. **Freq:** Monthly. **Key Personnel:** Shotaro Akaho, Assoc. Ed.; Francis Bond, Assoc. Ed.; Isao Echizen, Assoc. Ed. **ISSN:** 0916-8532. **URL:** http://www.jstage.jst.go.jp/browse/transinf/_vols.

46842 ■ Inflammation Research
Springer-Verlag Tokyo
No. 2, Funato Bldg.
1-11-11 Kudan-kita
Chiyoda-ku
Tokyo 102-0073, Japan
Ph: 81 368 317000
Fax: 81 368 317001
Publisher E-mail: info@springer.jp
Peer-reviewed journal covering the study of histopathology, immunological mechanisms, gene expression, mediators, experimental models, clinical investigations and the effects of drugs. **Freq:** Monthly. **Key Personnel:** Michael J. Parnham; Managing Editor, mparnham@birkhauser.ch; Ian Ahnfelt-Ronne, Editor, iar@novo.dk; Artur Bauhofer, Editor, a.bauhofer@web.de. **ISSN:** 1023-3830. **Subscription Rates:** EUR2,665.60 institutions enhanced access; EUR2,213 institutions print and e-access. **Remarks:** Advertising accepted; rates available upon request. **URL:** http://www.springer.com/birkhauser/biosciences/journal/11?changeHeader. **Circ:** (Not Reported)

46843 ■ Internal Medicine
Japanese Society of Internal Medicine
28-8, 3 chome
Hongo
Bunkyo-ku
Tokyo 113-8433, Japan
Ph: 81 338181556

Publisher E-mail: iminfo@naika.or.jp

Medical science journal. **Founded:** 1962. **Freq:** Monthly. **Key Personnel:** Masahiro Asaka, Editor-in-Chief; Keishi Kubo, Assoc. Ed.; Kenji Nakashima, Assoc. Ed. **ISSN:** 0918-2918. **Subscription Rates:** 20,000¥; US$270 other countries. **URL:** http://www.naika.or.jp/imonline/index.html. **Circ:** Paid 6,500

46844 ■ International Journal of Advanced Mechatronic Systems
Inderscience Enterprises Limited
c/o Prof. Mingcong Deng, Ed.-in-Ch.
Tokyo University of Agriculture & Technology
U.S. Department of Electrical & Electronic Engineering
2-24-16 Nakacho, Koganei
Tokyo 184-8588, Japan
Journal focusing on the research and experiments in the synergistic integration of mechanical engineering. **Freq:** 6/yr. **Key Personnel:** Prof. Mingcong Deng, Editor-in-Chief, deng@cc.tuat.ac.jp. **ISSN:** 1756-8412. **Subscription Rates:** EUR593 individuals print or online; EUR830 individuals print and online. **URL:** http://www.inderscience.com/browse/index.php?journalID=308.

46845 ■ International Journal of Asian Management
Springer-Verlag Tokyo
No. 2, Funato Bldg.
1-11-11 Kudan-kita
Chiyoda-ku
Tokyo 102-0073, Japan
Ph: 81 368 317000
Fax: 81 368 317001
Publisher E-mail: info@springer.jp
Journal publishing mainly original scholarly papers written by members of the International Federation of East Asian Management Association in order to advance academic understanding of Asian management theory and practice. **Freq:** Annual. **ISSN:** 1618-7504. **Remarks:** Advertising accepted; rates available upon request. **URL:** http://www.springer.com/business/journal/10276. **Circ:** (Not Reported)

46846 ■ International Journal of Clinical Oncology
Springer-Verlag Tokyo
No. 2, Funato Bldg.
1-11-11 Kudan-kita
Chiyoda-ku
Tokyo 102-0073, Japan
Ph: 81 368 317000
Fax: 81 368 317001
Publisher E-mail: info@springer.jp
Peer-reviewed journal containing original research papers on all aspects of clinical human oncology. **Founded:** 1966. **Freq:** Bimonthly. **Key Personnel:** Prof. Ikuo Konishi, Editor-in-Chief; Yoichi Arai, Assoc. Ed.; Toshiharu Kamura, Assoc. Ed.; Keisuke Aiba, Editorial Board; Takashi Nakatsuka, Assoc. Ed.; Sadao Amano, Editorial Board. **ISSN:** 1341-9625. **Subscription Rates:** EUR292 institutions; EUR350.40 institutions enhanced access. **Remarks:** Accepts advertising. **URL:** http://www.springer.com/medicine/oncology/journal/10147. **Circ:** (Not Reported)

46847 ■ International Journal of Japan Society for Precision Engineering
Japan Society for Precision Engineering
Kudan-Seiwa Bldg., 1-5-9
Kudan-kita
Chiyoda-ku
Tokyo 102-0073, Japan
Ph: 81 3 52265191
Fax: 81 3 52265192
Publisher E-mail: jspe_jspe@jspe.or.jp
Journal of engineering. **Founded:** 1963. **Freq:** Quarterly. **ISSN:** 0916-782X. **URL:** http://www.jspe.or.jp.

46848 ■ International Journal of Services Technology and Management
Inderscience Enterprises Limited
c/o Prof. Hajime Eto, Ed.
University of Tsukuba
Nakano 3-43-17-305, Nakano-ku
Tokyo 164-0001, Japan
Peer-reviewed journal covering the field of services innovation, services technologies and management. **Freq:** 8/yr. **Key Personnel:** Prof. Hajime Eto, Editor; Dr. M.A. Dorgham, Editor-in-Chief, editorial@inderscience.com. **ISSN:** 1460-6720. **Subscription Rates:** EUR735 individuals print or online; EUR1,025 individuals print and

online. **URL:** http://www.inderscience.com/browse/index.php?journalID=26.

46849 ■ International Medical News
International Medical Society of Japan
Inoue Bldg., No. 502 1-4-10
Kamiuma
Setagaya-ku
Tokyo 154-0011, Japan
Ph: 81 3 54860601
Fax: 81 3 54860599
Publisher E-mail: admin@imsj.or.jp
Medical science journal. **Founded:** 1952. **Freq:** Monthly. **ISSN:** 0535-1405. **URL:** http://www.imsj.or.jp/e/.

46850 ■ Ionizing Radiation
Japan Society of Applied Physics
Kudan-Kita Bldg., 5th Fl.
1-12-3 Kudan-Kita
Chiyoda-ku
Tokyo 102-0073, Japan
Ph: 81 3 32381041
Fax: 81 3 32216245
Physics journal. **Founded:** 1974. **Freq:** 3/year. **ISSN:** 0285-3604. **Subscription Rates:** 4,000¥. **Remarks:** Advertising accepted; rates available upon request. **URL:** http://annex.jsap.or.jp/radiation/radiation.html. **Circ:** (Not Reported)

46851 ■ ISIJ International
Iron and Steel Institute of Japan
Niikura Bldg., 2nd Fl.
2 Kanda, Tsukasacho, 2-chome
Chiyoda-Ku
Tokyo 101-0048, Japan
Ph: 81 3 52097011
Fax: 81 3 32571110
Publication covering worldwide metals. **Founded:** 1961. **Freq:** Monthly. **Trim Size:** A4. **Key Personnel:** Kaneaki Tsuzaki, Editor-in-Chief. **ISSN:** 0915-1559. **Subscription Rates:** 4,000¥ individuals regular; 6,000¥ individuals special; 5,000¥ members additional. **URL:** http://www.isij.or.jp/E_Katsudo/E_Kaiho/e_index.htm; http://www.isij.or.jp. **Formerly:** Transaction of the Iron and Steel Institute of Japan. **Ad Rates:** BW: 150,000¥, 4C: 300,000¥. **Circ:** Combined 1,600

46852 ■ Japan Architect
Japan Architect Company Ltd.
2-31-2 Yushima
Bunkyo-ku
Tokyo 113-0034, Japan
Ph: 81 3 38162532
Fax: 81 3 38128229
Publisher E-mail: ja-business@japan-architect.co.jp
Periodical containing information and detailed data of selected coverage of top-level Japanese architecture, projects, city planning and new trends. **Founded:** 1956. **Freq:** Quarterly. **ISSN:** 0021-4302. **Subscription Rates:** 10,000¥ individuals; 20,000¥ two years. **Remarks:** Advertising accepted; rates available upon request. **URL:** http://www.japan-architect.co.jp. **Circ:** Paid 18,000

46853 ■ Japan Automotive News
JAN Corp.
6-5-4 Shinbashi
Minato-ku
Tokyo 105-0004, Japan
Publisher E-mail: janinfo@japan-autonews.com
Newspaper covering automobiles. **Founded:** 1959. **Freq:** Monthly. **ISSN:** 0021-4329. **Subscription Rates:** 11,500¥ individuals in Asia; 12,000¥ individuals in North America, Europe, Oceania; 12,500¥ other countries Africa, South America. **Remarks:** Advertising accepted; rates available upon request. **URL:** http://www.japan-autonews.com. **Circ:** Paid 5,180

46854 ■ Japan Chemical Week
Chemical Daily Company Ltd.
16-8, Nihonbashi-Hamacho 3-Chome
Chuo-ku
Tokyo 103-8485, Japan
Ph: 81 33 6637931
Fax: 81 33 6632330
Publisher E-mail: intlsales@chemicaldaily.co.jp
Newspaper specializing in the chemical and related industries in Japan and Asia. **Freq:** Weekly. **ISSN:** 0047-1755. **Remarks:** Accepts advertising. **URL:** http://www.jcw-online.com/. **Ad Rates:** BW: 600,000¥. **Circ:** (Not Reported)

46855 ■ Japan Echo
Japan Echo Inc.
Nippon Press Center Bldg.
2-2-1 Uchisaiwai-cho
Chiyoda-ku
Tokyo 100-0011, Japan
Ph: 81 335 193511
Fax: 81 335 193519
Publication E-mail: editor@japanecho.co.jp
Publisher E-mail: editor@japanecho.co.jp
Journal covering essays, interviews, and topics of interest in Japan. **Subtitle:** An Interactive Journal of Informed Opinion. **Founded:** Sept. 1974. **Freq:** Bimonthly. **Print Method:** Offset. **Trim Size:** 210 x 270 mm. **Key Personnel:** Joji Harano, Publisher; Takashi Shiraishi, Editor-in-Chief. **ISSN:** 0388-0435. **Subscription Rates:** 8,400¥ individuals Japan, incl. 5% tax; 8,000¥ individuals. **URL:** http://www.japanecho.com/.

46856 ■ Japan Harvest
Japan Evangelical Missionary Association
Ochanomizu Christian Ctr. Bldg.
2-1 Kanda-Surugadai
Chiyoda-ku
Tokyo 101-0062, Japan
Ph: 81 3 32951949
Fax: 81 3 32951949
Magazine catering to the evangelical community. **Founded:** 1951. **Freq:** Quarterly. **ISSN:** 0021-440X. **Subscription Rates:** 2,500¥. **Remarks:** Advertising accepted; rates available upon request. **URL:** http://www.keikyo.com/jema/. **Circ:** Paid 1,200

46857 ■ Japan Heterocerists Journal
Japan Heterocerists' Society
c/o National Museum Society
Hyakuninchou 3 chome
Shinjuku-ku
Tokyo, Japan
Journal containing new information about moths. **Freq:** Annual. **URL:** http://www.moth.jp.

46858 ■ Japan Labor Review
The Japan Institute for Labour Policy and Training
4-8-23 Kami-Shakujii
Nerima-ku
Tokyo 177-8502, Japan
Ph: 81 3 59036111
Fax: 81 3 35941113
Publication E-mail: jlr@jil.go.jp
Publisher E-mail: jil@jil.go.jp
Journal of research in the field of labor studies, providing valuable information on Japanese labor issues to the broad range of overseas readers. **Founded:** 2004. **Freq:** Quarterly. **Key Personnel:** Hiroyuki Fujimura, Editor; Yuji Genda, Editor. **ISSN:** 1348-9364. **Subscription Rates:** Free. **URL:** http://www.jil.go.jp/english/JLR.htm.

46859 ■ Japan Mission Journal
Oriens Institute for Religious Research
2-28-5 Matsubara
Setagaya-ku
Tokyo 156-0043, Japan
Ph: 81 3 3322 7601
Fax: 81 3 3325 5322
Publication E-mail: jimu@oriens.or.jp
Publisher E-mail: jimu@oriens.or.jp
Periodical covering all aspects of evangelization and enculturation of Christianity in Japan. **Founded:** 1947. **Freq:** Quarterly. **ISSN:** 1344-7297. **Subscription Rates:** 4,200¥ individuals; US$35 individuals. **Remarks:** Advertising accepted; rates available upon request. **URL:** http://www.oriens.or.jp/english/e_jmj.html. **Circ:** Paid 1,000

46860 ■ Japan Racing Journal
Japan Association for International Horse Racing
Roppongi Hills Gate Tower
11-1, Roppongi 6-chome, Minato-ku
Tokyo 106-8401, Japan
Ph: 81 3 57857373
Fax: 81 3 57857376
Publisher E-mail: inter@jra.go.jp
Journal of the Japan Association for International Horse Racing. **Freq:** Bimonthly. **URL:** http://japanracing.jp/en/news-photos/racing-journal/index.html.

46861 ■ The Japan Times
The Japan Times Ltd.
5-4 Shibaura 4-chome

Minato-Ku
Tokyo 108-8071, Japan
Ph: 81 3 34535312
Publication E-mail: jtsales@japantimes.co.jp
Newspaper covering world and domestic news, business and politics. **Subtitle:** The World's Window on Japan. **Founded:** 1897. **Freq:** Daily. **ISSN:** 0289-1956. **Subscription Rates:** 4,480¥ individuals per month; 180¥ single issue English daily. **Remarks:** Advertising accepted; rates available upon request. **URL:** http://www.japantimes.co.jp/. **Circ:** (Not Reported)

46862 ■ The Japanese Journal of American Studies
University of Tokyo
The Center for Pacific and American Studies
Graduate School of Arts and Sciences
3-8-1 Komaba
Meguro-ku
Tokyo 153-8902, Japan
Ph: 81 354 546163
Fax: 81 354 546163
Publisher E-mail: office@jaas.gr.jp
Journal emphasizing the promotion of American Studies, trans-Atlantic approaches, cross-cultural and comparative perspectives. **Freq:** Annual. **Key Personnel:** Fumiko Nishizaki, Editor. **ISSN:** 0288-3570. **URL:** http://www.jaas.gr.jp/english/; http://wwwsoc.nii.ac.jp/jaas/periodicals/JJAS/.

46863 ■ Japanese Journal of Animal Psychology
Japanese Society for Animal Psychology
c/o K & U Co., Ltd.
MSK Bldg., 3rd Fl.
3-32-7 Hongo
Bunkyo-ku
Tokyo 113-0033, Japan
Publisher E-mail: doshin_ed@pri.kyoto-u.ac.jp
Journal of zoology. **Founded:** 1947. **Freq:** Semiannual. **Key Personnel:** Hiroshige Okaichi, Editor. **ISSN:** 0916-8419. **Subscription Rates:** 1,700¥ single issue. **Remarks:** Advertising accepted; rates available upon request. **Circ:** Controlled 500

46864 ■ Japanese Journal of Applied Physics
Japan Society of Applied Physics
Kudan-Kita Bldg., 5th Fl.
Kudan-Kita 1-12-3 Chiyoda-Ku
Tokyo 102-0073, Japan
Ph: 81 3 32381041
Fax: 81 3 32216245
Publisher E-mail: general-matters@jsap.or.jp
Physics journal. **Founded:** 1962. **Freq:** Monthly. **Key Personnel:** Osamu Ueda, Editor; Kazuhide Abe, Editor; Maki Suemitsu, Editor; Akihiro Kono, Editor; Hiroyoshi Naito, Editor; Yoshiaki Nakano, Assoc. Ed.; Masamitsu Haruna, Editor. **ISSN:** 0021-4922. **Subscription Rates:** 215,000¥ other countries airmail; 201,000¥ other countries surface airmail; 180,000¥ other countries surface mail; 180,000¥ individuals. **URL:** http://www.ipap.jp/jjap/. **Circ:** 3,900

46865 ■ Japanese Journal of Bacteriology
Business Center for Academic Societies Japan
Gakkai Ctr. C21
5-16-9 Honkomagome
Bunkyo-Ku
Tokyo 113-8622, Japan
Ph: 81 358 145800
Fax: 81 358 145823
Journal covering communicable diseases. **Founded:** 1944. **Freq:** Quarterly. **ISSN:** 0021-4930. **Subscription Rates:** 18,540¥. **Remarks:** Advertising accepted; rates available upon request. **URL:** http://wwwsoc.nii.ac.jp/jsb/journal/current.html. **Circ:** Paid 3,700

46866 ■ Japanese Journal of Biometrics
Biometric Society of Japan
c/o Statistical Information Institute for Consulting & Analysis
Nougakushorin Bldg., 5th Fl.
3-6 Kanda Jimbocho
Chiyoda-ku
Tokyo 101-0051, Japan
Fax: 81 3 32347472
Publisher E-mail: biometrics@sinfonica.or.jp
Journal covering biology. **Founded:** 1980. **Freq:** Biennial. **Key Personnel:** S. Matsui, Editor-in-Chief; N.

Minaka, Editor. **ISSN:** 0918-4430. **Remarks:** Accepts advertising. **URL:** http://wwwsoc.nii.ac.jp/jbs/index_e.html. **Circ:** (Not Reported)

46867 ■ Japanese Journal of Breast Cancer
Japanese Breast Cancer Society
C/O Cancer Institute Hospital
1-37-1, Kami-Ikebukuro
Toshima-ku
Tokyo 170-8455, Japan
Publication E-mail: t-mikami@kk-kyowa.ac.jp
Medical science journal. **Founded:** 1994. **Freq:** Quarterly. **Key Personnel:** Masakuni Noguchi, Editor-in-Chief. **ISSN:** 1340-6868.

46868 ■ Japanese Journal of Crop Science
Crop Science Society of Japan
Tokyo Secretariat
2F Shin-Kyoritsu Bldg.
Shinkawa 2-22-4, Chuo-Ku
Tokyo 104-0033, Japan
Fax: 81 3 35532047
Publisher E-mail: cssj-jim@bridge.ocn.ne.jp
Journal covering agriculture. **Founded:** 1927. **Freq:** Quarterly. **ISSN:** 0011-1848. **URL:** http://wwwsoc.nii.ac.jp/cssj/e/jcs/index.html. **Circ:** Paid 2,000

46869 ■ Japanese Journal of Infectious Diseases
National Institute of Infectious Diseases
Toyama 1-23-1
Shinjuku-ku
Tokyo 162-8640, Japan
Ph: 81 3 52851111
Fax: 81 3 52851150
Publication E-mail: jjid@nih.go.jp
Publisher E-mail: info@nih.go.jp
Medical science journal. **Founded:** 1948. **Freq:** Bimonthly. **Key Personnel:** Ichiro Kurane, Editor-in-Chief. **ISSN:** 1344-6304. **URL:** http://www.nih.go.jp/JJID/jjid.html. **Circ:** 1,100

46870 ■ Japanese Journal of Mathematics
Mathematical Society of Japan
34-8, Taito 1-chome
Taito-ku
Tokyo 110-0016, Japan
Ph: 81 3 38353483
Fax: 81 3 38353485
Mathematics journal. **Founded:** 1924. **Freq:** Semiannual December and April. **Key Personnel:** Yasuyuki Kawahigashi, Editor, yasuyuki@ms.u-tokyo.ac.jp; Takeshi Saito, Editor; Hiraku Nakajima, Editor, nakajima@math.kyoto-u.ac.jp. **ISSN:** 0289-2316. **Remarks:** Accepts advertising. **URL:** http://www.kurims.kyoto-u.ac.jp/~toshi/jjm/JJM_HP/jjm-index.htm. **Circ:** (Not Reported)

46871 ■ Japanese Journal of Medical Mycology
Business Center for Academic Societies Japan
Gakkai Ctr. C21
5-16-9 Honkomagome
Bunkyo-Ku
Tokyo 113-8622, Japan
Ph: 81 358 145800
Fax: 81 358 145823
Publication E-mail: kaiin@jsmm.org
Journal of microbiology. **Founded:** 1960. **Freq:** Quarterly. **Key Personnel:** Yuzuru Mikami, PhD, Editor-in-Chief; Susumu Kawamoto, Contact; Megumi Wakayama, Contact. **ISSN:** 0916-4804. **Subscription Rates:** US$10,300 individuals. **Remarks:** Advertising accepted; rates available upon request. **URL:** http://www.jsmm.org/. **Circ:** Paid 1,000

46872 ■ Japanese Journal of Ophthalmology
Springer-Verlag Tokyo
No. 2, Funato Bldg.
1-11-11 Kudan-kita
Chiyoda-ku
Tokyo 102-0073, Japan
Ph: 81 368 317000
Fax: 81 368 317001
Publisher E-mail: info@springer.jp
Journal published in English with the aim of disseminating the achievements of Japanese ophthalmologists worldwide. **Founded:** 1957. **Freq:** Bimonthly. **Key Personnel:** Hiroko Terasaki, Assoc. Ed.-in-Ch.; Mitsuru Sawa, Editor-in-Chief. **ISSN:** 0021-5155. **Subscription Rates:** EUR325 institutions print incl. free access or

e-only; EUR390 institutions print incl. enhanced access. **Remarks:** Advertising accepted; rates available upon request. **URL:** http://www.springer.com/medicine/ophthalmology/journal/10384. **Circ:** (Not Reported)

46873 ■ Japanese Journal of Ornithology
Ornithological Society of Japan
c/o National Science Museum
3-23-1, Hyakunin-cho
Shinjuku-ku
Tokyo 169-0073, Japan
Ph: 81 3 33647108
Fax: 81 3 33647104
Publisher E-mail: library@kahaku.go.jp
Journal covering biology. **Founded:** 1915. **Freq:** Quarterly. **Key Personnel:** Shoji Hamao, Editor-in-Chief. **ISSN:** 0913-400X. **Remarks:** Advertising accepted; rates available upon request. **URL:** http://wwwsoc.nii.ac.jp/osj/english/home_e.html. **Former name:** Tori. **Circ:** Paid 900

46874 ■ Japanese Journal of Physiology
Center for Academic Publications Japan
2-4-16 Yayoi
Bunkyo-Ku
Tokyo 113-0032, Japan
Ph: 81 3 38175821
Publication E-mail: jps@nv-med.com
Publisher E-mail: office_contact@capj.or.jp
Journal of physiology. **Founded:** 1951. **Freq:** Bimonthly. **Key Personnel:** Akinori Noma, Editor-in-Chief; Michiki Kasai, Assoc. Ed.; Masato Konishi, Assoc. Ed.; Ikuo Homma, Assoc. Ed.; Katsumasa Kawahara, Assoc. Ed.; Yasuaki Kawai, Assoc. Ed. **ISSN:** 0021-521X. **Subscription Rates:** US$160 institutions; US$80 individuals. **URL:** http://wwwsoc.nii.ac.jp/psj/jjp/editor.html. **Circ:** Paid 1,600

46875 ■ JAUW
Japanese Association of University Women
11-6-101 Samon-cho
Shinjuku-ku
Tokyo 160, Japan
Ph: 81 333 582882
Fax: 81 333 582889
Publisher E-mail: jauw@jauw.org
Japanese language publication covering women. **Freq:** Quarterly. **URL:** http://www.ifuw.org/fellowships/japan.htm.

46876 ■ Jikeikai Medical Journal
Jikei University School of Medicine
3-25-8 Nishi-Shinbashi
Minato-ku
Tokyo 105-8461, Japan
Medical science journal. **Founded:** 1954. **Freq:** Quarterly. **ISSN:** 0021-6968. **URL:** http://ir.jikei.ac.jp/handle/10328/1450. **Circ:** 1,000

46877 ■ JMA Management Review
Japan Management Association
Nihon Noritsu Kyokai
3-1-22 Shiba Koen
Minato-ku
Tokyo 105-8522, Japan
Ph: 81 334 341246
Fax: 81 334 340269
Publisher E-mail: global@jma.or.jp
Japanese language publication covering management. **Freq:** Monthly. **Remarks:** Advertising accepted; rates available upon request. **URL:** http://www.jma.or.jp/. **Circ:** 20,000

46878 ■ Joho-Shori
Information Processing Society of Japan
Joho-Shori Gakkai
Kagaku-Kaikan Bldg., 4th Fl.
1-5 Kanda-Surugadai
Chiyoda-ku
Tokyo 101-0062, Japan
Ph: 81 335 188374
Fax: 81 335 188375
Japanese language journal covering computer science. **Subtitle:** IPSJ Magazine. **Founded:** 1960. **Freq:** Weekly. **Print Method:** Offset. **Trim Size:** A4. **Key Personnel:** Takashi Masuda, President. **ISSN:** 0447-8053. **Remarks:** Accepts advertising. **URL:** http://www.jstage.jst.go.jp/browse/ipsjjip; http://www.ipsj.or.jp. **Ad Rates:** GLR: 141,750¥, BW: 141,750¥, 4C: 262,500¥. **Circ:** 27,000

46879 ■ Josei Seven
Shogakukan Inc.
2-3-1, Hitotsubashi
Chiyoda-ku
Tokyo 101-8001, Japan
Lifestyle magazine featuring news, fashion, cooking, money, and health and beauty. **Founded:** Aug. 5, 1969. **Freq:** Weekly (Mon.). **Key Personnel:** Masahiro Oga, President. **Subscription Rates:** 320¥ individuals. **URL:** http://www.shogakukan.co.jp/english/.

46880 ■ Journal of Advanced Computational Intelligence and Intelligent Informatics (JACIII)
Fuji Technology Press Ltd.
4F Toranomon Sangyo Bldg.
2-29 Toranomon
Minato-Ku
Tokyo 105-0001, Japan
Ph: 81 335 080051
Fax: 81 335 920648
Publisher E-mail: webmaster@fujipress.jp
Peer-reviewed journal covering the studies on computers. **Freq:** Bimonthly. **Key Personnel:** Kaoru Hirota, Editor-in-Chief; Lotfi A. Zadeh, Honorary Ed.; Toshio Fukuda, Editor-in-Chief; H. Asama, Editorial Member; Y. Dai, Editorial Member; D. Fogel, Advisory Ed. **ISSN:** 1343-0130. **Subscription Rates:** 111,500¥ individuals. **URL:** http://www.fujipress.jp/JACIII/.

46881 ■ Journal of Advanced Concrete Technology
Nihon Konkurito Kogaku Kyokai (Japan Concrete Institute)
Sogo Hanzomon Bldg., 12F
1-7 Kojimachi
Chiyoda-ku
Tokyo 102-0083, Japan
Ph: 81 332 631571
Fax: 81 332 632115
Publisher E-mail: jci-web@jci-net.or.jp
Journal promoting leading research, particularly on topics such as seismic design of RC structures and rehabilitation of damaged structures, autogenous shrinkage in early age concrete, concrete fracture mechanics, highly flowable concrete and non-metallic fiber-reinforced concrete. **Freq:** 3/yr. **Key Personnel:** Prof. Hirozo Mihashi, Editor-in-Chief. **ISSN:** 1346-8014. **Subscription Rates:** 16,000¥ institutions; 9,600¥ individuals; 6,500¥ individuals download only; 3,200¥ students. **URL:** http://act.jci-net.jp/index.htm.

46882 ■ Journal of American and Canadian Studies
Sophia University
7-1 Kioi-cho
Chiyoda-Ku
Tokyo 102-8554, Japan
Ph: 81 3 32383179
Fax: 81 3 32383539
Publication E-mail: instacs@sophia.as.jp
Humanities journal. **Founded:** 1988. **Freq:** Annual. **Key Personnel:** Tomoyuki Iino, Editor-in-Chief; Kazuyuki Matsuo, Board Member; Tsutomu Kanayama, Board Member; Thomas Hill, Board Member; Shitsuyo Masui, Board Member; Tomoyuki Iino, Board Member; Masaharu Nakamura, Board Member; Takahiro Ueyama, Board Member; Makoto Tanno, Board Member; Kenneth G. Okimoto, Board Member. **ISSN:** 0914-8035. **URL:** http://www.info.sophia.ac.jp/amecana/E2/Journalinfo.htm. **Circ:** Paid 2,000

46883 ■ Journal of Anesthesia
Springer-Verlag Tokyo
No. 2, Funato Bldg.
1-11-11 Kudan-kita
Chiyoda-ku
Tokyo 102-0073, Japan
Ph: 81 368 317000
Fax: 81 368 317001
Publisher E-mail: info@springer.jp
Journal publishing original articles, review articles, special articles, clinical reports, short communications, letters to the editor and book and multimedia reviews. **Founded:** 1987. **Freq:** Quarterly. **Key Personnel:** Michiaki Yamakage, Editor; Koh Shingu, Editor-in-Chief; Toshiaki Minami, Editor; Takashi Akata, Editor; Shigeru Saito, Editor; Masahiko Kawaguchi, Editor; Takashi Mashimo, Editor; Fumito Ichinose, Editor; Yuichi Kanmura, Editor; Katsuo Terui, Editor; Hideaki Tsuchida, Editor; Satoru Hashimoto, Editor. **ISSN:** 0913-8668.

Subscription Rates: EUR256 institutions print incl. free access; EUR307.20 institutions print incl. enhanced access. **Remarks:** Accepts advertising. **URL:** http://www.springer.com/medicine/anesthesiology/journal/540. **Circ:** (Not Reported)

46884 ■ Journal of Antibiotics
Japan Antibiotics Research Association
2-20-8 Kamiosaki
Shinagawa-ku
Tokyo 141-0021, Japan
Fax: 81 3 34910179
Publisher E-mail: gakkyo@antibiotics.or.jp
Pharmacy journal. **Subtitle:** An International Journal Devoted to Research. **Founded:** 1947. **Freq:** Monthly. **Key Personnel:** Satoshi Omura, Editor; Yoshikazu Takahashi, Editor. **ISSN:** 0021-8820. **Subscription Rates:** US$289 individuals print & online; EUR228 individuals print & online; 41,200¥ individuals print & online; 147 other countries print & online. **Remarks:** Advertising accepted; rates available upon request. **URL:** http://www.nature.com/ja/index.html; http://www.antibiotics.or.jp. **Circ:** Paid 2,000

46885 ■ Journal of Architecture, Planning and Environmental Engineering
Architectural Institute of Japan
26-20 Shiba 5-chome
Minato-Ku
Tokyo 108-8414, Japan
Ph: 81 334 562051
Fax: 81 334 562058
Publisher E-mail: info@aij.or.jp
Journal covering architecture. **Founded:** 1936. **Freq:** Monthly. **ISSN:** 1340-4210. **Subscription Rates:** 33,600¥. **URL:** http://ci.nii.ac.jp/vol_issue/nels/AN10438548_en.html.

46886 ■ Journal of Artificial Organs
Springer-Verlag Tokyo
No. 2, Funato Bldg.
1-11-11 Kudan-kita
Chiyoda-ku
Tokyo 102-0073, Japan
Ph: 81 368 317000
Fax: 81 368 317001
Publisher E-mail: info@springer.jp
Medical science journal. **Founded:** 1998. **Freq:** Quarterly. **Key Personnel:** Yoshiki Sawa, MD, Editor-in-Chief; Hikaru Matsuda, MD, Honorary Editorial Board; Tetsuzo Agishi, MD, Honorary Editorial Board; Yasunaru Kawashima, MD, Honorary Editorial Board; Kazuo Ota, MD, Honorary Editorial Board; Kazuhiko Atsumi, MD, Honorary Editorial Board; Satoshi Takano, MD, Honorary Editorial Board; Motokazu Hori, MD, Honorary Editorial Board; Michio Mito, MD, Honorary Editorial Board. **ISSN:** 1434-7229. **Subscription Rates:** US$314 institutions print incl. free access or e-only; US$376.80 institutions enhanced access. **Remarks:** Accepts advertising. **URL:** http://www.springer.com/medicine/surgery/journal/10047. **Circ:** (Not Reported)

46887 ■ Journal of Asian Architecture and Building Engineering
Architectural Institute of Japan
26-20 Shiba 5-chome
Minato-Ku
Tokyo 108-8414, Japan
Ph: 81 334 562051
Fax: 81 334 562058
Publication E-mail: jaabe@aij.or.jp
Publisher E-mail: info@aij.or.jp
Peer-reviewed international journal serving researchers in academic and research organizations and all practitioners in the building sector. **Freq:** Semiannual. **Key Personnel:** Prof. Hyoun Ho Rhee, Honorary Ed.; Prof. Yoshitake Doi, Field Ed.; Prof. Huiqin Hu, Editorial Member; Prof. Xilin Lu, Field Ed.; Prof. Ge Ming, Editorial Member; Prof. Jian Dai, Editorial Member; Prof. Kim Kwang Woo, Editorial Member; Prof. Xiaoqian Wang, Editorial Member. **ISSN:** 1346-7581. **URL:** http://www.aij.or.jp/eng/jaabe/index.htm.

46888 ■ Journal of Atherosclerosis and Thrombosis
Japan Atherosclerosis Society
c/o Kyowa Kikaku Ltd.
2-20-15 Shinbashi
Minato-ku
Tokyo 105-0004, Japan
Ph: 81 3 35714605
Fax: 81 3 35714606

Publisher E-mail: jas@kk-kyowa.co.jp
Medical science journal. **Founded:** 1994. **Freq:** Quarterly. **Key Personnel:** Shinichi Oikawa, Editor-in-Chief; Kenzo Tanaka, Honorable Member; Hiroshige Itakura, Honorable Member; Hajime Orimo, Honorable Member; Jun Sasaki, Auditor; Takao Fujinami, Honorable Member; Tamio Teramoto, Vice President; Toru Kita, President. **ISSN:** 1340-3478. **URL:** http://jas.umin.ac.jp.

46889 ■ Journal of Bone and Mineral Metabolism
Springer-Verlag Tokyo
No. 2, Funato Bldg.
1-11-11 Kudan-kita
Chiyoda-ku
Tokyo 102-0073, Japan
Ph: 81 368 317000
Fax: 81 368 317001
Publisher E-mail: info@springer.jp
Periodical aimed at providing an international forum for researchers and clinicians to present and discuss relevant issues in bone and mineral research. **Founded:** 1988. **Freq:** Bimonthly. **Key Personnel:** Fujio Suzuki, PhD, Ed. Emeritus; Yoshiki Seino, MD, Editor-in-Chief; Yoshiki Nishizawa, Editorial Ed.; Takayuki Hosoi, MD, Assoc. Ed.; Takuo Fujita, Ed. Emeritus; Shigeaki Kato, PhD, Assoc. Ed.; Masao Fukunaga, MD, Editorial Board; Toshio Matsumoto, MD, Assoc. Ed.; Teruki Sone, MD, Assoc. Ed. **ISSN:** 0914-8779. **Subscription Rates:** EUR325 institutions print incl. free access or e-only; EUR390 institutions enhanced access. **Remarks:** Accepts advertising. **URL:** http://www.springer.com/medicine/internal/journal/774. **Circ:** Paid 2,500

46890 ■ Journal of the Ceramic Society of Japan
Fuji Technology Press Ltd.
4F Toranomon Sangyo Bldg.
2-29 Toranomon
Minato-Ku
Tokyo 105-0001, Japan
Ph: 81 335 080051
Fax: 81 335 920648
Publication E-mail: submit@cersj.org
Publisher E-mail: webmaster@fujipress.jp
Journal of ceramics. **Founded:** 1987. **Freq:** Monthly. **Key Personnel:** Y. Sakka, Editor-in-Chief; L. Chen, Assoc. Ed.; H. Fujimori, Assoc. Ed. **ISSN:** 0914-5400. **URL:** http://www.ceramic.or.jp/ihensyuj/index.html. **Circ:** Paid 6,000

46891 ■ Journal of Chemical Engineering of Japan
Society of Chemical Engineers Japan
Kyoritsu Bldg.
4-6-19 Kohinata
Bunkyo-ku
Tokyo 112-0006, Japan
Ph: 81 3 39433527
Fax: 81 3 39433530
Publication E-mail: journal@scej.org
Publisher E-mail: journal@scej.org
Publishes original research in fields of chemical engineering ranging from fundamental principles to practical applications. **Founded:** 1968. **Freq:** Bimonthly. **Key Personnel:** Tomohiro Akiyama, Editor; Hiroshi Ooshima, Editor; Yoshiyuki Yamashita, Editor-in-Chief. **ISSN:** 0021-9592. **URL:** http://www.scej.org/jcej/.

46892 ■ Journal of Clinical and Experimental Medicine
Ishiyaku Publishers Inc.
7-10 Honkomagome 1-chome
Bunkyo-ku
Tokyo 113-8612, Japan
Ph: 81 3 53957600
Fax: 81 3 53957603
Medical science journal. **Founded:** 1946. **Freq:** Weekly. **ISSN:** 0039-2359. **Remarks:** Advertising accepted; rates available upon request. **URL:** http://www.ishiyaku.co.jp. **Circ:** Paid 8,800

46893 ■ Journal of Computer-Aided Chemistry
Chemical Society of Japan
1-5 Kanda-Surugadai
Chiyoda-Ku
Tokyo 101-8307, Japan
Ph: 81 332 926161
Fax: 81 332 926318
Publication E-mail: jcac@chemistry.or.jp

Publisher E-mail: info@chemistry.or.jp
Journal of the Chemical Society of Japan, Division of Chemical Information and Computer Sciences. **ISSN:** 1345-8647. **URL:** http://www.chemistry.or.jp/journals/index-e.html.

46894 ■ Journal of Dermatology
Japanese Dermatological Association
cosmos Hongo Bldg., 6th Fl.
1-4, Hongo 4-chome
Bunkyo-ku
Tokyo 113-0033, Japan
Journal of dermatology. **Founded:** 1974. **Freq:** Monthly. **Key Personnel:** Shinji Shimada, MD, Editor-in-Chief; Masutaka Furue, MD, Editor; Fukumi Furukawa, MD, Editor. **ISSN:** 0385-2407. **Subscription Rates:** US$123 individuals print and online; 76 individuals print & online; EUR114 individuals print & online; US$873 institutions print & online; 542 institutions print & online; EUR688 institutions print & online; US$1,062 institutions rest of the world. **URL:** http://www.dermatol.or.jp/Journal/JD/index-e.html; http://www.dermatol.or.jp/.

46895 ■ Journal of the Electronics Industry
Dempa Publications Inc.
1-11-15 Higashi Gotanda
Shinagawa-Ku
Tokyo 141-8715, Japan
Ph: 81 334 456111
Fax: 81 334 447515
Business publication. **Freq:** Monthly. **ISSN:** 0385-4515. **Subscription Rates:** US$150 other countries in Asia/Oceania; US$259 two years in Asia/Oceania; US$175 other countries; US$309 two years other countries. **URL:** http://www.dempa.net; http://aei.dempa.net/paidsub/index.html.

46896 ■ Journal of Ethology
Springer-Verlag Tokyo
No. 2, Funato Bldg.
1-11-11 Kudan-kita
Chiyoda-ku
Tokyo 102-0073, Japan
Ph: 81 368 317000
Fax: 81 368 317001
Publisher E-mail: info@springer.jp
Periodical featuring reviews and original papers relating to all aspects of animal behavior, including traditional ethology. **Founded:** 1982. **Freq:** 3/yr. **Key Personnel:** Kazuki Tsuji, Editorial Board; Yoshitaka Tsubaki, Ch. Ed., submit-j-ethol@ecology.kyoto-u.ac.jp; Martin Daly, Editorial Board; Kenji Karino, Editorial Board; Jae C. Choe, Editorial Board; Sachiko Koyama, Assoc. Ed. **ISSN:** 0289-0771. **Subscription Rates:** EUR285 institutions print incl. free access or e-only; EUR342 institutions print & enhanced access. **Remarks:** Accepts advertising. **URL:** http://www.springer.com/lifesci/zoology/journal/10164. **Circ:** (Not Reported)

46897 ■ Journal of Fluorine Chemistry
Elsevier Science
c/o T. Taguchi, Ed.
Tokyo University of Pharmacy & Life Science
Hachioji
Tokyo 192-0392, Japan
Publisher E-mail: nlinfo-f@elsevier.com
Journal publishing articles on pure and applied research on the chemistry and applications of fluorine. **Founded:** 1971. **Freq:** Monthly. **Key Personnel:** T. Nakajima, Editorial Board; W.R. Dolbier, Jr., Editor; G. Haufe, Editor. **ISSN:** 0022-1139. **Subscription Rates:** US$5,336 institutions all countries except Europe and Japan; EUR4,773 institutions European countries; 634,000¥ institutions; US$259 individuals all countries except Europe and Japan; EUR231 individuals European countries; 30,300¥ individuals. **Remarks:** Accepts advertising. **URL:** http://www.elsevier.com/wps/find/journaldescription.cws_home/504088/descriptiondescription. **Circ:** (Not Reported)

46898 ■ Journal of Forest Research
Springer-Verlag Tokyo
No. 2, Funato Bldg.
1-11-11 Kudan-kita
Chiyoda-ku
Tokyo 102-0073, Japan
Ph: 81 368 317000
Fax: 81 368 317001
Publisher E-mail: info@springer.jp
Journal covering all aspects of forest research, both basic and applied, with the aim of encouraging international communication between scientists in different fields who share a common interest in forest science. **Founded:** 1914. **Freq:** Bimonthly. **Key Personnel:** Sheauchi Cheng, Editorial Board; Katsumi Togashi, Editor-in-Chief, togashi@fr.a.u-tokyo.ac.jp; Edwin S. Miyata, Editorial Board; Peter Blandon, Editorial Board; Keigo Matsue, Editorial Board. **ISSN:** 1341-6979. **Subscription Rates:** EUR262 institutions print incl. free access or e-only; EUR314.40 institutions print incl. free enhanced access. **Remarks:** Advertising accepted; rates available upon request. **URL:** http://www.springer.com/lifesciences/forestry/journal/10310. **Circ:** (Not Reported)

46899 ■ Journal of Gastroenterology
Springer-Verlag Tokyo
No. 2, Funato Bldg.
1-11-11 Kudan-kita
Chiyoda-ku
Tokyo 102-0073, Japan
Ph: 81 368 317000
Fax: 81 368 317001
Publisher E-mail: info@springer.jp
Medical science journal. **Founded:** 1966. **Freq:** Monthly. **Key Personnel:** Akira Andoh, Assoc. Ed.; Takahisa Furuta, Assoc. Ed.; Mamoru Watanabe, Editor-in-Chief. **ISSN:** 0944-1174. **Subscription Rates:** EUR600 institutions print incl. free access or e-only; EUR720 institutions enhanced access. **Remarks:** Accepts advertising. **URL:** http://www.springer.com/medicine/internal/journal/535. **Circ:** Paid 4,500

46900 ■ Journal of General and Applied Microbiology
Microbiology Research Foundation
Center of Academic Publications Japan Bldg.
4-16, Yayoi 2 chome
Bunkyo-ku
Tokyo 113-0032, Japan
Publishes original papers pertaining to general and applied microbiology. **Founded:** 1955. **Freq:** Bimonthly. **Key Personnel:** Koji Yoda, Exec. Ed. **ISSN:** 0022-1260. **URL:** http://www.iam.u-tokyo.ac.jp/JGAM/general.html. **Circ:** Paid 680

46901 ■ Journal of Geodetic Society of Japan
Geodetic Society of Japan
c/o Japanese Association of Surveyors
1-3-4 Koishikawa
Bunkyo-ku
Tokyo 112-0002, Japan
Ph: 81 3 56843358
Fax: 81 3 56843366
Publisher E-mail: nihonsokuchi@jsurvey.jp
Journal of geography. **Founded:** 1954. **Freq:** Quarterly. **Key Personnel:** Satoshi Miura, Editor; Masaaki Mishina, Editor. **ISSN:** 0038-0830. **URL:** http://wwwsoc.nii.ac.jp/geod-soc/english/contact.html. **Circ:** Paid 775

46902 ■ Journal of Headache and Pain
Springer-Verlag Tokyo
No. 2, Funato Bldg.
1-11-11 Kudan-kita
Chiyoda-ku
Tokyo 102-0073, Japan
Ph: 81 368 317000
Fax: 81 368 317001
Publisher E-mail: info@springer.jp
Journal dedicated to researchers involved in all aspects of headache and pain, covering headache and pain syndromes in the following fields: genetics, neurology, internal medicine, clinical pharmacology, child neuropediatrics, anesthesiology, rheumatology, otology, dentistry, neurotraumatology, neurosurgery, psychiatry, pain management, and addiction. **Freq:** Bimonthly. **Key Personnel:** Paolo Martelletti, Editor-in-Chief. **ISSN:** 1129-2369. **Subscription Rates:** EUR340 institutions print incl. free access or e-only; EUR408 institutions print incl. enhanced access. **Remarks:** Advertising accepted; rates available upon request. **URL:** http://www.springer.com/medicine/journal/10194. **Circ:** (Not Reported)

46903 ■ Journal of Health Science
Pharmaceutical Society of Japan
12-15 Shibuya 2-chome
Shibuya-Ku
Tokyo 150-0002, Japan
Fax: 81 334 981835
Publication E-mail: ronb@pharm.or.jp
Publisher E-mail: doi@pharm.or.jp
Journal of health science. **Founded:** 1953. **Freq:** Bimonthly. **Key Personnel:** Hayao Ide, Editor-in-Chief;

Yoshito Kumagai, Editor; Shigeru Oshio, Assoc. Ed.; Toshio Okano, Editor; Momoko Chiba, Editor. **ISSN:** 1344-9702. **Subscription Rates:** US$56 members surface mail. **Remarks:** Advertising accepted; rates available upon request. **URL:** http://jhs.pharm.or.jp/index.html. **Circ:** Controlled 1,700

46904 ■ Journal of Hepato-Biliary-Pancreatic Sciences
Springer-Verlag Tokyo
No. 2, Funato Bldg.
1-11-11 Kudan-kita
Chiyoda-ku
Tokyo 102-0073, Japan
Ph: 81 368 317000
Fax: 81 368 317001
Publisher E-mail: info@springer.jp
Publishes original articles in the English language dealing with clinical investigations of and basic research on all aspects of the field of hepatic, biliary, and pancreatic surgery. **Founded:** 1993. **Freq:** Bimonthly. **Key Personnel:** Masao Tanaka, Editorial Board; Tadahiro Takada, Editor-in-Chief; Jiro Fujimoto, Editorial Board; B.J. Ammori, Editorial Board; Fumihiko Miura, Assoc. Ed.; John L. Cameron, Editorial Board. **ISSN:** 0944-1166. **Subscription Rates:** EUR346 institutions print incl. free access or e-only; EUR415.20 institutions enhanced access. **Remarks:** Accepts advertising. **URL:** http://www.springer.com/medicine/surgery/journal/534. **Formerly:** Journal of Hepato-Biliary-Pancreatic Surgery. **Circ:** (Not Reported)

46905 ■ Journal of Home Economics of Japan
Japan Society of Home Economics
Rm. 502, Gakuendai Hts.
502-2-1-15 Otsuka
Bunkyo-ku
Tokyo 112-0012, Japan
Ph: 81 3 39472627
Fax: 81 3 39472627
Publisher E-mail: kaseigakkai@tokyo.email.ne.jp
Journal of home economics. **Founded:** 1950. **Freq:** Monthly. **ISSN:** 0913-5227. **URL:** http://wwwsoc.nii.ac.jp/jshe/english/index.html6. **Circ:** Paid 5,350

46906 ■ Journal of Human Genetics
Nature Publishing Group
c/o Department of Human Genetics
Graduate School of Medicine
The University of Tokyo
7-3-1 Hongo, Bunkyo-ku
Tokyo 113-0033, Japan
Ph: 81 3 58028619
Publication E-mail: jhgedoc@m.u-tokyo.ac.jp
Journal featuring articles on human genetics, including medical genetics and human genome analysis. **Founded:** 1956. **Freq:** Monthly. **Key Personnel:** Katsushi Tokunaga, Editor-in-Chief; Akira Hata, Assoc. Ed.; Tetsuro Miki, Assoc. Ed.; Gozoh Tsujimoto, Assoc. Ed.; Mark Lathrop, Assoc. Ed. **ISSN:** 1434-5161. **Subscription Rates:** US$346 individuals online; US$384 individuals print and online; EUR289 individuals online; EUR321 individuals print and online; 54,900¥ individuals print and online; 49,400¥ individuals online; 207 other countries print and online; 186 other countries online. **Remarks:** Accepts advertising. **URL:** http://www.nature.com/jhg/index.html. **Circ:** Paid 1,200

46907 ■ Journal of Humanities and Natural Sciences
Tokyo Keizai University
1-7-34, Minami-cho
Kokubunji-shi
Tokyo 185-8502, Japan
Ph: 81 423287728
Fax: 81 423287769
Humanities journal. **Founded:** 1962. **Freq:** 3/yr. **ISSN:** 0495-8012. **URL:** http://www.tku.ac.jp/index.html. **Circ:** 2,200

46908 ■ Journal of IEICE
Institute of Electronics, Information and Communication Engineers
Kikai-Shinko-Kaikan Bldg., Annex 3F
5-22 Shibakoen 3 chome
Minato-ku
Tokyo 105-0011, Japan
Ph: 81 334 336692
Fax: 81 334 336616
Journal of electronics. **Founded:** 1917. **Freq:** Monthly. **ISSN:** 0913-5693. **Remarks:** Advertising accepted; rates

available upon request. **URL:** http://www.ieice.org/eng/books/kaishi.html. **Circ:** Paid 40,000

46909 ■ Journal of Infection and Chemotherapy
Springer-Verlag Tokyo
No. 2, Funato Bldg.
1-11-11 Kudan-kita
Chiyoda-ku
Tokyo 102-0073, Japan
Ph: 81 368 317000
Fax: 81 368 317001
Publisher E-mail: info@springer.jp
Pharmacy journal. **Founded:** 1995. **Freq:** Bimonthly. **Key Personnel:** Kyoichi Totsuka, PhD, Ed.-in-Ch. Emeritus; Masatoshi Konno, PhD, Ed.-in-Ch. Emeritus; Seiji Hori, PhD, Ed.-in-Ch. Emeritus; Yoshio Kobayashi, PhD, Editor-in-Chief; Keisuke Aiba, Assoc. Ed.; Satoshi Iwata, Assoc. Ed. **ISSN:** 1341-321X. **Subscription Rates:** US$339 institutions print incl. free access or e-only; US$406.80 institutions enhanced access. **Remarks:** Accepts advertising. **URL:** http://www.springer.com/medicine/internal/journal/10156. **Circ:** Paid 1,500

46910 ■ Journal of Ion Exchange
Japan Association of Ion Exchange
c/o Tomoe Okabe
2-62-8 Higashi-Ikebukuro
Tosima-ku
Tokyo 170-0013, Japan
Ph: 81 3 59501290
Fax: 81 3 59501292
Publisher E-mail: office.jaie@jaie.gr.jp
Journal devoting to the field of ion exchange and related fields either on academic or on industrial research developments. **Founded:** 1990. **Freq:** 3/yr. **Key Personnel:** Shogo Shimazu, Editor-in-Chief. **ISSN:** 0915-860X. **URL:** http://www.jaie.gr.jp/JIE_E.html.

46911 ■ Journal of Japan Biomagnetism and Bioelectromagnetics Society
Nihon Seitai Jiki Gakkai
Daigaku Igakubu
Iyo Denshi Kenkyu Shisetsu
3-1 Hongo 7-chome
Bunkyo-ku
Tokyo 113-0033, Japan
Journal covering biophysics. **Founded:** 1988. **Freq:** Semiannual. **ISSN:** 0915-0374.

46912 ■ Journal of Japan Medical Society of Paraplegia
Nihon Parapurejia Igakkai
Keio Gijuku Daigaku Igakubu Seikei
Gekagaku Kyoshitsu
35 Shinano-Machi
Shinjuku-ku
Tokyo 160-0016, Japan
Medical science journal. **Founded:** 1988. **Freq:** Annual. **ISSN:** 0914-6822.

46913 ■ Journal of Japan Salivary Gland Society
Nihon Daekisen Gakkai
2-1-1 Otsuka
Bunkyo-ku
Tokyo 1604, Japan
Fax: 81 3 59761478
Publisher E-mail: office@daekisen.org
Journal covering biology. **Founded:** 1959. **Freq:** Annual. **ISSN:** 0916-1104. **URL:** http://www.daekisen.org/.

46914 ■ Journal of Japan Spine Research Society
Nihon Sekitsui Geka Gakkai
Seikei Geka Kyoshitsu
35 Shinano-Machi
Shinjuku-ku
Tokyo 160-0016, Japan
Medical science journal. **Founded:** 1990. **Freq:** Annual. **ISSN:** 0915-6496.

46915 ■ Journal of Japanese Forestry Society
Japanese Forestry Society
7 Roku-Ban-cho
Chiyoda-ku
Tokyo 102-0085, Japan
Ph: 81 332612766
Publisher E-mail: office@forestry.jp
Journal of forestry. **Founded:** 1918. **Freq:** Bimonthly. **Key Personnel:** Katsumi Togashi, Editor-in-Chief. **ISSN:** 0021-485X. **Subscription Rates:** Included in

membership. **Remarks:** Advertising accepted; rates available upon request. **URL:** http://www.forestry.jp/contents/english/outline-eng.htm. **Circ:** Paid 4,000

46916 ■ Journal of Japanese Scientists
Japan Scientists Association
Chasu Bldg. 9F
1-9-15 Yushima
Bunkyo-Ku
Tokyo 113-0034, Japan
Fax: 81 3 38132363
Publisher E-mail: mail@jsa.gr.jp
Japanese language journal covering scientists. **Freq:** Monthly. **URL:** http://jsa.gr.jp/intl.

46917 ■ Journal of Japanese Society of Dialysis Therapy
Japanese Society for Dialysis Therapy
2-38-21 Hongo
Bunkyo-ku
Tokyo 113-0033, Japan
Ph: 81 358 000786
Fax: 81 358 000787
Publishes articles that are related to blood purification therapy. **Founded:** 1968. **Freq:** Monthly. **Key Personnel:** Akiyasu Yamashita, Vice-Chm.; Tadoa Akizawa, Chm. **URL:** http://www.jsdt.or.jp/index_e.html.

46918 ■ Journal of Japanese Society for Horticultural Science
Japanese Society for Horticultural Science
c/o Nakanishi Printing
Shimotachiuri Ogawa Higashi
Kamikyoku
Tokyo 602-8048, Japan
Ph: 81 754153661
Fax: 81 754153662
Publisher E-mail: jshs@nacos.com
Journal of horticultural science. **Founded:** 1925. **Freq:** Bimonthly. **Key Personnel:** Ken Ichi Arisumi, Editor; Eisuke Matsuo, Editor. **ISSN:** 1882-3351. **Subscription Rates:** 9,000¥. **Remarks:** Advertising accepted; rates available upon request. **URL:** http://www.jshs.jp/modules/tinyd13/index.php?id=2. **Circ:** Paid 3,000

46919 ■ Journal of Japanese Trade and Industry
Maruzen Company Ltd.
9-2 Nihombashi 3-chome
Chuo-Ku
PO Box 5050
Tokyo 103-8244, Japan
Ph: 81 3 32733234
Fax: 81 3 32731144
Publisher E-mail: export@maruzen.co.jp
Journal covering economics. **Founded:** 1982. **Freq:** Bimonthly. **ISSN:** 0285-9556. **Subscription Rates:** US$65 individuals. **Remarks:** Advertising accepted; rates available upon request. **URL:** http://www.maruzen.co.jp/home-eng/inter-d-per.html. **Circ:** Paid 35,000

46920 ■ Journal of Magnetics Society of Japan
Magnetics Society of Japan
5th Fl., Mitsui-Sumitomo, Kaijo Ogawamachi Bldg.
2-8 Kanda Ogawamachi
Chiyoda-ku
Tokyo 101-0052, Japan
Ph: 81 3 52810106
Fax: 81 3 52810107
Publisher E-mail: msj@bj.wakwak.com
Physics journal. **Founded:** 1977. **Freq:** Monthly. **Key Personnel:** Ken-Ichi Arai, President; Migaku Takahashi, Director. **ISSN:** 0285-0192. **Subscription Rates:** Included in membership. **URL:** http://www.wdc-jp.com/msj/english/journal/index.html.

46921 ■ Journal of Marine Science and Technology
Springer-Verlag Tokyo
No. 2, Funato Bldg.
1-11-11 Kudan-kita
Chiyoda-ku
Tokyo 102-0073, Japan
Ph: 81 368 317000
Fax: 81 368 317001
Publisher E-mail: info@springer.jp
Peer-reviewed journal providing information on current issues in marine science and technology by publishing original, full-length, refereed contributions on research and/or developments in this field. **Founded:** 1996. **Freq:** Quarterly. **Key Personnel:** Guttorm Alendal, Editorial Board; Emilio F. Campana, Editorial Board; Masahiko

Fujikubo, Editor-in-Chief; Volker Bertram, Assoc. Ed.; In-won Lee, Editorial Board; Takanori Hino, Dep. Ed.; Jun Kita, Editorial Board; Robert Latorre, Editorial Board; Reza Katebi, Editorial Board. **ISSN:** 0948-4280. **Subscription Rates:** US$207 institutions print incl. free access or e-only; US$248.40 institutions enhanced access. **Remarks:** Accepts advertising. **URL:** http://www.springer.com/engineering/mechanicaleng/journal/773. **Circ:** (Not Reported)

46922 ■ Journal of Material Cycles and Waste Management
Springer-Verlag Tokyo
No. 2, Funato Bldg.
1-11-11 Kudan-kita
Chiyoda-ku
Tokyo 102-0073, Japan
Ph: 81 368 317000
Fax: 81 368 317001
Publisher E-mail: info@springer.jp
Journal focusing on two areas: research in technical, political, and environmental problems of material cycles and waste management; and information that contributes to the development of an interdisciplinary science of material cycles and waste management. **Freq:** Quarterly. **Key Personnel:** Shin-ichi Sakai, Ch. Ed.; Kazuo Yamamoto, Ch. Ed. **ISSN:** 1438-4957. **Subscription Rates:** EUR250 institutions print incl. free access or e-only; EUR300 institutions print incl. enhanced access. **Remarks:** Advertising accepted; rates available upon request. **URL:** http://www.springer.com/environment/pollutionandremediation/journal/10163. **Circ:** (Not Reported)

46923 ■ Journal of Mathematical Sciences
University of Tokyo
Graduate School of Mathematical Sciences
3-8-1 Komaba
Meguro
Tokyo 153-8914, Japan
Ph: 81 3 54657001
Fax: 81 3 54657011
Publisher E-mail: www-admin@ms.u-tokyo.ac.jp
Mathematics journal. **Founded:** 1925. **Freq:** 3/yr. **Key Personnel:** Shuji Saito, Editorial Board, kiyoomi@ms.u-tokyo.ac.jp; Tadahisa Funaki, Editorial Board; Mikio Furuta, Editorial Board; Hitoshi Arai, Vice Ed.-in-Ch.; Tetsuji Tokihiro, Editorial Board; Yasuyuki Kawahigashi, Editor-in-Chief, yasuyuki@ms.u-tokyo.ac.jp. **ISSN:** 1340-5705. **URL:** http://journal.ms.u-tokyo.ac.jp/. **Merged with:** Journal of The Faculty of Science & Scientific Papers of The College of Arts and Sciences (Apr. 1992). **Circ:** Paid 850

46924 ■ Journal of Medical and Dental Sciences
Tokyo Medical and Dental University
1-5-45 Yushima
Bunkyo-ku
Tokyo 113-8510, Japan
Medical science journal. **Founded:** 1954. **Freq:** Quarterly. **Key Personnel:** Teruo Amagasa, Editor-in-Chief; Shoji Yamaoka, Editorial Board; Koichi Uemura, Editorial Board. **ISSN:** 1342-8810. **URL:** http://lib.tmd.ac.jp/jmd/. **Circ:** 1,000

46925 ■ Journal of Medical Ultrasonics
Springer-Verlag Tokyo
No. 2, Funato Bldg.
1-11-11 Kudan-kita
Chiyoda-ku
Tokyo 102-0073, Japan
Ph: 81 368 317000
Fax: 81 368 317001
Publisher E-mail: info@springer.jp
Journal providing a forum for researchers and practitioners to document advances and developments in the entire field of ultrasound in medicine and biology, encompassing both the medical and the engineering aspects of the science. **Freq:** Quarterly. **Key Personnel:** Nobuyuki Taniguchi, Editor-in-Chief; Terumi Hayashi, Scientific Advisory Board; Hideaki Ishida, Assoc. Ed. **ISSN:** 1346-4523. **Subscription Rates:** EUR267 institutions print incl. free access or e-only; EUR320.40 institutions print incl. enhanced access. **Remarks:** Advertising accepted; rates available upon request. **URL:** http://www.springer.com/medicine/radiology/journal/10396. **Circ:** (Not Reported)

46926 ■ Journal of Medicine & Philosophy
Oxford University Press
4-5-10-8F Shiba, Minato-ku
Tokyo 108-8386, Japan

Ph: 81 3 54445858
Fax: 81 3 34542929
Journal covering concerns of philosophy in medical research and practice. **Freq:** Bimonthly. **Key Personnel:** Edmund D. Pellegrino, Founding Ed.; H. Tristram Engelhardt, Jr., Sen. Ed.; Mark J. Cherry, Editor. **ISSN:** 0360-5310. **Subscription Rates:** US$513 institutions print & online; US$427 institutions online only; US$470 institutions print only; US$73 individuals; EUR465 institutions print & online; EUR387 institutions online only; EUR426 institutions print only; EUR66 individuals. **Remarks:** Accepts advertising. **URL:** http://jmp.oxfordjournals.org/. **Circ:** (Not Reported)

46927 ■ Journal of Meteorological Society of Japan
Meteorological Society of Japan
c/o Japan Meteorological Agency
1-3-4 Ote-Machi
Chiyoda-ku
Tokyo 100-0004, Japan
Ph: 81 3 32128341
Fax: 81 3 32164401
Publication E-mail: metsoc-j@aurora.ocn.ne.jp
Publisher E-mail: metsoc-j@aurora.ocn.ne.jp
Journal of meteorology. **Founded:** 1882. **Freq:** Bimonthly. **Key Personnel:** Kaoru Sato, Co-Ch. Ed.; Masaki Satoh, Editor-in-Chief. **ISSN:** 0026-1165. **URL:** http://www.jstage.jst.go.jp/browse/jmsj. **Circ:** Paid 2,000

46928 ■ Journal of Molecular Medicine
Springer-Verlag Tokyo
No. 2, Funato Bldg.
1-11-11 Kudan-kita
Chiyoda-ku
Tokyo 102-0073, Japan
Ph: 81 368 317000
Fax: 81 368 317001
Publisher E-mail: info@springer.jp
Journal publishing original papers, rapid communications, review articles and correspondence of the highest quality pertinent to all aspects of human biology and pathophysiology and the application of research involving gene technology, gene therapy, molecular structural analysis, genetic epidemiology and molecular and clinical pharmacology. **Freq:** Monthly. **Key Personnel:** Detlev Ganten, Editor-in-Chief; Gregg L. Semenza, Editor-in-Chief; Christiane Nolte-Berlin, Managing Editor; Chi Van Dang, Assoc. Ed.; Stephen L. Archer, Assoc. Ed.; Jun O. Liu, Assoc. Ed. **ISSN:** 0946-2716. **Subscription Rates:** EUR1,203 institutions print incl. free access or e-only; EUR1,443.60 institutions print incl. enhanced access. **Remarks:** Advertising accepted; rates available upon request. **URL:** http://www.springer.com/biomed/molecular/journal/109. **Circ:** (Not Reported)

46929 ■ Journal of Nippon Medical School
Medical Association of Nippon Medical School
1-1-5 Sendagi
Bunkyo-ku
Tokyo 113-8602, Japan
Fax: 81 338 223759
Publisher E-mail: jnms@nms.ac.jp
Medical science journal. **Founded:** 1927. **Freq:** Bimonthly. **Key Personnel:** Eiji Uchida, Editor in Chief; Hirobumi Asakura, Editor; Koji Adachi, Editor; Takashi Itoh, Editor; Zenya Naito, Editor; Timothy Minton, Editor; Akihiko Gemma, Editor. **ISSN:** 1345-4676. **Remarks:** Advertising accepted; rates available upon request. **URL:** http://www.nms.ac.jp/jnms/. **Circ:** Controlled 2,850

46930 ■ Journal of Nuclear Science and Technology
Atomic Energy Society of Japan
Nihon Genshiryoku Gakkai
3-7 Shimbashi 2-chome
Minato-ku
Tokyo 105-0004, Japan
Ph: 81 335 081261
Fax: 81 335 816128
Publication E-mail: atom@aesj.or.jp
Publisher E-mail: atom@aesj.or.jp
Journal covering nuclear science and technology. **Freq:** Monthly. **Key Personnel:** Tokohiko Yano, Editor-in-Chief. **ISSN:** 0022-3131. **Subscription Rates:** US$300 individuals. **URL:** http://wwwsoc.nii.ac.jp/aesj/jnst/index.htm; http://www.aesj.or.jp/publication/jnst.html. **Circ:** 1,500

46931 ■ Journal of Occupational Health
Japan Society for Occupational Health

IPEC Inc.
1-24-11 sugamo
Toshima-ku
Tokyo 170-0002, Japan
Ph: 81 3 59784067
Fax: 81 3 59784068
Publisher E-mail: joh-editor@info.uoeh-u.ac.jp
Publishes articles related to occupational and environmental health, including fundamental toxicological studies of industrial chemicals and other related studies. **Founded:** 1996. **Freq:** Bimonthly. **Key Personnel:** Akio Koizumi, Editor-in-Chief. **ISSN:** 1341-9145. **URL:** http://joh.med.uoeh-u.ac.jp. **Circ:** Paid 8,000

46932 ■ Journal of Oceanography
Oceanographic Society of Japan
c/o JOS/Mainichi Admin. Center for Academic Societies
9th Fl., Palace-side Bldg.
1-1-1 Hitotsubashi
Chiyoda-ku
Tokyo 100-0003, Japan
Fax: 81 332 111413
Journal containing scientific papers on marine sciences. **Freq:** Bimonthly. **Key Personnel:** Humio Mitsudera, Author; Isao Kudo, Author; Chen-Tung Arthur Chen, Editor. **ISSN:** 0916-8370. **Subscription Rates:** US$110 individuals regular member; US$80 members 65 and above; US$60 students member. **URL:** http://wwwsoc.nii.ac.jp/kaiyo/society/publish-e.html.

46933 ■ Journal of Operations Research Society of Japan
Elsevier Science Inc. - Japan Regional Office
9-15 Higashi-Azabu 1-chome
Minato-ku
Tokyo 106-0044, Japan
Ph: 81 335 896370
Fax: 81 335 896371
Publisher E-mail: jp.bkinfo@elsevier.com
Journal covering economics. **Founded:** 1957. **Freq:** Quarterly. **Key Personnel:** Masakiyo Miyazawa, Editor. **ISSN:** 0453-4514. **URL:** http://www.ingentaconnect.com/content/els/04534514. **Circ:** Paid 3,000

46934 ■ Journal of Oral Science
Nihon University School of Dentistry
1-8-13 Kanda-Surugadai
Chiyoda-ku
Tokyo 101-8310, Japan
Ph: 81 3 32198001
Fax: 81 3 32198310
Publisher E-mail: general@nc.dent.nihon-u.ac.jp
Journal of dentistry. **Founded:** 1958. **Freq:** Quarterly. **Key Personnel:** Noriaki Koshikawa, Editor-in-Chief; Masashi Miyazaki, Assoc. Ed.; Clive S. Langham, Language Ed. **ISSN:** 1343-4934. **URL:** http://www.dent.nihon-u.ac.jp/publ/e-pub00.html. **Circ:** Controlled 1,200

46935 ■ Journal of Orthopaedic Science
Springer-Verlag Tokyo
No. 2, Funato Bldg.
1-11-11 Kudan-kita
Chiyoda-ku
Tokyo 102-0073, Japan
Ph: 81 368 317000
Fax: 81 368 317001
Publisher E-mail: info@springer.jp
Periodical featuring the latest research and topical debates in all fields of clinical and experimental orthopedics. **Subtitle:** Official Journal of the Japanese Orthopaedic Association. **Founded:** 1996. **Freq:** Bimonthly. **Key Personnel:** Tetsuya Tamaki, Editor-in-Chief; Toru Fukubayashi, Assoc. Ed.; Kunio Takaoka, Assoc. Ed.; Yasuo Yamauchi, Assoc. Ed.; Savio Woo, Assoc. Ed.; Keiro Ono, Assoc. Ed. **ISSN:** 0949-2658. **Subscription Rates:** EUR342 institutions print incl. free access or e-only; EUR410.40 institutions enhanced access. **Remarks:** Accepts advertising. **URL:** http://www.springer.com/medicine/orthopedics/journal/776. **Circ:** Paid 2,800

46936 ■ Journal of Photochemistry and Photobiology, C
Elsevier (Singapore) Pte. Ltd.
c/o Masahiro Irie, Ed.-in-Ch.
Dept. of Chemistry
The Rikkyo (St. Paul) University
Nishi-Ikebukuro 3-34-1, Toshima-ku
Tokyo 171-8501, Japan

Publisher E-mail: asiabkinfo@elsevier.com
Official journal of the Japanese Photochemistry Association, providing a forum for mutual communication among scientists in various fields of photochemistry, covering such topics as fundamental molecular photochemistry in gas, liquid, and solid phases, organic photochemistry, inorganic photochemistry, supramolecular photochemistry, photochemical aspects of photosynthesis and photobiology, photoelectrochemistry, photocatalysis, solar energy conversion, photochemical devices, photofabrication, photofunctionalization, new chemistry for photonics, and other related areas. **Subtitle:** Photochemistry Reviews. **Founded:** 2000. **Freq:** Quarterly. **Key Personnel:** H. Inoue, Editor-in-Chief, inoue-haruo@tmu.ac.jp; M. Anpo, Editorial Board; I.R Gould, Editorial Board; H. Miyasaka, Assoc. Ed.; A. Harriman, Editorial Board; K. Morakoshi, Assoc. Ed.; B. Ohtani, Assoc. Ed.; U. Mazzucato, Editorial Board; T. Ichimura, Editorial Board; C.H. Tung, Editorial Board. **ISSN:** 1389-5567. **Subscription Rates:** EUR702 institutions for European countries and Iran; US$785 institutions for all countries except Europe, Japan and Iran; 93,200¥ institutions. **URL:** http://www.elsevier.com/wps/find/journaldescription.cws_home/620380/descriptiondescription.

46937 ■ Journal of Physical Society of Japan
Physical Society of Japan
Yushima Bldg., 5th Fl.
2-31-22 Yushima
Bunkyo-ku
Tokyo 113-0034, Japan
Fax: 81 3 58443290
Publication E-mail: jpsj_edit@ipap.jp
Physics journal. **Founded:** 1946. **Freq:** Monthly. **Key Personnel:** H. Takayama, Advisory Board; K. Asahi, Hd. Ed.; A. Furusaki, Assoc. Ed.; T. Deguchi, Assoc. Ed.; H. Amitsuka, Assoc. Ed.; A. Kawabata, Editor-in-Chief. **ISSN:** 0031-9015. **Subscription Rates:** 80,000¥ individuals; 86,000¥ other countries surface mail; 102,000¥ other countries airmail. **URL:** http://jpsj.ipap.jp/. **Circ:** Paid 4,000

46938 ■ Journal of Plant Research
Botanical Society of Japan
Toshin Bldg.
2-27-2 Hongo
Bunkyo-ku
Tokyo 113-0003, Japan
Ph: 81 3 38145675
Fax: 81 3 38145352
Publisher E-mail: bsj@bsj.or.jp
Journal covering botany. **Founded:** 1887. **Freq:** Bimonthly. **Key Personnel:** Hirokazu Tsukaya, Editor-in-Chief; Motoyuki Ashikara, Editor; Hidehiro Fukaki, Editor. **ISSN:** 0918-9440. **Subscription Rates:** 9,000¥ members; US$40 members; 180,000¥ institutions. **Remarks:** Accepts advertising. **URL:** http://bsj.or.jp. **Circ:** Paid 2,600

46939 ■ Journal of Reproduction and Development
Society for Reproduction and Development
c/o IPEC Inc.
1-24-11 Sugamo
Toshima
Tokyo 170-0002, Japan
Fax: 81 3 59784068
Publisher E-mail: info@reproduction.jp
Journal of veterinary science. **Founded:** 1955. **Freq:** Bimonthly. **Key Personnel:** Kei-Ichiro Maeda, Editor-in-Chief; Hiroshi Nagashima, Editorial Board; Masugi Nishihara, Editorial Board; Kiyoshi Okuda, Assoc. Edc.; Satoshi Ohkura, Managing Editor; Noboru Manabe, Contact. **ISSN:** 0916-8818. **Subscription Rates:** 9,000¥ nonmembers. **Remarks:** Advertising accepted; rates available upon request. **URL:** http://reproduction.jp/jrd/jrdtop.html. **Circ:** (Not Reported)

46940 ■ Journal of Robotics and Mechatronics
Fuji Technology Press Ltd.
4F Toranomon Sangyo Bldg.
2-29 Toranomon
Minato-Ku
Tokyo 105-0001, Japan
Ph: 81 335 080051
Fax: 81 335 920648
Publisher E-mail: webmaster@fujipress.jp
Peer-reviewed journal covering the field of computers. **Founded:** 1989. **Freq:** Bimonthly. **Key Personnel:** Ma-

---

Circulation: ★ = ABC; △ = BPA; ◆ = CAC; ● = CCAB; ❏ = VAC; ⊕ = PO Statement; ‡ = Publisher's Report; Boldface figures = sworn; Light figures = estimated.

Gale Directory of Publications & Broadcast Media/147th Ed.   **5117**

koto Kaneko, Former Ed. in Ch.; Kiyoshi Komoriya, Editor; Toshio Fukuda, Editorial Member; Kazuhiro Kosuge, Dep. Ch. Ed.; Fumihito Arai, Editorial Member; Tatsuo Arai, Editor-in-Chief; Masanori Hariyama, Editorial Member; Paolo Dario, Editorial Member; Yasuhisa Hasegawa, Editorial Member; Tsutomu Hasegawa, Editorial Member. **ISSN:** 0915-3942. **Subscription Rates:** 111,500¥ institutions. **URL:** http://www.fujipress.jp/JRM/index.html.

46941 ■ Journal of Space Technology and Science
Japanese Rocket Society
5-16-9 Honkomagome
Bunkyo-ku
Tokyo 113-0021, Japan
Ph: 81 3 58145801
Fax: 81 3 58145820
Journal of aeronautics. **Founded:** 1985. **Freq:** Semiannual. **Key Personnel:** Yoshiaki Ohkami, Editor. **ISSN:** 0911-551X. **Subscription Rates:** US$50.

46942 ■ Journal of Structural and Construction Engineering
Architectural Institute of Japan
26-20 Shiba 5-chome
Minato-Ku
Tokyo 108-8414, Japan
Ph: 81 334 562051
Fax: 81 334 562058
Publisher E-mail: info@aij.or.jp
Journal covering architecture. **Founded:** 1936. **Freq:** Monthly. **ISSN:** 1340-4202. **Subscription Rates:** 33,600¥. **URL:** http://ci.nii.ac.jp/vol_issue/nels/AN10438559_en.html.

46943 ■ Journal of Structural Engineering B
Architectural Institute of Japan
26-20 Shiba 5-chome
Minato-Ku
Tokyo 108-8414, Japan
Ph: 81 334 562051
Fax: 81 334 562058
Publisher E-mail: info@aij.or.jp
Journal covering civil engineering. **Founded:** 1985. **Freq:** Annual. **ISSN:** 0910-8033. **URL:** http://www.aij.or.jp/aijhome.htm.

46944 ■ Journal of Veterinary Medical Science
Maruzen Company Ltd.
9-2 Nihombashi 3-chome
Chuo-Ku
PO Box 5050
Tokyo 103-8244, Japan
Ph: 81 3 32733234
Fax: 81 3 32731144
Publisher E-mail: export@maruzen.co.jp
Journal of veterinary science. **Founded:** 1939. **Freq:** Monthly. **ISSN:** 0916-7250. **Subscription Rates:** US$294 individuals. **Remarks:** Advertising accepted; rates available upon request. **URL:** http://www.maruzen.co.jp/home-eng/inter-d-per.html. **Circ:** Paid 5,000

46945 ■ Journal of Visualization
Ohmsha Ltd.
3-1 Kanda-Nishiki-cho
Chiyoda-ku
Tokyo 101-8460, Japan
Ph: 81 3 32332425
Fax: 81 3 32332426
Publication E-mail: info@vsj.or.jp
Publisher E-mail: kaigaika@ohmsha.co.jp
Physics journal. **Founded:** 1998. **Freq:** Quarterly. **Key Personnel:** M. Kawahashi, Editor-in-Chief; D. Dabiri, Assoc. Ed.; N. Fujisawa, Assoc. Ed.; K. Koyamada, Assoc. Ed.; K. Hourigan, Assoc. Ed.; S.J. Lee, Assoc. Ed.; T. Leweke, Assoc. Ed.; N. Ninomiya, Assoc. Ed.; K. Okamoto, Assoc. Ed. **ISSN:** 1343-8875. **Subscription Rates:** 35,000¥ nonmembers including postage and handling charges; 15,000¥ members including postage and handling charges; EUR596 individuals including 36 for postage and handling; US$742 individuals including 44 for postage and handling. **URL:** http://www.ohmsha.co.jp/index_e.htm; http://www.springer.com/materials/mechanics/journal/12650.

46946 ■ Journal of Wood Science
Springer-Verlag Tokyo
No. 2, Funato Bldg.
1-11-11 Kudan-kita
Chiyoda-ku
Tokyo 102-0073, Japan
Ph: 81 368 317000
Fax: 81 368 317001
Publisher E-mail: info@springer.jp
Journal containing original articles on basic and applied research dealing with the science, technology, and engineering of wood, wood components, wood and wood-based products, and wood constructions. **Freq:** Bimonthly. **Key Personnel:** Yoshiyuki Nishio, Editor-in-Chief. **ISSN:** 1435-0211. **Subscription Rates:** EUR314 institutions print incl. free access or e-only; EUR376.80 institutions print incl. enhanced access. **Remarks:** Accepts advertising. **URL:** http://www.springer.com/lifesci/forestry/journal/10086. **Circ:** (Not Reported)

46947 ■ J@pan Inc Magazine
Japan Incorporated Communications K.K.
Minami-Aoyama 1st Bldg., 10th Fl.
7-8-1 Minami Aoyama, Minato-Ku
Tokyo 107-0062, Japan
Ph: 81 334 992099
Fax: 81 334 993109
Publication E-mail: subs@japaninc.com
Publisher E-mail: info@japaninc.com
English language magazine covering business and technology in Japan for professionals worldwide. **Subtitle:** Business Technology People. **Freq:** Monthly. **Key Personnel:** Terrie Lloyd, Publisher, terrie.lloyd@japaninc.com; Michael Condon, Editor-in-Chief, michael@japaninc.com. **ISSN:** 1345-4846. **Subscription Rates:** 3,600¥ individuals within Japan; 6,000¥ two years within Japan; 6,600¥ other countries; 12,000¥ two years outside Japan; 780¥ single issue; US$7.90 single issue. **Remarks:** Accepts advertising. **URL:** http://www.japaninc.com/the_magazine. **Formerly:** Computing Japan. **Ad Rates:** 4C: 550,000¥. **Circ:** 24,000

46948 ■ JSME International Journal Series A
Japan Society of Mechanical Engineers
Shinanomachi-Rengakan Bldg.
35 Shinano-Machi
Shinjuku-Ku
Tokyo 160-0016, Japan
Ph: 81 353 603505
Fax: 81 353 603509
Publisher E-mail: wwwadmin-e@jsme.or.jp
Journal of mechanical engineering. **Subtitle:** Solid Mechanics and Material Engineering. **Founded:** 1958. **Freq:** Quarterly. **Key Personnel:** Dr. Junji Tani, Editor-in-Chief. **ISSN:** 1344-7912. **Subscription Rates:** US$125 nonmembers; US$68 members. **Remarks:** Advertising accepted; rates available upon request. **URL:** http://www.jsme.or.jp. **Circ:** Paid 1,300

46949 ■ JSME International Journal Series B
Japan Society of Mechanical Engineers
Shinanomachi-Rengakan Bldg.
35 Shinano-Machi
Shinjuku-Ku
Tokyo 160-0016, Japan
Ph: 81 353 603505
Fax: 81 353 603509
Publisher E-mail: wwwadmin-e@jsme.or.jp
Journal of mechanical engineering. **Subtitle:** Fluids and Thermal Engineering. **Founded:** 1958. **Freq:** Quarterly. **ISSN:** 1340-8054. **Subscription Rates:** US$68 nonmembers; US$125 members. **URL:** http://www.jsme.or.jp; http://www.selcuk.edu.tr/dergi/engcomp/601800.html.

46950 ■ JSME International Journal Series C
Japan Society of Mechanical Engineers
Shinanomachi-Rengakan Bldg.
35 Shinano-Machi
Shinjuku-Ku
Tokyo 160-0016, Japan
Ph: 81 353 603505
Fax: 81 353 603509
Publication E-mail: journal@jsme.or.jp
Publisher E-mail: wwwadmin-e@jsme.or.jp
Journal of mechanical engineering. **Subtitle:** Dynamics, Control, Robotics, Design and Manufacturing. **Founded:** 1958. **Freq:** Quarterly. **Key Personnel:** Dr. Junji Tani, Editor-in-Chief. **ISSN:** 1344-7653. **Subscription Rates:** US$125 nonmembers; US$68 members. **URL:** http://www.jsme.or.jp/English/publication.html.

46951 ■ Juliet
Kodansha Ltd.
2-12-21 Otowa
Bunkyo-ku
Tokyo 112-8001, Japan
Ph: 81 3 3946 6201
Fax: 81 3 3944 9915
Magazine for girls featuring stories written in the style of a Harlequin romance. **Freq:** Bimonthly. **Key Personnel:** Sawako Noma, President. **URL:** http://www.kodanclub.com/cgi-local/magazine.cgi?id=18; http://www.kodanclub.com/.

46952 ■ Keio Economic Studies
Keio University
Keio Economic Society
2-19-30 Mita
Minato-ku
Tokyo 108-8346, Japan
Fax: 81 3 34547029
Journal covering economics. **Founded:** 1963. **Freq:** Semiannual. **Key Personnel:** Miki Seko, Editorial Committee; Hisashi Yano, Chm.; Mikio Nakayama, Editorial Committee. **ISSN:** 0022-9709. **Subscription Rates:** 1,500¥ individuals. **Remarks:** Advertising accepted; rates available upon request. **URL:** http://www.econ.keio.ac.jp/org/kes/en/kesj.html; http://www.econ.keio.ac.jp/org/kes/ja/pub/pkest.htm. **Circ:** Paid 800

46953 ■ The Keio Journal of Medicine
Keio University
School of Medicine
35 Shinanomachi
Shinjuku
Tokyo 160-8582, Japan
Ph: 81 3 33531211
Fax: 81 3 53617091
Publication devoted to the advancement and dissemination of the fundamental knowledge of medical science. **Founded:** 1952. **Freq:** Quarterly. **Key Personnel:** Kazuyuki Omae, MD, Editorial Advisory Board; Hideyuki Okano, MD, Editor; Takayuki Ohira, MD, Editor; Masafumi Nishizawa, PhD, Editor; Michiie Sakamoto, MD, Editor-in-Chief; Midori Awazu, MD, Editor; Akiko Tanikawa, MD, Editor; Michisuke Yuzaki, Editorial Advisory Board; Toshifumi Hibi, MD, Editor; Satoshi Ogawa, Editorial Advisory Board. **ISSN:** 0022-9717. **URL:** http://www.kjm.keio.ac.jp/. **Circ:** Paid 500

46954 ■ Kiss
Kodansha Ltd.
2-12-21 Otowa
Bunkyo-ku
Tokyo 112-8001, Japan
Ph: 81 3 3946 6201
Fax: 81 3 3944 9915
Comic magazine featuring stories about love and relationships for college girls and female office workers in their twenties. **Freq:** Semimonthly. **Key Personnel:** Sawako Noma, President. **URL:** http://www.kodansha.co.jp/english/manga/magazines.html.

46955 ■ Kogane
Koganemushi-Kenkyukai (The Japanese Society of Scarabaeoideans)
c/o Shinya Kawai
4-16-3, Shimouma
Setagaya-ku
Tokyo 154-0002, Japan
Publisher E-mail: kogane@kawamo.co.jp
Bulletins containing descriptions and exchanging information of world-wide scarabaeoid beetles. **Freq:** Semiannual. **ISSN:** 1346-0943. **URL:** http://kawamo.co.jp/kogane/.

46956 ■ Kyodo News
Shiodome Media Tower 15th Fl.
1-7-1 Higashi-Shimbashi
Minato-ku
Tokyo 105-7201, Japan
Fax: 81 3 62528306
Publisher E-mail: kokusai@kyodonews.jp
General online newspaper. **Founded:** 1945. **Freq:** Daily. **Remarks:** Advertising accepted; rates available upon request. **URL:** http://english.kyodonews.jp. **Circ:** (Not Reported)

46957 ■ Lamellicornia
Society of Lamellicornians
c/o Mr. Masaaki Ishida
23-5 Miyamae 3-chome
Suginami-ku
Tokyo 168-0081, Japan
Journal of entomology. **Founded:** 1985. **Freq:** Annual. **ISSN:** 0915-3020.

46958 ■ Landscape and Ecological Engineering
Springer-Verlag Tokyo
No. 2, Funato Bldg.
1-11-11 Kudan-kita
Chiyoda-ku
Tokyo 102-0073, Japan
Ph: 81 368 317000
Fax: 81 368 317001
Publisher E-mail: info@springer.jp
Journal publishing in the interests of protecting and improving the environment in the face of biodiversity loss, desertification, global warming, and other environmental conditions. **Freq:** Bimonthly. **Key Personnel:** Futoshi Nakamura, Editor-in-Chief; Nam-Choon Kim, Assoc. Ed.-in-Ch. **ISSN:** 1860-1871. **Subscription Rates:** EUR266 institutions print incl. free access or e-only; EUR319.20 institutions print incl. free enhanced access. **Remarks:** Advertising accepted; rates available upon request. **URL:** http://www.springer.com/lifesci/ecology/journal/11355. **Circ:** (Not Reported)

46959 ■ Language Teacher
Japan Association for Language Teaching
Urban Edge Bldg. 5F
1-37-9 Taito
Taito-ku
Tokyo 110-0016, Japan
Ph: 81 338 371630
Fax: 81 338 371631
Publication E-mail: tlt_ed1@jalt.org
Educational magazine. **Founded:** Apr. 1984. **Freq:** Monthly. **Key Personnel:** Paul Daniels, Co-Ed.; Katsumi Ito, Proofreader; Aleda Krause, Asst. Ed., Collating Ed.; Paul Lewis, Asst. Ed.; Junko Izawa, Proofer; Joyce Cunningham, Co-Ed. **ISSN:** 0289-7938. **URL:** http://www.jalt-publications.org/tlt/. **Ad Rates:** BW: 49,000¥. **Circ:** (Not Reported)

46960 ■ Library and Information Science
Mita Society for Library and Information Science
c/o School of Library & Information Science
Keio University
2-15-45 Mita
Minato-ku
Tokyo 108-8345, Japan
Publishes scholarly research papers and technical reports containing thoughts and findings not published previously in the fields of library and information science. **Founded:** 1963. **Freq:** Semiannual. **Key Personnel:** Teru Agata, Editorial Committee. **ISSN:** 0373-4447. **Subscription Rates:** US$20 individuals. **URL:** http://wwwsoc.nii.ac.jp/mslis/journal-e.html. **Circ:** Paid 1,500

46961 ■ Limnology
Springer-Verlag Tokyo
No. 2, Funato Bldg.
1-11-11 Kudan-kita
Chiyoda-ku
Tokyo 102-0073, Japan
Ph: 81 368 317000
Fax: 81 368 317001
Publisher E-mail: info@springer.jp
Journal covering the scientific study of bodies of water. **Founded:** 1931. **Freq:** 3/yr, April/August/December. **Trim Size:** A4. **Key Personnel:** Shin-Ichi Nakano, Assoc. Ed.; Syuhei Ban, Editor-in-Chief; Naoshige Goto, Managing Editor. **ISSN:** 1439-8621. **Subscription Rates:** EUR231 institutions print incl. free access; EUR277.20 institutions print incl. enhanced access. **Remarks:** Accepts advertising. **URL:** http://www.springer.com/lifesciences/ecology/journal/10201; http://www.jsidre.or.jp/. **Formerly:** Japanese Journal of Limnology (2000). **Circ:** Paid 1,200

46962 ■ Magazine Special
Kodansha Ltd.
2-12-21 Otowa
Bunkyo-ku
Tokyo 112-8001, Japan
Ph: 81 3 3946 6201
Fax: 81 3 3944 9915
Magazine featuring experimental comics and developing new genres. **Freq:** Monthly. **Key Personnel:** Sawako Noma, President. **URL:** http://www.kodansha.co.jp/english/manga/magazines.html.

46963 ■ Magazine Z
Kodansha Ltd.
2-12-21 Otowa
Bunkyo-ku
Tokyo 112-8001, Japan

Ph: 81 3 3946 6201
Fax: 81 3 3944 9915
Magazine featuring manga with characters that are based on computer games and television animation series for teenagers. **Freq:** Monthly. **Key Personnel:** Sawako Noma, President. **URL:** http://kc.kodansha.co.jp/magazine/index.php/18341/.

46964 ■ Mainichi Daily News
The Mainichi Newspapers Co
1-1-1 Hitotsubashi
Chiyoda-ku
Tokyo 100-8051, Japan
Ph: 81 332120885
Fax: 81 332112509
Newspaper featuring news, opinion and commentary. **Founded:** Feb. 21, 1872. **Freq:** Daily. **Key Personnel:** Yoshiyuki Watanabe, Mng. Dir. **URL:** http://mdn.mainichi.jp/.

46965 ■ Medical Entomology and Zoology
Japan Society of Medical Entomology and Zoology
c/o Mutsuo Kobayashi
Dept. of Medical Entomology
National Institute of Infectious Diseases
1-23-1 Shinjuku-ku
Tokyo 162-8640, Japan
Ph: 81 352 851111
Fax: 81 352 851147
Journal containing information about medical entomology and zoology. **Freq:** Quarterly. **Key Personnel:** Yasuhiro Yano, Editorial Board; Yasushi Otsuka, Editorial Board; Minoru Baba, Editorial Board; Pradya Somboon, Editorial Board; Takao Okazawa, Editorial Board; Jeffrey D. Wells, Editorial Board; Yoshio Tsuda, Editorial Board. **ISSN:** 0424-7086. **Subscription Rates:** US$45 individuals for overseas membership; 5,000¥ individuals. **Remarks:** Accepts advertising. **URL:** http://www.jsmez.gr.jp/eng/ejournal.html. **Circ:** (Not Reported)

46966 ■ Medical Molecular Morphology
Springer-Verlag Tokyo
No. 2, Funato Bldg.
1-11-11 Kudan-kita
Chiyoda-ku
Tokyo 102-0073, Japan
Ph: 81 368 317000
Fax: 81 368 317001
Publisher E-mail: info@springer.jp
Journal covering biology. **Founded:** 1993. **Freq:** Quarterly. **Key Personnel:** Yoshinori Otsuki, Editor-in-Chief. **ISSN:** 1860-1480. **Subscription Rates:** EUR256 institutions print incl. free access or e-only; EUR307.20 institutions print incl. enhanced access. **Remarks:** Accepts advertising. **URL:** http://www.springer.com/biomed/medicalmicrobiology/journal/795. **Formerly:** Medical Electron Microscopy. **Circ:** (Not Reported)

46967 ■ Metropolis
Crisscross KK
3F Maison Tomoe Bldg.
3-16-1 Minami-Aoyama
Minato-ku
Tokyo 107-0062, Japan
Ph: 81 3 34236932
Fax: 81 3 34236901
General interest magazine. **Subtitle:** Japan's No. 1 English Magazine. **Freq:** Weekly. **Key Personnel:** Steve Trautlein, Editor-in-Chief; Terrie Lloyd, CEO/Publisher; James Hadfield, Editor. **Subscription Rates:** 4,000¥ individuals 12 issues; 7,500¥ individuals 24 issues; 14,000¥ individuals 48 issues. **Remarks:** Advertising accepted; rates available upon request. **URL:** http://metropolis.co.jp/default.asp. **Circ:** ★30,000

46968 ■ Microbiology and Immunology
Center for Academic Publications Japan
2-4-16 Yayoi
Bunkyo-Ku
Tokyo 113-0032, Japan
Ph: 81 3 38175821
Publication E-mail: mi@capj.or.jp
Publisher E-mail: office_contact@capj.or.jp
Journal of microbiology and immunology. **Founded:** 1957. **Freq:** Monthly. **Print Method:** Pringed and Online. **Trim Size:** A4. **Key Personnel:** Yasuhiko Horiguchi, Editor-in-Chief, horiguti@biken.osaka-u.ac.jp; Toshinori Nakazama, Editorial Board, takayama@faculty.chiba-u.jp. **ISSN:** 0385-5600. **Subscription Rates:** US$457 institutions print & online; US$199 individuals print & on-

line; 232 institutions print & online; 100 individuals print & online; EUR294 institutions; EUR150 individuals Europe only. **Remarks:** Advertising accepted; rates available upon request. **URL:** http://editors.capj.or.jp/. **Circ:** Paid 1,000

46969 ■ Mitsubishi Electric Advance
Mitsubishi Electric Corp.
Tokyo Bldg.
2-7-3, Marunouchi
Chiyoda-ku
Tokyo 100-8310, Japan
Ph: 81 3 32182111
Journal of electrical engineering. **Founded:** 1977. **Freq:** Quarterly. **Key Personnel:** Kiyoshi Takakuwa, Editor-in-Chief. **ISSN:** 1345-3041. **URL:** http://global.mitsubishielectric.com/company/r_and_d/advance/advance.html. **Circ:** Paid 2,000

46970 ■ Modern Rheumatology
Springer-Verlag Tokyo
No. 2, Funato Bldg.
1-11-11 Kudan-kita
Chiyoda-ku
Tokyo 102-0073, Japan
Ph: 81 368 317000
Fax: 81 368 317001
Publisher E-mail: info@springer.jp
Journal publishing original papers in English on research pertinent to rheumatology and associated areas such as pathology, physiology, clinical immunology, microbiology, biochemistry, experimental animal models, and pharmacology. **Freq:** Bimonthly. **Key Personnel:** Tsuneyo Mimori, Editor-in-Chief; Takayuki Sumida, Assoc. Ed. **ISSN:** 1439-7595. **Subscription Rates:** EUR260 institutions print incl. free access or e-only; EUR312 institutions print incl. enhanced access. **Remarks:** Advertising accepted; rates available upon request. **URL:** http://www.springer.com/medicine/rheumatology/journal/10165. **Circ:** (Not Reported)

46971 ■ Monumenta Nipponica
Sophia University
7-1 Kioi-cho
Chiyoda-Ku
Tokyo 102-8554, Japan
Ph: 81 3 32383179
Fax: 81 3 32383539
Studies on Japanese history, literature, and culture. **Subtitle:** Studies in Japanese Culture. **Founded:** 1938. **Freq:** Semiannual. **Key Personnel:** Esther Sanders, Managing Editor; Kate Wildman Nakai, Editor; Francis Mathy, Editor; Wilhelm Schiffer, Editor; Edmund R. Skrzypczak, Editor; Michael Cooper, Editor; J.B. Kraus, Founder; Joseph Pittau, Editor. **ISSN:** 0027-0741. **Subscription Rates:** 4,600¥ individuals; US$40 other countries; EUR42 other countries. **Remarks:** Advertising accepted; rates available upon request. **URL:** http://monumenta.cc.sophia.ac.jp/. **Circ:** Paid 1,150

46972 ■ Morning
Kodansha Ltd.
2-12-21 Otowa
Bunkyo-ku
Tokyo 112-8001, Japan
Ph: 81 3 3946 6201
Fax: 81 3 3944 9915
Entertainment comic magazine featuring realistic stories about businessmen and office workers, sports professionals and college professors, samurai adventure, and military action for men. **Freq:** Weekly. **Key Personnel:** Sawako Noma, President. **URL:** http://www.kodansha.co.jp/english/manga/magazines.html.

46973 ■ Moto-Champ
Sanei-shobo Publishing Company Ltd.
Honshio 19
Shinjyuku-ku
Tokyo 160-8547, Japan
Ph: 81 3 53695111
Fax: 81 3 53695117
Consumer magazine covering motorcycles and scooters. **Founded:** 1980. **Freq:** Monthly. **Trim Size:** B5. **Key Personnel:** Masaru Chai, Editor. **Remarks:** Accepts advertising. **URL:** http://www.moto-champ.net/. **Formerly:** Osami Suzuki. **Ad Rates:** BW: 150,000¥, 4C: 500,000¥. **Circ:** (Not Reported)

46974 ■ Nakayoshi
Kodansha Ltd.
2-12-21 Otowa

Circulation: ★ = ABC; △ = BPA; ♦ = CAC; • = CCAB; ❑ = VAC; ⊕ = PO Statement; ‡ = Publisher's Report; Boldface figures = sworn; Light figures = estimated.

Gale Directory of Publications & Broadcast Media/147th Ed.

5119

Bunkyo-ku
Tokyo 112-8001, Japan
Ph: 81 3 3946 6201
Fax: 81 3 3944 9915
Comic magazine featuring cute, chic, and charming stories for young girls. **Freq:** Monthly. **Key Personnel:** Sawako Noma, President. **URL:** http://kc.kodansha.co.jp/magazine/index.php/01033.

46975 ■ National Geographic Japanese Edition
Nikkei Business Publications Inc.
1-17-3 Shirokane
Minato-ku
Tokyo 108-8646, Japan
Ph: 81 3 68118502
Fax: 81 3 54219058
Publisher E-mail: info@nikkeibp.com
Magazine covering "the unknown facts of Earth" that relate to nature, adventure, history, global environment, science, and culture. **Founded:** Apr. 1995. **Freq:** Monthly. **Print Method:** Four color offset lithography. **Trim Size:** 175 x 254 mm. **Key Personnel:** Yuko Tanaka, International Advertising Sales, phone 81 3 68118311, fax 81 3 54219804, yktanaka@nikkeibp.co.jp. **Remarks:** Accepts advertising. **URL:** http://www.nikkeibp.com/adinfo/printmedia/ngj.html. **Ad Rates:** BW: 740¥, 4C: 1,020¥. **Circ:** ★84,124

46976 ■ NEC Journal of Advanced Technology
NEC Creative Ltd.
NEC Mediaproducts, Ltd.
1-23, Heiwajima 4-chome
Oota-Ku
Tokyo 143-0006, Japan
Computer journal. **Freq:** Quarterly. **Subscription Rates:** US$58 individuals. **URL:** http://www.nec.co.jp; http://www.nec.co.jp/techrep/en/r_and_d/. **Formerly:** NEC Research & Development.

46977 ■ NEC Technical Journal
NEC Creative Ltd.
1-23, Heiwajima 4-chome
Oota-Ku
Tokyo 143-0006, Japan
Ph: 81 3 54713866
Fax: 81 3 54713867
Technical computer journal. **Freq:** Quarterly. **ISSN:** 1880-5884. **URL:** http://www.nec.co.jp/techrep/en/journal/index.html.

46978 ■ Nikkei Architecture
Nikkei Business Publications Inc.
1-17-3 Shirokane
Minato-ku
Tokyo 108-8646, Japan
Ph: 81 3 68118502
Fax: 81 3 54219058
Publisher E-mail: info@nikkeibp.com
Magazine featuring architects and architectural designs firms, general contractors, and home building and construction company. **Founded:** Apr. 1976. **Freq:** Biweekly. **Print Method:** Four color offset lithography. **Trim Size:** 208 x 280 mm. **Key Personnel:** Yuko Tanaka, International Advertising Sales, phone 81 3 68118311, fax 81 3 54219804, yktanaka@nikkeibp.co.jp. **Remarks:** Accepts advertising. **URL:** http://www.nikkeibp.com/adinfo/printmedia/pm_001006044.html. **Ad Rates:** BW: 738¥, 4C: 1,070¥. **Circ:** ★44,461

46979 ■ Nikkei Board Guide
Nikkei Business Publications Inc.
1-17-3 Shirokane
Minato-ku
Tokyo 108-8646, Japan
Ph: 81 3 68118502
Fax: 81 3 54219058
Publisher E-mail: info@nikkeibp.com
Magazine featuring information for electronic board development engineers. **Founded:** Apr. 1997. **Freq:** Quarterly. **Print Method:** Four color offset lithography. **Trim Size:** 208 x 280 mm. **Key Personnel:** Yuko Tanaka, International Advertising Sales, phone 81 3 68118311, fax 81 3 54219804, yktanaka@nikkeibp.co.jp. **Remarks:** Accepts advertising. **URL:** http://www.nikkeibp.com/adinfo/printmedia/pm_001002028.html. **Ad Rates:** BW: 270¥, 4C: 450¥. **Circ:** 60,000

46980 ■ Nikkei BP Government Technology
Nikkei Business Publications Inc.
1-17-3 Shirokane

Minato-ku
Tokyo 108-8646, Japan
Ph: 81 3 68118502
Fax: 81 3 54219058
Publisher E-mail: info@nikkeibp.com
Magazine featuring information technology for government sectors. **Founded:** Sept. 2003. **Freq:** Semiannual. **Print Method:** Four color offset lithography. **Trim Size:** 208 x 280 mm. **Key Personnel:** Yuko Tanaka, International Advertising Sales, phone 81 3 68118311, fax 81 3 54219804, yktanaka@nikkeibp.co.jp. **Remarks:** Accepts advertising. **URL:** http://www.nikkeibp.com/adinfo/printmedia/pm_001003037.html. **Ad Rates:** BW: 400¥, 4C: 600¥. **Circ:** 11,100

46981 ■ Nikkei Business
Nikkei Business Publications Inc.
1-17-3 Shirokane
Minato-ku
Tokyo 108-8646, Japan
Ph: 81 3 68118502
Fax: 81 3 54219058
Publisher E-mail: info@nikkeibp.com
Magazine covering information about company management and business operations. **Founded:** Sept. 1969. **Freq:** Weekly. **Print Method:** Offset lithography. **Trim Size:** 210 x 280 mm. **Key Personnel:** Yuko Tanaka, International Advertising Sales, phone 81 3 68118311, fax 81 3 54219804, yktanaka@nikkeibp.co.jp. **Remarks:** Accepts advertising. **URL:** http://www.nikkeibp.com/adinfo/printmedia/pm_001001010.html; http://business.nikkeibp.co.jp/english/index.html. **Ad Rates:** BW: 1,670¥, 4C: 2,520¥. **Circ:** ★308,561

46982 ■ Nikkei Business Associe
Nikkei Business Publications Inc.
1-17-3 Shirokane
Minato-ku
Tokyo 108-8646, Japan
Ph: 81 3 68118502
Fax: 81 3 54219058
Publisher E-mail: info@nikkeibp.com
Magazine covering business for young people. **Founded:** Apr. 2002. **Freq:** Semimonthly. **Print Method:** Four color offset lithography. **Trim Size:** 210 x 280 mm. **Key Personnel:** Yuko Tanaka, International Advertising Sales, phone 81 3 68118311, fax 81 3 54219804, yktanaka@nikkeibp.co.jp. **Remarks:** Accepts advertising. **URL:** http://www.nikkeibp.com/adinfo/printmedia/pm_001001012.html. **Ad Rates:** BW: 700¥, 4C: 1,000¥. **Circ:** ★71,610

46983 ■ Nikkei Communications
Nikkei Business Publications Inc.
1-17-3 Shirokane
Minato-ku
Tokyo 108-8646, Japan
Ph: 81 3 68118502
Fax: 81 3 54219058
Publisher E-mail: info@nikkeibp.com
Magazine featuring information on communications/network products, services and technologies for people engaged in the planning, building, and operating of corporate networks. **Founded:** Oct. 1985. **Freq:** Semimonthly. **Print Method:** Four color offset lithography. **Trim Size:** 208 x 280 mm. **Key Personnel:** Yuko Tanaka, International Advertising Sales, phone 81 3 68118311, fax 81 3 54219804, yktanaka@nikkeibp.co.jp. **Remarks:** Accepts advertising. **URL:** http://www.nikkeibp.com/adinfo/printmedia/pm_001003035.html. **Ad Rates:** BW: 540¥, 4C: 800¥. **Circ:** ★26,486

46984 ■ Nikkei Computer
Nikkei Business Publications Inc.
1-17-3 Shirokane
Minato-ku
Tokyo 108-8646, Japan
Ph: 81 3 68118502
Fax: 81 3 54219058
Publisher E-mail: info@nikkeibp.com
Magazine covering information technology. **Founded:** Oct. 1981. **Freq:** Semimonthly. **Print Method:** Four color offset lithography. **Trim Size:** 208 x 280 mm. **Key Personnel:** Yuko Tanaka, International Advertising Sales, phone 81 3 68118311, fax 81 3 54219804, yktanaka@nikkeibp.co.jp. **Remarks:** Accepts advertising. **URL:** http://www.nikkeibp.com/adinfo/printmedia/pm_001003029.html. **Ad Rates:** BW: 856¥, 4C: 1,236¥. **Circ:** ★48,862

46985 ■ Nikkei Construction
Nikkei Business Publications Inc.
1-17-3 Shirokane
Minato-ku
Tokyo 108-8646, Japan
Ph: 81 3 68118502
Fax: 81 3 54219058
Publisher E-mail: info@nikkeibp.com
Magazine featuring construction industry. **Founded:** Oct. 1989. **Freq:** Semimonthly. **Print Method:** Four color offset lithography. **Trim Size:** 210 x 280 mm. **Key Personnel:** Yuko Tanaka, International Advertising Sales, phone 81 3 68118311, fax 81 3 54219804, yktanaka@nikkeibp.co.jp. **Remarks:** Accepts advertising. **URL:** http://www.nikkeibp.com/adinfo/printmedia/pm_001003045.html. **Ad Rates:** BW: 459¥, 4C: 569¥. **Circ:** ★26,357

46986 ■ Nikkei Design
Nikkei Business Publications Inc.
1-17-3 Shirokane
Minato-ku
Tokyo 108-8646, Japan
Ph: 81 3 68118502
Fax: 81 3 54219058
Publisher E-mail: info@nikkeibp.com
Magazine covering buildings and stores design. **Founded:** July 1987. **Freq:** Monthly. **Print Method:** Four color offset lithography. **Trim Size:** 210 x 280 mm. **Key Personnel:** Yuko Tanaka, International Advertising Sales, phone 81 3 68118311, fax 81 3 54219804, yktanaka@nikkeibp.co.jp. **Remarks:** Accepts advertising. **URL:** http://www.nikkeibp.com/adinfo/printmedia/pm_001001016.html. **Ad Rates:** BW: 306¥, 4C: 522¥. **Circ:** Paid ★13,370

46987 ■ Nikkei Drug Information
Nikkei Business Publications Inc.
1-17-3 Shirokane
Minato-ku
Tokyo 108-8646, Japan
Ph: 81 3 68118502
Fax: 81 3 54219058
Publisher E-mail: info@nikkeibp.com
Magazine featuring drug information. **Founded:** Apr. 1998. **Freq:** Monthly. **Print Method:** Four color offset lithography. **Trim Size:** 210 x 297 mm. **Key Personnel:** Yuko Tanaka, International Advertising Sales, phone 81 3 68118311, fax 81 3 54219804, yktanaka@nikkeibp.co.jp. **Remarks:** Accepts advertising. **URL:** http://www.nikkeibp.com/adinfo/printmedia/pm_001005019.html. **Ad Rates:** BW: 532¥, 4C: 774¥. **Circ:** ★69,930

46988 ■ Nikkei Ecology
Nikkei Business Publications Inc.
1-17-3 Shirokane
Minato-ku
Tokyo 108-8646, Japan
Ph: 81 3 68118502
Fax: 81 3 54219058
Publisher E-mail: info@nikkeibp.com
Magazine covering ecology. **Founded:** June 1999. **Freq:** Monthly. **Print Method:** Four color offset lithography. **Trim Size:** 210 x 280 mm. **Key Personnel:** Yuko Tanaka, International Advertising Sales, phone 81 3 68118311, fax 81 3 54219804, yktanaka@nikkeibp.co.jp. **Remarks:** Accepts advertising. **URL:** http://www.nikkeibp.com/adinfo/printmedia/pm_001001014.html. **Ad Rates:** BW: 420¥, 4C: 580¥. **Circ:** ★16,632

46989 ■ Nikkei Electronics
Nikkei Business Publications Inc.
1-17-3 Shirokane
Minato-ku
Tokyo 108-8646, Japan
Ph: 81 3 68118502
Fax: 81 3 54219058
Publisher E-mail: info@nikkeibp.com
Publication covering the electronics industry. **Founded:** Apr. 1971. **Freq:** Biweekly. **Print Method:** Offset lithography. **Trim Size:** 208 x 280 mm. **Key Personnel:** Yasuo Tanokura, Editor-in-Chief; Matt Findel-Hawkins, Sales Dir., phone 44 20 79362855, fax 44 20 75836637. **Subscription Rates:** US$19,000 individuals. **Remarks:** Accepts advertising. **URL:** http://www.nikkeibp.com/adinfo/printmedia/ne.html. **Ad Rates:** BW: 580¥, 4C: 1,214¥. **Circ:** ★36,575

46990 ■ Nikkei Electronics China
Nikkei Business Publications Inc.

1-17-3 Shirokane
Minato-ku
Tokyo 108-8646, Japan
Ph: 81 3 68118502
Fax: 81 3 54219058
Publisher E-mail: info@nikkeibp.com
Magazine covering electronics. **Founded:** Nov. 2002. **Freq:** Monthly. **Print Method:** Four color offset lithography. **Trim Size:** 205 x 270 mm. **Key Personnel:** Yuko Tanaka, International Advertising Sales, phone 81 3 68118311, fax 81 3 54219804, yktanaka@nikkeibp.co. jp. **Remarks:** Accepts advertising. **URL:** http://www. nikkeibp.com/adinfo/printmedia/pm_001002023.html. **Ad Rates:** BW: US$1,060, 4C: US$4,150. **Circ:** △33,220

46991 ■ Nikkei Entertainment!
Nikkei Business Publications Inc.
1-17-3 Shirokane
Minato-ku
Tokyo 108-8646, Japan
Ph: 81 3 68118502
Fax: 81 3 54219058
Publisher E-mail: info@nikkeibp.com
Magazine featuring entertainment. **Founded:** Mar. 1997. **Freq:** Monthly. **Print Method:** Four color offset lithography. **Trim Size:** 210 x 280 mm. **Key Personnel:** Yuko Tanaka, International Advertising Sales, phone 81 3 68118311, fax 81 3 54219804, yktanaka@nikkeibp.co. jp. **Remarks:** Accepts advertising. **URL:** http://www. nikkeibp.com/adinfo/printmedia/pm_001007047.html. **Ad Rates:** BW: 760¥, 4C: 1,100¥. **Circ:** ★90,234

46992 ■ Nikkei Health
Nikkei Business Publications Inc.
1-17-3 Shirokane
Minato-ku
Tokyo 108-8646, Japan
Ph: 81 3 68118502
Fax: 81 3 54219058
Publisher E-mail: info@nikkeibp.com
Magazine covering health. **Founded:** Mar. 1998. **Freq:** Monthly. **Print Method:** Four color offset lithography. **Trim Size:** 210 x 280 mm. **Key Personnel:** Yuko Tanaka, International Advertising Sales, phone 81 3 68118311, fax 81 3 54219804, yktanaka@nikkeibp.co. jp. **Remarks:** Accepts advertising. **URL:** http://www. nikkeibp.com/adinfo/printmedia/pm_001005020.html. **Ad Rates:** BW: 600¥, 4C: 800¥. **Circ:** ★88,192

46993 ■ Nikkei Healthcare
Nikkei Business Publications Inc.
1-17-3 Shirokane
Minato-ku
Tokyo 108-8646, Japan
Ph: 81 3 68118502
Fax: 81 3 54219058
Publisher E-mail: info@nikkeibp.com
Magazine featuring healthcare information. **Founded:** Nov. 1989. **Freq:** Monthly. **Print Method:** Four color offset lithography. **Trim Size:** 208 x 280 mm. **Key Personnel:** Yuko Tanaka, International Advertising Sales, phone 81 3 68118311, fax 81 3 54219804, yktanaka@nikkeibp.co.jp. **Remarks:** Accepts advertising. **URL:** http://www.nikkeibp.com/adinfo/printmedia/pm_001005018.html. **Ad Rates:** BW: 351¥, 4C: 516¥. **Circ:** ★19,079

46994 ■ Nikkei Home Builder
Nikkei Business Publications Inc.
1-17-3 Shirokane
Minato-ku
Tokyo 108-8646, Japan
Ph: 81 3 68118502
Fax: 81 3 54219058
Publisher E-mail: info@nikkeibp.com
Magazine featuring home design and construction. **Founded:** June 1999. **Freq:** Monthly. **Print Method:** Four color offset lithography. **Trim Size:** 208 x 280 mm. **Key Personnel:** Yuko Tanaka, International Advertising Sales, phone 81 3 68118311, fax 81 3 54219804, yktanaka@nikkeibp.co.jp. **Remarks:** Accepts advertising. **URL:** http://www.nikkeibp.com/adinfo/printmedia/pm_001006046.html. **Ad Rates:** BW: 300¥, 4C: 450¥. **Circ:** ★22,754

46995 ■ Nikkei Information Strategy
Nikkei Business Publications Inc.
1-17-3 Shirokane
Minato-ku

Tokyo 108-8646, Japan
Ph: 81 3 68118502
Fax: 81 3 54219058
Publisher E-mail: info@nikkeibp.com
Magazine featuring new concepts of computerization and analyses of market trends. **Founded:** Apr. 1992. **Freq:** Monthly. **Print Method:** Four color offset lithography. **Trim Size:** 208 x 280 mm. **Key Personnel:** Yuko Tanaka, International Advertising Sales, phone 81 3 68118311, fax 81 3 54219804, yktanaka@nikkeibp.co. jp. **Remarks:** Accepts advertising. **URL:** http://www. nikkeibp.com/adinfo/printmedia/pm_001003030.html. **Ad Rates:** BW: 520¥, 4C: 760¥. **Circ:** ★20,809

46996 ■ Nikkei Linux
Nikkei Business Publications Inc.
1-17-3 Shirokane
Minato-ku
Tokyo 108-8646, Japan
Ph: 81 3 68118502
Fax: 81 3 54219058
Publisher E-mail: info@nikkeibp.com
Magazine covering information technology. **Founded:** Sept. 1999. **Freq:** Monthly. **Print Method:** Four color offset lithography. **Trim Size:** 208 x 280 mm. **Key Personnel:** Yuko Tanaka, International Advertising Sales, phone 81 3 68118311, fax 81 3 54219804, yktanaka@ nikkeibp.co.jp. **Remarks:** Accepts advertising. **URL:** http://www.nikkeibp.com/adinfo/printmedia/pm_ 001003033.html. **Ad Rates:** BW: 200¥, 4C: 450¥. **Circ:** ★15,185

46997 ■ Nikkei Medical
Nikkei Business Publications Inc.
1-17-3 Shirokane
Minato-ku
Tokyo 108-8646, Japan
Ph: 81 3 68118502
Fax: 81 3 54219058
Publisher E-mail: info@nikkeibp.com
Magazine featuring healthcare information. **Founded:** Apr. 1972. **Freq:** Monthly. **Print Method:** Four color offset lithography. **Trim Size:** 208 x 280 mm. **Key Personnel:** Yuko Tanaka, International Advertising Sales, phone 81 3 68118311, fax 81 3 54219804, yktanaka@ nikkeibp.co.jp. **Remarks:** Accepts advertising. **URL:** http://www.nikkeibp.com/adinfo/printmedia/pm_ 001005017.html. **Ad Rates:** BW: 1,116¥, 4C: 1,564¥. **Circ:** ★111,060

46998 ■ Nikkei Microdevices
Nikkei Business Publications Inc.
1-17-3 Shirokane
Minato-ku
Tokyo 108-8646, Japan
Ph: 81 3 68118502
Fax: 81 3 54219058
Publisher E-mail: info@nikkeibp.com
Magazine covering microdevices. **Founded:** July 1985. **Freq:** Monthly. **Print Method:** Four color offset lithography. **Trim Size:** 208 x 280 mm. **Key Personnel:** Yuko Tanaka, International Advertising Sales, phone 81 3 68118311, fax 81 3 54219804, yktanaka@nikkeibp.co. jp. **Remarks:** Accepts advertising. **URL:** http://www. nikkeibp.com/adinfo/printmedia/pm_001002025.html. **Ad Rates:** BW: 407¥, 4C: 627¥. **Circ:** ★14,200

46999 ■ Nikkei Monozukuri
Nikkei Business Publications Inc.
1-17-3 Shirokane
Minato-ku
Tokyo 108-8646, Japan
Ph: 81 3 68118502
Fax: 81 3 54219058
Publisher E-mail: info@nikkeibp.com
Magazine covering information about the manufacturing industry. **Founded:** Apr. 2004. **Freq:** Monthly. **Print Method:** Four color offset lithography. **Trim Size:** 208 x 280 mm. **Key Personnel:** Yuko Tanaka, International Advertising Sales, phone 81 3 68118311, fax 81 3 54219804, yktanaka@nikkeibp.co.jp. **Remarks:** Accepts advertising. **URL:** http://www.nikkeibp.com/adinfo/printmedia/pm_001002026.html. **Ad Rates:** BW: 478¥, 4C: 694¥. **Circ:** ★34,857

47000 ■ Nikkei Net Interactive
Nihon Keizai Shimbun Inc.
1-3-7 Otemachi
Chiyoda-Ku

Tokyo 100-8066, Japan
Ph: 81 3 62567158
Fax: 81 3 52233661
Publication E-mail: ecntct@nikkei.co.jp
Publisher E-mail: ecntct@nikkei.co.jp
Online business newspaper. **Freq:** Daily. **Subscription Rates:** 16,800¥ individuals. **Remarks:** Advertising accepted; rates available upon request. **URL:** http://www. nikkei.co.jp/enews/announce.html. **Circ:** (Not Reported)

47001 ■ Nikkei Network
Nikkei Business Publications Inc.
1-17-3 Shirokane
Minato-ku
Tokyo 108-8646, Japan
Ph: 81 3 68118502
Fax: 81 3 54219058
Publisher E-mail: info@nikkeibp.com
Magazine featuring network technology. **Founded:** Apr. 2000. **Freq:** Monthly. **Print Method:** Four color offset lithography. **Trim Size:** 208 x 280 mm. **Key Personnel:** Yuko Tanaka, International Advertising Sales, phone 81 3 68118311, fax 81 3 54219804, yktanaka@nikkeibp.co. jp. **Remarks:** Accepts advertising. **URL:** http://www. nikkeibp.com/adinfo/printmedia/pm_001003036.html. **Ad Rates:** BW: 480¥, 4C: 700¥. **Circ:** ★48,034

47002 ■ Nikkei PC Beginners
Nikkei Business Publications Inc.
1-17-3 Shirokane
Minato-ku
Tokyo 108-8646, Japan
Ph: 81 3 68118502
Fax: 81 3 54219058
Publisher E-mail: info@nikkeibp.com
Magazine featuring information for PC beginners. **Founded:** Sept. 1999. **Freq:** Monthly. **Print Method:** Four color offset lithography. **Trim Size:** 208 x 280 mm. **Key Personnel:** Yuko Tanaka, International Advertising Sales, phone 81 3 68118311, fax 81 3 54219804, yktanaka@nikkeibp.co.jp. **Remarks:** Accepts advertising. **URL:** http://www.nikkeibp.com/adinfo/printmedia/pm_001004040.html. **Ad Rates:** 4C: 450¥. **Circ:** 80,000

47003 ■ Nikkei PC21
Nikkei Business Publications Inc.
1-17-3 Shirokane
Minato-ku
Tokyo 108-8646, Japan
Ph: 81 3 68118502
Fax: 81 3 54219058
Publisher E-mail: info@nikkeibp.com
Magazine featuring personal computing. **Founded:** Mar. 1996. **Freq:** Monthly. **Print Method:** Four color offset lithography. **Trim Size:** 210 x 280 mm. **Key Personnel:** Yuko Tanaka, International Advertising Sales, phone 81 3 68118311, fax 81 3 54219804, yktanaka@nikkeibp.co. jp. **Remarks:** Accepts advertising. **URL:** http://www. nikkeibp.com/adinfo/printmedia/pm_001004039.html. **Ad Rates:** BW: 410¥, 4C: 700¥. **Circ:** ★161,939

47004 ■ Nikkei Personal Computing
Nikkei Business Publications Inc.
1-17-3 Shirokane
Minato-ku
Tokyo 108-8646, Japan
Ph: 81 3 68118502
Fax: 81 3 54219058
Publisher E-mail: info@nikkeibp.com
Magazine featuring information about computers. **Founded:** Oct. 1983. **Freq:** Semimonthly. **Print Method:** Four color offset lithography. **Trim Size:** 208 x 280 mm. **Key Personnel:** Yuko Tanaka, International Advertising Sales, phone 81 3 68118311, fax 81 3 54219804, yktanaka@nikkeibp.co.jp. **Remarks:** Accepts advertising. **URL:** http://www.nikkeibp.com/adinfo/printmedia/pm_001004038.html. **Ad Rates:** BW: 1,007¥, 4C: 1,460¥. **Circ:** ★177,199

47005 ■ Nikkei Restaurants
Nikkei Business Publications Inc.
1-17-3 Shirokane
Minato-ku
Tokyo 108-8646, Japan
Ph: 81 3 68118502
Fax: 81 3 54219058
Publisher E-mail: info@nikkeibp.com
Magazine featuring food service industry. **Founded:** Oct.

Circulation: ★ = ABC; △ = BPA; ◆ = CAC; • = CCAB; ❏ = VAC; ⊕ = PO Statement; ‡ = Publisher's Report; Boldface figures = sworn; Light figures = estimated.

1988. **Freq:** Monthly. **Print Method:** Four color offset lithography. **Trim Size:** 210 x 280 mm. **Key Personnel:** Yuko Tanaka, International Advertising Sales, phone 81 3 68118311, fax 81 3 54219804, yktanaka@nikkeibp.co. jp. **Remarks:** Accepts advertising. **URL:** http://www. nikkeibp.com/adinfo/printmedia/pm_001001015.html. **Ad Rates:** BW: 332¥, 4C: 504¥. **Circ:** ★19,137

47006 ■ Nikkei Software
Nikkei Business Publications Inc.
1-17-3 Shirokane
Minato-ku
Tokyo 108-8646, Japan
Ph: 81 3 68118502
Fax: 81 3 54219058
Publisher E-mail: info@nikkeibp.com
Magazine featuring computer software. **Founded:** May 1998. **Freq:** Monthly. **Print Method:** Four color offset lithography. **Trim Size:** 208 x 280 mm. **Key Personnel:** Yuko Tanaka, International Advertising Sales, phone 81 3 68118311, fax 81 3 54219804, yktanaka@nikkeibp.co. jp. **Remarks:** Accepts advertising. **URL:** http://www. nikkeibp.com/adinfo/printmedia/pm_001003034.html. **Ad Rates:** BW: 300¥, 4C: 500¥. **Circ:** ★20,928

47007 ■ Nikkei Solution Business
Nikkei Business Publications Inc.
1-17-3 Shirokane
Minato-ku
Tokyo 108-8646, Japan
Ph: 81 3 68118502
Fax: 81 3 54219058
Publisher E-mail: info@nikkeibp.com
Magazine covering business solutions. **Founded:** May 1996. **Freq:** Semimonthly. **Print Method:** Offset lithography. **Trim Size:** 210 x 280 mm. **Key Personnel:** Yuko Tanaka, International Advertising Sales, phone 81 3 68118311, fax 81 3 54219804, yktanaka@nikkeibp.co. jp. **Remarks:** Accepts advertising. **URL:** http://www. nikkeibp.com/adinfo/printmedia/pm_001003032.html. **Ad Rates:** BW: 275¥, 4C: 473¥. **Circ:** ★9,034

47008 ■ Nikkei Systems
Nikkei Business Publications Inc.
1-17-3 Shirokane
Minato-ku
Tokyo 108-8646, Japan
Ph: 81 3 68118502
Fax: 81 3 54219058
Publisher E-mail: info@nikkeibp.com
Magazine covering information technology. **Founded:** Mar. 2006. **Freq:** Monthly. **Print Method:** Four color offset lithography. **Trim Size:** 208 x 280 mm. **Key Personnel:** Yuko Tanaka, International Advertising Sales, phone 81 3 68118311, fax 81 3 54219804, yktanaka@ nikkeibp.co.jp. **Remarks:** Accepts advertising. **URL:** http://www.nikkeibp.com/adinfo/printmedia/pm_ 001003031.html. **Ad Rates:** BW: 390¥, 4C: 650¥. **Circ:** ★37,890

47009 ■ Nikkei Venture
Nikkei Business Publications Inc.
1-17-3 Shirokane
Minato-ku
Tokyo 108-8646, Japan
Ph: 81 3 68118502
Fax: 81 3 54219058
Publisher E-mail: info@nikkeibp.com
Magazine covering business venture. **Founded:** Oct. 1984. **Freq:** Monthly. **Print Method:** Four color offset lithography. **Trim Size:** 208 x 280 mm. **Key Personnel:** Yuko Tanaka, International Advertising Sales, phone 81 3 68118311, fax 81 3 54219804, yktanaka@nikkeibp.co. jp. **Remarks:** Accepts advertising. **URL:** http://www. nikkeibp.com/adinfo/printmedia/pm_001001013.html. **Ad Rates:** BW: 500¥, 4C: 770¥. **Circ:** ★59,790

47010 ■ The Nikkei Weekly
Nihon Keizai Shimbun Inc.
1-3-7 Otemachi
Chiyoda-Ku
Tokyo 100-8066, Japan
Ph: 81 3 62567158
Fax: 81 3 52233661
Publisher E-mail: ecntct@nikkei.co.jp
Business newspaper. **Founded:** 1962. **Freq:** Weekly (Mon.). **Key Personnel:** Nobuo Oneda, Editor. **ISSN:** 0918-5348. **Subscription Rates:** 21,600¥ individuals; 38,000¥ two years; US$129 individuals; C$195 individuals. **Remarks:** Advertising accepted; rates avail-

able upon request. **URL:** http://www.nni.nikkei.co.jp/e/fr/ tnw/index.htm. **Circ:** Paid 36,500

47011 ■ Nikkei WinPC
Nikkei Business Publications Inc.
1-17-3 Shirokane
Minato-ku
Tokyo 108-8646, Japan
Ph: 81 3 68118502
Fax: 81 3 54219058
Publisher E-mail: info@nikkeibp.com
Magazine featuring information about personal computers. **Founded:** Mar. 1995. **Freq:** Monthly. **Print Method:** Four color offset lithography. **Trim Size:** 280 x 280 mm. **Key Personnel:** Yuko Tanaka, International Advertising Sales, phone 81 3 68118311, fax 81 3 54219804, yktanaka@nikkeibp.co.jp. **Remarks:** Accepts advertising. **URL:** http://www.nikkeibp.com/adinfo/ printmedia/pm_001004043.html. **Ad Rates:** BW: 250¥, 4C: 550¥. **Circ:** ★43,791

47012 ■ Nippon Steel News
Nippon Steel Corp.
Marunouchi Pk. Bldg.
2-6-1, Marunouchi
Chiyoda Ward
Tokyo 100-8071, Japan
Ph: 81 332 424111
Fax: 81 332 755607
Journal of metallurgy. **Founded:** 1970. **Freq:** Monthly. **ISSN:** 0048-0452. **URL:** http://www.nsc.co.jp/en/ nsnews/.

47013 ■ Odontology
Springer-Verlag Tokyo
No. 2, Funato Bldg.
1-11-11 Kudan-kita
Chiyoda-ku
Tokyo 102-0073, Japan
Ph: 81 368 317000
Fax: 81 368 317001
Publisher E-mail: info@springer.jp
Peer-reviewed journal covering all disciplines involved in the field of dentistry and craniofacial research, including molecular studies related to oral health and disease. **Freq:** Semiannual. **Key Personnel:** Makoto Tsuchimo-chi, Editor-in-Chief; Ichiro Sasagawa, Managing Editor; Shingo Kurabuchi, Dep. Ed.; Yasumasa Akagawa, Assoc. Ed.; Takaaki Aoba, Assoc. Ed.; Jack L. Ferra-cane, Assoc. Ed. **ISSN:** 1618-1247. **Subscription Rates:** EUR156 institutions print incl. free access or e-only; EUR187.20 institutions enhanced access. **Remarks:** Advertising accepted; rates available upon request. **URL:** http://www.springer.com/east/home/ generic/search/results?SGWID=5-40109-701169595-0. **Circ:** (Not Reported)

47014 ■ One More Kiss
Kodansha Ltd.
2-12-21 Otowa
Bunkyo-ku
Tokyo 112-8001, Japan
Ph: 81 3 3946 6201
Fax: 81 3 3944 9915
Comic magazine featuring stories about love and beauty for women. **Freq:** Bimonthly. **Key Personnel:** Sawako Noma, President. **URL:** http://www.kodanclub.com/cgi-local/magazine.cgi?id=21; http://www.kodanclub.com/.

47015 ■ Optical Review
Optical Society of Japan
Imon Kudan-Kita Bldg., 5th Fl.
1-12-3 Kudan-kita
Chiyoda-ku
Tokyo 102-0073, Japan
Ph: 81 3 32381043
Fax: 81 3 32216245
Publisher E-mail: divisions@jsap.or.jp
Publishes research and review papers in all branches of optics. **Founded:** 1994. **Freq:** Bimonthly. **Key Personnel:** Ken-Ichi Ueda, Editor-in-Chief, ueda@ils.uec.ac.jp; K. Araki, Assoc. Ed.; H. Hori, Assoc. Ed. **ISSN:** 1340-6000. **URL:** http://annex.jsap.or.jp/OSJ/opticalreview/.

47016 ■ Paper Sky
Knee High Media Japan
1-23-3 Higashi Shibuya
Shibuya-ku
Tokyo 150-0011, Japan
Ph: 81 3 54699318
Fax: 81 3 54695656

Publication E-mail: international@khmj.com
Publisher E-mail: contact@khmj.com
Consumer magazine covering travel and lifestyle. **Freq:** in four seasonal editions. **Subscription Rates:** 1,000¥ individuals. **Remarks:** Accepts advertising. **URL:** http:// www.khmj.com; http://www.paper-sky.com. **Circ:** (Not Reported)

47017 ■ Pediatric Dental Journal
Japanese Society of Pediatric Dentistry Oral Health Association
1-43-9 Komagome TS Bldg.
Toshima-ku
Tokyo 170-0003, Japan
Journal of dentistry. **Founded:** 1991. **Freq:** Semiannual. **Key Personnel:** Dr. Kenshi Maki, PhD, Editor-in-Chief, k-maki@kyu-dent.ac.jp. **ISSN:** 0917-2394. **Subscription Rates:** US$10 individuals. **URL:** http://www.jspd.or. jp/english/02.htm.

47018 ■ Plant Production Science
Crop Science Society of Japan
Tokyo Secretariat
2F Shin-Kyoritsu Bldg.
Shinkawa 2-22-4, Chuo-Ku
Tokyo 104-0033, Japan
Fax: 81 3 35532047
Publisher E-mail: cssj-jim@bridge.ocn.ne.jp
Publishes original research reports on field crops and resource plants, their production and related subjects, covering a wide range of sciences; physiology, biotechnology, morphology, ecology, cropping system, production technology and post harvest. **Founded:** 1998. **Freq:** Quarterly. **Key Personnel:** Akira Yamauchi, Review Ed.; Osamu Ueno, Managing Editor; Mari Iwaya-Inoue, Editor-in-Chief. **ISSN:** 1343-943X. **Subscription Rates:** 6,000¥ individuals. **Remarks:** Advertising accepted; rates available upon request. **URL:** http://www.jstage.jst. go.jp/browse/pps. **Circ:** (Not Reported)

47019 ■ The Plaza
U-Kan Inc.
Yoyogi 2-32-1
Shibuya-ku
Tokyo 151-0053, Japan
Ph: 81 333 793881
Fax: 81 333 793882
Publisher E-mail: plaza@u-kan.co.jp
Journal in English and Japanese covering the preservation of global and intercultural human relations. **Founded:** Nov. 11, 1985. **Freq:** Quarterly. **Key Personnel:** Leo Shunji Nishida, Editor and Publisher. **URL:** http://u-kan.co.jp/indexE/indexE.html.

47020 ■ Polar Bioscience
National Institute of Polar Research
10-3 Midoricho
Tachikawa
Tokyo 190-8518, Japan
Ph: 81 42 5120608
Fax: 81 42 5283146
Publication E-mail: biosci20@nipr.ac.jp
Publication covering polar, sub-polar, marine and mountainous subjects, from a wide range of zoological, botanical and molecular disciplines. **Founded:** 1967. **Freq:** Annual. **Key Personnel:** M. Uchida, Editor; Takao Hoshiai, Editor-in-Chief; T. Odate, Editor; K. Furuya, Editor; T. Hirawake, Editor; S. Imura, Editor; H. Marchant, Editor; M. Fukuchi, Editor; S. Kojima, Editor; S. Kudoh, Executive Ed. **ISSN:** 1344-6231. **Remarks:** Advertising not accepted. **URL:** http://polaris.nipr.ac.jp/ ~penguin/polarbiosci/. **Formerly:** Proceedings of the Polar Biology Symposium of the National Institute of Polar Research. **Circ:** 1,000

47021 ■ Polymer Journal
Society of Polymer Science Japan
Shintomicho Bldg.
3-10-9 Irifune
Chuo-ku
Tokyo 104-0042, Japan
Ph: 81 3 55403776
Fax: 81 3 55403737
Publisher E-mail: kobunshi@spsj.or.jp
Journal covering scientific research and new information in all the fields of polymer science. **Founded:** 1970. **Freq:** Monthly. **Key Personnel:** Toshikazu Takata, Editor-in-Chief, fax 81 3 57342888, takata.t.ab@m. titech.ac.jp. **ISSN:** 0032-3896. **Subscription Rates:** US$314 individuals print and online; EUR248 individuals

print and online; 42,400¥ individuals print and online; 160 other countries print and online. **URL:** http://www.spsj.or.jp/c5/pj/pj.htm; http://matjournal.org/index.php?mid=jindex&stage=jlist1&jid=POLYMER. **Circ:** Paid 2,000

47022 ■ Population Ecology
Springer-Verlag Tokyo
No. 2, Funato Bldg.
1-11-11 Kudan-kita
Chiyoda-ku
Tokyo 102-0073, Japan
Ph: 81 368 317000
Fax: 81 368 317001
Publisher E-mail: info@springer.jp
Peer-reviewed journal containing original research articles and reviews on various aspects of population ecology. **Founded:** 1962. **Freq:** 3/yr. **Key Personnel:** Kazunori Sato, Assoc. Ed.; Dr. Takashi Saitoh, Ch. Ed., phone 44 1737 062590, fax 81 117 063450, popecol@fsc.hokudai.ac.jp; Andrew Liebhold, Assoc. Ed. **ISSN:** 1438-3896. **Subscription Rates:** EUR408 institutions print incl. free access or e-only; EUR489.60 institutions enhanced access. **Remarks:** Accepts advertising. **URL:** http://www.springer.com/lifesci/ecology/journal/10144. **Circ:** Paid 25,000

47023 ■ Ports and Harbors
International Association of Ports and Harbors
7F, S Twr., New Pier Takeshiba
1-16-1 Kaigan
Minato-ku
Tokyo 105-0022, Japan
Ph: 81 354 032770
Fax: 81 354 037651
Publisher E-mail: info@iaphworldports.org
Publication covering marine industries. **Founded:** 1956. **Freq:** Bimonthly 6/yr. **Key Personnel:** Penny Allen, Editor, phone 44 1737 379158; Satoshi Inoue, Sec. Gen., info@iaphworldports.org; Tony Slinn, Editor-in-Chief, phone 44 1737 379159, tony.slinn@lrfairplay.com. **ISSN:** 0554-0755. **Subscription Rates:** US$120 by mail includes postage; 80 by mail includes postage; EUR90 by mail includes postage. **Remarks:** Accepts advertising. **URL:** http://www.iaphworldports.org. **Ad Rates:** BW: 100,000¥, 4C: 3,043¥. **Circ:** 5,000

47024 ■ Primates
Springer-Verlag Tokyo
No. 2, Funato Bldg.
1-11-11 Kudan-kita
Chiyoda-ku
Tokyo 102-0073, Japan
Ph: 81 368 317000
Fax: 81 368 317001
Publisher E-mail: info@springer.jp
Journal of zoology. **Founded:** 1956. **Freq:** Quarterly. **Trim Size:** 277 x 210 mm. **Key Personnel:** James R. Anderson, Assoc. Ed.; Dr. Toshisada Nishida, Editor-in-Chief; Warren Y. Brockelman, Assoc. Ed. **ISSN:** 0032-8332. **Subscription Rates:** EUR358 institutions print incl. free access or e-only; EUR429.60 institutions print incl. enhanced access. **Remarks:** Advertising accepted; rates available upon request. **URL:** http://www.springer.com/lifesci/zoology/journal/10329. **Circ:** Paid 800

47025 ■ Priv.
Nikkei Business Publications Inc.
1-17-3 Shirokane
Minato-ku
Tokyo 108-8646, Japan
Ph: 81 3 68118502
Fax: 81 3 54219058
Publisher E-mail: info@nikkeibp.com
Lifestyle magazine featuring different women's interests. **Founded:** Mar. 2000. **Freq:** Quarterly. **Print Method:** Four color offset lithography. **Trim Size:** 208 x 280 mm. **Key Personnel:** Yuko Tanaka, International Advertising Sales, phone 81 3 68118311, fax 81 3 54219804, yktanaka@nikkeibp.co.jp. **Remarks:** Accepts advertising. **URL:** http://www.nikkeibp.com/adinfo/printmedia/pm_001007048.html. **Ad Rates:** 4C: 1,850¥. **Circ:** ★173,474

47026 ■ Proceedings of the Japan Academy, Series A
The Japan Academy
PO Box 5050
Tokyo 100-3191, Japan
Fax: 81 3 32789256
Journal featuring mathematical sciences. **Key Personnel:** Heisuke Hironaka, Editor-in-Chief; Shigefumi Mori,

Exec. Ed. **ISSN:** 0386-2194. **URL:** http://www.japan-acad.go.jp/en/publishing/pja_a.html.

47027 ■ Proceedings of the Japan Academy, Series B
The Japan Academy
PO Box 5050
Tokyo 100-3191, Japan
Fax: 81 3 32789256
Journal featuring scientific and academic progress in all fields of natural sciences. **Founded:** 1912. **Key Personnel:** Tamio Yamakawa, Editor-in-Chief; Masanori Otsuka, Exec. Ed. **ISSN:** 0386-2208. **URL:** http://www.japan-acad.go.jp/en/publishing/pja_b.html?pjaserb.htm.

47028 ■ Publications of Astronomical Society of Japan
Astronomical Society of Japan
c/o National Astronomical Observatory of Japan
2-21-1 Osawa
Mitaka-shi
Tokyo 181-8588, Japan
Ph: 81 422 311359
Fax: 81 422 315487
Publisher E-mail: office@pasj.asj.or.jp
Journal covering astronomy and astrophysics. **Founded:** 1949. **Freq:** Bimonthly. **Key Personnel:** T. Dotani, Managing Editor. **ISSN:** 0004-6264. **Subscription Rates:** 23,000¥ individuals. **Remarks:** Accepts advertising. **URL:** http://www.asj.or.jp. **Circ:** (Not Reported)

47029 ■ Quaternary Research
Japan Association for Quaternary Research
3F Rakuyo bld., 519 Waseda-tsurumaki-cho,
Shinjuku-ku
Tokyo 162-0041, Japan
Publisher E-mail: daiyonki@shunkosha.com
Earth sciences journal. **Subtitle:** Japan Association for Quaternary Research. **Founded:** 1957. **Freq:** 5/yr. **ISSN:** 0418-2642. **Subscription Rates:** US$83. **URL:** http://www.jstage.jst.go.jp/browse/jaqua/. **Circ:** Paid 1,900

47030 ■ Real Simple Japan
Nikkei Business Publications Inc.
1-17-3 Shirokane
Minato-ku
Tokyo 108-8646, Japan
Ph: 81 3 68118502
Fax: 81 3 54219058
Publisher E-mail: info@nikkeibp.com
Magazine featuring information for women who are searching for ways to balance their own needs, career, and family. **Founded:** Oct. 2005. **Freq:** Monthly. **Print Method:** Four color offset lithography. **Trim Size:** 228 x 276 mm. **Key Personnel:** Yuko Tanaka, International Advertising Sales, phone 81 3 68118311, fax 81 3 54219804, yktanaka@nikkeibp.co.jp. **Remarks:** Accepts advertising. **URL:** http://www.nikkeibp.com/adinfo/printmedia/pm_001007050.html. **Ad Rates:** 4C: 1,600¥. **Circ:** Paid ★105,285

47031 ■ Refrigeration
Japan Society of Refrigerating and Air Conditioning Engineers
Nihon Reito Kucho Gakkai
Sanei Bldg.
8 Sanei-cho
Shinjuku-ku
Tokyo 160-0008, Japan
Ph: 81 333 595231
Fax: 81 333 595233
English and Japanese language publication covering refrigeration. **Freq:** Monthly. **ISSN:** 0034-3714. **Subscription Rates:** Included in membership. **Remarks:** Advertising accepted; rates available upon request. **URL:** http://www.jsrae.or.jp/. **Circ:** 10,000

47032 ■ The Rigaku Journal
Rigaku Corp.
Rigaku Corp. 3-9-12 Matsubara-Cho
Akishima-shi
Tokyo 196-8666, Japan
Publisher E-mail: rinttyo@rigaku.co.jp
Scientific and technical journal containing articles relating to a wide range of X-ray diffraction and fluorescence applications. **Founded:** 1984. **Freq:** Semiannual. **Key Personnel:** Hideo Toraya, Editor-in-Chief; Kenichi Yaoita, Managing Editor, yaoita@rigaku.co.jp; Thomas

N. Blanton, Editor; Ting C. Huang, Assoc. Ed.-in-Ch.; Michael K. Mantler, Editor; Joe Ferrara, Editor. **ISSN:** 0913-543X. **URL:** http://www.rigaku.com/downloads/journal/.

47033 ■ The Rotary-No-Tomo
4th Fl., Kokuryu Shibakoen Bldg.
Shibakoen 2-6-15
Minato-ku
Tokyo 105-0011, Japan
Publisher E-mail: web@rotary-no-tomo.jp
Membership magazine of Rotary International covering current news about Rotary-related subjects in Japanese and English. **Freq:** Monthly. **Key Personnel:** Noriko Futagami, Editor. **URL:** http://www.rotary.or.jp/; http://www.rotary-no-tomo.jp/. **Circ:** 120,000

47034 ■ Rural and Environmental Engineering
Japanese Society of Irrigation Drainage and Reclamation Engineering
c/o Nogyo Doboku Kaikan
34-4 Shinbashi 5-Chome
Minato-ku
Tokyo 105-0004, Japan
Ph: 81 334 363418
Fax: 81 334 358494
Publisher E-mail: suido@jsidre.or.jp
Journal covering agriculture and environmental engineering. **Founded:** 1982. **Freq:** Semiannual. **Subscription Rates:** 6,000¥ individuals surface mail postage included; 4,000¥ individuals. **URL:** http://www.jsidre.or.jp/; http://www.jsidre.or.jp/publ/ree/index.htm.

47035 ■ SARAI
Shogakukan Inc.
2-3-1, Hitotsubashi
Chiyoda-ku
Tokyo 101-8001, Japan
Lifestyle magazine for the older generation. **Founded:** Sept. 7, 1989. **Freq:** Bimonthly. **Key Personnel:** Masahiro Oga, President. **Subscription Rates:** 480¥ individuals. **URL:** http://www.shogakukan.co.jp/english/.

47036 ■ Sensors and Materials
MYU
1-23-3-303 Sendagi
Bunkyo-ku
Tokyo 113-0022, Japan
Ph: 81 3 38227374
Fax: 81 3 38278547
Publisher E-mail: myukk@myu-inc.jp
Publishes original work in the experimental and theoretical fields, aimed at understanding sensing technology, related materials, associated phenomena, and applied systems. **Founded:** 1989. **Freq:** 8/yr. **Key Personnel:** Michael L. Reed, Editor; Susumu Sugiyama, Editor-in-Chief; Wolfgang Menz, Editor. **ISSN:** 0914-4935. **Subscription Rates:** US$400 individuals; 40,000¥ individuals. **URL:** http://www.myu-inc.jp/myukk/S&M/index.html.

47037 ■ Shakespeare Studies
Shakespeare Society of Japan
B1-23 Kenkyusha-Eigo Ctr. Bldg.
1-2, Kagurazaka
Shinjuku-ku
Tokyo 162-0825, Japan
Ph: 81 3 32608109
Publisher E-mail: info@s-sj.org
Journal of literature. **Founded:** 1962. **Freq:** Annual. **ISSN:** 0582-9402. **Subscription Rates:** 8,000¥ members; 5,000¥ students; 20,000¥ members associate. **URL:** http://www.s-sj.org/english/index.html. **Circ:** Paid 1,200

47038 ■ Shukan Shonen Magazine
Kodansha Ltd.
2-12-21 Otowa
Bunkyo-ku
Tokyo 112-8001, Japan
Ph: 81 3 3946 6201
Fax: 81 3 3944 9915
Entertainment comic magazine featuring stories ranging from sports to romance and cooking to humor. **Freq:** Weekly. **Key Personnel:** Sawako Noma, President. **URL:** http://kc.kodansha.co.jp/magazine/index.php/02065.

47039 ■ Shukan ST
The Japan Times Ltd.

5-4 Shibaura 4-chome
Minato-Ku
Tokyo 108-8071, Japan
Ph: 81 3 34535312
Newspaper covering education. **Founded:** 1990. **Freq:** Weekly. **ISSN:** 0915-7875. **Subscription Rates:** 13,200¥ individuals. **Remarks:** Advertising accepted; rates available upon request. **URL:** http://www.japantimes.co.jp/. **Circ:** Paid 150,000

47040 ■ Social Science Japan Journal
Oxford University Press
Institute of Social Science
University of Tokyo
7-3-1 Hongo
Bunkyo-ku
Tokyo 113-0033, Japan
Publisher E-mail: webenquiry.uk@oup.com
Peer-reviewed scholarly journal covering contemporary Japan. **Founded:** Apr. 1998. **Freq:** Semiannual. **Key Personnel:** Tom Gill, Managing Editor; Gregory Noble, Assoc. Ed.; Hiroshi Ishida, Assoc. Ed.; Tamio Nakamura, Assoc. Ed.; Akira Suehiro, Editor. **ISSN:** 1369-1465. **Remarks:** Accepts advertising. **URL:** http://www.glocom.org/books_and_journals/journal_abstracts/20030219_ja_s71/index.html. **Circ:** (Not Reported)

47041 ■ Soil Science and Plant Nutrition
Business Center for Academic Societies Japan
Gakkai Ctr. C21
5-16-9 Honkomagome
Bunkyo-Ku
Tokyo 113-8622, Japan
Ph: 81 358 145800
Fax: 81 358 145823
Journal covering agriculture. **Subtitle:** The Official Journal of the Japanese Society of Soil Science and Plant Nutrition. **Founded:** 1955. **Freq:** Quarterly. **Key Personnel:** Masanori Saito, Editor-in-Chief; toru Matoh, Editor-in-Chief; Sjinya Funakawa, Editor. **ISSN:** 0038-0768. **Subscription Rates:** US$553 institutions Americas (print and online); 330 institutions UK (print and online); EUR419 institutions Europe (print and online); US$647 institutions, other countries print and online; US$184 individuals Americas; 111 other countries; EUR141 individuals Euro zone; US$477 institutions Americas (online only); 285 institutions UK (online only); EUR362 institutions Europe (online only). **URL:** http://www.wiley.com/bw/journal.asp?ref=0038-0768.

47042 ■ Soils & Foundations
Japanese Geotechnical Society
2-chome Sengoku
Bunkyo-ku
Tokyo 112-0011, Japan
Ph: 81 339 468677
Fax: 81 339 468678
Publisher E-mail: jgs@jiban.or.jp
Journal covering civil engineering. **Founded:** 1953. **Freq:** Bimonthly. **Key Personnel:** Satoru Shibuya, Editor. **ISSN:** 0038-0806. **Subscription Rates:** 9,000¥ individuals surface mail; 13,000¥ individuals air mail. **Remarks:** Advertising accepted; rates available upon request. **URL:** http://www.jiban.or.jp/e/pub/pub.html. **Circ:** Paid 600

47043 ■ Structural Engineering Earthquake Engineering
Maruzen Company Ltd.
9-2 Nihombashi 3-chome
Chuo-Ku
PO Box 5050
Tokyo 103-8244, Japan
Ph: 81 3 32733234
Fax: 81 3 32731144
Publisher E-mail: export@maruzen.co.jp
Journal covering civil engineering. **Founded:** 1984. **Freq:** Semiannual. **ISSN:** 0289-8063. **Subscription Rates:** US$64 individuals. **URL:** http://www.maruzen.co.jp; http://www.maruzen.co.jp/home-eng/inter-d-per.html.

47044 ■ Studies in English Literature
English Literary Society of Japan
Kenkyusha Eigo Centre Bldg.
1-2 Kagurazaka
Shinjuku-ku
Tokyo 162-0825, Japan
Ph: 81 3 52611922
Publisher E-mail: ejimu@elsj.org
Journal of literature. **Founded:** 1919. **Freq:** 3/yr. **ISSN:** 0039-3649. **Remarks:** Advertising accepted; rates avail-

able upon request. **URL:** http://www.elsj.org/english/englishtop.html. **Circ:** Controlled 3,800

47045 ■ Surgery Today
Springer-Verlag Tokyo
No. 2, Funato Bldg.
1-11-11 Kudan-kita
Chiyoda-ku
Tokyo 102-0073, Japan
Ph: 81 368 317000
Fax: 81 368 317001
Publisher E-mail: info@springer.jp
Medical science journal. **Founded:** 1899. **Freq:** Monthly. **Key Personnel:** Michiaki Unno, Editorial Board; Kiyoshi Inokuchi, Ed. Emeritus; Mitsuo Shimada, Editorial Board; Yoshihiko Maehara, Editor-in-Chief; Hiroyasu Yokomise, Editorial Board; Eishi Nagai, Editorial Board. **ISSN:** 0941-1291. **Subscription Rates:** EUR718 institutions print incl. free access or e-only; EUR861.60 institutions enhanced access. **Remarks:** Accepts advertising. **URL:** http://www.springer.com/medicine/surgery/journal/595. **Circ:** Paid 1,500

47046 ■ Taikabutsu
Technical Association of Refractories - Japan
Taikabutsu Gijutsu Kyokai
New Ginza Bldg. 4th Fl.
7-3-13 Ginza
Chuo-ku
Tokyo 104-0061, Japan
Ph: 81 335 720705
Fax: 81 335 720175
Publisher E-mail: pjg00672@nifty.ne.jp
Japanese language publication covering metal. **Freq:** Monthly. **ISSN:** 0039-8993. **Subscription Rates:** 12,000¥ individuals surface mail; 15,000¥ individuals air mail. **Remarks:** Advertising accepted; rates available upon request. **URL:** http://www.tarj.org. **Circ:** (Not Reported)

47047 ■ Techniques in Coloproctology
Springer-Verlag Tokyo
No. 2, Funato Bldg.
1-11-11 Kudan-kita
Chiyoda-ku
Tokyo 102-0073, Japan
Ph: 81 368 317000
Fax: 81 368 317001
Publisher E-mail: info@springer.jp
International journal devoted to diagnostic and operative procedures carried out in the management of colorectal diseases with articles on imaging, clinical physiology, laparoscopy, open abdominal surgery and proctoperineology. **Freq:** 4/yr. **Key Personnel:** M. Pescatori, Editor-in-Chief; G. Gagliardi, Co-Ed. **ISSN:** 1123-6337. **Subscription Rates:** EUR290 institutions; EUR348 institutions enhanced access. **Remarks:** Advertising accepted; rates available upon request. **URL:** http://www.springer.com/medicine/surgery/journal/10151. **Circ:** (Not Reported)

47048 ■ Telecom Tribune
Shobunsha Blgd. No. 2
1-17-5 Uchikanda
Chiyoda-City
Tokyo 101-0047, Japan
Ph: 81 3 32946191
Fax: 81 3 32949066
Publisher E-mail: info@telecom-tribune.com
Publication reporting on telecommunications and technology issues in and around Japan. **Founded:** 1985. **Freq:** Monthly. **Key Personnel:** Akira Kadokura, Ed./Publisher; Koichi Ishii, Director. **ISSN:** 0912-9235. **URL:** http://www.techjapan.co.jp.

47049 ■ Tetsu-to-Hagane
Iron and Steel Institute of Japan
Niikura Bldg., 2nd Fl.
2 Kanda, Tsukasacho, 2-chome
Chiyoda-Ku
Tokyo 101-0048, Japan
Ph: 81 3 52097011
Fax: 81 3 32571110
Japanese language publication covering metals. **Founded:** 1915. **Freq:** Monthly. **Trim Size:** A4. **ISSN:** 0021-1575. **URL:** http://www.isij.or.jp/E_Katsudo/E_Kaiho/e_index.htm; http://www.isij.or.jp/. **Ad Rates:** BW: 100,000¥, 4C: 200,000¥. **Circ:** Combined 3,000

47050 ■ The Thermal and Nuclear Power
Thermal and Nuclear Power Engineering Society
Terayama Pacific Bldg.

1-23-11 Toranomon, Minato-ku
Tokyo 105-0001, Japan
Ph: 81 335 920380
Fax: 81 335 920335
Publisher E-mail: webadmin@tenpes.or.jp
Journal containing presented technical papers, introductory lectures, special reports with many photos. **Freq:** Monthly. **Subscription Rates:** Free. **URL:** http://www.tenpes.or.jp/index-e.html. **Circ:** 18,000

47051 ■ Tokyo Journal
NeXXus Communications K.K.
BIG Office Plz. 1002-1007
2-62-8 Higashi-Ikebukuro
Toshima-ku
Tokyo 170-0013, Japan
Ph: 81 339 845200
Fax: 81 339 866850
Publication E-mail: tj@nexxus.co.jp
Publisher E-mail: info@nexxus.co.jp
General interest magazine. **Freq:** Quarterly. **Key Personnel:** Mika Kojima, Managing Editor; Damian Peter Andrews, Copy Ed.; Dr. Stephan Hauser, Ed.-in-Ch./Publisher. **ISSN:** 0289-811X. **Subscription Rates:** 1,950¥ individuals domestic; 2,900¥ other countries; 3,900¥ other countries airmail; 3,750¥ two years domestic; 5,500¥ two years other countries; 7,500¥ two years other countries; airmail. **Remarks:** Accepts advertising. **URL:** http://www.tokyo.to/index.html. **Circ:** (Not Reported)

47052 ■ Tokyo Weekender
5th Fl., Chou Iikura Bldg.
8-5-8 Azabudai, Minato-ku
Tokyo 106-0041, Japan
Ph: 81 368 465615
Fax: 81 368 465616
Publisher E-mail: editor@weekenderjapan.com
Consumer magazine covering community news, social events and entertainment for the foreign and English community and tourists in Tokyo. **Founded:** 1970. **Freq:** Biweekly. **Key Personnel:** Stephen Young, Distribution Mgr.; Danielle Tate-Stratton, Asst. Ed.; Donald Eubank, Editor; Robert M. Poole, Contributing Ed.; Kieren Cashell, Contributor; Ray Pedersen, Publisher. **Subscription Rates:** US$20 individuals. **Remarks:** Accepts advertising. **URL:** http://www.weekender.co.jp. **Ad Rates:** BW: 350,000¥. **Circ:** 15,000

47053 ■ Tree Physiology
Oxford University Press
4-5-10-8F Shiba, Minato-ku
Tokyo 108-8386, Japan
Ph: 81 3 54445858
Fax: 81 3 34542929
Professional journal covering botany, forestry, and ecology. **Founded:** June 1986. **Freq:** Monthly. **Print Method:** Offset. **Trim Size:** 8 1/2 x 11. **Cols./Page:** 2. **Col. Width:** 8.3 centimeters. **Col. Depth:** 23.4 centimeters. **Key Personnel:** Marilyn C. Ball, Editor; James R. Ehleringer, Editor; Marc D. Abrams, Editor; Guillermo Goldstein, Editor; Annikki Makela, Editor; Peter Millard, Editor; Robert W. Pearcy, Editor; Frederick C. Meinzer, Editor; Ram Oren, Editor-in-Ch.; Joao S. Pereira, Editor; Gary Peter, Editor. **ISSN:** 0829-318X. **Subscription Rates:** 184 out of country corporate, print only; US$277 individuals corporate, print only; 148 out of country institution, print only; US$221 institutions print only; 22 individuals print; US$33 individuals print; EUR33 individuals print. **Remarks:** Accepts advertising. **URL:** http://treephys.oxfordjournals.org/. **Ad Rates:** BW: 550¥, 4C: 1,250¥. **Circ:** Paid 600, Non-paid 150

47054 ■ Tsuda Review
Tsuda College
2-1-1 Tsuda-Machi
Kodaira-shi
Tokyo 187-8577, Japan
Ph: 81 423425113
Journal of literature. **Founded:** 1956. **Freq:** Annual. **ISSN:** 0496-3547. **Circ:** 1,000

47055 ■ Venus: Japanese Journal of Malacology
Malacological Society of Japan
c/o National Science Museum
3-23-1 Hiyakunin-cho
Shinjuku-ku
Tokyo 169-0073, Japan
Publisher E-mail: msj_manager@hotmail.com
Journal of zoology. **Founded:** 1928. **Freq:** Quarterly.

Key Personnel: Akihiko Inaba, Editor. **ISSN:** 0042-3580. **Subscription Rates:** 7,500¥. **Circ:** Paid 900

47056 ■ Weekly Shonen Sunday
Shogakukan Inc.
2-3-1, Hitotsubashi
Chiyoda-ku
Tokyo 101-8001, Japan
Entertainment comic magazine Japanese boys. **Founded:** Mar. 15, 1959. **Freq:** Weekly (Wed.). **Key Personnel:** Masahiro Oga, President. **Subscription Rates:** 240¥ individuals. **URL:** http://www.shogakukan. co.jp/english/.

47057 ■ Young Magazine
Kodansha Ltd.
2-12-21 Otowa
Bunkyo-ku
Tokyo 112-8001, Japan
Ph: 81 3 3946 6201
Fax: 81 3 3944 9915
Magazine featuring original stories for young adult that ranges from action to science fiction, fantasy to high school drama, or motor sport to dropout adventure. **Freq:** Weekly. **Key Personnel:** Sawako Noma, President. **URL:** http://kc.kodansha.co.jp/magazine/index.php/02888.

47058 ■ Young Magazine Uppers
Kodansha Ltd.
2-12-21 Otowa
Bunkyo-ku
Tokyo 112-8001, Japan
Ph: 81 3 3946 6201
Fax: 81 3 3944 9915
Magazine featuring manga with sexy stories, martial art action, westerns, and slapstick for men. **Freq:** Biweekly. **Key Personnel:** Sawako Noma, President. **URL:** http://kc.kodansha.co.jp/magazine/index.php/02888.

47059 ■ AFN-Tokyo - 810 KHz
Det 10, Unit 5091
Yokota Air Base, Bldg. 3266
Fussa
Tokyo, Japan
Ph: 81 425 522511
Fax: 81 425 522511
E-mail: afn.publicity@yokota.af.mil
Format: News; Information. **Owner:** AFN Tokyo, at above address. **Operating Hours:** Continuous. **Wattage:** 50,000. **URL:** http://www.yokota.af.mil/afn.

47060 ■ Fukuoka - 3259 KHz
2-2-1 Jinnan
Shibuya-ku
Tokyo 150-8001, Japan
Ph: 81 3 34651111
Fax: 81 3 34698110
E-mail: nhkworld@nhk.jp
Format: News. **Owner:** Nippon Hoso Kyokai (NHK), at above address. **Operating Hours:** 0800-1300. **Wattage:** 600. **URL:** http://www.nhk.or.jp.

47061 ■ JOAB - 693 KHz
2-2-1 Jinnan
Shibuya-ku
Tokyo 150-8001, Japan
Ph: 81 3 34651111
Fax: 81 3 34098110
E-mail: nhkworld@nhk.jp
Format: Educational. **Owner:** Nippon Hoso Kyokai (NHK), at above address. **Operating Hours:** 2030-1640 (2030-1500, Sun. & Mon.). **Key Personnel:** Shigehiro Komaru, Chm.; Shigeo Fukuchi, President. **Wattage:** 500,000. **URL:** http://www.nhk.or.jp.

JOAC - See Nagasaki

JOAD - See Okinawa

JOAG - See Nagasaki

47062 ■ JOAK - 594 KHz
2-2-1 Jinnan
Shibuya-ku
Tokyo 150-8001, Japan
Ph: 81 3 34651111
Fax: 81 3 34811350
E-mail: nhkworld@nhk.jp
Format: News. **Owner:** Nippon Hoso Kyokai (NHK), at above address. **Operating Hours:** Continuous. **Key Personnel:** Shigeo Fukuchi, President; Hidemi Hyuga,

Exec. Dir. Gen. Wattage: 300,000. **Ad Rates:** Advertising accepted; rates available upon request. **URL:** http://www.nhk.or.jp.

47063 ■ JOAK - 82.5 MHz
2-2-1 Jinnan
Shibuya-ku
Tokyo 150-8001, Japan
Ph: 81 3 34651111
Fax: 81 3 34698110
Format: News. **Owner:** Nippon Hoso Kyokai (NHK), at above address. **Operating Hours:** Continuous. **Key Personnel:** Hidemi Hyuga, Exec. Dir. Gen. **Wattage:** 10,000. **URL:** http://www.nhk.or.jp.

JOAP - See Okinawa

JOAP - See Okinawa

47064 ■ JOAU - 80 MHz
1-chome Cho
Chiyoda-ku
Tokyo 102-8080, Japan
Ph: 81 3 32210080
Format: News. **Owner:** Tokyo FM Broadcasting Co., Ltd. (TFM), at above address. **Founded:** 1970. **Operating Hours:** Continuous. **Key Personnel:** Yasuo Okada, Sen. Mng. Dir.; Fumio Kotani, Mng. Dir.; Ichiro Sinji, Director. **Wattage:** 10,000. **Ad Rates:** Advertising accepted; rates available upon request. **URL:** http://www.tfm.co.jp/company/profile/.

47065 ■ JOAV - 81.3 MHz
Roppongi Hills Mori Tower 33F
10-1, Roppongi 6-chome
Tokyo 106-6188, Japan
Ph: 81 3 37971111
Fax: 81 3 37977906
Format: Eclectic. **Owner:** FM Japan Ltd. (J-Wave), at above address. **Founded:** 1988. **Operating Hours:** Continuous. **Key Personnel:** Toru Ogasawara, Exec. Dir.; Humihiko Imura, Chm.; Shuuzi Kusuda, Pres./CEO; Hideo Saitou, Dir. Gen.; Masuo Kanzaki, Director; Toyo Kurokouti, Director. **Wattage:** 10,000. **Ad Rates:** Advertising accepted; rates available upon request. **URL:** http://www.j-wave.co.jp/.

47066 ■ JOAX-TV - 4
1-6-1 Higashi Shimbashi
Minato-ku
Tokyo 105-7444, Japan
Ph: 81 3 62151111
Format: News; Full Service; Sports. **Owner:** Nippon Television Network Corporation (NTV), at above address. **Founded:** 1953. **Operating Hours:** 8 p.m.-6 p.m. **Wattage:** 50,000. **Ad Rates:** Advertising accepted; rates available upon request. **URL:** http://www.ntv.co.jp/.

47067 ■ JOBB - 828 KHz
2-2-1 Jinnan
Shibuya-ku
Tokyo 150-8001, Japan
Ph: 81 3 34651111
Fax: 81 3 34698110
E-mail: nhkworld@nhk.jp
Format: Educational. **Owner:** Nippon Hoso Kyokai (NHK), at above address. **Operating Hours:** 2030-1640 (2030-1500, Sun. & Mon.). **Key Personnel:** Shigehiro Komaru, Chm.; Shigeo Fukuchi, President. **Wattage:** 300,000. **Ad Rates:** Noncommercial. **URL:** http://www.nhk.or.jp.

JOBK - See Osaka

JOBK - See Osaka

JOBP - See Utsunomiya

47068 ■ JOCB - 909 KHz
2-2-1 Jinnan
Shibuya-ku
Tokyo 150-8001, Japan
Ph: 81 3 34651111
Fax: 81 3 34698110
E-mail: nhkworld@nhk.jp
Format: Educational. **Owner:** Nippon Hoso Kyokai (NHK), at above address. **Operating Hours:** 2030-1640 (2030-1500, Sun. & Mon.). **Wattage:** 10,000. **URL:** http://www.nhk.or.jp.

JOCC - See Asahikawa

JOCG - See Asahikawa

47069 ■ JOCK - 82.5 MHz

2-2-1 Jinnan
Shibuya-ku
Tokyo 150-8001, Japan
Ph: 81 3 34651111
Fax: 81 3 34698110
Format: News. **Owner:** Nippon Hoso Kyokai (NHK), at above address. **Operating Hours:** Continuous. **Wattage:** 10,000. **URL:** http://www.nhk.or.jp.

JOCK - See Nagoya

47070 ■ JOCX-TV - 8
4-8, Daiba 2-chome
Minato-ku
Tokyo 137-8088, Japan
Ph: 81 3 55008888
Format: News; Full Service; Sports. **Owner:** Fuji Television Network,Inc. (CX), at above address. **Founded:** 1959. **Key Personnel:** Hisashi Hieda, Chm./CEO; Kou Toyoda, Pres./COO; Ryosuke Yokoi, Sen. Exec. VP. **Wattage:** 50,000. **URL:** http://www.fujitv.co.jp.

JODC - See Hamamatsu

47071 ■ JODG - 576 KHz
2-1, Jinnan 2-chome
Shibuya-ku
Tokyo 150-8001, Japan
Ph: 81 3 34651111
Fax: 81 3 34698110
E-mail: nhkworld@nhk.jp
Format: News. **Owner:** Nippon Hoso Kyokai (NHK), at above address. **Operating Hours:** Continuous. **Key Personnel:** Shigetaka Komori, Chm.; Shigeo Fukuchi, President. **Wattage:** 1000. **Ad Rates:** Noncommercial. **URL:** http://www.nhk.or.jp.

47072 ■ JODW - 76.1 MHz
Higashi 1-chome
Shinagawa-ku
Tokyo 140-0002, Japan
Ph: 81 3 57817610
Fax: 81 3 34741761
E-mail: message@interfm.co.jp
Format: Eclectic. **Owner:** Inter-Wave Inc. (Inter FM), at above address. **Founded:** Apr. 1, 1996. **Operating Hours:** 0500-0400. **Wattage:** 10,000. **Ad Rates:** Advertising accepted; rates available upon request. **URL:** http://www.interfm.co.jp/.

JOEP - See Mito

47073 ■ JOEX-TV - 10
6-9-1, Roppongi
Minato-ku
Tokyo 106-8001, Japan
Ph: 81 3 64061111
Format: News; Information; Full Service. **Owner:** Asahi National Broadcasting Co., Ltd. (ANB), at above address. **Founded:** 1959. **Operating Hours:** 8:30 pm-6 pm. **Wattage:** 50,000. **URL:** http://www.tv-asahi.co.jp/.

47074 ■ JOFB - 702 KHz
2-2-1 Jinnan
Shibuya-ku
Tokyo 150-8001, Japan
Ph: 81 3 34651111
Fax: 81 3 34698110
E-mail: nhkworld@nhk.jp
Format: Educational. **Owner:** Nippon Hoso Kyokai (NHK), at above address. **Operating Hours:** 2030-1640 (2030-1500, Sun. & Mon.). **Key Personnel:** Shigeo Fukuchi, President; Shigehiro Komaru, Chm. **Wattage:** 10,000. **URL:** http://www.nhk.or.jp.

JOFC - See Fukui

JOFD - See Fukushima

JOFG - See Fukui

JOFG - See Fukui

JOFK - See Hiroshima

JOFK - See Hiroshima

JOFP - See Fukushima

JOFP - See Fukushima

JOGB - See Kumamoto

JOGK - See Kumamoto

JOGK - See Kumamoto

JOGP - See Yokohama

47075 ■ JOHB - 1089 KHz

2-2-1 Jinnan
Shibuya-ku
Tokyo 150-8001, Japan
Ph: 81 3 34651111
Fax: 81 3 34698110
E-mail: nhkworld@nhk.jp
Format: Educational. **Owner:** Nippon Hoso Kyokai (NHK), at above address. **Operating Hours:** 2030-1640 (2030- 1500, Sun. & Mon.). **Key Personnel:** Shigeo Fukuchi, President. **Wattage:** 10,000. **Ad Rates:** Noncommercial. **URL:** http://www.nhk.or.jp.

JOHC - See Kagoshima

JOHD - See Takamatsu

JOHG - See Kagoshima

JOHG - See Kagoshima

JOHK - See Sendai

JOHK - See Sendai

JOHP - See Takamatsu

JOHP - See Takamatsu

47076 ■ JOIB - 747 KHz
2-2-1 Jinnan
Shibuya-ku
Tokyo 150-8001, Japan
Ph: 81 3 34651111
Fax: 81 3 34698110
E-mail: nhkworld@nhk.jp
Format: Educational. **Owner:** Nippon Hoso Kyokai (NHK), at above address. **Operating Hours:** 2030-1640 (2030-1500, Sun. & Mon.). **Key Personnel:** Shigehiro Komaru, Chm.; Shigeo Fukuchi, President. **Wattage:** 500,000. **Ad Rates:** Noncommercial. **URL:** http://www.nhk.or.jp.

JOIC - See Toyama

JOID - See Oita

JOIG - See Toyama

JOIG - See Toyama

47077 ■ JOIK - 567 KHz
2-2-1 Jinnan
Shibuya-ku
Tokyo 150-8001, Japan
Ph: 81 3 34541111
Fax: 81 3 34811350
E-mail: nhkworld@nhk.jp
Format: News. **Owner:** Nippon Hoso Kyokai (NHK), at above address. **Operating Hours:** Continuous. **Key Personnel:** Shigeo Fukuchi, President; Hidemi Hyuga, Executive Dir. Gen. **Wattage:** 100,000. **URL:** http://www.nhk.or.jp.

JOIP - See Oita

JOIP - See Oita

JOIQ - See Muroran

JOIZ - See Muroran

JOJB - See Kanazawa

JOJC - See Yamagata

JOJG - See Yamagata

JOJG - See Yamagata

JOJK - See Kanazawa

JOJK - See Kanazawa

JOKB - See Okayama

JOKC - See Kofu

JOKD - See Kitami

JOKG - See Kofu

JOKG - See Kofu

JOKK - See Okayama

JOKK - See Okayama

JOKP - See Kitami

47078 ■ JOKR - 954 KHz
5-3-6, Akasaka
Minato-ku
Tokyo 107-8006, Japan
E-mail: radio@tbs.co.jp
Format: Eclectic. **Owner:** TBS Radio & Communications, Inc., at above address. **Founded:** 1951. **Operating Hours:** Continuous. **Key Personnel:** Keizo Zaitsu, Pres. /Rep. Dir.; Hiroshi Inoue, Chm./Rep. Dir.; Kazuo Hiramoto, Sen. Mng. Dir.; Yukio Kinugasa, Mng. Dir. **Wattage:** 100,000. **URL:** http://www.tbs.co.jp/.

47079 ■ JOLB - 1017 KHz

2-2-1 Jinnan
Shibuya-ku
Tokyo 150-8001, Japan
Ph: 81 3 34651111
Fax: 81 3 34698110
E-mail: nhkworld@nhk.jp
Format: Educational. **Owner:** Nippon Hoso Kyokai (NHK), at above address. **Operating Hours:** 2030-1640 (2030-1500, Sun. & Mon.). **Key Personnel:** Shigeo Fukuchi, President. **Wattage:** 50,000. **Ad Rates:** Noncommercial. **URL:** http://www.nhk.or.jp.

JOLC - See Tottori

47080 ■ JOLF - 1242 KHz
1-9-3, Yurakucho
Chiyoda-ku
Tokyo, Japan
Ph: 81 3 32871111
Format: Eclectic. **Owner:** Nippon Broadcasting System, Inc, at above address. **Founded:** 1954. **Operating Hours:** Continuous. **Key Personnel:** Shigemura Hazime, Pres./Chm. **Wattage:** 100,000. **Ad Rates:** Advertising accepted; rates available upon request. **URL:** http://www.jolf.co.jp/.

JOLG - See Tottori

JOLK - See Fukuoka

JOLK - See Fukuoka

JOLP - See Urawa

JOMC - See Miyazaki

JOMG - See Miyazaki

JOMP - See Chiba

47081 ■ JOMX-TV - 14
Media Ctr. 1-12 Koujimachi
Chiyoda-ku
Tokyo 102-8002, Japan
Ph: 81 3 55001414
Fax: 81 3 55001514
Owner: Tokyo Metropolitan Television Broadcasting Corporation, at above address. **Founded:** Apr. 30, 1993. **Key Personnel:** Wataru Gotoh, Chm./CEO. **Wattage:** 10,000. **URL:** http://www.mxtv.co.jp/.

JONB - See Nagano

JONK - See Nagano

JONP - See Tsu

JOOC - See Obihiro

JOOG - See Obihiro

JOOK - See Kyoto

JOOK - See Kyoto

JOOP - See Gifu

JOPB - See Shizuoka

JOPC - See Kushiro

JOPG - See Kushiro

JOPK - See Shizuoka

JOPK - See Shizuoka

JOQB - See Niigata

JOQC - See Morioka

47082 ■ JOQG - 83.1 MHz
2-2-1 Jinnan
Shibuya-ku
Tokyo 150-8001, Japan
Ph: 81 3 34651111
Fax: 81 3 34698110
Format: News. **Owner:** Nippon Hoso Kyokai (NHK), at above address. **Operating Hours:** Continuous. **Key Personnel:** Shigeo Fukuchi, President. **Wattage:** 1000. **Ad Rates:** Noncommercial. **URL:** http://www.nhk.or.jp.

JOQG - See Morioka

JOQK - See Niigata

JOQK - See Niigata

JOQP - See Hikone

JOQP - See Otsu

47083 ■ JOQR - 1134 KHz
Hamamatsu-cho 1-31
Minato-ku
Tokyo 160-8002, Japan
Ph: 81 3 54031111
Format: Eclectic. **Owner:** Nippon Cultural Broadcasting, Inc. (NCB), at above address. **Founded:** 1952.

Operating Hours: Continuous. **Wattage:** 100,000. **URL:** http://www.joqr.co.jp/.

JORB - See Kochi

JORK - See Kochi

47084 ■ JORX-TV - 6
5-3-6 Akasaka
Minato-ku
Tokyo 107-8006, Japan
Format: News. **Owner:** Tokyo Broadcasting System, Inc. (TBC), at above address. **Founded:** 1955. **Former name:** JOKR-TV (Oct. 1, 2001). **Operating Hours:** Continuous. **Key Personnel:** Hiroshi Inoue, Chm. & Rep. Dir.; Keizo Zaitsu, Pres. & Rep. Dir.; Kazuo Hiramoto, Sr. Mng. Dir.; Kiyoshi Wakabayashi, Director. **Wattage:** 50,000. **URL:** http://www.tbs.co.jp/eng/corporatedata/index.htm.

JOSB - See Kitakyushu

JOSK - See Kitakyushu

JOSP - See Saga

JOTB - See Matsue

JOTC - See Aomori

JOTG - See Aomori

JOTG - See Aomori

JOTK - See Matsue

JOTP - See Maebashi

47085 ■ JOTX-TV - 12
3-12, Toranomon 4-chome
Minato-ku
Tokyo 105-8012, Japan
Ph: 81 3 54707777
Fax: 81 3 54736393
Owner: TV Tokyo Corporation, at above address. **Founded:** 1964. **Key Personnel:** Masayuki Shimada, Co-CEO/Pres. **Wattage:** 50,000. **URL:** http://www.tv-tokyo.co.jp/.

JOUB - See Akita

JOUC - See Yamaguchi

47086 ■ JOUD - 77.1 MHz
2-11, Wakaba
Mihama-ku
Chiba 261-8586, Japan
Ph: 81 43 2765111
Fax: 81 43 2972781
Format: Eclectic. **Owner:** University Broadcasting Station, at above address. **Operating Hours:** 2100-1500. **Wattage:** 10,000. **URL:** http://www.u-air.ac.jp/.

JOUG - See Yamaguchi

JOUK - See Akita

JOUK - See Akita

47087 ■ JOVB - 1467 KHz
2-2-1 Jinnan
Shibuya-ku
Tokyo 150-8001, Japan
Ph: 81 3 34651111
Fax: 81 3 34698110
E-mail: nhkworld@nhk.jp
Format: Educational. **Owner:** Nippon Hoso Kyokai (NHK), at above address. **Operating Hours:** 2030-1640 (2030-1500, Sun. & Mon.). **Key Personnel:** Shigeo Fukuchi, President. **Wattage:** 1000. **URL:** http://www.nhk.or.jp.

JOVK - See Hakodate

JOXK - See Tokushima

JOXK - See Tokushima

47088 ■ JOZ - 3925 KHz
1-9-15, Akasaka
Minato-ku
Tokyo 107-8373, Japan
Ph: 81 3 35838151
Format: News. **Owner:** Nikkei Radio Broadcasting Corporation, at above address. **Founded:** 1954. **Operating Hours:** 2030-1400; 2030-1530 Thu.; 2030-1500 Fri.; 2030-1430 Sat.; 2. **Wattage:** 50,000. **URL:** http://www.radionikkei.jp/.

47089 ■ JOZB - 1512 KHz
2-2-1 Jinnan
Shibuya-ku
Tokyo 150-8001, Japan
Ph: 81 3 34651111

Fax: 81 3 34698110
E-mail: nhkworld@nhk.jp
Format: Educational. **Owner:** Nippon Hoso Kyokai (NHK), at above address. **Operating Hours:** 2030-1640 (2030-1500, Sun. & Mon.). **Key Personnel:** Shigeo Fukuchi, President. **Wattage:** 5000. **URL:** http://www.nhk.or.jp.

JOZK - See Matsuyama

JOZK - See Matsuyama

47090 ■ Tokyo - 9550 KHz
2-2-1 Jinnan
Shibuya-ku
Tokyo 150-8001, Japan
Ph: 81 3 34651111
Fax: 81 3 34698110
Format: News. **Owner:** Nippon Hoso Kyokai (NHK), at above address. **Operating Hours:** 0100-0730. **Key Personnel:** Shigehiro Komaru, Chm.; Shigeo Fukuchi, President; Hidemi Hyuga, Exec. Dir. Gen. **Wattage:** 900. **URL:** http://www.nhk.or.jp.

Tomakomai

47091 ■ Sapporo TV Hoso - 1440 KHz
1-1, Nishi 8-chome
Kita 1-jo, Chuo-ku
Sapporo 060-8705, Japan
Ph: 81 11 2411181
E-mail: radio@stv.jp
Format: Eclectic. **Owner:** The Sapporo Television Broadcasting Co., Ltd., at above address. **Founded:** 1962. **Operating Hours:** Continuous. **Wattage:** 1000. **URL:** http://www.stv.ne.jp/.

Tomo

47092 ■ JOEE-TV Tomo - 41
21-3, Moto-machi
Naka-ku
Hiroshima 730-8504, Japan
Ph: 81 82 2221155
E-mail: tv@rcc.net
Owner: Chugoku Broadcasting Co., Ltd. (RCC), at above address. **Founded:** 1959. **Wattage:** 10. **URL:** http://www.1350.jp/.

Tottori

47093 ■ JOJX-TV - 1
4-chome, 360 Rural Towns
Tottori 680-8572, Japan
Ph: 81 857 272111
Owner: Nihon-Kai Television Co., Ltd. (NKT), at above address. **Founded:** 1959. **Key Personnel:** Yoshiaki Baba, Chm./CEO; Akio Fujikawa, President. **Wattage:** 1000. **URL:** http://www.nkt-tv.co.jp/.

47094 ■ JOLC - 1125 KHz
2-2-1 Jinnan
Shibuya-ku
Tokyo 150-8001, Japan
Ph: 81 3 34651111
Fax: 81 3 34698110
E-mail: nhkworld@nhk.jp
Format: Educational. **Owner:** Nippon Hoso Kyokai (NHK), at above address. **Operating Hours:** 2030-1640 (2030-1500, Sun. & Mon.). **Key Personnel:** Shigeo Fukuchi, President. **Wattage:** 1000. **URL:** http://www.nhk.or.jp.

47095 ■ JOLG - 1368 KHz
2-2-1 Jinnan
Shibuya-ku
Tokyo 150-8001, Japan
Ph: 81 3 34651111
Fax: 81 3 34698110
E-mail: nhkworld@nhk.jp
Format: News. **Owner:** Nippon Hoso Kyokai (NHK), at above address. **Operating Hours:** Continuous. **Key Personnel:** Shigeo Fukuchi, President; Hidemi Hyuga, Exec. Dir. Gen. **Wattage:** 1000. **Ad Rates:** Noncommercial. **URL:** http://www.nhk.or.jp.

Toyama

47096 ■ Mathematics Journal of Toyama University
Toyama University
Dept. of Mathematics
3190 Gofuku
Toyama 930-8555, Japan
Ph: 81 764 456011
Mathematics journal. **Founded:** 1990. **Freq:** Annual. **ISSN:** 0916-6009. **URL:** http://www.u-toyama.ac.jp/en/index.html.

47097 ■ JOEE-TV Toyama - 44
21-3, Moto-machi
Naka-ku
Hiroshima 730-8504, Japan
Ph: 81 82 2221155
E-mail: tv@rcc.net
Owner: Chugoku Broadcasting Co., Ltd. (RCC), at above address. **Founded:** 1959. **Wattage:** 3. **Ad Rates:** Noncommercial. **URL:** http://www.rcc.co.jp.

47098 ■ JOIC - 1035 KHz
2-2-1 Jinnan
Shibuya-ku
Tokyo 150-8001, Japan
Ph: 81 3 34651111
Fax: 81 3 34698110
E-mail: nhkworld@nhk.jp
Format: Educational. **Owner:** Nippon Hoso Kyokai (NHK), at above address. **Operating Hours:** 2030-1640 (2030-1500, Sun. & Mon.). **Key Personnel:** Shigeo Fukuchi, President. **Wattage:** 1000. **Ad Rates:** Noncommercial. **URL:** http://www.nhk.or.jp.

47099 ■ JOIG - 648 KHz
2-2-1 Jinnan
Shibuya-ku
Tokyo 150-8001, Japan
Ph: 81 3 34651111
Fax: 81 3 34811350
E-mail: nhkworld@nhk.jp
Format: News. **Owner:** Nippon Hoso Kyokai (NHK), at above address. **Operating Hours:** Continuous. **Key Personnel:** Shigeo Fukuchi, President; Hidemi Hyuga, Exec. Dir. Gen. **Wattage:** 5000. **URL:** http://www.nhk.or.jp.

47100 ■ JOIG - 81.5 MHz
2-2-1 Jinnan
Shibuya-ku
Tokyo 150-8001, Japan
Ph: 81 3 34651111
Fax: 81 3 34698110
Format: News. **Owner:** Nippon Hoso Kyokai (NHK), at above address. **Operating Hours:** Continuous. **Key Personnel:** Hidemi Hyuga, Exec. Dir. Gen. **Wattage:** 1000. **Ad Rates:** Noncommercial. **URL:** http://www.nhk.or.jp.

47101 ■ JOLR - 738 KHz
10-18, Ushijima-cho
Toyama 930-8585, Japan
Ph: 81 76 4325555
E-mail: info@knb.ne.jp
Format: Eclectic. **Owner:** Kita-Nihon Broadcasting Co., Ltd. (KNB), at above address. **Founded:** 1952. **Operating Hours:** Continuous. **Wattage:** 5000. **URL:** http://www.knb.ne.jp.

47102 ■ JOLR-TV - 1
10-18, Cow Island Town
Toyama 930-8585, Japan
Ph: 81 76 4325555
E-mail: info@knb.ne.jp
Owner: Kita-Nihon Broadcasting Co., Ltd. (KNB), at above address. **Founded:** 1959. **Wattage:** 3000. **URL:** http://www.knb.ne.jp/.

47103 ■ JOOU - 82.7 MHz
2-11, Okuda
Toyama 930-8567, Japan
Format: Eclectic. **Owner:** Toyama FM Broadcasting Co., Ltd. at above address. **Founded:** 1985. **Operating Hours:** 0500-0400. **Key Personnel:** Araki Huzio, Chm.; Norihito Kitagawa Satoshi, President. **Wattage:** 1000. **Ad Rates:** Advertising accepted; rates available upon request. **URL:** http://www.fmtoyama.co.jp/.

47104 ■ JOTH-TV - 34
8-14, Shin-Nezuka-machi 1-chome
Toyama 939-8550, Japan
Ph: 81 76 4251111
E-mail: info@bbt.co.jp
Owner: Toyama Television Broadcasting Co., Ltd.

(BBT), at above address. **Founded:** 1969. **Wattage:** 10,000. **URL:** http://www.bbt.co.jp/.

47105 ■ Kita Nihin Hoso - 738 KHz
10-18, Ushijima-cho
Toyama 930-8585, Japan
Ph: 81 764 325555
E-mail: info@knb.ne.jp
Format: Eclectic. **Owner:** Kita-Nihon Broadcasting Co., Ltd. (KNB), at above address. **Operating Hours:** Continuous. **Wattage:** 5000. **URL:** http://www.knb.ne.jp/.

Tsu

47106 ■ JOMH-TV - 33
693-1, Kotani
Shibumi-cho
Tsu 514-8633, Japan
Owner: MIE Television Broadcasting Co., Ltd.(MTV), at above address. **Founded:** 1969. **Wattage:** 5000. **URL:** http://www.mietv.com/.

47107 ■ JONP - 81.8 MHz
2-2-1 Jinnan
Shibuya-ku
Tokyo 150-8001, Japan
Ph: 81 3 34651111
Fax: 81 3 34698110
Format: News. **Owner:** Nippon Hoso Kyokai (NHK), at above address. **Operating Hours:** Continuous. **Key Personnel:** Hidemi Hyuga, Exec. Dir. Gen. **Wattage:** 3000. **Ad Rates:** Noncommercial. **URL:** http://www.nhk.or.jp.

47108 ■ JONU - 78.9 MHz
1043-1, Kannon-cho
Tsu 514-8505, Japan
Ph: 81 59 2255533
E-mail: shitsumon@fmmie.co.jp
Format: Eclectic. **Owner:** Mie FM Broadcasting Co., Ltd., at above address. **Founded:** 1985. **Operating Hours:** Continuous. **Wattage:** 3000. **Ad Rates:** Advertising accepted; rates available upon request. **URL:** http://www.fmmie.jp.

Tsuchiura City

47109 ■ Resource Geology
Society of Resource Geology
2-18 Kamitakatsu-shinmachi
Tsuchiura City 300-0819, Japan
Publisher E-mail: srg@kt.rim.or.jp
Resource Geology is an international journal focusing economic geology, geochemistry and environmental geology. **Founded:** 1951. **Freq:** Quarterly. **Key Personnel:** Hidehiko Shimazaki, Editorial Board; Yoshimichi Kajiwara, Editor-in-Chief, yoshi_kaji@jcom.home.ne.jp; Shunso Ishihara, Honorary Ed. **ISSN:** 1344-1698. **Subscription Rates:** US$40 individuals; US$100 institutions. **URL:** http://www.kt.rim.or.jp/~srg/english.html. **Ad Rates:** BW: 60,000¥; 4C: 140,000¥. **Circ:** Paid 1,400

Tsukuba

47110 ■ International Journal of Knowledge Engineering and Soft Data Paradigms
Inderscience Enterprises Limited
c/o Dr. Mika Sato-Ilic, Ed.-in-Ch.
University of Tsukuba, Dept. of Risk Engineering
Faculty of Systems & Information Engineering
Tennodai 1-1-1
Tsukuba 305-8573, Japan
Journal covering the research conducted in the areas of knowledge engineering and soft data analysis. **Freq:** 4/yr. **Key Personnel:** Dr. Mika Sato-Ilic, Editor-in-Chief, mika@sk.tsukuba.ac.jp. **ISSN:** 1755-3210. **Subscription Rates:** EUR494 individuals print or online; EUR672 individuals print and online. **URL:** http://www.inderscience.com/browse/index.php?journalID=276.

47111 ■ Japanese Journal of Nematology
Japanese Nematological Society
Laboratory of Plant Nematology, Dept. of Plant Protection
National Agriculture Research Ctr.
3-1-1 Kannondai
Tsukuba 305-0866, Japan
Ph: 81 298 388839

Circulation: ★ = ABC; △ = BPA; ◆ = CAC; • = CCAB; □ = VAC; ⊕ = PO Statement; ‡ = Publisher's Report; Boldface figures = sworn; Light figures = estimated.

Gale Directory of Publications & Broadcast Media/147th Ed.

5127

Fax: 81 298 388837
Publisher E-mail: aiba@affrc.go.jp
Journal of zoology. **Founded:** 1972. **Freq:** Semiannual August & December. **Key Personnel:** Takayuki Mizukubo, Editor-in-Chief. **ISSN:** 0919-6765. **Subscription Rates:** US$35 students overseas. **URL:** http://senchug.ac.affrc.go.jp/e/index-e.html.

Urawa

47112 ■ JOLP - 85.1 MHz
2-2-1 Jinnan
Shibuya-ku
Tokyo 150-8001, Japan
Ph: 81 3 34651111
Fax: 81 3 34698110
Format: News. **Owner:** Nippon Hoso Kyokai (NHK), at above address. **Operating Hours:** Continuous. **Key Personnel:** Shigeo Fukuchi, President. **Wattage:** 5000. **URL:** http://www.nhk.or.jp.

47113 ■ JOUS-TV - 38
6-36-4, Tokiwa
Urawa 336-8538, Japan
Ph: 81 48 8243131
Owner: Television Saitama Co., Ltd. (TVS), at above address. **Founded:** 1979. **Wattage:** 5000. **URL:** http://www.teletama.jp/.

Utsunomiya

47114 ■ JOBP - 80.3 MHz
2-2-1 Jinnan
Shibuya-ku
Tokyo 150-8001, Japan
Ph: 81 3 34651111
Fax: 81 3 34698110
Format: News. **Owner:** Nippon Hoso Kyokai (NHK), at above address. **Operating Hours:** Continuous. **Key Personnel:** Hidemi Hyuga, Exec. Dir. Gen. **Wattage:** 1000. **URL:** http://www.nhk.or.jp.

47115 ■ JOGY-TV - 31
2-2-2, Akira
Uto Miyaiti
Utsunomiya 320-8531, Japan
Ph: 81 28 6230031
Owner: Tochigi Television Broadcasting Corporation (TTV), at above address. **Founded:** 1999. **Wattage:** 1000. **URL:** http://www.tochigi-tv.jp/.

47116 ■ JOSV - 76.4 MHz
1-19, Ichijo 3-chome
Utsunomiya 320-8550, Japan
Ph: 81 28 6387640
Format: Eclectic. **Owner:** FM Tochigi Co., Ltd. (Radio Berry), at above address. **Founded:** 1994. **Operating Hours:** Continuous. **Wattage:** 1000. **Ad Rates:** Advertising accepted; rates available upon request. **URL:** http://www.berry.co.jp/.

47117 ■ JOXF - 1530 KHz
12-11, Honcho
Utsunomiya 320-8601, Japan
Ph: 81 28 622 1111
Format: Eclectic. **Owner:** Tochigi Broadcasting Co., Ltd. (CRT), at above address. **Founded:** 1963. **Operating Hours:** 2100-2000; 2100-1500 Sun. **Wattage:** 5000. **URL:** http://www.crt-radio.co.jp.

Uwajima

47118 ■ JOAM - 1116 KHz
1-1-1 Hon-cho
Matsuyama 790-8510, Japan
Ph: 81 89 9153333
Fax: 81 89 9152370
Format: Eclectic. **Owner:** Nankai Broadcasting Co., Ltd.(RNB), at above address. **Founded:** 1954. **Operating Hours:** Continuous. **Wattage:** 1000. **URL:** http://www.rnb.co.jp/.

Wakayama

47119 ■ JOOM-TV - 30
151, Tani Sakai-shi
Wakayama 640-8533, Japan
Ph: 81 73 4555711
Owner: Wakayama Telecasting Corporation (WTV), at above address. **Founded:** 1974. **Key Personnel:** Naka-

hara Masaru, Pres./CEO. **Wattage:** 1000. **URL:** http://www.tv-wakayama.co.jp/.

47120 ■ JOVF - 1431 KHz
Cho 3-Chome
Wakayama 640-8577, Japan
Ph: 81 73 4281431
Format: Eclectic. **Owner:** Wakayama Broadcasting System (WBS), at above address. **Founded:** 1959. **Operating Hours:** 0500-0400 Mon.-Fri.; 0500-0300 Sat.; 0500-0015 Sun. **Wattage:** 5000. **URL:** http://wbs.co.jp.

Wakkanai

47121 ■ JOTS - 1368 KHz
Nishi 5, Chuo 2-chome
Kita 1
Sapporo 060-8501, Japan
Ph: 81 11 2325800
E-mail: info@hbc.co.jp
Format: Eclectic. **Owner:** Hokkaido Broadcasting Co., Ltd. (HBC), at above address. **Operating Hours:** Continuous. **Key Personnel:** Takashi Watanabe, President. **Wattage:** 1000. **URL:** http://www.hbc.co.jp/.

Yachiyo

47122 ■ JOEE-TV Yachiyo - 50
21-3, Moto-machi
Naka-ku
Hiroshima 730-8504, Japan
Ph: 81 82 2221155
E-mail: tv@rcc.net
Owner: Chugoku Broadcasting Co., Ltd. (RCC), at above address. **Founded:** 1959. **Wattage:** 3. **Ad Rates:** Advertising accepted; rates available upon request. **URL:** http://www.1350.jp/.

Yahiko

47123 ■ FM Radio Niigata - 86.5 MHz
4-3-5 Chuo Ku
Niigata, Japan
Ph: 81 25 2462311
Format: Eclectic. **Owner:** FM Radio Niigata Co., Ltd., at above address. **Operating Hours:** Continuous. **Wattage:** 1000. **Ad Rates:** Advertising accepted; rates available upon request. **URL:** http://www.fmniigata.com/.

47124 ■ JOWV - 79.0 MHz
2-1-1, Chou-ko
Niigata 950-8577, Japan
Ph: 81 25 2400079
Fax: 81 25 2465185
Format: Eclectic. **Owner:** Niigata Kenmin FM Broadcast Company, LTD. (FM PORT), at above address. **Founded:** 2000. **Operating Hours:** Continuous (off the air Sat.& Sun. 1600-2100). **Wattage:** 1000. **URL:** http://www.fmport.com.

Yamagata

47125 ■ Marine Micropaleontology
Elsevier Science
c/o R.W. Jordan, Ed.-in-Ch.
Department of Earth & Environment Sciences
Yamagata University
1-4-12 Kojirakawa-machi
Yamagata 990-8560, Japan
Ph: 81 23 6284645
Fax: 81 23 6284661
Publisher E-mail: nlinfo-f@elsevier.com
Journal covering articles on marine micropaleontology to solve fundamental geological and biological problems. **Founded:** 1976. **Freq:** 16/yr. **Key Personnel:** R.W. Jordan, Editor-in-Chief, sh081@kdw.kj.yamagata-u.ac.jp; F.J. Jorissen, Editor-in-Chief, frans.jorissen@univ-angers.fr; E. Alve, Editorial Board; J. Backman, Editorial Board; D. Boltovskoy, Editorial Board; X. Crosta, Editorial Board. **ISSN:** 0377-8398. **Subscription Rates:** US$1,849 institutions for all countries except Europe and Japan; 219,400¥ institutions; EUR1,654 other countries for European countries; EUR174 individuals for European countries; US$234 individuals for all countries except Europe and Japan; 26,900¥ individuals. **Remarks:** Accepts advertising. **URL:** http://www.elsevier.com/wps/find/journaldescription.cws_home/503351/description. **Circ:** (Not Reported)

47126 ■ JOCY-TV - 30
85 Ochiai Cho

Yamagata 990-8539, Japan
Ph: 81 23 6352111
Fax: 81 23 6352111
E-mail: arrange@sakuranbo.co.jp
Owner: Sakuranbo Television Broadcasting Corporation (SAY), at above address. **Founded:** 1997. **Key Personnel:** Soichi Yamamoto, President. **Wattage:** 10,000. **URL:** http://www.sakuranbo.co.jp/opening.html.

47127 ■ JOEF - 918 KHz
2-5, Hatago-machi
Yamagata 990-8555, Japan
E-mail: kokusai@ybc.co.jp
Format: Eclectic. **Owner:** Yamagata Broadcasting Co., Ltd. (YBC), at above address. **Founded:** 1953. **Operating Hours:** Continuous. **Wattage:** 5000. **URL:** http://www.ybc.co.jp/.

47128 ■ JOEF-TV - 10
2-5, Hatago-machi
Yamagata 990-8555, Japan
Ph: 81 23 6226161
E-mail: kokusai@ybc.co.jp
Owner: Yamagata Broadcasting Co., Ltd. (YBC), at above address. **Founded:** 1960. **Wattage:** 3000. **URL:** http://www.ybc.co.jp/.

47129 ■ JOEV - 80.4 MHz
14-69, Matsuyama 3-chome
Yamagata 990-9543, Japan
Ph: 81 23 6250804
Fax: 81 23 6250805
Format: Eclectic. **Owner:** Yamagata FM Broadcasting Co., Ltd. (YBC), at above address. **Founded:** 1989. **Operating Hours:** Continuous. **Key Personnel:** Jun Sato, President. **Wattage:** 1000. **Ad Rates:** Advertising accepted; rates available upon request. **URL:** http://www.boyfm.co.jp.

47130 ■ JOJC - 1521 KHz
2-2-1 Jinnan
Shibuya-ku
Tokyo 150-8001, Japan
Ph: 81 3 34651111
Fax: 81 3 34698110
E-mail: nhkworld@nhk.jp
Format: Educational. **Owner:** Nippon Hoso Kyokai (NHK), at above address. **Operating Hours:** 2030-1640 (2030-1500, Sun. & Mon.). **Key Personnel:** Shigeo Fukuchi, President. **Wattage:** 1000. **Ad Rates:** Noncommercial. **URL:** http://www.nhk.or.jp.

47131 ■ JOJG - 82.1 MHz
2-2-1 Jinnan
Shibuya-ku
Tokyo 150-8001, Japan
Ph: 81 3 34651111
Fax: 81 3 34698110
Format: News. **Owner:** Nippon Hoso Kyokai (NHK), at above address. **Operating Hours:** Continuous. **Key Personnel:** Hidemi Hyuga, Exec. Dir. Gen. **Wattage:** 1000. **Ad Rates:** Noncommercial. **URL:** http://www.nhk.or.jp.

47132 ■ JOJG - 540 KHz
2-2-1 Jinnan
Shibuya-ku
Tokyo 150-8001, Japan
Ph: 81 3 34651111
Fax: 81 3 34698110
Format: News. **Owner:** Nippon Hoso Kyokai (NHK), at above address. **Operating Hours:** Continuous. **Key Personnel:** Shigeo Fukuchi, President. **Wattage:** 5000. **Ad Rates:** Noncommercial. **URL:** http://www.nhk.or.jp.

47133 ■ JOWI-TV - 36
1-11-33, Hakusan
Yamagata 990-9536, Japan
Ph: 81 23 6248111
E-mail: soumu@tuy.co.jp
Owner: TV-U Yamagata,Inc. (TUY), at above address. **Founded:** 1989. **Wattage:** 10,000. **URL:** http://www.tuy.co.jp/.

47134 ■ JOYI-TV - 38
4-1, Shironishi-machi 5-chome
Yamagata 990-8511, Japan
Ph: 81 23 6451211
Owner: Yamagata Television System, Inc. (YTS), at above address. **Founded:** 1970. **Key Personnel:** Oka Masakazu, President. **Wattage:** 10,000. **URL:** http://www.yts.co.jp/.

Yamagata Hoso - See Yonezawa

Yamaguchi

47135 ■ JOPF - 765 KHz
Shunan Pk.
Yamaguchi 745-8686, Japan
Ph: 81 834 321114
Fax: 81 834 222195
Format: Eclectic. **Owner:** Yamaguchi Broadcasting Co., Ltd. (KΠY), at above address. **Founded:** 1956. **Operating Hours:** Continuous. **Wattage:** 5000. **URL:** http://www.kry.co.jp/.

JOPL - See Hagi

JOPM - See Shimonoseki

JOPN - See Iwakuni

47136 ■ JOUC - 1377 KHz
2-2-1 Jinnan
Shibuya-ku
Tokyo 150-8001, Japan
Ph: 81 3 34651111
Fax: 81 3 34698110
E-mail: nhkworld@nhk.jp
Format: Educational. **Owner:** Nippon Hoso Kyokai (NHK), at above address. **Operating Hours:** 2030-1640 (2030-1500, Sun. & Mon.). **Key Personnel:** Shigehiro Komaru, Chm.; Shigeo Fukuchi, President. **Wattage:** 5000. **Ad Rates:** Noncommercial. **URL:** http://www.nhk.or.jp.

47137 ■ JOUG - 675 KHz
2-2-1 Jinnan
Shibuya-ku
Tokyo 150-8001, Japan
Ph: 81 3 34651111
Fax: 81 3 34811350
E-mail: nhkworld@nhk.jp
Format: News. **Owner:** Nippon Hoso Kyokai (NHK), at above address. **Operating Hours:** Continuous. **Key Personnel:** Shigeo Fukuchi, President; Hidemi Hyuga, Exec. Dir. Gen. **Wattage:** 5000. **Ad Rates:** Noncommercial. **URL:** http://www.nhk.or.jp.

47138 ■ JOUU - 79.2 MHz
3-31, Midori-cho
Yamaguchi 753-8521, Japan
Ph: 81 83 9232100
Fax: 81 83 9248673
Format: Eclectic. **Owner:** FM Yamaguchi Co., Ltd. (FMY), at above address. **Founded:** 1985. **Operating Hours:** Continuous. **Wattage:** 1000. **Ad Rates:** Advertising accepted; rates available upon request. **URL:** http://www.fmy.co.jp/.

Yasuura

47139 ■ JOEE-TV Yasuura - 55
21-3, Moto-machi
Naka-ku
Hiroshima 730-8504, Japan
Ph: 81 82 2221155
E-mail: tv@rcc.net
Owner: Chugoku Broadcasting Co., Ltd. (RCC), at above address. **Founded:** 1959. **Wattage:** 1. **Ad Rates:** Noncommercial. **URL:** http://www.rcc.co.jp.

Yokohama

47140 ■ Mitsubishi Heavy Industries Technical Review
Mitsubishi Heavy Industries Ltd.
Technical Administration Dept.
3-1 Minatomirai 3-chome
Nishi-ku
Yokohama 220-8401, Japan
Ph: 81 3 67163111
Fax: 81 3 67165800
Journal of technology. **Founded:** 1964. **Freq:** Bimonthly. **ISSN:** 0026-6817. **URL:** https://www.mhi.co.jp/en/technology/review/index.html. **Circ:** 3,000

47141 ■ Poetry Kanto
Kanto Poetry Center
Kanto Gakuin University
Kamariya Minami 3-22-1
Kanazawa-ku
Yokohama 236-8502, Japan
Journal of literature. **Subtitle:** A Bridge Between. **Founded:** 1984. **Freq:** Annual. **Key Personnel:** Alan Botsford, Editor, alan@kanto-gakuin.ac.jp; Katsumasa Nishihara, Editor, katz@kanto-gakuin.ac.jp. **Remarks:** Advertising not accepted. **URL:** http://home.kanto-gakuin.ac.jp/~kg061001/index.html. **Circ:** Controlled 700

47142 ■ Systems and Synthetic Biology
Springer Netherlands
c/o Pawan K. Dhar, Ed.-in-Ch.
RIKEN Genomic Sciences Center
Yokohama, Japan
Publisher E-mail: permissions.dordrecht@springer.com
Journal covering molecular biology, engineering and mathematics. **Founded:** 1955. **Freq:** Quarterly. **Print Method:** Offset. **Cols./Page:** 5. **Col. Width:** 22 nonpareils. **Col. Depth:** 210 agate lines. **Key Personnel:** Alessandro Giuliani, Editor-in-Chief; David Gilbert, Editorial Board; Herbert Sauro, Editorial Board; Edward Oakeley, Editorial Board; Kenneth R. Showalter, Editorial Board; Hiraoki Kitano, Editorial Board; Charles DeLisi, Editorial Board; Jens Timmer, Editorial Board; Joseph Nadeau, Editorial Board; John Tyson, Editorial Board. **ISSN:** 1872-5325. **Subscription Rates:** EUR391 institutions print incl. free access or e-only; EUR469.20 institutions print incl. enhanced access. **URL:** http://www.springer.com/biomed/journal/11693.

47143 ■ The Yoke
Yokohama Association for International Communications and Exchanges
Yokohama International Organizations Center 5th Fl.
Pacifico Yokohama
1-1-1 Minato Mirai
Nishi-ku
Yokohama 220-0012, Japan
Ph: 81 452 221171
Fax: 81 452 212210
Publication E-mail: intlyoke@iris.or.jp
Publisher E-mail: yoke@yoke.or.jp
Magazine pertaining to social and cultural life of Yokahama. **Freq:** Bimonthly. **URL:** http://www.yoke.or.jp/theyoke/index.html.

47144 ■ JOGP - 81.9 MHz
2-2-1 Jinnan
Shibuya-ku
Tokyo 150-8001, Japan
Ph: 81 3 34651111
Fax: 81 3 34698110
Format: News. **Owner:** Nippon Hoso Kyokai (NHK), at above address. **Operating Hours:** Continuous. **Key Personnel:** Hidemi Hyuga, Exec. Dir. Gen. **Wattage:** 5000. **URL:** http://www.nhk.or.jp.

47145 ■ JOKM-TV - 42
2-23 Ku Ota Cho
Yokohama 231-8001, Japan
Ph: 81 45 6511711
Owner: Television Kanagama Inc. (TVK), at above address. **Founded:** 1972. **Key Personnel:** Kuni Yasushi Komiya, President. **Wattage:** 10,000. **URL:** http://www.tvk-yokohama.com/.

47146 ■ JORF - 1422 KHz
5-85, Naka-ku
Yokohama 231-8611, Japan
Ph: 81 45 2311531
E-mail: info@jorf.co.jp
Format: Eclectic. **Owner:** RF Radio Nippon Co., Ltd., at above address. **Founded:** 1958. **Operating Hours:** 0500-0400. **Wattage:** 50,000. **URL:** http://www.jorf.co.jp/.

47147 ■ JOTU - 84.7 MHz
2-2-1, Minato-Mirai
Nishi-ku
Yokohama Landmark Tower, 10th Fl.
Yokohama 220-8110, Japan
Ph: 81 45 2241000
Fax: 81 45 2241011
Format: Eclectic. **Owner:** Yokohama FM Broadcasting Co., Ltd., at above address. **Founded:** 1985. **Operating Hours:** Continuous Mon.-Fri.; 0500-0330 Sat.; 0500-2400 Sun. **Wattage:** 5000. **Ad Rates:** Advertising accepted; rates available upon request. **URL:** http://www.fmyokohama.co.jp/.

Yonago

47148 ■ JOHF - 900 KHz
1-71, Hukuwara Nishi 1-chome
Yonago 683-8670, Japan
Ph: 81 859 332111
Format: Eclectic. **Owner:** Broadcasting Systems of SAN-IN (BBS), at above address. **Founded:** 1954. **Operating Hours:** Continuous (off the air Sat. 1800-2030, Sun. 1600-1955). **Wattage:** 5000. **URL:** http://bss.jp/.

JOHL - See Tattori

San'in Hoso - See Izumo

Yonezawa

47149 ■ Yamagata Hoso - 918 KHz
2-5, Hatago-machi
Yamagata 990-8555, Japan
Ph: 81 23 6226161
Fax: 81 23 6254739
E-mail: kokusai@ybc.co.jp
Format: Eclectic. **Owner:** Yamagata Broadcasting Co., Ltd. (YBC), at above address. **Founded:** 1953. **Operating Hours:** Continuous. **Key Personnel:** Mitsuhiko Sato, President. **Wattage:** 1000. **URL:** http://www.ybc.co.jp/.

Yoshida

47150 ■ JOEE-TV Yoshida - 58
21-3, Moto-machi
Naka-ku
Hiroshima 730-8504, Japan
Ph: 81 82 2221155
E-mail: tv@rcc.net
Owner: Chugoku Broadcasting Co., Ltd. (RCC), at above address. **Founded:** 1959. **Wattage:** 10,000. **URL:** http://www.rcc.co.jp.

Yuki

47151 ■ JOEE-TV Yuki - 59
21-3, Moto-machi
Naka-ku
Hiroshima 730-8504, Japan
Ph: 81 82 2221155
E-mail: tv@rcc.net
Owner: Chugoku Broadcasting Co., Ltd. (RCC), at above address. **Founded:** 1959. **Wattage:** 10,000. **Ad Rates:** Noncommercial. **URL:** http://www.rcc.co.jp.

Circulation: ★ = ABC; △ = BPA; ♦ = CAC; • = CCAB; ❑ = VAC; ⊕ = PO Statement; ‡ = Publisher's Report; Boldface figures = sworn; Light figures = estimated.

Gale Directory of Publications & Broadcast Media/147th Ed.   5129

Amman

47152 ■ Dirasat Administrative Sciences
Deanship of Academic Research - University of Jordan
Deanship of Academic Research
University of Jordan
Amman, Jordan
Ph: 962 653 55000
Fax: 962 653 55599
Publisher E-mail: research@ju.edu.jo
Peer-reviewed journal featuring research papers and articles in administrative, economics, and accounting sciences. **Freq:** Annual. **Key Personnel:** Dr. Moudar Zgoul, Site Admin., m.zgoul@ju.edu.jo. **ISSN:** 1026-373X. **Subscription Rates:** 9 JD individuals; 11 JD institutions; US$30 other countries. **URL:** http://dar.ju.edu.jo/dirasatonline/articles.asp. **Circ:** Controlled 1,000

47153 ■ Dirasat Agricultural Sciences
Deanship of Academic Research - University of Jordan
Deanship of Academic Research
University of Jordan
Amman, Jordan
Ph: 962 653 55000
Fax: 962 653 55599
Publisher E-mail: research@ju.edu.jo
Peer-reviewed journal featuring research papers and articles in agricultural and animal sciences. **Freq:** 3/yr. **Key Personnel:** Dr. Moudar Zgoul, Contact, m.zgoul@ju.edu.jo. **ISSN:** 1026-3764. **Subscription Rates:** US$13.5 individuals; US$16.5 institutions; US$45 other countries. **URL:** http://dar.ju.edu.jo/dirasatonline/main.asp. **Circ:** Controlled 1,000

47154 ■ Dirasat Engineering Sciences
Deanship of Academic Research - University of Jordan
Deanship of Academic Research
University of Jordan
Amman, Jordan
Ph: 962 653 55000
Fax: 962 653 55599
Publisher E-mail: research@ju.edu.jo
Peer-reviewed journal publishing research contributions in the natural and engineering sciences. **Founded:** 1974. **Freq:** 2/yr. **Key Personnel:** Dr. Moudar Zgoul, Contact, m.zgoul@ju.edu.jo. **ISSN:** 1560-4551. **Subscription Rates:** 9 JD individuals; 11 JD institutions; US$30 other countries. **URL:** http://dar.ju.edu.jo/dirasatonline/main.asp. **Circ:** Controlled 1,000

47155 ■ Dirasat Human and Social Sciences
Deanship of Academic Research - University of Jordan
Deanship of Academic Research
University of Jordan
Amman, Jordan
Ph: 962 653 55000
Fax: 962 653 55599
Publisher E-mail: research@ju.edu.jo
Peer-reviewed journal featuring research papers and articles in the human and social sciences. **Founded:** 1974. **Freq:** 3/yr. **Key Personnel:** Dr. Moudar Zgoul, Contact, m.zgoul@ju.edu.jo. **ISSN:** 1026-3721. **Subscription Rates:** US$13.5 individuals; US$16.5 institutions; US$45 other countries. **URL:** http://dar.ju.edu.jo/dirasatonline/main.asp. **Circ:** Controlled 1,000

47156 ■ Dirasat Medical and Biological Sciences
Deanship of Academic Research - University of Jordan
Deanship of Academic Research
University of Jordan
Amman, Jordan
Ph: 962 653 55000
Fax: 962 653 55599
Publisher E-mail: research@ju.edu.jo
Peer-reviewed journal featuring research papers and articles in biological, medical, nursing, dentistry, and pharmaceutical sciences. **Freq:** Semiannual. **Key Personnel:** Dr. Moudar Zgoul, Contact, m.zgoul@ju.edu.jo. **ISSN:** 1026-3772. **Subscription Rates:** 9 JD individuals; 11 JD institutions; US$30 other countries. **URL:** http://dar.ju.edu.jo/dirasatonline/main.asp. **Circ:** Controlled 1,000

47157 ■ Dirasat Pure Sciences
Deanship of Academic Research - University of Jordan
Deanship of Academic Research
University of Jordan
Amman, Jordan
Ph: 962 653 55000
Fax: 962 653 55599
Publisher E-mail: research@ju.edu.jo
Journal publishing scholarly research in all fields of science. **Founded:** 1974. **Freq:** Semiannual. **Key Personnel:** Dr. Moudar Zgoul, Contact, m.zgoul@ju.edu.jo. **ISSN:** 1560-456X. **Subscription Rates:** 9 JD individuals; 11 JD institutions; US$30 other countries. **URL:** http://dar.ju.edu.jo/dirasatonline/main.asp. **Circ:** Controlled 1,000

47158 ■ Dirasat Sharia' and Law Sciences
Deanship of Academic Research - University of Jordan
Deanship of Academic Research
University of Jordan
Amman, Jordan
Ph: 962 653 55000
Fax: 962 653 55599
Publisher E-mail: research@ju.edu.jo
Peer-reviewed journal containing research papers and articles in law and Islamic studies. **Freq:** Semiannual. **Key Personnel:** Dr. Moudar Zgoul, Contact, dar.devit@ju.edu.jo. **ISSN:** 1026-3748. **Subscription Rates:** 9 JD individuals; 11 JD institutions; US$30 other countries. **URL:** http://dar.ju.edu.jo/dirasatonline/main.asp. **Circ:** Controlled 1,000

47159 ■ International Journal of Arabic-English Studies
Librairie du Liban Publishers
University of Jordan
PO Box 13315
Amman, Jordan
Ph: 962 653 49959
Fax: 962 655 15746
Publication E-mail: ijaes2000@yahoo.com
Publisher E-mail: info@ldlp.com
Journal promoting original research into cross-language and cross-cultural studies in general, and Arabic-English contrastive and comparative studies in particular, welcoming contributions to such areas of interest as comparative literature, contrastive textology, contrastive linguistics, lexicology, stylistics, and translation studies.

Founded: 2000. **Freq:** Annual. **Key Personnel:** Lewis Mukattash, Editor-in-Chief. **ISSN:** 1680-0982. **URL:** http://www.ijaes.org/.

47160 ■ Jordan Times
Jordan Press Foundation
Queen Rania Al Abdullah St.
PO Box 6710
Amman, Jordan
Ph: 962 656 00800
Fax: 962 656 96183
Publisher E-mail: jotimes@jpf.com.jo
Independent Arab political newspaper. **Freq:** Daily except. Sat. **Key Personnel:** Samir Barhoum, Editor-in-Chief, editor@jordantimes.com. **ISSN:** 1564-0221. **Subscription Rates:** US$265 individuals Arab countries; US$310 individuals Europe; US$350 individuals U.S., Australia & Japan. **Remarks:** Accepts advertising. **URL:** http://www.jordantimes.com/. **Circ:** (Not Reported)

47161 ■ Medical Journal of Islamic Academy of Sciences
Islamic Academy of Sciences
PO Box 830036
Amman, Jordan
Ph: 962 6 5522104
Fax: 962 6 5511803
Publisher E-mail: secretariat@ias-worldwide.org
Specialized medical journal of the Islamic Academy of Sciences. **Founded:** Aug. 1988. **Freq:** Quarterly. **Key Personnel:** Prof. Naci M. Bor, Editor-in-Chief, nacibor@bir.net.tr; Sinasi Ozsoylu, Editor, sinasiozsoylu@hotmail.com; Ethem Gelir, Assoc. Ed., ethemgelir@gmail.com. **ISSN:** 1016-3360. **Subscription Rates:** 40 JD individuals; 11 JD single issue. **Remarks:** Accepts advertising. **URL:** http://www.medicaljournal-ias.org/. **Circ:** (Not Reported)

47162 ■ Royal Wings (Jordan)
Royal Jordanian
PO Box 302
Amman, Jordan
Ph: 962 6 5202000
Fax: 962 6 5672527
Publisher E-mail: ammddrj@rj.com
In-flight magazine. **Founded:** July 1989. **Freq:** Bimonthly. **Remarks:** Accepts advertising. **URL:** http://www.rj.com/en/tabid/135/Default.aspx. **Circ:** (Not Reported)

47163 ■ Mood-FM - 92.00
PO Box 840890
Amman, Jordan
Ph: 962 6 5560066
Fax: 962 6 5656782
E-mail: info@mood.fm
Format: Music of Your Life; Oldies; World Beat. **Owner:** Mood-FM, at above address. **Operating Hours:** Continuous. **URL:** http://www.mood.fm.

47164 ■ TVMAX - 93
Al Rawashdeh Ctr. 2
Wadi Saqra St.
PO Box 940087
Amman, Jordan
Ph: 962 6 5511615

Fax: 962 6 5511617
E-mail: tvmax@orbit.net
Owner: Orbit Satellite Television and Radio Network, c/o Panther Media Group, PO Box 502211, Dubai Media City, Dubai, United Arab Emirates. **URL:** http://www. orbit.net.

47165 ■ TVMAX - 92
Al Rawashdeh Ctr. 2
Wadi Saqra St.
PO Box 940087
Amman, Jordan
Ph: 962 6 5511615
Fax: 962 6 5511617
E-mail: tvmax@orbit.net
Owner: Orbit Satellite Television and Radio Network, c/o Panther Media Group, PO Box 502211, Dubai Media City, Dubai, United Arab Emirates. **URL:** http://www. orbit.net.

47166 ■ TVMAX - 91
Al Rawashdeh Ctr. 2
Wadi Saqra St.
PO Box 940087
Amman, Jordan
Ph: 962 6 5511615
Fax: 962 6 5511617
E-mail: tvmax@orbit.net
Owner: Orbit Satellite Television and Radio Network, c/o Panther Media Group, PO Box 502211, Dubai Media City, Dubai, United Arab Emirates. **URL:** http://www. orbit.net.

47167 ■ TVMAX - 90
Al Rawashdeh Ctr. 2
Wadi Saqra St.
PO Box 940087
Amman, Jordan
Ph: 962 6 5511615

Fax: 962 6 5511617
E-mail: tvmax@orbit.net
Owner: Orbit Satellite Television and Radio Network, c/o Panther Media Group, PO Box 502211, Dubai Media City, Dubai, United Arab Emirates. **URL:** http://www. orbit.net.

Shmeisani

47168 ■ Play-FM - 99.6
Mihiar Center
PO Box 8496116
Shmeisani, Jordan
Ph: 962 6 4619060
Format: Ethnic; World Beat. **Key Personnel:** Zafer Younis, General Mgr., zafer@play.jo; Ramzi Halaby, Sales Mgr., ramzi@play.jo; Dan Harper, Production Mgr., dan@play.jo. **Ad Rates:** Advertising accepted; rates available upon request. **URL:** http://www.play.jo.

Almaty

47169 ■ Yevreiski Dom
Federation of Jewish Communities
Dzhambula str. 191

480008 Almaty, Kazakhstan
Ph: 7 3272 503950
Fax: 7 3272 775550
Magazine featuring articles concerning the Jewish

culture. **Key Personnel:** Yuri Koshtelyuk, Contact. **URL:** http://www.fjc.ru/departments/DeptInstIndex.asp?aid= 84076&countryid=80057.

Nairobi

47170 ■ African Journal of Biotechnology
African Journals Online
PO Box 5170-00200
Nairobi, Kenya
Publisher E-mail: info@ajol.info
Peer-reviewed journal covering applied biochemistry, industrial microbiology, molecular biology, genomic and proteomic, food and agricultural technologies, and metabolic engineering. **Founded:** Oct. 29, 1879. **Freq:** Monthly. **Print Method:** Offset. Accepts mats. **Cols./Page:** 6. **Col. Width:** 24 nonpareils. **Col. Depth:** 301 agate lines. **Key Personnel:** N.J. Tonukari, PhD, Editor, ajb_acadjourn@yahoo.com. **ISSN:** 1684-5315. **Subscription Rates:** Free online. **URL:** http://ajol.info/index.php/ajb.

47171 ■ African Journal of Ecology
East African Wild Life Society
PO Box 20110
Nairobi, Kenya
Ph: 254 20 3874145
Fax: 254 20 3870335
Publisher E-mail: info@eawildlife.org
African journal covering ecology. **Freq:** Quarterly. **ISSN:** 0141-6707. **Subscription Rates:** 399 institutions Europe, paper edition; US$633 U.S. and Canada institutions, paper edition; 439 institutions, other countries paper edition; 360 institutions Europe, online edition; US$570 U.S. and Canada institutions, online edition; 360 institutions, other countries online edition; 438 institutions paper & online, Europe; US$696 U.S. and Canada institutions, paper & online; 482 institutions, other countries paper & online. **URL:** http://www.eawildlife.org.

47172 ■ African Journal of Food, Agriculture, Nutrition and Development
African Journals Online
c/o Prof. Ruth K. Oniang'o, PhD, Ed. in Ch.
Jomo Kenyatta University of Agriculture
Rural Outreach Program
PO Box 29086-00625
Nairobi, Kenya
Ph: 254 202 727989
Fax: 254 202 727989
Publication E-mail: info@ajfand.net
Publisher E-mail: info@ajol.info
Peer-reviewed journal covering food and nutritional issues in Africa. **Freq:** 3/yr. **Key Personnel:** Prof. Ruth K. Oniang'o, PhD, Editor-in-Chief, oniango@iconnect.co.ke. **ISSN:** 1684-5358. **URL:** http://ajol.info/index.php/ajfand.

47173 ■ African Journal of Health Sciences
African Journals Online
PO Box 54840
Nairobi, Kenya
Publisher E-mail: info@ajol.info
Peer-reviewed journal covering health sciences and related disciplines in Africa. **Founded:** 1901. **Freq:** Quarterly. **Print Method:** Offset. **Cols./Page:** 8. **Col. Width:** 25 nonpareils. **Col. Depth:** 301 agate lines. **Key Personnel:** R. Barsoum, Editor; Dr. D.K. Koech, Editor-in-Chief, phone 254 20 2722541, fax 254 20 2720030, kemrilib@kemri.org; G.M.P. Mwaluko, Editor; W.L. Kilama, Editor; R. Owor, Editor; M.W. Kofi-Tsekpo, Editor; J.M. Mungai, Editor; L. Salako, Editor; V.P.K. Titanji, Editor; O.W. Prozesky, Editor. **ISSN:** 1022-9272. **URL:** http://ajol.info/index.php/ajhs.

47174 ■ African Journal of Science and Technology
African Network of Scientific and Technological Institutions
Reseau Africain d'Institutions Scientifiques et Technologiques
PO Box 30592
Nairobi, Kenya
Ph: 254 2 7622619
Fax: 254 2 7622538
Publisher E-mail: info@ansti.org
African journal covering science and technology in English and French. **Freq:** Semiannual. **Key Personnel:** Dr. Norbert Opiyo-Akech, Editor-in-Chief, opiyo-akech@uonbi.ac.ke. **URL:** http://www.ansti.org.

47175 ■ Bulletin of Animal Health and Production in Africa
Inter-African Bureau for Animal Resources
PO Box 30786
Nairobi, Kenya
Ph: 254 2 3674000
Fax: 254 2 3674341
Publication E-mail: info@ajol.info
Publisher E-mail: ibar.office@au-ibar.org
Peer-reviewed journal publishing articles related to animal health and production. **Key Personnel:** George Gitau, Tech. Support, gitau@au-ibar.org. **ISSN:** 0378-9721. **URL:** http://ajol.info/index.php/bahpa.

47176 ■ Daily Nation (Kenya)
Nation Media Group
Nation Center, Kimathi St.
PO Box 49010
Nairobi, Kenya
General newspaper. **Founded:** 1960. **Freq:** Mon.-Sat. **Cols./Page:** 6. **Col. Depth:** 36 centimeters. **Subscription Rates:** US$20.25 individuals 1 month + 3 issues free; US$58.50 individuals 3 months + 12 issues free; US$.75 individuals current issue. **Remarks:** Accepts advertising. **URL:** http://www.nation.co.ke/. **Circ:** Paid 205,000

47177 ■ Discovery and Innovation
African Journals Online
PO Box 14798
Nairobi, Kenya
Ph: 254 2 884401
Fax: 254 2 884406
Publisher E-mail: info@ajol.info
Peer-reviewed journal contains information on different scientific disciplines, including social sciences. **Freq:** Quarterly. **Key Personnel:** Prof. Keto E. Mshigeni, Editor-in-Chief, asp@aasciences.org; Prof. Samuel O. Akatch, Assoc. Ed.; Jonathan Tanui, Production Ed., j.tanui@afornet.org. **ISSN:** 1015-079X. **Subscription Rates:** 3,000 KSh individuals; 6,000 KSh institutions; US$160 individuals Africa; US$300 institutions Africa; US$300 other countries; US$500 institutions, other countries. **URL:** http://ajol.info/index.php/dai.

47178 ■ The East African
Nation Media Group
Nation Center, Kimathi St.
PO Box 49010
Nairobi, Kenya
Community newspaper. **Freq:** Weekly. **Remarks:** Accepts advertising. **URL:** http://www.theeastafrican.co.ke/. **Ad Rates:** BW: 213,000 KSh, 4C: 276,900 KSh. **Circ:** (Not Reported)

47179 ■ East African Agricultural and Forestry Journal
African Journals Online
PO Box 57811
Nairobi, Kenya
Publisher E-mail: info@ajol.info
Peer-reviewed journal containing information about food security. **Key Personnel:** Rachel Rege, Acting Ed., rrege@kari.org. **Subscription Rates:** 4,000 KSh individuals East Africa; 40 other countries; US$62 other countries. **URL:** http://ajol.info/index.php/eaafj.

47180 ■ East African Journal of Statistics
African Journals Online
Jomo Kenyatta University
U.S. Department of of Mathematics & Statistics
PO Box 62,000-00200
Nairobi, Kenya
Ph: 254 733 341025
Fax: 254 67 52164
Publisher E-mail: info@ajol.info
Peer-reviewed journal containing the latest findings in applied and theoretical statistics. **Freq:** Semiannual. **Key Personnel:** Prof. Romanus Odhiambo Otieno, Editor-in-Chief, romanusotieno@yahoo.com; John Lugovane, Contact, john@library.jkuat.ac.ke; L. Odongo, Editor. **ISSN:** 1811-7503. **Subscription Rates:** US$20 single issue East Africa; US$80 individuals East Africa; US$30 single issue other countries, US$120 other countries. **URL:** http://ajol.info/index.php/eajosta.

47181 ■ East African Medical Journal
African Journals Online
PO Box 41632
Nairobi, Kenya
Ph: 254 2 3864506
Fax: 254 2 3864514
Publisher E-mail: info@ajol.info
Peer-reviewed journal contains work reports and reviews of all aspects of medicine. **Freq:** Monthly. **Key Personnel:** Prof. W. Lore, Editor-in-Chief, eamj@wananchi.com; Nicolas Simiyu, Contact, simiyu@kma.co.ke. **ISSN:** 0012-835X. **URL:** http://ajol.info/index.php/eamj.

47182 ■ East and Central African Journal of Pharmaceutical Sciences
African Journals Online
Faculty of Pharmacy
College of Health Sciences
University of Nairobi
PO Box 19676-00202
Nairobi, Kenya
Ph: 254 20 2716962
Fax: 254 20 2716961

Circulation: ★ = ABC; △ = BPA; ♦ = CAC; • = CCAB; ❑ = VAC; ⊕ = PO Statement; ‡ = Publisher's Report; Boldface figures = sworn; Light figures = estimated.

Gale Directory of Publications & Broadcast Media/147th Ed. 5135

Publisher E-mail: info@ajol.info

Peer-reviewed journal covering information about research in pharmaceutical sciences. **Freq:** 3/yr. **Key Personnel:** Prof. C.K. Maitai, PhD, Editor-in-Chief, daru@uonbi.ac.ke; R.O. Adome, PhD, Editor; B. Hagos, PhD, Editor; I.O. Kibwage, PhD, Editor; G.N. Thoithi, PhD, Editor; E. Makannen, PhD, Editor. **ISSN:** 1026-552X. **URL:** http://ajol.info/index.php/ecajps.

47183 ▪ Habitat Debate
United Nations Centre for Human Settlements
PO Box 30030
Nairobi, Kenya
Ph: 254 20 7621234
Fax: 254 20 7624266
Publisher E-mail: infohabitat@unhabitat.org
Publication covering worldwide development. **Freq:** Quarterly. **Key Personnel:** Anna Kajumulo Tibaijuka, Exec. Dir. **Subscription Rates:** Free. **Remarks:** Advertising not accepted. **URL:** http://www.unhabitat.org/pmss/getPage.asp?page=latestPeriods. **Circ:** 10,000

47184 ▪ Innovation
African Centre for Technology Studies
PO Box 45917
ICRAF Complex
United Nations Ave.
Gigiri
Nairobi, Kenya
Ph: 254 20 7126889
Fax: 254 20 2339093
Publisher E-mail: info@acts.or.ke
Publication covering technology. **Freq:** Quarterly. **Remarks:** Advertising accepted; rates available upon request. **URL:** http://www.acts.or.ke. **Circ:** (Not Reported)

47185 ▪ International Journal of Tropical Insect Science
International Centre of Insect Physiology and Ecology
PO Box 30772
Nairobi, Kenya
Ph: 25 420 8632000
Fax: 25 420 8632001
Publisher E-mail: icipe@icipe.org
Publication covering insect science and application in English and French. **Freq:** Quarterly. **Key Personnel:** C. Borgemeister, Editor-in-Chief; T.R. Odhiambo, Founding Ed.; R. Anderson, Editorial Board. **ISSN:** 1742-7584. **Subscription Rates:** 286 institutions online and print; 234 institutions online only; US$550 institutions online and print; US$447 institutions online only; 167 individuals online and print; US$320 individuals online and print; 109 individuals online only; US$212 individuals online only. **URL:** http://www.icipe.org; http://journals.cambridge.org/action/displayJournal?jid=JTI. **Formerly:** Insect Science and Its Application.

47186 ▪ Journal of Civil Engineering
African Journals Online
U.S. Department of of Civil Engineering
PO Box 62000
Nairobi, Kenya
Publisher E-mail: info@ajol.info
Peer-reviewed journal covering all aspects of civil engineering activity. **Freq:** Annual. **Key Personnel:** Dr. Walter O. Oyawa, Editor-in-Chief, oyawaw@yahoo.com; Prof. Makoto Kimura, Editor; Prof. John G. Perry, Editor. **ISSN:** 1562-6121. **Subscription Rates:** 750 KSh individuals East Africa. **URL:** http://ajol.info/index.php/jce.

47187 ▪ Journal of Civil Engineering Research and Practice
African Journals Online
PO Box 62000-00200
Nairobi, Kenya
Ph: 254 67 52711
Fax: 245 67 52164
Publisher E-mail: info@ajol.info
Peer-reviewed journal covering the field of civil engineering. **Freq:** Semiannual. **Key Personnel:** Prof. Walter O. Oyawa, Editor-in-Chief, oyawaw@yahoo.com; Prof. Makoto Kimura, Editor-in-Chief. **ISSN:** 1729-5769. **Subscription Rates:** 2,500 KSh institutions East Africa; US$150 institutions, other countries; 1,000 KSh individuals East Africa; US$60 other countries. **URL:** http://ajol.info/index.php/jcerp.

47188 ▪ Journal of Food Technology in Africa
African Journals Online

City Sq.
PO Box 20175
Nairobi, Kenya
Fax: 254 2 242300
Publisher E-mail: info@ajol.info
Peer-reviewed journal covering all aspects of food science, technology, and nutrition. **Freq:** Quarterly. **Key Personnel:** Thomas R. Odhiambo, Contact; B.A. Wanga, Editor-in-Chief, africafoodjournal@yahoo.com; A.O. Adebayo, Editor. **ISSN:** 1028-6098. **URL:** http://ajol.info/index.php/jfta.

47189 ▪ Journal of Language, Technology & Entrepreneurship in Africa
African Journals Online
PO Box 14634-00800
Nairobi, Kenya
Ph: 254 20 3606595
Fax: 254 20 3606100
Publisher E-mail: info@ajol.info
Peer-reviewed journal containing information about language, technology, entrepreneurship, finance and communication. **Freq:** Semiannual. **Key Personnel:** Frederick K. Iraki, Editor, firaki@usiu.ac.ke; Prof. Mathew Buyu, Contact, mbuyu@usiu.ac.ke. **ISSN:** 1998-1279. **URL:** http://ajol.info/index.php/jolte.

47190 ▪ Journal of Tropical Microbiology and Biotechnology
African Journals Online
PO Box 62000-00200
Nairobi, Kenya
Publisher E-mail: info@ajol.info
Peer-reviewed journal covering the field of microbiology and biotechnology. **Key Personnel:** Dr. Hamadi Boga, Asst. Ed.-in-Ch., hamadiboga@yahoo.com; Prof. Jesse Machuka, Contact, machuka@mitsuminet.com. **ISSN:** 1607-4106. **Subscription Rates:** 1,500 KSh individuals; 4,000 KSh institutions; US$60 individuals Africa; US$150 institutions Africa; US$100 other countries; US$200 institutions, other countries. **URL:** http://ajol.info/index.php/jtmb.

47191 ▪ Kenya Veterinarian
African Journals Online
University of Nairobi
U.S. Department of of Clinical Studies
Faculty of Veterinary Medicine
PO Box 29053-00625
Nairobi, Kenya
Ph: 254 20 3003403
Publisher E-mail: info@ajol.info
Journal covering the field of veterinary. **Freq:** Semiannual. **Key Personnel:** Dr. John Demesi Mande, Editor-in-Chief, jmande@wananchi.com; Dr. Andrew N. Makanya, Assoc. Ed.; Dr. Raphael G. Wahome, Assoc. Ed. **ISSN:** 0256-5161. **Subscription Rates:** 5,000 TSh individuals Tanzania; 50,000 USh individuals Uganda; US$120 individuals Europe; 2,000 KSh individuals Kenya; US$150 individuals OTC. **URL:** http://ajol.info/index.php/kenvet.

47192 ▪ Kwani?
Kwani Trust
PO Box 2895
Nairobi, Kenya
Ph: 25 420 4441801
Fax: 25 420 4441802
Publication containing new journalism and fiction of experimental writing, poetry, cartoons photographs, literary travel writing, creative non-fiction. **Key Personnel:** Binyavanga Wainaina, Founding Ed., b.wainaina@kwani.org; Billy Kahora, Editor, b.kahora@kwani.org. **URL:** http://www.kwani.org.

47193 ▪ NJIWA
Eastern African Environmental Network
PO Box 14694-00800
Nairobi, Kenya
Ph: 254 20 3749534
Publisher E-mail: eaen@eaenet.or.ke
Publication covering conservation. **Freq:** Quarterly. **Remarks:** Advertising accepted; rates available upon request. **URL:** http://www.eaenet.or.ke/index.php?page=whatwedo&subpage=publications. **Circ:** (Not Reported)

47194 ▪ Our Planet
United Nations Environment Programme
United Nations Ave.
Gigiri
PO Box 30552

Nairobi, Kenya
Ph: 254 20 7621234
Fax: 254 20 7624489
Publisher E-mail: unepinfo@unep.org
Magazine reporting significant issues pertaining to environment such as water and climate change, each issue focusing on a particular subject. Discusses environmentally sustainable development. **Founded:** May 1996. **Key Personnel:** Klaus Toepfer, Editor. **Subscription Rates:** US$5 individuals. **URL:** http://www.unep.org/ourplanet/2010/sept/en/.

47195 ▪ Pachyderm
African Elephant Specialist Group
PO Box 68200
Nairobi, Kenya
Ph: 254 20 89060512
Fax: 254 20 890615
Publisher E-mail: afesg@iucn.org
Publication covering wildlife in English and French. **Freq:** Semiannual. **Remarks:** Advertising not accepted. **URL:** http://www.african-elephant.org/pachy/index.html. **Circ:** (Not Reported)

47196 ▪ Scopus
Nature Kenya
The East Africa Natural History Society
PO Box 44486
Nairobi, Kenya
Ph: 259 420 3749957
Publisher E-mail: info@naturekenya.org
Publication covering natural sciences. **Founded:** 1977. **Freq:** Semiannual. **Key Personnel:** Dr. Jeremy Lindsell, Editorial Board; Dr. David J. Pearson, Editorial Board; Dr. Luc Lens, Editorial Board; Dr. Leon A. Bennun, Editorial Board; Derek Pomeroy, Editorial Board; Darcy Ogada, Editorial Board; Dr. N.J. Cordeiro, Editorial Board; Dr. Mwangi Githiru, Editor, mwangi_githiru@yahoo.co.uk. **Subscription Rates:** 500 KSh members Kenya, Uganda, Tanzania; 800 KSh nonmembers; US$10 members others Countries, air mail; US$15 nonmembers others Countries, air mail. **URL:** http://www.naturekenya.org/Publications/Scopus.

47197 ▪ SWARA
East African Wild Life Society
PO Box 20110
Nairobi, Kenya
Ph: 254 20 3874145
Fax: 254 20 3870335
Publication E-mail: swaraeditor@gmail.com
Publisher E-mail: info@eawildlife.org
Publication covering wildlife conservation. **Freq:** Quarterly. **URL:** http://www.eawildlife.org.

47198 ▪ Coro-FM - 102.3
Harry Thuku Rd.
PO Box 30456-00100
Nairobi, Kenya
Ph: 254 2 341171
Fax: 254 2 250003
E-mail: corofm@swiftkenya.com
Format: Sports; Educational; News; Ethnic. **Owner:** Kenya Broadcasting Corporation, at above address. **Operating Hours:** Continuous. **Ad Rates:** Advertising accepted; rates available upon request. **URL:** http://www.kbc.co.ke.

47199 ▪ Hope-FM - 93.3
Valley Rd.
PO Box 42254
Nairobi, Kenya
Ph: 254 20 2730986
Fax: 254 20 2722418
E-mail: info@hopefm.org
Format: Contemporary Christian; Religious. **Owner:** Hope FM, at above address. **Operating Hours:** Continuous. **Ad Rates:** Advertising accepted; rates available upon request. **URL:** http://www.hopefm.org.

47200 ▪ Inooro Radio-FM - 98.9
PO Box 7468-00300
Nairobi, Kenya
Ph: 254 202721415
Fax: 254 202724220
E-mail: citizen@royalmedia.co.ke
Format: Agricultural; News; Sports; Talk. **Owner:** Royal Media Services Ltd, at above address. **Ad Rates:**

Advertising accepted; rates available upon request. **URL:** http://inoorofm.co.ke.

47201 ■ KBC-FM - 101.9
Harry Thuku Rd.

PO Box 30456-00100
Nairobi, Kenya
Ph: 254 20 318823
Fax: 254 20 220675

E-mail: md@kbc.co.ke
Format: Reggae; Hip Hop; Urban Contemporary. **Ad Rates:** Advertising accepted; rates available upon request. **URL:** http://www.kbc.co.ke.

Circulation: ★ = ABC; △ = BPA; ◆ = CAC; • = CCAB; ❏ = VAC; ⊕ = PO Statement; ‡ = Publisher's Report; Boldface figures = sworn; Light figures = estimated.

Gale Directory of Publications & Broadcast Media/147th Ed. 5137

Bishkek

47202 ■ The Times of Central Asia
175A, Abdrahmanova St., Office 304-305
720000 Bishkek, Kirgizstan
Ph: 996 312 661737
Fax: 996 312 665086
Publisher E-mail: gf@fiacconi.com
Newspaper. **Founded:** 1999. **Freq:** Daily. **Key Personnel:** Giorgio Fiacconi, Publisher. **ISSN:** 1607-3592. **Subscription Rates:** US$130 individuals printed edition (weekly); US$140 other countries printed edition (weekly); US$270 individuals combined edition (daily & weekly). **Remarks:** Accepts advertising. **URL:** http://www.timesca-europe.com/. **Circ:** (Not Reported)

Kyrgyz Radio - Cholpon-Ata - See Cholpon-Ata

Kyrgyz Radio - Haidarkan - See Haidarkan

Kyrgyz Radio - Jojomel - See Jojomel

Kyrgyz Radio - Orgochor - See Orgochor

Cholpon-Ata

47203 ■ Kyrgyz Radio - Cholpon-Ata - 1404 KHz
Jash Gvardiya blvd. 59
720010 Bishkek, Kirgizstan
E-mail: rkaktr@elcat.kg
Format: News. **Owner:** Kyrgyz National Broadcasting Corp., at above address. **Operating Hours:** 0000-1900. **Wattage:** 1000. **URL:** http://www.ktr.kg.

Haidarkan

47204 ■ Kyrgyz Radio - Haidarkan - 1404 KHz
Jash Gvardiya blvd. 59
720010 Bishkek, Kirgizstan
E-mail: rkaktr@elcat.kg
Format: News. **Owner:** Kyrgyz National Broadcasting Corp., at above address. **Operating Hours:** 0000-1900. **Key Personnel:** Toktosh Aytikeyeva, President. **Wattage:** 7000. **URL:** http://www.ktr.kg.

Jojomel

47205 ■ Kyrgyz Radio - Jojomel - 1404 KHz
Jash Gvardiya blvd. 59
720010 Bishkek, Kirgizstan
E-mail: rkaktr@elcat.kg
Format: News. **Owner:** Kyrgyz National Broadcasting Corp., at above address. **Operating Hours:** 0000-1900. **Wattage:** 20,000. **URL:** http://www.ktr.kg.

Orgochor

47206 ■ Kyrgyz Radio - Orgochor - 1404 KHz
Jash Gvardiya blvd. 59
720010 Bishkek, Kirgizstan
E-mail: rkaktr@elcat.kg
Format: News. **Owner:** Kyrgyz National Broadcasting Corp., at above address. **Operating Hours:** 0000-1900. **URL:** http://www.ktr.kg.

Circulation: ★ = ABC; △ = BPA; ♦ = CAC; ● = CCAB; ❑ = VAC; ⊕ = PO Statement; ‡ = Publisher's Report; Boldface figures = sworn; Light figures = estimated.

Gale Directory of Publications & Broadcast Media/147th Ed.   5139

Pyongyang

47207 ■ The Pyongyang Times
Pyongyang Times
Sochon-dong
Pyongyang, Democratic People's Republic of Korea
Ph: 850 2 18111
Fax: 850 2 3814598
Publisher E-mail: webmaster@kccbeijing.net
Newspaper. **Freq:** Daily. **URL:** http://www.kcckp.net/en/
periodic/times/index.php.

Circulation: ★ = ABC; △ = BPA; ◆ = CAC; • = CCAB; ❑ = VAC; ⊕ = PO Statement; ‡ = Publisher's Report; Boldface figures = sworn; Light figures = estimated.

Gale Directory of Publications & Broadcast Media/147th Ed. 5141

Andong-si

47208 ■ HLAW - 1017 KHz
709-1, Taehwa-dong
Andong-si 760-728, Republic of Korea
Ph: 82 54 8517114
Fax: 82 54 8543400
Format: Eclectic. **Owner:** Munhwa Broadcasting Corporation, 31, Yeouido-dong, Yeongdeungpo-gu, Seoul 150-728, Republic of Korea, Fax: 82 2 7823094. **Operating Hours:** Continuous. **Wattage:** 10,000. **Ad Rates:** Noncommercial. **URL:** http://www.andongmbc.co.kr.

Busan

47209 ■ Asia Pacific Journal of Tourism Research
Asia Pacific Tourism Association
School of Tourism Management
Dong-A University
1 Bumin-Dong 2-Ga
Seo-gu
Busan 602-072, Republic of Korea
Ph: 82 512008429
Fax: 82 512014335
Publisher E-mail: apta@daum.net
Asia Pacific journal covering tourism. **Freq:** Quarterly. **Key Personnel:** Kaye Chon, Editor-in-Chief; Philip L. Pearce, Consulting Ed. **ISSN:** 1094-1665. **Subscription Rates:** US$204 individuals print only; US$588 individuals online only; US$653 individuals print and online. **Remarks:** Advertising accepted; rates available upon request. **URL:** http://www.apta.asia/; http://www.tandf.co.uk/journals/titles/10941665.asp. **Circ:** 400

47210 ■ HLDA - 89.9 MHz
833-13, Bosaeng Bldg.
Dong-gu
Busan 601-060, Republic of Korea
Ph: 82 516445114
Owner: Buddhist Broadcasting System, 140 Dabo Bldg., 156-1, Mapo-dong, Seoul 121-050, Republic of Korea, Fax: 82 27055229. **Operating Hours:** 2000-1700. **Wattage:** 5000. **Ad Rates:** Advertising accepted; rates available upon request. **URL:** http://www.bbsi.co.kr; http://www.bbsradio.co.kr.

47211 ■ HLKU - 1161 KHz
316-2, Minrak-dong
Sooyoung-gu
Busan 613-728, Republic of Korea
Ph: 82 51 7601000
Fax: 82 51 7612161
Format: Eclectic. **Operating Hours:** Continuous. **Wattage:** 20,000. **URL:** http://www.busanmbc.co.kr; http://www.imbc.com.

47212 ■ MBC-Pusan - 95.9 MHz
316-2, Minrak-dong
Sooyoung-gu
Busan 613-728, Republic of Korea
Ph: 82 51 7601000
Fax: 82 51 7612162
Format: Eclectic. **Owner:** Munhwa Broadcasting Corporation, 34-3, Yeongdeungpo-gu, Seoul 150-877, Republic

of Korea, 82 2 32196208, Fax: 82 2 32196214. **Wattage:** 3000. **URL:** http://www.psmbc.co.kr; http://www.imbc.com.

Cheju

47213 ■ HLAJ - 774 KHz
321-22, Yeon-dong
Jeju-si, Jeju-do
Cheju 690-170, Republic of Korea
Ph: 82 64 7402114
Fax: 82 64 7469020
E-mail: master@jejumbc.com
Format: Eclectic. **Operating Hours:** Continuous. **Wattage:** 10,000. **URL:** http://www.jejumbc.com.

47214 ■ MBC-Cheju - 102.9 MHz
31, Yeouido-dong
Yeongdeungpo-gu
Seoul 150-728, Republic of Korea
Ph: 82 64 7402114
Fax: 82 64 7469020
Owner: Munhwa Broadcasting Corporation, at above address. **Wattage:** 774. **URL:** http://www.jejumbc.com/; http://www.imbc.com.

47215 ■ MBC-Cheju - 90.1 MHz
31, Yeouido-dong
Yeongdeungpo-gu
Seoul 150-728, Republic of Korea
Ph: 82 64 7402114
Fax: 82 64 7469020
Owner: Munhwa Broadcasting Corporation, at above address. **Wattage:** 3000. **URL:** http://www.jejumbc.com/; http://www.imbc.com.

Cheongju

47216 ■ KBS-Cheongju - 102.1 MHz
471 Kaishin-dong
Cheongju 360-790, Republic of Korea
Ph: 82 43 2607100
Fax: 82 43 2607199
Owner: Korean Broadcasting System, 18 Yoido-dong, Youngdungpo-gu, Seoul 150-790, Republic of Korea. **Key Personnel:** Won Kun Lee, Mng. Dir.; Kim Hong, Exec. VP. **Wattage:** 3000. **Ad Rates:** Noncommercial. **URL:** http://www.kbs.co.kr.

47217 ■ KBS-Uam-san - 89.3 MHz
471 Kaishin-dong
Cheongju 360-790, Republic of Korea
Ph: 82 43 2607100
Fax: 82 43 2607199
Owner: Korean Broadcasting System, 18 Yoido-dong, Youngdungpo-gu, Seoul 150-790, Republic of Korea, 82 2 7811000. **Key Personnel:** Won Kun Lee, PRGM. **Wattage:** 1000. **URL:** http://www.kbs.co.kr; http://english.kbs.co.kr/explore/contacts/expl_cnt.html.

Chinju

47218 ■ Advances in Algebra
Research India Publications
c/o Young Bae Jun, Ed.-in-Ch.
Gyeongsang National University

Dept. of Mathematics Education
Chinju 660-701, Republic of Korea
Publisher E-mail: info@ripublication.com
Journal covering theoretical and applied aspects of algebra. Topics include structure of finite groups and algebraic groups, combinatorics, algebraic geometry, super algebras, quantum groups, universal algebra, and theoretical computer science. **Founded:** 1912. **Freq:** Semiannual. **Print Method:** Offset. **Trim Size:** 7 7/8 x 10 1/2. **Key Personnel:** Zvi Arad, Editorial Board Member; Nanqing Ding, Editorial Board Member; Shaun Fallat, Editorial Board Member; Young Bae Jun, Editor-in-Chief, ybjun@gsnu.ac.kr; Bijan Davvaz, Editorial Board Member; Gerhard Hiss, Editorial Board Member. **ISSN:** 0973-6964. **Subscription Rates:** US$280 institutions and library; print plus online free; US$260 institutions and library; online only; US$180 individuals print plus online free; US$160 individuals online only; Rs 1,800 individuals. **URL:** http://www.ripublication.com/aa.htm.

47219 ■ MBC-Chinju - 91.1 MHz
31, Yeouido-dong
Yeongdeungpo-gu
Seoul 150-728, Republic of Korea
Ph: 82 55 7402114
Fax: 82 55 7402109
Format: Eclectic. **Owner:** Munhwa Broadcasting Corporation, at above address. **Wattage:** 3000. **URL:** http://www.jinjumbc.co.kr; http://www.imbc.com.

47220 ■ MBC-Chinju - 96.1 MHz
31, Yeouido-dong
Yeongdeungpo-gu
Seoul 150-728, Republic of Korea
Ph: 82 55 7402114
Fax: 82 55 7402109
Owner: Munhwa Broadcasting Corporation, at above address. **Wattage:** 3000. **URL:** http://www.jinjumbc.co.kr; http://www.imbc.com.

47221 ■ MBC-Chinju - 97.7 MHz
31, Yeouido-dong
Yeongdeungpo-gu
Seoul 150-728, Republic of Korea
Ph: 82 55 7402114
Fax: 82 55 7402109
Owner: Munhwa Broadcasting Corporation, at above address. **Wattage:** 1000. **URL:** http://www.jinjumbc.co.kr; http://www.imbc.com.

Chonju

47222 ■ MBC-Chonju - 99.1 MHz
31, Yeouido-dong
Yeongdeungpo-gu
Seoul 150-728, Republic of Korea
Ph: 82 63 2208000
Fax: 82 63 2261363
Owner: Munhwa Broadcasting Corporation, at above address. **Wattage:** 5000. **URL:** http://www.jmbc.co.kr/; http://www.imbc.com.

Chuncheon-si

47223 ■ HLAN - 774 KHz
238-3, Samchun-dong
Chuncheon-si 200-718, Republic of Korea
Ph: 82 33 2591215
Fax: 82 33 2546400
Format: Eclectic. **Operating Hours:** Continuous. **Wattage:** 10,000. **URL:** http://www.chmbc.co.kr.

Daegu

47224 ■ AFN Korea Radio & Television - 88.5 MHz
Camp Walker
Daegu, Republic of Korea
Operating Hours: Continuous. **Wattage:** 1000. **URL:** http://afnkorea.net/.

47225 ■ HLDI - 94.5 MHz
Metropolitan City Bldg.
156-1, Ui Jung-gu
Daegu 700-430, Republic of Korea
Ph: 82 27055114
Fax: 82 27055229
Owner: Buddhist Broadcasting System, 140 Dabo Bldg., 156-1, Mapo-dong, Seoul 121-050, Republic of Korea. **Operating Hours:** 2000-1700. **Wattage:** 3000. **URL:** http://www.bbsi.co.kr; http://www.bbsradio.co.kr.

Daejeon

47226 ■ ETRI Journal
Electronics and Telecommunications Research Institute
138 Gajeongno, Yuseong-Gu
Daejeon 305-700, Republic of Korea
Ph: 82 42 8606127
Fax: 82 42 8606737
Publisher E-mail: etrij@etri.re.kr
Academic journal in Korea in the field of electronics, information and telecommunications. **Founded:** 1993. **Freq:** Bimonthly. **Key Personnel:** Chunghyun Ahn, Editor, phone 82 42 8605826, fax 82 42 8606465, hyun@etri.re.kr; Byung-Han Ryu, Editor, rubh@etri.re.kr; Kyu-Seok Lee, Editor-in-Chief, phone 82 42 8605505, fax 82 42 8606836, kyulee@etri.re.kr; Alexander I. Rudnicky, Editor; Prof. Jinho Choi, Editor, j.choi@swansea.ac.uk; Jongdae Kim, Editor, phone 82 42 8606410, jdkim@etri.re.kr. **ISSN:** 1225-6463. **URL:** http://etrij.etri.re.kr. **Circ:** 3,700

47227 ■ International Journal of Theoretical and Applied Mechanics
Research India Publications
c/o Hyung Jin Sung, PhD, Ed.-in-Ch.
Dept. of Mechanical Engineering
Korea Advanced Institute of Science & Technology
373-1, Guseong-Dong, Yuseong-Gu
Daejeon 305-701, Republic of Korea
Fax: 82 42 8695027
Publisher E-mail: info@ripublication.com
Journal covering theoretical and applied mechanics including computational, and experimental aspects, and modeling, methods of analysis and instrumentation. **Founded:** 1927. **Freq:** 3/yr. **Print Method:** Offset. **Trim Size:** 5 3/8 x 7 3/4. **Cols./Page:** 2. **Col. Width:** 23 nonpareils. **Col. Depth:** 86 agate lines. **Key Personnel:** Hyung Jin Sung, PhD, Editor-in-Chief, hjsung@kaist.ac.kr; Tungyang Chen, Editorial Board; Russ Keanini, Editorial Board. **ISSN:** 0973-6085. **Subscription Rates:** US$320 institutions and library; print plus online free; US$300 institutions and library; online only; US$220 individuals print plus online free; US$200 individuals online only; Rs 1,800 individuals. **URL:** http://www.ripublication.com/ijtam.htm.

47228 ■ HLAD - 93.3 MHz
233-15, Jijok-dong
Yousung-gu
Daejeon 305-711, Republic of Korea
Ph: 82 42 8289330
Fax: 82 42 8289349
Owner: Far East Broadcasting Corporation, 89 Sangsu-dong Mapo-gu, Seoul 121-707, Republic of Korea, 82 2 3200114, Fax: 82 2 3200229. **Founded:** Dec. 1989. **Operating Hours:** 2000-1500. **Wattage:** 5000. **URL:** http://dfebc.net/; http://www.febc.or.kr.

MBC-Taegu - See Taegu

47229 ■ MBC-Taejon - 97.5 MHz
4-5 Doryong
Daejeon 305-740, Republic of Korea
Ph: 82 42 3303114
Fax: 82 42 3303700
Owner: Munhwa Broadcasting Corporation, 31, Yeouido-dong, Yeongdeungpo-gu, Seoul, Republic of Korea, 82 2 7892851, Fax: 82 2 7823094. **Wattage:** 5000. **Ad Rates:** Noncommercial. **URL:** http://www.tjmbc.co.kr; http://www.imbc.com.

47230 ■ MBC-Taejon - 92.5 MHz
4-5 Doryong
Daejeon 305-740, Republic of Korea
Ph: 82 42 3303114
Fax: 82 42 3303700
Format: Eclectic. **Owner:** Munhwa Broadcasting Corporation, 31, Yeouido-dong, Yeongdeungpo-gu, Seoul, Republic of Korea, 82 2 7892851, Fax: 82 2 7823094. **Wattage:** 1000. **URL:** http://www.tjmbc.co.kr; http://www.imbc.com.

Dongducheon

47231 ■ AFN Korea Radio & Television - 88.3 MHz
Camp Casey
Dongducheon, Republic of Korea
Operating Hours: Continuous. **Wattage:** 250. **URL:** http://afnkorea.net/.

47232 ■ AFN Korea Radio & Television - 1197 KHz
Camp Casey
Dongducheon, Republic of Korea
Operating Hours: 2005-0000 Mon.-Fri. **Wattage:** 1000. **URL:** http://afnkorea.net/.

Gangwon-do

47233 ■ HLDY - 90.1 MHz
500-1, Jangsa-dong
Sokcho
Gangwon-do 217-130, Republic of Korea
Ph: 82 33 6389000
Fax: 82 33 6373906
Format: Gospel. **Owner:** Far East Broadcasting Corporation, MPO Box 88, Seoul 121-707, Republic of Korea, 82 2 3200114, Fax: 82 2 3200229. **Founded:** Aug. 27, 2001. **Operating Hours:** 1900-1700. **Wattage:** 3000. **URL:** http://yeongdong.febc.net/; http://www.febc.or.kr.

Gwangju

47234 ■ HLCN - 819 KHz
300, Wolsan-dong
Nam-gu
Gwangju 503-728, Republic of Korea
Ph: 82 62 3602000
Fax: 82 62 3602155
Format: Eclectic. **Owner:** Munhwa Broadcasting Corporation, 31, Yeouido-dong, Yeongdeungpo-gu, Seoul 150-728, Republic of Korea, Fax: 82 2 7823094. **Operating Hours:** Continuous. **Wattage:** 20,000. **URL:** http://www.kjmbc.co.kr.

47235 ■ MBC-Kwangju - 93.9 MHz
31, Yeouido-dong
Yeongdeungpo-gu
Seoul 150-728, Republic of Korea
Ph: 82 62 3602000
Fax: 82 62 3602155
Format: Eclectic. **Owner:** Munhwa Broadcasting Corporation, at above address. **Wattage:** 5000. **URL:** http://www.imbc.com/; http://www.kjmbc.co.kr.

47236 ■ MBC-Kwangju - 95.1 MHz
31, Yeouido-dong
Yeongdeungpo-gu
Seoul 150-728, Republic of Korea
Ph: 82 62 3602000
Fax: 82 62 3602155
Owner: Munhwa Broadcasting Corporation, at above address. **Wattage:** 3000. **URL:** http://www.imbc.com; http://www.kjmbc.co.kr.

47237 ■ MBC-Kwangju - 91.5 MHz
31, Yeouido-dong
Yeongdeungpo-gu
Seoul 150-728, Republic of Korea

Ph: 82 62 3602000
Fax: 82 62 3602155
E-mail: gjmbc@kjmbc.co.kr
Owner: Munhwa Broadcasting Corporation, at above address. **Wattage:** 5000. **URL:** http://www.kjmbc.co.kr/; http://www.imbc.com.

Gyeongsangnam-do

47238 ■ HLDD - 98.1 MHz
No. 117, Joongang-dong
Changwon-si
Gyeongsangnam-do 641-843, Republic of Korea
Ph: 82 55 2699810
Fax: 82 55 2699729
Owner: Far East Broadcasting Corporation, MPO Box 88, Seoul 121-707, Republic of Korea, 82 2 3200114, Fax: 82 2 3200229. **Founded:** Mar. 1996. **Operating Hours:** 2000-1500. **Wattage:** 5000. **URL:** http://changwon.febc.net; http://www.febc.or.kr.

Jeju

47239 ■ HLAZ - 1566 KHz
No. 2761, Hagwi-ri
Aewol-up, Pukjejukun
Jeju 690-795, Republic of Korea
Ph: 82 64 7138100
Fax: 82 64 7138105
Format: Religious. **Owner:** Far East Broadcasting Corporation, MPO Box 88, Seoul 121-707, Republic of Korea, 82 2 3200114, Fax: 82 2 3200229. **Founded:** June 1973. **Operating Hours:** 22 hours Daily. **Wattage:** 250 KW/100 KW. **URL:** http://jeju.febc.net/; http://www.febc.or.kr.

HLAZ - See Sogwipo

47240 ■ KBS-Jeju - 621 KHz
302-3, Yeon-dong
Jeju 690-170, Republic of Korea
Format: Eclectic. **Owner:** Korean Broadcasting System, 18 Yoido-dong, Youngdungpo-gu, Seoul 150-790, Republic of Korea. **Former name:** HLCF-Sogwip'o. **Key Personnel:** Won Kun Lee, Mng. Dir.; Kim Hong, Exec. VP. **Wattage:** 10,000. **Ad Rates:** Noncommercial. **URL:** http://www.kbs.co.kr.

Jinhae

47241 ■ AFN Korea Radio & Television - 1512 KHz
Chinhae Naval Base
Jinhae, Republic of Korea
Format: News; Full Service. **Operating Hours:** Continuous. **Wattage:** 250. **URL:** http://afnkorea.net/.

Kyungnam

47242 ■ Advances in Theoretical and Applied Mathematics
Research India Publications
c/o Prof. Taekyun Kim, Ed.-in-Ch.
Jangjeon Research Institute for Mathematical Science & Physics
252-5, Hapcheon-Dong Hapcheon-Gun
Kyungnam 678-802, Republic of Korea
Publisher E-mail: info@ripublication.com
Journal covering theoretical and applied mathematics. Topics include statistics, probability, fluid mechanics, fuzzy mathematics, combinatorics, fractional analysis, solid mechanics, financial mathematics, differential equations, dynamical systems, numerical analysis, integral equations, mathematical physics, optimization, wavelets, signal theory, and discrete mathematics. **Founded:** 1958. **Freq:** 3/yr. **Print Method:** Offset. **Trim Size:** 8 3/8 x 10 7/8. **Cols./Page:** 2. **Col. Width:** 3 1/2 inches. **Col. Depth:** 10 inches. **Key Personnel:** Prof. Taekyun Kim, Editor-in-Chief, tkim64@hanmail.net; R.P. Agarwal, Editorial Board Member; N.U. Ahmed, Editorial Board Member; M.Z. Abu-Sbeih, Editorial Board Member; J. Appell, Editorial Board Member; M. Bohner, Editorial Board Member. **ISSN:** 0973-4554. **Subscription Rates:** US$380 institutions and library; print plus online free; US$140 individuals print plus online free; US$120 individuals online only; US$360 institutions and library; online only; Rs 1,800 individuals. **URL:** http://www.ripublication.com/atam.htm.

Masan

47243 ■ International Journal of Mathematical Sciences
Serials Publications
c/o J.K. Kim, Ed.-in-Ch.
Dept. of Mathematics, Education
Kyungnam University
Masan 631-701, Republic of Korea
Ph: 82 552 492211
Fax: 82 552 438609
Publisher E-mail: serials@satyam.net.in
Journal covering areas of applied, computational and industrial mathematics and statistics, and related areas of mathematical sciences. Topics include approximation theory, computation, systems control, differential equations and dynamical systems, financial math, fluid mechanic and solid mechanics, functional calculus and applications, numerical algorithms, optimization, statistics, wavelets and wavelet transforms, and inverse problems. **Founded:** 1891. **Freq:** Semiannual. **Print Method:** Offset. **Cols./Page:** 6. **Col. Width:** 18 nonpareils. **Col. Depth:** 294 agate lines. **Key Personnel:** Yang Xu, Editorial Board; J.K. Kim, Editor-in-Chief, jongkyuk@kyungnam.ac.kr. **ISSN:** 0972-754X. **Subscription Rates:** US$200 institutions print. **URL:** http://www.serialspublications.com/journals1.asp?jid=282&jtype=1.

47244 ■ MBC-Masan - 98.9 MHz
31, Yeouido-dong
Yeongdeungpo-gu
Seoul 150-728, Republic of Korea
Ph: 82 55 2505000
Fax: 82 55 2505001
Format: Eclectic. **Owner:** Munhwa Broadcasting Corporation, at above address. **Ad Rates:** Noncommercial. **URL:** http://www.masanmbc.co.kr; http://www.imbc.com.

47245 ■ MBC-Masan - 100.5 MHz
31, Yeouido-dong
Yeongdeungpo-gu
Seoul 150-728, Republic of Korea
Ph: 82 55 2505000
Fax: 82 55 2505001
Owner: Munhwa Broadcasting Corporation, at above address. **Wattage:** 1000. **URL:** http://www.masanmbc.co.kr; http://www.imbc.com.

Mokpo-si

47246 ■ HLKW - 100.5 MHz
878-9, San-dong
Mokpo-si 530-822, Republic of Korea
Ph: 82 61 2849000
Fax: 82 61 2849199
Owner: Far East Broadcasting Corporation, 89 Sangsu-dong Mapo-gu, Seoul 121-707, Republic of Korea, 82 2 3200114; Fax: 82 2 3200229. **Founded:** Apr. 20, 2001. **Key Personnel:** Billy Kim, Contact. **Wattage:** 1000. **Ad Rates:** Advertising accepted; rates available upon request. **URL:** http://www.febc.net.

Pohang

47247 ■ Bulletin of the Korean Mathematical Society
The Korean Mathematical Society
c/o Youngju Choie, Ed.-in-Ch.
Dept. of Mathematics, POSTECH
Pohang 790-784, Republic of Korea
Publisher E-mail: kms@kms.or.kr
Journal focusing on research in pure and applied mathematics. **Freq:** Quarterly February, May, August, November. **Key Personnel:** Youngju Choie, Editor-in-Chief, yjchoie@gmail.com; Sang Geun Hahn, Editor, sghahn@kaist.ac.kr; Bae Hyeong-Ohk, Editor, hobae@ajou.ac.kr. **ISSN:** 1015-8634. **Subscription Rates:** US$50 nonmembers; US$100 institutions; US$80 members ordinary; US$40 students members; US$240 members institution. **URL:** http://www.kms.or.kr/home/journal/old/bkms/.

47248 ■ HLCP-Pohang - 1305 KHz
655, Sangdo-dong
Pohang 790-790, Republic of Korea
Ph: 82 54 2807100
Fax: 82 54 2807199
Format: Eclectic. **Owner:** Korean Broadcasting System,

18 Yoido-dong, Youngdungpo-gu, Seoul 150-790, Republic of Korea, 82 2 7811000. **Wattage:** 10,000. **URL:** http://www.kbs.co.kr; http://english.kbs.co.kr/explore/contacts/expl_cnt.html.

47249 ■ MBC-Pohang - 97.9 MHz
31, Yeouido-dong
Yeongdeungpo-gu
Yosu 150-728, Republic of Korea
Ph: 82 54 2890114
Fax: 82 54 2892117
E-mail: webmaster@phmbc.co.kr
Owner: Munhwa Broadcasting Corporation, at above address. **Wattage:** 3000. **URL:** http://www.phmbc.co.kr; http://www.imbc.com.

Pyongtaek

47250 ■ AFN Korea Radio & Television - 1440 KHz
Camp Humphreys
Pyongtaek, Republic of Korea
Format: News; Full Service. **Operating Hours:** 8:05 pm-12:00 am Mon.-Fri. **Wattage:** 1000. **URL:** http://afnkorea.net/.

47251 ■ AFN Korea Radio & Television - 88.3 MHz
Camp Humphreys
Pyongtaek, Republic of Korea
Format: News; Full Service. **Wattage:** 50. **URL:** http://afnkorea.net/.

Seoul

47252 ■ American Chamber of Commerce in Korea
No. 4501, Trade Twr.
159-1 Samsung-dong, Kangham-gu
Seoul 135-729, Republic of Korea
Ph: 82 25642040
Fax: 82 25642050
Publisher E-mail: amchamrsvp@amchamkorea.org
Publication covering American Chamber of Commerce in Korea. **Freq:** Quarterly. **Key Personnel:** Tami Overby, Exec. VP. **Subscription Rates:** members free; 100,000¥ nonmembers. **URL:** http://www.amchamkorea.org/.

47253 ■ Archives of Pharmacal Research
Pharmaceutical Society of Korea
1489-3 Suhcho 3-Dong, Suhcho-Ku
Suhcho-ku
Seoul 137-071, Republic of Korea
Ph: 82 2 5843257
Fax: 82 2 5211781
Publisher E-mail: pskor@chollian.dacom.co.kr
Publishes research reports in the pharmaceutical-biomedical sciences. **Founded:** 1978. **Freq:** Monthly. **Key Personnel:** Dr. Young Choong Kim, Publisher; Dr. Sang Geon Kim, Editor-in-Chief; Dr. Eun-Seok Kim, Editor, sgk@snu.ac.kr. **ISSN:** 0253-6269. **Subscription Rates:** US$250 institutions; US$120 individuals; US$250 institutions, other countries; US$120 other countries. **Remarks:** Advertising accepted; rates available upon request. **URL:** http://apr.psk.or.kr/home/journal/. **Circ:** Paid 1,500

47254 ■ Asian-Australasian Journal of Animal Sciences
Asian-Australasian Association of Animal Production Societies
Rm. 708, Sammo Sporex
1638-32 Sillimbon-dong
Gwanak-gu
Seoul 151-730, Republic of Korea
Ph: 82 288 86558
Fax: 82 288 86559
Publication E-mail: jongkha@hotmail.com
Publication providing information on agriculture and biology. **Founded:** 1988. **Freq:** Monthly. **Trim Size:** A4. **Key Personnel:** Dr. Jong K. Ha, Editor-in-Chief; Hye J. Ann, Business Mgr. **ISSN:** 1011-2367. **Subscription Rates:** 150,000 W individuals; 70,000 W students; 250,000 W institutions. **Remarks:** Accepts advertising. **URL:** http://www.ajas.info/. **Ad Rates:** BW: US$300, 4C: US$500. **Circ:** 1,000

47255 ■ Asian Exchange
Asian Regional Exchange for New Alternatives
c/o Institute of Democracy & Society

Sungkonghoe University
1-1 Hang-dong
Guro-gu
Seoul 152 176, Republic of Korea
Ph: 82 2 26104751
Fax: 82 2 26104752
Publication covering social welfare. **Freq:** Semiannual. **ISSN:** 0256-7520. **Subscription Rates:** US$35 individuals Japan, Australia, New Zealand; US$25 individuals rest of Asia; US$25 individuals Africa, Latin America; US$40 individuals U.S. and Europe; 200 Yu individuals Hong Kong. **URL:** http://www.arenaonline.org/. **Circ:** 800

47256 ■ Asian Journal of Women's Studies
EWHA Womans University Press
Asian Ctr. for Women's Studies
Korean Women's Institute
EWHA Womans University
Seoul 120-750, Republic of Korea
Asian journal covering women's studies. **Subtitle:** AJWS. **Founded:** 1995. **Freq:** Quarterly. **Trim Size:** 14.5 x 22.5. **Key Personnel:** Pilwha Chang, Editor-in-Chief; Ji Eun Roh, Managing Editor; Kim Eun-Shil, Co-Ed.; Mala Khullar, Co-Ed. **ISSN:** 1225-9276. **Subscription Rates:** US$50 individuals; US$115 institutions; US$100 two years; US$230 two years institution; US$20 by mail. **URL:** http://kilden.forskningsradet.no/c17292/publikasjon/vis.html?tid=36288&strukt_tid=17292. **Ad Rates:** BW: US$100. **Circ:** Paid 700

47257 ■ Asian Perspective
Institute for Eastern Studies
28-42 Samchung-dong, Chongro-ku
Seoul 110-230, Republic of Korea
Political science journal. **Founded:** 1977. **Freq:** Quarterly. **Key Personnel:** Melvin Gurtov, Editor-in-Chief, mgurtov@aol.com. **ISSN:** 0258-9184. **Subscription Rates:** US$52 other countries. **Remarks:** Advertising accepted; rates available upon request. **URL:** http://www.asianperspective.org/. **Circ:** Paid 2,300

47258 ■ Biochemistry and Molecular Biology Reports
Korean Society for Biochemistry and Molecular Biology
Rm. 801, The Korea Science & Technology Center
635-4 Yeoksam-dong, Kangnam-gu
Seoul 135-703, Republic of Korea
Ph: 82 2 5087434
Fax: 82 2 5087578
Publisher E-mail: bmbreports@biochem.or.kr
Journal dealing with general areas of biochemistry. **Freq:** Bimonthly. **Key Personnel:** Jaesang Kim, Managing Editor; Soo Young Choi, Editor-in-Chief; Jaewhan Song, Managing Editor; Charles R. Cantor, Editorial Advisory Board; Zigang Dong, Overseas Ed.; Yong Song Gho, Review Ed.; Gordon G. Hammes, Editorial Advisory Board; Robert D. Wells, Editorial Advisory Board; Seung R. Paik, Review Ed. **ISSN:** 1225-8687. **Subscription Rates:** US$370 institutions plus 30.60 postage. **URL:** http://www.jbmb.or.kr/. **Formerly:** Korean Biochemical Journal; Journal of Biochemistry and Molecular Biology.

47259 ■ Bulletin of the Korean Chemical Society
Korean Chemical Society
34-1, 5-ga, Anam-dong
Seongbuk-gu
Seoul 136-075, Republic of Korea
Ph: 82 2 9532095
Fax: 82 2 9532093
Publication featuring research information in the field of pure and applied chemistry. **Freq:** Monthly. **Key Personnel:** Dr. Sun Yeoul Lee, Managing Editor; Hoosung Lee, Editor; Su-Moon Park, Editor-in-Chief, smpark@postech.edu. **ISSN:** 0253-2964. **Subscription Rates:** US$250 individuals. **Remarks:** Advertising not accepted. **URL:** http://journal.kcsnet.or.kr/. **Absorbed:** Korean Journal of Medicinal Chemistry. **Circ:** 2,300

47260 ■ The Choogan Chosun
The Chosun Ilbo
62-4 Taepyeongro 1-ga
Jung-gu
Seoul 100-101, Republic of Korea
Ph: 82 272 45114
Magazine covering general news and editorial. **Founded:** Oct. 20, 1968. **Freq:** Weekly. **URL:** http://comdev.chosun.com/homepage/html/publication_eng.html.

47261 ■ Chosen Ilbo
The Chosun Ilbo
62-4 Taepyeongro 1-ga
Jung-gu
Seoul 100-101, Republic of Korea
Ph: 82 272 45114
Publication E-mail: englishnews@chosun.com
General newspaper. **Founded:** 1920. **Freq:** Daily. **Trim Size:** 373 x 531 mm. **Key Personnel:** Bang Sang-Hoon, President. **Remarks:** Accepts advertising. **URL:** http://english.chosun.com. **Circ:** Combined ‡4,245,000

47262 ■ Communications of the Korean Mathematical Society
The Korean Mathematical Society
The Korea Science & Technology Center 202
635-4 Yeoksam-dong
Gangnam-gu
Seoul 135-703, Republic of Korea
Ph: 82 2 5650361
Fax: 82 2 5650364
Publisher E-mail: kms@kms.or.kr
Journal disseminating important research works of wide-ranging interests in the field of pure and applied mathematics. **Freq:** Quarterly January, July, October. **Key Personnel:** Chang Heon Kim, Editor, chkim@swu.ac.kr; Un Cig Ji, Editor, uncigji@cbucc.chungbuk.ac.kr; Yeol Je Cho, Editor-in-Chief, yjcho@gnu.ac.kr; Jae-Young Chung, Editor, jychung@kunsan.ac.kr. **ISSN:** 1225-1763. **Subscription Rates:** US$40 individuals; US$80 institutions; US$80 members ordinary; US$240 members institution; US$40 students members. **URL:** http://www.kms.or.kr/.

47263 ■ Current Applied Physics
Elsevier (Singapore) Pte. Ltd.
c/o Tae Won Noh, Ed.-in-Ch.
The Korean Physical Society
Yuksam-dong 635-4
Kangnam-Ku
Seoul 135703, Republic of Korea
Ph: 82 255 64737
Fax: 82 255 41643
Publisher E-mail: asiabkinfo@elsevier.com
International journal covering all the fields of applied science investigating the physics of the advanced materials for future applications. **Subtitle:** Physics, Chemistry and Materials Science. **Founded:** 2001. **Freq:** Bimonthly. **Key Personnel:** M. Aono, International Advisory Editorial Board; Tae Won Noh, Editor-in-Chief, twnoh@phya.snu.ac.kr; Livio Battezati, Regional Ed., livio.battezzati@unito.it; Evgeny Antipov, Regional Ed., antipov@icr.chem.msu.ru; Naresh S. Dalal, Regional Ed., dalal@chemmail.chem.fsu.edu; Kyunghwan Oh, Exec. Ed., koh@yonsei.ac.kr. **ISSN:** 1567-1739. **Subscription Rates:** EUR710 institutions European countries and Iran; 94,200¥ institutions; US$792 institutions all countries except Europe, Japan and Iran; EUR131 individuals European countries and Iran; US$175 individuals for all countries except Europe, Japan and Iran; 20,100¥ individuals. **URL:** http://www.elsevier.com/wps/find/journaldescription.cws_home/621284/descriptiondescription.

47264 ■ Development and Society
The Institute for Social Development and Policy Research
Seoul National University
Seoul 151-742, Republic of Korea
Ph: 82 28808799
Fax: 82 28736764
Publisher E-mail: isdpr@snu.ac.kr
Periodical that analyzes social causes and consequences of development. **Founded:** 1972. **Freq:** Semiannual June, & December. **Key Personnel:** Anthony Woodiwiss, Editor; Bae Yuri, Managing Editor. **ISSN:** 1598-8074. **URL:** http://www.devsoc.net/.

47265 ■ Feel
The Chosun Ilbo
62-4 Taepyeongro 1-ga
Jung-gu
Seoul 100-101, Republic of Korea
Ph: 82 272 45114
Consumer magazine covering fashion, culture, and the arts for women. **Founded:** Aug. 20, 1993. **URL:** http://comdev.chosun.com/homepage/html/publication_eng.html.

47266 ■ Global Journal of Pure and Applied Mathematics
Research India Publications
c/o Prof. Taekyun Kim, Ed.-in-Ch.
Division of General Education-Mathematics
Kwangwoon University
Seoul 139-704, Republic of Korea
Publisher E-mail: info@ripublication.com
Journal covering pure and applied mathematics. **Freq:** 6/yr. **Key Personnel:** Prof. Taekyun Kim, Editor-in-Chief, tkim@knu.ac.kr; M. Bohner, Assoc. Ed.; S. Mathur, Assoc. Ed. **ISSN:** 0973-1768. **Subscription Rates:** US$580 libraries and institution; print plus online free; US$560 libraries and institution; online only; US$240 individuals print plus online free; US$220 individuals online only; Rs 1,800 individuals. **URL:** http://www.ripublication.com/gjpam.htm.

47267 ■ International Journal of Applied Environmental Sciences
Research India Publications
c/o Prof. Soon-Ung Park, Ed.-in-Ch.
School of Earth & Environmental Sciences
Seoul National University
Seoul 151-742, Republic of Korea
Fax: 82 2 8806715
Publisher E-mail: info@ripublication.com
Journal covering environmental engineering and applied environmental science. **Founded:** Oct. 1982. **Freq:** 4/yr. **Print Method:** Offset. **Trim Size:** 7 7/8 x 10 1/2. **Key Personnel:** Prof. Soon-Ung Park, Editor-in-Chief; Dhari Al-Ajmi, Editorial Board Member; Viney P. Aneja, Editorial Board Member. **ISSN:** 0973-6077. **Subscription Rates:** US$380 institutions and library; print plus online free; US$360 institutions and library; online only; US$280 individuals print plus online free; US$260 individuals online only. **URL:** http://www.ripublication.com/ijaes.htm.

47268 ■ International Journal of Hybrid Intelligent Systems
IOS Press, B.V.
c/o Ajith Abraham, Ed.-in-Ch.
School of Computer Science & Engineering
410, 2nd Engineering Bldg.
221 Heuksok-Dong, Dongjak-gu
Seoul 156-756, Republic of Korea
Publisher E-mail: info@iospress.nl
Peer-reviewed journal on the theory and applications of hybrid and integrated intelligent systems, publishing papers that involve the use of two or more intelligent techniques and approaches, such as neural networks, traditional knowledge-based methods, fuzzy techniques, genetic algorithms, agent-based techniques, and case based reasoning. **Freq:** Quarterly. **Key Personnel:** Ajith Abraham, Editor-in-Chief, ajith.abraham@ieee.org; Gail A. Carpenter, Assoc. Ed.; Vasile Palade, Editor-in-Chief, vasile.palade@comlab.ox.ac.uk; B. Apolloni, Editorial Board. **ISSN:** 1448-5869. **Subscription Rates:** EUR90 individuals online only; US$105 individuals online only; EUR360 individuals online + online back volumes; US$486 individuals online + online back volumes; EUR338 individuals print and online; US$460 individuals print and online. **URL:** http://www.iospress.nl/loadtop/load.php?isbn=14485869.

47269 ■ International Journal of Information Technology, Communications and Convergence
Inderscience Enterprises Limited
c/o Prof. Jong Hyuk Park, Ed.-in-Ch.
Seoul National University of Technology
Dept. of Computer Science & Engineering
172 Gongreung 2-dong, Nowon-gu
Seoul 139-742, Republic of Korea
Journal covering the various theories and practical applications of future generation information technology. **Freq:** 4/yr. **Key Personnel:** Prof. Jong Hyuk Park, Editor-in-Chief, ijitcc.jhpark@gmail.com; Dr. Jong-Hyouk Lee, Managing Editor, hurryon@gmail.com; Dr. Javier A. Barria, Assoc. Ed. **ISSN:** 2042-3217. **Subscription Rates:** EUR494 individuals print or online; EUR672 individuals print and online. **URL:** http://www.inderscience.com/browse/index.php?journalID=358.

47270 ■ Journal
Technical Association of the Pulp and Paper Industry of Korea
Ste. 701, Chungmu Bldg.
44-13, Yoido-dong
Yongdupo-gu
Seoul 150-890, Republic of Korea

Ph: 82 2 7868620
Fax: 82 2 7868621
Publisher E-mail: ktappi@ktappi.or.kr
Journal covering paper. **Freq:** Quarterly. **Key Personnel:** Dr. Hye-Jung Youn, Assoc. Ed. **ISSN:** 0253-3200. **Remarks:** Advertising not accepted. **URL:** http://ktappi.or.kr/. **Circ:** (Not Reported)

47271 ■ Journal of Ceramic Processing Research
Hanyang University Ceramic Processing Research Center
17 Haengdang-dong
Seongdong-gu
Seoul 133-791, Republic of Korea
Ph: 82 222 201828
Fax: 82 222 917395
Publisher E-mail: jcpr@hanyang.ac.kr
Journal publishing peer-reviewed scientific papers covering the influence of processing routes on the microstructure and properties of ceramics and ceramic-based materials. **Freq:** Quarterly. **Key Personnel:** Prof. Kwang Bo Shim, Editor-in-Chief; Brian Ralph, Editor-in-Chief. **URL:** http://jcpr.kbs-lab.co.kr/english/ch0101.htm.

47272 ■ Journal of Computational Intelligence in Bioinformatics
Research India Publications
c/o Ajith Abraham, Consulting Ed.
Chung-Ang University
School of Computer Science & Engineering
221, Heuikseok-dong, Dongjak-gu
Seoul 156-756, Republic of Korea
Publisher E-mail: info@ripublication.com
Journal covering fundamental contributions in the field of bioinformatics. Topics include artificial intelligence and computational intelligence theory and their applications in bioinformatics. **Founded:** 1925. **Freq:** 3/yr. **Print Method:** Offset. **Trim Size:** 5 1/4 x 7 3/4. **Cols./Page:** 1. **Col. Width:** 49 nonpareils. **Col. Depth:** 87 agate lines. **Key Personnel:** Ajith Abraham, Consulting Ed.; Dr. Kezhi Mao, Editorial Board; Bhaskar Das Gupta, Editor-in-Chief. **ISSN:** 0973-385X. **URL:** http://www.ripublication.com/jcib.htm.

47273 ■ Journal of Economic Integration
Sejong University
Sejong Institution
98 Gunja-Dong, Gwangjin-Gu
Seoul 143-747, Republic of Korea
Ph: 82 2 34083973
Fax: 82 2 34083813
Publication E-mail: cie@sejong.ac.kr
Publisher E-mail: w3@sejong.ac.kr
Periodical covering business and economics. **Founded:** 1986. **Freq:** Quarterly. **Key Personnel:** Myung-Gun Choo, Editor; Frank Van Tongeren, Board of Ed.; Elena Ianchovichina, Board of Ed.; Hwan Ho Lee, Assoc. Ed.; Alan V. Deardorff, Board of Ed.; Barry Eichengreen, Board of Ed.; Danny Quah, Board of Ed.; Anne O. Krueger, Board of Ed.; Chulsu Kim, Assoc. Ed.; Jong Eun Lee, Managing Editor. **ISSN:** 1225-651X. **Subscription Rates:** US$40 individuals; US$120 institutions; US$50 individuals airmail; US$130 institutions airmail. **Remarks:** Advertising accepted; rates available upon request. **URL:** http://dasan.sejong.ac.kr. **Circ:** Paid 250

47274 ■ The Journal of Korean Radiological Society
Korean Radiological Society
69 Yangjaecheon-gil
Seocho-gu
Seoul 137-891, Republic of Korea
Ph: 82 257 88003
Fax: 82 252 97113
Publication E-mail: kjr@radiology.or.kr
Publisher E-mail: office@radiology.or.kr
Journal including English abstracts. **URL:** http://www.radiology.or.kr/eng/journal.html.

47275 ■ Journal of the Korean Society of Plastic and Reconstructive Surgery
Korean Society of Plastic and Reconstructive Surgery
Dae Han Sung Hyung Owe Gua
Seocho World officetel 1814
Seocho-dong 1355-3 Seocho-ku
Seoul 137-070, Republic of Korea
Ph: 82 2 34724252
Fax: 82 2 34724254

Publisher E-mail: kprs@chollian.net

Journal covering the Korean Society of Plastic Surgery, in Korean. **Freq:** Periodic. **ISSN:** 1015-6402. **Remarks:** Advertising accepted; rates available upon request. **URL:** http://www.plasticsurgery.or.kr/. **Circ:** (Not Reported)

47276 ■ The Journal of Microbiology
Microbiological Society of Korea
The Korea Science & Technology Ctr., Rm. 810
635-4 Yeogsam-dong
Gangnam-gu
Seoul 135-703, Republic of Korea
Ph: 82 2 34533321
Fax: 82 2 34533322
Publisher E-mail: msk@msk.or.kr
Microbiology journal. **Founded:** 1995. **Freq:** Bimonthly. **Key Personnel:** Sung Gyun Kang, Editor-in-Chief; Dae-Hyuk Kim, Managing Editor; Sang Ho Choi, Editor-in-Chief; Je Chul Lee, Editorial Board; Che Ok Jeon, Editor-in-Chief. **ISSN:** 1225-8873. **URL:** http://www.msk.or.kr/.

47277 ■ Journal of Plant Biology
Botanical Society of Korea
968-3 Pongchon-dong, Kwanak-gu
402 Keumsong Bldg.
Seoul 151-821, Republic of Korea
Ph: 82 288 40384
Fax: 82 288 40385
Publisher E-mail: botsockr@kornet.net
International journal devoted to biotechnology, biochemistry and macromolecular structure, cellular and developmental biology, ecology, genetics and genomics, molecular biology, morphology, physiology, and taxonomy of plants. **Founded:** 1958. **Freq:** Quarterly. **Key Personnel:** Dr. Woo Taek Kim, Editor; Gynheung An, Editor-in-Chief, genean@postech.ac.kr. **ISSN:** 1226-9239. **Remarks:** Advertising accepted; rates available upon request. **URL:** http://www.bosk.or.kr/english/sub01.asp. **Circ:** Paid 750

47278 ■ Korea Journal
Korean National Commission for UNESCO
50-14 Myong-dong 2-ga
Jung-gu
Seoul 100-810, Republic of Korea
Ph: 82 2 7551105
Fax: 82 2 7556667
Publication E-mail: kj@unesco.or.kr
Regional focus/area studies publication. **Subtitle:** Korean Studies. **Founded:** 1961. **Freq:** Quarterly. **Key Personnel:** Shin Jong Beom, Editor, jbshin@unesco.or.kr; Taeck-soo Chun, Publisher. **ISSN:** 0023-3900. **Subscription Rates:** 48,000 W individuals in Korea; US$60 other countries surface mail; 86,400 W two years Korea; US$108 other countries 3 years; US$65 individuals airmail Asia; US$70 U.S. and Canada Europe (airmail); US$75 other countries airmail; US$117 two years Asia (airmail); US$126 two years Europe, U.S., & Canada (airmail). **Remarks:** Advertising not accepted. **URL:** http://www.ekoreajournal.net/. **Circ:** 2,200

47279 ■ The Korea Post
2nd Fl., Daeok Bldg.
241-4 Oksu-dong
Songdong-gu
Seoul 133-839, Republic of Korea
Ph: 82 2 22981740
Fax: 82 2 22989506
Publisher E-mail: korpost@chol.com
General interest magazine. **Freq:** Monthly. **Subscription Rates:** 85,000 W individuals; US$140 other countries East Asia; US$145 other countries South East Asia; US$150 other countries U.S./Europe/Middle East/Oceania/South West Asia; US$170 other countries South America/Africa; 150,000 W two years; 210,000 W individuals three years. **Remarks:** Accepts advertising. **URL:** http://www.koreapost.com. **Ad Rates:** BW: US$3,931, 4C: US$6,316. **Circ:** (Not Reported)

47280 ■ Korea Times
The Korea Times Company Ltd.
43, Chungmuro 3-ga
Chung-ku
Seoul 100-013, Republic of Korea
Ph: 82 2 7242359
Fax: 82 2 7364061
Newspaper featuring news, opinion, and commentary.

Founded: 1950. **Freq:** Daily. **Key Personnel:** Chang-sup Lee, Ch. Editorial Writer; Moo-jong Park, Pres./Publisher; Jae-ku Chang, Chm. **ISSN:** 0023-3935. **Subscription Rates:** 20,000 W per month. **Remarks:** Advertising accepted; rates available upon request. **URL:** http://www.koreatimes.co.kr/www/index.asp. **Circ:** 150,000

47281 ■ The Korean Journal of Defense Analysis
Korea Institute for Defense Analyses
PO Box 250
Cheong Ryang
Seoul, Republic of Korea
Fax: 82 2 9611172
Publisher E-mail: wklee@kida.re.kr
Military journal. **Founded:** 1989. **Freq:** Quarterly. **ISSN:** 1016-3271. **Subscription Rates:** US$40 individuals. **URL:** http://www.kida.re.kr/eng/publication/publication_01_1.htm.

47282 ■ Korean Journal of Radiology
Korean Radiological Society
69 Yangjaecheon-gil
Seocho-gu
Seoul 137-891, Republic of Korea
Ph: 82 257 88003
Fax: 82 252 97113
Publisher E-mail: office@radiology.or.kr
Journal containing articles, case reports, pictorial essays and reviews that are relevant to the field of radiology. **Founded:** Mar. 2000. **Freq:** Quarterly. **Key Personnel:** Seong Ho Park, Dep. Ed.; Jung-Gi Im, MD, Founding Ed.; Man Chung Han, Honorary Ed.; Kyung Soo Lee, Editor. **Subscription Rates:** 100,000 W individuals; US$200 other countries. **URL:** http://www.kjronline.org/.

47283 ■ Koreana
Korea Foundation
10-11F, Diplomatic Center Bldg.
1376-1 Seocho 2-dong, Seocho-gu
Seoul 137-863, Republic of Korea
Ph: 82 234635600
Fax: 82 234636076
Publication E-mail: publication@kf.or.kr
Publication covering Korean culture. **Subtitle:** Korean Art & Culture. **Founded:** Mar. 1987. **Freq:** Quarterly. **Trim Size:** 207 x 270 mm. **Key Personnel:** Jeong-Yeop Park, Editor-in-Chief; Hahn Young-Hee, Editorial Dir.; Yim Sung-joon, Publisher. **ISSN:** 1016-0744. **Subscription Rates:** 18,000 W individuals Korea (surface mail), 1 year; 36,000 W two years Korea (surface mail), 2 year; 54,000 W individuals Korea (surface mail), 3 year; 4,500 W individuals Korea (surface mail); US$33 individuals Japan, HongKong, Taiwan and China, 1 year; US$60 two years Japan, HongKong, Taiwan and China, 2 year; US$81 individuals Japan, HongKong, Taiwan and China, 3 year; US$37 individuals elsewhere, 1year; US$68 two years elsewhere, 2year; US$93 individuals elsewhere, 3 year. **Remarks:** Advertising accepted; rates available upon request. **URL:** http://www.koreana.or.kr. **Circ:** Nonpaid 5,500

47284 ■ Natural Product Sciences
Korean Society of Pharmacognosy
Medicinal Studies Bldg., 1st Fl.
Soegyo-dong 448-13
Mapo-gu
Seoul 121-841, Republic of Korea
Ph: 82 25260370
Fax: 82 23260371
Publisher E-mail: head@kosphar.org
Pharmacy and pharmacology journal. **Freq:** Quarterly. **Key Personnel:** Jee H. Jung, Editor-in-Chief; Byung-Sun Min, Editorial Advisory Board; Youn Chul Kim, Editorial Advisory Board. **Subscription Rates:** US$30 members; US$40 other countries non-members. **URL:** http://www.ksp.or.kr/4s_02.html.

47285 ■ The Rotary Korea
Royal Bldg. 930
5 Dangjudong
Chongno-Ku
Seoul 110-0721, Republic of Korea
Ph: 82 2 7302511
Fax: 82 2 7302515
Publication E-mail: rotaryko@chollian.net

Publisher E-mail: rotaryko@chollian.net
Membership magazine of Rotary International covering current news about Rotary-related subjects in English and Korean. **Founded:** 1967. **Freq:** Monthly. **Key Personnel:** Hyo Soon Yim, Editor-in-Chief; Eun Ok Lee, Sen. Ed. **URL:** http://www.rotarykorea.org; http://www.rotary.org. **Circ:** 48,000

47286 ■ Seoul Journal of Economics
Seoul National University Institute of Economic Research
Seoul National University
Seoul 151-746, Republic of Korea
Fax: 82 288 84454
Publisher E-mail: sje@plaza.snu.ac.kr
Journal designed to carry both theoretical and empirical articles in all fields of economics. **Founded:** 1988. **Freq:** Quarterly. **Key Personnel:** In Ho Lee, Editor. **ISSN:** 1225-0279. **Subscription Rates:** 30,000 W individuals; 100,000 W institutions; US$100 institutions, other countries; US$30 other countries. **URL:** http://econ.snu.ac.kr/~journal/. **Circ:** Paid 300

47287 ■ The Sonyon Chosun
The Chosun Ilbo
62-4 Taepyeongro 1-ga
Jung-gu
Seoul 100-101, Republic of Korea
Ph: 82 272 45114
Children's newspaper. **Founded:** Jan. 10, 1970. **URL:** http://comdev.chosun.com/homepage/html/publication_eng.html.

47288 ■ The Sports Chosun
The Chosun Ilbo
62-4 Taepyeongro 1-ga
Jung-gu
Seoul 100-101, Republic of Korea
Ph: 82 272 45114
Sports newspaper. **Founded:** Mar. 21, 1990. **URL:** http://comdev.chosun.com/homepage/html/publication_eng.html; http://sports.chosun.com/.

47289 ■ The Wolgan Chosun
The Chosun Ilbo
62-4 Taepyeongro 1-ga
Jung-gu
Seoul 100-101, Republic of Korea
Ph: 82 272 45114
Consumer magazine covering general local news. **Subtitle:** The Monthly Chosun. **Founded:** Apr. 20, 1980. **Freq:** Monthly. **Print Method:** Paper. **Trim Size:** 148 x 225 mm. **ISSN:** 1228-2197. **Remarks:** Accepts advertising. **URL:** http://comdev.chosun.com/homepage/html/publication_eng.html; http://monthly.chosun.com/. **Ad Rates:** BW: 200 W, 4C: 200 W. **Circ:** Paid ‡100,000

47290 ■ The Wolgan Naksi
The Chosun Ilbo
62-4 Taepyeongro 1-ga
Jung-gu
Seoul 100-101, Republic of Korea
Ph: 82 272 45114
Consumer magazine covering fishing **Founded:** Apr. 10, 1984. **Freq:** Monthly. **URL:** http://comdev.chosun.com/homepage/html/publication_eng.html.

47291 ■ The Wolgan San
The Chosun Ilbo
62-4 Taepyeongro 1-ga
Jung-gu
Seoul 100-101, Republic of Korea
Ph: 82 272 45114
Consumer magazine covering mountaineering, mountain climbing and related activities. **Founded:** May 6, 1989. **Freq:** Monthly. **URL:** http://comdev.chosun.com/homepage/html/publication_eng.htmltop.

47292 ■ WTF Taekwondo
World Taekwondo Federation
4th Fl., Joyang Bldg. 113
Samseong-dong
Gangnam-gu
Seoul 135-090, Republic of Korea
Ph: 82 256 62505
Fax: 82 255 34728
Publisher E-mail: wtf@wtf.org
Publication covering martial arts. **Founded:** Aug. 5, 1976. **Freq:** Annual. **Trim Size:** 18.6 x 27.5 cm. **ISSN:** 1599-3779. **Subscription Rates:** US$60 two years

Circulation: ★ = ABC; △ = BPA; ◆ = CAC; • = CCAB; ❏ = VAC; ⊕ = PO Statement; ‡ = Publisher's Report; Boldface figures = sworn; Light figures = estimated.

Gale Directory of Publications & Broadcast Media/147th Ed.

5147

including postage. **Remarks:** Accepts advertising. **URL:** http://www.wtf.org/wtf_eng/site/news/magazine.html. **Ad Rates:** 4C: US$1,250. **Circ:** 1,900

47293 ■ Yonsei Medical Journal
Yonsei University College of Medicine
134 Shinchon-dong
Seodaemun-gu
Seoul 120-752, Republic of Korea
Ph: 82 2 22282034
Fax: 82 2 3934945
Publisher E-mail: ymj@yumc.yonsei.ac.kr
Periodical aiming at informing its readers of significant development in all areas related to medicine. **Founded:** 1960. **Freq:** Bimonthly. **Key Personnel:** In-Hung Choi, PhD, Editor-in-Chief; Chang-Ok Suh, PhD, Assoc. Ed.; Jung-Won Park, PhD, Exec. Ed. **ISSN:** 0513-5796. **URL:** http://www.eymj.org/. **Circ:** Paid 1,400

47294 ■ AFN Korea Radio & Television - 1530 KHz
American Forces Network
Yongsan
Seoul, Republic of Korea
Ph: 82 2 7247982
Fax: 82 2 7246970
Operating Hours: Continuous. **Wattage:** 5000. **URL:** http://afnkorea.net/.

47295 ■ AFN Korea Radio & Television - 102.7 MHz
American Forces Network
Yongsan
Seoul, Republic of Korea
Ph: 82 2 7247982
Fax: 82 2 7246970
Format: News. **Operating Hours:** Continuous. **Wattage:** 5000. **URL:** http://afnkorea.net/.

47296 ■ HLKV - 900 KHz
31, Yeouido-dong
Yeongdeungpo-gu
Seoul 150-728, Republic of Korea
Ph: 82 2 7892851
Fax: 82 2 7823094
Owner: Munwha Broadcasting Corporation, at above address. **Operating Hours:** Continuous. **Key Personnel:** Ki-Young Ohm, Pres./CEO. **Wattage:** 50,000. **Ad Rates:** Noncommercial. **URL:** http://www.imbc.com/.

47297 ■ HLKX - 106.9 MHz
MPO Box 88
Seoul 121-707, Republic of Korea
Ph: 82 2 3200114
Fax: 82 2 3200229
Owner: Far East Broadcasting Corporation, at above address. **Founded:** 1945. **Wattage:** 5000. **Ad Rates:** Noncommercial. **URL:** http://www.febc.or.kr.

47298 ■ HLKX - 1188 KHz
MPO Box 88
Seoul 121-707, Republic of Korea
Ph: 82 2 3200114
Fax: 82 2 3200229
Owner: Far East Broadcasting Company, at above address. **Founded:** 1956. **Key Personnel:** Billy Jan Hwan Kim, Chm. **Wattage:** 100,000. **URL:** http://www.febc.net.

47299 ■ HLKY - 93.9 MHz
917-1, Mok-dong
Yangchon-gu
Seoul 158-701, Republic of Korea
Ph: 82 226507000
Fax: 82 226500505
E-mail: faq@cbs.co.kr
Owner: Christian Broadcasting System, at above address. **Operating Hours:** Continuous. **Wattage:** 7000. **URL:** http://www.cbs.co.kr.

47300 ■ HLKY - 98.1 MHz
917-1, Mok-dong
Yangchon-gu
Seoul 158-701, Republic of Korea
Ph: 82 226507000
Fax: 82 226500505
E-mail: faq@cbs.co.kr
Format: Eclectic. **Owner:** Christian Broadcasting System, at above address. **Operating Hours:** Continuous. **Wattage:** 10,000. **Ad Rates:** Noncommercial. **URL:** http://www.cbs.co.kr.

47301 ■ HLKY - 837 KHz
917-1, Mok-dong
Yangchon-gu
Seoul 158-701, Republic of Korea
Ph: 82 2 26507820
Fax: 82 2 26500505
Owner: Christian Broadcasting System (Kidokkyo Pangsong), at above address. **Operating Hours:** Continuous. **Wattage:** 50,000. **URL:** http://www.cbs.co.kr.

47302 ■ HLSG - 101.9 MHz
140 Dabo Bldg.
156-1, Mapo-dong
Seoul 121-050, Republic of Korea
Ph: 82 27055114
Fax: 82 27055229
E-mail: webmaster@bbsi.co.kr
Owner: Buddhist Broadcasting System, at above address. **Operating Hours:** 2000-1700. **Wattage:** 5000. **URL:** http://www.bbsi.co.kr/.

47303 ■ MBC-Andong - 100.1 MHz
31, Yeouido-dong
Yeongdeungpo-gu
Seoul 150-728, Republic of Korea
Ph: 82 54 8517114
Fax: 82 54 8543400
Format: Eclectic. **Owner:** Munhwa Broadcasting Corporation, at above address. **Wattage:** 3000. **URL:** http://www.andongmbc.co.kr; http://www.imbc.com.

47304 ■ MBC-Andong - 91.3 MHz
31, Yeouido-dong
Yeongdeungpo-gu
Seoul 150-728, Republic of Korea
Ph: 82 54 8517114
Fax: 82 54 8543400
Owner: Munhwa Broadcasting Corporation, at above address. **Wattage:** 3000. **URL:** http://www.andongmbc.co.kr; http://www.imbc.com.

MBC-Cheju - See Cheju
MBC-Cheju - See Cheju

47305 ■ MBC-Cheongju - 99.7 MHz
31, Yeouido-dong
Yeongdeungpo-gu
Seoul 150-728, Republic of Korea
Ph: 82 43 2297114
Fax: 82 43 2299393
Owner: Munhwa Broadcasting Corporation, at above address. **Wattage:** 1000. **URL:** http://www.mbccj.co.kr; http://www.imbc.com.

47306 ■ MBC-Chinju - 93.5 MHz
31, Yeouido-dong
Yeongdeungpo-gu
Seoul 150-728, Republic of Korea
Ph: 82 55 7402114
Fax: 82 55 7402109
Format: Eclectic. **Owner:** Munhwa Broadcasting Corporation, at above address. **Wattage:** 1000. **URL:** http://www.jinjumbc.co.kr; http://www.imbc.com.

MBC-Chinju - See Chinju
MBC-Chinju - See Chinju
MBC-Chinju - See Chinju

47307 ■ MBC-Ch'ongju - 92.3 MHz
31, Yeouido-dong
Yeongdeungpo-gu
Seoul 150-728, Republic of Korea
Ph: 82 43 2297114
Fax: 82 43 2299393
Format: Eclectic. **Owner:** Munhwa Broadcasting Corporation, at above address. **Wattage:** 4000. **URL:** http://www.mbccj.co.kr; http://www.imbc.com.

MBC-Chonju - See Chonju

47308 ■ MBC-Chunchon - 92.3 MHz
31, Yeouido-dong
Yeongdeungpo-gu
Seoul 150-728, Republic of Korea
Ph: 82 33 2591215
Fax: 82 33 2546400
Format: Eclectic. **Owner:** Munhwa Broadcasting Corporation, at above address. **Wattage:** 4000. **URL:** http://www.chmbc.co.kr; http://www.imbc.com.

47309 ■ MBC-Chunchon - 94.5 MHz
31, Yeouido-dong
Yeongdeungpo-gu

Seoul 150-728, Republic of Korea
Ph: 82 33 2591215
Fax: 82 33 2546400
Owner: Munhwa Broadcasting Corporation, at above address. **Wattage:** 1000. **URL:** http://www.chmbc.co.kr; http://www.imbc.com.

47310 ■ MBC-Chungju - 94.1 MHz
31, Yeouido-dong
Yeongdeungpo-gu
Seoul 150-728, Republic of Korea
Ph: 82 43 8418114
Fax: 82 43 8418199
Format: Eclectic. **Owner:** Munhwa Broadcasting Corporation, at above address. **Operating Hours:** 7:55 pm-5 pm. **Wattage:** 500. **URL:** http://www.cjmbc.co.kr; http://www.imbc.com.

47311 ■ MBC-Chungju - 88.7 MHz
31, Yeouido-dong
Yeongdeungpo-gu
Seoul 150-728, Republic of Korea
Ph: 82 43 8418411
Fax: 82 43 8418199
Owner: Munhwa Broadcasting Corporation, at above address. **Wattage:** 3000. **URL:** http://www.cjmbc.co.kr; http://www.imbc.com.

47312 ■ MBC-Chungju - 96.1 MHz
31, Yeouido-dong
Yeongdeungpo-gu
Seoul 150-728, Republic of Korea
Ph: 82 43 8418114
Fax: 82 43 8418199
Format: Eclectic. **Owner:** Munhwa Broadcasting Corporation, at above address. **Wattage:** 1000. **URL:** http://www.cjmbc.co.kr; http://www.imbc.com.

MBC-Kwangju - See Gwangju
MBC-Kwangju - See Gwangju
MBC-Kwangju - See Gwangju
MBC-Masan - See Masan
MBC-Masan - See Masan

47313 ■ MBC-Mokpo - 102.3 MHz
31, Yeouido-dong
Yeongdeungpo-gu
Seoul 150-728, Republic of Korea
Ph: 82 61 2709000
Fax: 82 61 2709209
Owner: Munhwa Broadcasting Corporation, at above address. **Wattage:** 1000. **URL:** http://www.mokpombc.co.kr; http://www.imbc.com.

47314 ■ MBC-Mokpo - 89.1 MHz
31, Yeouido-dong
Yeongdeungpo-gu
Seoul 150-728, Republic of Korea
Ph: 82 61 2709000
Fax: 82 61 2709209
Format: Eclectic. **Owner:** Munhwa Broadcasting Corporation, at above address. **Wattage:** 2000. **URL:** http://www.mokpombc.co.kr; http://www.imbc.com.

47315 ■ MBC-Samcheok - 99.9 MHz
31, Yeouido-dong
Yeongdeungpo-gu
Seoul 150-728, Republic of Korea
Ph: 82 33 5713114
Fax: 82 33 5713155
Owner: Munhwa Broadcasting Corporation, at above address. **Wattage:** 1000. **URL:** http://www.scmbc.co.kr; http://www.imbc.com.

47316 ■ MBC-Samcheok - 101.5 MHz
31, Yeouido-dong
Yeongdeungpo-gu
Seoul 150-728, Republic of Korea
Ph: 82 33 5713114
Fax: 82 33 5713155
Format: Eclectic. **Owner:** Munhwa Broadcasting Corporation, at above address. **Wattage:** 1000. **URL:** http://www.scmbc.co.kr; http://www.imbc.com.

47317 ■ MBC-Samcheok - 98.1 MHz
31, Yeouido-dong
Yeongdeungpo-gu
Seoul 150-728, Republic of Korea
Ph: 82 33 5713114
Fax: 82 33 5713155
Owner: Munhwa Broadcasting Corporation, at above

address. **Wattage:** 3000. **URL:** http://www.scmbc.co.kr; http://www.imbc.com.

47318 ■ MBC-Seoul - 91.9 MHz
31, Yeouido-dong
Yeongdeungpo-gu
Seoul 150-728, Republic of Korea
Ph: 82 2 32196208
Fax: 82 2 32196214
Owner: Munhwa Broadcasting Corporation, at above address. **Wattage:** 10,000. **URL:** http://www.imbc.com.

47319 ■ MBC-Seoul - 95.9 MHz
31, Yeouido-dong
Yeongdeungpo-gu
Seoul 150-728, Republic of Korea
Ph: 82 2 32196208
Fax: 82 2 32196214
Format: Eclectic. **Owner:** Munhwa Broadcasting Corporation, at above address. **Wattage:** 10,000. **Ad Rates:** Advertising accepted; rates available upon request. **URL:** http://www.imbc.com.

47320 ■ MBC-Ulsan - 98.7 MHz
31, Yeouido-dong
Yeongdeungpo-gu
Seoul 150-728, Republic of Korea
Ph: 82 52 2901114
Fax: 82 52 2901117
Owner: Munhwa Broadcasting Corporation, at above address. **Wattage:** 3000. **Ad Rates:** Noncommercial. **URL:** http://www.usmbc.co.kr; http://www.imbc.com.

47321 ■ MBC-Ulsan - 97.5 MHz
31, Yeouido-dong
Yeongdeungpo-gu
Seoul 150-728, Republic of Korea
Ph: 82 52 2901114
Fax: 82 52 2901117
Format: Eclectic. **Owner:** Munhwa Broadcasting Corporation, at above address. **URL:** http://www.usmbc.co.kr; http://www.imbc.com.

47322 ■ MBC-Wonju - 98.9 MHz
31, Yeouido-dong
Yeongdeungpo-gu
Seoul 150-728, Republic of Korea
Ph: 82 33 7418114
Fax: 82 33 7418149
Owner: Munhwa Broadcasting Corporation, at above address. **Wattage:** 3000. **URL:** http://www.wjmbc.co.kr; http://www.imbc.com.

47323 ■ MBC-Wonju - 92.7 MHz
31, Yeouido-dong
Yeongdeungpo-gu
Seoul 150-728, Republic of Korea
Ph: 82 33 7418114

Fax: 82 33 7418149
Format: Eclectic. **Owner:** Munhwa Broadcasting Corporation, at above address. **Wattage:** 1000. **URL:** http://www.wjmbc.co.kr; http://www.imbc.com.

Sogwipo

47324 ■ HLAZ - 101.1 MHz
No. 2761, Hagwi-ri
Acwol-up, Pukjejukun
Jeju 690-795, Republic of Korea
Ph: 82 64 7138100
Fax: 82 64 7138105
Format: Eclectic. **Owner:** Far East Broadcasting Corporation, MPO Box 88, Seoul 121-707, Republic of Korea, 82 2 3200114, Fax: 82 2 3200229. **Founded:** June 1973. **Operating Hours:** 22 hours Daily. **Key Personnel:** Billy Kim, Director. **Wattage:** 1000. **Ad Rates:** Advertising accepted; rates available upon request. **URL:** http://jeju.febc.net; http://www.febc.net.

Songtan

47325 ■ AFN Korea Radio & Television - 1359 KHz
Osan Air Base
Songtan, Republic of Korea
Operating Hours: 2005-000, 0605-0900 Mon.-Fri. **Wattage:** 1000. **URL:** http://afnkorea.net/.

47326 ■ AFN Korea Radio & Television - 88.5 MHz
Osan Air Base
Songtan, Republic of Korea
Operating Hours: Continuous. **Wattage:** 50. **URL:** http://afnkorea.net/.

Suwon

47327 ■ Journal of Korean Society of Soil Science and Fertilizer
Korean Society of Soil Science and Fertilizer
National Institute of Agricultural Science and Technology
249 Seodun-dong
Kweonseon-gu
GyeongGi-Do
Suwon 441-709, Republic of Korea
Ph: 82 312 957335
Fax: 82 312 900207
Publisher E-mail: ksssf249@hanmail.net
Korean journal covering soil and fertilizer science, in Chinese, English and Korean. **Freq:** Bimonthly 4 Korean & 2 English edition. **Key Personnel:** Ki Cheol Eom, President; Sun Gang Yun, Vice President; Doug Young Chung, Vice President; Hae Nam Hyun, Contact; Du Hoi Choi, Vice President; Yeong Sang Jung, Contact;

Joong Geun Song, Vice President; Shin Jae Sung, Vice President; Chang Hoe Koo, Vice President. **ISSN:** 0367-6315. **Subscription Rates:** US$160 individuals. **Remarks:** Advertising accepted; rates available upon request. **URL:** http://www.ksssf.or.kr/. **Circ:** 850

Taegu

47328 ■ MBC-Taegu - 92.5 MHz
4-5 Doryong
Daejeon 305-740, Republic of Korea
Ph: 82 42 3303114
Fax: 82 42 3303700
Owner: Munhwa Broadcasting Corporation, 31, Yeouido-dong, Yeongdeungpo-gu, Seoul, Republic of Korea, 82 2 7892851, Fax: 82 2 7823094. **Wattage:** 5000. **Ad Rates:** Noncommercial. **URL:** http://www.tjmbc.co.kr; http://www.imbc.com.

Uijongbu

47329 ■ AFN Korea Radio & Television - 1161 KHz
Camp Red Cloud
Uijongbu, Republic of Korea
Operating Hours: Continuous. **Wattage:** 250. **URL:** http://afnkorea.net/.

47330 ■ AFN Korea Radio & Television - 88.5 MHz
Camp Red Cloud
Uijongbu, Republic of Korea
Operating Hours: Continuous. **Wattage:** 100. **URL:** http://afnkorea.net/.

Wonju-si

47331 ■ AFN Korea Radio & Television - 1440 KHz
Camp Long
Wonju-si, Republic of Korea
Operating Hours: Continuous. **Wattage:** 250. **URL:** http://afnkorea.net/.

Yosu

MBC-Pohang - See Pohang
47332 ■ MBC-Yosu - 98.3 MHz
31, Yeouido-dong
Yeongdeungpo-gu
Yosu 150-728, Republic of Korea
Ph: 82 61 6503333
Fax: 82 61 6528506
Owner: Munhwa Broadcasting Corporation, at above address. **Wattage:** 2000. **URL:** http://www.ysmbc.co.kr; http://www.imbc.com.

Circulation: ★ = ABC; △ = BPA; ◆ = CAC; • = CCAB; ❑ = VAC; ⊕ = PO Statement; ‡ = Publisher's Report; Boldface figures = sworn; Light figures = estimated.

Safat

47333 ■ Annals of the Arts and Social Sciences
Academic Publication Council
Kuwait University
PO Box 5969
Safat 13060, Kuwait
Ph: 965 498 4349
Fax: 965 484 5372
Publisher E-mail: ovpr_ra@kuc01.kuniv.edu.kw
Periodical publishing original and high quality research monographs; strengthening cultural and academic ties between Kuwaiti scholars and their Arab counterparts; expanding horizons of knowledge internationally; and highlighting Arab and Muslim scholars' scientific and cultural contributions to human knowledge and world civilization. **Freq:** Monthly. **Key Personnel:** Dr. Fatima Al-khalifa, Editor-in-Chief. **ISSN:** 1560-5248. **Subscription Rates:** 4 KD individuals; 6 KD individuals Arab countries; US$22 individuals; 22 KD institutions Kuwait & Arab countries; US$90 institutions, other countries; 7 KD two years; 10 KD two years Arab countries; US$37 two years; 37 KD institutions Kuwait & Arab countries, two years; US$100 institutions, other countries two years. **URL:** http://www.kjse.kuniv.edu.kw/aass/english/default.asp.

47334 ■ Arab Journal of Administrative Sciences
Academic Publication Council
Kuwait University
PO Box 5969
Safat 13060, Kuwait
Ph: 965 498 4349
Fax: 965 484 5372
Publication E-mail: ajoas@kuc01.kuniv.edu.kw
Publisher E-mail: ovpr_ra@kuc01.kuniv.edu.kw
Publication publishing research that develops tests, applications or advances management and administrative theory and practices as well as related book reviews, scientific reports and thesis abstracts in both Arabic and English. **Freq:** 3/yr. **Key Personnel:** Prof. Ali Abelrahim, Editor-in-Chief; Nadia M. Ali, Managing Editor; Prof. Mostafa A. Al-Shamy, Editorial Board. **ISSN:** 1029-855X. **Subscription Rates:** 3 KD individuals; 4 KD individuals Arab countries; US$15 individuals; 15 KD institutions Kuwait & Arab countries; US$60 institutions, other countries; 5 KD two years; 7 KD two years Arab countries; US$25 two years; 25 KD institutions Kuwait & Arab countries, two years; US$100 institutions, other countries two years. **URL:** http://pubcouncil.kuniv.edu.kw/AJAS/english/default.asp. **Circ:** Paid 2,000

47335 ■ Arab Journal for the Humanities
Academic Publication Council
Kuwait University
PO Box 5969
Safat 13060, Kuwait
Ph: 965 498 4349
Fax: 965 484 5372
Publication E-mail: ajh@kuniv.edu.kw
Publisher E-mail: ovpr_ra@kuc01.kuniv.edu.kw
Publication publishing papers in the fields of linguistics, literature, philosophy, history, the arts, and social sciences related to the humanities. **Founded:** 1981. **Freq:** Quarterly. **Key Personnel:** Suad Abdul Wahab Al-abdul Rahman, Editor-in-Chief; Nawal Al-Hazzani, Managing Editor. **ISSN:** 1026-9576. **Subscription Rates:** 3 KD individuals; 4 KD individuals Arab countries; US$15 individuals; 15 KD institutions Kuwait & Arab countries; US$60 institutions, other countries; 5 KD two years; 7 KD two years Arab countries; US$25 two years; 25 KD institutions Kuwait & Arab countries, two years; US$100 institutions, other countries two years. **URL:** http://pubcouncil.kuniv.edu.kw/ajh/Arabic/Default.asp. **Circ:** Paid 2,000

47336 ■ The Educational Journal
Academic Publication Council
Kuwait University
PO Box 5969
Safat 13060, Kuwait
Ph: 965 498 4349
Fax: 965 484 5372
Publication E-mail: joe@ku.edu.kw
Publisher E-mail: ovpr_ra@kuc01.kuniv.edu.kw
Journal featuring local and national research and studies focusing on education. **Founded:** 1983. **Freq:** Quarterly. **Key Personnel:** Prof. Saleh Abdullah Jasim, Editor-in-Chief. **ISSN:** 1029-810X. **Subscription Rates:** 750 KD individuals; US$1 individuals Arab countries; US$3 other countries. **URL:** http://pubcouncil.kuniv.edu.kw/joe/Arabic/Default.asp.

47337 ■ European Journal of Industrial Engineering
Inderscience Publishers
c/o Ali Allahverdi, Ed.
Kuwait University, Department of Industrial & Management Systems Engineering
College of Engineering & Petroleum
PO Box 5969
Safat 13060, Kuwait
Publisher E-mail: editor@inderscience.com
Peer-reviewed journal covering areas of industrial engineering. **Founded:** 2007. **Freq:** Quarterly. **Key Personnel:** Ali Allahverdi, Editor, ali.allahverdi@ku.edu.kw; Jose M. Framinan, Editor, jose@esi.us.es; Ruben Ruiz Garcia, Editor, rruiz@eio.upv.es; Turkay Dereli, Assoc. Ed.; Imed Kacem, Assoc. Ed.; Ruben Ruiz Garcia, Assoc. Ed. **ISSN:** 1751-5254. **Subscription Rates:** EUR494 individuals includes surface mail, print only; EUR672 individuals print and online; EUR840 individuals online only for 2-3 users. **URL:** http://www.inderscience.com/browse/index.php?journalCODE=ejie.

47338 ■ Journal of the Gulf and Arabian Peninsula Studies
Academic Publication Council
Kuwait University
PO Box 5969
Safat 13060, Kuwait
Ph: 965 498 4349
Fax: 965 484 5372
Publisher E-mail: ovpr_ra@kuc01.kuniv.edu.kw
Publishes papers addressing Gulf and Arabian Peninsula affairs, including economic, social and political perspectives. **Founded:** Jan. 1975. **Freq:** 3/yr. **Key Personnel:** Dr. Fatima Husain Al-Abdurazzak, Editor-in-Chief; Suhaila Fahad Al-Malek Al-Sabah, Managing Editor. **ISSN:** 0254-4288. **Subscription Rates:** 3 KD individuals; 4 KD individuals Arab countries; US$15 individuals; 15 KD institutions Kuwait & Arab countries; US$60 institutions, other countries; 5 KD two years; 7 KD two years Arab countries; US$25 two years; 25 KD institutions Kuwait & Arab countries, two years; US$100 institutions, other countries two years. **URL:** http://pubcouncil.kuniv.edu.kw/JGAPS.

47339 ■ Journal of the Social Sciences
Academic Publication Council
Kuwait University
PO Box 5969
Safat 13060, Kuwait
Ph: 965 498 4349
Fax: 965 484 5372
Publication E-mail: jss@kuc01.kuniv.edu.kw
Publisher E-mail: ovpr_ra@kuc01.kuniv.edu.kw
Journal featuring theoretical articles in the fields of social sciences. **Founded:** 1973. **Freq:** Quarterly. **Key Personnel:** Taiba A. Al-Asfour, Editor-in-Chief; Latifa al-Fahed, Managing Editor. **ISSN:** 0253-1097. **Subscription Rates:** US$15 individuals; US$60 institutions; US$100 two years; 3 KD individuals; 5 KD two years; 15 KD institutions. **URL:** http://pubcouncil.kuniv.edu.kw/jss/Arabic/Default.asp. **Circ:** Paid 3,000

47340 ■ The Kuwait Medical Journal
Kuwait Medical Association
PO Box 1202
Safat 13013, Kuwait
Ph: 965 53 17972
Fax: 965 53 12630
Publisher E-mail: kmj@kma.org.kw
Peer-reviewed journal featuring a collection of review articles, original articles, case reports in all areas within the medical sciences as well as general information concerning the Association. **Founded:** 1967. **Freq:** Quarterly. **Key Personnel:** Fuad Abdulla M. Hasan, Editor-in-Chief; Adel Khader Ayed, Editor. **ISSN:** 1607-8047. **Remarks:** Advertising accepted; rates available upon request. **URL:** http://www.kma.org.kw/KMJ/instructions.htm. **Circ:** Paid 7,000

47341 ■ Medical Principles and Practice
Kuwait University Health Science Centre
Karger
Faculty of Medicine 4th Fl.
PO Box 24923
Safat 13110, Kuwait
Fax: 965 25 330472
Publication E-mail: mpp@hsc.edu.kw
Concentrates on the recent advances made in basic medical sciences, clinical practice and associated disciplines within human medicine. **Founded:** 1976. **Freq:** Quarterly. **Key Personnel:** Christopher H.J. Ford, Editor; Azu Owunwanne, Editor-in-Chief. **ISSN:** 1011-7571. **Subscription Rates:** 1,435 Eg institutions print; EUR1,063 institutions print; US$1,341 institutions print; 1,579 Eg institutions print and online; EUR1,170 institutions print and online; US$1,476 institutions print and online. **URL:** http://content.karger.com. **Circ:** (Not Reported)

47342 ■ Kuwait Radio - Arabic Music - 95.0 MHz
PO Box 193

Circulation: ★ = ABC; △ = BPA; ♦ = CAC; • = CCAB; ❑ = VAC; ⊕ = PO Statement; ‡ = Publisher's Report; Boldface figures = sworn; Light figures = estimated.

Gale Directory of Publications & Broadcast Media/147th Ed.

5151

Safat 13002, Kuwait
Ph: 965 252 2450160
Fax: 965 252 2425642
E-mail: info@media.gov.kw
Owner: Radio of the State of Kuwait, at above address.
Operating Hours: Continuous. **Key Personnel:** Maher
N. Al-Mutawa, Dir., Engg.; Bader F. Al-Mazeedi, Dir.,
Engg. Communications; Yacoub Y. Dashty, Tech.
Adviser. **Ad Rates:** Advertising accepted; rates available upon request. **URL:** http://www.moinfo.gov.kw.

47343 ■ Kuwait Radio - Arabic Music - 90.5 MHz
PO Box 193
Safat 13002, Kuwait
Ph: 965 252 2450160
Fax: 965 252 2425642
E-mail: info@moinfo.gov.kw
Format: Classical. **Owner:** Radio of the State of Kuwait,
at above address. **Operating Hours:** Continuous. **Key
Personnel:** Maher N. Al-Mutawa, Dir., Engg.; Bader F.
Al-Mazeedi, Dir., Engg. Communications; Yacoub Y.
Dashty, Tech. Adviser. **Ad Rates:** Advertising accepted;
rates available upon request. **URL:** http://www.moinfo.
gov.kw.

47344 ■ Kuwait Radio - Arabic Music - 87.9 MHz
PO Box 397
Safat 13004, Kuwait
Ph: 965 252 2415301
Fax: 965 252 2414469
E-mail: info@moinfo.gov.kw
Format: Full Service; Classical. **Owner:** Radio of the
State of Kuwait, PO Box 967, Safat 13010, Kuwait, Fax:
965 252 2415498. **Operating Hours:** Continuous. **Ad
Rates:** Advertising accepted; rates available upon
request. **URL:** http://www.moinfo.gov.kw.

**47345 ■ Kuwait Radio - Arabic Music - 105.9
MHz**
PO Box 193
Safat 13002, Kuwait
Ph: 965 252 2450160
Fax: 965 252 2425642
E-mail: info@media.gov.kw
Format: Full Service. **Owner:** Radio of the State of
Kuwait, at above address. **Operating Hours:**
Continuous. **Key Personnel:** Maher N. Al-Mutawa, Dir.,
Engg.; Bader F. Al-Mazeediq, Dir., Engg. Communications; Yacoub Y. Dashty, Tech. Adviser. **Ad Rates:**
Advertising accepted; rates available upon request.
URL: http://www.moinfo.gov.kw.

47346 ■ Kuwait Radio - Easy FM - 92.5 MHz
PO Box 397
Safat 13004, Kuwait
Ph: 965 252 2415301
Fax: 965 252 2414469
E-mail: info@moinfo.gov.kw
Format: Eclectic. **Owner:** Radio of the State of Kuwait,
PO Box 967, Safat 13010, Kuwait, Fax: 965 252
2415498. **Operating Hours:** Continuous. **Wattage:**
5000. **Ad Rates:** Advertising accepted; rates available
upon request. **URL:** http://www.moinfo.gov.kw.

**47347 ■ Kuwait Radio - FM Super Station - 99.7
MHz**
PO Box 397
Safat 13004, Kuwait
Ph: 965 252 2457558
Fax: 965 252 2414469
E-mail: info@997rkfm.net
Format: News. **Owner:** Radio of the State of Kuwait,
PO Box 967, Safat 13010, Kuwait, Fax: 965 252
2415498. **Operating Hours:** Continuous. **Ad Rates:**
Advertising accepted; rates available upon request.
URL: http://www.moinfo.gov.kw.

47348 ■ Kuwait Radio - Holy Quran - 97.5 MHz
PO Box 397
Safat 13004, Kuwait
Ph: 965 252 2415301
Fax: 965 252 2414469
E-mail: info@media.gov.kw
Format: Religious. **Owner:** Radio of the State of Kuwait,
PO Box 967, Safat 13010, Kuwait, Fax: 965 252
2415498. **Operating Hours:** 0200-0700, 1700-0200.
Key Personnel: Maher N. Al-Mutawa, Dir., Engg.; Bader
F. Al-Mazeedi, Dir., Engg., Communications; Yacoub Y.
Dashty, Tech. Adviser. **Wattage:** 2000. **Ad Rates:**
Advertising accepted; rates available upon request.
URL: http://www.moinfo.gov.kw.

47349 ■ Kuwait Radio - Holy Quran - 93.3 MHz
PO Box 397
Safat 13004, Kuwait
Ph: 965 252 2415301
Fax: 965 252 2414469
E-mail: info@moinfo.gov.kw
Format: Religious. **Owner:** Radio of the State of Kuwait,
at above address. **Operating Hours:** Continuous. **Key
Personnel:** Maher N. Al-Mutawa, Dir., Engg.; Bader F.
Al-Mazeedi, Dir., Engg. Communications; Yacoub Y.
Dashty, Tech. Adviser. **Ad Rates:** Advertising accepted;
rates available upon request. **URL:** http://www.moinfo.
gov.kw.

47350 ■ Kuwait Radio - Holy Quran - 1341 KHz
PO Box 397
Safat 13004, Kuwait
Ph: 965 252 2415301
Fax: 965 252 2414469
E-mail: info@moinfo.gov.kw
Format: Religious. **Owner:** Radio of the State of Kuwait,
PO Box 967, Safat 13010, Kuwait, Fax: 965 252
2415498. **Operating Hours:** 0200-0700, 1700-2300.
Key Personnel: Maher N. Al-Mutawa, Dir., Engg.; Bader
F. Al-Mazeedi, Dir., Engg., Communications; Yacoub Y.
Dashty, Tech. Adviser. **Wattage:** 10,000. **Ad Rates:**
Advertising accepted; rates available upon request.
URL: http://www.moinfo.gov.kw.

47351 ■ Kuwait Radio - Holy Quran - 630 KHz
PO Box 397
Safat 13004, Kuwait
Ph: 965 252 2415301
Fax: 965 252 2414469
E-mail: info@moinfo.gov.kw
Format: Religious. **Owner:** Radio of the State of Kuwait,
PO Box 967, Safat 13010, Kuwait, Fax: 965 252
2415498. **Operating Hours:** Continuous. **Key Personnel:** Maher N. Al-Mutawa, Dir., Engg.; Bader F. Al-
Mazeedi, Dir., Engg., Communications; Yacoub Y.
Dashty, Tech. Adviser. **Wattage:** 10,000. **Ad Rates:**
Advertising accepted; rates available upon request.
URL: http://www.moinfo.gov.kw.

47352 ■ Kuwait Radio - Main Arabic - 98.9 MHz
PO Box 193
Safat 13002, Kuwait
Ph: 965 252 2450160
Fax: 965 252 2425642
E-mail: info@media.gov.kw
Owner: Radio of the State of Kuwait, at above address.
Operating Hours: Continuous. **Key Personnel:** Maher
N. Al-Mutawa, Dir., Engg.; Bader F. Al-Mazeedi, Dir.,
Engg. Communications; Yacoub Y. Dashty, Tech.
Adviser. **Wattage:** 20,000. **Ad Rates:** Advertising accepted; rates available upon request. **URL:** http://www.
moinfo.gov.kw.

47353 ■ Kuwait Radio - Main Arabic - 89.5 MHz
PO Box 397
Safat 13004, Kuwait
Ph: 965 252 2415301
Fax: 965 252 2414469
E-mail: info@moinfo.gov.kw
Format: News. **Owner:** Radio of the State of Kuwait,
PO Box 967, Safat 13010, Kuwait, Fax: 965 252
2415498. **Operating Hours:** Continuous. **Key Personnel:** Maher N. Al-Mutawa, Dir., Engg.; Bader F. Al-
Mazeedi, Dir., Engg., Communications; Yacoub Y.
Dashty, Tech. Adviser. **Ad Rates:** Advertising accepted;
rates available upon request. **URL:** http://www.moinfo.
gov.kw.

47354 ■ Kuwait Radio - Main Arabic - 963 KHz
PO Box 193
Safat 13002, Kuwait
Ph: 965 252 2450160
Fax: 965 252 2425642
E-mail: info@moinfo.gov.kw
Format: News. **Operating Hours:** 1200-1600, 2100-
0500, 0500-1200, 1600-2100. **Key Personnel:** Maher
N. Al-Mutawa, Dir., Engg.; Bader F. Al-Mazeedi, Dir.,
Engg., Communications; Yacoub Y. Dashty, Tech.
Adviser. **Wattage:** 20,000. **Ad Rates:** Advertising accepted; rates available upon request. **URL:** http://www.
moinfo.gov.kw.

47355 ■ Kuwait Radio - Main Arabic - 1134 KHz
PO Box 193
Safat 13002, Kuwait

Ph: 965 252 2450160
Fax: 965 252 2425642
E-mail: info@moinfo.gov.kw
Owner: Radio of the State of Kuwait, PO Box 967, Safat
13010, Kuwait, Fax: 965 252 2415498. **Operating
Hours:** Continuous. **Key Personnel:** Maher N. Al-
Mutawa, Dir., Engg.; Bader F. Al-Mazeedi, Dir., Engg.,
Communications; Yacoub Y. Dashty, Tech. Adviser. **Wattage:** 10,000. **Ad Rates:** Advertising accepted; rates
available upon request. **URL:** http://www.moinfo.gov.kw.

47356 ■ Kuwait Radio - Main Arabic - 540 KHz
PO Box 193
Safat 13002, Kuwait
Ph: 965 252 2450160
Fax: 965 252 2425642
E-mail: info@media.gov.kw
Format: News. **Owner:** Radio of the State of Kuwait,
PO Box 967, Safat 13010, Kuwait, Fax: 965 252
2415498. **Operating Hours:** Continuous. **Key Personnel:** Maher N. Al-Mutawa, Dir., Engg.; Bader F. Al-
Mazeedi, Dir., Engg., Communications; Yacoub Y.
Dashty, Tech. Adviser. **Wattage:** 600,000. **Ad Rates:**
Advertising accepted; rates available upon request.
URL: http://www.moinfo.gov.kw.

**47357 ■ Kuwait Radio - Second Arabic - 1341
KHz**
PO Box 397
Safat 13004, Kuwait
Ph: 965 252 2415301
Fax: 965 252 2414469
E-mail: info@moinfo.gov.kw
Owner: Radio of the State of Kuwait, PO Box 967, Safat
13010, Kuwait, Fax: 965 252 2415498. **Operating
Hours:** 0700-1700. **Key Personnel:** Maher N. Al-
Mutawa, Dir., Engg.; Bader F. Al-Mazeedi, Dir., Engg.,
Communications; Yacoub Y. Dashty, Tech. Adviser. **Wattage:** 10,000. **Ad Rates:** Advertising accepted; rates
available upon request. **URL:** http://www.moinfo.gov.kw.

**47358 ■ Kuwait Radio - Second Arabic Music -
1269 KHz**
PO Box 193
Safat 13002, Kuwait
Ph: 965 252 2450160
Fax: 965 252 2425642
E-mail: info@media.gov.kw
Owner: Radio of the State of Kuwait, PO Box 967, Safat
13010, Kuwait, Fax: 965 252 2415498. **Operating
Hours:** Continuous. **Key Personnel:** Maher N. Al-
Mutawa, Dir., Engg.; Bader F. Al-Mazeedi, Dir., Engg.,
Communications; Yacoub Y. Dashty, Tech. Adviser. **Wattage:** 100,000. **Ad Rates:** Advertising accepted; rates
available upon request. **URL:** http://www.moinfo.gov.kw.

**47359 ■ Kuwait Radio - Second Arabic Music -
103.7 MHz**
PO Box 397
Safat 13004, Kuwait
Ph: 965 252 2457558
Fax: 965 252 2414469
E-mail: info@media.gov.kw
Format: Full Service. **Owner:** Radio of the State of
Kuwait, PO Box 967, Safat 13010, Kuwait, Fax: 965 252
2415498. **Operating Hours:** Continuous. **Ad Rates:**
Advertising accepted; rates available upon request.
URL: http://www.moinfo.gov.kw.

47360 ■ Kuwait Radio - TV Sound - 100.5 MHz
PO Box 193
Safat 13002, Kuwait
Ph: 965 252 2450160
Fax: 965 252 2425642
E-mail: info@media.gov.kw
Format: Full Service. **Owner:** Radio of the State of
Kuwait, PO Box 967, Safat 13010, Kuwait, Fax: 965 252
2415498. **Operating Hours:** Continuous. **Key Personnel:** Maher N. Al-Mutawa, Dir., Engg.; Bader F. Al-
Mazeedi, Dir., Engg., Communications; Yacoub Y.
Dashty, Tech. Adviser. **Ad Rates:** Advertising accepted;
rates available upon request. **URL:** http://www.moinfo.
gov.kw.

Salmiya

47361 ■ Marina-FM - 88.8
Marina Mall, R2 Fl.
Salmiya, Kuwait

Ph: 965 5739456
Fax: 965 5739455
E-mail: info@psmedia.biz
Format: Ethnic; World Beat. **Owner:** Marina FM, at above address. **Operating Hours:** Continuous. **Key Personnel:** Talal Al-Yagout, Contact. **Ad Rates:** Advertising accepted; rates available upon request. **URL:** http://www.marinafm.com.

Surra

47362 ■ International Journal of Oil, Gas and Coal Technology
Inderscience Enterprises Limited
c/o Prof. M.R. Riazi, Ed.-in-Ch.
Kuwait University
U.S. Department of Chemical Engineering
PO Box 1084

Surra 45711, Kuwait
Peer-reviewed journal covering studies related to oil, natural gas, coal, and petrochemicals as well as manufacturing and refining of biofuels. **Freq:** 4/yr. **Key Personnel:** Prof. M.R. Riazi, Editor-in-Chief, mrriazi@gmail.com. **ISSN:** 1753-3309. **Subscription Rates:** EUR494 individuals print or online; EUR672 individuals print and online. **URL:** http://www.inderscience.com/browse/index.php?journalID=242.

Circulation: ★ = ABC; △ = BPA; ♦ = CAC; • = CCAB; ❑ = VAC; ⊕ = PO Statement; ‡ = Publisher's Report; Boldface figures = sworn; Light figures = estimated.

Gale Directory of Publications & Broadcast Media/147th Ed.   5153

Riga

47363 ■ Dari Pats
Dienas Zurnali
Mukusalas str. 41
Midlothian
LV-1004 Riga, Latvia
Ph: 371 6 7273311
Fax: 371 6 7292701
Publication E-mail: daripats@dienaszurnali.com
Publisher E-mail: pasts@dienaszurnali.lv
Magazine featuring home improvement and practical do it yourself guide. **Freq:** Monthly. **Remarks:** Accepts advertising. **URL:** http://dienaszurnali.lv/information_in_english; http://www.daripats.lv/index.php?&211. **Circ:** Paid 15,000

47364 ■ Darza Pasaule
Dienas Zurnali
Mukusalas str. 15
LV-1004 Riga, Latvia
Ph: 371 6 7297071
Publication E-mail: pasaule@dienaszurnali.lv
Publisher E-mail: pasts@dienaszurnali.lv
Magazine featuring gardening in Latvia. **Key Personnel:** Sandra Rusko, Editor-in-Chief, sandra.rusko@dienaszurnali.com. **Subscription Rates:** 18.95 Rb individuals; 9.48 Rb individuals 6 months. **Remarks:** Accepts advertising. **URL:** http://dienaszurnali.lv/information_in_english; http://darzapasaule.lv. **Circ:** (Not Reported)

47365 ■ Diena (Latvian Edition)
Joint Stock Company Diena
Mukusalas Str. 15
LV-1004 Riga, Latvia
Ph: 371 706 3150
Fax: 371 706 3167
Publisher E-mail: Info@asdiena.lv
General newspaper. **Founded:** Nov. 23, 1990. **Freq:** Mon.-Sat. **Key Personnel:** Aleksandrs Tralmaks, Director; Sarmite Elerte, Editor-in-Chief. **Remarks:** Accepts advertising. **URL:** http://www.asdiena.lv/eng/about/history.html. **Circ:** Controlled 65,000

47366 ■ Ilustreta Junioriem
Dienas Zurnali
Mukusalas str. 41
Midlothian
LV-1004 Riga, Latvia
Ph: 371 6 7273311
Fax: 371 6 7292701
Publisher E-mail: pasts@dienaszurnali.lv
Science magazine for the youth. **Freq:** Monthly. **Subscription Rates:** EUR21.98 individuals 6 months; EUR40.47 individuals. **URL:** http://dienaszurnali.lv/information_in_english; http://ekiosks.lv/ilustreta-junioriem.

47367 ■ Ilustreta Pasaules Vesture
Dienas Zurnali
Mukusalas str. 41
Midlothian
LV-1004 Riga, Latvia
Ph: 371 6 7273311
Fax: 371 6 7292701

Publication E-mail: ilustreta.vesture@dienaszurnali.com
Publisher E-mail: pasts@dienaszurnali.lv
Science magazine featuring articles on human history's most important and unusual events. **Freq:** Monthly. **URL:** http://dienaszurnali.lv/information_in_english; http://ekiosks.lv/ilustreta-pasaules-vesture.

47368 ■ Ilustreta Zinatne
Dienas Zurnali
Mukusalas str. 15
LV-1004 Riga, Latvia
Ph: 371 6 72292644
Publication E-mail: ilustreta.zinatne@dienaszurnali.com
Publisher E-mail: pasts@dienaszurnali.lv
Magazine featuring advances in modern science. **Freq:** Monthly. **Key Personnel:** Vents Thames, Editor-in-Chief, vents.star@ilustretazinatne.com; Dina Boehm, Editor, dina.bema@ilustretazinatne.com. **Subscription Rates:** 26.99 Rb individuals; 14.52 Rb individuals 6 months. **Remarks:** Accepts advertising. **URL:** http://dienaszurnali.lv/information_in_english; http://ekiosks.lv/ilustreta-zinatne; http://ilustretazinatne.lv/. **Circ:** (Not Reported)

47369 ■ Journal of Business Ethics Education
Dienas Zurnali
Mukusalas str. 41
Midlothian
LV-1004 Riga, Latvia
Ph: 371 6 7273311
Fax: 371 6 7292701
Publisher E-mail: pasts@dienaszurnali.lv
Journal assisting educators by providing conceptual tools managers needed to make choices those are ethically responsible and culturally sensitive as well as technically sound. **Key Personnel:** Olukunle Iyanda, Co-Ed.; John Hooker, Editor; Manuel Velasquez, Sen. Contributing Ed.; Norman Bowie, Sen. Contributing Ed. **Subscription Rates:** US$430 institutions library - hard copy; US$435 institutions library - hard copy & e-access; EUR360 institutions library - hard copy; EUR370 institutions library - hard copy & e-access; 240 institutions library - hard copy; 250 institutions library - hard copy & e-access. **URL:** http://www.neilsonjournals.com/JBEE/.

47370 ■ Journal of International Business Education
Dienas Zurnali
Mukusalas str. 41
Midlothian
LV-1004 Riga, Latvia
Ph: 371 6 7273311
Fax: 371 6 7292701
Publisher E-mail: pasts@dienaszurnali.lv
Journal covering developments in teaching methods and technologies, and new institutional frameworks for international business education. **Key Personnel:** Antonio Argandona, Editorial Board; Paul Beamish, Editorial Board; Paul Bracken, Editorial Board; David Conklin, Editorial Board; Elsie Echeverri-Carroll, Editorial Board; John Farley, Editorial Board. **Subscription Rates:** US$390 institutions library - hard copy; US$395 institutions library - hard copy & e-access; EUR330 institutions library - hard copy; EUR340 institutions library - hard copy & e-access; 220 institutions library - hard copy; 230 Rb institutions library - hard copy & e-access.

URL: http://www.neilsonjournals.com/JIBE/.

47371 ■ Journal of Organizational Behavior Education
Dienas Zurnali
Mukusalas str. 41
Midlothian
LV-1004 Riga, Latvia
Ph: 371 6 7273311
Fax: 371 6 7292701
Publisher E-mail: pasts@dienaszurnali.lv
Journal covering the teaching of organizational behavior. **Key Personnel:** Pino Audia, Editorial Board; Louis Barnes, Editorial Board; Jennifer Berdahl, Editorial Board. **Subscription Rates:** US$390 institutions library - hard copy only; US$395 institutions library - hard copy & e-access; EUR330 institutions library - hard copy only; EUR340 institutions library - hard copy & e-access; 220 institutions library - hard copy only; 230 institutions library - hard copy & e-access. **URL:** http://www.neilsonjournals.com/JOBE/.

47372 ■ Legendas
Dienas Zurnali
Mukusalas str. 41
Midlothian
LV-1004 Riga, Latvia
Ph: 371 6 7273311
Fax: 371 6 7292701
Publication E-mail: legends@dienaszurnali.com
Publisher E-mail: pasts@dienaszurnali.lv
Magazine featuring stories and novels of legendary people and events. **Freq:** Monthly. **Remarks:** Accepts advertising. **URL:** http://dienaszurnali.lv/information_in_english; http://ekiosks.lv/legendas. **Circ:** (Not Reported)

47373 ■ Musmajas
Dienas Zurnali
Mukusalas str. 15
LV-1004 Riga, Latvia
Ph: 371 6 7299105
Publication E-mail: athome@dienaszurnali.com
Publisher E-mail: pasts@dienaszurnali.lv
Magazine for cooking, gardening, and home design. **Key Personnel:** Aiva Kalve, Editor-in-Chief, aiva.forge@athome.com. **Subscription Rates:** 16.99 Rb individuals. **Remarks:** Accepts advertising. **URL:** http://dienaszurnali.lv/information_in_english; http://musmajas.lv. **Circ:** (Not Reported)

47374 ■ Una
Dienas Zurnali
Mukusalas str. 15
LV-1004 Riga, Latvia
Ph: 371 6 7297073
Publication E-mail: una@dienaszurnali.com
Publisher E-mail: pasts@dienaszurnali.lv
Magazine featuring lifestyle, health, fashion, stars and legends, travel news and culture. **Freq:** Monthly. **Key Personnel:** Gina Brisk, Editor-in-Chief, drove.brisk@una.com. **Subscription Rates:** 17.40 Rb individuals; 9.84 Rb individuals 6 months. **Remarks:** Accepts advertising. **URL:** http://dienaszurnali.lv/information_in_english; http://una.lv. **Circ:** Paid 18,000

47375 ■ Veseliba
Dienas Zurnali

Circulation: ★ = ABC; △ = BPA; ◆ = CAC; • = CCAB; ❑ = VAC; ⊕ = PO Statement; ‡ = Publisher's Report; Boldface figures = sworn; Light figures = estimated.

Gale Directory of Publications & Broadcast Media/147th Ed. 5155

Mukusalas str. 15
LV-1004 Riga, Latvia
Ph: 371 6 7297072
Publication E-mail: health@dienaszurnali.com
Publisher E-mail: pasts@dienaszurnali.lv
Magazine featuring articles on lifestyle and health. **Freq:** Monthly. **Key Personnel:** Solvita Velde, Editor-in-Chief, solvit.velde@health.com. **Subscription Rates:** 17.50 Rb individuals; 8.94 Rb individuals 6 months. **Remarks:** Accepts advertising. **URL:** http://dienaszurnali.lv/information_in_english; http://www.veseliba.lv/index.php?&93. **Circ:** Paid 17,000

47376 ■ Vides Vestis
Friends of the Earth Latvia
Kalniema 28
LV-1046 Riga, Latvia
Ph: 371 761 7174
Fax: 371 761 9043
Publisher E-mail: info@vak.lv
Publications covering ecology and conservation. **Founded:** 1997. **Freq:** Monthly. **Trim Size:** A4. **Remarks:** Accepts advertising. **URL:** http://www.videsvestis.lv; http://www.vak.lv/english/index.php. **Ad Rates:** BW: EUR200, 4C: EUR400. **Circ:** Paid 3,000, Nonpaid 2,000

47377 ■ Latvijas Radio 4 - 107.7 MHz
8 Doma laukums
LV-1505 Riga, Latvia
Ph: 371 34 67206722
Fax: 371 34 67206709
E-mail: radio@latvijasradio.lv
Format: Information. **Key Personnel:** Dzintris Kolats, Dir. Gen., phone 371 34 67206747, fax 371 34 67206709, dzintris.kolats@latvijasradio.lv. **URL:** http://www.latvijasradio.lv.

47378 ■ Latvijas Radio 1 - 90.7 MHz
8 Doma laukums
LV-1505 Riga, Latvia
Ph: 371 34 67206722
Fax: 371 34 67206709
E-mail: radio@latvijasradio.lv
Format: Public Radio. **Key Personnel:** Dzintris Kolats, Dir. Gen., phone 371 34 67206747, fax 371 34 67206709, dzintris.kolats@latvijasradio.lv. **URL:** http://www.latvijasradio.lv.

47379 ■ Latvijas Radio 3 - 103.7 MHz
8 Doma laukums
LV-1505 Riga, Latvia
Ph: 371 34 67206722

Fax: 371 34 67206709
E-mail: radio@latvijasradio.lv
Format: Classical. **Key Personnel:** Dzintris Kolats, Dir. Gen., phone 371 34 67206747, fax 371 34 67206709, dzintris.kolats@latvijasradio.lv. **URL:** http://www.latvijasradio.lv.

47380 ■ Latvijas Radio 2 - 91.5 MHz
8 Doma laukums
LV-1505 Riga, Latvia
Ph: 371 34 67206722
Fax: 371 34 67206709
E-mail: radio@latvijasradio.lv
Format: Public Radio. **Key Personnel:** Dzintris Kolats, Dir. Gen., phone 371 34 67206747, fax 371 34 67206709, dzintris.kolats@latvijasradio.lv. **URL:** http://www.latvijasradio.lv.

47381 ■ Radio SWH Rock-FM - 89.2
Skanstes iela 13
LV-1013 Riga, Latvia
Ph: 371 67370067
Fax: 371 67828283
E-mail: rock@radioswh.lv
Format: Album-Oriented Rock (AOR). **URL:** http://www.radioswh.lv/swhrock/page.php.

Aabey

47382 ■ National Broadcasting Network (NBN) - 89.4 MHz
Adnan El Hakim St.
Hala Bldg., Block A
Jnah
Beirut, Lebanon
Ph: 961 1 841027
Fax: 961 1 841029
E-mail: flash@nbn.com.lb
Format: News. **Owner:** National Broadcasting Network (NBN), at above address. **Ad Rates:** Advertising accepted; rates available upon request. **URL:** http://www.nbn.com.lb/.

Baalbek

47383 ■ NBN-TV - 49
Adnan El Hakim St., Jnah
Hala Bldg., Block A
Beirut, Lebanon
Ph: 961 1 841020
Fax: 961 1 841029
E-mail: flash@nbn.com.lb
Owner: National Broadcasting Network, at above address. **URL:** http://www.nbn.com.lb.

47384 ■ Sawt El Ghad - Baalbek - 97.1
Amaret Chalhoub, Jounieh-Beirut Hwy.
Jemejian Bldg., 4th Fl.
Beirut, Lebanon
Ph: 961 1 881555
Fax: 961 1 881999
E-mail: info@sawtelghad.com
Format: Contemporary Hit Radio (CHR); News. **Owner:** Sawt El Ghad, at above address. **Founded:** Sept. 10, 1997. **Operating Hours:** 7 a.m.-12 a.m. Mon.-Fri. **Key Personnel:** Loraine Kodelh, Contact, lorry@sawtelghad.com; Najwa Abou Khalil, Contact, najwa@sawtelghad.com; Nisrine Kabouch, Contact, nisrine@sawtelghad.com. **Wattage:** 2500. **URL:** http://www.sawtelghad.com.

Beirut

47385 ■ Achabaka
Dar Assayad
Saeed Frayha St.
PO Box 11-1038
Beirut, Lebanon
Ph: 961 5 457261
Fax: 961 5 452700
Publisher E-mail: beirutads@alanwar.com
Music and entertainment magazine. **Founded:** 1956. **Freq:** Weekly (Fri.). **Print Method:** Web offset. **Trim Size:** 205 x 275 mm. **Key Personnel:** Issam Freiha, Chm.; Marc Stephan, Production Mgr. **Subscription Rates:** US$250 individuals for Europe only; US$300 elsewhere. **Remarks:** Accepts advertising. **URL:** http://www.achabakamagazine.com/. **Ad Rates:** 4C: L1,500. **Circ:** Combined 113,583

47386 ■ Al Anwar
Dar Assayad
Saeed Frayha St.

PO Box 11-1038
Beirut, Lebanon
Ph: 961 5 457261
Fax: 961 5 452700
Publisher E-mail: beirutads@alanwar.com
Political and economic newspaper. **Founded:** 1959. **Freq:** Daily. **Key Personnel:** Rafic Khoury, Editor-in-Chief; Michel Raad, Editor-in-Chief; Fouad Daaboul, Managing Editor. **Subscription Rates:** US$500 individuals Europe; US$600 elsewhere. **Remarks:** Accepts advertising. **URL:** http://www.alanwar-leb.com/. **Circ:** Combined 47,899

47387 ■ Al Defaiya
Monch Publishing Group
Minkara Ctr., 6th Fl.
Madame Curie St.
Hamra
Beirut, Lebanon
Publication E-mail: defaiya@defaiya.com
Publisher E-mail: info@moench-group.com
Magazine featuring defense and aerospace technology in Arab world. **Subtitle:** Arabian Defense and Aerospace Magazine. **Founded:** 1993. **Freq:** Bimonthly. **Trim Size:** 206 x 271 mm. **Key Personnel:** Khaled Zahalan, Mng. Dir., zahalan@moench-group.com; Salim Abou Ismail, Editorial Mgr.; Stephen Orr, Co-Publisher, phone 49 228 6483105, fax 49 228 6483109, stephen.orr@moench-group.com. **Remarks:** Accepts advertising. **URL:** http://www.defaiya.com/; http://www.moench-group.com/defaiya.php. **Ad Rates:** BW: L4,150, 4C: L6,650. **Circ:** Combined 24,000

47388 ■ Al-Fares
Dar Assayad
Saeed Frayha St.
PO Box 11-1038
Beirut, Lebanon
Ph: 961 5 457261
Fax: 961 5 452700
Publisher E-mail: beirutads@alanwar.com
Lifestyle magazine for young men. **Freq:** Monthly. **Print Method:** Web offset. **Trim Size:** 230 x 300 mm. **Key Personnel:** Marc Stephan, Production Mgr.; George Trad, Editor-in-Chief; Issam Freiha, Chm. **Subscription Rates:** L150 individuals; L200 individuals. **Remarks:** Accepts advertising. **URL:** http://www.alfaresmagazine.com/pdf-website/whyalfares.html. **Ad Rates:** BW: L 3,675, 4C: L5,950. **Circ:** ★78,307

47389 ■ AL IDARI
Dar Assayad
PO Box 11-1038
Beirut, Lebanon
Publisher E-mail: beirutads@alanwar.com
Magazine featuring business and management issues in Arab World. **Founded:** 1975. **Freq:** Monthly. **Print Method:** Web offset. **Trim Size:** 205 x 275 mm. **Key Personnel:** Hassan Khoury, Editor-in-Chief; Marc Stephan, Production Mgr.; Issam Freiha, Chm. **Remarks:** Accepts advertising. **URL:** http://www.ssm.co.uk/media-search/details/al-idari/190/. **Ad Rates:** 4C: L 5,500. **Circ:** ★36,988

47390 ■ Arab Construction World (ACW)
Chatila Publishing House
PO Box 13-5121
Chouran
Beirut, Lebanon
Fax: 961 1 352419
Business journal covering developments and technologies in the building and road construction industries in the Middle East and North Africa. **Founded:** 1983. **Freq:** Monthly. **Trim Size:** 213 x 285 mm. **ISSN:** 1015-8316. **Subscription Rates:** US$45 individuals Lebanon; US$60 individuals Arab Countries; US$75 individuals Turkey, Cyprus, Iran and South Africa; US$105 individuals elsewhere; US$75 two years Lebanon; US$105 two years Arab Countries; US$135 two years Turkey, Cyprus, Iran, and South Africa; US$195 two years elsewhere; US$95 individuals Lebanon, 3 years; US$140 individuals Arab Countries, 3 years. **Remarks:** Accepts advertising. **URL:** http://www.acwmag.com/index.aspx?magazine_id=2. **Ad Rates:** BW: US$2,000, 4C: US$2,500. **Circ:** Combined ‡7,153

47391 ■ Arab Defence Journal
Dar Assayad
PO Box 11-1038
Beirut, Lebanon
Publication E-mail: office@contact.pr.net
Publisher E-mail: beirutads@alanwar.com
Magazine featuring aerospace, naval and land systems in Middle East. **Founded:** 1976. **Freq:** Monthly. **Trim Size:** 205 x 275 mm. **Key Personnel:** Faouzi Abou Farhat, Editor-in-Chief; Issam Freiha, Chm.; Marc Stephan, Production Mgr. **Remarks:** Accepts advertising. **URL:** http://www.arabdefencejournal.com. **Ad Rates:** BW: L 3,700, 4C: L4,900. **Circ:** ★25,000

47392 ■ Arab Water World (AWW)
Chatila Publishing House
PO Box 13-5121
Chouran
Beirut, Lebanon
Fax: 961 1 352419
English and Arabic language journal covering developments and technologies in the water and sewage industries in the Middle East and North Africa. **Founded:** 1977. **Freq:** 12/yr. **Trim Size:** 215 x 285 mm. **ISSN:** 1015-8332. **Subscription Rates:** US$45 individuals Lebanon; US$60 individuals Arab Countries; US$75 individuals Turkey, Cyprus, Iran and South Africa; US$105 other countries; US$75 two years Lebanon; US$105 two years Arab Countries; US$135 two years Turkey, Cyprus, Iran, and South Africa; US$195 other countries 2 years; US$95 individuals Lebanon, 3 years; US$140 individuals Arab Countries, 3 years. **Remarks:** Accepts advertising. **URL:** http://www.awwmag.com/index.aspx?magazine_id=1. **Ad Rates:** BW: L2,200, 4C: L2,750. **Circ:** 8,909

47393 ■ Assayad
Dar Assayad
Saeed Frayha St.
PO Box 11-1038
Beirut, Lebanon
Ph: 961 5 457261
Fax: 961 5 452700

Circulation: ★ = ABC; △ = BPA; ♦ = CAC; • = CCAB; ❑ = VAC; ⊕ = PO Statement; ‡ = Publisher's Report; Boldface figures = sworn; Light figures = estimated.

Gale Directory of Publications & Broadcast Media/147th Ed. 5157

Publisher E-mail: beirutads@alanwar.com
Magazine featuring Arab and Lebanese political, social and economic news. **Freq:** Weekly. **Trim Size:** 230 x 302 mm. **Key Personnel:** Marc Stephan, Production Mgr.; Issam Freiha, Chm. **Subscription Rates:** US$250 individuals for Europe; US$300 U.S. and other countries. **Remarks:** Accepts advertising. **URL:** http://www.al-sayad.com. **Ad Rates:** BW: L3,400, 4C: L5,900. **Circ:** 76,192

47394 ■ The Daily Star (Lebanon)
The Daily Star
Marine Twr., 6th Fl.
Rue de La Ste. Famille
Gemaizeh, Achrafieh
Beirut, Lebanon
Ph: 961 1 587277
Fax: 961 1 561333
General newspaper in English. **Founded:** June 1952. **Freq:** Daily 6/week. **Print Method:** Offset. **Trim Size:** 76 mm. **ISSN:** 1564-0310. **Subscription Rates:** US$93 individuals 3 months Lebanon; US$180 individuals 6 months Lebanon; US$333 individuals 12 months Lebanon; US$108 individuals 3 months Syria (Damascus); US$208 individuals 6 months Syria (Damascus); US$385 individuals 12 months Syria (Damascus); US$80 individuals 3 months Jordan (Aman); US$150 individuals 6 months Jordan (Aman); US$265 individuals 12 months Jordan (Aman); US$103 individuals 12 months Kuwait. **Remarks:** Accepts advertising. **URL:** http://www.dailystar.com.lb. **Circ:** Combined 10,550

47395 ■ Haigazian Armenological Review
Haigazian University
Department of Armenian Studies
Rue Mexique
Kantari
PO Box 11-1748
Beirut, Lebanon
Ph: 961 1 349230
Fax: 961 1 353012
Publication E-mail: review@haigazian.edu.lb
Publisher E-mail: info@haigazian.edu.lb
Journal covering studies in Armenia and the Armenian people. **Founded:** 1970. **Freq:** Annual. **Key Personnel:** Rev. Antranik Granian, Editor-in-Chief. **URL:** http://www.haigazian.edu.lb/Publications/Pages/HaigazianArmenologicalReview.

47396 ■ Hitek Magazine
Hazmieh Damascus Rd.
Karam Bldg., 3rd Fl., Near Sea Sweet
Beirut, Lebanon
Ph: 961 545 0212
Fax: 961 545 5477
Publisher E-mail: ktayar@arabcom.com
Trade magazine covering telecommunications. **Founded:** 1993. **Freq:** Monthly 9/yr. **Key Personnel:** Sylvia Snaige, Reporters; Walid Khoury, Reporters; Syed Noman, Reporters/Dir. Incharge; Jean Carlo Tayar, Reporters; Katia Tayar, Editor-in-Chief; Joseph Cherian, Editor, editor@hitekmag.com; Jean Louis Farwagi, Managing Editor, jlfarwagi@hitekmag.com. **Subscription Rates:** US$75 individuals; US$125 two years. **Remarks:** Accepts advertising. **URL:** http://www.robotarabia.com/hitekmag/. **Circ:** 10,000

47397 ■ Lebanese Review of Arab and International Arbitration
Ibrahim Najjar Law Firm
11 Madrassat El-Salam St.
PO Box 116/2270
Beirut, Lebanon
Ph: 961 1 202100
Fax: 961 1 201974
Publisher E-mail: inajjar@dm.net.lb
Journal covering topics relating to Lebanese, Arab and worldwide arbitration, including comparative law studies, legislation and statutes, judgments and arbitral awards in Lebanon and other Arab and international jurisdictions. **Founded:** 1996. **Freq:** Quarterly. **Key Personnel:** Ibrahim Najjar, Editor-in-Chief; Walid Kassir, Executive Board; Nabil N. Antaki, Editorial Board; Samir Abillamah, Editorial Board; Nathalie Najjar, Executive Board. **Subscription Rates:** US$75 individuals in Lebanon; US$135 individuals abroad; EUR105 individuals. **URL:** http://www.reviewofarbitration.com/.

47398 ■ Lebanese Science Journal
National Council for Scientific Research - Lebanon
PO Box 11-8281
Riad El-Solh 1107
59, Zahia Selman St.
Beirut, Lebanon
Ph: 961 1850 125
Fax: 961 1822 639
Publication E-mail: journal@cnrs.edu.lb
Publisher E-mail: hamze@cnrs.edu.lb
English and French language publication covering Lebanese and regional scientific research. **Subtitle:** Journal Scientifique Libanais. **Founded:** 1985. **Freq:** Semiannual. **Trim Size:** 16 x 23 1/2. **Key Personnel:** H.H. Kouyoumjian, Exec. Ed. **ISSN:** 1561-3410. **Subscription Rates:** Free. **Remarks:** Advertising not accepted. **URL:** http://www.cnrs.edu.lb/info/lsj.html. **Formed by the merger of:** Lebanese Science Bulletin; Lebanese Scientific Research Reports. **Circ:** (Not Reported)

47399 ■ Middle East Food (MEF)
Chatila Publishing House
PO Box 13-5121
Chouran
Beirut, Lebanon
Fax: 961 1 352419
English-Arabic journal covering developments and technologies in the food, catering and beverage industries of the Middle East and North Africa. **Founded:** 1985. **Freq:** Bimonthly. **Trim Size:** 213 x 285 mm. **ISSN:** 1015-8340. **Subscription Rates:** US$45 individuals Lebanon; US$60 individuals Arab Countries; US$75 individuals Turkey, Cyprus, Iran and South Africa; US$105 other countries; US$75 two years Lebanon; US$105 two years Arab Countries; US$135 two years Turkey, Cyprus, Iran, and South Africa; US$195 two years other countries; US$95 individuals Lebanon, 3 years; US$140 individuals Arab Countries, 3 years. **Remarks:** Accepts advertising. **URL:** http://www.mefmag.com/index.aspx?magazine_id=3. **Ad Rates:** BW: US$2,000, 4C: US$2,500. **Circ:** Combined ‡7,182

47400 ■ Monday Morning
Dimitri Trad Bldg.
Issa Maalouf St., Sioufi
PO Box 165612
Beirut, Lebanon
Ph: 961 1 200961
Fax: 961 1 335079
Publication E-mail: info@mmorning.com
Publisher E-mail: info@mmorning.com
Consumer news publication. **Founded:** 1971. **Freq:** Weekly. **Key Personnel:** C.B. Denman, Editor; Saer Karam, Editorial Dir./Gen. Mgr.; Melhem Karam, Editor-in-Chief. **Subscription Rates:** US$200 individuals; US$400 institutions; US$500 out of country. **URL:** http://www.mmorning.com. **Circ:** 11,000

47401 ■ Sahar
Dar Assayad
Saeed Frayha St.
PO Box 11-1038
Beirut, Lebanon
Ph: 961 5 457261
Fax: 961 5 452700
Publisher E-mail: beirutads@alanwar.com
Entertainment, fashion and lifestyle magazine for women. **Subtitle:** A Gem of a Magazine. **Founded:** Nov. 2005. **Freq:** Monthly. **Print Method:** Web offset. **Trim Size:** 230 x 300 mm. **Key Personnel:** Issam Freiha, Chm.; Marc Stephan, Production Mgr. **Remarks:** Accepts advertising. **URL:** http://www.dar-assayad.com/. **Circ:** 110,000

47402 ■ Today's Outlook
PO Box 90792
Jdeidet el Metn
Beirut, Lebanon
Ph: 961 1 696927
Fax: 961 1 696928
Publisher E-mail: todaysoutlook@gmail.com
Lifestyle magazine. **Freq:** Bimonthly. **Subscription Rates:** US$20 individuals; US$50 institutions; US$80 other countries; US$100 institutions, other countries. **Remarks:** Advertising accepted; rates available upon request. **URL:** http://www.todaysoutlook.com/. **Circ:** (Not Reported)

47403 ■ Future Television - 46
White House, Spears St., Sanayeh
PO Box 13-6052
Beirut, Lebanon
Ph: 961 1 355355
Fax: 961 1 753232
E-mail: future@future.com.lb
Format: Commercial TV; News. **Owner:** Future Television, at above address. **Founded:** 1993. **Operating Hours:** Continuous. **Ad Rates:** Advertising accepted; rates available upon request. **URL:** http://www.futuretvnetwork.com.

47404 ■ Future Television - 52
White House
Spears St., Sanayeh
PO Box 13-6052
Beirut, Lebanon
Ph: 961 1 355355
Fax: 961 1 753232
E-mail: future@future.com.lb
Format: Commercial TV; News. **Owner:** Future Television, at above address. **Founded:** Feb. 15, 1993. **Operating Hours:** Continuous. **Ad Rates:** Advertising accepted; rates available upon request. **URL:** http://www.futuretvnetwork.com.

47405 ■ Future Television - 28
White House, Spears St., Sanayeh
PO Box 13-6052
Beirut, Lebanon
Ph: 961 1 355355
Fax: 961 1 753232
E-mail: future@future.com.lb
Format: Commercial TV; News. **Owner:** Future Television, at above address. **Founded:** 1993. **Operating Hours:** Continuous. **Ad Rates:** Advertising accepted; rates available upon request. **URL:** http://www.futuretvnetwork.com.

47406 ■ Future Television - 37
White House, Spears St., Sanayeh
PO Box 13-6052
Beirut, Lebanon
Ph: 961 1 355355
Fax: 961 1 753232
E-mail: future@future.com.lb
Format: Commercial TV; News. **Owner:** Future Television, at above address. **Founded:** 1993. **Operating Hours:** Continuous. **Ad Rates:** Advertising accepted; rates available upon request. **URL:** http://www.futuretvnetwork.com.

47407 ■ Lebanese Broadcasting Corporation International - 9H
Adma, Zone Jaune, Rue 4 Bis
PO Box 165853
Zouk 111
Beirut, Lebanon
Ph: 961 9 850850
Fax: 961 9 850916
Format: News; Commercial TV; Sports. **Owner:** Lebanese Broadcasting Corporation International, at above address. **Operating Hours:** 0445-2200. **Key Personnel:** Pierre Al Daher, Station Mgr.; Nasim Boustany, Tech. Dir.; Selim El-Azar, Film Buyer. **Wattage:** 35,000. **Ad Rates:** Advertising accepted; rates available upon request. **URL:** http://www.lbcgroup.tv.

47408 ■ Lebanese Broadcasting Corporation International - 5H
Adma, Zone Jaune, Rue 4 Bis
PO Box 165853
Zouk 111
Beirut, Lebanon
Ph: 961 9 850850
Fax: 961 9 850916
Format: News; Commercial TV; Sports. **Owner:** Lebanese Broadcasting Corporation International, at above address. **Operating Hours:** 0445-2200. **Key Personnel:** Pierre Al Daher, Station Mgr. **Wattage:** 35,000. **Ad Rates:** Advertising accepted; rates available upon request. **URL:** http://www.lbcgroup.tv.

47409 ■ Lebanese Broadcasting Corporation International - 33H
Adma, Zone Jaune, Rue 4 Bis
PO Box 165853
Zouk 111
Beirut, Lebanon
Ph: 961 9 850850
Fax: 961 9 850916
Format: News; Commercial TV; Sports. **Owner:** Lebanese Broadcasting Corp. International, at above

address. **Operating Hours:** 0445-2200. **Key Personnel:** Pierre Al Daher, Station Mgr.; Nasim Boustany, Tech. Dir.; Selim El-Azar, Film Buyer. **Wattage:** 325,000. **Ad Rates:** Advertising accepted; rates available upon request. **URL:** http://www.lbcgroup.tv.

47410 ■ Lebanese Broadcasting Corporation International - 10H
Adma, Zone Jaune, Rue 4 Bis
PO Box 165853
Zouk 111
Beirut, Lebanon
Ph: 961 9 850850
Fax: 961 9 850916
Format: News; Commercial TV; Sports. **Owner:** Lebanese Broadcasting Corporation International, at above address. **Operating Hours:** 0445-2200. **Key Personnel:** Pierre Al Daher, Station Mgr.; Nasim Boustany, Tech. Dir.; Selim El-Azar, Film Buyer. **Wattage:** 35,000. **Ad Rates:** Advertising accepted; rates available upon request. **URL:** http://www.lbcgroup.tv.

47411 ■ Lebanese Broadcasting Corporation International - 12H
Adma, Zone Jaune, Rue 4 Bis
PO Box 165853
Zouk 111
Beirut, Lebanon
Ph: 961 9 850850
Fax: 961 9 850916
E-mail: info@lbcstreaming.com
Format: News; Commercial TV; Sports. **Owner:** Lebanese Broadcasting Corp. International, at above address. **Operating Hours:** 0445-2200. **Key Personnel:** Pierre Al Daher, Station Mgr.; Nasim Boustany, Tech. Dir.; Selim El-Azar, Film Buyer. **Wattage:** 60,000. **Ad Rates:** Advertising accepted; rates available upon request. **URL:** http://www.lbcgroup.tv.

47412 ■ Mix-FM - 104.4
Alfred Naccache Ave.
VDL Bldg.
Ashrafieh, Sassine
PO Box 16-6815
Beirut, Lebanon
Ph: 961 1 333288
Fax: 961 1 217788
E-mail: info@mixfm.com.lb
Format: Contemporary Hit Radio (CHR). **Operating Hours:** Continuous. **Ad Rates:** Advertising accepted; rates available upon request. **URL:** http://www.mixfm.com.lb.

47413 ■ Murr Television - 68
Fouad Chehab Ave., Achrafieh Fassouh
RML Bldg.
Beirut, Lebanon
Ph: 961 1 217000
Fax: 961 1 215215
E-mail: mtv@mtv.com.lb
Format: News; Sports; Commercial TV. **Owner:** Murr Television (MTV), at above address. **Operating Hours:** 0700-0200. **Key Personnel:** Michel El Murr, President. **URL:** http://www.lbcgroup.tv/lbc/en/home/.

47414 ■ Murr Television - 38
Fouad Chehab Ave. - Achrafieh Fassouh
RML Bldg.
Beirut, Lebanon
Ph: 961 1 217000
Fax: 961 1 215215
E-mail: mtv@mtv.com.lb
Format: News; Sports; Commercial TV. **Owner:** Murr Television (MTV), at above address. **Operating Hours:** 0700-0200. **Key Personnel:** Michel El Murr, President. **URL:** http://www.dm.net.lb/mtv/.

47415 ■ Murr Television - 48
Fouad Chehab Ave., Achrafieh Fassouh
RML Bldg.
Beirut, Lebanon
Ph: 961 1 217000
Fax: 961 1 215215
E-mail: mtv@mtv.com.lb
Format: News; Sports; Commercial TV. **Owner:** Murr Television (MTV), at above address. **Operating Hours:** 0700-0200. **Key Personnel:** Michel El Murr, President. **URL:** http://www.dm.net.lb/mtv/.

47416 ■ Murr Television - 28
Fouad Chehab Ave. - Achrafieh Fassouh
RML Bldg.
Beirut, Lebanon
Ph: 961 1 217000
Fax: 961 1 215215
E-mail: mtv@mtv.com.lb
Format: News; Sports; Commercial TV. **Owner:** Murr Television (MTV), at above address. **Operating Hours:** 0700-0200. **Key Personnel:** Michel El Murr, President. **URL:** http://www.dm.net.lb/mtv/.

National Broadcasting Network (NBN) - See Aabey

NBN-TV - See Baalbek

NBN-TV - See Beit Mery

NBN-TV - See Nabatieh

NBN-TV - See Zahle

47417 ■ NBN-TV Abay - 49
Adnan El Hakim St., Jnah
Hala Bldg., Block A
Beirut, Lebanon
Ph: 961 1 841020
Fax: 961 1 841029
E-mail: flash@nbn.com.lb
Owner: National Broadcasting Network, at above address. **URL:** http://www.nbn.com.lb.

47418 ■ NBN-TV Akroum - 29
Adnan El Hakim St., Jnah
Hala Bldg., Block A
Beirut, Lebanon
Ph: 961 1 841020
Fax: 961 1 841029
E-mail: flash@nbn.com.lb
Owner: National Broadcasting Network, at above address. **URL:** http://www.nbn.com.lb.

47419 ■ NBN-TV B.A. Haidar - 29
Adnan El Hakim St., Jnah
Hala Bldg., Block A
Beirut, Lebanon
Ph: 961 1 841020
Fax: 961 1 841029
E-mail: flash@nbn.com.lb
Owner: National Broadcasting Network, at above address. **URL:** http://www.nbn.com.lb.

47420 ■ NBN-TV Fatka - 63
Adnan El Hakim St., Jnah
Hala Bldg., Block A
Beirut, Lebanon
Ph: 961 1 841020
Fax: 961 1 841029
E-mail: flash@nbn.com.lb
Owner: National Broadcasting Network, at above address. **URL:** http://www.nbn.com.lb.

47421 ■ NBN-TV Keliat - 44
Adnan El Hakim St., Jnah
Hala Bldg., Block A
Beirut, Lebanon
Ph: 961 1 841020
Fax: 961 1 841029
E-mail: flash@nbn.com.lb
Owner: National Broadcasting Network, at above address. **URL:** http://www.nbn.com.lb.

47422 ■ NBN-TV Maad - 44
Adnan El Hakim St., Jnah
Hala Bldg., Block A
Beirut, Lebanon
Ph: 961 1 841020
Fax: 961 1 841029
E-mail: flash@nbn.com.lb
Owner: National Broadcasting Network, at above address. **URL:** http://www.nbn.com.lb.

47423 ■ NBN-TV Soltanieh - 29
Adnan El Hakim St., Jnah
Hala Bldg., Block A
Beirut, Lebanon
Ph: 961 1 841020
Fax: 961 1 841029
E-mail: flash@nbn.com.lb
Owner: National Broadcasting Network, at above address. **URL:** http://www.nbn.com.lb.

47424 ■ NBN-TV Turbo - 49
Adnan El Hakim St., Jnah
Hala Bldg., Block A
Beirut, Lebanon
Ph: 961 1 841020
Fax: 961 1 841029
E-mail: flash@nbn.com.lb
Owner: National Broadcasting Network, at above address. **URL:** http://www.nbn.com.lb.

Pax Radio - Beit Meri - See Beit Meri

47425 ■ Radio Orient - Beirut - 88.7 MHz
PO Box 13-60 52
Schouran
Beirut, Lebanon
Ph: 961 1 785004
Format: News; Sports; Adult Contemporary; Classical. **Owner:** Radio Orient, at above address. **Founded:** Feb. 1995. **Operating Hours:** Continuous. **Wattage:** 100,000. **Ad Rates:** Advertising accepted; rates available upon request. **URL:** http://www.futuretvnetwork.com/RO/radioorient-www/index.htm.

47426 ■ Radio Orient-FM - 88.7
PO Box 13-60 52
Beirut, Lebanon
Ph: 961 1 355355
Fax: 961 1 753232
E-mail: it@future-news.tv
Format: Sports; Urban Contemporary. **Owner:** Radio Orient, at above address. **Operating Hours:** Continuous. **Ad Rates:** Advertising accepted; rates available upon request. **URL:** http://www.futuretvnetwork.com.

47427 ■ Radio Orient-FM - 88.3
PO Box 13-6052
Sanayeh
Beirut, Lebanon
Ph: 961 1 370700
Format: Information; Ethnic; Sports; World Beat. **Owner:** Radio Orient, at above address. **Founded:** Feb. 1995. **Operating Hours:** Continuous. **Ad Rates:** Advertising accepted; rates available upon request. **URL:** http://www.futuretvnetwork.com.

Radio Orient - Jabal Tourbol - See Jabal Tourbol

Saout al Ghad - Deir al Achayer - See Deir al Achayer

Sawt El Ghad - Baalbek - See Baalbek

47428 ■ Sound of Music - Beirut - 106.5 MHz
Wadih Nassrallah Ctr., 7th Fl.
Anwar St.
Jdeideh
Beirut, Lebanon
Ph: 961 1 878819
E-mail: info@sawtelmousika.com
Format: Full Service. **Owner:** Sound of Music, at above address. **Founded:** Oct. 1998. **Operating Hours:** 0430-2400. **Wattage:** 25,000. **URL:** http://www.sawtelmousika.com.

47429 ■ TVMAX - 93
7th Fl., Block B, STARCO Ctr.
Beirut, Lebanon
Ph: 961 1 366066
Fax: 961 1 365292
E-mail: tvmax@orbit.net
URL: http://www.orbit.net.

47430 ■ TVMAX - 92
7th Fl., Block B, STARCO Ctr.
Beirut, Lebanon
Ph: 961 1 366066
Fax: 961 1 365292
E-mail: tvmax@orbit.net
URL: http://www.orbit.net.

47431 ■ TVMAX - 91
7th Fl., Block B, STARCO Ctr.
Beirut, Lebanon
Ph: 961 1 366066
Fax: 961 1 365292
E-mail: tvmax@orbit.net
URL: http://www.orbit.net.

47432 ■ TVMAX - 90
Sodeco Square St.
Beirut, Lebanon
Ph: 961 1 614066

Circulation: ★ = ABC; △ = BPA; ♦ = CAC; • = CCAB; ❑ = VAC; ⊕ = PO Statement; ‡ = Publisher's Report; Boldface figures = sworn; Light figures = estimated.

Gale Directory of Publications & Broadcast Media/147th Ed.   **5159**

Fax: 961 1 614062
E-mail: tvmax@orbit.net
Owner: Orbit Satellite Television and Radio Network, c/o Panther Media Group, PO Box 502211, Dubai Media City, Dubai, United Arab Emirates. **URL:** http://www. orbit.net.

47433 ■ Voice of the People-FM - 104
PO Box 145425
Beirut, Lebanon
Ph: 961 1 819014
Fax: 961 1 313605
Format: Ethnic; World Beat. **URL:** http://listen.to/shaab.

47434 ■ Voice of the People-FM - 103.7
PO Box 145425
Beirut, Lebanon
Ph: 961 1 819014
Fax: 961 1 313605
Format: Ethnic; World Beat. **URL:** http://listen.to/shaab.

Beit Meri

47435 ■ Pax Radio - Beit Meri - 103.1 MHz
6th Fl., Sea Sweet Bldg., Fouad Chehab Ave.
Beirut, Lebanon
Ph: 961 1 480077
Fax: 961 1 480077
E-mail: paxradio@hotmail.com
Owner: Pax Radio, at above address. **Operating Hours:** Continuous. **URL:** http://www.paxradio.com.

47436 ■ Radio Delta - Beit Meri - 102.0 MHz
Kahale Bldg., Old St.
PO Box 1306
Beit Meri el Metn, Lebanon
Ph: 961 4 972324
Fax: 961 4 870884
E-mail: info@radiodelta.com
Format: Full Service; Educational; Sports; News; Music of Your Life. **Owner:** Radio Delta, at above address. **Founded:** 1982. **Operating Hours:** 7:30 a.m.-4 p.m. **Key Personnel:** Robert Chamaa, Promotions Mgr., robert@radiodelta.com. **Wattage:** 50,000. **URL:** http://www.4com.net.lb/delta/; http://www.radiodelta.com/.

47437 ■ Radio Delta - Beit Meri - 101.7
Kahale Bldg., Old St.
PO Box 1306
Beit Meri el Metn, Lebanon
Ph: 961 4 972324
Fax: 961 4 870884
E-mail: info@radiodelta.com
Format: Full Service. **Owner:** Radio Delta, at above address. **Founded:** 1982. **Operating Hours:** Continuous. **Key Personnel:** Rony Njeim, General Mgr.; Robert Chamaa, Promotions Mgr., robert@radiodelta. com. **Wattage:** 50,000. **URL:** http://www.4com.net.lb/ delta/; http://www.radiodelta.com.

47438 ■ Radio Liban Libre - Beit Meri - 102.3 MHz
RLL Bldg., Adonis, Zouk Mosbeh
Zouk Mekhael
PO Box 110
Jounieh, Lebanon
Ph: 961 9 225577
Fax: 961 9 218235
E-mail: info@rll.com.lb
Format: Jazz. **Owner:** Free Lebanon for producing and broacasting, at above address. **Operating Hours:** Continuous. **Key Personnel:** Shawki Abou Sleiman, General Mgr. **Wattage:** 76,000. **URL:** http://www.rll.com. lb/.

Beit Meri el Metn

Radio Delta - Beit Meri - See Beit Meri

Radio Delta - Beit Meri - See Beit Meri

Radio Delta - Chouf - See Chouf

Radio Delta - Deir al Achayer - See Deir al Achayer

Radio Delta - Fatqa - See Fatqa

Radio Delta - Jabal Tourbol - See Jabal Tourbol

Radio Delta - Saida - See Saida

Radio Delta - Tarchich - See Tarchich

Radio Delta - Temnin al Fawka - See Temnin al Fawka

Radio Delta - Tripoli - See Tripoli

Radio Delta - Tyre - See Tyre

47439 ■ Radio One - 105.5
Zakhem Bldg., Ground Fl.
Beit Meri el Metn, Lebanon
Ph: 961 4 873333
E-mail: info@radioone.fm
Format: Adult Contemporary; Contemporary Hit Radio (CHR). **Owner:** Radio One, at above address. **Founded:** 1983. **Operating Hours:** Continuous. **Key Personnel:** Abdo Kahali, Station Mgr.; Raymond Gaspard, Chm./ CEO; Sarah Kreiker, Advertising Mgr. **Ad Rates:** Advertising accepted; rates available upon request. **URL:** http://www.radiooneglobal.com.

Beit Mery

47440 ■ NBN-TV - 63
Adnan El Hakim St., Jnah
Hala Bldg., Block A
Beirut, Lebanon
Ph: 961 1 841020
Fax: 961 1 841029
E-mail: flash@nbn.com.lb
Owner: National Broadcasting Network, at above address. **URL:** http://www.nbn.com.lb.

Chouf

47441 ■ Radio Delta - Chouf - 102.0 MHz
Kahale Bldg., Old St.
PO Box 1306
Beit Meri el Metn, Lebanon
Ph: 961 4 972324
Fax: 961 4 870884
E-mail: info@radiodelta.com
Format: Full Service; Educational; Sports; News; Music of Your Life. **Owner:** Radio Delta, at above address. **Operating Hours:** 7:30 a.m.-4 p.m. **Key Personnel:** Robert Chamaa, Promotions Mgr., robert@radiodelta. com. **URL:** http://www.4com.net.lb/delta/; http://www. radiodelta.com/.

Deir al Achayer

47442 ■ Radio Delta - Deir al Achayer - 102.0 MHz
Kahale Bldg., Old St.
PO Box 1306
Beit Meri el Metn, Lebanon
Ph: 961 4 972324
Fax: 961 4 870884
E-mail: info@radiodelta.com
Format: Full Service; Music of Your Life; News; Sports; Educational. **Owner:** Radio Delta, at above address. **Founded:** 1982. **Operating Hours:** 7:30 a.m.-4 p.m. **Key Personnel:** Robert Chamaa, Promotions Mgr., robert@radiodelta.com. **Wattage:** 25,000. **URL:** http:// www.4com.net.lb/delta/; http://www.radiodelta.com/.

47443 ■ Saout al Ghad - Deir al Achayer - 98.0 MHz
Zalka Main Rd.
PO Box 60073 Jal El Dib
Beirut, Lebanon
Ph: 961 4 721111
Fax: 961 4 721111
E-mail: info@sawtelghad.com
Format: Contemporary Hit Radio (CHR); News. **Owner:** Saout al Ghad, at above address. **Founded:** Sept. 10, 1997. **Key Personnel:** Mr. Wadih Abou Jaoude, General Mgr. **Wattage:** 84,000. **URL:** http://www.sawtelghad. com.

Faraya Mzaar

47444 ■ Radio Liban Libre - Faraya Mzaar - 102.7 MHz
RLL Bldg., Adonis, Zouk Mosbeh
Zouk Mekhael
PO Box 110
Jounieh, Lebanon
Ph: 961 9 225577
Fax: 961 9 218235
E-mail: info@rll.com.lb
Format: Jazz. **Owner:** Free Lebanon for producing and broacasting, at above address. **Operating Hours:** Continuous. **Key Personnel:** Chawki Abou Sleiman, General Mgr. **Wattage:** 50,000. **URL:** http://www.rll.com. lb.

Fatqa

47445 ■ Radio Delta - Fatqa - 101.7 MHz
Kahale Bldg., Old St.
PO Box 1306
Beit Meri el Metn, Lebanon
Ph: 961 4 972324
Fax: 961 4 870884
E-mail: info@radiodelta.com
Format: Full Service; Educational; Sports; News; Music of Your Life. **Owner:** Radio Delta, at above address. **Founded:** 1982. **Operating Hours:** 7:30 a.m.-4 p.m. **Key Personnel:** Robert Chamaa, Promotions Mgr., robert@radiodelta.com. **Wattage:** 1250. **URL:** http:// www.4com.net.lb/delta/; http://www.radiodelta.com/ profile.html.

Jabal Tourbol

47446 ■ Radio Delta - Jabal Tourbol - 102.0 MHz
Kahale Bldg., Old St.
PO Box 1306
Beit Meri el Metn, Lebanon
Ph: 961 4 972324
Fax: 961 4 870884
E-mail: info@radiodelta.com
Format: Full Service; Educational; News; Sports; Music of Your Life. **Owner:** Radio Delta, at above address. **Founded:** 1982. **Operating Hours:** 7:30 a.m.-4 p.m. **Key Personnel:** Robert Chamaa, Promotions Mgr., robert@radiodelta.com. **Wattage:** 10,000. **URL:** http:// www.4com.net.lb/delta/; http://www.radiodelta.com.

47447 ■ Radio Orient - Jabal Tourbol - 88.3 MHz
PO Box 13-60 52
Schouran
Beirut, Lebanon
Ph: 961 1 785004
Format: Eclectic. **Owner:** Radio Orient, at above address. **Wattage:** 200,000. **URL:** http://www. futuretvnetwork.com/RO/radioorient-www/profile.htm.

Jounieh

Radio Liban Libre - Beit Meri - See Beit Meri

Radio Liban Libre - Faraya Mzaar - See Faraya Mzaar

Metn

47448 ■ NRJ Beirut-FM - 99.0
Studiovision Bldg.
Naccache
Metn, Lebanon
Ph: 961 4 444000
Fax: 961 4 444149
Format: Contemporary Hit Radio (CHR); Blues. **URL:** http://www.nrjlebanon.com/.

47449 ■ NRJ-FM - 99
Studiovision Bldg.
Naccache
Metn, Lebanon
Ph: 961 4 444000
Fax: 961 4 444149
E-mail: info@nrjlebanon.com
Format: Contemporary Hit Radio (CHR); Ethnic. **Key Personnel:** Bernie Simmons, Contact; Dave Asher, Contact. **Ad Rates:** Advertising accepted; rates available upon request. **URL:** http://www.nrjlebanon.com.

Nabatieh

47450 ■ NBN-TV - 63
Adnan El Hakim St., Jnah
Hala Bldg., Block A
Beirut, Lebanon
Ph: 961 1 841020
Fax: 961 1 841029
E-mail: flash@nbn.com.lb
Owner: National Broadcasting Network, at above address. **URL:** http://www.nbn.com.lb.

Saida

47451 ■ Radio Delta - Saida - 101.9 MHz
Kahale Bldg., Old St.
PO Box 1306
Beit Meri el Metn, Lebanon
Ph: 961 4 972324

Fax: 961 4 870884
E-mail: info@radiodelta.com
Format: Full Service; Educational; Music of Your Life; News; Sports. **Owner:** Radio Delta, at above address. **Founded:** 1982. **Operating Hours:** 7.30 a.m. - 4 p.m. **Key Personnel:** Robert Chamaa, Promotions Mgr., robert@radiodelta.com. **Wattage:** 3500. **URL:** http://www.4com.net.lb/delta/; http://www.radiodelta.com/profile.html.

Tarchich

47452 ■ Radio Delta - Tarchich - 101.7 MHz
Kahale Bldg., Old St.
PO Box 1306
Beit Meri el Metn, Lebanon
Ph: 961 4 972324
Fax: 961 4 870884
E-mail: info@radiodelta.com
Format: Full Service; Educational; Sports; News; Music of Your Life. **Owner:** Radio Delta, at above address. **Founded:** 1982. **Operating Hours:** 7:30 a.m.-4 p.m. **Key Personnel:** Robert Chamaa, Promotions Mgr., robert@radiodelta.com. **Wattage:** 10,000. **URL:** http://www.radiodelta.com.

Temnin al Fawka

47453 ■ Radio Delta - Temnin al Fawka - 102.0

Kahale Bldg., Old St.
PO Box 1306
Beit Meri el Metn, Lebanon
Ph: 961 4 972324
Fax: 961 4 870884
E-mail: deltafm@inco.com.lb; info@radiodelta.com
Format: Full Service. **Owner:** Radio Delta, at above address. **Founded:** 1982. **Operating Hours:** Continuous. **Key Personnel:** Rony Njcim, General Mgr. **Wattage:** 10,000. **URL:** http://www.4com.net.lb/delta/; http://www.radiodelta.com.

Tripoli

47454 ■ Radio Delta - Tripoli - 101.7 MHz
Kahale Bldg., Old St.
PO Box 1306
Beit Meri el Metn, Lebanon
Ph: 961 4 972324
Fax: 961 4 870884
E-mail: info@radiodelta.com
Format: Full Service; Music of Your Life; Sports; News; Educational. **Owner:** Radio Delta, at above address. **Founded:** 1982. **Operating Hours:** 7:30 a.m.-4 p.m. **Key Personnel:** Robert Chamaa, Promotions Mgr., robert@radiodelta.com. **URL:** http://www.4com.net.lb/delta/; http://www.radiodelta.com/profile.html.

Tyre

47455 ■ Radio Delta - Tyre - 102.0 MHz
Kahale Bldg., Old St.
PO Box 1306
Beit Meri el Metn, Lebanon
Ph: 961 4 972324
Fax: 961 4 870884
E-mail: info@radiodelta.com
Format: Full Service; Music of Your Life; News; Sports; Educational. **Owner:** Radio Delta, at above address. **Founded:** 1982. **Operating Hours:** 7:30 a.m.-4 p.m. **Key Personnel:** Robert Chamaa, Promotions Mgr., robert@radiodelta.com. **URL:** http://www.4com.net.lb/delta/; http://www.radiodelta.com.

Zahle

47456 ■ NBN-TV - 44
Adnan El Hakim St., Jnah
Hala Bldg., Block A
Beirut, Lebanon
Ph: 961 1 841020
Fax: 961 1 841029
E-mail: flash@nbn.com.lb
Owner: National Broadcasting Network, at above address. **URL:** http://www.nbn.com.lb.

Circulation: ★ = ABC; △ = BPA; ◆ = CAC; • = CCAB; ❑ = VAC; ⊕ = PO Statement; ‡ = Publisher's Report; Boldface figures = sworn; Light figures = estimated.

Gale Directory of Publications & Broadcast Media/147th Ed.   5161

Maseru

47457 ■ PC-FM - 95.6
LNDC Center
Development House-Level 9
Maseru 100, Lesotho

Ph: 266 22 322122
Fax: 266 22 310888
Format: News; Talk; Information; Ethnic; New Age.
Owner: People's Choice Radio Station, at above
address. **Founded:** 1998. **Operating Hours:**

Continuous. **Key Personnel:** Khauta Mpeqa, Contact,
phone 266 223 22122, mkhauta@pcfm.co.ls; Kholu
Mamohato Qhobela, Station Mgr., kmqhobela@pcfm.co.
ls. **Ad Rates:** Advertising accepted; rates available upon
request. **URL:** http://www.pcfm.co.ls.

Zliten

47458 ■ Libyan Journal of Medicine
African Journals Online
PO Box 446

Zliten, Libyan Arab Jamahiriya
Publisher E-mail: info@ajol.info
Peer-reviewed journal covering medical education and health related issues. **Freq:** Quarterly. **Key Personnel:** Dr. Omran Bakoush, PhD, General Mgr., omran.

bakoush@med.lu.se; Mohamed Daw, Editor-in-Chief; Elhadi Aburawi, Editor; Elmahdi Elkhammas, MD, Dep. Ed.; Hani Benamer, Editor; Amin Bredan, Editor. **ISSN:** 1819-6357. **URL:** http://ajol.info/index.php/ljm.

Circulation: ★ = ABC; △ = BPA; ♦ = CAC; • = CCAB; ❑ = VAC; ⊕ = PO Statement; ‡ = Publisher's Report; Boldface figures = sworn; Light figures = estimated.

Gale Directory of Publications & Broadcast Media/147th Ed.

5165

Alytus

47459 ■ 99-FM - 99
Rotuses a. 2
62141 Alytus, Lithuania
Ph: 370 315 76120
Fax: 370 315 74646
E-mail: fm99@fm99.lt
Format: Ethnic; World Beat. **Operating Hours:** 18 hours Daily. **Ad Rates:** Advertising accepted; rates available upon request. **URL:** http://www.fm99.lt.

47460 ■ Ziniu radijas-FM - 95.3
Liberty Ave., 60
05120 Vilnius, Lithuania
Ph: 370 5 2431430
Fax: 370 5 2431433
Format: News. **Owner:** Ziniu radijas, at above address. **Founded:** Mar. 7, 2000. **URL:** http://www.ziniur.lt/.

Birzai

47461 ■ Ziniu radijas-FM - 96.0
Liberty Ave., 60
05120 Vilnius, Lithuania
Ph: 370 5 2431430
Fax: 370 5 2431433
Format: News. **Owner:** Ziniu radijas, at above address. **Founded:** Mar. 7, 2000. **URL:** http://www.ziniur.lt/.

Druskininkai

47462 ■ Ziniu radijas-FM - 100.0
Liberty Ave., 60
05120 Vilnius, Lithuania
Ph: 370 5 2431430
Fax: 370 5 2431433
Format: News. **Owner:** Ziniu radijas, at above address. **Founded:** Mar. 7, 2000. **URL:** http://www.ziniur.lt/.

Ignalina

47463 ■ Ziniu radijas-FM - 95.4
Liberty Ave., 60
05120 Vilnius, Lithuania
Ph: 370 5 2431430
Fax: 370 5 2431433
Format: News. **Owner:** Ziniu radijas, at above address. **Founded:** Mar. 7, 2000. **URL:** http://www.ziniur.lt/.

Kaunas

47464 ■ Caritas
Caritas Lithuania
Aukstaiciu 10
LT-44147 Kaunas, Lithuania
Ph: 370 37 205427
Fax: 370 37 205549
Publisher E-mail: caritas@lcn.lt
Publication covering Catholicism. **Freq:** Monthly. **ISSN:** 0236-2716. **Remarks:** Advertising accepted; rates available upon request. **URL:** http://www.caritas-europa.org/code/en/default.asp; http://www.periodicals.ru/import/good.phtml?id=347493&set_usr_lang=eng. **Circ:** 6,000

47465 ■ Medicina
Kaunas University of Medicine
Mickeviciaus 9
44307 Kaunas, Lithuania
Ph: 370 37 327201
Fax: 370 37 220733
Publication E-mail: medicina@med.kmu.lt
Publisher E-mail: rektoratas@kmu.lt
Peer-reviewed journal disseminating information to physicians from diverse backgrounds. **Founded:** 1920. **Freq:** Monthly. **Key Personnel:** Prof. Vilius Grabauskas, Editor-in-Chief. **ISSN:** 1010-660X. **Subscription Rates:** US$120 individuals; EUR80 individuals Europe; US$60 individuals 6 months; EUR40 individuals Europe, 6 months; US$30 individuals 3 months; EUR20 individuals Europe, 3 months. **URL:** http://medicina.kmu.lt/main-e.htm.

47466 ■ Seminars in Cardiology
Lithuanian Society of Cardiology
Eiveniu 2
LT-50009 Kaunas, Lithuania
Ph: 370 37 326449
Fax: 370 37 331395
Publisher E-mail: litcardio@gmail.com
Journal published jointly with the Lithuanian Heart Association. **Freq:** Quarterly. **Key Personnel:** Aleksandras Laucevicius, Editor-in-Chief; Margus Virgimaa, Assoc. Ed.; Andrejs Ergis, Assoc. Ed. **URL:** http://www.seminarsincardiology.com/archive-issues.php.

47467 ■ Gaudeamus-FM - 93.6
Gedimino g. 43 - 214
44240 Kaunas, Lithuania
E-mail: gaudeamus@ktu.lt
Format: Jazz. **Owner:** Kaunas University of Technology, at above address. **Key Personnel:** Giedrius Kuprevicius, Hd. **URL:** http://www.gaudeamus.fm/.

47468 ■ Geras-FM - 92
Gariunai St., 71
02300 Vilnius, Lithuania
Format: Classic Rock. **Owner:** UAB Geruda, at above address. **Key Personnel:** Evaldas Griskevicius, Director. **URL:** http://www.gerasfm.lt/.

47469 ■ KF-FM - 105.4
Savanoriu pr. 192-802
3000 Kaunas, Lithuania
Ph: 370 837 327427
Fax: 370 837 327447
E-mail: info@kf.lt
Format: Adult Contemporary. **Operating Hours:** Continuous. **Ad Rates:** Advertising accepted; rates available upon request. **URL:** http://www.kf.lt/?id=8.

47470 ■ Marijos Radijas-FM - 93.1 MHz
M.Dauksos g. 21/ V. Sladkeviciaus 1
44282 Kaunas, Lithuania
Ph: 370 37 377160
E-mail: direktorius@marijosradijas.lt
Format: Religious. **URL:** http://www.marijosradijas.lt.

47471 ■ Radijo Stotis Tau-FM - 102.9
Draugystes g. 19 - 357
51230 Kaunas, Lithuania
Ph: 370 837 352790
Fax: 370 837 352128
E-mail: info@tau.lt
Format: Ethnic; World Beat. **Operating Hours:** Continuous. **URL:** http://www.tau.lt.

47472 ■ Ziniu radijas-FM - 104.9
Liberty Ave., 60
05120 Vilnius, Lithuania
Ph: 370 5 2431430
Fax: 370 5 2431433
Format: News. **Owner:** Ziniu radijas, at above address. **Founded:** Mar. 7, 2000. **URL:** http://www.ziniur.lt/.

Klaipeda

47473 ■ Ziniu radijas-FM - 102.2
Liberty Ave., 60
05120 Vilnius, Lithuania
Ph: 370 5 2431430
Fax: 370 5 2431433
Format: News. **Owner:** Ziniu radijas, at above address. **Founded:** Mar. 7, 2000. **URL:** http://www.ziniur.lt/.

Marijampole

47474 ■ Ziniu radijas-FM - 93.4
Liberty Ave., 60
05120 Vilnius, Lithuania
Ph: 370 5 2431430
Fax: 370 5 2431433
Format: News. **Owner:** Ziniu radijas, at above address. **Founded:** Mar. 7, 2000. **URL:** http://www.ziniur.lt/.

Mazeikiai

47475 ■ Ziniu radijas-FM - 96.4
Liberty Ave., 60
05120 Vilnius, Lithuania
Ph: 370 5 2431430
Fax: 370 5 2431433
Format: News. **Owner:** Ziniu radijas, at above address. **Founded:** Mar. 7, 2000. **URL:** http://www.ziniur.lt/.

Panevezys

47476 ■ Ziniu radijas-FM - 107.9
Liberty Ave., 60
05120 Vilnius, Lithuania
Ph: 370 5 2431430
Fax: 370 5 2431433
Format: News. **Owner:** Ziniu radijas, at above address. **Founded:** Mar. 7, 2000. **URL:** http://www.ziniur.lt/.

Siauliai

47477 ■ Ziniu radijas-FM - 97.0
Liberty Ave., 60
05120 Vilnius, Lithuania
Ph: 370 5 2431430
Fax: 370 5 2431433
Format: News. **Owner:** Ziniu radijas, at above address. **Founded:** Mar. 7, 2000. **URL:** http://www.ziniur.lt/.

Taurage

47478 ■ Ziniu radijas-FM - 104.8
Liberty Ave., 60
05120 Vilnius, Lithuania
Ph: 370 5 2431430
Fax: 370 5 2431433
Format: News. **Owner:** Ziniu radijas, at above address.
Founded: Mar. 7, 2000. **URL:** http://www.ziniur.lt/.

Telsiai

47479 ■ Ziniu radijas-FM - 94.1
Liberty Ave., 60
05120 Vilnius, Lithuania
Ph: 370 5 2431430
Fax: 370 5 2431433
Format: News. **Owner:** Ziniu radijas, at above address.
Founded: Mar. 7, 2000. **URL:** http://www.ziniur.lt/.

Ukmerge

47480 ■ Ziniu radijas-FM - 100.6
Liberty Ave., 60
05120 Vilnius, Lithuania
Ph: 370 5 2431430
Fax: 370 5 2431433
Format: News. **Owner:** Ziniu radijas, at above address.
Founded: Mar. 7, 2000. **URL:** http://www.ziniur.lt/.

Utena

47481 ■ Ziniu radijas-FM - 92.3
Liberty Ave., 60
05120 Vilnius, Lithuania
Ph: 370 5 2431430
Fax: 370 5 2431433
Format: News. **Owner:** Ziniu radijas, at above address.
Founded: Mar. 7, 2000. **URL:** http://www.ziniur.lt/.

Vilnius

47482 ■ Lithuanian Journal of Physics
Lithuanian Physical Society
A. Gostauto 12
LT-2600 Vilnius, Lithuania
Ph: 37 526 20668
Fax: 37 521 25361
Publisher E-mail: lfd@itpa.lt
Scientific peer-reviewed journal covering physics. **Freq:**
Bimonthly. **ISSN:** 1392-1932. **URL:** http://www.itpa.lt/
LFD/Lfz/LFZ.html.

47483 ■ Geras-FM - 101.9
Gariunai St., 71
02300 Vilnius, Lithuania
Ph: 370 8 61117282
Format: Classic Rock. **Owner:** UAB Geruda, at above
address. **Key Personnel:** Evaldas Griskevicius, Director.
URL: http://www.gerasfm.lt/.

Geras-FM - See Kaunas

47484 ■ START-FM - 94.2
PO Box 1211
Vilnius, Lithuania
Ph: 370 5 2696933
E-mail: info@startfm.lt
Format: Easy Listening. **Owner:** START-FM, at above
address. **Founded:** Sept. 2005. **URL:** http://www.
startfm.lt/.

47485 ■ Ziniu radijas-FM - 97.3

Liberty Ave., 60
05120 Vilnius, Lithuania
Ph: 370 5 2431430
Fax: 370 5 2431433
Format: News. **Owner:** Ziniu radijas, at above address.
Founded: Mar. 7, 2000. **URL:** http://www.ziniur.lt/.

Ziniu radijas-FM - See Alytus
Ziniu radijas-FM - See Birzai
Ziniu radijas-FM - See Druskininkai
Ziniu radijas-FM - See Ignalina
Ziniu radijas-FM - See Kaunas
Ziniu radijas-FM - See Klaipeda
Ziniu radijas-FM - See Marijampole
Ziniu radijas-FM - See Mazeikiai
Ziniu radijas-FM - See Panevezys
Ziniu radijas-FM - See Siauliai
Ziniu radijas-FM - See Taurage
Ziniu radijas-FM - See Telsiai
Ziniu radijas-FM - See Ukmerge
Ziniu radijas-FM - See Utena
Ziniu radijas-FM - See Visaginas

Visaginas

47486 ■ Ziniu radijas-FM - 103.7
Liberty Ave., 60
05120 Vilnius, Lithuania
Ph: 370 5 2431430
Fax: 370 5 2431433
Format: News. **Owner:** Ziniu radijas, at above address.
Founded: Mar. 7, 2000. **URL:** http://www.ziniur.lt/.

Bettembourg

47487 ■ Radio LRB-FM - 103.9
Boite postale 8
L-3201 Bettembourg, Luxembourg
Ph: 352 524 48822
Fax: 352 524 48899
E-mail: info@radiolrb.lu
Format: World Beat. **Owner:** Radio Mania, at above address. **Operating Hours:** Continuous. **URL:** http://www.lrb.lu.

Capellen

47488 ■ AGEFI Luxembourg
111b Rte. d'Arlon
L-8311 Capellen, Luxembourg
Ph: 352 305 7571
Publisher E-mail: agefi@agefi.lu
Economic and financial newspaper. **Founded:** 1988.
Print Method: Offset. **Cols./Page:** 4. **Col. Width:** 67.5 millimeters. **Col. Depth:** 440 millimeters. **Key Personnel:** Christophe Labrique, Contact, publicite@agefi.lu; Adelin Remy, Contact; Francois Bodart, Contact; Olivier Minguet, Contact, ominguet@agefi.lu. **ISSN:** 1561-8366. **URL:** http://www.agefi.lu. **Circ:** Combined 24,000.

Gasperich

47489 ■ EldoRadio-FM - 107.2
47, Muehlenweg
L-2155 Gasperich, Luxembourg
Ph: 352 409 5091
Fax: 352 409 509609
E-mail: eldoradio@eldoradio.lu
Format: Top 40; Eighties; Contemporary Hit Radio (CHR); Ethnic. **Operating Hours:** Continuous. **Ad Rates:** Advertising accepted; rates available upon request. **URL:** http://www.eldoradio.lu.

47490 ■ EldoRadio-FM - 105
47, Muehlenweg
L-2155 Gasperich, Luxembourg
Ph: 352 409 5091
Fax: 352 409 509509
E-mail: eldoradio@eldoradio.lu
Format: Contemporary Hit Radio (CHR); Ethnic; Eighties. **Operating Hours:** Continuous. **Ad Rates:** Advertising accepted; rates available upon request. **URL:** http://www.eldoradio.lu.

Luxembourg

47491 ■ De Letzeburger Merkur
Chamber of Commerce of the Grand-Duchy of Luxembourg
7, Rue Alcide de Gasperi
Kirchberg
L-2981 Luxembourg, Luxembourg
Ph: 35 242 39391
Fax: 35 243 8326
Publisher E-mail: chamcom@cc.lu
Newspaper of the Chamber of Commerce in Luxembourg. **Remarks:** Accepts advertising. **URL:** http://www.cc.lu. **Ad Rates:** 4C: 1,350 LFr. **Circ:** Non-paid ‡24,300

47492 ■ Journal du Diabetique
Association Luxembourgeoise du Diabete
143, rue de Muhlenbach
L-2168 Luxembourg, Luxembourg
Ph: 352 485361
Fax: 352 26123748
Publisher E-mail: diabete@pt.lu
French and German language publication covering diabetes. **Freq:** Monthly. **Key Personnel:** Prof. T. Haak, Editor-in-Chief, haak@kirchheim-verlag.de. **ISSN:** 0341-8812. **Subscription Rates:** Included in membership; EUR39 individuals; 74.40 SFr individuals. **Remarks:** Advertising accepted; rates available upon request. **URL:** http://www.ald.lu; http://www.diabetes-journal.de. **Circ:** 800

47493 ■ Sew-Journal
Union of Science and Education
Syndicat Education et Sciences
1, rue Jean-Pierre Sauvage
Kirchberg
L-2514 Luxembourg, Luxembourg
Ph: 352 26096969
Fax: 352 26096969
Publisher E-mail: sew@ogbl.lu
Journal covering education, in German and French. **Freq:** Bimonthly. **Key Personnel:** Monique Adam, President, monique.adam@education.lu; Bach Christiane, Contact; Burg Martine, Contact; Derefa Rosy, Contact; Arendt Patrick, Contact; Christophe Diane, Contact. **Remarks:** Advertising accepted; rates available upon request. **URL:** http://www.sew.lu/cgi-bin/olefa?com=0O0O0O4O1O4O0O784528155O22697O00. **Circ:** (Not Reported)

47494 ■ ARA City Radio-FM - 103.3
2 rue de la Boucherie
L-1247 Luxembourg, Luxembourg
Ph: 352 26203040
E-mail: aracity@pt.lustudio; studio@aracityradio.com
Format: Eclectic. **Ad Rates:** Advertising accepted; rates available upon request. **URL:** http://www.aracityradio.com/.

47495 ■ ARA City Radio-FM - 105.2
2 rue de la Boucherie
L-1247 Luxembourg, Luxembourg
Ph: 352 26203040
E-mail: aracity@pt.lustudio; studio@aracityradio.com
Format: Eclectic. **Ad Rates:** Advertising accepted; rates available upon request. **URL:** http://www.aracityradio.com/.

47496 ■ Den Neien Radio-FM - 107.7
2, Rue Christophe Plantin
L-2339 Luxembourg, Luxembourg
Ph: 352 402401
Fax: 352 407998
E-mail: dnr@dnr.lu
Format: News; Contemporary Hit Radio (CHR); Ethnic; Sports. **Operating Hours:** 18 hours Daily. **Ad Rates:** Advertising accepted; rates available upon request. **URL:** http://www.dnr.lu.

47497 ■ Den Neien Radio-FM - 102.9
2, Rue Christophe Plantin
L-2339 Luxembourg, Luxembourg
Ph: 352 402401
Fax: 352 407998
E-mail: dnr@dnr.lu
Format: News; Contemporary Hit Radio (CHR); Sports; Ethnic. **Operating Hours:** Continuous. **Key Personnel:** Virginie Hanne, Contact; Myriam Colles, Contact. **Ad Rates:** Advertising accepted; rates available upon request. **URL:** http://www.dnr.lu.

47498 ■ Den Neien Radio-FM - 104.2
2, Rue Christophe Plantin
L-2339 Luxembourg, Luxembourg
Ph: 352 402401
Fax: 352 407998
E-mail: dnr@dnr.lu
Format: News; Contemporary Hit Radio (CHR); Ethnic; Sports. **Operating Hours:** Continuous. **Key Personnel:** Virginie Hanne, Contact; Myriam Colles, Contact. **Ad Rates:** Advertising accepted; rates available upon request. **URL:** http://www.dnr.lu.

47499 ■ Honnert-FM - 100.7
45a, av. Monterey
L-2163 Luxembourg, Luxembourg
Ph: 352 4400441
Format: Eclectic. **URL:** http://www.100komma7.lu.

Luxembourg-Gasperich

47500 ■ EldoRadio-FM - 105
45, Blvd. Pierre Frieden
L-1543 Luxembourg-Gasperich, Luxembourg
Ph: 352 4095091
Fax: 352 409509509
Format: Contemporary Hit Radio (CHR); Ethnic; Eighties. **Operating Hours:** Continuous. **Ad Rates:** Advertising accepted; rates available upon request. **URL:** http://www.eldoradio.lu.

Circulation: ★ = ABC; △ = BPA; ◆ = CAC; • = CCAB; ❏ = VAC; ⊕ = PO Statement; ‡ = Publisher's Report; Boldface figures = sworn; Light figures = estimated.

Gale Directory of Publications & Broadcast Media/147th Ed.

5169

Berovo

47501 ■ Antenna5 - Berovo - 97.9
Tetovska 35
91000 Skopje, Macedonia
Ph: 389 2 3111911
Format: Contemporary Hit Radio (CHR). **Owner:** Antenna5, at above address. **Key Personnel:** Zoran Petrov, Gen. Mgr./Music Ed. **URL:** http://www.antenna5.com.mk/about.aspxBroadcast.

Bitola

47502 ■ Antenna5 - Bitola - 93.9
Tetovska 35
91000 Skopje, Macedonia
Ph: 389 2 3111911
Format: Contemporary Hit Radio (CHR). **Owner:** Antenna5, at above address. **Key Personnel:** Zoran Petrov, Gen. Mgr./Music Ed. **URL:** http://www.antenna5.com.mk/about.aspxBroadcast.

47503 ■ Antenna5 - Bitola - 92.9
Tetovska 35
91000 Skopje, Macedonia
Ph: 389 2 3111911
Format: Contemporary Hit Radio (CHR). **Owner:** Antenna5, at above address. **Key Personnel:** Zoran Petrov, Gen. Mgr./Music Ed. **URL:** http://www.antenna5.com.mk/about.aspxBroadcast.

47504 ■ Radio-FM - 106.6
Krushevska 6 G
7000 Bitola, Macedonia
Ph: 389 47228106
Fax: 389 47203605
E-mail: 106radio@gmail.com
Format: Alternative/New Music/Progressive; Classical. **Operating Hours:** Continuous. **Key Personnel:** Kire Hristovski, General Mgr.; Marijan Hristovski, Mktg. Mgr.; Milan Hizvanovic, Editor-in-Chief; Zoran Mishevski, Commentator and Journalist. **Ad Rates:** Advertising accepted; rates available upon request. **URL:** http://www.106.com.mk.

Bogdanci

47505 ■ Antenna5 - Bogdanci - 89.2
Tetovska 35
91000 Skopje, Macedonia
Ph: 389 2 3111911
Format: Contemporary Hit Radio (CHR). **Owner:** Antenna5, at above address. **Key Personnel:** Zoran Petrov, Gen. Mgr./Music Ed. **URL:** http://www.antenna5.com.mk/about.aspxBroadcast.

47506 ■ Antenna5 - Bogdanci - 106.3
Tetovska 35
91000 Skopje, Macedonia
Ph: 389 2 3111911
Format: Contemporary Hit Radio (CHR). **Owner:** Antenna5, at above address. **Key Personnel:** Zoran Petrov, Gen. Mgr./Music Ed. **URL:** http://www.antenna5.com.mk/about.aspxBroadcast.

Delcevo

47507 ■ Antenna5 - Delcevo - 97.90
Tetovska 35
91000 Skopje, Macedonia
Ph: 389 2 3111911
Format: Contemporary Hit Radio (CHR). **Owner:** Antenna5, at above address. **Key Personnel:** Zoran Petrov, Gen. Mgr./Music Ed. **URL:** http://www.antenna5.com.mk/about.aspxBroadcast.

Demir Kapija

47508 ■ Antenna5 - Demir Kapija - 91.9
Tetovska 35
91000 Skopje, Macedonia
Ph: 389 2 3111911
Format: Contemporary Hit Radio (CHR). **Owner:** Antenna5, at above address. **Key Personnel:** Zoran Petrov, Gen. Mgr./Music Ed. **URL:** http://www.antenna5.com.mk/about.aspxBroadcast.

47509 ■ Antenna5 - Demir Kapija - 88.8
Tetovska 35
91000 Skopje, Macedonia
Ph: 389 2 3111911
Format: Contemporary Hit Radio (CHR). **Owner:** Antenna5, at above address. **Key Personnel:** Zoran Petrov, Gen. Mgr./Music Ed. **URL:** http://www.antenna5.com.mk/about.aspxBroadcast.

47510 ■ Antenna5 - Demir Kapija - 104.2
Tetovska 35
91000 Skopje, Macedonia
Ph: 389 2 3111911
Format: Contemporary Hit Radio (CHR). **Owner:** Antenna5, at above address. **Key Personnel:** Zoran Petrov, Gen. Mgr./Music Ed. **URL:** http://www.antenna5.com.mk/about.aspxBroadcast.

Dojran

47511 ■ Antenna5 - Dojran - 106.3
Tetovska 35
91000 Skopje, Macedonia
Ph: 389 2 3111911
Format: Contemporary Hit Radio (CHR). **Owner:** Antenna5, at above address. **Key Personnel:** Zoran Petrov, Gen. Mgr./Music Ed. **URL:** http://www.antenna5.com.mk/about.aspxBroadcast.

Dusegubica

47512 ■ Antenna5 - Dusegubica - 103.3
Tetovska 35
91000 Skopje, Macedonia
Ph: 389 2 3111911
Format: Contemporary Hit Radio (CHR). **Owner:** Antenna5, at above address. **Key Personnel:** Zoran Petrov, Gen. Mgr./Music Ed. **URL:** http://www.antenna5.com.mk/about.aspxBroadcast.

Galicnik

47513 ■ Antenna5 - Galicnik - 92.9
Tetovska 35

91000 Skopje, Macedonia
Ph: 389 2 3111911
Format: Contemporary Hit Radio (CHR). **Owner:** Antenna5, at above address. **Key Personnel:** Zoran Petrov, Gen. Mgr./Music Ed. **URL:** http://www.antenna5.com.mk/about.aspxBroadcast.

Gevgelija

47514 ■ Antenna5 - Gevgelija - 89.2
Tetovska 35
91000 Skopje, Macedonia
Ph: 389 2 3111911
Format: Contemporary Hit Radio (CHR). **Owner:** Antenna5, at above address. **Key Personnel:** Zoran Petrov, Gen. Mgr./Music Ed. **URL:** http://www.antenna5.com.mk/about.aspxBroadcast.

47515 ■ Antenna5 - Gevgelija - 106.3
Tetovska 35
91000 Skopje, Macedonia
Ph: 389 2 3111911
Format: Contemporary Hit Radio (CHR). **Owner:** Antenna5, at above address. **Key Personnel:** Zoran Petrov, Gen. Mgr./Music Ed. **URL:** http://www.antenna5.com.mk/about.aspxBroadcast.

Gostivar

47516 ■ Antenna5 - Gostivar - 106.9
Tetovska 35
91000 Skopje, Macedonia
Ph: 389 2 3111911
Format: Contemporary Hit Radio (CHR). **Owner:** Antenna5, at above address. **Key Personnel:** Zoran Petrov, Gen. Mgr./Music Ed. **URL:** http://www.antenna5.com.mk/about.aspxBroadcast.

47517 ■ Antenna5 - Gostivar - 105.5
Tetovska 35
91000 Skopje, Macedonia
Ph: 389 2 3111911
Format: Contemporary Hit Radio (CHR). **Owner:** Antenna5, at above address. **Key Personnel:** Zoran Petrov, Gen. Mgr./Music Ed. **URL:** http://www.antenna5.com.mk/about.aspxBroadcast.

Kavadarci

47518 ■ Antenna5 - Kavadarci - 91.9
Tetovska 35
91000 Skopje, Macedonia
Ph: 389 2 3111911
Format: Contemporary Hit Radio (CHR). **Owner:** Antenna5, at above address. **Key Personnel:** Zoran Petrov, Gen. Mgr./Music Ed. **URL:** http://www.antenna5.com.mk/about.aspxBroadcast.

47519 ■ Antenna5 - Kavadarci - 104.2
Tetovska 35
91000 Skopje, Macedonia
Ph: 389 2 3111911
Format: Contemporary Hit Radio (CHR). **Owner:** Antenna5, at above address. **Key Personnel:** Zoran Petrov, Gen. Mgr./Music Ed. **URL:** http://www.antenna5.com.mk/about.aspxBroadcast.

Kicevo

47520 ■ Antenna5 - Kicevo - 95.5
Tetovska 35
91000 Skopje, Macedonia
Ph: 389 2 3111911
Format: Contemporary Hit Radio (CHR). **Owner:** Antenna5, at above address. **Key Personnel:** Zoran Petrov, Gen. Mgr./Music Ed. **URL:** http://www.antenna5.com.mk/about.aspxBroadcast.

Kocani

47521 ■ Antenna5 - Kocani - 97.9
Tetovska 35
91000 Skopje, Macedonia
Ph: 389 2 3111911
Format: Contemporary Hit Radio (CHR). **Owner:** Antenna5, at above address. **Key Personnel:** Zoran Petrov, Gen. Mgr./Music Ed. **URL:** http://www.antenna5.com.mk/about.aspxBroadcast.

47522 ■ Antenna5 - Kocani - 104.8
Tetovska 35
91000 Skopje, Macedonia
Ph: 389 2 3111911
Format: Contemporary Hit Radio (CHR). **Owner:** Antenna5, at above address. **Key Personnel:** Zoran Petrov, Gen. Mgr./Music Ed. **URL:** http://www.antenna5.com.mk/about.aspxBroadcast.

Kratovo

47523 ■ Antenna5 - Kratovo - 106.9
Tetovska 35
91000 Skopje, Macedonia
Ph: 389 2 3111911
Format: Contemporary Hit Radio (CHR). **Owner:** Antenna5, at above address. **Key Personnel:** Zoran Petrov, Gen. Mgr./Music Ed. **URL:** http://www.antenna5.com.mk/about.aspxBroadcast.

47524 ■ Antenna5 - Kratovo - 105.5
Tetovska 35
91000 Skopje, Macedonia
Ph: 389 2 3111911
Format: Contemporary Hit Radio (CHR). **Owner:** Antenna5, at above address. **Key Personnel:** Zoran Petrov, Gen. Mgr./Music Ed. **URL:** http://www.antenna5.com.mk/about.aspxBroadcast.

Kriva Palanka

47525 ■ Antenna5 - Kriva Palanka - 95.5
Tetovska 35
91000 Skopje, Macedonia
Ph: 389 2 3111911
Format: Contemporary Hit Radio (CHR). **Owner:** Antenna5, at above address. **Key Personnel:** Zoran Petrov, Gen. Mgr./Music Ed. **URL:** http://www.antenna5.com.mk/about.aspxBroadcast.

47526 ■ Antenna5 - Kriva Palanka - 105.5
Tetovska 35
91000 Skopje, Macedonia
Ph: 389 2 3111911
Format: Contemporary Hit Radio (CHR). **Owner:** Antenna5, at above address. **Key Personnel:** Zoran Petrov, Gen. Mgr./Music Ed. **URL:** http://www.antenna5.com.mk/about.aspxBroadcast.

Krusevo

47527 ■ Antenna5 - Krusevo - 92.9
Tetovska 35
91000 Skopje, Macedonia
Ph: 389 2 3111911
Format: Contemporary Hit Radio (CHR). **Owner:** Antenna5, at above address. **Key Personnel:** Zoran Petrov, Gen. Mgr./Music Ed. **URL:** http://www.antenna5.com.mk/about.aspxBroadcast.

Kumanovo

47528 ■ Antenna5 - Kumanovo - 106.9
Tetovska 35
91000 Skopje, Macedonia
Ph: 389 2 3111911
Format: Contemporary Hit Radio (CHR). **Owner:** Antenna5, at above address. **Key Personnel:** Zoran Petrov, Gen. Mgr./Music Ed. **URL:** http://www.antenna5.com.mk/about.aspxBroadcast.

47529 ■ Antenna5 - Kumanovo - 106.3
Tetovska 35
91000 Skopje, Macedonia
Ph: 389 2 3111911
Format: Contemporary Hit Radio (CHR). **Owner:** Antenna5, at above address. **Key Personnel:** Zoran Petrov, Gen. Mgr./Music Ed. **URL:** http://www.antenna5.com.mk/about.aspxBroadcast.

47530 ■ Antenna5 - Kumanovo - 104.8
Tetovska 35
91000 Skopje, Macedonia
Ph: 389 2 3111911
Format: Contemporary Hit Radio (CHR). **Owner:** Antenna5, at above address. **Key Personnel:** Zoran Petrov, Gen. Mgr./Music Ed. **URL:** http://www.antenna5.com.mk/about.aspxBroadcast.

M. Radobil

47531 ■ Antenna5 - M. Radobil - 97.9
Tetovska 35
91000 Skopje, Macedonia
Ph: 389 2 3111911
Format: Contemporary Hit Radio (CHR). **Owner:** Antenna5, at above address. **Key Personnel:** Zoran Petrov, Gen. Mgr./Music Ed. **URL:** http://www.antenna5.com.mk/about.aspxBroadcast.

Makedonska Kamenica

47532 ■ Antenna5 - Makedonska Kamenica - 97.90
Tetovska 35
91000 Skopje, Macedonia
Ph: 389 2 3111911
Format: Contemporary Hit Radio (CHR). **Owner:** Antenna5, at above address. **Key Personnel:** Zoran Petrov, Gen. Mgr./Music Ed. **URL:** http://www.antenna5.com.mk/about.aspxBroadcast.

47533 ■ Antenna5 - Makedonska Kamenica - 104.8
Tetovska 35
91000 Skopje, Macedonia
Ph: 389 2 3111911
Format: Contemporary Hit Radio (CHR). **Owner:** Antenna5, at above address. **Key Personnel:** Zoran Petrov, Gen. Mgr./Music Ed. **URL:** http://www.antenna5.com.mk/about.aspxBroadcast.

Mavrovo

47534 ■ Antenna5 - Mavrovo - 95.5
Tetovska 35
91000 Skopje, Macedonia
Ph: 389 2 3111911
Format: Contemporary Hit Radio (CHR). **Owner:** Antenna5, at above address. **Key Personnel:** Zoran Petrov, Gen. Mgr./Music Ed. **URL:** http://www.antenna5.com.mk/about.aspxBroadcast.

47535 ■ Antenna5 - Mavrovo - 105.5
Tetovska 35
91000 Skopje, Macedonia
Ph: 389 2 3111911
Format: Contemporary Hit Radio (CHR). **Owner:** Antenna5, at above address. **Key Personnel:** Zoran Petrov, Gen. Mgr./Music Ed. **URL:** http://www.antenna5.com.mk/about.aspxBroadcast.

Negotino

47536 ■ Antenna5 - Negotino - 91.9
Tetovska 35
91000 Skopje, Macedonia
Ph: 389 2 3111911
Format: Contemporary Hit Radio (CHR). **Owner:** Antenna5, at above address. **Key Personnel:** Zoran Petrov, Gen. Mgr./Music Ed. **URL:** http://www.antenna5.com.mk/about.aspxBroadcast.

47537 ■ Antenna5 - Negotino - 88.8
Tetovska 35
91000 Skopje, Macedonia
Ph: 389 2 3111911
Format: Contemporary Hit Radio (CHR). **Owner:** Antenna5, at above address. **Key Personnel:** Zoran Petrov, Gen. Mgr./Music Ed. **URL:** http://www.antenna5.com.mk/about.aspxBroadcast.

47538 ■ Antenna5 - Negotino - 104.2
Tetovska 35
91000 Skopje, Macedonia
Ph: 389 2 3111911
Format: Contemporary Hit Radio (CHR). **Owner:** Antenna5, at above address. **Key Personnel:** Zoran Petrov, Gen. Mgr./Music Ed. **URL:** http://www.antenna5.com.mk/about.aspxBroadcast.

Ohrid

47539 ■ Antenna5 - Ohrid - 92.0
Tetovska 35
91000 Skopje, Macedonia
Ph: 389 2 3111911
Format: Contemporary Hit Radio (CHR). **Owner:** Antenna5, at above address. **Key Personnel:** Zoran Petrov, Gen. Mgr./Music Ed. **URL:** http://www.antenna5.com.mk/about.aspxBroadcast.

47540 ■ Antenna5 - Ohrid - 103.3
Tetovska 35
91000 Skopje, Macedonia
Ph: 389 2 3111911
Format: Contemporary Hit Radio (CHR). **Owner:** Antenna5, at above address. **Key Personnel:** Zoran Petrov, Gen. Mgr./Music Ed. **URL:** http://www.antenna5.com.mk/about.aspxBroadcast.

Pesocan

47541 ■ Antenna5 - Pesocan - 101.9
Tetovska 35
91000 Skopje, Macedonia
Ph: 389 2 3111911
Format: Contemporary Hit Radio (CHR). **Owner:** Antenna5, at above address. **Key Personnel:** Zoran Petrov, Gen. Mgr./Music Ed. **URL:** http://www.antenna5.com.mk/about.aspxBroadcast.

Popova Sapka

47542 ■ Antenna5 - Popova Sapka - 106.9
Tetovska 35
91000 Skopje, Macedonia
Ph: 389 2 3111911
Format: Contemporary Hit Radio (CHR). **Owner:** Antenna5, at above address. **Key Personnel:** Zoran Petrov, Gen. Mgr./Music Ed. **URL:** http://www.antenna5.com.mk/about.aspxBroadcast.

Prilep

47543 ■ Antenna5 - Prilep - 92.9
Tetovska 35
91000 Skopje, Macedonia
Ph: 389 2 3111911
Format: Contemporary Hit Radio (CHR). **Owner:** Antenna5, at above address. **Key Personnel:** Zoran Petrov, Gen. Mgr./Music Ed. **URL:** http://www.antenna5.com.mk/about.aspxBroadcast.

47544 ■ Antenna5 - Prilep - 106.3
Tetovska 35
91000 Skopje, Macedonia
Ph: 389 2 3111911
Format: Contemporary Hit Radio (CHR). **Owner:** Antenna5, at above address. **Key Personnel:** Zoran Petrov, Gen. Mgr./Music Ed. **URL:** http://www.antenna5.com.mk/about.aspxBroadcast.

Radovis

47545 ■ Antenna5 - FM Radovis - 91.9
Tetovska 35
91000 Skopje, Macedonia
Ph: 389 2 3111911
E-mail: mail@antenna5.fm
Format: World Beat. **Owner:** Antenna5, at above address. **URL:** http://www.antenna5.com.mk/about.aspxBroadcast.

Resen

47546 ■ Antenna5 - FM Resen - 92.9
Tetovska 35
91000 Skopje, Macedonia
Ph: 389 2 3111911
E-mail: mail@antenna5.fm
Format: World Beat. **Owner:** Antenna5, at above

address. **URL:** http://www.antenna5.com.mk/about. aspxBroadcast.

Skopje

Antenna5 - Berovo - See Berovo

Antenna5 - Bitola - See Bitola

Antenna5 - Bitola - See Bitola

Antenna5 - Bogdanci - See Bogdanci

Antenna5 - Bogdanci - See Bogdanci

Antenna5 - Delcevo - See Delcevo

Antenna5 - Demir Kapija - See Demir Kapija

Antenna5 - Demir Kapija - See Demir Kapija

Antenna5 - Demir Kapija - See Demir Kapija

Antenna5 - Dojran - See Dojran

Antenna5 - Dusegubica - See Dusegubica

Antenna5 - FM Radovis - See Radovis

Antenna5 - FM Resen - See Resen

47547 ■ Antenna5 - FM Skopje - 95.5
Tetovska 35
1000 Skopje, Macedonia
Ph: 389 23111911
Format: Top 40; World Beat; Full Service. **Owner:** Antenna5, at above address. **Operating Hours:** 19 hours Daily. **URL:** http://www.antenna5.com.mk.

Antenna5 - Galicnik - See Galicnik

Antenna5 - Gevgelija - See Gevgelija

Antenna5 - Gevgelija - See Gevgelija

Antenna5 - Gostivar - See Gostivar

Antenna5 - Gostivar - See Gostivar

Antenna5 - Kavadarci - See Kavadarci

Antenna5 - Kavadarci - See Kavadarci

Antenna5 - Kicevo - See Kicevo

Antenna5 - Kocani - See Kocani

Antenna5 - Kocani - See Kocani

Antenna5 - Kratovo - See Kratovo

Antenna5 - Kratovo - See Kratovo

Antenna5 - Kriva Palanka - See Kriva Palanka

Antenna5 - Kriva Palanka - See Kriva Palanka

Antenna5 - Krusevo - See Krusevo

Antenna5 - Kumanovo - See Kumanovo

Antenna5 - Kumanovo - See Kumanovo

Antenna5 - Kumanovo - See Kumanovo

Antenna5 - M. Radobil - See M. Radobil

Antenna5 - Makedonska Kamenica - See Makedonska Kamenica

Antenna5 - Makedonska Kamenica - See Makedonska Kamenica

Antenna5 - Mavrovo - See Mavrovo

Antenna5 - Mavrovo - See Mavrovo

Antenna5 - Negotino - See Negotino

Antenna5 - Negotino - See Negotino

Antenna5 - Negotino - See Negotino

Antenna5 - Ohrid - See Ohrid

Antenna5 - Ohrid - See Ohrid

Antenna5 - Pesocan - See Pesocan

Antenna5 - Popova Sapka - See Popova Sapka

Antenna5 - Prilep - See Prilep

Antenna5 - Prilep - See Prilep

Antenna5 - Stip - See Stip

Antenna5 - Stip - See Stip

Antenna5 - Stracin - See Stracin

Antenna5 - Struga - See Struga

Antenna5 - Struga - See Struga

Antenna5 - Strumica - See Strumica

Antenna5 - Strumica - See Strumica

Antenna5 - Sveti Nikole - See Sveti Nikole

Antenna5 - Tetovo - See Tetovo

Antenna5 - Tetovo - See Tetovo

Antenna5 - Valandovo - See Valandovo

Antenna5 - Veles - See Veles

Antenna5 - Vinica - See Vinica

Antenna5 - Vinica - See Vinica

Stip

47548 ■ Antenna5 - Stip - 91.9
Tetovska 35
91000 Skopje, Macedonia
Ph: 389 2 3111911
Format: Contemporary Hit Radio (CHR). **Owner:** Antenna5, at above address. **Key Personnel:** Zoran Petrov, Gen. Mgr./Music Ed. **URL:** http://www.antenna5. com.mk/about.aspxBroadcast.

47549 ■ Antenna5 - Stip - 104.8
Tetovska 35
91000 Skopje, Macedonia
Ph: 389 2 3111911
Format: Contemporary Hit Radio (CHR). **Owner:** Antenna5, at above address. **Key Personnel:** Zoran Petrov, Gen. Mgr./Music Ed. **URL:** http://www.antenna5. com.mk/about.aspxBroadcast.

47550 ■ Radio Cerenja-FM - 106.4
ul. Radanski pat br. 202
Stip, Macedonia
Ph: 389 32 384248
Fax: 389 32 390795
E-mail: edemir@soros.org.mk
Format: Full Service. **Founded:** Aug. 11, 1999. **Key Personnel:** Enise Demirova, General Mgr. **URL:** http:// www.cerenja.com.mk/.

Stracin

47551 ■ Antenna5 - Stracin - 105.5
Tetovska 35
91000 Skopje, Macedonia
Ph: 389 2 3111911
Format: Contemporary Hit Radio (CHR). **Owner:** Antenna5, at above address. **Key Personnel:** Zoran Petrov, Gen. Mgr./Music Ed. **URL:** http://www.antenna5. com.mk/about.aspxBroadcast.

Struga

47552 ■ Antenna5 - Struga - 92.0
Tetovska 35
91000 Skopje, Macedonia
Ph: 389 2 3111911
Format: Contemporary Hit Radio (CHR). **Owner:** Antenna5, at above address. **Key Personnel:** Zoran Petrov, Gen. Mgr./Music Ed. **URL:** http://www.antenna5. com.mk/about.aspxBroadcast.

47553 ■ Antenna5 - Struga - 103.3
Tetovska 35
91000 Skopje, Macedonia
Ph: 389 2 3111911
Format: Contemporary Hit Radio (CHR). **Owner:** Antenna5, at above address. **Key Personnel:** Zoran Petrov, Gen. Mgr./Music Ed. **URL:** http://www.antenna5. com.mk/about.aspxBroadcast.

Strumica

47554 ■ Antenna5 - Strumica - 91.9
Tetovska 35
91000 Skopje, Macedonia
Ph: 389 2 3111911
Format: Contemporary Hit Radio (CHR). **Owner:** Antenna5, at above address. **Key Personnel:** Zoran Petrov, Gen. Mgr./Music Ed. **URL:** http://www.antenna5.

com.mk/about.aspxBroadcast.

47555 ■ Antenna5 - Strumica - 100.5
Tetovska 35
91000 Skopje, Macedonia
Ph: 389 2 3111911
Format: Contemporary Hit Radio (CHR). **Owner:** Antenna5, at above address. **Key Personnel:** Zoran Petrov, Gen. Mgr./Music Ed. **URL:** http://www.antenna5. com.mk/about.aspxBroadcast.

Sveti Nikole

47556 ■ Antenna5 - Sveti Nikole - 91.9
Tetovska 35
91000 Skopje, Macedonia
Ph: 389 2 3111911
Format: Contemporary Hit Radio (CHR). **Owner:** Antenna5, at above address. **Key Personnel:** Zoran Petrov, Gen. Mgr./Music Ed. **URL:** http://www.antenna5. com.mk/about.aspxBroadcast.

Tetovo

47557 ■ Antenna5 - Tetovo - 106.9
Tetovska 35
91000 Skopje, Macedonia
Ph: 389 2 3111911
Format: Contemporary Hit Radio (CHR). **Owner:** Antenna5, at above address. **Key Personnel:** Zoran Petrov, Gen. Mgr./Music Ed. **URL:** http://www.antenna5. com.mk/about.aspxBroadcast.

47558 ■ Antenna5 - Tetovo - 105.5
Tetovska 35
91000 Skopje, Macedonia
Ph: 389 2 3111911
Format: Contemporary Hit Radio (CHR). **Owner:** Antenna5, at above address. **Key Personnel:** Zoran Petrov, Gen. Mgr./Music Ed. **URL:** http://www.antenna5. com.mk/about.aspxBroadcast.

Valandovo

47559 ■ Antenna5 - Valandovo - 106.3
Tetovska 35
91000 Skopje, Macedonia
Ph: 389 2 3111911
Format: Contemporary Hit Radio (CHR). **Owner:** Antenna5, at above address. **Key Personnel:** Zoran Petrov, Gen. Mgr./Music Ed. **URL:** http://www.antenna5. com.mk/about.aspxBroadcast.

Veles

47560 ■ Antenna5 - Veles - 91.9
Tetovska 35
91000 Skopje, Macedonia
Ph: 389 2 3111911
Format: Contemporary Hit Radio (CHR). **Owner:** Antenna5, at above address. **Key Personnel:** Zoran Petrov, Gen. Mgr./Music Ed. **URL:** http://www.antenna5. com.mk/about.aspxBroadcast.

Vinica

47561 ■ Antenna5 - Vinica - 97.9
Tetovska 35
91000 Skopje, Macedonia
Ph: 389 2 3111911
Format: Contemporary Hit Radio (CHR). **Owner:** Antenna5, at above address. **Key Personnel:** Zoran Petrov, Gen. Mgr./Music Ed. **URL:** http://www.antenna5. com.mk/about.aspxBroadcast.

47562 ■ Antenna5 - Vinica - 104.8
Tetovska 35
91000 Skopje, Macedonia
Ph: 389 2 3111911
Format: Contemporary Hit Radio (CHR). **Owner:** Antenna5, at above address. **Key Personnel:** Zoran Petrov, Gen. Mgr./Music Ed. **URL:** http://www.antenna5. com.mk/about.aspxBroadcast.

Circulation: ★ = ABC; △ = BPA; ◆ = CAC; • = CCAB; ❑ = VAC; ⊕ = PO Statement; ‡ = Publisher's Report; Boldface figures = sworn; Light figures = estimated.

Antananarivo

47563 ■ Aceem Radio-FM - 103.4
Escalier Ranavalona I Antaninarenina
Antananarivo 101, Madagascar
Ph: 261 202 265369
Fax: 261 202 256236
Format: Ethnic; World Beat. **Founded:** 1997. **Key Personnel:** Hery Rakotoarinia, Director. **URL:** http://www.aceem.com.

47564 ■ Foi-FM - 107.4 MHz
Rue Docteur Ralarosy
Antananarivo 101, Madagascar
Ph: 261 20 2231829
Format: Gospel; Religious. **Wattage:** 30. **URL:** http://fmfoi.ifrance.com.

47565 ■ Radio Madagasikara-FM - 99.2 MHz
BP 442

Anosy 101
Antananarivo 101, Madagascar
Ph: 261 20 2221745
Fax: 261 20 2232715
E-mail: rnmprog@dts.mg
Format: Ethnic; World Beat. **URL:** http://takelaka.dts.mg/radmad.

Blantyre

47566 ■ Malawi Medical Journal
African Journals Online
Private Bag 360
Chichiri
Blantyre, Malawi
Publisher E-mail: info@ajol.info
Peer-reviewed journal of the College of Medicine and Medical Association of Malawi. **Founded:** 1969. **Freq:** Quarterly. **Print Method:** Offset. **Trim Size:** 8 1/4 x 11. **Cols./Page:** 2. **Col. Width:** 46 nonpareils. **Col. Depth:** 126 agate lines. **Key Personnel:** Prof. M.E. Molyneux, Editor-in-Chief, mmolyneux@malawi.net; J.J. Wirima, Chm.; Prof. E. Parry, International Committee; Prof. C. Olweny, International Committee; Magriet Sacranie, Business Mgr.; J. Mukiibi, Sec.; Dr. R. Stektee, International Committee; Prof. P. Willcox, International Committee. **ISSN:** 0735-7028. **Subscription Rates:** US$30 other countries. **URL:** http://ajol.info/index.php/mmj.

47567 ■ Capital Radio Malawi-FM - 102.5
PO Box 437
Blantyre, Malawi
Ph: 265 1 820858
Fax: 265 1 823382
E-mail: stationmanager@capitalradiomalawi.com
Format: Adult Contemporary; News. **Owner:** Capital FM, at above address. **Founded:** Mar. 29, 1999. **Operating Hours:** 6 a.m.-10 p.m. Daily. **Key Personnel:** Alaudin S. Osman, Mng. Dir., phone 265 1 822001, al@capitalradiomalawi.com; Arlene Osman, Sales & Mktg. Mgr., phone 265 1 830290, arlene@capitalradiomalawi.com. **Ad Rates:** Advertising accepted; rates available upon request. **URL:** http://www.capitalradiomalawi.com.

Mangochi

47568 ■ Radio Maria Malawi-FM - 99.7 MHz
PO Box 408
Mangochi, Malawi
Ph: 265 1 599600
Fax: 265 1 599691
E-mail: radiomaria@malawi.net
Format: Contemporary Christian; Religious. **Operating Hours:** Continuous. **Ad Rates:** Noncommercial. **URL:** http://www.radiomaria.mw.

47569 ■ Radio Maria Malawi-FM - 94 MHz
PO Box 408
Mangochi, Malawi
Ph: 265 1 599600
Fax: 265 1 599691
E-mail: radiomaria@malawi.net
Format: Contemporary Christian; Religious. **Founded:** 1998. **Operating Hours:** Continuous. **Ad Rates:** Noncommercial. **URL:** http://www.radiomaria.mw.

47570 ■ Radio Maria Malawi-FM - 99.4 MHz
PO Box 408
Mangochi, Malawi
Ph: 265 1 599600
Fax: 265 1 599691
E-mail: radiomaria@malawi.net
Format: Contemporary Christian; Religious. **Operating Hours:** Continuous. **Ad Rates:** Noncommercial. **URL:** http://www.radiomaria.mw.

47571 ■ Radio Maria Malawi-FM - 99.2 MHz
PO Box 408
Mangochi, Malawi
Ph: 265 1 599600
Fax: 265 1 599691
E-mail: radiomaria@malawi.net
Format: Contemporary Christian; Religious. **Founded:** Aug. 24, 1999. **Operating Hours:** Continuous. **Ad Rates:** Noncommercial. **URL:** http://www.radiomaria.mw.

47572 ■ Radio Maria Malawi-FM - 88.5 MHz
PO Box 408
Mangochi, Malawi
Ph: 265 1 599600
Fax: 265 1 599691
E-mail: radiomaria@malawi.net
Format: Contemporary Christian; Religious. **Owner:** Radio Maria Malawi, at above address. **Founded:** 1998. **Operating Hours:** Continuous. **Ad Rates:** Noncommercial. **URL:** http://www.radiomaria.mw.

Zomba

47573 ■ Malawi Journal of Science and Technology
African Journals Online
University of Malawi
PO Box 278
Zomba, Malawi
Ph: 265 522622
Fax: 265 522760
Publisher E-mail: info@ajol.info
Peer-reviewed journal covering the study in applied and theoretical sciences. **Key Personnel:** Daveson Nyambani, Contact, publications@chanco.unima.mw. **ISSN:** 1019-7079. **Subscription Rates:** US$10 single issue. **URL:** http://ajol.info/index.php/mjst.

Circulation: ★ = ABC; △ = BPA; ♦ = CAC; • = CCAB; ❏ = VAC; ⊕ = PO Statement; ‡ = Publisher's Report; Boldface figures = sworn; Light figures = estimated.

Gale Directory of Publications & Broadcast Media/147th Ed. 5177

Bangi

47574 ■ Jurnal Ekonomi Malaysia
Penerbit Universiti Kebangsaan Malaysia
University Kebangsaan Malaysia
43600 Bangi, Malaysia
Ph: 60 3 89215321
Fax: 60 3 89254575
Publisher E-mail: penerbit@ukm.my
Business journal. **Founded:** 1980. **Freq:** Annual in December. **Key Personnel:** Ghafar Abd. Ismail, PhD, Editor-in-Chief. **ISSN:** 0127-1962. **URL:** http://pkukmweb.ukm.my/~fep/jurnal_ekonomi_malaysia.html. **Circ:** Paid 500

Besut

47575 ■ Minnal FM - Besut - 95.3
Tingkat 4, Wisma Radio
Peti Surat 11272
Angkasapuri
50740 Kuala Lumpur, Malaysia
Ph: 60 3 22887279
Fax: 60 3 22849137
E-mail: mail@minnalfm.com
Format: Classical; News; Information. **Owner:** Radio Televisyen Malaysia, Jabatan Penyiaran Malaysia, Angkasapuri, 50614 Kuala Lumpur, Malaysia. **Operating Hours:** Continuous. **URL:** http://www.minnalfm.com/.

Bintulu

47576 ■ Traxx FM - Bintulu - 98.5
2nd Fl., Wisma Radio
Angkasapuri
50740 Kuala Lumpur, Malaysia
Ph: 60 3 22887663
Fax: 60 3 22845750
Format: Contemporary Hit Radio (CHR); Talk; Information. **Owner:** Radio Televisyen Malaysia, Jabatan Penyiaran Malaysia, Angkasapuri, 50614 Kuala Lumpur, Malaysia. **Operating Hours:** Continuous. **URL:** http://www.traxxfm.net/.

Bukit Tinggi

47577 ■ Traxx FM - Bukit Tinggi - 92.9
2nd Fl., Wisma Radio
Angkasapuri
50740 Kuala Lumpur, Malaysia
Ph: 60 3 22887663
Fax: 60 3 22845750
Format: Contemporary Hit Radio (CHR); Talk; Information. **Owner:** Radio Televisyen Malaysia, Jabatan Penyiaran Malaysia, Angkasapuri, 50614 Kuala Lumpur, Malaysia. **Operating Hours:** Continuous. **URL:** http://www.traxxfm.net/.

Gurun

47578 ■ Traxx FM - Gurun - 98.7
2nd Fl., Wisma Radio
Angkasapuri
50740 Kuala Lumpur, Malaysia
Ph: 60 3 22887663

Fax: 60 3 22845750
Format: Contemporary Hit Radio (CHR); Talk; Information. **Owner:** Radio Televisyen Malaysia, Jabatan Penyiaran Malaysia, Angkasapuri, 50614 Kuala Lumpur, Malaysia. **Operating Hours:** Continuous. **URL:** http://www.traxxfm.net/.

Ipoh

47579 ■ Traxx FM - Ipoh - 90.1
2nd Fl., Wisma Radio
Angkasapuri
50740 Kuala Lumpur, Malaysia
Ph: 60 3 22887663
Fax: 60 3 22845750
Format: Contemporary Hit Radio (CHR); Talk; Information. **Owner:** Radio Televisyen Malaysia, Jabatan Penyiaran Malaysia, Angkasapuri, 50614 Kuala Lumpur, Malaysia. **Operating Hours:** Continuous. **URL:** http://www.traxxfm.net/.

Jeli

47580 ■ Minnal FM - Jeli - 92.4
Tingkat 4, Wisma Radio
Peti Surat 11272
Angkasapuri
50740 Kuala Lumpur, Malaysia
Ph: 60 3 22887279
Fax: 60 3 22849137
E-mail: mail@minnalfm.com
Format: Classical; News; Information. **Owner:** Radio Televisyen Malaysia, Jabatan Penyiaran Malaysia, Angkasapuri, 50614 Kuala Lumpur, Malaysia. **Operating Hours:** Continuous. **URL:** http://www.minnalfm.com/.

47581 ■ Traxx FM - Jeli - 90.8
2nd Fl., Wisma Radio
Angkasapuri
50740 Kuala Lumpur, Malaysia
Ph: 60 3 22887663
Fax: 60 3 22845750
Format: Contemporary Hit Radio (CHR); Talk; Information. **Owner:** Radio Televisyen Malaysia, Jabatan Penyiaran Malaysia, Angkasapuri, 50614 Kuala Lumpur, Malaysia. **Operating Hours:** Continuous. **URL:** http://www.traxxfm.net/.

Jerantut

47582 ■ Minnal FM - Jerantut - 91.9
Tingkat 4, Wisma Radio
Peti Surat 11272
Angkasapuri
50740 Kuala Lumpur, Malaysia
Ph: 60 3 22887279
Fax: 60 3 22849137
E-mail: mail@minnalfm.com
Format: Classical; News; Information. **Owner:** Radio Televisyen Malaysia, Jabatan Penyiaran Malaysia, Angkasapuri, 50614 Kuala Lumpur, Malaysia. **Operating Hours:** Continuous. **URL:** http://www.minnalfm.com/.

Johor Bahru

47583 ■ Traxx FM - Johor Bahru - 102.9

2nd Fl., Wisma Radio
Angkasapuri
50740 Kuala Lumpur, Malaysia
Ph: 60 3 22887663
Fax: 60 3 22845750
Format: Contemporary Hit Radio (CHR); Talk; Information. **Owner:** Radio Televisyen Malaysia, Jabatan Penyiaran Malaysia, Angkasapuri, 50614 Kuala Lumpur, Malaysia. **Operating Hours:** Continuous. **URL:** http://www.traxxfm.net/.

Kampar

47584 ■ International Journal of Modelling in Operations Management
Inderscience Enterprises Limited
c/o Dr. Keng-Boon Ooi, Ed.-in-Ch.
University Tunku Abdul Rahman, Faculty of Buyer's Guide & Finance
Perak Campus, Jalan Universiti
Bandar Barat
31900 Kampar, Malaysia
Journal covering the advancement of knowledge in the areas of services, engineering, business and management, and operations management. **Freq:** 4/yr. **Key Personnel:** Dr. Keng-Boon Ooi, Editor-in-Chief, editor. ijmom@gmail.com; Dr. Alain Yee-Loong Chong, Editor, alain.chong@gmail.com. **ISSN:** 2042-4094. **Subscription Rates:** EUR494 individuals print or online; EUR672 individuals print and online. **URL:** http://www.inderscience.com/browse/index.php?journalID=361.

Kota Baru

47585 ■ Traxx FM - Kota Baru - 104.7
2nd Fl., Wisma Radio
Angkasapuri
50740 Kuala Lumpur, Malaysia
Ph: 60 3 22887663
Fax: 60 3 22845750
Format: Contemporary Hit Radio (CHR); Talk; Information. **Owner:** Radio Televisyen Malaysia, Jabatan Penyiaran Malaysia, Angkasapuri, 50614 Kuala Lumpur, Malaysia. **Operating Hours:** Continuous. **URL:** http://www.traxxfm.net/.

Kota Belud

47586 ■ Traxx FM - Kota Belud - 102.5
2nd Fl., Wisma Radio
Angkasapuri
50740 Kuala Lumpur, Malaysia
Ph: 60 3 22887663
Fax: 60 3 22845750
Format: Contemporary Hit Radio (CHR); Talk; Information. **Owner:** Radio Televisyen Malaysia, Jabatan Penyiaran Malaysia, Angkasapuri, 50614 Kuala Lumpur, Malaysia. **Operating Hours:** Continuous. **URL:** http://www.traxxfm.net/.

Kota Kinabalu

47587 ■ Banci Estet Koko
Malaysian Cocoa Board
Locked Bag 211

Circulation: ★ = ABC; △ = BPA; ◆ = CAC; • = CCAB; ❑ = VAC; ⊕ = PO Statement; ‡ = Publisher's Report; Boldface figures = sworn; Light figures = estimated.

88999 Kota Kinabalu, Malaysia
Ph: 60 88 234477
Fax: 60 88 239575
Publisher E-mail: norhaini@koko.gov.my
Journal containing information about the numbers of cocoa estates, employment, payroll, input utilization, expenditure and value of fixed assets. **Freq:** Annual. **Subscription Rates:** M$15 individuals. **URL:** http://www.koko.gov.my/lkmbm/loader.cfm?&cat=Buku&type=Publications&id=1029.

47588 ■ Biotechnology & Molecular Biology Reviews
Academic Journals
c/o P. Ravindra, PhD, Ed.-in-Ch.
School of Engineering & IT
University Malaysia Sabah
88999 Kota Kinabalu, Malaysia
Publication E-mail: bmbr@academicjournals.org
Publisher E-mail: service@academicjournals.org
Journal covering reviews in biotechnology and molecular biology. **Freq:** Quarterly. **Key Personnel:** P. Ravindra, PhD, Editor-in-Chief, dr_ravindra@hotmail.com; David Maina Menge, PhD, Editor, dmenge@uci.edu; Evans Kaimoyo, PhD, Editor, ek246@cornell.edu. **ISSN:** 1538-2273. **Remarks:** Accepts advertising. **URL:** http://www.academicjournals.org/bmbr/index.htm. **Circ:** (Not Reported)

47589 ■ Borneo Review
Institute for Development Studies
Lot 2-5 Wisma SEDIA
Off Jalan Pintas, Penampang
Locked Bag 127
88994 Kota Kinabalu, Malaysia
Ph: 60 88 450500
Fax: 60 88 450599
Publishes research pertaining to economic, social, political and public administrative developments. **Founded:** 1990. **Freq:** Semiannual. **ISSN:** 0128-7397. **Remarks:** Advertising accepted; rates available upon request. **URL:** http://www.ids.org.my/old/publications/borneoreview/index.htm. **Circ:** (Not Reported)

47590 ■ Daily Express
Sabah Publishing House SDN BHD
PO Box 10139
88801 Kota Kinabalu, Sabah, Malaysia
Ph: 60 88238711
Fax: 60 88238611
General newspaper. **Founded:** Mar. 1963. **Freq:** Daily. **Key Personnel:** Puan Sri Yeh, Chm.; Clement Yeh Chang, Publisher. **Remarks:** Accepts advertising. **URL:** http://www.dailyexpress.com.my. **Circ:** (Not Reported)

47591 ■ Malaysian Cocoa Monitor
Malaysian Cocoa Board
Locked Bag 211
88999 Kota Kinabalu, Malaysia
Ph: 60 88 234477
Fax: 60 88 239575
Publisher E-mail: norhaini@koko.gov.my
Journal containing historical information on cocoa area, production, grindings, export and import statistics, prices, exchange rates and import tariffs. **Freq:** Semiannual. **Subscription Rates:** M$30 individuals local; M$50 other countries. **URL:** http://www.koko.gov.my/lkm/loader.cfm?page=industry/statistic/mcmonitor.cfm.

47592 ■ Overseas Chinese Daily
Sabah Publishing House SDN BHD
PO Box 10139
88801 Kota Kinabalu, Sabah, Malaysia
Ph: 60 88238711
Fax: 60 88238611
General newspaper. **Founded:** Mar. 1, 1936. **Key Personnel:** Puan Sri Yeh, Chairman; Clement Yeh Chang, Publisher. **Remarks:** Accepts advertising. **URL:** http://www.founder.net.my/ocdn. **Circ:** (Not Reported)

47593 ■ Traxx FM - Kota Kinabalu - 90.7
2nd Fl., Wisma Radio
Angkasapuri
50740 Kuala Lumpur, Malaysia
Ph: 60 3 22887663
Fax: 60 3 22845750
Format: Contemporary Hit Radio (CHR); Talk; Information. **Owner:** Radio Televisyen Malaysia, Jabatan Penyiaran Malaysia, Angkasapuri, 50614 Kuala Lumpur, Malaysia. **Operating Hours:** Continuous. **URL:** http://www.traxxfm.net/.

Kuala Besut

47594 ■ Traxx FM - Kuala Besut - 97.0
2nd Fl., Wisma Radio
Angkasapuri
50740 Kuala Lumpur, Malaysia
Ph: 60 3 22887663
Fax: 60 3 22845750
Format: Contemporary Hit Radio (CHR); Talk; Information. **Owner:** Radio Televisyen Malaysia, Jabatan Penyiaran Malaysia, Angkasapuri, 50614 Kuala Lumpur, Malaysia. **Operating Hours:** Continuous. **URL:** http://www.traxxfm.net/.

Kuala Dungun

47595 ■ Traxx FM - Kuala Dungun - 98.8
2nd Fl., Wisma Radio
Angkasapuri
50740 Kuala Lumpur, Malaysia
Ph: 60 3 22887663
Fax: 60 3 22845750
Format: Contemporary Hit Radio (CHR); Talk; Information. **Owner:** Radio Televisyen Malaysia, Jabatan Penyiaran Malaysia, Angkasapuri, 50614 Kuala Lumpur, Malaysia. **Operating Hours:** Continuous. **URL:** http://www.traxxfm.net/.

Kuala Lumpur

47596 ■ Al-Islam
Utusan Melayu (M) Bhd
46 M, Jalan Lima Off
Jalan Chan Sow Lin
55200 Kuala Lumpur, Malaysia
Ph: 60 3 92217055
Fax: 60 3 92227876
Publisher E-mail: online@utusan.com.my
Magazine featuring Islam and all aspects of its religious teachings. **Freq:** Monthly. **Trim Size:** 21 x 27.6 cm. **Key Personnel:** Datuk Abdul Aziz Ishak, Gp. Ed.-in-Ch. **Subscription Rates:** M$4.50 single issue. **Remarks:** Accepts advertising. **URL:** http://www.utusangroup.my/products/magazines. **Ad Rates:** BW: M$500, 4C: M$850. **Circ:** (Not Reported)

47597 ■ Asia-Pacific Military Balance
ADPR Consult (M) Sdn Bhd
PO Box 10762
No. 2, Jalan Sultan Sulaiman
50724 Kuala Lumpur, Malaysia
Ph: 60 3 77812903
Fax: 60 3 77812915
Publisher E-mail: enquiry@adprconsult.com.my
Periodical covering geo-strategic developments of consequence to the Asia-Pacific region from an Asian perspective. **Freq:** Semiannual. **ISSN:** 1511-3884. **Remarks:** Accepts advertising. **URL:** http://www.adprconsult.com.my/mag_apmb.html. **Ad Rates:** BW: M$3,700, 4C: M$5,000. **Circ:** (Not Reported)

47598 ■ Asian Defence Journal
SHP Media Sdn. Bhd.
C-17-1, 17th Fl., Tower C, Megan Ave. II
12, Jalan Yap Kwan Seng
PO Box 10836
50726 Kuala Lumpur, Malaysia
Ph: 60 3 21660852
Fax: 60 3 21610541
Publisher E-mail: info@shpmedia.com
Periodical covering military, geopolitical affairs and all spheres of defense activities and industries from an Asia-Pacific perspective. **Founded:** 1970. **Freq:** Monthly. **ISSN:** 0126-6403. **Remarks:** Accepts advertising. **URL:** http://www.shpmedia.com/pub_adj.htm. **Ad Rates:** BW: EUR2605, 4C: EUR3535. **Circ:** 20,000

47599 ■ Banker's Journal Malaysia
Institut Bank-Bank Malaysia
Wisma IBI, No. 5 Jalan Semantan
Damansara Hts.
50490 Kuala Lumpur, Malaysia
Ph: 60 3 20956833
Fax: 60 3 20952322
Publication E-mail: publish@ibbm.org.my

Publisher E-mail: ibbm@ibbm.org.my
Journal on banking and finance. **Freq:** Semiannual June and December. **ISSN:** 0126-9534. **Subscription Rates:** M$50 members IBBM (overseas); M$110 nonmembers overseas; M$25 members IBBM; M$35 nonmembers. **URL:** http://www.ibbm.org.my/files/KR_pub_BJM_AB.aspx.

47600 ■ Biomedical Imaging and Intervention Journal
University of Malaya Medical Centre
Lembah Pantai
59100 Kuala Lumpur, Malaysia
Ph: 60 3 79494422
Fax: 60 3 79562253
Publication E-mail: editor@biij.org
Publisher E-mail: ummc@ummc.edu.my
Journal dealing with the clinical and technical features of biomedical imaging and intervention, radiotherapy and oncology, minimally invasive image guided therapy, image processing and informatics, molecular medicine, medical physics and radiobiology in addition to radiography and bioengineering with relevance to imaging or intervention. **Subtitle:** A Multidisciplinary Open Access Online Journal. **Freq:** Quarterly. **Key Personnel:** Basri J.J. Abdullah, Editor, basri.abdullah@biij.org; Kwan-Hoong Ng, Editor, kwanhoong.ng@biij.org; Nahrizul Adib Kadri, Managing Editor, nahrizul.kadri@biij.org. **ISSN:** 1823-5530. **Subscription Rates:** Free. **URL:** http://www.biij.org/2005/1/e6/abstract.asp?ID=2.

47601 ■ Business Times
The New Straits Times Press (Malaysia) Bhd.
Balai Berita
31 Jalan Riong
59100 Kuala Lumpur, Malaysia
Ph: 60 322 823131
Fax: 60 322 821428
Publication E-mail: bt@nstp.com.my
Publisher E-mail: general@nstp.com.my
International business newspaper. **Founded:** 1976. **Freq:** Mon.-Sat. **Key Personnel:** Lokman Mansor, Dep. Ed.; Mustapha Kamil M. Janor, Exec. Ed. **Remarks:** Accepts advertising. **URL:** http://www.nstp.com.my/Corporate/nstp/products/productBT.htm; http://www.btimes.com.my/. **Circ:** (Not Reported)

47602 ■ FMM Directory of Malaysian Industries
Federation of Malaysian Manufacturers
Wisma FMM, No. 3
Persiaran Dagang
PJU 9, Bandar Sri Damansara
52200 Kuala Lumpur, Malaysia
Ph: 60 362 867200
Fax: 60 362 741266
Publisher E-mail: webmaster@fmm.org.my
Publication covering manufacturing. **Freq:** Annual. **Remarks:** Accepts advertising. **URL:** http://www.fmm.org.my/; http://www.fmm.org.my/p_ne_it.asp?NewsID=403&ThemeID=258&From=Theme. **Formerly:** FMM Forum. **Circ:** (Not Reported)

47603 ■ Harmoni
Utusan Melayu (M) Bhd
46 M, Jalan Lima Off
Jalan Chan Sow Lin
55200 Kuala Lumpur, Malaysia
Ph: 60 3 92217055
Fax: 60 3 92227876
Publisher E-mail: online@utusan.com.my
Magazine for women. **Freq:** fortnightly. **Trim Size:** 21 x 27.6 cm. **Key Personnel:** Datuk Abdul Aziz Ishak, Gp. Ed.-in-Ch. **Subscription Rates:** M$4 single issue. **Remarks:** Accepts advertising. **URL:** http://www.utusangroup.com.my/products/magazines. **Ad Rates:** 4C: M$3,000. **Circ:** (Not Reported)

47604 ■ i-Sihat
Utusan Melayu (M) Bhd
46 M, Jalan Lima Off
Jalan Chan Sow Lin
55200 Kuala Lumpur, Malaysia
Ph: 60 3 92217055
Fax: 60 3 92227876
Publisher E-mail: online@utusan.com.my
Magazine featuring health, beauty, healthy lifestyle, psychology, cosmetics, healthy food intake and fitness. **Freq:** Monthly. **Trim Size:** 21 x 27.6 cm. **Key Personnel:** Datuk Abdul Aziz Ishak, Gp. Ed.-in-Ch. **Subscription Rates:** M$5.50 single issue. **Remarks:** Accepts

advertising. **URL:** http://www.utusangroup.com.my/products/magazines. **Ad Rates:** 4C: M$3,000. **Circ:** (Not Reported)

47605 ■ INFOFISH International
Infofish
1st Fl. Wisma PKNS
Jalan Raja Laut
PO Box 10899
50728 Kuala Lumpur, Malaysia
Ph: 603 26914466
Fax: 603 26916804
Publisher E-mail: infish@po.jaring.my
Publication providing marketing information and technical advisory services for fishery products in the Asian and Pacific regions. **Founded:** 1981. **Freq:** Bimonthly. **ISSN:** 0127-2012. **Subscription Rates:** US$30 members; US$45 nonmembers. **Remarks:** Advertising accepted; rates available upon request. **URL:** http://www.infofish.org. **Circ:** 7,000

47606 ■ Journal of the Malaysian Branch of the Royal Asiatic Society
Malaysian Branch of the Royal Asiatic Society
2nd Fl., 4B Jalan Kemuja
Bangsar
59000 Kuala Lumpur, Malaysia
Ph: 60 3 22835345
Fax: 60 3 22822458
Publisher E-mail: mbras@tm.net.my
Scholarly publication. **Founded:** 1878. **Freq:** Semiannual June and December. **Key Personnel:** Cheah Boon Kheng, Editor; Dato H.S. Barlow, Editor. **ISSN:** 0126-7353. **Remarks:** Advertising accepted; rates available upon request. **URL:** http://www.mbras.org.my/; http://www.mbras.org.my/body_patrons.html. **Circ:** Paid 1,000

47607 ■ Journal of Rubber Research
Malaysian Rubber Board
Public Relations, Publications and Library Unit
148 Jalan Ampang
50450 Kuala Lumpur, Malaysia
Ph: 60 3 92062000
Fax: 60 3 21613139
Publisher E-mail: general@lgm.gov.my
Publishes results and reviews on all aspects of rubber. **Founded:** 1928. **Freq:** Quarterly. **ISSN:** 1511-1768. **Remarks:** Advertising accepted; rates available upon request. **URL:** http://journalseek.net/cgi-bin/journalseek/journalsearch.cgi?field=issn&query=1511-1768. **Circ:** Paid 1,000

47608 ■ Journal of Tropical Agriculture & Food Science
Malaysian Agricultural Research and Development Institute
Promotion and Sales Unit
PO Box 12301
50774 Kuala Lumpur, Malaysia
Ph: 60 389 437111
Fax: 60 389 483664
Publisher E-mail: enquiry@mardi.gov.my
Publishes results of scientific studies in the fields of tropical agriculture and food science. **Founded:** 1973. **Freq:** Biennial. **Print Method:** Offset. **Trim Size:** B5. **ISSN:** 1394-9829. **Remarks:** Advertising not accepted. **URL:** http://www.mardi.my/main.php?Content=sections&SubSectionID=603&SectionID=60 0. **Circ:** Paid 500

47609 ■ Juice
Catcha.com Private Ltd.
45-7 The Blvd. Mid Valley City
No. 08-01 HDB HUB
59200 Kuala Lumpur, Malaysia
Ph: 60 3 22970999
Fax: 60 3 22970888
Publisher E-mail: publicrelations@catchacorp.com
Lifestyle magazine. **Freq:** Weekly. **Remarks:** Accepts advertising. **URL:** http://www.catchacorp.com/publishing.html. **Circ:** Free 30,000

47610 ■ Kosmo!
Utusan Melayu (M) Bhd
46 M, Jalan Lima Off
Jalan Chan Sow Lin
55200 Kuala Lumpur, Malaysia
Ph: 60 3 92217055
Fax: 60 3 92227876
Publisher E-mail: online@utusan.com.my
Newspaper for new and modern generation. **Freq:** Daily.

Key Personnel: Meja Berita, Contact. **Remarks:** Accepts display and classified advertising. **URL:** http://www.kosmo.com.my/. **Ad Rates:** 4C: M$15. **Circ:** (Not Reported)

47611 ■ Malayan Nature Journal
Malayan Nature Society
JKR 641, Jalan Kelantan
Bukit Persekutuan
50480 Kuala Lumpur, Malaysia
Ph: 60 3 22879422
Fax: 60 3 22878773
Publisher E-mail: mns@mns.org.my
Natural science journal. **Founded:** Sept. 1940. **Freq:** Quarterly. **Key Personnel:** Geoffrey Davison, Editor. **ISSN:** 0025-1291. **URL:** http://www.mns.org.my/; http://www.mns.org.my/section.php?sid=22. **Circ:** Paid 2,500

47612 ■ Malaysia Society
Edipresse Asia
Ste. 2A-19-2, Level 19, Block 2A
Plz. Sentral, Jalan Stesen Sentral 5
Kuala Lumpur Sentral
50470 Kuala Lumpur, Malaysia
Ph: 60 3 27808833
Fax: 60 3 27808822
Magazine featuring the key people in Malaysia. **Freq:** Annual. **Key Personnel:** Florence Fang, Director; Sunita Chhabra, Ch. Ed. **URL:** http://www.edipresse.com/lifestyle/malaysia-society.

47613 ■ Malaysiakini
Mkini Dotcom Sdn. Bhd.
48 Jalan Kemuja
Bangsar Utama
59000 Kuala Lumpur, Malaysia
Ph: 60 322 835567
Fax: 60 322 892579
Publication E-mail: subscribe@malaysiakini.com
Independent newspaper covering Malaysia. **Subtitle:** Only the News that Matters. **Freq:** Daily. **Key Personnel:** Premesh Chandran, CEO, prem@malaysiakini.com; K. Kabilan, Editor, kabilan@malaysiakini.com. **Subscription Rates:** M$150 individuals; US$40 individuals. **Remarks:** Accepts advertising. **URL:** http://www.malaysiakini.com/. **Circ:** (Not Reported)

47614 ■ Malaysian Business
Berita Publishing Sdn Bhd
16-20 Jalen 4/109E
Desa Business Pk., Taman Desa
Off Jalan Kelang Lama
58100 Kuala Lumpur, Malaysia
Ph: 60 376 208111
Fax: 60 376 208026
English-language business publication. **Founded:** 1973. **Freq:** Biweekly. **Trim Size:** 275 x 210 mm. **Subscription Rates:** US$70.10 Singapore, Brunei Darussalam; US$104.80 India, Thailand, China, Japan and Australia; US$127.90 Europe and the Middle East; US$139.60 Argentina, Brazil, Africa, U.S. and Canada. **Remarks:** Advertising accepted; rates available upon request. **URL:** http://www.beritapublishing.com.my/Malaysian_Business/. **Circ:** (Not Reported)

47615 ■ Malaysian Chamber of Mines Year Book
Malaysian Chamber of Mines
W Block, Wisma Selangor Dredging, 8th Fl.
Jalan Ampang
50450 Kuala Lumpur, Malaysia
Ph: 60 3 21616171
Fax: 60 3 21616179
Publisher E-mail: mcom@mcom.com.my
Malaysian publication covering mining chambers. **Freq:** Annual. **Remarks:** Advertising accepted; rates available upon request. **URL:** http://www.mcom.com.my; http://www.mcom.com.my/publications.html. **Circ:** 500

47616 ■ Malaysian Journal of Economic Studies
Persatuan Ekonomi Malaysia
c/o University of Malaya
Faculty of Economics & Administration
50603 Kuala Lumpur, Malaysia
Journal publishing original research related to the Malaysian economy. **Freq:** Semiannual. **Key Personnel:** Tan Eu Chye, Hon. Sec.; Goh Kim Leng, Managing Editor; Shyamala Nagaraj, Chm. **ISSN:** 1511-4554. **URL:** http://www.pem.org.my/publications/journal-of-economic.htm. **Former name:** Kajian Ekonomi Malaysia.

47617 ■ Malaysian Journal of Library and Information Science
Faculty of Computer Science and Information Technology
University of Malaysia
University of Malaya
50603 Kuala Lumpur, Malaysia
Ph: 60 379 676300
Fax: 60 379 579249
Publication E-mail: edzan@um.edu.my
Publisher E-mail: dekan_fsktm@um.edu.my
Publishes original articles based on professional policies, practices, principles and progress in the field of library and information science. **Founded:** 1996. **Freq:** Semiannual. **Trim Size:** 17.5 x 25.5 cm. **Key Personnel:** Prof. Dr. Zainab Awang Ngah, Editor-in-Chief. **ISSN:** 1394-6234. **URL:** http://ejum.fsktm.um.edu.my/VolumeListing.aspx?JournalID=3.

47618 ■ Malaysian Journal of Science Series A: Life Sciences
University of Malaya
Department of Geography
Faculty of Arts & Social Sciences
50603 Kuala Lumpur, Malaysia
Ph: 60 3 79675504
Fax: 60 3 79675457
Publisher E-mail: sas_geog@um.edu.my
Periodical covering original research, communications, and reviews in the field of life sciences. **Founded:** 1971. **Freq:** 2/yr. **Key Personnel:** Yong Hoi Sen, Editor. **ISSN:** 1394-1712. **URL:** http://geografi.um.edu.my/Objective.html. **Circ:** 1,000

47619 ■ Malaysian Journal of Science Series B: Physical & Earth Sciences
University of Malaya
Department of Geography
Faculty of Arts & Social Sciences
50603 Kuala Lumpur, Malaysia
Ph: 60 3 79675504
Fax: 60 3 79675457
Publisher E-mail: sas_geog@um.edu.my
Periodical covering original research, communications, and reviews in the fields of physical and earth sciences. **Founded:** 1972. **Freq:** 2/yr. **Key Personnel:** Yong Hoi Sen, Editor. **ISSN:** 1394-3065.

47620 ■ Malaysian Journal of Tropical Geography
University of Malaya
Department of Geography
Faculty of Arts & Social Sciences
50603 Kuala Lumpur, Malaysia
Ph: 60 3 79675504
Fax: 60 3 79675457
Publisher E-mail: sas_geog@um.edu.my
Periodical containing original papers on the human, physical and theoretical aspects of geography and the environment of tropical and sub-tropical areas. **Founded:** 1980. **Freq:** Semiannual. **Key Personnel:** Lee Boon Thong, Editor. **ISSN:** 0127-1474. **Subscription Rates:** M$40. **URL:** http://geografi.um.edu.my/. **Circ:** Paid 400

47621 ■ Malaysian Naturalist
Malayan Nature Society
JKR 641, Jalan Kelantan
Bukit Persekutuan
50480 Kuala Lumpur, Malaysia
Ph: 60 3 22879422
Fax: 60 3 22878773
Publisher E-mail: mns@mns.org.my
Natural science journal. **Founded:** Sept. 1974. **Freq:** Quarterly. **ISSN:** 0127-0206. **Subscription Rates:** Included in membership. **Remarks:** Accepts advertising. **URL:** http://www.mns.org.my; http://www.mns.org.my/section.php?sid=21. **Circ:** (Not Reported)

47622 ■ Malaysia's Best Restaurants
Edipresse Asia
Ste. 2A-19-2, Level 19, Block 2A
Plz. Sentral, Jalan Stesen Sentral 5
Kuala Lumpur Sentral
50470 Kuala Lumpur, Malaysia
Ph: 60 3 27808833
Fax: 60 3 27808823
Magazine featuring the best restaurants in Malaysia. **Freq:** Annual. **Key Personnel:** Florence Fang, Director.

Circulation: ★ = ABC; △ = BPA; ◆ = CAC; • = CCAB; ❑ = VAC; ⊕ = PO Statement; ‡ = Publisher's Report; Boldface figures = sworn; Light figures = estimated.

Gale Directory of Publications & Broadcast Media/147th Ed.

5181

URL: http://www.edipresse.com/food-dining/malaysia-best-restaurant. **Circ:** ‡20,800

47623 ■ Man and Society
University of Malaya Press
Pantai Valley
50603 Kuala Lumpur, Malaysia
Ph: 60 3 79574361
Fax: 60 3 79574473
Publisher E-mail: terbit@um.edu.my
Sociology journal. **Founded:** 1972. **Freq:** Annual. **Key Personnel:** Dr. Jas Laile Suzana Jaafar, Editor-in-Chief. **ISSN:** 0126-8678. **Subscription Rates:** US$15. **Remarks:** Advertising accepted; rates available upon request. **URL:** http://umrefjournal.um.edu.my/journal/index.php?menu=view_detail&id=42. **Circ:** Paid 1,000

47624 ■ Mangga
Utusan Melayu (M) Bhd
46 M, Jalan Lima Off
Jalan Chan Sow Lin
55200 Kuala Lumpur, Malaysia
Ph: 60 3 92217055
Fax: 60 3 92227876
Publisher E-mail: online@utusan.com.my
Entertainment magazine for readers ages 15 to 35 years. **Freq:** Monthly. **Trim Size:** 16.2 x 25.5 cm. **Key Personnel:** Datuk Abdul Aziz Ishak, Gp. Ed.-in-Ch. **Subscription Rates:** M$3.50 single issue. **Remarks:** Accepts advertising. **URL:** http://www.utusangroup.com.my/products/magazines. **Ad Rates:** BW: M$2,080, 4C: M$3,250. **Circ:** ★121,465

47625 ■ Master Builders Journal
Master Builders Association - Malaysia
Persatuan Pemborong Binaan Malaysia
2-1 Jalan 2/109E, 1st Fl.
Desa Business Pk., Taman Desa
Off Jalan Kelang Lama
58100 Kuala Lumpur, Malaysia
Ph: 60 3 79848636
Fax: 60 3 79826811
Publisher E-mail: mbam01@mbam.org.my
Journal covering building industries. **Freq:** Quarterly. **Subscription Rates:** Free to members; M$40 individuals. **Remarks:** Accepts advertising. **URL:** http://www.mbam.org.my/. **Circ:** 3,000

47626 ■ Mastika
Utusan Melayu (M) Bhd
46 M, Jalan Lima Off
Jalan Chan Sow Lin
55200 Kuala Lumpur, Malaysia
Ph: 60 3 92217055
Fax: 60 3 92227876
Publisher E-mail: online@utusan.com.my
Magazine featuring local folklores and real life experiences. **Freq:** Monthly. **Trim Size:** 21 x 27.6 cm. **Key Personnel:** Datuk Abdul Aziz Ishak, Gp. Ed.-in-Ch. **Subscription Rates:** M$5.50 single issue. **Remarks:** Accepts advertising. **URL:** http://www.utusangroup.com.my/products/magazines. **Ad Rates:** BW: M$1,050, 4C: M$1,785. **Circ:** ★236,541

47627 ■ The Medical Journal of Malaysia
Malaysian Medical Association
4th Fl., Bangunan MMA, No. 124
Jalan Pahang
53000 Kuala Lumpur, Malaysia
Ph: 60 3 40411375
Fax: 60 3 40418187
Medical journal. **Founded:** 1890. **Freq:** Quarterly. **Print Method:** Offset. **Trim Size:** A4. **URL:** http://www.mma.org.my/Publications/MedicalJournalofMalaysia/tabid/69/Default.aspx. **Ad Rates:** BW: M$550, 4C: M$1,500. **Circ:** 8,000

47628 ■ Mingguan Malaysia
Utusan Melayu (M) Bhd
46 M, Jalan Lima Off
Jalan Chan Sow Lin
55200 Kuala Lumpur, Malaysia
Ph: 60 3 92217055
Fax: 60 3 92227876
Publisher E-mail: online@utusan.com.my
Newspaper featuring politics, life and social highlights. **Freq:** Weekly (Sun.). **Key Personnel:** Mohd. Zin Mahmud, Editor. **Remarks:** Accepts display and classified advertising. **URL:** http://www.utusangroup.com.my/

products/newspaper. **Ad Rates:** BW: M$48. **Circ:** Sun. ★483,240

47629 ■ Neurology Asia
ASEAN Neurological Association
c/o Neurology Laboratory
University Malaya Medical Centre
59100 Kuala Lumpur, Malaysia
Publication E-mail: editor@neurology-asia.org
Publisher E-mail: public@aseansec.org
Journal dealing with Asian neurology. **Founded:** 1996. **Freq:** Semiannual. **Key Personnel:** Chong Tin Tan, Editor-in-Chief; Li Kuo Tan, Webmaster; Heng Thay Chong, Assoc. Ed.; M. Faiz, Editorial Board; M.A. Mannan, Editorial Board; Sui Chee On, Editorial Board; Kwang-Woo Lee, Editorial Board; Einar Wilder-Smith, Assoc. Ed. **ISSN:** 1823-6138. **Subscription Rates:** US$30 individuals. **URL:** http://www.neurology-asia.org/.

47630 ■ New Straits Times
The New Straits Times Press (Malaysia) Bhd.
Balai Berita
31 Jalan Riong
59100 Kuala Lumpur, Malaysia
Ph: 60 322 823131
Fax: 60 322 821428
Publication E-mail: news@nstp.com.my
Publisher E-mail: general@nstp.com.my
Business newspaper. **Subtitle:** Incorporating Business Times. **Founded:** 1845. **Freq:** Daily. **Key Personnel:** Nuraina Abdul Samad, Managing Editor; Dato Syed Nadzri Syed Harun, Gp. Ed.; Md. Shariff Haron, Exec. Dir. **Subscription Rates:** Free. **Remarks:** Accepts advertising. **URL:** http://www.nst.com.my. **Formerly:** The Straits Times. **Circ:** 136,273

47631 ■ New Sunday Times
The New Straits Times Press (Malaysia) Bhd.
Balai Berita
31 Jalan Riong
59100 Kuala Lumpur, Malaysia
Ph: 60 322 823131
Fax: 60 322 821428
Publisher E-mail: general@nstp.com.my
English language newspaper for Malaysia. Featuring tabloid magazine sections Sunday Style and Cars, Bikes, Trucks. **Founded:** Dec. 1931. **Freq:** Weekly. **Remarks:** Accepts advertising. **URL:** http://www.nstp.com.my/Corporate/nstp/products/productSunTimes.htm. **Formerly:** The Sunday Times. **Circ:** 100,000

47632 ■ Pemikir
Utusan Melayu (M) Bhd
46 M, Jalan Lima Off
Jalan Chan Sow Lin
55200 Kuala Lumpur, Malaysia
Ph: 60 3 92217055
Fax: 60 3 92227876
Publisher E-mail: online@utusan.com.my
Magazine featuring topical issues from local and international scenes. **Freq:** Quarterly. **Trim Size:** 17 x 25 cm. **Key Personnel:** Datuk Abdul Aziz Ishak, Group Ed.-in-Ch. **Subscription Rates:** M$25.50 single issue. **Remarks:** Accepts advertising. **URL:** http://www.utusangroup.com.my/products/magazines. **Ad Rates:** BW: M$800, 4C: M$1,000. **Circ:** (Not Reported)

47633 ■ Rocket
Democratic Action Party of Malaysia
DAP Malaysia
Ibu Pejabat Kebangsaan
Jalan Yew
55100 Kuala Lumpur, Malaysia
Ph: 60 3 92005000
Fax: 60 3 92007000
Publication E-mail: rocket@dapmalaysia.org
Publisher E-mail: dap@dapmalaysia.org
Focuses on the general news from the Democratic Action Party, component parties and NGOs in Malaysia. **Founded:** 1967. **Freq:** 3/week. **Key Personnel:** Tan Seng Giaw, Contact. **ISSN:** 0048-8461. **Subscription Rates:** M$24 individuals. **URL:** http://www.dapmalaysia.org/newenglish/au_sr.htm.

47634 ■ Saji
Utusan Melayu (M) Bhd
46 M, Jalan Lima Off
Jalan Chan Sow Lin
55200 Kuala Lumpur, Malaysia
Ph: 60 3 92217055

Fax: 60 3 92227876
Publisher E-mail: online@utusan.com.my
Cooking magazine featuring delicious health food diets, coveted recipes and cooking tips. **Freq:** Monthly. **Trim Size:** 21 x 27.6 cm. **Key Personnel:** Datuk Abdul Aziz Ishak, Gp. Ed.-in-Ch. **Subscription Rates:** M$5.50 single issue. **Remarks:** Accepts advertising. **URL:** http://www.utusangroup.com.my/products/magazines. **Ad Rates:** 4C: M$2,200. **Circ:** ★57,567

47635 ■ Show Daily
ADPR Consult (M) Sdn Bhd
PO Box 10762
No. 2, Jalan Sultan Sulaiman
50724 Kuala Lumpur, Malaysia
Ph: 60 3 77812903
Fax: 60 3 77812915
Publisher E-mail: enquiry@adprconsult.com.my
Periodical featuring complete coverage of all press conferences, interviews with industry CEOs and top military brass, contract signing ceremonies, official VIP visits, live product demonstrations such as aerial displays and other newsworthy informat. **Freq:** Irregular. **Trim Size:** 235 x 305 mm. **Subscription Rates:** Free. **Remarks:** Accepts advertising. **URL:** http://www.adprconsult.com.my/mag_showdaily.html. **Ad Rates:** BW: US$2,030, 4C: US$2,900. **Circ:** (Not Reported)

47636 ■ Suara TEEAM
The Electrical and Electronics Association of Malaysia
No. 5-B Jalan Gelugor
Off Jalan Kenanga
55200 Kuala Lumpur, Malaysia
Ph: 60 392 214417
Fax: 60 392 218212
Publisher E-mail: teeam@po.jaring.my
Magazine containing news and information about the industry. **Key Personnel:** Chew Shee Fuee, Editor. **ISSN:** 0128-293X. **Remarks:** Accepts advertising. **URL:** http://teeam.com/p_publications.htm. **Ad Rates:** BW: M$500, 4C: M$950. **Circ:** (Not Reported)

47637 ■ Tech & U
The New Straits Times Press (Malaysia) Bhd.
Balai Berita
31 Jalan Riong
59100 Kuala Lumpur, Malaysia
Ph: 60 322 823131
Fax: 60 322 821428
Publisher E-mail: general@nstp.com.my
Business publication. **Freq:** Biweekly. **Key Personnel:** Ahmad Kushairi, News Ed.; Rozana Sani, Asst. News Ed. **URL:** http://www.nstp.com.my/Corporate/nstp/products/productTechU.htm. **Formerly:** Computimes (Malaysia). **Circ:** 163,287

47638 ■ URTV
Utusan Melayu (M) Bhd
46 M, Jalan Lima Off
Jalan Chan Sow Lin
55200 Kuala Lumpur, Malaysia
Ph: 60 3 92217055
Fax: 60 3 92227876
Publisher E-mail: online@utusan.com.my
Magazine featuring local and international entertainment circuits. **Freq:** Bimonthly. **Trim Size:** 26.5 x 38.3 cm. **Key Personnel:** Datuk Abdul Aziz Ishak, Gp. Ed.-in-Ch. **Subscription Rates:** M$3.50 single issue. **Remarks:** Accepts advertising. **URL:** http://www.utusangroup.com.my/products/magazines. **Circ:** ★53,860

47639 ■ Utusan Malaysia
Utusan Melayu (M) Bhd
46 M, Jalan Lima Off
Jalan Chan Sow Lin
55200 Kuala Lumpur, Malaysia
Ph: 60 3 92217055
Fax: 60 3 92227876
Publisher E-mail: online@utusan.com.my
Newspaper catering to the multicultural, sophisticated public in Malaysia. **Founded:** 1939. **Remarks:** Accepts advertising. **URL:** http://www.utusangroup.com.my/products/newspaper. **Circ:** Paid 228,802

47640 ■ Utusan Melayu Mingguan
Utusan Melayu (M) Bhd
46 M, Jalan Lima Off
Jalan Chan Sow Lin
55200 Kuala Lumpur, Malaysia
Ph: 60 3 92217055

Fax: 60 3 92227876
Publisher E-mail: online@utusan.com.my
Local community newspaper. **Freq:** Weekly. **Key Personnel:** Mohd. Zin Mahmud, Editor. **Remarks:** Accepts display and classified advertising. **URL:** http://www.utusangroup.com.my/products/newspaper. **Circ:** (Not Reported)

47641 ■ Wanita
Utusan Melayu (M) Bhd
46 M, Jalan Lima Off
Jalan Chan Sow Lin
55200 Kuala Lumpur, Malaysia
Ph: 60 3 92217055
Fax: 60 3 92227876
Publisher E-mail: online@utusan.com.my
Magazine for women in Malaysia. **Freq:** Monthly. **Trim Size:** 21 x 27.6 cm. **Key Personnel:** Datuk Abdul Aziz Ishak, Gp. Ed.-in-Ch. **Subscription Rates:** M$6.50 single issue. **Remarks:** Accepts advertising. **URL:** http://www.utusangroup.com.my/products/magazines. **Ad Rates:** 4C: M$6,300. **Circ:** ★38,844

47642 ■ Chinese Melody - 866
All Asia Broadcast Ctr.
Technology Pk. Malaysia
Lebuhraya Puchong - Sungai Besi
Bukit Jalil
57000 Kuala Lumpur, Malaysia
Ph: 60 3 95434129
Fax: 60 3 95437333
Format: Contemporary Hit Radio (CHR); Ethnic. **Owner:** Airtime Management & Programming Sdn Bhd, at above address. **Ad Rates:** Advertising accepted; rates available upon request. **URL:** http://www.astro.com.my/radio.

47643 ■ Era - 101
All Asia Broadcast Centre
Technology Pk. Malaysia
Lebuhraya Puchong - Sg Besi
Bukit Jalil
57000 Kuala Lumpur, Malaysia
Ph: 60 3 95438855
Fax: 60 3 95435675
E-mail: era@astro.com.my
Format: Full Service. **Owner:** Airtime Management & Programming Sdn Bhd, at above address. **Founded:** 1996. **Operating Hours:** Continuous. **Ad Rates:** Noncommercial. **URL:** http://www.lyngsat-address.com/df/ERA-Radio.html; http://www.era.fm/.

47644 ■ Era-FM - 103.3
All Asia Broadcast Ctr.
Bukit Jalil
57000 Kuala Lumpur, Malaysia
Ph: 60 3 95438888
Fax: 60 3 95435675
E-mail: webmaster@era.fm
Format: Ethnic; World Beat. **Ad Rates:** Advertising accepted; rates available upon request. **URL:** http://www.era.fm.

47645 ■ Golden Oldies - 861
All Asia Broadcast Ctr.
Technology Pk. Malaysia
Lebuhraya Puchong - Sg Besi
Bukit Jalil
57000 Kuala Lumpur, Malaysia
Ph: 60 3 95434129
Fax: 60 3 95437333
Format: Eclectic. **Owner:** Airtime Management & Programming Sdn Bhd, at above address. **Ad Rates:** Advertising accepted; rates available upon request. **URL:** http://www.astro.com.my/radio.

47646 ■ Hitz - 104 MHz
All Asia Broadcast Centre
Technology Pk. Malaysia
Lebuhraya Puchong - Sg Besi
Bukit Jalil
57000 Kuala Lumpur, Malaysia
Ph: 60 3 95438888
Fax: 60 3 95433888
E-mail: info@ampradio.net
Owner: Airtime Management & Programming Sdn Bhd, at above address. **Operating Hours:** Continuous. **Ad Rates:** Advertising accepted; rates available upon request. **URL:** http://www.astro.com.my; http://www.hitz.fm/.

47647 ■ Hitz-FM - 97.6
All Asia Broadcast Centre
Technology Pk.
Lebuhraya Puchong-Sg. Besi
Bukit Jalil
57000 Kuala Lumpur, Malaysia
Ph: 60 3 95438888
Fax: 60 3 95433888
E-mail: info@ampradio.net
Format: Top 40; Contemporary Hit Radio (CHR); News. **Owner:** All Asia Broadcast Centre, at above address. **Operating Hours:** Continuous. **Ad Rates:** Advertising accepted; rates available upon request. **URL:** http://www.hitz.fm.

47648 ■ Hitz-FM - 92.9
All Asia Broadcast Centre
Technology Pk.
Lebuhraya Puchong-Sg. Besi
Bukit Jalil
57000 Kuala Lumpur, Malaysia
Ph: 60 3 95438888
Fax: 60 3 95433888
E-mail: info@ampradio.net
Format: Top 40; Contemporary Hit Radio (CHR); News. **Owner:** All Asia Broadcast Centre, at above address. **Operating Hours:** Continuous. **Ad Rates:** Advertising accepted; rates available upon request. **URL:** http://www.hitz.fm.

47649 ■ India Beat - 864
All Asia Broadcast Ctr.
Technology Pk. Malaysia
Lebuhraya Puchong - Sungai Besi
Bukit Jalil
57000 Kuala Lumpur, Malaysia
Ph: 60 3 95434129
Fax: 60 3 95437333
Format: Ethnic; Contemporary Hit Radio (CHR). **Owner:** Airtime Management & Programming Sdn Bhd, at above address. **Ad Rates:** Advertising accepted; rates available upon request. **URL:** http://www.astro.com.my/radio.

47650 ■ Jazz - 865
All Asia Broadcast Ctr.
Technology Pk. Malaysia
Lebuhraya Puchong - Sungai Besi
Bukit Jalil
57000 Kuala Lumpur, Malaysia
Ph: 60 3 95434129
Fax: 60 3 95437333
Format: Jazz. **Owner:** Airtime Management & Programming Sdn Bhd, at above address. **Ad Rates:** Advertising accepted; rates available upon request. **URL:** http://www.astro.com.my/radio.

47651 ■ Light&Easy-FM - 94.6
Technology Pk.
Lebuhraya Puchong
Sg BesiBukit Jalil
57000 Kuala Lumpur, Malaysia
Ph: 60 3 95438888
Fax: 60 3 95430751
E-mail: lite@astro.com.my
Format: Soft Rock; Ethnic; Easy Listening. **Owner:** All Asia Broadcast Centre, at above address. **Operating Hours:** Continuous. **Ad Rates:** Advertising accepted; rates available upon request. **URL:** http://www.litefm.com.my.

47652 ■ LiteFM - 105.7
All Asia Broadcast Ctr.
Technology Pk.
Lebuhraya Puchong-Sg. Besi
Bukit Jalil
57000 Kuala Lumpur, Malaysia
Ph: 60 3 95438888
Fax: 60 3 95430751
E-mail: lite@astro.com.my
Format: Easy Listening. **Formerly:** Light&Easy-FM. **Ad Rates:** Advertising accepted; rates available upon request. **URL:** http://www.litefm.com.my.

Minnal FM - Besut - See Besut

Minnal FM - Jeli - See Jeli

Minnal FM - Jerantut - See Jerantut

47653 ■ Minnal FM - Kuala Lumpur - 92.3
Tingkat 4, Wisma Radio
Peti Surat 11272
Angkasapuri

50740 Kuala Lumpur, Malaysia
Ph: 60 3 22887279
Fax: 60 3 22849137
E-mail: mail@minnalfm.com
Format: Classical; News; Information. **Owner:** Radio Televisyen Malaysia, Jabatan Penyiaran Malaysia, Angkasapuri, 50614 Kuala Lumpur, Malaysia. **Operating Hours:** Continuous. **URL:** http://www.minnalfm.com/.

Minnal FM - Kuala Terengganu - See Kuala Terengganu

Minnal FM - Kuantan - See Kuantan

Minnal FM - Mersing - See Mersing

Minnal FM - Muar - See Muar

Minnal FM - Taiping - See Taiping

47654 ■ Mix - 105
All Asia Broadcast Centre
Technology Pk. Malaysia
Lebuhraya Puchong - Sg Besi
Bukit Jalil
57000 Kuala Lumpur, Malaysia
Ph: 60 3 95438888
Fax: 60 3 95433888
E-mail: mixfm@astro.com.my
Format: Full Service. **Owner:** Airtime Management & Programming Sdn Bhd, at above address. **Operating Hours:** 6 am-12 am Mon.-Fri. **Ad Rates:** Noncommercial. **URL:** http://www.mix.fm/04/.

47655 ■ My - 853
All Asia Broadcast Centre
Technology Pk. Malaysia
Lebuhraya Puchong - Sg Besi
Bukit Jalil
57000 Kuala Lumpur, Malaysia
Ph: 60 3 74919888
Fax: 60 3 95437333
E-mail: my@astro.com.my
Format: Full Service. **Owner:** Airtime Management & Programming Sdn Bhd, at above address. **Ad Rates:** Advertising accepted; rates available upon request. **URL:** http://www.astro.com.my; http://www.my.com.my.

Radio Television Malaysia - See Selangor

47656 ■ Radio Television Malaysia TV1 - 1
Ministry of Communication & Culture
Department of Broadcasting
Angkasapuri
50614 Kuala Lumpur, Malaysia
Ph: 60 3 22825333
Fax: 60 3 22825103
E-mail: feedback@rtm.gov.my
Format: News; Sports. **Owner:** Radio Television Malaysia, at above address. **Former name:** RTM1 (Dec. 28, 1978); The First Channel. **Operating Hours:** 6.00 a.m. - 5.40 a.m. **Key Personnel:** Datuk Ibrahim Yahaya, Dir. Gen. **Ad Rates:** Advertising accepted; rates available upon request. **URL:** http://www.rtm.gov.my/.

47657 ■ Radio Television Malaysia TV2 - 2
Ministry of Communication & Culture
Department of Broadcasting
Angkasapuri
50614 Kuala Lumpur, Malaysia
Ph: 60 3 22825333
Fax: 60 3 22825103
E-mail: feedback@rtm.gov.my
Format: News; Sports. **Owner:** Radio Television Malaysia, at above address. **Founded:** Nov. 17, 1969. **Former name:** The Second Channel. **Operating Hours:** 6.00 a.m. - 5.50 a.m. **Key Personnel:** Datuk Ibrahim Yahaya, Dir. Gen. **Ad Rates:** Advertising accepted; rates available upon request. **URL:** http://www.rtm.gov.my/.

47658 ■ Red-FM - 104.9
19th Fl., Bangunan AmAssurance
1 Jalan Lumut
50400 Kuala Lumpur, Malaysia
Ph: 60 3 40481988
Fax: 60 3 40444487
E-mail: info@starrfm.com.my
Format: News; Contemporary Hit Radio (CHR); Ethnic. **Operating Hours:** Continuous. **Key Personnel:** Jon Roy Fletcher, Executive, Airtime Sales, jon@starrfm.com.my; Zach Chiang, Executive Airtime Sales, zach@starrfm.com.my; Darren Low, Sales Mgr., darren@starrfm.com.my. **Ad Rates:** Advertising accepted; rates

Circulation: ★ = ABC; △ = BPA; ◆ = CAC; • = CCAB; ❑ = VAC; ⊕ = PO Statement; ‡ = Publisher's Report; Boldface figures = sworn; Light figures = estimated.

available upon request. **URL:** http://web.red.fm/Red_FM/Red_FM_%3A_Todays_Best_Music.html.

47659 ■ Sinar-FM - 96.7
All Asia Broadcast Center
Bukit Jalil
57000 Kuala Lumpur, Malaysia
Ph: 60 3 95438888
Fax: 60 3 95435675
E-mail: webmaster@sinar.fm
Format: Eighties; Album-Oriented Rock (AOR); Ethnic. **Owner:** Airtime Management and Programming Sdn. Bhd., at above address. **Ad Rates:** Advertising accepted; rates available upon request. **URL:** http://www.sinar.fm.

47660 ■ Sinar-FM - 93.8
All Asia Broadcast Center
Bukit Jalil
57000 Kuala Lumpur, Malaysia
Ph: 60 3 95438888
Fax: 60 3 95435675
E-mail: webmaster@sinar.fm
Format: Eighties; Album-Oriented Rock (AOR); Ethnic. **Ad Rates:** Advertising accepted; rates available upon request. **URL:** http://www.sinar.fm.

47661 ■ Sinar-FM - 96.9
All Asia Broadcast Center
Bukit Jalil
57000 Kuala Lumpur, Malaysia
Ph: 60 3 95438888
Fax: 60 3 95435675
E-mail: webmaster@sinar.fm
Format: Eighties; Album-Oriented Rock (AOR); Ethnic. **Owner:** Airtime Management and Programming Sdn. Bhd., at above address. **Ad Rates:** Advertising accepted; rates available upon request. **URL:** http://www.sinar.fm:

Traxx FM - Bintulu - See Bintulu

Traxx FM - Bukit Tinggi - See Bukit Tinggi

Traxx FM - Gurun - See Gurun

Traxx FM - Ipoh - See Ipoh

Traxx FM - Jeli - See Jeli

Traxx FM - Johor Bahru - See Johor Bahru

Traxx FM - Kota Baru - See Kota Baru

Traxx FM - Kota Belud - See Kota Belud

Traxx FM - Kota Kinabalu - See Kota Kinabalu

Traxx FM - Kuala Besut - See Kuala Besut

Traxx FM - Kuala Dungun - See Kuala Dungun

Traxx FM - Kuala Terengganu - See Kuala Terengganu

Traxx FM - Kuantan - See Kuantan

Traxx FM - Kuching - See Kuching

Traxx FM - Miri - See Miri

Traxx FM - Sandakan - See Sandakan

Traxx FM - Taiping - See Taiping

Traxx FM - Tangkak - See Tangkak

47662 ■ Xfresh-FM - 98.5
Administration Bldg., 3rd Fl.
All Asia Broadcast Ctr.
Technology Pk. Malaysia, Lebuhraya Puchong
Sungai Besi, Bukit Jalil
57000 Kuala Lumpur, Malaysia
Ph: 60 3 95438888
Fax: 60 3 95435675
Format: Ethnic. **Owner:** All Asia Networks PLC, at above address. **Ad Rates:** Advertising accepted; rates available upon request. **URL:** http://www.xfresh.com.

Kuala Terengganu

47663 ■ Minnal FM - Kuala Terengganu - 87.9
Tingkat 4, Wisma Radio
Peti Surat 11272
Angkasapuri
50740 Kuala Lumpur, Malaysia
Ph: 60 3 22887279
Fax: 60 3 22849137
E-mail: mail@minnalfm.com
Format: Classical; News; Information. **Owner:** Radio Televisyen Malaysia, Jabatan Penyiaran Malaysia, Angkasapuri, 50614 Kuala Lumpur, Malaysia. **Operating**

Hours: Continuous. **URL:** http://www.minnalfm.com/.

47664 ■ Traxx FM - Kuala Terengganu - 89.7
2nd Fl., Wisma Radio
Angkasapuri
50740 Kuala Lumpur, Malaysia
Ph: 60 3 22887663
Fax: 60 3 22845750
Format: Contemporary Hit Radio (CHR); Talk; Information. **Owner:** Radio Televisyen Malaysia, Jabatan Penyiaran Malaysia, Angkasapuri, 50614 Kuala Lumpur, Malaysia. **Operating Hours:** Continuous. **URL:** http://www.traxxfm.net/.

Kuantan

47665 ■ Minnal FM - Kuantan - 103.3
Tingkat 4, Wisma Radio
Peti Surat 11272
Angkasapuri
50740 Kuala Lumpur, Malaysia
Ph: 60 3 22887279
Fax: 60 3 22849137
E-mail: mail@minnalfm.com
Format: Classical; News; Information. **Owner:** Radio Televisyen Malaysia, Jabatan Penyiaran Malaysia, Angkasapuri, 50614 Kuala Lumpur, Malaysia. **Operating Hours:** Continuous. **URL:** http://www.minnalfm.com/.

47666 ■ Traxx FM - Kuantan - 105.3
2nd Fl., Wisma Radio
Angkasapuri
50740 Kuala Lumpur, Malaysia
Ph: 60 3 22887663
Fax: 60 3 22845750
Format: Contemporary Hit Radio (CHR); Talk; Information. **Owner:** Radio Televisyen Malaysia, Jabatan Penyiaran Malaysia, Angkasapuri, 50614 Kuala Lumpur, Malaysia. **Operating Hours:** Continuous. **URL:** http://www.traxxfm.net/.

Kuching

47667 ■ Pepper Market Bulletin
Malaysian Paper Board
Tanah Putih
PO Box 1653
93916 Kuching, Malaysia
Ph: 60 823 31811
Fax: 60 823 36877
Publisher E-mail: info@mpb.gov.my
Publication covering food. **Founded:** 1972. **Freq:** Quarterly. **Trim Size:** 19.5 x 26.5 cm. **ISSN:** 0126-5903. **URL:** http://www.mpb.gov.my/arkibbm.html. **Circ:** Combined 390

47668 ■ Radio Television Malaysia Sarawak - 1062 KHz
Broadcasting Department
Jalan P. Ramlee
93614 Kuching, Malaysia
Ph: 60 82 248422
Fax: 60 82 241914
E-mail: rtmkuc@rtm.net.my
Format: Eclectic. **Operating Hours:** 2200-0100 on weekdays; 2200-0600 on Sun. **Wattage:** 20,000. **URL:** http://www.rtmsarawak.gov.my/.

47669 ■ Radio Television Malaysia Sarawak - 621 KHz
Broadcasting Department
Jalan P. Ramlee
93614 Kuching, Malaysia
Ph: 60 8 2248422
Fax: 60 8 2241914
E-mail: rtmkuc@rtm.net.my
Format: Eclectic. **Operating Hours:** 2200-1600. **Wattage:** 20,000. **Ad Rates:** Noncommercial. **URL:** http://www.rtmsarawak.gov.my/.

47670 ■ Radio Television Malaysia Sarawak - 819 KHz
Broadcasting Department
Jalan P. Ramlee
93614 Kuching, Malaysia
Ph: 60 82 248422
Fax: 60 82 241914
E-mail: rtmkuc@rtm.net.my
Format: Eclectic. **Operating Hours:** 2200-1600. **Wattage:** 20,000. **URL:** http://www.rtmsarawak.gov.my/.

47671 ■ Radio Television Malaysia Sarawak - 4895 KHz
Broadcasting Department
Jalan P. Ramlee
93614 Kuching, Malaysia
Ph: 60 82 248422
Fax: 60 82 241914
E-mail: rtmkuc@rtm.net.my
Format: Eclectic. **Owner:** Radio Television Malaysia Sarawak, at above address. **Operating Hours:** 2100-1600. **Wattage:** 10,000. **Ad Rates:** Noncommercial. **URL:** http://www.rtmsarawak.gov.my/.

47672 ■ Radio Television Malaysia Sarawak - 7130 KHz
Broadcasting Department
Jalan P. Ramlee
93614 Kuching, Malaysia
Ph: 60 82 248422
Fax: 60 82 241914
E-mail: rtmkuc@rtm.net.my
Format: Educational. **Operating Hours:** 2100-1600. **Wattage:** 10,000. **URL:** http://www.rtmsarawak.gov.my/.

47673 ■ Radio Television Malaysia Sarawak - 846 KHz
Broadcasting Department
Jalan P. Ramlee
93614 Kuching, Malaysia
Ph: 60 82 248422
Fax: 60 82 241914
E-mail: rtmkuc@rtm.net.my
Format: Eclectic. **Owner:** Radio Television Malaysia Sarawak, at above address. **Operating Hours:** 2200-0100 on Weekdays; 2200-0600 on Sun. **Wattage:** 10,000. **Ad Rates:** Noncommercial. **URL:** http://www.rtmsarawak.gov.my/.

47674 ■ Radio Television Malaysia Sarawak - 954 KHz
Broadcasting Department
Jalan P. Ramlee
93614 Kuching, Malaysia
Ph: 60 82 248422
Fax: 60 82 241914
E-mail: rtmkuc@rtm.net.my
Format: Eclectic. **Owner:** Radio Television Malaysia Sarawak, at above address. **Operating Hours:** 2200-1600. **Wattage:** 10,000. **URL:** http://www.rtmsarawak.gov.my/.

47675 ■ Radio Television Malaysia Sarawak - 729 KHz
Broadcasting Department
Jalan P. Ramlee
93614 Kuching, Malaysia
Ph: 60 82 248422
Fax: 60 82 241914
E-mail: rtmkuc@rtm.net.my
Format: Eclectic. **Owner:** Radio Television Malaysia Sarawak, at above address. **Operating Hours:** 10 p.m.-4 a.m. on weekdays; 10 p.m. -2 a.m. on Sun. **Wattage:** 20,000. **Ad Rates:** Noncommercial. **URL:** http://www.rtmsarawak.gov.my/.

Radio Television Malaysia Sarawak - See Limbang

Radio Television Malaysia Sarawak - See Limbang

Radio Television Malaysia Sarawak - See Miri

Radio Television Malaysia Sarawak - See Miri

Radio Television Malaysia Sarawak - See Sibu

Radio Television Malaysia Sarawak - See Sibu

Radio Television Malaysia Sarawak - See Sri Aman

Radio Television Malaysia Sarawak - See Sri Aman

47676 ■ Traxx FM - Kuching - 89.9
2nd Fl., Wisma Radio
Angkasapuri
50740 Kuala Lumpur, Malaysia
Ph: 60 3 22887663
Fax: 60 3 22845750
Format: Contemporary Hit Radio (CHR); Talk; Information. **Owner:** Radio Televisyen Malaysia, Jabatan Penyiaran Malaysia, Angkasapuri, 50614 Kuala Lumpur, Malaysia. **Operating Hours:** Continuous. **URL:** http://www.traxxfm.net/.

Limbang

47677 ■ Radio Television Malaysia Sarawak - 873 KHz
Broadcasting Department
Jalan P. Ramlee
93614 Kuching, Malaysia
Ph: 60 8 2248422
Fax: 60 8 2241914
E-mail: rtmkuc@rtm.net.my
Format: Eclectic. **Operating Hours:** 2200-1600. **Wattage:** 20,000. **Ad Rates:** Noncommercial. **URL:** http://www.rtmsarawak.gov.my/.

47678 ■ Radio Television Malaysia Sarawak - 648 KHz
Broadcasting Department
Jalan P. Ramlee
93614 Kuching, Malaysia
Ph: 60 8 2248422
Fax: 60 8 2241914
E-mail: rtmkuc@rtm.net.my
Format: Eclectic. **Operating Hours:** 2100-1600. **Wattage:** 20,000. **Ad Rates:** Noncommercial. **URL:** http://www.rtmsarawak.gov.my/.

Malacca

47679 ■ Radio Malaya Malacca - 102.3 MHz
Jalan Timing Sari
Malacca, Malaysia
Ph: 60 6 2832314
Fax: 60 6 2832073
E-mail: rmm@mmu.edu.my
Format: Eclectic. **Founded:** 1946. **Operating Hours:** 2200-1600. **Wattage:** 1000. **Ad Rates:** Advertising accepted; rates available upon request. **URL:** http://melakafm.mmu.edu.my.

Melaka

47680 ■ Erasmus Law and Economics Review
c/o Dennis Khong, MAN
Faculty of Business & Law
Multimedia University
Jalan Ayer Keroh Lama
75450 Melaka, Malaysia
Publisher E-mail: denniswkkhong@gmail.com
Journal providing a new, open and free communication interface between lawyers, academics and economists, in order to reduce the law and economics approach especially among young lawyers and law students in Central Europe, and Asia and South America, which for their social, economical and political background are sharply different from the nations where law and economics was born and flourished. **Freq:** Annual. **Key Personnel:** Dr. Qi Zhou, Editor, qi.zhou@sheffield.ac.uk; Dr. Dennis W. K. Khong, Editor, dwkkhong@gmail.com. **ISSN:** 1824-3886. **URL:** http://www.eler.org/index.php.

47681 ■ International Journal of Precision Technology
Inderscience Publishers
c/o Dr. P. Brevern, Editorial Board Member
Multimedia University
Faculty of Engineering & Technology
Jalan Ayer Keroh Lama
75450 Melaka, Malaysia
Publisher E-mail: editor@inderscience.com
Peer-reviewed journal covering technological advances in precision engineering. **Founded:** 2007. **Freq:** 4/yr. **Key Personnel:** Prof. V.C. Venkatesh, Editor-in-Chief, vellore.venkatesh@unlv.edu; Dr. P. Brevern, Editorial Board Member; Prof. Fengzhou Fang, Editorial Board Member. **ISSN:** 1755-2060. **Subscription Rates:** EUR494 individuals includes surface mail, print only; EUR672 individuals print and online. **URL:** http://www.inderscience.com/browse/index.php?journalCODE=ijptech.

Mersing

47682 ■ Minnal FM - Mersing - 101.1
Tingkat 4, Wisma Radio
Peti Surat 11272
Angkasapuri
50740 Kuala Lumpur, Malaysia
Ph: 60 3 22887279
Fax: 60 3 22849137
E-mail: mail@minnalfm.com
Format: Classical; News; Information. **Owner:** Radio Televisyen Malaysia, Jabatan Penyiaran Malaysia, Angkasapuri, 50614 Kuala Lumpur, Malaysia. **Operating Hours:** Continuous. **Key Personnel:** Raja Sekaran, Director; S. Santa, Supvr. **URL:** http://www.minnalfm.com/english/frequency.html.

Miri

47683 ■ International Journal of Managerial and Financial Accounting
Inderscience Enterprises Limited
c/o Dr. Junaid M. Shaikh, Ed.-in-Ch.
Curtin University of Technology
Dept. of Accounting, School of Business
Sarawak Campus (Off Shore Campus), CDT 250
98009 Miri, Malaysia
Journal covering all aspects of managerial accounting as well as financial accounting prevailing worldwide. **Freq:** 4/yr. **Key Personnel:** Dr. Junaid M. Shaikh, Editor-in-Chief, junaid.s@curtin.edu.my. **ISSN:** 1753-6715. **Subscription Rates:** EUR494 individuals print or online; EUR672 individuals print and online. **URL:** http://www.inderscience.com/browse/index.php?journalID=252.

47684 ■ Radio Television Malaysia Sarawak - 1206 KHz
Broadcasting Department
Jalan P. Ramlee
93614 Kuching, Malaysia
Ph: 60 82 248422
Fax: 60 82 241914
E-mail: rtmkuc@rtm.net.my
Format: Eclectic. **Operating Hours:** 2200-0100 on weekdays; 2200-0600 on Sun. **Wattage:** 20,000. **Ad Rates:** Noncommercial. **URL:** http://www.rtmsarawak.gov.my/.

47685 ■ Radio Television Malaysia Sarawak - 91.9 MHz
Broadcasting Department
Jalan P. Ramlee
93614 Kuching, Malaysia
Ph: 60 82 248422
Fax: 60 82 241914
E-mail: rtmkuc@rtm.net.my
Format: Eclectic. **Operating Hours:** 2100-1600. **Wattage:** 20,000. **URL:** http://www.rtmsarawak.gov.my/.

47686 ■ Traxx FM - Miri - 104.5
2nd Fl., Wisma Radio
Angkasapuri
50740 Kuala Lumpur, Malaysia
Ph: 60 3 22887663
Fax: 60 3 22845750
Format: Contemporary Hit Radio (CHR); Talk; Information. **Owner:** Radio Televisyen Malaysia, Jabatan Penyiaran Malaysia, Angkasapuri, 50614 Kuala Lumpur, Malaysia. **Operating Hours:** Continuous. **URL:** http://www.traxxfm.net/.

Muar

47687 ■ Minnal FM - Muar - 103.3
Tingkat 4, Wisma Radio
Peti Surat 11272
Angkasapuri
50740 Kuala Lumpur, Malaysia
Ph: 60 3 22887279
Fax: 60 3 22849137
E-mail: mail@minnalfm.com
Format: Classical; News; Information. **Owner:** Radio Televisyen Malaysia, Jabatan Penyiaran Malaysia, Angkasapuri, 50614 Kuala Lumpur, Malaysia. **Operating Hours:** Continuous. **Key Personnel:** Raja Sekaran, Director; S. Santa, Supvr. **URL:** http://www.minnalfm.com/english/frequency.html.

Penang

47688 ■ The Classroom Teacher
SEAMEO Regional Centre for Education in Science and Mathematics
11700 Gelugor
11700 Penang, Malaysia
Ph: 60 465 22700
Fax: 60 465 22737
Publisher E-mail: director@recsam.edu.my
English and Malay publication covering science. **Founded:** 1995. **Freq:** Quarterly. **ISSN:** 1394-5688. **Remarks:** Advertising accepted; rates available upon request. **URL:** http://www.recsam.edu.my. **Circ:** 100

47689 ■ Journal of Science and Mathematics Education in Southeast Asia
SEAMEO Regional Centre for Education in Science and Mathematics
11700 Gelugor
11700 Penang, Malaysia
Ph: 60 465 22700
Fax: 60 465 22737
Publisher E-mail: director@recsam.edu.my
Southeast Asian journal covering science and math. **Founded:** 1970. **Freq:** Semiannual June and December. **Key Personnel:** Dr. Cheah Ui Hock, Editor-in-Chief; Devadason Robert Peter, Editor; Wahyudi Yososutikno, Editor. **ISSN:** 0126-7663. **Remarks:** Advertising accepted; rates available upon request. **URL:** http://www.recsam.edu.my/. **Circ:** 100

47690 ■ NAGA
WorldFish Center
11960 Bayan Lepas
Jalan Batu Maung, Batu Maung
PO Box 500
10670 Penang, Malaysia
Ph: 60 4 626 1606
Fax: 60 4 626 5530
Publisher E-mail: worldfishcenter@cgiar.org
Publication covering research on fisheries and aquatic resources. **Subtitle:** WorldFish Center Quarterly. **Founded:** 1986. **Freq:** Quarterly. **Print Method:** Offset. **Trim Size:** 8-1/2 x 11. **Key Personnel:** Sharmini Blok, Contact. **ISSN:** 1511-8533. **Subscription Rates:** US$20 individuals; Free developing countries. **Remarks:** Accepts advertising. **URL:** http://www.worldfishcenter.org/cms/list_article.aspx?catID=41&ddlID=145. **Formerly:** ICLARM Newsletter. **Ad Rates:** 4C: US$500, PCI: US$8. **Circ:** (Not Reported)

47691 ■ Suara SAM
Sahabat Alam Malaysia
21, Lindang Delima 15
11700 Penang, Malaysia
Ph: 604 6596960
Fax: 604 6596931
Periodical covering environmental issues. **Founded:** 1983. **Freq:** Quarterly. **ISSN:** 0127-6409. **Subscription Rates:** M$16. **Remarks:** Advertising accepted; rates available upon request. **Circ:** Paid 2,500

47692 ■ Third World Economics
Third World Network
131, Jalan Macalister
10400 Penang, Malaysia
Ph: 60 422 66159
Fax: 60 422 64505
Publication E-mail: twn@igc.apc.org
Publisher E-mail: twnet@po.jaring.my
Publication providing news and analyses that reflect the grassroots interests of people in the Third World. **Founded:** 1990. **Freq:** Biweekly. **ISSN:** 0128-4134. **Subscription Rates:** US$55 individuals third World Countries; US$75 individuals developed Countries; US$95 individuals developed Countries, airmail; US$75 individuals third World Countries, airmail. **URL:** http://www.twnside.org.sg/twe.htm.

47693 ■ Third World Resurgence
Third World Network
131, Jalan Macalister
10400 Penang, Malaysia
Ph: 60 422 66159
Fax: 60 422 64505
Publisher E-mail: twnet@po.jaring.my
Periodical providing a Third World perspective on the issues confronting the Third World, including the environment, health and basic needs, international affairs, politics, economics, culture, and so on. **Founded:** 1990. **Freq:** Monthly. **ISSN:** 0128-357X. **Subscription Rates:** US$45 institutions developed Countries; US$30 individuals developed Countries; US$20 individuals third World Countries; US$60 institutions developed Countries, airmail; US$45 individuals developed Countries, airmail; US$35 individuals third World Countries, airmail. **URL:** http://www.twnside.org.sg/twr.htm.

Circulation: ★ = ABC; △ = BPA; ♦ = CAC; • = CCAB; ❑ = VAC; ⊕ = PO Statement; ‡ = Publisher's Report; Boldface figures = sworn; Light figures = estimated.

Perlis

47694 ■ International Journal of Materials Engineering and Technology
Pushpa Publishing House
c/o Prof. M. Misbahul Amin, Ed.-in-Ch.
School of Materials Engineering
PPK Bahan Taman Muhibah UniMAP
University Malaysia Perlis, Jejawi
02600 Perlis, Malaysia
Publisher E-mail: arun@pphmj.com
Peer-reviewed journal covering issues on the properties of materials and their applications to equipment and structures. **Freq:** Semiannual. **Key Personnel:** Prof. M. Misbahul Amin, Editor-in-Chief, iijmet2008@atsyahoo.com. **Subscription Rates:** Rs 5,000 institutions print only; EUR240 institutions, other countries online only; EUR298 institutions, other countries print and online. **URL:** http://pphmj.com/journals/ijmet.htm.

Petaling Jaya

47695 ■ B & I Magazine
Eric Tan
Ste. 201, Block A, Mentari Business Pk.
Jalan PJS 8/5, Bandar Sunway
46150 Petaling Jaya, Malaysia
Ph: 60 356 319395
Fax: 60 356 374062
Publication E-mail: bni@tm.net.my
Publisher E-mail: b-i@b-i.biz
Building and construction magazine. **Founded:** 1991. **Freq:** Bimonthly. **Key Personnel:** Eric Tan, Editor. **Subscription Rates:** M$240 individuals Malaysia, postage included; US$90 other countries. **Remarks:** Accepts advertising. **URL:** http://www.b-i.com.my. **Ad Rates:** BW: M$2,200. **Circ:** 10,000

47696 ■ European Journal of Innovation Management
Emerald Group Publishing Ltd.
Monash University Malaysia
No. 2 Jalan Universiti
Bandar Sunway
46150 Petaling Jaya, Malaysia
Publisher E-mail: emerald@emeraldinsight.com
Journal aiming to be a European forum for disseminating vital information and knowledge in the field of innovation. Publishes high-quality papers written by both academics and practitioners, which capture leading edge developments, both in practice and theory. **Freq:** 4/yr. **Key Personnel:** Prof. Pervaiz K. Ahmed, Editor, pervaiz@buseco.monash.edu.my; Prof. Peter F. Kaminski, Editorial Advisory Board; Dr. Mohammed Rafiq, Co-Ed., m.rafiq@lboro.ac.uk; Dr. Catherine L. Wang, Co-Ed., catherine.wang@rhul.ac.uk; Prof. Antonis C. Simintiras, Editorial Advisory Board; Prof. Dale Littler, Editorial Advisory Board; Prof. Amar Dev Amar, Editorial Advisory Board; Andrew Smith, Publisher, agsmith@emeraldinsight.com. **ISSN:** 1460-1060. **URL:** http://info.emeraldinsight.com/products/journals/journals.htm?id=ejim.

47697 ■ Galaxie
Star Publications (M) Bhd
Menara Star, 15 Jalan 16/11
Selangor Darul Ehsan
46350 Petaling Jaya, Malaysia
Ph: 60 3 79671388
Fax: 60 3 79554039
Entertainment magazine. **Founded:** 1974. **Freq:** Biweekly. **ISSN:** 1511-0133. **Subscription Rates:** M$160 two years. **Remarks:** Accepts advertising. **URL:** http://thestar.com.my/info/thestar.asp. **Circ:** ★15,733

47698 ■ Golf Malaysia
Golf (Malaysia) Publications Sdn. Bhd.
No. 7-5 Block E2
Dataran Prima
Jalan PJU 1/42A
47301 Petaling Jaya, Malaysia
Ph: 60 378 805060
Fax: 60 378 805171
Golf magazine. **Founded:** 1980. **Freq:** Monthly. **Key Personnel:** Doug Neumann, Managing Editor, golfmsia@golfmalaysia.com.my; Juliana Cheah, Publisher. **ISSN:** 0127-1997. **URL:** http://www.golfmalaysia.com.my. **Circ:** Paid 25,000

47699 ■ IEM Journal
The Institution of Engineers, Malaysia

Institusi Jurutera, Malaysia
Lots 60/62, Jalan 52/4
Peti Surat 223, Jalan Sultan
Selangor Darul Ehsan
46720 Petaling Jaya, Malaysia
Ph: 60 796 84001
Fax: 60 795 77678
Publisher E-mail: sec@iem.org.my
Professional journal covering engineering. **Subtitle:** The Journal of the Institution of Engineers, Malaysia. **Freq:** Quarterly March, June, Sept. and Dec. **Trim Size:** A4. **Key Personnel:** Dr. Aminuddin bin Mohd Baki, Journal Ed. **ISSN:** 0126-513X. **Subscription Rates:** M$110 members. **URL:** http://www.myiem.org.my/content/journal-122.aspx. **Circ:** 15,000

47700 ■ Jurutera
The Institution of Engineers, Malaysia
Institusi Jurutera, Malaysia
Lots 60/62, Jalan 52/4
Peti Surat 223, Jalan Sultan
Selangor Darul Ehsan
46720 Petaling Jaya, Malaysia
Ph: 60 796 84001
Fax: 60 795 77678
Publisher E-mail: sec@iem.org.my
Engineering bulletin. **Freq:** Monthly. **Key Personnel:** Dr. Ramlee bin Karim, Ed. **Remarks:** Advertising accepted; rates available upon request. **URL:** http://www.myiem.org.my/content/publication-45.aspx. **Circ:** Paid 15,000

47701 ■ The Malaysian Surveyor
Institution of Surveyors, Malaysia
3rd Fl., Bangunan Juruukur
64-66 Jalan 52-4
46200 Petaling Jaya, Malaysia
Ph: 60 3 79551773
Fax: 60 3 79550253
Publisher E-mail: secretariat@ism.org.my
Publication focusing on the development of the surveying profession, innovations in surveying technology and surveyors' contribution towards the property market and building industry. **Subtitle:** The Professional Journal of the Institution of Surveyors. **Founded:** 1971. **Freq:** Quarterly. **ISSN:** 0126-6268. **Subscription Rates:** M$48 individuals Malaysia; US$30 individuals ASEAN countries; US$40 individuals Asia & Australia; US$55 individuals Europe & Africa, America. **Remarks:** Advertising accepted; rates available upon request. **URL:** http://www.ism.org.my/1_public/p_the_surveyor.asp. **Circ:** Paid 3,000

47702 ■ The Star
Star Publications (M) Bhd
Menara Star, 15 Jalan 16/11
Selangor Darul Ehsan
46350 Petaling Jaya, Malaysia
Ph: 60 3 79671388
Fax: 60 3 79554039
General newspaper. **Subtitle:** The People's Paper. **Founded:** 1971. **Freq:** Mon.-Sat. **Key Personnel:** Khim Lim Chye, Sen. News Ed.; Devid Rajah, News Ed.; Lourdes Joseph Charles, Dep. Exec. Ed.; David P.L. Yeoh, Dep. Gp. Ch. Ed.; P. Gunasegaram, Managing Editor; June H L Wong, Managing Editor; Datuk Seri Wong Chun Wai, Exec. Dir. **Remarks:** Accepts advertising. **URL:** http://thestar.com.my/. **Circ:** Mon.-Sat. ★926,000

47703 ■ FLY-FM - 95.8
2nd Fl., S Wing
Sri Pentas
No. 3, Persiaran Bandar Utama
Bandar Utama
47800 Petaling Jaya, Malaysia
Ph: 60 3 77105022
Fax: 60 3 77108098
Format: Ethnic; World Beat. **Ad Rates:** Advertising accepted; rates available upon request. **URL:** http://www.flyfm.com.my.

47704 ■ Fly-FM - 94
2nd Fl., S Wing
Sri Pentas
Persiaran Bandar Utama
47800 Petaling Jaya, Malaysia
Ph: 60 3 77105022
Fax: 60 3 77107098
Format: Contemporary Hit Radio (CHR); Ethnic; Talk. **Owner:** FLY FM, at above address. **Operating Hours:** 6 a.m-12 a.m Daily. **Ad Rates:** Advertising accepted;

rates available upon request. **URL:** http://www.flyfm.com.my.

47705 ■ Hot-FM - 90.1
Tingkat 2, S Wing
Sri Pentas, Persiaran Bandar Utama
47800 Petaling Jaya, Malaysia
Ph: 60 3 77108822
Fax: 60 3 77107098
Format: Ethnic; World Beat. **Operating Hours:** Continuous. **URL:** http://www.hotfm.com.my.

47706 ■ Hot-FM - 97.6
Tingkat 2, S Wing
Sri Pentas, Persiaran Bandar Utama
47800 Petaling Jaya, Malaysia
Ph: 60 3 77108822
Fax: 60 3 77107098
Format: Ethnic; World Beat. **Owner:** Hot FM, at above address. **Operating Hours:** Continuous. **URL:** http://www.hotfm.com.my/.

47707 ■ Hot-FM - 104.5
Tingkat 2, S Wing
Persiaran Bandar Utama
Selangor Darul Ehsan
47800 Petaling Jaya, Malaysia
Ph: 60 3 77108822
Fax: 60 3 77107098
Format: Ethnic; World Beat. **Operating Hours:** Continuous. **URL:** http://www.hotfm.com.my/.

47708 ■ Hot-FM - 88.2
Tingkat 2, South Wing, Sri Pentas
Persiaran Bandar Utama
47800 Petaling Jaya, Malaysia
Ph: 60 3 77105022
Fax: 60 3 77107098
Format: Ethnic; World Beat. **Owner:** Hot FM, at above address. **Operating Hours:** Continuous. **URL:** http://www.hotfm.com.my/.

Sabah

47709 ■ New Sabah Times
PO Box 15141
Kota Kinabalu
88861 Sabah, Malaysia
Ph: 60 882 30055
Fax: 60 882 41155
General newspaper. **Subtitle:** Sabah's First Established Paper. **Founded:** 1998. **Key Personnel:** Ch'ng Boon Heng, Editor-in-Chief, chng.boonheng@newsabahtimes.com.my; Fiona Siambun, Dep. Ch. Ed., fiona.siambun@newsabahtimes.com.my; Jerry Kamijan, Dep. Ch. Ed., jerry.kamijan@newsabahtimes.com.my. **URL:** http://www.newsabahtimes.com.my/.

Sandakan

47710 ■ Sandakan-FM - 90.1 MHz
Tingkat 6
Wisma Persekutuan
KM 11 Jalan Labuk
90500 Sandakan, Malaysia
Ph: 60 89 669842
Fax: 60 89 667202
E-mail: sandakanfm2u@gmail.com
Format: Ethnic. **Ad Rates:** Advertising accepted; rates available upon request. **URL:** http://sandakanfm.gov.my.

47711 ■ Traxx FM - Sandakan - 94.3
2nd Fl., Wisma Radio
Angkasapuri
50740 Kuala Lumpur, Malaysia
Ph: 60 3 22887663
Fax: 60 3 22845750
Format: Contemporary Hit Radio (CHR); Talk; Information. **Owner:** Radio Televisyen Malaysia, Jabatan Penyiaran Malaysia, Angkasapuri, 50614 Kuala Lumpur, Malaysia. **Operating Hours:** Continuous. **URL:** http://www.traxxfm.net/.

Selangor

47712 ■ Journal of Tropical Forest Science
Forest Research Institute Malaysia
52109 Kepong
52109 Selangor, Malaysia
Ph: 60 3 62797000
Fax: 60 3 62731314

Publisher E-mail: webgroup@frim.gov.my
Journal publishing original articles on current research related to tropical forestry and its associated sciences. **Founded:** 1988. **Freq:** Quarterly. **Trim Size:** 176 x 250. **Key Personnel:** K.A. Sarifah, Editor, sarifah@frim.gov.my; Y.F. Ho, Editor, hoyf@frim.gov.my. **ISSN:** 0128-1283. **Subscription Rates:** M$100 individuals; M$100 institutions; US$75 other countries individual; US$75 other countries institution. **URL:** http://www.frim.gov.my/Korporat/2003Publications/Links/Frim14.htm; http://www.frim.gov.my/publication.cfm. **Circ:** Paid 250

47713 ■ Radio Television Malaysia - 98.3 MHz
Department of Broadcasting
Ministry of Communication & Culture
Angkasapuri
50614 Kuala Lumpur, Malaysia
Ph: 60 3 22825333
Fax: 60 3 22825103
E-mail: feedback@rtm.gov.my
Format: Educational. **Owner:** Radio Television Malaysia, at above address. **Founded:** 1946. **Operating Hours:** Continuous. **Key Personnel:** Datuk Ibrahim Yahaya, Dir. Gen. **URL:** http://www.rtm.net.my.

Serdang

47714 ■ Asia-Pacific Journal of Molecular Biology & Biotechnology
Universiti Putra Malaysia
43400 Serdang, Malaysia
Ph: 60 3 89466000
Fax: 60 3 89487273
Periodical covering topics relating to molecular biology & biotechnology. **Founded:** 1993. **Freq:** Semiannual. **ISSN:** 0128-7451.

47715 ■ International Journal of Applied Engineering Research
Research India Publications
c/o Prof. Mohd Sapuan Salit, Ed.-in-Ch.
Department of Mechanical & Manufacturing Engineering
Universiti Putra Malaysia
UPM, Selangor
43400 Serdang, Malaysia
Publisher E-mail: info@ripublication.com
Journal covering engineering research and its applications. **Subtitle:** Research Journals on Environmental Sciences. **Freq:** Quarterly. **Key Personnel:** Prof. Mohd Sapuan Salit, Editor-in-Chief; Osama Badr, Editorial Board Member; Fatma Abou-Chadi, Editorial Board Member. **ISSN:** 0973-4562. **Subscription Rates:** US$580 institutions and library; print plus online free; US$560 institutions and library; online only; US$360 individuals print plus online free; US$320 individuals online only; Rs 5,400 individuals. **URL:** http://www.ripublication.com/ijaer.htm.

47716 ■ Pertanika Journal of Social Science and Humanities
Universiti Putra Malaysia Press
Serdang, Malaysia
Ph: 60 3 89468555
Fax: 60 3 89416172
Publisher E-mail: penerbit@putra.upm.edu.my
Social science journal. **Freq:** Semiannual. **Key Personnel:** Abdul Rahman Md Aroff, Editor. **ISSN:** 0128-7702. **Subscription Rates:** US$50 individuals; US$60 institutions. **URL:** http://www.rmc.upm.edu.my/jpertanika/index%20-%20JSSH.htm. **Circ:** Paid 200

47717 ■ Pertanika Journal of Tropical Agricultural Science
Universiti Putra Malaysia Press
Serdang, Malaysia
Ph: 60 3 89468555
Fax: 60 3 89416172
Publisher E-mail: penerbit@putra.upm.edu.my
Agricultural journal. **Founded:** 1978. **Freq:** Semiannual. **Print Method:** Digital Printing. **Trim Size:** 7 x 10. **Key Personnel:** Ruth Kiew, Editor. **ISSN:** 1511-3701. **Subscription Rates:** US$60. **Remarks:** Advertising accepted; rates available upon request. **URL:** http://www.rmc.upm.edu.my/jpertanika/index%20-%20JTAS.htm. **Circ:** (Not Reported)

Sibu

47718 ■ Radio Television Malaysia Sarawak - 6050 KHz
Broadcasting Department
Jalan P. Ramlee
93614 Kuching, Malaysia
Ph: 60 8 2248422
Fax: 60 8 2241914
E-mail: rtmkuc@rtm.net.my
Format: Eclectic. **Operating Hours:** 2200-0100 on weekdays; 2200-0600 on Sun. **Wattage:** 10,000. **Ad Rates:** Noncommercial. **URL:** http://www.rtmsarawak.gov.my/.

47719 ■ Radio Television Malaysia Sarawak - 909 KHz
Broadcasting Department
Jalan P. Ramlee
93614 Kuching, Malaysia
Ph: 60 8 2248422
Fax: 60 8 2241914
E-mail: rtmkuc@rtm.net.my
Format: Eclectic. **Operating Hours:** 2100-1600. **Wattage:** 20,000. **URL:** http://www.rtmsarawak.gov.my/.

Sri Aman

47720 ■ Radio Television Malaysia Sarawak - 1161 KHz
Broadcasting Department
Jalan P. Ramlee

93614 Kuching, Malaysia
Ph: 60 8 2248422
Fax: 60 8 2241914
E-mail: rtmkuc@rtm.net.my
Format: Eclectic. **Operating Hours:** 2200-0100 Weekdays; 2200-0600 Sun. **Wattage:** 20,000. **Ad Rates:** Noncommercial. **URL:** http://www.rtmsarawak.gov.my/.

47721 ■ Radio Television Malaysia Sarawak - 1044 KHz
Broadcasting Department
Jalan P. Ramlee
93614 Kuching, Malaysia
Ph: 60 8 2248422
Fax: 60 8 2241914
E-mail: rtmkuc@.rtm.net.my
Format: Eclectic. **Operating Hours:** 2100-1600. **Wattage:** 20,000. **URL:** http://www.rtmsarawak.gov.my/.

Taiping

47722 ■ Minnal FM - Taiping - 107.9
Tingkat 4, Wisma Radio
Peti Surat 11272
Angkasapuri
50740 Kuala Lumpur, Malaysia
Ph: 60 3 22887279
Fax: 60 3 22849137
E-mail: mail@minnalfm.com
Format: Classical; News; Information. **Owner:** Radio Televisyen Malaysia, Jabatan Penyiaran Malaysia, Angkasapuri, 50614 Kuala Lumpur, Malaysia. **Operating Hours:** Continuous. **URL:** http://www.minnalfm.com/.

47723 ■ Traxx FM - Taiping - 105.3
2nd Fl., Wisma Radio
Angkasapuri
50740 Kuala Lumpur, Malaysia
Ph: 60 3 22887663
Fax: 60 3 22845750
Format: Contemporary Hit Radio (CHR); Talk; Information. **Owner:** Radio Televisyen Malaysia, Jabatan Penyiaran Malaysia, Angkasapuri, 50614 Kuala Lumpur, Malaysia. **Operating Hours:** Continuous. **URL:** http://www.traxxfm.net/.

Tangkak

47724 ■ Traxx FM - Tangkak - 97.4
2nd Fl., Wisma Radio
Angkasapuri
50740 Kuala Lumpur, Malaysia
Ph: 60 3 22887663
Fax: 60 3 22845750
Format: Contemporary Hit Radio (CHR); Talk; Information. **Owner:** Radio Televisyen Malaysia, Jabatan Penyiaran Malaysia, Angkasapuri, 50614 Kuala Lumpur, Malaysia. **Operating Hours:** Continuous. **URL:** http://www.traxxfm.net/.

Circulation: ★ = ABC; △ = BPA; ◆ = CAC; • = CCAB; ❑ = VAC; ⊕ = PO Statement; ‡ = Publisher's Report; Boldface figures = sworn; Light figures = estimated.

Gale Directory of Publications & Broadcast Media/147th Ed.
5187

Male

47725 ■ Haveeru Daily
PO Box 20103
Ameenee Magu
Male, Maldives
Ph: 96 032 5671
Fax: 96 032 3103
Publisher E-mail: haveeru@dhaveeru.com.mv
General newspaper. **Founded:** 1979. **Freq:** Daily. **Print**

Method: Offset. **Trim Size:** 42.5 x 60.5 cm. **Cols./Page:**
50. **Key Personnel:** Ahmed Zahir, Managing Editor,
hiriga@haveeru.com.mv; Ali Rafeeq, Editor, alirafeeq@
haveeru.com.mv. **Remarks:** Accepts advertising. **URL:**
http://www.haveeru.com.mv/english/. **Former name:**
Haveeru. **Ad Rates:** GLR: MRu 40, BW: MRu 600, 4C;
MRu 400. **Circ:** (Not Reported)

47726 ■ Television Maldives - 7
Buruzu Magu

Male, Maldives
Ph: 960 334 2200
Fax: 960 332 5083
E-mail: info@tvm.gov.mv
Owner: Television Maldives, at above address.
Founded: Mar. 29, 1978. **Operating Hours:** 0300-0500
(Fri.); 1200-1620. **Wattage:** 1000. **Ad Rates:** Advertising accepted; rates available upon request. **URL:** http://
www.tvm.gov.mv/.

Circulation: ★ = ABC; △ = BPA; ◆ = CAC; • = CCAB; ❑ = VAC; ⊕ = PO Statement; ‡ = Publisher's Report; Boldface figures = sworn; Light figures = estimated.

Gale Directory of Publications & Broadcast Media/147th Ed.

5189

Birkirkara

47727 ■ BKR Radio-FM - 94.5
220 Valley Rd.
Birkirkara, Malta
Ph: 356 214 95897
Format: Contemporary Hit Radio (CHR). **Operating Hours:** 13 hours Daily. **Key Personnel:** Carmelo Calleja, Mng. Dir.; Kenneth Cefai, Financial Controller; Sandro Sammut, Station Engr.; George Peresso, Station Consultant. **Ad Rates:** Advertising accepted; rates available upon request. **URL:** http://www.bkr-radio.com.

Birzebbuga

47728 ■ Energy-FM - 96.4
8, Triq il-Kangu
Birzebbuga BBG 07, Malta
Ph: 356 216 52737
E-mail: info@energyfm964.com
Format: Contemporary Hit Radio (CHR); News. **Founded:** 1994. **Operating Hours:** 18 hours Daily. **Ad Rates:** Advertising accepted; rates available upon request. **URL:** http://www.energyfm964.com.

Cospicua

47729 ■ Kottoner 98-FM - 98.0
144 Matty Grima St,
Cospicua BML 1161, Malta
Ph: 356 21 677753
Fax: 356 21 667766
E-mail: 98fm@kottoner.com
Format: Classic Rock; Alternative/New Music/Progressive; World Beat. **Ad Rates:** Advertising accepted; rates available upon request. **URL:** http://www.kottoner.com/.

G'Mangia

47730 ■ Radju Malta-FM - 93.7
75, St. Luke's Rd.
G'Mangia MSD 09, Malta
Ph: 356 21225051
E-mail: info@pbs.com.mt
Format: News; Ethnic; Public Radio. **Operating Hours:** Continuous. **Ad Rates:** Advertising accepted; rates available upon request. **URL:** http://www.pbs.com.mt.

Gozo

47731 ■ Radju Bambina-FM - 98.3
Victory Sq. Xaghra Xra
Gozo NDR 103, Malta
Ph: 356 21551042
Fax: 356 21558715
E-mail: info@xaghraparish.org
Format: Religious. **Operating Hours:** Continuous. **URL:** http://www.xaghraparish.org.

47732 ■ Radju Lehen il-Belt Victoria-FM - 104
39, Pjazza San Gorg
Gozo NDR 103, Malta
Ph: 356 21565207

E-mail: lbv104@gmail.com
Format: Religious. **URL:** http://www.lbv104.com.

47733 ■ Radju Luminaria-FM - 106.9
Pjazza Dun Martin Camilleri
Nadur
Gozo NDR 104, Malta
Ph: 356 21552266
Fax: 356 21566660
Format: World Beat. **Operating Hours:** Continuous. **URL:** http://www.radjuluminaria.com.

Luqa

47734 ■ Calypso Ten 18-FM - 101.8
28, New St.
Valletta Rd.
Luqa, Malta
Ph: 356 500 43555
E-mail: info@calypsoradio.com
Format: Full Service. **Operating Hours:** Continuous. **URL:** http://www.calypsoradio.com/.

Msida

47735 ■ Campus-FM - 103.7
Old Humanities Bldg.
University of Malta
Tal-Qroqq
Msida, Malta
Ph: 356 21 333313
Fax: 356 21 314485
E-mail: campusfm@um.edu.mt
Format: Educational. **Founded:** 2002. **Operating Hours:** Continuous. **Key Personnel:** Ms. MaryLou Fava, Admin. Coord. **Ad Rates:** $2.50 for 10 seconds; $3.00 for 15 seconds; $3.50 for 20 seconds; $5.00 for 30 seconds; $6.00 for 40 seconds; $7.00 for 60 seconds. **URL:** http://campusfm.um.edu.mt/.

Naxxar

47736 ■ Christian Light Radio-FM - 105.4
PO Box 18
Naxxar, Malta
Ph: 356 21418686
E-mail: info@christianlightradio.com
Format: Contemporary Christian; Religious; Gospel. **Operating Hours:** Continuous. **URL:** http://www.christianlightradio.info.

Qala

47737 ■ Radju Lehen il-Qala-FM - 106.3
24, St. Francis St.
Qala 1030, Malta
Ph: 356 21 558556
E-mail: info@radjulehenil-qala.com
Format: Religious; Contemporary Christian; Ethnic. **Operating Hours:** Continuous. **URL:** http://www.radjulehenil-qala.com.

Qormi

47738 ■ Boats and Yachting
Boats & Yachting Ltd.
236 Mdina Rd.
Qormi QRM 08, Malta
Ph: 356 214 90539
Fax: 356 214 98893
Consumer magazine covering boating in Malta. **Founded:** 1991. **Freq:** Bimonthly. **Print Method:** Offset. **Remarks:** Accepts advertising. **URL:** http://www.boatsandyachting.com/about.asp. **Circ:** Combined 5,000

Saint Julians

47739 ■ The Malta Business Weekly
Standard Publications Ltd.
Standard House
Birkirkara Hill
Saint Julians STJ 1149, Malta
Ph: 356 21345888
Newspaper featuring business. **Freq:** Weekly. **Key Personnel:** Noel Grima, Editor-in-Chief, csultana@independent.com.mt; Noel Grima, Mng. Dir., nazzopardi@independent.com.mt. **Remarks:** Accepts advertising. **URL:** http://www.maltabusinessweekly.mt/mainpage.asp. **Circ:** (Not Reported)

47740 ■ The Malta Independent
Standard Publications Ltd.
Standard House
Birkirkara Hill
Saint Julians STJ 1149, Malta
Ph: 356 21345888
Newspaper featuring latest news, information, and events. **Key Personnel:** Stephen Calleja, Managing Editor, scalleja@independent.com.mt; Noel Azzopardi, Mng. Dir., nazzopardi@independent.com.mt; Noel Grima, Editor-in-Chief. **Remarks:** Accepts advertising. **URL:** http://www.independent.com.mt/mainpage.asp. **Circ:** (Not Reported)

47741 ■ The Malta Independent on Sunday
Standard Publications Ltd.
Standard House
Birkirkara Hill
Saint Julians STJ 1149, Malta
Ph: 356 21345888
Newspaper featuring latest news, information, and events. **Freq:** Weekly (Sun.). **Key Personnel:** Noel Grima, Editor-in-Chief, ngrima@independent.com.mt; Noel Azzopardi, Mng. Dir., nazzopardi@independent.com.mt. **Remarks:** Accepts advertising. **URL:** http://www.independent.com.mt/. **Circ:** (Not Reported)

Saint Julian's

47742 ■ Bay-FM - 89.7
Eden Pl.
St. George's Bay
Saint Julian's STJ 02, Malta
Ph: 356 23 710800
Fax: 356 23 710845
Format: Top 40; Blues. **Owner:** Eden Leisure Group, at above address. **Operating Hours:** 18 hours Daily. **Key**

Circulation: ★ = ABC; △ = BPA; ♦ = CAC; • = CCAB; ❑ = VAC; ⊕ = PO Statement; ‡ = Publisher's Report; Boldface figures = sworn; Light figures = estimated.

Gale Directory of Publications & Broadcast Media/147th Ed.

5191

Personnel: Marthese Azzopardi, Sales Mgr., m.azzopardi@bay.com.mt. **URL:** http://www.bay.com.mt.

Ta' Xbiex

47743 ■ Birds Eye View
BirdLife Malta
57/28 Triq Abate Rigord
Ta' Xbiex XBX 1120, Malta
Ph: 356 21347646
Fax: 356 21343239
Publisher E-mail: info@birdlifemalta.org
Magazine containing information on the activities and conservation campaigns organized by the society. **Key Personnel:** Tolga Temuge, Exec. Dir. **URL:** http://www.birdlifemalta.org/publications/magazines/adults/view.aspx?id=2.

47744 ■ Il-Merill
BirdLife Malta
57/28 Triq Abate Rigord
Ta' Xbiex XBX 1120, Malta
Ph: 356 21347646
Fax: 356 21343239
Publisher E-mail: info@birdlifemalta.org
Journal including various papers and short notes about different aspects of ornithology. **Founded:** 1970. **Freq:** Semiannual. **Key Personnel:** Joe Sultana, Editor. **URL:** http://www.birdlifemalta.org/publications/magazines/ornithologists/.

Valletta

47745 ■ Commercial Courier
Chamber of Commerce - Malta
Exchange Bldg.
Republic St.
Valletta VLT 05, Malta
Ph: 356 21 233873
Fax: 356 21 245223
Publisher E-mail: info@maltachamber.org.mt
Publication covering chambers of commerce. **Freq:** Monthly. **Remarks:** Advertising accepted; rates available upon request. **URL:** http://www.chamber.org.mt. **Circ:** 1,300

47746 ■ Id-Dijabete u Sahhtek
Maltese Diabetes Association
Ghaqda Kontra d-Dijabete
British Legion Premises
111 Melita St.
Valletta CMR 01, Malta
Ph: 356 21 221518
Publisher E-mail: info@diabetesmalta.org
Maltese language publication covering diabetes. **Freq:** 3/yr. **Key Personnel:** John Spiteri, Editor. **Subscription**

Rates: Included in membership. **URL:** http://www.diabetesmalta.org/. **Ad Rates:** BW: 60 ML, 4C: 85 ML. **Circ:** 900

47747 ■ Sunday Times (Malta)
Sunday Times
341 St. Paul St.
Valletta VLT 1211, Malta
Ph: 356 25594100
Fax: 356 25594116
Publication E-mail: mynews@timesofmalta.com
General newspaper. **Founded:** 1930. **Freq:** Weekly (Sun.). **Print Method:** Web offset. **Trim Size:** 29 x 41 cm. **Cols./Page:** 5. **Col. Width:** 4.6 centimeters. **Col. Depth:** 37 centimeters. **Remarks:** Accepts advertising. **URL:** http://www.timesofmalta.com/. **Ad Rates:** BW: 320 ML. **Circ:** Combined 40,000

47748 ■ Capital Radio-FM - 88.7
87 St. Ursula St.
Valletta, Malta
Ph: 356 21233078
Format: Contemporary Hit Radio (CHR); Eighties; Music of Your Life. **Founded:** July 1, 1998. **Operating Hours:** Continuous. **Key Personnel:** John Mallia, Station Dir.; Renald Bugeja, Program Dir. **Ad Rates:** Advertising accepted; rates available upon request. **URL:** http://www.capitalradio.com.mt.

Fort-de-France

47749 ■ Radio Saint Louis-FM - 99.5
Rue des Rameaux
Cour Vieux Habitants
97200 Fort-de-France, Martinique
Ph: 596 718604
Fax: 596 718605
E-mail: contact@radiosaintlouis.com
Format: Classical; Ethnic; Information; World Beat. **Operating Hours:** 18 hours Daily. **URL:** http://radiosaintlouis.com/cariboost1.

47750 ■ RBR-FM - 103.4
107 Ave. Leona Gabriel
Dillon City
97200 Fort-de-France, Martinique
Ph: 596 96600090
Fax: 596 96730653
E-mail: rbr@fr.fm
Format: Ethnic; World Beat. **Founded:** Nov. 1981. **Operating Hours:** Continuous. **Ad Rates:** Advertising accepted; rates available upon request. **URL:** http://apenntouchenoula.fr/rbr.

Le Francois

47751 ■ Radio Sud Est-FM - 89.3
Quartier Morne Pavillon
97240 Le Francois, Martinique
Ph: 596 512427
Fax: 596 514996
E-mail: radio-sud-est@wanadoo.fr
Format: Adult Contemporary; News. **URL:** http://www.radiosudest.com.

Circulation: ★ = ABC; △ = BPA; ♦ = CAC; • = CCAB; ❑ = VAC; ⊕ = PO Statement; ‡ = Publisher's Report; Boldface figures = sworn; Light figures = estimated.

Gale Directory of Publications & Broadcast Media/147th Ed.   5193

Curepipe

47752 ■ Internet Journal of Medical Update
African Journals Online
4 Malherbes St.
Curepipe, Mauritius
Publisher E-mail: info@ajol.info
Peer-reviewed journal containing review articles, original research work, and case reports for medical professionals. **Freq:** Semiannual. **Key Personnel:** Dr. Arun Kumar Agnihotri, Editor-in-Chief, phone 230 6751318, agnihotri_arun@hotmail.com; Dr. B.B. Gupta, Assoc. Ed.; Dr. Hari Shankar Joshi, Assoc. Ed.; Dr. Pei-Yi Chu, Assoc. Ed.; Dr. Smriti Agnihotri, Assoc. Ed.; Dr. Vineet Bhandari, Assoc. Ed. **ISSN:** 1694-0423. **URL:** http://ajol.info/index.php/ijmu.

Forest-Side

47753 ■ KOOL-FM - 97.3
1 Louis Pasteur St.
Forest-Side, Mauritius
Ph: 230 6021200
Fax: 230 6021292
Format: Eclectic. **Owner:** Mauritius Broadcasting Corporation, at above address. **Operating Hours:** Continuous. **Ad Rates:** Advertising accepted; rates available upon request. **URL:** http://mbc.intnet.mu; http://kool973.com.

Reduit

47754 ■ African Journal of Pharmacy & Pharmacology
Academic Journals
c/o Sharmilah Pamela Seetulsingh-Goorah, Ed.
Department of Health Sciences
Faculty of Science
University of Mauritius
Reduit, Mauritius
Publisher E-mail: service@academicjournals.org
Journal covering in all areas of pharmaceutical science. **Freq:** Monthly. **Key Personnel:** Sharmilah Pamela Seetulsingh-Goorah, Editor; Prof. Kehe Ruan, Editor. **Remarks:** Accepts advertising. **URL:** http://www.academicjournals.org/AJPP/. **Circ:** (Not Reported)

Circulation: ★ = ABC; △ = BPA; ◆ = CAC; ● = CCAB; ❑ = VAC; ⊕ = PO Statement; ‡ = Publisher's Report; Boldface figures = sworn; Light figures = estimated.

Gale Directory of Publications & Broadcast Media/147th Ed.   **5195**

Cabo San Lucas

47755 ■ Cabo Mil-FM - 96.3
Km 6 Carretera Transpeninsular
Fraccionamiento Cabo Bello
Apartado Postal 55
23410 Cabo San Lucas, Baja California Sur, Mexico
Ph: 52 624 1457963
Fax: 52 624 1457913
E-mail: fcervant@cabomil.com.mx
Format: Jazz; World Beat; Ethnic. **Owner:** Cabo Mil, at above address. **Founded:** Sept. 18, 1988. **Operating Hours:** Continuous. **URL:** http://www.cabomil.com.mx.

Celaya

47756 ■ Exa-FM - 104.5
Blvd. Adolfo Lopez Mateos, No. 117 Ote.
Celaya, Guanajuato, Mexico
Ph: 52 461 6127095
Format: Hispanic. **Owner:** TeleRadio, at above address. **URL:** http://www.teleradio.com.mx.

47757 ■ La Pachanga-AM - 840
Blvd. Adolfo Lopez Mateos, No. 117 Ote.
Celaya, Guanajuato, Mexico
Ph: 52 461 6120211
Format: Hispanic. **Owner:** TeleRadio, at above address. **URL:** http://www.teleradio.com.mx.

47758 ■ Romantica-AM - 740
Blvd. Adolfo Lopez Mateos, No. 1117 Ote.
Celaya, Guanajuato, Mexico
Ph: 52 461 6120211
Format: Hispanic. **Owner:** TeleRadio, at above address. **URL:** http://www.teleradio.com.mx.

Chihuahua

47759 ■ XEDI-AM - 1360
Reforma 2620
Edificio Reforma 2do piso.
Col. Lomas Alta
Del. Miguel Hidalgo
11950 Mexico City, Federal District, Mexico
Ph: 52 55 11050000
Fax: 52 55 11050016
E-mail: grupo@radiorama.com.mx
Format: Hispanic. **Owner:** Radiorama Corporativo, at above address. **Key Personnel:** Adrian Pereda Gomez, Contact, rgomez@radiorama.com.mx. **URL:** http://www.radiorama.com.mx/secciones.php?sec_id=32&ent_id=6.

47760 ■ XEFA-AM - 950
Reforma 2620
Edificio Reforma 2do piso.
Col. Lomas Alta
Del. Miguel Hidalgo
11950 Mexico City, Federal District, Mexico
Ph: 52 55 11050000
Fax: 52 55 11050016
E-mail: grupo@radiorama.com.mx
Format: Hispanic. **Owner:** Radiorama Corporativo, at above address. **Key Personnel:** Adrian Pereda Gomez, Contact, rgomez@radiorama.com.mx. **URL:** http://www.radiorama.com.mx/secciones.php?sec_id=32&ent_id=6.

47761 ■ XEFI-AM - 580
Reforma 2620
Edificio Reforma 2do piso.
Col. Lomas Alta
Del. Miguel Hidalgo
11950 Mexico City, Federal District, Mexico
Ph: 52 55 11050000
Fax: 52 55 11050016
E-mail: grupo@radiorama.com.mx
Format: Hispanic. **Owner:** Radiorama Corporativo, at above address. **Key Personnel:** Adrian Pereda Gomez, Contact, rgomez@radiorama.com.mx. **URL:** http://www.radiorama.com.mx/secciones.php?sec_id=32&ent_id=6.

47762 ■ XEFO-AM - 680
Reforma 2620
Edificio Reforma 2do piso.
Col. Lomas Alta
Del. Miguel Hidalgo
11950 Mexico City, Federal District, Mexico
Ph: 52 55 11050000
Fax: 52 55 11050016
E-mail: grupo@radiorama.com.mx
Format: Hispanic. **Owner:** Radiorama Corporativo, at above address. **Key Personnel:** Jose Luis Chavero Resendiz, Dir. Gen., jlchavero@radiorama.com.mx; Efrain Aizman Centeno, Promotions Dir., eaizman@radiorama.com.mx; Jaime Ramirez Arrevillaga, Sales Exec., jramirez@radiorama.com.mx. **URL:** http://www.radiorama.com.mx/secciones.php?sec_id=32&ent_id=6.

47763 ■ XEHES-AM - 1040
Reforma 2620
Edificio Reforma 2do piso.
Col. Lomas Alta
Del. Miguel Hidalgo
11950 Mexico City, Federal District, Mexico
Ph: 52 55 11050000
Fax: 52 55 11050016
E mail: grupo@radiorama.com.mx
Format: Hispanic. **Owner:** Radiorama Corporativo, at above address. **Key Personnel:** Jose Luis Chavero Resendiz, Dir. Gen., jlchavero@radiorama.com.mx; Efrain Aizman Centeno, Promotions Dir., eaizman@radiorama.com.mx; Jaime Ramirez Arrevillaga, Sales Exec., jramirez@radiorama.com.mx. **URL:** http://www.radiorama.com.mx/secciones.php?sec_id=32&ent_id=6.

47764 ■ XERPC-AM - 790
Reforma 2620
Edificio Reforma 2do piso.
Col. Lomas Alta
Del. Miguel Hidalgo
11950 Mexico City, Federal District, Mexico
Ph: 52 55 11050000
Fax: 52 55 11050016
E-mail: grupo@radiorama.com.mx
Format: Hispanic. **Owner:** Radiorama Corporativo, at above address. **Key Personnel:** Jose Luis Chavero Resendiz, Dir. Gen., jlchavero@radiorama.com.mx; Efrain Aizman Centeno, Promotions Dir., eaizman@radiorama.com.mx; Jaime Ramirez Arrevillaga, Sales Exec., jramirez@radiorama.com.mx. **URL:** http://www.radiorama.com.mx/secciones.php?sec_id=32&ent_id=6.

47765 ■ XHDI-FM - 88.5
Reforma 2620
Edificio Reforma 2do piso.
Col. Lomas Alta
Del. Miguel Hidalgo
11950 Mexico City, Federal District, Mexico
Ph: 52 55 11050000
Fax: 52 55 11050016
E-mail: grupo@radiorama.com.mx
Format: Hispanic. **Owner:** Radiorama Corporativo, at above address. **Key Personnel:** Jose Luis Chavero Resendiz, Dir. Gen., jlchavero@radiorama.com.mx; Efrain Aizman Centeno, Promotions Dir., eaizman@radiorama.com.mx; Jaime Ramirez Arrevillaga, Sales Exec., jramirez@radiorama.com.mx. **URL:** http://www.radiorama.com.mx/secciones.php?sec_id=32&ent_id=6.

47766 ■ XHFA-FM - 89.3
Reforma 2620
Edificio Reforma 2do piso.
Col. Lomas Alta
Del. Miguel Hidalgo
11950 Mexico City, Federal District, Mexico
Ph: 52 55 11050000
Fax: 52 55 11050016
E-mail: grupo@radiorama.com.mx
Format: Hispanic. **Owner:** Radiorama Corporativo, at above address. **Key Personnel:** Jose Luis Chavero Resendiz, Dir. Gen., jlchavero@radiorama.com.mx; Efrain Aizman Centeno, Promotions Dir., eaizman@radiorama.com.mx; Jaime Ramirez Arrevillaga, Sales Exec., jramirez@radiorama.com.mx. **URL:** http://www.radiorama.com.mx/secciones.php?sec_id=32&ent_id=6.

47767 ■ XHUA-FM - 90.1
Reforma
2620 Edificio Reforma 2do piso.
Col. Lomas
Alta Del. Miguel Hidalgo
11950 Mexico City, Federal District, Mexico
Ph: 52 55 11050000
Fax: 52 55 11050016
E-mail: grupo@radiorama.com.mx
Format: Hispanic. **Owner:** Radiorama Corporativo, at above address. **URL:** http://www.radiorama.com.mx/secciones.php?sec_id=32&ent_id=6.

Ciudad del Carmen

47768 ■ XEIT-AM - 1070
Reforma 2620
Edificio Reforma 2do piso.
Col. Lomas Alta
Del. Miguel Hidalgo
11950 Mexico City, Federal District, Mexico
Ph: 52 55 11050000
Fax: 52 55 11050016
E-mail: grupo@radiorama.com.mx
Format: Hispanic. **Owner:** Radiorama Corporativo, at above address. **Key Personnel:** Jose Luis Chavero Resendiz, Dir. Gen., jlchavero@radiorama.com.mx; Efrain Aizman Centeno, Promotions Dir., eaizman@radiorama.com.mx; Jaime Ramirez Arrevillaga, Sales Exec., jramirez@radiorama.com.mx. **URL:** http://www.radiorama.com.mx/secciones.php?sec_id=32&ent_id=6.

47769 ■ XEMAB-AM - 950
Reforma 2620
Edificio Reforma 2do piso.
Col. Lomas Alta
Del. Miguel Hidalgo
11950 Mexico City, Federal District, Mexico
Ph: 52 55 11050000
Fax: 52 55 11050016
E-mail: grupo@radiorama.com.mx
Format: Hispanic. **Owner:** Radiorama Corporativo, at above address. **Key Personnel:** Jose Luis Chavero Resendiz, Dir. Gen., jlchavero@radiorama.com.mx; Efrain Aizman Centeno, Promotions Dir., eaizman@radiorama.com.mx; Jaime Ramirez Arrevillaga, Sales Exec., jramirez@radiorama.com.mx. **URL:** http://www.radiorama.com.mx/secciones.php?sec_id=32&ent_id=6.

47770 ■ XHIT-FM - 99.7
Reforma 2620
Edificio Reforma 2do piso.
Col. Lomas Alta
Del. Miguel Hidalgo
11950 Mexico City, Federal District, Mexico
Ph: 52 55 11050000
Fax: 52 55 11050016
E-mail: grupo@radiorama.com.mx
Format: Hispanic. **Owner:** Radiorama Corporativo, at above address. **Key Personnel:** Jose Luis Chavero Resendiz, Dir. Gen., jlchavero@radiorama.com.mx; Efrain Aizman Centeno, Promotions Dir., eaizman@radiorama.com.mx; Jaime Ramirez Arrevillaga, Sales Exec., jramirez@radiorama.com.mx. **URL:** http://www.radiorama.com.mx/secciones.php?sec_id=32&ent_id=6.

Cuernavaca

47771 ■ Salud Publica de Mexico
Instituto Nacional de Salud Publica
Av. Universidad, 655
Col. Santa Maria Ahuacatitlan
62100 Cuernavaca, Morelos, Mexico
Ph: 52 777 1012900
Journal reviewing historical experiences in the field of health issues. **Freq:** Bimonthly. **Key Personnel:** Carlos Oropeza Abundez, Exec. Ed., eoropeza@insp3.insp.mx; Dr. Mauricio Hernandez Avila, Director. **ISSN:** 0036-3634. **Subscription Rates:** 250 MP individuals Mexico; 2,000 MP students Mexico; US$75 individuals Latin America; US$105 other countries; 60 MP single issue; US$15 single issue Latin America; US$20 single issue other countries. **URL:** http://www.scielosp.org/scielo.php?script=sci_serial&pid=0036-3634&lng=en&n. **Formerly:** Salubridad y Asistencia de Mexico.

Delicias

47772 ■ XEDCH-AM - 1180
Reforma 2620
Edificio Reforma 2do piso.
Col. Lomas Alta
Del. Miguel Hidalgo
11950 Mexico City, Federal District, Mexico
Ph: 52 55 11050000
Fax: 52 55 11050016
E-mail: grupo@radiorama.com.mx
Format: Hispanic. **Owner:** Radiorama Corporativo, at above address. **Key Personnel:** Adrian Pereda Gomez, Contact, rgomez@radiorama.com.mx. **URL:** http://www.radiorama.com.mx/secciones.php?sec_id=32&ent_id=6.

47773 ■ XEJK-AM - 980
Reforma 2620
Edificio Reforma 2do piso.
Col. Lomas Alta
Del. Miguel Hidalgo
11950 Mexico City, Federal District, Mexico
Ph: 52 55 11050000
Fax: 52 55 11050016
E-mail: grupo@radiorama.com.mx
Format: Hispanic. **Owner:** Radiorama Corporativo, at above address. **Key Personnel:** Jose Luis Chavero Resendiz, Dir. Gen., jlchavero@radiorama.com.mx; Efrain Aizman Centeno, Promotions Dir., eaizman@radiorama.com.mx; Jaime Ramirez Arrevillaga, Sales Exec., jramirez@radiorama.com.mx. **URL:** http://www.radiorama.com.mx/secciones.php?sec_id=32&ent_id=6.

Guadalajara

47774 ■ El Informador
Union Editorial S.A. de C.V.
Independencia No. 300
Col. Centro C.P.
44100 Guadalajara, Jalisco, Mexico
Ph: 52 333 6146340
General newspaper. **Freq:** Daily. **Subscription Rates:** 2,720 Ptas out of country. **URL:** http://www.informador.com.mx/.

Hermosillo

47775 ■ XHHLL-FM - 90.70
Nayarit No. 32
83000 Hermosillo, Sonora, Mexico
Ph: 52 662 2152090
Format: Ethnic. **Operating Hours:** Continuous. **Ad Rates:** Advertising accepted; rates available upon request. **URL:** http://www.lakaliente.com.mx.

Huixtla

47776 ■ XEKY-AM - 1280
Reforma 2620
Edificio Reforma 2do piso.
Col. Lomas Alta
Del. Miguel Hidalgo
11950 Mexico City, Federal District, Mexico
Ph: 52 55 11050000
Fax: 52 55 11050016
E-mail: grupo@radiorama.com.mx
Format: Hispanic. **Owner:** Radiorama Corporativo, at above address. **Key Personnel:** Jose Luis Chavero Resendiz, Dir. Gen., jlchavero@radiorama.com.mx; Efrain Aizman Centeno, Promotions Dir., eaizman@radiorama.com.mx; Jaime Ramirez Arrevillaga, Sales Exec., jramirez@radiorama.com.mx. **URL:** http://www.radiorama.com.mx/secciones.php?sec_id=32&ent_id=6.

47777 ■ XEMK-AM - 930
Reforma 2620
Edificio Reforma 2do piso.
Col. Lomas Alta
Del. Miguel Hidalgo
11950 Mexico City, Federal District, Mexico
Ph: 52 55 11050000
Fax: 52 55 11050016
E-mail: grupo@radiorama.com.mx
Format: Hispanic. **Owner:** Radiorama Corporativo, at above address. **Key Personnel:** Jose Luis Chavero Resendiz, Dir. Gen., jlchavero@radiorama.com.mx; Efrain Aizman Centeno, Promotions Dir., eaizman@radiorama.com.mx; Jaime Ramirez Arrevillaga, Sales Exec., jramirez@radiorama.com.mx. **URL:** http://www.radiorama.com.mx/secciones.php?sec_id=32&ent_id=6.

Jimenez

47778 ■ XHCJZ-FM - 105.1
Reforma 2620
Edificio Reforma 2do piso.
Col. Lomas Alta
Del. Miguel Hidalgo
11950 Mexico City, Federal District, Mexico
Ph: 52 55 11050000
Fax: 52 55 11050016
E-mail: grupo@radiorama.com.mx
Format: Hispanic. **Owner:** Radiorama Corporativo, at above address. **Key Personnel:** Jose Luis Chavero Resendiz, Dir. Gen., jlchavero@radiorama.com.mx; Efrain Aizman Centeno, Promotions Dir., eaizman@radiorama.com.mx; Jaime Ramirez Arrevillaga, Sales Exec., jramirez@radiorama.com.mx. **URL:** http://www.radiorama.com.mx/secciones.php?sec_id=32&ent_id=6.

Juarez

47779 ■ KXPL-AM - 1060
Reforma
2620 Edificio Reforma 2do piso.
Col. Lomas
Alta Del. Miguel Hidalgo
11950 Mexico City, Federal District, Mexico
Ph: 52 55 11050000
Fax: 52 55 11050016
E-mail: grupo@radiorama.com.mx
Format: Hispanic. **Owner:** Radiorama Corporativo, at

above address. **URL:** http://www.radiorama.com.mx/secciones.php?sec_id=32&ent_id=6.

Mexicali

47780 ■ Estudios Fronterizos
Universidad Autonoma de Baja California
Apartado postal 3-136
21100 Mexicali, Baja California, Mexico
Journal covering analysis of the border regions of the world. **Key Personnel:** Alain Musset, Contact. **ISSN:** 0187-697X. **URL:** http://www.uabc.mx/iis/ref/.

Mexico City

47781 ■ Almas
Guadalupe Missioners
Misioneros de Guadalupe
Cantera 29
Col. Tlalpan
Del. Tlalpan
14000 Mexico City, Federal District, Mexico
Ph: 15 556 552691
Publisher E-mail: padrinos@mg.org.mx
Mission publication in Spanish. **Freq:** Monthly. **Remarks:** Advertising not accepted. **URL:** http://www.revistaalmas.com.mx/mla.html. **Circ:** (Not Reported)

47782 ■ Boletin
Centre for Latin American Monetary Studies
Centro de Estudios Monetarios Latinoamericanos
Durango 54
Col. Roma
06700 Mexico City, Federal District, Mexico
Ph: 52 55 50616640
Publisher E-mail: cemla@cemla.org
Spanish language publication covering economics. **Founded:** 1995. **Freq:** Quarterly. **ISSN:** 0186-7229. **Remarks:** Advertising not accepted. **URL:** http://www.cemla.org/boletin-eng.htm. **Circ:** (Not Reported)

47783 ■ CIMMYT Annual Report
International Maize and Wheat Improvement Center
Centro Internacional de Mejoramiento de Maiz y Trigo
Apartado Postal 6-641
06600 Mexico City, Federal District, Mexico
Ph: 52 55 58042004
Fax: 52 555 8047558
English and Spanish language publication covering agricultural science. **Founded:** 1966. **Freq:** Annual. **Print Method:** Offset. **Trim Size:** 21 x 28 cm. **ISSN:** 0188-9214. **Subscription Rates:** Free. **Remarks:** Advertising not accepted. **URL:** http://www.cimmyt.org. **Circ:** 5,000

47784 ■ El Universal
El Universal, Compania Periodistica Nacional S.A. de C.V.
Bucareli 8
Mexico City, Federal District, Mexico
Ph: 52 570 91313
General newspaper. **Founded:** 1916. **Freq:** Daily. **Print Method:** Photo offset. **Subscription Rates:** 1,571.18 MP individuals daily. **Remarks:** Accepts advertising. **URL:** http://www.eluniversal.com.mx/. **Formerly:** El Universal; El Grafico; El Gran Diario de Mexico. **Ad Rates:** GLR: US$4.50, BW: US$12,500, 4C: US$13,000, PCI: US$4. **Circ:** Mon.-Fri. 350,000

47785 ■ International Journal of Business Competition and Growth
Inderscience Enterprises Limited
c/o Dr. Jerry Banks
Monterrey Institute of Technology & Higher Education, ITESM
Dept. of Marketing, Business Division
Graduate School of Administration & Management,
Mexico City Campus
14380 Mexico City, Federal District, Mexico
Journal covering the areas of competitiveness and robust business leadership research, highlighting systems thinking and business modeling issues. **Freq:** 4/yr. **Key Personnel:** Dr. Jerry Banks, Editorial Board. **ISSN:** 2042-3845. **Subscription Rates:** EUR494 individuals print or online; EUR672 individuals print and online. **Remarks:** Accepts advertising. **URL:** http://www.inderscience.com/browse/index.php?journalID=360board. **Circ:** (Not Reported)

47786 ■ Monetaria
Centre for Latin American Monetary Studies
Centro de Estudios Monetarios Latinoamericanos

Durango 54
Col. Roma
06700 Mexico City, Federal District, Mexico
Ph: 52 55 50616640
Publisher E-mail: cemla@cemla.org
Spanish language publication covering economics. **Founded:** 1978. **Freq:** Quarterly. **URL:** http://www. cemla.org/monetaria-eng.htm.

47787 ■ Money Affairs
Centre for Latin American Monetary Studies
Centro de Estudios Monetarios Latinoamericanos
Durango 54
Col. Roma
06700 Mexico City, Federal District, Mexico
Ph: 52 55 50616640
Publisher E-mail: cemla@cemla.org
Publication covering economics. **Founded:** 1988. **Freq:** Semiannual. **URL:** http://www.cemla.org/money-affairs-eng.htm.

47788 ■ Refugees
United Nations High Commission for Refugees - Regional Office Mexico
Office for Mexico, Belize, Central America, Cuba, and Panama
Apartado Postal 105-39
11581 Mexico City, Federal District, Mexico
Ph: 52 52802072
Fax: 52 52802133
Publisher E-mail: mexme@unhcr.ch
Publication covering refugees, in English, French, German, Italian, Japanese, Russian and Spanish. **Freq:** Quarterly. **ISSN:** 0572-791x. **Subscription Rates:** Free. **Remarks:** Advertising not accepted. **URL:** http://www. unhcr.org/pages/49c3646c4b8.html. **Circ:** 215,000

47789 ■ Rotarismo en Mexico
Paseo de la Reforma
No. 195-Piso 13
Col. Cuauhetemoc
06500 Mexico City, Federal District, Mexico
Ph: 52 554 94543
Fax: 52 551 03837
Publisher E-mail: rotarismoenmex@prodigy.net.mx
Membership magazine of Rotary International covering current news about Rotary-related subjects. **Founded:** 1974. **Freq:** Bimonthly. **Key Personnel:** C. P. Jorge Villanueva, Editor. **URL:** http://www.rotary.org/en/mediaandnews/morepublications/regionalmagazines/pages/ridefault.aspx. **Circ:** 13,500

47790 ■ Utillaje
Utillaje Inc.
Apartado Postal 19-467
03910 Mexico City, Federal District, Mexico
Ph: 52 55 55932787
Fax: 52 55 55636542
Publisher E-mail: informacion@utillaje.com
Classified magazine listing over 15,000 pieces of industrial machinery (Spanish). **Subtitle:** Directorio de maquinaria. **Founded:** 1993. **Freq:** Monthly. **Print Method:** Offset. **Trim Size:** 5 3/8 x 8 1/4. **Cols./Page:** 2. **Col. Width:** 2 1/4 inches. **Col. Depth:** 7 /12 inches. **ISSN:** 1065-9862. **Remarks:** Color advertising not accepted. **URL:** http://www.utillaje.com. **Ad Rates:** GLR: 7 MP, BW: 465 MP, 4C: 600 MP. **Circ:** Paid 500, Controlled 30,250

47791 ■ Ibero-FM - 90.9
Prol. Paseo de la Reforma 880
Col. Lomas de Santa Fe
01210 Mexico City, Federal District, Mexico
Ph: 52 55 59504390
Fax: 52 55 59504385
E-mail: contacto@ibero909.fm
Format: Eclectic. **Operating Hours:** Continuous. **Ad Rates:** Advertising accepted; rates available upon request. **URL:** http://impala.ibero909.fm.

KXPL-AM - See Juarez, Chihuahua

47792 ■ Stereo Joya-FM - 93.7
Constituyentes 1154
Col. Lomas Altas
11950 Mexico City, Federal District, Mexico
Ph: 52 55 7284800
Fax: 52 55 7284875
Format: Hispanic. **Owner:** Grupo Radio Centro, at above address. **Key Personnel:** Mariano Osorio,

Contact; Jesus Zuniga, Contact. **URL:** http://www. stereojoya.com.mx/.

47793 ■ Universal Stereo-FM - 92.1
Constituyentes 1154, 7 Piso
Col. Lomas Altas
11950 Mexico City, Federal District, Mexico
Ph: 52 55 7284800
Fax: 52 55 7284875
E-mail: universal@grc.com.mx
Format: Classic Rock. **Owner:** Grupo Radio Centro, at above address. **Key Personnel:** Adolfo Fernandez, Contact; Manuel Guerrero, Contact. **URL:** http://www. universalstereo.com.mx/.

XEDCH-AM - See Delicias, Chihuahua

XEDI-AM - See Chihuahua, Chihuahua

XEFA-AM - See Chihuahua, Chihuahua

XEFI-AM - See Chihuahua, Chihuahua

XEFO-AM - See Chihuahua, Chihuahua

XEHES-AM - See Chihuahua, Chihuahua

XEIO-AM - See Tuxtla Gutierrez, Chiapas

XEIT-AM - See Ciudad del Carmen, Campeche

XEJK-AM - See Delicias, Chihuahua

XEKQ-AM - See Tapachula, Chiapas

XEKY-AM - See Huixtla, Chiapas

XELM-AM - See Tuxtla Gutierrez, Chiapas

XEMAB-AM - See Ciudad del Carmen, Campeche

XEMK-AM - See Huixtla, Chiapas

XEOE-AM - See Tapachula, Chiapas

XERPC-AM - See Chihuahua, Chihuahua

XERPR-AM - See Tuxtla Gutierrez, Chiapas

XETAK-AM - See Tapachula, Chiapas

XETAP-AM - See Tapachula, Chiapas

XETUG-AM - See Tuxtla Gutierrez, Chiapas

XEUE-AM - See Tuxtla Gutierrez, Chiapas

XHCJZ-FM - See Jimenez, Coahuila

XHDI-FM - See Chihuahua, Chihuahua

XHFA-FM - See Chihuahua, Chihuahua

XHIT-FM - See Ciudad del Carmen, Campeche

XHSD-FM - See Silao, Guanajuato

XHUA-FM - See Chihuahua, Chihuahua

Oaxaca

47794 ■ XEOAX-AM - 680 KHz
Calzada Madero S/N Esq. Avenida
Tecnologico Centro Cultural
Oaxaca, Oaxaca, Mexico
Ph: 52 5016230
Format: Hispanic. **Owner:** Corporacion Oaxaquena de Radio y Television, at above address. **Key Personnel:** Lic. Salvador Musalem Santiago, Dir. Gon, direcciongeneral@cortv.com.mx. **URL:** http://www.cortv. com.mx.

47795 ■ XHOA-FM - 96.9 MHz
Calzada Madero S/N Esq. Avenida
Tecnologico Centro Cultural
Oaxaca, Oaxaca, Mexico
Ph: 52 5016230
Format: Hispanic. **Owner:** Corporacion Oaxaquena de Radio y Television, at above address. **Key Personnel:** Lic. Salvador Musalem Santiago, Dir. Gen., direcciongeneral@cortv.com.mx. **URL:** http://www.cortv. com.mx.

Puerto Escondido

47796 ■ XHEDO-FM - 94.1
Retorno D6 Esquina Retorno C6 Fraccionamiento Bacocho
71980 Puerto Escondido, Oaxaca, Mexico
Ph: 52 954 5822430
Format: Ethnic; World Beat. **Operating Hours:** Continuous. **Key Personnel:** Ricardo Cervantes Reyes, Contact. **URL:** http://www.esmeralda94-1.com.

San Luis Huexotla

47797 ■ Agrociencia
Colegio de Postgraduados
Guerrero Num. 9.
Reconciled Cor. Hidalgo
56251 San Luis Huexotla, Mexico, Mexico
Ph: 52 159 59284427
Fax: 52 159 59284427
Publication E-mail: agrocien90@yahoo.com.mx
Publisher E-mail: contacto@colpos.mx
Journal covering agricultural science. **Founded:** 1884. **Freq:** Mon.-Sat. (eve). **Print Method:** Offset. **Cols./Page:** 6. **Col. Width:** 25 nonpareils. **Col. Depth:** 301 agate lines. **Key Personnel:** Sergio S. Gonzales, Director. **ISSN:** 1405-3195. **Subscription Rates:** 750 MP individuals; US$1,500 institutions; 150 MP individuals other countries; US$150 institutions other countries; 300 MP students. **URL:** http://www.colpos.mx/agrocien/agrociencia.htm.

San Luis Potosi

47798 ■ XHAWD-FM - 107.1
Loma Blanca No. 198
Col. Loma Dorada
San Luis Potosi, San Luis Potosi, Mexico
Ph: 52 444 1288384
E-mail: contacto@magneticafm.com
Format: Ethnic; Information. **Operating Hours:** Continuous. **Wattage:** 5000. **Ad Rates:** Advertising accepted; rates available upon request. **URL:** http://www. magneticafm.com.

Silao

47799 ■ XHSD-FM - 99.3
Reforma
2620 Edificio Reforma 2do piso.
Col. Lomas
Alta Del. Miguel Hidalgo
11950 Mexico City, Federal District, Mexico
Ph: 52 55 11050000
Fax: 52 55 11050016
E-mail: ventas@radiorama.com.mx
Format: Hispanic. **Owner:** Radiorama Corporativo, at above address. **Key Personnel:** Jose Luis Chavero Resendiz, Dir. Gen., jlchavero@radiorama.com.mx; Efrain Aizman Centeno, Sales Exec., eaizman@radiorama. com.mx; Jaime Ramirez Arrevillaga, Sales Exec., jramirez@radiorama.com.mx. **URL:** http://www. radiorama.com.mx/secciones.php?sec_id=32&ent_id=6.

Tapachula

47800 ■ XEKQ-AM - 680
Reforma 2620
Edificio Reforma 2do piso.
Col. Lomas Alta
Del. Miguel Hidalgo
11950 Mexico City, Federal District, Mexico
Ph: 52 55 11050000
Fax: 52 55 11050016
E-mail: grupo@radiorama.com.mx
Format: Hispanic. **Owner:** Radiorama Corporativo, at above address. **Key Personnel:** Jose Luis Chavero Resendiz, Dir. Gen., jlchavero@radiorama.com.mx; Efrain Aizman Centeno, Promotions Dir., eaizman@radiorama. com.mx; Jaime Ramirez Arrevillaga, Sales Exec., jramirez@radiorama.com.mx. **URL:** http://www. radiorama.com.mx/secciones.php?sec_id=32&ent_id=6.

47801 ■ XEOE-AM - 810
Reforma 2620
Edificio Reforma 2do piso.
Col. Lomas Alta
Del. Miguel Hidalgo
11950 Mexico City, Federal District, Mexico
Ph: 52 55 11050000
Fax: 52 55 11050016
E-mail: grupo@radiorama.com.mx
Format: Hispanic. **Owner:** Radiorama Corporativo, at above address. **Key Personnel:** Jose Luis Chavero Resendiz, Dir. Gen., jlchavero@radiorama.com.mx; Efrain Aizman Centeno, Promotions Dir., eaizman@radiorama. com.mx; Jaime Ramirez Arrevillaga, Sales Exec., jramirez@radiorama.com.mx. **URL:** http://www. radiorama.com.mx/secciones.php?sec_id=32&ent_id=6.

Circulation: ★ = ABC; △ = BPA; ◆ = CAC; ● = CCAB; ❑ = VAC; ⊕ = PO Statement; ‡ = Publisher's Report; Boldface figures = sworn; Light figures = estimated.

47802 ■ XETAK-AM - 900
Reforma 2620
Edificio Reforma 2do piso.
Col. Lomas Alta
Del. Miguel Hidalgo
11950 Mexico City, Federal District, Mexico
Ph: 52 55 11050000
Fax: 52 55 11050016
E-mail: grupo@radiorama.com.mx
Format: Hispanic. **Owner:** Radiorama Corporativo, at above address. **Key Personnel:** Jose Luis Chavero Resendiz, Dir. Gen., jlchavero@radiorama.com.mx; Efrain Aizman Centeno, Promotions Dir., eaizman@radiorama.com.mx; Jaime Ramirez Arrevillaga, Sales Exec., jramirez@radiorama.com.mx. **URL:** http://www.radiorama.com.mx/secciones.php?sec_id=32&ent_id=6.

47803 ■ XETAP-AM - 960
Reforma 2620
Edificio Reforma 2do piso.
Col. Lomas Alta
Del. Miguel Hidalgo
11950 Mexico City, Federal District, Mexico
Ph: 52 55 11050000
Fax: 52 55 11050016
E-mail: grupo@radiorama.com.mx
Format: Hispanic. **Owner:** Radiorama Corporativo, at above address. **Key Personnel:** Jose Luis Chavero Resendiz, Dir. Gen., jlchavero@radiorama.com.mx; Efrain Aizman Centeno, Promotions Dir., eaizman@radiorama.com.mx; Jaime Ramirez Arrevillaga, Sales Exec., jramirez@radiorama.com.mx. **URL:** http://www.radiorama.com.mx/secciones.php?sec_id=32&ent_id=6.

Tuxtla Gutierrez

47804 ■ XEIO-AM - 840
Reforma 2620
Edificio Reforma 2do piso.
Col. Lomas Alta
Del. Miguel Hidalgo
11950 Mexico City, Federal District, Mexico
Ph: 52 55 11050000
Fax: 52 55 11050016

E-mail: grupo@radiorama.com.mx
Format: Hispanic. **Owner:** Radiorama Corporativo, at above address. **Key Personnel:** Jose Luis Chavero Resendiz, Dir. Gen., jlchavero@radiorama.com.mx; Efrain Aizman Centeno, Promotions Dir., eaizman@radiorama.com.mx; Jaime Ramirez Arrevillaga, Sales Exec., jramirez@radiorama.com.mx. **URL:** http://www.radiorama.com.mx/secciones.php?sec_id=32&ent_id=6.

47805 ■ XELM-AM - 1240
Reforma 2620
Edificio Reforma 2do piso.
Col. Lomas Alta
Del. Miguel Hidalgo
11950 Mexico City, Federal District, Mexico
Ph: 52 55 11050000
Fax: 52 55 11050016
E-mail: grupo@radiorama.com.mx
Format: Hispanic. **Owner:** Radiorama Corporativo, at above address. **Key Personnel:** Jose Luis Chavero Resendiz, Dir. Gen., jlchavero@radiorama.com.mx; Efrain Aizman Centeno, Promotions Dir., eaizman@radiorama.com.mx; Jaime Ramirez Arrevillaga, Sales Exec., jramirez@radiorama.com.mx. **URL:** http://www.radiorama.com.mx/secciones.php?sec_id=32&ent_id=6.

47806 ■ XERPR-AM - 1070
Reforma 2620
Edificio Reforma 2do piso.
Col. Lomas Alta
Del. Miguel Hidalgo
11950 Mexico City, Federal District, Mexico
Ph: 52 55 11050000
Fax: 52 55 11050016
E-mail: grupo@radiorama.com.mx
Format: Hispanic. **Owner:** Radiorama Corporativo, at above address. **Key Personnel:** Jose Luis Chavero Resendiz, Dir. Gen., jlchavero@radiorama.com.mx; Efrain Aizman Centeno, Promotions Dir., eaizman@radiorama.com.mx; Jaime Ramirez Arrevillaga, Sales Exec., jramirez@radiorama.com.mx. **URL:** http://www.radiorama.com.mx/secciones.php?sec_id=32&ent_id=6.

47807 ■ XETUG-AM - 950
Reforma 2620

Edificio Reforma 2do piso.
Col. Lomas Alta
Del. Miguel Hidalgo
11950 Mexico City, Federal District, Mexico
Ph: 52 55 11050000
Fax: 52 55 11050016
E-mail: grupo@radiorama.com.mx
Format: Hispanic. **Owner:** Radiorama Corporativo, at above address. **Key Personnel:** Jose Luis Chavero Resendiz, Dir. Gen., jlchavero@radiorama.com.mx; Efrain Aizman Centeno, Promotions Dir., eaizman@radiorama.com.mx; Jaime Ramirez Arrevillaga, Sales Exec., jramirez@radiorama.com.mx. **URL:** http://www.radiorama.com.mx/secciones.php?sec_id=32&ent_id=6.

47808 ■ XEUE-AM - 580
Reforma 2620
Edificio Reforma 2do piso.
Col. Lomas Alta
Del. Miguel Hidalgo
11950 Mexico City, Federal District, Mexico
Ph: 52 55 11050000
Fax: 52 55 11050016
E-mail: grupo@radiorama.com.mx
Format: Hispanic. **Owner:** Radiorama Corporativo, at above address. **Key Personnel:** Jose Luis Chavero Resendiz, Dir. Gen., jlchavero@radiorama.com.mx; Efrain Aizman Centeno, Promotions Dir., eaizman@radiorama.com.mx; Jaime Ramirez Arrevillaga, Sales Exec., jramirez@radiorama.com.mx. **URL:** http://www.radiorama.com.mx/secciones.php?sec_id=32&ent_id=6.

Veracruz

47809 ■ Ya-FM - 102.9
Ocampo No. 119 6 Piso
Edificio Pazos, Centro
91700 Veracruz, Chiapas, Mexico
Ph: 52 229 9890240
E-mail: ventas@gpazos.com
Format: News; Ethnic; Contemporary Hit Radio (CHR). **Operating Hours:** Continuous. **Ad Rates:** Advertising accepted; rates available upon request. **URL:** http://www.ya.fm.

Monte Carlo

47810 ■ Luxury Intelligence
Inderscience Enterprises Limited
c/o Prof. Mounir Kehal, Ed.-in-Ch.
ESC Rennes School of Business
2 rue Robert d'Abrissel CS 76522
35065 Rennes Cedex
98000 Monte Carlo, Monaco
Journal covering research and development on luxury brand and sector strategy and intelligence. **Subtitle:** An International Journal. **Freq:** 4/yr. **Key Personnel:** Prof. Mounir Kehal, Editor-in-Chief, mounir@sciencesdeluxe.com; Prof. Luana Carcano, Assoc. Ed. **ISSN:** 2041-3831. **Subscription Rates:** EUR494 individuals print or online; EUR672 individuals print and online. **URL:** http://www.inderscience.com/browse/index.php?journalID= 356.

Circulation: ★ = ABC; △ = BPA; ♦ = CAC; • = CCAB; ❏ = VAC; ⊕ = PO Statement; ‡ = Publisher's Report; Boldface figures = sworn; Light figures = estimated.

Gale Directory of Publications & Broadcast Media/147th Ed.   5201

Ulaanbaatar

47811 ■ Khumuun Bichig
MONTSAME News Agency
PO Box 1514
Ulaanbaatar, Mongolia
Fax: 976 11 327857
Publisher E-mail: foreignad@montsame

.mn
Newspaper in Mongolian traditional script. **Founded:** May 10, 1992. **Freq:** Weekly. **Remarks:** Accepts advertising. **URL:** http://www.mongolmessenger.mn/issue/060101.php. **Circ:** (Not Reported)

47812 ■ The Mongol Messenger
MONTSAME News Agency
PO Box 1514

Ulaanbaatar, Mongolia
Fax: 976 11 327857
Publisher E-mail: foreignad@montsame.mn
English language newspaper. **Founded:** July 1991. **Freq:** Weekly. **Subscription Rates:** US$52 individuals; US$90 other countries. **Remarks:** Accepts advertising. **URL:** http://www.mongolmessenger.mn/home/index.php. **Circ:** (Not Reported)

Circulation: ★ = ABC; △ = BPA; ♦ = CAC; • = CCAB; ❑ = VAC; ⊕ = PO Statement; ‡ = Publisher's Report; Boldface figures = sworn; Light figures = estimated.

Gale Directory of Publications & Broadcast Media/147th Ed. 5203

Casablanca

47813 ■ Tijaris
Islamic Centre for Development of Trade
Centre Islamique pour le Developpement du Commerce
Ave. des FAR
Tours des Habous
B.P. 13545 Casa Principal
Casablanca 20000, Morocco
Ph: 21 222 314974
Fax: 21 222 310110
Publisher E-mail: icdt@icdt-oic.org

Publication covering Islamic trade in Arabic, English and French. **Subtitle:** Magazine of International and Inter-Islamic Trade. **Freq:** Quarterly. **Key Personnel:** Allal Rachdi, Dir. Gen., dg@icdt-oic.org; Houcine Rahmouni, Advisory of the Dir. Gen., rahmouni@icdt-oic.org. **ISSN:** 0651-1578. **URL:** http://www.icdt-oic.org/Tijaris.aspx.

Rabat

47814 ■ African Journal of Mathematical Physics
GNPHE
University Mohamed V-Agdal

Focal point: Faculty of Science
Rabat, Morocco
Ph: 21 237 771834
Fax: 21 237 778973
Publication E-mail: ajmp@fsr.ac.ma
Scholarly journal reporting on current investigations in the fields of basic physics, mathematics and their applications. **Key Personnel:** A. Belhaj, Editorial Board; A. Awane, Editorial Board; M. Bennai, Editorial Board. **URL:** http://www.fsr.ac.ma/GNPHE/.

Circulation: ★ = ABC; △ = BPA; ◆ = CAC; • = CCAB; ❑ = VAC; ⊕ = PO Statement; ‡ = Publisher's Report; Boldface figures = sworn; Light figures = estimated.

Rangoon

47815 ■ VOA Burmese - 6185
c/o US Embassy
Merchant St.
Rangoon, Myanmar
E-mail: burmese@voanews.com
Format: News; Information; Educational. **Owner:** Voice of America, 330 Independence Ave. SW, Washington, DC 20237, 202203-4959, Fax: 202203-4960. **Operating Hours:** 2300-2400. **Key Personnel:** Than Lwin Htun, Contact. **URL:** http://www.voanews.com/burmese.

47816 ■ VOA Burmese - 11980
c/o US Embassy
Merchant St.
Rangoon, Myanmar
E-mail: burmese@voanews.com
Format: News; Information; Educational. **Owner:** Voice of America, 330 Independence Ave. SW, Washington, DC 20237, 202203-4959, Fax: 202203-4960. **Operating Hours:** 2300-2400. **Key Personnel:** Than Lwin Htun, Contact. **URL:** http://www.voanews.com/burmese.

47817 ■ VOA Burmese - 9505
c/o US Embassy
Merchant St.
Rangoon, Myanmar
E-mail: burmese@voanews.com
Format: News; Information; Educational. **Operating Hours:** 2330-2400. **Key Personnel:** Than Lwin Htun, Contact. **URL:** http://www.voanews.com/burmese.

47818 ■ VOA Burmese - 1575
c/o US Embassy
Merchant St.
Rangoon, Myanmar
E-mail: burmese@voanews.com
Format: News; Information; Educational. **Operating Hours:** 1430-1500. **Key Personnel:** Than Lwin Htun, Contact. **URL:** http://www.voanews.com/burmese.

47819 ■ VOA Burmese - 9325
c/o US Embassy
Merchant St.
Rangoon, Myanmar
E-mail: burmese@voanews.com
Format: News; Information; Educational. **Operating Hours:** 1430-1530. **Key Personnel:** Than Lwin Htun, Contact. **URL:** http://www.voanews.com/burmese.

47820 ■ VOA Burmese - 11910
c/o US Embassy
Merchant St.
Rangoon, Myanmar
E-mail: burmese@voanews.com
Format: News; Information; Educational. **Operating Hours:** 1430-1530. **Key Personnel:** Than Lwin Htun, Contact. **URL:** http://www.voanews.com/burmese.

47821 ■ VOA Burmese - 12120
c/o US Embassy
Merchant St.
Rangoon, Myanmar
E-mail: burmese@voanews.com
Format: News; Information; Educational. **Operating Hours:** 1430-1530. **Key Personnel:** Than Lwin Htun, Contact. **URL:** http://www.voanews.com/burmese.

Circulation: ★ = ABC; △ = BPA; ♦ = CAC; • = CCAB; ❑ = VAC; ⊕ = PO Statement; ‡ = Publisher's Report; Boldface figures = sworn; Light figures = estimated.

Windhoek

47822 ■ International Journal of Education Economics and Development
Inderscience Enterprises Limited
c/o Dr. Ravinder Rena, Ed.-in-Ch.
Harold Pupkewitz Graduate School of Business
Polytechnic of Namibia
13 Storch St., Private Bag 13388
Windhoek, Namibia
Publication E-mail: editor.ijeed@gmail.com
Peer-reviewed journal covering the economics of education. **Freq:** Quarterly. **Key Personnel:** Dr. Ravinder Rena, Editor-in-Chief. **ISSN:** 1759-5673. **Subscription Rates:** EUR494 individuals print or online; EUR672 individuals print and online. **URL:** http://www.inderscience.com/browse/index.php?journalCODE=ijeed.

47823 ■ The Namibia Economist
7 Schuster St.
PO Box 49
Windhoek 9000, Namibia
Ph: 264 612 21925
Fax: 264 612 20615
Business newspaper. **Founded:** Dec. 1986. **Freq:** Weekly. **Print Method:** Web offset. **Trim Size:** 420 x 580 mm. **Key Personnel:** Daniel Steinmann, Contact. **ISSN:** 1028-9413. **URL:** http://www.economist.com.na. **Circ:** Paid 7,000

47824 ■ The Namibian Newspaper
The Namibian
42 John Meinert St.
PO Box 20783
Windhoek, Namibia
Ph: 264 612 79660
Fax: 264 612 79602
General newspaper. **Freq:** Daily. **Key Personnel:** Gwen Lister, Editor. **Subscription Rates:** US$325 individuals weekly; US$1,500 individuals daily; US$700 individuals weekly; RSA; US$2,700 individuals daily; RSA; US$5,700 individuals weekly; SADC; US$16,900 individuals daily; SADC; US$5,800 individuals weekly; rest of Africa & Europe; US$17,200 individuals daily; rest of Africa & Europe; US$7,100 individuals weekly; rest of world; US$21,000 individuals daily; rest of world. **Remarks:** Accepts advertising. **URL:** http://www.namibian.com.na/. **Circ:** (Not Reported)

47825 ■ Radio Kudu-FM - 103.5
158 Jan Jonker St.
Windhoek 5369, Namibia
Ph: 264 61 247262
Fax: 264 61 247259
E-mail: radiokudu@radiokudu.com.na
Format: Contemporary Hit Radio (CHR). **Ad Rates:** Advertising accepted; rates available upon request. **URL:** http://www.kudufm.com/portal.

47826 ■ Radio Wave-FM - 96.7
PO Box 9953
Windhoek 9953, Namibia
Ph: 264 61 242350
Fax: 264 61 242322
E-mail: info@radiowave.com.na
Format: Contemporary Hit Radio (CHR); Information. **Operating Hours:** Continuous. **Ad Rates:** Advertising accepted; rates available upon request. **URL:** http://www.radiowave.com.na.

Bardibas

47827 ■ Radio Nepal - Bardibas - 1143 KHz
PO Box 634
Singha Durbar
Kathmandu, Nepal
Ph: 977 1 4211910
Fax: 977 1 4211952
E-mail: radio@engg.wlink.com.np
Format: News; Educational; Folk; Agricultural; Religious. **Owner:** Radio Broadcasting Service, at above address. **Operating Hours:** 4:56a.m.-11:05a.m.,11:11a.m.-5p.m. ,5p.m.-4:56a.m. Daily. **Key Personnel:** Er. Ramesh Jung Karkee, Chief Engineer, phone 977 1 4211667; Rajendra Prasad Sharma, Dep. Exec.Dir., phone 977 1 4211923; Sushil Koirala, Dep. Exec.Dir., phone 977 1 4211842. **Wattage:** 10,000. **Ad Rates:** $300-450 for 15 seconds; $600-900 for 30 seconds; $900-1,350 for 45 seconds; $1,200-1,800 for 60 seconds. **URL:** http://www.radionepal.org.

Butwal

47828 ■ Nepal Television - Butwal - 7
PO Box 3826
Singh Durbar
Kathmandu, Nepal
Ph: 977 1 4227453
Fax: 977 1 4228312
E-mail: neptv@vishnu.ccsl.com.np
Format: News; Information; Educational. **Owner:** Nepal Television, at above address. **Founded:** Jan. 1985. **Operating Hours:** 6:30a.m.-9p.m., 5:30p.m.-11p.m. weekdays; 12p.m.-5p.m.Weekend. **Wattage:** 10. **Ad Rates:** $2,900-9,300 for 10 seconds; $4,400-14,100 for 20 seconds; $6,100-16,500 for 30 seconds; $12,100-33,000 for 60 seconds. **URL:** http://www.explorenepal.com/ntv; http://www.nepaltelevision.com.np.

Chamere Danda

47829 ■ Nepal Television - Chamere Danda - 5
PO Box 3826
Singh Durbar
Kathmandu, Nepal
Ph: 977 1 4227453
Fax: 977 1 4228312
E-mail: neptv@vishnu.ccsl.com.np
Format: News; Information; Educational. **Owner:** Nepal Television, at above address. **Founded:** Jan. 1985. **Operating Hours:** 6:30a.m.-9p.m., 5:30p.m.-11p.m. weekdays; 12p.m.-5p.m.Weekend. **Wattage:** 1000. **Ad Rates:** $2,900-9,300 for 10 seconds; $4,400-14,100 for 20 seconds; $6,100-16,500 for 30 seconds; $12,100-33,000 for 60 seconds. **URL:** http://www.explorenepal.com/ntv; http://www.nepaltelevision.com.np.

Daunne

47830 ■ Nepal Television - Daunne - 12
PO Box 3826
Singh Durbar
Kathmandu, Nepal
Ph: 977 1 4227453

Fax: 977 1 4228312
E-mail: neptv@vishnu.ccsl.com.np
Format: News; Information; Educational. **Owner:** Nepal Television, at above address. **Founded:** Jan. 1985. **Operating Hours:** 6:30a.m.-9p.m., 5:30p.m.-11p.m. weekdays; 12p.m.-5p.m. Sat.-Sun. **Wattage:** 500. **Ad Rates:** $2,900-9,300 for 10 seconds; $4,400-14,100 for 20 seconds; $6,100-16,500 for 30 seconds; $12,100-33,000 for 60 seconds. **URL:** http://www.explorenepal.com/ntv; http://www.nepaltelevision.com.np.

Dhankuta

47831 ■ Radio Nepal - Dhankuta - 648 KHz
PO Box 634
Singha Durbar
Kathmandu, Nepal
Ph: 977 1 4211910
Fax: 977 1 4211952
E-mail: radio@engg.wlink.com.np
Format: Educational; News; Religious; Agricultural; Folk. **Owner:** Radio Broadcasting Service, at above address. **Operating Hours:** 4:56a.m.-12:30p.m.,12:56p.m.-4:59p.m.,5p.m.-11p.m. Daily. **Key Personnel:** Er. Ramesh Jung Karkee, Chief Engineer, phone 977 1 4211667; Mr. Rajendra Prasad Sharma, Dep. Exec.Dir., phone 977 1 4211923; Mr. Sushil Koirala, Dep. Exec. Dir., phone 977 1 4211842. **Wattage:** 100,000. **Ad Rates:** $300-450 for 15 seconds; $600-900 for 30 seconds; $900-1,350 for 45 seconds; $1,200-1,800 for 60 seconds. **URL:** http://www.radionepal.org.

Dipayal

47832 ■ Radio Nepal - Dipayal - 810 KHz
PO Box 634
Singha Durbar
Kathmandu, Nepal
Fax: 977 1 4211952
E-mail: radio@engg.wlink.com.np
Format: News; Educational; Folk; Agricultural; Religious. **Owner:** Radio Broadcasting Service, at above address. **Operating Hours:** 4:56a.m.-12:30p.m.,12:56p.m.-4:59p.m.,5p.m.-11p.m. Daily. **Key Personnel:** Er. Ramesh Jung Karkee, Chief Engineer, phone 977 1 4211667; Mr. Rajendra Prasad Sharma, Dep. Exec.Dir., phone 977 1 4211923; Mr. Sushil Koirala, Dep. Exec.Dir., phone 977 1 4211842. **Wattage:** 10,000. **Ad Rates:** $300-450 for 15 seconds; $600-900 for 30 seconds; $900-1,350 for 45 seconds; $1,200-1,800 for 60 seconds. **URL:** http://www.radionepal.org.

Hetaunda

47833 ■ Nepal Television - Hetaunda - 4
PO Box 3826
Singh Durbar
Kathmandu, Nepal
Ph: 977 1 4227453
Fax: 977 1 4228312
E-mail: neptv@vishnu.ccsl.com.np
Format: News; Information; Educational. **Owner:** Nepal Television, at above address. **Founded:** Jan. 1985. **Operating Hours:** 6:30a.m.-9p.m., 5:30p.m.-11p.m. week-

days; 12p.m.-5p.m.Weekend. **Wattage:** 100. **Ad Rates:** $2,900-9,300 for 10 seconds; $4,400-14,100 for 20 seconds; $6,100-16,500 for 30 seconds; $12,100-33,000 for 60 seconds. **URL:** http://www.explorenepal.com/ntv; http://www.nepaltelevision.com.np.

Ilam

47834 ■ Nepal Television - Ilam - 12
PO Box 3826
Singh Durbar
Kathmandu, Nepal
Ph: 977 1 4227453
Fax: 977 1 4228312
E-mail: neptv@vishnu.ccsl.com.np
Format: News; Information; Educational. **Owner:** Nepal Television, at above address. **Founded:** Jan. 1985. **Operating Hours:** 6:30a.m.-9p.m., 5:30p.m.-11p.m. weekdays; 12p.m.-5p.m. Sat.-Sun. **Wattage:** 5000. **Ad Rates:** $2,900-9,300 for 10 seconds; $4,400-14,100 for 20 seconds; $6,100-16,500 for 30 seconds; $12,100-33,000 for 60 seconds. **URL:** http://www.explorenepal.com/ntv; http://www.nepaltelevision.com.np.

Jaleswor

47835 ■ Nepal Television - Jaleswor - 11
PO Box 3826
Singh Durbar
Kathmandu, Nepal
Ph: 977 1 4227453
Fax: 977 1 4228312
E-mail: neptv@vishnu.ccsl.com.np
Format: News; Information; Educational. **Owner:** Nepal Television, at above address. **Founded:** Jan. 1985. **Operating Hours:** 6:30a.m.-9p.m., 5:30p.m.-11p.m. weekdays; 12p.m.-5p.m. Weekend. **Wattage:** 2000. **Ad Rates:** $2,900-9,300 for 10 seconds; $4,400-14,100 for 20 seconds; $6,100-16,500 for 30 seconds; $12,100-33,000 for 60 seconds. **URL:** http://www.explorenepal.com/ntv; http://www.nepaltelevision.com.np.

Kathmandu

47836 ■ Aankhijhyal
Nepal Forum for Environmental Journalists
Thapathali
PO Box 5143
Kathmandu, Nepal
Ph: 97 714 261991
Publisher E-mail: nefej@mos.com.np
Nepali language publication covering community development. **Freq:** Weekly. **URL:** http://www.nefej.org/.

47837 ■ The Himalayan Times
International Media Network Nepal Pvt. Ltd.
APCA House
Baidya Khana Rd.
Anam Nagar
PO Box 11651
Kathmandu, Nepal
Ph: 977 1 4771489
Fax: 977 1 4770701
Publication E-mail: editorial@thehimalayantimes.com
Newspaper. **Freq:** Daily. **Remarks:** Accepts advertising.

Circulation: ★ = ABC; △ = BPA; ◆ = CAC; • = CCAB; ❑ = VAC; ⊕ = PO Statement; ‡ = Publisher's Report; Boldface figures = sworn; Light figures = estimated.

URL: http://www.thehimalayantimes.com/. Circ: (Not Reported)

47838 ■ Journal of the Nepal Dental Association
Nepal Dental Association
PO Box 21506
Nagpokhari
Kathmandu, Nepal
Ph: 977 1 2120450
Publisher E-mail: info@jnda.com.np
Journal containing original research, clinical observations, or investigation on recent advances. **Freq:** Annual. **Key Personnel:** Dr. Siddharth Dixit, Editor-in-Chief. **URL:** http://www.jnda.com.np/home.php?fd=1&page=homepage.

47839 ■ Journal of the Nepal Medical Association
Nepal Medical Association
Siddhi Sadan
Exhibition Rd.
PO Box 189
Kathmandu, Nepal
Ph: 977 14 225860
Fax: 977 14 225300
Publisher E-mail: mail@nma.org.np
Scientific medical journal (English). **Founded:** 1963. **Freq:** Quarterly. **Key Personnel:** Ramesh Prasad Aacharya, Contact. **ISSN:** 0028-2715. **Remarks:** Advertising accepted; rates available upon request. **URL:** http://www.nma.org.np/; http://journals.sfu.ca/nepal/index.php/JNMA. **Circ:** Paid 1,250

47840 ■ Kathmandu Post
Mercantile Communications Pvt. Ltd.
PO Box 876
Durbar Marg
Kathmandu, Nepal
Ph: 977 4 445920
Fax: 977 1 4439360
Publisher E-mail: mc3@mos.com.np
Newspaper. **Freq:** Daily. **ISSN:** 1563-9770. **Remarks:** Accepts advertising. **URL:** http://www.nepalnews.com/ktmpost.htm. **Circ:** (Not Reported)

47841 ■ Kathmandu University Medical Journal
Kathmandu University, Kathmandu Medical College
Sinamangal
PO Box 21266
Kathmandu, Nepal
Publisher E-mail: editor@kumj.com.np
Journal devoted to basic, clinical and medical education. **Freq:** Quarterly. **Key Personnel:** Prof. Manindra Ranjan Baral, Editor-in-Chief; Prof. H. Dixit, Consultant Ed.; Prof. C.R. Pant, Asst. Publication Ed.; Dr. Narendra B. Rana, Editorial Advisory; Prof. A.C. Patowary, Editorial Advisory Board; Prof. Damber Bahadur Karki, Editorial Member. **ISSN:** 1812-2027. **URL:** http://www.kumj.com.np.

47842 ■ Nepal Agriculture Research Journal
Nepal Agricultural Research Council
PO Box 5459
Kathmandu, Nepal
Ph: 977 14 256837
Fax: 977 14 262500
Publisher E-mail: ed@narc.org.np
Publishes research articles pertaining to agriculture. **Founded:** 1997. **Freq:** Annual. **Key Personnel:** Krishna Raj Bhatta, Editor. **ISSN:** 1029-533X. **URL:** http://www.narc.org.np/publicaton/journal.php.

47843 ■ Nepali Times
Mercantile Communications Pvt. Ltd.
PO Box 876
Durbar Marg
Kathmandu, Nepal
Ph: 977 4 445920
Fax: 977 1 4439360
Publication E-mail: editors@nepalitimes.com
Publisher E-mail: mc3@mos.com.np
Newspaper. **Freq:** Weekly. **Key Personnel:** Kunda Dixit, Publisher; Rabi Thapa, Editor. **ISSN:** 1814-2613. **Subscription Rates:** NRs 1,600 individuals. **Remarks:** Accepts advertising. **URL:** http://www.nepalitimes.com/. **Circ:** (Not Reported)

47844 ■ New Business Age
Mercantile Communications Pvt. Ltd.
PO Box 876
Durbar Marg

Kathmandu, Nepal
Ph: 977 4 445920
Fax: 977 1 4439360
Publication E-mail: bizline@mos.com.np
Publisher E-mail: mc3@mos.com.np
General interest magazine. **Subtitle:** Information and Analysis. **Freq:** Monthly. **ISSN:** 1605-9271. **Remarks:** Advertising accepted; rates available upon request. **URL:** http://www.nepalnews.com/new_businessage.php. **Circ:** (Not Reported)

47845 ■ People's Review
Pushpa Raj Pradhan
Pipalbot
Dillibazar
Kathmandu, Nepal
Ph: 977 1 4438797
Publication E-mail: preview@ntc.net.np
Publisher E-mail: preview@ntc.net.np
Newspaper covering national news, views, analysis, commentary, opinion and business activities. **Subtitle:** A Political and Business Weekly. **Founded:** 1991. **Freq:** Weekly. **Key Personnel:** Pushpa Raj Pradhan, Ch. Ed. **ISSN:** 1563-9843. **URL:** http://www.peoplesreview.com.np.

47846 ■ Spotlight
Mercantile Communications Pvt. Ltd.
PO Box 876
Durbar Marg
Kathmandu, Nepal
Ph: 977 4 445920
Fax: 977 1 4439360
Publication E-mail: spot@mail.com.np
Publisher E-mail: mc3@mos.com.np
General interest magazine. **Freq:** Weekly. **ISSN:** 1563-9800. **Remarks:** Advertising accepted; rates available upon request. **URL:** http://www.nepalnews.com/spotlight.php. **Circ:** (Not Reported)

47847 ■ The Telegraph Weekly
Mercantile Communications Pvt. Ltd.
PO Box 876
Durbar Marg
Kathmandu, Nepal
Ph: 977 4 445920
Fax: 977 1 4439360
Publication E-mail: tgw@ntc.net.np
Publisher E-mail: mc3@mos.com.np
Newspaper. **Freq:** Weekly. **Key Personnel:** Niraj Aryal, Editor, nirajaryal@telegraphnepal.com; Narendra Prasad Upadhyaya, Editor-in-Chief, npu@telegraphnepal.com. **ISSN:** 1563-9797. **Remarks:** Accepts advertising. **URL:** http://www.telegraphnepal.com/. **Circ:** (Not Reported)

47848 ■ Voice of Child Workers
Child Workers in Nepal Concerned Center
Ravi Bhawan
Kathmandu, Nepal
Ph: 977 1 4282255
Publisher E-mail: cwin@mos.com.np
Publication covering child labor concerns. **Freq:** Quarterly. **Key Personnel:** Gauri Pradhan, Editor-in-Chief; Naresh Newar, Editor. **Subscription Rates:** NRs 50 individuals. **URL:** http://www.cwin.org.np. **Circ:** 5,000

47849 ■ Hits-FM - 91.2
Baneshwor
PO Box 21912
Kathmandu, Nepal
Ph: 977 1 4780534
E-mail: info@hitsfm.com.np
Format: Eclectic; Classic Rock; Jazz; Reggae; Hip Hop; Classical; Folk. **Owner:** Hits Nepal Pvt. Ltd., at above address. **Founded:** Jan. 1996. **Operating Hours:** Continuous. **Key Personnel:** Rajib Raj Bhandari, Chm.; Mahendra K. Shrestha, Director; Sanjib Raj Bhandari, Director; Binod Tuladhar, Director; Sonny Shrestha, Director; Jeevan Lal Shrestha, CEO. **URL:** http://www.hitsfm.com.np.

47850 ■ Kath-FM - 97.9
Pako, New Rd.
PO Box 5566
Kathmandu, Nepal
Ph: 977 1 224130
E-mail: kath979@sajilo.com
Format: Music of Your Life; Ethnic. **Operating Hours:** Continuous. **URL:** http://www.sajilo.com/kath979/.

47851 ■ Nepal Press Institute-FM - 105.4
PO Box 4128
Kathmandu, Nepal
Ph: 977 1 264155
Fax: 977 1 264154
E-mail: npiktm@wlink.com.np
Format: Educational; Information; Public Radio. **Wattage:** 100. **URL:** http://www.npiktm.org.

Nepal Television - Butwal - See Butwal

Nepal Television - Chamere Danda - See Chamere Danda

Nepal Television - Daunne - See Daunne

Nepal Television - Hetaunda - See Hetaunda

Nepal Television - Ilam - See Ilam

Nepal Television - Jaleswor - See Jaleswor

Nepal Television - Phulchoki - See Phulchoki

Nepal Television - Sarangkot - See Sarangkot

47852 ■ Nepal Television - Tansen (Palpa) - 5
PO Box 3826
Singh Durbar
Kathmandu, Nepal
Ph: 977 1 4227453
Fax: 977 1 4228312
E-mail: neptv@vishnu.ccsl.com.np
Format: News; Information; Educational. **Owner:** Nepal Television, at above address. **Founded:** Jan. 1985. **Operating Hours:** 6:30a.m.-9p.m., 5:30p.m.-11p.m. weekdays; 12p.m.-5p.m. Weekend. **Wattage:** 200. **Ad Rates:** $2,900-9,300 for 10 seconds; $4,400-14,100 for 20 seconds; $6,100-16,500 for 30 seconds; $12,100-33,000 for 60 seconds. **URL:** http://www.explorenepal.com/ntv; http://www.nepaltelevision.com.np.

Radio Nepal - Bardibas - See Bardibas

Radio Nepal - Dhankuta - See Dhankuta

Radio Nepal - Dipayal - See Dipayal

47853 ■ Radio Nepal - Kathmandu FM - 100 MHz
PO Box 634
Singha Durbar
Kathmandu, Nepal
Fax: 977 1 4211952
E-mail: radio@engg.wlink.com.np
Format: Educational; Folk; News; Agricultural; Religious. **Owner:** Radio Broadcasting Service, at above address. **Operating Hours:** 4:56a.m.-12:30p.m.,12:56p.m.-4:59p.m.,5p.m.-11p.m. Daily. **Key Personnel:** Er. Ramesh Jung Karkee, Chief Engineer, phone 977 1 4211667; Mr. Rajendra Prasad Sharma, Dep. Exec.Dir., phone 977 1 4211923; Mr. Sushil Koirala, Dep. Exec.Dir., phone 977 1 4211842. **Wattage:** 1000. **Ad Rates:** $300-450 for 15 seconds; $600-900 for 30 seconds; $900-1,350 for 45 seconds; $1,200-1,800 for 60 seconds. **URL:** http://www.radionepal.org.

47854 ■ Radio Nepal - Kathmandu MW - 792 KHz
PO Box 634
Singha Durbar
Kathmandu, Nepal
Fax: 977 1 4211952
E-mail: radio@engg.wlink.com.np
Format: Religious; Educational; News; Agricultural; Folk. **Owner:** Radio Broadcasting Service, at above address. **Founded:** Jan. 4, 1951. **Operating Hours:** 4:56a.m.-11:05a.m.,11:11a.m.-5p.m.,5p.m.-4:56a.m. Daily. **Key Personnel:** Er. Ramesh Jung Karkee, Chief Engineer, phone 977 1 4211667; Mr. Rajendra Prasad Sharma, Dep. Exec.Dir., phone 977 1 4211923; Mr. Sushil Koirala, Dep. Exec.Dir., phone 977 1 4211842. **Wattage:** 100,000. **Ad Rates:** $300-450 for 15 seconds; $600-900 for 30 seconds; $900-1,350 for 45 seconds; $1,200-1,800 for 60 seconds. **URL:** http://www.radionepal.org.

Radio Nepal - Khumaltar - See Khumaltar

Radio Nepal - Khumaltar - See Khumaltar

Radio Nepal - Khumaltar - See Khumaltar

Radio Nepal - Pokhara - See Pokhara

Radio Nepal - Surkhet - See Surkhet

Khumaltar

47855 ■ Radio Nepal - Khumaltar - 7165 KHz
PO Box 634
Singha Durbar

Kathmandu, Nepal
Fax: 977 1 4211952
E-mail: radio@engg.wlink.com.np
Format: News; Agricultural; Educational; Folk; Religious.
Owner: Radio Broadcasting Service, at above address.
Operating Hours: 4:56a.m.-11:05a.m.,11:11a.m.-5p.m.
,5p.m.-4:56a.m. Daily. **Key Personnel:** Er. Ramesh
Jung Karkee, Chief Engineer, phone 977 1 4211667; Mr.
Rajendra Prasad Sharma, Dep. Exec.Dir., phone 977 1
4211923; Sushil Koirala, Dep. Exec.Dir., phone 977 1
4211842. **Wattage:** 300,000. **Ad Rates:** $300-450 for
15 seconds; $600-900 for 30 seconds; $900-1,350 for
45 seconds; $1,200-1,800 for 60 seconds. **URL:** http://
www.radionepal.org.

47856 ■ Radio Nepal - Khumaltar - 5005 KHz
PO Box 634
Singha Durbar
Kathmandu, Nepal
Fax: 977 1 4211952
E-mail: radio@engg.wlink.com.np
Format: Religious; Educational; News; Agricultural;
Folk. **Owner:** Radio Broadcasting Service, at above
address. **Operating Hours:** 4:56a.m.-11:05a.m.,11:11a.
m.-5p.m.,5p.m.-4:56a.m. Daily. **Key Personnel:** Er.
Ramesh Jung Karkee, Chief Engineer, phone 977 1
4211667; Mr. Rajendra Prasad Sharma, Dep. Exec.Dir.,
phone 977 1 4211923; Sushil Koirala, Dep. Exec.Dir.,
phone 977 1 4211842. **Wattage:** 300,000. **Ad Rates:**
$300-450 for 15 seconds; $600-900 for 30 seconds;
$900-1,350 for 45 seconds; $1,200-1,800 for 60
seconds. **URL:** http://www.radionepal.org.

47857 ■ Radio Nepal - Khumaltar - 3230 KHz
PO Box 634
Singha Durbar
Kathmandu, Nepal
Ph: 977 1 4211910
Fax: 977 1 4211952
E-mail: radio@engg.wlink.com.np
Format: News; Educational; Folk; Agricultural; Religious.
Owner: Radio Broadcasting Service, at above address.
Operating Hours: 4:56a.m.-11:05a.m.,11:11a.m.-5p.m.
,5p.m.-4:56a.m. Daily. **Key Personnel:** Er. Ramesh
Jung Karkee, Chief Engineer, phone 977 1 4211667;
Rajendra Prasad Sharma, Dep. Exec.Dir., phone 977 1
4211923; Sushil Koirala, Dep. Exec.Dir., phone 977 1
4211842. **Wattage:** 300,000. **Ad Rates:** $300-450 for
15 seconds; $600-900 for 30 seconds; $900-1,350 for
45 seconds; $1,200-1,800 for 60 seconds. **URL:** http://
www.radionepal.org.

Phulchoki

47858 ■ Nepal Television - Phulchoki - 5
PO Box 3826
Singh Durbar
Kathmandu, Nepal
Ph: 977 1 4227453
Fax: 977 1 4228312
E-mail: neptv@vishnu.ccsl.com.np
Format: News; Information; Educational. **Owner:** Nepal
Television, at above address. **Founded:** Jan. 1985. **Op-
erating Hours:** 6:30a.m.-9p.m., 5:30p.m.-11p.m. week-
days; 12p.m.-5p.m. Weekend. **Wattage:** 5000. **Ad
Rates:** $2,900-9,300 for 10 seconds; $4,400-14,100 for
20 seconds; $6,100-16,500 for 30 seconds; $12,100-
33,000 for 60 seconds. **URL:** http://www.explorenepal.
com/ntv/; http://www.nepaltelevision.com.np.

Pokhara

47859 ■ BIG-FM - 101.2
PO Box 525
New Rd.
Pokhara, Nepal
Ph: 977 61 535063
E-mail: info@fmbig.com
Format: Information; News; Educational; Easy Listening.
Owner: Pokhara Broadcasting Company Pvt. Ltd., at
above address. **Founded:** Mar. 2009. **Wattage:** 1000.
URL: http://www.fmbig.com/.

47860 ■ Radio Nepal - Pokhara - 684 KHz
PO Box 634
Singha Durbar
Kathmandu, Nepal
Ph: 977 1 4211910
Fax: 977 1 4211952
E-mail: radio@engg.wlink.com.np
Format: News; Educational; Religious; Agricultural;
Folk. **Owner:** Radio Broadcasting Service, at above
address. **Founded:** Jan. 4, 1951. **Operating Hours:**
4:56a.m.-11:05a.m.,11:11a.m.-5p.m.,5p.m.-4:56a.m.
Daily. **Key Personnel:** Er. Ramesh Jung Karkee, Chief
Engineer, phone 977 1 4211667; Mr. Rajendra Prasad
Sharma, Dep. Exec.Dir., phone 977 1 4211923; Mr.
Sushil Koirala, Dep. Exec.Dir., phone 977 1 4211842.
Wattage: 100,000. **Ad Rates:** $300-450 for 15 seconds;
$600-900 for 30 seconds; $900-1,350 for 45 seconds;
$1,200-1,800 for 60 seconds. **URL:** http://www.
radionepal.org.

Rupandehi

47861 ■ Radio Lumbini-FM - 96.8
Aanandabane VDC

Ward No. 3, Manigram
Lumbini Zone
Rupandehi, Nepal
Ph: 977 61003
Fax: 977 61545
E-mail: lumbinifm@mos.com.np
Format: Public Radio; Information; Ethnic. **Owner:**
Radio Lumbini, at above address. **Founded:** Jan. 2000.
Ad Rates: Advertising accepted; rates available upon
request. **URL:** http://www.radiolumbini.netfirms.com.

Sarangkot

47862 ■ Nepal Television - Sarangkot - 7
PO Box 3826
Singh Durbar
Kathmandu, Nepal
Ph: 977 1 4227453
Fax: 977 1 4228312
E-mail: neptv@vishnu.ccsl.com.np
Format: News; Information; Educational. **Owner:** Nepal
Television, at above address. **Founded:** Jan. 1985. **Op-
erating Hours:** 6:30a.m.-9p.m., 5:30p.m.-11p.m. week-
days; 12p.m.-5p.m. Weekend. **Wattage:** 200. **Ad Rates:**
$2,900-9,300 for 10 seconds; $4,400-14,100 for 20
seconds; $6,100-16,500 for 30 seconds; $12,100-33,000
for 60 seconds. **URL:** http://www.explorenepal.com/ntv;
http://www.nepaltelevision.com.np.

Surkhet

47863 ■ Radio Nepal - Surkhet - 576 KHz
PO Box 634
Singha Durbar
Kathmandu, Nepal
Ph: 977 1 4211910
Fax: 977 1 4211952
E-mail: radio@engg.wlink.com.np
Format: News; Religious; Educational; Folk. **Owner:**
Radio Broadcasting Service, at above address.
Founded: Jan. 4, 1951. **Operating Hours:** Daily 4:56a.
m.-11:05a.m.,11:11a.m.-5p.m.,5p.m.-4:56a.m. **Key Per-
sonnel:** Er. Ramesh Jung Karkee, Chief Engineer,
phone 977 1 4211667; Mr. Rajendra Prasad Sharma,
Dep. Exec.Dir., phone 977 1 4211923; Mr. Sushil
Koirala, Dep. Exec.Dir., phone 977 1 4211842. **Watt-
age:** 100,000. **Ad Rates:** $300-450 for 15 seconds;
$600-900 for 30 seconds; $900-1,350 for 45 seconds;
$1,200-1,800 for 60 seconds. **URL:** http://www.
radionepal.org.

Almere

47864 ■ Eurostitch Magazine
Palmpolstraat 20
NL-1327 AB Almere, Netherlands
Ph: 31 365 314505
Fax: 31 365 349003
Publisher E-mail: info@eurostitch.com
Magazine on embroidery and textile plintiny. **Founded:**
Feb. 1993. **Freq:** Bimonthly Feb., Apr., Jun., Aug., Oct.,
and Dec. **Print Method:** Offset. **Subscription Rates:**
US$58 individuals; EUR53 individuals; 37 individuals.
Remarks: Accepts advertising. **URL:** http://www.
eurostitch.com/home.php?taal=eng&ed=200609. **Ad
Rates:** BW: EUR1,285, 4C: EUR2,365. **Circ:** Paid 15,000

Alphen aan den Rijn

47865 ■ Air & Space Law
Kluwer Law International
PO Box 316
NL-2400 AH Alphen aan den Rijn, Netherlands
Ph: 31 172 641500
Fax: 31 172 641555
Journal providing lawyers, policymakers and business-
people in the aviation and aerospace fields with articles
discussing and clarifying such issues as aircraft accident
investigation and liability legislation; air traffic control
and related issues like congestion and environmental
problems; multilateral conventions and EC law relating
to matters such as traffic rights and access to airports;
competition law; state aid; strategic alliances between
airlines, airports, and aerospace manufacturers; security,
credit and leasing interests involved in aircraft and
aircraft engine transactions; initiatives and new technologies in the aviation and aerospace industries; and the
commercialization of space enterprise. **Freq:** Bimonthly.
Key Personnel: Berend J.H. Crans, Editor; Peter van
Fenema, Editor; George N. Tompkins, Editor, **ISSN:**
0927-3379. **Subscription Rates:** EUR466 individuals
print or online; US$621 individuals print or online; 342
individuals print or online; EUR605 individuals print & online; US$807 individuals print & online; 445 individuals
print & online. **URL:** http://www.kluwerlawonline.com/
productinfo.php?pubcode=AILA.

47866 ■ Arbitration International
Kluwer Law International
PO Box 316
NL-2400 AH Alphen aan den Rijn, Netherlands
Ph: 31 172 641500
Fax: 31 172 641555
Journal covering the development and application of
international arbitration law. **Founded:** 1965. **Freq:**
Weekly (Fri.). **Print Method:** Offset. **Trim Size:** 11 1/2 x
15. **Cols./Page:** 5. **Col. Width:** 11.5 picas. **Col. Depth:**
14 inches. **Key Personnel:** Prof. Wiliam W. Park, Editor-
in-Chief; Prof. Anthony G. Guest, Editor; Nigel Blackaby,
Editor; Dr. Klaus Peter Berger, Editor; Salim Moollan,
Editor; Prof. Loukas Mistelis, Editor. **ISSN:** 0957-0411.
Subscription Rates: EUR516 individuals print or online;
US$688 individuals print or online; EUR379 individuals
print or online; EUR670 individuals print and online;
US$894 individuals print and online; 493 individuals
print and online. **URL:** http://www.kluwerlawonline.com/
productinfo.php?pubcode=ARBI.

47867 ■ Database Magazine
Array Publications B.V.
Lemelerberg 19-23
NL-2402 ZN Alphen aan den Rijn, Netherlands
Ph: 31 172 469030
Fax: 31 172 424381
Trade magazine covering database management
systems, data warehousing and business intelligence
for professionals. **Founded:** 1990. **Freq:** 8/yr. **Print
Method:** Offset. **Trim Size:** 210 x 285 mm. **Key Person-
nel:** Will Manusiwa, Account Mgr.; Hans Lamboo, Edi-
tor; Plooij Kraatz, Editor. **Subscription Rates:** EUR49.50
individuals The Netherlands; EUR61.50 other countries.
Remarks: Accepts advertising. **URL:** http://www.dbm.
nl/. **Ad Rates:** BW: 1,995 f. **Circ:** Paid ‡4,000

47868 ■ IT Service Magazine
Array Publications B.V.
Lemelerberg 19-23
NL-2402 ZN Alphen aan den Rijn, Netherlands
Ph: 31 172 469030
Fax: 31 172 424381
Trade magazine covering the field of information
technology management systems and network
management. **Freq:** 8/yr. **Print Method:** Offset. **Trim
Size:** 210 x 285 mm. **Key Personnel:** Nico Koets,
Contact. **Remarks:** Accepts advertising. **URL:** http://
www.itservice.nl/. **Ad Rates:** BW: 1,995 f, 4C: 1,550 f.
Circ: Combined ‡4,700

47869 ■ Journal of International Arbitration
Kluwer Law International
PO Box 316
NL-2400 AH Alphen aan den Rijn, Netherlands
Ph: 31 172 641500
Fax: 31 172 641555
Law periodical. **Founded:** 1984. **Freq:** Bimonthly. **Key
Personnel:** Dr. Michael J. Moser, Gen. Ed.; Friven
Guanhua Yeoh, Asst. Ed. **ISSN:** 0255-8106. **Subscrip-
tion Rates:** EUR662 individuals print or online; US$874
individuals print or online; 486 individuals print or online;
EUR861 individuals print and online; US$1,320 individu-
als print and online; 632 individuals print and online.
URL: http://www.kluwerlawonline.com/toc.php?
pubcode=JOIA.

47870 ■ Optimize
Array Publications B.V.
Lemelerberg 19-23
NL-2402 ZN Alphen aan den Rijn, Netherlands
Ph: 31 172 469030
Fax: 31 172 424381
Trade magazine for Oracle professionals in The Nether-
lands and Belgium. **Freq:** Bimonthly. **Print Method:**
Offset. **Trim Size:** 210 x 285 mm. **Key Personnel:** Dr.
W.M. Schoots, Contact; Saskia Kruijswijk, Contact. **Re-
marks:** Accepts advertising. **URL:** http://www.optimize.
nl/. **Ad Rates:** BW: 1,995 f. **Circ:** ‡3,500

47871 ■ Process Control
Array Publications B.V.
Lemelerberg 19-23
NL-2402 ZN Alphen aan den Rijn, Netherlands
Ph: 31 172 469030
Fax: 31 172 424381
Trade magazine covering laboratory technology and
process automation. **Freq:** 10/yr. **Print Method:** Offset.

Trim Size: 210 x 285 mm. **Key Personnel:** Eric van
Wijk, Account Mgr., phone 31 172 469030, fax 31 172
424381, eric.van.wijk@array.nl. **Remarks:** Accepts
advertising. **URL:** http://www.processcontrol.nl/. **Ad
Rates:** BW: 1,495 f. **Circ:** Combined 4,000

47872 ■ Software Release Magazine
Array Publications B.V.
Lemelerberg 19-23
NL-2402 ZN Alphen aan den Rijn, Netherlands
Ph: 31 172 469030
Fax: 31 172 424381
Trade magazine covering corporate software develop-
ment for professionals. **Freq:** 4/yr. **Print Method:** Offset.
Trim Size: 210 x 285 mm. **Subscription Rates:** EUR25
individuals The Netherlands; EUR37 individuals OTC.
Remarks: Accepts advertising. **URL:** http://www.release.
nl/English/Magazine. **Ad Rates:** BW: 1,995 f. **Circ:**
‡4,100

47873 ■ Telecommagazine
Array Publications B.V.
Lemelerberg 19-23
NL-2402 ZN Alphen aan den Rijn, Netherlands
Ph: 31 172 469030
Fax: 31 172 424381
Trade magazine covering network integration, data communication and telecommunication. **Founded:** May
1986. **Freq:** 10/yr. **Print Method:** Offset. **Trim Size:** 210
x 285 mm. **Key Personnel:** Bart Arkesteijn, Acct. Mgr.,
phone 31 172 469045, bart.arkesteijn@array.nl. **Remarks:** Accepts advertising. **URL:** http://www.
telecommagazine.nl/. **Ad Rates:** BW: 3,650 f. **Circ:**
7,369

Amersfoort

47874 ■ LEISA Magazine
Information on Low External Input and Sustainable
Agriculture
PO Box 2067
NL-3800 CB Amersfoort, Netherlands
Ph: 31 334 673870
Fax: 31 334 632410
Publisher E-mail: ileia@ileia.nl
Magazine covering sustainable farming in English,
French, Spanish, Bahasa, and Portuguese. **Founded:**
1984. **Freq:** Quarterly. **ISSN:** 0920-8771. **Subscription
Rates:** Free organizations & individuals in the South;
US$25 institutions in the North & international organiza-
tions; US$25 individuals. **URL:** http://www.leisa.info/.
Formerly: Leisa Newsletter. **Circ:** 17,000

Amsterdam

47875 ■ ACC Cardiosource Review Journal
Elsevier Science
PO Box 211
NL-1000 AE Amsterdam, Netherlands
Ph: 31 204 853757
Fax: 31 204 853432
Publisher E-mail: nlinfo-f@elsevier.com
Medical Journal focusing on the principles and knowl-
edge base of cardiovascular medicine as applied to clini-
cal problem solving. **Freq:** Monthly. **Key Personnel:**
S.S. Ballas, Managing Editor; K.D. Aaronson, MD,

Circulation: ★ = ABC; △ = BPA; ♦ = CAC; • = CCAB; ❑ = VAC; ⊕ = PO Statement; ‡ = Publisher's Report; Boldface figures = sworn; Light figures = estimated.

Assoc. Ed.; P.C. Block, MD, Assoc. Ed.; A.A. Bove, MD, Ed., Cardiosource; W.F. Armstrong, MD, Assoc. Ed.; D.S. Bach, MD, Assoc. Ed.; J.B. Froehlich, MD, Assoc. Ed.; R.R. Baliga, Assoc. Ed.; K.A. Eagle, MD; Editor-in-Chief; H.S. Gurm, MD, Assoc. Ed. **ISSN:** 1062-1458. **Subscription Rates:** US$196 institutions, other countries; US$99 students; US$354 institutions; US$196 individuals. **URL:** http://www.elsevier.com/wps/find/journaldescription.cws_home/523823/descriptiondescription.

47876 ■ Accident Analysis & Prevention
Elsevier Science
PO Box 211
NL-1000 AE Amsterdam, Netherlands
Ph: 31 204 853757
Fax: 31 204 853432
Publisher E-mail: nlinfo-f@elsevier.com
Peer-reviewed journal dealing with the factors leading to accidents and how best to avoid them. Stresses on issues like accident free design, biomechanics like threshold limits of injury, and all kinds of accident related statistical data analysis to help in policy-making decisions on safety measures. **Founded:** 1969. **Freq:** Bimonthly. **Key Personnel:** J. Broughton, Assoc. Ed.; R. Elvik, Editor, rune.elvik@toi.no; T. Assum, Editorial Advisory Board; A. Dellinger, Assoc. Ed.; K. Kim, Editor, karlk@hawaii.edu; E. Dahlen, Editorial Advisory Board. **ISSN:** 0001-4575. **Subscription Rates:** EUR290 individuals for European countries; 41,700¥ individuals; US$376 individuals all countries except Europe & Japan; US$2,104 institutions all countries except Europe & Japan; 249,700¥ institutions; EUR1,880 institutions for European countries. **Remarks:** Advertising accepted; rates available upon request. **URL:** http://www.elsevier.com/wps/find/journaldescription.cws_home/336/description. **Circ:** (Not Reported)

47877 ■ ACM Transactions on Computational Logic (TOCL)
Association for Computing Machinery
c/o Krzysztof R. Apt, Area Ed.
CWI
Kruislaan 413
NL-1098 SJ Amsterdam, Netherlands
Publication E-mail: acm-tocl@cs.utexas.edu
Publisher E-mail: acmhelp@acm.org
Journal of the Association for Computing Machinery focusing on the field of computational logic and all uses of logic in computer science. **Freq:** Quarterly. **Key Personnel:** Vladimir Lifschitz, Editor-in-Chief, vl@cs.utexas.edu; Yuliya Lierler, Editorial Asst., yuliya@cs.utexas.edu. **ISSN:** 1529-3785. **URL:** http://tocl.acm.org/.

47878 ■ Acta Politica
Palgrave Macmillan
Department of Political Science
Vrije Universiteit
De Boelelaan
1081 Amsterdam, Netherlands
Publication E-mail: acta.politica@fsw.vu.nl
Publisher E-mail: booksellers@palgrave.com
Journal covering topics on Dutch and comparative politics. **Founded:** 1971. **Freq:** Quarterly. **Print Method:** Offset. **Cols./Page:** 7. **Col. Width:** 8 picas. **Col. Depth:** 11.5 inches. **Key Personnel:** Kees Aarts, Editor; Kees van Kersbergen, Editor. **ISSN:** 0001-6810. **Subscription Rates:** 325 institutions, other countries print; US$604 institutions print; 58 other countries print and online; US$108 individuals print and online. **URL:** http://www.palgrave-journals.com/ap/index.html.

47879 ■ Acta Psychologica
Elsevier Science
PO Box 211
NL-1000 AE Amsterdam, Netherlands
Ph: 31 204 853757
Fax: 31 204 853432
Publisher E-mail: nlinfo-f@elsevier.com
Journal publishing original articles on experimental psychology. **Subtitle:** International Journal of Psychonomics. **Founded:** 1941. **Freq:** 9/yr. **Key Personnel:** R. Zwaan, Editor-in-Chief, zwaan@fsw.eur.nl; B. Hommel, Editorial Board; M. Bertamini, Assoc. Ed. **ISSN:** 0001-6918. **Subscription Rates:** 28,500¥ individuals; EUR198 individuals for European countries and Iran; US$259 individuals for all countries except Europe, Japan and Iran; 157,200¥ institutions; EUR1,185 institutions for European countries and Iran; US$1,323 institutions for all countries except Europe, Japan and Iran. **Remarks:** Accepts advertising. **URL:** http://www.elsevier.com/wps/find/journaldescription.cws_home/

505579/descriptiondescription. **Circ:** (Not Reported)

47880 ■ Acta Tropica
Elsevier Science
PO Box 211
NL-1000 AE Amsterdam, Netherlands
Ph: 31 204 853757
Fax: 31 204 853432
Publisher E-mail: nlinfo-f@elsevier.com
Journal covering biomedical and health sciences dealing with topics relevant to human and animal health in the tropics and the subtropics. The journal includes articles in the field of taxonomy, morphology, biochemistry, physiology, immunology, and epidemiology of communicable diseases. **Founded:** 1944. **Freq:** Monthly. **Key Personnel:** K. Berzins, Editor, phone 46 816 4170, fax 46 815 7356, klavs@imun.su.se; M.J. Wilson, Reviews Ed.; F. Guhl, Editor, fguhl@uniandes.edu.co. **ISSN:** 0001-706X. **Subscription Rates:** 275,500¥ institutions; EUR2,085 institutions for European countries and Iran; US$2,330 institutions for all countries except Europe, Japan and Iran; EUR268 individuals for European countries and Iran; US$360 individuals for all countries except Europe, Japan and Iran; 41,300¥ individuals. **Remarks:** Accepts advertising. **URL:** http://www.elsevier.com/wps/find/journaldescription.cws_home/506043/descriptiondescription. **Circ:** (Not Reported)

47881 ■ Advanced Engineering Informatics
Elsevier Science
PO Box 211
NL-1000 AE Amsterdam, Netherlands
Ph: 31 204 853757
Fax: 31 204 853432
Publisher E-mail: nlinfo-f@elsevier.com
Journal covering papers on computer applications that evaluate benefits, possibilities and risks of engineering informatics. **Founded:** 1986. **Freq:** 4/yr. **Key Personnel:** I. Smith, Editor, ian.smith@epfl.ch; T. Tomiyama, Editor, t.tomiyama@3me.tudelft.nl. **ISSN:** 1474-0346. **Subscription Rates:** 21,100¥ individuals for Japan; EUR138 individuals for European countries and Iran; US$184 other countries individual, except Europe, Japan and Iran; EUR1,231 institutions European countries and Iran; 1,374 f institutions, other countries except Europe, Japan and Iran; 163,200¥ institutions Japan. **URL:** http://www.elsevier.com/wps/find/journaldescription.cws_home/622240/descriptiondescription.

47882 ■ Advances in Colloid and Interface Science
Elsevier Science
PO Box 211
NL-1000 AE Amsterdam, Netherlands
Ph: 31 204 853757
Fax: 31 204 853432
Publisher E-mail: nlinfo-f@elsevier.com
Journal dedicated to experimental and theoretical developments in Interfacial and Colloidal Phenomena and their significance in Biology, Physics, chemistry and technology. **Founded:** 1965. **Freq:** 16/yr. **Key Personnel:** J. Berg, Editorial Board; R. Miller, Editor, miller@mpikg-golm.mpg.de. **ISSN:** 0001-8686. **Subscription Rates:** EUR2,708 institutions European countries and Iran; 359,800¥ institutions Japan; US$3,026 institutions, other countries except Europe, Japan and Iran; EUR173 individuals European countries and Iran; US$229 individuals other countries except Europe, Japan and Iran; 26,800¥ individuals Japan. **URL:** http://www.elsevier.com/wps/find/journaldescription.cws_home/500842/descriptiondescription.

47883 ■ Advances in Space Research
Elsevier Science
PO Box 211
NL-1000 AE Amsterdam, Netherlands
Ph: 31 204 853757
Fax: 31 204 853432
Publisher E-mail: nlinfo-f@elsevier.com
Publication covering advances in scientific space research in all domains. **Founded:** 1981. **Freq:** Periodic. **Key Personnel:** B. Paul, Co-Ed., bpaul@rri.res.in; J. Lastovicka, Editor-in-Chief, jla@ufa.cas.cz; T. Hei, Co-Ed., tkh1@columbia.edu. **ISSN:** 0273-1177. **Subscription Rates:** 556,000¥ institutions; EUR4,186 institutions for European countries and Iran; US$4,684 institutions for all countries except Europe, Japan and Iran. **Remarks:** Advertising not accepted. **URL:** http://www.elsevier.com/wps/find/journaldescription.cws_home/644/descriptiondescription. **Circ:** (Not Reported)

47884 ■ Aerospace Science and Technology
Elsevier Science

PO Box 211
NL-1000 AE Amsterdam, Netherlands
Ph: 31 204 853757
Fax: 31 204 853432
Publisher E-mail: nlinfo-f@elsevier.com
Journal publishing research information from designing to manufacturing in aerospace industry. **Founded:** 1997. **Freq:** 8/yr. **Key Personnel:** J.A. Ekaterinaris, Editor-in-Chief, ekaterin@iacm.forth.gr; M.S. Chandrasekhara, Assoc. Ed.; Shiyi Chen, Assoc. Ed.; I. Gursul, Assoc. Ed.; K. Kontis, Assoc. Ed.; P. Menounou, Assoc. Ed. **ISSN:** 1270-9638. **Subscription Rates:** US$454 institutions for all countries except Europe, Japan & Iran; EUR403 institutions for European countries & Iran; 53,300¥ institutions; 24,500¥ individuals; EUR159 individuals for European countries & Iran; US$212 individuals for all countries except Europe, Japan & Iran. **Remarks:** Accepts advertising. **URL:** http://www.elsevier.com/wps/find/journaldescription.cws_home/600735/descriptiondescription. **Circ:** (Not Reported)

47885 ■ Agricultural Systems
Elsevier Science
PO Box 211
NL-1000 AE Amsterdam, Netherlands
Ph: 31 204 853757
Fax: 31 204 853432
Publisher E-mail: nlinfo-f@elsevier.com
Journal dealing with interactions among agricultural systems. The emphasis is particularly on either methodological ways to understanding and managing interactions, or the application of holistic or quantitative systems methods to problems within agricultural systems and their interactions with other systems. **Founded:** 1976. **Freq:** Monthly. **Key Personnel:** Paul B.M. Berentsen, Editor, paul.berentsen@wur.nl; C. Stockle, Editor, cstockle@roadrunner.com; P.K. Thornton, Editor, p.thornton@cgiar.org. **ISSN:** 0308-521X. **Subscription Rates:** US$3,753 institutions for all countries except Europe, Japan & Iran; 445,800¥ institutions; EUR3,357 institutions for European countries & Iran; US$488 individuals for all countries except Europe, Japan & Iran; EUR438 individuals for European countries & Iran; 57,400¥ individuals. **Remarks:** Accepts advertising. **URL:** http://www.elsevier.com/wps/find/journaldescription.cws_home/405851/descriptiondescription. **Circ:** (Not Reported)

47886 ■ Agriculture, Ecosystems & Environment
Elsevier Science
PO Box 211
NL-1000 AE Amsterdam, Netherlands
Ph: 31 204 853757
Fax: 31 204 853432
Publisher E-mail: nlinfo-f@elsevier.com
Journal providing forum for discussion on how agricultural practices impact the environment and how changes outside agriculture influence agricultural systems. **Founded:** 1974. **Freq:** 16/yr. **Key Personnel:** M. Carter, Assoc. Ed., carterm@agr.gc.ca; J. Fuhrer, Editor-in-Chief, juerg.fuhrer@art.admin.ch; A. de Rouw, Assoc. Ed. **ISSN:** 0167-8809. **Subscription Rates:** 371,200¥ institutions for Japan; EUR2,801 institutions for European countries; US$3,183 institutions, other countries. **URL:** http://www.elsevier.com/wps/find/journaldescription.cws_home/503298/descriptiondescription.

47887 ■ AI Communications
IOS Press, B.V.
Nieuwe Hemweg 6B
NL-1013 BG Amsterdam, Netherlands
Ph: 31 20 6883355
Fax: 31 20 6203419
Publisher E-mail: info@iospress.nl
Peer-reviewed journal covering the whole AI community, scientific institutions as well as commercial and industrial companies, aiming to enhance contacts and information exchange between AI researchers and developers and to provide supranational information to those concerned with AI and advanced information processing. **Freq:** Quarterly. **Key Personnel:** S. Miksch, Editorial Board; F. Baader, Area Ch.; S. Russell, Editorial Board; Alves J.J. Alferes, Editorial Board; B. Nebel, Editorial Board; Enrico Giunchiglia, Editor-in-Chief, aicom@star.dist.unige.it. **ISSN:** 0921-7126. **Subscription Rates:** EUR463 individuals print and online; US$640 individuals print and online. **URL:** http://www.iospress.nl/loadtop/load.php?isbn=09217126.

47888 ■ American Journal of Ophthalmology
Elsevier Science B.V.
Radarweg 29
NL-1043 Amsterdam, Netherlands

Ph: 31 204 853911

Fax: 31 204 852457

Peer-reviewed and ophthalmology journal describing clinical investigations, clinical observations, and clinically relevant laboratory investigations related to ophthalmology. **Founded:** 1884. **Freq:** Monthly. **Print Method:** Offset. **Trim Size:** 8 1/8 x 10 7/8. **Cols./Page:** 2. **Col. Width:** 19.25 nonpareils. **Col. Depth:** 56 picas. **Key Personnel:** Thomas J. Liesegang, MD, Editor-in-Chief; Hans E. Grossniklaus, MD, Assoc. Ed. **ISSN:** 0002-9394. **Subscription Rates:** US$870 institutions, other countries; US$359 U.S. and other countries; US$243 students, other countries; US$85 U.S. and Canada students; US$654 U.S. and Canada institutions; US$171 U.S. and Canada. **URL:** http://www.elsevier.com/wps/find/journaldescription.cws_home/601028/descriptiondescription.

47889 ■ American Journal of Preventive Medicine
Elsevier Science B.V.
Radarweg 29
NL-1043 Amsterdam, Netherlands
Ph: 31 204 853911
Fax: 31 204 852457
Journal Covering basic and applied sciences that contribute to the promotion of health and the prevention of disease, disability, and premature death. **Founded:** 1984. **Freq:** Monthly. **Print Method:** Offset. **Trim Size:** 8 1/2 x 11. **Key Personnel:** K. Patrick, MD, Editor-in-Chief; C.S. Seidman, Managing Editor; F.D. Scutchfield, MD, Editor; R.B. Wallace, MD, Assoc. Ed.; B.A. Lytton, Assoc. Mng. Ed. **ISSN:** 0749-3797. **Subscription Rates:** US$905 institutions, other countries; US$2,296 other countries; US$277 individuals; US$834 institutions. **URL:** http://www.elsevier.com/wps/find/journaldescription.cws_home/600644/descriptiondescription. **Circ:** Paid ‡2,500, Non-paid ‡18

47890 ■ Amsterdam Monographs in American Studies
Rodopi
c/o R.V.A Janssens
University of Amsterdam
American Studies Dept.
Spuistraat 134
NL-1012 VB Amsterdam, Netherlands
Fax: 31 205 254625
Publisher E-mail: info@rodopi.nl
Journal devoted to the study of the history, culture and society of the United States. **Founded:** 1973. **Freq:** Monthly. **Print Method:** Offset. **Trim Size:** 7 7/8 x 10 1/2. **Cols./Page:** 3. **Col. Width:** 30 nonpareils. **Col. Depth:** 140 agate lines. **Key Personnel:** Rob Kroes, Founding Ed.; Ruud Janssens, Gen. Ed., r.v.a.janssens@uva.nl. **ISSN:** 0926-5600. **URL:** http://www.rodopi.nl/senj.asp?SerieId=AMAS.

47891 ■ Anaerobe
Elsevier Science B.V.
Radarweg 29
NL-1043 Amsterdam, Netherlands
Ph: 31 204 853911
Fax: 31 204 852457
Scholarly journal covering research on the biology of anaerobic microorganisms. **Freq:** Bimonthly. **Key Personnel:** Prof. J.G. Songer, Editor-in-Chief; M. Malamy, Editorial Board; D. Citron, Publication Committee. **ISSN:** 1075-9964. **Subscription Rates:** EUR670 institutions European countries and Iran; 72,400¥ institutions; US$597 institutions for all countries except Europe, Iran and Japan; EUR322 individuals European countries and Iran; US$318 individuals for all countries except Europe, Iran and Japan; 34,800¥ individuals. **URL:** http://www.elsevier.com/wps/find/journaldescription.cws_home/622780/descriptiondescription.

47892 ■ Analytical Biochemistry
Elsevier Science B.V.
Radarweg 29
NL-1043 Amsterdam, Netherlands
Ph: 31 204 853911
Fax: 31 204 852457
Peer-reviewed journal emphasizing methodology in the biological and biochemical sciences. **Founded:** 1960. **Freq:** Semimonthly. **Print Method:** Offset. **Trim Size:** 8 1/2 x 11. **Cols./Page:** 1. **Key Personnel:** William B. Jakoby, Editor-in-Chief; M.A. Batzer, Exec. Ed.; A.J.L. Cooper, Exec. Ed.; S. Daunert, Exec. Ed.; J.K. Baker, Exec. Ed.; P. Deininger, Exec. Ed.; G.M. Carman, Exec.

Ed.; R.H. Angeletti, Exec. Ed.; H. Goldfine, Exec. Ed. **ISSN:** 0003-2697. **Subscription Rates:** 360,600¥ individuals; US$2,746 institutions, other countries except Europe, Japan and Iran; EUR3,456 individuals European countries and Iran; 799,500¥ institutions; US$6,054 institutions, other countries except Europe, Japan and Iran; EUR7,654 institutions European countries and Iran. **Remarks:** Accepts advertising. **URL:** http://www.elsevier.com/wps/find/journaldescription.cws_home/622781/descriptiondescription. **Circ:** (Not Reported)

47893 ■ Analytical Cellular Pathology/Cellular Oncology
IOS Press, B.V.
c/o Gerrit Meijer, Ed.-in-Ch.
Dept. of Pathology
VU University Medical Ctr.
PO Box 7057
NL-1007 MB Amsterdam, Netherlands
Publisher E-mail: info@iospress.nl
Journal publishing scientific contributions from various biomedical and clinical disciplines involved in basic and translational cancer research on the cell and tissue level, technical and bioinformatics developments in this area and clinical applications. **Freq:** Monthly. **Key Personnel:** Gerrit Meijer, Editor-in-Chief, cellularoncology@vumc.nl; Peter Hamilton, Assoc. Ed., p.hamilton@qub.ac.uk; Thomas Ried, Assoc. Ed., riedt@mail.nih.gov; Hans Joenje, Editorial Board; Walter Giaretti, Assoc. Ed., walter.giaretti@istge.it; Calum Macaulay, Editorial Board; Ivar Petersen, Editorial Board; Manel Esteller, Editorial Board. **ISSN:** 1570-5870. **Subscription Rates:** EUR1,464 institutions print and online; US$2,120 institutions print and online. **URL:** http://www.iospress.nl/loadtop/load.php?isbn=15705870.

47894 ■ Andon
Society for Japanese Arts
Vereniging voor Japanse Kunst
Overste den Oudenlaan 7
Aerdenhout
NL-2111 WB Amsterdam, Netherlands
Ph: 31 23 5240129
Fax: 31 23 5248913
Publisher E-mail: info@society-for-japanese-arts.org
Publication covering the Japanese language. **Founded:** 1981. **Freq:** Quarterly. **Key Personnel:** Henk Herwig, Editor-in-Chief; Dick Raatgever, Advertising Mgr.; Anna Beerens, Advertising Mgr. **Subscription Rates:** EUR50 out of country for members outside Europe; EUR35 members for Dutch. **Remarks:** Advertising accepted; rates available upon request. **URL:** http://www.society-for-japanese-arts.org/andon.htm. **Circ:** (Not Reported)

47895 ■ Annals of Physics
Elsevier Science B.V.
Radarweg 29
NL-1043 Amsterdam, Netherlands
Ph: 31 204 853911
Fax: 31 204 852457
Peer-reviewed journal publishing original research in basic physics research. **Founded:** 1957. **Freq:** Monthly. **Trim Size:** 6 1/2 x 9 3/8. **Key Personnel:** F. Wilczek, Editor-in-Chief, annals@mit.edu; L. Radzihovsky, Editor, radzihov@colorado.edu; E. Braaten, Editor, braaten@pacific.mps.ohio-state.edu; C. Nayak, Editor, nayak@physics.ucla.edu; D. Kharzeev, Editor, kharzeev@bnl.gov; J. Peacock, Editor, jap@roe.ac.uk. **ISSN:** 0003-4916. **Subscription Rates:** US$5,012 institutions for all countries except Europe, Iran and Japan; US$400 individuals for all countries except Europe, Iran and Japan; 40,000¥ individuals; EUR400 individuals European countries and Iran; EUR6,419 institutions European countries and Iran; 670,100¥ institutions. **Remarks:** Accepts advertising. **URL:** http://www.elsevier.com/wps/find/journaldescription.cws_home/622784/descriptiondescription. **Circ:** (Not Reported)

47896 ■ Anti-Cancer Drugs
Lippincott Williams & Wilkins
c/o Mels Sluyser, PhD, Ed.-in-Ch.
The Netherlands Cancer Institute
Plesmanlaan 121
NL-1066 Amsterdam, Netherlands
Publisher E-mail: customerservice@lww.com
Journal providing current information on the clinical and experimental effects of toxic and non-toxic cancer agents and is specifically directed towards breakthroughs in cancer treatment. **Subtitle:** An International Journal on Anti-Cancer Agents. **Freq:** 10/yr. **Key Personnel:** Mels Sluyser, PhD, Editor-in-Chief, m.sluyser@planet.nl. **ISSN:** 0959-4973. **Subscription Rates:**

US$614.80 individuals; US$2,724.20 institutions; US$296 individuals in-training; US$649 other countries individual; US$2,873.80 other countries institutional; US$296 other countries in-training. **URL:** http://journals.lww.com/anti-cancerdrugs/pages/default.aspx; http://www.lww.com/product/Anti-Cancer-Drugs/?0959-4973.

47897 ■ Applied and Computational Harmonic Analysis
Elsevier Science B.V.
Radarweg 29
NL-1043 Amsterdam, Netherlands
Ph: 31 204 853911
Fax: 31 204 852457
Journal publishing information on harmonic analysis and related works, such as phase-space analysis and image compression. Emphasis on wavelet analysis and signal processing. **Freq:** Bimonthly. **Trim Size:** 8 1/2 x 11. **Key Personnel:** C.K. Chui, Editor-in-Chief; R.R. Coifman, Editor-in-Chief; I. Daubechies, Editor-in-Chief; D.L. Donoho, Assoc. Ed.; M.V. Wickerhauser, Software Ed.; R. Balan, Editorial Advisory Board; M. Vetterli, Assoc. Ed.; R. Gundy, Editorial Advisory Board. **ISSN:** 1063-5203. **Subscription Rates:** EUR1,010 institutions European countries and Iran; US$789 institutions all countries except Europe, Japan & Iran; 105,600¥ institutions; US$354 individuals all countries except Europe, Japan & Iran; EUR450 individuals European countries and Iran; 47,100¥ individuals. **URL:** http://www.elsevier.com/wps/find/journaldescription.cws_home/622786/descriptiondescription.

47898 ■ Archives of Biochemistry and Biophysics
Elsevier Science B.V.
Radarweg 29
NL-1043 Amsterdam, Netherlands
Ph: 31 204 853911
Fax: 31 204 852457
Journal presenting articles in the areas of biochemistry and biophysics. **Founded:** 1943. **Freq:** Semimonthly. **Print Method:** Offset. **Trim Size:** 8 1/2 x 11. **Key Personnel:** H. Sies, Editor-in-Chief; P. Fitzpatrick, Editor-in-Chief; A. Scarpa, Editor-in-Chief; M. Kester, Editorial Board; W.M. Atkins, Editorial Board; E. Cadenas, Editorial Board; G.E. Arteel, Editorial Board; J.P. Jin, Editorial Board. **ISSN:** 0003-9861. **Subscription Rates:** 835,800¥ institutions; US$6,050 institutions; EUR7,995 institutions; EUR323 students; US$283 students; 33,800¥ students; US$601 individuals; US$691 individuals; 72,100¥ individuals. **Remarks:** Accepts advertising. **URL:** http://www.elsevier.com/wps/find/journaldescription.cws_home/622787/descriptiondescription. **Circ:** (Not Reported)

47899 ■ Asian Journal of Water, Environment and Pollution
IOS Press, B.V.
Nieuwe Hemweg 6B
NL-1013 BG Amsterdam, Netherlands
Ph: 31 20 6883355
Fax: 31 20 6203419
Publisher E-mail: info@iospress.nl
Journal focusing on Asia, where besides water, there are several other issues related to environment, such as global warming and its impact; intense land/use and shifting pattern of agriculture; issues related to fertilizer applications and pesticide residues in soil and water; and solid and liquid waste management particularly in industrial and urban areas. **Freq:** Quarterly. **Key Personnel:** Prof. V. Subramanian, Editor-in-Chief, ajwep@capital-publishing.com. **ISSN:** 0972-9860. **Subscription Rates:** EUR253 institutions print and online; US$330 institutions print and online; EUR60 individuals online; US$70 individuals online. **URL:** http://www.iospress.nl/loadtop/load.php?isbn=09729860.

47900 ■ Atomic Data and Nuclear Data Tables
Elsevier Science B.V.
Radarweg 29
NL-1043 Amsterdam, Netherlands
Ph: 31 204 853911
Fax: 31 204 852457
Journal publishing compilations of experimental and theoretical information in atomic physics, nuclear physics, and related fields. **Founded:** 1973. **Freq:** Bimonthly. **Trim Size:** 8 1/2 x 11. **Key Personnel:** D.R. Schultz, Editor, schultzd@ornl.gov; S.M. Austin, Assoc. Ed.; A. Dalgarno, Assoc. Ed. **ISSN:** 0092-640X. **Subscription Rates:** US$1,425 institutions all countries except Europe, Japan & Iran; EUR1,811 institutions European countries and Iran; 189,300¥ institutions; US$714

Circulation: ★ = ABC; △ = BPA; ◆ = CAC; • = CCAB; ❑ = VAC; ⊕ = PO Statement; ‡ = Publisher's Report; Boldface figures = sworn; Light figures = estimated.

individuals European countries and Iran; EUR1,811 individuals all countries except Europe, Japan & Iran; 85,500¥ individuals. **URL:** http://www.elsevier.com/wps/find/journaldescription.cws_home/622789/descriptiondescription.

47901 ■ Autovisie
TTG—De Telegraaf Tijdschriften Groep B.V.
Basiweg 30
PO Box 36
NL-1000 AC Amsterdam, Netherlands
Ph: 31 20 5852913
Publisher E-mail: redactie@autovisie.nl
Consumer magazine covering automobiles. **Founded:** 1955. **Freq:** Semimonthly. **Key Personnel:** Ton Roks, Editor, t.roks@ttg.nl; Wim Hoogland, General Ed. **Remarks:** Accepts advertising. **URL:** http://www.autovisie.nl; http://www.ttg.nl/autovisie/index.xml?__toolbar=0. **Circ:** Paid 60,000

47902 ■ Babel
John Benjamins Publishing Co.
Klaprozenweg 105
PO Box 36224
NL-1033 NN Amsterdam, Netherlands
Ph: 31 206 304747
Fax: 31 206 739773
Publisher E-mail: benjamins@presswarehouse.com
Peer-reviewed journal designed primarily for translators and interpreters. **Freq:** Quarterly. **Key Personnel:** Rene Haeseryn, Editor-in-Chief; Pierre-Francois Caille, Founding Ed. **ISSN:** 0521-9744. **Subscription Rates:** EUR188 institutions backvolumes; EUR80 individuals special; EUR188 institutions print + online. **URL:** http://www.benjamins.com/cgi-bin/t_seriesview.cgi?series=Babel.

47903 ■ Best Practice & Research Clinical Endocrinology & Metabolism
Elsevier Science
PO Box 211
NL-1000 AE Amsterdam, Netherlands
Ph: 31 204 853757
Fax: 31 204 853432
Publisher E-mail: nlinfo-f@elsevier.com
Journal reporting on the key clinical issues of diagnosis, treatment and patient management. **Freq:** 6/yr. **Key Personnel:** Christoph A. Meier, Editor-in-Chief; R. Rosenfeld, Editorial Board; S. Melmed, Editorial Board; S. O'Rahilly, Editorial Board; D. LeRoith, Editorial Board; W. Kiess, Editorial Board; D. Dunger, Editorial Board; A. Moses, Editorial Board; L. Giudice, Editorial Board; G. Van den Berghe, Editorial Board; P. Mullis, Editorial Board. **ISSN:** 1521-690X. **Subscription Rates:** EUR587 institutions for European countries & Iran; US$519 institutions for all countries except Europe, Japan & Iran; 67,000¥ institutions; EUR334 individuals for European countries & Iran; US$296 individuals for all countries except Europe, Japan & Iran; 36,000¥ individuals. **Remarks:** Advertising accepted; rates available upon request. **URL:** http://www.elsevier.com/wps/find/journaldescription.cws_home/623001/description. **Circ:** (Not Reported)

47904 ■ Best Practice & Research Clinical Hematology
Elsevier Science
PO Box 211
NL-1000 AE Amsterdam, Netherlands
Ph: 31 204 853757
Fax: 31 204 853432
Publisher E-mail: nlinfo-f@elsevier.com
Journal devoted to latest in clinical practice and thinking within the topic of hematology. **Freq:** Quarterly. **Key Personnel:** J.M. Rowe, MD, Editor-in-Chief, rowe@jimmy.harvard.edu; C. Hershko, Editorial Board; A.V. Hoffbrand, Editorial Board. **ISSN:** 1521-6926. **Subscription Rates:** EUR315 individuals for European countries & Iran; EUR485 institutions for European countries & Iran; 34,100¥ individuals; 52,600¥ institutions; US$279 individuals for all countries except Europe, Japan & Iran; US$432 institutions for all countries except Europe, Japan & Iran; EUR159 elsewhere resident, for European countries & Iran; 17,000¥ institutions, other countries resident; US$141 elsewhere resident. **Remarks:** Advertising accepted; rates available upon request. **URL:** http://www.elsevier.com/wps/find/journaldescription.cws_home/623003/descriptiondescription. **Circ:** (Not Reported)

47905 ■ Biochemical and Biophysical Research Communications
Elsevier Science B.V.
Radarweg 29
NL-1043 Amsterdam, Netherlands
Ph: 31 204 853911

Fax: 31 204 852457
International scientific journal devoted to the rapid dissemination of timely and significant experimental results in the diverse fields of modern biology, including cell biology. **Founded:** 1959. **Freq:** 52/yr. **Print Method:** Offset. **Trim Size:** 6 7/8 x 10. **Key Personnel:** W.J. Lennarz, Editor-in-Chief, wlennarz@notes.cc.sunysb.edu; W. Baumeister, Editor, baumeist@biochem.mpg.de; C.H. Chung, Editor, chc-bbrc@plaza.snu.ac.kr; K. Takatsu, Editor, takatsuk@med.u-toyama.ac.jp; E. Carafoli, Editor, ernesto.carafoli@unipd.it; M. Muramatsu, Editor, bbrcmura@saitama-med.ac.jp; S. Orrenius, Editor, sten.orrenius@ki.se. **ISSN:** 0006-291X. **Subscription Rates:** 971,600¥ institutions; US$7,443 institutions for all countries except Europe, Iran and Japan; EUR9,303 institutions for European countries and Iran; US$4,188 individuals for all countries except Europe, Iran and Japan; EUR5,207 individuals for European countries and Iran; 543,900¥ individuals. **Remarks:** Accepts advertising. **URL:** http://www.elsevier.com/wps/find/journaldescription.cws_home/622790/descriptiondescription. **Circ:** (Not Reported)

47906 ■ Biochimica et Biophysica Acta (BBA)
Elsevier Science
PO Box 211
NL-1000 AE Amsterdam, Netherlands
Ph: 31 204 853757
Fax: 31 204 853432
Publisher E-mail: nlinfo-f@elsevier.com
A broad base journal on biochemistry, biophysics, molecular biology with reference to structure and function. **Founded:** 1947. **Freq:** 100/yr. **Key Personnel:** U. Brandt, Exec. Ed.; P. Brzezinski, Exec. Ed.; E. Arner, Exec. Ed. **Subscription Rates:** 2,377,002¥ institutions for Japan; EUR17,879 institutions for European countries & Iran; US$19,999 institutions for all countries except Europe, Japan & Iran. **Remarks:** Accepts advertising. **URL:** http://www.elsevier.com/wps/find/journaldescription.cws_home/506062/description. **Circ:** (Not Reported)

47907 ■ Biochimica et Biophysica Acta (BBA)-General Subjects
Elsevier Science
PO Box 211
NL-1000 AE Amsterdam, Netherlands
Ph: 31 204 853757
Fax: 31 204 853432
Publisher E-mail: nlinfo-f@elsevier.com
Journal reporting on research investigations from cutting edge fields in life sciences mainly covering biochemical and biophysical features such as glycobiology and novel compounds. **Freq:** Monthly. **Key Personnel:** Sharon S. Krag, Exec. Ed.; Elias Arner, Exec. Ed.; Mark T. Hamann, Section Ed. **ISSN:** 0304-4165. **Subscription Rates:** 408,500¥ institutions; EUR3,074 institutions for European countries & Iran; US$3,438 institutions for all countries except Europe, Japan & Iran; US$400 individuals for all countries except Europe, Japan & Iran; EUR299 individuals for European countries & Iran; 46,000¥ individuals. **Remarks:** Accepts advertising. **URL:** http://www.elsevier.com/wps/find/journaldescription.cws_home/506066/description. **Circ:** (Not Reported)

47908 ■ Biochimica et Biophysica Acta (BBA)-Molecular Basis of Disease
Elsevier Science
PO Box 211
NL-1000 AE Amsterdam, Netherlands
Ph: 31 204 853757
Fax: 31 204 853432
Publisher E-mail: nlinfo-f@elsevier.com
Journal dealing with the biochemistry and molecular genetics of disease processes and their models. **Subtitle:** One of the Nine Topical Sections of Biochimica et Biophysica Acta. **Freq:** Monthly. **Key Personnel:** J.N. Keller, Exec. Ed.; R.P.J. Oude Elferink, Exec. Ed.; P.A. Andreasen, Section Ed. **ISSN:** 0925-4439. **Subscription Rates:** 230,400¥ institutions; EUR1,737 institutions for European countries & Iran; US$1,941 institutions for all countries except Europe, Japan & Iran; 34,700¥ individuals; EUR225 individuals for European countries & Iran; US$302 individuals for all countries except Europe, Japan & Iran. **Remarks:** Accepts advertising. **URL:** http://www.elsevier.com/wps/find/journaldescription.cws_home/506068/description. **Circ:** (Not Reported)

47909 ■ Biochimica et Biophysica Acta (BBA)-Molecular and Cell Biology of Lipids
Elsevier Science
PO Box 211
NL-1000 AE Amsterdam, Netherlands
Ph: 31 204 853757

Fax: 31 204 853432
Publisher E-mail: nlinfo-f@elsevier.com
Peer-reviewed journal focusing on analysis and characterization of the lipidome thatincludes all forms of lipids, their transport and metabolism through interactions with other biomolecules in a cell, tissue or whole organism. The novel lipids, their biosynthesis and metabolism are also discussed. **Freq:** Monthly. **Key Personnel:** R. Zechner, Exec. Ed.; S. Cockcroft, Section Ed.; Y. Igarashi, Section Ed.; W. Dowhan, Exec. Ed.; P. Dawson, Section Ed.; P. Calder, Section Ed. **ISSN:** 1388-1981. **Subscription Rates:** 427,800¥ institutions; EUR3,223 institutions for European countries & Iran; US$3,605 institutions for all countries except Europe, Japan & Iran; EUR297 institutions for European countries & Iran; US$398 individuals for all countries except Europe, Japan & Iran; 45,700¥ individuals. **Remarks:** Accepts advertising. **URL:** http://www.elsevier.com/wps/find/journaldescription.cws_home/506067/description. **Circ:** (Not Reported)

47910 ■ Biochimica et Biophysica Acta (BBA)-Proteins & Proteomics
Elsevier Science
PO Box 211
NL-1000 AE Amsterdam, Netherlands
Ph: 31 204 853757
Fax: 31 204 853432
Publisher E-mail: nlinfo-f@elsevier.com
Peer-reviewed journal covering protein structure conformation, and dynamics, protein-ligand interactions, enzyme mechanisms, models and kinetics, physical properties and spectroscopy. **Freq:** Monthly. **Key Personnel:** A. Fontana, Section Ed.; P.F. Cook, Exec. Ed.; F. Lottspeich, Exec. Ed.; J.M. Zhou, Section Ed.; D.E. Wemmer, Section Ed.; V. Turk, Section Ed. **ISSN:** 1570-9639. **Subscription Rates:** EUR3,671 institutions for European countries & Iran; US$4,106 institutions for all countries except Europe, Japan & Iran; 487,100¥ institutions; EUR337 individuals for European countries & Iran; US$452 individuals for all countries except Europe, Japan & Iran; 51,900¥ individuals. **Remarks:** Accepts advertising. **URL:** http://www.elsevier.com/wps/find/journaldescription.cws_home/635707/description. **Circ:** (Not Reported)

47911 ■ Bioelectrochemistry
Elsevier Science
PO Box 211
NL-1000 AE Amsterdam, Netherlands
Ph: 31 204 853757
Fax: 31 204 853432
Publisher E-mail: nlinfo-f@elsevier.com
Peer-reviewed journal focusing on electrochemical principles in biology and biological aspects of electrochemistry in connection with the Bioelectrochemical Society. **Founded:** 1974. **Freq:** Bimonthly. **Key Personnel:** E. Neumann, Principal Ed., phone 49 521 1062063, fax 49 521 1062053, eberhard.neumann@uni-bielefeld.de; F.A. Armstrong, Advisory Board; N. Hu, Advisory Board; A. Kuhn, Advisory Board; P. Vadgama, Advisory Board; J. Lipowski, Advisory Board. **ISSN:** 1567-5394. **Subscription Rates:** US$2,712 institutions for all countries except Europe, Japan & Iran; 322,100¥ institutions; EUR2,423 institutions for European countries & Iran. **Remarks:** Accepts advertising. **URL:** http://www.elsevier.com/wps/find/journaldescription.cws_home/504080/description. **Circ:** (Not Reported)

47912 ■ Blood Cells, Molecules, & Diseases
Elsevier Science B.V.
Radarweg 29
NL-1043 Amsterdam, Netherlands
Ph: 31 204 853911
Fax: 31 204 852457
Scholarly journal covering hematology, cell biology, immunology and genetics. **Freq:** 8/yr. **Key Personnel:** Edward J. Benz, Jr., Contributing Ed., phone 617632-2159, fax 617632-2161, edward_benz@dfci.harvard.edu; M.A. Lichtman, MD, Editor-in-Chief, phone 585275-2205, fax 585271-1876, mal@urmc.rochester.edu; J.W. Adamson, MD, Contributing Ed., phone 858552-8585, fax 858552-7485, jadamson@ucsd.edu. **ISSN:** 1079-9796. **Subscription Rates:** EUR1,277 institutions for European countries and Iran; US$1,072 institutions for all countries except Europe, Iran and Japan; 133,200¥ institutions; US$143 students for all countries except Europe, Iran and Japan; 16,900¥ students; EUR163 students for European countries and Iran; US$339 individuals for all countries except Europe, Iran and Japan; EUR388 individuals for European countries and Iran; 40,700¥ individuals. **URL:** http://www.elsevier.com/wps/find/journaldescription.cws_home/622796/descriptiondescription.

47913 ■ Brain and Language
Elsevier Science B.V.
Radarweg 29
NL-1043 Amsterdam, Netherlands
Ph: 31 204 853911
Fax: 31 204 852457
Interdisciplinary journal publishing original research data on human language and other forms of communication as they relate to brain structure and function. **Founded:** 1974. **Freq:** 12/yr. **Trim Size:** 5 7/8 x 9. **Key Personnel:** H.A. Whitaker, PhD, Founding Ed.; S.L. Small, PhD, Editor-in-Chief. **ISSN:** 0093-934X. **Subscription Rates:** US$800 individuals all countries except Europe, Japan and Iran; US$378 students all countries except Europe, Japan and Iran; US$1,685 institutions all countries except Europe, Japan and Iran; EUR2,089 institutions for European countries and Iran; 218,200¥ institutions; EUR443 students for European countries and Iran; 46,100¥ students; EUR986 individuals for European countries and Iran; 103,100¥ individuals. **Remarks:** Accepts advertising. **URL:** http://www.elsevier.com/wps/find/journaldescription.cws_home/622799/descriptiondescription. **Circ:** (Not Reported)

47914 ■ Brain Research Bulletin
Elsevier Science
PO Box 211
NL-1000 AE Amsterdam, Netherlands
Ph: 31 204 853757
Fax: 31 204 853432
Publisher E-mail: nlinfo-f@elsevier.com
Peer-reviewed journal publishing research articles and reviews in all areas of the neurosciences in connection with the International Behavioral Neuroscience Society. **Founded:** 1976. **Freq:** 18/yr. **Key Personnel:** Andres Buonanno, Editor-in-Chief; J.P. Aggleton, Editorial Board; E.D. Abercrombie, Editorial Board; M. Bickford, Editorial Board; T. Carlsted, Editorial Board; I. Curthoys, Editorial Board; B. Ghetti, Editorial Board; E.A. Debski, Editorial Board; L. Hein, Editorial Board. **ISSN:** 0361-9230. **Subscription Rates:** US$2,063 individuals for all countries except Europe, Japan & Iran; 243,400¥ individuals; EUR1,835 individuals for European countries & Iran; EUR4,371 institutions for European countries & Iran; US$4,890 institutions for all countries except Europe, Japan & Iran; 550,500¥ institutions. **Remarks:** Accepts advertising. **URL:** http://www.elsevier.com/wps/find/journaldescription.cws_home/525456/description. **Circ:** (Not Reported)

47915 ■ Breast Disease
IOS Press, B.V.
Nieuwe Hemweg 6B
NL-1013 BG Amsterdam, Netherlands
Ph: 31 20 6883355
Fax: 31 20 6203419
Publisher E-mail: info@iospress.nl
Peer-reviewed journal devoting each volume to an in-depth analysis of the scientific and public implications of recent research on a specific problem in breast cancer. **Freq:** 4/yr. **Key Personnel:** Edison T. Liu, Founding Ed.; Jeffrey E. Green, Editor-in-Chief, jegreen@nih.gov. **ISSN:** 0888-6008. **Subscription Rates:** EUR418 individuals print and online; US$544 individuals print and online. **URL:** http://www.iospress.nl/loadtop/load.php?isbn=08886008.

47916 ■ Bridge Structures
IOS Press, B.V.
Nieuwe Hemweg 6B
NL-1013 BG Amsterdam, Netherlands
Ph: 31 20 6883355
Fax: 31 20 6203419
Publisher E-mail: info@iospress.nl
Peer-reviewed journal presenting the transformation of theoretical knowledge into guidelines and specifications that are compliant with the technical constraint of bridge engineering design and encompassing, but not restricted to analysis, assessment, construction, design, fabrication, maintenance, management and rehabilitation of bridge structures. **Subtitle:** Assessment, Design and Construction. **Freq:** 4/yr. **Key Personnel:** Khaled M. Mahmoud, Editor-in-Chief, khaled@kmbtc.com; Paul Fanning, Editorial Board; Fabio Brancaleoni, Editorial Board; Dennis Mertz, Editorial Board; Peter Irwin, Editorial Board; John W. Fisher, Editorial Board; Gerhard Sedlacek, Editorial Board; Michel Virlogeux, Editorial Board; Hai Fan Xiang, Editorial Board. **ISSN:** 1573-2487. **Subscription Rates:** EUR333 institutions print and online; US$450 institutions print + online. **Remarks:** Accepts advertising. **URL:** http://www.tandf.co.uk/

journals/titles/15732487.asp. **Circ:** (Not Reported)

47917 ■ Building and Environment
Elsevier Science
PO Box 211
NL-1000 AE Amsterdam, Netherlands
Ph: 31 204 853757
Fax: 31 204 853432
Publisher E-mail: nlinfo-f@elsevier.com
Journal dealing with building research and architectural science. **Founded:** 1965. **Freq:** Monthly. **Key Personnel:** Joseph A. Clarke, Assoc. Ed.; Vivian Loftness, Assoc. Ed.; Xudong Yang, Assoc. Ed.; Qingyan Chen, Editor-in-Chief, yanchen@purdue.edu. **ISSN:** 0360-1323. **Subscription Rates:** US$2,500 institutions for all countries except Europe, Japan & Iran; 296,600¥ institutions; EUR2,235 institutions for European countries & Iran; EUR284 individuals for European countries & Iran; US$319 individuals for all countries except Europe, Japan & Iran; 37,600¥ individuals. **Remarks:** Accepts advertising. **URL:** http://www.elsevier.com/wps/find/journaldescription.cws_home/296/descriptiondescription. **Circ:** (Not Reported)

47918 ■ Bulletin des Sciences Mathematiques
Elsevier Science
PO Box 211
NL-1000 AE Amsterdam, Netherlands
Ph: 31 204 853757
Fax: 31 204 853432
Publisher E-mail: nlinfo-f@elsevier.com
Bulletin publishing original papers on all branches of pure mathematics. **Founded:** 1997. **Freq:** 8/yr. **Key Personnel:** D. Eisenbud, Editorial Board; L. Carleson, Editorial Board; B. Gaveau, Editorial Board; F. Golse, Editorial Board; V.I. Arnold, Editorial Board; H. Hedenmalm, Editorial Board; G. Pisier, Editorial Board; D. Nualart, Editorial Board. **ISSN:** 0007-4497. **Subscription Rates:** EUR174 institutions for European countries & Iran; 95,000¥ institutions; US$801 institutions for all countries except Europe, Japan & Iran; EUR174 individuals for European countries & Iran; US$234 individuals for all countries except Europe, Japan & Iran; 26,900¥ individuals. **Remarks:** Accepts advertising. **URL:** http://www.elsevier.com/wps/find/journaldescription.cws_home/600729/descriptiondescription. **Circ:** (Not Reported)

47919 ■ Butt
BUTT magazine
Kleine-Gartmanplantsoen 21-I
NL-1017 RP Amsterdam, Netherlands
Publisher E-mail: mail@buttmagazine.com
Magazine for and about homosexuals. **Freq:** Quarterly. **Key Personnel:** Gert Jonkers, Contact. **Remarks:** Accepts advertising. **URL:** http://www.buttmagazine.com. **Circ:** (Not Reported)

47920 ■ Cancer Biomarkers
IOS Press, B.V.
Nieuwe Hemweg 6B
NL-1013 BG Amsterdam, Netherlands
Ph: 31 20 6883355
Fax: 31 20 6203419
Publisher E-mail: info@iospress.nl
Journal concentrating on molecular biomarkers in cancer research, publishing original research findings on the subject of the identification of markers associated with the disease processes whether or not they are an integral part of the pathological lesion. **Freq:** 12/yr. **Key Personnel:** Sudhir Srivastava, PhD, Editor-in-Chief, submissions@iospress.com; T. Block, Editorial Board; J. Marks, Editorial Board. **ISSN:** 1574-0153. **Subscription Rates:** EUR1,114 institutions print and online; US$1,465 institutions print and online. **URL:** http://www.iospress.nl/loadtop/load.php?isbn=15740153.

47921 ■ Carbohydrate Polymers
Elsevier Science
PO Box 211
NL-1000 AE Amsterdam, Netherlands
Ph: 31 204 853757
Fax: 31 204 853432
Publisher E-mail: nlinfo-f@elsevier.com
Journal devoted to the study of the industrial applications of carbohydrate polymers in areas such as food, textiles, paper, wood, adhesives, pharmaceuticals, oil field applications and industrial chemistry. **Subtitle:** A Journal Devoted to Scientific and Technological Aspects of Industrially Relevant Polysaccharides. **Founded:** 1981. **Freq:** 16/yr. **Key Personnel:** John R. Mitchell, Editor, john.mitchell@nottingham.ac.uk; J.F. Kennedy,

Editor, jfk@advscitec.co.uk; B.E. Christensen, Editorial Board; I. Arvanitoyannis, Editorial Board; Y. Fang, Editorial Board; Y. Du, Editorial Board. **ISSN:** 0144-8617. **Subscription Rates:** 26,000¥ individuals; US$223 individuals for all countries except Europe, Japan & Iran; EUR198 individuals for European countries & Iran; US$4,047 institutions for all countries except Europe, Japan & Iran; EUR3,620 institutions for European countries & Iran; 480,100¥ institutions. **Remarks:** Accepts advertising. **URL:** http://www.elsevier.com/wps/find/journaldescription.cws_home/405871/description. **Circ:** (Not Reported)

47922 ■ Carros Magazine
Readershouse/Hearst
Aletta Jacobslaan 7
NL-1006 BP Amsterdam, Netherlands
Ph: 31 20 5551010
Publisher E-mail: info@rhbm.nl
Consumer magazine covering luxury automobiles. **Subtitle:** The Top Automobile Magazine. **Founded:** 1994. **Freq:** 8/yr. **Cols./Page:** 5. **Key Personnel:** Carlo Brantsen, Head Ed.; Martin Van Der Zeeuw, End Ed.; Frank Kloppert, Editor. **Subscription Rates:** EUR25 individuals; EUR10 individuals 3 issues (Netherlands only). **Remarks:** Accepts advertising. **URL:** http://www.carros.nl/. **Ad Rates:** BW: EUR3,250. **Circ:** Combined 30,000

47923 ■ Cell Biology International
Elsevier Science B.V.
Radarweg 29
NL-1043 Amsterdam, Netherlands
Ph: 31 204 853911
Fax: 31 204 852457
Scholarly journal covering cell biology for plant and animal scientists. **Freq:** Monthly. **Key Personnel:** S.T. Christensen, Asst. Ed.; D. Wheatley, Editor-in-Chief; A. Forer, Editorial Board; C. Jensen, Editorial Board; I.L. Cameron, Editorial Board; C.R. Green, Regional Ed.; H. Carvallo, Regional Ed.; J. Cosson, Editorial Board; C. De La Torre, Editorial Board. **ISSN:** 0165-6995. **Subscription Rates:** EUR990 institutions European countries; 106,900¥ institutions; US$877 institutions for all countries except Europe and Japan. **URL:** http://www.elsevier.com/wps/find/journaldescription.cws_home/622803/descriptiondescription.

47924 ■ Cement and Concrete Composites
Elsevier Science
PO Box 211
NL-1000 AE Amsterdam, Netherlands
Ph: 31 204 853757
Fax: 31 204 853432
Publisher E-mail: nlinfo-f@elsevier.com
Journal reporting on the latest developments in the field of cement-concrete composites technology and in the production, use and performance of cement-based construction materials in general. **Freq:** 10/yr. **Key Personnel:** R.N. Swamy, Honorary Ed.; J.E. Bolander, Editor-in-Chief, jebolander@ucdavis.edu; Dale P. Bentz, Assoc. Ed., dale.bentz@nist.gov; A. Brandt, Editorial Board; S. Chandra, Editorial Board; N. Banthia, Editorial Board. **ISSN:** 0958-9465. **Subscription Rates:** EUR1,520 institutions for European countries & Iran; US$1,702 institutions for all countries except Europe, Japan & Iran; 202,100¥ institutions. **Remarks:** Accepts advertising. **URL:** http://www.elsevier.com/wps/find/journaldescription.cws_home/405892/description. **Circ:** (Not Reported)

47925 ■ Ceramics International
Elsevier Science
PO Box 211
NL-1000 AE Amsterdam, Netherlands
Ph: 31 204 853757
Fax: 31 204 853432
Publisher E-mail: nlinfo-f@elsevier.com
Journal focusing on basic knowledge of ceramic science and their application to the development of better ceramic materials. **Freq:** 8/yr. **Key Personnel:** J.F. Baumard, Editor-in-Chief; P. Vincenzini, Gen. Ed.; J.K. Guo, Editor-in-Chief; K. Koumoto, Editor-in-Chief; R. Pampuch, Editor-in-Chief. **ISSN:** 0272-8842. **Subscription Rates:** 299,800¥ institutions; US$2,527 institutions for all countries except Europe, Japan & Iran; EUR2,259 institutions for European countries & Iran. **Remarks:** Accepts advertising. **URL:** http://www.elsevier.com/wps/find/journaldescription.cws_home/405926/description. **Circ:** (Not Reported)

47926 ■ Chemical Engineering Journal
Elsevier Science
PO Box 211

NL-1000 AE Amsterdam, Netherlands
Ph: 31 204 853757
Fax: 31 204 853432
Publisher E-mail: nlinfo-f@elsevier.com
Journal devoted to advances in research and development in the field of chemical engineering. **Freq:** 30/yr. **Key Personnel:** L.R. Weatherley, Editorial Board; J. Santamaria, Co-Ed.; M. Deshusses, Co-Ed.; G. Marin, Co-Ed.; K.L. Yeung, Co-Ed.; B. Andersson, Editorial Board. **ISSN:** 1385-8947. **Subscription Rates:** EUR3,099 institutions for European countries and Iran; US$3,465 institutions for all Countries except Europe, Japan and Iran; 411,600¥ institutions. **Remarks:** Accepts advertising. **URL:** http://www.elsevier.com/wps/find/journaldescription.cws_home/601273/descriptiondescription. **Circ:** (Not Reported)

47927 ■ Chemosphere
Elsevier Science
PO Box 211
NL-1000 AE Amsterdam, Netherlands
Ph: 31 204 853757
Fax: 31 204 853432
Publisher E-mail: nlinfo-f@elsevier.com
Journal dedicated to research in the field of environmental science. **Founded:** 1972. **Freq:** 44/yr. **Key Personnel:** H. Fiedler, Editor, phone 41 22 9178187, fax 41 22 7973460, heidelore.fiedler@unep.org; L.L. Needham, Editor, lln1@cdc.gov; J. Albaies, Editorial Board; R. Malisch, Editorial Board; S. Safe, Editorial Board; J. Rivera, Editorial Board. **ISSN:** 0045-6535. **Subscription Rates:** US$605 individuals for all countries except Europe, Japan & Iran; EUR540 individuals for European countries & Iran; 71,600¥ individuals for Japan; US$6,322 institutions for all countries except Europe, Japan & Iran; EUR5,650 institutions for European countries & Iran; 750,500¥ institutions Japan. **Remarks:** Accepts advertising. **URL:** http://www.elsevier.com/find/journaldescription.cws_home/362/description. **Circ:** (Not Reported)

47928 ■ Clinical Therapeutics
Elsevier Science
PO Box 211
NL-1000 AE Amsterdam, Netherlands
Ph: 31 204 853757
Fax: 31 204 853432
Publisher E-mail: nlinfo-f@elsevier.com
Peer-reviewed journal focusing on the developments in the drug therapies. **Subtitle:** The International Peer-Reviewed Journal of Drug Therapy. **Founded:** 1977. **Freq:** Monthly. **Key Personnel:** P.D. Walson, MD, Editor-in-Chief; Prof. G. Akoun, Editorial Advisory Board; M. Aman, PhD, Editorial Advisory Board. **ISSN:** 0149-2918. **Subscription Rates:** US$218 individuals plus any supplements; US$243 individuals air-expedited shipment; US$225 institutions, other countries plus any supplements; US$252 institutions, other countries air-expedited shipment. **URL:** http://www.clinicaltherapeutics.com/; http://www.elsevier.com/wps/find/journaldescription.cws_home/525050/descrip tion.

47929 ■ Cognitive Development
Elsevier Science
PO Box 211
NL-1000 AE Amsterdam, Netherlands
Ph: 31 204 853757
Fax: 31 204 853432
Publisher E-mail: nlinfo-f@elsevier.com
Journal on Cognitive Development. **Freq:** Quarterly. **Key Personnel:** D. Kuhn, Editor; P. Bloom, Editorial Board; A. Demetriou, Editorial Board. **ISSN:** 0885-2014. **Subscription Rates:** US$170 individuals for all countries except Europe, Japan & Iran; 20,000¥ individuals; EUR151 individuals for European countries & Iran; US$462 institutions for all countries except Europe, Japan & Iran; EUR413 institutions for European countries & Iran; 55,000¥ institutions. **Remarks:** Accepts advertising. **URL:** http://www.elsevier.com/wps/find/journaldescription.cws_home/620192/description. **Circ:** (Not Reported)

47930 ■ Cognitive Psychology
Elsevier Science B.V.
Radarweg 29
NL-1043 Amsterdam, Netherlands
Ph: 31 204 853911
Fax: 31 204 852457
Journal publishing research data on studies of memory, language processing, perception, problem-solving, and thinking. **Freq:** 8/yr. **Trim Size:** 5 7/8 x 9. **Key Personnel:** G.D. Logan, Editor; D. Baldwin, Assoc. Ed.; T. Carr, Assoc. Ed. **ISSN:** 0010-0285. **Subscription Rates:**

US$898 institutions all countries except Europe, Japan & Iran; US$171 individuals all countries except Europe, Japan & Iran; EUR172 students all countries except Europe, Japan & Iran; EUR131 individuals; 18,800¥ individuals; 117,900¥ institutions; EUR1,129 institutions; EUR132 students; 19,000¥ students. **Remarks:** Accepts advertising. **URL:** http://www.elsevier.com/wps/find/journaldescription.cws_home/622807/descriptiondescription. **Circ:** (Not Reported)

47931 ■ Cognitive Systems Research
Elsevier Science
PO Box 211
NL-1000 AE Amsterdam, Netherlands
Ph: 31 204 853757
Fax: 31 204 853432
Publisher E-mail: nlinfo-f@elsevier.com
Peer-reviewed journal focusing on research of cognitive processes in natural and artificial systems. **Founded:** 1999. **Freq:** Quarterly. **Key Personnel:** V. Honavar, Co-Ed.-in-Ch., honavar@cs.iastate.edu; R. Sun, Co-Ed.-in-Ch., rsun@rpi.edu; G. Oden, Co-Ed.-in-Ch., gregg-oden@uiowa.edu; T. Shallice, Advisory Member; C.L. Giles, Advisory Member; G. Lakoff, Advisory Member. **ISSN:** 1389-0417. **Subscription Rates:** US$559 institutions for all countries except Europe, Japan & Iran; EUR498 institutions for European countries & Iran; 65,700¥ institutions; US$123 individuals for all countries except Europe, Japan & Iran; 14,200¥ individuals; EUR91 individuals for European countries & Iran. **Remarks:** Accepts advertising. **URL:** http://www.elsevier.com/wps/find/journaldescription.cws_home/620288/description. **Circ:** (Not Reported)

47932 ■ Communications in Nonlinear Science and Numerical Simulation
Elsevier Science
PO Box 211
NL-1000 AE Amsterdam, Netherlands
Ph: 31 204 853757
Fax: 31 204 853432
Publisher E-mail: nlinfo-f@elsevier.com
Peer-reviewed journal covering techniques in non-linear science and complexity focusing on research on mathematical modelling, analytical approaches and numerical techniques. **Founded:** 1996. **Freq:** Monthly. **Key Personnel:** S. Ruffo, Editor, stefano.ruffo@unifi.it; G.Q. Chen, International Advisory Editors Board, gqchen@pku.edu.cn; A.C.J. Luo, Editor, aluo@siue.edu; Stefano Ruffo, Editor, stefano.ruffo@unifi.it; G. Unal, Assoc. Ed., gunal@itu.edu.tr. **ISSN:** 1007-5704. **Subscription Rates:** EUR687 institutions for European countries & Iran; US$767 institutions for all countries except Europe, Japan & Iran; 91,000¥ institutions; EUR184 individuals for European countries & Iran; US$248 individuals for all countries except Europe, Japan & Iran; 25,900¥ individuals. **Remarks:** Accepts advertising. **URL:** http://www.elsevier.com/wps/find/journaldescription.cws_home/622724/description. **Circ:** (Not Reported)

47933 ■ Composite Structures
Elsevier Science
PO Box 211
NL-1000 AE Amsterdam, Netherlands
Ph: 31 204 853757
Fax: 31 204 853432
Publisher E-mail: nlinfo-f@elsevier.com
Journal focusing on advances in the use of composite materials in structural applications. **Founded:** 1983. **Freq:** Monthly. **Key Personnel:** I.H. Marshall, Founding Ed.; S. Adali, Editorial Board; R. Akkerman, Editorial Board; M. Qatu, Editorial Board; P. Gaudenzi, Editorial Board; W. Becker, Editorial Board. **ISSN:** 0263-8223. **Subscription Rates:** 707,400¥ institutions; EUR5,328 institutions for European countries & Iran; US$5,961 institutions for all countries except Europe, Japan & Iran. **Remarks:** Accepts advertising. **URL:** http://www.elsevier.com/wps/find/journaldescription.cws_home/405928/descriptiondescription. **Circ:** (Not Reported)

47934 ■ Composites Part A
Elsevier Science
PO Box 211
NL-1000 AE Amsterdam, Netherlands
Ph: 31 204 853757
Fax: 31 204 853432
Publisher E-mail: nlinfo-f@elsevier.com
Peer-reviewed journal focusing on the science and technology of composite materials. **Subtitle:** Applied Science and Manufacturing. **Freq:** Monthly. **Key Personnel:** M. Wisnom, Editor-in-Chief, composites-part-a@bristol.ac.uk; A.A. Baker, Editorial Board; H. Hamada, Editorial Board; P.T. Curtis, Editorial Board; M.G. Bader, Editorial Board; S.G. Advani, North American Ed.,

advani@me.udel.edu; N. Takeda, Asian Ed., takeda@smart.k.u-tokyo.ac.jp. **ISSN:** 1359-835X. **Subscription Rates:** US$3,282 institutions for all countries except Europe, Japan & Iran; EUR2,931 institutions for European countries & Iran; 389,200¥ institutions; US$129 individuals for all countries except Europe, Japan & Iran; EUR111 individuals for European countries & Iran; 15,100¥ individuals. **Remarks:** Accepts advertising. **URL:** http://www.elsevier.com/wps/find/journaldescription.cws_home/30399/description. **Circ:** (Not Reported)

47935 ■ Computational Statistics & Data Analysis
Elsevier Science
PO Box 211
NL-1000 AE Amsterdam, Netherlands
Ph: 31 204 853757
Fax: 31 204 853432
Publisher E-mail: nlinfo-f@elsevier.com
Peer-reviewed journal covering research and applications of computational statistics and data analysis. **Founded:** 1983. **Freq:** Monthly. **Key Personnel:** S.P. Azen, Editor-in-Chief, sazen@usc.edu; E.J. Kontoghiorghes, Co-Ed., csda@cfe-csda.org; J.C. Lee, Co-Ed., jaeclee@korea.ac.kr; D.A. Belsley, Advisory Board; P.M. Bentler, Advisory Board; N.R. Draper, Advisory Board. **ISSN:** 0167-9473. **Subscription Rates:** US$2,926 institutions for all countries except Europe, Japan & Iran; EUR2,615 institutions for European countries & Iran; 346,800¥ institutions. **Remarks:** Accepts advertising. **URL:** http://www.elsevier.com/find/journaldescription.cws_home/505539/description. **Circ:** (Not Reported)

47936 ■ Computer Speech & Language
Elsevier Science B.V.
Radarweg 29
NL-1043 Amsterdam, Netherlands
Ph: 31 204 853911
Fax: 31 204 852457
Scholarly journal covering speech and language of humans and machines. **Freq:** Quarterly. **Key Personnel:** S. Narayanan, Editor; J. Hajic, Editorial Board; S. Clark, Editorial Board; E.T. Briscoe, Editor; R.K. Moore, Editor-in-Chief; S. Furui, Editorial Board. **ISSN:** 0885-2308. **Subscription Rates:** US$200 individuals for all countries except Europe, Iran and Japan; 21,100¥ individuals; EUR196 individuals for European countries and Iran; EUR606 institutions for European countries and Iran; US$543 institutions for all countries except Europe, Iran and Japan; 65,500¥ institutions. **URL:** http://www.elsevier.com/wps/find/journaldescription.cws_home/622808/descriptiondescription.

47937 ■ Computer Vision and Image Understanding
Elsevier Science B.V.
Radarweg 29
NL-1043 Amsterdam, Netherlands
Ph: 31 204 853911
Fax: 31 204 852457
Peer-reviewed journal focusing on the computer analysis of pictorial information. **Freq:** Monthly. **Trim Size:** 8 1/2 x 11. **Key Personnel:** A.C. Kak, Editor-in-Chief; N. Ahuja, Area Ed.; R. Bergevin, Area Ed.; Y. Aloimonos, Area Ed.; L.S. Davis, Area Ed.; B.C. Vemuri, Area Ed. **ISSN:** 1077-3142. **Subscription Rates:** EUR2,033 institutions European countries and Iran; US$1,595 institutions, other countries except Europe, Japan and Iran; 212,600¥ institutions Japan; US$699 individuals except Europe, Japan and Iran; 96,100¥ individuals Japan; EUR899 individuals European countries and Iran. **URL:** http://www.elsevier.com/wps/find/journaldescription.cws_home/622809/descriptiondescription.

47938 ■ Consciousness and Cognition
Elsevier Science B.V.
Radarweg 29
NL-1043 Amsterdam, Netherlands
Ph: 31 204 853911
Fax: 31 204 852457
Journal focusing on a natural science approach to consciousness, voluntary control, and self. **Founded:** 1992. **Freq:** Quarterly. **Trim Size:** 6 7/8 x 10. **Key Personnel:** W.P. Banks, Editor-in-Chief; A. Revonsuo, Assoc. Ed.; J. Enns, Assoc. Ed. **ISSN:** 1053-8100. **Subscription Rates:** EUR874 institutions European countries and Iran; US$576 institutions all countries except Europe, Japan & Iran; 91,400¥ institutions; 21,200¥ students; US$144 students all countries except Europe, Japan & Iran; EUR201 students European countries and Iran; US$256 individuals all countries except Europe, Japan & Iran; 41,000¥ individuals; EUR391 individuals European countries and Iran. **URL:** http://www.elsevier.

com/wps/find/journaldescription.cws_home/622810/descrip tiondescription.

47939 ■ Contemporary Educational Psychology
Elsevier Science B.V.
Radarweg 29
NL-1043 Amsterdam, Netherlands
Ph: 31 204 853911
Fax: 31 204 852457
Journal of empirical research, theory in the application of psychological methods, and research to problems in education. **Founded:** 1976. **Freq:** Quarterly. **Trim Size:** 5 7/8 x 9. **Key Personnel:** P.A. Alexander, MD, Editor; R. Bruning, Editorial Board; S.M. Alessi, Editorial Board; M. Ainley, Editorial Board; M. Bong, Editorial Board. **ISSN:** 0361-476X. **Subscription Rates:** 97,100¥ institutions; US$775 institutions; EUR929 institutions; US$145 students; 16,000¥ students; EUR111 students; US$145 individuals; 16,000¥ individuals; EUR111 individuals. **Remarks:** Accepts advertising. **URL:** http://www.elsevier.com/wps/find/journaldescription.cws_home/622811/descriptiondescription. **Circ:** (Not Reported)

47940 ■ Contemporary Pragmatism
Editions Rodopi B.V.
Tijnmuiden 7
NL-1046 AK Amsterdam, Netherlands
Ph: 31 206 114821
Fax: 31 204 472979
Publisher E-mail: info@rodopi.nl
Interdisciplinary, international journal for discussions of applying pragmatism, broadly understood, to today's issues. **Freq:** Semiannual. **Key Personnel:** John Shook, Editor, jshook@pragmatism.org; Paulo Ghiraldelli, Editorial Board; Randall Dipert, Editorial Board; James Bohman, Editorial Board; Nancy Frankenberry, Editorial Board; Pascal Engel, Editorial Board; Randall Auxier, Editorial Board; Jose Miguel Esteban, Editorial Board; Susana De Castro Amaral, Editorial Board. **ISSN:** 1572-3429. **Subscription Rates:** EUR38 individuals; US$49 individuals (postage included); EUR90 libraries; US$133 libraries plus postage. **URL:** http://www.rodopi.nl/senj.asp?serieid=cp.

47941 ■ Cretaceous Research
Elsevier Science
PO Box 211
NL-1000 AE Amsterdam, Netherlands
Ph: 31 204 853757
Fax: 31 204 853432
Publisher E-mail: nlinfo-f@elsevier.com
Journal dealing with research on Cretaceous period including Jurassic and Tertiary. **Freq:** Bimonthly. **Key Personnel:** H.W. Bailey, Editorial Board; D.J. Horne, Assoc. Ed., d.j.horne@qmul.ac.uk; C.J. Wood, Assoc. Ed., chrisjwood@btopenworld.com; J.W.M. Jagt, Assoc. Ed., john.jagt@maastricht.nl; D. Batten, Assoc. Ed., david.batten@manchester.ac.uk; B.T. Huber, Editorial Board. **ISSN:** 0195-6671. **Subscription Rates:** US$373 individuals for all countries except Europe, Japan & Iran; EUR417 individuals for European countries & Iran; 45,100¥ individuals; US$1,264 institutions for all countries except Europe, Japan & Iran; EUR1,421 institutions for European countries & Iran; 153,500¥ institutions. **Remarks:** Accepts advertising. **URL:** http://www.elsevier.com/wps/find/journaldescription.cws_home/022812/description. **Circ:** (Not Reported)

47942 ■ Cryobiology
Elsevier Science B.V.
Radarweg 29
NL-1043 Amsterdam, Netherlands
Ph: 31 204 853911
Fax: 31 204 852457
International scientific journal publishing research in the field of low temperature biology and medicine. **Subtitle:** The Official Journal of the Society for Cryobiology **Subject Matter.** **Founded:** 1964. **Freq:** Bimonthly. **Print Method:** Offset. **Trim Size:** 6 7/8 x 10. **Key Personnel:** D.E. Pegg, Editor-in-Chief; W.J. Armitage, Assoc. Ed.; M. Toner, Assoc. Ed. **ISSN:** 0011-2240. **Subscription Rates:** EUR940 institutions European countries and Iran; 97,900¥ institutions; US$701 institutions for all countries except Europe, Iran and Japan; EUR134 students European countries and Iran; 13,900¥ students; US$118 students for all countries except Europe, Iran and Japan. **Remarks:** Accepts advertising. **URL:** http://www.elsevier.com/wps/find/journaldescription.cws_home/622814/descriptiondescription. **Circ:** (Not Reported)

47943 ■ Current Biology
Elsevier Science
PO Box 211
NL-1000 AE Amsterdam, Netherlands
Ph: 31 204 853757
Fax: 31 204 853432
Publisher E-mail: nlinfo-f@elsevier.com
Journal for researchers, educators, and students of biology. **Freq:** 24/yr. **Key Personnel:** Geoffrey North, Editor, geoff@current-biology.com; Ulysses Lateiner, Managing Editor, ulateiner@cell.com; Cyrus Martin, Asst. Ed., cmartin@cell.com. **ISSN:** 0960-9822. **Subscription Rates:** US$1,479 institutions print; 1,479¥ institutions print, outside US; EUR202 U.S. and Canada print and online; EUR75 individuals print and online; 305¥ individuals print and online; US$194 U.S. and Canada online. **Remarks:** Advertising accepted; rates available upon request. **URL:** http://www.current-biology.com. **Circ:** (Not Reported)

47944 ■ Current Opinion in Biotechnology
Elsevier Science
PO Box 211
NL-1000 AE Amsterdam, Netherlands
Ph: 31 204 853757
Fax: 31 204 853432
Publisher E-mail: nlinfo-f@elsevier.com
Journal dealing with advances in biotechnology. **Freq:** Bimonthly. **Key Personnel:** Greg Stephanopoulos, Editor; Victor de Lorenzo, Editor; Julian Davies, Editorial Board; Lee Hood, Editorial Board; George Poste, Editorial Board. **ISSN:** 0958-1669. **Subscription Rates:** US$739 individuals for all countries except Europe, Japan & Iran; EUR677 individuals for European countries & Iran; 81,900¥ individuals; US$2,619 institutions for all countries except Europe, Japan & Iran; EUR2,341 institutions for European countries & Iran; 324,900¥ institutions. **Remarks:** Accepts advertising. **URL:** http://www.elsevier.com/wps/find/journaldescription.cws_home/601293/description. **Circ:** (Not Reported)

47945 ■ Current Opinion in Cell Biology
Elsevier Science
PO Box 211
NL-1000 AE Amsterdam, Netherlands
Ph: 31 204 853757
Fax: 31 204 853432
Publisher E-mail: nlinfo-f@elsevier.com
Journal devoted to current trends in cell biology. **Freq:** Bimonthly. **Key Personnel:** Tom Misteli, Editor; Graham Warren, Editor; Vann Bennett, Editorial Board; Timothy Hunt, Editorial Board; Richard O. Hynes, Editorial Board. **ISSN:** 0955-0674. **Subscription Rates:** US$368 individuals for all countries except Europe, Japan & Iran; EUR338 individuals for European countries & Iran; 41,100¥ individuals; US$1,996 institutions for all countries except Europe, Japan & Iran; EUR1,786 institutions for European countries & Iran; 247,600¥ institutions. **Remarks:** Accepts advertising. **URL:** http://www.elsevier.com/wps/find/journaldescription.cws_home/601296/description?navopenmenu=4. **Circ:** (Not Reported)

47946 ■ Current Opinion in Chemical Biology
Elsevier Science
PO Box 211
NL-1000 AE Amsterdam, Netherlands
Ph: 31 204 853757
Fax: 31 204 853432
Publisher E-mail: nlinfo-f@elsevier.com
Journal on chemical biology. **Founded:** 1997. **Freq:** Bimonthly. **Key Personnel:** Donald Hilvert, Editor; Carolyn Bertozzi, Editor; Gerald F. Joyce, Editorial Board; Duilio Arigoni, Editorial Board; Peter B. Dervan, Editorial Board; Stephen J. Benkovic, Editorial Board; Ronald Breslow, Editorial Board; Kevin T. Chapman, Editorial Board; Jacqueline K. Barton, Editorial Board; Michael H. Gelb, Editorial Board; Harry B. Gray, Editorial Board; Milan Mrksich, Editorial Board. **ISSN:** 1367-5931. **Subscription Rates:** US$361 individuals for all countries except Europe, Japan & Iran; 40,300¥ individuals; EUR332 individuals for European countries & Iran; US$2,033 institutions for all countries except Europe, Japan & Iran; 252,200¥ institutions; EUR1,819 institutions for European countries & Iran. **Remarks:** Accepts advertising. **URL:** http://www.elsevier.com/wps/find/journaldescription.cws_home/601299/description. **Circ:** (Not Reported)

47947 ■ Current Opinion in Genetics & Development
Elsevier Science
PO Box 211
NL-1000 AE Amsterdam, Netherlands
Ph: 31 204 853757
Fax: 31 204 853432
Publisher E-mail: nlinfo-f@elsevier.com
Journal on currents trends in the field of genetics. **Freq:** Bimonthly. **Key Personnel:** R.A. Firtel, Editor; D. Ish-Horowicz, Editor; Thomas Jessell, Editorial Board; Robin Allshire, Editorial Board; David Baltimore, Editorial Board; Tony Hunter, Editorial Board. **ISSN:** 0959-437X. **Subscription Rates:** US$366 individuals for all countries except Europe, Japan & Iran; 40,900¥ individuals; EUR336 individuals for European countries & Iran; US$1984 institutions for all countries except Europe, Japan & Iran; 246,200¥ institutions; EUR1,776 institutions for European countries & Iran. **Remarks:** Accepts advertising. **URL:** http://www.elsevier.com/wps/find/journaldescription.cws_home/601302/descriptiondescription. **Circ:** (Not Reported)

47948 ■ Current Opinion in Microbiology
Elsevier Science
PO Box 211
NL-1000 AE Amsterdam, Netherlands
Ph: 31 204 853757
Fax: 31 204 853432
Publisher E-mail: nlinfo-f@elsevier.com
Journal on current trends in the field of microbiology. **Freq:** Bimonthly. **Key Personnel:** Julian Davies, Editor-in-Chief; Pascale Cossart, Editor-in-Chief; Mick Chandler, Editorial Board; Howard Bussey, Editorial Board; Stanley N. Cohen, Editorial Board; Jeff Errington, Editorial Board; Herb Arst, Editorial Board; Rita R. Colwell, Editorial Board; Mitch Sogin, Editorial Board. **ISSN:** 1369-5274. **Subscription Rates:** US$376 individuals for all countries except Europe, Japan & Iran; EUR346 individuals for European countries & Iran; 42,000¥ individuals; US$2,040 institutions for all countries except Europe, Japan & Iran; EUR1,825 institutions for European countries & Iran; 253,100¥ institutions. **Remarks:** Accepts advertising. **URL:** http://www.elsevier.com/wps/find/journaldescription.cws_home/601308/descriptiondescription. **Circ:** (Not Reported)

47949 ■ Current Opinion in Plant Biology
Elsevier Science
PO Box 211
NL-1000 AE Amsterdam, Netherlands
Ph: 31 204 853757
Fax: 31 204 853432
Publisher E-mail: nlinfo-f@elsevier.com
Journal devoted to the current trends in the field of plant biology. **Freq:** Bimonthly. **Key Personnel:** Detlef Weigel, Editor; Jeff Dangl, Editorial Board; Frederick M. Ausubel, Editorial Board; Dorothea Bartels, Editorial Board; Mike Bevan, Editorial Board; Simon Bright, Editorial Board. **ISSN:** 1369-5266. **Subscription Rates:** US$361 individuals for all countries except Europe, Japan & Iran; 40,300¥ individuals; EUR332 individuals for European countries & Iran; US$1,968 institutions for all countries except Europe, Japan & Iran; 244,100¥ institutions; EUR1,761 institutions for European countries & Iran. **Remarks:** Accepts advertising. **URL:** http://www.elsevier.com/wps/find/journaldescription.cws_home/601314/description. **Circ:** (Not Reported)

47950 ■ Current Problems in Cancer
Elsevier Science
PO Box 211
NL-1000 AE Amsterdam, Netherlands
Ph: 31 204 853757
Fax: 31 204 853432
Publisher E-mail: nlinfo-f@elsevier.com
Journal discussing on management of all types of malignancies. **Freq:** Bimonthly. **Key Personnel:** Peter A.S. Johnstone, MD, Editor-in-Chief; Shivaani Kummar, MD, Assoc. Ed.; Keith A. Delman, MD, Assoc. Ed. **ISSN:** 0147-0272. **Subscription Rates:** US$361 institutions; US$194 individuals; US$77 students; US$306 institutions; US$156 individuals; US$94 students. **Remarks:** Accepts advertising. **URL:** http://www.elsevier.com/wps/find/journaldescription.cws_home/623361/description. **Circ:** (Not Reported)

47951 ■ Currents of Encounter
Rodopi
c/o Hendrick M. Vroom, Ed.
Free University
Faculty of Theology
PO Box 7161
NL-1007 MC Amsterdam, Netherlands
Fax: 31 204 446635
Publisher E-mail: info@rodopi.nl
Journal covering interreligious relations, analyzing, and monitoring the role of religion in society. **Subtitle:** Studies on the Contact between Christianity and Other

---

Religions, Beliefs, and Cultures. **Founded:** 1963. **Freq:** Weekly (Wed.). **Print Method:** Offset. **Cols./Page:** 5. **Col. Width:** 11.5 picas. **Col. Depth:** 197 agate lines. **Key Personnel:** Jerald D. Gort, Editor; Lourens Minnema, Editor; Henry Jansen, Editor. **ISSN:** 0923-6201. **URL:** http://www.rodopi.nl/senj.asp?SerieId= CURRENTS.

47952 ■ Cytokine
Elsevier Science B.V.
Radarweg 29
NL-1043 Amsterdam, Netherlands
Ph: 31 204 853911
Fax: 31 204 852457
Scholarly journal covering molecular biology, biochemistry, immunology and related fields. **Freq:** Monthly. **Key Personnel:** S.L. Gaffen, Assoc. Ed.; Gordon W. Duff, Editor; S.K. Durum, Editor. **ISSN:** 1043-4666. **Subscription Rates:** US$1,692 institutions for all countries except Europe, Iran and Japan; 205,400¥ institutions; EUR1,905 institutions European countries and Iran; US$785 individuals for all countries except Europe, Iran and Japan; EUR773 individuals European countries and Iran; 83,400¥ individuals. **Remarks:** Accepts advertising. **URL:** http://www.elsevier.com/wps/find/ journaldescription.cws_home/622815/ descriptiondescription. **Circ:** (Not Reported)

47953 ■ Desalination
Elsevier Science
PO Box 211
NL-1000 AE Amsterdam, Netherlands
Ph: 31 204 853757
Fax: 31 204 853432
Publisher E-mail: nlinfo-f@elsevier.com
International journal in the field of water desalting and purification, covering advanced technologies for water treatment and various aspects of desalting. **Subtitle:** The International Journal on the Science and Technology of Desalting and Water Purification. **Founded:** 1966. **Freq:** 48/yr. **Key Personnel:** Nidal Hilal, Editor-in-Chief; P. Cornel, Editorial Board; I.S. Kim, Editorial Board; Y. Cohen, Editorial Board; D. Hasson, Editorial Board; J. Glater, Editorial Board. **ISSN:** 0011-9164. **Subscription Rates:** EUR6,325 institutions for European countries; 844,800¥ institutions; US$7,122 institutions, other countries for all countries except Europe and Japan. **Remarks:** Accepts advertising. **URL:** http://www. elsevier.com/wps/find/journaldescription.cws_home/ 502683/descrip tiondescription. **Circ:** (Not Reported)

47954 ■ Developmental Biology
Elsevier Science B.V.
Radarweg 29
NL-1043 Amsterdam, Netherlands
Ph: 31 204 853911
Fax: 31 204 852457
Peer-reviewed journal publishing original research on mechanisms of development, differentiation, growth, regeneration, and tissue repair at the molecular, cellular, and genetic levels (in plants and animals). **Founded:** 1959. **Freq:** Semimonthly. **Print Method:** Offset. **Trim Size:** 8 1/2 x 11. **Key Personnel:** C. Birchmeier, Editor, phone 49 30 94062403, fax 49 30 94063765, cbirch@ mdc-berlin.de; C.P. Blobel, Editorial Board; R. Krumlauf, Editor-in-Chief, phone 816926-4051, fax 816926-2008, rek@stowers-institut.org; H.J. Yost, Editorial Board; S. Cohen, Editor, scohen@imcb.a-star.edu.sg; M. Levine, Editor, phone 510642-5014, fax 510643-5785, mlevine@ berkeley.edu. **ISSN:** 0012-1606. **Subscription Rates:** 1,048,400¥ institutions; US$7,661 institutions for all countries except Europe, Iran and Japan; EUR10,040 institutions European countries and Iran; 55,600¥ students; US$466 students for all countries except Europe, Iran and Japan; EUR533 students European countries and Iran; 67,600¥ individuals; US$566 individuals for all countries except Europe, Iran and Japan; EUR649 individuals European countries and Iran. **Remarks:** Accepts advertising. **URL:** http://www. elsevier.com/wps/find/journaldescription.cws_home/ 622816/descriptiondescription. **Circ:** (Not Reported)

47955 ■ Developmental & Comparative Immunology
Elsevier Science
PO Box 211
NL-1000 AE Amsterdam, Netherlands
Ph: 31 204 853757
Fax: 31 204 853432
Publisher E-mail: nlinfo-f@elsevier.com
Journal covering research on development of the immune system and comparative immunology in connection with International Society of Developmental and

Comparative Immunology. **Subtitle:** Ontogeny, Phylogeny, Aging. **Founded:** 1977. **Freq:** 12/yr. **Key Personnel:** E.L. Cooper, Founding Ed.; K. Soderhall, Editor-in-Chief, kenneth.soderhall@ebc.uu.se. **ISSN:** 0145-305X. **Subscription Rates:** 319,200¥ institutions Japan; EUR2,403 institutions European countries and Iran; US$2,687 institutions, other countries except Europe, Japan and Iran. **URL:** http://www.elsevier.com/wps/find/ journaldescription.cws_home/275/descriptiondescription.

47956 ■ Developmental Review
Elsevier Science B.V.
Radarweg 29
NL-1043 Amsterdam, Netherlands
Ph: 31 204 853911
Fax: 31 204 852457
Journal reports on issues with important implications for the fields of pediatrics, psychiatry, and education. **Subtitle:** Perspectives in Behavior and Cognition. **Founded:** 1981. **Freq:** Quarterly. **Trim Size:** 5 7/8 x 9. **Key Personnel:** M.L. Howe, Assoc. Ed.; C.J. Brainerd, Editor; P. Bauer, Editorial Board; S.J. Ceci, Editorial Board; V.F. Reyna, Assoc. Ed.; D.F. Bjorklund, Editorial Board. **ISSN:** 0273-2297. **Subscription Rates:** US$546 institutions all countries except Europe, Japan & Iran; 65,700¥ institutions; EUR629 institutions European countries and Iran; US$101 students all countries except Europe, Japan & Iran; EUR79 students European countries and Iran; 11,300¥ students; US$100 individuals all countries except Europe, Japan & Iran; EUR79 individuals European countries and Iran; 11,100¥ individuals. **Remarks:** Accepts advertising. **URL:** http://www.elsevier.com/wps/ find/journaldescription.cws_home/622817/ descriptiondescription. **Circ:** (Not Reported)

47957 ■ Diachronica
John Benjamins Publishing Co.
Klaprozenweg 105
PO Box 36224
NL-1033 NN Amsterdam, Netherlands
Ph: 31 206 304747
Fax: 31 206 739773
Publisher E-mail: benjamins@presswarehouse.com
Peer-reviewed journal covering all aspects of changes across all global languages. **Founded:** 1965. **Freq:** 3/yr. **Print Method:** Offset. **Cols./Page:** 3. **Col. Width:** 25 nonpareils. **Col. Depth:** 140 agate lines. **Key Personnel:** Joseph C. Salmons, Exec. Ed.; Brian D. Joseph, Assoc. Ed.; Martha Ratliff, Assoc. Ed.; Sheila Embleton, Assoc. Ed.; Elly van Gelderen, Book Review Ed.; E.F.K. Koerner, Consulting Ed. **ISSN:** 0176-4225. **Subscription Rates:** EUR246 individuals print + online; EUR70 individuals special. **URL:** http://www.benjamins.com/cgi-bin/t_seriesview.cgi?series=DIA.

47958 ■ Digital Signal Processing
Elsevier Science B.V.
Radarweg 29
NL-1043 Amsterdam, Netherlands
Ph: 31 204 853911
Fax: 31 204 852457
Peer-reviewed journal containing information regarding creativity in the field of signal processing. **Founded:** 1994. **Freq:** Bimonthly. **Trim Size:** 8 1/2 x 11. **Key Personnel:** J. Campbell, Editorial Board; M. Rangaswamy, Editor, muralidhar.rangaswamy@hanscom.af. mil; P.M. Djuric, Editorial Board; J. Li, Editorial Board; T. Sarkar, Editorial Board; M. Bellanger, Editorial Board; F.J. Harris, Editor, fred.harris@sdsu.edu; S. Furui, Editorial Board; J.A. Cadzow, Editorial Board. **ISSN:** 1051-2004. **Subscription Rates:** 75,400¥ institutions; US$578 institutions for all countries except Europe, Iran and Japan; EUR724 institutions European countries and Iran; US$259 individuals for all countries except Europe, Iran and Japan; 33,700¥ individuals; EUR323 individuals European countries and Iran. **URL:** http://www.elsevier. com/wps/find/journaldescription.cws_home/622818/ descriptiondescription.

47959 ■ Disease Markers
IOS Press, B.V.
Nieuwe Hemweg 6B
NL-1013 BG Amsterdam, Netherlands
Ph: 31 20 6883355
Fax: 31 20 6203419
Publisher E-mail: info@iospress.nl
Journal publishing original research findings on the subject of the identification of markers associated with the disease processes whether or not they are an integral part of the pathological lesion. **Freq:** Monthly. **Key Personnel:** Sudhir Srivastava, PhD, Editor, phone 703239-2260, fax 703323-3668; B. Levin, Editorial Board; P.E. Barker, Editorial Board; P.G. Anker, Editorial

Board; M.J. Birrer, Editorial Board; S.G. Baker, Editorial Board; T.M. Block, Editorial Board; P. Bofetta, Editorial Board; D. Alberts, Editorial Board. **ISSN:** 0278-0240. **Subscription Rates:** EUR1,514 institutions print and online; US$2,315 institutions print and online. **URL:** http:// www.iospress.nl/loadtop/load.php?isbn=02780240.

47960 ■ Dyes and Pigments
Elsevier Science
PO Box 211
NL-1000 AE Amsterdam, Netherlands
Ph: 31 204 853757
Fax: 31 204 853432
Publisher E-mail: nlinfo-f@elsevier.com
Journal publishing the scientific and technical aspects on synthesis of dyes, pigments and their intermediates, their physical or chemical properties, physical aspects of their preparation, their photochemical, ecological or biological properties and the relationship between color and chemical constitution. **Founded:** 1980. **Freq:** Monthly. **Key Personnel:** Prof. S. Burkinshaw, Editor, s.m.burkinshaw@leeds.ac.uk; Prof. H. Tian, Assoc. Ed., tianhe@ecust.edu.cn; Prof. B.M. Heron, Assoc. Ed., b.m.heron@leeds.ac.uk. **ISSN:** 0143-7208. **Subscription Rates:** 396,400¥ institutions; EUR2,988 institutions European countries; US$3,343 institutions, other countries; 34,000¥ individuals; EUR221 individuals; US$296 individuals. **Remarks:** Accepts advertising. **URL:** http://www.elsevier.com/wps/find/ journalbibliographicinfo.cws_home/405894/d escription. **Circ:** (Not Reported)

47961 ■ EAIE Forum
European Association for International Education
PO Box 11189
NL-1001 GD Amsterdam, Netherlands
Ph: 31 20 445100
Fax: 31 20 3445119
Publisher E-mail: eaie@eaie.nl
Publication covering exchange students. **Freq:** Continuous 3/yr. **Key Personnel:** Michael Cooper, Editor. **ISSN:** 1389-0808. **Subscription Rates:** Included in membership. **Remarks:** Advertising accepted; rates available upon request. **URL:** http://www.eaie.org/ publications/forum. **Circ:** 2,000

47962 ■ Ecotoxicology and Environmental Safety
Elsevier Science B.V.
Radarweg 29
NL-1043 Amsterdam, Netherlands
Ph: 31 204 853911
Fax: 31 204 852457
Journal reporting research of the biologic and toxic effects of natural or synthetic chemical pollutants on animal, plant, or microbial ecosystems. **Founded:** 1977. **Freq:** 8/yr. **Trim Size:** 8 1/2 x 11. **Key Personnel:** Irena Twardowska, Editor, irena@ipis.zabrze.pl; N. Denslow, Assoc. Ed. **ISSN:** 0147-6513. **Subscription Rates:** 192,400¥ institutions; EUR1,843 institutions European countries and Iran; US$1,391 institutions all countries except Europe, Japan & Iran; EUR391 students European countries and Iran; 40,700¥ students; US$343 students all countries except Europe, Japan & Iran; 82,000¥ individuals; US$685 individuals all countries except Europe, Japan & Iran; EUR786 individuals European countries and Iran. **Remarks:** Accepts advertising. **URL:** http://www.elsevier.com/wps/find/journaldescription.cws_ home/622819/descriptiondescription. **Circ:** (Not Reported)

47963 ■ Electric Power Systems Research
Elsevier Science
PO Box 211
NL-1000 AE Amsterdam, Netherlands
Ph: 31 204 853757
Fax: 31 204 853432
Publisher E-mail: nlinfo-f@elsevier.com
International journal publishing original papers concerned with generation, transmission, distribution and utilization of electrical energy. **Founded:** 1978. **Freq:** 12/yr. **Key Personnel:** Prof. C.A. Nucci, Editor-in-Chief, carloalberto.nucci@unibo.it; Dr. C.R. Haden, Exec. Ed.; Dr. J.D. Morgan, Assoc. Ed., jderaldmorgan@hotmail. com. **ISSN:** 0378-7796. **Subscription Rates:** 420,900¥ institutions for Japan; EUR3,170 institutions for European countries and Iran; US$3,562 institutions all countries except Europe, Japan and Iran. **URL:** http://www. elsevier.com/wps/find/journaldescription.cws_home/ 504085/description.

47964 ■ Elegance
TTG—De Telegraaf Tijdschriften Groep B.V.
PO Box 851

NL-1000 AW Amsterdam, Netherlands
Ph: 31 204 802835
Fax: 31 205 854177
Publication E-mail: abonnementen@elegance.nl
Publisher E-mail: redactie@autovisie.nl
Consumer magazine covering lifestyle, fashion, travel and home for women. **Freq:** Monthly. **Print Method:** Offset. **Trim Size:** 230 x 297 mm. **Key Personnel:** Lenny Gerdes, Editor-in-Chief. **Subscription Rates:** EUR53.95 individuals; EUR5.25 single issue. **Remarks:** Accepts advertising. **URL:** http://www.ttg.nl/elegance/abonnement/. **Circ:** Combined †55,885

47965 ■ English Text Construction
John Benjamins Publishing Co.
Klaprozenweg 105
PO Box 36224
NL-1033 NN Amsterdam, Netherlands
Ph: 31 206 304747
Fax: 31 206 739773
Publisher E-mail: benjamins@presswarehouse.com
Peer-reviewed journal focusing on English text construction. **Freq:** Semiannual. **Key Personnel:** An Laffut, Editor; Keith Carlon, Managing Editor; Dirk Van Hulle, Editor. **ISSN:** 1874-8767. **Subscription Rates:** EUR157 institutions backvolumes; EUR70 individuals special; EUR157 institutions print + online. **URL:** http://www.benjamins.com/cgi-bin/t_seriesview.cgi?series=ETC.

47966 ■ English World-Wide
John Benjamins Publishing Co.
Klaprozenweg 105
PO Box 36224
NL-1033 NN Amsterdam, Netherlands
Ph: 31 206 304747
Fax: 31 206 739773
Publisher E-mail: benjamins@presswarehouse.com
Peer-reviewed journal covering English language focusing on findings in the dialectology and sociolinguistics of the English-speaking communities. **Founded:** 1922. **Freq:** 3/yr. **Print Method:** Flexograph. **Cols./Page:** 6. **Col. Width:** 26 nonpareils. **Col. Depth:** 301 agate lines. **Key Personnel:** Edgar W. Schneider, Editor. **ISSN:** 0172-8865. **Subscription Rates:** EUR284 individuals print + online; EUR80 individuals special. **URL:** http://www.benjamins.com/cgi-bin/t_seriesview.cgi?series=EWW.

47967 ■ Entomologia Experimentalis et Applicata
John Wiley & Sons Inc.
Wiley-Blackwell
c/o Dr. S.B.J. Menken, Ed.-in-Ch.
Institute for Biodiversity & Ecosystem Dynamics
Kruislaan 318
NL-1098 SM Amsterdam, Netherlands
Journal covering the fields of experimental biology and ecology of insects and other terrestrial arthropods, with both pure and applied scopes. **Freq:** Monthly. **Key Personnel:** Dr. S.B.J. Menken, Editor-in-Chief, menken@science.uva.nl. **ISSN:** 0013-8703. **Subscription Rates:** US$2,688 institutions Americas (print and online); 1,455 institutions UK (print and online); EUR1,847 institutions Europe (print and online); US$3,135 institutions, other countries print and online; US$2,443 institutions Americas (print or online only); 1,322 institutions UK (print or online only); EUR1,680 institutions Europe (print or online only); US$2,850 institutions, other countries print or online only. **Remarks:** Accepts advertising. **URL:** http://www.wiley.com/bw/journal.asp?ref=0013-8703. **Circ:** (Not Reported)

47968 ■ Environmental & Experimental Botany
Elsevier Science
PO Box 211
NL-1000 AE Amsterdam, Netherlands
Ph: 31 204 853757
Fax: 31 204 853432
Publisher E-mail: nlinfo-f@elsevier.com
Peer-reviewed Scientific journal publishing research papers on the physical, chemical and biological mechanisms and processes. **Founded:** 1961. **Freq:** 9/yr. **Print Method:** Typeset. **Trim Size:** 7 1/8 x 9 7/8. **Cols./Page:** 2. **Col. Width:** 2 7/8 inches. **Col. Depth:** 7 3/8 inches. **Key Personnel:** Jean Claude Kader, Editor-in-Chief, jean-claude.kader@jussieu.org; J. Barcelo, Editorial Board; G.B. Begonia, Editorial Board. **ISSN:** 0098-8472. **Subscription Rates:** 34,000¥ individuals; US$296 individuals European countries & Iran; EUR221 individuals all countries except Europe, Japan & Iran; EUR1,167 institutions European countries & Iran; US$1,304 institu-

tions all countries except Europe, Japan & Iran; 154,500¥ institutions. **URL:** http://www.elsevier.com/wps/find/journaldescription.cws_home/267/descriptiondescription. **Circ:** 800

47969 ■ Environmental Policy and Law
IOS Press, B.V.
Nieuwe Hemweg 6B
NL-1013 BG Amsterdam, Netherlands
Ph: 31 20 6883355
Fax: 31 20 6203419
Publisher E-mail: info@iospress.nl
Publication covering environmental law in English and French. **Founded:** 1975. **Freq:** Bimonthly. **Key Personnel:** Dr. Wolfgang E. Burhenne, Editor-in-Chief, phone 49 228 2692240, fax 49 228 2692251, icel@intlawpol.org. **ISSN:** 0378-777X. **Subscription Rates:** EUR557 individuals regular; US$777 individuals regular. **Remarks:** Advertising accepted; rates available upon request. **URL:** http://www.i-c-e-l.org/; http://www.iospress.nl/. **Circ:** (Not Reported)

47970 ■ Environmental Research
Elsevier Science B.V.
Radarweg 29
NL-1043 Amsterdam, Netherlands
Ph: 31 204 853911
Fax: 31 204 852457
Journal covering the toxic effects of environmental agents in humans and animals. **Subtitle:** A Multidisciplinary Journal of Environmental Sciences, Ecology, and Public Health. **Freq:** 8/yr. **Trim Size:** 8 1/2 x 11. **Key Personnel:** E.K. Silbergeld, Editor-in-Chief, esilberg@jhsph.edu; P.J. Landrigan, Ed. Emeritus; Y. Aoki, Assoc. Ed.; M.E. Cebrian, Assoc. Ed.; P. Grandjean, Assoc. Ed.; J. Burger, Assoc. Ed.; B. Gulson, Assoc. Ed.; S. Araki, Assoc. Ed.; A.R. Flegal, Assoc. Ed. **ISSN:** 0013-9351. **Subscription Rates:** US$1,379 individuals all countries except Europe, Japan & Iran; EUR1,577 individuals European countries and Iran; 164,600¥ individuals; EUR3,554 institutions European countries and Iran; US$2,698 institutions all countries except Europe, Japan & Iran; 370,900¥ institutions. **URL:** http://www.elsevier.com/wps/find/journaldescription.cws_home/622821/descrip tiondescription.

47971 ■ Environmental Toxicology and Pharmacology
Elsevier Science Inc.
c/o N.P.E. Vermeulen, Ed.-in-Ch.
Dept. of Pharmacochemistry
Vrije Universiteit
De Boelelaan 1083
NL-1081 Amsterdam, Netherlands
Ph: 31 20 5987590
Fax: 31 20 5987610
Publisher E-mail: usinfo-ehelp@elsevier.com
Journal featuring environmental toxicology and pharmacology and its effects on animals and man. **Founded:** 1996. **Freq:** 6/yr. **Print Method:** Offset. **Cols./Page:** 6. **Col. Width:** 26 nonpareils. **Col. Depth:** 301 agate lines. **Key Personnel:** F. Fonnum, Editorial Board; M.D. Coleman, Assoc. Ed., phone 44 121 2043916, m.d.coleman@aston.ac.uk; W. Hao, Assoc. Ed., phone 86 10 82802352, fax 86 10 82428655, whao@bjmu.edu.cn; J.H. Koeman, Founding Ed., jh.koeman@zonnet.nl; P. Beaune, Editorial Board; R.P. Bos, Editorial Board; N.P.E. Vermeulen, Editor-in-Chief, etap@few.vu.nl; P.M. Danselle, Editorial Board. **ISSN:** 1382-6689. **Subscription Rates:** EUR1,598 institutions European countries & Iran; 212,500¥ institutions; US$1,789 institutions, other countries except Europe, Japan and Iran; EUR173 individuals European countries & Iran; US$233 other countries except Europe, Japan and Iran; 26,900¥ individuals. **URL:** http://www.elsevier.com/wps/find/journaldescription.cws_home/523024/descriptiondescription.

47972 ■ Epilepsy & Behavior
Elsevier Science B.V.
Radarweg 29
NL-1043 Amsterdam, Netherlands
Ph: 31 204 853911
Fax: 31 204 852457
Peer-reviewed scholarly, medical journal covering epilepsy, clinical neurology, neurosurgery, neuropsychiatry, neuropsychology, neurophysiology, neuropharmacology, and neuroimaging. **Freq:** Monthly. **Key Personnel:** S.C. Schachter, MD, Editor-in-Chief; J. Barry, Editorial Board; A.P. Aldenkamp, Editorial Board; F. Andermann, Editorial Board; C. Elger, PhD, Assoc. Ed.; O. Devinsky, MD, Assoc. Ed. **ISSN:** 1525-5050. **Subscription Rates:**

US$276 U.S. and other countries except Europe, Iran and Japan; EUR314 individuals European countries and Iran; 32,600¥ individuals Japan; EUR1,434 institutions European countries and Iran; US$1,132 institutions, other countries except Europe, Iran and Japan; 149,800¥ institutions Japan. **Remarks:** Accepts advertising. **URL:** http://www.elsevier.com/wps/find/journaldescription.cws_home/622822/descriptiondescription. **Circ:** (Not Reported)

47973 ■ European Journal of Ageing
Springer-Verlag Tokyo
Institute for Research in Extramural Medicine & Dept. of Psychiatry
VU University Medical Centre - LASA
Van der Boechorststraat 7
NL-1081 BT Amsterdam, Netherlands
Fax: 31 204 446775
Publisher E-mail: info@springer.jp
Journal address the field of gerontology and ageing with a particular focus on social, behavioral and health related scientific research originating from Europe. **Freq:** Quarterly. **Key Personnel:** Prof. Hans-Werner Wahl, Editor-in-Chief, fax 49 622 1548112, eja@dzfa.uni-heidelberg.de; Prof. Dorly J.H. Deeg, Editor-in-Chief, eja@vumc.nl; Svein Olav Daatland, Consulting Ed. **ISSN:** 1613-9372. **Subscription Rates:** EUR579 institutions print incl. free access or e-only; EUR694.80 institutions print incl. enhanced access. **Remarks:** Advertising accepted; rates available upon request. **URL:** http://www.springer.com/socialsciences/socialsciences%2Cgeneral/journal/10433. **Circ:** (Not Reported)

47974 ■ European Journal of Arts Education
European League of Institutes of the Arts
Beulingstraat 8
NL-1017 BA Amsterdam, Netherlands
Ph: 31 20 6265417
Fax: 31 20 6267751
Publisher E-mail: info@elia-artschools.org
European journal covering arts education. **Freq:** Semiannual. **Key Personnel:** Malcolm Miles, Editor. **ISSN:** 1571-9936. **URL:** http://www.elia-artschools.org.

47975 ■ European Journal of Transport and Infrastructure Research
Delft University Press
Niewe Hemweg 6B
1013 BG Amsterdam, Netherlands
Ph: 31 20 6883355
Fax: 31 20 6203419
Publisher E-mail: info.dupress@iospress.nl
Journal aiming to present results of original scientific research to a diverse readership of scientists, practitioners, and policy-makers. **Key Personnel:** Prof. B. van Wee, Editor-in-Chief. **ISSN:** 1567-7141. **URL:** http://www.ejtir.tbm.tudelft.nl/.

47976 ■ European Management Journal
Elsevier Science
PO Box 211
NL-1000 AE Amsterdam, Netherlands
Ph: 31 204 853757
Fax: 31 204 853432
Publisher E-mail: nlinfo-f@elsevier.com
Peer-reviewed journal featuring the latest thinking and research on major management topics. **Founded:** 1983. **Freq:** Bimonthly. **Key Personnel:** Herve Laroche, Editor, laroche@escp-eap.net; Douglas MacBeth, Assoc. Ed., d.k.macbeth@soton.ac.uk; K. Glaister, Editorial Board. **ISSN:** 0263-2373. **Subscription Rates:** 116,700¥ institutions; EUR878 institutions for Europe; US$981 institutions all countries except Europe and Japan; 21,800¥ individuals; EUR164 individuals for Europe; US$185 individuals all countries except Europe and Japan. **Remarks:** Accepts advertising. **URL:** http://www.elsevier.com/wps/find/journaldescription.cws_home/115/description. **Circ:** (Not Reported)

47977 ■ Evolution and Human Behavior
Elsevier Science B.V.
Radarweg 29
NL-1043 Amsterdam, Netherlands
Ph: 31 204 853911
Fax: 31 204 852457
Scientific research journal covering the study of human behavior. **Founded:** 1979. **Freq:** Bimonthly. **Print Method:** Offset. **Key Personnel:** S. Gaulin, Editor-in-Chief; M. Daly, Consulting Ed.; M. Wilson, Consulting Ed. **ISSN:** 1090-5138. **Subscription Rates:** US$1,368 institutions, other countries; US$1,208 institutions; US$454 individuals; US$523 other countries. **Remarks:**

Circulation: ★ = ABC; △ = BPA; ♦ = CAC; • = CCAB; ❑ = VAC; ⊕ = PO Statement; ‡ = Publisher's Report; Boldface figures = sworn; Light figures = estimated.

Gale Directory of Publications & Broadcast Media/147th Ed.   **5223**

Accepts advertising. **URL:** http://www.elsevier.com/wps/find/journaldescription.cws_home/505760/descriptiondescription. **Circ:** (Not Reported)

47978 ■ Experimental Cell Research
Elsevier Science B.V.
Radarweg 29
NL-1043 Amsterdam, Netherlands
Ph: 31 204 853911
Fax: 31 204 852457
Peer-reviewed journal on cell biology and cancer research featuring experimental studies on the general organization and activity of cells. **Founded:** 1949. **Freq:** 20/yr. **Trim Size:** 8 1/2 x 11. **Key Personnel:** U. Lendahl, Editor-in-Chief; C. Hoog, Assoc. Ed.; D.P. Barlow, Editorial Board; G. Carpenter, Assoc. Ed.; J. Bartek, Editorial Board; J. Campisi, Editorial Board. **ISSN:** 0014-4827. **Subscription Rates:** US$6,252 institutions for all countries except Europe, Iran and Japan; EUR7,182 institutions European countries and Iran; 750,100¥ institutions; US$681 individuals for all countries except Europe, Iran and Japan; EUR776 individuals European countries and Iran; 81,200¥ individuals. **Remarks:** Accepts advertising. **URL:** http://www.elsevier.com/wps/find/journaldescription.cws_home/622826/descriptiondescription. **Circ:** 1,986

47979 ■ Experimental Eye Research
Elsevier Science B.V.
Radarweg 29
NL-1043 Amsterdam, Netherlands
Ph: 31 204 853911
Fax: 31 204 852457
Scholarly journal covering the anatomy, physiology, and biochemistry of the eye, and related fields. **Freq:** Monthly. **Key Personnel:** Joe G. Hollyfield, Editor-in-Chief, hollyfj@ccf.org; Bela Anand-Apte, Exec. Ed.; Muayyad R. Al-Ubaidi, Exec. Ed.; Carlos Belmonte, Exec. Ed.; Michael Iuvone, Exec. Ed. **ISSN:** 0014-4835. **Subscription Rates:** 384,200¥ institutions; EUR3,558 institutions European countries and Iran; US$3,162 institutions for all countries except Europe, Iran and Japan; EUR531 individuals European countries and Iran; US$527 individuals for all countries except Europe, Iran and Japan; 57,300¥ individuals. **Remarks:** Accepts advertising. **URL:** http://www.elsevier.com/wps/find/journaldescription.cws_home/622827/descriptiondescription. **Circ:** (Not Reported)

47980 ■ Experimental and Molecular Pathology
Elsevier Science B.V.
Radarweg 29
NL-1043 Amsterdam, Netherlands
Ph: 31 204 853911
Fax: 31 204 852457
Journal presenting articles on disease processes in relation to structural and biochemical alterations in mammalian tissues and fluids, and on the application of new techniques of analytical chemistry, histochemistry, pharmacology, toxicology, and electron microscopy to problems of pathology in man and animals. **Founded:** 1962. **Freq:** Bimonthly. **Trim Size:** 6 7/8 x 10. **Key Personnel:** J.M. Cruse, Editor-in-Chief; M.I. Greene, Sen. Ed.; R.E. Lewis, Dep. Ed.-in-Ch.; K. Boekelheide, Editorial Board; F. Coulston, Founding Ed.; E. Farber, Editorial Board. **ISSN:** 0014-4800. **Subscription Rates:** US$1,305 institutions for all countries except Europe, Japan and Iran; EUR1,642 institutions European countries and Iran; 171,400¥ institutions; US$321 students; EUR367 students; 38,100¥ students; 79,800¥ individuals; EUR766 individuals European countries and Iran; US$583 individuals for all countries except Europe, Japan and Iran. **Remarks:** Accepts advertising. **URL:** http://www.elsevier.com/wps/find/journaldescription.cws_home/622825/descriptiondescription. **Circ:** (Not Reported)

47981 ■ Experimental Neurology
Elsevier Science B.V.
Radarweg 29
NL-1043 Amsterdam, Netherlands
Ph: 31 204 853911
Fax: 31 204 852457
International journal publishing original research results in neuroscience with emphasis on new findings in neural development, regeneration, plasticity, and transplantation. **Founded:** 1959. **Freq:** Monthly. **Trim Size:** 8 1/2 x 11. **Key Personnel:** Sid Gilman, Editor-in-Chief; S. Goldman, Section Ed. **ISSN:** 0014-4886. **Subscription Rates:** US$3,686 institutions for all countries except Europe, Iran and Japan; EUR4,749 institutions for European countries and Iran; 496,000¥ institutions; EUR689 students for European countries and iran; US$602 students for all countries except Europe, Iran

and Japan; 71,800¥ students. **Remarks:** Accepts advertising. **URL:** http://www.elsevier.com/wps/find/journaldescription.cws_home/622828/descriptiondescription. **Circ:** (Not Reported)

47982 ■ Experimental Parasitology
Elsevier Science B.V.
Radarweg 29
NL-1043 Amsterdam, Netherlands
Ph: 31 204 853911
Fax: 31 204 852457
Journal emphasizing modern approaches to parasitology, including molecular biology and immunology. **Founded:** 1952. **Freq:** Monthly. **Trim Size:** 6 7/8 x 10. **Key Personnel:** J. Bradley, Editorial Board; John Horton, Editor-in-Chief, epeditor@aol.com; P. Craig, Editorial Board. **ISSN:** 0014-4894. **Subscription Rates:** EUR2,162 institutions European countries and Iran; US$1,641 institutions all countries except Europe, Japan & Iran; 225,900¥ institutions; EUR963 individuals European countries and Iran; US$736 individuals all countries except Europe, Japan & Iran; 100,400¥ individuals; 17,500¥ students; EUR168 students European countries and Iran; US$147 students all countries except Europe, Japan & Iran. **URL:** http://www.elsevier.com/wps/find/journaldescription.cws_home/622829/descriptiondescription.

47983 ■ Explorations in Economic History
Elsevier Science B.V.
Radarweg 29
NL-1043 Amsterdam, Netherlands
Ph: 31 204 853911
Fax: 31 204 852457
Journal covering the application of economic analysis to history. **Founded:** 1970. **Freq:** Quarterly. **Trim Size:** 6 x 9. **Key Personnel:** D. Irwin, Editorial Board; S.L. Engerman, Assoc. Ed.; R.H. Steckel, Editor-in-Chief; S.N. Broadberry, Editorial Board; H. Bodenhorn, Editorial Board; M. Botticini, Editorial Board; G. Clark, Editorial Board; D.L. Costa, Editorial Board. **ISSN:** 0014-4983. **Subscription Rates:** US$623 institutions all countries except Europe, Japan & Iran; 86,200¥ institutions; EUR825 institutions European countries and Iran; US$283 individuals all countries except Europe, Japan & Iran; EUR373 individuals European countries and Iran; 38,900¥ institutions; US$61 students all countries except Europe, Japan & Iran; EUR70 students European countries and Iran; 7,300¥ students. **URL:** http://www.elsevier.com/wps/find/journaldescription.cws_home/622830/descrip tiondescription.

47984 ■ Fantastic Man
Fantastic Man Magazine
Kleine-Gartmanplantsoen 21
NL-1017 RP Amsterdam, Netherlands
Ph: 31 20 3209032
Fax: 31 842 248511
Publisher E-mail: office@fantasticman.com
Magazine of men's style. **Freq:** Semiannual. **Subscription Rates:** EUR20 individuals; EUR41 other countries airmail. **URL:** http://www.fantasticmanmagazine.com.

47985 ■ Few-Body Systems
Springer-Verlag
c/o B.L.G. Bakker, Ed.-in-Ch.
Dept. of Physics & Astronomy
Vrije University
De Boelelaan 1081
NL-1081 HV Amsterdam, Netherlands
Fax: 31 204 447992
Publisher E-mail: springer@springer.at
Journal publishing original research work, both experimental and theoretical, in the field of few-body systems. **Key Personnel:** J.A. Tjon, Editorial Board; B.L.G. Bakker, Editor-in-Chief, blgbkkr@nat.vu.nl; C.D. Roberts, Field Ed., fax 630252-6008, cdroberts@anl.gov; A. Kievsky, Field Ed., fax 39 50 2214887, alejandro.kievsky@pi.infn.it; D.A. Micha, Editorial Board. **ISSN:** 0177-7963. **Remarks:** Accepts advertising. **URL:** http://www.springer.com/springerwiennewyork/physics/journal/601. **Circ:** (Not Reported)

47986 ■ Finite Fields and Their Applications
Elsevier Science B.V.
Radarweg 29
NL-1043 Amsterdam, Netherlands
Ph: 31 204 853911
Fax: 31 204 852457
Peer-reviewed technical journal covering the finite field theory and applications. **Freq:** Bimonthly. **Key Personnel:** Gary L. Mullen, Editor-in-Chief; Simeon Ball, Editorial Board; Michael Fried, Editorial Board. **ISSN:** 1071-5797. **Subscription Rates:** 70,600¥ institutions;

US$529 institutions for all countries except Europe, Iran and Japan; EUR674 institutions European countries and Iran; EUR295 individuals European countries and Iran; 30,900¥ individuals; US$232 individuals for all countries except Europe, Iran and Japan. **Remarks:** Accepts advertising. **URL:** http://www.elsevier.com/wps/find/journaldescription.cws_home/622831/descriptiondescription. **Circ:** (Not Reported)

47987 ■ Food Microbiology
Elsevier Science B.V.
Radarweg 29
NL-1043 Amsterdam, Netherlands
Ph: 31 204 853911
Fax: 31 204 852457
Journal containing information on the microbiology of foods. **Founded:** 1994. **Freq:** 8/yr. **Key Personnel:** R.L. Buchanan, Contributing Ed.; G. Duffy, Contributing Ed.; M.L. Tortorello, Editor. **ISSN:** 0740-0020. **Subscription Rates:** US$438 individuals all countries except Europe, Japan & Iran; EUR423 individuals European countries and Iran; 45,600¥ individuals; US$1,036 institutions all countries except Europe, Japan & Iran; 126,000¥ institutions; EUR1,166 institutions European countries and Iran. **URL:** http://www.elsevier.com/wps/find/journaldescription.cws_home/622833/descrip tiondescription.

47988 ■ Forest Ecology and Management
Elsevier Science
PO Box 211
NL-1000 AE Amsterdam, Netherlands
Ph: 31 204 853757
Fax: 31 204 853432
Publisher E-mail: nlinfo-f@elsevier.com
Scientific journal containing articles relating to forest management and conservation, including the application of biological, ecological and social knowledge to the man-made and natural forests. **Subtitle:** An International Journal. **Founded:** 1977. **Freq:** 24/yr. **Key Personnel:** R.F. Fisher, Editorial Advisory Board; D. Binkley, Editor, dan.binkley@colostate.edu; P.M. Attiwill, Editor-in-Chief, attiwill@unimelb.edu.au. **ISSN:** 0378-1127. **Subscription Rates:** EUR537 individuals for European countries and Iran; US$604 individuals for all countries except Europe, Japan and Iran; 71,600¥ individuals for Japan; 604,300¥ institutions for Japan; EUR5,107 institutions for European countries and Iran; US$4,552 institutions for all countries except Europe, Japan and Iran. **URL:** http://www.elsevier.com/wps/find/journaldescription.cws_home/503310/description.

47989 ■ Frame
Uitgeverij Bis B.V.
Oude Braak 16
NL-1012 PS Amsterdam, Netherlands
Ph: 31 20 423717
Fax: 31 20 4280653
Professional magazine covering interior architecture and design for retail, exhibition, leisrre and workplace segments. **Founded:** Dec. 1997. **Freq:** Bimonthly. **Print Method:** Offset. **Trim Size:** 230 x 297 mm. **Cols./Page:** 3. **Key Personnel:** Elles Middeljans, Publisher, elles@framemag.com. **ISSN:** 1388-4239. **Remarks:** Accepts advertising. **URL:** http://www.framemag.com/. **Circ:** Combined 17,000

47990 ■ Free Radical Biology and Medicine
Elsevier Science
PO Box 211
NL-1000 AE Amsterdam, Netherlands
Ph: 31 204 853757
Fax: 31 204 853432
Publication E-mail: frbm@elsevier.com
Publisher E-mail: nlinfo-f@elsevier.com
International journal dealing with chemical, biochemical, physiological, pathological, pharmacological, toxicological and medical approaches to free radicals and oxidative biology in connection with International Society for Free Radical Research (SFRR). **Founded:** 1985. **Freq:** 24/yr. **Key Personnel:** Kelvin J.A. Davies, Editor-in-Chief; Victor M. Darley-Usmar, Assoc. Ed.; Phyllis A. Dennery, Assoc. Ed. **ISSN:** 0891-5849. **Subscription Rates:** EUR616 individuals for European countries and Iran; US$695 individuals for all countries except Europe, Japan and Iran; 81,900¥ individuals for Japan; EUR3,318 institutions for European countries and Iran; 440,700¥ institutions for Japan; US$3,709 institutions for all countries except Europe, Japan and Iran. **URL:** http://www.elsevier.com/wps/find/journaldescription.cws_home/525469/description.

47991 ■ Frontiers in Neuroendocrinology
Elsevier Science B.V.
Radarweg 29

NL-1043 Amsterdam, Netherlands
Ph: 31 204 853911
Fax: 31 204 852457
Scholarly journal covering brain-endocrine interactions. **Freq:** Quarterly. **Key Personnel:** J.E. Levine, Editor; B.S. McEwen, Editorial Board; J. Balthazart, Editor; J.I. Koenig, Editorial Board; P. Kelly, Editorial Board; J.D. Blaustein, Editorial Board; E.R. De Kloet, Editorial Board; Z. Naor, Editorial Board; S. Lightman, Editorial Board. **ISSN:** 0091-3022. **Subscription Rates:** 74,800¥ institutions; EUR716 institutions European countries and Iran; US$571 institutions for all countries except Europe, Iran and Japan; EUR322 individuals European countries and Iran; 33,900¥ individuals; US$259 individuals for all countries except Europe, Iran and Japan. **Remarks:** Accepts advertising. **URL:** http://www.elsevier.com/wps/find/journaldescription.cws_home/622834/descriptiondescription. **Circ:** (Not Reported)

47992 ■ Functions of Language (FOL)
John Benjamins Publishing Co.
Klaprozenweg 105
PO Box 36224
NL-1033 NN Amsterdam, Netherlands
Ph: 31 206 304747
Fax: 31 206 739773
Publisher E-mail: benjamins@presswarehouse.com
Peer-reviewed journal of linguistics which explores the functionalist perspective on the organization and use of natural language. Topics covered include prosodic phenomena in phonology, the clause in its communicative context, and regularities of pragmatics, conversation and discourse, as well as the interaction between the various levels of analysis. **Founded:** 1931. **Freq:** Semiannual. **Print Method:** Photo offset. **Key Personnel:** Lachlan J. MacKenzie, Editor; Geoff Thompson, Editor; Miriam Taverniers, Managing Editor. **ISSN:** 0929-998X. **Subscription Rates:** EUR218 individuals print + online; EUR70 individuals special. **URL:** http://www.benjamins.com/cgi-bin/t_seriesview.cgi?series=FOL.

47993 ■ Fundamenta Informaticae
IOS Press, B.V.
Nieuwe Hemweg 6B
NL-1013 BG Amsterdam, Netherlands
Ph: 31 20 6883355
Fax: 31 20 6203419
Publisher E-mail: info@iospress.nl
International journal publishing original research results in all areas of mathematical foundations of computer science and their applications. **Freq:** 32/yr. **Key Personnel:** Andrzej Skowron, Editor-in-Chief, skowron@mimuw.edu.pl; Damian Niwinski, Editor-in-Chief, niwinski@mimuw.edu.pl. **ISSN:** 0169-2968. **Subscription Rates:** EUR1,904 individuals regular; US$2,675 individuals regular. **URL:** http://www.iospress.nl/loadtop/load.php?isbn=01692968.

47994 ■ Fungal Genetics and Biology
Elsevier Science B.V.
Radarweg 29
NL-1043 Amsterdam, Netherlands
Ph: 31 204 853911
Fax: 31 204 852457
Journal publishing experimental investigations relating structure and function to growth, reproduction, morphogenesis, and differentiation of fungi and their traditional allies. **Founded:** 1977. **Freq:** Monthly. **Trim Size:** 6 7/8 x 10. **Key Personnel:** D. Bell-Pederson, Assoc. Ed.; M.H. Lebrun, Assoc. Ed.; N. Gow, Editor-in-Chief; G. Goldman, Assoc. Ed.; F. Martin, Assoc. Ed. **ISSN:** 1087-1845. **Subscription Rates:** EUR1,033 institutions European countries and Iran; US$801 institutions all countries except Europe, Japan & Iran; 108,200¥ institutions; EUR423 individuals European countries and Iran; US$329 individuals all countries except Europe, Japan & Iran; 44,200¥ individuals; EUR142 students European countries and Iran; US$125 students all countries except Europe, Japan & Iran; 14,800¥ students. **URL:** http://www.elsevier.com/wps/find/journaldescription.cws_home/622835/descriptiondescription. **Formerly:** Experimental Mycology.

47995 ■ Future Generation Computer Systems
Elsevier Science
c/o Peter Sloot, Ed.-in-Ch.
University of Amsterdam
Dept. of Computer Science
Kruislaan 403
NL-1098 SJ Amsterdam, Netherlands
Publisher E-mail: nlinfo-f@elsevier.com
International journal dealing with the new developments in Grid Applications and application support, Grid methods and middleware, Grid Theory. **Subtitle:** The International Journal of Grid Computing: Theory, Methods and Applications. **Founded:** 1984. **Freq:** 8/yr. **Key Personnel:** Peter Sloot, Editor-in-Chief, sloot@science.uva.nl; H.E. Bal, Editor; L. Grandinetti, Editor; J.J. Dongarra, Editor; Rajkumar Buyya, Editor; Carl Kesselman, Editor; C. de Laat, Editor; G.C. Fox, Editor; B. Jones, Editor. **ISSN:** 0167-739X. **Subscription Rates:** EUR1,138 institutions for European countries; US$1,273 institutions for all countries except Europe and Japan; 151,400¥ institutions; EUR160 individuals; US$214 individuals; 24,700¥ individuals. **Remarks:** Accepts advertising. **URL:** http://www.elsevier.com/wps/journaldescription.cws_home/505611/descrip tion. **Circ:** (Not Reported)

47996 ■ Games and Economic Behavior
Elsevier Science B.V.
Radarweg 29
NL-1043 Amsterdam, Netherlands
Ph: 31 204 853911
Fax: 31 204 852457
Journal publishing original and survey papers on game-theoretic modeling in the social, biological, and mathematical sciences. **Founded:** 1989. **Freq:** 6/yr. **Trim Size:** 6 x 9. **Key Personnel:** E. Kalai, Editor-in-Chief; S. Neff, Managing Editor; R.J. Aumann, Advisory Ed.; K.J. Arrow, Advisory Ed.; D. Austen-Smith, Advisory Ed.; J. Andreoni, Advisory Ed.; F. Bloch, Advisory Ed.; P. Battigalli, Advisory Ed.; D. Blackwell, Advisory Ed. **ISSN:** 0899-8256. **Subscription Rates:** 129,700¥ institutions; EUR1,141 institutions European countries and Iran; US$982 institutions all countries except Europe, Japan and Iran; EUR151 individuals European countries and Iran; US$107 individuals for all countries except Europe, Japan and Iran; 16,000¥ individuals; US$110 students all Countries except Europe, Japan and Iran; EUR87 students European countries and Iran; 9,100¥ students. **URL:** http://www.elsevier.com/wps/find/journaldescription.cws_home/622836/descrip tiondescription.

47997 ■ Geotextiles and Geomembranes
Elsevier Science
PO Box 211
NL-1000 AE Amsterdam, Netherlands
Ph: 31 204 853757
Fax: 31 204 853432
Publisher E-mail: nlinfo-f@elsevier.com
Peer-reviewed journal dealing with various topics pertaining to geosynthetics, research, behavior, performance analysis, testing, design, construction methods, case histories and field experience. Seeks to advance scientific and engineering development of geotextiles, geomembranes, related products and associated technologies, in connection with International Geosynthetics Society. **Founded:** 1984. **Freq:** 6/yr. **Key Personnel:** Dr. R. Kerry Rowe, Editor, kerry@civil.queensu.ca. **ISSN:** 0266-1144. **Subscription Rates:** 151,000¥ institutions for Japan; EUR1,136 institutions for European countries; US$1,272 institutions for all countries except Europe and Japan; US$184 individuals; 21,100¥ individuals; EUR138 individuals. **Remarks:** Accepts advertising. **URL:** http://www.elsevier.com/wps/find/journaldescription.cws_home/405897/descrip tion. **Circ:** (Not Reported)

47998 ■ Geothermics
Elsevier Science
PO Box 211
NL-1000 AE Amsterdam, Netherlands
Ph: 31 204 853757
Fax: 31 204 853432
Publisher E-mail: nlinfo-f@elsevier.com
Journal publishing research papers on various aspects of geothermal energy. **Subtitle:** International Journal of Geothermal Research and its Applications. **Founded:** 1972. **Freq:** 4/yr. **Key Personnel:** S.K. Garg, Editor, garg@saic.com. **ISSN:** 0375-6505. **Subscription Rates:** EUR1,407 institutions for European countries and Iran; 187,000¥ institutions Japan; US$1,575 institutions for all countries except Europe, Japan and Iran. **URL:** http://www.elsevier.com/wps/find/journaldescription.cws_home/389/description.

47999 ■ German Monitor
Editions Rodopi B.V.
Tijnmuiden 7
NL-1046 AK Amsterdam, Netherlands
Ph: 31 206 114821
Fax: 31 204 472979
Publisher E-mail: info@rodopi.nl
Journal featuring articles and information about German. **Key Personnel:** Prof. Pol O. Dochartaigh, Editor, p.odochartaigh@ulster.ac.uk. **ISSN:** 0927-1910. **URL:** http://www.rodopi.nl/senj.asp?SerieId=GM.

48000 ■ Gesture
John Benjamins Publishing Co.
Klaprozenweg 105
PO Box 36224
NL-1033 NN Amsterdam, Netherlands
Ph: 31 206 304747
Fax: 31 206 739773
Publisher E-mail: benjamins@presswarehouse.com
Peer-reviewed journal publishing articles reporting original research, as well as survey and review articles, on all aspects of gesture, including, but not limited to the relationship between gesture and speech; the role gesture may play in communication in all the circumstances of social interaction; gesture and cognition; and the development of gesture in children. **Freq:** Semiannual. **Key Personnel:** Adam Kendon, Editor; Cornelia Muller, Editor. **ISSN:** 1568-1475. **Subscription Rates:** EUR322 individuals print + online; EUR85 individuals special. **URL:** http://www.benjamins.com/cgi-bin/t_seriesview.cgi?series=GEST.

48001 ■ Ghanaian Newsrunner
Poederooienstraat 66
NL-1106 CK Amsterdam, Netherlands
Ph: 31 20 6977764
Fax: 31 20 6971978
Publisher E-mail: info@newsrunner.com
Magazine for the Ghanaian community in the Netherlands. **Founded:** 1995. **Freq:** Biweekly. **Subscription Rates:** Free. **URL:** http://www.newsrunner.com/.

48002 ■ Global Environmental Change
Elsevier Science
PO Box 211
NL-1000 AE Amsterdam, Netherlands
Ph: 31 204 853757
Fax: 31 204 853432
Publisher E-mail: nlinfo-f@elsevier.com
Peer-reviewed international journal covering social and natural sciences. Publishes research and review articles in the field of global environmental change. **Subtitle:** Human and Policy Dimensions. **Freq:** Quarterly. **Key Personnel:** Katrina Brown, Editor, k.brown@uea.ac.uk; Neil Adger, Editor, n.adger@uea.ac.uk; Neil Jennings, Asst. Ed., gec@uea.ac.uk; J. Fang, International Editorial Board; Mike Hulme, International Editorial Board; B. Campbell, International Editorial Board. **ISSN:** 0959-3780. **Subscription Rates:** EUR831 institutions for European countries; 110,700¥ institutions; US$930 institutions for all countries except Europe and Japan; EUR128 individuals for European countries; 18,400¥ individuals; US$166 individuals for all countries except Europe and Japan. **Remarks:** Accepts advertising. **URL:** http://www.elsevier.com/wps/find/journaldescription.cws_home/30425/descript ion; http://www.elsevier.com/wps/find/journaldescription.cws_home/30425/descript iondescription. **Circ:** (Not Reported)

48003 ■ Global and Planetary Change
Elsevier Science
PO Box 211
NL-1000 AE Amsterdam, Netherlands
Ph: 31 204 853757
Fax: 31 204 853432
Publisher E-mail: nlinfo-f@elsevier.com
Journal highlighting changes in earth history and the analysis and prediction of current and future changes. Includes topics such as changes in the chemical composition of the oceans and atmosphere, climate change, sea level variations, human geography, global geophysics and tectonics, global ecology and biogeography. **Founded:** 1988. **Freq:** 20/yr. **Key Personnel:** K. McGuffie, Editor, kendal.mcguffie@uts.edu.au; T.M. Cronin, Editor, phone 703648-6363, fax 703648-6953, tcronin@usgs.gov; Sierd Cloetingh, Editor, cloeting@falw.vu.nl. **ISSN:** 0921-8181. **Subscription Rates:** US$2,105 institutions all countries except Europe and Japan; EUR1,883 institutions for European countries; 250,000¥ institutions; EUR262 individuals European countries; US$295 individuals all countries except Europe and Japan; 34,300¥ individuals. **Remarks:** Accepts advertising. **URL:** http://www.elsevier.com/wps/find/journaldescription.cws_home/503335/descrip tiondescription. **Circ:** (Not Reported)

48004 ■ Graphical Models
Elsevier Science B.V.
Radarweg 29
NL-1043 Amsterdam, Netherlands
Ph: 31 204 853911
Fax: 31 204 852457
Peer-reviewed journal focusing on the synthesis methods and computational methods underlying computer generated or processed imagery. **Founded:** 1983. **Freq:** Bimonthly. **Trim Size:** 8 1/2 x 11. **Key Personnel:** Norman.l. Badler, Ed. Emeriti; Ingrid. Carlbom, Ed. Emeriti; Jarek. Rossignac, Editor-in-Chief. **ISSN:** 1524-0703. **Subscription Rates:** EUR487 individuals European countries and Iran; US$385 other countries except Europe, Iran and Japan; 51,000¥ individuals Japan; US$842 institutions, other countries except Europe, Japan and Iran; 112,500¥ institutions Japan; EUR1,078 institutions European countries and Iran. **URL:** http://www.elsevier.com/wps/find/journaldescription.cws_home/622839/descriptiondescription. **Formerly:** Graphical Models and Image Processing.

48005 ■ Grazer Philosophische Studien
Editions Rodopi B.V.
Tijnmuiden 7
NL-1046 AK Amsterdam, Netherlands
Ph: 31 206 114821
Fax: 31 204 472979
Publisher E-mail: info@rodopi.nl
Peer-reviewed journal containing articles on philosophical problems that are related to analytic tradition. **Freq:** Semiannual. **Key Personnel:** Johannes L. Brandl, Editor; Martina Furst, Managing Editor, martina.fuerst@uni-graz.at. **ISSN:** 0165-9227. **URL:** http://www.rodopi.nl/senj.asp?SerieId=GPS.

48006 ■ The Grey Journal
Grey Literature Network Service
Javastraat 194-HS
NL-1095 CP Amsterdam, Netherlands
Ph: 31 20 3312420
Publication E-mail: journal@greynet.org
Publisher E-mail: info@greynet.org
Flagship journal for the grey literature community, crossing continents, disciplines, and sectors both public and private. **Subtitle:** An International Journal on Grey Literature. **Freq:** 3/yr. **Key Personnel:** Dr. Dominic J. Farace, Editor; Julia Gelfand, Assoc. Ed.; Dr. Joachim Schopfel, Assoc. Ed. **ISSN:** 1574-1796. **Subscription Rates:** EUR110 individuals; EUR225 institutions. **URL:** http://www.greynet.org/thegreyjournal.html.

48007 ■ Gynecologic Oncology
Elsevier Science B.V.
Radarweg 29
NL-1043 Amsterdam, Netherlands
Ph: 31 204 853911
Fax: 31 204 852457
Journal dedicated to publishing clinical and investigative articles concerning tumors of the female reproductive tract. **Subtitle:** The Official Publication of the Society of Gynecologic Oncologists. **Founded:** 1972. **Freq:** Monthly. **Trim Size:** 8 1/2 x 11. **Key Personnel:** D.M. Gershenson, MD, Ed. Emeritus; Anil K. Sood, MD, Dep. Ed.; Stephen C. Rubin, MD, Dep. Ed.; Barbara A. Goff, MD, Dep. Ed.; Robert E. Bristow, MD, Dep. Ed.; B. Karlan, MD, Editor-in-Chief, karlanb@cshs.org. **ISSN:** 0090-8258. **Subscription Rates:** US$3,120 institutions all countries except Europe, Japan & Iran; 426,500¥ institutions; EUR4,084 institutions; US$122 students all countries except Europe, Japan & Iran; 13,900¥ students; EUR95 students; 95,800¥ individuals; EUR917 individuals; US$496 individuals all countries except Europe, Japan & Iran. **Remarks:** Accepts advertising. **URL:** http://www.elsevier.com/wps/find/journaldescription.cws_home/622840/descrip tiondescription. **Circ:** (Not Reported)

48008 ■ Habitat International
Elsevier Science
PO Box 211
NL-1000 AE Amsterdam, Netherlands
Ph: 31 204 853757
Fax: 31 204 853432
Publisher E-mail: nlinfo-f@elsevier.com
Peer-reviewed journal focusing on human settlements, their planning, design, production and management. The main concern is on urbanization in the developing world. **Founded:** 1976. **Freq:** Quarterly. **Key Personnel:** C.L. Choguill, Editor, cchoguill@hotmail.com; M.B.G. Choguill, Asst. Ed. **ISSN:** 0197-3975. **Subscription Rates:** EUR252 individuals European countries;

US$326 individuals except Europe and Japan; 36,100¥ individuals; US$1,695 institutions except Europe and Japan; EUR1,518 institutions European countries; 201,300¥ institutions. **Remarks:** Accepts advertising. **URL:** http://www.elsevier.com/wps/find/journaldescription.cws_home/479/descriptiondescription. **Circ:** (Not Reported)

48009 ■ Hearing Research
Elsevier Science
PO Box 211
NL-1000 AE Amsterdam, Netherlands
Ph: 31 204 853757
Fax: 31 204 853432
Publisher E-mail: nlinfo-f@elsevier.com
Journal dealing with auditory neurophysiology, ultra-structure, psychoacoustics and behavioral studies of hearing in animals, and models of auditory functions. **Founded:** 1978. **Freq:** 24/yr. **Key Personnel:** Barbara Canlon, Editor-in-Chief, barbara.canlon@ki.se. **ISSN:** 0378-5955. **Subscription Rates:** 796,300¥ institutions for Japan; EUR6,001 institutions for European countries and Iran; US$6,716 institutions all countries except Europe, Japan and Iran; 48,500¥ individuals for Japan; EUR361 individuals for European countries and Iran; US$405 individuals all countries except Europe, Japan and Iran. **URL:** http://www.elsevier.com/wps/find/journaldescription.cws_home/506060/description.

48010 ■ Heart, Lung and Circulation
Elsevier Science
PO Box 211
NL-1000 AE Amsterdam, Netherlands
Ph: 31 204 853757
Fax: 31 204 853432
Publisher E-mail: nlinfo-f@elsevier.com
Journal forming a common ground for discussion on clinical and research activities in the fields of basic cardiovascular science, clinical cardiology and cardiac surgery, with a focus on emerging issues in cardiovascular disease. **Freq:** Bimonthly. **Key Personnel:** Prof. Richmond Jeremy, Editor-in-Chief; Deborah Edward, PhD, Editorial Mgr., deborah.edward@sydney.edu.au; K.R. Boheler, Editorial Board. **ISSN:** 1443-9506. **Subscription Rates:** 24,700¥ individuals; US$566 institutions; US$256 individuals; US$186 individuals; 54,500¥ institutions; EUR414 institutions. **Remarks:** Accepts advertising. **URL:** http://www.elsevier.com/wps/find/journaldescription.cws_home/702903/description. **Circ:** (Not Reported)

48011 ■ Historia Mathematica
Elsevier Science B.V.
Radarweg 29
NL-1043 Amsterdam, Netherlands
Ph: 31 204 853911
Fax: 31 204 852457
Journal is concerned with the history of all aspects of the mathematical sciences in all parts of the world and from all historical periods. **Founded:** 1974. **Freq:** Quarterly. **Trim Size:** 6 7/8 x 10. **Key Personnel:** Benno van Dalen, Assoc. Ed.; Craig Fraser, Assoc. Ed.; Umberto Bottazzini, Assoc. Ed.; June Barrow Green, Co-Ed.-in-Ch.; Adrian Rice, Book Review Ed.; Antoni Malet, Book Review Ed. **ISSN:** 0315-0860. **Subscription Rates:** 55,300¥ institutions; EUR529 institutions European countries and Iran; US$414 institutions all countries except Europe, Japan & Iran; US$147 individuals European countries and Iran; US$120 individuals all countries except Europe, Japan & Iran; 15,500¥ individuals. **Remarks:** Accepts advertising. **URL:** www.elsevier.com/wps/find/journaldescription.cws_home/622841/descrip tiondescription. **Circ:** (Not Reported)

48012 ■ Historiographia Linguistica (HL)
John Benjamins Publishing Co.
Klaprozenweg 105
PO Box 36224
NL-1033 NN Amsterdam, Netherlands
Ph: 31 206 304747
Fax: 31 206 739773
Publisher E-mail: benjamins@presswarehouse.com
Peer-reviewed journal covering the history of the sciences concerned with language such as linguistics, philology, anthropology, sociology, pedagogy, psychology, neurology, and other disciplines. **Subtitle:** International Journal for the History of the Language Sciences. **Founded:** 1978. **Freq:** 3/yr. **Trim Size:** 8 1/2 x 11. **Key Personnel:** E.F.K. Koerner, Editor; John Considine, Assoc. Ed.; Nicola McLelland, Review Ed. **ISSN:** 0302-5160. **Subscription Rates:** EUR338 individuals print + online; EUR85 individuals special. **URL:** http://www.benjamins.com/cgi-bin/t_seriesview.cgi?series=HL.

48013 ■ Hormones and Behavior
Elsevier Science B.V.
Radarweg 29
NL-1043 Amsterdam, Netherlands
Ph: 31 204 853911
Fax: 31 204 852457
Journal covering the evolutionary significance of hormone-behavior and cellular and molecular mechanisms of hormonal actions on tissues relevant to behavior. **Founded:** 1969. **Freq:** 10/yr. **Trim Size:** 6 x 9. **Key Personnel:** Dr. A.M. Etgen, Editor; E. Adkins-Regan, Editor; A.S. Clark, Editorial Board; M.M. McCarthy, Editorial Board; K. Wallen, Editorial Board; A.H. Bass, Editorial Board. **ISSN:** 0018-506X. **Subscription Rates:** US$1,575 institutions European countries and Iran; EUR1,916 institutions all countries except Europe, Japan & Iran; 200,100¥ institutions; US$346 individuals all countries except Europe, Japan & Iran; 41,400¥ individuals; EUR397 individuals European countries and Iran; EUR239 students all countries except Europe, Japan & Iran; 24,800¥ students; US$208 students European countries and Iran. **Remarks:** Accepts advertising. **URL:** http://www.elsevier.com/wps/find/journaldescription.cws_home/622842/descrip tiondescription. **Circ:** (Not Reported)

48014 ■ Human Movement Science
Elsevier Science
PO Box 211
NL-1000 AE Amsterdam, Netherlands
Ph: 31 204 853757
Fax: 31 204 853432
Publisher E-mail: nlinfo-f@elsevier.com
Peer-reviewed journal covering psychological, neuro-physiological and biomechanical/biophysical research on various kinds of movements studied by the human body. **Founded:** 1983. **Freq:** Bimonthly. **Key Personnel:** P.J. Beek, Editor; J.J. Adam, Editorial Board; J. Piek, Section Ed.; H. Bekkering, Editorial Board; H.T.A. Whiting, Founding Ed.; M. Schieppati, Section Ed.; W. Berg, Editorial Board; R. Blickhan, Editorial Board. **ISSN:** 0167-9457. **Subscription Rates:** 117,600¥ institutions; EUR887 institutions for Europe; US$994 institutions all countries except Europe and Japan; 20,400¥ individuals; EUR141 individuals for Europe; US$183 individuals all countries except Europe and Japan. **Remarks:** Accepts advertising. **URL:** http://www.elsevier.com/wps/find/journaldescription.cws_home/505584/description. **Circ:** (Not Reported)

48015 ■ Human Resource Management Review
Elsevier Science
PO Box 211
NL-1000 AE Amsterdam, Netherlands
Ph: 31 204 853757
Fax: 31 204 853432
Publisher E-mail: nlinfo-f@elsevier.com
Journal pertaining to human resource management and similar fields. **Freq:** Quarterly. **Key Personnel:** R.W. Griffeth, Editor, griffeth@ohio.edu; S. Alvarez, Editorial Board; M.L. Ambrose, Editorial Board; D. Balkin, Assoc. Ed.; R.P. Steel, Assoc. Ed.; J. Hayton, Editorial Board; C.L. Adkins, Editorial Board; K.M. Bartol, Editorial Board; D.G. Allen, Editorial Board. **ISSN:** 1053-4822. **Subscription Rates:** EUR150 individuals for European countries; US$166 individuals for all countries except Europe and Japan; 19,700¥ individuals; EUR507 institutions for European countries; US$565 institutions for all countries except Europe and Japan; 67,100¥ institutions. **Remarks:** Accepts advertising. **URL:** http://www.elsevier.com/wps/find/journaldescription.cws_home/620229/descrip tiondescription. **Circ:** (Not Reported)

48016 ■ Infant Behavior and Development
Elsevier Science Inc.
c/o G. Savelsbergh, Ed.
Dept. of Movement Behaviour
Vrije Universiteit
Amsterdam, Netherlands
Publisher E-mail: usinfo-ehelp@elsevier.com
Journal covering empirical (fundamental and clinical), theoretical, methodological reviews. **Subtitle:** An International and Interdisciplinary Journal. **Freq:** 4/yr. **Key Personnel:** G. Savelsbergh, Editor; L.P. Lipsitt, Founding Ed.; G.P. Aylward, Consulting Ed.; J.E. Bates, Consulting Ed.; L. Beckwith, Consulting Ed.; J. Belsky, Consulting Ed.; E.M. Blass, Consulting Ed.; L.A. Camras, Consulting Ed.; J. Colombo, Consulting Ed. **ISSN:** 0163-6383. **Subscription Rates:** EUR508 institutions European countries and Iran; 67,500¥ institutions; US$569 institutions, other countries except Europe, Japan and Iran; US$170 other countries except Europe and Iran; 20,000¥ individuals; EUR151 individuals

for European countries and Iran; US$170 individuals all countries except Europe, Japan and Iran. **URL:** http://www.elsevier.com/wps/find/journaldescription.cws_home/620197/descriptiondescription.

48017 ■ Informatica
IOS Press, B.V.
Nieuwe Hemweg 6B
NL-1013 BG Amsterdam, Netherlands
Ph: 31 20 6883355
Fax: 31 20 6203419
Publisher E-mail: info@iospress.nl
Journal providing an international forum for high-quality original research and publishing papers on mathematical simulation and optimization, recognition and control, programming theory and systems, automation systems and elements. **Freq:** Quarterly. **Key Personnel:** Dr. Jonas Mockus, Editor-in-Chief, jmockus@gmail.com; J.K. Ho, International Editorial Board; B. Jaumard, International Editorial Board; M. Iri, International Editorial Board; L. Telksnys, Editor, telksnys@ktl.mii.lt; M. Sapagovas, Editor, m.sapagovas@ktl.mii.lt; R. Seinauskas, Editor, rsei@sc-uni.ktu.lt; F. Al Khayyal, International Editorial Board; G. Dzemyda, Exec. Ed., dzemyda@ktl.mii.lt; A. Avizienis, International Editorial Board. **ISSN:** 0868-4952. **Subscription Rates:** EUR258 individuals print and online; US$360 individuals print and online. **URL:** http://www.iospress.nl/loadtop/load.php?isbn=08684952.

48018 ■ Information Design Journal
John Benjamins Publishing Co.
Klaprozenweg 105
PO Box 36224
NL-1033 NN Amsterdam, Netherlands
Ph: 31 206 304747
Fax: 31 206 739773
Publisher E-mail: benjamins@presswarehouse.com
Peer-reviewed journal featuring research and practice in information design. **Freq:** 3/yr. **Key Personnel:** Peter Simlinger, Gen. Ed.; Carel Jansen, Editor; Aaron Marcus, Editor; Karen Schriver, Editor; David Sless, Editor. **ISSN:** 0142-5471. **Subscription Rates:** EUR196 institutions backvolumes; EUR75 individuals special; EUR202 institutions print + online. **URL:** http://www.benjamins.com/cgi-bin/t_seriesview.cgi?series=IDJ.

48019 ■ Information Economics and Policy
Elsevier Science
PO Box 211
NL-1000 AE Amsterdam, Netherlands
Ph: 31 204 853757
Fax: 31 204 853432
Publisher E-mail: nlinfo-f@elsevier.com
Peer-reviewed journal publishing contributions relating to policy-oriented research about the production, distribution and use of information. **Founded:** 1984. **Freq:** Quarterly. **Key Personnel:** S. Greenstein, Editor; A. Geuna, Editor; T, Valletti, Editor; D. Waterman, Editor; P. Belleflamme, Assoc. Ed.; S. Brusoni, Assoc. Ed. **ISSN:** 0167-6245. **Subscription Rates:** US$72 individuals all countries except Europe and Japan; EUR64 individuals European countries; 8,800¥ individuals; US$686 institutions all countries except Europe and Japan; EUR613 institutions European countries; 81,500¥ institutions. **Remarks:** Accepts advertising. **URL:** http://www.elsevier.com/wps/find/journaldescription.cws_home/505549/descrip tion. **Ciro:** (Not Reported)

48020 ■ Information Processing & Management
Elsevier Science
PO Box 211
NL-1000 AE Amsterdam, Netherlands
Ph: 31 204 853757
Fax: 31 204 853432
Publisher E-mail: nlinfo-f@elsevier.com
Peer-reviewed journal relating to process and management of information. **Subtitle:** An International Journal. **Founded:** 1963. **Freq:** Bimonthly. **Key Personnel:** Noriko Kando, Assoc. Ed.; T. Aparac, Editorial Board; Kalervo Jarvelin, Assoc. Ed.; D. Harman, Editorial Board; Tefko Saracevic, Editorial Board; P. Borlund, Editorial Board; C.J. van Rijsbergen, Editorial Board; ChengXiang Zhai, Assoc. Ed.; C. Cool, Editorial Board. **ISSN:** 0306-4573. **Subscription Rates:** EUR271 individuals European countries and Iran; 39,000¥ individuals Japan; US$352 individuals all countries except Europe, Japan and Iran; 243,100¥ institutions Japan; US$2,046 institutions all countries except Europe, Japan and Iran; EUR1,829 institutions European countries and Iran. **URL:** http://www.elsevier.com/wps/find/journaldescription.cws_home/244/description.

48021 ■ Information Services & Use
IOS Press, B.V.
Nieuwe Hemweg 6B
NL-1013 BG Amsterdam, Netherlands
Ph: 31 20 6883355
Fax: 31 20 6203419
Publisher E-mail: info@iospress.nl
Journal targeting leaders in information management and applications, attempting to keep them fully informed of fast-moving developments in fields such as: online systems, offline systems, electronic publishing, library automation, education and training, word processing and telecommunications. **Freq:** Quarterly. **Key Personnel:** Dr. Elliot R. Siegel, Editor-in-Chief, siegel.consulting@gmail.com; Arthur W. Elias, Ed. Emeritus; Arnoud De Kemp, Editor-in-Chief, dekemp@digiprimo.com. **ISSN:** 0167-5265. **Subscription Rates:** EUR418 individuals print and online; US$585 individuals print and online. **URL:** http://www.iospress.nl/loadtop/load.php?isbn=01675265.

48022 ■ Interaction Studies
John Benjamins Publishing Co.
Klaprozenweg 105
PO Box 36224
NL-1033 NN Amsterdam, Netherlands
Ph: 31 206 304747
Fax: 31 206 739773
Publisher E-mail: benjamins@presswarehouse.com
Peer-reviewed journal publishing advanced information in interdisciplinary area of Interaction Studies in biological and artificial systems. **Freq:** 3/yr. **Key Personnel:** Kerstin Dautenhahn, Editor; James Hurford, Assoc. Ed.; Marc Bekoff, Assoc. Ed.; Angelo Cangelosi, Editor; Guy Theraulaz, Assoc. Ed.; Jacqueline Nadel, Assoc. Ed. **ISSN:** 1572-0373. **Subscription Rates:** EUR303 individuals print + online; EUR80 individuals special. **URL:** http://www.benjamins.com/cgi-bin/t_seriesview.cgi?series=is.

48023 ■ Intercultural Theology and Study of Religions
Editions Rodopi B.V.
Tijnmuiden 7
NL-1046 AK Amsterdam, Netherlands
Ph: 31 206 114821
Fax: 31 204 472979
Publisher E-mail: info@rodopi.nl
Journal covering the field of religion and theology. **Key Personnel:** Prof. Claude Ozankom, Editor. **ISSN:** 1872-4477. **URL:** http://www.rodopi.nl/senj.asp?SerieId=ITSR.

48024 ■ International Biodeterioration and Biodegradation
Elsevier Science B.V.
Radarweg 29
NL-1043 Amsterdam, Netherlands
Ph: 31 204 853911
Fax: 31 204 852457
Professional publication covering biodeterioration and biodegration. **Subtitle:** The Official Journal of the International Biodeterioration and Biodegradation Society. **Founded:** 1987. **Freq:** 8/yr. **Key Personnel:** R.J. Koestler, Editor-in-Chief; L.H.G. Morton, Editorial Board, lhgmorton@uclan.ac.uk; R. Boopathy, Editor, ramaraj.boopathy@nicholls.edu; V. Koestler, Editorial Asst., eicibb@hotmail.com; M. Sylvestre, Editor, michel.sylvestre@iaf.inrs.ca; D. Allsopp, Editorial Board, d.allsopp@tiscali.co.uk. **ISSN:** 0964-8305. **Subscription Rates:** EUR1,700 institutions European countries and Iran; US$147 individuals all countries except Europe, Iran and Japan; EUR110 individuals European countries and Iran; 16,800¥ individuals for Japan; 226,100¥ institutions for Japan; 1,902 f institutions, other countries except Europe, Japan and Iran. **Remarks:** Accepts advertising. **URL:** http://www.elsevier.com/wps/find/journaldescription.cws_home/405899/descriptiondescription. **Formerly:** International Biodeterioration. **Circ:** (Not Reported)

48025 ■ International Journal of Artificial Intelligence in Education
IOS Press, B.V.
Nieuwe Hemweg 6B
NL-1013 BG Amsterdam, Netherlands
Ph: 31 20 6883355
Fax: 31 20 6203419
Publisher E-mail: info@iospress.nl
Journal publishing papers concerned with the application of AI to education in order to help the development of principles for the design of computer-based learning systems. **Freq:** Quarterly. **Key Personnel:** James Lester, Editor-in-Chief; Michael Baker, Editorial Board; Joost Breuker, Editorial Board; Christopher Dede, Editorial Board; Judy Kay, Assoc. Ed.; Richard Cox, Editorial Board; Tak-Wai Chan, Editorial Board; Jeremy Roschelle, Editorial Board; Valerie Shute, Editorial Board. **ISSN:** 1560-4292. **Subscription Rates:** EUR243 institutions print and online; US$345 institutions print and online. **URL:** http://www.iospress.nl/loadtop/load.php?isbn=15604292.

48026 ■ International Journal of Corpus Linguistics
John Benjamins Publishing Co.
Klaprozenweg 105
PO Box 36224
NL-1033 NN Amsterdam, Netherlands
Ph: 31 206 304747
Fax: 31 206 739773
Publisher E-mail: benjamins@presswarehouse.com
Peer-reviewed journal covering language as a social phenomenon that can be investigated empirically on the basis of authentic spoken texts. **Founded:** 1980. **Freq:** 4/yr. **Print Method:** Offset. **Trim Size:** 8 1/2 x 11. **Cols./Page:** 3. **Col. Width:** 42 nonpareils. **Col. Depth:** 133 agate lines. **Key Personnel:** Michaela Mahlberg, Editor; Wolfgang Teubert, Consulting Ed.; Svenja Adolphs, Review Ed. **ISSN:** 1384-6655. **Subscription Rates:** EUR366 individuals print + online; EUR85 individuals special. **URL:** http://www.benjamins.com/cgi-bin/t_seriesview.cgi?series=ijcl.

48027 ■ International Journal of Hybrid Intelligent Systems
IOS Press, B.V.
Nieuwe Hemweg 6B
NL-1013 BG Amsterdam, Netherlands
Ph: 31 20 6883355
Fax: 31 20 6203419
Publication E-mail: ijhis@hybridsystem.com
Publisher E-mail: info@iospress.nl
Peer-refereed journal focusing on the theory and applications of hybrid and integrated intelligent systems, providing the academic community with a medium for presenting original research and applications related to the simultaneous use of two or more intelligent techniques. **Freq:** Quarterly. **Key Personnel:** Ajith Abraham, Editor-in-Chief, ajith.abraham@ieee.org; Lakhmi C. Jain, Editor-in-Chief, lakhmi.jain@unisa.edu.au; Vasile Palade, Editor-in-Chief, vasile.palade@comlab.ox.ac.uk. **ISSN:** 1448-5869. **Subscription Rates:** EUR338 individuals print & online; US$460 individuals print & online. **URL:** http://www.iospress.nl/loadtop/load.php?isbn=15701263.

48028 ■ International Journal of Industrial Organization
Elsevier Science
PO Box 211
NL-1000 AE Amsterdam, Netherlands
Ph: 31 204 853757
Fax: 31 204 853432
Publisher E-mail: nlinfo-f@elsevier.com
Peer-reviewed journal focusing on the theoretical and experiential queries in industrial organization. **Founded:** 1983. **Freq:** Bimonthly. **Key Personnel:** P. Bajari, Editor; B. Caillaud, Editor; N. Gandal, Editor; H.J. Paarsch, Co-Ed.; V. Nocke, Co-Ed.; J. Gans, Co-Ed.; G.Z. Jin, Co-Ed.; J.P. Choi, Co-Ed.; R.A. Jensen, Co-Ed. **ISSN:** 0167-7187. **Subscription Rates:** US$107 individuals for all countries except Europe and Japan; 13,500¥ individuals; EUR100 individuals European countries; US$1,633 institutions for all countries except Europe and Japan; EUR1,461 institutions European countries; 194,200¥ institutions. **Remarks:** Accepts advertising. **URL:** http://www.elsevier.com/wps/find/journaldescription.cws_home/505551/descrip tiondescription. **Circ:** (Not Reported)

48029 ■ International Journal of Injury Control and Safety Promotion
Taylor & Francis Ltd.
c/o Consumer Safety Institute
PO Box 75169
NL-1070 AD Amsterdam, Netherlands
Peer-reviewed journal publishing articles concerning all phases of injury control, including prevention, acute care and rehabilitation. **Freq:** 4/yr. **Key Personnel:** Wim Rogmans, Editor, w.rogmans@eurosafe.com; Geetam Tiwari, Editor-in-Chief, icspjournal@gmail.com; Shrikant Bangdiwala, Editor-in-Chief; R. Kisser, Editorial Board; M. Hijar, Editorial Board; A. Butchart, Editorial Board.

Circulation: ★ = ABC; △ = BPA; ◆ = CAC; ● = CCAB; ❑ = VAC; ⊕ = PO Statement; ‡ = Publisher's Report; Boldface figures = sworn; Light figures = estimated.

ISSN: 1745-7300. **Subscription Rates:** 405 institutions print and online; 384 institutions online; 122 individuals print only; US$672 institutions print and online; US$639 institutions online; US$203 individuals print only; EUR534 institutions print and online; EUR507 institutions online; EUR161 individuals. **Remarks:** Accepts advertising. **URL:** http://www.tandf.co.uk/journals/titles/17457300.asp. **Circ:** (Not Reported)

48030 ■ International Journal of Mechanical Sciences
Elsevier Science
PO Box 211
NL-1000 AE Amsterdam, Netherlands
Ph: 31 204 853757
Fax: 31 204 853432
Publisher E-mail: nlinfo-f@elsevier.com
Peer-reviewed journal on mechanical sciences for engineers and scientists. **Founded:** 1960. **Freq:** Monthly. **Key Personnel:** S.R. Reid, Editor-in-Chief; K. Davey, Assoc. Ed.; T.X. Yu, Assoc. Ed.; N. Jones, Editorial Board; S. Abrate, Editorial Board; A.G. Atkins, Editorial Board. **ISSN:** 0020-7403. **Subscription Rates:** EUR3,313 institutions for European countries; US$3,706 institutions except Europe and Japan; 439,900¥ institutions; EUR268 individuals European countries; EUR35,700 individuals except Europe and Japan; US$301 individuals for all countries except Europe and Japan. **Remarks:** Accepts advertising. **URL:** http://www.elsevier.com/wps/find/journaldescription.cws_home/206/descriptio ndescription. **Circ:** (Not Reported)

48031 ■ International Journal of Pharmaceutics
Elsevier Science
PO Box 211
NL-1000 AE Amsterdam, Netherlands
Ph: 31 204 853757
Fax: 31 204 853432
Publication E-mail: ijp@pharmacy.ac.uk
Publisher E-mail: nlinfo-f@elsevier.com
Peer-reviewed journal covering all topics related to Pharmaceutics. **Founded:** 1978. **Freq:** 38/yr. **Key Personnel:** A.T. Florence, Editor-in-Chief, ataylorflorence@aol.com; T. Nagai, Advisor; A.T. Florence, Editor. **ISSN:** 0378-5173. **Subscription Rates:** EUR611 individuals European countries and Iran; US$685 individuals all countries except Europe, Japan and Iran; 82,500¥ individuals Japan; EUR9,189 institutions European countries and Iran; 1,220,500¥ institutions Japan; US$10,280 institutions, other countries except Europe, Japan and Iran. **URL:** http://www.elsevier.com/wps/find/journaldescription.cws_home/505513/descriptiondescription.

48032 ■ International Journal of Regulation and Governance
IOS Press, B.V.
Nieuwe Hemweg 6B
NL-1013 BG Amsterdam, Netherlands
Ph: 31 20 6883355
Fax: 31 20 6203419
Publisher E-mail: info@iospress.nl
Journal providing a forum for investigation, analysis of energy, telecommunications, water, environment, and transport. **Freq:** 2/yr. **Key Personnel:** L. Srivastava, Editor-in-Chief, leena@teri.res.in; A. Eberhard, Editorial Board; R. Lawton, Editorial Board; S. Thomas, Editorial Board; Nurul M. Islam, Editorial Board; S.L. Rao, Editorial Board; S. Sundar, Editorial Board; M. Munasinghe, Editorial Board; B. Tenenbaum, Editorial Board. **ISSN:** 0972-4907. **Subscription Rates:** EUR117 institutions print and online; US$140 institutions print and online. **URL:** http://www.iospress.nl/loadtop/load.php?isbn=09724907.

48033 ■ Interpreting
John Benjamins Publishing Co.
Klaprozenweg 105
PO Box 36224
NL-1033 NN Amsterdam, Netherlands
Ph: 31 206 304747
Fax: 31 206 739773
Publisher E-mail: benjamins@presswarehouse.com
Peer-reviewed journal featuring research and practice in interpreting. **Freq:** Semiannual. **Key Personnel:** Miriam Shlesinger, Editor; Franz Pochhacker, Editor. **ISSN:** 1384-6647. **Subscription Rates:** EUR197 individuals backvolumes; EUR75 institutions special; EUR197 individuals print + online. **URL:** http://www.benjamins.com/cgi-bin/t_seriesview.cgi?series=INTP.

48034 ■ Intervention Research
IOS Press, B.V.
c/o Marcel Veenswijk, Ed.-in-Ch.
Dept. of Culture, Organization & Management

Vrije Universiteit
De Boelelaan 1081c
NL-1081 BG Amsterdam, Netherlands
Ph: 31 20 5986732
Fax: 31 20 5986765
Publisher E-mail: info@iospress.nl
Journal establishing a platform (and filling a gap) for organizational (culture) scholars in the field of intervention and cultural change in organizations, presenting papers that connect contextual developments to organizational change programs and intervention strategies to individual coping strategies, taking full account of areas of uncertainty and ambiguity. **Freq:** Quarterly. **Key Personnel:** Marcel Veenswijk, Editor-in-Chief, m.veenswijk@fsw.vu.nl; Robyn Thomas, Editorial Board; Paul Bate, Assoc. Ed.; Joanne Martin, Editorial Board; Eero Vaara, Editorial Board; Simon Bekker, Assoc. Ed.; Allen Batteau, Editorial Board; Stefan Sveningsson, Editorial Board; Andrew Brown, Editorial Board. **ISSN:** 1573-417X. **Subscription Rates:** EUR341 institutions print and online; US$409 institutions print and online. **URL:** http://www.iospress.nl/loadtop/load.php?isbn=1573417x.

48035 ■ Japan and the World Economy
Elsevier Science
PO Box 211
NL-1000 AE Amsterdam, Netherlands
Ph: 31 204 853757
Fax: 31 204 853432
Publisher E-mail: nlinfo-f@elsevier.com
Peer-reviewed journal covering research in economics, finance, managerial sciences focusing on the problems of economic interdependence between Japan and its trading partners. **Subtitle:** International Journal of Theory and Policy. **Founded:** 1988. **Freq:** Quarterly. **Key Personnel:** Yasushi Hamao, Editor; Robert Dekle, Editor; K. Dewenter, Assoc. Ed.; T.M. Greaney, Assoc. Ed.; Y. Iwamoto, Assoc. Ed.; D. Joines, Assoc. Ed. **ISSN:** 0922-1425. **Subscription Rates:** US$98 individuals except Japan and Europe; 8,900¥ individuals; EUR84 individuals in Europe; US$671 institutions; 79,700¥ institutions; EUR600 institutions. **Remarks:** Accepts advertising. **URL:** http://www.elsevier.com/wps/find/journaldescription.cws_home/505557/descrip tion. **Circ:** (Not Reported)

48036 ■ Journal of Accounting and Economics
Elsevier Science
PO Box 211
NL-1000 AE Amsterdam, Netherlands
Ph: 31 204 853757
Fax: 31 204 853432
Publisher E-mail: nlinfo-f@elsevier.com
Peer-reviewed journal focusing on the economic analyses of accounting problems. **Founded:** 1979. **Freq:** Bimonthly. **Key Personnel:** Jerold L. Zimmerman, Editor; Ross L. Watts, Editor; T.Z. Lys, Editor; R.W. Holthausen, Editor; S.P. Kothari, Editor; M. Hanlon, Editor. **ISSN:** 0165-4101. **Subscription Rates:** 177,600¥ institutions; US$1,497 institutions for all countries except Europe and Japan; EUR1,336 institutions for European countries; US$57 students for all countries except Europe and Japan; 6,600¥ students; EUR52 students for European countries; US$89 individuals for all countries except Europe and Japan; 11,200¥ individuals; EUR85 individuals for European countries. **Remarks:** Accepts advertising. **URL:** http://www.elsevier.com/wps/find/journaldescription.cws_home/505556/description. **Circ:** (Not Reported)

48037 ■ Journal of Accounting and Public Policy
Elsevier Science
PO Box 211
NL-1000 AE Amsterdam, Netherlands
Ph: 31 204 853757
Fax: 31 204 853432
Publisher E-mail: nlinfo-f@elsevier.com
Journal dealing with the files of accounting and public policy. **Founded:** 1982. **Freq:** Bimonthly. **Key Personnel:** Lawrence A. Gordon, Editor-in-Chief; Martin P. Loeb, Editor; F.L. Ayres, Editorial Board; P.J. Beck, Editorial Board; M.D. Beneish, Editorial Board; J. Aharony, Editorial Board. **ISSN:** 0278-4254. **Subscription Rates:** US$131 individuals for all countries except Europe and Japan; 15,700¥ individuals; EUR118 individuals for European countries; US$817 institutions for all countries except Europe and Japan; 97,000¥ institutions; EUR730 institutions for European countries. **Remarks:** Accepts advertising. **URL:** http://www.elsevier.com/wps/find/journaldescription.cws_home/505721/description. **Circ:** (Not Reported)

48038 ■ Journal of Algebra
Elsevier Science B.V.
Radarweg 29
NL-1043 Amsterdam, Netherlands
Ph: 31 204 853911
Fax: 31 204 852457
Journal publishing original research in the field of algebra. **Founded:** 1964. **Freq:** Semimonthly. **Trim Size:** 6 x 9. **Key Personnel:** M. Broue, Editor-in-Chief, jalgebra@ihp.jussieu.fr; Luchezar L. Avramov, Editorial Board, avramov@math.unl.edu; Gerhard Hiss, Editor, gerhard.hiss@math.rwth-aachen.de. **ISSN:** 0021-8693. **Subscription Rates:** 793,500¥ institutions; US$5,969 institutions all countries except Europe, Japan & Iran; EUR7,598 institutions European countries and Iran; 35,500¥ individuals; EUR300 individuals European countries and Iran; US$300 individuals all countries except Europe, Japan & Iran. **URL:** http://www.elsevier.com/wps/find/journaldescription.cws_home/622850/descrip tiondescription.

48039 ■ Journal of Algorithms in Cognition, Informatics and Logic
Elsevier Science B.V.
Radarweg 29
NL-1043 Amsterdam, Netherlands
Ph: 31 204 853911
Fax: 31 204 852457
Journal presenting papers on algorithms. **Subtitle:** Cognition, Informatics and Logic. **Founded:** 1980. **Freq:** 4/yr. **Trim Size:** 5 7/8 x 9. **ISSN:** 0196-6774. **URL:** http://www.elsevier.com/wps/find/journaldescription.cws_home/622851/descriptiondescription. **Formerly:** Journal of Algorithms.

48040 ■ Journal of Alloys and Compounds
Elsevier Science
University of Amsterdam
Van der Waals-Zeeman Laboratory
Valckenierstraat 65-67
NL-1018 XE Amsterdam, Netherlands
Publisher E-mail: nlinfo-f@elsevier.com
Journal covering Materials Science, Solid-State Chemistry and Physics. **Founded:** 1959. **Freq:** 42/yr. **Key Personnel:** Holger Kleinke, Editor, jalcom@uwaterloo.ca; K.H.J. Buschow, Editor-in-Chief, k.h.j.buschow@uva.nl; G.J. Miller, Honorary Ed.; A.V. Andreev, Editorial Advisory Board; H. Sato, Editorial Advisory Board; Hongge Pan, Editor, honggepan@zju.edu.cn; D.C. Johnson, Editorial Advisory Board; Hiroki Sakaguchi, Editor, sakaguch@chem.tottori-u.ac.jp; H. Franzen, Honorary Ed.; J. Raub, Honorary Ed.; J. Huot, Editorial Advisory Board; R. Nesper, Editorial Advisory Board. **ISSN:** 0925-8388. **Subscription Rates:** 1,620,300¥ institutions; EUR12,220 institutions; US$13,728 institutions; 91,800¥ individuals; EUR708 individuals; US$793 individuals. **Remarks:** Accepts advertising. **URL:** http://www.elsevier.com/wps/find/journaldescription.cws_home/522468/description. **Circ:** (Not Reported)

48041 ■ Journal of Alzheimer's Disease
IOS Press, B.V.
Nieuwe Hemweg 6B
NL-1013 BG Amsterdam, Netherlands
Ph: 31 20 6883355
Fax: 31 20 6203419
Publisher E-mail: info@iospress.nl
Peer-reviewed International multidisciplinary journal focusing to facilitate progress in understanding the etiology, pathogenesis, epidemiology, genetics, behavior, treatment and psychology of Alzheimer's disease. **Freq:** 8/yr. **Key Personnel:** George Perry, PhD, Editor-in-Chief, george.perry@utsa.edu; Beth Kumar, Managing Editor, editorial@j-alz.com; Mark A. Smith, PhD, Editor-in-Chief, mark.smith@case.edu. **ISSN:** 1387-2877. **Subscription Rates:** US$2,620 institutions print; EUR1,902 institutions print. **URL:** http://www.j-alz.com/.

48042 ■ Journal of the American College of Surgeons
Elsevier Science B.V.
Radarweg 29
NL-1043 Amsterdam, Netherlands
Ph: 31 204 853911
Fax: 31 204 852457
Peer-reviewed journal covering general surgery, surgical specialties, and experimental surgery. **Founded:** July 1905. **Freq:** Monthly. **Print Method:** Offset. **Trim Size:** 8 1/8 x 10 3/4. **Cols./Page:** 2. **Col. Width:** 3 1/2 inches. **Col. Depth:** 10 inches. **Key Personnel:** Timothy J. Eberlein, MD, Editor-in-Chief; Timothy Buchman, Dep.

Ed.; Joan S. Chmiel, PhD, Statistician; Nancy L. Ascher, Dep. Ed.; Stanley W. Ashley, Dep. Ed.; Barbara L. Bass, Dep. Ed. **ISSN:** 1072-7515. **Subscription Rates:** US$240 students, other countries; US$85 students for USA; US$750 institutions; US$232 individuals for USA and Canada; US$436 institutions for USA; US$406 individuals. **Remarks:** Accepts advertising. **URL:** http://www.elsevier.com/wps/find/journaldescription.cws_home/600623/descriptiondescription. **Circ:** Paid ‡13,176, Controlled ‡6,832

48043 ■ Journal of Analytical and Applied Pyrolysis
Elsevier Science
PO Box 211
NL-1000 AE Amsterdam, Netherlands
Ph: 31 204 853757
Fax: 31 204 853432
Publisher E-mail: nlinfo-f@elsevier.com
Peer-reviewed journal focusing on qualitative and quantitative results with reference to pyrolysis. **Founded:** 1979. **Freq:** Bimonthly. **Key Personnel:** K.J. Voorhees, Editor, kvoorhee@mines.edu; M. Blazso, Editor, blazso@chemres.hu; M. Day, Editorial Board. **ISSN:** 0165-2370. **Subscription Rates:** EUR3,117 institutions in Europe; US$3,488 institutions except Europe and Japan; 414,300¥ institutions; EUR156 individuals; US$209 individuals; 24,100¥ individuals. **Remarks:** Accepts advertising. **URL:** http://www.elsevier.com/wps/find/journaldescription.cws_home/502687/descriptiondescription. **Circ:** (Not Reported)

48044 ■ Journal of Anthropological Archaeology
Elsevier Science B.V.
Radarweg 29
NL-1043 Amsterdam, Netherlands
Ph: 31 204 853911
Fax: 31 204 852457
Journal covering the development of theory and methodology for the systematic understanding of the organization, operation, and evolution of human societies. **Founded:** 1982. **Freq:** Quarterly. **Trim Size:** 6 7/8 x 10. **Key Personnel:** J.M. O'Shea, Editor, joshea@umich.edu; R. Whallon, Founding and Consulting Ed.; P.D. Jordan, Editorial Board; P. McAnany, Founding and Consulting Ed.; M. Zvelebil, Founding and Consulting Ed.; G.R. Milner, Editorial Board; T. Hunt, Founding and Consulting Ed.; R.W. Chapman, Editorial Board; K.A. Spielmann, Editorial Board. **ISSN:** 0278-4165. **Subscription Rates:** US$96 individuals all countries except Europe, Japan & Iran; 12,300¥ individuals; EUR116 individuals European countries and Iran; US$428 institutions all countries except Europe, Japan & Iran; 59,200¥ institutions; EUR568 institutions European countries and Iran. **Remarks:** Accepts advertising. **URL:** http://www.elsevier.com/wps/find/journaldescription.cws_home/622852/descriptiondescription. **Circ:** (Not Reported)

48045 ■ Journal of Applied Developmental Psychology
Elsevier Science
PO Box 211
NL-1000 AE Amsterdam, Netherlands
Ph: 31 204 853757
Fax: 31 204 853432
Publisher E-mail: nlinfo-f@elsevier.com
Journal covering various studies related to the application of behavioral science research in developmental and life span psychology. **Freq:** Bimonthly. **Key Personnel:** J. Torney-Purta, Editor; J. Colombo, Editorial Board; R. Bibace, Editorial Board; A.A. Benasich, Editorial Board; D. Moshman, Book Review Ed.; M.H. Bornstein, Editorial Board; Beale M. Spencer, Editorial Board; D.R. Anderson, Editorial Board; R. Bakeman, Editorial Board; K. Wentzel, Editor; C. Howes, Editorial Board; A. Diamond, Editorial Board. **ISSN:** 0193-3973. **Subscription Rates:** EUR177 individuals for European countries; 23,400¥ individuals; US$198 individuals for all countries except Europe and Japan; 68,000¥ institutions; US$574 institutions for all countries except Europe and Japan; EUR514 institutions for European countries. **Remarks:** Accepts advertising. **URL:** http://www.elsevier.com/wps/find/journaldescription.cws_home/620199/description. **Circ:** (Not Reported)

48046 ■ Journal of Applied Geophysics
Elsevier Science
PO Box 211
NL-1000 AE Amsterdam, Netherlands
Ph: 31 204 853757
Fax: 31 204 853432
Publisher E-mail: nlinfo-f@elsevier.com
Journal covering environmental, geotechnical, engineering and hydrological aspects of geophysics, in addition to conventional subjects such as mining and petroleum geophysics. **Founded:** 1963. **Freq:** Monthly. **Key Personnel:** Klaus Holliger, Editor-in-Chief, klaus.holliger@unil.ch; M. Chouteau, Editor-in-Chief, chouteau@geo.polymtl.ca; A.M. Hirt, Editorial Board; V. Pereyra, Editorial Board; M.H. Loke, Editorial Board; D. Patella, Editorial Board; S. Friedel, Editorial Board; K. Mickus, Editorial Board; K. Titov, Editorial Board. **ISSN:** 0926-9851. **Subscription Rates:** EUR1,327 institutions for European countries; US$1,483 institutions for all countries except Europe and Japan; 175,900¥ institutions; EUR174 individuals; US$234 individuals; 26,900¥ individuals. **Remarks:** Accepts advertising. **URL:** http://www.elsevier.com/wps/find/journaldescription.cws_home/503333/descrip tion. **Former name:** Geoexploration. **Circ:** (Not Reported)

48047 ■ Journal of Applied Mathematics and Mechanics
Elsevier Science
PO Box 211
NL-1000 AE Amsterdam, Netherlands
Ph: 31 204 853757
Fax: 31 204 853432
Publisher E-mail: nlinfo-f@elsevier.com
Journal covering latest developments in high-level mathematical investigations of modern physical and mechanical problems. **Founded:** 1958. **Freq:** Bimonthly. **Key Personnel:** Yu S. Osipov, Editorial Board; Yu P. Gupalo, Dep. Ed.; F.L. Chernousko, Editor-in-Chief; S.S. Grigoryan, Editorial Board; L.V. Ovsyannikov, Editorial Board; N.F. Morozov, Editorial Board. **ISSN:** 0021-8928. **Subscription Rates:** 551,000¥ institutions; US$4,640 institutions for all countries except Europe and Japan; EUR4,151 institutions for European countries. **Remarks:** Accepts advertising. **URL:** http://www.elsevier.com/wps/find/journaldescription.cws_home/248/descriptio n. **Foreign language name:** Prikladnaya Matematika i Mekhanika. **Circ:** (Not Reported)

48048 ■ Journal of Approximation Theory
Elsevier Science B.V.
Radarweg 29
NL-1043 Amsterdam, Netherlands
Ph: 31 204 853911
Fax: 31 204 852457
Journal is devoted to new advances in pure and applied approximation theory. **Founded:** 1968. **Freq:** Monthly. **Trim Size:** 6 x 9. **Key Personnel:** Paul Nevai, Editor-in-Chief; A. Ron, Editor-in-Chief; T.A. Hogan, Editorial Asst. **ISSN:** 0021-9045. **Subscription Rates:** 392,700¥ institutions; US$2,963 institutions all countries except Europe, Japan & Iran; EUR3,759 institutions European countries and Iran; US$1,390 individuals all countries except Europe, Japan & Iran; EUR1,758 individuals European countries and Iran; 183,600¥ individuals. **URL:** http://www.elsevier.com/wps/find/journaldescription.cws_home/622853/descriptiondescription.

48049 ■ Journal of Arid Environments
Elsevier Science
PO Box 211
NL-1000 AE Amsterdam, Netherlands
Ph: 31 204 853757
Fax: 31 204 853432
Publisher E-mail: nlinfo-f@elsevier.com
Journal covering climate, geomorphology, geology, geography, botany, zoology, anthropology, sociology, and technical development in arid, semi-arid, and desert environments. **Freq:** 12/yr. **Key Personnel:** Prof. D.A. Ravetta, Editor-in-Chief; Prof. D. Eldridge, Assoc. Ed.; Prof. S.J. Milton, Assoc. Ed.; Prof. D.S.G. Thomas, Assoc. Ed.; E.R. Vivoni, Assoc. Ed. **ISSN:** 0140-1963. **Subscription Rates:** EUR670 individuals for European countries; US$598 individuals for all countries except Europe and Japan; 72,400¥ individuals; US$1,880 individuals for all countries except Europe and Japan; 228,600¥ individuals; EUR2,117 individuals for European countries. **Remarks:** Accepts advertising. **URL:** http://www.elsevier.com/wps/find/journaldescription.cws_home/622855/descrip tion. **Circ:** (Not Reported)

48050 ■ Journal of Asian Earth Sciences
Elsevier Science
PO Box 211
NL-1000 AE Amsterdam, Netherlands
Ph: 31 204 853757
Fax: 31 204 853432
Publisher E-mail: nlinfo-f@elsevier.com
Peer-reviewed journal covering all aspects of research related to the solid Earth Sciences of Asia worldwide. **Founded:** 1986. **Freq:** 18/yr. **Key Personnel:** Y. Isozaki, Editor; T.M. Kusky, Editor; J.R. Ali, Editorial Board; M. Faure, Editor; J.G. Liou, Editor; D. Brown, Editorial Board; P.D. Clift, Editorial Board; I. Metcalfe, Editor; Bor-Ming Jahn, Editor-in-Chief, phone 88 622 7839910, jahn@earth.sinica.edu.tw; Y. Huh, Editorial Board; P.A. Cawood, Editorial Board; T. Kato, Editorial Board. **ISSN:** 1367-9120. **Subscription Rates:** US$87 individuals for all countries except Europe, Japan and Iran; EUR77 individuals for European countries and Iran; 10,300¥ individuals; US$1,603 institutions for all countries except Europe, Japan and Iran; 190,500¥ institutions; EUR1,434 institutions for European countries and Iran. **Remarks:** Accepts advertising. **URL:** http://www.elsevier.com/wps/find/journaldescription.cws_home/235/descriptiondescription. **Circ:** (Not Reported)

48051 ■ Journal of Asian Economics
Elsevier Science
PO Box 211
NL-1000 AE Amsterdam, Netherlands
Ph: 31 204 853757
Fax: 31 204 853432
Publisher E-mail: nlinfo-f@elsevier.com
Journal providing a forum for publication of increasingly growing research in Asian economic studies and a unique forum for continental Asian economic studies. **Founded:** 1990. **Freq:** Bimonthly. **Trim Size:** 7 x 10. **Cols./Page:** 1. **Col. Width:** 30 picas. **Col. Depth:** 42 picas. **Key Personnel:** R. Bahl, Exec. Ed.; C.Y. Chu, Exec. Ed.; S. Bhuyan, Book Review Ed.; J. Behrman, Exec. Ed.; K. Hamada, Assoc. Ed., koichi.hamada@yale.edu; S.L. Husted, Assoc. Ed.; G.M. Bodnar, Exec. Ed.; M. Dutta, Founding Ed. **ISSN:** 1049-0078. **Subscription Rates:** US$107 individuals all countries except Europe & Japan; 15,300¥ individuals; EUR111 individuals European countries & Iran; EUR550 institutions European countries & Iran; 72,300¥ institutions; US$631 institutions all countries except Europe & Japan. **URL:** http://www.elsevier.com/wps/find/journaleditorialboard.cws_home/620171/editorialboard.

48052 ■ Journal of Asian Pacific Communication
John Benjamins Publishing Co.
Klaprozenweg 105
PO Box 36224
NL-1033 NN Amsterdam, Netherlands
Ph: 31 206 304747
Fax: 31 206 739773
Publisher E-mail: benjamins@presswarehouse.com
Peer-reviewed journal covering language and communication studies in the Asia Pacific region. **Founded:** May 1971. **Freq:** 2/yr. **Print Method:** Offset. **Trim Size:** 7 7/8 x 10 1/2. **Cols./Page:** 2 and 3. **Col. Width:** 2 1/4 inches. **Col. Depth:** 10 inches. **Key Personnel:** Howard Giles, Editor-in-Chief; Herbert D. Pierson, Editor-in-Chief. **ISSN:** 0957-6851. **Subscription Rates:** EUR218 individuals print + online; EUR75 individuals special. **URL:** http://www.benjamins.com/cgi-bin/t_seriesview.cgi?series=japc.

48053 ■ Journal of Autoimmunity
Elsevier Science
PO Box 211
NL-1000 AE Amsterdam, Netherlands
Ph: 31 204 853757
Fax: 31 204 853432
Publisher E-mail: nlinfo-f@elsevier.com
Journal publishing articles on different aspects of autoimmunity. Covers mechanism of self-recognition, regulation of autoimmune responses, experimental autoimmune diseases, diagnostic auto antibody tests, and the epidemiology, pathophysiology, and treatment of autoimmune diseases. **Freq:** 8/yr. **Key Personnel:** J.F. Bach, Founding Ed.; Eric M. Gershwin, Co-Ed.-in-Ch.; Yehuda Shoenfeld, Co-Ed.-in-Ch. **ISSN:** 0896-8411. **Subscription Rates:** US$1,044 institutions for all countries except Europe and Japan; 127,000¥ institutions for Japan; EUR1,174 institutions for European countries; EUR359 individuals for European countries; US$226 individuals for all countries except Europe and Japan; 38,600¥ individuals for Japan. **Remarks:** Accepts advertising. **URL:** http://www.elsevier.com/wps/find/journaldescription.cws_home/622856/descrip tion. **Circ:** (Not Reported)

48054 ■ Journal of Business Research
Elsevier Science

Circulation: ★ = ABC; △ = BPA; ♦ = CAC; • = CCAB; ❑ = VAC; ⊕ = PO Statement; ‡ = Publisher's Report; Boldface figures = sworn; Light figures = estimated.

Gale Directory of Publications & Broadcast Media/147th Ed. 5229

PO Box 211
NL-1000 AE Amsterdam, Netherlands
Ph: 31 204 853757
Fax: 31 204 853432
Publisher E-mail: nlinfo-f@elsevier.com
Journal applying theory built from business research to practical situations in the business world. **Founded:** 1978. **Freq:** Monthly. **Key Personnel:** A.G. Woodside, Editor; M. Laroche, Managing Editor; T. Ellson, Assoc. Ed. **ISSN:** 0148-2963. **Subscription Rates:** EUR213 individuals for European countries; US$240 individuals for all countries except Europe and Japan; 28,300¥ individuals; US$2,366 institutions for all countries except Europe and Japan; 280,700¥ institutions; EUR2,114 institutions for European countries. **Remarks:** Accepts advertising. **URL:** http://www.elsevier.com/wps/find/journaldescription.cws_home/505722/descrip tion. **Circ:** (Not Reported)

48055 ■ Journal of Business Venturing
Elsevier Science
PO Box 211
NL-1000 AE Amsterdam, Netherlands
Ph: 31 204 853757
Fax: 31 204 853432
Publisher E-mail: nlinfo-f@elsevier.com
Journal providing a platform for exchange of valuable ideas on various aspects of entrepreneurship. **Subtitle:** Entrepreneurship, Entrepreneurial Finance, Innovation and Regional Development. **Founded:** 1985. **Freq:** Bimonthly. **Key Personnel:** S. Subramony, Managing Editor, subramonys@darden.virginia.edu; S. Venkataraman, Sen. Ed.; C. Schade, Assoc. Ed. **ISSN:** 0883-9026. **Subscription Rates:** 23,200¥ individuals; EUR173 individuals for European countries; US$196 individuals for all countries except Europe and Japan; US$1,153 institutions for all countries except Europe and Japan; EUR1,033 institutions for European countries; 137,100¥ institutions. **Remarks:** Accepts advertising. **URL:** http://www.elsevier.com/wps/find/journaldescription.cws_home/505723/descrip tion. **Circ:** (Not Reported)

48056 ■ Journal of Cereal Science
Elsevier Science
PO Box 211
NL-1000 AE Amsterdam, Netherlands
Ph: 31 204 853757
Fax: 31 204 853432
Publisher E-mail: nlinfo-f@elsevier.com
Journal focusing on the functional and nutritional value of cereal grains and their products such as starch derivatives, syrups, protein concentrates, and isolates. **Founded:** 1983. **Freq:** Bimonthly. **Key Personnel:** D. Lafiandra, Editor; R.J. Hamer, Editor; P.R. Shewry, Reviews Ed.; F. MacRitchie, Editor-in-Chief; R. Graybosch, Editor; P. Colonna, Editorial Ed. **ISSN:** 0733-5210. **Subscription Rates:** 23,800¥ individuals; EUR221 individuals for European countries; US$223 individuals for all countries except Europe and Japan; EUR1,042 institutions for European countries; US$924 institutions for all countries except Europe and Japan; 112,400¥ institutions. **Remarks:** Accepts advertising. **URL:** http://www.elsevier.com/wps/find/journaldescription.cws_home/622859/description. **Circ:** (Not Reported)

48057 ■ Journal of Chemical Health and Safety
Elsevier Science
PO Box 211
NL-1000 AE Amsterdam, Netherlands
Ph: 31 204 853757
Fax: 31 204 853432
Publisher E-mail: nlinfo-f@elsevier.com
Journal concerned with the currents developments in chemical health and safety issues, ranging from OSHA and EPA regulations to the safe handling of hazardous waste, from the latest innovations in effective chemical hygiene practices to the courts' most recent rulings on safety-related lawsuits. **Freq:** 6/yr. **Key Personnel:** H.J. Elston, Editor, helston@fgi.net; W. Kingsley, Founding Ed., wkk29@aol.com; W.C. Gottschall, Ed. Emeritus. **ISSN:** 1871-5532. **Subscription Rates:** US$548 institutions; EUR490 institutions; 65,000¥ institutions. **Remarks:** Accepts advertising. **URL:** http://www.elsevier.com/wps/find/journaldescription.cws_home/707512/descrip tiondescription. **Formerly:** Chemical Health and Safety (Jan. 1, 2006). **Circ:** (Not Reported)

48058 ■ The Journal of Chemical Thermodynamics
Elsevier Science
PO Box 211
NL-1000 AE Amsterdam, Netherlands
Ph: 31 204 853757
Fax: 31 204 853432

Publisher E-mail: nlinfo-f@elsevier.com
Peer-reviewed journal sharing information on new measurements in experimental thermodynamics and thermophysics including calorimetry, phase equilibria, equilibrium thermodynamic properties and transport properties. **Freq:** Monthly. **Key Personnel:** Prof. R.D. Weir, Editor; Prof. J.P.M. Trusler, Editor; Prof. A. Padua, Editor. **ISSN:** 0021-9614. **Subscription Rates:** US$2,592 institutions all countries except Europe and Japan; EUR2,915 institutions; 315,000¥ institutions for Japan; EUR265 individuals; US$355 individuals; 40,700 f JPN. **Remarks:** Accepts advertising. **URL:** http://www.elsevier.com/wps/find/journaldescription.cws_home/622860/description. **Circ:** (Not Reported)

48059 ■ Journal of Chromatography A
Elsevier Science
PO Box 211
NL-1000 AE Amsterdam, Netherlands
Ph: 31 204 853757
Fax: 31 204 853432
Publisher E-mail: nlinfo-f@elsevier.com
Peer-reviewed journal on separation techniques including chromatography, electrochromatography, electrophoresis, hyphenated and other multi-dimensional techniques, sample preparation as well as detection methods such as mass spectrometry. **Founded:** 1958. **Freq:** 52/yr. **Key Personnel:** J.G. Dorsey, Editor, dorsey@chem.fsu.edu; R.W. Giese, Editor; C.F. Poole, Editor; M.L. Riekkola, Editor; P.J. Schoenmakers, Editor; N. Tanaka, Editor. **ISSN:** 0021-9673. **Subscription Rates:** EUR15,415 institutions; 2,046,800¥ institutions for Japan; US$17,243 institutions for all countries except Europe and Japan. **Remarks:** Accepts advertising. **URL:** http://www.elsevier.com/wps/find/journaldescription.cws_home/502688/description. **Circ:** (Not Reported)

48060 ■ Journal of Colloid and Interface Science
Elsevier Science B.V.
Radarweg 29
NL-1043 Amsterdam, Netherlands
Ph: 31 204 853911
Fax: 31 204 852457
Journal publishing original research data on fundamental principles and their applications in chemistry, physics, engineering, biology, and applied mathematics. **Founded:** 1946. **Freq:** Semimonthly. **Trim Size:** 8 1/2 x 11. **Key Personnel:** D.T. Wasan, Editor-in-Chief; M. Malmsten, Co-Ed.; J. Eastoe, Co-Ed. **ISSN:** 1121-9797. **Subscription Rates:** EUR3,151 individuals; US$2,483 individuals all countries except Europe, Japan & Iran; 328,900¥ individuals; 750,200¥ institutions; EUR7,184 institutions; US$5,634 institutions all countries except Europe, Japan & Iran. **Remarks:** Accepts advertising. **URL:** http://www.elsevier.com/wps/find/journaldescription.cws_home/622861/descrip tiondescription. **Circ:** (Not Reported)

48061 ■ Journal of Combinatorial Theory, Series A
Elsevier Science B.V.
Radarweg 29
NL-1043 Amsterdam, Netherlands
Ph: 31 204 853911
Fax: 31 204 852457
Journal publishing mathematical research on the theoretical and physical aspects of the study of finite and discrete structures in all branches of science. **Founded:** 1971. **Freq:** 8/yr. **Trim Size:** 6 x 9. **Key Personnel:** H. Barcelo, Editor-in-Chief; G.C. Rota, Founding Ed.; B. Leclerc, Editorial Board; G. Andrews, Editorial Board; C.J. Colbourn, Advisory Board; V. Welker, Advisory Board. **ISSN:** 0097-3165. **Subscription Rates:** EUR196 individuals European countries and Iran; US$159 individuals all countries except Europe, Japan & Iran; 20,500¥ individuals; EUR2,270 institutions all countries except Europe, Japan & Iran; 292,600¥ institutions; US$2,801 institutions European countries and Iran. **URL:** http://www.elsevier.com/wps/find/journaldescription.cws_home/622862/descriptiondescription.

48062 ■ Journal of Combinatorial Theory, Series B
Elsevier Science B.V.
Radarweg 29
NL-1043 Amsterdam, Netherlands
Ph: 31 204 853911
Fax: 31 204 852457
Peer-reviewed journal publishing mathematical research on the theoretical and physical aspects of the study of finite and discrete structures in science. **Freq:** Bimonthly. **Trim Size:** 6 x 9. **Key Personnel:** N.C. Wormald, Editor-

in-Chief; M. Ellingham, Managing Editor; A.G. Thomason, Editor-in-Chief; Y. Kohayakawa, Managing Editor; Frank Harary, Founding Ed.; Gian-Carlo Rota, Founding Ed. **ISSN:** 0095-8956. **Subscription Rates:** EUR150 individuals European countries and Iran; US$117 individuals for all countries except Europe,Iran and Japan; 15,600¥ individuals; 210,400¥ institutions; US$1,574 institutions for all countries except Europe, Iran and Japan; EUR2,016 institutions for European countries and Iran. **URL:** http://www.elsevier.com/wps/find/journaldescription.cws_home/622863/descriptiondescription.

48063 ■ Journal of Computational Methods in Sciences and Engineering
IOS Press, B.V.
Nieuwe Hemweg 6B
NL-1013 BG Amsterdam, Netherlands
Ph: 31 20 6883355
Fax: 31 20 6203419
Publisher E-mail: info@iospress.nl
Journal publishing of new research results on computational methods in sciences and engineering. **Freq:** Bimonthly. **Key Personnel:** Prof. Theodore Elias Simos, Editor-in-Chief, simos@uop.gr; Prof. George Maroulis, Editor-in-Chief, maroulis@upatras.gr; R. Mickens, Editorial Board. **ISSN:** 1472-7978. **Subscription Rates:** EUR657 institutions print and online; US$922 institutions print and online. **URL:** http://www.iospress.nl/loadtop/load.php?isbn=14727978.

48064 ■ Journal of Computational Physics
Elsevier Science B.V.
Radarweg 29
NL-1043 Amsterdam, Netherlands
Ph: 31 204 853911
Fax: 31 204 852457
Peer-reviewed journal covering the computational aspects of physical problems. **Founded:** 1966. **Freq:** 24/yr. **Trim Size:** 8 1/2 x 11. **Key Personnel:** R. Fedkiw, Assoc. Ed., fedkiw@cs.stanford.edu; G. Tryggvason, Editor, gretar@wpi.edu; R. Abgrall, Assoc. Ed., abgrall@math.u-bordeaux.fr; P. Degond, Assoc. Ed., pierre.degond@math.univ-toulouse.fr; J.P. Boyd, Assoc. Ed., jpboyd@umich.edu; B. Koren, Assoc. Ed., barry.koren@cwi.nl. **ISSN:** 0021-9991. **Subscription Rates:** EUR675 individuals for European countries and Iran; US$590 individuals for all countries except Europe, Iran and Japan; 70,400¥ individuals; EUR7,846 institutions for European countries and Iran; US$6,215 institutions for all countries except Europe, Iran and Japan; 819,200¥ institutions. **Remarks:** Accepts advertising. **URL:** http://www.elsevier.com/wps/find/journaldescription.cws_home/622866/descriptiondescription. **Circ:** (Not Reported)

48065 ■ Journal of Computer and System Sciences
Elsevier Science B.V.
Radarweg 29
NL-1043 Amsterdam, Netherlands
Ph: 31 204 853911
Fax: 31 204 852457
Journal focuses on the publication of original research in computer science and system science, with particular attention given to the pertinent mathematical theory and its applications. **Freq:** 8/yr. **Trim Size:** 8 1/2 x 11. **Key Personnel:** E.K. Blum, Managing Editor; M. Rabin, Editor; D.E. Knuth, Editor; R.E. Miller, Editor; R.M. Karp, Editor; C.H. Papadimitriou, Editor; D.S. Scott, Editor; H. Rogers, Jr., Editor; J. Hopcroft, Editor. **ISSN:** 0022-0000. **Subscription Rates:** EUR150 individuals European countries and Iran; US$122 individuals all countries except Europe, Japan & Iran; 15,600¥ individuals; 278,700¥ institutions; EUR2,669 institutions European countries and Iran; US$2,168 institutions all countries except Europe, Japan & Iran. **URL:** http://www.elsevier.com/wps/find/journaldescription.cws_home/622867/descriptiondescription.

48066 ■ Journal of Cultural Heritage
Elsevier Science
PO Box 211
NL-1000 AE Amsterdam, Netherlands
Ph: 31 204 853757
Fax: 31 204 853432
Publisher E-mail: nlinfo-f@elsevier.com
Scientific journal covering cultural heritage for scientists involved in Conservation and Awareness of Cultural Heritage. **Subtitle:** A Multidisciplinary Journal of Science & Technology for Conservation & Awareness. **Founded:** 2000. **Freq:** Quarterly. **Trim Size:** 21 x 27 cm. **Key Personnel:** P.A. Vigato, Editor-in-Chief; F. Al-Khrayesh, Editorial Board; J. Asmus, Editorial Board.

ISSN: 1296-2074. **URL:** http://www.elsevier.com/wps/find/journaldescription.cws_home/620738/descriptiondescription.

48067 ■ Journal of Development Economics
Elsevier Science
PO Box 211
NL-1000 AE Amsterdam, Netherlands
Ph: 31 204 853757
Fax: 31 204 853432
Publisher E-mail: nlinfo-f@elsevier.com
Peer-reviewed journal dealing with all aspects of economic development right from policy issues to structural problems of underdevelopment. **Founded:** 1974. **Freq:** Bimonthly. **Key Personnel:** Maitreesh Ghatak, Editor; T.J. Besley, Assoc. Ed.; C. Broda, Assoc. Ed.; C.R. Udry, Co-Ed.; W. Easterly, Co-Ed.; E. Verhoogen, Co-Ed. **ISSN:** 0304-3878. **Subscription Rates:** EUR2,068 institutions for European countries; US$2,314 institutions for all countries except Europe and Japan; 275,000¥ institutions, other countries; 20,800¥ individuals; US$152 individuals for all countries except Europe and Japan; EUR146 individuals for European countries. **Remarks:** Accepts advertising. **URL:** http://www.elsevier.com/wps/find/journaldescription.cws_home/505546/description. **Circ:** (Not Reported)

48068 ■ Journal of Differential Equations
Elsevier Science B.V.
Radarweg 29
NL-1043 Amsterdam, Netherlands
Ph: 31 204 853911
Fax: 31 204 852457
Peer-reviewed journal addressing the theory and application of differential equations. **Founded:** 1965. **Freq:** Semimonthly. **Trim Size:** 6 x 9. **Key Personnel:** Shui-Nee Chow, Editor-in-Chief; John Mallet-Paret, Editor-in-Chief; Konstantin Mischaikow, Editor-in-Chief; Jack K. Hale, Founding Ed.; Sigurd Angenent, Editorial Board; John Ball, Editorial Board; Alberto Bressan, Editorial Board; K. Lu, Editorial Board; Marshall Slemrod, Editorial Board. **ISSN:** 0022-0396. **Subscription Rates:** EUR5,537 institutions European countries and Iran; 578,500¥ institutions; US$4,422 institutions for all countries except Europe, Iran and Japan. **URL:** http://www.elsevier.com/wps/find/journaldescription.cws_home/622868/descriptiondescription.

48069 ■ Journal of E-Governance
IOS Press, B.V.
Nieuwe Hemweg 6B
NL-1013 BG Amsterdam, Netherlands
Ph: 31 20 6883355
Fax: 31 20 6203419
Publisher E-mail: info@iospress.nl
Journal dedicated to publishing facts and analysis on strategic developments and opinions of leading commentators on economic, policy, regulation and applications of electronic business over the Internet and other communications networks. **Subtitle:** Digest of Electronic Commerce Policy and Regulation. **Freq:** Quarterly. **Key Personnel:** Russell Pipe, MD, Editor; Thanom Diinkham, Managing Editor; Timothy G. Donovan, Assoc. Ed.; Prof. John Eger, Assoc. Ed.; Prof. Toshio Obi, Assoc. Ed. **ISSN:** 1878-7673. **Subscription Rates:** EUR453 institutions print and online; US$645 institutions print and online. **URL:** http://www.iospress.nl/loadtop/load.php?isbn=10844678. **Formerly:** I-Ways.

48070 ■ Journal of Economic Psychology
Elsevier Science
PO Box 211
NL-1000 AE Amsterdam, Netherlands
Ph: 31 204 853757
Fax: 31 204 853432
Publisher E-mail: nlinfo-f@elsevier.com
Journal covering socio-psychological aspects of economic phenomena and processes. **Founded:** 1981. **Freq:** Bimonthly. **Key Personnel:** G. Antonides, Editor-in-Chief; D. Read, Editor-in-Chief; F. Bolger, Assoc. Ed. **ISSN:** 0167-4870. **Subscription Rates:** EUR212 individuals for European countries; US$240 individuals for all countries except Europe and Japan; 28,100¥ individuals; 92,600¥ institutions; US$779 institutions for all countries except Europe and Japan; EUR698 institutions for European countries. **Remarks:** Accepts advertising. **URL:** http://www.elsevier.com/wps/find/journaldescription.cws_home/505589/descriptiondescription. **Circ:** (Not Reported)

48071 ■ Journal of Economic and Social Measurement
IOS Press, B.V.

Nieuwe Hemweg 6B
NL-1013 BG Amsterdam, Netherlands
Ph: 31 20 6883355
Fax: 31 20 6203419
Publisher E-mail: info@iospress.nl
Publication covering economics. **Freq:** Quarterly. **Key Personnel:** Dr. Charles G. Renfro, Editor-in-Chief. **ISSN:** 0747-9662. **Subscription Rates:** EUR125 individuals online only; US$145 individuals online only. **URL:** http://www.iospress.nl/loadtop/load.php?isbn=07479662.

48072 ■ Journal of English for Academic Purposes
Elsevier Science
PO Box 211
NL-1000 AE Amsterdam, Netherlands
Ph: 31 204 853757
Fax: 31 204 853432
Publisher E-mail: nlinfo-f@elsevier.com
Peer-reviewed journal focusing on linguistic, sociolinguistic and psycholinguistic description of English with relevance to academics. **Founded:** 2002. **Freq:** Quarterly. **Key Personnel:** L. Hamp-Lyons, Editor, lizhl@hkucc.hku.hk; K. Hyland, Editorial Board; Pearson C. Casanave, Reviews Ed., casanave@redshift.com. **ISSN:** 1475-1585. **Subscription Rates:** 10,600¥ individuals; US$92 individuals for all countries except Europe and Japan; EUR81 individuals for European countries; US$720 institutions for all countries except Europe and Japan; 85,500¥ institutions for Japan; EUR643 institutions for European countries. **Remarks:** Accepts advertising. **URL:** http://www.elsevier.com/wps/find/journaldescription.cws_home/622440/descriptiondescription. **Circ:** (Not Reported)

48073 ■ Journal of Environmental Management
Elsevier Science B.V.
Radarweg 29
NL-1043 Amsterdam, Netherlands
Ph: 31 204 853911
Fax: 31 204 852457
Peer-reviewed journal containing information on all aspects of management and use of the environment, both natural and man-made. **Founded:** 1994. **Freq:** Monthly. **Key Personnel:** A. Gill, Editor-in-Chief, jem@sfo.com; M. Ruth, Editorial Board; G. Huang, Editorial Board; J. Marion, Editorial Board; C. Allan, Editorial Board; L. Firbank, Editorial Board; B. Tansel, Assoc. Ed.; A. Gilbert, Editorial Board. **ISSN:** 0301-4797. **Subscription Rates:** 182,400¥ institutions; US$1,502 institutions for all countries except Europe, Iran and Japan; EUR1,689 institutions European countries and Iran; EUR426 individuals European countries and Iran; US$380 individuals for all countries except Europe and Japan; 46,000¥ individuals. **URL:** http://www.elsevier.com/wps/find/journaldescription.cws_home/622871/descriptiondescription.

48074 ■ Journal of Environmental Psychology
Elsevier Science B.V.
Radarweg 29
NL-1043 Amsterdam, Netherlands
Ph: 31 204 853911
Fax: 31 204 852457
Journal containing information on the scientific development and maturation of the study of environmental psychology. **Founded:** 1994. **Freq:** Quarterly. **Key Personnel:** H. Heft, Review Ed., heft@denison.edu; I. Donald, Editorial Advisory Board; R. Gifford, Managing Editor, rgifford@uvic.ca; M. Bonnes, Editorial Advisory Board; C. Werner, Editorial Advisory Board; S. Ahrentzen, Editorial Advisory Board; T. Daniel, Editorial Advisory Board; T. Garling, Editorial Advisory Board. **ISSN:** 0272-4944. **Subscription Rates:** EUR141 individuals European countries and Iran; 15,300¥ individuals; US$128 individuals all countries except Europe, Japan & Iran; EUR489 institutions for European Countries; 53,000¥ institutions; US$434 institutions all countries except Europe, Japan & Iran. **URL:** http://www.elsevier.com/wps/find/journaldescription.cws_home/622872/descriptiondescription.

48075 ■ Journal of Experimental Child Psychology
Elsevier Science B.V.
Radarweg 29
NL-1043 Amsterdam, Netherlands
Ph: 31 204 853911
Fax: 31 204 852457
Peer-reviewed journal covering the psychology of child behavior. **Founded:** 1964. **Freq:** Monthly. **Trim Size:** 5 7/8 x 9. **Key Personnel:** M. Bruck, Editorial Board; J.A.

LeFevre, Assoc. Ed.; D. Geary, Editorial Board; P.J. Bauer, Editorial Board; J. Plumert, Assoc. Ed.; B.P. Ackerman, Editorial Board; D.F. Bjorklund, Editor; P. Quinn, Editorial Board; R. Flom, Editorial Board; P. Klaczynski, Editorial Board; Lee H. Swanson, Editorial Board. **ISSN:** 0022-0965. **Subscription Rates:** US$1,715 institutions all countries except Europe, Iran and Japan; EUR1,974 institutions for European countries and Iran; 205,900¥ institutions; EUR257 students for European countries and Iran; US$331 students all countries except Europe, Iran and Japan; 36,900¥ students; EUR258 individuals European countries and Iran; US$333 individuals for all countries except Europe and Japan; 37,100¥ institutions. **URL:** http://www.elsevier.com/wps/find/journaldescription.cws_home/622873/descriptiondescription.

48076 ■ Journal of Experimental Social Psychology
Elsevier Science B.V.
Radarweg 29
NL-1043 Amsterdam, Netherlands
Ph: 31 204 853911
Fax: 31 204 852457
Peer-reviewed journal publishing original research and theory on social interaction. **Founded:** 1965. **Freq:** Bimonthly. **Trim Size:** 5 7/8 x 9. **Key Personnel:** J. Cooper, Editor, jcoops@princeton.edu; N. Shelton, Assoc. Ed. **ISSN:** 0022-1031. **Subscription Rates:** US$1,073 institutions for all countries except Europe, Iran and Japan; EUR1,289 institutions for European countries and Iran; 134,400¥ institutions; EUR175 students European countries and Iran; US$154 students for all countries except Europe, Iran and Japan; 18,300¥ students; 22,200¥ individuals; EUR153 individuals for European countries and Iran; US$199 individuals for all countries except Europe, Iran and Japan. **URL:** http://www.elsevier.com/wps/find/journaldescription.cws_home/622874/descriptiondescription.

48077 ■ Journal of Financial Intermediation
Elsevier Science B.V.
Radarweg 29
NL-1043 Amsterdam, Netherlands
Ph: 31 204 853911
Fax: 31 204 852457
Publication offering a unifying perspective on the evolution of institutions and the financial intermediation process. **Founded:** 1990. **Freq:** Quarterly. **Trim Size:** 5 7/8 x 9. **Key Personnel:** S.I. Greenbaum, Editorial Advisory Committee; F. Allen, Editorial Advisory Committee; E.-L. von Thadden, Editorial Advisory Committee. **ISSN:** 1042-9573. **Subscription Rates:** US$499 institutions for all countries except Europe, Iran and Japan; EUR642 institutions for European countries and Iran; 67,300¥ institutions; EUR84 individuals for European countries and Iran; 8,900¥ individuals; US$67 individuals for all countries except Europe, Iran and Japan. **URL:** http://www.elsevier.com/wps/find/journaldescription.cws_home/622875/descriptiondescription.

48078 ■ Journal of Fluency Disorders
Elsevier Science
PO Box 211
NL-1000 AE Amsterdam, Netherlands
Ph: 31 204 853757
Fax: 31 204 853432
Publisher E-mail: nlinfo-f@elsevier.com
Peer-reviewed journal relating to fluency disorders, in connection with the International Fluency Association. **Founded:** 1975. **Freq:** 4/yr. **Key Personnel:** E.G. Conture, Editorial Consultant; A. Craig, Editor, a.craig@med.usyd.edu.au; Charles E. Healey, Book Review Ed., ehealey1@unl.edu. **ISSN:** 0094-730X. **Subscription Rates:** US$151 individuals all countries except Europe, Japan and Iran; EUR115 individuals European countries and Iran; 16,700¥ individuals Japan; US$831 institutions all countries except Europe, Japan and Iran; EUR748 institutions European countries and Iran; 99,000¥ institutions Japan. **URL:** http://www.elsevier.com/wps/find/journaldescription.cws_home/505771/description.

48079 ■ Journal of Food Composition and Analysis
Elsevier Science B.V.
Radarweg 29
NL-1043 Amsterdam, Netherlands
Ph: 31 204 853911
Fax: 31 204 852457
Journal publishing data on the chemical composition of human foods. **Founded:** 1987. **Freq:** 8/yr. **Trim Size:** 6 7/8 x 10. **Key Personnel:** M. Heinonen, Editorial Board; K.K. Stewart, Consulting/Founding Ed.; J. Crews,

Managing Editor; H. Corke, Editorial Board; K. Phillips, Assoc. Ed.; B. Burlingame, PhD, Editor-in-Chief; N. Ismail, Editorial Board. **ISSN:** 0889-1575. **Subscription Rates:** US$550 institutions all countries except Europe, Japan & Iran; 75,200¥ institutions; EUR721 institutions European countries and Iran; US$108 students all countries except Europe, Japan & Iran; EUR126 students European countries and Iran; 13,200¥ students; EUR289 individuals European countries and Iran; US$221 individuals all countries except Europe, Japan & Iran; 30,300¥ individuals. **URL:** http://www.elsevier.com/wps/find/journaldescription.cws_home/622878/descriptiondescription.

48080 ■ Journal of Functional Analysis
Elsevier Science B.V.
Radarweg 29
NL-1043 Amsterdam, Netherlands
Ph: 31 204 853911
Fax: 31 204 852457
Peer-reviewed journal presenting original research papers in all scientific disciplines in which functional analysis plays an important role. **Founded:** May 1967. **Freq:** Semimonthly. **Trim Size:** 6 x 9. **Cols./Page:** 1. **Key Personnel:** A. Connes, Editor-in-Chief; P. Malliavin, Editor-in-Chief; D. Stroock, Editor-in-Chief. **ISSN:** 0022-1236. **Subscription Rates:** EUR5,408 institutions European countries and Iran; 29,800¥ individuals; US$225 individuals all countries except Europe, Iran and Japan; EUR224 individuals European countries; US$4,229 institutions all countries except Europe,Iran and Japan; 565,000¥ institutions. **Remarks:** Accepts advertising. **URL:** http://www.elsevier.com/wps/find/journaldescription.cws_home/622879/description. **Circ:** (Not Reported)

48081 ■ Journal of Geodynamics
Elsevier Science
PO Box 211
NL-1000 AE Amsterdam, Netherlands
Ph: 31 204 853757
Fax: 31 204 853432
Publisher E-mail: nlinfo-f@elsevier.com
Interdisciplinary journal covering solid earth research in geodetic, geophysical, geological and geochemical geodynamics. **Founded:** 1984. **Freq:** 10/yr. **Key Personnel:** R. Stephenson, Editor-in-Chief, r.stephenson@abdn.ac.uk; K. Benn, Editorial Board Member; I.M. Artemieva, Editorial Board Member; W. Jacoby, Editorial Board Member; S. Zerbini, Editorial Board Member; G. Ranalli, Advisory Ed.; J.R. Kayal, Editorial Board Member; P. Wu, Editorial Board Member; B.F. Chao, Editorial Board Member; K. Wang, Editorial Board Member; S.B. Nielsen, Editorial Board Member; V. Mocanu, Editorial Board Member. **ISSN:** 0264-3707. **Subscription Rates:** 251,300¥ institutions; EUR1,893 institutions for European countries and Iran; US$2,119 institutions for all countries except Europe, Japan and Iran; US$292 individuals for all countries except Europe, Japan and Iran; 33,500¥ individuals; EUR217 individuals for European countries and Iran. **Remarks:** Advertising not accepted. **URL:** http://www.elsevier.com/wps/find/journaldescription.cws_home/874/descriptiondescription. **Circ:** (Not Reported)

48082 ■ Journal of Hazardous Materials
Elsevier Science
PO Box 211
NL-1000 AE Amsterdam, Netherlands
Ph: 31 204 853757
Fax: 31 204 853432
Publisher E-mail: nlinfo-f@elsevier.com
Journal publishing articles on the hazards of certain materials on people and the environment, and ways of dealing with it. **Founded:** 1976. **Freq:** 33/yr. **Key Personnel:** M. Fingas, Editorial Board; G. Lyberatos, Editor, lyberatos@chemeng.upatras.gr. **ISSN:** 0304-3894. **Subscription Rates:** US$765 individuals except European countries, Japan and Iran; EUR679 individuals European countries and Iran; 90,200¥ individuals Japan; US$4,896 institutions except European countries, Japan and Iran; EUR4,376 institutions European countries and Iran; 581,200¥ institutions Japan. **URL:** http://www.elsevier.com/wps/find/journaldescription.cws_home/502691/description.

48083 ■ Journal of Historical Pragmatics
John Benjamins Publishing Co.
Klaprozenweg 105
PO Box 36224
NL-1033 NN Amsterdam, Netherlands
Ph: 31 206 304747
Fax: 31 206 739773
Publisher E-mail: benjamins@presswarehouse.com
Peer-reviewed journal providing an interdisciplinary forum for theoretical, empirical and methodological work at the intersection of pragmatics and historical linguistics, focusing on socio-historical and pragmatic aspects of historical texts in their sociocultural context of communication. **Freq:** Semiannual. **Key Personnel:** Andreas H. Jucker, Editor; Irma Taavitsainen, Editor. **ISSN:** 1566-5852. **Subscription Rates:** EUR218 individuals. **URL:** http://www.benjamins.com/cgi-bin/t_seriesview.cgi?series=JHP.

48084 ■ Journal of Housing Economics
Elsevier Science B.V.
Radarweg 29
NL-1043 Amsterdam, Netherlands
Ph: 31 204 853911
Fax: 31 204 852457
Journal containing information on economic research related to housing and analytical techniques on housing-related questions. **Founded:** 1993. **Freq:** Quarterly. **Trim Size:** 6 x 9. **Key Personnel:** H.O. Pollakowski, Editor; A. Anas, Editorial Board; D.R. Capozza, Editorial Board; J.K. Brueckner, Editorial Board; R. Arnott, Editorial Board; D. DiPasquale, Editorial Board. **ISSN:** 1051-1377. **Subscription Rates:** US$67 individuals all countries except Europe, Japan & Iran; 8,900¥ individuals; EUR84 individuals European countries and Iran; EUR585 institutions European countries and Iran; US$444 institutions all countries except Europe, Japan & Iran; 60,900¥ institutions. **URL:** http://www.elsevier.com/wps/find/journaldescription.cws_home/622881/descrip tiondescription.

48085 ■ Journal of Human Evolution
Elsevier Science
PO Box 211
NL-1000 AE Amsterdam, Netherlands
Ph: 31 204 853757
Fax: 31 204 853432
Publisher E-mail: nlinfo-f@elsevier.com
Peer-reviewed journal dealing with all aspects of human evolution. **Freq:** Monthly. **Key Personnel:** William H. Kimbel, Editor, kimbel@asu.edu; Steve Leigh, Editor, sleigh@uiuc.edu; Rebecca Ackermann, Book Review Ed. **ISSN:** 0047-2484. **Subscription Rates:** EUR657 individuals European countries; US$657 individuals all countries except Europe and Japan; 70,800¥ individuals; US$1,773 institutions all countries except Europe and Japan; 215,400¥ institutions; EUR1,996 institutions European countries. **Remarks:** Accepts advertising. **URL:** http://www.elsevier.com/wps/find/journaldescription.cws_home/622882/descriptiondescription. **Circ:** (Not Reported)

48086 ■ Journal of Integrated Design & Process Science
IOS Press, B.V.
Nieuwe Hemweg 6B
NL-1013 BG Amsterdam, Netherlands
Ph: 31 20 6883355
Fax: 31 20 6203419
Publisher E-mail: info@iospress.nl
Peer-reviewed journal covering interdisciplinary notions of design and process, encouraging papers crossing the boundaries back and forth in mathematical landscape as well as among mathematics, physics, economics, management science, and engineering. **Freq:** Quarterly. **Key Personnel:** Azad M. Madni, Editor-in-Chief, amadni@intelsystech.com; C.V. Ramamoorthy, Honorary Ed.-in-Ch. **ISSN:** 1092-0617. **Subscription Rates:** EUR388 institutions print and online; US$483 institutions print and online. **URL:** http://www.iospress.nl/loadtop/load.php?isbn=10920617.

48087 ■ Journal of Intelligent & Fuzzy Systems
IOS Press, B.V.
Nieuwe Hemweg 6B
NL-1013 BG Amsterdam, Netherlands
Ph: 31 20 6883355
Fax: 31 20 6203419
Publisher E-mail: info@iospress.nl
Journal providing information on fuzzy logic and intelligent systems in the fields of computer science, engineering and manufacturing. **Subtitle:** Applications in Engineering and Technology. **Freq:** Bimonthly. **Trim Size:** 11 x 8 1/2. **Key Personnel:** Reza Langari, Editor-in-Chief, phone 979845-6918, fax 979845-3081, rlangari@tamu.edu; Lotfi A. Zadeh, Honorary Ed.; Timothy J. Ross, Founding Ed.; Mo M. Jamshidi, Founding Ed.; M. Gupta, Editorial Advisory Board; O.P. Malik, Editorial Advisory Board; Vladik Kreinovich, Book Review Ed.; F. Hadaegh, Editorial Advisory Board; B.K. Bose, Editorial Advisory Board; A. Abraham, Editorial Advisory Board. **ISSN:** 1064-1246. **Subscription Rates:** EUR657 institutions print and online; US$917 institutions print and online. **Remarks:** Accepts advertising. **URL:** http://www.iospress.nl/html/10641246.php. **Ad Rates:** 4C: 1,835 f. **Circ:** 3,850

48088 ■ Journal of Invertebrate Pathology
Elsevier Science B.V.
Radarweg 29
NL-1043 Amsterdam, Netherlands
Ph: 31 204 853911
Fax: 31 204 852457
Journal publishing research concerned with the nature and study of infectious and noninfectious diseases of invertebrates. **Founded:** 1959. **Freq:** 9/yr. **Trim Size:** 8 1/2 x 11. **Key Personnel:** B.A. Federici, Editor-in-Chief; R. Anderson, Assoc. Ed.; J. Becnel, Assoc. Ed. **ISSN:** 0022-2011. **Subscription Rates:** 220,700¥ institutions; US$1,664 institutions all countries except Europe, Japan & Iran; EUR2,115 institutions European countries and Iran; 98,200¥ individuals; US$744 individuals all countries except Europe, Japan & Iran; EUR940 individuals European countries and Iran. **URL:** http://www.elsevier.com/wps/find/journaldescription.cws_home/622883/descriptiondescription.

48089 ■ Journal of the Japanese and International Economics
Elsevier Science B.V.
Radarweg 29
NL-1043 Amsterdam, Netherlands
Ph: 31 204 853911
Fax: 31 204 852457
Journal publishing academic analyses of the Japanese economy and its interdependence with other national economies. **Founded:** 1987. **Freq:** Quarterly. **Trim Size:** 6 x 9. **Key Personnel:** T. Hoshi, Editor-in-Chief; J. Corbett, Board of Assoc. Ed.; T. Okazaki, Book Review Ed. **ISSN:** 0889-1583. **Subscription Rates:** EUR848 institutions European countries and Iran; 898,800¥ institutions; US$601 institutions all countries except Europe, Japan & Iran; EUR84 individuals European countries and Iran; 8,900¥ individuals; US$60 individuals all countries except Europe, Japan & Iran. **URL:** http://www.elsevier.com/wps/find/journaldescription.cws_home/622903/descriptiondescription.

48090 ■ Journal of Language & Politics
John Benjamins Publishing Co.
Klaprozenweg 105
PO Box 36224
NL-1033 NN Amsterdam, Netherlands
Ph: 31 206 304747
Fax: 31 206 739773
Publisher E-mail: benjamins@presswarehouse.com
Peer-reviewed journal representing a forum for analyzing and discussing the various dimensions in the interplay of language and politics. **Freq:** 3/yr. **Key Personnel:** Ruth Wodak, Editor; Paul Chilton, Editor; Christopher Hart, Book Review Ed. **ISSN:** 1569-2159. **Subscription Rates:** EUR382 individuals print + online; EUR85 individuals special. **URL:** http://www.benjamins.com/cgi-bin/t_seriesview.cgi?series=jlp.

48091 ■ The Journal of Logic and Algebraic Programming
Elsevier Science Inc.
c/o J.A. Bergstra, Ed.-in-Ch.
Faculty of Science
University of Amsterdam
Kruislaan 403
NL-1098 Amsterdam, Netherlands
Ph: 31 20 5257591
Fax: 31 20 5257490
Publisher E-mail: usinfo-ehelp@elsevier.com
Journal covering survey, historical studies and techniques for programming in its broadest sense. **Founded:** 2000. **Print Method:** Offset. **Trim Size:** 7 x 10. **Cols./Page:** 1. **Col. Width:** 56 nonpareils. **Col. Depth:** 105 agate lines. **Key Personnel:** J.V. Tucker, Editor-in-Chief, j.v.tucker@swan.ac.uk; L. Aceto, Editorial Board; E.G. Wagner, Editorial Board; H. Zantema, Editorial Board; A. Ponse, Editorial Board; U. Berger, Editorial Board; J.C.M. Baeten, Editorial Board; J.A. Bergstra, Editor-in-Chief, janb@science.uva.nl. **ISSN:** 1567-8326. **Subscription Rates:** US$1,403 institutions, other countries except Europe, Japan and Iran; EUR1,254 institutions for European countries and Iran; 166,900¥ institutions; EUR167 individuals for European countries and Iran; US$225 other countries except Europe, Japan and Iran; 25,900¥ individuals. **URL:** http://www.elsevier.com/wps/find/journaldescription.cws_home/621520/descriptiondescription.

48092 ■ Journal of Loss Prevention in the Process Industries
Elsevier Science
PO Box 211
NL-1000 AE Amsterdam, Netherlands
Ph: 31 204 853757
Fax: 31 204 853432
Publisher E-mail: nlinfo-f@elsevier.com
Journal on loss prevention with respect to the chemical industries. **Freq:** 6/yr. **Key Personnel:** Paul Amyotte, Editor, paul.amyotte@dal.ca; S.S. Grossel, Founding Regional Ed., psadi28@aol.com; Genserik Reniers, Assoc. Ed., genserik.reniers@ua.ac.be. **ISSN:** 0950-4230. **Subscription Rates:** 199,600¥ institutions in Japan; US$1,679 institutions; EUR1,504 institutions in Europe; 24,200¥ individuals; EUR157 individuals; US$210 individuals. **Remarks:** Accepts advertising. **URL:** http://www.elsevier.com/wps/find/journaldescription.cws_home/30444/description. **Circ:** (Not Reported)

48093 ■ Journal of Magnetic Resonance
Elsevier Science B.V.
Radarweg 29
NL-1043 Amsterdam, Netherlands
Ph: 31 204 853911
Fax: 31 204 852457
Scholarly journal covering nuclear magnetic resonance and related topics. **Freq:** Monthly. **Key Personnel:** W.S. Warren, Editorial Board; S.J. Opella, Editor; L. Frydman, Assoc. Ed. **ISSN:** 1090-7807. **Subscription Rates:** 658,900¥ institutions; US$4,976 institutions for all countries except Europe, Iran and Japan; EUR6,309 institutions European countries and Iran; EUR1,646 individuals European countries and Iran; 171,800¥ individuals; US$1,288 individuals for all countries except Europe, Iran and Japan. **Remarks:** Accepts advertising. **URL:** http://www.elsevier.com/wps/find/journaldescription.cws_home/622884/descriptiondescription. **Circ:** (Not Reported)

48094 ■ Journal of Materials Processing Technology
Elsevier Science
PO Box 211
NL-1000 AE Amsterdam, Netherlands
Ph: 31 204 853757
Fax: 31 204 853432
Publisher E-mail: nlinfo-f@elsevier.com
Journal covering processing technology of metals and other traditional and advanced materials. **Founded:** 1978. **Freq:** 12/yr. **Key Personnel:** J.M. Allwood, Editor-in-Chief; C.K. Chua, Editorial Board; T. Altan, Editorial Board; G. Hirt, Editorial Board; P. Groche, Editorial Board; F.W. Travis, Founding Ed. **ISSN:** 0924-0136. **Subscription Rates:** EUR5,096 institutions; US$6,854 institutions for all countries except Europe and Japan; 809,300¥ institutions. **Remarks:** Accepts advertising. **URL:** http://www.elsevier.com/wps/find/journaldescription.cws_home/505656/descriptiondescription. **Circ:** (Not Reported)

48095 ■ Journal of Mathematical Psychology
Elsevier Science B.V.
Radarweg 29
NL-1043 Amsterdam, Netherlands
Ph: 31 204 853911
Fax: 31 204 852457
Journal publishing empirical and theoretical papers in mathematical psychology. **Founded:** 1964. **Freq:** Bimonthly. **Trim Size:** 8 1/2 x 11. **Key Personnel:** R. Schweickert, Consulting Ed.; J.C. Falmagne, Consulting Ed.; F.G. Ashby, Consulting Ed.; R.D. Luce, Consulting Ed.; J.R. Busemeyer, Consulting Ed.; W. Batchelder, Consulting Ed.; P. Suppes, Consulting Ed.; S. Ullman, Consulting Ed. **ISSN:** 0022-2496. **Subscription Rates:** EUR1,791 institutions European countries and Iran; 179,400¥ institutions; US$1,224 institutions all countries except Europe, Japan & Iran; EUR178 students European countries and Iran; 25,800¥ students; US$232 students all countries except Europe, Japan & Iran; EUR179 individuals European countries and Iran; 25,900¥ individuals; US$233 individuals all countries except Europe, Japan & Iran. **URL:** http://www.elsevier.com/wps/find/journaldescription.cws_home/622887/descriptiondescription.

48096 ■ Journal of Memory and Language
Elsevier Science B.V.
Radarweg 29
NL-1043 Amsterdam, Netherlands
Ph: 31 204 853911

Fax: 31 204 852457
Journal contributing to the formulation of scientific issues and theories in the areas of language comprehension and production; and human learning and memory. **Founded:** 1985. **Freq:** 8/yr. **Trim Size:** 6 7/8 x 10. **Key Personnel:** R. Greene, Assoc. Ed.; A.G. Samuel, Editorial Board; K. Bock, Editorial Board. **ISSN:** 0749-596X. **Subscription Rates:** 148,300¥ institutions; EUR1,420 institutions European countries and Iran; US$1,218 institutions all countries except Europe, Japan and Iran; US$502 individuals all countries except Europe, Japan and Iran; EUR583 individuals European countries and Iran; 60,700¥ individuals; US$238 students for all countries except Europe, Japan and Iran; EUR274 students European countries and Iran; 28,400¥ students. **URL:** http://www.elsevier.com/wps/find/journaldescription.cws_home/622888/descriptiondescription.

48097 ■ Journal of Molecular Biology
Elsevier Science
PO Box 211
NL-1000 AE Amsterdam, Netherlands
Ph: 31 204 853757
Fax: 31 204 853432
Publisher E-mail: nlinfo-f@elsevier.com
Journal covering current research works in all aspects of molecular biology. **Freq:** 50/yr. **Key Personnel:** Peter Wright, Editor-in-Chief; Jonathan Karn, Exec. Ed. **ISSN:** 0022-2836. **Subscription Rates:** US$1,070 individuals for all countries except Europe and Japan; 124,200¥ individuals; EUR1,149 individuals for European countries; 996,200¥ institutions; US$8,201 institutions for all countries except Europe and Japan; EUR9,223 institutions for European Countries. **Remarks:** Accepts advertising. **URL:** http://www.elsevier.com/wps/find/journaldescription.cws_home/622890/descriptiondescription. **Circ:** (Not Reported)

48098 ■ Journal of Molecular Liquids
Elsevier Science
PO Box 211
NL-1000 AE Amsterdam, Netherlands
Ph: 31 204 853757
Fax: 31 204 853432
Publisher E-mail: nlinfo-f@elsevier.com
Peer-reviewed journal focusing on the molecular characterization of particular liquid systems mainly their structure, dynamics and intermolecular forces. **Founded:** 1970. **Freq:** 21/yr. **Key Personnel:** W. Schroer, Editor-in-Chief; R. Buchner, Editorial Board; M. Besnard, Editorial Board. **ISSN:** 0167-7322. **Subscription Rates:** 438,300¥ institutions; US$3,689 institutions for all countries except Europe and Japan; EUR3,297 institutions for European countries; US$293 individuals; EUR218 individuals; 33,700¥ individuals. **Remarks:** Accepts advertising. **URL:** http://www.elsevier.com/wps/find/journaldescription.cws_home/500849/descriptiondescription. **Circ:** (Not Reported)

48099 ■ Journal of Molecular Spectroscopy
Elsevier Science B.V.
Radarweg 29
NL-1043 Amsterdam, Netherlands
Ph: 31 204 853911
Fax: 31 204 852457
Peer-reviewed journal publishing experimental and theoretical articles on subjects relevant to molecular spectroscopy and its modern applications. **Founded:** 1957. **Freq:** Monthly. **Trim Size:** 6 7/8 x 10. **Key Personnel:** R.W. Field, Editorial Board; A.J. Merer, Ed. Emeritus; N. Picque, Editorial Board; S. Urban, Editorial Board; L. Ziurys, Editorial Board; T.A. Miller, Editor; S. Tashkun, Editorial Board. **ISSN:** 0022-2852. **Subscription Rates:** 238,700¥ individuals; EUR2,284 individuals European countries and Iran; US$1,804 individuals for all countries except Europe, Iran and Japan; 521,800¥ institutions; US$3,923 institutions for all countries except Europe, Iran and Japan; EUR4,995 institutions European countries and Iran. **Remarks:** Accepts advertising. **URL:** http://www.elsevier.com/wps/find/journaldescription.cws_home/622891/descriptiondescription. **Circ:** (Not Reported)

48100 ■ Journal of Multivariate Analysis
Elsevier Science B.V.
Radarweg 29
NL-1043 Amsterdam, Netherlands
Ph: 31 204 853911
Fax: 31 204 852457
Journal publishing articles on fundamental theoretical aspects of multivariate analysis. **Founded:** 1971. **Freq:** 10/yr. **Trim Size:** 6 x 9. **Key Personnel:** J. De Leeuw, Editor-in-Chief; B. Arnold, Editor; D.M. Dabrowska, Edi-

tor; Y. Kano, Editor; J. Jiang, Editor; C. Genest, Editor; D. Marinucci, Editor; P. Kim, Editor. **ISSN:** 0047-259X. **Subscription Rates:** 267,300¥ institutions all countries except Europe, Japan & Iran; EUR2,563 institutions European countries and Iran; US$848 individuals all countries except Europe, Japan & Iran; EUR1,072 individuals European countries and Iran; 111,700¥ individuals. **URL:** http://www.elsevier.com/wps/find/journaldescription.cws_home/622892/descrip tiondescription.

48101 ■ Journal of Network and Computer Applications
Elsevier Science B.V.
Radarweg 29
NL-1043 Amsterdam, Netherlands
Ph: 31 204 853911
Fax: 31 204 852457
Scholarly journal covering networked computer systems. **Freq:** Bimonthly. **Key Personnel:** L. Bononi, Editorial Board; M. Atiquzzaman, Mng. Ed.-in-Ch., atiq@ou.edu. **ISSN:** 1084-8045. **Subscription Rates:** EUR1,108 institutions European countries and Iran; US$985 institutions for all countries except Europe, Iran and Japan; 119,800¥ institutions; US$272 individuals for all countries except Europe, Iran and Japan; 28,000¥ individuals; EUR261 individuals for European countries and Iran. **Remarks:** Accepts advertising. **URL:** http://www.elsevier.com/wps/find/journaldescription.cws_home/622893/descriptiondescription. **Circ:** (Not Reported)

48102 ■ Journal of Neurolinguistics
Elsevier Science
PO Box 211
NL-1000 AE Amsterdam, Netherlands
Ph: 31 204 853757
Fax: 31 204 853432
Publisher E-mail: nlinfo-f@elsevier.com
Peer-reviewed journal providing a forum for synergy of the language sciences and the neurosciences including disciplines from linguistics and cognitive psychology to neurology and neuropsychiatry. **Founded:** 1988. **Freq:** 6/yr. **Key Personnel:** H. Cohen, Editor, henri.cohen@parisdescartes.fr; A. Avrutin, Editorial Board; R. Borowsky, Editorial Board. **ISSN:** 0911-6044. **Subscription Rates:** US$939 institutions all countries except Europe, Japan and Iran; EUR840 institutions European countries and Iran; 111,400¥ institutions Japan; 19,700¥ individuals Japan; US$178 individuals all countries except Europe, Japan and Iran; EUR137 individuals for European countries and Iran. **URL:** http://www.elsevier.com/wps/find/journaldescription.cws_home/866/description.

48103 ■ Journal of Non-Newtonian Fluid Mechanics
Elsevier Science
PO Box 211
NL-1000 AE Amsterdam, Netherlands
Ph: 31 204 853757
Fax: 31 204 853432
Publisher E-mail: nlinfo-f@elsevier.com
Journal dealing with rheological sciences and its applications on the macroscopic and microscopic scale. **Founded:** 1976. **Freq:** 24/yr. **Key Personnel:** G.H. McKinley, Editorial Board; R. Keunings, Editor, roland.keunings@inma.ucl.ac.be. **ISSN:** 0377-0257. **Subscription Rates:** US$4,464 institutions all countries except Europe, Japan and Iran; EUR3,989 institutions European countries and Iran; 530,400¥ institutions Japan; US$293 individuals all countries except Europe, Japan and Iran; 33,700¥ individuals Japan; EUR218 individuals for European countries and Iran. **URL:** http://www.elsevier.com/wps/find/journaldescription.cws_home/502693/description.

48104 ■ Journal of Number Theory
Elsevier Science B.V.
Radarweg 29
NL-1043 Amsterdam, Netherlands
Ph: 31 204 853911
Fax: 31 204 852457
Journal publishing selected research articles on contemporary number theory and related areas. **Founded:** 1962. **Freq:** Monthly. **Trim Size:** 6 x 9. **Key Personnel:** David Goss, Editor-in-Chief, jnt@math.ohio-state.edu; C. Consani, Editorial Board; M. Beck, Editorial Board; B. Conrad, Editorial Board; D. Zagier, Editorial Board; P. Bayer, Editorial Board. **ISSN:** 0022-314X. **Subscription Rates:** 168,800¥ individuals; EUR1,615 individuals; US$1,281 individuals; 338,600¥ institutions; EUR3,242 institutions; US$2,555 institutions. **URL:** http://www.elsevier.com/wps/find/journaldescription.cws_home/622894/descriptiondescription.

Circulation: ★ = ABC; △ = BPA; ♦ = CAC; • = CCAB; ❑ = VAC; ⊕ = PO Statement; ‡ = Publisher's Report; Boldface figures = sworn; Light figures = estimated.

Gale Directory of Publications & Broadcast Media/147th Ed.   5233

48105 ■ Journal for Nurse Practitioners
Elsevier Science
PO Box 211
NL-1000 AE Amsterdam, Netherlands
Ph: 31 204 853757
Fax: 31 204 853432
Publisher E-mail: nlinfo-f@elsevier.com
Peer-reviewed journal covering legislative, regulatory, and clinical practice issues. **Founded:** 2006. **Freq:** 10/yr. **Key Personnel:** Marilyn W. Edmunds, PhD, Editor; Susie Adams, PhD, Editorial Board; Claudia Barksdale, PhD, Editorial Board; Alison Mitchell, Editorial Board; Debra J. Barksdale, PhD, Editorial Board; Joan E. King, PhD, Editorial Board. **ISSN:** 1555-4155. **Subscription Rates:** US$203 institutions outside U.S.; US$64 individuals within U.S.; US$153 institutions within U.S.; US$96 individuals outside U.S. **Remarks:** Accepts advertising. **URL:** http://www.elsevier.com/wps/find/journaldescription.cws_home/706147/description. **Circ:** (Not Reported)

48106 ■ Journal of Organometallic Chemistry
Elsevier Science
PO Box 211
NL-1000 AE Amsterdam, Netherlands
Ph: 31 204 853757
Fax: 31 204 853432
Publisher E-mail: nlinfo-f@elsevier.com
Journal covering theoretical aspects, structural chemistry, synthesis, physical and chemical properties including reaction mechanisms, and practical applications of organometallic compounds. **Founded:** 1964. **Freq:** 26/yr. **Key Personnel:** R.D. Adams, Editor, adams@mail.chem.sc.edu; G. Bertrand, Editor, guy.bertrand@ucr.edu; W.A. Herrman, Editor, herrmannfreising@hotmail.com. **ISSN:** 0022-328X. **Subscription Rates:** 99,600¥ individuals; EUR752 institutions European countries; US$847 individuals for all countries except Europe and Japan; 1,697,400¥ institutions; EUR12,771 institutions for European countries; US$14,286 institutions for all countries except Europe and Japan. **Remarks:** Advertising accepted; rates available upon request. **URL:** http://www.elsevier.com/wps/find/journaldescription.cws_home/504090/descriptiondescription. **Circ:** (Not Reported)

48107 ■ Journal of Parallel and Distributed Computing
Elsevier Science B.V.
Radarweg 29
NL-1043 Amsterdam, Netherlands
Ph: 31 204 853911
Fax: 31 204 852457
Journal publishing original research papers and timely review articles on the theory, design, evaluation, and practices of parallel and distributed computing systems. **Founded:** 1984. **Freq:** Monthly. **Trim Size:** 8 1/2 x 11. **Key Personnel:** S. Sahni, Editor, sahni@cise.ufl.edu; A. Gottlieb, Editor, gottlieb@nyu.edu; K. Hwang, Editor, kaihwang@usc.edu; A. Ferreira, Subject Area Ed.; H.J. Siegel, Chm., Advisory Board, hj@colostate.edu; D.P. Agrawal, Subject Area Ed.; M.J. Atallah, Subject Area Ed.; I. Ahmad, Subject Area Ed.; S.S. Iyengar, Subject Area Ed. **ISSN:** 0743-7315. **Subscription Rates:** US$1,276 institutions all countries except Europe, Japan & Iran; EUR1,642 institutions European countries and Iran; 171,500¥ institutions; EUR367 students European countries and Iran; 38,100¥ students; US$321 students all countries except Europe, Japan & Iran; 78,200¥ individuals; EUR749 individuals European countries and Iran; US$585 individuals all countries except Europe, Japan & Iran. **URL:** http://www.elsevier.com/wps/find/journaldescription.cws_home/622895/descriptiondescription.

48108 ■ Journal of Pediatric Neurology
IOS Press, B.V.
Nieuwe Hemweg 6B
NL-1013 BG Amsterdam, Netherlands
Ph: 31 20 6883355
Fax: 31 20 6203419
Publisher E-mail: info@iospress.nl
Multidisciplinary, peer-reviewed medical journal publishing articles in the fields of child neurology, pediatric neurosurgery, pediatric neuroradiology, child psychiatry and pediatric neuroscience. **Freq:** Quarterly. **Key Personnel:** Huseyin Caksen, MD, Editor-in-Chief, jpn@yyu.edu.tr; Colin Ferrie, MD, Assoc. Ed.; Raj Kumar, MD, Asian Ed., jpn@sushrut.sgpgi.ac.in; John B.P. Stephenson, MD, Assoc. Ed.; Jafri M. Abdullah, MD, Assoc. Ed. **ISSN:** 1304-2580. **Subscription Rates:** EUR278 individuals print and online; US$390 individuals print and online; EUR75 individuals online; US$85 individuals online. **URL:** http://www.iospress.nl/loadtop/load.php?isbn=13042580; http://www.jpneurology.org/.

48109 ■ Journal of Phonetics
Elsevier Science
PO Box 211
NL-1000 AE Amsterdam, Netherlands
Ph: 31 204 853757
Fax: 31 204 853432
Publisher E-mail: nlinfo-f@elsevier.com
Peer-reviewed journal on phonetics. **Freq:** Quarterly. **Key Personnel:** G. Docherty, Advisory Ed.; O-S. Bohn, Assoc. Ed.; D. Byrd, Editorial Board. **ISSN:** 0095-4470. **Subscription Rates:** EUR191 individuals European countries; US$170 individuals except Europe and Japan; 20,500¥ individuals; US$686 institutions except Europe and Japan; 83,600¥ institutions; EUR771 institutions European countries. **Remarks:** Accepts advertising. **URL:** http://www.elsevier.com/wps/find/journaldescription.cws_home/622896/descriptiondescription. **Circ:** (Not Reported)

48110 ■ Journal of Pidgin and Creole Languages (JPCL)
John Benjamins Publishing Co.
Klaprozenweg 105
PO Box 36224
NL-1033 AM Amsterdam, Netherlands
Ph: 31 206 304747
Fax: 31 206 739773
Publisher E-mail: benjamins@presswarehouse.com
Journal covering all aspects of pidginization and creolization. **Founded:** 1964. **Freq:** Semiannual. **Cols./Page:** 5. **Col. Width:** 27 nonpareils. **Col. Depth:** 224 agate lines. **Key Personnel:** Donald Winford, Editor. **ISSN:** 0920-9034. **Subscription Rates:** EUR80 individuals; EUR296 institutions print and online. **URL:** http://www.benjamins.com/cgi-bin/t_seriesview.cgi?series=jpcl.

48111 ■ Journal of Policy Modeling
Elsevier Science
PO Box 211
NL-1000 AE Amsterdam, Netherlands
Ph: 31 204 853757
Fax: 31 204 853432
Publisher E-mail: nlinfo-f@elsevier.com
Journal dealing with the international policy issues. **Founded:** 1979. **Freq:** 6/yr. **Key Personnel:** Antonio Maria Costa, Editor-in-Chief; J.D. Sachs, Editorial Board; S. Ichimura, Editorial Board; E.S. Phelps, Editorial Board; L.E. Westphal, Editorial Board; K.P. Sauvant, Editorial Board. **ISSN:** 0161-8938. **Subscription Rates:** US$116 individuals for all countries except Europe and Japan; 15,300¥ individuals; EUR115 individuals European countries; EUR843 institutions European countries; 112,200¥ institutions; US$945 institutions all countries except Europe and Japan. **Remarks:** Accepts advertising. **URL:** http://www.elsevier.com/wps/find/journaldescription.cws_home/505735/descriptiondescription. **Circ:** (Not Reported)

48112 ■ Journal of Power Sources
Elsevier Science
PO Box 211
NL-1000 AE Amsterdam, Netherlands
Ph: 31 204 853757
Fax: 31 204 853432
Publisher E-mail: nlinfo-f@elsevier.com
Peer-reviewed journal covering aspects of science, technology and commercialization of primary/secondary batteries and fuel cells. **Founded:** 1976. **Freq:** Semimonthly. **Key Personnel:** P.T. Moseley, Editor, pmoseley@ilzro.org; Z. Ogumi, Editor, ogumi@scl.kyoto-u.ac.jp; D.A.J. Rand, Editor, david.rand@csiro.au; B. Scrosati, Editor, scrosati@uniroma1.it; C.K. Dyer, Editor, chris.dyer@verizon.net. **ISSN:** 0378-7753. **Subscription Rates:** US$5,351 institutions for all countries except Europe and Japan; EUR4,783 institutions for European countries; 635,500¥ institutions. **Remarks:** Accepts advertising. **URL:** http://www.elsevier.com/wps/find/journaldescription.cws_home/504093/descriptiondescription. **Circ:** (Not Reported)

48113 ■ Journal of Proteomics
Elsevier Science
PO Box 211
NL-1000 AE Amsterdam, Netherlands
Ph: 31 204 853757
Fax: 31 204 853432
Publisher E-mail: nlinfo-f@elsevier.com
Journal covering the development of new techniques to solve theoretical and experimental problems in the area of life sciences, mainly in biochemistry and biophysics. **Founded:** 1979. **Freq:** Monthly. **Key Personnel:** Juan J. Calvete, Editor-in-Chief; J.J. Diaz, Exec. Ed.; I. Miller, Exec. Ed. **ISSN:** 1874-3919. **Subscription Rates:** EUR1,980 institutions for European countries; US$2,209 institutions for all countries except Europe and Japan; 262,400¥ institutions; EUR174 individuals; US$234 individuals; 26,900¥ individuals. **Remarks:** Accepts advertising. **URL:** http://www.elsevier.com/wps/find/journaldescription.cws_home/713351/descriptiondescription. **Formerly:** Journal of Biochemical and Biophysical Methods. **Circ:** (Not Reported)

48114 ■ Journal of Research in Personality
Elsevier Science B.V.
Radarweg 29
NL-1043 Amsterdam, Netherlands
Ph: 31 204 853911
Fax: 31 204 852457
Journal publishing articles on issues in the field of personality study, including the genetic, physiological, motivational, learning, perceptual, cognitive, and social processes of both normal and abnormal personalities in humans and animals. **Founded:** 1965. **Freq:** Bimonthly. **Trim Size:** 5 7/8 x 9. **Key Personnel:** Peter Borkenau, Assoc. Ed.; Richard E. Lucas, Editor-in-Chief; Mathias Allemand, Consulting Ed.; Jeremy Biesanz, Consulting Ed.; Phebe Cramer, Assoc. Ed.; Michael Ashton, Consulting Ed. **ISSN:** 0092-6566. **Subscription Rates:** EUR1,076 institutions European countries and Iran; US$789 institutions all countries except Europe, Japan & Iran; 112,100¥ institutions; EUR111 individuals European countries and Iran; US$145 individuals all countries except Europe, Japan & Iran; 16,000¥ individuals; US$90 students all countries except Europe, Japan & Iran; 9,900¥ students; EUR68 students European countries and Iran. **URL:** http://www.elsevier.com/wps/find/journaldescription.cws_home/622897/descriptiondescription.

48115 ■ Journal of Sea Research
Elsevier Science
PO Box 211
NL-1000 AE Amsterdam, Netherlands
Ph: 31 204 853757
Fax: 31 204 853432
Publisher E-mail: nlinfo-f@elsevier.com
Peer-reviewed journal on marine research. **Founded:** 1997. **Freq:** 8/yr. **Key Personnel:** T. Watmough, Asst. Ed.; Carlo Heip, Editor-in-Chief, carlo.heip@nioz.nl; M.J. Williams, Assoc. Ed., meryljwilliams@gmail.com; J. Hewitt, Assoc. Ed., j.hewitt@niwa.co.nz; Herman Ridderinkhof, Assoc. Ed., herman.ridderinkhof@nioz.nl; A.G.J. Buma, Editorial Board. **ISSN:** 1385-1101. **Subscription Rates:** EUR722 institutions for European countries; US$809 institutions for all countries except Europe and Japan; 95,700¥ institutions; EUR152 individuals European countries; US$172 individuals all countries except Europe and Japan; 20,400¥ individuals. **Remarks:** Accepts advertising. **URL:** http://www.elsevier.com/wps/find/journaldescription.cws_home/600318/descriptiondescription. **Circ:** (Not Reported)

48116 ■ The Journal of Socio-Economics
Elsevier Science B.V.
Radarweg 29
NL-1043 Amsterdam, Netherlands
Ph: 31 204 853911
Fax: 31 204 852457
Peer-reviewed economics journal focusing on economics research as well as interdisciplinary discourses. **Founded:** 1972. **Freq:** Bimonthly. **Print Method:** Offset. **Trim Size:** 6 7/8 x 10. **Cols./Page:** 1. **Key Personnel:** Morris Altman, Editor, morris.altman@vuw.ac.nz; J. Tomer, Co-Ed., jtomer@juno.com; R. Hattwick, Founding Ed.; P. Anand, Editorial Board; L.R. Anderson, Editorial Board; R. Ashford, Editorial Board. **ISSN:** 1053-5357. **Subscription Rates:** EUR661 institutions for European countries and Iran; US$738 institutions, other countries except Europe, japan and Iran; 87,600¥ institutions; US$107 other countries except Europe, Iran and Japan; EUR111 individuals European countries and Iran; 15,300¥ individuals Japan. **URL:** http://www.elsevier.com/wps/find/journaldescription.cws_home/620175/descriptiondescription.

48117 ■ Journal of Sound and Vibration
Elsevier Science
PO Box 211
NL-1000 AE Amsterdam, Netherlands
Ph: 31 204 853757
Fax: 31 204 853432
Publisher E-mail: nlinfo-f@elsevier.com
Peer-reviewed Scientific journal on sound and vibration. **Freq:** 26/yr. **Key Personnel:** R.J. Astley, Subject Ed.; Y.

Auregan, Subject Ed.; C.L. Morfey, Ed. Emeritus; L. Huang, Subject Ed. **ISSN:** 0022-460X. **Subscription Rates:** EUR9,469 institutions for Europe; 1,022,900¥ institutions; US$8,458 institutions for all countries except Europe and Japan. **Remarks:** Accepts advertising. **URL:** http://www.elsevier.com/wps/find/journaldescription.cws_home/622899/descriptiondescription. **Circ:** (Not Reported)

48118 ■ The Journal of Steroid Biochemistry and Molecular Biology
Elsevier Science
PO Box 211
NL-1000 AE Amsterdam, Netherlands
Ph: 31 204 853757
Fax: 31 204 853432
Publisher E-mail: nlinfo-f@elsevier.com
Peer-reviewed journal dealing with experimental or theoretical developments in areas related to steroids. **Founded:** 1970. **Freq:** Semimonthly 25/yr. **Key Personnel:** B. Potter, Assoc. Ed.; J. Adamski, Editor-in-Chief; A. Odermatt, Assoc. Ed. **ISSN:** 0960-0760. **Subscription Rates:** 705,100¥ institutions; EUR5,314 institutions for Europe; US$5,943 institutions, other countries for all countries except Europe and Japan; EUR400 individuals for Europe; 53,200¥ individuals; US$450 individuals for all countries except Europe and Japan. **Remarks:** Accepts advertising. **URL:** http://www.elsevier.com/wps/find/journaldescription.cws_home/333/description. **Circ:** (Not Reported)

48119 ■ Journal of Structural Biology
Elsevier Science B.V.
Radarweg 29
NL-1043 Amsterdam, Netherlands
Ph: 31 204 853911
Fax: 31 204 852457
Journal publishing papers dealing with the structural analysis of biological matter at all levels of organization by means of light, electron microscopy, x-ray diffraction, and nuclear magnetic resonance which yields structural information. **Founded:** 1957. **Freq:** Monthly. **Trim Size:** 8 1/2 x 11. **Key Personnel:** A.C. Steven, Editor-in-Chief; W. Baumeister, Editor-in-Chief; B. Carragher, Assoc. Ed. **ISSN:** 1047-8477. **Subscription Rates:** US$1,451 institutions all countries except Europe, Japan & Iran; 199,100¥ institutions; EUR1,907 institutions European countries and Iran; US$98 students all countries except Europe, Japan & Iran; 11,500¥ students; EUR111 students European countries and Iran; EUR810 individuals European countries and Iran; US$620 individuals all countries except Europe, Japan & Iran; 84,400¥ individuals. **URL:** http://www.elsevier.com/wps/find/journaldescription.cws_home/622900/descriptiondescription.

48120 ■ Journal of Substance Abuse Treatment (JSAT)
Elsevier Science
PO Box 211
NL-1000 AE Amsterdam, Netherlands
Ph: 31 204 853757
Fax: 31 204 853432
Publisher E-mail: nlinfo-f@elsevier.com
Medical journal featuring original reviews, training and educational articles, special commentary, and especially research articles that are meaningful to the treatment of nicotine, alcohol, and other drugs of dependence. **Founded:** 1984. **Freq:** 8/yr **Print Method:** Offset. **Trim Size:** 8 1/2 x 11. **Cols./Page:** 2. **Key Personnel:** J. Copeland, Editorial Board; D. Garnick, Editorial Board; G. Chang, Editorial Board; R.E. Booth, Editorial Board; W. Fals-Stewart, Editorial Board; Chantal A. Lambert-Harris, Managing Editor; L.B. Cottler, Editorial Board; Mark P. McGovern, Editor-in-Chief; M. Galanter, Editorial Board. **ISSN:** 0740-5472. **Subscription Rates:** US$1,187 institutions, other countries; US$327 individuals in US; US$1,055 institutions; US$378 individuals. **Remarks:** Advertising accepted; rates available upon request. **URL:** http://www.elsevier.com/wps/find/journaldescription.cws_home/525475/descriptiondescription. **Circ:** (Not Reported).

48121 ■ The Journal of Supercritical Fluids
Elsevier Science B.V.
Radarweg 29
NL-1043 Amsterdam, Netherlands
Ph: 31 204 853911
Fax: 31 204 852457
Journal containing articles on theories and fluids. **Founded:** 1988. **Freq:** Monthly. **Cols./Page:** 2. **Col. Width:** 19.5 picas. **Col. Depth:** 56 picas. **Key Person-**

nel: Gerd Brunner, Regional Ed., fax 49 40 428784072, brunner@tu-harburg.de; Erdogan Kiran, Editor-in-Chief, phone 540231-1375, fax 540231-5022, ekiran@vt.edu; Richard L. Smith, Jr., Regional Ed., phone 81 22 7955863, fax 81 22 7955863, smith@scf.che.tohoku.ac.jp. **ISSN:** 0896-8446. **Subscription Rates:** US$1,703 institutions all countries except Europe, Japan & Iran; 202,100¥ institutions; EUR1,520 institutions European countries and Iran; 97,900¥ individuals; US$830 individuals all countries except Europe, Japan & Iran; EUR736 individuals European countries and Iran. **URL:** http://www.elsevier.com/wps/find/journaldescription.cws_home/600250/descrip tiondescription. **Circ:** Paid 229, Controlled 34

48122 ■ Journal of Surgical Research
Elsevier Science B.V.
Radarweg 29
NL-1043 Amsterdam, Netherlands
Ph: 31 204 853911
Fax: 31 204 852457
Journal publishing original articles on clinical and laboratory investigations related to surgical practice and teaching. **Subtitle:** Official Publication of the Association for Academic Surgery. **Founded:** 1967. **Freq:** 14/yr. **Trim Size:** 8 1/2 x 11. **Key Personnel:** W.W. Souba, MD, Editor; D.W. McFadden, MD, Editor; D.R. Meldrum, MD, Assoc. Ed. **ISSN:** 0022-4804. **Subscription Rates:** US$907 individuals; US$1,046 institutions, other countries. **Remarks:** Accepts advertising. **URL:** http://www.elsevier.com/wps/find/journaldescription.cws_home/622901/descriptiondescription; http://www.journalofsurgicalresearch.com/. **Circ:** (Not Reported)

48123 ■ Journal of Systems and Software
Elsevier Science
PO Box 211
NL-1000 AE Amsterdam, Netherlands
Ph: 31 204 853757
Fax: 31 204 853432
Publisher E-mail: nlinfo-f@elsevier.com
Peer-reviewed journal publishing papers relating to all aspects of computers. **Founded:** 1979. **Freq:** 12/yr. **Key Personnel:** D.N. Card, Editorial Board; H. van Vliet, Editor-in-Chief, hans@cs.vu.nl; D.H. Bae, Editorial Board. **ISSN:** 0164-1212. **Subscription Rates:** 296,000¥ institutions for Japan; EUR2,233 institutions for European countries and Iran; US$2,497 institutions all countries except Europe, Japan and Iran. **URL:** http://www.elsevier.com/wps/find/journaldescription.cws_home/505732/description.

48124 ■ Journal of Terramechanics
Elsevier Science
PO Box 211
NL-1000 AE Amsterdam, Netherlands
Ph: 31 204 853757
Fax: 31 204 853432
Publisher E-mail: nlinfo-f@elsevier.com
Journal publishing scientific articles relating to the field of terramechanics. **Founded:** 1964. **Freq:** 6/yr. **Key Personnel:** R. Lal Kushwaha, Editor-in-Chief, lal.kushwaha@usask.ca; S. Shoop, Editorial Advisory Board; J. Lever, Editorial Advisory Board; George Mason, Editor, george.l.mason@erdc.usace.army.mil; A. Anderson, Editorial Advisory Board; C. Fervers, Editorial Advisory Board. **ISSN:** 0022-4898. **Subscription Rates:** 128,800¥ institutions for Japan; EUR970 institutions for Europe; US$1,086 institutions, other countries. **Remarks:** Accepts advertising. **URL:** http://www.elsevier.com/wps/find/journaldescription.cws_home/302/description. **Circ:** (Not Reported)

48125 ■ Journal of The Franklin Institute
Elsevier Science
PO Box 211
NL-1000 AE Amsterdam, Netherlands
Ph: 31 204 853757
Fax: 31 204 853432
Publisher E-mail: nlinfo-f@elsevier.com
Journal covering recent advances in the fields of engineering and applied mathematics. The areas of interest include information and communication systems, signal processing, wavelets, sensor fusion, computer and communication networks, neural networks, control theory, nonlinear dynamics, fractals and chaos theory. **Subtitle:** Engineering and Applied Mathematics. **Founded:** 1826. **Freq:** 10/yr. **Key Personnel:** Michael Basin, Editor-in-Chief; Janet English-Cartwright, Managing Editor. **ISSN:** 0016-0032. **Subscription Rates:** US$2,505 institutions all countries except Europe, Japan

and Iran; EUR2,228 institutions European countries and Iran; 295,800¥ institutions Japan. **URL:** http://www.elsevier.com/wps/find/journaldescription.cws_home/334/description.

48126 ■ Journal of Urban Economics
Elsevier Science B.V.
Radarweg 29
NL-1043 Amsterdam, Netherlands
Ph: 31 204 853911
Fax: 31 204 852457
Journal publishing articles that illustrate empirical, theoretical, positive, or normative approaches to urban economics. **Founded:** 1974. **Freq:** Bimonthly. **Trim Size:** 6 x 9. **Key Personnel:** J.K. Brueckner, Editorial Board; S. Bucovetsky, Editorial Board; N.E. Coulson, Editorial Board; A. Anas, Editorial Board; K.J. Bogart, Asst. to the Ed., jue@maxwell.syr.edu; E. Glaeser, Editorial Board; G. Duranton, Co-Ed.; W. Hoyt, Editorial Board; T. Holmes, Editorial Board. **ISSN:** 0094-1190. **Subscription Rates:** EUR1,714 institutions European countries and Iran; US$1,317 institutions all countries except Europe, Japan & Iran; 179,000¥ institutions; 15,800¥ individuals; EUR140 individuals European countries and Iran; US$107 individuals all countries except Europe, Japan & Iran. **URL:** http://www.elsevier.com/wps/find/journaldescription.cws_home/622905/descriptiondescription.

48127 ■ Journal of Vestibular Research
IOS Press, B.V.
Nieuwe Hemweg 6B
NL-1013 BG Amsterdam, Netherlands
Ph: 31 20 6883355
Fax: 31 20 6203419
Publisher E-mail: info@iospress.nl
Peer-reviewed journal publishing experimental and observational studies, review papers and theoretical papers based on current knowledge of the vestibular system. **Subtitle:** Equilibrium and Orientation. **Freq:** Bimonthly. **Key Personnel:** Joseph M. Furman, MD, Editor-in-Chief, jvr@jvr-web.org; Adolfo Bronstein, MD, Editorial Board; Yuriko Sugiuchi, MD, Editorial Board; Bernard Hess, PhD, Editorial Board; Robert H. Schor, PhD, Assoc. Ed.; Pierre-Paul Vidal, MD, Editorial Board; Izumi Koizuka, MD, Editorial Board; Mans Magnusson, MD, Editorial Board; Paul Smith, PhD, Editorial Board. **ISSN:** 0957-4271. **Subscription Rates:** EUR757 individuals; US$1,077 individuals. **URL:** http://www.jvr-web.org/; http://www.iospress.nl/loadtop/load.php?isbn=09574271.

48128 ■ Journal of Visual Communication and Image Representation
Elsevier Science B.V.
Radarweg 29
NL-1043 Amsterdam, Netherlands
Ph: 31 204 853911
Fax: 31 204 852457
Peer-reviewed journal containing information on visual communication and image representation. **Founded:** 1994. **Freq:** 8/yr. **Trim Size:** 8 1/2 x 11. **Key Personnel:** Jay C.C. Kuo, Editor-in-Chief; Yehoshua Y. Zeevi, Editor-in-Chief; Kiyoharu Aizawa, Editorial Board. **ISSN:** 1047-3203. **Subscription Rates:** US$894 institutions for all countries except Europe, Iran and Japan; EUR1,142 institutions European countries and Iran; 119,000¥ institutions; EUR397 individuals European countries and Iran; US$311 individuals for all countries except Europe and Japan; 41,500¥ individuals. **URL:** http://www.elsevier.com/wps/find/journaldescription.cws_home/622906/descriptiondescription.

48129 ■ Journal of Visual Languages and Computing
Elsevier Science
PO Box 211
NL-1000 AE Amsterdam, Netherlands
Ph: 31 204 853757
Fax: 31 204 853432
Publisher E-mail: nlinfo-f@elsevier.com
Journal focusing on all aspects of visual languages and its impact on the art of computing. **Freq:** Bimonthly. **Key Personnel:** S.K. Chang, Editor; S. Levialdi, Editor; L.A. Belady, Advisory Ed.; P. Bottoni, Assoc. Ed.; A. Del Bimbo, Assoc. Ed.; E. Glinert, Assoc. Ed. **ISSN:** 1045-926X. **Subscription Rates:** EUR234 individuals for European countries & Iran; US$264 individuals for all countries except Europe, Japan & Iran; 25,300¥ individuals; EUR682 institutions for European countries & Iran; 73,700¥ institutions; US$606 institutions for all countries except Europe, Japan & Iran. **Remarks:** Accepts advertising. **URL:** http://www.elsevier.com/wps/

Circulation: ★ = ABC; △ = BPA; ♦ = CAC; • = CCAB; ❏ = VAC; ⊕ = PO Statement; ‡ = Publisher's Report; Boldface figures = sworn; Light figures = estimated.

find/journaldescription.cws_home/622907/description. **Circ:** (Not Reported)

48130 ■ Journal of Vocational Behavior
Elsevier Science B.V.
Radarweg 29
NL-1043 Amsterdam, Netherlands
Ph: 31 204 853911
Fax: 31 204 852457
Journal publishing empirical and theoretical articles in the areas of vocational behavior and lifelong career development across the life span. **Founded:** 1971. **Freq:** Bimonthly. **Trim Size:** 6 x 9. **Key Personnel:** M.L. Savickas, Editor, ms@neoucom.edu; N.E. Betz, Editorial Board; D.L. Blustein, Editorial Board; L.T. Eby, Editorial Board; R.W. Lent, Editorial Board; N.A. Fouad, Editorial Board. **ISSN:** 0001-8791. **Subscription Rates:** US$1,220 institutions; EUR1,557 institutions; 162,800¥ institutions; EUR346 students; 36,000¥ students; US$272 students; 70,000¥ individuals; EUR671 individuals; US$529 individuals. **URL:** http://www.elsevier.com/wps/find/journaldescription.cws_home/622908/descriptiondescription.

48131 ■ Journal of Volcanology and Geothermal Research
Elsevier Science
PO Box 211
NL-1000 AE Amsterdam, Netherlands
Ph: 31 204 853757
Fax: 31 204 853432
Publisher E-mail: nlinfo-f@elsevier.com
Journal covering all aspects of volcanology and geothermal research. **Subtitle:** An International Journal on the Geophysical, Geochemical, Petrological, Economic and Environmental Aspects of Volcanology and Geothermal Research. **Founded:** 1976. **Freq:** 40/yr. **Key Personnel:** J.W. Neuberg, Editor-in-Chief, j.neuberg@see.leeds.ac.uk; M.T. Mangan, Editor-in-Chief, mmangan@usgs.gov; G. Chiodini, Editor-in-Chief, chiod@ov.ingv.it; L. Wilson, Editor-in-Chief, l.wilson@lancaster.ac.uk; S. Allen, Editorial Board; A. Aiuppa, Editorial Board; Joan Marti, Editor-in-Chief, joan.marti@ija.csic.es; J.G. Brophy, Editorial Board; E. Del Pezzo, Editorial Board. **ISSN:** 0377-0273. **Subscription Rates:** US$3,894 institutions for all countries except Europe, Japan & Iran; EUR3,473 institutions for European countries & Iran; 460,600¥ institutions; EUR235 individuals for European countries & Iran; US$266 individuals for all countries except Europe, Japan & Iran; 30,800¥ individuals. **Remarks:** Accepts advertising. **URL:** http://www.elsevier.com/wps/find/journaldescription.cws_home/503346/description. **Circ:** (Not Reported)

48132 ■ Journal of Wind Engineering & Industrial Aerodynamics
Elsevier Science
PO Box 211
NL-1000 AE Amsterdam, Netherlands
Ph: 31 204 853757
Fax: 31 204 853432
Publisher E-mail: nlinfo-f@elsevier.com
Peer-reviewed journal dealing with wind engineering in connection with the International Association for Wind Engineering. **Subtitle:** The Journal of the International Association for Wind Engineering. **Founded:** 1975. **Freq:** Monthly. **Key Personnel:** Ted Stathopoulos, Editor, statho@cbs-engr.concordia.ca; J.E. Cermak, Editorial Board; N.J. Cook, Editorial Board; D. Lindley, Editorial Board; A. Kareem, Editorial Board; J. Gandemer, Editorial Board. **ISSN:** 0167-6105. **Subscription Rates:** 428,200¥ institutions for Japan; EUR3,224 institutions for European countries & Iran; US$3,625 institutions for all countries except Europe, Japan & Iran; EUR157 individuals for European countries & Iran; US$210 individuals for all countries except Europe, Japan & Iran; 24,200¥ individuals. **Remarks:** Accepts advertising. **URL:** http://www.elsevier.com/wps/find/journaldescription.cws_home/505658/description. **Circ:** (Not Reported)

48133 ■ Language Problems and Language Planning
John Benjamins Publishing Co.
Klaprozenweg 105
PO Box 36224
NL-1033 NN Amsterdam, Netherlands
Ph: 31 206 304747
Fax: 31 206 739773
Publisher E-mail: benjamins@presswarehouse.com
Peer-reviewed journal covering political, sociological, and economic aspects of language and language use. Also covering relationships between and amongst language communities, and the adaptation, manipula-

tion, and standardization of language for international use. **Freq:** 3/yr. **Key Personnel:** Probal Dasgupta, Editor; Humphrey Tonkin, Editor; Frank Nuessel, Book Review Ed. **ISSN:** 0272-2690. **Subscription Rates:** EUR202 individuals print + online; EUR70 individuals special. **URL:** http://www.benjamins.nl/cgi-bin/t_seriesview.cgi?series=LPLP.

48134 ■ Languages in Contrast
John Benjamins Publishing Co.
Klaprozenweg 105
PO Box 36224
NL-1033 NN Amsterdam, Netherlands
Ph: 31 206 304747
Fax: 31 206 739773
Publisher E-mail: benjamins@presswarehouse.com
Peer-reviewed journal featuring contrastive studies of two or more languages. **Freq:** Semiannual. **Key Personnel:** Silvia Bernardini, Editor; Hilde Hasselgard, Editor. **ISSN:** 1387-6759. **Subscription Rates:** EUR75 individuals special; EUR175 institutions backvolumes; EUR175 institutions print + online. **URL:** http://www.benjamins.com/cgi-bin/t_seriesview.cgi?series=LiC.

48135 ■ Learning and Motivation
Elsevier Science B.V.
Radarweg 29
NL-1043 Amsterdam, Netherlands
Ph: 31 204 853911
Fax: 31 204 852457
Journal publishing original experimental research on the analysis of basic phenomena and mechanisms of learning, memory, and motivation. **Founded:** 1970. **Freq:** Quarterly. **Trim Size:** 5 7/8 x 9. **Key Personnel:** W.A. Roberts, Editor; K. Cheng, Assoc. Ed.; M. Papini, Assoc. Ed. **ISSN:** 0023-9690. **Subscription Rates:** US$751 institutions all countries except Europe, Japan & Iran; 116,400¥ institutions; EUR1,116 institutions European countries and Iran; EUR110 individuals European countries and Iran; US$142 individuals all countries except Europe, Japan & Iran; 15,800¥ individuals; 15,800¥ students; US$142 students all countries except Europe, Japan & Iran; EUR110 students European countries and Iran. **URL:** http://www.elsevier.com/wps/find/journaldescription.cws_home/622909/descriptiondescription.

48136 ■ Leven
Nederlandse Vegetariersbond
Nieuwezijds Voorburgwal 153
NL-1012 RK Amsterdam, Netherlands
Ph: 31 20 3300044
Fax: 31 20 4203737
Publication E-mail: info@vegetariers.nl
Publisher E-mail: info@vegetariers.nl
Consumer magazine covering vegetarian food and lifestyle. **Print Method:** Offset. **Cols./Page:** 3. **ISSN:** 0166-0802. **Remarks:** Accepts advertising. **URL:** http://www.vegetariers.nl/magazine_leven.aspx. **Circ:** Paid ‡8,500

48137 ■ Liber Quarterly
Walter de Gruyter GmbH & Co. KG
c/o Trix Bakker, Ed.
Head Humanities Library
Vrije Universiteit
De Boelelaan 1103
1081 HV Amsterdam, Netherlands
Ph: 31 20 4445220
Publisher E-mail: info@degruyter.com
Journal providing reports on the practical aspects of library management and information science. **Freq:** Quarterly. **Key Personnel:** Trix Bakker, Editor, t.bakker@ubvu.vu.nl. **ISSN:** 1435-5205. **Subscription Rates:** EUR254 individuals. **URL:** http://www.degruyter.de/journals/lq/detailEn.cfm.

48138 ■ Linguistic Variations Yearbook
John Benjamins Publishing Co.
Klaprozenweg 105
PO Box 36224
NL-1033 NN Amsterdam, Netherlands
Ph: 31 206 304747
Fax: 31 206 739773
Publisher E-mail: benjamins@presswarehouse.com
Peer-reviewed journal devoted to the study of the nature and scope of linguistic variation from the point of view of the minimalist program, investigating to what extent the study of linguistic variation can shed light on the broader issue of language particular vs. language universal properties and design. **Freq:** Annual. **Key Personnel:** Jeroen Van Craenenbroeck, Gen. Ed.; Johan Rooryck, Assoc. Ed.; Pierre Pica, Founding Ed. **ISSN:** 1568-1483.

Subscription Rates: EUR112 individuals print + online. **URL:** http://www.benjamins.com/cgi-bin/t_seriesview.cgi?series=livy.

48139 ■ Lingvisticae Investigationes
John Benjamins Publishing Co.
Klaprozenweg 105
PO Box 36224
NL-1033 NN Amsterdam, Netherlands
Ph: 31 206 304747
Fax: 31 206 739773
Publisher E-mail: benjamins@presswarehouse.com
Peer-reviewed journal covering lexicon, grammar, phonology and semantics. **Founded:** 1961. **Freq:** Semiannual. **Print Method:** Offset. **Trim Size:** 8 1/2 x 11. **Cols./Page:** 3. **Col. Width:** 28 nonpareils. **Col. Depth:** 140 agate lines. **Key Personnel:** Maurice Gross, Founder Ed.; Eric Laporte, Editor; Gaston Gross, Editor. **ISSN:** 0378-4169. **Subscription Rates:** EUR373 individuals print + online; EUR85 individuals special. **URL:** http://www.benjamins.com/cgi-bin/t_seriesview.cgi?series=LI.

48140 ■ LOVER
Internationaal Informatiecentrum en Archief voor de Vrouwenbeweging
Obiplein 4
NL-1094 RB Amsterdam, Netherlands
Ph: 31 20 6650820
Fax: 31 20 6655812
Publication E-mail: lover@iiav.nl
Publisher E-mail: info@iiav.nl
Dutch language publication covering feminism. **Founded:** 1974. **Freq:** Quarterly. **Key Personnel:** Padu Boerstra, Editor, padu@dds.nl. **ISSN:** 1651-8042. **URL:** http://www.aletta.nu/aletta/nl/producten/tijdschrift_lover. **Circ:** 2,000

48141 ■ Marine Structures
Elsevier Science
PO Box 211
NL-1000 AE Amsterdam, Netherlands
Ph: 31 204 853757
Fax: 31 204 853432
Publisher E-mail: nlinfo-f@elsevier.com
Journal focusing on latest developments in research, design, fabrication and in-service experience in the area of marine structures. **Founded:** 1988. **Freq:** 4/yr. **Key Personnel:** Torgeir Moan, Editor, tormo@marin.ntnu.no. **ISSN:** 0951-8339. **Subscription Rates:** 221,600¥ institutions for Japan; EUR1,670 institutions for European countries; US$1,867 institutions, other countries except Europe, Japan and Iran. **URL:** http://www.elsevier.com/wps/find/journaldescription.cws_home/405903/description.

48142 ■ Matatu
Editions Rodopi B.V.
Tijnmuiden 7
NL-1046 AK Amsterdam, Netherlands
Ph: 31 206 114821
Fax: 31 204 472979
Publisher E-mail: info@rodopi.nl
Journal covering the African literary and cultural studies. **Subtitle:** Journal for African Culture and Society. **Key Personnel:** Holger G. Ehling, Founding Ed. **ISSN:** 0932-9714. **URL:** http://www.rodopi.nl/senj.asp?SerieId=MATATU.

48143 ■ Materials Characterization
Elsevier Science
PO Box 211
NL-1000 AE Amsterdam, Netherlands
Ph: 31 204 853757
Fax: 31 204 853432
Publisher E-mail: nlinfo-f@elsevier.com
International journal focusing on theoretical and practical aspects of the structure and behavior of materials, characterization techniques for elucidating microstructure of materials. The journal brought out in connection with International Metallographic Society. **Founded:** 1968. **Freq:** Monthly. **Key Personnel:** I. Kaus, Assoc. Ed.; I. Baker, Editor-in-Chief; P. Munroe, Assoc. Ed.; J.D. Robson, Assoc. Ed.; D.W. Hetzner, Assoc. Ed.; D.P. Field, Assoc. Ed. **ISSN:** 1044-5803. **Subscription Rates:** 170,400¥ institutions; US$1,442 institutions all countries except Europe and Japan; EUR1,284 institutions for European countries. **Remarks:** Accepts advertising. **URL:** http://www.elsevier.com/wps/find/journaldescription.cws_home/505786/description. **Circ:** (Not Reported)

48144 ■ Materials Science and Engineering
Elsevier Science
PO Box 211
NL-1000 AE Amsterdam, Netherlands
Ph: 31 204 853757
Fax: 31 204 853432
Publisher E-mail: nlinfo-f@elsevier.com
Journal providing an international forum for theoretical and experimental studies on electronic, ionic, magnetic and optical properties of materials in bulk as well as thin films. **Subtitle:** B. **Founded:** 1988. **Freq:** 30/yr. **Key Personnel:** Prof. M. Balkanski, Founding Ed.; Prof. H. Kamimura, Founding Ed.; Prof. D. Schleich, Dep. Ed.; Prof. P. Kumta, Editor-in-Chief. **ISSN:** 0921-5107. **Subscription Rates:** 639,100¥ institutions; US$5,410 institutions for all countries except Europe and Japan; EUR4,814 institutions for Europe. **Remarks:** Accepts advertising. **URL:** http://www.elsevier.com/wps/find/journaldescription.cws_home/504099/descriptiondescription. **Circ:** (Not Reported)

48145 ■ Materials Science and Engineering
Elsevier Science
PO Box 211
NL-1000 AE Amsterdam, Netherlands
Ph: 31 204 853757
Fax: 31 204 853432
Publisher E-mail: nlinfo-f@elsevier.com
Journal reporting on a wide spectrum of materials science and engineering covering surveys of work accomplished till date, current trends in research and applications, and future prospects. **Subtitle:** R: Reports. **Founded:** 1986. **Freq:** 12/yr. **Key Personnel:** A.G. Cullis, Editor; S.S. Lau, Editor; F.W. Saris, Founding Ed. **ISSN:** 0927-796X. **Subscription Rates:** 241,600¥ institutions; EUR2,040 institutions for Europe; US$1,814 institutions. **Remarks:** Accepts advertising. **URL:** http://www.elsevier.com/wps/find/journaldescription.cws_home/505673/descrip tiondescription. **Circ:** (Not Reported)

48146 ■ Materials Science and Engineering
Elsevier Science
PO Box 211
NL-1000 AE Amsterdam, Netherlands
Ph: 31 204 853757
Fax: 31 204 853432
Publisher E-mail: nlinfo-f@elsevier.com
Journal involving theoretical and experimental studies of the properties and behavior of a wide range of materials with respect to their structure and engineering application. **Subtitle:** A. **Founded:** 1967. **Freq:** 30/yr. **Key Personnel:** Prof. Enrique J. Lavernia, Editor; Prof. E. Werner, Editor; Prof. M. Kato, Editor; Prof. J.D. Whittenberger, Editor; J. Driver, Editorial Board. **ISSN:** 0921-5093. **Subscription Rates:** 1,382,700¥ institutions for Japan; EUR10,430 institutions for Europe; US$24,300 institutions, other countries; 23,500¥ individuals for Japan; EUR176 individuals for Europe; US$197 other countries. **Remarks:** Accepts advertising. **URL:** http://www.elsevier.com/wps/find/journaldescription.cws_home/504098/description. **Circ:** (Not Reported)

48147 ■ Materials Science in Semiconductor Processing
Elsevier Science
PO Box 211
NL-1000 AE Amsterdam, Netherlands
Ph: 31 204 853757
Fax: 31 204 853432
Publisher E-mail: nlinfo-f@elsevier.com
Journal providing a platform for exchange of ideas in experimental and theoretical materials research stimulated by and applied to semiconductor processing. **Freq:** 6/yr. **Key Personnel:** D. Eaglesham, Editorial Advisory Board; R.A. Chapman, Editorial Advisory Board; L. Colombo, Editorial Advisory Board. **ISSN:** 1369-8001. **Subscription Rates:** 71,400¥ institutions for Japan; EUR538 institutions for Europe; US$604 institutions, other countries. **Remarks:** Accepts advertising. **URL:** http://www.elsevier.com/wps/find/journaldescription.cws_home/600849/description. **Circ:** (Not Reported)

48148 ■ Mathematical Social Sciences
Elsevier Science
PO Box 211
NL-1000 AE Amsterdam, Netherlands
Ph: 31 204 853757
Fax: 31 204 853432
Publisher E-mail: nlinfo-f@elsevier.com
Journal on mathematical modeling in relation to economics, psychology, political sciences, sociology and other social sciences. **Founded:** 1981. **Freq:** Bimonthly. **Key Personnel:** J.F. Laslier, Editor, jean-francois.laslier@polytechnique.edu; C. Poujouly, Editorial Asst.; F. Aleskerov, Editorial Board; A. Bogomolnaia, Editorial Board; C. Bevia, Editorial Board; F. Bloch, Editorial Board; A. Chateauneuf, Editorial Board; S.J. Brams, Editorial Board; A. Citanna, Editorial Board. **ISSN:** 0165-4896. **Subscription Rates:** US$116 individuals for all countries except Europe and Japan; 12,900¥ individuals; EUR89 individuals for European countries; 174,300¥ institutions; US$1,465 institutions for all countries except Europe and Japan; EUR1,312 institutions for European countries. **Remarks:** Accepts advertising. **URL:** http://www.elsevier.com/wps/find/journaldescription.cws_home/505565/descrip tiondescription. **Circ:** (Not Reported)

48149 ■ Matrix Biology
Elsevier Science
PO Box 211
NL-1000 AE Amsterdam, Netherlands
Ph: 31 204 853757
Fax: 31 204 853432
Publisher E-mail: nlinfo-f@elsevier.com
Journal focusing on studies exploiting most scientific technologies including molecular biology, cell biology, immunochemistry, structural biology, computational biology, theoretical biology, and macromolecular chemistry involving extra cellular matrix and its biological role in connection with International Society for Matrix Biology. **Founded:** 1999. **Freq:** 8/yr. **Key Personnel:** Bjorn R. Olsen, Editor-in-Chief; Renato Iozzo, Review Ed.; Steffen Gay, Founding Ed. **ISSN:** 0945-053X. **Subscription Rates:** US$235 individuals for all countries except Europe and Japan; S 208 individuals for European countries; 27,500¥ individuals; US$1,029 institutions for all countries except Europe and Japan; 122,600¥ institutions; EUR922 institutions for European countries. **Remarks:** Accepts advertising. **URL:** http://www.elsevier.com/wps/find/journaldescription.cws_home/601342/descrip tiondescription. **Circ:** (Not Reported)

48150 ■ Mechanics of Materials
Elsevier Science
PO Box 211
NL-1000 AE Amsterdam, Netherlands
Ph: 31 204 853757
Fax: 31 204 853432
Publisher E-mail: nlinfo-f@elsevier.com
Peer-reviewed journal disseminating knowledge in the fields technological materials such as metals, polymers, ceramics, various advanced composites, wood, etc., geotechnical materials such as rock and soil, and on thermo mechanical processes pertaining to solid earth geophysics. **Subtitle:** An International Journal. **Founded:** 1982. **Freq:** 12/yr. **Key Personnel:** S. Nemat-Nasser, Editor-in-Chief, mechmat@starlite.ucsd.edu. **ISSN:** 0167-6636. **Subscription Rates:** 281,200¥ institutions for Japan; EUR2,118 institutions for European countries and Iran; US$2,382 institutions, other countries except Europe, Japan and Iran. **URL:** http://www.elsevier.com/wps/find/journaldescription.cws_home/505659/description.

48151 ■ Mechatronics
Elsevier Science
PO Box 211
NL-1000 AE Amsterdam, Netherlands
Ph: 31 204 853757
Fax: 31 204 853432
Publisher E-mail: nlinfo-f@elsevier.com
Peer-reviewed journal focusing on precision mechanical engineering, electronic control and systems thinking in the design and manufacture of products, published in connection with International Federation of Automatic Control. **Founded:** 1991. **Freq:** 8/yr. **Key Personnel:** N. Aspragathos, Assoc. Ed.; Maarten Steinbuch, Editor-in-Chief, phone 31 40 2475444, fax 31 40 2461418, m.steinbuch@tue.nl; K. Bouazza-Marouf, Assoc. Ed. **ISSN:** 0957-4158. **Subscription Rates:** 189,500¥ institutions; US$1,595 institutions all countries except Europe and Japan; EUR1,428 institutions European countries; US$107 individuals all countries except Europe and Japan; 12,800¥ individuals; EUR94 individuals European countries. **Remarks:** Accepts advertising. **URL:** http://www.elsevier.com/wps/find/journaldescription.cws_home/933/descriptiondescription. **Circ:** (Not Reported)

48152 ■ Meeleven
Postbus 10887
NL-1001 EW Amsterdam, Netherlands
Ph: 31 20 5317600
Fax: 31 20 4203528
Publication E-mail: meeleven@deregenboog.org
Publisher E-mail: info@deregenboog.org
Magazine covering the foundation and its work. **Founded:** Nov. 1977. **Freq:** Quarterly. **ISSN:** 1324-0606. **Remarks:** Advertising not accepted. **URL:** http://www.deregenboog.org. **Circ:** Non-paid 9,500

48153 ■ The Mental Lexicon
John Benjamins Publishing Co.
Klaprozenweg 105
PO Box 36224
NL-1033 NN Amsterdam, Netherlands
Ph: 31 206 304747
Fax: 31 206 739773
Publisher E-mail: benjamins@presswarehouse.com
Peer-reviewed journal providing an international forum for research that bears on the issues of the representation and processing of words in the mind and brain. **Freq:** 3/yr. **Key Personnel:** Gonia Jarema, Editor; Gary Libben, Editor. **ISSN:** 1871-1340. **Subscription Rates:** EUR70 individuals special; EUR266 individuals print + online. **URL:** http://www.benjamins.com/cgi-bin/t_seriesview.cgi?series=ml.

48154 ■ Metabolic Engineering
Elsevier Science B.V.
Radarweg 29
NL-1043 Amsterdam, Netherlands
Ph: 31 204 853911
Fax: 31 204 852457
Scholarly journal covering research in metabolic control analysis and related fields. **Founded:** Jan. 1999. **Freq:** Bimonthly. **Key Personnel:** Barry C. Buckland, Assoc. Ed.; Greg Stephanopoulos, Editor-in-Chief; Joanne Kelleher, Assoc. Ed. **ISSN:** 1096-7176. **Subscription Rates:** EUR586 institutions European countries and Iran; US$434 institutions for all countries except Europe, Iran and Japan; 61,300¥ institutions; EUR257 individuals European countries and Iran; US$194 individuals for all countries except Europe, Iran and Japan; 26,800¥ individuals. **Remarks:** Accepts advertising. **URL:** http://www.elsevier.com/wps/find/journaldescription.cws_home/622913/descriptiondescription. **Circ:** (Not Reported)

48155 ■ Metal Finishing
Elsevier Science B.V.
Radarweg 29
NL-1043 Amsterdam, Netherlands
Ph: 31 204 853911
Fax: 31 204 852457
Magazine informing on the practical and technical aspects of finishing metal and plastic products, including waste treatment and pollution control. **Founded:** 1903. **Freq:** Monthly. **Print Method:** Sheetfed and Web Offset. **Trim Size:** 8 1/8 x 10 7/8. **Cols./Page:** 3. **Col. Width:** 26 nonpareils. **Col. Depth:** 132 agate lines. **Key Personnel:** Susan Canalizo, Art Dir./Production Mgr.; Greg Valero, Publisher; Drew Amorosi, Managing Editor. **ISSN:** 0026-0576. **Subscription Rates:** EUR252 institutions European countries and Iran; US$284 institutions, other countries except Europe, Japan and Iran; 33,700¥ institutions Japan; US$123 institutions for USA; US$173 institutions, Canada and Mexico. **Remarks:** Accepts advertising. **URL:** http://www.elsevier.com/wps/find/journaldescription.cws_home/522931/descriptiondescription. **Circ:** (Not Reported)

48156 ■ Methods
Elsevier Science B.V.
Radarweg 29
NL-1043 Amsterdam, Netherlands
Ph: 31 204 853911
Fax: 31 204 852457
Journal containing information on providing methodology of central significance to the neurosciences. **Founded:** 1994. **Freq:** Monthly. **Trim Size:** 8 1/2 x 11. **Key Personnel:** Kenneth W. Adolph, Editor; Kathryn Calame, Editorial Board; Tasuku Honjo, Editorial Board; Daniel M. Lane, Editorial Board. **ISSN:** 1046-2023. **Subscription Rates:** EUR818 institutions European countries and Iran; US$610 institutions all countries except Europe, Japan & Iran; 85,400¥ institutions; EUR172 students European countries and Iran; US$150 students all countries except Europe, Japan & Iran; 18,000¥ students; EUR346 individuals European countries and Iran; US$260 individuals all countries except Europe, Japan & Iran; 36,000¥ individuals. **URL:** http://www.elsevier.com/wps/find/journaldescription.cws_home/622914/descrip tiondescription. **Formerly:** NeuroProtocols.

Circulation: ★ = ABC; △ = BPA; ◆ = CAC; ● = CCAB; ❑ = VAC; ⊕ = PO Statement; ‡ = Publisher's Report; Boldface figures = sworn; Light figures = estimated.

Gale Directory of Publications & Broadcast Media/147th Ed.

5237

48157 ∎ Microbes and Infection
Elsevier Science
PO Box 211
NL-1000 AE Amsterdam, Netherlands
Ph: 31 204 853757
Fax: 31 204 853432
Publisher E-mail: nlinfo-f@elsevier.com
Peer-reviewed journal concerned with latest developments in research on infection and immunity. **Founded:** 1999. **Freq:** 15/yr. **Key Personnel:** S.H.E. Kaufmann, Special Issue Ed.; D.M. Ojcius, Editor-in-Chief; G. Milon, Review Ed.; A. Adachi, Editor; S. Akira, Editor; M. Behr, Editor. **ISSN:** 1286-4579. **Subscription Rates:** 171,200¥ institutions; US$1,444 institutions for all countries except Europe and Japan; EUR1,290 institutions for European countries; EUR394 individuals; US$528 individuals; 60,700¥ individuals. **Remarks:** Accepts advertising. **URL:** http://www.elsevier.com/wps/find/journaldescription.cws_home/601557/description. **Circ:** (Not Reported)

48158 ∎ Microbial Pathogenesis
Elsevier Science
PO Box 211
NL-1000 AE Amsterdam, Netherlands
Ph: 31 204 853757
Fax: 31 204 853432
Publisher E-mail: nlinfo-f@elsevier.com
Journal covering molecular and cellular mechanisms in infectious disease. Discusses infectious agents of bacterial, fungal, viral, and protozoal origins. **Freq:** Monthly. **Key Personnel:** A.B. Rickinson, Assoc. Ed.; Prof. R. Ahmed, Editorial Board; Dr. J.P. Gorvel, Editor-in-Chief. **ISSN:** 0882-4010. **Subscription Rates:** EUR304 individuals European countries; US$301 individuals countries except Europe and Japan; 32,800¥ individuals; US$971 institutions all countries except Europe and Japan; 117,600¥ institutions; EUR1,090 institutions for European countries. **Remarks:** Accepts advertising. **URL:** http://www.elsevier.com/wps/find/journaldescription.cws_home/622915/description. **Circ:** (Not Reported)

48159 ∎ Microvascular Research
Elsevier Science B.V.
Radarweg 29
NL-1043 Amsterdam, Netherlands
Ph: 31 204 853911
Fax: 31 204 852457
Journal publishing information on research in the microvascular field and related fields. **Founded:** 1968. **Freq:** Bimonthly. **Trim Size:** 6 7/8 x 10. **Key Personnel:** D. Shepro, Honorary Editorial Consultant; M.E. Beckner, Assoc. Ed.; S. Bertuglia, Assoc. Ed.; M.W. Dewhirst, Assoc. Ed.; P.A. D'Amore, Editor-in-Chief; J.G.N. Garcia, Editor-in-Chief; M. Boric, Assoc. Ed.; E. Dejana, Assoc. Ed.; E. Bouskela, Assoc. Ed.; P. Conti, Assoc. Ed.; D. English, Assoc. Ed.; A.M. Dvorak, Assoc. Ed. **ISSN:** 0026-2862. **Subscription Rates:** US$1,489 institutions all countries except Europe, Japan & Iran; 205,700¥ institutions; EUR1,968 institutions European countries and Iran; EUR573 students European countries and Iran; US$501 students all countries except Europe, Japan & Iran; 59,700¥ students; EUR878 individuals European countries and Iran; US$667 individuals all countries except Europe, Japan & Iran; 91,500¥ individuals. **URL:** http://www.elsevier.com/wps/find/journaldescription.cws_home/622916/description.

48160 ∎ Misjpoge
Netherlands Society for Jewish Genealogy
PO Box 94703
NL-1090 GS Amsterdam, Netherlands
Publisher E-mail: info@nljewgen.org
Dutch language publication covering genealogy. **Subtitle:** Verenigingsblad van de Nederlandse Kring voor Joodse Genealogie. **Founded:** 1988. **Freq:** Quarterly. **Print Method:** Offset. **Trim Size:** A5. **ISSN:** 0921-8114. **Remarks:** Advertising not accepted. **URL:** http://www.nljewgen.org/eng/content/periodl.html. **Circ:** 650

48161 ∎ Model Assisted Statistics and Applications
IOS Press, B.V.
Nieuwe Hemweg 6B
NL-1013 BG Amsterdam, Netherlands
Ph: 31 20 6883355
Fax: 31 20 6203419
Publisher E-mail: info@iospress.nl
Peer-reviewed journal welcoming original papers in the field of sampling theory, econometrics, time-series, design of experiments, and multivariate analysis. **Freq:**

Quarterly. **Key Personnel:** Dr. Sarjinder Singh, Editor-in-Chief, sarjinder@yahoo.com; Stephen Horn, Managing Editor; Dr. R. Arnab, Assoc. Ed.; Dr. Guohua Zou, Assoc. Ed.; Dr. Marcin Kozak, Assoc. Ed.; Dr. S.S. Osahan, Assoc. Ed.; Michael Scheltgen, Asst. Ed.; Dr. S.R. Puertas, Assoc. Ed.; Dr. M.L. Bansal, Assoc. Ed. **ISSN:** 1574-1699. **Subscription Rates:** EUR293 individuals print and online; US$420 individuals print and online; EUR80 individuals online; US$95 individuals online. **URL:** http://www.iospress.nl/loadtop/load.php?isbn=15741699.

48162 ∎ Molecular Aspects of Medicine
Elsevier Science
PO Box 211
NL-1000 AE Amsterdam, Netherlands
Ph: 31 204 853757
Fax: 31 204 853432
Publisher E-mail: nlinfo-f@elsevier.com
Journal integrating biochemistry and molecular and cell biology to physiology, pharmacology and pathology to infuse molecular perspective in the field of medicine and clinical knowledge in the field of basic sciences. **Founded:** 1975. **Freq:** Bimonthly. **Key Personnel:** A. Azzi, Editor-in-Chief; J. Guinovart, Assoc. Ed.; R. Huber, Assoc. Ed.; A. Miyajima, Assoc. Ed.; H.J. Forman, Assoc. Ed.; G. Poli, Assoc. Ed.; C. De Duve, Editorial Board; P. Ascenzi, Assoc. Ed.; E. Arner, Editorial Board. **ISSN:** 0098-2997. **Subscription Rates:** 196,800¥ institutions; EUR1,481 institutions for Europe; US$1,658 institutions all countries except Europe and Japan; EUR157 individuals; US$210 individuals; 24,200¥ individuals. **Remarks:** Accepts advertising. **URL:** http://www.elsevier.com/wps/find/journaldescription.cws_home/457/description; http://www.elsevier.com/wps/find/journaldescription.cws_home/457/descriptiondescription. **Circ:** (Not Reported)

48163 ∎ Molecular and Biochemical Parasitology
Elsevier Science
PO Box 211
NL-1000 AE Amsterdam, Netherlands
Ph: 31 204 853757
Fax: 31 204 853432
Publisher E-mail: nlinfo-f@elsevier.com
Journal devoted to the research in molecular biology and biochemistry of parasitic protozoa and helminths and also host-parasite interactions. **Founded:** 1980. **Freq:** Monthly. **Key Personnel:** A.P. Waters, Editor, waters@bio.gla.ac.uk; P.T. Loverde, Editor, loverde@uthscsa.edu; C.E. Clayton, Editorial Board; B. Ullman, Editorial Board; A.G. Craig, Reviews Ed., agcraig@liverpool.ac.uk; D.R. Allred, Editorial Board. **ISSN:** 0166-6851. **Subscription Rates:** 619,400¥ institutions; EUR4,659 institutions for European countries; US$5,212 institutions for all countries except Europe and Japan; EUR254 individuals; US$341 individuals; 39,100¥ individuals. **Remarks:** Accepts advertising. **URL:** http://www.elsevier.com/wps/find/journaldescription.cws_home/506086/description. **Circ:** (Not Reported)

48164 ∎ Molecular and Cellular Neurosciences
Elsevier Science B.V.
Radarweg 29
NL-1043 Amsterdam, Netherlands
Ph: 31 204 853911
Fax: 31 204 852457
Peer-reviewed journal containing information on molecular, cellular and tissue levels. **Founded:** 1994. **Freq:** Monthly. **Key Personnel:** O. Isacson, Editor-in-Chief, isacson@hms.harvard.edu; G.M. Beaudoin, Review Ed. **ISSN:** 1044-7431. **Subscription Rates:** US$1,306 institutions for all countries except Europe, Iran and Japan; EUR1,652 institutions European countries and Iran; 172,600¥ institutions; EUR271 individuals European countries and Iran; 28,300¥ individuals; US$236 individuals for all countries except Europe, Iran and Japan; US$109 students for all countries except Europe, Iran and Japan; 13,100¥ students; EUR126 students European countries and Iran. **URL:** http://www.elsevier.com/wps/find/journaldescription.cws_home/622917/description.

48165 ∎ Molecular and Cellular Probes
Elsevier Science
PO Box 211
NL-1000 AE Amsterdam, Netherlands
Ph: 31 204 853757
Fax: 31 204 853432
Publisher E-mail: nlinfo-f@elsevier.com
Medical journal disseminating information on the location, diagnosis, and monitoring of inherited and infectious disease aided by molecular, immunological and proteomic techniques. **Freq:** Bimonthly. **Key Person-**

nel: A. Fox, Editor-in-Chief; R.P. Viscidi, Editor; A. Beaudet, Editorial Board; G. Allmaier, Editorial Board; J.M. Connor, Editorial Board; G. Conrads, Editorial Board; R.B. Gasser, Editor; M. Franklin, Editorial Board; J.T. Epplen, Editor. **ISSN:** 0890-8508. **Subscription Rates:** EUR263 individuals European countries; 28,500¥ individuals; US$258 individuals all countries except Europe and Japan; EUR659 institutions European countries; US$587 institutions all countries except Europe and Japan; 71,200¥ institutions. **Remarks:** Accepts advertising. **URL:** http://www.elsevier.com/wps/find/journaldescription.cws_home/622918/description; http://www.elsevier.com/wps/find/journaldescription.cws_home/622918/descrip tiondescription. **Circ:** (Not Reported)

48166 ∎ Molecular Genetics and Metabolism
Elsevier Science B.V.
Radarweg 29
NL-1043 Amsterdam, Netherlands
Ph: 31 204 853911
Fax: 31 204 852457
Journal publishing papers on original research in the fields of biochemistry, physiologic chemistry, and metabolic biology. **Founded:** 1969. **Freq:** Monthly. **Trim Size:** 8 1/2 x 11. **Key Personnel:** E.R.B. McCabe, Editor-in-Chief; D. Bessman, Editorial Board; M. Bennett, Editorial Board; R. Beitner, Editorial Board; N. Blau, Editorial Board; S.D. Cederbaum, Editorial Board. **ISSN:** 1096-7192. **Subscription Rates:** US$1,474 institutions all countries except Europe, Japan & Iran; EUR1,899 institutions European countries and Iran; 198,400¥ institutions; US$185 students all countries except Europe, Japan & Iran; US$563 individuals all countries except Europe, Japan & Iran; EUR642 individuals European countries and Iran; 67,000¥ individuals; EUR211 students European countries and Iran; 22,100¥ students. **URL:** http://www.elsevier.com/wps/find/journaldescription.cws_home/622920/descriptiondescription. **Formerly:** Biochemical and Molecular Medicine.

48167 ∎ Molecular Immunology
Elsevier Science
PO Box 211
NL-1000 AE Amsterdam, Netherlands
Ph: 31 204 853757
Fax: 31 204 853432
Publisher E-mail: nlinfo-f@elsevier.com
Journal dealing with immunological facts at the molecular, cellular and functional levels of natural and acquired immunity. **Founded:** 1964. **Freq:** 16/yr. **Key Personnel:** M.R. Daha, Editor; J.A. Villadangos, Editor-in-Chief; Z. Fishelson, Advisory Ed.; M. Daeron, Advisory Ed.; A. Erdei, Advisory Ed.; A. Ferreira, Advisory Ed. **ISSN:** 0161-5890. **Subscription Rates:** EUR3,599 institutions European countries; 478,300¥ institutions; US$4,027 institutions all countries except Europe and Japan; EUR400 individuals European countries; US$450 individuals all countries except Europe and Japan; 53,100¥ individuals. **Remarks:** Accepts advertising. **URL:** http://www.elsevier.com/wps/find/journaldescription.cws_home/253/descriptio ndescription. **Circ:** (Not Reported)

48168 ∎ Molecular Phylogenetics and Evolution
Elsevier Science B.V.
Radarweg 29
NL-1043 Amsterdam, Netherlands
Ph: 31 204 853911
Fax: 31 204 852457
Journal containing information on a forum for molecular studies that advance our understanding of phylogeny and evolution. **Founded:** 1992. **Freq:** Monthly. **Trim Size:** 8 1/2 x 11. **Key Personnel:** M. Goodman, Editor-in-Chief; G. Bernardi, Editor; A. Larson, Editor; A.L. Hughes, Editor; D.E. Wildman, Dep. Ed.; S. Richter, Editor; B. Schierwater, Editor; A. Litt, Editor. **ISSN:** 1055-7903. **Subscription Rates:** US$939 institutions; 129,500¥ institutions; EUR1,237 institutions; EUR255 students; 26,600¥ students; US$222 students; EUR506 individuals; US$386 individuals; 52,800¥ individuals. **URL:** http://www.elsevier.com/wps/find/journaldescription.cws_home/622921/descrip tiondescription.

48169 ∎ Narrative Inquiry
John Benjamins Publishing Co.
Klaprozenweg 105
PO Box 36224
NL-1033 NN Amsterdam, Netherlands
Ph: 31 206 304747
Fax: 31 206 739773
Publisher E-mail: benjamins@presswarehouse.com
Peer-reviewed journal featuring a forum for theoretical, empirical, and methodological work on narrative. **Freq:**

Semiannual. **Key Personnel:** Michael Bamberg, Editor; Allyssa McCabe, Editor. **ISSN:** 1387-6740. **Subscription Rates:** EUR80 individuals special; EUR296 institutions backvolumes; EUR296 institutions print + online. **URL:** http://www.benjamins.com/cgi-bin/t_seriesview.cgi?series=NI.

48170 ■ Nature, Culture and Literature
Editions Rodopi B.V.
Tijnmuiden 7
NL-1046 AK Amsterdam, Netherlands
Ph: 31 206 114821
Fax: 31 204 472979
Publisher E-mail: info@rodopi.nl
Journal featuring the ecological perspective of literary and cultural studies. **Key Personnel:** Dr. Hubert F. van den Berg, Editor, h.f.van.den.berg@let.rug.nl; Axel Goodbody, Editor. **ISSN:** 1572-4344. **URL:** http://www.rodopi.nl/senj.asp?SerieId=NCL.

48171 ■ Naunyn-Schmiedeberg's Archives of Pharmacology
Springer-Verlag
c/o Dr. M.C. Michel, Mng. Ed.
Dept. Pharmacology & Pharmacotherapy
Meibergdreef 15
NL-1105 AZ Amsterdam, Netherlands
Fax: 31 20 6965976
Journal dealing with all aspects of Pharmacology. **Founded:** 1873. **Freq:** 6/yr. **Key Personnel:** D. Dobrev, Editor; Dr. M.C. Michel, Managing Editor, naunyn@amc.uva.nl; M. Fromm, Editor; G. Tsujimoto, Editor; E. Schlicker, Editor; P. Molenaar, Editor; M.D. Hamon, Editor; H. Foth, Editor; S. Hegde, Editor. **ISSN:** 0028-1298. **Subscription Rates:** EUR2,619 institutions print incl. free access; EUR3,142.80 institutions print incl. enhanced access. **Remarks:** Advertising accepted; rates available upon request. **URL:** http://www.springer.com/biomed/pharmaceuticalscience/journal/210. **Circ:** (Not Reported)

48172 ■ Neural Networks
Elsevier Science
PO Box 211
NL-1000 AE Amsterdam, Netherlands
Ph: 31 204 853757
Fax: 31 204 853432
Publisher E-mail: nlinfo-f@elsevier.com
Peer-reviewed interdisciplinary journal for all researchers in the field of psychology, neurobiology, mathematics, physics, computer science, and engineering, in connection with the International Neural Network Society, European Neural Network Society and Japanese Neural Network Society. **Founded:** 1988. **Freq:** 10/yr. **Key Personnel:** John G. Taylor, Co-Ed.-in-Ch., john.g.taylor@kcl.ac.uk; Mitsuo Kawato, Editorial Board; Stephen Grossberg, Co-Ed.-in-Ch., steve@cns.bu.edu; Kenji Doya, Co-Ed.-in-Ch.; Dana Z. Anderson, Editorial Board; Bruno Apolloni, Editorial Board. **ISSN:** 0893-6080. **Subscription Rates:** US$362 individuals for all countries except Europe, Japan & Iran; 43,000¥ individuals; EUR325 individuals for European countries & Iran; EUR1,913 institutions for European countries & Iran; US$2,139 institutions for all countries except Europe, Japan & Iran; 254,100¥ institutions. **Remarks:** Accepts advertising. **URL:** http://www.elsevier.com/wps/find/journaldescription.cws_home/841/description. **Circ:** (Not Reported)

48173 ■ Neurobiology of Disease
Elsevier Science B.V.
Radarweg 29
NL-1043 Amsterdam, Netherlands
Ph: 31 204 853911
Fax: 31 204 852457
Scholarly journal covering basic and clinical neuroscience. **Freq:** Monthly. **Key Personnel:** W.C. Mobley, Ed. Emeriti; J.T. Greenamyre, Editor, phone 412648-9793, fax 412648-9766, jgreena@pitt.edu; S. Gilman, Editor-in-Chief, phone 734936-1808, fax 734936-1752, sgilman@umich.edu. **ISSN:** 0969-9961. **Subscription Rates:** US$724 institutions for all countries except Europe, Iran and Japan; 99,900¥ institutions; EUR956 institutions European countries and Iran; 27,700¥ individuals; EUR275 individuals for European countries and Iran; US$232 individuals for all countries except Europe, Iran and Japan; 21,500¥ students; US$181 students for all countries except Europe, Iran and Japan; EUR207 students European countries and Iran. **Remarks:** Accepts advertising. **URL:** http://www.elsevier.com/wps/find/journaldescription.cws_home/622923/descriptiondescription. **Circ:** (Not Reported)

48174 ■ NeuroImage
Elsevier Science B.V.
Radarweg 29
NL-1043 Amsterdam, Netherlands
Ph: 31 204 853911
Fax: 31 204 852457
Journal containing information on all neuroscientific data. **Freq:** 20/yr. **Trim Size:** 8 1/2 x 11. **Key Personnel:** Paul Fletcher, Editor-in-Chief; Michael Breakspear, Handling Ed.; K.J. Friston, Ed. Emeriti; Katrin Amunts, Section Ed.; John Ashburner, Handling Ed.; Michael Breakspear, Handling Ed.; R. Leahy, Handling Ed.; Sonja Kotz, Handling Ed. **ISSN:** 1053-8119. **Subscription Rates:** 323,300¥ institutions; US$2,483 institutions all countries except Europe, Japan & Iran; EUR3,094 institutions European countries and Iran; EUR375 individuals European countries and Iran; US$327 individuals all countries except Europe, Japan & Iran; 39,200¥ individuals; 19,500¥ students; US$162 students. **URL:** http://www.elsevier.com/wps/find/journaldescription.cws_home/622925/descriptiondescription.

48175 ■ Neuropsychiatrie de l'Enfance et de l'Adolescence
Elsevier Science
PO Box 211
NL-1000 AE Amsterdam, Netherlands
Ph: 31 204 853757
Fax: 31 204 853432
Publisher E-mail: nlinfo-f@elsevier.com
Journal on child-adolescent psychiatry. **Freq:** 8/yr. **Key Personnel:** M. Basquin, Editor-in-Chief; P. Ferrari, Assoc. Ed.; P. Mazet, Assoc. Ed.; G. Schmit, Assoc. Ed.; A. Plantade, Assoc. Ed.; Sophie de Jocas, Editorial Asst. **ISSN:** 0222-9617. **URL:** http://www.elsevier.com/wps/find/journaldescription.cws_home/621376/description.

48176 ■ Neuropsychologia
Elsevier Science
PO Box 211
NL-1000 AE Amsterdam, Netherlands
Ph: 31 204 853757
Fax: 31 204 853432
Publisher E-mail: nlinfo-f@elsevier.com
Peer-reviewed journal dealing with all aspects of cognitive and behavioral neuroscience. **Founded:** 1963. **Freq:** 14/yr. **Key Personnel:** S. Bentin, Editorial Advisory Board; M.D. Rugg, Editor-in-Chief, mrugg@uci.edu; R. Adolphs, Editorial Advisory Board; J.P. Aggleton, Editorial Advisory Board; M.T. Banich, Editorial Advisory Board; D.P. Carey, Editorial Advisory Board. **ISSN:** 0028-3932. **Subscription Rates:** US$665 individuals for all countries except Europe, Japan & Iran; 78,800¥ individuals; EUR593 individuals for European countries & Iran; 456,300¥ institutions; EUR3,438 institutions for European countries & Iran; US$3,844 institutions for all countries except Europe, Japan & Iran. **Remarks:** Accepts advertising. **URL:** http://www.elsevier.com/wps/find/journaldescription.cws_home/247/description. **Circ:** (Not Reported)

48177 ■ Neuroscience Letters
Elsevier Science
PO Box 211
NL-1000 AE Amsterdam, Netherlands
Ph: 31 204 853757
Fax: 31 204 853432
Publisher E-mail: nlinfo-f@elsevier.com
Journal for neuroscientists. **Founded:** 1975. **Freq:** 57/yr. **Key Personnel:** S.G. Waxman, Editor-in-Chief; Ausim Azizi, Dep. Ed.; Joel Black, Dep. Ed.; T. Cummins, Assoc. Ed.; J.R. Binder, Assoc. Ed.; B.A. Barres, Assoc. Ed. **ISSN:** 0304-3940. **Subscription Rates:** 1,094,100¥ institutions; US$9,211 institutions for all countries except Europe, Japan & Iran; EUR8,236 institutions for European countries & Iran. **Remarks:** Accepts advertising. **URL:** http://www.elsevier.com/wps/find/journaldescription.cws_home/506081/description. **Circ:** (Not Reported)

48178 ■ Neuroscience Research
Elsevier Science
PO Box 211
NL-1000 AE Amsterdam, Netherlands
Ph: 31 204 853757
Fax: 31 204 853432
Publisher E-mail: nlinfo-f@elsevier.com
Journal covering all branches of neuroscience. **Subtitle:** The Official Journal of the Japan Neuroscience Society. **Founded:** 1984. **Freq:** Monthly. **Key Personnel:** T. Tsu-

moto, Editor-in-Chief; A. Iriki, Editor-in-Chief; M. Ito, Founding Ed.; J. Tanji, Advisory Board; S. Nakanishi, Advisory Board; T. Wiesel, Advisory Board. **ISSN:** 0168-0102. **Subscription Rates:** 218,200¥ institutions; US$1,838 institutions for all countries except Europe, Japan & Iran; EUR1,644 institutions for European countries & Iran. **Remarks:** Accepts advertising. **URL:** http://www.elsevier.com/wps/find/journaldescription.cws_home/506082/description. **Circ:** (Not Reported)

48179 ■ Neurotoxicology and Teratology
Elsevier Science
PO Box 211
NL-1000 AE Amsterdam, Netherlands
Ph: 31 204 853757
Fax: 31 204 853432
Publisher E-mail: nlinfo-f@elsevier.com
Peer-reviewed journal publishing research papers related to the areas of adult neurotoxicology and developmental neurotoxicology, in connection with Behavioral Toxicology Society and the Neurobehavioral Teratology Society. **Founded:** 1979. **Freq:** Bimonthly. **Key Personnel:** Jane Adams, PhD, Editor-in-Chief, jane.adams@umb.edu; Kent W. Anger, Editorial Advisory Board; David Bellinger, Editorial Advisory Board; Scott E. Bowen, Editorial Advisory Board; Judy Buelke-Sam, Editorial Advisory Board; Christina Chambers, Editorial Advisory Board. **ISSN:** 0892-0362. **Subscription Rates:** EUR2,061 institutions for European countries & Iran; US$2,306 institutions for all countries except Europe, Japan & Iran; 273,500¥ institutions; EUR173 individuals for European countries & Iran; US$233 individuals for all countries except Europe, Japan & Iran; 26,800¥ individuals. **Remarks:** Accepts advertising. **URL:** http://www.elsevier.com/wps/find/journaldescription.cws_home/525481/description. **Circ:** (Not Reported)

48180 ■ New Astronomy
Elsevier Science
PO Box 211
NL-1000 AE Amsterdam, Netherlands
Ph: 31 204 853757
Fax: 31 204 853432
Publisher E-mail: nlinfo-f@elsevier.com
Journal publishing articles in all fields of astronomy and astrophysics. **Subtitle:** An International Journal in Astronomy and Astrophysics. **Freq:** 8/yr. **Key Personnel:** P.S. Conti, Receiving Ed.; M. Fukugita, Receiving Ed.; G.F. Gilmore, Receiving Ed. **ISSN:** 1384-1076. **Subscription Rates:** 110,200¥ institutions for Japan; US$927 institutions for all countries except Europe, Japan & Iran; EUR830 institutions for European countries & Iran; US$225 individuals for all countries except Europe, Japan & Iran; 26,400¥ individuals for Japan; EUR198 individuals for European countries & Iran. **Remarks:** Accepts advertising. **URL:** http://www.elsevier.com/wps/find/journaldescription.cws_home/601274/description. **Circ:** (Not Reported)

48181 ■ New Astronomy Reviews
Elsevier Science
PO Box 211
NL-1000 AE Amsterdam, Netherlands
Ph: 31 204 853757
Fax: 31 204 853432
Publisher E-mail: nlinfo-f@elsevier.com
Journal focusing on the fields of astronomy and astrophysics. **Subtitle:** An International Review Journal. **Founded:** 1958. **Freq:** Monthly. **Key Personnel:** J. Audouze, Editor, audouze@iap.fr; Jack Lissauer, Editor, jack.j.lissauer@nasa.gov; L. Kiseleva, Editorial Board; R. Wijers, Editor, r.a.m.j.wijers@uva.nl; P.S. Conti, Editor, pconti@jila.colorado.edu; M. Bailey, Editorial Board; S.V.W. Beckwith, Editorial Board. **ISSN:** 1387-6473. **Subscription Rates:** 156,700¥ institutions; US$1,321 institutions for all countries except Europe, Japan & Iran; EUR1,180 institutions for European countries & Iran; 33,500¥ individuals; EUR217 individuals for European countries & Iran; US$292 individuals for all countries except Europe, Japan & Iran. **Remarks:** Accepts advertising. **URL:** http://www.elsevier.com/wps/find/journaldescription.cws_home/426/description. **Circ:** (Not Reported)

48182 ■ Nitric Oxide
Elsevier Science B.V.
Radarweg 29
NL-1043 Amsterdam, Netherlands
Ph: 31 204 853911
Fax: 31 204 852457
Scholarly journal covering a variety of topics in biology and chemistry. **Subtitle:** Biology and Chemistry. **Freq:** 8/yr. **Key Personnel:** Jack R. Lancaster, PhD, Editor-in-

---

Chief; Ulrich Forstermann, Assoc. Ed.; Takaaki Akaike, Assoc. Ed.; Joshua M. Hare, Assoc. Ed.; Joseph Beckman, Editorial Advisory Board; Christian Bogdan, Editorial Advisory Board. **ISSN:** 1089-8603. **Subscription Rates:** 78,100¥ institutions Japan; US$573 institutions, other countries; EUR749 institutions European countries and Iran; EUR330 individuals European countries and Iran; US$253 U.S. and other countries except Europe, Japan and Iran; 34,600¥ individuals Japan. **Remarks:** Accepts advertising. **URL:** http://www.elsevier.com/wps/find/journaldescription.cws_home/622926/descriptiondescription. **Circ:** (Not Reported)

48183 ■ North American Journal of Economics and Finance
Elsevier Science B.V.
Radarweg 29
NL-1043 Amsterdam, Netherlands
Ph: 31 204 853911
Fax: 31 204 852457
Scholarly journal sponsored by the North American Economics and Finance Association. **Subtitle:** A Journal of Theory and Practice. **Founded:** 1990. **Freq:** 3/yr. **Trim Size:** 6 7/8 x 10. **Key Personnel:** H. Beladi, Managing Editor, psiklos@wlu.ca; M.T. Bohl, Co-Ed.; D.D. VanHoose, Co-Ed. **ISSN:** 1062-9408. **Subscription Rates:** US$121 individuals all countries except Europe, Japan and Iran; US$563 institutions all countries except Europe, Japan and Iran; 15,900¥ individuals; 66,900¥ institutions; EUR504 institutions for European countries; EUR115 individuals for European countries. **Remarks:** Accepts advertising. **URL:** http://www.elsevier.com/wps/find/journaldescription.cws_home/620163/descriptiondescription. **Formerly:** North American Review of Economics and Finance. **Circ:** Paid 300, Non-paid 50

48184 ■ Nuclear Data Sheets
Elsevier Science B.V.
Radarweg 29
NL-1043 Amsterdam, Netherlands
Ph: 31 204 853911
Fax: 31 204 852457
Journal publishing nuclear structure data evaluations and bibliography. **Founded:** 1966. **Freq:** Monthly. **Trim Size:** 8 1/2 x 11. **Key Personnel:** J.K. Tuli, Editor. **ISSN:** 0090-3752. **Subscription Rates:** 258,500¥ institutions; US$1,940 institutions all countries except Europe, Japan and Iran; EUR2,476 institutions European countries and Iran. **URL:** http://www.elsevier.com/wps/find/journaldescription.cws_home/622927/descriptiondescription.

48185 ■ Nuclear Physics A
Elsevier Science
PO Box 211
NL-1000 AE Amsterdam, Netherlands
Ph: 31 204 853757
Fax: 31 204 853432
Publisher E-mail: nlinfo-f@elsevier.com
Journal publishing contributions on nuclear and hadronic physics. Covers nuclear structure and dynamics, intermediate and high energy heavy ion physics, hadronic physics, electromagnetic and weak interactions, and nuclear astrophysics. **Subtitle:** Nuclear and Hadronic Physics. **Founded:** 1956. **Freq:** 68/yr. **Key Personnel:** E. Levin, Assoc. Ed.; G. Baym, Assoc. Ed.; B. Friman, Assoc. Ed.; T. Hatsuda, Assoc. Ed.; B. Jacak, Assoc. Ed. **ISSN:** 0375-9474. **Subscription Rates:** US$9,015 individuals for all countries except Europe, Japan & Iran; EUR8,058 individuals for European countries & Iran; 1,069,600¥ individuals Japan. **Remarks:** Advertising accepted; rates available upon request. **URL:** http://www.elsevier.com/wps/find/journaldescription.cws_home/505715/description. **Circ:** (Not Reported)

48186 ■ Nuclear Physics B
Elsevier Science
PO Box 211
NL-1000 AE Amsterdam, Netherlands
Ph: 31 204 853757
Fax: 31 204 853432
Publisher E-mail: nlinfo-f@elsevier.com
Journal publishing research articles in the area of high energy physics and quantum field theory. Focuses on particle physics, field theory and statistical systems, and physical mathematics. **Subtitle:** Particle Physics, Field Theory and Statistical Systems, Physical Mathematics. **Founded:** 1967. **Freq:** 36/yr. **Key Personnel:** T. Nakada, Supervisory Ed.; D. Kutasov, Supervisory Ed.; A. Schwimmer, Supervisory Ed.; H. Ooguri, Supervisory Ed.; H. Saleur, Supervisory Ed.; L. Maiani, Supervisory

Ed. **ISSN:** 0550-3213. **Subscription Rates:** US$7,405 institutions for all countries except Europe, Japan & Iran; EUR6,620 institutions for European countries & Iran; 879,400¥ institutions Japan. **Remarks:** Advertising accepted; rates available upon request. **URL:** http://www.elsevier.com/wps/find/journaldescription.cws_home/505716/description. **Circ:** (Not Reported)

48187 ■ Nuclear Physics B
Elsevier Science
PO Box 211
NL-1000 AE Amsterdam, Netherlands
Ph: 31 204 853757
Fax: 31 204 853432
Publisher E-mail: nlinfo-f@elsevier.com
Journal covering latest developments and inventions reported at important conferences on high-energy physics and related areas such as particle physics, harmonic physics, cosmology, astrophysics and gravitation, field theory and statistical systems, and physical mathematics. **Subtitle:** Proceedings Supplements (PS). **Founded:** 1987. **Freq:** Monthly. **Key Personnel:** G. Veneziano, Editorial Board; S.J. Brodsky, Editorial Board; G. Parisi, Editorial Board; B. de Wit, Editorial Board; A. Schwimmer, Editorial Board; S. Weinberg, Editorial Board. **ISSN:** 0920-5632. **Subscription Rates:** US$4,471 institutions for all countries except Europe, Japan & Iran; EUR3,996 institutions for European countries & Iran; 530,900¥ institutions. **Remarks:** Advertising accepted; rates available upon request. **URL:** http://www.elsevier.com/wps/find/journaldescription.cws_home/505717/description. **Circ:** (Not Reported)

48188 ■ Nurse Education Today
Elsevier Science
PO Box 211
NL-1000 AE Amsterdam, Netherlands
Ph: 31 204 853757
Fax: 31 204 853432
Publisher E-mail: nlinfo-f@elsevier.com
Journal publishing research articles in nursing, midwifery and health professional education. **Freq:** 8/yr. **Key Personnel:** Martin Johnson, Editor; Sian Maslin-Prothero, Assoc. Ed.; Mike Cook, International Advisory Board; Wendy Hall, Review Ed., hall@nursing.ubc.ca; P.L. Bradshaw, International Advisory Board; P. Burnard, International Advisory Board. **ISSN:** 0260-6917. **Subscription Rates:** US$174 individuals for all countries except Europe, Japan & Iran; EUR184 individuals for European countries & Iran; 20,000¥ individuals Japan; US$796 institutions for all countries except Europe, Japan & Iran; EUR900 institutions for European countries & Iran; 96,800¥ institutions Japan. **Remarks:** Advertising accepted; rates available upon request. **URL:** http://www.elsevier.com/wps/find/journaldescription.cws_home/623061/description. **Circ:** (Not Reported)

48189 ■ Nutrition
Elsevier Science
PO Box 211
NL-1000 AE Amsterdam, Netherlands
Ph: 31 204 853757
Fax: 31 204 853432
Publisher E-mail: nlinfo-f@elsevier.com
Professional journal covering nutrition research and science. **Subtitle:** The International Journal of Applied & Basic Nutritional Sciences. **Founded:** 1984. **Freq:** Monthly. **Trim Size:** 8 1/8 x 10 7/8. **Cols./Page:** 2. **Key Personnel:** Michael M. Meguid, MD, Editor-in-Chief; D. Labadarios, PhD, Regional Ed.; P. Little, MD, Co-Ed. **ISSN:** 0899-9007. **Subscription Rates:** US$965 institutions, other countries; US$397 individuals in US; US$891 institutions; US$449 individuals. **URL:** http://www.elsevier.com/wps/find/journaldescription.cws_home/525614/descriptiondescription.

48190 ■ Operations Research Letters
Elsevier Science
c/o Jan Karel Lenstra, Ed.-in-Ch.
CWI
PO Box 94079
NL-1090 GB Amsterdam, Netherlands
Publisher E-mail: nlinfo-f@elsevier.com
Magazine dealing with all the aspects of operations research and the management and decision sciences. **Founded:** 1982. **Freq:** Bimonthly. **Key Personnel:** Jan Karel Lenstra, Editor-in-Chief, jan.karel.lenstra@cwi.nl; George L. Nemhauser, Founding Ed.; Samuel Burer, Assoc. Ed., samuel-burer@uiowa.edu. **ISSN:** 0167-6377. **Subscription Rates:** EUR811 institutions for European countries & Iran; US$909 institutions for all countries except Europe, Japan & Iran; 107,700¥

institutions. **Remarks:** Advertising accepted; rates available upon request. **URL:** http://www.elsevier.com/wps/find/journaldescription.cws_home/505567/descriptiondescription. **Circ:** (Not Reported)

48191 ■ Optical Fiber Technology
Elsevier Science B.V.
Radarweg 29
NL-1043 Amsterdam, Netherlands
Ph: 31 204 853911
Fax: 31 204 852457
Journal containing information on fiber amplifiers for the electronic regeneration. **Founded:** 1994. **Freq:** Bimonthly. **Trim Size:** 8 1/2 x 11. **Key Personnel:** E. Desurvire, Founding Ed.; M. Chbat, Assoc. Ed.; B. Desthieux, Editor-in-Chief, bertrand_desthieux@hotmail.com; J. Minelly, Assoc. Ed.; E. Snitzer, Honorary Ed.; S. Kinoshita, Assoc. Ed.; M. Nakazawa, Honorary Ed.; J.M. Dudley, Assoc. Ed.; G. Keiser, Assoc. Ed. **ISSN:** 1068-5200. **Subscription Rates:** EUR813 institutions; US$643 institutions; 85,200¥ institutions; EUR96 individuals; US$130 individuals; 14,700¥ individuals. **URL:** http://www.elsevier.com/wps/find/journaldescription.cws_home/622928/descrip tiondescription.

48192 ■ Optical Materials
Elsevier Science
PO Box 211
NL-1000 AE Amsterdam, Netherlands
Ph: 31 204 853757
Fax: 31 204 853432
Publisher E-mail: nlinfo-f@elsevier.com
Journal publishing original articles and review papers on design, synthesis, characterization and applications of optical materials. **Subtitle:** An International Journal on the Physics and Chemistry of Optical Materials and their Applications, including Devices. **Founded:** 1991. **Freq:** Monthly. **Key Personnel:** G. Boulon, Editor-in-Chief, georges.boulon@pcml.univ-lyon1.fr; D. Hreniak, Editorial Asst., hreniak@int.pan.wroc.pl; G.C. Righini, Assoc. Ed.; J. Cybinska, Editorial Asst., jcybinska@interia.pl; T.T. Basiev, Assoc. Ed.; J.P. Huignard, Assoc. Ed.; H.J. Eichler, Assoc. Ed.; C. Klingshirn, Assoc. Ed.; M. Nikl, Assoc. Ed.; J. Zyss, Assoc. Ed.; T.T. Basiev, Assoc. Ed. **ISSN:** 0925-3467. **Subscription Rates:** EUR1,447 institutions for European countries & Iran; US$1,625 institutions for all countries except Europe, Japan & Iran; 192,100¥ institutions. **Remarks:** Advertising accepted; rates available upon request. **URL:** http://www.elsevier.com/wps/find/journaldescription.cws_home/522512/descriptiondescription. **Circ:** (Not Reported)

48193 ■ Optics Communications
Elsevier Science
PO Box 211
NL-1000 AE Amsterdam, Netherlands
Ph: 31 204 853757
Fax: 31 204 853432
Publisher E-mail: nlinfo-f@elsevier.com
Journal dealing with various areas of modern optics. **Founded:** 1969. **Freq:** Semimonthly. **Key Personnel:** W.P. Schleich, Editor, phone 49 731 5023080, fax 49 731 5023086, optcom@uni-ulm.de; S. Maier, Editor, phone 44 20 75946063, fax 44 20 75942077, optcommjournal@imperial.ac.uk; B.J. Eggleton, Editor, phone 61 2 93513604, optcom@physics.usyd.edu.au; Niel Broderick, Advisory Board; Howard J. Carmichael, Advisory Board; Franco Gori, Advisory Board. **ISSN:** 0030-4018. **Subscription Rates:** 991,600¥ institutions; US$8,352 institutions for all countries except Europe, Japan & Iran; EUR7,467 institutions for European countries & Iran; EUR1,243 individuals for European countries & Iran; 165,200¥ individuals; US$1,398 individuals for all countries except Europe, Japan & Iran. **Remarks:** Advertising accepted; rates available upon request. **URL:** http://www.elsevier.com/wps/find/journaldescription.cws_home/505711/descriptiondescription. **Circ:** (Not Reported)

48194 ■ Optics & Laser Technology
Elsevier Science
PO Box 211
NL-1000 AE Amsterdam, Netherlands
Ph: 31 204 853757
Fax: 31 204 853432
Publisher E-mail: nlinfo-f@elsevier.com
Journal focusing on research covering application and development of the technology of optics and lasers. **Freq:** 8/yr. **Key Personnel:** S. James, Editor, s.w.james@cranfield.ac.uk; M. Abushagur, Editorial Advisory Board; H. Albrecht, Editorial Advisory Board. **ISSN:** 0030-3992. **Subscription Rates:** 204,600¥ institutions; US$1,724 institutions for all countries except Europe,

Japan & Iran; EUR1,540 institutions for European countries & Iran. **Remarks:** Advertising accepted; rates available upon request. **URL:** http://www.elsevier.com/wps/find/journaldescription.cws_home/30464/descriptiondescription. **Circ:** (Not Reported)

48195 ■ Ore Geology Reviews
Elsevier Science
PO Box 211
NL-1000 AE Amsterdam, Netherlands
Ph: 31 204 853757
Fax: 31 204 853432
Publisher E-mail: nlinfo-f@elsevier.com
Journal focusing on the latest developments in many fields concerning the study and exploration of ore deposits. **Subtitle:** Journal for Comprehensive Studies of Ore Genesis and Ore Exploration. **Founded:** 1986. **Freq:** 8/yr. **Key Personnel:** N.J. Cook, Editor-in-Chief, phone 61 8 83030686, fax 61 8 83035673, nigel.cook@adelaide.edu.au; G.B. Arehart, Editorial Board; F.P. Bierlein, Editorial Board; I. Graham, Editorial Board; J. Mao, Editorial Board; J. Lexa, Editorial Board. **ISSN:** 0169-1368. **Subscription Rates:** US$1,288 institutions for all countries except Europe, Japan & Iran; EUR1,151 institutions for European countries & Iran; 153,000¥ institutions; EUR159 individuals for European countries & Iran; US$212 individuals for all countries except Europe, Japan & Iran; 24,500¥ individuals. **Remarks:** Advertising accepted; rates available upon request. **URL:** http://www.elsevier.com/wps/find/journaldescription.cws_home/503354/descriptiondescription. **Circ:** (Not Reported)

48196 ■ Organizational Behavior and Human Decision Processes
Elsevier Science B.V.
Radarweg 29
NL-1043 Amsterdam, Netherlands
Ph: 31 204 853911
Fax: 31 204 852457
Scientific journal publishing articles on research and development in human organizational psychology, including the decision processes. **Founded:** 1966. **Freq:** Bimonthly. **Trim Size:** 8 1/2 x 11. **Key Personnel:** Jeffrey R. Edwards, Editorial Board; David A. Harrison, Editorial Board; Paul E. Levy, Assoc. Ed.; Linn van Dyne, Assoc. Ed.; William P. Bottom, Assoc. Ed.; Daan van Knippenberg, Assoc. Ed. **ISSN:** 0749-5978. **Subscription Rates:** 260,700¥ institutions; US$1,999 institutions for all countries except Europe, Iran and Japan; EUR2,495 institutions European countries and Iran; 54,100¥ students; US$414 students for all countries except Europe, Iran and Japan; EUR516 students European countries and Iran; 114,800¥ individuals; US$887 individuals for all countries except Europe, Iran and Japan; EUR1,100 individuals European countries and Iran. **Remarks:** Accepts advertising. **URL:** http://www.elsevier.com/wps/find/journaldescription.cws_home/622929/descriptiondescription. **Circ:** (Not Reported)

48197 ■ Overleven
KWF Kankerbestrijding - Dutch Cancer Society
Delflandlaan 17
NL-1062 EA Amsterdam, Netherlands
Ph: 31 020 5700500
Fax: 31 020 6750302
Publisher E-mail: info@kwfkankerbestrijding.nl
Consumer magazine covering cancer news for hospitals and doctors' offices. **Founded:** June 2002. **ISSN:** 1380-0825. **URL:** http://www.brandingmedia.eu/html/overleven.html.

48198 ■ Pacific-Basin Finance Journal
Elsevier Science
PO Box 211
NL-1000 AE Amsterdam, Netherlands
Ph: 31 204 853757
Fax: 31 204 853432
Publisher E-mail: nlinfo-f@elsevier.com
Journal publishing academic research on capital markets of the Asia-Pacific countries. **Founded:** 1993. **Freq:** 5/yr. **Key Personnel:** C. Cao, Co-Ed.; Ghon S. Rhee, Co-Ed.; J.K. Kang, Co-Ed.; F. Allen, Editorial Board; A. Ang, Editorial Board; A. Bris, Editorial Board. **ISSN:** 0927-538X. **Subscription Rates:** 8,500¥ individuals; EUR60 individuals for European countries & Iran; US$63 individuals for all countries except Europe, Japan & Iran; 83,200¥ institutions; EUR625 institutions for European countries & Iran; US$701 institutions for all countries except Europe, Japan & Iran. **Remarks:** Advertising accepted; rates available upon request. **URL:** http://www.elsevier.com/wps/find/journaldescription.cws_home/523619/descriptiondescription. **Circ:** (Not Reported)

48199 ■ Pharmacological Research
Elsevier Science
PO Box 211
NL-1000 AE Amsterdam, Netherlands
Ph: 31 204 853757
Fax: 31 204 853432
Publisher E-mail: nlinfo-f@elsevier.com
Journal publishing papers on basic and applied pharmacological research in both animals and human being. Includes papers on research areas such as biochemical and molecular pharmacology, cardiovascular and renal pharmacology, smooth muscle and gastrointestinal tract, clinical pharmacology, respiratory tract, inflammation studies and toxicology, neuropharmacology, psychopharmacology, and neuroendocrinology, chemotherapy, and immunopharmacology. **Freq:** 12/yr. **Key Personnel:** T. Florio, Editorial Board; E. Cerbai, Editorial Board; F. Battaini, Editorial Board; J. Doucet, Editorial Board; F. Visioli, PhD, Editor-in-Chief, pharmacolres@snv.jussieu.fr; S.P. Duckles, Editorial Board. **ISSN:** 1043-6618. **Subscription Rates:** 175,300¥ institutions for Japan; EUR1,622 institutions for European countries & Iran; US$1,441 institutions for all countries except Europe, Japan & Iran; EUR179 individuals for European countries & Iran; US$241 individuals for all countries except Europe, Japan & Iran; 27,700¥ individuals for Japan. **Remarks:** Advertising accepted; rates available upon request. **URL:** http://www.elsevier.com/wps/find/journaldescription.cws_home/622931/descriptiondescription. **Circ:** (Not Reported)

48200 ■ Physica B
Elsevier Science
c/o F.R. de Boer, Ed.
Van der Waals-Zeeman Laboratory
Valckenierstraat 65
NL-1018 XE Amsterdam, Netherlands
Ph: 31 205 255717
Publisher E-mail: nlinfo-f@elsevier.com
Peer-reviewed journal dealing with both theoretical and experimental aspects of condensed matter and solid state physics. **Subtitle:** Condensed Matter. **Founded:** 1975. **Freq:** 24/yr. **Key Personnel:** L. Degiorgi, Editor, phone 41 633 1072, degiorgi@solid.phys.ethz.ch; R. Jochemsen, Editor, phone 31 71 5275442, jochemsen@physics.leidenuniv.nl; F.R. de Boer, Editor, f.r.deboer@uva.nl; H. Wada, Editor, phone 81 92 6422549, fax 81 92 6422553, wada@phys.kyushu-u.ac.jp; R. Blinc, Advisory Editorial Board; P. Fulde, Advisory Editorial Board. **ISSN:** 0921-4526. **Subscription Rates:** 1,005,400¥ institutions; US$8,470 institutions for all countries except Europe, Japan & Iran; EUR7,571 institutions for all countries except Europe, Japan & Iran. **Remarks:** Advertising accepted; rates available upon request. **URL:** http://www.elsevier.com/wps/find/journaldescription.cws_home/505712/description. **Circ:** (Not Reported)

48201 ■ Physica E
Elsevier Science
PO Box 211
NL-1000 AE Amsterdam, Netherlands
Ph: 31 204 853757
Fax: 31 204 853432
Publisher E-mail: nlinfo-f@elsevier.com
Peer-reviewed journal dealing with fundamental and applied aspects of physics in low-dimensional systems, including semiconductor heterostructures, mesoscopic systems, quantum wells and superlattices, two-dimensional electron systems, and quantum wires and dots. The areas of interest including optical and transport properties, many-body effects, integer and fractional quantum Hall effects, single electron effects and devices, and novel phenomena. **Subtitle:** Low-Dimensional Systems and Nanostructures. **Founded:** 1997. **Freq:** 10/yr. **Key Personnel:** G. Abstreiter, Advisory Editorial Board; T. Chakraborty, Editor, phone 204474-7041, fax 204474-7622, tapash@physics.umanitoba.ca; M.W. Wu, Editor, phone 86 551 3603524, mwwu@ustc.edu.cn. **ISSN:** 1386-9477. **Subscription Rates:** 239,100¥ institutions; US$2,020 institutions for all countries except Europe, Japan & Iran; EUR1,803 institutions for European countries & Iran. **Remarks:** Accepts advertising. **URL:** http://www.elsevier.com/wps/find/journaldescription.cws_home/600554/description. **Circ:** (Not Reported)

48202 ■ Physics and Chemistry of the Earth
Elsevier Science
PO Box 211
NL-1000 AE Amsterdam, Netherlands
Ph: 31 204 853757
Fax: 31 204 853432
Publisher E-mail: nlinfo-f@elsevier.com
Peer-reviewed journal. Part A covers geology, geochemistry, tectonophysics, seismology, volcanology, paleomagnetism and rock magnetism, electromagnetism and potential fields, marine and environmental sciences, and geodesy. Part B covers hydrology and water resources research, engineering and management, oceanography and oceanic chemistry, shelf, sea, lake and river sciences, meteorology and atmospheric sciences, climatology, and glaciology. Part C covers solar, heliospheric and solar-planetary sciences, geology, geophysics, atmospheric sciences of planets, satellites, and small bodies, and cosmochemistry and exobiology. **Founded:** 1956. **Freq:** 18/yr. **Key Personnel:** J.H. Gottsmann, Editor-in-Chief, j.gottsmann@bristol.ac.uk; H.P. Plag, Editor-in-Chief, hpplag@unr.edu; H.H.G. Savenije, Editor-in-Chief, h.h.g.savenije@tudelft.nl. **ISSN:** 1474-7065. **Subscription Rates:** US$3,241 institutions for all countries except Europe, Japan and Iran; 384,800¥ institutions; EUR2,896 institutions for European countries and Iran. **Remarks:** Advertising accepted; rates available upon request. **URL:** http://www.elsevier.com/wps/find/journaldescription.cws_home/413/descriptiondescription. **Absorbed:** Physics and Chemistry of the Earth, Part A (2002); Physics and Chemistry of the Earth, Part B (2002); Physics and Chemistry of the Earth, Part C (2002). **Circ:** (Not Reported)

48203 ■ Physics Reports
Elsevier Science
PO Box 211
NL-1000 AE Amsterdam, Netherlands
Ph: 31 204 853757
Fax: 31 204 853432
Publisher E-mail: nlinfo-f@elsevier.com
Journal focusing on current trends on a wide spectrum of topics in physics. **Subtitle:** A Review Section of Physics Letters. **Founded:** 1971. **Freq:** 60/yr. **Key Personnel:** M Kamionkowski, Editorial Board, kamion@tapir.caltech.edu; J. Eichler, Editorial Board, eichler@helmholtz-berlin.de; D.L. Mills, Editorial Board, dlmills@uci.edu. **ISSN:** 0370-1573. **Subscription Rates:** EUR6,783 institutions for European countries & Iran; 899,600¥ institutions; US$7,589 institutions for all countries except Europe, Japan & Iran. **Remarks:** Advertising accepted; rates available upon request. **URL:** http://www.elsevier.com/wps/find/journaldescription.cws_home/505703/description. **Circ:** (Not Reported)

48204 ■ Planetary and Space Science
Elsevier Science
PO Box 211
NL-1000 AE Amsterdam, Netherlands
Ph: 31 204 853757
Fax: 31 204 853432
Publisher E-mail: nlinfo-f@elsevier.com
Official journal of the Planetary and Solar System Sciences Section of the European Geophysical Society. Covers cosmochemistry and origin; small bodies, dust, and rings; terrestrial planets and satellites; outer planets and satellites; planetary atmospheres; planetary magnetospheres and ionospheres; exobiology; celestial mechanics; and the history of planetary and space research. **Founded:** 1959. **Freq:** 15/yr. **Key Personnel:** R. Schulz, Editor-in-Chief; J.E. Arlot, Advisory Ed.; R. Courtin, Advisory Ed. **ISSN:** 0032-0633. **Subscription Rates:** US$4,151 institutions for all countries except Europe, Japan and Iran; 492,500¥ institutions; EUR3,712 institutions for European countries and Iran; EUR401 individuals for European countries and Iran; US$450 individuals for all countries except Europe, Japan and Iran; 53,300¥ individuals. **Remarks:** Advertising not accepted. **URL:** http://www.elsevier.com/wps/find/journaldescription.cws_home/200/descriptiondescription. **Circ:** (Not Reported)

48205 ■ Plant Physiology and Biochemistry
Elsevier Science
PO Box 211
NL-1000 AE Amsterdam, Netherlands
Ph: 31 204 853757
Fax: 31 204 853432
Publisher E-mail: nlinfo-f@elsevier.com
Peer-reviewed journal focusing on current advances in embraces physiology, biochemistry, molecular biology, biophysics, structure and genetics at different levels, from the molecular to the whole plant and environment. **Founded:** 1962. **Freq:** Monthly. **Key Personnel:** Jean-

Circulation: ★ = ABC; △ = BPA; ♦ = CAC; • = CCAB; ❑ = VAC; ⊕ = PO Statement; ‡ = Publisher's Report; Boldface figures = sworn; Light figures = estimated.

Claude Kader, Editor-in-Chief, jean-claude.kader@jussieu.org; R. Antunes de Azevedo, Advisory Board; H. Asard, Advisory Board; S. Baud, Advisory Board; D.P. Briskin, Advisory Board; D. Dixon, Advisory Board. **ISSN:** 0981-9428. **Subscription Rates:** 123,400¥ institutions; EUR929 institutions for European countries & Iran; US$1,043 institutions for all countries except Europe, Japan & Iran; 34,000¥ individuals for Japan; EUR221 individuals for European countries & Iran; US$296 individuals for all countries except Europe, Japan & Iran. **Remarks:** Advertising accepted; rates available upon request. **URL:** http://www.elsevier.com/wps/find/journaldescription.cws_home/600784/description. **Circ:** (Not Reported)

48206 ■ Plasmid
Elsevier Science B.V.
Radarweg 29
NL-1043 Amsterdam, Netherlands
Ph: 31 204 853911
Fax: 31 204 852457
Journal focuses on the biology of extrachromosoinal genetic elements in both prokaryotic eukaryotic systems, including their biological behavior, molecular structure, genetic function, their genetic products, and their use of genetic tools. **Subtitle:** A Journal of Mobile Genomes and Genome. **Founded:** 1977. **Freq:** Bimonthly. **Trim Size:** 6 7/8 x 10. **Key Personnel:** R. Bernander, Editor; R. Calendar, Editor; D. Chattoraj, MD, Editor-in-Chief; M. Espinosa, Editor; S.B. Levy, Editor; A.M. Chakrabarty, Editor; M. Chandler, Editor; I. Kobayashi, Editor; M. Salas, Editor. **ISSN:** 0147-619X. **Subscription Rates:** EUR1,171 institutions European countries and Iran; US$931 institutions all countries except Europe, Japan & Iran; 122,500¥ institutions; EUR387 individuals European countries and Iran; EUR387 individuals all countries except Europe, Japan & Iran; 40,400¥ individuals; US$96 students all countries except Europe, Japan & Iran; 11,300¥ students; EUR108 students European countries and Iran. **Remarks:** Accepts advertising. **URL:** http://www.elsevier.com/wps/find/journaldescription.cws_home/622933/descriptiondescription. **Circ:** (Not Reported)

48207 ■ Poetics
Elsevier Science
PO Box 211
NL-1000 AE Amsterdam, Netherlands
Ph: 31 204 853757
Fax: 31 204 853432
Publisher E-mail: nlinfo-f@elsevier.com
Peer-reviewed journal devoted to theoretical and empirical research on culture, the media and the arts with emphasis on psychology, sociology, and economics. **Subtitle:** Journal of Empirical Research on Culture, the Media and the Arts. **Founded:** 1972. **Freq:** Bimonthly. **Key Personnel:** K. van Rees, Editor; P. Dimaggio, Assoc. Ed.; Teun van Dijk, Founding Ed.; S. Baumann, Advisory Ed.; K. Cerulo, Advisory Ed.; D. Grazian, Advisory Ed. **ISSN:** 0304-422X. **Subscription Rates:** 75,700¥ institutions; EUR572 institutions for European countries & Iran; US$639 institutions for all countries except Europe, Japan & Iran; 13,300¥ individuals; EUR90 individuals for European countries & Iran; US$119 individuals for all countries except Europe, Japan & Iran. **Remarks:** Advertising accepted; rates available upon request. **URL:** http://www.elsevier.com/wps/find/journaldescription.cws_home/505592/descriptiondescription. **Circ:** (Not Reported)

48208 ■ Polish Analytical Philosophy
Editions Rodopi B.V.
Tijnmuiden 7
NL-1046 AK Amsterdam, Netherlands
Ph: 31 206 114821
Fax: 31 204 472979
Publisher E-mail: info@rodopi.nl
Journal focusing on analytical philosophy. **Key Personnel:** Jacek Juliusz Jadacki, Editor-in-Chief; Leszek Nowak, Editor. **ISSN:** 1389-6768. **URL:** http://www.rodopi.nl/senj.asp?SerieId=POLISHANA.

48209 ■ Polymer
Elsevier Science
PO Box 211
NL-1000 AE Amsterdam, Netherlands
Ph: 31 204 853757
Fax: 31 204 853432
Publisher E-mail: nlinfo-f@elsevier.com
Journal publishing original research, related to all areas of polymer science and technology. **Subtitle:** The International Journal for the Science and Technology of Polymers. **Freq:** 26/yr. **Key Personnel:** Matthias Ballauff, Editor, matthias.ballauff@helmholtz-berlin.de; T.

Hashimoto, Sen. Ed., hashimoto.takeji@jaea.go.jp; Y. Imanishi, Honorary Ed.; S.Z.D. Cheng, Sen. Ed., cheng@uakron.edu; W.W. Adams, Editorial Advisory Board; R.J. Composto, Editorial Advisory Board. **ISSN:** 0032-3861. **Subscription Rates:** 1,061,200¥ institutions; US$8,942 institutions for all countries except Europe, Japan & Iran; EUR7,992 institutions for European countries & Iran; EUR582 individuals for European countries & Iran; US$656 individuals for all countries except Europe, Japan & Iran; 77,300¥ individuals. **Remarks:** Advertising accepted; rates available upon request. **URL:** http://www.elsevier.com/wps/find/journaldescription.cws_home/30466/description. **Circ:** (Not Reported)

48210 ■ Powder Technology
Elsevier Science
PO Box 211
NL-1000 AE Amsterdam, Netherlands
Ph: 31 204 853757
Fax: 31 204 853432
Publisher E-mail: nlinfo-f@elsevier.com
Journal focusing on the science and technology of Wet and Dry Particulate Systems. **Subtitle:** An International Journal on the Science and Technology of Wet and Dry Particulate Systems. **Founded:** 1968. **Freq:** 27/yr. **Key Personnel:** J.P.K. Seville, Editor-in-Chief, phone 44 24 76522923, fax 44 24 76418922, powdertechnology@warwick.ac.uk; M. Adams, Editorial Board; H. Arastoopour, Editorial Board. **ISSN:** 0032-5910. **Subscription Rates:** 548,500¥ institutions; US$4,617 institutions for all countries except Europe, Japan & Iran; EUR4,128 institutions for European countries & Iran. **Remarks:** Advertising accepted; rates available upon request. **URL:** http://www.elsevier.com/wps/find/journaldescription.cws_home/504094/descriptiondescription. **Circ:** (Not Reported)

48211 ■ Pragmatics & Cognition
John Benjamins Publishing Co.
Klaprozenweg 105
PO Box 36224
NL-1033 NN Amsterdam, Netherlands
Ph: 31 206 304747
Fax: 31 206 739773
Publisher E-mail: benjamins@presswarehouse.com
Peer-reviewed journal covering philosophy, linguistics, semiotics, cognitive science, neuroscience, artificial intelligence, ethology, and cognitive anthropology. **Founded:** 1981. **Freq:** 3/yr. **Print Method:** Offset. **Trim Size:** 8 1/4 x 11 1/4. **Cols./Page:** 3. **Col. Width:** 27 nonpareils. **Col. Depth:** 140 agate lines. **Key Personnel:** Yorick Wilks, Assoc. Ed.; Itiel E. Dror, Assoc. Ed.; Stephen Stich, Assoc. Ed.; Jens Allwood, Assoc. Ed.; Benny Shanon, Assoc. Ed.; Marcelo Dascal, Editor. **ISSN:** 0929-0907. **Subscription Rates:** EUR425 individuals print + online; EUR80 individuals special. **URL:** http://www.benjamins.com/cgi-bin/t_seriesview.cgi?series=P%26C.

48212 ■ Pratiques Psychologiques
Elsevier Science
PO Box 211
NL-1000 AE Amsterdam, Netherlands
Ph: 31 204 853757
Fax: 31 204 853432
Publisher E-mail: nlinfo-f@elsevier.com
Journal covering all aspects of psychology. **Founded:** 2004. **Freq:** Quarterly. **Key Personnel:** Jean-Luc Bernaud, Publishing Dir.; Dana Castro, Editor-in-Chief; G. Lemmel, Editorial Board. **ISSN:** 1269-1763. **URL:** http://www.elsevier.com/wps/find/journaldescription.cws_home/681012/description.

48213 ■ Precambrian Research
Elsevier Science
PO Box 211
NL-1000 AE Amsterdam, Netherlands
Ph: 31 204 853757
Fax: 31 204 853432
Publisher E-mail: nlinfo-f@elsevier.com
Journal publishing studies on all aspects of geology. **Founded:** 1974. **Freq:** 32/yr. **Key Personnel:** W. Mueller, Editor, phone 418545-5013, fax 418545-5012, wmueller@uqac.ca; P.A. Cawood, Editor, phone 61 8 64883422, fax 61 8 64881090, pcawood@tsrc.uwa.edu.au; R.R. Parrish, Editor, phone 44 115 9363427, fax 44 115 9363302, rrp@nigl.nerc.ac.uk. **ISSN:** 0301-9268. **Subscription Rates:** 418,400¥ institutions for Japan; EUR3,152 institutions for European countries and Iran; US$3,528 institutions all countries except Europe, Japan and Iran; 52,600¥ individuals for Japan; EUR391 individuals for European countries and Iran; US$441 individuals

all countries except Europe, Japan and Iran. **URL:** http://www.elsevier.com/wps/find/journaldescription.cws_home/503357/description.

48214 ■ Preventive Medicine
Elsevier Science B.V.
Radarweg 29
NL-1043 Amsterdam, Netherlands
Ph: 31 204 853911
Fax: 31 204 852457
Medical journal covering epidemiology and public health, with a clinical section geared toward physicians; emphasizes chronic lifestyle-related diseases. **Founded:** Mar. 1972. **Freq:** Monthly. **Trim Size:** 8 1/2 x 11. **Key Personnel:** Alfredo Morabia, PhD, Editor-in-Chief, preventive.medicine@qc.cuny.edu; Michael C. Constanza, PhD, Editor; Herman van Oyen, MD, Assoc. Ed. **ISSN:** 0091-7435. **Subscription Rates:** 170,300¥ institutions; US$1,238 institutions, other countries except Europe, Japan and Iran; EUR1,629 institutions European countries and Iran; 71,800¥ individuals; US$526 other countries except Europe, Japan and Iran; EUR689 individuals European countries and Iran; 15,100¥ students; US$129 students except Europe, Japan and Iran; EUR146 students European countries and Iran. **Remarks:** Accepts advertising. **Circ:** (Not Reported)

48215 ■ Probus
Walter de Gruyter GmbH & Co. KG
c/o Leo W. Wetzels, Ed.-in-Ch.
Dept. of Linguistics, Vrije Universiteit Amsterdam
De Boelelaan 1105
NL-1081 HV Amsterdam, Netherlands
Publisher E-mail: info@degruyter.com
Peer-reviewed journal dealing with historical and synchronic research in the field of Latin and Romance linguistics, with special emphasis on phonology, morphology, syntax, language acquisition and sociolinguistics. **Subtitle:** International Journal of Latin and Romance Linguistics. **Freq:** Semiannual. **Print Method:** Offset. **Trim Size:** 240 mm. x 160 mm. **Key Personnel:** Leo W. Wetzels, Editor-in-Chief, wlm.wetzels@let.vu.nl. **ISSN:** 0921-4771. **Subscription Rates:** EUR209 individuals print or online; EUR240 individuals print and online; EUR115 single issue. **Remarks:** Accepts advertising. **URL:** http://www.degruyter.de/journals/probus/detailEn.cfm. **Ad Rates:** BW: 350 f. **Circ:** (Not Reported)

48216 ■ Progress in Surface Science
Elsevier Science
PO Box 211
NL-1000 AE Amsterdam, Netherlands
Ph: 31 204 853757
Fax: 31 204 853432
Publisher E-mail: nlinfo-f@elsevier.com
Journal publishing contributions on various aspects of surface science by invited authors of repute. Seeks to promote exchange of views amongst surface scientists in various fields. **Founded:** 1971. **Freq:** Monthly. **Key Personnel:** A.W. Kleyn, Editorial Board, kleyn@rijnh.nl; H. Petek, Editor-in-Chief, progss@pitt.edu; M. Bonn, Editorial Board, bonn@amolf.nl. **ISSN:** 0079-6816. **Subscription Rates:** US$2,561 institutions for all countries except Europe and Japan; 303,800¥ institutions; EUR2,288 institutions European countries; US$171 individuals; 19,700¥ individuals; EUR129 individuals. **Remarks:** Accepts advertising. **URL:** http://www.elsevier.com/wps/find/journaldescription.cws_home/411/description. **Circ:** (Not Reported)

48217 ■ Protein Expression and Purification
Elsevier Science B.V.
Radarweg 29
NL-1043 Amsterdam, Netherlands
Ph: 31 204 853911
Fax: 31 204 852457
Journal providing information about protein isolation and techniques practicing various molecular biological procedures. **Founded:** 1994. **Freq:** Monthly. **Trim Size:** 8 1/2 x 11. **Key Personnel:** Z.F. Burton, Exec. Ed.; R.R. Burgess, Editor-in-Chief; J.M. Cregg, Exec. Ed.; W.H. Campbell, Exec. Ed.; S. Black, Editorial Board; B.G. Fox, Editorial Board; Y.C. Chao, Editorial Board; J.J. Dunn, Exec. Ed.; G. Georgiou, Editorial Board. **ISSN:** 1046-5928. **Subscription Rates:** EUR1,208 institutions European countries and Iran; 126;300¥ institutions; US$916 institutions except Europe, Iran and Japan; EUR257 students European countries and Iran; US$227 students except Europe, Iran and Japan; 26,800¥ students; EUR519 individuals European countries and Iran; US$394 individuals except Europe, Iran and Japan; 54,100¥ individuals. **URL:** http://www.elsevier.com/wps/

find/journaldescription.cws_home/622935/
descriptiondescription.

48218 ■ Psychologie Francaise
Elsevier Science
PO Box 211
NL-1000 AE Amsterdam, Netherlands
Ph: 31 204 853757
Fax: 31 204 853432
Publisher E-mail: nlinfo-f@elsevier.com
Journal publishing papers relating to psychology, in connection with Societe francaise de psychologie. **Founded:** 2004. **Freq:** Quarterly. **Key Personnel:** Denis Brouillet, Editor-in-Chief; Gerard Poussin, Editorial Board; Eric Raufaste, Editorial Board. **ISSN:** 0033-2984. **URL:** http://www.elsevier.com/wps/find/journaldescription.cws_home/681015/description.

48219 ■ Radiation Physics and Chemistry
Elsevier Science
PO Box 211
NL-1000 AE Amsterdam, Netherlands
Ph: 31 204 853757
Fax: 31 204 853432
Publisher E-mail: nlinfo-f@elsevier.com
Journal focusing on research and developments in radiation physics, radiation chemistry and radiation processing. **Subtitle:** The Journal for Radiation Physics, Radiation Chemistry and Radiation Processing. **Founded:** 1969. **Freq:** Monthly. **Key Personnel:** C. Chantler, Editor-in-Chief, chantler@unimelb.edu.au; A. Miller, Editor-in-Chief, arne.miller@risoe.dk; L. Wojnarovits, Editor-in-Chief, wojn@iki.kfki.hu. **ISSN:** 0969-806X. **Subscription Rates:** US$623 individuals for countries except Europe, Japan and Iran; 73,500¥ individuals in Japan; EUR554 individuals for European countries and Iran; EUR2,644 institutions for European countries and Iran; US$2,955 institutions for countries except Europe, Japan and Iran; 350,500¥ institutions in Japan. **URL:** http://www.elsevier.com/wps/find/journaldescription.cws_home/331/description.

48220 ■ Regulatory Toxicology and Pharmacology
Elsevier Science B.V.
Radarweg 29
NL-1043 Amsterdam, Netherlands
Ph: 31 204 853911
Fax: 31 204 852457
Journal presents significant development, public opinion, scientific data, ideas that bridge the gap between scientific information, legal aspects of Toxicological, and Pharmacological regulations. **Subtitle:** Official Journal of the International Society of Regulatory Toxicology and Pharmacology. **Founded:** 1981. **Freq:** 9/yr. **Trim Size:** 8 1/2 x 11. **Key Personnel:** Gio B. Gori, Editor; Jay I. Goodman, Assoc. Ed.; Friedhelm Korte, Assoc. Ed. **ISSN:** 0273-2300. **Subscription Rates:** EUR1,527 institutions European countries and Iran; 159,100¥ institutions; US$1,177 institutions all countries except Europe, Japan & Iran; EUR677 individuals European countries and Iran; US$522 individuals all countries except Europe, Japan & Iran; 70,800¥ individuals; EUR208 students European countries and Iran; US$182 students all countries except Europe, Japan & Iran; 21,800¥ students. **Remarks:** Accepts advertising. **URL:** http://www.elsevier.com/wps/find/journaldescription.cws_home/622939/descriptiondescription. **Circ:** (Not Reported)

48221 ■ Research in Economics
Elsevier Science B.V.
Radarweg 29
NL-1043 Amsterdam, Netherlands
Ph: 31 204 853911
Fax: 31 204 852457
Scholarly journal covering research in all fields of economics worldwide. **Subtitle:** An International Review of Economics. **Founded:** 1947. **Freq:** Quarterly. **Key Personnel:** G. Codognato, Assoc. Ed.; G. Cazzavillan, Editor; A. Brugiavini, Co-Ed.; L. Anderlini, Assoc. Ed.; J. Banks, Assoc. Ed.; P. Reichlin, Co-Ed. **ISSN:** 1090-9443. **Subscription Rates:** EUR766 institutions European countries and Iran; 82,800¥ institutions; US$681 institutions all countries except Europe, Japan and Iran; 8,900¥ individuals; EUR84 individuals European countries and Iran; US$98 individuals all countries except Europe, Japan and Iran. **Remarks:** Accepts advertising. **URL:** http://www.elsevier.com/wps/find/journaldescription.cws_home/622941/descriptiondescription. **Circ:** (Not Reported)

48222 ■ Residence
TTG—De Telegraaf Tijdschriften Groep B.V.

PO Box 905
NL-1000 AX Amsterdam, Netherlands
Publication E-mail: residence@residence.nl
Publisher E-mail: redactie@autovisie.nl
Consumer magazine covering interior design and homes. **Freq:** Monthly. **Print Method:** Offset. **Trim Size:** 230 x 297 mm. **Key Personnel:** Marian De Schipper, Text Ed.; Trudy Veenhoven, Design; Marco De Vries, Text Ed.; Steven Van Manen, Editor-in-Chief; Lilian Polderman, Editorial Board; Rensker Schriemer, Editorial Board. **Remarks:** Accepts advertising. **URL:** http://www.ttg.nl/residence/index.xml?__toolbar=0. **Ad Rates:** 4C: EUR6,105. **Circ:** Paid ‡33,556

48223 ■ Review of Cognitive Linguistics
John Benjamins Publishing Co.
Klaprozenweg 105
PO Box 36224
NL-1033 NN Amsterdam, Netherlands
Ph: 31 206 304747
Fax: 31 206 739773
Publisher E-mail: benjamins@pressrwarehouse.com
Peer-reviewed journal aiming to establish itself as an international forum for the publication of high-quality original research on all areas of linguistic enquiry from a cognitive perspective. **Freq:** Annual. **Key Personnel:** Francisco Jose Ruiz De Mendoza Ibanez, Editor-in-Chief; Maria Sandra Pena Cervel, Review Ed. **ISSN:** 1572-0268. **Subscription Rates:** EUR180 individuals print + online; EUR70 individuals special. **URL:** http://www.benjamins.com/cgi-bin/t_seriesview.cgi?series=RCL. **Formerly:** Annual Review of Cognitive Linguistics.

48224 ■ Review of Economic Dynamics
Elsevier Science B.V.
Radarweg 29
NL-1043 Amsterdam, Netherlands
Ph: 31 204 853911
Fax: 31 204 852457
Scholarly journal covering economics for the Society for Economic Dynamics. **Freq:** Quarterly. **Key Personnel:** M. Boldrin, Assoc. Ed.; D. Backus, Editor; G.D. Hansen, Assoc. Ed.; M. Bassetto, Editor; R.E. Lucas, Jr., Editor; U.J. Jermann, Editor. **ISSN:** 1094-2025. **Subscription Rates:** US$641 institutions for all countries except Europe, Iran and Japan; 77,100¥ institutions; EUR737 institutions European countries and Iran; EUR140 individuals European countries and Iran; US$107 individuals for all countries except Europe, Iran and Japan; 15,000¥ individuals; US$110 students for all countries except Europe, Iran and Japan; 8,000¥ students; EUR74 students European countries and Iran. **Remarks:** Accepts advertising. **URL:** http://www.elsevier.com/wps/find/journaldescription.cws_home/622942/descriptiondescription. **Circ:** (Not Reported)

48225 ■ Revista Europea de Estudios Latinoamericanos y del Caribe
Centre for Latin American Research and Documentation
Keizersgracht 395-397
NL-1016 EK Amsterdam, Netherlands
Ph: 31 20 5253498
Fax: 31 20 6255127
Publisher E-mail: secretariat@cedla.uva.nl
Publication covering academic studies in anthropology, archeology, demography, economics, ecology, political science, and history, specifically pertaining Latin America and the Caribbean. **Subtitle:** European Review of Latin American and Caribbean Studies. **Founded:** June 1965. **Freq:** Semiannual. **Trim Size:** 16 x 24 cm. **Key Personnel:** K. Willingham, Desk Ed., k.willingham@cedla.nl; Dr. Barbara Hogenboom, Book Review Ed., b.b.hogenboom@cedla.nl; Dr. Mario A. Fumerton, Editor, mario.fumerton@let.uu.nl; Prof. Michiel Baud, Managing Editor, j.m.baud@cedla.nl. **ISSN:** 0924-0608. **Subscription Rates:** EUR45 institutions and libraries; EUR20 individuals includes postage by surface mail; EUR10 individuals for priority mail (airmail). **Remarks:** Advertising not accepted. **URL:** http://www.cedla.uva.nl/50_publications/erlacs.html. **Formerly:** Boletin de Estudios Latinoamericanos y del Caribe (1989). **Circ:** (Not Reported)

48226 ■ Rhinology
European Rhinologic Society
PO Box 22 660
NL-1100 DD Amsterdam, Netherlands
Fax: 31 20 5666490
Publication E-mail: info@rhinologyjournal.com
Publisher E-mail: ers2006isian@congreszon.fi
Publication covering otorhinolaryngology. **Founded:**

1963. **Freq:** Quarterly. **Key Personnel:** Dr. Valerie J. Lund, Editor-in-Chief; Dr. Wilfred T.V. Germeraad, Managing Editor; Dr. Egbert H. Huizing, Honorary Ed. **ISSN:** 0300-0729. **Subscription Rates:** Included in membership. **Remarks:** Advertising accepted; rates available upon request. **URL:** http://www.rhinologyjournal.com. **Circ:** 1,500

48227 ■ Rotarian
Redactie De Rotarian
Stichting Rotary Administratie Nederland
Amstel 266
NL-1017 AM Amsterdam, Netherlands
Ph: 31 206 232405
Fax: 31 206 227642
Publisher E-mail: rotarian@rotarynederland.nl
Membership magazine of Rotary International covering current news about Rotary-related subjects. **Founded:** 1947. **Freq:** Monthly 11/yr. **Key Personnel:** Marcel Harlaar, Editor. **URL:** http://www.rotary.nl/; http://www.rotary.org/en/mediaandnews/morepublications/regionalmagazines/pages/ridefault.aspx. **Circ:** ★20,000

48228 ■ Russian Literature
Elsevier Science Inc.
c/o W.G. Weststeijn, Ed.-in-Ch.
University of Amsterdam
Slavic Seminar, Spuistraat 210
1012 Amsterdam, Netherlands
Ph: 31 20 5253070
Fax: 31 20 5253052
Publisher E-mail: usinfo-ehelp@elsevier.com
Peer-reviewed journal focusing on the special topics of Russian literature with contributions on related subjects in Croatian, Serbian, Czech, Slovak and Polish literatures. **Founded:** Nov. 11, 1973. **Freq:** 8/yr. **Print Method:** Offset. **Trim Size:** 5 1/2 x 8 1/2. **Cols./Page:** 1. **Col. Width:** 50 nonpareils. **Col. Depth:** 100 agate lines. **Key Personnel:** A.A. Hansen-Love, Editorial Board; E.A de Haard, Managing Editor; W. Schmid, Editorial Board; R.L. Jackson, Editorial Board; L.M. O'Toole, Editorial Board; W.G. Weststeijn, Editor-in-Chief. **ISSN:** 0304-3479. **Subscription Rates:** EUR1,160 institutions for European countries and Iran; 153,800¥ institutions; US$1,297 institutions, other countries except Europe, Japan and Iran; US$103 other countries except Europe, Japan and Iran; 9,900¥ individuals Japan; EUR78 individuals for European countries and Iran. **URL:** http://www.elsevier.com/wps/find/journaldescription.cws_home/505594/descriptiondescription.

48229 ■ Scandinavian Journal of Management
Elsevier Science
PO Box 211
NL-1000 AE Amsterdam, Netherlands
Ph: 31 204 853757
Fax: 31 204 853432
Publisher E-mail: nlinfo-f@elsevier.com
Journal focusing on management in private and public organizations. **Subtitle:** Official Journal of the Nordic Academy of Management. **Founded:** 1989. **Freq:** Quarterly. **Key Personnel:** Y. Benschop, Editorial Board; N. Brunsson, Editorial Board; Robyn Thomas, Editorial Board; Juha Laurila, Editorial Board; Janne Tienari, Editor, janne.tienari@hse.fi; Andreas Werr, Assoc. Editor. **ISSN:** 0956-5221. **Subscription Rates:** 119,800¥ institutions; EUR901 institutions for European countries & Iran; US$1,007 institutions for all countries except Europe, Japan & Iran. **Remarks:** Accepts advertising. **URL:** http://www.elsevier.com/wps/find/journaldescription.cws_home/872/descriptiondescription. **Circ:** (Not Reported)

48230 ■ Seminars in Cell & Developmental Biology
Elsevier Science B.V.
Radarweg 29
NL-1043 Amsterdam, Netherlands
Ph: 31 204 853911
Fax: 31 204 852457
Scholarly journal covering cell and developmental biology for scientists. **Freq:** 9/yr. **Key Personnel:** John Davey, Editor-in-Chief; Matthew Freeman, Editorial Advisory Board; David R. Garrod, Editorial Advisory Board. **ISSN:** 1084-9521. **Subscription Rates:** EUR241 individuals European countries and Iran; 25,800¥ individuals; US$230 individuals for all countries except Europe, Iran and Japan; EUR900 institutions European countries and Iran; 97,100¥ institutions; US$799 institutions for all countries except Europe, Iran and Japan. **Remarks:** Accepts advertising. **URL:** http://www.elsevier.com/wps/find/journaldescription.cws_home/

Circulation: ★ = ABC; △ = BPA; ◆ = CAC; ● = CCAB; □ = VAC; ⊕ = PO Statement; ‡ = Publisher's Report; Boldface figures = sworn; Light figures = estimated.

622944/descriptiondescription. Circ: (Not Reported)

48231 ■ Shock and Vibration
IOS Press, B.V.
Nieuwe Hemweg 6B
NL-1013 BG Amsterdam, Netherlands
Ph: 31 20 6883355
Fax: 31 20 6203419
Publisher E-mail: info@iospress.nl
Journal containing information relevant to shock and vibration engineering. Topics range from vibration testing and control to statistical energy analysis. **Freq:** Bimonthly. **Key Personnel:** Prof. Daniel J. Inman, Editor-in-Chief, dinman@vt.edu; Walter D. Pilkey, Founding Ed.; S. Adhikari, Assoc. Ed., s.adhikari@swansea.ac.uk. **ISSN:** 1070-9622. **Subscription Rates:** EUR677 individuals regular; US$947 individuals regular. **Remarks:** Accepts advertising. **URL:** http://www.saviac.org/MIsc/journals.htm; http://www.iospress.nl/loadtop/load.php?isbn=10709622. **Ad Rates:** 4C: EUR1,835. **Circ:** 4,900

48232 ■ Sign Language and Linguistics
John Benjamins Publishing Co.
Klaprozenweg 105
PO Box 36224
NL-1033 NN Amsterdam, Netherlands
Ph: 31 206 304747
Fax: 31 206 739773
Publisher E-mail: benjamins@presswarehouse.com
Peer-reviewed journal covering sign languages in the larger context of natural language. **Founded:** 1909. **Freq:** Semiannual. **Print Method:** Web press. **Trim Size:** 11 x 17. **Cols./Page:** 6. **Col. Width:** 2 1/16 inches. **Col. Depth:** 21 1/2 inches. **Key Personnel:** Gaurav Mathur, Review Ed.; Josep Quer, Editor; Roland Pfau, Editor. **ISSN:** 1387-9316. **Subscription Rates:** EUR214 individuals print + online; EUR70 individuals special. **URL:** http://www.benjamins.com/cgi-bin/t_seriesview.cgi?series=SL%26L.

48233 ■ Social Science Research
Elsevier Science B.V.
Radarweg 29
NL-1043 Amsterdam, Netherlands
Ph: 31 204 853911
Fax: 31 204 852457
Journal publishing papers devoted to quantitative social science research and methodology. **Founded:** 1972. **Freq:** Bimonthly. **Trim Size:** 6 x 9. **Key Personnel:** J.D. Wright, Editor, jwright@mail.ucf.edu; C. Brody, Board of Advisory Ed.; D. Elesh, Board of Advisory Ed.; P.H. Rossi, Founding Ed.; K.L. Wilson, Board Advisory Ed. **ISSN:** 0049-089X. **Subscription Rates:** EUR970 institutions European countries and Iran; US$756 institutions all countries except Europe, Japan and Iran; 101,500¥ institutions; US$126 individuals all countries except Europe, Japan and Iran; EUR170 individuals European countries and Iran; 17,800¥ individuals; US$46 students for all Countries except Europe, Japan and Iran; 5,800¥ students; EUR57 students European countries and Iran. **URL:** http://www.elsevier.com/wps/find/journaldescription.cws_home/622946/descriptiondescription.

48234 ■ Space Communications
IOS Press, B.V.
Nieuwe Hemweg 6B
NL-1013 BG Amsterdam, Netherlands
Ph: 31 20 6883355
Fax: 31 20 6203419
Publisher E-mail: info@iospress.nl
Professional, peer-reviewed journal providing a broad coverage of every facet of space communications, including mobile and broadband communications, video and audio broadcasting, Internet and Interactive applications, message and data collection, navigation and positioning, integrated applications, telemetry and deep space communications and communications aspects of remote sensing. **Subtitle:** An International Journal. **Freq:** Quarterly. **Key Personnel:** M. Bousquet, Editor-in-Chief, michel.bousquet@isae.fr. **ISSN:** 0924-8625. **Subscription Rates:** EUR125 individuals online only; US$145 individuals online only; EUR588 institutions online + online back volumes; US$805 institutions online + online back volumes; EUR458 individuals print and online; US$630 individuals print and online. **URL:** http://www.iospress.nl/loadtop/load.php?isbn=09248625.

48235 ■ Spanish in Context
John Benjamins Publishing Co.
Klaprozenweg 105
PO Box 36224
NL-1033 NN Amsterdam, Netherlands

Ph: 31 206 304747
Fax: 31 206 739773
Publisher E-mail: benjamins@presswarehouse.com
Peer-reviewed journal publishing original theoretical, empirical and methodological studies into pragmatics and sociopragmatics, variationist and interactional sociolinguistics, sociology of language, discourse and conversation analysis, functional contextual analyses, bilingualism, and crosscultural and intercultural communication with the aim of extending our knowledge of Spanish and of these disciplines themselves. **Freq:** Semiannual. **Key Personnel:** Rosina Marquez Reiter, Exec. Ed.; Francisco Yus, Review Ed.; Francisco Moreno Fernandez, Co-Ed. **ISSN:** 1571-0718. **Subscription Rates:** EUR218 individuals print + online; EUR70 individuals special. **URL:** http://www.benjamins.com/cgi-bin/t_seriesview.cgi?series=sic.

48236 ■ Statistical Journal of the IAOS
IOS Press, B.V.
Nieuwe Hemweg 6B
NL-1013 BG Amsterdam, Netherlands
Ph: 31 20 6883355
Fax: 31 20 6203419
Publisher E-mail: info@iospress.nl
Journal striving to inform the professional world of statisticians, applied economists, social scientists and policy analysts of new work going on within official statistics, international organizations, government departments, universities and research institutions; establishing a forum for critical discussion of the entire range of problems - organizational, methodological, analytical and conceptual facing statistical services and other institutions doing statistical work; helping promote innovative and interesting research and studies, and contribute to filling the gap between official and academic statisticians, between national statistical work and international work and between the statistical community and the public. **Freq:** Quarterly. **Key Personnel:** Dr. Siu-Ming Tam, Editor-in-Chief, siu-ming.tam@abs.gov.au. **ISSN:** 1874-7655. **Subscription Rates:** EUR528 institutions print and online; US$750 institutions print and online. **URL:** http://isi.cbs.nl/iaos/; http://www.iospress.nl/loadtop/load.php?isbn=18747655. **Formerly:** Statistical Journal of the United Nations Economic Commission for Europe.

48237 ■ Stochastic Processes and Their Applications
Elsevier Science
PO Box 211
NL-1000 AE Amsterdam, Netherlands
Ph: 31 204 853757
Fax: 31 204 853432
Publisher E-mail: nlinfo-f@elsevier.com
Publication covering theory and applications of stochastic processes. **Freq:** Monthly. **Key Personnel:** T. Mikosch, Editor-in-Chief, mikosch@math.ku.dk; K. Alexander, Assoc. Ed.; E.D. Andjel, Assoc. Ed. **ISSN:** 0304-4149. **Subscription Rates:** US$2,572 institutions for all countries except Europe, Japan and Iran; 305,300¥ institutions; EUR2,300 institutions for European countries and Iran; 31,200¥ individuals; EUR202 individuals for European countries and Iran; US$271 individuals for all countries except Europe, Japan and Iran. **Remarks:** Advertising not accepted. **URL:** http://www.elsevier.com/wps/find/journaldescription.cws_home/505572/descriptiondescription. **Circ:** (Not Reported)

48238 ■ Strength, Fracture and Complexity
IOS Press, B.V.
Nieuwe Hemweg 6B
NL-1013 BG Amsterdam, Netherlands
Ph: 31 20 6883355
Fax: 31 20 6203419
Publisher E-mail: info@iospress.nl
Journal devoted to solving the strength and fracture unifiedly in non linear and systematized manner as complexity system. **Freq:** Quarterly. **Key Personnel:** Takeo Yokobori, Editor-in-Chief; Alan H. Cottrell, Honorary Ed.; A. Carpinteri, Editor. **ISSN:** 1567-2069. **Subscription Rates:** EUR473 institutions print and online; US$565 institutions print and online; EUR110 individuals online only; US$130 individuals online only. **URL:** http://www.iospress.nl/loadtop/load.php?isbn=15672069.

48239 ■ Studies in Language
John Benjamins Publishing Co.
Klaprozenweg 105
PO Box 36224
NL-1033 NN Amsterdam, Netherlands
Ph: 31 206 304747

Fax: 31 206 739773
Publisher E-mail: benjamins@presswarehouse.com
Peer-reviewed journal covering issues on contemporary linguistics from discourse-pragmatic, functional, and typological perspectives. **Freq:** 4/yr. **Key Personnel:** Thomas E. Payne, Review Ed.; Bernard Comrie, Managing Editor; Balthasar Bickel, Managing Editor. **ISSN:** 0378-4177. **Subscription Rates:** EUR562 individuals print + online; EUR95 individuals special. **URL:** http://www.benjamins.com/cgi-bin/t_seriesview.cgi?series=SL.

48240 ■ Tailoring Biotechnologies
The Network University
Nijnburg 2a
NL-1081 GG Amsterdam, Netherlands
Ph: 31 205 040008
Fax: 31 204 420977
Publisher E-mail: info@netuni.uva.nl
Peer-reviewed Journal dedicated to biotechnology, agriculture, sustainable development and food security issues mainly in developing countries. **Freq:** 3/yr. **Subscription Rates:** EUR58 institutions; EUR42 individuals. **URL:** http://www.biotech-monitor.nl/. **Formerly:** Biotechnology and Development Monitor.

48241 ■ Target
John Benjamins Publishing Co.
Klaprozenweg 105
PO Box 36224
NL-1033 NN Amsterdam, Netherlands
Ph: 31 206 304747
Fax: 31 206 739773
Publisher E-mail: benjamins@presswarehouse.com
Peer-reviewed journal promoting the scholarly study of translational phenomena from a thoroughly interdisciplinary and international point of view. **Subtitle:** International Journal of Translation Studies. **Freq:** Semiannual. **Key Personnel:** Jose Lambert, Gen. Ed.; Lieven D'hulst, Review Ed.; Gideon Toury, Founding Ed. **ISSN:** 0924-1884. **Subscription Rates:** EUR230 individuals backvolumes; EUR230 individuals print + online; EUR80 individuals special. **URL:** http://www.benjamins.com/cgi-bin/t_seriesview.cgi?series=Target.

48242 ■ Technology and Health Care
IOS Press, B.V.
Nieuwe Hemweg 6B
NL-1013 BG Amsterdam, Netherlands
Ph: 31 20 6883355
Fax: 31 20 6203419
Publisher E-mail: info@iospress.nl
Journal covering the overlapping areas between physics, engineering, informatics and human biology, basic medical sciences, clinical medicine and presenting a forum for the discussion of socio-economic aspects related to medical technology. **Freq:** Bimonthly. **Key Personnel:** Prof. P.F. Niederer, Editor-in-Chief, peter.niederer@biomed.ee.ethz.ch. **ISSN:** 0928-7329. **Subscription Rates:** EUR547 institutions print and online; US$777 institutions print and online. **URL:** http://www.iospress.nl/loadtop/load.php?isbn=09287329.

48243 ■ Technovation
Elsevier Science
PO Box 211
NL-1000 AE Amsterdam, Netherlands
Ph: 31 204 853757
Fax: 31 204 853432
Publisher E-mail: nlinfo-f@elsevier.com
Journal on technological innovation, entrepreneurship and technology management. **Subtitle:** The International Journal of Technological Innovation, Entrepreneurship and Technology Management. **Founded:** 1981. **Freq:** Monthly. **Key Personnel:** G. Hayward, Ed. Emeritus; Jonathan Linton, Editor-in-Chief, linton@management.uottawa.ca; T. Khalil, Sen. Ed., tkhalil@miami.edu; J. Sapsed, Book Review Ed., j.d.sapsed@bton.ac.uk; D. Archibugi, Editorial Board; M. Von Zedtwitz, Contact, max@post.harvard.edu; C. Watanabe, Information Technology and National Policy, chihiro@me.titech.ac.jp; F. Betz, Editorial Board. **ISSN:** 0166-4972. **Subscription Rates:** US$1,998 institutions for all countries except Europe, Japan & Iran; 237,200¥ institutions; EUR1,787 institutions for European countries & Iran. **Remarks:** Accepts advertising. **URL:** http://www.elsevier.com/wps/find/journaldescription.cws_home/422925/description. **Circ:** (Not Reported)

48244 ■ Telematics and Informatics
Elsevier Science
PO Box 211
NL-1000 AE Amsterdam, Netherlands
Ph: 31 204 853757

Fax: 31 204 853432
Publisher E-mail: nlinfo-f@elsevier.com
Peer-reviewed interdisciplinary journal examining the social, economic and cultural impacts of new technologies. **Founded:** 1984. **Freq:** Quarterly. **Key Personnel:** L. Floridi, Editorial Advisory Board; T. Jacobson, Editorial Advisory Board; J.C. Burgelman, Editorial Advisory Board; N.B. Fairweather, Editorial Advisory Board; N. Dower, Editorial Advisory Board; S. Braman, Editorial Advisory Board; J. Hong, Editorial Advisory Board; J. Servaes, Editor-in-Chief, telematicsandinformatics@gmail.com; J.D.H. Downing, Editorial Advisory Board. **ISSN:** 0736-5853. **Subscription Rates:** 156,100¥ institutions; US$1,318 institutions for all countries except Europe and Japan; EUR1,176 institutions for European countries; US$146 individuals; 16,800¥ individuals; EUR110 individuals. **Remarks:** Accepts advertising. **URL:** http://www.elsevier.com/wps/find/journaldescription.cws_home/703/descriptio n. **Circ:** (Not Reported)

48245 ■ Terminology
John Benjamins Publishing Co.
Klaprozenweg 105
PO Box 36224
NL-1033 NN Amsterdam, Netherlands
Ph: 31 206 304747
Fax: 31 206 739773
Publisher E-mail: benjamins@presswarehouse.com
Peer-reviewed journal focusing on multidisciplinary communication. **Subtitle:** International Journal of Theoretical and Applied Issues in Specialized Communication. **Freq:** Semiannual. **Key Personnel:** Marie-Claude L'Homme, Editor; Kyo Kageura, Editor. **ISSN:** 0929-9971. **Subscription Rates:** EUR236 individuals; EUR236 individuals backvolumes; EUR236 individuals print + online; EUR70 individuals special. **URL:** http://www.benjamins.com/cgi-bin/t_seriesview.cgi?series=TERM.

48246 ■ Tetrahedron
Elsevier Science
PO Box 211
NL-1000 AE Amsterdam, Netherlands
Ph: 31 204 853757
Fax: 31 204 853432
Publisher E-mail: nlinfo-f@elsevier.com
International journal publishing original research papers and critical reviews in organic chemistry. **Subtitle:** The International Journal for the Rapid Publication of Full Original Research Papers and Critical Reviews in Organic Chemistry. **Founded:** 1957. **Freq:** 52/yr. **Key Personnel:** Prof. L. Ghosez, Editor, l.ghosez@iecb.u-bordeaux.fr; Prof. Lin Guo-Qiang, Editor, tetrahed@mail.sioc.ac.cn; Prof. S.F. Martin, Editor, tet@cm.utexas.edu; Prof. W.B. Motherwell, Editor, w.b.motherwell@ucl.ac.uk; Prof. B. Ganem, Exec. Board. **ISSN:** 0040-4020. **Subscription Rates:** 2,296,200¥ institutions; EUR17,209 institutions for European countries & Iran; US$19,341 institutions for all countries except Europe, Japan & Iran; EUR688 individuals for European countries & Iran; 90,800¥ individuals; US$772 individuals for all countries except Europe, Japan & Iran. **Remarks:** Accepts advertising. **URL:** http://www.elsevier.com/wps/find/journaldescription.cws_home/942/description. **Circ:** (Not Reported)

48247 ■ Theatre Research International
International Federation for Theatre Research
Federation Internationale pour la Recherche Theatrale
Department of Theatre Studies
University of Amsterdam
Nieuwe Doelenstraat 16
1012 Amsterdam, Netherlands
Fax: 31 20 5252938
Publisher E-mail: membership@firt-iftr.org
Worldwide research publication covering theater. **Freq:** 3/yr. **Key Personnel:** Charlotte Canning, Assoc. Ed., charlottecanning@mail.utexas.edu; Elaine Aston, Senior Ed., e.aston@lancaster.ac.uk. **ISSN:** 0307-8833. **Subscription Rates:** 58 individuals print only; 144 institutions print and electronic; 139 individuals back volumes. **Remarks:** Advertising accepted; rates available upon request. **URL:** https://www.firt-iftr.org/en/theatre-research-international. **Circ:** 1,000

48248 ■ Thermochimica Acta
Elsevier Science
PO Box 211
NL-1000 AE Amsterdam, Netherlands
Ph: 31 204 853757
Fax: 31 204 853432

Publisher E-mail: nlinfo-f@elsevier.com
Peer-reviewed journal publishing original research contributions focusing on all aspects of thermoanalytical calarometric methods and their Application to Experimental Chemistry, Physics, Biology and Engineering. **Founded:** 1970. **Freq:** 30/yr. **Key Personnel:** L.D. Hansen, Consulting Ed.; C. Schick, Editor, christoph.schick@uni-rostock.de; S. Vyazovkin, Editor, vyazovkin@uab.edu. **ISSN:** 0040-6031. **Subscription Rates:** EUR10,339 institutions for European countries and Iran; 1,372,200¥ institutions for Japan; US$11,565 institutions for all countries except Europe, Japan and Iran. **URL:** http://ees.elsevier.com/tca; http://www.elsevier.com/wps/find/journaldescription.cws_home/500855/descrip tiondescription.

48249 ■ Thrombosis Research
Elsevier Science B.V.
Radarweg 29
NL-1043 Amsterdam, Netherlands
Ph: 31 204 853911
Fax: 31 204 852457
Journal covering peer-reviewed original research on thrombosis, hemostasis and fibrinolysis for the international scientific community. **Founded:** 1972. **Freq:** Monthly. **Print Method:** Offset. **Trim Size:** 6 3/4 x 10. **Cols./Page:** 2. **Col. Width:** 42 nonpareils. **Col. Depth:** 152 agate lines. **Key Personnel:** Per Morten Sandset, Editor-in-Chief; Jeffrey Stephen Ginsberg, Editorial Board; Dr. Charles Francis, Editor-in-Chief; Yukio Osaki, Sen. Assoc. Ed.; B. Brenner, Assoc. Ed.; N. Key, Sen. Assoc. Ed. **ISSN:** 0049-3848. **Subscription Rates:** US$269 individuals all countries except Europe, Japan and Iran; 31,800¥ individuals; EUR242 individuals European countries and Iran; 355,800¥ institutions; US$2,997 institutions all countries except Europe, Japan and Iran; EUR2,679 institutions European countries and Iran. **URL:** http://www.elsevier.com/wps/find/journaldescription.cws_home/369/descriptio ndescription. **Circ:** ‡1,580

48250 ■ Topology
Elsevier Science
PO Box 211
NL-1000 AE Amsterdam, Netherlands
Ph: 31 204 853757
Fax: 31 204 853432
Publisher E-mail: nlinfo-f@elsevier.com
Peer-reviewed journal on mathematics with particular focus on areas related to topology or geometry. **Founded:** 1962. **Freq:** Quarterly. **ISSN:** 0040-9383. **Subscription Rates:** US$113 individuals for all countries except Europe, Japan & Iran; 15,000¥ individuals; EUR112 individuals for European countries & Iran; EUR796 individuals for European countries & Iran; 105,800¥ institutions; US$891 institutions for all countries except Europe, Japan & Iran. **Remarks:** Accepts advertising. **URL:** http://www.elsevier.com/wps/find/journaldescription.cws_home/261/description. **Circ:** (Not Reported)

48251 ■ Topology and its Applications
Elsevier Science
c/o J. Van Mill, Ed.-in-Ch.
Vrije Universiteit, Faculteit der Exacte Wetenschappen
Divisie Wiskunde en Informatica
De Boelelaan 1081a
NL-1081 HV Amsterdam, Netherlands
Publisher E-mail: nlinfo-f@elsevier.com
Peer-reviewed journal publishing original research articles in topology. **Founded:** 1971. **Freq:** 18/yr. **Key Personnel:** K. Kuperberg, Advisory Board; J. Van Mill, Editor-in-Chief, vanmill@cs.vu.nl; J.E. Vaughan, Editor-in-Chief, vaughanj@uncg.edu; J. Keesling, Advisory Board; P. Goerss, Managing Editor, pgoerss@math.northwestern.edu; A.S. Dow, Advisory Board; A. Dranishnikov, Editorial Board; J. Nagata, Advisory Board; R.L. Devaney, Editorial Board. **ISSN:** 0166-8641. **Subscription Rates:** EUR2,736 institutions for European countries & Iran; 363,800¥ institutions; US$3,060 institutions for all countries except Europe, Japan & Iran. **Remarks:** Accepts advertising. **URL:** http://www.elsevier.com/wps/find/journaldescription.cws_home/505624/description. **Circ:** (Not Reported)

48252 ■ Toxicology
Elsevier Science
PO Box 211
NL-1000 AE Amsterdam, Netherlands
Ph: 31 204 853757
Fax: 31 204 853432

Publisher E-mail: nlinfo-f@elsevier.com
Peer-reviewed journal publishing original research in all areas of toxicology. **Founded:** 1973. **Freq:** 36/yr. **Key Personnel:** H.W.J. Marquardt, Editor-in-Chief, marquardt@uke.uni-hamburg.de; K. B. Wallace, Editor-in-Chief, kwallace@d.umn.edu; M. Arand, Editorial Board; O. Aruoma, Editorial Board; M. Aschner, Editorial Board; G. Begum, Editorial Board. **ISSN:** 0300-483X. **Subscription Rates:** US$6,857 institutions for all countries except Europe, Japan & Iran; 814,700¥ institutions for Japan; EUR6,130 institutions for European countries & Iran. **Remarks:** Accepts advertising. **URL:** http://www.elsevier.com/wps/find/journaldescription.cws_home/505518/description. **Circ:** (Not Reported)

48253 ■ Toxicology and Applied Pharmacology
Elsevier Science B.V.
Radarweg 29
NL-1043 Amsterdam, Netherlands
Ph: 31 204 853911
Fax: 31 204 852457
Journal publishing original scientific research on tissue structure or function resulting from the administration of chemicals, drugs, or natural products to animals or humans. **Founded:** 1959. **Freq:** Semimonthly. **Trim Size:** 8 1/2 x 11. **Key Personnel:** Michael P. Waalkes, Editor, taap-ed-office@nc.rr.com; Scott W. Burchiel, Assoc. Ed.; George B. Corcoran, Assoc. Ed. **ISSN:** 0041-008X. **Subscription Rates:** 79,100¥ individuals; EUR759 individuals for European countries and Iran; US$594 individuals for all countries except Europe and Japan; 555,700¥ institutions; US$4,151 institutions for all countries except Europe and Japan; EUR5,324 institutions for European countries and Iran. **Remarks:** Accepts advertising. **URL:** http://www.elsevier.com/wps/find/journaldescription.cws_home/622951/descrip tiondescription. **Circ:** (Not Reported)

48254 ■ Transportation Research Part A: Policy and Practice
Elsevier Science
PO Box 211
NL-1000 AE Amsterdam, Netherlands
Ph: 31 204 853757
Fax: 31 204 853432
Publisher E-mail: nlinfo-f@elsevier.com
Peer-reviewed journal presenting research on transportation systems. **Subtitle:** An International Journal. **Founded:** 1967. **Freq:** 10/yr. **Print Method:** Offset. **Trim Size:** 7 1/2 x 10 3/4. **Cols./Page:** 1. **Col. Width:** 78 nonpareils. **Col. Depth:** 137 agate lines. **Key Personnel:** D.A. Niemeier, Editor-in-Chief, dniemeier@ucdavis.edu; J.A. Carrasco, Assoc. Ed., j.carrasco@udec.cl; R. Donnelly, Assoc. Ed., donnellyr@pbworld.com. **ISSN:** 0965-8564. **Subscription Rates:** EUR285 individuals for European countries and Iran; US$370 individuals for all countries except Europe, Japan and Iran; 41,000¥ individuals for Japan; 231,900¥ institutions for Japan; US$1,953 institutions for all countries except Europe, Japan and Iran; EUR1,746 institutions for European countries and Iran. **Remarks:** Accepts advertising. **URL:** http://www.elsevier.com/wps/find/journaldescription.cws_home/547/descriptiondescription. **Circ:** ‡1,500

48255 ■ Transportation Research Part F
Elsevier Science
PO Box 211
NL-1000 AE Amsterdam, Netherlands
Ph: 31 204 853757
Fax: 31 204 853432
Publisher E-mail: nlinfo-f@elsevier.com
Peer-reviewed journal focusing on the behavioral and psychological aspects of traffic and transport. **Subtitle:** Traffic Psychology and Behaviour. **Founded:** 1998. **Freq:** Bimonthly. **Key Personnel:** J.A. Groeger, Editor; D. Parker, Editorial Board; M. Sullman, Editorial Board; F. Saad, Editorial Board; L. Aberg, Editorial Board; T.A. Ranney, Editorial Board; B. Schlag, Editorial Board; D. Yagil, Editorial Board. **ISSN:** 1369-8478. **Subscription Rates:** EUR855 institutions for European countries & Iran; 113,700¥ institutions; US$957 institutions for all countries except Europe, Japan & Iran; EUR137 individuals for European countries & Iran; 19,700¥ individuals; US$178 individuals for all countries except Europe, Japan & Iran. **Remarks:** Accepts advertising. **URL:** http://www.elsevier.com/wps/find/journaldescription.cws_home/600660/description. **Circ:** (Not Reported)

48256 ■ Trends in Analytical Chemistry
Elsevier Science
PO Box 211
NL-1000 AE Amsterdam, Netherlands
Ph: 31 204 853757

Circulation: ★ = ABC; △ = BPA; ♦ = CAC; • = CCAB; ❑ = VAC; ⊕ = PO Statement; ‡ = Publisher's Report; Boldface figures = sworn; Light figures = estimated.

Fax: 31 204 853432
Publisher E-mail: nlinfo-f@elsevier.com
Journal dealing with all aspects of new developments in analytical chemistry. **Founded:** 1981. **Freq:** 11/yr. **Key Personnel:** A. Crawford, Staff Ed., phone 44 12 52314708, fax 44 78 91979457, alex.crawford06@btinternet.com; A. Townshend, Consulting Ed.; Y. Gohshi, Consulting Ed. **ISSN:** 0165-9936. **Subscription Rates:** US$269 individuals for all countries except Europe, Japan & Iran; EUR238 individuals for European countries & Iran; 31,800¥ individuals. **Remarks:** Accepts advertising. **URL:** http://www.elsevier.com/wps/find/journaldescription.cws_home/502695/descriptiondescription; http://www.elsevier.com/wps/find/journaldescription.cws_home/502695/descrip tion. **Circ:** (Not Reported)

48257 ■ Trends in Biochemical Sciences
Elsevier Science
PO Box 211
NL-1000 AE Amsterdam, Netherlands
Ph: 31 204 853757
Fax: 31 204 853432
Publisher E-mail: nlinfo-f@elsevier.com
Journal dealing about recent advances in biochemistry and molecular biology. **Founded:** 1976. **Freq:** Monthly. **Key Personnel:** V. Ashton, Asst. Ed.; Sarah Cullinan, Editor; K. Shah, Editorial Coord. **ISSN:** 0968-0004. **Subscription Rates:** EUR245 individuals for European countries & Iran; US$223 individuals for all countries except Europe, Japan & Iran; 27,100¥ individuals; US$2,042 institutions for all countries except Europe, Japan & Iran; 253,300¥ institutions; EUR1,826 institutions for European countries & Iran. **Remarks:** Accepts advertising. **URL:** http://www.elsevier.com/wps/find/journaldescription.cws_home/405916/descriptiondescription; http://www.cell.com/trends/biochemical-sciences. **Circ:** (Not Reported)

48258 ■ Trends in Biotechnology
Elsevier Science
PO Box 211
NL-1000 AE Amsterdam, Netherlands
Ph: 31 204 853757
Fax: 31 204 853432
Publisher E-mail: nlinfo-f@elsevier.com
Journal dealing with various areas of applied biosciences. **Founded:** 1983. **Freq:** Monthly. **Key Personnel:** Petra Gross, Editor; A. Colman, Advisory Editorial Board; J. Chataway, Advisory Editorial Board; V. Demidov, Advisory Editorial Board; M. Ferrari, Advisory Editorial Board; D. Cowan, Advisory Editorial Board. **ISSN:** 0167-7799. **Subscription Rates:** EUR223 individuals for European countries & Iran; US$245 individuals for all countries except Europe, Japan & Iran; 27,100¥ individuals; US$2,043 institutions for all countries except Europe, Japan & Iran; 253,400¥ institutions for Japan; EUR1,827 institutions for European countries & Iran. **Remarks:** Advertising accepted; rates available upon request. **URL:** http://www.elsevier.com/wps/find/journaldescription.cws_home/405917/descriptiondescription; http://www.cell.com/trends/biotechnology. **Circ:** (Not Reported)

48259 ■ Trends in Cell Biology
Elsevier Science
PO Box 211
NL-1000 AE Amsterdam, Netherlands
Ph: 31 204 853757
Fax: 31 204,853432
Publisher E-mail: nlinfo-f@elsevier.com
Peer-reviewed journal focusing on recent advances in the field of cell-biological research. **Founded:** 1991. **Freq:** Monthly. **Key Personnel:** J. Gray, Advisory Editorial Board; W.C. Earnshaw, Advisory Editorial Board; S. Emr, Advisory Editorial Board; D. Drubin, Advisory Editorial Board; D. Goldfarb, Advisory Editorial Board; P. Cossart, Advisory Editorial Board; W. Baumeister, Advisory Editorial Board. **ISSN:** 1962-8924. **Subscription Rates:** EUR223 individuals for European countries & Iran; US$245 individuals for all countries except Europe, Japan & Iran; 27,100¥ individuals; US$2,042 institutions for all countries except Europe, Japan & Iran; 253,300¥ institutions; EUR2,042 institutions for European countries & Iran. **Remarks:** Advertising accepted; rates available upon request. **URL:** http://www.elsevier.com/wps/find/journaldescription.cws_home/422552/descriptiondescription; http://www.cell.com/trends/cell-biology. **Circ:** (Not Reported)

48260 ■ Trends in Cognitive Sciences
Elsevier Science
PO Box 211
NL-1000 AE Amsterdam, Netherlands
Ph: 31 204 853757
Fax: 31 204 853432
Publisher E-mail: nlinfo-f@elsevier.com
Journal covering psychology, artificial intelligence, linguistics, philosophy, computer science, anthropology, physiology and neuroscience. **Freq:** Monthly. **Key Personnel:** R. Adolphs, Advisory Editorial Board; Stavroula Kousta, Editor; S. Fiske, Advisory Editorial Board. **ISSN:** 1364-6613. **Subscription Rates:** 253,400¥ institutions; EUR1,827 institutions for European countries & Iran; US$2,043 institutions for all countries except Europe, Japan & Iran; 27,100¥ individuals; EUR223 individuals for European countries & Iran; US$245 individuals for all countries except Europe, Japan & Iran. **Remarks:** Accepts advertising. **URL:** http://www.elsevier.com/wps/find/journaldescription.cws_home/600356/description. **Circ:** (Not Reported)

48261 ■ Trends in Ecology & Evolution
Elsevier Science
PO Box 211
NL-1000 AE Amsterdam, Netherlands
Ph: 31 204 853757
Fax: 31 204 853432
Publisher E-mail: nlinfo-f@elsevier.com
Journal dealing with all aspects of ecology and evolutionary biology, from molecular to global. **Founded:** 1986. **Freq:** Monthly. **Key Personnel:** Katrina A. Lythgoe, Editor; J. Bakker, Advisory Editorial Board; S.C.H. Barrett, Advisory Editorial Board; G. Arnqvist, Advisory Editorial Board; Linsey Meredith, Content Development Ed.; Katja Bargum, Actg. Ed. **ISSN:** 0169-5347. **Subscription Rates:** EUR223 individuals for European countries & Iran; US$245 individuals for all countries except Europe, Japan & Iran; 27,100¥ individuals; US$2,043 institutions for all countries except Europe, Japan & Iran; 253,400¥ institutions for Japan; EUR1,827 institutions for European countries & Iran. **Remarks:** Advertising accepted; rates available upon request. **URL:** http://www.cell.com/trends/ecology-evolution; http://www.elsevier.com/wps/find/journaldescription.cws_home/30339/descriptiondescription. **Circ:** (Not Reported)

48262 ■ Trends in Food Science & Technology
Elsevier Science
PO Box 211
NL-1000 AE Amsterdam, Netherlands
Ph: 31 204 853757
Fax: 31 204 853432
Publisher E-mail: nlinfo-f@elsevier.com
Peer-reviewed journal focusing on the science and technology of food analysis, development, manufacture, storage and marketing. **Subtitle:** An Official Journal of the European Federation of Food Science and Technology (EFFoST), and the International Union of Food Science and Technology (IUFoST). **Founded:** 1990. **Freq:** Monthly. **Key Personnel:** Paul Finglas, Exec. Ed., paul.finglas@bbsrc.ac.uk; F. Toldra, European Ed., ftoldra@iata.csic.es; R. Yada, North American Ed., ryada@uoguelph.ca; J.M. Aguilera, Advisory Editorial Board; K. Arihara, Advisory Editorial Board; A. Costa, Advisory Editorial Board. **ISSN:** 0924-2244. **Subscription Rates:** US$1,786 institutions for all countries except Europe, Japan & Iran; 212,100¥ institutions; EUR1,595 institutions for European countries & Iran; 29,000¥ individuals; US$246 individuals for all countries except Europe, Japan & Iran; EUR218 individuals for European countries & Iran. **Remarks:** Accepts advertising. **URL:** http://www.elsevier.com/wps/find/journaldescription.cws_home/601278/descriptiondescription. **Circ:** (Not Reported)

48263 ■ Trends in Genetics
Elsevier Science
PO Box 211
NL-1000 AE Amsterdam, Netherlands
Ph: 31 204 853757
Fax: 31 204 853432
Publisher E-mail: nlinfo-f@elsevier.com
Peer-reviewed journal focusing on research in genetics, developmental biology and genomics. **Founded:** 1985. **Freq:** Monthly. **Key Personnel:** P. Borst, Editorial Board; G. Fink, Editorial Board; Treasa Creavin, Editor; J. Hodgkin, Editorial Board; K.V. Anderson, Editorial Board; M. Justice, Editorial Board. **ISSN:** 0168-9525. **Subscription Rates:** 27,100¥ individuals; US$245 individuals for all countries except Europe, Japan & Iran; EUR223 individuals for European countries & Iran; 253,400¥ institutions; US$2,043 institutions for all countries except Europe, Japan & Iran; EUR1,827 institutions for European countries & Iran. **Remarks:** Advertising accepted; rates available upon request. **URL:** http://www.elsevier.com/wps/find/journaldescription.cws_home/405918/descriptiondescription. **Circ:** (Not Reported)

48264 ■ Trends in Microbiology
Elsevier Science
PO Box 211
NL-1000 AE Amsterdam, Netherlands
Ph: 31 204 853757
Fax: 31 204 853432
Publisher E-mail: nlinfo-f@elsevier.com
Peer-reviewed journal dealing with all aspects of microbiology. **Founded:** 1993. **Freq:** Monthly. **Key Personnel:** W. Ford Doolittle, Advisory Editorial Board; Norma Andrews, Advisory Editorial Board; Richard Moxon, Advisory Editorial Board; Stefan Kaufmann, Advisory Editorial Board; Brett Finlay, Advisory Editorial Board; William Goldman, Advisory Editorial Board; Gail Teitzel, Editor; Adriano Aguzzi, Advisory Editorial Board; Barry Bloom, Advisory Editorial Board; Robin Weiss, Advisory Editorial Board. **ISSN:** 0966-842X. **Subscription Rates:** US$1,826 institutions; US$245 individuals. **Remarks:** Advertising accepted; rates available upon request. **URL:** http://www.cell.com/trends/microbiology; http://www.elsevier.com/wps/find/journaldescription.cws_home/424100/descrip tiondescription. **Circ:** (Not Reported)

48265 ■ Trends in Neurosciences
Elsevier Science
PO Box 211
NL-1000 AE Amsterdam, Netherlands
Ph: 31 204 853757
Fax: 31 204 853432
Publisher E-mail: nlinfo-f@elsevier.com
Peer-reviewed journal covering all aspects of neuroscience. **Founded:** 1978. **Freq:** Monthly. **Key Personnel:** Sian Lewis, Editor; Helen Barbour, Actg. Ed.; A. Bjorklund, Advisory Editorial Board. **ISSN:** 0166-2236. **Subscription Rates:** EUR223 individuals for European countries & Iran; US$245 individuals for all countries except Europe, Japan & Iran; 27,100¥ individuals; US$1,827 institutions for all countries except Europe, Japan & Iran; 253,400¥ institutions; EUR2,043 institutions for European countries & Iran. **Remarks:** Advertising accepted; rates available upon request. **URL:** http://www.cell.com/trends/neurosciences; http://www.elsevier.com/wps/find/journaldescription.cws_home/405919/descrip tiondescription. **Circ:** (Not Reported)

48266 ■ Trends in Parasitology
Elsevier Science
PO Box 211
NL-1000 AE Amsterdam, Netherlands
Ph: 31 204 853757
Fax: 31 204 853432
Publisher E-mail: nlinfo-f@elsevier.com
Journal dealing with current research in all aspects of parasitology including vaccine and drug development, molecular biology, biochemistry, genetics and bioinformatics, veterinary parasitology, vector biology and control, and disease epidemiology. **Founded:** 1985. **Freq:** Monthly. **Key Personnel:** R. Lynn Sherrer, Editor. **ISSN:** 1471-4922. **Subscription Rates:** EUR223 individuals for European countries & Iran; US$245 individuals for all countries except Europe, Japan & Iran; 27,100¥ individuals; US$2,041 institutions for all countries except Europe, Japan & Iran; 253,200¥ institutions; EUR1,825 institutions for European countries & Iran. **Remarks:** Advertising accepted; rates available upon request. **URL:** http://www.cell.com/trends/parasitology; http://www.elsevier.com/wps/find/journaldescription.cws_home/405915/descrip tiondescription. **Circ:** (Not Reported)

48267 ■ Trends in Pharmacological Sciences
Elsevier Science
PO Box 211
NL-1000 AE Amsterdam, Netherlands
Ph: 31 204 853757
Fax: 31 204 853432
Publisher E-mail: nlinfo-f@elsevier.com
Journal focusing on techniques to theoretical pharmacology and toxicology. **Founded:** 1979. **Freq:** Monthly. **Key Personnel:** Joanna Schaffhausen, Editor. **ISSN:** 0165-6147. **Subscription Rates:** EUR1,826 institutions for European countries & Iran; US$2,042 institutions for all countries except Europe, Japan & Iran; 253,300¥ institutions; EUR223 individuals for European countries & Iran; US$245 individuals for all countries except Europe, Japan & Iran; 27,100¥ individuals. **Remarks:** Advertising accepted; rates available upon request. **URL:** http://www.trends.com/tips/default.htm; http://www.elsevier.com/wps/find/journaldescription.cws_home/405920/descrip tiondescription. **Circ:** (Not Reported)

48268 ■ Utrecht Studies in Language and Communication
Editions Rodopi B.V.
Tijnmuiden 7
NL-1046 AK Amsterdam, Netherlands
Ph: 31 206 114821
Fax: 31 204 472979
Publisher E-mail: info@rodopi.nl
Journal covering theoretical insights in language. **Key Personnel:** Wolfgang Herrlitz, Editor; Paul van den Hoven, Editor. **ISSN:** 0927-7706. **URL:** http://www.rodopi.nl/senj.asp?SerieId=USLC.

48269 ■ Variants
Editions Rodopi B.V.
Tijnmuiden 7
NL-1046 AK Amsterdam, Netherlands
Ph: 31 206 114821
Fax: 31 204 472979
Publisher E-mail: info@rodopi.nl
Journal of the European Society for Textual Scholarship, examining literary creation and the relationship between reading and writing. **Subtitle:** The Journal of the European Society for Textual Scholarship. **Key Personnel:** Barbara Bordalejo, Editor; Wim Van Mierlo, Review Ed. **ISSN:** 1573-3084. **URL:** http://www.rodopi.nl/senj.asp?serieid=variants.

48270 ■ Web Intelligence and Agent Systems
IOS Press, B.V.
Nieuwe Hemweg 6B
NL-1013 BG Amsterdam, Netherlands
Ph: 31 20 6883355
Fax: 31 20 6203419
Publisher E-mail: info@iospress.nl
Peer-reviewed journal aiming to achieve a disciplinary balance between Web technology and intelligent agent technology by deepening the understanding of computational, logical, cognitive, physical, and social foundations, as well as the enabling technologies for developing and applying Web-based intelligence and autonomous agents systems. **Freq:** Quarterly. **Key Personnel:** Prof. Jiming Liu, Editor-in-Chief, phone 852 34117088, fax 852 34117892, jiming@comp.hkbu.edu.hk; Dr. Prabhakar Raghavan, Assoc. Ed., pragh@yahoo-inc.com; Carles Sierra, Editorial Board; Prof. Boi V. Faltings, Assoc. Ed., phone 41 216 932735, fax 41 216 935225, boi.faltings@epfl.ch; Maria Gini, Editorial Board; Dr. Philips S. Yu, Assoc. Ed., phone 914784-7141, fax 914784-6205, psyu@us.ibm.com; Jeffrey Bradshaw, Editorial Board; Peter Brusilovsky, Editorial Board; Prof. Ning Zhong, Editor-in-Chief, phone 81 272 657366, fax 81 272 657366, zhong@maebashi-it.ac.jp; Karl Aberer, Editorial Board. **ISSN:** 1570-1263. **Subscription Rates:** EUR438 individuals print and online; US$605 individuals print and online. **URL:** http://www.iospress.nl/loadtop/load.php?isbn=15701263.

48271 ■ Wordt Vervolgd
Amnesty International Dutch Section
Amnesty International Afdeling Nederland
PO Box 1968
NL-1000 BZ Amsterdam, Netherlands
Ph: 31 206 264436
Publisher E-mail: amnesty@amnesty.nl
Dutch language publication covering human rights. **Subtitle:** Word Vervolgd. **Founded:** Sept. 1968. **Freq:** Monthly. **Print Method:** Offset. **Trim Size:** 210 x 295 cm. **ISSN:** 0165-4241. **URL:** http://www.amnesty.nl/wordtvervolgd_formulier. **Formerly:** Frontaal. **Ad Rates:** BW: US$1,850, 4C: US$2,050. **Circ:** Non-paid 32,500.

48272 ■ World New Music Magazine
International Society for Contemporary Music - Netherlands
c/o Muziek Centrum Nederland
Rokin 111
NL-1012 KN Amsterdam, Netherlands
Ph: 31 20 3446060
Publisher E-mail: info@iscm.org
Magazine covering music. **Freq:** Annual. **Remarks:** Advertising accepted; rates available upon request. **URL:** http://www.iscm.org. **Circ:** (Not Reported)

48273 ■ Written Language and Literacy
John Benjamins Publishing Co.
Klaprozenweg 105
PO Box 36224
NL-1033 NN Amsterdam, Netherlands
Ph: 31 206 304747

Fax: 31 206 739773
Publisher E-mail: benjamins@presswarehouse.com
Peer-reviewed journal covering neurolinguistic, psycholinguistic, educational and sociolinguistic accounts of the structure and functions of written language, the processes and acquisition of reading and writing, and the use and development of literacy in different social and cultural settings. **Freq:** Semiannual. **Key Personnel:** Ludo Verhoeven, Assoc. Ed.; Robert Schreuder, Assoc. Ed.; Martin Neef, Gen. Ed. **ISSN:** 1387-6732. **Subscription Rates:** EUR194 individuals print + online; EUR70 individuals special. **URL:** http://www.benjamins.com/cgi-bin/t_seriesview.cgi?series=WL%26L.

48274 ■ Zuidelyk Afrika
Netherlands Institute for Southern Africa
Nederlands Instituut voor Zuidelyk Afrika
Postbus 10707
NL-1001 ES Amsterdam, Netherlands
Ph: 31 205 206210
Fax: 31 205 206249
Publisher E-mail: niza@niza.nl
Publication on Southern Africa covering political and social developments, daily life, culture, literature, and travel. **Subtitle:** Maatschappij - Cultuur - Reizen (Society - Culture - Travel). **Founded:** Mar. 1997. **Freq:** Quarterly. **Print Method:** Offset. **Trim Size:** 290 x 235 mm. **ISSN:** 1386-4297. **Remarks:** Accepts advertising. **URL:** http://www.niza.nl. **Ad Rates:** BW: EUR600, 4C: EUR1,145. **Circ:** Paid 2,500.

Apeldoorn

48275 ■ Direct Mailings
ZOA Refugee Care - Netherlands
ZOA Vluchtelingenzorg
Sleutelbloemstraat 8
PO Box 4130
NL-7320 AC Apeldoorn, Netherlands
Ph: 31 553 663339
Fax: 31 553 668799
Publisher E-mail: info@zoa.nl
Dutch language publication covering refugees worldwide. **Subtitle:** ZOA Nieuws. **Freq:** Periodic. **Key Personnel:** Dr. Z. De Haan, Contact. **ISSN:** 0165-9308. **Remarks:** Advertising not accepted. **URL:** http://www.zoaweb.org. **Circ:** Non-paid 55,000.

Arnhem

48276 ■ European Urology
European Association of Urology
PO Box 30016
NL-6803 AA Arnhem, Netherlands
Ph: 31 263 890680
Fax: 31 263 890674
Peer-reviewed journal containing articles and topical reviews on a wide range of urological problems. **Freq:** Monthly. **URL:** http://www.uroweb.org/publications/european-urology/.

Beekbergen

48277 ■ World Poultry Science Journal
World's Poultry Science Association - The Netherlands
Association Universelle d'Aviculture Scientifique
PO Box 31
NL-7360 AA Beekbergen, Netherlands
Ph: 31 55 5063250
Fax: 31 55 5064858
Journal covering worldwide poultry science. **Freq:** Quarterly. **ISSN:** 0043-9339. **Subscription Rates:** 134 institutions online only; 174 institutions online/print; US$248 institutions online only; 90 individuals online & print; 79 individuals online only. **URL:** http://www.wpsa.com/journal/wpsj.html. **Circ:** 7,000.

Bussum

48278 ■ Analysis in Theory and Applications
Baltzer Science Publishers
PO Box 221
NL-1400 AE Bussum, Netherlands
Ph: 31 356 954250
Fax: 31 256 954258
Publisher E-mail: subscribe@baltzer.nl
Scientific journal covering the fields of approximation theory and expansions, Fourier and harmonic analysis

and related areas. **Key Personnel:** M. T. Cheng, Editor-in-Chief; C. K. Chui, Editor-in-Chief. **ISSN:** 1000-9221. **Subscription Rates:** US$279 institutions. **URL:** http://www.springerlink.com/content/1672-4070/. **Formerly:** Approximation Theory and its Applications.

48279 ■ Anti-Cancer Agents in Medicinal Chemistry
Bentham Science Publishers Ltd.
PO Box 294
NL-1400 AG Bussum, Netherlands
Publisher E-mail: subscriptions@bentham.org
Journal covering all the latest and outstanding developments in medicinal chemistry and rational drug design for the discovery of new anti-cancer agents. **Freq:** 10/yr. **Key Personnel:** Michelle Prudhomme, Editor-in-Chief, michelle.prudhomme@univ-bpclermont.fr; Peter M. Fischer, Co-Ed.; Sean Michael Kerwin, Co-Ed. **ISSN:** 1871-5206. **Subscription Rates:** US$3,390 institutions corporate, print; US$3,390 institutions corporate, online; US$4,070 institutions corporate, print and online; US$1,870 institutions academic, print; US$1,870 institutions academic, online; US$2,060 institutions academic, print and online; US$430 individuals. **Remarks:** Accepts advertising. **URL:** http://www.bentham.org/cmcaca. **Formerly:** Current Medicinal Chemistry. Anti-Cancer Agents. **Circ:** (Not Reported)

48280 ■ Cardiovascular & Hematological Disorders - Drug Targets
Bentham Science Publishers Ltd.
PO Box 294
NL-1400 AG Bussum, Netherlands
Publisher E-mail: subscriptions@bentham.org
Journal covering all the latest and outstanding developments on the medicinal chemistry, pharmacology, molecular biology, genomics and biochemistry of contemporary molecular targets involved in cardiovascular and hematological disorders, e.g. disease specific proteins, receptors, enzymes, genes. **Freq:** Quarterly. **Key Personnel:** Garry X. Shen, Editor-in-Chief; Lynn Boshkov, Assoc. Ed.; Leslie Miller, Assoc. Ed. **ISSN:** 1871-529X. **Subscription Rates:** US$1,310 individuals corporate, print; US$1,310 individuals corporate, online; US$1,570 individuals corporate, print and online; US$730 individuals academic, print; US$730 individuals academic, online; US$800 individuals academic, print and online; US$180 individuals print. **Remarks:** Accepts advertising. **URL:** http://www.bentham.org/cdtchd. **Formerly:** Current Drug Targets. Cardiovascular & Hematological Disorders. **Circ:** (Not Reported)

48281 ■ Clinical Practice and Epidemiology in Mental Health
Bentham Science Publishers Ltd.
PO Box 294
NL-1400 AG Bussum, Netherlands
Publisher E-mail: subscriptions@bentham.org
Online journal covering all aspects of cerebrospinal fluid in health and disease. **Key Personnel:** Prof. Hagop S. Akiskal, Editorial Board; Dr. Benedikt Amann, Editorial Board; Prof. Mauro Giovanni Carta, Editor-in-Chief, mgcarta@tiscali.it; Dr. Maria Carolina Hardoy, Assoc. Ed.; Prof. Ricardo Araya, Editorial Board. **ISSN:** 1745-0170. **Remarks:** Accepts advertising. **URL:** http://www.bentham.org/open/cpemh/index.htm. **Circ:** (Not Reported)

48282 ■ CNS & Neurological Disorders - Drug Targets
Bentham Science Publishers Ltd.
PO Box 294
NL-1400 AG Bussum, Netherlands
Publisher E-mail: subscriptions@bentham.org
Journal covering all the latest and outstanding developments on the medicinal chemistry, pharmacology, molecular biology, genomics and biochemistry of contemporary molecular targets involved in neurological and central nervous system (CNS) disorders, e.g. disease specific proteins, receptors, enzymes, genes. **Freq:** Bimonthly. **Key Personnel:** Stephen D. Sakper, PhD, Editor-in-Chief, stephen_skaper@hotmail.com; Claire F. Evans, Co-Ed.; John H. Kehne, Co-Ed. **ISSN:** 1871-5273. **Subscription Rates:** US$2,090 institutions corporate, print; US$2,090 institutions corporate, online; US$2,510 institutions corporate, print & online; US$1,150 individuals academic, print; US$1,150 individuals academic, online; US$1,270 individuals academic, print & online; US$270 individuals print. Re-

Circulation: ★ = ABC; △ = BPA; ◆ = CAC; • = CCAB; ❑ = VAC; ⊕ = PO Statement; ‡ = Publisher's Report; Boldface figures = sworn; Light figures = estimated.

Gale Directory of Publications & Broadcast Media/147th Ed.   5247

marks: Accepts advertising. **URL:** http://www.bentham.org/cdtcnsnd. **Formerly**: Current Drug Targets. CNS & Neurological Disorders. **Circ:** (Not Reported)

48283 ■ Current Bioinformatics
Bentham Science Publishers Ltd.
PO Box 294
NL-1400 AG Bussum, Netherlands
Publisher E-mail: subscriptions@bentham.org
Journal covering biomedicine, genomics, computational proteomics, systems biology and metabolic pathway engineering. **Freq:** Quarterly. **Print Method:** Offset. **Cols./Page:** 4. **Col. Width:** 28 nonpareils. **Col. Depth:** 182 agate lines. **Key Personnel:** I. Ghosh, Editorial Advisory Board; J. Fang, Editorial Advisory Board; A. Giuliani, Editorial Advisory Board; I. Marin, Editorial Advisory Board; G. Etherington, Editorial Advisory Board; R. Janardan, Editorial Advisory Board; I.J. Del-Favero, Editorial Advisory Board; J. Dickerson, Editorial Advisory Board; C. Creevey, Editorial Advisory Board. **ISSN:** 1574-8936. **Subscription Rates:** US$980 individuals corporate, print; US$980 individuals corporate, online; US$1,180 individuals corporate, print and online; US$610 individuals academic, print; US$610 individuals academic, online; US$670 individuals academic, print and online; US$180 individuals print. **Remarks:** Accepts advertising. **URL:** http://www.bentham.org/cbio/index.htm. **Circ:** (Not Reported)

48284 ■ Current Clinical Pharmacology
Bentham Science Publishers Ltd.
PO Box 294
NL-1400 AG Bussum, Netherlands
Publisher E-mail: subscriptions@bentham.org
Journal covering the latest advances in the field of clinical pharmacology. **Freq:** Quarterly. **Key Personnel:** Jos H. Beijnen, Editor-in-Chief; R. Agarwal, Editorial Advisory Board; K. Allegaert, Editorial Advisory Board. **ISSN:** 1574-8847. **Subscription Rates:** US$980 institutions corporate, print; US$980 institutions corporate, online; US$1,180 institutions corporate, print and online; US$610 institutions academic, print; US$610 institutions academic, online; US$670 institutions academic, print and online; US$180 individuals. **URL:** http://www.bentham.org/ccp/index.htm.

48285 ■ Current Computer-Aided Drug Design
Bentham Science Publishers Ltd.
PO Box 294
NL-1400 AG Bussum, Netherlands
Publisher E-mail: subscriptions@bentham.org
Journal providing information on recent developments in drug design based on computational techniques and their applications in drug discovery. **Freq:** Quarterly. **Key Personnel:** Satya P. Gupta, Editor-in-Chief; S. Hannongbua, Editorial Advisory Board; A.K. Debnath, Editorial Advisory Board; P.G. Seybold, Editorial Advisory Board; A.T. Balaban, Editorial Advisory Board; S. Balaz, Editorial Advisory Board; R. Benigni, Editorial Advisory Board; E. Aki-Sener, Editorial Advisory Board. **ISSN:** 1573-4099. **Subscription Rates:** US$960 individuals corporate, print; US$960 individuals corporate, online; US$1,150 individuals corporate, print and online; US$460 individuals academic, print; US$460 individuals academic, online; US$510 individuals academic, print and online; US$190 individuals print. **Remarks:** Advertising accepted; rates available upon request. **URL:** http://www.bentham.org/ccadd/index.htm. **Circ:** (Not Reported)

48286 ■ Current Drug Discovery Technologies
Bentham Science Publishers Ltd.
PO Box 294
NL-1400 AG Bussum, Netherlands
Publisher E-mail: subscriptions@bentham.org
Journal providing comprehensive overviews of all the major modern techniques and technologies used in drug design and discovery. **Freq:** Quarterly. **Key Personnel:** R. Breslow, Editorial Advisory Board; Y. Audigier, Editorial Advisory Board; D. Boison, Editorial Advisory Board. **ISSN:** 1570-1638. **Subscription Rates:** US$1,010 individuals corporate, print; US$1,010 institutions corporate, online; US$1,210 institutions corporate, print & online; US$570 individuals academic, print; US$570 individuals academic, online; US$630 individuals academic, print and online; US$180 individuals print. **Remarks:** Accepts advertising. **URL:** http://www.bentham.org/cddt/. **Circ:** (Not Reported)

48287 ■ Current Drug Metabolism
Bentham Science Publishers Ltd.
PO Box 294
NL-1400 AG Bussum, Netherlands
Publisher E-mail: subscriptions@bentham.org
Journal serving as an international forum for the publication of novel and pioneering original work as well as timely reviews in drug metabolism. **Freq:** 10/yr. **Key Personnel:** Chandra Prakash, PhD, Editor-in-Chief, chandra.prakash@biogenidec.com; Amin Rostami-Hodjegan, Assoc. Ed.; Ken-ichi Fujita, Assoc. Ed.; Lee Jia, Assoc. Ed.; Nico P.E. Vermeulen, Assoc. Ed. **ISSN:** 1389-2002. **Subscription Rates:** US$4,190 institutions print or online, corporate; US$2,150 institutions print or online, academic; US$430 individuals print, personal; US$3,490 individuals print, corporate; US$1,950 individuals print, academic; US$3,490 individuals online, corporate; 1,950 f individuals online, academic. **Remarks:** Accepts advertising. **URL:** http://www.bentham.org/cdm. **Circ:** (Not Reported)

48288 ■ Current Drug Safety
Bentham Science Publishers Ltd.
PO Box 294
NL-1400 AG Bussum, Netherlands
Publisher E-mail: subscriptions@bentham.org
Journal covering the latest advances in the field of drug safety. **Freq:** Quarterly. **Key Personnel:** Frank M.C. Besag, Co-Ed.-in-Ch.; D. Berry, Editorial Advisory Board. **ISSN:** 1574-8863. **Subscription Rates:** US$980 institutions corporate, print; US$980 institutions corporate, online; US$1,180 institutions corporate, print and online; US$610 institutions academic, print; US$610 institutions academic, online; US$670 institutions academic, print and online; US$180 individuals. **URL:** http://www.bentham.org/cds/index.htm.

48289 ■ Current Drug Therapy
Bentham Science Publishers Ltd.
PO Box 294
NL-1400 AG Bussum, Netherlands
Publisher E-mail: subscriptions@bentham.org
Journal covering the latest advances in the field of drug therapy. **Freq:** Quarterly. **Key Personnel:** Joachim F. Wernicke, Editor-in-Chief; E. Aguglia, Editorial Advisory Board; L. Arboleya, Editorial Advisory Board. **ISSN:** 1574-8855. **Subscription Rates:** US$980 institutions corporate, print; US$980 institutions corporate, online; US$1,180 institutions corporate, print and online; US$610 institutions academic, print; US$610 institutions academic, online; US$670 institutions academic, print and online; US$180 individuals. **URL:** http://www.bentham.org/cdth/index.htm.

48290 ■ Current Hypertension Reviews
Bentham Science Publishers Ltd.
PO Box 294
NL-1400 AG Bussum, Netherlands
Publisher E-mail: subscriptions@bentham.org
Journal publishing frontier reviews on all the latest advances on hypertension and its related areas, e.g. nephrology, clinical care, and therapy. **Freq:** Quarterly. **Key Personnel:** Prof. Kazuomi Kario, Editor-in-Chief; L. Alcocer, Editorial Advisory Board; A. Avolio, Editorial Advisory Board. **ISSN:** 1573-4021. **Subscription Rates:** US$960 individuals corporate, print; US$960 individuals corporate, online; US$460 individuals academic, print; US$460 individuals academic, online; US$190 individuals. **Remarks:** Accepts advertising. **URL:** http://www.bentham.org/chr/index.htm. **Circ:** (Not Reported)

48291 ■ Current Nutrition & Food Science
Bentham Science Publishers Ltd.
PO Box 294
NL-1400 AG Bussum, Netherlands
Publisher E-mail: subscriptions@bentham.org
Journal publishing frontier reviews on all the latest advances on basic and clinical nutrition and food sciences. **Freq:** Quarterly. **Key Personnel:** Fidel Toldra, Editor-in-Chief; F. Branca, Editorial Advisory Board; K. Brownell, Editorial Advisory Board; K. Arihara, Editorial Advisory Board; J. Bauditz, Editorial Advisory Board; W.S. Agras, Editorial Advisory Board; F. Bozzetti, Editorial Advisory Board; J. Anderson, Editorial Advisory Board; C.M. Bulik, Editorial Advisory Board. **ISSN:** 1573-4013. **Subscription Rates:** US$960 institutions corporate, print; US$960 institutions corporate, online; US$190 individuals print; US$460 institutions academic, print; US$460 institutions academic, online. **Remarks:** Accepts advertising. **URL:** http://www.bentham.org/cnf/index.htm. **Circ:** (Not Reported)

48292 ■ Current Organic Synthesis
Bentham Science Publishers Ltd.
PO Box 294
NL-1400 AG Bussum, Netherlands
Publisher E-mail: subscriptions@bentham.org
Book series devoted to publishing the latest and most important advances in organic synthesis. **Freq:** 4/yr. **Key Personnel:** Atta ur Rahman, Editor-in-Chief; A. Krief, Assoc. Ed. **ISSN:** 1570-1794. **Remarks:** Accepts advertising. **URL:** http://www.bentham.org/cos/. **Circ:** (Not Reported)

48293 ■ Current Pharmaceutical Biotechnology
Bentham Science Publishers Ltd.
PO Box 294
NL-1400 AG Bussum, Netherlands
Publisher E-mail: subscriptions@bentham.org
Journal cover all the latest and outstanding developments in pharmaceutical biotechnology. **Freq:** 8/yr. **Key Personnel:** Alain Rolland, PhD, Assoc. Ed.; Seng H. Cheng, Assoc. Ed.; Zeno Foldes-Papp, PhD, Editor-in-Chief; Seth P. Monkarsh, Assoc. Ed.; Steven J. Shire, Assoc. Ed. **ISSN:** 1389-2010. **Subscription Rates:** US$1,500 institutions academic, print; US$350 individuals; US$1,500 institutions academic, online; US$1,650 institutions academic, print and online; US$2,710 institutions corporate, print; US$2,710 institutions corporate, online; US$3,250 institutions corporate, print and online. **Remarks:** Accepts advertising. **URL:** http://www.bentham.org/cpb. **Circ:** (Not Reported)

48294 ■ Current Pharmaceutical Design
Bentham Science Publishers Ltd.
PO Box 294
NL-1400 AG Bussum, Netherlands
Publisher E-mail: subscriptions@bentham.org
Journal covering all subject areas of major importance to modern drug design, including medicinal chemistry, pharmacology, drug targets, and disease mechanism. **Freq:** 36/yr. **Key Personnel:** William A. Banks, Editor-in-Chief. **ISSN:** 1381-6128. **Subscription Rates:** US$13,820 individuals corporate, print; US$13,820 individuals corporate, online; US$16,580 individuals corporate, print and online; US$6,980 individuals academic, print; US$6,980 individuals academic, online; US$7,680 individuals academic, print and online; US$7,680 individuals print. **URL:** http://www.bentham.org/cpd/.

48295 ■ Current Pharmacogenomics and Personalized Medicine
Bentham Science Publishers Ltd.
PO Box 294
NL-1400 AG Bussum, Netherlands
Publisher E-mail: subscriptions@bentham.org
Journal providing comprehensive overviews of all current research on pharmacogenomics and pharmacogenetics. **Freq:** Quarterly. **Key Personnel:** Vural Ozdemir, Editor-in-Chief; Eleni Aklillu, International Editorial Advisory Board; Jeanne Fourie, International Editorial Advisory Board; Edmund J.D. Lee, Consultant Ed.; Junichi Azuma, International Editorial Advisory Board; Neal L. Benowitz, International Editorial Advisory Board; Charles Cantor, International Editorial Advisory Board; Yasuhiro Fujiwara, International Editorial Advisory Board. **ISSN:** 1875-6921. **Subscription Rates:** US$1,260 institutions corporate, print; US$1,260 institutions corporate, online; US$1,510 institutions corporate, print and online; US$700 institutions academic, print; US$700 institutions academic, online; US$770 institutions academic, print and online; US$160 individuals print. **Remarks:** Accepts advertising. **URL:** http://www.bentham.org/cppm/index.htm. **Formerly**: Current Pharmacogenomics. **Circ:** (Not Reported)

48296 ■ Current Proteomics
Bentham Science Publishers Ltd.
PO Box 294
NL-1400 AG Bussum, Netherlands
Publisher E-mail: subscriptions@bentham.org
Journal covering development of proteomics. **Freq:** 4/yr. **Key Personnel:** Bernd Rehm, Editor-in-Chief; H.T. Chang, Editorial Board; P. Cash, Editorial Board; J.S. Cottrell, Editorial Board; N.L. Anderson, Editorial Board; A. Bairoch, Editorial Board; S.T. Chen, Editorial Board; R. Aebersold, Editorial Board. **ISSN:** 1570-1646. **Subscription Rates:** US$1,010 institutions corporate, print

or online; US$1,210 institutions corporate print & online; US$570 institutions academic print or online; US$630 individuals academic print & online; US$180 individuals print. **Remarks:** Accepts advertising. **URL:** http://bentham.org/cp. **Circ:** (Not Reported)

48297 ■ Current Signal Transduction Therapy
Bentham Science Publishers Ltd.
PO Box 294
NL-1400 AG Bussum, Netherlands
Publisher E-mail: subscriptions@bentham.org
Journal involved in drug design and discovery. **Freq:** 3/yr. **Key Personnel:** Gyorgy Keri, Co-Ed.-in-Ch.; Axel Ullrich, Co-Ed.-in-Ch.; L. Buday, Editorial Advisory Board. **ISSN:** 1574-3624. **Subscription Rates:** US$980 institutions corporate, print; US$980 institutions corporate, online; US$1,180 institutions academic, print and online; US$610 institutions academic, print; US$610 institutions academic, online; US$670 institutions academic, print and online; US$180 individuals. **URL:** http://www.bentham.org/cstt/index.htm.

48298 ■ Current Topics in Medicinal Chemistry
Bentham Science Publishers Ltd.
PO Box 294
NL-1400 AG Bussum, Netherlands
Publisher E-mail: subscriptions@bentham.org
Journal providing a forum for the review of areas of keen and topical interest to medicinal chemists and others in the allied disciplines. **Freq:** 18/yr. **Key Personnel:** Allen B. Reitz, PhD, Editor-in-Chief, allen.reitz@ihvr.org; M. Abou-Gharbia, Editorial Advisory Board; F.I. Carroll, Editorial Advisory Board; R.W. Joseph, Assoc. Ed.; G. Hartman, Editorial Advisory Board. **ISSN:** 1568-0266. **Subscription Rates:** US$3,060 institutions academic, print; US$520 individuals; US$3,060 institutions academic, online; US$3,370 institutions academic, print and online; US$4,560 institutions corporate, print; US$4,560 institutions corporate, online; US$5,470 institutions corporate, print and online. **Remarks:** Accepts advertising. **URL:** http://www.bentham.org/ctmc. **Circ:** (Not Reported)

48299 ■ Current Women's Health Reviews
Bentham Science Publishers Ltd.
PO Box 294
NL-1400 AG Bussum, Netherlands
Publisher E-mail: subscriptions@bentham.org
Journal publishing frontier reviews on all the latest advances on obstetrics and gynecology. **Freq:** Quarterly. **Key Personnel:** Jose M. Belizan, Editor-in-Chief; N.E. Avis, Editorial Advisory Board; P.C. Arck, Editorial Advisory Board; A. Arici, Editorial Advisory Board; M.J. Birrer, Editorial Advisory Board; A.B. Caughey, Editorial Advisory Board; O.B. Christiansen, Editorial Advisory Board; N.J. Alexander, Editorial Advisory Board; S. Daya, Editorial Advisory Board. **ISSN:** 1573-4048. **Subscription Rates:** US$190 individuals print; US$960 institutions corporate, online; US$460 institutions academic, online; US$460 institutions academic, print; US$960 institutions corporate, print. **Remarks:** Accepts advertising. **URL:** http://www.bentham.org/cwhr/index.htm. **Circ:** (Not Reported)

48300 ■ Drug Metabolism Letters
Bentham Science Publishers Ltd.
PO Box 294
NL-1400 AG Bussum, Netherlands
Publisher E-mail: subscriptions@bentham.org
Journal covering major advances in drug metabolism and disposition. **Freq:** Quarterly. **Key Personnel:** Shufeng Zhou, Assoc. Ed.; Chandra Prakash, PhD, Editor-in-Chief, chandra.prakash@biogenidec.com; Kenichi Fujita, Assoc. Ed.; Lee Jia, Assoc. Ed. **ISSN:** 1872-3128. **Subscription Rates:** US$890 institutions corporate, print; US$890 institutions corporate, online; US$1,070 institutions corporate, print and online; US$430 institutions academic, print; US$430 institutions academic, online; US$470 institutions academic, print and online. **URL:** http://www.bentham.org/dml/index.htm.

48301 ■ Infectious Disorders - Drug Targets
Bentham Science Publishers Ltd.
PO Box 294
NL-1400 AG Bussum, Netherlands
Publisher E-mail: subscriptions@bentham.org
Journal covering all the latest and outstanding developments on the medicinal chemistry, pharmacology,

molecular biology, genomics and biochemistry of contemporary molecular targets involved in infectious disorders, e.g. disease specific proteins, receptors, enzymes, genes. **Freq:** Quarterly. **Key Personnel:** Dr. Jean-Marc Sabatier, Editor-in-Chief, sabatier.jm1@libertysurf.fr. **ISSN:** 1871-5265. **Subscription Rates:** US$1,700 institutions print; US$1,700 institutions online; US$950 institutions academic, print or online; US$220 individuals print only. **Remarks:** Accepts advertising. **URL:** http://www.bentham.org/cdtid. **Formerly:** Current Drug Targets Infectious Disorders. **Circ:** (Not Reported)

48302 ■ Inflammation & Allergy - Drug Targets
Bentham Science Publishers Ltd.
PO Box 294
NL-1400 AG Bussum, Netherlands
Publisher E-mail: subscriptions@bentham.org
Journal covering all the latest and outstanding developments on the medicinal chemistry, pharmacology, molecular biology, genomics and biochemistry of contemporary molecular targets involved in inflammation and allergy, e.g. disease specific proteins, receptors, enzymes, genes. **Freq:** 5/yr. **Key Personnel:** S. Holgate, Regional Ed.; C.R. MacKay, Regional Ed. **ISSN:** 1871-5281. **Subscription Rates:** US$1,600 institutions print; US$1,600 institutions online; US$900 institutions academic, print or online; US$220 individuals print. **Remarks:** Accepts advertising. **URL:** http://www.bentham.org/cdtia. **Formerly:** Current Drug Targets. Inflammation & Allergy. **Circ:** (Not Reported)

48303 ■ Japanese Heart Journal
Baltzer Science Publishers
PO Box 221
NL-1400 AE Bussum, Netherlands
Ph: 31 356 954250
Fax: 31 256 954258
Publisher E-mail: subscribe@baltzer.nl
Scientific journal covering original work in the fields of clinical or experimental cardiovascular research. **Key Personnel:** Ryozo Nagai, M.D., Editor-in-Chief. **ISSN:** 0021-4868. **Subscription Rates:** US$344 institutions. **URL:** http://square.umin.ac.jp/jhj/.

48304 ■ Recent Patents on Cardiovascular Drug Discovery
Bentham Science Publishers Ltd.
PO Box 294
NL-1400 AG Bussum, Netherlands
Publisher E-mail: subscriptions@bentham.org
Journal covering current pharmaceutical design and current medicinal chemistry. **Freq:** 3/yr. **Print Method:** Offset. **Trim Size:** 8 1/2 x 11. **Cols./Page:** 2. **Col. Width:** 26 nonpareils. **Col. Depth:** 102 agate lines. **Key Personnel:** H. Chen, Editorial Advisory Board; Khurshid Zaman, Editor-in-Chief; C. Charles, Editorial Advisory Board. **ISSN:** 1574-8901. **Subscription Rates:** US$430 individuals print only; US$1,520 institutions corporate, print; US$1,520 institutions corporate, online; US$1,820 institutions corporate, print and online; US$940 institutions academic, print; US$940 institutions academic, online; US$1,030 institutions academic, print and online. **URL:** http://www.bentham.org/prc/index.htm.

48305 ■ Recent Patents on Drug Delivery & Formulation
Bentham Science Publishers Ltd.
PO Box 294
NL-1400 AG Bussum, Netherlands
Publisher E-mail: subscriptions@bentham.org
Journal covering important and recent annotated patents on drug delivery and formulation. **Freq:** 3/yr. **Key Personnel:** Khurshid Zaman, Editor; A. Agrawal, Editorial Advisory Board; M. Amiji, Editorial Advisory Board. **ISSN:** 1872-2113. **Subscription Rates:** US$1,400 institutions corporate, print; US$1,400 institutions corporate, online; US$1,680 institutions corporate, print and online; US$870 institutions academic, print; US$870 institutions academic, online; US$960 institutions academic, print and online; US$400 individuals. **URL:** http://www.bentham.org/ddf/index.htm.

48306 ■ Recent Patents on Nanotechnology
Bentham Science Publishers Ltd.
PO Box 294
NL-1400 AG Bussum, Netherlands
Publisher E-mail: subscriptions@bentham.org
Journal covering important and recent annotated patents on nanotechnology. **Freq:** 3/yr. **Key Personnel:** Edu-

ardo Ruiz- Hitzky, Editor-in-Chief; P. Alexandridis, Editorial Advisory Board; S. Barth, Editorial Advisory Board. **ISSN:** 1872-2105. **Subscription Rates:** US$1,400 institutions corporate, print; US$1,400 institutions corporate, online; US$1,680 institutions corporate, print and online; US$870 institutions academic, print; US$870 institutions academic, online; US$960 institutions academic, print and online; US$400 individuals. **URL:** http://www.bentham.org/nanotec/index.htm.

48307 ■ Topics in Catalysis
Baltzer Science Publishers
PO Box 221
NL-1400 AE Bussum, Netherlands
Ph: 31 356 954250
Fax: 31 256 954258
Publisher E-mail: subscribe@baltzer.nl
Scientific journal covering the main trends in catalysis. **Key Personnel:** Gabor A. Somorjai, Editor-in-Chief; John Meurig Thomas, Founding Ed.; Robert Raja, Editorial Board; T. Maschmeyer, Editorial Board. **ISSN:** 1022-5528. **Remarks:** Accepts advertising. **URL:** http://www.springer.com/chemistry/journal/11244. **Circ:** (Not Reported)

Delft

48308 ■ Computer-Aided Design
Elsevier Science Inc.
Delft University of Technology
Delft, Netherlands
Publisher E-mail: usinfo-ehelp@elsevier.com
Peer-reviewed journal focusing on the research and developments in the application of computers to the design process. **Freq:** Monthly. **Print Method:** Offset. **Cols./Page:** 5. **Col. Width:** 12 picas. **Col. Depth:** 16 inches. **Key Personnel:** R. Martin, Editorial Board; S.M. Hu, Editorial Board; C.M. Hoffmann, Editorial Board; B.H.M. Gerritsen, Editorial Board; G. Elber, Editorial Board; K.C. Hui, Editorial Board; G. Jared, Editorial Board; P. Brunet, Editorial Board; R. Gadh, Editorial Board; I. Horvath, Editor-in-Chief; K. Lee, Editor-in-Chief; N.M. Patrikalakis, Editor-in-Chief. **ISSN:** 0010-4485. **Subscription Rates:** 265,000¥ institutions; EUR1,996 institutions for European countries and Iran; US$2,232 institutions, other countries except Europe, Japan and Iran; US$199 other countries except Europe, Japan and Iran; 24,400¥ individuals; EUR185 individuals for European countries and Iran. **URL:** http://www.elsevier.com/wps/find/journaldescription.cws_home/30402/descriptiondescription.

48309 ■ Hydrology and Earth System Sciences Discussions
Copernicus GmbH
c/o Hubert H.G. Savenije, Ch. Exec. Ed.
Delft University of Technology, Water Resources
PO Box 5048
NL-2600 Delft, Netherlands
Publisher E-mail: info@copernicus.org
International journal for the publication of original research in hydrology, placed within a holistic Earth system science context. **Key Personnel:** Hubert H.G. Savenije, Ch. Exec. Ed.; Murugesu Sivapalan, Exec. Ed.; Jesus Carrora, Exec. Ed.; Kevin Bishop, Editor, phone 46 18 673131, fax 46 18 673156, kevin.bishop@ma.slu.se. **ISSN:** 1027-5606. **Subscription Rates:** EUR1,329 individuals print; EUR122 single issue print; EUR598 members print; EUR55 members print (single); EUR130 other countries air mail. **URL:** http://www.hydrol-earth-syst-sci.net/volumes_and_issues.html.

48310 ■ International Shipbuilding Progress
IOS Press Inc.
c/o Dr. Rene R.H.M. Huijsmans, Ed.-in-Ch.
Faculty, 3ME, TU Delft
Ships Hydromechanics Section
Mekelweg 2
NL-2628 CD Delft, Netherlands
Ph: 31 15 2783598
Fax: 31 15 2781836
Publisher E-mail: sales@iospress.com
Journal covering scientific work and advancing subjects related to the field of marine technology. **Founded:** 1975. **Freq:** Quarterly. **Print Method:** Offset. **Trim Size:** 11 x 17. **Cols./Page:** 5. **Col. Width:** 24 nonpareils. **Col. Depth:** 210 agate lines. **Key Personnel:** Dr. Rene R.H.M. Huijsmans, Editor-in-Chief, r.h.m.huijsmans@tudelft.nl. **ISSN:** 0020-868X. **Subscription Rates:** EUR85 individuals online only; US$100 individuals online only;

Circulation: ★ = ABC; △ = BPA; ◆ = CAC; • = CCAB; ▢ = VAC; ⊕ = PO Statement; ‡ = Publisher's Report; **Boldface figures** = sworn; Light figures = estimated.

EUR328 individuals print and online; US$455 individuals print and online; EUR444 institutions print and online; US$615 institutions print and online. **URL:** http://www.iospress.nl/.

48311 ■ Journal of Molecular Catalysis B

Elsevier Science Inc.
c/o R.A. Sheldon, Ed.-in-Ch.
Delft University of Technology
Julianalaan 136
NL-2628 Delft, Netherlands
Fax: 31 15 2781415
Publisher E-mail: usinfo-ehelp@elsevier.com
Journal focused on research and developments in the applications of whole-cell and cell-free enzymes. **Subtitle:** Enzymatic. **Founded:** 1995. **Freq:** 24/yr. **Key Personnel:** R.A. Sheldon, Editor-in-Chief, r.a.sheldon@tnw.tudelft.nl; Y. Asano, Editor, asano@pu-toyama.ac.jp; J.D. Stewart, Editor, jds2@chem.ufl.edu. **ISSN:** 1381-1177. **Subscription Rates:** EUR175 individuals European countries and Iran; US$236 other countries except Europe, Japan and Iran; 27,200¥ individuals; 178,200¥ institutions; EUR1,343 institutions for European countries and Iran; US$1,503 institutions, other countries except Europe, Japan and Iran. **URL:** http://www.elsevier.com/wps/find/journaldescription.cws_home/525211/descriptiondescription.

48312 ■ Journal on Satisfiability, Boolean Modeling and Computation

IOS Press Inc.
c/o Hans Van Maaren, Ed.-in-Ch.
Delft University of Technology, Faculty of Electrical Engg.
Mathematics & Computer Science, Dept. of Software Technology
Mekelweg 4
NL-2628 CD Delft, Netherlands
Publisher E-mail: sales@iospress.com
Peer-reviewed journal covering computational logic, constraint programming, quantified Boolean logic, pseudo Boolean methods, zero-one programming, integer programming, and operations research. **Founded:** May 22, 2006. **Freq:** Quarterly. **Print Method:** Offset. **Trim Size:** 8 x 10 3/4. **Cols./Page:** 3. **Key Personnel:** Sharad Malik, Editorial Board; Joao Marques-Silva, Editorial Board; Daniel Le Berre, Editorial Board; Hans Van Maaren, Editor-in-Chief, h.vanmaaren@tudelft.nl; Endre Boros, Editorial Board; Dimitris Achlioptas, Editorial Board; Armin Biere, Editorial Board; Fahiem Bacchus, Editorial Board; Chu Min Li, Editorial Board. **ISSN:** 1574-0617. **Subscription Rates:** EUR541 individuals; US$750 individuals. **URL:** http://www.iospress.nl/loadtop/load.php?isbn=15740617; http://jsat.ewi.tudelft.nl/.

48313 ■ Safety Science

Elsevier Science
c/o B. Ale, Assoc. Ed.
Delft University of Technology
Jaffalaan 5
NL-2600 GA Delft, Netherlands
Publisher E-mail: nlinfo-f@elsevier.com
Journal focusing on research in the science and technology of human safety. **Founded:** 1977. **Freq:** 10/yr. **Key Personnel:** R. Amalberti, Editorial Board; D. Dejoy, Editorial Board; B. Ale, Assoc. Ed., b.j.m.ale@tudelft.nl. **ISSN:** 0925-7535. **Subscription Rates:** 30,900¥ individuals; EUR215 individuals for European countries & Iran; US$278 individuals for all countries except Europe, Japan & Iran; 176,600¥ institutions; EUR1,329 institutions for European countries & Iran; US$1,486 institutions for all countries except Europe, Japan & Iran. **Remarks:** Accepts advertising. **URL:** http://www.elsevier.com/wps/find/journaldescription.cws_home/505657/descriptiondescription. **Circ:** (Not Reported)

48314 ■ Sedimentary Geology

Elsevier Science Inc.
c/o G.J. Weltje, Ed.-in-Ch.
Fac. of Applied Earth Sciences
Technische Universiteit Delft
Mijnbouwstraat 120
NL-2628 RX Delft, Netherlands
Publisher E-mail: usinfo-ehelp@elsevier.com
Journal covering regional or geodynamical aspects of sedimentary systems and basin analysis. **Founded:** 1967. **Freq:** 40/yr. **Print Method:** Offset. **Trim Size:** 5 1/2 x 8 1/2. **Cols./Page:** 1. **Col. Width:** 50 nonpareils. **Col. Depth:** 100 agate lines. **Key Personnel:** G.J. Weltje, Editor-in-Chief, g.j.weltje@tudelft.nl; T.P. Burchette, Editorial Board; H. Bahlburg, Editorial Board; C.R. Fielding, Editorial Board; S. Driese, Editorial Board.

ISSN: 0037-0738. **Subscription Rates:** EUR214 individuals for European countries and Iran; US$240 other countries except Europe, Japan and Iran; 27,900¥ individuals; EUR3,569 institutions for European countries and Iran; 474,100¥ institutions; US$3,993 institutions except Europe, Japan and Iran. **URL:** http://www.elsevier.com/wps/find/journaldescription.cws_home/503361/descriptiondescription.

48315 ■ Sensors and Actuators A

Elsevier Science Inc.
c/o Prof. P.J. French, Ed.-in-Ch.
Technische Universiteit Delft
Delft, Netherlands
Publisher E-mail: usinfo-ehelp@elsevier.com
Journal devoted to research and development of physical transducers (sensors and actuators). **Subtitle:** Physical. **Founded:** 1981. **Freq:** 16/yr. **Key Personnel:** Prof. J.E. Wood, Editor; Dr. H.A.C. Tilmans, Editor; Prof. Satoshi Konishi, Editor; Prof. P.J. French, Editor-in-Chief; Prof. V.M. Bright, Editor; W. Benecke, Editorial Board. **ISSN:** 0924-4247. **Subscription Rates:** 586,000¥ institutions; US$4,941 institutions, other countries except Europe, Japan and Iran; EUR4,417 institutions for European countries and Iran. **URL:** http://www.elsevier.com/wps/find/journaldescription.cws_home/504103/descriptiondescription.

48316 ■ Spectrochimica Acta Part B

Elsevier Science Inc.
c/o M. De Loos-Vollebregt, Ed.
Delft University of Technology
Fac. Applied Sciences
DCT-TOCK, Julianalaan 136
2628 Delft, Netherlands
Publisher E-mail: usinfo-ehelp@elsevier.com
Journal covering atomic emission, atomic absorption, atomic fluorescence, mass spectrometry and X-ray spectrometry. **Subtitle:** Atomic Spectroscopy. **Founded:** 1939. **Freq:** 12/yr. **Print Method:** Offset. **Trim Size:** 5 1/2 x 8 1/2. **Cols./Page:** 1. **Col. Width:** 50 nonpareils. **Col. Depth:** 100 agate lines. **Key Personnel:** R.E. Sturgeon, Editor; J.M. Mermet, Chairman Editorial Advisory Board, jeanmichel.mermet@wanadoo.fr; M. De Loos Vollebregt, Editor, m.t.c.deloos-vollebregt@tudelft.nl; A. Bogaerts, Chairman Editorial Advisory Board, annemie.bogaerts@ua.ac.be; J.A. Aguilera, Editorial Advisory Board. **ISSN:** 0584-8547. **Subscription Rates:** 546,300¥ institutions; US$4,601 institutions, other countries except Europe, Japan and Iran; EUR4,115 institutions for European countries and Iran; 42,600¥ individuals; EUR320 individuals for European countries and Iran; US$358 other countries except Europe, Japan and Iran. **URL:** http://www.elsevier.com/wps/find/journaldescription.cws_home/525437/descriptiondescription.

Doorwerth

48317 ■ Weed Research

European Weed Research Society
Europaische Gesellschaft fur Herbologie
c/o drs Ben Post
Postbus 28
NL-6865 ZG Doorwerth, Netherlands
Fax: 31 26 3706896
Publisher E-mail: membership@ewrs.org
Peer-reviewed journal covering weed in science in the English language. **Freq:** Bimonthly. **Key Personnel:** Jon Marshall, Editor-in-Chief. **ISSN:** 0043-1737. **Subscription Rates:** US$1,209 institutions print + online; US$1,411 institutions, other countries print + online; 93654 institutions print + online; EUR830 institutions print + online. **URL:** http://www.ewrs.org/weedresearch.asp; http://www.wiley.com/bw/journal.asp?ref=0043-1737&site=1.

Dordrecht

48318 ■ Acta Applicandae Mathematicae

Springer Netherlands
Van Godewijckstraat 30
3311 GX Dordrecht, Netherlands
Ph: 31 786 576210
Fax: 31 786 576744
Publisher E-mail: permissions.dordrecht@springer.com
Journal covering mathematical applications. **Subtitle:** An International Journal on Applying Mathematics and Mathematical Applications. **Freq:** 3/yr. **Key Personnel:** L. Desvillettes, Editor-in-Chief; Giorgio Koch, Editorial Advisory Board; M. Diehl, Corresponding Ed.; Svetlana Boyarchenko, Assoc. Ed.; E. Carlen, Assoc. Ed.; J.A. Carrillo, Assoc. Ed. **ISSN:** 0167-8019. **Subscription**

Rates: EUR2,020 institutions print incl. free access or e-only; EUR2,424 institutions print incl. enhanced access. **Remarks:** Advertising accepted; rates available upon request. **URL:** http://www.springerlink.com/content/1572-9036/. **Circ:** (Not Reported)

48319 ■ Acta Biotheoretica

Springer Netherlands
Van Godewijckstraat 30
3311 GX Dordrecht, Netherlands
Ph: 31 786 576210
Fax: 31 786 576744
Publisher E-mail: permissions.dordrecht@springer.com
Journal dedicated to philosophical and mathematical features in biology and biomedical sciences. **Subtitle:** An International Journal on the Mathematical and Philosophical Foundation of Biological and Biomedical Science. **Freq:** Quarterly. **Key Personnel:** A. Stevens, Assoc. Ed.; L. Hemerik, Assoc. Ed.; J. Demongeot, Assoc. Ed.; T.A.C. Reydon, Assoc. Ed.; U. An Der Heiden, Assoc. Ed.; T. De Cock Buning, Managing Editor; W.J. Bock, Editorial Board; D. von Engelhardt, Editorial Board; J. Viret, Editorial Board. **ISSN:** 0001-5342. **Subscription Rates:** EUR462 institutions print incl. free access or e-only; EUR554.40 institutions print incl. enhanced access. **Remarks:** Advertising accepted; rates available upon request. **URL:** http://www.springer.com/philosophy/philosophyofsciences/journal/10441. **Circ:** (Not Reported)

48320 ■ Advances in Computational Mathematics

Springer Netherlands
Van Godewijckstraat 30
3311 GX Dordrecht, Netherlands
Ph: 31 786 576210
Fax: 31 786 576744
Publisher E-mail: permissions.dordrecht@springer.com
Scientific journal covering computational mathematics. **Key Personnel:** Charles A. Micchelli, Editor-in-Chief; Yuesheng Xu, Managing Editor. **ISSN:** 1019-7168. **Subscription Rates:** EUR954 institutions print or online only; EUR1,144 institutions print and online. **URL:** http://www.springerlink.com/content/101738/.

48321 ■ Aerobiologia

Springer Netherlands
Van Godewijckstraat 30
3311 GX Dordrecht, Netherlands
Ph: 31 786 576210
Fax: 31 786 576744
Publisher E-mail: permissions.dordrecht@springer.com
Journal containing review articles in the interdisciplinary fields of aerobiology and interaction of human, plant and animal systems on the biosphere. **Subtitle:** International Journal of Aerobiology. **Freq:** Quarterly. **Key Personnel:** Paolo Mandrioli, Editor-in-Chief; M.L. Muilenberg, Editorial Board; S. Grinshpun, Editorial Board; P. De Nuntiis, Editorial Board; A. Ariatti, Editorial Board; W.D. Griffiths, Editorial Board; E. Levetin, Editorial Board; G. Frenguelli, Editorial Board; W.E. Krumbein, Editorial Board. **ISSN:** 0393-5965. **Subscription Rates:** EUR431 institutions print incl. free access or e-only; EUR517.20 institutions print incl. enhanced access. **URL:** http://www.springer.com/environment/journal/10453.

48322 ■ African Archaeological Review

Springer Netherlands
Van Godewijckstraat 30
3311 GX Dordrecht, Netherlands
Ph: 31 786 576210
Fax: 31 786 576744
Publisher E-mail: permissions.dordrecht@springer.com
Publication covering anthropology, archeology, and folklore. **Freq:** Quarterly. **Key Personnel:** Adria LaViolette, Editor; Scott MacEachern, Editor; Diane Gifford-Gonzalez, Editorial Board; Nicholas David, Editorial Board; George Abungu, Editorial Board; Steven A. Brandt, Editorial Board; Peter J. Mitchell, Editorial Board; Kathy Schick, Editorial Board. **ISSN:** 0263-0338. **Subscription Rates:** EUR385 institutions print incl. free access or e-only; EUR462 institutions print incl. enhanced access. **Remarks:** Accepts advertising. **URL:** http://www.springerlink.com/content/0263-0338/. **Circ:** (Not Reported)

48323 ■ Agroforestry Systems

Springer Netherlands
Van Godewijckstraat 30
3311 GX Dordrecht, Netherlands
Ph: 31 786 576210
Fax: 31 786 576744
Publisher E-mail: permissions.dordrecht@springer.com
Peer-reviewed journal covering all areas of agroforestry.

Freq: 3/yr. Key Personnel: Fergus Sinclair, Honorary Ed.; P.K. Ramachandran Nair, Honorary Ed.; D.P Garrity, Honorary Ed. ISSN: 0167-4366. Subscription Rates: EUR1,322 institutions print incl. free access or e-only; EUR1,586.40 institutions print incl. enhanced access. Remarks: Accepts advertising. URL: http://www.springer.com/lifesci/forestry/journal/10457. Circ: (Not Reported)

48324 ■ American Journal of Community Psychology
Springer Netherlands
Van Godewijckstraat 30
3311 GX Dordrecht, Netherlands
Ph: 31 786 576210
Fax: 31 786 576744
Publisher E-mail: permissions.dordrecht@springer.com
Journal focusing on the community as a psychological force in the development, prevention, and treatment of individual dysfunctions. Founded: 1973. Freq: 8/yr. Print Method: Offset. Trim Size: 6 x 9. Cols./Page: 1. Col. Width: 54 nonpareils. Col. Depth: 103 agate lines. Key Personnel: Charles D. Spielberger, Founding Ed.; Jacob Kraemer Tebes, Editor-in-Chief. ISSN: 0091-0562. Subscription Rates: EUR1,309 institutions print & online; EUR1,570.80 institutions print & enhanced access. Remarks: Accepts advertising. URL: http://www.springer.com/psychology/communitypsychology/journal/10464. Circ: (Not Reported)

48325 ■ Annals of Mathematics and Artificial Intelligence
Springer Netherlands
Van Godewijckstraat 30
3311 GX Dordrecht, Netherlands
Ph: 31 786 576210
Fax: 31 786 576744
Publisher E-mail: permissions.dordrecht@springer.com
Scientific journal covering mathematics and computational techniques in artificial intelligence. Freq: Quarterly. Key Personnel: Martin Charles Golumbic, Editor-in-Chief. ISSN: 1012-2443. Subscription Rates: EUR1,278 institutions print or online only; EUR1,533 institutions print and enhanced access. URL: http://www.springerlink.com/content/101739/.

48326 ■ Annals of Operations Research
Springer Netherlands
Van Godewijckstraat 30
3311 GX Dordrecht, Netherlands
Ph: 31 786 576210
Fax: 31 786 576744
Publisher E-mail: permissions.dordrecht@springer.com
Peer-reviewed journal covering operations research. Freq: Annual. Key Personnel: Peter L. Hammer, Founding Ed.; Endre Boros, Editor-in-Chief. ISSN: 0254-5330. Subscription Rates: EUR3,114 institutions print incl. free access or e-only; EUR3,736.80 institutions print incl. enhanced access. URL: http://www.springerlink.com/content/101740/.

48327 ■ Applied Mathematics and Mechanics
Springer Netherlands
Van Godewijckstraat 30
3311 GX Dordrecht, Netherlands
Ph: 31 786 576210
Fax: 31 786 576744
Publisher E-mail: permissions.dordrecht@springer.com
Scientific journal covering applied mathematics. Freq: 12/yr. Key Personnel: Zhe-wei Zhou, Editor-in-Chief. ISSN: 0253-4827. Subscription Rates: EUR1,030 institutions print incl. free access or e-only; EUR1,236 institutions print incl. enhanced access. URL: http://www.springerlink.com/content/106588/.

48328 ■ Archives of Sexual Behavior
Springer Netherlands
Van Godewijckstraat 30
3311 GX Dordrecht, Netherlands
Ph: 31 786 576210
Fax: 31 786 576744
Publisher E-mail: permissions.dordrecht@springer.com
Journal focusing on sexual behavior. Subtitle: The Official Publication of the International Academy of Sex Research. Founded: 1971. Freq: Bimonthly. Print Method: Offset. Trim Size: 6 x 9. Cols./Page: 1. Col. Width: 54 nonpareils. Col. Depth: 103 agate lines. Key Personnel: Gerianne M. Alexander, Editorial Board; Hayley Wood, Managing Editor; Richard Green, Founding Ed.; Kenneth J. Zucker, Editor. ISSN: 0004-0002. Subscription Rates: EUR1,621 institutions print or online; EUR1,945.20 institutions print or online. Remarks: Advertising accepted; rates available upon request.

URL: http://www.springer.com/psychology/sexualbehaviour/journal/10508. Circ: (Not Reported)

48329 ■ Autonomous Agents and Multi-Agent Systems
Springer Netherlands
Van Godewijckstraat 30
3311 GX Dordrecht, Netherlands
Ph: 31 786 576210
Fax: 31 786 576744
Publisher E-mail: permissions.dordrecht@springer.com
Journal covering theory and practice of autonomous agents and multi-agent systems. Freq: 3/yr. Key Personnel: Elisabeth Andre, Assoc. Ed.; Keith Decker, Assoc. Ed.; Craig Boutilier, Assoc. Ed.; Jeffrey S. Rosenschein, Editor-in-Chief; Michael Wooldridge, Assoc. Ed. ISSN: 1387-2532. Subscription Rates: EUR974 institutions print or online; EUR1,168.80 institutions print and online. Remarks: Accepts advertising. URL: http://www.springerlink.com/content/102852/. Circ: (Not Reported)

48330 ■ BioControl
Springer Netherlands
Van Godewijckstraat 30
3311 GX Dordrecht, Netherlands
Ph: 31 786 576210
Fax: 31 786 576744
Publisher E-mail: permissions.dordrecht@springer.com
Journal providing basic and applied research on biological control of invertebrate, vertebrate and weed pests, and plant diseases. Freq: Bimonthly. Key Personnel: Eric Wajnberg, Editor-in-Chief; Dirk Badendreier, Assoc. Ed.; John K. Scott, Assoc. Ed. ISSN: 1386-6141. Subscription Rates: EUR715 institutions print or online only; EUR858 institutions print and enhanced access. URL: http://www.springer.com/lifesci/entomology/journal/10526.

48331 ■ Biodegradation
Springer Netherlands
Van Godewijckstraat 30
3311 GX Dordrecht, Netherlands
Ph: 31 786 576210
Fax: 31 786 576744
Publisher E-mail: permissions.dordrecht@springer.com
Journal devoted to issues in biological treatment like biotransformation, mineralization, detoxification, recycling, treatment of chemicals or waste materials through microbes, microbial associations, or recombinant organisms. Freq: Bimonthly. Key Personnel: Ronald L. Crawford, Editor-in-Chief; A.B. Cunningham, Editorial Board; C.M. Aelion, Mng. Ed. Board; J.A. Field, Mng. Ed. Board; V. Andreoni, Editorial Board; Jaak Ryckeboer, Mng. Ed. Board; Edward J. Bouwer, Mng. Ed. Board; Hans-Peter E. Kohler, Mng. Ed. Board; W. Bae, Editorial Board. ISSN: 0923-9820. Subscription Rates: EUR1,343 institutions print incl. free access or e-only; EUR1,611.60 institutions print incl. enhanced access. Remarks: Advertising accepted; rates available upon request. URL: http://www.springer.com/environment/soilscience/journal/10532. Circ: (Not Reported)

48332 ■ Biogeochemistry
Springer Netherlands
Van Godewijckstraat 30
3311 GX Dordrecht, Netherlands
Ph: 31 786 576210
Fax: 31 786 576744
Publisher E-mail: permissions.dordrecht@springer.com
Peer-reviewed journal reporting on issues related to geochemical control of the ecosystems. The areas of interest include individual elements or specific classes of natural or anthropogenic compounds in ecosystems. Freq: 3/yr. Key Personnel: Katja Lajtha, Editor-in-Chief; Robert W. Howarth, Founding Ed.; Troy W. Baisden, Assoc. Ed. ISSN: 0168-2563. Subscription Rates: EUR2,422 institutions print incl. free access or e-only; EUR2,906.40 institutions print incl. enhanced access. Remarks: Advertising accepted; rates available upon request. URL: http://www.springer.com/geosciences/journal/10533. Circ: (Not Reported)

48333 ■ Biologia Plantarum
Springer Netherlands
Van Godewijckstraat 30
3311 GX Dordrecht, Netherlands
Ph: 31 786 576210
Fax: 31 786 576744
Publisher E-mail: permissions.dordrecht@springer.com
Journal on experimental botany covering plant physiology, molecular biology, biochemistry, biophysics, biotechnology, genetics, structural botany and pathology.

Freq: Quarterly. Key Personnel: J. Pospisilova, Editor-in-Chief; J. Fajkus, Assoc. Ed.; J. Burketova, Assoc. Ed. ISSN: 0006-3134. Subscription Rates: EUR1,344 institutions print incl. free access or e-only; EUR1,612.80 institutions print incl. enhanced access. Remarks: Advertising accepted; rates available upon request. URL: http://www.springer.com/lifesci/plantsciences/journal/10535. Circ: (Not Reported)

48334 ■ Biology and Philosophy
Springer Netherlands
Van Godewijckstraat 30
3311 GX Dordrecht, Netherlands
Ph: 31 786 576210
Fax: 31 786 576744
Publisher E-mail: permissions.dordrecht@springer.com
Journal is highly broad based with topics covering a wide spectrum debating mainly on how the advances in the various fields implicate the humanity in general. Freq: 5/yr. Key Personnel: Kim Sterelny, Editor-in-Chief; Peter Godfrey-Smith, Assoc. Ed.; Jane Maienschein, Assoc. Ed.; Paul Griffiths, Assoc. Ed.; Daniel Alexandrov, Editorial Board; Robert Brandon, Editorial Board. ISSN: 0169-3867. Subscription Rates: EUR889 institutions print incl. free access or e-only; EUR1,066.80 institutions print incl. enhanced access. Remarks: Advertising accepted; rates available upon request. URL: http://www.springer.com/philosophy/philosophyofsciences/journal/10539. Circ: (Not Reported)

48335 ■ Boundary-Layer Meteorology
Springer Netherlands
Van Godewijckstraat 30
3311 GX Dordrecht, Netherlands
Ph: 31 786 576210
Fax: 31 786 576744
Publisher E-mail: permissions.dordrecht@springer.com
Journal dealing with physical, chemical and biological processes in the atmospheric boundary Layer. Freq: 3/yr. Key Personnel: P.A. Taylor, Co-Ed.; John R. Garratt, Co-Ed.; R.E. Munn, Founding Ed.; S.E. Belcher, Editorial Board; I.P. Castro, Editorial Board. ISSN: 0006-8314. Subscription Rates: EUR3,284 institutions print incl. free access or e-only; EUR3,940.80 institutions print incl. enhanced access. URL: http://www.springer.com/earthsciences/meteorology/journal/10546.

48336 ■ Brain and Mind
Springer Netherlands
Van Godewijckstraat 30
3311 GX Dordrecht, Netherlands
Ph: 31 786 576210
Fax: 31 786 576744
Publisher E-mail: permissions.dordrecht@springer.com
Journal dealing with all aspects of neuroscience and neurophilosophy. Subtitle: A Transdisciplinary Journal of Neuroscience and Neurophilosophy. Freq: 3/yr. ISSN: 1389-1987. Remarks: Advertising accepted; rates available upon request. URL: http://www.springer.com/biomed/neuroscience/journal/10547. Circ: (Not Reported)

48337 ■ Breast Cancer Research and Treatment
Springer Netherlands
Van Godewijckstraat 30
3311 GX Dordrecht, Netherlands
Ph: 31 786 576210
Fax: 31 786 576744
Publisher E-mail: permissions.dordrecht@springer.com
Peer-reviewed journal dealing with treatment and investigations on breast cancer. Freq: 3/yr. Key Personnel: Marc E. Lippman, Editor-in-Chief; Stephen P. Ethier, Assoc. Ed.; Daniel F. Hayes, Assoc. Ed. ISSN: 0167-6806. Subscription Rates: EUR3,034 institutions print incl. free access or e-only; EUR3,640.80 institutions print incl. enhanced access. Remarks: Advertising accepted; rates available upon request. URL: http://www.springer.com/medicine/oncology/journal/10549. Circ: (Not Reported)

48338 ■ Bulletin of the Brazilian Mathematical Society, New Series
Springer Netherlands
Van Godewijckstraat 30
3311 GX Dordrecht, Netherlands
Ph: 31 786 576210
Fax: 31 786 576744
Publisher E-mail: permissions.dordrecht@springer.com
Journal covering mathematics. Freq: Quarterly. Print Method: Offset. Cols./Page: 6. Col. Width: 2 1/16 inches. Col. Depth: 21 1/2 inches. Key Personnel: Jacob Palis, Managing Editor, jpalis@impa.br; Djairo G.

De Figueiredo, Editorial Board, djairo@ime.unicamp.br; Blaine Lawson, Editorial Board, blaine@math.sunysb.edu; Srinivasa S.R. Varadhan, Editorial Board, varadhan@cims.nyu.edu; Manfredo P. Do Carmo, Editorial Board, manfredo@impa.br; Lennart Carleson, Editorial Board, carleson@math.kth.se; Louis Nirenberg, Editorial Board, nirenberg@cims.nyu.edu; John Coates, Editorial Board, j.h.coates@dpmms.cam.ac.uk; Steven L. Kleiman, Editorial Board, kleiman@math.mit.edu. **ISSN:** 1678-7544. **Subscription Rates:** EUR528 institutions print incl. free access or e-only; EUR633.60 institutions print incl. enhanced access. **Remarks:** Accepts advertising. **URL:** http://www.springer.com/math/journal/574. **Circ:** (Not Reported)

48339 ■ Bulletin of Earthquake Engineering
Springer Netherlands
Van Godewijckstraat 30
3311 GX Dordrecht, Netherlands
Ph: 31 786 576210
Fax: 31 786 576744
Publisher E-mail: permissions.dordrecht@springer.com
Peer-reviewed journal dealing with the broad spectrum of earthquake engineering. **Freq:** Quarterly. **Key Personnel:** Atilla Ansal, Editor; Jacob M. Eisenberg, Editorial Board; Philippe Bisch, Editorial Board; Franco Braga, Editorial Board; Nuray Aydinoglu, Editorial Board; Pierre-Yves Bard, Editorial Board; Panayotis Gr. Carydis, Editorial Board; Mauro Dolce, Editorial Board; Nicholas N. Ambraseys, Editorial Board; Alberto Castellani, Editorial Board; Martin Koller, Editorial Board; Costas Syrmakezis, Editorial Board. **ISSN:** 1570-761X. **Subscription Rates:** EUR351 institutions print incl. free access or e-only; EUR421.20 institutions print incl. enhanced access. **URL:** http://www.springer.com/earthsciences/journal/10518.

48340 ■ Bulletin of Mathematical Biology
Springer Netherlands
Van Godewijckstraat 30
3311 GX Dordrecht, Netherlands
Ph: 31 786 576210
Fax: 31 786 576744
Publisher E-mail: permissions.dordrecht@springer.com
Journal devoting to research at the junction of computational, theoretical and experimental biology, in connection with Society for Mathematical Biology. **Subtitle:** A Journal Devoted to Research at the Junction of Computational, Theoretical and Experimental Biology Official Journal of The Society for Mathematical Biology. **Freq:** 8/yr. **Key Personnel:** P.K. Maini, Editor; S.R. Lubkin, Board Chair; J. Velasco-Hernandez, Book Review Ed. **ISSN:** 0092-8240. **Subscription Rates:** EUR1,030 institutions print including free access or e-only; EUR1,236 institutions print including enhanced access. **URL:** http://www.springerlink.com/content/119979/.

48341 ■ Cancer and Metastasis Reviews
Springer Netherlands
Van Godewijckstraat 30
3311 GX Dordrecht, Netherlands
Ph: 31 786 576210
Fax: 31 786 576744
Publisher E-mail: permissions.dordrecht@springer.com
Journal devoted to current advances in the biology and treatment of malignancies. **Freq:** Quarterly. **Key Personnel:** George Poste, Founding Ed.; Isaiah J. Fidler, Editorial Advisory Board; Garth L. Nicolson, Founding Ed.; Avraham Raz, Editor-in-Chief; Kenneth V. Honn, Editor-in-Chief; Joszef Timar, Editorial Advisory Board. **ISSN:** 0167-7659. **Subscription Rates:** EUR810 institutions print including free access or e-only; EUR972 institutions print including enhanced access. **Remarks:** Advertising accepted; rates available upon request. **URL:** http://www.springerlink.com/content/0167-7659. **Circ:** (Not Reported)

48342 ■ Cardiac Electrophysiology Review
Springer Netherlands
Van Godewijckstraat 30
3311 GX Dordrecht, Netherlands
Ph: 31 786 576210
Fax: 31 786 576744
Publisher E-mail: permissions.dordrecht@springer.com
Journal focusing on mechanisms and therapy, heart failure and chronic atrial fibrillation. **Freq:** Quarterly. **Print Method:** Offset. **Trim Size:** 8 1/2 x 11. **Cols./Page:** 3. **Col. Width:** 28 nonpareils. **Col. Depth:** 130 agate lines. **ISSN:** 1385-2264. **URL:** http://www.springerlink.com/content/1385-2264.

48343 ■ Cardiovascular Drugs and Therapy
Springer Netherlands

Van Godewijckstraat 30
3311 GX Dordrecht, Netherlands
Ph: 31 786 576210
Fax: 31 786 576744
Publisher E-mail: permissions.dordrecht@springer.com
Journal devoted to recent advances in cardio vascular pharmacology. **Freq:** Bimonthly. **Key Personnel:** Lionel H. Opie, Founding Ed.; Henry N. Neufeld, Founding Ed.; Willem J. Remme, Editor-in-Chief. **ISSN:** 0920-3206. **Subscription Rates:** EUR899 institutions print including free access or e-only; EUR1,078.80 institutions print including enhanced access. **Remarks:** Advertising accepted; rates available upon request. **URL:** http://www.springerlink.com/content/0920-3206. **Circ:** (Not Reported)

48344 ■ Catalysis Letters
Springer Netherlands
Van Godewijckstraat 30
3311 GX Dordrecht, Netherlands
Ph: 31 786 576210
Fax: 31 786 576744
Publisher E-mail: permissions.dordrecht@springer.com
Scientific journal covering catalysis. **Freq:** Quarterly. **Key Personnel:** Gabor A. Somorjai, Editor-in-Chief; Sir John Meurig Thomas, Editor-in-Chief. **ISSN:** 1011-372X. **Subscription Rates:** EUR3,606 institutions print or online only; EUR4,327.20 institutions print and enhanced access. **Remarks:** Accepts advertising. **URL:** http://www.springer.com/chemistry/journal/10562. **Circ:** (Not Reported)

48345 ■ Catalysis Surveys from Asia
Springer Netherlands
Van Godewijckstraat 30
3311 GX Dordrecht, Netherlands
Ph: 31 786 576210
Fax: 31 786 576744
Publisher E-mail: permissions.dordrecht@springer.com
Scientific journal covering catalysis. **Freq:** Quarterly. **Key Personnel:** Prof. Koichi Eguchi, Editor; Sang Heup Moon, Advisory Board; Prof. Yoshio Ono, Founding Ed. **ISSN:** 1571-1013. **Subscription Rates:** EUR454 institutions print or online only; EUR544 institutions print and enhanced access. **Remarks:** Accepts advertising. **URL:** http://www.springer.com/chemistry/journal/10563; http://www.springerlink.com/content/1571-1013. **Formerly:** Catalysis Surveys from Japan. **Circ:** (Not Reported)

48346 ■ Celestial Mechanics & Dynamical Astronomy
Springer Netherlands
Van Godewijckstraat 30
3311 GX Dordrecht, Netherlands
Ph: 31 786 576210
Fax: 31 786 576744
Publisher E-mail: permissions.dordrecht@springer.com
Journal covering celestial mechanics and its applications, as well as related fields. **Subtitle:** An International Journal of Space Dynamics. **Freq:** Quarterly. **Key Personnel:** Sylvio Ferraz-Mello, Editor-in-Chief; J. Burns, Assoc. Ed.; Alessandra Celletti, Assoc. Ed.; K.T. Alfriend, Assoc. Ed.; A. Elipe, Assoc. Ed. **ISSN:** 0923-2958. **Subscription Rates:** EUR2,208 institutions print incl. free access or e-only; EUR2,649 institutions print incl. enhanced access. **Remarks:** Advertising accepted; rates available upon request. **URL:** http://www.springer.com/astronomy/journal/10569. **Circ:** (Not Reported)

48347 ■ Cell Biology and Toxicology
Springer Netherlands
Van Godewijckstraat 30
3311 GX Dordrecht, Netherlands
Ph: 31 786 576210
Fax: 31 786 576744
Publisher E-mail: permissions.dordrecht@springer.com
Journal covering cell biology, genetic, molecular and cellular toxicology. **Subtitle:** An International Journal Devoted to Research at the Cellular Level. **Freq:** Bimonthly. **Key Personnel:** Michael J. Welsh, Consulting Ed.; John R.W. Masters, Editor-in-Chief; Gary Williams, Founding Ed. **ISSN:** 0742-2091. **Subscription Rates:** EUR628 institutions print incl. free access or e-only; EUR753.60 institutions print incl. enhanced access. **Remarks:** Advertising accepted; rates available upon request. **URL:** http://www.springer.com/lifesci/cellbiology/journal/10565. **Circ:** (Not Reported)

48348 ■ Central European Journal of Biology
Springer Netherlands
Van Godewijckstraat 30
3311 GX Dordrecht, Netherlands
Ph: 31 786 576210
Fax: 31 786 576744

Publisher E-mail: permissions.dordrecht@springer.com
Journal covering research biology. **Founded:** 1967. **Print Method:** Offset. **Cols./Page:** 6. **Col. Width:** 26 nonpareils. **Col. Depth:** 294 agate lines. **Key Personnel:** Ewa Golonka, Managing Editor; Peter J. Artymiuk, Editorial Advisory Board; Sergey Y. Bershitsky, Editorial Advisory Board; Alexander B. Chetverin, Editorial Advisory Board; Mariusz Z. Ratajczak, Editor-in-Chief. **ISSN:** 1895-104X. **Subscription Rates:** EUR1,005 institutions print & online; EUR1,206 institutions print & enchanced access. **URL:** http://www.springer.com/lifesciences/journal/11535.

48349 ■ Central European Journal of Medicine
Springer Netherlands
Van Godewijckstraat 30
3311 GX Dordrecht, Netherlands
Ph: 31 786 576210
Fax: 31 786 576744
Publisher E-mail: permissions.dordrecht@springer.com
Journal publishing research results in the field of medicine. **Founded:** 1968. **Freq:** Bimonthly. **Print Method:** Offset. **Trim Size:** 8 1/8 x 10 7/8. **Cols./Page:** 3. **Col. Width:** 27 nonpareils. **Col. Depth:** 140 agate lines. **Key Personnel:** Graham R.V. Hughes, Editorial Advisory Board; John J. Mann, Editor-in-Chief; Stephen T. Holgate, Editorial Advisory Board; Maciej Banach, Managing Editor; Gautam Chaudhuri, Editorial Advisory Board. **ISSN:** 1895-1058. **Subscription Rates:** EUR1,162 institutions print & online; EUR1,394.40 institutions print & enchanced access. **URL:** http://www.springer.com/medicine/journal/11536.

48350 ■ Chemosensory Perception
Springer Netherlands
Van Godewijckstraat 30
3311 GX Dordrecht, Netherlands
Ph: 31 786 576210
Fax: 31 786 576744
Publisher E-mail: permissions.dordrecht@springer.com
Journal covering chemical, sensory, and neurological science. **Freq:** Quarterly. **Key Personnel:** Kathryn Deibler, PhD, Editorial Board; Terry Acree, Exec. Ed.; Jeannine Delwiche, Editor-in-Chief. **ISSN:** 1936-5802. **Subscription Rates:** EUR326 institutions print including free access or e-only; EUR391.20 institutions print including enhanced access. **URL:** http://www.springer.com/foodscience/journal/12078.

48351 ■ Chinese Science Bulletin
Springer Netherlands
Van Godewijckstraat 30
3311 GX Dordrecht, Netherlands
Ph: 31 786 576210
Fax: 31 786 576744
Publisher E-mail: permissions.dordrecht@springer.com
Journal covering various fields of natural science. **Freq:** 36/yr. **Print Method:** Offset. **Trim Size:** 13 3/4 x 22 5/8. **Cols./Page:** 6. **Col. Width:** 26 nonpareils. **Col. Depth:** 21 1/2 inches. **Key Personnel:** Qimin Zhan, Editor; Niu Yaoling, Editor; Weihua Wu, Editor; Zhu Zuoyan, Editor-in-Chief; Guo Zhengtang, Editor; Chen Dongmin, Editor. **ISSN:** 1001-6538. **Subscription Rates:** EUR1,499 institutions print incl. free access or e-only; EUR1,798.80 institutions print incl. enhanced access. **URL:** http://www.springer.com/new%26forthcomingtitles%28default%29/journal/11434.

48352 ■ Climatic Change
Springer Netherlands
Van Godewijckstraat 30
3311 GX Dordrecht, Netherlands
Ph: 31 786 576210
Fax: 31 786 576744
Publisher E-mail: permissions.dordrecht@springer.com
Earth sciences periodical. **Subtitle:** An Interdisciplinary, International Journal Devoted to the Description, Causes and Implications of Climatic Change. **Freq:** Monthly. **Key Personnel:** Stephen H. Schneider, Editor-in-Chief; Katarina Kivel, Asst. Ed.; N. Arnell, Editorial Board. **ISSN:** 0165-0009. **Subscription Rates:** EUR3,376 institutions print incl. free access or e-only; EUR4,051 institutions print incl. enhanced access. **URL:** http://www.springer.com/earthsciences/meteorology/journal/10584.

48353 ■ Clinical and Experimental Medicine
Springer Netherlands
Van Godewijckstraat 30
3311 GX Dordrecht, Netherlands
Ph: 31 786 576210
Fax: 31 786 576744

Publisher E-mail: permissions.dordrecht@springer.com
Journal covering clinical chemistry, hematology, immunology, oncology and virology. **Founded:** June 1985. **Freq:** Quarterly. **Print Method:** Offset. **Trim Size:** 8 1/8 x 10 3/4. **Cols./Page:** 3. **Col. Width:** 27 nonpareils. **Key Personnel:** L. Casciola-Rosen, Editorial Board; A. Mantovani, Editorial Board; P.M. Mannucci, Editorial Board; M.E. Gershwin, Editorial Board; C.A. Dinarello, Editorial Board; E.C. LeRoy, Editorial Board; B. Barlogie, Editorial Board; F. Tedesco, Editorial Board; A. Macario, Editorial Board; S. Marcovina, Editorial Board; Franco Dammacco, Editor-in-Chief; S. Romagnani, Editorial Board. **ISSN:** 1591-8890. **Subscription Rates:** EUR920 institutions print incl. free access or e-only; EUR1,104 institutions print incl. enhanced access. **Remarks:** Accepts advertising. **URL:** http://www.springer.com/medicine/internal/journal/10238. **Circ:** (Not Reported)

48354 ■ Clinical & Experimental Metastasis
Springer Netherlands
Van Godewijckstraat 30
3311 GX Dordrecht, Netherlands
Ph: 31 786 576210
Fax: 31 786 576744
Publisher E-mail: permissions.dordrecht@springer.com
Journal focusing on research in the field of metastasis. **Freq:** 8/yr. **Key Personnel:** Danny R. Welch, Editor-in-Chief, dwelch@path.uab.edu; Tatsuro Irimura, Editor-in-Chief, irimura@mol.f.u-tokyo.ac.jp; Suzanne A. Eccles, Editor-in-Chief, sue.eccles@icr.ac.uk; I.J. Fidler, Editorial Board; A. Albini, Editorial Board; Kurt Hellmann, Ed. Emeritus; M. Bar-Eli, Editorial Board; Garth L. Nicolson, Ed. Emeritus; A.F. Chambers, Editorial Board; D. Edwards, Editorial Board. **ISSN:** 0262-0898. **Subscription Rates:** EUR1,568 institutions print incl. free access or e-only; EUR1,881.60 institutions print incl. enhanced access. **Remarks:** Advertising accepted; rates available upon request. **URL:** http://www.springer.com/biomed/cancer/journal/10585. **Circ:** (Not Reported)

48355 ■ Clinical Neuroradiology
Springer Netherlands
Van Godewijckstraat 30
3311 GX Dordrecht, Netherlands
Ph: 31 786 576210
Fax: 31 786 576744
Publisher E-mail: permissions.dordrecht@springer.com
Journal covering diagnostic and therapeutic contributions. **Subtitle:** Official Publication of the German, Austrian and Swiss Societies of Neuroradiology. **Founded:** Aug. 1938. **Freq:** Quarterly. **Print Method:** Offset. **Trim Size:** 8 1/2 x 11. **Cols./Page:** 2 and 3. **Col. Width:** 21 and 14 picas. **Col. Depth:** 10 inches. **Key Personnel:** L. Solymosi, Editor-in-Chief; M. Bendszus, Editor; H. Urbach, Editor; C. Ozdoba, Editor; T. Krings, Editor. **ISSN:** 0939-7116. **Subscription Rates:** EUR204.67 institutions print incl. free access or e-only; EUR245.61 institutions print incl. enhanced access. **Remarks:** Accepts advertising. **URL:** http://www.springer.com/medicine/radiology/journal/62. **Circ:** (Not Reported)

48356 ■ CME
Springer Netherlands
Van Godewijckstraat 30
3311 GX Dordrecht, Netherlands
Ph: 31 786 576210
Fax: 31 786 576744
Publisher E-mail: permissions.dordrecht@springer.com
Journal focused on training for medical practice. **Founded:** 1970. **Freq:** Monthly. **Print Method:** Offset. **Trim Size:** 10 x 12 7/8. **Cols./Page:** 8. **Col. Width:** 6.5 picas. **Col. Depth:** 77 picas. **Key Personnel:** Dr. Helmut Lydtin, Editorial Board. **ISSN:** 1614-371X. **Subscription Rates:** EUR266 institutions print incl. free access or e-only. **URL:** http://www.springer.com/medicine/journal/11298.

48357 ■ Coloproctology
Springer Netherlands
Van Godewijckstraat 30
3311 GX Dordrecht, Netherlands
Ph: 31 786 576210
Fax: 31 786 576744
Publisher E-mail: permissions.dordrecht@springer.com
Journal covering surgery, dermatology, urology, gynecology, and coloproctology. **Freq:** 6/yr. **Key Personnel:** Dr. Thorolf Hager, Editor, th.hager@web.de; Prof. Alexander Herold, Editorial Board; Prof. Heinz-Jurgen Krammer, Editorial Board. **ISSN:** 0174-2442. **Subscription Rates:** EUR191.59 institutions print incl. free access or e-only; EUR229.91 institutions print incl. enhanced access. Re-

marks: Advertising accepted; rates available upon request. **URL:** http://www.springer.com/medicine/surgery/journal/53. **Circ:** (Not Reported)

48358 ■ Computer Supported Cooperative Work (CSCW)
Springer Netherlands
Van Godewijckstraat 30
3311 GX Dordrecht, Netherlands
Ph: 31 786 576210
Fax: 31 786 576744
Publisher E-mail: permissions.dordrecht@springer.com
Journal focusing on the theoretical, practical, technical, and social issues in computer supported cooperative work. **Subtitle:** The Journal of Collaborative Computing. **Freq:** 6/yr. **Key Personnel:** Kjeld Schmidt, Editor-in-Chief; Prasun Dewan, Assoc. Ed.; Paul Luff, Book Review Ed.; Geraldine Fitzpatrick, Assoc. Ed.; Mark Ackerman, Assoc. Ed.; Gloria Mark, Assoc. Ed. **ISSN:** 0925-9724. **Subscription Rates:** EUR736 institutions print incl. free access or e-only; EUR883.20 institutions print incl. enhanced access. **Remarks:** Advertising accepted; rates available upon request. **URL:** http://www.springer.com/computer/journal/10606. **Circ:** (Not Reported)

48359 ■ Contemporary Family Therapy
Springer Netherlands
Van Godewijckstraat 30
3311 GX Dordrecht, Netherlands
Ph: 31 786 576210
Fax: 31 786 576744
Publisher E-mail: permissions.dordrecht@springer.com
Journal publishing the latest developments to family therapy. **Subtitle:** An International Journal. **Founded:** 1979. **Freq:** Quarterly. **Print Method:** Offset. **Trim Size:** 6 x 9. **Cols./Page:** 1. **Col. Width:** 63 nonpareils. **Col. Depth:** 98 agate lines. **Key Personnel:** Dorothy S. Becvar, PhD, Editor-in-Chief; Jukka Aaltonen, Editorial Advisory Board; David Baptiste, Editorial Advisory Board. **ISSN:** 0892-2764. **Subscription Rates:** EUR896 institutions print including free access or e-only; EUR1,075.20 institutions print including enhanced access. **Remarks:** Accepts advertising. **URL:** http://www.springerlink.com/content/0892-2764. **Circ:** (Not Reported)

48360 ■ Contemporary Islam
Springer Netherlands
Van Godewijckstraat 30
3311 GX Dordrecht, Netherlands
Ph: 31 786 576210
Fax: 31 786 576744
Publisher E-mail: permissions.dordrecht@springer.com
Peer-reviewed journal covering the study of Islam and contemporary Muslim life. **Subtitle:** Dynamics of Muslim Life. **Founded:** 1958. **Freq:** 3/yr. **Print Method:** Web offset. **Trim Size:** 9 3/4 x 16. **Cols./Page:** 6. **Col. Width:** 20 nonpareils. **Col. Depth:** 116 agate lines. **Key Personnel:** Dr. Filippo Osella, Editorial Board; Dr. Gary R. Bunt, Editorial Board; Prof. Miriam Cooke, Editorial Board; Dr. Karin Van Nieuwkerk, Editorial Board; Dr. Caroline Osella, Editorial Board; Dr. Gabriele Marranci, Founding Ed.; Dr. Noha Nasser, Editorial Board; Prof. Daniel Varisco, Editor; Dr. Ala Al-Hamarneh, Editorial Board; Dr. Anne Sofie Roald, Editorial Board. **ISSN:** 1872-0218. **Subscription Rates:** EUR363 institutions print incl. free access or e-only; EUR435.60 institutions print incl. enhanced access. **URL:** http://www.springer.com/humanities/religiousstudies/journal/11562.

48361 ■ Crime, Law and Social Change
Springer Netherlands
Van Godewijckstraat 30
3311 GX Dordrecht, Netherlands
Ph: 31 786 576210
Fax: 31 786 576744
Publisher E-mail: permissions.dordrecht@springer.com
Peer-reviewed law periodical. **Subtitle:** An Interdisciplinary Journal. **Freq:** Bimonthly. **Key Personnel:** Peter K. Manning, Sen. Ed.; Anamika Twyman-Ghoshal, Book Review Ed.; Nikos Passas, Editor-in-Chief. **ISSN:** 0925-4994. **Subscription Rates:** EUR1,317 institutions print incl. free access or e-only; EUR1,580.40 institutions print incl. enhanced access. **Remarks:** Accepts advertising. **URL:** http://www.springer.com/socialsciences/criminology/journal/10611. **Circ:** (Not Reported)

48362 ■ Criminal Law Forum
Springer Netherlands
Van Godewijckstraat 30
3311 GX Dordrecht, Netherlands
Ph: 31 786 576210
Fax: 31 786 576744

Publisher E-mail: permissions.dordrecht@springer.com
Peer-reviewed journal dealing with theoretical and practical aspects of criminal law, in connection with the Society for the Reform of Criminal Law. **Freq:** Quarterly. **Key Personnel:** Shane Darcy, Assoc. Ed.; William A. Schabas, Editor-in-Chief; Nicolaos Strapatsas, Assoc. Ed. **ISSN:** 1046-8374. **Subscription Rates:** EUR467 institutions print incl. free access or e-only; EUR560.40 institutions print incl. enhanced access. **Remarks:** Advertising accepted; rates available upon request. **URL:** http://www.springer.com/law/journal/10609. **Circ:** (Not Reported)

48363 ■ Critical Criminology
Springer Netherlands
Van Godewijckstraat 30
3311 GX Dordrecht, Netherlands
Ph: 31 786 576210
Fax: 31 786 576744
Publisher E-mail: permissions.dordrecht@springer.com
Journal dealing with social, political and economic justice, in connection with the Division of Critical Criminology in the American Society of Criminology. **Freq:** Quarterly. **Key Personnel:** Shahid Alvi, Editor-in-Chief; Joanna S. Goodey, Editor; Walter Dekeseredy, Editorial Board. **ISSN:** 1205-8629. **Subscription Rates:** EUR433 institutions print incl. free access or e-only; EUR519.60 institutions print incl. enhanced access. **Remarks:** Advertising accepted; rates available upon request. **URL:** http://www.springer.com/socialsciences/criminology/journal/10612. **Circ:** (Not Reported)

48364 ■ De Economist
Springer Netherlands
Van Godewijckstraat 30
3311 GX Dordrecht, Netherlands
Ph: 31 786 576210
Fax: 31 786 576744
Publisher E-mail: permissions.dordrecht@springer.com
Publication covering economics. **Subtitle:** Quarterly Review of the Royal Netherlands Economic Association. **Founded:** 1852. **Freq:** Quarterly. **Key Personnel:** C. Van Ewijk, Editorial Board; P.J.A. Van Els, Editorial Board/Book Review Ed.; J.L. De Bruyn Kops, Founding Ed.; R.J.M. Alessie, Editorial Board; S.K. Kuipers, Honorary Ed.; F.J.H. Don, Editorial Board. **ISSN:** 0013-063X. **Subscription Rates:** EUR475 institutions print incl. free access or e-only; EUR570 institutions print incl. enhanced access. **Remarks:** Accepts advertising. **URL:** http://www.springer.com/economics/journal/10645. **Circ:** (Not Reported)

48365 ■ Der Anaesthesist
Springer Netherlands
Van Godewijckstraat 30
3311 GX Dordrecht, Netherlands
Ph: 31 786 576210
Fax: 31 786 576744
Publisher E-mail: permissions.dordrecht@springer.com
Journal covering anesthesia and intensive medicine up to the pain therapy. **Founded:** July 1, 1937. **Freq:** Monthly. **Print Method:** Offset. **Trim Size:** 13 1/2 x 23. **Cols./Page:** 6. **Col. Width:** 12.5 picas. **Col. Depth:** 301 agate lines. **Key Personnel:** Dr. Rolf Rossaint, Editor; Prof. Axel R. Heller, Editor, axel.heller@uniklinikum-dresden.de; Dr. Markus Weigand, Editor, markus.weigand@chiru.med.uni-giessen.de. **ISSN:** 0003-2417. **Subscription Rates:** EUR488 institutions print incl. free access or e-only; EUR585.60 institutions print incl. enhanced access. **Remarks:** Accepts advertising. **URL:** http://www.springer.com/medicine/anesthesiology/journal/101. **Circ:** (Not Reported)

48366 ■ Der Chirurg
Springer Netherlands
Van Godewijckstraat 30
3311 GX Dordrecht, Netherlands
Ph: 31 786 576210
Fax: 31 786 576744
Publisher E-mail: permissions.dordrecht@springer.com
Journal covering information about surgery. **Founded:** 1954. **Freq:** Monthly. **Print Method:** Offset. **Cols./Page:** 6. **Col. Width:** 26 nonpareils. **Col. Depth:** 294 agate lines. **Key Personnel:** Dr. Joachim Jahne, Editor; Dr. E. Kern, Ed. Emeritus; Dr. Jorg Rudiger Siewert, Editor; Prof. Jurgen Bauch, Editor; Prof. Volker Schumpelick, Editor; Prof. Michael Betzler, Editor. **ISSN:** 0009-4722. **Subscription Rates:** EUR514 institutions print incl. free access or e-only; EUR616.80 institutions print incl. enhanced access. **Remarks:** Accepts advertising. **URL:** http://www.springer.com/medicine/surgery/journal/104. **Circ:** (Not Reported)

Circulation: ★ = ABC; △ = BPA; ◆ = CAC; • = CCAB; ❑ = VAC; ⊕ = PO Statement; ‡ = Publisher's Report; Boldface figures = sworn; Light figures = estimated.

48367 ■ Der Gastroenterologe
Springer Netherlands
Van Godewijckstraat 30
3311 GX Dordrecht, Netherlands
Ph: 31 786 576210
Fax: 31 786 576744
Publisher E-mail: permissions.dordrecht@springer.com
Journal covering gastroenterology and hepatology. **Freq:** Bimonthly. **Key Personnel:** Dr. Bernd Kohler, Editor; Prof. Wolfgang Schepp, Editor, gastroenterologie@kh-bogenhausen.de; Prof. Ralf Jakobs, Editor, jakobsr@klilu.de. **ISSN:** 1861-9681. **Subscription Rates:** EUR250 institutions print incl. free access or e-only; EUR300 institutions print incl. enhanced access. **URL:** http://www.springer.com/medicine/internal/journal/11377.

48368 ■ Der Nephrologe
Springer Netherlands
Van Godewijckstraat 30
3311 GX Dordrecht, Netherlands
Ph: 31 786 576210
Fax: 31 786 576744
Publisher E-mail: permissions.dordrecht@springer.com
Journal covering training for all active nephrology physicians. **Founded:** Aug. 1882. **Freq:** Bimonthly. **Print Method:** Offset. **Cols./Page:** 6. **Col. Width:** 25 nonpareils. **Col. Depth:** 294 agate lines. **Key Personnel:** Prof. Friedrich Luft, Editorial Board; Prof. Bernd Grabensee, Editorial Board; Prof. Martin Zeier, Editorial Board; Prof. Danilo Fliser, Editorial Board; Prof. Ulrich Kunzendorf, Editorial Board; Prof. Hermann Haller, Editorial Board; Prof. Uwe Heemann, Editorial Board. **ISSN:** 1862-040X. **Subscription Rates:** EUR250 institutions print incl. free access or e-only; EUR300 institutions print incl. enhanced access. **URL:** http://www.springer.com/medicine/nephrology/journal/11560.

48369 ■ Der Nervenarzt
Springer Netherlands
Van Godewijckstraat 30
3311 GX Dordrecht, Netherlands
Ph: 31 786 576210
Fax: 31 786 576744
Publisher E-mail: permissions.dordrecht@springer.com
Peer-reviewed journal covering all areas of nerve-medical research. **Founded:** 1958. **Freq:** Monthly. **Print Method:** Offset. **Cols./Page:** 6. **Col. Width:** 12 nonpareils. **Col. Depth:** 290 agate lines. **Key Personnel:** Dr. Thomas Brandt, Editor, thomas.brandt@med.uni-muenchen.de; Prof. Henning Sass, Editor, hsass@ukaachen.de; Werner Hacke, Editor, werner_hacke@med.uni-heidelberg.de. **ISSN:** 0028-2804. **Subscription Rates:** EUR478 institutions print incl. free access or e-only; EUR573.60 institutions print incl. enhanced access. **Remarks:** Accepts advertising. **URL:** http://www.springer.com/medicine/journal/115. **Circ:** (Not Reported)

48370 ■ Der Radiologe
Springer Netherlands
Van Godewijckstraat 30
3311 GX Dordrecht, Netherlands
Ph: 31 786 576210
Fax: 31 786 576744
Publisher E-mail: permissions.dordrecht@springer.com
Peer-reviewed journal focused on study of radiology. **Freq:** Monthly. **Print Method:** Offset. **Cols./Page:** 6. **Col. Width:** 26 nonpareils. **Col. Depth:** 301 agate lines. **Key Personnel:** Dr. Maximilian Reiser, Editor, karin.darda-okunek@med.uni-muenchen.de; Prof. Thomas Helmberger, Editor, thomas.helmberger@kh-bogenhausen.de. **ISSN:** 0033-832X. **Subscription Rates:** EUR564 institutions print incl. free access or e-only; EUR676.80 institutions print incl. enhanced access. **Remarks:** Accepts advertising. **URL:** http://www.springer.com/medicine/radiology/journal/117. **Circ:** (Not Reported)

48371 ■ Der Schmerz
Springer Netherlands
Van Godewijckstraat 30
3311 GX Dordrecht, Netherlands
Ph: 31 786 576210
Fax: 31 786 576744
Publisher E-mail: permissions.dordrecht@springer.com
Peer-reviewed journal covering physicians of all fields. **Freq:** Bimonthly. **Print Method:** Offset. **Cols./Page:** 6. **Col. Width:** 24 nonpareils. **Col. Depth:** 301 agate lines. **Key Personnel:** Dr. Hans-Georg Schaible, Editor, hansgeorg.schaible@mti.uni-jena.de; Prof. Luke Radbruch, Editor, palliativmedizin@ukaachen.de. **ISSN:** 0932-433X. **Subscription Rates:** EUR397 institutions print

incl. free access or e-only; EUR476.40 institutions print incl. enhanced access. **Remarks:** Accepts advertising. **URL:** http://www.springer.com/medicine/journal/482. **Circ:** (Not Reported)

48372 ■ Designs, Codes and Cryptography
Springer Netherlands
Van Godewijckstraat 30
3311 GX Dordrecht, Netherlands
Ph: 31 786 576210
Fax: 31 786 576744
Publisher E-mail: permissions.dordrecht@springer.com
Peer-reviewed journal publishing theoretical and practical papers in the fields of design theory, coding theory and cryptography. Mainly covers the algebraic and geometric aspects of any of the above fields. **Subtitle:** An International Journal. **Freq:** 3/yr. **Key Personnel:** Dieter Jungnickel, Editor-in-Chief; Jennifer D. Key, Editor-in-Chief; Peter Wild, Editor-in-Chief; C. Boyd, Editorial Board; P. Charpin, Editorial Board; P. Camion, Editorial Board; C.J. Colbourn, Editorial Board; K.T. Arasu, Editorial Board. **ISSN:** 0925-1022. **Subscription Rates:** EUR1,654 institutions print incl. free access or e-only; EUR1,984:80 institutions print incl. enhanced access. **Remarks:** Advertising accepted; rates available upon request. **URL:** http://www.springerlink.com/content/0925-1022. **Circ:** (Not Reported)

48373 ■ Dialectical Anthropology
Springer Netherlands
Van Godewijckstraat 30
3311 GX Dordrecht, Netherlands
Ph: 31 786 576210
Fax: 31 786 576744
Publisher E-mail: permissions.dordrecht@springer.com
Peer-reviewed journal for critical minds in anthropology, the arts and humanities, and social and political sciences. **Founded:** 1975. **Freq:** Quarterly. **Key Personnel:** Kirk Dombrowski, Editor-in-Chief; Stanley Diamond, Founding Ed.; Anthony Marcus, Editor-in-Chief; Ananthakrishnan Aiyer, Editor-in-Chief; Albert Sgambati, Literary Ed.; Winnie Lem, Editorial Committee; Susana Narotzky, Editorial Committee; George Baca, Editorial Committee; Kathy Powell, Editorial Committee; Raymond Pettit, Editorial Committee/Book Review Ed. **ISSN:** 0304-4092. **Subscription Rates:** EUR483 institutions print incl. free access or e-only; EUR579.60 institutions print incl. enhanced access. **Remarks:** Accepts advertising. **URL:** http://www.springer.com/socialsciences/archaeology%26anthropology/journal/10624. **Circ:** (Not Reported)

48374 ■ Digestive Diseases and Sciences
Springer Netherlands
Van Godewijckstraat 30
3311 GX Dordrecht, Netherlands
Ph: 31 786 576210
Fax: 31 786 576744
Publisher E-mail: permissions.dordrecht@springer.com
Peer-reviewed medical journal focusing on gastroenterology and related fields. **Founded:** 1934. **Freq:** Monthly. **Print Method:** Offset. **Trim Size:** 8 1/4 x 11. **Cols./Page:** 2. **Col. Width:** 19 picas. **Col. Depth:** 52 picas. **Key Personnel:** Henry Lin, Assoc. Ed.; Emmet B. Keeffe, MD, Editor-in-Chief; Edward Whang, MD, Editorial Board; Stanley Ashley, MD, Editorial Board. **ISSN:** 0163-2116. **Subscription Rates:** EUR1,585 institutions print or online; EUR1,902 institutions print & enhanced access. **URL:** http://www.springer.com/medicine/internal/journal/10620. **Ad Rates:** BW: 1,225 f, 4C: 1,505 f. **Circ:** 1,700

48375 ■ Discrete Event Dynamic Systems
Springer Netherlands
Van Godewijckstraat 30
3311 GX Dordrecht, Netherlands
Ph: 31 786 576210
Fax: 31 786 576744
Publisher E-mail: permissions.dordrecht@springer.com
Peer-reviewed journal publishing articles on the modeling and control of discrete event dynamical systems. **Subtitle:** Theory and Applications. **Freq:** 4/yr. **Key Personnel:** Han-fu Chen, Editorial Board; Christos Cassandras, Editorial Board; Alessandro Giua, Editorial Board; Y.C. Ho, Founding & Advisory Ed.; X.R. Cao, Editor-in-Chief; David Yao, Department Ed.; Stephane Lafortune, Department Ed.; Rene Boel, Department Ed. **ISSN:** 0924-6703. **Subscription Rates:** EUR744 institutions print including free access or e-only; EUR892.80 institutions print including enhanced access. **Remarks:** Advertising accepted; rates available upon request. **URL:** http://www.springerlink.com/content/0924-6703. **Circ:** (Not Reported)

48376 ■ Distributed and Parallel Databases
Springer Netherlands
Van Godewijckstraat 30
3311 GX Dordrecht, Netherlands
Ph: 31 786 576210
Fax: 31 786 576744
Publisher E-mail: permissions.dordrecht@springer.com
Journal publishing advances in research, systems development efforts, and user experiences in distributed and parallel database systems. **Subtitle:** An International Journal. **Freq:** 3/yr. **Key Personnel:** Athman Bouguettaya, Editorial Board; Ahmed K. Elmagarmid, Editor-in-Chief; Amit P. Sheth, Editor-in-Chief. **ISSN:** 0926-8782. **Subscription Rates:** EUR941 institutions print including free access or e-only; EUR1,129.20 institutions print including enhanced access. **Remarks:** Advertising accepted; rates available upon request. **URL:** http://www.springerlink.com/content/0926-8782. **Circ:** (Not Reported)

48377 ■ Documenta Ophthalmologica
Springer Netherlands
Van Godewijckstraat 30
3311 GX Dordrecht, Netherlands
Ph: 31 786 576210
Fax: 31 786 576744
Publisher E-mail: permissions.dordrecht@springer.com
Journal on applications of clinical electrophysiology of vision published in connection with International Society for Clinical Electrophysiology of Vision. Provides information on methods to improve diagnosis and clinical management of patients using visual electrophysiology. **Subtitle:** The Journal of Clinical Electrophysiology and Vision - The Official Journal of the International Society for Clinical Electrophysiology and Vision. **Freq:** 3/yr. **Key Personnel:** Mineo Kondo, Assoc. Ed.; Laura Frishman, Editor-in-Chief; Scott Brodie, Assoc. Ed.; Michael Bach, Assoc. Ed.; David Birch, Editorial Board; Colin Barber, Editorial Board; Geoffrey Arden, Editorial Board; Mitchell Brigell, Editorial Board; Ido Perlman, Editorial Board. **ISSN:** 0012-4486. **Subscription Rates:** EUR1,337 institutions print incl. free access or e-only; EUR1,604.40 institutions print incl. enhanced access. **Remarks:** Advertising accepted; rates available upon request. **URL:** http://springerlink.metapress.com/content/1573-2622/. **Circ:** (Not Reported)

48378 ■ Economic Change and Restructuring
Springer Netherlands
Van Godewijckstraat 30
3311 GX Dordrecht, Netherlands
Ph: 31 786 576210
Fax: 31 786 576744
Publisher E-mail: permissions.dordrecht@springer.com
Journal dealing with research on transitional economies and policy research and economic analysis. **Subtitle:** Empirical and Policy Research on the Transitional and Emerging Economies. **Freq:** Quarterly. **Key Personnel:** Roberta Benini, Editor; Wojciech W. Charemza, Editor; George Hondroyiannis, Editor. **ISSN:** 1573-9414. **Subscription Rates:** EUR532 institutions print incl. free access or e-only; EUR638.40 institutions print incl. enhanced access. **Remarks:** Advertising accepted; rates available upon request. **URL:** http://www.springer.com/economics/journal/10644. **Formerly:** Economics of Planning (Jan. 9, 2006). **Circ:** (Not Reported)

48379 ■ Economic Theory
Springer Netherlands
Van Godewijckstraat 30
3311 GX Dordrecht, Netherlands
Ph: 31 786 576210
Fax: 31 786 576744
Publisher E-mail: permissions.dordrecht@springer.com
Journal covering macroeconomics, social choice and welfare, financial economics, money and banking, industrial organization. **Freq:** Monthly. **Print Method:** Offset. **Cols./Page:** 6. **Col. Width:** 2 inches. **Col. Depth:** 21 1/2 inches. **Key Personnel:** Mukul Majumdar, Advisory Board; Dan Kovenock, Co-Ed.; Nicholas C. Yannelis, Editor; Mark Machina, Co-Ed.; Timothy J. Kehoe, Co-Ed.; Edward C. Prescott, Co-Ed.; Mordecai Kurz, Advisory Board; Charalambos D. Aliprantis, Founding Ed. **ISSN:** 0938-2259. **Subscription Rates:** EUR1,651 institutions print & online; EUR1,981.20 institutions print & enchanced access. **URL:** http://www.springer.com/economics/economictheory/journal/199.

48380 ■ Education Assessment, Evaluation and Accountability
Springer Netherlands
Van Godewijckstraat 30

3311 GX Dordrecht, Netherlands
Ph: 31 786 576210
Fax: 31 786 576744
Publisher E-mail: permissions.dordrecht@springer.com
Journal focusing on evaluation of teachers, administrators, educational specialist positions, and higher education faculty performance. **Key Personnel:** Leijf Moos, Editor-in-Chief; John MacBeath, Editor-in-Chief; Yin Cheong Cheng, Editorial Board; Ben Levin, Editorial Board; Brad Portin, Editorial Board; Neil Dempster, Editorial Board; Mats Ekholm, Editorial Board; Peter Gronn, Editorial Board; Stephan Huber, Editorial Board; Mary James, Editorial Board. **ISSN:** 1874-8597. **Subscription Rates:** EUR404 institutions print & online; EUR484.80 institutions print & enchanced access. **Remarks:** Advertising accepted; rates available upon request. **URL:** http://www.springerlink.com/content/121162/?p=95c98cfdedaf436c853e107acc8047a4&pi=0. **Formerly:** Journal of Personnel Evaluation in Education. **Circ:** (Not Reported)

48381 ■ European Journal of Clinical Microbiology & Infectious Diseases
Springer Netherlands
Van Godewijckstraat 30
3311 GX Dordrecht, Netherlands
Ph: 31 786 576210
Fax: 31 786 576744
Publisher E-mail: permissions.dordrecht@springer.com
Journal covering bacterial, viral, fungal, pathogenesis, diagnosis, epidemiology, therapy and prevention of infectious diseases. **Freq:** Monthly. **Key Personnel:** N. Jung, Editorial Asst.; J. Clement, Advisory Board; P.J. Collignon, Advisory Board; Alex van Belkum, Editor-in-Chief; B.A. Cunha, Advisory Board; D.W. Denning, Advisory Board; G.M. Eliopoulos, Advisory Board. **ISSN:** 0934-9723. **Subscription Rates:** EUR955 institutions print incl. free access or e-only; EUR1,146 institutions print incl. enhanced access. **Remarks:** Accepts advertising. **URL:** http://www.springer.com/biomed/medicalmicrobiology/journal/10096. **Circ:** (Not Reported)

48382 ■ European Journal on Criminal Policy and Research
Springer Netherlands
Van Godewijckstraat 30
3311 GX Dordrecht, Netherlands
Ph: 31 786 576210
Fax: 31 786 576744
Publisher E-mail: permissions.dordrecht@springer.com
Peer-reviewed journal focusing on the European dimension of crime and looks at its research and policy implications. **Freq:** Quarterly. **Key Personnel:** Ernesto U. Savona, Editor-in-Chief; Stefano Caneppele, Managing Editor; Rosemary Barberet, Editorial Board; Marcelo F. Aebi, Editorial Board; Ronald V. Clarke, Editorial Board; Alenka Selih, Editorial Board. **ISSN:** 0928-1371. **Subscription Rates:** EUR272 institutions print incl. free access or e-only; EUR326.40 institutions print incl. enhanced access. **Remarks:** Advertising accepted; rates available upon request. **URL:** http://www.springer.com/socialsciences/criminology/journal/10610. **Circ:** (Not Reported)

48383 ■ European Journal of Plastic Surgery
Springer Netherlands
Van Godewijckstraat 30
3311 GX Dordrecht, Netherlands
Ph: 31 786 576210
Fax: 31 786 576744
Publisher E-mail: permissions.dordrecht@springer.com
Journal covering microsurgery, tissue expansion, craniofacial surgery, trauma, malignancy, and aesthetic surgery. **Founded:** Oct. 6, 1966. **Freq:** Bimonthly. **Print Method:** Offset. **Cols./Page:** 5. **Col. Width:** 1 15/16 inches. **Col. Depth:** 15 1/2 inches. **Key Personnel:** I.T. Jackson, Editor-in-Chief; L. Clodius, Editorial Board; E. Arnaud, Editorial Board; Z.M. Arnez, Editorial Board; P. Blondeel, Editorial Board; A. Batchelor, Editorial Board; B. Coessens, Editorial Board; N. Ashammakhi, Editorial Board; Z. Can, Editorial Board; H.M. Costa, Co-Ed. **ISSN:** 0930-343X. **Subscription Rates:** EUR837 institutions print incl. free access or e-only; EUR1,004.40 institutions print incl. enhanced access. **Remarks:** Accepts advertising. **URL:** http://www.springer.com/medicine/surgery/journal/238. **Circ:** (Not Reported)

48384 ■ European Radiology Supplements
Springer Netherlands
Van Godewijckstraat 30
3311 GX Dordrecht, Netherlands
Ph: 31 786 576210

Fax: 31 786 576744
Publisher E-mail: permissions.dordrecht@springer.com
Peer-reviewed journal describing scientific knowledge in radiology. **Founded:** Dec. 4, 1981. **Print Method:** Web offset. **Trim Size:** 9 3/4 x 14 1/8. **Cols./Page:** 4. **Col. Width:** 2.25 inches. **Col. Depth:** 14.25 inches. **Key Personnel:** N. Gourtsoyiannis, Section Ed.; S.A. Taylor, Section Ed.; T.R. Fleiter, Section Ed.; M.R. Torkzad, Section Ed.; A.K. Dixon, Editor-in-Chief; J. Lissner, Founding Ed.; Albert L. Baert, Editor; A. De Backer, Section Ed.; T.J. Vogl, Dep. Ed. **ISSN:** 0938-7994. **Subscription Rates:** EUR1,275 institutions print & online; EUR1,530 institutions print including enhanced access. **Remarks:** Accepts advertising. **URL:** http://www.springer.com/medicine/radiology/journal/330. **Circ:** (Not Reported)

48385 ■ Evolution: Education and Outreach
Springer Netherlands
Van Godewijckstraat 30
3311 GX Dordrecht, Netherlands
Ph: 31 786 576210
Fax: 31 786 576744
Publisher E-mail: permissions.dordrecht@springer.com
Peer-reviewed journal covering evolutionary theory. **Freq:** Quarterly. **Key Personnel:** Dr. Niles Eldredge, PhD, Editor-in-Chief; Gregory Eldredge, Editor-in-Chief; Mick Wycoff, Managing Editor. **ISSN:** 1936-6426. **Subscription Rates:** EUR316 institutions print including free access or e-only; EUR379.20 institutions print including enhanced access. **URL:** http://www.springer.com/lifesci/journal/12052.

48386 ■ Feminist Legal Studies
Springer Netherlands
Van Godewijckstraat 30
3311 GX Dordrecht, Netherlands
Ph: 31 786 576210
Fax: 31 786 576744
Publisher E-mail: permissions.dordrecht@springer.com
Law periodical. **Founded:** 1999. **Freq:** Triennial. **Trim Size:** 15.6 x 23.5 cm. **Key Personnel:** Rosemary Hunter, Academic Ed.; Donatella Alessandrini, Editorial Board. **ISSN:** 0966-3622. **Subscription Rates:** EUR277 institutions print incl. free access or e-only; EUR332.40 institutions print incl. enhanced access. **Remarks:** Accepts advertising. **URL:** http://www.springer.com/law/journal/10691. **Circ:** (Not Reported)

48387 ■ Financial Markets and Portfolio Management
Springer Netherlands
Van Godewijckstraat 30
3311 GX Dordrecht, Netherlands
Ph: 31 786 576210
Fax: 31 786 576744
Publisher E-mail: permissions.dordrecht@springer.com
Journal covering all areas of finance and management. **Freq:** Quarterly. **Print Method:** Offset. **Trim Size:** 12 1/2 x 22 3/4. **Cols./Page:** 6. **Col. Width:** 11.2 nonpareils. **Col. Depth:** 294 agate lines. **Key Personnel:** Wolfgang Drobetz, Editorial Board; Jonathan Berk, Editorial Board; Philippe Jorion, Editorial Board; Manuel Ammann, Managing Editor; Francis Longstaff, Editorial Board; Jean-Pierre Danthine, Editorial Board; Thomas Stucki, Editorial Board; Rolf Banz, Editorial Board; Markus Rudolf, Editorial Board; Gunter Franke, Editorial Board. **ISSN:** 1555-4961. **Subscription Rates:** EUR196 institutions print incl. free access or e-only; EUR235.20 institutions print incl. enhanced access. **URL:** http://www.springer.com/business/journal/11408.

48388 ■ Flexible Services and Manufacturing Journal
Springer Netherlands
Van Godewijckstraat 30
3311 GX Dordrecht, Netherlands
Ph: 31 786 576210
Fax: 31 786 576744
Publisher E-mail: permissions.dordrecht@springer.com
Journal focusing on research on theoretical and application issues in the field of flexible manufacturing. **Subtitle:** Design, Analysis, and Operation of Manufacturing and Assembly Systems. **Freq:** Quarterly. **Key Personnel:** Sally Brailsford, Editor; Frank Chen, Editor; Jian Chen, Editor; Mabel Chou, Editor; Hans-Otto Guenther, Editor-in-Chief; Meltem Denizel, Editor; Karl F. Doerner, Editor; Matthias Ehrgott, Editor; Nesim Erkip, Editor; Edwin O. Fischer, Editor. **ISSN:** 1936-6582. **Subscription Rates:** EUR582 institutions print incl. free access or e-only; EUR698.40 institutions print incl. enhanced access. **Remarks:** Advertising accepted; rates available upon

request. **URL:** http://www.springerlink.com/content/0920-6299. **Former name:** International Journal of Flexible Manufacturing Systems (Jan. 1, 2008). **Circ:** (Not Reported)

48389 ■ Food Biophysics
Springer Netherlands
Van Godewijckstraat 30
3311 GX Dordrecht, Netherlands
Ph: 31 786 576210
Fax: 31 786 576744
Publisher E-mail: permissions.dordrecht@springer.com
Journal covering physical and chemical studies of food structure. **Founded:** Jan. 14, 1971. **Print Method:** Offset. **Trim Size:** 11 x 17. **Cols./Page:** 5. **Col. Width:** 23 nonpareils. **Col. Depth:** 224 agate lines. **Key Personnel:** Douglas G. Dalgleish, Editorial Board; Jose M. Aguilera, Editorial Board; Richard D. Ludescher, Editor-in-Chief; Erik Van Der Linden, Assoc. Ed.; Dane Bicanic, Editorial Board; John Coupland, Editorial Board; Srinivasan Damodaran, Editorial Board; John Brady, Assoc. Ed. **ISSN:** 1557-1858. **Subscription Rates:** EUR248 institutions print & online; EUR297.60 institutions print & enchanced access. **URL:** http://www.springer.com/foodscience/journal/11483.

48390 ■ Forschung im Ingenieurwesen
Springer Netherlands
Van Godewijckstraat 30
3311 GX Dordrecht, Netherlands
Ph: 31 786 576210
Fax: 31 786 576744
Publisher E-mail: permissions.dordrecht@springer.com
Journal covering research engineering sciences. **Subtitle:** Engineering Research. **Freq:** Quarterly. **Print Method:** Offset. **Trim Size:** 11 x 17. **Cols./Page:** 4. **Col. Width:** 11.5 picas. **Col. Depth:** 15 inches. **Key Personnel:** Prof. Stephan Kabelac, Editor-in-Chief, kabelac@hsu-hh.de. **ISSN:** 0015-7899. **Subscription Rates:** EUR851 institutions print incl. free access or e-only; EUR1021.20 institutions print incl. enhanced access. **Remarks:** Accepts advertising. **URL:** http://www.springer.com/engineering/mechanicaleng/journal/10010. **Circ:** (Not Reported)

48391 ■ Forum der Psychoanalyse
Springer Netherlands
Van Godewijckstraat 30
3311 GX Dordrecht, Netherlands
Ph: 31 786 576210
Fax: 31 786 576744
Publisher E-mail: permissions.dordrecht@springer.com
Journal covering clinical theory and practice of the psychoanalysis. **Subtitle:** Zeitschrift fur klinische Theorie und Praxis. **Founded:** 1978. **Freq:** Quarterly. **Print Method:** Offset. **Trim Size:** Tab 16. **Cols./Page:** 5. **Col. Width:** 22 nonpareils. **Col. Depth:** 224 agate lines. **Key Personnel:** Dr. Michael Ermann, Editor, ermann-forum@t-online.de; Dr. Carl Nedelmann, Editor, carl.nedelmann@dpv-mail.de; Prof. Jurgen Korner, Editor, koerner@zedat.fu-berlin.de. **ISSN:** 0178-7667. **Subscription Rates:** EUR200 institutions print incl. free access or e-only; EUR240 institutions print incl. enhanced access. **Remarks:** Advertising accepted; rates available upon request. **URL:** http://www.springer.com/psychology/journal/451. **Circ:** (Not Reported)

48392 ■ Foundations of Science
Springer Netherlands
Van Godewijckstraat 30
3311 GX Dordrecht, Netherlands
Ph: 31 786 576210
Fax: 31 786 576744
Publisher E-mail: permissions.dordrecht@springer.com
Journal covering methodological and philosophical topics of science. **Subtitle:** The Official Journal of the Association for Foundations of Science, Language and Cognition. **Founded:** 1985. **Freq:** Quarterly. **Print Method:** Offset. **Trim Size:** 11 1/2 x 14. **Cols./Page:** 4. **Col. Width:** 24 nonpareils. **Col. Depth:** 171 agate lines. **Key Personnel:** Jan Broekaert, Asst. Ed.; Liane Gabora, Asst. Ed.; Diederik Aerts, Editor-in-Chief. **ISSN:** 1233-1821. **Subscription Rates:** EUR488 institutions print incl. free access or e-only; EUR585.60 institutions print incl. enhanced access. **Remarks:** Accepts advertising. **URL:** http://www.springer.com/philosophy/philosophyofsciences/journal/10699. **Circ:** (Not Reported)

48393 ■ Frontiers of Biology in China
Springer Netherlands
Van Godewijckstraat 30
3311 GX Dordrecht, Netherlands

Circulation: ⋆ = ABC; △ = BPA; ♦ = CAC; • = CCAB; ❑ = VAC; ⊕ = PO Statement; ‡ = Publisher's Report; Boldface figures = sworn; Light figures = estimated.

Gale Directory of Publications & Broadcast Media/147th Ed.   5255

Ph: 31 786 576210
Fax: 31 786 576744
Publisher E-mail: permissions.dordrecht@springer.com
Peer-reviewed journal covering biology, botany, zoology, biophysics, biomathematics and biotechnology. **Freq:** Quarterly. **Print Method:** Offset. **Cols./Page:** 6. **Col. Width:** 24 nonpareils. **Col. Depth:** 298 agate lines. **Key Personnel:** Lizhe An, Editorial Board; Weihua Wu, Editor-in-Chief; Nathalie Beaujean, Editorial Board; Sixue Chen, Editorial Board; Xuemei Chen, Editorial Board; Zhizhong Gong, Editorial Board; Jiming Jiang, Editorial Board; Yi Zhang, Editorial Board; Jun Wang, Editorial Board; Jiemin Wong, Editorial Board. **ISSN:** 1673-3509. **Subscription Rates:** EUR466 institutions print incl. free access or e-only; EUR559.20 institutions print incl. enhanced access. **URL:** http://www.springer.com/lifesci/journal/11515.

48394 ■ Frontiers of Chemistry in China
Springer Netherlands
Van Godewijckstraat 30
3311 GX Dordrecht, Netherlands
Ph: 31 786 576210
Fax: 31 786 576744
Publisher E-mail: permissions.dordrecht@springer.com
Peer-reviewed journal devoted to chemist in academic institution. **Founded:** 1985. **Freq:** Quarterly. **Print Method:** Offset. **Trim Size:** 8 1/4 x 10 7/8. **Cols./Page:** 3. **Col. Width:** 27 nonpareils. **Col. Depth:** 140 agate lines. **Key Personnel:** Yuliang Yang, Editor-in-Chief; Guibin Jiang, Assoc. Ed.-in-Ch. **ISSN:** 1673-3495. **Subscription Rates:** EUR492 institutions print incl. free access or e-only; EUR590.40 institutions print incl. enhanced access. **URL:** http://www.springer.com/chemistry/journal/11458.

48395 ■ Frontiers of Economics in China
Springer Netherlands
Van Godewijckstraat 30
3311 GX Dordrecht, Netherlands
Ph: 31 786 576210
Fax: 31 786 576744
Publisher E-mail: permissions.dordrecht@springer.com
Peer-reviewed journal covering the field of economics in China. **Freq:** Quarterly. **Print Method:** Offset. **Trim Size:** 12 1/2 x 22 3/4. **Cols./Page:** 6. **Col. Width:** 1.833 nonpareils. **Col. Depth:** 295 agate lines. **Key Personnel:** Zhou Liqun, Editor-in-Chief; Bai Chong-En, Editorial Board; Guoqiang Tian, Editorial Board; Chung-Hua Shen, Editorial Board; Justin Yifu Lin, Editorial Board; Ho-Mou Wu, Editorial Board; Li Junjiang, Editorial Board; Liu Wei, Editorial Board; Liu Zhibiao, Editorial Board; Changying Li, Deputy Ed.-in-Ch. **ISSN:** 1673-3444. **Subscription Rates:** EUR430 institutions print incl. free access or e-only; EUR516 institutions print incl. enhanced access. **URL:** http://www.springer.com/economics/journal/11459.

48396 ■ Frontiers of Education in China
Springer Netherlands
Van Godewijckstraat 30
3311 GX Dordrecht, Netherlands
Ph: 31 786 576210
Fax: 31 786 576744
Publisher E-mail: permissions.dordrecht@springer.com
Journal promoting education in China. **Founded:** Apr. 1865. **Freq:** Quarterly. **Print Method:** Offset. **Cols./Page:** 6. **Col. Width:** 2 inches. **Col. Depth:** 21 1/2 inches. **Key Personnel:** Chen Xuefei, Editorial Board; Chen Shijian, Editorial Board; Hu Jianhua, Editorial Board; Yao Yun, Assoc. Ed.-in-Ch.; David A. Pariser, Editorial Board; Chen Yukun, Editorial Board; Henze Juergen, Editorial Board; Gao Baoli, Editorial Board; Hu Zhongping, Editorial Board; Gu Mingyuan, Editor-in-Chief. **ISSN:** 1673-341X. **Subscription Rates:** EUR430 institutions print incl. free access or e-only; EUR516 institutions print incl. enhanced access. **URL:** http://www.springer.com/education/journal/11516.

48397 ■ Frontiers of Electrical and Electronic Engineering in China
Springer Netherlands
Van Godewijckstraat 30
3311 GX Dordrecht, Netherlands
Ph: 31 786 576210
Fax: 31 786 576744
Publisher E-mail: permissions.dordrecht@springer.com
Journal covering electrical, micro-electronics, photoelectric engineering and electromagnetism. **Freq:** Quarterly. **Print Method:** Offset. **Cols./Page:** 5. **Col. Width:** 20 nonpareils. **Col. Depth:** 196 agate lines. **Key Personnel:** Zhong Yixin, Assoc. Ed.-in-Ch.; Huiyu Xia, Manag-

ing Editor; Cui Xiang, Editorial Board; Bi Guangguo, Editorial Board; Bai Er-Wei, Editorial Board; Li Yanda, Editor-in-Chief; Wang Weining, Managing Editor; Chi Huisheng, Editorial Board. **ISSN:** 1673-3460. **Subscription Rates:** EUR387 institutions print incl. free access or e-only; EUR464.40 institutions print incl. enhanced access. **URL:** http://www.springer.com/engineering/electronics/journal/11460.

48398 ■ Frontiers of Forestry in China
Springer Netherlands
Van Godewijckstraat 30
3311 GX Dordrecht, Netherlands
Ph: 31 786 576210
Fax: 31 786 576744
Publisher E-mail: permissions.dordrecht@springer.com
Journal featuring advanced forestry research in China. **Freq:** Quarterly. **Print Method:** Offset. **Trim Size:** 8 1/4 x 10 3/4. **Cols./Page:** 3. **Col. Width:** 28 nonpareils. **Col. Depth:** 134 agate lines. **Key Personnel:** Dai Silan, Editorial Board; Guofang Shen, Editor-in-Chief; Gu Wanchun, Editorial Board; Feng Zongwei, Editorial Board; Guo Lanbin, Editorial Board; Dong Naijun, Editorial Board; Chen Xiaoyang, Editorial Board; Feng Zhongke, Editorial Board; Chen Junyu, Editorial Board; Chen Jiquan, Editorial Board. **ISSN:** 1673-3517. **Subscription Rates:** EUR367 institutions print incl. free access or e-only; EUR440.40 institutions print incl. enhanced access. **URL:** http://www.springer.com/lifesci/forestry/journal/11461.

48399 ■ Frontiers of History in China
Springer Netherlands
Van Godewijckstraat 30
3311 GX Dordrecht, Netherlands
Ph: 31 786 576210
Fax: 31 786 576744
Publisher E-mail: permissions.dordrecht@springer.com
Peer-reviewed journal covering history of Chinese culture. **Freq:** Quarterly. **Print Method:** Offset. **Cols./Page:** 6. **Col. Width:** 25 nonpareils. **Col. Depth:** 301 agate lines. **Key Personnel:** Chen Chunsheng, Editorial Board; Li Xueqin, Editor-in-Chief; Chen Hua, Editorial Board. **ISSN:** 1673-3401. **Subscription Rates:** EUR430 institutions print incl. free access or e-only; EUR516 institutions print incl. enhanced access. **URL:** http://www.springer.com/humanities/history/journal/11462.

48400 ■ Frontiers of Law in China
Springer Netherlands
Van Godewijckstraat 30
3311 GX Dordrecht, Netherlands
Ph: 31 786 576210
Fax: 31 786 576744
Publisher E-mail: permissions.dordrecht@springer.com
Journal covering new legislative law. **Freq:** Quarterly. **Key Personnel:** Huang Jin, Editorial Board; Chen Guiming, Editorial Board; Rao Geping, Editorial Board; He Jiahong, Editor-in-Chief; Bian Jianlin, Editorial Board; Feng Jun, Editorial Board; Chen Xingliang, Editorial Board; Liu Chuntian, Editorial Board; Che Pizhao, Editorial Board; Wu Zhipan, Editorial Board. **ISSN:** 1673-3428. **Subscription Rates:** EUR546 institutions print incl. free access or e-only; EUR655.20 institutions print incl. enhanced access. **URL:** http://www.springer.com/law/journal/11463.

48401 ■ Frontiers of Mathematics in China
Springer Netherlands
Van Godewijckstraat 30
3311 GX Dordrecht, Netherlands
Ph: 31 786 576210
Fax: 31 786 576744
Publisher E-mail: permissions.dordrecht@springer.com
Journal covering different fields of mathematics and sciences. **Founded:** 1986. **Freq:** Quarterly. **Print Method:** Offset. **Trim Size:** 8 1/2 x 11. **Cols./Page:** 3. **Key Personnel:** Kungching Chang, Editor-in-Chief; Chen Mu-Fa, Assoc. Ed.-in-Ch.; Zhengyan Lin, Editorial Board; Bao Gang, Editorial Board; Kening Lu, Editorial Board; Bolin Guo, Editorial Board; Yongchuan Chen, Editorial Board; Deng Bangming, Editorial Board; Tang Tao, Assoc. Ed.-in-Ch. **ISSN:** 1673-3452. **Subscription Rates:** EUR546 institutions print incl. free access or e-only; EUR655.20 institutions print incl. enhanced access. **URL:** http://www.springer.com/math/journal/11464.

48402 ■ Frontiers of Mechanical Engineering in China
Springer Netherlands
Van Godewijckstraat 30
3311 GX Dordrecht, Netherlands

Ph: 31 786 576210
Fax: 31 786 576744
Publisher E-mail: permissions.dordrecht@springer.com
Peer-reviewed journal covering the field of mechanical engineering. **Freq:** Quarterly. **Print Method:** Offset. **Trim Size:** 10 x 12 3/4. **Cols./Page:** 6. **Col. Width:** 28 nonpareils. **Col. Depth:** 181 agate lines. **Key Personnel:** Fei Renyuan, Assoc. Ed.-in-Ch.; Yubao Chen, Editorial Board; Masao Sakane, Editorial Board; Tielin Shi, Assoc. Ed.-in-Ch.; Yang Shuzi, Editor-in-Chief; Guo Dongming, Editorial Board; Chen Darong, Editorial Board; Jay Lee, Editorial Board; Peihua Gu, Editorial Board. **ISSN:** 1673-3479. **Subscription Rates:** EUR483 institutions print incl. free access or e-only; EUR579.60 institutions print incl. enhanced access. **URL:** http://www.springer.com/engineering/mechanicaleng/journal/11465.

48403 ■ Frontiers of Philosophy in China
Springer Netherlands
Van Godewijckstraat 30
3311 GX Dordrecht, Netherlands
Ph: 31 786 576210
Fax: 31 786 576744
Publisher E-mail: permissions.dordrecht@springer.com
Journal for professors and students interested in Chinese culture. **Freq:** Quarterly. **Print Method:** Offset. **Cols./Page:** 6. **Col. Width:** 25 nonpareils. **Col. Depth:** 21 1/2 inches. **Key Personnel:** John Cobb, Editorial Board; Wu Yujun, Managing Editor; Guo Guichun, Editorial Board; Wan Junren, Editorial Board; Yuan Guiren, Editor-in-Chief; Tian Ping, Assoc. Ed.-in-Ch.; Haifang Sun, Managing Editor; Feng Jun, Editorial Board; Ju Shier, Editorial Board. **ISSN:** 1673-3436. **Subscription Rates:** EUR546 institutions print incl. free access or e-only; EUR655.20 institutions print incl. enhanced access. **URL:** http://www.springer.com/philosophy/journal/11466.

48404 ■ Frontiers of Physics in China
Springer Netherlands
Van Godewijckstraat 30
3311 GX Dordrecht, Netherlands
Ph: 31 786 576210
Fax: 31 786 576744
Publisher E-mail: permissions.dordrecht@springer.com
Journal covering physics. **Freq:** Quarterly. **Print Method:** Offset. **Trim Size:** 13 x 21 1/2. **Cols./Page:** 6. **Col. Width:** 12.5 picas. **Key Personnel:** Hu Gang, Assoc. Ed.-in-Ch.; Feng Shi-Ping, Editorial Board; Deng Xiao hua, Editorial Board; Li Shi-Qun, Assoc. Ed.-in-Ch.; Kuang Le-man, Editorial Board; Chen Hong, Editorial Board; Dai Zi-Gao, Editorial Board; Lu Guo, Assoc. Ed.-in-Ch.; Chao Kuang-Ta, Editor-in-Chief; Ding Da-jun, Editorial Board Member. **ISSN:** 1673-3487. **Subscription Rates:** EUR483 institutions print incl. free access or e-only; EUR579.60 institutions print incl. enhanced access. **URL:** http://www.springer.com/physics/journal/11467.

48405 ■ Genetica
Springer Netherlands
Van Godewijckstraat 30
3311 GX Dordrecht, Netherlands
Ph: 31 786 576210
Fax: 31 786 576744
Publisher E-mail: permissions.dordrecht@springer.com
Journal publishing latest genetic research. **Subtitle:** An International Journal of Genetics and Evolution. **Freq:** 3/yr. **Key Personnel:** Pierre Capy, Editor; Ronny C. Woodruff, Editor; S. Abe, Assoc. Ed. **ISSN:** 0016-6707. **Subscription Rates:** EUR2,960 institutions print incl. free access or e-only; EUR3,552 institutions print incl. enhanced access. **Remarks:** Advertising accepted; rates available upon request. **URL:** http://www.springer.com/lifesci/journal/10709. **Circ:** (Not Reported)

48406 ■ GeoInformatica
Springer Netherlands
Van Godewijckstraat 30
3311 GX Dordrecht, Netherlands
Ph: 31 786 576210
Fax: 31 786 576744
Publisher E-mail: permissions.dordrecht@springer.com
Journal publishing novel results emerging from the research in the area of computer science applied to geographic information systems. **Subtitle:** An International Journal on Advances of Computer Science for Geographic Information Systems. **Freq:** Quarterly. **Key Personnel:** George Benwell, Regional Ed.; Andrew U. Frank, Editor-in-Chief; Patrick Bergougnoux, Founding Ed.-in-Ch.; Niki Pissinou, Editorial Board; Gary Hunter,

Editorial Board; Peter Burrough, Editorial Board; Flavio Bonfatti, Editorial Board; Shashi Shekhar, Editor-in-Chief; John Herring, Editorial Board. **ISSN:** 1384-6175. **Subscription Rates:** EUR779 institutions print including free access or e-only; EUR934.80 institutions print including enhanced access. **Remarks:** Advertising accepted; rates available upon request. **URL:** http://www.springerlink.com/content/1384-6175. **Circ:** (Not Reported)

48407 ■ Geometriae Dedicata
Springer Netherlands
Van Godewijckstraat 30
3311 GX Dordrecht, Netherlands
Ph: 31 786 576210
Fax: 31 786 576744
Publisher E-mail: permissions.dordrecht@springer.com
Journal dealing with geometry and its relationship to topology, group theory and the theory of dynamical systems. **Founded:** 1972. **Freq:** Annual. **Key Personnel:** William Mark Goldman, Editor-in-Chief; Benson Farb, Honorary Ed.; R.J. Zimmer, Honorary Ed.; Lawrence Ein, Editorial Board; R. Spatzier, Editorial Board. **ISSN:** 0046-5755. **Subscription Rates:** EUR1,603 institutions print incl. free access or e-only; EUR1,923.60 institutions print incl. enhanced access. **Remarks:** Advertising accepted; rates available upon request. **URL:** http://www.springer.com/math/geometry/journal/10711. **Circ:** (Not Reported)

48408 ■ Grammars
Springer Netherlands
Van Godewijckstraat 30
3311 GX Dordrecht, Netherlands
Ph: 31 786 576210
Fax: 31 786 576744
Publisher E-mail: permissions.dordrecht@springer.com
Journal covering natural languages and mathematical research. **Subtitle:** A Journal of Mathematical Research on Formal and Natural Languages. **Founded:** Nov. 15, 1973. **Print Method:** Offset. **Trim Size:** 13 x 21 1/2. **Cols./Page:** 6. **Col. Width:** 12 1/2 picas. **Col. Depth:** 129 picas. **ISSN:** 1386-7393. **Remarks:** Accepts advertising. **URL:** http://www.springer.com/linguistics/computationallinguistics/journal/10721. **Circ:** (Not Reported)

48409 ■ Grundwasser
Springer Netherlands
Van Godewijckstraat 30
3311 GX Dordrecht, Netherlands
Ph: 31 786 576210
Fax: 31 786 576744
Publisher E-mail: permissions.dordrecht@springer.com
Magazine covering underground water and development from science and practices. **Subtitle:** Zeitschrift der Fachsektion Hydrogeologie in der Deutschen. **Freq:** Quarterly. **Print Method:** Offset. **Cols./Page:** 6. **Col. Width:** 25 nonpareils. **Col. Depth:** 301 agate lines. **Key Personnel:** Dr. Mario Schirmer, Editor; Prof. Christoph Schuth, Editor; Patricia Schull, Editor. **ISSN:** 1430-483X. **Subscription Rates:** EUR222 institutions print incl. free access or e-only; EUR266.40 institutions print incl. enhanced access. **Remarks:** Accepts advertising. **URL:** http://www.springer.com/earthsciences/hydrogeology/journal/767. **Circ:** (Not Reported)

48410 ■ Gynakologische Endokrinologie
Springer Netherlands
Van Godewijckstraat 30
3311 GX Dordrecht, Netherlands
Ph: 31 786 576210
Fax: 31 786 576744
Publisher E-mail: permissions.dordrecht@springer.com
Peer-reviewed journal covers Gynaekologie and the reproduction medicine. **Freq:** Quarterly. **Print Method:** Offset. **Cols./Page:** 6. **Col. Width:** 26 nonpareils. **Col. Depth:** 301 agate lines. **Key Personnel:** Prof. Klaus Diedrich, Editor; Prof. Thomas Strowitzki, Editor. **ISSN:** 1610-2894. **Subscription Rates:** EUR272 institutions print incl. free access or e-only; EUR326.40 institutions print incl. enhanced access. **Remarks:** Accepts advertising. **URL:** http://www.springer.com/medicine/gynecology/journal/10304. **Circ:** (Not Reported)

48411 ■ Gynecological Surgery
Springer Netherlands
Van Godewijckstraat 30
3311 GX Dordrecht, Netherlands
Ph: 31 786 576210
Fax: 31 786 576744

Publisher E-mail: permissions.dordrecht@springer.com
Peer-reviewed journal covering the surgical aspects of endoscopic imaging, and allied techniques such as interventional endoscopy and ultrasound. **Founded:** 2004. **Freq:** Quarterly. **Print Method:** Offset. **Cols./Page:** 6. **Col. Width:** 25 nonpareils. **Col. Depth:** 301 agate lines. **Key Personnel:** Ivo Brosens, Editor-in-Chief; Margit Dueholm, Editorial Advisory Board; J. Stencl, Editorial Board; Z. Holub, Editorial Board; P. Bartos, Editorial Board; A. Wattiez, Editorial Board; Frank Willem Jansen, Editorial Board. **ISSN:** 1613-2076. **Subscription Rates:** EUR647 institutions print incl. free access or e-only; EUR776.40 institutions print incl. enhanced access. **URL:** http://www.springer.com/medicine/gynecology/journal/10397.

48412 ■ Health Care Analysis
Springer Netherlands
Van Godewijckstraat 30
3311 GX Dordrecht, Netherlands
Ph: 31 786 576210
Fax: 31 786 576744
Publisher E-mail: permissions.dordrecht@springer.com
Journal seeking to analyze health care from multiple perspectives: public policy and health-related education, health services organization and decision-making health care professional practice. **Subtitle:** An International Journal of Health Care Philosophy and Policy. **Freq:** Quarterly. **Key Personnel:** Andrew Robert Edgar, Editor; Steve Edwards, Editorial Board; Heather Draper, Editorial Board; Henk Ten Have, Editorial Board; Paul Menzel, Editorial Board; Alan Cribb, Editorial Board; Chris Hackler, Editorial Board; Donna Dickenson, Editorial Board; Margaret Battin, Advisory Board; Richard Ashcroft, Editorial Board. **ISSN:** 1065-3058. **Subscription Rates:** EUR679 institutions print including free access or e-only; EUR814.80 institutions print including enhanced access. **Remarks:** Accepts advertising. **URL:** http://www.springerlink.com/content/1065-3058. **Circ:** (Not Reported)

48413 ■ HealthCare Ethics Committee Forum
Springer Netherlands
Van Godewijckstraat 30
3311 GX Dordrecht, Netherlands
Ph: 31 786 576210
Fax: 31 786 576744
Publisher E-mail: permissions.dordrecht@springer.com
Peer-reviewed journal on ethics in healthcare featuring topics of interest to practicing physicians, nurses, social workers, risk managers, attorneys, ethicists, and other HEC committee members. **Subtitle:** An Interprofessional Journal on Healthcare Institutions' Ethical and Legal Issues. **Freq:** Quarterly. **Key Personnel:** Henk A.M.J. Ten Have, European Ed.; Mark J. Cherry, Editor-in-Chief; Stuart F. Spicker, Founding Ed.; George Khushf, Admin. and Organisational Ethics; Roberta M. Berry, Editorial Board; Nicholas Capaldi, Editorial Board. **ISSN:** 0956-2737. **Subscription Rates:** EUR328 institutions print incl. free access or e-only; EUR393 institutions print incl. enhanced access. **Remarks:** Advertising accepted; rates available upon request. **URL:** http://springerlink.metapress.com/content/102899/. **Circ:** (Not Reported)

48414 ■ Helminthologia
Springer Netherlands
Van Godewijckstraat 30
3311 GX Dordrecht, Netherlands
Ph: 31 786 576210
Fax: 31 786 576744
Publisher E-mail: permissions.dordrecht@springer.com
Peer-reviewed journal focusing on the latest research in helminthology. **Freq:** Quarterly. **Key Personnel:** Vladimira Hanzelova, Editorial Board; H. Auer, Advisory Board; Marian Varady, Editor-in-Chief; Pavol Dubinsky, Editorial Board; Marta Spakulova, Editorial Board; C. Arme, Advisory Board; Valeria Letkova, Editorial Board; Slavka Sabolova-Barlakova, Asst. of the Mng. Ed.; Lydia Cislakova, Editorial Board. **ISSN:** 0440-6605. **Subscription Rates:** EUR502 institutions print incl. free access or e-only; EUR602.40 institutions print incl. enhanced access. **URL:** http://www.springer.com/biomed/journal/11687.

48415 ■ Higher Education
Springer Netherlands
Van Godewijckstraat 30
3311 GX Dordrecht, Netherlands
Ph: 31 786 576210
Fax: 31 786 576744

Publisher E-mail: permissions.dordrecht@springer.com
Journal focusing on higher education and educational planning in a global scenario in institutions such as universities, polytechnics, colleges, and in those imparting vocational education. **Subtitle:** The International Journal of Higher Education and Educational Planning. **Founded:** 1972. **Freq:** 6/yr. **Key Personnel:** Grant Harman, Editor-in-Chief, gharman@une.edu.au; Noel J. Entwistle, Advisory Ed.; Philip G Altbach, Editorial Advisory Board. **ISSN:** 0018-1560. **Subscription Rates:** EUR1,143 institutions print incl. free access or e-only; EUR1,371.60 institutions print incl. enhanced access. **Remarks:** Advertising accepted; rates available upon request. **URL:** http://springerlink.metapress.com/content/102901/. **Circ:** (Not Reported)

48416 ■ HNO
Springer Netherlands
Van Godewijckstraat 30
3311 GX Dordrecht, Netherlands
Ph: 31 786 576210
Fax: 31 786 576744
Publisher E-mail: permissions.dordrecht@springer.com
Journal covering the requirements of ambulatory practice. **Subtitle:** German Society of Oto-Rhino-Laryngology, Head and Neck Surgery. **Freq:** Monthly. **Print Method:** Offset. **Cols./Page:** 6. **Col. Width:** 21 nonpareils. **Col. Depth:** 308 agate lines. **Key Personnel:** Prof. Peter K. Plinkert, Editor, peter_plinkert@med.uni-heidelberg.de; Prof. Alexander Berghaus, Editor, alexander.berghaus@med.uni-muenchen.de; Prof. Friedrich Bootz, Editor, friedrich.bootz@ukb.uni-bonn.de. **ISSN:** 0017-6192. **Subscription Rates:** EUR433 institutions print incl. free access or e-only; EUR519.60 institutions print incl. enhanced access. **Remarks:** Accepts advertising. **URL:** http://www.springer.com/medicine/otorhinolaryngology/journal/106. **Circ:** (Not Reported)

48417 ■ Holz als Roh- und Werkstoff
Springer Netherlands
Van Godewijckstraat 30
3311 GX Dordrecht, Netherlands
Ph: 31 786 576210
Fax: 31 786 576744
Publisher E-mail: permissions.dordrecht@springer.com
Journal covering wood and wood products. **Subtitle:** European Journal of Wood and Wood Products. **Freq:** 4/yr. **Key Personnel:** Prof. G. Wegener, Editor; Prof. P. Glos, Editor; Prof. J. Fromm, Editorial Board. **ISSN:** 0018-3768. **Subscription Rates:** EUR1,275 institutions print incl. free access or e-only; EUR1,530 institutions print incl. enhanced access. **Remarks:** Accepts advertising. **URL:** http://www.springer.com/lifesci/forestry/journal/107. **Circ:** (Not Reported)

48418 ■ Human Ecology
Springer Netherlands
Van Godewijckstraat 30
3311 GX Dordrecht, Netherlands
Ph: 31 786 576210
Fax: 31 786 576744
Publisher E-mail: permissions.dordrecht@springer.com
Journal focusing on interactions between people and environment. **Subtitle:** An Interdisciplinary Journal. **Founded:** 1972. **Freq:** Bimonthly. **Print Method:** Offset. **Trim Size:** 6 x 0. **Cols./Page:** 1. **Col. Width:** 54 nonpareils. **Col. Depth:** 103 agate lines. **Key Personnel:** Daniel G. Bates, Editor; Flora E. Lu, Book Review Ed.; Susan H. Lees, Editorial Board. **ISSN:** 0300-7839. **Subscription Rates:** EUR1,315 institutions print or online; EUR1,578 institutions print & enhanced access. **Remarks:** Accepts advertising. **URL:** http://www.springer.com/socialsciences/archaeology%26anthropology/journal/10745. **Circ:** (Not Reported)

48419 ■ Hydrobiologia
Springer Netherlands
Van Godewijckstraat 30
3311 GX Dordrecht, Netherlands
Ph: 31 786 576210
Fax: 31 786 576744
Publisher E-mail: permissions.dordrecht@springer.com
Peer-reviewed journal focusing on the fields of fundamental limnology and marine biology. **Subtitle:** The International Journal of Aquatic Sciences. **Freq:** Annual. **Key Personnel:** Henri J. Dumont, Honorary Ed.-in-Ch.; Koen Martens, Editor-in-Chief; David M. Harper, Advisory Board; Jim A. Cambray, Editorial Board; Luis Mauricio Bini, Editorial Board. **ISSN:** 0018-8158. **Subscription Rates:** EUR10,708 institutions print incl. free access

Circulation: ★ = ABC; △ = BPA; ♦ = CAC; • = CCAB; ❑ = VAC; ⊕ = PO Statement; ‡ = Publisher's Report; Boldface figures = sworn; Light figures = estimated.

Gale Directory of Publications & Broadcast Media/147th Ed.   **5257**

or e-only; EUR12,849.60 institutions print incl. enhanced access. **URL:** http://www.springerlink.com/content/1573-5117/.

48420 ■ Hyperfine Interactions
Springer Netherlands
Van Godewijckstraat 30
3311 GX Dordrecht, Netherlands
Ph: 31 786 576210
Fax: 31 786 576744
Publisher E-mail: permissions.dordrecht@springer.com
Scientific journal covering research in solid-state physics, atomic physics, nuclear physics, and chemistry. **Freq:** Triennial. **Key Personnel:** Hans-Jurgen Kluge, Editor-in-Chief; Guido Langouche, Editor-in-Chief. **ISSN:** 0304-3834. **Subscription Rates:** EUR3,310 institutions print incl. free access or e-only; EUR3,972 institutions print incl. enhanced access. **Remarks:** Accepts advertising. **URL:** http://www.springerlink.com/content/101746/; http://www.springer.com/physics/elementary/journal/10751. **Circ:** (Not Reported)

48421 ■ Informatik-Spektrum
Springer Netherlands
Van Godewijckstraat 30
3311 GX Dordrecht, Netherlands
Ph: 31 786 576210
Fax: 31 786 576744
Publisher E-mail: permissions.dordrecht@springer.com
Journal about technical and scientific progress in computer science and its applications. **Subtitle:** Organ der Gesellschaft fur Informatik e.V. und mit ihr assoziierter Organisationen. **Founded:** 1976. **Freq:** 6/yr. **Print Method:** Offset. **Trim Size:** 8 1/8 x 10 7/8. **Cols./Page:** 3. **Col. Width:** 2 1/4 inches. **Col. Depth:** 10 inches. **Key Personnel:** Hermann Engesser, Editor-in-Chief, hermann.engesser@springer.com; Dr. B. Bartsch-Sporl, Editor, brigitte@bsr-consulting.de. **ISSN:** 0170-6012. **Subscription Rates:** EUR620 institutions print incl. free access or e-only; EUR744 institutions print incl. enhanced access. **Remarks:** Accepts advertising. **URL:** http://www.springer.com/computer/journal/287. **Circ:** (Not Reported)

48422 ■ Information Technology and Management
Springer Netherlands
Van Godewijckstraat 30
3311 GX Dordrecht, Netherlands
Ph: 31 786 576210
Fax: 31 786 576744
Publisher E-mail: permissions.dordrecht@springer.com
Journal covering the impact of different technologies on information system design, functionality, operations and management. **Freq:** Quarterly. **Key Personnel:** Ritu Agarwal, Editorial Board; Nabil R. Adam, Editorial Board; Varghese S. Jacob, Editor-in-Chief; H. Pirkul, Editor-in-Chief; Amitava Dutta, Editorial Board; Gary J. Koehler, Editorial Board. **ISSN:** 1385-951X. **Subscription Rates:** EUR525 institutions print including free access or e-only; EUR630 institutions print including enhanced access. **Remarks:** Advertising accepted; rates available upon request. **URL:** http://www.springerlink.com/content/1385-951X. **Circ:** (Not Reported)

48423 ■ Integrated Assessment
Springer Netherlands
Van Godewijckstraat 30
3311 GX Dordrecht, Netherlands
Ph: 31 786 576210
Fax: 31 786 576744
Publisher E-mail: permissions.dordrecht@springer.com
Peer-reviewed scientific journal covering integrated assessment. **Freq:** Quarterly. **Key Personnel:** Hadi Dowlatabadi, Editor-in-Chief, hadi.d@ubc.ca; Anton Pitts, Editor, apitts@interchange.ubc.ca; James Tansey, Editor, james.tansey@gmail.com; Michael M. Burgess, Section Ed., mburgess@ethics.ubc.ca. **ISSN:** 1389-5176. **Remarks:** Accepts advertising. **URL:** http://journals.sfu.ca/int_assess/index.php/iaj/search/results; http://www.springerlink.com/content/104581/. **Circ:** (Not Reported)

48424 ■ Intensivmedizin und Notfallmedizin
Springer Netherlands
Van Godewijckstraat 30
3311 GX Dordrecht, Netherlands
Ph: 31 786 576210
Fax: 31 786 576744
Publisher E-mail: permissions.dordrecht@springer.com
Journal on intensive medicine and emergency medicine. **Subtitle:** German Interdisciplinary Journal of Intensive Care Medicine. **Founded:** 1953. **Freq:** 8/yr. **Print Method:** Offset. **Trim Size:** 8 1/8 x 10 7/8. **Cols./Page:** 3. **Col. Width:** 2 1/4 inches. **Col. Depth:** 10 inches. **Key Personnel:** Dr. H.P. Schuster, Coord. Ed., dres.schuster@t-online.de; Prof. H.A. Adams, Advisory Board, adams.ha@mh-hannover.de; Prof. G. Baumann, Advisory Board, gert.baumann@charite,de. **ISSN:** 0175-3851. **Subscription Rates:** EUR789 institutions print incl. free access or e-only; EUR946.80 institutions print incl. enhanced access. **Remarks:** Advertising accepted; rates available upon request. **URL:** http://www.springer.com/steinkopff/inneremedizin/journal/390. **Circ:** (Not Reported)

48425 ■ International Journal for the Advancement of Counseling
Springer Netherlands
Van Godewijckstraat 30
3311 GX Dordrecht, Netherlands
Ph: 31 786 576210
Fax: 31 786 576744
Publisher E-mail: permissions.dordrecht@springer.com
Journal covering the exchange of counselling activities worldwide. **Freq:** Quarterly. **Key Personnel:** Don C. Locke, Co-Ed.; Arthur M. Horne, Co-Ed.; Frederick D. Harper, Co-Ed. **ISSN:** 0165-0653. **Subscription Rates:** EUR475 institutions print or online; EUR570 institutions print & enchanced access. **URL:** http://www.springerlink.com/content/102909/.

48426 ■ International Journal of Computer Assisted Radiology and Surgery
Springer Netherlands
Van Godewijckstraat 30
3311 GX Dordrecht, Netherlands
Ph: 31 786 576210
Fax: 31 786 576744
Publisher E-mail: permissions.dordrecht@springer.com
Peer-reviewed journal for interdisciplinary research, development and applications of image guided diagnosis and therapy. **Subtitle:** A Journal for Interdisciplinary Research, Development and Applications of Image Guided Diagnosis and Therapy. **Founded:** 1960. **Freq:** Bimonthly. **Print Method:** Offset. **Trim Size:** 8 1/8 x 10 7/8. **Cols./Page:** 3. **Col. Width:** 2 1/4 inches. **Col. Depth:** 10 inches. **Key Personnel:** R. Fahlbusch, Dep. Ed.; L. Berliner, Dep. Ed.; H.K. Huang, Dep. Ed.; A.G. Farman, Dep. Ed.; M.W. Vannier, Editor-in-Chief; M. Hashizume, Dep. Ed.; K. Doi, Dep. Ed.; T. Dohi, Dep. Ed.; H.U. Lemke, Editor-in-Chief; D. Caramella, Dep. Ed. **ISSN:** 1861-6410. **Subscription Rates:** EUR483 institutions print incl. free access or e-only; EUR579.60 institutions print incl. enhanced access. **Remarks:** Accepts advertising. **URL:** http://www.springer.com/medicine/radiology/journal/11548. **Circ:** (Not Reported)

48427 ■ International Journal for Educational and Vocational Guidance
Springer Netherlands
Van Godewijckstraat 30
3311 GX Dordrecht, Netherlands
Ph: 31 786 576210
Fax: 31 786 576744
Publisher E-mail: permissions.dordrecht@springer.com
Journal devoted to work and leisure, career development, career counseling and guidance. **Founded:** 1972. **Freq:** 3/yr. **Print Method:** Offset. **Trim Size:** 10 1/4 x 13 3/4. **Cols./Page:** 4. **Col. Width:** 2 1/4 inches. **Col. Depth:** 13 inches. **Key Personnel:** Raoul Van Esbroeck, Editor; Jean Pierre Dauwalder, Advisory Board; Tony G. Watts, Editorial Board; Diana Aisenson, Advisory Board; Jose Antonia Benavent, Advisory Board; Jean Guichard, Editorial Board; Bernadette Dumora, Advisory Board; Spencer Niles, Editorial Board; Norm Amundson, Advisory Board. **ISSN:** 0251-2513. **Subscription Rates:** EUR301 institutions print incl. free access or e-only; EUR361.20 institutions print incl. enhanced access. **Remarks:** Accepts advertising. **URL:** http://www.springer.com/education/journal/10775. **Circ:** (Not Reported)

48428 ■ International Journal of Historical Archaeology
Springer Netherlands
Van Godewijckstraat 30
3311 GX Dordrecht, Netherlands
Ph: 31 786 576210
Fax: 31 786 576744
Publisher E-mail: permissions.dordrecht@springer.com
Scholarly Journal covering historical archaeology. **Founded:** June 1997. **Freq:** Quarterly. **Trim Size:** 6 x 9. **Cols./Page:** 1. **Col. Width:** 27 picas. **Key Personnel:** Charles E. Orser, Jr., Editor; Martin Hall, Editorial Board; J. Barto Arnold III, Consulting Ed.; Colm Donnelly, Edito-

rial Board; Kathleen A. Deagan, Editorial Board; Anders Andren, Editorial Board; David Barker, Editorial Board. **ISSN:** 1092-7697. **Subscription Rates:** EUR325 institutions print including free access or e-only; EUR390 institutions print including enhanced access. **Remarks:** Accepts advertising. **URL:** http://www.springerlink.com/content/104876/. **Circ:** (Not Reported)

48429 ■ International Journal for Philosophy of Religion
Springer Netherlands
Van Godewijckstraat 30
3311 GX Dordrecht, Netherlands
Ph: 31 786 576210
Fax: 31 786 576744
Publisher E-mail: permissions.dordrecht@springer.com
Publication covering philosophy and religion. **Freq:** Bimonthly. **Key Personnel:** James A. Keller, Book Review Ed.; Eugene Thomas Long, Editor-in-Chief; Frank R. Harrison III, President; Billy Joe Lucas, Board of Assoc. Ed.; Gareth B. Matthews, Board of Assoc. Ed. **ISSN:** 0020-7047. **Subscription Rates:** EUR645 institutions print incl. free access or e-only; EUR774 institutions print incl. enhanced access. **Remarks:** Accepts advertising. **URL:** http://www.springer.com/philosophy/philosophyofreligion/journal/11153. **Circ:** (Not Reported)

48430 ■ International Journal of Politics, Culture, and Society
Springer Netherlands
Van Godewijckstraat 30
3311 GX Dordrecht, Netherlands
Ph: 31 786 576210
Fax: 31 786 576744
Publication E-mail: ijpcs@newschool.edu
Publisher E-mail: permissions.dordrecht@springer.com
Peer-reviewed journal covering the field of sociology. **Freq:** Quarterly. **Key Personnel:** Jeffrey Goldfarb, Editor; Elzbieta Matynia, Editor; Luca Follis, Assoc. Ed./Mng. Ed.; Vera L. Zolberg, Editor; Fanon Howell, Assoc. Ed./Mng. Ed.; Despina Lalaki, Assoc. Ed./Mng. Ed. **ISSN:** 0891-4486. **Subscription Rates:** EUR882 institutions print incl. free access or e-only; EUR1,058.40 institutions print incl. enhanced access. **Remarks:** Accepts advertising. **URL:** http://www.springer.com/socialsciences/sociology/journal/10767?detailsPage=editorialBoard. **Circ:** (Not Reported)

48431 ■ International Journal for the Semiotics of Law
Springer Netherlands
Van Godewijckstraat 30
3311 GX Dordrecht, Netherlands
Ph: 31 786 576210
Fax: 31 786 576744
Publisher E-mail: permissions.dordrecht@springer.com
French and English language journal covering the semiotics of law worldwide. **Freq:** Quarterly. **Key Personnel:** Bernard S. Jackson, Honorary Board Membership; Anne Wagner, Editor-in-Chief; Bruce Arrigo, Editorial Board. **ISSN:** 0952-8059. **Subscription Rates:** US$373 institutions including postage & handling; US$447.60 institutions including postage & handling. **URL:** http://www.springerlink.com/content/104162/. **Foreign language name:** Revue Internationale de Semiotique Jurdique.

48432 ■ International Review of Education
Springer Netherlands
Van Godewijckstraat 30
3311 GX Dordrecht, Netherlands
Ph: 31 786 576210
Fax: 31 786 576744
Publisher E-mail: permissions.dordrecht@springer.com
Publication covering worldwide education, in English, French and German. **Founded:** 1955. **Freq:** Bimonthly. **Key Personnel:** S. Halimi, Editorial Board; Hassana Alidou, Consulting Ed.; L.W. Anderson, Consulting Ed.; H. Abadzi, Consulting Ed.; C. Adick, Editorial Board; A. Ouane, Editorial Board; Virman Man, Exec. Ed. **ISSN:** 0020-8566. **Subscription Rates:** EUR448 institutions print + online; EUR537.60 institutions print + enhanced access. **Remarks:** Advertising not accepted. **URL:** http://www.springer.com/education/comparativeeducation/journal/11159. **Circ:** Paid ‡1,200

48433 ■ Invertebrate Neuroscience
Springer Netherlands
Van Godewijckstraat 30
3311 GX Dordrecht, Netherlands
Ph: 31 786 576210
Fax: 31 786 576744
Publisher E-mail: permissions.dordrecht@springer.com
Journal covering invertebrate neuroscience. **Freq:**

Quarterly. **Key Personnel:** David B. Sattelle, Editor-in-Chief, david.sattelle@dpag.ox.ac.uk; Andrew Jones, Technical Reports Ed., andrew.jones@dpag.ox.ac.uk; D. Shepherd, Editorial Board; V. Dyakonova, Editorial Board; E.R. Brown, Editorial Board; Steven D. Buckingham, Review Ed., steven.buckingham@dpag.ox.ac.uk; J.R. Bloomquist, Editorial Board; M. Darlison, Editorial Board; K. Elekes, Editorial Board. **ISSN:** 1354-2516. **Subscription Rates:** EUR422 institutions print incl. free access or e-only; EUR506.40 institutions print incl. enhanced access. **Remarks:** Accepts advertising. **URL:** http://www.springer.com/biomed/neuroscience/journal/10158. **Circ:** (Not Reported)

48434 ■ Ionics
Springer Netherlands
Van Godewijckstraat 30
3311 GX Dordrecht, Netherlands
Ph: 31 786 576210
Fax: 31 786 576744
Publisher E-mail: permissions.dordrecht@springer.com
Journal devoted to science and technology of ionic motion. **Subtitle:** International Journal of Ionics The Science and Technology of Ionic Motion. **Freq:** 6/yr. **Key Personnel:** E. Wachsman, Editor-in-Chief; W. Weppner, Editor-in-Chief, ww@tf.uni-kiel.de; A.K. Arof, Editor, akarof@um.edu.my; S.P.S. Badwal, Editor, badwal@mst.csiro.au; Christian Julien, Editor, christian.julien@insp.jussieu.fr; S. Bredikhin, Editor, bredikh@issp.ac.ru; S. Chandra, Editor, schandra@bhu.ac.in; Liquan Chen, Editor, lqchen@aphy.iphy.ac.cn; U. Guth, Editor, guth@htwm.de; N. Inoue, Editor, ninoue@sci.ehime-u.ac.jp. **ISSN:** 0947-7047. **Subscription Rates:** EUR701 institutions print incl. free access or e-only; EUR841.20 institutions print incl. enhanced access. **URL:** http://www.springer.com/chemistry/physical/journal/11581.

48435 ■ The Jetix Magazine
Future Publishing Ltd.
Postbus 1015
NL-3300 BA Dordrecht, Netherlands
Publication E-mail: mailbox@zpress-magazines.nl
Publisher E-mail: future@subscription.co.uk
Children's magazine of video games and entertainment. **Key Personnel:** Alex Klein, Director. **Subscription Rates:** 10.99 individuals quarterly direct debit; 43.99 individuals credit card. **URL:** http://www.jetixmagazine.nl/.

48436 ■ Journal of Academic Ethics
Springer Netherlands
Van Godewijckstraat 30
3311 GX Dordrecht, Netherlands
Ph: 31 786 576210
Fax: 31 786 576744
Publisher E-mail: permissions.dordrecht@springer.com
Peer-reviewed journal focusing on ethical issues in the field of research, teaching, administration and governance from the post-secondary education perspective. **Freq:** Quarterly. **Key Personnel:** Deborah C. Poff, Editor-in-Chief; Alex C. Michalos, Co-Ed.; Myles Brand, Editorial Board. **ISSN:** 1570-1727. **Subscription Rates:** EUR308 institutions print incl. free access or e-only; EUR369.60 institutions print incl. enhanced access. **Remarks:** Advertising accepted; rates available upon request. **URL:** http://www.springer.com/education/leadership%26administration/journal/10805. **Circ:** (Not Reported)

48437 ■ Journal of Applied Electrochemistry
Springer Netherlands
Van Godewijckstraat 30
3311 GX Dordrecht, Netherlands
Ph: 31 786 576210
Fax: 31 786 576744
Publisher E-mail: permissions.dordrecht@springer.com
Journal covering technologically oriented aspects of electrochemistry. **Freq:** Monthly. **Key Personnel:** Geraldine G. Botte, Editor; C. Comninellis, Editorial Advisory Board. **ISSN:** 0021-891X. **Subscription Rates:** EUR2,694 institutions print or online; EUR3,232.80 institutions print & online. **Remarks:** Accepts advertising. **URL:** http://www.springerlink.com/content/100178/. **Circ:** (Not Reported)

48438 ■ Journal of Archaeological Research
Springer Netherlands
Van Godewijckstraat 30
3311 GX Dordrecht, Netherlands
Ph: 31 786 576210
Fax: 31 786 576744
Publisher E-mail: permissions.dordrecht@springer.com
Journal targeting archaeological students and professionals covering comparative research, critical articles, and peer-review analyses of studies. **Key Personnel:** Richard E. Blanton, Assoc. Ed.; Laura Lee Junker, Assoc. Ed.; Clive Gamble, Assoc. Ed.; Joao Zilhao, Assoc. Ed.; Richard Bradley, Assoc. Ed.; Jane E. Buikstra, Assoc. Ed.; Bruce D. Smith, Assoc. Ed.; Gary M. Feinman, Editor; Douglas T. Price, Editor; Susan Alcock, Assoc. Ed. **ISSN:** 1059-0161. **Subscription Rates:** EUR603 institutions print or online; EUR723.60 institutions print & online. **Remarks:** Advertising accepted; rates available upon request. **URL:** http://www.springerlink.com/content/104889/. **Circ:** (Not Reported)

48439 ■ Journal of the Association for Research in Otolaryngology
Springer Netherlands
Van Godewijckstraat 30
3311 GX Dordrecht, Netherlands
Ph: 31 786 576210
Fax: 31 786 576744
Publisher E-mail: permissions.dordrecht@springer.com
Peer-reviewed journal covering otolaryngology and communications sciences, including hearing, balance, the chemical senses, voice, speech, and laryngeal function. **Freq:** Quarterly. **Key Personnel:** Ruth Anne Eatock, Editor-in-Chief; Robert P. Carlyon, Assoc. Ed.; Karen B. Avraham, Assoc. Ed. **ISSN:** 1525-3961. **Subscription Rates:** EUR355 institutions print incl. free access or e-only; EUR426 institutions print incl. enhanced access. **Remarks:** Accepts advertising. **URL:** http://www.springer.com/medicine/otorhinolaryngology/journal/10162. **Circ:** (Not Reported)

48440 ■ Journal of Atmospheric Chemistry
Springer Netherlands
Van Godewijckstraat 30
3311 GX Dordrecht, Netherlands
Ph: 31 786 576210
Fax: 31 786 576744
Publisher E-mail: permissions.dordrecht@springer.com
Geoscience journal. **Freq:** Triennial. **Key Personnel:** Elliot L. Atlas, Editor-in-Chief; Andreas Wahner, Editorial Board; Yutaka Kondo, Editorial Board; Claire Granier, Editorial Board; B. Brune, Editorial Board. **ISSN:** 0167-7764. **Subscription Rates:** EUR1,464 institutions print incl. free access or e-only; EUR1,756 institutions print incl. enhanced access. **Remarks:** Accepts advertising. **URL:** http://www.springer.com/earthsciences/meteorology/journal/10874. **Circ:** (Not Reported)

48441 ■ Journal of Autism and Developmental Disorders
Springer Netherlands
Van Godewijckstraat 30
3311 GX Dordrecht, Netherlands
Ph: 31 786 576210
Fax: 31 786 576744
Publisher E-mail: permissions.dordrecht@springer.com
Peer-reviewed journal containing research studies, interventions and theoretical papers on the severe psychopathologies in childhood. **Subtitle:** Journal of Autism. **Founded:** 1971. **Freq:** Bimonthly. **Key Personnel:** Mohammed Ghaziuddin, Editorial Board; Sandra L. Harris, Assoc. Ed.; Christopher L. McDougle, Assoc. Ed.; Catherine Barthelemy, Editorial Board; Tony Charman, Assoc. Ed.; Fred R. Volkmar, Editor-in-Chief; Joel Bregman, Editorial Board. **ISSN:** 0162-3257. **Subscription Rates:** EUR1,477 institutions print or online; EUR1,772.40 institutions print & enhanced access. **Remarks:** Advertising not accepted. **URL:** http://www.springer.com/psychology/child%26schoolpsychology/journal/10803. **Circ:** (Not Reported)

48442 ■ Journal of Bamboo and Rattan
Springer Netherlands
Van Godewijckstraat 30
3311 GX Dordrecht, Netherlands
Ph: 31 786 576210
Fax: 31 786 576744
Publisher E-mail: permissions.dordrecht@springer.com
Peer-reviewed journal covering all aspects of fast growing, multi-purpose pliable species. Discusses scientific issues relating to bamboo and rattan. **Freq:** Quarterly. **Key Personnel:** Jules J.A. Janssen, Editor-in-Chief. **ISSN:** 1569-1586. **Remarks:** Advertising accepted; rates available upon request. **URL:** http://www.springer.com/environment/environmentalmanagement/journal/10866. **Circ:** (Not Reported)

48443 ■ Journal of Behavioral Education
Springer Netherlands
Van Godewijckstraat 30
3311 GX Dordrecht, Netherlands
Ph: 31 786 576210
Fax: 31 786 576744
Publisher E-mail: permissions.dordrecht@springer.com
Journal covering research on the application of behavioral principles and technology to education. **Freq:** Quarterly. **Key Personnel:** Brian K. Martens, Editor-in-Chief; Scott Ardoin, Assoc. Ed.; Sheila Alber-Morgan, Editorial Board. **ISSN:** 1053-0819. **Subscription Rates:** EUR475 institutions print including free access or e-only; EUR570 institutions print including enhanced access. **Remarks:** Accepts advertising. **URL:** http://www.springerlink.com/content/105719/. **Circ:** (Not Reported)

48444 ■ Journal of Bioethical Inquiry
Springer Netherlands
Van Godewijckstraat 30
3311 GX Dordrecht, Netherlands
Ph: 31 786 576210
Fax: 31 786 576744
Publisher E-mail: permissions.dordrecht@springer.com
Journal covering core areas of conventional bioethics, such as research, clinical practice and medical technology. **Freq:** Quarterly. **Key Personnel:** Paul Komesaroff, Editorial Board; Kate Cregan, Editor-in-Chief; Cameron Stewart, Assoc. Ed.; Colin Thomson, Assoc. Ed. **ISSN:** 1176-7529. **Subscription Rates:** EUR285 institutions print incl. free access or e-only; EUR342 institutions print incl. enhanced access. **URL:** http://www.springer.com/medicine/journal/11673.

48445 ■ Journal of Biomedical Science
Springer Netherlands
Van Godewijckstraat 30
3311 GX Dordrecht, Netherlands
Ph: 31 786 576210
Fax: 31 786 576744
Publisher E-mail: permissions.dordrecht@springer.com
Journal covering biomedicine. **Founded:** 1994. **Freq:** Bimonthly 6/yr. **Trim Size:** 210 x 280 mm. **Key Personnel:** Michael Ming-Chiao Lai, Editor-in-Chief; Benjamin Berkhout, Editor; Julie Y.H. Chan, Editor; Y.S. Chan, Editor; Wen-Chang Chang, Editor; Ding-Shinn Chen, Editor; Chen-Kung Chou, Editor; John T. Kung, Editor; Jung-Yaw Lin, Editor; Ling-Pai Ting, Editor. **ISSN:** 1021-7770. **Subscription Rates:** US$711 institutions print including free access or e-only; US$853.20 institutions print including enhanced access. **Remarks:** Accepts advertising. **URL:** http://www.springer.com/biomed/journal/11373; http://www.jbiomedsci.com/. **Circ:** (Not Reported)

48446 ■ Journal of Business Ethics
Springer Netherlands
Van Godewijckstraat 30
3311 GX Dordrecht, Netherlands
Ph: 31 786 576210
Fax: 31 786 576744
Publisher E-mail: permissions.dordrecht@springer.com
Business journal. **Freq:** 7/yr. **Key Personnel:** Alex C. Michalos, Editor-in-Chief; Deborah C. Poff, Editor; Sally Gunz, Section Ed.; Lawrence B. Chonko, Editorial Board; Johannes Brinkmann, Editorial Board; Gedeon J. Rossouw, Editorial Board; Richard F. Beltramini, Editorial Board; Loren Falkenberg, Section Ed. **ISSN:** 0167-4544. **Subscription Rates:** EUR2,368 institutions print incl. free access or e-only; EUR2,841 institutions print incl. enhanced access. **Remarks:** Accepts advertising. **URL:** http://www.springer.com/philosophy/ethics/journal/10551; http://www.springerlink.com/content/0167-4544. **Circ:** (Not Reported)

48447 ■ Journal of Cardiovascular Translational Research
Springer Netherlands
Van Godewijckstraat 30
3311 GX Dordrecht, Netherlands
Ph: 31 786 576210
Fax: 31 786 576744
Publisher E-mail: permissions.dordrecht@springer.com
Journal covering practice of clinical cardiovascular medicine. **Freq:** Bimonthly. **Key Personnel:** Nabil Dib, Editor-in-Chief; Jennifer Hall, PhD, Editor; Kendra Bartels, Managing Editor. **ISSN:** 1937-5387. **Subscription Rates:** EUR387 institutions print including free access or e-only; EUR464.40 institutions print including enhanced access. **URL:** http://www.springer.com/medicine/internal/journal/12265.

Circulation: ★ = ABC; △ = BPA; ♦ = CAC; • = CCAB; ❑ = VAC; ⊕ = PO Statement; ‡ = Publisher's Report; Boldface figures = sworn; Light figures = estimated.

Gale Directory of Publications & Broadcast Media/147th Ed.   5259

48448 ■ Journal of Clinical Monitoring and Computing
Springer Netherlands
Van Godewijckstraat 30
3311 GX Dordrecht, Netherlands
Ph: 31 786 576210
Fax: 31 786 576744
Publisher E-mail: permissions.dordrecht@springer.com
Medical journal for anesthesiologists and designers of patient and drug monitoring equipment. **Subtitle:** Including a Specialty Section on Surgical Neuromonitoring. **Founded:** Jan. 1985. **Freq:** Bimonthly. **Print Method:** Offset. **Trim Size:** 8 1/8 x 10 7/8. **Cols./Page:** 2. **Col. Width:** 3 3/8 inches. **Col. Depth:** 10 inches. **Key Personnel:** Vincenzo Lanza, MD, Editor-in-Chief; Paul G. Barash, MD, Editorial Board; Biagio Allaria, PhD, Editorial Board; M. Fisher, MD, Editorial Board; Gerard Bashein, MD, Editorial Board; Maurizio Renna, MD, Coord. Ed.; J.A. Blom, PhD, Editorial Board; Harvey L. Edmonds, Jr., Editorial Board; Ronald Dueck, MD, Editorial Board; J. Bruhn, MD, Editorial Board. **ISSN:** 1387-1307. **Subscription Rates:** EUR907 institutions print incl. free access or e-only; EUR1,088.40 institutions print incl. enhanced access. **Remarks:** Accepts advertising. **URL:** http://www.springerlink.com/content/102923/. **Formerly:** Journal of Clinical Monitoring; International Journal of Clinical Monitoring and Computing. **Circ:** Paid 1,300

48449 ■ Journal of Cluster Science
Springer Netherlands
Van Godewijckstraat 30
3311 GX Dordrecht, Netherlands
Ph: 31 786 576210
Fax: 31 786 576744
Publisher E-mail: permissions.dordrecht@springer.com
Peer-reviewed scientific journal. **Subtitle:** including Nanoclusters and Nanoparticles. **Founded:** 1990. **Freq:** Quarterly. **Print Method:** Offset. **Key Personnel:** Lord Lewis, Emeritus Editorial Board; W.T. Wong, Editorial Board; A.P. Alivisatos, Editorial Board; M.I. Bruce, Editorial Board; L.F. Dahl, Editorial Board; Richard D. Adams, Editor; Charles M. Lukehart, Editor; Dr. Boon K. Teo, Editor. **ISSN:** 1040-7278. **Subscription Rates:** EUR836 institutions print or online; EUR1003.20 institutions print & enhanced access. **Remarks:** Accepts advertising. **URL:** http://www.springer.com/chemistry/journal/10876. **Circ:** (Not Reported)

48450 ■ Journal of Computational Electronics
Springer Netherlands
Van Godewijckstraat 30
3311 GX Dordrecht, Netherlands
Ph: 31 786 576210
Fax: 31 786 576744
Publisher E-mail: permissions.dordrecht@springer.com
Journal focusing on research investigations on various aspects of modeling and simulation of modern electronics including optical, electronic, mechanical, and quantum mechanical aspects, as well as research on the underlying mathematical algorithms and computational details. **Freq:** 4/yr. **Key Personnel:** Paolo Lugli, Editorial Board; Joseph W. Jerome, Editorial Board; Robert Eisenberg, Editorial Board; Christian Ringhofer, Editorial Board; Aldo Di Carlo, Editorial Board; Gerhard Wachutka, Editorial Board; Karl Hess, Editor-in-Chief; Narayan Aluru, Editorial Board; Stephen Goodnick, Editorial Board; David K. Ferry, Editor-in-Chief. **ISSN:** 1569-8025. **Subscription Rates:** US$488 institutions print including free access or e-only; US$585.60 institutions print including enhanced access. **Remarks:** Advertising accepted; rates available upon request. **URL:** http://www.springerlink.com/content/1569-8025. **Circ:** (Not Reported)

48451 ■ Journal of Computational Neuroscience
Springer Netherlands
Van Godewijckstraat 30
3311 GX Dordrecht, Netherlands
Ph: 31 786 576210
Fax: 31 786 576744
Publisher E-mail: permissions.dordrecht@springer.com
Journal providing a common ground for integrating computational and experimental work in the neurosciences based on approaches including anatomy, electrophysiology, biophysics, imaging, and molecular biology. **Freq:** 3/yr. **Key Personnel:** Alain Destexhe, Editor-in-Chief; Upinder Bhalla, Action Ed.; Erik De Schutter, Action Ed. **ISSN:** 0929-5313. **Subscription Rates:** EUR926 institutions print including free access or e-only; EUR1,111.20 institutions print including enhanced

access. **Remarks:** Advertising accepted; rates available upon request. **URL:** http://www.springerlink.com/content/0929-5313. **Circ:** (Not Reported)

48452 ■ Journal in Computer Virology
Springer Netherlands
Van Godewijckstraat 30
3311 GX Dordrecht, Netherlands
Ph: 31 786 576210
Fax: 31 786 576744
Publisher E-mail: permissions.dordrecht@springer.com
Journal dedicated to viral and antiviral computer technologies. **Freq:** Quarterly. **Key Personnel:** Eric Filiol, Editor-in-Chief; David M. Chess, Editorial Board; Fred Cohen, Editorial Board; Caroline Fontaine, Editorial Board; Cestmir Halbich, Editorial Board; Marko Helenius, Editorial Board; Ferenc Leitold, Editorial Board; Ludovic Me, Editorial Board; Markus Schmall, Editorial Board; Diomidis Spinellis, Editorial Board. **ISSN:** 1772-9890. **Subscription Rates:** EUR453 institutions print incl. free access or e-only; EUR543.60 institutions print incl. enhanced access. **Remarks:** Accepts advertising. **URL:** http://www.springer.com/computer/journal/11416. **Circ:** (Not Reported)

48453 ■ Journal of Consumer Policy
Springer Netherlands
Van Godewijckstraat 30
3311 GX Dordrecht, Netherlands
Ph: 31 786 576210
Fax: 31 786 576744
Publisher E-mail: permissions.dordrecht@springer.com
Journal covering advertising, marketing and public relations. **Subtitle:** Consumer Issues in Law, Economics, and Behavioral Sciences. **Freq:** Quarterly. **Key Personnel:** Alan Mathios, Editor; Christian Twigg-Flesner, Editor; John Thogersen, Editor; Lucia Reisch, Editor; Stephen Weatherill, Editor; Suzanne C. Beckmann, Editorial Board. **ISSN:** 0168-7034. **Subscription Rates:** EUR554 institutions print incl. free access or e-only; EUR664.80 institutions print incl. enhanced access. **Remarks:** Accepts advertising. **URL:** http://www.springer.com/socialsciences/socialsciences%2Cgeneral/journal/10603. **Circ:** (Not Reported)

48454 ■ Journal of Dynamical and Control Systems
Springer Netherlands
Van Godewijckstraat 30
3311 GX Dordrecht, Netherlands
Ph: 31 786 576210
Fax: 31 786 576744
Publisher E-mail: permissions.dordrecht@springer.com
Peer-reviewed journal covering the entire spectrum of issues related to dynamical systems. **Freq:** Quarterly. **Key Personnel:** Andrei A. Agrachev, Editor-in-Chief, agrachev@sissa.it; Revaz V. Gamkrelidze, Editor-in-Chief, gam@ipsun.ras.ru; Dmitry V. Anosov, Managing Editor, anosov@mi.ras.ru; Werner Balser, Managing Editor, balser@mathematik.uni-ulm.de; Martin J. Corless, Editor, corless@ecn.purdue.edu; Yulii Ilyashenko, Managing Editor, yuilyashenko@glas.apc.org; Matthias Kawski, Managing Editor, kawski@asu.edu; Yuri Sachkov, Managing Editor, sachkov@sys.botik.ru; Bernard Bonnard, Editorial Board, bbonnard@u-bourgogne.fr; John Burns, Editorial Board, burns@sun.icam.vt.edu. **ISSN:** 1079-2724. **Subscription Rates:** EUR682 institutions print incl. free access or e-only; EUR818.40 institutions print incl. enhanced access. **Remarks:** Accepts advertising. **URL:** http://www.springerlink.com/content/1079-2724. **Circ:** (Not Reported)

48455 ■ Journal of Dynamics and Differential Equations
Springer Netherlands
Van Godewijckstraat 30
3311 GX Dordrecht, Netherlands
Ph: 31 786 576210
Fax: 31 786 576744
Publisher E-mail: permissions.dordrecht@springer.com
Mathematics journal. **Freq:** Quarterly. **Print Method:** Offset. **Key Personnel:** Alberto Bressan, Editorial Board; Franco Flandoli, Editorial Board; Constantine M. Dafermos, Editorial Board; Wolfgang-Jurgen Beyn, Editorial Board; Shui-Nee Chow, Editorial Board; Genevieve Raugel, Editor-in-Chief; John M. Ball, Editorial Board; George R. Sell, Editor-in-Chief; Yingfei Yi, Editor-in-Chief. **ISSN:** 1040-7294. **Subscription Rates:** EUR895 institutions print or online; EUR1,074 institutions print & enhanced access. **Remarks:** Accepts advertising. **URL:** http://www.springer.com/math/dyn.systems/journal/10884. **Circ:** (Not Reported)

48456 ■ Journal of East Asian Linguistics
Springer Netherlands
Van Godewijckstraat 30
3311 GX Dordrecht, Netherlands
Ph: 31 786 576210
Fax: 31 786 576744
Publisher E-mail: permissions.dordrecht@springer.com
Journal on the study of East Asian languages primarily Chinese, Japanese and Korean. Journal identifies the significant role of the languages in shaping future linguistic theories. **Freq:** Quarterly. **Key Personnel:** C.-T. James Huang, Editor; Mamoru Saito, Editor; Kate Pilson, Editorial Asst.; Lisa Cheng, Editorial Board; Junko Ito, Editorial Board; Chung-hye Han, Editorial Board; Jennifer L. Conrad, Copy Ed.; Christine Kamprath, Copy Ed.; Andrew Simpson, Editor; Teresa A. Griffith, Copy Ed. **ISSN:** 0925-8558. **Subscription Rates:** EUR534 institutions print incl. free access or e-only; EUR640.80 institutions print incl. enhanced access. **Remarks:** Advertising accepted; rates available upon request. **URL:** http://www.springer.com/linguistics/comparativelinguistics/journal/10831. **Circ:** (Not Reported)

48457 ■ The Journal of Economic Inequality
Springer Netherlands
Van Godewijckstraat 30
3311 GX Dordrecht, Netherlands
Ph: 31 786 576210
Fax: 31 786 576744
Publisher E-mail: permissions.dordrecht@springer.com
Journal focusing on the issues related to economic and social inequalities. **Freq:** Quarterly. **Key Personnel:** Jacques Silber, Founding Ed.; Amartya Sen, Advisory Board; Sudhir Anand, Editorial Board; Yoram Amiel, Editorial Board; Jean-Yves Duclos, Editor-in-Chief; Kaushik Basu, Editorial Board; Anthony Atkinson, Advisory Board. **ISSN:** 1569-1721. **Subscription Rates:** EUR427 institutions print incl. free access or e-only; EUR512.40 institutions print incl. enhanced access. **Remarks:** Advertising accepted; rates available upon request. **URL:** http://www.springerlink.com/content/1573-8701/?contentstatus=accepted. **Circ:** (Not Reported)

48458 ■ Journal of Experimental Criminology
Springer Netherlands
Van Godewijckstraat 30
3311 GX Dordrecht, Netherlands
Ph: 31 786 576210
Fax: 31 786 576744
Publisher E-mail: permissions.dordrecht@springer.com
Journal focusing on fully experimental and partially experimental research in the building up of evidence based crime and justice policy. **Freq:** Quarterly. **Key Personnel:** David Weisburd, Editor-in-Chief, dweisbur@gmu.edu; Lorraine Mazerolle, Assoc. Ed., l.mazerolle@griffith.edu.au; Rochelle Schnurr, Managing Editor, expericrim@savion.cc.huji.ac.il; Mimi Ajzenstadt, Assoc. Ed., mimi@mscc.huji.ac.il; David B. Wilson, Assoc. Ed., dwilsonb@gmu.edu. **ISSN:** 1573-3750. **Subscription Rates:** EUR414 institutions print incl. free access or e-only; EUR496.80 institutions print incl. enhanced access. **Remarks:** Advertising accepted; rates available upon request. **URL:** http://www.springer.com/socialsciences/criminology/journal/11292. **Circ:** (Not Reported)

48459 ■ Journal of Financial Services Research
Springer Netherlands
Van Godewijckstraat 30
3311 GX Dordrecht, Netherlands
Ph: 31 786 576210
Fax: 31 786 576744
Publisher E-mail: permissions.dordrecht@springer.com
Journal dealing with the financial services sector. **Freq:** 3/yr. **Key Personnel:** Joel Houston, Assoc. Ed.; David J. Cummins, Assoc. Ed.; Charles Calomiris, Assoc. Ed.; Haluk Unal, Managing Editor; Stijn Claessens, Editor; Robert Marquez, Editor. **ISSN:** 0920-8550. **Subscription Rates:** EUR848 institutions print including free access or e-only; EUR1,017.60 institutions print including enhanced access. **Remarks:** Advertising accepted; rates available upon request. **URL:** http://www.springerlink.com/content/0920-8550. **Circ:** (Not Reported)

48460 ■ Journal of Fusion Energy
Springer Netherlands
Van Godewijckstraat 30
3311 GX Dordrecht, Netherlands
Ph: 31 786 576210
Fax: 31 786 576744

Publisher E-mail: permissions.dordrecht@springer.com Journal focusing on thermonuclear fusion. **Founded:** 1981. **Freq:** Quarterly. **Print Method:** Offset. **Trim Size:** 8 3/8 x 10 3/4. **Cols./Page:** 1. **Col. Width:** 54 nonpareils. **Col. Depth:** 103 agate lines. **Key Personnel:** Stephen O. Dean, Editor; Igor Anisimov, Assoc. Ed.; Niek Lopes Cardozo, Assoc. Ed. **ISSN:** 0164-0313. **Subscription Rates:** EUR875 institutions print or online; US$1,050 institutions print & enhanced access. **Remarks:** Advertising accepted; rates available upon request. **URL:** http://www.springer.com/physics/ particleandnuclearphysics/journal/10894. **Circ:** (Not Reported)

48461 ■ Journal of Gambling Studies
Springer Netherlands
Van Godewijckstraat 30
3311 GX Dordrecht, Netherlands
Ph: 31 786 576210
Fax: 31 786 576744
Publisher E-mail: permissions.dordrecht@springer.com Psychology journal sponsored by The National Council on Compulsive Gambling. Inc. **Freq:** Quarterly. **Key Personnel:** Jon E. Grant, Editor-in-Chief; Gary Anders, Editorial Board; Donald W. Black, Editorial Board. **ISSN:** 1050-5350. **Subscription Rates:** EUR1,067 institutions print including free access or e-only. **Remarks:** Accepts advertising. **URL:** http://www.springerlink.com/content/ 105582/. **Circ:** (Not Reported)

48462 ■ Journal of Genetic Counseling
Springer Netherlands
Van Godewijckstraat 30
3311 GX Dordrecht, Netherlands
Ph: 31 786 576210
Fax: 31 786 576744
Publisher E-mail: permissions.dordrecht@springer.com Journal covering issues of advancing technical developments and concerns of individuals at genetic risk for genetic counseling, medical social workers, geneticists and others. **Freq:** 6/yr. **Key Personnel:** Allyn McConkie-Rosell, Advisory Ed.; Pat McCarthy Veach, Asst. Ed.; Bonnie S. LeRoy, Editor-in-Chief. **ISSN:** 1059-7700. **Subscription Rates:** EUR616 institutions print incl. free access or e-only; EUR739.20 institutions print incl. enhanced access. **Remarks:** Accepts advertising. **URL:** http://www.springerlink.com/content/104800/. **Circ:** (Not Reported)

48463 ■ Journal of Geographical Systems
Springer Netherlands
Van Godewijckstraat 30
3311 GX Dordrecht, Netherlands
Ph: 31 786 576210
Fax: 31 786 576744
Publisher E-mail: permissions.dordrecht@springer.com Journal dedicated to geographical information, analysis, theory, and decision. **Freq:** Quarterly. **Key Personnel:** Manfred M. Fischer, Editor-in-Chief, manfred.fischer@ wu-wien.ac.at; Antonio Paez, Editor-in-Chief, paezha@ mcmaster.ca; L. Anselin, Editorial Board; R.G.V. Baker, Editorial Board; R.S. Bivand, Editorial Board; S. Dragicevic, Editorial Board; D.A. Griffith, Editorial Board; A.S. Fotheringham, Editorial Board; A.U. Frank, Editorial Board; M.F. Goodchild, Editorial Board. **ISSN:** 1435-5930. **Subscription Rates:** EUR360 institutions print incl. free access or e-only; EUR432 institutions print incl. enhanced access. **URL:** http://www.springer.com/ economics/regionalscience/journal/10109.

48464 ■ Journal of Geometry
Springer Netherlands
Van Godewijckstraat 30
3311 GX Dordrecht, Netherlands
Ph: 31 786 576210
Fax: 31 786 576744
Publisher E-mail: permissions.dordrecht@springer.com Journal featuring current research developments in the fields of geometry, algebra, finite geometries, combinatorial geometry, and special geometries. **Founded:** 1971. **Freq:** 3/yr. **Trim Size:** 17 x 24 cm. **Key Personnel:** Hans Havlicek, Editor; Werner Heise, Editor; Hans-Joachim Kroll, Editor, kroll@ma.tum.de; Martin Barner, Editor; Walter Benz, Editor; Pier Vittorio Ceccherini, Editor; James W.P. Hirschfeld, Editor; Helmut Karzel, Editor; Joseph Zaks, Editor. **ISSN:** 0047-2468. **Subscription Rates:** EUR692 institutions print incl. free access or e-only; EUR830.40 institutions print incl. enhanced access. **URL:** http://www.springer.com/birkhauser/ mathematics/journal/22.

48465 ■ Journal of Global Optimization
Springer Netherlands

Van Godewijckstraat 30
3311 GX Dordrecht, Netherlands
Ph: 31 786 576210
Fax: 31 786 576744
Publisher E-mail: permissions.dordrecht@springer.com Journal on global optimization. **Subtitle:** An International Journal Dealing with Theoretical and Computational Aspects of Seeking Global Optima and Their Applications in Science, Management and Engineering. **Freq:** Quarterly. **Key Personnel:** Panos M. Pardalos, Editor-in-Chief; R. Horst, Advisory Ed.; H. Tuy, Advisory Ed.; H.P. Benson, Editorial Board; I.M. Bomze, Editorial Board. **ISSN:** 0925-5001. **Subscription Rates:** EUR1,882 institutions print incl. free access or e-only; EUR2,258.40 institutions print incl. enhanced access. **Remarks:** Advertising accepted; rates available upon request. **URL:** http://www.springerlink.com/content/ 0925-5001. **Circ:** (Not Reported)

48466 ■ Journal of Grid Computing
Springer Netherlands
Van Godewijckstraat 30
3311 GX Dordrecht, Netherlands
Ph: 31 786 576210
Fax: 31 786 576744
Publisher E-mail: permissions.dordrecht@springer.com Journal dealing with the Grid computing and its advantages. **Freq:** Quarterly. **Key Personnel:** Peter Kacsuk, Editor-in-Chief; Ian Foster, Editor-in-Chief; David Abramson, Editorial Board; Malcolm Atkinson, Editorial Board; Henri Bal, Editorial Board; Fran Berman, Editorial Board. **ISSN:** 1570-7873. **Subscription Rates:** EUR380 institutions print incl. free access or e-only; EUR456 institutions print incl. enhanced access. **Remarks:** Advertising accepted; rates available upon request. **URL:** http://www.springerlink.com/content/ 111140/. **Circ:** (Not Reported)

48467 ■ Journal of Housing and the Built Environment
Springer Netherlands
Van Godewijckstraat 30
3311 GX Dordrecht, Netherlands
Ph: 31 786 576210
Fax: 31 786 576744
Publisher E-mail: permissions.dordrecht@springer.com Journal dealing with housing, spatial planning, building and urban development. **Freq:** Quarterly. **Key Personnel:** Peter J. Boelhouwer, Editor-in-Chief; Gideon Bolt, Editor; Tuna Tasan-Kok, Editor; John Doling, Editorial Advisory Board; Pascal De Decker, Editor; Jan Rouwendal, Editor; Jeroen van der Veer, Editor; Andreas Faludi, Editorial Advisory Board; Edwin Deutsch, Editorial Advisory Board; Marietta Haffner, Editorial Advisory Board. **ISSN:** 1566-4910. **Subscription Rates:** EUR352 institutions print incl. free access or e-only; EUR422.40 institutions print incl. enhanced access. **Remarks:** Advertising accepted; rates available upon request. **URL:** http://www.springer.com/geography/ humangeography/journal/10901. **Circ:** (Not Reported)

48468 ■ Journal of Immigrant and Minority Health
Springer Netherlands
Van Godewijckstraat 30
3311 GX Dordrecht, Netherlands
Ph: 31 786 576210
Fax: 31 786 576744
Publisher E-mail: permissions.dordrecht@springer.com Journal covering immigrant health worldwide. **Freq:** Quarterly. **Key Personnel:** Karen Jaynes Williams, PhD, Book Ed.; Kathrin S. Mautino, Editorial Board; Linda S. Lloyd, Editorial Board; Sana Loue, Editor. **ISSN:** 1557-1912. **Subscription Rates:** EUR432 institutions print or online; EUR518.40 institutions print + enhanced access. **Remarks:** Accepts advertising. **URL:** http://www. springerlink.com/content/1557-1912/. **Formerly:** Journal of Immigrant Health. **Circ:** (Not Reported)

48469 ■ Journal of Inorganic and Organometallic Polymers and Materials
Springer Netherlands
Van Godewijckstraat 30
3311 GX Dordrecht, Netherlands
Ph: 31 786 576210
Fax: 31 786 576744
Publisher E-mail: permissions.dordrecht@springer.com Journal encompasses a broad range of synthetic and natural substances which contain main group, transition, and inner transition elements. **Founded:** May 1, 1991. **Freq:** Quarterly. **Key Personnel:** Didier Astruc, Editorial Board; Martel Zeldin, Editor; Harry R. Allcock, Editorial

Board; Alaa S. Abd-El-Aziz, Editor. **ISSN:** 1574-1443. **Subscription Rates:** EUR653 institutions print or online; EUR783.60 institutions print and online. **Remarks:** Advertising accepted; rates available upon request. **URL:** http://www.springerlink.com/content/105725/. **Circ:** (Not Reported)

48470 ■ Journal of Low Temperature Physics
Springer Netherlands
Van Godewijckstraat 30
3311 GX Dordrecht, Netherlands
Ph: 31 786 576210
Fax: 31 786 576744
Publisher E-mail: permissions.dordrecht@springer.com Physics journal covering Superconductivity. **Founded:** 1969. **Freq:** Bimonthly. **Print Method:** Offset. **Trim Size:** 6 x 9. **Cols./Page:** 1. **Col. Width:** 54 nonpareils. **Col. Depth:** 103 agate lines. **Key Personnel:** J. Brooks, Editorial Board and Policy Committee; C.F. Barenghi, Editorial Board and Policy Committee; S. Balibar, Editorial Board and Policy Committee; W.P. Halperin, Editorial Board and Policy Committee; Mikko Paalanen, Editor-in-Chief; J. Beamish, Editorial Board and Policy Committee; Neil Sullivan, Editor-in-Chief; Horst Meyer, Editor-in-Chief; John G. Daunt, Founding Ed. **ISSN:** 0022-2291. **Subscription Rates:** EUR2,904 institutions print incl. free access or e-only; EUR3,484.80 institutions print incl. enhanced access. **Remarks:** Advertising accepted; rates available upon request. **URL:** http://www. springerlink.com/content/104917/; http://www.springer. com/materials/journal/10909. **Circ:** (Not Reported)

48471 ■ Journal of Management and Governance
Springer Netherlands
Van Godewijckstraat 30
3311 GX Dordrecht, Netherlands
Ph: 31 786 576210
Fax: 31 786 576744
Publisher E-mail: permissions.dordrecht@springer.com Journal covering inquiry into the cognitive and relational foundations of governance, and into the analysis and design of governance. **Freq:** Quarterly. **Key Personnel:** Roberto Di Pietra, Editor-in-Chief; Thomas Ahrens, Co-Ed.; Lino Cinquini, Co-Ed.; Igor Filatotchev, Co-Ed.; Rosario Faraci, Co-Ed. **ISSN:** 1385-3457. **Subscription Rates:** EUR507 institutions print or online; EUR608.40 institutions print and online. **Remarks:** Accepts advertising. **URL:** http://www.springerlink.com/content/ 102940/. **Circ:** (Not Reported)

48472 ■ Journal of Maritime Archaeology
Springer Netherlands
Van Godewijckstraat 30
3311 GX Dordrecht, Netherlands
Ph: 31 786 576210
Fax: 31 786 576744
Publisher E-mail: permissions.dordrecht@springer.com Journal featuring maritime archaeology, both terrestrial and underwater. **Freq:** Semiannual. **Key Personnel:** Jonathan R. Adams, Editor; Lucy Blue, Editorial Board; Richard Bradley, Editorial Board; Carl Olof Cederlund, Editorial Board; Tim Champion, Editorial Board; Annalies Corbin, Editorial Board; Kevin Crisman, Editorial Board; Christopher Dobbs, Editorial Board; Justin Dix, Editorial Board; Helen Farr, Editorial Board. **ISSN:** 1557-2285. **Subscription Rates:** EUR189 institutions print incl. free access or e-only; EUR226.80 institutions print incl. enhanced access. **URL:** http://www.springer.com/ socialsciences/anthropologyandarchaeology/journal/ 11457.

48473 ■ Journal of Materials Science
Springer Netherlands
Van Godewijckstraat 30
3311 GX Dordrecht, Netherlands
Ph: 31 786 576210
Fax: 31 786 576744
Publisher E-mail: permissions.dordrecht@springer.com Journal focused on studying the relationship between structure, properties, and uses of materials for structural scientists. **Freq:** Semimonthly. **Key Personnel:** C.B. Carter, Editor-in-Chief; Rees D. Rawlings, Editor; Mark Aindow, Dep. Ed.-in-Ch.; Helen M. Chan, Editor; Kamanio Chattopadhyay, Distinguished Advisory Board; Robert Cook, Editorial Board; Jan H. Evans-Freeman, Editor; Christopher F. Blanford, Editor; Wayne D. Kaplan, Editor. **ISSN:** 0022-2461. **Subscription Rates:** EUR10,011 institutions print incl. free access or e-only; EUR12,013.20 institutions print incl. enhanced access. **Remarks:** Accepts advertising. **URL:** http://www.

springer.com/materials/journal/10853. **Circ:** (Not Reported)

48474 ■ Journal of Mathematical Chemistry
Springer Netherlands
Van Godewijckstraat 30
3311 GX Dordrecht, Netherlands
Ph: 31 786 576210
Fax: 31 786 576744
Publisher E-mail: permissions.dordrecht@springer.com
Scientific journal covering mathematical chemistry. **Freq:** Quarterly. **Key Personnel:** Paul G. Mezey, Editor-in-Chief. **ISSN:** 0259-9791. **Subscription Rates:** EUR1,233 institutions print incl. free access or e-only; EUR1,479 institutions print incl. enhanced access. **Remarks:** Accepts advertising. **URL:** http://www.springerlink.com/content/0259-9791; http://www.springer.com/chemistry/physical/journal/10910. **Circ:** (Not Reported)

48475 ■ Journal of Mathematical Modelling and Algorithms
Springer Netherlands
Van Godewijckstraat 30
3311 GX Dordrecht, Netherlands
Ph: 31 786 576210
Fax: 31 786 576744
Publisher E-mail: permissions.dordrecht@springer.com
Journal focusing on algorithmic in the field of discrete mathematics. **Freq:** Quarterly. **Key Personnel:** Victor J. Rayward-Smith, Editor-in-Chief; J. MacGregor Smith, Regional Ed.; F. Archetti, Editorial Board. **ISSN:** 1570-1166. **Subscription Rates:** EUR369 institutions print incl. free access or e-only; EUR442.80 institutions print incl. enhanced access. **Remarks:** Advertising accepted; rates available upon request. **URL:** http://www.springer.com/math/journal/10852. **Circ:** (Not Reported)

48476 ■ Journal of Medical Humanities
Springer Netherlands
Van Godewijckstraat 30
3311 GX Dordrecht, Netherlands
Ph: 31 786 576210
Fax: 31 786 576744
Publisher E-mail: permissions.dordrecht@springer.com
Journal covering interdisciplinary inquiry in medicine and medical education. **Freq:** Quarterly. **Key Personnel:** Tod S. Chambers, Editorial Board; Kathleen Pachucki, Asst. Ed.; Catherine Belling, Assoc. Ed.; Stephanie Brown Clark, Editorial Board; Martha Stoddard Holmes, Assoc. Ed.; Bradley E. Lewis, Assoc. Ed.; Thomas R. Cole, Editorial Board; Therese Jones, Editor. **ISSN:** 1041-3545. **Subscription Rates:** US$718 institutions including postage & handling; US$861.60 institutions including postage & handling. **Remarks:** Accepts advertising. **URL:** http://www.springerlink.com/content/104920/. **Circ:** (Not Reported)

48477 ■ Journal of Neuro-Oncology
Springer Netherlands
Van Godewijckstraat 30
3311 GX Dordrecht, Netherlands
Ph: 31 786 576210
Fax: 31 786 576744
Publisher E-mail: permissions.dordrecht@springer.com
Journal dealing with all aspects of research relating to cancer of the central nervous system, providing a platform for exchange of ideas among neurologists, neurosurgeons, radiotherapists, medical oncologists, neuropathologists, neurodiagnosticians, and laboratory-based oncologists engaged in similar research. **Freq:** 3/yr. **Key Personnel:** Linda M. Liau, Editor-in-Chief; Joachim Baehring, Editorial Board; Charles S. Cobbs, Editorial Board. **ISSN:** 0167-594X. **Subscription Rates:** EUR2,512 institutions print incl. free access or e-only; EUR3,014.40 institutions enhanced access. **Remarks:** Advertising accepted; rates available upon request. **URL:** http://www.springer.com/medicine/oncology/journal/11060. **Circ:** (Not Reported)

48478 ■ Journal of Neuroimmune Pharmacology
Springer Netherlands
Van Godewijckstraat 30
3311 GX Dordrecht, Netherlands
Ph: 31 786 576210
Fax: 31 786 576744
Publisher E-mail: permissions.dordrecht@springer.com
Peer-reviewed biomedical journal focusing on neuroimmune pathways in disease and for treatment of neurologic and europsychiatric disorders. **Freq:** Quarterly. **Key Personnel:** Martin Adler, Editorial Board; Aftab Ansari, Editorial Board; Thomas J. Rogers, PhD, Sen. Ed., rogerst@temple.edu; Alexander Kabanov, Section Ed., akabanov@unmc.edu; Linda Chang, Section Ed.,

ichang@hawaii.edu; Howard E. Gendelman, MD, Editor-in-Chief, hegendel@nmc.edu; Stanley Appel, Editorial Board, sappel@tmh.tmc.edu; Steve Jacobson, Section Ed., jacobsons@ninds.nih.gov; Guy Cabral, Section Ed., gacabral@vcu.edu. **ISSN:** 1557-1890. **Subscription Rates:** EUR500 institutions print incl. free access or e-only; EUR600 institutions print incl. enhanced access. **Remarks:** Accepts advertising. **URL:** http://www.springer.com/biomed/neuroscience/journal/11481. **Circ:** (Not Reported)

48479 ■ Journal of Nonverbal Behavior
Springer Netherlands
Van Godewijckstraat 30
3311 GX Dordrecht, Netherlands
Ph: 31 786 576210
Fax: 31 786 576744
Publisher E-mail: permissions.dordrecht@springer.com
Peer-reviewed journal publishing information on all major areas of nonverbal behavior. **Founded:** 1976. **Freq:** Quarterly. **Print Method:** Offset. **Trim Size:** 6 x 9. **Cols./Page:** 1. **Col. Width:** 63 nonpareils. **Col. Depth:** 98 agate lines. **Key Personnel:** Howard S. Friedman, Editor; Jessica Dennis, Managing Editor. **ISSN:** 0191-5886. **Subscription Rates:** EUR931 institutions print or online; EUR1,117.20 institutions print & enhanced access. **Remarks:** Advertising accepted; rates available upon request. **URL:** http://www.springer.com/psychology/personality%26socialpsychology/journal/10919. **Circ:** (Not Reported)

48480 ■ Journal of Optimization Theory and Applications
Springer Netherlands
Van Godewijckstraat 30
3311 GX Dordrecht, Netherlands
Ph: 31 786 576210
Fax: 31 786 576744
Publisher E-mail: permissions.dordrecht@springer.com
Mathematics journal. **Founded:** 1967. **Freq:** Monthly. **Print Method:** Offset. **Trim Size:** 6 x 9. **Cols./Page:** 1. **Col. Width:** 27 picas. **Col. Depth:** 42 picas. **Key Personnel:** Mark J. Balas, Assoc. Ed.; J. Abadie, Assoc. Ed.; Mordecai Avriel, Assoc. Ed.; Angelo Miele, Editor-in-Chief. **ISSN:** 0022-3239. **Subscription Rates:** US$2,543 institutions print or online; US$3,051.60 institutions print & enchanced access. **Remarks:** Advertising accepted; rates available upon request. **URL:** http://www.springer.com/math/journal/10957?detailsPage=editorialBoard. **Circ:** (Not Reported)

48481 ■ Journal of Orofacial Orthopedics/Fortschritte der Kieferorthopadie
Springer Netherlands
Van Godewijckstraat 30
3311 GX Dordrecht, Netherlands
Ph: 31 786 576210
Fax: 31 786 576744
Publisher E-mail: permissions.dordrecht@springer.com
Peer-reviewed journal covering the study of orofacial orthopedics. **Subtitle:** Official Journal of the German Orthodontic Society/Offizielle Zeitschrift der Deutschen Gesellschaft fur Kieferorthopadie. **Freq:** Bimonthly. **Key Personnel:** Dr. Irmtrud Jonas, Editor-in-Chief, judith.gremmler@uniklinik-freiburg.de; Dr. P. Diedrich, Editor-in-Chief, pdiedrich@ukaachen.de; Prof. U. Hirschfelder, Asst. Ed.-in-Ch.; Dr. B. Kahl-Nieke, President. **ISSN:** 1434-5293. **Subscription Rates:** EUR275.70 institutions print incl. free access or e-only; EUR330.84 institutions print incl. enhanced access. **Remarks:** Accepts advertising. **URL:** http://www.springer.com/medicine/dentistry/journal/56. **Circ:** (Not Reported)

48482 ■ Journal of Pest Science
Springer Netherlands
Van Godewijckstraat 30
3311 GX Dordrecht, Netherlands
Ph: 31 786 576210
Fax: 31 786 576744
Publisher E-mail: permissions.dordrecht@springer.com
Journal of pest science providing authoritative coverage of new developments and advances in plant protection. **Freq:** Quarterly. **Key Personnel:** Heidrun Vogt, Subject Ed.; Sven Bacher, Subject Ed.; Anita Juen, Subject Ed.; Tim Haye, Subject Ed.; Bernd Freier, Subject Ed.; Miklos Toth, Subject Ed.; Myron Zalucki, Subject Ed.; Michael Traugott, Editor-in-Chief, michael.traugott@uibk.ac.at. **ISSN:** 1612-4758. **Subscription Rates:** EUR578 institutions print incl. free access or e-only; EUR693.60 institutions print incl. enhanced access. **URL:** http://www.springer.com/lifesci/agriculture/journal/10340.

48483 ■ Journal of Pharmaceutical Innovation
Springer Netherlands
Van Godewijckstraat 30
3311 GX Dordrecht, Netherlands
Ph: 31 786 576210
Fax: 31 786 576744
Publisher E-mail: permissions.dordrecht@springer.com
Peer-reviewed journal covering innovative research in pharmaceutical industry. **Freq:** Quarterly. **Key Personnel:** James K. Drennen III, Editor-in-Chief; Emanuel Diliberto, Editorial Advisory Board; Colman Casey, Editorial Advisory Board. **ISSN:** 1872-5120. **Subscription Rates:** EUR364 institutions print including free access or e-only; EUR436.80 institutions print including enhanced access. **URL:** http://www.springer.com/biomed/pharmaceuticalscience/journal/12247?detailsPage=description.

48484 ■ Journal of Polymer Research
Springer Netherlands
Van Godewijckstraat 30
3311 GX Dordrecht, Netherlands
Ph: 31 786 576210
Fax: 31 786 576744
Publisher E-mail: permissions.dordrecht@springer.com
Journal covering basic and applied research in the field of polymer science and technology. **Freq:** 6/yr. **Key Personnel:** Wen-Yen Chiu, Assoc. Ed.; Show-An Chen, Editor-in-Chief; Hsin-Lung Chen, Assoc. Ed.; An-Chung Su, Assoc. Ed.; Feng-Chih Chang, Editorial Board; Emo Chiellini, Editorial Board; Bernard Lotz, Editorial Board; Helmut Ritter, Editorial Board; Eamor M. Woo, Editorial Board. **ISSN:** 1022-9760. **Subscription Rates:** EUR338 institutions print incl. free access or e-only; EUR405.60 institutions print incl. enhanced access. **Remarks:** Advertising accepted; rates available upon request. **URL:** http://www.springerlink.com/content/1572-8935/. **Circ:** (Not Reported)

48485 ■ Journal of Polymers and the Environment
Springer Netherlands
Van Godewijckstraat 30
3311 GX Dordrecht, Netherlands
Ph: 31 786 576210
Fax: 31 786 576744
Publisher E-mail: permissions.dordrecht@springer.com
Peer-reviewed interdisciplinary journal covering polymers and environmental issues related to them. **Freq:** Quarterly. **Key Personnel:** Jonathan Dordick, Editorial Board; Richard Farrell, Editorial Board; Ann-Christine Albertsson, Editorial Board; Anthony Andrady, Editorial Board; Richard Ashby, Editorial Board; Yoshiharu Doi, Editorial Board; Emo Chiellini, Editorial Board; Stephen P. McCarthy, Editor. **ISSN:** 1566-2543. **Subscription Rates:** EUR505 institutions print or online; EUR606 institutions print & enhanced access. **Remarks:** Advertising accepted; rates available upon request. **URL:** http://www.springer.com/chemistry/polymer/journal/10924. **Formerly:** Journal of Environmental Polymer Degradation. **Circ:** (Not Reported)

48486 ■ The Journal of Primary Prevention
Springer Netherlands
Van Godewijckstraat 30
3311 GX Dordrecht, Netherlands
Ph: 31 786 576210
Fax: 31 786 576744
Publisher E-mail: permissions.dordrecht@springer.com
Journal covering research, literature reviews and book reviews in the field of primary prevention. **Freq:** Bimonthly. **Key Personnel:** Preston A. Britner, PhD, Editor; Ken McLeroy, PhD, Assoc. Ed.; Melissa F. Peskin, PhD, Assoc. Ed. **ISSN:** 0278-095X. **Subscription Rates:** EUR996 institutions print incl. free access or e-only; EUR1,195.20 institutions print incl. enhanced access. **Remarks:** Advertising accepted; rates available upon request. **URL:** http://www.springer.com/publichealth/journal/10935. **Circ:** (Not Reported)

48487 ■ Journal of Productivity Analysis
Springer Netherlands
Van Godewijckstraat 30
3311 GX Dordrecht, Netherlands
Ph: 31 786 576210
Fax: 31 786 576744
Publisher E-mail: permissions.dordrecht@springer.com
Journal focusing on productivity-related developments. **Freq:** 3/yr. **Key Personnel:** Ana M. Aizcorbe, Assoc. Ed.; Antonio M. Alvarez, Assoc. Ed.; Timo Kuosmanen, Assoc. Ed.; Tim J. Coelli, Assoc. Ed.; Mark F.J. Steel, Assoc. Ed.; Lawrence M. Seiford, Assoc. Ed.; Emmanuel Thanassoulis, Editor; Robin C. Sickles, Editor-in-

Chief, rsickles@rice.edu; Paul W. Wilson, Editor; Jose H. Dula, PhD, Assoc. Ed. **ISSN:** 0895-562X. **Subscription Rates:** EUR828 institutions print including free access or e-only; EUR993.60 institutions print including enhanced access. **Remarks:** Advertising accepted; rates available upon request. **URL:** http://www.springerlink.com/content/0895-562X. **Circ:** (Not Reported)

48488 ▪ Journal of Psycholinguistic Research
Springer Netherlands
Van Godewijckstraat 30
3311 GX Dordrecht, Netherlands
Ph: 31 786 576210
Fax: 31 786 576744
Publisher E-mail: permissions.dordrecht@springer.com
International journal covering the social, anthropological, developmental, semantic, biological, psychopathological, and educational aspects of the communicative process. **Founded:** 1972. **Freq:** Bimonthly. **Print Method:** Offset. **Trim Size:** 6 x 9. **Cols./Page:** 1. **Col. Width:** 54 nonpareils. **Col. Depth:** 103 agate lines. **Key Personnel:** Robert W. Rieber, Editor; Ray Dougherty, Assoc. Ed.; Rafael Javier, Assoc. Ed. **ISSN:** 0090-6905. **Subscription Rates:** EUR1,649 institutions print or online; EUR1,978.80 institutions print & enchanced access. **Remarks:** Advertising accepted; rates available upon request. **URL:** http://www.springer.com/psychology/journal/10936. **Circ:** (Not Reported)

48489 ▪ Journal of Psychopathology & Behavioral Assessment
Springer Netherlands
Van Godewijckstraat 30
3311 GX Dordrecht, Netherlands
Ph: 31 786 576210
Fax: 31 786 576744
Publisher E-mail: permissions.dordrecht@springer.com
Psychology journal. **Founded:** 1979. **Freq:** Quarterly. **Print Method:** Offset Uses mats. **Trim Size:** 6 x 9. **Cols./Page:** 1. **Col. Width:** 54 nonpareils. **Col. Depth:** 103 agate lines. **Key Personnel:** Randall T. Salekin, Editor-in-Chief; Henry E. Adams, Founding Ed. **ISSN:** 0882-2689. **Subscription Rates:** EUR938 institutions print or online; EUR1,125.60 institutions print & enchanced access. **Remarks:** Advertising accepted; rates available upon request. **URL:** http://www.springer.com/psychology/psychologygeneral/journal/10862. **Circ:** (Not Reported)

48490 ▪ Journal of Risk and Uncertainty
Springer Netherlands
Van Godewijckstraat 30
3311 GX Dordrecht, Netherlands
Ph: 31 786 576210
Fax: 31 786 576744
Publisher E-mail: permissions.dordrecht@springer.com
Journal publishing original contributions relating to decision analysis, economics and psychology dealing with choice under uncertainty. **Freq:** 3/yr. **Key Personnel:** Kip W. Viscusi, Editor-in-Chief; Christina Stoddard, Managing Editor; Colin Camerer, Assoc. Ed. **ISSN:** 0895-5646. **Subscription Rates:** EUR889 institutions print including free access or e-only; EUR1,066.80 institutions print including enhanced access. **Remarks:** Advertising accepted; rates available upon request. **URL:** http://www.springerlink.com/content/0895-5646. **Circ:** (Not Reported)

48491 ▪ Journal of Scheduling
Springer Netherlands
Van Godewijckstraat 30
3311 GX Dordrecht, Netherlands
Ph: 31 786 576210
Fax: 31 786 576744
Publisher E-mail: permissions.dordrecht@springer.com
Peer-reviewed journal covering advances in scheduling research. **Founded:** June 1998. **Freq:** Bimonthly. **Key Personnel:** Edmund Burke, Editor-in-Chief; Michael L. Pinedo, Editor; Steef van de Velde, Editor. **ISSN:** 1094-6136. **Subscription Rates:** EUR686 institutions print including free access or e-only; EUR823.20 institutions print including enhanced access. **Remarks:** Advertising accepted; rates available upon request. **URL:** http://www.springerlink.com/content/1094-6136. **Circ:** (Not Reported)

48492 ▪ Journal of Science Teacher Education
Springer Netherlands
Van Godewijckstraat 30
3311 GX Dordrecht, Netherlands
Ph: 31 786 576210
Fax: 31 786 576744

Publisher E-mail: permissions.dordrecht@springer.com
Official journal of the Association for Science Teacher Education. Serves as a forum for disseminating research and theoretical position statements concerning the preparation and in-service education of science teachers. **Subtitle:** The Official Journal of the Association for Science Teacher Education. **Freq:** 6/yr. **Key Personnel:** John R. Staver, Editor-in-Chief; Emily Wischow, Managing Editor; John Settlage, Assoc. Ed. **ISSN:** 1046-560X. **Subscription Rates:** EUR405 institutions print incl. free access or e-only; EUR486 institutions print incl. enhanced access. **Remarks:** Accepts advertising. **URL:** http://www.springer.com/education/scienceeducation/journal/10972. **Circ:** (Not Reported)

48493 ▪ Journal of Statistical Physics
Springer Netherlands
Van Godewijckstraat 30
3311 GX Dordrecht, Netherlands
Ph: 31 786 576210
Fax: 31 786 576744
Publisher E-mail: permissions.dordrecht@springer.com
Physics journal covering statistical mechanics and thermodynamics of equilibrium and nonequilibrium processes. **Founded:** 1969. **Freq:** Semimonthly. **Print Method:** Offset. **Trim Size:** 6 x 9. **Cols./Page:** 1. **Col. Width:** 54 nonpareils. **Col. Depth:** 103 agate lines. **Key Personnel:** Cedric Villani, Assoc. Ed., cedric.villani@umpa.ens-lyon.fr; Jorge Kurchan, Assoc. Ed., jorge@pmmh.espci.fr; Herbert Spohn, Assoc. Ed., spohn@mathematik.tu-muenchen.de; Bernard Derrida, Assoc. Ed., derrida@lps.ens.fr; John Cardy, Assoc. Ed., cardy@thphys.ox.ac.uk; Deepak Dhar, Assoc. Ed., ddhar@theory.tifr.res.in; Eric Carlen, Assoc. Ed., carlen@math.rutgers.edu; Joel L. Lebowitz, Editor-in-Chief, lebowitz@math.rutgers.edu. **ISSN:** 0022-4715. **Subscription Rates:** EUR3,984 institutions print or online; US$4,780.80 institutions print & enchanced access. **Remarks:** Advertising accepted; rates available upon request. **URL:** http://www.springer.com/physics/complexity/journal/10955?detailsPage=description. **Circ:** (Not Reported)

48494 ▪ Journal of Structural and Functional Genomics
Springer Netherlands
Van Godewijckstraat 30
3311 GX Dordrecht, Netherlands
Ph: 31 786 576210
Fax: 31 786 576744
Publisher E-mail: permissions.dordrecht@springer.com
Peer-reviewed journal covering the field of structural and functional genomics. **Freq:** Quarterly. **Key Personnel:** Lucia Banci, Editorial Board; Andrzej Joachimiak, Editor-in-Chief; Shigeyuki Yokoyama, Assoc. Ed.; Wayne A. Hendrickson, Advisory Board; Thomas C. Terwilliger, Assoc. Ed.; Gaetano T. Montelione, Assoc. Ed. **ISSN:** 1345-711X. **Subscription Rates:** EUR525 institutions print incl. free access or e-only; EUR630 institutions print incl. enhanced access. **Remarks:** Advertising accepted; rates available upon request. **URL:** http://www.springer.com/lifesci/biochemistry/journal/10969. **Circ:** (Not Reported)

48495 ▪ Journal of Superconductivity and Novel Magnetism
Springer Netherlands
Van Godewijckstraat 30
3311 GX Dordrecht, Netherlands
Ph: 31 786 576210
Fax: 31 786 576744
Publisher E-mail: permissions.dordrecht@springer.com
Peer-reviewed journal focusing on spintronics, magnetic semiconductors, properties of magnetic multilayers, magneto resistive materials and structures and magnetic oxides. **Freq:** 8/yr. **Key Personnel:** Vladimir Z. Kresin, Co-Ed.; Stephan Von Molnar, Editorial Board; K.A. Muller, Letters Ed.; Antonio Barone, Editorial Board; Stuart A. Wolf, Co-Ed.; Ivan Bozovic, Editorial Board; Annette Bussmann-Holder, Editorial Board; Israel Felner, Editorial Board; Jochen Mannhart, Editorial Board. **ISSN:** 1557-1939. **Subscription Rates:** EUR1,213 institutions print incl. free access or e-only; EUR1,455.60 institutions print incl. enhanced access. **Remarks:** Accepts advertising. **URL:** http://www.springer.com/materials/journal/10948. **Circ:** (Not Reported)

48496 ▪ Journal of Systems Science and Complexity
Springer Netherlands
Van Godewijckstraat 30
3311 GX Dordrecht, Netherlands

Ph: 31 786 576210
Fax: 31 786 576744
Publisher E-mail: permissions.dordrecht@springer.com
Journal publishing high-quality and original papers on theories, methodologies and applications of systems science and complexity science. **Freq:** Quarterly. **Key Personnel:** Lei Guo, Editor-in-Chief; Shouyang Wang, Managing Editor; Guanrong Chen, Editorial Board; Xiao-Shan Gao, Managing Editor; Xiuli Chao, Editorial Board; Yu Chen, Editorial Board; Daizhan Cheng, Editorial Board; Jianqing Fan, Editorial Board; ShuCherng Fang, Editorial Board; Jing Han, Editorial Board. **ISSN:** 1009-6124. **Subscription Rates:** EUR581 institutions print incl. free access or e-only; EUR697.20 institutions print incl. enhanced access. **URL:** http://www.springer.com/math/applications/journal/11424.

48497 ▪ Journal of Systems Science and Systems Engineering
Springer Netherlands
Van Godewijckstraat 30
3311 GX Dordrecht, Netherlands
Ph: 31 786 576210
Fax: 31 786 576744
Publisher E-mail: permissions.dordrecht@springer.com
Journal covering theory, methodology and applications relating to systems science and systems engineering. **Founded:** 1992. **Freq:** Quarterly. **Key Personnel:** Jifa Gu, Editor-in-Chief; Chunjun Zhao, Editor-in-Chief; Jian Chen, Editor. **ISSN:** 1004-3756. **Subscription Rates:** EUR319 institutions print incl. free access or e-only; EUR382.80 institutions print incl. enhanced access. **URL:** http://www.springer.com/engineering/journal/11518.

48498 ▪ Journal of Thrombosis and Thrombolysis
Springer Netherlands
Van Godewijckstraat 30
3311 GX Dordrecht, Netherlands
Ph: 31 786 576210
Fax: 31 786 576744
Publisher E-mail: permissions.dordrecht@springer.com
Journal for contemporary cardiologists, hematologists and clinician-scientists actively involved in treatment decisions and clinical investigation of thrombotic disorders involving the cardiovascular and cerebrovascular systems with its principal focus centering on the pathobiology of thrombosis and the use of anticoagulants, platelet antagonists and thrombolytic agents in scientific investigation and patient care. **Freq:** Quarterly. **Key Personnel:** Richard C. Becker, MD, Editor-in-Chief; Christopher Cannon, MD, Assoc. Ed.; Karin Przyklenk, Assoc. Ed. **ISSN:** 0929-5305. **Subscription Rates:** EUR1,074 institutions print incl. free access or e-only; EUR1,288.80 institutions print incl. enhanced access. **Remarks:** Advertising accepted; rates available upon request. **URL:** http://www.springerlink.com/content/0929-5305. **Circ:** (Not Reported)

48499 ▪ Journal of World Prehistory
Springer Netherlands
Van Godewijckstraat 30
3311 GX Dordrecht, Netherlands
Ph: 31 786 576210
Fax: 31 786 576744
Publisher E-mail: permissions.dordrecht@springer.com
Peer-reviewed journal publishing timely and authoritative research syntheses from all fields of archaeology. **Freq:** Quarterly. **Print Method:** Offset. **Key Personnel:** Alex Bentley, Advisory Ed.; Matthew Betts, Advisory Ed.; Peter Biehl, Assoc. Ed.; Timothy F. Taylor, Editor-in-Chief. **ISSN:** 0892-7537. **Subscription Rates:** EUR754 institutions print or online; EUR904.80 institutions print & enhanced access. **Remarks:** Accepts advertising. **URL:** http://www.springer.com/socialsciences/anthropologyandarchaeology/journal/10963. **Circ:** (Not Reported)

48500 ▪ Knee Surgery, Sports Traumatology, Arthroscopy
Springer Netherlands
Van Godewijckstraat 30
3311 GX Dordrecht, Netherlands
Ph: 31 786 576210
Fax: 31 786 576744
Publisher E-mail: permissions.dordrecht@springer.com
Peer-reviewed journal covering processes that underlie evolution, development, structure, function, etiology. **Freq:** Monthly. **Key Personnel:** Rene Verdonk, Editor-in-Chief; H. Alfredson, Editorial Board; R. Cugat, Editorial Board. **ISSN:** 0942-2056. **Subscription Rates:**

Circulation: ★ = ABC; △ = BPA; ♦ = CAC; ● = CCAB; ❑ = VAC; ⊕ = PO Statement; ‡ = Publisher's Report; Boldface figures = sworn; Light figures = estimated.

EUR1,553 institutions print incl. free access or e-only; EUR1,863.60 institutions print incl. enhanced access. **Remarks:** Accepts advertising. **URL:** http://www. springer.com/medicine/orthopedics/journal/167. **Circ:** (Not Reported)

48501 ■ Knowledge and Information Systems
Springer Netherlands
Van Godewijckstraat 30
3311 GX Dordrecht, Netherlands
Ph: 31 786 576210
Fax: 31 786 576744
Publisher E-mail: permissions.dordrecht@springer.com
Peer-reviewed journal focusing on knowledge systems and advanced information systems, including their theoretical foundations, infrastructure and enabling technologies. **Subtitle:** An International Journal. **Freq:** 3/yr. **Key Personnel:** Nick Cercone, Honorary Ed.-in-Ch., ncercone@yorku.ca; Xindong Wu, Editor-in-Chief, kais@cs.uvm.edu; Benjamin W. Wah, Honorary Ed.-in-Ch., b-wah@uiuc.edu. **ISSN:** 0219-1377. **Subscription Rates:** EUR1,047 institutions print incl. free access or e-only; EUR1,256.40 institutions print incl. enhanced access. **Remarks:** Advertising accepted; rates available upon request. **URL:** http://www.springer.com/computer/informationsystems/journal/10115. **Circ:** (Not Reported)

48502 ■ La radiologia medica
Springer Netherlands
Van Godewijckstraat 30
3311 GX Dordrecht, Netherlands
Ph: 31 786 576210
Fax: 31 786 576744
Publisher E-mail: permissions.dordrecht@springer.com
Peer-reviewed journal covering biomedical engineering. **Subtitle:** Official Journal of the Italian Society of Medical Radiology. **Founded:** 1914. **Freq:** 8/yr. **Key Personnel:** Roberto Pozzi Mucelli, Editor-in-Chief, roberto.pozzimucelli@univr.it; G. Guglielmi, Dep. Ed.; M.A. Cova, Editorial Asst. **ISSN:** 0033-8362. **Subscription Rates:** EUR486 institutions print incl. free access or e-only; EUR583.20 institutions print incl. enhanced access. **URL:** http://www.springer.com/medicine/radiology/journal/11547.

48503 ■ La Lettre de medecine physique et de readaptation
Springer Netherlands
Van Godewijckstraat 30
3311 GX Dordrecht, Netherlands
Ph: 31 786 576210
Fax: 31 786 576744
Publisher E-mail: permissions.dordrecht@springer.com
Journal promoting physical therapy and integration. **Freq:** Quarterly. **Key Personnel:** Samy Bendaya, Editor; Anne Peskine, Asst. Ed.; Patricia Blondel, Asst. Ed. **ISSN:** 1778-4298. **Subscription Rates:** EUR222.82 institutions print incl. free access or e-only; EUR267.60 institutions print incl. enhanced access. **Remarks:** Advertising accepted; rates available upon request. **URL:** http://www.springer.com/medicine/journal/11659. **Circ:** (Not Reported)

48504 ■ Landslides
Springer Netherlands
Van Godewijckstraat 30
3311 GX Dordrecht, Netherlands
Ph: 31 786 576210
Fax: 31 786 576744
Publisher E-mail: permissions.dordrecht@springer.com
Journal covering biomedical engineering. **Subtitle:** Journal of the International Consortium on Landslides. **Freq:** Quarterly. **Key Personnel:** Prof. Kyoji Sassa, Editor-in-Chief; P. Bobrowsky, Assoc. Ed.; E. Derbyshire, Advisory Member; K. Ishihara, Advisory Member; J. Hutchinson, Advisory Member; E. Eder, Advisory Member. **ISSN:** 1612-510X. **Subscription Rates:** EUR324 institutions print incl. free access or e-only; EUR388.80 institutions print incl. enhanced access. **URL:** http://www.springer.com/new%26forthcomingtitles%28default%29/journal/10346.

48505 ■ Language Policy
Springer Netherlands
Van Godewijckstraat 30
3311 GX Dordrecht, Netherlands
Ph: 31 786 576210
Fax: 31 786 576744
Publisher E-mail: permissions.dordrecht@springer.com
Journal covering linguistics, language policy, sociolinguistics, and language education. **Freq:** Quarterly. **Key Personnel:** Teresa McCarty, Assoc. Ed.; Stephen May, Assoc. Ed.; Bernard Spolsky, Ed. Emeritus; Kendall King, Editor; Francois Grin, Editorial Board. **ISSN:** 1568-

4555. **Subscription Rates:** EUR284 institutions print incl. free access or e-only; EUR340.80 institutions print incl. enhanced access. **Remarks:** Advertising accepted; rates available upon request. **URL:** http://www.springer.com/linguistics/appliedlinguistics/journal/10993. **Circ:** (Not Reported)

48506 ■ Language Resources and Evaluation
Springer Netherlands
Van Godewijckstraat 30
3311 GX Dordrecht, Netherlands
Ph: 31 786 576210
Fax: 31 786 576744
Publisher E-mail: permissions.dordrecht@springer.com
Journal devoted to the acquisition, creation, annotation, and use of language resources, together with methods for evaluation of resources, technologies, and applications. **Freq:** Quarterly. **Key Personnel:** Nicoletta Calzolari, Editor-in-Chief; Bente Maegaard, Advisory Board; Khalid Choukri, Advisory Board; Joseph Mariani, Advisory Board; Junichi Tsujii, Advisory Board; Steven Bird, Editorial Board. **ISSN:** 1574-020X. **Subscription Rates:** EUR709 institutions print incl. enhanced access; EUR850.80 institutions print incl. enhanced access. **Remarks:** Advertising accepted; rates available upon request. **URL:** http://www.springer.com/linguistics/computationallinguistics/journal/10579. **Formerly:** Computers and the Humanities. **Circ:** (Not Reported)

48507 ■ Law and Philosophy
Springer Netherlands
Van Godewijckstraat 30
3311 GX Dordrecht, Netherlands
Ph: 31 786 576210
Fax: 31 786 576744
Publisher E-mail: permissions.dordrecht@springer.com
Law periodical. **Freq:** Bimonthly. **Key Personnel:** Douglas N. Husak, Editor-in-Chief; Maimon Schwarzschild, Editorial Board; Wil Waluchow, Book Review Ed.; L. Alexander, Editorial Board; S. Byrd, Editorial Board. **ISSN:** 0167-5249. **Subscription Rates:** EUR804 institutions print incl. free access or e-only; EUR964 institutions print incl. enhanced access. **Remarks:** Accepts advertising. **URL:** http://www.springer.com/law/journal/10982. **Circ:** (Not Reported)

48508 ■ Liverpool Law Review
Springer Netherlands
Van Godewijckstraat 30
3311 GX Dordrecht, Netherlands
Ph: 31 786 576210
Fax: 31 786 576744
Publisher E-mail: permissions.dordrecht@springer.com
Law periodical. **Freq:** 3/yr. **Key Personnel:** Ian Campbell, Editorial Board; Dr. Lorie Charlesworth, Editor-in-Chief; Prof. John Cooke, Editorial Board; Michael Meehan, Editorial Board; Dr. Preeti Nijhar, Editorial Board; Dr. Anna Carline, Book Review Ed.; Huw Thomas, Editorial Board; Dr. Anthony Harvey, Editorial Board; Prof. George Mair, Editorial Board. **ISSN:** 0144-932X. **Subscription Rates:** EUR277 institutions print incl. free access or e-only; EUR332.40 institutions print incl. enhanced access. **Remarks:** Accepts advertising. **URL:** http://www.springer.com/law/journal/10991. **Circ:** (Not Reported)

48509 ■ L1-Educational Studies in Language and Literature
Springer Netherlands
Van Godewijckstraat 30
3311 GX Dordrecht, Netherlands
Ph: 31 786 576210
Fax: 31 786 576744
Publisher E-mail: permissions.dordrecht@springer.com
Journal on educational studies in language and literature. **Key Personnel:** Mary Kooy, Editor-in-Chief; Gert Rijlaarsdam, Editor-in-Chief; Ana Atorresi, Editorial Board. **ISSN:** 1567-6617. **URL:** http://www.springer.com/west/home?SGWID=4-102-70-35603799-0&changeHeader=true.

48510 ■ Manuelle Medizin
Springer Netherlands
Van Godewijckstraat 30
3311 GX Dordrecht, Netherlands
Ph: 31 786 576210
Fax: 31 786 576744
Publisher E-mail: permissions.dordrecht@springer.com
Online journals on biomedical sciences - pharmaceutical research, eco health, molecular medicine, neuroscience, human genetics and genomic medicine. **Subtitle:** Chirotherapie, Manuelle Therapie. **Freq:** Bimonthly. **Print Method:** Offset. **Cols./Page:** 6. **Col. Width:** 12 inches.

Col. Depth: 21 inches. **Key Personnel:** Prof. L. Beyer, Editor; Dr. Ulrich W. Bohni, Publisher. **ISSN:** 0025-2514. **Subscription Rates:** EUR352 institutions print incl. free access or e-only; EUR422.40 institutions print incl. enhanced access. **Remarks:** Advertising accepted; rates available upon request. **URL:** http://www.springer.com/medicine/journal/337. **Circ:** (Not Reported)

48511 ■ Marketing Letters
Springer Netherlands
Van Godewijckstraat 30
3311 GX Dordrecht, Netherlands
Ph: 31 786 576210
Fax: 31 786 576744
Publisher E-mail: permissions.dordrecht@springer.com
Journal focusing on research in marketing. **Subtitle:** A Journal of Research in Marketing. **Freq:** 4/yr. **Key Personnel:** Rajeev Batra, Editorial Board; Greg Allenby, Editorial Board; Randolph E. Bucklin, Editor-in-Chief; Mary Frances Luce, Editorial Board; Rajesh Chandy, Editorial Board; Joel E. Urbany, Editor-in-Chief; Charles B. Weinberg, Editorial Board; Barton Weitz, Editorial Board; Frank Kardes, Editorial Board. **ISSN:** 0923-0645. **Subscription Rates:** EUR595 institutions print including free access or e-only; EUR714 institutions print including enhanced access. **Remarks:** Advertising accepted; rates available upon request. **URL:** http://springerlink.metapress.com/content/100312/. **Circ:** (Not Reported)

48512 ■ Maternal and Child Health Journal
Springer Netherlands
Van Godewijckstraat 30
3311 GX Dordrecht, Netherlands
Ph: 31 786 576210
Fax: 31 786 576744
Publisher E-mail: permissions.dordrecht@springer.com
Journal covering the maternal and child health field. **Freq:** Quarterly. **Key Personnel:** Pierre Buekens, Editorial Board; Milton Kotelchuck, Founding Ed.; Greg R. Alexander, Editor; Anita Farel, Editorial Board; Donna J. Petersen, Editor. **ISSN:** 1092-7875. **Subscription Rates:** US$684 institutions including postage & handling; US$820.80 institutions including postage & handling. **Remarks:** Accepts advertising. **URL:** http://www.springerlink.com/content/105600/. **Circ:** (Not Reported)

48513 ■ Mathematical Physics, Analysis and Geometry
Springer Netherlands
Van Godewijckstraat 30
3311 GX Dordrecht, Netherlands
Ph: 31 786 576210
Fax: 31 786 576744
Publisher E-mail: permissions.dordrecht@springer.com
Journal covering theory and application of analysis and geometry to physics. **Subtitle:** An International Journal devoted to the Theory and Applications of Analysis and Geometry to Physics. **Freq:** Quarterly. **Key Personnel:** S. Albeverio, Editorial Board; J.M. Bony, Editorial Board; L.D. Faddeev, Editorial Board; G. Papanicolaou, Editorial Board; E. Bedford, Editorial Board; L.H. Eliasson, Editorial Board; D. Shepelsky, Editorial Board; Henry McKean, Editor-in-Chief; Alexander Its, Editor-in-Chief; Anne Boutet De Monvel, Editor-in-Chief. **ISSN:** 1385-0172. **Subscription Rates:** EUR362 institutions print incl. free access or e-only; EUR434.40 institutions print incl. enhanced access. **Remarks:** Accepts advertising. **URL:** http://www.springerlink.com/content/102957/. **Circ:** (Not Reported)

48514 ■ Meccanica
Springer Netherlands
Van Godewijckstraat 30
3311 GX Dordrecht, Netherlands
Ph: 31 786 576210
Fax: 31 786 576744
Publisher E-mail: permissions.dordrecht@springer.com
International journal focusing on current research in mechanics with research contributions from Italy and rest of the world in connection with Italian Association of Theoretical and Applied Mechanics (AIMETA). **Subtitle:** An International Journal of Theoretical and Applied Mechanics AIMETA. **Founded:** 1966. **Freq:** Bimonthly. **Key Personnel:** Vincenzo Parenti Castelli, Editor, meccanica.aimeta@mail.ing.unibo.it; Piero Bassanini, Assoc. Ed.; Guido Buresti, Assoc. Ed. **ISSN:** 0025-6455. **Subscription Rates:** EUR946 institutions print incl. free access or e-only; EUR1,235.20 institutions print incl. enhanced access. **Remarks:** Advertising accepted; rates available upon request. **URL:** http://springerlink.metapress.com/content/102958/. **Circ:** (Not Reported)

48515 ■ Metabolic Brain Disease
Springer Netherlands
Van Godewijckstraat 30
3311 GX Dordrecht, Netherlands
Ph: 31 786 576210
Fax: 31 786 576744
Publisher E-mail: permissions.dordrecht@springer.com
Medical journal. **Freq:** Quarterly. **Print Method:** Offset.
Key Personnel: Vilmary Friederichs, Managing Editor;
James A. Ferrendelli, Editorial Board; Kathryn J. Jones,
Editorial Board; Richard C. Wiggins, Dep. Ch. Ed.; Dr.
David W. McCandless, Ed.-in-Ch./Founding Ed.; Roger
Butterworth, Dep. Ch. Ed.; Vivienne Russell, Dep. Ch.
Ed. **ISSN:** 0885-2490. **Subscription Rates:** EUR980
institutions print or online; EUR1,176 institutions print &
enhanced access. **Remarks:** Accepts advertising. **URL:**
http://www.springer.com/biomed/neuroscience/journal/
11011. **Circ:** (Not Reported)

48516 ■ Mycopathologia
Springer Netherlands
Van Godewijckstraat 30
3311 GX Dordrecht, Netherlands
Ph: 31 786 576210
Fax: 31 786 576744
Publisher E-mail: permissions.dordrecht@springer.com
Journal covering the study of fungi in disease and
biodeterioration. **Founded:** 1938. **Freq:** 8/yr. **Key Personnel:** Deepak Bhatnagar, Editor; Richard Baird, Editor; Vishnu Chaturvedi, Editor-in-Chief, eic@
mycopathologia.net. **ISSN:** 0301-486X. **Subscription
Rates:** US$1,878 institutions including postage &
handling; US$2,253.60 institutions including postage &
handling. **URL:** http://www.springerlink.com/content/
102966/.

48517 ■ Natural Computing
Springer Netherlands
Van Godewijckstraat 30
3311 GX Dordrecht, Netherlands
Ph: 31 786 576210
Fax: 31 786 576744
Publisher E-mail: permissions.dordrecht@springer.com
Journal dealing with the aspects of natural sciences and
computer sciences. **Freq:** Quarterly. **Key Personnel:** G.
Rozenberg, Editor-in-Chief; Herman P. Spaink, Editor-
in-Chief; M. Hagiya, Editor; J.N. Kok, Assoc. Ed.; N.C.
Seeman, Editor; D. Corne, Editor; M. Hirvensalo, Area
Ed.; G. Paun, Editor; L. Kari, Editor. **ISSN:** 1567-7818.
Subscription Rates: EUR453 individuals print incl. free
access or e-only; EUR543.60 individuals print incl.
enhanced access. **Remarks:** Advertising accepted;
rates available upon request. **URL:** http://www.springer.
com/computer/foundations/journal/11047. **Circ:** (Not
Reported)

48518 ■ Netnomics
Springer Netherlands
Van Godewijckstraat 30
3311 GX Dordrecht, Netherlands
Ph: 31 786 576210
Fax: 31 786 576744
Publisher E-mail: permissions.dordrecht@springer.com
Scientific journal covering electronic networking and
economic research. **Key Personnel:** Stefan Voss, Edi-
tor, stefan.voss@uni-hamburg.de. **ISSN:** 1385-9587.
Subscription Rates: US$152 individuals. **URL:** http://
www.springerlink.com/content/102537/.

48519 ■ Neurochemical Research
Springer Netherlands
Van Godewijckstraat 30
3311 GX Dordrecht, Netherlands
Ph: 31 786 576210
Fax: 31 786 576744
Publisher E-mail: permissions.dordrecht@springer.com
Journal focusing on the neurosciences. **Founded:** 1976.
Freq: Monthly. **Print Method:** Offset. **Trim Size:** 8 3/3 x
10 3/4. **Cols./Page:** 1. **Col. Width:** 54 nonpareils. **Col.
Depth:** 103 agate lines. **Key Personnel:** Jan Albrecht,
Editor; Naren L. Banik, Editor; George H. DeVries,
Assoc. Ed.; Vladimir J. Balcar, Editor; Karl E. Akerman,
Editor; Dusan Dobrota, Editor; Ralf Dringen, Editor; Le-
ontino Battistin, Editor; Dr. Abel Lajtha, Editor-in-Chief;
Henry Sershen, Managing Editor; Samuel Gandy, Edi-
tor; Gianfrancesco Goracci, Editor. **ISSN:** 0364-3190.
Subscription Rates: US$2,668 institutions print or on-
line; US$3,201.60 institutions print & enchanced access.
Remarks: Advertising accepted; rates available upon
request. **URL:** http://www.springer.com/biomed/

neuroscience/journal/11064. **Circ:** (Not Reported)

48520 ■ Numerical Algorithms
Springer Netherlands
Van Godewijckstraat 30
3311 GX Dordrecht, Netherlands
Ph: 31 786 576210
Fax: 31 786 576744
Publisher E-mail: permissions.dordrecht@springer.com
Scientific journal covering numerical algorithms. **Freq:**
Quarterly. **Key Personnel:** Claude Brezinski, Editor-in-
Chief. **ISSN:** 1017-1398. **Subscription Rates:** EUR1,577
institutions print incl. free access or e-only; EUR1,892
institutions print incl. enhanced access. **Remarks:** Ac-
cepts advertising. **URL:** http://www.springerlink.com/
content/101751/. **Circ:** (Not Reported)

48521 ■ Optimization and Engineering
Springer Netherlands
Van Godewijckstraat 30
3311 GX Dordrecht, Netherlands
Ph: 31 786 576210
Fax: 31 786 576744
Publisher E-mail: permissions.dordrecht@springer.com
Journal covering optimizational theory and applications
in engineering science. **Subtitle:** International Multidis-
ciplinary Journal to Promote Optimization Theory and
Applications in Engineering Sciences. **Freq:** Quarterly.
Key Personnel: Hans Georg Bock, Subject Ed.; Tamas
Terlaky, Editor-in-Chief; Yinyu Ye, Subject Ed. **ISSN:**
1389-4420. **Subscription Rates:** EUR439 institutions
print including free access or e-only; EUR526.80 institutions print including enhanced access. **Remarks:** Accepts advertising. **URL:** http://www.springerlink.com/
content/105609/. **Circ:** (Not Reported)

48522 ■ Order
Springer Netherlands
Van Godewijckstraat 30
3311 GX Dordrecht, Netherlands
Ph: 31 786 576210
Fax: 31 786 576744
Publisher E-mail: permissions.dordrecht@springer.com
Journal covering theory of ordered sets and its
application. **Subtitle:** A Journal on the Theory of
Ordered Sets and its Applications. **Freq:** 3/yr. **Key Personnel:** Dwight Duffus, Editor-in-Chief; William T. Trotter, Editorial Board; M. Aschenbrenner, Editorial Board.
ISSN: 0167-8094. **Subscription Rates:** EUR480 institutions print including free access or e-only; EUR576 institutions print including enhanced access. **Remarks:** Accepts advertising. **URL:** http://www.springerlink.com/
content/100324/. **Circ:** (Not Reported)

**48523 ■ Origins of Life and Evolution of the Bio-
sphere**
Springer Netherlands
Van Godewijckstraat 30
3311 GX Dordrecht, Netherlands
Ph: 31 786 576210
Fax: 31 786 576744
Publisher E-mail: permissions.dordrecht@springer.com
Journal covering the international society for the study
of the origin of life. **Subtitle:** The Journal of the
International Astrobiology Society. **Freq:** Bimonthly. **Key
Personnel:** Alan W. Schwartz, Editor-in-Chief, alan@
sci.ru.nl; A. Brack, Editorial Board; H. Cleaves, Editorial
Board. **ISSN:** 0169-6149. **Subscription Rates:** EUR800
institutions print including free access or e-only; EUR960
institutions print including enhanced access. **URL:** http://
www.springerlink.com/content/102974/.

48524 ■ Periodica Mathematica Hungarica
Springer Netherlands
Van Godewijckstraat 30
3311 GX Dordrecht, Netherlands
Ph: 31 786 576210
Fax: 31 786 576744
Publisher E-mail: permissions.dordrecht@springer.com
Journal covering original articles on pure and applied
mathematics published in connection with Janos Bolyai
Mathematical Society. **Freq:** Semiannual. **Key Person-
nel:** Attila Petho, Editorial Board; Jozsef Fritz, Editorial
Board; Imre Barany, Editorial Board; Istvan Berkes,
Editorial Board; Jozsef Beck, Editorial Board; Maria B.
Szendrei, Editor-in-Chief. **ISSN:** 0031-5303. **Subscrip-
tion Rates:** EUR894 institutions print incl. free access or
e-only; EUR1,072.80 institutions print incl. enhanced
access. **Remarks:** Advertising accepted; rates available
upon request. **URL:** http://www.springer.com/math/
journal/10998. **Circ:** (Not Reported)

48525 ■ Pharmaceutical Research
Springer Netherlands
Van Godewijckstraat 30
3311 GX Dordrecht, Netherlands
Ph: 31 786 576210
Fax: 31 786 576744
Publisher E-mail: permissions.dordrecht@springer.com
Research journal. **Subtitle:** An Official Journal of the
American Association of Pharmaceutical Scientists.
Freq: Monthly. **Print Method:** Offset. **Trim Size:** 8 1/2 x
11. **Key Personnel:** Ken-ichi Inui, Editor; Sandra Aller-
heiligen, Editorial Advisory Board; Wim Jiskoot, Editor;
Paul M. Bummer, Editor; Lawrence Ng, Editorial Advisory
Board; Robin H. Bogner, Editorial Advisory Board; Peter
W. Swaan, Editor-in-Chief. **ISSN:** 0724-8741. **Subscrip-
tion Rates:** EUR1,977 institutions print incl. free access
or e-only; EUR2,372.40 institutions print incl. enhanced
access. **Remarks:** Accepts advertising. **URL:** http://
www.springerlink.com/content/105282/. **Circ:** (Not
Reported)

48526 ■ Philosophical Studies
Springer Netherlands
Van Godewijckstraat 30
3311 GX Dordrecht, Netherlands
Ph: 31 786 576210
Fax: 31 786 576744
Publisher E-mail: permissions.dordrecht@springer.com
Journal covering philosophy in the analytic tradition.
Subtitle: An International Journal for Philosophy in the
Analytic Tradition. **Founded:** 1950. **Freq:** 3/yr. **Key Per-
sonnel:** Karen Bennett, Board of Consulting Ed.; Phillip
Bricker, Board of Consulting Ed.; Alex Byrne, Board of
Consulting Ed.; John P. Burgess, Board of Consulting
Ed.; Michael Devitt, Board of Consulting Ed.; Jeffrey
King, Board of Consulting Ed.; Richard Feldman, Board
of Consulting Ed.; David Chalmers, Board of Consulting
Ed.; Stewart Cohen, Editor-in-Chief; Keith Lehrer, Sen.
Advisory Ed.; Thomas A. Blackson, Book Symposium
Ed. **ISSN:** 0031-8116. **Subscription Rates:** EUR2,270
institutions print including free access or e-only;
EUR2,724 institutions print including enhanced access.
Remarks: Accepts advertising. **URL:** http://www.
springerlink.com/content/102978/. **Circ:** (Not Reported)

48527 ■ Photonic Network Communications
Springer Netherlands
Van Godewijckstraat 30
3311 GX Dordrecht, Netherlands
Ph: 31 786 576210
Fax: 31 786 576744
Publisher E-mail: permissions.dordrecht@springer.com
Peer-reviewed journal covering photonic networking.
Freq: 3/yr. **Key Personnel:** Imrich Chlamtac, Advisory
Board; David Cotter, Editorial Board; Ulrich Killat, Edito-
rial Board; Harmen R. Van As, Editor-in-Chief; Polina
Bayvel, Editorial Board. **ISSN:** 1387-974X. **Subscrip-
tion Rates:** EUR646 institutions print including free ac-
cess or e-only; EUR775.20 institutions print including
enhanced access. **Remarks:** Accepts advertising. **URL:**
http://www.springerlink.com/content/103282/. **Circ:** (Not
Reported)

48528 ■ Photosynthesis Research
Springer Netherlands
Van Godewijckstraat 30
3311 GX Dordrecht, Netherlands
Ph: 31 786 576210
Fax: 31 786 576744
Publisher E-mail: permissions.dordrecht@springer.com
Journal for the International Society of Photosynthesis
Research. **Subtitle:** Official Journal of the International
Society of Photosynthesis Research. **Freq:** 3/yr. **Key
Personnel:** David B. Knaff, Editor-in-Chief; J.T. Beatty,
Assoc. Ed.; T.M. Bricker, Assoc. Ed. **ISSN:** 0166-8595.
Subscription Rates: EUR2,346 institutions print includ-
ing free access or e-only; EUR2,815.20 institutions print
including enhanced access. **Remarks:** Accepts
advertising. **URL:** http://www.springerlink.com/content/
100325/; http://www.springer.com/lifesciences/
plantsciences/journal/11120; http://www.springerlink.
com/content/0166-8595. **Circ:** (Not Reported)

48529 ■ Photosynthetica
Springer Netherlands
Van Godewijckstraat 30
3311 GX Dordrecht, Netherlands
Ph: 31 786 576210
Fax: 31 786 576744
Publisher E-mail: permissions.dordrecht@springer.com
Scientific journal dedicated to all aspects of
photosynthesis. **Subtitle:** International Journal for

Circulation: ★ = ABC; △ = BPA; ♦ = CAC; • = CCAB; ❏ = VAC; ⊕ = PO Statement; ‡ = Publisher's Report; Boldface figures = sworn; Light figures = estimated.

Photosynthesis Research. **Freq:** Quarterly. **Key Personnel:** Prof. Jan Naus, Editor-in-Chief; Ivana Stetinova, Exec. Ed.; C. Buschmann, Editorial Board. **ISSN:** 0300-3604. **Subscription Rates:** EUR1,173 institutions print incl. free access or e-only; EUR1,407.60 institutions print incl. enhanced access. **Remarks:** Advertising accepted; rates available upon request. **URL:** http://www.springer.com/lifesci/plantsciences/journal/11099. **Circ:** (Not Reported)

48530 ■ Phytoparasitica
Springer Netherlands
Van Godewijckstraat 30
3311 GX Dordrecht, Netherlands
Ph: 31 786 576210
Fax: 31 786 576744
Publisher E-mail: permissions.dordrecht@springer.com
Journal covering plant protection sciences worldwide. **Founded:** 1973. **Freq:** 5/yr. **Key Personnel:** S. Freeman, Editorial Board; A. Freidberg, Editorial Board; A. Gamliel, Editorial Board; I. Ishaaya, Editorial Board; J. Katan, Editorial Board; Vivian R. Priel, Exec. Ed.; B. Raccah, Editor-in-Chief. **ISSN:** 0334-2123. **Subscription Rates:** EUR342 institutions print or online only; EUR410.40 institutions print and enhanced access. **URL:** http://www.springer.com/life+sci/plant+sciences/journal/12600.

48531 ■ Pituitary
Springer Netherlands
Van Godewijckstraat 30
3311 GX Dordrecht, Netherlands
Ph: 31 786 576210
Fax: 31 786 576744
Publisher E-mail: permissions.dordrecht@springer.com
Peer-reviewed journal covering the pituitary and its disorders. **Subtitle:** The Official Journal of the Pituitary Society. **Freq:** Quarterly. **Key Personnel:** Shlomo Melmed, Editor-in-Chief; Nelson Horseman, Editor; Rudolf Fahlbusch, Editor. **ISSN:** 1386-341X. **Subscription Rates:** EUR513 institutions print including free access or e-only; EUR615.60 institutions print including enhanced access. **Remarks:** Accepts advertising. **URL:** http://www.springerlink.com/content/103316/. **Circ:** (Not Reported)

48532 ■ Plant Cell, Tissue and Organ Culture
Springer Netherlands
Van Godewijckstraat 30
3311 GX Dordrecht, Netherlands
Ph: 31 786 576210
Fax: 31 786 576744
Publisher E-mail: permissions.dordrecht@springer.com
Journal covering biotechnology of higher plants. **Subtitle:** Journal of Plant Biotechnology. **Freq:** 3/yr. **Key Personnel:** Dr. Christian Walter, Assoc. Ed.; Dr. Carole Bassett, Assoc. Ed.; Dr. Schuyler S. Korban, Editor-in-Chief; Dr. Margherita Beruto, Assoc. Ed.; Dr. Donald Briskin, Assoc. Ed.; Dr. Zong-Ming Cheng, Assoc. Ed.; Geert Jan De Klerk, Assoc. Ed.; Dr. Noelle Dorion, Assoc. Ed.; Dr. Klaus Eimert, Assoc. Ed.; Dr. Fredy Altpeter, Assoc. Ed.; Dr. Viola Hanke, Assoc. Ed. **ISSN:** 0167-6857. **Subscription Rates:** EUR2,902 institutions print including free access or e-only; EUR3,482.40 institutions print including enhanced access. **Remarks:** Accepts advertising. **URL:** http://www.springerlink.com/content/100327/. **Circ:** (Not Reported)

48533 ■ Plant Ecology
Springer Netherlands
Van Godewijckstraat 30
3311 GX Dordrecht, Netherlands
Ph: 31 786 576210
Fax: 31 786 576744
Publisher E-mail: permissions.dordrecht@springer.com
Journal covering comprehensive plant ecology. **Subtitle:** An International Journal. **Freq:** 2/yr. **Key Personnel:** D.C. Glenn-Lewin, Advisory Board; E. Bergmeier, Editorial Board; I. Dickie, Book Review Ed.; J. Rozema, Editorial Board; R.G. Baker, Editorial Board; M.J.A. Werger, Advisory Board; M.J. Hutchings, Advisory Board; Neal L. Enright, Editor-in-Chief; R. Dirzo, Advisory Board; G. Stewart, Editorial Board. **ISSN:** 1385-0237. **Subscription Rates:** EUR3,967 institutions print including free access or e-only; EUR4,760.40 institutions print including enhanced access. **Remarks:** Accepts advertising. **URL:** http://www.springerlink.com/content/100328/. **Formerly:** Vegetatio. **Circ:** (Not Reported)

48534 ■ Plant Foods for Human Nutrition
Springer Netherlands
Van Godewijckstraat 30
3311 GX Dordrecht, Netherlands
Ph: 31 786 576210

Fax: 31 786 576744
Publisher E-mail: permissions.dordrecht@springer.com
Journal covering improvement and evaluation of plant food for humans. **Freq:** Quarterly. **Key Personnel:** O. Paredes-Lopez, Editor-in-Chief; Wanda Chenoweth, Assoc. Editorial Board; Michael Liebman, Assoc. Editorial Board. **ISSN:** 0921-9668. **Subscription Rates:** US$616 institutions including postage & handling; US$739.20 institutions including postage & handling. **Remarks:** Accepts advertising. **URL:** http://www.springerlink.com/content/102980/. **Formerly:** Qualitas Plantarum. **Circ:** (Not Reported)

48535 ■ Plant Molecular Biology
Springer Netherlands
Van Godewijckstraat 30
3311 GX Dordrecht, Netherlands
Ph: 31 786 576210
Fax: 31 786 576744
Publisher E-mail: permissions.dordrecht@springer.com
Journal contributing to all areas of plant biology including comparative genomics, functional genomics, proteomics, bioinformatics, computational biology, biochemical and regulatory networks, and biotechnology. **Subtitle:** An International Journal on Molecular Biology, Molecular Genetics and Biochemistry. **Founded:** 1981. **Freq:** 6/yr. **Key Personnel:** Wilhelm Gruissem, Editor-in-Chief; L. Comai, Assoc. Ed.; D.A. Chamovitz, Assoc. Ed.; P. Cubas, Assoc. Ed.; G.P. Bolwell, Assoc. Ed.; J.J. Casal, Assoc. Ed. **ISSN:** 0167-4412. **Subscription Rates:** EUR3,747 individuals print incl. free access or e-only; EUR4,496.40 individuals print incl. enhanced access. **Remarks:** Advertising accepted; rates available upon request. **URL:** http://www.springer.com/lifesci/plantsciences/journal/11103. **Circ:** (Not Reported)

48536 ■ Plant and Soil
Springer Netherlands
Van Godewijckstraat 30
3311 GX Dordrecht, Netherlands
Ph: 31 786 576210
Fax: 31 786 576744
Publisher E-mail: permissions.dordrecht@springer.com
Journal covering plant-soil relationships worldwide. **Subtitle:** An International Journal on Plant-Soil Relationships. **Freq:** Semimonthly. **Key Personnel:** Pieter Poot, Managing Editor; Hans Lambers, Editor-in-Chief; Lieve Bultynck, Managing Editor. **ISSN:** 0032-079X. **Subscription Rates:** EUR6,243 institutions print including free access or e-only; EUR7,491.60 institutions print including enhanced access. **Remarks:** Accepts advertising. **URL:** http://www.springerlink.com/content/100326/. **Circ:** (Not Reported)

48537 ■ Plasma Chemistry and Plasma Processing
Springer Netherlands
Van Godewijckstraat 30
3311 GX Dordrecht, Netherlands
Ph: 31 786 576210
Fax: 31 786 576744
Publisher E-mail: permissions.dordrecht@springer.com
Journal covering the technical applications of plasmas. **Founded:** Mar. 1981. **Freq:** Quarterly. **Print Method:** Offset. **Key Personnel:** Steven Girshick, Editor; Emil Pfender, Editorial Board; Stan Veprek, Editor. **ISSN:** 0272-4324. **Subscription Rates:** EUR1,105 institutions print or online; EUR1,326 institutions print & enchanced access. **Remarks:** Accepts advertising. **URL:** http://www.springer.com/physics/classicalcontinuumphysics/journal/11090. **Circ:** (Not Reported)

48538 ■ Policy Sciences
Springer Netherlands
Van Godewijckstraat 30
3311 GX Dordrecht, Netherlands
Ph: 31 786 576210
Fax: 31 786 576744
Publisher E-mail: permissions.dordrecht@springer.com
Political science journal. **Subtitle:** Integrating Knowledge and Practice to Advance Human Dignity. **Freq:** Quarterly. **Key Personnel:** Toddi Steelman, Editor; William Ascher, International Editorial Board; Jorge E. Rivera, Assoc. Ed.; Murray B. Rutherford, Book Review Ed.; Michael W. Reisman, International Editorial Board; David Pelletier, Assoc. Ed.; Gary D. Brewer, International Editorial Board; Richard Wallace, Assoc. Ed.; Robert E. Goodin, International Editorial Board; Andrew R. Willard, International Editorial Board; Rodney Muth, International Editorial Board. **ISSN:** 0032-2687. **Subscription Rates:** EUR654 institutions print incl. free access or e-only; EUR784 institutions print incl. enhanced access. **URL:**

http://www.springer.com/socialsciences/politicalscience/journal/11077.

48539 ■ Population Research and Policy Review
Springer Netherlands
Van Godewijckstraat 30
3311 GX Dordrecht, Netherlands
Ph: 31 786 576210
Fax: 31 786 576744
Publisher E-mail: permissions.dordrecht@springer.com
Journal covering policy implications of research in population for government officials and scholars. **Subtitle:** In Cooperation with the Southern Demographic Association (SDA). **Freq:** Bimonthly. **Key Personnel:** Thomas W. Pullum, Editor-in-Chief; Mark D. Hayward, Assoc. Ed.; Tom Burch, Editorial Board; Robert A. Hummer, Assoc. Ed.; Cynthia Osborne, Assoc. Ed.; David A. Swanson, Editorial Board. **ISSN:** 0167-5923. **Subscription Rates:** EUR800 institutions print including free access or e-only; EUR960 institutions print including enhanced access. **Remarks:** Accepts advertising. **URL:** http://www.springer.com/socialsciences/demography/journal/11113; http://www.springerlink.com/content/0167-5923. **Circ:** (Not Reported)

48540 ■ Potential Analysis
Springer Netherlands
Van Godewijckstraat 30
3311 GX Dordrecht, Netherlands
Ph: 31 786 576210
Fax: 31 786 576744
Publisher E-mail: permissions.dordrecht@springer.com
Journal covering interactions between potential theory, probability theory, geometry and functional analysis. **Subtitle:** An International Journal Devoted to the Interactions between Potential Theory, Probability Theory, Geometry and Functional Analysis. **Freq:** Quarterly. **Key Personnel:** Laurent Saloff-Coste, Editor-in-Chief; D. Smets, Editorial Board; V.G. Mazya, Editorial Board; M.T. Barlow, Assoc. Board; N. Trudinger, Editorial Board; K.D. Elworthy, Editorial Board; M. Rockner, Editorial Board; P.J. Fitzsimmons, Editorial Board; L. Zambotti, Editorial Board; Dominique Bakry, Editorial Board. **ISSN:** 0926-2601. **Subscription Rates:** EUR816 institutions print including free access or e-only; EUR979.20 institutions print including enhanced access. **Remarks:** Accepts advertising. **URL:** http://www.springerlink.com/content/100331/. **Circ:** (Not Reported)

48541 ■ Precision Agriculture
Springer Netherlands
Van Godewijckstraat 30
3311 GX Dordrecht, Netherlands
Ph: 31 786 576210
Fax: 31 786 576744
Publisher E-mail: permissions.dordrecht@springer.com
Journal dealing with the multidisciplinary nature of precision agriculture. **Subtitle:** An International Journal on Advances in Precision Agriculture. **Freq:** Bimonthly. **Key Personnel:** Jim A. Schepers, Co-Ed.; Mike Wong, Editorial Board; Newell R. Kitchen, Editorial Board; Svend Christensen, Editorial Board; Michael D. Steven, Editorial Board; Sakae Shibusawa, Editorial Board; Viacheslav I. Adamchuk, Editorial Board; Herman Auernhammer, Editorial Board; Margaret A. Oliver, Co-Ed.; John Stafford, Co-Ed. **ISSN:** 1385-2256. **Subscription Rates:** EUR571 institutions print including free access or e-only; EUR685.20 institutions print including enhanced access. **Remarks:** Advertising accepted; rates available upon request. **URL:** http://www.springerlink.com/content/1385-2256. **Circ:** (Not Reported)

48542 ■ Public Choice
Springer Netherlands
Van Godewijckstraat 30
3311 GX Dordrecht, Netherlands
Ph: 31 786 576210
Fax: 31 786 576744
Publisher E-mail: permissions.dordrecht@springer.com
Journal covering areas common to both economics and political science. **Freq:** 8/yr. **Key Personnel:** William F. Shughart II, Sen. Ed., shughart@olemiss.edu; Charles K. Rowley, Editorial Board; Robert D. Tollison, Editorial Board. **ISSN:** 0048-5829. **Subscription Rates:** EUR1,887 institutions; EUR2,264.40 institutions enhanced access. **Remarks:** Advertising accepted; rates available upon request. **URL:** http://www.springerlink.com/content/0048-5829. **Circ:** (Not Reported)

48543 ■ Quality of Life Research
Springer Netherlands
Van Godewijckstraat 30
3311 GX Dordrecht, Netherlands

Ph: 31 786 576210
Fax: 31 786 576744
Publisher E-mail: permissions.dordrecht@springer.com
Journal covering quality of life aspects of treatment, care and rehabilitation worldwide. **Subtitle:** An International Journal of Quality of Life Aspects of Treatment, Care and Rehabilitation. **Freq:** 10/yr. **Key Personnel:** Elena M. Andresen, Assoc. Ed.; Aeilko H. Zwindermann, International Advisory Board; Carla Bann, Assoc. Ed.; Michael Erhart, Assoc. Ed.; Cynthia Gross, Assoc. Ed.; Leah Kleinman, Assoc. Ed.; Youngmee Kim, Assoc. Ed.; Paul Krabbe, Assoc. Ed.; Simon A. Pickard, International Advisory Board. **ISSN:** 0962-9343. **Subscription Rates:** EUR2,163 institutions print & online; EUR2,595.60 institutions print & enchanced access. **Remarks:** Accepts advertising. **URL:** http://www.springerlink.com/content/100213/. **Circ:** (Not Reported)

48544 ■ Quality & Quantity
Springer Netherlands
Van Godewijckstraat 30
3311 GX Dordrecht, Netherlands
Ph: 31 786 576210
Fax: 31 786 576744
Publisher E-mail: permissions.dordrecht@springer.com
Journal focusing on the scientific development of social research. **Subtitle:** International Journal of Methodology. **Freq:** Bimonthly. **Key Personnel:** Vittorio Capecchi, Editor; Robert B. Smith, Advisory Ed.; Luca Ricolfi, Advisory Ed.; Philippe Ciboia, Advisory Ed.; Massimo Buscema, Assoc. Ed.; Massimo Buscema, Editorial Sec., shunmax@libero.it; Raymond Boudon, Assoc. Ed.; Mohamed Cherkaoui, Advisory Ed.; Juan I. Piovani, Advisory Ed.; Guido Maurelli, Advisory Ed. **ISSN:** 0033-5177. **Subscription Rates:** EUR1,458 institutions print incl. free access or e-only; EUR1,749.60 institutions enhanced access. **Remarks:** Advertising accepted; rates available upon request. **URL:** http://www.springer.com/socialsciences/socialsciences%2Cgeneral/journal/11135. **Circ:** (Not Reported)

48545 ■ Queueing Systems
Springer Netherlands
Van Godewijckstraat 30
3311 GX Dordrecht, Netherlands
Ph: 31 786 576210
Fax: 31 786 576744
Publisher E-mail: permissions.dordrecht@springer.com
Journal covering queueing systems for researchers. **Subtitle:** Theory and Applications. **Freq:** Quarterly. **Key Personnel:** Onno J. Boxma, Advisory Board; I. Adan, Assoc. Ed.; V. Anantharam, Assoc. Ed. **ISSN:** 0257-0130. **Subscription Rates:** EUR1,622 institutions print including free access or e-only; EUR1,946.40 institutions print including enhanced access. **Remarks:** Accepts advertising. **URL:** http://www.springerlink.com/content/101752/. **Circ:** (Not Reported)

48546 ■ The Ramanujan Journal
Springer Netherlands
Van Godewijckstraat 30
3311 GX Dordrecht, Netherlands
Ph: 31 786 576210
Fax: 31 786 576744
Publisher E-mail: permissions.dordrecht@springer.com
Journal on mathematics. **Subtitle:** An International Journal Devoted to the Areas of Mathematics Influenced by Ramanujan. **Freq:** 3/yr. **Key Personnel:** Richard Askey, Editorial Board; George Andrews, Editorial Board; Krishnaswami Alladi, Editor-in-Chief; Jonathan Borwein, Editorial Board; Heng Huat Chan, Editorial Board; David Bressoud, Editorial Board; Bruce Berndt, Coord. Ed.; Frank Garvan, Coord. Ed.; Peter Borwein, Editorial Board. **ISSN:** 1382-4090. **Subscription Rates:** EUR527 institutions print including free access or e-only; EUR632.40 institutions print including enhanced access. **URL:** http://www.springer.com/mathematics/numbers/journal/11139.

48547 ■ Reading and Writing
Springer Netherlands
Van Godewijckstraat 30
3311 GX Dordrecht, Netherlands
Ph: 31 786 576210
Fax: 31 786 576744
Publisher E-mail: permissions.dordrecht@springer.com
Interdisciplinary journal covering the processes involved in reading and writing, including linguistics, information processing, and related disciplines. **Subtitle:** An Interdisciplinary Journal. **Freq:** 9/yr. **Key Personnel:** Brian Byrne, Editorial Board; Anne Cunningham, Edito-

rial Board; Joanne F. Carlisle, Editorial Board; P.G. Aaron, Editorial Board; Malatesha R. Joshi, Editor; Marketa Caravolas, Editorial Board; Peter E. Bryant, Editorial Board; William Tunmer, Assoc. Ed. **ISSN:** 0922-4777. **Subscription Rates:** EUR927 institutions print including free access or e-only; EUR1,112.40 individuals print including enhanced access. **Remarks:** Accepts advertising. **URL:** http://www.springer.com/linguistics/languages%26literature/journal/11145; http://www.springerlink.com/content/0922-4777. **Circ:** (Not Reported)

48548 ■ Real-Time Systems
Springer Netherlands
Van Godewijckstraat 30
3311 GX Dordrecht, Netherlands
Ph: 31 786 576210
Fax: 31 786 576744
Publisher E-mail: permissions.dordrecht@springer.com
Journal covering time-critical computing systems. **Subtitle:** The International Journal of Time-Critical Computing Systems. **Freq:** 3/yr. **Key Personnel:** Krithi Ramamritham, Editor-in-Chief; Tarek F. Abdelzaher, Editor-in-Chief; John A. Stankovic, Advisory Board; Wei Zhao, Advisory Board; Giorgio C. Buttazzo, Editor-in-Chief; Wolfgang A. Halang, Founding Ed. **ISSN:** 0922-6443. **Subscription Rates:** EUR1,127 institutions print including free access or e-only; EUR1,352.40 institutions print including enhanced access. **Remarks:** Accepts advertising. **URL:** http://www.springerlink.com/content/100334/. **Circ:** (Not Reported)

48549 ■ Reliable Computing
Springer Netherlands
Van Godewijckstraat 30
3311 GX Dordrecht, Netherlands
Ph: 31 786 576210
Fax: 31 786 576744
Publisher E-mail: permissions.dordrecht@springer.com
Journal covering interval computations. **Subtitle:** An International Journal devoted to Reliable Mathematical Computations based on Finite Representations and Guaranteed Accuracy. **Freq:** Bimonthly. **Key Personnel:** Boris S. Dobronets, Editorial Board; Gotz Alefeld, Editorial Board; Annie Cuyt, Editorial Board; Vyacheslav M. Nesterov, Editor-in-Chief; Siegfried M. Rump, Editorial Board. **ISSN:** 1385-3139. **Remarks:** Accepts advertising. **URL:** http://www.springerlink.com/content/102987/. **Circ:** (Not Reported)

48550 ■ Research in Higher Education
Springer Netherlands
Van Godewijckstraat 30
3311 GX Dordrecht, Netherlands
Ph: 31 786 576210
Fax: 31 786 576744
Publisher E-mail: permissions.dordrecht@springer.com
Journal covering higher education research. **Subtitle:** Journal of the Association for Institutional Research. **Freq:** 8/yr. **Key Personnel:** James C. Hearn, Assoc. Ed.; Robert K. Toutkoushian, Consulting Ed.; Yonghong Jade Xu, Consulting Ed.; Ernest T. Pascarella, Assoc. Ed.; Paul D. Umbach, Consulting Ed.; Scott L. Thomas, Consulting Ed.; Alberto F. Cabrera, Consulting Ed.; Paul T. Brinkman, Consulting Ed.; Deborah Faye Carter, Consulting Ed.; John C. Smart, Editor. **ISSN:** 0361-0365. **Subscription Rates:** EUR1,175 institutions print including free access or e-only; EUR1,410 institutions print including enhanced access. **Remarks:** Accepts advertising. **URL:** http://www.springerlink.com/content/101599/. **Circ:** (Not Reported)

48551 ■ Review of Accounting Studies
Springer Netherlands
Van Godewijckstraat 30
3311 GX Dordrecht, Netherlands
Ph: 31 786 576210
Fax: 31 786 576744
Publisher E-mail: permissions.dordrecht@springer.com
Journal covering theoretical, empirical and experimental accounting research. **Freq:** Quarterly. **Key Personnel:** Stephen Penman, Editor; Stanley Baiman, Managing Editor; Stefan J. Reichelstein, Editor; Richard Sloan, Managing Editor; Doron Nissim, Editor; Peter Easton, Editor. **ISSN:** 1380-6653. **Subscription Rates:** EUR646 institutions print including free access or e-only; EUR775.20 institutions print including enhanced access. **Remarks:** Accepts advertising. **URL:** http://www.springerlink.com/content/102988/. **Circ:** (Not Reported)

48552 ■ The Review of Austrian Economics
Springer Netherlands

Van Godewijckstraat 30
3311 GX Dordrecht, Netherlands
Ph: 31 786 576210
Fax: 31 786 576744
Publisher E-mail: permissions.dordrecht@springer.com
Journal covering Austrian economics. **Freq:** Quarterly. **Key Personnel:** Leland Yeager, Advisory Ed.; Israel M. Kirzner, Advisory Ed.; Steve Horwitz, Book Review Ed.; Peter J. Boettke, Editor-in-Chief; Stefan Voigt, Assoc. Ed.; Benjamin Powell, Assoc. Ed. **ISSN:** 0889-3047. **Subscription Rates:** EUR512 institutions print including free access or e-only; EUR614.40 institutions print including enhanced access. **URL:** http://www.springerlink.com/content/100335/.

48553 ■ Review of Derivatives Research
Springer Netherlands
Van Godewijckstraat 30
3311 GX Dordrecht, Netherlands
Ph: 31 786 576210
Fax: 31 786 576744
Publisher E-mail: permissions.dordrecht@springer.com
Journal covering derivatives research for financial institutions, institutional investors and corporations. **Freq:** 3/yr. **Key Personnel:** Gurdip Bakshi, Editor; Dilip Madan, Editor; Charles Cao, Assoc. Ed.; Liuren Wu, Assoc. Ed.; Myron Scholes, Advisory Ed.; Robert Merton, Advisory Ed.; Marti G. Subrahmanyam, Founding Ed.; Tan Wang, Assoc. Ed.; Menachem Brenner, Founding Ed.; Stephen Ross, Advisory Ed.; Mark Loewenstein, Assoc. Ed. **ISSN:** 1380-6645. **Subscription Rates:** EUR391 institutions print & online; EUR469.20 institutions print & enchanced access. **Remarks:** Accepts advertising. **URL:** http://www.springerlink.com/content/102989/. **Circ:** (Not Reported)

48554 ■ Review of Industrial Organization
Springer Netherlands
Van Godewijckstraat 30
3311 GX Dordrecht, Netherlands
Ph: 31 786 576210
Fax: 31 786 576744
Publisher E-mail: permissions.dordrecht@springer.com
Journal covering industrial organization worldwide. **Subtitle:** An International Journal Published for the Industrial Organization Society. **Freq:** Quarterly. **Key Personnel:** John Howard Brown, Editorial Board; Dennis C. Mueller, Editorial Board; William G. Shepherd, Special Ed.; Christopher M. Snyder, Editorial Board; Michael Mazzeo, Editorial Board; David Besanko, Editorial Board; Vivek Ghosal, Editorial Board; Lawrence J. White, Gen. Ed.; Sara Fisher Ellison, Editorial Board; Jeroen Hinloopen, Editorial Board; Laura Rondi, Editorial Board. **ISSN:** 0889-938X. **Subscription Rates:** EUR852 institutions print including free access or e-only; EUR1,022.40 institutions print including enhanced access. **Remarks:** Accepts advertising. **URL:** http://www.springerlink.com/content/100336/. **Circ:** (Not Reported)

48555 ■ Review of Quantitative Finance and Accounting
Springer Netherlands
Van Godewijckstraat 30
3311 GX Dordrecht, Netherlands
Ph: 31 786 576210
Fax: 31 786 576744
Publisher E-mail: permissions.dordrecht@springer.com
Journal covering research work which involves the interaction of finance with accounting, economics and quantitative methods, focused on finance and accounting. **Freq:** Quarterly. **Key Personnel:** Lee Cheng-few, Editor-in-Chief; Richard T. Baillie, Assoc. Ed.; Charles Q. Cao, Assoc. Ed. **ISSN:** 0924-865X. **Subscription Rates:** EUR1,134 institutions print including free access or e-only; EUR1,360.80 institutions print including enhanced access. **Remarks:** Advertising accepted; rates available upon request. **URL:** http://www.springerlink.com/content/0924-865X. **Circ:** (Not Reported)

48556 ■ Reviews in Endocrine & Metabolic Disorders
Springer Netherlands
Van Godewijckstraat 30
3311 GX Dordrecht, Netherlands
Ph: 31 786 576210
Fax: 31 786 576744
Publisher E-mail: permissions.dordrecht@springer.com
Journal covering research and treatment in endocrine and metabolic disorders for scientists and clinicians. **Freq:** Quarterly. **Key Personnel:** Kenneth D. Burman, Assoc. Ed.; Shlomo Melmed, Editorial Board; Ken Ho,

Circulation: ★ = ABC; △ = BPA; ♦ = CAC; • = CCAB; ❏ = VAC; ⊕ = PO Statement; ‡ = Publisher's Report; Boldface figures = sworn; Light figures = estimated.

Gale Directory of Publications & Broadcast Media/147th Ed.

5267

Assoc. Ed.; Ram K. Menon, Co-Ed.; Alan Chait, Editorial Board; Steven W. Lamberts, Assoc. Ed.; Michael C. Sheppard, Assoc. Ed.; Michael P. Conn, Co-Ed.; Ernesto Canalis, Editorial Board; Michael G. Besser, Editorial Board; Derek Le Roith, Founding Ed.; Irving M. Spitz, Editorial Board. **ISSN:** 1389-9155. **Subscription Rates:** EUR512 institutions print including free access or e-only; EUR614.40 institutions print including enhanced access. **URL:** http://www.springerlink.com/content/104970/.

48557 ■ Reviews in Fish Biology and Fisheries
Springer Netherlands
Van Godewijckstraat 30
3311 GX Dordrecht, Netherlands
Ph: 31 786 576210
Fax: 31 786 576744
Publisher E-mail: permissions.dordrecht@springer.com
Peer-reviewed journal covering fish and fisheries biology worldwide. **Freq:** Quarterly. **Key Personnel:** Michael A. Banks, Editorial Board; Howard Bern, Editorial Board; Devin M. Bartley, Editorial Board; Stephen Blaber, Editorial Board; Jennifer L. Nielsen, Editor-in-Chief; James Bohnsack, Editorial Board. **ISSN:** 0960-3166. **Subscription Rates:** EUR880 institutions print including free access or e-only; EUR1,056 institutions print including enhanced access. **URL:** http://www.springerlink.com/content/100215/; http://www.springer.com/lifesci/ecology/journal/11160.

48558 ■ Russian Linguistics
Springer Netherlands
Van Godewijckstraat 30
3311 GX Dordrecht, Netherlands
Ph: 31 786 576210
Fax: 31 786 576744
Publisher E-mail: permissions.dordrecht@springer.com
Journal covering Russian language studies. **Subtitle:** International Journal for the Study of Russian and other Slavic Languages. **Freq:** 3/yr. **Key Personnel:** Regina Sippl-Jahn, Editorial Sec.; G.G. Corbett, Editorial Board; Alexander V. Issatschenko, Founder; D.J. Birnbaum, Editorial Board; Roger Comtet, Editor; Werner Lehfeldt, Editorial Board; Jos Schaeken, Editor; Ulrich Schweier, Editor; D. Weiss, Editorial Board. **ISSN:** 0304-3487. **Subscription Rates:** EUR633 institutions print including free access or e-only; EUR759.60 institutions print including enhanced access. **Remarks:** Accepts advertising. **URL:** http://www.springerlink.com/content/102991/; http://www.springer.com/education%26language/linguistics/journal/11185. **Circ:** (Not Reported).

48559 ■ Science & Education
Springer Netherlands
Van Godewijckstraat 30
3311 GX Dordrecht, Netherlands
Ph: 31 786 576210
Fax: 31 786 576744
Publisher E-mail: permissions.dordrecht@springer.com
Journal covering the history, philosophy, and sociology of science and mathematics. **Subtitle:** Contributions from History, Philosophy and Sociology of Science and Mathematics. **Freq:** 10/yr. **Key Personnel:** Michael R. Matthews, Editor-in-Chief; Fouad Abd-El-Khalick, Editorial Committee; Kevin de Berg, Editorial Committee. **ISSN:** 0926-7220. **Subscription Rates:** EUR1,078 institutions print including free access or e-only; EUR1,293.60 institutions print including enhanced access. **Remarks:** Accepts advertising. **URL:** http://www.springerlink.com/content/102992/. **Circ:** (Not Reported)

48560 ■ Sensing and Imaging
Springer Netherlands
Van Godewijckstraat 30
3311 GX Dordrecht, Netherlands
Ph: 31 786 576210
Fax: 31 786 576744
Publisher E-mail: permissions.dordrecht@springer.com
Journal covering subsurface sensing technologies and applications. **Subtitle:** An International Journal. **Freq:** Quarterly. **Key Personnel:** Cam Nguyen, Founding Ed.; Donald A. Bender, Editorial Board; Nathan Ida, Editorial Board; Renato G. Basisio, Editorial Board; Guido Biffi Gentili, Editorial Board; Alex Brandelik, Editorial Board; James Lin, Editorial Board; David Daniels, Editorial Board; T. Lasri, Editorial Board; Ernesto Cespedes, Editor. **ISSN:** 1557-2064. **Subscription Rates:** EUR456 institutions print or online; EUR547.20 institutions print and online. **Remarks:** Accepts advertising. **URL:** http://www.springerlink.com/content/104979/. **Formerly:** Subsurface Sensing Technologies and Applications. **Circ:** (Not Reported)

48561 ■ Social Indicators Research
Springer Netherlands
Van Godewijckstraat 30
3311 GX Dordrecht, Netherlands
Ph: 31 786 576210
Fax: 31 786 576744
Publisher E-mail: permissions.dordrecht@springer.com
Journal covering social sciences. **Subtitle:** An International and Interdisciplinary Journal for Quality-of-Life Measurement. **Founded:** 1974. **Freq:** 15/yr. **Key Personnel:** Alex C. Michalos, Editor; Hirotsugu Aiga, Editorial Board; Barbara Baldazzi, Editorial Board. **ISSN:** 0303-8300. **Subscription Rates:** EUR2,473 institutions print incl. free access or e-only; EUR2,967.60 institutions print incl. enhanced access. **Remarks:** Accepts advertising. **URL:** http://www.springer.com/socialsciences/sociology/journal/11205. **Circ:** (Not Reported)

48562 ■ Social Justice Research
Springer Netherlands
Van Godewijckstraat 30
3311 GX Dordrecht, Netherlands
Ph: 31 786 576210
Fax: 31 786 576744
Publisher E-mail: permissions.dordrecht@springer.com
Professional journal. **Freq:** Quarterly. **Print Method:** Offset. **Key Personnel:** Kasumi Yoshimura, Editorial Asst.; John T. Jost, Assoc. Ed.; James H. Liu, Assoc. Ed.; Brian Lowery, Assoc. Ed.; Susan Opotow, Assoc. Ed.; Curtis D. Hardin, Editor-in-Chief. **ISSN:** 0885-7466. **Subscription Rates:** EUR804 institutions print or online; EUR964.80 institutions print & enhanced access. **Remarks:** Accepts advertising. **URL:** http://www.springer.com/psychology/personality%26socialpsychology/journal/11211?detailsPage=description.. **Circ:** (Not Reported)

48563 ■ Software Quality Journal
Springer Netherlands
Van Godewijckstraat 30
3311 GX Dordrecht, Netherlands
Ph: 31 786 576210
Fax: 31 786 576744
Publisher E-mail: permissions.dordrecht@springer.com
Journal covering quality management in the effective construction of software systems. **Freq:** Quarterly. **Print Method:** Offset. **Cols./Page:** 6. **Col. Width:** 25 nonpareils. **Col. Depth:** 291 agate lines. **Key Personnel:** James D..Arthur, Editorial Board; Rachel Harrison, Editor-in-Chief; James Bieman, Editorial Board; Geoff R. Dromey, Editorial Board; Marek Reformat, Editorial Board; Tracy Hall, Editorial Board; Margaret Ross, Regional Ed.; Norman Fenton, Editorial Board; Giuliano Antoniol, Editorial Board. **ISSN:** 0963-9314. **Subscription Rates:** EUR683 institutions print incl. free access or e-only; EUR819.60 institutions print incl. enhanced access. **Remarks:** Advertising accepted; rates available upon request. **URL:** http://www.springer.com/computer/swe/journal/11219. **Circ:** (Not Reported)

48564 ■ Solar Physics
Springer Netherlands
Van Godewijckstraat 30
3311 GX Dordrecht, Netherlands
Ph: 31 786 576210
Fax: 31 786 576744
Publisher E-mail: permissions.dordrecht@springer.com
Journal covering articles on the internal structure of the sun and its evolution to the outer corona. **Subtitle:** A Journal for Solar and Solar-Stellar Research and the Study of Solar Terrestrial Physics. **Founded:** 1967. **Freq:** Semiannual. **Print Method:** Offset. **Cols./Page:** 6. **Col. Width:** 20 nonpareils. **Col. Depth:** 301 agate lines. **Key Personnel:** G. Poletto, Editorial Board; Lidia van Driel-Gesztelyi, Editor; J.O. Stenflo, Honorary Member; P. Charbonneau, Editorial Board; P. Heinzel, Editorial Board; John Leibacher, Editor; Jingxiu Wang, Editorial Board; Takashi Sakurai, Editor. **ISSN:** 0038-0938. **Subscription Rates:** EUR4,845 institutions print incl. free access or e-only; EUR5,814 institutions print incl. enhanced access. **Remarks:** Advertising accepted; rates available upon request. **URL:** http://www.springer.com/astronomy/astrophysics/journal/11207. **Circ:** (Not Reported)

48565 ■ Somatic Cell and Molecular Genetics
Springer Netherlands
Van Godewijckstraat 30.
3311 GX Dordrecht, Netherlands
Ph: 31 786 576210
Fax: 31 786 576744
Publisher E-mail: permissions.dordrecht@springer.com
Journal presenting genetics research. **Founded:** 1975. **Freq:** Quarterly. **Print Method:** Offset. **Trim Size:** 7 x 10. **Cols./Page:** 1. **Col. Width:** 54 nonpareils. **Col. Depth:** 103 agate lines. **Key Personnel:** Richard Davidson, Editor; Elliot Kaufman, PhD, Editor-in-Chief, erk@uic.edu. **ISSN:** 0740-7750. **Remarks:** Advertising accepted; rates available upon request. **URL:** http://www.springer.com/biomed/humangenetics/journal/11188. **Circ:** (Not Reported)

48566 ■ Space Science Reviews
Springer Netherlands
Van Godewijckstraat 30
3311 GX Dordrecht, Netherlands
Ph: 31 786 576210
Fax: 31 786 576744
Publisher E-mail: permissions.dordrecht@springer.com
Journal covering astrophysics, physics of planetary systems, solar physics, and magnetospheric physics. **Freq:** Quarterly. **Print Method:** Offset. **Cols./Page:** 8. **Col. Width:** 1 1/2 inches. **Col. Depth:** 21 inches. **Key Personnel:** E.C. Stone, Editorial Board; P. Charbonneau, Editorial Board; Hans Bloemen, Editor-in-Chief; Markus J. Aschwanden, Editorial Committee; Christopher T. Russell, Editorial Committee; James L. Burch, Editorial Committee; J. Luhmann, Editorial Board; Rudolf Von Steiger, Editorial Committee. **ISSN:** 0038-6308. **Subscription Rates:** EUR3,541 institutions print incl. free access or e-only; EUR4,249.20 institutions print incl. enhanced access. **Remarks:** Accepts advertising. **URL:** http://www.springer.com/astronomy/extraterrestrialphysics/journal/11214. **Circ:** (Not Reported)

48567 ■ Sport Sciences for Health
Springer Netherlands
Van Godewijckstraat 30
3311 GX Dordrecht, Netherlands
Ph: 31 786 576210
Fax: 31 786 576744
Publisher E-mail: permissions.dordrecht@springer.com
Journal covering clinical research on physiology and pathophysiology. **Subtitle:** Official Journal of the Faculty of Exercise Sciences - University of Milan. **Founded:** 1979. **Freq:** 3/yr. **Print Method:** Offset. **Trim Size:** 8 1/2 x 10 7/8. **Cols./Page:** 3. **Col. Width:** 26 nonpareils. **Col. Depth:** 117 agate lines. **Key Personnel:** A. Veicsteinas, Co-Ed.; G. Michielon, Asst. Ed.; G. Alberti, Assoc. Ed.; G. Cometti, Advisory Board; E. Arcelli, Assoc. Ed.; G. Merati, Asst. Ed.; F. Carandente, Assoc. Ed.; L. Luzi, Co-Ed.; Giuliano Pizzini, Editor-in-Chief; A. La Torre, Assoc. Ed. **ISSN:** 1824-7490. **Subscription Rates:** EUR255 institutions print incl. free access or e-only; EUR306 institutions print incl. enhanced access. **URL:** http://www.springer.com/medicine/orthopedics/journal/11332.

48568 ■ Statistics and Computing
Springer Netherlands
Van Godewijckstraat 30
3311 GX Dordrecht, Netherlands
Ph: 31 786 576210
Fax: 31 786 576744
Publisher E-mail: permissions.dordrecht@springer.com
Journal covering topics on statistical and computer science. **Freq:** Quarterly. **Print Method:** Web offset. **Cols./Page:** 6. **Col. Width:** 12.2 picas. **Col. Depth:** 21 1/2 inches. **Key Personnel:** Pierre L'Ecuyer, Editorial Board; Gilles Celeux, Editor-in-Chief; Hans Lenz, Editorial Board; John Hinde, Editorial Board; Mauro Piccioni, Editorial Board; Siddhartha Chib, Editorial Board; Steven Gilmour, Editorial Board; Jim Griffin, Editorial Board; Chris Meek, Editorial Board; Petros Dellaportas, Editorial Board. **ISSN:** 0960-3174. **Subscription Rates:** EUR835 institutions print incl. free access or e-only; EUR1,002 institutions print incl. enhanced access. **Remarks:** Accepts advertising. **URL:** http://www.springerlink.com/content/0960-3174. **Circ:** (Not Reported)

48569 ■ Studia Logica
Springer Netherlands
Van Godewijckstraat 30
3311 GX Dordrecht, Netherlands
Ph: 31 786 576210
Fax: 31 786 576744
Publisher E-mail: permissions.dordrecht@springer.com
Journal covering philosophy and methodology of science. **Subtitle:** An International Journal for Symbolic Logic. **Founded:** 1979. **Freq:** 3/yr. **Print Method:** Offset. **Trim Size:** 7 x 10. **Cols./Page:** 2. **Col. Width:** 45

nonpareils. **Col. Depth:** 126 agate lines. **Key Personnel:** Gerhard Brewka, Consulting Board; Nuel D. Belnap, Consulting Board; Walter A. Carnielli, Consulting Board; M.E. Adams, Consulting Board; Andre Fuhrmann, Consulting Board; Dov M. Gabbay, Consulting Board; Sergei N. Artemov, Consulting Board; Maxwell John Cresswell, Consulting Board; Guram Bezhanishvili, Assoc. Ed.; Janusz Czelakowski, Assoc. Ed.; Ryszard Wojcicki, Editor-in-Chief. **ISSN:** 0039-3215. **Subscription Rates:** EUR1,360 institutions print incl. free access or e-only; EUR1,632 institutions print incl. enhanced access. **Remarks:** Accepts advertising. **URL:** http://www.springer.com/philosophy/logicandphilosophyoflanguage/journal/11225. **Circ:** (Not Reported)

48570 ■ Studies in Philosophy and Education
Springer Netherlands
Van Godewijckstraat 30
3311 GX Dordrecht, Netherlands
Ph: 31 786 576210
Fax: 31 786 576744
Publisher E-mail: permissions.dordrecht@springer.com
Peer-reviewed journal focusing on philosophical, theoretical, normative and conceptual problems. **Founded:** Dec. 13, 1984. **Print Method:** Offset. **Trim Size:** 11 x 14. **Cols./Page:** 4. **Col. Width:** 28 nonpareils. **Col. Depth:** 196 agate lines. **Key Personnel:** Francis T. Villemain, Founder; Gert Biesta, Editor-in-Chief; James W. Garrison, Advisory Ed.; Ann Chinnery, Book Review Ed. **ISSN:** 0039-3746. **Subscription Rates:** EUR594 institutions print & online; EUR712.80 institutions print & enchanced access. **URL:** http://www.springer.com/west/home/generic/search/results?SGWID=4-40109-70-35667985-0.

48571 ■ Supportive Care in Cancer
Springer Netherlands
Van Godewijckstraat 30
3311 GX Dordrecht, Netherlands
Ph: 31 786 576210
Fax: 31 786 576744
Publisher E-mail: permissions.dordrecht@springer.com
Journal covering medical, technical and surgical topics concerning supportive therapy. **Founded:** Jan. 1927. **Freq:** Monthly. **Print Method:** Offset. **Trim Size:** 8 1/2 x 11. **Cols./Page:** 3. **Col. Width:** 2.25 picas. **Col. Depth:** 9.5 picas. **Key Personnel:** J.J. Body, Editorial Consultant; D. Walsh, Editorial Consultant; S. Eychmuller, Editorial Consultant; J. Epstein, Assoc. Ed.-in-Ch.; J. Herrstedt, Assoc. Ed.-in-Ch.; R. Arnold, Assoc. Ed.; E. Bruera, Editorial Consultant; K. White, Assoc. Ed.; R.A. Ammann, Editorial Consultant; F.D. Ashbury, Editor-in-Chief. **ISSN:** 0941-4355. **Subscription Rates:** EUR947 institutions print incl. free access or e-only; EUR1,136.40 institutions print incl. enhanced access. **Remarks:** Accepts advertising. **URL:** http://www.springer.com/medicine/oncology/journal/520. **Circ:** (Not Reported)

48572 ■ Surgical and Radiologic Anatomy
Springer Netherlands
Van Godewijckstraat 30
3311 GX Dordrecht, Netherlands
Ph: 31 786 576210
Fax: 31 786 576744
Publisher E-mail: permissions.dordrecht@springer.com
Journal devoted to physicians, surgeons and radiologists. **Founded:** 1954. **Freq:** 10/yr. **Print Method:** Offset. **Trim Size:** 8 1/2 x 11. **Cols./Page:** 2 and 3. **Col. Width:** 26 and 42 nonpareils. **Col. Depth:** 139 agate lines. **Key Personnel:** B. Grignon, Assoc. Ed.; S. Velut, Assoc. Ed.; F. Duparc, Editor-in-Chief; C. Avisse, Assoc. Ed.; F. Anderhuber, Assoc. Ed.; E.J. Voiglio, Assoc. Ed.; B. Moriggl, Assoc. Ed.; T. Sato, Assoc. Ed. **ISSN:** 0930-1038. **Subscription Rates:** EUR770 institutions print incl. free access or e-only; EUR924 institutions print incl. enhanced access. **Remarks:** Accepts advertising. **URL:** http://www.springer.com/medicine/internal/journal/276. **Circ:** (Not Reported)

48573 ■ Surveys in Geophysics
Springer Netherlands
Van Godewijckstraat 30
3311 GX Dordrecht, Netherlands
Ph: 31 786 576210
Fax: 31 786 576744
Publisher E-mail: permissions.dordrecht@springer.com
Peer-reviewed international review journal of geophysics and planetary sciences, affiliated with the European Geophysical Society. Covers the solid Earth, its oceans and atmosphere; solar-terrestrial phenomena; planets and space physics; hydrology; atmospheric physics;

meteorology; the magnetosphere and ionosphere; the geophysics of the moon and the terrestrial-type planets; and the physics of exploration for natural resources, including new developments in the methods and techniques of applied geophysics. **Subtitle:** Areas. **Freq:** Bimonthly. **Key Personnel:** Michael J. Rycroft, Managing Editor, michaelrycroft@btinternet.com; A. Cazenave, Editorial Board; P. Fabian, Assoc. Ed.; M. Coradini, Editorial Board. **ISSN:** 0169-3298. **Subscription Rates:** EUR954 institutions print incl. free access or e-only; EUR1,144 institutions print incl. enhanced access. **URL:** http://www.springer.com/earthsciences/geophysics/journal/10712.

48574 ■ Sustainability Science
Springer Netherlands
Van Godewijckstraat 30
3311 GX Dordrecht, Netherlands
Ph: 31 786 576210
Fax: 31 786 576744
Publisher E-mail: permissions.dordrecht@springer.com
Journal providing a platform for building sustainability science. **Freq:** Bimonthly. **Print Method:** Offset. **Trim Size:** 11 1/4 x 16. **Cols./Page:** 4. **Col. Width:** 14 picas. **Col. Depth:** 17 1/2 inches. **Key Personnel:** William Ascher, Editorial Advisor; Peter Marcotullio, Editor; Ronald D. Brunner, Editor; Luiz Di Bernardo, Editor; Joanne Kauffman, Editor; Cris Brack, Editor; Peter A. Wilderer, Editorial Advisor; Zafar Adeel, Editor; Kazuhiko Takeuchi, Editor-in-Chief; Garry Brewer, Editorial Advisor. **ISSN:** 1862-4065. **Subscription Rates:** EUR231 institutions print incl. free access or e-only; EUR277.20 institutions print incl. enhanced access. **URL:** http://www.springer.com/environment/environmentalmanagement/journal/11625.

48575 ■ Synthese
Springer Netherlands
Van Godewijckstraat 30
3311 GX Dordrecht, Netherlands
Ph: 31 786 576210
Fax: 31 786 576744
Publisher E-mail: permissions.dordrecht@springer.com
Journal covering epistemology, methodology and philosophy of science. **Subtitle:** An International Journal for Epistemology, Methodology and Philosophy of Science. **Freq:** 3/yr. **Print Method:** Offset. **Trim Size:** 9 x 11. **Cols./Page:** 3. **Col. Width:** 2 1/4 inches. **Col. Depth:** 9 3/4 inches. **Key Personnel:** John Symons, Editor-in-Chief; Vincent F. Hendricks, Editor-in-Chief; Robert van Rooij, Area Ed.; Raymond Dacey, Area Ed.; Luciano Floridi, Area Ed.; Jaakko Hintikka, Advisory Board; Peter Gardenfors, Advisory Board; Mark Bedau, Area Ed.; Wiebe van der Hoek, Editor-in-Chief. **ISSN:** 0039-7857. **Subscription Rates:** EUR2,379 institutions print incl. free access or e-only; EUR2,854.80 institutions print incl. enhanced access. **Remarks:** Accepts advertising. **URL:** http://www.springer.com/philosophy/logic/journal/11229. **Circ:** (Not Reported)

48576 ■ Systemic Practice and Action Research
Springer Netherlands
Van Godewijckstraat 30
3311 GX Dordrecht, Netherlands
Ph: 31 786 576210
Fax: 31 786 576744
Publisher E-mail: permissions.dordrecht@springer.com
Journal focusing the effects of technological advancement on society. **Freq:** Bimonthly. **Print Method:** Offset. **Trim Size:** 11 x 16 1/2. **Cols./Page:** 6. **Col. Width:** 10 1/4 inches. **Col. Depth:** 15.5 inches. **Key Personnel:** Russell Ackoff, International Advisory Committee; Ronald S.J. Tuninga, Assoc. Ed.; Jennifer Wilby, Book Reviews Ed.; Gabriele Bammer, International Advisory Committee; Stafford Beer, International Advisory Committee; John Brocklesby, International Advisory Committee; Simon Bell, Dep. Ed.; Peter Checkland, International Advisory Committee; David Coghlan, International Advisory Committee. **ISSN:** 1094-429X. **Subscription Rates:** EUR919 institutions print including free access or e-only; EUR1,102.80 institutions print including enhanced access. **Remarks:** Advertising accepted; rates available upon request. **URL:** http://www.springerlink.com/content/1094-429X. **Circ:** (Not Reported)

48577 ■ Theoretical Medicine and Bioethics
Springer Netherlands
Van Godewijckstraat 30
3311 GX Dordrecht, Netherlands
Ph: 31 786 576210
Fax: 31 786 576744

Publisher E-mail: permissions.dordrecht@springer.com
Journal dealing with the study of philosophy and methodology of medical practice and research. **Subtitle:** Philosophy of Medical Research and Practice. **Freq:** Bimonthly. **Key Personnel:** Daniel P. Sulmasy, Editor-in-Chief; Kazem Sadegh-Zadeh, Founding Ed.; Lynn A. Jansen, Co-Ed.; Joseph Mfutso-Bengo, Assoc. Ed.; Bernadette Tobin, Assoc. Ed. **ISSN:** 1386-7415. **Subscription Rates:** EUR682 institutions print incl. free access or e-only; EUR818.40 institutions print incl. enhanced access. **Remarks:** Accepts advertising. **URL:** http://springerlink.metapress.com/content/103004/. **Circ:** (Not Reported)

48578 ■ Theory and Decision
Springer Netherlands
Van Godewijckstraat 30
3311 GX Dordrecht, Netherlands
Ph: 31 786 576210
Fax: 31 786 576744
Publisher E-mail: permissions.dordrecht@springer.com
Journal dedicated to all aspects of decision making in psychology, management science, economics, the theory of games, statistics, operations research, artificial intelligence, cognitive science and analytical philosophy. **Subtitle:** An International Journal for Multidisciplinary Advances in Decision Science. **Freq:** Quarterly. **Key Personnel:** Mohammed Abdellaoui, Editor-in-Chief; J. Eichberger, Board of Coord. Ed.; D. Bouyssou, Board of Consulting Ed.; A. Montesano, Board of Consulting Ed.; H. Bleichrodt, Board of Coord. Ed.; F. Bloch, Board of Coord. Ed.; G.L. Eberlein, Honorary Board Member; A.C. Michalos, Honorary Board Member; B.R. Munier, Honorary Board Member; M. Allais, Board of Consulting Ed.; P. Suppes, Board of Consulting Ed.; M. Weber, Board of Consulting Ed. **ISSN:** 0040-5833. **Subscription Rates:** EUR1,153 institutions print incl. free access or e-only; EUR1,383.60 institutions print incl. enhanced access. **Remarks:** Advertising accepted; rates available upon request. **URL:** http://www.springer.com/economics/economictheory/journal/11238. **Circ:** (Not Reported)

48579 ■ Theory and Society
Springer Netherlands
Van Godewijckstraat 30
3311 GX Dordrecht, Netherlands
Ph: 31 786 576210
Fax: 31 786 576744
Publisher E-mail: permissions.dordrecht@springer.com
Scholarly journal covering theoretically informed analyses of social processes. **Subtitle:** Renewal and Critique in Social Theory. **Freq:** 6/yr. **Key Personnel:** Janet Gouldner, Exec. Ed., jgouldner@ucdavis.edu; Karen G. Lucas, Managing Editor, lucask@umsl.edu; Alvin W. Gouldner, Founding Ed.; Roger Brubaker, Editor; Anthony Giddens, Editor; Jaime Becker, Asst. Mng. Ed.; Raewyn Connell, Editor; Richard Swedberg, Editor. **ISSN:** 0304-2421. **Subscription Rates:** EUR720 institutions print incl. free access or e-only; EUR864 institutions print incl. enhanced access. **Remarks:** Advertising accepted; rates available upon request. **URL:** http://www.springer.com/socialsciences/sociology/journal/11186. **Circ:** (Not Reported)

48580 ■ Transition Metal Chemistry
Springer Netherlands
Van Godewijckstraat 30
3311 GX Dordrecht, Netherlands
Ph: 31 786 576210
Fax: 31 786 576744
Publisher E-mail: permissions.dordrecht@springer.com
Journal dealing with the properties and related topics on metal-based compounds. **Freq:** 8/yr. **Key Personnel:** Prof. David R.M. Walton, Founding Ed.; P.J. Dyson, Editorial Board; M.E. Light, Editorial Board; P. Chiusoli, Editorial Board; W.P. Griffith, Editorial Board; Dr. Marcus C. Durrant, Editor-in-Chief; M.V. Twigg, Editorial Board; R. Vilar, Editorial Board; S.L. James, Editorial Board. **ISSN:** 0340-4285. **Subscription Rates:** EUR2,643 institutions print incl. free access or e-only; EUR3,171.60 institutions print incl. enhanced access. **Remarks:** Accepts advertising. **URL:** http://www.springer.com/chemistry/journal/11243. **Circ:** (Not Reported)

48581 ■ Transport in Porous Media
Springer Netherlands
Van Godewijckstraat 30
3311 GX Dordrecht, Netherlands
Ph: 31 786 576210
Fax: 31 786 576744
Publisher E-mail: permissions.dordrecht@springer.com
Journal dealing with the physical and chemical aspects

Circulation: ★ = ABC; △ = BPA; ◆ = CAC; • = CCAB; ❏ = VAC; ⊕ = PO Statement; ‡ = Publisher's Report; Boldface figures = sworn; Light figures = estimated.

of transport of extensive quantities such as mass of a fluid phase, mass of a component of a phase, momentum and energy, in single and multiphase flow in a (possibly deformable) porous medium domain, as encountered in a variety of scientific and engineering disciplines. **Freq:** Triennial. **Key Personnel:** Jacob Bear, Editor; M. Blunt, Editorial Board; S. Kimura, Editorial Board. **ISSN:** 0169-3913. **Subscription Rates:** EUR2,036 institutions print incl. free access or e-only; EUR2,443.20 institutions print incl. enhanced access. **URL:** http://www.springer.com/geosciences/journal/11242.

48582 ▪ Transportation
Springer Netherlands
Van Godewijckstraat 30
3311 GX Dordrecht, Netherlands
Ph: 31 786 576210
Fax: 31 786 576744
Publisher E-mail: permissions.dordrecht@springer.com
Journal focusing on formulation of policy, the preparation and evaluation of plans, and the day-to-day operational management of transport systems. **Freq:** Bimonthly. **Key Personnel:** David T. Hartgen, Editor; Martin G. Richards, Editor-in-Chief; Kay Axhausen, Editor; Theo Arrentze, Editorial Advisory Board. **ISSN:** 0049-4488. **Subscription Rates:** EUR881 institutions print incl. free access or e-only; EUR1,057.20 institutions print incl. enhanced access. **Remarks:** Advertising accepted; rates available upon request. **URL:** http://www.springer.com/economics/regionalscience/journal/11116. **Circ:** (Not Reported)

48583 ▪ Tropical Animal Health and Production
Springer Netherlands
Van Godewijckstraat 30
3311 GX Dordrecht, Netherlands
Ph: 31 786 576210
Fax: 31 786 576744
Publisher E-mail: permissions.dordrecht@springer.com
Journal covering research, investigation and observation in any field of animal health, welfare and production in tropical and subtropical environments. **Freq:** 8/yr. **Key Personnel:** Leslie Harrison, Editor-in-Chief, leslie.harrison@ed.ac.uk; H. Everts, Consultant Scientific Ed.; M. Martin Curran, Consultant Scientific Ed. **ISSN:** 0049-4747. **Subscription Rates:** EUR1,200 institutions print incl. free access or e-only; EUR1,440 institutions print incl. enhanced access. **Remarks:** Advertising accepted; rates available upon request. **URL:** http://www.springer.com/medicine/journal/11250. **Circ:** (Not Reported)

48584 ▪ Urban Ecosystems
Springer Netherlands
Van Godewijckstraat 30
3311 GX Dordrecht, Netherlands
Ph: 31 786 576210
Fax: 31 786 576744
Publisher E-mail: permissions.dordrecht@springer.com
Journal devoted to ecology of urban environments and their policy implications. **Freq:** Quarterly. **Key Personnel:** Christopher P. Dunn, Editorial Board; Mark Felton, Editorial Board; Christine C. Harwell, Editorial Board; Gordon A. Bradley, Editorial Board; Paige S. Warren, Editorial Board; Sarel Cilliers, Editorial Board; Mark A. Harwell, Editorial Board; Glenn R. Guntenspergen, Editor-in-Chief; Lawrence A. Baker, Editorial Board. **ISSN:** 1083-8155. **Subscription Rates:** EUR396 institutions print including free access or e-only; EUR475.20 institutions print including enhanced access. **URL:** http://www.springerlink.com/content/100227/.

48585 ▪ User Modeling and User-Adapted Interaction
Springer Netherlands
Van Godewijckstraat 30
3311 GX Dordrecht, Netherlands
Ph: 31 786 576210
Fax: 31 786 576744
Publisher E-mail: permissions.dordrecht@springer.com
Journal devoted to modeling. **Freq:** 5/yr. **Key Personnel:** Peter Brusilovsky, Editorial Board; Liliane Ardissono, Editorial Board; Susan Dumais, Editorial Board; Sandra Carberry, Editorial Board; David Chin, Editorial Board; Alfred Kobsa, Editor; Gordon McCalla, Editorial Board; Mathias Bauer, Editorial Board; Lorrie Cranor, Editorial Board; Nicola Henze, Editorial Board. **ISSN:** 0924-1868. **Subscription Rates:** EUR677 institutions print including free access or e-only; EUR812.40 institutions print including enhanced access. **URL:** http://www.springer.com/computer/hci/journal/11257.

48586 ▪ Vietnam Journal of Mathematics
Springer Netherlands
Van Godewijckstraat 30

3311 GX Dordrecht, Netherlands
Ph: 31 786 576210
Fax: 31 786 576744
Publisher E-mail: permissions.dordrecht@springer.com
Journal of mathematics covering articles on regional and international scientific community. **Key Personnel:** Masami Ito, Editorial Board, ito@ksuvx0.kyoto-su.ac.jp; Le Hai Khoi, Editorial Board, lhkhoi@ioit.ncst.ac.vn; Dinh Van Huynh, Editorial Board; Phan Quoc Khanh, Editorial Board; Nguyen Khoa Son, Editor-in-Chief, nkson@thevinh.ac.vn; Hans George Bock, Editorial Board, bock@iwr.uni-heidelberg.de; Nguyen Huu Duc, Editorial Board; Do Cong Khanh, Editorial Board; Dinh Dung, Editorial Board, ddung@ioit.ncst.ac.vn; Nguyen Huu Viet Hung, Editorial Board. **ISSN:** 0866-7179. **URL:** http://www.springer.com/mathematics/journal/10013.

48587 ▪ Wireless Networks
Springer Netherlands
Van Godewijckstraat 30
3311 GX Dordrecht, Netherlands
Ph: 31 786 576210
Fax: 31 786 576744
Publisher E-mail: permissions.dordrecht@springer.com
Peer-reviewed scientific journal covering wireless communication and telecommunication. **Freq:** 8/yr. **Key Personnel:** Imrich Chlamtac, Editor-in-Chief. **ISSN:** 1022-0038. **Subscription Rates:** EUR762 institutions print incl. free access or e-only; EUR914 institutions print incl. enhanced access. **URL:** http://www.springerlink.com/content/101756/.

48588 ▪ World Wide Web
Springer Netherlands
Van Godewijckstraat 30
3311 GX Dordrecht, Netherlands
Ph: 31 786 576210
Fax: 31 786 576744
Publisher E-mail: permissions.dordrecht@springer.com
Peer-reviewed journal covering all aspects of the world wide web. **Freq:** Quarterly. **Key Personnel:** Marek Rusinkiewicz, Editor-in-Chief; Yanchun Zhang, Editor-in-Chief. **ISSN:** 1386-145X. **Subscription Rates:** EUR453 institutions print or online only; EUR543 institutions print and enhanced access. **URL:** http://www.springerlink.com/content/101757/.

Eindhoven

48589 ▪ E-Polymers
European Polymer Federation
Den Dolech 2
NL-5612 AZ Eindhoven, Netherlands
Online journal making novel scientific and technological results available both in academia and industry. **Key Personnel:** Hartwig Hocker, Editor-in-Chief, hoecker@e-polymers.org; Dr. Merina Rajan, Tech. Ed., rajan@e-polymers.org; Prof. Stanislaw Penczek, Editor-in-Chief, penczek@e-polymers.org; Prof. Stanislaw Slomkowski, Executive Ed., slomkowski@e-polymers.org. **ISSN:** 1618-7229. **URL:** http://www.e-polymers.org/.

48590 ▪ The Follies Journal
The Folly Fellowship
Tarantostraat 41
NL-5632 RE Eindhoven, Netherlands
Ph: 31 402423648
Professional journal covering landscape architecture. **Subtitle:** The International Magazine for Follies, Grottoes and Garden Buildings. **Founded:** 1988. **Freq:** Quarterly. **Key Personnel:** Michael Cousins, Editor, mcousins@grottoes.freeserve.co.uk; Pieter Boogaart, Managing Editor, prboogaart@hetnet.nl. **ISSN:** 0963-9004. **Subscription Rates:** 12 individuals; 8 members back issue; Free to members. **Remarks:** Accepts advertising. **URL:** http://www.follies.org.uk/journal.htm. **Circ:** (Not Reported)

48591 ▪ Gerontechnology
International Society for Gerontechnology
Den Dolech 2, Matrix 1.05
PO Box 513
NL-5600 MB Eindhoven, Netherlands
Ph: 31 402 475040
Fax: 31 402 475923
Publisher E-mail: info@gerontechnology.info
Journal with a commitment to tuning the balance between ageing, technology and the emerging knowledge-based society, reflecting the broad categories of interest in this field: health, housing, mobility, communication, leisure, and work. **Subtitle:** International

Journal on the Fundamental Aspects of Technology to Serve the Ageing Society. **Freq:** Quarterly. **ISSN:** 1569-1101. **Subscription Rates:** EUR100 members print and online; EUR25 students members, online; EUR400 libraries print and online; EUR500 institutions non-profit organisation; EUR1,500 institutions commercial organisation; EUR2,500 regional chapter. **URL:** http://www.gerontechjournal.net.

48592 ▪ Journal of Biomechanics
Mosby Inc.
Dept. of Biomedical Engineering
Wh4. 131
Eindhoven University of Technology
PO Box 513
NL-5600 MB Eindhoven, Netherlands
Publisher E-mail: custserv.ehs@elsevier.com
Journal publishing reports of original and substantial findings using the principles of mechanics to explore biological problems. **Freq:** 16/yr. **Key Personnel:** Rik Huiskes, Ed. Emeritus; Farshid Guilak, Editor-in-Chief; K. Ito, Editorial Consultant; G.A. Ateshian, Editorial Consultant; Frank P.T. Baaijens, Assoc. Ed.; R.N. Hinrichs, Editorial Board ASB Rep.; N. Stergiou, Editorial Board ASB Rep.; P. Prendergast, Editorial Consultant; T.P. Andriacchi, Editorial Advisory Board. **ISSN:** 0021-9290. **Subscription Rates:** US$513 other countries except Europe, Japan and Iran; 318 individuals; 60,600¥ individuals; 543,000¥ institutions; US$4,573 institutions for European countries and Iran; US$4,089 institutions, other countries except Europe, Japan and Iran. **Remarks:** Accepts advertising. **URL:** http://www.jbiomech.com/; http://www.elsevier.com/wps/find/journaldescription.cws_home/321/descriptiondescription. **Circ:** (Not Reported)

Enschede

48593 ▪ International Journal of Applied Earth Observation and Geoinformation
Elsevier Science
ITC International Institute for Geo-Information Science &
Dept. of Earth Observation Sciences (EOS)
NL-7500 AA Enschede, Netherlands
Publisher E-mail: nlinfo-f@elsevier.com
Publication covering photogrammetry. **Founded:** 2002. **Freq:** Quarterly. **Key Personnel:** Peter M. Atkinson, Assoc. Ed.; A.U. Frank, Assoc. Ed.; J. Dungan, Assoc. Ed.; A. Stein, Editor-in-Chief, stein@itc.nl; Y. Liu, Assoc. Ed.; M. Molenaar, Editorial Board. **ISSN:** 0303-2434. **Subscription Rates:** 56,500¥ institutions; US$479 institutions for all countries except Europe, Japan and Iran; EUR426 institutions for European countries and Iran; 9,900¥ individuals; US$83 individuals for all countries except Europe, Japan and Iran; EUR74 individuals for European countries and Iran. **Remarks:** Advertising accepted; rates available upon request. **URL:** http://www.elsevier.com/wps/find/journaldescription.cws_home/622741/descriptiondescription. **Formerly:** ITC Journal. **Circ:** (Not Reported)

48594 ▪ International Journal of Healthcare Technology and Management
Inderscience Enterprises Limited
c/o Dr. Koos Krabbendam, Assoc. Ed.
School of Business Public Administration & Technology
University of Twente
PO Box 217
7500 AE Enschede, Netherlands
Peer-reviewed journal covering the fields of management, economics, and the management of technology in healthcare. **Freq:** 6/yr. **Key Personnel:** Dr. Koos Krabbendam, Assoc. Ed.; Dr. M.A. Dorgham, Editor-in-Chief, editorial@inderscience.com; Dr. Eliezer Geisler, Assoc. Ed. **ISSN:** 1368-2156. **Subscription Rates:** EUR593 individuals print or online; EUR830 individuals print and online. **URL:** http://www.inderscience.com/browse/index.php?journalID=16.

48595 ▪ International Journal of Web-Based Communities
Inderscience Publishers
c/o Dr. Piet Kommers, Exec. Ed.
University of Twente, Faculty of Behavioral Science
Bldg. Cubicus, Rm. B319
PO Box 217
NL-7500 AE Enschede, Netherlands
Publisher E-mail: editor@inderscience.com
Peer-reviewed journal offering state of the art to practitioners such as communication managers, officers of public information services, web masters and those

who are responsible for online communities, publishing and integrating scientific results and acting as a catalyst to the rapidly developing culture of web communities. **Freq:** Quarterly. **Key Personnel:** Dr. Piet Kommers, Exec. Ed., kommers@edte.utwente.nl; Prof. Kazys Baniulis, Editorial Board Member; Dr. Pedro Isaias, Assoc. Ed.; Margriet Simmerling, Tech. Ed.; Dr. Labib Arafeh, Editorial Board Member; Dr. Rafik Aliev, Editorial Board Member. **ISSN:** 1477-8394. **Subscription Rates:** EUR494 individuals print only (surface mail); EUR840 individuals online only (2-3 users); EUR672 individuals print and online; EUR534 individuals print only (airmail). **URL:** http://www.inderscience.com/browse/index.php?journalCODE=ijwbc.

48596 ■ ISPRS Journal of Photogrammetry and Remote Sensing
Elsevier Science Inc.
c/o George Vosselman, Ed.-in-Ch.
ITC, Dept. of Earth Observation Science
Hengelosestraat 99
PO Box 6
Enschede, Netherlands
Ph: 31 53 487 4344
Fax: 31 53 487 4335
Publisher E-mail: usinfo-ehelp@elsevier.com
Peer-reviewed journal devoted to individuals who are members of the (ISPRS) photogrammetry and remote sensing, National Members (National Societies) and employees of ISPRS photogrammetry and remote sensing sustaining members. **Founded:** 1965. **Freq:** 6/yr. **Print Method:** Offset. **Trim Size:** 8 1/2 x 11. **Cols./Page:** 3. **Col. Width:** 2 1/4 inches. **Col. Depth:** 9 1/2 inches. **Key Personnel:** George Vosselman, Editor-in-Chief, vosselman@itc.nl; Eberhard Gulch, Assoc. Ed., phone 49 711121 2610, fax 49 711121 2556, eberhard.guelch@hft-stuttgart.de; Olaf Hellwich, Assoc. Ed., phone 49 303142 2796, fax 49 303142 1104, hellwich@fpk.tu-berlin.de; Q. Weng, Assoc. Ed., qweng@indstate.edu. **ISSN:** 0924-2716. **Subscription Rates:** 14,000¥ individuals; US$118 other countries except Europe, Japan and Iran; EUR106 individuals for European countries and Iran; EUR675 institutions for European countries and Iran; 89,600¥ institutions; US$757 institutions, other countries except Europe, Japan and Iran. **URL:** http://www.elsevier.com/wps/find/journaldescription.cws_home/503340/descriptiondescription.

48597 ■ Journal of Back and Musculoskeletal Rehabilitation
IOS Press, B.V.
c/o Prof. Hermie J. Hermens, Ed.-in-Ch.
Roessingh Research & Development
Roessinghsbleekweg 33b
NL-7522 AH Enschede, Netherlands
Ph: 31 53 4875702
Fax: 31 53 4340849
Publisher E-mail: info@iospress.nl
Peer-reviewed journal focusing on presenting practical information about the interdisciplinary approach to musculoskeletal rehabilitation for clinicians who treat patients with back and musculoskeletal pain complaints, providing readers with both a general fund of knowledge on the assessment and management of specific problems and new information considered to be state-of-the-art in the field. **Freq:** Quarterly. **Key Personnel:** Prof. Hermie J. Hermens, Editor-in-Chief, h.hermens@rrd.nl; Karen Snowden Nucker, Founding Ed.; Richard Aspden, Regional Ed., phone 44 1224 552767, fax 44 1224 559533, r.aspden@abdn.ac.uk. **ISSN:** 1053-8127. **Subscription Rates:** EUR458 individuals print and online; US$635 individuals print and online. **URL:** http://www.iospress.nl/loadtop/load.php?isbn=10538127.

Groningen

48598 ■ Cognitive Systems
European Society for the Study of Cognitive Systems
University of Groningen
Grote Kruisstraat 2/1
NL-9712 TS Groningen, Netherlands
Fax: 31 503 636304
Publisher E-mail: esscs@ppsw.rug.nl
Publication covering artificial intelligence. **Freq:** Periodic. **URL:** http://www.esscs.org/journal.php.

48599 ■ Computers in Industry
Elsevier Science Inc.
Faculty of Management & Organisation
University of Groningen

PO Box 800
9700 Groningen, Netherlands
Fax: 31 50 3632275
Publisher E-mail: usinfo-ehelp@elsevier.com
Peer-reviewed journal covering use of information and communication technology. **Founded:** 1980. **Freq:** 9/yr. **Key Personnel:** D.N. Batanov, Editorial Board; P. Bernus, Editorial Board; H. Wortmann, Editor-in-Chief; H.S. Jagdev, Editor-in-Chief; W. Shen, Assoc. Ed.; F.B. Vernadat, Assoc. Ed. **ISSN:** 0166-3615. **Subscription Rates:** 180,400¥ institutions; EUR1,358 institutions European countries and Iran; US$1,529 institutions, other countries except Europe, Japan and Iran. **URL:** http://www.elsevier.com/wps/find/journaldescription.cws_home/505646/descriptiondescription.

48600 ■ European Journal of Cardiovascular Nursing
Mosby Inc.
c/o T. Jaarsma, Ed.-in-Ch.
Dept. of Cardiology
University Medical Center Groningen
PO Box 30 001
NL-9700 RB Groningen, Netherlands
Publisher E-mail: custserv.ehs@elsevier.com
Journal for cardiology nurses. **Freq:** Quarterly. **Key Personnel:** T. Jaarsma, Editor-in-Chief, tiny.jaarsma@liu.se; D.R. Thompson, Co-Ed., david.thompson@acu.edu.au; P. Davidson, Editorial Board; B. Fridlund, Co-Ed., bengt.fridlund@omv.lu.se; K. Dracup, Editorial Board; H. Arthur, Editorial Board; A. Stromberg, Co-Ed., aanst@imv.liu.se; A. Brostrom, Editorial Board; C. Deaton, Editorial Board; K. King, Editorial Board; I. Ekman, Editorial Board. **ISSN:** 1474-5151. **Subscription Rates:** US$156 other countries except Europe, Japan and Iran; EUR138 individuals for European countries and Iran; 18,400¥ individuals; US$345 institutions, other countries except Europe, Japan and Iran; EUR308 institutions for European countries and Iran; 40,800¥ institutions. **Remarks:** Accepts advertising. **URL:** http://www.elsevier.com/wps/find/journaldescription.cws_home/622273/descriptiondescription; http://www.us.elsevierhealth.com/product.jsp?isbn=14745151. **Circ:** (Not Reported)

48601 ■ Indagationes Mathematicae
Elsevier Science Inc.
c/o H.W. Broer, Ed.-in-Ch.
Rijksuniversiteit Groningen
Groningen, Netherlands
Publisher E-mail: usinfo-ehelp@elsevier.com
Journal covering mathematical science. **Founded:** 1951. **Freq:** Quarterly. **Print Method:** Offset. **Trim Size:** 8 x 10 3/4. **Cols./Page:** 3. **Col. Width:** 27 nonpareils. **Col. Depth:** 140 agate lines. **Key Personnel:** F. Beukers, Editor; L.A. Peletier, Editor; M. Crainic, Editor; B. de Pagter, Editor; F. de Hollander, Editor. **ISSN:** 0019-3577. **Subscription Rates:** US$524 institutions, other countries except Europe, Japan and Iran; 62,300¥ institutions; EUR467 institutions for European countries and Iran. **URL:** http://www.elsevier.com/wps/find/journaldescription.cws_home/505620/descriptiondescription.

48602 ■ Indo-Iranian Journal
Brill Academic Publishers
c/o Hans Bakker, Ed.-in-Ch.
University of Groningen
PO Box 716
NL-9700 AS Groningen, Netherlands
Publisher E-mail: marketing@brill.nl
Peer-reviewed journal featuring Indo-Iranian language focusing on South Asia and pre-Islamic Iran's medieval and ancient languages and culture. **Founded:** 1957. **Freq:** Quarterly. **Key Personnel:** Hans Bakker, Editor-in-Chief, h.t.bakker@rug.nl; Jonathan Silk, Editor-in-Chief, j.a.silk.indoiranianjournal@gmail.com. **ISSN:** 0019-7246. **Subscription Rates:** EUR137 individuals; US$186 individuals; EUR414 institutions; US$563 institutions; EUR376 institutions online only; US$512 institutions online only. **URL:** http://www.brill.nl/iij.

48603 ■ International Journal of Lean Enterprise Research
Inderscience Enterprises Limited
PO Box Prof. Jannes Slomp, Ed.-in-Ch.
University of Groningen, Lean Operations Research Center
Faculty of Economics & Business
PO Box 800
9700 AV Groningen, Netherlands
Journal featuring the discussion on the principles and implementation of lean thinking. **Freq:** 4/yr. **Key Person-**

nel: Prof. Jannes Slomp, Editor-in-Chief, j.slomp@rug.nl. **ISSN:** 1754-2294. **Subscription Rates:** EUR494 individuals print or online; EUR672 individuals print and online. **URL:** http://www.inderscience.com/browse/index.php?journalID=258.

48604 ■ Wieler Revue
Wieler Revue b.v.
Postbus 5070
NL-9700 GB Groningen, Netherlands
Ph: 31 505 445830
Consumer magazine covering cycle racing worldwide. **Freq:** 17/yr. **Print Method:** Offset. **Trim Size:** 210 x 280 mm. **Col. Width:** 185 millimeters. **Col. Depth:** 250 millimeters. **Key Personnel:** D. Smeding, Mktg. & Sales. **Remarks:** Accepts advertising. **URL:** http://www.wielerrevue.nl. **Circ:** Combined 22,740

Haarlem

48605 ■ Computer!Totaal
IDG the Netherlands
Richard Holkade 8
2033 PZ Haarlem, Netherlands
Ph: 31 23 5461111
Fax: 31 23 546 1155
Publisher E-mail: info@idg.nl
Magazine covering articles on purchase and use of hardware and software. **Founded:** Jan. 1, 1992. **Freq:** Monthly. **Remarks:** Accepts advertising. **URL:** http://www.idg.com/www/IDGProducts.nsf/0/35B70897E98456A1852575F300582007. **Ad Rates:** 4C: 10,800 f. **Circ:** 134,000

The Hague

48606 ■ Amsterdam Real Estate City Book
Europe Real Estate Publishers
PO Box 84416
NL-2508 AK The Hague, Netherlands
Ph: 31 703 023300
Fax: 31 703 023330
Publisher E-mail: sales@europe-re.com
Publication featuring in-depth analysis of living, working, and shopping in Amsterdam. **Key Personnel:** Marinus Dijkman, Editor-in-Chief. **Subscription Rates:** EUR45 individuals (inclusive vat / exclusive post & package). **Remarks:** Accepts advertising. **URL:** http://www.amsterdam-re.com. **Circ:** (Not Reported)

48607 ■ Asian International Arbitration Journal
Kluwer Datalex
Kluwer Publishing Co.
PO Box 85889
The Hague, Netherlands
Ph: 31 78 6546454
Fax: 31 78 6546474
Publisher E-mail: services@wkap.nl
Journal covering legal arbitration throughout Asia. **Founded:** 2005. **Freq:** Semiannual. **Print Method:** Offset. **Trim Size:** 11 1/2 x 17. **Cols./Page:** 6. **Col. Width:** 24 nonpareils. **Col. Depth:** 336 agate lines. **Key Personnel:** Michael Pryles, Gen. Ed.; Philip Chan, Gen. Ed.; Sabiha Shiraz, Managing Editor; Zabrina Hamid, Asst. Ed. **ISSN:** 1574-3330. **Subscription Rates:** EUR260 individuals; US$266 individuals; 147 individuals online only. **URL:** http://www.kluwerlawonline.com/productinfo.php?pubcode=AIAJ.

48608 ■ Autokampioen
ANWB Media
PO Box 93557
NL-2509 AN The Hague, Netherlands
Publisher E-mail: orderverwerking@anwb.nl
Consumer magazine covering automobile techniques, racing and new products. **Founded:** 1908. **Freq:** Semimonthly. **Print Method:** Offset. **Cols./Page:** 4. **ISSN:** 0005-0997. **Subscription Rates:** EUR76.50 members; EUR89.76 nonmembers; EUR7.50 single issue. **Remarks:** Accepts advertising. **URL:** http://www.anwb.nl/webwinkel/tijdschriften/autokampioen. **Ad Rates:** BW: 3,428 f, 4C: 5,050 f. **Circ:** Controlled 55,000

48609 ■ Caravanserai
International Sufi Movement
Mouvement Soufi International
Banstraat 24
NL-2517 GJ The Hague, Netherlands
Publication E-mail: ic@sufimovement.org
Publisher E-mail: ihq@sufimovement.org
Publication covering Sufism. **Freq:** Annual. **Remarks:** Advertising not accepted. **URL:** http://www.

Circulation: ★ = ABC; △ = BPA; ♦ = CAC; • = CCAB; ❑ = VAC; ⊕ = PO Statement; ‡ = Publisher's Report; Boldface figures = sworn; Light figures = estimated.

Gale Directory of Publications & Broadcast Media/147th Ed.   5271

sufimovement.org/caravan.htm. **Circ:** (Not Reported)

48610 ■ Common Market Law Review
Kluwer Datalex
Kluwer Publishing Co.
PO Box 85889
The Hague, Netherlands
Ph: 31 78 6546454
Fax: 31 78 6546474
Publisher E-mail: services@wkap.nl
Law journal. **Founded:** 1991. **Freq:** Bimonthly. **Print Method:** Offset. **Trim Size:** 13 1/2 x 22. **Cols./Page:** 8. **Col. Width:** 1 5/8 inches. **Col. Depth:** 21 inches. **Key Personnel:** Alan Dashwood, Editor; Piet Jan Slot, Editor. **ISSN:** 0165-0750. **Subscription Rates:** US$965 individuals; EUR682 individuals; 502 individuals; EUR887 individuals combo; US$1,254 individuals combo; 652 individuals combo. **URL:** http://www2.warwick.ac.uk/fac/soc/law/elj/directory/c/cmlr/; http://www.kluwerlawonline.com/productinfo.php?pubcode=COLA.

48611 ■ De Architect
Postbus 49
NL-2501 The Hague, Netherlands
Ph: 31 703 789911
Fax: 31 703 854321
Publication E-mail: architect@sdu.nl
Publisher E-mail: architect@sdu.nl
Professional design magazine covering architecture, town planning, interior design and technology. **Founded:** 1970. **Freq:** 16/yr. **Key Personnel:** Harm Tilman, Contact, phone 31 703 780406, h.tilman@sdu.nl; Sander Woertman, Contact, phone 31 703 780316, s.woertman@sdu.nl; Nienke Abma-Stuivenberg, Contact, phone 31 703 780310, n.abma@sdu.nl. **ISSN:** 0925-6830. **Subscription Rates:** EUR55 individuals. **Remarks:** Accepts advertising. **URL:** http://dearchitect.sdu.nl/do/welkom. **Circ:** Combined 8,192

48612 ■ Democraat
Political Party Democrats 66
Politieke Partij Democraten 66
PO Box 660
NL-2501 CR The Hague, Netherlands
Ph: 31 703 566066
Fax: 31 703 641917
Publication E-mail: r.de.vries@d66.nl
Publisher E-mail: international@d66.nl
Dutch language publication covering political parties. **Founded:** 1967. **Freq:** Quarterly. **URL:** http://www.d66.nl; http://democrats.nl/d66.html. **Circ:** Non-paid 12,500

48613 ■ EC Tax Review
Kluwer Datalex
Kluwer Publishing Co.
PO Box 85889
The Hague, Netherlands
Ph: 31 78 6546454
Fax: 31 78 6546474
Publisher E-mail: services@wkap.nl
Journal covering information about European taxation. **Founded:** Oct. 1957. **Freq:** 6/yr. **Print Method:** Offset. **Trim Size:** 8 3/8 x 10 7/8. **Cols./Page:** 2 and 3. **Col. Width:** 20 and 13.5 picas. **Col. Depth:** 54 picas. **Key Personnel:** B.J. Kiekebeld, Editor. **ISSN:** 0928-2750. **Subscription Rates:** EUR474 individuals; US$632 individuals; 349 individuals; EUR616 individuals combo; US$822 individuals combo; 454 individuals combo. **URL:** http://www.kluwerlawonline.com/productinfo.php?pubcode=ECTA.

48614 ■ Europa Nostra
Europa Nostra Pan European Federation for Heritage
35 Lange Voorhout
NL-2514 EC The Hague, Netherlands
Ph: 31 70 3024050
Fax: 31 70 3617865
Publisher E-mail: info@europanostra.org
English and French language publication covering historic preservation. **Founded:** 1999. **Freq:** Annual. **Key Personnel:** Prof. Gianni Perbellini, Contact. **URL:** http://www.europanostra.org. **Formerly:** European Cultural Heritage Review.

48615 ■ European Business Law Review
Kluwer Datalex
Kluwer Publishing Co.
PO Box 85889
The Hague, Netherlands
Ph: 31 78 6546454
Fax: 31 78 6546474

Publisher E-mail: services@wkap.nl
Journal covering analysis of business law including both European Community law and the laws of the member states and other European countries. **Key Personnel:** Mads Andenas, Editor-in-Chief. **ISSN:** 0959-6941. **Subscription Rates:** EUR962 individuals print and online; US$1,282 individuals print and online; 707 individuals print and online; EUR740 individuals; US$986 individuals; 544 individuals. **URL:** http://www.kluwerlawonline.com/productinfo.php?pubcode=EULR.

48616 ■ Forum
Confederation of Netherlands Industry and Employers
PO Box 93002
NL-2509 AA The Hague, Netherlands
Ph: 31 703 490349
Fax: 31 703 490300
Publication E-mail: forum@vno.ncw.nl
Publisher E-mail: informatie@vno-ncw.nl
Dutch language publication covering politics, economy and entrepreneurship. **Subtitle:** Voor Ondernemend Nederland. **Founded:** Sept. 1, 1995. **Freq:** Semiweekly. **Key Personnel:** Paul van Lith, Contact, lith@vno-ncw.nl. **ISSN:** 1384-2102. **Remarks:** Accepts advertising. **URL:** http://www.vno-ncw.nl. **Circ:** Non-paid 30,000

48617 ■ Hivos Magazine
Humanist Institute for Co-Operation with Developing Countries
Instituto Humanista para la Cooperacion con los Paises en Desarrollo
PO Box 85565
NL-2508 CG The Hague, Netherlands
Ph: 31 703 765500
Fax: 31 703 624600
Publisher E-mail: info@hivos.nl
Dutch language magazine covering worldwide development. **Freq:** Quarterly. **Key Personnel:** A.P. Van Den Ham, Dir. Prog. and Proj.; M.M. Monteiro, Chm. **URL:** http://www.hivos.nl/english.

48618 ■ The International Sports Law Journal
Asser International Sports Law Centre
PO Box 30461
NL-2500 GL The Hague, Netherlands
Ph: 31 70 3420300
Fax: 31 70 3420359
Publisher E-mail: info@asser.nl
Journal commenting upon and informing those interested in sports and the law - whether academics, practitioners or others - about "legally relevant" developments in the world of sport in a national and international perspective. **Founded:** 2002. **URL:** http://www.asser.nl/Default.aspx?site_id=11&level1=13908&level2=13941.

48619 ■ Kampioen
ANWB Media
PO Box 93557
NL-2509 AN The Hague, Netherlands
Publication E-mail: kampioen@anwb.nl
Publisher E-mail: orderverwerking@anwb.nl
Magazine of The Royal Touring Club of The Netherlands for members covering travel, tourism, camping, winter sports and related issues. **Founded:** June 1885. **Freq:** 11/yr. **Cols./Page:** 3. **Remarks:** Accepts advertising. **URL:** http://www.kampioen.nl/published/kmp/content/paginas/HOMEPAGE.nl.html. **Circ:** Controlled 3,531,785

48620 ■ KCK
ANWB Media
PO Box 93557
NL-2509 AN The Hague, Netherlands
Publication E-mail: kck@anwb.nl
Publisher E-mail: orderverwerking@anwb.nl
Consumer magazine covering camping. **Founded:** 1941. **Freq:** Monthly. **Print Method:** Offset. **Cols./Page:** 3. **Key Personnel:** Harinck William Dick, Managing Editor; Gerhard-Paul Wisgerhof, Editor. **ISSN:** 0165-4128. **Subscription Rates:** EUR45 individuals; EUR6.25 single issue; EUR61.95 members; EUR72.50 nonmembers. **Remarks:** Accepts advertising. **URL:** http://kampeerencaravankampioen.nl/published/kck/content/paginas/kck-het-tijdschrift.nl.html. **Circ:** Controlled 158,581

48621 ■ Leiden Journal of International Law
Cambridge University Press
c/o Larissa Van Den Herik, Ed.-in-Ch.
PO Box 13228
NL-2501 EE The Hague, Netherlands
Publisher E-mail: customer_service@cup.org
Journal covering international law including international

legal theory and dispute settlement. **Founded:** 1979. **Freq:** Bimonthly. **Print Method:** Offset. **Trim Size:** 8 1/2 x 11. **Cols./Page:** 3. **Col. Depth:** 140 agate lines. **Key Personnel:** Larissa Van Den Herik, Editor-in-Chief, ljil@law.leidenuniv.nl; Jean D'Aspremont, Editor; Fleur Johns, Editor. **ISSN:** 0922-1565. **Subscription Rates:** 192 institutions online and print; US$311 institutions online and print; 171 institutions online; US$275 institutions online; 31 individuals print only; US$46 individuals print only. **URL:** http://journals.cambridge.org/action/displayJournal?jid=LJL. **Circ:** 500

48622 ■ Marineblad
Koninklijke Vereniging van Marineofficieren
Wassaenaarseweg 2 B
NL-2596 The Hague, Netherlands
Ph: 31 70 3839504
Fax: 31 70 3835911
Publication E-mail: marineblad@kvmo.nl
Publisher E-mail: info@kvmo.nl
Journal covering naval and defense issues. **Founded:** 1886. **Freq:** Monthly 11/yr. **ISSN:** 0025-3340. **URL:** http://www.kvmo.nl/marineblad/index.html. **Circ:** Controlled 6,000

48623 ■ Op Pad
ANWB Media
PO Box 93557
NL-2509 AN The Hague, Netherlands
Publication E-mail: oppad@anwb.nl
Publisher E-mail: orderverwerking@anwb.nl
Consumer magazine covering camping, hiking, cycling and canoeing. **Founded:** 1983. **Freq:** 8/yr. **Print Method:** Offset. **Cols./Page:** 3. **Key Personnel:** Bert Gorissen, Editor; Petra Strijdhorst, Editor; Shiva Janssen, Editor. **ISSN:** 0168-3845. **Subscription Rates:** EUR45.95 individuals for non members; EUR43.95 other countries; EUR5.50 single issue. **Remarks:** Accepts advertising. **URL:** http://www.oppad.nl/published/opp/content/pages/homepage/homepage-oppad.nlhtml. **Ad Rates:** 4C: 4.998 f. **Circ:** Controlled 35,796

48624 ■ Oud Hollad
Brill Academic Publishers
Netherlands Institute for Art History
PO Box 90418
NL-2509 LK The Hague, Netherlands
Publication E-mail: oudholland@rkd.nl
Publisher E-mail: marketing@brill.nl
Journal featuring information on visual arts and art history. **Subtitle:** Quarterly for Dutch Art History. **Founded:** 1883. **Freq:** Quarterly. **Key Personnel:** Nathalie Dufais, Editor, dufais@rkd.nl. **ISSN:** 0030-672X. **Subscription Rates:** EUR72 individuals print only; US$176 individuals print only; EUR130 institutions print and electronic; US$176 institutions print and electronic; EUR108 institutions online only; US$147 institutions online only; EUR119 institutions print only; US$162 institutions print only. **URL:** http://www.brill.nl/ohd.

48625 ■ Pharmacy Education
International Pharmaceutical Federation
PO Box 84200
NL-2508 The Hague, Netherlands
Ph: 31 70 3021970
Fax: 31 70 3021999
Publisher E-mail: fip@fip.org
Journal providing a forum for communication between academic teachers and practitioners, with an emphasis on new and established teaching and learning methods; new curriculum and syllabus directions; guidance on structuring courses and assessing achievement as well as the dissemination of new ideas. **Subtitle:** An International Journal for Pharmaceutical Education. **Freq:** Quarterly. **Key Personnel:** Prof. Ian Bates, Editor-in-Chief, pharmacy.education@pharmacy.ac.uk; J. Atkinson, Editorial Board; Sarah Carter, Editor; Prof. Peter Bouhuijs, Editorial Board; Prof. Kevin Taylor, Editorial Board; Prof. Zubin Austin, Editorial Board; Mr. Mike Rouse, Editorial Board. **ISSN:** 1560-2214. **Remarks:** Accepts advertising. **URL:** http://www.fip.org/news_publications?page=publications; http://pharmacyeducation.fip.org/. **Circ:** (Not Reported)

48626 ■ Pro Motor
ANWB Media
PO Box 93557
NL-2509 AN The Hague, Netherlands
Publisher E-mail: orderverwerking@anwb.nl
Consumer magazine covering motorcycles for hobbyists. **Founded:** 1990. **Freq:** 10/yr. **Print Method:** Offset.

Cols./Page: 3. **ISSN:** 1381-0154. **Subscription Rates:** 4,895 f Free to qualified subscribers; EUR578 members; EUR578 single issue. **Remarks:** Accepts advertising. **URL:** http://www.promotor.nl/published/prm/content/pages/homepage_prm.nl.html. **Ad Rates:** 4C: 3 f. **Circ:** Controlled 38,217

48627 ■ Reizen
ANWB Media
PO Box 93557
NL-2509 AN The Hague, Netherlands
Publisher E-mail: orderverwerking@anwb.nl
Consumer magazine covering adventure and tourism. **Founded:** 1937. **Freq:** 11/yr. **Print Method:** Offset. **Cols./Page:** 4. **ISSN:** 0921-0032. **Subscription Rates:** EUR29.90 individuals. **URL:** http://www.anwb.nl/webwinkel/tijdschriften/REIZEN-magazine. **Circ:** 55,350

48628 ■ Terra et Aqua
International Association of Dredging Cos.
Alexanderveld 84
NL-2585 DB The Hague, Netherlands
Ph: 31 703 523334
Fax: 31 703 512654
Publication E-mail: terra@iadc-dredging.com
Publisher E-mail: info@iadc-dredging.com
Marine industries publication. **Subtitle:** International Journal on Public Works, Ports and Waterways. **Freq:** Quarterly. **Key Personnel:** Marsha R. Cohen, Editor. **ISSN:** 0376-6411. **Subscription Rates:** Free upon request. **Remarks:** Advertising not accepted. **URL:** http://www.iadc-dredging.com; http://www.terra-et-aqua.com/. **Circ:** (Not Reported)

48629 ■ Waterkampioen
ANWB Media
PO Box 93557
NL-2509 AN The Hague, Netherlands
Publisher E-mail: orderverwerking@anwb.nl
Consumer magazine covering water sports, water travel, ship building and related activities. **Founded:** 1927. **Freq:** 20/yr. **Print Method:** Offset. **Cols./Page:** 3. **ISSN:** 0043-1451. **Subscription Rates:** EUR77.95 members; EUR89.95 nonmembers; EUR7.50 single issue; EUR4.55 single issue; EUR7 individuals Belgium; EUR9 individuals Europe; EUR11 individuals outside Europe. **Remarks:** Accepts advertising. **URL:** http://www.waterkampioen.nl/published/wkm/content/pages/homepage.nl.html. **Ad Rates:** BW: 4,436 f, 4C: 6,042 f. **Circ:** Controlled 37,940

Heerlen

48630 ■ Technology and Disability
IOS Press, B.V.
c/o Dr. Ir. Mathijs Soede, Ed.-in-Ch.
Centre of Research in Technology & Care
Zuyd University
PO Box 550
NL-6400 AN Heerlen, Netherlands
Ph: 31 45 4006521
Publisher E-mail: info@iospress.nl
Journal communicating knowledge about the field of assistive technology devices and services, within the context of the lives of end users-persons with disabilities and their family members, covering research and development efforts, education and training programs, service and policy activities and consumer experiences. **Freq:** Quarterly. **Key Personnel:** Dr. Ir. Mathijs Soede, Editor-in-Chief, m.soede@hszuyd.nl; R. Andrich, Editorial Board. **ISSN:** 1055-4181. **Subscription Rates:** EUR458 institutions print and online; US$630 institutions print and online. **URL:** http://www.iospress.nl/loadtop/load.php?isbn=10554181.

Hilversum

48631 ■ Mental Health Reforms
Global Initiative on Psychiatry
PO Box 1282
NL-1200 BG Hilversum, Netherlands
Ph: 31 356 838727
Fax: 31 356 833646
Publisher E-mail: hilversum@gip-global.org
Publication covering human rights and mental health reform. **Founded:** 1999. **Freq:** Quarterly. **Subscription Rates:** EUR40 individuals; EUR7.50 single issue + postal costs. **Remarks:** Advertising not accepted. **URL:** http://www.gip-global.org/p/28/133/ms9-0/mental-health-reforms. **Circ:** 1,000

48632 ■ Amsterdam-FM - 104.4
Postbus 813

NL-1200 AV Hilversum, Netherlands
Ph: 31 35 6263040
Format: Ethnic; Contemporary Hit Radio (CHR). **Founded:** July 8, 2006. **Operating Hours:** Continuous. **Ad Rates:** Advertising accepted; rates available upon request. **URL:** http://www.100p.nl.

48633 ■ Apeldoorn-FM - 88.2
Postbus 813
NL-1200 AV Hilversum, Netherlands
Ph: 31 35 6263040
Format: Ethnic; World Beat. **Operating Hours:** Continuous. **Ad Rates:** Advertising accepted; rates available upon request. **URL:** http://www.100p.nl.

48634 ■ Arnhem-FM - 87.8
Postbus 813
NL-1200 AV Hilversum, Netherlands
Ph: 31 35 6263040
Format: Ethnic; World Beat. **Operating Hours:** Continuous. **Ad Rates:** Advertising accepted; rates available upon request. **URL:** http://www.100p.nl.

48635 ■ Enschede-FM - 99.1
Postbus 813
NL-1200 AV Hilversum, Netherlands
Ph: 31 35 6263040
E-mail: sales@100p.nl
Format: Ethnic; World Beat. **Owner:** 100%NL, at above address. **Operating Hours:** Continuous. **URL:** http://www.100p.nl.

48636 ■ Flevoland-FM - 104.4
Postbus 813
NL-1200 AV Hilversum, Netherlands
Ph: 31 35 6263040
E-mail: sales@100p.nl
Format: Ethnic; World Beat. **Owner:** 100%NL, at above address. **Operating Hours:** 18 hours Daily. **URL:** http://www.100p.nl.

48637 ■ Haarlem-FM - 93.8
Postbus 813
NL-1200 AV Hilversum, Netherlands
Ph: 31 35 6263040
E-mail: sales@100p.nl
Format: Ethnic; World Beat. **Owner:** 100%NL, at above address. **Operating Hours:** 18 hours Daily. **URL:** http://www.100p.nl.

Houten

48638 ■ Basin Research
European Association of Geoscientists and Engineers
PO Box 59
NL-3990 DB Houten, Netherlands
Ph: 31 88 995055
Fax: 31 30 6343524
Publisher E-mail: eage@eage.org
Geoscience publication. **Freq:** Bimonthly. **Key Personnel:** P. Decelles, Editorial Board; J. Cartwright, Editorial Board; H.D. Sinclair, Editorial Board; W. Cavazza, Editorial Board; J.F. Dewey, Editorial Board; P.A. Allen, Editorial Board; Michelle Kominz, Editor, michelle.kominz@wmioh.odu; Joffroy Nunn, Editor, joff@gool.lcu.edu; R.S. Anderson, Editorial Board; D.W. Burbank, Editorial Board. **ISSN:** 0950-091X. **Remarks:** Advertising not accepted. **URL:** http://www.eage.org/index.php?evp=1180&ActiveMenu=21&Opendivs=s10,s14,s27; http://www.wiley.com/bw/journal.asp?ref=0950-091X. **Circ:** (Not Reported)

48639 ■ First Break
European Association of Geoscientists and Engineers
PO Box 59
NL-3990 DB Houten, Netherlands
Ph: 31 88 995055
Fax: 31 30 6343524
Publisher E-mail: eage@eage.org
Geoscience publication. **Freq:** Monthly. **Key Personnel:** Salima Gader, Contact, sgr@eage.org. **ISSN:** 0263-5046. **Subscription Rates:** EUR901.95 institutions. **URL:** http://www.eage.org/index.php?evp=1168&ActiveMenu=9&Opendivs=s10,s14,s15; http://www.firstbreak.org/. **Circ:** 25,000

48640 ■ Geophysical Prospecting
European Association of Geoscientists and Engineers
PO Box 59
NL-3990 DB Houten, Netherlands
Ph: 31 88 995055

Fax: 31 30 6343524
Publisher E-mail: eage@eage.org
Geoscience publication. **Freq:** Bimonthly. **Key Personnel:** Tijmen Jan Moser, Editor-in-Chief; Helmut Jakubowicz, Dep. Ed.; Evgeny Landa, Dep. Ed. **ISSN:** 0016-8025. **Remarks:** Accepts advertising. **URL:** http://www.eage.org/index.php?evp=1188&ActiveMenu=29&Opendivs=s10,s14,s35. **Ad Rates:** BW: 1,520 f, 4C: 3,195 f. **Circ:** ‡8,841

Leiden

48641 ■ Advanced Composite Materials
Brill Academic Publishers
PO Box 9000
NL-2300 PA Leiden, Netherlands
Ph: 31 71 5353500
Fax: 31 71 5317532
Publisher E-mail: marketing@brill.nl
Peer-reviewed journal covering the field of composite materials and their structures. **Freq:** 4/yr. **Key Personnel:** Y. Kogo Chiba, Editor-in-Chief; Chun-Gon Kim, Editor-in-Chief. **ISSN:** 0924-3046. **Subscription Rates:** EUR845 institutions print and electronic; US$1,150 institutions print and electronic; EUR704 institutions online only; US$958 institutions online only; EUR774 institutions print only; US$1,054 institutions print only. **URL:** http://www.brill.nl/acm.

48642 ■ Advanced Robotics
Brill Academic Publishers
PO Box 9000
NL-2300 PA Leiden, Netherlands
Ph: 31 71 5353500
Fax: 31 71 5317532
Publisher E-mail: marketing@brill.nl
Journal dealing with the aspects of research on robotics science and engineering by highlighting the work done in Japan, in connection with the Robotics Society of Japan. **Freq:** 15/yr. **Key Personnel:** Dr. Kazuhiro Kosuge, Advisory Board; Fumihito Arai, Editor; Koh Hosoda, Committee of RSJ International Journal; Shigeki Sugano, Editor-in-Chief. **ISSN:** 0169-1864. **Subscription Rates:** EUR2,036 institutions electronic and print; US$2,790 institutions electronic and print; EUR1,697 institutions online only; US$2,310 institutions online only; EUR1,867 institutions print only; US$2,541 institutions print only. **URL:** http://www.brill.nl/default.aspx?partid=18&pid=9713.

48643 ■ African and Asian Studies
Brill Academic Publishers
PO Box 9000
NL-2300 PA Leiden, Netherlands
Ph: 31 71 5353500
Fax: 31 71 5317532
Publisher E-mail: marketing@brill.nl
Journal publishing original research by social scientists in the area of anthropology, sociology, history, political science and related social sciences about African and Asian societies and cultures and their relationships. **Freq:** 4/yr. **Key Personnel:** Tukumbi Lumumba Kasongo, Editor; Prof. Funwi Ayuninjam, Editorial Board; Prof. Jerry Bentley, Editorial Board; Prof. Mohamadou Diallo, Editorial Board. **ISSN:** 1569-2094. **Subscription Rates:** EUR91 individuals print; US$124 individuals print; EUR301 institutions electronic and print; US$410 institutions electronic and print; EUR251 institutions online only; US$376 institutions online only. **URL:** http://www.brill.nl/product.asp?id=10254.

48644 ■ African Diaspora
Brill Academic Publishers
PO Box 9000
NL-2300 PA Leiden, Netherlands
Ph: 31 71 5353500
Fax: 31 71 5317532
Publication E-mail: afdi@brill.nl
Publisher E-mail: marketing@brill.nl
Peer-reviewed journal featuring articles on African culture focusing on their migration and diaspora. **Subtitle:** A Journal of Transnational Africa in a Global World. **Freq:** Semiannual. **Key Personnel:** Kristine Krause, Editorial Board; Rijk van Dijk, Editorial Board; John Thornton, Editorial Board. **ISSN:** 1872-5457. **Subscription Rates:** EUR52 individuals; US$71 individuals; EUR157 institutions; US$215 institutions; EUR143 institutions online only; US$195 institutions online only. **URL:** http://www.brill.nl/afdi.

48645 ■ Amphibia-Reptilia
Brill Academic Publishers

PO Box 9000
NL-2300 PA Leiden, Netherlands
Ph: 31 71 5353500
Fax: 31 71 5317532
Publisher E-mail: marketing@brill.nl
Publication covering herpetology. **Founded:** 1980. **Freq:** 4/yr. **Trim Size:** 160 x 240 mm. **Key Personnel:** Dr. Mathieu Denoel, Editor; Dr. Luca Luiselli, Assoc. Ed.; Dr. D. James Harris, Editor. **ISSN:** 0173-5373. **Subscription Rates:** EUR151 individuals print; US$206 individuals print; EUR498 institutions electronic & print; US$678 institutions electronic & print; EUR415 institutions online only; US$565 institutions online only; EUR457 institutions print; US$622 institutions print. **Remarks:** Advertising accepted; rates available upon request. **URL:** http://www.brill.nl/default.aspx?partid=212&pid=7101. **Circ:** (Not Reported)

48646 ■ Ancient Civilizations from Scythia to Siberia
Brill Academic Publishers
PO Box 9000
NL-2300 PA Leiden, Netherlands
Ph: 31 71 5353500
Fax: 31 71 5317532
Publisher E-mail: marketing@brill.nl
Journal covering the history, archaeology, numismatics, epigraphy, and papyrology of material culture. **Subtitle:** An International Journal of Comparative Studies in History and Archaeology. **Founded:** May 22, 1897. **Freq:** 2/yr. **Print Method:** Offset. **Trim Size:** 10 x 16. **Cols./Page:** 5. **Col. Width:** 11 picas. **Col. Depth:** 16 inches. **Key Personnel:** G. Bongard-Levin, Editor-in-Chief; G. Gnoli, Editor-in-Chief; A. Ivantchik, Editor-in-Chief; N. Boroffka, Editorial Board; P. Callieri, Editorial Board. **ISSN:** 0929-077X. **Subscription Rates:** EUR95 individuals print only; US$129 individuals print only; EUR316 institutions print and electronic; US$429 institutions print and electronic; EUR263 institutions online only; US$358 institutions online only; EUR289 institutions print only; US$394 institutions print only. **URL:** http://www.brill.nl/acss.

48647 ■ Animal Biology
Brill Academic Publishers
PO Box 9000
NL-2300 PA Leiden, Netherlands
Ph: 31 71 5353500
Fax: 31 71 5317532
Publisher E-mail: marketing@brill.nl
Journal covering zoology, including ecology, behavior, evolution, morphology, neurobiology, developmental biology, physiology, cognition, endocrinology, systematic, genomic and theoretical biology. **Founded:** 1949. **Freq:** 4/yr. **Print Method:** Web offset. **Trim Size:** 11 1/2 x 14 1/2. **Cols./Page:** 4. **Col. Width:** 2 3/8 inches. **Col. Depth:** 13 1/4 inches. **Key Personnel:** M. Muller, Managing Editor, animal.biology@wur.nl. **ISSN:** 1570-7555. **Subscription Rates:** EUR151 individuals print only; US$206 individuals print only; EUR498 institutions print and electronic; US$678 institutions print and electronic; EUR415 institutions online only; US$565 institutions online only; EUR457 institutions print only; US$622 institutions print only. **URL:** http://www.brill.nl/ab.

48648 ■ Applied Herpetology
Brill Academic Publishers
PO Box 9000
NL-2300 PA Leiden, Netherlands
Ph: 31 71 5353500
Fax: 31 71 5317532
Publisher E-mail: marketing@brill.nl
Journal addressing research on amphibians and reptiles with a focus on biodiversity, conservation, environmental monitoring, farming, natural products development and wildlife management. **Freq:** 4/yr. **Key Personnel:** Dr. M.J. Tyler, Editor-in-Chief; Dr. A. Hailey, Managing Editor. **ISSN:** 1570-7539. **URL:** http://www.brill.nl/ah.

48649 ■ Arab Law Quarterly
Brill Academic Publishers
PO Box 9000
NL-2300 PA Leiden, Netherlands
Ph: 31 71 5353500
Fax: 31 71 5317532
Publisher E-mail: marketing@brill.nl
Journal covering Arab laws, both Sharia and secular. Subject areas covered include Arab laws in transnational affairs, commercial law, Islamic law, and international comparative law. **Founded:** 1892. **Freq:** 4/yr. **Print Method:** Letterpress. **Trim Size:** 13 x 22. **Cols./Page:** 6. **Col. Width:** 2 1/16 inches. **Col. Depth:**

22 inches. **Key Personnel:** M.A.K. Afridi, Editorial Board; Husain Al Baharna, Editorial Board; Dr. Ahmed Al-Melhem, Editorial Board; Dr. Sabah Al-Mukhtar, Editorial Board; Ann E. Mayer, Editorial Board; Mark S.W. Hoyle, Editor-in-Chief, markhoyle@tanfieldchambers.co.uk. **ISSN:** 0268-0556. **Subscription Rates:** EUR193 individuals print only; US$263 individuals print only; EUR701 institutions print and electronic; US$954 institutions print and electronic; EUR584 institutions online only; US$795 institutions online only; EUR642 institutions print only; US$875 institutions print only. **URL:** http://www.brill.nl/alq.

48650 ■ Arabica
Brill Academic Publishers
PO Box 9000
NL-2300 PA Leiden, Netherlands
Ph: 31 71 5353500
Fax: 31 71 5317532
Publisher E-mail: marketing@brill.nl
Journal covering studies, documents, and notes on the language, literature, history and civilization of the Arab world, with emphasis on multidisciplinary studies and contemporary problems concerning Arab societies. **Founded:** 1944. **Freq:** 6/yr. **Print Method:** Offset. **Trim Size:** 8 1/2 x 11. **Cols./Page:** 3. **Col. Width:** 28 nonpareils. **Col. Depth:** 140 agate lines. **Key Personnel:** M. Arkoun, Editor; A. Cheikh-Moussa, Editor; J. Chabbi, Editorial Board; M.A. Amir-Moezzi, Editorial Board. **ISSN:** 0570-5398. **Subscription Rates:** EUR150 individuals print only; US$206 individuals print only; EUR496 institutions print and electronic; US$675 institutions print and electronic; EUR413 institutions online only; US$562 institutions online only; EUR454 institutions print only; US$618 institutions print only. **URL:** http://www.brill.nl/arab.

48651 ■ Archive for the Psychology of Religion
Brill Academic Publishers
PO Box 9000
NL-2300 PA Leiden, Netherlands
Ph: 31 71 5353500
Fax: 31 71 5317532
Publisher E-mail: marketing@brill.nl
Peer-reviewed journal covering psychology of religion. **Founded:** Apr. 1925. **Freq:** Annual. **Print Method:** Offset. **Trim Size:** 9 x 12. **Cols./Page:** 2. **Col. Width:** 42 nonpareils. **Col. Depth:** 140 agate lines. **Key Personnel:** Heinz Streib, Editor; James Day, Editor; Ralph W. Hood, Jr., Editor. **ISSN:** 0084-6724. **Subscription Rates:** EUR50 individuals print only; US$68 individuals print only; EUR163 institutions print and electronic; US$222 institutions print and electronic; EUR136 institutions online only; US$185 institutions online only; EUR150 institutions print only; US$204 institutions print only. **URL:** http://www.brill.nl/default.aspx?partid=18&pid=22615.

48652 ■ Aries
Brill Academic Publishers
PO Box 9000
NL-2300 PA Leiden, Netherlands
Ph: 31 71 5353500
Fax: 31 71 5317532
Publisher E-mail: marketing@brill.nl
Peer-reviewed journal devoted to a developing new domain of research in the humanities, usually referred to as "Western Esotericism", covering a variety of alternative currents in western religious history, including the so-called "hermetic philosophy" and related currents in the early modern period; alchemy, paracelsianism and rosicrucianism; Christian kabbalah and its later developments; theosophical and illuminist currents; and various occultist and related developments during the 19th and 20th centuries, up to and including popular contemporary currents such as the New Age movement. **Subtitle:** Journal for the Study of Western Esotericism. **Freq:** 2/yr. **Key Personnel:** Roland Edighoffer, Editor; Wouter J. Hanegraaff, Editor; Antoine Faivre, Editor. **ISSN:** 1567-9896. **Subscription Rates:** EUR58 individuals print; US$79 individuals print; EUR131 institutions electronic & print; US$178 institutions electronic & print; EUR109 institutions online only; US$148 institutions online only; EUR120 institutions print; US$163 institutions print. **URL:** http://www.brill.nl/arie.

48653 ■ Asian Journal of Social Science
Brill Academic Publishers
PO Box 9000
NL-2300 PA Leiden, Netherlands
Ph: 31 71 5353500
Fax: 31 71 5317532
Publisher E-mail: marketing@brill.nl
Journal focusing on theoretical issues of the social sci-

ences in the context of Asian empirical realities. **Founded:** 1973. **Freq:** 6/yr. **Print Method:** Offset. **Trim Size:** 10 x 16. **Cols./Page:** 5. **Col. Width:** 11.5 picas. **Col. Depth:** 216 agate lines. **Key Personnel:** Syed Farid Alatas, Editor; Chan Kwok Bun, Editorial Board; Vineeta Sinha, Dep. Ed. **ISSN:** 1568-4849. **Subscription Rates:** EUR92 individuals print only; US$125 institutions print only; EUR452 institutions print and electronic; US$615 institutions print and electronic; EUR377 institutions online only; US$513 institutions online only; EUR415 institutions print only; US$564 institutions print only. **URL:** http://www.brill.nl/ajss.

48654 ■ Asian Medicine
Brill Academic Publishers
PO Box 9000
NL-2300 PA Leiden, Netherlands
Ph: 31 71 5353500
Fax: 31 71 5317532
Publisher E-mail: marketing@brill.nl
Multidisciplinary journal aimed at researchers and practitioners of Asian Medicine in Asia as well as in Western countries, publishing academic essays that explore the historical, anthropological, sociological and philological dimensions of Asian medicine, as well as practice reports from clinicians based in Asia and in Western countries. **Subtitle:** Tradition and Modernity. **Freq:** 2/yr. **Key Personnel:** Geoffrey Samuel, Editor; J.S. Alter, Editorial Board; Vivienne Lo, Editor; D. Bensky, Editorial Board; N.S. Bhatt, Editorial Board. **ISSN:** 1573-420X. **Subscription Rates:** EUR55 individuals print; US$75 individuals print; EUR166 institutions electronic & print; US$225 institutions electronic & print; EUR138 institutions online only; US$188 institutions online only; EUR152 institutions print only; US$207 institutions print. **URL:** http://www.brill.nl/asme.

48655 ■ Austrian Review of International and European Law
Brill Academic Publishers
PO Box 9000
NL-2300 PA Leiden, Netherlands
Ph: 31 71 5353500
Fax: 31 71 5317532
Publisher E-mail: marketing@brill.nl
Journal covering discussion of international and European law, with emphasis on Austrian law. **Key Personnel:** Gerhard Loibl, Editor. **URL:** http://www.brill.nl/product_id18742.htm.

48656 ■ Behaviour
Brill Academic Publishers
PO Box 9000
NL-2300 PA Leiden, Netherlands
Ph: 31 71 5353500
Fax: 31 71 5317532
Publisher E-mail: marketing@brill.nl
Journal featuring contributions to the biological analysis of the causation, ontogeny, function, and evolution of behavior of all animal species, including humans. **Founded:** 1958. **Freq:** Monthly. **Print Method:** Web offset. **Trim Size:** 9 3/4 x 16. **Cols./Page:** 6. **Col. Width:** 20 nonpareils. **Col. Depth:** 116 agate lines. **Key Personnel:** Th.C.M. Bakker, Assoc. Ed.; R. Cocroft, Assoc. Ed.; P.C.H. Albers, Managing Editor; B.D. Wisenden, Managing Editor. **ISSN:** 0005-7959. **Subscription Rates:** EUR1,374 institutions print and electronic; US$1,870 institutions print and electronic; EUR1,145 institutions online only; US$1,558 institutions online only; EUR1,260 institutions print only; US$1,714 institutions print only. **URL:** http://www.brill.nl/beh.

48657 ■ Biblical Interpretation
Brill Academic Publishers
PO Box 9000
NL-2300 PA Leiden, Netherlands
Ph: 31 71 5353500
Fax: 31 71 5317532
Publisher E-mail: marketing@brill.nl
Journal reporting on many aspects of current biblical criticism for understanding of different interpretations including feminist readings, semiotic, post-structuralist, reader-response and other types of literary readings, liberation-theological readings, ecological readings, and psychological readings and so on. **Subtitle:** A Journal of Contemporary Approaches. **Freq:** 5/yr. **Key Personnel:** H. Pyper, Editor; D.E. Orton, Founding Ed. **ISSN:** 0927-2569. **Subscription Rates:** EUR97 individuals print only; US$132 individuals print only; EUR319 institutions print and electronic; US$435 institutions print and electronic; EUR266 institutions online only; US$362 institutions online only; EUR293 institutions print only; US$398 institu-

tions print only. **URL:** http://www.brill.nl/m_catalogue_sub6_id7141.htm.

48658 ■ Brill's Annual of Afroasiatic Languages and Linguistics
Brill Academic Publishers
PO Box 9000
NL-2300 PA Leiden, Netherlands
Ph: 31 71 5353500
Fax: 31 71 5317532
Publisher E-mail: marketing@brill.nl
Peer-reviewed journal featuring the study of Afroasiatic languages and linguistics. **Freq:** Annual. **Key Personnel:** Sabrina Bendjaballah, Editor, sabrina.benjaballah@linguist.jussieu.fr; Chris Reintges, Editor, creintges@linguist.jussieu.fr; Jean Lowenstamm, Editor. **ISSN:** 1876-6633. **Subscription Rates:** EUR41 individuals; US$56 individuals; EUR124 institutions; US$169 institutions; EUR113 individuals online only; US$154 individuals online only. **URL:** http://www.brill.nl/baall.

48659 ■ Bulletin Antieke Beschaving (BABESCH)
PEETERS - Leuven
PO Box 11062
2301 Leiden, Netherlands
Publisher E-mail: peeters@peeters-leuven.be
Peer-reviewed journal focusing on research and fieldwork in classical archaeology. **Founded:** 1926. **Freq:** Annual. **Key Personnel:** E.M. Moormann, Editor, editorinchief@babesch.org. **ISSN:** 0165-9367. **Subscription Rates:** EUR95 individuals. **URL:** http://www.peeters-leuven.be/journoverz.asp?nr=54; http://www.babesch.org/.

48660 ■ Cainozoic Research
Backhuys Publishers BV
PO Box 321
NL-2300 AH Leiden, Netherlands
Ph: 31 71 5170208
Fax: 31 71 5171856
Publisher E-mail: info@backhuys.com
Journal focusing on Cainozoic palaeontology and stratigraphy of the North Sea Basin. **Freq:** Semiannual. **Key Personnel:** David J. Ward, Managing Editor, d.ward@dial.pipex.com; Dr. W.A. Berggren, Assoc. Ed. **ISSN:** 1570-0399. **URL:** http://www.euronet.nl/users/backhuys/cares.htm.

48661 ■ China Information
Sage Publications Inc.
PO Box 9515
NL-2300 RA Leiden, Netherlands
Fax: 31 715 272526
Publication E-mail: chinainformation@let.leidenuniv.nl
Publisher E-mail: info@sagepub.com
Peer-reviewed journal focusing on the politics, economics, law, ecology, culture, and society of contemporary China and overseas Chinese communities. **Subtitle:** A Journal on Contemporary China Studies. **Freq:** 3/yr. **Key Personnel:** Tak-Wing Ngo, Editor; Woei Lien Chong, Assoc. Ed. **ISSN:** 0920-203X. **Subscription Rates:** US$740 institutions print & e-access; US$666 institutions e-access; US$679 individuals e-access; US$470 institutions all online content; US$725 institutions print only; US$72 individuals print only. **Remarks:** Accepts advertising. **URL:** http://www.hum.leidenuniv.nl/chinees/china-tools/tijdschriften/moderne-china.html; http://www.sagepub.com/journals/Journal201679. **Circ:** (Not Reported)

48662 ■ Comparative Sociology
Brill Academic Publishers
PO Box 9000
NL-2300 PA Leiden, Netherlands
Ph: 31 71 5353500
Fax: 31 71 5317532
Publisher E-mail: marketing@brill.nl
Journal presenting a detailed account of studies made in different cultures on a comparative basis. **Freq:** Bimonthly. **Key Personnel:** David Sciulli, Editor, compsoc@tamu.edu; Dr. Mehdi P. Amineh, Book Review Ed., m.p.amineh@uva.nl; Sander De Rijke, Book Review Ed. **ISSN:** 1569-1322. **Subscription Rates:** EUR150 individuals print only; US$204 individuals print only; EUR566 institutions electronic and print; US$770 institutions electronic and print; EUR472 institutions online only; US$642 institutions online only; EUR519 institutions print only; US$706 institutions print only. **URL:** http://www.brill.nl/m_catalogue_sub6_id9998.htm.

48663 ■ Composite Interfaces
Brill Academic Publishers
PO Box 9000
NL-2300 PA Leiden, Netherlands
Ph: 31 71 5353500
Fax: 31 71 5317532
Publisher E-mail: marketing@brill.nl
Journal covering issues in interface-related phenomena. Topics include surface treatment of reinforcing fibers and fillers, effect of interface structure on mechanical properties, physical properties, curing and rheology, coupling agents, synthesis of matrices designed to promote adhesion, molecular and atomic characterization of interfaces, interfacial morphology, dynamic mechanical study of interphases, interfacial compatibilization, adsorption and tribology. **Founded:** 1948. **Freq:** 9/yr. **Print Method:** Offset. **Trim Size:** 8 1/2 x 11. **Cols./Page:** 3 and 2. **Col. Width:** 26 and 41 nonpareils. **Col. Depth:** 133 agate lines. **Key Personnel:** H. Ishida, Editor-in-Chief, hatsuo.ishida@case.edu; F.H.J. Maurer, Editorial Board; C.-S. Ha, Assoc. Ed.; A. Takahara, Editor. **ISSN:** 0927-6440. **Subscription Rates:** EUR1,443 institutions online only; US$1,964 institutions online only. **URL:** http://www.brill.nl/ci.

48664 ■ Computing Letters
Brill Academic Publishers
PO Box 9000
NL-2300 PA Leiden, Netherlands
Ph: 31 71 5353500
Fax: 31 71 5317532
Publisher E-mail: marketing@brill.nl
Journal covering research results in computing. **Founded:** May 1892. **Freq:** Quarterly. **Print Method:** Letterpress and offset. **Cols./Page:** 6. **Col. Width:** 25 nonpareils. **Col. Depth:** 301 agate lines. **Key Personnel:** Prof. T.E. Simos, Editor-in-Chief; Prof. G. Maroulis, Editor-in-Chief. **URL:** http://www.compulett.org/; http://www.brill.nl/default.aspx?partid=18&pid=22693.

48665 ■ Crustaceana
Brill Academic Publishers
PO Box 9000
NL-2300 PA Leiden, Netherlands
Ph: 31 71 5353500
Fax: 31 71 5317532
Publisher E-mail: marketing@brill.nl
Journal dealing with crustacean research. **Subtitle:** International Journal of Crustacean Research. **Freq:** 12/yr. **Key Personnel:** J.C. von Vaupel Klein, Managing Editor, jcvvk@xs4all.nl. **ISSN:** 0011-216X. **Subscription Rates:** EUR966 institutions electronic and print; US$1,355 institutions electronic and print; EUR830 institutions online only; US$1,130 institutions online only; EUR913 institutions print only; US$1,243 institutions print only. **URL:** http://www.brill.nl/cr.

48666 ■ Dead Sea Discoveries
Brill Academic Publishers
PO Box 9000
NL-2300 PA Leiden, Netherlands
Ph: 31 71 5353500
Fax: 31 71 5317532
Publisher E-mail: marketing@brill.nl
International journal dealing with the study of Dead Sea Scrolls. The primary interest is to study the findings in Judean Desert for Biblical Studies, and the study of early Jewish and Christian history. **Subtitle:** A Journal of Current Research on the Scrolls and Related Literature. **Freq:** 3/yr. **Key Personnel:** A. Lange, Editorial Board; J.J. Collins, Editorial Board; Hindy Najman, Exec. Ed.; M.J. Bernstein, Editorial Board; Eibert J. C. Tigchelaar, Exec. Ed. **ISSN:** 0929-0761. **Subscription Rates:** EUR100 individuals print; EUR207 institutions online only; EUR228 institutions print; US$136 individuals print; US$310 institutions print; US$282 institutions online only. **Remarks:** Advertising accepted; rates available upon request. **URL:** http://www.brill.nl/dsd. **Circ:** (Not Reported)

48667 ■ Designed Monomers and Polymers
Brill Academic Publishers
PO Box 9000
NL-2300 PA Leiden, Netherlands
Ph: 31 71 5353500
Fax: 31 71 5317532
Publisher E-mail: marketing@brill.nl
Peer-reviewed journal in the field of macromolecular design and application, including macromolecular science, initiators, macroinitiators for macromolecular design, kinetics, mechanism and modeling aspects of polymerization. **Subtitle:** An International Journal on Monomer and Macromolecular Synthesis. **Freq:** 6/yr. **Key Personnel:** Y. Yagci, Regional Co-Ed.; G.R. Newkome, Editorial Board; T. Nakaya, Editorial Board; J.P. Kennedy, Editorial Board; M.K. Mishra, Editor; J.V. Crivello, Editorial Board. **ISSN:** 1385-772X. **Subscription Rates:** US$856 institutions online only; US$1,165 institutions online only. **URL:** http://www.brill.nl/default.aspx?partid=18&pid=9721.

48668 ■ Die Welt des Islams
Brill Academic Publishers
PO Box 9000
NL-2300 PA Leiden, Netherlands
Ph: 31 71 5353500
Fax: 31 71 5317532
Publisher E-mail: marketing@brill.nl
Journal focusing on the history and culture of the people of Islam from the end of the eighteenth century until present times. **Subtitle:** International Journal for the Study of Modern Islam. **Founded:** 1981. **Freq:** 4/yr. **Print Method:** Offset. **Trim Size:** 8 1/4 x 11 1/4. **Cols./Page:** 3. **Col. Width:** 27 nonpareils. **Col. Depth:** 140 agate lines. **Key Personnel:** Stefan Reichmuth, Editor. **ISSN:** 0043-2539. **Subscription Rates:** EUR95 individuals print only; US$129 individuals print only; EUR313 institutions print and electronic; US$426 institutions print and electronic; EUR261 institutions online only; US$355 institutions online only; EUR287 institutions print only; US$391 institutions print only. **URL:** http://www.brill.nl/default.aspx?partid=18&pid=7202.

48669 ■ East Central Europe
Brill Academic Publishers
PO Box 9000
NL-2300 PA Leiden, Netherlands
Ph: 31 71 5353500
Fax: 31 71 5317532
Publisher E-mail: marketing@brill.nl
Peer-reviewed journal covering social science and humanities on East Central Europe. **Freq:** Semiannual. **Key Personnel:** Maciej Janowski, Editor-in-Chief. **ISSN:** 0094-3037. **Subscription Rates:** EUR48 individuals; US$65 individuals; EUR145 institutions; US$198 institutions; EUR132 institutions online only; US$180 institutions online only. **URL:** http://www.brill.nl/eceu.

48670 ■ European Journal of East Asian Studies
Brill Academic Publishers
PO Box 9000
NL-2300 PA Leiden, Netherlands
Ph: 31 71 5353500
Fax: 31 71 5317532
Publisher E-mail: marketing@brill.nl
Journal covering the whole of the broader East Asian region, including Southeast as well as Northeast Asia. **Freq:** 2/yr. **Key Personnel:** Philippe Regnier, Editor-in-Chief; Ruediger Frank, Dep. Ch. Ed. **ISSN:** 1568-0584. **Subscription Rates:** EUR44 individuals print only; US$60 individuals print only; EUR161 institutions electronic and print; US$219 institutions electronic and print; EUR134 institutions online only; US$182 institutions online only; EUR147 institutions print only; US$200 institutions print only. **URL:** http://www.brill.nl/m_catalogue_sub6_id9449.htm.

48671 ■ European Journal of Jewish Studies
Brill Academic Publishers
PO Box 9000
NL-2300 PA Leiden, Netherlands
Ph: 31 71 5353500
Fax: 31 71 5317532
Publisher E-mail: marketing@brill.nl
Peer-reviewed journal covering Jewish studies. **Subtitle:** The Journal of the European Association for Jewish Studies. **Founded:** 1971. **Freq:** 2/yr. **Print Method:** Offset. **Trim Size:** 8 1/2 x 11. **Cols./Page:** 2. **Col. Width:** 42 nonpareils. **Col. Depth:** 140 agate lines. **Key Personnel:** Giuseppe Veltri, PhD, Editor; Shlomo Z. Berger, Editorial Board; Michael Brenner, Editorial Board; Diana Matut, Managing Editor. **ISSN:** 1025-9996. **Subscription Rates:** EUR55 individuals; US$75 individuals; EUR110 institutions; US$150 institutions; EUR100 institutions online only; US$136 institutions online only. **URL:** http://www.brill.nl/default.aspx?partid=18&pid=26429.

48672 ■ Exchange
Brill Academic Publishers
PO Box 9000
NL-2300 PA Leiden, Netherlands
Ph: 31 71 5353500

Circulation: ★ = ABC; △ = BPA; ◆ = CAC; • = CCAB; ❑ = VAC; ⊕ = PO Statement; ‡ = Publisher's Report; Boldface figures = sworn; Light figures = estimated.

Gale Directory of Publications & Broadcast Media/147th Ed.   5275

Fax: 31 71 5317532
Publisher E-mail: marketing@brill.nl
Journal devoting to missiology and ecumenical studies, charting developments in both fields across the broad spectrum of Christian and other religious traditions. **Subtitle:** A Journal of Missiological and Ecumenical Research. **Founded:** 1972. **Freq:** 4/yr. **Key Personnel:** Freek L. Bakker, Exec. Ed. **ISSN:** 0166-2740. **Subscription Rates:** EUR70 individuals print only; US$95 individuals print only; EUR230 institutions print and electronic; US$331 institutions print and electronic; EUR192 institutions online only; US$261 institutions online only; EUR211 institutions print only; US$287 institutions print only. **URL:** http://www.brill.nl/m_catalogue_sub6_id7220.htm.

48673 ■ Global Responsibility to Protect
Brill Academic Publishers
PO Box 9000
NL-2300 PA Leiden, Netherlands
Ph: 31 71 5353500
Fax: 31 71 5317532
Publisher E-mail: marketing@brill.nl
Journal focusing on study and practice of the responsibility to protect. **Freq:** Quarterly. **Key Personnel:** Alex J. Bellamy, Editor; Sara E. Davies, Editor. **ISSN:** 1875-9858. **Subscription Rates:** EUR70 individuals print only; US$95 individuals print only; EUR216 institutions print and electronic; US$294 institutions print and electronic; EUR180 institutions online only; US$245 institutions online only; EUR198 institutions print only; US$270 institutions print only. **URL:** http://www.brill.nl/gr2p.

48674 ■ Grotiana
Brill Academic Publishers
PO Box 9000
NL-2300 PA Leiden, Netherlands
Ph: 31 71 5353500
Fax: 31 71 5317532
Publisher E-mail: marketing@brill.nl
Peer-reviewed journal covering the life and works of Hugo Grotius. **Freq:** Annual. **Key Personnel:** Dr. Hans W. Blom, Editor-in-Chief, blom@fsw.eur.nl. **ISSN:** 0167-3831. **Subscription Rates:** EUR42 individuals; US$57 individuals; EUR62 institutions; US$84 institutions; EUR56 institutions online only; US$76 institutions online only. **URL:** http://www.brill.nl/grot.

48675 ■ Historiography East and West
Brill Academic Publishers
PO Box 9000
NL-2300 PA Leiden, Netherlands
Ph: 31 71 5353500
Fax: 31 71 5317532
Publisher E-mail: marketing@brill.nl
Journal dealing with representation of history rather than history itself. The emphasis has been on comparison of Asian practice with Western historio-gra-phi-cal traditions in history writing. **Freq:** 2/yr. **Key Personnel:** Prof. Axel Schneider, Managing Editor; Prof. Susanne Weigelin-Schwiedrzik, Managing Editor. **ISSN:** 1570-1867. **URL:** http://www.brill.nl/m_catalogue_sub6_id10982.htm.

48676 ■ Hobbes Studies
Brill Academic Publishers
PO Box 9000
NL-2300 PA Leiden, Netherlands
Ph: 31 71 5353500
Fax: 31 71 5317532
Publisher E-mail: marketing@brill.nl
Peer-reviewed journal publishing articles related to Thomas Hobbes. **Freq:** Semiannual. **Key Personnel:** Martin A. Bertman, Editor-in-Chief; Juhana Lemetti, Assoc. Ed., juhana.lemetti@helsinki.fi. **ISSN:** 0921-5891. **Subscription Rates:** EUR42 individuals; US$57 individuals; EUR90 institutions; US$121 institutions; EUR81 institutions online only; US$110 institutions online only. **URL:** http://www.brill.nl/default.aspx?partid=212&pid=29360.

48677 ■ Index Islamicus
Brill Academic Publishers
PO Box 9000
NL-2300 PA Leiden, Netherlands
Ph: 31 71 5353500
Fax: 31 71 5317532
Publisher E-mail: marketing@brill.nl
Bibliographical reference volume covering literature on Islam, the Middle East and the Muslim world. **Subtitle:** New Books, Articles and Reviews on Islam and the Muslim World. **Founded:** 1928. **Freq:** 4/yr. **Key Personnel:** Heather Bleaney, Editor. **ISSN:** 1360-0982. **Subscription Rates:** EUR1,223 institutions; US$1,665

institutions. **Remarks:** Advertising not accepted. **URL:** http://www.brill.nl/default.aspx?partid=18&pid=10433; http://www.indexislamicus.com/. **Circ:** (Not Reported)

48678 ■ Insect Systematics & Evolution
Brill Academic Publishers
PO Box 9000
NL-2300 PA Leiden, Netherlands
Ph: 31 71 5353500
Fax: 31 71 5317532
Publisher E-mail: marketing@brill.nl
Journal featuring insect evolution and systematics. **Subtitle:** An International Journal of Systematic Entomology. **Freq:** Quarterly. **Key Personnel:** Dr L. Krogmann, Editor-in-Chief. **ISSN:** 1399-560X. **Subscription Rates:** EUR313 institutions print and electronic; US$426 institutions print and electronic; EUR261 institutions online only; US$355 institutions online only; EUR287 institutions print only; US$391 institutions print only. **URL:** http://www.brill.nl/ise.

48679 ■ International Community Law Review
Brill Academic Publishers
PO Box 9000
NL-2300 PA Leiden, Netherlands
Ph: 31 71 5353500
Fax: 31 71 5317532
Publisher E-mail: marketing@brill.nl
Journal exploring the implications of various traditions of international law, as well as current hegemonic trends. **Founded:** 1979. **Freq:** 4/yr. **Print Method:** Offset. **Trim Size:** 8 1/2 x 11. **Cols./Page:** 3. **Col. Width:** 14 picas. **Col. Depth:** 59 picas. **Key Personnel:** Malgosia Fitzmaurice, Editor-in-Chief; Panos Merkouris, Managing Editor. **ISSN:** 1871-9740. **Subscription Rates:** EUR80 individuals print only; US$118 institutions print only; EUR310 institutions print and electronic; US$456 institutions print and electronic; EUR379 institutions online only; US$410 institutions online only. **URL:** http://www.brill.nl/iclr.

48680 ■ International Criminal Law Review
Martinus Nijhoff
Plantijnstraat 2
NL-2321 JC Leiden, Netherlands
Ph: 31 715 353500
Fax: 31 715 317532
Journal publishing in-depth analytical research that deals with the substantive and procedural law on the international level; important cases from national jurisdictions which have a bearing on general issues; criminological and sociological; and historical research. **Freq:** 4/yr. **Key Personnel:** Michael Bohlander, Editor-in-Chief, michael.bohlander@durham.ac.uk; Hirad Abtahi, Editorial Board; Diane Marie Amann, Editorial Board. **ISSN:** 1567-536X. **Subscription Rates:** EUR90 individuals; US$122 individuals; EUR355 institutions; US$456 institutions; EUR307 institutions; US$418 institutions. **URL:** http://www.brill.nl/m_catalogue_sub6_id18491.htm.

48681 ■ International Journal of Myriapodology
Brill Academic Publishers
PO Box 9000
NL-2300 PA Leiden, Netherlands
Ph: 31 71 5353500
Fax: 31 71 5317532
Publisher E-mail: marketing@brill.nl
Journal featuring research articles on myriapods. **Freq:** Semiannual. **Key Personnel:** Prof. Henrik Enghoff, Editor-in-Chief, henghoff@snm.ku.dk; Dr. Pavel Stoev, Managing Editor, stoev@nmnh.bas.bg. **ISSN:** 1875-2535. **Subscription Rates:** EUR74 individuals print only; US$99 individuals print only; EUR223 institutions electronic and print; US$304 institutions electronic and print; EUR186 institutions online only; US$253 institutions online only; EUR205 institutions print only; US$278 institutions print only. **URL:** http://www.brill.nl/ijm.

48682 ■ International Journal of the Platonic Tradition
Brill Academic Publishers
PO Box 9000
NL-2300 PA Leiden, Netherlands
Ph: 31 71 5353500
Fax: 31 71 5317532
Publisher E-mail: marketing@brill.nl
Journal covering the platonic tradition from philosophical, historical, and religious perspectives. **Founded:** 1980. **Freq:** Semiannual. **Print Method:** Offset. **Trim Size:** 8 1/4 x 10 3/4. **Cols./Page:** 3. **Col. Width:** 13 3/5 picas. **Col. Depth:** 136 agate lines. **Key Personnel:** Prof. John F. Finamore, Editor-in-Chief. **ISSN:** 1872-5082. **Subscription Rates:** EUR55 individuals print only;

US$75 individuals print only; EUR182 institutions print and electronic; US$248 institutions print and electronic; EUR152 institutions online only; US$207 institutions online only; EUR167 institutions print only; US$228 institutions print only. **URL:** http://www.brill.nl/jpt.

48683 ■ International Organizations Law Review
Martinus Nijhoff
Plantijnstraat 2
NL-2321 JC Leiden, Netherlands
Ph: 31 715 353500
Fax: 31 715 317532
Journal functioning as a discussion forum for academics and practitioners active in the field of the law of international organizations. **Freq:** Annual. **Key Personnel:** Niels M. Blokker, Editor-in-Chief; Ramses A. Wessel, Editor-in-Chief; James D. Fry, Managing Editor. **ISSN:** 1572-3739. **Subscription Rates:** EUR85 individuals list price; US$116 individuals list price; EUR281 institutions list price; US$382 institutions list price; EUR257 institutions print only; US$350 institutions print only. **URL:** http://www.brill.nl/m_catalogue_sub6_id21691.htm.

48684 ■ Iran and the Caucasus
Brill Academic Publishers
PO Box 9000
NL-2300 PA Leiden, Netherlands
Ph: 31 71 5353500
Fax: 31 71 5317532
Publisher E-mail: marketing@brill.nl
Peer-reviewed journal covering the history of the Iranian and Caucasian people. **Freq:** 2/yr. **Key Personnel:** Garnik S. Asatrian, Editor-in-Chief, caucas@armline.am; Victoria Arakelova, Assoc. Ed.; Giusto Traina, Assoc. Ed.; Carlo Cereti, International Editorial Board; Victoria Arakelova, Assoc. Ed.; Hayrapet Margarian, International Editorial Board. **ISSN:** 1609-8498. **Subscription Rates:** US$54 individuals; US$150 institutions; US$136 institutions online only; EUR40 individuals; EUR110 institutions; EUR100 institutions online only. **URL:** http://www.brill.nl/ic.

48685 ■ Islamic Law and Society
Brill Academic Publishers
PO Box 9000
NL-2300 PA Leiden, Netherlands
Ph: 31 71 5353500
Fax: 31 71 5317532
Publisher E-mail: marketing@brill.nl
Journal dealing with classical and modern Islamic law, in Muslim and non-Muslim countries. **Freq:** 4/yr. **Key Personnel:** David S. Powers, Editor-in-Chief; Susan Spectorsky, Editorial Board; Baber Johansen, Editorial Board; Aharon Layish, Editorial Board. **ISSN:** 0928-9380. **Subscription Rates:** EUR108 individuals print only; US$147 individuals print only; EUR355 institutions print and electronic; US$484 institutions print and electronic; EUR296 institutions online only; US$403 institutions online only; EUR326 institutions print only; US$443 institutions print only. **Remarks:** Advertising accepted; rates available upon request. **URL:** http://www.brill.nl/ils. **Circ:** (Not Reported)

48686 ■ Journal of Adhesion Science and Technology
Brill Academic Publishers
PO Box 9000
NL-2300 PA Leiden, Netherlands
Ph: 31 71 5353500
Fax: 31 71 5317532
Publisher E-mail: marketing@brill.nl
Journal focusing on the theories and mechanisms of adhesion covering adhesion principles in all areas of technology. **Freq:** 16/yr. **Key Personnel:** Dr. K.L. Mittal, Editor-in-Chief, klm@mstconf.com; I. Benedek, Editorial Board; J.C Berg, Editorial Board; A.K. Bhowmick, Editorial Board; F. Simon, Editorial Board; A.D. Crocombe, Editorial Board; C. Cetinkaya, Editorial Board. **ISSN:** 0169-4243. **Subscription Rates:** EUR2,416 institutions print and electronic; US$3,288 institutions print and electronic; EUR2,013 institutions online only; US$2,740 institutions online only; EUR2,214 institutions print only; US$3,014 institutions print only. **URL:** http://www.brill.nl/m_catalogue_sub6_id9737.htm.

48687 ■ Journal of Ancient Near Eastern Religions
Brill Academic Publishers
PO Box 9000
NL-2300 PA Leiden, Netherlands
Ph: 31 71 5353500
Fax: 31 71 5317532
Publisher E-mail: marketing@brill.nl
Peer-reviewed journal dealing with the religions of area

generally referred to the Ancient Near East. **Freq:** 2/yr. **Key Personnel:** Theo Van Den Hout, Editorial Board; Chris Woods, Editor. **ISSN:** 1569-2116. **Subscription Rates:** EUR47 individuals; US\$64 individuals; EUR141 institutions; US\$191 institutions; EUR128 institutions online only; US\$174 institutions online only. **URL:** http://www.brill.nl/jane.

48688 ■ Journal of Arabic Literature
Brill Academic Publishers
PO Box 9000
NL-2300 PA Leiden, Netherlands
Ph: 31 71 5353500
Fax: 31 71 5317532
Publisher E-mail: marketing@brill.nl
Journal covering various aspects of Arabic literature. **Founded:** 1970. **Freq:** 3/yr. **Key Personnel:** Muhsin Jassim Al-Musawi, Exec. Ed.; Suzanne Pinckney Stetkevych, Editorial Board; James T. Monroe, Editorial Board; Federico Corriente, Editorial Board. **ISSN:** 0085-2376. **Subscription Rates:** EUR72 individuals print only; US\$98 individuals print only; EUR236 institutions print and electronic; US\$322 institutions print and electronic; EUR197 institutions online only; US\$268 institutions online only; EUR217 institutions print only; US\$295 institutions print only. **URL:** http://www.brill.nl/m_catalogue_sub6_id7314.htm.

48689 ■ Journal of Asian and African Studies
E.J. Brill
PO Box 9000
NL-2300 PA Leiden, Netherlands
Ph: 31 715 353500
Fax: 31 715 317532
Publisher E-mail: cs@brill.nl
Publication covering ethnic, cultural, and racial issues and their study. **Freq:** Quarterly. **Key Personnel:** Prof. Jerry Bentley, Editorial Board; Prof. Christopher Ehret, Editorial Board; Prof. Mohamadou Diallo, Editorial Board; Prof. Kempe Ronald Hope, Editorial Board. **ISSN:** 1569-2094. **Subscription Rates:** US\$358 institutions online only; US\$430 institutions; US\$131 individuals; EUR96 individuals; EUR289 institutions; EUR263 institutions online only. **URL:** http://puck.ingentaselect.com; http://www.brill.nl/default.aspx?partid=212&pid=10254.

48690 ■ Journal of Biomaterials Science, Polymer Edition
Brill Academic Publishers
PO Box 9000
NL-2300 PA Leiden, Netherlands
Ph: 31 71 5353500
Fax: 31 71 5317532
Publisher E-mail: marketing@brill.nl
Journal covering fundamental research on the molecular and cellular properties of polymeric biomaterials and the mechanisms of interaction between such biomaterials and living organisms. **Founded:** June 1985. **Freq:** 14/yr. **Print Method:** Offset. **Trim Size:** 8 1/8 x 10 3/4. **Cols./Page:** 3. **Col. Width:** 27 nonpareils. **Key Personnel:** S.L. Cooper, Editor, coopers@chemeng.ohio-state.edu; K. Kataoka, Editor, kataoka@bmw.mm.t.u-tokyo.ac.jp; Prof. Michel Vert, Editor, crba@univ-montpl.fr. **ISSN:** 0920-5063. **Subscription Rates:** EUR2,128 institutions print and electronic; US\$2,896 institutions print and electronic; EUR1,773 institutions online only; US\$2,413 institutions online only; EUR1,950 institutions print only; U3\$2,654 institutions print only. **URL:** http://www.brill.nl/default.aspx?partid=18&pid=9739.

48691 ■ Journal of Cognition and Culture
Brill Academic Publishers
PO Box 9000
NL-2300 PA Leiden, Netherlands
Ph: 31 71 5353500
Fax: 31 71 5317532
Publisher E-mail: marketing@brill.nl
Journal providing an interdisciplinary forum for exploring the mental foundations of culture and the culture foundations of mental life. **Freq:** 2/yr. **Key Personnel:** Dr. Thomas E. Lawson, Exec. Ed.; Dr. Pascal Boyer, Exec. Ed.; Dr. Justin L. Barrett, Book Review Ed. **ISSN:** 1567-7095. **Subscription Rates:** EUR91 individuals print only; US\$124 individuals print only; EUR224 institutions electronic and print; US\$306 institutions electronic and print; EUR187 institutions online only; US\$255 institutions online only; EUR206 institutions print only; EUR281 institutions print only. **URL:** http://www.brill.nl/jocc.

48692 ■ Journal of Early Modern History
Brill Academic Publishers
PO Box 9000
NL-2300 PA Leiden, Netherlands
Ph: 31 71 5353500
Fax: 31 71 5317532
Publisher E-mail: marketing@brill.nl
Journal covering early modern history including topics such as culture. **Founded:** 1882. **Freq:** 6/yr. **Print Method:** Offset. **Trim Size:** 13 3/4 x 22 5/8. **Cols./Page:** 6. **Col. Width:** 26 nonpareils. **Col. Depth:** 21 1/2 inches. **Key Personnel:** James D. Tracy, Exec. Ed.; Simon Ditchfield, Book Review Ed.; Kate Fleet, Book Review Ed. **ISSN:** 1385-3783. **Subscription Rates:** EUR73 individuals print only; US\$99 individuals print only; EUR311 institutions print and electronic; US\$423 institutions print and electronic; EUR259 institutions online only; US\$352 institutions online only; EUR285 institutions print only; US\$387 institutions print only. **URL:** http://www.brill.nl/default.aspx?partid=18&pid=7320.

48693 ■ Journal of the Economic and Social History of the Orient
Brill Academic Publishers
PO Box 9000
NL-2300 PA Leiden, Netherlands
Ph: 31 71 5353500
Fax: 31 71 5317532
Publisher E-mail: marketing@brill.nl
Journal focusing on the economic and social history of the Ancient Near East from ancient times to the beginning of the nineteenth century. **Founded:** 1958. **Freq:** 5/yr. **Key Personnel:** Norman Yoffee, Editorial Board; Kenneth Hall, Editorial Board; Harriet Zurndorfer, Editorial Board; David Washbrook, Editorial Board. **ISSN:** 0022-4995. **Subscription Rates:** EUR80 individuals print only; US\$109 individuals print only; EUR481 institutions electronic and print; US\$654 institutions electronic and print; EUR401 institutions online only; US\$589 institutions online only; EUR441 institutions print only; US\$600 institutions print only. **URL:** http://www.brill.nl/m_catalogue_sub6_id7324.htm.

48694 ■ Journal of Egyptian History
Brill Academic Publishers
PO Box 9000
NL-2300 PA Leiden, Netherlands
Ph: 31 71 5353500
Fax: 31 71 5317532
Publisher E-mail: marketing@brill.nl
Journal covering various aspects of ancient Egyptian history. **Key Personnel:** Christian Cannuyer, Editorial Board; Aidan Dodson, Editorial Board; Thomas Schneider, Editor-in-Chief; Leo Depuydt, Editorial Board; Andrea Gnirs-Loprieno, Editorial Board; Karl Jansen-Winkeln, Editorial Board. **ISSN:** 1874-1657. **Subscription Rates:** EUR40 individuals print only; US\$54 institutions print only; EUR136 institutions print and electronic; US\$185 institutions print and electronic; EUR113 institutions online only; US\$154 institutions online only; EUR124 institutions print only; US\$169 institutions print only. **URL:** http://www.brill.nl/default.aspx?partid=18&pid=27057.

48695 ■ Journal of Electromagnetic Waves and Applications
Brill Academic Publishers
PO Box 9000
NL-2300 PA Leiden, Netherlands
Ph: 31 71 5353500
Fax: 31 71 5317532
Publisher E-mail: marketing@brill.nl
Journal dealing with all aspects of electromagnetic wave theory and its applications. **Freq:** 18/yr. **Key Personnel:** Dr. J.A. Kong, Founding Ed.-in-Ch., jpier@ewt.mit.edu; W.C. Chew, Editor-in-Chief; A. Biswas, Editorial Board; A.C. Priou, Editorial Board. **ISSN:** 0920-5071. **Subscription Rates:** EUR3,052 institutions electronic and print; US\$4,153 institutions electronic and print; EUR2,543 institutions online only; US\$3,461 institutions online only; EUR2,797 institutions print only; US\$3,807 institutions print only. **Remarks:** Advertising accepted; rates available upon request. **URL:** http://www.brill.nl/m_catalogue_sub6_id9748.htm. **Circ:** (Not Reported)

48696 ■ Journal of Empirical Theology
Brill Academic Publishers
PO Box 9000
NL-2300 PA Leiden, Netherlands
Ph: 31 71 5353500
Fax: 31 71 5317532
Publisher E-mail: marketing@brill.nl
Journal covering theological articles and book reviews based upon empirical research and empirical methodology. **Freq:** 2/yr. **Key Personnel:** Chris A.M. Hermans, Exec. Ed.; A. Bucher, Board of Ed.; F.V. Anthony, Board of Consulting Ed.; J. Astley, Board of Consulting Ed.; F. Clooney, Board of Consulting Ed.; D. Browning, Board of Ed.; K. Gabriel, Board of Consulting Ed.; Theo Van Der Zee, Book Review Ed. **ISSN:** 0922-2936. **Subscription Rates:** EUR42 individuals print only; US\$57 individuals print only; EUR139 institutions electronic and print; US\$190 institutions electronic and print; EUR116 institutions online only; US\$158 institutions online only; EUR128 institutions print only; US\$174 institutions print only. **URL:** http://www.brill.nl/m_catalogue_sub6_id11324.htm.

48697 ■ Journal of Ethnopharmacology
Elsevier Science
c/o R. Verpoorte, Ed.-in-Ch.
Gorlaeus Laboratorium
Leiden University
HB024, Einsteinweg 55
NL-2333 CC Leiden, Netherlands
Publisher E-mail: nlinfo-f@elsevier.com
Journal devoted to the understanding of use of plants fungi, animals, microorganisms and minerals, and their biological and pharmacological effects based on the principles put forth in international conventions. **Founded:** 1979. **Freq:** 18/yr. **Key Personnel:** P.J. Houghton, Editor, peter.houghton@kcl.ac.uk; R. Verpoorte, Editor-in-Chief, jethnoph@chem.leidenuniv.nl; De-An Guo, Assoc. Ed.; P.K. Mukherjee, Assoc. Ed.; Schmeda G. Hirschmann, Assoc. Ed.; G. Bourdy, Editorial Board; S. Alban, Editorial Board; V. da Silva Bolzani, Editorial Board; E. Yesilada, Assoc. Ed.; M.J. Balick, Editorial Board. **ISSN:** 0378-8741. **Subscription Rates:** 390,700¥ institutions; EUR2,946 institutions for Europe; US\$3,294 institutions; US\$556 individuals; EUR415 individuals; 63,900¥ individuals. **Remarks:** Accepts advertising. **URL:** http://www.elsevier.com/wps/find/journaldescription.cws_home/506035/descriptiondescription. **Circ:** (Not Reported)

48698 ■ Journal for European Environmental & Planning Law
Brill Academic Publishers
PO Box 9000
NL-2300 PA Leiden, Netherlands
Ph: 31 71 5353500
Fax: 31 71 5317532
Publisher E-mail: marketing@brill.nl
Journal covering the European environmental planning, policies, and law. **Freq:** Quarterly. **Key Personnel:** Prof. Wolfgang Kock, Editor-in-Chief, wolfgang.koeck@ufz.de. **ISSN:** 1613-7272. **Subscription Rates:** EUR91 individuals print only; US\$124 individuals print; EUR302 institutions print and electronic; US\$412 institutions print and electronic; EUR252 institutions online only; US\$343 institutions online only; EUR277 institutions print only; US\$377 institutions print only. **URL:** http://www.brill.nl/jeep.

48699 ■ The Journal of Jewish Thought and Philosophy
Brill Academic Publishers
PO Box 9000
NL-2300 PA Leiden, Netherlands
Ph: 31 71 5353500
Fax: 31 71 5317532
Publisher E-mail: marketing@brill.nl
Journal covering Jewish thought, philosophy, and intellectual history. **Founded:** 1924. **Freq:** 2/yr. **Print Method:** Offcot. **Cols./Page:** 6. **Col. Width:** 12 nonpareils. **Col. Depth:** 294 agate lines. **Key Personnel:** Elliot R. Wolfson, Editor-in-Chief; Dana Hollander, Managing Editor; Catherine Chalier, Editor; Robert Gibbs, Editor; Irene Kajon, Editor; Michael Zank, Editor. **ISSN:** 1053-699X. **Subscription Rates:** EUR86 individuals print only; US\$117 individuals print only; EUR286 institutions print and electronic; US\$388 institutions print and electronic; EUR238 institutions online only; US\$324 institutions online only; EUR262 institutions print only; US\$356 institutions print only. **URL:** http://www.brill.nl/default.aspx?partid=18&pid=24577.

48700 ■ Journal of Phenomenological Psychology
Brill Academic Publishers
PO Box 9000
NL-2300 PA Leiden, Netherlands
Ph: 31 71 5353500
Fax: 31 71 5317532
Publisher E-mail: marketing@brill.nl
Peer-reviewed journal covering philosophy, psychology, and phenomenology. **Founded:** 1969. **Freq:** Semiannual. **Trim Size:** 6 x 9. **Cols./Page:** 1. **Key Personnel:** Frederick J. Wertz, Editor; Mufid James Hannush, Review Ed. **ISSN:** 0047-2662. **Subscription**

Circulation: ★ = ABC; △ = BPA; ◆ = CAC; • = CCAB; ❑ = VAC; ⊕ = PO Statement; ‡ = Publisher's Report; Boldface figures = sworn; Light figures = estimated.

Gale Directory of Publications & Broadcast Media/147th Ed.

5277

Rates: EUR45 individuals print; US$61 individuals print; EUR148 institutions electronic & print; US$201 institutions electroni & print; EUR123 institutions online only; US$181 institutions electronic & print; EUR135 institutions print; US$184 institutions print. **Remarks:** Accepts advertising. **URL:** http://www.brill.nl/default.aspx?partid=18&pid= 9387. **Circ:** Paid 350

48701 ■ Journal of Reformed Theology
Brill Academic Publishers
PO Box 9000
NL-2300 PA Leiden, Netherlands
Ph: 31 71 5353500
Fax: 31 71 5317532
Publisher E-mail: marketing@brill.nl
Peer-reviewed journal covering systematic, historical, and biblical theology. **Founded:** 1995. **Freq:** 3/yr. **Print Method:** Offset. **Cols./Page:** 6. **Col. Width:** 26 nonpareils. **Col. Depth:** 294 agate lines. **Key Personnel:** Eddy Van Der Borght, Editor-in-Chief. **ISSN:** 1872-5163. **Subscription Rates:** EUR58 individuals print only; US$79 individuals print only; EUR145 institutions print and electronic; US$197 institutions print and electronic; EUR121 institutions online only; US$165 institutions online only; EUR133 institutions print only; US$182 institutions print only. **URL:** http://www.brill.nl/jrt.

48702 ■ Journal of Religion in Africa
Brill Academic Publishers
PO Box 9000
NL-2300 PA Leiden, Netherlands
Ph: 31 71 5353500
Fax: 31 71 5317532
Publisher E-mail: marketing@brill.nl
Journal covering the religious traditions and their forms in Africa. Also includes religious texts in original African language. **Founded:** 1967. **Freq:** 4/yr. **Print Method:** Offset. **Trim Size:** 14 x 22. **Cols./Page:** 6. **Col. Width:** 12 picas. **Col. Depth:** 290.5 picas. **Key Personnel:** Brad Weiss, Editor; Adeline Masquelier, Editor. **ISSN:** 0022-4200. **Subscription Rates:** EUR130 individuals print only; US$177 individuals print only; EUR276 institutions print and electronic; US$375 institutions print and electronic; EUR230 institutions online only; US$313 institutions online only; EUR253 institutions print only; US$344 institutions print only. **URL:** http://www.brill.nl/default.aspx?partid=18&pid=7322.

48703 ■ Journal of Religion in Europe
Brill Academic Publishers
PO Box 9000
NL-2300 PA Leiden, Netherlands
Ph: 31 71 5353500
Fax: 31 71 5317532
Publisher E-mail: marketing@brill.nl
Peer-reviewed journal focusing on European religious practices. **Freq:** 3/yr. **Key Personnel:** Hans G. Kippenberg, Editor; Kocku von Stuckrad, Editor. **ISSN:** 1874-8910. **Subscription Rates:** EUR55 individuals; US$75 individuals; EUR167 institutions; US$228 institutions; EUR152 institutions online only; US$207 institutions online only. **URL:** http://www.brill.nl/jre.

48704 ■ Journal for the Study of Judaism
Brill Academic Publishers
PO Box 9000
NL-2300 PA Leiden, Netherlands
Ph: 31 71 5353500
Fax: 31 71 5317532
Publisher E-mail: marketing@brill.nl
Journal focusing on the history, literature and religious ideas on Judaism in the Persian, Hellenistic and Roman period. **Subtitle:** In the Persian, Hellenistic and Roman Period. **Founded:** 1970. **Freq:** 5/yr. **Key Personnel:** Garcia F. Martinez, Exec. Ed.; G. Stemberger, Editorial Board; J. Sievers, Editorial Board; E.J.C. Tigchelaar, Exec. Ed., jsj@rug.nl; H. Najman, Editor; J. Duhaime, Editorial Board; J.J. Collins, Editorial Board; Klostergaard A. Petersen, Editorial Board. **ISSN:** 0047-2212. **Subscription Rates:** EUR124 individuals print only; US$169 individuals print only; EUR341 institutions print and electronic; US$465 institutions print and electronic; EUR284 institutions online only; US$387 institutions online only; EUR312 institutions print only; US$426 institutions print only. **URL:** http://www.brill.nl/jsj.

48705 ■ KronoScope
Brill Academic Publishers
PO Box 9000
NL-2300 PA Leiden, Netherlands
Ph: 31 71 5353500
Fax: 31 71 5317532
Publisher E-mail: marketing@brill.nl
Journal providing a framework for an interdisciplinary dialogue about the nature of time. **Subtitle:** Journal for the Study of Time. **Freq:** 2/yr. **Key Personnel:** J.T. Fraser, Founding Ed.; Claudia Clausius, Managing Editor. **ISSN:** 1567-715X. **Subscription Rates:** EUR143 institutions online only; US$195 institutions online only. **URL:** http://www.brill.nl/m_catalogue_sub6_id9587.htm.

48706 ■ Late Antique Archaeology
Brill Academic Publishers
PO Box 9000
NL-2300 PA Leiden, Netherlands
Ph: 31 71 5353500
Fax: 31 71 5317532 .
Publisher E-mail: marketing@brill.nl
Journal covering information relating to the historical reconstruction of Mediterranean society, from AD 283 to approximately the middle of the 7th century. **Founded:** 1999. **Freq:** Annual. **Print Method:** Offset: **Trim Size:** 13 x 21. **Cols./Page:** 6. **Col. Width:** 2 1/16 inches. **Col. Depth:** 21 1/2 inches. **Key Personnel:** Luke Lavan, Managing Editor. **ISSN:** 1570-6893. **URL:** http://www.brill.nl/default.aspx?partid=18&pid=10809.

48707 ■ The Law and Practice of International Courts and Tribunals
Martinus Nijhoff
Plantijnstraat 2
NL-2321 JC Leiden, Netherlands
Ph: 31 715 353500
Fax: 31 715 317532
Journal aiming to provide articles and information on the law and practice of international courts and tribunals with particular emphasis on procedural questions. **Subtitle:** A Practitioners' Journal. **Freq:** Annual. **Key Personnel:** Eduardo Valencia-Ospina, Editor-in-Chief; Loretta Malintoppi, Managing Editor. **ISSN:** 1569-1853. **Subscription Rates:** EUR93 individuals; US$127 individuals; EUR306 institutions; US$416 institutions; EUR281 institutions print only; US$382 institutions print only. **URL:** http://www.brill.nl/m_catalogue_sub6_id18287.htm.

48708 ■ Medieval Encounters
Brill Academic Publishers
PO Box 9000
NL-2300 PA Leiden, Netherlands
Ph: 31 71 5353500
Fax: 31 71 5317532
Publisher E-mail: marketing@brill.nl
Journal encouraging a dialogue across cultural, linguistic and disciplinary boundaries on the interactions of Jewish, Christian and Muslim cultures from the fourth through to the sixteenth century. **Subtitle:** Jewish, Christian and Muslim Culture in Confluence and Dialogue. **Founded:** 1999. **Freq:** 4/yr. **Key Personnel:** Cynthia Robinson, Editor. **ISSN:** 1380-7854. **Subscription Rates:** EUR81 individuals print only; US$110 individuals print only; EUR268 institutions print and electronic; US$365 institutions print and electronic; EUR223 institutions online only; US$304 institutions online only; EUR245 institutions print only; EUR334 institutions print only. **Remarks:** Advertising accepted; rates available upon request. **URL:** http://www.brill.nl/m_catalogue_sub6_id7354.htm. **Circ:** (Not Reported)

48709 ■ Method & Theory in the Study of Religion
Brill Academic Publishers
PO Box 9000
NL-2300 PA Leiden, Netherlands
Ph: 31 71 5353500
Fax: 31 71 5317532
Publisher E-mail: marketing@brill.nl
Journal focusing on the theoretical and methodological issues in the study of religion from the academic point of view. **Subtitle:** Journal of the North American Association for the Study of Religion. **Founded:** 1989. **Freq:** Quarterly. **Key Personnel:** Armin Geertz, Editorial Board; Thomas E. Lawson, Editorial Board; John Morgan, Founding Ed.; Lorne Dawson, Editorial Board; Gary Lease, Editorial Board; Gregory Alles, Editorial Board; Tomoko Masuzawa, Editorial Board; Ann Baranowski, Founding Ed.; Donald Wiebe, Editorial Board; Prof. Matthew Day, Editor, mday@fsu.edu. **ISSN:** 0943-3058. **Subscription Rates:** EUR67 individuals print only; US$91 individuals print only; EUR222 institutions print and electronic; US$298 institutions print and electronic; EUR185 institutions online only; EUR252 institutions online only; EUR204 institutions print only; US$277 institutions print only. **URL:** http://www.brill.nl/m_catalogue_sub6_id7362.htm.

48710 ■ Middle East Journal of Culture and Communication
Brill Academic Publishers
PO Box 9000
NL-2300 PA Leiden, Netherlands
Ph: 31 71 5353500
Fax: 31 71 5317532
Publisher E-mail: marketing@brill.nl
Journal focusing on the culture and communication in Middle Eastern region. **Freq:** 3/yr. **Key Personnel:** Lina Khatib, Editor; Tarik Sabry, Editor; Dina Matar, Editor. **ISSN:** 1873-9857. **Subscription Rates:** EUR55 individuals print only; US$75 individuals print only; EUR198 institutions print and electronic; US$269 institutions print and electronic; EUR165 institutions online only; US$225 institutions online only; EUR182 institutions print only; US$248 institutions print only. **URL:** http://www.brill.nl/mjcc.

48711 ■ Middle East Law and Governance
Brill Academic Publishers
PO Box 9000
NL-2300 PA Leiden, Netherlands
Ph: 31 71 5353500
Fax: 31 71 5317532
Publisher E-mail: marketing@brill.nl
Peer-reviewed journal covering law and governance issues in the Middle Eastern region. **Freq:** Semiannual. **Key Personnel:** Anver Emon, Editor; Ellen Lust-Okar, Editor; Audrey Macklin, Editor. **ISSN:** 1876-3367. **Subscription Rates:** EUR52 individuals; US$71 individuals; EUR157 institutions; US$215 institutions; EUR143 institutions online only; US$195 institutions online only. **URL:** http://www.brill.nl/melg.

48712 ■ Mnemosyne
E.J. Brill
PO Box 9000
NL-2300 PA Leiden, Netherlands
Ph: 31 715 353500
Fax: 31 715 317532
Publication E-mail: mnemosyne@let.vu.nl
Publisher E-mail: cs@brill.nl
Periodical focusing on history. **Subtitle:** A Journal of Classical Studies. **Freq:** Quarterly. **Key Personnel:** G.J. Boter, Editorial Board; A. Chaniotis, Editorial Board; K. Coleman, Editorial Board; I.J.F. de Jong, Editorial Board. **ISSN:** 0026-7074. **Subscription Rates:** EUR130 individuals; US$177 individuals; EUR490 institutions; US$666 institutions; EUR408 institutions online only; US$555 institutions online only. **Remarks:** Advertising accepted; rates available upon request. **URL:** http://www.brill.nl/default.aspx?partid=212&pid=7366. **Circ:** (Not Reported)

48713 ■ Nematology
Brill Academic Publishers
PO Box 9000
NL-2300 PA Leiden, Netherlands
Ph: 31 71 5353500
Fax: 31 71 5317532
Publisher E-mail: marketing@brill.nl
Journal dealing with all aspects of nematological research. **Subtitle:** International Journal of Fundamental and Applied Nematological Research. **Freq:** 6/yr. **Key Personnel:** Roland Perry, Editor-in-Chief, roland.perry@bbsrc.ac.uk; David Hunt, Editor-in-Chief, d.hunt@cabi.org; Ralf Udo Ehlers, Editorial Board; Pierre Abad, Editorial Board; Howard Ferris, Editorial Board; John Jones, Editorial Board; David J. Chitwood, Editorial Board. **ISSN:** 1388-5545. **Subscription Rates:** EUR816 institutions print and electronic; US$1,111 institutions print and electronic; EUR680 institutions online only; US$925 institutions online only; EUR748 institutions print only; US$1,018 institutions print only. **URL:** http://www.brill.nl/m_catalogue_sub6_id8548.htm.

48714 ■ Nordic Journal of International Law
Brill Academic Publishers
PO Box 9000
NL-2300 PA Leiden, Netherlands
Ph: 31 71 5353500
Fax: 31 71 5317532
Publisher E-mail: marketing@brill.nl
Journal providing a platform in the Nordic countries for exchange of ideas on legal developments in the international and European countries. **Subtitle:** Acta Scandinavica Juris Gentium. **Founded:** 1930. **Freq:** 4/yr. **Key Personnel:** Anna Maria Nawrot, Managing Editor; Frederik Danelius, Editorial Board; Gudmundur Alfredsson, Co-Ed.; Michael Bogdan, Book Review Ed.; Sten Harck, Co-Ed.; Thordis Ingadottir, Editorial Board; Christina Johnsson, Editor-in-Chief. **ISSN:** 0902-7351. **Subscription Rates:** EUR151 individuals print only; US$206 individuals print only; EUR499 institutions print and electronic; US$679 institutions print and electronic; EUR416 institutions online only; US$566 institutions on-

line only; EUR458 institutions print only; US$623 institutions print only. **URL:** http://www.brill.nl/m_catalogue_sub6_id18325.htm.

48715 ■ Novum Testamentum
Brill Academic Publishers
PO Box 9000
NL-2300 PA Leiden, Netherlands
Ph: 31 71 5353500
Fax: 31 71 5317532
Publisher E-mail: marketing@brill.nl
Journal dedicated to the study of the New Testament and related subjects. **Subtitle:** An International Quarterly for New Testament and Related Studies. **Freq:** 4/yr. **Key Personnel:** C. Breytenbach, Exec. Ed.; J. Thom, Exec. Ed. **ISSN:** 0048-1009. **Subscription Rates:** EUR86 individuals print only; US$117 individuals print only; EUR286 institutions print and electronic; US$388 institutions print and electronic; EUR238 institutions online only; US$324 institutions online only; EUR262 institutions print only; US$356 institutions print only. **URL:** http://www.brill.nl/m_catalogue_sub6_id7400.htm.

48716 ■ Phronesis
Brill Academic Publishers
PO Box 9000
NL-2300 PA Leiden, Netherlands
Ph: 31 71 5353500
Fax: 31 71 5317532
Publisher E-mail: marketing@brill.nl
Scholarly journal on the study of ancient Greek and Roman thought in the context of philosophy, psychology, metaphysics, epistemology and the philosophy of science and medicine from its origins down to the end of the sixth century A.D. **Subtitle:** A Journal for Ancient Philosophy. **Founded:** 1955. **Freq:** 5/yr. **Key Personnel:** Prof. Verity Harte, Editor, verity.harte@yale.edu; Prof. Christof Rapp, Editor; K.A. Algra, Editorial Board; J. Barnes, Editorial Board. **ISSN:** 0031-8868. **Subscription Rates:** EUR90 individuals; EUR274 institutions; EUR249 institutions online only; US$122 individuals; US$373 institutions; US$339 institutions online only. **URL:** http://www.brill.nl/m_catalogue_sub6_id7431.htm.

48717 ■ Proceedings of the Boston Area Colloquium in Ancient Philosophy
Brill Academic Publishers
PO Box 9000
NL-2300 PA Leiden, Netherlands
Ph: 31 71 5353500
Fax: 31 71 5317532
Publisher E-mail: marketing@brill.nl
Journal covering ancient philosophical topics such as a new way of linking Aristotle's Metaphysics and De Anima through a dynamic understanding of substance. **Founded:** Oct. 1963. **Freq:** Annual. **Print Method:** Offset. **Cols./Page:** 6. **Col. Width:** 2 1/10 inches. **Col. Depth:** 21 inches. **Key Personnel:** John J. Cleary, Editor; Gary M. Gurtler S.J., Editor. **ISSN:** 1059-986X. **URL:** http://www.brill.nl/m_catalogue_sub6_id9064.htm.

48718 ■ Psychological Research Psychologische Forschung
Springer-Verlag
c/o Bernard Hommel, Ed.
Dept. of Psychology
Leiden University
2300 Leiden, Netherlands
Journal publishing articles that help in fundamental understanding of human perception, attention, memory, and action. **Freq:** 6/yr. **Key Personnel:** P.A. Frensch, Editorial Advisory Board; Digby Elliot, Editorial Advisory Board; H. Heuer, Assoc. Ed.; Axel Buchner, Editorial Advisory Board; Asher Cohen, Editorial Advisory Board; Ulrich Ansorge, Editorial Advisory Board. **ISSN:** 0340-0727. **Subscription Rates:** EUR1,406 institutions print incl. free access; EUR1,687.20 institutions print incl. enhanced access. **Remarks:** Advertising accepted; rates available upon request. **URL:** http://www.springer.com/psychology/journal/426. **Circ:** (Not Reported)

48719 ■ Religion and Human Rights
Brill Academic Publishers
PO Box 9000
NL-2300 PA Leiden, Netherlands
Ph: 31 71 5353500
Fax: 31 71 5317532
Publisher E-mail: marketing@brill.nl
Journal covering the interactions, conflicts and reconciliations between religions or beliefs, and systems for the promotion and protection of human rights. **Subtitle:** An International Journal. **Founded:** 1888. **Freq:** 3/yr. **Print**

Method: Offset. **Cols./Page:** 6. **Col. Width:** 2 1/16 inches. **Col. Depth:** 21 1/2 inches. **Key Personnel:** Dr. Nazila Ghanea, Managing Editor; Prof. Gudmundur Alfredsson, Advisory Board. **ISSN:** 1871-031X. **Subscription Rates:** EUR54 individuals print only; US$73 individuals print only; EUR180 institutions print and electronic; US$245 institutions print and electronic; EUR150 institutions online only; US$204 institutions online only; EUR165 institutions print only, US$224 Institutions print only. **URL:** http://www.brill.nl/rhrs.

48720 ■ Religion and Theology
Brill Academic Publishers
PO Box 9000
NL-2300 PA Leiden, Netherlands
Ph: 31 71 5353500
Fax: 31 71 5317532
Publisher E-mail: marketing@brill.nl
Peer-reviewed journal covering contemporary developments in religion and theology. **Subtitle:** A Journal of Contemporary Religious Discourse. **Founded:** 1994. **Freq:** 2/yr. **Print Method:** Offset. **Trim Size:** 10 1/4 x 13. **Cols./Page:** 6. **Col. Width:** 13 inches. **Col. Depth:** 240 agate lines. **Key Personnel:** Gerhard A. van den Heever, Exec. Ed., religion&theology@unisa.ac.za. **ISSN:** 1023-0807. **Subscription Rates:** EUR65 individuals; US$88 individuals; EUR197 institutions; US$268 institutions; EUR179 institutions online only; US$244 institutions online only. **URL:** http://www.brill.nl/default.aspx?partid=18&pid=7460.

48721 ■ Research in Phenomenology
Brill Academic Publishers
PO Box 9000
NL-2300 PA Leiden, Netherlands
Ph: 31 71 5353500
Fax: 31 71 5317532
Publisher E-mail: marketing@brill.nl
Professional journal covering phenomenological philosophy. **Founded:** 1970. **Freq:** 3/yr. **Trim Size:** 6 x 9. **Cols./Page:** 1. **Key Personnel:** John Sallis, Editor. **ISSN:** 0085-5553. **Subscription Rates:** EUR79 individuals print; US$108 individuals print; EUR262 institutions electronic & print; US$356 institutions electronic & print; EUR218 institutions online only; US$297 institutions online only; EUR240 institutions print; US$327 institutions print. **Remarks:** Accepts advertising. **URL:** http://www.brill.nl/default.aspx?partid=18&pid=9390. **Circ:** Paid 200

48722 ■ Russian History
Brill Academic Publishers
PO Box 9000
NL-2300 PA Leiden, Netherlands
Ph: 31 71 5353500
Fax: 31 71 5317532
Publisher E-mail: marketing@brill.nl
Journal featuring articles on the history of Russia. **Freq:** Quarterly. **Key Personnel:** Lawrence N. Langer, Editor-in-Chief. **ISSN:** 0094-288X. **Subscription Rates:** EUR58 individuals print only; US$79 individuals print only; EUR193 institutions print and electronic; US$263 institutions print and electronic; EUR161 institutions online only; US$219 institutions online only; EUR177 institutions print only; US$241 institutions print only. **URL:** http://www.brill.nl/ruhi.

48723 ■ Seeing and Perceiving
Brill Academic Publishers
PO Box 9000
NL-2300 PA Leiden, Netherlands
Ph: 31 71 5353500
Fax: 31 71 5317532
Publisher E-mail: marketing@brill.nl
Journal covering geospatial and information technology. **Subtitle:** An International Journal on Computation, Perception, Attention and Action. **Founded:** 1957. **Freq:** 6/yr. **Print Method:** Offset. **Cols./Page:** 6. **Col. Width:** 12 picas. **Col. Depth:** 21 1/2 inches. **Key Personnel:** Concetta Morrone, Editor-in-Chief; Adam Reeves, Editor-in-Chief, reeves@neu.edu. **ISSN:** 1878-4755. **Subscription Rates:** EUR156 individuals print only; US$212 individuals print only; EUR516 institutions print and electronic; US$703 institutions print and electronic; EUR430 institutions online only; US$585 institutions online only; EUR473 institutions print only; US$644 institutions print only. **URL:** http://www.brill.nl/sp. **Formerly:** Spatial Vision.

48724 ■ Social Sciences and Missions
Brill Academic Publishers
PO Box 9000
NL-2300 PA Leiden, Netherlands
Ph: 31 71 5353500
Fax: 31 71 5317532

Publication E-mail: ssmbrill@gmail.com
Publisher E-mail: marketing@brill.nl
Peer-reviewed journal on social sciences and Christian missions. **Freq:** Semiannual. **Key Personnel:** Eric Morier-Genoud, Editor; Wendy Urban-Mead, Editor. **ISSN:** 1874-8937. **Subscription Rates:** EUR55 individuals; US$75 individuals; EUR116 institutions; US$157 institutions; EUR105 institutions online only; US$143 institutions online only. **URL:** http://www.brill.nl/ssm.

48725 ■ Southeastern Europe
Brill Academic Publishers
PO Box 9000
NL-2300 PA Leiden, Netherlands
Ph: 31 71 5353500
Fax: 31 71 5317532
Publisher E-mail: marketing@brill.nl
Peer-reviewed journal publishing research articles on the new developments in Southeastern Europe. **Freq:** Annual. **Key Personnel:** Anna Krasteva, Editor; Stefano Bianchini, Editor. **ISSN:** 0094-4467. **Subscription Rates:** EUR30 individuals; US$41 individuals; EUR90 institutions; US$123 institutions; EUR82 institutions online only; US$112 institutions online only. **URL:** http://www.brill.nl/seeu.

48726 ■ The Soviet and Post-Soviet Review
Brill Academic Publishers
PO Box 9000
NL-2300 PA Leiden, Netherlands
Ph: 31 71 5353500
Fax: 31 71 5317532
Publisher E-mail: marketing@brill.nl
Peer-reviewed journal featuring articles on modern Russia's social history. **Freq:** Semiannual. **Key Personnel:** Christopher J. Ward, Editor-in-Chief. **ISSN:** 1075-1262. **Subscription Rates:** EUR29 individuals; US$39 individuals; EUR88 institutions; US$120 institutions; EUR80 institutions online only; US$109 institutions online only. **URL:** http://www.brill.nl/spsr.

48727 ■ Terrestrial Arthropod Reviews
Brill Academic Publishers
PO Box 9000
NL-2300 PA Leiden, Netherlands
Ph: 31 71 5353500
Fax: 31 71 5317532
Publisher E-mail: marketing@brill.nl
Journal featuring articles on terrestrial arthropods. **Freq:** Semiannual. **Key Personnel:** Jorge A. Santiago-Blay, PhD, Editor-in-Chief, blayjorge@gmail.com. **ISSN:** 1874-9828. **Subscription Rates:** EUR74 individuals print only; US$99 individuals print only; EUR223 institutions print and electronic; US$304 institutions print and electronic; EUR186 institutions online only; US$253 institutions online only; EUR205 institutions print only; US$278 institutions print only. **URL:** http://www.brill.nl/tar.

48728 ■ T'oung Pao
Brill Academic Publishers
PO Box 9000
NL-2300 PA Leiden, Netherlands
Ph: 31 71 5353500
Fax: 31 71 5317532
Publisher E-mail: marketing@brill.nl
Peer-reviewed journal publishing information on all aspects of traditional China. **Subtitle:** International Journal of Chinese Studies. **Freq:** 2/yr. **Key Personnel:** P.-E. Will, Editor; Ter B. Haar, Editor. **ISSN:** 0082-5433. **Subscription Rates:** EUR91 individuals; US$124 individuals; EUR260 institutions; US$353 institutions; EUR236 institutions online only; US$321 institutions online only. **Remarks:** Advertising accepted; rates available upon request. **URL:** http://www.brill.nl/m_catalogue_sub6_id7547.htm. **Circ:** (Not Reported)

48729 ■ Vetus Testamentum
International Organization for the Study of The Old Testament
Organisation Internationale pour l'Etude de l'Ancien Testament
Faculty of Theology, Leiden Univ.
PO Box 9515
NL-2300 RA Leiden, Netherlands
Ph: 31 715 272577
Fax: 31 715 272571
Publication covering the Bible in English, French and German. **Freq:** Quarterly. **Key Personnel:** A. Van Der Kooij, Executive Ed.; A. Lemaire, Editorial Board; R.P. Gordon, Book Review Ed.; H.G.M. Williamson, Editorial Board; C. Newsom, Editorial Board; H. Spieckermann, Editorial Board; G. Knoppers, Editorial Board; Trebolle J. Barrera, Editorial Board; H.M. Barstad, Editorial

Board; A. Hurvitz, Editorial Board. **ISSN:** 0042-4935. **Subscription Rates:** EUR115 individuals print; US$156 individuals print; EUR410 institutions print and electronic; US$558 institutions print and electronic; EUR342 institutions online only; US$465 institutions online only; EUR376 institutions print; US$512 institutions print. **URL:** http://www.brill.nl/vt.

48730 ■ Zutot
Brill Academic Publishers
PO Box 9000
NL-2300 PA Leiden, Netherlands
Ph: 31 71 5353500
Fax: 31 71 5317532
Publisher E-mail: marketing@brill.nl
Journal featuring articles on Jewish studies. **Subtitle:** Perspectives on Jewish Culture. **Freq:** Annual. **Key Personnel:** Shlomo Berger, Editor; Michael Brocke, Editor; Irene Zwiep, Editor. **ISSN:** 1571-7283. **Subscription Rates:** EUR31 individuals print only; US$42 individuals print only; EUR102 institutions print and electronic; US$138 institutions print and electronic; EUR85 institutions online only; US$116 institutions online only; EUR94 institutions print only; US$128 institutions print only. **URL:** http://www.brill.nl/zuto.

Maarssen

48731 ■ Fietsmarkt
Blauw Media Uitgeverij B.V.
Straatweg 28
NL-3604 BB Maarssen, Netherlands
Ph: 31 346 574040
Fax: 31 346 576056
Publication E-mail: fietsmarkt.redactie@blauwmedia.com
Publisher E-mail: info@blauwmedia.com
Trade journal covering the Dutch and Belgian bicycle and scooter industry. **Founded:** 1995. **Freq:** 8/yr. **Print Method:** Offset. **Trim Size:** 210 x 297 mm. **ISSN:** 1383-6604. **URL:** http://www.blauwmediauitgeverij.nl/fietsmarkt. **Ad Rates:** BW: EUR1,475, 4C: EUR2,710. **Circ:** Combined 3,600

48732 ■ Mannenmode
Blauw Media Uitgeverij B.V.
Straatweg 28
NL-3604 BB Maarssen, Netherlands
Ph: 31 346 574040
Fax: 31 346 576056
Publication E-mail: mannenmode.redactie@blauwmedia.com
Publisher E-mail: info@blauwmedia.com
Trade magazine for the men's fashion industry. **Founded:** Jan. 1984. **Freq:** Quarterly. **Print Method:** Offset. **Trim Size:** 235 x 322 mm. **Key Personnel:** Henk Louwmans, Publisher, phone 31 346 582467, louwmans@blauwmedia.com. **Subscription Rates:** EUR47.20 individuals The Netherlands; EUR49.50 individuals Belgium. **URL:** http://www.vakbladmannenmode.nl. **Ad Rates:** BW: EUR1,445, 4C: EUR2,480. **Circ:** Paid 2,400

48733 ■ Tred
Blauw Media Uitgeverij B.V.
Straatweg 28
NL-3604 BB Maarssen, Netherlands
Ph: 31 346 574040
Fax: 31 346 576056
Publication E-mail: tred.redactie@blauwmedia.com
Publisher E-mail: info@blauwmedia.com
Trade magazine covering the shoe industry in the Netherlands and Belgium. **Founded:** Feb. 1979. **Freq:** Annual. **Print Method:** Offset. **Trim Size:** 235 x 322 mm. **Key Personnel:** Henk Louwmans, Publisher, phone 31 346 582467, h.louwmans@blauwmedia.com. **ISSN:** 0169-6173. **Subscription Rates:** EUR89.99 individuals the Netherlands; EUR97.25 individuals Belgium. **URL:** http://www.vakbladtred.nl. **Ad Rates:** BW: EUR1,415, 4C: EUR2,445. **Circ:** Combined 3,100

48734 ■ Trend Boutique
Blauw Media Uitgeverij B.V.
Straatweg 28
NL-3604 BB Maarssen, Netherlands
Ph: 31 346 574040
Fax: 31 346 576056
Publication E-mail: trendboutique.advertenties@blauwmedia.com
Publisher E-mail: info@blauwmedia.com
Trade journal covering leather goods and fashion accessories for retailers. **Freq:** Bimonthly. **Print Method:** Offset. **Trim Size:** 235 x 322 mm. **Key Personnel:**

Ronald Mulder, Advertising; Henk Louwans, Publisher. **Subscription Rates:** EUR42.25 The Netherlands; EUR46.10 Belgium; EUR72.10 other countries. **Remarks:** Accepts advertising. **URL:** http://www.vakbladtrendboutique.nl/. **Ad Rates:** BW: EUR1,020, 4C: EUR1,785. **Circ:** Combined 2,200

48735 ■ Trends
Blauw Media Uitgeverij B.V.
Straatweg 28
NL-3604 BB Maarssen, Netherlands
Ph: 31 346 574040
Fax: 31 346 576056
Publisher E-mail: info@blauwmedia.com
Trade journal for glass, porcelain, pottery, luxury household goods, applied arts and giftware retailers, wholesalers, manufacturers and others. **Freq:** Monthly. **Print Method:** Offset. **Trim Size:** 210 x 297 mm. **Remarks:** Accepts advertising. **URL:** http://www.vakbladtred.nl/. **Circ:** 4,500

Maastricht

48736 ■ European Economic Review
Elsevier Science Inc.
University of Maastricht
Faculty of Economics & Business Administration
Tongersestraat 53
NL-6211 LM Maastricht, Netherlands
Publisher E-mail: usinfo-ehelp@elsevier.com
Journal for the development and application of economics science in Europe. **Founded:** 1969. **Freq:** 8/yr. **Print Method:** Offset. **Trim Size:** 6 x 10 1/2. **Cols./Page:** 3. **Col. Width:** 10 picas. **Col. Depth:** 9 5/8 inches. **Key Personnel:** T. Gylfason, Editor; Z. Eckstein, Editor; S. Baliga, Assoc. Ed.; H. Fang, Assoc. Ed.; G.A. Pfann, Editor, eer@ke.unimaas.nl; Y. Chen, Assoc. Ed.; H. Bleichrodt, Assoc. Ed.; J. Albrecht, Assoc. Ed.; A. Dukes, Assoc. Ed.; E. Gal-Or, Editor; J. Von Hagen, Editor. **ISSN:** 0014-2921. **Subscription Rates:** US$1,835 institutions, other countries except Europe, Japan and Iran; EUR1,835 institutions for European countries and Iran; 243,300¥ institutions; US$66 other countries except Europe, Japan and Iran; EUR62 individuals for European countries and Iran; 8,700¥ individuals. **URL:** http://www.elsevier.com/wps/find/journaldescription.cws_home/505541/descriptiondescription. **Circ:** (Not Reported)

48737 ■ Journal of Behavior Therapy and Experimental Psychiatry
Mosby Inc.
c/o A. Arntz, Co-Ed.
Dept. of Medical, Clinical & Experimental Psychology
PO Box 616
6200 Maastricht, Netherlands
Publisher E-mail: custserv.ehs@elsevier.com
Journal publishing experimental tests of psychological approaches to mental disorders, though contributions from biology and / or non-experimental disciplines. **Founded:** 1970. **Freq:** Quarterly. **Key Personnel:** A. Arntz, Co-Ed., btep@maastrichtuniversity.nl; M. Van Den Hout, Co-Ed., m.vandenhout@fss.uu.nl; J. Reyna, Consulting Ed.; J. Wolpe, Co-Founding Ed.; J. Forsyth, Editorial Board; J.G. Asmundson, Editorial Board; L.E. Alden, Editorial Board; M. Basoglu, Editorial Board; R. Bentall, Editorial Board. **ISSN:** 0005-7916. **Subscription Rates:** EUR152 individuals European countries and Iran; US$189 other countries except Europe, Japan and Iran; 21,700¥ individuals; EUR903 institutions European countries and Iran; US$1,012 institutions, other countries except Europe, Japan and Iran; 120,000¥ institutions. **Remarks:** Accepts advertising. **URL:** http://www.elsevier.com/wps/find/journaldescription.cws_home/339/descriptiondescription. **Circ:** (Not Reported)

48738 ■ Journal of Chemical Neuroanatomy
Elsevier Science
c/o Harry W.M. Steinbusch, Ed.-in-Ch.
European Graduate School of Neuroscience (EURON)
Department of Psychiatry & Neuropsychology
Maastricht University, Postbus 616
6200 Maastricht, Netherlands
Publisher E-mail: nlinfo-f@elsevier.com
Peer-reviewed journal reporting on the functional and biochemical aspects of the nervous system with its microanatomical organization. The study including highly sensitive techniques chemical microassays, hybridoma technology, immunocytochemistry, in situ hybridization and receptor radioautography and so on. **Founded:** 1994. **Freq:** 8/yr. **Key Personnel:** Harry W.M. Steinbusch, Editor-in-Chief, cheneu@np.unimaas.nl; G.S. Aston-Jones, Editorial Advisory Board; J.C. Bittencourt,

Editorial Advisory Board. **ISSN:** 0891-0618. **Subscription Rates:** EUR1,458 institutions; US$1,628 institutions all countries except Europe and Japan; 193,300¥ institutions for Japan; EUR174 individuals; US$235 individuals; 27,000¥ individuals. **Remarks:** Accepts advertising. **URL:** http://www.elsevier.com/wps/find/journaldescription.cws_home/524994/description. **Circ:** (Not Reported)

Meppel

48739 ■ Kijk op Oost Nederland
Periodiek en Partners
Postbus 41
NL-7940 AA Meppel, Netherlands
Ph: 31 572855333
Fax: 31 572855300
Publisher E-mail: uitg@giethoorn-tenbrink.nl
Professional magazine covering business. **Founded:** 1981. **Freq:** 8/year. **Print Method:** Offset. **Trim Size:** 225 x 297 mm. **Remarks:** Accepts advertising. **URL:** http://www.gmgroep.nl/kijkopoostnederland/. **Circ:** Combined 8,229

Nieuwegein

48740 ■ Beatles Unlimited Magazine
Beatles Unlimited
PO Box 602
NL-3430 AP Nieuwegein, Netherlands
Ph: 31 306 063678
Fan magazine covering the Beatles in Dutch, English and German. **Founded:** Nov. 10, 1963. **Freq:** Bimonthly. **Print Method:** Offset. **ISSN:** 1384-296X. **Subscription Rates:** EUR37 individuals by registered mail; EUR38.50 individuals by paypal; US$56 individuals registered mail; EUR40.50 individuals non European Union countries. **URL:** http://www.beatles-unlimited.com. **Circ:** 3,575

48741 ■ Nederlands Tandartsenblad
Nederlandse Maatschappij tot bevordering der Tandheelkunde
Geelgors 1
3435 CA Nieuwegein, Netherlands
Ph: 31 30 6076251
Publication E-mail: nt@nmt.nl
Publisher E-mail: nmt@nmt.nl
Professional magazine covering dentistry in the Netherlands. **Freq:** Semimonthly. **Key Personnel:** Reinier van de Vrie, Contact, phone 31 30 6076303, r.vandevrie@nmt.nl; Evert Berkel, Contact, e.berkel@nmt.nl. **Subscription Rates:** EUR172.50 nonmembers; EUR27 individuals outside Europe; EUR10.25 single issue. **Remarks:** Accepts advertising. **URL:** http://www.ntblad.nl/. **Circ:** (Not Reported)

Nigtevecht

48742 ■ International Journal of Risk and Safety in Medicine
IOS Press, B.V.
c/o C.J. Van Boxtel, Ed.
Korte Velterslaan 10
NL-1393 PB Nigtevecht, Netherlands
Ph: 31 294 251448
Publisher E-mail: info@iospress.nl
Journal concerned with rendering the practice of medicine as safe as it can be, promoting the highest possible quality of care, and examining how those risks which are inevitable can be contained and managed with particular attention given to a number of major fields, including drugs and vaccines, surgery and anesthesia, gynecology and obstetrics, medical equipment and materials, and alternative medicine. **Freq:** Quarterly. **Key Personnel:** C.J. Van Boxtel, Editor, cvboxtel@xs4all.nl; C. Vincent, Assoc. Ed., c.vincent@imperial.ac.uk. **ISSN:** 0924-6479. **Subscription Rates:** EUR150 individuals online only; US$180 individuals online only; EUR728 individuals online + online back volumes; US$1,008 individuals online + online back volumes; EUR558 individuals print and online; US$775 individuals print and online. **URL:** http://www.iospress.nl/loadtop/load.php?isbn=09246479.

Nijmegen

48743 ■ Early Science and Medicine
Brill Academic Publishers
c/o Dr. Christoph Luthy, PhD, Ed.
Faculty of Philosophy
Radboud University Nijmegen
PO Box 9103

NL-6500 HD Nijmegen, Netherlands
Publisher E-mail: marketing@brill.nl
Peer-reviewed journal devoted to the history of science, medicine and technology from the earliest times through the end of the eighteenth century. It lays emphasis on the text-based traditions that connect antiquity with the Middle Ages, the Renaissance, and the early modern period. **Subtitle:** A Journal for the Study of Science, Technology and Medicine in the Pre-modern Period. **Freq:** 6/yr. **Key Personnel:** Christoph Luthy, PhD, Editor; Andre Goddu, Book Review Ed.; Stefano Caroti, Editorial Board; Ann Hanson, Editorial Board; Michael Hunter, Editorial Board; Anita Guerrini, Editorial Ed. **ISSN:** 1383-7427. **Subscription Rates:** EUR65 individuals; US$88 individuals; EUR271 institutions; US$369 institutions; EUR246 institutions online only; US$335 institutions online only. **URL:** http://www.ru.nl/filosofie/geschiedenis/onderzoek/center_for_the/center_documents/esm/; http://www.brill.nl/m_catalogue_sub6_id7207.htm.

48744 ■ European Journal of Psychological Assessment
Hogrefe & Huber Publishers
c/o Eric E.J. De Bruyn, Ed.-in-Ch.
Behavioral Science Institute
Radboud University
PO Box 9104
NL-6500 HE Nijmegen, Netherlands
Ph: 31 24 6312123
Fax: 31 24 3612776
Publisher E-mail: customerservice@hogrefe-publishing.com
Journal covering articles on theoretical and applied developments in psychology. **Founded:** 1986. **Freq:** Quarterly. **Print Method:** Offset. **Trim Size:** 8 1/4 x 11. **Key Personnel:** Karl Schweizer, Editor, k.schweizer@psych.uni-frankfurt.de; Eric E.J. De Bruyn, Editor-in-Chief, e.debruyn@pwo.ru.nl; Michael Schreiner, Editorial Asst., schreiner@psych.uni-frankfurt.de; Valentin Bucik, Assoc. Ed.; Antonio Godoy, Assoc. Ed. **ISSN:** 1015-5759. **Subscription Rates:** EUR306 institutions; EUR224 institutions; US$168 individuals; EUR120 individuals; US$102 single issue; EUR74 single issue; US$95 members special rates for IAAP; EUR68 members special rates for IAAP. **Remarks:** Accepts advertising. **URL:** http://www.hogrefe.com/index.php?mod=journals&action=1&site=ejpa. **Ad Rates:** BW: 600 f. **Circ:** 800

48745 ■ Neurocomputing
Elsevier Science Inc.
c/o T. Heskes, Ed.-in-Ch.
Radboud University Nijmegen, ICIS
Toernooiveld 1
NL-6500 Nijmegen, Netherlands
Ph: 31 24 3652696
Fax: 31 24 3554074
Publisher E-mail: usinfo-ehelp@elsevier.com
Peer-reviewed journal featuring recent fundamental contributions in the field of neurocomputing. **Founded:** 1989. **Freq:** 18/yr. **Key Personnel:** T. Heskes, Editor-in-Chief, neucom-eo@elsevier.com. **ISSN:** 0925-2312. **Subscription Rates:** 342,000¥ institutions; EUR2,579 institutions for European countries and Iran; US$2,884 institutions, other countries except Europe, Japan and Iran. **URL:** http://www.elsevier.com/wps/find/journaldescription.cws_home/505628/descriptiondescription.

Renkum

48746 ■ Journal of Vegetation Science
International Association for Vegetation Science
Internationale Vereinigung fur Vegetationskunde
c/o Nina A.C. Smits
Wes Beekhuizenweg 3
NL-6871 VJ Renkum, Netherlands
Publisher E-mail: nina.smits@wur.nl
Journal covering botany. **Freq:** Bimonthly. **Key Personnel:** Alessandro Chiarucci, Editor-in-Chief, chiarucci@unisi.it. **ISSN:** 1100-9233. **Subscription Rates:** US$133 institutions print and online student members; 147 institutions print and online student members; EUR102 institutions print and online student members; EUR112 institutions print & online. **Remarks:** Advertising not accepted. **URL:** http://www.iavs.org/. **Circ:** (Not Reported)

Rijswijk

48747 ■ Immunogenetics
Springer-Verlag Tokyo
Biomedical Primate Research Centre

Dept. of Immunobiology
Lange Kleiweg 139
PO Box 3306
NL-2280 GH Rijswijk, Netherlands
Ph: 31 15 2842688
Fax: 31 15 2843987
Publisher E-mail: info@springer.jp
Journal publishing original papers, brief communications, and reviews on research in immunogenetics of cell interaction, immunogenetics of tissue differentiation and development, phylogeny of alloantigens and of immune response, genetic control of immune response and disease susceptibility, and genetics and biochemistry of alloantigens. **Freq:** Monthly. **Key Personnel:** Dr. Ronald E. Bontrop, Editor-in-Chief; P. Demant, Editorial Board; Masanori Kasahara, Co-Ed.; S. Beck, Editorial Board; R. Miller, Editorial Board; M. Carrington, Editorial Board; Dr. Martin F. Flajnik, Co-Ed.; J.D. Hansen, Editorial Board; D. Devine, Desk Ed.; N. Barclay, Editorial Board. **ISSN:** 0093-7711. **Subscription Rates:** EUR2,400 institutions print incl. free access or e-only; EUR2,880 institutions print incl. enhanced access. **Remarks:** Advertising accepted; rates available upon request. **URL:** http://www.springer.com/biomed/immunology/journal/251. **Circ:** (Not Reported)

Rotterdam

48748 ■ Best Practice & Research
Elsevier Science Inc.
c/o E.J. Kuipers, Ed.-in-Ch.
Department of Gastroenterology & Hepatology
Gravendijkwal 230
NL-3015 CE Rotterdam, Netherlands
Publisher E-mail: usinfo-ehelp@elsevier.com
Journal providing information on current clinical practice and specialty of gastroenterology. **Subtitle:** Clinical Gastroenterology. **Founded:** 1978. **Freq:** 6/yr. **Print Method:** Offset. **Trim Size:** 13 3/4 x 21 1/2. **Cols./Page:** 6. **Col. Width:** 5 nonpareils. **Col. Depth:** 21 1/2 inches. **Key Personnel:** V. Isakov, Editorial Board; E.J. Kuipers, Editor-in-Chief; M. Manns, Editorial Board; P. Marteau, Editorial Board; K.E.L. McColl, Editorial Board; J. Neuberger, Editorial Board; F. Pallone, Editorial Board. **ISSN:** 1521-6918. **Subscription Rates:** US$580 institutions, other countries except Europe, Japan and Iran; 70,600¥ institutions; EUR655 institutions for European countries and Iran; 52,300¥ individuals Japan; US$429 other countries except Europe, Japan and Iran; EUR484 individuals for European countries and Iran. **URL:** http://www.elsevier.com/wps/find/journaldescription.cws_home/623002/descriptiondescription.

48749 ■ Corporate Reputation Review
Palgrave Macmillan
PO Box 1738
3000 Rotterdam, Netherlands
Publisher E-mail: booksellers@palgrave.com
International publication for corporate communication and reputation management professionals in private and public sector organizations. Journal publishing latest and best practice - expert practitioners address the strategic development and maintenance of corporate reputation; rigorous research; highlighting new and cutting-edge thinking on the important areas of corporate reputation. **Founded:** 1997. **Freq:** Quarterly. **Key Personnel:** Cees B.M. Van Riel, Editor-in-Chief; Charles Fombrun, Editor-in-Chief; Paul Argenti, Assoc. Ed. **ISSN:** 1363-3589. **Subscription Rates:** 319 institutions, other countries print; US$510 institutions print; 136 other countries print and online; US$218 individuals print and online. **URL:** http://www.palgrave-journals.com/crr/index.html.

48750 ■ Het Houtblad
Postbus 8632
NL-3009 AP Rotterdam, Netherlands
Ph: 31 10 2894078
Fax: 31 10 2894076
Publisher E-mail: info@houtblad.nl
Professional magazine covering issues for architects, builders, the timber trade and the woodworking industry. **Founded:** 1989. **Freq:** Monthly 8/yr. **Print Method:** Offset. **Trim Size:** 185 X 259 mm. **ISSN:** 0923-5574. **Subscription Rates:** EUR89 individuals. **Remarks:** Accepts advertising. **URL:** http://www.houtblad.nl/nieuws/1. **Ad Rates:** BW: EUR2,006. **Circ:** Controlled ‡16,500

48751 ■ Journal of Purchasing & Supply Management
Elsevier Science Inc.
RSM Erasmus University
Rm. T10-54
PO Box 1738
Rotterdam, Netherlands
Ph: 31 104081980
Fax: 31 10 4089014
Publisher E-mail: usinfo-ehelp@elsevier.com
Journal devoted to purchasing and supply management. **Freq:** 4/yr. **Key Personnel:** Stephan M. Wagner, Assoc. Ed.; Louise Knight, Assoc. Ed.; Nigel Caldwell, Assoc. Ed.; George Zsidisin, Assoc. Ed.; E. Bartezzaghi, Editorial Advisory Board; J. Anderson, Editorial Advisory Board; M. Christopher, Editorial Advisory Board; Finn Wynstra, Editor, jpsm-editor@rsm.nl. **ISSN:** 1478-4092. **Subscription Rates:** EUR564 institutions for European countries and Iran; US$632 institutions, other countries except Europe, Japan and Iran; 74,900¥ institutions; EUR121 individuals for European countries and Iran; 16,400¥ individuals; US$153 other countries except Europe, Japan and Iran. **URL:** http://www.elsevier.com/wps/find/journaldescription.cws_home/642704/descriptiondescription.

48752 ■ Statistica Neerlandica
John Wiley & Sons Inc.
Wiley-Blackwell
c/o P.H. Franses, Ed.
Dept. of Econometrics
Erasmus University
Rotterdam, Netherlands
Peer-reviewed journal containing research and expository material about new developments in probability, statistics, and operations research. **Freq:** Quarterly. **Key Personnel:** P.H. Franses, Editor, franses@few.eur.nl; P.M.C. de Boer, Managing Editor, pmdeboer@few.eur.nl; Ivo Adan, Assoc. Ed. **ISSN:** 0039-0402. **Subscription Rates:** US$79 individuals Americas (print and online); EUR70 individuals Euro zone (print and online); 47 other countries print and online; US$647 institutions Americas (print and online); 385 institutions UK (print and online); EUR489 institutions Europe (print and online); US$571 institutions developing countries (print and online); US$755 institutions, other countries print and online; US$588 institutions Americas (print or online only); 350 institutions UK (print or online only). **Remarks:** Accepts advertising. **URL:** http://www.wiley.com/bw/journal.asp?ref=0039-0402. **Circ:** (Not Reported)

48753 ■ Strabismus
Taylor & Francis Ltd.
Erasmus MC
Dept. of Ophthalmology
PO Box 2040
NL-3015 GD Rotterdam, Netherlands
Ph: 31 10 7040704
Peer-reviewed journal containing the following sections: editorials, original papers, research reports, reviews, symposium proceedings, letters to the editor, selected abstracts and book reviews. **Freq:** 4/yr. **Key Personnel:** H.J. Simonsz, MD, Editor-in-Chief, simonsz@compuserve.com. **ISSN:** 0927-3972. **Subscription Rates:** US$535 individuals print & online; US$535 institutions online only; US$535 institutions print & online; US$535 individuals online only. **Remarks:** Accepts advertising. **URL:** http://www.informaworld.com/smpp/title~db=all~content=t713734563. **Circ:** (Not Reported)

Tilburg

48754 ■ International Journal of Cooperative Information Systems
World Scientific Publishing Company Private Ltd.
c/o M.P. Papazoglou, Ed.-in-Ch.
Tilburg University
INFOLAB, Rm. B711
PO Box 90153
NL-5000 LE Tilburg, Netherlands
Ph: 31 13 4662349
Fax: 31 13 4663069
Publisher E-mail: wspc@wspc.com.sg
Journal addressing the intricacies of cooperative work in the framework of distributed interoperable information systems, providing a forum for the presentation and dissemination of research covering all aspects of CIS design, requirements, functionality, implementation, deployment, and evolution, publishing papers describing original ideas and new results, on topics that include, but are not limited to: CIS Principles - cooperation, intel-

ligence, autonomy; architectures and communication protocols for CIS open architectures, blackboard systems, multiagent planning frameworks, speech acts, advanced information services in support of interoperability; information agents' models and organisations, application of information agent technology in virtuallaboratories, concurrent engineering and other groupware frameworks. **Freq:** Quarterly. **Key Personnel:** Gunter Schlageter, Editor-in-Chief, fax 49 233 1987314, gunter.schlageter@fernuni-hagen.de; M.P. Papazoglou, Editor-in-Chief, m.p.papazoglou@uvt.n1; B. Bhargava, Assoc. Ed., bb@cs.purdue.edu; E. Bertino, Assoc. Ed., bertino@disi.unige.it; A. Borgida, Assoc. Ed., borgida@cs.rutgers.edu; M. Jarke, Assoc. Ed., jarke@informatik.rwth-aachen.de. **ISSN:** 0218-8430. **Subscription Rates:** US$691 institutions and libraries; print and electronic; US$663 institutions and libraries; electronic only; US$34 individuals for postage; S$1,115 institutions and libraries; print and electronic; S$1,070 institutions and libraries; electronic only; S$45 individuals for postage; EUR613 institutions and libraries; print and electronic; EUR588 institutions and libraries; electronic only; EUR23 individuals for postage. **Remarks:** Advertising accepted; rates available upon request. **URL:** http://www.worldscinet.com/ijcis/ijcis.shtml. **Circ:** (Not Reported)

Utrecht

48755 ■ Ars Disputandi
Igitur, Utrecht Publishing & Archiving Services
Heidelberglaan 3
NL-3584 CS Utrecht, Netherlands
Ph: 31 302 536635
Publication E-mail: ad-editor@igitur.uu.nl
Publisher E-mail: info@igitur.uu.nl
Online journal providing a forum for the exchange of ideas and arguments, promoting research and discussion of issues in the philosophy of religion by providing for the fast publication of contributions to ongoing debates. **Subtitle:** The Online Journal for Philosophy of Religion. **Key Personnel:** Marcel Sarot, Editor; Michael Scott, Editor; Maarten Wisse, Editor. **ISSN:** 1566-5399. **URL:** http://www.arsdisputandi.org/.

48756 ■ European Journal of Developmental Psychology
Psychology Press
c/o Willem Koops, Ed.
Utrecht University
Dept. of Social Sciences
PO Box 80.140
NL-3508 TC Utrecht, Netherlands
Journal dedicated to psychological development and developmental psychopathology during infancy, childhood and adolescence in the context of theoretical, empirical, methodological perspectives. Journal is published in connection with European Society for Developmental Psychology. **Freq:** Bimonthly. **Key Personnel:** Michel Deleau, Assoc. Ed.; Willem Koops, Founding Ed.; Christiane Spiel, Assoc. Ed.; Anne Borge, Assoc. Ed.; Paul Harris, Editorial Board. **ISSN:** 1740-5629. **Subscription Rates:** US$589 institutions online only; US$298 individuals; US$620 institutions print & online; EUR239 individuals; EUR471 institutions online only; EUR496 institutions print and online; 373 institutions print and online; 354 institutions online; 182 individuals. **Remarks:** Advertising accepted; rates available upon request. **URL:** http://www.tandf.co.uk/journals/titles/17405629.asp. **Circ:** (Not Reported)

48757 ■ European Journal of Public Health
European Public Health Association
Otterstraat 118-124
PO Box 1568
NL-3500 BN Utrecht, Netherlands
Ph: 31 302 729709
Fax: 31 302 729729
Publisher E-mail: office@eupha.org
Journal containing information on current international health issues, focusing on the European region. **Freq:** Quarterly. **Key Personnel:** Johan P. MacKenbach, Editor; Peter Allebeck, Editor-in-Chief. **ISSN:** 1101-1262. **Subscription Rates:** US$733 individuals; EUR416 institutions print and online; US$834 institutions print and online; US$765 institutions print; 366 individuals print; US$47 members; US$654 institutions online only; 327 institutions online only; EUR490 institutions online only; EUR573 institutions print only. **Remarks:** Accepts advertising. **URL:** http://eurpub.oxfordjournals.org/. **Circ:** (Not Reported)

48758 ■ Geneesmiddelenbulletin
Postbus 2190
3500 GD Utrecht, Netherlands
Ph: 31 30 2823360
Fax: 31 20 7978500
Trade journal covering pharmaceuticals. **Subtitle:** Gebu. **Founded:** 1967. **Freq:** Monthly. **Key Personnel:** Josef Tukker, Editor-in-Chief. **ISSN:** 0304-4629. **Subscription Rates:** Free to qualified subscribers free to all Doctors, Pharmacists, Members. **URL:** http://gebu.artsennet.nl/. **Circ:** Non-paid 47,000

48759 ■ Global Business and Economics Review
Inderscience Enterprises Limited
c/o Peter-Jan Engelen, Ed.-in-Ch.
Utrecht University
Utrecht School of Economics
Janskerkhof 12
3512BL Utrecht, Netherlands
Peer-reviewed journal focusing on the discussion and analysis of advanced concepts, initial treatments, and fundamental research in all fields of business and economics. **Freq:** 4/yr. **Key Personnel:** Peter-Jan Engelen, Editor-in-Chief, p.j.engelen@econ.uu.nl. **ISSN:** 1097-4954. **Subscription Rates:** EUR494 individuals print or online; EUR672 individuals print and online. **URL:** http://www.inderscience.com/browse/index.php?journalID=168.

48760 ■ International Journal of Integrated Care
Igitur, Utrecht Publishing & Archiving Services
Heidelberglaan 3
NL-3584 CS Utrecht, Netherlands
Ph: 31 302 536635
Publication E-mail: ijic@igitur.uu.nl
Publisher E-mail: info@igitur.uu.nl
Peer-reviewed journal publishing papers on integration of health and social services and the relation between primary health care and hospital care. **Key Personnel:** Dr. Guus Schrijvers, Editor, a.j.p.schrijvers@umcutrecht.nl; Dr. Maria de Lourdes Ferrer Goodwin, Managing Editor; Dr. Jon Glasby, Editor, j.glasby@bham.ac.uk. **ISSN:** 1568-4156. **URL:** http://www.ijic.org.

48761 ■ Journal of Community & Applied Social Psychology
John Wiley & Sons Inc.
c/o Sandra Schruijer, Ed.
University of Utrecht
Bijlhouwerstraat 6
NL-3511 ZC Utrecht, Netherlands
Publisher E-mail: info@wiley.com
Journal concerning social psychological analysis and those involved, such as clinical and social psychologists, psychiatrists and health professionals. **Freq:** Bimonthly. **Trim Size:** 6 1/2 x 9 3/4. **Key Personnel:** Flora Cornish, Assoc. Ed.; Christopher Sonn, Assoc. Ed.; Arjan Bos, Assoc. Ed.; Esther Wiesenfeld, Assoc. Ed.; Sandra Schruijer, Editor. **ISSN:** 1052-9284. **Subscription Rates:** 170 individuals print only; US$335 other countries print only; US$1,143 institutions, other countries print only; US$1,258 institutions, other countries print with online access. **Remarks:** Accepts advertising. **URL:** http://as.wiley.com/WileyCDA/WileyTitle/productCd-CASP.html; http://onlinelibrary.wiley.com/journal/10.1002/(ISSN)1099-1298. **Formerly:** Social Behaviour. **Circ:** Paid 2,800

48762 ■ Journal of Economic and Social Geography
Royal Dutch Geographical Society
Koninklijk Nederlands Aardrijkskundig Genootschap
PO Box 805
NL-3500 AV Utrecht, Netherlands
Ph: 31 30 2534056
Fax: 31 30 2535523
Publisher E-mail: info@knag.nl
Journal covering geography. **Founded:** 1910. **Freq:** 5/yr. **Trim Size:** 29 x 16.8 cm. **Key Personnel:** Frank Van Oort, Editor-in-Chief, phone 31 30 2532230, fax 31 30 2532037, f.vanoort@geo.uu.nl; Bouke van Gorp, Exec. Ed., phone 31 30 2534915, fax 31 30 2532037, b.vangorp@geo.uu.nl; Justin Beaumont, Book Review Ed., phone 31 50 3636910, j.r.beaumont@rug.nl; Veronique Schutjens, Editorial Board; Jouke Van Dijk, Editorial Board. **ISSN:** 0040-747X. **Subscription Rates:** 52 other countries print or online; US$89 individuals Americas (print and online); EUR79 individuals Euro zone (print and online); 286 institutions print and online; US$496 institutions Americas (print and online); EUR362 institutions Europe (print and online); US$496 institutions, other countries print and online; 286 institutions print only; US$450 institutions Americas (print only); EUR329 institutions Europe (print only). **Remarks:** Accepts advertising. **URL:** http://www.blackwellpublishing.com; http://www.knag.nl/english/index.html. **Ad Rates:** BW: 275. **Circ:** (Not Reported)

48763 ■ Mechanisms of Development
International Society of Developmental Biologists
Netherlands Institute for Developmental Biology
Hubrecht Laboratory
Uppsalalaan 8
NL-3584 CT Utrecht, Netherlands
Ph: 31 302 121883
Fax: 31 302 516464
Publisher E-mail: paul@niob.knaw.nl
Publication covering biology. **Freq:** Monthly. **Key Personnel:** D. Wilkinson, Editor-in-Chief, modgep@nimr.mrc.ac.uk; C. Klaembt, Editor, klaembt@uni-muenster.de; J.U. Lohmann, Editor, jlohmann@meristemania.org; M.E. Halpern, Editorial Board; D. Stainer, Editor, phone 415502-5679, fax 415476-3892, didier_stainier@biochem.ucsf.edu; Y. Saga, Editor, ysaga@lab.nig.ac.jp. **ISSN:** 0925-4773. **Subscription Rates:** 372,600¥ institutions; US$3,141 institutions, other countries except Europe, Japan and Iran; EUR2,808 institutions for European countries and Iran; EUR218 individuals for European countries and Iran; 33,700¥ individuals; US$293 other countries except Europe, Japan and Iran. **Remarks:** Advertising accepted; rates available upon request. **URL:** http://www.elsevier.com/wps/find/journaldescription.cws_home/506090/descriptiondescription. **Circ:** (Not Reported)

48764 ■ Netherlands Quarterly of Human Rights
Netherlands Institute of Human Rights
Studie- en Informatiecentrum Mensenrechten
Janskerkhof 3
NL-3512 BK Utrecht, Netherlands
Publisher E-mail: sim@law.uu.nl
The Netherlands Quarterly of Human Rights is an international journal with contributions concerning the human rights situation in the world and the promotion and protection of human rights in international law. **Freq:** Quarterly. **Key Personnel:** Annelies Hess Bosch, Managing Editor; Kevin Boyle, Board of Ed.; Andrew Clapham, Board of Ed.; Peter Baehr, Editor-in-Chief. **ISSN:** 0169-3441. **Remarks:** Advertising accepted; rates available upon request. **Circ:** (Not Reported)

48765 ■ Resources, Conservation and Recycling
Elsevier Science Inc.
c/o E. Worrell, Ed.
Copernicus Inst.
Dept. of Science, Technology & Society
Universiteit Utrecht, Heidelberglaan 2
NL-3584 CS Utrecht, Netherlands
Ph: 31 30 2808374
Fax: 31 30 2808301
Publisher E-mail: usinfo-ehelp@elsevier.com
Journal emphasizes the transformation processes involved in a transition toward more sustainable production and consumption systems. **Founded:** 1988. **Freq:** Monthly. **Print Method:** Offset. Uses mats. **Trim Size:** 13 1/8 x 21. **Cols./Page:** 6. **Col. Width:** 25 nonpareils. **Col. Depth:** 294 agate lines. **Key Personnel:** P.S. Phillips, Editorial Board; A.G. Buekens, Editorial Board; R.U. Ayres, Editorial Board; P.H. Brunner, Editorial Board; P.M. Weaver, Assoc. Ed.; T. Jackson, Editorial Board; M.H. Wong, Editorial Board; L.F. Diaz, Editorial Board; P. Glavic, Editorial Board; E. Worrell, Editor, e.worrell@ecofys.nl. **ISSN:** 0921-3449. **Subscription Rates:** US$2,222 institutions, other countries except Europe, Japan and Iran; EUR1,986 institutions for European countries and Iran; 263,800¥ institutions; EUR262 individuals for European countries and Iran; US$352 other countries except Europe, Japan and Iran; 40,400¥ individuals. **URL:** http://www.elsevier.com/wps/find/journaldescription.cws_home/503358/descriptiondescription.

48766 ■ Tijdschrift voor economische en sociale geografie
John Wiley & Sons Inc.
Wiley-Blackwell
c/o Bouke van Gorp, Exec. Dir.
Utrecht University
PO Box 80115
NL-3508 TC Utrecht, Netherlands

Ph: 31 30 2534915
Fax: 31 30 2532037
Journal containing contemporary issues in human geography. **Freq:** 5/yr. **Key Personnel:** Frank van Oort, Editor-in-Chief, f.vanoort@geo.uu.nl; Bouke van Gorp, Exec. Ed., b.vangorp@geo.uu.nl. **ISSN:** 0040-747X. **Subscription Rates:** US$89 individuals Americas (print and online); EUR79 individuals Euro zone (print and online); 52 other countries non-Euro zone (print and online); 286 institutions UK (print and online); US$496 institutions Americas (print and online); EUR362 institutions Europe (print and online); 577 institutions, other countries print and online; 259 institutions UK (print or online only); US$450 institutions Americas (print or online only); EUR329 institutions Europe (print or online only). **Remarks:** Accepts advertising. **URL:** http://www.wiley.com/bw/journal.asp?ref=0040-747X. **Circ:** (Not Reported)

48767 ■ Utrecht Law Review
Igitur, Utrecht Publishing & Archiving Services
Heidelberglaan 3
NL-3584 CS Utrecht, Netherlands
Ph: 31 302 536635
Publication E-mail: ulr@uu.nl
Publisher E-mail: info@igitur.uu.nl
Journal offering a scientific platform for cross-border legal research, concerning research in which the boundaries of the classic branches of the law (private law, criminal law, constitutional and administrative law, European and public international law) are crossed and connections are made between these areas of the law, amongst others from a comparative law perspective. **Key Personnel:** Dr. Antoine M. Hol, Editor-in-Chief; Dr. Titia Kloos, Managing Editor. **ISSN:** 1871-515X. **URL:** http://www.utrechtlawreview.org/.

48768 ■ Veterinary Sciences Tomorrow
Igitur, Utrecht Publishing & Archiving Services
Heidelberglaan 3
NL-3584 CS Utrecht, Netherlands
Ph: 31 302 536635
Publication E-mail: vetscite@vet.uu.nl
Publisher E-mail: info@igitur.uu.nl
International electronic journal for scientists, academic teachers, graduate students and policy makers, publishing refereed reviews, interpretation and opinion on topics relevant to the veterinary sciences, including animal health and welfare. **Freq:** Quarterly. **Key Personnel:** Prof. Marian C. Horzinek, Editor-in-Chief; Dr. Virgil E. Schijns, Editor; Dr. Anjop Venker-van Haagen, Editor. **ISSN:** 1569-0830. **Remarks:** Accepts advertising. **URL:** http://www.vetscite.org/. **Circ:** (Not Reported)

Voorburg

48769 ■ Bernoulli
Bernoulli Society for Mathematical Statistics and Probability
c/o Ms. Margaret de Ruiter-Molloy, Membership Off.
428 Prinses Beatrixlaan
PO Box 950
NL-2270 AZ Voorburg, Netherlands
Ph: 31 70 3375726
Fax: 31 70 3860025
Publisher E-mail: mmly@cbs.nl
Publication covering statistics and probability. **Freq:** Quarterly. **Key Personnel:** Richard Davis, Editor-in-Chief, rdavis@stat.columbia.edu; Peter McCullagh, Assoc. Ed.; David Cox, Assoc. Ed.; Peter Hall, Assoc. Ed.; Thomas Lee, Assoc. Ed.; Amarjit Budhiraja, Assoc. Ed.; David Applebaum, Assoc. Ed., d.applebaum@sheffield.ac.uk; Nancy Reid, Assoc. Ed.; Johan Segers, Assoc. Ed. **ISSN:** 1350-7265. **Subscription Rates:** US$446 institutions hardcopy and on-line; EUR25 members developed rate; EUR15 members developing rate. **Remarks:** Advertising not accepted. **URL:** http://www.bernoulli-society.org/index.php/publications/bernoulli-journal/bernoulli-journal. **Circ:** Paid 2,000

48770 ■ Journal of Time Series Analysis
Bernoulli Society for Mathematical Statistics and Probability
c/o Ms. Margaret de Ruiter-Molloy, Membership Off.
428 Prinses Beatrixlaan
PO Box 950
NL-2270 AZ Voorburg, Netherlands
Ph: 31 70 3375726
Fax: 31 70 3860025
Publisher E-mail: mmly@cbs.nl
Journal covering statistics. **Freq:** Bimonthly. **Key Personnel:** M.B. Priestley, Editor, phone 44 161 2003660, fax 44 161 2003669, m.b.priestley@umist.ac.uk. **ISSN:** 0143-9782. **Subscription Rates:** US$128 individuals America (print & online); EUR161 individuals Europe Zone (print & online); 108 individuals Non-Europe Zone (print & online); 139 other countries print & online; US$210 members America (print & online); EUR147 members Europe Zone (print & online); 97 members Non-Europe Zone (print & online); 126 members rest of the world (print & online); US$128 students America (print & online); 97 students, other countries print & online. **Remarks:** Accepts advertising. **URL:** http://www.blackwellpublishing.com; http://www.blackwellpublishing.com/subs.asp?ref=0143-9782. **Circ:** (Not Reported)

Wageningen

48771 ■ The Journal of Agricultural Education and Extension
Routledge
Taylor & Francis Group Ltd.

Wageningen University
Wageningen, Netherlands
Publisher E-mail: webmaster.books@tandf.co.uk
Peer-reviewed journal covering scientific articles on the dynamics in innovation support structures. **Freq:** Quarterly. **Key Personnel:** Volker Hoffmann, Book Review Ed.; Angela Pachuau, Editorial Asst.; Cees Leeuwis, Editorial Committee; Harm Biemans, Editorial Committee; Anne Van Den Ban, Editorial Committee; Marianne Cerf, Editorial Committee; Martin Mulder, Editor-in-Chief; Prof. Ricardo Ramirez, Editorial Committee; Hilde Tobi, Editorial Committee. **ISSN:** 1389-224X. **Subscription Rates:** 227 institutions print + online; 215 institutions online; 81 individuals; US$377 institutions print + online; US$358 institutions online; US$136 individuals; EUR300 institutions print and online; EUR286 institutions online only; EUR108 individuals. **URL:** http://www.tandf.co.uk/journals/titles/1389224X.asp.

48772 ■ NJAS
Netherlands Royal Society for Agricultural Sciences
Koninklijke Landbouwkundige Vereniging
PO Box 79
NL-6700 AB Wageningen, Netherlands
Ph: 31 317 455191
Fax: 31 317 483976
Publisher E-mail: office.klv@wur.nl
Publication covering agricultural science. **Subtitle:** Wageningen Journal of Life Sciences. **Founded:** 1953. **Freq:** Quarterly. **Trim Size:** 170 x 242 mm. **Key Personnel:** Dr. Ekko Van Ierland, Editorial Board; Dr. Paul Struik, Editor; Dr. Kor Oldenbroek, Editorial Board; Dr. Jan Wienk, Editor; Dr. Tiny Van Boekel, Editorial Board. **ISSN:** 1573-5214. **Subscription Rates:** EUR30 members Netherlands; EUR30 members outside Netherlands; EUR15 members online; EUR355 nonmembers. **Remarks:** Accepts advertising. **URL:** https://www.klv.nl/EN/ABOUTKLV/Pages/Membershipfees.aspx. **Circ:** (Not Reported)

Wijchen

48773 ■ CBM
Magenta Uitgeverij
Bijsterhuizen 31-47
NL-6604 LV Wijchen, Netherlands
Ph: 31 243 454150
Fax: 31 243 976071
Publication E-mail: cbm@computerweb.nl
Professional magazine for computer resellers and retailers. **Founded:** Jan. 1, 1997. **Freq:** Monthly. **Subscription Rates:** EUR53 individuals Nederland; EUR60 individuals Europe; EUR73 individuals overige landen. **Remarks:** Accepts advertising. **URL:** http://www.computerweb.com.nl/. **Ad Rates:** BW: EUR1,500, 4C: EUR2,625. **Circ:** Combined 6,300

Circulation: ★ = ABC; △ = BPA; ◆ = CAC; • = CCAB; ❑ = VAC; ⊕ = PO Statement; ‡ = Publisher's Report; Boldface figures = sworn; Light figures = estimated.

Curacao

48774 ■ Radio Hoyer 1-FM - 101.9
Plasa Horacio Hoyer 21
Curacao, Netherlands Antilles
Ph: 599 9 4611678
Fax: 599 9 4616528

E-mail: hoyer@cura.net
Format: News; Sports; Ethnic. **Founded:** 1954. **Ad Rates:** Advertising accepted; rates available upon request. **URL:** http://www.radiohoyer.com.

48775 ■ Radio Hoyer 2-FM - 105.1
Plasa Horacio Hoyer 21
Curacao, Netherlands Antilles
Ph: 599 9 4611678
Fax: 599 9 4616528
E-mail: hoyer@cura.net
Format: News; Sports; Ethnic. **Founded:** 1954. **Operating Hours:** Continuous. **Ad Rates:** Advertising accepted; rates available upon request. **URL:** http://www.radiohoyer.com.

Circulation: ★ = ABC; △ = BPA; ◆ = CAC; • = CCAB; ▢ = VAC; ⊕ = PO Statement; ‡ = Publisher's Report; Boldface figures = sworn; Light figures = estimated.

Gale Directory of Publications & Broadcast Media/147th Ed.

5285

Albany

48776 ■ Cancer Informatics
Libertas Academica Ltd.
PO Box 302-874
North Harbour
Albany 0751, New Zealand
Ph: 64 9 4763930
Fax: 64 9 3531397
Peer-reviewed journal covering the role of computational biology and bioinformatics in cancer treatment. **Key Personnel:** James Willey, Editor-in-Chief; Richard H.J. Begent, MD, Honorary Editorial Board; Constantin F Aliferis, PhD, Honorary Editorial Board; Dr. J.T. Efird, Assoc. Ed.; Trachette L. Jackson, Assoc. Ed.; Georgios S. Stamatakos, Assoc. Ed. **ISSN:** 1176-9351. **URL:** http://la-press.com/journals.php?pa=home&journal_id=10.

48777 ■ Evolutionary Bioinformatics Online
Libertas Academica Ltd.
PO Box 302-874
North Harbour
Albany 0751, New Zealand
Ph: 64 9 4763930
Fax: 64 9 3531397
Peer-reviewed journal focusing on evolutionary bioinformatics. **Key Personnel:** Dennis Wall, Editor-in-Chief; Patrick Aloy, Ph.D., Editorial Board; Miguel Andrade, Ph.D., Editorial Board. **ISSN:** 1176-9343. **URL:** http://la-press.com/journals.php?pa=home&journal_id=17.

48778 ■ Health Care and Informatics Review Online
Enigma Publishing Ltd.
Unit 3, Bldg. H
Apollo Technical Park
5 Orbit Dr.
Albany, New Zealand
Ph: 64 991 29106
Fax: 64 991 29101
Publisher E-mail: enigma@enigmapublishing.com
Journal dedicated to reviewing and interpreting significant developments in healthcare delivery, focusing on knowledge gained through the practical experience of managing health issues and the material is relevant to a wide variety of managers and practitioners. **Freq:** Quarterly. **ISSN:** 1176-4201. **URL:** http://hcro.enigma.co.nz/website/index.cfm.

Alexandra

48779 ■ National-AM - 639
Radio New Zealand House, Level 2
155 The Terrace
PO Box 123
Wellington, New Zealand
Ph: 64 4 4741999
Fax: 64 4 4741459
E-mail: rnz@radionz.co.nz
Format: Eclectic. **Owner:** Radio New Zealand, at above address. **Operating Hours:** Continuous. **Ad Rates:** Noncommercial. **URL:** http://www.radionz.co.nz/listen/amfm.

48780 ■ Newstalk ZB-FM Central Otago - 95.1
54 Cook St.
Private Bag 92198
Auckland, New Zealand
Ph: 64 9 3730000
Format: News; Talk. **Owner:** The Radio Network, at above address. **Key Personnel:** Paul Holmes, Contact; Leighton Smith, Contact, leighton@newstalkzb.co.nz; Danny Watson, Contact, danny@newstalkzb.co.nz. **URL:** http://www.newstalkzb.co.nz/featdetail.asp?recnumber=1.

48781 ■ Southern Star-FM - 88.4
53 Upper Queen St.
Auckland, New Zealand
Ph: 64 9 3073100
Fax: 64 9 3096888
Format: Contemporary Christian. **Owner:** Rhema Broadcasting Group, at above address. **URL:** http://www.sstar.co.nz/.

Amberley

48782 ■ Hurunui News
Allied Press Ltd.
5 Markham St.
Amberley, New Zealand
Ph: 64 3 3148335
Fax: 64 3 3148071
Publication E-mail: hurunui@alliedpress.co.nz
Publisher E-mail: corporate@alliedpress.co.nz
Newspaper covering local events and issues in the Hurunui District. **Freq:** Monthly. **URL:** http://www.alliedpress.co.nz/papers.php?pub=hurunui.

Auckland

48783 ■ AA Directions
New Zealand Automobile Association
99 Albert St.
PO Box 5
Auckland, New Zealand
Ph: 64 996 68800
Fax: 64 996 68891
Publisher E-mail: info@aa.co.nz
Magazine featuring travel and lifestyle articles, news and views. **Freq:** Quarterly. **Key Personnel:** Kathryn Webster, Editor. **Subscription Rates:** Free to members. **URL:** http://www.aa.co.nz/membership/benefits/magazines/Pages/default.aspx.

48784 ■ Afro-Asian Journal of Finance and Accounting
Inderscience Enterprises Limited
c/o Prof. Ben Jacobsen, Ed.-in-Ch.
Massey University, Dept. of Commerce
New Zealand Institute of Advanced Study
Private Bag 102 904 NSMC
Auckland 1311, New Zealand
Journal focusing on finance and accounting issues in Africa, the Middle-East, and Asia. **Freq:** 4/yr. **Key Personnel:** Prof. Ben Jacobsen, Editor-in-Chief, b.jacobsen@massey.ac.nz; Prof. Prem Lal Joshi, Managing Editor, prem@acadjoshi.com. **ISSN:** 1751-6447. **Subscription Rates:** EUR494 individuals online or print; EUR672 individuals online and print. **URL:** http://www.inderscience.com/browse/index.php?journalID=214.

48785 ■ Auckland University Law Review
University of Auckland
Faculty of Law
PO Box 92019
Auckland 1142, New Zealand
Ph: 64 937 37599
Fax: 64 937 37473
Publisher E-mail: lawreception@auckland.ac.nz
Law periodical. **Freq:** Annual. **Key Personnel:** Elizabeth Chan, Sen. Ed.; Martien Duis, Sen. Ed.; Max Harris, Editor-in-Chief; Alice Krzanich, Sen. Ed.; Patricia Ieong, Editor-in-Chief; Patrick Lilly, Sen. Ed.; Rachel McMaster, Sen. Ed.; Hamish McQueen, Sen. Ed.; Lewis Mills, Sen. Ed.; Benedict Tompkins, Sen. Ed. **ISSN:** 0067-0510. **Subscription Rates:** US$45 individuals New Zealand; US$45 individuals Australian and South Pacific; US$45 elsewhere elsewhere. **URL:** http://aulr.auckland.ac.nz/.

48786 ■ Australian Women's Weekly
Australian Consolidated Press NZ Ltd.
Private Bag 92512
Auckland 1036, New Zealand
Ph: 64 9 3082700
Fax: 64 9 3082878
Magazine for women. **Freq:** Monthly. **Key Personnel:** Leonie Barlow, Editor; Karen Shayler, Advertising Mgr. **Subscription Rates:** NZ$59.95 individuals; NZ$118.90 two years. **Remarks:** Accepts advertising. **URL:** http://www.acpmedia.co.nz/acpmagazines/auswomensweekly/tabid/119/Default.aspx. **Ad Rates:** 4C: NZ$10,000. **Circ:** ★80,727

48787 ■ Boating New Zealand
Fairfax New Zealand Ltd.
274 Church St.
Penrose
Auckland, New Zealand
Ph: 64 9 6341800
Fax: 64 9 6342948
Publisher E-mail: webmaster@fairfaxnz.co.nz
Magazine for boating enthusiasts. **Founded:** 1986. **Print Method:** Web offset. **Trim Size:** 330 x 277 mm. **Key Personnel:** Kent Gray, Editor, editor@boatingnz.co.nz; Tim Porter, Manager, tim.porter@boatingnz.co.nz. **Remarks:** Accepts advertising. **URL:** http://www.fairfaxnz.co.nz/publications/general/info79.html. **Circ:** ★15,256

48788 ■ Catering Plus
TPL Media
308 Gt South Rd.
Greenlane
Auckland 1051, New Zealand
Ph: 64 9 5293000
Fax: 64 9 5293001
Publisher E-mail: info@tplmedia.co.nz
Magazine featuring information on special event catering, industry personnel, food safety and hygiene, equipment highlights and staffing issues. **Freq:** Bimonthly. **Key Personnel:** Cynthia Daly, Editor, phone 64 9 5293015, cynthiad@tplmedia.co.nz; Yash Narula, Sales Mgr., phone 64 9 5293009, yashn@tplmedia.co.nz; Matt Wilke, Business Mgr. **Subscription Rates:** NZ$45

Circulation: ★ = ABC; △ = BPA; ◆ = CAC; • = CCAB; ❑ = VAC; ⊕ = PO Statement; ‡ = Publisher's Report; Boldface figures = sworn; Light figures = estimated.

individuals. **Remarks:** Accepts advertising. **URL:** http://www.cateringplus.co.nz; http://www.tplmedia.co.nz/Publications/Magazines/tabid/121/Default.aspx. **Ad Rates:** 4C: NZ$1,980. **Circ:** ‡2,528

48789 ■ Commercial Horticulture Magazine
The Reference Publishing Co.
PO Box 26269
Epsom
Auckland, New Zealand
Ph: 64 93582749
Fax: 64 93582741
Publication E-mail: commhort@nursery.net.nz
Publisher E-mail: refpub@nursery.co.nz
Trade magazine of the nursery and garden trade in New Zealand. **Subtitle:** The Magazine of the Nursery Industry. **Freq:** Monthly. **Trim Size:** 210 x 297 mm. **Key Personnel:** Marian Kennelly, Sales Mgr.; Des Snell, Manager. **ISSN:** 0113-7018. **Subscription Rates:** US$69 individuals within New Zealand; $A 82.50 in Australia; US$55 in US; 33 UK. **Remarks:** Accepts advertising. **URL:** http://www.nursery.net.nz. **Ad Rates:** GLR: NZ$25, BW: NZ$735, 4C: NZ$995. **Circ:** Paid 2,000

48790 ■ D-Photo
ParksideMedia
PO Box 46020
Herne Bay
Auckland 1147, New Zealand
Ph: 64 9 3601480
Fax: 64 9 3601470
Publisher E-mail: admin@parkside.co.nz
Magazine for novice and amateur photographers. **Freq:** Bimonthly. **Key Personnel:** Tim Grey, Editor. **Subscription Rates:** NZ$40 two years; $A 26 individuals; US$61 elsewhere rest of world. **Remarks:** Accepts advertising. **URL:** http://www.dphoto.co.nz/. **Circ:** 12,000

48791 ■ Dairyman
Rural Press Ltd.
300 Great S Rd., Level 1
Greenlane
PO Box 4233
Auckland 1140, New Zealand
Ph: 64 9 5235056
Newspaper covering the dairy industry in New Zealand. **Freq:** Monthly. **Key Personnel:** Craig Chapman, General Mgr., craig.chapman@ruralpress.com; Fiona Mackinnon, Advertising Mgr., advertising.nz@ruralpress.com; Jeff Smith, Editor, jeff.smith@ruralpress.com. **Subscription Rates:** NZ$25 individuals. **Remarks:** Accepts advertising. **URL:** http://www.ruralpress.com/publications/detail_nz.asp. **Circ:** ‡25,500

48792 ■ Fashion Quarterly
Australian Consolidated Press NZ Ltd.
Private Bag 92512
Auckland 1036, New Zealand
Ph: 64 9 3082700
Fax: 64 9 3082878
Consumer magazine covering fashion and beauty. **Founded:** 1980. **Freq:** Quarterly. **Key Personnel:** Fiona Hawtin, Editor; Jackie Jones, Advertising Mgr. **Subscription Rates:** $A 36.10 individuals. **Remarks:** Accepts advertising. **URL:** http://www.acpmedia.co.nz/ACPMagazines/FashionQuarterly/tabid/86/Default.aspx. **Ad Rates:** 4C: NZ$6,500. **Circ:** Controlled 23,713

48793 ■ Fish and Game New Zealand
Fairfax New Zealand Ltd.
274 Church St., Level 1
Penrose
Auckland, New Zealand
Ph: 64 9 6341800
Fax: 64 9 6342948
Publisher E-mail: webmaster@fairfaxnz.co.nz
Magazine featuring freshwater trout, salmon and upland game birds in New Zealand. **Trim Size:** 210 x 297 mm. **Key Personnel:** Tim Porter, General Mgr., tim.porter@fairfaxmags.co.nz. **Remarks:** Accepts advertising. **URL:** http://www.fairfaxnz.co.nz/publications/general/info78.html. **Ad Rates:** 4C: NZ$2,500. **Circ:** *17,435

48794 ■ Food & Beverage Today
TPL Media
308 Gt South Rd.
Greenlane
Auckland 1051, New Zealand
Ph: 64 9 5293000

Fax: 64 9 5293001
Publisher E-mail: info@tplmedia.co.nz
Magazine featuring coffee. **Subtitle:** the taste of success. **Freq:** Bimonthly. **Trim Size:** 210 x 297 mm. **Key Personnel:** Cynthia Daly, Editor, phone 64 9 5293015, cynthiad@tplmedia.co.nz; Ashlyn Braganza, Sales Mgr., phone 64 9 5293006, ashlynb@tplmedia.co.nz. **Subscription Rates:** US$75 individuals New Zealand; US$100 other countries online. **Remarks:** Accepts advertising. **URL:** http://www.coffeeculturemag.co.nz; http://www.tplmedia.co.nz/Publications/Magazines/tabid/121/Default.aspx. **Formerly:** Coffee Culture. **Ad Rates:** 4C: NZ$2,580. **Circ:** 6,587

48795 ■ Home New Zealand
Australian Consolidated Press NZ Ltd.
Private Bag 92512
Auckland 1036, New Zealand
Ph: 64 9 3082700
Fax: 64 9 3082878
Magazine featuring modern homes that are destined to become classics. **Freq:** Bimonthly. **Trim Size:** 225 x 297 mm. **Key Personnel:** Jeremy Hansen, Editor. **Subscription Rates:** NZ$9.50 single issue. **Remarks:** Accepts advertising. **URL:** http://www.acpmedia.co.nz/ACPMagazines/HOMENewZealand/tabid/128/Default.aspx. **Former name:** NZ Home & Entertaining. **Ad Rates:** 4C: NZ$5,950. **Circ:** 14,805

48796 ■ Horticulture News
Rural Press Ltd.
300 Great S Rd., Level 1
Greenlane
PO Box 4233
Auckland 1140, New Zealand
Ph: 64 9 5235056
Fax: 64 9 5241170
Newspaper covering the horticultural industry in New Zealand. **Freq:** Monthly. **Key Personnel:** Rebecca Stuart, General Mgr., rebecca.stuart@ruralpress.com; Fiona Mackinnon, Advertising Mgr., advertising.nz@ruralpress.com. **Subscription Rates:** $A 35 individuals; $A 60 two years; $A 5 single issue. **Remarks:** Accepts advertising. **URL:** http://www.ruralpress.com/publications/detail_nz.asp. **Circ:** ‡4,000

48797 ■ Impact
World Vision - New Zealand
Private Bag 92078
Auckland, New Zealand
Ph: 64 9 5807700
Fax: 64 9 5807799
Publisher E-mail: nzcommunications@worldvision.org.nz
Magazine giving an overview of the current work of the organization. **Freq:** Quarterly. **Subscription Rates:** free. **URL:** http://www.worldvision.org.nz/aboutwvnz/about_wvnz.aspx.

48798 ■ International Journal of Biomechatronics and Biomedical Robotics
Inderscience Enterprises Limited
c/o Prof. Shane Xie, Ed.-in-Ch.
The University of Auckland
Dept. of Mechanical Engineering
Private Bag 92019
Auckland 1142, New Zealand
Journal featuring the developments in biomechatronics and robot assistive technologies for medical and bio applications. **Freq:** 4/yr. **Key Personnel:** Prof. Shane Xie, Editor-in-Chief, s.xie@auckland.ac.nz. **ISSN:** 1757-6792. **Subscription Rates:** EUR494 individuals print or online; EUR672 individuals print and online. **URL:** http://www.inderscience.com/browse/index.php?journalID=322.

48799 ■ International Journal of Learning and Change
Inderscience Publishers
Business School, The University of Auckland
PO Box 92019
Auckland, New Zealand
Publisher E-mail: editor@inderscience.com
Journal covering contemporary issues from the perspectives of process, structure, meaning and methods of individual and organisational learning and their impact on the organisational change process. **Freq:** Quarterly. **Key Personnel:** Dr. Shantha Liyanage, Editor-in-Chief, shantha.liyanage@mgsm.edu.au; Thomas Andersson, Editorial Board Member; Prof. Barry Bozeman, Editorial Board Member; Prof. Jan Annerstedt, Assoc. Ed.; Prof.

Jon Sigurdson, Assoc. Ed. **ISSN:** 1740-2875. **Subscription Rates:** EUR494 individuals print or online; EUR672 individuals print and online. **URL:** http://www.inderscience.com/browse/index.php?journalCODE=ijlc.

48800 ■ Journal of Sociolinguistics
John Wiley & Sons Inc.
Wiley-Blackwell
c/o Dr. Allan Bell, Ed.
Institute of Culture, Discourse & Communication
Auckland University of Technology
PO Box 92006
Auckland 1121, New Zealand
Ph: 64 9 9179683
Fax: 64 9 9179978
Journal publishing articles in the field of research on language and society. **Freq:** 5/yr. **Key Personnel:** David Britain, Assoc. Ed.; Dr. Allan Bell, Editor, allan.bell@aut.ac.nz; Walt Wolfram, Editorial Board; Lesley Milroy, Editorial Board; Karin Aronsson, Editorial Board; P.J. Trudgill, Honorary Board; Michael Clyne, Editorial Board; Aidan Coveney, Editorial Board. **ISSN:** 1360-6441. **Subscription Rates:** US$98 individuals print + online; 59 individuals print + online; US$644 institutions print + online; US$585 institutions print or online; 382 institutions print + online; EUR88 individuals print + online; 347 institutions print or online; EUR485 institutions print + online; EUR440 institutions print or online; US$749 institutions, other countries print + online. **Remarks:** Advertising accepted; rates available upon request. **URL:** http://www.wiley.com/bw/journal.asp?ref=1360-6441. **Circ:** (Not Reported)

48801 ■ KiaOra
Australian Consolidated Press NZ Ltd.
Private Bag 92512
Auckland 1036, New Zealand
Ph: 64 9 3082700
Fax: 64 9 3082878
Magazine for Air New Zealand travelers. **Subtitle:** Air New Zealand inflight magazine. **Freq:** Monthly. **Key Personnel:** Jenny Farrell, Editor; Portia Treadwell, Advertising Mgr. **Remarks:** Accepts advertising. **URL:** http://www.acpmedia.co.nz/ACPMagazines/KiaOraAirNewZealandinflightmagazine/tabid/110/Default.aspx. **Ad Rates:** 4C: NZ$9,000. **Circ:** 45,000

48802 ■ The Lifestyle Farmer
Rural Press Ltd.
300 Great S Rd., Level 1
Greenlane
PO Box 4233
Auckland 1140, New Zealand
Ph: 64 9 5241179
Newspaper featuring New Zealand farmers. **Freq:** Monthly. **Key Personnel:** Rebecca Stuart, Advertising Mgr., rebecca.stuart@ruralpress.com; Fiona Mackinnon, Advertising Mgr., advertising.nz@ruralpress.com. **Subscription Rates:** NZ$50 individuals; NZ$90 two years; NZ$5.90 single issue. **Remarks:** Accepts advertising. **URL:** http://www.ruralpress.com/publications/detail_nz.asp; http://www.farmonline.co.nz/farmmags/lifestylefarmer/index.aspx. **Circ:** (Not Reported)

48803 ■ Little Treasures
Australian Consolidated Press NZ Ltd.
Private Bag 92512
Auckland 1036, New Zealand
Ph: 64 9 3082700
Fax: 64 9 3082878
Magazine for parents. **Freq:** Bimonthly. **Trim Size:** 210 x 275 mm. **Key Personnel:** Emily Simpson, Editor. **Subscription Rates:** NZ$4.66 single issue; NZ$18.49 individuals. **Remarks:** Accepts advertising. **URL:** http://www.acpmedia.co.nz/ACPMagazines/LittleTreasures/tabid/123/Default.aspx. **Ad Rates:** 4C: NZ$6,000. **Circ:** *30,713

48804 ■ Meteorite
Pallasite Press
PO Box 296
Silverdale
Auckland, New Zealand
Ph: 64 942 69311
Fax: 64 942 69312
Publisher E-mail: jschiff@ihug.co.nz
Magazine covering geology and science worldwide. **Founded:** Feb. 1995. **Freq:** Quarterly. **Trim Size:** 205 x 275 mm. **Key Personnel:** Aaron Schiff, Design & Layout, afs@ihug.co.nz; Alan Rubin, Consultant Sci.; Kathy Campbell, Consultant Sci.; Sally Sutton, Transla-

tor; Richard O. Norton, Contributing Ed.; Joel Schiff, Editor, jschiff@ihug.co.nz; Christine Schiff, Business Mgr. **ISSN:** 1173-2245. **Subscription Rates:** US$35 individuals. **Remarks:** Accepts advertising. **URL:** http://homepages.ihug.co.nz/~afs/about.html. **Ad Rates:** BW: NZ$350. **Circ:** (Not Reported)

48805 ■ New Zealand Author
New Zealand Society of Authors
PO Box 7701
Wellesley St.
Auckland 1141, New Zealand
Ph: 64 937 94801
Fax: 64 937 94801
New Zealand publication covering writers. **Freq:** Bimonthly. **ISSN:** 0114-8230. **Remarks:** Advertising accepted; rates available upon request. **URL:** http://www.authors.org.nz. **Circ:** 1,300

48806 ■ New Zealand Baptist
Baptist Churches of New Zealand
PO Box 12149
Penrose
Auckland 1642, New Zealand
Ph: 64 9 5260333
Fax: 64 9 5260334
Publisher E-mail: info@baptist.org.nz
New Zealand newspaper covering the Baptist religion. **Freq:** Monthly no January issue. **Print Method:** Offset. **Trim Size:** 290 x 420. **Cols./Page:** 6. **ISSN:** 0027-7177. **Subscription Rates:** US$30 individuals + GST; New Zealand; US$45 individuals Australia; US$50 other countries. **URL:** http://www.baptist.org.nz/default.asp?id=30. **Ad Rates:** BW: NZ$825, 4C: NZ$1,100. **Circ:** 9,800

48807 ■ New Zealand Classic Car
ParksideMedia
PO Box 46020
Herne Bay
Auckland 1147, New Zealand
Ph: 64 9 3601480
Fax: 64 9 3601470
Publisher E-mail: admin@parkside.co.nz
Motoring magazine. **Founded:** 1991. **Freq:** Monthly. **Key Personnel:** Allan Walton, Editor; Bruce Mountain, Advertising Mgr.; Greg Vincent, Publisher. **Subscription Rates:** NZ$49 individuals six months; NZ$85 individuals; NZ$155 two years; NZ$199 other countries. **Remarks:** Accepts advertising. **URL:** http://www.classiccar.co.nz/. **Ad Rates:** 4C: NZ$2,800. **Circ:** 10,743

48808 ■ New Zealand Dental Journal
New Zealand Dental Association
GEON Group
107 Kerwyn Ave.
Highbrook
Auckland 2161, New Zealand
Ph: 64 9 9252986
Fax: 64 9 9252931
Publisher E-mail: nzdainfo@nzda.org.nz
New Zealand journal covering dentistry. **Freq:** Quarterly March, June, September and December. **Key Personnel:** Sonia Fredrick, Contact, sonia.fredrick@geongroup.com; Murray Thomson, Editor. **Subscription Rates:** US$138 members overseas; US$138 nonmembers New Zealand; US$200 nonmembers Australia/South Pacific; US$245 nonmembers rest of world; Free members in New Zealand. **Remarks:** Advertising accepted; rates available upon request. **URL:** http://www.nzda.org.nz/pub/index.php?id=93. **Circ:** (Not Reported)

48809 ■ New Zealand Doctor
CMPMedica (NZ) Ltd
3 Shea Ter.
Takapuna
PO Box 31 348
Milford
Auckland, New Zealand
Ph: 64 9 4884278
Fax: 64 9 4896240
Newspaper catering to primary health sector. Covers issues such as health politics, clinical and technical developments and business management. **Founded:** 1989. **Freq:** Semimonthly published Wednesday, every fortnight except Jan. **Key Personnel:** Colin Abercrombie, Mng. Dir., phone 64 9 4884260, fax 64 9 4896240, cabercrombie@nz.cmpmedica.com; Barbara Fountain, Editor, phone 64 9 4884266, editor@nzdoctor.co.nz;

Amanda Cameron, Dep. Ed., phone 64 9 4884273, acameron@nzdoctor.co.nz. **Subscription Rates:** NZ$288 individuals Australia; NZ$169 individuals New Zealand; NZ$406 individuals U.K., South African & rest of the world; NZ$340 U.S. and Canada. **Remarks:** Accepts classified advertising. **URL:** http://www.nzdoctor.co.nz/. **Circ:** (Not Reported)

48810 ■ New Zealand Fishing News
Fairfax New Zealand Ltd.
274 Church St., Level 1
Penrose
Auckland, New Zealand
Ph: 64 9 6341800
Fax: 64 9 6342948
Publisher E-mail: webmaster@fairfaxnz.co.nz
Magazine featuring angling and sportfishing craft. **Freq:** Monthly. **Print Method:** Web offset. **Trim Size:** 380 x 272 mm. **Key Personnel:** Grant Dixon, Editor, grant.dixon@fishnz.co.nz. **Remarks:** Accepts advertising. **URL:** http://www.fairfaxnz.co.nz/publications/general/info34.html. **Ad Rates:** BW: NZ$1,797, 4C: NZ$3,113. **Circ:** ★26,780

48811 ■ New Zealand Fishing World
Image Centre Publishing
34 Westmoreland St. W
Grey Lynn
Auckland, New Zealand
Ph: 64 9 3605700
Fax: 64 9 3605702
Publisher E-mail: info@image-centre.com
Magazine covering locations, gamefishing, hot spots, boat reviews, techniques, and more. **Freq:** Bimonthly. **Key Personnel:** Geoff Thomas, Editor. **Subscription Rates:** US$16.55 individuals New Zealand; US$71.75 two years individual. **Remarks:** Accepts advertising. **URL:** http://www.nzfishingworld.co.nz. **Ad Rates:** BW: NZ$3,600. **Circ:** ★9,391

48812 ■ New Zealand Gardener
Fairfax New Zealand Ltd.
317 New North Rd.
Eden Ter.
Auckland 1021, New Zealand
Ph: 64 9 9096800
Fax: 64 9 9096802
Publisher E-mail: webmaster@fairfaxnz.co.nz
Magazine featuring New Zealand's most beautiful gardens. **Freq:** Monthly. **Key Personnel:** Lynda Halliman, Editor; Angela Moon-Jones, Advertising Mgr. **Remarks:** Accepts advertising. **URL:** http://www.fairfaxnz.co.nz/publications/general/info28.html; http://www.nzgardener.co.nz/. **Circ:** ★35,880

48813 ■ New Zealand Geographer
New Zealand Geographical Society Inc.
c/o School of Geography, Geology & Environmental Science
The University of Auckland
PO Box 92019
Auckland, New Zealand
Ph: 64 937 37599
Publication E-mail: nzgs@auckland.ac.nz
Publisher E-mail: nzgs@auckland.ac.nz
Geography publication. **Founded:** 1944. **Freq:** Semiannual. **Print Method:** Offset. **Trim Size:** A4. **Key Personnel:** Eric Pawson, Mng. Ed. & Ch.; Janine Wiles, Book Review Ed. **ISSN:** 0028-8144. **Subscription Rates:** NZ$155 institutions; NZ$100 school; NZ$70 individuals; NZ$190 institutions Australia and Pacific; NZ$240 institutions elsewhere; NZ$80 individuals Australia and Pacific; NZ$90 individuals elsewhere. **Remarks:** Advertising accepted; rates available upon request. **URL:** http://www.nzgs.co.nz/NZG.aspx. **Circ:** (Not Reported)

48814 ■ New Zealand Grapegrower
Rural Press Ltd.
300 Great S Rd., Level 1
Greenlane
PO Box 4233
Auckland 1140, New Zealand
Ph: 64 9 5235056
Fax: 64 9 5241170
Newspaper covering the viticulture industry in New Zealand. **Freq:** Quarterly. **Key Personnel:** Rebecca Stuart, General Mgr., rebecca.stuart@ruralpress.com; Fiona Mackinnon, Advertising Mgr., advertising.nz@ruralpress.

com; Daniel Pilkington, Editor, daniel.pilkington@ruralpress.com. **Subscription Rates:** NZ$30 individuals; NZ$5.50 single issue. **Remarks:** Accepts advertising. **URL:** http://www.ruralpress.com/publications/detail_nz.asp. **Circ:** ‡3,000

48815 ■ New Zealand Horse and Pony
Fairfax New Zealand Ltd.
274 Church St.
Penrose
Auckland, New Zealand
Ph: 64 9 6341800
Fax: 64 9 6342948
Publisher E-mail: webmaster@fairfaxnz.co.nz
Magazine for equestrian community. **Founded:** 1959. **Print Method:** offset. **Trim Size:** 29.7 x 21 cm. **Key Personnel:** Rowan Dixon, Editor, editor@horse-pony.co.nz; Tim Porter, Manager, tim.porter@fairfaxmags.co.nz. **Remarks:** Accepts advertising. **URL:** http://www.fairfaxnz.co.nz/publications/general/info12.html. **Ad Rates:** 4C: NZ$1,400. **Circ:** ★12,792

48816 ■ New Zealand Journal of Geography
New Zealand Geographical Society Inc.
c/o School of Geography, Geology & Environmental Science
The University of Auckland
PO Box 92019
Auckland, New Zealand
Ph: 64 937 37599
Publisher E-mail: nzgs@auckland.ac.nz
New Zealand geographic journal. **Founded:** 1946. **Freq:** Semiannual. **Print Method:** Offset. **Trim Size:** A5. **Key Personnel:** Eric Pawson, Mng. Ed. & Ch.; Janine Wiles, Book Review Ed. **Remarks:** Advertising accepted; rates available upon request. **URL:** http://www.nzgs.co.nz/nzjg.aspx. **Circ:** (Not Reported)

48817 ■ The New Zealand Journal of History
University of Auckland
Faculty of Law
PO Box 92019
Auckland 1142, New Zealand
Ph: 64 937 37599
Fax: 64 937 37473
Publisher E-mail: lawreception@auckland.ac.nz
Periodical focusing on history. **Freq:** Semiannual April and October. **Key Personnel:** Raewyn Dalziel, Editorial Board; Judith Bassett, Editorial Board; Nisha Saheed, Business Mgr.; Caroline Daley, Editor; Judith Binney, Editorial Board; Malcolm Campbell, Editorial Board; Deborah Montgomerie, Editor; Greg Ryan, Review Ed. **ISSN:** 0028-8322. **Subscription Rates:** NZ$50 individuals; NZ$60 other countries; NZ$30 students; NZ$35 students, other countries. **Remarks:** Accepts advertising. **URL:** http://www.arts.auckland.ac.nz/uoa/home/about/departments-and-schools/history-1/newzealandjournalofhistory. **Ad Rates:** BW: NZ$120. **Circ:** 800

48818 ■ New Zealand Lifestyle Block
Fairfax New Zealand Ltd.
274 Church St.
Penrose
Auckland, New Zealand
Ph: 64 9 6341800
Fax: 64 9 6342948
Publisher E-mail: webmaster@fairfaxnz.co.nz
Magazine featuring horticulture. **Freq:** Monthly. **Print Method:** offset. **Trim Size:** 210 x 275 mm. **Key Personnel:** Nadene Hall, Editor, editor@nzlifestyleblock.co.nz. **Remarks:** Accepts advertising. **URL:** http://www.fairfaxnz.co.nz/publications/general/info31.html. **Formerly:** New Zealand Growing Today. **Ad Rates:** 4C: NZ$2,016. **Circ:** ★8,412

48819 ■ New Zealand Listener
New Zealand Magazines Ltd.
Piccadilly House
74 New North Rd.
Eden Ter.
Auckland, New Zealand
Ph: 64 9 3090296
Publisher E-mail: info@nzmag.com
Consumer magazine covering current affairs, television, radio, the arts and books. **Founded:** 1939. **Freq:** Weekly (Sat.). **Trim Size:** 200 x 275 mm. **Key Personnel:** Pamela Stirling, Editor; Guy Somerset, Arts & Books Ed.; Chris Gwin, Circulation Sales Mgr.; Victoria Pre-

Circulation: ★ = ABC; △ = BPA; ♦ = CAC; • = CCAB; ❑ = VAC; ⊕ = PO Statement; ‡ = Publisher's Report; Boldface figures = sworn; Light figures = estimated.

Gale Directory of Publications & Broadcast Media/147th Ed.   **5289**

ston, Ed. Asst.; Sarah Sandley, Sh. Exec.; Mary Jane Boland, Dep. Ed.; Louise Wilson, Advertising Dir., louise.wilson@nzmagazines.co.nz; Steve Philp, Art Dir. **Subscription Rates:** $A 155 individuals; $A 82 individuals 6 months. **Remarks:** Accepts advertising. **URL:** http://www.wilsonandhorton.co.nz; http://www.listener.co.nz/. **Ad Rates:** BW: $A 4,800, 4C: $A 7,100. **Circ:** Combined 80,939

48820 ■ New Zealand Performance Car
ParksideMedia
PO Box 46020
Herne Bay
Auckland 1147, New Zealand
Ph: 64 9 3601480
Fax: 64 9 3601470
Publisher E-mail: admin@parkside.co.nz
Lifestyle and motoring magazine. **Founded:** 1996. **Freq:** Monthly. **Trim Size:** 210 x 297 mm. **Key Personnel:** Brad Lord, Editor; Keith Guyett, Advertising Mgr.; Greg Vincent, Publisher. **Subscription Rates:** NZ$95 individuals; NZ$49 individuals six months; NZ$155 individuals Australia; NZ$210 other countries. **Remarks:** Accepts advertising. **URL:** http://www.performancecar.co.nz/. **Circ:** ★17,432

48821 ■ New Zealand Trucking
Fairfax New Zealand Ltd.
274 Church St., Level 1
Penrose
Auckland, New Zealand
Ph: 64 9 6341800
Fax: 64 9 6345600
Publisher E-mail: webmaster@fairfaxnz.co.nz
Magazine for road transport enthusiasts. **Freq:** 11/yr. **Print Method:** offset. **Trim Size:** 235 x 320 mm. **Key Personnel:** John Murphy, Editor, editor@nztrucking.co.nz; Tim Porter, Manager, tim.porter@fairfaxmags.co.nz. **Remarks:** Accepts advertising. **URL:** http://www.fairfaxnz.co.nz/publications/general/info33.html. **Ad Rates:** BW: NZ$1,480, 4C: NZ$2,500. **Circ:** ★10,009

48822 ■ North & South
Australian Consolidated Press NZ Ltd.
Private Bag 92512
Auckland 1036, New Zealand
Ph: 64 9 3082700
Fax: 64 9 3082878
Publication E-mail: northsouth@acpmagazines.co.nz
News magazine featuring New Zealand. **Subtitle:** Thinking New Zealand. **Founded:** Apr. 1986. **Freq:** Monthly. **Trim Size:** 225 x 297 mm. **Key Personnel:** Paula Blind, Advertising Mgr.; Virginia Larson, Editor. **Subscription Rates:** NZ$63 individuals; NZ$117 two years. **Remarks:** Accepts advertising. **URL:** http://www.acpmedia.co.nz/ACPMagazines/NorthSouth/tabid/127/Default.aspx. **Ad Rates:** 4C: NZ$7,500. **Circ:** 299,000

48823 ■ NZ Catholic
PO Box 147-000
Ponsonby
Auckland 1034, New Zealand
Ph: 64 936 03067
Fax: 64 936 03065
Catholic newspaper. **Founded:** 1996. **Freq:** Semimonthly. **Key Personnel:** Michael Otto, Sen. Journalist; Gavin Abraham, Managing Editor; Pat McCarthy, Assoc. Ed.; Dennis Augustine, Promotions & Adv. Mgr. **ISSN:** 1174-0086. **Subscription Rates:** NZ$70 individuals; NZ$130 two years; NZ$120 other countries. **Remarks:** Accepts advertising. **URL:** http://www.nzcatholic.org.nz. **Ad Rates:** BW: NZ$950, 4C: NZ$1,140. **Circ:** Paid 20,000

48824 ■ NZBusiness
Adrenalin Publishing Ltd.
14C Vega Pl.
Mairangi Bay
Auckland, New Zealand
Ph: 64 9 8173818
Publisher E-mail: yvonnec@xtra.co.nz
Magazine featuring topics of interest to business owners and operators. **Freq:** 11/yr. **Key Personnel:** Cathy Parker, Publisher, cathy@adrenalin.co.nz; Yvonne Carter, Publisher, yvonnec@xtra.co.nz; Glenn Baker, Editor, editor@nzbusiness.co.nz. **Subscription Rates:** NZ$75 individuals New Zealand only; NZ$130 other countries for Australian; NZ$140 elsewhere. **Remarks:** Accepts advertising. **URL:** http://www.adrenalin.co.nz/afa.asp?idWebPage=13002; http://www.nzbusiness.co.

nz/. **Ad Rates:** 4C: NZ$3,565. **Circ:** ★7,428

48825 ■ NZ4WD
Adrenalin Publishing Ltd.
14C Vega Pl.
Mairangi Bay
Auckland, New Zealand
Ph: 64 9 8173818
Publication E-mail: info@nz4wd.co.nz
Publisher E-mail: yvonnec@xtra.co.nz
Magazine featuring information to the 4WD vehicle buyer and driver. **Founded:** 1996. **Freq:** 11/yr. **Trim Size:** 210 x 297 mm. **Key Personnel:** Cathy Parker, Publisher, cathy@adrenalin.co.nz; John Oxley, Editor, john@adrenalin.co.nz. **Subscription Rates:** NZ$43 individuals in New Zealand; NZ$140 individuals Australia/Pacific Islands; NZ$150 individuals rest of the world. **Remarks:** Accepts advertising. **URL:** http://www.adrenalin.co.nz/afa.asp?idWebPage=13002; http://www.nz4wd.co.nz/. **Ad Rates:** BW: NZ$1,100, 4C: NZ$2,450. **Circ:** ★2,619

48826 ■ NZV8
ParksideMedia
PO Box 46020
Herne Bay
Auckland 1147, New Zealand
Ph: 64 9 3601480
Fax: 64 9 3601470
Publisher E-mail: admin@parkside.co.nz
Magazine featuring V8-engined vehicles. **Freq:** Monthly. **Key Personnel:** Todd Wylie, Editor, editor@nzv8mag.co.nz; Dan Gibson, Advertising Mgr., htebbutt@parkside.co.nz; Greg Vincent, Publisher, gvincent@parkside.co.nz. **Subscription Rates:** NZ$85; NZ$159 two years; NZ$139 Australia; NZ$210 other countries. **Remarks:** Accepts advertising. **URL:** http://www.v8.co.nz. **Circ:** (Not Reported)

48827 ■ onHoliday
Fairfax New Zealand Ltd.
Freepost 5319
PO Box 790
Shortland St.
Auckland, New Zealand
Publication E-mail: info@fairfaxmagazines.co.nz
Publisher E-mail: webmaster@fairfaxnz.co.nz
Magazine providing inspirational travel, plus food and lifestyle ideas reflecting the true kiwi spirit of adventure both at home and abroad. **Freq:** Quarterly. **Key Personnel:** Wendy Barnard, Editorial Asst. **Subscription Rates:** US$45 individuals; US$82 two years individual; US$75 individuals Australia; US$115 other countries. **URL:** http://www.fairfaxnz.co.nz/publications/advertising/ad112.html.

48828 ■ The Open Society
New Zealand Association of Rationalists and Humanists
Rationalist House
64 Symonds St.
Auckland 1010, New Zealand
Ph: 64 9 3735131
Fax: 64 9 3798233
Publisher E-mail: admin@nzarh.org.nz
Journal serving New Zealand's non-religious community. **Founded:** 1927. **Freq:** Quarterly. **Key Personnel:** Hayden Wood, Editor-in-Chief. **ISSN:** 0028-8632. **Subscription Rates:** NZ$20 individuals including postage & GST; NZ$30 other countries overseas, postage included; NZ$5 single issue including postage & GST. **URL:** http://www.nzarh.org.nz/journal.htm.

48829 ■ Transportant
Logistics and Transport New Zealand
c/o John Partridge, Devel. Executive
PO Box 1281
Shortland St.
Auckland, New Zealand
Ph: 64 936 84970
Fax: 64 936 84971
Publisher E-mail: info@cilt.co.nz
Journal containing articles on transport issues and events. **Freq:** Quarterly. **Subscription Rates:** NZ$40 individuals; NZ$7 individuals single. **Remarks:** Accepts advertising. **URL:** http://www.cilt.co.nz/Category?Action=View& Category_id=67& Highlight=Transportant. **Circ:** (Not Reported)

48830 ■ Traveltrade
TPL Media
308 Gt South Rd.

Greenlane
Auckland 1051, New Zealand
Ph: 64 9 5293000
Fax: 64 9 5293001
Publisher E-mail: info@tplmedia.co.nz
Magazine featuring travel and tourism in New Zealand. **Freq:** 22/yr. **Key Personnel:** Gordon Gillan, Managing Editor, phone 64 9 5293026, gordon@traveltrade.co.nz; Tracy Fairey, Sales Mgr., phone 64 9 5293021, tracy@traveltrade.co.nz. **Subscription Rates:** NZ$100 individuals online; NZ$85 individuals. **Remarks:** Accepts advertising. **URL:** http://www.traveltrade.co.nz; http://www.tplmedia.co.nz/Publications/Magazines/tabid/121/Default.aspx. **Circ:** ‡1,393

48831 ■ Truck & Machinery Trader
Fairfax New Zealand Ltd.
274 Church St., Level 1
Penrose
Auckland, New Zealand
Ph: 64 9 6341800
Fax: 64 9 6345600
Publisher E-mail: webmaster@fairfaxnz.co.nz
Magazine featuring machinery and equipment. **Freq:** 11/yr. **Print Method:** offset. **Key Personnel:** Tim Porter, Manager, tim.porter@fairfaxnz.co.nz. **Remarks:** Accepts advertising. **URL:** http://www.fairfaxnz.co.nz/publications/general/info26.html. **Ad Rates:** BW: NZ$650, 4C: NZ$1,300. **Circ:** ★12,390

48832 ■ Wine Technology in New Zealand
TPL Media
308 Gt South Rd.
Greenlane
Auckland 1051, New Zealand
Ph: 64 9 5293000
Fax: 64 9 5293001
Publication E-mail: editor@winetech.co.nz
Publisher E-mail: info@tplmedia.co.nz
Magazine for winemakers and grapegrowers. **Freq:** Bimonthly. **Key Personnel:** Graham Hawkes, Editor, grahamh@tplmedia.co.nz; Ashlyn Braganza, Advertising Mgr., ashlynb@tplmedia.co.nz. **Subscription Rates:** NZ$50 individuals online; NZ$40 individuals. **Remarks:** Accepts advertising. **URL:** http://www.winetech.co.nz; http://www.tplmedia.co.nz/Publications/Magazines/tabid/121/Default.aspx. **Circ:** ‡2052

48833 ■ Zootaxa
Magnolia Press
PO Box 41383
St. Lukes
Auckland 1346, New Zealand
Publication E-mail: zootaxa@mapress.com
Publisher E-mail: magnolia@mapress.com
International journal for animal taxonomists. **Key Personnel:** Z.Q. Zhang, Ch. Ed./Founder, zhangz@landcareresearch.co.nz. **ISSN:** 1175-5326. **Subscription Rates:** US$3,100 individuals all issues online edition. **URL:** http://www.mapress.com/zootaxa.

48834 ■ b-FM - 95
PO Box 4560
Auckland 1001, New Zealand
Ph: 64 9 3094831
Fax: 64 9 3667224
E-mail: 95bfm@95bfm.com
Format: Alternative/New Music/Progressive; Talk; News. **Founded:** 1969. **Operating Hours:** Continuous. **Key Personnel:** Ben Cochrane, Mng. Dir., ben@thebusinessltd.co.nz; Paul Deady, News & Editorial Dir., pauld@95bfm.com; Pennie Blair, Operations Mgr., accounts@95bfm.com. **URL:** http://www.95bfm.co.nz/.

48835 ■ The Breeze-FM - 94
Level 3, 239 Ponsonby Rd.
Ponsonby
Auckland, New Zealand
Ph: 64 9 3735000
Fax: 64 9 3734000
Format: Easy Listening. **Owner:** MediaWorks New Zealand, 3 Flower St., Eden Ter., Auckland, New Zealand, 64 9 9289000. **Operating Hours:** 6 a.m.-12 a.m. Daily. **URL:** http://wellington.thebreeze.co.nz/; http://www.mediaworks.co.nz/.

48836 ■ Classic Hits-FM - 97.4
54 Cook St.
Private Bag 92-198
Auckland, New Zealand

Ph: 64 9 3730000
Fax: 64 9 3674797
E-mail: dallasg@trn.co.nz
Format: Classic Rock. **Operating Hours:** Continuous.
Ad Rates: Advertising accepted; rates available upon request. **URL:** http://www.classichits.co.nz.

Coast-AM - See Christchurch

Coast-AM - See Dunedin

Coast-AM - See Hawera

Coast-AM - See Napier

Coast-AM - See New Plymouth

Coast-AM - See Palmerston North

Coast-AM - See Whangarei

48837 ■ Coast-FM - 105.4
PO Box 92198
Auckland, New Zealand
E-mail: coast@thecoast.net.nz
Format: News; Music of Your Life. **URL:** http://www.thecoast.net.nz.

Coast-FM - See Invercargill

Coast-FM - See Tauranga

Coast-FM - See Wellington

Coast-FM Kapiti - See Wellington

48838 ■ Easy Mix-FM - 98.2
Private Bag 92198
Auckland, New Zealand
Ph: 64 9 3730000
E-mail: studio@easymix.co.nz
Format: Adult Contemporary. **Owner:** The Radio Network, at above address. **URL:** http://www.easymix.co.nz/.

Easy Mix-FM - See Napier

Easy Mix-FM - See Rotorua

Easy Mix-FM - See Tauranga

48839 ■ Flava-FM - 96.1
54 Cook St.
Private Bag 92198
Auckland 1111, New Zealand
Ph: 64 9 3730000
Fax: 64 9 3674802
E-mail: wassup@flava.co.nz
Format: Hip Hop; Blues. **Owner:** The Radio Network, at above address. **URL:** http://www.flava.co.nz/.

48840 ■ Fleet-FM - 88.3
PO Box 78104
Auckland 1245, New Zealand
Ph: 64 9 3070789
E-mail: studio@fleetfm.co.nz
Format: Eclectic. **Founded:** July 18, 2003. **Operating Hours:** 18 hours Daily. **Ad Rates:** Noncommercial. **URL:** http://www.fleetfm.co.nz.

48841 ■ GEORGE-FM - 96.8
Level 1, 105 Ponsonby Rd.
PO Box 47664
Auckland, New Zealand
Ph: 64 0 3604495
Fax: 64 9 3600044
Format: Eclectic; Full Service. **Owner:** MediaWorks, PO Box 47-560, Auckland 1144, New Zealand, 64 9 9289200, Fax: 64 9 3611677. **Founded:** 1998. **URL:** http://www.georgefm.co.nz/.

48842 ■ Hauraki-FM - 99.0
54 Cook St.
Private Bag 92198
Auckland, New Zealand
Ph: 64 9 3730000
Fax: 64 9 3674802
Format: Classic Rock. **Owner:** The Radio Network, at above address. **Key Personnel:** Grant Lee, General Mgr., grantlee@radionetwork.co.nz. **URL:** http://www.hauraki.co.nz/; http://www.radiohauraki.co.nz/Stations/Hauraki/.

48843 ■ Life-FM - 99.8
Symonds St.
Private Bag 92636
Auckland, New Zealand
Ph: 64 9 3661251
Fax: 64 9 3096888

E-mail: studio@lifefm.co.nz
Format: Religious; Contemporary Christian. **Owner:** Rhema Broadcasting Group, at above address. **Founded:** 1997. **Ad Rates:** Advertising accepted; rates available upon request. **URL:** http://www.lifefm.co.nz.

48844 ■ Mai-FM - 88.6
PO Box 68-886
Newton
Auckland, New Zealand
Ph: 64 9 9777800
Fax: 64 9 9777801
E-mail: web@maifm.co.nz
Format: Adult Contemporary; Urban Contemporary; Full Service. **Owner:** Mai Media Ltd, at above address. **Key Personnel:** Mereana Hawthorn, General Mgr.; David Bridgman, Contact; Toni Ulrich, Natl. Sales Mgr.; Sacha Morecho, Office Mgr. **URL:** http://www.maifm.co.nz.

48845 ■ More-FM - 91.8
Level 3, 239 Ponsonby Rd.
Symonds St.
PO Box 8880
Auckland, New Zealand
Ph: 64 3334000
Fax: 64 3734000
Format: World Beat; Ethnic; Talk. **Operating Hours:** Continuous. **Ad Rates:** Advertising accepted; rates available upon request. **URL:** http://www.morefm.co.nz.

48846 ■ Newstalk ZB-AM - 873
54 Cook St.
Private Bag 92198
Auckland, New Zealand
Ph: 64 9 3730000
Fax: 64 9 3674802
E-mail: news@newstalkzb.co.nz
Format: News; Talk. **Owner:** The Radio Network, at above address. **Key Personnel:** Kerre Woodham, Contact, kerre@newstalkzb.co.nz. **URL:** http://www.newstalkzb.co.nz/default.asp; http://www.radionetwork.co.nz/.

Newstalk ZB-AM Northland - See Whangarei

Newstalk ZB-AM Northland - See Whangarei

Newstalk ZB-AM Southland - See Invercargill

Newstalk ZB-AM Waikato - See Hamilton

48847 ■ Newstalk ZB-FM - 89.4
54 Cook St.
PO Box 92198
Auckland, New Zealand
Ph: 64 9 3730000
E-mail: news@newstalkzb.co.nz
Format: News; Talk. **Owner:** Radio Network, at above address. **Operating Hours:** Continuous. **Ad Rates:** Advertising accepted; rates available upon request. **URL:** http://www.newstalkzb.co.nz.

Newstalk ZB-FM Central Otago - See Alexandra

Newstalk ZB-FM Central Otago - See Wanaka

48848 ■ 95b-FM - 95.0
Shortland St.
PO Box 4560
Auckland 1001, New Zealand
Ph: 64 9 3094831
Fax: 64 9 3667224
E-mail: 95bfm@95bfm.com; studio@95bfm.com
Format: Eclectic. **Key Personnel:** Pat Fife, Sales Mgr., pat@95bfm.com; Pennie Blair, Operations Mgr., pennie@95bfm.com. **URL:** http://www.95bfm.co.nz/.

48849 ■ 104.6-FM - 104.6
PO Box 44-215
Auckland 1246, New Zealand
Ph: 64 9 8158600
E-mail: info@104.6planetfm.org.nz
Format: News; Information; Educational; Eclectic; Ethnic; World Beat. **Operating Hours:** Continuous. **Ad Rates:** $15 for 30 seconds. **URL:** http://www.104.6planetfm.org.nz/.

48850 ■ Radio New Zealand National-AM - 756
Radio New Zealand House
155 The Terrace
PO Box 123
Wellington, New Zealand
Ph: 64 4 4741999
Fax: 64 4 4741459

E-mail: rnz@radionz.co.nz
Format: News; Information. **Owner:** Radio New Zealand, at above address. **URL:** http://www.radionz.co.nz/national/home.

48851 ■ Radio Rhema-AM - 1251
Private Bag 92-636
Symonds St.
Auckland, New Zealand
Ph: 64 9 3075180
Fax: 64 9 3096888
Format: Religious; Contemporary Christian. **Owner:** Rhema Broadcasting Group, at above address. **Operating Hours:** Continuous. **URL:** http://www.rhema.co.nz/.

48852 ■ Radio Sport - 1332
Private Bag 92198
Auckland, New Zealand
Ph: 64 9 3730000
Fax: 64 9 3674644
E-mail: sport@radiosport.co.nz
Format: Sports. **Owner:** The Radio Network, at above address. **Key Personnel:** Peter Everatt, Operations Mgr., phone 64 9 3674705, petereveratt@radionetwork.co.nz; Malcolm Jordam, Prog. Ed., phone 64 9 3674672, malcolm@radiosport.co.nz; Chris Gregory, Program Dir., phone 64 9 3674604, chrisgregory@radionetwork.co.nz. **URL:** http://www.radiosport.co.nz/.

Radio Sport-AM Southland - See Invercargill

48853 ■ Radio Tarana-AM - 1386
PO Box 5956
Wellesley St.
Auckland, New Zealand
Ph: 64 9 3032286
Fax: 64 9 3033066
E-mail: info@tarana.co.nz
Format: Ethnic; News; Religious; Talk. **Founded:** June 15, 1996. **Key Personnel:** Hemant Parikh, Contact, phone 64 21 629359, hemant@tarana.co.nz; Surya Patel, Sales, phone 64 21 581386; Gopal Bhatia, Sales. **Ad Rates:** Advertising accepted; rates available upon request. **URL:** http://www.tarana.co.nz.

48854 ■ Solid Gold-FM - 93.4
PO Box 47560
Ponsonby
Auckland, New Zealand
Ph: 64 800 765434
Fax: 64 800 465332
Format: Oldies; Classic Rock. **Owner:** MediaWorks New Zealand, 3 Flower St., Eden Ter., Auckland, New Zealand, 64 9 9289000. **Founded:** Oct. 13, 1997. **Ad Rates:** Advertising accepted; rates available upon request. **URL:** http://www.solidgoldfm.co.nz; http://www.mediaworks.co.nz/.

Southern Star-AM - See Invercargill

Southern Star-FM - See Alexandra

48855 ■ UP-FM - 107.5
206 Symond St., Level 1
Newton
Auckland, New Zealand
Ph: 64 9 3778736
E-mail: info@upfm.dj
Format: Urban Contemporary. **Key Personnel:** Jarra Borman, Advertising, phone 64 21 873646; Mike Smith, Advertising, phone 64 21 447169. **Ad Rates:** Advertising accepted; rates available upon request. **URL:** http://www.upfm.dj.

48856 ■ ZM-FM - 91.0
PO Box 92198
Auckland, New Zealand
Ph: 64 800 342596
Fax: 64 9 3674804
E-mail: zm@zmonline.com
Format: Contemporary Hit Radio (CHR). **Ad Rates:** Advertising accepted; rates available upon request. **URL:** http://www.91zm.co.nz.

Bay of Islands

48857 ■ Cool Blue-FM - 96.1
PO Box 124
Paihia
Bay of Islands, New Zealand
Ph: 64 27 4434007

Circulation: ★ = ABC; △ = BPA; ♦ = CAC; • = CCAB; ❑ = VAC; ⊕ = PO Statement; ‡ = Publisher's Report; Boldface figures = sworn; Light figures = estimated.

E-mail: coolblueradio@coolblueradio.com
Format: Eclectic. **URL:** http://www.coolblue.co.nz.

Blenheim

48858 ■ Classic Hits-FM Marlborough - 96.9
12a Kinross St.
PO Box 225
Blenheim, New Zealand
Ph: 64 3 5780129
Fax: 64 3 5780981
Format: Adult Contemporary. **Owner:** The Radio Network, 54 Cook St., Private Bag 92198, Auckland, New Zealand, 64 9 3730000, Fax: 64 9 3674797. **Key Personnel:** Jennifer L., Contact, jenniferl@radionetwork.co.nz. **Ad Rates:** Advertising accepted; rates available upon request. **URL:** http://www.classichits.co.nz/?Region=Marlborough.

48859 ■ Fresh-FM - 89.2
143 Collingwood St.
Nelson 7010, New Zealand
Ph: 64 3 5469891
Fax: 64 3 5469892
E-mail: nelson@freshfm.net
Format: Ethnic. **Key Personnel:** Mike Williams, Station Mgr., mike@freshfm.net; Jo Ann Firestone, Program Dir., joann@freshfm.net. **URL:** http://www.freshfm.net/.

48860 ■ National-AM - 567
Radio New Zealand House, Level 2
155 The Terrace
PO Box 123
Wellington, New Zealand
Ph: 64 4 4741999
Fax: 64 4 4741459
E-mail: rnz@radionz.co.nz
Format: Eclectic. **Owner:** Radio New Zealand, at above address. **Operating Hours:** Continuous. **Ad Rates:** Noncommercial. **URL:** http://www.radionz.co.nz/listen/amfm.

Christchurch

48861 ■ Archaeology in New Zealand
New Zealand Archaeological Association Inc.
c/o Katharine Watson, Ed.
Underground Overground Archaeology Ltd.
28 Pratt St.
New Brighton
Christchurch, New Zealand
Ph: 64 3 276563985
Publisher E-mail: kylie.bop@clear.net.nz
Publication covering archeology in New Zealand. **Freq:** Quarterly. **Key Personnel:** Katharine Watson, Editor, katharine_watson@xtra.co.nz. **ISSN:** 0113-7832. **Subscription Rates:** NZ$70 individuals the subscribers. **URL:** http://www.nzarchaeology.org; http://www.nzarchaeology.org/ainz.html.

48862 ■ Auckland Today
Academy Publishing
Academy House
818 Colombo St., Level 3
PO Box 1879
Christchurch 8013, New Zealand
Ph: 64 3 9615050
Fax: 64 3 9615112
Publisher E-mail: ian@academy.net.nz
Executive magazine highlighting the successful growth and development of business in Auckland region. **Founded:** 1993. **Freq:** Bimonthly. **Trim Size:** 260 x 360 mm. **Subscription Rates:** US$24.95 individuals. **Remarks:** Accepts advertising. **URL:** http://www.magazinestoday.co.nz/Magazines/AucklandToday.html. **Circ:** Paid ★20,162

48863 ■ Australian AG Contractor and Large Scale Farmer
Agrimedia Ltd.
Ashcroft House
Tancreds Rd., R D 2
PO Box 37-151
Christchurch, New Zealand
Ph: 64 3 3296555
Fax: 64 3 3296550
Publisher E-mail: admin@agrimedia.co.nz
Magazine for rural contractors and farmers. **Freq:** Bimonthly. **Key Personnel:** Paul Titus, Editor, phone 64 3 3816912, titus@paradise.net.nz. **Subscription Rates:**

Free. **Remarks:** Accepts advertising. **URL:** http://www.agrimedia.co.nz/publications.php. **Ad Rates:** BW: NZ$2,025. **Circ:** (Not Reported)

48864 ■ Canterbury Today
Academy Publishing
Academy House
818 Colombo St., Level 3
PO Box 1879
Christchurch 8013, New Zealand
Ph: 64 3 9615050
Fax: 64 3 9615112
Publisher E-mail: ian@academy.net.nz
Business-to-business tabloid newspaper. **Founded:** 1985. **Freq:** Bimonthly. **Trim Size:** 260 x 360 mm. **Subscription Rates:** US$24.95 individuals. **Remarks:** Accepts advertising. **URL:** http://www.magazinestoday.co.nz/Magazines/CanterburyToday.html. **Circ:** Combined 21,899

48865 ■ Central Today
Academy Publishing
Academy House
818 Colombo St., Level 3
PO Box 1879
Christchurch 8013, New Zealand
Ph: 64 3 9615050
Fax: 64 3 9615112
Publisher E-mail: ian@academy.net.nz
Magazine highlighting the successful growth and development of business in Central North Island region. **Founded:** 1999. **Freq:** Bimonthly. **Trim Size:** 260 x 360 mm. **Subscription Rates:** US$24.95 individuals. **Remarks:** Accepts advertising. **URL:** http://www.magazinestoday.co.nz/Magazines/CentralToday.html. **Circ:** Combined 18,862

48866 ■ The Christchurch Star
APN New Zealand Ltd.
Southern Div.
PO Box 1467
Christchurch, New Zealand
Community newspaper. **Founded:** 1863. **Freq:** Semiweekly (Wed. and Fri.). **Remarks:** Accepts advertising. **URL:** http://www.soldonapn.co.nz/regionals/star. **Circ:** Non-paid 117,707

48867 ■ The Guardian
New Zealand Democratic Party
PO Box 18-907
New Brighton
Christchurch 8641, New Zealand
Ph: 64 3 3829544
Fax: 64 3 3829544
Publication covering political parties. **Freq:** Quarterly. **ISSN:** 0113-0078. **Subscription Rates:** US$10 individuals includes subscription to the guardian. **Remarks:** Advertising accepted; rates available upon request. **URL:** http://www.democrats.org.nz/OurNews/TheGuardian/tabid/118/Default.aspx. **Circ:** 2,500

48868 ■ History Now
University of Canterbury
History Dept.
Private Bag 4800
Christchurch 8140, New Zealand
Ph: 64 3 3367001
Publication E-mail: history@canterbury.ac.nz
Publisher E-mail: info@canterbury.ac.nz
Illustrated journal covering research, new developments and publications in history for teachers and a general audience. **Subtitle:** Te Pae Tawhito o te Wa. **Founded:** 1996. **Freq:** Semiannual. **Trim Size:** A4. **ISSN:** 1173-3438. **Remarks:** Accepts advertising. **URL:** http://www.hist.canterbury.ac.nz. **Formerly:** Historical News. **Ad Rates:** BW: NZ$50, 4C: NZ$80. **Circ:** (Not Reported)

48869 ■ Hospitality Today
Academy Publishing
Academy House
818 Colombo St., Level 3
PO Box 1879
Christchurch 8013, New Zealand
Ph: 64 3 9615050
Fax: 64 3 9615112
Publisher E-mail: ian@academy.net.nz
Newspaper containing articles about succesful businesses and businessmen in the hospitality industry. **Freq:** Bimonthly. **Trim Size:** 260 x 360 mm. **Subscription Rates:** NZ$20 individuals. **URL:** http://www.

academy.net.nz/?location=hospitality_today. **Circ:** Combined 13,406

48870 ■ Jewellery Time
Jewellers and Watchmakers of New Zealand
10a Athelstan St.
Barrington
Christchurch 8024, New Zealand
Ph: 64 3 3376576
Fax: 64 3 3376576
Publisher E-mail: info@jwnz.co.nz
Magazine serving as a focal point of industry communication. **Key Personnel:** Debra Douglas, Editor, phone 64 9 5217446, fax 64 9 5217446, chaucer@xtra.co.nz. **URL:** http://www.jwnz.co.nz/.

48871 ■ New Zealand AgriBusiness
Agrimedia Ltd.
Ashcroft House
Tancreds Rd., R D 2
PO Box 37-151
Christchurch, New Zealand
Ph: 64 3 3296555
Fax: 64 3 3296550
Publisher E-mail: admin@agrimedia.co.nz
Magazine featuring rural trade information for the agribusiness sector. **Freq:** 6/yr. **Key Personnel:** Kathy Davis, Editor, phone 64 3 5775640, kathydavis@clear.net.nz. **Subscription Rates:** Free. **Remarks:** Accepts advertising. **URL:** http://www.agrimedia.co.nz/publications.php. **Ad Rates:** BW: NZ$2,025. **Circ:** (Not Reported)

48872 ■ New Zealand AgriVet
Agrimedia Ltd.
Ashcroft House
Tancreds Rd., R D 2
PO Box 37-151
Christchurch, New Zealand
Ph: 64 3 3296555
Fax: 64 3 3296550
Publisher E-mail: admin@agrimedia.co.nz
Magazine covering rural veterinary practice. **Freq:** Bimonthly. **Key Personnel:** Kathy Davis, Editor, phone 64 3 5775640, kathydavis@clear.net.nz. **Remarks:** Accepts advertising. **URL:** http://www.agrimedia.co.nz/publications.php. **Ad Rates:** BW: NZ$1,590. **Circ:** (Not Reported)

48873 ■ New Zealand College of Midwives
376 Manchester St.
Christchurch 8014, New Zealand
Ph: 64 3 3772732
Fax: 64 3 3775662
Publisher E-mail: nzcom@nzcom.org.nz
Publication covering New Zealand College of Midwives. **Freq:** Semiannual April and October. **Key Personnel:** Janice Bateman, Contact, phone 44 3 961512, janice@targetmedia.co.nz. **ISSN:** 0114-7870. **Subscription Rates:** US$7 members single copy; US$12 nonmembers single copy. **Remarks:** Advertising accepted; rates available upon request. **URL:** http://www.midwife.org.nz/index.cfm/1,114,0,0,html/NZCOM-Journal. **Circ:** 2,500

48874 ■ New Zealand Journal of Mathematics
New Zealand Mathematical Society
c/o Dr.Alex James, Sec.
Dept. of Mathematics & Statistics
University of Canterbury
Private Bag 4800
Christchurch 8140, New Zealand
Publication E-mail: nzjmath@math.auckland.ac.nz
Publisher E-mail: a.james@math.canterbury.ac.nz
Journal of the New Zealand Mathematical Society, published jointly with University of Auckland. **Freq:** Semiannual. **Key Personnel:** Marston Conder, Editorial Board, conder@math.auckland.ac.nz; Prof. Gaven Martin, Editor, g.j.martin@massey.ac.nz; Douglas Bridges, Editorial Board, d.bridges@math.canterbury.ac.nz. **ISSN:** 1171-6096. **Subscription Rates:** NZ$50 individuals; NZ$10 students; NZ$25 students overseas; NZ$25 individuals reciprocsl members. **URL:** http://www.math.auckland.ac.nz/NZJM/. **Formerly:** Journal of Mathematics.

48875 ■ New Zealand Rural Contractor and Large Scale Farmer
Agrimedia Ltd.
Ashcroft House
Tancreds Rd., R D 2

PO Box 37-151
Christchurch, New Zealand
Ph: 64 3 3296555
Fax: 64 3 3296550
Publisher E-mail: admin@agrimedia.co.nz
Magazine for agricultural contractors and farmers. **Freq:** Bimonthly. **Key Personnel:** Paul Titus, Editor, phone 64 3 3816912, titus@paradise.net.nz. **Subscription Rates:** Free. **Remarks:** Accepts advertising. **URL:** http://www. agrimedia.co.nz/publications.php. **Ad Rates:** BW: NZ$2,025. **Circ:** (Not Reported)

48876 ■ The New Zealand Shipping Gazette
Mercantile Gazette Marketing Ltd.
8 Sheffield Cres.
PO Box 20034
Christchurch 05003, New Zealand
Ph: 64 3 3583219
Fax: 64 3 3584490
Publisher E-mail: subscriptions@mgpublications.co.nz
Trade magazine covering the shipping industry for importers, exporters, manufacturers and companies allied to the shipping industry. **Founded:** 1876. **Freq:** Weekly. **Remarks:** Accepts advertising. **URL:** http://www.mgpublications.co.nz/; http://www.shipdata.co.nz. **Circ:** (Not Reported)

48877 ■ Principals Today
Academy Publishing
Academy House
818 Colombo St., Level 3
PO Box 1879
Christchurch 8013, New Zealand
Ph: 64 3 9615050
Fax: 64 3 9615112
Publisher E-mail: ian@academy.net.nz
Magazine covering information on the education market in New Zealand for decision makers. **Founded:** 1989. **Freq:** Quarterly. **Trim Size:** A3. **Subscription Rates:** US$24.95 individuals 6 issues. **Remarks:** Accepts advertising. **URL:** http://www.magazinestoday.co.nz/Magazines/PrincipalsToday.html. **Circ:** Combined ★8,221

48878 ■ Retirement Today
Academy Publishing
Academy House
818 Colombo St., Level 3
PO Box 1879
Christchurch 8013, New Zealand
Ph: 64 3 9615050
Fax: 64 3 9615112
Publisher E-mail: ian@academy.net.nz
Magazine featuring articles for 65 above age group or those considering retirement. **Key Personnel:** Janice Bateman, Sales and Mktg. Mgr., phone 44 3 9615127, janice@targetmedia.co.nz. **Subscription Rates:** Free. **URL:** http://www.magazinestoday.co.nz/Magazines/RetirementToday.html. **Circ:** Combined 40,000

48879 ■ Wellington Today
Academy Publishing
Academy House
818 Colombo St., Level 3
PO Box 1879
Christchurch 8013, New Zealand
Ph: 64 3 9615050
Fax: 64 3 9615112
Publisher E-mail: ian@academy.net.nz
Magazine emphasizing important elements of business strategy. **Freq:** Bimonthly. **Trim Size:** 260 x 360 mm. **Subscription Rates:** US$24.95 individuals. **URL:** http://www.magazinestoday.co.nz/Magazines/WellingtonToday.html.

48880 ■ The Breeze-FM - 94.5
7th Fl., 151 Kilmore St.
Christchurch, New Zealand
Ph: 64 3 3791290
Fax: 64 3 3665301
E-mail: christchurch@thebreeze.co.nz
Format: Easy Listening. **Owner:** Mediaworks New Zealand, 3 Flower St., Eden Ter., Auckland, New Zealand, 64 9 9289000. **Key Personnel:** Rob McDonald, General Mgr.; Dave Crowther, Sales Mgr.; Rik Van Dijk, Program Dir.; Shellee Arnold, Promotions Mgr.; Adam Perry, Creative Dir. **URL:** http://christchurch.thebreeze.co.nz/; http://www.mediaworks.co.nz/.

48881 ■ Classic Hits-FM - 97.7
Level 8, 155 Worcester St.
PO Box 1484
Christchurch, New Zealand
Ph: 64 3 3799600
Fax: 64 3 3633556
E-mail: redandblack@classichits.co.nz
Format: Classic Rock. **Owner:** The Radio Network, 54 Cook St., Private Bag 92198, Auckland, New Zealand, 64 9 3730000, Fax: 64 9 3674797. **Key Personnel:** Dave Fitzgerald, Contact. **URL:** http://www.classichits.co.nz/.

48882 ■ Coast-AM - 1593
Private Bag 92198
Auckland, New Zealand
E-mail: coast@thecoast.net.nz
Format: Oldies. **Owner:** The Radio Network, at above address. **Key Personnel:** Rick Morin, Contact; Mike Oliver, Contact. **URL:** http://www.thecoast.net.nz.

48883 ■ More-FM - 92.1
102 Victoria St.
PO Box 25 209
Christchurch, New Zealand
Ph: 64 3 3771999
Fax: 64 3 3771993
Format: Contemporary Hit Radio (CHR); Information. **Owner:** MediaWorks NZ Limited, 3 Flower St., Eden Ter., Auckland, New Zealand, 64 3 3779730, Fax: 64 9 3665991. **Operating Hours:** Continuous. **Ad Rates:** Advertising accepted; rates available upon request. **URL:** http://www.morefm.net.nz.

48884 ■ Plains-FM - 96.9
Cor. Madras & St. Asaph St.
PO Box 22297
Christchurch 8001, New Zealand
Ph: 64 3 3657997
Fax: 64 3 3400967
E-mail: info@plainsfm.org.nz
Format: Talk; Information; World Beat; Educational. **Operating Hours:** Continuous. **Key Personnel:** Nicki Reece, Station Mgr., nicki@plainsfm.org.nz; Margaret Henderson, Office Admin., margaret@plainsfm.org.nz; Naoko Kudo, Operations Mgr., naoko@plainsfm.org.nz; Edward Swift, Mornings Producer, edward@plainsfm.org.nz. **Ad Rates:** Advertising accepted; rates available upon request. **URL:** http://www.plainsfm.org.nz.

48885 ■ RDU-FM - 98.5
PO Box 31-244
Christchurch, New Zealand
Ph: 64 3 3642983
Format: Alternative/New Music/Progressive. **Operating Hours:** 6 a.m.-1 a.m. **Key Personnel:** Simone Hall, Office Mgr., simone@rdu.org.nz; Benet Hitchcock, Program Dir., benet@rdu.org.nz; James Meharry, Station Dir., james@rdu.org.nz; Karyn South, Mng. Dir., karyn@rdu.org.nz. **URL:** http://www.rdu.org.nz/.

48886 ■ Tahu-FM - 90.5
PO Box 13469
Christchurch, New Zealand
Ph: 64 3 3713900
Fax: 64 3 3713901
E-mail: mail@tahu.co.nz
Format: Hip Hop; Blues; Ethnic. **Operating Hours:** Continuous. **Ad Rates:** Advertising accepted; rates available upon request. **URL:** http://www.tahufm.com.

Tahu-FM - See Invercargill

Tahu-FM - See Kaikoura

48887 ■ ZB-AM - 1098
Level 8, 155 Worcester St.
PO Box 1484
Christchurch, New Zealand
Ph: 64 3 3799600
Fax: 64 3 3633510
Format: News; Talk; Information. **Owner:** Radio Network, 54 Cook St., Private Bag 92198, Auckland, New Zealand, 64 9 3730000, Fax: 64 9 3674802. **Operating Hours:** Continuous. **Key Personnel:** Andrew Britt, General Mgr., phone 64 3 3633504, fax 64 3 3633510, andrewbritt@radionetwork.co.nz; Chris Simon, Sales Mgr., chrissimon@radionetwork.co.nz. **URL:** http://www.newstalkzb.co.nz; http://www.radionetwork.co.nz.

Cromwell

48888 ■ Junctures
Otago Polytechnic
PO Box 16
Cromwell 9310, New Zealand
Ph: 64 344 59900
Fax: 64 344 59909
Publisher E-mail: info@op.ac.nz
Journal providing a forum for discussion on themes of interest to a wide range of disciplines. **Subtitle:** Journal for Thematic Dialogue. **Freq:** Semiannual. **Key Personnel:** Dr. Susan Ballard, Editor, sballard@tekotago.ac.nz; Prof. Leoni Schmidt, Editorial Board. **ISSN:** 1176-5119. **Subscription Rates:** NZ$100 institutions; NZ$140 institutions, other countries; NZ$40 individuals; NZ$65 other countries. **URL:** http://www.junctures.org.

Dunedin

48889 ■ JNZL: Journal of New Zealand Literature
University of Otago Press
Level 1, 398 Cumberland St.
PO Box 56
Dunedin, New Zealand
Ph: 64 3 4791100
Fax: 64 3 4798385
Publisher E-mail: university.press@otago.ac.nz
Peer-reviewed journal covering literature and writing. **Founded:** 1983. **Freq:** Annual. **ISSN:** 0112-1227. **Subscription Rates:** US$25 institutions standard; US$20 individuals student; US$25 overseas (includes economy air postage). **URL:** http://www.waikato.ac.nz/wfass/jnzl/.

48890 ■ Journal of Neuroendocrinology
John Wiley & Sons Inc.
Wiley-Blackwell
c/o David R. Grattan, Ed.-in-Ch.
Centre for Neuroendocrinology
& U.S. Department of of Anatomy & Structural Biology
School of Medical Science, University of Otago, PO Box 913
Dunedin, New Zealand
Peer-reviewed journal on classical neuroendocrinology including vertebrate and invertebrate endocrinology and broadening its base to encompass regulation of behavioral, cognitive, developmental, degenerative and metabolic processes. **Freq:** Monthly. **Key Personnel:** Greti Aguilera, Sen. Ed., greti_aguilera@nih.gov; Colin H. Brown, Sen. Ed., colin.brown@otago.ac.uk; Kevin L. Grove, Sen. Ed., grovek@ohsu.edu; David R. Grattan, Editor-in-Chief, phone 64 3 4797442, fax 64 3 4797254, dave.grattan@anatomy.otago.ac.nz; Stephen G. Matthews, Editorial Advisory Board. **ISSN:** 0953-8194. **Subscription Rates:** US$258 individuals print and online; EUR231 individuals print and online; 153 other countries print and online; US$3,214 institutions print and online; EUR2,208 institutions print and online; 1,738 institutions print and online; US$2,922 institutions print or online; EUR2,007 institutions print or online; 1,580 institutions print or online; US$3,408 institutions, other countries print or online. **Remarks:** Advertising accepted; rates available upon request. **URL:** http://www.wiley.com/bw/journal.asp?ref=0953-8194. **Circ:** (Not Reported)

48891 ■ Landfall
University of Otago Press
Level 1, 398 Cumberland St.
PO Box 56
Dunedin, New Zealand
Ph: 64 3 4791100
Fax: 64 3 4798385
Publisher E-mail: university.press@otago.ac.nz
Publication featuring poems, stories, fiction, non-fiction, reviews, commentaries and portfolios of art. **Founded:** 1947. **Freq:** Semiannual. **Trim Size:** 167 x 215 mm. **ISSN:** 0023-7930. **Subscription Rates:** NZ$29.95 single issue; $A 24.95 single issue; US$20 single issue. **Remarks:** Accepts advertising. **URL:** http://www.otago.ac.nz/press/landfall. **Ad Rates:** BW: NZ$190. **Circ:** Paid 1,250

48892 ■ Otago Daily Times
Allied Press Ltd.
52 Stuart St.
PO Box 517
Dunedin, New Zealand
Ph: 64 3 4774760
Fax: 64 3 4747424

Circulation: ★ = ABC; △ = BPA; ♦ = CAC; • = CCAB; ❏ = VAC; ⊕ = PO Statement; ‡ = Publisher's Report; Boldface figures = sworn; Light figures = estimated.

Gale Directory of Publications & Broadcast Media/147th Ed.

5293

Publisher E-mail: corporate@alliedpress.co.nz
Newspaper featuring news and events in New Zealand.
Freq: Mon.-Sat. **Remarks:** Accepts advertising. **URL:**
http://www.alliedpress.co.nz/papers.php?pub=odt. **Circ:**
Combined 45,000

48893 ■ Southern Rural Life
Allied Press Ltd.
52 Stuart St.
PO Box 517
Dunedin, New Zealand
Ph: 64 3 4774760
Fax: 64 3 4747424
Publication E-mail: srl@alliedpress.co.nz
Publisher E-mail: corporate@alliedpress.co.nz
Newspaper covering rural life in Otago and Southland
areas. **Freq:** Biweekly. **Subscription Rates:** Free. **URL:**
http://www.alliedpress.co.nz/papers.php?pub=srl. **Circ:**
‡20,000

48894 ■ Classic Hits-FM - 89.4
Westpac Bldg., Level 2
106 George St.
Dunedin, New Zealand
Ph: 64 3 4748400
Fax: 64 3 4748422
E-mail: dunedin@classichits.co.nz
Format: Adult Contemporary. **Owner:** The Radio
Network, 54 Cook St., Private Bag 92198, Auckland,
New Zealand, 64 9 3730000, Fax: 64 9 3674797. **URL:**
http://www.classichits.co.nz/.

48895 ■ Coast-AM - 954
Private Bag 92198
Auckland, New Zealand
E-mail: coast@thecoast.net.nz
Format: Oldies. **Owner:** The Radio Network, at above
address. **Key Personnel:** Rick Morin, Contact; Ray
Makelow, Contact. **Ad Rates:** Advertising accepted;
rates available upon request. **URL:** http://www.thecoast.
net.nz/.

48896 ■ Radio One-FM - 91.0
OUSA Bldg.
640 Cumberland St.
Dunedin, New Zealand
Ph: 64 3 4795834
Format: Alternative/New Music/Progressive. **Owner:**
University of Otago, at above address. **Operating
Hours:** Continuous. **Key Personnel:** Rob Falconer,
Production Mgr., phone 64 3 4795892, production@r1.
co.nz. **URL:** http://www.r1.co.nz/.

Dunedin North

48897 ■ Journal of Pacific Archaeology
New Zealand Archaeological Association Inc.
PO Box 6337
Dunedin North 9059, New Zealand
Publisher E-mail: kylie.bop@clear.net.nz
Peer-reviewed professional journal covering prehistoric
and historic archaeology in New Zealand. **Freq:** Annual.
Key Personnel: Atholl Anderson, Editor, atholl.
anderson@anu.edu.au. **ISSN:** 0110-540X. **URL:** http://
www.nzarchaeology.org/jpa.html. **Formerly:** New
Zealand Journal of Archaeology.

Gisborne

48898 ■ New Zealand Snowboarder
27 Seddon Cres.
Gisborne, New Zealand
Ph: 64 6 8687974
Fax: 64 6 8687971
Publication E-mail: hq@nzsnowboarder.nzl.com
Publisher E-mail: hq@nzsnowboarder.nzl.com
Consumer magazine covering snowboarding in New
Zealand. **Founded:** 1993. **Freq:** May, July and
September. **Key Personnel:** Ste'en Webster, Editor;
Phil Erickson, Director; Dylan Butt, Assoc. Ed. **Subscrip-
tion Rates:** NZ$34 individuals; NZ$60 individuals
Australia; NZ$95 other countries. **Remarks:** Accepts
advertising. **URL:** http://www.nzsnowboarder.nzl.com.
Circ: (Not Reported)

48899 ■ Classic Hits-FM - 90.9
PO Box 1040
Gisborne, New Zealand
Ph: 64 6 8672139
Fax: 64 6 8678309

E-mail: gisborne@classichits.co.nz
Format: Classic Rock. **Owner:** The Radio Network, 54
Cook St., Private Bag 92198, Auckland, New Zealand,
64 9 3730000, Fax: 64 9 3674797. **Key Personnel:**
Darryl Mallet, Contact. **URL:** http://www.classichits.co.
nz.

48900 ■ Turanga-FM - 95.5
PO Box 1224
Gisborne, New Zealand
Ph: 64 6 8686821
Fax: 64 6 8681564
E-mail: turangafm@turangafm.maori.nz
Format: Ethnic; Religious. **Founded:** 1992. **Operating
Hours:** Continuous. **Key Personnel:** Raa Walker,
Program Dir., raawalker@surf.co.nz; Fred Maynard, Sta-
tion Mgr., fred@turangafm.maori.nz; Avon Brown,
Advertising Sales Contact, avon@turangafm.maori.nz.
Ad Rates: Advertising accepted; rates available upon
request. **URL:** http://www.turangafm.co.nz.

48901 ■ Turanga-FM - 91.7
PO Box 1224
Gisborne, New Zealand
Ph: 64 6 8686821
Fax: 64 6 8681564
E-mail: turangafm@turangafm.maori.nz
Format: Ethnic; Religious. **Operating Hours:**
Continuous. **Key Personnel:** Fred Maynard, Station
Mgr., fred@turangafm.maori.nz; Raa Walker, Program
Dir., raawalker@surf.co.nz; Avon Brown, Advertising
Sales Contact, avon@turangafm.maori.nz. **Ad Rates:**
Advertising accepted; rates available upon request.
URL: http://www.turangafm.co.nz.

Gore

48902 ■ The Ensign
Allied Press Ltd.
47 Mersey St.
Gore, New Zealand
Ph: 64 3 2089280
Fax: 64 3 2088949
Publication E-mail: ensign@alliedpress.co.nz
Publisher E-mail: corporate@alliedpress.co.nz
Newspaper covering local events and issues in Eastern
and Northern Southland and West Otago. **Founded:**
1878. **Freq:** Semiweekly (Wed. and Fri.). **URL:** http://
www.alliedpress.co.nz/papers.php?pub=ens. **Circ:**
‡11,500

48903 ■ Hokonui Gold-FM - 94.8
76a Main St.
PO Box 292
Gore 9700, New Zealand
Ph: 64 3 2089325
Fax: 64 3 2089326
E-mail: office@hokonuigold.co.nz
Format: Easy Listening; Oldies; Sports; Agricultural;
News. **Owner:** Radio Network Ltd., 54 Cook St., Private
Bag 92 198, Auckland, New Zealand, 64 9 3730000,
Fax: 64 9 3674802. **Founded:** 1993. **Formerly:** 4ZG.
Operating Hours: Continuous. **Key Personnel:** Nick
Jeffrey, General Mgr., nick@hokonuigold.co.nz. **Ad
Rates:** Advertising accepted; rates available upon
request. **URL:** http://www.hokonuigold.co.nz.

Greymouth

48904 ■ Greymouth Star
Allied Press Ltd.
5-9 Werita St.
PO Box 3
Greymouth, New Zealand
Ph: 64 3 7687121
Fax: 64 3 7686205
Publication E-mail: editor@greystar.co.nz
Publisher E-mail: corporate@alliedpress.co.nz
Newspaper covering events and issues in the Westland
region. **Founded:** Mar. 18, 1866. **Freq:** Daily. **URL:**
http://www.alliedpress.co.nz/papers.php?pub=gs.

48905 ■ The West Coast Messenger
Allied Press Ltd.
3 Werita St.
Greymouth, New Zealand
Ph: 64 3 7689456
Fax: 64 3 7689455
Publication E-mail: messenger@greystar.co.nz

Publisher E-mail: corporate@alliedpress.co.nz
Newspaper covering issues and events in Westport,
Greymouth and Hokitika. **Freq:** Weekly (Wed.). **URL:**
http://www.alliedpress.co.nz/papers.php?pub=ms.

48906 ■ Classic Hits-FM - 91.1
51 Mackay St.
PO Box 378
Greymouth, New Zealand
Ph: 64 3 7687069
Fax: 64 3 7687067
E-mail: joels@radionetwork.co.nz
Format: Classic Rock. **Owner:** The Radio Network, 54
Cook St., Private Bag 92198, Auckland, New Zealand,
64 9 3730000, Fax: 64 9 3674797. **Key Personnel:** Phil
Lemon, Contact, philip@classichits.co.nz. **URL:** http://
www.classichits.co.nz.

Hamilton

48907 ■ AgTrader
Rural Press Ltd.
Federated Farmers Bldg., Level 4
169 London St.
Hamilton, New Zealand
Ph: 64 7 8390603
Newspaper containing articles for buyers and sellers of
agricultural machinery. **Freq:** Monthly. **Key Personnel:**
Rebecca Stuart, Advertising Mgr., rebecca.stuart@
ruralpress.com; Craig Chapman, General Mgr., craig.
chapman@ruralpress.com. **Subscription Rates:** US$25
individuals; US$50 two years. **Remarks:** Accepts
advertising. **URL:** http://www.ruralpress.com/
publications/detail_nz.asp. **Circ:** ‡82,000

48908 ■ Apex
New Zealand Association for Gifted Children
c/o Prof. Roger Moltzen, Ed.
Dept. of Education Studies
University of Waikato
Private Bag 3105
Hamilton, New Zealand
Ph: 64 783 84695
Fax: 64 783 84434
Publisher E-mail: president@giftedchildren.org.nz
Magazine for educators and other professionals. **Key
Personnel:** Prof. Roger Moltzen, Editor, rim@waikato.
ac.nz; Prof. Tracy Riley, Editor, t.l.riley@massey.ac.nz.
Subscription Rates: NZ$36 individuals; NZ$70 two
years; NZ$100 individuals three years; NZ$150 individu-
als five years. **URL:** http://www.giftedchildren.org.nz/
apex/.

48909 ■ New Zealand Journal of Zoology
Royal Society of New Zealand
c/o Dr. C.M. King, Ed.
Department of Biological Sciences
University of Waikato
Private Bag 3105
Hamilton, New Zealand
Ph: 64 7 8562889
Fax: 64 7 8384324
Journal covering fields of zoological science concerning
New Zealand, the Pacific Basin, and Antarctica. **Freq:**
Quarterly. **Key Personnel:** Dr C.M. King, Editor, nzjz@
rsnz.org. **ISSN:** 0301-4223. **Subscription Rates:**
US$130 individuals print only; US$333 individuals online
only; US$350 individuals print and online; NZ$180
individuals online. **URL:** http://www.rsnz.org/publish/
nzjz/.

48910 ■ Ramp
A Ramp Magazine
Dept. of Media Arts
Wintec
Private Bag 3036
Hamilton, New Zealand
Fax: 64 7 8580227
Publication E-mail: rampmagazine@mediarts.net.nz
Publisher E-mail: editor@rampmagazine.org
Magazine featuring original writing and art. **Remarks:**
Accepts advertising. **URL:** http://www.rampmagazine.
org/. **Circ:** (Not Reported)

48911 ■ Tourism Management
Elsevier Science
c/o Chris Ryan, Ed.
Tourism Programme, Centre for Management Studies
University of Waikato
PO Box 3015

Hamilton, New Zealand
Ph: 64 783 84259
Fax: 64 783 84063
Publisher E-mail: nlinfo-f@elsevier.com
Journal providing information for those engaged in planning and management of travel and tourism. **Subtitle:** Research, Policies, Practice. **Freq:** Bimonthly. **Key Personnel:** Chris Ryan, Editor, caryan@waikato.ac.nz; D. Buhalis, International Editorial Board; G.J. Ashworth, International Editorial Board; K. Hollinshead, International Editorial Board; D. Getz, International Editorial Board; Stephen Page, Assoc. & Reviews Ed., s.j.page@ stir.ac.uk. **ISSN:** 0261-5177. **Subscription Rates:** US$210 individuals for all countries except Europe, Japan & Iran; 25,000¥ individuals; EUR187 individuals for European countries & Iran; US$1,533 institutions for all countries except Europe, Japan & Iran; EUR1,371 institutions for European countries & Iran; 181,900¥ institutions. **Remarks:** Accepts advertising. **URL:** http://www.elsevier.com/wps/find/journaldescription.cws_home/30472/description. **Circ:** (Not Reported)

48912 ■ The Breeze-FM - 99.3
Tower Bldg., 12th Fl.
48 Ward St.
Hamilton, New Zealand
Ph: 64 7 8382693
Fax: 64 7 8382893
Format: Easy Listening. **Owner:** Mediaworks New Zealand, 3 Flower St., Eden Ter., Auckland, New Zealand, 64 9 9289000. **Operating Hours:** 5 a.m.-12 a.m. Daily. **URL:** http://waikato.thebreeze.co.nz/; http://www.mediaworks.co.nz/.

48913 ■ Classic Hits-FM Waikato - 98.6
PO Box 489
Hamilton, New Zealand
Ph: 64 7 8580700
Fax: 64 7 8580730
E-mail: bunty@classichits.co.nz
Format: Adult Contemporary. **Owner:** The Radio Network, 54 Cook St., Private Bag 92198, Auckland, New Zealand, 64 9 3730000, Fax: 64 9 3674797. **URL:** http://www.classichits.co.nz/?Region=Waikato.

48914 ■ Newstalk ZB-AM Waikato - 1296
54 Cook St.
Private Bag 92198
Auckland, New Zealand
Ph: 64 9 3730000
Format: News; Talk. **Owner:** The Radio Network, at above address. **Key Personnel:** Paul Holmes, Contact; Leighton Smith, Contact, leighton@newstalkzb.co.nz; Danny Watson, Contact, danny@newstalkzb.co.nz. **URL:** http://www.newstalkzb.co.nz/featdetail.asp? recnumber=1.

Hastings

48915 ■ Hawke's Bay Today
APN News & Media Ltd.
113 Karamu Rd.
PO Box 180
Hastings, New Zealand
Ph: 04 6 8730800
Fax: 64 6 8730812
Publisher E-mail: info@apn.com.au
General newspaper. **Founded:** May 3, 1999. **Freq:** Daily (eve.). **Key Personnel:** Anthony Phillips, Editor, phone 64 687 30842, editor@hbtoday.co.nz. **Subscription Rates:** US$1.20 individuals; US$2 individuals ordinary post Monday to Friday; US$2 individuals ordinary post Saturday; US$2 individuals fast post: Monday to Friday; US$3 individuals Saturday. **Remarks:** Accepts advertising. **URL:** http://www.hbtoday.co.nz/. **Merged with:** Dannevirke's Evening News. **Circ:** Paid ‡36,665

Hawera

48916 ■ Coast-AM - 1557
Private Bag 92198
Auckland, New Zealand
E-mail: coast@thecoast.net.nz
Format: Oldies. **Owner:** The Radio Network, at above address. **Key Personnel:** Rick Morin, Contact; Ray Mankelow, Contact. **Ad Rates:** Advertising accepted; rates available upon request. **URL:** http://www.thecoast.net.nz.

Hokitika

48917 ■ West Coast Times
Allied Press Ltd.
18 Weld St.
PO Box 122
Hokitika, New Zealand
Ph: 64 3 7558422
Fax: 64 3 7558204
Publication E-mail: wctimes@greystar.co.nz
Publisher E-mail: corporate@alliedpress.co.nz
Newspaper covering local events in Hokitika area. **Founded:** 1865. **Freq:** Daily (morn.). **URL:** http://www.alliedpress.co.nz/papers.php?pub=wct.

Inglewood

48918 ■ Crossroads-FM - 107.1
9 Ngahere St.
Taranaki
Inglewood 4651, New Zealand
E-mail: big_dave@ihug.co.nz
Format: Oldies; Classic Rock; Jazz; Blues; Easy Listening; Country. **Operating Hours:** Continuous. **URL:** http://crossroadsfm.greenmountainmusic.com/.

Invercargill

48919 ■ Classic Hits-FM Southland - 98.8
Radio Network House, 1st Fl.
PO Box 802
Invercargill, New Zealand
Ph: 64 3 2187209
Fax: 64 3 2111532
Format: Adult Contemporary. **Owner:** The Radio Network, 54 Cook St., Private Bag 92198, Auckland, New Zealand, 64 9 3730000, Fax: 64 9 3674797. **Key Personnel:** John McDowell, Contact, boggy@ classichits.co.nz. **Ad Rates:** Advertising accepted; rates available upon request. **URL:** http://www.classichits.co.nz/?Region=Southland.

48920 ■ Coast-FM - 92.4
Private Bag 92198
Auckland, New Zealand
E-mail: coast@thecoast.net.nz
Format: Oldies. **Owner:** The Radio Network, at above address. **Key Personnel:** Rick Morin, Contact; Mike Oliver, Contact. **Ad Rates:** Advertising accepted; rates available upon request. **URL:** http://www.thecoast.net.nz.

48921 ■ Hauraki-FM Southland - 93.2
Radio Network House, 1st Fl.
PO Box 802
Invercargill, New Zealand
Ph: 64 3 2111500
Fax: 64 3 2111532
E-mail: carmelcrooks@radionetwork.co.nz
Format: Classic Rock. **Owner:** The Radio Network, 54 Cook St., Private Bag 92198, Auckland, New Zealand, 64 9 3730000, Fax: 64 9 3674802. **Key Personnel:** Nick Jeffrey, Oper./Sales Mgr., phone 64 3 2111515, nickjeffrey@radionetwork.co.nz. **URL:** http://www.radiohauraki.co.nz/.

48922 ■ Newstalk ZB-AM Southland - 864
54 Cook St.
Private Bag 92198
Auckland, New Zealand
Ph: 64 9 3730000
Format: News; Talk. **Owner:** The Radio Network, at above address. **Key Personnel:** Paul Holmes, Contact; Leighton Smith, Contact, leighton@newstalkzb.co.nz; Danny Watson, Contact, danny@newstalkzb.co.nz. **URL:** http://www.newstalkzb.co.nz/featdetail.asp? recnumber=1.

48923 ■ Radio Sport-AM Southland - 558
Private Bag 92198
Auckland, New Zealand
Ph: 64 9 3730000
Fax: 64 9 3674644
E-mail: sport@radiosport.co.nz
Format: Sports. **Owner:** The Radio Network, at above address. **Key Personnel:** Chris Gregory, Program Dir., phone 64 9 3674604, chrisgregory@radionetwork.co.nz; Malcolm Jordan, Prog. Ed., phone 64 9 3674672,

malcolm@radiosport.co.nz. **URL:** http://www.radiosport.co.nz/.

48924 ■ Southern Star-AM - 1314
53 Upper Queen St.
Auckland, New Zealand
Ph: 64 9 3073100
Fax: 64 9 3096888
Format: Contemporary Christian. **Owner:** Rhema Broadcasting Group, at above address. **URL:** http://www.sstar.co.nz/.

48925 ■ Tahu-FM - 99.6
PO Box 13469
Christchurch, New Zealand
Ph: 64 3 3713900
Fax: 64 3 3713901
E-mail: mail@tahu.co.nz
Format: Hip Hop; Urban Contemporary; Ethnic. **URL:** http://www.tahufm.com/.

Kaikohe

48926 ■ Radio New Zealand National-AM - 981
Radio New Zealand House
155 The Terrace
PO Box 123
Wellington, New Zealand
Ph: 64 4 4741999
Fax: 64 4 4741459
E-mail: rnz@radionz.co.nz
Format: News; Information. **Owner:** Radio New Zealand, at above address. **URL:** http://www.radionz.co.nz/.

Kaikoura

48927 ■ Tahu-FM - 91.1
PO Box 13469
Christchurch, New Zealand
Ph: 64 3 3713900
Fax: 64 3 3713901
E-mail: mail@tahu.co.nz
Format: Hip Hop; Urban Contemporary; Ethnic. **URL:** http://www.tahufm.com/.

Kaitaia

48928 ■ Northland Age
Northland Age Ltd.
PO Box 45
Kaitaia, New Zealand
Ph: 64 940 80330
Fax: 64 940 82955
Publication E-mail: editor@northlandage.co.nz
Publisher E-mail: info@northlandage.co.nz
Community newspaper. **Freq:** Biweekly Tuesday and Thursday. **Key Personnel:** Joanne Nattrass, General Mgr.; Sharon Adams, Advertising; Peter Jackson, Editor. **Subscription Rates:** US$60 individuals six months local delivery; US$110 individuals local delivery; US$115 individuals six months postal delivery; US$230 individuals postal delivery. **Remarks:** Accepts advertising. **URL:** http://www.northlandage.co.nz/. **Ad Rates:** PCI; NZ$5.45. **Circ:** *6,525

48929 ■ Radio New Zealand National-AM - 837
Radio New Zealand House
155 The Terrace
PO Box 123
Wellington, New Zealand
Ph: 64 4 4741999
Fax: 64 4 4741459
E-mail: rnz@radionz.co.nz
Format: News; Information. **Owner:** Radio New Zealand, at above address. **URL:** http://www.radionz.co.nz/national/home.

Kapiti

48930 ■ National-AM - 567
Radio New Zealand House, Level 2
155 The Terrace
PO Box 123
Wellington, New Zealand
Ph: 64 4 4741999
Fax: 64 4 4741459
E-mail: rnz@radionz.co.nz
Format: Eclectic. **Owner:** Radio New Zealand, at above

Circulation: * = ABC; △ = BPA; ♦ = CAC; • = CCAB; ❑ = VAC; ⊕ = PO Statement; ‡ = Publisher's Report; Boldface figures = sworn; Light figures = estimated.

Gale Directory of Publications & Broadcast Media/147th Ed.

5295

address. **Operating Hours:** Continuous. **Ad Rates:** Noncommercial. **URL:** http://www.radionz.co.nz/listen/amfm.

Mairangi Bay

48931 ■ American Journal of Cancer
Adis International Ltd.
41 Centorian Dr.
PO Box 65901
Mairangi Bay 0754, New Zealand
Ph: 64 9 4770700
Fax: 64 9 4770766
Publication E-mail: cancer@adis.co.nz
Journal providing a forum for discussing, evaluating and disseminating the latest information on rational therapy and effective patient management within the discipline of oncology. **Freq:** Bimonthly. **Key Personnel:** Michelle I. Wilde, Editor; Treena Hall, Publication Mgr.; Aman U. Buzdar, Consulting Ed. **ISSN:** 1175-6357. **URL:** http://pt.wkhealth.com/pt/re/onc/authors.htm.

48932 ■ American Journal of Cardiovascular Drugs
Adis International Ltd.
41 Centorian Dr.
PO Box 65901
Mairangi Bay 0754, New Zealand
Ph: 64 9 4770700
Fax: 64 9 4770766
Journal promoting rational therapy and disease management within the discipline of cardiology by providing a regular program of independent review articles covering all aspects of the management of cardiovascular disorders, particularly the place in therapy of newer and established agents and procedures. **Freq:** Bimonthly. **Key Personnel:** Michael A. Lincoff, MD, Consulting Ed.; J.P. Cooke, Editorial Board; Amitabh Prakash, MD, Editor; S. Goldstein, Editorial Board; A. Lafont, Editorial Board. **ISSN:** 1175-3277. **Subscription Rates:** US$145 individuals print and electronic; US$180 individuals electronic only. **URL:** http://cardiovascular.adisonline.com/pt/re/cvd/home.htm.

48933 ■ American Journal of Clinical Dermatology
Adis International Ltd.
41 Centorian Dr.
PO Box 65901
Mairangi Bay 0754, New Zealand
Ph: 64 9 4770700
Fax: 64 9 4770766
Publication E-mail: derm@adis.co.nz
Journal providing up-to-date information on rational therapy and effective patient management in dermatology. **Freq:** Bimonthly. **Key Personnel:** Kathy Fraser, Editor; D. Abeck, Editorial Board; F. Belli, Editorial Board; C.J. Cockerell, Editorial Board; T. Alster, Editorial Board; K.E. Andersen, Editorial Board. **ISSN:** 1175-0561. **Subscription Rates:** US$180 individuals print and electronic; US$145 individuals electronic only. **URL:** http://dermatology.adisonline.com/.

48934 ■ Clinical Drug Investigation
Adis International Ltd.
41 Centorian Dr.
PO Box 65901
Mairangi Bay 0754, New Zealand
Ph: 64 9 4770700
Fax: 64 9 4770766
Publication E-mail: cdi@adis.co.nz
Journal focusing on findings of drug research. **Freq:** Monthly. **Key Personnel:** Jasbir Singh, Editor. **ISSN:** 1173-2563. **Subscription Rates:** US$225 individuals print and electronic; US$190 individuals electronic. **URL:** http://druginvestigation.adisonline.com/.

48935 ■ Clinical Pharmacokinetics
Adis International Ltd.
41 Centorian Dr.
PO Box 65901
Mairangi Bay 0754, New Zealand
Ph: 64 9 4770700
Fax: 64 9 4770766
Publication E-mail: journalcpk@adis.co.nz
Journal focusing on research in the field of pharmacokinetics. **Freq:** Monthly. **Key Personnel:** Amitabh Prakash, MD, Editor; Trevor M. Speight, Consulting Ed.; G.D. Anderson, Editorial Board. **ISSN:** 0312-5963. **Subscription Rates:** US$290 individuals print

and electronic; US$245 individuals electronic only. **URL:** http://pharmacokinetics.adisonline.com/.

Mana

48936 ■ Kiwi Parent
Parents Centres New Zealand
Unit 4, Bridgepoint
13 Marina View
Mana, New Zealand
Ph: 64 423 32022
Fax: 64 423 32063
Publisher E-mail: info@parentscentre.org.nz
Magazine providing information about parenting. **Freq:** Bimonthly. **Key Personnel:** Leigh Bredenkamp, Editor, leighb@e-borne.co.nz. **Subscription Rates:** NZ$30 individuals; NZ$60 two years. **Remarks:** Accepts advertising. **URL:** http://www.parentscentre.org.nz/kiwiparent/default.asp; http://www.kiwiparent.co.nz/. **Circ:** Controlled ‡15,000

Masterton

48937 ■ Wairarapa Times-Age
Wairarapa Times-Age Company Ltd.
Cor. Chapel & Perry St.
PO Box 445
Masterton, New Zealand
Ph: 64 637 89999
Fax: 64 637 82371
General newspaper. **Founded:** 1874. **Freq:** Mon.-Sat. **Remarks:** Accepts advertising. **URL:** http://www.times-age.co.nz. **Circ:** 7,302

48938 ■ Arrow-FM - 92.7
Empire Bldg.
92 Queen St.
Masterton, New Zealand
Ph: 64 6 3780255
E-mail: quiver@arrowfm.co.nz
Format: Eclectic; Public Radio. **Founded:** Mar. 2, 1986. **Operating Hours:** Continuous. **Ad Rates:** Noncommercial; underwriting available. **URL:** http://www.arrowfm.co.nz.

Napier

48939 ■ Circle
Association of Anglican Women
Raffles & Bower St.
Napier, New Zealand
Ph: 64 6 8358230
Fax: 64 6 8350680
Member publication covering the Anglican Catholic Church. **Freq:** Quarterly. **Trim Size:** A5. **Key Personnel:** Elizabeth Crawley, President, phone 64 6 8446303, kevincrawley@xtra.co.nz; Gloria Robertshawe, Sec., phone 64 6 8354391, marglo.rob@clear.net.nz; Chris Parkes, Editor, phone 64 7.5767143, chrisdave.parkes@xtra.co.nz. **Remarks:** Advertising not accepted. **URL:** http://www.waiapu.com/index.php?page=anglican-women. **Circ:** (Not Reported)

48940 ■ Classic Hits-FM Hawke's Bay - 89.5
Broadcasting House
105 Dickens St.
PO Box 241
Napier, New Zealand
Ph: 64 6 8338400
Fax: 64 6 8338421
Format: Contemporary Hit Radio (CHR). **Owner:** The Radio Network, 54 Cook St., Private Bag 92198, Auckland, New Zealand, 64 9 3730000, Fax: 64 9 3674797. **Key Personnel:** Martin Good, Contact, martingood@classichits.co.nz. **URL:** http://www.classichits.co.nz/.

48941 ■ Coast-AM - 1530
Private Bag 92198
Auckland, New Zealand
E-mail: coast@thecoast.net.nz
Format: Oldies. **Owner:** The Radio Network, at above address. **Key Personnel:** Rick Morin, Contact; Ray Mankelow, Contact. **Ad Rates:** Advertising accepted; rates available upon request. **URL:** http://www.thecoast.net.nz.

48942 ■ Easy Mix-FM - 90.3
Private Bag 92198
Auckland, New Zealand
Ph: 64 9 3730000

E-mail: studio@easymix.co.nz
Format: Adult Contemporary. **Owner:** The Radio Network, at above address. **Key Personnel:** Alison Leonard, Contact. **URL:** http://www.easymix.co.nz.

48943 ■ 2HBS-FM - 88.8
PO Box 3103
Onekawa
Napier, New Zealand
Ph: 64 6 8453888
E-mail: soundwavefm@xtra.co.nz
Format: Eclectic. **URL:** http://www.geocities.com/capecanaveral/9885/sw2.html.

Nelson

48944 ■ Classic Hits-FM - 89.8
Broadcasting House
41 Selwyn Pl.
PO Box 43
Nelson, New Zealand
Ph: 64 3 5481064
Fax: 64 3 5462580
Format: Adult Contemporary. **Owner:** The Radio Network, 54 Cook St., Private Bag 92198, Auckland, New Zealand, 64 9 3730000, Fax: 64 9 3674797. **Key Personnel:** Kent Robertson, Contact, kent@classichits.co.nz. **URL:** http://www.classichits.co.nz.

48945 ■ Fresh-FM - 95.4
143 Collingwood St.
Nelson 7010, New Zealand
Ph: 64 3 5469891
Fax: 64 3 5469892
E-mail: nelson@freshfm.net
Format: Ethnic. **Key Personnel:** Mike Williams, Station Mgr., mike@freshfm.net; Jo Ann Firestone, Program Dir., joann@freshfm.net. **URL:** http://www.freshfm.net/.

48946 ■ Fresh-FM - 99.4
c/o NMIT
Private Bag 19
Nelson 7042, New Zealand
Ph: 64 3 5469891
Fax: 64 3 5469892
E-mail: nelson@freshfm.net
Format: Ethnic. **Key Personnel:** Mike Williams, Station Mgr., mike@freshfm.net; Jo Ann Firestone, Program Dir., joann@freshfm.net. **URL:** http://www.freshfm.net/.

Fresh-FM - See Blenheim

New Plymouth

48947 ■ Classic Hits-FM Taranaki - 90.7
PO Box 141
New Plymouth, New Zealand
Ph: 64 6 7592460
Fax: 64 6 7592440
Format: Adult Contemporary. **Owner:** The Radio Network, 54 Cook St., Private Bag 92198, Auckland, New Zealand, 64 9 3670000, Fax: 64 9 3674797. **Key Personnel:** Charlotte Butler, Contact, gumboots@classichits.co.nz. **URL:** http://www.classichits.co.nz.

48948 ■ Classic Hits-FM Taranaki - 90.0
PO Box 141
New Plymouth, New Zealand
Ph: 64 6 7592460
Fax: 64 6 7592440
Format: Adult Contemporary. **Owner:** The Radio Network, 54 Cook St., Private Bag 92198, Auckland, New Zealand, 64 9 3730000, Fax: 64 9 3674797. **Key Personnel:** Charlotte Butler, Contact, gumboots@classichits.co.nz. **URL:** http://www.classichits.co.nz.

48949 ■ Coast-AM - 1359
Private Bag 92198
Auckland, New Zealand
E-mail: coast@thecoast.net.nz
Format: Oldies. **Owner:** The Radio Network, at above address. **Key Personnel:** Rick Morin, Contact; Ray Mankelow, Contact. **Ad Rates:** Advertising accepted; rates available upon request. **URL:** http://www.thecoast.net.nz.

48950 ■ Hauraki-FM Taranaki - 90.8
PO Box 141
New Plymouth, New Zealand
Ph: 64 6 7592460
Fax: 64 6 7592440
Format: Classic Rock. **Owner:** The Radio Network, 54

Cook St., Private Bag 92198, Auckland, New Zealand, 64 9 3730000, Fax: 64 9 3674802. **Key Personnel:** Richard Williams, General Mgr., phone 64 6 7592469, fax 64 6 7592442, richardwilliams@radionetwork.co.nz. **URL:** http://www.radiohauraki.co.nz.

48951 ■ National-AM - 918
Radio New Zealand House, Level 2
155 The Terrace
PO Box 123
Wellington, New Zealand
Ph: 64 4 4741999
Fax: 64 4 4741459
E-mail: rnz@radionz.co.nz
Format: Eclectic. **Owner:** Radio New Zealand, at above address. **Operating Hours:** Continuous. **Ad Rates:** Noncommercial. **URL:** http://www.radionz.co.nz/listen/amfm.

North Shore

48952 ■ Diesel Industry News
Adrenalin Publishing Ltd.
PO Box 65092
Mairangi Bay
North Shore 0754, New Zealand
Ph: 64 9 4784771
Fax: 64 9 4784779
Publication E-mail: info@motorequipmentnews.co.nz
Publisher E-mail: yvonnec@xtra.co.nz
Magazine featuring repairing and servicing diesel powered machinery. **Key Personnel:** Cathy Parker, Publisher, phone 64 9 4770360, cathy@adrenalin.co.nz; Robert Barry, Editor, phone 64 9 4784771, robert@adrenalin.co.nz. **Subscription Rates:** NZ$59 individuals; NZ$110 individuals Australia/Pacific Island; NZ$120 individuals International. **Remarks:** Accepts advertising. **URL:** http://www.dieselindustrynews.co.nz. **Circ:** (Not Reported)

North Shore City

48953 ■ BeautyNZ
Adrenalin Publishing Ltd.
PO Box 65092
North Shore City 0754, New Zealand
Publisher E-mail: yvonnec@xtra.co.nz
Magazine exclusively for members of the Association of Beauty Therapist. **Freq:** Bimonthly. **Key Personnel:** Cathy Parker, Publisher, phone 64 9 4770360, cathy@adrenalin.co.nz; Kathryn Calvert, Editor, phone 64 9 4770368, editor@beautynzmag.co.nz. **Remarks:** Accepts advertising. **URL:** http://www.adrenalin.co.nz/afa.asp?idWebPage=13002; http://www.beautynzmag.co.nz/. **Circ:** 3,200

48954 ■ DEMM Engineering & Manufacturing Magazine
Adrenalin Publishing Ltd.
PO Box 65092
Mairangi Bay
North Shore City 0754, New Zealand
Ph: 64 9 4784771
Fax: 64 9 4784779
Publisher E-mail: yvonnec@xtra.co.nz
Magazine for engineering and manufacturing industries. **Freq:** Monthly. **Trim Size:** 210 x 297 mm. **Key Personnel:** Cathy Parker, Publisher, phone 64 9 4770360, cathy@adrenalin.co.nz; Glenn Baker, Editor, phone 64 9 4800393, editor@demm.co.nz; Frank Atkinson, Advertising Mgr., phone 64 9 4770362, frank@demm.co.nz. **Subscription Rates:** NZ$59 individuals; NZ$110 individuals to Australia; NZ$120 individuals rest of world. **Remarks:** Accepts advertising. **URL:** http://www.demm.co.nz. **Ad Rates:** BW: NZ$1,780, 4C: NZ$2,650. **Circ:** 9,017

48955 ■ Electrical + Automation Technology
Adrenalin Publishing Ltd.
PO Box 65092
Mairangi Bay
North Shore City 0754, New Zealand
Ph: 64 9 4784771
Fax: 64 9 4784779
Publisher E-mail: yvonnec@xtra.co.nz
Magazine featuring electrical and automation process industries. **Freq:** 6/yr. **Key Personnel:** Cathy Parker, Publisher, phone 64 9 4770360, cathy@adrenalin.co.nz; Lynnaire Johnston, Editor, phone 64 9 4835300, editor@

electricalautomation.co.nz; Frank Atkinson, Advertising Mgr., phone 64 9 4770362, frank@adrenalin.co.nz. **Subscription Rates:** NZ$48 individuals; NZ$70 individuals to Australia and Pacific Island; NZ$80 other countries. **Remarks:** Accepts advertising. **URL:** http://www.electricalautomation.co.nz. **Ad Rates:** BW: NZ$2,615, 4C: NZ$3,350. **Circ:** ★10,315

48956 ■ Motor Equipment News
Adrenalin Publishing Ltd.
PO Box 65092
Mairangi Bay
North Shore City 0754, New Zealand
Publication E-mail: info@motorequipmentnews.co.nz
Publisher E-mail: yvonnec@xtra.co.nz
Magazine featuring automotive repair, service and parts industry. **Freq:** 11/yr. **Trim Size:** 247 x 378 mm. **Key Personnel:** Cathy Parker, Publisher, phone 64 9 4770360, cathy@adrenalin.co.nz; Robert Barry, Editor, phone 64 9 4770367, robert@adrenalin.co.nz; Dan Prestige, Advertising Mgr., phone 64 9 4770361, ben@adrenalin.co.nz. **Subscription Rates:** NZ$59 individuals; NZ$110 individuals to Australia and Pacific Island; NZ$120 other countries. **Remarks:** Accepts advertising. **URL:** http://www.motorequipmentnews.co.nz. **Ad Rates:** BW: NZ$2,730, 4C: NZ$3,295. **Circ:** ★11,330

48957 ■ New Zealand Company Vehicle
Adrenalin Publishing Ltd.
PO Box 65092
Mairangi Bay
North Shore City 0754, New Zealand
Ph: 64 9 4784771
Fax: 64 9 4784779
Publisher E-mail: yvonnec@xtra.co.nz
Magazine featuring automobile for fleet market. **Subtitle:** and Executive Cars. **Freq:** 6/yr. **Trim Size:** 210 x 297 mm. **Key Personnel:** Cathy Parker, Publisher, phone 64 9 4770360, cathy@adrenalin.co.nz; Robert Barry, Editor, phone 64 9 4770367, robert@adrenalin.co.nz; Dan Prestige, Advertising Mgr., phone 64 9 447 0361, dan@adrenalin.co.nz. **Subscription Rates:** NZ$48 individuals; NZ$70 individuals to Australia and Pacific Islands; NZ$80 other countries. **Remarks:** Accepts advertising. **URL:** http://www.companyvehicle.co.nz. **Ad Rates:** BW: NZ$2,005, 4C: NZ$2,410. **Circ:** Controlled ★7,048

48958 ■ New Zealand 4WD
Adrenalin Publishing Ltd.
PO Box 65092
North Shore City 0754, New Zealand
Publisher E-mail: yvonnec@xtra.co.nz
Magazine featuring 4-wheel-drive vehicles. **Founded:** 1996. **Freq:** 11/yr. **Trim Size:** 210 x 297 mm. **Key Personnel:** Cathy Parker, Publisher, phone 64 9 4770360, cathy@adrenalin.co.nz; John Oxley, Editor, phone 64 9 4784771, editor@nz4wd.co.nz; Dan Prestige, Contact, phone 64 9 4770361, dan@nz4wd.co.nz. **Subscription Rates:** NZ$49 individuals; NZ$150 other countries; NZ$140 individuals to Australia and Pacific Islands. **Remarks:** Accepts advertising. **URL:** http://www.nz4wd.co.nz. **Ad Rates:** BW: NZ$1,910, 4C: NZ$2,290. **Circ:** 3,403

48959 ■ NZ Business
Adrenalin Publishing Ltd.
14C Vega Pl.
PO Box 65092
North Shore City 0754, New Zealand
Ph: 64 9 4784771
Fax: 64 9 4784779
Publisher E-mail: yvonnec@xtra.co.nz
Magazine featuring small to medium business in New Zealand. **Subtitle:** Big on Small Business. **Freq:** 11/yr. **Trim Size:** 210 x 297 mm. **Key Personnel:** Cathy Parker, Publisher, phone 64 9 4770360, cathy@adrenalin.co.nz; Glenn Baker, Editor, phone 64 9 4800393, editor@nzbusiness.co.nz; Yvonne Carter, Publisher, phone 64 9 8173818, yvonnec@xtra.co.nz. **Subscription Rates:** NZ$80 individuals; NZ$130 individuals Australia; NZ$140 other countries. **Remarks:** Accepts advertising. **URL:** http://www.nzbusiness.co.nz. **Ad Rates:** BW: NZ$2,235, 4C: NZ$3,110. **Circ:** 7,579

Oamaru

48960 ■ Classic Hits-FM - 98.4
Thames St.

PO Box 426
Oamaru, New Zealand
Ph: 64 3 4341395
Fax: 64 3 4331087
E-mail: waitaki@classichits.co.nz
Format: Classic Rock. **Owner:** The Radio Network, 54 Cook St., Private Bag 92198, Auckland, New Zealand, 64 9 3730000, Fax: 64 9 3674797. **Key Personnel:** Becky Morgan, Contact. **URL:** http://www.classichits.co.nz/.

Oneroa

48961 ■ Gulf News (Waiheke)
Pendragon Press Ltd.
April Arcade
124 Ocean View Rd.
PO Box 5
Oneroa, New Zealand
Ph: 64 937 25055
Fax: 64 937 25055
Community newspaper. **Freq:** Weekly. **Key Personnel:** Liz Waters, Editor and Publisher; Merrie Hewetson, Business Mgr.; Kelly Bouzaid, Advertising Mgr. **ISSN:** 1170-0483. **Remarks:** Accepts advertising. **URL:** http://www.waihekegulfnews.co.nz. **Circ:** ‡3,129

Palmerston North

48962 ■ Australasian Journal of Disaster and Trauma Studies
Massey University
School of Psychology
Private Bag 11-222
Palmerston North, New Zealand
Ph: 64 6 2569099
Fax: 64 6 3505673
Publisher E-mail: psych.admin.pn@massey.ac.nz
Scholarly, electronic journal covering disaster and trauma studies in Australia, New Zealand and the Pacific rim. **Founded:** Feb. 1997. **Freq:** Biennial. **Key Personnel:** Prof. Douglas Paton, Editor, douglas.paton@utas.edu.au. **ISSN:** 1174-4707. **Subscription Rates:** Free. **Remarks:** Advertising not accepted. **URL:** http://www.massey.ac.nz/~trauma. **Circ:** (Not Reported)

48963 ■ Australian & New Zealand Journal of Statistics
John Wiley & Sons Inc.
Wiley-Blackwell
c/o Prof. Stephen Haslett, Mng. Ed.
Institute of Fundamental Sciences - Statistics
Massey University
Private Bag 11222
Palmerston North 4442, New Zealand
Ph: 64 6 3504966
Journal focusing on statistics. **Freq:** Quarterly. **Key Personnel:** M. Anderson, Applications Editorial Board Member; J. Brown, Applications Editorial Board Member; Prof. Stephen Haslett, Managing Editor, k.mengersen@qut.edu.au. **ISSN:** 1369-1473. **Subscription Rates:** US$130 individuals print and online; US$84 members print and online; US$290 institutions print and online; US$264 institutions print or online; EUR257 Institutions print and online; EUR100 members Euro zone; 66 individuals print and online; EUR233 institutions print or online; US$396 institutions, other countries print and online; US$360 institutions, other countries print or online. **Remarks:** Accepts advertising. **URL:** http://www.wiley.com/bw/journal.asp?ref=1369-1473&site=1. **Circ:** (Not Reported)

48964 ■ New Zealand Studies in Applied Linguistics
Applied Linguistics Association of New Zealand
c/o Dr. Gillian Skyrme
School of Language Studies
Massey University
Private Bag 11 222
Palmerston North, New Zealand
Publisher E-mail: r.erlam@auckland.ac.nz
Peer-reviewed journal featuring studies and issues in Applied Linguistics. **Freq:** Semiannual. **Key Personnel:** Prof. John Bitchener, Editor, john.bitchener@aut.ac.nz. **ISSN:** 1173-5562. **URL:** http://www.alanz.ac.nz/journal/.

48965 ■ NZ Journal of Teachers' Work
Massey University
School of Psychology
Private Bag 11-222

Palmerston North, New Zealand
Ph: 64 6 2569099
Fax: 64 6 3505673
Publisher E-mail: psych.admin.pn@massey.ac.nz
National, peer-reviewed journal containing articles of interest to early childhood, primary, secondary and tertiary teachers. **Key Personnel:** John O'Neill, Gen. Ed.; Sharon Wright, Exec. Ed., s.r.wright@massey.ac.nz. **ISSN:** 1176-6662. **Subscription Rates:** Free for teachers. **URL:** http://www.teacherswork.ac.nz.

48966 ▪ Classic Hits-FM Manawatu - 97.8
619 Main St.
PO Box 1045
Palmerston North, New Zealand
Ph: 64 6 3503550
Fax: 64 6 3503580
E-mail: manawatu@classichits.co.nz
Format: Adult Contemporary. **Owner:** The Radio Network, 54 Cook St., Private Bag 92198, Auckland, New Zealand, 64 9 3730000, Fax: 64 9 3674797. **Key Personnel:** Richard Dryden, Contact. **URL:** http://www.classichits.co.nz/?Region=Manawatu.

48967 ▪ Coast-AM - 1548
Private Bag 92198
Auckland, New Zealand
E-mail: coast@thecoast.net.nz
Format: Oldies. **Owner:** The Radio Network, at above address. **Key Personnel:** Rick Morin, Contact; Ray Mankelow, Contact. **Ad Rates:** Advertising accepted; rates available upon request. **URL:** http://www.thecoast.net.nz.

48968 ▪ More FM Manawatu - 92.2
The Hub
Westside Bldg., Level 3
Cor. The Sq. & Rangitkei St.
Palmerston North, New Zealand
Ph: 64 6 3560922
Fax: 64 6 3584069
Format: Full Service; Adult Contemporary. **Formerly:** XS-FM. **Key Personnel:** Darren Wallace, Program Dir., darrenw@morefm.co.nz; Willie Furnell, General Mgr., willief@morefm.co.nz; Craig Loach, Sales Mgr., craigl@morefm.co.nz. **URL:** http://www.morefmmanawatu.co.nz/.

48969 ▪ 999-AM - 999
PO Box 4666
Palmerston North, New Zealand
Ph: 64 6 3579340
Fax: 64 6 3579345
E-mail: info@accessmanawatu.co.nz
Format: Eclectic; News; Ethnic. **Key Personnel:** Fraser Greig, Station Mgr., fraser@accessmanawatu.co.nz; Janine Flanagan, Accounts/Admin., janine@accessmanawatu.co.nz. **URL:** http://www.accessmanawatu.co.nz/.

48970 ▪ Vision 100-FM - 100
Pete's Post Bag 100
Manawatu
Palmerston North, New Zealand
Ph: 64 27 4154970
E-mail: office@vision100.com
Format: Classic Rock; Album-Oriented Rock (AOR); Urban Contemporary. **Owner:** VISION 100 Ltd., at above address. **Founded:** Aug. 17, 1999. **Key Personnel:** Grant Seton, Director. **Ad Rates:** Advertising accepted; rates available upon request. **URL:** http://www.vision100.com/.

Paraparaumu

48971 ▪ Classic Hits-FM Kapiti - 92.7
Shop 5, Coastlands Mall
PO Box 596
Paraparaumu, New Zealand
Ph: 64 4 9029886
Fax: 64 4 2983086
Format: Adult Contemporary. **Owner:** The Radio Network, 54 Cook St., Private Bag 92198, Auckland, New Zealand, 64 9 3730000, Fax: 64 9 3674797. **Key Personnel:** Dave Smart, Contact, dave@classichits.co.nz. **URL:** http://www.classichits.co.nz/?Region=Kapiti.

Piopio

48972 ▪ Maniapoto-FM - 92.7
Te Kumi Marae
State Hwy. 3
PO Box 416
Te Kuiti, New Zealand
Ph: 64 7 8781160
Fax: 64 7 8783002
Format: Ethnic. **Key Personnel:** Jaqui Taituha, Manager. **URL:** http://www.irirangi.net/iwi-stations.aspx.

Queenstown

48973 ▪ National-AM - 1134
Radio New Zealand House, Level 2
155 The Terrace
PO Box 123
Wellington, New Zealand
Ph: 64 4 4741999
Fax: 64 4 4741459
E-mail: rnz@radionz.co.nz
Format: Eclectic. **Owner:** Radio New Zealand, at above address. **Operating Hours:** Continuous. **Ad Rates:** Noncommercial. **URL:** http://www.radionz.co.nz/listen/amfm.

Rotorua

48974 ▪ Classic Hits-FM - 97.5
1140 Fenton St.
PO Box 1147
Rotorua, New Zealand
Ph: 64 7 3489089
Fax: 64 7 3495527
Format: Classic Rock. **Owner:** The Radio Network, 54 Cook St., Private Bag 92198, Auckland, New Zealand, 64 9 3730000, Fax: 64 9 3674797. **Key Personnel:** Luke Valentine, Contact, luke@classichits.co.nz. **URL:** http://www.classichits.co.nz/.

48975 ▪ Country Radio-FM - 88.4
23 McKenzie Rd.
Rotorua, New Zealand
Ph: 64 7 3454792
E-mail: radionet@wave.co.nz
Format: Country; News. **Ad Rates:** Advertising accepted; rates available upon request. **URL:** http://www.globaltech.co.nz.

48976 ▪ Country Radio-FM - 88.7
23 McKenzie Rd.
Rotorua, New Zealand
Ph: 64 7 3454792
E-mail: barknet@clear.net.nz
Format: Country. **Owner:** Country Radio Network, at above address. **Key Personnel:** Peter Thompson, Contact, petert@globaltech.co.nz. **URL:** http://www.globaltech.co.nz/radio.html.

48977 ▪ Easy Mix-FM - 95.1
Private Bag 92198
Auckland, New Zealand
Ph: 64 9 3730000
E-mail: studio@easymix.co.nz
Format: Adult Contemporary. **Owner:** The Radio Network, at above address. **Key Personnel:** Alison Leonard, Contact. **URL:** http://www.easymix.co.nz.

Takaka

48978 ▪ Fresh-FM - 95.2
84 Commercial St.
Takaka 7110, New Zealand
Ph: 64 3 5258779
Fax: 64 3 5258779
E-mail: takaka@freshfm.net
Format: Ethnic. **Key Personnel:** Mike Williams, Station Mgr., mike@freshfm.net; Jo Ann Firestone, Program Dir., joann@freshfm.net. **URL:** http://www.freshfm.net/.

Taupo

48979 ▪ Classic Hits-FM - 96.7
Cor. Paora Hapi and Gascoigne Sts.
PO Box 967
Taupo, New Zealand
Ph: 64 7 3760550
Fax: 64 7 3780030
Format: Classic Rock. **Owner:** The Radio Network, 54

Cook St., Private Bag 92198, Auckland, New Zealand, 64 9 3730000, Fax: 64 9 3674797. **Key Personnel:** Brendon Weatherly, Contact, brendon@classichits.co.nz. **URL:** http://www.classichits.co.nz/.

Tauranga

48980 ▪ Avoscene
New Zealand Avocado Growers Association
Level 5, Harrington House
Harrington St.
PO Box 13267
Tauranga 3141, New Zealand
Ph: 64 7 5716147
Fax: 64 7 5716145
Publisher E-mail: info@nzavocado.co.nz
Magazine containing articles on relevant issues facing the industry. **Freq:** Quarterly. **Subscription Rates:** US$100 individuals New Zealand; US$100 other countries; US$15 single issue. **URL:** http://nzavocado.co.nz/Avo.scene.html.

48981 ▪ Classic Hits-FM Bay of Plenty - 95.0
4th Fl., Harrington House
Harrington St.
PO Box 642
Tauranga, New Zealand
Ph: 64 7 5789139
Fax: 64 7 5778522
E-mail: bk@classichits.co.nz
Format: Adult Contemporary. **Owner:** The Radio Network, 54 Cook St., Private Bag 92198, Auckland, New Zealand, 64 9 3730000, Fax: 64 9 3674797. **Key Personnel:** Nichola Maclean, Contact, nicholamaclean@radionetwork.co.nz. **URL:** http://www.classichits.co.nz/?Region=Bay%20Of%20Plenty.

48982 ▪ Coast-FM - 97.3
Private Bag 92198
Auckland, New Zealand
E-mail: coast@thecoast.net.nz
Format: Oldies. **Owner:** The Radio Network, at above address. **Key Personnel:** Rick Morin, Contact; Ray Mankelow, Contact. **Ad Rates:** Advertising accepted; rates available upon request. **URL:** http://www.thecoast.net.nz.

48983 ▪ Easy Mix-FM - 99.0
Private Bag 92198
Auckland, New Zealand
Ph: 64 9 3730000
E-mail: studio@easymix.co.nz
Format: Adult Contemporary. **Owner:** The Radio Network, at above address. **Key Personnel:** Alison Leonard, Contact. **URL:** http://www.easymix.co.nz.

Te Kuiti

48984 ▪ Maniapoto-FM - 99.6
Te Kumi Marae
State Hwy. 3
PO Box 416
Te Kuiti, New Zealand
Ph: 64 7 8781160
Fax: 64 7 8783002
Format: Ethnic. **Key Personnel:** Jaqui Taituha, Manager. **URL:** http://www.irirangi.net/iwi-stations.aspx.

48985 ▪ Maniapoto-FM - 96.5
Te Kumi Marae
State Hwy. 3
PO Box 416
Te Kuiti, New Zealand
Ph: 64 7 8781160
Fax: 64 7 8783002
Format: Ethnic. **Key Personnel:** Jaqui Taituha, Manager. **URL:** http://www.irirangi.net/iwi-stations.aspx.

48986 ▪ Maniapoto-FM - 91.9
Te Kumi Marae
State Hwy. 3
PO Box 416
Te Kuiti, New Zealand
Ph: 64 7 8781160
Fax: 64 7 8783002
Format: Ethnic. **Key Personnel:** Jaqui Taituha, Manager. **URL:** http://www.irirangi.net/iwi-stations.aspx.

Maniapoto-FM - See Piopio

Timaru

48987 ■ Courier Country
Allied Press Ltd.
12-14 George St.
PO Box 179
Timaru, New Zealand
Ph: 64 3 6879228
Fax: 64 3 6881753
Publication E-mail: timaru@timarucourier.co.nz
Publisher E-mail: corporate@alliedpress.co.nz
Newspaper covering information and events in North
Otago to Mid-Canterbury. **Subscription Rates:** Free.
URL: http://www.alliedpress.co.nz/papers.php?pub=
ccountry. **Circ:** 15,200

48988 ■ Classic Hits-FM - 98.7
Sophia St.
PO Box 275
Timaru, New Zealand
Ph: 64 3 6846846
Fax: 64 3 6886733
Format: Classic Rock. **Owner:** The Radio Network, 54
Cook St., Private Bag 92198, Auckland, New Zealand,
64 9 3730000, Fax: 64 9 3674797. **Key Personnel:**
Mark Whaley, Contact. **URL:** http://www.classichits.co.
nz/.

48989 ■ Classic Hits-FM - 94.7
Sophia St.
PO Box 275
Timaru, New Zealand
Ph: 64 3 6848152
Fax: 64 3 6846846
Format: Classic Rock. **Owner:** The Radio Network, 54
Cook St., Private Bag 92198, Auckland, New Zealand,
64 9 3730000, Fax: 64 9 3674797. **Key Personnel:**
Mark Whaley, Contact. **URL:** http://www.classichits.co.
nz/.

48990 ■ National-AM - 918
Radio New Zealand House, Level 2
155 The Terrace
PO Box 123
Wellington, New Zealand
Ph: 64 4 4741999
Fax: 64 4 4741459
E-mail: rnz@radionz.co.nz
Format: Eclectic. **Owner:** Radio New Zealand, at above
address. **Operating Hours:** Continuous. **Ad Rates:**
Noncommercial. **URL:** http://www.radionz.co.nz/listen/
amfm.

Turangi

48991 ■ Triple T-FM - 91.9
33 Town Ctr.
PO Box 198
Turangi, New Zealand
Ph: 64 7 3860935
Fax: 64 7 3860994
E-mail: t97.2fm@xtra.co.nz
Format: Ethnic; World Beat. **Operating Hours:**
Continuous. **Key Personnel:** Katipo Te Hiini, Mng. Dir.,
katipo@tuwharetoafm.co.nz; Aaron Moeke, Program
Dir., aaron@tuwharetoafm.co.nz; Charmaine Haenga,
Admin. **Ad Rates:** Advertising accepted; rates available
upon request. **URL:** http://www.tuwharetoa.irirangi.net.

Upper Hutt

48992 ■ Break In
New Zealand Association of Radio Transmitters
19 Main St., Ste. 9
Upper Hutt 5018, New Zealand
Ph: 64 4 9392189
Fax: 64 4 9392190
Publisher E-mail: nzart@nzart.org.nz
Technical publication of the New Zealand Association of
Radio Transmitters. **Freq:** Bimonthly. **Key Personnel:**
John Walker, Editor, editor@nzart.org.nz. **ISSN:** 0006-
9523. **Remarks:** Accepts advertising. **URL:** http://www.
nzart.org.nz/breakin/index.html. **Circ:** (Not Reported)

Waitomo Caves

48993 ■ Tall Poppies
New Zealand Association for Gifted Children
PO Box 46
Waitomo Caves, New Zealand
Ph: 64 3 9601252
Publication E-mail: tallpoppies@giftedchildren.org.nz
Publisher E-mail: president@giftedchildren.org.nz
Magazine for families of the gifted children and
professionals. **Freq:** 3/yr. **Subscription Rates:** Included
in membership. **URL:** http://www.giftedchildren.org.nz/
national/tallpoppies.php.

Wanaka

48994 ■ Newstalk ZB-FM Central Otago - 90.6
54 Cook St.
Private Bag 92198
Auckland, New Zealand
Ph: 64 9 3730000
Format: News; Talk. **Owner:** The Radio Network, at
above address. **Key Personnel:** Paul Holmes, Contact;
Leighton Smith, Contact, leighton@newstalkzb.co.nz.
URL: http://www.newstalkzb.co.nz/featdetail.asp?
recnumber=1.

Wanganui

48995 ■ New Zealand Camellia Bulletin
New Zealand Camellia Society
c/o Mrs. V. Cave, Ed.
Seafield R.D. 4
Wanganui, New Zealand
Publisher E-mail: vonniecave@farmside.co.nz
Publication of the New Zealand Camellia Society.
Founded: 1959. **Freq:** Quarterly. **Trim Size:** A5. **Key
Personnel:** Vonnie Cave, Editor, vonniecave@farmside.
co.nz. **Remarks:** Accepts advertising. **URL:** http://www.
nzcamelliasociety.co.nz/. **Ad Rates:** BW: US$200, 4C:
US$300. **Circ:** (Not Reported)

48996 ■ Wanganui Chronicle
Wanganui Newspapers
59 Taupo Quay
PO Box 433
Wanganui, New Zealand
Ph: 64 646 3490710
Fax: 64 646 3490721
Publisher E-mail: news@wanganuichronicle.co.nz
General newspaper. **Founded:** 1856. **Freq:** Daily. **Key
Personnel:** Andy Jarden, General Mgr., phone 64 634
90713, andy.jarden@wanganuichronicle.co.nz; Allison
Hollard, Advertising Mgr., alison.hollard@
wanganuichronicle.co.nz; Ross Pringle, Editor, phone
64 634 90717, ross.pringle@wanganuichronicle.co.nz;
Louisa Hewitt, Circulation Mgr., phone 64 634 90715,
louisa.hewitt@wanganuichronicle.co.nz. **Remarks:** Accepts advertising. **URL:** http://www.wanganuichronicle.
co.nz. **Circ:** Combined ‡15,255

48997 ■ Classic Hits-FM - 89.6
PO Box 632
Wanganui, New Zealand
Ph: 64 6 3458564
Fax: 64 6 3456402
Format: Classic Rock. **Owner:** The Radio Network, 54
Cook St., Private Bag 92198, Auckland, New Zealand,
64 9 3730000, Fax: 64 9 3674797. **Key Personnel:**
Rachel Prankerd, Contact, rach@classichits.co.nz. **URL:**
http://www.classichits.co.nz/.

Wellington

48998 ■ The Adventure
Scripture Union in New Zealand
PO Box 760
Wellington, New Zealand
Ph: 64 438 50485
Fax: 64 438 50483
Publisher E-mail: info@scriptureunion.org.nz
Magazine containing news, events, activities and stories
about the organization's works in New Zealand. **Freq:**
5/yr. **Subscription Rates:** Free. **URL:** http://www.
scriptureunion.org.nz/theadventureform.htm.

48999 ■ AFR Smart Investor
Fairfax Business Media
40 Boulcott, Level 3

PO Box 2595
Wellington 2000, New Zealand
Ph: 64 4 496 9800
Fax: 64 4 496 9841
Magazine covering financial investment ideas for
Australian investors. **Freq:** Monthly. **Trim Size:** 220 x
275 mm. **Key Personnel:** Nicole Pedersen-McKinnon,
Editor; Michael Grenenger, Advertising Dir.; Michael Gill,
CEO/Ed.-In-Ch. **Subscription Rates:** $A 85 individuals
including GST; $A 155 two years. **Remarks:** Accepts
advertising. **URL:** http://www.afrsmartinvestor.com.au/.
Circ: (Not Reported)

**49000 ■ Australian and New Zealand Journal of
Statistics**
New Zealand Statistical Association
PO Box 1731
Wellington, New Zealand
Australian journal covering statistics. **Freq:** Quarterly.
Key Personnel: Stephen Haslett, Managing Editor;
Prof. Mervyn J. Silvapulle, Theory and Methods Ed.,
anzjs@buseco.monash.edu.au; Dr. Petra Graham, Book
Review Ed. **ISSN:** 1369-1473. **Subscription Rates:**
US$280 institutions print only; 194 institutions print only;
EUR247 institutions Europe; US$382 other countries print
only; US$137 individuals print & online; 69 individuals
for non Euro zone & U.K; EUR105 individuals print & online; US$322 institutions print & online; 224 institutions
print & online; EUR285 institutions print & online. **Remarks:** Accepts advertising. **URL:** http://nzsa.rsnz.org;
http://www.statsoc.org.au; http://www.
blackwellpublishing.com. **Formerly:** The Australian
Journal of Statistics and The New Zealand Statistician.
Circ: (Not Reported)

49001 ■ Booknotes
New Zealand Book Council
Level 7, Alan Burns Insurance House
69 Boulcott St.
Wellington 6011, New Zealand
Ph: 64 449 91569
Fax: 64 449 91424
Publisher E-mail: admin@bookcouncil.org.nz
Publication covering books. **Freq:** Quarterly. **Key Per-
sonnel:** David Larsen, Editor; Kate De Goldi, Writer;
David Hill, Contact. **Subscription Rates:** Included in
membership. **Remarks:** Accepts advertising. **URL:** http://
www.bookcouncil.org.nz. **Ad Rates:** BW: NZ$250. **Circ:**
(Not Reported)

49002 ■ Booksellers News
Booksellers New Zealand
Level 1, Survey House
PO Box 13248
21-29 Broderick Rd.
Johnsonville
Wellington, New Zealand
Ph: 64 447 85511
Fax: 64 447 85519
Publisher E-mail: info@booksellers.co.nz
Trade magazine of New Zealand booksellers. **Freq:**
Bimonthly. **Key Personnel:** Carmen Wilson, Mktg. &
Promotions Mgr.; Holly Robinson, Promotions Coord.;
Linda Henderson, CEO. **Remarks:** Accepts advertising.
URL: http://www.booksellers.co.nz/tr_news.htm. **Circ:**
(Not Reported)

**49003 ■ Chartered Accountants Journal of New
Zealand**
Institute of Chartered Accountants of New Zealand
Level 7, Tower Bldg.
50 Cstomhouse Quay
PO Box 11342
Wellington 6142, New Zealand
Ph: 64 4 4747840
Fax: 64 4 4736303
Publisher E-mail: customer@nzica.com
Journal covering New Zealand chartered accountants.
Freq: 11/yr. **Key Personnel:** Dinu Harry, President.
ISSN: 1172-9929. **Subscription Rates:** US$12 single
issue; US$11 other countries single copy; US$120
members additional copy; US$107 members other
countries (additional copy); US$14 nonmembers single
copy; US$12.50 nonmembers New Zealand; US$120
nonmembers overseas. **Remarks:** Advertising accepted;
rates available upon request. **URL:** http://www.nzica.
com/. **Circ:** 12,941

49004 ■ Circular
Bus and Coach Association of New Zealand Inc.
PO Box 9336

Circulation: ★ = ABC; △ = BPA; ♦ = CAC; • = CCAB; ❑ = VAC; ⊕ = PO Statement; ‡ = Publisher's Report; Boldface figures = sworn; Light figures = estimated.

Gale Directory of Publications & Broadcast Media/147th Ed.

5299

Wellington, New Zealand
Ph: 64 449 97334
Fax: 64 449 97353
Publisher E-mail: info@busandcoach.co.nz
Magazine featuring road tests of new buses or coaches. **Freq:** Monthly. **Subscription Rates:** NZ$125 individuals 11 issues; NZ$155 individuals overseas. **Remarks:** Accepts advertising. **URL:** http://www.busandcoach.co.nz/services/circulars.asp. **Circ:** (Not Reported)

49005 ■ Creative Wood
National Association of Woodturners New Zealand Inc.
PO Box 51-014
Wellington 6230, New Zealand
Ph: 64 423 23128
Fax: 64 423 23129
Publisher E-mail: evond@xtra.co.nz
Official magazine of the National Association of Woodturners New Zealand Inc. **Freq:** Quarterly. **Print Method:** Offset. **Trim Size:** A4. **Key Personnel:** John Mackinven, Book Review Ed.; Richard Frost, Contact, richard@tasmanimage.co.nz. **ISSN:** 1175-4702. **Remarks:** Accepts advertising. **URL:** http://www.naw.org.nz/magazine/. **Formerly:** NZ Woodturner. **Ad Rates:** BW: NZ$640, 4C: NZ$900. **Circ:** 1,000

49006 ■ DANZ
Dance Aotearoa New Zealand
Wellington Arts Ctr.
Ground Fl., 69 Abel Smith St.
PO Box 9885
Wellington 6141, New Zealand
Ph: 64 801 9885
Publisher E-mail: danz@danz.org.nz
Official magazine of Dance Aotearoa New Zealand covering dance. **Freq:** Quarterly. **Trim Size:** A4. **Key Personnel:** Tania Kopytko, Exec, Dir. **URL:** http://www.danz.org.nz. **Circ:** Paid 500

49007 ■ e.nz magazine
The Institution of Professional Engineers New Zealand
158 The Ter.
PO Box 12 241
Wellington, New Zealand
Ph: 64 447 39444
Fax: 64 447 48933
Publication E-mail: e.nz@ipenz.org.nz
Publisher E-mail: ipenz@ipenz.org.nz
Magazine of The Institution of Professional Engineers New Zealand. **Subtitle:** The Magazine of Technical Enterprise. **Freq:** Bimonthly. **Key Personnel:** Nick Helm, Managing Editor, nhelm@ipenz.org.nz; Hazel Penfold, Writer/Ed., phone 64 447 49650; Chris Burr, Sales Mgr., phone 64 447 48947, chris@ipenz.org.nz. **Subscription Rates:** US$40 individuals in New Zealand. **Remarks:** Accepts advertising. **URL:** http://e.nz-magazine.co.nz; http://www.ipenz.org/ipenz/. **Circ:** (Not Reported)

49008 ■ Forest and Bird Magazine
Forest and Bird
Level 1, 90 Ghuznee St.
PO Box 631
Wellington, New Zealand
Ph: 64 438 57374
Fax: 64 438 57373
Publisher E-mail: office@forestandbird.org.nz
Magazine for members of The Royal Forest and Bird Protection Society of New Zealand. **Freq:** Quarterly. **Key Personnel:** Peter Maddison, President; Mike Britton, General Mgr., m.britton@forestandbird.org.nz. **Subscription Rates:** Included in membership. **Remarks:** Accepts advertising. **URL:** http://www.forestandbird.org.nz/what-we-do/publications/forest-bird-magazine. **Circ:** Paid 20,000

49009 ■ Hi Society
Medical Assurance Society
PO Box 13402
Johnsonville
Wellington, New Zealand
Ph: 64 447 88863
Magazine of the Medical Assurance Society. **Freq:** Quarterly. **URL:** http://www.medicals.co.nz/Membership/MemberBenefits/.

49010 ■ Journal
New Zealand Society for Music Therapy
New Zealand School of Music
Mt. Cook Campus
PO Box 2332

Wellington, New Zealand
Publisher E-mail: info@musictherapy.org.nz
Publication covering music therapy. **Founded:** 1974. **Freq:** Annual. **Key Personnel:** Daphne Rickson, President, phone 44 4 8015799, daphne.rickson@nzsm.ac.nz. **URL:** http://www.musictherapy.org.nz/index.php?q=journal.htm. **Ad Rates:** BW: US$100. **Circ:** 200

49011 ■ Journal of the Royal Society of New Zealand
Royal Society of New Zealand
4 Halswell St.
PO Box 598
Wellington 6011, New Zealand
Ph: 64 4 4727421
Fax: 64 4 4731841
Peer-reviewed Journal covering research papers on the science of New Zealand and the Pacific region. **Freq:** Quarterly. **Key Personnel:** Charles Daugherty, Sen. Ed. **ISSN:** 0303-6758. **Subscription Rates:** NZ$333 individuals online only; US$130 individuals print only; US$350 institutions print and online. **URL:** http://www.royalsociety.org.nz/publications/journals/nzjr/.

49012 ■ Journal of Symbolic Logic
University of Illinois Press
Victoria University
School of Mathematics & Computer Science
Box 600
Wellington 6001, New Zealand
Publisher E-mail: uipress@uillinois.edu
Academic journal covering the discipline of symbolic logic. **Freq:** Quarterly. **Key Personnel:** Jeremy Avigad, Coord.Ed. **ISSN:** 0022-4812. **Subscription Rates:** US$615 individuals; US$625 institutions included in membership. **URL:** http://www.aslonline.org/journals-journal.html.

49013 ■ Kai Tiaki
New Zealand Nurses Organization
PO Box 2128
Wellington 6140, New Zealand
Ph: 64 4 4999533
Fax: 64 4 3829993
Publisher E-mail: nzno@nzno.org.nz
Journal covering nursing practice, research, politics, news, and issues related to employment in the field. **Subtitle:** Nursing New Zealand. **Founded:** Feb. 1908. **Freq:** Monthly. **Print Method:** Web Offset. **Trim Size:** A4. **Key Personnel:** Teresa O'Connor, Editor, phone 64 3 5480018, teresao@nzno.org.nz; Anne Manchester, Editor, phone 64 4 4946386, annem@nzno.org.nz. **ISSN:** 1173-2032. **Subscription Rates:** Included in membership; NZ$150 nonmembers; NZ$200 institutions; NZ$220 institutions, other countries. **Remarks:** Accepts advertising. **URL:** http://www.nzno.org.nz/services/journals_-_kai_tiaki. **Formerly:** Nursing New Zealand; New Zealand Nursing Journal. **Ad Rates:** BW: NZ$1,500, 4C: NZ$2,100. **Circ:** ‡44,000

49014 ■ Kotuitui
Royal Society of New Zealand
4 Halswell St.
PO Box 598
Wellington 6011, New Zealand
Ph: 64 4 4727421
Fax: 64 4 4731841
Publication E-mail: kotuitui@rsnz.org
Peer-reviewed Journal covering all social science disciplines. **Key Personnel:** Nick Lewis, Co-Ed.; Paul Spoonley, Co-Ed. **ISSN:** 1177-083X. **Subscription Rates:** NZ$205 individuals; US$130 individuals; NZ$495 institutions; US$350 institutions. **URL:** http://www.royalsociety.org.nz/publications/journals/nzjs/.

49015 ■ Library Life
Library and Information Association of New Zealand
PO Box 12-212
Wellington 6144, New Zealand
Ph: 64 447 35834
Fax: 64 449 91480
Publication E-mail: megan@lianza.org.nz
Publisher E-mail: admin@lianza.org.nz
Publication covering libraries. **Subtitle:** Te Ran Ora. **Founded:** 1978. **Freq:** Monthly 11/yr. **Key Personnel:** Jo Beck, Editor. **ISSN:** 1176-8088. **URL:** http://www.lianza.org.nz/publications/. **Ad Rates:** BW: NZ$450, 4C: NZ$1,350. **Circ:** 1,600

49016 ■ The Maori Law Review
Tom Bennion
Harbour City Tower, Ste. 512
29 Brandon St.
Wellington, New Zealand
Ph: 64 4 4735755
Fax: 64 4 4735751
Publication E-mail: tom@bennion.co.nz
Publisher E-mail: tom@bennion.co.nz
Journal covering laws affecting the Maori, the indigenous people of New Zealand/Aotearoa. **Freq:** Monthly 11/yr (combined Dec./Jan.). **Key Personnel:** Thomas Bennion, Editor; James Maddock, Assoc. Ed. **ISSN:** 1172-8434. **Subscription Rates:** NZ$100 individuals print only; NZ$100 other countries print only. **Remarks:** Advertising not accepted. **URL:** http://www.bennion.co.nz/. **Circ:** (Not Reported)

49017 ■ MIS Australia
Fairfax Business Media
40 Boulcott, Level 3
PO Box 2595
Wellington 2000, New Zealand
Ph: 64 4 496 9800
Fax: 64 4 496 9841
Publication covering IT management information. **Founded:** 1993. **Freq:** Monthly 11/yr. **ISSN:** 1327-9688. **Subscription Rates:** $A 84 individuals; $A 118 individuals outside Australia. **URL:** http://mis-asia.com/home; http://subscribe.fairfax.com.au.

49018 ■ New Zealand Economic Papers
New Zealand Association of Economists
97 Cuba St.
PO Box 568
Wellington, New Zealand
Ph: 64 4 8017139
Fax: 64 4 8017106
Publisher E-mail: economists@nzae.org.nz
Publication covering economics. **Founded:** 1967. **Freq:** 2/yr. **Trim Size:** 230 x 150 cm. **Key Personnel:** Ananish Chaudhuri, Editor. **ISSN:** 0077-9954. **Subscription Rates:** NZ$90; NZ$100 New Zealand, airmail; NZ$120 Australia, airmail; NZ$130 other countries airmail; Free For members. **Remarks:** Advertising not accepted. **URL:** http://www.nzae.org.nz/papers/. **Circ:** (Not Reported)

49019 ■ New Zealand Education Gazette
APN Educational Media
Level 1, Saatchi & Saatchi Bldg.
Wellington, New Zealand
Ph: 64 4 4711600
Fax: 64 4 4711080
Publisher E-mail: production3@apn-ed.co.nz
Official publication of the Ministry of Education covering education for schools. **Freq:** Weekly (Mon.) every two (occasionally three) weeks except January. **Key Personnel:** John Gerritsen, Editor, editor@edgazette.govt.nz. **Subscription Rates:** NZ$145 individuals print version; Free to schools; US$225 out of country. **Remarks:** Accepts advertising. **URL:** http://www.edgazette.govt.nz. **Ad Rates:** PCI: NZ$19.50. **Circ:** 17,200

49020 ■ New Zealand Freemason
Grand Lodge of Antient Free and Accepted Masons of New Zealand
Marion Sq.
PO Box 6439
Wellington 6141, New Zealand
Ph: 64 4 3856622
Fax: 64 4 3855749
Publication E-mail: editor@freemasons.co.nz
Publisher E-mail: secretary@freemasons.co.nz
Magazine covering freemasonry in New Zealand. **Freq:** Quarterly. **URL:** http://www.freemasons.co.nz/cms/news/new-zealand-freemason-magazine/. **Circ:** ‡12,000

49021 ■ New Zealand Journal of Agricultural Research
Royal Society of New Zealand
4 Halswell St.
PO Box 598
Wellington 6011, New Zealand
Ph: 64 4 4727421
Fax: 64 4 4731841
Journal covering aspects of animal and pastoral science relevant to temperate and subtropical regions. **Freq:** Quarterly. **Key Personnel:** David Swain, Editor, nzjar@rsnz.org. **ISSN:** 0028-8233. **Subscription Rates:** NZ$495 institutions print and online; NZ$205 individuals

print and online; US$130 individuals print and online; US$350 institutions print and online. **URL:** http://www.royalsociety.org.nz/site/publish/journals/nzjar/default.aspx.

49022 ■ New Zealand Journal of Botany
Royal Society of New Zealand
4 Halswell St.
PO Box 598
Wellington 6011, New Zealand
Ph: 64 4 4727421
Fax: 64 4 4731841
Journal covering all aspects of the botany, mycology, and phycology of the South Pacific, Australia, South America, southern Africa, and Antarctica. **Subtitle:** The International Journal Of Austral Botany. **Freq:** Quarterly. **Key Personnel:** Kevin Gould, Sen. Ed.; Kevin Burns, Assoc. Ed.; Julian Heyes, Assoc. Ed. **ISSN:** 0028-825X. **Subscription Rates:** NZ$495 institutions print and on-line; NZ$205 individuals print and online; US$130 individuals print and online; US$350 institutions print and online. **URL:** http://www.royalsociety.org.nz/publications/journals/nzjb/.

49023 ■ New Zealand Journal of Crop and Horticultural Science
Royal Society of New Zealand
4 Halswell St.
PO Box 598
Wellington 6011, New Zealand
Ph: 64 4 4727421
Fax: 64 4 4731841
Journal covering aspects of crop and horticultural science. **Freq:** Quarterly. **Key Personnel:** Sandra Stanislawek, Editor, nzjchs@royalsociety.org.nz. **ISSN:** 0114-0671. **Subscription Rates:** NZ$495 institutions print and online; NZ$205 individuals print and online; US$130 individuals print and online; US$350 institutions print and online. **URL:** http://www.rsnz.org/publish/nzjchs/.

49024 ■ New Zealand Journal of Educational Studies
New Zealand Council for Educational Research
10th Fl., W Block, Education House
178-182 Willis St.
Wellington 6011, New Zealand
Ph: 64 438 47939
Fax: 64 438 47933
Publication E-mail: nzjes@nzare.org.nz
Journal covering educational studies. **Freq:** Semiannual. **Key Personnel:** Dr. Liz Gordon, Editor. **Subscription Rates:** US$115 individuals; US$115 institutions; US$57.50 students. **Remarks:** Advertising not accepted. **URL:** http://www.nzare.org.nz/publications.html. **Former name:** NZ Journal of Educational Studies. **Circ:** (Not Reported)

49025 ■ New Zealand Journal of Geology and Geophysics
Royal Society of New Zealand
4 Halswell St.
PO Box 598
Wellington 6011, New Zealand
Ph: 64 4 4727421
Fax: 64 4 4731841
Journal covering all aspects of the earth sciences relevant to New Zealand, the Pacific, and Antarctica. **Subtitle:** An international journal of Pacific Rim Geosciences. **Freq:** Quarterly. **Trim Size:** A4. **Key Personnel:** Fred Davey, Sen. Ed. **ISSN:** 0028-8306. **Subscription Rates:** US$333 individuals online only; US$350 institutions print and online. **URL:** http://www.royalsociety.org.nz/publications/journals/nzjg/.

49026 ■ New Zealand Journal of Human Resources Management
Human Resources Institute of New Zealand
Level 1, 11 Chews Ln.
PO Box 11 450
Wellington, New Zealand
Ph: 64 449 92966
Fax: 64 449 92965
Publisher E-mail: hrinz@hrinz.org.nz
Peer-reviewed official journal of the Human Resources Institute of New Zealand. **Key Personnel:** Dr. Jarrod Haar, Editor. **ISSN:** 1175-5407. **URL:** http://www.nzjhrm.org.nz/.

49027 ■ New Zealand Journal of Marine and Freshwater Research
Royal Society of New Zealand
4 Halswell St.
PO Box 598
Wellington 6011, New Zealand
Ph: 64 4 4727421
Fax: 64 4 4731841
Peer-reviewed Journal covering all aspects of aquatic science. **Freq:** Quarterly. **Key Personnel:** Doug Mounfort, Sen. Ed. **ISSN:** 0028-8330. **Subscription Rates:** NZ$333 individuals online only; US$130 individuals print only; US$350 individuals print and online. **URL:** http://www.royalsociety.org.nz/publications/journals/nzjm/.

49028 ■ New Zealand Journal of Outdoor Education
Outdoors New Zealand
PO Box 6027
Marion Sq.
Wellington 6141, New Zealand
Ph: 64 4 3857287
Fax: 64 4 3857366
Publisher E-mail: info@outdoorsnz.org.nz
Journal emphasizing Australian outdoor education perspectives and understandings of the environment. **Freq:** Semiannual. **Key Personnel:** Dr. Mike Brown, Editor. **Subscription Rates:** US$4 individuals; US$20 nonmembers non members; NZ$50 other countries overseas. **URL:** http://www.wilderdom.com/journals.htmajoe.

49029 ■ New Zealand Population Review
Population Association of New Zealand
PO Box 225
Wellington, New Zealand
Ph: 64 4 4638225
Fax: 64 4 4638088
Publisher E-mail: cyril.mako@minedu.govt.nz
Peer-reviewed journal featuring refereed articles. **Freq:** Semiannual. **URL:** http://panz.rsnz.org/?page_id=5.

49030 ■ The New Zealand Railway Observer
New Zealand Railway & Locomotive Society Inc.
PO Box 5134
Wellington 6145, New Zealand
Ph: 64 4 5684938
Fax: 64 4 5865554
Publication E-mail: nzrls@actrix.co.nz
Publisher E-mail: nzrls@actrix.co.nz
Trade magazine covering current and historical issues relating to rail transport in New Zealand. **Founded:** 1944. **Freq:** Bimonthly. **Cols./Page:** 4. **Col. Width:** 87 millimeters. **Col. Depth:** 265 millimeters. **Key Personnel:** W.W. Prebble, Publications Off./Dir.; G.T. Carter, Ed./Pres.; A.L.R. Merrifield, Newsletter Ed.; R.G. Thompson, Sec.; A.M. Spencer, Treas.; D.A. Kent, Director; R.W. Seaton, Director; D.H. Rudd, Director. **ISSN:** 0028-8624. **Subscription Rates:** NZ$60 single issue. **URL:** http://www.railsoc.org.nz. **Circ:** Combined 1,450

49031 ■ New Zealand Veterinary Journal
New Zealand Veterinary Association
PO Box 11-212
Wellington, New Zealand
Ph: 64 4 4710484
Fax: 64 4 4710494
Publication E-mail: nzvj@massey.ac.nz
Publisher E-mail: nzva@vets.org.nz
Peer-reviewed New Zealand journal covering veterinary medicine. **Founded:** 1952. **Freq:** Bimonthly. **Print Method:** Offset. **Trim Size:** A4. **Key Personnel:** Peter Jolly, PhD, Managing Editor, peter.jolly@vets.org.nz; Michele Cooke, PhD, Asst. Ed. **ISSN:** 0048-0169. **Subscription Rates:** US$235 individuals; NZ$320 individuals; $A 305 individuals; NZ$640 individuals multi-user single-site; $A 610 individuals multi-user single-site; US$470 individuals multi-user single-site. **Remarks:** Accepts advertising. **URL:** http://www.vetjournal.org.nz. **Alt. Formats:** CD-ROM. **Ad Rates:** BW: NZ$1,200, 4C: NZ$2,400. **Circ:** Paid 2,000

49032 ■ Red Cross News
New Zealand Red Cross
L3 Red Cross House
69 Molesworth St.
Thorndon
Wellington 6038, New Zealand

Ph: 64 447 23750
Publisher E-mail: national@redcross.org.nz
Magazine highlighting issues in New Zealand and the Pacific. **Freq:** Quarterly. **Key Personnel:** Kelly Mitchell, Editor, kelly.mitchell@redcross.org.nz; John Ware, CEO; Wendy Potter, Operations Mgr. **Subscription Rates:** Free. **URL:** http://www.redcross.org.nz.

49033 ■ The Reserve Bank of New Zealand
Reserve Bank of New Zealand
2 The Ter.
PO Box 2498
Wellington 6011, New Zealand
Ph: 64 4 4722029
Fax: 64 4 4738554
Publisher E-mail: rbnz-info@rbnz.govt.nz
Publication for the banking, finance, and accounting industries. **Freq:** Quarterly. **ISSN:** 1174-7943. **Remarks:** Advertising not accepted. **URL:** http://www.rbnz.govt.nz/. **Circ:** (Not Reported)

49034 ■ Social Policy Journal of New Zealand
Ministry of Social Development
PO Box 1556
Wellington 6140, New Zealand
Ph: 64 4 9163300
Fax: 64 4 9180099
Publisher E-mail: information@msd.govt.nz
Political science publication. **Freq:** 3/yr. **Key Personnel:** Marlene Levine, Editor, phone 64 4 916 3809, marlene.levine001@msd.govt.nz. **ISSN:** 1177-9837. **URL:** http://www.msd.govt.nz.

49035 ■ Tectonophysics
Elsevier Science
c/o Martha K. Savage, Ed.-in-Ch.
PO Box 600
Wellington, New Zealand
Ph: 64 4 4635961
Fax: 64 4 4955186
Publisher E-mail: nlinfo-f@elsevier.com
Journal dealing with geotectonics and the geology and physics of the interior of the Earth. **Subtitle:** The International Journal of Integrated Solid Earth Sciences. **Founded:** 1964. **Freq:** 68/yr. **Key Personnel:** M. Liu, Editor-in-Chief, lium@missouri.edu; Martha K. Savage, Editor-in-Chief, martha.savage@vuw.ac.nz; Jean Pierre Burg, Editor-in-Chief; H. Thybo, Editor-in-Chief, thybo@geo.ku.dk. **ISSN:** 0040-1951. **Subscription Rates:** 72,000¥ individuals; US$614 individuals for all countries except Europe, Japan & Iran; EUR546 individuals for European countries & Iran; EUR5,764 institutions for European Countries; 766,100¥ institutions; US$6,447 institutions for all countries except Europe, Japan & Iran. **Remarks:** Accepts advertising. **URL:** http://www.elsevier.com/wps/find/journaldescription.cws_home/503362/description. **Circ:** (Not Reported)

49036 ■ Water and Wastes in New Zealand
New Zealand Water and Wastes Association
PO Box 1316
Wellington 6140, New Zealand
Ph: 64 4 4728925
Fax: 64 4 4728926
Publisher E-mail: water@nzwwa.org.nz
Journal containing up-to-date technical innovations, equipment and products, government regulations and legislation, environmental law, and industry news. **Freq:** Bimonthly 5/yr. **Key Personnel:** Noeline Strange, Contact. **Subscription Rates:** Included in membership. **Remarks:** Accepts advertising. **URL:** http://www.waternz.org.nz/publications.html. **Ad Rates:** BW: NZ$1,400, 4C: NZ$2,200. **Circ:** ‡1,450

49037 ■ Classic Hits-FM - 90
PO Box 300
Wellington, New Zealand
Ph: 64 4 8024710
Fax: 64 4 3853366
E-mail: daveandcamille@classichits.co.nz
Format: Classic Rock. **Owner:** The Radio Network, 54 Cook St., Private Bag 92198, Auckland, New Zealand, 64 9 3730000, Fax: 64 9 3674797. **Key Personnel:** Dave Smart, Contact; Camille Guzzwell, Contact. **URL:** http://www.classichits.co.nz.

49038 ■ Coast-FM - 99.4
Private Bag 92198
Auckland, New Zealand
E-mail: coast@thecoast.net.nz
Format: Oldies. **Owner:** The Radio Network, at above

Circulation: ★ = ABC; △ = BPA; ◆ = CAC; • = CCAB; □ = VAC; ⊕ = PO Statement; ‡ = Publisher's Report; Boldface figures = sworn; Light figures = estimated.

address. **Key Personnel:** Rick Morin, Contact; Ray Mankelow, Contact. **Ad Rates:** Advertising accepted; rates available upon request. **URL:** http://www.thecoast. net.nz.

49039 ■ Coast-FM Kapiti - 95.7
Private Bag 92198
Auckland, New Zealand
E-mail: coast@thecoast.net.nz
Format: Oldies. **Owner:** The Radio Network, at above address. **Key Personnel:** Rick Morin, Contact; Ray Mankelow, Contact. **URL:** http://www.thecoast.net.nz.

49040 ■ Hauraki-FM - 93.1
PO Box 300
Wellington, New Zealand
Ph: 64 4 8024710
Fax: 64 4 3854210
Format: Classic Rock. **URL:** http://www.radiohauraki.co. nz/Stations/Hauraki/.

49041 ■ More-FM - 99
15 Walter St., Level 3
Wellington, New Zealand
Ph: 64 4 3822200
Fax: 64 4 3854288
Format: Adult Contemporary; News. **URL:** http://www. morefm.com/.

49042 ■ National-AM - 567
Radio New Zealand House, Level 2
155 The Terrace
PO Box 123
Wellington, New Zealand
Ph: 64 4 4741999
Fax: 64 4 4741459
E-mail: rnz@radionz.co.nz
Format: Eclectic. **Owner:** Radio New Zealand, at above address. **Operating Hours:** Continuous. **Ad Rates:** Noncommercial. **URL:** http://www.radionz.co.nz/listen/ amfm.

National-AM - See Alexandra

National-AM - See Blenheim

National-AM - See Kapiti

National-AM - See New Plymouth

National-AM - See Queenstown

National-AM - See Timaru

National-AM - See Whangarei

49043 ■ 90-FM - 90
Cor. Abel Smith & Taranaki Sts.
PO Box 300
Wellington, New Zealand
E-mail: reception@radionetwork.co.nz
Format: Adult Contemporary; Oldies; News; Sports. **Owner:** Radio Network, 54 Cook St., Private Bag 92-198, Auckland, New Zealand, 64 9 3730000, Fax: 64 9 3674802. **Operating Hours:** 6 a.m.-12 a.m. **Key Personnel:** Rhys Nimmo, General Mgr., phone 64 4 3826676, fax 64 4 3854210, rhysnimmo@radionetwork. co.nz; Grant Lee, General Mgr., phone 64 9 3674623, fax 64 9 3674802, grantlee@radionetwork.co.nz; Jason Pine, Operations Mgr., phone 64 4 8024759, fax 64 4 3853366, jasonpine@radionetwork.co.nz. **Ad Rates:**

Advertising accepted; rates available upon request. **URL:** http://www.radionetwork.co.nz/.

49044 ■ Radio Active-FM - 89
PO Box 11-971
Wellington, New Zealand
Ph: 64 4 8019899
Fax: 64 4 8019879
E-mail: accommodation@radioactive.co.nz
Format: Alternative/New Music/Progressive; World Beat; Jazz. **Operating Hours:** Continuous. **Key Personnel:** Dave Gibbons, Station Mgr.; Carl Jackson, Music Dir./Prog. **URL:** http://www.radioactive.co.nz.

Radio New Zealand National-AM - See Auckland

Radio New Zealand National-AM - See Kaikohe

Radio New Zealand National-AM - See Kaitaia

49045 ■ RNZ-FM - 101.3
Level 2, Radio New Zealand House
155 The Ter.
Wellington, New Zealand
Ph: 64 4 4741999
Fax: 64 4 4741459
E-mail: rnz@radionz.co.nz
Format: Public Radio; News; Eclectic. **Owner:** Radio New Zealand, at above address. **Founded:** 1925. **Operating Hours:** Continuous. **Key Personnel:** Peter Cavanagh, Ch. Executive/Ed.-in-Ch. **URL:** http://www. radionz.co.nz/.

49046 ■ Te Upoko O Te Ika-AM - 1161
Level 2, Grand Central Plz.
76-86 Manners Mall St.
PO Box 11 812
Wellington, New Zealand
Ph: 64 4 8015002
Fax: 64 4 8015009
E-mail: wena@teupoko.co.nz
Format: Ethnic. **Operating Hours:** Continuous. **Key Personnel:** Wena Tait, General Mgr. **Ad Rates:** $35 for 30 seconds; $40 for 45 seconds; $55 for 60 seconds. **URL:** http://www.teupoko.irirangi.net.

Whakatane

49047 ■ Bayrock-FM - 97.7
PO Box 383
Whakatane 3158, New Zealand
Ph: 64 7 3086239
E-mail: bayrock@bayrock.co.nz
Format: Classic Rock; Album-Oriented Rock (AOR). **Owner:** Radio Bay of Plenty Ltd., at above address. **Founded:** Dec. 26, 1993. **Ad Rates:** Advertising accepted; rates available upon request. **URL:** http://www. bayrock.co.nz.

49048 ■ 1XX-FM - 90.5
PO Box 383
Whakatane 3158, New Zealand
Ph: 64 7 3086239
Fax: 64 7 3071242
E-mail: reception@1xx.co.nz
Format: Adult Contemporary; Sports; News; Oldies. **Owner:** Radio Bay Of Plenty Ltd., at above address. **Founded:** June 30, 1971. **Operating Hours:**

Continuous. **Key Personnel:** Julie Richmond, Contact. **URL:** http://www.1xx.co.nz/.

Whanganui

49049 ■ Awa-FM - 91.2
Level 2, Anderson's Bldg.
49 Ridgway St.
PO Box 430
Whanganui 5001, New Zealand
Ph: 64 6 3471402
Fax: 64 6 3472339
E-mail: awafm@awafm.co.nz
Format: Ethnic; World Beat. **Founded:** June 17, 1991. **Key Personnel:** Geoff Mariu, Mng. Dir., geoff@awafm. co.nz; Kahurangi Simon, Program Dir., kahurangi@ awafm.co.nz. **URL:** http://www.awa.irirangi.net.

Whangarei

49050 ■ Coast-AM - 900
Private Bag 92198
Auckland, New Zealand
E-mail: coast@thecoast.net.nz
Format: Oldies. **Owner:** The Radio Network, at above address. **Key Personnel:** Rick Morin, Contact; Ray Mankelow, Contact. **Ad Rates:** Advertising accepted; rates available upon request. **URL:** http://www.thecoast. net.nz.

49051 ■ National-AM - 837
Radio New Zealand House, Level 2
155 The Terrace
PO Box 123
Wellington, New Zealand
Ph: 64 4 4741999
Fax: 64 4 4741459
E-mail: rnz@radionz.co.nz
Format: Eclectic. **Owner:** Radio New Zealand, at above address. **Operating Hours:** Continuous. **Ad Rates:** Noncommercial. **URL:** http://www.radionz.co.nz/listen/ amfm.

49052 ■ Newstalk ZB-AM Northland - 1215
54 Cook St.
Private Bag 92198
Auckland, New Zealand
Ph: 64 9 3730000
Format: News; Talk. **Owner:** The Radio Network, at above address. **Key Personnel:** Paul Holmes, Contact; Leighton Smith, Contact, leighton@newstalkzb.co.nz; Danny Watson, Contact, danny@newstalkzb.co.nz. **URL:** http://www.newstalkzb.co.nz/featdetail.asp? recnumber=1.

49053 ■ Newstalk ZB-AM Northland - 1026
54 Cook St.
Private Bag 92198
Auckland, New Zealand
Ph: 64 9 3730000
Format: News; Talk. **Owner:** The Radio Network, at above address. **Key Personnel:** Paul Holmes, Contact; Leighton Smith, Contact, leighton@newstalkzb.co.nz; Danny Watson, Contact, danny@newstalkzb.co.nz. **URL:** http://www.newstalkzb.co.nz/featdetail.asp? recnumber=1.

Managua

49054 ■ La Boletina
Fundacion Puntos de Encuentro
De la Rotonda El Gueguense
4 cuadras al Oeste
Managua, Nicaragua

Ph: 50 526 81227
Fax: 50 526 66305
Publication E-mail: boletina@puntos.org.ni
Publisher E-mail: puntos@puntos.org
Spanish language publication covering feminism. **Subtitle:** Un aporte de Puntos de Encuentro a la comunicacion entre mujeves. **Founded:** May 1991. **Freq:** 4/yr.

Print Method: Offset. **Trim Size:** 6 1/2 x 8. **Key Personnel:** Helena Ramos, Contact; Martha Juarez, Editor, martha.juarez@puntos.org.ni. **ISSN:** 1024-2759. **Subscription Rates:** US$10 individuals Nicaragua; US$20 individuals Central America; US$25 other countries. **URL:** http://www.puntos.org.ni/servicios/actividades/default.php?acti=350. **Circ:** 26,000

Aba

49055 ■ Journal of Medical Investigation and Practice
African Journals Online
School of Clinical Medicine
Abia State University Teaching Hospital
PMB 7004
Aba, Nigeria
Publisher E-mail: info@ajol.info
Peer-reviewed journal covering the field of biomedical science. **Key Personnel:** Prof. I.E.K. Mba, Editor-in-Chief, adisayinka@softhome.net. **ISSN:** 9783-1230. **Subscription Rates:** N 200 individuals; N 300 institutions; US$25 other countries; US$30 institutions, other countries. **URL:** http://ajol.info/index.php/jomip.

49056 ■ Journal for Phytomedicine and Therapeutics
African Journals Online
National Institute for Pharmaceutical Research & Development
PMB 21
Garki
Abuja, Nigeria
Publisher E-mail: info@ajol.info
Peer-reviewed journal containing information related to pharmaceutical, medical sciences and development. **Freq:** Semiannual. **Key Personnel:** Dr. Uford Inyang, Contact, phone 234 9 5239039, fax 234 9 5231043, uinyang@niprd.org; Maimuna E. Abdulrahim, Sec., maimunaesse@yahoo.com. **ISSN:** 1118-1028. **Subscription Rates:** N 1,000 individuals; N 2,000 institutions; US$60 other countries; US$100 institutions, other countries. **URL:** http://ajol.info/index.php/jopat.

Abuja (Lagos)

49057 ■ The Nigerian Engineer
Nigerian Society of Engineers
National Engineering Center
off National Mosque-Labour House Rd.
Central Business Area
Abuja, Lagos, Nigeria
Ph: 234 9 6735096
Publication E-mail: nsehqr@linkserve.com
Publisher E-mail: info@nseng.org
Nigerian publication covering engineering. **Subtitle:** Technical Transaction. **Freq:** Quarterly. **Subscription Rates:** Free to members. **Remarks:** Accepts advertising. **URL:** http://www.nse.org.ng. **Ad Rates:** BW: N 50,000, 4C: N 400,000. **Circ:** Paid 2,000

49058 ■ Women on the Move
Centre for Development and Population Activities - Nigeria
Ground Fl., Bel House
22, Port Harcourt Cres.
Off Gimbiya St.
Area 11, Garki
Abuja, Lagos, Nigeria
Ph: 234 9 4618863
Fax: 234 9 4618864
Publisher E-mail: cedpanig@cedpa.org
Publication covering family planning. **Freq:** Periodic.
Subscription Rates: US$2 single issue. **Remarks:** Advertising not accepted. **URL:** http://www.cedpa.org/; http://www.cedpa.org/content/general/detail/764/. **Circ:** (Not Reported)

Ago Iwoye

49059 ■ OYE
African Journals Online
Department of English Language
Faculty of Arts
Olabisi Onabanjo University
P.M.B. 2002
Ago Iwoye, Ogun, Nigeria
Publisher E-mail: info@ajol.info
Peer-reviewed journal containing articles relevant to the development of the humanities. **Subtitle:** Ogun Journal of Arts. **Freq:** Annual. **Key Personnel:** Prof. J.O. Oyegoke, Editor, oyeeditor@yahoo.com; E.O. Oduwole, Business Mgr., ebunoduwole2k2@yahoo.com. **ISSN:** 0795-9475. **Subscription Rates:** US$15 individuals. **URL:** http://ajol.info/index.php/oye.

Akure

49060 ■ Nigeria Journal of Pure and Applied Physics
African Journals Online
U.S. Department of of Physics
Federal University
Akure, Ondo, Nigeria
Publisher E-mail: info@ajol.info
Peer-reviewed journal focusing on the results of research in all branches of pure and applied physics. **Key Personnel:** Dr. Moses Oludare Ajewole, Editor-in-Chief, phone 234 34 241305, njpapfuta@yahoo.com. **ISSN:** 1596-0862. **Subscription Rates:** US$25 individuals. **URL:** http://ajol.info/index.php/njpap.

Asaba

49061 ■ Journal of Applied Chemistry and Agricultural Research
African Journals Online
U.S. Department of of Agronomy
Delta State University
Asaba Campus
PMB 95074
Asaba, Nigeria
Publisher E-mail: info@ajol.info
Peer-reviewed journal covering the field of agricultural, biological and applied chemical science. **Freq:** Annual. **Key Personnel:** Dr. Steve O. Emosairue, Editor-in-Chief, soemosa@yahoo.co.uk; A.I. Essien, Editor-in-Chief. **ISSN:** 1117-2894. **Subscription Rates:** N 1,500 individuals; N 2,000 institutions; US$40 other countries. **URL:** http://ajol.info/index.php/jacar.

Benin City

49062 ■ African Journal of Reproductive Health
African Journals Online
Women's Health & Action Research Ctr.
4 Alofoje Ave., Off Uwasota St.
PO Box 10231
Ugbowo
Benin City, Nigeria
Ph: 234 526 00151
Fax: 234 526 02334
Publisher E-mail: info@ajol.info
Peer-reviewed journal focusing on reproductive health in Africa. **Founded:** 1902. **Freq:** Semiannual. **Print Method:** Offset. **Cols./Page:** 6. **Col. Width:** 24 nonpareils. **Col. Depth:** 301 agate lines. **Key Personnel:** Aghedo Osaretin, Managing Editor; Clifford Odimegwu, Asst. Ed.; Friday Okonofua, Editor, wharc@hyperia.com. **ISSN:** 1118-4841. **URL:** http://ajol.info/index.php/ajrh.

49063 ■ Annals of Biomedical Science
African Journals Online
Department of Child Health
University of Benin Teaching Hospital
P.M.B. 1111
Benin City, Nigeria
Publisher E-mail: info@ajol.info
Peer-reviewed journal covering all aspects of clinical and medical research as well as from fields of basic and applied biomedical sciences. **Freq:** Semiannual. **Key Personnel:** Dr. NKD Halim, Editor-in-Chief, dayehalim@yahoo.com. **ISSN:** 1596-6569. **Subscription Rates:** N 500 individuals; US$30 individuals Africa; US$35 individuals Europe; US$40 other countries. **URL:** http://ajol.info/index.php/abs.

49064 ■ Journal of Medicine and Biomedical Research
African Journals Online
U.S. Department of of Obstetrics & Gynaecology
School of Medicine, College of Medical Sciences
University of Benin
Benin City, Nigeria
Ph: 234 52 600437
Fax: 234 52 602091
Publisher E-mail: info@ajol.info
Peer-reviewed journal containing information about primary health care. **Freq:** Semiannual. **Key Personnel:** Prof. F.E. Okonofua, Editor, wharc@hyperia.com; Prof. AO Isah, Assoc. Ed.; Dr. V. Iyawe, Assoc. Ed. **ISSN:** 1596-6941. **URL:** http://ajol.info/index.php/jmbr.

49065 ■ Journal of the Nigerian Association of Mathematical Physics
African Journals Online
U.S. Department of of Physics
University of Benin
Benin City, Nigeria
Publisher E-mail: info@ajol.info
Peer-reviewed journal covering the importance of mathematics to physics, chemistry, engineering or other sciences. **Freq:** Annual. **Key Personnel:** Dr. John O.A. Idiodi, Editor-in-Chief, idiodi@myway.com. **ISSN:** 1116-4336. **Subscription Rates:** N 4,000 individuals; US$200 other countries. **URL:** http://ajol.info/index.php/jonamp.

49066 ■ Tropical Freshwater Biology
African Journals Online
52 Ewah Rd.
PQ Box 3441
Benin City, Nigeria

Publisher E-mail: info@ajol.info

Peer-reviewed journal covering the field of freshwater biology in the tropical and subtropical regions of the world. **Freq:** Annual. **Key Personnel:** Dr. Anthony E. Ogbeibu, Editor, ogbeibu@yahoo.com. **ISSN:** 0795-0101. **Subscription Rates:** US$70 individuals. **URL:** http://ajol.info/index.php/tfb.

49067 ■ Tropical Journal of Pharmaceutical Research
Pharmacotherapy Group
Faculty of Pharmacy
University of Benin
Benin City, Nigeria
Ph: 234 802 3360318
Fax: 234 52 602257
Publisher E-mail: okhamafe@uniben.edu
Journal promoting pharmaceutical sciences and related disciplines including biotechnology, cell and molecular biology, medical and life sciences, and related engineering fields. **Key Personnel:** Prof. Augustine O. Okhamafe, Editor-in-Chief; Dr. Patrick O. Erah, Editor, p_erah@yahoo.com. **ISSN:** 1596-5996. **URL:** http://pharmacotherapy.ourprofile.org/; http://www.tjpr.org/.

49068 ■ West African Journal of Pharmacology and Drug Research
African Journals Online
U.S. Department of of Pharmacology & Toxicology
University of Benin
P.M.B. 1154
Benin City, Nigeria
Publisher E-mail: info@ajol.info
Peer-reviewed journal covering all aspects of drug action and related topics including chemotherapy and toxicology. **Freq:** Semiannual. **Key Personnel:** Prof. E.K.I. Omogbai, Editor-in-Chief, omog@uniben.edu; P.A. Akah, Assoc. Ed. **ISSN:** 0303-691X. **Subscription Rates:** 60 individuals; US$100 individuals. **URL:** http://ajol.info/index.php/wajpdr.

Calabar

49069 ■ Global Journal of Agricultural Sciences
African Journals Online
Dept. of Animal Science
University of Calabar
PO Box 3651
Unical Post Office
Calabar, Cross River, Nigeria
Publisher E-mail: info@ajol.info
Peer-reviewed journal providing information on problems facing farmers in the Third World and the ways of solving them with particular attention to Nigeria. **Freq:** Semiannual. **Key Personnel:** Prof. Barth N. Ekueme, Managing Editor, bachudo@yahoo.com. **ISSN:** 1596-2903. **Subscription Rates:** US$25 single issue; US$100 individuals. **URL:** http://ajol.info/index.php/gjass.

49070 ■ Global Journal of Educational Research
African Journals Online
Dept. of Geology
University of Calabar
PO Box 3651
Unical Post Office
Calabar, Cross River, Nigeria
Publisher E-mail: info@ajol.info
Peer-reviewed journal promoting research in all areas of education, including curriculum development, educational technology, foundation, administration. **Freq:** Semiannual. **Key Personnel:** Prof. Barth N. Ekueme, Managing Editor, bachudo@yahoo.com. **Subscription Rates:** US$25 single issue foreign; N 750 single issue domestic; US$50 other countries; N 1,500 individuals. **URL:** http://www.ajol.info/journal_index.php?jid=189&ab=gjedr.

49071 ■ Global Journal of Environmental Sciences
African Journals Online
c/o Prof. Barth N. Ekeume, Mng. Ed.
University of Calabar
PO Box 3651
Unical Post Office
Calabar, Cross River, Nigeria
Publisher E-mail: info@ajol.info
Peer-reviewed journal promoting research in all areas of Environmental Sciences including waste management, pollution control, and remediation of hazards. **Freq:** Semiannual. **Key Personnel:** Prof. Barth N. Ekueme,

Managing Editor, bachudo@yahoo.com. **ISSN:** 1596-6194. **Subscription Rates:** N 750 single issue; N 1,500 individuals; US$25 single issue international; US$50 other countries. **URL:** http://ajol.info/index.php/gjes.

49072 ■ Global Journal of Geological Sciences
African Journals Online
Dept. of Geology
University of Calabar
PO Box 3561
Calabar, Cross River, Nigeria
Publisher E-mail: info@ajol.info
Peer-reviewed journal promoting research in all areas of geological sciences, including petrology, mineralogy, geophysics, hydrogeology, engineering geology, petroleum geology, palaeontology, environmental geology, and economic geology. **Freq:** Semiannual. **Key Personnel:** Prof. Barth N. Ekwueme, Managing Editor, bachudo@yahoo.com. **ISSN:** 1596-6798. **Subscription Rates:** US$50 individuals; N 1,500 individuals. **URL:** http://ajol.info/index.php/gjgs.

49073 ■ Global Journal of Humanities
African Journals Online
Dept. of Geology
University of Calabar
PO Box 3651
Unical Post Office
Calabar, Cross River, Nigeria
Publisher E-mail: info@ajol.info
Peer-reviewed journal promoting research in all areas of humanities, including philosophy, languages, linguistics, literature, history, fine/applied arts, theater arts, architecture. **Freq:** Semiannual. **Key Personnel:** Prof. Barth N. Ekueme, Editor-in-Chief, bachudo@yahoo.com. **ISSN:** 1596-6232. **Subscription Rates:** US$40 single issue foreign; N 1,500 single issue domestic; US$80 individuals foreign; N 3,000 individuals domestic. **URL:** http://ajol.info/index.php/gjh.

49074 ■ Global Journal of Medical Sciences
African Journals Online
Dept. of Internal Medicine
College of Medical Sciences
University of Calabar
Calabar, Cross River, Nigeria
Publisher E-mail: info@ajol.info
Peer-reviewed journal promoting research in all areas of medical endeavour and health care from basic science to evidence-based clinical management. **Freq:** Semiannual. **Key Personnel:** Prof. Barth N. Ekueme, Managing Editor, bachudo@yahoo.com. **ISSN:** 1596-2911. **Subscription Rates:** US$25 single issue; US$50 individuals. **URL:** http://ajol.info/index.php/gjms.

49075 ■ Global Journal of Pure and Applied Sciences
Bachudo Science Co. Ltd.
Dept. of Geology
University of Calabar
PO Box 3651
Unical Post Office
Calabar, Cross River, Nigeria
Peer-reviewed journal covering research in biological sciences, agricultural sciences, chemical sciences, mathematical and computer sciences, physics, engineering, environmental sciences and medicine. **Freq:** Quarterly. **ISSN:** 1118-0579. **Subscription Rates:** US$160 other countries; US$3,000 individuals. **URL:** http://www.ajol.info/journal_index.php?jid=87.

49076 ■ Global Journal of Social Sciences
African Journals Online
Dept. of Geology
University of Calabar
PO Box 3651
Unical Post Office
Calabar, Cross River, Nigeria
Publisher E-mail: info@ajol.info
Peer-reviewed journal promoting research in all areas of sociology, anthropology, management sciences, geography, and regional planning. **Freq:** Semiannual. **Key Personnel:** Prof. Barth N. Ekueme, Managing Editor, bachudo@yahoo.com. **ISSN:** 1596-6216. **URL:** http://ajol.info/index.php/gjss.

49077 ■ Journal of Medical Laboratory Science
African Journals Online
U.S. Department of of Medical Microbiology
College of Medical Sciences

University of Calabar
Calabar, Cross River, Nigeria
Publisher E-mail: info@ajol.info
Peer-reviewed journal covering biomedical science. **Freq:** Semiannual. **Key Personnel:** Prof. Simon J. Utsalo, Editor-in-Chief, sjutsalo@yahoo.com; Dr. M.F. Useh, Assoc. Ed.; Dr. E.O. Irokanulor, Assoc. Ed. **ISSN:** 1116-1043. **Subscription Rates:** N 900 individuals; N 1,500 institutions; US$50 individuals Africa; 60 individuals UK; US$90 other countries. **URL:** http://ajol.info/index.php/jmls.

49078 ■ Mary Slessor Journal of Medicine
African Journals Online
Dept. of Medical Microbiology
College of Medical Sciences
University of Calabar
Calabar, Cross River, Nigeria
Publisher E-mail: info@ajol.info
Peer-reviewed journal focusing on medicine. **Founded:** 1968. **Freq:** Semiannual. **Print Method:** Web press. **Trim Size:** 8 1/2 x 11. **Cols./Page:** 3. **Key Personnel:** Prof. Chuks G. Ejezie, Editor-in-Chief, gcejezie@netscape.net; Prof. A.I. Obiekezie, Editor; Prof. S.J. Etuk, Editor. **ISSN:** 1119-409X. **Subscription Rates:** US$30 individuals. **URL:** http://ajol.info/index.php/msjm.

49079 ■ Nigerian Journal of Physiological Sciences
African Journals Online
Dept. of Physiology
College of Medical Sciences
University of Calabar
Calabar, Cross River, Nigeria
Ph: 234 803 5524412
Publisher E-mail: info@ajol.info
Peer-reviewed journal focusing on clinical research in physiological sciences. **Founded:** 1984. **Freq:** Semiannual. **Print Method:** Offset. **Trim Size:** 8 1/2 x 11. **Cols./Page:** 2. **Col. Width:** 47 nonpareils. **Col. Depth:** 127 agate lines. **Key Personnel:** Dr. A.R.A. Alada, Editor-in-Chief, dralada@yahoo.com; Prof. E.E. Osim, Contact, emeosim@yahoo.com. **ISSN:** 0794-859X. **Subscription Rates:** US$105.50 institutions airmail deliveries, an additional 60 per volume; US$60 individuals. **URL:** http://ajol.info/index.php/njps.

49080 ■ Journal of College of Medicine
African Journals Online
University of Nigeria Teaching Hospital
P.M.B. 1129
Enugu, Nigeria
Publisher E-mail: info@ajol.info
Peer-reviewed journal covering clinical, experimental, cultural, historical and other topics about healthcare. **Freq:** Semiannual. **Key Personnel:** Prof. Basden J.C. Onwubere, Acting Ed.-in-Ch., bjconwub@yahoo.com; Uche Okafor, Asst. Ed.-in-Ch. **URL:** http://ajol.info/index.php/jcm.

49081 ■ Orient Journal of Medicine
African Journals Online
PO Box 3153
Enugu, Nigeria
Publisher E-mail: info@ajol.info
Peer-reviewed journal containing articles in clinical or laboratory medical sciences. **Freq:** Quarterly. **Key Personnel:** Dr. U.F. Ezepue, Editor, ifenna@skannet.com. **ISSN:** 1115-0521. **Subscription Rates:** 20 individuals; US$40 other countries. **URL:** http://ajol.info/index.php/ojm.

Enugu (Anambra)

49082 ■ Nigerian Journal of Otorhinolaryngology
African Journals Online
Dept. of Otorhinolaryngology
College of Medicine
University of Nigeria Teaching Hospital
Enugu, Anambra, Nigeria
Publisher E-mail: info@ajol.info
Peer-reviewed journal focusing on otorhinolaryngology. **Founded:** Mar. 1986. **Freq:** Semiannual March and September. **Print Method:** Offset. **Trim Size:** 8 1/4 x 11. **Cols./Page:** 2. **Col. Width:** 46 nonpareils. **Col. Depth:** 126 agate lines. **Key Personnel:** Prof. P.A. Okeowo, Editorial Adviser; Dr. R.E.L. Okujaye, Editorial Adviser; Dr. O.A. Somefun, Asst. Ed.; Prof. B.C. Okafor, Editorial Adviser; Dr. A.O. Imogu, Editorial Asst.; Dr.

O.G.B. Nwaorgu, Editorial Asst.; Prof. F.O. Ogisi, Editorial Adviser; Dr. Basil C. Ezeanolue, Editor, editornjorl@yahoo.com. **ISSN:** 9783-1230. **Subscription Rates:** N 600 individuals; US$15 individuals; US$25 individuals; N 1,200 institutions; US$20 institutions; US$30 institutions. **URL:** http://ajol.info/index.php/njorl.

Ibadan

49083 ■ African Journal of International Affairs and Development
African Journals Online
PO Box 30678
Ibadan, Oyo, Nigeria
Ph: 234 2 8101963
Fax: 234 2 8104165
Publisher E-mail: info@ajol.info
Peer-reviewed journal covering the study of Africa in global affairs and development. **Founded:** 1995. **Freq:** Semiannual. **Key Personnel:** Dr. Jide Owoeye, Editor-in-Chief, collegepresspublishers@yahoo.com. **ISSN:** 0117-272X. **Subscription Rates:** US$15 individuals Africa; US$25 other countries; US$20 institutions Africa; US$40 institutions, other countries. **URL:** http://ajol.info/index.php/ajiad.

49084 ■ African Journal of Library, Archives and Information Science
African Journals Online
c/o Prof. M.A. Tiamiyu, Ed.-in-Ch.
University of Ibadan
PO Box 20492
Ibadan, Oyo, Nigeria
Ph: 234 267 3552629
Publisher E-mail: info@ajol.info
Peer-reviewed journal covering library, archives, and information science. **Founded:** 1874. **Freq:** Semiannual. **Print Method:** Offset. **Trim Size:** 13 x 21. **Cols./Page:** 6. **Col. Width:** 23 nonpareils. **Col. Depth:** 224 agate lines. **Key Personnel:** Prof. M.A. Tiamiyu, Editor-in-Chief, mutatiamiyu@yahoo.com; Prof. L.O. Aina, Managing Editor. **ISSN:** 0795-4778. **Subscription Rates:** N 2,000 individuals; N 3,000 institutions. **URL:** http://ajol.info/index.php/ajlais.

49085 ■ African Journal of Livestock Extension
African Journals Online
Dept. of Agricultural Ext. & Rural Development
Faculty of Agriculture & Forestry
University of Ibadan
Ibadan, Oyo, Nigeria
Publisher E-mail: info@ajol.info
Peer-reviewed journal focusing on species of livestock. **Founded:** 1976. **Freq:** Annual. **Print Method:** Offset. **Trim Size:** 8 1/2 x 10 7/8. **Cols./Page:** 3 and 2. **Col. Width:** 14 and 21 picas. **Col. Depth:** 10 1/4 inches. **Key Personnel:** Dr. A.E. Adekoya, Editorial Adviser; Dr. G.R.K. Sharma, Editor-in-Chief, sharmagrk@yahoo.com. **ISSN:** 1596-4019. **URL:** http://ajol.info/index.php/ajlex.

49086 ■ African Journal for the Psychological Study of Social Issues
African Journals Online
c/o Prof. S.K. Balogun, Ed.-in-Ch.
Dept. of Psychology
University of Ibadan
Ibadan, Oyo, Nigeria
Ph: 234 803 3322424
Publisher E-mail: info@ajol.info
Peer-reviewed journal dedicated to the scientific investigation of psychological and social issues and related phenomena in Africa. **Founded:** 1848. **Freq:** Semiannual. **Cols./Page:** 6. **Col. Width:** 1.83 inches. **Col. Depth:** 21 1/2 inches. **Key Personnel:** Prof. S.K. Balogun, Editor-in-Chief, phone 234 80 33322424, shyngle61@yahoo.com. **ISSN:** 9783-2184. **Subscription Rates:** US$12 out of country; US$8 individuals African countries. **URL:** http://ajol.info/index.php/ajpssi.

49087 ■ Archives of Ibadan Medicine
African Journals Online
2.Awosika Ave.
Bodija Estate
PO Box 20222
Ibadan, Oyo, Nigeria
Publisher E-mail: info@ajol.info
Peer-reviewed journal focusing on issues related to the development of medicine. **Freq:** Semiannual. **Key Per-**

sonnel: Dr. EO Olapade-Olaopa, Editor-in-Chief, phone 234 810 1113, abb@infoweb.com.ng. **ISSN:** 1467-6958. **Subscription Rates:** N 1000 individuals; R 20 individuals; US$50 individuals rest of World; US$150 other countries corporate. **URL:** http://ajol.info/index.php/aim.

49088 ■ Journal of Agriculture and Social Research
African Journals Online
Department of Agriculture Ext. & Rural Development
University Ibadan
Ibadan, Oyo, Nigeria
Publisher E-mail: info@ajol.info
Peer-reviewed journal on agriculture and social research. **Freq:** Semiannual. **Key Personnel:** Prof. Laogun Obafemi, Consulting Ed.; Dr. O.A. Angba, Assoc. Ed.; Dr. A.C. Agumagu, Consulting Ed.; E.A. Onemolease, Assoc. Ed.; Dr. M.A. Bankole, Assoc. Ed.; Prof. J.O. Akintola, Consulting Ed.; Dr. O.I. Oladele, Editor-in-Chief, deledimeji@hotmail.com; Olufemi M. Adesope, Managing Editor, molsyfem@yahoo.com; Prof. C.C. Asiabaka, Consulting Ed. **ISSN:** 1595-7470. **Subscription Rates:** N 400 individuals; N 800 institutions; US$6 institutions per copy; US$3 individuals per copy. **URL:** http://ajol.info/index.php/jasr.

49089 ■ Journal of Environmental Extension
African Journals Online
U.S. Department of of Agricultural Extension & Rural Development
Faculty of Agriculture & Forestry
University of Ibadan
Ibadan, Oyo, Nigeria
Publisher E-mail: info@ajol.info
Peer-reviewed journal containing ideas on formulation, packaging, dissemination and consequential impacts of ideas/policies relating to the quality and sustainability of the environment. **Freq:** Annual. **Key Personnel:** Dr. Adegbenga E. Adekoya, Contact, vichenfel@yahoo.com. **ISSN:** 1595-5125. **URL:** http://ajol.info/index.php/jext.

49090 ■ Journal of Librarianship and Information Science in Africa
African Journals Online
U.S. Department of of Library, Archival & Information Studies
University of Ibadan
Ibadan, Oyo, Nigeria
Publisher E-mail: info@ajol.info
Peer-reviewed journal containing information for librarians, information scientists, and other information professionals especially in Africa. **Freq:** Semiannual. **Key Personnel:** Prof. G.O. Alegbeleye, Contact, galegbe@mail.skannet.com. **ISSN:** 1595-8922. **Subscription Rates:** US$45 institutions Africa; 40 institutions UK; US$55 other countries; US$25 individuals Africa; 20 individuals UK; US$30 other countries. **URL:** http://ajol.info/index.php/jlisa.

49091 ■ Journal of Mining and Geology
African Journals Online
U.S. Department of of Geology
Univeroity of Ibadan
Ibadan, Oyo, Nigeria
Publisher E-mail: info@ajol.info
Peer-reviewed journal covering the fields of the geosciences, mining, metallurgy, materials science and geoenvironmental studies. **Freq:** Semiannual. **Key Personnel:** A. Azubuike Elueze, Editor-in-Chief, aa.elueze@mail.ui.edu.ng. **ISSN:** 1116-2775. **Subscription Rates:** N 1,000 single issue; US$60 other countries. **URL:** http://ajol.info/index.php/jmg.

49092 ■ Moor Journal of Agricultural Research
African Journals Online
Obafemi Awolowo University
Moor Plantation
P.M.B. 5029
Ibadan, Oyo, Nigeria
Ph: 234 2 2311728
Publisher E-mail: info@ajol.info
Peer-reviewed journal covering the field of agriculture in Nigeria. **Freq:** Semiannual. **Key Personnel:** Dr. L.B. Taiwo, Assoc. Ed., lbtaiwo@yahoo.com; Prof. O. Omueti, Editor-in-Chief; Dr. G.A. Oluwatosin, Editor. **ISSN:** 1595-4153. **Subscription Rates:** US$30 individuals; US$15 single issue. **URL:** http://ajol.info/index.php/mjar.

49093 ■ Nigerian Journal of Animal Production
African Journals Online
Institute for Agricultural Research & Training
Moore Plantation
Ibadan, Oyo, Nigeria
Publisher E-mail: info@ajol.info
Peer-reviewed journal covering the field of animal production in Nigeria. **Freq:** Semiannual. **Key Personnel:** Dr. O.O. Oduguwa, Editor-In-Chief, oduguwa2002@yahoo.com. **ISSN:** 0331-2064. **Subscription Rates:** N 500 nonmembers; US$128 other countries. **URL:** http://ajol.info/index.php/njap.

49094 ■ Nigerian Journal of Clinical and Counselling Psychology
African Journals Online
U.S. Department of of Guidance & Counselling
University of Ibadan
Ibadan, Oyo, Nigeria
Publisher E-mail: info@ajol.info
Peer-reviewed journal covering the applied field of clinical and counselling psychology. **Freq:** Semiannual. **Key Personnel:** Dr. Helen O. Nwagwu, Editor, hnwagwu@yahoo.com. **ISSN:** 1118-4035. **Subscription Rates:** US$18 individuals. **URL:** http://ajol.info/index.php/njccp.

49095 ■ Nigerian Journal of Economic History
African Journals Online
U.S. Department of of History
Faculty of Arts
University of Ibadan
Ibadan, Oyo, Nigeria
Publisher E-mail: info@ajol.info
Peer-reviewed journal containing the scholarly study of Africa's past economic issues. **Key Personnel:** Dr. Ini Udoka, Editor-in-Chief, uduakudoka01@yahoo.com; Dr. Olutayo Charles Adesina, Contact, editornjeh@yahoo.com. **ISSN:** 1595-0795. **Subscription Rates:** N 600 individuals; US$15 individuals; 10 individuals; N 1,000 institutions; US$25 institutions; 15 institutions. **URL:** http://ajol.info/index.php/njeh.

49096 ■ Nigerian Journal of Genetics
African Journals Online
National Ctr. for Genetic Resources & Biotechnology
P.M.B. 5382
Ibadan, Oyo, Nigeria
Fax: 234 2 2312567
Publisher E-mail: info@ajol.info
Peer-reviewed journal containing articles on basic genetics and applied breeding. **Freq:** Annual. **Key Personnel:** Prof. Con Ikeobi, Contact, ikeobi@yahoo.co.uk. **ISSN:** 0189-9686. **Subscription Rates:** N 1,100 individuals; N 1,600 institutions; US$35 other countries; US$50 institutions, other countries. **URL:** http://ajol.info/index.php/njg.

49097 ■ Nigerian Journal of Horticultural Science
African Journals Online
Dept. of Agronomy
University of Ibadan
Ibadan, Oyo, Nigeria
Publisher E-mail: info@ajol.info
Peer-reviewed journal focusing on horticulture in Nigeria. **Founded:** 1977. **Key Personnel:** Dr. J.A. Fagbayide, Editor-in-Chief, jufak2002@yahoo.com; Prof. J.D. Olarewaju, Editorial Board; Dr. R.K.A. Egharevba, Editorial Board; Prof. J.O. Babatola, Editorial Board; Dr. Adenike O. Olufolaji, Editor-in-Chief; Dr. V.C. Umeh, Editorial Board. **ISSN:** 1118-2733. **Subscription Rates:** N 5,000 institutions; US$100 institutions Africa; US$250 institutions, other countries; N 2,000 individuals; US$50 individuals Africa; US$100 other countries. **URL:** http://ajol.info/index.php/njhs.

49098 ■ Nigerian Journal of Ophthalmology
African Journals Online
c/o OSN Secretariat
Ojulowo Eye Hospital
PO Box 851
Ibadan, Oyo, Nigeria
Publisher E-mail: info@ajol.info
Peer-reviewed journal of the Ophthalmological Society of Nigeria. **Freq:** Semiannual. **Key Personnel:** Prof. Oyin Olurin, Editorial Board; Dr. O.E. Babalola, Editorial Board; Dr. N.O. Magulike, Editorial Board; Dr. Ian Murdoch, Editorial Board; Prof. A.M. Baiyeroju, Editorial Board; Dr. C.O. Bekibele, Editor-in-Chief, cob150@

Circulation: ★ = ABC; △ = BPA; ◆ = CAC; • = CCAB; ❑ = VAC; ⊕ = PO Statement; ‡ = Publisher's Report; Boldface figures = sworn; Light figures = estimated.

Gale Directory of Publications & Broadcast Media/147th Ed.

5307

yahoo.com; Dr. Linda Lawrence, Editorial Board; Dr. Manish Nagpal, Editorial Board; Dr. O.T. Edema, Editorial Board; Dr. C. Chuka-Okosa, Editorial Board; Prof. O.O. Osuntokun, Editorial Board; Dr. H.A. Ajibode, Editorial Board. **ISSN:** 0189-9171. **Subscription Rates:** N 2,000 individuals; 50 individuals; US$75 other countries. **URL:** http://ajol.info/index.php/njo.

49099 ▪ Nigerian Journal of Paediatrics
African Journals Online
c/o Dept. of Paediatrics
University College Hospital
Ibadan, Oyo, Nigeria
Publisher E-mail: info@ajol.info
Peer-reviewed journal covering pediatrics in Nigeria. **Founded:** 1960. **Freq:** Quarterly. **Print Method:** Offset. **Trim Size:** 6 7/8 x 10. **Cols./Page:** 3. **Col. Width:** 26 nonpareils. **Col. Depth:** 140 agate lines. **Key Personnel:** Wilson Aderele, Editor-in-Chief, wiaderele@yahoo.com. **ISSN:** 0302-4660. **Subscription Rates:** US$200 individuals; 100 individuals. **URL:** http://ajol.info/index.php/njp.

49100 ▪ Nigerian Journal of Plastic Surgery
African Journals Online
U.S. Department of of Surgery
University College Hospital
Ibadan, Oyo, Nigeria
Publisher E-mail: info@ajol.info
Peer-reviewed journal covering all areas related to plastic and reconstructive surgery as well as to trauma surgery. **Freq:** Semiannual. **Key Personnel:** Prof. O.M. Oluwatosin, Editor, emiolaitan@yahoo.com; Aranmolate Segun, Assoc. Ed.; M.K. Asuku, Assoc. Ed. **ISSN:** 0794-9316. **Subscription Rates:** N 1,500 individuals; US$20 other countries; N 2,500 institutions; US$50 institutions, other countries. **URL:** http://ajol.info/index.php/njpsur.

49101 ▪ Tropical Journal of Animal Science
African Journals Online
U.S. Department of of Animal Science, Rm. 313
University of Ibadan
Ibadan, Oyo, Nigeria
Publisher E-mail: info@ajol.info
Peer-reviewed journal covering the field of animal science. **Freq:** Semiannual. **Key Personnel:** Dr. E.A. Iyayi, Editor-in-Chief, tropjas@yahoo.co.uk. **ISSN:** 1119-4308. **Subscription Rates:** N 4,000 individuals; US$40 individuals. **URL:** http://ajol.info/index.php/tjas.

49102 ▪ Tropical Journal of Obstetrics and Gynaecology
African Journals Online
U.S. Department of of Obstetrics & Gynaecology
University College Hospital
Ibadan, Oyo, Nigeria
Publisher E-mail: info@ajol.info
Peer-reviewed journal containing articles in obstetrics, gynaecology, reproductive health and allied disciplines in the tropics. **Freq:** Semiannual. **Key Personnel:** Prof. A.O. Omigbodun, Editor, tropical@skannet.com. **ISSN:** 0189-5178. **Subscription Rates:** 15 individuals. **URL:** http://ajol.info/index.php/tjog.

49103 ▪ Tropical Veterinarian
African Journals Online
Tropical of Veterinarian
Faculty of Veterinary Medicine
University of Ibadan
Ibadan, Oyo, Nigeria
Publisher E-mail: info@ajol.info
Peer-reviewed journal devoted to all aspects of veterinary science. **Freq:** Quarterly. **Key Personnel:** S.O. Akpavie, Editor-in-Chief, tropivet@skannet.com; BO Oke, Assoc. Ed.; MO Abatan, Assoc. Ed. **ISSN:** 0794-4845. **Subscription Rates:** N 5,000 institutions; US$120 institutions; N 1,000 individuals; N 80 individuals USA. **URL:** http://ajol.info/index.php/tv.

49104 ▪ West African Journal of Medicine
African Journals Online
U.S. Department of of Surgery
University College Hospital
Ibadan, Oyo, Nigeria
Publisher E-mail: info@ajol.info
Peer-reviewed journal covering the field of medical science in West Africa. **Freq:** Quarterly. **Key Personnel:** Prof. A.E. Ohwovoriole, Editor-in-Chief, wajmeditorinchief@yahoo.com. **ISSN:** 0189-160X. **URL:** http://ajol.info/index.php/wajm.

Idi-Araba

49105 ▪ Nigerian Dental Journal
African Journals Online
Editorial Office, Rm. 221
School of Dental Sciences, 2nd Fl.
College of Medicine, University of Lagos
PMB 12003
Idi-Araba, Lagos, Nigeria
Publisher E-mail: info@ajol.info
Peer-reviewed journal focusing on the subject of dental practice in the developing world. **Freq:** Semiannual. **Key Personnel:** Dr. Folakemi Oredugba, Editor-in-Chief, fola_ored@yahoo.com; Dr. W.L. Adeyemo, Contact, lanreadeyemo@yahoo.com. **ISSN:** 0189-1006. **Subscription Rates:** US$10 individuals; 5 individuals; N 5,000 institutions; US$150 institutions; 75 institutions; N 500 single issue; US$5 single issue; 2.50 single issue. **URL:** http://ajol.info/index.php/ndj.

Ikeja

49106 ▪ Democracy & Development
African Journals Online
Ctr. for Democracy & Development
PO Box 15700
Ikeja, Lagos, Nigeria
Publisher E-mail: info@ajol.info
Peer-reviewed journal covering democracy, security, and development in Africa. **Subtitle:** Journal of West African Affairs. **Freq:** Semiannual. **Key Personnel:** Dr. Jibrin Ibrahim, Editor-in-Chief, jibo72@yahoo.com; Prof. Okechukwu Ibeanu, Editor; Dr. Dziodzi Tsikata, Book Review Ed. **ISSN:** 1465-0142. **URL:** http://ajol.info/index.php/dad.

49107 ▪ Nigerian Hospital Practice
African Journals Online
PO Box 6420
Ikeja, Lagos, Nigeria
Publisher E-mail: info@ajol.info
Peer-reviewed journal covering medical education in Nigeria. **Freq:** Bimonthly. **Key Personnel:** Prof. E.A. Dosumu, Contact, nigerhpract@yahoo.com; Lucky Okolie, Contact, phone 234 802 3594150. **ISSN:** 1597-7889. **Subscription Rates:** N 3,500 individuals; N 5,000 institutions; US$100 other countries individual; US$150 institutions, other countries. **URL:** http://ajol.info/index.php/nhp.

49108 ▪ Nigerian Medical Practitioner
African Journals Online
PO Box 6420
Ikeja, Lagos, Nigeria
Publisher E-mail: info@ajol.info
Peer-reviewed journal containing research articles of interest to medical and allied health practitioners. **Freq:** Monthly. **Key Personnel:** Prof. O.A. Sofola, Editor-in-Chief, nigermedpract@atsyahoo.com; Prof. S.A. Ogun, Editor, nigermedpract@yahoo.com; Lucky Okolie, Business Mgr. **ISSN:** 0189-0964. **Subscription Rates:** N 3,500 individuals; N 5,000 institutions; US$100 other countries. **URL:** http://ajol.info/index.php/nmp.

Ikoyi

49109 ▪ Economic and Policy Review
African Journals Online
Maku House, 1st Fl.
109, Awolowo Rd.
Ikoyi, Lagos, Nigeria
Publisher E-mail: info@ajol.info
Peer-reviewed journal covering economics and business in Nigeria. **Freq:** Quarterly. **Key Personnel:** Tega Agbanobi, Publisher, tega.agbanobi@nesgroup.org; Onyinye Uzuana, Contact, onyinye.uzuana@nesgroup.org. **URL:** http://ajol.info/index.php/epr/index. **Former name:** NESG Economic Indicators.

Ile-Ife

49110 ▪ African Journal of Oral Health
African Journals Online
c/o Prof. Eyitope O. Ogunbodede, Ed.-in-Ch.
Faculty of Dentistry
Obafemi Awolowo University
Ile-Ife, Nigeria
Ph: 234 803 7195770

Publisher E-mail: info@ajol.info
Peer-reviewed journal covering oral health research and practice in the African continent. **Founded:** 1905. **Freq:** Quarterly. **Print Method:** Offset. **Cols./Page:** 6. **Col. Width:** 2 inches. **Col. Depth:** 21 1/2 inches. **Key Personnel:** Prof. Eyitope O. Ogunbodede, Editor-in-Chief; Dr. J.O. Taiwo, Assoc. Ed.; Dr. P.A. Akeredolu, Assoc. Ed.; Prof. Cynthia M. Pine, Assoc. Ed.; Prof. Titus Schleyer, Assoc. Ed.; Prof. Tony Smith, Assoc. Ed. **ISSN:** 0189-5710. **Subscription Rates:** N 6,500 institutions; US$120 institutions; US$220 other countries; N 3,200 individuals; US$70 individuals; US$98 individuals; N 2,000 students; US$35 students; US$50 students; N 12,000 institutions 2 years. **URL:** http://www.ajoh.org/.

49111 ▪ African Journal of Traditional, Complementary and Alternative Medicines
African Journals Online
c/o Prof. Clement O. Adewunmi, Ed.-in-Ch.
Drug Research & Production Unit, Faculty of Pharmacy
Obafemi Awolowo University
Ile-Ife, Nigeria
Publisher E-mail: info@ajol.info
Peer-reviewed journal covering research in applied medicinal plants, traditional medicines, complementary alternative medicines, food and agricultural technologies, and promotion of healthy use of medicinal products. **Founded:** 1998. **Freq:** 3/yr. **Print Method:** Offset. **Cols./Page:** 6. **Col. Width:** 21 1/2 nonpareils. **Col. Depth:** 294 agate lines. **Key Personnel:** Prof. Clement O. Adewunmi, Editor-in-Chief, editor@africanethnomedicines.net; John A.O. Ojewole, Editor-in-Chief, ojewolej@ukzn.ac.za. **ISSN:** 0189-6016. **Subscription Rates:** US$50 single issue print; US$500 institutions libraries; US$150 individuals print. **URL:** http://ajol.info/index.php/ajtcam.

49112 ▪ Gender and Behaviour
African Journals Online
U.S. Department of of Psychology
Obafemi Awolowo University
Ile-Ife, Nigeria
Publisher E-mail: info@ajol.info
Peer-reviewed journal containing information about psychological and behavioural aspects of gender in general. **Freq:** Semiannual. **Key Personnel:** Fatima Adamu, Editor; Dolapo Amole, Editor; Emma Mensah, Editor. **ISSN:** 0117-7322. **Subscription Rates:** US$40 individuals; US$100 institutions. **URL:** http://ajol.info/index.php/gab.

49113 ▪ IFE PsychologIA
African Journals Online
Dept. of Psychology
PO Box 1548
Ile-Ife, Nigeria
Publisher E-mail: info@ajol.info
Peer-reviewed journal of psychology in Africa and worldwide. **Founded:** 1951. **Freq:** Semiannual. **Print Method:** Letterpress. **Trim Size:** 8 1/2 x 10 1/2. **Cols./Page:** 2. **Col. Width:** 40 nonpareils. **Col. Depth:** 122 agate lines. **Key Personnel:** Prof. A.A. Olowu, Editor-in-Chief, ifepsy@yahoo.com. **ISSN:** 1117-1421. **Subscription Rates:** US$120 individuals any country; US$120 institutions any country. **URL:** http://ajol.info/index.php/ifep.

49114 ▪ Journal of the Obafemi Awolowo University Medical Student's Association
African Journals Online
College of Health Sciences
Obafemi Awolowo University
Ile-Ife, Nigeria
Publisher E-mail: info@ajol.info
Peer-reviewed journal covering medically related topics. **Freq:** Annual. **Key Personnel:** Dr. Deola Adesanya, Editor-in-Chief, ifemedjc@yahoo.com. **ISSN:** 0331-3727. **URL:** http://ajol.info/index.php/ifemed.

49115 ▪ Nigerian Journal of Natural Products and Medicine
African Journals Online
Dept. of Pharmacognosy
Faculty of Pharmacy
Obafemi Awolowo University
Ile-Ife, Nigeria
Ph: 234 36 232 595
Fax: 234 36 231 733
Publisher E-mail: info@ajol.info
Peer-reviewed journal of natural products and medicine

of Nigeria. **Founded:** 1996. **Freq:** Annual. **Key Personnel:** S.A. Adesanya, PhD, Editor-in-Chief, jadesany@yahoo.co.uk; A.O. Odukoya, PhD, Assoc. Ed.; M.S. Abubakar, PhD, Assoc. Ed. **Subscription Rates:** N 500 individuals; N 1,000 institutions; US$50 individuals; US$100 institutions. **URL:** http://ajol.info/index.php/njnpm. ■

49116 ■ Nigerian Music Review
African Journals Online
PO Box 1033
Obafemi Awolowo University
Ile-Ife, Nigeria
Ph: 234 803 4549393
Publisher E-mail: info@ajol.info
Peer-reviewed journal focusing on musicology, ethnomusicology, African music, music education, performance, composition and music technology. **Founded:** 1976. **Freq:** Annual. **Print Method:** Offset. **Trim Size:** 8 1/2 x 11. **Cols./Page:** 3 and 2. **Col. Width:** 26 and 40 nonpareils. **Col. Depth:** 136 agate lines. **Key Personnel:** Dr. Femi Adedeji, Assoc. Ed.; Prof. Tunji Vidal, Editor-in-Chief; Dr. Yemi Olaniyan, Editor. **ISSN:** 1116-428X. **Subscription Rates:** N 700 individuals single volume with postage; US$20 individuals single volume with postage; 10 individuals single volume with postage; N 850 institutions single volume with postage; US$25 institutions single volume with postage; 15 institutions single volume with postage. **URL:** http://ajol.info/index.php/nmr. ■

Ilorin

49117 ■ African Journal of Clinical and Experimental Microbiology
African Journals Online
c/o Prof. Boaz Adegboro, Ed.
Faculty of Health Sciences
University of Ilorin
PO Box 5395
Ilorin, Kwara, Nigeria
Ph: 234 312 22076
Publisher E-mail: info@ajol.info
Peer-reviewed journal covering medical microbiology including bacteriology, viriology, rickettsiology, chiaydiology, mycology, mycobacteriology, actinomyceles, arasitology, epidemiology of infectious diseases, general clinical microbiology, and clinical veterinary microbiology. **Founded:** 1892. **Freq:** 3/yr. **Print Method:** Offset. **Trim Size:** 14 x 23. **Cols./Page:** 6. **Col. Width:** 2 1/16 inches. **Col. Depth:** 21.5 picas. **Key Personnel:** Prof. Boaz Adegboro, Editor, ajcem2002@yahoo.com.; A.O. Coker, Editorial Adviser; T.O. Odugbemi, Editorial Adviser. **ISSN:** 1595-689X. **URL:** http://www.ajol.info/journal_index.php?jid=47&ab=ajcem.

49118 ■ Agrosearch
African Journals Online
Faculty of Agriculture
University of Ilorin
PMB 1515
Ilorin, Kwara, Nigeria
Publisher E-mail: info@ajol.info
Journal containing research findings in all areas of agriculture, food sciences and development. **Freq:** Semiannual. **Key Personnel:** Prof. O.A. Omotesho, Editor-in-Chief, phone 234 80 33510678, agrosearching@yahoo.com. **ISSN:** 1117-9996. **Subscription Rates:** N 500 individuals; N 1000 institutions. **URL:** http://ajol.info/index.php/agrosh.

49119 ■ BIOKEMISTRI
Bioline International
Dept. of Biochemistry
University of Ilorin
Ilorin, Kwara, Nigeria
Publication E-mail: biokemistri@yahoo.com
Publisher E-mail: bioline.international@utoronto.ca
Journal on biochemistry. **Freq:** Semiannual (June and December). **Key Personnel:** J.T. Ekanem, PhD, Editor-in-Chief. **ISSN:** 0795-8080. **Subscription Rates:** 60 individuals including handling, packaging and postage; US$100 individuals including handling, packaging and postage; N 8,500 individuals including handling, packaging and postage. **URL:** http://www.bioline.org.br/bk.

49120 ■ Journal of Agricultural Research and Development
African Journals Online

Faculty of Agriculture
University of Ilorin
P.M.B. 1515
Ilorin, Kwara, Nigeria
Publisher E-mail: info@ajol.info
Peer-reviewed journal covering all fields of agriculture. **Freq:** Semiannual. **Key Personnel:** Prof. Abiodun A. Adeloye, Editor-in-Chief, jard_unilorin@yahoo.com; Dr. O.A. Adekunle, Business Mgr.; Prof. O.A. Omotesho, Dep. Ed.-in-Ch. **ISSN:** 1596-5511. **Subscription Rates:** N 2,500 individuals; N 1,750 students; US$75 other countries; N 4,500 libraries. **URL:** http://ajol.info/index.php/jard.

49121 ■ Nigerian Journal of Guidance and Counselling
African Journals Online
U.S. Department of of Guidance & Counselling
University of Ilorin
Ilorin, Kwara, Nigeria
Publisher E-mail: info@ajol.info
Peer-reviewed journal containing articles on issues related to counseling and psychology. **Freq:** Annual. **Key Personnel:** Prof. Adeyemi I. Idowu, Editor-in-Chief, tnjgcwebs@yahoo.com. **ISSN:** 0794-0831. **URL:** http://ajol.info/index.php/njgc.

49122 ■ Tropical Journal of Health Sciences
African Journals Online
College of Medicine
University of Ilorin
PMB 1515
Ilorin, Kwara, Nigeria
Publication E-mail: tjhsilorin@yahoo.com
Publisher E-mail: info@ajol.info
Peer-reviewed journal covering the field of health sciences. **Freq:** Semiannual. **Key Personnel:** Prof. A.B. Okesina, Editor-in-Chief, drokesina@yahoo.com. **ISSN:** 1117-4153. **Subscription Rates:** N 250 individuals college staff; N 150 students; N 350 individuals; N 450 institutions; US$15 other countries. **URL:** http://ajol.info/index.php/tjhc.

Jos

49123 ■ African Journal of Paediatric Surgery
African Journals Online
Paediatric Surgery Unit
Dept. of Surgery
Jos University Teaching Hospital
PO Box 2076
Jos, Plateau, Nigeria
Publisher E-mail: info@ajol.info
Peer-reviewed journal devoted to pediatric surgery. **Freq:** Semiannual. **Key Personnel:** Dr. Aba Francis Uba, Editor-in-Chief, phone 234 80371 54469, afranu@yahoo.com; A. Hesse, Editor; S.O. Ekenze, Editor. **ISSN:** 0189-6725. **Subscription Rates:** N 6,000 institutions; N 4,000 individuals. **URL:** http://ajol.info/index.php/ajps-n.

49124 ■ Highland Medical Research Journal
African Journals Online
PO Box 887
Jos, Plateau, Nigeria
Ph: 243 803 7035957
Fax: 243 807 3454172
Publisher E-mail: info@ajol.info
Peer-reviewed journal covering scientific research in various fields of medical science. **Freq:** Semiannual. **Key Personnel:** Dr. B.M. Mandong, Editor-in-Chief, mafala2004@yahoo.com. **ISSN:** 1596-2407. **Subscription Rates:** R 15 individuals; R 20 individuals non African; R 25 institutions; R 30 institutions non African; N 500 individuals; N 1,200 institutions. **URL:** http://ajol.info/index.php/hmrj.

49125 ■ Journal of Aquatic Sciences
African Journals Online
Fisheries Research Unit
Department of Zoology
University of Jos
Jos, Plateau, Nigeria
Publisher E-mail: info@ajol.info
Peer-reviewed journal covering aquatic sciences. **Founded:** 1986. **Freq:** Semiannual. **Key Personnel:** Dr. Edosa Omoregie, Editor-in-Chief, phone 234 80 60220010, omoregie@unijos.edu.ng; Prof. J.W. Wade, Editor; Prof. A.J. Matty, Editor. **ISSN:** 0189-8779. **Subscription Rates:** N 550 individuals; US$100 individuals;

50 individuals; N 2,500 institutions; US$220 institutions; 110 institutions. **URL:** http://ajol.info/index.php/jas.

49126 ■ Journal of Medicine in the Tropics
University of Jos
Faculty of Medical Sciences
c/o The Deans Office
University of Jos
PMB 2084
Jos, Plateau, Nigeria
Ph: 23 473 55952
Peer-reviewed journal covering the research in the field of medicine and related sciences. **Freq:** Semiannual. **Key Personnel:** Dr. Basil N. Okeahialam, Editor-in-Chief. **ISSN:** 0795-9168. **Subscription Rates:** US$50 institutions Africa; US$70 institutions, other countries; US$50 individuals Africa; US$60 other countries; N 1,000 individuals Nigeria; US$30 single issue international; N 500 single issue. **URL:** http://ajol.info/index.php/jmt.

49127 ■ Journal of Pharmacy and Bioresources
African Journals Online
Faculty of Pharmaceutical Sciences
University of Jos
Jos, Plateau, Nigeria
Publisher E-mail: info@ajol.info
Peer-reviewed journal covering areas of pharmaceutical and life sciences. **Freq:** Semiannual. **Key Personnel:** Prof. E.N. Sokomba, Editor-in-Chief, phone 234 803 7006372, jpb@unijos.edu.ng. **ISSN:** 0189-8442. **Subscription Rates:** N 950 individuals single volume; N 1,900 institutions single volume; N 500 single issue; N 1000 single issue for corporate. **URL:** http://ajol.info/index.php/jpb.

49128 ■ Nigerian Journal of Pharmaceutical Research
African Journals Online
Dept. of Pharmaceutical Chemistry
Faculty of Pharmaceutical Sciences
University of Jos
Jos, Plateau, Nigeria
Ph: 234 803 8131246
Publisher E-mail: info@ajol.info
Peer-reviewed journal of pharmaceutical research in Nigeria. **Founded:** 1981. **Freq:** Annual. **Print Method:** Offset. **Trim Size:** 8 1/2 x 11. **Cols./Page:** 2. **Col. Width:** 47 nonpareils. **Col. Depth:** 127 agate lines. **Key Personnel:** Prof. T.A. Iranloye, Editor-in-Chief, naap2004jos@yahoo.com; Sunday Otimenyin, Tech. Support, phone 234 802 8557051, sundayo@unijos.edu.ng. **ISSN:** 0189-8434. **Subscription Rates:** N 300 individuals; US$20 individuals. **URL:** http://ajol.info/index.php/njpr.

Lagos

49129 ■ African Journal of Agricultural Research
Academic Journals
73023 Victoria Island
Lagos, Lagos, Nigeria
Publication E-mail: ajar@academicjournals.org
Publisher E-mail: service@academicjournals.org
Journal covering all areas of agriculture in Africa. **Freq:** Monthly. **Key Personnel:** Prof. N.A. Amusa, Editor. **ISSN:** 1991-637X. **Remarks:** Accepts advertising. **URL:** http://www.academicjournals.org/AJAR/. **Circ:** (Not Reported)

49130 ■ African Journal of Biochemistry Research
Academic Journals
73023 Victoria Island
Lagos, Lagos, Nigeria
Publication E-mail: ajbr@academicjournals.org
Publisher E-mail: service@academicjournals.org
Journal covering in all areas of biochemistry. **Freq:** Monthly. **Key Personnel:** Prof. Johnson Lin, Acting Ed.; Carlos H. I. Ramos, Assoc. Ed.; Gregory Lloyd Blatch, Assoc. Ed. **ISSN:** 1996-0778. **Remarks:** Accepts advertising. **URL:** http://www.academicjournals.org/AJBR/. **Circ:** (Not Reported)

49131 ■ African Journal of Business Management
Academic Journals
73023 Victoria Island
Lagos, Lagos, Nigeria

Circulation: ★ = ABC; △ = BPA; ♦ = CAC; • = CCAB; ❏ = VAC; ⊕ = PO Statement; ‡ = Publisher's Report; Boldface figures = sworn; Light figures = estimated.

Gale Directory of Publications & Broadcast Media/147th Ed.   5309

Publication E-mail: ajbm@academicjournals.org
Publisher E-mail: service@academicjournals.org
Peer-reviewed Journal covering business research.
Freq: Monthly. **Key Personnel:** Dr. De la Rey van der Waldt, Editor-in-Chief. **ISSN:** 1990-3839. **Remarks:** Accepts advertising. **URL:** http://www.academicjournals.org/AJBM/index.htm. **Circ:** (Not Reported)

49132 ■ African Journal of Food Science
Academic Journals
73023 Victoria Island
Lagos, Lagos, Nigeria
Publication E-mail: ajfs@academicjournals.org
Publisher E-mail: service@academicjournals.org
Journal covering in all areas of food science. **Freq:** Monthly. **Key Personnel:** Prof. A.H. Subratty, Editor; Mr. Barakat S.M. Mahmoud, Assoc. Ed. **ISSN:** 1996-0794. **Remarks:** Accepts advertising. **URL:** http://www.academicjournals.org/AJFS/index.htm. **Circ:** (Not Reported)

49133 ■ African Journal of Microbiology Research
Academic Journals
73023 Victoria Island
Lagos, Lagos, Nigeria
Publication E-mail: ajmr.acadjourn@gmail.com
Publisher E-mail: service@academicjournals.org
Journal covering in all areas of microbiology. **Freq:** Monthly. **Key Personnel:** Prof. Stefan Schmidt, Editor; Mamadou Gueye, Assoc. Ed.; Carolina Mary Knox, Assoc. Ed. **ISSN:** 1996-0808. **Remarks:** Accepts advertising. **URL:** http://www.academicjournals.org/AJMR/. **Circ:** (Not Reported)

49134 ■ African Journal of Plant Science
Academic Journals
73023 Victoria Island
Lagos, Lagos, Nigeria
Publication E-mail: ajps@academicjournals.org
Publisher E-mail: service@academicjournals.org
Peer-reviewed Journal covering all areas of plant science and botany. **Freq:** Monthly. **Key Personnel:** Prof. Diaga Diouf, Editor. **ISSN:** 1996-0824. **Remarks:** Accepts advertising. **URL:** http://www.academicjournals.org/AJPS/index.htm. **Circ:** (Not Reported)

49135 ■ African Journal of Political Science & International Relations
Academic Journals
73023 Victoria Island
Lagos, Lagos, Nigeria
Publication E-mail: ajpsir@acadjourn.org
Publisher E-mail: service@academicjournals.org
Journal covering Africa's political science and international relations. **Freq:** Monthly. **Key Personnel:** Ayandiji Daniel Aina, Assoc. Ed.; Prof. F.J. Kolapo, Assoc. Ed. **ISSN:** 1996-0832. **Remarks:** Accepts advertising. **URL:** http://www.academicjournals.org/AJPSIR/. **Circ:** (Not Reported)

49136 ■ African Journal of Pure & Applied Chemistry
Academic Journals
73023 Victoria Island
Lagos, Lagos, Nigeria
Publication E-mail: ajpac@academicjournals.org
Publisher E-mail: service@academicjournals.org
Journal covering research analysis on applied chemistry. **Freq:** Monthly. **Key Personnel:** Prof. Tebello Nyokong, Acting Ed.; Prof. F. Tafesse, Assoc. Ed. **ISSN:** 1996-0840. **Remarks:** Accepts advertising. **URL:** http://www.academicjournals.org/AJPAC/index.htm. **Circ:** (Not Reported)

49137 ■ Educational Research & Reviews
Academic Journals
73023 Victoria Island
Lagos, Lagos, Nigeria
Publisher E-mail: service@academicjournals.org
Journal covering all areas of education including education policies and management. **Freq:** Monthly. **Key Personnel:** Dr. Ken Alston, Editor; Prof. Malcom Vick, Assoc. Ed. **ISSN:** 1990-3839. **Remarks:** Accepts advertising. **URL:** http://www.academicjournals.org/ERR2/index.htm. **Circ:** (Not Reported)

49138 ■ International NGO Journal
Academic Journals
73023 Victoria Island
Lagos, Lagos, Nigeria
Publication E-mail: ngo@academicjournals.org
Publisher E-mail: service@academicjournals.org
Journal covering activities of Non Governmental Organization. **Freq:** Monthly. **Key Personnel:** Dr. Philomena Imonivwerha, Editor. **ISSN:** 1993-8225. **Remarks:** Accepts advertising. **URL:** http://www.academicjournals.org/INGOJ/index.htm. **Circ:** (Not Reported)

49139 ■ Journal of Cell & Animal Biology
Academic Journals
73023 Victoria Island
Lagos, Lagos, Nigeria
Publication E-mail: jcab@academicjournals.org
Publisher E-mail: service@academicjournals.org
Journal covering in all areas of cell and animal biology. **Freq:** Monthly. **Key Personnel:** Jacob Tavern Ross, Editor; Hamada Mohamed Mahmoud, Co-Ed. **ISSN:** 1996-0867. **Remarks:** Accepts advertising. **URL:** http://www.academicjournals.org/JCAB/index.htm. **Circ:** (Not Reported)

49140 ■ Lagos Journal of Library and Information Science
African Journals Online
Nigerian Institutes of Advanced Legal Studies
University of Lagos Campus
PMB 12820 Marina
Lagos, Lagos, Nigeria
Publisher E-mail: info@ajol.info
Peer-reviewed journal containing information about international library and information community. **Freq:** Semiannual. **Key Personnel:** Charles O. Omekwu, PhD, Editor-in-Chief, charles.omekwu@unn.edu.ng. **ISSN:** 1596-9487. **Subscription Rates:** N 500 individuals; N 1,000 institutions; US$30 other countries. **URL:** http://ajol.info/index.php/ljlis.

49141 ■ Nigerian Journal of Health and Biomedical Sciences
African Journals Online
College of Medicine of the University of Lagos
Dept. of Physiology
PO Box 12003
Lagos, Lagos, Nigeria
Publisher E-mail: info@ajol.info
Peer-reviewed journal of health and biomedical science of Nigeria. **Freq:** Semiannual. **Key Personnel:** Dr. I.I. Olatunji-Bello, Editor-in-Chief, yemibello@lycos.com; Dr. Tolu Odugbemi, Publisher, toluodugbemi@yahoo.com; A.O. Atoyebi, Production Ed. **ISSN:** 1595-8272. **Subscription Rates:** N 1,000 individuals; 50 individuals; US$100 individuals; N 1,200 institutions; 50 institutions; US$100 institutions; C$80 institutions. **URL:** http://ajol.info/index.php/njhbs.

49142 ■ Nigerian Quarterly Journal of Hospital Medicine
African Journals Online
College of Medicine
University of Lagos
P.M.B. 12003
Lagos, Lagos, Nigeria
Ph: 234 1 5835629
Publisher E-mail: info@ajol.info
Peer-reviewed journal containing articles in medicine, dentistry, pharmaceutical, and basic medical sciences. **Freq:** Quarterly. **Key Personnel:** Prof. Ossretin Albert T. Ebuehi, Editor-in-Chief, ebuehi@yahoo.com. **ISSN:** 0189-2657. **Subscription Rates:** US$40 individuals Africa; US$75 Institutions Africa; US$75 individuals Europe; US$150 institutions Europe; US$100 U.S. and Canada; US$200 institutions, Canada USA. **URL:** http://ajol.info/index.php/nqjhm.

49143 ■ Scientific Research & Essays
Academic Journals
73023 Victoria Island
Lagos, Lagos, Nigeria
Publication E-mail: sre@academicjournals.org
Publisher E-mail: service@academicjournals.org
Journal covering applied research in science, medicine, agriculture and engineering. **Freq:** Bimonthly. **Key Personnel:** Dr. NJ Tonukari, Editor-in-Chief, sre@academicjournals.org; Dr. M. Sivakumar, PhD, Assoc. Ed. **ISSN:** 1992-2248. **Remarks:** Accepts advertising. **URL:** http://www.academicjournals.org/SRE/. **Circ:** (Not Reported)

49144 ■ Cool-FM - 96.9
267A, Etim Inyang Cres. Victoria Island Annex
P.M.B. 10096

Victoria Island
Lagos, Lagos, Nigeria
Ph: 234 1 2623053
Fax: 234 1 2610393
E-mail: info@coolfm.us
Format: Urban Contemporary. **Operating Hours:** Continuous. **Ad Rates:** Advertising accepted; rates available upon request. **URL:** http://www.coolfm.us.

Makurdi

49145 ■ International Journal of Development and Policy Studies
African Journals Online
PO Box 827
Makurdi, Benue, Nigeria
Publisher E-mail: info@ajol.info
Peer-reviewed journal containing information about social policy. **Key Personnel:** Tyoor F.M. Terhemba, Contact, phone 234 80 36309129, qdmrcnigeria@yahoo.com. **ISSN:** 0795-0632. **URL:** http://ajol.info/index.php/qijdps.

49146 ■ Nigerian Journal of Fisheries
African Journals Online
Benue State University
PMB 102119
Makurdi, Benue, Nigeria
Publisher E-mail: info@ajol.info
Peer-reviewed journal covering all aspects of fisheries for progressive development. **Founded:** 1976. **Freq:** Semiannual. **Key Personnel:** Dr. P.A. Araoye, Editor-in-Chief, araoyepa@yahoo.com; I.T. Omoniyi, Dep. Ed. **Subscription Rates:** N 500 individuals; US$35 individuals; N 3,500 libraries; US$100 libraries; N 3,500 institutions; US$100 institutions. **URL:** http://ajol.info/index.php/njf.

Minna

49147 ■ Information Technologist
African Journals Online
U.S. Department of of Library & Information Technology
Federal University of Technology
Minna, Niger, Nigeria
Publisher E-mail: info@ajol.info
Peer-reviewed journal covering the field of information and communication technology, including library and information science. **Subtitle:** An International Journal of Information Communication Technology. **Freq:** Semiannual. **Key Personnel:** Dr. Everest C. Madu, Editor-in-Chief, evamadu@yahoo.co.uk. **ISSN:** 1597-4316. **Subscription Rates:** US$70 individuals; US$90 institutions. **URL:** http://ajol.info/index.php/ict.

Nnewi

49148 ■ Journal of Biomedical Investigation
African Journals Online
U.S. Department of of Pharmacology/Therapeutics
Faculty of Medicine, College of Health Sciences
Nnamdi Azikiwe University
PMB 5001
Nnewi, Anambra, Nigeria
Publisher E-mail: info@ajol.info
Peer-reviewed journal covering biomedical sciences. **Freq:** Semiannual. **Key Personnel:** Charles Onyenekwe, Editor-in-Chief, phone 234 80 37077065, charleschinedum2002@yahoo.com; Ed Nwobodo, Editor; Sam Meludu, Bus. Ed. **ISSN:** 1597-0043. **Subscription Rates:** US$50 individuals. **URL:** http://ajol.info/index.php/jbi.

49149 ■ Nigerian Journal of Clinical Practice
African Journals Online
Dept. of Surgery
Nnamdi Azikiwe University Teaching Hospital
Nnewi, Anambra, Nigeria
Publisher E-mail: info@ajol.info
Peer-reviewed journal promoting clinical and academic excellence in medicine and dentistry and allied sciences. **Founded:** 1997. **Freq:** Semiannual. **Print Method:** Offset. Uses mats. **Trim Size:** 11 1/4 x 16. **Cols./Page:** 4. **Col. Width:** 28 nonpareils. **Col. Depth:** 205 agate lines. **Key Personnel:** Prof. Stanley N.C. Anyanwu, Editor, sncanyanwu@yahoo.com; Dr. Joseph I. Ikechebelu, Contact; Dr. I. Evbuomwan, Asst. Ed. **ISSN:** 1119-3077. **Subscription Rates:** US$100 single issue; US$350 two years African; US$200 individuals African; US$250

individuals non African. **URL:** http://ajol.info/index.php/njcp.

49150 ■ Nigerian Medical Journal
Nigerian Medical Association
Dept. of Surgery
Nnamdi Azikiwe University Teaching Hospital
P.M.B. 5025
Nnewi, Anambra, Nigeria
Publisher E-mail: info@nigeriannma.org
Journal of the Nigerian Medical Association. **Freq:** Bimonthly. **Key Personnel:** Dr. B.A. Ekele, Assoc. Ed.; Prof. Stanley Anyanwu, Editor; Dr. A. Aderibigbe, Assoc. Ed.; Dr. I.A.O. Ujah, Assoc. Ed.; Dr. M.C. Izegbu, Assoc. Ed.; Dr. R.A. Adebayo, Assoc. Ed. **Subscription Rates:** N 1,000 members; N 1,500 nonmembers individuals; N 2,300 nonmembers institutions; US$110 individuals Africa; US$275 individuals U.S., Australia and Asia; EUR135 individuals; US$220 other countries others; N 300 members 1 copy; N 400 nonmembers 1 copy, individuals; N 500 nonmembers 1 copy, institutions. **URL:** http://www.nigeriannma.org/journal.htm.

49151 ■ Tropical Journal of Medical Research
African Journals Online
Dept. of Medicine, Faculty of Medicine
College of Health Sciences
Nnamdi Azikiwe University
PMB 5001
Nnewi, Anambra, Nigeria
Ph: 234 80 34048668
Publisher E-mail: info@ajol.info
Peer-reviewed journal containing research work, review articles, important case report, short communications, and innovations in medicine and related fields. **Freq:** Semiannual. **Key Personnel:** Prof. M.C. Nwosu, Editor-in-Chief, mnqnwosu@yahoo.com. **ISSN:** 1119-0388. **Subscription Rates:** US$30 individuals; 20 individuals. **URL:** http://ajol.info/index.php/tjmr.

49152 ■ Plant Products Research Journal
African Journals Online
U.S. Department of of Biochemistry
University of Nigeria
Nsukka, Nigeria
Publisher E-mail: info@ajol.info
Peer-reviewed journal covering all aspects of plant biology. **Freq:** Semiannual. **Key Personnel:** Prof. Obioma U. Njoku, Editor-in-Chief, obynjoku203@yahoo.com. **ISSN:** 1119-2283. **Subscription Rates:** US$50 individuals. **URL:** http://ajol.info/index.php/pprj.

49153 ■ West African Journal of Radiology
African Journals Online
U.S. Department of of Radiology
University of Nigeria Teaching Hospital
Nsukka, Nigeria
Ph: 234 42 303105
Publisher E-mail: info@ajol.info
Peer-reviewed journal covering the science and technology of radiology and radiotherapy. **Founded:** 1982. **Key Personnel:** Dr. B.C. Umerah, Editor-in-Chief, benumerah@yahoo.com; Dr. IJ Okoye, Asst. Ed., okoyeij2002@yahoo.co.uk. **ISSN:** 1115-3474. **Subscription Rates:** N 500 individuals; N 600 institutions; US$30 U.S. and Canada Africa, Europe; US$50 institutions, Canada Africa, Europe, USA; US$35 other countries; US$55 institutions, other countries. **URL:** http://ajol.info/index.php/wajr.

Nsukka (Anambra)

49154 ■ Agro-Science
University of Nigeria
c/o Prof. Michael I. Uguru, Ed.-in-Ch.
Dept. of Crop Science
University of Nigeria
Nsukka, Anambra, Nigeria
Ph: 234 803 7723307
Publication E-mail: info@agrosciencejournal.com
Journal covering crop science, animal science, animal health, soil and environment, agricultural economics, agricultural extension, home economics, food and nutrition, post harvest technology, agricultural engineering and mechanization. **Founded:** June 1978. **Freq:** Semiannual January and July. **Print Method:** Web. **Trim Size:** 8 1/4 x 10 3/4. **Cols./Page:** 3. **Col. Width:** 2 5/16 inches. **Col. Depth:** 9 3/4 inches. **Key Personnel:** Prof. Michael I. Uguru, Editor-in-Chief, chiefeditor@

agrosciencejournal.com. **ISSN:** 1119-7455. **URL:** http://www.agrosciencejournal.com/about-agro-journal-nigeria.html.

49155 ■ Animal Research International
African Journals Online
U.S. Department of of Zoology
University of Nigeria
PO Box 3146
Nsukka, Anambra, Nigeria
Publisher E-mail: info@ajol.info
Peer-reviewed journal covering information on the results of scientific research into the fauna of Africa. **Freq:** 3/yr. **Key Personnel:** Prof. F.C. Okafor, Editor; Dr. Joseph E. Eyo, Assoc. Ed., divinelovejoe@yahoo.com. **Subscription Rates:** US$350 individuals; US$300 students; US$600 institutions; N 2,000 individuals; N 1,400 students; N 5,000 institutions. **URL:** http://ajol.info/index.php/ari.

49156 ■ Bio-Research
African Journals Online
Faculty of Biological Sciences
University of Nigeria
Nsukka, Anambra, Nigeria
Publisher E-mail: info@ajol.info
Peer-reviewed journal covering biological research and biotechnology. **Freq:** Semiannual. **Key Personnel:** Prof. I.C. Ononogbu, Editor-in-Chief, phone 234 42 770644, obynjoku203@yahoo.com; O. Obidoa, Editor; N.M. Inyang, Editor. **ISSN:** 1596-7409. **Subscription Rates:** N 3,500 individuals; US$50 individuals Africa; US$60 other countries. **URL:** http://ajol.info/index.php/br.

49157 ■ Journal of Pharmaceutical and Allied Sciences
African Journals Online
Dept. of Pharmaceutics
University of Nigeria
Nsukka, Anambra, Nigeria
Ph: 234 804 3180627
Fax: 234 804 2770644
Publisher E-mail: info@ajol.info
Peer-reviewed journal of pharmaceutical and allied sciences. **Founded:** Jan. 1967. **Freq:** Semiannual. **Print Method:** Offset. **Trim Size:** 8 3/8 x 10 7/8. **Cols./Page:** 3. **Col. Width:** 13 picas. **Col. Depth:** 56 1/2 picas. **Key Personnel:** Dr. M. Iwuagwu, Editorial Advisory Board; Dr. Amit Misra, Editorial Advisory Board; Prof. C.T. Andrade, Editorial Advisory Board; Dr. Emmanuel Chinedum Ibezim, Editor-in-Chief, ecibezim@yahoo.com; Dr. L. Ezeanyika, Editorial Advisory Board; Prof. C.N. Aguwa, Editorial Advisory Board. **ISSN:** 1596-8499. **Subscription Rates:** N 1,000 individuals within Nigeria; 20 individuals outside Nigeria including postage; US$35 individuals outside Nigeria including postage. **URL:** http://ajol.info/index.php/jophas.

Obubra

49158 ■ Journal of Agriculture, Forestry and the Social Sciences
Cross River University of Technology
Department of Animal Science and Fisheries
Obubra Campus
State PMB 1123
Obubra, Cross River, Nigeria
Peer-reviewed Journal covering Agriculture, Forestry and the Social Sciences focusing towards sustainable agriculture. **Freq:** Semiannual June/ December. **Key Personnel:** Essien Antigha, Coordinating Ed., antigha2005@yahoo.com. **ISSN:** 1597-0906. **URL:** http://ajol.info/index.php/joafss.

Oshodi

49159 ■ Daily Champion
PO Box 2276
Oshodi, Lagos, Nigeria
Ph: 234 145 25807
Fax: 234 145 24421
Publisher E-mail: letters@champion-newspapers.com
General newspaper. **Key Personnel:** Seyi Fasugba, Editor; Sam Ameh, Editor; Ugo Onuoha, Editor-in-Chief. **URL:** http://www.champion-newspapers.com/.

49160 ■ Nigerian Food Journal
African Journals Online
NITEL Training Ctr.

Cappa Bus stop
PO Box 2
Oshodi, Lagos, Nigeria
Ph: 234 1 4749019
Fax: 234 803 5487198
Publisher E-mail: info@ajol.info
Peer-reviewed journal covering all aspects of food science and technology. **Founded:** 1983. **Freq:** Annual. **Key Personnel:** Prof. Maduebibisi Iwe, Editor-in-Chief, maduoiwe@yahoo.com; Prof. O.M. Oyawoye, Assoc. Ed.; Dr. Abimbola Uzomah, Assoc. Ed. **ISSN:** 0189-7241. **Subscription Rates:** N 3,000 individuals; N 5,000 institutions; US$100 individuals Africa; US$150 other countries. **URL:** http://ajol.info/index.php/nifoj.

Owerri

49161 ■ Animal Production Research Advances
African Journals Online
Department of Animal Science & Technology
Federal University of Technology
PMB 1526
Owerri, Imo, Nigeria
Publisher E-mail: info@ajol.info
Peer-reviewed journal covering information about the production of all animal species utilized as food. **Freq:** Quarterly. **Key Personnel:** Dr. Charles Okoli, Editor-in-Chief, phone 234 80 56647100, dr_charleso@yahoo.com. **ISSN:** 0794-4721. **Subscription Rates:** N 3,000 individuals; US$180 other countries; N 6,000 institutions; US$360 institutions, other countries. **URL:** http://ajol.info/index.php/apra.

49162 ■ Global Approaches to Extension Practice
African Journals Online
U.S. Department of of Agricultural Extension
Federal University of Technology
PMB 1526
Owerri, Imo, Nigeria
Publisher E-mail: info@ajol.info
Peer-reviewed journal containing information about agricultural extension, extension communications technology, indigenous knowledge systems, program planning in extension and extension administration. **Subtitle:** A Journal of Agricultural Extension. **Freq:** Semiannual. **Key Personnel:** Dr. Edna C. Matthews-Njoku, Editor-in-Chief, dredna04@yahoo.co.uk; Dr. O.M. Adesope, Editor. **ISSN:** 0794-1005. **Subscription Rates:** N 600 individuals; US$10 individuals; N 1,000 institutions; US$20 institutions. **URL:** http://ajol.info/index.php/gaep.

49163 ■ International Journal of Agriculture and Rural Development
African Journals Online
U.S. Department of Agricultural Extension
School of Agriculture & Agricultural Technology
Federal University of Technology
PMB 1526
Owerri, Imo, Nigeria
Publisher E-mail: info@ajol.info
Peer-reviewed journal covering the areas of agriculture and rural development in the tropics. **Freq:** Semiannual. **Key Personnel:** Prof. C.C. Asiabaka, Editor-in-Chief, phone 234 80 37219323, ijards@yahoo.com; Dr. OM Adesope, Contact, omadesope@yahoo.co.uk. **ISSN:** 1595-9716. **Subscription Rates:** N 1,000 individuals; US$50 individuals Africa; US$100 other countries; N 1,500 institutions; US$60 institutions Africa; US$120 institutions, other countries. **URL:** http://ajol.info/index.php/ijard.

49164 ■ Journal of Research in National Development
African Journals Online
U.S. Department of of Maritime Management of Technology
Federal University of Technology
Owerri, Imo, Nigeria
Publisher E-mail: info@ajol.info
Peer-reviewed journal covering topics on social sciences. **Freq:** Semiannual. **Key Personnel:** Dr. Kenneth U. Nnadi, Contact, phone 234 803 7523584, kennethnnadi@yahoo.com. **ISSN:** 1596-8308. **Subscription Rates:** N 1,000 individuals. **URL:** http://ajol.info/index.php/jorind.

Circulation: ★ = ABC; △ = BPA; ◆ = CAC; • = CCAB; ▢ = VAC; ⊕ = PO Statement; ‡ = Publisher's Report; Boldface figures = sworn; Light figures = estimated.

Gale Directory of Publications & Broadcast Media/147th Ed.   5311

Port Harcourt

49165 ■ African Journal of Applied Zoology and Environmental Biology
African Journals Online
U.S. Department of of Animal & Environmental Biology
University of Port Harcourt
PO Box 47
Choba Park
Port Harcourt, Rivers, Nigeria
Publisher E-mail: info@ajol.info
Peer-reviewed journal covering the scientific research on the flora and fauna of Africa. **Freq:** Annual. **Key Personnel:** Prof. F.O.I. Arene, Editor, phone 234 80 33387952, foiarene@yahoo.com; J.O. Lawal, Assoc. Ed.; A.S. Ali, Assoc. Ed. **ISSN:** 1119-023X. **Subscription Rates:** US$400 individuals. **URL:** http://ajol.info/index.php/ajazeb.

49166 ■ Journal of Applied Sciences and Environmental Management
African Journals Online
Department of Pure & Industrial Chemistry
University of Port Harcourt
PO Box 402
Choba
Port Harcourt, Rivers, Nigeria
Publisher E-mail: info@ajol.info
Peer-reviewed journal covering the effects of toxic from natural or synthetic chemicals occurring in the human environment to plants, animals or humans. **Freq:** Quarterly. **Key Personnel:** Dr. M. Horsfall, Exec. Ed., horsfalljnr@yahoo.com; Deborah O. Eromosele, Contact, editorjasem@yahoo.com. **ISSN:** 1119-8362. **URL:** http://ajol.info/index.php/jasem.

49167 ■ Journal of Modeling, Design & Management of Engineering Systems
African Journals Online
U.S. Department of of Chemical Engineering
University of Port Harcourt
PMB 5323
Port Harcourt, Rivers, Nigeria
Publisher E-mail: info@ajol.info
Peer-reviewed journal covering topics on engineering and related fields. **Freq:** Semiannual. **Key Personnel:** Dr. A.O. Kuye, Editor, jmdmes@atsyahoo.co.uk; Dr. Chika Oko, Editor. **ISSN:** 1596-3497. **Subscription Rates:** US$80 individuals; US$100 institutions. **URL:** http://ajol.info/index.php/jmdmes.

49168 ■ Journal of Technology and Education in Nigeria
African Journals Online
University of Port Harcourt
PMB 5323
Port Harcourt, Rivers, Nigeria
Publisher E-mail: info@ajol.info
Peer-reviewed journal covering agriculture, food science, technology/engineering, science and applied science, and vocational/technical education. **Freq:** Annual. **Key Personnel:** A.C. Agumagu, PhD, Editor-in-Chief, aceetee@yahoo.com; O.M. Adesope, PhD, Managing Editor, omadesope@yahoo.co.uk; Dr. B.O. Esonu, Assoc. Ed.; Dr. C.O. Anyim, Assoc. Ed.; Dr. C.I. Ezedinma, Assoc. Ed.; C.E. Orji, Assoc. Ed. **ISSN:** 1118-5570. **Subscription Rates:** N 600 individuals; N 900 institutions. **URL:** http://ajol.info/index.php/joten.

49169 ■ Port Harcourt Medical Journal
African Journals Online
27 Old Aba Rd.
PO Box 5575
Port Harcourt, Rivers, Nigeria
Publisher E-mail: info@ajol.info
Journal containing medical information about basic and clinical medicine, including dentistry. **Freq:** 3/yr. **Key Personnel:** Prof. N. Eke, Editor-in-Chief, pharcourtmedj@yahoo.com. **ISSN:** 0795-3038. **Subscription Rates:** N 2,000 individuals; N 5,000 institutions; US$50 other countries. **URL:** http://ajol.info/index.php/phmedj.

Sagamu

49170 ■ Nigerian Journal of Orthopaedics and Trauma
African Journals Online
P.M.B.
Sagamu, Ogun, Nigeria

Publisher E-mail: info@ajol.info
Peer-reviewed journal of orthopedics and trauma. **Freq:** Semiannual. **Key Personnel:** Loa Thanni, Editor-in-Chief, njotrauma@yahoo.com. **ISSN:** 1596-4582. **Subscription Rates:** US$30 individuals developing countries; US$40 institutions developing coutries; US$60 individuals developed countries; US$80 institutions developed countries. **URL:** http://ajol.info/index.php/njotra.

Shomolu

49171 ■ Nigerian Journal of Psychiatry
African Journals Online
PO Box 8869
Shomolu, Lagos, Nigeria
Publisher E-mail: info@ajol.info
Peer-reviewed journal covering all areas of psychiatry. **Freq:** 3/yr. **Key Personnel:** Dr. Gbenga Okulate, Contact, okulateus@yahoo.com. **ISSN:** 0189-1774. **Subscription Rates:** N 750 single issue. **URL:** http://ajol.info/index.php/njpsyc.

Sokoto

49172 ■ Annals of African Medicine
Bioline International
Usmanu Danfodiyo University Teaching Hospital
Sokoto, Sokoto, Nigeria
Ph: 234 602 31514
Fax: 234 602 31514
Publisher E-mail: bioline.international@utoronto.ca
Journal serving as a medium for the publication of research findings in the broad field of medicine in Africa and other developing countries, and elsewhere which have relevance to Africa. **Freq:** Semiannual. **Key Personnel:** Bello B. Shehu, Contact; P.M. Mshelbwala, Assoc. Ed.; Prof. Emmanuel A. Ameh, Editor-in-Chief. **ISSN:** 1596-3519. **Subscription Rates:** Rs 2,000 individuals; Rs 2,000 institutions; US$200 other countries; US$200 institutions, other countries. **URL:** http://ajol.info/index.php/aam; http://www.bioline.org.br/info?id=am&doc=about.

49173 ■ European Journal of General Medicine
Bioline International
Usmanu Danfodiyo University Teaching Hospital
Sokoto, Sokoto, Nigeria
Ph: 234 602 31514
Fax: 234 602 31514
Publisher E-mail: bioline.international@utoronto.ca
Peer-reviewed medical journal covering the fields of general medicine. **Freq:** Quarterly. **Key Personnel:** Kursat Uzun, MD, Editor-in-Chief; Reha Erkoc, Assoc. Ed.; Bekir Atik, Assoc. Ed. **ISSN:** 1304-3897. **URL:** http://www.ejgm.org.

49174 ■ Sahel Medical Journal
African Journals Online
Usmanu Danfodiyo University
Teaching Hospital
P.M.B. 2370
Sokoto, Sokoto, Nigeria
Publisher E-mail: info@ajol.info
Peer-reviewed journal focusing on information about medical sciences in Nigeria. **Freq:** Quarterly. **Print Method:** Offset. **Trim Size:** 6 1/2 x 9. **Cols./Page:** 2. **Col. Width:** 38 nonpareils. **Col. Depth:** 125 agate lines. **Key Personnel:** Prof. Simeon A. Isezuo, Editor-in-Chief, phone 234 60 860676, fax 234 60 231514, simeonisezuo@yahoo.com; Bello T. Saddique, Contact, uduthsmj98@yahoo.com. **ISSN:** 1118-8561. **Subscription Rates:** N 1,000 institutions; N 2,500 individuals; US$20 institutions Africa; US$75 individuals Africa; US$60 institutions, other countries; US$200 other countries; US$50 institutions Canada; US$150 individuals Canada. **URL:** http://ajol.info/index.php/smj2.

Umuahia

49175 ■ Nigerian Agricultural Journal
African Journals Online
National Root Crops Research Impute Umudike
PMB 7006
Umuahia, Nigeria
Publisher E-mail: info@ajol.info
Peer-reviewed journal covering agriculture in Nigeria and Africa. **Freq:** Annual. **Key Personnel:** Prof. C.F.I. Onwuka, Editor-in-Chief, chysonka@yahoo.com; Prof.

C.F.L. Onwuka, Dep. Ed.-in-Ch.; Dr. G.N. Asumugha, Business Mgr. **ISSN:** 0300-368X. **Subscription Rates:** US$100 institutions; US$50 individuals; US$30 students. **URL:** http://ajol.info/index.php/naj.

Uturu

49176 ■ Journal of Experimental and Clinical Anatomy
African Journals Online
Dept. of Anatomy
College of Medicine & Health Sciences
Abia State University
Uturu, Imo, Nigeria
Publisher E-mail: info@ajol.info
Peer-reviewed journal on experimental and clinical anatomy. **Founded:** 1827. **Freq:** 2/yr (June and December). **Print Method:** Offset. **Cols./Page:** 6. **Col. Width:** 25 nonpareils. **Col. Depth:** 301 agate lines. **Key Personnel:** Dr. C.I.P. Anibeze, Editor, phone 234 8033180232, fax 234 42452881, jeca2001ng@yahoo.com; Dr. G.E. Anyanwu, Editorial Asst.; Dr. HB Fawehinmi, Editorial Asst. **ISSN:** 1596-2393. **Subscription Rates:** US$50 elsewhere post free; N 500 individuals; N 1,000 individuals per volume; N 2,000 institutions per volume. **URL:** http://ajol.info/index.php/jeca.

49177 ■ Journal of Health and Visual Sciences
African Journals Online
U.S. Department of of Optometry
College of Medicine & Health Sciences
Abia State University
PMB 2000
Uturu, Imo, Nigeria
Publisher E-mail: info@ajol.info
Peer-reviewed journal covering various topics in the field of opthalmology and visual science. **Freq:** Semiannual. **Key Personnel:** Sam A. Igwe, Editor-in-Chief, nwosuigwe@yahoo.com. **ISSN:** 1119-2006. **URL:** http://ajol.info/index.php/jhvs.

Victoria Island

49178 ■ Lagos Business School Management Review
African Journals Online
Pan African University
2 Ahmed Onibudo St.
PO Box 73688
Victoria Island, Lagos, Nigeria
Publisher E-mail: info@ajol.info
Peer-reviewed journal containing information on management research relevant to Africa's economy. **Freq:** Semiannual. **Key Personnel:** Dr. Obinna Muogboh, Managing Editor, omuogboh@lbs.edu.ng; Christopher Kolade, Editor-in-Chief; Chantal Epie, Managing Editor. **ISSN:** 1118-3713. **Subscription Rates:** US$30 individuals; US$40 institutions. **URL:** http://ajol.info/index.php/lbsmr.

Yaba

49179 ■ Lagos Historical Review
African Journals Online
U.S. Department of of History & Strategic Studies, Rm. 401
Arts Block
University of Lagos
Akoka
Yaba, Lagos, Nigeria
Publisher E-mail: info@ajol.info
Peer-reviewed journal covering papers with a historical focus. **Freq:** Annual. **Key Personnel:** Dr. Funke Adeboye, Editor, funks29adeboye@yahoo.co.uk; Dr. Ademola Adeleke, Contact, sarlek@yahoo.com. **ISSN:** 1596-5031. **Subscription Rates:** US$35 individuals; US$45 institutions. **URL:** http://ajol.info/index.php/lhr.

49180 ■ Nigerian Libraries
African Journals Online
University Library
University of Lagos
Akoka
Yaba, Lagos, Nigeria
Publisher E-mail: info@ajol.info
Peer-reviewed journal covering library science information in Nigerian libraries. **Freq:** Semiannual. **Key Personnel:** Dr. S. Olajire Olanlokun, Editor-in-Chief, library@unilag.edu. **ISSN:** 0029-0122. **Subscription**

Rates: N 300 individuals; US$65 individuals Africa; US$60 other countries. **URL:** http://ajol.info/index.php/jnla.

Zaria

49181 ■ Annals of Nigerian Medicine
African Journals Online
c/o Dr. J.G. Makama, Ed.-in-Ch.
Ahmadu Bello University Teaching Hospital
Dept. of Paediatrics
Zaria, Kaduna, Nigeria
Ph: 234 803 7264939
Publisher E-mail: info@ajol.info
Peer-reviewed and medical journal. **Founded:** Apr. 1, 1974. **Freq:** Semiannual. **Print Method:** Offset. **Trim Size:** 9 3/4 x 15 1/2. **Cols./Page:** 5. **Col. Width:** 22 nonpareils. **Col. Depth:** 217 agate lines. **Key Personnel:** Dr. J.G. Makama, Editor-in-Chief, editorannigmed@yahoo.com; Dr. M. Ahmed, Dep. Ed., anmjournal@yahoo.com; Dr. M. Tanko, Assoc. Ed. **ISSN:** 0331-3131. **Subscription Rates:** N 1,500 individuals; N 2,500 institutions; US$25 individuals outside Nigeria; US$50 institutions outside Nigeria. **URL:** http://ajol.info/index.php/anmed.

49182 ■ Journal of Community Medicine and Primary Health Care
African Journals Online
U.S. Department of Community Medicine
Ahmadu Bello University
Zaria, Kaduna, Nigeria
Ph: 234 803 7175805
Publisher E-mail: info@ajol.info
Peer-reviewed journal covering all aspects of public health and primary health care. **Freq:** Semiannual. **Key Personnel:** Dr. Clara Ladi Ejembi, Editor-in-Chief, acpn_journal@yahoo.com; Dr. M.O. Araoye, Asst. Ed.-in-Ch. **ISSN:** 0794-7410. **URL:** http://ajol.info/index.php/jcmphc.

49183 ■ Nigerian Journal of Chemical Research
African Journals Online
U.S. Department of of Chemistry
Ahmadu Bello University
Zaria, Kaduna, Nigeria
Publisher E-mail: info@ajol.info
Peer-reviewed journal covering all areas of chemistry. **Freq:** Annual. **Key Personnel:** E.J. Ekanem, Editor-in-Chief, ngjnchres@yahoo.com. **Subscription Rates:** N 500 individuals. **URL:** http://ajol.info/index.php/njcr.

49184 ■ Nigerian Journal of Soil & Environmental Research
African Journals Online
Department of Soil Science/IAE
Ahmadu Bello University
Zaria, Kaduna, Nigeria
Publisher E-mail: info@ajol.info
Peer-reviewed journal concerned with soils and environmental issues of tropical interest. **Founded:** 1958. **Freq:** Annual. **Print Method:** Letterpress. **Cols./Page:** 2. **Col. Width:** 40 nonpareils. **Col. Depth:** 128 agate lines. **Key Personnel:** Prof. E.N.O. Iwuafor, Contact, phone 234 803 7871804, enoiwuafor@yahoo.com. **ISSN:** 1595-6121. **Subscription Rates:** N 500 individuals per copy; US$10 individuals per copy. **URL:** http://ajol.info/index.php/njser. **Formerly:** Nigerian Journal of Soil Research.

49185 ■ Nigerian Journal of Surgical Research
The Nigerian Journal of Surgical Research
c/o Pediatric Surgery Unit
Ahmadu Bello University Teaching Hospital
Zaria, Kaduna, Nigeria
Ph: 234 69 333 311
Fax: 234 69 334 150
Publisher E-mail: info@njsr.net
Journal covering developments and advances in the field of surgery and related clinical and basic sciences in Nigeria and the rest of Africa. **Founded:** 1922. **Freq:** Quarterly. **Print Method:** Offset. **Cols./Page:** 5. **Col. Width:** 28 nonpareils. **Col. Depth:** 195 agate lines. **Key**

Personnel: Emmanuel A. Ameh, Editor-in-Chief, ssrsnjsr@skannet.com. **ISSN:** 1595-1103. **Subscription Rates:** US$60 other countries; N 4,000 individuals. **URL:** http://www.bioline.org.br/sr.

49186 ■ Nigerian Veterinary Journal
African Journals Online
Ahmadu Bello University
Main Campus, Samaru
Zaria, Kaduna, Nigeria
Publisher E-mail: info@ajol.info
Peer-reviewed journal covering Nigerian veterinary medicine. **Founded:** 1971. **Freq:** Semiannual. **Print Method:** Offset. **Trim Size:** 8 1/4 x 10 3/4. **Cols./Page:** 3. **Col. Width:** 13.5 picas. **Col. Depth:** 58 picas. **Key Personnel:** Dr. S.V.O. Shoyinka, Editor-in-Chief; Dr. M.C.O. Eziebe, Asst. Ed.-in-Ch.; Dr. B.D. Remi-Adewumi, Editor-in-Chief, nvj3003@yahoo.com. **ISSN:** 0331-3026. **Subscription Rates:** N 2,000 institutions including postage and handling; US$100 institutions including postage and handling; N 500 individuals including postage and handling; US$25 individuals including postage and handling. **URL:** http://ajol.info/index.php/nvj.

49187 ■ Samaru Journal of Information Studies
African Journals Online
U.S. Department of of Library & Information Science
Ahmadu Bello University
Zaria, Kaduna, Nigeria
Publisher E-mail: info@ajol.info
Peer-reviewed journal covering the field of library and information science. **Freq:** Semiannual. **Key Personnel:** Prof. Zakari Mohammed, Editor-in-Chief, zakmoh2000@yahoo.com; Ezra Shiloba Gbaje, Shiloba@yahoo.com; John Agada, PhD, Consulting Ed. **ISSN:** 1596-5414. **Subscription Rates:** N 1000 individuals; US$12 other countries; N 1,500 institutions; US$30 institutions, other countries. **URL:** http://ajol.info/index.php/sjis.

Circulation: ★ = ABC; △ = BPA; ♦ = CAC; • = CCAB; ❑ = VAC; ⊕ = PO Statement; ‡ = Publisher's Report; Boldface figures = sworn; Light figures = estimated.

Gale Directory of Publications & Broadcast Media/147th Ed.   5313

Baerum

49188 ■ The Norway Post
Idomeneo A.S.
Holmaveien 21
PO Box 25
1306 Baerum
N-1306 Baerum, Norway
Ph: 47 671 76875
Fax: 47 671 76851
Online, English language general newspaper. **Key Personnel:** Rolleiv Solholm, Editor-in-Chief, phone 47 67176850, fax 47 67176851. **Remarks:** Accepts advertising. **URL:** http://www.norwaypost.no/. **Circ:** (Not Reported)

49189 ■ SkiSport
Ski Forum A/S
Postboks 6
Post Terminal
N-1306 Baerum, Norway
Publisher E-mail: skisport@skisport.no
Consumer magazine covering Nordic and Alpine skiing. **Founded:** 1948. **Freq:** 8/yr. **Print Method:** Offset. **Key Personnel:** Allan Aabech, Editor; Ellen Aabech, Contact. **ISSN:** 0333-3973. **Subscription Rates:** 390 individuals; 530 other countries. **Remarks:** Accepts advertising. **URL:** http://www.skisport.no. **Former name:** Skiidrett; Ski; SkiSport/Ski Forum AS. **Ad Rates:** BW: 10,000 NKr, 4C: 14,000 NKr. **Circ:** 10,000

Bergen

49190 ■ Aquaculture Nutrition
John Wiley & Sons Inc.
Wiley-Blackwell
c/o Dr. Rune Waagbo, Ed.-in-Ch.
National Institute of Nutrition & Seafood Research (NIFES)
PO Box 2029
N-5817 Bergen, Norway
Publication E-mail: an@nifes.no
Journal focusing on the nutrition of all cultivated aquatic animals. **Freq:** Bimonthly. **Key Personnel:** Dr. Rune Waagbo, Editor-in-Chief; Dr. Gro-Ingunn Hemre, Editor, gro-ingunn.hemre@nifes.no; Gordon Bell, Editorial Board; George Kissil, Editorial Board; Kari Ruohonen, Editorial Board. **ISSN:** 1353-5773. **Subscription Rates:** US$370 individuals print and online; US$114 members print and online (KAS); US$1,215 institutions print and online; US$1,104 institutions print or online; 660 institutions print and online; EUR301 individuals print and online; EUR103 members print and online (KAS); EUR838 institutions print and online; EUR761 institutions print or online; US$1,418 institutions, other countries print and online. **Remarks:** Accepts advertising. **URL:** http://www.wiley.com/bw/journal.asp?ref=1353-5773&site=1. **Circ:** (Not Reported)

49191 ■ Scandinavian Journal of Immunology
John Wiley & Sons Inc.
Wiley-Blackwell
Broegelmann Research Laboratory
The Gade Institute
University of Bergen
Armauer Hansen Bldg.
N-5021 Bergen, Norway
Ph: 47 55974648
Fax: 47 55975817
Publication E-mail: sji@gades.uib.no
Peer-reviewed journal focusing on the field of immune reactions covering investigations from all over the world. **Freq:** Monthly. **Key Personnel:** J.B. Natvig, Sen. Advisory Board; R. Jonsson, Editor-in-Chief, roland.jonsson@gades.uib.no; J.D. Capra, Sen. Advisory Board; Z. Dembic, Assoc. Ed.; M. Harboe, Sen. Advisory Board; S. Meri, Assoc. Ed.; H.G. Ljunggren, Dep. Ed.-in-Ch., hans-gustaf.ljunggren@ki.se; P. Garred, Assoc. Ed.; P. Brandtzaeg, Sen. Advisory Board; W. Agace, Editorial Board; O. Bakke, Editorial Board. **ISSN:** 0300-9475. **Subscription Rates:** US$50 members print + online, EUR45 members print + online; 30 members print + online; US$1,752 institutions print + online; US$1,365 institutions print, online; 894 institutions print + online; EUR1,136 institutions print + online; EUR1,033 institutions print, online; US$1,752 institutions, other countries print + online; US$1,593 institutions, other countries print + online. **URL:** http://www.wiley.com/bw/journal.asp?ref=0300-9475&site=1.

Jar

49192 ■ Kulde Skandinavia
Kuldeforlaget
Marielundsveien 5
N-1358 Jar, Norway
Ph: 47 671 20659
Fax: 47 671 2061790
Publication E-mail: postmaster@kulde.biz
Trade magazine covering refrigeration and heat pumps. **Founded:** 1984. **Freq:** Bimonthly. **Print Method:** Offset. **Trim Size:** 210 x 296 mm. **Cols./Page:** 4. **Col. Width:** 42 millimeters. **Key Personnel:** Ase Rostad, Advertising Mgr., ase.rostad@kulde.biz; Halvor Rostad, Editor, rostad@kulde.biz. **ISSN:** 0801-7093. **Subscription Rates:** 450 NKr individuals. **Remarks:** Accepts advertising. **URL:** http://www.kulde.biz. **Ad Rates:** BW: 2 NKr, 4C: 2 NKr. **Circ:** Controlled 3,550

Moss

49193 ■ Byggaktuelt
Reed Business Information Norway A.S.
Vaerftsgata 7
Postboks 1024
N-1510 Moss, Norway
Ph: 47 699 12400
Publication E-mail: info@reedbusiness.no
Publisher E-mail: firmapost@reedbusiness.no
Trade magazine for the building and construction industry. **Founded:** Sept. 1985. **Print Method:** Offset. **Trim Size:** 185 x 270 mm. **Cols./Page:** 4. **Col. Width:** 43 millimeters. **Key Personnel:** Pal Engeseth, Contact, ple@reedbusiness.no; Anton Granhus, Contact, axg@reedbusiness.no. **ISSN:** 0800-7713. **URL:** http://www.byggaktuelt.no. **Circ:** Combined 12,445

Nesbru

49194 ■ SEIL Magasinet
MediaNavigering A.S.
PO Box 253
N-1379 Nesbru, Norway
Ph: 47 66 774060
Fax: 47 66 774061
Publication E-mail: morten.jensen@seilmagasinet.no
Publisher E-mail: post@seilmagainet.no
Consumer magazine covering sailing. **Founded:** 1975. **Freq:** Biennial. **Print Method:** Offset. **Trim Size:** 198 x 269 mm. **Cols./Page:** 4. **Col. Width:** 46 millimeters. **Col. Depth:** 269 millimeters. **ISSN:** 1501-8105. **Subscription Rates:** 659 NKr individuals. **Remarks:** Accepts advertising. **URL:** http://www.seilmagasinet.no. **Circ:** Combined 16,000

Oslo

49195 ■ Climate Research
Inter-Research Science Center
Centre for Ecological & Evolutionary Synthesis (CEES)
Dept. of Biology, University of Oslo
Blindern
PO Box 1066
N-0316 Oslo, Norway
Ph: 47 22 854584
Fax: 47 22 854001
Publisher E-mail: ir@int-res.com
Journal focusing on the effects of climate on human life and ecosystems, dealing with environmental sciences. **Key Personnel:** Mikhail A. Semenov, Editor-in-Chief, mikhail.semenov@bbsrc.ac.uk; Nils Chr. Stenseth, Editor-in-Chief, n.c.stenseth@bio.uio.no; Bryson C. Bates, Editor, bryson.batesat@csiro.au. **ISSN:** 0936-577X. **Subscription Rates:** EUR796 individuals print and online; EUR816 individuals Germany; EUR842 other countries air mail; EUR716 individuals online only. **URL:** http://www.int-res.com/journals/cr/.

49196 ■ Dagens Naeringsliv
Norges Handels & Sjofartstidende
Christian Krohgs gate 16
PO Box 1182
Sentrum
N-0107 Oslo, Norway
Ph: 47 22001000
Business publication. **Freq:** Daily. **Key Personnel:** Amund Djuve, Ed.-in-Ch./Mng. Dir., amund.djuve@dn.no; Gunnar Bjorkavag, CEO. **URL:** http://www.dn.no/avis/; http://www.nhst.no/dn/. **Circ:** 79,628

49197 ■ European Journal of Behavior Analysis
Norsk Atferdsanalytisk Forening
Kapellveien 6
N-0487 Oslo, Norway
Ph: 47 33 806570
Fax: 47 21 012449
Journal for the original publication of experimental reports and theoretical/conceptual papers relevant to the analysis of the behavior of individual organisms. **Freq:** Semiannual. **Key Personnel:** Erik Arntzen, Editor, erik.arntzen@equivalence.net; Arne Brekstad, Editor, arne.brekstad@psykologi.uio.no; Julie Vargas, Editorial Board; Per Holth, Editor, per.holth@hiak.no; Dermot Holmes Barnes, Editorial Board; F.C. Mace, Editorial Board; Terje Sagvolden, Editorial Board; Bryan Roche, Editorial Board. **ISSN:** 1502-1149. **Subscription Rates:**

100 NKr individuals; US$12 individuals; EUR13 individuals. **URL:** http://www.ejoba.org/.

49198 ■ Flynytt
Norsk Aero Klubb
Radhusgaten 5B
Postboks 383
Sentrum
N-0102 Oslo, Norway
Ph: 47 230 10450
Fax: 47 230 10451
Publication E-mail: flynytt@nak.no
Publisher E-mail: post@nlf.no
Journal covering aviation and military issues. **Founded:** 1933. **URL:** http://www.nak.no/flynytt/. **Circ:** Combined 5,200

49199 ■ Frisor
Norges Frisormester Forbund
Postboks 7071
N-0306 Oslo, Norway
Ph: 47 230 87960
Fax: 47 230 87970
Publisher E-mail: nff@nff.no
Trade magazine for hair dressers and salon owners. **Founded:** 1901. **Freq:** Bimonthly. **Key Personnel:** Olav Eikemo, Director, phone 47 23087963, olav.eikemo@nffs.no; Jarl M. Garder, Editor, phone 47 230 87961, jarl.m.garder@nffs.no. **Remarks:** Accepts advertising. **URL:** http://www.nffs.no. **Ad Rates:** BW: 119 NKr, 4C: 147 NKr. **Circ:** Paid 2,500, Non-paid 10,000

49200 ■ Hold Pusten
Norsk Radiografforbund
Radhusgata 4
N-0105 Oslo, Norway
Ph: 47 23100470
Fax: 47 23100480
Publisher E-mail: nrf@radlograf.no
Professional magazine of the Norwegian Radiographers Association covering radiography. **Founded:** Mar. 1974. **Freq:** Monthly. **Print Method:** Offset. **Trim Size:** 210 x 297 mm. **Cols./Page:** 3. **Col. Width:** 57 millimeters. **Col. Depth:** 260 millimeters. **Key Personnel:** Ola Jacob Amundsen, Editor; Anne Lise Faengsrud, Contact, anne-lise@addmedia.no. **ISSN:** 0332-9410. **Remarks:** Accepts advertising. **URL:** http://katalogen.fagpressen.no/blader/0048.html. **Ad Rates:** BW: 6,800 NKr, 4C: 8,800 NKr. **Circ:** Combined ‡1,970

49201 ■ Liberalt Forum
Liberal Party of Norway
Venstre
Moellergaten 16
N-0179 Oslo, Norway
Ph: 47 22 404350
Fax: 47 22 404351
Publisher E-mail: venstre@venstre.no
Norwegian language publication covering political parties. **Freq:** Biweekly. **Remarks:** Advertising accepted; rates available upon request. **URL:** http://www.venstre.no/sentralt/organisasjon/. **Circ:** (Not Reported)

49202 ■ Meieriposten
Norske Meierifolks Landsforening
Postboks 9370
Gronland
N-0135 Oslo, Norway
Ph: 47 230 02710
Publication E-mail: meieriposten@nml.no
Publisher E-mail: firmapost@nml.no
Trade magazine covering the dairy and ice cream industry in Norway and elsewhere. **Founded:** 1914. **Freq:** Monthly except July. **Trim Size:** 185 x 260 mm. **Cols./Page:** 3. **Col. Width:** 58 millimeters. **Key Personnel:** Jostein Kolberg, Editor, jostein.kolberg@nml.no. **ISSN:** 0025-8776. **Subscription Rates:** 480 NKr individuals; 680 NKr out of country by airmail. **Remarks:** Accepts advertising. **URL:** http://www.nml.no/Default.asp?WCI=DisplayGroup&WCE=21&DGI=21. **Ad Rates:** BW: 4,400 NKr, 4C: 8,240 NKr, PCI: 9 NKr. **Circ:** Paid 2,050

49203 ■ Microporous and Mesoporous Materials
Elsevier Science
c/o Michael Stocker, Ed.-in-Ch.
SINTEF Materials & Chemistry
PO Box 124
Blindern
N-0314 Oslo, Norway
Ph: 47 400 03730

Fax: 47 220 67350
Publisher E-mail: nlinfo-f@elsevier.com
Journal covering all aspects of porous solids classified as either microporous (pore width up to 2 nm) or mesoporous (pore width ca.2 to ca.50 nm). **Freq:** 30/yr. **Key Personnel:** Michael Stocker, Editor-in-Chief, michael.stocker@sintef.no; K. Kuroda, Editor, kuroda@waseda.jp; J. Weitkamp, Founding Ed. **ISSN:** 1387-1811. **Subscription Rates:** US$3,916 institutions all countries except Europe and Japan; EUR3,500 institutions for Europe; 465,100¥ institutions for Europe; EUR378 individuals for Europe; 50,900¥ individuals; US$425 individuals all countries except Europe and Japan. **Remarks:** Accepts advertising. **URL:** http://www.elsevier.com/wps/find/journaldescription.cws_home/600760/description. **Circ:** (Not Reported)

49204 ■ Monitor 21
Program for Research and Documentation for a Sustainable Society
University of Oslo
PO Box 1116
Blindern
N-0317 Oslo, Norway
Ph: 47 228 58900
Fax: 47 228 58790
Publisher E-mail: informasjon@prosus.uio.no
Publication covering the future. **Subtitle:** Et Informasionsblad on Bcerelaftig Utrililing. **Freq:** Quarterly. **ISSN:** 1502-5381. **Remarks:** Advertising not accepted. **URL:** http://www.prosus.uio.no/info/m21/index.htm. **Circ:** (Not Reported)

49205 ■ The Norseman
The Norse Federation
Nordmanns-Forbundet
Radhusgaten 23 B
NO-0158 Oslo, Norway
Ph: 47 233 57170
Fax: 47 233 57175
Publisher E-mail: norseman@norseman.no
English and Norwegian language publication covering Norway. **Freq:** 5/yr (Jan., March, May, Sept. (2 issues), & Nov.). **Key Personnel:** Bjarne Bore, Editor-in-Chief. **ISSN:** 0029-1846. **Remarks:** Advertising accepted; rates available upon request. **URL:** http://www.norseman.no. **Circ:** (Not Reported)

49206 ■ Posthornet
Mollergaten 10
N-0179 Oslo, Norway
Ph: 47 23061561
Fax: 47 23062271
Publisher E-mail: post@aktuell.no
Trade magazine covering the postal organization in Norway. **Freq:** Monthly. **Trim Size:** 246 x 370 mm. **Cols./Page:** 6. **Col. Width:** 36.8 millimeters. **Col. Depth:** 370 millimeters. **Key Personnel:** Kristian Brustad, Contact, kristian.brustad@lomedia.no. **Subscription Rates:** Free. **Remarks:** Accepts advertising. **URL:** http://www.frifagbevegelse.no/aktuell/posthornet/. **Circ:** Non-paid 31,000

49207 ■ Scandinavian Journal of Disability Research
Routledge
Taylor & Francis Group Ltd.
NOVA Norwegian Social Research
PO Box 3223
Elisenberg
Oslo, Norway
Ph: 47 2254 1286
Fax: 47 2254 1201
Publisher E-mail: webmaster.books@tandf.co.uk
Peer-reviewed journal aiming to disseminate leading social research on disability, focusing on the relation between persons with disabilities and their environments, incorporating research from a variety of perspectives including: educational, sociological, sociopsychological, historical, legal, economical and sociomedical. **Freq:** 4/yr. **Key Personnel:** John Eriksen, Editor; Anita Ghai, Consulting Ed.; Robert C. Bogdan, Consulting Ed.; Hilary Brown, Consulting Ed.; Per Solvang, Book Review Ed.; Ingemar Emanuelsson, Consulting Ed.; Marcel Calvez, Consulting Ed.; Lars Grue, Consulting Ed.; Erland Hjelmquist, Consulting Ed. **ISSN:** 1501-7419. **Subscription Rates:** US$153 institutions online; 92 institutions online; US$80 individuals; 49 individuals; US$161 institutions print + online; 97 institutions print + online; EUR129 institutions print and online; EUR123 institutions online only; EUR63 individuals. **Re-**

marks: Accepts advertising. **URL:** http://www.tandf.co.uk/journals/titles/15017419.asp. **Circ:** (Not Reported)

49208 ■ Scandinavian Journal of Educational Research
Routledge
Taylor & Francis Group Ltd.
c/o Dr. Oyvind Lund Martinsen, Ed.
Institute for Leadership & Organizational Management
Norwegian Scholarship of Management
Nydalsveien 37
N-0442 Oslo, Norway
Publisher E-mail: webmaster.books@tandf.co.uk
Peer-reviewed journal focusing on central ideas and themes in educational thinking and research. **Freq:** Bimonthly. **Key Personnel:** Prof. Edmund Edvardsen, Editorial Board; Prof. Berit Askling, Editorial Board; Prof. Ingrid Calgren, Editorial Board; Prof. Oyvind Lund Martinsen, Editor; Prof. Sven Erik Nordenbo, National Ed.; Prof. Marja-Leena Stenstrom, National Ed. **ISSN:** 0031-3831. **Subscription Rates:** 677 institutions print + online; US$1,123 institutions print + online; 643 institutions online; US$1,067 institutions online; 195 individuals; US$325 individuals; EUR894 institutions print and online; EUR850 institutions online only; EUR259 individuals. **URL:** http://www.tandf.co.uk/journals/titles/00313831.asp.

49209 ■ Transportforum
Transportbedriftenes Landsforening
PO Box 5477, Majorstuen
N-0305 Oslo, Norway
Ph: 47 23088600
Fax: 47 23088601
Publication E-mail: transportforum@transport.no
Publisher E-mail: tl@transport.no
Trade magazine covering the transportation industry in Norway, including bus, trucks, and light rail. **Founded:** 1929. **Freq:** Monthly 11/yr. **Print Method:** Offset. **Trim Size:** 210 x 297 mm. **Key Personnel:** Marit Grottheim, Editor-in-Chief, marit.grottheim@transport.no. **Subscription Rates:** 490 NKr individuals. **Remarks:** Accepts advertising. **URL:** http://www.transport.no/tf. **Ad Rates:** BW: 10,750 NKr, 4C: 15,850 NKr. **Circ:** Combined 5,000

49210 ■ Universitas
University of Oslo
Student Organizations, Universitas
Boks 89
Blindern
N-0314 Oslo, Norway
Ph: 47 22 853336
Fax: 47 22 853274
Publication E-mail: universitas@studorg.uio.no
Student newspaper. **Founded:** 1949. **Freq:** 34/yr. **Key Personnel:** Aksel Kjaer Vidnes, Editor, a.k.vidnes@universitas.uio.no. **URL:** http://universitas.no/. **Circ:** Controlled 15,000

Sogndal

49211 ■ Nordic Journal of Music Therapy
Sogn og Fjordane Univiversity College
PO Box 133
Sogndal, Norway
Ph: 47 576 76000
Fax: 47 576 76100
Publisher E-mail: post@hisf.no
Peer-reviewed journal publishing articles on music therapy in the Nordic countries of Denmark, Finland, Iceland, Norway and Sweden and the Baltic Countries of Estonia, Latvia and Lithuania. **Founded:** 1992. **Freq:** Semiannual. **Key Personnel:** Dr. Christian Gold, Editor-in-Chief, christian.gold@uni.no; Dr. Cochavit Elefant, Assoc. Ed., cochavit.elefant@grieg.uib.no. **ISSN:** 0809-8131. **Subscription Rates:** US$80 individuals print only; US$338 individuals online only; US$375 individuals print & online. **Remarks:** Accepts advertising. **URL:** http://njmt.b.uib.no: **Ad Rates:** BW: 1,800 NKr. **Circ:** (Not Reported)

Stabekk

49212 ■ Banneret
Det Norske Baptistsamfunn
Micheletsvei 62c
N-1368 Stabekk, Norway
Ph: 47 67 103560
Fax: 47 67 103569
Publication E-mail: banneret.redaksjon@baptist.no

Publisher E-mail: post@baptist.no
Magazine covering news for members of the Baptist Union. **Founded:** 1879. **Freq:** Monthly. **Trim Size:** Offset. **Cols./Page:** 3. **Col. Width:** 50 millimeters. **Key Personnel:** Roger Dahl, Editor. **Subscription Rates:** 450 NKr individuals. **URL:** http://www.baptist.no/php/news_cats.php?cat_id=21.

Stavange

49213 ■ International Journal of Strategic Engineering Asset Management
Inderscience Enterprises Limited
c/o Prof. Jayantha P. Liyanage, Ed.-in-Ch.
University of Stavanger
Centre for Industrial Asset Management
Faculty of Science & Technology
N-4036 Stavange, Norway
Journal focusing on engineering asset management. **Freq:** 4/yr. **Key Personnel:** Prof. Jayantha P. Liyanage, Editor-in-Chief, j.p.liyanage@uis.no. **ISSN:** 1759-9733. **Subscription Rates:** EUR494 individuals print or online; EUR672 individuals print and online. **URL:** http://www.inderscience.com/browse/index.php?journalID=348.

Tromso

49214 ■ Polar Research
John Wiley & Sons Inc.
Wiley-Blackwell
c/o Helle V. Goldman, Ch. Ed.
Norwegian Polar Institute
Polar Environmental Centre
N-9296 Tromso, Norway
Ph: 47 77 750618
Fax: 47 77 750501
Peer-reviewed journal covering research in all scientific disciplines relevant to the polar regions. **Freq:** 3/yr. **Key Personnel:** Helle V. Goldman, Ch. Ed., goldman@npolar.no. **ISSN:** 0800-0395. **Subscription Rates:** US$500 institutions Americas (print and online); EUR312 institutions Europe (print and online); 246 institutions UK (print and online); US$483 institutions, other countries print and online; US$450 institutions Americas (online only); EUR282 institutions Europe (online only); 450 institutions UK (online only); US$435 institutions, other countries online only. **URL:** http://www.wiley.com/bw/journal.asp?ref=0800-0395.

Trondheim

49215 ■ Acta Anaesthesiologica Scandinavica
John Wiley & Sons Inc.

Wiley-Blackwell
c/o Sven Erik Gisvold
Dept. of Anaesthesia
St. Olav Hospital
University Hospital of Trondheim
N-7006 Trondheim, Norway
Ph: 47 73868108
Fax: 47 73868117
International Journal focusing on anaesthesiology and intensive care, pain, and emergency medicine. **Subtitle:** An International Journal of Anaesthesiology and Intensive Care, Pain and Emergency Medicine. **Founded:** 1957. **Freq:** 10/yr. **Key Personnel:** Lars S. Rasmussen, Editor-in-Chief, lars.rasmussen@rh.regionh.dk; Seppo Alahuhta, Editorial Board, phone 358 8 3152262, fax 358 8 3155577, seppo.alahuhta@oulo.fi; Anne Berit Guttormsen, Editorial Board, phone 47 95890534, fax 47 55976898, anne.guttormsen@helse-bergen.no. **ISSN:** 0001-5172. **Subscription Rates:** US$256 members print and online (Americas); US$583 institutions print and online (Americas); US$530 institutions print (Americas); 346 institutions print and online; 152 members print and online (other countries); US$680 institutions, other countries print and online; US$617 institutions, other countries print; EUR400 institutions print; EUR228 members print and online; EUR440 institutions print and online. **Remarks:** Accepts advertising. **URL:** http://www.wiley.com/bw/submit.asp?ref=0001-5172&site=1. **Circ:** (Not Reported)

49216 ■ International Journal of Computational Intelligence Research
Research India Publications
c/o A. Abraham, PhD, Ed.-in-Ch.
Norwegian University of Science & Technology
Trondheim, Norway
Publisher E-mail: info@ripublication.com
Journal covering research on computational intelligence in theoretical and methodological aspects, and its applications. **Founded:** Mar. 1977. **Freq:** 4/yr. **Print Method:** Offset. **Trim Size:** 7 7/8 x 10 1/2. **Cols./Page:** 3. **Key Personnel:** A. Abraham, PhD, Editor-in-Chief. **ISSN:** 0973-1873. **Subscription Rates:** US$380 institutions and library; print plus online free; US$360 institutions and library; online only; US$160 individuals print plus online free; US$140 individuals online only; Rs 1,800 individuals. **URL:** http://www.ripublication.com/ijcir.htm.

49217 ■ International Journal of Grid & Utility Computing
Inderscience Publishers

c/o Prof. Ajith Abraham, Ed.-in-Ch.
O.S. Bragstads plass 2E
NO-7491 Trondheim, Norway
Publisher E-mail: editor@inderscience.com
Peer-reviewed journal covering grid and utility computing technology. **Founded:** 2005. **Freq:** 4/yr. **Key Personnel:** Prof. Ajith Abraham, Editor-in-Chief, ajith.abraham@ieee.org; Prof. Vaclav Snasel, Editor-in-Chief, vaclav.snasel@vsb.cz; Dr. Florin Pop, Managing Editor, florin.pop@cs.pub.ro. **ISSN:** 1741-847X. **Subscription Rates:** EUR494 individuals includes surface mail, print only; EUR672 individuals print and online. **URL:** http://www.inderscience.com/browse/index.php?journalCODE=ijguc.

49218 ■ Nordic Journal for Architectural Research
Nordic Association for Architectural Research
Faculty for Architecture & Fine Arts
The Norwegian University of Science & Technology
NTNU
N-7491 Trondheim, Norway
Ph: 47 735 95007
Publisher E-mail: eivind.kasa@ark.ntnu.no
Journal covering Nordic architectural research. **Freq:** Quarterly. **Key Personnel:** Ruth Woods, Editor; Eivind Kasa, Editor; Jerker Lundequist, Editor; Birgit Cold, Editor. **Subscription Rates:** 310 NKr individuals; 215 NKr students. **Remarks:** Accepts advertising. **URL:** http://www.arkitekturforskning.net. **Circ:** (Not Reported)

49219 ■ Norsk Geologisk Tidsskrift
Taylor & Francis Group Journals
Dept. of Geography
Norwegian University of Science & Technology
7491 Trondheim, Norway
Publisher E-mail: customerservice@taylorandfrancis.com
Journal providing information about human geography. **Subtitle:** Norwegian Journal of Geography. **Freq:** Quarterly. **Print Method:** Offset. **Cols./Page:** 6. **Col. Width:** 21 nonpareils. **Col. Depth:** 126 agate lines. **Key Personnel:** Michael Jones, Editor-in-Chief; Ivar Berthling, Co-Ed.; Anders Lundberg, Co-Ed. **ISSN:** 0029-1951. **Subscription Rates:** 162 institutions print and online; 154 institutions online; 79 individuals; US$268 institutions print and online; US$255 institutions online; US$131 individuals; EUR213 institutions print and online; EUR203 institutions online only; EUR105 individuals. **URL:** http://www.tandf.co.uk/journals/titles/00291951.asp.

Circulation: ★ = ABC; △ = BPA; ◆ = CAC; • = CCAB; ❑ = VAC; ⊕ = PO Statement; ‡ = Publisher's Report; Boldface figures = sworn; Light figures = estimated.

Muscat

49220 ■ Business Today
Apex Publishing
PO Box 2616
Muscat 112, Oman
Ph: 968 247 99388
Fax: 968 247 93316
Journal covering business and economics. **Founded:** 1998. **Freq:** Monthly. **Key Personnel:** Charles F. Kettering, Editor; Mohana Prabhakar, Managing Editor. **Subscription Rates:** 18 Rlo individuals 12 issues; US$36 individuals 24 issues; US$55 other countries. **Remarks:** Accepts advertising. **URL:** http://www.businesstoday.co.om/; http://www.apexstuff.com/bt/200702/index.asp. **Circ:** (Not Reported)

49221 ■ International Journal of Food Properties
Taylor & Francis Group Journals
Dept. of Food Science & Nutrition
College of Agricultural & Marine Sciences
Sultan Qaboos University
PO Box 34, Al Khod 123
Muscat, Oman
Publisher E-mail: customerservice@taylorandfrancis.com
Journal focusing on all scientific and applied aspects of food properties. **Freq:** Quarterly. **Key Personnel:** Shafiur M. Rahman, Editor-in-Chief; K.A. Buckle, Editorial Board; X.D. Chen, Editorial Board; S.I. Ali, Editorial Board; K. Chang, Editorial Board; Bhesh Bhandari, Editorial Board; G.V. Barbosa-Canovas, Editorial Board; M.O. Balaban, Editorial Board; M. Barigou, Editorial Board; Shyam S. Sablani, Assoc. Ed. **ISSN:** 1094-2912. **Subscription Rates:** 1,056 institutions print + online; US$1,746 institutions print + online; 1,004 institutions online; 255 individuals personal; US$423 individuals personal; US$1,659 institutions online; EUR1,389 institutions print and online; EUR1,320 institutions online only; EUR338 individuals. **URL:** http://www.tandf.co.uk/journals/titles/10942912.asp.

49222 ■ Oman Daily Observer
The Oman Establishment for Press, News, Publication and Advertising
PO Box 974
Muscat 113, Oman
Publication E-mail: editor@omanobserver.com
Newspaper. **Founded:** 1981. **Freq:** Daily. **Key Personnel:** Ibrahim Bin Saif Al Hamdani, Editor-in-Chief. **Remarks:** Accepts advertising. **URL:** http://omanobserver.com/. **Circ:** (Not Reported)

49223 ■ Oman Today
Apex Publishing
PO Box 2616
Muscat 112, Oman
Ph: 968 247 99388
Fax: 968 247 93316
General interest periodical. **Founded:** 1980. **Freq:** Monthly. **Key Personnel:** Emma Ventura, Editor. **Subscription Rates:** US$45 individuals Gulf Countries (via airmail); 10 Rlo individuals in Oman; US$57 other countries by airmail. **Remarks:** Accepts advertising. **URL:** http://www.apexstuff.com/; http://www.apexstuff.com/ot/200709/index.asp. **Circ:** Paid 40,000

49224 ■ Oman Tribune
PO Box 463
Muscat 113, Oman
Ph: 968 24491919
Fax: 968 24498444
Publication E-mail: webmaster@omantribune.com
Publisher E-mail: eomantribune@mantribune.com
Newspaper covering news and events in Oman. **Freq:** Daily. **Key Personnel:** Abdul Hamied Bin Suleiman Al Taie, Editor-in-Chief; Ajith Das, News Ed. **Remarks:** Accepts advertising. **URL:** http://www.omantribune.com/. **Circ:** (Not Reported)

49225 ■ Times of Oman
Muscat Press and Publishing House
PO Box 770
Ruwi
Muscat 112, Oman
Ph: 968 24811953
Fax: 968 24813153
Publication E-mail: online@timesofoman.com
Newspaper. **Founded:** 1975. **Freq:** Daily. **Key Personnel:** Essa Bin Mohammed Al-Zedjali, Founder/Chm./Ed.-in-Ch. **Remarks:** Accepts advertising. **URL:** http://www.timesofoman.com/. **Ad Rates:** BW: 1,590 Rlo, 4C: 3,180 Rlo. **Circ:** 20,000

Ruwi

49226 ■ Al Ghorfa
Oman Chamber of Commerce and Industry
PO Box 1400
Ruwi 112, Oman
Ph: 968 24707674
Fax: 968 24708497
Publication E-mail: alghorfa@chamberoman.com
Publisher E-mail: occi@chamberoman.com
Arabic language publication covering chambers of commerce, with some English-language articles. **Founded:** 1978. **Freq:** Bimonthly. **Trim Size:** A4. **Key Personnel:** Hilal bin Khamis Al Naqbi, Editor; Khalil bin Abdullah Al Khnji, Editor-in-Chief; Hamoud bin Hamad Al Mahrouqi, Managing Editor. **Subscription Rates:** Free. **Remarks:** Accepts advertising. **URL:** http://www.chamberoman.com/. **Ad Rates:** 4C: US$780. **Circ:** Non-paid 10,500

Circulation: ★ = ABC; △ = BPA; ◆ = CAC; • = CCAB; ❑ = VAC; ⊕ = PO Statement; ‡ = Publisher's Report; Boldface figures = sworn; Light figures = estimated.

Gale Directory of Publications & Broadcast Media/147th Ed.   5319

Abbottabad

49227 ■ Journal of Ayub Medical College
Ayub Medical College
Karakoram Hwy.
Abbottabad 22040, Pakistan
Ph: 92 992 381907
Fax: 92 992 382321
Publication E-mail: jamc@ayubmed.edu.pk
Publisher E-mail: ayubmed@ayubmed.edu.pk
Medical journal. **Freq:** Quarterly. **Key Personnel:** Dr. Muhammad Ayub, Managing Editor; Dr. Tariq S. Mufti, Editor-in-Chief; A.K. Saeed, Editor; Saqib Lodhi, Editorial Board; Sultan Farooqi, Advisory Board; Iftikhar Qayum, Editorial Board; Shamim M. Anwar, Editorial Board; Shuja Tahir, Advisory Board. **ISSN:** 1025-9589. **URL:** http://www.ayubmed.edu.pk/JAMC/.

Faisalabad

49228 ■ Academic Journal of Cancer Research
International Digital Organization for Scientific Information
P-08, Omer Homes
Satyana Rd.
Bat. 15, Campus de Beaulieu
Faisalabad 35042, Pakistan
Ph: 92 41 8501147
Fax: 92 41 8501146
Publication E-mail: idosi@idosi.org; idosi.editor@gmail.com
Journal covering cancer research. **Freq:** Semiannual. **Key Personnel:** Muhammad Zeeshan, Managing Editor; Dr. Hanaa Hussien Abd El-Baky, Editor-in-Chief. **ISSN:** 1995-8943. **URL:** http://www.idosi.org/ajcr/ajcr.htm.

49229 ■ Academic Journal of Financial Management
International Digital Organization for Scientific Information
P-08, Omer Homes
Satyana Rd.
Bat. 15, Campus de Beaulieu
Faisalabad 35042, Pakistan
Ph: 92 41 8501147
Fax: 92 41 8501146
Journal covering financial management. **Freq:** Semiannual. **Key Personnel:** Muhammad Zeeshan, Managing Editor. **ISSN:** 1995-8978. **Subscription Rates:** EUR200 individuals; EUR250 institutions; EUR100 single issue. **URL:** http://www.idosi.org/ajfm/ajfm.htm.

49230 ■ Advances in Biological Research
International Digital Organization for Scientific Information
P-08, Omer Homes
Satyana Rd.
Bat. 15, Campus de Beaulieu
Faisalabad 35042, Pakistan
Ph: 92 41 8501147
Fax: 92 41 8501146
Publication E-mail: idosi.editor@gmail.com
Journal covering biological research. **Freq:** Bimonthly. **Key Personnel:** Dr. Ramesh Katam, Editor-in-Chief; Dr.

Shaban Sharaf El-Deen, Editor-in-Chief; Muhammad Zeeshan, Managing Editor. **ISSN:** 1992-0067. **URL:** http://www.idosi.org/abr/abr.htm.

49231 ■ Agricultural Journal
Medwell Journals
ANSInet Bldg.
308-Lasani Town
Sargodha Rd.
Faisalabad, Pakistan
Ph: 92 41 5004000
Fax: 92 41 8815599
Journal covering agriculture in Asia. **Freq:** Bimonthly. **Key Personnel:** Muhammad Kamran, Editor-in-Chief. **ISSN:** 1816-9155. **URL:** http://www.medwelljournals.com/journalhome.php?jid=1816-9155.

49232 ■ American-Eurasian Journal of Agricultural & Environmental Sciences
International Digital Organization for Scientific Information
P-08, Omer Homes
Satyana Rd.
Bat. 15, Campus de Beaulieu
Faisalabad 35042, Pakistan
Ph: 92 41 8501147
Fax: 92 41 8501146
Publication E-mail: bahaamekki@gmail.com
Journal covering agricultural and environmental sciences. **Freq:** Bimonthly. **Key Personnel:** Dr. Bahaa el din Mekki, Editor-in-Chief; Dr. Sophia Rhizopoulou, Editor-in-Chief; Dr. Nsalambi Nkongolo, Editor-in-Chief. **ISSN:** 1818-6769. **URL:** http://www.idosi.org/aejaes/aejaes.htm.

49233 ■ American-Eurasian Journal of Botany
International Digital Organization for Scientific Information
P-08, Omer Homes
Satyana Rd.
Bat. 15, Campus de Beaulieu
Faisalabad 35042, Pakistan
Ph: 92 41 8501147
Fax: 92 41 8501146
Journal covering botany. **Freq:** Quarterly. **Key Personnel:** Dr. Ahmed Hasson, Editor-in-Chief; Muhammad Zeeshan, Managing Editor; Dr. A.N. Misra, Editor-in-Chief. **ISSN:** 1995-8951. **URL:** http://www.idosi.org/aejb/aejb.htm.

49234 ■ American-Eurasian Journal of Scientific Research
International Digital Organization for Scientific Information
P-08, Omer Homes
Satyana Rd.
Bat. 15, Campus de Beaulieu
Faisalabad 35042, Pakistan
Ph: 92 41 8501147
Fax: 92 41 8501146
Journal covering scientific research. **Freq:** Quarterly. **Key Personnel:** Dr. Mokhtar Abdel-Kader, Editor-in-Chief; Dr. Ghulam Jilani, Editor-in-Chief; Dr. Duponnois Robin, Editor-in-Chief. **ISSN:** 1818-6785. **URL:** http://www.idosi.org/aejsr/aejsr.htm.

49235 ■ Asian Journal of Cell Biology
Asian Network for Scientific Information
308-Lasani Town, Sargodha Rd.
Faisalabad 38850, Pakistan
Ph: 92 41 8787087
Fax: 92 41 8815544
Peer-reviewed journal publishing original papers on the structure, function and macromolecular organization of cells and cell components focusing on cellular dynamics, motility and differentiation, particularly if related to cellular biochemistry, molecular biology, immunology, neurobiology, and developmental biology. **Freq:** Quarterly. **Key Personnel:** Dr. Brij B. Singh, Assoc. Ed.; Dr. Ayman El-Kenawy, Assoc. Ed.; Dr. Nesrin Ozsoy, Assoc. Ed.; Dr. Yonggang Wang, Assoc. Ed. **ISSN:** 1814-0068. **URL:** http://scialert.net/jindex.php?issn=1814-0068.

49236 ■ Asian Journal of Information Technology
Medwell Journals
ANSInet Bldg.
308-Lasani Town
Sargodha Rd.
Faisalabad, Pakistan
Ph: 92 41 5004000
Fax: 92 41 8815599
Journal focusing on the field of information technology. **Freq:** Monthly. **Key Personnel:** Dr. Kasim Mousa Al-Aubidy, Editor-in-Chief. **ISSN:** 1682-3915. **URL:** http://www.medwelljournals.com/journalhome.php?jid=1682-3915.

49237 ■ Asian Journal of Plant Sciences
Asian Network for Scientific Information
308-Lasani Town, Sargodha Rd.
Faisalabad 38850, Pakistan
Ph: 92 41 8787087
Fax: 92 41 8815544
Peer-reviewed journal covering all aspects of plant science. **Freq:** 0/yr. **Key Personnel:** Dr. Ilakan Ulukan, Regional Ed.; Dr. Bhaskar C. Behera, Regional Ed.; Dr. Dexian He, Regional Ed. **ISSN:** 1682-3974. **URL:** http://scialert.net/jindex.php?issn=1682-3974; http://ansinet.com/current.php?issn=1682-3974.

49238 ■ Australian Journal of Basic and Applied Sciences
International Network for Scientific Information
Haseeb Shaheed Colony, P-112, No. 10
Hilal Rd.
Faisalabad, Pakistan
Ph: 92 333 6616624
Fax: 92 333 2227333
Publisher E-mail: editor@insinet.net
Journal covering basic and applied sciences. **Freq:** Quarterly. **Key Personnel:** Dr. Deborah Mooney, Editorial Board Member; Dr. Kadambot Siddique, Editorial Board Member; Dr. Yan Chen, Editorial Board Member. **ISSN:** 1991-8178. **URL:** http://www.insinet.net/ajbas.html.

49239 ■ Biotechnology
Asian Network for Scientific Information
308-Lasani Town, Sargodha Rd.
Faisalabad 38850, Pakistan

Ph: 92 41 8787087
Fax: 92 41 8815544
Peer-reviewed journal featuring articles relating to aspects of biotechnology. **Freq:** Quarterly. **Key Personnel:** Dr. Dheeraj Verma, Technical Ed.; Dr. Charles Knill, Regional Ed.; Dr. Khalil I. Al-Mughrabi, Regional Ed.; Dr. Rekha R. Warier, Technical Ed.; Dr. Hala El-Adawi, Assoc. Ed.; Dr. Seiji Shibasaki, Assoc. Ed. **ISSN:** 1682-296X. **URL:** http://scialert.net/jindex.php?issn=1682-296x; http://ansinet.com/current.php?issn=1682-296x.

49240 ■ Botany Research Journal
Medwell Journals
ANSInet Bldg.
308-Lasani Town
Sargodha Rd.
Faisalabad, Pakistan
Ph: 92 41 5004000
Fax: 92 41 8815599
Journal focusing on the field of botany. **Freq:** Bimonthly. **Key Personnel:** Dr. Muhammad Sohail, Dir. of Publications. **ISSN:** 1995-4751. **URL:** http://www.medwelljournals.com/journalhome.php?jid=1995-4751.

49241 ■ Global Journal of Biotechnology & Biochemistry
International Digital Organization for Scientific Information
P-08, Omer Homes
Satyana Rd.
Bat. 15, Campus de Beaulieu
Faisalabad 35042, Pakistan
Ph: 92 41 8501147
Fax: 92 41 8501146
Journal covering biotechnology and biochemistry. **Freq:** Semiannual. **Key Personnel:** Dr. Gholamreza Salehi Jouzani, Editor-in-Chief; Dr. Mohamed El-Sherif A. Shabeb, Editor-in-Chief; Dr. Idress Hamad Attitalla, Editor-in-Chief. **ISSN:** 1995-9001. **URL:** http://www.idosi.org/gjbb/gjbb.htm.

49242 ■ Global Journal of Environmental Research
International Digital Organization for Scientific Information
P-08, Omer Homes
Satyana Rd.
Bat. 15, Campus de Beaulieu
Faisalabad 35042, Pakistan
Ph: 92 41 8501147
Fax: 92 41 8501146
Journal covering environment research. **Freq:** Quarterly. **Key Personnel:** Dr. Mohamed El-Sherif A. Shabeb, Editor-in-Chief; Dr. Ramesh Katam, Editor-in-Chief; Dr. Ismail Bin Sahid, Editor-in-Chief. **ISSN:** 1990-925X. **URL:** http://www.idosi.org/gjer/gjer.htm.

49243 ■ Global Journal of Molecular Sciences
International Digital Organization for Scientific Information
P-08, Omer Homes
Satyana Rd.
Bat. 15, Campus de Beaulieu
Faisalabad 35042, Pakistan
Ph: 92 41 8501147
Fax: 92 41 8501146
Journal covering molecular sciences. **Freq:** Semiannual. **Key Personnel:** Dr. Mohamed El-Sherif A. Shabeb, Editor-in-Chief; Dr. Wahid Mohamed Ahmed, Editor-in-Chief; Muhammad Zeeshan, Managing Editor. **ISSN:** 1990-9241. **URL:** http://www.idosi.org/gjms/gjms.htm.

49244 ■ Global Journal of Pharmacology
International Digital Organization for Scientific Information
P-08, Omer Homes
Satyana Rd.
Bat. 15, Campus de Beaulieu
Faisalabad 35042, Pakistan
Ph: 92 41 8501147
Fax: 92 41 8501146
Journal covering pharmacology. **Freq:** 3/yr. **Key Personnel:** Muhammad Zeeshan, Managing Editor; Prof. Wahid M. Ahmed, Editor-in-Chief; Prof. Samy I. Shalaby, Editor-in-Chief. **ISSN:** 1992-0075. **URL:** http://www.idosi.org/gjp/gjp.htm.

49245 ■ Global Veterinaria
International Digital Organization for Scientific Information
P-08, Omer Homes

Satyana Rd.
Bat. 15, Campus de Beaulieu
Faisalabad 35042, Pakistan
Ph: 92 41 8501147
Fax: 92 41 8501146
Journal covering all aspects of veterinary sciences. **Freq:** Bimonthly. **Key Personnel:** Dr. Wahid Mohamed Ahmed, Editor-in-Chief, wahidmma@hotmail.com; Muhammad Zeeshan, Managing Editor. **ISSN:** 1992-6197. **URL:** http://www.idosi.org/gv/gv.htm.

49246 ■ Humanity & Social Sciences Journal
International Digital Organization for Scientific Information
P-08, Omer Homes
Satyana Rd.
Bat. 15, Campus de Beaulieu
Faisalabad 35042, Pakistan
Ph: 92 41 8501147
Fax: 92 41 8501146
Journal covering humanity and social sciences. **Freq:** Quarterly. **Key Personnel:** Dr. Sefika Sule Ercetin, Editor-in-Chief; Dr. Alay Ahmad, Editor-in-Chief; Dr. A.H. Roslan Harahap, Editor-in-Chief. **ISSN:** 1818-4960. **URL:** http://www.idosi.org/hssj/hss.htm.

49247 ■ Information Technology Journal
Asian Network for Scientific Information
308-Lasani Town, Sargodha Rd.
Faisalabad 38850, Pakistan
Ph: 92 41 8787087
Fax: 92 41 8815544
International official journal of Asian Network for Scientific Information publishing original articles, reviews and short communications of a high scientific and ethical standard, covering such subjects as: computer science, information systems, computer systems and information engineering and software engineering. **Freq:** 8/yr. **ISSN:** 1812-5638. **Subscription Rates:** US$1,800 individuals print and online; US$2,100 institutions print and online; US$300 single issue. **URL:** http://www.ansinet.com/current.php?issn=1812-5638.

49248 ■ International Business Management
Medwell Journals
ANSInet Bldg.
308-Lasani Town
Sargodha Rd.
Faisalabad, Pakistan
Ph: 92 41 5004000
Fax: 92 41 8815599
Journal focusing on the field of business management. **Freq:** Bimonthly. **Key Personnel:** Dr. Tatiana Bouzdine Chameeva, Editor-in-Chief. **ISSN:** 1993-5250. **URL:** http://www.medwelljournals.com/journalhome.php?jid=1993-5250.

49249 ■ International Journal of Botany
Asian Network for Scientific Information
308-Lasani Town, Sargodha Rd.
Faisalabad 38850, Pakistan
Ph: 92 41 8787087
Fax: 92 41 8815544
Peer-reviewed journal accepting research papers on all aspects of plant science, including cell and molecular biology, ecology, mycology and plant pathology, phycology, physiology and biochemistry, structure and development, systematics, phytogeography, and paleobotany. **Freq:** Quarterly. **Key Personnel:** Dr. Arunrat Chaveerach, Assoc. Ed.; Dr. Ahmad Abdul Hameed, Assoc. Ed.; Prof. Mustafa Temel, Assoc. Ed. **ISSN:** 1811-9700. **URL:** http://www.ansinet.com/current.php?issn=1811-9700; http://scialert.net/jindex.php?issn=1811-9700.

49250 ■ International Journal of Electrical and Power Engineering
Medwell Journals
ANSInet Bldg.
308-Lasani Town
Sargodha Rd.
Faisalabad, Pakistan
Ph: 92 41 5004000
Fax: 92 41 8815599
Journal covering the study of electrical engineering. **Freq:** Bimonthly. **Key Personnel:** Prof. Boukhemis Chetate, Editor-in-Chief. **ISSN:** 1990-7958. **URL:** http://www.medwelljournals.com/journalhome.php?jid=1990-7958.

49251 ■ International Journal of Molecular Medicine and Advance Sciences
Medwell Journals
ANSInet Bldg.
308-Lasani Town
Sargodha Rd.
Faisalabad, Pakistan
Ph: 92 41 5004000
Fax: 92 41 8815599
Journal covering the field of molecular medicine and advance sciences. **Freq:** Bimonthly. **Key Personnel:** Dr. Armando Rojas Rubio, Editor-in-Chief. **ISSN:** 1813-176X. **URL:** http://www.medwelljournals.com/journalhome.php?jid=1813-176x.

49252 ■ International Journal of Pharmacology
Asian Network for Scientific Information
308-Lasani Town, Sargodha Rd.
Faisalabad 38850, Pakistan
Ph: 92 41 8787087
Fax: 92 41 8815544
Journal publishing full-length papers, short communications and rapid communications on the mechanisms of action of chemical substances affecting biological systems, accepting articles on behavioral pharmacology, neuropharmacology and analgesia, cardiovascular pharmacology, pulmonary, gastrointestinal and urogenital pharmacology, endocrine pharmacology, immunopharmacology and inflammation, and molecular and cellular pharmacology. **Freq:** Bimonthly. **Key Personnel:** Dr. Suvakanta Dash, Regional Ed.; Dr. Bangning Yu, Assoc. Ed. **ISSN:** 1811-7775. **URL:** http://www.ansinet.com/current.php?issn=1811-7775; http://scialert.net/jindex.php?issn=1811-7775.

49253 ■ International Journal of Planetary and Space Research
International Digital Organization for Scientific Information
P-08, Omer Homes
Satyana Rd.
Bat. 15, Campus de Beaulieu
Faisalabad 35042, Pakistan
Ph: 92 41 8501147
Fax: 92 41 8501146
Journal covering planetary and space research. **Freq:** Semiannual. **Key Personnel:** Muhammad Zeeshan, Managing Editor. **ISSN:** 1993-145X. **Subscription Rates:** EUR200 individuals; EUR300 institutions. **URL:** http://www.idosi.org/ijpsr/ijpsr.htm.

49254 ■ International Journal of Poultry Science
Asian Network for Scientific Information
308-Lasani Town, Sargodha Rd.
Faisalabad 38850, Pakistan
Ph: 92 41 8787087
Fax: 92 41 8815544
Peer-reviewed journal publishing original papers on all aspects of poultry science. **Freq:** Monthly. **Key Personnel:** Muhammad Sarwar, Managing Editor; Dr. Sanjay Jahhao, Advisory Board. **ISSN:** 1682-8356. **URL:** http://scialert.net/jindex.php?issn=1682-8356; http://www.ansinet.com/current.php?issn=1682-8356.

49255 ■ International Journal of Quality and Innovation
Inderscience Enterprises Limited
c/o Prof. Niaz Ahmad, Ed.-in-Ch.
National Textile University
Sheikhupura Rd.
Faisalabad 37610, Pakistan
Journal covering quality and innovation in the business. **Freq:** Quarterly. **Key Personnel:** Prof. Niaz Ahmad, Editor-in-Chief, rector@ntu.edu.pk. **ISSN:** 1756-6975. **Subscription Rates:** EUR494 individuals print or online; EUR672 individuals print and online. **URL:** http://www.inderscience.com/browse/index.php?journalCODE=ijqi.

49256 ■ International Journal of Soft Computing
Medwell Journals
ANSInet Bldg.
308-Lasani Town
Sargodha Rd.
Faisalabad, Pakistan
Ph: 92 41 5004000
Fax: 92 41 8815599
Journal covering the field of soft computing. **Freq:** Bimonthly. **Key Personnel:** Dr. Mu-Chun Su, Editor-in-Chief. **ISSN:** 1816-9503. **URL:** http://www.medwelljournals.com/journalhome.php?jid=1816-9503.

49257 ■ International Journal of Systems Signal Control and Engineering Application
Medwell Journals
ANSInet Bldg.
308-Lasani Town
Sargodha Rd.
Faisalabad, Pakistan
Ph: 92 41 5004000
Fax: 92 41 8815599
Journal containing articles on system analysis, modeling, simulation, signal processing, control synthesis and related topics. **Freq:** Bimonthly. **Key Personnel:** Dr. Zhiwei Gao, Editor-in-Chief. **ISSN:** 1997-5422. **URL:** http://www.medwelljournals.com/journalhome.php?jid=1997-5422.

49258 ■ International Journal of Tropical Medicine
Medwell Journals
ANSInet Bldg.
308-Lasani Town
Sargodha Rd.
Faisalabad, Pakistan
Ph: 92 41 5004000
Fax: 92 41 8815599
Journal covering the field of tropical medicine. **Freq:** Bimonthly. **Key Personnel:** Dr. R. Manojkumar, Editor-in-Chief. **ISSN:** 1816-3319. **URL:** http://www.medwelljournals.com/journalhome.php?jid=1816-3319.

49259 ■ Journal of Agronomy
Asian Network for Scientific Information
308-Lasani Town, Sargodha Rd.
Faisalabad 38850, Pakistan
Ph: 92 41 8787087
Fax: 92 41 8815544
Peer-reviewed journal publishing original articles, reviews and short communications of a high scientific and ethical standard in the field of crop sciences: crop physiology, crop production and management, agroclimatology and modeling, plant-soil relationships, crop quality and post-harvest physiology, farming and cropping systems, agro-ecosystems and the environment. **Freq:** Quarterly. **Key Personnel:** Dr. Anil Kumar, Assoc. Ed.; Dr. Moosa Meskarbashee, Assoc. Ed.; Dr. Talaat A. Ahmed, Assoc. Ed.; Dr. Pitipong Thobunluepop, Assoc. Ed.; Dr. Suleyman Taban, Assoc. Ed. **ISSN:** 1812-5379. **URL:** http://scialert.net/jindex.php?issn=1812-5379; http://www.ansinet.com/current.php?issn=1812-5379.

49260 ■ Journal of Animal and Veterinary Advances
Medwell Journals
ANSInet Bldg.
308-Lasani Town
Sargodha Rd.
Faisalabad, Pakistan
Ph: 92 41 5004000
Fax: 92 41 8815599
Journal covering the field of veterinary science. **Freq:** Monthly. **Key Personnel:** Dr. Richard Avery Zinn, Editor-in-Chief. **ISSN:** 1680-5593. **URL:** http://www.medwelljournals.com/journalhome.php?jid=1680-5593.

49261 ■ Journal of Applied Sciences
Asian Network for Scientific Information
308-Lasani Town, Sargodha Rd.
Faisalabad 38850, Pakistan
Ph: 92 41 8787087
Fax: 92 41 8815544
International journal publishing original articles, reviews and short communications of a high scientific and ethical standard in applied sciences, including chemistry, environmental sciences, business and economics, physics, mathematics and statistics, geology, engineering, computer science and social sciences. **Freq:** Semimonthly. **Key Personnel:** Dr. Hakan Ulukan, Editorial Board. **ISSN:** 1812-5654. **Subscription Rates:** US$3,500 individuals print and online; US$4,000 institutions print and online; US$300 single issue. **URL:** http://www.ansinet.com/current.php?issn=1812-5654.

49262 ■ Journal of Applied Sciences Research
International Network for Scientific Information
Haseeb Shaheed Colony, P-112, No. 10
Hilal Rd.
Faisalabad, Pakistan
Ph: 92 333 6616624
Fax: 92 333 2227333
Publisher E-mail: editor@insinet.net
Journal covering research in applied sciences. **Freq:** Monthly. **Key Personnel:** Dr. Kadambot Siddique, Editorial Board Member; Dr. Deborah Mooney, Editorial Board Member. **ISSN:** 1816-157X. **URL:** http://www.insinet.net/jasr.html.

49263 ■ Journal of Aquaculture Feed Science and Nutrition
Medwell Journals
ANSInet Bldg.
308-Lasani Town
Sargodha Rd.
Faisalabad, Pakistan
Ph: 92 41 5004000
Fax: 92 41 8815599
Journal covering the field of aquaculture and nutrition. **Freq:** Quarterly. **Key Personnel:** Dr. Simon J. Davies, Editor-in-Chief. **ISSN:** 2070-1667. **URL:** http://www.medwelljournals.com/journalhome.php?jid=2070-1667.

49264 ■ Journal of Biological Sciences
Asian Network for Scientific Information
308-Lasani Town, Sargodha Rd.
Faisalabad 38850, Pakistan
Ph: 92 41 8787087
Fax: 92 41 8815544
Peer-reviewed journal accepting articles on biological research. **Freq:** 8/yr. **Key Personnel:** Dr. Mehmet Ozaslan, Editor-in-Chief; Dr. Hakan Ulukan, Regional Ed.; Dr. Hala El-Adawi, Assoc. Ed. **ISSN:** 1727-3048. **URL:** http://scialert.net/jindex.php?issn=1727-3048; http://www.ansinet.com/current.php?issn=1727-3048.

49265 ■ Journal of Economics Theory
Medwell Journals
ANSInet Bldg.
308-Lasani Town
Sargodha Rd.
Faisalabad, Pakistan
Ph: 92 41 5004000
Fax: 92 41 8815599
Journal covering the field of economics based on rigorous theoretical reasoning. **Freq:** Bimonthly. **Key Personnel:** Dr. Muhammad Sohail, Dir. of Publications; Dr. Run Yu, Editor. **ISSN:** 1994-8212. **URL:** http://www.medwelljournals.com/journalhome.php?jid=1994-8212.

49266 ■ Journal of Engineering and Applied Sciences
Medwell Journals
ANSInet Bldg.
308-Lasani Town
Sargodha Rd.
Faisalabad, Pakistan
Ph: 92 41 5004000
Fax: 92 41 8815599
Journal covering the field of engineering and applied science. **Freq:** Monthly. **Key Personnel:** Dr. Ibrahim Badran, Editor-in-Chief. **ISSN:** 1816-949X. **URL:** http://www.medwelljournals.com/journalhome.php?jid=1816-949x.

49267 ■ Journal of Entomology
Asian Network for Scientific Information
300-Lasani Town, Sargodha Rd.
Faisalabad 38850, Pakistan
Ph: 92 41 8787087
Fax: 92 41 8815544
International journal publishing original articles, reviews and short communications of a high scientific and ethical standard in entomology. **Freq:** Quarterly. **Key Personnel:** Dr. Sobhy Abdel-Shafy, Tech. Ed.; Dr. Alinaghi Mirmoayedi, Assoc. Ed.; Dr. Ayman A. El-Badry, Assoc. Ed. **ISSN:** 1812-5670. **Subscription Rates:** US$900 individuals; US$1,100 institutions; US$300 single issue. **URL:** http://scialert.net/jindex.php?issn=1812-5670.

49268 ■ Journal of Fisheries International
Medwell Journals
ANSInet Bldg.
308-Lasani Town
Sargodha Rd.
Faisalabad, Pakistan
Ph: 92 41 5004000
Fax: 92 41 8815599
Journal focusing on the study of fisheries. **Freq:** Bimonthly. **Key Personnel:** Dr. Gordon Huang, Editor-in-Chief. **ISSN:** 1817-3381. **URL:** http://www.medwelljournals.com/journalhome.php?jid=1817-3381.

49269 ■ Journal of Food Technology
Medwell Journals
ANSInet Bldg.
308-Lasani Town
Sargodha Rd.
Faisalabad, Pakistan
Ph: 92 41 5004000
Fax: 92 41 8815599
Journal covering the field of food technology. **Freq:** Bimonthly. **Key Personnel:** Dr. Wayne R. Leifert, Editor-in-Chief. **ISSN:** 1684-8462. **URL:** http://www.medwelljournals.com/journalhome.php?jid=1684-8462.

49270 ■ Journal of Medical Sciences
Asian Network for Scientific Information
308-Lasani Town, Sargodha Rd.
Faisalabad 38850, Pakistan
Ph: 92 41 8787087
Fax: 92 41 8815544
Peer-reviewed journal covering all aspects of medical sciences. **Freq:** 8/yr. **Key Personnel:** Dr. Suvakanta Dash, Regional Ed.; Dr. Aliyu Mohammed, Assoc. Ed.; Dr. Nabeel Khouri, Assoc. Ed. **ISSN:** 1682-4474. **URL:** http://scialert.net/jindex.php?issn=1682-4474; http://ansinet.com/current.php?issn=1682-4474.

49271 ■ Journal of Mobile Communication
Medwell Journals
ANSInet Bldg.
308-Lasani Town
Sargodha Rd.
Faisalabad, Pakistan
Ph: 92 41 5004000
Fax: 92 41 8815599
Journal focusing on the study of mobile communication. **Freq:** Bimonthly. **Key Personnel:** Dr. Ioannis Mylonakis, Editor-in-Chief. **ISSN:** 1990-794X. **URL:** http://www.medwelljournals.com/journalhome.php?jid=1990-794x.

49272 ■ Journal of Modern Mathematics and Statistics
Medwell Journals
ANSInet Bldg.
308-Lasani Town
Sargodha Rd.
Faisalabad, Pakistan
Ph: 92 41 5004000
Fax: 92 41 8815599
Journal covering the field of modern mathematics and statistics. **Freq:** Bimonthly. **Key Personnel:** Dr. Muhammad Sohail, Dir. of Publications. **ISSN:** 1994-5388. **URL:** http://www.medwelljournals.com/journalhome.php?jid=1994-5388.

49273 ■ Journal of Molecular Genetics
Medwell Journals
ANSInet Bldg.
308-Lasani Town
Sargodha Rd.
Faisalabad, Pakistan
Ph: 92 41 5004000
Fax: 92 41 8815599
Journal covering the field of molecular genetics. **Freq:** Quarterly. **Key Personnel:** Dr. Richard Y. Zhao, Editor-in-Chief. **ISSN:** 2070-4267. **URL:** http://www.medwelljournals.com/journalhome.php?jid=2070-4267.

49274 ■ Middle East Journal of Scientific Research
International Digital Organization for Scientific Information
P-08, Omer Homes
Satyana Rd.
Bat. 15, Campus de Beaulieu
Faisalabad 35042, Pakistan
Ph: 92 41 8501147
Fax: 92 41 8501146
Journal covering scientific research. **Freq:** Monthly. **Key Personnel:** Dr. Hamed M. Eel-Shora, Editor-in-Chief; Dr. Sefika Sule Ercetin, Editor-in-Chief; Muhammad Zeeshan, Managing Editor. **ISSN:** 1990-9233. **URL:** http://www.idosi.org/mejsr/mejsr.htm.

49275 ■ Online Journal of Earth Sciences
Medwell Journals
ANSInet Bldg.
308-Lasani Town
Sargodha Rd.
Faisalabad, Pakistan
Ph: 92 41 5004000

Circulation: ★ = ABC; △ = BPA; ♦ = CAC; • = CCAB; ❑ = VAC; ⊕ = PO Statement; ‡ = Publisher's Report; Boldface figures = sworn; Light figures = estimated.

Gale Directory of Publications & Broadcast Media/147th Ed.   5323

Fax: 92 41 8815599
Journal covering the field of earth science. **Freq:** Bimonthly. **Key Personnel:** Dr. Baddari Kamel, Editor-in-Chief. **ISSN:** 1991-7708. **URL:** http://www.medwelljournals.com/journalhome.php?jid=1991-7708.

49276 ■ Pakistan Journal of Biological Sciences
Asian Network for Scientific Information
308-Lasani Town, Sargodha Rd.
Faisalabad 38850, Pakistan
Ph: 92 41 8787087
Fax: 92 41 8815544
Peer-reviewed journal covering all aspects of biological sciences. **Freq:** Semimonthly. **Key Personnel:** Dr. Aziz Bin Ahmad, Assoc. Ed.; Dr. Yannick Maneuf, Assoc. Ed.; Prof. Fahrettin Tilki, Assoc. Ed. **ISSN:** 1028-8880. **URL:** http://scialert.net/jindex.php?issn=1028-8880; http://www.ansinet.com/current.php?issn=1028-8880.

49277 ■ Pakistan Journal of Nutrition
Asian Network for Scientific Information
308-Lasani Town, Sargodha Rd.
Faisalabad 38850, Pakistan
Ph: 92 41 8787087
Fax: 92 41 8815544
Peer-reviewed journal publishing original papers on all aspects of nutritional sciences. **Freq:** Bimonthly. **Key Personnel:** H.M. Naeem, Managing Editor; Dr. Z.Y. Chen, Contact; Dr. Azlin Mustapha, Contact. **ISSN:** 1680-5194. **URL:** http://scialert.net/jindex.php?issn=1680-5194; http://ansinet.com/current.php?issn=1680-5194.

49278 ■ Plant Pathology Journal
Asian Network for Scientific Information
308-Lasani Town, Sargodha Rd.
Faisalabad 38850, Pakistan
Ph: 92 41 8787087
Fax: 92 41 8815544
Peer-reviewed journal covering issues relating to plant pathology. **Freq:** Quarterly. **Key Personnel:** Dr. Mohamed A. Elwakil, Editor-in-Chief. **ISSN:** 1812-5387. **URL:** http://scialert.net/jindex.php?issn=1812-5387; http://ansinet.com/current.php?issn=1812-5387. **Formerly:** Pakistan Journal of Plant Pathology.

49279 ■ Plant Sciences Research
Medwell Journals
ANSInet Bldg.
308-Lasani Town
Sargodha Rd.
Faisalabad, Pakistan
Ph: 92 41 5004000
Fax: 92 41 8815599
Journal focusing on the culture and management of plants, protection of the environment, and conservation of natural resources. **Freq:** Bimonthly. **Key Personnel:** Dr. Muhammad Sohail, Dir. of Publications. **ISSN:** 1995-476X. **URL:** http://www.medwelljournals.com/journalhome.php?jid=1995-476x.

49280 ■ Research Journal of Agriculture and Biological Sciences
International Network for Scientific Information
Haseeb Shaheed Colony, P-112, No. 10
Hilal Rd.
Faisalabad, Pakistan
Ph: 92 333 6616624
Fax: 92 333 2227333
Publisher E-mail: editor@insinet.net
Journal covering agriculture and biological sciences. **Freq:** Bimonthly. **Key Personnel:** Dr. Kyung Dong Lee, Editorial Board Member; Dr. Richard A. Heckmann, Editorial Board Member; Dr. Buniyamin Yildirim, Editorial Board Member. **ISSN:** 1816-1561. **URL:** http://www.insipub.com/rjabs.html.

49281 ■ Research Journal of Agronomy
Medwell Journals
ANSInet Bldg.
308-Lasani Town
Sargodha Rd.
Faisalabad, Pakistan
Ph: 92 41 5004000
Fax: 92 41 8815599
Journal covering the field of agronomy. **Freq:** Bimonthly. **Key Personnel:** Dr. Muhammad Sohail, Dir. of Publications. **ISSN:** 1815-9354. **URL:** http://www.medwelljournals.com/journalhome.php?jid=1815-9354.

49282 ■ Research Journal of Animal Sciences
Medwell Journals
ANSInet Bldg.
308-Lasani Town
Sargodha Rd.
Faisalabad, Pakistan
Ph: 92 41 5004000
Fax: 92 41 8815599
Journal covering the field of animal science. **Freq:** Bimonthly. **Key Personnel:** Dr. Muhammad Sohail, Dir. of Publications. **ISSN:** 1993-5269. **URL:** http://www.medwelljournals.com/journalhome.php?jid=1993-5269.

49283 ■ Research Journal of Animal and Veterinary Sciences
International Network for Scientific Information
Haseeb Shaheed Colony, P-112, No. 10
Hilal Rd.
Faisalabad, Pakistan
Ph: 92 333 6616624
Fax: 92 333 2227333
Publisher E-mail: editor@insinet.net
Journal covering animal and veterinary sciences. **Freq:** Annual. **Key Personnel:** Dr. Joseph M. Erwin, Editorial Board Member; Dr. Bahy Ahmed Ali, Editorial Board Member; Dr. Adem Kamalak, Editorial Board Member. **ISSN:** 1816-2746. **URL:** http://www.insipub.com/rjavs.html.

49284 ■ Research Journal of Applied Sciences
Medwell Journals
ANSInet Bldg.
308-Lasani Town
Sargodha Rd.
Faisalabad, Pakistan
Ph: 92 41 5004000
Fax: 92 41 8815599
Journal covering the field of applied sciences. **Freq:** Monthly. **Key Personnel:** Dr. Abdellatif Mtibaa, Editor-in-Chief. **ISSN:** 1815-932X. **URL:** http://www.medwelljournals.com/journalhome.php?jid=1815-932x.

49285 ■ Research Journal of Biological Sciences
Medwell Journals
ANSInet Bldg.
308-Lasani Town
Sargodha Rd.
Faisalabad, Pakistan
Ph: 92 41 5004000
Fax: 92 41 8815599
Journal covering the field of biological sciences. **Freq:** Bimonthly. **Key Personnel:** Dr. Cham Bill Elliot, Editor-in-Chief. **ISSN:** 1815-8846. **URL:** http://www.medwelljournals.com/journalhome.php?jid=1815-8846.

49286 ■ Research Journal of Cell and Molecular Biology
International Network for Scientific Information
Haseeb Shaheed Colony, P-112, No. 10
Hilal Rd.
Faisalabad, Pakistan
Ph: 92 333 6616624
Fax: 92 333 2227333
Publisher E-mail: editor@insinet.net
Journal covering cell and molecular biology. **Freq:** Semiannual. **Key Personnel:** Dr. Elsayed Elsayed Hafez, Editor-in-Chief, elsayed_hafez@yahoo.com. **ISSN:** 1991-8828. **URL:** http://www.insipub.com/rjcmb.html.

49287 ■ Research Journal of Dairy Sciences
Medwell Journals
ANSInet Bldg.
308-Lasani Town
Sargodha Rd.
Faisalabad, Pakistan
Ph: 92 41 5004000
Fax: 92 41 8815599
Journal covering the field of dairy science. **Freq:** Bimonthly. **Key Personnel:** Dr. Vasileios Bampidis, Editor-in-Chief. **ISSN:** 1993-5277. **URL:** http://www.medwelljournals.com/journalhome.php?jid=1993-5277.

49288 ■ Research Journal of Fisheries and Hydrobiology
International Network for Scientific Information
Haseeb Shaheed Colony, P-112, No. 10
Hilal Rd.
Faisalabad, Pakistan
Ph: 92 333 6616624

Fax: 92 333 2227333
Publisher E-mail: editor@insinet.net
Journal covering fisheries and hydrobiology. **Freq:** Semiannual. **Key Personnel:** Dr. Ibrahim El-Shishtawy Hassan Belal, Editorial Board; Dr. Mohsen Abdel-Tawwab, Editorial Board; Dr. Richard A. Heckmann, Editorial Board. **ISSN:** 1816-9112. **URL:** http://www.insipub.com/rjfh.html.

49289 ■ Research Journal of Medical Sciences
Medwell Journals
ANSInet Bldg.
308-Lasani Town
Sargodha Rd.
Faisalabad, Pakistan
Ph: 92 41 5004000
Fax: 92 41 8815599
Journal covering the field of medical science. **Freq:** Bimonthly. **Key Personnel:** Dr. Gianfranco D. Alpini, Editor-in-Chief. **ISSN:** 1815-9346. **URL:** http://www.medwelljournals.com/journalhome.php?jid=1815-9346.

49290 ■ Research Journal of Medicine and Medical Sciences
International Network for Scientific Information
Haseeb Shaheed Colony, P-112, No. 10
Hilal Rd.
Faisalabad, Pakistan
Ph: 92 333 6616624
Fax: 92 333 2227333
Publisher E-mail: editor@insinet.net
Journal covering medicine and medical sciences. **Freq:** Semiannual. **Key Personnel:** Dr. Neal Davies, Editorial Board Member; Dr. Ugur Cavlak, Editorial Board Member; Dr. Murat Cavit, Editorial Board Member. **ISSN:** 1816-272X. **URL:** http://www.insipub.com/rjmms.html.

49291 ■ Research Journal of Pharmacology
Medwell Journals
ANSInet Bldg.
308-Lasani Town
Sargodha Rd.
Faisalabad, Pakistan
Ph: 92 41 5004000
Fax: 92 41 8815599
Journal covering the field of pharmacology. **Freq:** Bimonthly. **Key Personnel:** Dr. Hassan Malekinejad, Editor-in-Chief. **ISSN:** 1815-9362. **URL:** http://www.medwelljournals.com/journalhome.php?jid=1815-9362.

49292 ■ Research Journal of Poultry Sciences
Medwell Journals
ANSInet Bldg.
308-Lasani Town
Sargodha Rd.
Faisalabad, Pakistan
Ph: 92 41 5004000
Fax: 92 41 8815599
Journal covering the field of poultry science. **Freq:** Bimonthly. **Key Personnel:** Dr. Muhammad Sohail, Dir. of Publications. **ISSN:** 1993-5285. **URL:** http://www.medwelljournals.com/journalhome.php?jid=1993-5285.

49293 ■ Research Journal of Telecommunication and Information Technology
International Network for Scientific Information
Haseeb Shaheed Colony, P-112, No. 10
Hilal Rd.
Faisalabad, Pakistan
Ph: 92 333 6616624
Fax: 92 333 2227333
Publisher E-mail: editor@insinet.net
Journal covering telecommunication and information technology. **Freq:** Annual. **Key Personnel:** Dr. Ahmad T. Al-Taani, Editorial Board Member; Dr. Kevin Curran, Editorial Board Member. **ISSN:** 1816-2738. **URL:** http://www.insipub.com/rjtit.html.

49294 ■ Surgery Journal
Medwell Journals
ANSInet Bldg.
308-Lasani Town
Sargodha Rd.
Faisalabad, Pakistan
Ph: 92 41 5004000
Fax: 92 41 8815599
Journal focusing on the study of surgery. **Freq:** Bimonthly. **Key Personnel:** Muhammad Kamran, Editor-in-Chief. **ISSN:** 1816-3211. **URL:** http://www.medwelljournals.com/eboard.php?jid=1816-3211.

49295 ■ Universal Science and Engineering for Marine Environment
International Digital Organization for Scientific Information
P-08, Omer Homes
Satyana Rd.
Bat. 15, Campus de Beaulieu
Faisalabad 35042, Pakistan
Ph: 92 41 8501147
Fax: 92 41 8501146
Journal covering coastal environment. **Freq:** 3/yr. **Key Personnel:** Dr. Sarwoko Mangkoedihardjo, Editor-in-Chief; Muhammad Zeeshan, Managing Editor; Dr. Masoud Hedayatifard, Assoc. Ed.-in-Ch. **ISSN:** 1992-0083. **Subscription Rates:** EUR300 individuals; EUR375 institutions; EUR125 single issue. **URL:** http://www.idosi.org/useme/useme.htm.

49296 ■ Veterinary Research
Medwell Journals
ANSInet Bldg.
308-Lasani Town
Sargodha Rd.
Faisalabad, Pakistan
Ph: 92 41 5004000
Fax: 92 41 8815599
Journal covering the field of veterinary research. **Freq:** Bimonthly. **Key Personnel:** Dr. Wael A. Khamas, Editor-in-Chief. **ISSN:** 1993-5412. **URL:** http://www.medwelljournals.com/journalhome.php?jid=1993-5412.

49297 ■ World Applied Sciences Journal
International Digital Organization for Scientific Information
P-08, Omer Homes
Satyana Rd.
Bat. 15, Campus de Beaulieu
Faisalabad 35042, Pakistan
Ph: 92 41 8501147
Fax: 92 41 8501146
Peer-reviewed journal covering world applied sciences. **Freq:** Monthly. **Key Personnel:** Dr. Ghasem Najafpour, Editor-in-Chief; Dr. Wahid Mohamed Ahmed, Editor-in-Chief; Dr. Sofika Ercetin Sule, Editor-in-Chief. **ISSN:** 1818-4952. **Subscription Rates:** EUR1,800 individuals; EUR2,400 institutions. **URL:** http://www.idosi.org/wasj/wasj.htm.

49298 ■ World Information Technology Journal
International Digital Organization for Scientific Information
P-08, Omer Homes
Satyana Rd.
Bat. 15, Campus de Beaulieu
Faisalabad 35042, Pakistan
Ph: 92 41 8501147
Fax: 92 41 8501146
Journal covering world information technology. **Freq:** Semiannual. **Key Personnel:** Dr. Omer M. Al-Jarrah, Editor-in-Chief; Muhammad Zeeshan, Managing Editor; Seyed Vahid Jalali, Editor-in-Chief. **ISSN:** 1818-4944. **URL:** http://www.idosi.org/witj/witj.htm.

49299 ■ World Journal of Agricultural Sciences
International Digital Organization for Scientific Information
P-08, Omer Homes
Satyana Rd.
Bat. 15, Campus de Beaulieu
Faisalabad 35042, Pakistan
Ph: 92 41 8501147
Fax: 92 41 8501146
Journal covering agricultural sciences. **Freq:** Bimonthly. **Key Personnel:** Dr. Bahaa El-Din Bastawy Mekki, Editor-in-Chief; Dr. Thomas Stuart Jayne, Editor-in-Chief; Dr. Mohamed S.A. Shabeb, Editor-in-Chief. **ISSN:** 1817-3047. **URL:** http://www.idosi.org/wjas/wjas.htm.

49300 ■ World Journal of Chemistry
International Digital Organization for Scientific Information
P-08, Omer Homes
Satyana Rd.
Bat. 15, Campus de Beaulieu
Faisalabad 35042, Pakistan
Ph: 92 41 8501147
Fax: 92 41 8501146
Journal covering chemistry. **Freq:** Quarterly. **Key Personnel:** Dr. Sultan T. Abu-Orabi, Assoc. Ed.; Dr. Ali Kamel Khalafalla, Editor-in-Chief; Muhammad Zeeshan,

Managing Editor. **ISSN:** 1817-3071. **URL:** http://www.idosi.org/wjc/wjc.htm.

49301 ■ World Journal of Dairy & Food Sciences
International Digital Organization for Scientific Information
P-08, Omer Homes
Satyana Rd.
Bat. 15, Campus de Beaulieu
Faisalabad 35042, Pakistan
Ph: 92 41 8501147
Fax: 92 41 8501146
Journal covering daily and food sciences. **Freq:** Quarterly. **Key Personnel:** Dr. Mahmut Dogan, Editor-in-Chief; Dr. Wahid Mohamed Ahmed, Editor-in-Chief; Dr. Anita Rani Jindal, Editor-in-Chief. **ISSN:** 1817-308X. **URL:** http://www.idosi.org/wjdfs/wjdfs.htm.

49302 ■ World Journal of Medical Sciences
International Digital Organization for Scientific Information
P-08, Omer Homes
Satyana Rd.
Bat. 15, Campus de Beaulieu
Faisalabad 35042, Pakistan
Ph: 92 41 8501147
Fax: 92 41 8501146
Journal covering medical sciences. **Freq:** Quarterly. **Key Personnel:** Dr. P.D. Gupta, Editor-in-Chief, raiwind786@hotmail.com; Dr. Mahmoud Al-Sheyyab, Assoc. Ed.-in-Ch.; Dr. Jafar A. Qasem, Assoc. Ed.-in-Ch. **ISSN:** 1817-3055. **URL:** http://www.idosi.org/wjms/wjms.htm.

49303 ■ World Journal of Zoology
International Digital Organization for Scientific Information
P-08, Omer Homes
Satyana Rd.
Bat. 15, Campus de Beaulieu
Faisalabad 35042, Pakistan
Ph: 92 41 8501147
Fax: 92 41 8501146
Journal covering zoology. **Freq:** Quarterly. **Key Personnel:** Dr. Wahid Mohamed Ahmed, Editor-in-Chief; Dr. Marwan M. Muwalla, Editor-in-Chief; Muhammad Zeeshan, Managing Editor. **ISSN:** 1817-3098. **URL:** http://www.idosi.org/wjz/zoology.htm.

Hyderabad

49304 ■ Pakistan Broadcasting Corporation, Hyderabad-I - 1008 KHz
G-5 Constitutional Ave.
Islamabad 4400, Pakistan
Ph: 92 221 784065
E-mail: cfmpbchq@isb.comsats.net.pk; info@radio.gov.pk
Format: Educational; Music of Your Life; News. **Owner:** Pakistan Broadcasting Corporation, at above address. **Founded:** 1955. **Operating Hours:** 8:10 a.m.-12:05 a.m. **Wattage:** 120,000. **URL:** http://www.radio.gov.pk/index.asp.

49305 ■ Pakistan Broadcasting Corporation, Hyderabad-II - 1098 KHz
G-5 Constitutional Ave.
Islamabad 4400, Pakistan
Ph: 92 221 784065
E-mail: cfmpbchq@isb.comsats.net.pk; info@radio.gov.pk
Format: News; Music of Your Life; Educational. **Owner:** Pakistan Broadcasting Corporation, at above address. **Operating Hours:** 8:10 a.m.-12:05 a.m. **Wattage:** 10,000. **URL:** http://www.radio.gov.pk/index.asp.

Islamabad

49306 ■ Pakistan Journal of Agricultural Research
Pakistan Agricultural Research Council
PO Box 1031
Islamabad, Pakistan
Ph: 92 519 203071
Fax: 92 519 202968
Publisher E-mail: webmaster@parc.gov.pk
Journal covering agriculture. **Founded:** 1949. **Freq:** Quarterly. **ISSN:** 0251-0480. **Subscription Rates:** PRs 500 individuals; PRs 125 single issue; US$40 other countries; US$10 other countries single copy. **URL:**

http://www.parc.gov.pk/Pjar/pjar.html. **Circ:** Paid 1,000

49307 ■ Pakistan Journal of Hydrocarbon Research
Hydrocarbon Development Institute of Pakistan
Plot No. 18, St. 6, H-9/1
Islamabad, Pakistan
Ph: 92 51 9258301
Fax: 92 51 9258310
Publisher E-mail: info@hdip.com.pk
Journal reporting on pure and applied research in oil and gas exploration. **Founded:** 1989. **Freq:** Semiannual. **Key Personnel:** Shakeel Ahmed, Dir. Gen./Ch. Executive. **ISSN:** 1017-0626. **URL:** http://www.hdip.com.pk. **Circ:** Paid 500

49308 ■ Pakistan Journal of Medical Research
Pakistan Medical Research Council
Shahrah-e-Jumhuriat, Sector G-5/2
PO Box 2598
Islamabad 44000, Pakistan
Ph: 92 920 7386
Fax: 92 921 6774
Publisher E-mail: pmrc@comsats.net.pk
Journal covering clinical and biomedical research. **Founded:** July 1958. **Freq:** Quarterly. **Key Personnel:** Zulifiqar a. Bhutta, Editorial Advisory Board; Gregory Pappas, Editorial Advisory Board; Adnan A. Hyder, Editorial Advisory Board; Rashid Chotani, Editorial Advisory Board; Tariq Bhutta, Editorial Advisory Board; Sania Nishtar, Editorial Advisory Board; Huma Qureshi, Editor; Agha Sadaruddin, Asst. Ed.; Muhammad Yamin Satti, Tech. & Editorial Asst. **ISSN:** 0030-9842. **Subscription Rates:** PRs 800 individuals inland, post-paid; PRs 200 single issue post-paid; US$300 other countries post-paid. **URL:** http://www.pmrc.org.pk/pjmr_main.htm. **Circ:** Paid 1,000

49309 ■ Pakistan Journal of Scientific and Industrial Research
Pakistan Council of Scientific and Industrial Research
Constitution Ave.
Sector G-5/2
Islamabad, Pakistan
Ph: 92 51 9225395
Fax: 92 51 9219266
Publication E-mail: info@pjsir.org
Journal that reports on issues relating to scientific and industrial research. **Founded:** 1958. **Freq:** Monthly. **Key Personnel:** Ghulam Qadir Shaikh, Editor; Shagufta Y. Iqbal, Editor; Gulzar Hussain Jhatial, Editor. **ISSN:** 0030-9885. **Subscription Rates:** PRs 2000 individuals; US$400 other countries; PRs 350 single issue; US$70 other countries single copy. **URL:** http://www.pjsir.org/auth-instructions.php. **Circ:** Paid 800

49310 ■ PakTribune
House 6, Khyaban-e-Iqbal, Margalla Rd.
F-7/3
Islamabad, Pakistan
Ph: 92 51 111888666
Fax: 92 51 2871236
Publisher E-mail: editor@paktribune.com
Online news service for Pakistan. **Freq:** Daily. **Key Personnel:** Riaz Jafri, Editor-in-Chief, editor@paktribune.com. **Remarks:** Accepts advertising. **URL:** http://paktribune.com. **Circ:** (Not Reported)

49311 ■ Progressive Farming
Pakistan Agricultural Research Council
PO Box 1031
Islamabad, Pakistan
Ph: 92 519 203071
Fax: 92 519 202968
Publisher E-mail: webmaster@parc.gov.pk
Journal covering agriculture. **Founded:** 1981. **Freq:** Bimonthly. **URL:** http://www.parc.gov.pk/info_ser.html. **Circ:** Paid 1,000

49312 ■ Pulse Weekly
Mezzaine No.8, 47-W Dossul Arcade
Jinnah Ave., Blue Area
Islamabad, Pakistan
Ph: 92 51 812257
Newspaper. **Freq:** Weekly. **Key Personnel:** Dr. Shireen Mazari, Editor-in-Chief. **Remarks:** Accepts advertising. **URL:** http://www.angelfire.com/hi2/pulse. **Circ:** (Not Reported)

Circulation: ★ = ABC; △ = BPA; ♦ = CAC; • = CCAB; ❑ = VAC; ⊕ = PO Statement; ‡ = Publisher's Report; Boldface figures = sworn; Light figures = estimated.

49313 ■ Pakistan Broadcasting Corporation, Abbottabad - 1602 KHz
G-5 Constitutional Ave.
Islamabad 4400, Pakistan
Ph: 92 992 6070
E-mail: cfmpbchq@isb.comsats.net.pk; info@radio.gov.pk
Format: News; Music of Your Life; Educational. **Owner:** Pakistan Broadcasting Corporation, at above address. **Founded:** 1989. **Operating Hours:** 1:45 p.m.-7:15 p.m. **Wattage:** 250. **URL:** http://www.radio.gov.pk/index.asp.

49314 ■ Pakistan Broadcasting Corporation, Bahawalpur - 1341 KHz
G-5 Constitutional Ave.
Islamabad 4400, Pakistan
Ph: 92 6217162
E-mail: cfmpbchq@isb.comsats.net.pk; info@radio.gov.pk
Format: Educational; News; Music of Your Life. **Owner:** Pakistan Broadcasting Corporation, at above address. **Founded:** Aug. 18, 1975. **Operating Hours:** 1:50 p.m.-11:10 p.m. **Wattage:** 10,000. **URL:** http://www.radio.gov.pk/index.asp.

49315 ■ Pakistan Broadcasting Corporation, Chitral - 1584 KHz
G-5 Constitutional Ave.
Islamabad 4400, Pakistan
Ph: 92 933 412636
E-mail: cfmpbchq@isb.comsats.net.pk; info@radio.gov.pk
Format: Music of Your Life; Educational; News. **Owner:** Pakistan Broadcasting Corporation, at above address. **Operating Hours:** 3:45 p.m.-8:30 p.m. **Wattage:** 250. **URL:** http://www.radio.gov.pk/index.asp.

49316 ■ Pakistan Broadcasting Corporation, Dera Ismail Khan - 1404 KHz
G-5 Constitutional Ave.
Islamabad 4400, Pakistan
Ph: 92 961 810241
E-mail: cfmpbchq@isb.comsats.net.pk; info@radio.gov.pk
Format: Music of Your Life; Educational; News. **Owner:** Pakistan Broadcasting Corporation, at above address. **Founded:** 1981. **Operating Hours:** 1:55 p.m.-9:05 p.m. **Wattage:** 10,000. **URL:** http://www.radio.gov.pk/index.asp.

49317 ■ Pakistan Broadcasting Corporation, Faisalabad - 1476 KHz
G-5 Constitutional Ave.
Islamabad 4400, Pakistan
Ph: 92 41 9220148
E-mail: cfmpbchq@isb.comsats.net.pk; info@radio.gov.pk
Format: Educational; News; Music of Your Life. **Owner:** Pakistan Broadcasting Corporation, at above address. **Founded:** Sept. 15, 1982. **Operating Hours:** 8 a.m.-5:15 p.m. **Wattage:** 10,000. **URL:** http://www.radio.gov.pk/index.asp.

49318 ■ Pakistan Broadcasting Corporation, Gilgit - 1512 KHz
G-5 Constitutional Ave.
Islamabad 4400, Pakistan
Ph: 92 572 3259
E-mail: cfmpbchq@isb.comsats.net.pk; info@radio.gov.pk
Format: Music of Your Life; News; Educational. **Owner:** Pakistan Broadcasting Corporation, at above address. **Founded:** 1977. **Operating Hours:** 3:04 p.m.-10 p.m. **Wattage:** 10,000. **URL:** http://www.radio.gov.pk/index.asp.

Pakistan Broadcasting Corporation, Hyderabad-I - See Hyderabad

Pakistan Broadcasting Corporation, Hyderabad-II - See Hyderabad

49319 ■ Pakistan Broadcasting Corporation, Islamabad - 101 MHz
G-5, Constitutional Ave.
Islamabad, Pakistan
Ph: 92 51 81003558
E-mail: info@radio.gov.pk
Format: Classical; Folk; Contemporary Hit Radio (CHR). **Owner:** Pakistan Broadcasting Corporation, at above address. **Founded:** Oct. 1998. **Operating Hours:** 1745-2230. **Wattage:** 100,000. **URL:** http://www.radio.gov.pk/index.asp.

49320 ■ Pakistan Broadcasting Corporation, Islamabad - 585 KHz
G-5 Constitutional Ave.
Islamabad 4400, Pakistan
Ph: 92 51 81003558
E-mail: cfmpbchq@isb.comsats.net.pk; info@radio.gov.pk
Format: News; Educational; Music of Your Life. **Owner:** Pakistan Broadcasting Corporation, at above address. **Founded:** 1977. **Operating Hours:** 5:45 p.m.-10:30 p.m. **Wattage:** 1,000,000. **URL:** http://www.radio.gov.pk/index.asp.

Pakistan Broadcasting Corporation, Karachi-I - See Karachi

Pakistan Broadcasting Corporation, Karachi-II - See Karachi

49321 ■ Pakistan Broadcasting Corporation, Khairpur - 927 KHz
G-5 Constitutional Ave.
Islamabad 4400, Pakistan
Ph: 92 7924425
E-mail: cfmpbchq@isb.comsats.net.pk; info@radio.gov.pk
Format: News; Educational. **Owner:** Pakistan Broadcasting Corporation, at above address. **Founded:** May 7, 1986. **Operating Hours:** 8:24 a.m.-11:08 p.m. **Wattage:** 100,000. **URL:** http://www.radio.gov.pk/index.asp.

49322 ■ Pakistan Broadcasting Corporation, Khuzdar - 567 KHz
G-5 Constitutional Ave.
Islamabad 4400, Pakistan
Ph: 92 871 412730
E-mail: cfmpbchq@isb.comsats.net.pk; info@radio.gov.pk
Format: Sports; News; Music of Your Life; Educational. **Owner:** Pakistan Broadcasting Corporation, at above address. **Founded:** 1981. **Operating Hours:** 5:15 p.m.-11:10 p.m. **Wattage:** 300,000. **URL:** http://www.radio.gov.pk/index.asp.

49323 ■ Pakistan Broadcasting Corporation, Lahore-I - 630 KHz
G-5 Constitutional Ave.
Islamabad 4400, Pakistan
Ph: 92 42 9200681
E-mail: cfmpbchq@isb.comsats.net.pk; info@radio.gov.pk
Format: Music of Your Life; News; Educational. **Owner:** Pakistan Broadcasting Corporation, at above address. **Founded:** 1937. **Operating Hours:** 8:20 a.m.-12 a.m. **Wattage:** 100,000. **URL:** http://www.radio.gov.pk/index.asp.

Pakistan Broadcasting Corporation, Lahore-II - See Lahore

49324 ■ Pakistan Broadcasting Corporation, Loralai - 1251 KHz
G-5 Constitutional Ave.
Islamabad 4400, Pakistan
Ph: 92 821 410785
E-mail: cfmpbchq@isb.comsats.net.pk; info@radio.gov.pk
Format: News; Music of Your Life; Educational. **Owner:** Pakistan Broadcasting Corporation, at above address. **Founded:** 1996. **Operating Hours:** 4:45 p.m.-9:15 p.m. **Wattage:** 10,000. **URL:** http://www.radio.gov.pk/index.asp.

49325 ■ Pakistan Broadcasting Corporation, Multan - 1035 KHz
G-5 Constitutional Ave.
Islamabad 4400, Pakistan
Ph: 92 61 43688
E-mail: cfmpbchq@isb.comsats.net.pk; info@radio.gov.pk
Format: News; Music of Your Life; Educational. **Owner:** Pakistan Broadcasting Corporation, at above address. **Founded:** 1970. **Operating Hours:** 8 a.m.-12 a.m. **Wattage:** 120,000. **URL:** http://www.radio.gov.pk/index.asp.

49326 ■ Pakistan Broadcasting Corporation, Peshawar - 540 KHz
G-5, Constitutional Ave.
Islamabad 4400, Pakistan
Ph: 92 91 9210293
E-mail: info@radio.gov.pk
Format: Talk; Full Service. **Owner:** Pakistan Broadcasting Corporation, at above address. **Founded:** July 16, 1942. **Operating Hours:** 0800-2302. **Wattage:** 10,000. **URL:** http://www.radio.gov.pk/index.asp.

Pakistan Broadcasting Corporation, Peshawar-II - See Peshawar

49327 ■ Pakistan Broadcasting Corporation, Quetta - 855 KHz
G-5, Constitutional Ave.
Islamabad, Pakistan
Ph: 92 81 9202393
E-mail: info@radio.gov.pk
Format: Talk; Full Service. **Owner:** Pakistan Broadcasting Corporation, at above address. **Founded:** Oct. 17, 1956. **Operating Hours:** 0810-2310. **Wattage:** 10,000. **URL:** http://www.radio.gov.pk/index.asp.

49328 ■ Pakistan Broadcasting Corporation, Quetta - 756 KHz
G-5, Constitutional Ave.
Islamabad, Pakistan
Ph: 92 81 9202393
E-mail: info@radio.gov.pk
Format: Full Service. **Owner:** Pakistan Broadcasting Corporation, at above address. **Founded:** Oct. 17, 1956. **Operating Hours:** 0810-2310. **Wattage:** 10,000. **URL:** http://www.radio.gov.pk/index.asp.

Pakistan Broadcasting Corporation, Quetta-I - See Quetta

Pakistan Broadcasting Corporation, Quetta-II - See Quetta

49329 ■ Pakistan Broadcasting Corporation, Rawalpindi - 102
G-5 Constitutional Ave.
Islamabad 4400, Pakistan
E-mail: cfmpbchq@isb.comsats.net.pk; info@radio.gov.pk
Format: News. **Owner:** Pakistan Broadcasting Corporation, at above address. **Founded:** 1949. **Operating Hours:** 7 a.m.-9 a.m.; 6 p.m.-11 p.m. **Wattage:** 100,000. **URL:** http://www.radio.gov.pk/index.asp.

Pakistan Broadcasting Corporation, Rawalpindi - See Rawalpindi

49330 ■ Pakistan Broadcasting Corporation, Sibbi - 1584 KHz
G-5 Constitutional Ave.
Islamabad 4400, Pakistan
E-mail: cfmpbchq@isb.comsats.net.pk; info@radio.gov.pk
Format: Educational; News; Music of Your Life. **Owner:** Pakistan Broadcasting Corporation, at above address. **Founded:** 1989. **Operating Hours:** 12:55 p.m.-4:15 p.m. **Wattage:** 250. **URL:** http://www.radio.gov.pk/index.asp.

49331 ■ Pakistan Broadcasting Corporation, Skardu - 1557 KHz
G-5 Constitutional Ave.
Islamabad 4400, Pakistan
Ph: 92 575 2441
E-mail: cfmpbchq@isb.comsats.net.pk; info@radio.gov.pk
Format: Educational; News; Music of Your Life. **Owner:** Pakistan Broadcasting Corporation, at above address. **Founded:** 1977. **Operating Hours:** 3 p.m.-10 p.m. **Wattage:** 10,000. **URL:** http://www.radio.gov.pk/index.asp.

49332 ■ Pakistan Broadcasting Corporation, Turbat - 1584 KHz
G-5 Constitutional Ave.
Islamabad 4400, Pakistan
Ph: 92 861 412330
E-mail: cfmpbchq@isb.comsats.net.pk; info@radio.gov.pk
Format: Music of Your Life; News; Educational. **Owner:** Pakistan Broadcasting Corporation, at above address. **Founded:** 1981. **Operating Hours:** 4:04 p.m.-11:10 p.m. **Wattage:** 250. **URL:** http://www.radio.gov.pk/index.asp.

49333 ■ Pakistan Broadcasting Corporation, Zhob - 1449 KHz
G-5 Constitutional Ave.
Islamabad 4400, Pakistan
Ph: 92 822 412268
E-mail: info@radio.gov.pk
Format: News; Music of Your Life; Educational. **Owner:** Pakistan Broadcasting Corporation, at above address. **Founded:** 1996. **Operating Hours:** 5 p.m.-9:07 p.m.

Wattage: 10,000. **URL:** http://www.radio.gov.pk/index. asp.

49334 ■ Radio Pakistan-AM - 585 KHz
G-5 Constitutional Ave.
Islamabad, Pakistan
Ph: 92 51 81003558
E-mail: info@radio.gov.pk
Format: Educational; Information; News. **Owner:** Pakistan Broadcasting Corporation, at above address. **Wattage:** 1000. **URL:** http://www.radio.gov.pk.

49335 ■ Radio Pakistan-AM - 1260 KHz
G-5 Constitutional Ave.
Islamabad, Pakistan
Ph: 92 51 522975
E-mail: info@radio.gov.pk
Format: Educational; Information; News. **Owner:** Pakistan Broadcasting Corporation, at above address. **URL:** http://www.radio.gov.pk.

49336 ■ Radio Pakistan-AM - 585 KHz
G-5 Constitutional Ave.
Islamabad, Pakistan
Ph: 92 51 81003558
E-mail: info@radio.gov.pk
Format: Educational; Information; News. **Owner:** Pakistan Broadcasting Corporation, at above address. **URL:** http://www.radio.gov.pk.

49337 ■ Radio Pakistan-AM - 630 KHz
G-5 Constitutional Ave.
Islamabad, Pakistan
Ph: 92 42 9200681
E-mail: info@radio.gov.pk
Format: Educational; Information; News. **Owner:** Pakistan Broadcasting Corporation, at above address. **Operating Hours:** Continuous. **URL:** http://www.radio. gov.pk.

49338 ■ Radio Pakistan-FM - 101 MHz
G-5 Constitutional Ave.
Islamabad, Pakistan
E-mail: info@radio.gov.pk
Format: News; Public Radio. **Owner:** Pakistan Broadcasting Corporation, at above address. **Operating Hours:** Continuous. **URL:** http://www.radio.gov.pk.

Karachi

49339 ■ Aurora
The DAWN Group of Newspapers
Haroon House
Dr. Ziauddin Ahmed Rd. .
Karachi 74200, Pakistan
Ph: 92 111 444777
Fax: 92 21 5693995
Publisher E-mail: webmaster@dawn.com
Trade magazine covering products, marketing, advertising and the media for advertising executives. **Freq:** Bimonthly. **Subscription Rates:** US$22 individuals Africa, Asia, Central and Latin America; US$26 individuals Australia, North Central and Latin America; PRs 100 individuals. **Remarks:** Accepts advertising. **URL:** http:// www.dawn.com/fixed/group/publicat.htm7; http://www dawn.com/fixed/subs/aurora.htm. **Circ:** (Not Reported)

49340 ■ Business Recorder
Recorder House
531 Business Recorder Rd.
Karachi 74550, Pakistan
Ph: 92 225 0311
Fax: 92 228 644
Publication E-mail: cir.khi@br-mail.com; ed.khi@br-mail. com
Trade newspaper covering business and economics in Pakistan. **Freq:** Daily. **Key Personnel:** M.A. Zuberi, Editor-in-Chief. **URL:** http://www.brecorder.com/.

49341 ■ Current Analytical Chemistry
Bentham Science Publishers Ltd.
c/o Atta-ur-Rahman, Ed.-in-Ch.
International Centre for Chemical
and Biological Sciences
University of Karachi
Karachi 75270, Pakistan
Publisher E-mail: subscriptions@bentham.org
Journal publishing authoritative reviews, written by experts in the field on all the most recent advances in analytical chemistry. **Freq:** Quarterly. **Key Personnel:**

Atta-ur Rahman, Editor-in-Chief; S. Achilefu, Editorial Advisory Board. **ISSN:** 1573-4110. **Subscription Rates:** US$860 individuals print corporate; US$860 individuals corporate online; US$1,030 individuals print and online corporate; US$420 individuals academic print; US$420 individuals academic online; US$460 individuals academic print and online; US$170 individuals. **Remarks:** Accepts advertising. **URL:** http://www.bentham.org/cac/ index.htm. **Circ:** (Not Reported)

49342 ■ Current Bioactive Compounds
Bentham Science Publishers Ltd.
c/o Atta-ur-Rahman, Ed.-in-Ch.
International Centre for Chemical
and Biological Sciences
University of Karachi
Karachi 75270, Pakistan
Publisher E-mail: subscriptions@bentham.org
Journal providing updates to researchers about new bioactive compounds with proven activities in various biological screenings and pharmacological models. **Freq:** Quarterly. **Key Personnel:** Atta-ur Rahman, Editor-in-Chief; A.T. Balaban, Editorial Advisory Board; E. Block, Editorial Advisory Board; Iqbal M. Choudhary, Editor-in-Chief; L. Bohlin, Editorial Advisory Board; W. Fenical, Editorial Advisory Board. **ISSN:** 1573-4072. **Subscription Rates:** US$460 institutions academic print; US$460 institutions academic online; US$510 institutions academic print and online; US$190 individuals print; US$960 institutions corporate print; US$960 institutions corporate online; US$1,150 institutions corporate print and online. **Remarks:** Accepts advertising. **URL:** http://www.bentham.org/cbc/index. htm. **Circ:** (Not Reported)

49343 ■ Current Nanoscience
Bentham Science Publishers Ltd.
c/o Atta-ur-Rahman, Ed.-in-Ch.
International Centre for Chemical
and Biological Sciences
University of Karachi
Karachi 75270, Pakistan
Publisher E-mail: subscriptions@bentham.org
Journal publishing authoritative reviews and original research reports, written by experts in the field on all the most recent advances in nanoscience and nanotechnology. **Freq:** Quarterly. **Key Personnel:** Atta-ur Rahman, Editor-in-Chief; M. Fan, Assoc. Ed.; C. Berry, Editorial Advisory Board. **ISSN:** 1573-4137. **Subscription Rates:** US$460 institutions academic, print; US$190 individuals; US$460 institutions academic, online; US$510 institutions academic, print and online; US$960 institutions corporate, print; US$960 institutions corporate, online; PRs 1,150 institutions corporate, print and online. **Remarks:** Accepts advertising. **URL:** http:// www.bentham.org/cnano/index.htm. **Circ:** (Not Reported)

49344 ■ Current Pharmaceutical Analysis
Bentham Science Publishers Ltd.
c/o Atta-ur-Rahman, Ed.-in-Ch.
International Centre for Chemical
and Biological Sciences
University of Karachi
Karachi 75270, Pakistan
Publisher E-mail: subscriptions@bentham.org
Journal publishing authoritative reviews, written by experts in the field on all the most recent advances in pharmaceutical and biomedical analysis. **Freq:** Quarterly. **Key Personnel:** Atta-ur Rahman, Editor-in-Chief; A. Bolton, Editorial Advisory Board; N.D. Danielson, Editorial Advisory Board; H.Y. Aboul-Enein, Editorial Advisory Board; J. Angerer, Editorial Advisory Board. **ISSN:** 1573-4129. **Subscription Rates:** US$460 institutions academic, print; US$190 individuals; US$460 institutions academic, online; US$960 institutions corporate, online; US$960 institutions corporate, print. **Remarks:** Accepts advertising. **URL:** http://www. bentham.org/cpa/index.htm. **Circ:** (Not Reported)

49345 ■ Daily Jang
Jang Group of Newspapers
Printing House
I.I. Chundrigar Rd.
Karachi 74200, Pakistan
Ph: 92 212 637111
Fax: 92 212 636066
Urdu language general newspaper. **Freq:** Daily. Re-

marks: Accepts advertising. **URL:** http://jang.com.pk/ jang/feb2009-daily/14-02-2009/index.html. **Circ:** (Not Reported)

49346 ■ Dawn
The DAWN Group of Newspapers
Haroon House
Dr. Ziauddin Ahmed Rd.
Karachi 74200, Pakistan
Ph: 92 111 444777
Fax: 92 21 5693995
Publisher E-mail: webmaster@dawn.com
English language general newspaper. **Founded:** Oct. 26, 1941. **Freq:** Daily. **Key Personnel:** Abbas Nasir, Editor; Quaid-i-Azam Mohammad Ali Jinnah, Founder; Hameed Haroon, Publisher. **Remarks:** Accepts advertising. **URL:** http://www.dawn.com/fixed/group/ publicat.htm1. **Circ:** 138,000

49347 ■ Dawn Magazine
The DAWN Group of Newspapers
Haroon House
Dr. Ziauddin Ahmed Rd.
Karachi 74200, Pakistan
Ph: 92 111 444777
Fax: 92 21 5693995
Publisher E-mail: webmaster@dawn.com
Consumer magazine covering local lifestyle and issues. **Freq:** Weekly (Sun.). **URL:** http://www.dawn.com/ weekly/dmag/dmag.htm.

49348 ■ Eastern Worker
Bureau of Labour Publications
8 Business Ctr., Ground Fl.
Mumtaz Hasan Rd.
PO Box 5833
Karachi 74000, Pakistan
Ph: 92 21 2414975
Publisher E-mail: blplabourlaws@yahoo.com
Journal featuring articles on labor and industrial relations. **Subtitle:** Journal on Labour Laws, Labour-Management Relations & Socio-Economic Affairs. **Founded:** 1950. **Freq:** Bimonthly. **Key Personnel:** P. Shafi, PhD, Editor. **Subscription Rates:** Rs 1,200 individuals. **Remarks:** Advertising accepted; rates available upon request. **URL:** http://www.blplabourlaws.com/. **Circ:** Paid 1,000

49349 ■ Fashion Mag
Jang Group of Newspapers
Printing House
I.I. Chundrigar Rd.
Karachi 74200, Pakistan
Ph: 92 212 637111
Fax: 92 212 636066
Pakistani women's fashion magazine. **Freq:** Weekly. **Remarks:** Accepts advertising. **URL:** http://thenews. com.pk/archive/fashion/FashionMAG.aspx. **Circ:** (Not Reported)

49350 ■ Hamdard Islamicus
Hamdard Foundation Pakistan
Al-Majeed, Hamdard Centre
Nazimabad No.3
Karachi 74600, Pakistan
Ph: 92 216 616001
Fax: 92 216 611755
Publisher E-mail: hfp@hamdardfoundation.org
Journal featuring articles pertaining to the Islamic religion. **Founded:** 1978. **Freq:** Quarterly. **ISSN:** 0250-7196. **URL:** http://www.hamdardfoundation.org. **Circ:** Paid 2,000

49351 ■ Hamdard Medicus
Hamdard Foundation Pakistan
Al-Majeed, Hamdard Centre
Nazimabad No.3
Karachi 74600, Pakistan
Ph: 92 216 616001
Fax: 92 216 611755
Publisher E-mail: hfp@hamdardfoundation.org
Journal featuring articles covering medical sciences. **Subtitle:** Journal of Science and Medicine. **Founded:** 1957. **Freq:** Quarterly. **ISSN:** 0250-4723. **Remarks:** Advertising accepted; rates available upon request. **URL:** http://www.hamdardfoundation.org. **Circ:** Paid 2,000

49352 ■ Hamdard Naunehal
Hamdard Foundation Pakistan

Circulation: ★ = ABC; △ = BPA; ♦ = CAC; ✦ = CCAB; ❏ = VAC; ⊕ = PO Statement; ‡ = Publisher's Report; Boldface figures = sworn; Light figures = estimated.

Gale Directory of Publications & Broadcast Media/147th Ed.   5327

Al-Majeed, Hamdard Centre
Nazimabad No.3
Karachi 74600, Pakistan
Ph: 92 216 616001
Fax: 92 216 611755
Publication E-mail: hamdard@khi.pk.net.com.ph
Publisher E-mail: hfp@hamdardfoundation.org
Magazine covering articles of children's interest. Providing a platform for their views and talents. **Founded:** 1952. **Freq:** Monthly. **Key Personnel:** Masood Ahmed Barakaatee, Ch. Ed.; Sadia Rashid, Publisher; Furqan Ahmad Shamsi, Advertising Dir.; Khwaja Arshad Hussain, Accounts Dir.; Shaheed Hakeem Muhammad Said, Founder. **ISSN:** 0259-3734. **Subscription Rates:** PRs 15 single issue; PRs 160 individuals. **URL:** http://www.hamdardfoundation.org/naunehal.php.

49353 ■ Herald
The DAWN Group of Newspapers
Haroon House
Dr. Ziauddin Ahmed Rd.
Karachi 74200, Pakistan
Ph: 92 111 444777
Fax: 92 21 5693995
Publisher E-mail: webmaster@dawn.com
Consumer magazine covering current affairs and news in English. **Freq:** Monthly. **Key Personnel:** Idrees Bakhtiar, Assoc. Ed.; Moosa Kaleem, Reporter; Madiha Sattar, Sen. Asst. Ed.; Muhammad Badar Alam, Editor; Niloufer Patel, Dir., Circulation; Masood Hamid, Dir., Mktg. **Remarks:** Accepts advertising. **URL:** http://www.dawn.com/fixed/group/publicat.htm7. **Circ:** (Not Reported)

49354 ■ Images
The DAWN Group of Newspapers
Haroon House
Dr. Ziauddin Ahmed Rd.
Karachi 74200, Pakistan
Ph: 92 111 444777
Fax: 92 21 5693995
Publisher E-mail: webmaster@dawn.com
Consumer magazine covering local issues and lifestyle. **Freq:** Weekly (Sun.). **URL:** http://www.dawn.com/weekly/images/images.htm; http://www.dawn.com/fixed/group/publicat.htm.

49355 ■ Infectious Diseases Journal
Creative Endeavors
3/C, 10th St.
Khayaban-e-Shamsheer, Phase V
DHA
Karachi 75000, Pakistan
Journal featuring articles and information related to various infectious diseases. **Freq:** Quarterly. **Key Personnel:** Dr. Salman Faridi, Editor; Naila Baig Ansari, Publisher, nb@ansari.com. **ISSN:** 1027-0299. **URL:** http://www.angelfire.com/id/journal/index.html.

49356 ■ Investor's Business & Financial Journal
Jang Group of Newspapers
Printing House
I.I. Chundrigar Rd.
Karachi 74200, Pakistan
Ph: 92 212 637111
Fax: 92 212 636066
Journal covering business and finance for investors. **Freq:** Monthly. **Remarks:** Accepts advertising. **URL:** http://jang.com.pk/thenews/investors/oct2006/index.html. **Circ:** (Not Reported)

49357 ■ Journal of College of Physicians and Surgeons Pakistan
College of Physicians and Surgeons Pakistan
7th Central St.
Defence Housing Authority
Karachi 75500, Pakistan
Ph: 92 21 9207100
Fax: 92 21 9207120
Publication E-mail: publications@cpsp.edu.pk
Publisher E-mail: administration@cpsp.edu.pk
Journal featuring articles, case reports, review articles, short communications, commentaries and survey reports on medical subjects. **Founded:** 1991. **Freq:** Monthly. **Key Personnel:** Jamshed Akhtar, Editor; Zafar Ullah Chaudhry, Editor-in-Chief; Muhammad Zafaruddin, Managing Editor; Abdul Sattar Memon, Assoc. Ed.; Abdul Ghaffar, Editorial Asst. **ISSN:** 1022-386X. **Remarks:** Advertising accepted; rates available upon request. **URL:** http://www.cpsp.edu.pk/index.php?code=

MjF8TGVmdHxqY3BzcC5waHB8MA==. **Circ:** Paid 5,000

49358 ■ Journal of the Pakistan Medical Association
Pakistan Medical Association
P.M.A. House
Aga Khan III Rd.
Karachi 74400, Pakistan
Ph: 92 21 5418192
Fax: 92 21 5418192
Publication E-mail: jpma_jpma@hotmail.com
Publisher E-mail: jpma_jpma@hotmail.com
Medical journal. **Founded:** 1950. **Freq:** Monthly. **Key Personnel:** Fatema Jawad, Editor-in-Chief, editor@jpma.org.pk; Najum F. Mahmudi, Mng. Sec.; Dr. Masood A. Shaikh, Chm.; Huma Qureshi, Assoc. Ed.-in-Ch.; Qudsia Anjum Fasih, Assoc. Ed., associate@jpma.org.pk. **ISSN:** 0030-9982. **Subscription Rates:** PRs 3,000 individuals; US$110 individuals. **URL:** http://www.jpma.org.pk. **Circ:** Paid 6,000

49359 ■ Labour Code of Pakistan
Bureau of Labour Publications
8 Business Ctr., Ground Fl.
Mumtaz Hasan Rd.
PO Box 5833
Karachi 74000, Pakistan
Ph: 92 21 2414975
Publisher E-mail: blplabourlaws@yahoo.com
Journal featuring articles related to labor and industrial relations in Pakistan. **Founded:** 1953. **Freq:** Irregular. **Key Personnel:** P. Shafi, PhD, Editor; M. Shafi, Editor. **Subscription Rates:** PRs 500 individuals. **URL:** http://www.blplabourlaws.com/plc.htm.

49360 ■ Letters in Drug Design & Discovery
Bentham Science Publishers Ltd.
c/o Atta-ur-Rahman, Ed.-in-Ch.
International Centre for Chemical
and Biological Sciences
University of Karachi
Karachi 75270, Pakistan
Ph: 92 21 34824924
Fax: 92 21 34819018
Publisher E-mail: subscriptions@bentham.org
Journal publishing original letters on all areas of rational drug design and discovery including medicinal chemistry, in-silico drug design, combinatorial chemistry, high-throughput screening, drug targets, and structure-activity relationships. **Freq:** 8/yr. **Key Personnel:** Atta-ur Rahman, Editor-in-Chief; Y. Okada, Regional Ed.; D.J. Waxman, Assoc. Ed.; E.J. Lavoie, Assoc. Ed.; A. Makriyannis, Assoc. Ed.; J.L. Neumeyer, Regional Ed.; B. Wang, Assoc. Ed.; M. Asanuma, Editorial Advisory Board. **ISSN:** 1570-1808. **Subscription Rates:** US$1,060 institutions academic, print; US$400 individuals print; US$1,060 institutions academic, online; US$1,920 institutions corporate, online; US$1,920 institutions corporate, print. **Remarks:** Accepts advertising. **URL:** http://www.bentham.org/lddd/. **Circ:** (Not Reported)

49361 ■ Letters in Organic Chemistry
Bentham Science Publishers Ltd.
c/o Atta-ur-Rahman, Ed.-in-Ch.
International Centre for Chemical
and Biological Sciences
University of Karachi
Karachi 75270, Pakistan
Ph: 92 21 34824924
Fax: 92 21 34819018
Publisher E-mail: subscriptions@bentham.org
Journal publishing original letters on all areas of organic chemistry including synthesis, bioorganic, medicinal, natural products, organometallic, supramolecular, molecular recognition and physical organic chemistry. **Freq:** 8/yr. **Key Personnel:** Atta-ur Rahman, Editor-in-Chief; M. Fan, Regional Ed.; M. Yus, Regional Ed.; P. Vanelle, Assoc. Ed.; J. Cossy, Editorial Advisory Board; C. Bolm, Editorial Advisory Board. **ISSN:** 1570-1786. **Subscription Rates:** US$1,160 institutions academic, print; US$400 individuals; US$1,160 institutions academic, online; US$1,280 institutions academic, print and online; US$2,120 institutions corporate, print; US$2,120 institutions corporate, online; PRs 2,540 institutions corporate, print and online. **Remarks:** Accepts advertising. **URL:** http://www.bentham.org/loc/index.htm. **Circ:** (Not Reported)

49362 ■ Management Accountant
Institute of Cost and Management Accountants of Pakistan
ICMAP Bldg., ST-18/C, Block 6
Gulshan-e-Iqbal
PO Box 17642
Karachi 75300, Pakistan
Ph: 92 21 9243900
Fax: 92 21 9243342
Publisher E-mail: ed@icmap.com.pk
Journal covering professional management accountancy, information technology and other topics in order to keep students and members updated. **Founded:** 1962. **Freq:** Monthly. **Key Personnel:** Hasan A. Bilgrami, President; Mohammad Hanif, Vice President; Zia-ul Mustafa Awan, Honorary Sec. **ISSN:** 1027-7536. **Subscription Rates:** PRs 3,000 individuals for fellow member; PRs 2,500 individuals for associate member. **Remarks:** Advertising accepted; rates available upon request. **URL:** http://www.icmap.com.pk/ma.htm. **Circ:** Paid 10,000

49363 ■ Medicinal Chemistry
Bentham Science Publishers Ltd.
c/o Atta-ur-Rahman, Ed.-in-Ch.
International Centre for Chemical
and Biological Sciences
University of Karachi
Karachi 75270, Pakistan
Ph: 92 21 34824924
Fax: 92 21 34819018
Publisher E-mail: subscriptions@bentham.org
Journal covering all the latest outstanding developments in medicinal chemistry and rational drug design. **Freq:** Bimonthly. **Key Personnel:** Atta-ur Rahman, Editor-in-Chief; S. Balaz, Editorial Advisory Board; William J. Hoekstra, Co-Ed.; D. Fabbro, Editorial Advisory Board; K.C. Chou, Assoc. Ed.; S. Ahmed, Editorial Advisory Board; Andreas Hilgeroth, Co-Ed.; Z. Debyser, Editorial Advisory Board; B. Christensen, Editorial Advisory Board. **ISSN:** 1573-4064. **Subscription Rates:** US$610 institutions academic, print; US$190 individuals; US$610 institutions academic, online; US$670 institutions academic, print and online; US$980 institutions corporate, print; US$980 institutions corporate, online; PRs 1,180 institutions corporate, print and online. **Remarks:** Accepts advertising. **URL:** http://www.bentham.org/mc/index.htm. **Circ:** (Not Reported)

49364 ■ Mini-Reviews in Organic Chemistry
Bentham Science Publishers Ltd.
c/o Atta-ur-Rahman, Ed.-in-Ch.
International Centre for Chemical
and Biological Sciences
University of Karachi
Karachi 75270, Pakistan
Publisher E-mail: subscriptions@bentham.org
Journal publishing original reviews on all areas of organic chemistry including synthesis, bioorganic, medicinal, natural products, organometallic, supramolecular, molecular recognition, and physical organic chemistry. **Freq:** Quarterly. **Key Personnel:** Atta-ur Rahman, Editor-in-Chief; A. Attygalle, Editorial Advisory Board; H.M.L. Davies, Assoc. Ed.; A. Krief, Assoc. Ed.; Z.J. Witczak, Assoc. Ed.; W. Boland, Editorial Advisory Board. **ISSN:** 1570-193X. **Subscription Rates:** US$570 institutions academic, print; US$180 individuals; US$570 institutions academic, online; US$630 institutions academic, print and online; US$1,010 institutions corporate, print; US$1,010 institutions corporate, online; PRs 1,210 institutions corporate, print and online. **Remarks:** Accepts advertising. **URL:** http://bentham.org/mroc/. **Circ:** (Not Reported)

49365 ■ The News International
Jang Group of Newspapers
Printing House
I.I. Chundrigar Rd.
Karachi 74200, Pakistan
Ph: 92 212 637111
Fax: 92 212 636066
English language newspaper covering news in Pakistan. **Freq:** Daily. **Key Personnel:** Mir Shakil-Ur-Rahman, Editor-in-Chief. **ISSN:** 1563-9479. **Remarks:** Accepts advertising. **URL:** http://www.thenews.com.pk/. **Ad Rates:** BW: PRs 2,600. **Circ:** 140,000

49366 ■ Pakistan Accountant
Institute of Chartered Accountants of Pakistan

Chartered Accountants Ave.
Clifton
Karachi 75600, Pakistan
Ph: 92 21 111000422
Fax: 92 21 9251626
Journal covering accounting. **Founded:** 1963. **Freq:** Bimonthly. **Key Personnel:** Adnan Zaman, Editor-in-Chief. **ISSN:** 0030-9621. **Subscription Rates:** PRs 200 individuals; US$40 other countries; PRs 150 students; PRs 30 students single copy; PRs 40 single issue; US$10 other countries single copy. **URL:** http://www.icap.org.pk. **Circ:** Paid 1,400

49367 ■ Pakistan Christian Post
912-B UNI Shopping Centre
A. H. Rd. Saddar
Karachi, Pakistan
Publication E-mail: pakistanchristianpost@comcast.net
Publisher E-mail: pakistanchristianpost@comcast.net
Newspaper for Pakistani Christians. **Freq:** Monthly. **Key Personnel:** Dr. Nazir S. Bhatti, Editor, nazirbhattipcc@aol.com; Salim Balouch, Resident Ed. - Pakistan; Dr. Stephen Gill, Resident Ed. - Canada. **Remarks:** Accepts advertising. **URL:** http://www.pakistanchristianpost.com. **Circ:** (Not Reported)

49368 ■ Pakistan Journal of Botany
Pakistan Botanical Society
Dr. Abdul Ghaffar , Ch.Ed.
Dept. of Botany
University of Karachi
Karachi 75270, Pakistan
Ph: 92 221 4387867
Publisher E-mail: pakjbot@yahoo.com
Journal covering crop physiology and current advances in ecological and environmental sciences. **Founded:** 1969. **Freq:** Semiannual. **Key Personnel:** Dr. M. Ashraf, Subject Ed., ashrafm@fsd.paknet.com.pk; Dr. Abdul Ghaffar, Editor-in-Chief, shaji@super.net.pk; Dr. Shahida Hasnain, Subject Ed., genetic@brain.net.pk. **ISSN:** 0556-3321. **URL:** http://www.pakbs.org/pjbot/pjhtmls/PJB.html. **Circ:** Controlled 1,000

49369 ■ Pakistan Journal of Medical Sciences
Professional Medical Publications
Rm. No. 522, 5th Fl., Panorama Centre
Bldg. No. 2, Saddar
PO Box 8766
Karachi, Pakistan
Ph: 92 21 5689285
Fax: 92 21 5689860
Publication E-mail: pjms@pjms.com.pk
Publisher E-mail: pulse@pulsepakistan.com
Journal covering case reports of interesting and rare diseases and original research articles. **Founded:** 1984. **Freq:** Quarterly. **Key Personnel:** Shaukat Ali Jawaid, Managing Editor; Maqbool H. Jafary, Ch. Ed.; Mubarak Ali, Production Ed.; Mohammad Perwaiz Iqbal, Editorial Board; Azam Samdani, Editorial Board; Nazeer B. Khan, Editorial Board; H.R. Ahmad, Editorial Board; A. Samad, Editorial Board. **ISSN:** 1681-715X. **Subscription Rates:** PRs 2,000 individuals Pakistan; US$50 individuals Middle East; US$70 U.S. and Canada; US$35 other countries saarc countries; US$50 other countries China and Japan. **Remarks:** Advertising accepted; rates available upon request. **URL:** http://www.pjms.com.pk/. **Circ:** Paid 2,000

49370 ■ Pakistan Journal of Pathology
Pakistan Association of Pathologists
Sindlab Private Ltd.
Z-74, D.M.C. Society, Tariq Rd.
Karachi 74800, Pakistan
Ph: 92 91 9212041
Publisher E-mail: mnasimkhan@hotmail.com
Journal reporting on the latest news on pathology. **Founded:** 1990. **Freq:** Monthly. **Key Personnel:** Farooq Ahmad Khan, Editor-in-Chief. **ISSN:** 1024-6193. **Subscription Rates:** Included in membership. **Remarks:** Advertising accepted; rates available upon request. **URL:** http://www.pakpathologists.org/. **Circ:** (Not Reported)

49371 ■ Pakistan Journal of Pharmaceutical Sciences
University of Karachi
Faculty of Pharmacy
Faculty of Pharmacy
University of Karachi

Karachi 75270, Pakistan
Publication E-mail: pakjps@hotmail.com
Publisher E-mail: info@uok.edu.pk
Journal covering issues relating to pharmaceutical chemistry, pharmaceutics, pharmacognosy, pharmacology, and related studies in toxicology. **Freq:** Quarterly. **Key Personnel:** Dr. Muhammad Arif, Advisory Board; Dr. Ghazala H. Rizwani, Editor-in-Chief; Dr. Mansoor Ahmed, Advisory Board; Abdel-Aziz El-Basyouni Mohamed Wahbi, International Advisory Board; Dr. Shed Waseemuddin Ahmed, Editor-in-Chief, ahmed55@yahoo.com; Zafar Alam Mahmood, International Advisory Board; Judith Hohmann, International Advisory Board; Iqbal Ramzan, International Advisory Board. **ISSN:** 1011-601X. **URL:** http://www.pjps.pk; http://www.uok.edu.pk/faculties/pharmacy/publications.php.

49372 ■ Pakistan Textile Journal
B4 2nd Fl., 64/21, Miran Mohd Shah Rd.
Karachi, Pakistan
Ph: 92 21 4533616
Fax: 92 21 5206188
Publication E-mail: ptj@cyber.net.pk
Publisher E-mail: ptj@cyber.net.pk
Journal that reports on innovations in spinning, weaving, threading, knitting, non-woven, embroidery, dyeing, fabrics and garments. **Founded:** 1950. **Freq:** Monthly. **Key Personnel:** Amina Baqai, Editor-in-Chief; Dr. Noor Ahmed Memon, Assoc Ed. **ISSN:** 0048-2757. **Subscription Rates:** US$250 other countries America and Australia; US$200 other countries Asia and Europe; PRs 2520 individuals. **Remarks:** Accepts advertising. **URL:** http://www.ptj.com.pk. **Ad Rates:** BW: US$550, 4C: US$805. **Circ:** Paid 2,500

49373 ■ Progress
Pakistan Petroleum Ltd.
PIDC House
Dr. Ziauddin Ahmed Rd.
PO Box 3942
Karachi 75530, Pakistan
Ph: 92 21 5651480
Fax: 92 21 5680005
Publisher E-mail: info@ppl.com.pk
Provides news about the Pakistani oil and gas industry. **Founded:** 1956. **Freq:** Monthly. **ISSN:** 0033-0574. **URL:** http://www.ppl.com.pk/media/Magazine/Pages/default.aspx. **Circ:** Paid 4,750

49374 ■ Pulse International
Professional Medical Publications
Rm. No. 522, 5th Fl., Panorama Centre
Bldg. No. 2, Saddar
PO Box 8766
Karachi, Pakistan
Ph: 92 21 5689285
Fax: 92 21 5689860
Publication E-mail: pulse@pulsepakistan.com
Publisher E-mail: pulse@pulsepakistan.com
Medical journal. **Founded:** 1978. **Freq:** Biweekly. **Print Method:** Offset. **Key Personnel:** Mubarak Ali, Sen. Sub-Ed.; Shaukat Ali Jawaid, Ch. Ed.; Prof. Mahmood Ali Malik, Contributors; Dr. Maqbool H. Jafary, Honorary Ed.-in-Ch.; Prof. Masood Jawaid, Contributors. **Subscription Rates:** PRs 2000 individuals; US$70 U.S. and Canada; US$50 other countries Middle East, China/Japan; US$35 other countries SAARC Countries; 40 other countries UK. **Remarks:** Accepts advertising. **URL:** http://www.pulsepakistan.com/. **Ad Rates:** BW: PRs 30,000, 4C: PRs 45,000. **Circ:** Paid 8,000

49375 ■ The Review
The DAWN Group of Newspapers
Haroon House
Dr. Ziauddin Ahmed Rd.
Karachi 74200, Pakistan
Ph: 92 111 444777
Fax: 92 21 5693995
Publisher E-mail: webmaster@dawn.com
Consumer magazine covering local issues and lifestyle. **Freq:** Weekly (Thurs.). **URL:** http://www.dawn.com/weekly/review/review.htm.

49376 ■ Spider
The DAWN Group of Newspapers
Haroon House
Dr. Ziauddin Ahmed Rd.
Karachi 74200, Pakistan
Ph: 92 111 444777

Fax: 92 21 5693995
Publication E-mail: letters@spider.tm
Publisher E-mail: webmaster@dawn.com
Consumer magazine covering the Internet for beginners or advanced users. **Founded:** 1998. **Freq:** Monthly. **Key Personnel:** Cecil J. Chen, Asst. Ed., cecil@spider.tm; Mir Abbas Hasnain Hunzai, Mktg. Mgr.; Niloufer Patel, Circulation Dir.; Masood Hamid, Mktg. Dir.; Reba Shahid, Editor, reba@spider.tm. **Remarks:** Accepts advertising. **URL:** http://www.spider.tm. **Ad Rates:** BW: PRs 450, 4C: PRs 200. **Circ:** (Not Reported)

49377 ■ Star
The DAWN Group of Newspapers
Haroon House
Dr. Ziauddin Ahmed Rd.
Karachi 74200, Pakistan
Ph: 92 111 444777
Fax: 92 21 5693995
Publisher E-mail: webmaster@dawn.com
English language newspaper. **Founded:** 1953. **Freq:** Daily (eve.). **Remarks:** Accepts advertising. **URL:** http://www.dawn.com/fixed/group/publicat.htm6. **Circ:** (Not Reported)

49378 ■ US
Jang Group of Newspapers
Printing House
I.I. Chundrigar Rd.
Karachi 74200, Pakistan
Ph: 92 212 637111
Fax: 92 212 636066
Publication E-mail: us.mag@thenews.com.pk
Consumer youth magazine. **Subtitle:** Magazine for the Youth. **Freq:** Weekly. **Remarks:** Accepts advertising. **URL:** http://jang.com.pk; http://jang.com.pk/thenews/feb2009-weekly/us-13-02-2009/index.html. **Circ:** (Not Reported)

49379 ■ You
Jang Group of Newspapers
Printing House
I.I. Chundrigar Rd.
Karachi 74200, Pakistan
Ph: 92 212 637111
Fax: 92 212 636066
Women's magazine. **Freq:** Weekly. **Remarks:** Accepts advertising. **URL:** http://jang.com.pk/thenews/aug2007-weekly/you-28-08-2007/index.html. **Circ:** (Not Reported)

49380 ■ Young World
The DAWN Group of Newspapers
Haroon House
Dr. Ziauddin Ahmed Rd.
Karachi 74200, Pakistan
Ph: 92 111 444777
Fax: 92 21 5693995
Publisher E-mail: webmaster@dawn.com
Consumer magazine for young people. **Freq:** Weekly (Sun.). **URL:** http://www.dawn.com/weekly/yworld/yworld.htm.

49381 ■ City-FM - 89
11 Dockyard Rd.
West Wharf Industrial Area
Karachi, Pakistan
Ph: 92 21 2331095
Fax: 92 21 2331099
E-mail: sales@cityfm89.com
Format: Ethnic; World Beat. **Operating Hours:** Continuous. **Ad Rates:** Advertising accepted; rates available upon request. **URL:** http://www.cityfm89.com.

49382 ■ Pakistan Broadcasting Corporation, Karachi-I - 828 KHz
G-5 Constitutional Ave.
Islamabad 4400, Pakistan
E-mail: cfmpbchq@isb.comsats.net.pk; info@radio.gov.pk
Format: News; Music of Your Life; Educational. **Owner:** Pakistan Broadcasting Corporation, at above address. **Founded:** 1948. **Operating Hours:** 8:10 a.m.-12 a.m. **Wattage:** 100,000. **URL:** http://www.radio.gov.pk/index.asp.

49383 ■ Pakistan Broadcasting Corporation, Karachi-II - 639 KHz
G-5 Constitutional Ave.
Islamabad 4400, Pakistan

Circulation: ★ = ABC; △ = BPA; ◆ = CAC; • = CCAB; ❑ = VAC; ⊕ = PO Statement; ‡ = Publisher's Report; Boldface figures = sworn; Light figures = estimated.

E-mail: cfmpbchq@isb.comsats.net.pk; info@radio.
gov.pk
Format: Educational; Music of Your Life; News. **Owner:**
Pakistan Broadcasting Corporation, at above address.
Founded: 1948. **Operating Hours:** 8:10 a.m.-12 a.m.
Wattage: 100,000. **URL:** http://www.radio.gov.pk/index.
asp.

Lahore

49384 ■ Daily Times
41-N, Industrial Area
Gulberg II
Lahore, Pakistan
Ph: 92 42 5878614
Fax: 92 42 5878620
Publication E-mail: editorial@dailytimes.com.pk
Publisher E-mail: letters@dailytimes.com.pk
Newspaper. **Subtitle:** Your Right to Know - A new Voice
for Pakistan. **Freq:** Daily. **Key Personnel:** Zeeshan
Bhutta, Resident Ed., bhutta@dailytimes.com.pk. **Re-
marks:** Accepts advertising. **URL:** http://www.dailytimes.
com.pk. **Circ:** (Not Reported)

49385 ■ The Friday Times
72 FCC Gulberg IV
Lahore, Pakistan
Ph: 92 425 763510
Fax: 92 425 751025
Publisher E-mail: tft@lhr.comsats.net.pk
Political newspaper. **Freq:** Weekly (Fri.). **Key Personnel:** Najam Sethi, Editor-in-Chief, najamsethi@
thefridaytimes.com; Jugnu Mohsin, Managing Editor,
jugnumohsin@thefridaytimes.com; Raza Rumi, News
Ed., razarumi@thefridaytimes.com; M Imran Yousf, Asst.
Mktg. Mgr., marketing@thefridaytimes.com; Anjum Ali,
Distribution Mgr., anjumali@thefridaytimes.com. **Subscription Rates:** US$25 individuals. **URL:** http://www.
thefridaytimes.com/. **Formerly:** The Friday Times. **Feature Editors:** Salma Mahmud, *Features*, features@
thefridaytimes.com.

49386 ■ Pakistan Pediatric Journal
Association of Pediatricians of Pakistan
37/B, GOR-2, Bahawalpur House
Lahore, Pakistan
Medical journal. **Freq:** Quarterly. **Key Personnel:** Prof.
Said ul Haque, Ch. Ed. **ISSN:** 0304-4904. **URL:** http://
www.ppa.org.pk/main/index.asp.

49387 ■ Psychology Quarterly
Government College
Psychology Department
Katchery Rd.
Lahore 5400, Pakistan
Ph: 92 42 9213340
Publisher E-mail: registrar@gcu.edu.pk
Journal covering psychology. **Founded:** 1964. **Freq:**
Quarterly. **Key Personnel:** Syed Azhar Ali Rizvi, Editor.
ISSN: 0033-3093. **URL:** http://www.gcu.edu.pk/. **Circ:**
Paid 300

49388 ■ Renaissance
51-K Model Town
Lahore, Pakistan
Ph: 92 42 5865145
Fax: 92 42 5864856
Publisher E-mail: info@monthly-renaissance.com
Islamic journal. **Founded:** 1991. **Freq:** Monthly. **Key
Personnel:** Shakeel Ur-Rehman, Managing Editor,
shakeel@monthly-renaissance.com; Shehzad Saleem,
Editor, shehzad@monthly-renaissance.com; Javed Ah-
mad Ghamidi, Ch. Ed., ghamidi@monthly-renaissance.
com. **ISSN:** 1605-0045. **Subscription Rates:** US$30
other countries. **Remarks:** Accepts advertising. **URL:**
http://www.monthly-renaissance.com/. **Ad Rates:** BW:
US$15. **Circ:** (Not Reported)

49389 ■ Weekly Cutting Edge
Fisco Press Pvt. Ltd.
Flat No. 1, St. No. 38

Umar Market
Canal Park Gulberg-II
Lahore, Pakistan
Ph: 92 42 5787978
Fax: 92 42 8492837
Publication E-mail: weeklycuttingedge@gmail.com
Publisher E-mail: info@weeklycuttingedge.com
Newspaper featuring news and events. **Key Personnel:**
Dr. Niloufer Mahdi, Editor; Akhtar Mahmood, Circulation
Mgr.; Muhammad Atique, Mktg. Exec. **Remarks:** Ac-
cepts advertising. **URL:** http://www.weeklycuttingedge.
com/index.htm. **Circ:** (Not Reported)

**49390 ■ Pakistan Broadcasting Corporation,
Lahore-II - 1080 KHz**
G-5 Constitutional Ave.
Islamabad 4400, Pakistan
Ph: 92 42 9200681
E-mail: cfmpbchq@isb.comsats.net.pk; info@radio.
gov.pk
Format: Educational; Music of Your Life; News. **Owner:**
Pakistan Broadcasting Corporation, at above address.
Operating Hours: 8:20 a.m.-12 a.m. **Wattage:** 50,000.
URL: http://www.radio.gov.pk/index.asp.

Larkana

49391 ■ Pakistan Journal of Surgery
Society of Surgeons of Pakistan
c/o Prof. Ahmed Memon
Surgical Unit III
Chandka Medical College
Larkana, Pakistan
Publisher E-mail: surgicon2009@yahoo.com
Medical journal. **Freq:** Quarterly. **Key Personnel:** Prof.
Mahmood Ayyaz, Editor; Prof. Zakiuddin G. Oonwala,
Editor; Dr. Sham Nadeem Alam, Managing Editor,
shamsalam@hotmail.com. **ISSN:** 0258-8552. **Subscrip-
tion Rates:** PRs 1500 individuals; PRs 2000 individuals
India; 100 U.S.; US$50 individuals U.K. **URL:** http://
www.pjs.com.pk/.

Peshawar

49392 ■ The Frontier Post
The Frontier Publications Private Ltd.
27 Abdara Rd.
PO Box 1161
University Town
Peshawar, Pakistan
Ph: 92 300 5182252
Publisher E-mail: tfpost@brain.net.pk
General newspaper. **Subtitle:** National Daily Published
From Peshwar And Quetta. **Freq:** Daily. **Key Person-
nel:** Jalil Afridi, Managing Editor; Rahmat Shah Afridi,
Editor-in-Chief; Mahmood Afridi, Editor. **Remarks:** Ac-
cepts advertising. **URL:** http://thefrontierpost.com.pk/.
Circ: (Not Reported)

49393 ■ Journal of Pakistan Psychiatric Society
Pakistan Psychiatric Society
c/o Saeed Farooq, Ed.
Journal of Pakistan Psychiatric Society
29-30 Habib Medical Complex
Dabgari Gardens
Peshawar, Pakistan
Publisher E-mail: jppslrh@yahoo.com
Journal focusing on the field of psychiatry. **Founded:**
Jan. 2005. **Freq:** Semiannual. **Key Personnel:** Saeed
Farooq, Editor; Akhtar Sherin, Assoc. Ed.; Muhammad
Irfan, Assoc. Ed. **ISSN:** 1726-8710. **URL:** http://www.
jpps.com.pk/.

49394 ■ Pakistan Journal of Forestry
Pakistan Forest Institute
BPO Forest Institute
NWFP
Peshawar, Pakistan
Ph: 92 521 40580
Publisher E-mail: dg@pfi.pwr.sdnpk.undp.org
Journal covering forestry. **Founded:** 1951. **Freq:**

Quarterly. **Key Personnel:** K.M. Siddiqui, Editor. **ISSN:**
0030-9818. **URL:** http://journalseek.net/cgi-bin/
journalseek/journalsearch.cgi?field=issn&query=0030-
9818. **Circ:** Paid 400

49395 ■ Statesman
Mashriq Group of Newspapers
Bilal Town, GT Rd.
PO Box 1107
Peshawar, Pakistan
Ph: 92 91 2651151
Fax: 92 91 2651197
Publisher E-mail: shakilsunil@yahoo.com
General interest periodical. **Founded:** 1955. **Freq:**
Weekly. **Key Personnel:** Syed Ayaz Badshah, Editor-in-
Chief. **ISSN:** 0039-0313. **URL:** http://dailymashriq.com.
pk/mashriq.html. **Circ:** Paid 5,000

**49396 ■ Pakistan Broadcasting Corporation,
Peshawar-II - 729 KHz**
G-5 Constitutional Ave.
Islamabad 4400, Pakistan
Ph: 92 91 9210293
E-mail: cfmpbchq@isb.comsats.net.pk; info@radio.
gov.pk
Format: News; Music of Your Life; Educational. **Owner:**
Pakistan Broadcasting Corporation, at above address.
Founded: July 16, 1942. **Operating Hours:** 8 a.m.-
11:02 p.m. **Wattage:** 100,000. **URL:** http://www.radio.
gov.pk/index.asp.

49397 ■ Radio Buraq Peshawar-FM - 104
RB 104 2nd Fl., Jasmine Arcade
Fakhr-e-Alam Rd.
Peshawar, Pakistan
Ph: 92 91 5271731
Fax: 92 91 5271733
E-mail: infopsh@radio-buraq.com
Format: Full Service. **Operating Hours:** Continuous.
URL: http://www.radio-buraq.com.

Quetta

**49398 ■ Pakistan Broadcasting Corporation,
Quetta-I - 756 KHz**
G-5 Constitutional Ave.
Islamabad 4400, Pakistan
Ph: 92 81 9202393
E-mail: cpsradio@isb.comsats.net.pk; info@radio.
gov.pk
Format: Educational; Music of Your Life; News. **Owner:**
Pakistan Broadcasting Corporation, at above address.
Founded: Oct. 17, 1956. **Operating Hours:** 8:10 a.m.-
11:10 p.m. **Wattage:** 150,000. **URL:** http://www.radio.
gov.pk/index.asp.

**49399 ■ Pakistan Broadcasting Corporation,
Quetta-II - 855 KHz**
G-5 Constitutional Ave.
Islamabad 4400, Pakistan
Ph: 92 81 9202393
E-mail: cfmpbchq@isb.comsats.net.pk; info@radio.
gov.pk
Format: Educational; Music of Your Life; News. **Owner:**
Pakistan Broadcasting Corporation, at above address.
Founded: Oct. 17, 1956. **Operating Hours:** 8:10 a.m.-
11:10 p.m. **Wattage:** 10,000. **URL:** http://www.radio.gov.
pk/index.asp.

Rawalpindi

**49400 ■ Pakistan Broadcasting Corporation,
Rawalpindi - 1260 KHz**
G-5, Constitutional Ave.
Islamabad, Pakistan
Ph: 92 51 522975
E-mail: info@radio.gov.pk
Format: Talk; Full Service. **Owner:** Pakistan Broadcast-
ing Corporation, at above address. **Founded:** 1949.
Operating Hours: 0800-2308. **Wattage:** 100,000. **URL:**
http://www.radio.gov.pk/index.asp.

Panama City

49401 ■ Focus on Panama
Focus Publications (Int.) S.A.
PO Box 0819-06908
El Dorado
Panama City, Panama
Ph: ( )507 225 6638
Fax: ( )507 225 0466
Publication E-mail: focusint@sinfo.net

Publisher E-mail: focusint@sinfo.net
Consumer magazine covering travel and tourism in
Panama. **Founded:** 1970. **Freq:** Semiannual. **Print
Method:** Web offset. **Trim Size:** 5 1/4 x 8 1/4. **Subscription
Rates:** US$10 single issue. **URL:** http://www.
focuspublicationsint.com. **Circ:** Non-paid 60,000

49402 ■ Radio Maria-AM - 1310
Avenida Los Peridistas
Casa D-5

El Dorado
Panama City, Panama
Ph: ( )507 2606762
Fax: ( )507 2606349
E-mail: info.pan@radiomaria.org
Format: Contemporary Christian; Religious; Gospel.
Operating Hours: 18 hours Daily. **URL:** http://www.
radiomariapanama.org.

Circulation: ★ = ABC; △ = BPA; ♦ = CAC; • = CCAB; ❑ = VAC; ⊕ = PO Statement; ‡ = Publisher's Report; Boldface figures = sworn; Light figures = estimated.

Gale Directory of Publications & Broadcast Media/147th Ed. 5331

Port Moresby

49403 ■ Post-Courier
South Pacific Post Proprietary Ltd.
PO Box 85

Lawes Rd.
Port Moresby, Papua New Guinea
Ph: 675 3091000
Fax: 675 3212721
Publication E-mail: editorial@spp.com.pg

Publisher E-mail: postcourier@spp.com.pg
General newspaper. **Founded:** 1969. **Freq:** Daily. **Key Personnel:** Bob Howarth, Mng. Dir. **Remarks:** Accepts advertising. **URL:** http://www.postcourier.com.pg. **Ad Rates:** PCI: 22.95 K. **Circ:** Combined 28,835

Circulation: ★ = ABC; △ = BPA; ♦ = CAC; • = CCAB; ❑ = VAC; ⊕ = PO Statement; ‡ = Publisher's Report; Boldface figures = sworn; Light figures = estimated.

Gale Directory of Publications & Broadcast Media/147th Ed.

5333

Asuncion

49404 ■ Obedira-FM - 102.1
Comandante Gamarra 1202 e/ Isabel La Catolica
Barrio San Antonio
Asuncion, Paraguay
Ph: 595 21 425042
Fax: 595 21 480048
E-mail: info@obedira.com.py
Format: Ethnic; World Beat. **Operating Hours:**
Continuous. **Ad Rates:** Advertising accepted; rates
available upon request. **URL:** http://www.obedira.com.
py.

49405 ■ 1ro de Marzo-AM - 780
Avenida Peron casi Concepcion de Prieto
Asuncion, Paraguay
Ph: 595 21 300380
Format: Ethnic; Sports. **Operating Hours:** Continuous.
Ad Rates: Advertising accepted; rates available upon
request. **URL:** http://www.780am.com.py.

49406 ■ Radio Canal 100-FM - 100.1
Las Perlas 4269 casi Choferes del Chaco
Asuncion, Paraguay
Ph: 595 21 603426
Fax: 595 21 606295
Format: Ethnic; World Beat. **Operating Hours:**
Continuous. **URL:** http://www.canal100.com.py.

49407 ■ Radio Nanduti-AM - 1020
Carmen Soler 1194 y Choferes del Chaco
Asuncion, Paraguay
Ph: 595 21 604308
Format: News. **Operating Hours:** Continuous. **URL:**
http://www.nanduti.com.py.

49408 ■ 780-AM - 780
Avenida Peron casi Concepcion de Prieto
Asuncion, Paraguay
Ph: 595 21 300380
Format: Ethnic; World Beat. **Operating Hours:**
Continuous. **URL:** http://www.780am.com.py.

49409 ■ Venus-FM - 105.1
Av. Republica Argentina y Souza
Asuncion, Paraguay
Ph: 595 21 610151
E-mail: 105.1@venus.com.py
Format: World Beat; Ethnic; Talk. **Operating Hours:**
Continuous. **Key Personnel:** Gustavo Riveros, Admin.
Mgr.; Jorge Luis Frutos, Director. **URL:** http://www.
venus.com.py.

Caaguazu

49410 ■ Horizonte-FM - 106.3
Carlos Antonio Lopez C
Bernardino Caballero 3400
Caaguazu, Paraguay
Ph: 595 522 42070
E-mail: info@fmhorizonte.com.py
Format: Ethnic; World Beat; Folk. **Owner:** FM Hori-
zonte, at above address. **Operating Hours:** Continuous.
Key Personnel: Dr. Roque A. Gomez, Director,
roquegomez1063@hotmail.com. **URL:** http://www.
fmhorizonte.com.py.

Encarnacion

49411 ■ Itapua-FM - 102.5
Arq. Tomas R. Pereira C

Mcal. Estigarribia
Encarnacion, Paraguay
Ph: 595 71 205802
Fax: 595 71 205347
E-mail: adm@itapuafm.com.py
Format: Sports; Information; Ethnic; World Beat. **Oper-
ating Hours:** 16 hours Daily. **Key Personnel:** Ing. Pablo
Borecki, Director; Jose Ishibashi, Director; Alberto
Vazquez, Director. **Ad Rates:** Advertising accepted;
rates available upon request. **URL:** http://www.itapuafm.
com.py.

Lambare

49412 ■ Cardinal-AM - 730
Comendador Nicolas Bo 1334
Lambare, Paraguay
Ph: 595 21 300170
Fax: 595 21 303089
Format: Ethnic; World Beat. **Owner:** Cardinal Radio, at
above address. **Operating Hours:** Continuous. **Ad
Rates:** Advertising accepted; rates available upon
request. **URL:** http://www.cardinal.com.py.

49413 ■ Cardinal-FM - 92.3
Comendador Nicolas Bo 1334
Lambare, Paraguay
Ph: 595 21 303052
Format: Ethnic; World Beat. **Operating Hours:** 18
hours Daily. **Ad Rates:** Advertising accepted; rates avail-
able upon request. **URL:** http://www.cardinal.com.py.

Abancay

49414 ■ Radio Estacion Solar-FM - 103.3
Av. Seoane 375 - 377
Abancay, Peru
Ph: 51 83 324087
E-mail: corporacionsolar@speedy.com.pe
Format: Hispanic; Top 40. **URL:** http://www.corporacionsolar.com/solar_fm.html.

Arequipa

49415 ■ Radio Universal-FM - 93.5
Av. La Paz 507
Arequipa, Peru
Ph: 51 54 405477
E-mail: universalradio2@yahoo.com
Format: Ethnic; World Beat. **Operating Hours:** Continuous. **URL:** http://www.geocities.com/radio_continental/.

49416 ■ Radio Yaravi-FM - 106.3
Calle Los Robles 139 Urb. Orrantia
Arequipa, Peru
Ph: 51 54 213172
E-mail: yaravi@radioyaravi.org.pe
Format: Hispanic. **URL:** http://www.radioyaravi.org.pe/.

Chepen

49417 ■ Radio San Sebastian-FM - 103.3
Jiron Atahualpa 795
Chepen, Peru
Ph: 51 44 562038
E-mail: radiosansebastian@yahoo.es
Format: Contemporary Christian; Religious. **Operating Hours:** 12 1/2 hours Daily. **URL:** http://www.todochepen.com/radiosansebastian.

Chiclayo

49418 ■ El Rotario Peruano
c/o Juan Scander Juayeq
Los Sauces 312, Santa Victoria
Chiclayo, Peru
Ph: 51 74 227127
Fax: 51 74 233651
Publisher E-mail: jscander@gmail.com
Membership magazine of Rotary International covering current news about Rotary-related subjects. **Founded:** 1933. **Freq:** Quarterly. **Key Personnel:** Juan Scander Juayeq, Contact. **URL:** http://www.rotary.org/en/mediaandnews/morepublications/regionalmagazines/pages/ridefault.aspx. **Circ:** 3,500

49419 ■ Radio Maranon-AM - 580
Francisco de Orellana 343
AP 50
Chiclayo, Peru
Ph: 51 76 431147
Format: World Beat; Ethnic. **Operating Hours:** Continuous. **URL:** http://www.radiomaranon.org.pe.

Huancayo

49420 ■ Radio Antena Sur-FM - 90.3
Av. 13 de Noviembre 398
El Tambo
Huancayo, Peru
Ph: 51 64 254888
Format: Hispanic. **Key Personnel:** Rolando Gonzalo, General Mgr., gerencia@radioantenasur.com; Rocio Aliaga, Advertising Mgr., rocioaliaga@radioantenasur.com; Roy Diaz, Contact, programacion@radioantenasur.com. **URL:** http://www.radioantenasur.com.pe.

Huanuco

49421 ■ Radio Huanuco-FM - 94.7
Jiron Tarapaca 693
Huanuco, Peru
Ph: 51 62 517946
Format: World Beat; Ethnic. **Operating Hours:** Continuous. **Ad Rates:** Advertising accepted; rates available upon request. **URL:** http://www.radiohuanuco.com.

Huarochiri

49422 ■ Radio Matucana-FM - 102.9
Jr. Amazonas 150
Huarochiri, Peru
Ph: 51 2443214
E-mail: radiomatucana@lycos.es
Format: World Beat. **Operating Hours:** Continuous. **URL:** http://usuarios.lycos.es/radiomatucana.

Lima

49423 ■ Anales de la Facultad de Medicina
Universidad Nacional Mayor de San Marcos
Facultad de Medicina
Av. Grau 755
Lima 01, Peru
Ph: 51 1 6197000
Publisher E-mail: ofinfmed@unmsm.edu.pe
Journal dedicated to medical practice. **Founded:** 1973. **Freq:** Semiannual. **Print Method:** Offset. **Trim Size:** 6 x 9. **Cols./Page:** 1. **Col. Width:** 50 nonpareils. **Col. Depth:** 98 agate lines. **Key Personnel:** Dr. Jose Pacheco Romero, Editor; Dr. Eleazar Aliaga Viera, Editor; Dr. Carlos Battilana Guanilo, Editor. **ISSN:** 1025-5583. **URL:** http://medicina.unmsm.edu.pe/anales/presentacion.asp.

49424 ■ Negocios Internacionales
ComexPeru Peruvian Foreign Trading Society
ComexPeru Sociedad de Comercio Exterior del Peru
Bartolome Herrera 254
Miraflores
Lima 18, Peru
Ph: 51 1 44225784
Fax: 51 1 44225942
Publisher E-mail: postmast@comexperu.org.pe
Spanish language publication covering trade. **Freq:** Monthly. **URL:** http://www.comexperu.org.pe. **Ad Rates:** 4C: US$1,800. **Circ:** 6,000

49425 ■ Quehacer
Development Studies and Promotion Center
Centro de Estudios y Promocion del Desarrollo
Jr. Leon de la Fuente No. 110
Lima 17, Peru
Ph: 51 1 6138300
Fax: 51 1 6138308
Publisher E-mail: postmaster@desco.org.pe
Spanish language publication covering community development. **Founded:** Oct. 1, 1979. **Freq:** Bimonthly. **Key Personnel:** Juan Larco, Editor; Abelardo Sanchez Leon, Director. **ISSN:** 0250-9806. **Subscription Rates:** US$70 individuals for International (all destinations). **Remarks:** Advertising accepted; rates available upon request. **URL:** http://www.desco.org.pe. **Circ:** 4,000

49426 ■ Resomeu Senaual
Development Studies and Promotion Center
Centro de Estudios y Promocion del Desarrollo
Jr. Leon de la Fuente No. 110
Lima 17, Peru
Ph: 51 1 6138300
Fax: 51 1 6138308
Publisher E-mail: postmaster@desco.org.pe
Spanish language publication covering community development. **Freq:** Weekly. **ISSN:** 0250-9792. **URL:** http://www.desco.org.pe. **Circ:** 500

49427 ■ Doble Nueve-FM - 99.1
Avenida Santa Cruz 1530
Lima, Peru
Ph: 51 1 98088011
E-mail: 99fm@radiodoblenueve.com
Format: Contemporary Hit Radio (CHR); Alternative/New Music/Progressive. **Operating Hours:** Continuous. **Ad Rates:** Advertising accepted; rates available upon request. **URL:** http://www.radiodoblenueve.com.

49428 ■ Milenia Radio-AM - 1530
Avenida Arnaldo Marquez 1944
Lima, Peru
Ph: 51 1 4612222
Fax: 51 1 4617757
E-mail: milenia@radiomilenia.com.pe
Format: Educational; Information; World Beat. **Operating Hours:** Continuous. **Ad Rates:** Noncommercial. **URL:** http://www.radiomilenia.com.pe.

49429 ■ Radio Bacan Sat-AM - 1130
Jr. Bernardo Alcedo No. 375
Lima, Peru
Ph: 51 1 2652333
Fax: 51 1 4727162
Format: Ethnic; World Beat. **Operating Hours:** Continuous. **URL:** http://www.radiobacan.com.

49430 ■ Radio Comas-AM - 1300
Av. Estados Unidos 327
Lima, Peru
Ph: 51 1 5250859
Fax: 51 1 5250094
Format: Educational. **URL:** http://www.radiocomas.com.

49431 ■ Radio Comas-FM - 101.7
Av. Estados Unidos 327
Urb. Huaquillay

Circulation: ★ = ABC; △ = BPA; ♦ = CAC; • = CCAB; ❑ = VAC; ⊕ = PO Statement; ‡ = Publisher's Report; Boldface figures = sworn; Light figures = estimated.

Gale Directory of Publications & Broadcast Media/147th Ed. 5337

Comas
Lima, Peru
Ph: 51 1 5250859
Fax: 51 1 5250094
E-mail: comasfm@radiocomas.com
Format: Ethnic; World Beat. **URL:** http://www.
radiocomas.com.

49432 ■ Radio Filarmonia-FM - 102.7
Av. Pedro de Osma 501
Barranco
Lima, Peru
Ph: 51 1 2522222
Fax: 51 1 2515325
E-mail: radio@filarmonia.org
Format: Classical; Jazz; Ethnic. **Operating Hours:**
Continuous. **URL:** http://www.filarmonia.org.

49433 ■ Radio Impacto-FM - 90.7
Av. los Geranios 233
Urb Residencial
Huaral
Lima, Peru
Ph: 51 1 2461651
E-mail: impacto@radioimpactoperu.com
Format: Hispanic. **Key Personnel:** Dr. Juan Verastegui,
General Mgr. **URL:** http://www.radioimpactoperu.com/
portal/modules/news.

49434 ■ Radio Nacional del Peru-AM - 850
Av. Petit Thouars 447
Lima 1, Peru
Ph: 51 1 4331404
Format: World Beat. **Owner:** Radio Nacional Del Peru,
at above address. **Operating Hours:** Continuous. **Ad
Rates:** Advertising accepted; rates available upon
request. **URL:** http://www.radionacional.com.pe.

49435 ■ Radio Nacional del Peru-FM - 103.9
Av. Petit Thouars 447
Lima, Peru
Ph: 51 1 4331404
Fax: 51 1 4336650
Format: World Beat. **Operating Hours:** Continuous. **Ad
Rates:** Advertising accepted; rates available upon
request. **URL:** http://www.radionacional.com.pe.

49436 ■ Radio del Pacifico-AM - 640
Av. Guzman Blanco 465 - piso 7
Lima, Peru
Ph: 51 1 4337879

Fax: 51 1 4333276
E-mail: administracion@grupopacifico.org
Format: Hispanic; Contemporary Christian. **Owner:**
Grupo Pacifico de Comunicaciones, at above address.
Key Personnel: Amarildo Vicuna, Contact, gerencia@
grupopacifico.org. **URL:** http://www.grupopacifico.org/
radio.html.

49437 ■ Radio San Borja-FM - 91.1
Av. Javier Prado Este 2340
San Borja
Lima 41, Peru
Ph: 51 1 224 2386
E-mail: administracion@radiosanborja.com
Format: Hispanic. **URL:** http://www.radiosanborja.com.

Moquegua

49438 ■ Radio Altamar-FM - 102.3
Ubicacion Estudios y Planta
Jr. Callao Nro 221
Moquegua, Peru
Ph: 51 53 481106
Fax: 51 53 482634
E-mail: altamar102@yahoo.es
Format: Ethnic; World Beat. **Ad Rates:** Advertising ac-
cepted; rates available upon request. **URL:** http://www.
radioaltamar.tk.

Piura

49439 ■ Radio Cutivalu-AM - 700 KHz
San Ignacio de Loyola No. 300 - Urb. Miraflores
Piura, Peru
Ph: 51 73 343370
Format: Ethnic; World Beat. **Operating Hours:** 14.30
hours Daily. **URL:** http://www.radiocutivalu.org.

Puno

49440 ■ Pachamama Radio-AM - 850
Jr. Acora 222
Puno, Peru
Ph: 51 352200
Format: Educational; Ethnic; World Beat. **Operating
Hours:** Continuous. **Key Personnel:** Dr. Mauricio Rod-
riguez, Dir. Gen.; Marlene Choque, Contact, publicidad@
pachamamaradio.org.pe; Grover Cutipa, Contact,
pruduccion@pachamamaradio.org.pe; Juan Sotomayor,
Contact, juan.sotomayor@pachamamaradio.org.pe.

URL: http://www.pachamamaradio.org.pe.

San Isidro

49441 ■ Made in Germany
Peruvian - German Chamber of Commerce and
Industry
Camara de Comercio e Industria Peruano-Alemana
Av. Camino Real 348, of. 1502
San Isidro 27, Peru
Ph: 51 1 4418616
Fax: 51 1 4426014
Publisher E-mail: info@camara-alemana.org.pe
Spanish language publication covering chambers of
commerce. **Freq:** Quarterly. **Subscription Rates:** 15
individuals; US$20 individuals + shipping. **URL:** http://
peru.ahk.de/index.php?id=424. **Circ:** 5,000

San Juan de Lurigancho

49442 ■ Canto Grande-FM - 97.7
Av. Del Parque 721
Urb. Canto Grande 2 Etapa
San Juan de Lurigancho, Peru
Ph: 51 7156014
Format: Ethnic; World Beat. **Ad Rates:** Advertising ac-
cepted; rates available upon request. **URL:** http://www.
cantograndefm.com.

Sullana

49443 ■ Radio Capullana-AM - 970
141 St. , 2nd Fl.
Sullana, Peru
Ph: 51 73 503071
E-mail: publicidad@radiocapullana.com
Format: Ethnic. **Founded:** July 28, 1986. **Operating
Hours:** Continuous. **Key Personnel:** Midian Agurto
Rosa Lizama, Admin. **URL:** http://www.radiocapullana.
com/laradio.html.

Tacna

49444 ■ Radio Uno-FM - 93.7
Calle 2 de Mayo N 263
Tacna, Peru
Ph: 51 425555
Format: Ethnic; News. **Operating Hours:** Continuous.
Ad Rates: Advertising accepted; rates available upon
request. **URL:** http://www.radiouno.com.pe.

Angeles City

49445 ■ GV-FM - 99.1
GV Compound, Rizal Ext.
Angeles City, Philippines
Ph: 63 45 8881596
Fax: 63 45 3221311
Format: Top 40; Contemporary Hit Radio (CHR); Information. **Operating Hours:** Continuous. **Wattage:** 20,000. **Ad Rates:** Advertising accepted; rates available upon request. **URL:** http://www.gvfm991.com.

Bacolod City

49446 ■ DYBM-FM - 99.1
Cordova Ave.
Mountain View Subd.
Mandalagan
Bacolod City 6100, Philippines
Ph: 63 34 4339991
Fax: 63 34 4410235
Format: Adult Contemporary. **URL:** http://www.crossover.com.ph/.

49447 ■ DYHT-FM - 94.3
4th Fl., State Condo. Bldg.
1 Salcedo St.
Legaspi Village
Makati City, Metro Manila 1229, Philippines
Ph: 63 2 8120529
Fax: 63 2 8163680
Format: Eclectic. **Owner:** Radio Mindanao Network, at above address. **Ad Rates:** Advertising accepted; rates available upon request. **URL:** http://www.rmn.ph/fmstations/dyht.

49448 ■ DYIF-FM - 95.5 MHz
3rd Fl., CBS Development
Corp. Bldg.
Lacson St.
Mandalagan
Bacolod City 6100, Philippines
Ph: 63 34 4411670
Fax: 63 34 7090766
E-mail: starfm_bacolod@bomboradyo.com
Format: Adult Contemporary. **Owner:** Bombo Radyo Philippines, 2406 Florete Bldg., Edison cor. Nobel St., Makati City 1200, Philippines, 63 2 8430116, Fax: 63 2 8173631. **Key Personnel:** Errol Emil Adrian V. Ledesma, Station Mgr. **Wattage:** 10,000. **URL:** http://www.bomboradyo.com/archive/new/stationprofile/starfmbacolod/index.h t m.

49449 ■ DYVS - 1233 KHz
Km. 7, Pahanocoy
PO Box 393
Bacolod City, Philippines
Ph: 62 34 4442112
Fax: 62 34 4442112
E-mail: dyvs@febc.org.ph
Format: Eclectic. **Owner:** Far East Broadcasting Co., at above address. **Founded:** Sept. 29, 1974. **Operating Hours:** 2100-1600. **Key Personnel:** Ralph Belzunce, Station Mgr. **Wattage:** 5000. **URL:** http://febc.ph.

Baguio City

49450 ■ Asian Journal of Pentecostal Studies
Faculty of Asia Pacific Theological Seminary
PO Box 377
Baguio City 2600, Philippines
Ph: 63 744 427068
Fax: 63 744 426378
Publisher E-mail: info@apts.edu
Serves as a forum for theological discussion in Asia and elsewhere. **Founded:** 1998. **Freq:** Semiannual January and July. **ISSN:** 0118-8534. **Subscription Rates:** 300 PP individuals; US$15 individuals Asia; US$20 elsewhere; 600 PP individuals; US$30 individuals Asia; US$40 elsewhere; 750 PP individuals; 40 individuals Asia; US$50 elsewhere. **URL:** http://www.apts.edu/index.cfm?menuid=88&parentid=54.

49451 ■ DWHB-FM - 103.9
4 Fl., State Condo. Bldg.
1 Salcedo St.
Legaspi Village
Makati City 1229, Philippines
Ph: 63 2 8120529
Fax: 63 2 8108362
Format: Adult Contemporary. **Owner:** Radio Mindanao Network, at above address. **Ad Rates:** Advertising accepted; rates available upon request. **URL:** http://www.rmn.ph/fmstations/dwhb.

49452 ■ DWIM-FM - 89.5 MHz
87 Lourdes Subd.
Baguio City, Philippines
Ph: 63 74 4427926
Fax: 63 74 6192897
E-mail: starfmbaguio@mountainview.com.ph
Format: Adult Contemporary. **Owner:** Bombo Radyo Philippines, 2406 Florete Bldg., Edison cor. Nobel St., Makati City 1200, Philippines, 63 2 8430116, Fax: 63 2 8173631. **Key Personnel:** Mrs. Floribel Caja Sales, Station Mgr. **Wattage:** 4500. **URL:** http://www.bomboradyo.com/archive/new/stationprofile/starfmbaguio/index.ht m.

Bislig

49453 ■ DXHP - 999 KHz
State Condo. Bldg., 4th Fl.
1 Salcedo St.
Legaspi Village
Makati City, Philippines
Ph: 63 2 8120530
Fax: 63 2 8108362
Format: Eclectic. **Owner:** Radio Mindanao Network, at above address. **Operating Hours:** 2100-1600. **Wattage:** 101,000. **URL:** http://www.rmn.com.ph/.

Bukidnon

49454 ■ DXDB - 594 KHz
Unit 201, Sunrise Condominium
226 Ortigas Ave.
San Juan, Philippines
Ph: 63 2 7249850
Fax: 63 2 7249962

E-mail: cmnftd@cmn-ftd.org
Format: News. **Owner:** Catholic Media Network, at above address. **Operating Hours:** 18 hours Daily. **Key Personnel:** Medda M. Carpio, Accounting Mgr.; Ma. Cecilia C. Roxas, Program Mgr.; Jean Paul Varela, Network Mgr. **Wattage:** 5000. **URL:** http://www.catholicmedianetwork.org.

49455 ■ DXMB - 648 KHz
State Condo. Bldg., 4th Fl.
1 Salcedo St.
Legaspi Village
Makati City, Philippines
Ph: 63 2 8120530
Fax: 63 2 8108362
Format: Eclectic. **Owner:** Radio Mindanao Network, at above address. **Operating Hours:** 2100-1600. **Wattage:** 5000. **URL:** http://www.rmn.com.ph/.

Butuan City

49456 ■ DXBC - 693 KHz
State Condo. Bldg., 4th Fl.
1 Salcedo St.
Legaspi Village
Makati City, Philippines
Ph: 63 2 8120530
Fax: 63 2 8108362
Format: Eclectic. **Owner:** Radio Mindanao Network, at above address. **Operating Hours:** 2100-1600. **Wattage:** 10,000. **URL:** http://www.rmn.com.ph/.

49457 ■ DXXX-FM - 100.7
4th Fl., State Condo. Bldg.
1 Salcedo St.
Legaspi Village
Makati City, Metro Manila 1229, Philippines
Ph: 63 2 8120529
Fax: 63 2 8163680
Format: Eclectic. **Owner:** Radio Mindanao Network, at above address. **Ad Rates:** Advertising accepted; rates available upon request. **URL:** http://www.rmn.ph/fmstations/dxxx.

Cagayan de Oro City

49458 ■ DXCC - 828 KHz
4th Fl. State Condo. Bldg.
1 Salcedo St.
Legaspi Village
Makati City, Philippines
Ph: 63 2 8120530
Fax: 63 2 8108362
Format: Eclectic. **Owner:** Radio Mindanao Network, at above address. **Operating Hours:** 2100-1600. **Wattage:** 10,000. **URL:** http://www.rmn.com.ph/.

49459 ■ DXVM-FM - 99.1
4th Fl., State Condo. Bldg.
1 Salcedo St.
Legaspi Village
Makati City, Metro Manila 1229, Philippines
Ph: 63 2 8120529
Fax: 63 2 8163680
Format: Eclectic. **Owner:** Radio Mindanao Network, at

Circulation: ★ = ABC; △ = BPA; ◆ = CAC; • = CCAB; ❑ = VAC; ⊕ = PO Statement; ‡ = Publisher's Report; Boldface figures = sworn; Light figures = estimated.

above address. **Ad Rates:** Advertising accepted; rates available upon request. **URL:** http://www.rmn.ph/fmstations/dxvm.

49460 ■ Home Radio Cagayan de Oro-FM - 93.5
Apolinar Velez St., Cor. Arch. Hayes St.
Cagayan de Oro City, Philippines
Ph: 63 88 8579350
E-mail: homecdo@yahoo.com
Format: Adult Contemporary. **Owner:** ALIW Broadcasting Corporation, 5 Fl., Citystate Centre, 709 Shaw Blvd., Pasig, Philippines, 63 2 6373965, Fax: 63 2 6339158. **Wattage:** 10,000. **Ad Rates:** $792 for 15 seconds; $1320 for 30 seconds; $1980 for 45 seconds; $2640 for 60 seconds. **URL:** http://www.homeradiofm.net/cagayandeoro.php.

Calbayog

49461 ■ DYCC - 936 KHz
State Condo. Bldg., 4th Fl.
1 Salcedo St.
Legaspi Village
Makati City, Philippines
Ph: 63 2 8120530
Fax: 63 2 8108362
Format: Eclectic. **Owner:** Radio Mindanao Network, at above address. **Operating Hours:** 2100-1600. **Wattage:** 1000. **URL:** http://www.rmn.com.ph/.

Cebu City

49462 ■ Philippine Quarterly of Culture and Society
University of San Carlos
P. del Rosario St.
Cebu City 6000, Philippines
Ph: 63 32 2531000
Fax: 63 32 2554341
Publisher E-mail: information@usc.edu.ph
Journal featuring articles on subjects pertaining to Philippine culture and society. **Founded:** 1973. **Freq:** Quarterly. **Key Personnel:** Harold Olofson, Editor; Lawrence M. Liao, Advisory Editorial Board; Theodore Murnane, Advisory Editorial Board; Erlinda K. Alburo, Advisory Editorial Board; John A. Peterson, Advisory Editorial Board; Socorro A. Gultiano, Advisory Editorial Board. **ISSN:** 0115-0243. **Remarks:** Advertising accepted; rates available upon request. **URL:** http://www.usc.edu.ph/; http://www.usc.edu.ph/administration/san_carlos_publication_publications_available.jsp. **Circ:** Paid 280

49463 ■ Philippine Scientist
University of San Carlos
P. del Rosario St.
Cebu City 6000, Philippines
Ph: 63 32 2531000
Fax: 63 32 2554341
Publisher E-mail: information@usc.edu.ph
Deals with research in various natural science fields, emphasizing marine biology and entomology. **Founded:** 1964. **Freq:** Annual. **Key Personnel:** Lawrence M. Liao, Editor. **ISSN:** 0079-1466. **Remarks:** Advertising accepted; rates available upon request. **URL:** http://www.usc.edu.ph/; http://www.usc.edu.ph/administration/san_carlos_publication_publications_available.jspphilippine_scientist. **Circ:** Paid 200

49464 ■ Sun.Star Network
Sun.Star Network Exchange
Sun. Star Bldg.
3rd Fl., Sun. Star Bldg.
P. del Rosario cor. P. Cui Sts.
Cebu City 6000, Philippines
Ph: 63 322 546100
Fax: 63 322 546530
Publication E-mail: sunnex@sunstar.com.ph
Publisher E-mail: sunnex@sunstar.com.ph
General newspaper. **Key Personnel:** Leah F. Ybanez, Admin. Asst.; Victor R. Sotto, Web Tech. Support; Laureen R. Mondonedo, Asst. Content Ed.; Marlen D. Limpag, Managing Editor; Mildred V. Galarpe, Network Coord.; Joy R. Flores, Editor; Alfredo Pasaylo, Jr., Asst. Ed.; Nini B. Cabaero, Editor-in-Chief; Ariel B. Catubig, Asst. Content Ed.; Tashuana Alemania, Asst. Content Ed. **Remarks:** Accepts advertising. **URL:** http://www.sunstar.com.ph. **Circ:** (Not Reported)

49465 ■ Zee Lifestyle
Zee Publications Inc.
PDI Bldg.
Archbishop Reyes Ave.
Cebu City 6000, Philippines
Ph: 63 32 2342636
Publisher E-mail: info@zeelifestylecebu.com
Magazine featuring lifestyle, fashion and travel in Cebu and Davao. **Key Personnel:** Eva C. Gullas, Publisher, ecg@zeelifestylecebu.com; Cybill Gayatin, Editor-in-Chief, cybill@zeelifestylecebu.com; Katsy Borromeo, Managing Editor, katsy@zeelifestylecebu.com. **Subscription Rates:** US$32 individuals; 1,000 PP individuals Cebu and Manila. **Remarks:** Accepts advertising. **URL:** http://zeelifestylecebu.com/. **Circ:** 25,000

49466 ■ Crossover-FM - 90.7
Rm. 210, Dona Luisa Bldg.
Fuente Osmena
Cebu City, Philippines
Fax: 63 32 4125043
Format: Blues; Jazz. **Ad Rates:** Advertising accepted; rates available upon request. **URL:** http://www.crossover.com.ph.

49467 ■ DYAC-FM - 90.7
Rm. 210, Dona Luisa Bldg.
Fuente Osmena
Cebu City, Philippines
Ph: 63 32 4125043
Format: Adult Contemporary. **URL:** http://www.crossover.com.ph/.

49468 ■ DYHP - 612 KHz
State Condo. Bldg., 4th Fl.
1 Salcedo St.
Legaspi Village
Makati City, Philippines
Ph: 63 2 8120530
Fax: 63 2 8108362
Format: Eclectic. **Owner:** Radio Mindanao Network, at above address. **Operating Hours:** 2100-1600. **Wattage:** 10,000. **URL:** http://www.rmn.com.ph/.

49469 ■ DYMX-FM - 95.5 MHz
140 M. Velez St.
Cebu City, Philippines
Ph: 63 32 2430340
Fax: 63 32 2549143
E-mail: starfm_cebu@bomboradyo.com
Format: Adult Contemporary. **Owner:** Bombo Radyo Philippines, 2406 Florete Bldg., Edison cor. Nobel St., Makati City 1200, Philippines, 63 2 8430116, Fax: 63 2 8173631. **Founded:** 1995, **Key Personnel:** Ernesto F. Yap, Jr., Station Mgr. **Wattage:** 25,000. **URL:** http://www.bomboradyo.com/archive/new/stationprofile/starfmcebu/index.htm.

49470 ■ DYXL-FM - 93.9
4th Fl., State Condo. Bldg.
1 Salcedo St.
Legaspi Village
Makati City, Metro Manila 1229, Philippines
Ph: 63 2 8120529
Fax: 63 2 8163680
Format: Eclectic. **Owner:** Radio Mindanao Network, at above address. **Ad Rates:** Advertising accepted; rates available upon request. **URL:** http://www.rmn.ph/fmstations/dyxl.

49471 ■ Home Radio Cebu-FM - 106.7
Ground Fl., Fortune Life Bldg., Jones Ave.
Cebu City, Philippines
Ph: 63 3 22532973
Fax: 63 3 22534252
E-mail: homecebu@yahoo.com
Format: Adult Contemporary. **Owner:** ALIW Broadcasting Corporation, 5 Fl., Citystate Centre, 709 Shaw Blvd., Pasig City, Philippines, 63 2 4701750, Fax: 63 2 4701138. **Wattage:** 25,000. **Ad Rates:** $792 for 15 seconds; $1320 for 30 seconds; $1980 for 45 seconds; $2640 for 60 seconds. **URL:** http://www.homeradiofm.net/cebu.php.

Cotabato City

49472 ■ DXFD-FM - 93.7 MHz
5th St., Don E. Sero, RH-5
Cotabato City, Philippines
Ph: 63 64 3902989

E-mail: starfm_cot@yahoo.com.ph
Format: Adult Contemporary. **Owner:** Bombo Radyo Philippines, 2406 Florete Bldg., Edison cor. Nobel St., Makati City 1200, Philippines, 63 2 8430116, Fax: 63 2 8173631. **Key Personnel:** Mr. Garry A. Aragoncillo, Station Mgr. **Wattage:** 5000. **URL:** http://www.bomboradyo.com/archive/new/stationprofile/starfmcotabato/index.htm.

49473 ■ DXMY - 729 KHz
State Condo. Bldg., 4th Fl.
1 Salcedo St.
Legaspi Village
Makati City, Philippines
Ph: 63 2 8120530
Fax: 63 2 8108362
Format: Eclectic. **Owner:** Radio Mindanao Network, at above address. **Operating Hours:** 2100-1600. **Wattage:** 5000. **URL:** http://www.rmn.com.ph/.

Dagupan City

49474 ■ DWHT-FM - 107.9
4 Fl., State Condo. Bldg.
1 Salcedo St.
Legaspi Village
Makati City 1229, Philippines
Ph: 63 2 8120529
Fax: 63 2 8108362
Format: Oldies; Talk; News. **Owner:** Radio Mindanao Network, at above address. **Ad Rates:** Advertising accepted; rates available upon request. **URL:** http://www.rmn.ph/fmstations/dwht.

49475 ■ DWHY-FM - 100.7 MHz
Bombo Radyo Broadcast Ctr.
Maramba Bankers Village
Bonuan Catacdang
Dagupan City 2400, Philippines
Ph: 63 75 5229908
E-mail: starfmdagupan@bomboradyo.com
Format: Adult Contemporary. **Owner:** Bombo Radyo Philippines, 2406 Florete Bldg., Edison cor. Nobel St., Makati City 1200, Philippines, 63 2 8430116, Fax: 63 2 8173631. **Founded:** June 12, 1993. **Key Personnel:** Christian E. Queyquep, Station Mgr. **Wattage:** 10,000. **URL:** http://www.bomboradyo.com/archive/new/stationprofile/starfmdagupan/index.htm.

49476 ■ DWON-FM - 104.7
4th Fl., State Condo. Bldg.
1 Salcedo St.
Legaspi Village
Makati City 1229, Philippines
Ph: 63 2 8120529
Fax: 63 2 8108362
Format: Adult Contemporary. **Owner:** Radio Mindanao Network, at above address. **Ad Rates:** Advertising accepted; rates available upon request. **URL:** http://www.rmn.ph/fmstations/dwon.

49477 ■ DZWN - 1125 KHz
Bombo Radio Broadcast Ctr.
Maramba Banker's Village
Bonuan Catacdang
Dagupan City 2400, Philippines
Ph: 63 75 5158819
Fax: 63 75 6532258
Format: News. **Owner:** Bombo Radyo Philippines, 2406 Florete Bldg., Edison Cor. Nobel St., Makati, Philippines, 63 2 8430116, 63 2 8430122, Fax: 63 2 8173631. **Operating Hours:** 2100-1600. **Key Personnel:** Chris Estolas, Station Mgr. **Wattage:** 10,000. **URL:** http://www.bomboradyo.com.

Daraga

49478 ■ DWAS - 1125 KHz
PO Box 78
Legaspi City 4500, Philippines
Ph: 63 52 4820460
Fax: 63 52 8200620
E-mail: dwas@febc.org.ph
Format: Eclectic. **Owner:** Far East Broadcasting Co., 62 Karuhatan Rd., Valenzuela City 1441, Philippines, Fax: 63 2 2925790. **Founded:** Dec. 8, 1973. **Operating Hours:** weekdays 5:30 a.m.-9 p.m.; Sun.-Sat. 5:30 a.m.-12 a.m. **Key Personnel:** Banjamin Munoz, Station Mgr. **Wattage:** 5000. **URL:** http://febc.ph.

Davao City

49479 ■ Crossover-FM - 93.1
251-F Valrose Bldg.
C.M. Recto Ave.
Davao City, Philippines
Ph: 63 82 2220931
Format: Blues; Jazz. **Ad Rates:** Advertising accepted; rates available upon request. **URL:** http://www.crossover.com.ph.

49480 ■ DXDC - 621 KHz
State Condo. Bldg., 4th Fl.
1 Salcedo St.
Legaspi Village
Makati City, Philippines
Ph: 63 2 8120530
Fax: 63 2 8108362
Format: Eclectic. **Owner:** Radio Mindanao Network, at above address. **Operating Hours:** 2100-1600. **Wattage:** 25,000. **URL:** http://www.rmn.com.ph/.

49481 ■ DXFE - 1197 KHz
Circumferential Rd.
Dona Vicente Village
Davao City 8000, Philippines
Ph: 63 82 2276530
Fax: 63 82 2242184
E-mail: dxfe@febc.org.ph
Format: Eclectic. **Owner:** Far East Broadcasting Co., at above address. **Founded:** 1971. **Operating Hours:** 2100-1600: **Key Personnel:** Rev. Arnel C. Tan, Station Mgr. **Wattage:** 5000. **URL:** http://febc.ph.

49482 ■ DXFX-FM - 96.3 MHz
Bombo Radyo Broadcast Ctr.
San Pedro St.
Davao City 8000, Philippines
Ph: 63 82 2225924
Fax: 63 82 2226007
E-mail: starfm_davao@bomboradyo.com
Format: Adult Contemporary. **Owner:** Bombo Radyo Philippines, 2406 Florete Bldg., Edison cor. Nobel St., Makati City 1200, Philippines, 63 2 8430116, Fax: 63 2 8173631. **Key Personnel:** Rogelio G. Caballo, Station Mgr. **Wattage:** 10,000. **URL:** http://www.bomboradyo.com/archive/new/stationprofile/starfmdavao/index.htm.

49483 ■ DXLR-FM - 93.1
251-F Valrose Bldg.
C.M. Recto Ave.
Davao City, Philippines
Ph: 63 82 2220931
Fax: 63 82 2222931
Format: Adult Contemporary. **URL:** http://www.crossover.com.ph/.

49484 ■ DXXL-FM - 93.9
4th Fl., State Condo. Bldg.
1 Salcedo St.
Legaspi Village
Makati City, Metro Manila 1229, Philippines
Ph: 63 2 8120529
Fax: 63 2 8163680
Format: Eclectic. **Owner:** Radio Mindanao Network, at above address. **Ad Rates:** Advertising accepted; rates available upon request. **URL:** http://www.rmn.ph/fmstations/dxxl.

49485 ■ Home Radio Davao-FM - 98.7
4D3F Atu Plz.
Duterte St.
Davao City, Philippines
Ph: 63 82 2222337
E-mail: dzqmfm@yahoo.com
Format: Adult Contemporary. **Owner:** ALIW Broadcasting Corporation, 5 Fl., Citystate Centre, 709 Shaw Blvd., Pasig City, Philippines, 63 2 6373965, Fax: 63 2 6339158. **Wattage:** 10,000. **Ad Rates:** $792 for 15 seconds; $1320 for 30 seconds; $1980 for 45 seconds; $2640 for 60 seconds. **URL:** http://www.homeradiofm.net/davao.php.

Davao Oriental

49486 ■ DXHM - 549 KHz
Unit 201, Sunrise Condominium
226 Ortigas Ave., North Greenhills
San Juan, Metro Manila 1503, Philippines
Ph: 63 2 7249850

Fax: 63 2 7249962
E-mail: cmnftd@cmn-ftd.org
Format: News; Religious. **Owner:** Catholic Media Network, at above address. **Operating Hours:** 15 hours Daily. **Key Personnel:** Rev. Patricio H. Alo, Station Dir.; Rev. Fr. Edito Bano, Station Mgr. **Wattage:** 5000. **URL:** http://www.catholicmedianetwork.org.

Dipolog City

49487 ■ The Daily Dipolognon
Reyes Bldg.
Gonzales St.
Dipolog City, Philippines
Ph: 63 62 2122673
Publisher E-mail: webmaster@dipolognon.com
Newspaper. **Freq:** Daily. **Key Personnel:** Mr. Rheynolds R. Gaylan, Contact, rheynolds@dipolognon.com. **Remarks:** Accepts advertising. **URL:** http://www.dipolognon.com/. **Circ:** (Not Reported)

49488 ■ DXDR - 981 KHz
State Condo. Bldg., 4th Fl.
1 Salcedo St.
Legaspi Village
Makati City, Philippines
Ph: 63 2 8120530
Fax: 63 2 8108362
Format: Eclectic. **Owner:** Radio Mindanao Network, at above address. **Operating Hours:** 2100-1600. **Wattage:** 5000. **URL:** http://www.rmn.com.ph/.

49489 ■ DXFB-FM - 93.3 MHz
2nd Fl., Lordel Bldg.
Gen. Luna cor. Osmena Sts.
Dipolog City 7100, Philippines
Ph: 63 65 2126596
Fax: 63 65 2126596
E-mail: stardip@mozcom.com
Format: Adult Contemporary. **Owner:** Bombo Radyo Philippines, 2406 Florete Bldg., Edison cor. Nobel St., Makati City 1200, Philippines, 63 2 8430116, Fax: 63 2 8173631. **Key Personnel:** Harriet Ybanez-Paquibot, Station Mgr. **Wattage:** 5000. **URL:** http://www.bomboradyo.com/archive/new/stationprofile/starfmdipolog/index.htm.

49490 ■ DXZZ-FM - 94.1
4th Fl., State Condo. Bldg.
1 Salcedo St.
Legaspi Village
Makati City, Metro Manila 1229, Philippines
Ph: 63 2 8120529
Fax: 63 2 8163680
Format: Eclectic. **Owner:** Radio Mindanao Network, at above address. **Ad Rates:** Advertising accepted; rates available upon request. **URL:** http://www.rmn.ph/fmstations/dxzz.

General Santos City

49491 ■ DXCK-FM - 91.9
4th Fl., State Condo. Bldg.
1 Salcedo St.
Legaspi Village
Makati City, Metro Manila 1229, Philippines
Ph: 63 2 8120529
Fax: 63 2 8163680
Format: Eclectic. **Owner:** Radio Mindanao Network, at above address. **Ad Rates:** Advertising accepted; rates available upon request. **URL:** http://www.rmn.ph/fmstations/dxck.

49492 ■ DXCP - 585 KHz
Unit 201, Sunrise Condominium
226 Ortigas Ave.
San Juan 1503, Philippines
Ph: 63 2 7249850
E-mail: cmnftd@cmn-ftd.org
Format: News. **Owner:** Catholic Media Network, at above address. **Operating Hours:** 16 hours Daily. **Key Personnel:** Medda M. Carpio, Accounting Mgr.; Ma. Cecilia C. Roxas, Program Mgr.; Jean Paul Varela, Network Mgr. **Wattage:** 5000. **URL:** http://www.catholicmedianetwork.org.

49493 ■ DXES - 801 KHz
Bombo Radyo Broadcast Ctr.
Amao Rd., Brgy. Bula
General Santos City 9500, Philippines

Ph: 63 83 5527080
Fax: 63 83 5527080
E-mail: bombogensan@hotmail.com
Format: News. **Owner:** Bombo Radyo Philippines, 2046 Florete Bldg., Edison Cor. Nobel St., Makati, Metro Manila, Philippines, 63 2 8430116, 63 2 8430122, Fax: 63 2 8173631. **Operating Hours:** 4:30 a.m.-12 p.m. Mon.-Sat.; 4 a.m.-11:30 a.m. Sun. **Key Personnel:** Ricky E. Collado, Station Mgr. **Wattage:** 10,000. **URL:** http://www.bomboradyo.com.

49494 ■ DXMD - 152 KHz
State Condo. Bldg., 4th Fl.
1 Salcedo St.
Legaspi Village
Makati City, Philippines
Ph: 63 2 8120530
Fax: 63 2 8108362
Format: Eclectic. **Owner:** Radio Mindanao Network, at above address. **Wattage:** 10,000. **URL:** http://www.rmn.com.ph/.

49495 ■ Home Radio General Santos-FM - 98.3
Sleepbest Hotel, Pioneer Ave.
General Santos City, Philippines
Ph: 63 83 5536137
E-mail: dxqs983@yahoo.com
Format: Adult Contemporary. **Owner:** ALIW Broadcasting Corporation, 5 Fl., Citystate Centre, 709 Shaw Blvd., Pasig, Philippines, 63 2 4701750, Fax: 63 2 4701138. **Wattage:** 10,000. **Ad Rates:** $792 for 15 seconds; $1320 for 30 seconds; $1980 for 45 seconds; $2640 for 60 seconds. **URL:** http://www.homeradiofm.net/generalsantos.php.

Iligan City

49496 ■ DXIC - 711 KHz
State Condo. Bldg., 4th Fl.
1 Salcedo St.
Legaspi Village
Makati City, Philippines
Ph: 63 2 8120530
Fax: 63 2 8108362
Format: Eclectic. **Owner:** Radio Mindanao Network, at above address. **Operating Hours:** 2100-1600. **Wattage:** 10,000. **URL:** http://www.rmn.com.ph/.

49497 ■ DXYX-FM - 102.3
4th Fl., State Condo. Bldg.
1 Salcedo St.
Legaspi Village
Makati City, Metro Manila 1229, Philippines
Ph: 63 2 8120529
Fax: 63 2 8163680
Format: Eclectic. **Owner:** Radio Mindanao Network, at above address. **Ad Rates:** Advertising accepted; rates available upon request. **URL:** http://www.rmn.ph/fmstations/dxyx.

Iloilo City

49498 ■ DYIC-FM - 95.1
4th Fl., State Condo. Bldg.
1 Salcedo St.
Legaspi Village
Makati City, Metro Manila 1229, Philippines
Ph: 63 2 8120529
Fax: 63 2 8163680
Format: Top 40; News. **Owner:** Radio Mindanao Network, at above address. **Ad Rates:** Advertising accepted; rates available upon request. **URL:** http://www.rmn.ph/fmstations/dyic.

49499 ■ DYRF-FM - 99.5 MHz
3rd Fl., R. Florete Bldg.
cor. Rizal Fermin Caram Ave.
Iloilo City 5000, Philippines
Ph: 63 33 3379087
Fax: 63 33 3379777
E-mail: starfm_iloilo@bomboradyo.com
Format: Adult Contemporary. **Owner:** Bombo Radyo Philippines, 2406 Florete Bldg., Edison cor. Nobel St., Makati City 1200, Philippines, 63 2 8430116, Fax: 63 2 8173631. **Key Personnel:** Mr. Alquin Rubidy, Station Mgr. **Wattage:** 10,000. **URL:** http://www.bomboradyo.com/archive/new/stationprofile/starfmiloilo/index.htm.

49500 ■ DYRI - 774 KHz
3rd Fl., St. Anne Bldg.

Circulation: ★ = ABC; △ = BPA; ♦ = CAC; • = CCAB; ❑ = VAC; ⊕ = PO Statement; ‡ = Publisher's Report; Boldface figures = sworn; Light figures = estimated.

Luna St., Lapaz
Iloilo City 5000, Philippines
Ph: 63 33 5089152
Fax: 63 33 5085615
E-mail: rmn_iloilo@yahoo.com
Format: News. **Owner:** Radio Mindanao Network, 4 Fl., State Condominium Bldg., 1 Salcedo St., Legaspi Village, Makati City, Metro Manila, Philippines, 63 2 8120529, Fax: 63 2 8163680. **Operating Hours:** 4 a.m.- 11:30 p.m. Daily. **Wattage:** 10,000. **URL:** http://www.rmn.com.ph; http://www.rmniloilo.com.ph.

Intramuros

49501 ■ Manila Bulletin
Muralla Cor. Recoletos Sts.
PO Box 769.
Intramuros, Metro Manila 1002, Philippines
Publication E-mail: editorial@mb.com.ph
Publisher E-mail: bulletin@mb.com.ph
General newspaper. **Freq:** Daily. **Print Method:** Offset. **Key Personnel:** Atty. Hermogenes P. Pobre, Publisher; Vicente Edgardo C. Bartilad, Editor-in-Chief; Diego C. Cagahastian, News Ed. **Subscription Rates:** 6,656 PP individuals 52 Sunday issues (Metro Manila subscribers only); 3,328 PP individuals 26 Sunday issues (Metro Manila subscribers only). **Remarks:** Accepts advertising. **URL:** http://www.mb.com.ph/; http://www.mb.com.ph/subscribe.html. **Circ:** (Not Reported)

49502 ■ Tempo
Manila Bulletin
Muralla Cor. Recoletos Sts.
PO Box 769.
Intramuros, Metro Manila 1002, Philippines
Publisher E-mail: bulletin@mb.com.ph
Newspaper. **Freq:** Daily. **Subscription Rates:** 2,912 PP individuals. **Remarks:** Accepts advertising. **URL:** http://www.tempo.com.ph/. **Circ:** (Not Reported)

49503 ■ DZRV - 846 KHz
121 Arzobispo St.
PO Box 132
Intramuros, Metro Manila 1184, Philippines
Ph: 63 2 5277631
Fax: 63 2 5273956
E-mail: rcam@pldtdsl.net
Format: Full Service; Religious. **Owner:** Roman Catholic Archdiocese of Manila, at above address. **Operating Hours:** 4:00 AM - 2:15 AM (following day). **Key Personnel:** Fr. Anton CT Pascual, Pres./COO. **Wattage:** 50,000. **URL:** http://www.veritas846.ph; http://www.rcam.org/.

Kalibo

49504 ■ DYIN - 1107 KHz
Bombo Radio Broadcast Ctr.
Oyo Torong St., Cor. J. Magno St.
Kalibo 5600, Philippines
Ph: 63 36 2683141
Fax: 63 36 2683141
E-mail: bombo_kalibo@yahoo.com
Format: News. **Owner:** Bombo Radyo Philippines, 2406 Florete Bldg., Edison Cor. Nobel St., Makati City, Philippines, 63 2 8430116, Fax: 63 2 8173631. **Operating Hours:** 4:30 a.m.-12 p.m. Mon.-Sat.; 4:30 a.m.-11:30 p.m. Sun. **Key Personnel:** Eril Ibardolasa, Station Mgr. **Wattage:** 5000. **URL:** http://www.bomboradyo.com.

49505 ■ DYKR - 1161 KHz
State Condo. Bldg., 4th Fl.
1 Salcedo St.
Legaspi Village
Makati City, Philippines
Ph: 63 2 8120530
Fax: 63 2 8108362
Format: Eclectic. **Owner:** Radio Mindanao Network, at above address. **Operating Hours:** 2100-1600. **Wattage:** 5000. **URL:** http://www.rmn.com.ph/.

Koronadal

49506 ■ DXKI - 1062 KHz
Barangay Morales
Koronadal 9506, Philippines
Ph: 63 83 2285066
Fax: 63 83 2285066
E-mail: dxki@febc.org.ph
Format: Eclectic. **Owner:** Far East Broadcasting Co.,

62 Karuhatan Rd., Valenzuela City 1441, Philippines, 63 2 2925603, Fax: 63 2 2925790. **Founded:** Dec. 19, 1964. **Operating Hours:** 2100-1600. **Key Personnel:** Alex S. Gunay, Station Mgr. **Wattage:** 5000. **URL:** http://febc.ph/.

Laguna

49507 ■ The Philippine Agricultural Scientist
University of the Philippines at Los Banos
College of Agriculture
College
Laguna 4031, Philippines
Ph: 63 495 362379
Fax: 63 495 362379
Publication E-mail: philagri@laguna.net
Publisher E-mail: philagri@laguna.net
Features original research papers and reviews on plant, animal, soil and food sciences, agricultural biotechnology and agri-business. **Founded:** 1911. **Freq:** Quarterly. **Key Personnel:** Evelyn Mae Tecson-Mendoza, PhD, Editor-in-Chief; Hosanna H. Espanto, Assoc. Ed.; Juanito B. Reyes, Production Ed. **ISSN:** 0031-7454. **Subscription Rates:** 1,500 PP individuals; US$210 other countries. **Remarks:** Accepts advertising. **URL:** http://www.laguna.net/philippagricsci. **Circ:** Paid 25,000

49508 ■ The Philippine Entomologist
Philippine Association of Entomologists
c/o Department of Entomology
University of the Phillipines at Los Banos College
Laguna 4031, Philippines
Ph: 63 49 536 1315
Publication E-mail: oil@admi.uplb.edu.ph
Publisher E-mail: oil@admi.uplb.edu.ph
Journal covering entomology. **Founded:** 1968. **Freq:** Semiannual. **Key Personnel:** Dr. Candida B. Adalla, President. **ISSN:** 0048-3753. **Subscription Rates:** US$600 institutions non members; US$50 other countries. **Remarks:** Advertising accepted; rates available upon request. **URL:** http://www.laguna.net/pae/. **Circ:** Paid 1,000

Laoag City

49509 ■ The Ilocos Times
Ilocos Publishing Corp.
Barangay 23
M.H. del Pilar St.
Laoag City 2900, Philippines
Ph: 63 77 7720976
Fax: 63 77 7711378
Publisher E-mail: publisher@ilocostimes.com
Newspaper. **Subtitle:** The Bastion of Press Freedom. **Freq:** Weekly. **Key Personnel:** Efren S. Ramos, Jr., Editor and Publisher; Dominic B. De La Cruz, Staff Reporter; Rex Dominique S. Ramos, Circulation Mgr.; Michael T. Esmino, Assoc. Ed./Columnist. **Remarks:** Accepts advertising. **URL:** http://www.ilocostimes.com/. **Circ:** 5,000

49510 ■ Campus Radio-FM - 97.1
3 Fl., New Pacific Bldg.
Abadilla St.
Laoag City, Philippines
Ph: 63 77 7731437
E-mail: campusradiolaoag@yahoo.com
Format: Contemporary Hit Radio (CHR). **Operating Hours:** Continuous. **URL:** http://www.angelfire.com/nd/campusradiolaoag/campus.html.

49511 ■ DWHP-FM - 99.5
4 Fl., State Condo. Bldg.
1 Salcedo St.
Legaspi Village
Makati City 1229, Philippines
Ph: 63 2 8120529
Fax: 63 2 8108362
Format: Adult Contemporary. **Owner:** Radio Mindanao Network, at above address. **Ad Rates:** Advertising accepted; rates available upon request. **URL:** http://www.rmn.ph/fmstations/dwhp.

Legaspi City

DWAS - See Daraga

Los Banos

49512 ■ DZLB - 97.4 MHz

UP-Los Banos College
2nd Fl., College of Development Communication
Los Banos 4031, Philippines
Ph: 63 49 5362433
E-mail: dzlbfm@yahoo.com
Format: News; Talk; Soft Rock; Classic Rock. **Owner:** University of the Philippines, Los Banos, at above address. **Operating Hours:** 4-10 p.m. **Wattage:** 20,000. **URL:** http://listen.to/lbfm.

Maasin

49513 ■ DYDM - 1548 KHz
Unit 201, Sunrise Condominium
226 Ortigas Ave.
San Juan, Philippines
Ph: 63 2 7249850
Fax: 63 2 7249962
Format: News. **Owner:** Catholic Media Network, at above address. **Operating Hours:** 13 hours Daily. **Key Personnel:** Precioso Cantilas, Station Pres.; Fr. Amiel Aborneo, Station Dir.; Mr. Rafael Gerong, Station Mgr.; Aurora Salazar, Sales Mgr.; Zaldy Olita, News Dir. **Wattage:** 5000. **URL:** http://www.catholicmedianetwork.org.

Makati City

49514 ■ AmCham Business Journal
American Chamber of Commerce of the Philippines
2/F Corinthian Plz., Paseo de Roxas
CPO 2562
Makati City 1229, Philippines
Ph: 63 2 8187911
Fax: 63 2 8113081
Publication E-mail: publications@amchamphilippines.com
Publisher E-mail: info@amchamphilippines.com
General business magazine circulated worldwide containing business updates, corporate information, current trends in the different industries and the general business outlook within the Philippines. **Freq:** Monthly. **Print Method:** Offset. **Trim Size:** 8 3/4 x 11 3/4. **Subscription Rates:** 3,500 PP individuals; US$250 other countries. **Remarks:** Advertising accepted; rates available upon request. **URL:** http://www.amchamphilippines.com/index.php?page=publications&publications=details&id=1. **Circ:** (Not Reported)

49515 ■ Computer World Philippines
Media G8way Publishing Corp.
Unit P5 VGP Ctr.
6772 Ayala Ave.
Makati City 1226, Philippines
Ph: 632 812 8401
Fax: 632 894 2487
Newspaper covering information systems management for professionals. **Founded:** July 15, 1991. **Freq:** Monthly. **Trim Size:** 28 x 43 cm. **Cols./Page:** 6. **Col. Width:** 3.7 centimeters. **Col. Depth:** 40 centimeters. **Key Personnel:** Ibarra C. Gutierrez, Editor-in-Chief, icgutierrez@computerworld.com.ph; Deb C. Gutierrez, Sales and Marketing Dir., dacgutierrez@mediag8way.com. **Subscription Rates:** 1,350 PP individuals; 2,700 PP two years. **Remarks:** Accepts advertising. **URL:** http://www.computerworld.com.ph/?_s=4. **Circ:** (Not Reported)

49516 ■ Enterprise
Media G8way Publishing Corp.
Unit P5 VGP Ctr.
6772 Ayala Ave.
Makati City 1226, Philippines
Ph: 632 812 8401
Fax: 632 894 2487
Magazine pertaining to computers. **Freq:** Monthly. **Key Personnel:** Michael David C. Tan, Assoc. Ed., mdctan@enterprise.ph; Ibarra C. Gutierrez, Editor-in-Chief, icgutierrez@mediag8way.com. **Subscription Rates:** US$1,200 individuals; US$2,160 two years. **Remarks:** Advertising accepted; rates available upon request. **URL:** http://www.enterprise.ph/?_s=8&_ss=236. **Circ:** 60,000

49517 ■ Home Life
Society of St. Paul, Inc.
c/o Cris Robert Cano Cellan, Ed.
7708 St. Paul Rd.
San Antonio Village
Makati City, Metro Manila 1203, Philippines

Publication E-mail: homelife@stpauls.ph
Magazine featuring different sections for different members of the family. **Founded:** 1953. **Freq:** Monthly. **Key Personnel:** Cris Robert Cano Cellan, Editor; Miguel C. Arguelles, Fiction Ed.; Leoncio P. Deriada, Poetry Ed. **ISSN:** 0115-2971. **Subscription Rates:** 363 PP individuals for Metro Manila, p&p included; 407 PP individuals for the provinces, p&p included. **URL:** http://backup.rome67ad.com/st-pauls/homelife-mainmenu-35.html. **Circ:** Paid 60,000.

49518 ■ PC World Philippines
Media G8way Publishing Corp.
Unit P5 VGP Ctr.
6772 Ayala Ave.
Makati City 1226, Philippines
Ph: 632 812 8401
Fax: 632 894 2487
Trade magazine covering productivity and buying information for computer users. **Founded:** Mar. 1989. **Freq:** Monthly. **Trim Size:** 21.59 x 27.94 cm. **Cols./Page:** 3. **Col. Width:** 5.5 centimeters. **Col. Depth:** 25 centimeters. **Key Personnel:** Ibarra C. Gutierrez, Editor-in-Chief, icgutierrez@enterprise.ph; Jean Paulo T. de Jesus, Editor, sean@pcworld.com.ph; Michael David C. Tan, Assoc. Ed., mdctan@enterprise.ph. **Remarks:** Accepts advertising. **URL:** http://www.pcworld.com.ph. **Former name:** PC Digest. **Circ:** 65,000.

49519 ■ Philippine Daily Inquirer
The Philippine Daily Inquirer Inc.
Chino Roces Ave.
Cor. Yague & Mascardo Sts.
PO Box 2353
Makati City 1263, Philippines
Ph: 63 2 8978808
Fax: 63 2 8974793
Publisher E-mail: feedback@inquirer.com.ph
General newspaper. **Founded:** Dec. 1985. **Freq:** Daily. **Key Personnel:** Isagani M. Yambot, Publisher; Letty Jimenez-Magsanoc, Editor-in-Chief; Jose Ma. D. Nolasco, Managing Editor. **Remarks:** Accepts advertising. **URL:** http://services.inquirer.net. **Circ:** (Not Reported)

49520 ■ Philippine Journal of Development
Philippine Institute for Development Studies
Rm. 304, NEDA Makati Bldg.
106 Amorsolo St.
Legaspi Village
Makati City 1229, Philippines
Ph: 63 289 35705
Fax: 63 289 39589
Publisher E-mail: publications@pidsnet.pids.gov.ph
Studies economics in business, sociology, politics, public administration and foreign relations as they relate to the development of the Philippines. **Founded:** 1974. **Freq:** Semiannual. **Key Personnel:** Sheila V. Siar, Assoc. Ed.; Jennifer P.T. Liguton, Managing Editor; Dr. Michael M. Alba, Editorial Board; Dr. Gonzalo M. Jurado, Editorial Board Chp. **ISSN:** 0115-9143. **Subscription Rates:** 900 PP individuals including mailing; US$55 individuals including mailing; 400 PP single issue. **Remarks:** Advertising not accepted. **URL:** http://www3.pids.gov.ph/ris/journalindex.htm. **Circ:** Paid 500

49521 ■ Philippine Journal of Ophthalmology
Philippine Academy of Ophthalmology
Unit 815, Medical Plz. Makati
Amorsolo St.
Cor. De la Rosa St.
Makati City 1000, Philippines
Ph: 63 2 8135318
Fax: 63 2 8135331
Publisher E-mail: secretariat_pao@globelines.com.ph
Journal covering ophthalmology. **Founded:** 1969. **Freq:** Quarterly. **Key Personnel:** Dr. Romeo V. Fajardo, Editorial Board; Patricia M. Khu, MD, Editor-in-Chief; Carlos G. Naval, MD, Managing Editor. **ISSN:** 0031-7659. **Subscription Rates:** US$30 individuals; US$50 institutions. **Remarks:** Advertising accepted; rates available upon request. **URL:** http://www.pao.org.ph/pjo.php. **Circ:** Paid 1,000

49522 ■ Philippine Society
Edipresse Asia
Manila Bank Bldg., 11th Fl., Unit 11-A
6772 Ayala Ave.
Makati City, Philippines
Ph: 63 2 8140771

Fax: 63 2 8120790
Magazine featuring the 400 most powerful and influential individuals in the Philippines. **Freq:** Annual. **Key Personnel:** Irene Francisco, Director; Anton San Diego, Ch. Ed. **URL:** http://www.edipresse.com/lifestyle/philippines-society. **Circ:** ‡45,000

49523 ■ Philippine Tatler
Edipresse Asia
Manila Bank Bldg., 11th Fl., Unit 11-A
6772 Ayala Ave.
Makati City, Philippines
Ph: 63 2 8140771
Fax: 63 2 8120790
Publication E-mail: cmail@philtatler.com
Magazine featuring the latest trends in contemporary society. **Freq:** Monthly. **Key Personnel:** Irene Francisco, Director; Anton San Diego, Ch. Ed. **URL:** http://www.edipresse.com/lifestyle/philippine-tatler. **Circ:** ‡45,000

49524 ■ Philippines' Best Restaurants
Edipresse Asia
Manila Bank Bldg., 11th Fl., Unit 11-A
6772 Ayala Ave.
Makati City, Philippines
Ph: 63 2 8140771
Fax: 63 2 8120790
Publication E-mail: cmail@philtatler.com
Magazine featuring the best restaurants in the Philippines. **Freq:** Annual. **Key Personnel:** Irene Francisco, Director; Anton San Diego, Ch. Ed.; Lynne Palma, General Mgr. **URL:** http://www.edipresseasia.com/magazines.php?MagID=PHBRG.

DWHB-FM - See Baguio City

DWHP-FM - See Laoag City

DWHT-FM - See Dagupan City

49525 ■ DWKC-FM - 93.9
4th Fl., Guadalupe Commercial Complex Bldg.
Edsa, Guadalupe
Makati City 1212, Philippines
Ph: 63 2 8822375
Fax: 63 2 8822374
E-mail: ifmmanila@rmn.ph
Format: Adult Contemporary. **Owner:** Radio Mindanao Network, at above address. **Ad Rates:** Advertising accepted; rates available upon request. **URL:** http://www.rmn.ph/fmstations/dwkc.

DWNX-FM - See Naga City

DWON-FM - See Dagupan City

DXBC - See Butuan City

DXCC - See Cagayan de Oro City

DXCK-FM - See General Santos City

DXDC - See Davao City

DXDR - See Dipolog City

DXHP - See Bislig

DXIC - See Iligan City

DXKE-FM - See Surigao City

DXKR - See Marbel

DXMB - See Bukidnon

DXMD - See General Santos City

DXMY - See Cotabato City

DXPR - See Pagadian City

DXRS - See Surigao City

DXRZ - See Zamboanga City

DXVM-FM - See Cagayan de Oro City

DXWD-FM - See Pagadian City

DXWR-FM - See Zamboanga City

DXXL-FM - See Davao City

DXXX-FM - See Butuan City

DXYX-FM - See Iligan City

DXZZ-FM - See Dipolog City

DYCC - See Calbayog

DYHP - See Cebu City

DYHT-FM - See Bacolod City

DYIC-FM - See Iloilo City

DYKR - See Kalibo

DYVR - See Roxas City

DYVR-FM - See Roxas City

DYXL-FM - See Cebu City

DYXY-FM - See Tacloban City

49526 ■ DZFE - 98.7 MHz
Rm. 2608, Cityland 10, Tower 1
HV de la Costa St., Salcedo Village
Makati City, Metro Manila 1227, Philippines
Ph: 63 2 8103835
Fax: 63 2 8402864
E-mail: dzfe@i-manila.com.ph
Format: Contemporary Christian; Gospel; Classical. **Owner:** Far East Broadcasting Co., 62 Karuhatan Rd., Valenzuela City 1441, Philippines, 63 2 2925603, 63 2 2921152, Fax: 63 2 2925790. **Founded:** 1954. **Operating Hours:** 6 a.m. - 10 p.m. Mon. - Sat. **Wattage:** 5000. **URL:** http://dzfe.febc.ph/; http://febc.ph/.

DZFE - See Manila

49527 ■ DZIQ-AM - 990
3rd Fl., Media Resource Plz.
2530 Mola cor. Pasong Tirad St.
Pasong Tamo
Makati City, Philippines
Ph: 63 2 4089734
Fax: 63 2 4030513
Format: News; Public Radio; Information. **Owner:** Philippine Daily Inquirer, Makati Central Post Office, PO Box 2353, Makati City 1263, Philippines, 63 2 8978808, Fax: 63 2 8974793. **URL:** http://www.dziq.am/.

DZXL - See Manila

49528 ■ DZXL-AM - 558
4th Fl., Guadalupe Commercial Complex Bldg.
Edsa
Guadalupe
Makati City, Philippines
Ph: 63 2 8822370
E-mail: rmnmanila@rmn.ph
Format: Sports. **Owner:** RMN Networks, 4th Fl., State Condo. Bldg., 1 Salcedo St., Legaspi Village, Makati City, Philippines, 63 2 8120529, Fax: 63 2 8108362. **Founded:** Aug. 28, 1952. **Operating Hours:** Continuous. **Wattage:** 50,000. **Ad Rates:** Advertising accepted; rates available upon request. **URL:** http://www.rmn.ph/amstations/dzxl.

49529 ■ RMN Manila-AM - 558 KHz
Guadalupe Commercial Complex Bldg., 4th Fl.
Edsa
Guadalupe
Makati City, Philippines
Ph: 63 2 8822370
E-mail: rmnmanila@rmn.ph
Format: News; Sports. **Ad Rates:** Advertising accepted; rates available upon request. **URL:** http://www.rmn.ph.

49530 ■ Yes-FM - 101.1
FJE Bldg., 105 Esteban St.
Legaspi Village
Makati City, Philippines
Ph: 63 2 8404747
E-mail: yes_candy@yahoo.com
Format: Ethnic; Information; Eclectic. **Owner:** Manila Broadcasting Co., at above address. **Operating Hours:** Continuous. **Ad Rates:** Advertising accepted; rates available upon request. **URL:** http://www.angelfire.com/al2/adonato/mbc1.html.

Mandaluyong City

49531 ■ Accountant's Journal
Philippine Institute of Certified Public Accountants
PICPA Bldg.
700 Shaw Blvd.
Mandaluyong City, Metro Manila, Philippines
Ph: 63 2 723 0691
Fax: 63 2 723 6305
Publisher E-mail: picpamsd@pldtdsl.net
Journal covering accounting. **Freq:** Quarterly. **Remarks:** Advertising accepted; rates available upon request. **URL:** http://www.picpa.com.ph/. **Circ:** (Not Reported)

49532 ■ Candy Magazine
Summit Media
6F & 7F Robinsons Cybergate Ctr., Tower 3
Robinsons Pioneer Complex
Pioneer St.
Mandaluyong City 1550, Philippines

Circulation: ★ = ABC; △ = BPA; ◆ = CAC; • = CCAB; ❏ = VAC; ⊕ = PO Statement; ‡ = Publisher's Report; Boldface figures = sworn; Light figures = estimated.

Ph: 63 2 4518888
Fax: 63 2 6317788
Publisher E-mail: customercare@summitmedia.com.ph
Consumer magazine covering fashion, beauty, and other issues for Filipino girls and teenagers. **Freq:** Monthly. **Key Personnel:** Mia Custodio, Editor-in-Chief, mia@candymag.com; Denise Congco, Assoc. Publisher, ads@candymag.com; Mimi Tiu, Managing Editor. **Subscription Rates:** 1020 PP individuals. **Remarks:** Accepts advertising. **URL:** http://www.candymag.com; http://www.summitmedia.com.ph/magazines/candy. **Circ:** 40,000

49533 ■ Cosmopolitan Philippines
Summit Media
6F & 7F Robinsons Cybergate Ctr., Tower 3
Robinsons Pioneer Complex
Pioneer St.
Mandaluyong City 1550, Philippines
Ph: 63 2 4518888
Fax: 63 2 6317788
Publisher E-mail: customercare@summitmedia.com.ph
Consumer magazine covering fashion, beauty, and other issues for women. **Founded:** Apr. 25, 1997. **Freq:** Monthly. **Key Personnel:** Zo Aguila, Editor-in-Chief, zo.aguila@summitmedia.com.ph; Trixie Reyna, Managing Editor, trixie@cosmo.ph; Maan Chipeco-de Guzman, Advertising Mgr., maan.chipeco@summitmedia.com.ph; Anna Vitug-Dy, Digital Publisher, annamarie.dy@summitmedia.com.ph; Ichi Apostol, Team Publisher, cristina.apostol@summitmedia.com.ph. **Subscription Rates:** 1,275 PP individuals; 356.25 PP individuals 3 months; 675 PP individuals 6 months. **Remarks:** Accepts advertising. **URL:** http://www.cosmomagazine.com.ph; http://www.summitmedia.com.ph/magazines/cosmopolitan/. **Circ:** 72,000

49534 ■ Design and Architecture
Santa Barbara Publishing Corp.
105 Labrador Bldg.
Epifanio Delos Santos Ave.
Mandaluyong City, Metro Manila, Philippines
Ph: 63 253 27974
Fax: 63 253 10838
Magazine related to architecture. **Founded:** 1992. **Freq:** Quarterly. **Key Personnel:** Sylvia Rose Montilla, Editor-in-Chief. **ISSN:** 0116-9718. **Subscription Rates:** 750 PP individuals; US$49 individuals USA & Europe, surface mail; US$27 individuals airmail; US$44 individuals Asia, surface mail; US$19 individuals airmail. **Remarks:** Accepts advertising. **URL:** http://www.nsclub.net/dna/. **Circ:** Paid 2,500

49535 ■ Disney Princess Magazine
Summit Media
6F & 7F Robinsons Cybergate Ctr., Tower 3
Robinsons Pioneer Complex
Pioneer St.
Mandaluyong City 1550, Philippines
Ph: 63 2 4518888
Fax: 63 2 6317788
Publisher E-mail: customercare@summitmedia.com.ph
Fun-to-learn magazine, bringing together Ariel, Belle, Sleeping Beauty, Cinderella and other princesses with magical stories, collectible posters, Princess projects and fun activities. **Freq:** 11/yr. **Trim Size:** 8.5 x 11. **Key Personnel:** Maita De Jesus, Editor-in-Chief, maita.dejesus@summitmedia.com.ph; Christine Ko, Team Publisher, christine.ko@summitmedia.com.ph. **Subscription Rates:** 1,275 PP individuals; 2,400 PP two years. **Remarks:** Accepts advertising. **URL:** http://www.summitmedia.com.ph/magazines/disneyprincess/. **Circ:** 22,000

49536 ■ For Him Magazine Philippines
Summit Media
6F & 7F Robinsons Cybergate Ctr., Tower 3
Robinsons Pioneer Complex
Pioneer St.
Mandaluyong City 1550, Philippines
Ph: 63 2 4518888
Fax: 63 2 6317788
Publisher E-mail: customercare@summitmedia.com.ph
Magazine for men. **Freq:** Monthly. **Trim Size:** 8 1/2 x 11. **Key Personnel:** Lou Albano, Managing Editor, lou.albano@summitmedia.com.ph; Chad Rosario, Assoc. Publisher, chad.rosario@summitmedia.com.ph; Allan A. Madrilejos, Editor-in-Chief, allan.madrilejos@summitmedia.com.ph. **Subscription Rates:** 1,275 PP

individuals; 356.25 PP individuals 3 months; 675 PP individuals 6 months. **Remarks:** Advertising accepted; rates available upon request. **URL:** http://www.fhm.com.ph/; http://www.summitmedia.com.ph/magazines/fhm/. **Circ:** 150,000

49537 ■ Good Housekeeping Philippines
Summit Media
6F & 7F Robinsons Cybergate Ctr., Tower 3
Robinsons Pioneer Complex
Pioneer St.
Mandaluyong City 1550, Philippines
Ph: 63 2 4518888
Fax: 63 2 6317788
Publisher E-mail: customercare@summitmedia.com.ph
Consumer magazine covering home, parenting, health, food and other issues for women. **Founded:** June 1998. **Freq:** 11/yr. **Trim Size:** 8 1/2 x 11. **Key Personnel:** Melody Lalata, Assoc. Publisher, cristina.apostol@summitmedia.com.ph. **Subscription Rates:** 285 PP individuals 3 months; 540 PP individuals 6 months; 1,020 PP individuals. **Remarks:** Accepts advertising. **URL:** http://www.summitmedia.com.ph/magazines/goodhousekeeping. **Circ:** 50,000

49538 ■ High School Musical
Summit Media
6F & 7F Robinsons Cybergate Ctr., Tower 3
Robinsons Pioneer Complex
Pioneer St.
Mandaluyong City 1550, Philippines
Ph: 63 2 4518888
Fax: 63 2 6317788
Publisher E-mail: customercare@summitmedia.com.ph
Magazine for High School Musical fans. **Freq:** 10/yr. **Trim Size:** 8.5 x 11. **Key Personnel:** Christine Ko, Team Publisher, christine.ko@summitmedia.com.ph; Ines Bautista-Yao, Editor-in-Chief, ines.bautista@summitmedia.com.ph. **Remarks:** Accepts advertising. **URL:** http://www.summitmedia.com.ph/magazines/highschoolmusical/. **Circ:** 20,000

49539 ■ Preview
Summit Media
6F & 7F Robinsons Cybergate Ctr., Tower 3
Robinsons Pioneer Complex
Pioneer St.
Mandaluyong City 1550, Philippines
Ph: 63 2 4518888
Fax: 63 2 6317788
Publisher E-mail: customercare@summitmedia.com.ph
Consumer magazine covering fashion, beauty, and celebrities for Filipino women. **Freq:** 11/yr. **Key Personnel:** Tara Santos, Assoc. Publisher, tara.santos@summitmedia.com.ph; Pauline Suaco-Juan, Editor-in-Chief, pauline.suaco@summitmedia.com.ph. **Subscription Rates:** 427.50 PP individuals 3 months; 810 PP individuals 6 months; 1,530 PP individuals. **Remarks:** Accepts advertising. **URL:** http://www.summitmedia.com.ph/magazines/preview/. **Circ:** 45,000

49540 ■ Seventeen Philippines
Summit Media
6F & 7F Robinsons Cybergate Ctr., Tower 3
Robinsons Pioneer Complex
Pioneer St.
Mandaluyong City 1550, Philippines
Ph: 63 2 4518888
Fax: 63 2 6317788
Publisher E-mail: customercare@summitmedia.com.ph
Consumer magazine for teenage girls. **Freq:** 11/yr. **Key Personnel:** Mia Fausto, Editor-in-Chief, mia.fausto@summitmedia.com.ph; Denise Congco, Assoc. Publisher, denise.congco@summitmedia.com.ph. **Subscription Rates:** 242.25 PP individuals 3 months; 459 PP individuals 6 months; 867 PP individuals. **Remarks:** Accepts advertising. **URL:** http://www.summitmedia.com.ph/magazines/seventeen/. **Circ:** 30,000

49541 ■ Smart Parenting
Summit Media
6F & 7F Robinsons Cybergate Ctr., Tower 3
Robinsons Pioneer Complex
Pioneer St.
Mandaluyong City 1550, Philippines
Ph: 63 2 4518888
Fax: 63 2 6317788
Publisher E-mail: customercare@summitmedia.com.ph
Magazine featuring information on raising children. **Freq:** 11/yr. **Key Personnel:** Mia Fausto-Cruz, Editor-in-Chief,

mia.fausto@summitmedia.com.ph; Melody Lalata, Assoc. Publisher, melody.lalata@summitmedia.com.ph. **Subscription Rates:** 1,020 PP individuals; 1,920 PP two years. **Remarks:** Accepts advertising. **URL:** http://www.summitmedia.com.ph/magazines/smartparenting/; http://www.smartparenting.com.ph/parentchat/. **Circ:** 20,000

49542 ■ Star Teacher
Summit Media
6F & 7F Robinsons Cybergate Ctr., Tower 3
Robinsons Pioneer Complex
Pioneer St.
Mandaluyong City 1550, Philippines
Ph: 63 2 4518888
Fax: 63 2 6317788
Publisher E-mail: customercare@summitmedia.com.ph
Magazine for teachers featuring information that will help them in the classroom as well as information that will help them with their personal lives. **Freq:** Quarterly. **Key Personnel:** Ines Bautista-Yao, Editor-in-Chief, ines.bautista@summitmedia.com.ph. **Remarks:** Accepts advertising. **URL:** http://www.summitmedia.com.ph/magazines/starteacher/; http://www.starteacher.ph/. **Circ:** 8,000

49543 ■ Yes!
Summit Media
6F & 7F Robinsons Cybergate Ctr., Tower 3
Robinsons Pioneer Complex
Pioneer St.
Mandaluyong City 1550, Philippines
Ph: 63 2 4518888
Fax: 63 2 6317788
Publisher E-mail: customercare@summitmedia.com.ph
Consumer magazine covering celebrities and entertainment. **Freq:** Monthly. **Key Personnel:** Joann Maglipon, Editor-in-Chief, joann.maglipon@summitmedia.com.ph; Danio Caw, Team Publisher, danio.caw@summitmedia.com.ph. **Subscription Rates:** 1020 PP individuals. **Remarks:** Accepts advertising. **URL:** http://www.summitmedia.com.ph/magazines/yes/. **Circ:** 150,000

49544 ■ Yummy
Summit Media
6F & 7F Robinsons Cybergate Ctr., Tower 3
Robinsons Pioneer Complex
Pioneer St.
Mandaluyong City 1550, Philippines
Ph: 63 2 4518888
Fax: 63 2 6317788
Publisher E-mail: customercare@summitmedia.com.ph
Modern food magazine featuring delicious recipes, food styling, useful cooking, and food shopping tips. **Freq:** 11/yr. **Trim Size:** 8.5 x 11. **Key Personnel:** Danio Caw, Team Publisher, danio.caw@summitmedia.com.ph; Becky Kho, Editor-in-Chief, becky.kho@summitmedia.com.ph. **Subscription Rates:** 1,275 PP individuals; 2,400 PP two years. **Remarks:** Accepts advertising. **URL:** http://www.summitmedia.com.ph/magazines/yummy/. **Circ:** 30,000

Mandaue

49545 ■ DYAB - 1512 KHz
ABS-CBN Broadcast Complex
Jagobiao
Mandaue 6014, Philippines
Ph: 63 32 5643202
E-mail: leo_lastimosa@abs-cbn.com
Format: Eclectic. **Owner:** ABS-CBN Broadcasting Network Inc., Sgt. E.A. Esguerra Ave. cor. Mother Ignacia St., Quezon City, Metro Manila 1103, Philippines. **Operating Hours:** 2100-1600. **Wattage:** 15,000. **URL:** http://www.abs-cbn.com; http://dyabcebu.tripod.com/.

Manila

49546 ■ ADB Business Opportunities
Asian Development Bank
6 ADB Ave.
Mandaluyong
Manila 0980, Philippines
Ph: 63 263 24444
Fax: 63 263 62444
Publication covering economic development. **Freq:** Monthly. **URL:** http://www.adb.org/business/opportunities/.

49547 ■ Asian Development Review
Asian Development Bank
6 ADB Ave.
Mandaluyong
Manila 0980, Philippines
Ph: 63 263 24444
Fax: 63 263 62444
Publication on Asian development. **Freq:** Semiannual. **ISSN:** 0116-1105. **Subscription Rates:** US$12 individuals. **URL:** http://www.adb.org/Documents/Periodicals/ADR/default.asp.

49548 ■ Cabletow
Grand Lodge of the Philippines
New Plaridel Masonic Temple, 2nd Fl.
1440 San Marcelino St.
PO Box 990
Ermita
Manila 1000, Philippines
Ph: 63 2 522 2218
Publication E-mail: glp_cabletow@yahoo.com
Publisher E-mail: inform@glphils.org
Magazine featuring articles about freemasonry in the Philippines. **Freq:** Bimonthly. **Key Personnel:** J. Flor R. Nicholas, Editor-in-Chief. **URL:** http://glphils.org/glp2007/reference.html.

49549 ■ Daily Tribune
The Tribune Publishing Co. Inc.
The Penthouse Stes.
GLC Bldg.
T.M. Kalaw cor. A. Mabini Sts.
Ermita
Manila, Philippines
Ph: 63 2 5215511
Publication E-mail: webmaster@tribune.net.ph
Newspaper for general interest. **Freq:** Daily. **Key Personnel:** Ninez Cacho-Olivares, Publisher/Ed.-in-Ch., nco@tribune.net.ph; Romulo Marinas, News Ed. **Remarks:** Accepts advertising. **URL:** http://www.tribune.net.ph/. **Ad Rates:** BW: 96,228 PP. **Circ:** (Not Reported)

49550 ■ Journal of Philippine Statistics
National Statistics Office
Ramon Magsaysay Blvd.
Box 779
Sta. Mesa
Manila 1008, Philippines
Ph: 63 2 7160807
Fax: 63 2 7156503
Provides essential statistical information on population, education, health, vital statistics, travel, social welfare, foreign trade, prices and law enforcement. **Founded:** 1940. **Freq:** Quarterly. **Key Personnel:** Preciosa Astillero, Editor; Carmelita N. Ericta, Admin., c.ericta@census.gov.ph. **ISSN:** 0022-3603. **Subscription Rates:** US$30 single issue. **URL:** http://www.census.gov.ph/. **Circ:** Paid 250

49551 ■ Lila
Saint Scholastica's College Institute of Women's Studies
931 Estrada St., Malate
Manila 1004, Philippines
Ph: 63 252 23551
Fax: 63 252 30693
Publisher E-mail: iwsmnl@yahoo.com
Deals with women's issues in the Asia-Pacific region for the community of women who lead in academia and related areas. **Subtitle:** Asia Pacific Women's Studies Journal. **Founded:** 1991. **Freq:** Semiannual. **Key Personnel:** Mary John Mananzan, Editor. **ISSN:** 0117-343X. **URL:** http://www.ssc.edu.ph/sscweb_content/iws_publications.htm. **Circ:** Paid 500

49552 ■ Malaya
People's Independent Media Inc.
Leyland Bldg.
Railroad St.
Port Area
Manila 1018, Philippines
Ph: 63 2 5271841
Fax: 63 2 5271836
Publisher E-mail: business_malaya@yahoo.com
Newspaper for general interest. **Founded:** 1981. **Freq:** Daily. **Key Personnel:** Joy de los Reyes, Editor-in-Chief; Amado P. Macasaet, Publisher. **Subscription Rates:** 3,900 PP individuals regular; 3,510 PP two years discounted. **Remarks:** Accepts advertising. **URL:** http://

www.malaya.com.ph/. **Ad Rates:** BW: 89,910 PP. **Circ:** (Not Reported)

49553 ■ Manila Journal of Science
De La Salle University
College of Science
2401 Taft Ave.
Manila 1004, Philippines
Journal presenting scientific research and reviews. **Founded:** 1975. **Freq:** Semiannual. **ISSN:** 0118-9913. **Remarks:** Advertising accepted; rates available upon request. **URL:** http://www.dlsu.edu.ph/. **Circ:** Paid 300

49554 ■ Philippine Headline News Online
1991 M.H. del Pilar
Malate
Manila, Philippines
Ph: 63 2 5232040
Fax: 63 2 5217366
Publication E-mail: info@newsflash.org
Publisher E-mail: info@newsflash.org
Online newspaper providing insights of events in the Philippines. **Freq:** Daily. **Key Personnel:** Sol Jose Vanzi, Editor, sjvanzi@newsflash.org. **URL:** http://www.newsflash.org/.

49555 ■ Philippine Journal of Linguistics
Linguistic Society of the Philippines
De La Salle University
2401 Taft Ave.
Manila 1004, Philippines
Journal presenting original studies in descriptive, comparative, historical, and area linguistics as well as papers on the application of theory to language teaching. **Founded:** 1970. **Freq:** Semiannual. **Key Personnel:** Ma. Lourdes S. Bautista, Editor. **ISSN:** 0048-3796. **Subscription Rates:** 500 PP individuals; US$20 other countries. **URL:** http://www.dlsu.edu.ph/inside/organizations/lsp/journal.asp. **Circ:** Paid 500

49556 ■ Philippine Journal of Nursing
Philippine Nurses Association
1663 F.T. Benitez St.
Malate
Manila 1004, Philippines
Ph: 63 2 5210937
Fax: 63 2 5251596
Publisher E-mail: philippinenursesassociation@yahoo.com.ph
Nursing journal. **Founded:** 1953. **Freq:** Quarterly. **ISSN:** 0048-3818. **Subscription Rates:** 100 PP. **Remarks:** Advertising accepted; rates available upon request. **URL:** http://www.pna-ph.org/journal.asp. **Circ:** Paid 13,000

49557 ■ Philippine Labor Review
Department of Labor and Employment
Institute for Labor Studies
5th Fl., DOLE Bldg.
Gen. Luna St., Intramuros
Manila 1002, Philippines
Ph: 63 2 5273490
Fax: 63 2 5273448
Publication E-mail: publications@ilsdole.gov.ph
Journal containing papers on labor and employment, the economy, industry, and other labor-related topics. **Founded:** 1976. **Freq:** Semiannual. **ISSN:** 0115-2629. **Subscription Rates:** 65 PP individuals. **URL:** http://www.ilsdole.gov.ph/publications/philippine-labor-review. **Circ:** Paid 2,000

49558 ■ Philippiniana Sacra
University of Santo Tomas
Ecclesiastical Faculties
Ecclesiastical Publications Office
Espana St.
Manila 1015, Philippines
Ph: 63 2 4061611
Journal containing scholarly research in the fields of ecclesiastical disciplines. **Founded:** 1966. **Freq:** 3/yr. **Key Personnel:** Fr. Javier I. Gonzales, Editor. **ISSN:** 0115-9577. **Subscription Rates:** 900 PP individuals; US$15 other countries air mail; 300 PP single issue; US$15 single issue other countries. **URL:** http://www.ust.edu.ph/index.php/inside-ust/34/150-philippiniana-sacra.html. **Circ:** Paid 500

49559 ■ SABRAO Journal of Breeding and Genetics
Society for the Advancement of Breeding Researches in Asia and Oceania
c/o Dr. Edilberto Redona, Ed.
DAPO Box 7777
Manila, Metro Manila, Philippines
Ph: 63 2 5805600
Fax: 63 2 5805699
Publication devoted to the basic and practical aspects of breeding research in economic organisms. **Founded:** 1969. **Freq:** Semiannual. **Key Personnel:** Dr. Edilberto Redona, Editor, e.redona@cgiar.org. **ISSN:** 1029-7073. **Subscription Rates:** US$15 individuals Bangladesh, Bhutan, Cambodia, China, India; US$20 other countries; US$15 individuals. **URL:** http://open.irri.org/sabrao/index.php?option=com_content&task=view&id=28&Itemid=32. **Ad Rates:** BW: US$75. **Circ:** (Not Reported)

49560 ■ Unitas
University of Santo Tomas Publishing House
Beato Angelico Bldg.
UST Compound
Espana, Sampaloc
Manila 1008, Philippines
Ph: 63 2 7313101
Fax: 63 2 7313522
Journal containing articles and studies, a university forum, coverage of the world of books and review articles. **Founded:** 1922. **Freq:** Quarterly. **Key Personnel:** Isidro C. Abano, Editor. **ISSN:** 0041-7149. **Subscription Rates:** 400 PP individuals; US$30 other countries; 110 PP single issue; US$58 other countries. **URL:** http://library.ust.edu.ph/journalweb/unitas_index.htm. **Circ:** Paid 500

49561 ■ DZFE - 98.7 MHz
2608 Cityland 10, Tower 1
HV de la Costa St.
Salcedo Village
Makati City, Metro Manila 1227, Philippines
Ph: 63 2 8103835
Fax: 63 2 8402864
E-mail: dzfe@i-manila.com.ph
Format: Classical. **Owner:** Far East Broadcasting Co., 62 Karuhatan Rd., Valenzuela City 1441, Philippines, Fax: 63 2 2925790. **Founded:** 1954. **Operating Hours:** 6.00 a.m. - 10 p.m. **Wattage:** 20,000. **URL:** http://www.febc.ph.

49562 ■ DZXL - 558 KHz
4th Fl. Guadalupe Commercial Complex Bldg.
Edsa, Guadalupe
Makati City, Metro Manila, Philippines
Ph: 63 2 8822375
Fax: 63 2 8822374
E-mail: ifmmanila@rmn.ph
Format: Eclectic. **Owner:** Radio Mindanao Network, 4th Fl., State Condo. Bldg., 1 Salcedo St., Legaspi Vill., Makati City, Philippines, Fax: 63 2 8163680. **Operating Hours:** 2100-1600. **Wattage:** 50,000. **URL:** http://www.rmn.com.ph/.

49563 ■ Green Giant-FM - 87.5
Velasco Bldg., Rm. 504
2401 Taft Ave.
Manila, Metro Manila, Philippines
Format: Educational. **Owner:** De La Salle University, at above address. **URL:** http://greengiantfm.dlsu.edu.ph/; http://www.dlsu.edu.ph/.

Marbel

49564 ■ DXKR - 639 KHz
State Condo. Bldg., 4th Fl.
1 Salcedo St.
Legaspi Village
Makati City 9506, Philippines
Ph: 63 2 8120530
Fax: 63 2 8108362
Format: Eclectic. **Owner:** Radio Mindanao Network, at above address. **Operating Hours:** 2100-1600. **Wattage:** 5000. **URL:** http://www.rmn.com.ph/.

Naga City

49565 ■ DWNX-FM - 91.1
4th Fl., State Condo. Bldg.
1 Salcedo St.

Circulation: ★ = ABC; △ = BPA; ♦ = CAC; • = CCAB; ❑ = VAC; ⊕ = PO Statement; ‡ = Publisher's Report; Boldface figures = sworn; Light figures = estimated.

Gale Directory of Publications & Broadcast Media/147th Ed.   5345

Legaspi Village
Makati City, Metro Manila 1229, Philippines
Ph: 63 2 8120529
Fax: 63 2 8163680
Format: Top 40; News. **Owner:** Radio Mindanao Network, at above address. **Ad Rates:** Advertising accepted; rates available upon request. **URL:** http://www.rmn.ph/fmstations/dwnx.

Pagadian City

49566 ■ DXPR - 603 KHz
4th Fl., State Condo Bldg.
1 Salcedo St.
Legaspi Vill.
Makati City, Metro Manila, Philippines
Ph: 63 2 8120529
Fax: 63 2 8163680
Format: Public Radio. **Owner:** Radio Mindanao Network, at above address. **Operating Hours:** 2100-1600. **Wattage:** 5000. **Ad Rates:** $0 for 36 seconds. **URL:** http://www.rmn.com.ph/.

49567 ■ DXWD-FM - 96.7
4th Fl., State Condo. Bldg.
1 Salcedo St.
Legaspi Village
Makati City, Metro Manila 1229, Philippines
Ph: 63 2 8120529
Fax: 63 2 8163680
Format: Eclectic. **Owner:** Radio Mindanao Network, at above address. **Ad Rates:** Advertising accepted; rates available upon request. **URL:** http://www.rmn.ph/fmstations/dxwd.

Pasay City

49568 ■ Ani
Cultural Center for the Philippines
CCP Complex, Roxas Blvd.
Pasay City 1300, Philippines
Ph: 63 283 21125
Fax: 63 283 23683
Publication E-mail: aniyearbook@yahoo.com
Publisher E-mail: ccp@culturalcenter.gov.ph
Journal covering contemporary literature by Filipino creative writers and scholars. **Founded:** 1986. **Freq:** Annual. **Key Personnel:** Herminio S. Beltran, Editor. **ISSN:** 0116-4791. **Subscription Rates:** 175 PP individuals. **URL:** http://www.culturalcenter.gov.ph. **Circ:** Paid 2,000

49569 ■ DWSM-FM - 102.7 MHz
10th Fl., EGI Rufino Bldg.
Taft cor. Gil Puyat Sts.
Pasay City 1300, Philippines
Ph: 63 2 5520391
Fax: 63 2 5520393
E-mail: starfm_manila@bomboradyo.com
Format: Oldies. **Owner:** Bombo Radyo Philippines, 2406 Florete Bldg., Edison cor. Nobel St., Makati City 1200, Philippines, 63 2 8430116, Fax: 63 2 8173631. **Key Personnel:** Rey Dela Cruz, Station Mgr. **Wattage:** 25,000. **URL:** http://www.bomboradyo.com/archive/new/stationprofile/starfmmanila/index.ht m.

49570 ■ DZRH - 666 KHz
MBC Bldg., CCP Complex
Roxas Blvd.
Pasay City, Metro Manila, Philippines
Ph: 63 2 8326115
Fax: 63 2 8326113
E-mail: dzrh@mbcradio.net
Format: Eclectic. **Owner:** Manila Broadcasting Co., at above address. **Operating Hours:** 2100-1600. **Key Personnel:** Joe Taruc, Contact. **Wattage:** 50,000. **URL:** http://dzrh.tripod.com.

Pasig City

49571 ■ IBP Journal
Integrated Bar of the Philippines
IBP Bldg.
No. 15 Julia Vargas Ave.
Ortigas Center
Pasig City, Metro Manila, Philippines
Ph: 63 2 6314697
Fax: 63 2 6313014
Publisher E-mail: ibpsecretariat@ibp.ph
Journal covering law. **Founded:** 1973. **Freq:** Quarterly.

Key Personnel: Rose Marie M. King, Editor-in-Chief; Ruben F. Balane, Contact; Emerico O. De Guzman, Managing Editor. **Subscription Rates:** 500 PP. **Remarks:** Accepts advertising. **URL:** http://www.ibp.ph/. **Formerly:** IBP Law Journal. **Ad Rates:** 4C: 47,300 PP. **Circ:** Paid 20,000

49572 ■ Mabuhay
Eastgate Publishing Corporation
704 Prestige Tower Condominium
Ortigas Center
Pasig City 1605, Philippines
Ph: 63 2 6334004
In-flight magazine of the Philippine Airlines, featuring travel and tourism, culture and arts. **Freq:** Monthly. **Trim Size:** 213 x 296 mm. **Remarks:** Accepts advertising. **URL:** http://eastgateph.com/site/mabuhaymagazine. html. **Circ:** (Not Reported)

49573 ■ Philippine Journal of Internal Medicine
Philippine College of Physicians
Unit 2201-2203, 22nd Fl.
San Miguel Ave. Cor. Shaw Blvd.
Ortigas Center
Pasig City 1600, Philippines
Ph: 63 2 9102250
Fax: 63 2 9102251
Publisher E-mail: secretariat@pcp.org.ph
Medical science journal. **Founded:** 1963. **Freq:** Bimonthly. **ISSN:** 0556-0071. **URL:** http://www.pcp.org. ph/.

49574 ■ DWAV-FM - 89.1
Unit 201, Strata 2000 Bldg.
F. Ortigas Jr. Ave.
Ortigas Ctr.
Pasig City 1605, Philippines
Ph: 63 2 6329283
Fax: 63 2 6349283
E-mail: wave891@wave891.fm
Format: Easy Listening; Blues. **Owner:** The Radio Partners Inc., Unit 904, Paragon Plz., EDSA cor. Reliance St., Mandaluyong City 1550, Philippines, 63 2 6373449, Fax: 63 2 6373449. **Operating Hours:** Continuous. **Key Personnel:** James Bonnevie, Account Mgr., jdgoodlife@wave891.fm. **Wattage:** 25,000 ERP. **URL:** http://www.wave891.fm/; http://www.theradiopartners.com/.

49575 ■ DWIZ - 882 KHz
5th Fl., Citystate Ctr.
709 Shaw Blvd.
Pasig City, Philippines
Ph: 63 2 4701750
Fax: 63 2 4701473
E-mail: postmaster.aliwbroadcasting@gmail.com
Format: Information; News. **Owner:** Aliw Broadcasting Corp., at above address. **Operating Hours:** Continuous weekdays & Sat.; 5a.m.- 12 a.m. Sun; . **Wattage:** 50,000. **URL:** http://www.dwiz882.com.

49576 ■ DWKX-FM - 103.5
Unit 1508, Jollibee Plz.
F. Ortigas Jr. Rd.
Ortigas Ctr.
Pasig City, Metro Manila 1605, Philippines
Ph: 63 2 6382529
Fax: 63 2 6363394
E-mail: info@1035max.fm
Format: Adult Contemporary. **Owner:** Advanced Media Broadcasting System, Inc., at above address. **Key Personnel:** Patt Perado, Sales Dir., patt@1035max.fm; Bing Bayron-Galano, Sen. Account Mgr., bing@1035max.fm; Reden Pamintuan, Account Mgr., reden@1035max.fm. **URL:** http://1035max.fm/.

49577 ■ DWNU-FM - 107.5
Ground Fl., AIC Gold Tower
Emerald Ave., Ortigas Ctr.
Pasig City 1600, Philippines
Ph: 63 2 6346513
Fax: 63 2 6346516
Format: Reggae; Alternative/New Music/Progressive; Blues; Talk. **Operating Hours:** Continuous. **Wattage:** 25,000. **Ad Rates:** Advertising accepted; rates available upon request. **URL:** http://www.nu107fm.com.

49578 ■ DWQZ-FM - 97.9
5th Fl. Citystate Ctr.
709 Shaw Blvd.
Pasig City 1600, Philippines

Ph: 63 2 6373965
Format: Easy Listening. **Owner:** Aliw Broadcasting Corporation, at above address. **Founded:** 1998. **URL:** http://www.homeradiofm.net/.

49579 ■ Monster Radio RX-FM - 93.1
17F Unit C, Strata 2000 Bldg.
F. Ortigas Ave.
Ortigas Center
Pasig City 1605, Philippines
Format: Alternative/New Music/Progressive; Hip Hop; Contemporary Hit Radio (CHR). **Owner:** Audiovisual Communications Inc., at above address. **Ad Rates:** Advertising accepted; rates available upon request. **URL:** http://www2.rx931.com.

Puerto Princesa

49580 ■ DYPR - 765 KHz
Palawan Broadcast Ctr.
61 Mabini St.
Puerto Princesa 5300, Philippines
Ph: 63 48 4332534
E-mail: dypr@mozcom.com
Format: News; Public Radio. **Owner:** Palawan Broadcasting Corporation, at above address. **Founded:** 1965. **Operating Hours:** 4:30 a.m.-10:30 p.m. **Wattage:** 10,000. **Ad Rates:** Advertising accepted; rates available upon request. **URL:** http://www.pto-princesa.com/dypr.

Quezon City

49581 ■ Asian Fisheries Science
Asian Fisheries Society
c/o The Editor
PO Box 2725
Quezon City Central Post Office
Quezon City, Metro Manila 1167, Philippines
Publisher E-mail: info@asianfisheriessociety.org
Journal covering all aspects of Asian fisheries and aquaculture research. **Founded:** 1987. **Freq:** Quarterly. **Key Personnel:** Dr. Shi-Yen Shiau, Editor-in-Chief; Teodora Bagarinao, Editorial Board; Aida R. Rubiano, Asst. Ed.; Dr. Mahfuzuddin Ahmed, Assoc. Ed.; John L. Sumner, Assoc. Ed.; Yang Yi, Editorial Board. **ISSN:** 0116-6514. **Remarks:** Advertising accepted; rates available upon request. **URL:** http://www.asianfisheriessociety. org/. **Circ:** (Not Reported)

49582 ■ Asian Migrant
Scalabrini Migration Center
4 13th St.
New Manila
Quezon City, Metro Manila 1112, Philippines
Ph: 63 272 43512
Fax: 63 272 14296
Publisher E-mail: smc@smc.org.ph
Magazine covering various aspects of Asian migration. **Founded:** 1987. **Freq:** Quarterly. **ISSN:** 1013-8064. **Subscription Rates:** US$20 individuals. **URL:** http://www.smc.org.ph; http://www.smc.org.ph/am.htm.

49583 ■ Asian Migration News
Scalabrini Migration Center
4 13th St.
New Manila
Quezon City, Metro Manila 1112, Philippines
Ph: 63 272 43512
Fax: 63 272 14296
Publication E-mail: smc@smc.org.ph
Publisher E-mail: smc@smc.org.ph
Online publication providing scholars, policy makers, advocates and students with a summary of news and events related to migration in Asia. **Freq:** Biweekly. **Key Personnel:** Maruja Asis, Editor; Fabio Baggio, Editor. **Subscription Rates:** US$22 individuals. **URL:** http://www.smc.org.ph/amnews/amnews.htm.

49584 ■ Asian and Pacific Migration Journal
Scalabrini Migration Center
4 13th St.
New Manila
Quezon City, Metro Manila 1112, Philippines
Ph: 63 272 43512
Fax: 63 272 14296
Publisher E-mail: smc@smc.org.ph
Journal covering research and analysis on migration and refugee movements from and within Asia and the Pacific. **Founded:** 1992. **Freq:** Quarterly. **ISSN:** 0117-1968. **Subscription Rates:** US$70 individuals Asia,

Pacific and Oceania; hard copy; US$85 individuals Americas, Europe and Africa; hard copy; US$50 individuals Americas, Europe and Africa. **URL:** http://www.smc.org.ph/home.htm; http://www.smc.org.ph/apmj.htm.

49585 ■ Asian Review of Public Administration
Eastern Regional Organization for Public Administration
Organizacion Regional del Oriente para la Administracion Publica
University of the Philippines
National College of Public Administration and Governance Bldg.
Diliman
Quezon City 1101, Philippines
Ph: 63 2 9297789
Fax: 63 2 9297789
Publisher E-mail: eropa@eropa.org.ph
Publication covering public administration. **Founded:** 1989. **Print Method:** Offset. **Trim Size:** 5 x 7. **URL:** http://www.eropa.org.ph/activities/ARPA.php.

49586 ■ Business World
BusinessWorld Publishing Corp.
Raul L. Locsin Bldg. I
95 Balete Dr. Ext.
New Manila
Quezon City, Metro Manila 1112, Philippines
Ph: 63 2 5359901
Fax: 63 2 5359926
Publication E-mail: editor@bworld.com.ph
Business and financial newspaper. **Founded:** 1967. **Freq:** Daily. **Key Personnel:** Raul L. Locsin, Founder; Wilfredo G. Reyes, Managing Editor; Arnold E. Belleza, Executive Ed. **ISSN:** 0116-3930. **Subscription Rates:** 4,200 PP individuals; 7,600 PP two years; 2,200 PP individuals 6 months. **Remarks:** Accepts advertising. **URL:** http://www.bworldonline.com/assets/main.php?id=aboutus. **Circ:** Paid 54,000

49587 ■ The Buzz Magasin
ABS-CBN Publishing Inc.
Eugenio Lopez Communications Ctr., 4th Fl.
Eugenio Lopez Dr.
Quezon City 1104, Philippines
Ph: 63 2 4152272
Fax: 63 2 4151215
Publisher E-mail: metromag@abs-cbn.com
Entertainment magazine for showbiz news enthusiasts. **Subtitle:** Mga Tsismis Sa TV, Dito Binubusisi!. **Trim Size:** 9 x 12. **Key Personnel:** Benjie Felipe, Editor-in-Chief. **Subscription Rates:** 60 PP individuals. **Remarks:** Accepts advertising. **URL:** http://www.metromagazine.ph. **Circ:** (Not Reported)

49588 ■ CHALK
ABS-CBN Publishing Inc.
Eugenio Lopez Communications Ctr., 4th Fl.
Eugenio Lopez Dr.
Quezon City 1104, Philippines
Ph: 63 2 4152272
Fax: 63 2 4151215
Publication E-mail: chalk@abs.pinoycentral.com
Publisher E-mail: metromag@abs-cbn.com
College lifestyle magazine. **Subtitle:** College Never Looked This Good. **Founded:** Aug. 2000. **Freq:** Monthly. **Trim Size:** 8.25 x 11. **Key Personnel:** Vicky Montenegro, Editor-in-Chief, vicky_montenegro@abs.pinoycentral.com. **Remarks:** Accepts advertising. **URL:** http://www.metrozines.com/contactus.php. **Circ:** (Not Reported)

49589 ■ Diliman Review
University of the Philippines
2nd Fl., Palma Hall Annex
Diliman
Quezon City, Metro Manila 1101, Philippines
Fax: 63 2 9818500
Covers topics ranging from science and technology to literature and society, history and economics, politics and religion. **Founded:** 1952. **Freq:** Quarterly. **Key Personnel:** Priscelina Patajo-Legasto, PhD, Editor, priscelina.legasto@up.edu.ph. **ISSN:** 0012-2858. **URL:** http://www.up.edu.ph/oldsystem/dil_rev_call4papers.htm.

49590 ■ Dream Weddings
Dream Weddings Publication-Philippines
94C Sct. de Guia
Diliman
Quezon City, Philippines

Publisher E-mail: info@dreamweddingsphilippines.com
Lifestyle magazine. **Freq:** Monthly. **Key Personnel:** Nona Castillejos-Clemente, Editor-in-Chief. **Subscription Rates:** Free for members. **Remarks:** Accepts advertising. **URL:** http://www.dreamweddingsphilippines.com/. **Circ:** (Not Reported)

49591 ■ East Asian Pastoral Review
East Asian Pastoral Institute
U.P. Campus
PO Box 221
Quezon City 1101, Philippines
Ph: 63 242 65901
Fax: 63 242 66143
Publication E-mail: eapisec@admu.edu.ph
Publisher E-mail: eapisec@admu.edu.ph
Journal covering religion and theology. **Subtitle:** A Quarterly with Focus on Asia for all Church Ministers and Theology in Context, Interested Laity and Theological Students. **Founded:** 1980. **Freq:** Quarterly. **Key Personnel:** Fernando Macalinao, Editor; Luc Mees, Assoc. Ed. **ISSN:** 0116-0257. **URL:** http://eapi.admu.edu.ph/eapr.htm. **Circ:** Paid 2,000

49592 ■ Electrical Engineer Magazine
Institute of Integrated Electrical Engineers of the Philippines Inc.
No. 41 Monte de Piedad St.
Cubao
Quezon City, Metro Manila 1109, Philippines
Ph: 63 2 7227383
Fax: 63 2 7273545
Publisher E-mail: iiee@iiee.org.ph
Journal related to electrical engineering. **Founded:** 1975. **Freq:** Bimonthly. **Remarks:** Advertising accepted; rates available upon request. **URL:** http://www.iiee.org.ph/home/index.php/the-electrical-engineer. **Circ:** Paid 17,000

49593 ■ FOOD
ABS-CBN Publishing Inc.
Eugenio Lopez Communications Ctr., 4th Fl.
Eugenio Lopez Dr.
Quezon City 1104, Philippines
Ph: 63 2 4152272
Fax: 63 2 4151215
Publication E-mail: food@abs.pinoycentral.com
Publisher E-mail: metromag@abs-cbn.com
Culinary magazine. **Subtitle:** The Philippines' Largest Selling Culinary Magazine. **Founded:** Oct. 1995. **Freq:** Monthly. **Trim Size:** 8.25 x 11. **Key Personnel:** Norma Chikiamco, Editor-in-Chief, norma_chikiamco@abs.pinoycentral.com. **Subscription Rates:** 1,092 PP individuals. **Remarks:** Accepts advertising. **URL:** http://www.metrozines.com/search.php?search_mag=Y&search_txt=Food. **Circ:** (Not Reported)

49594 ■ Haring Ibon
Haribon Foundation
2nd Fl., Santos & Sons Bldg.
No. 973 Aurora Blvd.
Cubao
Quezon City, Philippines
Ph: 63 2 4344642
Fax: 63 2 4344696
Publisher E-mail: act@haribon.org.ph
English and Filipino language publication covering conservation. **Freq:** Quarterly. **Remarks:** Accepts advertising. **URL:** http://www.haribon.org.ph; http://www.haribon.org.ph/Topic/54/Publication. **Circ:** (Not Reported)

49595 ■ INNOTECH Journal
SEAMEO Regional Centre for Educational Innovation and Technology
UP PO Box 207
University of the Philippines
Diliman
Quezon City 1101, Philippines
Ph: 63 292 47681
Fax: 63 292 10224
Publisher E-mail: info@seameo-innotech.org
Journal containing information on educational trends and issues. **Freq:** Semiannual. **ISSN:** 0115-7418. **URL:** http://www.seameo-innotech.org/resources/journals/journals.asp.

49596 ■ I.T. Matters
BusinessWorld Online, Inc.
Raul L. Locsin Bldg. I

95 Balete Dr. Ext.
New Manila
Quezon City 1112, Philippines
Ph: 63 2 5359901
Fax: 63 2 5359926
Online newspaper covering the information technology (IT) industry. **Subtitle:** More than the Bits and Bytes. **Freq:** Daily. **Key Personnel:** Wilfredo G. Reyes, News Ed.; Raul L. Locsin, Founder; Cris V. Paraso, City Ed.; Alicia A. Herrera, Assoc. Ed.; Vergel O. Santos, Chm., Editorial Board; Arnold E. Belleza, Executive Ed.; Michael O. Cerdenia, Hd., Editorial Multimedia Gp. **URL:** http://www.itmatters.com.ph/.

49597 ■ Journal of Asian Mission
Asia Theological Association
c/o Asia Graduate School of Theology
54 Scout Madrinan
Quezon City, Metro Manila 1100, Philippines
Publisher E-mail: info@ataasia.com
Journal featuring theories and practices of mission for missionary task and evangelization of Asia. **Freq:** Semiannual. **URL:** http://www.ataasia.com/publications/publications.html.

49598 ■ Kritika Kultura
Ateneo de Manila University Press
ADMU Campus
Bellarmine Hall
Katipunan Ave., Loyola Hts.
Quezon City 1108, Philippines
Ph: 63 2 4265984
Publication E-mail: kritikakultura@admu.edu.ph
Publisher E-mail: unipress@admu.edu.ph
Electronic journal of language and literary/cultural studies in the Philippines. **Key Personnel:** Ma. Luisa F. Torres Reyes, Editor-in-Chief, mreyes@ateneo.edu; Mary Thomas, Managing Editor; Peter Horn, International Board of Ed.; Rajeev S. Patke, International Board of Ed.; Anette Horn, International Board of Ed.; Ivery De Pano, Managing Editor; Temario Rivera, International Board of Ed.; Jan Baetens, International Board of Ed. **URL:** http://www.ateneo.edu/index.php?p=1806.

49599 ■ Metro
ABS-CBN Publishing Inc.
Eugenio Lopez Communications Ctr., 4th Fl.
Eugenio Lopez Dr.
Quezon City 1104, Philippines
Ph: 63 2 4152272
Fax: 63 2 4151215
Publication E-mail: metromag@abs-cbn.com
Publisher E-mail: metromag@abs-cbn.com
Lifestyle and fashion magazine for women. **Subtitle:** The Independent Woman. **Freq:** Monthly. **Trim Size:** 9 x 10.75. **Key Personnel:** Mel Cuevas, Editor-in-Chief. **Remarks:** Accepts advertising. **URL:** http://publishing.abs-cbn.com/metro.htm. **Circ:** (Not Reported)

49600 ■ Metro hiM
ABS-CBN Publishing Inc.
Eugenio Lopez Communications Ctr., 4th Fl.
Eugenio Lopez Dr.
Quezon City 1104, Philippines
Ph: 63 2 4152272
Fax: 63 2 4151215
Publication E-mail: metro_him@abs.pinoycentral.com
Publisher E-mail: metromag@abs-cbn.com
Magazine for young independent men. **Subtitle:** Man Made Better. **Trim Size:** 9 x 12. **Key Personnel:** Carlo Tadiar, Editor-in-Chief, carlo_tadiar@abs.pinoycentral.com. **Remarks:** Accepts advertising. **URL:** http://www.metrozines.com/search.php?search_mag=Y&search_txt=Metro%20Him. **Circ:** (Not Reported)

49601 ■ Metro Home & Entertaining
ABS-CBN Publishing Inc.
Eugenio Lopez Communications Ctr., 4th Fl.
Eugenio Lopez Dr.
Quezon City 1104, Philippines
Ph: 63 2 4152272
Fax: 63 2 4151215
Publication E-mail: metrohome@abs.pinoycentral.com
Publisher E-mail: metromag@abs-cbn.com
Magazine for interior designers and homeowners. **Subtitle:** The best guide to premium homes and premium living. **Founded:** 2003. **Trim Size:** 9 x 12. **Key Personnel:** Carlo Tadiar, Editor-in-Chief, carlo_tadiar@abs.pinoycentral.com. **Subscription Rates:** 2,100 PP

Circulation: ★ = ABC; △ = BPA; ◆ = CAC; ● = CCAB; ❑ = VAC; ⊕ = PO Statement; ‡ = Publisher's Report; Boldface figures = sworn; Light figures = estimated.

Gale Directory of Publications & Broadcast Media/147th Ed.

5347

individuals. **Remarks:** Accepts advertising. **URL:** http://www.metrozines.com/contactus.php. **Circ:** (Not Reported)

49602 ■ Metro Society
ABS-CBN Publishing Inc.
Eugenio Lopez Communications Ctr., 4th Fl.
Eugenio Lopez Dr.
Quezon City 1104, Philippines
Ph: 63 2 4152272
Fax: 63 2 4151215
Publication E-mail: metro_society@abs.pinoycentral.com
Publisher E-mail: metromag@abs-cbn.com
Magazine featuring the lifestyle of high society and powerful men and women of politics and industry. **Subtitle:** Society By Society. **Trim Size:** 9 x 12. **Key Personnel:** Maritess Garcia, Contact. **Remarks:** Accepts advertising. **URL:** http://www.metrozines.com/search.php?search_mag=Y&search_txt=Metro%20Society. **Circ:** (Not Reported)

49603 ■ Metro Weddings
ABS-CBN Publishing Inc.
Eugenio Lopez Communications Ctr., 4th Fl.
Eugenio Lopez Dr.
Quezon City 1104, Philippines
Ph: 63 2 4152272
Fax: 63 2 4151215
Publication E-mail: metrowed@abs.pinoycentral.com
Publisher E-mail: metromag@abs-cbn.com
Bridal magazine. **Subtitle:** Your Bridal Bible. **Trim Size:** 9 x 10.75. **Key Personnel:** Romina Urra-Gonzales, Editor-in-Chief, romina_urra@abs.pinoycentral.com. **Remarks:** Accepts advertising. **URL:** http://www.metrozines.com/search.php?search_mag=Y&search_txt=Metro%20Weddings. **Circ:** (Not Reported)

49604 ■ MetroActive
ABS-CBN Publishing Inc.
Eugenio Lopez Communications Ctr., 4th Fl.
Eugenio Lopez Dr.
Quezon City 1104, Philippines
Ph: 63 2 4152272
Fax: 63 2 4151215
Publication E-mail: metroactive@abs.pinoycentral.com
Publisher E-mail: metromag@abs-cbn.com
Lifestyle magazine for sports-minded male professionals. **Subtitle:** Your guide to an active lifestyle. **Trim Size:** 9 x 10.75. **Key Personnel:** Vladimir Bunoan, Editor-in-Chief. **Remarks:** Accepts advertising. **URL:** http://publishing.abs-cbn.com/metro-active.htm. **Circ:** (Not Reported)

49605 ■ PAID
Freedom from Debt Coalition
11 Matimpiin St.
Barangay Pinyahan
Quezon City 1100, Philippines
Ph: 63 2 9211985
Fax: 63 2 9246399
Publisher E-mail: mail@fdc.ph
English and Filipino language publication covering economic development. **Freq:** Quarterly. **ISSN:** 0119-1527. **Remarks:** Advertising not accepted. **URL:** http://www.freedomfromdebtcoalition.org/; http://www.fdc.ph/index.php?option=com_docman&task=cat_view&gid=44&&Itemid=89. **Circ:** 1,000

49606 ■ Philippine Journal of Psychology
Psychological Association of the Philippines
Philippine Social Science Council
PSSC Bldg.
Commonwealth Ave.
Diliman
Quezon City 1101, Philippines
Publication E-mail: pjp@philippinepsychology.net
Publisher E-mail: pjp@philippinepsychology.net
Publishes original studies and research work by psychologists and other social scientists in fields related to psychology. **Founded:** 1968. **Freq:** Semiannual. **Key Personnel:** Allen Tan, Editorial Board; Melissa Reyes, Editorial Board; Regina Hechanova, Editorial Board; Cecilia Conaco, Editorial Board; Dr. Ma. Emma Concepcion D. Liwag, Editor. **Subscription Rates:** US$20 other countries; US$10 single issue. **Remarks:** Advertising accepted; rates available upon request. **URL:** http://www.philjol.info/index.php/PJP. **Circ:** Paid 175

49607 ■ Philippine Journal of Public Administration
University of the Philippines
National College of Public Administration and Governance
Diliman
Quezon City 1101, Philippines
Ph: 63 2 9283861
Fax: 63 2 9261432
Publisher E-mail: ncpag@broline.com
Journal covering public administration. **Subtitle:** Journal of the National College of Public Administration and Governance. **Founded:** 1957. **Freq:** Quarterly. **Key Personnel:** Victoria A. Bautista, Contact. **ISSN:** 0031-7675. **URL:** http://www.philjol.info/index.php/PJPA/user/register. **Circ:** Paid 1,000

49608 ■ Philippine Law Journal
University of the Philippines
Law Publishing House
Diliman
Quezon City 1101, Philippines
Ph: 63 2 920 5514
Journal covering law. **Founded:** 1914. **Freq:** Quarterly. **Key Personnel:** Melissa Parreno, Editor, melissa.parreno@gmail.com. **ISSN:** 0031-7721. **Subscription Rates:** 500 PP individuals; US$75 other countries. **URL:** http://law.upd.edu.ph/; http://journals.upd.edu.ph/index.php/plj/index. **Circ:** Paid 821

49609 ■ Philippine Planning Journal
University of the Philippines
School of Urban and Regional Planning
E Jacinto St.
Diliman
Quezon City 1101, Philippines
Ph: 63 2 9206853
Publication E-mail: weplan_at_surp@up.edu.ph
Publisher E-mail: weplan_at_surp@up.edu.ph
Journal covering different thematic issues such as transportation, housing, and environmental concerns. **Founded:** 1969. **Freq:** Semiannual. **ISSN:** 0048-3850. **Remarks:** Advertising accepted; rates available upon request. **URL:** http://www.upd.edu.ph/~surp/research/ppj.html. **Circ:** Paid 600

49610 ■ Philippine Review of Economics
University of the Philippines
School of Economics
The Philippine Review of Economics
Rm. 232, School of Economics
University of the Philippines Diliman
Quezon City, Metro Manila 1101, Philippines
Publication E-mail: pre.upse@up.edu.ph
Devoted to the publication of theoretical and empirical work in economic development. **Freq:** Semiannual June and December. **Key Personnel:** Emmanuel F. Esguerra, Editor; Cristina C. David, Board of Ed.; Raul V. Fabella, Board of Ed.; Cielito F. Habito, Board of Ed. **ISSN:** 1655-1516. **Subscription Rates:** US$20 students, other countries; US$30 other countries per issue; US$40 institutions, other countries per issue. **URL:** http://www.econ.upd.edu.ph/respub/pre.php.

49611 ■ Philippine Rotary
Phillipine Rotary
87 Visayas Ave.
Project 6
Quezon City, Metro Manila 1100, Philippines
Ph: 63 2 9267453
Fax: 63 2 9291912
Publication E-mail: office@philrotary.com
Publisher E-mail: office@philrotary.com
Official regional membership magazine of Rotary International covering current news about Rotary-related subjects of Philippines in English. **Founded:** 1977. **Freq:** Monthly. **Print Method:** Offset. **Trim Size:** 8.25 x 10.75. **Key Personnel:** Mar Un Ocampo III, Editor-in-Chief; Sonny T. Ventura, Managing Editor. **Subscription Rates:** 540 PP individuals; 45 PP single issue; 270 PP individuals 6 months. **URL:** http://www.bluenimbus.com/philrotary/; http://www.rotary.org/en/mediaandnews/morepublications/regionalmagazines/pages/ridefault.aspx. **Circ:** 15,000

49612 ■ Philippine Social Sciences Review
University of the Philippines
College of Social Sciences and Philosophy
Palma Hall
Diliman

Quezon City 1101, Philippines
Ph: 63 2 9818500
Fax: 63 2 9263486
Publication E-mail: cssppub@kssp.upd.edu.ph
Publisher E-mail: dekano@kssp.upd.edu.ph
Social science journal. **Founded:** 1929. **Freq:** Quarterly. **Key Personnel:** Jorge V. Tigno, Editor-in-Chief; Eric Julian Manalastas, Managing Editor. **ISSN:** 0117-1828. **URL:** http://journals.upd.edu.ph/index.php/pssr. **Circ:** Controlled 1,000

49613 ■ Philippine Sociological Review
Philippine Sociological Society
PO Box 205
Diliman
Quezon City, Metro Manila 1101, Philippines
Ph: 63 2 4265990
Publisher E-mail: projects@pssc.org.ph
Sociology journal. **Founded:** 1953. **Freq:** Annual. **Key Personnel:** Prof. Emma Porio, Contact, eporio@ateneo.edu. **ISSN:** 0031-7810. **Remarks:** Advertising accepted; rates available upon request. **URL:** http://www.philjol.info/index.php/PSR. **Circ:** Paid 500

49614 ■ Philippine Studies
Ateneo de Manila University Press
ADMU Campus
Bellarmine Hall
Katipunan Ave., Loyola Hts.
Quezon City 1108, Philippines
Ph: 63 2 4265984
Publication E-mail: philstudies@admu.edu.ph
Publisher E-mail: unipress@admu.edu.ph
Journal featuring articles, notes, and reviews in the humanities, literature, history, social sciences, philosophy, and Philippine arts. **Subtitle:** Quarterly Publication of Philippine Thought and Culture. **Founded:** 1953. **Freq:** Quarterly. **Key Personnel:** Filomeno V. Aguilar, Jr., Editor. **ISSN:** 0031-7837. **Subscription Rates:** 750 PP individuals print and online; 1,000 PP institutions print and online; US$70 other countries print or online; US$60 other countries print or online only; US$75 institutions, other countries print or online only; US$85 institutions, other countries print and online. **Remarks:** Advertising accepted; rates available upon request. **URL:** http://www.philippinestudies.net/ojs/index.php/ps. **Circ:** Paid 650

49615 ■ Pink
ABS-CBN Publishing Inc.
Eugenio Lopez Communications Ctr., 4th Fl.
Eugenio Lopez Dr.
Quezon City 1104, Philippines
Ph: 63 2 4152272
Fax: 63 2 4151215
Publication E-mail: metromag@abs-cbn.com
Publisher E-mail: metromag@abs-cbn.com
Shopping guide magazine for teens. **Subtitle:** A Girl's Guide to Shopping. **Founded:** 2002. **Trim Size:** 8.25 x 11. **Key Personnel:** Jane Kingsu, Editor-in-Chief. **Remarks:** Accepts advertising. **URL:** http://publishing.abs-cbn.com/pink.htm. **Circ:** (Not Reported)

49616 ■ Planet Philippines
Buzzword Media Corporation
Rm. 14, Ground Fl., Maya Bldg.
678 EDSA
Cubao
Quezon City, Metro Manila 1109, Philippines
Publisher E-mail: buzzwordmedia@yahoo.com
General interest magazine. **Freq:** Biweekly. **Key Personnel:** Wilson G. Bailon, Editor-in-Chief. **Remarks:** Accepts advertising. **URL:** http://www.planetphilippines.com/. **Circ:** (Not Reported)

49617 ■ StarStudio
ABS-CBN Publishing Inc.
Eugenio Lopez Communications Ctr., 4th Fl.
Eugenio Lopez Dr.
Quezon City 1104, Philippines
Ph: 63 2 4152272
Fax: 63 2 4151215
Publication E-mail: starstudio@abs.pinoycentral.com
Publisher E-mail: metromag@abs-cbn.com
Entertainment magazine. **Subtitle:** We Bring You Closer to The Stars. **Freq:** Monthly. **Trim Size:** 9 x 11.25. **Key Personnel:** Jerome Gomez, Editor-in-Chief, jerome_gomez@abs.pinoycentral.com. **Remarks:** Accepts advertising. **URL:** http://www.metrozines.com/contactus.php. **Circ:** 150,000

49618 ■ Women in Action
Isis International
3 Marunong St.
Barangay Central
Quezon City, Metro Manila 1100, Philippines
Ph: 63 2 9281956
Fax: 63 2 9241065
Magazine keeping readers up-to-date on the women's movement worldwide. **Founded:** 1984. **Freq:** 3/yr. **Key Personnel:** Lilian Mercado Careon, Contact; Cai Yiping, Exec. Dir. **ISSN:** 1011-5048. **Subscription Rates:** 300 PP individuals; US$30 individuals for Asia, the Pacific and Middle East; US$35 other countries. **Remarks:** Accepts advertising. **URL:** http://www.isiswomen.org. **Circ:** Paid 2,000

49619 ■ Working Mom
ABS-CBN Publishing Inc.
Eugenio Lopez Communications Ctr., 4th Fl.
Eugenio Lopez Dr.
Quezon City 1104, Philippines
Ph: 63 2 4152272
Fax: 63 2 4151215
Publication E-mail: mwm@abs.pinoycentral.com
Publisher E-mail: metromag@abs-cbn.com
Magazine for married or single moms. **Subtitle:** Your Guide To A Balanced Life. **Print Method:** offset. **Trim Size:** 9 x 11.25. **Key Personnel:** Francine Marquez, Editor-in-Chief, francine_marquez@abs.pinoycentral. com. **Remarks:** Accepts advertising. **URL:** http://www. metrozines.com/contactus.php. **Circ:** (Not Reported)

49620 ■ DREAM-FM - 106.7
762 Quirino Hwy.
Novaliches
Quezon City, Philippines
Format: Jazz; Blues. **Owner:** DREAM FM, at above address. **Key Personnel:** Chrissy Francisco, Contact; Elaine Marie Icasiano, Contact; Michael Carl Chua, Contact. **URL:** http://1067dreamfm.com/.

49621 ■ DWBM-FM - 105.1
6 Tirad Pass
Sta. Mesa Hts.
Quezon City, Philippines
Ph: 63 2 7311667
Fax: 63 2 7124213
Format: Jazz; Blues. **Owner:** Mareco Broadcasting Network Inc., at above address. **URL:** http://www. crossover.com.ph/.

49622 ■ DWLS-FM - 97.1
14th Fl. & 15th Fl. GMA Network Ctr.
EDSA Cor. Timog Ave.
Diliman
Quezon City 1104, Philippines
Ph: 63 2 9827777
Fax: 63 2 9282044
Format: Adult Contemporary. **Owner:** GMA Network Inc., at above address. **URL:** http://www.gmanetwork. com/about.

49623 ■ DZEC - 1062 KHz
Maligaya Bldg. II
887 EDSA
Quezon City, Philippines
Ph: 63 2 9951325
Fax: 63 2 9951392
E-mail: production@net-25.com
Format: News; Information. **Owner:** Eagle Broadcasting Corp., at above address. **Operating Hours:** 2100-1600. **Key Personnel:** Mr. Art de Guzman, Contact, adeguzman@net-25.com. **Wattage:** 40,000. **URL:** http:// www.net-25.com.

49624 ■ DZMM - 630 KHz
Chronicle Bldg.
Mother Ignacia St. cor Sgt. Esguerra Ave.
Quezon City, Philippines
Ph: 63 2 4166300
E-mail: dzmm630@abs-cbn.com
Format: News; Public Radio; Information. **Owner:** ABS-CBN Broadcasting Corporation, at above address. **Operating Hours:** Continuous. **Key Personnel:** Eugenio Lopez III, Chm./CEO. **Wattage:** 50,000. **URL:** http://www. abs-cbn.com; http://www.dzmm.com.ph/.

49625 ■ NET 25 - 25
887 Maligaya Bldg. No. 2, Edsa
Quezon City 1100, Philippines

Ph: 63 2 9951388
Fax: 63 2 9951392
Owner: Eagle Broadcasting Corporation, at above address. **Founded:** July 27, 1999. **Key Personnel:** Mr. Caesar R. Vallejos, Sales and Mktg. Dir., cvallejos@net-25.com. **URL:** http://www.net-25.com/index.html.

Roxas City

49626 ■ DYRX-FM - 103.7 MHz
Arnaldo Blvd.
Roxas City, Philippines
Ph: 63 36 6210119
Fax: 63 36 6214967
E-mail: star_roxas@bomboradyo.com
Format: Adult Contemporary. **Owner:** Bombo Radyo Philippines, 2406 Florete Bldg., Edison cor. Nobel St., Makati City 1200, Philippines, 63 2 8430116, Fax: 63 2 8173631. **Key Personnel:** Michael B. Loja, Station Mgr. **Wattage:** 5000. **URL:** http://www.bomboradyo.com/ archive/new/stationprofile/starfmroxas/index.htm.

49627 ■ DYVR - 657 KHz
State Condo. Bldg., 4th Fl.
1 Salcedo St.
Legaspi Village
Makati City, Philippines
Ph: 63 2 8120530
Fax: 63 2 8108362
Format: Eclectic. **Owner:** Radio Mindanao Network, at above address. **Operating Hours:** 2100-1600. **Wattage:** 5000. **URL:** http://www.rmn.com.ph/.

49628 ■ DYVR-FM - 93.9
4th Fl., State Condo. Bldg.
1 Salcedo St.
Legaspi Village
Makati City, Metro Manila 1229, Philippines
Ph: 63 2 8120529
Fax: 63 2 8163680
Format: Eclectic. **Owner:** Radio Mindanao Network, at above address. **Ad Rates:** Advertising accepted; rates available upon request. **URL:** http://www.rmn.ph/ fmstations/dyvr.

San Juan

DXCP - See General Santos City

DXDB - See Bukidnon

DXHM - See Davao Oriental

DXSN - See Surigao City

49629 ■ DXVP - 1467 KHz
Unit 201, Sunrise Condominium
226 Ortigas Ave.
San Juan 1503, Philippines
Ph: 63 2 7249850
Fax: 63 2 7249962
Format: News. **Owner:** Catholic Media Network, at above address. **Operating Hours:** 13 hours Daily. **Key Personnel:** Fr. Serge Dela Noche, Station Mgr.; Ma. Cecilia C. Roxas, Program Mgr.; Jean Paul Varela, Network Mgr. **Wattage:** 5000. **URL:** http://www catholicmedianetwork.org.

DYDM - See Maasin

DYRD - See Tagbilaran

49630 ■ DZEA - 909 KHz
Unit 201, Sunrise Condominium
226 Ortigas Ave.
San Juan 2900, Philippines
Ph: 63 2 7249850
Fax: 63 2 7249962
Format: News. **Owner:** Catholic Media Network, at above address. **Operating Hours:** 16 hours Daily. **Key Personnel:** Medda M. Carpio, Accounting Mgr.; Ma. Cecilia C. Roxas, Program Mgr.; Jean Paul Varela, Network Mgr. **Wattage:** 5000. **URL:** http://www. catholicmedianetwork.org.

DZNS - See Vigan

49631 ■ DZVT - 1395 KHz
Unit 201, Sunrise Condominium
226 Ortigas Ave.
San Juan, Philippines
Ph: 63 2 7249850
Fax: 63 2 7249962

E-mail: cmnftd@cmn-ftd.org
Format: News. **Owner:** Catholic Media Network, at above address. **Operating Hours:** 15 hours Daily. **Wattage:** 5000. **URL:** http://www.catholicmedianetwork.org.

Surigao City

49632 ■ DXKE-FM - 94.1
4th Fl., State Condo. Bldg.
1 Salcedo St.
Legaspi Village
Makati City, Metro Manila 1229, Philippines
Ph: 63 2 8120529
Fax: 63 2 8163680
Format: Eclectic. **Owner:** Radio Mindanao Network, at above address. **Ad Rates:** Advertising accepted; rates available upon request. **URL:** http://www.rmn.ph/ fmstations/dxke.

49633 ■ DXRS - 1206 KHz
State Condo. Bldg., 4th Fl.
1 Salcedo St.
Legaspi Village
Makati City, Philippines
Ph: 63 2 8120530
Fax: 63 2 8108362
Format: Eclectic. **Owner:** Radio Mindanao Network, at above address. **Operating Hours:** 2100-1600. **Wattage:** 5000. **URL:** http://www.rmn.com.ph/.

49634 ■ DXSN - 1017 KHz
Unit 201, Sunrise Condominium
226 Ortigas Ave., North Greenhills
San Juan, Metro Manila, Philippines
Ph: 63 2 7249850
Fax: 63 2 7249962
E-mail: cmnftd@cmn-ftd.org
Format: News. **Owner:** Catholic Media Network, at above address. **Operating Hours:** 14 hours Daily. **Key Personnel:** Fr. Francis Lucas, Pres./CEO; Fr. Josefito Mira, Station Mgr. **Wattage:** 5000. **URL:** http://www. catholicmedianetwork.org.

Tacloban City

49635 ■ DYTX-FM - 95.1 MHz
YPL Bldg.
Sto. Nino St. cor. Imelda Ave.
Tacloban City, Philippines
Ph: 63 32 2430340
Fax: 63 32 2549143
E-mail: star_tacfm@yahoo.com
Format: Adult Contemporary; News; Information. **Owner:** Bombo Radyo Philippines, 2406 Florete Bldg., Edison cor. Nobel St., Makati City 1200, Philippines, 63 2 8430116, Fax: 63 2 8173631. **Key Personnel:** Virn I. Villagracia, Station Mgr. **Wattage:** 10,000. **URL:** http:// www.bomboradyo.com/archive/new/stationprofile/ starfmtacloban/index. h tm.

49636 ■ DYXY-FM - 99.1
4th Fl., State Condo. Bldg.
1 Salcedo St.
Legaspi Village
Makati City, Metro Manila 1229, Philippines
Ph: 63 2 8120529
Fax: 63 2 8163680
Format: Eclectic. **Owner:** Radio Mindanao Network, at above address. **Ad Rates:** Advertising accepted; rates available upon request. **URL:** http://www.rmn.ph/ fmstations/dyxy.

Tagbilaran

49637 ■ The Bohol Chronicle
Bohol Chronicle Press
56 B. Inting St.
Tagbilaran 6300, Philippines
Ph: 63 38 4113100
Fax: 63 38 4113100
Publication E-mail: ads@boholchronicle.com
Publisher E-mail: editor@boholchronicle.com
Newspaper. **Founded:** 1954. **Freq:** Semiweekly. **Key Personnel:** Peter P. Dejaresco, Assoc. Ed., peterd@ boholchronicle.com. **Subscription Rates:** 1,500 PP individuals towns-mail, within Region VII; 1,800 PP individuals outside region VII; US$150 other countries; 1,200 PP individuals city delivery (Sun.& Wed.). **URL:** http://www.boholchronicle.com.

Circulation: ★ = ABC; △ = BPA; ♦ = CAC; • = CCAB; ❑ = VAC; ⊕ = PO Statement; ‡ = Publisher's Report; Boldface figures = sworn; Light figures = estimated.

49638 ■ DYRD - 1161 KHz
Unit 201, Sunrise Condominium
226 Ortigas Ave., North Greenhills
San Juan, Metro Manila 6300, Philippines
Ph: 63 2 7249850
Fax: 63 2 7249962
Format: News. **Owner:** Catholic Media Network, at above address. **Operating Hours:** 2100-1600. **Key Personnel:** Peter P. Dejaresco, General Mgr.; Fred Araneta, Program Dir.; Kit Bagaipo, News Dir. **Wattage:** 5000. **URL:** http://www.dyrdam.com.

Taguig City

49639 ■ NRCD Research Journal of the Philippines
National Research Council of the Philippines
Pambansang Sanggunian S.A. Pananaliksik ng Pilipinas
General Santos Ave.
Bicutan
Taguig City, Philippines
Ph: 63 2 8378142
Fax: 63 2 8390275
Publisher E-mail: nrcpinfo@yahoo.com
Philippine journal covering scientific research. **Freq:** Periodic. **ISSN:** 0117-3294. **URL:** http://www.nrcp.dost.gov.ph/.

49640 ■ Philippine Journal of Nutrition
Philippine Association of Nutrition
General Santos Ave.
Bicutan
Taguig City, Metro Manila 1631, Philippines
Ph: 63 283 91842
Fax: 63 283 91842
Peer-reviewed journal covering nutrition and dietetics. **Founded:** 1949. **Freq:** Quarterly. **Key Personnel:** Dr. Aida Aguinaldo, Editor-in-Chief. **ISSN:** 0031-7640. **Remarks:** Advertising accepted; rates available upon request. **URL:** http://pan.fnri.dost.gov.ph/index.php?option=com_content&task=view&id=27&Itemid=54. **Circ:** (Not Reported)

49641 ■ Philippine Journal of Science
Industrial Technology Development Institute
DOST Compound
Gen. Santos Ave.
Bicutan
Taguig City 1631, Philippines
Ph: 63 28372071
Fax: 63 28373167
Journal covering basic sciences. **Founded:** 1906. **Freq:** Quarterly. **Key Personnel:** Dr. William G. Padolina, Editor-in-Chief; Maria Judith L. Sablan, Managing Editor; Virginia P. Dolotina, Circulation Mgr. **ISSN:** 0031-7683. **Subscription Rates:** 1,000 PP institutions two issues; 800 PP individuals two issues; US$200 other countries two issues. **URL:** http://www.stii.dost.gov.ph/pjsweb/frames/. **Circ:** Paid 1,300

Tandag

49642 ■ DXJS - 873 KHz
Capitol Hills

Tandag 8300, Philippines
Format: Eclectic. **Owner:** Philippine Broadcasting Service, Bureau of Broadcast Services, 4th Fl. PIA Bldg., Visayas Ave., Quezon City 1100, Philippines. **Operating Hours:** 2100-1600. **Key Personnel:** Thelma Castano, Station Mgr., phone 63 82 2111855, fax 63 82 2113967. **Wattage:** 10,000. **URL:** http://www.pbs.gov.ph/.

Tuguegarao City

49643 ■ DZGR - 891 KHz
Bombo Radyo Broadcast Ctr.
Taft St. Ext., Barangay 5
Tuguegarao City 3500, Philippines
Ph: 63 78 8442758
Fax: 63 78 8440211
E-mail: bombotuguegarao@yahoo.com
Format: News. **Owner:** Bombo Radyo, 2406 Florete Bldg., Edison Cor. Nobel St., Makati City, Philippines, 63 2 8430116, 63 2 8430122, Fax: 63 2 8173631. **Operating Hours:** 4:30 a.m.-12 p.m. Mon.-Sat.; 4:30-11:30 p.m. Sun. **Key Personnel:** Bobby Daguio, Station Mgr. **Wattage:** 5000. **URL:** http://www.bomboradyo.com.

Valenzuela City

49644 ■ DZAS - 702 KHz
62 Karuhatan Rd.
Valenzuela City 1441, Philippines
Ph: 63 2 2921152
Fax: 63 2 2925790
E-mail: dzas@febc.org.ph
Format: Religious; News; Gospel; Information. **Owner:** Far East Broadcasting Co., at above address. **Founded:** June 1948. **Formerly:** KZAS (June 1948). **Operating Hours:** 4:45 a.m.-12 a.m. Mon.-Sat.; 5:30 a.m.-12 a.m. Sun. **Wattage:** 50,000. **URL:** http://febc.ph.

Vigan

49645 ■ DZNS - 963 KHz
Unit 201, Sunrise Condominium
226 Ortigas Ave., North Greenhills
San Juan, Metro Manila, Philippines
Ph: 63 2 7249850
Fax: 63 2 7249962
E-mail: cmnftd@cmn-ftd.org
Format: News. **Owner:** Catholic Media Network, at above address. **Operating Hours:** 14 hours Daily. **Key Personnel:** Rev. Ernesto A. Salgado, D.D., Station Dir.; Fr. Arwin Romulo Y. Rebollido, Exec. Dir. **Wattage:** 5000. **URL:** http://www.catholicmedianetwork.org.

49646 ■ DZVV - 603 KHz
Bombo Radyo Broadcast Ctr.
Tamag
Vigan 2700, Philippines
Ph: 63 77 7222850
Fax: 63 77 6321125
E-mail: bombovgn@yahoo.com
Format: News. **Owner:** Bombo Radyo Philippines, 2046 Florete Bldg., Edison Cor. Nobel St., Makati City, Metro Manila, Philippines, 63 2 8430116, 63 2 8430122, Fax: 63 2 8173631. **Operating Hours:** 4:30 a.m-12 p.m.

Mon.-Sat.; 4:30 a.m.-11:30 Sun. **Key Personnel:** Evelyn Quinto-Pascua, Station Mgr. **Wattage:** 5000. **URL:** http://www.bomboradyo.com.

Zamboanga City

49647 ■ Daily Zamboanga Times
Mayor Jaldon St.
Canelar
Zamboanga City, Philippines
Newspaper. **Freq:** Daily. **Key Personnel:** Roy Ramos, Editor-in-Chief. **URL:** http://www.zambotimes.com/.

49648 ■ DXAS - 1116 KHz
PO Box 349
Tugbungan
Zamboanga City 7000, Philippines
Ph: 63 62 9915764
Fax: 63 62 9924420
E-mail: dxas@febc.org.ph
Format: Eclectic. **Owner:** Far East Broadcasting Co., 62 Karuhatan Rd., Valenzuela City 1441, Philippines, Fax: 63 2 2925790. **Founded:** Oct. 28, 1978. **Operating Hours:** Sun. 6a.m.-9.30a.m.; weekdays,Sat. 5a.m.-8.15a.m.,6p.m.-8.45p.m. **Key Personnel:** Peter Jorge Que, Station Mgr. **Wattage:** 5000. **URL:** http://febc.ph.

49649 ■ DXCB-FM - 93.9 MHz
4th Fl., AJS Bldg.
Valderosa St.
Zamboanga City 7000, Philippines
Ph: 63 2 9932099
Fax: 63 2 9932099
E-mail: starfm_zamboanga@bomboradyo.com
Format: Adult Contemporary. **Owner:** Bombo Radyo Philippines, 2406 Florete Bldg., Edison cor. Nobel St., Makati City 1200, Philippines, 63 2 8430116, Fax: 63 2 8173631. **Key Personnel:** Mr. Gil Jay Lazo, Station Mgr. **Wattage:** 10,000. **URL:** http://www.bomboradyo.com/archive/new/stationprofile/starfmzamboanga/index htm.

49650 ■ DXRZ - 900 KHz
State Condo. Bldg., 4th Fl.
1 Salcedo St.
Legaspi Village
Makati City, Philippines
Ph: 63 2 8120530
Fax: 63 2 8108362
Format: Eclectic. **Owner:** Radio Mindanao Network, at above address. **Operating Hours:** 2100-1600. **Wattage:** 5000. **URL:** http://www.rmn.com.ph/.

49651 ■ DXWR-FM - 96.3
4th Fl., State Condo. Bldg.
1 Salcedo St.
Legaspi Village
Makati City, Metro Manila 1229, Philippines
Ph: 63 2 8120529
Fax: 63 2 8163680
Format: Eclectic. **Owner:** Radio Mindanao Network, at above address. **Ad Rates:** Advertising accepted; rates available upon request. **URL:** http://www.rmn.ph/fmstations/dxwr

Bydgoszcz

49652 ■ Acta Angiologica
Via Medica
ul. K. Ujejskiego 75
PL-85-168 Bydgoszcz, Poland
Ph: 48 52 3655232
Fax: 48 52 3655782
Publisher E-mail: viamedica@viamedica.pl
Journal covering vascular disorders. **Freq:** Quarterly.
Key Personnel: Arkadiusz Jawien, Editor-in-Chief,
ajawien@ceti.com.pl. **ISSN:** 1234-950X. **Subscription
Rates:** 164 Zl individuals print; 235 Zl institutions print;
EUR41 individuals print; EUR59 institutions print. **Remarks:** Accepts advertising. **URL:** http://www.viamedica.
pl/en/gazety/xgazAang/index.phtml. **Circ:** (Not Reported)

49653 ■ Advances in Palliative Medicine
Via Medica
ul. Marii Sklodowskiej-Curie 9
PL-85-094 Bydgoszcz, Poland
Ph: 48 52 5853461
Publisher E-mail: viamedica@viamedica.pl
Journal focusing on palliative medicine. **Freq:** Quarterly.
Key Personnel: Malgorzata Krajnik, Editor-in-Chief.
ISSN: 1898-3863. **Remarks:** Accepts advertising. **URL:**
http://www.viamedica.pl/en/gazety/xgazEang/stopka.
phtml. **Circ:** (Not Reported)

49654 ■ Psychiatry in General Practice
Via Medica
ul. Kurpinskiego 19
PL-85-096 Bydgoszcz, Poland
Ph: 48 52 5854039
Fax: 48 52 5853766
Publisher E-mail: viamedica@viamedica.pl
Journal covering psychiatry. **Freq:** Quarterly. **Key Personnel:** Aleksander Araszkiewicz, Editor-in-Chief. **ISSN:**
1643-0956. **URL:** http://www.viamedica.pl/en/gazety/
czasopisma.phtml.

Gdansk

49655 ■ Arterial Hypertension
Via Medica
Grupa Via Medica
ul. Swietokrzyska 73
PL-80-180 Gdansk, Poland
Ph: 48 58 3209494
Fax: 48 58 3209460
Publication E-mail: redakcja@viamedica.pl
Publisher E-mail: viamedica@viamedica.pl
Journal covering field of arterial hypertension. **Founded:**
1997. **Freq:** Bimonthly. **Key Personnel:** Andrzej Tykarski, Editor-in-Chief. **ISSN:** 1428-5851. **Subscription
Rates:** 92 Zl individuals print; 184 Zl institutions print;
EUR23 individuals print; EUR46 institutions print. **Remarks:** Accepts advertising. **URL:** http://www.viamedica.
pl/en/gazety/xgaz5ang/index.phtml; http://www.nt.
viamedica.pl/. **Circ:** (Not Reported)

**49656 ■ Endocrinology, Obesity and Metabolic
Disorders**
Via Medica
Via Medica
ul. Swietokrzyska 73

PL-80-180 Gdansk, Poland
Ph: 48 58 3209494
Fax: 48 58 3209460
Publisher E-mail: viamedica@viamedica.pl
Journal covering fields of metabolic disorders, endocrinology, and obesity. **Freq:** Quarterly. **Key Personnel:**
Prof. Marek Bolanowski, Editor-in-Chief. **ISSN:** 1734-
3321. **Subscription Rates:** 62 Zl individuals print; 124
Zl institutions print; EUR16 individuals print; EUR31 institutions print. **Remarks:** Accepts advertising. **URL:** http://
www.viamedica.pl/en/gazety/xgazMang/index.phtml;
http://www.endokrynologia.viamedica.pl/. **Circ:** (Not
Reported)

49657 ■ Folia Morphologica
Via Medica
ul. Debinki 1
PL-80-211 Gdansk, Poland
Ph: 48 58 3491401
Fax: 48 58 3491421
Publisher E-mail: viamedica@viamedica.pl
Journal covering morphology. **Freq:** Quarterly. **Key Personnel:** Janusz Morys, Editor-in-Chief, jmorys@amg.
gda.pl. **ISSN:** 0015-5659. **Subscription Rates:** 198 Zl
individuals online; 421 Zl institutions online; EUR50
individuals online; EUR106 institutions online. **Remarks:**
Accepts advertising. **URL:** http://www.viamedica.pl/en/
gazety/gazetax1ang/index.phtml. **Circ:** (Not Reported)

49658 ■ Nuclear Medicine Review
Via Medica
ul. Debinki 7
PL-80-211 Gdansk, Poland
Ph: 48 58 3492204
Fax: 48 58 3492204
Publication E-mail: plass@amg.gda.pl
Publisher E-mail: viamedica@viamedica.pl
Journal covering all nuclear medicine topics. **Freq:**
Semiannual. **Key Personnel:** Julian Liniecki, Editor-in-
Chief. **ISSN:** 1506-9680. **Subscription Rates:** 91.35 Zl
individuals online; 185 Zl institutions online; EUR23
individuals online; EUR47 institutions online. **Remarks:**
Accepts advertising. **URL:** http://www.viamedica.pl/en/
gazety/gazetax2ang/index.phtml; http://www.nmr.
viamedica.pl/. **Circ:** (Not Reported)

49659 ■ Nursing Topics
Via Medica
ul. Do Studzienki 38
PL-80-227 Gdansk, Poland
Ph: 48 58 3491292
Fax: 48 58 3491292
Publisher E-mail: viamedica@viamedica.pl
Peer-reviewed journal covering field of nursing.
Founded: 1993. **Key Personnel:** Dr. Aleksandra
Gaworska-Krzeminska, Editor-in-Chief, a.gawor@friend.
pl. **ISSN:** 1233-9989. **Subscription Rates:** 60 Zl
individuals print; 120 Zl institutions print; EUR15 individuals print; EUR30 institutions print. **Remarks:** Accepts
advertising. **URL:** http://www.viamedica.pl/en/gazety/
xgazUang/index.phtml. **Circ:** (Not Reported)

49660 ■ Psychooncology
Via Medica
ul. Pomorska 68
PL-80-343 Gdansk, Poland
Ph: 48 58 5571414
Fax: 48 58 5571414

Publisher E-mail: viamedica@viamedica.pl
Journal covering psychological aspects of oncological
diseases. **Freq:** Semiannual. **Key Personnel:** Mikolaj
Majkowicz, Editor-in-Chief, joannakozaka@wp.pl. **ISSN:**
1429-8538. **URL:** http://www.viamedica.pl/en/gazety/
xgazRang/index.phtml.

Katowice

49661 ■ Acta Chromatographica
University of Silesia
Institute of Chemistry
12 Bankowa st.
40-007 Katowice, Poland
Publishing papers on all aspects of theory and practice
of chromatography. **Key Personnel:** J. Bojarski, Editorial Board; D. Agbaba, Editorial Board; G. Morlock, Editorial Board; W. Wasiak, Editorial Board; F. Geiss, Editorial Board; M. Sajewicz, Co-Ed.; K. Ciazynska-
Halarewicz, Tech. Ed.; T.H. Dzido, Editorial Board; T.
Kowalska, Co-Ed. **ISSN:** 1233-2356. **URL:** http://acta-
chromatographica.us.edu.pl/.

49662 ■ Polish Surgery
Via Medica
ul. Ziolowa 45/47
PL-40-635 Katowice, Poland
Ph: 48 32 2029577
Fax: 48 32 2061728
Publisher E-mail: viamedica@viamedica.pl
Journal covering Polish surgery. **Freq:** Quarterly. **Key
Personnel:** Krzysztof Ziaja, Editor-in-Chief. **ISSN:** 1507-
5524. **Subscription Rates:** 84 Zl individuals; 120 Zl
institutions; EUR21 individuals; EUR30 institutions. **Remarks:** Accepts advertising. **URL:** http://www.viamedica.
pl/en/gazety/xgazCang/index.phtml. **Circ:** (Not Reported)

Kornik

49663 ■ Dendrobiology
Polska Akademia Nauk
Instytut Dendrologii
ul. Parkowa 5
PL-62-035 Kornik, Poland
Ph: 48 61 8170 033
Fax: 48 61 8170 166
Publisher E-mail: idkornik@man.poznan.pl
Journal featuring articles and reviews related to biology
of trees and shrubs. **Key Personnel:** Piotr Karolewski,
Editor-in-Chief, pkarolew@man.poznan.pl; Marian J. Giertych, Editorial Sec., giertych@man.poznan.pl. **ISSN:**
1641-1307. **URL:** http://www.idpan.poznan.pl/
dendrobiology/.

Krakow

49664 ■ Acta Physica Polonica B
Jagiellonian University
Institute of Physics
ul. Reymonta 4
30-059 Krakow, Poland
Ph: 48 12 6336377
Fax: 48 12 6337086

Circulation: ★ = ABC; △ = BPA; ♦ = CAC; • = CCAB; ❑ = VAC; ⊕ = PO Statement; ‡ = Publisher's Report; Boldface figures = sworn; Light figures = estimated.

Gale Directory of Publications & Broadcast Media/147th Ed.   5351

Publication E-mail: acta@if.uj.edu.pl
Peer-reviewed journal covering all aspects of physics. **Founded:** 1920. **Freq:** Monthly. **Key Personnel:** Wojciech Slominski, Contact; Michal Praszalowicz, Editor; Marek Kutschera, Contact. **ISSN:** 0587-4254. **Subscription Rates:** EUR330 other countries; 1,020 Zl individuals. **URL:** http://th-www.if.uj.edu.pl/acta/.

49665 ■ Diametros
Jagiellonian University
Institute of Philosophy
ul. Grodzka 52
Pl-31-041 Krakow, Poland
Ph: 48 12 6631732
Fax: 48 12 4224916
Publication E-mail: diametros@iphils.uj.edu.pl
Publisher E-mail: diametros@iphils.uj.edu.pl
Journal covering various aspects of philosophy. **Subtitle:** An Online Journal of Philosophy. **Founded:** 2004. **Freq:** Quarterly. **Key Personnel:** Wlodzimierz Galewicz, Editor; Tomasz Kuninski, Editorial Board; Teresa Galewicz, Editorial Board; Steffen Huber, Editorial Board; Olga Dryla, Editorial Sec.; Jan Wawrzyniak, Editorial Board; Jacek Malczewski, Editorial Board; Jaroslaw Kucharski, Editorial Board. **URL:** http://www.diametros.iphils.uj.edu.pl/.

49666 ■ International Journal of Biometrics
Inderscience Enterprises Limited
c/o Khalid Saeed, Ed.-in-Ch.
AGH University of Science & Technology
Al. Mickiewicza 30
30-059 Krakow, Poland
Journal covering studies in the field of human authentication. **Freq:** 4/yr. **Key Personnel:** Khalid Saeed, Editor-in-Chief, saeed@agh.edu.pl. **ISSN:** 1755-8301. **Subscription Rates:** EUR494 individuals print or online; EUR672 individuals print and online. **URL:** http://www.inderscience.com/browse/index.php?journalID=285.

49667 ■ Pharmacological Reports
Institute of Pharmacology
Polish Academy of Sciences
Smetna 12
31-343 Krakow, Poland
Ph: 48 126 623220
Fax: 48 126 374500
Publisher E-mail: ifpan@if-pan.krakow.pl
Peer-reviewed journal covering all aspects of pharmacology. **Freq:** Bimonthly. **Key Personnel:** Beata Kreiner, Managing Editor; Grazyna Skuza, Dep. Ed.; Wladyslaw Lason, Editor-in-Chief, lason@if-pan.krakow.pl. **Subscription Rates:** 270 Zl individuals in Poland; 45 Zl single issue in Poland; US$180 other countries plus postage; US$210 institutions, other countries plus postage; US$45 institutions other countries (single copy); US$30 other countries single issue; 520 Zl institutions in Poland; 85 Zl single issue institutional. **URL:** http://www.if-pan.krakow.pl/pjp/. **Formerly:** Polish Journal of Pharmacology.

49668 ■ Polish Gerontology
Via Medica
ul. Sniadeckich 10
31-531 Krakow, Poland
Ph: 48 12 4248800
Fax: 48 12 4248854
Publisher E-mail: viamedica@viamedica.pl
Journal covering field of biological processes of aging. **Freq:** Quarterly. **Key Personnel:** Prof. Tomasz Grodzicki, Editor-in-Chief. **ISSN:** 1425-4956. **Subscription Rates:** 54 Zl individuals print; 108 Zl institutions print; EUR14 individuals print; EUR27 institutions print. **Remarks:** Accepts advertising. **URL:** http://www.viamedica.pl/en/gazety/xgazKang/index.phtml. **Circ:** (Not Reported)

Lodz

49669 ■ Cardiovascular Forum
Via Medica
ul. Kniaziewicza 1/5
PL-91-347 Lodz, Poland
Ph: 48 42 2516015
Fax: 48 42 2516015
Publisher E-mail: viamedica@viamedica.pl
Journal covering developments in cardiology, diagnostic and treatment in cardiovascular medicine. **Founded:** 1996. **Freq:** Quarterly. **Key Personnel:** Jaroslaw Drozdz, Editor-in-Chief, drozdz@ptkardio.pl. **ISSN:**

1425-3674. **Remarks:** Accepts advertising. **URL:** http://www.viamedica.pl/en/gazety/xgaz3ang/index.phtml. **Circ:** (Not Reported)

49670 ■ International Review of Pragmatics
Brill Academic Publishers
c/o Prof. Piotr Cap, Mng. Ed.
Department of Pragmatics
University of Lodz
Al. Kosciuszki 65
PL-90514 Lodz, Poland
Publisher E-mail: marketing@brill.nl
Peer-reviewed journal on pragmatics and all aspects of human communication. **Freq:** Semiannual. **Key Personnel:** Prof. Piotr Cap, Managing Editor, piotr.cap@gmail.com. **ISSN:** 1877-3095. **Subscription Rates:** EUR51 individuals; US$69 individuals; EUR154 institutions; US$210 institutions; EUR140 institutions online only; US$191 institutions online only. **URL:** http://www.brill.nl/irp.

49671 ■ Journal of Applied Analysis
Walter de Gruyter Inc.
c/o Marek Balcerzak, Ed.-in-Ch.
Institute of Mathematics
Technical University of Lodz
Wolczanska 215
93-005 Lodz, Poland
Publisher E-mail: info@degruyterny.com
Peer-reviewed Journal covering mathematical analysis and its applications to physics, mechanics, economics, computer sciences and engineering. **Founded:** 1995. **Freq:** Semiannual. **Key Personnel:** Marek Balcerzak, Editor-in-Chief; K. Ciesielski, Editor-in-Chief. **ISSN:** 1425-6908. **Subscription Rates:** EUR92 individuals print or online; EUR106 individuals print + online; EUR51 single issue. **URL:** http://www.degruyter.com/journals/jaa/detailEn.cfm.

Lublin

49672 ■ Annals of Agricultural and Environmental Medicine
Institute of Agricultural Medicine
Instytut Medycyny Wsi
Jaczewskiego 2
PO Box 185
PL-20-950 Lublin, Poland
Ph: 48 81 7184410
Fax: 48 817 478646
Publisher E-mail: aaem@galen.imw.lublin.pl
Journal covering agricultural and environmental medicine, including forestry, food production, chemical pollutants, and occupational diseases. **Founded:** 1994. **Freq:** Semiannual. **Print Method:** Offset. **Trim Size:** 8 1/4 x 10 7/8. **Cols./Page:** 3 and 2. **Col. Width:** 26 and 40 nonpareils. **Col. Depth:** 140 agate lines. **Key Personnel:** Jolanta Szymanska, Editor-in-Chief, adpunctum@adres.pl; Leszek Wdowiak, Editorial Board; Ewa Cisak, Co-Ed., ewac@galen.imw.lublin.pl. **ISSN:** 1232-1966. **Subscription Rates:** US$100 institutions; US$60 individuals; 50 Zl institutions Europe; 40 Zl individuals Europe. **URL:** http://www.aaem.pl/index.html.

Poznan

49673 ■ Acta Scientarum Polonorum - Technologia Alimentaria
Agricultural University of Poznan Press
Wolynska 33
PL-60-637 Poznan, Poland
Journal covering food science. **Founded:** Sept. 1892. **Freq:** Daily Monday through Friday. **Print Method:** Offset. **Cols./Page:** 6. **Col. Width:** 25 nonpareils. **Col. Depth:** 294 agate lines. **Key Personnel:** Waldemar Uchman, Chm., waluchm@up.poznan.pl. **ISSN:** 1644-0730. **URL:** http://www.food.actapol.net/.

Pulawy

49674 ■ The Bulletin of the Veterinary Institute in Pulawy
National Veterinary Research Institute
Al. Partyzantow 57
24-100 Pulawy, Poland
Ph: 48 81 8893000
Fax: 48 81 8862595
Publisher E-mail: sekretariat@piwet.pulawy.pl
Journal devoted to veterinary science and related fields. **Freq:** Quarterly. **Key Personnel:** Jacek Roszkowski, Editor-in-Chief, phone 48 81 8893232, roszk@piwet.

pulawy.pl; Dariusz Bednarek, Assoc. Ed. **Subscription Rates:** US$240 individuals; EUR100 individuals. **URL:** http://bulletin.piwet.pulawy.pl/.

Sejny

49675 ■ Krasnogruda
Pogranicze Foundation
Fundacja Pogranicze
ul. Pilsudskiego St. 37
PL-16-500 Sejny, Poland
Ph: 48 87 5162765
Fax: 48 87 5162765
Publisher E-mail: prognanic@free.ngo.pl
Magazine containing culture, art, history, literature, national and religious information. **Subtitle:** Nations Cultures and Small Homelands of Central-Eastern Europe. **Freq:** Quarterly. **ISSN:** 1230-7645. **Subscription Rates:** 60 Zl individuals; US$80 out of country. **URL:** http://www.pogranicze.sejny.pl/archiwum/english/krasnogruda/.

Szczecin

49676 ■ Acta Ichthyologica et Piscatoria
Wydawnictwo Naukowe Akademii Rolniczej W Szczecinie
ul. Doktora Judyman 22
PL-71-466 Szczecin, Poland
Ph: 48 914 541639
Publication E-mail: editor@aiep.pl
Publisher E-mail: wydawnictwo@biot.ar.szczecin.pl
Journal covering experimental data of ichthyology and fisheries. **Founded:** 1951. **Freq:** Semiannual. **Print Method:** Letterpress. **Cols./Page:** 2. **Col. Width:** 38 nonpareils. **Col. Depth:** 118 agate lines. **Key Personnel:** Wojciech Piasecki, Editor-in-Chief; George W. Benz, Assoc. Ed.; Barbara F. Nowak, Assoc. Ed. **ISSN:** 0137-1592. **Subscription Rates:** US$70 individuals. **URL:** http://www.aiep.pl/index.php.

Warsaw

49677 ■ Acta Arithmetica
Polish Academy of Sciences
Institute of Mathematics
PO Box 21
ul. Sniadeckich 8
00-956 Warsaw, Poland
Fax: 48 226 293997
Publication E-mail: actarith@impan.gov.pl
Publisher E-mail: publ@impan.gov.pl
Scholarly journal on the theory of numbers. **Key Personnel:** A. Schinzel, Contact; D. Goldfeld, Contact; J. Browkin, Contact; J. Kaczorowski, Editor; A.N. Andrianov, Contact; R. Tijdeman, Contact; W.M. Schmidt, Contact. **ISSN:** 0065-1036. **Subscription Rates:** EUR580 individuals; EUR30 single issue. **URL:** http://journals.impan.gov.pl/aa/.

49678 ■ Acta Biochimica Polonica
L. Pasteura 3
02-093 Warsaw, Poland
Ph: 48 225 892471
Fax: 48 225 892471
Publication E-mail: abp@nencki.gov.pl
Publisher E-mail: abp@nencki.gov.pl
Journal dealing with enzymology and metabolism, membranes and bioenergetics, gene structure and expression, protein, nucleic acid and carbohydrate structure and metabolism, in connection with Polish Biochemical Society and Polish Academy of Sciences. **Founded:** 1954. **Freq:** Quarterly. **Key Personnel:** Grzegorz Wegrzyn, Editor-in-Chief; Lech Wojtczak, Chm.; Daniela Barszcz, Assoc. Ed.; Ewa Bartnik, Assoc. Ed.; Andrzej Dzugaj, Assoc. Ed.; Anna Filipek, Assoc. Ed. **ISSN:** 0001-527X. **Subscription Rates:** US$200 institutions; US$100 individuals including postage and handling. **URL:** http://www.actabp.pl/index.html.

49679 ■ Acta Geophysica
Versita
Solipska 14A/1 St.
PL-02-482 Warsaw, Poland
Ph: 48 22 7015015
Fax: 48 22 4335126
Publisher E-mail: info@versita.com
Journal covering general and applied geophysics. **Key Personnel:** Jaroslaw Napiorkowski, Editor-in-Chief; Iwona Brzuska, Managing Editor; Dumitru Baleanu,

Assoc. Ed. **ISSN:** 1895-6572. **URL:** http://www.versita. com/science/geosciences/ag/.

49680 ■ Acta Neurobiologiae Experimentalis
The Nencki Institute Of Experimental Biology
3 Pasteur St.
PL-02-093 Warsaw, Poland
Ph: 48 226 598571
Fax: 48 228 225342
Publisher E-mail: dyrekcja@nencki.gov.pl
Journal covering the research results on brain. **Founded:** 1962. **Freq:** Quarterly. **Print Method:** Offset. **Trim Size:** 8 1/4 x 11 1/4. **Cols./Page:** 2. **Col. Width:** 40 nonpareils. **Col. Depth:** 140 agate lines. **Key Personnel:** Krzysztof Turlejski, Ch. Ed.; Jennifer Cook, English Language Ed.; Malgorzata Galysz-Wrobel, Managing Editor, phone 48 22 5892274, m.galysz@ nencki.gov.pl. **ISSN:** 0003-6935. **Subscription Rates:** EUR200 individuals. **URL:** http://www.ane.pl/.

49681 ■ Acta Palaeontologica Polonica
Instytut Paleobiologii PAN
ul. Twarda 51/55
00-818 Warsaw, Poland
Ph: 48 22 6978850
Fax: 48 22 6206225
Publication E-mail: app@twarda.pan.pl
Publisher E-mail: paleo@twarda.pan.pl
Peer-reviewed journal covering the field of paleontology. **Founded:** 1956. **Freq:** Quarterly. **Key Personnel:** Richard L. Cifelli, Editor, rlc@ou.edu; Jaroslaw Stolarski, Editor, stolacy@twarda.pan.pl; Brian Davis, Asst. Ed., bmdavi@ou.edu. **ISSN:** 0567-7920. **Subscription Rates:** EUR18 single issue individual; EUR20 institutions single issue; EUR65 individuals; EUR75 institutions. **URL:** http://www.app.pan.pl/home.html.

49682 ■ Acta Protozoologica
The Nencki Institute Of Experimental Biology
3 Pasteur St.
PL-02-093 Warsaw, Poland
Ph: 48 226 598571
Fax: 48 228 225342
Publisher E-mail: dyrekcja@nencki.gov.pl
Journal covering the experimental and theoretical contributions of protistology, and cell biology of lower eukaryote. **Founded:** 1963. **Freq:** Quarterly. **Key Personnel:** Malgorzata Prajer, Co-Ed.; Krzysztof Wiackwowski, Editor-in-Chief; Helmut Berger, Editorial Board; Tom Fenchel, Editorial Board; Janusz Fyda, Co-Ed.; Hanna Fabczak, Editorial Board; Sarah Poynton, Editorial Board; David J. Patterson, Editorial Board; GenoVeva F. Esteban, Editorial Board; Linda Basson, Editorial Board. **ISSN:** 0065-1583. **Subscription Rates:** EUR120 individuals; EUR200 institutions. **URL:** http:// www.eko.uj.edu.pl/ap/.

49683 ■ Acta Zoologica Lituanica
Versita
Solipska 14A/1 St.
PL-02-482 Warsaw, Poland
Ph: 48 22 7015015
Fax: 48 22 4335126
Publisher E-mail: info@versita.com
Journal containing articles on the study of animal ecology and related fields. **Key Personnel:** Linas Balciauskas, Editor-in-Chief; Dalius Butkauskas, Editor; Mindaugas Dagys, Editor; Gediminas Valkiunas, Editor; Rimantas Rakauskas, Editor. **ISSN:** 1392-1657. **URL:** http://www.versita.com/science/lifesciences/azl/.

49684 ■ Advances in Cell Biology
Versita
Solipska 14A/1 St.
PL-02-482 Warsaw, Poland
Ph: 48 22 7015015
Fax: 48 22 4335126
Publisher E-mail: info@versita.com
Journal containing articles on cell biology. **Key Personnel:** Jerzy Kawiak, Editor-in-Chief; Lilia Hryniewiecka, Assoc. Ed.; Jan Zeromski, Assoc. Ed. **URL:** http://www.versita.com/science/lifesciences/acb/.

49685 ■ Advances in Cognitive Psychology
Versita
Solipska 14A/1 St.
PL-02-482 Warsaw, Poland
Ph: 48 22 7015015
Fax: 48 22 4335126

Publisher E-mail: info@versita.com
Journal covering the field of cognitive psychology. **Key Personnel:** Piotr Jaskowski, Editor-in-Chief; Anita Bialunska, Managing Editor; Denis Burnham, Editor. **ISSN:** 1895-1171. **URL:** http://www.versita.com/science/psychology/acp/.

49686 ■ Advances in Materials Science
Versita
Solipska 14A/1 St.
PL-02-482 Warsaw, Poland
Ph: 48 22 7015015
Fax: 48 22 4335126
Publisher E-mail: info@versita.com
Journal covering topics on materials science and engineering. **Key Personnel:** Andrzej Zielinski, Editor-in-Chief; Janusz Cwiek, Co-Ed.; Jerzy Labanowski, Co-Ed. **ISSN:** 1730-2439. **URL:** http://www.versita.com/science/engineering/ams/.

49687 ■ Advances in Medical Sciences
Versita
Solipska 14A/1 St.
PL-02-482 Warsaw, Poland
Ph: 48 22 7015015
Fax: 48 22 4335126
Publication E-mail: editorial_office@umwb.edu.pl
Publisher E-mail: info@versita.com
Journal covering all areas of medical sciences. **Founded:** 1955. **Freq:** Semiannual. **Key Personnel:** Jacek Niklinski, Editor-in-Chief; Jan Dlugosz, Dep. Ed.; Richard McCallum, International Ed. **ISSN:** 1896-1126. **URL:** http://www.versita.com/science/medicine/advms/; http://www.advms.pl/node/2.

49688 ■ Advances in Rehabilitation
Versita
Solipska 14A/1 St.
PL-02-482 Warsaw, Poland
Ph: 48 22 7015015
Fax: 48 22 4335126
Publisher E-mail: info@versita.com
Journal containing papers on psychological, sociological, and occupational rehabilitation. **Key Personnel:** Aleksander Ronikier, Editor-in-Chief; Andrzej Gryglewicz, Dep./Mng. Ed. **ISSN:** 0860-6161. **URL:** http:// www.versita.com/science/healthsciences/air/.

49689 ■ Annals of Warsaw University of Life Sciences, Land Reclamation
Versita
Solipska 14A/1 St.
PL-02-482 Warsaw, Poland
Ph: 48 22 7015015
Fax: 48 22 4335126
Publisher E-mail: info@versita.com
Journal focusing on the research, critical reviews and short communications on land reclamation. **Founded:** 1957. **Freq:** Annual. **Key Personnel:** Jozef Mosiej, Editor-in-Chief; Gunno Renman, Editor; Janusz Kubrak, Editor. **ISSN:** 1898-8857. **URL:** http://www.versita.com/science/environment/annlr/.

49690 ■ Anthropological Review
Versita
Solipska 14A/1 St.
PL-02-482 Warsaw, Poland
Ph: 48 22 7015015
Fax: 48 22 4335126
Publisher E-mail: info@versita.com
Journal covering the field of physical anthropology. **Founded:** 1997. **Freq:** Annual. **Key Personnel:** Jan D. Strzalko, Editor. **ISSN:** 1898-6773. **URL:** http://www.versita.com/science/socialsciences/ar/.

49691 ■ Archives of Industrial Hygiene and Toxicology
Versita
Solipska 14A/1 St.
PL-02-482 Warsaw, Poland
Ph: 48 22 7015015
Fax: 48 22 4335126
Publisher E-mail: info@versita.com
Peer-reviewed journal covering all aspects of environmental and occupational health and toxicology. **Freq:** Quarterly. **Key Personnel:** Nevenka Kopjar, Editor-in-Chief. **ISSN:** 0004-1254. **URL:** http://www.versita.com/science/medicine/aiht/.

49692 ■ Archives of Polish Fisheries
Versita
Solipska 14A/1 St.
PL-02-482 Warsaw, Poland
Ph: 48 22 7015015
Fax: 48 22 4335126
Publisher E-mail: info@versita.com
Journal focusing on all aspects of fish and fisheries research. **Freq:** Quarterly. **Key Personnel:** Boguslaw Zdanowski, Editor-in-Chief; Andrzej Kapusta, Managing Editor. **ISSN:** 1230-6428. **URL:** http://www.versita.com/science/lifesciences/apf/.

49693 ■ Artificial Satellites
Versita
Solipska 14A/1 St.
PL-02-482 Warsaw, Poland
Ph: 48 22 7015015
Fax: 48 22 4335126
Publisher E-mail: info@versita.com
Journal focusing on the aspects of geodesy and geodynamics. **Key Personnel:** Wieslaw Kosek, Editor-in-Chief. **ISSN:** 0208-841X. **URL:** http://www.versita.com/science/geosciences/as/.

49694 ■ Balkan Journal of Medical Genetics
Versita
Solipska 14A/1 St.
PL-02-482 Warsaw, Poland
Ph: 48 22 7015015
Fax: 48 22 4335126
Publisher E-mail: info@versita.com
Journal covering all branches of medical genetics. **Key Personnel:** Efremov G.D., Editor-in-Chief; Toncheva D.I., Editor. **ISSN:** 1311-0160. **URL:** http://www.versita.com/science/medicine/bjmg/.

49695 ■ Baltic Journal of Law & Politics
Versita
Solipska 14A/1 St.
PL-02-482 Warsaw, Poland
Ph: 48 22 7015015
Fax: 48 22 4335126
Publisher E-mail: info@versita.com
Journal reporting the law and politics of the Baltic Region. **Key Personnel:** Tomas Berkmanas, Editor-in-Chief; Saulius Pivoras, Sen. Ed.; Barry Hart Dubner, Editor; Mark Summers, Editor; Linas Meskys, Editor; Jay Daniel Mininger, Editor. **URL:** http://www.versita.com/science/law/bjlp/.

49696 ■ Biologija
Versita
Solipska 14A/1 St.
PL-02-482 Warsaw, Poland
Ph: 48 22 7015015
Fax: 48 22 4335126
Publisher E-mail: info@versita.com
Journal covering the field of biology. **Freq:** Quarterly. **Key Personnel:** Dr. Vytautas Petras Rancelis, Editor-in-Chief. **ISSN:** 1392-0146. **URL:** http://www.versita.com/science/lifesciences/biologija/.

49697 ■ Biomedical Human Kinetics
Versita
Solipska 14A/1 St.
PL-02-482 Warsaw, Poland
Ph: 48 22 7015015
Fax: 48 22 4335126
Publisher E-mail: info@versita.com
Journal covering biomedical areas related to physical activity. **Key Personnel:** Krzysztof Mazurek, Editor-in-Chief; Romuald Stupnicki, Managing Editor. **URL:** http://www.versita.com/science/healthsciences/bhk/.

49698 ■ Bulletin of the Polish Academy of Sciences Mathematics
Institute of Mathematics of the Polish Academy of Sciences
PO Box 21
ul. Sniadeckich 8
00-956 Warsaw, Poland
Ph: 48 225 228100
Fax: 48 226 293997
Publisher E-mail: instytut.matematyczny@impan.gov.pl
A mathematical bulletin. **Founded:** 1953. **Key Personnel:** Stanislaw Kwapien, Dep. Ed.; Jerzy Kaczorowski, Editorial Board; Carl De Boor, Editorial Board; Czeslaw Bessaga, Editorial Board; Bogdan Bojarski, Editorial Board; Henryk Iwaniec, Editorial Board; Zbigniew

Ciesielski, Editorial Board. **ISSN:** 0239-7269. **Subscription Rates:** EUR100 individuals; EUR33 single issue. **URL:** http://journals.impan.gov.pl/ba/index.html.

49699 ■ Central European Journal of Chemistry
Versita
Solipska 14A/1 St.
PL-02-482 Warsaw, Poland
Ph: 48 22 7015015
Fax: 48 22 4335126
Publisher E-mail: info@versita.com
Journal covering all areas of chemistry, including research and review articles, rapid and short communications, and book reviews. **Freq:** Quarterly. **Key Personnel:** Krzysztof Matyjaszewski, Editor-in-Chief; Masha Dorogova, Managing Editor; Tania Dey, Assoc. Ed. **ISSN:** 1895-1066. **URL:** http://www.versita.com/science/chemistry/cejc/.

49700 ■ Central European Journal of Geosciences
Versita
Solipska 14A/1 St.
PL-02-482 Warsaw, Poland
Ph: 48 22 7015015
Fax: 48 22 4335126
Publisher E-mail: info@versita.com
Peer-reviewed journal covering all fields of earth sciences. **Freq:** Quarterly. **Key Personnel:** Robert J. Bodnar, Editor-in-Chief, rjb@vt.edu. **ISSN:** 2081-9900. **URL:** http://www.versita.com/science/geosciences/cejg/.

49701 ■ Central European Journal of Mathematics
Versita
Solipska 14A/1 St.
PL-02-482 Warsaw, Poland
Ph: 48 22 7015015
Fax: 48 22 4335126
Publisher E-mail: info@versita.com
Journal covering all areas of mathematics, including research and review articles, rapid and short communications, and book reviews. **Freq:** Quarterly. **Key Personnel:** Fedor Bogomolov, Editor-in-Chief; Drazen Adamovic, Editor; Zeljko Cuckovic, Editor; Vasyl Andriychuk, Editor; Tatiana Sworowska, Managing Editor; Zeljko Cuckovic, Editor. **ISSN:** 1895-1074. **URL:** http://www.versita.com/science/mathematics/cejm/.

49702 ■ Central European Journal of Physics
Versita
Solipska 14A/1 St.
PL-02-482 Warsaw, Poland
Ph: 48 22 7015015
Fax: 48 22 4335126
Publisher E-mail: info@versita.com
Journal covering all areas of physics, including research and review articles, rapid and short communications, and book reviews. **Freq:** Quarterly. **Key Personnel:** Vladimir Zakharov, Editor-in-Chief; Istvan Simon, Editor; Jiri Bicak, Editorial Advisory Board; Tsuneya Ando, Editorial Advisory Board; Hesheng Chen, Editorial Advisory Board; Tomasz Hornowski, Editor; Krzysztof Malarz, Managing Editor; Jim Allen, Editorial Advisory Board; Vladimir Fortov, Editorial Advisory Board. **ISSN:** 1895-1082. **URL:** http://www.versita.com/science/physics/cejp/.

49703 ■ Chemical Papers
Versita
Solipska 14A/1 St.
PL-02-482 Warsaw, Poland
Ph: 48 22 7015015
Fax: 48 22 4335126
Publisher E-mail: info@versita.com
Journal covering the field of pure and applied chemistry and chemical engineering. **Key Personnel:** Milan Polakovic, Editor-in-Chief, milan.polakovic@stuba.sk; Raquel Aires Barros, Assoc. Ed., rbarros@ist.utl.pt; Jed F. Fisher, Assoc. Ed., jed.f.fisher.57@nd.edu; Philippe H. Kahn, Assoc. Ed., kahn@univ-paris-diderot.fr; Maurizio Masi, Assoc. Ed., maurizio.masi@polimi.it; Antonio Vicente, Assoc. Ed., avicente@deb.uminho.pt. **ISSN:** 0336-6352. **URL:** http://www.versita.com/science/chemistry/cp/.

49704 ■ Chwila rozrywki
Edipresse Publications S.A.
Ul. Wiejska 19
PL-00-480 Warsaw, Poland
Ph: 48 22 5842438
Fax: 48 22 5842410
Publisher E-mail: groupe@edipresse.com
Magazine featuring real life stories, including tips and advice for improving the everyday life. **Freq:** Monthly. **Key Personnel:** Malgorzata Franke, Director; Urszula Zubczynska, Ch. Ed. **URL:** http://www.edipresse.com/entertainment/chwila-rozrywki.

49705 ■ Dom & Wnetrze
Edipresse Publications S.A.
Ul. Wiejska 19
PL-00-480 Warsaw, Poland
Ph: 48 22 5842200
Fax: 48 22 5842318
Publication E-mail: info@domiwnetrze.pl
Publisher E-mail: groupe@edipresse.com
Magazine covering architecture and interior decorating. **Founded:** 1991. **Freq:** Monthly. **Key Personnel:** Agnieszka Smit, Director; Ewa Mierzejewska, Ch. Ed. **URL:** http://polki.pl/dom_i_wnetrze.html; http://www.edipresse.com/home-design/dom-wnetrze. **Circ:** ‡20,283

49706 ■ Ecological Questions
Versita
Solipska 14A/1 St.
PL-02-482 Warsaw, Poland
Ph: 48 22 7015015
Fax: 48 22 4335126
Publisher E-mail: info@versita.com
Journal focusing on research about the environmental changes caused by natural processes and human activities. **Key Personnel:** Marian Rejewski, Editor-in-Chief; Marta Luscinska, Managing Editor; Ewa Kazmierczak, Editor. **ISSN:** 1644-7298. **URL:** http://www.versita.com/science/environment/eq/.

49707 ■ Economics and Organization of Enterprise
Versita
Solipska 14A/1 St.
PL-02-482 Warsaw, Poland
Ph: 48 22 7015015
Fax: 48 22 4335126
Publisher E-mail: info@versita.com
Journal covering the field of management, organizations and ergonomics. **Key Personnel:** Wieslaw M. Grudzewski, Editor; Irena Hejduk, Dep. Ed.; Andrzej Herman, Dep. Ed.; Wojciech Wiszniewski, Dep. Ed. **ISSN:** 0860-6846. **URL:** http://www.versita.com/science/business/eoe/.

49708 ■ Ekologija
Versita
Solipska 14A/1 St.
PL-02-482 Warsaw, Poland
Ph: 48 22 7015015
Fax: 48 22 4335126
Publisher E-mail: info@versita.com
Journal covering the field of ecology. **Key Personnel:** Irena Eitminaviciute, Editor-in-Chief; Vincas Buda, Dep. Ed.-in-Ch. **ISSN:** 0235-7224. **URL:** http://www.versita.com/science/environment/ekologija/.

49709 ■ European Countryside
Versita
Solipska 14A/1 St.
PL-02-482 Warsaw, Poland
Ph: 48 22 7015015
Fax: 48 22 4335126
Publisher E-mail: info@versita.com
Journal focusing on the ecology of rural landscape, rural sociology, demography and gender, multi-functional rural development, and agriculture. **Key Personnel:** Milada Stastna, Editor-in-Chief; Antonin Vaishar, Managing Editor. **ISSN:** 1803-8417. **URL:** http://www.versita.com/science/environment/ec/.

49710 ■ Folia Neuropathologica
Termedia Publishing House
Medical Research Centre
5 Painskiego St.
PL-02-106 Warsaw, Poland
Ph: 48 226 086543
Fax: 48 226 685532
Publisher E-mail: termedia@termedia.pl
Journal dedicated to neuropathology and allied disciplines in neurosciences, in connection with Polish Association of Neuropathologists and M. Mossakowski Medical Research Centre Polish Academy of Sciences. **Freq:** Quarterly. **Key Personnel:** Ewa Matyja, Editor-in-Chief; Milena Laure-Kamionowska, Assoc. Ed. **ISSN:** 1641-4640. **Subscription Rates:** 160 Zl institutions print and online; 80 Zl individuals print and online. **URL:** http://www.termedia.pl/magazine.php?magazine_id=20&magazine_subpage=CURRENT. **Circ:** 450

49711 ■ Folia Oeconomica Stetinensia
Versita
Solipska 14A/1 St.
PL-02-482 Warsaw, Poland
Ph: 48 22 7015015
Fax: 48 22 4335126
Publisher E-mail: info@versita.com
Peer-reviewed journal containing methodological papers and doctoral and postdoctoral thesis in the field of economics. **Freq:** Annual. **Key Personnel:** Waldemar Tarczynski, Editor-in-Chief, wtarc@uoo.univ.szczecin.pl; Jerzy Dudzinski, Editor; Ignacy Dziedziczak, Editor. **ISSN:** 1730-4237. **URL:** http://www.versita.com/science/business/fos/.

49712 ■ Formalized Mathematics
Versita
Solipska 14A/1 St.
PL-02-482 Warsaw, Poland
Ph: 48 22 7015015
Fax: 48 22 4335126
Publisher E-mail: info@versita.com
Journal covering the field of formalized and mechanically checked mathematics. **Key Personnel:** Roman Matuszewski, Editor-in-Chief; Grzegorz Bancerek, Scientific Ed.; Pauline N. Kawamoto, Language Ed. **ISSN:** 1426-2630. **URL:** http://www.versita.com/science/mathematics/fm/.

49713 ■ Geodesy and Cartography
Versita
Solipska 14A/1 St.
PL-02-482 Warsaw, Poland
Ph: 48 22 7015015
Fax: 48 22 4335126
Publisher E-mail: info@versita.com
Peer-reviewed journal covering the study, establishment and improvement of geodesy and mapping technologies. **Key Personnel:** Jonas Skeivalas, Editor-in-Chief; Eimuntas Parseliunas, Managing Editor. **ISSN:** 1392-1541. **URL:** http://www.versita.com/science/geosciences/gc/.

49714 ■ Geologija
Versita
Solipska 14A/1 St.
PL-02-482 Warsaw, Poland
Ph: 48 22 7015015
Fax: 48 22 4335126
Publisher E-mail: info@versita.com
Peer-reviewed journal covering various geological disciplines. **Freq:** Quarterly. **Key Personnel:** Algirdas Gaigalas, Editor-in-Chief; Juozas Paskevicius, Managing Editor; Algirdas Grigelis, Managing Editor. **ISSN:** 1392-110X. **URL:** http://www.versita.com/science/geosciences/geologija/.

49715 ■ Hacquetia
Versita
Solipska 14A/1 St.
PL-02-482 Warsaw, Poland
Ph: 48 22 7015015
Fax: 48 22 4335126
Publisher E-mail: info@versita.com
Journal covering the field of taxonomy, floristics, faunistic, vegetation ecology, biocoenology and palynology. **Key Personnel:** Urban Silc, Editor-in-Chief. **ISSN:** 1581-4661. **URL:** http://www.versita.com/science/lifesciences/hacquetia/.

49716 ■ Hot Moda & Shopping
Edipresse Publications S.A.
Ul. Wiejska 19
PL-00-480 Warsaw, Poland
Ph: 48 22 5842357
Fax: 48 22 5842356
Publisher E-mail: groupe@edipresse.com
Magazine covering shopping and fashion appeals for women. **Freq:** Monthly. **Key Personnel:** Magdalena Modrzewska, Director; Anna Jurgas, Ch. Ed. **URL:** http://www.edipresse.com/womens/hot-moda-shopping. **Circ:** ‡7,073

49717 ■ Human Movement
Versita

Solipska 14A/1 St.
PL-02-482 Warsaw, Poland
Ph: 48 22 7015015
Fax: 48 22 4335126
Publisher E-mail: info@versita.com
Journal focusing on the broad spectrum of human movement. **Freq:** Semiannual. **Key Personnel:** Alicja Rutkowska-Kucharska, Editor-in-Chief; Wieslaw Osinski, Assoc. Ed.; Andrzej Klimek, Assoc. Ed. ISSN: 1732-3991. **URL:** http://www.versita.com/science/healthsciences/hm/.

49718 ■ Information Processing Letters
Elsevier Science Inc.
Institute of Informatics
Warsaw University
ul. Banacha 2
02-097 Warsaw, Poland
Publisher E-mail: usinfo-ehelp@elsevier.com
Journal devoted to information processing. **Founded:** 1971. **Freq:** 24/yr. **Trim Size:** 8 3/8 x 10 7/8. **Cols./Page:** 2. **Key Personnel:** A. Tarlecki, Managing Editor, tarlecki@mimuw.edu.pl; S.E. Hambrusch, Board of Ed., seh@cs.purdue.edu; Y. Desmedt, Board of Ed., ipl@adastral.ucl.ac.uk; J. Chomicki, Board of Ed., chomicki@cse.buffalo.edu; W.L. Hsu, Board of Ed., hsu@iis.sinica.edu.tw; A.A. Bertossi, Board of Ed., bertossi@cs.unibo.it; J.L. Fiadeiro, Board of Ed., jose@fiadeiro.org; F.Y.L. Chin, Board of Ed., ipl@cs.hku.hk. ISSN: 0020-0190. **Subscription Rates:** US$2,337 institutions, other countries except Europe, Japan and Iran; 277,500¥ institutions; EUR2,091 institutions for European countries and Iran; US$286 other countries except Europe, Japan and Iran; EUR213 individuals for European countries and Iran; 32,900¥ individuals. **URL:** http://www.elsevier.com/wps/find/journaldescription.cws_home/505612/descriptiondescription.

49719 ■ International Journal of Applied Mathematics and Computer Science
Versita
Solipska 14A/1 St.
PL-02-482 Warsaw, Poland
Ph: 48 22 7015015
Fax: 48 22 4335126
Publisher E-mail: info@versita.com
Journal covering research concerned on the application of mathematical methods to computer science and engineering. **Key Personnel:** Jozef Korbicz, Editor-in-Chief, j.korbicz@issi.uz.zgora.pl; Dariusz Ucinski, Dep. Ed., d.ucinski@issi.uz.zgora.pl. ISSN: 1641-876X. **URL:** http://www.versita.com/science/computerscience/amcs/.

49720 ■ International Journal of Strategic Property Management
Versita
Solipska 14A/1 St.
PL-02-482 Warsaw, Poland
Ph: 48 22 7015015
Fax: 48 22 4335126
Publisher E-mail: info@versita.com
Peer-reviewed journal covering all areas of strategic property management. **Key Personnel:** Edmundas K. Zavadskas, Editor-in-Chief; Arturas Kaklauskas, Editor-in-Chief; Brian Sloan, Editor-in-Chief. ISSN: 1648-715X. **URL:** http://www.versita.com/science/business/ijspm/.

49721 ■ Issues of Business and Law
Versita
Solipska 14A/1 St.
PL-02-482 Warsaw, Poland
Ph: 48 22 7015015
Fax: 48 22 4335126
Publisher E-mail: info@versita.com
Peer-reviewed journal focusing on the fields of business economics, management and law. **Key Personnel:** Juozas Ruzevicius, Editor-in-Chief; Izolda Krutkiene, Managing Editor; Jens J. Dahlgaard, Editor. ISSN: 1822-9530. **URL:** http://www.versita.com/science/business/ibl/.

49722 ■ Journal of Human Kinetics
Versita
Solipska 14A/1 St.
PL-02-482 Warsaw, Poland
Ph: 48 22 7015015
Fax: 48 22 4335126
Publisher E-mail: info@versita.com
Journal covering research in the science of human movement studies. **Key Personnel:** Zbigniew

Waskiewicz, Editor-in-Chief; Adam Zajac, Managing Editor. ISSN: 1640-5544. **URL:** http://www.versita.com/science/healthsciences/johk/.

49723 ■ Journal of Konbin
Versita
Solipska 14A/1 St.
PL-02-482 Warsaw, Poland
Ph: 48 22 7015015
Fax: 48 22 4335126
Publisher E-mail: info@versita.com
Journal focusing on the safety and reliability of "human being-technologyenvironment" system. **Key Personnel:** Janusz Szpytko, Editor-in-Chief; Krzysztof Bubrzyk, Dep./Mng. Ed. ISSN: 1895-8281. **URL:** http://versita.com/science/engineering/jok/.

49724 ■ Journal of Medical Biochemistry
Versita
Solipska 14A/1 St.
PL-02-482 Warsaw, Poland
Ph: 48 22 7015015
Fax: 48 22 4335126
Publisher E-mail: info@versita.com
Journal covering all aspects of clinical chemistry, medical biochemistry and related fields. **Key Personnel:** Prof. Nada Majkic-Singh, Editor-in-Chief; Prof. Svetlana Ignjatovic, Dep./Mng. Ed. ISSN: 1452-8258. **URL:** http://www.versita.com/science/medicine/jmb/.

49725 ■ Journal of Plant Protection Research
Versita
Solipska 14A/1 St.
PL-02-482 Warsaw, Poland
Ph: 48 22 7015015
Fax: 48 22 4335126
Publisher E-mail: info@versita.com
Journal focusing on the study of plant protection. **Key Personnel:** Henryk Pospieszny, Editor-in-Chief; Stefan Pruszynski, Dep. Ed.; Danuta Wolna, Managing Editor. ISSN: 1427-4345. **URL:** http://www.versita.com/science/agriculture/jppr/.

49726 ■ Journal of Teacher Education for Sustainability
Versita
Solipska 14A/1 St.
PL-02-482 Warsaw, Poland
Ph: 48 22 7015015
Fax: 48 22 4335126
Publisher E-mail: info@versita.com
Journal covering the issues of sustainability in teacher education. **Key Personnel:** Astrida Skrinda, Editor-in-Chief; Carol Fortino, Editor; Detlev Lindau-Bank, Editor; Pat Irwin, Editor; Sirpa Tani, Editor; Charles Hopkins, Editor. ISSN: 1691-4147. **URL:** http://www.versita.com/science/education/jtes/.

49727 ■ Journal of Telecommunications and Information Technology
Instytut Lacznosci
ul. Szachowa 1
PL-04-894 Warsaw, Poland
Ph: 48 225 128100
Fax: 48 225 128625
Publisher E-mail: info@itl.waw.pl
Journal publishing papers from researchers working in several modern and important fields of telecommunications and computer science. **Key Personnel:** Pawel Szczepanski, Editor-in-Chief; Maria Lopuszniak, Managing Editor. ISSN: 1509-4553. **URL:** http://www.itl.waw.pl/publikacje/kwartalnik-jtit.

49728 ■ Journal of Water and Land Development
Versita
Solipska 14A/1 St.
PL-02-482 Warsaw, Poland
Ph: 48 22 7015015
Fax: 48 22 4335126
Publisher E-mail: info@versita.com
Journal covering all aspects of water and land management studies. **Freq:** Annual. **Key Personnel:** Waldemar Mioduszewski, Editor-in-Chief; Szczepan L. Dabkowski, Editor; Magdalena Borys, Editor. ISSN: 1429-7426. **URL:** http://www.versita.com/science/environment/jwld/.

49729 ■ Kwietnik
Agora S.A.
Czerska 8/10

PL-00-732 Warsaw, Poland
Ph: 48 22 5556880
Fax: 48 22 5556674
Publication E-mail: kwietnik@agora.pl
Publisher E-mail: kwietnik@agora.pl
Journal covering gardening and horticulture. **Founded:** Jan. 1995. **Freq:** Monthly. **Trim Size:** 204 x 275 mm. **Key Personnel:** Agnieszka Starega, Hd. of Advertising Department; Jolanta Zdanowska, Editor-in-Chief; Anna Wieczorek, Hd. of Mktg. Department; Adam Popielski, Dep. Dir.; Cezary Jeksa, Publisher. ISSN: 1233-3808. **Remarks:** Accepts advertising. **URL:** http://www.agora.pl/agora_eng/1,66708,764415.html. **Circ:** 42,200

49730 ■ Latvian Journal of Physics and Technical Sciences
Versita
Solipska 14A/1 St.
PL-02-482 Warsaw, Poland
Ph: 48 22 7015015
Fax: 48 22 4335126
Publisher E-mail: info@versita.com
Journal covering the study of applied physics in engineering, astronomy and spectroscopy. **Key Personnel:** Yuris Ekmanis, Editor-in-Chief; Yurgis Vilemas, Editor; Jans Kapala, Editor. ISSN: 0868-8257. **URL:** http://www.versita.com/science/physics/ljpts/.

49731 ■ Limes
Versita
Solipska 14A/1 St.
PL-02-482 Warsaw, Poland
Ph: 48 22 7015015
Fax: 48 22 4335126
Publisher E-mail: info@versita.com
Peer-reviewed journal focusing on the historical and cultural studies of borderlands in Poland, Lithuania and Belarus. **Key Personnel:** Tomas Kacerauskas, Editor-in-Chief; Jovile Bareviciute, Managing Editor; Basia Nikiforova, Dep. Ed.-in-Ch. ISSN: 2029-0187. **URL:** http://www.versita.com/science/socialsciences/limes/.

49732 ■ Linguistica Pragensia
Versita
Solipska 14A/1 St.
PL-02-482 Warsaw, Poland
Ph: 48 22 7015015
Fax: 48 22 4335126
Publisher E-mail: info@versita.com
Journal focusing on the achievements of Czech linguists. **Key Personnel:** Prof. Libuse Duskova, Editor-in-Chief; Prof. Jarmila Tarnyikova, Assoc. Ed.; Michaela Lastovickova, Editor. ISSN: 0862-8432. **URL:** http://versita.com/science/linguistics/lingprag/.

49733 ■ Lodz Papers in Pragmatics
Versita
Solipska 14A/1 St.
PL-02-482 Warsaw, Poland
Ph: 48 22 7015015
Fax: 48 22 4335126
Publisher E-mail: info@versita.com
Journal covering all aspects of human communication. **Key Personnel:** Prof. Piotr Cap, Editor-in-Chief, strus_pl@yahoo.com. ISSN: 1895-6106. **URL:** http://versita.metaproc.com/content/120719/?p=6b94263c5f5b4ed0bec57bbf340480e9&p_o=0.

49734 ■ Macedonian Journal of Medical Sciences
Versita
Solipska 14A/1 St.
PL-02-482 Warsaw, Poland
Ph: 48 22 7015015
Fax: 48 22 4335126
Publisher E-mail: info@versita.com
Journal containing research articles in health and biological sciences. **Key Personnel:** Mirko Spiroski, PhD, Editor-in-Chief, mspiroski@yahoo.com; Jean Gogusev, PhD, Editor-in-Chief, gogusev@necker.fr; Dejan Trajkov, MD, Editor-in-Chief, dejantmk@yahoo.com. ISSN: 1857-5749. **URL:** http://www.versita.com/science/medicine/mjms/.

49735 ■ Mamo, to ja
Edipresse Publications S.A.
Ul. Wiejska 19
PL-00-480 Warsaw, Poland
Ph: 48 22 5842335
Fax: 48 22 5842366

Circulation: ★ = ABC; △ = BPA; ♦ = CAC; • = CCAB; ❏ = VAC; ⊕ = PO Statement; ‡ = Publisher's Report; Boldface figures = sworn; Light figures = estimated.

Publication E-mail: info@mamo-to-ja.pl
Publisher E-mail: groupe@edipresse.com
Magazine focusing on young modern parents. **Freq:** Monthly. **Key Personnel:** Agnieszka Smit, Director; Magdalena Klimkowska, Ch. Ed. **URL:** http://www.edipresse.com/parentschildren/mamo-ja. **Circ:** ‡98,937

49736 ■ Mathematica Slovaca
Versita
Solipska 14A/1 St.
PL-02-482 Warsaw, Poland
Ph: 48 22 7015015
Fax: 48 22 4335126
Publisher E-mail: info@versita.com
Journal containing articles from all areas in mathematics. **Key Personnel:** Sylvia Pulmannova, Editor-in-Chief, pulmann@mat.savba.sk; Prof. Anatolij Dvurecenskij, Managing Editor, dvurecen@mat.savba.sk. **ISSN:** 0139-9918. **URL:** http://www.versita.com/science/mathematics/maslo/.

49737 ■ Medicina Sportiva
Versita
Solipska 14A/1 St.
PL-02-482 Warsaw, Poland
Ph: 48 22 7015015
Fax: 48 22 4335126
Publisher E-mail: info@versita.com
Journal covering various aspects of physical activity and exercise sciences. **Freq:** Quarterly. **Key Personnel:** Zbigniew Szygula, Editor-in-Chief; Wojciech Gawronski, Dep./Mng. Ed. **ISSN:** 1734-2260. **URL:** http://www.versita.com/science/healthsciences/ms/.

49738 ■ Mineralogia
Versita
Solipska 14A/1 St.
PL-02-482 Warsaw, Poland
Ph: 48 22 7015015
Fax: 48 22 4335126
Publisher E-mail: info@versita.com
Journal focusing on the field of mineralogical sciences. **Key Personnel:** Andrzej Skowronski, Editor-in-Chief. **ISSN:** 1899-8291. **URL:** http://www.versita.com/science/geosciences/minerpolon/.

49739 ■ Nukleonika
Institute of Nuclear Chemistry and Technology
16 Dorodna St.
03-195 Warsaw, Poland
Ph: 48 225 041220
Fax: 48 228 111532
Publication E-mail: nukleon@ichtj.waw.pl
Publisher E-mail: sekdyrn@orange.ichtj.waw.pl
Peer-reviewed journal publishing articles on various aspects of nuclear sciences. **Subtitle:** International Journal of Nuclear Research. **Founded:** 1956. **Freq:** Quarterly. **Key Personnel:** Prof. Andrzej G. Chmielewski, PhD, Editor-in-Chief, a.chmielewski@ichtj.waw.pl; Hilmar Forstel, Editorial Board; Janusz Z. Beer, Editorial Board; Gregory R. Choppin, Editorial Board; Wladyslaw Dabrowski, Editorial Board; Krzysztof Andrzejewski, Editorial Board; Grazyna Bystrzejewska-Piotrowska, Editorial Board; Jacqueline Belloni, Editorial Board. **ISSN:** 0029-5922. **Subscription Rates:** US$27 single issue individual; back volumes; US$50 single issue institutional; back volumes; US$105 individuals; US$200 institutions. **URL:** http://www.ichtj.waw.pl/ichtj/general/nukleon.htm.

49740 ■ Oceanological and Hydrobiological Studies
Versita
Solipska 14A/1 St.
PL-02-482 Warsaw, Poland
Ph: 48 22 7015015
Fax: 48 22 4335126
Publisher E-mail: info@versita.com
Journal covering all aspects of the marine environment and hydrobiology. **Freq:** Quarterly. **Key Personnel:** Prof. Marcin Plinski, Editor-in-Chief; Grzegorz Kozlowski, Dep./Mng. Ed. **ISSN:** 1730-413X. **URL:** http://www.versita.com/science/lifesciences/oandhs/.

49741 ■ Old and New Concepts of Physics
Versita
Solipska 14A/1 St.
PL-02-482 Warsaw, Poland
Ph: 48 22 7015015
Fax: 48 22 4335126

Publisher E-mail: info@versita.com
Journal containing articles related to physics. **Key Personnel:** E. Kapuscik, Editor-in-Chief; M. Skulimowski, Managing Editor. **ISSN:** 1733-8026. **URL:** http://www.versita.com/science/physics/cphys/.

49742 ■ Opto-Electronics Review
Versita
Solipska 14A/1 St.
PL-02-482 Warsaw, Poland
Ph: 48 22 7015015
Fax: 48 22 4335126
Publisher E-mail: info@versita.com
Journal covering the field of opto-electronics. **Key Personnel:** Prof. Antoni Rogalski, Editor-in-Chief, rogan@wat.edu.pl; Jerzy Zielinski, Dep. Ed.-in-Ch.; Janusz Sadowski, Managing Editor. **ISSN:** 1230-3402. **URL:** http://www.versita.com/science/physics/oer/.

49743 ■ Organizacija
Versita
Solipska 14A/1 St.
PL-02-482 Warsaw, Poland
Ph: 48 22 7015015
Fax: 48 22 4335126
Publisher E-mail: info@versita.com
Peer-reviewed journal covering the managerial aspects of organizational science, business information systems and human resources management. **Key Personnel:** Joze Zupancic, Editor-in-Chief; Marko Ferjan, Editor; Bostjan Gomiscek, Editor. **ISSN:** 1318-5454. **URL:** http://www.versita.com/science/business/organizacija/.

49744 ■ Paladyn
Versita
Solipska 14A/1 St.
PL-02-482 Warsaw, Poland
Ph: 48 22 7015015
Fax: 48 22 4335126
Publisher E-mail: info@versita.com
Journal featuring advances in behavioral robotics. **Subtitle:** Journal of Behavioral Robotics. **Key Personnel:** Andrzej Ruta, Assoc. Ed., aruta@versita.com; Gregor SchOner, Editor-in-Chief; Ildar Farkhatdinov, Assoc. Ed.; Andrea Bonarini, Editor; Ben Krose, Editor; Daniel Polani, Editor. **ISSN:** 2080-9778. **URL:** http://www.versita.com/science/engineering/paladyn/.

49745 ■ Party Celebrity lives
Edipresse Publications S.A.
Ul. Wiejska 19
PL-00-480 Warsaw, Poland
Ph: 48 22 5842200
Fax: 48 22 5842356
Publisher E-mail: groupe@edipresse.com
Magazine covering the lives of celebrities. **Freq:** Biweekly. **Key Personnel:** Aneta Wikariak, Ch. Ed. **URL:** http://www.edipresse.com/celebrity-news/party-celebrity-lives. **Circ:** ‡472,261

49746 ■ Philologia
Versita
Solipska 14A/1 St.
PL-02-482 Warsaw, Poland
Ph: 48 22 7015015
Fax: 48 22 4335126
Publisher E-mail: info@versita.com
Journal covering the field of humanities and social sciences. **Key Personnel:** Biljana Cubrovic, Editor-in-Chief. **ISSN:** 1451-5342. **URL:** http://versita.metapress.com/content/120779/?p=eecaf312acd446f1b9b7241b4dee6178&p_o=0.

49747 ■ Physical Education and Sport
Versita
Solipska 14A/1 St.
PL-02-482 Warsaw, Poland
Ph: 48 22 7015015
Fax: 48 22 4335126
Publisher E-mail: info@versita.com
Journal covering the areas of physical activity and sport sciences. **Key Personnel:** Krzysztof Mazurek, Editor-in-Chief; Romuald Stupnicki, Managing Editor. **ISSN:** 0043-9630. **URL:** http://www.versita.com/science/healthsciences/pes/.

49748 ■ Polish Journal of Chemical Technology
Versita
Solipska 14A/1 St.
PL-02-482 Warsaw, Poland
Ph: 48 22 7015015

Fax: 48 22 4335126
Publisher E-mail: info@versita.com
Peer-reviewed journal covering the field of fundamental and applied chemistry. **Key Personnel:** Ryszard Jozef Kalenczuk, Editor-in-Chief; Maria Ursula Tomaszewska, Dep./Mng. Ed. **ISSN:** 1509-8117. **URL:** http://www.versita.com/science/chemistry/pjcht/.

49749 ■ Polish Journal of Medical Physics and Engineering
Versita
Solipska 14A/1 St.
PL-02-482 Warsaw, Poland
Ph: 48 22 7015015
Fax: 48 22 4335126
Publisher E-mail: info@versita.com
Journal covering the field of medical physics and engineering. **Key Personnel:** Natalia Golnik, Editor-in-Chief. **ISSN:** 1425-4689. **URL:** http://www.versita.com/science/engineering/pjmpe/.

49750 ■ Polish Journal of Natural Sciences
Versita
Solipska 14A/1 St.
PL-02-482 Warsaw, Poland
Ph: 48 22 7015015
Fax: 48 22 4335126
Publisher E-mail: info@versita.com
Journal covering all aspects of natural sciences. **Freq:** Quarterly. **Key Personnel:** Janusz Falkowski, Editor-in-Chief. **ISSN:** 1643-9953. **URL:** http://www.versita.com/science/agriculture/pjns/.

49751 ■ Polish Journal of Surgery
Versita
Solipska 14A/1 St.
PL-02-482 Warsaw, Poland
Ph: 48 22 7015015
Fax: 48 22 4335126
Publisher E-mail: info@versita.com
Journal covering all aspect of surgery. **Key Personnel:** Adam Dziki, Editor-in-Chief. **ISSN:** 0032-373X. **URL:** http://www.versita.com/science/medicine/pjs/.

49752 ■ Polish Maritime Research
Versita
Solipska 14A/1 St.
PL-02-482 Warsaw, Poland
Ph: 48 22 7015015
Fax: 48 22 4335126
Publisher E-mail: info@versita.com
Journal covering research and scientific problems on ships, marine and offshore technology. **Freq:** Quarterly. **Key Personnel:** Przemyslaw Wierzchowski, Editor; Tadeusz Borzecki, Editor-in-Chief; Piotr Bzura, Managing Editor. **ISSN:** 1233-2585. **URL:** http://www.versita.com/science/engineering/pmr/.

49753 ■ Polish Pneumology and Allergology
Via Medica
ul. Plocka 26
PL-01-138 Warsaw, Poland
Ph: 48 22 4312144
Fax: 48 22 4312454
Publisher E-mail: viamedica@viamedica.pl
Journal covering pneumology and allergology. **Freq:** Quarterly. **Key Personnel:** Prof. Dorota Gorecka, Editor-in-Chief. **ISSN:** 0867-7077. **Subscription Rates:** 90 Zl individuals print; 180 Zl institutions print; EUR23 individuals print; EUR45 institutions print. **Remarks:** Accepts advertising. **URL:** http://www.viamedica.pl/en/gazety/xgazSang/index.phtml. **Circ:** (Not Reported)

49754 ■ Polish Psychological Bulletin
Versita
Solipska 14A/1 St.
PL-02-482 Warsaw, Poland
Ph: 48 22 7015015
Fax: 48 22 4335126
Publisher E-mail: info@versita.com
Journal covering research in psychology. **Key Personnel:** Dariusz Dolinski, Editor-in-Chief; Michal Grycz, Managing Editor. **ISSN:** 0079-2993. **URL:** http://www.versita.com/science/psychology/ppb/.

49755 ■ Polish Sexology
Via Medica
ul. Husarska 6b
PL-02-489 Warsaw, Poland
Fax: 48 22 6211552
Publisher E-mail: viamedica@viamedica.pl
Journal covering all branches of sexology. **Founded:**

2003. **Freq:** Semiannual. **Key Personnel:** Slawomir Jakima, Editor-in-Chief. **ISSN:** 1731-6677. **Subscription Rates:** 32 Zl individuals print; 64 Zl institutions print. **Remarks:** Accepts advertising. **URL:** http://www.viamedica.pl/en/gazety/xgazFang/index.phtml. **Circ:** (Not Reported)

49756 ■ Poznan Studies in Contemporary Linguistics
Versita
Solipska 14A/1 St.
PL-02-482 Warsaw, Poland
Ph: 48 22 7015015
Fax: 48 22 4335126
Publisher E-mail: info@versita.com
Journal focusing on contemporary linguistic theories and interdisciplinary study of language. **Key Personnel:** Katarzyna Dziubalska-Kolaczyk, Editor, dkasia@ifa.amu.edu.pl. **ISSN:** 0137-2459. **URL:** http://www.versita.com/pscl.

49757 ■ Prawdziwe Zycie
Edipresse Publications S.A.
Ul. Wiejska 19
PL-00-480 Warsaw, Poland
Ph: 48 22 5842438
Fax: 48 22 5842410
Publisher E-mail: groupe@edipresse.com
Magazine featuring real life stories. **Freq:** Monthly. **Key Personnel:** Malgorzata Franke, Director; Urszula Zubczynska, Ch. Ed. **URL:** http://www.edipresse.com/entertainment/prawdziwe-%C5%BCycie.

49758 ■ Przedszkolak
Edipresse Publications S.A.
Ul. Wieska 19
PL-00-480 Warsaw, Poland
Ph: 48 22 5842335
Fax: 48 22 5842201
Publisher E-mail: groupe@edipresse.com
Magazine for parents with children between 3 and 7 years old. **Freq:** Bimonthly. **Key Personnel:** Agnieszka Smit, Director; Magdalena Klimkowska, Ch. Ed. **URL:** http://www.edipresse.com/parentschildren/przedszkolak.

49759 ■ Przekroj
Edipresse Publications S.A.
Ul. Wiejska 19
PL-00-490 Warsaw, Poland
Publisher E-mail: groupe@edipresse.com
Magazine focusing on the current affairs in Poland. **Founded:** 1940. **Freq:** Weekly. **Key Personnel:** Ewa Redel-Bydlowska, Director. **URL:** http://www.przekroj.pl/. **Circ:** ‡68,815

49760 ■ Przyjaciolka
Edipresse Publications S.A.
Ul. Wiejska 19
PL-00-480 Warsaw, Poland
Ph: 48 22 5842438
Fax: 48 22 5842436
Publication E-mail: info@przyjaciolka.pl
Publisher E-mail: groupe@edipresse.com
Magazine featuring fashion stories, beauty, health and psychology advice and interviews. **Founded:** 1948. **Freq:** Bimonthly. **Key Personnel:** Malgorzata Franke, Director; Agnieszka Swiecka, Ch. Ed. **URL:** http://www.edipresse.com/womens/przyjaci%C3%B3lka; http://www.przyjaciolka.pl/. **Circ:** ‡460,291

49761 ■ Psychology of Language and Communication
Versita
Solipska 14A/1 St.
PL-02-482 Warsaw, Poland
Ph: 48 22 7015015
Fax: 48 22 4335126
Publisher E-mail: info@versita.com
Journal containing articles on psychological studies about language and communication processes in children and adults. **Key Personnel:** Barbara Bokus, Editor-in-Chief; Hristo Kyuchukov, Assoc. Ed.; Tiia Tulviste, Assoc. Ed. **ISSN:** 1234-2238. **URL:** http://www.versita.com/science/psychology/plc/.

49762 ■ Radiology and Oncology
Versita
Solipska 14A/1 St.
PL-02-482 Warsaw, Poland
Ph: 48 22 7015015

Fax: 48 22 4335126
Publisher E-mail: info@versita.com
Journal focusing on the field of radiology and oncology. **Key Personnel:** Gregor Sersa, Editor-in-Chief; Viljem Kovac, Exec. Ed.; Andrej Cor, Dep. Ed. **ISSN:** 1318-2099. **URL:** http://www.versita.com/science/medicine/ro/.

49763 ■ Ring
Versita
Solipska 14A/1 St.
PL-02-482 Warsaw, Poland
Ph: 48 22 7015015
Fax: 48 22 4335126
Publisher E-mail: info@versita.com
Journal covering issues in bird ringing, migration and bird numbers monitoring. **Key Personnel:** Przemyslaw Busse, Editor-in-Chief; Agnieszka Ozarowska, Dep./Mng. Ed. **ISSN:** 0035-5429. **URL:** http://www.versita.com/science/lifesciences/ring/.

49764 ■ Scalable Computing
Warsaw School of Social Psychology
ul. Chodakowska 19/31
03-815 Warsaw, Poland
Publisher E-mail: bwm@swps.edu.pl
Journal for scalable computing practice and experience. **Subtitle:** Practice and Experience. **Key Personnel:** Alexander Denisjuk, Mng. & Tech. Ed.; Peter Arbenz, Editor, arbenz@inf.ethz.ch; Bogdan Czejdo, Editor, czejdo@loyno.edu; Marcin Paprzycki, Editor, marcin.paprzycki@ibspan.waw.pl; David Du, Editor, du@cs.umn.edu; Yakov Fet, Editor, fet@ssd.sscc.ru; Frederic Desprez, Editor, frederic.desprez@inria.fr; Luigi Brugnano, Editor, brugnano@math.unifi.it; Dorothy Bollman, Editor, bollman@cs.uprm.edu. **URL:** http://www.scpe.org/.

49765 ■ South East European Journal of Economics and Business
Versita
Solipska 14A/1 St.
PL-02-482 Warsaw, Poland
Ph: 48 22 7015015
Fax: 48 22 4335126
Publisher E-mail: info@versita.com
Journal covering the field of economics and business in South East Europe. **Key Personnel:** Besim Culahovic, Editor-in-Chief; Dzevad Sehic, Dep./Mng. Ed.; Fikret Causevic, Dep./Mng. Ed. **ISSN:** 1840-118X. **URL:** http://www.versita.com/science/business/seejeb/.

49766 ■ Suicidology
Via Medica
Sobieski St. 9
PL-02-957 Warsaw, Poland
Ph: 48 22 4582659
Publisher E-mail: viamedica@viamedica.pl
Journal covering field of suicidology. **Freq:** Annual. **Key Personnel:** Prof. Brunon Holyst, Editor-in-Chief. **ISSN:** 1895-3786. **URL:** http://www.viamedica.pl/en/gazety/xgazOang/index.phtml.

49767 ■ Town Planning and Architecture
Versita
Solipska 14A/1 St.
PL-02-482 Warsaw, Poland
Ph: 48 22 7015015
Fax: 48 22 4335126
Publisher E-mail: info@versita.com
Peer-reviewed journal containing research in the fields of town planning and architecture. **Founded:** 1995. **Key Personnel:** Jurgis Vanagas, Editor-in-Chief; Audrius Novickas, Managing Editor. **ISSN:** 1392-1630. **URL:** http://www.versita.com/science/environment/tpa/.

49768 ■ Trener
Polish Football Association
Federation Polonaise de Football
ul. Miodowa 1
PL-00-080 Warsaw, Poland
Ph: 48 22 5512300
Fax: 48 22 5512240
Polish language publication covering soccer. **Freq:** Semimonthly. **Remarks:** Advertising accepted; rates available upon request. **URL:** http://www.pzpn.pl/. **Circ:** 2,000

49769 ■ Twoj Maluszek
Edipresse Publications S.A.

Ul. Wiejska 19
PL-00-480 Warsaw, Poland
Ph: 48 22 5842335
Fax: 48 22 5842201
Publisher E-mail: groupe@edipresse.com
Magazine containing practical advice and information for urban parents with babies and toddlers. **Freq:** Monthly. **Key Personnel:** Agnieszka Smit, Director; Magdalena Klimkowska, Ch. Ed. **URL:** http://www.edipresse.com/parentschildren/tw%C3%B3j-maluszek. **Circ:** ↓146,473

49770 ■ Twoje dziecko
Edipresse Publications S.A.
Ul. Wiejska 19
PL-00-490 Warsaw, Poland
Ph: 48 22 5842335
Fax: 48 22 5842366
Publication E-mail: info@twoje-dziecko.pl
Publisher E-mail: groupe@edipresse.com
Magazine focusing on health and education of babies. **Founded:** 1950. **Freq:** Monthly. **Key Personnel:** Agnieszka Smit, Director; Agata Telezynska, Ch. Ed. **URL:** http://www.edipresse.com/parentschildren/twoje-dziecko. **Circ:** ‡70,524

49771 ■ Uczucia i tesknoty
Edipresse Publications S.A.
Ul. Wiejska 19
PL-00-480 Warsaw, Poland
Ph: 48 22 5842200
Fax: 48 22 5842521
Publisher E-mail: groupe@edipresse.com
Magazine featuring real life stories and information on better living. **Freq:** Monthly. **Key Personnel:** Malgorzata Franke, Director; Urszula Zubczynska, Ch. Ed. **URL:** http://www.edipresse.com/entertainment/uczucia-i-tesknoty; http://www.edipresse.pl/. **Circ:** ‡63,514

49772 ■ Uroda
Edipresse Publications S.A.
Ul. Wiejska 19
PL-00-480 Warsaw, Poland
Ph: 48 22 5842200
Fax: 48 22 5842500
Publication E-mail: uroda@pdw.pl
Publisher E-mail: groupe@edipresse.com
Magazine providing information on women's lifestyle. **Freq:** Monthly. **Key Personnel:** Agnieszka Smit, Director; Danuta Bybrowska, Ch. Ed. **URL:** http://www.edipresse.com/womens/uroda; http://uroda.pl/. **Circ:** ‡76,342

49773 ■ Vestnik Zoologii
Versita
Solipska 14A/1 St.
PL-02-482 Warsaw, Poland
Ph: 48 22 7015015
Fax: 48 22 4335126
Publisher E-mail: info@versita.com
Peer-reviewed journal covering all fields of zoology. **Freq:** Bimonthly. **Key Personnel:** Igor Akimov, Editor-in-Chief; Vitaliy Kharchenko, Managing Editor; Vladislav Monchenko, Managing Editor. **ISSN:** 0084-5604. **URL:** http://www.versita.com/science/lifesciences/vzool/.

49774 ■ Vita
Edipresse Publications S.A.
Ul. Wiejska 19
PL-00-480 Warsaw, Poland
Ph: 48 22 5842438
Fax: 48 22 5842410
Publication E-mail: info@vita.pl
Publisher E-mail: groupe@edipresse.com
Magazine featuring information on health and well-being. **Freq:** Monthly. **Key Personnel:** Malgorzata Franke, Director; Agnieszka Swiecka, Ch. Ed. **URL:** http://www.edipresse.com/health-fitness/vita; http://www.vita.pl/. **Circ:** ‡72,677

49775 ■ Warsaw Insider
Valkea Media
ul. Elblaska 15/17
PL-01-747 Warsaw, Poland
Ph: 48 22 6398567
Fax: 48 22 6398569
Publication E-mail: insider@warsawinsider.pl
Lifestyle and entertainment magazine featuring good living and fast times in Warsaw. **Freq:** Monthly. **Print Method:** offset. **Key Personnel:** Agnieszka Le Nart,

Circulation: ★ = ABC; △ = BPA; ♦ = CAC; • = CCAB; ❑ = VAC; ⊕ = PO Statement; ‡ = Publisher's Report; Boldface figures = sworn; Light figures = estimated.

Gale Directory of Publications & Broadcast Media/147th Ed.   5357

Editor-in-Chief, alenart@valkea.com. **Subscription Rates:** 56 Zl individuals 6 months; 109 Zl individuals; EUR32 individuals Europe, 6 months; EUR59 individuals Europe; EUR44 other countries 6 months; EUR76 other countries. **Remarks:** Accepts advertising. **URL:** http://www.warsawinsider.pl/. **Circ:** 20,000

49776 ■ Zoologica Poloniae
Versita
Solipska 14A/1 St.
PL-02-482 Warsaw, Poland
Ph: 48 22 7015015
Fax: 48 22 4335126
Publisher E-mail: info@versita.com
Journal covering all aspects of general zoology. **Key Personnel:** Antoni Ogorzalek, Editor-in-Chief; Jan Kotusz, Dep./Mng. Ed. **ISSN:** 0044-510X. **URL:** http://www.versita.com/science/lifesciences/zp/.

Wroclaw

49777 ■ Cellular & Molecular Biology Letters
Springer Netherlands
c/o Jan Szopa, Ed.-in-Ch.
Institute of Biochemistry & Molecular Biology
University of Wroclaw
ul. Przybyszewskiego 63-77
51148 Wroclaw, Poland
Publisher E-mail: permissions.dordrecht@springer.com
Journal covering biochemistry, biophysics and biotechnology. **Subtitle:** An International Journal. **Founded:** 1996. **Freq:** Quarterly. **Print Method:** Offset. **Trim Size:** 14 x 22. **Cols./Page:** 6. **Col. Width:** 12 picas. **Col. Depth:** 290.5 picas. **Key Personnel:** Alastair Aitken, Editorial Board; Walter B. Gratzer, Editorial Board; Guru V. Betageri, Editorial Board; Wlodzimierz Korohoda, Editorial Board; Tadeusz Chojnacki, Editorial Board; Stephen A. Krawetz, Editorial Board; Yechezkel Barenholz, Editorial Board. **ISSN:** 1425-8153. **Subscription Rates:** EUR368 institutions print incl. free access or e-only; EUR441.60 institutions print incl. enhanced access. **URL:** http://www.springer.com/lifesci/cellbiology/journal/11658.

49778 ■ Geochronometria
WIND- J. Wojewoda Publishing Company
Kuropatwia 2

PL-44-100 Wroclaw, Poland
Journal covering the methods of absolute chronology and using them in different fields of earth and other natural sciences and archaeology. **Key Personnel:** Anna Pazdur, Editor-in-Chief; Grzegorz Adamiec, Consulting Ed.; Danuta Michczynska, Asst. Ed. **ISSN:** 1733-8387. **URL:** http://www.geochronometria.pl/.

49779 ■ Interdisciplinary Problems of Stroke
Via Medica
ul. Borowska 213
PL-50-556 Wroclaw, Poland
Ph: 48 71 7343100
Fax: 48 71 7343109
Publisher E-mail: viamedica@viamedica.pl
Journal covering problems of stroke. **Freq:** Semiannual. **Key Personnel:** Ryszard Podemski, Editor-in-Chief, profrpo@neurol.am.wroc.pl. **ISSN:** 1505-6740. **Subscription Rates:** 32 Zl individuals print; 64 Zl institutions print; EUR8 individuals print; EUR16 institutions print. **Remarks:** Accepts advertising. **URL:** http://www.viamedica.pl/en/gazety/xgazDang/index.phtml. **Circ:** (Not Reported)

49780 ■ International Journal of Intelligent Information and Database Systems
Inderscience Publishers
c/o Prof. Ngoc Thanh Nguyen, Ed.-in-Ch.
Wroclaw University of Technology
Institute of Informatics
Str. Janiszewskiego 11/17
50-370 Wroclaw, Poland
Publisher E-mail: editor@inderscience.com
Peer-reviewed journal covering new intelligent technologies for information processing data. **Founded:** 2007. **Freq:** 6/yr. **Key Personnel:** Prof. Ngoc Thanh Nguyen, Editor-in-Chief, thanh@pwr.wroc.pl; Prof. Shyi-Ming Chen, Assoc. Ed.; Prof. Tu Bao Ho, Assoc. Ed. **ISSN:** 1751-5858. **Subscription Rates:** EUR494 individuals includes surface mail, print only; EUR672 individuals print and online. **URL:** http://www.inderscience.com/browse/index.php?journalCODE=ijiids.

Zabrze

49781 ■ Annales Academiae Medicae Silesiensis
Via Medica

ul. 3 Maja 13/15
PL-41-800 Zabrze, Poland
Ph: 48 32 2712511
Fax: 48 32 2714617
Publisher E-mail: viamedica@viamedica.pl
Journal covering developments in medical sciences. **Freq:** 6/yr. **Key Personnel:** Prof. Wladyslaw Grzeszczak, Editor-in-Chief. **ISSN:** 0208-5607. **Remarks:** Accepts advertising. **URL:** http://www.viamedica.pl/en/gazety/czasopisma.phtml. **Circ:** (Not Reported)

49782 ■ Experimental and Clinical Diabetology
Via Medica
ul. 3 Maja 13/15
PL-41-800 Zabrze, Poland
Ph: 48 32 2712511
Fax: 48 32 2714617
Publisher E-mail: viamedica@viamedica.pl
Journal covering developments in the field of diabetology. **Freq:** Semiannual. **Key Personnel:** Wladyslaw Grzeszczak, Editor-in-Chief. **ISSN:** 1643-3165. **Subscription Rates:** 136 Zl individuals print; 196 Zl institutions print; EUR34 individuals print; EUR49 institutions print. **Remarks:** Accepts advertising. **URL:** http://www.viamedica.pl/en/gazety/xgaz9ang/index.phtml. **Circ:** (Not Reported)

49783 ■ Polish Journal of Endocrinology
Via Medica
Plac Traugutta 2
PL-41-908 Zabrze, Poland
Ph: 48 32 2786126
Fax: 48 32 2786126
Publication E-mail: endoklin@sum.edu.pl; endokrynologia.polska@viamedica.pl
Publisher E-mail: viamedica@viamedica.pl
Journal covering clinical and experimental endocrinology. **Founded:** 1949. **Freq:** Bimonthly. **Key Personnel:** Prof. Beata Kos-Kudla, Editor-in-Chief. **ISSN:** 0423-104X. **Subscription Rates:** 120 Zl individuals print; 240 Zl institutions print; EUR30 individuals print; EUR61 institutions print. **Remarks:** Accepts advertising. **URL:** http://www.viamedica.pl/en/gazety/xgazPang/index.phtml. **Circ:** (Not Reported)

Almargem do Bispo

49784 ■ Saude e Lar
Publicadora Atlantico
Rua N Senhora da Piedade
Sabugo
P-2715 Almargem do Bispo, Portugal
Ph: 351 21 9626200
Fax: 351 21 9626201
Consumer magazine covering health, family, home and education. **Founded:** 1940. **Freq:** Monthly. **Print Method:** Offset. **Key Personnel:** Dr. Samuel Ribeiro, Director; Maria Augusta Lopes, Editor-in-Chief. **Subscription Rates:** EUR28 individuals. **Remarks:** Advertising not accepted. **URL:** http://www.saudelar.com/. **Circ:** (Not Reported)

Aveiro

49785 ■ Diario de Aveiro
Group Diario de Coimbra
Av. De. Lourenco Peixinho 15-1-G
P-3800 Aveiro, Portugal
Ph: 351 234 234000031
Fax: 351 234 234000032
Publication E-mail: diarioaveiro@diarioaveiro.pt
Publisher E-mail: alucas@esoterica.pt
General newspaper. **Freq:** Daily. **Print Method:** Web offset. **Cols./Page:** 6. **Col. Width:** 45 millimeters. **Col. Depth:** 33.3 centimeters. **Key Personnel:** Adriano Lucas, Director, alucas@cpu.pt; Jose Carlos Galiano Pinheiro, Director, jornaldc@esoterica.pt. **Subscription Rates:** EUR105 individuals; EUR45 individuals for students. **Remarks:** Accepts advertising. **URL:** http://www.diarioaveiro.pt/. **Circ:** Controlled 5,050

49786 ■ International Journal of Machining and Machinability of Materials
Inderscience Publishers
c/o Prof. Paulo J. Davim, Ed.-in-Ch.
University of Aveiro
Department of Mechanical Engineering
Campus Santiago
3810-193 Aveiro, Portugal
Publisher E-mail: editor@inderscience.com
Peer-reviewed journal covering machining and machinability of materials. **Freq:** 8/yr. **Key Personnel:** Prof. Paulo J. Davim, Editor-in-Chief, pdavim@ua.pt; Prof. Antoniomaria Di Ilio, Editorial Board Member; Prof. Kai Cheng, Editorial Board Member; Prof. Kai Cheng, Editorial Board Member; Prof. Eduardo Bianchi, Editorial Board Member; Prof. Alexandre Abrao, Editorial Board Member; Prof. Viktor P. Astakhov, Editorial Board Member; Prof. Kevin Chou, Editorial Board Member; Prof. V.N. Gaitonde, Editorial Board Member. **ISSN:** 1748-5711. **Subscription Rates:** EUR735 individuals print only (surface mail); EUR1,240 individuals online only (2-3 users); EUR1,025 individuals print and online; EUR795 individuals print only (airmail). **URL:** http://www.inderscience.com/browse/index.php?journalCODE=ijmmm.

49787 ■ International Journal of Materials Engineering Innovation
Inderscience Enterprises Limited
c/o Prof. J. Paulo Davim, Ed.-in-Ch.
Department of Mechanical Engineering

University of Aveiro
Campus Santiago
P-3810-193 Aveiro, Portugal
Peer-reviewed journal focusing on the innovation in materials engineering. **Freq:** Quarterly. **Key Personnel:** Prof. J. Paulo Davim, Editor-in-Chief, pdavim@ua.pt; Prof. J.M.F. Ferreira, Editor-in-Chief, jmf@ua.pt. **ISSN:** 1757-2754. **Subscription Rates:** EUR494 individuals print or online; EUR672 individuals print and online. **URL:** http://www.inderscience.com/browse/index.php?journalCODE=ijmatei.

49788 ■ International Journal of Molecular Engineering
Inderscience Enterprises Limited
c/o Prof. Nasar Ali, Assoc. Ed.
University of Aveiro
Dept. of Mechanical Engineering
3810-193 Aveiro, Portugal
Journal covering the fields of fundamental chemistry, biology, and physics of molecular engineering. **Freq:** 4/yr. **Key Personnel:** Prof. Nasar Ali, Assoc. Ed.; Dr. M.A. Dorgham, Editor-in-Chief, editorial@inderscience.com. **ISSN:** 1743-8241. **Subscription Rates:** EUR494 individuals print or online; EUR672 individuals print and online. **URL:** http://www.inderscience.com/browse/index.php?journalID=146.

49789 ■ International Journal of Surface Science & Engineering
Inderscience Publishers
c/o Prof. J. Paulo Davim, Ed.-in-Ch.
University of Aveiro
Department of Mechanical Engineering
Campus Santiago
3810-193 Aveiro, Portugal
Publisher E-mail: editor@inderscience.com
Peer-reviewed journal covering field of surface science & tribology. **Founded:** 2007. **Freq:** 6/yr. **Key Personnel:** Prof. J. Paulo Davim, Editor-in-Chief, pdavim@ua.pt; Prof. Liangchi Zhang, Editor-in-Chief, liangchi.zhang@unsw.edu.au; Prof. Hong Hocheng, Assoc. Ed. **ISSN:** 1749-785X. **Subscription Rates:** EUR593 individuals includes surface mail, print only; EUR830 individuals print and online. **URL:** http://www.inderscience.com/browse/index.php?journalCODE=ijsurfse.

Coimbra

49790 ■ Diario de Coimbra
Group Diario de Coimbra
Rua Adriano Lucas
Apartado 542
P-3020 Coimbra 351 239492, Portugal
Ph: 351 239499999
Publication E-mail: redac@diariocoimbra.pt
Publisher E-mail: alucas@esoterica.pt
General newspaper. **Freq:** Daily. **Print Method:** Web offset. **Cols./Page:** 6. **Col. Width:** 45 millimeters. **Key Personnel:** Adriano Lucas, Editor-in-Chief, alucas@cpu.pt; Jose Carlos Galiano Pinheiro, Director, jornaldc@esoterica.pt. **Remarks:** Accepts advertising. **URL:** http://www.diariocoimbra.pt/. **Circ:** Controlled 10,200

Cruz Quebrada-Dafundo

49791 ■ Auto Hoje (Car Today)
Motor Press Lisbon
Rua Policarpo Anjos, No. 4
P-1495-742 Cruz Quebrada-Dafundo, Portugal
Ph: 351 214 154500
Fax: 351 214 154501
Consumer magazine covering automobile reports, new models and car tests. **Founded:** 1989. **Freq:** Weekly. **Print Method:** Offset. **Trim Size:** 27.7 x 36 cm. **Cols./Page:** 4. **Key Personnel:** Sandro Meda, Director. **Remarks:** Accepts advertising. **URL:** http://www.autohoje.com/. **Circ:** Paid 19,923

49792 ■ Automagazine
Motor Press Lisbon
Rua Policarpo Anjos, No. 4
P-1495-742 Cruz Quebrada-Dafundo, Portugal
Ph: 351 214 154500
Fax: 351 214 154501
Consumer magazine covering automobiles and motor sports. **Founded:** 1992. **Freq:** Monthly. **Print Method:** Offset. **Trim Size:** 22.5 x 29.5 cm. **Cols./Page:** 4. **Key Personnel:** Jose Moreno, Director; Rita Vidreiro, Advertising Mgr.; Luis Pimenta, Editor. **Subscription Rates:** 320 Esc individuals. **Remarks:** Accepts advertising. **URL:** http://automagazine.blogspot.com/. **Circ:** Controlled 19,912

49793 ■ Bike Magazine
Motor Press Lisbon
Rua Policarpo Anjos, No. 4
P-1495-742 Cruz Quebrada-Dafundo, Portugal
Ph: 351 214 154500
Fax: 351 214 154501
Consumer magazine covering mountain biking. **Founded:** 1994. **Freq:** Monthly. **Print Method:** Offset. **Trim Size:** 22.5 x 29.5 cm. **Cols./Page:** 3. **Key Personnel:** Vitor Sousa, Editor; Alexander Silva, Director. **Remarks:** Accepts advertising. **URL:** http://www.bikemagazine.pt/. **Circ:** Paid 5,650

49794 ■ Guia do Automovel
Motor Press Lisbon
Rua Policarpo Anjos, No. 4
P-1495-742 Cruz Quebrada-Dafundo, Portugal
Ph: 351 214 154500
Fax: 351 214 154501
Consumer magazine covering automobiles. **Founded:** 1985. **Freq:** Monthly. **Print Method:** Offset. **Trim Size:** 13.5 x 19.5 cm. **Cols./Page:** 3. **Key Personnel:** Antonio Amorim, Director; Rita Vidreiro, Advertising Dir. **Remarks:** Accepts advertising. **URL:** http://www.guiadoautomovel.pt/. **Circ:** Paid 42,496

49795 ■ Motociclismo
Motor Press Lisbon
Rua Policarpo Anjos, No. 4
P-1495-742 Cruz Quebrada-Dafundo, Portugal
Ph: 351 214 154500
Fax: 351 214 154501
Consumer magazine covering the motorcycle market in Portugal. **Founded:** 1991. **Freq:** Monthly. **Print Method:** Offset. **Trim Size:** 22.5 x 29.5 cm. **Cols./Page:** 3. **Key Personnel:** Luis Carlos Sousa, Director. **Remarks:** Ac-

---

Circulation: ★ = ABC; △ = BPA; ♦ = CAC; • = CCAB; ❑ = VAC; ⊕ = PO Statement; ‡ = Publisher's Report; Boldface figures = sworn; Light figures = estimated.

cepts advertising. **URL:** http://www.motociclismo.it/. **Circ:** Controlled 15,889

49796 ■ Pais & Filhos
Motor Press Lisbon
Rua Policarpo Anjos, No. 4
P-1495-742 Cruz Quebrada-Dafundo, Portugal
Ph: 351 214 154500
Fax: 351 214 154501
Consumer magazine covering parenting, beauty, and fashion. **Founded:** 1991. **Freq:** Monthly. **Print Method:** Offset. **Trim Size:** 22.5 x 29.5 cm. **Cols./Page:** 2. **Key Personnel:** Maria Jorge Costa, Director. **Remarks:** Accepts advertising. **URL:** http://www.paisefilhos.pt/. **Circ:** Paid 30,712

Fatima

49797 ■ Soul
World Apostolate of Fatima
International Secretariat
Rua S Vicente Paulo, 32
Apartado 1
P-2495-438 Fatima, Portugal
Ph: 351 249532865
Fax: 351 249539864
Publication E-mail: service@bluearmy.com
Publisher E-mail: info@worldfatima.com
Catholic publication. **Freq:** Bimonthly. **Subscription Rates:** 9.95 Esc U.S.; 12.95 Esc Canada; US$13.95 elsewhere. **URL:** http://www.wafusa.org/pulications/soul/soul.html.

Funchal

49798 ■ International Journal of Agile and Extreme Software Development
Inderscience Publishers
c/o Pedro Campos, Assoc. Ed.
University of Madeira
Department of Mathematics & Engineering
Funchal, Portugal
Publisher E-mail: editor@inderscience.com
Peer-reviewed journal providing a platform for enhancing and sharing knowledge about research topics, new methods and practices and the real life application of agile approaches and to facilitate the rapid and wide diffusion of results and experiences that promote such efforts. **Freq:** Quarterly. **Key Personnel:** E. Michael Maximilien, Editor-in-Chief, maxim@us.ibm.com; Dr. Pedro Campos, Assoc. Ed.; Robert Biddle, Editorial Board Member. **ISSN:** 1743-5137. **Subscription Rates:** EUR494 individuals print only (surface mail); EUR840 individuals online only (2-3 users); EUR672 individuals print and online. **URL:** http://www.inderscience.com/browse/index.php?journalCODE=ijaesd.

Leira

49799 ■ Diario de Leiria
Group Diario de Coimbra
Edificio Mariuga
Rua Sao Franciso 7-4-Esq.
P-2400 Leira 351 244814, Portugal
Ph: 351 244000031
Fax: 351 244000032
Publication E-mail: jornald@esoterica.pt
Publisher E-mail: alucas@esoterica.pt
General newspaper. **Freq:** Daily. **Print Method:** Web offset. **Cols./Page:** 6. **Key Personnel:** Adriano Lucas, Director, alucas@cpu.pt; Jose Carlos Galiano Pinheiro, Director, jornaldc@esoterica.pt. **Remarks:** Accepts advertising. **URL:** http://www.diarioleiria.pt/. **Circ:** Controlled 2,010

Lisboa

49800 ■ International Journal of Organisational Design and Engineering
Inderscience Enterprises Limited
c/o Rodrigo Magalhaes, Ed.-in-Ch.
INOV Centre for Organizational Design & Engineering
Rua Alves Redol, 9
1000-029 Lisboa, Portugal
Journal covering the development of organizational design and engineering. **Freq:** 4/yr. **Key Personnel:** Rodrigo Magalhaes, Editor-in-Chief, rodrigo.magalhaes@inov.pt. **ISSN:** 1758-9797. **Subscription Rates:** EUR494 individuals print or online; EUR672 individuals print and online. **URL:** http://www.

inderscience.com/browse/index.php?journalID=344.

Lisbon

49801 ■ Acta Ethologica
Springer-Verlag
c/o Rui F. Oliveira, Ed.-in-Ch.
Unidade de Investigacao em Eco-Etologia
Instituto Superior de Psicologia Aplicada-ISPA
Rua Jardim do Tabaco 44
P-1100 Lisbon, Portugal
Fax: 351 21 8860954
Journal devoted to the field of ethology primarily on the behavior biology of humans and other animals. Published in connection with Instituto Superior de Psicologia Aplicada (ISPA), with the co-operation of Portuguese Society of Ethology. **Freq:** Semiannual. **Key Personnel:** Rui F. Oliveira, Editor-in-Chief, ruiol@ispa.pt; Peter McGregor, Assoc. Ed.; Ingo Schlupp, Assoc. Ed.; Joana Jordao, Editorial Asst.; Eduardo Barata, Assoc. Ed.; Emanuel Goncalves, Assoc. Ed.; Kurt Kotrschal, Assoc. Ed.; Juan Carlos Senar, Ch. Ed., jcsenar@mail.bcn.es. **ISSN:** 0873-9749. **Subscription Rates:** EUR154 institutions print incl. free access; EUR184.80 institutions print incl. enhanced access. **Remarks:** Advertising accepted; rates available upon request. **URL:** http://www.springer.com/lifesciences/behavioural/journal/10211. **Circ:** (Not Reported)

49802 ■ Disputatio
Centro de Filosofia
Faculdade de Letras da Universidade de Lisboa
Alameda da Universidade
1600-214 Lisbon, Portugal
Ph: 35 121 7920091
Fax: 35 121 7920091
Publisher E-mail: c.filosofia@fl.ul.pt
Peer-reviewed journal covering all aspects of analytical philosophy. Focuses on current issues in the philosophies of language, logic and mind. **Subtitle:** International Journal of Philosophy. **Freq:** Semiannual May, and Nov. **Key Personnel:** Joao Branquinho, Editor; Celia Teixeira, Managing Editor, celia.teixeira@gmail.com. **ISSN:** 0873-626X. **URL:** http://disputatio.com.

49803 ■ ISRM News Journal
International Society for Rock Mechanics
Av. Brasil, 101
P-1700 Lisbon, Portugal
Ph: 351 218 443419
Fax: 351 218 443021
Publisher E-mail: secretariat.isrm@lnec.pt
Professional journal covering the field of rock mechanics worldwide. **Founded:** 1992. **Freq:** Annual. **Trim Size:** A4. **Remarks:** Accepts advertising. **URL:** http://www.isrm.net/gca/?id=206. **Ad Rates:** BW: US$1,000, 4C: US$1,300. **Circ:** 6,000

49804 ■ Natural Products
Trade Science Inc.
c/o A.P. Rauter, Editorial Board
Departamento de Quimica e Bioquimica
Faculdade de Ciencias da Universidade de Lisboa
Ed. C8, 5 piso, Campo Grande
1749-016 Lisbon, Portugal
Publisher E-mail: help@tsijournals.com
Journal covering literature reviews on the chemistry and biochemistry of alkaloids, terpinoids, steroids, fatty acids, and heterocyclic, aliphatic, aromatic, and alicyclic natural products. **Subtitle:** An Indian Journal. **Founded:** 1943. **Freq:** 4/yr. **Print Method:** Offset. **Trim Size:** 8 1/4 x 11 1/8. **Cols./Page:** 3. **Col. Width:** 27 nonpareils. **Col. Depth:** 140 agate lines. **Key Personnel:** A.P. Rauter, Editorial Board; Alicia B. Pomilio, Editorial Board; Bahar Ahmed, Editorial Board. **ISSN:** 0974-7508. **Subscription Rates:** Rs 2,400 individuals; Rs 240 other countries. **URL:** http://www.tsijournals.com/npaij/.

49805 ■ Revista de Ciencias Agrarias
Agronomic Scientific Society of Portugal
Sociedade de Ciencias Agrarias de Portugal
Rua de Junqueira 299
P-1300 Lisbon, Portugal
Ph: 351 213633719
Publisher E-mail: info.scap@sapo.pt
Portuguese publication covering agricultural science. **Founded:** 1971. **Freq:** Periodic. **Key Personnel:** Marco Aurelio Leite Nunes, Editor. **ISSN:** 0871-018X. **Remarks:** Advertising accepted; rates available upon request. **URL:** http://www.ufra.edu.br/. **Circ:** (Not Reported)

49806 ■ Revistacap
Associacao do Comercio Automovel de Portugal
Av. Torre de Belem, 29
P-1400-342 Lisbon, Portugal
Ph: 351 21 3035300
Fax: 351 21 3021474
Publisher E-mail: mail@acap.pt
Portuguese language publication covering automotive industries. **Freq:** Bimonthly Periodic trimester. **Remarks:** Advertising accepted; rates available upon request. **URL:** http://www.acap.pt. **Circ:** (Not Reported)

Madalena do Pico

49807 ■ Radio Pico-FM - 100.2
Avenida Machado Serpa n 54
9950 Madalena do Pico, Portugal
Ph: 351 292 622727
Fax: 351 292 622874
E-mail: radiopico@sapo.pt
Format: Information; Ethnic; Contemporary Hit Radio (CHR). **Operating Hours:** 13 hours Daily. **Key Personnel:** Jose Antonio Soares, President, phone 351 912 208057; Fernando Silva Teixeira, Vice President, phone 351 917 840823. **URL:** http://www.radiopico.com.

Ponta Delgada

49808 ■ Radio Horizonte-FM - 104.4
Rua Nova da Misericordia, 271
P-9500 Ponta Delgada, Portugal
Ph: 351 296 653911
Fax: 351 296 653910
E-mail: horizonte2@horizonteacores.com
Format: Jazz; Ethnic. **Operating Hours:** Continuous. **URL:** http://www.horizonteacores.com.

Porto

49809 ■ O Informador Fiscal
c/o Mr. Rua Dias Ferreira, No. 370, 1 pt.
Apartado 8012
P-4100-246 Porto, Portugal
Ph: 351 22 3394030
Fax: 351 22 3394029
Publication E-mail: info@o-informador-fiscal.pt
Publisher E-mail: info@o-informador-fiscal.pt
Professional magazine covering finance. **Founded:** 1935. **Freq:** Semimonthly. **Print Method:** Offset. **Key Personnel:** Nuno Ferreira, Editor, nferreira@o-informador-fiscal.pt. **Subscription Rates:** EUR99.50. **Remarks:** Advertising not accepted. **URL:** http://www.o-informador-fiscal.pt/. **Alt. Formats:** CD-ROM. **Circ:** (Not Reported)

Ribeira Grande

49810 ■ Radio Nova Cidade-FM - 105.5
Apartado 70
P-9600 Ribeira Grande, Portugal
Ph: 351 296 472738
Fax: 351 296 472812
E-mail: radionovacidade@gmail.com
Format: Ethnic; Information; World Beat. **URL:** http://www.radionovacidade.pt.

Velas

49811 ■ Radio Lumena-FM - 92.2
Rua Cunha da Silveira 25
Apartado 8
9800 Velas, Portugal
Ph: 351 295 412575
Fax: 351 295 412810
E-mail: radiolumena@radiolumena.com
Format: Ethnic; Contemporary Hit Radio (CHR). **Key Personnel:** Jose Machado, Contact, josemachado@radiolumena.com; Norberto Silveira, Contact; Cecilia Maciel, Contact, ceciliamaciel@radiolumena.com; Nazaria Viegas, Contact. **Ad Rates:** Advertising accepted; rates available upon request. **URL:** http://www.radiolumena.com.

49812 ■ Radio Lumena-FM - 107.01
Rua Cunha da Silveira 25
Apartado 8
9800 Velas, Portugal
Ph: 351 295 412575
Fax: 351 295 412810

E-mail: infor@radiolumena.com
Format: Contemporary Hit Radio (CHR); Ethnic. **Key Personnel:** Jose Machado, Contact, josemachado@radiolumena.com; Norberto Silveira, Contact; Cecilia Maciel, Contact, ceciliamaciel@radiolumena.com; Nazaria Viegas, Contact. **Ad Rates:** Advertising accepted; rates available upon request. **URL:** http://www.radiolumena.com.

Viseu

49813 ■ Diario Regional Viseu
Group Diario de Coimbra
Rua Alexandre Herculaus 198-1-Esq.
P-3510 Viseu 351 232425, Portugal
Ph: 351 232000030
Fax: 351 232000032

Publication E-mail: diario-viseu@clix.pt
Publisher E-mail: alucas@esoterica.pt
General newspaper. **Freq:** Mon.-Sat. **Print Method:** Web offset. **Cols./Page:** 6. **Key Personnel:** Adriano Lucas, Director & Pres., alucas@cpu.pt; Jose Carlos Galiano Pinheiro, Director. **Remarks:** Accepts advertising. **URL:** http://www.diarioviseu.pt. **Former name:** Diario Regional. **Circ:** Controlled 1,025

49814 ■ International Journal of Simulation and Process Modelling
Inderscience Publishers
c/o Dr. Nuno Melao, Ed.
Universidade Catolica Portuguesa
Departamento de Economia, Gestao e Ciencias Sociais
Estrada da Circunvalacao
P-3504-505 Viseu, Portugal

Publisher E-mail: editor@inderscience.com
Peer-reviewed journal aiming to provide a unified discussion forum for academics, researchers and practitioners interested in the modelling and simulation of business processes, production processes, service and administrative processes and public sector processes. **Freq:** Quarterly. **Key Personnel:** Dr. Nuno Melao, Editor, nmelao@crb.ucp.pt; Prof. Andrew Seila, Editor, seila@arches.uga.edu; Prof. Libero Nigro, Assoc. Ed.; Dr. Sanjay Jain, Assoc. Ed.; Dr. Peter Ball, Assoc. Ed.; Dr. Yinong Chen, American Ed.; Dr. Young-Jun Son, Assoc. Ed.; Prof. Alexander Verbraeck, European Ed. **ISSN:** 1740-2123. **Subscription Rates:** EUR494 individuals print only (surface mail); EUR840 individuals online only (2-3 users); EUR534 individuals print only (airmail); EUR672 individuals print and online. **URL:** http://www.inderscience.com/browse/index.php?journalCODE=ijspm.

Circulation: ★ = ABC; △ = BPA; ◆ = CAC; ● = CCAB; ❑ = VAC; ⊕ = PO Statement; ‡ = Publisher's Report; Boldface figures = sworn; Light figures = estimated.

Gale Directory of Publications & Broadcast Media/147th Ed.

5361

Al Arish

49815 ■ Qatar Broadcasting Service - Al Arish - 954 KHz
PO Box 1414
Doha, Qatar
Ph: 974 4894444
Fax: 974 4882888
E-mail: info@qatarradio.net
Format: Eclectic. **Owner:** Qatar Broadcasting Service, at above address. **Operating Hours:** 2:45 a.m.-9:30 p.m. **Wattage:** 1,500,000. **Ad Rates:** Advertising accepted; rates available upon request. **URL:** http://www.qatarradio.net.

Al-Jumaliyah

49816 ■ Qatar Broadcasting Service - Al-Jumaliyah - 102.6 MHz
PO Box 1414
Doha, Qatar
Ph: 974 4894444
Fax: 974 4870712
E-mail: info@qatarradio.net
Format: News. **Owner:** Qatar Broadcasting Service, at above address. **Operating Hours:** 3 a.m.-9:30 p.m. **Wattage:** 20,000. **Ad Rates:** Advertising accepted; rates available upon request. **URL:** http://www.qatarradio.net.

49817 ■ Qatar Broadcasting Service - Al-Jumaliyah - 90.8 MHz
PO Box 1414
Doha, Qatar
Ph: 974 4894444
Fax: 974 4870712
E-mail: info@qatarradio.net
Format: Eclectic. **Owner:** Qatar Broadcasting Service, at above address. **Operating Hours:** 2:45 a.m.-9:30 p.m. **Wattage:** 40,000. **Ad Rates:** Advertising accoptod; rates available upon request. **URL:** http://www.qatarradio.net.

Al Khaisah

49818 ■ Qatar Broadcasting Service - Al Khaisah - 675 KHz
PO Box 1414
Doha, Qatar
Ph: 974 4894444
Fax: 974 4882888
E-mail: info@qatarradio.net
Format: Eclectic. **Owner:** Qatar Broadcasting Service, at above address. **Operating Hours:** 2:45 a.m.-9:30 p.m. **Wattage:** 50,000. **Ad Rates:** Advertising accepted; rates available upon request. **URL:** http://www.qatarradio.net.

Al Khisah

49819 ■ Qatar Broadcasting Service - Al Khisah - 1233 KHz
PO Box 1414
Doha, Qatar
Ph: 974 4894444
Fax: 974 4870712
E-mail: info@qatarradio.net
Format: Eclectic. **Owner:** Qatar Broadcasting Service, at above address. **Operating Hours:** 3 a.m.-10 a.m., 1 p.m.-7 p.m. **Wattage:** 100,000. **Ad Rates:** Advertising accepted; rates available upon request. **URL:** http://www.qatarradio.net.

49820 ■ Qatar Broadcasting Service - Al Khisah - 999 KHz
PO Box 1414
Doha, Qatar
Ph: 974 4894444
Fax: 974 4870712
E-mail: info@qatarradio.net
Format: Eclectic. **Owner:** Qatar Broadcasting Service, at above address. **Operating Hours:** 2:45 a.m.-7 a.m., 1 p.m.-7 p.m. **Wattage:** 50,000. **Ad Rates:** Advertising accepted; rates available upon request. **URL:** http://www.qatarradio.net.

Doha

49821 ■ The Gulf Times
Gulf Publishing & Printing Company
PO Box 533
Doha, Qatar
Ph: 974 43 50478
Fax: 974 43 50474
Publication E-mail: edit@gulf-times.com
Publisher E-mail: editor@gulf-times.com
Newspaper covering a wide range of international and local news in English for the country of Qatar. **Founded:** 1978. **Freq:** Daily. **Key Personnel:** Dr. Marzook Basher Binmarzook, Editor-in-Chief, phone 974 4350475; C.P. Ravindran, Production Ed.; Neil Cook, Managing Editor, phone 974 4350473. **Remarks:** Accepts advertising. **URL:** http://www.gulf-times.com/site/topics/index.asp?cu_no=2&temp_type=44. **Circ:** 15,000

49822 ■ Qatar Info Magazine
Qatar Info
PO Box 6124
Doha, Qatar
Ph: 974 4371773
Fax: 974 4371776
General interest periodical. **Freq:** Quarterly. **Key Personnel:** Bernadette M. Igbenabor, Editor. **URL:** http://www.qatar-info.com/monthly/front.html.

49823 ■ Qatar Medical Journal
Ministry of Public Health
PO Box 3050
Doha, Qatar
Ph: 97 443 92132
Fax: 97 443 14564
Journal covering medical sciences. **Founded:** 1980. **Freq:** Monthly. **Key Personnel:** Dr. Abdurrazak Gehani, Editor-in-Chief; Dr. Mohammed Hammoudeh, Editor-in-Chief. **ISSN:** 0253-8253. **URL:** http://www.hmc.org.qa/hmc/qmj/index.htm.

Qatar Broadcasting Service - Al Arish - See Al Arish

Qatar Broadcasting Service - Al-Jumaliyah - See Al-Jumaliyah

Qatar Broadcasting Service - Al-Jumaliyah - See Al-Jumaliyah

Qatar Broadcasting Service - Al Khaisah - See Al Khaisah

Qatar Broadcasting Service - Al Khisah - See Al Khisah

Qatar Broadcasting Service - Al Khisah - See Al Khisah

49824 ■ Qatar Broadcasting Service - Doha - 1602 KHz
PO Box 1414
Doha, Qatar
Ph: 974 4894444
Fax: 974 4870712
E-mail: info@qatarradio.net
Format: Eclectic. **Owner:** Qatar Broadcasting Service, at above address. **Operating Hours:** 2:45 a.m.-7 a.m., 1 p.m.-7 p.m. **Wattage:** 1000. **Ad Rates:** Advertising accepted; rates available upon request. **URL:** http://www.qatarradio.net.

49825 ■ Qatar Broadcasting Service - Doha - 97.5 MHz
PO Box 1414
Doha, Qatar
Ph: 974 4894444
Fax: 974 4870712
E-mail: info@qatarradio.net
Owner: Qatar Broadcasting Service, at above address. **Operating Hours:** 3 a.m.- 9:30 p.m. **Wattage:** 10,000. **Ad Rates:** Advertising accepted; rates available upon request. **URL:** http://www.qatarradio.net.

49826 ■ TVMAX - 93
PO Box 22810
Doha, Qatar
Ph: 974 4477177
Fax: 974 4315988
E-mail: tvmax@orbit.net
URL: http://www.orbit.net.

49827 ■ TVMAX - 92
PO Box 22810
Doha, Qatar
Ph: 974 4477177
Fax: 974 4315988
E-mail: tvmax@orbit.net
Owner: Orbit Satellite Television and Radio Network, c/o Panther Media Group, PO Box 502211, Dubai Media City, Dubai, United Arab Emirates. **URL:** http://www.orbit.net.

49828 ■ TVMAX - 91
PO Box 22810
Doha, Qatar
Ph: 974 4477177
Fax: 974 4315988
E-mail: tvmax@orbit.net
Owner: Orbit Satellite Television and Radio Network, c/o Panther Media Group, PO Box 502211, Dubai Media City, Dubai, United Arab Emirates. **URL:** http://www.orbit.net.

49829 ■ TVMAX - 90
PO Box 22810
Doha, Qatar
Ph: 974 4477177
Fax: 974 4315988

Circulation: ★ = ABC; △ = BPA; ♦ = CAC; • = CCAB; ❑ = VAC; ⊕ = PO Statement; ‡ = Publisher's Report; Boldface figures = sworn; Light figures = estimated.

E-mail: tvmax@orbit.net
Owner: Orbit Satellite Television and Radio Network, c/o Panther Media Group, PO Box 502211, Dubai Media City, Dubai, United Arab Emirates. **URL:** http://www. orbit.net.

Arad

49830 ■ International Journal of Advanced Intelligence Paradigms
Inderscience Enterprises Limited
c/o Prof. Valentina E. Balas, Ed.-in-Ch.
Aurel Vlaicu University of Arad, Faculty of Engineering
Dept. of Automation & Applied Informatics
77 B-dul Revolutiei
310130 Arad, Romania
Journal covering all areas for implementing advanced intelligent systems and their applications. **Freq:** 4/yr. **Key Personnel:** Prof. Valentina E. Balas, Editor-in-Chief, balas@inext.ro. **ISSN:** 1755-0386. **Subscription Rates:** EUR494 individuals print or online; EUR672 individuals print and online. **URL:** http://www.inderscience.com/browse/index.php?journalID=272.

Bucharest

49831 ■ Avantaje
Edipresse Publications S.A.
Strada Buzesti 50-52
R-011015 Bucharest, Romania
Ph: 40 21 3193559
Fax: 40 21 3193568
Publication E-mail: avantaje@edipresse.ro
Publisher E-mail: groupe@edipresse.com
Magazine focusing on the fashion and lifestyle of women. **Freq:** Monthly. **Key Personnel:** Cristina Simion, Director; Daniela Palade Teodorescu, Ch. Ed. **URL:** http://www.edipresse.com/womens/avantaje; http://www.avantaje.ro/. **Circ:** ‡23,612

49832 ■ Balkan Journal of Geometry and its Applications
The Balkan Society of Geometers
Department of Mathematics I
University Politehnica of Bucharest
Splaiul Independentei 313
RO-060042 Bucharest, Romania
Fax: 40 21 4115365
Publisher E-mail: udriste@mathem.pub.ro
Journal covering papers ranging from pure and applied mathematics and mainly presented at Balkan meetings. The areas of interest include synthetic geometry, computational geometry and applications in physics, chemistry, biology, engineering and architecture. **Freq:** Semiannual. **Key Personnel:** I.D. Albu, Members; C. Udriste, Editor-in-Chief; M. Anastasiei, Members; Dr. Constantin Udriste, Contact. **ISSN:** 1224-2780. **Subscription Rates:** EUR60 individuals; EUR100 institutions. **URL:** http://www.mathem.pub.ro/bjga/.

49833 ■ Buletin AGIR
General Association of Engineers in Romania
Calea Victoriei 118, 1st Fl.
R-70179 Bucharest, Romania
Ph: 40 21 3168994
Fax: 40 21 3125531
Publisher E-mail: office@agir.ro
Romanian language publication covering engineering. **Freq:** Quarterly. **Remarks:** Advertising accepted; rates available upon request. **URL:** http://www.agir.ro/en/publicatii.php. **Circ:** (Not Reported)

49834 ■ Economistul - The Economist
General Association of Romanian Economists
Calea Grivitei N 21, Sector 1
R-010702 Bucharest, Romania
Ph: 40 21 3122248
Fax: 40 21 3129717
Publisher E-mail: ager@edeconomica.com
Romanian language publication covering economics. **Founded:** June 29, 1990. **Freq:** Daily. **Key Personnel:** Dr. Ioan Erhan, Dir. Gen. **ISSN:** 1221-8669. **Remarks:** Advertising accepted; rates available upon request. **URL:** http://www.economistul.eu/. **Circ:** 30,000

49835 ■ Elle Decoration
Edipresse Publications S.A.
Strada Buzesti 50-52
R-011015 Bucharest, Romania
Ph: 40 21 3193559
Fax: 40 21 3193568
Publisher E-mail: groupe@edipresse.com
Magazine focusing on designs for homes and interiors. **Freq:** Monthly. **Key Personnel:** Ileana Raducanu, Ch. Ed.; Laura Lipan, Advertising Mgr.; Cristia Simion, Director. **URL:** http://www.edipresse.ro/edipresse_ro/magazine_details.php?id=7. **Circ:** ‡9,469

49836 ■ Elle Mariaj
Edipresse Publications S.A.
Strada Buzesti 50-52
R-011015 Bucharest, Romania
Ph: 40 21 3193559
Fax: 40 21 3193568
Publisher E-mail: groupe@edipresse.com
Magazine covering fashion, weddings, shopping, beauty, deco and travel. **Freq:** Semiannual. **Key Personnel:** Cristina Simion, Director; Roxana Voloseniuc, Ch. Ed. **URL:** http://www.edipresse.com/womens/elle-mariaj. **Circ:** ‡4,387

49837 ■ Higher Education in Europe
European Centro for Higher Education
Centre Europeen pour l'Enseignement Superieur
39, Stirbei Voda St.
R-010102 Bucharest, Romania
Ph: 40 211 3130839
Fax: 40 211 3123567
Publisher E-mail: info@cepes.ro
Publication covering European higher education in English, French and Russian. **Founded:** 1975. **Freq:** Quarterly. **Key Personnel:** Philip Altbach, Editorial Board; Ion Dumitrache, Editorial Board. **ISSN:** 0379-7724. **Remarks:** Accepts advertising. **URL:** http://www.cepes.ro/publications/default.htm. **Circ:** (Not Reported)

49838 ■ Intamplari Adevarate
Edipresse Publications S.A.
Strada Buzesti 50-52
R-11015 Bucharest, Romania
Ph: 40 21 3193559
Fax: 40 21 3193568
Publisher E-mail: groupe@edipresse.com
Magazine featuring real life stories. **Freq:** Biweekly. **Key Personnel:** Vlad Macri, Ch. Ed.; Cristina Simion, Director. **URL:** http://www.edipresse.com/entertainment/intamplari-adevarate. **Circ:** ‡30,880

49839 ■ Lucru de Mana
Edipresse Publications S.A.
Strada Buzesti 50-52
R-011015 Bucharest 1, Romania
Ph: 40 21 2300235
Fax: 40 21 2302877
Publication E-mail: lucrudemana@edipresse.ro
Publisher E-mail: groupe@edipresse.com
Magazine featuring needlework techniques. **Freq:** Quarterly. **Key Personnel:** Christina Simion, Director; Alina Miron, Ch. Ed. **URL:** http://www.edipresse.com/knittingsewing/lucru-de-m%C3%A2n%C3%A3. **Circ:** ‡12,516

49840 ■ Nuclear Energy
Romanian Association for Nuclear Energy
Str. Polona, Nr. 65, Sector 1
Bucharest, Romania
Ph: 40 21 2038200
Fax: 40 21 2119400
Publisher E-mail: irotaru@nuclearelectrica.ro
Romanian and English language publication covering nuclear energy. **Freq:** Annual. **Key Personnel:** Iosif Constantin Bilegan, Editor-in-Chief, ibilegan@nuclearelectrica.ro. **Subscription Rates:** Free members. **Remarks:** Advertising accepted; rates available upon request. **URL:** http://www.aren.ro. **Circ:** (Not Reported)

49841 ■ Povestea Mea
Edipresse Publications S.A.
18 Mircea Eliade Blvd., 10th Fl.
Bucharest, Romania
Ph: 40 21 3193559
Fax: 40 21 3193568
Publisher E-mail: groupe@edipresse.com
Magazine featuring real life romantic stories. **Founded:** 1996. **Freq:** Weekly. **Key Personnel:** Cristina Simion, Director; Vlad Macri, Ch. Ed. **URL:** http://www.edipresse.com/entertainment/povestea-mea. **Circ:** ‡31,077

49842 ■ Psychologies
Edipresse Publications S.A.
Strada Buzesti 50-52
R-011015 Bucharest 1, Romania
Ph: 40 21 3193559
Fax: 40 21 3193568
Publisher E-mail: groupe@edipresse.com
Magazine featuring the lifestyle and personality development of women. **Freq:** Quarterly. **Key Personnel:** Luliana Alexa, Ch. Ed.; Cristina Simion, Director. **URL:** http://www.edipresse.com/womens/psychologies; http://www.psychologies.ro/. **Circ:** ‡10,845

49843 ■ Romanian Journal of Society and Politics
Civic Education Project
Bd. Unirii, nr. 76
Bl. J3A, sc. A, ap 2
Sector 3
Bucharest, Romania
Ph: 40 1 3206532
Publisher E-mail: freyberg_inan@yahoo.com
Journal providing a forum for the publication of peer-reviewed and original social science research on

---

Circulation: ★ = ABC; △ = BPA; ♦ = CAC; • = CCAB; ❑ = VAC; ⊕ = PO Statement; ‡ = Publisher's Report; Boldface figures = sworn; Light figures = estimated.

Romania and the Romanians - in Romania, the Republic of Moldova, and the Diaspora. **Founded:** 2000. **Freq:** Semiannual. **Key Personnel:** Liliana Popescu, Exec. Ed. **URL:** http://www.h-net.org/announce/show.cgi?ID=127057.

49844 ■ TRANSURB
Romanian Union of Public Transport
Uniunea Romana De Transport Public - URTP
6-8 Gh. Magheru Blvd., 6th Fl., Rm. 15-16, District 1
010332 Bucharest, Romania
Ph: 40 314 025702
Fax: 40 314 025701
Publisher E-mail: office@urtp.ro
Romanian language publication covering transportation. **Freq:** Quarterly. **Key Personnel:** Viorica Sarman, Editor, viorica.sarman@urtp.ro; Constantin Donea, President, c_donea@urtp.ro. **Subscription Rates:** Free. **Remarks:** Advertising accepted; rates available upon request. **URL:** http://www.urtp.ro/old/engl/publicatii.htmlrev. **Circ:** (Not Reported)

49845 ■ Univers Ingineresc
General Association of Engineers in Romania
Calea Victoriei 118, 1st Fl.
R-70179 Bucharest, Romania
Ph: 40 21 3168994
Fax: 40 21 3125531
Publisher E-mail: office@agir.ro
Romanian and English language publication covering engineering. **Founded:** Feb. 1990. **Freq:** Bimonthly. **ISSN:** 1223-0294. **Remarks:** Advertising accepted; rates available upon request. **URL:** http://www.agir.ro/en/publicatii.php. **Circ:** (Not Reported)

49846 ■ Ziua
Strada Ion Campineanu Numarul 4
Sect. 1
Bucharest, Romania
Ph: 40 315 9111
Fax: 40 310 3119
Publisher E-mail: ziua@ziua.ro
General newspaper. **Founded:** June 15, 1994. **Cols./Page:** 8. **Col. Width:** 40 millimeters. **Key Personnel:** Sorin Rosca Stanescu, Director; Roland Catalin Pena, Editor-in-Chief, fefe@ziua.ro. **Remarks:** Accepts advertising. **URL:** http://www.ziua.ro. **Circ:** Paid 80,000

Cluj-Napoca

49847 ■ Journal for the Study of Religions and Ideologies
Seminarul de Cercetare a Religiilor si Ideologiilor
Catedra de Filosofie Sistematica
Universitatea "Babes-Bolyai"
Et. 1, sala 130
St. M. Kogalniceanu nr. 1
3400 Cluj-Napoca, Romania
Ph: 40 744 698826
Publisher E-mail: s_c_i_r_i@yahoo.com
Peer-reviewed journal for the professors and young researchers interested in the study of religions and ideologies. **Freq:** 3/yr. **Key Personnel:** Michael Jones, Exec. Ed.; Sandu Frunza, Editor; Codruta Cuceu, Editorial Board; Diana Cotrau, Editorial Board; Iulia Grad, Editorial Board; Horatiu Crisan, Editorial Board; Mihaela Paraschivescu, Editorial Board; Adrian Costache, Editorial Board; Andreia Schindler, Editorial Board; Theodora-Eliza Vacarescu, Editorial Board. **ISSN:** 1583-0039. **URL:** http://www.jsri.ro/.

Tg-Mures

49848 ■ BYTE Romania
Computer Press Agora S.R.L.
Str. T. Vladimirescu 63/1
PO Box 230
R-4300 Tg-Mures, Romania
Publisher E-mail: byte@gora.ro
Magazine covering computers. **Founded:** 1995. **Key Personnel:** Mircea Sarbu, Editorial Dir., msarbu@agora.ro; Darvas Attila, Editor-in-Chief, adarvas@agora.ro; Daniel Moldovan, Sen. Ed., dmoldovan@agora.ro; Mircea Sabau, Editor, msabau@agora.ro; Budai Laszlo, Editor; Iosif Fettich, Assoc. Ed., ifettich@agora.ro; Romulus Maier, Gen. Dir., rmaier@agora.ro; Adrian Pop, Exec. Dir., adipop@agora.ro; Gabriela Bucsa, Mktg. Mgr., gbucsa@agora.ro. **ISSN:** 1223-9801. **Remarks:** Accepts advertising. **URL:** http://www.byte.ro/redactia/contacts.html. **Circ:** (Not Reported)

Timisoara

49849 ■ Timisoara Medical Journal (TMJ)
Pius Branzeu Center
Victor Babes University of Medicine and Pharmacy
2 Eftimie Murgu St.
RO-300041 Timisoara, Romania
Ph: 40 256 216510
Fax: 40 256 216510
Publisher E-mail: office@tmj.ro
Journal publishing original papers of general interest in clinical and laboratory medicine, clinical and experimental research, clinical epidemiology and basic science research. **Freq:** Quarterly. **Key Personnel:** Stefan I. Dragulescu, Editor-in-Chief; Gheorghe I. Mihalas, Assoc. Ed.; Carmen Todea, Assoc. Ed.; Stefan Ioan Stratul, Assoc. Ed.; Mihai Ionac, Exec. Ed.; Dan Bogdan Navolan, Assoc. Ed. **ISSN:** 1583-5251. **Subscription Rates:** EUR24 individuals local; EUR27 individuals; EUR50 institutions local or national; EUR50 other countries individuals; EUR70 institutions, other countries. **URL:** http://www.tmj.ro/.

Birobidzhan

49850 ■ GTRK Bira - Birobidzhan - 216 KHz
Ulitsa Sovetskaya 13
682290 Birobidzhan, Russia
E-mail: gtrkbira@on-line.jar.ru
Format: News. **Owner:** Vserossiyskaya Gosudarstven-naya Teleradiokompaniya (VGTRK), Leningradskiy Pr. 22/2, 125124 Moscow, Russia, Fax: 7 95 2142347. **Operating Hours:** 8 p.m.-4 p.m. **Key Personnel:** Oleg Dobrodeyev, Chm. **Wattage:** 30,000. **URL:** http://www.vgtrk.com.

Bratsk

49851 ■ Golos Angary - 68.63 MHz
Pigorov St. 1/2
PO Box 2219
665730 Bratsk, Russia
Ph: 7 3953 441313
Fax: 7 3953 441313
E-mail: office@rga.ru
Format: Full Service. **Owner:** Radiocompany Golos Angary, Ltd., at above address. **Founded:** May 6, 1996. **Operating Hours:** Continuous. **Key Personnel:** Yury Osintsev, CEO; Artem Smirnov, Music Ed.; Tanya Efanova, Manager; Julia Belorybtseva, Manager; Nastia Mukatova, Program Dir.; Natasha Alyukina, Manager; Natasha Smirnova, Hd. of Advertising. **Wattage:** 100. **Ad Rates:** $108-276 for 15 seconds; $156-391 for 30 seconds; $185-472 for 45 seconds. **URL:** http://www.rga.ru.

Cherepovets

49852 ■ Ekho Moskvy - Cherepovets - 105.2 MHz
Ulitsa Novyy Arbat 11
119992 Moscow, Russia
Ph: 7 495 6959229
E-mail: info@echo.msk.ru
Format: News; Information. **Owner:** Ekho Moskvy, at above address. **Operating Hours:** Continuous. **Key Personnel:** Yuri Fedutinov, Dir. Gen. **Ad Rates:** Advertising accepted; rates available upon request. **URL:** http://www.echo.msk.ru.

Chita

49853 ■ GTRK Chitinskaya - Chita - 66.32 MHz
Ulitsa Kostyushko-Grigorovicha 27
672090 Chita, Russia
Ph: 7 3022 354370
Fax: 7 3022 267523
E-mail: chrtv@chita.rfn.ru
Format: News. **Owner:** Vserossiyskaya Gosudarstven-naya Teleradiokompaniya (VGTRK), Leningradskiy Pr. 22/2, 125124 Moscow, Russia, Fax: 7 95 2142347. **Operating Hours:** 10:10 p.m.-11 p.m.; 9:10 p.m.-10 p.m., 10 a.m.-11 a.m. **Key Personnel:** Elena Knyazev, Hd. **URL:** http://chita.rfn.ru.

GTRK Chitinskaya - Kholbon - See Kholbon

Dalnegorsk

49854 ■ Radio VBC - 936 KHz
Uborevicha St.
20 Radio House
690091 Vladivostok, Russia
Ph: 7 4232 510586
Fax: 7 4232 261726
E-mail: info@radiovbc.ru
Format: News; Information. **Founded:** Sept. 1999. **Key Personnel:** Alexander Kolchurin, CEO. **Wattage:** 5000. **Ad Rates:** Advertising accepted; rates available upon request. **URL:** http://www.radiovbc.ru.

Ekaterinburg

49855 ■ Physics of Metals and Metallography
Maik Nauka/Interperiodica Publishing
ul. S. Kovalevskoi, 18
620990 Ekaterinburg, Russia
Ph: 7 343 3740230
Fax: 7 343 3745244
Publication E-mail: fmm@imp.uran.ru
Publisher E-mail: compmg@maik.ru
Journal publishing articles involving the theory of metals and metal alloys, their electrical and magnetic properties, as well as their structure, phase transformations and principal mechanical properties. **Founded:** 1955. **Freq:** Monthly. **Key Personnel:** Vladimir V. Ustinov, Editor-in-Chief; Yurii A. Izyumov, Dep. Ed.-in-Ch.; Nikolai V. Mushnikov, Exec. Ed.-in-Ch. **ISSN:** 0031-918X. **Subscription Rates:** EUR4,936 institutions print incl. free access or e-only; EUR5,923.20 institutions print incl. enhanced access. **Remarks:** Advertising not accepted. **URL:** http://www.maik.ru/cgi-bin/journal.pl?name=physmet&page=main. **Circ:** (Not Reported)

Gorno-Altaysk

GTRK Gornyy Altay - Shebalino - See Shebalino

GTRK Gornyy Altay - Ust-Kan - See Ust-Kan

GTRK Gornyy Altay - Ust-Ulagan - See Ust-Ulagan

Irkutsk

49856 ■ Geography and Natural Resources
Publishing House of the Siberian Branch of the Russian Academy of Sciences
Institute of Geography
Box 4027
664033 Irkutsk, Russia
Ph: 7 3952 426422
Publication E-mail: gipr@izdatgeo.ru
Journal covering theoretical problems of geography and nature management. **Freq:** 4/yr. **Key Personnel:** A.N. Antipov, Editor-in-Chief. **ISSN:** 0206-1619. **URL:** http://www.sibran.ru/English/geogre.htm.

Ishim

49857 ■ Nashe Radio - Ishim - 107.8 MHz
923-1701 St. Baumanskaya

105082 Moscow, Russia
Ph: 7 495 9250449
E-mail: nashe@nashe.ru
Format: Classic Rock; News. **Owner:** Nashe Radio, at above address. **Key Personnel:** Mikhail Zotov, Dir. Gen.; Oleg Khlebnikov, Program Dir.; Maria Rumyantsev, Business Mgr. **Ad Rates:** Advertising accepted; rates available upon request. **URL:** http://www.nashe.ru.

Kaliningrad

49858 ■ Radio Baltik Plyus - 72.11 MHz
ul. Narvskaya, 58
236000 Kaliningrad, Russia
Ph: 7 4012 341888
Fax: 7 4012 341444
E-mail: balticplus@kaliningrad.ru
Format: Eclectic. **Owner:** Radio Baltik Plyus, at above address. **Wattage:** 1000. **URL:** http://www.balticpl.ru.

Kazan

49859 ■ Hit-FM - Kazan - 91.1 MHz
ul. Khoroshevskaya 3 d. 12
123298 Moscow, Russia
Ph: 7 495 9951036
E-mail: hitfm@hitfm.ru
Format: Contemporary Hit Radio (CHR); Top 40. **Owner:** Hit-FM, at above address. **Operating Hours:** Continuous. **Key Personnel:** Vladimir Bazhin, Gen. Producer; Irina Furmanchuk, Editor-in-Chief, hohloma@hitfm.ru. **Ad Rates:** Advertising accepted; rates available upon request. **URL:** http://www.hitfm.ru.

49860 ■ Puls Radio - 103.3 MHz
Ulitsa Decembrists 2
420066 Kazan, Russia
Ph: 7 8432 491033
E-mail: radiopuls@mail.ru
Format: Contemporary Hit Radio (CHR); News. **Owner:** Puls Radio, at above address. **Founded:** Apr. 1995. **Wattage:** 1000. **URL:** http://www.pulsfm.ru.

Khanty-Mansiysk

49861 ■ Nashe Radio - Khanty-Mansiysk - 105.3 MHz
923-1701 St. Baumanskaya
105082 Moscow, Russia
Ph: 7 495 9250449
E-mail: nashe@nashe.ru
Format: Classic Rock; News. **Owner:** Nashe Radio, at above address. **Key Personnel:** Mikhail Zotov, Dir. Gen.; Oleg Khlebnikov, Program Dir.; Maria Rumyantsev, Business Mgr. **Ad Rates:** Advertising accepted; rates available upon request. **URL:** http://www.nashe.ru.

Kholbon

49862 ■ GTRK Chitinskaya - Kholbon - 69.80 MHz
Ulitsa Kostyushko-Grigorovicha 27
672090 Chita, Russia
Ph: 7 3022 354370
Fax: 7 3022 267523

Circulation: ★ = ABC; △ = BPA; ◆ = CAC; • = CCAB; ❑ = VAC; ⊕ = PO Statement; ‡ = Publisher's Report; Boldface figures = sworn; Light figures = estimated.

Gale Directory of Publications & Broadcast Media/147th Ed.   5367

E-mail: gnchrtv@mail.ru
Format: News. **Owner:** Vserossiyskaya Gosudarstven-naya Teleradiokompaniya (VGTRK), Leningradskiy Pr. 22/2, 125124 Moscow, Russia, Fax: 7 95 2142347. **Operating Hours:** 10:10 p.m.-11 p.m.; 9:10 p.m.-10 p.m., 10 a.m.-11 a.m. **Key Personnel:** Oleg Dobrodeyev, Chm. **URL:** http://www.vgtrk.com.

Krasnoyarsk

49863 ■ Avtoradio-AM - 810 KHz
ul. P. zheleznyak 16 B
660022 Krasnoyarsk, Russia
Ph: 7 3912 541741
E-mail: info@avtoradio.net
Format: Information; Adult Contemporary; News. **Owner:** Avtoradio, at above address. **Operating Hours:** 6 a.m. - 1 a.m. **Wattage:** 10,000. **Ad Rates:** Advertising accepted; rates available upon request. **URL:** http://www.avtoradio.net.

49864 ■ GTRK Krasnoyarskaya - Krasnoyarsk - 216 KHz
Sovetskaya 128
660100 Krasnoyarsk, Russia
Ph: 7 391 2438800
Fax: 7 391 2431675
E-mail: newsradio@kgtrk.ru
Format: News. **Owner:** Vserossiyskaya Gosudarstven-naya Teleradiokompaniya (VGTRK), Leningradskiy Pr. 22/2, 125124 Moscow, Russia, Fax: 7 95 2142347. **Operating Hours:** 10 p.m.-6 p.m. **Key Personnel:** Nely-ubin Vasily Vladimirovich, Director. **Wattage:** 150,000. **URL:** http://www.vgtrk.com.

Kurkino

49865 ■ Radio Center - 1503 KHz
Nikolskaya Str. 7
109012 Moscow, Russia
Ph: 7 495 7454076
Fax: 7 495 6480111
E-mail: 1503am@radiocenter.net
Format: Religious; Classical. **Owner:** Radio Station Center, at above address. **Founded:** Mar. 1, 1992. **Operating Hours:** 2p.m. - 9a.m. **Key Personnel:** An-drey V. Nekrasov, General Mgr. **URL:** http://www.radiocenter.net.

Megion

49866 ■ Nashe Radio - Megion - 101.6 MHz
15-16 St. Baumanskaya
105082 Moscow, Russia
Ph: 7 495 9250449
E-mail: nashe@nashe.ru
Format: Classic Rock; News. **Owner:** Nashe Radio, at above address. **Key Personnel:** Mikhail Zotov, Dir. Gen.; Oleg Khlebnikov, Program Dir.; Maria Rumyant-sev, Business Mgr. **Ad Rates:** Advertising accepted; rates available upon request. **URL:** http://www.nashe.ru.

Moscow

49867 ■ Acarina
KMK Scientific Press Ltd.
c/o Dr. K.G. Mikhailov
Zoological Museum MGU
Bolshaya Nikitskaya Str. 6
125009 Moscow, Russia
Publication E-mail: kmk2000@online.ru
Publisher E-mail: kmk2000@online.ru
Peer-reviewed journal covering the morphology, tax-onomy, zoogeography, evolution and development of ticks and mites. **Founded:** 1993. **Freq:** Semiannual. **Key Personnel:** Dr. Olga V. Voltzit, Editor-in-Chief, voltzit@zmmu.msu.ru; Dr. A.V. Tolstikov, Consulting Ed., atolus@yahoo.com; S.V. Mironov, Consulting Ed., astigmata@zin.ru; H.M. Andre, Advisory Board; V.N. Be-lozerov, Advisory Board; Andre V. Bochkov, Assoc. Ed., prostigmata@zin.ru; G. Alberti, Advisory Board; J. Dab-ert, Advisory Board; D. Walter, Advisory Board. **ISSN:** 0132-8077. **Subscription Rates:** US$60 individuals; US$95.27 individuals; US$40 individuals. **Remarks:** Advertising accepted; rates available upon request. **URL:** http://kmk.entomology.ru/acarina.htm; http://insects.ummz.lsa.umich.edu/acarina. **Circ:** (Not Re-ported)

49868 ■ Aeroflot Premium
SPN Publishing Company
4a Novodanilovskaya nab
117105 Moscow, Russia
Magazine for business-class Passengers flying with Aeroflot-Russian Airlines. **Founded:** Sept. 2007. **Freq:** Monthly. **Key Personnel:** Oleg Kuzmenko, Editor-in-Chief; Alexey Ivanov, Advertising Dir.; Stanislav Belya-kov, Mktg. Dir. **Remarks:** Accepts advertising. **URL:** http://eng.spn.ru/publishing/journals/aeroflot_premium. **Circ:** 25,000

49869 ■ Airfleet
Airfleet Review
PO Box 77
125057 Moscow, Russia
Ph: 7 95 4575244
Publication E-mail: af@airfleet.ru
Periodical covering the armed forces. **Freq:** Bimonthly. **ISSN:** 1561-8250. **Remarks:** Accepts advertising. **URL:** http://www.airfleet.ru/index.php?lang=1. **Circ:** (Not Reported)

49870 ■ Anesthesiology & Intensive Care
Meditsina Publishers
Bolshaya Pirogovskaya, 5, Bldg. 2
119435 Moscow, Russia
Ph: 7 95 2453355
Fax: 7 95 2453355
Publisher E-mail: meditsina@mtu-net.ru
Journal covering problems of anesthesiology and resuscitation in Russia public health. **Founded:** 1992. **Freq:** Bimonthly. **Key Personnel:** Prof. Armen A. Bun-yatyan, Editor-in-Chief. **ISSN:** 0300-9092. **Remarks:** Accepts advertising. **URL:** http://www.medlit.ru/medeng/anest5.htm. **Circ:** (Not Reported)

49871 ■ Annals of Ophthalmology
Meditsina Publishers
Bolshaya Pirogovskaya, 5, Bldg. 2
119435 Moscow, Russia
Ph: 7 95 2453355
Fax: 7 95 2453355
Publisher E-mail: meditsina@mtu-net.ru
Journals covering problems of theory and practice of Russian and foreign ophthalmology. **Founded:** 1884. **Freq:** Bimonthly. **Key Personnel:** Prof. Mikhail M. Kras-nov, Editor-in-Chief. **ISSN:** 0042-465X. **Remarks:** Ac-cepts advertising. **URL:** http://www.medlit.ru/medeng/vof5.htm. **Circ:** (Not Reported)

49872 ■ Annals of the Russian Academy of Medical Sciences
Meditsina Publishers
Bolshaya Pirogovskaya, 5, Bldg. 2
119435 Moscow, Russia
Ph: 7 95 2453355
Fax: 7 95 2453355
Publisher E-mail: meditsina@mtu-net.ru
Journal covering problems of medical science and public health practice. **Founded:** 1946. **Freq:** Monthly. **Key Personnel:** Prof. Nikolai P. Bochkov, Editor-in-Chief. **ISSN:** 0869-6047. **Remarks:** Accepts advertising. **URL:** http://www.medlit.ru/medeng/vestr5.htm. **Circ:** (Not Reported)

49873 ■ Annals of Surgery
Meditsina Publishers
Bolshaya Pirogovskaya, 5, Bldg. 2
119435 Moscow, Russia
Ph: 7 95 2453355
Fax: 7 95 2453355
Publisher E-mail: meditsina@mtu-net.ru
Journals covering latest advances in all surgical areas. **Founded:** 1996. **Freq:** Bimonthly. **Key Personnel:** Prof. Leo A. Bokeria, Editor-in-Chief. **ISSN:** 1560-9502. **Re-marks:** Accepts advertising. **URL:** http://www.medlit.ru/medeng/annal5.htm. **Circ:** (Not Reported)

49874 ■ Annals of Traumatology & Orthopedics
Meditsina Publishers
Bolshaya Pirogovskaya, 5, Bldg. 2
119435 Moscow, Russia
Ph: 7 95 2453355
Fax: 7 95 2453355
Publisher E-mail: meditsina@mtu-net.ru
Journal covering urgent problems of current traumatol-ogy and orthopedics. **Founded:** 1994. **Freq:** Quarterly. **Key Personnel:** Prof. Sergei P. Mironov, Editor-in-Chief. **ISSN:** 0869-8678. **Remarks:** Accepts advertising. **URL:**

http://www.medlit.ru/medeng/vto5.htm. **Circ:** (Not Reported)

49875 ■ Applied Biochemistry and Microbiology
Maik Nauka/Interperiodica Publishing
c/o Bach Institute of Biochemistry
Leninskii pr. 33
117071 Moscow, Russia
Ph: 7 495 9546530
Fax: 7 495 9542732
Publisher E-mail: compmg@maik.ru
Journal presenting original papers on research in the fields of biochemistry and microbiology that have or may have practical applications. **Founded:** 1965. **Freq:** Bimonthly. **Key Personnel:** Prof. Aleksei M. Bezboro-dov, Dep. Ed.-in-Ch.; Prof. Vladimir O. Popov, Editor-in-Chief; Aleksander M. Boronin, Editorial Board. **ISSN:** 0003-6838. **Subscription Rates:** EUR4,631 institutions print incl. free access or e-only; EUR5,557.20 institutions print incl. enhanced access. **URL:** http://www.maik.rssi.ru/cgi-perl/journal.pl?lang=eng&name=appbio.

49876 ■ Astronomical and Astrophysical Transactions
Taylor & Francis Group Journals
Sternberg Astronomical Institute
Lomonosov Moscow State University 13
Universitetskij pr.
119992 Moscow, Russia
Publisher E-mail: customerservice@taylorandfrancis.com
Journal focusing on all modern and classical fields of astronomy and astrophysics, as well as material con-cerned with astronomical instrumentation and related fundamental sciences. **Freq:** Bimonthly. **Key Person-nel:** Nikolai G. Bochkarev, Editor-in-Chief; B. Carr, Edito-rial Board; G.S. Bisnovatyi-Kogan, Editorial Board; A.G. Doroshkevich, Editorial Board; Vera P. Arkhipova, Assoc. Ed.; V.V. Burdyuzha, Editorial Board; E.V. Kononovich, Editorial Board; Yu. N. Efremov, Editorial Board; Yu. V. Barkin, Editorial Board. **ISSN:** 1055-6796. **Subscription Rates:** US$3,123 institutions print + online; US$3,123 individuals print + online; US$348 individuals personal; US$348 institutions online; US$2,966 institutions online. **URL:** http://www.informaworld.com/smpp/title~content=t713453505.

49877 ■ Astronomy Letters
Maik Nauka/Interperiodica Publishing
Profsoyuznaia St. 90
117997 Moscow, Russia
Ph: 7 953 361600
Fax: 7 953 360666
Publication E-mail: pazh@maik.ru
Publisher E-mail: compmg@maik.ru
Journal publishing the results of original research in all branches of modern astronomy and astrophysics includ-ing high energy astrophysics, cosmology, space as-tronomy, theoretical astrophysics, radioastronomy, extra galactic astronomy, stellar astronomy and investigation of the Solar system. **Founded:** 1975. **Freq:** Monthly. **Key Personnel:** Rashid A. Sunyaev, Editor-in-Chief; Dmitrii A. Varshalovich, Editorial Board; Leonid I. Matveenko, Dep. Ed.-in-Ch.; Sergei A. Grebenev, Exec. Ed.-in-Ch.; Nikolai N. Chugai, Editorial Board; Vladimir Yu Astakhov, Ed. of the English Translation. **ISSN:** 1063-7737. **Subscription Rates:** EUR2,232 institutions print incl. free access or e-only; EUR2,678.40 institutions print incl. enhanced access. **Remarks:** Advertising not accepted. **URL:** http://www.maik.ru/cgi-bin/journal.pl?name=letters&page=main. **Circ:** (Not Reported)

49878 ■ Astronomy Reports
Maik Nauka/Interperiodica Publishing
Profsoyuznaia St. 90
117997 Moscow, Russia
Ph: 7 953 361600
Fax: 7 953 360666
Publication E-mail: astrep@maik.ru
Publisher E-mail: compmg@maik.ru
Journal publishing original papers on astronomy, includ-ing theoretical and observational astrophysics, physics of the Sun, planetary astrophysics, radioastronomy, stel-lar astronomy, celestial mechanics and astronomy methods and instrumentation. **Founded:** 1924. **Freq:** Monthly. **Key Personnel:** Alexander A. Boyarchuk, Editor-in-Chief; Dmitrii V. Bisikalo, Editorial Board; Ana-tolii M. Cherepashchuk, Dep. Ed.-in-Ch.; Viktor K. Abal-akin, Editorial Board; Alexander V. Tutukov, Exec. Ed.-in-Ch.; Venera R. Sokolova, Staff Ed. **ISSN:** 1063-7729. **Subscription Rates:** EUR3,431 institutions print incl.

free access or e-only; EUR4,117.20 institutions print incl. enhanced access. **Remarks:** Advertising not accepted. **URL:** http://www.maik.ru/cgi-bin/journal.pl?name=asteng&page=main. **Circ:** (Not Reported)

49879 ■ Atelier Rundschau
Edipresse Publications S.A.
Ul. Bakuninskaya 71
Bldg. 10, 6th Fl.
107082 Moscow, Russia
Ph: 7 495 7751435
Fax: 7 495 7751434
Publisher E-mail: groupe@edipresse.com
Magazine featuring the fashion industry. **Freq:** Monthly. **Key Personnel:** Irina Surovtseva, Director; Tatiana Kovaleva, Ch. Ed. **URL:** http://www.edipresse.com/b2b/atelier-rundschau. **Circ:** ‡18,320

49880 ■ Automatic Control and Computer Sciences
Maik Nauka/Interperiodica Publishing
Profsoyuznaia St. 90
117997 Moscow, Russia
Ph: 7 953 361600
Fax: 7 953 360666
Publication E-mail: gobzemis@edi.lv
Publisher E-mail: compmg@maik.ru
Journal covering automatic control and distributed processing and signal processing. **Freq:** 3/yr. **Key Personnel:** Andrejs Gobzemis, Editor-in-Chief. **ISSN:** 0146-4116. **Subscription Rates:** EUR2,387 institutions print incl. free access or e-only; EUR2,864 institutions print incl. enhanced access. **URL:** http://www.maik.rssi.ru/cgi-perl/journal.pl?lang=eng&name=autcont.

49881 ■ Automatic Documentation and Mathematical Linguistics
Maik Nauka/Interperiodica Publishing
Prof. Ruggero S. Gilyarevskii, Ed.-in-Ch.
Usievicha st., 20, A-190
125190 Moscow, Russia
Ph: 7 495 1554495
Fax: 7 495 9430060
Publisher E-mail: compmg@maik.ru
Journal covering all aspects of automatization of information processes and systems, as well as algorithms and methods for automatic language analysis. **Key Personnel:** Prof. Ruggero S. Gilyarevskii, Editor-in-Chief, giliarevski@viniti.ru; A.I. Chernyi, Assoc. Ed. **ISSN:** 0005-1055. **Subscription Rates:** EUR2,290 institutions print incl. free access or e-only; EUR2,748 institutions print incl. enhanced access. **URL:** http://www.maik.rssi.ru/cgi-perl/journal.pl?lang=eng&name=autdoc.

49882 ■ Automation and Remote Control
Maik Nauka/Interperiodica Publishing
Profsoyuznaya ul. 65
117997 Moscow, Russia
Ph: 7 95 3348770
Publication E-mail: redacsia@ipu.rssi.ru
Publisher E-mail: compmg@maik.ru
Journal covering entirely control theory problems and applications. **Founded:** 1936. **Freq:** 12/yr. **Key Personnel:** Nikolai A. Kuznetsov, Editor-in-Chief; P.P. Parkhomenko, Dep. Ed.-in-Ch.; D.A. Novikov, Exec. Ed.-in-Ch. **ISSN:** 0005-1179. **Subscription Rates:** EUH5,448 institutions print incl. free access or e-only; EUR6,537.60 institutions print incl. enhanced access. **URL:** http://www.maik.rssi.ru/cgi-perl/journal.pl?lang=eng&name=autorc.

49883 ■ Biochemistry (Moscow)
Maik Nauka/Interperiodica Publishing
GSP-1 Maronovskii per. 26
119049 Moscow, Russia
Ph: 7 495 2382479
Fax: 7 495 2382479
Publication E-mail: biochem@maik.ru
Publisher E-mail: compmg@maik.ru
Scientific journal covering the fields of biochemistry and biochemical aspects of molecular biology, bio-organic chemistry, microbiology, immunology, physiology, and biomedical sciences. **Founded:** 1956. **Freq:** Monthly. **Key Personnel:** A.A. Bogdanov, Dep. Ed.-in-Ch.; V.P. Skulachev, Editor-in-Chief; V.A. Shuvalov, Editorial Board; E.V. Dyatlovitskaya, Editorial Board; A.A. Baykov, Editorial Board; R.D. Ozrina, Exec. Ed.-in-Ch.; D. Baltimore, Editorial Board; G.I. Abelev, Editorial Board; V.A. Gvozdev, Editorial Board. **ISSN:** 0006-2979. **Subscription Rates:** EUR5,813 institutions; EUR6,975.60 institutions enhanced access. **URL:** http://www.maik.

rssi.ru/cgi-bin/journal.pl?name=biochmsc&page=sub.

49884 ■ Boat International Russia
Boat International Group
3/1 Gruzinskiy pereulok, off. 219
123056 Moscow, Russia
Ph: 7 495 6265593
Fax: 7 495 6265593
Publisher E-mail: info@boatinternational.co.uk
Magazine covering luxury yacht in Russia. **Freq:** Bimonthly. **Trim Size:** 235 x 275 mm. **Key Personnel:** Tony Harris, CEO/Publisher; Tony Euden, Publishing Dir., tony.euden@boatinternationalmedia.com. **Remarks:** Accepts advertising. **URL:** http://www.boatinternationalmedia.com/mags/mag03.htm. **Ad Rates:** 4C: 4,300 Rb. **Circ:** 15,000

49885 ■ Bulletin of the Crimean Astrophysical Observatory
Maik Nauka/Interperiodica Publishing
Profsoyuznaia St. 90
117997 Moscow, Russia
Ph: 7 953 361600
Fax: 7 953 360666
Publication E-mail: suv@crao.crimea.ua
Publisher E-mail: compmg@maik.ru
Journal focusing on observational and theoretical astrophysics, as well as related topics on geophysics and solar physics. **Freq:** Annual. **Key Personnel:** Nikolai V. Steshenko, Editor-in-Chief; Alla N. Rostopchina-Shakhovskaya, Dep. Ed.-in-Ch. **ISSN:** 0190-2717. **Subscription Rates:** EUR638 institutions print incl. free access or e-only; EUR765.60 institutions print incl. enhanced access. **URL:** http://www.maik.rssi.ru/cgi-perl/journal.pl?lang=eng&name=bullcia.

49886 ■ Clinical Laboratory Diagnosis
Meditsina Publishers
Bolshaya Pirogovskaya, 5, Bldg. 2
119435 Moscow, Russia
Ph: 7 95 2453355
Fax: 7 95 2453355
Publisher E-mail: meditsina@mtu-net.ru
Journal covering theoretical and practical problems of clinical laboratory diagnosis. **Founded:** 1955. **Freq:** Monthly. **Key Personnel:** Prof. Vadim V. Mensshikov, Editor-in-Chief. **ISSN:** 0869-2084. **Remarks:** Accepts advertising. **URL:** http://www.medlit.ru/medeng/klinl5.htm. **Circ:** (Not Reported)

49887 ■ Coke and Chemistry
Maik Nauka/Interperiodica Publishing
ul. 2d Baumanskaya
105005 Moscow, Russia
Ph: 7 495 7779524
Publication E-mail: koks@metallurgizdat.com
Publisher E-mail: compmg@maik.ru
Journal covering the scientific developments and applications in the field of coal beneficiation and preparation for coking, coking processes, design of coking ovens and equipment, by-product recovery, automation of technological processes, ecology, and economics. **Freq:** 4/yr. **Key Personnel:** Prof. Grigorii M. Karpin, Editor-in-Chief; A.V. Lobastov, Dep, Ed.-in-Ch. **ISSN:** 1068-364X. **Subscription Rates:** EUR2,352 institutions print incl. free access or e-only; EUR2,822.40 institutions print incl. enhanced access. **URL:** http://www.maik.rssi.ru/cgi-perl/journal.pl?lang=eng&name=cokechem.

49888 ■ Colloid Journal
Maik Nauka/Interperiodica Publishing
Profsoyuznaia St. 90
117997 Moscow, Russia
Ph: 7 953 361600
Fax: 7 953 360666
Publication E-mail: colljour@maik.ru
Publisher E-mail: compmg@maik.ru
Russia journal that publishes the results of research in the area of chemical science dealing with the disperse state of matter and surface phenomena in disperse systems. **Founded:** 1935. **Freq:** Bimonthly. **Key Personnel:** Anatolii I. Rusanov, Editor-in-Chief; Vladimir L. Vakula, Editor; E.D. Shchukin, Editorial Board; Victor M. Rudoy, Exec. Ed.-in-Ch.; A.M. Cazabat, International Advisory Board; Pavel Yu. Butyagin, Editorial Board; O.G. Us'yarov, Dep. Ed.-in-Ch.; Alexander K. Shchekin, Editorial Board. **ISSN:** 1061-933X. **Subscription Rates:** EUR4,767 institutions; EUR5,720.40 institutions enhanced access. **URL:** http://www.maik.rssi.ru/cgi-perl/journal.pl?lang=eng&name=colljour.

49889 ■ Computational Mathematics and Mathematical Physics
Maik Nauka/Interperiodica Publishing
ul. Vavilova 40
119991 Moscow, Russia
Ph: 7 499 1355508
Fax: 7 499 1356159
Publication E-mail: comp_mat@ccas.ru
Publisher E-mail: compmg@maik.ru
Journal including surveys and original papers on computational mathematics, computational methods of mathematical physics, informatics and other mathematical sciences. **Freq:** Monthly. **Key Personnel:** Prof. Yurii S. Osipov, Editor-in-Chief; Prof. Movlud K. Kerimov, Dep. Ed.-in-Ch.; Alexander A. Abramov, Editorial Board; Irina V. Ruzanova, Editor; Aleksei A. Arsenyev, Editorial Board; Grigorii I. Shishkin, Editorial Board. **ISSN:** 0965-5425. **Subscription Rates:** EUR4,524 institutions print incl. free access or e-only; EUR5,428.80 institutions print incl. enhanced access. **Remarks:** Advertising not accepted. **URL:** http://www.maik.ru/cgi-bin/journal.pl?name=commat&page=main. **Circ:** (Not Reported)

49890 ■ Cosmic Research
Maik Nauka/Interperiodica Publishing
Bol'shaya Gruzinskaya 10
123242 Moscow, Russia
Ph: 7 495 2542490
Fax: 7 495 3332378
Publication E-mail: vkurt@asc.rssi.ru
Publisher E-mail: compmg@maik.ru
Journal that publishes scientific papers covering all subjects of space science and technology. **Founded:** 1963. **Freq:** Bimonthly. **Key Personnel:** Aleksandr S. Lidvansky, Editor; Timur M. Eneev, Editor-in-Chief; Vyacheslav M. Linkin, Editorial Board; Dr. Mikhail I. Panasyuk, Editorial Board; Oleg M. Rzhiga, Editorial Board; Garrii A. Popov, Editorial Board. **ISSN:** 0010-9525. **Subscription Rates:** EUR4,551 institutions print incl. free access or e-only; EUR5,461.20 institutions print incl. enhanced access. **URL:** http://www.maik.rssi.ru/cgi-perl/journal.pl?name=cosres&page=main.

49891 ■ Crystallography Reports
Maik Nauka/Interperiodica Publishing
Kristallografiya
Leninskii pr. 59
117333 Moscow, Russia
Ph: 7 499 1356070
Fax: 7 499 1351011
Publication E-mail: redcryst@ns.crys.ras.ru
Publisher E-mail: compmg@maik.ru
Journal publishing original papers, short communications, and reviews on different aspects of crystallography: diffraction and scattering of X-rays, electrons and neutrons; X-ray, electron, and neutron diffraction determination of crystal structure of inorganic and organic materials, including proteins and other biological objects; optical and radiowave spectroscopy; growth, real structure and physical properties of crystals; thin films and partly disordered systems; and the methods used in these studies. **Freq:** Bimonthly. **Key Personnel:** Alisa F. Konstantinova, Exec. Ed.-in-Ch.; Kirill S. Aleksandrov, Editorial Board; Viktor L. Aksenov, Dep. Ed.-in-Ch.; Khachik S. Bagdasarov, Editorial Board. **ISSN:** 1063-7745. **Subscription Rates:** EUR3,197 institutions print incl. free access or e-only; EUR3,836.40 institutions print incl. enhanced access. **Remarks:** Advertising not accepted. **URL:** http://www.maik.ru/cgi-bin/journal.pl?name=cryst&page=main. **Circ:** (Not Reported)

49892 ■ Diana Creative
Edipresse Publications S.A.
Ul. Bakuninskaya 71
Bldg. 10, 6th Fl.
107082 Moscow, Russia
Ph: 7 495 7751435
Fax: 7 495 7751434
Publisher E-mail: groupe@edipresse.com
Magazine featuring needlecraft patterns and techniques. **Freq:** Monthly. **Key Personnel:** Galina Mednikova, Ch. Ed.; Galina Arefieva, Director. **URL:** http://www.edipresse.com/knittingsewing/diana-creative. **Circ:** ‡20,715

49893 ■ Diana Moden
Edipresse Publications S.A.
Ul. Bakuninskaya 71
Bldg. 10, 6th Fl.
107082 Moscow, Russia
Ph: 7 495 7751435

Circulation: ★ = ABC; △ = BPA; ◆ = CAC; • = CCAB; ❑ = VAC; ⊕ = PO Statement; ‡ = Publisher's Report; Boldface figures = sworn; Light figures = estimated.

Gale Directory of Publications & Broadcast Media/147th Ed.   5369

Fax: 7 495 7751434
Publisher E-mail: groupe@edipresse.com
Magazine featuring knitting patterns. **Freq:** 9/yr. **Key Personnel:** Svetlana Kostenko, Ch. Ed.; Irina Surovtseva, Director. **URL:** http://www.edipresse.com/knittingsewing/diana-moden; http://www.diana-moden.ru/. **Circ:** ‡50,230

49894 ■ Doklady Biochemistry and Biophysics
Maik Nauka/Interperiodica Publishing
Profsoyuznaia St. 90
117997 Moscow, Russia
Ph: 7 953 361600
Fax: 7 953 360666
Publisher E-mail: compmg@maik.ru
Journal that looks into a wide variety of topics in biophysics, with emphasis on the action of gamma rays, X-rays, light, and ultrasound on living organisms. **Founded:** 1964. **Freq:** Bimonthly. **Key Personnel:** Yurii S. Osipov, Editor-in-Chief; Evgenii F. Mishenko, Dep. Ed.-in-Ch.; Alexander F. Andreev, Editorial Board; Gorimir G. Chernyi, Editorial Board; Yurii V. Gulyaev, Editorial Board. **ISSN:** 1607-6729. **Subscription Rates:** EUR3,618 institutions print incl. free access or E-Only; EUR4,341.60 institutions print incl. enhanced access. **URL:** http://www.maik.rssi.ru/cgi-bin/journal.pl?name=danbcbp&page=main. **Merged with:** Doklady Biophysics; Doklady Biochemistry.

49895 ■ Doklady Biological Sciences
Maik Nauka/Interperiodica Publishing
Profsoyuznaia St. 90
117997 Moscow, Russia
Ph: 7 953 361600
Fax: 7 953 360666
Publisher E-mail: compmg@maik.ru
Journal containing English translations of current Russian research in medical sciences. **Founded:** 1933. **Freq:** Bimonthly. **Key Personnel:** Evgenii F. Mishenko, Dep. Ed.-in-Ch.; Vladimir L. Ushakov, Editor; Stanislav V. Emel'yanov, Editorial Board; Yurii S. Osipov, Editor-in-Chief; Gorimir G. Chernyi, Editorial Board; Oleg A. Bogatikov, Editorial Board; Alexander A. Boyarchuk, Editorial Board; Georgii A. Zavarzin, Editorial Board; Alexander F. Andreev, Editorial Board; Yurii D. Tret'yakov, Editorial Board. **ISSN:** 0012-4966. **Subscription Rates:** EUR3,954 institutions print incl. free access or E-only; EUR4,744.80 institutions print incl. enhanced access. **URL:** http://www.maik.rssi.ru/cgi-perl/journal.pl?lang=eng&name=danbio.

49896 ■ Doklady Chemistry
Maik Nauka/Interperiodica Publishing
Ul.Profsoyuznaya 90
117997 Moscow, Russia
Ph: 7 495 3347380
Publication E-mail: dan@maik.ru
Publisher E-mail: compmg@maik.ru
Publishes the most significant new research in chemistry being done in Russia today. **Founded:** 1933. **Freq:** Monthly. **Key Personnel:** Yurii S. Osipov, Editor-in-Chief; Valentin P. Dymnikov, Editorial Board; Vladimir M. Kotlyakov, Editorial Board. **ISSN:** 0012-5008. **Subscription Rates:** EUR4,061 institutions; EUR4,873.20 institutions enhanced access. **URL:** http://www.maik.rssi.ru/journals/danchem.htm.

49897 ■ Doklady Earth Sciences
Maik Nauka/Interperiodica Publishing
Profsoyuznaia St. 90
117997 Moscow, Russia
Ph: 7 953 361600
Fax: 7 953 360666
Publisher E-mail: compmg@maik.ru
Publishes brief scientific reports on previously unpublished significant new research in mathematics as well as on its applications. **Founded:** 1933. **Freq:** 9/yr. **Key Personnel:** Yurii S. Osipov, Editor-in-Chief; Evgenii F. Mishenko, Dep. Ed.-in-Ch.; Irina V. Isavnina, Managing Editor; Alexander A. Boyarchuk, Editorial Board; Vladimir M. Kotlyakov, Editorial Board. **ISSN:** 1028-334X. **Subscription Rates:** EUR5,214 institutions; EUR6,256.80 institutions enhanced access. **URL:** http://www.maik.rssi.ru/journals/earthsci.htm.

49898 ■ Doklady Mathematics
Maik Nauka/Interperiodica Publishing
Profsoyuznaia St. 90
117997 Moscow, Russia
Ph: 7 953 361600
Fax: 7 953 360666
Publication E-mail: dan@maik.ru

Publisher E-mail: compmg@maik.ru
Journal publishing brief scientific reports on previously unpublished significant new research in mathematics and its applications, including the materials from the following areas: mathematics, mathematical physics, computer science, control theory and computers. **Freq:** Bimonthly. **Key Personnel:** Yurii S. Osipov, Editor-in-Chief; Irina V. Ruzanova, Editor; Evgenii F. Mishenko, Dep. Ed.-in-Ch. **ISSN:** 1064-5624. **Subscription Rates:** EUR2,388 institutions print incl. free access or e-only; EUR2,865.60 institutions print incl. enhanced access. **Remarks:** Advertising not accepted. **URL:** http://www.maik.ru/cgi-bin/journal.pl?name=danmath&page=main. **Circ:** (Not Reported)

49899 ■ Doklady Physical Chemistry
Maik Nauka/Interperiodica Publishing
Profsoyuznaia St. 90
117997 Moscow, Russia
Ph: 7 953 361600
Fax: 7 953 360666
Publisher E-mail: compmg@maik.ru
Journal publishing the most significant new research in physical chemistry being done in Russia today. **Founded:** 1933. **Freq:** Monthly. **Key Personnel:** Evgenii F. Mishenko, Dep. Ed.-in-Ch.; Stanislav V. Emel'yanov, Editorial Board; Gorimir G. Chernyi, Editorial Board; Oleg A. Bogatikov, Editorial Board; Alexander F. Andreev, Editorial Board; Alexander A. Boyarchuk, Editorial Board; Yurii S. Osipov, Editor-in-Chief; Valerii V. Kozlov, Editorial Board. **ISSN:** 0012-5016. **Subscription Rates:** EUR5,475 institutions print incl. free access or e-only; EUR6,570 institutions print incl. enhanced access. **URL:** http://www.springerlink.com/content/106526/; http://www.maik.rssi.ru/cgi-perl/journal.pl?lang=eng&name=danpc.

49900 ■ Doklady Physics
Maik Nauka/Interperiodica Publishing
Profsoyuznaia St. 90
117997 Moscow, Russia
Ph: 7 953 361600
Fax: 7 953 360666
Publication E-mail: dan@maik.ru
Publisher E-mail: compmg@maik.ru
Publishes the most significant new research in physics being done in Russia today. **Founded:** 1933. **Freq:** Monthly. **Key Personnel:** Evgenii F. Mishenko, Dep. Ed.-in-Ch.; Yurii S. Osipov, Editor-in-Chief; Rem V. Petrov, Editorial Board. **ISSN:** 1028-3358. **Subscription Rates:** EUR3,354 institutions; EUR4,024.80 institutions enhanced access. **URL:** http://www.maik.rssi.ru/cgi-bin/journal.pl?name=danphys&page=main.

49901 ■ Doping Journal
Do Vostrebovania
121359 Moscow, Russia
Publisher E-mail: postmaster@dopingjournal.org
Journal providing online-only peer-reviewed publication of the results and conclusions of original research on doping, with a particular emphasis on novel findings in chemistry and biology of doping chemicals, nonchemical agents, nutritional supplements, and healthy natural alternatives for the doping usage. **Key Personnel:** Alexei R. Koudinov, Managing Editor; Giuseppe Lippi, Editor; Hakan Gur, Editor. **ISSN:** 1812-948X. **URL:** http://dopingjournal.org/mydopingjindex.html.

49902 ■ Epidemiology & Infectious Diseases
Meditsina Publishers
Bolshaya Pirogovskaya, 5, Bldg. 2
119435 Moscow, Russia
Ph: 7 95 2453355
Fax: 7 95 2453355
Publisher E-mail: meditsina@mtu-net.ru
Journal covering epidemiological surveys, diagnosis, treatment and prevention of infectious diseases. **Founded:** 1996. **Freq:** Bimonthly. **Key Personnel:** Prof. Valentin I. Pokrovsky, Editor-in-Chief. **ISSN:** 1560-9529. **Remarks:** Accepts advertising. **URL:** http://www.medlit.ru/medeng/eib5.htm. **Circ:** (Not Reported)

49903 ■ The Exile
Ul Novaya Basmanaya 10
Pod 6, Etazh 4 1/2
117418 Moscow, Russia
Ph: 7 495 6233565
Fax: 7 495 6235442
Publisher E-mail: office@exile.ru
Critical and radical newspaper with original views on modern life in Russia. **Subtitle:** Moscow's Only Alternative. **Founded:** 1997. **Freq:** Biweekly. **Key Per-**

sonnel: Mark Ames, Editor-in-Chief, editor@exile.ru. **Remarks:** Accepts advertising. **URL:** http://exiledonline.com/. **Circ:** (Not Reported)

49904 ■ Flooring Professional Magazine
Impress Media, Inc.
4th Roschinsky proezd, 20 bld. 5,9
115191 Moscow, Russia
Ph: 7 495 9267340
Fax: 7 495 9267215
Publication E-mail: info@impressmedia.ru
Publisher E-mail: info@impressmedia.ru
Magazine featuring flooring and floor covers. **Freq:** 6/yr. **Key Personnel:** Annette Wassenaar, Gen. Mgr.; Roman Khaburgaev, Editor-in-Chief, editor@flooringmagazine.ru. **Subscription Rates:** US$45. **Remarks:** Accepts advertising. **URL:** http://www.flooringmagazine.ru/english.php. **Circ:** 8,000

49905 ■ Forensic Medical Examination
Meditsina Publishers
Bolshaya Pirogovskaya, 5, Bldg. 2
119435 Moscow, Russia
Ph: 7 95 2453355
Fax: 7 95 2453355
Publisher E-mail: meditsina@mtu-net.ru
Journal covering theory and practice of forensic medicine. **Founded:** 1958. **Freq:** Bimonthly. **Key Personnel:** Prof. Yuri I. Pigolkin, Editor-in-Chief. **ISSN:** 0039-4521. **Remarks:** Accepts advertising. **URL:** http://www.medlit.ru/medeng/sudm5.htm. **Circ:** (Not Reported)

49906 ■ Geochemistry International
Maik Nauka/Interperiodica Publishing
Ul. Kosygina 19
119991 Moscow, Russia
Ph: 7 499 1378722
Fax: 7 499 9382054
Publisher E-mail: compmg@maik.ru
Journal covering cosmochemistry, geochemistry of magmatic, metamorphic, hydrothermal, and sedimentary processes, organic geochemistry, applied geochemistry, and chemistry of the environment. **Founded:** 1956. **Freq:** Monthly. **Key Personnel:** Evgenii B. Kurdyukov, Editor; Andrei V. Girnis, Editor; Igor D. Ryabchikov, Dep. Ed.-in-Ch.; Oleg A. Bogatikov, Editorial Board; Prof. Claude J. Allegre, Editorial Board; Erik M. Galimov, Editor-in-Chief; Alexander T. Bazilevsky, Editorial Board; Sergei F. Karpenko, Exec. Ed.-in-Ch.; Igor V. Chernyshev, Editorial Board. **ISSN:** 0016-7029. **Subscription Rates:** EUR4,512 institutions print incl. free access or e-only; EUR5,414.40 institutions print incl. enhanced access. **URL:** http://www.maik.rssi.ru/cgi-bin/journal.pl?name=geochem&page=main.

49907 ■ Geology of Ore Deposits
Maik Nauka/Interperiodica Publishing
Staromonetnyi per. 35
119017 Moscow, Russia
Ph: 7 499 2308483
Fax: 7 499 9511587
Publisher E-mail: compmg@maik.ru
Journal containing original scientific articles and reviews on a wide range of problems in theoretical and applied science. **Founded:** 1959. **Freq:** Bimonthly. **Key Personnel:** Nikolai P. Laverov, Editorial Board; Vladimir V. Yarmolyuk, Dep. Ed.-in-Ch.; Vsevolod Yu. Prokof'ev, Exec. Ed.-in-Ch.; Nikolai S. Bortnikov, Editor-in-Chief; Dmitrii V. Grichuk, Editorial Board; Aleksandr I. Khanchuk, Editorial Board; Vadim I. Kazansky, Editorial Board; Lev S. Borodin, Editorial Board; Dmitrii V. Rundquist, Dep. Ed.-in-Ch.; Lev Z. Bykhovsky, Editorial Board; Dr. Viktor S. Popov, Editor; Boris I. Omel'yanenko, Editorial Board. **ISSN:** 1075-7015. **Subscription Rates:** EUR1,755 institutions print incl. free access or e-only; EUR2,106 institutions print incl. enhanced access. **URL:** http://www.maik.rssi.ru/cgi-bin/journal.pl?name=geolore&page=main.

49908 ■ Geomagnetism and Aeronomy
Maik Nauka/Interperiodica Publishing
Maronovskii per. 26
GSP-1
119049 Moscow, Russia
Ph: 7 499 2307945
Publication E-mail: geomag@naukaran.ru
Publisher E-mail: compmg@maik.ru
Journal covering the fields of interplanetary space, geo-effective solar events, the magnetosphere, the ionosphere, the upper and middle atmosphere, and the action of solar variability and activity on atmospheric

parameters and climate. **Founded:** 1961. **Freq:** Bimonthly. **Key Personnel:** Oleg M. Raspopov, Editor-in-Chief; Aleksei D. Danilov, Editorial Board; Elisaveta E. Antonova, Editorial Board; Sergei A. Pulinets, Editorial Board; Dmitrii D. Sokolov, Editorial Board; Aleksandr V. Gurevich, Editorial Board; Natal'ya G. Kleymenova, Editorial Board; Anatolii A. Nusinov, Editorial Board; Gennadii A. Fonarev, Editorial Board; Kim G. Ivanov, Dep. Ed.-in-Ch.; Yurii V. Safronov, Editor; Mlkhail I. Verigin, Editorial Board. **ISSN:** 0016-7932. **Subscription Rates:** EUR1,443 institutions print incl. free access or e-only; EUR1,731.60 institutions print incl. enhanced access. **URL:** http://www.maik.rssi.ru/cgi-bin/journal.pl?name=geomag&page=main.

49909 ■ Geotectonics
Maik Nauka/Interperiodica Publishing
Geological Institute
Pyzhevskii per. 7
109017 Moscow, Russia
Ph: 7 495 9516685
Fax: 7 495 9510443
Publication E-mail: gin@ran.msk.su
Publisher E-mail: compmg@maik.ru
Journal publishing articles on general and regional tectonics, structural geology, geodynamics, and experimental tectonics, and considers the relation of tectonics to the deep structure of the earth, magmatism, metamorphism, and mineral resources. **Founded:** 1965. **Freq:** Bimonthly. **Key Personnel:** Yurii M. Pushcharovsky, Editor-in-Chief; Yurii N. Avsyuk, Editorial Board; Valentin S. Burtman, Sec. of the Editorial Board; Sergey V. Ruzhentsev, Dep. Ed.-in-Ch.; Elena A. Konstantinovskaia, Editorial Board; Enrico Bonatti, Editorial Board. **ISSN:** 0016-8521. **Subscription Rates:** EUR1,070 institutions print incl. free access or e-only; EUR1,284 institutions print incl. enhanced access. **Remarks:** Accepts advertising. **URL:** http://www.maik.ru/cgi-bin/journal.pl?name=geoteng&page=main. Circ: (Not Reported)

49910 ■ Haematology & Trasfusiology
Meditsina Publishers
Bolshaya Pirogovskaya, 5, Bldg. 2
119435 Moscow, Russia
Ph: 7 95 2453355
Fax: 7 95 2453355
Publisher E-mail: meditsina@mtu-net.ru
Journals covering problems of hematology and blood transfusion. **Founded:** 1956. **Freq:** Bimonthly. **Key Personnel:** Prof. Andrei I. Vorobyev, Editor-in-Chief. **ISSN:** 0234-5730. **Remarks:** Accepts advertising. **URL:** http://www.medlit.ru/medeng/gemat5.htm. **Circ:** (Not Reported)

49911 ■ Health Care of the Russian Federation
Meditsina Publishers
Bolshaya Pirogovskaya, 5, Bldg. 2
119435 Moscow, Russia
Ph: 7 95 2453355
Fax: 7 95 2453355
Publisher E-mail: meditsina@mtu-net.ru
Journal covering health status and development of public health service in the republics, territories, regions and districts of the Russian Federation. **Founded:** 1957. **Freq:** Bimonthly. **Key Personnel:** Prof. Anatoly I. Putapov, Editor-in-Chief. **ISSN:** 0044-197X. **Remarks:** Accepts advertising. **URL:** http://www.medlit.ru/medeng/zdrav5.htm. Circ: (Not Reported)

49912 ■ Herald of the Russian Academy of Sciences
Maik Nauka/Interperiodica Publishing
Maronovskii per. 26
119991 Moscow, Russia
Ph: 7 499 2382123
Fax: 7 499 2382510
Publication E-mail: west@maik.ru
Publisher E-mail: compmg@maik.ru
Journal presenting the viewpoints of various disciplines on many important subjects related to the natural, technical and social sciences, addressing the scientist's role in society and the role of scientific knowledge in the modern world. **Freq:** Bimonthly. **Key Personnel:** Vladislav V. Pirozhkov, Editorial Board; Yurii S. Osipov, Editor-in-Chief; Boris O. Alekseev, Editor; Eugene P. Chelyshev, Editorial Board; Valentin L. Yanin, Editorial Board. **ISSN:** 1019-3316. **Subscription Rates:** EUR3,208 institutions print incl. free access or e-only; EUR3,849.60 institutions print incl. enhanced access.

Remarks: Advertising not accepted. **URL:** http://www.maik.ru/cgi-bin/journal.pl?name=herald&page=main. **Circ:** (Not Reported)

49913 ■ High Energy Chemistry
Maik Nauka/Interperiodica Publishing
Profsoyuznaia St. 90
117997 Moscow, Russia
Ph: 7 953 361600
Fax: 7 953 360666
Publisher E-mail: compmg@maik.ru
Publishes original papers on radiation chemistry, photochemistry, plasma chemistry, laser chemistry, and other aspects of high energy chemistry. **Founded:** 1967. **Freq:** Bimonthly. **Key Personnel:** Vadim V. Gustov, Exec. Ed.-in-Ch.; Victor P. Shantarovich, Editorial Board; Viktor F. Plyusnin, Editorial Board; Gleb A. Abakumov, Editorial Board; Valerii P. Kazakov, Editorial Board; Aleksandr K. Chibisov, Editorial Board; Lyudmila I. Yashina, Staff Ed.; Vladimir F. Razumov, Editor-in-Chief; Stanislav V. Zatonsky, Editor; Valerii L. Ermolaev, Editorial Board; Dmitrii I. Slovetskii, Editorial Board; Dr. Boris G. Ershov, Editorial Board. **ISSN:** 0018-1439. **Subscription Rates:** EUR4,873 institutions; EUR5,847.60 institutions enhanced access. **URL:** http://www.maik.ru/cgi-perl/journal.pl?lang=eng&name=highen&page=main.

49914 ■ High Temperature
Maik Nauka/Interperiodica Publishing
Ul. Krasnokazarmennaya 17a
111116 Moscow, Russia
Ph: 7 495 3620788
Publication E-mail: tvt@iht.mpei.ac.ru
Publisher E-mail: compmg@maik.ru
Examines theoretical and experimental results of research in high-temperature physics as they apply to modern engineering problems. **Founded:** 1963. **Freq:** Bimonthly. **Key Personnel:** Eduard E. Son, Dep. Ed.-in-Ch.; Henri A. Bronstein, Editor; Vladimir E. Fortov, Editor-in-Chief; Anatoly D. Rahkel, Exec. Ed.-in-Ch.; Vladimir G. Asmolov, Editorial Board; Alexander I. Leontiev, Editorial Board. **ISSN:** 0018-151X. **Subscription Rates:** EUR4,916 institutions; EUR5,899.20 institutions enhanced access. **URL:** http://www.maik.rssi.ru/cgi-bin/journal.pl?name=hightemp&page=main.

49915 ■ Human Physiology
Maik Nauka/Interperiodica Publishing
Maronovskii per. 26
119049 Moscow, Russia
Ph: 7 499 2382322
Publication E-mail: h-physiol@naukaran.ru
Publisher E-mail: compmg@maik.ru
Publishes studies on the physiology of work, speech, and sport, emphasizing their relationship to the physiology of the brain and the neurophysiology of psychological activity. **Founded:** 1975. **Freq:** Bimonthly. **Key Personnel:** Valentin D. Sonkin, Dep. Ed.-in-Ch.; Deborah A. Farber, Editorial Board; Galina N. Boldyreva, Editorial Board; Vera M. Vladimirskaya, Exec. Ed.-in-Ch.; Olga L. Vinogradova, Editorial Board; Ludmila V. Belova, Staff Ed.; Nikolai I. Volkov, Editorial Board; Georgii M. Zarakovskii, Dep. Ed.-in-Ch. **ISSN:** 0362-1197. **Subscription Rates:** EUR3,625 institutions; EUR4,350 institutions enhanced access. **URL:** http://www.maik.rssi.ru/cgi-perl/journal.pl?lang=eng&name=humphys.

49916 ■ Hygiene & Sanitation
Meditsina Publishers
Bolshaya Pirogovskaya, 5, Bldg. 2
119435 Moscow, Russia
Ph: 7 95 2453355
Fax: 7 95 2453355
Publisher E-mail: meditsina@mtu-net.ru
Journal covering general sanitary problems. **Founded:** 1922. **Freq:** Bimonthly. **Key Personnel:** Prof. Gennady I. Rumyantsev, Editor-in-Chief. **ISSN:** 0016-9900. **Remarks:** Accepts advertising. **URL:** http://www.medlit.ru/medeng/gig5.htm. **Circ:** (Not Reported)

49917 ■ Industria Mody
Edipresse Publications S.A.
Ul. Bakuninskaya 71
Bldg. 10, 6th Fl.
107082 Moscow, Russia
Ph: 7 495 7751435
Fax: 7 495 7751434
Publisher E-mail: groupe@edipresse.com
Magazine focusing on the latest fashion trends. **Freq:** Quarterly. **Key Personnel:** Alexander Khilkevich, Ch. Ed.; Irina Surovtseva, Director. **URL:** http://www.

edipresse.com/b2b/industria-mody; http://www.konliga.ru/publications/fashion/. **Circ:** ‡1,900

49918 ■ Inflight Review
SPN Publishing Company
4a Novodanilovskaya nab
117105 Moscow, Russia
Magazine for passengers of Rossiya State Transport Company. **Founded:** 1990. **Freq:** Monthly. **Key Personnel:** Irina Tiusonina, Editor-in-Chief; Alina Bashkeeva, Dep. Ed.; Eugeny Grigoriev, Production Mgr **Remarks:** Accepts advertising. **URL:** http://www.spn.ru/publishing/ir. **Ad Rates:** 4C: 225,000 Rb. **Circ:** 70,000

49919 ■ Inorganic Materials
Maik Nauka/Interperiodica Publishing
Leninskii pr. 31, Rm. 71
119991 Moscow, Russia
Ph: 7 495 9543483
Publication E-mail: neorganmat@igic.ras.ru
Publisher E-mail: compmg@maik.ru
Journal containing reviews, original papers, and news about chemistry, physics, and applications of various inorganic materials. **Founded:** 1965. **Freq:** Monthly. **Key Personnel:** Anatolii S. Vlasov, Editorial Board; Vadim I. Nefedov, Editor-in-Chief; Valentin A. Fedorov, Dep. Ed.-in-Ch.; Mikhail F. Churbanov, Dep. Ed.-in-Ch.; Yurii D. Tret'yakov, Dep. Ed.-in-Ch.; Galina F. Gubskaya, Exec. Ed.-in-Ch.; Svetlana S. Baikova, Staff Ed.; Gennadii S. Burkhanov, Editorial Board. **ISSN:** 0020-1685. **Subscription Rates:** EUR5,651 institutions print incl. free access or e-only; EUR6,781 institutions print incl. enhanced access. **URL:** http://www.maik.rssi.ru/cgi-bin/journal.pl?name=inorgmat&page=main.

49920 ■ Integral Transforms and Special Functions
Taylor & Francis Group Journals
Dordodnicyn Computing Centre of the Russian Academy of Sciences
Vavilov St. 40
119991 Moscow, Russia
Publisher E-mail: customerservice@taylorandfrancis.com
Peer-reviewed journal focusing on the use of integral transforms and special functions in the fields of pure and applied mathematics, physics, engineering, and computer science. **Freq:** Monthly. **Key Personnel:** Prof. E.I. Moiseev, Editor-in-Chief, emoiseev@ccas.ru; Prof. H.J. Glaeske, Assoc. Ed., glaeske@minet.uni-jena.de; V.M. Babich, Editorial Board; Prof. H.M. Srivastava, Assoc. Ed., harimsv@math.uvic.ca; Prof. Yu. A. Brychkov, Managing Editor, brychkov@ccas.ru; Prof. Vu Kim Tuan, Assoc. Ed., vu@westga.edu. **ISSN:** 1056-2469. **Subscription Rates:** US$4,338 institutions print + online; US$3,904 institutions online; EUR3,453 institutions print + online; 3,238 institutions print + online; 2,914 institutions online; EUR3,108 institutions online. **URL:** http://www.tandf.co.uk/journals/titles/10652469.asp.

49921 ■ International Textiles
Edipresse Publications S.A.
Ul. Bakuninskaya 71
Bldg. 10, 6th Fl.
107082 Moscow, Russia
Ph: 7 495 7751435
Fax: 7 495 7751434
Publication E-mail: b2bsite@konliga.ru
Publisher E-mail: groupe@edipresse.com
Magazine highlighting the fashion industry. **Freq:** Bimonthly. **Key Personnel:** Irina Surovtseva, Director; Alexander Khilkevich, Ch. Ed. **URL:** http://www.edipresse.com/b2b/international-textiles; http://www.konliga.ru/publications/intextiles/. **Circ:** ‡235

49922 ■ Iren
Edipresse Publications S.A.
Ul. Bakuninskaya 71
Bldg. 10, 6th Fl.
107082 Moscow, Russia
Ph: 7 495 7751435
Fax: 7 495 7751434
Publisher E-mail: groupe@edipresse.com
Magazine featuring knitted fashion inspired by French haute-couture. **Freq:** 6/yr. **Key Personnel:** Galina Mednikova, Ch. Ed.; Galina Arefieva, Director. **URL:** http://www.edipresse.com/b2b/knittingsewing/iren. **Circ:** ‡27,340

49923 ■ Izvestiya
Turpion - Moscow Ltd.
MIAN

Circulation: ★ = ABC; △ = BPA; ♦ = CAC; • = CCAB; ❑ = VAC; ⊕ = PO Statement; ‡ = Publisher's Report; Boldface figures = sworn; Light figures = estimated.

Gale Directory of Publications & Broadcast Media/147th Ed. 5371

8 Gubkina St., Rm. 915
119991 Moscow, Russia
Ph: 7 495 1354509
Fax: 7 495 9300604
Publisher E-mail: admin@turpion.ru
Peer-reviewed Journal covering mathematics. **Subtitle:** Mathematics. **Founded:** 1937. **Freq:** Bimonthly. **Key Personnel:** V.V. Kozlov, Editor-in-Chief; A.G. Sergeev, Dep. Ed.; V.I. Arnold, Editorial Board. **ISSN:** 1064-5632. **Subscription Rates:** US$1,930 individuals print & only; 1,047 individuals rest of the world; US$1,737 individuals online; 942 individuals online; US$386 single issue; 209 single issue. **URL:** http://www.turpion.org/php/homes/pa.phtml?jrnid=im.

49924 ■ Izvestiya, Atmospheric and Oceanic Physics
Maik Nauka/Interperiodica Publishing
Pyzhevskii per. 3
119017 Moscow, Russia
Ph: 7 495 9512174
Fax: 7 495 2331652
Publication E-mail: japho@omega.ifaran.ru
Publisher E-mail: compmg@maik.ru
Publishes original scientific research and review articles on vital issues in the physics of the earths atmosphere and hydrosphere and climate theory. **Founded:** 1965. **Freq:** Bimonthly. **Key Personnel:** Georgii S. Golitsyn, Editor-in-Chief; A.S. Ginzburg, Exec. Ed.-in-Ch.; A.P. Ivanov, Editorial Board; Dr. V.V. Yefimov, Editorial Board; Dr. I.L. Karol, Editorial Board; A.S Sarkisyan, Dep. Ed.-in-Ch. **ISSN:** 0001-4338. **Subscription Rates:** EUR1,632 institutions; EUR1,958.40 institutions enhanced access. **URL:** http://www.maik.rssi.ru/cgi-perl/journal.pl?lang=eng&name=physatm.

49925 ■ Izvestiya, Physics of the Solid Earth
Maik Nauka/Interperiodica Publishing
Ul. Bolshaya Gruzinskaya 10
123995 Moscow, Russia
Ph: 7 495 2549341
Fax: 7 495 2549088
Publication E-mail: journal@ifz.ru
Publisher E-mail: compmg@maik.ru
Publishes results of original theoretical and experimental research in relevant areas of the physics of the earths interior and applied geophysics. **Founded:** 1965. **Freq:** Monthly. **Key Personnel:** Dr. Vladimir B. Smirnov, Exec. Ed.-in-Ch.; Alexander O. Gliko, Editor-in-Chief; Valerii P. Trubitsyn, Dep. Ed.-in-Ch.; Dr Yurii O. Kuz'min, Editorial Board; Dr. Andrei F. Grachev, Editorial Board; Vitaly V. Adushkin, Editorial Board; Dr. Lev P. Vinnik, Editorial Board; Dr. Sergei M. Molodenskii, Dep. Ed.-in-Ch.; Dr. Anatolii G. Yagola, Editorial Board. **ISSN:** 1069-3513. **Subscription Rates:** EUR1,548 institutions; EUR1,857.60 institutions enhanced access. **Remarks:** Advertising not accepted. **URL:** http://www.maik.rssi.ru/cgi-bin/journal.pl?name=physeth&page=main. **Circ:** (Not Reported)

49926 ■ Journal of Advances in Chemical Physics
Cambridge International Science Publishing
N.N. Semenov Institute of Chemical Physics
Russian Academy of Sciences
ul. Kosygina 4
119991 Moscow, Russia
Publication E-mail: jacp@cisp-publishing.com
Publisher E-mail: cisp@cisp-publishing.com
Journal covering areas of chemical physics. **Freq:** 6/yr. **Key Personnel:** A.L. Buchachenko, Editor-in-Chief. **URL:** http://www.cisp-publishing.com/acatalog/Journals.html.

49927 ■ Journal of Analytical Chemistry
Maik Nauka/Interperiodica Publishing
Vernadsky Institute of Geochemistry & Analytical Chemistry
Ul. Kosygina 19
119991 Moscow, Russia
Ph: 7 495 9390210
Fax: 7 495 9382054
Publication E-mail: janchem@mail.ru
Publisher E-mail: compmg@maik.ru
Journal covering theoretical and some applied aspects of analytical chemistry. **Founded:** 1946. **Freq:** Monthly. **Key Personnel:** Yurii A. Zolotov, Editor-in-Chief; Elena A. Rykova, Editor; Vadim M. Ivanov, Dep. Ed.-in-Ch.; Gennadii M. Kolesov, Exec. Ed.-in-Ch.; Mikhail K. Beklemishev, Editorial Board; Boris K. Zuev, Editorial Board. **ISSN:** 1061-9348. **Subscription Rates:** EUR5,406 institutions print incl. free access or e-only; EUR6,487.20

institutions print incl. enhanced access. **URL:** http://www.maik.rssi.ru/cgi-bin/journal.pl?name=anchem&page=main.

49928 ■ Journal of Computer and Systems Sciences International
Maik Nauka/Interperiodica Publishing
ul. Viktorenko 7
125319 Moscow, Russia
Ph: 7 495 7717038
Publication E-mail: info@gosniias.msk.ru
Publisher E-mail: compmg@maik.ru
Journal featuring papers on the theory and methods of control with particular attention given to computer methods and technologies. **Founded:** 1963. **Freq:** Bimonthly. **Key Personnel:** Evgenii A. Fedosov, Editor-in-Chief; Vladimir I. Kukhtenko, Dep. Ed.-in-Ch.; Alexander M. Formal'skii, Editorial Board; Marina V. Andzhievskaya, Staff Ed.; Konstantin I. Kii, Ed. of the English Translation; Larisa V. Vishnyakova, Exec. Ed.-in-Ch.; Felix L. Chernousko, Dep. Ed.-in-Ch.; Boris E. Fedunov, Editorial Board; Innokentii N. Beloglazov, Editorial Board; Nikolai N. Bolotnik, Editorial Board; Vadin N. Vagin, Editorial Board; Sergei Yu. Zheltov, Editorial Board. **ISSN:** 1064-2307. **Subscription Rates:** EUR3,747 institutions print incl. free access or e-only; EUR4,496.40 institutions print incl. enhanced access. **Remarks:** Advertising not accepted. **URL:** http://www.maik.ru/cgi-bin/journal.pl?name=compsys&page=main. **Circ:** (Not Reported)

49929 ■ Journal of Ichthyology
Maik Nauka/Interperiodica Publishing
Maronovskii pr. 26
119049 Moscow, Russia
Ph: 7 495 2381468
Fax: 7 495 1245983
Publication E-mail: admaron@naukaran.ru
Publisher E-mail: compmg@maik.ru
Journal featuring articles in the fields of fish ecology, morphology, genetics, physiology, embryology, systematics, and fisheries biology. **Founded:** 1961. **Freq:** Irregular. **Key Personnel:** Nikolai V. Parin, Editor-in-Chief; Dr. Nikolai N. Smirnov, Editor; Dr. Mikhail I. Shatunovsky, Dep. Ed.-in-Ch.; Dmitrii S. Pavlov, Dep. Ed.-in-Ch.; Dr. Mikhail V. Mina, Dep. Ed.-in-Ch. **ISSN:** 0032-9452. **Subscription Rates:** EUR4,086 institutions print incl. free access or e-only; EUR4,903.20 institutions print incl. enhanced access. **Remarks:** Advertising accepted; rates available upon request. **URL:** http://www.maik.rssi.ru/cgi-perl/journal.pl?lang=eng&name=ichth. **Circ:** (Not Reported)

49930 ■ Journal of Neurosurgical Problems
Meditsina Publishers
Bolshaya Pirogovskaya, 5, Bldg. 2
119435 Moscow, Russia
Ph: 7 95 2453355
Fax: 7 95 2453355
Publisher E-mail: meditsina@mtu-net.ru
Journals covering theoretical, practical and organizational problems of modern neurosurgery. **Founded:** 1937. **Freq:** Quarterly. **Key Personnel:** Prof. Alexander N. Konovalov, Editor-in-Chief. **ISSN:** 0042-8817. **Remarks:** Accepts advertising. **URL:** http://www.medlit.ru/medeng/index2.htm. **Circ:** (Not Reported)

49931 ■ Kinetics and Catalysis
Maik Nauka/Interperiodica Publishing
Leninskii pr. 47
119991 Moscow, Russia
Ph: 7 495 1355358
Fax: 7 495 1355328
Publication E-mail: kincat@ioc.ac.ru
Publisher E-mail: compmg@maik.ru
Publishes theoretical and experimental materials on homogeneous and heterogeneous kinetics and catalysis. **Founded:** 1960. **Freq:** Bimonthly. **Key Personnel:** Prof. Il'ya I. Moiseev, Dep. Ed.-in-Ch.; Prof. Vladimir B. Kazansky, Editor-in-Chief; Vilen V. Azatyan, Editorial Board. **ISSN:** 0023-1584. **Subscription Rates:** EUR5,271 institutions; EUR6,325.20 institutions enhanced access. **URL:** http://www.maik.rssi.ru/cgi-bin/journal.pl?name=kincat&page=sub.

49932 ■ Knit&Mode
Edipresse Publications S.A.
Ul. Bakuninskaya 71
Bldg. 10, 6th Fl.
107082 Moscow, Russia
Ph: 7 495 7751435
Fax: 7 495 7751434
Publication E-mail: n.filkina@konliga.ru

Publisher E-mail: groupe@edipresse.com
Magazine featuring knitting and fashion. **Freq:** 11/yr. **Key Personnel:** Galina Arefieva, Director; Galina Mednikova, Ch. Ed. **URL:** http://www.edipresse.com/knittingsewing/knitmode. **Circ:** ‡15,900

49933 ■ Kollektsia Idei
Edipresse Publications S.A.
Ul. Bakuninskaya 71
Bldg. 10, 6th Fl.
107082 Moscow, Russia
Ph: 7 495 7751435
Fax: 7 495 7751434
Publication E-mail: ideas@konliga.ru
Publisher E-mail: groupe@edipresse.com
Magazine providing craft ideas and activities for children and their parents. **Freq:** Biweekly. **Key Personnel:** Galina Arefieva, Director; Elena Tsygarovskaya, Ch. Ed. **URL:** http://www.edipresse.com/parentschildren/kollektsia-idei. **Circ:** ‡24,800

49934 ■ Kulinarny Practicum
Edipresse Publications S.A.
Ul. Bakuninskaya 71
Bldg. 10, 6th Fl.
107082 Moscow, Russia
Ph: 7 495 7751435
Fax: 7 495 7751434
Publisher E-mail: groupe@edipresse.com
Magazine focusing on cooking and dining at home. **Freq:** 10/yr. **Key Personnel:** Daria Nemtsova, Director; Elena Gurova, Ch. Ed. **URL:** http://www.edipresse.com/fooddining/kulinarny-practicum. **Circ:** ‡120,000

49935 ■ Laser Physics
Maik Nauka/Interperiodica Publishing
Moscow State Engineering Physics Institute
31 Kashirskoe Shosse
115409 Moscow, Russia
Ph: 7 495 1482780
Fax: 7 495 1482780
Publication E-mail: yevseyev@theor.mephi.ru
Publisher E-mail: compmg@maik.ru
Journal offering a comprehensive view of theoretical and experimental laser research and applications by top authors with articles covering every aspect of modern laser physics and quantum electronics, emphasizing physical effects in various media (solid, gaseous, liquid) leading to the generation of laser radiation; peculiarities of propagation of laser radiation; problems involving impact of laser radiation on various substances and the emerging physical effects, including coherent ones; the applied use of lasers and laser spectroscopy; the processing and storage of information. **Founded:** 1990. **Freq:** Monthly. **Key Personnel:** Pavel P. Pashinin, Editor-in-Chief; Aleksey M. Zheltikov, Editorial Board, zheltikov@phys.msu.ru; Sergey N. Bagayev, Editorial Board, bagayev@laser.nsc.ru; Zhores I. Alferov, Editorial Board, zhores.alferov@pop.ioffe.rssi.ru; Vanderlei S. Bagnato, Editorial Board, vander@if.sc.usp.br. **ISSN:** 1054-660X. **Subscription Rates:** EUR3,209 institutions print incl. free access or e-only; EUR3,850.80 institutions print incl. enhanced access. **Remarks:** Advertising not accepted. **URL:** http://www.lasphys.com/lasphys.htm. **Circ:** (Not Reported)

49936 ■ Lechaim
Federation of Jewish Communities
Rizhskaya sq., 1/3
127055 Moscow, Russia
Ph: 7 495 7923110
Magazine featuring news, memoirs, Torah studies, Jewish culture and art, literature and exclusive interviews. **Freq:** Monthly. **Key Personnel:** Boruch Gorin, Ch. Ed. **URL:** http://www.fjc.ru/departments/DeptDetail.asp?AID=84076. **Circ:** ‡54,000

49937 ■ Lena Rukodelie
Edipresse Publications S.A.
Ul. Bakuninskaya 71
Bldg. 10, 6th Fl.
107082 Moscow, Russia
Ph: 7 495 7751435
Fax: 7 495 7751434
Publisher E-mail: groupe@edipresse.com
Magazine featuring illustrations and instructions for needlework. **Freq:** Monthly. **Key Personnel:** Galina Arefieva, Director; Galina Mednikova, Ch. Ed. **URL:** http://www.edipresse.com/knittingsewing/lena-rukodelie. **Circ:** ‡20,600

49938 ■ Lithology and Mineral Resources
Maik Nauka/Interperiodica Publishing
Geological Institute (GIN), Russian Academy of Sciences
Pyzhevskii per. 7
109017 Moscow, Russia
Ph: 8 495 9516685
Publication E-mail: rnedumov@yandex.ru
Publisher E-mail: compmg@maik.ru
Journal covering a wide range of problems related to the formation of sedimentary rocks and ores. **Founded:** 1963. **Freq:** Bimonthly. **Key Personnel:** Dr. Galina Yu. Butuzova, Dep. Ed.-in-Ch.; Dibya R. Sakya, PhD, Editor; Vladimir N. Kholodov, Editor-in-Chief; Yurii O. Gavrilov, PhD, Editorial Board; Nikolai P. Chamov, Editorial Board; Boris P. Zolotarev, Editorial Board; Oleg V. Yapaskurt, Editorial Board; Grigorii A. Mashkovtsev, Editorial Board; Dr. Ivar O. Murdmaa, Editorial Board. **ISSN:** 0024-4902. **Subscription Rates:** EUR4,974 institutions print incl. free access or e-only; EUR5,968.80 institutions print incl. enhanced access. **URL:** http://www.maik.rssi.ru/cgi-bin/journal.pl?name=litmin&page=guid.

49939 ■ Malenkaya Diana
Edipresse Publications S.A.
Ul. Bakuninskaya 71
Bldg. 10, 6th Fl.
107082 Moscow, Russia
Ph: 7 495 7751435
Fax: 7 495 7751434
Publication E-mail: n.filkina@konliga.ru
Publisher E-mail: groupe@edipresse.com
Magazine featuring knitwear fashion and knitting for young people. **Freq:** Monthly. **Key Personnel:** Galina Arefieva, Director; Galina Mednikova, Ch. Ed. **URL:** http://www.edipresse.com/knittingsewing/malenkaya-diana-little-diana. **Circ:** ‡72,350

49940 ■ Mama, eto ya!
Edipresse Publications S.A.
Ul. Bakuninskaya 71
Bldg. 10, 6th Fl.
107082 Moscow, Russia
Ph: 7 495 7751435
Fax: 7 495 7751434
Publisher E-mail: groupe@edipresse.com
Magazine covering young mothers' pregnancy to the toddler years. **Freq:** Monthly. **Key Personnel:** Daria Nemtsova, Director; Yana Kononova, Ch. Ed. **URL:** http://www.edipresse.com/parentschildren/mama-eto-ya. **Circ:** ‡86,740

49941 ■ Medical Care
Meditsina Publishers
Bolshaya Pirogovskaya, 5, Bldg. 2
119435 Moscow, Russia
Ph: 7 95 2453355
Fax: 7 95 2453355
Publisher E-mail: meditsina@mtu-net.ru
Journal covering medical care in Russia. **Founded:** 1993. **Freq:** Bimonthly. **Key Personnel:** Prof. Andrei M. Stochik, Editor-in-Chief. **ISSN:** 0869-7760. **Remarks:** Accepts advertising. **URL:** http://www.medlit.ru/medeng/mp5.htm. **Circ:** (Not Reported)

49942 ■ Medico-Social Expert Evaluation and Rehabilitation
Meditsina Publishers
Bolshaya Pirogovskaya, 5, Bldg. 2
119435 Moscow, Russia
Ph: 7 95 2453355
Fax: 7 95 2453355
Publisher E-mail: meditsina@mtu-net.ru
Journal for specialists of institutions engaged in the problems of disability and invalids. **Founded:** 1998. **Freq:** Quarterly. **Key Personnel:** Prof. Sergei N. Puzin, Editor-in-Chief. **ISSN:** 1560-9537. **Remarks:** Accepts advertising. **URL:** http://www.medlit.ru/medeng/msoz5.htm. **Circ:** (Not Reported)

49943 ■ Molecular Genetics, Microbiology & Virology
Meditsina Publishers
Bolshaya Pirogovskaya, 5, Bldg. 2
119435 Moscow, Russia
Ph: 7 95 2453355
Fax: 7 95 2453355
Publisher E-mail: meditsina@mtu-net.ru
Journal covering theoretical and applied problems of molecular genetics of pro and eukaryotes, molecular microbiology and molecular virology. **Founded:** 1983. **Freq:** Quarterly. **Key Personnel:** Prof. Evgeny D. Sverdlov, Editor-in-Chief. **ISSN:** 0208-0613. **Remarks:** Accepts advertising. **URL:** http://www.medlit.ru/medeng/molg5.htm. **Circ:** (Not Reported)

49944 ■ Molecular Medicine
Meditsina Publishers
Bolshaya Pirogovskaya, 5, Bldg. 2
119435 Moscow, Russia
Ph: 7 95 2453355
Fax: 7 95 2453355
Publisher E-mail: meditsina@mtu-net.ru
Journal covering molecular-cellular regularities of diseases onset, design of novel methods of human diseases diagnosis, prospects of creating highly effective new generation medicines basing on the latest achievements in molecular biology and gene engineering. **Founded:** 2003. **Freq:** Bimonthly. **Key Personnel:** Prof. Michael A. Paltsev, Editor-in-Chief. **ISSN:** 1728-2918. **Remarks:** Accepts advertising. **URL:** http://www.medlit.ru/medeng/molmed5.htm. **Circ:** (Not Reported)

49945 ■ Moscow Mathematical Journal
Independent University of Moscow
Bolshoy Vlasyevskiy Pereulok 11
119002 Moscow, Russia
Ph: 7 495 2414086
Fax: 7 499 7951015
Publication E-mail: mmj@mccme.ru
Publisher E-mail: ium@mccme.ru
Journal presenting research and research-expository papers in mathematics from all over the world in order to bring together different branches of science and to achieve the broadest possible outlook on mathematics. **Freq:** Quarterly. **Key Personnel:** Yu Ilyashenko, Editor; Michael Tsfasman, Editor. **Subscription Rates:** US$270 individuals list price; US$135 individuals special price. **URL:** http://www.ams.org/distribution/mmj/.

49946 ■ Moscow News
4, Zubovsky Blvd.
119021 Moscow, Russia
Ph: 7 495 6456565
Publication E-mail: info@mnweekly.ru
Publisher E-mail: info@mnweekly.ru
Publication featuring news, opinion, and commentary. **Founded:** 1930. **Key Personnel:** Sergei Roy, Editor-in-Chief, roy@mn.ru. **ISSN:** 0027-1306. **Subscription Rates:** 660 Rb individuals. **Remarks:** Accepts advertising. **URL:** http://www.mnweekly.ru. **Ad Rates:** BW: 2,900 Rb. **Circ:** 75,000

49947 ■ Natalia
Edipresse Publications S.A.
Ul. Bakuninskaya 71
Bldg. 10, 6th Fl.
107082 Moscow, Russia
Ph: 7 495 7751435
Fax: 7 495 7751434
Publisher E-mail: groupe@edipresse.com
Magazine featuring various knitting styles and patterns. **Freq:** 6/yr. **Key Personnel:** Natalia Zhuravleva, Ed.; Galina Arefieva, Director. **URL:** http://www.edipresse.com/knittingsewing/natalia; http://www.natalia-knitting.ru/. **Circ:** ‡14,300

49948 ■ Obstetrics & Gynaecology
Meditsina Publishers
Bolshaya Pirogovskaya, 5, Bldg. 2
119435 Moscow, Russia
Ph: 7 95 2453355
Fax: 7 95 2453355
Publisher E-mail: meditsina@mtu-net.ru
Journal covering modern achievements in the obstetrics, gynaecology and other related fields. **Founded:** 1922. **Freq:** Bimonthly. **Key Personnel:** Prof. Gennady T. Sukhikh, Editor-in-Chief. **ISSN:** 0300-9092. **Remarks:** Accepts advertising. **URL:** http://www.medlit.ru/medeng/akush5.htm. **Circ:** (Not Reported)

49949 ■ Oceanology
Maik Nauka/Interperiodica Publishing
Nakhimovskii pr. 36
117997 Moscow, Russia
Ph: 7 495 1246381
Publication E-mail: varhipk@ocean.ru
Publisher E-mail: compmg@maik.ru
Journal publishing original papers in all fields of theoretical and experimental research in physical, chemical, biological, geological and technical oceanology. **Founded:** 1961. **Freq:** Bimonthly. **Key Personnel:** Mikhail N. Koshlyakov, Dep. Ed.-in-Ch.; Boris N. Filyushkin, Exec. Ed.-in-Ch.; M.S. Barash, Editorial Board; Yury S. Dolotov, Dep. Ed.-in-Ch.; A.G. Zatsepin, Editorial Board; Mikhail V. Flint, Dep. Ed.-in-Ch. **ISSN:** 0001-4370. **Subscription Rates:** EUR1,496 institutions print incl. free access or e-only; EUR1,795.20 institutions print incl. enhanced access. **Remarks:** Advertising not accepted. **URL:** http://www.maik.ru/cgi-bin/journal.pl?name=ocean&page=main. **Circ:** (Not Reported)

49950 ■ Oil & Gas Eurasia
Eurasia Press, Inc.
67 Koptevskaya Ul., Office 111,
125009 Moscow, Russia
Ph: 7 495 7818837
Fax: 7 495 7818836
Magazine highlighting oilfield technology and equipment in non-technical language for senior managers in Russian companies. **Freq:** Monthly 10/yr. **Trim Size:** 210 x 297. **Key Personnel:** Pat Davis Szymczak, Ed.-in-Ch. & Publisher, p.szymczak@eurasiapress.com; Bojan Soc, Managing Editor, me@eurasiapress.com. **Subscription Rates:** US$300 individuals print. **Remarks:** Accepts advertising. **URL:** http://www.oilandgaseurasia.com/?action=About. **Ad Rates:** 4C: 4,350 Rb. **Circ:** Combined △12,723

49951 ■ Pathological Physiology & Experimental Therapy
Meditsina Publishers
Bolshaya Pirogovskaya, 5, Bldg. 2
119435 Moscow, Russia
Ph: 7 95 2453355
Fax: 7 95 2453355
Publisher E-mail: meditsina@mtu-net.ru
Journal covering materials on pressing problems of modern theoretical medicine. **Founded:** 1957. **Freq:** Quarterly. **Key Personnel:** Prof. Boris B. Moroz, Editor-in-Chief. **ISSN:** 0031-2991. **Remarks:** Accepts advertising. **URL:** http://www.medlit.ru/medeng/patf5.htm. **Circ:** (Not Reported)

49952 ■ Pattern Recognition and Image Analysis
Maik Nauka/Interperiodica Publishing
ul. Vavilova 40
119991 Moscow, Russia
Ph: 7 499 1359033
Fax: 7 499 1359033
Publication E-mail: igourevi@ccas.ru
Publisher E-mail: compmg@maik.ru
Peer-reviewed journal featuring top papers in pattern recognition, image recognition, analysis, understanding and processing and publishing concise articles covering theory, methodology and practical applications including topics such as mathematical theory of pattern recognition, raw data representation, computer vision, image processing, machine learning, computer graphics, data and knowledge bases, neural nets, software, specialized computer architectures, applications and related areas. **Freq:** Quarterly. **Key Personnel:** Prof. Yuri I. Zhuravlev, Editor-in-Chief; Prof. Gunilla Borgefors, Editorial Board; Prof. Sergey V. Ablameyko, Editorial Board; Prof. Horst Bunke, Editorial Board; Prof. Stanislav V. Emelyanov, Editorial Board; Prof. Olivier Faugeras, Editorial Board. **ISSN:** 1054-6618. **Subscription Rates:** EUR1,262 institutions print incl. free access or e-only; EUR1,514.40 institutions print incl. enhanced access. **Remarks:** Advertising not accepted. **URL:** http://www.maik.ru/cgi-bin/journal.pl?name=patrec&page=main. **Circ:** (Not Reported)

49953 ■ Pediatric Surgery
Meditsina Publishers
Bolshaya Pirogovskaya, 5, Bldg. 2
119435 Moscow, Russia
Ph: 7 95 2453355
Fax: 7 95 2453355
Publisher E-mail: meditsina@mtu-net.ru
Journal covering general pediatric surgery. **Founded:** 1996. **Freq:** Bimonthly. **Key Personnel:** Prof. Yuri F. Isakov, Editor-in-Chief. **ISSN:** 1560-9510. **Remarks:** Accepts advertising. **URL:** http://www.medlit.ru/medeng/dx5.htm. **Circ:** (Not Reported)

Circulation: * = ABC; △ = BPA; ♦ = CAC; • = CCAB; □ = VAC; ⊕ = PO Statement; ‡ = Publisher's Report; Boldface figures = sworn; Light figures = estimated.

49954 ■ Petroleum Chemistry
Maik Nauka/Interperiodica Publishing
Neftekhimiya
Leninskii pr. 29
117912 Moscow, Russia
Ph: 7 495 9554308
Fax: 7 495 9554325
Publication E-mail: petroch@ips.ac.ru
Publisher E-mail: compmg@maik.ru
Journal offering original papers on and reviews of theoretical and experimental studies concerned with current problems of petroleum chemistry and processing such as chemical composition of crude oils and natural gas liquids; petroleum refining (cracking, hydrocracking, and catalytic reforming); catalysts for petrochemical processes (hydrogenation, isomerization, oxidation, hydroformylation, etc.); activation and catalytic transformation of hydrocarbons and other components of petroleum, natural gas, and other complex organic mixtures; new petrochemicals including lubricants and additives; environmental problems; and information on scientific meetings relevant to these areas. **Founded:** 1961. **Freq:** Bimonthly. **Key Personnel:** Salambek N. Khadzhiev, Editor-in-Chief; Dr. Evgenii I. Bagrii, Dep. Ed.-in-Ch.; Dr. Lyubov K. Altunina, Editorial Board; Dr. Oleg P. Parenago, Exec. Ed.-in-Ch.; Guram N. Gordadze, Editorial Board; Ramiz G. Rizaev, Editorial Board. **ISSN:** 0965-5441. **Subscription Rates:** EUR5,103 institutions print incl. free access or e-only; EUR6,123.60 institutions print incl. enhanced access. **Remarks:** Advertising not accepted. **URL:** http://www.maik.ru/cgi-bin/journal.pl?name=petrchem&page=main. **Circ:** (Not Reported)

49955 ■ Petrology
Maik Nauka/Interperiodica Publishing
Staromonetny per. 35
109017 Moscow, Russia
Ph: 7 499 2308298
Fax: 7 495 9511587
Publication E-mail: petrolog@igem.ru
Publisher E-mail: compmg@maik.ru
Journal of magmatic, metamorphic, and experimental petrology, mineralogy, and geochemistry offering comprehensive information on all multidisciplinary aspects of theoretical, experimental and applied petrology. **Freq:** Bimonthly. **Key Personnel:** Prof. Oleg A. Bogatikov, Editor-in-Chief; Prof. Sergei P. Korikovsky, Dep. Ed.-in-Ch.; Prof. Andrey V. Girnis, Exec. Ed.-in-Ch.; V.A. Glebovitskii, Editorial Board; Prof. N.I. Dobretsov, Editorial Board; N.P. Yushkin, Editorial Board; Dr. A.B. Kotov, Editorial Board; Prof. F.A. Letnikov, Editorial Board; Prof. A.A. Marakushev, Editorial Board. **ISSN:** 0869-5911. **Subscription Rates:** EUR1,780 institutions print incl. free access or e-only; EUR1,136 institutions print incl. enhanced access. **Remarks:** Advertising not accepted. **URL:** http://www.maik.ru/cgi-bin/journal.pl?name=petreng&page=main. **Circ:** (Not Reported)

49956 ■ Physics of Atomic Nuclei
Maik Nauka/Interperiodica Publishing
Profsoyuznaia St. 90
117997 Moscow, Russia
Ph: 7 953 361600
Fax: 7 953 360666
Publication E-mail: yadfiz@maik.ru
Publisher E-mail: compmg@maik.ru
Russian journal on elementary particles and nuclei. Experimental and theoretical studies of nuclear physics are covered. **Founded:** 1965. **Freq:** Monthly. **Key Personnel:** Yurii G. Abov, Editor-in-Chief; Andrei R. Isaakyan, Editor; V.V. Kulikov, Exec. Ed.-in-Ch. **ISSN:** 1063-7788. **Subscription Rates:** EUR5,827 institutions; EUR6,992.40 institutions enhanced access. **URL:** http://www.maik.rssi.ru/cgi-bin/journal.pl?name=nuclphys&page=main.

49957 ■ Physics of Particles and Nuclei Letters
Maik Nauka/Interperiodica Publishing
Profsoyuznaia St. 90
117997 Moscow, Russia
Ph: 7 953 361600
Fax: 7 953 360666
Publication E-mail: pepan@jinr.ru
Publisher E-mail: compmg@maik.ru
Journal publishing articles with results of the original theoretical, experimental, scientific-technical, methodical and applied research, covering subjects such as theoretical physics, elementary particle physics, relativistic nuclear physics, nuclear physics and related problems in other branches of physics, neutron physics, condensed matter physics, physics and technique at low temperature, physics and technique of accelerators, physical experimental instruments and methods, physical computer experiments, applied research in these branches of physics and radiology, ecology and nuclear medicine. **Freq:** Bimonthly. **Key Personnel:** Alexei N. Sissakian, Editor-in-Chief; A.I. Malakhov, Dep. Ed.-in-Ch.; D.V. Shirkov, Dep. Ed.-in-Ch. **ISSN:** 1547-4771. **Subscription Rates:** EUR5,302 institutions print incl. free access or e-only; EUR6,362.40 institutions print incl. enhanced access. **URL:** http://www.maik.ru/cgi-bin/journal.pl?name=physpnlt&page=address.

49958 ■ Physitherapy, Balneology and Rehabilitation
Meditsina Publishers
Bolshaya Pirogovskaya, 5, Bldg. 2
119435 Moscow, Russia
Ph: 7 95 2453355
Fax: 7 95 2453355
Publisher E-mail: meditsina@mtu-net.ru
Journal for physiotherapy doctors. **Founded:** 2002. **Freq:** Bimonthly. **Key Personnel:** Prof. Vasily M. Bogolyubov, Editor-in-Chief. **ISSN:** 1681-3456. **Remarks:** Accepts advertising. **URL:** http://www.medlit.ru/medeng/fizter5.htm. **Circ:** (Not Reported)

49959 ■ Plasma Physics Reports
Maik Nauka/Interperiodica Publishing
Profsoyuznaya ul. 90
117997 Moscow, Russia
Ph: 7 495 3360700
Publication E-mail: plasphys@maik.ru
Publisher E-mail: compmg@maik.ru
Journal covering such topics as high-temperature plasma physics connected with the problem of controlled nuclear fusion based on magnetic and inertial confinement; physics of cosmic plasma, including magnetosphere plasma, sun and stellar plasma, etc.; gas discharge plasma and plasma generated by laser and particle beams and also publishing papers on such related topics as plasma electronics, generation of radiation in plasma and plasma diagnostics. **Founded:** 1975. **Freq:** Monthly. **Key Personnel:** Vitalii D. Shafranov, Editor-in-Chief; Nikolai L. Aleksandrov, Editorial Board; Lev M. Kovrizhnykh, Dep. Ed.-in-Ch.; A.S. Sakharov, Editor; Vladimir V. Arsenin, Editorial Board; Victor I. Ilgisonis, Editorial Board. **ISSN:** 1063-780X. **Subscription Rates:** EUR4,103 institutions print incl. free access or e-only; EUR4,923.60 institutions print incl. enhanced access. **Remarks:** Advertising not accepted. **URL:** http://www.maik.ru/cgi-bin/journal.pl?name=plasphys&page=main. **Circ:** (Not Reported)

49960 ■ Polymer Science
Maik Nauka/Interperiodica Publishing
Leninskii pr. 29
119991 Moscow, Russia
Ph: 7 495 9554895
Fax: 7 495 6338520
Publication E-mail: vms@ips.ac.ru
Publisher E-mail: compmg@maik.ru
Offers a comprehensive view of all multidisciplinary aspects of theoretical and experimental polymer research and application. **Founded:** 1959. **Freq:** Monthly. **Key Personnel:** Prof. Eduard F. Oleinik, Dep. Ed.-in-Ch.; Prof. Vyacheslav V. Kireev, Exec. Ed.-in-Ch.; Aleksandr A. Berlin, Editorial Board. **ISSN:** 0965-545X. **URL:** http://www.maik.rssi.ru/cgi-bin/journal.pl?name=polscia&page=main. **Circ:** Paid 1,000

49961 ■ Polymer Science, Series C
Maik Nauka/Interperiodica Publishing
Profsoyuznaia St. 90
117997 Moscow, Russia
Ph: 7 953 361600
Fax: 7 953 360666
Publisher E-mail: compmg@maik.ru
Journal including only invited papers, such as reviews, and personal points of view in the fast developing areas of polymer science. **Founded:** 1959. **Freq:** Annual. **Key Personnel:** Prof. Eduard F. Oleinik, Dep. Ed.-in-Ch.; Vyacheslav V. Kireev, Exec. Ed.-in-Ch.; Aleksandr A. Berlin, Editorial Board. **ISSN:** 1811-2382. **URL:** http://www.maik.rssi.ru/cgi-bin/journal.pl?name=polscic&page=main.

49962 ■ Problems of Biological, Medical and Pharmaceutical Chemistry
Meditsina Publishers
Bolshaya Pirogovskaya, 5, Bldg. 2
119435 Moscow, Russia
Ph: 7 95 2453355
Fax: 7 95 2453355
Publisher E-mail: meditsina@mtu-net.ru
Journal covering practical and theoretical aspects of biological, medical and pharmaceutical chemistry. **Founded:** 1998. **Freq:** Quarterly. **Key Personnel:** Prof. Evgeny S. Severin, Editor-in-Chief. **ISSN:** 1560-9596. **Remarks:** Accepts advertising. **URL:** http://www.medlit.ru/medeng/vblox5.htm. **Circ:** (Not Reported)

49963 ■ Problems of Endocrinology
Meditsina Publishers
Bolshaya Pirogovskaya, 5, Bldg. 2
119435 Moscow, Russia
Ph: 7 95 2453355
Fax: 7 95 2453355
Publisher E-mail: meditsina@mtu-net.ru
Journal covering advances made in the field of endocrinology by Russian and foreign researchers. **Founded:** 1955. **Freq:** Bimonthly. **Key Personnel:** Prof. Viktor P. Fedotov, Editor-in-Chief. **ISSN:** 0375-9660. **Remarks:** Accepts advertising. **URL:** http://www.medlit.ru/medeng/probe5.htm. **Circ:** (Not Reported)

49964 ■ Problems of Health Resort Treatment, Physiotherapy & Exercise Therapy
Meditsina Publishers
Bolshaya Pirogovskaya, 5, Bldg. 2
119435 Moscow, Russia
Ph: 7 95 2453355
Fax: 7 95 2453355
Publisher E-mail: meditsina@mtu-net.ru
Journal covering physiological and therapeutic effect of physical and health resorts. **Founded:** 1923. **Freq:** Bimonthly. **Key Personnel:** Prof. Alexander N. Razumov, Editor-in-Chief. **ISSN:** 0042-8787. **Remarks:** Accepts advertising. **URL:** http://www.medlit.ru/medeng/vkur5.htm. **Circ:** (Not Reported)

49965 ■ Problems of Social Hygiene, Health Care & History of Medicine
Meditsina Publishers
Bolshaya Pirogovskaya, 5, Bldg. 2
119435 Moscow, Russia
Ph: 7 95 2453355
Fax: 7 95 2453355
Publisher E-mail: meditsina@mtu-net.ru
Journal covering problems of social hygiene, development of public health service and history of medicine. **Founded:** 1994. **Freq:** Bimonthly. **Key Personnel:** Prof. Oleg P. Schepin, Editor-in-Chief. **ISSN:** 0869-866X. **Remarks:** Accepts advertising. **URL:** http://www.medlit.ru/medeng/prsoz5.htm. **Circ:** (Not Reported)

49966 ■ Problems of Tuberculosis
Meditsina Publishers
Bolshaya Pirogovskaya, 5, Bldg. 2
119435 Moscow, Russia
Ph: 7 95 2453355
Fax: 7 95 2453355
Publisher E-mail: meditsina@mtu-net.ru
Journal covering problems of epidemiology and organization of tuberculosis control and its prophylaxis, clinic and treatment. **Founded:** 1923. **Freq:** Bimonthly. **Key Personnel:** Prof. Mikhail I. Perelman, Editor-in-Chief. **ISSN:** 0032-9533. **Remarks:** Accepts advertising. **URL:** http://www.medlit.ru/medeng/prtub5.htm. **Circ:** (Not Reported)

49967 ■ Problems of Virology
Meditsina Publishers
Bolshaya Pirogovskaya, 5, Bldg. 2
119435 Moscow, Russia
Ph: 7 95 2453355
Fax: 7 95 2453355
Publisher E-mail: meditsina@mtu-net.ru
Journal covering advances in virology in Russia and abroad. **Founded:** 1956. **Freq:** Bimonthly. **Key Personnel:** Prof. Dmitry K. Lvov, Editor-in-Chief. **ISSN:** 0507-4088. **Remarks:** Accepts advertising. **URL:** http://www.medlit.ru/medeng/vvir5.htm. **Circ:** (Not Reported)

49968 ■ Protection of Metals
Maik Nauka/Interperiodica Publishing
Maronovskii per. 26
119991 Moscow, Russia
Ph: 7 495 9554684
Publication E-mail: m-protect@maik.ru
Publisher E-mail: compmg@maik.ru
Journal covering all aspects of the theory and practice of corrosion and corrosion protection of metallic

materials. **Founded:** 1964. **Freq:** Bimonthly. **Key Personnel:** Vadim M. Novakovskii, Asst. Ed.; Yurii M. Polukarov, Editorial Board, polukarov@lmm.physchem.msk.ru; Andrei I. Marshakov, Editorial Board; Nikolai P. Aleshin, Editorial Board; Vladimir A. Kotenev, Dep. Ed.-in-Ch.; Vladimir V. Arslanov, Editorial Board; Aslan Yu Tsivadze, Editor-in-Chief. **ISSN:** 0033-1732. **Subscription Rates:** EUR4,743 institutions print incl. free access or e-only; EUR5,691.60 institutions print incl. enhanced access. **URL:** http://www.maik.rssi.ru/cgi-perl/journal.pl?name=protmet&page=main.

49969 ■ Quantum Electronics
Turpion - Moscow Ltd.
MIAN
8 Gubkina St., Rm. 915
119991 Moscow, Russia
Ph: 7 495 1354509
Fax: 7 495 9300604
Publisher E-mail: admin@turpion.ru
Journal covering laser research and its applications. **Founded:** 1971. **Freq:** Monthly. **Key Personnel:** O.N. Krokhin, Editor-in-Chief; I.B. Kovsh, Assoc. Ed.; A.S. Semenov, Assoc. Ed. **ISSN:** 1063-7818. **Subscription Rates:** US$4,159 individuals print and online, rest of world; 2,312 individuals print and online, rest of world; US$3,743 individuals online; 2,081 individuals online, rest of world; US$416 single issue; 231 single issue. **URL:** http://www.turpion.org/php/homes/pa.phtml?jrnid=qe.

49970 ■ Regular & Chaotic Dynamics
Turpion - Moscow Ltd.
MIAN
8 Gubkina St., Rm. 915
119991 Moscow, Russia
Ph: 7 495 1354509
Fax: 7 495 9300604
Publisher E-mail: admin@turpion.ru
Peer-reviewed Journal featuring original research results in the analysis of regular and stochastic behavior in determined dynamic systems that arise in classical mechanics, physics and in other areas. **Founded:** 1996. **Freq:** Quarterly. **Key Personnel:** V.V. Kozlov, Editor-in-Chief; L.A. Gazizullina, Managing Editor; A.V. Borisov, Assoc. Ed. **ISSN:** 1560-3547. **URL:** http://www.turpion.org/php/homes/pa.phtml?jrnid=rd.

49971 ■ Russian Art
Edipresse Publications S.A.
Ul. Bakuninskaya 71
Bldg. 10, 6th Fl.
107082 Moscow, Russia
Ph: 7 495 7751435
Fax: 7 495 7751434
Publication E-mail: russart@konliga.ru
Publisher E-mail: groupe@edipresse.com
Magazine covering the Russian world of art. **Freq:** Quarterly. **Key Personnel:** Raisa Neyaglova-Kolosova, Director. **URL:** http://www.edipresse.com/en/par_pays/russie/edipresse_konliga/magazines/russian_art. **Circ:** ‡7,000

49972 ■ Russian Chemical Reviews
Turpion - Moscow Ltd.
c/o Tatyana Teplova, Mng. Ed.
N D. Zelinsky Institute of Organic Chemistry
Russian Academy of Sciences
Leninsky Prospekt, 47
119992 Moscow, Russia
Ph: 70 951 358797
Fax: 70 951 358860
Publisher E-mail: admin@turpion.ru
Periodical covering most aspects of modern chemistry. **Founded:** 1960. **Freq:** Monthly. **Key Personnel:** Tatyana N. Teplova, Managing Editor, ukh@ioc.ac.ru; Oleg M. Nefedov, Editor-in-Chief; M. Yu Antipin, Editorial Board; L.A. Gribov, Editorial Board; S.M. Aldoshin, Editorial Board; S.O. Bachurin, Editorial Board. **ISSN:** 0036-021X. **Subscription Rates:** US$2,632 individuals print and online; 1,577 individuals print and online; US$2,369 individuals online; 1,419 individuals online; US$263 single issue; 158 single issue. **URL:** http://www.uspkhim.ru/rcr.html.

49973 ■ Russian Digital
SPN Publishing Company
4a Novodanilovsky nab
117105 Moscow, Russia
Magazine featuring world of digital electronics and technologies on the Russian market. **Founded:** 2000. **Freq:** Monthly. **Key Personnel:** Mikhail Genin, Editor-in-Chief. **Remarks:** Accepts advertising. **URL:** http://www.spn.ru/publishing. **Ad Rates:** 4C: 208,500 Rb. **Circ:** 130,000

49974 ■ Russian Entomological Journal
KMK Scientific Press Ltd.
c/o Dr. K.G. Mikhailov
Zoological Museum MGU
Bolshaya Nikitskaya Str. 6
125009 Moscow, Russia
Publisher E-mail: kmk2000@online.ru
Journal emphasizing the morphology, taxonomy, zoogeography, evolution and development of insects, both living and fossil, as well as plant protection problems. **Founded:** 1992. **Freq:** Quarterly. **Key Personnel:** Dr. Kirill G. Mikhailov, Editorial Board; Dr. L.N. Medvedev, Editor-in-Chief; Dr. A.V. Sviridov, Editorial Board; Dr. V.E. Gokhman, Editorial Board; Dr. A.V. Antropov, Editorial Board; Dr. A.V. Matalin, Editorial Board; Prof. A.P. Rasnitsyn, Editorial Board. **ISSN:** 0132-8069. **Subscription Rates:** US$50 individuals print online; US$60 institutions print online. **Remarks:** Accepts advertising. **URL:** http://kmk.entomology.ru/rej.htm. **Ad Rates:** BW: US$50, 4C: US$100. **Circ:** (Not Reported)

49975 ■ Russian Journal of Bioorganic Chemistry
Maik Nauka/Interperiodica Publishing
Shemyakin-Ovchinnikov Institute of Bioorganic Chemistry
ul. Miklukho-Maklaya 16/10
117997 Moscow, Russia
Ph: 7 495 3307783
Fax: 7 495 3357103
Publication E-mail: rjbc@ibch.ru
Publisher E-mail: compmg@maik.ru
Journal for scientists, teachers at universities and higher schools, students, and researchers at industrial, medical, agricultural and environmental- control laboratories, publishing reviews and the results of original experimental and theoretical investigations on the structure functions, structure-activity relationships, and synthesis of biopolymers such as proteins, nucleic acids, polysaccharides, mixed biopolymers and their complexes and low molecular-mass biologically active compounds (peptides, sugars, lipids, and antibiotics). **Founded:** 1975. **Freq:** Bimonthly. **Key Personnel:** Vadim T. Ivanov, Editor-in-Chief; Evgenii V. Grishin, Dep. Ed.-in-Ch.; Sergei A. Luk'yanov, Dep. Ed.-in-Ch. **ISSN:** 1068-1620. **Subscription Rates:** EUR3,402 institutions print incl. free access or e-only; EUR4,082.40 institutions print incl. enhanced access. **Remarks:** Advertising not accepted. **URL:** http://www.maik.ru/cgi-bin/journal.pl?name=biochem&page=main. **Circ:** (Not Reported)

49976 ■ Russian Journal of Biotechnology
Maik Nauka/Interperiodica Publishing
Proezd 1-st Dorozhnyi 1
113545 Moscow, Russia
Publisher E-mail: compmg@maik.ru
Journal published only in Russian containing articles with experimental data and analytical reviews that cover all aspects of modern biotechnology: the search, creation, and investigation of producers of biologically active substances, improvement of the technique of the production, and use of biologicals and environmental problems biotechnology causes or is capable of solving. **Freq:** Quarterly. **Key Personnel:** Vladimir G. Debabov, Editor-in-Chief. **ISSN:** 0234-2758. **Remarks:** Advertising not accepted. **URL:** http://www.maik.ru/cgi-bin/journal.pl?name=biotech&page=main. **Circ:** (Not Reported)

49977 ■ Russian Journal of Inorganic Chemistry
Maik Nauka/Interperiodica Publishing
Kurnakov Institute of General & Inorganic Chemistry
Leninskii pr. 31
119991 Moscow, Russia
Ph: 7 495 9543397
Publication E-mail: neochem@igic.ras.ru
Publisher E-mail: compmg@maik.ru
Journal covering research into the synthesis and properties of inorganic compounds, coordination compounds, high-temperature semiconductors, physicochemical analysis of inorganic systems, theoretical inorganic chemistry and related topics. **Founded:** 1956. **Freq:** Monthly. **Key Personnel:** Nikolai T. Kuznetsov, Editor-in-Chief; L.A. Aslanov, Editorial Board; V.T. Kalinnikov,

Editorial Board; F.A. Cotton, Editorial Board; C. Furlani, Editorial Board; V.V. Boldyrev, Editorial Board; I.L. Eremenko, Editorial Board; Svetlana P. Petrosyants, Exec. Ed.-in-Ch. **ISSN:** 0036-0236. **Subscription Rates:** EUR5,613 institutions print incl. free access or e-only; EUR6,735.60 institutions print incl. enhanced access. **URL:** http://www.maik.rssi.ru/cgi-bin/journal.pl?name=inrgchem&page=main.

49978 ■ Russian Journal of Oncology
Meditsina Publishers
Bolshaya Pirogovskaya, 5, Bldg. 2
119435 Moscow, Russia
Ph: 7 95 2453355
Fax: 7 95 2453355
Publisher E-mail: meditsina@mtu-net.ru
Journal covering clinical and experimental oncology. **Founded:** 1996. **Freq:** Bimonthly. **Key Personnel:** Prof. Valery I. Chissov, Editor-in-Chief. **ISSN:** 1028-9984. **Remarks:** Accepts advertising. **URL:** http://www.medlit.ru/medeng/onkj5.htm. **Circ:** (Not Reported)

49979 ■ Russian Journal of Pediatrics
Meditsina Publishers
Bolshaya Pirogovskaya, 5, Bldg. 2
119435 Moscow, Russia
Ph: 7 95 2453355
Fax: 7 95 2453355
Publisher E-mail: meditsina@mtu-net.ru
Journal covering problems in health care of children and adolescents. **Founded:** 1997. **Freq:** Bimonthly. **Key Personnel:** Prof. Alexander A. Baranov, Editor-in-Chief. **ISSN:** 1560-9561. **Remarks:** Accepts advertising. **URL:** http://www.medlit.ru/medeng/pedj5.htm. **Circ:** (Not Reported)

49980 ■ Russian Journal of Physical Chemistry
Maik Nauka/Interperiodica Publishing
Maronovskii per. 26
119991 Moscow, Russia
Ph: 7 495 2382188
Publication E-mail: belenkina@maik.ru
Publisher E-mail: compmg@maik.ru
Offers a comprehensive review of theoretical and experimental research not only from the Russian Academy of Sciences but also from the entire Commonwealth of Independent States. **Founded:** 1930. **Freq:** Monthly. **Key Personnel:** Dr. Valerii V. Lunin, Editor-in-Chief; Nikolai F. Stepanov, Dep. Ed.-in-Ch.; Vitalii P. Chizhkov, Editorial Board; Dr. Leonid M. Kustov, Exec. Ed.-in-Ch.; Dr. Mikhail V. Alfimov, Editorial Board; Dr. Anatolii L. Buchachenko, Editorial Board. **ISSN:** 0036-0244. **Subscription Rates:** EUR5,545 institutions; EUR6,654 institutions enhanced access. **URL:** http://www.maik.ru/cgi-perl/journal.pl?lang=eng&name=physcha.

49981 ■ Russian Journal of Skin and Sexually Transmitted Diseases
Meditsina Publishers
Bolshaya Pirogovskaya, 5, Bldg. 2
119435 Moscow, Russia
Ph: 7 95 2453355
Fax: 7 95 2453355
Publisher E-mail: meditsina@mtu-net.ru
Journal covering dermatology, venereology, and dermatooncology. **Founded:** 1998. **Freq:** Bimonthly. **Key Personnel:** Prof. Oleg L. Ivanov, Editor-in-Chief. **ISSN:** 1560-9588. **Remarks:** Accepts advertising. **URL:** http://www.medlit.ru/medeng/kozvn5.htm. **Circ:** (Not Reported)

49982 ■ Russian Journal of Stomatology
Meditsina Publishers
Bolshaya Pirogovskaya, 5, Bldg. 2
119435 Moscow, Russia
Ph: 7 95 2453355
Fax: 7 95 2453355
Publisher E-mail: meditsina@mtu-net.ru
Journal covering information on etiology, clinical picture, differential diagnosis, treatment and prevention of diseases of the face and oral cavity. **Founded:** 1997. **Freq:** Bimonthly. **Key Personnel:** Prof. Mikhail N. Puzin, Editor-in-Chief. **ISSN:** 1560-9553. **Remarks:** Accepts advertising. **URL:** http://www.medlit.ru/medeng/stom5.htm. **Circ:** (Not Reported)

49983 ■ Russian Journal of Theriology
KMK Scientific Press Ltd.
c/o Dr. K.G. Mikhailov
Zoological Museum MGU

Circulation: ★ = ABC; △ = BPA; ◆ = CAC; ● = CCAB; ❑ = VAC; ⊕ = PO Statement; ‡ = Publisher's Report; Boldface figures = sworn; Light figures = estimated.

Gale Directory of Publications & Broadcast Media/147th Ed.   5375

Bolshaya Nikitskaya Str. 6
125009 Moscow, Russia
Publisher E-mail: kmk2000@online.ru
Peer-reviewed journal covering all areas of theriology (taxonomy, phylogeny and evolution, morphology, palaeontology, ecology, zoogeography, faunistics). **Founded:** 2002. **Freq:** Semiannual. **Key Personnel:** Dr. A.O. Averianov, Editor; Alexei V. Abramov, Asst. Ed. **ISSN:** 1682-3540. **Subscription Rates:** US$40 individuals; US$60 institutions. **URL:** http://kmk.entomology.ru/rjt.htm.

49984 ■ Russian Medical Journal
Meditsina Publishers
Bolshaya Pirogovskaya, 5, Bldg. 2
119435 Moscow, Russia
Ph: 7 95 2453355
Fax: 7 95 2453355
Publisher E-mail: meditsina@mtu-net.ru
Journal covering practical problems in the diagnosis and treatment of the major nosological entities as well as the problems of social hygiene and public health organization. **Founded:** 1995. **Freq:** Bimonthly. **Key Personnel:** Prof. Oleg V. Aleksandrov, Editor-in-Chief. **ISSN:** 0869-7760. **Remarks:** Accepts advertising. **URL:** http://www.medlit.ru/medeng/medj5.htm. **Circ:** (Not Reported)

49985 ■ Russian Metallurgy
Maik Nauka/Interperiodica Publishing
Leninskii pr. 49
119991 Moscow, Russia
Ph: 8 499 1359678
Fax: 8 499 1354383
Publication E-mail: eliz@imet.ac.ru
Publisher E-mail: compmg@maik.ru
Journal publishing articles on topics such as physico-chemical properties of metallurgical materials (ores, slags, mattes, and melts of metals and alloys); physico-chemical processes (thermodynamics and kinetics of pyrometallurgical, hydrometal-lurgical, electrochemical, and other processes); theoretical aspects of the processes of metallurgical production; metal forming; thermoplastic and thermochemical treatment; computation and experimental determination of phase diagrams and thermokinetic diagrams; mechanisms and kinetics of phase transformations in metallic materials; relations between the chemical composition, phase and structural states of structural and functional materials and their physicochemical and service properties; interaction between metallicmaterials and external media; effects of radiation on these materials. **Freq:** Bimonthly. **Key Personnel:** Oleg A. Bannykh, Editor-in-Chief; Yurii V. Tsvetkov, Dep. Ed.-in-Ch.; Dr. Kira B. Povarova, Dep. Ed.-in-Ch. **ISSN:** 0036-0295. **Subscription Rates:** EUR2,742 institutions print incl. free access or e-only; EUR3,290.40 institutions print incl. enhanced access. **Remarks:** Advertising not accepted. **URL:** http://www.maik.ru/cgi-bin/journal.pl?name=rusmet&page=main. **Circ:** (Not Reported)

49986 ■ Sabrina
Edipresse Publications S.A.
Ul. Bakuninskaya 71
Bldg. 10, 6th Fl.
107082 Moscow, Russia
Ph: 7 495 7751435
Fax: 7 495 7751434
Publisher E-mail: groupe@edipresse.com
Magazine featuring knitwear and knitting patterns. **Freq:** Monthly. **Key Personnel:** Galina Arefieva, Director; Galina Mednikova, Ch. Ed. **URL:** http://www.edipresse.com/knittingsewing/sabrina. **Circ:** ‡74,880

49987 ■ Sabrina Baby
Edipresse Publications S.A.
Ul. Bakuninskaya 71
Bldg. 10, 6th Fl.
107082 Moscow, Russia
Ph: 7 495 7751435
Fax: 7 495 7751434
Publisher E-mail: groupe@edipresse.com
Magazine featuring knitting patterns for baby and toddler knitwear. **Freq:** 6/yr. **Key Personnel:** Galina Arefieva, Director; Galina Mednikova, Ch. Ed. **URL:** http://www.edipresse.com/knittingsewing/sabrina-baby. **Circ:** ‡6,110

49988 ■ Samaya
Edipresse Publications S.A.
Ul. Bakuninskaya 71

Bldg. 10, 6th Fl.
107082 Moscow, Russia
Ph: 7 495 7751435
Fax: 7 495 7751434
Publication E-mail: samaya@konliga.ru
Publisher E-mail: groupe@edipresse.com
Magazine featuring practical advice for young modern working women. **Freq:** Monthly. **Key Personnel:** Daria Nemtsova, Director; Anastasia Koroleva, Ch. Ed. **URL:** http://www.edipresse.com/womens/samaya; http://www.samaya.ru/. **Circ:** ‡117,350

49989 ■ Sbornik
Turpion - Moscow Ltd.
MIAN
8 Gubkina St., Rm. 915
119991 Moscow, Russia
Ph: 7 495 1354509
Fax: 7 495 9300604
Publisher E-mail: admin@turpion.ru
Peer-reviewed Journal featuring research papers keeping pace with modern trends in contemporary mathematics. **Subtitle:** Mathematics. **Founded:** 1866. **Freq:** Bimonthly. **Key Personnel:** F.H Goldman, Ed. of the English Edition; A.A. Gonchar, Editor-in-Chief; A.T. Fomenko, Editorial Board; A.S. Mishchenko, Editorial Board; A.K. Gushchin, Editorial Board; A.N. Parshin, Editorial Board; S.P. Suetin, Exec. Sec.; V.M. Tikhomirov, Editorial Board. **ISSN:** 1064-5616. **Subscription Rates:** US$2,432 individuals print & online; 1,319 individuals rest of world; US$2,189 individuals online; 1,187 individuals online; US$486 single issue; 264 single issue. **URL:** http://www.turpion.org/php/homes/pa.phtml?jrnid=sm.

49990 ■ Sociology of Medicine
Meditsina Publishers
Bolshaya Pirogovskaya, 5, Bldg. 2
119435 Moscow, Russia
Ph: 7 95 2453355
Fax: 7 95 2453355
Publisher E-mail: meditsina@mtu-net.ru
Journal covering medical and sociological regularities in human health formation and maintenance. **Founded:** 2003. **Freq:** Bimonthly. **Key Personnel:** Prof. Andrey V. Reshetnikov, Editor-in-Chief. **ISSN:** 1723-2810. **Remarks:** Accepts advertising. **URL:** http://www.medlit.ru/medeng/socmed5.htm. **Circ:** (Not Reported)

49991 ■ Stratigraphy and Geological Correlation
Maik Nauka/Interperiodica Publishing
Pyzhevskii per 7
Geological Institute RAS
119017 Moscow, Russia
Ph: 7 495 9512164
Fax: 7 495 9510443
Publication E-mail: zakharov@ginras.ru
Publisher E-mail: compmg@maik.ru
Journal researchers, university professors, students and geologists interested in understanding stratigraphy and the chronological features of the world's geological record, providing coverage of the fundamental and applied aspects of stratigraphy and the correlation of geological events and processes in time and space. **Freq:** Bimonthly. **Key Personnel:** Dr. Victor A. Zakharov, Asst. Ed.; Mikhail A. Semikhatov, Editor-in-Chief, semikhatov@ginran.ru. **ISSN:** 0869-5938. **Subscription Rates:** EUR1,782 institutions print incl. free access or e-only; EUR2,138.40 institutions print incl. enhanced access. **Remarks:** Advertising not accepted. **URL:** http://www.maik.ru/cgi-bin/journal.pl?name=strteng&page=main. **Circ:** (Not Reported)

49992 ■ Studies on Russian Economic Development
Maik Nauka/Interperiodica Publishing
Nakhimovskii pr. 47
117418 Moscow, Russia
Ph: 7 495 1293633
Publisher E-mail: compmg@maik.ru
Journal providing up-to-date information on socioeconomic problems in Russia and CIS countries of interest to those in the world of international business relations and Russian and international political studies. **Freq:** Bimonthly. **Key Personnel:** Viktor V. Ivanter, Editor-in-Chief; Andrei G. Fonotov, Advisory Board; Aleksandr G. Granberg, Advisory Board; Andrei Belousov, Advisory Board; Feliks N. Klotsvog, Advisory Board; Nikolai Ya Petrakov, Advisory Board. **ISSN:** 1075-7007. **Subscription Rates:** EUR1,274 institutions print incl. free access

or e-only; EUR1,528.80 institutions print incl. enhanced access. **Remarks:** Advertising not accepted. **URL:** http://www.maik.ru/cgi-bin/journal.pl?name=rusec&page=main. **Circ:** (Not Reported)

49993 ■ Susanna Rukodeliye
Edipresse Publications S.A.
Ul. Bakuninskaya 71
Bldg. 10, 6th Fl.
107082 Moscow, Russia
Ph: 7 495 7751435
Fax: 7 495 7751434
Publication E-mail: n.filkina@konliga.ru
Publisher E-mail: groupe@edipresse.com
Magazine featuring a variety of clothing, needlework and original patchwork patterns and instructions. **Freq:** Bimonthly. **Key Personnel:** Galina Arefieva, Director; Galina Mednikova, Ch. Ed. **URL:** http://www.edipresse.com/knittingsewing/susanna-rukodeliye. **Circ:** ‡20,980

49994 ■ Susanna Vjazanie
Edipresse Publications S.A.
Ul. Bakuninskaya 71
Bldg. 10, 6th Fl.
107082 Moscow, Russia
Ph: 7 495 7751435
Fax: 7 495 7751434
Publication E-mail: n.filkina@konliga.ru
Publisher E-mail: groupe@edipresse.com
Magazine featuring Italian knitware fashion. **Freq:** Monthly. **Key Personnel:** Galina Arefieva, Director; Galina Mednikova, Ch. Ed. **URL:** http://www.edipresse.com/knittingsewing/susanna-vjazanie-knitting. **Circ:** ‡75,000

49995 ■ Therapeutic Archives
Meditsina Publishers
Bolshaya Pirogovskaya, 5, Bldg. 2
119435 Moscow, Russia
Ph: 7 95 2453355
Fax: 7 95 2453355
Publisher E-mail: meditsina@mtu-net.ru
Journal covering clinical and clinico-experimental studies. **Founded:** 1923. **Freq:** Monthly. **Key Personnel:** Prof. Evgeny I. Chazov, Editor-in-Chief. **ISSN:** 0040-3660. **Remarks:** Accepts advertising. **URL:** http://www.medlit.ru/medeng/tarh5.htm. **Circ:** (Not Reported)

49996 ■ Thermal Engineering
Maik Nauka/Interperiodica Publishing
ul. Krasnokazarmennaya 14
111250 Moscow, Russia
Ph: 7 495 3625598
Fax: 7 495 3625598
Publication E-mail: teploen@mpei.ru
Publisher E-mail: compmg@maik.ru
Journal publishing articles analyzing the current state and perspectives of energy development, design and operation of power engineering equipment such as that at thermal and nuclear power stations, energy conservation and pollution control, the theoretical fundamentals of heat engineering, and non-traditional heat sources. **Freq:** Monthly. **Key Personnel:** Viktor I. Dobrokhotov, Editor-in-Chief; Irina A. Nasokina, Dep. Ed.-in-Ch.; Peter A. Antikain, Editorial Board. **ISSN:** 0040-6015. **Subscription Rates:** EUR2,730 institutions print incl. free access or e-only; EUR3,276 institutions print incl. enhanced access. **Remarks:** Advertising not accepted. **URL:** http://www.maik.ru/cgi-bin/journal.pl?name=thermeng&page=main. **Circ:** (Not Reported)

49997 ■ Thoracic & Cardiovascular Surgery
Meditsina Publishers
Bolshaya Pirogovskaya, 5, Bldg. 2
119435 Moscow, Russia
Ph: 7 95 2453355
Fax: 7 95 2453355
Publisher E-mail: meditsina@mtu-net.ru
Journals covering theoretical and organizational problems of chest surgery and allied fields. **Founded:** 1959. **Freq:** Bimonthly. **Key Personnel:** Prof. Viktor S. Savelyev, Editor-in-Chief. **ISSN:** 0236-2791. **Remarks:** Accepts advertising. **URL:** http://www.medlit.ru/medeng/grudn5.htm. **Circ:** (Not Reported)

49998 ■ Vjazanie Vashe Hobby
Edipresse Publications S.A.
Ul. Bakuninskaya 71
Bldg. 10, 6th Fl.
107082 Moscow, Russia
Ph: 7 495 7751435
Fax: 7 495 7751434

Publisher E-mail: groupe@edipresse.com
Magazine featuring knitting patterns. **Freq:** Monthly. **Key Personnel:** Galina Arefieva, Director; Galina Mednikova, Ch. Ed. **URL:** http://www.edipresse.com/knittingsewing/vjazanie-vashe-hobby. **Circ:** ‡64,900

49999 ■ Vyshitye Kartiny
Edipresse Publications S.A.
Ul. Bakuninskaya 71
Bldg. 10, 6th Fl.
107082 Moscow, Russia
Ph: 7 495 7751435
Fax: 7 495 7751434
Publisher E-mail: groupe@edipresse.com
Magazine featuring patterns for various types of embroidery. **Freq:** Monthly. **Key Personnel:** Galina Arefieva, Director; Galina Mednikova, Ch. Ed. **URL:** http://www.edipresse.com/knittingsewing/vyshitye-kartiny-embroidery. **Circ:** ‡18,100

50000 ■ Avtoradio - 90.3 MHz
ul. 8 March, d.8
127083 Moscow, Russia
Ph: 7 495 2583344
Format: Contemporary Hit Radio (CHR); Educational. **Owner:** Avtoradio, at above address. **Founded:** Apr. 5, 1993. **Operating Hours:** Continuous. **Wattage:** 5000. **URL:** http://www.avtoradio.ru.

Ekho Moskvy - Cherepovets - See Cherepovets

50001 ■ Ekho Moskvy - Moskva - 91.2 MHz
Ekho Moskvy
11 Novvy Arbat
119019 Moscow, Russia
Ph: 7 95 2 029229
Fax: 7 95 2 029102
E-mail: echo@echo.msk.ru
Format: Eclectic. **Owner:** Ekho Moskvy, at above address. **Wattage:** 1000. **URL:** http://www.echo.msk.ru.

Ekho Moskvy - Tula - See Tula

Europa Plus - Vladivostok - See Vladivostok

50002 ■ Hit FM - 107 MHz
3rd Khoroshevskaya ul, d. 12
123298 Moscow, Russia
Ph: 7 495 9951036
E-mail: hitfm@hitfm.ru
Format: Eclectic. **Key Personnel:** Bazhin Vladimir, Gen. Producer; Khokhloma Irina, Editor-in-Chief; Vitalius Starykh, Musical Ed.; Frost Natalie, Traffic Mgr. **URL:** http://www.hitfm.ru.

Hit-FM - Kazan - See Kazan

50003 ■ Hit-FM - Moskva - 107.4 MHz
3-4 Khoroshevskaya ul., d. 12
123298 Moscow, Russia
Ph: 7 495 9951036
E-mail: hitfm@hitfm.ru
Format: Eclectic. **Owner:** Hit-FM, at above address. **Key Personnel:** Vladimir Bazhin, Gen. Producer; Irina Furmanchuk, Editor-in-Chief, hohloma@hitfm.ru. **Wattage:** 10,000. **URL:** http://www.hittm.ru.

Hit-FM - Murmansk - See Murmansk

Hit-FM - Yessentuki - See Yessentuki

Nashe Radio - Ishim - See Ishim

Nashe Radio - Khanty-Mansiysk - See Khanty-Mansiysk

Nashe Radio - Megion - See Megion

Nashe Radio - Noyabrsk - See Noyabrsk

Nashe Radio - Orenburg - See Orenburg

Nashe Radio - Pokachi - See Pokachi

Nashe Radio - Tobolsk - See Tobolsk

Radio Center - See Kurkino

50004 ■ Radio Zinzine-FM - 90.8
Ul. Trifonovskaya, 57
129272 Moscow, Russia
Ph: 7 495 2219909
Fax: 7 495 2219909
E-mail: svetlana@relax-fm.ru
Format: Folk. **Operating Hours:** Continuous. **Ad Rates:** Advertising accepted; rates. available upon request. **URL:** http://www.relaxfm.ru.

Radiostantsiya Radonezh - See Noginsk

50005 ■ Relax-FM - 90.8
Ul. Trifonovskaya, 57
129272 Moscow, Russia
Ph: 7 495 2219909
Fax: 7 495 2219909
E-mail: svetlana@relax-fm.ru
Format: Blues; Jazz. **Founded:** Sept. 11, 2002. **Operating Hours:** 18 hours Daily. **Ad Rates:** Advertising accepted; rates available upon request. **URL:** http://www.relax-fm.ru.

Murmansk

50006 ■ Hit-FM - Murmansk - 105.4 MHz
3 Khoroshevskaya ul., d. 12
123298 Moscow, Russia
Ph: 7 495 9 951036
E-mail: hitfmp@hitfm.ru
Format: Eclectic. **Owner:** Hit-FM, at above address. **Key Personnel:** Vladimir Bazhin, Gen. Producer; Irina Furmanchuk, Editor-in-Chief, hohloma@hitfm.ru. **Wattage:** 4000. **URL:** http://www.hitfm.ru.

Nizhniy Tagil

50007 ■ Radio Ekofond - 103.0 MHz
pr. Lenin 64
622001 Nizhniy Tagil, Russia
Ph: 7 3435 960017
Fax: 7 3435 251801
E-mail: san@ekoradio.ru
Format: Contemporary Hit Radio (CHR). **Owner:** Vserossiyskaya Gosudarstvennaya Teleradiokompaniya (VGTRK, Gov.), Leningradskiy Pr. 22/2, 125124 Moscow, Russia, Fax: 7 495 2142347. **Founded:** Jan. 20, 1997. **Operating Hours:** Continuous. **Key Personnel:** Oleg Dobrodeyev, Chm. **Wattage:** 1000. **Ad Rates:** Advertising accepted; rates available upon request. **URL:** http://www.ekoradio.ru.

Noginsk

50008 ■ Radiostantsiya Radonezh - 846 KHz
Ulitsa Pyatnitskaya 25
115326 Moscow, Russia
Ph: 7 495 9506356
Fax: 7 495 9506356
E-mail: radonezh@radonezh.ru
Format: Religious. **Owner:** Radiostantsiya Radonezh, at above address. **Operating Hours:** 1700-2000. **Wattage:** 150,000. **URL:** http://www.radonezh.ru.

Novosibirsk

50009 ■ Applied Physics B
Springer-Verlag Tokyo
Institute of Laser Physics
Sibirian Br.
Russian Academy of Sciences
Pr. Lavrentyev 13/3
630090 Novosibirsk, Russia
Publisher E-mail: info@springer.jp
Journal covering the broad field of laser physics, linear and nonlinear optics, ultrafast phenomena, photonic devices, optical and laser materials, quantum optics, laser spectroscopy of atoms, molecules and clusters, and use of laser radiation in biophotonics, chemistry and biochemistry. **Subtitle:** Lasers and Optics. **Freq:** 8/yr. **Key Personnel:** F. Trager, Editor-in-Chief, fax 49 561 8044518, traeger@physik.uni-kassel.de; Rainer Blatt, Board of Co-Ed., rainer.blatt@uibk.ac.at; G. Huber, Board of Co-Ed., huber@physnet.uni-hamburg.de; K. Buse, Board of Co-Ed., kbuse@uni-bonn.de; T. Yabuzaki, Board of Co-Ed., yabuzaki@isc.osakac.ac.jp; Y.R. Shen, Board of Co-Ed., shenyr@physics.berkeley.edu; F.K. Tittel, Board of Co-Ed., fkt@rice.edu; S.N. Bagaev, Board of Co-Ed., bagayev@laser.nsc.ru. **ISSN:** 0946-2171. **Subscription Rates:** EUR4,807 institutions print incl. free access or e-only; EUR5,768.40 institutions print incl. enhanced access. **Remarks:** Advertising accepted; rates available upon request. **URL:** http://www.springer.com/physics/optics/journal/340. **Circ:** (Not Reported)

50010 ■ Earth's Cryosphere
Publishing House of the Siberian Branch of the Russian Academy of Sciences
Pr. Akademika Koptyuga 3
630090 Novosibirsk, Russia
Ph: 7 383 3356430
Publication E-mail: crio@izdatgeo.ru
Journal covering the study of the cryosphere of the Earth and other planets. **Founded:** 1997. **Freq:** 4/yr. **Key Personnel:** V.P. Mel'nikov, Editor-in-Chief. **URL:** http://www.sibran.ru/English/kriose.htm.

50011 ■ Journal Chemistry for Sustainable Development
Publishing House of the Siberian Branch of the Russian Academy of Sciences
Morskoy pr. 2
630090 Novosibirsk, Russia
Ph: 7 383 3301758
Publication E-mail: csd@ad-sbras.nsc.ru
Journal covering all aspects of chemical research. **Founded:** 1993. **Freq:** Bimonthly. **Key Personnel:** Prof. Nikolay Z. Lyakhov, Editor-in-Chief, lyakhov@solid.nsk.su; L. Altunina, Editorial Board. **ISSN:** 1817-1818. **URL:** http://www.sibran.ru/English/CSDE.HTM.

50012 ■ Journal of Mining Sciences
Publishing House of the Siberian Branch of the Russian Academy of Sciences
Krasnyi pr. 54
630091 Novosibirsk, Russia
Ph: 7 3832 170048
Journal covering mining sciences. **Key Personnel:** V.N. Oparin, Editor-in-Chief. **ISSN:** 0015-3273. **URL:** http://www.sibran.ru/English/ftprpe.htm.

50013 ■ Siberian Journal of Ecology
Publishing House of the Siberian Branch of the Russian Academy of Sciences
Ul. Sovetskaia, 18-341
630099 Novosibirsk, Russia
Ph: 7 383 2224104
Publication E-mail: phsb@ad-sbras.nsc.ru
Journal covering aspects of ecology. **Key Personnel:** I.Yu. Koropachinsky, Editor-in-Chief. **ISSN:** 0869-8619. **URL:** http://www.sibran.ru/English/secje.htm.

50014 ■ Siberian Journal of Numerical Mathematics
Publishing House of the Siberian Branch of the Russian Academy of Sciences
Pr. Akademika Lavrent'eva 6
630090 Novosibirsk, Russia
Ph: 7 3832 356545
Fax: 7 3832 308783
Publication E-mail: sibjnm@sscc.ru; sibjnm@oapmg.sscc.ru
Journal covering mathematics models, and theory and practice of computational methods of mathematics. **Key Personnel:** A.S. Alekseyev, Editor-in-Chief. **URL:** http://www.sibran.ru/English/sjvme.htm.

50015 ■ Thermophysics and Aeromechanics
Maik Nauka/Interperiodica Publishing
Institute of Thermophysics SB RAS
Lavrent'ev Ave. 1
630090 Novosibirsk, Russia
Ph: 8 383 3165035
Publication E-mail: tanda@itp.nsc.ru
Publisher E-mail: compmg@maik.ru
Journal publishing original reports, reviews and discussions on the following topics: hydrogasdynamics, heat and mass transfer, turbulence, means and methods of aero- and thermophysical experiment, physics of low-temperature plasma and physical and technical problems of energetics. **Freq:** Quarterly. **Key Personnel:** E.P. Volchkov, Editor-in-Chief. **ISSN:** 0869-8643. **Subscription Rates:** EUR1,096 institutions print incl. free access or e-only; EUR1,228.80 institutions print incl. enhanced access. **Remarks:** Advertising not accepted. **URL:** http://www.maik.ru/cgi-bin/journal.pl?name=thphaero& page=main. **Circ:** (Not Reported)

Noyabrsk

50016 ■ Nashe Radio - Noyabrsk - 105.3 MHz
923-1701 St. Baumanskaya
105082 Moscow, Russia
Ph: 7 495 9250449
E-mail: nashe@nashe.ru
Format: Classic Rock; News. **Owner:** Nashe Radio, at above address. **Key Personnel:** Mikhail Zotov, Dir. Gen.; Oleg Khlebnikov, Program Dir.; Maria Rumyantsev, Business Mgr. **Ad Rates:** Advertising accepted; rates available upon request. **URL:** http://www.nashe.ru.

Circulation: ★ = ABC; △ = BPA; ◆ = CAC; ● = CCAB; ❑ = VAC; ⊕ = PO Statement; ‡ = Publisher's Report; Boldface figures = sworn; Light figures = estimated.

Gale Directory of Publications & Broadcast Media/147th Ed.

5377

Orenburg

50017 ■ Nashe Radio - Orenburg - 105.8 MHz
923-1701 St. Baumanskaya
105 082 Moscow, Russia
Ph: 7 495 1050449
E-mail: nashe@nashe.ru
Format: Classic Rock; News. **Owner:** Nashe Radio, at above address. **Key Personnel:** Mikhail Zotov, Dir. Gen.; Oleg Khlebnikov, Program Dir.; Maria Rumnyantsev, Commercial Dir. **Ad Rates:** Advertising accepted; rates available upon request. **URL:** http://www.nashe.ru.

Perm

50018 ■ Radio Maximum - 103.2 MHz
Ulitsa Gorkogo 18
614000 Perm, Russia
Ph: 7 8432 2910703
Fax: 7 8432 2129975
E-mail: radio@maximum.perm.ru
Format: News; Contemporary Hit Radio (CHR). **Owner:** Vserossiyskaya Gosudarstvennaya Teleradiokompaniya (VGTRK, Gov.), Leningradskiy Pr. 22/2, 125124 Moscow, Russia, Fax: 7 495 2142347. **Wattage:** 5000. **URL:** http://www.maximum.perm.ru/.

Pokachi

50019 ■ Nashe Radio - Pokachi - 102.3 MHz
15-16 St. Baumanskaya
105082 Moscow, Russia
Ph: 7 495 9250449
E-mail: nashe@nashe.ru
Format: Classic Rock; News. **Owner:** Nashe Radio, at above address. **Key Personnel:** Mikhail Zotov, Dir. Gen.; Oleg Khlebnikov, Program Dir.; Maria Rumyantsev, Business Mgr. **Ad Rates:** Advertising accepted; rates available upon request. **URL:** http://www.nashe.ru.

Saint Petersburg

50020 ■ Cell and Tissue Biology
Maik Nauka/Interperiodica Publishing
Tsitologiya
Mendeleevskaya line, 1
199034 Saint Petersburg, Russia
Ph: 7 812 3285255
Fax: 7 812 2970341
Publication E-mail: cytology@mail.cytspb.rssi.ru
Publisher E-mail: compmg@maik.ru
Journal focusing on vast aspects of cell research. **Freq:** 3/yr. **Key Personnel:** Nikolai N. Nikolsky, Editor-in-Chief; V.M. Mikhelson, Dep. Ed.-in-Ch.; I.A. Gamaley, Exec. Ed.-in-Ch. **ISSN:** 1990-519X. **Subscription Rates:** EUR1,274 institutions print incl. free access or e-only; EUR1,528.80 institutions print incl. enhanced access. **URL:** http://www.maik.rssi.ru/cgi-perl/journal.pl?lang=eng&name=bioceti.

50021 ■ Entomological Review
Maik Nauka/Interperiodica Publishing
Universitetskaya nab 1
199034 Saint Petersburg, Russia
Ph: 7 812 3281212
Fax: 7 812 1140444
Publication E-mail: blaps@zin.ru
Publisher E-mail: compmg@maik.ru
Publishes papers dealing with all aspects of theoretical and applied entomology. Covers systematics, faunistics, zoogeography, evolution, ecology, morphology, physiology of insects, spiders and mites, as well as biological and chemical control of pest. **Founded:** 1959. **Freq:** 9/yr. **Key Personnel:** Gleb S. Medvedev, Editor-in-Chief; Boris A. Korotyaev, Editorial Board; Rustem D. Zhantiev, Editorial Board; Vladimir I. Tansky, Editorial Board; Dr. Vadim F. Zaitsev, Dep. Ed.-in-Ch.; Dr. Vera A. Richter, Exec. Ed.-in-Ch.; Sergey A. Belokobylsky, Editorial Board; Alexandr F. Emelyanov, Editorial Board; Igor K. Lopatin, Editorial Board. **ISSN:** 0013-8738. **Subscription Rates:** EUR4,747, institutions, EUR5,696.40 institutions enhanced access. **URL:** http://www.maik.rssi.ru/cgi-bin/journal.pl?name=enteng&page=main.

50022 ■ Glass Physics and Chemistry
Maik Nauka/Interperiodica Publishing
nab. Makarova 2
199034 Saint Petersburg, Russia
Ph: 7 812 3288584
Fax: 7 812 3282241
Publication E-mail: gpcj@isc.nw.ru

Publisher E-mail: compmg@maik.ru
Journal presenting the results of research on the inorganic and physical chemistry of glasses, ceramics, nanoparticles, nanocomposites, as well as on high-temperature oxides and coatings by Russian and foreign authors. **Founded:** 1975. **Freq:** Bimonthly. **Key Personnel:** Vladimir Ya Shevchenko, Editor-in-Chief. **ISSN:** 1087-6596. **Subscription Rates:** EUR2,990 institutions print incl. free access or e-only; EUR3,588 institutions print incl. enhanced access. **URL:** http://www.maik.rssi.ru/cgi-perl/journal.pl?lang=eng&name=physglas.

50023 ■ Journal of Evolutionary Biochemistry and Physiology
Maik Nauka/Interperiodica Publishing
Sechenov Institute of Evolutionary Physiology & Biochemistry
Thorez av. 44
194223 Saint Petersburg, Russia
Ph: 7 812 5527901
Fax: 7 812 5523012
Publisher E-mail: compmg@maik.ru
Journal featuring the most recent research findings on the evolution of basic forms of metabolism, comparative and developmental physiology, and biochemistry and the biochemical evolution of the animal world. **Founded:** 1965. **Freq:** Bimonthly. **Key Personnel:** Vladimir L. Svidersky, Editor-in-Chief; Nikolai P. Vesselkin, Dep. Ed.-in-Ch.; Alexandr N. Knyazev, Exec. Ed. **ISSN:** 0022-0930. **Subscription Rates:** EUR4,666 institutions print incl. free access or e-only; EUR5,599.20 institutions print incl. enhanced access. **URL:** http://www.maik.rssi.ru/cgi-bin/journal.pl?name=evolbp&page=main.

50024 ■ Physics of the Solid State
Maik Nauka/Interperiodica Publishing
Mendeleevskaya liniya 1
199034 Saint Petersburg, Russia
Ph: 7 812 3286286
Publication E-mail: sst@journals.ioffe.rssi.ru
Publisher E-mail: compmg@maik.ru
Journal presenting the latest results from Russia's leading researchers in condensed matter physics at the Russian Academy of Sciences and other institutions, covering all areas of solid state physics including solid state optics, solid state acoustics, electronic and vibrational spectra, phase transition, ferroelectricity, magnetism and superconductivity. **Founded:** 1959. **Freq:** Monthly. **Key Personnel:** K.S. Aleksandrov, Editorial Board; V.V. Lemanov, Dep. Ed.-in-Ch.; A.A. Kaplyanskii, Editor-in-Chief; L.A. Morozova, Staff Ed.; E.G. Ponyatovskii, Editorial Board. **ISSN:** 1063-7834. **Subscription Rates:** EUR6,222 institutions print incl. free access or e-only; EUR7,466.40 institutions print incl. enhanced access. **Remarks:** Advertising not accepted. **URL:** http://www.maik.ru/journal.pl?name=physsost&page=main. **Circ:** (Not Reported)

50025 ■ Reviews on Advanced Materials Science
Institute of Problems of Mechanical Engineering
V.O., Bolshoj pr., 61
199178 Saint Petersburg, Russia
Ph: 78 123 214778
Fax: 78 123 214771
Peer-reviewed journal publishing reviews, contemporary issues and international conference proceedings in the area of theoretical and experimental studies of advanced materials, giving importance on nanostructured materials, semiconductors and high-transition-temperature superconductors. **Freq:** Bimonthly. **Key Personnel:** L. Kabacoff, International Editorial Board; T.G. Langdon, International Editorial Board; D. Hui, International Editorial Board; I.A. Archakov, Editor; K. Chong, International Editorial Board; C.S. Pande, International Editorial Board; P. Jena, International Editorial Board; M.I. Baraton, International Editorial Board; B.I. Smirnov, International Editorial Board. **ISSN:** 1606-5131. **URL:** http://www.ipme.ru/e-journals/RAMS/.

50026 ■ Russian Journal of General Chemistry
Maik Nauka/Interperiodica Publishing
Mendeleevskaya liniya 1
199034 Saint Petersburg, Russia
Ph: 7 812 3284628
Publication E-mail: chem@thesa.ru
Publisher E-mail: compmg@maik.ru
Journal covering all aspects of chemistry, especially general and boundary problems, and focuses on new achievements in the field. **Founded:** 1961. **Freq:** Monthly. **Key Personnel:** Prof. Anatoly I. Rusanov, Editor-in-Chief; Prof. Aleksei B. Nikolskii, Dep. Ed.-in-

Ch.; Prof. Boris I. Ionin, Managing Editor. **ISSN:** 1070-3632. **Subscription Rates:** EUR5,690 institutions print incl. free access or e-only; EUR6,828 institutions print incl. enhanced access. **URL:** http://www.maik.ru/cgi-bin/journal.pl?name=genchem&page=main.

50027 ■ Russian Journal of Organic Chemistry
Maik Nauka/Interperiodica Publishing
Mendeleevskaya liniya 1
199034 Saint Petersburg, Russia
Ph: 7 812 2184628
Publication E-mail: beletska@org.chem.msu.ru
Publisher E-mail: compmg@maik.ru
Journal covering all aspects of modern organic chemistry including organic synthesis, theoretical organic chemistry, structure and mechanism, and the application of organometallic compounds in organic synthesis. **Founded:** 1965. **Freq:** Monthly. **Key Personnel:** Irina P. Beletskaya, Editor-in-Chief; O.N. Chupakhin, Editorial Board; V.N. Charushin, Editorial Board; A.V. Cheprakov, Editorial Board; U.M. Djemilev, Editorial Board; A.I. Konovalov, Editorial Board; O.G. Kulinkovich, Editorial Board; R.R. Kostikov, Editorial Board; V.A. Tartakovskii, Dep. Ed.-in-Ch.; R.A. Cherkasov, Editorial Board; I.V. Tzelinskii, Editorial Board; G.A. Tolstikov, Editorial Board. **ISSN:** 1070-4280. **Subscription Rates:** EUR5,613 institutions print incl. free access or e-only; EUR6,735.60 institutions print incl. enhanced access. **URL:** http://www.maik.rssi.ru/cgi-perl/journal.pl?lang=eng&name=orgchem.

50028 ■ The St. Petersburg Times
4 St. Isaac's Sq.
190000 Saint Petersburg, Russia
Ph: 7 812 3256080
Fax: 7 812 3256080
Publication E-mail: letters@sptimes.ru
General newspaper. **Founded:** May 1993. **Freq:** Semiweekly Tues.- Fri. **Key Personnel:** Shura Collinson, Bus. Ed.; collinson@sptimes.ru; Anna Brun, Advertising Dir., brun@sptimes.ru; Vyacheslav Korolev, Subscription Mgr., korolev@sptimes.ru; Matthew Brown, Dep. ed., brown@sptimes.ru; Tobin Auber, Editor, auber@sptimes.ru; Derk Sauer, CEO; Tatyana Turikova, Gen. Dir., turikova@sptimes.ru. **Subscription Rates:** 250 Rb individuals 1 month; 1,450 Rb individuals 6 months (50 issues); 2,900 Rb individuals 100 issues. **Remarks:** Accepts advertising. **URL:** http://www.sptimes.ru. **Ad Rates:** BW: 130,000 Rb. **Circ:** 20,000

50029 ■ Canal-Melodia - 91.1 MHz
Professora Popova 47
197376 Saint Petersburg, Russia
Ph: 7 812 3460974
Fax: 7 812 2349712
Format: Eclectic. **Wattage:** 5000. **Ad Rates:** Advertising accepted; rates available upon request. **URL:** http://www.melodia.ru/.

50030 ■ Radio Eremitazh - 90.1 MHz
per. Krapivny 5, ofice 205
194044 Saint Petersburg, Russia
Ph: 7 812 5421260
Fax: 7 812 5425019
E-mail: radio@rhfm.ru
Format: Jazz; News. **Owner:** Radio Eremitazh, at above address. **Founded:** 2000. **Key Personnel:** Tatiana Vasilyevna Bazhanova, Dir. Gen.; Irina Ivanovna Vdovina, Exec. Dir., irina@rhfm.ru; Smirnov Maxim, Sound Dir.; Cumins Sergey, Sound Dir.; Aleksey Zakharov, Program Dir., zaharison@mail.ru. **Wattage:** 1000. **Ad Rates:** Advertising accepted; rates available upon request. **URL:** http://www.rhfm.ru.

50031 ■ Radio Khit - 90.6 MHz
Ulitsa Shevchenko 27
199406 Saint Petersburg, Russia
Ph: 7 812 3256806
Fax: 7 812 3251713
E-mail: reklama@radiohit.ru
Format: Adult Contemporary; News. **Owner:** Radio khit, at above address. **Founded:** Apr. 25, 1998. **Wattage:** 1000. **URL:** http://www.radiohit.ru.

50032 ■ Radio Maria - 1053 KHz
PO Box 732
190068 Saint Petersburg, Russia
Fax: 7 812 3259426
E-mail: logos@radiomaria.ru
Format: Religious; Contemporary Christian; News. **Operating Hours:** Continuous. **Key Personnel:** Yevgeny Matseo, Founder; Alexander Rusakov, Fund Dir. **Watt-**

age: 10,000. **URL:** http://radiomaria.ucoz.ru.

50033 ■ Radio Teos - 1089 KHz
ul Michurinskaya, 14/3-78
197046 Saint Petersburg, Russia
Ph: 8 812 4980483
Fax: 8 812 4980483
E-mail: spb@radioteos.ru
Format: Religious; Gospel; News. **Operating Hours:**
16 hours Daily. **Key Personnel:** Denis Kozlov, PR Mgr.,
dkozlov@radioteos.ru. **Wattage:** 20,000. **URL:** http://
www.radiotserkov.ru.

Shebalino

**50034 ■ GTRK Gornyy Altay - Shebalino - 1350
KHz**
Ulitsa Choros-Girkina 38
659700 Gorno-Altaysk, Russia
E-mail: info@gtrk.gorny.ru
Format: Full Service. **Owner:** Vserossiyskaya Gosudarstvennaya Teleradiokompaniya (VGTRK), Leningradskiy Private 22/2, 125124 Moscow, Russia. **Operating
Hours:** 2310-2400, 1110-1200 Mon.-Fri. **Key Personnel:** Oleg Dobrodeyev, Chm. **Wattage:** 5000. **URL:**
http://www.vgtrk.com.

Syktyvkar

50035 ■ Europa Plus Komi-FM - 100.3
108A ul. Internatsionalnaya
167982 Syktyvkar, Russia
Ph: 7 821 2217012
E-mail: europaplus@europaplus.komi.ru
Format: World Beat. **URL:** http://www.lyngsat-address.
com/df/Eueropa-Plus-Komi.html.

Tobolsk

50036 ■ Nashe Radio - Tobolsk - 107.9 MHz
923-1701 St. Baumanskaya
105082 Moscow, Russia
Ph: 7 495 9250449
E-mail: nashe@nashe.ru
Format: Classic Rock; News. **Owner:** Nashe Radio, at
above address. **Key Personnel:** Mikhail Zotov, Dir.
Gen.; Oleg Khlebnikov, Program Dir.; Maria Rumyantsev, Business Mgr. **Ad Rates:** Advertising accepted;
rates available upon request. **URL:** http://www.nashe.ru.

Tula

50037 ■ Ekho Moskvy - Tula - 106.9 MHz
Ulitsa Novyy Arbat 11
119992 Moscow, Russia
Ph: 7 495 6959229
E-mail: echo@echo.msk.ru
Format: News; Information. **Owner:** Ekho Moskvy, at
above address. **Operating Hours:** Continuous. **Key
Personnel:** Yuri Fedutinov, Dir. Gen. **Wattage:** 1000.
Ad Rates: Advertising accepted; rates available upon
request. **URL:** http://www.echo.msk.ru.

Ust-Kan

**50038 ■ GTRK Gornyy Altay - Ust-Kan - 1350
KHz**
Ulitsa Choros-Gurkina 38
659700 Gorno-Altaysk, Russia
E-mail: info@gtrk.gorny.ru

Format: News. **Owner:** Vserossiyskaya Gosudarstven-
naya Teleradiokompaniya (VGTRK), Leningradskiy
Private 22/2, 125124 Moscow, Russia. **Operating
Hours:** 2310-2400, 1110-1200 Mon.-Fri. **Key Person-
nel:** Oleg Dobrodeyev, CEO. **Wattage:** 5000. **Ad Rates:**
Advertising accepted; rates available upon request.
URL: http://www.vgtrk.com.

Ust-Ulagan

**50039 ■ GTRK Gornyy Altay - Ust-Ulagan - 1350
KHz**
Ulitsa Choros-Gurkina 38
659700 Gorno-Altaysk, Russia
E-mail: info@gtrk.gorny.ru
Format: News. **Owner:** Vserossiyskaya Gosudarstven-
naya Teleradiokompaniya (VGTRK), Leningradskiy
Private 22/2, 125124 Moscow, Russia. **Operating
Hours:** 2310-2400, 1110-1200 Mon.-Fri. **Key Person-
nel:** Oleg Dobrodeyev, Chm. **Wattage:** 5000. **Ad Rates:**
Advertising accepted; rates available upon request.
URL: http://www.vgtrk.com.

Vladivostok

50040 ■ Russian Journal of Marine Biology
Maik Nauka/Interperiodica Publishing
Institute of Marine Biology, Far East Division of the
RAS
Ul. Palchevskogo 17
690041 Vladivostok, Russia
Ph: 7 4232 311172
Fax: 7 4232 310900
Publication E-mail: biolm@imb.dvo.ru
Publisher E-mail: compmg@maik.ru
Covers a wide range of research and some applied
aspects of marine biology as a synthetic science related
to various fields of study on marine biota and
environment. **Founded:** 1975. **Freq:** Bimonthly. **Key
Personnel:** Andrei V. Adrianov, Editor-in-Chief; Vladimir
V. Gulbin, Exec. Ed.-in-Ch.; Viktor E. Vaskovsky, Edito-
rial Board; Vyacheslav P. Shuntov, Dep. Ed.-in-Ch.; Ser-
gei L. Kondrashev, Dep. Ed.-in-Ch. **ISSN:** 1063-0740.
Subscription Rates: EUR2,840 institutions; EUR3,408
institutions enhanced access. **URL:** http://www.maik.
rssi.ru/cgi-perl/journal.pl?lang=eng&name=marbio.

50041 ■ Vladivostok News
Vladivostok Novosti Ltd.
13 Narodny Prospect
690014 Vladivostok, Russia
Ph: 7 423 2415590
Fax: 7 423 2415615
English language general newspaper. **Founded:** Apr.
1992. **Freq:** Weekly. **Key Personnel:** Maria Shiman-
skaya, Translator, shimanskaya@vladnews.ru; Alyona
Sokolova, Editor, sokolova@vladnews.ru; Nikolai Pe-
sochenski, Web Admin., sergeant@vladnews.ru. **URL:**
http://vn.vladnews.ru/.

50042 ■ Europa Plus - Vladivostok - 1557 KHz
Ulitsa Akademika Koroleva 19
127427 Moscow, Russia
Ph: 7 95 6178257
Fax: 7 95 9563508
E-mail: main@europaplus.ru
Format: News; Contemporary Hit Radio (CHR). **Owner:**
Europa Plus, at above address. **Operating Hours:**
Continuous. **Key Personnel:** Georges Polinskya,
President. **Ad Rates:** Advertising accepted; rates avail-

able upon request. **URL:** http://www.europaplus.ru.

50043 ■ Radio VBC - 612 KHz
Uborevicha St.
20-A Radio House
690091 Vladivostok, Russia
Ph: 7 4232 510586
Fax: 7 4232 261726
E-mail: info@radiovbc.ru
Format: Full Service. **Owner:** Radio VBC, at above
address. **Operating Hours:** Continuous. **Key Person-
nel:** Vladimir Evgenevich, Gen. Dir. **Wattage:** 10,000.
Ad Rates: Advertising accepted; rates available upon
request. **URL:** http://www.radiovbc.ru.

Radio VBC - See Dalnegorsk

Volgograd

50044 ■ Social Evolution & History
Izdatel'skii Dom Uchitel'
82-53 Bystrova St.
400067 Volgograd, Russia
Ph: 7 8442 448553
Fax: 7 8442 448553
Publisher E-mail: uchitel@avtlg.ru
Journal founded to meet the needs of those seeking an
understanding of how human societies developed in the
past and continue to develop in the present, devoted to
social evolution specifically. **Freq:** Semiannual March
and September. **Key Personnel:** Herbert Barry III,
Editor. **ISSN:** 1681-4363. **Subscription Rates:** US$50
institutions; US$33 single issue institution; US$25
individuals; US$17 single issue individual; US$16
students; US$10 single issue student. **URL:** http://www.
nsu.ru/filf/pha/journals/seh.htm.

Yekaterinburg

50045 ■ Radio Studencheskiy Kanal - 90.2 MHz
Ulitsa Repina 15
620109 Yekaterinburg, Russia
Ph: 7 343 2421477
Fax: 7 343 2421477
E-mail: radiosk@isnet.ru
Format: Contemporary Hit Radio (CHR). **Owner:** Radio
Studencheskiy Kanal, at above address. **Wattage:** 1000.
URL: http://www.radiosk.ru.

50046 ■ Studiya Gorod - 909 KHz
Private Lenina 24a-449
620014 Yekaterinburg, Russia
E-mail: info@gorodfm.ru
Format: News; Talk. **Founded:** Dec. 24, 1990. **Key
Personnel:** Oxana Butorova, Proj. Mgr., phone 7 343
3775577; Dmitriy Pudovkin, Technical Dir., pud@radio.
ur.ru. **Wattage:** 10,000. **Ad Rates:** Advertising accepted;
rates available upon request. **URL:** http://www.gorodfm.
ru.

Yessentuki

50047 ■ Hit-FM - Yessentuki - 104.2 MHz
c/o Hit-FM
3 Khoroshevskaya ul., d. 12
123298 Moscow, Пшзэіа
Ph: 7 495 9951036
E-mail: hitfmp@hifm.ru
Format: Eclectic. **Owner:** Hit-FM, at above address.
Wattage: 500. **URL:** http://www.hitfm.ru.

Kigali

50048 ■ HIV Plus
Institut Africain pour le Developpement Economique et
Social - Rwanda
BP 866
Kigali, Rwanda

Ph: 250 84713
Fax: 250 84713
Publication E-mail: mail@hivplusmag.com
Journal providing access to latest research on treatment
and research breakthroughs in HIV related topics and
raises awareness of HIV-related cultural and policy

developments in the United States and throughout the
world. **Freq:** Bimonthly. **Key Personnel:** Michael W.E.
Edwards, Editor-in-Chief; Joe Valentino, Publisher. **Subscription Rates:** Free. **Remarks:** Advertising accepted;
rates available upon request. **URL:** http://www.
hivplusmag.com. **Circ:** (Not Reported)

Circulation: ★ = ABC; △ = BPA; ♦ = CAC; • = CCAB; ❑ = VAC; ⊕ = PO Statement; ‡ = Publisher's Report; Boldface figures = sworn; Light figures = estimated.

Gale Directory of Publications & Broadcast Media/147th Ed.   5381

Basseterre

50049 ■ Winn-FM - 98.9
Unit C24, The Sands
Newtown Bay Rd.
Basseterre, St. Kitts and Nevis
Ph: 869466-9586
Fax: 869466-7904
E-mail: info@winnfm.com
Format: Sports; Eclectic; News. **Operating Hours:** 12 hours Daily. **URL:** http://www.winnfm.com.

Charlestown

50050 ■ Voice of Nevis (VON) Radio-AM - 895
Bath Plains
Nevis
PO Box 195
Charlestown, St. Kitts and Nevis
Ph: 869469-1616
Fax: 869469-5329
E-mail: feedback@vonradio.com
Format: Agricultural; Country; Information; Talk; News. **Founded:** June 18, 1988. **Operating Hours:** 16 hours Daily. **Key Personnel:** Evered Herbert, General Mgr., gmanager@vonradio.com. **Ad Rates:** Advertising accepted; rates available upon request. **URL:** http://www.vonradio.com.

Lodge Village

50051 ■ GoodWill-FM - 103.3
PO Box 98
Lodge Village, St. Kitts and Nevis
Ph: 869465-7795
Fax: 869465-9556
E-mail: info@goodwillfm.com
Format: Religious. **Operating Hours:** 8 a.m. to 5 p.m. Mon.-Fri.; 8 a.m. to 1 p.m. Sat.-Sun. **URL:** http://www.goodwillfm.com.

Castries

50052 ■ Radio Caribbean International-FM - 101.1
11 Mongiraud St.

Box 121
Castries, St. Lucia
Ph: (758)452-2636
Fax: (758)452-2637

E-mail: rci@candw.lc
Format: Ethnic; News; Information. **URL:** http://www.rcistlucia.com/now/default.aspx.

Circulation: ★ = ABC; △ = BPA; ◆ = CAC; • = CCAB; ❏ = VAC; ⊕ = PO Statement; ‡ = Publisher's Report; Boldface figures = sworn; Light figures = estimated.

Gale Directory of Publications & Broadcast Media/147th Ed.

5385

San Marino

50053 ■ European Weightlifter
European Weightlifting Federation

Via Gino Giacomini, 83
San Marino 47890, San Marino
Ph: 39 378 995639
Fax: 39 378 913795

Publisher E-mail: secretariat@ewf.sm
Magazine of the European Weightlifting Federation.
Freq: Annual. **URL:** http://www.ewf.sm/publications.php.

Dhahran

50054 ■ Arabian Journal for Science and Engineering
King Fahd University of Petroleum and Minerals
PO Box 5033
Dhahran 31261; Saudi Arabia
Ph: 966 3 8605418
Fax: 966 3 8605458
Publication E-mail: ajse@kfupm.edu.sa
Publisher E-mail: ajse@kfupm.edu.sa
Journal of science and engineering. **Founded:** 1975.
Freq: Bimonthly. **Key Personnel:** Dr. Bassam M. El Ali,
Managing Editor, belali@kfupm.edu.sa. **ISSN:** 0377-
9211. **Remarks:** Advertising accepted; rates available
upon request. **URL:** http://www.kfupm.edu.sa/
publications/ajse/. **Circ:** Paid 800

Dubai

50055 ■ ARN-FM - 96.7
PO Box 502012
Dubai, Saudi Arabia
Ph: 966 971 43912000
Fax: 966 971 43912007
E-mail: info@arnonline.com
Format: Eclectic; News; Sports. **Owner:** Arabian Radio
Network, at above address. **Founded:** 2004. **Operating
Hours:** Continuous. **Key Personnel:** Sam Armitage,
Sales Mgr., phone 966 971 43062222, fax 966 971
43479965, sarmitage@arnonline.com; Sumantra Ghosh,
Sen. Sales Mgr., sghosh@arabmediagroup.ae. **Ad
Rates:** Advertising accepted; rates available upon
request. **URL:** http://www.arnonline.com.

Jeddah

50056 ■ Islamic Capitals and Cities Magazine
Organization of Islamic Capitals and Cities
PO Box 13621
Jeddah 21414, Saudi Arabia
Ph: 66 626 9821414
Fax: 66 626 981053
Publisher E-mail: secrtriat@oicc.org
Magazine covering Islamic capitals and cities. **Freq:**
Semiannual. **Subscription Rates:** US$20 individuals.
URL: http://www.oicc.org/; http://www.oicc.org/
oiccenglish/publications.htm.

50057 ■ Saudi Gazette
Okaz Organization for Press and Publication
PO Box 5034
Jeddah 21422, Saudi Arabia
Ph: 966 2 6722775
Fax: 966 2 6712355
General newspaper. **Founded:** 1976. **Freq:** Daily. **ISSN:**
1319-0326. **Subscription Rates:** 720 SRI individuals;
1,225 SRI two years. **Remarks:** Accepts advertising.
URL: http://www.saudigazette.com.sa. **Ad Rates:** BW:
22 SRI, 4C: 33 SRI. **Circ:** Paid 60,000

50058 ■ Saudi Heart Journal
Saudi Heart Foundation
PO Box 6615

Jeddah 21452, Saudi Arabia
Journal of cardiovascular diseases. **Founded:** 1989.
Freq: 2/yr. **Key Personnel:** Hassan Raffa, Editor. **ISSN:**
1018-077X. **Remarks:** Advertising accepted; rates available upon request. **Circ:** Free 5,000

Riyadh

50059 ■ Annals of Thoracic Medicine
Medknow Publications Pvt Ltd.
PO Box 106911
Riyadh 11676, Saudi Arabia
Ph: 966 1 2488966
Fax: 966 1 2487431
Journal featuring clinical investigations in the multidisci-
plinary specialties of chest medicine, including pulmonol-
ogy, cardiology, thoracic surgery, transplantation, sleep
and breathing, and airway diseases. **Founded:** 1973.
Freq: Quarterly. **Print Method:** Offset. **Trim Size:** 6 3/4
x 10. **Cols./Page:** 2. **Col. Width:** 32 nonpareils. **Col.
Depth:** 109 agate lines. **Key Personnel:** Dr. Mohamed
S. Al-Moamary, Editor-in-Chief, almoamary@yahoo.com;
Prof. Ahmed S. BaHammam, Assoc. Ed.; Prof. Emad A.
Koshak, Assoc. Ed. **ISSN:** 1817-1737. **Subscription
Rates:** Rs 2,500 individuals; Rs 2,500 institutions;
US$75 other countries; US$150 institutions, other
countries. **URL:** http://www.thoracicmedicine.org/.

50060 ■ Arab News
Saudi Research & Publishing Co.
PO Box 478
Riyadh 11411, Saudi Arabia
Ph: 966 1 4419933
Fax: 966 1 4400453
General newspaper. **Subtitle:** Saudi Arabia's First
English Daily. **Founded:** 1975. **Freq:** Daily. **Key Person-
nel:** Khaled Al-Maeena, Editor-in-Chief, almaeena@
arabnews.com. **ISSN:** 0254-833X. **Remarks:** Accepts
advertising. **URL:** http://www.arabnews.com/. **Circ:** 52

50061 ■ Business Process Management Journal
Emerald Group Publishing Ltd.
Department of Information System
College of Computer & Information Sciences
King Saud University
PO Box 51178
Riyadh 11543, Saudi Arabia
Publisher E-mail: emerald@emeraldinsight.com
Journal for researchers and practitioners to disseminate
and acquire leading-edge knowledge relating to latest
development in BPM concepts, practices, tools and
technologies. **Freq:** 6/yr. **Key Personnel:** Prof. Majed
Al-Mashari, Editor, malmashari@yahoo.com; Lucy
Sootheran, Publisher, lsootheran@emeraldinsight.com;
Mohamed Zairi, Founding Ed. **ISSN:** 1463-7154. **URL:**
http://info.emeraldinsight.com/products/journals/journals.
htm?id=bpmj.

50062 ■ Journal of King Saud University
King Saud University
PO Box 2454
Riyadh 11451, Saudi Arabia
Fax: 966 1 4677580
Publisher E-mail: rectoroffice@ksu.edu.sa
Journal of engineering. **Subtitle:** Engineering Sciences.

Founded: 1989. **Freq:** Semiannual. **Trim Size:** 21 x 24
cm. **Key Personnel:** Prof. Anis H. Fakeeha, Editor-in-
Chief. **ISSN:** 1018-3639. **Subscription Rates:** US$10
individuals including postage. **Remarks:** Advertising accepted; rates available upon request. **URL:** http://www.
ksu.edu.sa/sites/Colleges/Engineering/Pages/KSUJ-
EngSci.aspx. **Circ:** Paid 2,000

**50063 ■ Journal of King Saud University:
Agricultural Sciences**
King Saud University Libraries
PO Box 2454
Riyadh 11451, Saudi Arabia
Ph: 966 1 4670112
Fax: 966 1 4677580
Publication E-mail: agrijor@ksu.edu.sa
Publisher E-mail: rectoroffice@ksu.edu.sa
Agricultural scientific journal. **Founded:** 1989. **Freq:**
Semiannual. **ISSN:** 1018-3590. **Subscription Rates:**
US$5 elsewhere; 10 SRI individuals. **Remarks:** Accepts
advertising. **URL:** http://wwww.ksu.edu.sa/printpress/
JDetails.asp?m=348&v=43&i=1&b=6. **Circ:** Paid 2,000

**50064 ■ Journal of King Saud University:
Architecture and Planning**
King Saud University Libraries
PO Box 2454
Riyadh 11451, Saudi Arabia
Ph: 966 1 4670112
Fax: 966 1 4677580
Publication E-mail: ksucapj@ksu.edu.sa
Publisher E-mail: rectoroffice@ksu.edu.sa
Journal of architecture. **Founded:** 1989. **Freq:** Annual.
Trim Size: 21 x 24 cm. **Key Personnel:** Mohammed Al-
Sahli, Manager. **ISSN:** 1018-3604. **Subscription Rates:**
US$10 individuals. **Remarks:** Advertising accepted;
rates available upon request. **URL:** http://wwww.ksu.
edu.sa/printpress/JDetails.asp?m=350&v=43&i=1&b=8.
Circ: Paid 3,000

50065 ■ Journal of King Saud University: Arts
King Saud University Libraries
PO Box 2454
Riyadh 11451, Saudi Arabia
Ph: 966 1 4670112
Fax: 966 1 4677580
Publisher E-mail: rectoroffice@ksu.edu.sa
Journal of art, literature and social sciences. **Founded:**
1989. **Freq:** Semiannual. **Trim Size:** 21 x 24 cm. **Key
Personnel:** Mohammed Al-Sahli, Manager. **ISSN:** 1018-
3612. **Subscription Rates:** US$10 individuals. **URL:**
http://wwww.ksu.edu.sa/printpress/JDetails.asp?m=
343&v=43&i=1&b=1. **Circ:** Paid 3,000

**50066 ■ Journal of King Saud University:
Computer & Information Sciences**
King Saud University Libraries
PO Box 2454
Riyadh 11451, Saudi Arabia
Ph: 966 1 4670112
Fax: 966 1 4677580
Publication E-mail: journal@ccis.ksu.edu.sa
Publisher E-mail: rectoroffice@ksu.edu.sa
Computer science journal. **Founded:** 1994. **Freq:**
Annual. **Trim Size:** 21 x 24 cm. **Key Personnel:** Khalid
A. Al Hamoudi, Editor. **ISSN:** 1319-1578. **Subscription**

Rates: US$10 individuals. **Remarks:** Advertising accepted; rates available upon request. **URL:** http://wwww.ksu.edu.sa/printpress/JDetails.asp?m=349&v=43&i=1&b=7. **Circ:** Paid 3,000

50067 ■ Journal of King Saud University: Educational Sciences & Islamic Studies
King Saud University Libraries
PO Box 2454
Riyadh 11451, Saudi Arabia
Ph: 966 1 4670112
Fax: 966 1 4677580
Publisher E-mail: rectoroffice@ksu.edu.sa
Journal of Islamic religion and theology. **Founded:** 1989. **Freq:** Semiannual. **Trim Size:** 21 x 24 cm. **Key Personnel:** Mohammed Al-Sahli, Manager. **ISSN:** 1018-3620. **Subscription Rates:** US$10 individuals. **URL:** http://wwww.ksu.edu.sa/printpress/JDetails.asp?m=344&v=43&i=1&b=2. **Circ:** Paid 2,000

50068 ■ Journal of King Saud University: Science
King Saud University Libraries
PO Box 2454
Riyadh 11451, Saudi Arabia
Ph: 966 1 4670112
Fax: 966 1 4677580
Publication E-mail: siournal@ksu.edu.sa
Publisher E-mail: rectoroffice@ksu.edu.sa
Science journal. **Founded:** 1989. **Freq:** Semiannual. **Key Personnel:** Mohammed Al-Sahli, Manager. **ISSN:** 1083-3647. **Subscription Rates:** US$10 individuals. **Remarks:** Advertising accepted; rates available upon request. **URL:** http://wwww.ksu.edu.sa/printpress/JDetails.asp?m=355&v=44&i=1&b=4. **Circ:** Paid 3,000

50069 ■ The Saudi Journal of Gastroenterology
Saudi Gastroenterology Association
Endoscopy Unit
King Khalid University Hospital
PO Box 2925
Riyadh 11461, Saudi Arabia
Ph: 966 1 4679130
Fax: 966 1 4679130
Publisher E-mail: rectoroffice@ksu.edu.sa
Medical journal. **Founded:** 1995. **Freq:** Quarterly. **Key Personnel:** Ibrahim A. Al-Mofleh, Editor. **ISSN:** 1319-3767. **Subscription Rates:** Rs 2400 individuals; US$200 other countries; Rs 2400 institutions; US$200 institutions, other countries. **URL:** http://www.saudijgastro.com/.

50070 ■ Saudi Journal of Kidney Diseases and Transplantation
Saudi Center for Organ Transplantation
PO Box 27049
Riyadh 11417, Saudi Arabia
Ph: 966 1 4451100
Fax: 966 1 4453934
Publication E-mail: sjkdt@sjkdt.org
Publisher E-mail: sjkdt@sjkdt.org
Journal of urology and nephrology. **Founded:** 1990. **Freq:** Quarterly. **Key Personnel:** Faissal A.M. Shaheen, Exec. Ed.; Abdullah A. Al-Khader, Editor-in-Chief; Besher A. Al-Attar, MD, Sci. Ed.; Mohammad Ziad Souqiyyeh, MD, Sci. Ed.; Mohammed Ikram, Asst. Ed.; Abdul Rahman, Founder-Ed.; Ramprasad Kurpad, MD, Sci. Ed.; K.M.S. Aziz, PhD, Sci. Ed. **ISSN:** 1319-2442. **Remarks:** Advertising accepted; rates available upon request. **URL:** http://www.sjkdt.org/. **Circ:** Paid 3,500

50071 ■ Saudi Medical Journal
Riyadh Armed Forces Hospital
PO Box 7897
Riyadh 11159, Saudi Arabia
Ph: 966 14 791000
Fax: 966 14 761810
Publication E-mail: info@smj.org.sa
Publisher E-mail: info@smj.org.sa
Peer-reviewed medical publication. **Subtitle:** Integrating Medical Sciences and Health Care. **Founded:** 1979. **Freq:** Monthly. **Key Personnel:** Dr. Fahdah Alokaily, Assoc. Ed., falokaily@smj.org.sa; Dr. Saud Al Omani, Editor-in-Chief, salomani@smj.org.sa. **ISSN:** 0379-5284. **Subscription Rates:** 375 SRI individuals; US$100 other countries. **Remarks:** Advertising accepted; rates available upon request. **URL:** http://www.smj.org.sa/. **Circ:** (Not Reported)

50072 ■ Urology Annals
Medknow Publications Pvt Ltd.
c/o Dr. Khalid Fouda Neel, Ed.-in-Ch.
Department of Surgery (37)
King Khalid University Hospital & College of Medicine
PO Box 2925
Riyadh 11461, Saudi Arabia
Peer-reviewed journal featuring articles in urology. **Freq:** Semiannual. **Key Personnel:** Dr. Khalid Fouda Neel, Editor-in-Chief, kfouda@ksu.edu.sa; Dr. Abdul Monem Gomha, Asst. Ed., abdulmonem.gomha2atsgmail.com. **ISSN:** 0974-7796. **Subscription Rates:** Rs 1,500 individuals print only; Rs 3,000 institutions print only; US$150 other countries print only; US$300 institutions, other countries print only. **Remarks:** Accepts advertising.

URL: http://www.urologyannals.com. **Circ:** (Not Reported)

50073 ■ TVMAX - 93
King Abdulaziz St.
Old Airport Rd.
Behind Al Mutlaq Hotel
PO Box 60465
Riyadh 11546, Saudi Arabia
Ph: 966 920004444
E-mail: tvmax@orbit.net
URL: http://www.orbit.net.

50074 ■ TVMAX - 92
King Abdulaziz St.
Old Airport Rd.
Behind Al Mutlaq Hotel
PO Box 60465
Riyadh 11545, Saudi Arabia
Ph: 966 920004444
Fax: 966 4774604
E-mail: tvmax@orbit.net
Owner: Orbit Satellite Television and Radio Network, c/o Panther Media Group, PO Box 502211, Dubai Media City, Dubai, United Arab Emirates. **URL:** http://www.orbit.net.

50075 ■ TVMAX - 91
King Abdulaziz St.
Old Airport Rd.
Behind Al Mutlaq Hotel
PO Box 60465
Riyadh 11545, Saudi Arabia
Ph: 966 920004444
Fax: 966 4774604
E-mail: tvmax@orbit.net
Owner: Orbit Satellite Television and Radio Network, c/o Panther Media Group, PO Box 502211, Dubai Media City, Dubai, United Arab Emirates. **URL:** http://www.orbit.net.

50076 ■ TVMAX - 90
King Abdulaziz St.
Old Airport Rd.
Behind Al Mutlaq Hotel
PO Box 60465
Riyadh 11545, Saudi Arabia
Ph: 966 920004444
Fax: 966 4774604
E-mail: tvmax@orbit.net
Owner: Orbit Satellite Television and Radio Network, c/o Panther Media Group, PO Box 502211, Dubai Media City, Dubai, United Arab Emirates. **URL:** http://www.orbit.net.

Dakar

50077 ■ Africa Development
CODESRIA - Council for the Development of Social
Science Research in Africa
Ave. Cheikh Anta Diop x
Canal IV
BP 3304
Dakar, Senegal
Ph: 22 182 59822
Fax: 22 182 41289
Publisher E-mail: codesria@codesria.sn
Journal focusing on issues about the development of
the society. **Founded:** 1976. **Freq:** Quarterly. **Key Personnel:** Alexander Bangirana, Editor; Oyekunle Oyediran, Editorial Asst. **ISSN:** 0850-3907. **Subscription Rates:** US$32 institutions for African; US$45 institutions, other countries; US$30 individuals. **URL:** http://www.codesria.org/spip.php?rubrique39&lang=fr.

50078 ■ Africa Media Review
CODESRIA - Council for the Development of Social
Science Research in Africa
Ave. Cheikh Anta Diop x
Canal IV
BP 3304
Dakar, Senegal
Ph: 22 182 59822
Fax: 22 182 41289
Publisher E-mail: codesria@codesria.sn
Journal focusing on interconnections between media,
communication, and social processes in Africa. **Freq:**
3/yr. **Key Personnel:** Audrey Gadzekpo, Publisher,
audreygadzekpo@gmail.com; Peter Nwosu, Editor,
drnwosup@yahoo.com; Aghi Bahi, Editor, bahi_aghi@
yahoo.fr. **ISSN:** 0258-4913. **URL:** http://www.codesria.
org/Links/Publications/Journals/africa_media_review.
htm.

50079 ■ African Journal of International Affairs
CODESRIA - Council for the Development of Social
Science Research in Africa
Ave. Cheikh Anta Diop x
Canal IV
BP 3304
Dakar, Senegal
Ph: 22 182 59822
Fax: 22 182 41289
Publisher E-mail: codesria@codesria.sn
Journal focusing on contemporary issues in African
International Affairs. **Freq:** Semiannual. **Key Personnel:**
Adebayo Olukoshi, Editor-in-Chief, olukoshi@yahoo.
com; Tukumbi Lumumba Kasango, Editor-in-Chief,
tl25@cornell.edu; Cyril Obi, Publisher, obicy@yahoo.
com. **ISSN:** 0850-7902. **Subscription Rates:** US$10
individuals; US$15 other countries. **URL:** http://www.
codesria.org/spip.php?rubrique44&lang=fr.

50080 ■ CODESRIA Bulletin
CODESRIA - Council for the Development of Social
Science Research in Africa
Ave. Cheikh Anta Diop x
Canal IV
BP 3304
Dakar, Senegal
Ph: 22 182 59822
Fax: 22 182 41289
Publisher E-mail: codesria@codesria.sn
Journal featuring exchange of information and encouraging research cooperation among African researchers.
Freq: Quarterly. **Key Personnel:** Alexander Bangirana,
Editor; Oyekunle Oyediran, Editorial Asst. **Subscription
Rates:** Free to qualified subscribers. **URL:** http://www.
codesria.org/spip.php?rubrique52&lang=fr. **Circ:** 5000

50081 ■ Journal of Higher Education in Africa
CODESRIA - Council for the Development of Social
Science Research in Africa
Ave. Cheikh Anta Diop x
Canal IV
BP 3304
Dakar, Senegal
Ph: 22 182 59822
Fax: 22 182 41289
Publication E-mail: jhea@codesria.sn
Publisher E-mail: codesria@codesria.sn
Journal featuring analysis, information, and critique on
contemporary issues of higher education. **Freq:**
Semiannual. **Key Personnel:** Francis Nyamnjoh,
Publisher, nyamnjoh@gmail.com; Yann Lebeau, Editor,
y.lebeau@uea.ac.uk; Oyekunle Oyediran, Managing
Editor. **ISSN:** 0851-7762. **Subscription Rates:** US$100
institutions; US$200 institutions, other countries; US$60
individuals. **URL:** http://www.codesria.org/spip.php?
rubrique54&lang=fr.

Circulation: ★ = ABC; △ = BPA; ◆ = CAC; • = CCAB; ❑ = VAC; ⊕ = PO Statement; ‡ = Publisher's Report; Boldface figures = sworn; Light figures = estimated.

Gale Directory of Publications & Broadcast Media/147th Ed.   5391

Belgrade

50082 ■ Energy and Buildings
Elsevier Science
c/o Prof. Branilav B. Todorovic, Ed.
Faculty of Mechanical Engineering
Belgrade University
Kraljice Marije 16
YU-11120 Belgrade, Serbia
Publisher E-mail: nlinfo-f@elsevier.com
International journal publishing articles on energy use in buildings. **Founded:** 1978. **Freq:** 12/yr. **Key Personnel:** Prof. Branislav B. Todorovic, Editor, todorob@eunet.yu; Francis Allard, Editorial Board; Constantinos A. Balaras, Editorial Board. **ISSN:** 0378-7788. **Subscription Rates:** 255,100¥ institutions for Japan; EUR1,923 institutions for Europe; US$2,158 institutions all countries except Europe and Japan. **Remarks:** Accepts advertising. **URL:** http://www.elsevier.com/wps/find/journaldescription.cws_home/504083/description. **Circ:** (Not Reported)

50083 ■ Science of Sintering
International Institute for the Science of Sintering
Knez-Mhailova 35/IV
PO Box 315
YU-11001 Belgrade, Serbia
Ph: 381 11 637367
Fax: 381 11 637239
Publication E-mail: scisint@sanu.ac.rs
Publisher E-mail: scisint@sanu.ac.rs
Publication covering metallurgy. **Founded:** Jan. 1969. **Freq:** 3/yr. **Trim Size:** A4. **Key Personnel:** Dr. M.V. Nikolic, Assoc. Ed.; maria@mi.sanu.ac.yu; Momcilo M. Ristic, Editor-in-Chief, momcilo.ristic@sanu.ac.yu; Dr. Dragan Uskokovic, Managing Editor, phone 381 11 636994, fax 381 11 185263, dragan.uskokovic@itn.sanu.ac.rs. **ISSN:** 0350-820X. **Subscription Rates:** EUR110 individuals. **Remarks:** Accepts advertising. **URL:** http://www.iiss.sanu.ac.rs/journal.htm. **Formerly:** Physics of Sintering (1973). **Ad Rates:** DW: US$100. **Circ:** (Not Reported)

50084 ■ OK Radio-FM - 94.2
1 Branka Momirova 12
YU-11000 Belgrade, Serbia
Ph: 381 11 2085111
Fax: 381 11 2085136
E-mail: studio@okradio.net
Format: Ethnic; World Beat. **Owner:** Ok Radio Group Ltd., at above address. **Operating Hours:** Continuous. **Ad Rates:** Advertising accepted; rates available upon request. **URL:** http://www.okradio.net.

50085 ■ Radio Jat-FM - 102.7
Kraljice Marije 57/55
YU-11000 Belgrade, Serbia
Ph: 381 11 7839078
E-mail: marketing@radiojat.rs
Format: Urban Contemporary; Contemporary Hit Radio (CHR); Full Service. **Founded:** Mar. 21, 1999. **Operating Hours:** Continuous. **Key Personnel:** Sladjana Kujundzic, Mktg. Mgr., phone 381 63 632423; Dragica Gajic, Mktg. Mgr., phone 381 63 221418; Momcilo Kostic, Actg. Mgr. **Ad Rates:** Advertising accepted; rates avail-

able upon request. **URL:** http://www.radiojat.rs/cms/news.php.

50086 ■ Radio Novosti-FM - 104.7
Radio Novosti d.o.o
Trg Nikole Pasica 7
YU-11000 Belgrade, Serbia
Ph: 381 11 3398187
Fax: 381 11 3398041
E-mail: radiom@novosti.rs
Format: Ethnic; World Beat. **Operating Hours:** Continuous. **URL:** http://www.radionovosti.com.

50087 ■ Top-FM - 106.8 MHz
TC Pozeska 85b/I
YU-11000 Belgrade, Serbia
Ph: 381 113551666
Fax: 381 113058111
E-mail: office@topfm.rs
Format: Top 40; Adult Contemporary; Contemporary Hit Radio (CHR). **Operating Hours:** Continuous. **Ad Rates:** Advertising accepted; rates available upon request. **URL:** http://www.topfm.co.yu.

Jagodina

50088 ■ Radio Morava-FM - 98.4
Jug Bogdanova 11
YU-35000 Jagodina, Serbia
Ph: 381 35 242523
Fax: 381 35 242523
E-mail: info@radiomorava.rs
Format: Ethnic; World Beat. **Ad Rates:** Advertising accepted; rates available upon request. **URL:** http://www.radiomorava.rs.

Kragujevac

50089 ■ Radio FM9 - 95.9
Kneza Mihaila 10
34000 Kragujevac, Serbia
Ph: 381 34 333500
Format: Easy Listening. **Owner:** Radio9, at above address. **URL:** http://www.radio9.net/.

Nis

50090 ■ Acta Stomatologica Naissi
University of Nis, Faculty of Medicine and Clinic of Stomatology in Nis
Clinic of Stomatology
52 Brace Taskovic St.
18000 Nis, Serbia
Publisher E-mail: asn@medfak.ni.ac.yu
Journal publishing articles on research, patient care, and education in the field of dentistry especially relevant to the field on stomatology. **Founded:** 1984. **Freq:** Quarterly. **Key Personnel:** Nikola Buric, Editor-in-Chief; Ljubomir Todorovic, Editorial Board. **ISSN:** 0352-5252. **Subscription Rates:** EUR50 individuals; EUR100 institutions. **URL:** http://www.medfak.ni.ac.rs/ASN/index.htm.

50091 ■ Microelectronics Reliability
Elsevier Science

c/o Prof. N.D. Stojadinovic, Ed.-in-Ch.
Faculty of Electronic Engineering
University of Nis
Beogradska 14
YU-18000 Nis, Serbia
Publisher E-mail: nlinfo-f@elsevier.com
Peer-reviewed journal focusing on latest research works and related information on the reliability of microelectronic devices, circuits and systems. **Founded:** 1962. **Freq:** Monthly. **Key Personnel:** Prof. M.G. Pecht, Editor-in-Chief, pecht@calce.umd.edu; Prof. N.D. Stojadinovic, Editor-in-Chief, nstojadinovic@elfak.ni.ac.yu; Dr. J.H. Stathis, Assoc. Ed.; G. Ghibaudo, Assoc. Ed.; H.S. Momose, Editorial Advisory Board; Prof. Hei Wong, Assoc. Ed., eehwong@cityu.edu.hk. **ISSN:** 0026-2714. **Subscription Rates:** 487,300¥ institutions; EUR3,671 institutions for Europe; US$4,108 institutions all countries except Europe and Japan. **Remarks:** Accepts advertising. **URL:** http://www.elsevier.com/wps/find/journaldescription.cws_home/274/description. **Circ:** (Not Reported)

Novi Sad

50092 ■ Radio Buca-FM - 89
9 Jugovica 17
YU-21000 Novi Sad, Serbia
Ph: 381 214739152
Fax: 381 21549099
E-mail: info@radiobuca.rs
Format: Ethnic; World Beat. **Operating Hours:** Continuous. **Ad Rates:** Advertising accepted; rates available upon request. **URL:** http://www.radiobuca.co.yu.

50093 ■ Radio 021-FM - 92.2
Svetozara Miletica 45
YU-21000 Novi Sad, Serbia
Ph: 381 421216
Fax: 381 423271
Format: Ethnic; World Beat. **Operating Hours:** Continuous. **Key Personnel:** Slobodan Stojsic, Director. **Ad Rates:** Advertising accepted; rates available upon request. **URL:** http://www.021.rs.

Sremska Kamenica

50094 ■ Archive of Oncology
Institute of Oncology of Vojvodina
Institutski Put 4
YU-21204 Sremska Kamenica, Serbia
Ph: 381 21 4805500
Fax: 381 21 6613741
Publisher E-mail: info@onko.onk.ns.ac.yu
Journal dedicated to oncology. **Founded:** 1908. **Freq:** Quarterly. **Print Method:** Offset. **Cols./Page:** 6. **Col. Width:** 12 picas. **Col. Depth:** 24 inches. **Key Personnel:** Ljubomir Vujaklija, Editor; Vladimir Baltiae, Editor-in-Chief. **ISSN:** 1450-9520. **Subscription Rates:** EUR40 individuals Europe; US$70 elsewhere; 3,000 Din individuals; EUR50 institutions Europe; US$100 institutions, other countries; 4,000 Din institutions. **URL:** http://www.onk.ns.ac.rs/archive/home.asp.

Circulation: ★ = ABC; △ = BPA; ♦ = CAC; • = CCAB; ❑ = VAC; ⊕ = PO Statement; ‡ = Publisher's Report; Boldface figures = sworn; Light figures = estimated.

Gale Directory of Publications & Broadcast Media/147th Ed.

5393

Victoria

50095 ■ **Seychelles Nation**
The Seychelles Nation Newspaper
Long Pier Rd.

PO Box 800
Victoria, Mahe, Seychelles
Ph: 248 225 775
Fax: 248 321 006

Government newspaper. **Freq:** Daily Mon.-Fri. **Key Personnel:** Denis Rose, Director. **Remarks:** Accepts advertising. **URL:** http://www.nation.sc/. **Circ:** (Not Reported)

Freetown

50096 ■ The Pool Newspaper
Third Fl., Ste. No. 1, Short St.
Freetown, Sierra Leone

Ph: 232 222 20102
Fax: 232 222 20102
Publisher E-mail: pool@justice.com
Community newspaper. **Freq:** 3/week. **Key Personnel:**
Sayoh Kamara, News Ed.; Unisa Deen Kargbo, Sub

Ed.; Adizatu Bangura, Sec.; Musa Karim, Office Asst.;
Osman F. Koroma, Editor; Musu Kamara, Graphics
Designer; Chernor Ojuku Sesay, Managing Editor. **URL:**
http://poolnewspaper.tripod.com/homepage.html. **Circ:**
3,000

Circulation: ★ = ABC; △ = BPA; ♦ = CAC; • = CCAB; ❏ = VAC; ⊕ = PO Statement; ‡ = Publisher's Report; Boldface figures = sworn; Light figures = estimated.

Gale Directory of Publications & Broadcast Media/147th Ed.

5397

Nanyang

50097 ■ Educational Research for Policy and Practice
Springer Netherlands
National Institute of Education
Nanyang Technology University
Nanyang, Singapore
Publisher E-mail: permissions.dordrecht@springer.com
Journal covering quantitative and qualitative contribution of educational research. **Founded:** 1978. **Freq:** 3/yr. **Print Method:** Offset. **Trim Size:** 13 x 21. **Cols./Page:** 6. **Col. Width:** 2 1/16 inches. **Col. Depth:** 21 1/2 inches. **Key Personnel:** Agnes Chang, Assoc. Ed.; Mary Hill, Editorial Board; Geoff Masters, Assoc. Ed.; Gerald W. Fry, Editorial Board; M.S. Khaparde, Assoc. Ed.; Y.C. Cheng, Editorial Board; Lee Chong Nim, Editorial Board; Zhou Mansheng, Assoc. Ed.; Ryo Watanabe, Assoc. Ed.; Robyn Baker, Editorial Board; Oon-Seng Tan, Editor-in-Chief. **ISSN:** 1570-2081. **Subscription Rates:** US$224 institutions; US$268.80 institutions enhanced access. **URL:** http://www.springer.com/west/home/generic/search/results?SGWID=4-40109-70-35692155-0.

Pasir Panjang

50098 ■ ASEAN Economic Bulletin
Institute of Southeast Asian Studies
30 Heng Mui Keng Ter.
Pasir Panjang 119614, Singapore
Ph: 65 677 80955
Fax: 65 677 81735
Publisher E-mail: admin@iseas.edu.sg
Publication covering economics. **Freq:** 3/yr. **Key Personnel:** K. Kesavapany, Chp.; Renuka Mahadevan, Editor; Sanchita Basu, Asst. Ed.; Nick Freeman, Editor. **ISSN:** 0217-4472. **Subscription Rates:** US$63 individuals in Asia/Australia/NZ/Japan; US$78 individuals in European/N&S America/Africa/; US$71 individuals in Singapore/Malaysia/Brunei; US$117 institutions in Asia/Australia/NZ/Japan; US$146 institutions in European/N&S America/Africa/; US$113 institutions in Singapore/Malaysia/Brunei. **URL:** http://bookshop.iseas.edu.sg.

50099 ■ Contemporary Southeast Asia
Institute of Southeast Asian Studies
30 Heng Mui Keng Ter.
Pasir Panjang 119614, Singapore
Ph: 65 677 80955
Fax: 65 677 81735
Publication E-mail: pubsunit@iseas.edu.sg
Publisher E-mail: admin@iseas.edu.sg
Political science publication. **Subtitle:** A Journal of International and Strategic Affairs. **Founded:** Jan. 1979. **Freq:** 3/yr. **Print Method:** Offset. **Trim Size:** 9 x 6. **Key Personnel:** K.S. Nathan, Editor, ksnathan@iseas.edu.sg; Thyaga S. Rajan, Editorial Asst.; Dayaneetha De Silva, Production Ed.; Ho Khai Leong, Assoc. Ed.; K. Kesavapany, Chp.; Tin Maung Than, Assoc. Ed. **ISSN:** 0129-797X. **Subscription Rates:** S$76 individuals Singapore/Malaysia/Brunei; S$119 institutions Singapore/Malaysia/Brunei; US$49 individuals Asia/Australia/NZ/Japan; US$77 institutions Asia/Australia/

NZ/Japan; US$59 individuals Europe/N & S America/Africa/Middle East; US$94 institutions Europe/N & S America/Africa/Middle East. **Remarks:** Accepts advertising. **URL:** http://bookshop.iseas.edu.sg. **Ad Rates:** BW: US$250. **Circ:** Paid 800

50100 ■ SOJOURN
Institute of Southeast Asian Studies
30 Heng Mui Keng Ter.
Pasir Panjang 119614, Singapore
Ph: 65 677 80955
Fax: 65 677 81735
Publisher E-mail: admin@iseas.edu.sg
Journal covering sociology and social issues. **Subtitle:** Journal of Social Issues in Southeast Asia. **Founded:** Feb. 1986. **Freq:** Semiannual. **Print Method:** Offset. **Trim Size:** 9 X 6. **ISSN:** 0217-9520. **Subscription Rates:** US$42 individuals Singapore, Malaysia, Brunei; US$75 institutions Singapore/Malaysia/Brunei; US$33 individuals Asia/Australia/NZ/Japan; US$62 institutions Asia/Australia/NZ/Japan; US$45 individuals Europe/N&S America/Africa/Middle East; US$84 institutions Europe/N&S America/Africa/Middle East. **Remarks:** Accepts advertising. **URL:** http://bookshop.iseas.edu.sg/ISEAS/Journal.jsp?cSeriesCode=SJ24/2. **Ad Rates:** BW: S$250. **Circ:** Paid 700

Singapore

50101 ■ Acta Biomaterialia
Elsevier (Singapore) Pte. Ltd.
3 Killiney Rd., No. 08-01
Winsland House 1
Singapore 239519, Singapore
Ph: 65 6 3490222
Fax: 65 6 7331510
Publisher E-mail: asiabkinfo@elsevier.com
International journal publishing peer-reviewed original research reports, review papers and communications in the broadly defined field of biomaterials science. **Founded:** 2005. **Freq:** 9/yr. **Key Personnel:** Prof. W.R. Wagner, Editor-in-Chief; K.S. Anseth, Editorial Board. **ISSN:** 1742-7061. **Subscription Rates:** 126,900¥ institutions; US$1,070 institutions all countries except Europe, Japan and Iran; EUR957 institutions European countries and Iran. **URL:** http://www.elsevier.com/wps/find/journaldescription.cws_home/702994/descriptiondescription.

50102 ■ Ad Hoc Networks
Elsevier (Singapore) Pte. Ltd.
3 Killiney Rd., No. 08-01
Winsland House 1
Singapore 239519, Singapore
Ph: 65 6 3490222
Fax: 65 6 7331510
Publisher E-mail: asiabkinfo@elsevier.com
International and archival journal providing a publication vehicle for complete coverage of all topics of interest to those involved in ad hoc and sensor networking areas. **Founded:** 2003. **Freq:** 8/yr. **Key Personnel:** I.F. Akyildiz, Editor; T. Abdelzahar, Editorial Board; S. Basagni, Editorial Board; N. Bulusu, Editorial Board; J. McNair, Editorial Board; F. Dressler, Editorial Board; A. Durresi, Editorial Board; M. Cesana, Editorial Board. **ISSN:** 1570-

8705. **Subscription Rates:** US$548 institutions all countries except Europe, Japan and Iran; EUR515 institutions European countries and Iran; 61,100¥ institutions Japan. **URL:** http://www.elsevier.com/wps/find/journaldescription.cws_home/672380/descriptiondescription.

50103 ■ Annals, Academy of Medicine, Singapore
Academy of Medicine, Singapore
142 Neil Rd.
Runme Shaw Bldg.
Singapore 088871, Singapore
Ph: 65 62238968
Fax: 65 62255155
Publication E-mail: annals@ams.edu.sg
Publisher E-mail: main@academyofmedicine.edu.sg
Periodical serving the various specialties that form the membership of the Academy of Medicine, Singapore. **Founded:** 1972. **Freq:** Bimonthly. **Key Personnel:** Vernon M.S. Oh, Editor; Ng Beng Yeong, Assoc. Ed.; Yap Hui Kim, Dep. Ed.; Eng King Tan, Editor. **ISSN:** 0304-4602. **Subscription Rates:** Free to members. **URL:** http://www.annals.edu.sg/.

50104 ■ Asia Europe Journal
Springer-Verlag GmbH & Company KG
Asia Europe Foundation
31 Heng Mui Keng Ter.
Singapore 119595, Singapore
Ph: 65 68749736
Fax: 65 68721206
Publication E-mail: asiaeuropejournal@asef.org
Publisher E-mail: webmaster@springer.com
Peer-reviewed journal covering the interdisciplinary and intercultural studies and research between Asia and Europe in the social sciences and humanities, covering various aspects of bilateral relations, comparative studies, Asian area studies in a European perspective or European studies from an Asian viewpoint. **Subtitle:** Intercultural Studies in the Social Sciences and Humanities. **Freq:** Quarterly. **Key Personnel:** Albrecht Rothacher, Editor-in-Chief; Horst Guenter Krenzler, Advisory Board; Chia Siow Yue, Advisory Board; Taciana Fisac, Advisory Board; Paul Lim, Advisory Board; Martin Bull, Advisory Board. **ISSN:** 1610-2932. **Subscription Rates:** EUR177 institutions; EUR212.40 institutions enhanced access. **Remarks:** Advertising accepted; rates available upon request. **URL:** http://www.springer.com/socialsciences/socialsciences%2Cgeneral/journal/10308. **Circ:** (Not Reported)

50105 ■ Asian Airlines & Aerospace
Global Business Press Pte. Ltd.
Level 34, Centennial Tower
3 Temasek Ave.
Singapore 039190, Singapore
Ph: 65 65497706
Fax: 65 65497011
Periodical containing special features, and profiles of the region's airline and aerospace industry. **Subtitle:** Asia's Leading Aviation Monthly. **Founded:** 1993. **Freq:** Monthly. **Trim Size:** 210 x 275 mm. **ISSN:** 1394-1798. **URL:** http://www.asianairlines-airports.com/. **Ad Rates:** BW: US$3,850, 4C: US$5,500. **Circ:** 5,434

Circulation: ★ = ABC; △ = BPA; ◆ = CAC; • = CCAB; ❑ = VAC; ⊕ = PO Statement; ‡ = Publisher's Report; Boldface figures = sworn; Light figures = estimated.

Gale Directory of Publications & Broadcast Media/147th Ed. 5399

50106 ■ Asian Case Research Journal
World Scientific Publishing Company Private Ltd.
c/o Lau Geok Theng, Ch. Ed.
NUS Business School
National University of Singapore
1 Business Link
Singapore 117592, Singapore
Publisher E-mail: wspc@wspc.com.sg
Journal aiming to provide case instructors such as academics, consultants, and company in-house trainers, a selection of high-quality cases on Asian companies and MNCs operating in the Asia-Pacific. **Founded:** 1997. **Freq:** Semiannual. **Key Personnel:** Lau Geok Theng, Ch. Ed., bizlaugt@nus.edu.sg; Nitin Pangarkar, Assoc. Ed.; Sum Chee Chuong, Assoc. Ed.; Winston Kwok Chee Chiu, Assoc. Ed.; Dr. Yeo Wee Yong, Assoc. Ed.; Kwok Siew Geok, Editorial Asst., bizksg@nus.edu.sg. **ISSN:** 0218-9275. **Subscription Rates:** US$117 institutions and libraries; print & electronic; US$112 institutions and libraries; electronic only; US$11 individuals for postage; EUR105 institutions and libraries; print & electronic; EUR101 institutions and libraries; electronic only; EUR7 individuals for postage; S$191 institutions and libraries; print & electronic; S$183 institutions and libraries; electronic only; S$14 individuals for postage. **Remarks:** Advertising accepted; rates available upon request. **URL:** http://www.worldscinet.com/acrj/acrj.shtml. **Circ:** (Not Reported)

50107 ■ Asian Defence and Diplomacy
Global Business Press Pte. Ltd.
Level 34, Centennial Tower
3 Temasek Ave.
Singapore 039190, Singapore
Ph: 65 65497706
Fax: 65 65497011
Publication providing substantive reports and analysis on defense and security issues. **Subtitle:** The Leading Magazine for Information on Region. **Founded:** 1994. **Freq:** Monthly. **Trim Size:** 210 x 275 mm. **ISSN:** 1394-178X. **Subscription Rates:** US$68 individuals Singapore; US$60 individuals Asia Pacific; US$120 individuals Americas & Africa; M$120 individuals Malaysia; US$100 individuals Europe & Middle East. **URL:** http://www.asiandefence-diplomacy.com/. **Ad Rates:** BW: US$4,130, 4C: US$5,900. **Circ:** 10,088

50108 ■ Asian Diver
Asian Diver Magazine
MediaCorp Publishing Pte Ltd.
Techpoint No. 01-06/08
10 Ang Mo Kio St. 65
Singapore 569059, Singapore
Ph: 65 64838399
Fax: 65 64842512
Magazine covering diving. **Founded:** 1992. **Freq:** 7/yr. **Key Personnel:** Jonathan Meur, Editor, jon@asiangeo.com. **ISSN:** 0218-3064. **Subscription Rates:** S$45 individuals singapore & Malaysia; US$45 individuals other parts of Asia; US$50 individuals outside Asia; US$50 individuals Australia, Vew Zealand, South Pacific. **Remarks:** Accepts advertising. **URL:** http://www.asiandiver.com/. **Circ:** (Not Reported)

50109 ■ Asian Furniture
Toucan Publications Ltd.
322-C King George's Ave.
Singapore 0820, Singapore
Ph: 65 2997121
Fax: 65 2997545
Magazine on furniture and furnishings.

50110 ■ Asian Home Gourmet
18 Cross St., No. 12-01/08
China Sq. Central
Singapore 048423, Singapore
Ph: 65 621 20100
Fax: 65 622 63935
Publisher E-mail: order@asianhomegourmet.com.sg
Culinary magazine. **Freq:** Quarterly. **URL:** http://www.asianhomegourmet.com/.

50111 ■ Asian Journal of Communication
Asian Media Information & Communication Centre
Jurong Point PO Box 360
Singapore 916412, Singapore
Ph: 65 679 27570
Fax: 65 679 27129
Publisher E-mail: enquiries@amic.org.sg
Asian journal covering communications. **Founded:** 1990. **Freq:** 4/yr. **Print Method:** Offset. **Trim Size:** 6 x

9. **Key Personnel:** Katherine T. Frith, Editorial Advisory Board; Eddie C.Y. Kuo, Founding Ed.; Hao Xiaoming, Editor. **ISSN:** 0129-2986. **Subscription Rates:** US$125 individuals print only; US$485 individuals online only; US$539 individuals print & online. **Remarks:** Advertising accepted; rates available upon request. **URL:** http://www.amic.org.sg. **Circ:** 750

50112 ■ Berita Harian
Singapore Press Holdings Ltd.
News Ctr.
1000 Toa Payoh N
Singapore 318994, Singapore
Ph: 65 63196319
Fax: 65 63198150
Publisher E-mail: sphcorp@sph.com.sg
Newspaper for the local Malay community. **Founded:** July 1, 1957. **Freq:** Daily. **Print Method:** Web offset. **Key Personnel:** Mohd Guntor Sadali, Editor, guntor@sph.com.sg. **Subscription Rates:** US$173.30 individuals; US$346.60 two years. **Remarks:** Accepts advertising. **URL:** http://www.sph.com.sg/ourproducts_newspaper_beritaharian.shtml. **Ad Rates:** 4C: S$3,450. **Circ:** Mon.-Fri. 62,000

50113 ■ Berita Minggu
Singapore Press Holdings Ltd.
News Ctr.
1000 Toa Payoh N
Singapore 318994, Singapore
Ph: 65 63196319
Fax: 65 63198150
Publisher E-mail: sphcorp@sph.com.sg
Newspaper featuring Malay community stories. **Founded:** July 10, 1960. **Freq:** Sunday. **Print Method:** Web offset. **Key Personnel:** Mohd Guntor Sadali, Editor. **Subscription Rates:** US$173.30 individuals; US$346.60 two years. **Remarks:** Accepts advertising. **URL:** http://www.sph.com.sg/ourproducts_newspaper_beritaminggu.shtml. **Ad Rates:** 4C: S$3,650. **Circ:** 62,000

50114 ■ The Best of Singapore
Edipresse Asia
211 Henderson Rd., No. 07-04
Henderson Industrial Pk.
Singapore 159552, Singapore
Ph: 65 63231606
Fax: 65 63231692
Magazine featuring Singapore's top shops, services and brands. **Freq:** Annual. **Key Personnel:** Gilbert Cheah, Director; Joseph Lim, Ch. Ed. **URL:** http://www.edipresse.com/lifestyle/best-singapore. **Circ:** ‡20,000

50115 ■ BigO
Options Publications Private Ltd.
PO Box 784
Marine Parade
Singapore 914410, Singapore
Ph: 65 634 84007
Publication E-mail: mybigo@bigozine.com
Singapore's rock magazine. **Freq:** Weekly. **Key Personnel:** Stephen Tan, Contact; Philip Cheah, Contact. **Subscription Rates:** Free. **Remarks:** Accepts advertising. **URL:** http://www.bigo.com.sg/. **Circ:** (Not Reported)

50116 ■ Biomolecular Frontiers
National University of Singapore
Department of Biochemistry
Yong Loo Lin School of Medicine
8 Medical Dr., Blk. MD7, No. 02-03
Singapore 117597, Singapore
Publisher E-mail: qsmanager@nus.edu.sg
Journal featuring articles about biology and chemistry. **Subtitle:** An International Journal of Life Sciences from Singapore. **Key Personnel:** Tang Bor Luen, Contact, phone 65 161040, bchtbl@nus.edu.sg. **ISSN:** 1793-2327. **URL:** http://www.biomolfrontiers.nus.edu.sg/.

50117 ■ The Business Times
Singapore Press Holdings Ltd.
News Ctr.
1000 Toa Payoh N
Singapore 318994, Singapore
Ph: 65 63196319
Fax: 65 63198150
Publisher E-mail: sphcorp@sph.com.sg
Newspaper containing book reviews, film reviews, music reviews and theater reviews. **Founded:** Oct. 1, 1976. **Freq:** Daily. **Key Personnel:** Alvin Tay, Editor, alvintay@

sph.com.sg; Vikram Khanna, Assoc. Ed., vikram@sph.com.sg; Rahul Pathak, Assoc. Ed., radulp@sph.com.sg. **Subscription Rates:** US$81.60 individuals. **Remarks:** Accepts advertising. **URL:** http://www.businesstimes.com.sg; http://www.sph.com.sg/ourproducts_newspaper_bt.shtml. **Ad Rates:** 4C: S$2,600. **Circ:** Mon.-Fri. 35,700

50118 ■ The Catholic News
2 Highland Rd., 01-03
Singapore 549102, Singapore
Ph: 65 685 83055
Fax: 65 685 82055
Publisher E-mail: cathnews@catholic.org.sg
Periodical containing Catholic church news from Asia and around the world. **Freq:** Semimonthly 26/yr. **Key Personnel:** Johnson Fernandez, Managing Editor, johnfern@catholic.org.sg; Cecilia Teo, Office Mgr., cecteo@catholic.org.sg. **Subscription Rates:** S$29 individuals. **Remarks:** Accepts advertising. **URL:** http://www.catholicnews.sg/index.php; http://www.veritas.org.sg; http://www.catholic.org.sg. **Ad Rates:** BW: S$1,050. **Circ:** 20,000

50119 ■ China
National University of Singapore
21 Lower Kent Ridge Rd.
Singapore 119077, Singapore
Ph: 65 6516 6666
Fax: 65 6775 9330
Publisher E-mail: qsmanager@nus.edu.sg
Journal serving the scholars in China with advances in a wide range of fields pertaining to China Studies. **Subtitle:** An International Journal. **Freq:** Semiannual. **Key Personnel:** Zheng Yongnian, Editor; Gungwu Wang, Advisory Board; Elspeth Thomson, Assoc. Ed.; Thomas P. Bernstein, Editorial Board; John P. Burns, Editorial Board; Jessica Loon, Production Ed. **ISSN:** 0219-7472. **Subscription Rates:** US$40 institutions online or print; US$56 institutions print and online; US$16 individuals. **URL:** http://www.nus.edu.sg/npu/cij/homepage/tableofc.html; http://muse.jhu.edu/journals/china/.

50120 ■ Chinese Management Studies
Emerald Group Publishing Ltd.
c/o Prof. Check Teck Foo, Ed.
Aventis School of Management
Le Meridien Hotel, No. 03-08
100 Orchard Rd.
Singapore 238840, Singapore
Publisher E-mail: emerald@emeraldinsight.com
Journal covering Chinese enterprise management. **Founded:** 2007. **Freq:** Quarterly. **Key Personnel:** Prof. Check Teck Foo, Editor, ctfoo@baruch.sg; Martyn Lawrence, Publisher, mlawrence@emeraldinsight.com. **ISSN:** 1750-614X. **URL:** http://info.emeraldinsight.com/products/journals/journals.htm?id=cms.

50121 ■ Chinese Medical Association Journal
Elsevier (Singapore) Pte. Ltd.
3 Killiney Rd., No. 08-01
Winsland House 1
Singapore 239519, Singapore
Ph: 65 6 3490222
Fax: 65 6 7331510
Publisher E-mail: asiabkinfo@elsevier.com
Official, peer-reviewed publication of the Chinese Medical Association. **Freq:** Monthly. **Key Personnel:** Shou-Dong Lee, Editor-in-Chief; Fa-Yauh Lee, Dep. Ed.-in-Ch.; Han-Chieh Lin, Editor. **ISSN:** 1726-4901. **Subscription Rates:** EUR465 individuals; 71,900¥ individuals; US$609 institutions. **Remarks:** Accepts advertising. **URL:** http://www.elsevier.com/wps/find/journaldescription.cws_home/708698/descriptiondescription. **Circ:** (Not Reported)

50122 ■ Chirurgie de la Main
Elsevier (Singapore) Pte. Ltd.
3 Killiney Rd., No. 08-01
Winsland House 1
Singapore 239519, Singapore
Ph: 65 6 3490222
Fax: 65 6 7331510
Publisher E-mail: asiabkinfo@elsevier.com
Official journal of la Societe francaise de chirurgie de la main, published in French and English. **Founded:** 1981. **Freq:** Bimonthly. **Key Personnel:** Thierry Tubert, Editor-in-Chief; M. Ebelin, Assoc. Ed.; R. Legre, Assoc. Ed.; S. Baux, Editorial Board; Y. Allieu, Editorial Board; G. Dautel, Editorial Board. **ISSN:** 1297-3203. **URL:** http://www.elsevier.com/wps/find/journaldescription.cws_home/

621365/descriptiondescription.

50123 ■ Citta Bella
Singapore Press Holdings Ltd.
News Ctr.
1000 Toa Payoh N
Singapore 318994, Singapore
Ph: 65 63196319
Fax: 65 63198150
Publisher E-mail: sphcorp@sph.com.sg
Chinese language magazine for women. **Founded:** Nov. 1993. **Freq:** Monthly. **Trim Size:** 205 x 275 mm. **Subscription Rates:** S$48 individuals. **Remarks:** Accepts advertising. **URL:** http://www.sph.com.sg/magazine/cittabella.html. **Ad Rates:** BW: S$2,100, 4C: S$2,800. **Circ:** 30,000

50124 ■ Comptes Rendus
Elsevier (Singapore) Pte. Ltd.
3 Killiney Rd., No. 08-01
Winsland House 1
Singapore 239519, Singapore
Ph: 65 6 3490222
Fax: 65 6 7331510
Publisher E-mail: asiabkinfo@elsevier.com
Journal covering paleontoloty, prehistoric science, and the evolution and history of science. **Founded:** 2002. **Freq:** 8/yr. **Key Personnel:** Jean Dercourt, Publishing Dir.; J. Aubouin, Editorial Board; Y. Coppens, Editorial Board; Yves Coppens, Editor-in-Chief; P. Taquet, Editor-in-Chief; Kevin Padian, Editor-in-Chief; Philippe Taquet, Editor-in-Chief; M. Durand-Delgas, Editorial Board. **ISSN:** 1631-0683. **URL:** http://www.elsevier.com/wps/find/journaldescription.cws_home/623404/descriptiondescription.

50125 ■ Computer Era
Eastern Holdings Ltd.
1100 Lower Delta Rd., No. 04-01
EPL Bldg.
Singapore 169206, Singapore
Ph: 65 637 92888
Fax: 65 637 92803
Publication E-mail: computerera@epl.com.sg
Publisher E-mail: eastern1@singnet.com.sg
Magazine on computers. **Founded:** 1981. **Freq:** Semiannual. **Remarks:** Accepts advertising. **URL:** http://www.computerera.com.sg. **Circ:** (Not Reported)

50126 ■ Computer Products
Global Sources
c/o Media Data Systems Pte. Ltd.
Raffles City
PO Box 0203
Singapore 911707, Singapore
Ph: 65 65472800
Fax: 65 65472888
Publisher E-mail: service@globalsources.com
Trade magazine covering Asian sources of computer products and news. **Founded:** 1983. **Freq:** Monthly. **Print Method:** Web. **Trim Size:** 8 1/16 x 10 5/8. **Cols./Page:** 2. **Subscription Rates:** US$130 two years; US$75 individuals. **Remarks:** Accepts advertising. **URL:** http://www.globalsources.com. **Absorbed:** Asian Sources Multimedia Products. **Formerly:** Asian Sources Computer Products. **Circ:** (Not Reported)

50127 ■ Computerworld Singapore
IDG Communications (S) Private Ltd.
80 Marine Parade Rd.
No. 17-01A Pky. Parade
Singapore 449269, Singapore
Ph: 65 63458383
Fax: 65 63456735
Publication providing relevant news to Singapore's computer software professionals. **Freq:** Weekly. **Key Personnel:** Teng Fang Yih, Editor. **Subscription Rates:** S$48 through eNETS. **Remarks:** Accepts advertising. **URL:** http://mis-asia.com/magazines/computerworld_singapore. **Circ:** (Not Reported)

50128 ■ COSMOS
World Scientific Publishing Company Private Ltd.
5 Toh Tuck Link
Singapore 596224, Singapore
Ph: 99965 646 65775
Fax: 99965 646 77667
Publisher E-mail: wspc@wspc.com.sg
Journal publishing expository or review articles, articles on new research results, or a combination of both, with the aim of promoting interdisciplinary research in Science and Mathematics. **Freq:** Semiannual. **Key Personnel:** Barry Halliwell, Editorial Advisor; Lee Seng Luan, Managing Editor; Yang Chen Ning, Editorial Advisor; Andrew Wee Thye Shen, Editor-in-Chief; Sir Michael Atiyah, Editorial Advisor; Chou Loke, Editorial Advisor; Gilbert Strang, Editorial Advisor; Pierre-Louis Lions, Editorial Advisor; Louis H.Y. Chen, Editorial Advisor; Jerome Friedman, Editorial Advisor. **ISSN:** 0219-6077. **Subscription Rates:** US$154 institutions and libraries; electronic + print; EUR126 institutions and libraries; electronic + print; S$245 institutions and libraries; electronic + print; US$148 institutions and libraries; electronic only; EUR121 institutions and libraries; electronic only; S$235 institutions and libraries; electronic only; US$13 individuals for postage; EUR9 individuals for postage; S$17 individuals for postage. **Remarks:** Advertising accepted; rates available upon request. **URL:** http://www.worldscinet.com/cosmos/cosmos.shtml. **Circ:** (Not Reported)

50129 ■ CW Magazine
Peter Knipp Holdings Private Ltd.
7 Jalan Kilang, 5th Fl.
Singapore 159407, Singapore
Ph: 65 62737707
Fax: 65 62701763
Asia's leading food and beverage portal. **Subtitle:** New Asia Cuisine & Wine Scene. **Freq:** Bimonthly. **Remarks:** Advertising accepted; rates available upon request. **URL:** http://www.asiacuisine.com.sg/; http://www.pkh.com.sg/press/release/CW.html. **Formerly:** CW Magazine. **Circ:** 12,000

50130 ■ DENTAL ASIA
Pablo Publishing Pte Ltd.
Block 61, Kallang Pl., No. 07-01
Singapore 339156, Singapore
Ph: 65 63967877
Fax: 65 63967177
Publisher E-mail: info@pabloasia.com
Magazine featuring dental industry in Asia. **Subtitle:** Asia's Premier Journal for Dental Practice and Technology. **Freq:** Bimonthly. **Key Personnel:** Alexis Ang, Editor, alexisang@pabloasia.com; William Pang, Publisher, williampang@pabloasia.com. **Subscription Rates:** US$77.04 individuals English and Chinese edition; US$139.10 two years English and Chinese edition; US$78 individuals to Asia Pacific, English & Chinese edition; US$140 two years to Asia Pacific, English & Chinese edition; US$90 individuals to America/Europe, English & Chinese edition; US$162 two years to America/Europe, English & Chinese edition. **Remarks:** Accepts advertising. **URL:** http://www.dentalasia.net/. **Circ:** (Not Reported)

50131 ■ The Dental Mirror
National University of Singapore
c/o Faculty of Dentistry
National University of Singapore
National University Hospital
5 Lower Kent Ridge Rd.
Singapore 119074, Singapore
Ph: 65 67724989
Fax: 65 67785742
Publication E-mail: denbox2@nus.edu.sg
Publisher E-mail: qsmanager@nus.edu.sg
Journal of dentistry. **Freq:** Semiannual. **Key Personnel:** Dr. Arlene Teo, Editor. **URL:** http://www.dentistry.nus.edu.sg/faculty/mirror.htm.

50132 ■ Digital Investigation
Elsevier (Singapore) Pte. Ltd.
3 Killiney Rd., No. 08-01
Winsland House 1
Singapore 239519, Singapore
Ph: 65 6 3490222
Fax: 65 6 7331510
Publisher E-mail: asiabkinfo@elsevier.com
Journal bringing together the growing global community interested in digital forensics, encompassing law enforcement, research, corporate information security, legal professionals and government. **Freq:** Quarterly. **Key Personnel:** E. Casey, Editor-in-Chief, eoghan@disclosedigital.com; Geoff Fellows, Editorial Board; Olivier De Vel, Editorial Board; Pete Forster, Editorial Board. **ISSN:** 1742-2876. **Subscription Rates:** 46,900¥ individuals; EUR355 individuals European Countries and Iran; US$397 individuals all Countries except Europe,
Iran and Japan; 104,200¥ institutions; EUR786 institutions European countries and Iran; US$873 institutions countries except Europe, Iran and Japan. **URL:** http://www.elsevier.com/wps/find/journaldescription.cws_home/702130/descrip tiondescription.

50133 ■ Digital Nanyang Chronicle
The Nanyang Chronicle
School of Communication & Information
Nanyang Technological University
31 Nanyang Link
Singapore 639798, SIngapore
Ph: 65 679 06446
Fax: 65 6794 0096
Publication E-mail: chronicle@ntu.edu.sg
Publisher E-mail: chronicle@ntu.edu.sg
Independent student newspaper. **Founded:** July 1994. **Freq:** Bimonthly. **Key Personnel:** Charles Shereen Naaz, Editor-in-Chief; Elizabeth Law Shi Ming, Managing Editor; Hui Xian Kwan, Sub-Ed. **Remarks:** Advertising accepted; rates available upon request. **URL:** http://www3.ntu.edu.sg/chronicle/. **Circ:** 20,000

50134 ■ Discrete Optimization
Elsevier (Singapore) Pte. Ltd.
3 Killiney Rd., No. 08-01
Winsland House 1
Singapore 239519, Singapore
Ph: 65 6 3490222
Fax: 65 6 7331510
Publisher E-mail: asiabkinfo@elsevier.com
Journal publishing research papers on the mathematical, computational and applied aspects of all areas of integer programming and combinatorial optimization. **Founded:** 2004. **Freq:** Quarterly. **Key Personnel:** Nimrod Megiddo, Editor-in-Chief; Gregory Gutin, Assoc. Ed.; Daniel Bienstock, Assoc. Ed.; Endre Boros, Assoc. Ed.; Horst Hamacher, Assoc. Ed.; Michel Minoux, Assoc. Ed. **ISSN:** 1572-5286. **Subscription Rates:** EUR640 institutions European countries and Iran; 76,100¥ institutions; US$640 institutions all countries except Europe, Japan, and Iran; US$147 individuals all countries except Europe, Japan, and Iran; 16,900¥ individuals; EUR111 individuals European countries and Iran. **URL:** http://www.elsevier.com/wps/find/journaldescription.cws_home/702998/descriptiondescription.

50135 ■ Drug Discovery Today
Elsevier (Singapore) Pte. Ltd.
3 Killiney Rd., No. 08-01
Winsland House 1
Singapore 239519, Singapore
Ph: 65 6 3490222
Fax: 65 6 7331510
Publisher E-mail: asiabkinfo@elsevier.com
Journal discussing the varied strategies used in ensuring drug action, especially with regard to biopharmaceuticals, including stem-cell therapy, vaccination, gene therapy, tissue modelling, tissue and non-tissue implants and many others. **Subtitle:** Therapeutic Strategies. **Founded:** 2004. **Freq:** Quarterly. **Key Personnel:** S.L. Carney, Editor. **ISSN:** 1359-6446. **URL:** http://www.drugdiscoverytoday.com/.

50136 ■ Drug Discovery Today
Elsevier (Singapore) Pte. Ltd.
3 Killiney Rd., No. 08-01
Winsland House 1
Singapore 239519, Singapore
Ph: 65 6 3490222
Fax: 65 6 7331510
Publisher E-mail: asiabkinfo@elsevier.com
Journal comparing different technological tools and techniques used from the discovery of new drug targets through to the launch of new medicines. **Subtitle:** Technologies. **Founded:** 2004. **Freq:** Quarterly. **Key Personnel:** Kelvin Lam, Editor-in-Chief; Henk Timmerman, Editor-in-Chief; Graeme Milligan, Advisory Editorial Board; Thomas Baillie, Advisory Editorial Board; Chris Lipinski, Advisory Editorial Board; Nick Terrett, Advisory Editorial Board. **ISSN:** 1740-6749. **Subscription Rates:** EUR2,353 institutions European countries and Iran; 312,600¥ institutions; US$2,646 institutions all countries except Europe, Japan and Iran. **URL:** http://www.elsevier.com/wps/find/journaldescription.cws_home/702730/descrip tiondescription.

50137 ■ Drug Discovery Today
Elsevier (Singapore) Pte. Ltd.
3 Killiney Rd., No. 08-01
Winsland House 1
Singapore 239519, Singapore

Ph: 65 6 3490222
Fax: 65 6 7331510
Publisher E-mail: asiabkinfo@elsevier.com
Journal covering the analysis of the molecules and pathways that fail or are subverted during the aetiology and pathogenesis of human disease. **Subtitle:** Disease Mechanisms. **Founded:** 2004. **Freq:** Quarterly. **Key Personnel:** Toren Finkel, Editor-in-Chief; Charles Lowenstein, Editor-in-Chief; Luciano Adorini, Advisory Editorial Board. **ISSN:** 1740-6765. **Subscription Rates:** EUR2,208 institutions European countries and Iran; 293,300¥ institutions; US$2,483 institutions all countries except Europe, Japan and Iran. **URL:** http://www.elsevier.com/wps/find/journaldescription.cws_home/702728/descriptiondescription.

50138 ■ Drug Discovery Today
Elsevier (Singapore) Pte. Ltd.
3 Killiney Rd., No. 08-01
Winsland House 1
Singapore 239519, Singapore
Ph: 65 6 3490222
Fax: 65 6 7331510
Publisher E-mail: asiabkinfo@elsevier.com
Journal discussing the non-human experimental models through which inference is drawn regarding the molecular aetiology and pathogenesis of human disease. **Subtitle:** Disease Models. **Founded:** 2004. **Freq:** Quarterly. **Key Personnel:** Andrew McCulloch, Editor-in-Chief; Jan Tornell, Editor-in-Chief. **ISSN:** 1740-6757. **Subscription Rates:** EUR2,229 institutions European countries and Iran; 296,000¥ institutions; US$2,506 institutions all countries except Europe, Japan and Iran. **URL:** http://www.elsevier.com/wps/find/journaldescription.cws_home/702727/descriptiondescription.

50139 ■ Drug Discovery Today
Elsevier (Singapore) Pte. Ltd.
3 Killiney Rd., No. 08-01
Winsland House 1
Singapore 239519, Singapore
Ph: 65 6 3490222
Fax: 65 6 7331510
Publisher E-mail: asiabkinfo@elsevier.com
Journal covering systems biology, knowledge management and integration, bio/cheminformatics, virtual screening, in silico modeling, e-clinical trials and text mining. **Subtitle:** Biosilico. **Key Personnel:** C. Watson, Editor; S. Carney, Assoc. Ed.; J. Clough, Assoc. Ed. **ISSN:** 1741-8364. **URL:** http://www.elsevier.com/wps/find/journaldescription.cws_home/703022/descriptiondescription.

50140 ■ Ecological Indicators
Elsevier (Singapore) Pte. Ltd.
3 Killiney Rd., No. 08-01
Winsland House 1
Singapore 239519, Singapore
Ph: 65 6 3490222
Fax: 65 6 7331510
Publisher E-mail: asiabkinfo@elsevier.com
Journal providing a forum for the discussion of the applied scientific development and review of traditional indicator approaches as well as for theoretical, modelling and quantitative applications such as index development. **Subtitle:** Integrating Sciences for Monitoring, Assessment and Management. **Founded:** 2001. **Freq:** Bimonthly. **Key Personnel:** F. Muller, Editor-in-Chief; V. Dale, Editorial Board; J.P. Bennett, Editorial Board; J. Karr, Editorial Board; F. Colijn, Editorial Board; R. Costanza, Editorial Board. **ISSN:** 1470-160X. **Subscription Rates:** 73,600¥ institutions European countries and Iran; EUR555 institutions all countries except Europe, Japan and Iran; EUR175 individuals European countries and Iran; US$236 individuals all Countries except Europe, Japan and Iran; 27,200¥ individuals. **URL:** http://www.elsevier.com/wps/find/journaldescription.cws_home/621241/descriptiondescription.

50141 ■ Ecological Informatics
Elsevier (Singapore) Pte. Ltd.
3 Killiney Rd., No. 08-01
Winsland House 1
Singapore 239519, Singapore
Ph: 65 6 3490222
Fax: 65 6 7331510
Publisher E-mail: asiabkinfo@elsevier.com
International journal devoted to the publication of high quality, peer-reviewed articles on all aspects of ecoinformatics, computational ecology and systems ecology, and special issues on topics of current interest. **Subtitle:**

An International Journal on Ecoinformatics and Computational Ecology. **Founded:** 2006. **Freq:** Bimonthly. **Key Personnel:** Friedrich Recknagel, Editor-in-Chief, phone 61 8 83033953, fax 61 8 83036222, friedrich.recknagel@adelaide.edu.au; Bruce Beck, Editorial Board; Sovan Lek, Editorial Board, lek@cict.fr. **ISSN:** 1574-9541. **Subscription Rates:** US$541 institutions all countries except Europe, Japan and Iran; EUR563 institutions European countries and Iran; 56,300¥ institutions; US$147 individuals all countries except Europe, Japan and Iran; 16,800¥ individuals; EUR110 individuals European countries and Iran. **URL:** http://www.elsevier.com/wps/find/journaldescription.cws_home/705192/descriptiondescription.

50142 ■ 8 Days
Media Corporation Publishing Private Ltd.
Caldecott Broadcast Centre
Andrew Rd.
Singapore 299939, Singapore
Ph: 65 63333888
Fax: 65 62515628
Publication E-mail: subhelp@mediacorp.com.sg
Publisher E-mail: feedback@mediacorp.com.sg
Movie, music and food magazine. **Freq:** Weekly. **Key Personnel:** Yeo Siew Kim, Sr. Assoc. Dir., yeo_siew_kim@mediacorppublishing.com. **Subscription Rates:** S$90 individuals. **Remarks:** Advertising accepted; rates available upon request. **URL:** http://www.corporate.mediacorp.sg/print/. **Circ:** (Not Reported)

50143 ■ Electronic & Components
Global Sources
c/o Media Data Systems Pte. Ltd.
Raffles City
PO Box 0203
Singapore 911707, Singapore
Ph: 65 65472800
Fax: 65 65472888
Publisher E-mail: service@globalsources.com
Trade magazine covering Asian sources of electronic components and news. **Founded:** 1979. **Freq:** Monthly. **Print Method:** Web. **Trim Size:** 8 1/16 x 10 5/8. **Cols./Page:** 2. **Subscription Rates:** US$130 two years; US$75 individuals. **Remarks:** Accepts advertising. **URL:** http://www.diamondpublications.com/scripts/prodView.asp?idProduct=351. **Formerly:** Asian Sources Electronic Components. **Circ:** (Not Reported)

50144 ■ Electronic Journal of Foreign Language Teaching
Centre for Language Studies
Faculty of Arts & Social Sciences
National University of Singapore
9 Arts Link
Singapore 117570, Singapore
Academic journal disseminating scholarly information on research and development in the field of second and foreign language teaching and learning in Asia and beyond. **Freq:** Semiannual. **Key Personnel:** Chan Wai Meng, Editor; Titima Suthiwan, Assoc. Ed. **ISSN:** 0219-9874. **URL:** http://e-flt.nus.edu.sg.

50145 ■ Emerging Markets Review
Elsevier (Singapore) Pte. Ltd.
3 Killiney Rd., No. 08-01
Winsland House 1
Singapore 239519, Singapore
Ph: 65 6 3490222
Fax: 65 6 7331510
Publisher E-mail: asiabkinfo@elsevier.com
Journal featuring articles from all disciplines that relate to emerging markets such as finance, economics, political economy, industrial organization, law and economics, and institutional economics. **Founded:** 2000. **Freq:** Quarterly. **Key Personnel:** J. Estrada, Assoc. Ed.; A. Ang, Assoc. Ed.; J.A. Batten, Editor, jabatten@gmail.com; B. Esty, Assoc. Ed.; K. Chan, Assoc. Ed.; S. Claessens, Assoc. Ed. **ISSN:** 1566-0141. **Subscription Rates:** US$66 individuals all countries except Europe, Japan and Iran; EUR62 individuals European countries and Iran; 8,500¥ individuals; US$300 institutions for all Countries except Europe, Japan and Iran; EUR268 institutions European countries and Iran; 35,500¥ institutions. **URL:** http://www.elsevier.com/wps/find/journaldescription.cws_home/620356/descriptiondescription.

50146 ■ Ezyhealth Singapore
Ezyhealth Holdings Pte. Ltd.
53A Science Park Dr.
The Faraday

Singapore Science Pk.
Singapore 118234, Singapore
Ph: 65 639 59393
Fax: 65 639 59394
Health, beauty, and fitness magazine. **Founded:** 1999. **Freq:** Monthly. **Subscription Rates:** Free. **URL:** http://www.ezyhealth.com. **Ad Rates:** 4C: S$3,800. **Circ:** Free 100,000

50147 ■ The Family Doctor
World Organization of Family Doctors
College of Medicine Bldg.
16 College Rd., No. 01-02
Singapore 169854, Singapore
Ph: 65 6224 2886
Fax: 65 6324 2029
Publisher E-mail: gfdadmin@globalfamilydoctor.com
Publication covering family medicine. **Freq:** Annual. **Subscription Rates:** S$69.50 Free members; S$69.50 nonmembers. **Remarks:** Advertising not accepted. **URL:** http://www.globalfamilydoctor.com. **Circ:** 130,000

50148 ■ FDM Asia
Eastern Holdings Ltd.
1100 Lower Delta Rd., No. 04-01
EPL Bldg.
Singapore 169206, Singapore
Ph: 65 637 92888
Fax: 65 637 92803
Publisher E-mail: eastern1@singnet.com.sg
Magazine for professionals in the woodworking and furniture manufacturing industry. **Founded:** 1986. **Freq:** 8/yr. **Key Personnel:** Sim Eric, Advertising Sales Mgr., phone 65 63792888; Kenneth Tan, Managing Editor. **Remarks:** Accepts advertising. **URL:** http://www.fdmasia.com/. **Circ:** (Not Reported)

50149 ■ Female Business
Singapore Press Holdings Ltd.
News Ctr.
1000 Toa Payoh N
Singapore 318994, Singapore
Ph: 65 63196319
Fax: 65 63198150
Publisher E-mail: sphcorp@sph.com.sg
Magazine for Singapore's dynamic career women. **Trim Size:** 210 x 275 mm. **Remarks:** Accepts advertising. **URL:** http://www.sph.com.sg/magazine/female_business.html. **Ad Rates:** 4C: S$4,500. **Circ:** 25,000

50150 ■ Food & Beverage Asia
Pablo Publishing Pte Ltd.
Block 61, Kallang Pl., No. 07-01
Singapore 339156, Singapore
Ph: 65 63967877
Fax: 65 63967177
Publisher E-mail: info@pabloasia.com
Magazine featuring innovations, trends and technologies of food and drinks manufacturing industries in Asia. **Subtitle:** Incorporating the Publications of the Singapore Institute of Food Science and Technology. **Founded:** 2002. **Key Personnel:** Denice Cabel, Editor, denice@pabloasia.com. **Subscription Rates:** US$77.04 individuals English and Chinese edition; US$139.10 two years English and Chinese edition; US$78 individuals to Asia Pacific, English & Chinese edition; US$140 two years to Asia Pacific, English & Chinese edition; US$90 individuals to America/Europe, English & Chinese edition; US$162 two years to America/Europe, English & Chinese edition. **Remarks:** Accepts advertising. **URL:** http://www.foodbeverageasia.com/. **Circ:** (Not Reported)

50151 ■ Gene Expression Patterns
Elsevier (Singapore) Pte. Ltd.
3 Killiney Rd., No. 08-01
Winsland House 1
Singapore 239519, Singapore
Ph: 65 6 3490222
Fax: 65 6 7331510
Publisher E-mail: asiabkinfo@elsevier.com
Journal devoted to the rapid publication of cloning and expression papers, papers reporting patterns of expression of interesting or important genes during development, or the results of molecular or gene expression screens analyzing interesting developmental events or stages. **Founded:** 2001. **Freq:** 8/yr. **Key Personnel:** C. Klaembt, Editor, klaembt@uni-muenster.de; Y. Saga, Editor, ysaga@lab.nig.ac.jp; N. Stainier, Editor, didier.stainier@ucsf.edu. **ISSN:** 1567-133X. **Subscription Rates:** 277,500¥ institutions; US$2,339 institutions all

Countries except Europe, Japan and Iran; EUR2,092 institutions European countries and Iran; EUR172 individuals European countries and Iran; US$231 individuals for all countries except Europe, Japan and Iran; 26,600¥ individuals. **URL:** http://www.elsevier.com/wps/find/journaldescription.cws_home/628039/descriptiondescription.

50152 ■ Global Sources Auto Parts & Accessories
Global Sources
c/o Media Data Systems Pte. Ltd.
Raffles City
PO Box 0203
Singapore 911707, Singapore
Ph: 65 65472800
Fax: 65 65472888
Publisher E-mail: service@globalsources.com
Magazine covering products and suppliers of auto parts and accessories. **Freq:** Monthly. **Subscription Rates:** US$75 by mail 4-6 weeks; US$120 two years by mail, 4-6 weeks; US$20 single issue through air courier, 3-7 days. **Remarks:** Accepts advertising. **URL:** http://www.globalsources.com/SITE/C2/APA.HTM?pi_sys_id=magol&pi_pub=APA&piproj=10AWJP&pi_act=1. **Circ:** (Not Reported)

50153 ■ Global Sources Baby & Childrens Products
Global Sources
c/o Media Data Systems Pte. Ltd.
Raffles City
PO Box 0203
Singapore 911707, Singapore
Ph: 65 65472800
Fax: 65 65472888
Publisher E-mail: service@globalsources.com
Magazine featuring baby and children's products and suppliers. **Freq:** Monthly. **Subscription Rates:** US$75 by mail 4-6 weeks; US$120 two years by mail, 4-6 weeks; US$20 single issue through air courier, 3-7 days. **Remarks:** Accepts advertising. **URL:** http://www.globalsources.com/SITE/C2/BCP.HTM?pi_sys_id=magol&pi_pub=BCP&pi_proj=10AWJP&pi_act=1. **Circ:** (Not Reported)

50154 ■ Global Sources Fashion Accessories
Global Sources
c/o Media Data Systems Pte. Ltd.
Raffles City
PO Box 0203
Singapore 911707, Singapore
Ph: 65 65472800
Fax: 65 65472888
Publisher E-mail: service@globalsources.com
Magazine featuring products and suppliers of fashion accessories. **Freq:** Monthly. **Subscription Rates:** US$75 by mail 4-6 weeks; US$120 two years by mail, 4-6 weeks; US$20 single issue through air courier, 3-7 days. **Remarks:** Accepts advertising. **URL:** http://www.globalsources.com/SITE/C2/FA.HTM?pi_sys_id=magol&pi_pub=FA&pi_proj=10AWJP&pi_act=1. **Circ:** (Not Reported)

50155 ■ Global Sources Garments & Textiles
Global Sources
c/o Media Data Systems Pte. Ltd.
Raffles City
PO Box 0203
Singapore 911707, Singapore
Ph: 65 65472800
Fax: 65 65472888
Publisher E-mail: service@globalsources.com
Magazine featuring products and suppliers of garments and textiles. **Freq:** Monthly. **Subscription Rates:** US$75 by mail 4-6 weeks; US$120 two years by mail, 4-6 weeks; US$20 single issue through air courier, 3-7 days. **Remarks:** Accepts advertising. **URL:** http://www.globalsources.com/SITE/C2/GT.HTM?pi_sys_id=magol&pi_pub=GAT&pi_proj=10AWJP&pi_act=1. **Circ:** (Not Reported)

50156 ■ Global Sources Gifts & Premiums
Global Sources
c/o Media Data Systems Pte. Ltd.
Raffles City
PO Box 0203
Singapore 911707, Singapore
Ph: 65 65472800
Fax: 65 65472888

Publisher E-mail: service@globalsources.com
Magazine featuring gifts, premium export products and suppliers. **Freq:** Monthly. **Subscription Rates:** US$75 by mail 4-6 weeks; US$120 two years by mail, 4-6 weeks; US$20 single issue through air courier, 3-7 days. **Remarks:** Accepts advertising. **URL:** http://www.globalsources.com/SITE/C2/GP.HTM?pi_sys_id=magol&pi_pub=GH&pi_proj=10AWJP&pi_act=1. **Circ:** (Not Reported)

50157 ■ Global Sources Hardware & DIY
Global Sources
c/o Media Data Systems Pte. Ltd.
Raffles City
PO Box 0203
Singapore 911707, Singapore
Ph: 65 65472800
Fax: 65 65472888
Publisher E-mail: service@globalsources.com
Magazine covering hardware and DIY products and suppliers. **Freq:** Monthly. **Subscription Rates:** US$75 by mail 4-6 weeks; US$120 two years by mail, 4-6 weeks; US$20 single issue through air courier, 3-7 days. **Remarks:** Accepts advertising. **URL:** http://www.globalsources.com/SITE/C2/HW.HTM?pi_sys_id=magol&pi_pub=HW&pi_proj=10AWJP&pi_act=1. **Circ:** (Not Reported)

50158 ■ Global Sources Home Products
Global Sources
c/o Media Data Systems Pte. Ltd.
Raffles City
PO Box 0203
Singapore 911707, Singapore
Ph: 65 65472800
Fax: 65 65472888
Publisher E-mail: service@globalsources.com
Magazine featuring home products and suppliers. **Freq:** Monthly. **Subscription Rates:** US$75 by mail 4-6 weeks; US$120 two years by mail, 4-6 weeks; US$20 single issue through air courier, 3-7 days. **Remarks:** Accepts advertising. **URL:** http://www.globalsources.com/SITE/C2/HP.HTM?pi_sys_id=magol&pi_pub=HP&pi_proj=10AWJP&pi_act=1. **Circ:** (Not Reported)

50159 ■ Global Sources Sports & Leisure
Global Sources
c/o Media Data Systems Pte. Ltd.
Raffles City
PO Box 0203
Singapore 911707, Singapore
Ph: 65 65472800
Fax: 65 65472888
Publisher E-mail: service@globalsources.com
Magazine featuring sports and leisure products and suppliers. **Freq:** Monthly. **Subscription Rates:** US$75 by mail 4-6 weeks; US$120 two years by mail, 4-6 weeks; US$20 single issue through air courier, 3-7 days. **Remarks:** Accepts advertising. **URL:** http://www.globalsources.com/SITE/C2/SL.HTM?pi_sys_id=magol&pi_pub=SL&pi_proj=10AWJP&pi_act=1. **Circ:** (Not Reported)

50160 ■ Global Sources Telecom Products
Global Sources
c/o Media Data Systems Pte. Ltd.
Raffles City
PO Box 0203
Singapore 911707, Singapore
Ph: 65 65472800
Fax: 65 65472888
Publisher E-mail: service@globalsources.com
Magazine featuring telecom products and suppliers. **Freq:** Monthly. **Subscription Rates:** US$75 by mail 4-6 weeks; US$120 two years by mail, 4-6 weeks; US$20 single issue through air courier, 3-7 days. **Remarks:** Accepts advertising. **URL:** http://www.globalsources.com/SITE/C2/TS.HTM?pi_sys_id=magol&pi_pub=TS&pi_proj=10AWJP&pi_act=1. **Circ:** (Not Reported)

50161 ■ Golf
Eastern Holdings Ltd.
1100 Lower Delta Rd., No. 04-01
EPL Bldg.
Singapore 169206, Singapore
Ph: 65 637 92888
Fax: 65 637 92803
Publisher E-mail: eastern1@singnet.com.sg
Periodical covering local, regional, and international golf

events. **Freq:** Monthly. **Subscription Rates:** Free. **Remarks:** Accepts advertising. **URL:** http://www.epl.com.sg/publications/golf.asp. **Circ:** (Not Reported)

50162 ■ Hardwage Mag
Hardware Zone Private Ltd.
20 Ayer Rajah Cres.
NO. 09-04/05, Technopreneur Centre
Singapore 139964, Singapore
Ph: 65 6 8722725
Fax: 65 6 8722724
Publisher E-mail: info.sg@hwzcorp.com
Computer hardware magazine. **Freq:** Monthly. **Subscription Rates:** S$82.80 individuals; S$165.50 two years. **Remarks:** Advertising accepted; rates available upon request. **URL:** http://www.hardwaremag.com. **Circ:** (Not Reported)

50163 ■ Harmful Algae
Elsevier (Singapore) Pte. Ltd.
3 Killiney Rd., No. 08-01
Winsland House 1
Singapore 239519, Singapore
Ph: 65 6 3490222
Fax: 65 6 7331510
Publisher E-mail: asiabkinfo@elsevier.com
Journal providing a forum to promote knowledge of harmful microalgae, including cyanobacteria, as well as monitoring, management and control of these organisms. **Founded:** 2002. **Freq:** Bimonthly. **Key Personnel:** Sandra E. Shumway, Editor-in-Chief, sandra.shumway@uconn.edu; G.J. Doucette, Editorial Advisory Board; Theodore Smayda, Editor-in-Chief, tsmayda@gso.uri.edu; D.M. Anderson, Editorial Advisory Board; M. Burkholder, Editorial Advisory Board; P.J. Hansen, Editorial Advisory Board; Y. Fukuyo, Editorial Advisory Board. **ISSN:** 1568-9883. **Subscription Rates:** US$489 institutions all countries except Europe, Japan and Iran; EUR437 institutions European countries and Iran; 57,900¥ institutions; US$103 individuals all countries except Europe, Japan and Iran; 12,100¥ individuals; US$107 students all countries except Europe, Japan and Iran; EUR94 students European countries and Iran; 12,500¥ students. **URL:** http://www.elsevier.com/wps/find/journaldescription.cws_home/622278/descriptiondescription.

50164 ■ Her World
Singapore Press Holdings Ltd.
News Ctr.
1000 Toa Payoh N
Singapore 318994, Singapore
Ph: 65 63196319
Fax: 65 63198150
Publisher E-mail: sphcorp@sph.com.sg
Women's magazine on fashion, beauty and relationships. **Founded:** July 1960. **Freq:** Monthly. **Key Personnel:** Rachel Tan, Editor. **Subscription Rates:** US$58 individuals. **Remarks:** Accepts advertising. **URL:** http://www.herworld.com/; http://www.sph.com.sg. **Ad Rates:** BW: S$3,220, 4C: S$4,290. **Circ:** 62,530

50165 ■ Her World Brides
Singapore Press Holdings Ltd.
News Ctr.
1000 Toa Payoh N
Singapore 318994, Singapore
Ph: 65 63196319
Fax: 65 63198150
Publication E-mail: maghwbrides@sph.com.sg
Publisher E-mail: sphcorp@sph.com.sg
Magazine for modern brides. **Founded:** Feb. 27, 1998. **Freq:** Quarterly. **Subscription Rates:** US$32 individuals; US$64 two years. **Remarks:** Accepts advertising. **URL:** http://www.hwbrides.com.sg/. **Ad Rates:** BW: US$2,250, 4C: US$3,000. **Circ:** 13,193

50166 ■ Highway Magazine
Automobile Association of Singapore
336 River Valley Rd., No. 03-00
AA Ctr.
Singapore 238366, Singapore
Ph: 65 63338811
Fax: 65 67335094
Publisher E-mail: aasmail@aas.com.sg
Publication of the Automobile Association of Singapore. **Freq:** Bimonthly. **URL:** http://www.aas.com.sg/.

50167 ■ Home & Decor
Singapore Press Holdings Ltd.

Circulation: ★ = ABC; △ = BPA; ♦ = CAC; • = CCAB; ❑ = VAC; ⊕ = PO Statement; ‡ = Publisher's Report; Boldface figures = sworn; Light figures = estimated.

News Ctr.
1000 Toa Payoh N
Singapore 318994, Singapore
Ph: 65 63196319
Fax: 65 63198150
Publication E-mail: hdecor@sph.com.sg
Publisher E-mail: sphcorp@sph.com.sg
Decor magazine for Singapore. **Founded:** 1999. **Freq:** Monthly. **Key Personnel:** Sophie Kho, Editor. **Subscription Rates:** US$60 individuals; US$120 two years. **Remarks:** Accepts advertising. **URL:** http://www. homeanddecor.com.sg/. **Ad Rates:** BW: S$1,800, 4C: S$2,700. **Circ:** 27,000

50168 ■ Hydrocarbon Asia
AP Energy Business Publications Private Ltd.
63 Robinson Rd., No. 02-16
Singapore 68894, Singapore
Ph: 65 622 23422
Fax: 65 622 25587
Refining, gas processing and petrochemical business and technical magazine. **Freq:** Monthly. **Key Personnel:** Khin Bo, Editor. **Subscription Rates:** US$110 individuals. **Remarks:** Accepts advertising. **URL:** http:// www.hcasia.safan.com/. **Ad Rates:** BW: US$3,300. **Circ:** (Not Reported)

50169 ■ Icon Moments
Singapore Press Holdings Ltd.
News Ctr.
1000 Toa Payoh N
Singapore 318994, Singapore
Ph: 65 63196319
Fax: 65 63198150
Publisher E-mail: sphcorp@sph.com.sg
Fashion, beauty and lifestyle magazine featuring Chinese watch and jewelry. **Freq:** Annual. **Trim Size:** 220 x 297 mm. **Remarks:** Accepts advertising. **URL:** http://www.sph.com.sg/article.display.php?id=695. **Ad Rates:** 4C: S$4,000. **Circ:** Combined 20,000

50170 ■ Infinite Dimensional Analysis, Quantum Probability and Related Topics
World Scientific Publishing Company Private Ltd.
5 Toh Tuck Link
Singapore 596224, Singapore
Ph: 99965 646 65775
Fax: 99965 646 77667
Publisher E-mail: wspc@wspc.com.sg
Publication focusing on infinite dimensional analysis and quantum probability. **Founded:** 1998. **Freq:** Quarterly. **Key Personnel:** T. Hida, Editor-in-Chief, thida@ccmfs. meijo-u.ac.jp; Vyacheslav P Belavkin, Assoc. Ed., vpb@ maths.nott.ac.uk; Vladimir I. Bogachev, Assoc. Ed., vbogach@mech.math.msu.su; L. Accardi, Managing Editor, fax 39 620 22539, accardi@volterra.mat. uniroma2.it; Sergio Albeverio, Editor, albeverio@uni-bonn.de; Giuseppe Da Prato, Editor, daprato@sns.it. **ISSN:** 0219-0257. **Subscription Rates:** US$505 institutions and libraries; print + electronic; US$34 individuals for postage; US$485 institutions and libraries; electronic only; S$836 institutions and libraries; electronic + print; S$803 institutions and libraries; electronic only; S$45 individuals for postage; EUR436 institutions and libraries; electronic + print; EUR419 institutions and libraries; electronic only; EUR26 individuals for postage. **URL:** http://www.worldscinet.com/idaqp/idaqp.shtml.

50171 ■ Information Fusion
Elsevier (Singapore) Pte. Ltd.
3 Killiney Rd., No. 08-01
Winsland House 1
Singapore 239519, Singapore
Ph: 65 6 3490222
Fax: 65 6 7331510
Publisher E-mail: asiabkinfo@elsevier.com
Journal presenting, within a single forum, all of the developments in the field of multi-sensor, multi-source information fusion and thereby promoting the synergism among the many disciplines that are contributing to its growth. **Freq:** Quarterly. **Key Personnel:** B.V. Dasarathy, Editor-in-Chief, belurd@gmail.com; A.A. Goshtasby, Editorial Board; A. Appriou, Editorial Board; J. Beyerer, Editorial Board; N.S.V. Rao, Editorial Board; S. Das, Editorial Board; H. Leung, Editorial Board. **ISSN:** 1566-2535. **Subscription Rates:** EUR126 individuals European Countries and Iran; 16,900¥ individuals; US$143 individuals all countries except Europe, Iran and Japan; US$580 institutions all countries except Europe, Iran and Japan; 68,800¥ institutions; EUR520 institutions European countries and Iran. **URL:** http://

www.elsevier.com/locate/inffus.

50172 ■ Infosecurity
Elsevier (Singapore) Pte. Ltd.
3 Killiney Rd., No. 08-01
Winsland House 1
Singapore 239519, Singapore
Ph: 65 6 3490222
Fax: 65 6 7331510
Publisher E-mail: asiabkinfo@elsevier.com
Journal covering in-depth analysis of specific business and management issues relating to information security, focusing on evidence-based experiences and applications from within all industry sectors. **Freq:** 7/yr. **Key Personnel:** S. Mathieson, Editor. **ISSN:** 1742-6847. **Subscription Rates:** US$259 institutions all countries except Europe, Japan and Iran; 30,300¥ institutions; EUR229 institutions European countries and Iran. **URL:** http://www.infosecurity-magazine.com/; http://www. elsevier.com/wps/find/journaldescription.cws_home/ 713933/descrip tiondescription.

50173 ■ Innovation
World Scientific Publishing Company Private Ltd.
Office of Research National University of Singapore
University Hall
Lee Kong Chian Wing, UHL, No. 05-02S
21 Lower Kent Ridge Rd.
Singapore 119077, Singapore
Ph: 65 65164811
Fax: 65 67756467
Publisher E-mail: wspc@wspc.com.sg
Publication devoted to the sharing of ideas and discussion of public sector innovation. **Subtitle:** The Magazine of Research and Technology. **Founded:** 2000. **Freq:** 3/yr. **Key Personnel:** Candace Lim, Editor, candacelim@nus.edu.sg. **ISSN:** 0219-4023. **Subscription Rates:** S$34 individuals Asia Pacific and Australasia, India, China, HK; US$19 individuals U.S./Canada/ South America/JPN/Korea/Middle East; EUR19 individuals; S$65 two years Asia Pacific/Australia, India, China, HK; US$37 two years U.S./Canada/South America/JPN/Korea/Middle East; EUR37 two years. **Remarks:** Accepts advertising. **URL:** http://www. innovationmagazine.com/. **Ad Rates:** BW: S$1,800, 4C: S$2,350. **Circ:** 10,000

50174 ■ Integrator
Disabled People's Association
No. 04-77 German Ctr.
25 International Business Park
Singapore 609916, Singapore
Ph: 65 68991220
Fax: 65 68991232
Publisher E-mail: dpa@dpa:org.sg
Newspaper covering the disabled. **Freq:** Quarterly. **Key Personnel:** Leo Chen Ian, President; Chang Siew Ngoh, Vice President. **Remarks:** Advertising accepted; rates available upon request. **URL:** http://www.dpa.org.sg/ Publications/integrator.asp. **Circ:** 800

50175 ■ International Immunopharmacology
Elsevier (Singapore) Pte. Ltd.
3 Killiney Rd., No. 08-01
Winsland House 1
Singapore 239519, Singapore
Ph: 65 6 3490222
Fax: 65 6 7331510
Publisher E-mail: asiabkinfo@elsevier.com
Journal publishing original research papers pertinent to the overlapping areas of immunology, pharmacology, cytokine biology, immunotherapy, immunopathology and immunotoxicology. **Founded:** 2001. **Freq:** Monthly. **Key Personnel:** Prof. J.E. Talmadge, Editor-in-Chief, jtalmadg.immpharm@atlarge.net; Dr. F. Abe, Assoc. Ed., fabe@unmc.edu; Dr. Alun K. Brown, Assoc. Ed., alun. brown@kcl.ac.uk. **ISSN:** 1567-5769. **Subscription Rates:** EUR2,782 institutions European countries and Iran; US$3,111 institutions all countries except Europe, Japan and Iran; 369,200¥ institutions; 54,400¥ individuals; US$473 individuals all countries except Europe, Japan and Iran; EUR353 individuals European countries and Iran. **URL:** http://www.elsevier.com/wps/find/ journaldescription.cws_home/621330/descrip tiondescription.

50176 ■ International Journal of Algebra and Computation
World Scientific Publishing Company Private Ltd.
5 Toh Tuck Link
Singapore 596224, Singapore
Ph: 99965 646 65775
Fax: 99965 646 77667

Publisher E-mail: wspc@wspc.com.sg
Journal publishing original papers in mathematics. **Founded:** 1995. **Freq:** 8/yr. **Key Personnel:** J. Rhodes, Founding Ed./Ed.-in-Ch., rhodes@math.berkeley.edu; J. Meakin, Managing Editor, jmeakin@math.unl.edu; R.I. Grigorchuk, Editorial Board, grigorch@mi.ras.ru; S. Smale, Honorary Ed.; S.W. Margolis, Managing Editor, margolis@math.biu.ac.il; J. Stallings, Honorary Ed., stall@cartan.berkeley.edu. **ISSN:** 0218-1967. **Subscription Rates:** US$1,267 institutions and libraries; print & electronic; US$50 individuals for postage; US$1,216 institutions and libraries; electronic only; EUR1,079 institutions and libraries; print & electronic; EUR1,036 institutions and libraries; electronic only; EUR34 individuals for postage; S$2,023 institutions and libraries; print & electronic; S$1,942 institutions and libraries; electronic only; S$67 individuals for postage. **URL:** http://www. worldscinet.com/ijac/ijac.shtml.

50177 ■ International Journal of Chinese & Oriental Languages Processing
Chinese and Oriental Languages Information Processing Society
School of Computing, Lower Kent Ridge
National Univ. of Singapore
Singapore 119260, Singapore
Publisher E-mail: luakt@colips.org
Periodical devoted to the publication of original theoretical and applied research in Chinese and oriental languages. **Founded:** 1991. **Freq:** Semiannual. **Key Personnel:** Lua Kim Teng, Editor, luakt@colips. org; Zhang Min, Exec. Ed., mzhang@i2r.a-star.edu.sg. **ISSN:** 0219-5968. **URL:** http://www.colips.org/journal/ index.htm. **Also known as:** Journal of Chinese Language and Computing. **Formerly:** Communications of COLIPS. **Circ:** Paid 400

50178 ■ International Journal of Complexity in Leadership and Management
Inderscience Enterprises Limited
c/o Prof. Thow Yick Liang, Ed.-in-Ch.
Singapore Management University
Lee Kong Chian School of Business
50 Stamford Rd.
Singapore 178899, Singapore
Journal focusing on the complexity of leadership and management. **Freq:** 4/yr. **Key Personnel:** Prof. Thow Yick Liang, Editor-in-Chief, tyliang@smu.edu.sg; Dr. Pak Tee Ng, Editor, paktee.ng@nie.edu.sg. **ISSN:** 1759-0256. **Subscription Rates:** EUR494 individuals print or online; EUR672 individuals print and online. **URL:** http:// www.inderscience.com/browse/index.php?journalID= 345.

50179 ■ International Journal of Computational Methods (IJCM)
World Scientific Publishing Company Private Ltd.
c/o G.R. Liu, Ch. Ed.
Dept. of Mechanical Engineering
National University of Singapore
10 Kent Ridge Cres.
Singapore 119260, Singapore
Publisher E-mail: wspc@wspc.com.sg
Journal reporting recent developments in theory, algorithm, programming, coding, numerical simulation and/or novel application of computational techniques to problems in engineering, science, and other disciplines related to computations. **Key Personnel:** R.C. Batra, Ch. Ed., rbatra@vt.edu; G. Yagawa, Ch. Ed., yagawa@ q.t.u-tokyo.ac.jp; B.C. Tan, Managing Editor, mpetanbc@ nus.edu.sg; Z.H. Zhong, Ch. Ed., zhong_zhihua@sina. com; G.R. Liu, Ch. Ed., mpeliugr@nus.edu.sg; J.S. Chen, Editorial Board. **ISSN:** 0219-8762. **Subscription Rates:** US$351 institutions and libraries; electronic + print; US$337 institutions and libraries; electronic only; US$34 individuals for postage; EUR23 individuals for postage; EUR302 institutions and libraries; electronic + print; EUR290 institutions and libraries; electronic only; S$45 individuals for postage; S$551 institutions and libraries; electronic + print; S$529 institutions and libraries; electronic only. **URL:** http://www.worldscinet.com/ ijcm/mkt/aims_scope.shtml.

50180 ■ International Journal of Geometric Methods in Modern Physics (IJGMMP)
World Scientific Publishing Company Private Ltd.
5 Toh Tuck Link
Singapore 596224, Singapore
Ph: 99965 646 65775
Fax: 99965 646 77667
Publisher E-mail: wspc@wspc.com.sg
Journal focusing on application of geometric methods to quantum field theory, non-perturbative quantum gravity,

string and brane theory, quantum mechanics, semi-classical approximations in quantum theory, quantum thermodynamics and statistical physics, quantum computation and control theory. **Freq:** 8/yr. **Key Personnel:** G. Sardanashvily, Managing Editor, sard@grav.phys.msu.su; A. Ashtekar, Editorial Board; A. Cattaneo, Editorial Board; A. Borowiec, Editorial Board; Yong-Shi Wu, Editorial Board; B. Fedosov, Editorial Board; D. Alekseevsky, Editorial Board; G. Giachetta, Assoc. Ed., giovanni.giachetta@unicam.it; T. Ratiu, Editorial Board; F. Cantrijn, Editorial Board. **ISSN:** 0219-8878. **Subscription Rates:** US$549 institutions and libraries; electronic + print; EUR482 institutions and libraries; electronic + print; S$878 institutions and libraries; electronic + print; US$527 institutions and libraries; electronic only; EUR463 institutions and libraries; electronic only; S$843 institutions and libraries; electronic only; US$50 individuals for postage; EUR34 individuals for postage; S$67 individuals for postage. **Remarks:** Advertising accepted; rates available upon request. **URL:** http://www.worldscinet.com/ijgmmp/ijgmmp.shtml. **Circ:** (Not Reported)

50181 ■ International Journal of Humanoid Robotics (IJHR)
World Scientific Publishing Company Private Ltd.
c/o Ming Xie, Ed.-in-Ch.
School of Mechanical & Aerospace Engineering
Nanyang Technological University
Singapore 639798, Singapore
Publisher E-mail: wspc@wspc.com.sg

Journal publishing mental and physical development of humanoid robots, recent achievements and the future trends in robotics R&D and on Curriculum Development in Humanoid Robot Education. **Freq:** Quarterly. **Key Personnel:** Christian Balkenius, Editor; Ming Xie, Editor-in-Chief, mmxie@ntu.edu.sg; Jean-Guy Fontaine, Editor-in-Chief, jean-guy.fontaine@iit.it; Manuel Armada, Editor; Juyang Weng, Editor-in-Chief, weng@cse.msu.edu; Gerd Hirzinger, Advisory Board, gerd.hirzinger@dlr.de. **ISSN:** 0219-8436. **Subscription Rates:** US$414 institutions and libraries; electronic + print; US$397 institutions and libraries; electronic only; US$34 individuals for postage; EUR360 institutions and libraries; electronic + print; EUR346 institutions and libraries; electronic only; EUR23 individuals print only; S$652 institutions and libraries; electronic + print; S$626 institutions and libraries; electronic only; S$45 individuals for postage. **URL:** http://www.worldscinet.com/ijhr/ijhr.shtml.

50182 ■ International Journal of Image and Graphics
World Scientific Publishing Company Private Ltd.
5 Toh Tuck Link
Singapore 596224, Singapore
Ph: 99965 646 65775
Fax: 99965 646 77667
Publisher E-mail: wspc@wspc.com.sg

Journal publishing efficient and effective image and graphics technologies and systems, and providing a central forum for scientists, researchers, engineers and vendors from different disciplines to exchange ideas, identify problems, investigate relevant issues, share common interests, explore new directions, and initiate possible collaborative research and system development. **Freq:** Quarterly. **Key Personnel:** David Zhang, Editor-in-Chief, csdzhang@comp.polyu.edu.hk; E. Pissaloux, Regional Ed.; J. Rokne, Regional Ed.; E. Wu, Regional Ed.; A.P. Britto, Assoc. Ed.; J. Chai, Assoc. Ed. **ISSN:** 0219-4678. **Subscription Rates:** US$410 institutions and libraries; electronic + print; EUR364 institutions and libraries; electronic + print; S$663 institutions and libraries; electronic + print; US$394 institutions and libraries; electronic only; EUR349 institutions and libraries; electronic only; S$636 institutions and libraries; electronic only; US$34 individuals for postage; EUR23 individuals for postage; S$45 individuals for postage. **Remarks:** Advertising accepted; rates available upon request. **URL:** http://www.worldscinet.com/ijig/ijig.shtml. **Circ:** (Not Reported)

50183 ■ International Journal of Information Acquisition
World Scientific Publishing Company Private Ltd.
5 Toh Tuck Link
Singapore 596224, Singapore
Ph: 99965 646 65775
Fax: 99965 646 77667
Publisher E-mail: wspc@wspc.com.sg

Peer-reviewed journal promoting interaction and the exchange of original investigations and inventions, research findings and results, academic philosophies and opinions in information acquisition science and technology, seeking to advance the fundamental theories, key technologies and the critical applications in information acquisition science and technology. **Freq:** Quarterly. **Key Personnel:** Dr. Tao Mei, Editor-in-Chief; Dr. Max Meng, Assoc. Ed.; Dr. Harold Szu, Assoc. Ed. **ISSN:** 0219-8789. **Subscription Rates:** US$393 institutions and libraries; electronic + print; US$377 institutions and libraries; electronic only; US$39 individuals for postage; S$623 institutions and libraries; electronic + print; S$598 institutions and libraries; electronic only; S$52 individuals for postage; EUR323 institutions and libraries; electronic + print; EUR310 institutions and libraries; electronic only; EUR31 individuals for postage. **Remarks:** Advertising accepted; rates available upon request. **URL:** http://www.worldscinet.com/ijia/ijia.shtml. **Circ:** (Not Reported)

50184 ■ International Journal of Innovation Management
World Scientific Publishing Company Private Ltd.
5 Toh Tuck Link
Singapore 596224, Singapore
Ph: 99965 646 65775
Fax: 99965 646 77667
Publisher E-mail: wspc@wspc.com.sg

Publication focusing on the advancement of academic research and management practice in the field of innovation management. **Founded:** 1997. **Freq:** Quarterly. **Key Personnel:** Joe Tidd, Managing Editor, phone 65 127 3686758, fax 65 127 3685865, j.tidd@sussex.ac.uk; P. Nightingale, Book Review Ed.; J. Bower, Editorial Review Board, d.j.bower@gcal.ac.uk. **ISSN:** 1363-9196. **Subscription Rates:** US$782 institutions and libraries; print + electronic; EUR666 institutions and libraries; print + electronic; S$1,277 institutions and libraries; print + electronic; US$451 institutions and libraries; electronic only; EUR639 institutions and libraries; electronic only; S$1,226 institutions and libraries; electronic only; US$47 individuals for postage; EUR36 individuals for postage; S$62 individuals for postage. **URL:** http://www.worldscinet.com/ijim/ijim.shtml.

50185 ■ International Journal of Modern Physics A
World Scientific Publishing Company Private Ltd.
5 Toh Tuck Link
Singapore 596224, Singapore
Ph: 99965 646 65775
Fax: 99965 646 77667
Publisher E-mail: wspc@wspc.com.sg

Periodical containing review articles and original papers covering the latest research developments in particles and fields, gravitation and cosmology. **Founded:** 1986. **Freq:** 32/yr. **Key Personnel:** H.S. Chen, Editorial Board; I. Tsutsui, Managing Editor, izumi.tsutsui@kek.jp; V.A. Rubakov, Managing Editor, rubakov@ms2.inr.ac.ru; L. Brink, Managing Editor, tfelb@fy.chalmers.se; P. Fisher, Editorial Board; A.P. Balachandran, Managing Editor, erobb@phy.syr.edu; M. Ninomiya, Managing Editor, ninomiya@yukawa.kyoto-u.ac.jp; Harry W.K. Cheung, Editorial Board; J. Nash, Editorial Board; T. Ferbel, Editorial Board. **ISSN:** 0217-751X. **Subscription Rates:** US$6,434 institutions and libraries; electronic + print; EUR5,408 institutions and libraries; electronic + print; S$10,380 institutions and libraries; electronic + print; US$6,177 institutions and libraries; electronic only; EUR5,192 institutions and libraries; electronic only; S$9,965 institutions and libraries; electronic only; US$125 individuals add postage; EUR98 individuals add postage; S$166 individuals add postage. **URL:** http://www.worldscinet.com/ijmpa/ijmpa.shtml. **Circ:** Paid 500

50186 ■ International Journal of Modern Physics C
World Scientific Publishing Company Private Ltd.
5 Toh Tuck Link
Singapore 596224, Singapore
Ph: 99965 646 65775
Fax: 99965 646 77667
Publisher E-mail: wspc@wspc.com.sg

Periodical covering computational physics, physical computation and related subjects. **Subtitle:** Computational Physics and Physical Computation. **Founded:** 1990. **Freq:** Monthly. **Key Personnel:** H.J. Herrmann, Managing Editor, hans@ica1.uni-stuttgart.de; P.M.C. De Oliveira, Managing Editor, pmco@if.uff.br; K. Binder, Assoc. Ed.; H.Q. Lin, Managing Editor, hqlin@phy.cuhk.edu.hk; D. Sornette, Assoc. Ed. **ISSN:** 0129-1831. **Subscription Rates:** US$1,738 institutions and libraries; print & electronic; US$1,668 institutions and libraries; electronic only; US$59 individuals add postage; EUR1,401 institutions and libraries; print & electronic; EUR1,345 institutions and libraries; electronic only; EUR46 individuals add postage; S$2,770 institutions and libraries; print & electronic; S$2,659 institutions and libraries; electronic only; S$78 individuals add postage. **URL:** http://journals.wspc.com.sg/ijmpc/ijmpc.shtml; http://www.worldscinet.com/ijmpc/ijmpc.shtml. **Formerly:** International Journal of Modern Physics C: Physics and Computers.

50187 ■ International Journal of Modern Physics D
World Scientific Publishing Company Private Ltd.
5 Toh Tuck Link
Singapore 596224, Singapore
Ph: 99965 646 65775
Fax: 99965 646 77667
Publisher E-mail: wspc@wspc.com.sg

Journal covering astrophysics, gravitation and cosmology. **Subtitle:** Gravitation, Astrophysics and Cosmology. **Founded:** 1992. **Freq:** 14/yr. **Key Personnel:** D.V. Ahluwalia, Special Papers Ed., dharamvir.ahluwalia@canterbury.ac.nz; Ruth Gregory, Managing Editor, fax 44 191 3343051, r.a.w.gregory@durham.ac.uk; Jorge Pullin, Managing Editor, phone 225578-0464, fax 225578-0464, pullin@lsu.edu. **ISSN:** 0218-2718. **Subscription Rates:** US$1,542 institutions and libraries; print & electronic; US$1,480 institutions and libraries; electronic; US$70 individuals add postage; EUR1,287 institutions and libraries; print & electronic; EUR1,236 institutions and libraries; electronic; S$2,411 institutions and libraries; print & electronic; S$2,315 institutions and libraries; electronic; S$93 individuals add postage. **URL:** http://www.worldscinet.com/ijmpd/ijmpd.shtml.

50188 ■ International Journal of Modern Physics E
World Scientific Publishing Company Private Ltd.
5 Toh Tuck Link
Singapore 596224, Singapore
Ph: 99965 646 65775
Fax: 99965 646 77667
Publisher E-mail: wspc@wspc.com.sg

Periodical covering the topics on experimental, theoretical and computational nuclear science. **Subtitle:** Nuclear Physics. **Founded:** 1992. **Freq:** Bimonthly. **Key Personnel:** W. Greiner, Managing Editor, greiner@fias.uni-frankfurt.de; D.H. Feng, Editor; E.M. Henley, Managing Editor, fax 206685-0635, henley@alpher.npl.washington.edu; R.F. Casten, Editor; H. Ejiri, Editor; Dmitri E. Kharzeev, Managing Editor, kharzeev@bnl.gov. **ISSN:** 0218-3013. **Subscription Rates:** US$1,223 institutions and libraries; electronic and print; US$1,174 institutions and libraries; electronic only; S$1,876 institutions and libraries; electronic only; US$59 individuals add postage; EUR988 institutions and libraries; electronic and print; EUR948 institutions and libraries; electronic only; S$78 institutions add postage; EUR46 individuals add postage; S$1,954 institutions and libraries; electronic and print. **URL:** http://www.worldscinet.com/ijmpe/ijmpe.shtml. **Formerly:** International Journal of Modern Physics E: Report on Nuclear Physics.

50189 ■ International Journal of Nanoscience
World Scientific Publishing Company Private Ltd.
5 Toh Tuck Link
Singapore 596224, Singapore
Ph: 99965 646 65775
Fax: 99965 646 77667
Publisher E-mail: wspc@wspc.com.sg

Inter-disciplinary, internationally-reviewed research journal covering all aspects of nanometer scale science and technology, seeking articles in any contemporary topical area, from basic science of nanoscale physics and chemistry to applications in nanodevices, quantum engineering and quantum computing. **Freq:** Bimonthly. **Key Personnel:** A.T.S. Wee, Managing Editor, phyweets@nus.edu.sg; J.G. Hou, Managing Editor, jghou@ustc.edu.cn; A. Zakhidov, Managing Editor, zakhidov@utdallas.edu. **ISSN:** 0219-581X. **Subscription Rates:** US$887 institutions and libraries; print and electronic; EUR715 institutions and libraries; print and electronic; US$852 institutions and libraries; electronic only; EUR686 institutions and libraries; electronic only; US$47 individuals for postage; S$1,416 institutions and libraries; print and electronic; S$1,359 institutions and libraries; electronic only; S$62 individuals for postage; EUR36 individuals for postage. **Remarks:** Advertising accepted; rates available upon request. **URL:** http://www.worldscinet.com/ijn/ijn.shtml. **Circ:** (Not Reported)

50190 ■ International Journal of Neural Systems
World Scientific Publishing Company Private Ltd.
5 Toh Tuck Link

Circulation: ★ = ABC; △ = BPA; ♦ = CAC; • = CCAB; ❑ = VAC; ⊕ = PO Statement; ‡ = Publisher's Report; Boldface figures = sworn; Light figures = estimated.

Singapore 596224, Singapore
Ph: 99965 646 65775
Fax: 99965 646 77667
Publisher E-mail: wspc@wspc.com.sg
Periodical containing peer-reviewed journal covering information processing in natural and artificial neural systems. **Founded:** 1989. **Freq:** Bimonthly. **Key Personnel:** Hojjat Adeli, Editor-in-Chief; Cihan H. Dagli, Editorial Advisory Board. **ISSN:** 0129-0657. **Subscription Rates:** US$968 institutions and libraries; print & electronic; US$47 individuals add postage; US$929 institutions and libraries; electronic only; EUR780 institutions and libraries; print & electronic; EUR749 institutions and libraries; electronic only; EUR36 individuals add postage; S$1,544 institutions and libraries; print & electronic; S$1,482 institutions and libraries; electronic only; S$62 individuals add postage. **URL:** http://www.worldsci.net.com/ijns/ijns.shtml.

50191 ■ International Journal of Osteopathic Medicine
Elsevier (Singapore) Pte. Ltd.
3 Killiney Rd., No. 08-01
Winsland House 1
Singapore 239519, Singapore
Ph: 65 6 3490222
Fax: 65 6 7331510
Publisher E-mail: asiabkinfo@elsevier.com
Peer-reviewed journal publishing basic science research, clinical epidemiology and health social science in relation to osteopathy and neuromusculoskeletal medicine. **Freq:** Quarterly. **Key Personnel:** Dr. Janine Leach, Editorial Board; Carol Fawkes, International Advisory Board; Robert Moran, Editor; Nicholas Lucas, Editor; Ann Moore, Editorial Advisor; Michael Patterson, Editorial Board; Tamar Pincus, Editorial Board; Steven Vogel, Editor; Peter Gibbons, Editorial Board. **ISSN:** 1746-0689. **Subscription Rates:** 37,700¥ institutions; US$318 institutions for all countries except Europe, Japan and Iran; EUR284 for European countries and Iran; 13,400¥ individuals; US$111 individuals for all countries except Europe, Japan and Iran; EUR101 individuals for European countries and Iran. **URL:** http://www.elsevier.com/wps/find/journaldescription.cws_home/705245/descriptiondescription.

50192 ■ International Journal of PIXE
World Scientific Publishing Company Private Ltd.
5 Toh Tuck Link
Singapore 596224, Singapore
Ph: 99965 646 65775
Fax: 99965 646 77667
Publisher E-mail: wspc@wspc.com.sg
Periodical covering the latest developments in the various aspects of particle-induced X-ray emission. **Founded:** 1990. **Freq:** Quarterly. **Key Personnel:** K. Ishii, Editor-in-Chief; K.G. Malmqvist, Managing Editor, garbokf@seldc52; M. Kasahara, Managing Editor, kasahara@energy.kyoto-u.ac.jp; F. Aldape, Editorial Board; E. Clayton, Editorial Board. **ISSN:** 0129-0835. **Subscription Rates:** US$655 institutions and libraries; print & electronic; US$629 institutions and libraries; electronic only; US$34 individuals for postage; EUR526 institutions and libraries; print & electronic; EUR505 institutions and libraries; electronic only; EUR26 individuals for postage; S$1,042 institutions and libraries; print & electronic; S$1,000 institutions and libraries; electronic only; S$45 individuals for postage. **URL:** http://www.worldscinet.com/ijpixe/ijpixe.shtml.

50193 ■ International Journal of Surgery
Elsevier (Singapore) Pte. Ltd.
3 Killiney Rd., No. 08-01
Winsland House 1
Singapore 239519, Singapore
Ph: 65 6 3490222
Fax: 65 6 7331510
Publisher E-mail: asiabkinfo@elsevier.com
Peer-reviewed journal dedicated to publishing original research, review articles, and more, offering significant contributions to knowledge in clinical surgery, experimental surgery, surgical education and history. **Freq:** Bimonthly. **Key Personnel:** David Rosin, Editor-in-Chief, rdrosin@uk-consultants.co.uk; Riaz Agha, Managing Editor, editor@journal-surgery.com; Alfio Ferlito, Asst. Ed. **ISSN:** 1743-9191. **URL:** http://www.elsevier.com/wps/find/journaldescription.cws_home/705107/descriptiondescription.

50194 ■ International Journal of Technoentrepreneurship
Inderscience Publishers

c/o Prof. Francois Therin, Ed.
U21 Global
5 Shenton Way, No. 1-1 UIC Bldg.
Singapore 068808, Singapore
Publisher E-mail: editor@inderscience.com
Peer-reviewed journal covering high tech entrepreneurship and intrapreneurship. **Founded:** 2007. **Freq:** 4/yr. **Key Personnel:** Prof. Francois Therin, Editor, francois.therin@u21global.com; Dr. William Lekse, Assoc. Ed.; Dr. Marie-Josee Roy, Assoc. Ed. **ISSN:** 1746-5370. **Subscription Rates:** EUR494 individuals print (includes surface mail); EUR672 individuals print and online. **URL:** http://www.inderscience.com/browse/index.php?journalCODE=ijte.

50195 ■ International Journal on Wireless & Optical Communications
World Scientific Publishing Company Private Ltd.
5 Toh Tuck Link
Singapore 596224, Singapore
Ph: 99965 646 65775
Fax: 99965 646 77667
Publisher E-mail: wspc@wspc.com.sg
Journal publishing technical papers in the emerging and important fields of wireless and optical communications and networks, the state of the art techniques and high quality research work in fast-moving fields. **Freq:** 3/yr. **Key Personnel:** Tjeng T. Tjhung, Editor-in-Chief; Mohammed Aitiquzzaman, Editor; Serge Fdida, Editor. **ISSN:** 0219-7995. **Subscription Rates:** US$135 institutions electronic + print; EUR122 institutions electronic + print; S$225 institutions electronic + print; US$128 institutions electronic only; EUR116 institutions electronic only; S$214 institutions electronic only; US$54 individuals print only; EUR51 individuals print only; S$92 individuals print only. **Remarks:** Advertising accepted; rates available upon request. **URL:** http://www.worldscinet.com/ijwoc/mkt/aims_scope.shtml. **Circ:** (Not Reported)

50196 ■ Investor's Guide to Singapore
Singapore International Chamber of Commerce
John Hancock Twr.
6 Raffles Quay, No. 10-01
Singapore 048580, Singapore
Ph: 65 65000988
Fax: 65 62242785
Publication E-mail: publications@sicc.com.sg
Publisher E-mail: general@sicc.com.sg
Journal covering business, economics and investments. **Founded:** 1973. **Freq:** Annual. **ISSN:** 0129-5276. **Remarks:** Accepts advertising. **URL:** http://www.sicc.com.sg. **Circ:** Paid 4,000

50197 ■ ITBM - RBM
Elsevier (Singapore) Pte. Ltd.
3 Killiney Rd., No. 08-01
Winsland House 1
Singapore 239519, Singapore
Ph: 65 6 3490222
Fax: 65 6 7331510
Publisher E-mail: asiabkinfo@elsevier.com
Journal providing information and knowledge in the field of biomedical technologies, and devoted to fundamental as well as clinical research. **Founded:** 1979. **Freq:** Bimonthly. **Key Personnel:** Didier Pinaudeau, Editor-in-Chief, didier.pinaudeau@chu-lyon.fr; Christine Sempe, Publishing Ed., c.sempe@elsevier.fr. **ISSN:** 1297-9562. **URL:** http://www.elsevier.com/wps/find/journaldescription.cws_home/600219/descriptiondescription.

50198 ■ Journal of Applied Logic
Elsevier (Singapore) Pte. Ltd.
3 Killiney Rd., No. 08-01
Winsland House 1
Singapore 239519, Singapore
Ph: 65 6 3490222
Fax: 65 6 7331510
Publisher E-mail: asiabkinfo@elsevier.com
Journal publishing papers in the areas of logic which can be applied in other disciplines as well as application papers in those disciplines, the unifying theme being logics arising from modelling the human agent. **Founded:** 2003. **Freq:** Quarterly. **Key Personnel:** Dov M. Gabbay, Exec. Ed.; Andrew J.I. Jones, Exec. Ed.; Jane Spurr, Editorial Office Mgr., jane@dcs.kcl.ac.uk. **ISSN:** 1570-8683. **Subscription Rates:** US$67 individuals for all countries except Europe, Japan and Iran; 7,600¥ individuals; US$62 individuals for European countries and Iran; US$515 institutions for all countries except Europe, Japan and Iran; 57,600¥ institutions;

EUR487 institutions for European countries and Iran. **URL:** http://www.elsevier.com/wps/find/journaldescription.cws_home/672712/descriptiondescription.

50199 ■ Journal of Asian Evangelical Theology
Asia Theological Association
c/o TCA College
PO Box 616
Singapore 914021, Singapore
Publisher E-mail: info@ataasia.com
Journal focusing on evangelical theology. **Freq:** Semiannual. **Key Personnel:** Siga Arles, Editor; Wallace Louie, Joint Ed. **Subscription Rates:** Free to members. **URL:** http://www.ataasia.com/publications/publications.html.

50200 ■ Journal of Biological Systems
World Scientific Publishing Company Private Ltd.
5 Toh Tuck Link
Singapore 596224, Singapore
Ph: 99965 646 65775
Fax: 99965 646 77667
Publisher E-mail: wspc@wspc.com.sg
Journal aiming to promote interdisciplinary approaches in biology and in medicine. **Founded:** 1993. **Freq:** Quarterly. **Key Personnel:** R.V. Jean, Ch. Ed., rvjcm611121@yahoo.ca; R.C. Brunet, Assoc. Ed.; E.R. Dougherty, Assoc. Ed. **ISSN:** 0218-3390. **Subscription Rates:** S$962 institutions and libraries; electronic + print; EUR529 institutions and libraries; electronic + print; US$590 institutions and libraries; electronic + print; S$924 institutions and libraries; electronic only; EUR508 institutions and libraries; electronic only; US$566 institutions and libraries; electronic only; S$45 individuals for postage; EUR23 individuals for postage; US$34 individuals for postage. **URL:** http://www.worldscinet.com/jbs/jbs.shtml.

50201 ■ Journal of Chinese Overseas
National University of Singapore
21 Lower Kent Ridge Rd.
Singapore 119077, Singapore
Ph: 65 6516 6666
Fax: 65 6775 9330
Publisher E-mail: qsmanager@nus.edu.sg
Journal featuring research articles, reports, and book reviews about Chinese overseas. **Freq:** Quarterly. **Key Personnel:** Tan Chee-Beng, Editor; Ng Chin-keong, Editor. **ISSN:** 1793-0391. **Subscription Rates:** S$65 individuals; US$50 other countries; US$70 institutions, other countries. **URL:** http://www.nus.edu.sg/npu/jco/index.html; http://muse.jhu.edu/login?uri=/journals/journal_of_chinese_overseas/v004/4.

50202 ■ Journal of Computational Acoustics
World Scientific Publishing Company Private Ltd.
5 Toh Tuck Link
Singapore 596224, Singapore
Ph: 99965 646 65775
Fax: 99965 646 77667
Publisher E-mail: wspc@wspc.com.sg
Journal aiming to provide an international forum for the dissemination of the state-of-the-art information in the field of computational acoustics. **Freq:** Semiannual. **Key Personnel:** D. Lee, Editor-in-Chief, phone 352674-9350, fax 352674-9351, dinglee1@aol.com; J.S. Papadakis, Sen. Ed., panos@iacm.forth.gr; Leif Bjorno, Sen. Ed., profbjorno@yahoo.dk. **ISSN:** 0218-396X. **Subscription Rates:** US$578 institutions and libraries; electronic and print; EUR518 institutions and libraries; electronic and print; S$941 institutions and libraries; electronic and print; US$555 institutions and libraries; electronic only; EUR497 institutions and libraries; electronic only; S$903 institutions and libraries; electronic only; US$39 individuals for postage; EUR26 individuals for postage; S$52 individuals for postage. **URL:** http://www.worldscinet.com/jca/jca.shtml.

50203 ■ Journal of Developmental Entrepreneurship
World Scientific Publishing Company Private Ltd.
5 Toh Tuck Link
Singapore 596224, Singapore
Ph: 99965 646 65775
Fax: 99965 646 77667
Publisher E-mail: wspc@wspc.com.sg
Journal for scholars who study issues of developmental entrepreneurship and professionals involved in governmental and non-governmental efforts to facilitate entrepreneurship in economic and community development programs around the world, providing a forum for the dissemination of descriptive, empirical, and theoreti-

cal research that focuses on issues concerning micro-enterprise and small business development, especially under conditions of adversity. **Freq:** Quarterly. **Key Personnel:** Peter Koveos, Editor, jde@som.syr.edu; Michael H Morris, Ed. Emeritus; Robert H. Brockhaus, Editorial Board; George Burman, Assoc. Ed.; Timothy Bates, Editorial Board; David Pistrui, Editorial Board; Pedro Ivan Tichauer, Asst. to the Ed.; Catherine Foster Alter, Editorial Board; Minet Schindehutte, Assoc. Ed. **ISSN:** 1084-9467. **Subscription Rates:** US$284 institutions and libraries; print and electronic; US$273 institutions and libraries; electronic only; US$34 individuals for postage; EUR231 institutions and libraries; print and electronic; EUR222 institutions and libraries; electronic only; EUR23 individuals for postage; S$450 institutions and libraries; print and electronic; S$432 institutions and libraries; electronic only; S$45 individuals for postage. **Remarks:** Advertising accepted; rates available upon request. **URL:** http://www.worldscinet.com/jde/jde.shtml. **Circ:** (Not Reported)

50204 ■ Journal of Enterprising Culture
World Scientific Publishing Company Private Ltd.
5 Toh Tuck Link
Singapore 596224, Singapore
Ph: 99965 646 65775
Fax: 99965 646 77667
Publisher E-mail: wspc@wspc.com.sg
Journal publishing conceptual, research, and/or case based works that can be of practical value to business persons, educators, students and advocates. **Freq:** Quarterly. **Key Personnel:** Teck-Meng Tan, Editor-in-Chief; Soke-Yin Wong, Managing Editor; Ravinder A. Zutshi, Managing Editor; Wee-Liang Tan, Managing Editor, jec@smu.edu.sg; Horst Albach, International Advisory Board; Bhabatosh Banerjee, International Advisory Board. **ISSN:** 0218-4958. **Subscription Rates:** US$292 institutions and libraries; electronic + print; US$280 institutions and libraries; electronic only; US$34 individuals for postage; S$449 institutions and libraries; electronic only; EUR256 institutions and libraries; electronic + print; EUR246 institutions electronic only; S$45 individuals for postage; EUR23 individuals for postage; S$468 institutions and libraries; electronic + print. **URL:** http://www.worldscinet.com/jec/jec.shtml.

50205 ■ Journal of Environmental Assessment Policy and Management
World Scientific Publishing Company Private Ltd.
5 Toh Tuck Link
Singapore 596224, Singapore
Ph: 99965 646 65775
Fax: 99965 646 77667
Publisher E-mail: wspc@wspc.com.sg
Interdisciplinary, peer-reviewed international journal covering policy and decision-making relating to environmental assessment (EA) in the broadest sense. **Founded:** 1999. **Freq:** Quarterly. **Key Personnel:** William R. Sheate, Editorial Board, w.sheate@imperial.ac.uk; Fredrik Burstrom von Malmborg, Editorial Board, fredrik.vonmalmborg@naturvardsverket.se; Dr. Bram Noble, Assoc. Ed., b.noble@usask.ca. **ISSN:** 1464-3332. **Subscription Rates:** US$532 institutions and libraries; print & electronic; US$511 institutions and libraries; electronic; US$34 individuals for postage; EUR454 institutions, other countries and libraries; print & electronic; EUR436 institutions, other countries and libraries; electronic; S$872 institutions and libraries; print & electronic; S$837 institutions and libraries; electronic; S$45 individuals for postage; EUR26 individuals for postage. **URL:** http://www.worldscinet.com/jeapm/jeapm.shtml.

50206 ■ Journal of Graph Algorithms and Applications
World Scientific Publishing Company Private Ltd.
5 Toh Tuck Link
Singapore 596224, Singapore
Ph: 99965 646 65775
Fax: 99965 646 77667
Publication E-mail: jgaa@cs.brown.edu
Publisher E-mail: wspc@wspc.com.sg
Peer-reviewed journal covering the analysis, design, implementation, and applications of graph algorithms. **Key Personnel:** Roberto Tamassia, Editor-in-Chief, phone 401863-7639, rt@cs.brown.edu; Giuseppe Liotta, Managing Editor, liotta@diei.unipg.it; Ioannis G. Tollis, Editor-in-Chief, tollis@utdallas.edu; T.C. Hu, Advisory Board, hu@cs.ucsd.edu; Emilio Di Giacomo, Publication Ed., digiacomo@diei.unipg.it; I. Chlamtac, Advisory Board; Dr. Susanne Albers, Editorial Board, salbers@

informatik.uni-freiburg.de; Prof. Lars Arge, PhD, Editorial Board, large@daimi.au.dk; Ulrik Brandes, Editorial Board, ulrik.brandes@uni-konstanz.de; G.N. Frederickson, Advisory Board, gnf@cs.purdue.edu. **ISSN:** 1526-1719. **URL:** http://jgaa.info/.

50207 ■ Journal of Integrative Neuroscience
World Scientific Publishing Company Private Ltd.
5 Toh Tuck Link
Singapore 596224, Singapore
Ph: 99965 646 65775
Fax: 99965 646 77667
Publisher E-mail: wspc@wspc.com.sg
Journal promoting an unbiased and permanent forum for a synthesis of the brain sciences through the auspices of theory and neurogenic or neurosurgical experimentation, encompassing all aspects of integration in the brain in order to elucidate brain operations across multiple levels in a hierarchy. **Freq:** Quarterly. **Key Personnel:** Roman R. Poznanski, PhD, Editor-in-Chief, roman.poznanski@cgu.edu; Charles Capaday, Editorial Board; Melvyn D. Goldfinger, Assoc. Ed., mel.goldfinger@wright.edu; Francis S. Roman, PhD, Assoc. Ed., froman@up.univ-mrs.fr; Theodore W. Berger, PhD, Editorial Board; Stephen W. Kercel, PhD, Editorial Board. **ISSN:** 0219-6352. **Subscription Rates:** US$413 institutions and libraries; print and electronic; EUR369 institutions and libraries; print and electronic; US$396 institutions and libraries; electronic only; EUR354 institutions and libraries; electronic only; US$39 individuals for postage; S$671 institutions and libraries; print and electronic; S$644 institutions and libraries; electronic only; S$52 individuals for postage; EUR26 individuals for postage. **Remarks:** Advertising accepted; rates available upon request. **URL:** http://www.worldscinet.com/jin/jin.shtml. **Circ:** (Not Reported)

50208 ■ Journal of Knot Theory and Its Ramifications
World Scientific Publishing Company Private Ltd.
5 Toh Tuck Link
Singapore 596224, Singapore
Ph: 99965 646 65775
Fax: 99965 646 77667
Publisher E-mail: wspc@wspc.com.sg
Periodical serving as a forum for new developments in knot theory. **Founded:** 1992. **Freq:** 8/yr. **Key Personnel:** M. Wadati, Managing Editor, wadati@rs.kagu.tus.ac.jp; V.G. Turaev, Academic Ed.; R. Benedetti, Academic Ed.; M. Boileau, Academic Ed.; C. Blanchet, Academic Ed.; L.H. Kauffman, Editor-in-Chief, kauffman@uic.edu. **ISSN:** 0218-2165. **Subscription Rates:** US$1,677 institutions and libraries; electronic + print; US$1,610 institutions and libraries; electronic only; US$59 individuals for postage; EUR46 individuals for postage; EUR1,349 institutions and libraries; electronic + print; EUR1,295 institutions and libraries; electronic only; S$78 individuals for postage; S$2,671 institutions and libraries; electronic + print; S$2,564 institutions and libraries; electronic only. **URL:** http://www.worldscinet.com/jktr/jktr.shtml.

50209 ■ Journal of Men's Health
Elsevier (Singapore) Pte. Ltd.
3 Killiney Rd., No. 08-01
Winsland House 1
Singapore 239519, Singapore
Ph: 65 6 3490222
Fax: 65 6 7331510
Publisher E-mail: asiabkinfo@elsevier.com
Journal offering comprehensive, accessible resource of knowledge directly applicable to the daily care of patients, and offering key information and insight about men's health and gender medicine to other healthcare professionals, men's health and other organizations, patient groups and policy makers. **Freq:** Quarterly. **Key Personnel:** Prof. S. Meryn, MD, Editor-in-Chief; Dr. I. Banks, MD, Assoc. Ed.; Dr. J.A. Fromson, MD, Assoc. Ed. **ISSN:** 1875-6867. **Subscription Rates:** US$163 individuals all countries except Europe, Japan and Iran; 19,300¥ individuals; EUR147 individuals European countries and Iran; US$722 institutions all countries except Europe, Japan and Iran; EUR643 institutions European countries and Iran; 85,500¥ institutions. **URL:** http://www.elsevier.com/wps/find/journaldescription.cws_home/714640/descrip tiondescription. **Formerly:** The Journal of Men's Health & Gender.

50210 ■ Journal of Musculoskeletal Research
World Scientific Publishing Company Private Ltd.
5 Toh Tuck Link
Singapore 596224, Singapore

Ph: 99965 646 65775
Fax: 99965 646 77667
Publisher E-mail: wspc@wspc.com.sg
International, interdisciplinary journal aimed at publishing up-to-date contributions on clinical and basic research on the musculoskeletal system. **Founded:** 1997. **Freq:** Quarterly. **Key Personnel:** Chen Po-Quang, Editor-in-Chief, phone 886 2 23970800, fax 886 2 23225110, pqchen@ccms.ntu.edu.tw; Kai-Nan An, Editor-in-Chief, phone 507538-1717, fax 507284-5392, an.kainan@mayo.edu; Freddie H. Fu, Editorial Board; Li-Shan Chou, Editorial Board; Albert King, Editorial Board; Ken N. Kuo, Editorial Board; Yogu Hu, Editorial Board; Eiji Itoi, Editorial Board. **ISSN:** 0218-9577. **Subscription Rates:** US$235 institutions and libraries; electronic and print; EUR221 institutions and libraries; electronic and print; S$402 institutions and libraries; electronic and print; US$226 institutions and libraries; electronic only; EUR212 institutions and libraries; electronic only; S$386 institutions and libraries; electronic only; US$39 individuals for postage; EUR31 individuals for postage; S$52 individuals for postage. **URL:** http://www.worldscinet.com/jmr/jmr.shtml.

50211 ■ Journal of Pediatric Urology
Elsevier (Singapore) Pte. Ltd.
3 Killiney Rd., No. 08-01
Winsland House 1
Singapore 239519, Singapore
Ph: 65 6 3490222
Fax: 65 6 7331510
Publisher E-mail: asiabkinfo@elsevier.com
Journal publishing submitted research and clinical articles relating to pediatric prology to advance and improve the education and the diffusion of knowledge of new and improved methods of teaching and practising pediatric urology in all its branches. **Founded:** 2004. **Freq:** Bimonthly. **Key Personnel:** David Frank, Editor, phone 44 117 3428838; T. Boemers, Editorial Board; P. Caione, Editorial Board; M. Bajpai, Editorial Board; P. Bugmann, Editorial Board; Prof. Pierre Mouriquand, Editor, pierre.mouriquand@chu-lyon.fr; S. Etker, Editorial Board; J.C. Djurhuus, Editorial Board; J. Fishwick, Editorial Board. **ISSN:** 1477-5131. **Subscription Rates:** EUR488 institutions European countries and Iran; US$546 institutions all Countries except Europe, Japan and Iran; 64,900¥ institutions; 32,600¥ individuals; US$276 individuals; EUR245 individuals. **URL:** http://www.elsevier.com/wps/find/journaldescription.cws_home/703405/descrip tiondescription.

50212 ■ Law Gazette
The Law Society of Singapore
39 S Bridge Rd.
Singapore 058673, Singapore
Ph: 65 65382500
Fax: 65 65335700
Publisher E-mail: lawsoc@lawsoc.org.sg
Law journal. **Subtitle:** An Official Publication of the Law Society of Singapore. **Freq:** Monthly. **Key Personnel:** Wong Meng Meng, President. **Remarks:** Accepts advertising. **URL:** http://www.lawgazette.com.sg. **Ad Rates:** 4C: S$2,800. **Circ:** Paid 5,000

50213 ■ LawLink
The Alumni Relations Committee, NUS Law School
13 Law Link
Kent Ridge
Singapore 117590, Singapore
Fax: 65 677 90979
Publication E-mail: lawweb@nus.edu.sg
Publisher E-mail: lawlink@nus.edu.sg
Alumni magazine of the National University of Singapore Law School. **Freq:** Semiannual. **ISSN:** 0219-6441. **URL:** http://law.nus.edu.sg/alumni/lawlink.html.

50214 ■ Lianhe Wanbao
Singapore Press Holdings Ltd.
News Ctr.
1000 Toa Payoh N
Singapore 318994, Singapore
Ph: 65 63196319
Fax: 65 63198150
Publisher E-mail: sphcorp@sph.com.sg
Daily evening newspaper focusing on human interests and community events. **Founded:** Mar. 16, 1983. **Freq:** Daily. **Print Method:** Web offset. **Key Personnel:** Koh Lin Hoe, Editor. **Remarks:** Accepts advertising. **URL:** http://www.sph.com.sg/ourproducts_newspaper_lhwb.shtml. **Ad Rates:** 4C: S$3,000. **Circ:** Mon.-Fri. 107,200

Circulation: ★ = ABC; △ = BPA; ♦ = CAC; • = CCAB; ❏ = VAC; ⊕ = PO Statement; ‡ = Publisher's Report; Boldface figures = sworn; Light figures = estimated.

Gale Directory of Publications & Broadcast Media/147th Ed.   5407

50215 ■ Lianhe Zaobao
Singapore Press Holdings Ltd.
News Ctr.
1000 Toa Payoh N
Singapore 318994, Singapore
Ph: 65 63196319
Fax: 65 63198150
Publication E-mail: zaobao@zaobao.com.sg
Publisher E-mail: sphcorp@sph.com.sg
Morning newspaper giving insights into local and foreign news. **Founded:** Mar. 16, 1983. **Freq:** Daily. **Key Personnel:** Lim Jim Koon, Editor. **Subscription Rates:** US$271.50 individuals; US$543 two years. **Remarks:** Accepts advertising. **URL:** http://www.sph.com.sg/ourproducts_newspaper_lhzbs.shtml; http://www.zaobao.com. **Ad Rates:** 4C: S$3,000. **Circ:** Mon.-Fri. 176,600

50216 ■ Lien
Alliance Francaise
1 Sarkies Rd.
Singapore 258130, Singapore
Ph: 65 67378422
Fax: 65 67333023
Publisher E-mail: irenechew@alliancefrancaise.org.sg
Online Franco-Singaporean arts magazine. **Freq:** Bimonthly. **Remarks:** Advertising accepted; rates available upon request. **URL:** http://www.alliancefrancaise.org.sg/. **Circ:** (Not Reported)

50217 ■ Modern Physics Letters A
World Scientific Publishing Company Private Ltd.
5 Toh Tuck Link
Singapore 596224, Singapore
Ph: 99965 646 65775
Fax: 99965 646 77667
Publisher E-mail: wspc@wspc.com.sg
Periodical containing research papers covering current research developments in gravitation, cosmology, nuclear physics, and particles and fields. **Founded:** 1986. **Freq:** 40/yr. **Key Personnel:** S.L. Olsen, Editorial Board, solsen@phys.hawaii.edu; T. Eguchi, Editorial Board, eguchi@danjuro.phys.s.u-tokyo.ac.jp; Harry W.K. Cheung, Editorial Board, cheung@fnal.gov; J. Shan, Editorial Board, jins@mail.ihep.ac.cn; A.P. Balachandran, Editorial Board, chkirkpa@syr.edu. **ISSN:** 0217-7323. **Subscription Rates:** S$6,977 institutions and libraries; print & electronic; S$6,698 institutions and libraries; electronic; S$180 individuals for postage; EUR3,635 institutions, other countries and libraries; print & electronic; EUR3,490 institutions, other countries and libraries; electronic; US$4,218 institutions and libraries; print & electronic; US$4,049 institutions and libraries; electronic; US$135 individuals for postage; EUR106 individuals for postage. **URL:** http://www.worldscinet.com/mpla/mpla.shtml. **Circ:** Paid 550

50218 ■ Modern Physics Letters B
World Scientific Publishing Company Private Ltd.
5 Toh Tuck Link
Singapore 596224, Singapore
Ph: 99965 646 65775
Fax: 99965 646 77667
Publisher E-mail: wspc@wspc.com.sg
Periodical featuring important and useful research findings in condensed matter physics, statistical physics, applied physics and high-Tc superconductivity. **Founded:** 1987. **Freq:** 30/yr. **Key Personnel:** W. Schommers, Editor-in-Chief, phone 49 7247 822432, wolfram.schommers@iwr.fzk.de; Wang Yu Peng, Editor-in-Chief, yupeng@aphy.iphy.ac.cn; Fa Yueh Wu, Editor-in-Chief, fywu@neu.edu. **ISSN:** 0217-9849. **Subscription Rates:** US$3,397 institutions and libraries; print & electronic; EUR2,812 institutions and libraries; electronic; S$144 institutions for postage; US$108 individuals for postage; S$5,184 institutions and libraries; electronic; S$5,400 institutions and libraries; print & electronic; US$3,261 institutions and libraries; electronic; EUR85 individuals for postage; EUR2,812 institutions and libraries; print & electronic. **URL:** http://www.worldscinet.com/mplb/mplb.shtml. **Circ:** Paid 350

50219 ■ Motherhood
Eastern Holdings Ltd.
1100 Lower Delta Rd., No. 04-01
EPL Bldg.
Singapore 169206, Singapore
Ph: 65 637 92888
Fax: 65 637 92803
Publisher E-mail: eastern1@singnet.com.sg
Magazine for an online parenting audience. **Freq:** Monthly. **Key Personnel:** Shenielle Aloysis, Editor,

shenielle@epl.com.sg; Jeffrey Foo, Sales Mgr., jeffreyfoo@epl.com.sg. **Subscription Rates:** US$126 individuals 3 years, newsstand; US$96 two years; US$54 individuals. **Remarks:** Advertising accepted; rates available upon request. **URL:** http://www.motherhood.com.sg. **Circ:** (Not Reported)

50220 ■ Motherhood Handbook
Eastern Holdings Ltd.
1100 Lower Delta Rd., No. 04-01
EPL Bldg.
Singapore 169206, Singapore
Ph: 65 637 92888
Fax: 65 637 92803
Publisher E-mail: eastern1@singnet.com.sg
Publication providing information on concise and succinct information on pregnancy, birth, and early baby care. **Freq:** Annual. **Remarks:** Accepts advertising. **URL:** http://www.epl.com.sg/publications/default.asp?mag=motherhood_hb. **Circ:** (Not Reported)

50221 ■ Motoring
Eastern Holdings Ltd.
1100 Lower Delta Rd., No. 04-01
EPL Bldg.
Singapore 169206, Singapore
Ph: 65 637 92888
Fax: 65 637 92803
Publisher E-mail: eastern1@singnet.com.sg
Automotive publication. **Founded:** 1990. **Remarks:** Accepts advertising. **URL:** http://www.epl.com.sg/publications/motoring.asp. **Circ:** (Not Reported)

50222 ■ Motoring Annual
Eastern Holdings Ltd.
1100 Lower Delta Rd., No. 04-01
EPL Bldg.
Singapore 169206, Singapore
Ph: 65 637 92888
Fax: 65 637 92803
Publisher E-mail: eastern1@singnet.com.sg
Magazine featuring the latest in automotive industry. **Freq:** Annual. **Remarks:** Accepts advertising. **URL:** http://www.epl.com.sg/publications/motoring.asp?mag=motor_annual. **Circ:** (Not Reported)

50223 ■ MSDN Magazine. Southeast Asia Edition
Charlton Media Group
15B Stanley St.
Singapore 68734, Singapore
Ph: 65 622 37660
Publisher E-mail: rowena@charltonmedia.com
Localized guide to Microsoft software, providing real-world solutions. **Key Personnel:** Keith Ward, Editor-in-Chief. **Remarks:** Accepts advertising. **URL:** http://msdn.microsoft.com/en-au/magazine/default.aspx. **Circ:** (Not Reported)

50224 ■ My Paper
Singapore Press Holdings Ltd.
News Ctr.
1000 Toa Payoh N
Singapore 318994, Singapore
Ph: 65 63196319
Fax: 65 63198150
Publication E-mail: myviews@sph.com.sg
Publisher E-mail: sphcorp@sph.com.sg
Free Chinese newspaper bilingual, young adults aged 20-40. **Founded:** June 1, 2006. **Freq:** Mon.-Fri. **Key Personnel:** April Pung Koon King, Editor, pungkk@sph.com.sg; Yeow Kai Chai, Editor, kaichai@sph.com.sg. **Remarks:** Accepts advertising. **URL:** http://www.sph.com.sg/ourproducts_newspaper_mypaper.shtml; http://www.mypaper.sg/. **Ad Rates:** 4C: S$4,000. **Circ:** Free 300,000

50225 ■ Nature Watch
Nature Society (Singapore, Singapore)
510 Geylang Rd.
No. 02-05, The Sunflower
Singapore 389466, Singapore
Ph: 65 6741 2036
Fax: 65 6741 0871
Publisher E-mail: contact@nss.org.sg
Periodical featuring articles of interest to nature lovers. **Freq:** Quarterly. **URL:** http://habitatnews.nus.edu.sg/pub/naturewatch; http://www.nss.org.sg/naturewatch.html.

50226 ■ The New Paper on Sunday
Singapore Press Holdings Ltd.
News Ctr.
1000 Toa Payoh N
Singapore 318994, Singapore
Ph: 65 63196319
Fax: 65 63198150
Publisher E-mail: sphcorp@sph.com.sg
Newspaper for members of the family, expatriates, single and busy people. **Founded:** Apr. 11, 1999. **Freq:** Sunday. **Key Personnel:** Ivan Fernandez, Editor. **Remarks:** Accepts advertising. **URL:** http://www.sph.com.sg/ourproducts_newspaper_tnps.shtml. **Ad Rates:** 4C: S$2,400. **Circ:** Sun. 109,300

50227 ■ Newman
Lexicon Group Ltd.
371 Beach Rd.
03-18 Keypoint
Singapore 199597, Singapore
Ph: 65 629 20300
Fax: 65 629 34294
Publisher E-mail: corp.info@lexicon.com.sg
Singapore's magazine for men. **Freq:** Monthly. **Key Personnel:** Susy Lee, Sen. Sales Mgr.; Chong Chye Wan, President, chong.chyewan@inovatif.com.my; Casey Khoo, Vice President, casey.khoo@inovatif.com.my. **Subscription Rates:** S$60 individuals; S$108 two years. **Remarks:** Accepts advertising. **URL:** http://www.lexicon.com.sg/singapore/print/newman__msia_ad.asp. **Ad Rates:** BW: S$4,000. **Circ:** (Not Reported)

50228 ■ NTU
Nanyang Technological University
50 Nanyang Ave.
Singapore 639798, Singapore
Ph: 65 67911744
Fax: 65 67911604
Publisher E-mail: adm_intnl@ntu.edu.sg
Magazine featuring campus life. **Freq:** Bimonthly. **Key Personnel:** Mike Tan, Manager, phone 65 65138017, mttan@ntu.edu.sg. **URL:** http://atntu.ntu.edu.sg/Pages/Home.aspx.

50229 ■ NUS Economic Journal
National University of Singapore
21 Lower Kent Ridge Rd.
Singapore 119260, Singapore
Ph: 65 65166666
Journal covering business and economics. **Founded:** 1962. **Freq:** Annual. **Key Personnel:** Cadence Wong Yim Hwa, Editor. **ISSN:** 0218-3269. **Subscription Rates:** S$10. **Remarks:** Advertising accepted; rates available upon request. **URL:** http://www.nus.edu.sg/. **Circ:** Paid 10,000

50230 ■ NuYou
Singapore Press Holdings Ltd.
News Ctr.
1000 Toa Payoh N
Singapore 318994, Singapore
Ph: 65 63196319
Fax: 65 63198150
Publisher E-mail: sphcorp@sph.com.sg
Chinese fashion, beauty and lifestyle magazine for savvy career women aged 20-39. **Founded:** 1976. **Trim Size:** 210 x 275 mm. **Subscription Rates:** US$60 individuals. **Remarks:** Accepts advertising. **URL:** http://www.sph.com.sg/article.display.php?id=1280; http://www.nuyou.com.sg/. **Ad Rates:** 4C: S$2,600. **Circ:** 25,000

50231 ■ NuYou Time
Singapore Press Holdings Ltd.
News Ctr.
1000 Toa Payoh N
Singapore 318994, Singapore
Ph: 65 63196319
Fax: 65 63198150
Publisher E-mail: sphcorp@sph.com.sg
Chinese language magazine featuring watches. **Founded:** 2001. **Freq:** Annual. **Trim Size:** 210 x 275 mm. **Remarks:** Accepts advertising. **URL:** http://www.sph.com.sg/article.display.php?id=684. **Ad Rates:** 4C: S$3,200. **Circ:** 20,000

50232 ■ Optical Switching and Networking
Elsevier (Singapore) Pte. Ltd.
3 Killiney Rd., No. 08-01
Winsland House 1
Singapore 239519, Singapore

Ph: 65 6 3490222
Fax: 65 6 7331510
Publisher E-mail: asiabkinfo@elsevier.com
Journal providing complete coverage of all topics of interest to those involved in the optical and opto-electronic networking areas. **Subtitle:** A Computer Networks Journal. **Founded:** 2004. **Freq:** Quarterly. **Key Personnel:** F. Neri, Editor-in-Chief; D. Datta, Editorial Board; F. Callegati, Editorial Board; G. Rouskas, Editor-in-Chief; A. Fumagalli, Editorial Board; E. Karasan, Editorial Board. **ISSN:** 1573-4277. **Subscription Rates:** US$438 institutions for all countries except Europe, Japan and Iran; 51,500¥ institutions; EUR438 institutions European countries and Iran; US$118 individuals; EUR87 individuals European countries and Iran; 13,600¥ individuals. **URL:** http://www.elsevier.com/wps/find/journaldescription.cws_home/703621/descriptiondescription.

50233 ■ Organic Electronics
Elsevier (Singapore) Pte. Ltd.
3 Killiney Rd., No. 08-01
Winsland House 1
Singapore 239519, Singapore
Ph: 65 6 3490222
Fax: 65 6 7331510
Publisher E-mail: asiabkinfo@elsevier.com
Journal establishing a dedicated channel for physicists, material scientists, and chemists, who are interested in organic electronic devices, such as, but not limited to, organic light emitting devices, thin film transistors, photovoltaic cells, etc. **Founded:** 2000. **Freq:** 8/yr. **Key Personnel:** P. Heremans, Editor, heremans@imec.be; V.M. Agranovich, Assoc. Ed., agran@isan.troitsk.ru; E. Umbach, Assoc. Ed., umbach@physik.uni-wuerzburg.de; N. Peyghambarian, Assoc. Ed., nnp@u.arizona.edu; M. Fujihira, Assoc. Ed., mfujihir@bio.titech.ac.jp; C. Adachi, Editor, adachi@cstf.kyushu-u.ac.jp; R.A.J. Janssen, Editor, r.a.j.janssen@tue.nl. **ISSN:** 1566-1199. **Subscription Rates:** EUR651 institutions European countries and Iran; US$651 institutions all countries except Europe, Japan and Iran; 86,500¥ institutions; US$155 individuals all countries except Europe, Japan and Iran; EUR117 individuals European countries and Iran; 17,800¥ individuals. **URL:** http://www.elsevier.com/wps/find/journaldescription.cws_home/620806/descriptiondescription.

50234 ■ PANELS & FURNITURE ASIA
Pablo Publishing Pte Ltd.
Block 61, Kallang Pl., No. 07-01
Singapore 339156, Singapore
Ph: 65 63967877
Fax: 65 63967177
Publisher E-mail: info@pabloasia.com
Magazine covering the panel processing industry and panel production in Asia. **Subtitle:** For Panel Manufacturing, Furniture From Panels & Flooring. **Freq:** Bimonthly. **Key Personnel:** Irena Josoeb, Editor, irenaj@pabloasia.com; William Pang, Publisher, williampang@pabloasia.com; Kelly Shen, General Mgr., pabloshanghai@tom.com. **Subscription Rates:** US$77.04 individuals English and Chinese edition; US$139.10 two years English and Chinese edition; US$78 individuals to Asia Pacific, English & Chinese edition; US$140 two years to Asia Pacific, English & Chinese edition; US$90 individuals to America/Europe, English & Chinese edition; US$162 two years to America/Europe, English & Chinese edition. **Remarks:** Accepts advertising. **URL:** http://www.panelsfurnitureasia.com/index.htm. **Circ:** (Not Reported)

50235 ■ Parallel Processing Letters
World Scientific Publishing Company Private Ltd.
5 Toh Tuck Link
Singapore 596224, Singapore
Ph: 99965 646 65775
Fax: 99965 646 77667
Publisher E-mail: wspc@wspc.com.sg
Periodical covering parallel processing. **Founded:** 1991. **Freq:** Quarterly. **Key Personnel:** Selim G. Akl, Editor-in-Chief, akl@cs.queensu.ca; Irene LaFleche, Editorial Asst., irene@cs.queensu.ca; A. Adamatzky, Editorial Board, andrew.adamatzky@uwe.ac.uk. **ISSN:** 0129-6264. **Subscription Rates:** US$591 institutions and libraries; print & electronic; US$636 institutions and libraries; electronic; US$34 institutions for postage; EUR567 institutions and libraries; print & electronic; EUR544 institutions and libraries; electronic; S$1,087 institutions and libraries; print & electronic; S$1,044

institutions and libraries; electronic; EUR26 institutions for postage; S$45 institutions for postage. **URL:** http://www.worldscinet.com/ppl/ppl.shtml.

50236 ■ Pervasive and Mobile Computing
Elsevier (Singapore) Pte. Ltd.
3 Killiney Rd., No. 08-01
Winsland House 1
Singapore 239519, Singapore
Ph: 65 6 3490222
Fax: 65 6 7331510
Publisher E-mail: asiabkinfo@elsevier.com
Professional, peer-reviewed journal publishing high-quality scientific articles (both theory and practice) covering all aspects of pervasive computing and communications. **Founded:** 2005. **Freq:** Bimonthly. **Key Personnel:** Sajal K. Das, Editor-in-Chief, das@cse.uta.edu; J. Cao, Area Ed., csjcao@comp.polyu.edu.hk; C. Bisdikian, Area Ed., bisdik@us.ibm.com; Marco Conti, Assoc. Ed.-in-Ch., marco.conti@iit.cnr.it; T. Camp, Area Ed., tcamp@mines.edu; A. Misra, Area Ed., archan@us.ibm.com. **ISSN:** 1574-1192. **Subscription Rates:** US$715 institutions for all countries except Europe, Japan and Iran; 77,800¥ institutions; EUR577 institutions European countries and Iran; US$155 individuals for all countries except Europe, Japan and Iran; EUR117 individuals European countries and Iran; 17,800¥ individuals. **URL:** http://www.elsevier.com/wps/find/journaldescription.cws_home/704220/descriptiondescription.

50237 ■ Petromin
AP Energy Business Publications Private Ltd.
63 Robinson Rd., No. 02-16
Singapore 68894, Singapore
Ph: 65 622 23422
Fax: 65 622 25587
Upstream oil and gas magazine. **Founded:** 1983. **Freq:** Monthly 10/yr. **ISSN:** 0129-1122. **Subscription Rates:** US$120 individuals 6 issues. **Remarks:** Accepts advertising. **URL:** http://www.petromin.safan.com. **Ad Rates:** BW: US$3,630. **Circ:** (Not Reported)

50238 ■ Photodiagnosis and Photodynamic Therapy
Elsevier (Singapore) Pte. Ltd.
3 Killiney Rd., No. 08-01
Winsland House 1
Singapore 239519, Singapore
Ph: 65 6 3490222
Fax: 65 6 7331510
Publisher E-mail: asiabkinfo@elsevier.com
International journal for the dissemination of scientific knowledge and clinical developments of photodiagnosis and photodynamic therapy in all medical specialties. **Founded:** 2004. **Freq:** Quarterly. **Key Personnel:** Prof. K. Moghissi, Editor-in-Chief; R. Allison, Assoc. Ed.; H. Barr, Assoc. Ed.; P. Barber, Editorial Board; M. Adamek, Editorial Board; A. Batlle, Editorial Board. **ISSN:** 1572-1000. **Subscription Rates:** EUR152 individuals European countries and Iran; US$152 individuals for all countries except Europe, Japan and Iran; 21,200¥ individuals; US$332 institutions for all countries except Europe, Japan and Iran; 46,500¥ institutions; EUR332 institutions European countries and Iran; 106 individuals for UK. **URL:** http://www.elsevier.com/wps/find/journaldescription.cws_home/701993/descriptiondescription.

50239 ■ Physics of Life Reviews
Elsevier (Singapore) Pte. Ltd.
3 Killiney Rd., No. 08-01
Winsland House 1
Singapore 239519, Singapore
Ph: 65 6 3490222
Fax: 65 6 7331510
Publisher E-mail: asiabkinfo@elsevier.com
International journal publishing review articles on physics of living systems, complex phenomena in biological systems, and related fields of artificial life, robotics, mathematical bio-semiotics, and artificial intelligent systems. **Founded:** 2004. **Freq:** Quarterly. **Key Personnel:** A. Meystel, Editorial Board, meystel@ece.drexel.edu; Ernesto Di Mauro, Editorial Board, ernesto.dimauro@uniroma1.it; T. Fukuda, Editorial Board, fukuda@mein.nagoya-u.ac.jp; V. Zakharov, Editorial Board, zakharov@math.arizona.edu; M. Frank-Kamenetskii, Editorial Board, mfk@bu.edu; Leonid I. Perlovsky, Editor-in-Chief, leonid@deas.harvard.edu; L. Zadeh, Editorial Board, zadeh@cs.berkeley.edu; L. Peliti, Editorial Board, luca.peliti@na.infn.it. **ISSN:** 1571-

0645. **Subscription Rates:** EUR536 institutions for European countries and Iran; US$536 institutions, other countries all countries except Europe, Japan and Iran; 63,900¥ institutions; US$123 individuals all countries except Europe, Japan and Iran; EUR91 individuals for European countries and Iran; 14,200¥ individuals. **URL:** http://www.elsevier.com/wps/find/journaldescription.cws_home/680835/descriptiondescription.

50240 ■ Planews
Singapore Institute of Planners
93 Toa Payoh Central, No. 05-01
Toa Payoh Community Bldg.
Singapore 319194, Singapore
Ph: 65 62515503
Fax: 65 62524533
Publisher E-mail: info@sip.org.sg
Journal of housing and urban planning. **Founded:** 1972. **Freq:** Semiannual. **ISSN:** 0129-3184. **Remarks:** Advertising accepted; rates available upon request. **URL:** http://www.sip.org.sg/Planews/planews.htm. **Circ:** Paid 1,000

50241 ■ Plastics & Rubber Singapore Journal
Plastics and Rubber Institute of Singapore
Tanglin PO Box 354
Singapore 912412, Singapore
Publication E-mail: chmcsoh@nus.edu.sg
Technical publication on the science and technology that drives the plastics and rubber industries. **Subtitle:** An Official Publication of the Plastics and Rubber Institute of Singapore. **Key Personnel:** Prof. Hardy Chan, Contact. **Subscription Rates:** Free all members. **Remarks:** Advertising accepted; rates available upon request. **URL:** http://www.pris.org.sg/journals.html. **Circ:** (Not Reported)

50242 ■ Regional Best Restaurants
Edipresse Asia
211 Henderson Rd., No. 07-04
Henderson Industrial Pk.
Singapore 159552, Singapore
Ph: 65 63231606
Fax: 65 63231692
Magazine featuring the best restaurants of Singapore, Malaysia, Indonesia and Hong Kong. **Freq:** Annual. **Key Personnel:** Gilbert Cheah, Director; Joseph Lim, Ch. Ed. **URL:** http://www.edipresse.com/food-dining/regional-best-restaurants. **Circ:** ‡16,000

50243 ■ Regional Outlook
Institute of Southeast Asian Studies
30 Heng Mui Keng Ter.
Pasir Panjang
Singapore 119614, Singapore
Ph: 65 67780955
Fax: 65 67781735
Publisher E-mail: admin@iseas.edu.sg
Periodical providing a succinct analysis of current political and economic trends in the ten countries of Southeast Asia. **Subtitle:** Southeast Asia. **Founded:** 1992. **Freq:** Annual. **Key Personnel:** Lee Poh Onn, Editor. **ISSN:** 0218-3056. **Subscription Rates:** US$23.90 individuals. **URL:** http://www.iseas.edu.sg/routlook.htm.

50244 ■ Research and Practice in Human Resource Management
Singapore Human Resources Institute
2 Serangoon Rd.
Level 6, Tekka Mall
Singapore 218227, Singapore
Ph: 65 64380012
Fax: 65 62994864
Publisher E-mail: enquiries@shri.org.sg
Publishes articles in fields of interest to scholars and practitioners of personnel management and human resource management. **Founded:** 1993. **Freq:** Semiannual. **Key Personnel:** Dr. Cecil Pearson, Editor, cecil.pearson@cbs.curtin.edu.au; Dr. Alan Nankervis, Editor, alan.nankervis@rmit.edu.au; Prof. Samir Chatterjee, Coord. Ed., samir.chatterjee@cbs.curtin.edu.au. **ISSN:** 0218-5180. **Subscription Rates:** S$100 individuals; S$45 single issue back issues. **URL:** http://www.shri.org.sg/rphrm.curtin.edu.au.

50245 ■ Review of Pacific Basin Financial Markets and Policies
World Scientific Publishing Company Private Ltd.
5 Toh Tuck Link
Singapore 596224, Singapore
Ph: 99965 646 65775

Circulation: ★ = ABC; △ = BPA; ♦ = CAC; • = CCAB; □ = VAC; ⊕ = PO Statement; ‡ = Publisher's Report; Boldface figures = sworn; Light figures = estimated.

Gale Directory of Publications & Broadcast Media/147th Ed.   5409

Fax: 99965 646 77667

Publisher E-mail: wspc@wspc.com.sg

Publication focusing on global interdisciplinary research in finance, economics and accounting. **Founded:** 1998. **Freq:** Quarterly.. **Key Personnel:** Lee Chang-Few, Managing Editor, lee@business.rutgers.edu; Raj Aggarwal, Assoc. Ed.; Paul C. H. Chiu, Assoc. Ed.; James R. Barth, Assoc. Ed.; Eric C. Chang, Assoc. Ed.; James S. Ang, Assoc. Ed.; Sheng Shen Chen, Assoc. Ed.; Jack C. Francis, Assoc. Ed.; Yasuo Hoshino, Assoc. Ed. **ISSN:** 0219-0915. **Subscription Rates:** EUR337 institutions and libraries; electronic + print; EUR324 institutions and libraries; electronic only; EUR26 institutions for postage; S$944 institutions and libraries; electronic + print; US$377 institutions electronic only; US$34 institutions for postage; US$393 institutions electronic + print; S$618 institutions and libraries; electronic only; S$45 institutions for postage. **URL:** http://www.worldscinet.com/rpbfmp/rpbfmp.shtml.

50246 ■ Reviews in Mathematical Physics
World Scientific Publishing Company Private Ltd.
5 Toh Tuck Link
Singapore 596224, Singapore
Ph: 99965 646 65775
Fax: 99965 646 77667
Publisher E-mail: wspc@wspc.com.sg
Periodical publishing papers of relevance to mathematical physicists, mathematicians and theoretical physicists interested in interdisciplinary topic. **Founded:** 1989. **Freq:** 10/yr. **Key Personnel:** J. Yngvason, Editor-in-Chief, rmp@esi.ac.at; I.M. Sigal, Editor; M. Ge, Editor; P. Kulish, Editor; S. Albeverio, Assoc. Ed.; M. Aizenman, Assoc. Ed. **ISSN:** 0129-055X. **Subscription Rates:** US$1,679 institutions and libraries; electronic + print; US$1,612 institutions and libraries; electronic only; US$53 individuals for postage; EUR41 individuals for postage; EUR1,410 institutions and libraries; electronic + print; EUR1,354 institutions and libraries; electronic only; EUR70 individuals for postage; S$2,710 institutions and libraries; electronic only; S$2,602 institutions and libraries; electronic + print. **URL:** http://www.worldscinet.com/rmp/rmp.shtml. **Circ:** Paid 150

50247 ■ RSYC
Republic of Singapore Yacht Club
52 W Coast Ferry Rd.
Singapore 126887, Singapore
Ph: 65 676 89288
Fax: 65 676 89280
Publication E-mail: pr@rsyc.org.sg
Publisher E-mail: info@rsyc.org.sg
Official magazine of the Republic of Singapore Yacht Club. **Freq:** Bimonthly. **Key Personnel:** Eddie Sun, Banquet Mgr., eddie@rsyc.org.sg; Frank Schulz-Utermoehl, General Mgr. **Remarks:** Accepts advertising. **URL:** http://www.rsyc.org.sg/article/index.htm. **Ad Rates:** 4C: S$700. **Circ:** 2,200

50248 ■ Rubber Industry Report
International Rubber Study Group
111 North Bridge Rd.
No. 23-06 Peninsula Plz.
Singapore 179098, Singapore
Ph: 65 68372411
Fax: 65 63394369
Publication E-mail: contact_irsg@rubberstudy.com
Publisher E-mail: contact_irsg@rubberstudy.com
Trade magazine covering analysis of the rubber market worldwide. **Freq:** 10/yr. **ISSN:** 0020-8655. **Subscription Rates:** S$2,500 individuals; S$1000 single issue. **Remarks:** Advertising not accepted. **URL:** http://www.rubberstudy.com/pub-industry-report.aspx. **Formerly:** International Rubber Digest. **Circ:** (Not Reported)

50249 ■ Rubber Statistical Bulletin
International Rubber Study Group
111 North Bridge Rd.
No. 23-06 Peninsula Plz.
Singapore 179098, Singapore
Ph: 65 68372411
Fax: 65 63394369
Publication E-mail: contact_irsg@rubberstudy.com
Publisher E-mail: contact_irsg@rubberstudy.com
Trade magazine covering statistics on production and imports and exports of natural and synthetic rubber by country. **Freq:** Quarterly. **ISSN:** 0035-9548. **Subscription Rates:** S$2,500 individuals; S$1,000 single issue. **Remarks:** Advertising not accepted. **URL:** http://www.rubberstudy.com/pub-stats-bulletin.aspx. **Circ:** (Not Reported)

50250 ■ SEAMEO Regional Language Centre Guidelines
SEAMEO Regional Language Centre
30 Orange Grove Rd.
Singapore 258352, Singapore
Ph: 65 68857855
Fax: 65 67342753
Publisher E-mail: enquiries@relc.org.sg
Publication focusing on language teaching and learning disciplines. **Founded:** 1979. **Freq:** 3/yr. **Key Personnel:** Chan Yue Weng, Editor; tay Sor Har, Centre Directory, admin@relc.org.sq. **ISSN:** 0129-7767. **Subscription Rates:** US$70 individuals; US$392 institutions. **URL:** http://www.relc.org.sg. **Circ:** Paid 1,000

50251 ■ Shin Min Daily News
Singapore Press Holdings Ltd.
News Ctr.
1000 Toa Payoh N.
Singapore 318994, Singapore
Ph: 65 63196319
Fax: 65 63198150.
Publisher E-mail: sphcorp@sph.com.sg
Newspaper providing local and international issues. **Founded:** May 18, 1967. **Freq:** Daily. **Key Personnel:** Tom Lam Huat, Editor. **Remarks:** Accepts advertising. **URL:** http://www.sph.com.sg/ourproducts_newspaper_shinmin.shtml. **Ad Rates:** 4C: S$3,000. **Circ:** Mon.-Fri. 139,600

50252 ■ Simply Her
Singapore Press Holdings Ltd.
News Ctr.
1000 Toa Payoh N
Singapore 318994, Singapore
Ph: 65 63196319
Fax: 65 63198150
Publisher E-mail: sphcorp@sph.com.sg
Lifestyle magazine for modern and working women. **Founded:** Oct. 2004. **Trim Size:** 200 x 270 mm. **Key Personnel:** Caroline Ngui, Editor. **Subscription Rates:** US$50.40 individuals; US$100.80 two years. **Remarks:** Accepts advertising. **URL:** http://www.simplyher.com.sg/article.display.php?id=116; http://www.simplyher.com.sg/. **Ad Rates:** BW: S$2,270, 4C: S$3,500. **Circ:** 50,000

50253 ■ Singapore Architect
Singapore Institute of Architects
79B Neil Rd.
Singapore 088904, Singapore
Ph: 65 62262668
Fax: 65 62262663
Publisher E-mail: info@sia.org.sg
Official magazine of the Singapore Institute of Architects, promoting quality Singapore architecture as well as providing a forum for its architects. **Freq:** Bimonthly. **Subscription Rates:** US$86 individuals Singapore; US$151 individuals Malaysia and Brunei; US$238 individuals Asia Pacific; US$297 individuals all other countries. **Remarks:** Advertising accepted; rates available upon request. **URL:** http://www.sia.org.sg/. **Formerly:** S.I.A. Journal (SIAJ). **Circ:** (Not Reported)

50254 ■ Singapore Economic Review
World Scientific Publishing Company Private Ltd.
c/o Euston Quah, Ed.
School of Humanities & Social Sciences
Nanyang Technological University
Nanyang Ave.
Singapore 639798, Singapore
Publisher E-mail: wspc@wspc.com.sg
Periodical focusing on the publication of high-quality theoretical and empirical papers on all aspects of economics. **Founded:** 1956. **Freq:** 3/yr. **Key Personnel:** Euston Quah, Editor, ecsquahe@nus.edu.sg; Ahmed Khalid, Assoc. Ed.; Hian Teck Hoon, Co-Ed.; Anthony Chin, Assoc. Ed.; Ngee Choon Chia, Co-Ed.; Christos Sakellariou, Assoc. Ed. **ISSN:** 0217-5908. **Subscription Rates:** US$188 institutions and libraries; print & electronic; US$180 institutions and libraries; electronic only; US$21 individuals for postage; EUR135 institutions and libraries; print & electronic; EUR130 institutions and libraries; electronic only; EUR16 individuals for postage; S$280 institutions and libraries; print & electronic; S$269 institutions and libraries; electronic only; S$28 individuals for postage. **Remarks:** Advertising accepted; rates available upon request. **URL:** http://www.worldscinet.com/ser/ser.shtml. **Circ:** Paid 800

50255 ■ The Singapore Family Physician
College of Family Physicians Singapore

16 College Rd., No. 01-02
Singapore 169854, Singapore
Ph: 65 622 30606
Fax: 65 622 20204
Publisher E-mail: contact@cfps.org.sg
Medical journal. **Freq:** Quarterly. **Key Personnel:** Dr. Matthew Ng Joo Ming, Contact. **Remarks:** Accepts advertising. **URL:** http://www.cfps.org.sg/. **Circ:** ‡1,000

50256 ■ Singapore Journal of Legal Studies
National University of Singapore
Faculty of Law
National University of Singapore
13 Law Link
Singapore 117590, Singapore
Publication E-mail: lawsjls@nus.edu.sg
Publisher E-mail: qsmanager@nus.edu.sg
Publication focusing on legal developments in Singapore. **Founded:** 1959. **Freq:** Biennial. **Key Personnel:** Prof. Margaret Fordham, Editor, lawfordh@nus.edu.sg; Prof. Yeo Meng Heong, Ch. Ed., lawyeos@nus.edu.sg; Prof. Yvonne CL Lee, Deputy Ch. Ed., lawylcl@nus.edu.sg. **ISSN:** 0218-2173. **Subscription Rates:** S$45 single issue; S$35 single issue other than Singapore; US$60 single issue North America; US$55 individuals other jurisdictions. **Remarks:** Advertising accepted; rates available upon request. **URL:** http://law.nus.edu.sg/sjls/index.html. **Circ:** Paid 1,850

50257 ■ Singapore Journal of Physics
Institute of Physics, Singapore
c/o Dept. of Physics
National University of Singapore
2 Science Dr. 3
Singapore 117542, Singapore
Ph: 65 687 43056
Fax: 65 677 76126
Publisher E-mail: ips@physics.nus.edu.sg
Journal containing research papers, research notes and review articles. **Freq:** Semiannual. **URL:** http://www.physics.nus.edu.sg/~phyips/sjp.html.

50258 ■ Singapore Law Review
National University of Singapore
21 Lower Kent Ridge Rd.
Singapore 119077, Singapore
Ph: 65 6516 6666
Fax: 65 6775 9330
Publisher E-mail: qsmanager@nus.edu.sg
Periodical aimed at promoting legal thinking, legal writing and discussions amongst the students of the Law Faculty. **Founded:** 1969. **Freq:** Annual. **Key Personnel:** Melanie Hong, Ch. Ed.; Charissa Lu, Dep. Ch. Ed. **ISSN:** 0080-9691. **Remarks:** Advertising accepted; rates available upon request. **URL:** http://www.singaporelawreview.org/. **Circ:** Paid 1,350

50259 ■ Singapore Management Review
Singapore Institute of Management
461 Clementi Rd.
Singapore 599491, Singapore
Ph: 65 62489777
Publisher E-mail: research@sim.edu.sg
Publication focusing on the latest business issues in Singapore and around the Asian region. **Subtitle:** Asia-Pacific Journal of Management Theory and Practice. **Founded:** 1979. **Freq:** Semiannual. **Key Personnel:** Dr. Benjamin Tan Lin Boon, Editor-in-Chief; Roland Tan Chee Teik, Assoc. Ed.; Dr. Doreen Thang Chze Lin, Assoc. Ed. **ISSN:** 0129-5977. **Subscription Rates:** US$39.50 two years. **URL:** http://www.sim.edu.sg/mbs/pub/gen/mbs_pub_gen_content.cfm?mnuid=93.

50260 ■ Singapore Medical Journal
Singapore Medical Association
Alumni Medical Ctr.
2 College Rd., Level 2
Singapore 169850, Singapore
Ph: 65 622 31264
Fax: 65 622 47827
Singapore journal covering medicine. **Founded:** 1960. **Freq:** Monthly. **Key Personnel:** Li Li Loy, Advertising Exec., lili@sma.org.sg. **ISSN:** 0037-5675. **Remarks:** Accepts advertising. **URL:** http://www.sma.org.sg/advertising/smj.html. **Circ:** 4,700

50261 ■ Singapore National Academy of Science Journal
National University of Singapore
21 Lower Kent Ridge Rd.

Singapore 119077, Singapore
Ph: 65 6775 6666
Journal covering biology and botany. **Founded:** 1977. **Freq:** Annual. **Key Personnel:** A.N. Rao, Editor. **ISSN:** 0129-3729. **Subscription Rates:** S$32. **Circ:** Paid 1,500

50262 ■ Singapore Tatler
Edipresse Asia
211 Henderson Rd., No. 07-04
Henderson Industrial Pk.
Singapore 159552, Singapore
Ph: 65 63231606
Fax: 65 63231692
Publication E-mail: general@edipresse.com.sg
Magazine covering the high society luxury and fashion of Singapore. **Freq:** Monthly. **Key Personnel:** Gilbert Cheah, Director; Jane Ngiam, Ch. Ed. **URL:** http://www.edipresse.com/lifestyle/singapore-tatler. **Circ:** ‡13,000

50263 ■ Singapore Tatler Homes
Edipresse Asia
211 Henderson Rd., No. 07-04
Henderson Industrial Pk.
Singapore 159552, Singapore
Ph: 65 63231606
Fax: 65 63231692
Magazine featuring the top luxury homes in Singapore and the region, including the interior designs, appliances and accessories. **Freq:** Quarterly. **Key Personnel:** Gilbert Cheah, Director; Joseph Lim, Ch. Ed. **URL:** http://www.edipresse.com/home-design/singapore-tatler-homes. **Circ:** ‡14,000

50264 ■ Singapore Tatler Society
Edipresse Asia
211 Henderson Rd., No. 07-04
Henderson Industrial Pk.
Singapore 159552, Singapore
Ph: 65 63231606
Fax: 65 63231692
Publication E-mail: general@edipresse.com.sg
Magazine featuring the society people, places and events in Singapore. **Freq:** Annual. **Key Personnel:** Gilbert Cheah, Director; Jane Ngiam, Ch. Ed. **URL:** http://www.edipresse.com/lifestyle/singapore-tatler-society. **Circ:** ‡12,200

50265 ■ Singapore Tatler Weddings
Edipresse Asia
211 Henderson Rd., No. 07-04
Henderson Industrial Pk.
Singapore 159552, Singapore
Ph: 65 63231606
Fax: 65 63231692
Magazine featuring the high society weddings in Singapore. **Freq:** Annual. **Key Personnel:** Gilbert Cheah, Director; Joseph Lim, Ch. Ed. **URL:** http://www.edipresse.com/lifestyle/singapore-tatler-weddings. **Circ:** ‡14,000

50266 ■ Singapore Visitor
Lexicon Group Ltd.
371 Beach Rd.
03-18 Keypoint
Singapore 199597, Singapore
Ph: 65 629 20300
Fax: 65 629 34294
Publisher E-mail: corp.info@lexicon.com.sg
A comprehensive guide that focuses on issues of much relevance and interest to the visiting businessman in the areas of WORK, PLAY and LIVE while in Singapore. **Freq:** Monthly. **Key Personnel:** Ho Sum Kwong, Editor-in-Chief; Agatha Koh, Editorial Dir.; Marguerita Tan, Editor. **URL:** http://www.lexicon.com.sg/singapore/print/index.asp. **Ad Rates:** 4C: S$3,500. **Circ:** (Not Reported)

50267 ■ Singapore's Best Restaurants
Edipresse Asia
211 Henderson Rd., No. 07-04
Henderson Industrial Pk.
Singapore 159552, Singapore
Ph: 65 63231606
Fax: 65 63231692
Magazine featuring the best fine dining restaurants in Singapore. **Freq:** Annual. **Key Personnel:** Gilbert Cheah, Director; Joseph Lim, Ch. Ed. **URL:** http://www.edipresse.com/food-dining/singapores-best-restaurants. **Circ:** ‡33,000

50268 ■ Smart Investor
Lexicon Group Ltd.
371 Beach Rd.
03-18 Keypoint
Singapore 199597, Singapore
Ph: 65 629 20300
Fax: 65 629 34294
Publication E-mail: smartinvestor@panpacmedia.com
Publisher E-mail: corp.info@lexicon.com.sg
Magazine that explores opportunities and options available to the serious retail investor. **Freq:** Monthly. **Key Personnel:** Yusli Yusoff, Sen. Business Mgr., yusli@lexicon.com.sg. **Remarks:** Accepts advertising. **URL:** http://www.lexicon.com.sg/singapore/print/si_ad.asp; http://www.smartinvestor.com.sg. **Ad Rates:** BW: S$3,000. **Circ:** (Not Reported)

50269 ■ South Seas Society Journal
South Seas Society
PO Box 709
Singapore 901409, Singapore
Fax: 65 64665510
Journal covering Asian history. **Founded:** 1940. **Freq:** Annual. **Key Personnel:** Gwee Yee Hean, Editor. **ISSN:** 0081-2889. **Subscription Rates:** US$20. **Remarks:** Advertising not accepted. **Circ:** Paid 600

50270 ■ Southeast Asian Affairs
Institute of Southeast Asian Studies
30 Heng Mui Keng Ter.
Pasir Panjang
Singapore 119614, Singapore
Ph: 65 67780955
Fax: 65 67781735
Publisher E-mail: admin@iseas.edu.sg
Annual review of significant trends and developments in Southeast Asia. **Founded:** 1974. **Freq:** Annual. **Key Personnel:** Daljit Singh, Editor; Chin Kin Wah, Editor. **ISSN:** 0377-5437. **Subscription Rates:** US$27 individuals; S$40 individuals. **URL:** http://www.iseas.edu.sg/saa.html.

50271 ■ Space
Lexicon Group Ltd.
371 Beach Rd.
03-18 Keypoint
Singapore 199597, Singapore
Ph: 65 629 20300
Fax: 65 629 34294
Publisher E-mail: corp.info@lexicon.com.sg
Magazine on architecture and interior design. **Freq:** Quarterly. **Key Personnel:** Casey Khoo, Vice President, casey.khoo@inovatif.com.my; S. Vithiah, Sen. Sales Mgr., vithiah@inovatif.com.my; Chong Chye Wan, President, chong.chyewan@inovatif.com.my. **Subscription Rates:** S$28 individuals; S$56 two years. **URL:** http://www.lexicon.com.sg/singapore/print/space__msia_ad.asp. **Ad Rates:** 4C: S$2,700. **Circ:** (Not Reported)

50272 ■ Statistical Methodology
Elsevier (Singapore) Pte. Ltd.
3 Killiney Rd., No. 08-01
Winsland House 1
Singapore 239519, Singapore
Ph: 65 6 3490222
Fax: 65 6 7331510
Publisher E-mail: asiabkinfo@elsevier.com
Journal publishing articles of high quality reflecting the varied facets of contemporary statistical theory as well as of significant applications. **Founded:** 2004. **Freq:** 6/yr. **Key Personnel:** G.J. Babu, Editor-in-Chief, stamet@stat.psu.edu; M.C. Jones, Assoc. Ed.; M. Aoshima, Assoc. Ed.; Y.P. Chaubey, Assoc. Ed.; P. Zeephongsekul, Assoc. Ed.; G. Shieh, Assoc. Ed. **ISSN:** 1572-3127. **Subscription Rates:** US$443 institutions all countries except Europe, Japan and Iran; 52,300¥ institutions; EUR443 institutions European countries and Iran; EUR134 individuals European countries and Iran; US$179 individuals all countries except Europe, Japan and Iran; 20,600¥ individuals. **URL:** http://www.elsevier.com/wps/find/journaldescription.cws_home/702016/descriptiondescription.

50273 ■ The Straits Times
Singapore Press Holdings Ltd.
News Ctr.
1000 Toa Payoh N
Singapore 318994, Singapore
Ph: 65 63196319

Fax: 65 63198150
Publisher E-mail: sphcorp@sph.com.sg
Newspaper focusing on Singapore and the Asian region. **Founded:** July 15, 1845. **Freq:** Daily. **Key Personnel:** Han Fook Kwang, Editor; Alan John, Dep. Ed.; Bertha Henson, Assoc. Ed.; Felix Soh, Digital Media Ed.; Mathew Pereira, Sports Ed.; Zuraidah Ibrahim, Dep. Ed.; Patrick Daniel, Editor-in-Chief. **Subscription Rates:** US$295.60 individuals; US$591.20 two years. **Remarks:** Accepts advertising. **URL:** http://www.straitstimes.com/Home.html. **Circ:** Paid 400,000

50274 ■ Style
MediaCorp Publishing
Caldecott Broadcast Centre
Andrew Rd.
Singapore 299939, Singapore
Ph: 65 633 33888
Fax: 65 625 15628
Publisher E-mail: feedback@mediacorp.com.sg
Trend-setting fashion and lifestyle buying guide. **URL:** http://www.corporate.mediacorp.sg/publishing/index.htm.

50275 ■ Surface Review and Letters
World Scientific Publishing Company Private Ltd.
5 Toh Tuck Link
Singapore 596224, Singapore
Ph: 99965 646 65775
Fax: 99965 646 77667
Publisher E-mail: wspc@wspc.com.sg
Periodical focusing on the elucidation of properties and processes that occur at the boundaries of materials. **Founded:** 1994. **Freq:** Bimonthly. **Key Personnel:** S.Y. Tong, Editor-in-Chief, apdtong@cityu.edu.hk; D.K. Saldin, Exec. Editor. **ISSN:** 0218-625X. **Subscription Rates:** US$1,425 institutions and libraries; electronic + print; EUR1,231 institutions and libraries; electronic + print; S$2,362 institutions and libraries; electronic + print; US$1,368 institutions and libraries; electronic only; EUR1,182 institutions and libraries; electronic only; S$2,268 institutions and libraries; electronic only; US$47 individuals for postage; EUR36 individuals for postage; S$62 individuals for postage. **URL:** http://www.worldscinet.com/srl/srl.shtml.

50276 ■ Tamil Murasu
Singapore Press Holdings Ltd.
News Ctr.
1000 Toa Payoh N
Singapore 318994, Singapore
Ph: 65 63196319
Fax: 65 63198150
Publisher E-mail: sphcorp@sph.com.sg
Newspaper for Tamil speaking community in Singapore covering local and foreign news. **Founded:** 1935. **Freq:** Daily. **Key Personnel:** Nirmala Murugaian, Editor. **Subscription Rates:** US$185.70 individuals; US$371.40 two years. **Remarks:** Accepts advertising. **URL:** http://www.sph.com.sg/ourproducts_newspaper_tamilmurasu.shtml. **Ad Rates:** 4C: S$4,000. **Circ:** 14,400

50277 ■ Teens Annual
Eastern Holdings Ltd.
1100 Lower Delta Rd., No. 04-01
EPL Bldg.
Singapore 169206, Singapore
Ph: 65 637 92888
Fax: 65 637 92803
Publisher E-mail: eastern1@singnet.com.sg
Teen magazine focusing on fashion, health, and beauty. **Freq:** Annual. **Remarks:** Accepts advertising. **URL:** http://www.epl.com.sg/publications/teens.asp?mag=teens_annual. **Circ:** (Not Reported)

50278 ■ Thumbs Up
Singapore Press Holdings Ltd.
News Ctr.
1000 Toa Payoh N
Singapore 318994, Singapore
Ph: 65 63196319
Fax: 65 63198150
Publisher E-mail: sphcorp@sph.com.sg
Newspaper for students between primary 3 to 6. **Founded:** Jan. 15, 2000. **Freq:** Weekly. **Key Personnel:** Ms. Lim Soon Lan, Editor. **Remarks:** Accepts advertising. **URL:** http://www.sph.com.sg/ourproducts_newspaper_thumbsup.shtml. **Ad Rates:** 4C: S$700. **Circ:** Mon.-Fri. 39,200

50279 ■ Today's Parents
Lexicon Group Ltd.

Circulation: ★ = ABC; △ = BPA; ♦ = CAC; • = CCAB; □ = VAC; ⊕ = PO Statement; ‡ = Publisher's Report; Boldface figures = sworn; Light figures = estimated.

Gale Directory of Publications & Broadcast Media/147th Ed.   5411

371 Beach Rd.
03-18 Keypoint
Singapore 199597, Singapore
Ph: 65 629 20300
Fax: 65 629 34294
Publisher E-mail: corp.info@lexicon.com.sg
Magazine covering the latest information on the parenting scene, sex, health and nutrition, and family. **Freq:** Monthly. **Key Personnel:** Yusli Yusoff, Sen. Business Mgr., yusli@lexicon.com.sg. **URL:** http://www.lexicon.com.sg/singapore/print/tp_ad.asp; http://www.todaysparent.com. **Ad Rates:** BW: S$2,200, 4C: S$2,700. **Circ:** (Not Reported)

50280 ■ Torque
Singapore Press Holdings Ltd.
News Ctr.
1000 Toa Payoh N
Singapore 318994, Singapore
Ph: 65 63196319
Fax: 65 63198150
Publisher E-mail: sphcorp@sph.com.sg
Magazine for local car enthusiasts. **Founded:** 1990. **Freq:** Monthly. **Key Personnel:** Lee Nian Tjoe, Editor. **Subscription Rates:** US$66 individuals. **Remarks:** Accepts advertising. **URL:** http://www.sph.com.sg/article.display.php?id=665; http://www.torque.com.sg/. **Circ:** 25,000

50281 ■ Travel Trade Gazette Asia
TTG Asia Media Private Ltd.
1 Science Park Rd.
No. 04-07 The Capricorn
Singapore Science Park II
Singapore 117528, Singapore
Ph: 65 63957575
Fax: 65 65362972
Publisher E-mail: ttgnewsdesk@ttgasia.com
Publication focusing on travel and tourism. **Freq:** Weekly. **Key Personnel:** Michael Crow, Publisher. **Remarks:** Accepts advertising. **URL:** http://www.ttgasia.com/. **Ad Rates:** BW: US$10,744, 4C: US$12,492. **Circ:** ‡16,800

50282 ■ TTGmice
TTG Asia Media Private Ltd.
1 Science Park Rd.
No. 04-07 The Capricorn
Singapore Science Park II
Singapore 117528, Singapore
Ph: 65 63957575
Fax: 65 65362972
Publisher E-mail: ttgnewsdesk@ttgasia.com
Publication providing information on meetings, incentive travel, conventions and exhibitions industry in the Asia-Pacific regional markets. **Founded:** 1994. **Freq:** Monthly. **Key Personnel:** Raini Hamdi, Gp. Ed., raini.hamdi@ttgasia.com; Kris Chan, Business Mgr., kris.chan@ttgasia.com; Michael Crow, Publisher, michael.chow@ttgasia.com; Vincent Lim, Sales Dir., vincent.lim@ttgasia.com. **Subscription Rates:** US$70 individuals Asia-Pacific; US$90 other countries non Asia-Pacific. **Remarks:** Accepts advertising. **URL:** http://www.ttgmice.com/index.php?option=com_content&task=view&id=1697&itemid=100&issueid=47. **Formerly:** Incentives & Meetings Asia. **Ad Rates:** BW: US$7,900. **Circ:** (Not Reported)

50283 ■ Urban Forestry & Urban Greening
Elsevier (Singapore) Pte. Ltd.
3 Killiney Rd., No. 08-01
Winsland House 1
Singapore 239519, Singapore
Ph: 65 6 3490222
Fax: 65 6 7331510
Publisher E-mail: asiabkinfo@elsevier.com
International journal aimed at presenting high-quality research with urban and peri-urban woody and non-woody vegetation and its use, planning, design, establishment and management as its main topics. **Freq:** Quarterly. **Key Personnel:** Cecil C. Konijnendijk, Editor-in-Chief, phone 45 33247230, cecil@woodscapeconsult.com; Nina Bassuk, Editorial Board; Arne Arnberger, Editorial Board; David J. Nowak, Regional Ed., dnowak@fs.fed.us; Simon Bell, Editorial Board; John Dwyer, Editorial Board; Robert Brown, Editorial Board; Alicia Chacalo, Editorial Board; Mary Forrest, Editorial Board. **ISSN:** 1618-8667. **Subscription Rates:** EUR309 institutions for European countries and Iran; US$322

institutions all countries except Europe, Japan and Iran; 39,500¥ institutions; EUR145 individuals for European countries and Iran; US$140 individuals all countries except Europe, Japan and Iran; 19,000¥ individuals; EUR109 students for European countries and Iran; 13,300¥ students; US$105 students all countries except Europe, Japan and Iran; EUR309 institutions for Germany, Austria, Switzerland. **URL:** http://www.elsevier.com/wps/find/journaldescription.cws_home/701803/descriptiondescription.

50284 ■ Water & Wastewater Asia
Pablo Publishing Pte Ltd.
Block 61, Kallang Pl., No. 07-01
Singapore 339156, Singapore
Ph: 65 63967877
Fax: 65 63967177
Publisher E-mail: info@pabloasia.com
Magazine featuring changes and developments within the water and wastewater industries worldwide. **Subtitle:** Incorporating the Official Newsletter of the Singapore Water Association. **Freq:** Bimonthly. **Key Personnel:** Ong Tze Kian, Editor, ongtzekian@pabloasia.com. **Subscription Rates:** US$77.04 individuals English and Chinese edition; US$139.10 two years English and Chinese edition; US$78 individuals to Asia Pacific, English & Chinese edition; US$140 two years to Asia Pacific, English & Chinese edition; US$90 individuals to America/Europe, English & Chinese edition; US$162 two years to America/Europe, English & Chinese edition. **Remarks:** Accepts advertising. **URL:** http://www.waterwastewaterasia.com/. **Circ:** (Not Reported)

50285 ■ Wedding & Travel
Fullhouse Communications Private Ltd.
246 MacPherson Rd., No. 06-01
Betime Bldg.
Singapore 348578, Singapore
Ph: 65 68427266
Fax: 65 68427133
Wedding magazine. **Freq:** Semiannual. **URL:** http://www.fullhouse.com.sg/today_issue.htm.

50286 ■ White Cane
Singapore Association of the Visually Handicapped
47 Toa Payoh Rise
Singapore 298104, Singapore
Ph: 65 625 14331
Fax: 65 625 37191
Publisher E-mail: enquiries@savh.org.sg
Journal of the Singapore Association of the Visually Handicapped. **Freq:** Annual. **Key Personnel:** Mr. Tan Guan Heng, President; Mr Lee Soo Hoon Phillip, Vice President; Mr. Khoo Kong Ngian, Vice President; Danny Chia Choon Guan, Honorary Sec. **URL:** http://www.savh.org.sg/.

50287 ■ Wine & Dine
Lexicon Group Ltd.
371 Beach Rd.
03-18 Keypoint
Singapore 199597, Singapore
Ph: 65 629 20300
Fax: 65 629 34294
Publisher E-mail: corp.info@lexicon.com.sg
Magazine covering food, wine, travel and good living. **Freq:** Monthly. **Key Personnel:** Joey Tan, Assoc. Publisher, joey.tan@lexicon.com.sg. **URL:** http://www.lexicon.com.sg/singapore/print/wd_ad.asp; http://www.wineanddine.com.sg. **Ad Rates:** BW: S$3,500, 4C: S$4,500. **Circ:** 40,000

50288 ■ Woman's World
Eastern Holdings Ltd.
1100 Lower Delta Rd., No. 04-01
EPL Bldg.
Singapore 169206, Singapore
Ph: 65 637 92888
Fax: 65 637 92803
Publication E-mail: womansworld@epl.com.sg
Publisher E-mail: eastern1@singnet.com.sg
Woman's lifestyle magazine. **Freq:** Monthly. **Remarks:** Accepts advertising. **URL:** http://www.epl.com.sg/publications/woman.asp?mag=woman. **Circ:** (Not Reported)

50289 ■ Young Parents
Singapore Press Holdings Ltd.
News Ctr.
1000 Toa Payoh N
Singapore 318994, Singapore
Ph: 65 63196319

Fax: 65 63198150
Publication E-mail: magyoungparentssales@sph.com.sg
Publisher E-mail: sphcorp@sph.com.sg
Magazine for parents. **Founded:** 1986. **Freq:** Monthly. **Key Personnel:** Stephanie Yeo, Editor; Eugene Low, Dep. Mng. Dir.; Adrian Cheong, Asst. Mgr. **Subscription Rates:** US$60 individuals; US$120 two years. **Remarks:** Accepts advertising. **URL:** http://www.youngparents.com.sg/. **Ad Rates:** BW: S$1,600, 4C: S$2,200. **Circ:** 15,000

50290 ■ Young Parents Baby
Singapore Press Holdings Ltd.
News Ctr.
1000 Toa Payoh N
Singapore 318994, Singapore
Ph: 65 63196319
Fax: 65 63198150
Publisher E-mail: sphcorp@sph.com.sg
Magazine for parents with babies up to 2 years of age. **Freq:** Quarterly. **Key Personnel:** Stephanie Yeo, Editor. **Remarks:** Accepts advertising. **URL:** http://www.sph.com.sg/article.display.php?id=1282. **Circ:** 25,000

50291 ■ Young Parents Preschool Guide
Singapore Press Holdings Ltd.
News Ctr.
1000 Toa Payoh N
Singapore 318994, Singapore
Ph: 65 63196319
Fax: 65 63198150
Publisher E-mail: sphcorp@sph.com.sg
Magazine for young parents who have a preschool child. **Founded:** Oct. 2003. **Freq:** Annual. **Remarks:** Accepts advertising. **URL:** http://www.sph.com.sg/article.display.php?id=1282. **Circ:** 30,000

50292 ■ zbCOMMA
Singapore Press Holdings Ltd.
News Ctr.
1000 Toa Payoh N
Singapore 318994, Singapore
Ph: 65 63196319
Fax: 65 63198150
Publisher E-mail: sphcorp@sph.com.sg
Chinese newspaper featuring youth issues. **Founded:** Feb. 22, 1991. **Freq:** Weekly (Fri.). **Key Personnel:** Ms. Lim Soon Lan, Editor. **Remarks:** Accepts advertising. **URL:** http://www.sph.com.sg/ourproducts_newspaper_zbcomma.shtml. **Formerly:** Friday Weekly. **Ad Rates:** 4C: S$700. **Circ:** 60,000

50293 ■ Capital Radio 95.8 FM - 95.8 FM
Caldecott Broadcast Ctr.
Andrew Rd.
Singapore 299939, Singapore
Ph: 65 63 333888
Fax: 65 62 515628
Format: News; Full Service; Oldies. **Owner:** Media Corporation Radio, at above address. **Operating Hours:** Continuous. **Key Personnel:** Ho Kwon Ping, Chm.; Shaun Seow, CEO. **Ad Rates:** $50-330 per unit. **URL:** http://www.capital958.sg/.

50294 ■ Class 95 FM - 95 MHz
Caldecott Broadcast Centre
4th Storey Radio Bldg., Andrew Rd.
Singapore 299939, Singapore
Ph: 65 63333888
E-mail: class95@mediacorp.com.sg
Format: Adult Contemporary; Oldies. **Owner:** Media Corporation Radio, at above address. **Operating Hours:** Continuous. **Key Personnel:** Ho Kwon Ping, Chm.; Shaun Seow, CEO, Media Corp Radio. **Ad Rates:** $50-650 per unit. **URL:** http://www.class95.sg/.

50295 ■ Gold 90.5 FM - 90.5 MHz
Caldecott Broadcast Centre
Level 4, Radio Bldg.
Andrew Rd.
Singapore 299939, Singapore
Ph: 65 63597567
Fax: 65 63559050
E-mail: gold905@mediacorp.com.sg
Format: Oldies. **Owner:** Media Corporation Radio, at above address. **Founded:** 1998. **Operating Hours:** Continuous. **Key Personnel:** Ho Kwon Ping, Chm.; Media Corp Radio; Shaun Seow, CEO, Media Corp

Radio. **Ad Rates:** $50-280 per unit. **URL:** http://www. gold90.com.sg.

50296 ■ The International Channel 96.3 FM - 96.3 MHz
Caldecott Broadcast Ctr.
4th Fl., Radio Bldg., Andrew Rd.
Singapore 299939, Singapore
Ph: 65 63333888
Fax: 65 62515628
E-mail: fm963@mediacorpradio.com
Format: Full Service. **Owner:** Media Corporation Radio, at above address. **Operating Hours:** 6.50a.m.-12a.m. Mon.-Fri; 7a.m.-12a.m. Sat. & Sun. **Key Personnel:** Ho Kwon Ping, Chm.; Shaun Seow, CEO. **Ad Rates:** Advertising accepted; rates available upon request. **URL:** http://www.international963.sg/.

50297 ■ Love 97.2 FM - 97.2 MHz
Caldecott Broadcast Ctr.
Andrew Rd., Radio Bldg.
Singapore 299939, Singapore
Ph: 65 63333888
Fax: 65 62515628
Format: Easy Listening; Adult Contemporary; Oldies. **Owner:** Media Corporation Radio, at above address. **Operating Hours:** Continuous. **Key Personnel:** Ho Kwon Ping, Chm.; Shaun Seow, CEO. **Ad Rates:** $50-450 per unit. **URL:** http://www.love972.sg/index.htm.

50298 ■ Mediacorp TV Pte. Ltd. - Channel 8 - 8
Caldecott Broadcast Ctr.
Andrew Rd.
Singapore 299939, Singapore
Ph: 65 63333888
Fax: 65 62515628
Format: News. **Owner:** Mediacorp TV Pte. Ltd., at above address. **Operating Hours:** Continuous. **Key Personnel:** Khiew Voon Kwang, Senior Vice President. **Ad Rates:** Advertising accepted; rates available upon request. **URL:** http://www.corporate.mediacorp.sg/; http://ch8.mediacorptv.com/.

50299 ■ Mediacorp TV Pte. Ltd. - Channel 5 - 5
Caldecott Broadcast Ctr.
Andrew Rd.
Singapore 299939, Singapore
Ph: 65 63333888
Fax: 65 62515628
E-mail: feedback@mediacorp.com.sg
Format: Sports; News. **Owner:** Mediacorp TV Pte. Ltd., at above address. **Operating Hours:** Continuous. **Ad Rates:** Advertising accepted; rates available upon request. **URL:** http://ch5.mediacorptv.com/.

50300 ■ 987FM - 98.7 MHz
Caldecott Broadcast Ctr.
4th Storey, Radio Bldg., Andrew Rd.
Singapore 299939, Singapore
Ph: 65 63333888
Fax: 65 62515628
Format: Top 40. **Owner:** Media Corporation Radio, at above address. **Founded:** 1989. **Formerly:** Perfect Ten 98.7 FM. **Operating Hours:** Continuous. **Key Personnel:** Ho Kwon Ping, Chm.; Shaun Seow, CEO, Media Corp Radio. **Ad Rates:** $50-350 per unit. **URL:** http://www.987fm.sg/.

50301 ■ 938LIVE - 93.8 MHz
Caldecott Broadcast Ctr.
4th Fl., Radio Bldg., Andrew Rd.
Singapore 299939, Singapore
Ph: 65 68222268
Fax: 65 62520938
E-mail: 938live@mediacorp.com.sg
Format: News; Information. **Owner:** Media Corporation Radio, at above address. **Founded:** 2005. **Formerly:** News Radio 93.8 FM. **Operating Hours:** 6 a.m.-12 a.m. Daily. **Key Personnel:** Ho Kwon Ping, Chm.; Gerardine Tan, Sen. Prog. Dir., phone 65 63597312; Justin Tan, Station Admin. Exec., phone 65 63597314. **Ad Rates:** $60-290 per unit. **URL:** http://www.938live.sg/.

50302 ■ Oli 96.8 FM - 96.8 MHz
Caldecott Broadcast Ctr.

4th Fl., Radio Bldg., Andrew Rd.
Singapore 299939, Singapore
Ph: 65 66911968
Fax: 65 63597500
Format: Adult Contemporary. **Owner:** Media Corporation Radio, at above address. **Founded:** 1936. **Operating Hours:** Continuous. **Key Personnel:** Ho Kwon Ping, Chm.; M. Susila, Asst. Admin. Exec., phone 65 63597340, msusila@mediacorp.com; James Yip, CEO, Media Corp Radio. **Ad Rates:** Advertising accepted; rates available upon request. **URL:** http://www.oli.sg/.

50303 ■ Power 98 FM - 98.0 MHz
Bukit Merah Central
PO Box 1315
Singapore 911599, Singapore
Ph: 65 63731924
Fax: 65 62783039
E-mail: makeithappen@safraradio.com.sg
Format: News; Sports; Soft Rock. **Owner:** SAFRA Radio, at above address. **Founded:** 1994. **Operating Hours:** Continuous. **Ad Rates:** Advertising accepted; rates available upon request. **URL:** http://www.power98.com.sg.

50304 ■ RADIO 91.3 FM - 91.3 Mhz
c/o UnionWorks Pte. Ltd.
1000 Toa Payoh N
Singapore 318994, Singapore
Ph: 65 63191900
Format: News; Contemporary Hit Radio (CHR). **Owner:** Unionworks Pte. Ltd., at above address. **Founded:** 1991. **Formerly:** Heart 91.3 (2000); WKRZ 91.3 FM. **Operating Hours:** Continuous. **Ad Rates:** Advertising accepted; rates available upon request. **URL:** http://www.radio913.com/.

50305 ■ Ria 89.7 FM - 89.7 MHz
Caldecott Broadcast Ctr.
Andrew Rd.
Singapore 299939, Singapore
Ph: 656333 3888
Fax: 656251 5628
Format: Contemporary Hit Radio (CHR); News. **Owner:** Media Corporation Radio, at above address. **Operating Hours:** Continuous. **Key Personnel:** Ho Kwon Ping, Chm.; Shaun Seow, CEO. **Ad Rates:** $12-80 per unit. **URL:** http://www.ria.sg/index_ria_89.7.htm.

50306 ■ Symphony 92.4 FM - 92.4 MHz
Caldecott Broadcast Ctr.
4th Fl., Radio Bldg., Andrew Rd.
Singapore 299939, Singapore
Ph: 65 63333888
Fax: 65 62515628
E-mail: symphony@mediacorp.com.sg
Format: Classical. **Owner:** Media Corporation Radio, at above address. **Founded:** July 18, 1969. **Operating Hours:** 6 a.m.-12 a.m. Daily. **Key Personnel:** Ho Kwon Ping, Chm.; Shaun Seow, CEO, Media Corp Radio. **Ad Rates:** $100 per unit. **URL:** http://www.symphony.sg/.

50307 ■ UFM1003 - 100.3 MHz
SPH News Ctr.
1000 Toa Payoh N
Singapore 318994, Singapore
Ph: 65 63 3191900
E-mail: feedback@radio1003.com
Format: News. **Owner:** UnionWorks Pte. Ltd., at above address. **Founded:** Mar. 10, 2001. **Operating Hours:** Continuous. **Ad Rates:** Advertising accepted; rates available upon request. **URL:** http://www.radio1003.com.

50308 ■ Warna 94.2 FM - 94.2 MHz
Caldecott Broadcast Ctr.
Andrew Rd.
Singapore 299939, Singapore
Ph: 65 63 333888
Fax: 65 62 515628
Format: Full Service; News. **Owner:** Media Corporation Radio, at above address. **Operating Hours:** Continuous. **Key Personnel:** Ho Kwon Ping, Chm.; Shaun Seow, CEO. **Ad Rates:** $20-150 per unit. **URL:** http://www.warna.sg/.

50309 ■ Y.E.S. 93.3 FM - 93.3 MHz
Caldecott Broadcast Ctr.
Andrew Rd.
Singapore 299939, Singapore
Ph: 65 63 333888
Fax: 65 62 515628
Format: Adult Contemporary; News. **Owner:** Media Corporation Radio, at above address. **Operating Hours:** Continuous. **Key Personnel:** Ho Kwon Ping, Chm.; Shaun Seow, CEO. **Ad Rates:** $50-430 per unit. **URL:** http://www.yes933.sg/.

Singapore City

50310 ■ Annual Review of Singapore Cases
Singapore Academy of Law
1 Supreme Court Ln., Level 6
Singapore City 178879, Singapore
Ph: 65 63324388
Fax: 65 63344940
Journal featuring Singapore reported and unreported cases, together with a discussion of relevant cases from other jurisdictions that impact on local law. **Founded:** 2000. **Freq:** Annual. **Key Personnel:** Teo Keang Sood, Author/Ed. **Subscription Rates:** US$53.50 individuals. **URL:** http://www.sal.org.sg/Lists/BookTitles/DispForm. aspx?ID=38.

50311 ■ Asian Security Review
Alphabet Media
12 Prince Edward Rd.
No. 03-01, Podium A Bestway Bldg.
Singapore City 079212, Singapore
Ph: 65 63363136
Fax: 65 6324 1228
Magazine focusing on homeland security and critical infrastructure protection. **Freq:** 6/yr. **Key Personnel:** James Smith, Mng. Dir., james.smith@alphabet-media.com; Robin Hicks, Editor, phone 65 6324 7620, robin.hicks@alphabet-media.com. **Remarks:** Accepts advertising. **URL:** http://www.asiansecurity.org/. **Circ:** 10,000

50312 ■ FutureGov
Alphabet Media
12 Prince Edward Rd.
No. 03-01, Podium A Bestway Bldg.
Singapore City 079212, Singapore
Ph: 65 63363136
Fax: 65 6324 1228
Magazine featuring institutional reform in the public sector, and research into improving the business of government. **Freq:** 6/yr. **Key Personnel:** James Smith, Mng. Dir., phone 65 6324 7612, james.smith@alphabet-media.com. **Remarks:** Accepts advertising. **URL:** http://www.futuregov.net/. **Formerly:** Public Sector Technology & Management. **Circ:** 8,950

50313 ■ Inter Se Print
Singapore Academy of Law
1 Supreme Court Ln., Level 6
Singapore City 178879, Singapore
Ph: 65 63324388
Fax: 65 63344940
Magazine featuring the life of a particular area of practice or topic with people profiles, interview segments, and reviews of relevant legal publications in the area. **Freq:** Semiannual. **Subscription Rates:** S$10 single issue. **URL:** http://www.sal.org.sg/digitallibrary/List/inter%205e%20Magazine/DisoForm.aspx?ID=49.

50314 ■ Singapore Academy of Law Journal
Singapore Academy of Law
1 Supreme Court Ln., Level 6
Singapore City 178879, Singapore
Ph: 65 63324388
Fax: 65 63344940
Journal featuring articles related to Singapore law as well as Asia-Pacific and common law legal systems, and comparative and international law. **Founded:** 1989. **Freq:** Semiannual. **Key Personnel:** Prof. Michael Furmston, Editor; Prof. Francis Reynolds, Editor. **Subscription Rates:** S$32.10 individuals. **URL:** http://www.sal.org.sg/Lists/BookTitles/DispForm.aspx?ID=69.

Circulation: ★ = ABC; △ = BPA; ♦ = CAC; • = CCAB; ❑ = VAC; ⊕ = PO Statement; ‡ = Publisher's Report; Boldface figures = sworn; Light figures = estimated.

Gale Directory of Publications & Broadcast Media/147th Ed.   5413

Bratislava

50315 ■ Acta Physica Slovaca
Institute of Physics
Slovak Academy of Sciences
Dubravska cesta 9
845 11 Bratislava, Slovakia
Ph: 421 2 59410501
Fax: 421 2 54776085
Publisher E-mail: danka.haasova@savba.sk
Journal covering aspects of the experimental and theoretical physics. **Founded:** 1973. **Key Personnel:** Andrej Gendiar, Technical Ed., aps@savba.sk; Vladimir Buzek, Editor, buzek@savba.sk. **ISSN:** 0323-0465. **Subscription Rates:** EUR234 individuals print and online, by surface mail; EUR252 single issue print and online, by air mail; EUR39 individuals single issue, surface mail; EUR42 individuals single issue, air mail; EUR39 individuals. **URL:** http://www.physics.sk/aps/.

50316 ■ Acta Virologica
Academic Electronic Press
Institute of Virology
Slovak Academy of Sciences
Dubravska cesta 9
SK-845 05 Bratislava, Slovakia
Ph: 42 125 9302412
Fax: 42 125 4776380
Publisher E-mail: koresp@aepress.sk
Journal focusing on molecular and cellular virology. **Freq:** 4/yr. **Key Personnel:** Gustav Russ, Editor-in-Chief; Jaroslav Zemla, Editor. **ISSN:** 0001-723X. **URL:** http://www.aepress.sk/acta/av.htm.

50317 ■ Central-European Value Studies
Rodopi
c/o Prof. Emil Visnovsky, Ed.
Dept. of Social & Biological Communication
Slovak Academy of Sciences
Klemensova 19
SL-81364 Bratislava, Slovakia
Ph: 94 421 754775683
Fax: 94 421 754770442
Publisher E-mail: info@rodopi.nl
Journal covering all areas of value inquiry, including social and political thought, ethics, applied philosophy, feminism, pragmatism, religious values, medical and health values, values in science and technology, law and society, and theory of culture. **Key Personnel:** Prof. Emil Visnovsky, Editor, visnovsky@yahoo.com. **URL:** http://www.rodopi.nl/senj.asp?SerieId=CEVS.

50318 ■ Computing and Informatics
Slovak Academy of Sciences
Institute of Informatics
Dubravska cesta 9
845 07 Bratislava, Slovakia
Ph: 42 125 9411204
Fax: 42 125 4771004
Publisher E-mail: cai.ui@savba.sk
Professional journal covering computer science. **Founded:** 1982. **Freq:** Bimonthly. **Trim Size:** B5. **Key Personnel:** Dr. Ladislav Hluchy, Editor-in-Chief; V. Sgurev, Editorial Board; E. Tyugu, Editorial Board; J. Fodor, Editorial Board; Ivan Plander, Founding Ed. **ISSN:** 1335-9150. **Subscription Rates:** US$140 individuals.

Remarks: Advertising not accepted. **URL:** http://www.cai.sk/. **Former name:** Computers and Artificial Intelligence. **Circ:** Paid 300

50319 ■ Endocrine Regulations
Academic Electronic Press
c/o Richard Kvetnansky, Editor-in-Chief
Institute of Experimental Endocrinology
Slovak Academy of Sciences
Vlarska 3
833 06 Bratislava, Slovakia
Publisher E-mail: koresp@aepress.sk
International journal on experimental and clinical endocrinology and diabetes. **Freq:** Quarterly. **Key Personnel:** Richard Kvetnansky, Editor-in-Chief; Julian Podoba, Honorary Ed.; Karel Pacak, Assoc. Ed. **ISSN:** 1210-0668. **URL:** http://www.aepress.sk/endo/erhome.htm.

50320 ■ Journal of Hydrology and Hydromechanics
Slovak Academy of Sciences
Institute of Hydrology
Racianska 75
831 02 Bratislava, Slovakia
Ph: 421 2 44259404
Fax: 421 2 44259404
Journal covering basic disciplines of water sciences. **Founded:** 1953. **Key Personnel:** Viliam Novak, Editor; Jiri Myska, Editor. **Remarks:** Accepts advertising. **URL:** http://ih.savba.sk/jhh/; http://www.sav.sk/index.php?lang=en&charset=ascii&doc=publish-journal&journal_no=14. **Circ:** (Not Reported)

50321 ■ Measurement Science Review
Slovak Academy of Sciences
Institute of Measurement Science
Dubravska cesta 9
841 04 Bratislava, Slovakia
Ph: 421 2 54774033
Fax: 421 2 54775943
Publication E-mail: measurement@savba.sk
Publisher E-mail: measurement@savba.sk
Journal covering the theory of measurement science. **Key Personnel:** Prof. Ivan Frollo, Editor-in-Chief. **ISSN:** 1335-8871. **URL:** http://www.measurement.sk/.

50322 ■ The Slovak Spectator
The Rock s.r.o.
Lazaretska 12
811 08 Bratislava, Slovakia
Ph: 421 2 59233300
Publication E-mail: spectator@spectator.sk
Publisher E-mail: spectator@spectator.sk
Newspaper featuring local news, culture and business in Slovakia. **Freq:** Weekly. **Key Personnel:** Jan Pallo, Publisher, jan.pallo@spectator.sk; Beata Balogova, Editor-in-Chief, beata.balogova@spectator.sk. **Remarks:** Accepts advertising. **URL:** http://www.spectator.sk/. **Ad Rates:** BW: EUR2,250. **Circ:** 8,500

50323 ■ SPEX
The Rock s.r.o.
Lazaretska 12

811 08 Bratislava, Slovakia
Ph: 421 2 59233300
Publisher E-mail: spectator@spectator.sk
Magazine featuring researched and well-written stories in the areas of culture, company, executive profiles, lifestyles, social events, issues of concern and major news events in the capital and every region in Slovakia. **Key Personnel:** Jan Pallo, Publisher, jan.pallo@spectator.sk; Tom Nicholson, Editor, tom.nicholson@spectator.sk; Beata Balogova, Editor-in-Chief, beata.balogova@spectator.sk. **Remarks:** Accepts advertising. **URL:** http://www.spectator.sk/info_pages/view/10. **Circ:** (Not Reported)

50324 ■ Fun Radio-FM - 94.3
Leskova 5
PO Box 525
815 25 Bratislava, Slovakia
Ph: 421 2 52494626
Fax: 421 2 57787110
Format: Ethnic; World Beat. **Operating Hours:** Continuous. **Ad Rates:** Advertising accepted; rates available upon request. **URL:** http://www.funradio.sk.

Kosice

50325 ■ Acta Montanistica Slovaca
Technical University of Kosice
Faculty of Mining, Ecology, Process Control and Geo-technologies
c/o Prof. Ing. Tibor Sasvari, PhD, Ed.-in-Ch.
Letna 9
04200 Kosice, Slovakia
Ph: 421 55 6022945
Fax: 421 55 6023128
Publication E-mail: actamont@tuke.sk
Journal covering articles on basic and applied research in various fields including as geology and geological survey, earth resources, underground engineering and geotechnics, mining mechanization, deep hole drilling, surveying and engineering geodesy, ecotechnology and mineralogy, automation and applied informatics in raw materials extraction, and utilization and processing. **Founded:** 1996. **Freq:** Quarterly. **Print Method:** Offset. **Trim Size:** 8 1/2 x 11. **Cols./Page:** 3. **Col. Width:** 2 1/3 inches. **Col. Depth:** 10 inches. **Key Personnel:** Prof. Ing. Tibor Sasvari, PhD, Editor-in-Chief; Andrew Harrison, Assoc. Ed.; Juraj Janocko, Assoc. Ed. **ISSN:** 1335-1788. **URL:** http://actamont.tuke.sk.

Skalica

50326 ■ Radio G3-FM - 89.2
Bajanova 17
909 01 Skalica, Slovakia
Ph: 421 34 6600971
Fax: 421 34 6600972
E-mail: radiog3@radiog3.sk
Format: Ethnic; World Beat. **URL:** http://www.radiog3.sk.

Trencin

50327 ■ Radio GO DeeJay-FM - 89.8 MHz
PO Box 31
911 01 Trencin, Slovakia
Ph: 421 905 607367
E-mail: studio@djgo.sk
Format: Ethnic; World Beat. **Operating Hours:**
Continuous. **Ad Rates:** Advertising accepted; rates
available upon request. **URL:** http://www.djgo.sk.

Zilina

50328 ■ Radio Frontinus-FM - 104.6 MHz
Dolne Rudiny 3
010 01 Zilina, Slovakia
Ph: 421 41 7633367
Fax: 421 41 7641111
Format: Ethnic; World Beat. **Operating Hours:**
Continuous. **URL:** http://www.frontinus.sk.

50329 ■ Radio Zet-FM - 94.5
Horny val 3
010 01 Zilina, Slovakia
Ph: 421 908 264462
E-mail: radio@radiozet.sk
Format: Contemporary Hit Radio (CHR). **Owner:** Radio
Zet, at above address. **Operating Hours:** Continuous.
Ad Rates: Advertising accepted; rates available upon
request. **URL:** http://www.radiozet.sk.

Bojnice

50330 ■ Radio Beta-FM - 93.9 MHz
Okrajova 12
SLO-97201 Bojnice, Slovenia
Ph: 386 421 465403033
Fax: 386 421 465403111
E-mail: studio@beta.sk
Format: Ethnic; World Beat. **Operating Hours:**
Continuous. **Ad Rates:** Advertising accepted; rates
available upon request. **URL:** http://www.beta.sk.

Hajdina

50331 ■ Biota
Drustvo za Proucevanje Ptic in Varstvo Narave
c/o Milan Vogrin, EDC
Zg. Hajdina 83c
SI-2288 Hajdina, Slovenia
Publisher E-mail: milan.vogrin@guest.arnes.si
Journal publishing papers from all fields of biology and
ecology in their widest sense. **Subtitle:** Journal for Biol-
ogy and Ecology. **Freq:** Semiannual. **Key Personnel:**
Milan Vogrin, Editor-in-Chief, milan.vogrin@guest.arnes.
si. **URL:** http://www.dppvn.eu/revija-biota/.

Koper

**50332 ■ International Journal of Sustainable
Economy**
Inderscience Enterprises Limited
c/o Dr. Egon Zizmond, Ed.-in-Ch.
University of Primorska
Faculty of Management
SI-6000 Koper, Slovenia
Journal covering the field of economic theory and
analysis towards the sustainable economy. **Freq:** 4/yr.
Key Personnel: Dr. Egon Zizmond, Editor-in-Chief,
egon.zizmond@fm-kp.si. **ISSN:** 1756-5804. **Subscrip-
tion Rates:** EUR494 individuals print or online; EUR672
individuals print and online. **URL:** http://www
inderscience.com/browse/index.php?journalID=301.

Ljubljana

50333 ■ Acta Agriculturae Slovenica
University of Ljubljana
Biotechnical Faculty
Jamnikarjeva 101
SI-1000 Ljubljana, Slovenia
Ph: 38 613 203000
Fax: 38 612 565782
Publisher E-mail: info@bf.uni-lj.si
Scientific journal covering agronomy and zootechny.
Freq: Quarterly. **Key Personnel:** Prof. Ivan Kreft, PhD,
Editor-in-Chief, ivan.kreft@guest.arnes.si; Franc Krama-
ric, Tech. Ed. **ISSN:** 1581-9175. **Subscription Rates:**
EUR25 individuals; EUR17 single issue. **URL:** http://aas.
bf.uni-lj.si/index-en.htm.

50334 ■ Acta Chimica Slovenica (ACSi)
Slovenian Chemical Society
c/o Aleksander Pavko, EDC
Faculty of Chemistry & Chemical Technology
University of Ljubljana
Askerceva 5

SI-10000 Ljubljana, Slovenia
Ph: 386 1 2419506
Fax: 386 1 2419530
Publisher E-mail: chem.soc@ki.si
Providing a forum for the publication of considerable
original work in the chemical and allied research topics.
Founded: 1998. **Freq:** Quarterly. **Key Personnel:**
Branko Stanovnik, Chm.; Aleksander Pavko, Editor-in-
Chief, acsi@fkkt.uni-lj.si; Marija Bester-Rogac, Assoc.
Ed. **ISSN:** 1318-0207. **Subscription Rates:** EUR110
individuals including postage. **URL:** http://acta.chem-
soc.si; http://www.chem-soc.si/.

50335 ■ Acta Entomologica Slovenica
The Slovenian Museum of Natural History
Presernova 20
p.p. 290
SI-1001 Ljubljana, Slovenia
Ph: 386 1 2410940
Fax: 386 1 2410953
Publisher E-mail: uprava@pms-lj.si
Journal covering scientific works, overview articles and
book reviews in the field of entomology. **Freq:**
Semiannual. **Print Method:** Offset. **Trim Size:** 11 x 17.
Cols./Page: 5. **Col. Depth:** 1 3/4 inches. **Key Person-
nel:** Dr. Martin Baehr, Editorial Board; Dr. Werner Holz-
inger, Editorial Board; Dr. Andrej Gogala, Editor,
agogala@pms-lj.si; Dr. Jan Carnelutti, Editorial Board;
Dr. Tomi Trilar, Editorial Board; Dr. Bozidar Drovenik,
Editorial Board. **Subscription Rates:** EUR21 individuals.
URL: http://www2.pms-lj.si/publications/acta.html.

50336 ■ Acta Geographica Slovenica
Anton Melik Geographical Institute
PO Box 306
SI-1001 Ljubljana, Slovenia
Publisher E-mail: gi@zrc-sazu.si
Journal focusing on Slovene geography. **Founded:**
1948. **Freq:** Semiannual. **Print Method:** Offset. **Trim
Size:** 8 1/2 x 10 7/8. **Cols./Page:** 3. **Col. Width:** 28
nonpareils. **Col. Depth:** 129 agate lines. **Key Person-
nel:** Blaz Komac, PhD, Editor; Matija Zorn, PhD, Manag-
ing Editor; Matej Gabrovec, PhD, International Editorial
Board; Ivan Gams, PhD, International Editorial Board;
Andrej Kranjc, PhD, International Editorial Board. **ISSN:**
1581-6613. **URL:** http://giam.zrc-sazu.si/index.php?q=
en/node/90.

50337 ■ Illiesia
The Slovenian Museum of Natural History
Presernova 20
p.p. 290
SI-1001 Ljubljana, Slovenia
Ph: 386 1 2410940
Fax: 386 1 2410953
Publisher E-mail: uprava@pms-lj.si
Journal publishing papers dealing with research on
plecoptera. **Subtitle:** International Journal of Stonefly
Research. **Key Personnel:** Bill P. Stark, Editor; Ignac
Sivec, Editor; B. Kondratieff, Advisory Board. **ISSN:**
1855-5810. **Subscription Rates:** Free. **URL:** http://mrc.
pms-lj.si/illiesia/index.html.

**50338 ■ International Journal of Microstructure
and Materials Properties**
Inderscience Publishers

Dr. Janez Grum, Ed.-in-Ch.
University of Ljubljana
Faculty of Mechanical Engineering
Askerceva 6
SLO-1000 Ljubljana, Slovenia
Publisher E-mail: editor@inderscience.com
Peer-reviewed journal publishing contributions on vari-
ous mechanical, electrical, magnetic and optical proper-
ties of metal, ceramic and polymeric materials in terms
of the crystal structure and microstructure. **Freq:** 6/yr.
Key Personnel: Dr. Janez Grum, Editor-in-Chief, janez.
grum@fs.uni-lj.si; Dr. Charlie R. Brooks, Editorial Board
Member; Dr. Helen V. Atkinson, Editorial Board Member.
ISSN: 1741-8410. **Subscription Rates:** EUR593 individuals print only (surface mail); EUR1,010 individuals
online only (2-3 users); EUR830 individuals print and online; EUR643 individuals print only (airmail). **URL:** http://
www.inderscience.com/browse/index.php?
journalCODE=ijmmp.

**50339 ■ Journal of International Relations and
Development**
Palgrave Macmillan
Centre of International Relations
Faculty of Social Sciences
SI-1001 Ljubljana, Slovenia
Publication E-mail: jird@fdv.uni-lj.si
Publisher E-mail: booksellers@palgrave.com
Peer-reviewed journal covering international relations
and international political economy. **Freq:** Quarterly.
Key Personnel: Stefano Guzzini, International Advisory
Board; Milan Brglez, International Advisory Board;
Patrick Thaddeus Jackson, Editor-in-Chief. **ISSN:** 1408-
6980. **Subscription Rates:** 306 institutions, other
countries print; US$582 institutions print; 61 other
countries print and online; US$113 individuals print and
online. **URL:** http://www.palgrave-journals.com/jird/
index.html.

50340 ■ Mladina Magazine
Mladina
Dunajska cesta 51
SI-1000 Ljubljana, Slovenia
Ph: 386 123 06500
Fax: 386 123 06510
Publication E-mail: desk@mladina.si
Publisher E-mail: desk@mladina.si
Local political and lifestyle magazine. **Founded:** 1943.
Freq: Weekly. **Key Personnel:** Grega Repovz, Editor,
grega.repovz@mladina.si; Jana Jausovec, Editorial
Asst., jana.jausovec@mladina.si. **Remarks:** Accepts
advertising. **URL:** http://www.mladina.si. **Circ:** Paid
80,000

50341 ■ Scopolia
The Slovenian Museum of Natural History
Presernova 20
p.p. 290
SI-1001 Ljubljana, Slovenia
Ph: 386 1 2410940
Fax: 386 1 2410953

Publisher E-mail: uprava@pms-lj.si
Journal focusing on Slovenian Museum of Natural
History. **Freq:** 2/yr. **Key Personnel:** Tone Wraber,
Contact; Lojze Marincek, Contact; Kazimir Tarman,
Contact; Nikola Tvrtkovic, Contact; Ignac Sivec, Contact;
Janez Gregori, Editor. **Subscription Rates:** 600 Din
individuals. **URL:** http://www2.pms-lj.si/publications/
scopolia.html.

Maribor
50342 ■ MARS-FM - 95.9 Mhz
Gosposvetska cesta 87/b SI
2000 Maribor, Slovenia
Ph: 386 2 2525495
E-mail: mars@radiomars.si
Format: News; Information. **URL:** http://www.radiomars.
si/program/info/rsnafrekvencimars.aspx.

50343 ■ Radio Student-FM - 89.3
Gosposvetska cesta 87/b SI
2000 Maribor, Slovenia
Ph: 386 2 2526650
Fax: 386 2 2525489
E-mail: mars@radiomars.si
Format: Information; Educational; News. **URL:** http://
www.radiomars.si/program/info/rsnafrekvencimars.aspx.

Gizo

50344 ■ **Radio Hapi Isles-AM - 1035**
PO Box 78
Gizo, Solomon Islands
Ph: 677 60160
Fax: 677 60160
Format: Educational; Full Service; Information. **Owner:** Solomon Islands Broadcasting Corporation, PO Box 654, Honiara, Solomon Islands, 677 20051, Fax: 677

23159. **Founded:** 1976. **Operating Hours:** 6 am-10 pm Sunday - Saturday. **Ad Rates:** Advertising accepted; rates available upon request. **URL:** http://www. sibconline.com.sb.

Honiara

50345 ■ **Radio Hapi Isles-AM - 1035**
PO Box 654
Honiara, Solomon Islands

Ph: 677 20051
Fax: 677 23159
E-mail: sibcnews@solomon.com.sb
Format: Educational; Full Service; Information. **Owner:** Solomon Islands Broadcasting Corporation, at above address. **Operating Hours:** 6 am-10 pm Sunday-Saturday. **Ad Rates:** Advertising accepted; rates available upon request. **URL:** http://www.sibconline.com.sb.

Arcadia

50346 ■ International Journal of Emotional Psychology and Sport Ethics
African Journals Online
PO Box 56541
Arcadia 0007, Republic of South Africa
Publisher E-mail: info@ajol.info
Peer-reviewed journal covering sports and human behaviour. **Freq:** Semiannual. **Key Personnel:** Ogbonnaya Urorgi, Editor-in-Chief, ugoh5000@yahoo.com.au; Dr. Jonathan Aizoba, Contact, jaizoba2002@yahoo.co. uk. **ISSN:** 1119-7048. **Subscription Rates:** N 5,000 individuals; US$150 other countries. **URL:** http://ajol. info/index.php/ijepse.

Auckland Park

50347 ■ Ergonomics SA
Ergonomics Society of South Africa
c/o Schu Schutte
CSIR Mining Technology
PO Box 91230
Auckland Park 2006, Republic of South Africa
Ph: 27 113 580202
Fax: 27 114 823267
Publisher E-mail: pschutte@csir.co.za
Journal of the Ergonomics Society of South Africa. **Freq:** Semiannual. **Key Personnel:** Prof. P.A. Scott, Editor-in-Chief. **ISSN:** 1010-2728. **URL:** http://www. ergonomicssa.com/journal.html.

50348 ■ Health SA Gesondheid
African Journals Online
University of Johannesburg
PO Box 524
Auckland Park 2006, Republic of South Africa
Ph: 27 11 5592254
Fax: 27 11 5592257
Publisher E-mail: info@ajol.info
Peer-reviewed journal containing information about interdisciplinary health research. **Freq:** Quarterly. **Key Personnel:** Charlene Downing, Contact; Liselle Viljoen, Managing Editor. **ISSN:** 1025-9848. **URL:** http://ajol.info/index.php/hsa.

50349 ■ Journal for Language Teaching
African Journals Online
Afrikaans Department
Rand Afrikaans University
PO Box 524
Auckland Park 2006, Republic of South Africa
Publisher E-mail: info@ajol.info
Peer-reviewed journal containing academic research articles about language education and language related matters. **Freq:** Semiannual. **Key Personnel:** Thys Human, Editor, thysh@uj.ac.za. **ISSN:** 0259-9570. **Subscription Rates:** R 100 individuals; R 240 institutions. **URL:** http://ajol.info/index.php/jlt. **Circ:** 350

50350 ■ Channel Africa-AM - 7230
PO Box 91313
Auckland Park 2006, Republic of South Africa
Format: News; Talk. **Owner:** Channel Africa, at above address. **Founded:** 1994. **Operating Hours:** 5am-11:15pm Daily. **Key Personnel:** Mr. David Moloto,

General Mgr., phone 27 11 7144541, fax 27 11 7142072, molotod@sabc.co.za; Mr. Lungi Daweti, Program Mgr., phone 27 11 7143963, fax 27 11 7142072, dawetimj@ sabc.co.za; Ms. Mamolefe Segakweng, Mktg. Mgr., phone 27 11 7143413, fax 27 11 7142072. **URL:** http:// www.channelafrica.org.

50351 ■ Classic-FM - 102.7 MHz
PO Box 782
Auckland Park 2006, Republic of South Africa
Ph: 27 11 4031027
Fax: 27 11 4035451
E-mail: info@classicfm.co.za
Format: Classical; News. **Founded:** Sept. 1, 1997. **Operating Hours:** Continuous. **Key Personnel:** Mike Ford, Contact; Julia Burger, Contact. **Wattage:** 35,000. **URL:** http://www.classicfm.co.za/.

Bedfordview

50352 ■ SA Journal of Sports Medicine
South African Sports Medicine Association
PO Box 2491
Bedfordview 2008, Republic of South Africa
Ph: 27 117 173372
Fax: 27 117 173379
Publisher E-mail: info@sasma.org.za
Journal covering sport medicine and science in South Africa. **Freq:** Quarterly. **Key Personnel:** Tariq Cassim, Editor; Gertrude Fani, Editor. **URL:** http://www.sajsm. org.za/index.php/sajsm.

Bellville

50353 ■ African Finance Journal
African Finance Association
Africa Centre for Investment Analysis (ACIA)
University of Stellenbosch Business School
PO Box 610
Bellville 7535, Republic of South Africa
Ph: 27 219 184469
Fax: 27 219 184262
Journal promoting knowledge about finance in the context of development in Africa, focusing on latest research works in the fields of Finance, Accounting and Economics and looking for a balanced approach between theoretical and empirical studies. **Freq:** Semiannual. **Key Personnel:** Nicholas Biekpe, Executive Ed.; Melvin Ayogu, Co-Ed.; Menzie D. Chinn, Co-Ed.; Lemma Senbet, Advisory Ed.; Campbell Harvey, Advisory Ed.; Lloyd P. Blenman, Co-Ed.; Kalu Ojah, Co-Ed. **ISSN:** 1605-9786. **Subscription Rates:** US$60 members Africa; US$160 members libraries & corporate (Africa); US$30 members students (Africa). **URL:** http:// www.africagrowth.com/afj.htm.

Bloemfontein

50354 ■ Acta Theologica
University of the Orange Free State
PO Box 339
Bloemfontein 9300, Republic of South Africa
Ph: 27 514 019111
Publisher E-mail: info.stg@ufs.ac.za
Journal covering religion and theology. **Founded:** 1912.

Freq: Bimonthly 6/yr (during the academic year). **Print Method:** Offset. **Trim Size:** 5 1/2 x 8. **Cols./Page:** 1. **Col. Width:** 57 nonpareils. **Col. Depth:** 105 agate lines. **Key Personnel:** Dr. L. Hoffman, Exec. Ed., hoffmanl. hum@ufs.ac.za. **ISSN:** 1015-8758. **URL:** http://www. uovs.ac.za/faculties/content.php?id=3980&FCode=09.

50355 ■ Navorsinge van die Nasionale Musium, Bloemfontein
National Museum, Bloemfontein
PO Box 266
Bloemfontein 9300, Republic of South Africa
Ph: 27 514 479609
Fax: 27 514 476273
Publisher E-mail: direk@nasmus.co.za
Journal covering research related to the disciplines of the National Museum Bloemfontein, including natural sciences, human sciences, anthropology, archaeology, history, and others. **Founded:** 1952. **Freq:** Annual. **ISSN:** 0067-9208. **Remarks:** Advertising not accepted. **URL:** http://www.nasmus.co.za/. **Circ:** (Not Reported)

50356 ■ O-FM - 94
PO Box 7117
Bloemfontein 9300, Republic of South Africa
Ph: 27 51 5050900
Fax: 27 51 5050905
E-mail: info@ofm.co.za
Format: Adult Contemporary; Top 40; News; Music of Your Life; Sports. **Operating Hours:** Continuous. **Key Personnel:** Tim Zunckel, Program Mgr., timz@ofm.co. za; Gary Stroebel, CEO, gary@ofm.co.za; Nick Efstathiou, Mktg. Mgr., nick@ofm.co.za. **URL:** http://www. ofm.co.za/.

Bloubergstrand

50357 ■ South African Journal of Wildlife Research
Southern African Wildlife Management Association
Natuurbestuurvereniging van Suidelike Afrika
PO Box 217
Bloubergstrand 7436, Republic of South Africa
Publisher E-mail: elma@mweb.co.za
Journal covering African wildlife research. **Freq:** Semiannual. **Key Personnel:** Dr. Michael Somers, Editor, phone 27 12 4202627, fax 27 12 4206096, michael. somers@up.ac.za. **Subscription Rates:** R 575 individuals; US$170 other countries. **URL:** http://www.sawma. co.za/.

Brandhof

50358 ■ Journal of Bone and Joint Surgery
South African Orthopaedic Association
PO Box 12918
Brandhof 9324, Republic of South Africa
Ph: 27 51 4303280
Fax: 27 51 4303284
Publisher E-mail: info@saoa.org.za
Journal covering orthopedics. **Freq:** Monthly. **Key Personnel:** James Scott, Editor. **ISSN:** 0301-620X. **Subscription Rates:** 182 individuals combined volume (24 issues & 5 supplements); 82 individuals British volume (with 3 supplements); 114 individuals American volume

---

Circulation: ★ = ABC; △ = BPA; ♦ = CAC; • = CCAB; ❑ = VAC; ⊕ = PO Statement; ‡ = Publisher's Report; Boldface figures = sworn; Light figures = estimated.

(with 2 supplements). **Remarks:** Accepts advertising. **URL:** http://www.jbjs.org.uk/. **Circ:** Paid ‡4,500

Bruma

50359 ■ South African Journal of Industrial Engineering
Southern African Institute for Industrial Engineering
PO Box 141
Bruma 2026, Republic of South Africa
Ph: 27 11 5596143
Fax: 27 11 269759
Publisher E-mail: admin@saiie.co.za
Journal covering industrial engineering. **Founded:** Jan. 1927. **Freq:** Semiannual. **Print Method:** Offset. **Trim Size:** 8 1/2 x 11. **Cols./Page:** 3. **Col. Width:** 2.25 picas. **Col. Depth:** 9.5 picas. **Key Personnel:** Prof. Susan Adendorff, Editor, susan@up.ac.za. **ISSN:** 1012-277X. **URL:** http://www.saiie.co.za/index.php?option=com_content&view=category&layout=blog&id=58&Itemid=55.

Cape Town

50360 ■ Achiever
Cape Media
28 Main Rd.
Rondebosch
Cape Town 7700, Republic of South Africa
Ph: 27 21 6817000
Fax: 27 21 6854445
Publisher E-mail: info@capemedia.co.za
Magazine providing skills development, training and industry information to South Africa's decision-makers and stake holders. **Freq:** 4/yr. **Key Personnel:** Nadia Gamieldien, Editor. **Remarks:** Accepts advertising. **URL:** http://www.capemedia.co.za/achiever; http://www.achieveronline.co.za/. **Circ:** 10,000

50361 ■ African Natural History
Iziko Museums of Cape Town
PO Box 61
Cape Town 8000, Republic of South Africa
Ph: 27 214 813800
Fax: 27 214 813993
Publisher E-mail: info@iziko.org.za
Journal covering the field of natural history, relevant to the eastern African region. **Founded:** 1925. **Freq:** Annual. **Print Method:** Offset. **Col. Width:** 2 1/16 inches. **Col. Depth:** 294 agate lines. **Key Personnel:** Herbert Klinger, Editor. **ISSN:** 1816-8396. **URL:** http://www.iziko.org.za/iziko/publications/african_nat_hist.html.

50362 ■ African Security Review
Institute for Security Studies
PO Box 3077
Cape Town 8001, Republic of South Africa
Ph: 27 214 617211
Fax: 27 214 617213
Publisher E-mail: capetown@issafrica.org
Journal covering security and related issues in sub-Saharan Africa. **Founded:** Sept. 29, 1915. **Freq:** Quarterly during the academic year. **Print Method:** Offset. **Cols./Page:** 6. **Col. Width:** 2 1/16 inches. **Col. Depth:** 21 inches. **ISSN:** 1024-6029. **URL:** http://www.iss.co.za/Publications/Asrindex.html.

50363 ■ BBQ Scorecard
Cape Media
28 Main Rd.
Rondebosch
Cape Town 7700, Republic of South Africa
Ph: 27 21 6817000
Fax: 27 21 6854445
Publication E-mail: bbqscorecard@capemedia.co.za
Publisher E-mail: info@capemedia.co.za
Magazine featuring business, including insight and understanding about the scorecard system. **Freq:** Quarterly. **Key Personnel:** Lonwabo Panca, Contact. **URL:** http://www.capemedia.co.za/bbq-scorecard. **Circ:** 10,000

50364 ■ The Big Issue
PO Box 5094
Cape Town 8000, Republic of South Africa
Ph: 27 214 616690
Fax: 27 214 616662
Publisher E-mail: info@bigissue.org.za
The Big Issue is about providing employment and developing 'employable' people. **Founded:** 1996. **Freq:** Monthly. **Print Method:** Web. **Trim Size:** 275 x 210.

Key Personnel: Donald J. Paul, Editor; Bronwen Dyke, Dep. Ed. **Remarks:** Accepts advertising. **URL:** http://www.bigissue.org.za. **Ad Rates:** BW: R 8,000. **Circ:** (Not Reported)

50365 ■ Black Business Quarterly
Cape Media
28 Main Rd.
Rondebosch
Cape Town 7700, Republic of South Africa
Ph: 27 21 6817000
Fax: 27 21 6854445
Publication E-mail: bbq@capemedia.co.za
Publisher E-mail: info@capemedia.co.za
Magazine featuring top black business leadership. **Freq:** Quarterly. **Key Personnel:** Sibulele Phumeza Siko, Editor. **Remarks:** Accepts advertising. **URL:** http://www.capemedia.co.za/bbq. **Circ:** 10,000

50366 ■ Bloemnews
Media24
Nasper Ctr.
Heerengracht 40
PO Box 2271
Cape Town 8000, Republic of South Africa
Ph: 27 21 4062489
Fax: 27 21 4063753
Publisher E-mail: dvos@naspers.com
Local community newspaper serving Bloemfontein, Heidedal and Mangaung. **Freq:** Weekly. **Key Personnel:** Ben Burger, Editor, phone 27 51 4047901, bburger@volksblad.com; Rouxnette McKeating, Sen. Sales Mgr., phone 27 51 4047637, rmckeating@volksblad.com. **Remarks:** Accepts advertising. **URL:** http://www.media24.com/en/newspapers/community-newspapers/central-newspapers/bloemnews.html. **Circ:** (Not Reported)

50367 ■ Blue Chip
Cape Media
28 Main Rd.
Rondebosch
Cape Town 7700, Republic of South Africa
Ph: 27 21 6817000
Fax: 27 21 6854445
Publication E-mail: bluechip@capemedia.co.za
Publisher E-mail: info@capemedia.co.za
Magazine for financial services industry, featuring key global and local developments, trends and issues. **Freq:** Bimonthly. **Key Personnel:** Mark Fortuin, Contact. **Remarks:** Accepts advertising. **URL:** http://www.capemedia.co.za/blue-chip; http://www.bluechipjournal.co.za/. **Circ:** 10,000

50368 ■ Caledon Kontreinuus
Media24
Nasper Ctr.
Heerengracht 40
PO Box 2271
Cape Town 8000, Republic of South Africa
Ph: 27 21 4062489
Fax: 27 21 4063753
Publisher E-mail: dvos@naspers.com
Local community newspaper serving Caledon, Genadendal, Greyton. **Freq:** Weekly. **Key Personnel:** De Waal Steyn, Editor, phone 27 28 3123717, dewaal.steyn@hermanustimes.co.za. **Remarks:** Accepts advertising. **URL:** http://www.media24.com/en/newspapers/community-newspapers/boland-newspapers/caledon-kontreinuus.html. **Circ:** (Not Reported)

50369 ■ Cape Business News
30 Study St.
PO Box 60567
Cape Town 7441, Republic of South Africa
Ph: 27 215 574061
Fax: 27 215 574707
Publication E-mail: info@businessnewsonline.co.za
Publisher E-mail: subs@cbn.co.za
Business newspaper. **Founded:** Aug. 1980. **Freq:** Monthly. **Print Method:** Web Offset. **Key Personnel:** Yvonne Van Der Westhuizen, Contact, phone 44 21 5565492, fax 44 21 5565492; Johan Moolman, Editor, phone 44 21 5574061, fax 44 21 5574707. **ISSN:** 1563-5600. **Subscription Rates:** R 216 individuals print. **Remarks:** Accepts advertising. **URL:** http://www.cbn.co.za/. **Circ:** Paid 6,713

50370 ■ Carletonville Herald
Media24
Nasper Ctr.
Heerengracht 40
PO Box 2271
Cape Town 8000, Republic of South Africa
Ph: 27 21 4062489
Fax: 27 21 4063753
Publisher E-mail: dvos@naspers.com
Local community newspaper serving Carletonville, Welverdiend, Glenharvie, Fochville, Deelkraal and Oberholzer. **Key Personnel:** Hennie Stander, Editor, phone 27 18 2930750, hstander@media24.com. **Remarks:** Accepts advertising. **URL:** http://www.media24.com/en/newspapers/community-newspapers/northern-newspapers/carltonville-herald.html; http://www.carletonvilleherald.com. **Circ:** 5,664

50371 ■ City Vision
Media24
Nasper Ctr.
Heerengracht 40
PO Box 2271
Cape Town 8000, Republic of South Africa
Ph: 27 21 4062489
Fax: 27 21 4063753
Publisher E-mail: dvos@naspers.com
Local community newspaper serving Alexandra, Kathorus, Soweto. **Freq:** Semiweekly. **Key Personnel:** Vukile Sonandzi, Editor, phone 27 21 9177474, vukile.sonandzi@cityvision.co.za; Damian Samuels, Sales Mgr., phone 27 21 9177467, dsamuels@cityvision.co.za. **Remarks:** Accepts advertising. **URL:** http://www.media24.com/en/newspapers/community-newspapers/wp-newspapers/city-vision.html. **Circ:** 80,787

50372 ■ Current Allergy & Clinical Immunology
Allergy Society of South Africa
PO Box 88
Observatory 7935
Cape Town 7935, Republic of South Africa
Ph: 27 21 4479019
Fax: 27 21 4480846
Publisher E-mail: allsa@gem.co.za
Journal devoted to clinical aspects of immunology with emphasis on allergy. **Freq:** Quarterly. **Key Personnel:** Prof. Paul C. Potter, Founding Ed.; Prof. Eugene G. Weinberg, Editor; Prof. Heather J. Zar, Editor; Anne Hahn, Production Ed., Advertising Mgr. **ISSN:** 1609-3607. **Remarks:** Accepts advertising. **URL:** http://www.allergysa.org/; http://www.allergysa.org/journals/journal2006mar.htm. **Circ:** (Not Reported)

50373 ■ Die Breederivier Gazette
Media24
Nasper Ctr.
Heerengracht 40
PO Box 2271
Cape Town 8000, Republic of South Africa
Ph: 27 21 4062489
Fax: 27 21 4063753
Publisher E-mail: dvos@naspers.com
Local community newspaper serving Breede River and Winelands. **Founded:** June 2002. **Freq:** Weekly (Fri.). **Key Personnel:** Ernie Roworth, Advertising Mgr., eroworth@worcesterstandard.com. **Remarks:** Accepts advertising. **URL:** http://www.media24.com/en/newspapers/community-newspapers/boland-newspapers/die-breederivier-gazette.html. **Circ:** 10,280

50374 ■ DistrictMail
Media24
Nasper Ctr.
Heerengracht 40
PO Box 2271
Cape Town 8000, Republic of South Africa
Ph: 27 21 4062489
Fax: 27 21 4063753
Publisher E-mail: dvos@naspers.com
Local community newspaper serving Greater Helderberg region. **Freq:** Weekly (Thurs.). **Key Personnel:** Barrie de Beer, Publisher, barrie.debeer@helderberg.com; Theresa Olivier, Editor, tolivier@helderberg.com. **Remarks:** Accepts advertising. **URL:** http://www.media24.com/en/newspapers/community-newspapers/boland-newspapers/districtmail.html. **Circ:** 30,000

50375 ■ Eikestadnuus
Media24
Nasper Ctr.

Heerengracht 40
PO Box 2271
Cape Town 8000, Republic of South Africa
Ph: 27 21 4062489
Fax: 27 21 4063753
Publisher E-mail: dvos@naspers.com
Regional community newspaper serving Stellenbosch, Franschhoek, Somerset West, Strand and Gordon's Bay. **Freq:** Weekly. **Key Personnel:** Elsab Retief, Editor, eretief@eikestadnuus.com. **Remarks:** Accepts advertising. **URL:** http://www.media24.com/en/newspapers/community-newspapers/boland-newspapers/eikestadnuus.html. **Circ:** 9,000

50376 ■ Energy Forecast
Cape Media
28 Main Rd.
Rondebosch
Cape Town 7700, Republic of South Africa
Ph: 27 21 6817000
Fax: 27 21 6854445
Publisher E-mail: info@capemedia.co.za
Magazine for decision makers on oil and gas, power, energy and renewable energy industries and sectors. **Key Personnel:** Les Bownes, Contact. **Remarks:** Accepts advertising. **URL:** http://www.capemedia.co.za/energy; http://www.energyforecastonline.co.za/. **Circ:** 10,000

50377 ■ Explore South Africa
Cape Media
28 Main Rd.
Rondebosch
Cape Town 7700, Republic of South Africa
Ph: 27 21 6817000
Fax: 27 21 6854445
Publisher E-mail: info@capemedia.co.za
Magazine covering tourism, business and trade. **Freq:** 4/yr. **Key Personnel:** Illana Strauss Dillon, Contact. **Remarks:** Accepts advertising. **URL:** http://www.capemedia.co.za/explore-south-africa. **Circ:** ★10,000

50378 ■ Fairlady
Media24
PO Box 1802
Cape Town 8000, Republic of South Africa
Publisher E-mail: dvos@naspers.com
Magazine for South African women. **Freq:** Monthly. **Trim Size:** 210 x 275 mm. **Key Personnel:** Liezl de Swardt, Publisher, phone 27 21 4465259, fax 27 11 3220700, liezl.deswardt@media24.com; Suzy Brokensha, Editor, phone 27 21 4465243, sbrokensha@fairlady.com. **Remarks:** Accepts advertising. **URL:** http://www.fairlady.com/; http://www.media24.com/index.php?option=com_flexicontent&view=items&cid=182&id=236&Itemid=383. **Ad Rates:** 4C: R 37,020. **Circ:** ★71,898

50379 ■ Gazette
Media24
Nasper Ctr.
Heerengracht 40
PO Box 2271
Cape Town 8000, Republic of South Africa
Ph: 27 21 4062489
Fax: 27 21 4063753
Publisher E-mail: dvos@naspers.com
Local community newspaper serving Stellenbosch area. **Key Personnel:** Elsabe Retief, Editor, eikestadnuus@naspers.com. **Remarks:** Accepts advertising. **URL:** www.media24.com/en/home/item/710-gazette.html. **Formerly:** Stellenbosch Gazette. **Circ:** 13,000

50380 ■ HelderMail
Media24
Nasper Ctr.
Heerengracht 40
PO Box 2271
Cape Town 8000, Republic of South Africa
Ph: 27 21 4062489
Fax: 27 21 4063753
Publisher E-mail: dvos@naspers.com
Local community newspaper serving Helderberg area. **Freq:** Weekly (Tues.). **Key Personnel:** Theresa Olivier, Editor, tolivier@helderberg.com; Shamiel Salie, Advertising Mgr., shamiel.salie@helderberg.com; Barrie de Beer, Publisher, barrie.debeer@helderberg.com. **Remarks:** Accepts advertising. **URL:** http://www.media24.com/en/newspapers/community-newspapers/boland-newspapers/heldermail.html. **Circ:** 30,000

50381 ■ Hermanus Times
Media24
Nasper Ctr.
Heerengracht 40
PO Box 2271
Cape Town 8000, Republic of South Africa
Ph: 27 21 4062489
Fax: 27 21 4063753
Publisher E-mail: dvos@naspers.com
Local community newspaper serving Overstrand region. **Freq:** Weekly. **Key Personnel:** De Waal Steyn, Editor, phone 27 28 3123717, fax 27 28 3124316, editor@hermanustimes.co.za. **Remarks:** Accepts advertising. **URL:** http://www.media24.com/en/newspapers/community-newspapers/boland-newspapers/hermanus-times.html. **Circ:** 7,921

50382 ■ Idees
Media24
PO Box 1802
Cape Town 8000, Republic of South Africa
Publisher E-mail: dvos@naspers.com
Magazine for South African women. **Freq:** Monthly. **Key Personnel:** Terena le Roux, Publisher, phone 27 21 4063300, fax 27 21 4062929, tleroux@media24.com; Terena le Roux, Editor, tleroux@media24.com. **Remarks:** Accepts advertising. **URL:** http://www.idees.co.za; http://www.media24.com/en/magazines/creative-living-magazines/idees.html. **Circ:** 85,642

50383 ■ Institute for Security Studies Monographs
Institute for Security Studies
PO Box 3077
Cape Town 8001, Republic of South Africa
Ph: 27 214 617211
Fax: 27 214 617213
Publisher E-mail: capetown@issafrica.org
Journal focusing on national security concerns, human rights, governance, personal and community security, justice, refugee movements and internal displacement, food security, and sustainable livelihoods. **Freq:** 15/yr. **Subscription Rates:** Rs 370 individuals. **URL:** http://www.iss.co.za/pgcontent.php?UID=60.

50384 ■ International Journal of Shoulder Surgery
Medknow Publications Pvt Ltd.
PO Box 15741
Panorama
Cape Town 7506, Republic of South Africa
Peer-reviewed journal covering the basic science, diagnostic and therapeutic aspects of disorders of the shoulder girdle. **Founded:** 1947. **Freq:** Quarterly. **Print Method:** Offset. **Trim Size:** 8 3/8 x 10 7/8. **Cols./Page:** 3. **Col. Width:** 28 nonpareils. **Col. Depth:** 137 agate lines. **Key Personnel:** Joe F. de Beer, Editor; Deepak N. Bhatia, Editor. **ISSN:** 0973-6042. **URL:** http://www.internationalshoulderjournal.org/.

50385 ■ Kroonnuus
Media24
Nasper Ctr.
Heerengracht 40
PO Box 2271
Cape Town 8000, Republic of South Africa
Ph: 27 21 4062489
Fax: 27 21 4063753
Publisher E-mail: dvos@naspers.com
Local community newspaper serving Kroonstad. **Freq:** Weekly (Tues.). **Key Personnel:** Tharine Geldenhuys, Editor, phone 27 56 2123171, tgeldenhuys@volksblad.com; Elrina de Beer, Sales Mgr., phone 27 51 3571304, edebeer@volksblad.com. **Remarks:** Accepts advertising. **URL:** http://www.media24.com/en/newspapers/community-newspapers/central-newspapers/kroonnuus.html. **Circ:** 8,332

50386 ■ Landbouweekblad
Media24
PO Box 1802
Cape Town 8000, Republic of South Africa
Publisher E-mail: dvos@naspers.com
Magazine featuring agricultural sector in South Africa. **Key Personnel:** Jean du Preez, Publisher, phone 27 21 4062309, fax 27 21 4062940, lbw@landbou.com. **Remarks:** Accepts advertising. **URL:** http://www.media24.com/en/magazines/specialist-magazines/landbouweekblad.html. **Circ:** 42,628

50387 ■ Leadership in HIV/AIDS
Cape Media
28 Main Rd.
Rondebosch
Cape Town 7700, Republic of South Africa
Ph: 27 21 6817000
Fax: 27 21 6854445
Publisher E-mail: info@capemedia.co.za
Magazine providing support and information about HIV/AIDS to industry. **Freq:** Bimonthly. **Key Personnel:** Karen Nimmo, Contact. **Remarks:** Accepts advertising. **URL:** http://www.capemedia.co.za/hiv; http://www.hivaidsonline.co.za/. **Circ:** 10,000

50388 ■ Leef met hart & siel
Media24
Nasper Ctr.
Heerengracht 40
PO Box 2271
Cape Town 8000, Republic of South Africa
Ph: 27 21 4062489
Fax: 27 21 4063753
Publisher E-mail: dvos@naspers.com
Magazine for women. **Freq:** Monthly. **Trim Size:** 210 x 275 mm. **Key Personnel:** Liezl de Swardt, Publisher, phone 27 21 4465259, liezl.deswardt@media24.com; Christine Ferreira, Editor, phone 27 11 2634974, cferreira@leef.co.za. **Remarks:** Accepts advertising. **URL:** http://www.media24.com/en/magazines/woman360/leef-met-hart-en-siel.html. **Ad Rates:** 4C: R 16,640. **Circ:** ★40,886

50389 ■ Maluti
Media24
Nasper Ctr.
Heerengracht 40
PO Box 2271
Cape Town 8000, Republic of South Africa
Ph: 27 21 4062489
Fax: 27 21 4063753
Publisher E-mail: dvos@naspers.com
Local community newspaper serving Bethlehem. **Freq:** Weekly (Wed.). **Key Personnel:** Lynda Greyling, Editor, phone 27 58 3035411, lgreyling@volksblad.com; Nicoline Harrington, Sales Mgr., nharrington@volksblad.com. **Remarks:** Accepts advertising. **URL:** http://www.media24.com/en/newspapers/community-newspapers/central-newspapers/maluti.html. **Circ:** 7,861

50390 ■ Max Power
Media24
PO Box 1802
Cape Town 8000, Republic of South Africa
Publisher E-mail: dvos@naspers.com
Lifestyle magazine featuring cars. **Key Personnel:** Ashfaaq Bux, Editor, phone 27 21 4461322, fax 27 83 7809997, abux@media24.com; John Relihan, Publisher, jrelihan@media24.com; Aziza Patandin, Office Mgr., phone 27 21 4461306, aziza.patandin@media24.com. **Remarks:** Accepts advertising. **URL:** http://www.media24.com/generic.aspx?i_BusinessUnitID=2&lang=Eng&i_CategoryID=83. **Circ:** (Not Reported)

50391 ■ Medical Technology
Society of Medical Laboratory Technologists of South Africa
Vereniging van Geneeskundige Laboratorium Tegnoloe van Suid-Afrika
PO Box 6014
Roggebaai
Cape Town 8012, Republic of South Africa
Ph: 27 21 4194857
Fax: 27 21 4212566
Publisher E-mail: info@smltsa.org.za
Publication covering medical technology, in Afrikaans and English. **Freq:** Semiannual. **Key Personnel:** Dr. A.J. Esterhuyse, Editor-in-Chief, esterhuysejs@cput.ac.za. **ISSN:** 1011-5528. **Subscription Rates:** Included in membership; US$57 individuals. **URL:** http://www.smltsa.org.za/journal/index.htm.

50392 ■ Meyerton Ster
Media24
Nasper Ctr.
Heerengracht 40
PO Box 2271
Cape Town 8000, Republic of South Africa
Ph: 27 21 4062489
Fax: 27 21 4063753

Circulation: ★ = ABC; △ = BPA; ◆ = CAC; • = CCAB; ❏ = VAC; ⊕ = PO Statement; ‡ = Publisher's Report; Boldface figures = sworn; Light figures = estimated.

Publisher E-mail: dvos@naspers.com

Local community newspaper serving Vaalpark, Kragbron, Clydesdale and Sasolburg. **Key Personnel:** Thys Foord, Mng. Dir., phone 27 16 9507066, tfoord@media24.com; Retha Fichat, Editor, phone 27 16 9507070, rfichat@media24.com. **Remarks:** Accepts advertising. **URL:** http://www.media24.com/en/newspapers/community-newspapers/meyerton-ster.html. **Circ:** 7,581

50393 ■ Move!
Media24
Nasper Ctr.
Heerengracht 40
PO Box 2271
Cape Town 8000, Republic of South Africa
Ph: 27 21 4062489
Fax: 27 21 4063753
Publisher E-mail: dvos@naspers.com

Magazine for black women. **Subtitle:** A Magazine for women. **Founded:** Feb. 2005. **Key Personnel:** Jonathan Harris, Publisher, phone 27 11 5055602, jonathan.harris@thought24.co.za; Makhosazana Zwane-Siguqa, Editor, phone 27 11 5055643, mzwane@movemag.co.za. **Remarks:** Accepts advertising. **URL:** http://www.media24.com/en/magazines/thought24/move.html. **Circ:** 41,336

50394 ■ Noord-Vrystaatse Gazette
Media24
Nasper Ctr.
Heerengracht 40
PO Box 2271
Cape Town 8000, Republic of South Africa
Ph: 27 21 4062489
Fax: 27 21 4063753
Publisher E-mail: dvos@naspers.com

Local community newspaper serving Parys, Koppies, Vredefort, Bothaville and Viljoenskroon. **Key Personnel:** Thys Foord, Mng. Dir., phone 27 16 9507066, tfoord@media24.com; Retha Fichat, Editor, phone 27 16 9507070, rfichat@media24.com; Am van Rooyen, Sales Mgr., phone 27 16 9507012, avanroo@media24.com. **Remarks:** Accepts advertising. **URL:** http://www.media24.com/generic.aspx?i_BusinessUnitID=2&lang=Eng&i_CategoryID=59. **Circ:** 7,451

50395 ■ Noordkaap
Media24
Nasper Ctr.
Heerengracht 40
PO Box 2271
Cape Town 8000, Republic of South Africa
Ph: 27 21 4062489
Fax: 27 21 4063753
Publisher E-mail: dvos@naspers.com

Local community newspaper serving Kimberley and surrounding areas. **Freq:** Weekly. **Key Personnel:** Ruan Bruwer, Editor, phone 27 53 8312331, ruan.bruwer@volksblad.com. **Remarks:** Accepts advertising. **URL:** http://www.media24.com/en/newspapers/community-newspapers/central-newspapers/noordkaap.html. **Circ:** 21,593

50396 ■ Northwest Gazette
Media24
Nasper Ctr.
Heerengracht 40
PO Box 2271
Cape Town 8000, Republic of South Africa
Ph: 27 21 4062489
Fax: 27 21 4063753
Publisher E-mail: dvos@naspers.com

Local community newspaper serving Potchefstroom, Carletonville, Ventersdorp en Fochville. **Key Personnel:** Thys Foord, Mng. Dir., phone 27 16 9507066, tfoord@media24.com; Hennie Stander, Editor, phone 27 18 2930750, hstander@media24.com. **Remarks:** Accepts advertising. **URL:** http://www.media24.com/en/newspapers/community-newspapers/northern-newspapers/noordwes-gazette.html. **Circ:** 29,786

50397 ■ Ons Stad
Media24
Nasper Ctr.
Heerengracht 40
PO Box 2271
Cape Town 8000, Republic of South Africa
Ph: 27 21 4062489
Fax: 27 21 4063753

Publisher E-mail: dvos@naspers.com

Local community newspaper serving Bloemfontein. **Freq:** Weekly. **Key Personnel:** Marietjie Gericke, Editor, phone 27 51 4047696, mgericke@volksblad.com; Jeannine van Zyl, Advertising Mgr., phone 27 51 4047856, jvanzyl2@volksblad.com. **Remarks:** Accepts advertising. **URL:** http://www.media24.com/en/newspapers/community-newspapers/central-newspapers/ons-stad.html. **Circ:** 36,681

50398 ■ Opportunity
Cape Media
28 Main Rd.
Rondebosch
Cape Town 7700, Republic of South Africa
Ph: 27 21 6817000
Fax: 27 21 6854445
Publication E-mail: opportunity@capemedia.co.za
Publisher E-mail: info@capemedia.co.za

Magazine featuring Africa's trade and investment opportunities. **Freq:** Bimonthly. **Key Personnel:** Venesia Fowler, Contact. **Remarks:** Accepts advertising. **URL:** http://www.capemedia.co.za/opportunity; http://www.opportunityonline.co.za/. **Circ:** 10,000

50399 ■ Overberg Venster
Media24
Nasper Ctr.
Heerengracht 40
PO Box 2271
Cape Town 8000, Republic of South Africa
Ph: 27 21 4062489
Fax: 27 21 4063753
Publisher E-mail: dvos@naspers.com

Local community newspaper serving Overberg region. **Freq:** Weekly. **Key Personnel:** De Waal Steyn, Manager, phone 27 28 312 3717, nuus@overbergvenster.co.za. **Remarks:** Accepts advertising. **URL:** http://www.media24.com/en/newspapers/community-newspapers/boland-newspapers/overberg-venster.html. **Circ:** 7,145

50400 ■ Paarl Post
Media24
Nasper Ctr.
Heerengracht 40
PO Box 2271
Cape Town 8000, Republic of South Africa
Ph: 27 21 4062489
Fax: 27 21 4063753
Publisher E-mail: dvos@naspers.com

Local community newspaper serving Paarl, Wellington, Franschhoek, Simondium and Klapmuts. **Freq:** Weekly (Thurs.). **Key Personnel:** Anne Kruger, Editor, phone 27 21 8703701, edit@paarlpost.co.za. **Remarks:** Accepts advertising. **URL:** http://www.paarlpost.co.za/; http://www.media24.com/en/newspapers/community-newspapers/boland-newspapers/paarl-post.html. **Circ:** 16,000

50401 ■ Port Elizabeth Express
Media24
Nasper Ctr.
Heerengracht 40
PO Box 2271
Cape Town 8000, Republic of South Africa
Ph: 27 21 4062489
Fax: 27 21 4063753
Publisher E-mail: dvos@naspers.com

Local community newspaper serving Port Elizabeth metropolitan area. **Freq:** Weekly. **Key Personnel:** Elizabeth Ferreira, Editor, phone 27 41 5036059, fax 27 41 5036138. **Remarks:** Accepts advertising. **URL:** http://www.media24.com/en/newspapers/community-newspapers/eastern-cape-newspapers/pe-express.html. **Circ:** 89,800

50402 ■ Potchefstroom Herald
Media24
Nasper Ctr.
Heerengracht 40
PO Box 2271
Cape Town 8000, Republic of South Africa
Ph: 27 21 4062489
Fax: 27 21 4063753
Publisher E-mail: dvos@naspers.com

Local community newspaper serving Potchefstroom and Ventersdorp. **Freq:** Weekly (Fri.). **Key Personnel:** Thys Foord, Mng. Dir., phone 27 16 9507066, tfoord@media24.com; Hennie Stander, Editor, phone 27 18 2930750, hstander@media24.com; Madelein Nel, Sales

Mgr., phone 27 18 2930750, mnel@media24.com. **Remarks:** Accepts advertising. **URL:** http://www.potchherald.co.za/; http://www.media24.com/en/newspapers/community-newspapers/northern-newspapers/potchefstroom-herald.html. **Circ:** 7,805

50403 ■ Psychologies South Africa
Media24
Nasper Ctr.
Heerengracht 40
PO Box 2271
Cape Town 8000, Republic of South Africa
Ph: 27 21 4062489
Fax: 27 21 4063753
Publisher E-mail: dvos@naspers.com

Magazine for women. **Freq:** Bimonthly. **Trim Size:** 210 x 275 mm. **Key Personnel:** Liezl de Swartdt, Publisher, phone 27 21 4465259, liezl.deswardt@media24.com; Tracy Melass, Editor, phone 27 21 4461411, tracy.melass@media24.com. **Remarks:** Accepts advertising. **URL:** http://www.media24.com/en/magazines/woman360/psychologies.html. **Ad Rates:** 4C: R 27,000. **Circ:** 42,000

50404 ■ QwaQwa News
Media24
Nasper Ctr.
Heerengracht 40
PO Box 2271
Cape Town 8000, Republic of South Africa
Ph: 27 21 4062489
Fax: 27 21 4063753
Publisher E-mail: dvos@naspers.com

Local community newspaper serving QwaQwa, Bethlehem, Kestell, Lyttelton, Phofung, Phuthadithaba, Roodepoort and Witsieshoek. **Freq:** Weekly (Thurs.). **Key Personnel:** Andy Galloway, Editor, phone 27 51 4047910, agallowa@volksblad.com; Alda Roux, Advertising Mgr., phone 27 51 4047831, alda@volksblad.com; Nicoline Harrington, Sales Mgr., phone 27 58 3035411, nharrington@volksblad.com. **Remarks:** Accepts advertising. **URL:** http://www.media24.com/en/newspapers/community-newspapers/central-newspapers/express-qwaqwa-and-eastern-free-state.htm. **Circ:** 4,069

50405 ■ Rapport
Media24
Nasper Ctr.
Heerengracht 40
PO Box 2271
Cape Town 8000, Republic of South Africa
Ph: 27 21 4062489
Fax: 27 21 4063753
Publisher E-mail: dvos@naspers.com

Political newspaper in South Africa and Namibia. **Freq:** Sunday. **Key Personnel:** Johann Maarman, Editor and Publisher, phone 27 21 4063228, jmaarman@rapport.co.za; Liza Albrecht, Editor, phone 27 11 7139002, liza.albrecht@rapport.co.za. **Remarks:** Accepts advertising. **URL:** http://www.news24.com/Rapport/Home/; http://www.media24.com/en/newspapers/rcp-media/rapport.html. **Circ:** (Not Reported)

50406 ■ Road Ahead
Cape Media
28 Main Rd.
Rondebosch
Cape Town 7700, Republic of South Africa
Ph: 27 21 6817000
Fax: 27 21 6854445
Publication E-mail: roadahead@capemedia.co.za
Publisher E-mail: info@capemedia.co.za

Magazine covering information for the road transport sector. **Freq:** Quarterly. **Key Personnel:** Greg Penfold, Contact, greg@capemedia.co.za. **Remarks:** Accepts advertising. **URL:** http://www.capemedia.co.za/road-ahead. **Circ:** 10,000

50407 ■ SA Crime Quarterly
Institute for Security Studies
PO Box 3077
Cape Town 8001, Republic of South Africa
Ph: 27 214 617211
Fax: 27 214 617213
Publisher E-mail: capetown@issafrica.org

Magazine providing concise analysis of developments in crime trends, and the state's response. **Freq:** Quarterly. **Key Personnel:** Chandre Gould, Contributing Ed., cgould@issafrica.org. **Subscription Rates:** R 115 individuals South Africa; US$25 individuals African countries; US$35 individuals international. **URL:** http://www.iss.co.za/pgcontent.php?UID=649.

50408 ■ SARIE My inspirasie
Media24
Nasper Ctr.
Heerengracht 40
PO Box 2271
Cape Town 8000, Republic of South Africa
Ph: 27 21 4062489
Fax: 27 21 4063753
Publisher E-mail: dvos@naspers.com
Magazine for women. **Freq:** Monthly. **Trim Size:** 210 x 275 mm. **Key Personnel:** Liezl de Swardt, Publisher, phone 27 21 4465259, fax 27 11 3220700, liezl.deswardt@media24.com; Michelle van Breda, Editor, phone 27 21 4465128, mvanbre@sarie.com. **Remarks:** Accepts advertising. **URL:** http://www.sarie.com/; http://www.media24.com/en/magazines/woman360/sarie.html.
Ad Rates: 4C: R 30,855. **Circ:** ★125,612

50409 ■ Sasolburg Ster
Media24
Nasper Ctr.
Heerengracht 40
PO Box 2271
Cape Town 8000, Republic of South Africa
Ph: 27 21 4062489
Fax: 27 21 4063753
Publisher E-mail: dvos@naspers.com
Local community newspaper serving Vaalpark, Kragbron, Clydesdale and Sasolburg. **Key Personnel:** Thys Foord, Mng. Dir., phone 27 16 9507066, tfoord@media24.com; Retha Fichat, Editor, phone 27 16 9507070, rfichat@media24.com; Am van Rooyen, Sales Mgr., phone 27 16 9507012, avanroo@media24.com. **Remarks:** Accepts advertising. **URL:** http://www.media24.com/en/newspapers/community-newspapers/northern-newspapers/sasolburg-ster.html. **Circ:** 11,565

50410 ■ Service
Cape Media
28 Main Rd.
Rondebosch
Cape Town 7700, Republic of South Africa
Ph: 27 21 6817000
Fax: 27 21 6854445
Publisher E-mail: info@capemedia.co.za
Magazine incorporating the buyer's guide for local government. **Freq:** Bimonthly. **Key Personnel:** Leueen Dollman, Contact. **Remarks:** Accepts advertising. **URL:** http://www.capemedia.co.za/service; http://www.servicepublication.co.za/. **Circ:** 10,000

50411 ■ Shipyear
Cape Media
28 Main Rd.
Rondebosch
Cape Town 7700, Republic of South Africa
Ph: 27 21 6817000
Fax: 27 21 6854445
Publisher E-mail: info@capemedia.co.za
Magazine for the shipping and marine industry. **Freq:** Annual. **Key Personnel:** Les Bownes, Contact. **Remarks:** Accepts advertising. **URL:** http://www.capemedia.co.za/ship-year; http://www.shipyearonline.co.za/. **Circ:** 10,000

50412 ■ South African Journal of Bioethics and Law
African Journals Online
University of Witwatersrand
Private Bag X1
Pinelands
Cape Town 7430, Republic of South Africa
Publisher E-mail: info@ajol.info
Peer-reviewed journal covering topics related to biomedical, law, and human rights issues. **Freq:** Semiannual. **Key Personnel:** Ames Dhai, Editor, amaboo.dhai@wits.ac.za; Gertrude Fani, Editor; Siobhan Tillemans, Editor; Robert Matzdorff, Editor; JP van Niekerk, Editor; Emma Buchanan, Editor, emmab@hmpg.co.za. **URL:** http://ajol.info/index.php/sajbl.

50413 ■ South African Journal of Child Health
African Journals Online
Private Bag X1
Pinelands
Cape Town 7430, Republic of South Africa

Ph: 27 21 6578200
Fax: 27 21 6834509
Publisher E-mail: info@ajol.info
Peer-reviewed journal covering the field of medical child health. **Freq:** Quarterly. **Key Personnel:** Nonhlanhla P. Khumalo, Editor, nkhumalo@shmpg.co.za; Elsa Lampropoulos, Contact, elamprop@hmpg.co.za. **URL:** http://ajol.info/index.php/sajchh.

50414 ■ Swartlander
Media24
Nasper Ctr.
Heerengracht 40
PO Box 2271
Cape Town 8000, Republic of South Africa
Ph: 27 21 4062489
Fax: 27 21 4063753
Publisher E-mail: dvos@naspers.com
Regional community newspaper serving Malmesbury, Moorreesburg, Piketberg, Porterville, Riebeeck-West and Riebeeck-Kasteel, Darling and Yzerfontein. **Freq:** Weekly. **Key Personnel:** Gerard Grobler, Publisher, phone 27 22 4823817, gerard.grobler@media24.com; Danie Le Roux, Sales Mgr., phone 27 83 7276568, dleroux@swartlander.co.za. **Remarks:** Accepts advertising. **URL:** http://www.media24.com/generic.aspx?i_BusinessUnitID=1&lang=Eng&i_CategoryID=33. **Circ:** 4,300

50415 ■ TOPbike
Media24
PO Box 1802
Cape Town 8000, Republic of South Africa
Publisher E-mail: dvos@naspers.com
Magazine for biking enthusiasts. **Key Personnel:** Jaco Kirsten, Editor, phone 27 21 4461330; Egbert de Waal, Publisher; Aziza Patandin, Office Mgr., phone 27 21 4461306, fax 27 73 1821151, aziza.patadin@media24.com. **Remarks:** Accepts advertising. **URL:** http://www.media24.com/generic.aspx?i_BusinessUnitID=1&lang=Eng&i_CategoryID=84. **Circ:** (Not Reported)

50416 ■ TopCar
Media24
Nasper Ctr.
Heerengracht 40
PO Box 2271
Cape Town 8000, Republic of South Africa
Ph: 27 21 4062489
Fax: 27 21 4063753
Publisher E-mail: dvos@naspers.com
Magazine for car and car culture enthusiasts. **Key Personnel:** Pierro Steyn, Editor, phone 27 21 4461032, fax 27 83 2800546, psteyn@media24.com; Charlene Beukus, Publisher. **Remarks:** Accepts advertising. **URL:** http://www.media24.com/index.php?option=com_flexicontent&view=items&cid=192&id=230&Itemid=377. **Circ:** 31,990

50417 ■ topMotor
Media24
PO Box 1802
Cape Town 8000, Republic of South Africa
Publisher E-mail: dvos@naspers.com
Motoring magazine for car and car culture enthusiasts. **Key Personnel:** Pierro Steyn, Editor, phone 27 21 4461032, fax 27 83 2800546, psteyn@media24.com; John Relihan, Publisher, jrelihan@media24.com; Aziza Patandin, Office Mgr., phone 27 21 4461306, aziza.patandin@media24.com. **Remarks:** Accepts advertising. **URL:** http://www.media24.com/generic.aspx?i_BusinessUnitID=2&lang=Eng&i_CategoryID=87. **Circ:** (Not Reported)

50418 ■ True Love
Media24
Nasper Ctr.
Heerengracht 40
PO Box 2271
Cape Town 8000, Republic of South Africa
Ph: 27 21 4062489
Fax: 27 21 4063753
Publisher E-mail: dvos@naspers.com
Magazine for young and modern black women ages 18-35. **Founded:** 1972. **Freq:** Monthly. **Trim Size:** 210 x 275 mm. **Key Personnel:** Jonathan Harris, Publisher, phone 27 11 5055602. **Remarks:** Accepts advertising. **URL:** http://www.media24.com/generic.aspx?i_BusinessUnitID=2&lang=Eng&i_CategoryID=99. **Ad**

Rates: 4C: R 40,350. **Circ:** ★99,889

50419 ■ Tuis
Media24
Nasper Ctr.
Heerengracht 40
PO Box 2271
Cape Town 8000, Republic of South Africa
Ph: 27 21 4062489
Fax: 27 21 4063753
Publisher E-mail: dvos@naspers.com
Magazine for home-owners. **Freq:** Monthly. **Key Personnel:** Charlene Beukes, Publisher, phone 27 21 4465061, fax 27 21 4461014, cbeukes@media24.com; Anneke Blaise, Editor, phone 27 21 4062101, fax 27 21 4062929, editor@homemag.co.za. **Remarks:** Accepts advertising. **URL:** http://www.media24.com/en/magazines/creative-living-magazines/tuis.html. **Circ:** 84,715

50420 ■ tvplus
Media24
Nasper Ctr.
Heerengracht 40
PO Box 2271
Cape Town 8000, Republic of South Africa
Ph: 27 21 4062489
Fax: 27 21 4063753
Publication E-mail: tvplus@media24.com
Publisher E-mail: dvos@naspers.com
Magazine for heavy television viewers. **Freq:** Monthly. **Key Personnel:** Willem Breytenbach, Publisher, phone 27 21 4461030; Natalie Cavernelis, Editor, phone 27 21 4461215. **Subscription Rates:** R 383.55; R 503.78 individuals in Namibia; R 841.78 individuals in Zimbabwe; R 745.78 other countries. **Remarks:** Accepts advertising. **URL:** http://www.media24.com/index.php?option=com_flexicontent&view=items&cid=229&id=213&Itemid=279. **Circ:** 150,254

50421 ■ TygerBurger
Media24
Nasper Ctr.
Heerengracht 40
PO Box 2271
Cape Town 8000, Republic of South Africa
Ph: 27 21 4062489
Fax: 27 21 4063753
Publisher E-mail: dvos@naspers.com
Local community newspaper serving suburbs of Cape Town. **Freq:** Weekly. **Key Personnel:** Marita Meyer, Editor, mmeyer@tygerburger.co.za. **Remarks:** Accepts advertising. **URL:** http://www.media24.com/en/newspapers/community-newspapers/wp-newspapers/tygerburger.html. **Circ:** Combined 126,461

50422 ■ Vaal Vision
Media24
Nasper Ctr.
Heerengracht 40
PO Box 2271
Cape Town 8000, Republic of South Africa
Ph: 27 21 4062489
Fax: 27 21 4063753
Publisher E-mail: dvos@naspers.com
Local community newspaper serving Bophelong, Sebokeng, Sharpeville, Zamdela, Rust-ter-Vaal, Roshnee, Springcol, Unitaspark, Steelpark and John Deo. **Key Personnel:** Thys Foord, Mng. Dir., phone 27 16 9507066, tfoord@media24.com; Nthabiseng More, phone 27 16 9507009, nthabiseng.nhlapo@media24.com. **Remarks:** Accepts advertising. **URL:** http://www.media24.com/en/newspapers/community-newspapers/northern-newspapers/vaal-vision.html. **Circ:** 64,946

50423 ■ Vaal Weekly
Media24
Nasper Ctr.
Heerengracht 40
PO Box 2271
Cape Town 8000, Republic of South Africa
Ph: 27 21 4062489
Fax: 27 21 4063753
Publisher E-mail: dvos@naspers.com
Local community newspaper serving Vanderbijlpark, Vereeniging, Meyerton, Sasolburg, Bophelong, Muvhango, Boipatong, Sharpeville, Sebokeng and Evaton. **Freq:** Weekly. **Key Personnel:** Thys Foord, Mng. Dir., phone 27 16 9507066, tfoord@media24.com; Nith-

Circulation: ★ = ABC; △ = BPA; ♦ = CAC; • = CCAB; ❏ = VAC; ⊕ = PO Statement; ‡ = Publisher's Report; Boldface figures = sworn; Light figures = estimated.

abiseng Nhlapo, Editor, phone 27 16 9507009. **Remarks:** Accepts advertising. **URL:** http://www.vaalweekblad.co.za/; http://www.media24.com/en/newspapers/community-newspapers/northern-newspapers/vaal-weekly.html. **Circ:** 8,702

50424 ■ Vanderbijlpark Ster
Media24
Nasper Ctr.
Heerengracht 40
PO Box 2271
Cape Town 8000, Republic of South Africa
Ph: 27 21 4062489
Fax: 27 21 4063753
Publisher E-mail: dvos@naspers.com
Local community newspaper serving Bedworthpark, Bonnan, Flora Gardens and Vanderbijlpark. **Key Personnel:** Thys Foord, Mng. Dir., phone 27 16 9507066, tfoord@media24.com; Retha Fichat, Editor, phone 27 16 9507070, rfichat@media24.com. **Remarks:** Accepts advertising. **URL:** http://www.media24.com/en/newspapers/community-newspapers/northern-newspapers/vanderbijlpark-ster.html. **Circ:** 25,020

50425 ■ Vereeniging Ster
Media24
Nasper Ctr.
Heerengracht 40
PO Box 2271
Cape Town 8000, Republic of South Africa
Ph: 27 21 4062489
Fax: 27 21 4063753
Publisher E-mail: dvos@naspers.com
Local community newspaper serving Dadaville, Roshnee, Rust ter Vaal, Springcol, Vereeniging, Viljoensdrift and Waldrift. **Key Personnel:** Thys Foord, Mng. Dir., phone 27 16 9507066, tfoord@media24.com; Retha Fichat, Editor, phone 27 16 9507070, rfichat@media24.com. **Remarks:** Accepts advertising. **URL:** http://www.media24.com/en/newspapers/community-newspapers/northern-newspapers/vereeniging-ster.html. **Circ:** 22,592

50426 ■ Volksblad
Media24
Nasper Ctr.
Heerengracht 40
PO Box 2271
Cape Town 8000, Republic of South Africa
Ph: 27 21 4062489
Fax: 27 21 4063753
Publisher E-mail: dvos@naspers.com
Community newspaper. **Founded:** 1904. **Freq:** Daily. **Key Personnel:** Ainsley Moos, Editor, phone 27 51 4047877; Jeannine van Zyl, Advertising Mgr., phone 27 51 4047855, jvanzyl2@volksblad.com. **Remarks:** Accepts advertising. **URL:** http://www.volksblad.com/Content/; http://www.media24.com/en/newspapers/dailies/volksblad.html. **Circ:** 28,062

50427 ■ Vrystaat
Media24
Nasper Ctr.
Heerengracht 40
PO Box 2271
Cape Town 8000, Republic of South Africa
Ph: 27 21 4062489
Fax: 27 21 4063753
Publisher E-mail: dvos@naspers.com
Local community newspaper serving Eastern Free State. **Freq:** Weekly (Thurs.). **Key Personnel:** Susan Mare, Editor, phone 27 58 3035411, smare@volksblad.com; Augnischa van Eck, Sales Mgr., phone 7 58 3571304, avaneck@volksblad.com. **Remarks:** Accepts advertising. **URL:** http://www.media24.com/generic.aspx?i_BusinessUnitID=2&lang=Eng&i_CategoryID=54. **Circ:** 4,673

50428 ■ Weskus News
Media24
Nasper Ctr.
Heerengracht 40
PO Box 2271
Cape Town 8000, Republic of South Africa
Ph: 27 21 4062489
Fax: 27 21 4063753
Publisher E-mail: dvos@naspers.com
Local community newspaper serving Atlantis, Mamre and Darling. **Key Personnel:** Jacques Dommisse, Publisher, phone 27 82 8880440, jacques.dommisse@

media24.com; Willie Martin, Editor, phone 27 83 6498991, weskusnuus@telkomsa.net. **Remarks:** Accepts advertising. **URL:** http://www.media24.com/generic.aspx?i_BusinessUnitID=2&lang=Eng&i_CategoryID=34. **Circ:** 15,000

50429 ■ Weslander
Media24
Nasper Ctr.
Heerengracht 40
PO Box 2271
Cape Town 8000, Republic of South Africa
Ph: 27 21 4062489
Fax: 27 21 4063753
Publisher E-mail: dvos@naspers.com
Regional community newspaper serving West Coast Peninsula. **Freq:** Weekly. **Key Personnel:** Jacques Dommisse, Publisher, phone 27 82 8880440, jacques.dommisse@media24.com; Alida Buckle, Editor, abuckle@weslander.co.za; Stefan Kolver, Advertising Mgr., phone 27 22 7131251. **Remarks:** Accepts advertising. **URL:** http://www.media24.com/en/newspapers/community-newspapers/boland-newspapers/weslander.html. **Circ:** 11,300

50430 ■ Cape Talk-AM - 567
Somerset Sq., Ste. 7d
Highfield Rd.
Cape Town, Republic of South Africa
Ph: 27 21 4464700
Fax: 27 21 4464800
Format: News; Sports; Talk. **Owner:** Cape Talk, at above address. **Key Personnel:** Colleen Louw, Station Mgr., ctnews@capetalk.co.za; Africa Melane, Programming Oper. Mgr., africa@capetalk.co.za; Shelley Doyle, Contact, shelley@capetalk.co.za. **Ad Rates:** Advertising accepted; rates available upon request. **URL:** http://www.capetalk.co.za.

50431 ■ Fine Music Radio-FM - 101.3
PO Box 1013
Cape Town 8000, Republic of South Africa
Ph: 27 214 011013
Fax: 27 214 011014
E-mail: fmr@fmr.co.za
Format: Classical; Jazz; News. **Operating Hours:** Continuous. **Key Personnel:** Victoria Cawood, Station Mgr. **Ad Rates:** Advertising accepted; rates available upon request. **URL:** http://www.fmr.co.za.

50432 ■ K-FM - 94.5
Private Bag X945
Cape Town 8000, Republic of South Africa
Ph: 27 21 4464700
Fax: 27 21 4464800
E-mail: 945webmaster@kfm.co.za
Format: Oldies; Adult Contemporary; Talk; News. **Key Personnel:** Colleen Louw, Station Mgr.; Juanita Bloemetje, Finance, juanita@kfm.co.za; Leila Ryloon, Advertising, leilar@primedia.co.za. **URL:** http://www.kfm.co.za/.

50433 ■ KFM-FM - 94.5
Somerset Sq., Ste. 7d
Highfield Rd.
PO Box X945
Cape Town 8000, Republic of South Africa
Ph: 27 21 4464700
Fax: 27 21 4464800
E-mail: 945webmaster@kfm.co.za
Format: Alternative/New Music/Progressive; Information; News. **Operating Hours:** Continuous. **Key Personnel:** Ian Bredenkamp, Program Mgr., ianb@primedia.co.za; Yumnah Hendricks, Contact, comments@kfm.co.za; Janine Willemans, Contact, janinew@primedia.co.za; Colleen Louw, Station Mgr.; Shelley Doyle, Contact, shelley@primedia.co.za; Karl Gostner, General Mgr. **Ad Rates:** Advertising accepted; rates available upon request. **URL:** http://www.kfm.co.za.

50434 ■ Lotus FM - Cape Town - 97.8 MHz
100 Old Fort Rd.
Private Bag 1337
Durban 4000, Republic of South Africa
Ph: 27 31 3625445
Fax: 27 31 3625202
E-mail: lotus@lotusfm.co.za
Format: Public Radio. **Operating Hours:** Continuous. **Key Personnel:** Kamsiliya Arumugam, Contact, phone 27 31 3625448, kamsiliya@lotusfm.co.za; Sagren Nai-

doo, Contact, phone 27 31 3625211, sagren@lotusfm.co.za. **URL:** http://www.lotusfm.co.za/portal/site/LotusFM/menuitem.a13733dc3e9a0bad5729 4f945401aeb9/.

50435 ■ Radio 786-FM - 100.4
c/o Murton & Klipfontein Rds.
2nd Fl., Rycom Center
Rylands Estate
Cape Town 7764, Republic of South Africa
Ph: 27 21 6991786
Fax: 27 21 6990786
E-mail: admin@radio786.co.za
Format: Ethnic; Information; News; Talk. **Operating Hours:** Continuous. **Ad Rates:** Advertising accepted; rates available upon request. **URL:** http://www.radio786.co.za.

Centurion

50436 ■ AFMA Matrix
Animal Feed Manufacturers Association
PO Box 8144
Centurion 0046, Republic of South Africa
Ph: 27 126 639097
Fax: 27 126 639612
Publisher E-mail: admin@afma.co.za
Publication covering farm feed (English and Afrikaans). **Founded:** Mar. 1998. **Freq:** Quarterly. **Print Method:** Lithograph. **Trim Size:** 210 x 297 mm. **Key Personnel:** De Wet Boshoff, Exec.Dir., admin@afma.co.za. **Remarks:** Advertising accepted; rates available upon request. **URL:** http://www.afma.co.za. **Circ:** 2,000

50437 ■ African Journal of Research in Mathematics, Science and Technology Education
SA ePublications
1021 Bank Ave.
PO Box 9785
Centurion 0046, Republic of South Africa
Ph: 27 126 439500
Fax: 27 126 633543
Publisher E-mail: info@sabinet.co.za
Journal devoted to theory and practice in science, mathematics and technology education. **Freq:** Semiannual. **Key Personnel:** Sarah Howie, Contact; Victor Polaki, Contact; Peter Hewson, Contact. **ISSN:** 1028-8457. **URL:** http://www.journals.co.za/ej/ejour_saarmste.html.

50438 ■ English in Africa
SA ePublications
1021 Bank Ave.
PO Box 9785
Centurion 0046, Republic of South Africa
Ph: 27 126 439500
Fax: 27 126 633543
Publisher E-mail: info@sabinet.co.za
Journal covering the study of African literature in English. **Founded:** 1974. **Freq:** Semiannual. **Key Personnel:** Craig MacKenzie, Editor; David Attwell, Editorial Board. **ISSN:** 0376-8902. **URL:** http://www.journals.co.za/ej/ejour_iseaeng.html.

50439 ■ IMFO
SA ePublications
1021 Bank Ave.
PO Box 9785
Centurion 0046, Republic of South Africa
Ph: 27 126 439500
Fax: 27 126 633543
Publisher E-mail: info@sabinet.co.za
Journal covering local government management, development, education and training, municipal services and the profession of the municipal finance officer. **Subtitle:** Official Journal of the Institute of Municipal Finance Officers. **Freq:** Quarterly. **Key Personnel:** Bossie Du Plessis, Editor; Burgert Gildenhuys, Editorial Committee; Jeff Makhetha, Editorial Committee. **ISSN:** 1607-520X. **URL:** http://www.journals.co.za/ej/ejour_imfo.html.

50440 ■ IMIESA
SA ePublications
1021 Bank Ave.
PO Box 9785
Centurion 0046, Republic of South Africa
Ph: 27 126 439500
Fax: 27 126 633543

Publisher E-mail: info@sabinet.co.za
Journal focusing on local government activities and public works, management structures, and municipal service delivery. Also covering municipal engineering, and impact of national and international developments on local projects. **Freq:** 11/yr. **Key Personnel:** Tony Stone, Managing Editor; Elizabeth Shorten, Publisher. **ISSN:** 0257-1978. **URL:** http://www.journals.co.za/ej/ejour_imiesa.html.

50441 ■ Journal for Christian Scholarship
SA ePublications
1021 Bank Ave.
PO Box 9785
Centurion 0046, Republic of South Africa
Ph: 27 126 439500
Fax: 27 126 633543
Publisher E-mail: info@sabinet.co.za
Online journal for Christian education. **Founded:** 1978. **Freq:** Quarterly. **Print Method:** Offset. **Trim Size:** 8 3/8 x 10 7/8. **Cols./Page:** 3. **Col. Width:** 27 nonpareils. **Col. Depth:** 137 agate lines. **Key Personnel:** Dr. Roy A. Clouser, Editorial Staff; Prof. D.F.M. Strauss, Editor; Prof. W.J. Richards, Editorial Staff; Prof. O.A. Henning, Editorial Staff. **ISSN:** 1013-1116. **URL:** http://www.journals.co.za/ej/ejour_tcwet.html.

50442 ■ Journal of Engineering, Design and Technology
SA ePublications
1021 Bank Ave.
PO Box 9785
Centurion 0046, Republic of South Africa
Ph: 27 126 439500
Fax: 27 126 633543
Publisher E-mail: info@sabinet.co.za
Peer-reviewed journal covering the engineering, design and technology sectors. **Founded:** 1938. **Freq:** Biennial. **Print Method:** off site. **Cols./Page:** 12 picas. **Col. Depth:** 21 1/2 inches. **Key Personnel:** Dr. Theo C. Haupt, Editor. **ISSN:** 1726-0531. **URL:** http://www.journals.co.za/ej/ejour_jedt.html.

50443 ■ Journal of Literary Studies
SA ePublications
1021 Bank Ave.
PO Box 9785
Centurion 0046, Republic of South Africa
Ph: 27 126 439500
Fax: 27 126 633543
Publisher E-mail: info@sabinet.co.za
Journal covering literary studies including literary theory, methodology, research, and related matters. **Founded:** 1955. **Freq:** Quarterly. **Trim Size:** 8 3/8 x 10 7/8. **Cols./Page:** 2. **Key Personnel:** Andre P. Brink, Assoc. Ed.; Stanley Ridge, Assoc. Ed.; Ina Grabe, Editor. **ISSN:** 0256-4718. **URL:** http://www.journals.co.za/ej/ejour_litstud.html.

50444 ■ Old Testament Essays
SA ePublications
1021 Bank Ave.
PO Box 9785
Centurion 0046, Republic of South Africa
Ph: 27 126 439500
Fax: 27 126 633543
Publisher E-mail: info@sabinet.co.za
Journal covering a collection of stories and essays from the old testament, detailing the lives of prophets and people who lived before the time of Jesus Christ. **Founded:** 1887. **Freq:** 3/yr. **Print Method:** Offset. **Cols./Page:** 6. **Col. Width:** 25 nonpareils. **Col. Depth:** 301 agate lines. **Key Personnel:** P.J. Botha, Editor; W.S. Boshoff, Assoc. Ed.; S.D. Snyman, Assoc. Ed. **ISSN:** 1010-9919. **URL:** http://www.journals.co.za/ej/ejour_oldtest.html.

50445 ■ Perspectives in Education
SA ePublications
1021 Bank Ave.
PO Box 9785
Centurion 0046, Republic of South Africa
Ph: 27 126 439500
Fax: 27 126 633543
Publisher E-mail: info@sabinet.co.za
Journal covering topics on contemporary educational issues. **Founded:** 1863. **Freq:** Quarterly. **Print Method:** Offset. **Trim Size:** 14 x 22 3/4. **Cols./Page:** 6. **Col. Width:** 25 nonpareils. **Col. Depth:** 301 agate lines. Key

Personnel: J.G. Maree, Editor-in-Chief; J.D. Jansen, Co-Ed.; B. Avalos, Editorial Board. **ISSN:** 0081-2463. **URL:** http://www.journals.co.za/ej/ejour_persed.html.

50446 ■ SA Irrigation
SA ePublications
1021 Bank Ave.
PO Box 9785
Centurion 0046, Republic of South Africa
Ph: 27 126 439500
Fax: 27 126 633543
Publisher E-mail: info@sabinet.co.za
Journal covering policies, legislation, and regulations pertaining to the use of water for agricultural purposes. Also features water conservation practices, engineering designs, techniques, and equipment. **Founded:** 1969. **Freq:** Bimonthly. **Print Method:** Offset. **Trim Size:** 5 1/2 x 8 1/2. **Cols./Page:** 1. **Col. Width:** 50 nonpareils. **Col. Depth:** 100 agate lines. **Key Personnel:** Raymond Campling, Managing Editor; Debbie Besseling, Editor; Elizabeth Shorten, Publisher. **ISSN:** 0257-5081. **URL:** http://www.journals.co.za/ej/ejour_sh_sairr.html.

50447 ■ SA Journal of Human Resource Management
SA ePublications
1021 Bank Ave.
PO Box 9785
Centurion 0046, Republic of South Africa
Ph: 27 126 439500
Fax: 27 126 633543
Publisher E-mail: info@sabinet.co.za
Journal covering industrial psychology and human resource management in South Africa. **Freq:** 3/yr. **ISSN:** 1683-7584. **URL:** http://www.journals.co.za/ej/ejour_sajhrm.html.

50448 ■ SA Journal of Industrial Psychology
SA ePublications
1021 Bank Ave.
PO Box 9785
Centurion 0046, Republic of South Africa
Ph: 27 126 439500
Fax: 27 126 633543
Publisher E-mail: info@sabinet.co.za
Journal covering industrial psychology. **Founded:** 1973. **Freq:** Quarterly. **Print Method:** Offset. **Trim Size:** 5 1/2 x 8 1/2. **Cols./Page:** 1. **Col. Width:** 50 nonpareils. **Col. Depth:** 100 agate lines. **Key Personnel:** N. Anderson, Editorial Board; G. Roodt, Managing Editor; K. Ortlepp, Book Review Ed. **ISSN:** 0258-5200. **URL:** http://journals.sabinet.co.za/ej/ejour_psyc.html.

50449 ■ Scriptura
SA ePublications
1021 Bank Ave.
PO Box 9785
Centurion 0046, Republic of South Africa
Ph: 27 126 439500
Fax: 27 126 633543
Publisher E-mail: info@sabinet.co.za
Journal publishing contributions in the field of theology. **Subtitle:** International Journal of Bible, Religion and Theology in Southern Africa. **Founded:** 1889. **Freq:** 3/yr. **Print Method:** Letterpress and offset. **Trim Size:** 6 1/4 x 9 1/4. **Cols./Page:** 1. **Key Personnel:** Ernst Conradie, Co-Ed.; J. Botha, Editorial Board; J.M. Amanze, Editorial Board; D.M. Balia, Editorial Board; Hendrick Bosman, Co-Ed.; Elna Mouton, Co-Ed. **ISSN:** 0254-1807. **URL:** http://www.journals.co.za/ej/ejour_script.html.

50450 ■ South African Computer Journal
SA ePublications
1021 Bank Ave.
PO Box 9785
Centurion 0046, Republic of South Africa
Ph: 27 126 439500
Fax: 27 126 633543
Publisher E-mail: info@sabinet.co.za
Journal covering computer science and information systems. **Founded:** 1964. **Freq:** 3/yr. **Trim Size:** 6 1/4 x 9 1/2. **Key Personnel:** Prof. Lucas Venter, Editor; Prof. Paula Kotze, Editor, jbishop@cs.up.ac.za; Prof. Richard J. Boland, Editorial Board, boland@spider.cwrv.edu. **ISSN:** 1015-7999. **Subscription Rates:** R 120 individuals; US$60 elsewhere. **URL:** http://www.journals.co.za/ej/ejour_comp.html; http://journals.sabinet.co.za/comp/.

50451 ■ South African Journal of Business Management
SA ePublications
1021 Bank Ave.
PO Box 9785
Centurion 0046, Republic of South Africa
Ph: 27 126 439500
Fax: 27 126 633543
Publisher E-mail: info@sabinet.co.za
Journal covering marketing and communication management, human resource management, business management, accounting and financial management, public management and administration, and tourism management. **Freq:** Quarterly. **Key Personnel:** S. Adendorff, Editorial Committee; F. Ahwireng-Obeng, Editorial Committee; C. Firer, Editorial Committee. **ISSN:** 0378-9098. **URL:** http://www.journals.co.za/ej/ejour_busman.html.

50452 ■ South African Journal of Cultural History
SA ePublications
1021 Bank Ave.
PO Box 9785
Centurion 0046, Republic of South Africa
Ph: 27 126 439500
Fax: 27 126 633543
Publisher E-mail: info@sabinet.co.za
Journal covering social dimensions of HIV/AIDS in African context. Including inputs from the disciplines of sociology, demography, epidemiology, social geography, economics, psychology, anthropology, philosophy, health communication, media, cultural studies, public health, education, nursing science and social work. **Founded:** 1968. **Freq:** Semiannual. **Print Method:** Offset. **Trim Size:** 5 1/2 x 8 1/2. **Cols./Page:** 1. **Col. Width:** 50 nonpareils. **Col. Depth:** 100 agate lines. **Key Personnel:** Estelle E. Pretorius, Editor. **ISSN:** 1018-0745. **URL:** http://www.journals.co.za/ej/ejour_culture.html.

50453 ■ South African Journal of Diabetes and Vascular Disease
SA ePublications
1021 Bank Ave.
PO Box 9785
Centurion 0046, Republic of South Africa
Ph: 27 126 439500
Fax: 27 126 633543
Publisher E-mail: info@sabinet.co.za
Journal covering the topics of diabetes and vascular disease. **Freq:** Semiannual. **Key Personnel:** Prof. W.F. Mollentze, Editor; Prof. F. Bonnici, National Editorial Board; Prof. A.J. Brink, Consulting Ed. **ISSN:** 1811-6515. **URL:** http://www.journals.co.za/ej/ejour_sajdvd.html.

50454 ■ South African Journal of Information Management
SA ePublications
1021 Bank Ave.
PO Box 9785
Centurion 0046, Republic of South Africa
Ph: 27 126 439500
Fax: 27 126 633543
Publisher E-mail: info@sabinet.co.za
Peer-reviewed journal covering information management including knowledge management, record management, strategic management, information economy, information systems management, data mining and warehousing, and relevant applications of information technology. **Founded:** 1969. **Freq:** Quarterly. **Print Method:** Offset. **Trim Size:** 5 1/2 x 8 1/2. **Cols./Page:** 1. **Col. Width:** 50 nonpareils. **Col. Depth:** 100 agate lines. **Key Personnel:** Ivan Altin, Editorial Board; Prof. Hans Boon, Editorial Board; Prof. Chun Wei Choo, Editorial Board. **ISSN:** 1560-683X. **URL:** http://www.journals.co.za/ej/ejour_info.html.

50455 ■ Southern African Journal of Critical Care
SA ePublications
1021 Bank Ave.
PO Box 9785
Centurion 0046, Republic of South Africa
Ph: 27 126 439500
Fax: 27 126 633543
Publisher E-mail: info@sabinet.co.za
Journal featuring clinical investigations in the multidisciplinary specialties of chest medicine, such as pulmonology, cardiology, thoracic surgery, transplantation, sleep

and breathing, airways disease, and more. **Freq:** Semiannual. **Key Personnel:** Prof. Daniel J. Ncayiyana, Editor; Andrew Argent, Assoc. Ed. **ISSN:** 1562-8264. **URL:** http://www.journals.co.za/ej/ejour_m_sajcc.html.

50456 ■ Tax Breaks Newsletter
SA ePublications
1021 Bank Ave.
PO Box 9785
Centurion 0046, Republic of South Africa
Ph: 27 126 439500
Fax: 27 126 633543
Publisher E-mail: info@sabinet.co.za
Journal covering tips on how to legally pay the least tax possible. **Founded:** 1974. **Freq:** Monthly. **Print Method:** Offset. **Trim Size:** 5 1/2 x 8 1/2. **Cols./Page:** 1. **Col. Width:** 50 nonpareils. **Col. Depth:** 100 agate lines. **Key Personnel:** Kathy Thersby, Editor. **ISSN:** 0093-8548. **URL:** http://www.journals.co.za/ej/ejour_montb.html.

50457 ■ Transactions of the Centre for Business Law
SA ePublications
1021 Bank Ave.
PO Box 9785
Centurion 0046, Republic of South Africa
Ph: 27 126 439500
Fax: 27 126 633543
Publisher E-mail: info@sabinet.co.za
Journal publishing contributions, originating from postgraduate research in the area of mercantile, commercial or business law. **Freq:** Semiannual. **Key Personnel:** T. Murray, Contact, murray.bib@mail.uovs.ac.za. **URL:** http://www.journals.co.za/ej/ejour_medsor.html.

50458 ■ Jacaranda-FM - 94.2
1 Samrand Ave.
Kosrnosdal
PO Box 11961
Centurion 0046, Republic of South Africa
Ph: 27 839109421
Fax: 27 866021757
E-mail: enquiries@jacarandafm.com
Format: Ethnic; World Beat; News. **Owner:** Jacaranda Broadcast Centre, at above address. **Ad Rates:** Advertising accepted; rates available upon request. **URL:** http://www.jacarandafm.com.

Claremont

50459 ■ Acta Juridica
JUTA Law
1st fl. Suncare Bldg.
21 Dreyer St.
Claremont 7708, Republic of South Africa
Ph: 27 21 6592300
Fax: 27 21 6592360
Publication E-mail: sue.wright@uct.ac.za
Law journal. **Founded:** 1958. **Freq:** Annual. **Print Method:** Offset. **Trim Size:** 10 x 14. **Cols./Page:** 5. **Col. Width:** 1 7/8 inches. **Col. Depth:** 14 inches. **Key Personnel:** I.F. Du Bois, Editor; J. Glazewski, Editor; A. Fagan, Editor; Prof. E.R. Kalula, Editor-in-Chief; S. Jagwanth, Editor; Tshepo H. Mongalo, Editor. **ISSN:** 0008-0950. **Subscription Rates:** R 535 individuals. **URL:** http://www.jutalaw.co.za/catalogue/itemdisplay.jsp?item_id=12080&nav_id=2009&tier_id=3723&qsHasChildren=true.

50460 ■ African Human Rights Law Journal
JUTA Law
1st fl. Suncare Bldg.
21 Dreyer St.
Claremont 7708, Republic of South Africa
Ph: 27 21 6592300
Fax: 27 21 6592360
Peer-reviewed Journal dealing with human rights related topics of relevance to Africa, Africans and scholars of Africa. **Founded:** 1961. **Freq:** Semiannual. **Print Method:** Offset. **Cols./Page:** 3. **Col. Width:** 27 nonpareils. **Col. Depth:** 130 agate lines. **Key Personnel:** Annelize Nienaber, Asst. Ed.; Frans Viljoen, Editor; Christof Heyns, Editor. **ISSN:** 1609-073X. **Subscription Rates:** R 645 individuals. **URL:** http://www.jutalaw.co.za/catalogue/itemdisplay.jsp?item_id=3591&nav_id=2009&tier_id=3723&qsHasChildren=true.

50461 ■ Jutas Business Law
JUTA Law

1st fl. Suncare Bldg.
21 Dreyer St.
Claremont 7708, Republic of South Africa
Ph: 27 21 6592300
Fax: 27 21 6592360
Peer-reviewed Journal covering aspects of law that affect the business world. **Founded:** 1905. **Freq:** Quarterly. **Print Method:** Offset. **Cols./Page:** 6. **Col. Width:** 12.25 picas. **Col. Depth:** 301 agate lines. **Key Personnel:** C. Visser, Editor. **ISSN:** 1021-7061. **Subscription Rates:** R 720 individuals. **URL:** http://www.jutalaw.co.za/catalogue/itemdisplay.jsp?item_id=3596&nav_id=2009&tier_id=3723&qsHasChildren=true.

50462 ■ SA Mercantile Law Journal
JUTA Law
1st fl. Suncare Bldg.
21 Dreyer St.
Claremont 7708, Republic of South Africa
Ph: 27 21 6592300
Fax: 27 21 6592360
Journal covering mercantile and business law. **Founded:** 1964. **Freq:** 3/yr. **Print Method:** Web offset. **Trim Size:** 11 3/8 x 14 7/8. **Cols./Page:** 5. **Col. Width:** 23 nonpareils. **Col. Depth:** 194 agate lines. **Key Personnel:** Prof. J.P. Niekerk, Editor; W. Jacobs, Editorial Asst.; Prof. A.D.M. Forte, Editorial Advisory Board. **ISSN:** 1015-0099. **URL:** http://www.journals.co.za/ej/ejour_ju_samlj.html.

50463 ■ South African Journal of Criminal Justice
JUTA Law
1st fl. Suncare Bldg.
21 Dreyer St.
Claremont 7708, Republic of South Africa
Ph: 27 21 6592300
Fax: 27 21 6592360
Legal journal covering criminal law, criminal procedure, evidence, international criminal law and criminology with a particular emphasis on Southern Africa. **Founded:** Mar. 1958. **Freq:** 3/yr. **Print Method:** Web offset. **Trim Size:** 8 1/2 x 11. **Cols./Page:** 3. **Col. Width:** 2 1/4 inches. **Col. Depth:** 10 inches. **Key Personnel:** K Phelps, Editor; J.M. Burchell, Editor-in-Chief; P.J. Schwikkard, Editor. **ISSN:** 1011-8627. **Subscription Rates:** R 645 individuals. **URL:** http://www.jutalaw.co.za/catalogue/itemdisplay.jsp?item_id=3599&nav_id=2009&tier_id=3723&qsHasChildren=true.

50464 ■ South African Journal on Human Rights
JUTA Law
1st fl. Suncare Bldg.
21 Dreyer St.
Claremont 7708, Republic of South Africa
Ph: 27 21 6592300
Fax: 27 21 6592360
Professional journal covering public law in South Africa. **Founded:** 1985. **Freq:** Quarterly. **Key Personnel:** Wesahl Agherdien, Editor; Glenda Fick, Editor; Catherine Albertyn, Editor. **ISSN:** 0258-7203. **Subscription Rates:** R 700 individuals postage and packaging charges. **Remarks:** Advertising not accepted. **URL:** http://www.jutalaw.co.za/catalogue/itemdisplay.jsp?item_id=3600. **Circ:** (Not Reported)

50465 ■ Stellenbosch Law Review
JUTA Law
1st fl. Suncare Bldg.
21 Dreyer St.
Claremont 7708, Republic of South Africa
Ph: 27 21 6592300
Fax: 27 21 6592360
Journal covering topical legal issues in various fields. **Founded:** 1972. **Freq:** Triennial. **Print Method:** Offset. **Trim Size:** 8 1/2 x 11. **Cols./Page:** 3. **Col. Width:** 27 nonpareils. **Col. Depth:** 140 agate lines. **Key Personnel:** Prof. JE Du Plessis, Editor; Prof. AJ van der Walt, Editorial Committee; R. Stevens, Editorial Committee. **ISSN:** 1016-4359. **Subscription Rates:** R 630 institutions. **URL:** http://www.jutalaw.co.za/catalogue/itemdisplay.jsp?item_id=3603&nav_id=2009&tier_id=3723&qsHasChildren=true.

Cresta

50466 ■ The Southern African Treasurer
Association of Corporate Treasurers of Southern Africa
PO Box 5853
Cresta 2118, Republic of South Africa

Ph: 27 114 821512
Fax: 27 114 821996
Publisher E-mail: agalatis@actsa.org.za
Journal containing articles about the treasury industry. **Freq:** Quarterly. **URL:** http://www.actsa.org.za.

Durban

50467 ■ blunt
Atoll Media
Umgeni Business Pk.
47 Intersite Ave., 1st Fl.
Durban 4098, Republic of South Africa
Ph: 27 31 2632772
Fax: 27 31 2632771
Magazine for youth who likes board riding, music, and art. **Freq:** 10/yr. **Key Personnel:** Yusuf Laher, Editor, yusuf@bluntmag.co.za; Olaf Oleesan, Asst. Ed., olaf@bluntmag.co.za. **Subscription Rates:** R 550 other countries. **Remarks:** Accepts advertising. **URL:** http://www.bluntmag.co.za/. **Circ:** ★13,207

50468 ■ Saltwater GIRL
Atoll Media
Umgeni Business Pk.
47 Intersite Ave., 1st Fl.
Durban 4098, Republic of South Africa
Ph: 27 31 2632772
Fax: 27 31 2632771
Magazine for free-thinking teenage girls. **Freq:** 10/yr. **Key Personnel:** Mea Neethling, Editor, mea@swg.co.za. **Subscription Rates:** R 175 individuals; R 350 two years. **Remarks:** Accepts advertising. **URL:** http://www.swg.co.za/site/default.asp. **Circ:** ★32,360

50469 ■ Saltwater GIRL SURF
Atoll Media
Umgeni Business Pk.
47 Intersite Ave., 1st Fl.
Durban 4098, Republic of South Africa
Ph: 27 31 2632772
Fax: 27 31 2632771
Magazine for female surfers in South Africa. **Freq:** 4/yr. **Key Personnel:** Mea Neethling, Editor, mea@swg.co.za; John McCarthy, Publisher, john@atollmedia.co.za; Lari Brown, Managing Editor, lari@swg.co.za. **Subscription Rates:** R 66 individuals. **Remarks:** Accepts advertising. **URL:** http://www.swgsurf.co.za/. **Circ:** (Not Reported)

50470 ■ South African Health Review
Health Systems Trust
34 Essex Ter., Westville, 3630
PO Box 808
Durban 4000, Republic of South Africa
Ph: 27 31 2669090
Fax: 27 31 2669199
Journal focusing on comparative exploration of the nation's health. **Founded:** 2006. **Freq:** Annual. **Print Method:** Offset. Uses mats. **Cols./Page:** 5. **Col. Width:** 2 1/16 inches. **Col. Depth:** 13 1/8 inches. **URL:** http://www.hst.org.za/generic/29.

50471 ■ World Airnews
PO Box 35082
Northway
Durban 4065, Republic of South Africa
Ph: 27 31 5641319
Fax: 27 31 5637115
Publisher E-mail: info@airnews.co.za
Aviation journal covering aviation development news and features in Africa. **Subtitle:** Africa's Journal for the Discerning Aviation Professional. **Founded:** Mar. 1973. **Freq:** Monthly. **Print Method:** Litho. **Trim Size:** 210 x 280 mm. **Cols./Page:** 3. **Col. Width:** 60 millimeters. **Col. Depth:** 185 millimeters. **Key Personnel:** Tom Chalmers, Managing Editor; Joan Chalmers, Asst. Editor; Tracy Sugdon, Production Mgr. **ISSN:** 0261-2399. **Subscription Rates:** R 200 individuals; R 20 single issue. **Remarks:** Accepts advertising. **URL:** http://www.airnews.co.za/home/. **Ad Rates:** BW: US$2,100; 4C: US$3,480. **Circ:** Paid 9,250, Non-paid 4,200

50472 ■ Zigzag
Atoll Media
Umgeni Business Pk.
47 Intersite Ave., 1st Fl.
Durban 4098, Republic of South Africa
Ph: 27 31 2632772

Fax: 27 31 2632771
Journal covering surf and beach culture in South Africa.
Freq: 10/yr. **Key Personnel:** Will Bendix, Editor, will@
zigzag.co.za; Karen O'Moore, Publisher, komoore@
touchline.co.za. **Subscription Rates:** R 200 individuals;
R 400 two years; R 565 other countries. **Remarks:** Accepts advertising. **URL:** http://www.zigzag.co.za/. **Circ:**
★15,252

50473 ■ Lotus-FM - 106.8
100 Old Fort Rd.
Durban 4000, Republic of South Africa
Ph: 27 31 3625445
Fax: 27 31 3625202
E-mail: lotus@lotusfm.co.za
Format: Contemporary Hit Radio (CHR); News. **Operating Hours:** ACTS. **Ad Rates:** Advertising accepted;
rates available upon request. **URL:** http://www.lotusfm.
co.za.

50474 ■ Lotus-FM - 87.7
100 Old Fort Rd.
PO Box 1337
Durban 4000, Republic of South Africa
Ph: 27 31 3625445
Fax: 27 31 3625202
E-mail: lotus@lotusfm.co.za
Format: Contemporary Hit Radio (CHR); News. **Operating Hours:** Continuous. **Ad Rates:** Advertising accepted; rates available upon request. **URL:** http://www.
lotusfm.co.za.

Lotus FM - Cape Town - See Cape Town

Lotus FM - Durban North - See Durban North

Lotus FM - Glencoe - See Glencoe

Lotus FM - Ladysmith - See Ladysmith

Lotus FM - Pietermaritzburg - See Pietermaritzburg

Lotus FM - Port Elizabeth - See Port Elizabeth

Lotus FM - Port Shepstone - See Port Shepstone

50475 ■ Ukhozi-FM - 90.8
100 Old Fort Rd.
PO Box 1588
Durban 4000, Republic of South Africa
Ph: 27 31 3625403
Format: Full Service. **Key Personnel:** Mr. Welcome
Nzimande, Station Mgr., phone 27 31 3625402, fax 27
31 3625203, nzimande@sabc.co.za; Bheki Msane,
Program Mgr., fax 27 31 3625203; Lindelani Ngema,
Promotions Mgr., phone 27 31 3625325, ngemalv@
sabc.co.za. **URL:** http://www.ukhozifm.co.za/portal/site/
UkhoziFM.

Durban North

50476 ■ Lotus FM - Durban North - 89.4 MHz
100 Old Fort Rd.
Private Bag 1337
Durban 4000, Republic of South Africa
Ph: 27 31 3625445
Fax: 27 31 3625202
E-mail: lotuc@lotusfm.co.za
Format: Public Radio. **Operating Hours:** Continuous.
Key Personnel: Kamsiliya Arumugam, Contact, phone
27 31 3625448, kamsiliya@lotusfm.co.za; Sagren Naidoo, Contact, phone 27 31 3625211, sagren@lotusfm.
co.za. **URL:** http://www.lotusfm.co.za/portal/site/
LotusFM/menuitem.a13733dc3e9a0bad5729 4
f945401aeb9/.

Elsenburg

50477 ■ Agriprobe
Western Cape Department of Agriculture
PO Box X1
Elsenburg 7607, Republic of South Africa
Ph: 27 218 085111
Fax: 27 218 085120
Journal covering the western cape department of
agriculture. **Founded:** 1888. **Freq:** Quarterly. **Print
Method:** Offset. **Cols./Page:** 5. **Col. Width:** 24
nonpareils. **Col. Depth:** 224 agate lines. **Key Personnel:** Liesl Muller, Editor; Ilse Trautmann, Editor; Charlene Nieuwoudt, Editor. **ISSN:** 1810-9799. **URL:** http://
www.capegateway.gov.za/; http://www.elsenburg.com/
agriprobe.html.

Erasmusrand

50478 ■ South African Journal of Plant and Soil
Soil Science Society of South Africa
Grondkundevereniging van Suid-Afrika
PO Box 65217
Erasmusrand 0165, Republic of South Africa
South African journal covering plants and soil, in English
and Afrikaans. **Freq:** Quarterly. **Key Personnel:** V.L.
Tolmay, Sci. Ed., tolmayv@arc.agric.za; Dr. Ian Raper,
Managing Editor; Edda Hubrig, Publishing Ed.; Engela
Van Dyk, Publishing Ed.; R. Barnard, Editorial Committee; D. Marais, Editorial Committee. **ISSN:** 0257-1862.
Subscription Rates: R 450 individuals; R 520 institutions; US$250 other countries incl. postage. **URL:** http://
www.soils.org.za; http://www.plantandsoil.co.za/.

Garden View

50479 ■ Engineering News
Creamer Media (Pty) Ltd.
PO Box 75316
Garden View 2047, Republic of South Africa
Ph: 27 116 223744
Fax: 27 116 229350
Publisher E-mail: newsdesk@engineeringnews.co.za
Trade magazine covering engineering. **Founded:** 1981.
Freq: Weekly. **Print Method:** Web Offset. **Trim Size:**
275 x 210 mm. **Key Personnel:** Erna Oasthuizen,
Sales, Mktg. and Online Mgr.; Martin Zhuwakinyu, Asst.
Ed. News; Reinette Classen, Subscription Mgr.; Terence
Creamer, Dep. Ed.; Liezel Hill, Dep. Ed. **ISSN:** 0257-
8646. **Subscription Rates:** R 423 individuals; R 1,500
individuals sub-Saharan Countries, airmail; R 2,000
individuals row, airmail. **Remarks:** Accepts advertising.
URL: http://www.engineeringnews.co.za/; http://www.
researchchannel.co.za; http://www.creamermedia.co.za.
Formerly: Martin Creamer Engineering News. **Ad
Rates:** 4C: R 13,500. **Circ:** Combined ★15,003

50480 ■ Mining Weekly
Creamer Media (Pty) Ltd.
PO Box 75316
Garden View 2047, Republic of South Africa
Ph: 27 116 223744
Fax: 27 116 229350
Publisher E-mail: newsdesk@engineeringnews.co.za
Trade magazine covering mining in Africa. **Founded:**
1995. **Freq:** Weekly. **Print Method:** Web Offset. **Trim
Size:** 210 x 275 mm. **Key Personnel:** Erna Oasthuizen,
Sales Mktg. & Online Mgr.; Terence Creamer, Engineering News Ed.; Martin Creamer, Editor. **ISSN:** 1562-9619.
Subscription Rates: R 282 individuals; R 1,500
individuals airmail Sub-Saharan; R 2,000 other countries; US$209 individuals airmail Sub-Saharan; US$278
other countries. **Remarks:** Accepts advertising. **URL:**
http://www.miningweekly.co.za/; http://www.
researchchannel.co.za; http://www.creamermedia.co.za;
http://www.polity.org.za. **Formerly:** Martin Creamer's
Mining Weekly. **Ad Rates:** 4C: R 12,100. **Circ:** Combined ★14,850

Gauteng

50481 ■ Food Review
South African Association for Food Science and
Technology
PO Box 35233
Menlo Pk.
Gauteng 0102, Republic of South Africa
Ph: 27 12 3492788
Fax: 27 86 6984784
Publisher E-mail: saafost.irene@telkomsa.net
Publication covering food. **Founded:** 1966. **Freq:**
Monthly. **Subscription Rates:** Included in membership.
Remarks: Advertising accepted; rates available upon
request. **URL:** http://www.saafost.org.za/. **Circ:** 5,000

50482 ■ Professional Nursing Today
Medpharm Publications
The Centurion Wine & Art Ctr.
123 Amcor Rd., Ground Level
Gauteng 0157, Republic of South Africa
Ph: 64 126 647460
Fax: 64 126 646276
Journal covering primary health care, women's, men's
health, infection control, and wound care. **Founded:**
July 1920. **Freq:** Bimonthly. **Print Method:** Offset. **Trim**

Size: 8 1/4 x 11. **Cols./Page:** 3. **Col. Width:** 13.5 picas.
Col. Depth: 140 agate lines. **Key Personnel:** Dr. Vicky
Pinkney-Atkinson, Editor, vicki@phango.org.za. **ISSN:**
1607-6672. **Subscription Rates:** Rs 250 individuals.
URL: http://www.medpharm.co.za/?q=node/13; http://
www.pntonline.co.za/index.php/PNT.

50483 ■ SA Pharmaceutical Journal
Medpharm Publications
The Centurion Wine & Art Ctr.
123 Amcor Rd., Ground Level
Gauteng 0157, Republic of South Africa
Ph: 64 126 647460
Fax: 64 126 646276
Peer-reviewed journal covering various aspects of
pharmacy. **Founded:** 1873. **Freq:** Monthly 10/yr. **Print
Method:** Offset. **Cols./Page:** 6. **Col. Width:** 25
nonpareils. **Col. Depth:** 287 agate lines. **Key Personnel:** Lorraine Osman, Exec. Ed., lorraine@pharmail.co.
za; Dr. Douw Greeff, Editorial Advisor. **ISSN:** 1015-1362.
Subscription Rates: Rs 28.40 individuals. **URL:** http://
www.medpharm.co.za/?q=node/14; http://www.sapj.co.
za/index.php/SAPJ.

Glencoe

50484 ■ Lotus FM - Glencoe - 90.0 MHz
100 Old Fort Rd.
Private Bag 1337
Durban 4000, Republic of South Africa
Ph: 27 31 3625445
Fax: 27 31 3625202
E-mail: lotus@lotusfm.co.za
Format: Public Radio. **Operating Hours:** Continuous.
Key Personnel: Kamsiliya Arumugam, Contact, phone
27 31 3625448, kamsiliya@lotusfm.co.za; Sagren Naidoo, Contact, phone 27 31 3625211, sagren@lotusfm.
co.za. **URL:** http://www.lotusfm.co.za/portal/site/
LotusFM/menuitem.a13733dc3e9a0bad5729 4
f945401aeb9/.

Glenstantia

50485 ■ Impact Radio-FM - 103
PO Box 33626
Glenstantia 0010, Republic of South Africa
Ph: 27 12 3488111
Fax: 27 12 3482335
E-mail: radio@impactradio.co.za
Format: Religious; Contemporary Christian; News;
Gospel; Top 40. **Operating Hours:** 5:45 a.m.-11.45 p.m.
Ad Rates: $88-200 for 20 seconds; $110-250 for 30
seconds; $146.30-332.50 for 40 seconds. **URL:** http://
www.impactradio.co.za.

Grahamstown

50486 ■ African Journal of AIDS Research
National Inquiry Services Centre (Pty.) Ltd.
1 Dundas St.
PO Box 377
Grahamstown 6140, Republic of South Africa
Ph: 27 466 229698
Fax: 27 466 229550
Publisher E-mail: sales@nisc.co.za
Peer-reviewed Journal publishing papers that make an
original contribution to the understanding of social
dimensions of HIV/AIDS in African contexts, including
articles from the disciplines of sociology, demography,
epidemiology, social geography, economics, psychology,
anthropology, philosophy, health communication, media,
cultural studies, public health, education, nursing science and social work. **Freq:** 3/yr. **Key Personnel:** Dr.
Kevin Kelly, Managing Editor, kk@cadre.org.za; Dr. Sue
Cooling, Editorial Asst., ajar@ru.ac.za; Prof. Peter
Aggleton, PhD, Editorial Board. **ISSN:** 1608-5906. **Subscription Rates:** R 528 individuals print and online; R
468 individuals online; R 780 institutions print and online; R 780 institutions online. **URL:** http://www.nisc.co.
za/journals?id=1.

50487 ■ African Journal of Biomedical Research
African Journals Online
PO Box 377
Grahamstown 6140, Republic of South Africa
Ph: 27 466 229698
Fax: 27 466 229550

Circulation: ★ = ABC; △ = BPA; ◆ = CAC; • = CCAB; ❑ = VAC; ⊕ = PO Statement; ‡ = Publisher's Report; Boldface figures = sworn; Light figures = estimated.

Publisher E-mail: info@ajol.info
Peer-reviewed journal covering biomedical sciences.
Founded: 1939. **Freq:** 3/yr. **Print Method:** Offset. **Trim Size:** 13 x 21 1/4. **Cols./Page:** 6. **Col. Width:** 12 picas. **Col. Depth:** 295 agate lines. **Key Personnel:** Prof. Raphael A. Elegbe, Editor-in-Chief, phone 234 802 3255893, fax 234 802 8100147, ajbrui@hotmail.com; Dr. S.B. Olaleye, Tech. Support, sb.olaleye@mail.ui.edu.ng. **ISSN:** 1119-5096. **URL:** http://ajol.info/index.php/ajbr.

50488 ■ African Journal of Economic Policy
African Journals Online
PO Box 377
Grahamstown 6140, Republic of South Africa
Ph: 27 466 229698
Fax: 27 466 229550
Publisher E-mail: info@ajol.info
Peer-reviewed journal covering trade policy research and training programs in economics. **Founded:** 1890. **Freq:** Semiannual. **Print Method:** Offset. **Cols./Page:** 6. **Col. Width:** 26 nonpareils. **Col. Depth:** 301 agate lines. **Key Personnel:** Abiodun Bankole, Editor, asbanky@yahoo.com. **ISSN:** 1116-4875. **Subscription Rates:** US$30 institutions Africa; US$60 institutions, other countries; US$20 individuals Africa; US$40 other countries. **URL:** http://ajol.info/index.php/ajep.

50489 ■ African Journal of Marine Science
African Journals Online
PO Box 377
Grahamstown 6140, Republic of South Africa
Publisher E-mail: info@ajol.info
Peer-reviewed journal covering marine research. Topics range from estuarine and coastal waters to the open ocean, and from chemical and physical to biological oceanography. **Founded:** 1912. **Freq:** 3/yr. **Print Method:** Offset. **Cols./Page:** 6. **Col. Width:** 25 nonpareils. **Col. Depth:** 301 agate lines. **Key Personnel:** Mike Schramm, Publishing Ed., phone 27 466 229698, fax 27 466 229550, mike@nisc.co.za; Stan C. Pillar, Editor-in-Chief, scpillar@deat.gov.za; Paul D. Cowley, Editor. **ISSN:** 1814-232X. **URL:** http://ajol.info/index.php/ajms.

50490 ■ African Sociological Review
CODESRIA - Council for the Development of Social Science Research in Africa
c/o D. Wisch
Dept. of Sociology
Rhodes University
PO Box 94
Grahamstown 6140, Republic of South Africa
Publisher E-mail: codesria@codesria.sn
Journal publishing contributions that deal with matters related to African and general social analysis. **Freq:** Semiannual. **Key Personnel:** Olajide Oloyede, Publisher, jide.oloyede@gmail.co; Jean-Bernard Ouedraogo, Editor, jberno@yahoo.com; Jimi O. Adesina, Editorial Advisory Board; Elisio Macamo, Publisher, elisio.macamo@unibas.ch; Harri Englund, Editorial Advisory Board; Onalenna D. Selolwane, Editor, selolwan@mopipi.ub.pw. **ISSN:** 1027-4332. **Subscription Rates:** R 50 individuals in Africa; R 80 institutions in Africa; US$50 individuals elsewhere; US$80 institutions elsewhere. **URL:** http://www.codesria.org/spip.php?rubrique42&lang=fr. **Foreign language name:** Revue Africaine de Sociologie.

50491 ■ African Studies Monographs
African Journals Online
PO Box 377
Grahamstown 6140, Republic of South Africa
Ph: 27 466 229698
Fax: 27 466 229550
Publisher E-mail: info@ajol.info
Peer-reviewed journal covering matters of philosophy, history, literature, arts and culture, environment, gender, politics, administration crisis management, and others. **Key Personnel:** Dr. Oghenekaro Moses Ogbinaka, Editor, karogbi@yahoo.com. **ISSN:** 1119-7196. **Subscription Rates:** N 300 individuals; US$10 institutions; N 350 institutions; US$15 institutions. **URL:** http://ajol.info/index.php/astumo.

50492 ■ Agricultural and Food Science Journal of Ghana
African Journals Online
PO Box 377
Grahamstown 6140, Republic of South Africa

Ph: 27 466 229698
Fax: 27 466 229550
Publisher E-mail: info@ajol.info
Peer-reviewed journal covering observational and experimental research and critical reviews in agriculture and food science. **Freq:** Annual. **Key Personnel:** Dr. G.K.S. Aflakpui, Editor-in-Chief, phone 233516-0391, fax 233516-0396, gksaflakpui@cropsresearch.org; Dr. J.V.K. Afun, Editor; K. Obeng-Antwi, Editor; B. Banful, Editor; Dr. E.A. Asiedu, Editor; R.K. Bam, Editor. **ISSN:** 0855-5591. **Subscription Rates:** Cd 120,000 individuals; US$45 other countries. **URL:** http://ajol.info/index.php/afsjg.

50493 ■ Annals of Ibadan Postgraduate Medicine
African Journals Online
PO Box 377
Grahamstown 6140, Republic of South Africa
Ph: 27 466 229698
Fax: 27 466 229550
Publisher E-mail: info@ajol.info
Journal covering the field of medical sciences. **Key Personnel:** Rufus Olusola Akinyemi, Contact, phone 234 803 3704384, ibadanpgmed@yahoo.com. **ISSN:** 1597-1627. **URL:** http://ajol.info/index.php/aipm.

50494 ■ Ethiopian Pharmaceutical Journal
African Journals Online
PO Box 377
Grahamstown 6140, Republic of South Africa
Ph: 27 466 229698
Fax: 27 466 229550
Publisher E-mail: info@ajol.info
Peer-reviewed journal devoted to research concerning all aspects of pharmaceutical sciences. **Freq:** Semiannual. **Print Method:** Web press. **Trim Size:** 8 1/4 x 11. **Cols./Page:** 3. **Col. Width:** 26 nonpareils. **Col. Depth:** 133 agate lines. **Key Personnel:** N.A. Armstrong, Member of the Editorial Board; P. Houghton, Member of the Editorial Board; A. Mazumder, Member of the Editorial Board; Abebe Endale, Assoc. Ed., aendale@phar.aau.edu.et; E. Dagne, Member of the Editorial Board; Kaleab Asres, Editor-in-Chief, kasres@gmail.com; N. Mekonnen, Member of the Editorial Board; Ephrem Engidawork, Assoc. Ed., ephrem@phar.aau.edu.et; P.C. Schmidt, Member of the Editorial Board. **ISSN:** 1029-5933. **Subscription Rates:** E$15 individuals; US$5 elsewhere postage included. **URL:** http://ajol.info/index.php/epj.

50495 ■ Ghana Journal of Agricultural Science
African Journals Online
PO Box 377
Grahamstown 6140, Republic of South Africa
Ph: 27 466 229698
Fax: 27 466 229550
Publisher E-mail: info@ajol.info
Peer-reviewed journal of agricultural science, covering articles on West African agriculture. **Freq:** Semiannual. **Key Personnel:** D.K. Acquaye, Editor; Eric Asante, Production Ed., erasantegh@yahoo.com; Prof. Barth N. Ekueme, Managing Editor. **ISSN:** 0855-0042. **Subscription Rates:** US$7 single issue; US$18 individuals. **URL:** http://ajol.info/index.php/gjas.

50496 ■ Global Journal of Engineering Research
African Journals Online
PO Box 377
Grahamstown 6140, Republic of South Africa
Ph: 27 466 229698
Fax: 27 466 229550
Publisher E-mail: info@ajol.info
Peer-reviewed journal publishing original research papers of high standard, containing material of significant contribution to civil engineering, with emphasis being placed on material that is applicable to the solution of practical problems. **Freq:** Semiannual. **Key Personnel:** Prof. Barth N. Ekueme, Managing Editor, bachudo@yahoo.com. **ISSN:** 1596-292X. **Subscription Rates:** US$40 single issue; US$80 individuals. **URL:** http://ajol.info/index.php/gjer.

50497 ■ Global Journal of Mathematical Sciences
African Journals Online
PO Box 377
Grahamstown 6140, Republic of South Africa
Ph: 27 466 229698
Fax: 27 466 229550

Publisher E-mail: info@ajol.info
Peer-reviewed journal publishing research work in all areas of mathematical sciences and application at all levels including, but not limited to basic research leading to development of new theories, techniques and application to science, industry and society, promoting the exchange of information and ideas between all classes of mathematicians and /or the rest of society. **Freq:** Semiannual. **Key Personnel:** Prof. Barth N. Ekueme, Managing Editor, bachudo@yahoo.com. **ISSN:** 1596-6208. **Subscription Rates:** N 750 single issue local; N 3,000 individuals local; US$25 single issue international; US$100 other countries. **URL:** http://ajol.info/index.php/gjmas.

50498 ■ International Journal of Natural and Applied Sciences
African Journals Online
PO Box 377
Grahamstown 6140, Republic of South Africa
Ph: 27 466 229698
Fax: 27 466 229550
Publisher E-mail: info@ajol.info
Peer-reviewed journal covering all areas of natural and applied sciences. **Freq:** Quarterly. **Key Personnel:** Dr. J.C. Anosike, Editor-in-Chief, jc_anosike@yahoo.com; Dr. Charles I. Okoli, Contact, tapasinstitute@yahoo.com. **ISSN:** 0794-4713. **Subscription Rates:** N 3,000 individuals; N 6,000 institutions; US$180 other countries; US$360 institutions, other countries. **URL:** http://ajol.info/index.php/ijonas.

50499 ■ International Journal of Tropical Agriculture and Food Systems
African Journals Online
PO Box 377
Grahamstown 6140, Republic of South Africa
Ph: 27 466 229698
Fax: 27 466 229550
Publisher E-mail: info@ajol.info
Peer-reviewed journal covering all areas of agriculture and food production. **Freq:** Quarterly. **Key Personnel:** Dr. Emmanuel U. Onweremadu, Editor-in-Chief, tapasinstitute@yahoo.com; F.N. Nnadi, Managing Editor; Dr. I.I. Ibeawuchi, Managing Editor. **ISSN:** 0794-4713. **Subscription Rates:** N 5,000 individuals; N 8,000 institutions; US$150 other countries; US$300 institutions, other countries. **URL:** http://ajol.info/index.php/ijotafs.

50500 ■ Journal of Applied Science, Engineering and Technology
African Journals Online
PO Box 377
Grahamstown 6140, Republic of South Africa
Ph: 27 466 229698
Fax: 27 466 229550
Publisher E-mail: info@ajol.info
Peer-reviewed journal covering the field of engineering, physical sciences, technology and biotechnology. **Freq:** Semiannual. **Key Personnel:** Prof. Olusegun Omole, Editor-in-Chief, dean_tech@mail.ui.edu.ng; Dr. Abel O. Olorunnisola, Business Mgr., abelolorunnisola@yahoo.com; Dr. Adenike Osofisan, Assoc. Ed. **ISSN:** 1596-3233. **Subscription Rates:** N 500 individuals; N 1000 institutions. **URL:** http://ajol.info/index.php/jaset.

50501 ■ Journal of Child and Adolescent Mental Health
African Journals Online
PO Box 377
Grahamstown 6140, Republic of South Africa
Ph: 27 466 229698
Fax: 27 466 229550
Publisher E-mail: info@ajol.info
Peer-reviewed journal covering the field of child and adolescent mental health from countries in Southern Africa. **Freq:** Semiannual. **Key Personnel:** Mike Schramm, Publishing Mgr., mike@nisc.co.za; Alan J. Flisher, Editor-in-Chief, aflisher@curie.uct.ac.za; Prof. Soraya Seedat, Editor, sseedat@sun.ac.za. **ISSN:** 1728-0583. **URL:** http://ajol.info/index.php/jcamh; http://www.nisc.co.za/journals?id=4.

50502 ■ Journal of Philosophy and Culture
African Journals Online
PO Box 377
Grahamstown 6140, Republic of South Africa
Ph: 27 466 229698
Fax: 27 466 229550

Publisher E-mail: info@ajol.info
Peer-reviewed journal covering the field of philosophy, culture, and allied disciplines. **Freq:** Semiannual. **Key Personnel:** Dr. Raymond N. Osei, Editor, clasphil1@yahoo.com; Peter Grant, Contact, petgrant@yahoo.com. **ISSN:** 0855-6660. **Subscription Rates:** Cd 150,000 individuals; Cd 90,000 students; Cd 200,000 institutions; US$10 other countries; US$15 institutions, other countries. **URL:** http://ajol.info/index.php/jpc.

50503 ■ Journal of Social Development in Africa
PO Box 377
PO Box 66022, Kopje
Grahamstown, Republic of South Africa
Ph: 27 46 6228058
Fax: 27 46 6229550
Scholarly journal covering social, political and economic development in Southern Africa. **Founded:** 1986. **Freq:** Semiannual. **Trim Size:** A5. **Cols./Page:** 1. **Col. Width:** 104 millimeters. **Col. Depth:** 166 millimeters. **Key Personnel:** Edwin Kaseke, Editorial Board; Rodreck Mupedziswa, Editorial Board; Victor Muzvidziwa, Editorial Board; Gary Craig, Editorial Advisor; Lena Dominelli, Editorial Advisor; John F. Jones, Editorial Advisor; Fikile Mazibuko, Editorial Advisor; Lynne Healy, Editorial Advisor; James Midgley, Editorial Advisor; Carole Pearce, Editor, zimreview@mango.zw. **ISSN:** 1012-1080. **Subscription Rates:** Z$300 individuals; Z$150 students; US$35 individuals developing world; US$65 other countries; US$20 individuals airmail. **URL:** http://ajol.info/index.php/jsda. **Circ:** Combined 150

50504 ■ Makerere Journal of Higher Education
African Journals Online
PO Box 377
Grahamstown 6140, Republic of South Africa
Ph: 27 466 229698
Fax: 27 466 229550
Publisher E-mail: info@ajol.info
Peer-reviewed journal containing issues related with higher education. **Freq:** Annual. **Key Personnel:** Prof. Jude Ssempebwa, Editor-in-Chief, phone 256 41 532992, fax 256 41 541303, majohe@educ.mak.ac.ug; Beatrice Sekabembe, Contact, phone 256 41 541524, sekabembe@yahoo.com; Prof. Samuel Olajide Owolabi, Editor-in-Chief. **ISSN:** 1816-6822. **Subscription Rates:** 25 USh single issue; US$20 other countries. **URL:** http://ajol.info/index.php/majohe.

50505 ■ Nigeria Journal of Business Administration
African Journals Online
PO Box 377
Grahamstown 6140, Republic of South Africa
Ph: 27 466 229698
Fax: 27 466 229550
Publisher E-mail: info@ajol.info
Peer-reviewed journal covering the research in the management sciences and the exchange of information between the academic, professional, and business worlds. **Freq:** Semiannual. **Key Personnel:** Prof. A.B. Agbadudu, Editor-in-Chief, njba@uniben.edu; Dr. I.O. Osamwonyi, Contact, osamwonyi@uniben.edu. **ISSN:** 0794-0672. **Subscription Rates:** N 500 individuals; US$50 individuals Africa; US$75 other countries; N 2,000 individuals; US$100 individuals Africa; US$200 institutions, other countries. **URL:** http://ajol.info/index.php/njbm.

50506 ■ Nigerian Journal of Parasitology
African Journals Online
PO Box 377
Grahamstown 6140, Republic of South Africa
Ph: 27 466 229698
Fax: 27 466 229550
Publication E-mail: parasitologyjournal@yahoo.com
Publisher E-mail: info@ajol.info
Peer-reviewed journal devoted primarily to pure applied research technical studies. **Founded:** 1980. **Freq:** Annual. **Print Method:** Offset. **Trim Size:** 8 1/2 x 11. **Cols./Page:** 2. **Col. Width:** 47 nonpareils. **Col. Depth:** 127 agate lines. **Key Personnel:** Prof. J.P. Fabiyi, Editorial Board; Dr. C.I. Eneanya, Editorial Board; Prof. L.D. Edungbola, Editorial Board; Prof. C.O.E. Onwuliri, Editorial Board; Prof. E.I. Braide, Editorial Board; Prof. M.G. Ogbe, Editorial Board; R.I.S. Agbede, Editorial Board; Prof. B.E.B. Nwoke, Editorial Board; Prof. Chiedu Felix Mafiana, Editor-in-Chief, phone 234 80 33444595,

editor.njp@gmail.com. **ISSN:** 1117-4145. **Subscription Rates:** US$70 individuals; N 1,000 individuals. **URL:** http://ajol.info/index.php/njpar.

50507 ■ Nigerian Journal of Physics
African Journals Online
PO Box 377
Grahamstown 6140, Republic of South Africa
Ph: 27 466 229698
Fax: 27 466 229550
Publisher E-mail: info@ajol.info
Peer-reviewed journal covering the field of pure and applied physics. **Freq:** Semiannual. **Key Personnel:** Prof. F.C. Eze, Editor-in-Chief, eze_fc@yahoo.com; Prof. T.C. Akpa, Dep. Ed., t.akpa@nnra.gov.ng. **ISSN:** 1595-0611. **Subscription Rates:** US$120 individuals. **URL:** http://ajol.info/index.php/njphy.

50508 ■ Nigerian Journal of Soil Science
African Journals Online
PO Box 377
Grahamstown 6140, Republic of South Africa
Ph: 27 466 229698
Fax: 27 466 229550
Publisher E-mail: info@ajol.info
Peer-reviewed journal focusing on soil science. **Founded:** 1962. **Freq:** Annual. **Print Method:** Offset. **Trim Size:** 9 x 11 5/8. **Key Personnel:** Prof. S.O. Ojeniyi, Editor-in-Chief, soj_oje@yahoo.co.uk; Prof. T.A. Okusami, Dep. Ed.-in-Ch.; Prof. Akin Olayinka, Business Mgr. **ISSN:** 1597-4488. **Subscription Rates:** US$50 individuals; N 500 individuals. **URL:** http://ajol.info/index.php/njss.

50509 ■ Ostrich
National Inquiry Services Centre (Pty.) Ltd.
1 Dundas St.
PO Box 377
Grahamstown 6140, Republic of South Africa
Ph: 27 466 229698
Fax: 27 466 229550
Publisher E-mail: sales@nisc.co.za
Peer-reviewed Journal covering general field of ornithology in Africa and its islands. **Subtitle:** Journal of African Ornithology. **Freq:** Semiannual. **Key Personnel:** Prof. Ara Monadjem, Editor, ara@all-out.org; Mark D. Anderson, Assoc. Ed.; Dr. Michel Louette, Assoc. Ed. **ISSN:** 0030-6525. **Subscription Rates:** R 980 institutions print and online; R 588 individuals print and online; R 850 institutions online; R 510 individuals online. **URL:** http://www.nisc.co.za/journals?id=6.

50510 ■ Philosophical Papers
African Journals Online
PO Box 377
Grahamstown 6140, Republic of South Africa
Ph: 27 466 229698
Fax: 27 466 229550
Publisher E-mail: info@ajol.info
Peer-reviewed journal of analytic philosophy based in South Africa. **Founded:** 1972. **Freq:** 3/yr. **Print Method:** Letterpress. Uses mats. **Trim Size:** 8 1/2 x 11. **Cols./Page:** 2. **Col. Width:** 3 1/2 inches. **Col. Depth:** 10 inches. **Key Personnel:** Lorraine Code, International Board of Consultant; Emmanuel Chukwudi, International Board of Consultant; Lindsay Kelland, Managing Editor, philosophical.papers@ru.ac.za; Marius Vermaak, Editorial Board; Lynne Rudder Baker, International Board of Consultant; Andy Clark, International Board of Consultant; Thomas Martin, Editorial Board; Francis Williamson, Editorial Board; Tyler Burge, International Board of Consultant; Jonathan Barnes, International Board of Consultant; Prof. Ward E. Jones, Editor; Terrence Horgan, International Board of Consultant. **ISSN:** 0556-8641. **URL:** http://ajol.info/index.php/pp.

50511 ■ Rhodes Journalism Review
Rhodes University
Department of Journalism & Media Studies
PO Box 94
Grahamstown 6140, Republic of South Africa
Ph: 27 46 6037100
Fax: 27 46 6037101
Publisher E-mail: journqueries@ru.ac.za
Publication of the Department of Journalism & Media Studies at Rhodes University. **Key Personnel:** Anthea Garman, Editor. **Subscription Rates:** R 80 individuals. **Remarks:** Accepts advertising. **URL:** http://rjr.ru.ac.za. **Ad Rates:** 4C: R 11,000. **Circ:** (Not Reported)

50512 ■ Securities Market Journal
African Journals Online
PO Box 377
Grahamstown 6140, Republic of South Africa
Ph: 27 466 229698
Fax: 27 466 229550
Publisher E-mail: info@ajol.info
Peer-reviewed journal containing issues related to the capital market. **Freq:** Annual. **Key Personnel:** Dr. I.O. Osamwonyi, Publisher, osamwonyi@uniben.edu. **Subscription Rates:** N 500 individuals; US$50 individuals Africa; US$75 other countries; N 2,000 institutions; US$100 institutions Africa; US$200 institutions, other countries. **URL:** http://ajol.info/index.php/smj.

50513 ■ Shakespeare in Southern Africa
Shakespeare Society of Southern Africa
Rhodes University
PO Box 94
Grahamstown 6140, Republic of South Africa
Ph: 27 466 226093
Publisher E-mail: shakespeare@ru.ac.za
Journal of the Shakespeare Society of Southern Africa. **Founded:** 1987. **Freq:** Annual. **Key Personnel:** Prof. Brian Pearce, Editor. **Subscription Rates:** Included in membership; R 100 individuals South Africa, Zambia, Zimbabwe; US$30 other countries; 22 other countries. **URL:** http://www.ru.ac.za/static/institutes/shake/journal.html.

50514 ■ South African Journal Clinical Nutrition
African Journals Online
PO Box 377
Grahamstown 6140, Republic of South Africa
Ph: 27 466 229698
Fax: 27 466 229550
Publication E-mail: publishing@samedical.org
Publisher E-mail: info@ajol.info
Peer-reviewed journal containing papers related to clinical nutrition. **Freq:** Quarterly. **Key Personnel:** Prof. Demetre Labadarios, Editor, editor@sajcn.co.za; Daniel J. Ncayiyana, Editor; J.P. De V. Van Niekerk, Dep. Ed. **ISSN:** 0038-2469. **URL:** http://ajol.info/index.php/sajcn.

50515 ■ Southern African Linguistics and Applied Language Studies
African Journals Online
NISC Pty Ltd.
PO Box 377
19 Worcester St.
Grahamstown 6140, Republic of South Africa
Publisher E-mail: info@ajol.info
Peer-reviewed journal covering topics on research into all the languages of southern Africa, including English and Afrikaans. **Freq:** Quarterly. **Key Personnel:** Mike Schramm, Pub. Mgr., phone 27 46 6229698, fax 24 46 6229550, mike@nisc.co.za; Prof. Jacobus A. Naude, Editor-in-Chief, naudej@ufs.ac.za. **ISSN:** 1607-3614. **Subscription Rates:** R 550 institutions; US$300 institutions; R 228 individuals; US$145 individuals. **URL:** http://ajol.info/index.php/salas.

50516 ■ Sudan Journal of Medical Sciences
African Journals Online
PO Box 377
Grahamstown 6140, Republic of South Africa
Ph: 27 466 229698
Fax: 27 466 229550
Publisher E-mail: info@ajol.info
Peer-reviewed journal containing issues relevant to basic and clinical sciences. **Freq:** 3/yr. **Key Personnel:** Prof. Mohammad AM Ibnouf, Editor-in-Chief, sudanjms@yahoo.co.uk; Dr. Aamir Yassin, Contact, phone 249 9 13103535. **ISSN:** 1858-5051. **Subscription Rates:** S 10 individuals. **URL:** http://ajol.info/index.php/sjms.

50517 ■ Tanzania Dental Journal
African Journals Online
PO Box 377
Grahamstown 6140, Republic of South Africa
Ph: 27 466 229698
Fax: 27 466 229550
Publisher E-mail: info@ajol.info
Peer-reviewed journal covering all aspects of oral health. **Freq:** Semiannual. **Key Personnel:** Dr. Febronia Kokulengya Kahabuka, Editor-in-Chief, fkahabuka@muchs.ac.tz; Dr. Flora Fabian, Contact, phone 255 744 485678, ffabian@muchs.ac.tz. **ISSN:** 0856-0625. **Subscription**

Circulation: ★ = ABC; △ = BPA; ♦ = CAC; ● = CCAB; ❑ = VAC; ⊕ = PO Statement; ‡ = Publisher's Report; Boldface figures = sworn; Light figures = estimated.

Gale Directory of Publications & Broadcast Media/147th Ed.   5431

Rates: US$20 individuals; US$30 institutions. **URL:** http://ajol.info/index.php/tdj.

Greyville

50518 ■ Sunday Tribune (South Africa)
Independent News & Media PLC
PO Box 47549
Greyville 4023, Republic of South Africa
Fax: 27 031 3082911
Publication E-mail: tribletter@nn.independent.co.za
General newspaper. **Founded:** 1937. **Freq:** Weekly (Sun.). **Cols./Page:** 10. **Key Personnel:** Brian Porter, Advertising Dir., phone 27 313 3082470, brian.porter@inl.co.za; Phillida Ellis, Mktg. Mgr., phone 27 313 082434, phillida.ellis@inl.co.za; Philani Mgwaba, Editor. **Subscription Rates:** R 250 individuals; 17.57 individuals; EUR20.19 individuals. **Remarks:** Accepts advertising. **URL:** http://www.sundaytribune.co.za/. **Ad Rates:** BW: R 115.36. **Circ:** Paid 113,195.

Halfway House

50519 ■ Civil Engineering
South African Institution of Civil Engineering
Private Bag X200
Halfway House 1685, Republic of South Africa
Ph: 27 11 8055947
Fax: 27 11 8055971
Publisher E-mail: civilinfo@saice.org.za
Journal covering civil engineering. **Founded:** 1906. **Freq:** Monthly. **Print Method:** Web offset. **Trim Size:** 210 x 148 mm. **Cols./Page:** 6. **Col. Width:** 12.2 picas. **Col. Depth:** 21 1/2 inches. **Key Personnel:** Barbara Spence, Advertising; Verelene de Koker, Editor, vdekoker@saice.org.za; Dawie Botha, Exec. Dir. **ISSN:** 1021-2000. **URL:** http://www.civils.org.za/.

50520 ■ Clean Air Journal
National Association for Clean Air
Nasionale Vereniging vir Skoon Lug
PO Box 8370
Halfway House 1685, Republic of South Africa
Ph: 27 71 6839770
Fax: 27 11 8057010
Publication covering pollution control, in Afrikaans and English. **Freq:** Biennial. **Key Personnel:** Rory Macnamara, Editor. **ISSN:** 1017-1703. **Remarks:** Advertising accepted; rates available upon request. **URL:** http://www.journals.co.za/ej/ejour_cleanair.html. **Circ:** 550

Hatfield

50521 ■ African Entomology
Entomological Society of Southern Africa
Entomologiese Vereniging van Suidelike Afrika
PO Box 13162
Hatfield 0028, Republic of South Africa
Publisher E-mail: avzyl@iafrica.com
Journal covering African entomology (Afrikaans and English). **Subtitle:** Journal of the Entomological Society of Southern Africa. **Founded:** 1993. **Freq:** Semiannual. **ISSN:** 1021-3589. **Remarks:** Accepts advertising. **URL:** http://journals.sabinet.co.za/essa. **Ad Rates:** BW: US$420. **Circ:** (Not Reported)

50522 ■ Aloe
Succulent Society of South Africa
Vetplantvereniging van Suid-Afika
PO Box 12580
Hatfield 0028, Republic of South Africa
Ph: 27 12 9933588
Fax: 27 12 9933588
Publisher E-mail: sssa@succulents.net
Publication covering gardening. **Freq:** Quarterly. **ISSN:** 0002-6301. **Subscription Rates:** Free. **Remarks:** Advertising accepted; rates available upon request. **URL:** https://www.succulentsociety.co.za/. **Circ:** (Not Reported)

Hillcrest

50523 ■ South African Journal of Economic and Management Sciences
University of Pretoria
Faculty of Economic and Management Sciences
Sciences Bldg.
University of Pretoria, Lynnwood Rd.
Hillcrest 0002, Republic of South Africa
Ph: 27 124 203111

Fax: 27 124 204555
Publisher E-mail: csc@up.ac.za
Journal covering marketing and communication management, human resource management, business management, accounting and financial management, public management and administration, and tourism management. **Founded:** 1917. **Freq:** 3/yr. **Print Method:** Offset. **Cols./Page:** 8. **Col. Width:** 21 nonpareils. **Col. Depth:** 301 agate lines. **ISSN:** 1015-8812. **URL:** http://www.journals.co.za/ej/ejour_ecoman.html.

Houghton

50524 ■ Jewish Affairs
South African Jewish Board of Deputies
PO Box 87557
Houghton 2041, Republic of South Africa
Ph: 27 114 861434
Fax: 27 116 464940
Publisher E-mail: sajbod@iafrica.com
Journal covering essays of scholarly research on subjects of Jewish interest, especially South African Jewish life. **Founded:** 1942. **Freq:** Quarterly. **Print Method:** Litho. **Trim Size:** 297 x 210 mm. **Cols./Page:** 2. **Col. Width:** 22 millimeters. **Col. Depth:** 72 millimeters. **Key Personnel:** David Saks, Editor. **ISSN:** 0021-6313. **Subscription Rates:** US$172 individuals. **Remarks:** Accepts advertising. **URL:** http://www.jewish.org.za. **Ad Rates:** BW: R 2,400, 4C: R 3,600. **Circ:** Combined ⊕1,000

Howick

50525 ■ African Wildlife
Wildlife and Environment Society of South Africa
1 Karkloof Rd.
PO Box 394
Howick 3290, Republic of South Africa
Ph: 27 33 3303931
Fax: 27 33 3304576
Publication E-mail: wildmag@yebo.co.za
Publisher E-mail: marketing@wessa.co.za
Publication covering wildlife environment. **Subtitle:** People Caring for the Earth. **Founded:** 1946. **Freq:** Quarterly. **Trim Size:** A4. **ISSN:** 0256-6273. **Remarks:** Advertising accepted; rates available upon request. **URL:** http://www.wessa.org.za/index.php/African-Wildlife/African-Wildlife-Introduction.html. **Circ:** 10,000

Jeffreys Bay

50526 ■ Kouga Express
Media24
7B Oosterland Bldg.
Jeffreys St.
Jeffreys Bay 6330, Republic of South Africa
Publisher E-mail: dvos@naspers.com
Local community newspaper serving Jeffreysbay, Humansdorp, Kareedouw, Krakeel, Joubertinia, Patensie, Hankey, Loerie, Louterwater, Ashtonbay, Stormsrivier en Uniondale. **Freq:** Weekly (Thurs.). **Key Personnel:** Lizelle Delport-van Wyk, Editor, phone 27 42 2932973, kougaexp@media24.com. **Remarks:** Accepts advertising. **URL:** http://www.media24.com/en/newspapers/community-newspapers/eastern-cape-newspapers/kouga-express.html; http://www.kougaexpress.co.za/. **Circ:** 20,250

Johannesburg

50527 ■ Beeld
Media24
Kingsweg 69
Auckland Pk.
Johannesburg 2006, Republic of South Africa
Publisher E-mail: dvos@naspers.com
Community newspaper. **Freq:** Daily. **Key Personnel:** Tim du Plessis, Editor, timdup@beeld.com. **Remarks:** Accepts advertising. **URL:** http://www.beeld.com/Content/. **Circ:** 101,972

50528 ■ Building Women
3S Shorten Publications
PO Box 92026
Johannesburg 2117, Republic of South Africa
Ph: 27 11 5313300
Fax: 27 11 4401516

Publisher E-mail: enquiries@media3s.co.za
Journal about women in the building industry. **Founded:** 1994. **Freq:** Bimonthly. **Print Method:** Offset. **Cols./Page:** 6. **Col. Width:** 21 nonpareils. **Col. Depth:** 13 inches. **Key Personnel:** Mahadi Moloi, Managing Editor; Lee Furter, Editor-in-Chief; Elizabeth Shorten, Publisher & Mng. Dir. **URL:** http://www.media3s.co.za/shortens/html/Product7.asp.

50529 ■ Business Day
BDFM Publishers (Pty) Ltd.
4 Biermann Ave.
Rosebank
Johannesburg 2196, Republic of South Africa
Business newspaper. **Freq:** Daily. **Key Personnel:** Kevin O'Grady, Contact; Peter Bruce, Contact. **Subscription Rates:** R 2,137.44 individuals. **Remarks:** Accepts advertising. **URL:** http://www.businessday.co.za/home.aspx?Page=BD4P1236& MenuItem=BD4P1236; http://www.bmie.co.za/. **Ad Rates:** BW: R 49,680, 4C: R 70,740. **Circ:** (Not Reported)

50530 ■ Journal of African Elections
Electoral Institute of Southern Africa
14 Park Rd.
PO Box 740
Johannesburg 2006, Republic of South Africa
Ph: 27 113 816000
Fax: 27 114 826163
Peer-reviewed journal covering research in the human sciences related to developments and change in Africa. **Founded:** 1952. **Freq:** Semiannual. **Print Method:** Offset. Uses mats. **Trim Size:** 10 x 13. **Cols./Page:** 5. **Col. Width:** 11.5 picas. **Col. Depth:** 65 picas. **Key Personnel:** David Caroll, Editorial Board; Jorgen Elklit, Editorial board; Denis Kadima, Editor; Sean Jacobs, Editorial Board; Amanda Gouws, Editorial Board; Claude Kabemba, Editorial Board. **ISSN:** 1609-4700. **Subscription Rates:** R 160 individuals. **URL:** http://www.eisa.org.za/EISA/publications/jae.htm.

50531 ■ Journal of Marketing
Marketing Federation of Southern Africa
JSE Bldg., 17 Diagonal St.
Newtown
Johannesburg 2000, Republic of South Africa
Ph: 27 11 8323500
Fax: 27 11 7263639
Publisher E-mail: info@mfsa.co.za
Journal containing information on marketing, sales, media, advertising, communications and technology. **Freq:** Bimonthly. **Key Personnel:** Jeremy Maggs, Editor. **ISSN:** 1811-9565. **Remarks:** Accepts advertising. **URL:** http://www.journals.co.za/ej/ejour_mfsa.html. **Circ:** (Not Reported)

50532 ■ Obstetrics and Gynaecology Forum
African Journals Online
Craighall
PO Box 412748
Johannesburg 2024, Republic of South Africa
Ph: 27 11 7889139
Fax: 27 11 7889136
Publisher E-mail: info@ajol.info
Peer-reviewed journal containing articles related to women's healthcare, focusing on the practice of obstetrics and gynecology. **Freq:** Quarterly. **Key Personnel:** Prof. B.G. Lindeque, Editor-in-Chief, inhouse@iafrica.com; Prof. J. Moodley, Editor; Prof. H.J. Odendaal, Editor; Prof. Z. van der Spuy, Editor; Prof. EWW Sonnendecker, Ed. Emeritus. **ISSN:** 1027-9148. **URL:** http://ajol.info/index.php/ogf.

50533 ■ The Shopsteward
Congress of South African Trade Unions
1 Leyds St.
Braamfontein
Johannesburg 2000, Republic of South Africa
Ph: 27 11 3394911
Fax: 27 11 3395080
Journal covering news and events, policies and programmes, views and opinions from the federation and its affiliates. **Freq:** 8/yr. **Key Personnel:** Zwelinzima Vavi, Editor-in-Chief; Patrick Craven, Editor, patricl@cosatu.org.za. **ISSN:** 1608-036X. **Subscription Rates:** R 80 individuals; R 290 individuals Southern Africa; air mail; R 310 elsewhere air mail; R 180 other countries surface mail. **Remarks:** Accepts advertising. **URL:** http://www.cosatu.org.za/show.php?include=docs/intropages/2009/webcont0803. **Circ:** (Not Reported)

50534 ■ South African Gastroenterology Review
African Journals Online
PO Box 412748
Craighall
Johannesburg, Republic of South Africa
Publisher E-mail: info@ajol.info
Peer-reviewed journal covering articles pertinent to the practicing gastroenterologist in South Africa. **Freq:** Quarterly. **Print Method:** Offset. **Trim Size:** 8 1/2 x 11. **Cols./Page:** 3. **Col. Width:** 14 picas. **Col. Depth:** 58 picas. **Key Personnel:** Dr. Herbie Schneider, Editor; Dr. Keith Pettengell, Editor, phone 27 11 7889139, fax 27 11 7889136, inhouse@iafrica.com; Dr. John P. Wright, Editor. **ISSN:** 1812-1659. **URL:** http://ajol.info/index.php/sagr.

50535 ■ South African Psychiatry Review
African Journals Online
PO Box 412748
Johannesburg 2024, Republic of South Africa
Publisher E-mail: info@ajol.info
Peer-reviewed journal focusing on primary care practitioners and specialist mental health care professionals. **Freq:** Quarterly. **Print Method:** Offset. **Trim Size:** 7 7/8 x 10 5/8. **Cols./Page:** 1. **Col. Width:** 84 nonpareils. **Col. Depth:** 133 agate lines. **Key Personnel:** Sean Kaliski, Assoc. Ed.; Cliff Allwood, Assoc. Ed.; Joseph R. Calabrese, Advisory Board; Michael Berk, Assoc. Ed.; Brian Harvey, Assoc. Ed.; Dan Mkize, Assoc. Ed.; Peter Cleaton-Jones, Advisory Board; Robin Emsley, Assoc. Ed.; Christopher P. Szabo, Editor-in-Chief, christopher.szabo@wits.ac.za. **ISSN:** 1811-7805. **URL:** http://ajol.info/index.php/ajpsy.

50536 ■ Southern African Journal of Anaesthesia and Analgesia
African Journals Online
PO Box 412748
Craighall
Johannesburg 2024, Republic of South Africa
Publisher E-mail: info@ajol.info
Peer-reviewed journal providing information on specialist professionals and general practitioners. **Freq:** Quarterly. **Print Method:** Offset. **Trim Size:** 7 5/8 x 10 5/8. **Cols./Page:** 1. **Col. Width:** 84 nonpareils. **Col. Depth:** 133 agate lines. **Key Personnel:** Prof. C. Lundgren, Editor-in-Chief, phone 27 11 7889139, fax 27 11 7889136, inhouse@iafrica.com; Dr. R.A. Dyer, Asst. Ed.; Prof. S. Bhagwanjee, Editorial Board. **ISSN:** 1027-9148. **URL:** http://ajol.info/index.php/sajaa.

50537 ■ Transport World Africa
3S Shorten Publications
PO Box 92026
Johannesburg 2117, Republic of South Africa
Ph: 27 11 5313300
Fax: 27 11 4401516
Publisher E-mail: enquiries@media3s.co.za
Magazine covering shipping, aviation, road, and rail, and the interaction between these sectors, with emphasis on Africa. **Founded:** 1851. **Freq:** Bimonthly. **Print Method:** Offset. **Cols./Page:** 6. **Col. Width:** 19 nonpareils. **Col. Depth:** 200 agate lines. **Subscription Rates:** Cr$225 individuals; US$85 other countries. **Remarks:** Accepts advertising. **URL:** http://www.3smedia.co.za/index.php?id=25. **Circ:** (Not Reported)

50538 ■ Umsebenzi
South African Communist Party
PO Box 1027
Johannesburg 2000, Republic of South Africa
Ph: 27 11 3393621
Fax: 27 11 3396880
Publisher E-mail: info@sacp.org.za
Magazine covering politics. **Subtitle:** Voice of the South African Communist Party. **Freq:** Semimonthly. **Subscription Rates:** US$83 U.S.; US$7 single issue U.S. **URL:** http://www.sacp.org.za/list.php?type=Umsebenzi.

50539 ■ Y-FM - 99.2
Postnet Ste. 148
Private Bag x31
Johannesburg 2132, Republic of South Africa
Ph: 27 11 8807070
Fax: 27 11 8806966
E-mail: support@yfm.co.za
Format: Urban Contemporary; Full Service; Information; Hip Hop. **Founded:** 1997. **Operating Hours:** Continuous. **Key Personnel:** Kanthan Pillay, CEO;

Tamaria Motsepe, Mktg. Mgr.; Meshni Hutheram, Direct Sales Mgr.; Tumelo Diaho-Monaheng, Program Mgr. **Ad Rates:** $330-3267 for 30 seconds. **URL:** http://www.yworld.co.za.

50540 ■ YFM-FM - 99.2
Regent's Pl. Office 1A
1st Fl., Cradock Ave.
Rosebank
Johannesburg 2132, Republic of South Africa
Ph: 27 11 8807070
Fax: 27 11 8806966
Format: Ethnic; Urban Contemporary; Hip Hop; Alternative/New Music/Progressive; News. **Owner:** YFM, at above address. **Founded:** 1997. **Key Personnel:** Kanthan Pillay, CEO, phone 27 11 8807070. **Ad Rates:** Advertising accepted; rates available upon request. **URL:** http://www.yfm.co.za.

Kaapstad

50541 ■ Die Burger
Media24
Posbus 692
Kaapstad 8000, Republic of South Africa
Publisher E-mail: dvos@naspers.com
Community newspaper. **Freq:** Daily. **Key Personnel:** Zelda Jongbloed, Dep. Ed., phone 27 21 4062107, zjongbloed@dieburger.com; Henry Jeffreys, Editor, phone 27 21 4062812, hjeffreys@dieburger.com; Jo-ann Floris, News Ed., phone 27 41 5036111, jfloris@dieburger.com. **Remarks:** Accepts advertising. **URL:** http://www.dieburger.com/; http://www.media24.com/en/newspapers/dailies/die-burger.html. **Circ:** 104,808

Kloof

50542 ■ Dataweek
Technews (Pty) Ltd.
PO Box 626
Kloof 3640, Republic of South Africa
Ph: 27 31 7640593
Fax: 27 31 7640386
Publication E-mail: dataweek@technews.co.za
Publisher E-mail: info@technews.co.za
Trade magazine covering electronics and communications technology. **Subtitle:** Electronics & Communications Technology. **Freq:** Bimonthly. **Trim Size:** A4. **Key Personnel:** Brett van den Bosch, Editor; Malckey Tehini, Business Mgr., phone 27 11 5435808, malckey@technews.co.za. **Remarks:** Accepts advertising. **URL:** http://www.dataweek.co.za. **Ad Rates:** BW: R 10,300, 4C: R 12,600. **Circ:** Free 4,000

Kranskop

50543 ■ Radio Khwezi-FM - 107.7
PO Box 49415
Kranskop 3268, Republic of South Africa
Ph: 27 324815520
Fax: 27 324815523
E-mail: mail@khwezi.org.za
Format: Ethnic; News; Information; Educational; Eclectic. **Operating Hours:** Continuous. **Key Personnel:** Fano Sibisi, Station Mgr., fano@khwezi.org.za; Beni Husslig, Dep. Station Mgr., beni@khwezi.org.za; Peter Rice, Contact, peter@khwezi.org.za. **Ad Rates:** Advertising accepted; rates available upon request. **URL:** http://www.khwezi.org.za.

KwaZulu-Natal

50544 ■ Rotary Africa
PO Box 563
Westville
KwaZulu-Natal 3630, Republic of South Africa
Ph: 27 312 671848
Fax: 27 312 671849
Publisher E-mail: rotaryafrica@mweb.co.za
Membership magazine of Rotary International covering current news about Rotary-related subjects for Africa (in English). **Founded:** 1927. **Freq:** Monthly. **Print Method:** Litho. **Trim Size:** A4. **Key Personnel:** Sharon Robertson, Admin. Asst., sharon@rotaryafrica.za.org; Sarah van Heerden, Editor. **Subscription Rates:** R 200 individuals; R 400 two years; R 105 individuals 6 months. **URL:** http://www.rotaryafrica.za.org. **Circ:** Paid ⊕7,000

50545 ■ South African Historical Journal
South African Historical Society
c/o Prof. Julie Parle, Pres.
University of KwaZulu-Natal
Howard College
King George V Ave.
KwaZulu-Natal 4041, Republic of South Africa
Ph: 27 31 2602624
Fax: 27 31 2602621
Publisher E-mail: parlej@ukzn.ac.za
Peer-reviewed journal covering South African history. **Founded:** 1852. **Freq:** Quarterly. **Print Method:** Offset. **Trim Size:** 13 x 22. **Cols./Page:** 6. **Col. Width:** 2 1/16 inches. **Col. Depth:** 21 inches. **Key Personnel:** Cynthia Kros, Coordinating Ed.; Isabel Hofmeyr, Editor. **ISSN:** 0258-2473. **Subscription Rates:** US$137 individuals print only; US$652 individuals print and online. **URL:** http://www.sahs.org.za/index.php/journal.html.

Ladysmith

50546 ■ Lotus FM - Ladysmith - 87.9 MHz
100 Old Fort Rd.
Private Bag 1337
Durban 4000, Republic of South Africa
Ph: 27 31 3625445
Fax: 27 31 3625202
E-mail: lotus@lotusfm.co.za
Format: Public Radio. **Operating Hours:** Continuous. **Key Personnel:** Kamsiliya Arumugam, Contact, phone 27 31 3625448, kamsiliya@lotusfm.co.za; Sagren Naidoo, Contact, phone 27 31 3625211, sagren@lotusfm.co.za. **URL:** http://www.lotusfm.co.za/portal/site/LotusFM/menuitem.a13733dc3e9a0bad5729 4 f945401aeb9/.

Lenasia

50547 ■ African Safety Promotion
African Journals Online
c/o Lyndsey Louri
PO Box 1087
Lenasia 1820, Republic of South Africa
Ph: 27 118 571142
Fax: 27 118 571770
Publisher E-mail: info@ajol.info
Peer-reviewed journal covering the field of injury prevention and safety promotion in Africa. **Subtitle:** A Journal of Injury and Violence Prevention. **Founded:** 1929. **Freq:** Semiannual. **Print Method:** Offset. **Cols./Page:** 6. **Col. Width:** 26 nonpareils. **Col. Depth:** 301 agate lines. **Key Personnel:** Lyndsey Lourie, Contact, lourilc@unisa.ac.za. **ISSN:** 1728-774X. **URL:** http://ajol.info/index.php/asp.

50548 ■ MW-AM - 1548
PO Box 2580
Lenasia 1820, Republic of South Africa
Ph: 27 11 8547022
Fax: 27 11 8547024
Format: Ethnic; Religious. **Founded:** Apr. 10, 1997. **Operating Hours:** 5a.m-11p.m Daily. **Key Personnel:** Ismail Variava, Program Mgr., isv@radioislam.co.za. **URL:** http://radioislam.orgza.info/a/index.php.

Linton Grange

50549 ■ BayFM - 107.9
PO Box 10991
Linton Grange 6015, Republic of South Africa
Fax: 27 866586143
E-mail: info@bayfm.co.za
Format: Adult Contemporary; Talk; Top 40. **Founded:** 1995. **Formerly:** CBFM (2004). **Operating Hours:** Continuous. **Ad Rates:** $70-250 for 30 seconds. **URL:** http://www.bayfm.co.za.

Lynnwood Ridge

50550 ■ Quest
Academy of Science of South Africa
PO Box 72135
Lynnwood Ridge 0040, Republic of South Africa
Ph: 27 128 436482
Fax: 27 866 810143
Publisher E-mail: admin@assaf.org.za
Magazine for covering South Africa's scientific research in the natural sciences, technology, humanities, and all

Circulation: ★ = ABC; △ = BPA; ◆ = CAC; • = CCAB; ❑ = VAC; ⊕ = PO Statement; ‡ = Publisher's Report; Boldface figures = sworn; Light figures = estimated.

Gale Directory of Publications & Broadcast Media/147th Ed.   **5433**

areas that use evidence-based research. **Subtitle:** Science for South Africa. **Founded:** 1967. **Freq:** Quarterly. **Print Method:** Offset. **Trim Size:** 13 x 21 1/2. **Cols./Page:** 6. **Col. Width:** 2 inches. **Col. Depth:** 21 1/2 inches. **Key Personnel:** George Ellis, Editorial Board; Wieland Gevers, Editorial Board; Jonathan Jansen, Editorial Board; Dr. Briget Farham, Editorial Board; Graham Baker, Editorial Board. **ISSN:** 1729-830X. **URL:** http://www.assaf.co.za/?page_id=349; http://www.questsciencemagazine.co.za/.

50551 ■ South African Journal of Science
Academy of Science of South Africa
PO Box 72135
Lynnwood Ridge 0040, Republic of South Africa
Ph: 27 128 436482
Fax: 27 866 810143
Publisher E-mail: admin@assaf.org.za
Multidisciplinary journal covering life sciences, agriculture, biology, geography, geology, anthropology, and climatology. **Founded:** 1886. **Freq:** Monthly 10/yr. **Print Method:** Offset. **Trim Size:** 8 x 10 1/2. **Cols./Page:** 3. **Col. Width:** 2 1/4 inches. **Col. Depth:** 140 agate lines. **Key Personnel:** Graham Baker, Editor; Michael Cherry, Editor-in-Chief. **ISSN:** 0038-2353. **Subscription Rates:** R 400 individuals; R 610 institutions; US$145 U.S. overseas. **URL:** http://www.assaf.co.za/?page_id=346; http://www.sajs.co.za/index.php/SAJS/about/editorialTEAM.

Matieland

50552 ■ Agrekon
Agricultural Economics Association of South Africa
Private Bag X3060
Matieland 7602, Republic of South Africa
Journal promoting research and discussions on agricultural and economic issues related to southern Africa. **Freq:** Quarterly. **Key Personnel:** Nick Vink, Editor, nv@sun.ac.za. **ISSN:** 0303-1853. **Subscription Rates:** R 150 individuals in South Africa (Rand monetary area); R 150 elsewhere in Africa; US$40 individuals outside Africa; R 50 individuals single copy; Free AEASA members. **URL:** http://www.aeasa.org.za/; http://www.journals.co.za/ej/ejour_agrekon.html.

50553 ■ SATJ
University of Stellenbosch
Centre for Theatre and Performance Studies
c/o Director - CTPS
Drama Dept.
PO Box X1
Matieland 7602, Republic of South Africa
Ph: 27 218 083216
Fax: 27 218 083086
Publication E-mail: satj@sun.ac.za
Publisher E-mail: satj@sun.ac.za
Journal covering theater and the performing arts, with emphasis on South Africa. Featuring the history, theory and practice of the performing arts, as well as the methodology of research of theater. **Subtitle:** South African Theatre Journal. **Founded:** 1876. **Freq:** Annual. **Print Method:** Offset. **Trim Size:** 14 x 22 3/4. **Cols./Page:** 6. **Col. Width:** 26 nonpareils. **Col. Depth:** 301 agate lines. **Key Personnel:** Temple Haupfleisch, Editor; Edwin Hees, Asst. Ed.; Rebecca Smart, Tech. Ed. **ISSN:** 1013-7548. **Subscription Rates:** R 40 individuals South Africa; US$40 individuals abroad; R 60 institutions South Africa; US$60 institutions abroad. **URL:** http://sun025.sun.ac.za/portal/page/portal/Arts/Departments/drama/research/Tab3.

50554 ■ South African Music Studies
Society for Research in Music
PO Box 3211
Matieland 7602, Republic of South Africa
Ph: 27 82 8815825
Fax: 27 86 5253704
Publication E-mail: sasrim@gmail.com
Publisher E-mail: sasrim@gmail.com
Journal covering South African and other music. **Founded:** 1981. **Freq:** Annual. **Trim Size:** 18.5 x 25 cm. **Key Personnel:** Kofi Agawu, Editorial Board; Gregory Barz, Editorial Board. **ISSN:** 0258-509X. **Subscription Rates:** US$100 individuals; R 600 institutions; R 100 members ordinary; R 120 institutions; R 40 students; R 14 individuals by surface; R 90 individuals by air; R 250 institutions by surface or by air. **Remarks:** Accepts advertising. **URL:** http://www.sasrim.ac.za/

index.php?page=3. **Also known as:** SAMUS. **Formerly:** South African Journal of Musicology. **Ad Rates:** BW: R 600. **Circ:** Paid 125, Non-paid 14

50555 ■ M-FM - 92.6
PO Box 3426
Matieland 7602, Republic of South Africa
Ph: 27 21 8083098
Fax: 27 21 8084814
E-mail: mfm@mfm.sun.ac.za
Format: Eclectic; Talk; Educational; Information; News; Adult Contemporary. **Operating Hours:** Continuous. **Key Personnel:** Martin de Abreu, Station Mgr., sm@mfm.sun.ac.za; Steyn du Toit, Program Mgr., program@mfm.sun.ac.za; Jacques Visagie, Operations Mgr., ops@mfm.sun.ac.za; Charlene Wicomb, Admin./Finance Mgr., admin@mfm.sun.ac.za. **Ad Rates:** $20-65 for 15 seconds; $40-160 for 30 seconds. **URL:** http://www.mfm.co.za/.

Mmabatho

50556 ■ Potchefstroom Electronic Law Journal
North West University
Faculty of Law
PO Box X2046
Mmabatho 2735, Republic of South Africa
Ph: 27 183 892111
Fax: 27 183 925775
Publisher E-mail: lester.mpolokeng@nwu.ac.za
Journal covering development in South Africa. **Founded:** 1982. **Freq:** Semiannual. **Print Method:** Offset. **Trim Size:** 6 x 9. **Cols./Page:** 1. **Col. Width:** 56 nonpareils. **Col. Depth:** 100 agate lines. **Key Personnel:** Prof. Christa Rautenbach, Exec. Ed.; Prof. Jan Swanepoel, Co-Ed., prfjs@puk.ac.za. **ISSN:** 1727-3781. **Subscription Rates:** Free. **URL:** http://www.puk.ac.za/fakulteite/regte/per/index.html.

Mount Edgecombe

50557 ■ African Journal on Conflict Resolution
African Centre for the Constructive Resolution or Disputes
2 Golf Course Dr.
Mount Edgecombe 4320, Republic of South Africa
Ph: 27 31 5023908
Fax: 27 31 5024160
Publisher E-mail: info@accord.org.za
Journal focusing on conflict resolution with inputs emerging from African universities, colleges and organizations. **Founded:** 1999. **Freq:** Semiannual. **Key Personnel:** Prof. Jannie Malan, Editor; Prof. Jakes Gerwel, Editor; Tor Sellstrom, Editor. **Subscription Rates:** US$749 individuals. **URL:** http://www.accord.org.za/publications/ajcr.

50558 ■ Conflict Trends Magazine
African Centre for the Constructive Resolution or Disputes
2 Golf Course Dr.
Mount Edgecombe 4320, Republic of South Africa
Ph: 27 31 5023908
Fax: 27 31 5024160
Publisher E-mail: info@accord.org.za
Magazine offering at-a-glance overviews of both developments in conflicts and positive steps towards renaissance on the continent of Africa, including in-depth articles focusing on conflict analysis. **Freq:** Quarterly. **Key Personnel:** Vasu Gounden, Editor-in-Chief; Venashri Pillay, Managing Editor. **ISSN:** 1561-9818. **URL:** http://www.journals.co.za/ej/ejour_accordc.html.

Newtown

50559 ■ Kaya-FM - 95.9
PO Box 434
Newtown 2113, Republic of South Africa
Ph: 27 11 6349500
Fax: 27 11 6349574
E-mail: pr@kayafm.co.za
Format: Adult Contemporary; Talk; Jazz; Sports; Music of Your Life. **Founded:** Aug. 1997. **Operating Hours:** Continuous. **Ad Rates:** $150-2460 for 30 seconds. **URL:** http://www.kayafm.co.za/.

Overport

50560 ■ Transformation
PO Box 37432

Overport 4067, Republic of South Africa
Publication E-mail: transform@ukzn.ac.za
Journal covering contemporary South African society in transition, the surrounding region, and the global context affecting southern African developments. **Founded:** 1987. **Freq:** 3/yr. **Key Personnel:** John Daniel, Editor; Shirley Brooks, Editor; Gerhard Mare, Editor; Lindy Stiebel, Editor; Imraan Valodia, Editor; Monique Marks, Editor; Bill Freund, Editor. **Subscription Rates:** R 120 individuals; R 240 institutions; 40 individuals U.K. and Europe; 50 institutions U.K. and Europe; US$60 individuals; US$75 institutions; US$22 single issue; 15 single issue U.K. and Europe. **URL:** http://www.transformation.und.ac.za.

Paarl

50561 ■ Encounter Southern Africa
Southern Africa Places
PO Box 3422
Paarl 7620, Republic of South Africa
Ph: 27 218 723210
Fax: 27 218 723212
Consumer magazine covering travel and tourism in Southern Africa. **Remarks:** Accepts advertising. **URL:** http://www.encounter.co.za. **Circ:** (Not Reported)

Parklands

50562 ■ Essentials
Box 1346
Parklands 2121, Republic of South Africa
Ph: 27 011 8890808
Fax: 27 011 8890792
Publication E-mail: essentialsfeedback@caxton.co.za
Consumer magazine covering inspirational and other issues for women. **Subtitle:** Inspiration to make the most of your life. **Founded:** Nov. 1994. **Freq:** Monthly. **Print Method:** gravure. **Trim Size:** 210 x 276 cm. **Key Personnel:** Danielle Weakley, Editor. **Subscription Rates:** R 158 individuals 12 months; R 79 individuals 6 months. **Remarks:** Accepts advertising. **URL:** http://www.essentials.co.za/index.php?pIGcms_nodesIGcms_nodesUID=d5c9ea8351878f5897bc6d759a63920f. **Ad Rates:** BW: R 33,400. **Circ:** Paid ★76,295

Parkview

50563 ■ Vulture News
Vulture Study Group
Private Bag X11
Parkview 2122, Republic of South Africa
Ph: 27 11 6468617
Fax: 27 11 4861506
Publisher E-mail: vsg@ewt.org.za
Publication covering wildlife conservation. **Freq:** Semiannual. **ISSN:** 1606-7479. **Subscription Rates:** R 250 individuals. **URL:** https://www.ewt.org.za/Getinvolved/ourpublications.aspxVultureNews.

Pietermaritzburg

50564 ■ African Journal of Aquatic Science
National Inquiry Services Centre (Pty.) Ltd.
81 Tatham Rd.
Pietermaritzburg 3201, Republic of South Africa
Ph: 27 333 442789
Fax: 27 333 442789
Publisher E-mail: sales@nisc.co.za
Aquatic Science journal covering African waters. Areas of interest including limnology, hydrobiology, estuarine and coastal marine science, ecology, conservation, biomonitoring, management, water quality, ecotoxicology, biological interactions, physical properties and human impacts on aquatic systems. **Freq:** 3/yr. **Key Personnel:** Mike Schramm, Publishing Mgr., publishing@nisc.co.za; Dr. Wynand Vlok, President, wynand.vlok@gmail.com; Dr. Jan Roos, Vice President, roosjc.sci@ufs.ac.za; Mike Coke, Editor, mdcoke@futurenet.co.za; Prof. Brian Marshall, Editorial Review Board. **ISSN:** 1608-5914. **Subscription Rates:** R 578.50 individuals print and online; R 468 individuals online only, Africa; R 890 institutions print and online, South Africa; R 785 institutions online only, Africa. **URL:** http://www.dwaf.gov.za/iwqs/sasaqs/journal.htm; http://www.nisc.co.za/journals?id=2.

50565 ■ African Journal of Range and Forage Science
NISC Proprietary Ltd.
PO Box 41
Hilton
Pietermaritzburg 3245, Republic of South Africa
Ph: 27 331 3903113
Fax: 27 86 6227576
Publication E-mail: pscoging@pan.uzulu.ac.za
Publisher E-mail: sales@nisc.co.za
African journal dedicated to promoting the understanding of processes that affect forage production of rangelands and pastures in Africa. Printed in English. **Founded:** 1985. **Freq:** 3/yr. **Print Method:** Litho. **Trim Size:** 210 x 277 mm. **Key Personnel:** Nicky Allsopp, Editorial Advisory Panel; Luthando Dziba, Assoc. Ed.; Freyni du Toit, Admin. Mgr. **ISSN:** 1022-0119. **Subscription Rates:** R 965 institutions print & online; R 750 institutions online only; R 579 individuals; R 450 individuals online only. **Remarks:** Advertising accepted; rates available upon request. **URL:** http://www.nisc.co.za/journals?id=3. **Circ:** Paid 196

50566 ■ African Zoology
Zoological Society of Southern Africa
School of Biological & Conservation Sciences
University of KwaZulu-Natal
Post Bag X01
Pietermaritzburg 3209, Republic of South Africa
Ph: 27 332 605127
Fax: 27 332 605105
Journal publishing research articles and short communications on zoology in Africa and surrounding oceans, seas and islands. **Freq:** Semiannual. **Key Personnel:** Dr. G.N. Bronner, Assoc. Ed., gbronner@botzoo.uct.ac.za; Nico Dippenaar, Managing Editor, nicod@pixie.co.za; Prof. Hannes van Wyk, Editor, jhvw@sun.ac.za; Prof. LeFras Mouton, Editor, pnm@sun.ac.za. **ISSN:** 1562-7020. **URL:** http://www.zssa.co.za/.

50567 ■ ESARBICA Journal
African Journals Online
U.S. Department of of Information Studies
School of Human & Social Studies
University of KwaZulu-Natal
Private Bag X01
Pietermaritzburg 3209, Republic of South Africa
Ph: 27 33 2605972
Fax: 27 33 2605092
Publisher E-mail: info@ajol.info
Peer-reviewed journal covering the field of knowledge management and indigenous knowledge systems. **Subtitle:** Journal of the Eastern and Southern Africa Regional Branch of the International Council on Archives. **Freq:** Annual. **Key Personnel:** Dr. Patrick Ngulube, Editor, ngulubep@ukzn.ac.za; Peter Sebina, Dep. Ed. **ISSN:** 0376-4753. **Subscription Rates:** US$20 individuals. **URL:** http://ajol.info/index.php/esarjo.

50568 ■ Indilinga
Indilinga: African Journal of Indigenous Knowledge Systems
PO Box 266
Msunduzi
Pietermaritzburg 3231, Republic of South Africa
Publisher E-mail: qmkabela@gmail.com
Journal dealing with circular orientation of indigenous African communities. **Subtitle:** African Journal of Indigenous Knowledge Systems. **Freq:** Semiannual. **Key Personnel:** Queeneth Mkabela, Editor-in-Chief, qmkabela@gmail.com; Sihawu Ngubane, Managing Editor; Solvi Lillejord, Assoc. Ed. **ISSN:** 1683-0296. **Subscription Rates:** R 500 institutions; US$150 other countries; US$250 institutions, other countries; R 300 individuals. **URL:** http://ajol.info/index.php/indilinga.

50569 ■ Scientia Horticulturae
Elsevier Science Inc.
c/o J.P. Bower, Ed.-in-Ch.
Dept. of Horticultural Science
University of KwaZulu-Natal
P/Bag X01 Scottsville
Pietermaritzburg 3209, Republic of South Africa
Publisher E-mail: usinfo-ehelp@elsevier.com
Journal publishing original research on horticultural crops. **Founded:** 1973. **Freq:** 16/yr. **Print Method:** Offset. **Trim Size:** 5 1/2 x 8 1/2. **Cols./Page:** 1. **Col.**
Width: 50 nonpareils. **Col. Depth:** 100 agate lines. **Key Personnel:** G.H. Barry, Editorial Advisory Board; W. Hackett, Editorial Advisory Board; R.L. Geneve, Editorial Advisory Board; X.X. Deng, Editor-in-Chief; G.C. Douglas, Editorial Board Members; J.P. Bower, Editor-in-Chief; W. Guo, Editorial Board Member; S.J. Wellensiek, Founding Ed.; V. Kesavan, Editorial Board Member. **ISSN:** 0304-4238. **Subscription Rates:** 273,600¥ institutions; US$2,311 institutions, other countries except Europe, Japan and Iran; EUR1,065 institutions for European countries and Iran. **URL:** http://www.elsevier.com/wps/find/journaldescription.cws_home/503316/descriptiondescription.

50570 ■ Lotus FM - Pietermaritzburg - 88.3 MHz
100 Old Fort Rd.
Private Bag 1337
Durban 4000, Republic of South Africa
Ph: 27 31 3625445
Fax: 27 31 3625202
E-mail: lotus@lotusfm.co.za
Format: Public Radio. **Operating Hours:** Continuous. **Key Personnel:** Kamsiliya Arumugam, Contact, phone 27 31 3625448, kamsiliya@lotusfm.co.za; Sagren Naidoo, Contact, phone 27 31 3625211, sagren@lotusfm.co.za. **URL:** http://www.lotusfm.co.za/portal/site/LotusFM/menuitem.a13733dc3e9a0bad5729 4 f945401aeb9/.

Pinegowrie

50571 ■ Gadget
Media Africa
PO Box 752
Pinegowrie 2123, Republic of South Africa
Ph: 27 117 827003
Fax: 27 117 827063
Online consumer magazine covering technology. **Subtitle:** The Magazine of Personal Technology. **Freq:** Daily. **Key Personnel:** Sean Bacher, Editor; Arthur Goldstuck, Editor-in-Chief, phone 27 11 7827003, fax 27 11 7827063, arthurg@internet.org.za. **Subscription Rates:** Free email. **URL:** http://www.gadget.co.za.

50572 ■ LMS—Laboratory Marketing Spectrum
Wilbury & Claymore
PO Box 2177
Pinegowrie 2123, Republic of South Africa
Ph: 27 117 874696
Fax: 27 117 871819
Publisher E-mail: info@wilbury.co.za
Trade magazine covering laboratory equipment. **Founded:** 1983. **Freq:** Bimonthly. **Print Method:** Offset litho. **Trim Size:** 210 x 297 mm. **Subscription Rates:** R 171 individuals; US$45 other countries airmail. **Remarks:** Accepts advertising. **URL:** http://wilbury.co.za/brands/. **Former name:** Labquip. **Circ:** ★5,833

Pinelands

50573 ■ Journal of Endocrinology, Metabolism and Diabetes of South Africa
African Journals Online
Private Bag X1
Pinelands 7430, Republic of South Africa
Ph: 27 21 5306520
Fax: 27 21 5314126
Publisher E-mail: info@ajol.info
Peer-reviewed journal covering topics about endocrinology, metabolism, and diabetes. **Freq:** 3/yr. **Key Personnel:** Prof. Stephen Hough, Editor, fsh@sun.ac.za; Daniel J. Ncayiyana, Editor; J.P. van Niekerk, Dep. Ed.; Fraser Pirie, Editor; Emma Buchanan, Asst. Ed. **ISSN:** 0038-2469. **URL:** http://ajol.info/index.php/jemdsa.

50574 ■ South African Journal of Obstetrics and Gynaecology
African Journals Online
Private Bag X1
Pinelands 7430, Republic of South Africa
Ph: 27 21 5306520
Fax: 27 21 5314126
Publisher E-mail: info@ajol.info
Peer-reviewed journal focusing on obstetrics and gynecology. **Freq:** 3/yr. **Print Method:** Offset. **Trim Size:** 8 1/4 x 10 7/8. **Cols./Page:** 3 and 2. **Col. Width:** 26 and 40 nonpareils. **Col. Depth:** 116 agate lines. **Key Personnel:** Athol Kent, Editor, atholkent@mweb.co.za; Emma Buchanan, Asst. Ed.; M. Marivate, Assoc. Ed. **ISSN:**
0038-2329. **URL:** http://ajol.info/index.php/sajog.

50575 ■ South African Journal of Psychiatry
African Journals Online
Private Bag X1
Pinelands 7430, Republic of South Africa
Ph: 27 21 5306520
Fax: 27 21 5314126
Publisher E-mail: info@ajol.info
Peer-reviewed journal covering information on psychiatry. **Freq:** Quarterly. **Key Personnel:** C.W. van Staden, Editor, cwvanstaden@icon.co.za. **ISSN:** 0038-2469. **URL:** http://ajol.info/index.php/sajpsyc.

50576 ■ South African Journal of Radiology
African Journals Online
Private Bag X1
Pinelands 7430, Republic of South Africa
Ph: 27 21 5306520
Fax: 27 21 5314126
Publisher E-mail: info@ajol.info
Peer-reviewed journal about scientific knowledge in radiology. **Founded:** Jan. 1942. **Freq:** Quarterly. **Print Method:** Sheet-fed offset. **Trim Size:** 8 x 10 7/8. **Cols./Page:** 3. **Col. Width:** 26 nonpareils. **Col. Depth:** 133 agate lines. **Key Personnel:** Mala Modi, Editorial Board; Jan Lotz, Editor-in-Chief, lotz@sun.ac.za; Alan Scher, Editorial Board; Sawas Andronikou, Editorial Board; Steve Beningfield, Editorial Board; Peter Corr, Editorial Board; Julia Casciola, Production Ed.; Leonie Scholtz, Editorial Board; Malan van Rensburg, Editorial Board. **ISSN:** 0038-2469. **URL:** http://ajol.info/index.php/sajr.

50577 ■ South African Journal of Surgery
African Journals Online
Private Bag X1
Pinelands 7430, Republic of South Africa
Ph: 27 21 5306520
Fax: 27 21 5314126
Publisher E-mail: info@ajol.info
Peer-reviewed journal containing papers related to surgery. **Key Personnel:** Susan Parkes, Editor, susan.parkes@wits.ac.za; J.E.J. Krige, Editor; G.J. Oettle, Editor. **ISSN:** 0038-2361. **URL:** http://ajol.info/index.php/sajs.

Port Elizabeth

50578 ■ Obiter
Nelson Mandela Metropolitan University
Faculty of Law
PO Box 77000
Port Elizabeth 6031, Republic of South Africa
Ph: 27 41 5042593
Fax: 27 41 5042574
Publisher E-mail: info@nmmu.ac.za
Journal covering various aspects of law. **Founded:** 1927. **Freq:** 3/yr. **Print Method:** Offset. **Trim Size:** 6 x9. **Cols./Page:** 1. **Col. Width:** 52 nonpareils. **Col. Depth:** 100 agate lines. **Key Personnel:** Prof. Adriaan Van der Walt, Editor, adriaan.vanderwalt@nmmu.ac.za; Hilda Fisher, Contact, hilda.fisher@nmmu.ac.za. **ISSN:** 1682-5853. **Subscription Rates:** R 210 individuals. **URL:** http://www.nmmu.ac.za/default.asp?id=7855&bhcp=1.

50579 ■ Lotus FM - Port Elizabeth - 98.3 MHz
100 Old Fort Rd.
Private Bag 1337
Durban 4000, Republic of South Africa
Ph: 27 31 3625445
Fax: 27 31 3625202
E-mail: lotus@lotusfm.co.za
Format: Public Radio. **Operating Hours:** Continuous. **Key Personnel:** Kamsiliya Arumugam, Contact, phone 27 31 3625448, kamsiliya@lotusfm.co.za; Sagren Naidoo, Contact, phone 27 31 3625211, sagren@lotusfm.co.za. **URL:** http://www.lotusfm.co.za/portal/site/LotusFM/menuitem.a13733dc3e9a0bad5729 4 f945401aeb9/.

Port Shepstone

50580 ■ Lotus FM - Port Shepstone - 88.2 MHz
100 Old Fort Rd.
Private Bag 1337
Durban 4000, Republic of South Africa
Ph: 27 31 3625445
Fax: 27 31 3625202

Circulation: ★ = ABC; △ = BPA; ♦ = CAC; • = CCAB; ❏ = VAC; ⊕ = PO Statement; ‡ = Publisher's Report; Boldface figures = sworn; Light figures = estimated.

Gale Directory of Publications & Broadcast Media/147th Ed.   5435

E-mail: lotus@lotusfm.co.za
Format: Public Radio. **Operating Hours:** Continuous. **Key Personnel:** Kamsiliya Arumugam, Contact, phone 27 31 3625448, kamsiliya@lotusfm.co.za; Sagren Naidoo, Contact, phone 27 31 3625211, sagren@lotusfm.co.za. **URL:** http://www.lotusfm.co.za/portal/site/LotusFM/menuitem.a13733dc3e9a0bad5729 4 f945401aeb9/.

Pretoria

50581 ■ Africa Insight
African Journals Online
PO Box 630
Pretoria 0001, Republic of South Africa
Publisher E-mail: info@ajol.info
Peer-reviewed journal promoting insight into the process of change in Africa. Topics include political trends and events, democratization, economic issues, regional cooperation, international relations, education and training, and health hazards. **Founded:** June 11, 1890. **Freq:** Quarterly. **Print Method:** Offset. **Trim Size:** 13 x 21. **Cols./Page:** 6. **Col. Width:** 25 nonpareils. **Col. Depth:** 301 agate lines. **Key Personnel:** Elizabeth La Roux, Editor-in-Chief; Robyn Grimsley, Asst. Ed., robyn@ai.org.za. **ISSN:** 0256-2804. **Subscription Rates:** US$45 elsewhere; US$120 by mail individual; R 200 individuals for South Africa, Lesotho, Namibia and Swaziland; R 400 institutions for South Africa, Lesotho, Namibia and Swaziland; US$90 elsewhere institutional and corporate; US$150 by mail institutional and corporate; US$15 single issue; R 35 single issue. **URL:** http://ajol.info/index.php/ai.

50582 ■ Africa Institute Occasional Papers
Africa Institute
Africa Institute of South Africa
PO Box 630
Pretoria 0001, Republic of South Africa
Peer-reviewed journal focusing on political, socio economic, international and development issues in contemporary Africa. **URL:** http://www.einaudi.cornell.edu/africa/publications/occasional.asp.

50583 ■ African Journal of Cross-Cultural Psychology and Sport Facilitation
African Journals Online
PO Box 392
Pretoria, Republic of South Africa
Publisher E-mail: info@ajol.info
Peer-reviewed journal covering theoretical propositions and research in behavioral disorders, marriage and family issues in Africa and other parts of the world. Also includes health psychology, mental health studies, anthropological investigations, and ecumenical behaviors. **Freq:** Annual. **Key Personnel:** Prof. Dele Braimoh, Managing Editor, dbraimoh@yahoo.com; Dr. J. Aizoba, Editorial Board, jaizoba2002@yahoo.co.uk; Dr. O.O. Omotayo, Editorial Board. **ISSN:** 1119-7056. **Subscription Rates:** N 5,000 individuals; US$150 other countries. **URL:** http://ajol.info/index.php/ajcpsf.

50584 ■ Africanus
University of South Africa
Department of Development Administration
PO Box 392
Pretoria 0003, Republic of South Africa
Ph: 27 124 296813
Publisher E-mail: dbeerfc@unisa.ac.za
Journal covering the Transvaal region of South Africa. **Founded:** Oct. 7, 1916. **Freq:** Annual. **Print Method:** Offset. **Trim Size:** 13 x 21 1/2. **Cols./Page:** 6. **Col. Width:** 2 1/16 inches. **Col. Depth:** 21 1/2 inches. **Key Personnel:** Prof. Linda Cornwell, Editor, cornwl@unisa.ac.za; Prof. Frik de Beer, Editorial Committee, debeerfc@unisa.ac.za.; Prof. Peter Stewart, Editorial Committee, stewapds@unisa.ac.za. **ISSN:** 0304-615X. **Subscription Rates:** R 17.50 individuals; US$5 individuals. **URL:** http://www.unisa.ac.za/default.asp?Cmd=ViewContent&ContentID=932.

50585 ■ Artthrob
PO Box 30
Faerie Glen
Pretoria 0043, Republic of South Africa
Publisher E-mail: editor@artthrob.co.za
Magazine covering contemporary art in South Africa. **Subtitle:** Contemporary Art in South Africa. **Founded:** Aug. 1997. **Print Method:** Online. **Key Personnel:** Sue Williamson, Founding Ed.; Michael Smith, Managing Editor; Peter Machen, Durban Ed.; Anthea Buys, Gauteng Ed.; Chad Rossouw, Online Ed. **URL:** http://www.artthrob.co.za; http://www.artthrob.co.za/01feb/exchange.html.

50586 ■ Communicatio
University of South Africa
Department of Communication
PO Box 392
Pretoria 0003, Republic of South Africa
Journal covering communication theory and research. **Subtitle:** South African Journal for Communication Theory and Research. **Founded:** 1924. **Freq:** Semiannual. **Print Method:** Offset. Accepts mats. **Trim Size:** 6 x 9. **Cols./Page:** 1. **Col. Width:** 54 nonpareils. **Col. Depth:** 105 agate lines. **Key Personnel:** Prof. Pieter J. Fourie, Editor. **ISSN:** 0250-0167. **Subscription Rates:** R 40 individuals; US$30 individuals. **URL:** http://www.unisa.ac.za/Default.asp?Cmd=ViewContent&ContentID=934.

50587 ■ Control Engineering Practice
Elsevier Science Inc.
c/o I.K. Craig, Ed.-in-Ch.
Dept. of Electrical
Electronic & Computer Engineering
University of Pretoria
Pretoria 0002, Republic of South Africa
Publisher E-mail: usinfo-ehelp@elsevier.com
Journal providing information on automation control techniques and industrially related academics. **Founded:** 1993. **Freq:** Monthly. **Print Method:** Offset. **Trim Size:** 8 1/2 x 11. **Cols./Page:** 3. **Col. Width:** 28 nonpareils. **Col. Depth:** 140 agate lines. **Key Personnel:** E.F. Camacho, Editor, eduardo@cartuja.us.es; L. Guzzella, Editor, guzzella@imrt.mavt.ethz.ch; D. Hrovat, Editor, dhroval@ford.com; D.G. Hulbert, Editor, daveh@mintek.co.za; G.W. Irwin, Editor, g.irwin@ee.qub.ac.uk; T.H. Lee, Editor, eleleeth@nus.edu.sg; T. Samad, Editor, samad@ieee.org; Y. Xi, Editor, ygxi@sjtu.edu.cn; I.K. Craig, Editor, icraig@postino.up.ac.za; A. Kugi, Editor-in-Chief. **ISSN:** 0967-0661. **Subscription Rates:** 12,800¥ individuals; US$107 other countries except Europe, Japan and Iran; EUR97 individuals for European countries and Iran; US$2,111 institutions, other countries except Europe, Japan and Iran; EUR1,888 institutions for European countries and Iran; 250,500¥ institutions. **URL:** http://www.elsevier.com/wps/find/journaldescription.cws_home/123/descriptiondescription.

50588 ■ De Arte
University of South Africa
Department of Art History, Visual Arts and Musicology
Sunnyside Campus, Bldg. 12C
PO Box 392
Pretoria 0003, Republic of South Africa
Ph: 27 11 6709000
Publisher E-mail: uarth@unisa.ac.za
Journal covering visual arts, art history, art criticism and related disciplines. **Founded:** 1871. **Freq:** Quarterly. **Print Method:** Offset. **Cols./Page:** 6. **Col. Width:** 26 nonpareils. **Col. Depth:** 294 agate lines. **Key Personnel:** Valerie Bester, Co-Ed.; Bernadette Van Haute, Editor; Joey de Jager, Editorial Committee. **ISSN:** 0004-3389. **URL:** http://www.unisa.ac.za/default.asp?Cmd=ViewContent&ContentID=7176.

50589 ■ De Rebus
The Law Society of South Africa
304 Brooks St.
PO Box 36626
Pretoria 0102, Republic of South Africa
Ph: 27 123 668800
Fax: 27 123 620969
Publication E-mail: derebus@mweb.co.za
Publisher E-mail: lssa@lssa.org.za
Professional magazine covering law for attorneys in South Africa. **Subtitle:** The South African Attorneys Journal. **Founded:** 1958. **Freq:** Monthly. **Print Method:** Litho. **Trim Size:** 210 x 297 mm. **Cols./Page:** 4. **Col. Width:** 41 millimeters. **Col. Depth:** 250 millimeters. **Key Personnel:** Philip Van Der Merwe, Editor. **ISSN:** 0250-0329. **Subscription Rates:** R 37,000 individuals; R 28,400 students for bona fide full-time; R 28,400 individuals for retired attorneys; R 59,000 other countries other African postal union countries; R 71,500 students, other countries surface mail. **Remarks:** Accepts advertising. **URL:** http://lssa.org.za; http://www.derebus.org.za. **Ad Rates:** BW: R 7,171, 4C: R 11,208. **Circ:** Combined ★20,004

50590 ■ Education as Change
Department of Curriculum Studies, RAU
Rm. F211, Aldoel Bldg.
Cnr of George Storrar & Leyds St.
Groenkloof Campus
Pretoria, Republic of South Africa
Ph: 27 124 202966
Fax: 27 124 203003
Publisher E-mail: marieta.nieman@up.ac.za
Peer-reviewed journal publishing contributions from the field of education. **Founded:** 1878. **Freq:** Semiannual. **Print Method:** Offset. **Cols./Page:** 6. **Col. Width:** 24 nonpareils. **Col. Depth:** 303 agate lines. **Key Personnel:** Elizabeth Henning, Editor, phone 27 11 5593696, journal-ed@uj.ac.za; Leila Kajee, Assoc. Ed.; Katalin Morgan, Managing Editor. **ISSN:** 1947-9417. **Subscription Rates:** US$58 individuals; US$216 institutions online only; US$240 institutions print and online. **URL:** http://www.journals.co.za/ej/ejour_edchange.html; http://www.informaworld.com/smpp/title~content=t909559414~db=all.

50591 ■ Freeskier
University of South Africa
Department of Music
PO Box 392
Muckleneuk
Pretoria 0003, Republic of South Africa
Ph: 27 116 709000
Magazine dedicated to skiing. **Key Personnel:** Matt Harvey, Ed. /Digital media Dir., harvey@freeskier.com; Christopher Jerard, Publisher, cj@freeskier.com; Bradford Fayfield, Founder/ CEO. **Subscription Rates:** US$9.95 individuals; R 14.95 two years. **URL:** http://freeskier.com/.

50592 ■ Fundamina
Southern African Society of Legal Historians
Dept. of Jurisprudence
Pretoria 0003, Republic of South Africa
Ph: 27 012 4298412
Publisher E-mail: kroezij@unisa.ac.za
Journal covering legal history. **Subtitle:** A Journal of Legal History. **Founded:** 1942. **Freq:** Annual. **Print Method:** Offset. **Trim Size:** 9 x 11. **Cols./Page:** 3. **Col. Width:** 2 1/4 inches. **Col. Depth:** 9 3/4 inches. **Key Personnel:** H. Van Den Bergh, Editor; R. Feenstra, Honorary Ed. **ISSN:** 1021-545X. **URL:** http://www.legalhistory.org.za/Journal_Contents.htm.

50593 ■ Journal of African Earth Sciences
Elsevier Science
c/o P. Eriksson, Ed.-in-Ch.
University of Pretoria
Dept. of Earth Sciences
Pretoria 0002, Republic of South Africa
Ph: 27 124 202238
Fax: 27 123 625219
Publisher E-mail: nlinfo-f@elsevier.com
Peer-reviewed journal covering all aspects of geological investigations, especially the search for natural resources, on the African continent and surrounding Gondwana fragments. **Founded:** 1983. **Freq:** 15/yr. **Key Personnel:** P. Eriksson, Editor-in-Chief, pat.eriksson@up.ac.za; Prof. Sospeter M. Muhongo, Editor-in-Chief, phone 255 754 400900, s.muhongo@icsu-africa.org; H.A.B. Kampunzu, Ed. Emeriti; C.A. Kogbe, Founding Ed.; J. Lang, Ed. Emeriti. **ISSN:** 1464-343X. **Subscription Rates:** EUR164 individuals for European countries and Iran; US$183 individuals for all countries except Europe, Japan and Iran; 21,500¥ individuals; 361,200¥ institutions; EUR2,721 institutions for European countries and Iran; US$3,044 institutions for all countries except Europe, Japan and Iran. **Remarks:** Accepts advertising. **URL:** http://www.elsevier.com/wps/find/journaldescription.cws_home/691/descriptiondescription. **Circ:** (Not Reported)

50594 ■ Journal of Zoology
Zoological Society of London
c/o Nigel Bennett, Ed.-in-Ch.
Dept. of Zoology & Entomology
Mammals Research Institute
University of Pretoria
Pretoria 00002, Republic of South Africa
Peer-reviewed journal covering zoology. **Freq:** Monthly. **Key Personnel:** Dr. Gunther Zupanc, Editor; Nigel Bennett, Editor-in-Chief, ncbennett@zoology.up.ac.za; Tim Halliday, Editor. **ISSN:** 0952-8369. **Subscription Rates:** 1,332 institutions UK (print and online); US$2,462 institutions Americas (print and online); EUR1,692 institutions

Europe (print and online); US$2,872 other countries; 1,211 institutions UK (print only); US$2,238 institutions Americas (print only); EUR1,529 institutions Europe (print only); US$2,611 other countries print only. **Remarks:** Advertising not accepted. **URL:** http://www.blackwellpublishing.com/journal.asp?ref=0952-8369& site=1; http://www.zsl.org/info/publications/. **Circ:** (Not Reported)

50595 ■ Language Matters
University of South Africa
Department of Linguistics
Unisa Press
PO Box 392
Muckleneuk
Pretoria 0003, Republic of South Africa
Ph: 27 11 6709000
Peer-reviewed journal covering different aspects of the languages of South Africa. **Subtitle:** Studies in the Languages of Southern Africa. **Freq:** Semiannual. **Key Personnel:** Lawrie Barnes, Editor; Khombe Mangwanda, Assoc. Ed.; Christine Marshall, Assoc. Ed. **ISSN:** 1753-5395. **Subscription Rates:** US$75 individuals print only; US$246 individuals online only; US$273 individuals print and online. **URL:** http://www.informaworld.com/smpp/title~content=t777285708~db=all.

50596 ■ Management Dynamics
Southern African Institute for Management Scientists
Faculty of Economic & Management Sciences
University of Pretoria
Pretoria 0002, Republic of South Africa
Ph: 27 124 203816
Fax: 27 123 625058
Publisher E-mail: ronel.rensburg@up.ac.za
Journal covering topics on business-related disciplines including strategic management, marketing, operations, human resources, organizational behavior, consumer behavior, research methods, information systems, customer satisfaction, business education, and electronic commerce. **Subtitle:** Journal of the Southern African Institute for Management Scientists. **Founded:** 1954. **Freq:** Quarterly. **Print Method:** Offset. **Trim Size:** 8 1/2 x 11. **Cols./Page:** 2 and 3. **Col. Width:** 26 and 42 nonpareils. **Col. Depth:** 139 agate lines. **Key Personnel:** Christo Boshoff, Editor, phone 27 41 5042577, fax 27 41 5832644; Fred Geel, Admin. Asst. **ISSN:** 1019-567X. **URL:** http://thor.sabinet.co.za.

50597 ■ Musicus
University of South Africa
Department of Music
PO Box 392
Muckleneuk
Pretoria 0003, Republic of South Africa
Ph: 27 116 709000
Journal covering music syllabi, examinations, aural tests, sight-reading, and interpretation and analysis of examination pieces. **Founded:** 1947. **Freq:** Semiannual. **Print Method:** Offset. **Trim Size:** 7 1/2 x 10. **Cols./Page:** 2 and 3. **Col. Width:** 26 and 40 nonpareils. **Col. Depth:** 140 agate lines. **Key Personnel:** Japie Human, Contact; Alexander Jenner, Contact. **ISSN:** 0193-8371. **Subscription Rates:** R 45 individuals; US$30 individuals. **URL:** http://www.unisa.ac.za/default.asp?Cmd=ViewContent&ContentID=940.

50598 ■ Onderstepoort Journal of Veterinary Research
Onderstepoort Veterinary Institute
1134 Park St.
Hatfield
PO Box 8783
Pretoria 0001, Republic of South Africa
Ph: 27 12 4279700
Fax: 27 12 3423948
Professional journal covering veterinary research. **Founded:** 1933. **Freq:** Quarterly. **Trim Size:** 205 x 280 mm. **Cols./Page:** 2. **Col. Width:** 8 centimeters. **Col. Depth:** 230 millimeters. **Key Personnel:** Prof. J. Boomker, Editor, joop.boomker@up.ac.za. **ISSN:** 0030-2465. **Subscription Rates:** US$456 individuals South Africa. **Remarks:** Advertising not accepted. **URL:** http://www.journals.co.za/ej/ejour_opvet.html. **Circ:** Combined 300

50599 ■ Sahara J
African Journals Online
HSRC
Private Bag X41
Pretoria 0001, Republic of South Africa
Publisher E-mail: info@ajol.info
Peer-reviewed journal covering all topics of social aspects of HIV/AIDS. **Subtitle:** Journal of Social Aspects of HIV/AIDS Research Alliance. **Freq:** Quarterly. **Key Personnel:** Prof. Karl Peltzer, Editor, phone 27 12 3022637, fax 27 12 3022001, saharaj@hsrc.ac.za; Mercy Banyini, Tech. Support, phone 27 12 3022608, mbanyini@hsrc.ac.za. **ISSN:** 1729-0376. **URL:** http://ajol.info/index.php/saharaj.

50600 ■ Servamus
SARP Publishers
PO Box 828
Pretoria 0001, Republic of South Africa
Ph: 27 12 3285282
Safety & Security Magazine. **Founded:** 1907. **Freq:** Monthly. **Print Method:** Web. **Trim Size:** 210 x 275 mm. **Key Personnel:** Kotie Geldenhuys, Journalist, phone 27 12 3454641, kotie@servamus.co.za; Annalise Kempen, Editor, phone 27 12 3454622, fax 27 12 3455627, annalise@servamus.co.za. **ISSN:** 1015-2385. **URL:** http://www.servamus.co.za/. **Formerly:** Nongqai; Justitia; SARP; SAP. **Ad Rates:** BW: R 4,690, 4C: R 7,540. **Circ:** Paid 30,000

50601 ■ South African Journal of Agricultural Extension
African Journals Online
Dept. LEVLO
University of Pretoria
Pretoria 0002, Republic of South Africa
Ph: 27 12 4203246
Fax: 27 12 4203247
Publisher E-mail: info@ajol.info
Peer-reviewed journal focusing on agricultural extension of South Africa. **Freq:** Annual. **Print Method:** Offset. **Cols./Page:** 2. **Col. Width:** 34 nonpareils. **Col. Depth:** 117 agate lines. **Key Personnel:** Dr. Fanie Terblanche, Editor, jo.coertse@up.ac.za. **ISSN:** 0301-603X. **Subscription Rates:** R 100 individuals; US$20 individuals. **URL:** http://ajol.info/index.php/sajae.

50602 ■ South African Journal of Animal Science
South African Society of Animal Science
PO Box 13884
Hatfield
Pretoria 0028, Republic of South Africa
Ph: 27 124 205017
Fax: 27 124 203290
Publication E-mail: editor@sasas.co.za
Publisher E-mail: secretary@sasas.co.za
Journal covering animal science, including farm livestock and aquatic and wildlife species. **Founded:** 1972. **Freq:** Quarterly. **Trim Size:** 21 x 29.7 mm. **ISSN:** 0375-1589. **Subscription Rates:** 50 individuals internet only; 125 individuals internet only 1 user; 3,380 individuals internet only 1 user; 2,705 institutions; 95 individuals. **Remarks:** Accepts advertising. **URL:** http://www.sasas.co.za/. **Circ:** (Not Reported)

50603 ■ South African Journal of Labour Relations
University of South Africa
Graduate School of Business Leadership and the Department of Business Management
PO Box 392
Pretoria 0003, Republic of South Africa
Ph: 27 11 6520000
Fax: 27 11 6520299
Publisher E-mail: sbl@unisa.ac.za
Journal covering employment relations in South and Southern Africa. **Founded:** Apr. 1961. **Freq:** Quarterly. **Print Method:** Offset. **Trim Size:** 8 x 10 7/8. **Cols./Page:** 3. **Col. Width:** 13.5 picas. **Col. Depth:** 10 inches. **Key Personnel:** Prof. B.J. Erasmus, Editor; Prof. B.J. Swanepoel, Assoc. Ed. **ISSN:** 0379-8410. **URL:** http://www.journals.co.za/ej/ejour_labour.html.

50604 ■ Southern African Journal of Accountability and Auditing Research
Southern African Institute of Government Auditors
PO Box 36303
Menlo Pk.
Pretoria 0102, Republic of South Africa
Ph: 27 123 621221
Fax: 27 123 621418
Journal covering accountability and auditing related topics. **Founded:** 1920. **Freq:** Annual. **Print Method:** Offset. **Trim Size:** 11 1/4 x 16. **Cols./Page:** 4. **Col. Width:** 14 picas. **Col. Depth:** 17 1/2 inches. **Key Personnel:** H. De Jager, Editor; E.D. Agyeman, Editor; W.P. Barth, Editor. **ISSN:** 1028-9011. **URL:** http://www.saiga.co.za/publications-sajaar.htm.

50605 ■ Southern African Journal of HIV Medicine
South African Medical Association
Mediese Vereniging van Suid Afrika
PO Box 74789
Lynnwood Ridge
Pretoria 0040, Republic of South Africa
Ph: 27 124812010
Fax: 27 124812061
Publisher E-mail: mariethag@samedical.org
Peer-reviewed journal publishing papers related to HIV medicine. **Freq:** Quarterly. **Key Personnel:** Linda-Gail Bekker, Editor, linda-gail.bekker@hiv-research.org.za. **ISSN:** 0038-2469. **URL:** http://www.sajhivmed.org.za/index.php/sajhivmed; http://www.ajol.info/journal_index.php?jid=247&ab=sajhivm.

50606 ■ Southern Forest
Southern African Institute of Forestry
Postnet, Ste. 329
Private Bag X4
Menlo Park
Pretoria 0102, Republic of South Africa
Ph: 27 123 481745
Fax: 27 123 481745
Publisher E-mail: forestry@mweb.co.za
Journal containing scientific papers of interest to Southern Africa. **Subtitle:** A Journal of Forest Science. **Freq:** Triennial. **Key Personnel:** Dr. Andrew Morris, Editor, saif@mweb.co.za. **ISSN:** 1991-931X. **Subscription Rates:** R 567 individuals print + online; R 474 individuals online only; US$273 individuals print + online (international); R 945 institutions print + online; R 790 institutions online only. **URL:** http://www.saif.org.za/index.php?page=SH-forestry-journal. **Formerly:** Southern African Forestry Journal; Southern Hemisphere Forestry Journal.

50607 ■ Tydskrif vir letterkunde
African Journals Online
Humanities Bldg. 15-28
University of Pretoria
Pretoria 0002, Republic of South Africa
Ph: 27 12 4202341
Fax: 27 12 4202349
Publisher E-mail: info@ajol.info
Peer-reviewed journal covering articles on African literature. **Founded:** 1951. **Freq:** Semiannual. **Trim Size:** 8 1/2 x 11. **Cols./Page:** 3. **Col. Width:** 7 1/4 inches. **Col. Depth:** 9 1/2 inches. **Key Personnel:** Prof. Hein Willemse, Editor-in-Chief, tvl@postino.up.ac.za; Jakes Gerwel, Advisory Board; Eliza Botha, Advisory Board. **ISSN:** 0041-476X. **Subscription Rates:** R 130 individuals; US$70 individuals; R 190 institutions local subscriber; US$45 institutions foreign subscriber. **URL:** http://ajol.info/index.php/tvl.

50608 ■ Water Wheel
South African Water Research Commission
Marumati Bldg.
Frederika Street & 18th Ave.
Rietfontein
Pretoria 0003, Republic of South Africa
Ph: 27 123 300340
Fax: 27 123 312565
Publisher E-mail: info@awrc.org.za
Magazine covering various aspects of water and water research. **Founded:** 1910. **Freq:** Bimonthly. **Print Method:** Offset. **Trim Size:** 8 1/2 x 11. **Cols./Page:** 3. **Col. Width:** 27 nonpareils. **Col. Depth:** 140 agate lines. **ISSN:** 0258-2244. **URL:** http://www.wrc.org.za/Pages/KH_WaterWheel.aspx?dt=4&ms=55; .

50609 ■ Radio Pulpit-FM - 97.2
PO Box 3436
Pretoria 0001, Republic of South Africa
Ph: 27 12 3341200
Fax: 27 12 3337251
E-mail: gospel@radiokansel.co.za
Format: Religious; Contemporary Christian. **Founded:**

Circulation: ★ = ABC; △ = BPA; ◆ = CAC; • = CCAB; ❑ = VAC; ⊕ = PO Statement; ‡ = Publisher's Report; Boldface figures = sworn; Light figures = estimated.

Gale Directory of Publications & Broadcast Media/147th Ed.

5437

1981. **Operating Hours:** 4am-12am Sun, Wed, Fri; 4am-11am Mon., Tue., Thur., Sat. **Key Personnel:** Dr. Roelf Petersen, Contact. **Ad Rates:** $105-630 for 30 seconds. **URL:** http://www.radiokansel.co.za/.

Randburg

50610 ■ SA Architect
South African Institute of Architects
Private Bag 10063
Randburg 2125, Republic of South Africa
Ph: 27 117 821315
Fax: 27 117 828771
Publisher E-mail: admin@saia.org.za
Publication covering architecture. **Founded:** 1899. **Freq:** Bimonthly. **Remarks:** Advertising accepted; rates available upon request. **URL:** http://www.saia.org.za/publications.php. **Formerly:** South Arican Architect. **Circ:** (Not Reported)

Rivonia

50611 ■ Muratho
South African Translators Institute
PO Box 1710
Rivonia 2128, Republic of South Africa
Ph: 27 11 8032681
Fax: 27 86 5114971
Publisher E-mail: registrar@translators.org.za
Journal of the South African Translators Institute. **Freq:** Semiannual. **URL:** http://translators.org.za/sati_cms/index.php?frontend_action=display_text_content&content_id=1.

50612 ■ Highveld-FM - 94.7
PO Box 3438
Rivonia 2128, Republic of South Africa
Ph: 27 11 8838947
Fax: 27 11 5063393
E-mail: webmaster947@highveld.co.za
Format: News; Contemporary Hit Radio (CHR). **Operating Hours:** Continuous. **Ad Rates:** Advertising accepted; rates available upon request. **URL:** http://www.highveld.co.za.

50613 ■ 702-AM - 702
PO Box 5572
Rivonia 2128, Republic of South Africa
Ph: 27 11 5063702
E-mail: comment@702.co.za
Format: Talk; Sports; Information; News. **Owner:** Primedia Broadcasting Pty. Ltd., PO Box 3438, Rivonia 2128, Republic of South Africa. **Operating Hours:** 12a.m.-9p.m. Mon.-Fri.; 12a.m.-10p.m. Sat.; 1a.m.-10p.m. Sun. **URL:** http://www.702.co.za/.

50614 ■ Talk Radio-AM - 702
Primedia House, 2nd Fl.
5 Gwen Ln., Sandown
PO Box 5572
Rivonia 2128, Republic of South Africa
Ph: 27 11 5063702
Fax: 27 86 5012014
E-mail: comment@702.co.za
Format: Talk. **Owner:** Primedia, PO Box 3438, Rivonia 2128, Republic of South Africa. **Ad Rates:** Advertising accepted; rates available upon request. **URL:** http://www.702.co.za.

Roggebaai

50615 ■ Design Indaba Magazine
Interactive Africa
PO Box 7735
Roggebaai 8012, Republic of South Africa
Ph: 27 21 4659966
Fax: 27 21 4659978
Publication E-mail: magazine@designindaba.com
Publisher E-mail: admin@interactive.africa.com
Magazine advancing the cause of design as a communication fundamental, a business imperative and a powerful tool in industry and commerce. **Freq:** Quarterly. **Key Personnel:** Dale Cupido, Contact. **Subscription Rates:** R 160 individuals; R 290 two years; US$55 other countries; US$85 two years international; 32 individuals; 50 two years international. **URL:** http://www.designindabamag.com. **Circ:** 5,000

50616 ■ The South African Radiographer
Society of Radiographers of South Africa

Vereniging van Radiograwe van Suid-Afrika
PO Box 6014
Roggebaai 8012, Republic of South Africa
Ph: 27 21 4194857
Fax: 27 21 4212566
Publication covering medical technology, in Afrikaans and English. **Freq:** Semiannual. **Key Personnel:** P. Corr, Editorial Board; L. Munro, Editor-in-Chief. **ISSN:** 0258-0241. **Subscription Rates:** Included in membership. **Remarks:** Advertising accepted; rates available upon request. **URL:** http://www.sorsa.org.za. **Circ:** 1,800

Rondebosch

50617 ■ Archaeologies
AltaMira Press
c/o Nick Shepherd, Ed.
Centre for African Studies
University of Cape Town Private Bag
Rondebosch 07700, Republic of South Africa
Ph: 27 21 6502308
Fax: 27 21 6861505
Publisher E-mail: custserv@rowman.com
Journal focused on the world archaeologies. **Freq:** 3/yr. **Key Personnel:** Madeleine Regan, Managing Editor, archaeologies@ideasandwords.com.au; Nick Shepherd, Editor, shepherd@humanities.uct.ac.za. **Subscription Rates:** US$60 individuals; US$150 institutions; US$144 individuals 3 years; US$360 institutions 3 years; US$25 individuals single copy; US$50 institutions single copy. **Remarks:** Accepts advertising. **URL:** http://www.altamirapress.com/RLA/journals/archaeologies. **Circ:** (Not Reported)

50618 ■ Journal of the Musical Arts in Africa
African Journals Online
South African College of Music
University of Cape Town
Rondebosch 7701, Republic of South Africa
Ph: 27 21 6502626
Fax: 27 21 6502627
Publisher E-mail: info@ajol.info
Peer-reviewed journal covering musical arts in the African continent. **Freq:** Annual. **Key Personnel:** Prof. Anri Herbst, Editor-in-Chief, anri.herbst@uct.ac.za; Mike Shramm, Contact, mike@nisc.co.za. **ISSN:** 1812-1004. **URL:** http://ajol.info/index.php/jmaa.

50619 ■ Journal for the Study of Religion
African Journals Online
U.S. Department of of Religious Studies
University of Cape Town
Rondebosch 7701, Republic of South Africa
Publisher E-mail: info@ajol.info
Peer-reviewed journal covering the study of religion in Southern Africa. **Freq:** Semiannual. **Key Personnel:** David Chidester, Editor, davidc@iafrica.com. **ISSN:** 1011-7601. **Subscription Rates:** R 100 individuals; R 75 students; US$40 other countries; R 125 institutions; US$50 institutions, other countries; R 75 individuals; US$20 individuals. **URL:** http://ajol.info/index.php/jsr.

50620 ■ Language Sciences
Elsevier Science Inc.
c/o N. Love, Ed.
Dept. of Linguistics
University of Cape Town
Private Bag
Rondebosch 7700, Republic of South Africa
Publisher E-mail: usinfo-ehelp@elsevier.com
Journal devoted to language science and anthropologists, philosophers, psychologists and also sociologists. **Founded:** 1978. **Freq:** 6/yr. **Print Method:** Offset. **Trim Size:** 8 1/2 x 11. **Cols./Page:** 3. **Col. Width:** 14 picas. **Col. Depth:** 59 picas. **Key Personnel:** L. Campbell, Assoc. Ed.; S.J. Cowley, Assoc. Ed.; E.J. Francis, Assoc. Ed.; K. Allan, Assoc. Ed.; C. Goddard, Assoc. Ed.; A. Deumert, Assoc. Ed.; N.J. Enfield, Assoc. Ed.; N. Love, Editor, nigel.love@uct.ac.za; P. Carr, Assoc. Ed.; N.S. Baron, Assoc. Ed. **ISSN:** 0388-0001. **Subscription Rates:** US$929 institutions, other countries except Europe, Japan and Iran; 123,200¥ institutions; EUR929 institutions for European countries and Iran; EUR150 individuals for European countries and Iran; US$196 other countries except Europe, Japan and Iran; 21,600¥ individuals. **URL:** http://www.elsevier.com/wps/find/journaldescription.cws_home/867/descriptiondescription.

50621 ■ Marine Ornithology
Pacific Seabird Group
c/o John Cooper, Ed.-in-Ch.
Avian Demography Unit
Dept. of Statistical Sciences
University of Cape Town
Rondebosch 7701, Republic of South Africa
Publication E-mail: marine.ornithology@ec.gc.ca
Peer-reviewed international journal on marine seabirds. **Founded:** 1976. **Freq:** Biennial. **Key Personnel:** John Cooper, Editor-in-Chief, jcooper@adu.uct.ac.za; Scott Hatch, Editor, shatch@usgs.gov; Rob Barrett, Editor, robb@tmu.uit.no. **Subscription Rates:** US$90 institutions; US$40 individuals; US$20 individuals low/mid income country. **URL:** http://www.marineornithology.org/. **Formerly:** Cormorant (1976).

50622 ■ Monday Paper
University of Cape Town
Department of Communication
PO Box X3
Rondebosch 7701, Republic of South Africa
Ph: 27 21 6509111
Newspaper for staff of University of Cape Town. **Founded:** 1981. **Freq:** Weekly. **Print Method:** Form-Fed. **Key Personnel:** Megan Morris, Editor, megan.morris@uct.ac.za; Myolisi Gophe, Writer, myolisi.gophe@uct.ac.za; Helen Theron, Sr. Ed., helen.theron@uct.ac.za. **Remarks:** Accepts advertising. **URL:** http://www.uct.ac.za/mondaypaper/. **Circ:** (Not Reported)

50623 ■ The South African Geographical Journal
Society of South African Geographers
Dept. of Environmental & Geographical Science
University of Cape Town
Rondebosch 7701, Republic of South Africa
Ph: 27 216 502873
Publisher E-mail: meadows@enviro-uct.ac.za
Scholarly journal covering all aspects of geography, particularly with relevance to southern Africa. **Subtitle:** Die Suid-Afrikaanse Geografiese Tydskrif. **Founded:** 1920. **Freq:** Semiannual. **Trim Size:** A4. **Key Personnel:** M.E. Meadows, PhD, Editor; M.F. Ramutsindela, PhD, Editor. **ISSN:** 0373-6245. **Subscription Rates:** R 46 individuals; R 23 single issue. **Remarks:** Accepts advertising. **URL:** http://www.journals.co.za/ej/ejour_sageo.html. **Circ:** Paid 400

Saldanha

50624 ■ Scientia Militaria
Stellenbosch University
Faculty of Military Science (SA Military Academy)
Private Bag X2
Saldanha 7395, Republic of South Africa
Ph: 27 22 7023107
Fax: 27 22 7023060
Publisher E-mail: lizelb@ma2.sun.ac.za
Journal covering matters related to South African military. **Key Personnel:** Dr. Abel Esterhuyse, Editor; Dr. Francois Vrey, Asst. Ed.; Dr. Ian Liebenberg, Editor. **ISSN:** 1022-8136. **URL:** http://www0.sun.ac.za/scientiamilitaria/.

Salt River

50625 ■ Voice of the Cape-FM - 100.4
2 Queenspark Ave.
Salt River 7924, Republic of South Africa
Ph: 27 21 4423500
Fax: 27 21 4477271
E-mail: munadia@vocfm.co.za
Format: Ethnic; Religious; News. **Ad Rates:** Advertising accepted; rates available upon request. **URL:** http://www.vocfm.co.za.

Sandton

50626 ■ Huisgenoot
Media24
PO Box 786291
Sandton 2146, Republic of South Africa
Publication E-mail: huisgenoot_inteken@media24.com
Publisher E-mail: dvos@naspers.com
Lifestyle magazine for Afrikaans-speaking South Africans. **Freq:** Weekly. **Key Personnel:** Willem Breytenbach, Publisher; Esmar Weideman, Editor. **Remarks:** Accepts advertising. **URL:** http://www.

huisgenoot.com/. **Circ:** 355,487

50627 ■ Mshana
Media24
PO Box 785266
Sandton 2146, Republic of South Africa
Ph: 27 21 4461343
Publication E-mail: info@mshana.co.za
Publisher E-mail: dvos@naspers.com
Entertainment magazine for urban teenager. **Founded:** Mar. 2007. **Freq:** Monthly. **Trim Size:** 171 x 245 mm. **Key Personnel:** John Relihan, Publisher, phone 27 21 4461027; Anita Pyke, Editorial Publisher, phone 27 21 4461369, apyke@media24.com. **Subscription Rates:** R 6.95 single issue. **Remarks:** Accepts advertising. **URL:** http://www.media24.com/generic.aspx?i_BusinessUnitID=2&lang=Eng&i_CategoryID=79. **Ad Rates:** 4C: R 9,120. **Circ:** (Not Reported)

Saxonwold

50628 ■ The Military History Journal
South African National Museum of Military History
PO Box 52090
Saxonwold 2132, Republic of South Africa
Ph: 27 116 465513
Fax: 27 116 465256
Publisher E-mail: milmus@icon.co.za
Journal covering research and issues concerning military history. **Subtitle:** Incorporating Museum Review. **Founded:** 1967. **Freq:** Semiannual. **Print Method:** On paper. **Trim Size:** 201 x 297 mm. **ISSN:** 0026-4016. **Remarks:** Advertising not accepted. **URL:** http://www.militarymuseum.co.za. **Circ:** (Not Reported)

Scottsville

50629 ■ Neotestamentica
New Testament Society of South Africa
School of Religion & Theology
University of KwaZulu-Natal
PO Box X01
Scottsville 3209, Republic of South Africa
Publisher E-mail: neotestamentica@ukzn.ac.za
Peer-reviewed journal covering various aspects of the New Testament Society, ranging from historical to hermeneutical and methodological studies. **Founded:** 1965. **Freq:** Semiannual. **Key Personnel:** Prof. Jonathan A. Draper, Editor, draper@ukzn.ac.za; Prof. Gert J. Steyn, Book Review Ed., gert.steyn@up.ac.za. **Subscription Rates:** R 75 individuals plus 5 for postage; US$40 other countries plus 5 for postage. **URL:** http://www.neotestamentica.net/.

Silverton

50630 ■ Radio Rippel-FM - 90.5
PO Box 912-1905
Silverton 0127, Republic of South Africa
Ph: 27 123 492574
Fax: 27 123 492578
Format: Full Service; Contemporary Hit Radio (CHR). **Operating Hours:** 16 hours Daily. **Key Personnel:** Rina Browne, Admin. Mgr., rina@rippel.co.za; Rene Ehlers, Mktg. Mgr., rene@rippel.co.za; Hennie Koortzen, General Mgr., hennie@rippel.co.za. **Ad Rates:** Advertising accepted; rates available upon request. **URL:** http://www.rippel.co.za.

Stellenbosch

50631 ■ International Journal of Postharvest Technology and Innovation
Inderscience Publishers
c/o Dr. Umezuruike Linus Opara, Ed.-in-Ch.
Stellenbosch University
Faculty of AgriSciences
Stellenbosch 7602, Republic of South Africa
Publisher E-mail: editor@inderscience.com
Peer-reviewed journal offering a scientific forum for dissemination of innovative research findings and industry best practices on postharvest handling techniques, agro-processing and marketing of food and biological products of plant and animal origin. **Freq:** Quarterly. **Key Personnel:** Dr. Umezuruike Linus Opara, Editor-in-Chief, opara@sun.ac.za; Prof. Adel A. Kader, Consulting Ed.; Dr. Nigel H. Banks, Consulting Ed. **ISSN:** 1744-7550. **Subscription Rates:** EUR494 individuals print only;

EUR840 individuals online only (2-3 users); EUR672 individuals print and online. **URL:** http://www.inderscience.com/browse/index.php?journalCODE=ijpti.

50632 ■ Journal of East African Natural History
Nature Kenya
The East Africa Natural History Society
c/o Benny Bytebier, Ed.-in-Ch.
Stellenbosch University
Biochemistry Dept.
Stellenbosch X1 7602, Republic of South Africa
Publication E-mail: office@naturekenya.org
Publisher E-mail: info@naturekenya.org
Journal covering East African natural history. **Subtitle:** A Journal of Biodiversity. **Freq:** Semiannual. **Key Personnel:** Lorna Depew, Editor; Benny Bytebier, Editor-in-Chief, bytebier@ukzn.ac.za. **ISSN:** 0012-8317. **Subscription Rates:** US$40 nonmembers plus postage and handling charges; US$25 members; US$40 individuals back issues. **URL:** http://www.naturekenya.org/JournalEANH.htm.

50633 ■ Lithos
Elsevier Science Inc.
c/o Ian Buick, Ed.-in-Ch.
University of Stellenbosch
Matieland 7602
Stellenbosch, Republic of South Africa
Publisher E-mail: usinfo-ehelp@elsevier.com
Journal of petrology, mineralogy and geochemistry. **Subtitle:** An International Journal of Petrology, Mineralogy and Geochemistry. **Founded:** 1968. **Freq:** 28/yr. **Print Method:** Offset. **Trim Size:** 8 1/2 x 11. **Key Personnel:** S. Claesson, Editorial Board; Ian Buick, Editor-in-Chief, buick@sun.ac.za; G.E. Bebout, Editorial Board; J.C. Duchesne, Editorial Board; Y. Dilek, Editorial Board; S. Foley, Editorial Board; Andrew C. Kerr, Editor-in-Chief, kerra@cf.ac.uk; T. Andersen, Editorial Board; W.A. Bohrson, Editorial Board; M. Cho, Editorial Board; Nelson G. Eby, Editor-in-Chief, nelson_eby@uml.edu. **ISSN:** 0024-4937. **Subscription Rates:** EUR347 individuals for European countries and Iran; US$390 other countries except Europe; 45,800¥ individuals; US$1,813 institutions, other countries except Europe, Japan and Iran; 241,100¥ institutions; EUR1,813 institutions for European countries and Iran. **URL:** http://www.elsevier.com/wps/find/journaldescription.cws_home/503348/descriptiondescription.

50634 ■ Per Liguam
University of Stellenbosch
PO Box X1
Stellenbosch 7602, Republic of South Africa
Ph: 27 218 089111
Journal covering topics of interest to teachers, researchers, academics, language practitioners and other people involved in applied language studies. **Subtitle:** Journal of Language Learning. **Founded:** 1893. **Freq:** Semiannual. **Print Method:** Offset. **Trim Size:** 8 x 10 1/2. **Cols./Page:** 3. **Col. Width:** 27 nonpareils. **Col. Depth:** 128 agate lines. **Key Personnel:** Elaine Ridge, Editor, er@maties.sun.ac.za. **ISSN:** 0259-2312. **URL:** http://journals.sabinet.co.za/ej/ejour_perling.html.

50635 ■ South African Journal for Research in Sport, Physical Education and Recreation
African Journals Online
U.S. Department of of Sport Science
University of Stellenbosch
Private Bag X1
Matieland
Stellenbosch 7602, Republic of South Africa
Ph: 27 21 8084915
Fax: 27 21 8084817
Publisher E-mail: info@ajol.info
Peer-reviewed journal containing information about the different field of sports. **Freq:** Semiannual. **Key Personnel:** Prof. Floris J.G. Van Der Merwe, Editor; Prof. Elmarie Terblanche, Contact, et2@sun.ac.za; Dr. Kallie van Deventer, Editor, sajrsper@sun.ac.za. **ISSN:** 0379-9069. **Subscription Rates:** R 100 individuals; R 50 students; US$50 other countries. **URL:** http://ajol.info/index.php/sajrs.

50636 ■ Studies in Economics and Econometrics
Bureau for Economic Research
Vineyard Centre, Cor. Adam Tas & Devon Valley Rd.
Unit N, 1st Fl.
Onder-Papegaaiberg
Stellenbosch 7600, Republic of South Africa

Ph: 27 218 872810
Fax: 27 218 839225
Publisher E-mail: hhman@sun.ac.za
Journal covering economics. **Founded:** 1914. **Freq:** 3/yr. **Print Method:** Offset. **Trim Size:** 9 13/16 x 16. **Cols./Page:** 6. **Col. Width:** 18 nonpareils. **Col. Depth:** 224 agate lines. **ISSN:** 0379-6205. **URL:** http://www.journals.co.za/ej/ejour_bersee.html.

Sunnyside

50637 ■ Acta Criminologica
Criminological Society of Southern Africa
PO Box 28936
Sunnyside 0132, Republic of South Africa
Journal covering research findings and statistical information in the field of criminal justice. **Founded:** 1969. **Freq:** 3/yr. **Print Method:** Offset. **Cols./Page:** 6. **Col. Width:** 2 1/16 inches. **Col. Depth:** 21 1/2 inches. **Key Personnel:** Dr. Robert Peacock, Editor, robert.peacock@arts.monash.edu. **ISSN:** 1012-8093. **URL:** http://www.journals.co.za/ej/ejour_crim.html; http://www.journals.co.za/crim/acta/index.html.

Tygerberg

50638 ■ African Journal of Herpetology
Herpetological Association of Africa
c/o Mandi Alblas
Dept. of Biomedical Sciences
PO Box 19063
Tygerberg 7505, Republic of South Africa
Ph: 27 21 9389394
Fax: 27 21 9389317
Publisher E-mail: aa2@sun.ac.za
Journal covering systematics, genetics, physiology, ecology, behavioral ecology, ethnology, and morphology of African reptiles and amphibians. **Freq:** Semiannual. **Key Personnel:** G. John Measey, Editor, measey@sanbi.org. **URL:** http://web.wits.ac.za/Academic/Science/APES/Research/MWLab/HAA/AfricanJournalofHerpetology/.

50639 ■ South African Family Practice
African Journals Online
University of Stellenbosch
PO Box 19063
Tygerberg 7505, Republic of South Africa
Ph: 27 21 9389449
Fax: 27 21 9389153
Publisher E-mail: info@ajol.info
Peer-reviewed journal providing information on practicing family doctors and researchers. **Founded:** 1978. **Freq:** Bimonthly. **Print Method:** Offset. **Trim Size:** 11 1/2 x 15. **Cols./Page:** 4. **Col. Width:** 28 nonpareils. **Col. Depth:** 185 agate lines. **Key Personnel:** Prof. Pierre JT de Villiers, Editor, pjtdv@sun.ac.za. **ISSN:** 1726-426X. **URL:** http://ajol.info/index.php/safp.

Umhlanga

50640 ■ African Journal of Marine Science
Natal Sharks Board
PO Box 2
Umhlanga 4320, Republic of South Africa
Ph: 27 315 660400
Fax: 27 315 660499
Journal containing a series of papers on the biology and catch statistics of the shark species commonly caught in the net. **Key Personnel:** Paul D. Cowley, Editor; Hans M. Verheye, Editor; Mark J. Gibbons, Editor; Robert J.M. Crawford, Editor; Stan C. Pillar, Editor-in-Chief, scpillar@deat.gov.za; Grant C. Pitcher, Editor. **ISSN:** 1814-232X. **URL:** http://www.nisc.co.za/journals?id=10. **Formerly:** South African Journal of Marine Science.

Vlaeberg

50641 ■ 567-AM - 567
Private Bag 567
Vlaeberg 8018, Republic of South Africa
Ph: 27 21 4460567
Fax: 27 21 4464800
E-mail: 567webmaster@capetalk.co.za
Format: Talk; Sports; Information; News. **Operating Hours:** 12am-9p.m. Mon.-Fri.; 12am-10pm Sat.; 1am-10pm Sun. **Key Personnel:** Colleen Louw, Station Mgr., feedback@capetalk.co.za; Africa Melane, Prog. Opera-

Circulation: ★ = ABC; △ = BPA; ◆ = CAC; • = CCAB; ▢ = VAC; ⊕ = PO Statement; ‡ = Publisher's Report; Boldface figures = sworn; Light figures = estimated.

Gale Directory of Publications & Broadcast Media/147th Ed.   5439

tions Mgr., africa@capetalk.co.za; Shelley Doyle, PR & Promo., shelley@capetalk.co.za; Pippa Cohen, Sales Mgr., pippa@capetalk.co.za. **URL:** http://www.capetalk.co.za/.

Walmer

50642 ■ Algoa FM - 94.8
PO Box 5973
Walmer 6065, Republic of South Africa
Ph: 27 41 5059497
Fax: 27 41 5835555
E-mail: info@algoafm.co.za
Format: Adult Contemporary; Full Service; Oldies. **Owner:** African Media Entertainment, 5th Fl., Park Terras, 33 Princess of Wales, Parktown, Johannesburg 2162, Republic of South Africa, 27 11 4840000, Fax: 27 11 4841444. **Operating Hours:** Continuous. **Key Per-**

sonnel: Dave Tiltman, Mng. Dir.; Dennis Karantges, Sales Mgr.; Alfie Jay, Program Mgr.; Toinette Koumpan, Promotions Mgr., marketing@algoafm.co.za. **URL:** http://www.brfm.co.za.

Wits

50643 ■ South African Actuarial Journal
African Journals Online
Department of Statistics & Actuarial Science
University of the Witwatersrand
Private Bag 3
Wits 2050, Republic of South Africa
Ph: 27 11 6465332
Fax: 27 11 3396640
Publisher E-mail: info@ajol.info
Peer-reviewed journal covering actuarial research of relevance to South Africa. **Freq:** Annual. **Key Person-**

nel: Rob Thomson, Editor, rthomson@icon.co.za; Jo-Anne Friedlander, Contact, jjf@userfriendly.co.za. **ISSN:** 1680-2179. **Subscription Rates:** R 75 individuals. **URL:** http://ajol.info/index.php/saaj.

50644 ■ South African Journal of Chemistry
South African Chemical Institute
Suid-Afrikaanse Chemiese Instituut
The Secretary
PO Box 407
Wits 2050, Republic of South Africa
Ph: 27 11 7176741
Fax: 27 11 7176779
Publisher E-mail: saci.chem@wits.ac.za
South African journal covering chemistry. **Freq:** Quarterly. **Key Personnel:** T.A. Ford, Editor-in-Chief. **Subscription Rates:** R 300 institutions. **URL:** http://www.saci.co.za/index.html.

Badajoz

50645 ■ Journal of Digital Contents
Formatex Research Centre
C/Zurbaran
1 2a Planta
Oficina 1
E-06002 Badajoz, Spain
Ph: 34 924 258615
Fax: 34 924 263053
Publisher E-mail: info@formatex.org
International journal of interest to professionals in the digital design area. **Subtitle:** An International Journal. **Freq:** Quarterly. **ISSN:** 1696-313X. **URL:** http://www. formatex.org/jdc/jdc.htm.

Barcelona

50646 ■ AEBDC News
Spanish Association of Dance Sport and Competition Dancing
Asociacion Espanola de Baile Deportivo y de Competicion
C. St. Quinti, 37-45
ESC. A Entr. 2
E-08041 Barcelona, Spain
Ph: 34 93 4565167
Fax: 34 93 4557078
Publication E-mail: newtopdance@gmail.com
Publisher E-mail: info@aebdc.org
Spanish language publication covering dance. **Founded:** Jan. 2000. **Freq:** Bimonthly. **Subscription Rates:** Free. **Remarks:** Advertising accepted; rates available upon request. **URL:** http://www.aebdc.org. **Circ:** (Not Reported)

50647 ■ Afers Internacionals
Cidob
Elisabets, 12
E-08001 Barcelona, Spain
Ph: 34 933 026495
Magazine covering the study of international themes in politics and social science. **Founded:** 1983. **Freq:** Triennial. **Trim Size:** 16.6 x 23.5 cm. **Key Personnel:** Josep Ribera, Director. **ISSN:** 1133-6595. **Subscription Rates:** EUR31 individuals. **URL:** http://www.cidob.org/en/publicaciones/revistas/revista_cidob_d_afers_internacionals. **Circ:** (Not Reported)

50648 ■ AIDS Reviews
Permanyer Publications
Mallorca, 310
08037 Barcelona, Spain
Ph: 34 932 075920
Fax: 34 934 576642
Publisher E-mail: permanyer@permanyer.com
Journal publishing information on HIV/AIDS. Includes information on clinical aspects, therapy, drug resistance, vaccines, virology, evolution, immunology, pathogenesis, diagnostics, epidemiology, opportunistic infections, and prevention. **Freq:** Quarterly. **Key Personnel:** Genoveffa Franchini, Editor; Walid Heneine, Editor; Anne-Mieke Vandamme, Editor; Vincent Soriano, Editor-in-Chief. **ISSN:** 1139-6121. **Subscription Rates:** EUR100 individuals print version; EUR85 individuals electronic version; EUR200 institutions print version; EUR170 institutions electronic version. **URL:** http://www.aidsreviews.com.

50649 ■ Archipielago
Editorial Archipielago
Cardener, 23 LOW IZDA
E-08024 Barcelona, Spain
Ph: 34 932 108503
Fax: 34 932 108503
Publication E-mail: publicidad@archipielago-ed.com
Publisher E-mail: redaccion@archipielago-ed.com
Magazine covering modern culture. **Freq:** Bimonthly 5/yr. **Trim Size:** 18.5 x 26 cm. **Key Personnel:** Mateo Gamon, Contact; Amador Fernandez-Savater, Director; Dante Bernardi, Contact; Julia Varela, Editorial Board; Isabel Escudero, Director. **ISSN:** 0214-2686. **Subscription Rates:** EUR35.50 individuals Spain; EUR55 other countries; EUR125 other countries rest of world. **URL:** http://www.archipielago-ed.com/.

50650 ■ Arquitectura y Diseno
RBA Edipresse
Perez Galdos 36
E-08012 Barcelona, Spain
Ph: 34 93 4157374
Fax: 34 93 2177378
Magazine featuring topics on design and architecture. **Freq:** Monthly. **Key Personnel:** Aurea Diaz, Director; Soledad Lorenzo, Ch. Ed. **URL:** http://www.rbarevistas.com/revista.php?id=37. **Circ:** ‡47,513

50651 ■ Arxus de Miscel-lania Zoologica
Museu de Ciencies Naturals de la Ciutadella, Museu de Zoologia
Parc de la Ciutadella, s/n
E-08003 Barcelona, Spain
Ph: 34 93 2562200
Fax: 34 933 104999
Publisher E-mail: museuciencies@bcn.cat
Journal publishing papers on fauna, chorology, and descriptive ecology, mostly of the Western Mediterranean area. **Key Personnel:** Francesc Uribe, Editor; Montserrat Ferrer, Managing Editor; Oleguer Escola, Editorial Committee. **ISSN:** 1698-0476. **URL:** http://w10.bcn.es/APPS/wprmuseuciencies/Museu.GeneradorPagines?idioma=3&seccio=11_2.

50652 ■ Aula
Editorial Grao
Hurtado 29
E-08022 Barcelona, Spain
Ph: 34 934 080464
Fax: 34 933 524337
Professional magazine covering education. **Subtitle:** De Innovacion Educativa. **Founded:** 1992. **Freq:** Monthly. **Print Method:** Offset. **Trim Size:** 21 x 29.5 cm. **Cols./Page:** 3. **ISSN:** 1131-995X. **URL:** http://aula.grao.com/revistas/presentacion.asp?ID=3. **Ad Rates:** BW: EUR425, 4C: EUR725. **Circ:** Paid 4,300

50653 ■ L'Avenc
L'Avenc S.L.
Passeig de Sant Joan, 26, 2n 1a
E-08007 Barcelona, Spain
Ph: 34 93 2457921
Fax: 34 93 2654416
Publisher E-mail: lavenc@lavenc.com
Catalan language magazine covering Catalonia's history, culture and thinking and historical investigation and its analysis. **Founded:** 1977. **Freq:** Monthly 3/yr. **Trim Size:** 20.5 x 30.5 cm. **Key Personnel:** Josep M. Munoz, Director, jmmunoz@lavenc.cat. **ISSN:** 0210-0150. **Subscription Rates:** EUR55 individuals Spain; EUR105 individuals Europe; EUR155 other countries; EUR93 two years spain; EUR180 two years Europe; EUR260 other countries 2 years. **URL:** http://www.lavenc.com. **Ad Rates:** BW: 150000 Ptas. **Circ:** 8,000

50654 ■ The Barcelona Review
Correu Vell, 12 - 2
E-08002 Barcelona, Spain
Fax: 34 933 191596
Publisher E-mail: editor@barcelonareview.com
Magazine focusing on contemporary fiction. **Freq:** Bimonthly. **Key Personnel:** Jill Adams, Editor, editor@barcelonareview.com. **URL:** http://www.barcelonareview.com.

50655 ■ Cancer & Chemotherapy Reviews
Permanyer Publications
Mallorca, 310
08037 Barcelona, Spain
Ph: 34 932 075920
Fax: 34 934 576642
Publisher E-mail: permanyer@permanyer.com
Journal covering medical oncology and hemato-oncology. **Freq:** Quarterly. **Key Personnel:** Eduardo Diaz-Rubio, Editor-in-Chief; Pedro Perez-Segura, Editor. **ISSN:** 1885-740X. **Subscription Rates:** EUR100 individuals; EUR200 institutions. **URL:** http://www.cancerchemotherapyreviews.com/.

50656 ■ Cirugia Cardiovascular
Permanyer Publications
Mallorca, 310
08037 Barcelona, Spain
Ph: 34 932 075920
Fax: 34 934 576642
Publisher E-mail: permanyer@permanyer.com
Journal covering aspects of teaching and research within thoracic and cardiovascular surgery. **Freq:** Quarterly. **Key Personnel:** Carlos A. Mestres, Editor-in-Chief; Enrique Perez de la Sota, Assoc. Ed. **ISSN:** 1134-0096. **Subscription Rates:** EUR100 individuals; EUR200 institutions. **URL:** http://www.cirugiacardiovascular.org/home.asp.

50657 ■ Clara
RBA Edipresse
Perez Galdos 36
E-08012 Barcelona, Spain
Ph: 34 93 4157374
Fax: 34 93 2177378
Magazine covering beauty, fashion, children, health, relationships, news, cooking, decorating, travel, leisure and culture. **Founded:** 1992. **Freq:** Monthly. **Key Personnel:** Nuria Polo, Ch. Ed.; Laura Gonzalez, Director. **URL:** http://www.rba.es/Areas-de-Negocio/Revistas; http://www.rbaedipresse.es/revista.php?id=31. **Circ:** ‡161,874

50658 ■ Clara Deco
Edipresse Publications S.A.
Clara Muntaner 40-42
E-08011 Barcelona, Spain
Ph: 34 93 5087000

Circulation: ★ = ABC; △ = BPA; ♦ = CAC; • = CCAB; ▢ = VAC; ⊕ = PO Statement; ‡ = Publisher's Report; Boldface figures = sworn; Light figures = estimated.

Gale Directory of Publications & Broadcast Media/147th Ed.

5441

Fax: 34 93 4541322
Publisher E-mail: groupe@edipresse.com
Reference magazine for interior designing. **Founded:** 2003. **Freq:** Monthly. **Key Personnel:** Aurora Gonzalo, Ch. Ed.; Assumpta Soria Badia, Director. **URL:** http://www.edipresse.com/en/par_pays/espagne/rba_edipresse/magazines/clara_deco.

50659 ■ Comer Bien
RBA Edipresse
Perez Galdos 36
E-08012 Barcelona, Spain
Ph: 34 93 4157374
Fax: 34 93 2177378
Magazine featuring recipes for healthy home cooking. **Freq:** Monthly. **Key Personnel:** Laura Gonzalez, Director; Julia Blazquez, Ch. Ed. **URL:** http://www.rbarevistas.com/revista.php?id=2. **Circ:** ‡49,079

50660 ■ Computer Science Review
Elsevier Science Inc.
c/o J. Diaz, Ed.-in-Ch.
Fac. d'Informatica
Universitat Politecnica de Catalunya
Pau Gargallo, 5
E-08028 Barcelona, Spain
Publisher E-mail: usinfo-ehelp@elsevier.com
Journal covering computer science and related fields. **Founded:** 2007. **Freq:** 4/yr. **Print Method:** Offset. **Trim Size:** 8 1/2 x 11. **Cols./Page:** 1. **Col. Width:** 72 nonpareils. **Col. Depth:** 126 agate lines. **Key Personnel:** J.C. Bermond, Editorial Board; D. Achlioptas, Editorial Board; P. Flajolet, Editorial Board; X. Deng, Editorial Board; Y. Gurevich, Editorial Board; N. Alon, Editorial Board; J. Nesetril, Editor-in-Chief, nesetril@kam.mff.cuni.cz; J. Karhumaki, Editorial Board; G. Ausiello, Editorial Board; J. Bergstra, Editorial Board; J. Diaz, Editor-in-Chief, diaz@lsi.upc.edu. **ISSN:** 1574-0137. **Subscription Rates:** EUR241 institutions for European countries and Iran; 39,200¥ institutions; EUR328 institutions, other countries except Europe, Japan and Iran. **URL:** http://www.elsevier.com/wps/find/journaldescription.cws_home/710138/descriptiondescription.

50661 ■ Cosas de Cocina
Edipresse Publications S.A.
Perez Galdos 36
E-08012 Barcelona, Spain
Ph: 34 93 4157374
Fax: 34 93 2177378
Publisher E-mail: groupe@edipresse.com
Magazine featuring menu ideas, seasonal recipes and easy-to-make dishes. **Freq:** Monthly. **Key Personnel:** Aurea Diaz, Director; Nuria San Frutos, Ch. Ed. **URL:** http://www.edipresse.com/en/par_pays/espagne/rba_edipresse/magazines/cosas_de_cocina. **Circ:** ‡60,144

50662 ■ Cuerpomente
Edipresse Publications S.A.
Perez Galdos 36
E-08012 Barcelona, Spain
Publisher E-mail: groupe@edipresse.com
Magazine covering natural medicine, psychology and nutrition. **Freq:** Monthly. **Key Personnel:** Josan Ruiz, Ch. Ed.; Laura Gonzalez, Director. **URL:** http://www.cuerpomente.es/. **Circ:** ‡66,291

50663 ■ Dirigido
Dirigido por
Consell de Cent, 304-2-1
E-08007 Barcelona, Spain
Ph: 34 934 876202
Fax: 34 934 280896
Publisher E-mail: redaccion@dirigidopor.com
Magazine covering thematic issues in cinematography. **Founded:** 1972. **Freq:** Monthly. **Print Method:** Offset. **Trim Size:** 22 x 29.7 cm. **Key Personnel:** Angel Fabregat, President. **Subscription Rates:** US$143 individuals U.S.; 350 Ptas individuals. **URL:** http://www.dirigidopor.com/dirigidopor/Dirigido.html. **Ad Rates:** BW: EUR630. **Circ:** (Not Reported)

50664 ■ Drug News & Perspectives
Prous Science S.A.
Provenza 388
08025 Barcelona, Spain
Ph: 34 93 4592220
Fax: 34 93 4581535
Publisher E-mail: service@prous.com
A highly diversified and fully illustrated drug news-

magazine for scientists and managers in pharmaceutical research and development. **Founded:** 1988. **Freq:** 10/yr. **Key Personnel:** Patrick Sofarelli, Contact, psofarelli@prous.com. **ISSN:** 0214-0934. **Subscription Rates:** US$1,520 individuals. **Remarks:** Accepts advertising. **URL:** http://journals.prous.com/journals/servlet/xmlxsl/pk_journals.xml_home_pr. **Circ:** (Not Reported)

50665 ■ Ecologia Politica
Icaria Editorial
Arc de Sant Cristofol, 11-23
E-08003 Barcelona, Spain
Ph: 34 933 011723
Fax: 34 932 954916
Publisher E-mail: icaria@icariaeditorial.com
Magazine covering ecological issues worldwide. **Subtitle:** Cuadernos de Debate Internacional. **Freq:** Semiannual. **Trim Size:** 19 x 24 cm. **Key Personnel:** Joan Martinez Alier, Coord. **ISSN:** 1130-6378. **Subscription Rates:** 9 individuals. **URL:** http://www.icariaeditorial.com.

50666 ■ El Ciervo
El Ciervo 96 S.A.
Calvet, 56
E-08021 Barcelona, Spain
Ph: 34 932 005145
Magazine covering Christian thought and culture. **Subtitle:** Revista De Pensamiento Y Cultura. **Founded:** 1951. **Freq:** Monthly 10/yr. **Trim Size:** 24.5 x 33.7 cm. **ISSN:** 0045-6869. **Subscription Rates:** EUR49 individuals Spain; EUR64 individuals Europe; EUR73 out of country. **URL:** http://www.elciervo.es. **Circ:** (Not Reported)

50667 ■ El Farmaceutico
Ediciones Mayo S.A.
Aribau, 185-187, 2 planta
E-08021 Barcelona, Spain
Ph: 34 932 090255
Fax: 34 932 020643
Publisher E-mail: edmayo@edicionesmayo.es
Professional journal covering pharmacy topics for pharmacists in Spain. **Founded:** 1984. **Freq:** Continuous 19/yr with control & 2 extra issues. **Print Method:** Offset. **Trim Size:** 205 x 270 mm. **Cols./Page:** 3. **Col. Width:** 50 millimeters. **ISSN:** 0213-7283. **Remarks:** Accepts advertising. **URL:** http://www.edicionesmayo.es. **Ad Rates:** BW: 2,600 Ptas. **Circ:** Non-paid 20,000

50668 ■ El Farmaceutico Hospitales
Ediciones Mayo S.A.
Aribau, 185-187, 2 planta
E-08021 Barcelona, Spain
Ph: 34 932 090255
Fax: 34 932 020643
Publisher E-mail: edmayo@edicionesmayo.es
Professional magazine for pharmacy services departments in hospitals, specialists in intensive care medicine, preventive medicine, and related medical professionals. **Founded:** 1990. **Freq:** Bimonthly. **Print Method:** Offset. **Trim Size:** 205 x 270 mm. **Cols./Page:** 3. **Col. Depth:** 225 millimeters. **ISSN:** 0214-4697. **Remarks:** Accepts advertising. **URL:** http://www.edicionesmayo.es. **Ad Rates:** BW: 2,265 Ptas, 4C: 2,155 Ptas. **Circ:** Controlled 2,800

50669 ■ El Jueves
Edipresse Publications S.A.
Viladomat 135, 3
E-08015 Barcelona, Spain
Ph: 34 93 2922217
Fax: 34 93 2375824
Publisher E-mail: groupe@edipresse.com
Magazine focusing on politics, economy and society. **Freq:** Weekly. **Key Personnel:** Andres Ponton, Director. **URL:** http://www.revistas-ari.es/index.php/editoras/category/34. **Circ:** ‡74,441

50670 ■ El Mueble
Edipresse Publications S.A.
Perez Galdos 36
E-08012 Barcelona, Spain
Ph: 34 93 4157374
Fax: 34 93 2177378
Publisher E-mail: groupe@edipresse.com
Magazine containing selections of furnishings and accessories. **Freq:** Monthly. **Key Personnel:** Esther Giralt, Director. **URL:** http://www.revistas-ari.es/index.php/editoras/category/34; http://www.rba.es/. **Circ:** ‡217,434

50671 ■ El Mueble Casas de Campo
Edipresse Publications S.A.
Perez Galdos 36
E-08012 Barcelona, Spain
Ph: 34 93 4157374
Fax: 34 93 2177378
Publisher E-mail: groupe@edipresse.com
Magazine highlighting the country home decorating styles. **Freq:** Monthly. **Key Personnel:** Nacho Benavides, Director. **URL:** http://www.revistas-ari.es/index.php/editoras/category/34. **Circ:** ‡43,155

50672 ■ El Mueble Cocinas y Banos
Edipresse Publications S.A.
Perez Galdos 36
E-08012 Barcelona, Spain
Ph: 34 93 4157374
Fax: 34 93 2177378
Publisher E-mail: groupe@edipresse.com
Magazine featuring kitchen and bathroom designs. **Freq:** Monthly. **Key Personnel:** Nuria Garcia, Director. **URL:** http://www.revistas-ari.es/index.php/editoras/category/34. **Circ:** ‡20,535

50673 ■ Europa de les Nacions
Escarre International Center for the Ethnic Minorities and Nations
Centre Internacional Escarre per a les Minories Etniques i les Nacions
Rocafort, 242, bis
Catalonia
E-08029 Barcelona, Spain
Ph: 34 934 443800
Fax: 34 934 443809
Publisher E-mail: webmaster@ciemen.cat
Publication covering national sovereignty in Catalan and English. **Subtitle:** La Revista Del Ciemen. **Freq:** Quarterly. **ISSN:** 1136-5749. **URL:** http://www.ciemen.org/nacions.htm.

50674 ■ Forum
Ediciones Mayo S.A.
Aribau, 185-187, 2 planta
E-08021 Barcelona, Spain
Ph: 34 932 090255
Fax: 34 932 020643
Publisher E-mail: edmayo@edicionesmayo.es
Professional magazine covering medical meetings worldwide. **Founded:** 1982. **Freq:** Bimonthly. **Print Method:** Offset. **Trim Size:** 230 x 300 mm. **Cols./Page:** 3. **Col. Depth:** 242 millimeters. **ISSN:** 0212-9965. **Remarks:** Accepts advertising. **URL:** http://www.edicionesmayo.es. **Ad Rates:** 4C: EUR2,450. **Circ:** (Not Reported)

50675 ■ Guaraguao
Centro de Estudios y Cooperacion para America Latina
Pisuerga 2, 1o 3o
E-08028 Barcelona, Spain
Magazine covering contemporary Latin American culture. **Subtitle:** Revista de Cultura Latino Americana. **Founded:** 1996. **Freq:** Semiannual. **Trim Size:** 16 x 24 cm. **Key Personnel:** Raquel Tellosa, Editor. **ISSN:** 1137-2354. **Subscription Rates:** EUR100 individuals. **Remarks:** Accepts advertising. **URL:** http://www.revistaguaraguao.org/. **Ad Rates:** BW: 100 Ptas. **Circ:** (Not Reported)

50676 ■ Habitania
RBA Edipresse
Perez Galdos 36
E-08012 Barcelona, Spain
Ph: 34 93 4157374
Fax: 34 93 2177378
Publication E-mail: habitania@rba.es
Magazine focusing on the art of living. **Freq:** Monthly. **Key Personnel:** Natalia Klamburg, Ch. Ed.; Aurea Diaz, Director. **URL:** http://www.rbarevistas.com/revista.php?id=11. **Circ:** ‡44,184

50677 ■ Hepatology Reviews
Permanyer Publications
Mallorca, 310
08037 Barcelona, Spain
Ph: 34 932 075920
Fax: 34 934 576642
Publisher E-mail: permanyer@permanyer.com
Journal covering information on recent advances in liver disease. **Freq:** Quarterly. **Key Personnel:** Rafael Esteban, Editor-in-Chief; Maria Buti, Editor. **ISSN:** 1697-431X. **Subscription Rates:** EUR100 individuals print; EUR200 institutions print; EUR85 individuals electronic;

EUR170 institutions electronic. **URL:** http://www.hepatologyreviews.com/.

50678 ■ Historia, Antropologia y Fuentes Orales
Asociacion Historia y Fuente Oral
Sta. Llucia, 1
E-08002 Barcelona, Spain
Ph: 34 933 181195
Fax: 34 933 178327
Publisher E-mail: hayfo.revista@gmail.com
Magazine covering history and contemporaneity and oral tradition. **Subtitle:** Oral History, Anthropology and Sources. **Freq:** Semiannual. **Trim Size:** 17 x 24 cm. **Key Personnel:** Mercedes Vilanova, Director. **ISSN:** 1136-1700. **Subscription Rates:** EUR20 individuals Spain; EUR45 individuals rest of world. **URL:** http://www.hayfo.com/.

50679 ■ Historia National Geographic
Edipresse Publications S.A.
Perez Galdos 36
E-08012 Barcelona, Spain
Publisher E-mail: groupe@edipresse.com
Magazine highlighting history through portraits, investigative reports and photography. **Freq:** Monthly. **Key Personnel:** Cati Miloro, Director; Josep Maria Casals, Ch. Ed. **URL:** http://www.historiang.com/. **Circ:** ‡142,798

50680 ■ IDP
Universitat Oberta de Catalunya
Av. Tibidabo 39-43
E-08035 Barcelona, Spain
Ph: 34 93 2532323
Fax: 34 93 4175129
Publisher E-mail: secretaria_rectorat@uoc.edu
Journal on internet, law and politics. **Founded:** 1912. **Freq:** Monthly. **Print Method:** Offset. **Trim Size:** 8 1/4 x 11 5/16. **Cols./Page:** 2. **Col. Width:** 3 1/2 inches. **Col. Depth:** 9 1/2 inches. **Key Personnel:** Dr. Pere Fabra, Director. **ISSN:** 1699-8154. **URL:** http://www.uoc.edu/idp/5/cat/index.html.

50681 ■ International Microbiology
Spanish Society for Microbiology
Jordi Ferran 14, Ent.
E-08028 Barcelona, Spain
Ph: 34 934 482373
Fax: 34 933 341079
Publication E-mail: int.microbiol@microbios.org
Publisher E-mail: secretaria.sem@semicro.es
Journal dealing with all fields of microbiology and it addresses the international scientific community. **Founded:** 1998. **Freq:** Quarterly. **Key Personnel:** Lynn Margulis, Assoc. Ed.; Moselio Schaechter, Assoc. Ed.; John Skehel, Assoc. Ed. **ISSN:** 1139-6709. **Subscription Rates:** EUR300 individuals plus postage and handling. **URL:** http://www.im.microbios.org/

50682 ■ Labores del Hogar
Edipresse Publications S.A.
Perez Galdos 36
E-08012 Barcelona, Spain
Publisher E-mail: groupe@edipresse.com
Magazine featuring needlework patterns with text and illustrations. **Freq:** Monthly. **Key Personnel:** Laura Gonzalez, Director; Eulalia Ubach, Ch. Ed. **URL:** http://www.rbarevistas.com/revista.php?id=7. **Circ:** ‡53,427

50683 ■ Lecturas
Edipresse Publications S.A.
Perez Galdos 36
E-08012 Barcelona, Spain
Publisher E-mail: groupe@edipresse.com
Magazine featuring celebrities. **Freq:** Weekly. **Key Personnel:** Carmen Grasa, Ch. Ed.; Mamen Lorenzo, Ch. Ed. **URL:** http://www.rbarevistas.com/revista.php?id=13. **Circ:** ‡198,930

50684 ■ Lecturas Cocina Facil
Edipresse Publications S.A.
Perez Galdos 36
E-08012 Barcelona, Spain
Publisher E-mail: groupe@edipresse.com
Magazine providing simple and original recipes. **Freq:** Monthly. **Key Personnel:** Laura Gonzalez, Director; Mar Esteban, Ch. Ed. **URL:** http://www.rbaedipresse.es/revista.php?id=3. **Circ:** ‡81,446

50685 ■ Lecturas Especial Cocina
Edipresse Publications S.A.
Perez Galdos 36
E-08012 Barcelona, Spain

Ph: 34 93 4157374
Fax: 34 93 2177378
Publisher E-mail: groupe@edipresse.com
Magazine providing simple and easy to cook recipes for every season. **Freq:** 3/yr. **Key Personnel:** Laura Gonzalez, Director; Julia Bianquez, Ch. Ed. **URL:** http://www.edipresse.com/en/par_pays/espagne/rba_edipresse/magazines/lecturas_especial_cocina. **Circ:** ‡78,346

50686 ■ Lecturas Moda
Edipresse Publications S.A.
Perez Galdos 36
E-08012 Barcelona, Spain
Publisher E-mail: groupe@edipresse.com
Magazine featuring the latest trends in the international fashion industry. **Freq:** Semiannual. **Key Personnel:** Laura Gonzalez, Director; Xandra Sarret, Ch. Ed. **URL:** http://www.rbarevistas.com/revista.php?id=22.

50687 ■ Linea Saludable
Edipresse Publications S.A.
Perez Galdos 36
E-08012 Barcelona, Spain
Ph: 34 93 4157374
Fax: 34 93 2177378
Publisher E-mail: groupe@edipresse.com
Magazine focusing on nutrition, sports and relaxation. **Freq:** Monthly. **Key Personnel:** Laura Gonzalez, Ch. Ed.; Carme Vietez, Director. **URL:** http://www.edipresse.com/en/par_pays/espagne/rba_edipresse/magazines/linea_saludable. **Circ:** ‡68,000

50688 ■ Mente Sana
RBA Edipresse
Perez Galdos 36
E-08012 Barcelona, Spain
Ph: 34 93 4157374
Fax: 34 93 2177378
Magazine focusing on healthy living and guide to well-being. **Freq:** Monthly. **Key Personnel:** Jorge Bucay, Editor. **URL:** http://www.mentesana.es/. **Circ:** ‡118,513

50689 ■ Mundo Recambio y Taller (Spares and Workshop World)
Mundo Recambio y Taller
Paris 150 4b 3a
E-08036 Barcelona, Spain
Ph: 34 934 395564
Fax: 34 934 306853
Publisher E-mail: mryt@ceiarsis.com
Trade magazine covering the automotive aftermarket. **Subtitle:** La revista tecnica de la Automocion. **Founded:** June 1980. **Freq:** Monthly. **Print Method:** Offset. **Cols./Page:** 4. **Key Personnel:** Yvonne Rubio, Director. **ISSN:** 1139-8647. **Subscription Rates:** EUR180 individuals banners; EUR100 individuals banner 468x60 px.; EUR180 individuals minibanner 140x170 px. **Remarks:** Accepts advertising. **URL:** http://www.mundorecambioytaller.com/. **Ad Rates:** BW: EUR782, 4C: EUR1,230. **Circ:** Paid 2,500, Non-paid 7,500

50690 ■ Opera Actual
Opera Actual S.L.
Bruc, 6 Ppal 2a
E-08010 Barcelona, Spain
Ph: 34 933 191300
Fax: 34 933 107338
Publication E-mail: suscripciones@operaactual.com
Magazine covering opera. **Founded:** 1991. **Freq:** Bimonthly. **Key Personnel:** Maria Jose Ibars, Administration; Roger Alier, Pres./Founder; Joaquin Calvo, Vice President; Marcelo Cervello, Vice President; Francisco Garcia-Rosado, Director; Fernando Sans Riviere, Director. **Subscription Rates:** EUR51 individuals Spain; EUR89 individuals Europe; EUR100 individuals U.S. **URL:** http://www.operaactual.com/.

50691 ■ Patrones
Edipresse Publications S.A.
Perez Galdos 36
E-08012 Barcelona, Spain
Publisher E-mail: groupe@edipresse.com
Magazine highlighting the fashion catwalks. **Freq:** Monthly. **Key Personnel:** Laura Gonzalez, Director; Xandra Sarret, Ch. Ed. **URL:** http://www.rbaedipresse.es/revista.php?id=6. **Circ:** ‡33,397

50692 ■ PC Actual
RBA Edipresse
Perez Galdos 36
E-08012 Barcelona, Spain
Ph: 34 93 4157374

Fax: 34 93 2177378
Computer magazine featuring the latest trends and information on IT. **Freq:** Monthly. **Key Personnel:** Cati Miloro, Director; Javier Perez Cortijo, Ch. Ed. **URL:** http://www.pcactual.com/. **Circ:** ‡61,365

50693 ■ Peluquerias Hair Styles
Ediciones Prensa y Video, S.L.
Plz. de las Navas, 11
E-08004 Barcelona, Spain
Ph: 34 93 292 5840
Fax: 34 93 292 5841
Publication E-mail: info@hair-styles.com
Publisher E-mail: info@hair-styles.com
Trade magazine for hairdressers. **Founded:** Feb. 1969. **Freq:** Monthly. **Cols./Page:** 4. **ISSN:** 1134-5608. **Subscription Rates:** US$94 individuals surface mail; EUR70 individuals surface mail; EUR91 individuals airmail; US$124 individuals airmail. **Remarks:** Accepts advertising. **URL:** http://www.hair-styles.com. **Alt. Formats:** CD-ROM; Large-print. **Circ:** (Not Reported)

50694 ■ Quaderns d'Arquitectura
Col. legi d'Aquitectues de Catalunya
c/o Gustavo Gill
C/Ressello, 87-89
E-08029 Barcelona, Spain
Ph: 34 933 228161
Fax: 34 933 229205
Publisher E-mail: coac@coac.net
Magazine covering architectural works and art worldwide. **Freq:** 5/yr. **Trim Size:** 24 x 31 cm. **Key Personnel:** Lluis Ortega, Editor; Gustavo Gill, Contact, pedidos@ggili.com. **Subscription Rates:** EUR62 individuals ordinary mail in Spain; EUR73 individuals orinary mail in UE; EUR80 other countries. **Remarks:** Advertising accepted; rates available upon request. **URL:** http://quaderns.coac.net/q/index.html. **Circ:** (Not Reported)

50695 ■ Revista Espanola de Ortodoncia
Permanyer Publications
Mallorca, 310
08037 Barcelona, Spain
Ph: 34 932 075920
Fax: 34 934 576642
Publisher E-mail: permanyer@permanyer.com
Journal covering orthodontics and related fields. **Founded:** 1971. **Freq:** Quarterly. **Key Personnel:** Eliseo Plasencia, Scientific Commitee, eliseo.plasencia@permanyer.com; Joseph A. Canut, Founding Ed.; Andreu Puigdollers, Editor, andreu.puigdollers@permanyer.com. **ISSN:** 0210-0576. **Subscription Rates:** EUR65 individuals online; EUR85 individuals Spain; EUR100 other countries European Union; EUR130 other countries. **URL:** http://www.revistadeortodoncia.com/.

50696 ■ Saber Vivir
RBA Edipresse
Perez Galdos 36
E-08012 Barcelona, Spain
Ph: 34 93 4157374
Fax: 34 93 2177378
Magazine focusing on health living. **Freq:** Monthly. **Key Personnel:** Charo Sierra, Ch. Ed.; Laura Gonzalez, Director. **URL:** http://www.rbarevistas.com/revista.php?id=42. **Circ:** ‡142,798

50697 ■ Scientia Marina
Institut Ciencies del Mar de Barcelona
Passeig Martim de la Barceloneta 37-49
E-08003 Barcelona, Spain
Ph: 34 93 2309500
Fax: 34 93 2309555
Publication E-mail: scimar@icm.csic.es
Journal covering marine sciences worldwide. **Subtitle:** International Journal on Marine Sciences. **Founded:** 1955. **Freq:** Quarterly. **Trim Size:** A4. **Cols./Page:** 2. **Col. Width:** 8 centimeters. **Key Personnel:** Albert Palanques, Asst. Ed.; I. Palomera, Scientific Ed.; M. Pascual, Scientific Ed.; D. Vaque, Editor-in-Chief; Jordi Font, Asst. Ed.; Paloma Martin, Asst. Ed.; T. Packard, Asst. Ed. **ISSN:** 0214-8358. **Subscription Rates:** EUR165 individuals Spain; EUR200 other countries. **URL:** http://www.icm.csic.es/scimar. **Circ:** Combined 290

50698 ■ Show Press
Prensa del Espectaculo S.L.
Paris, 151-155
esc. izda
Despacho, 7
E-08036 Barcelona, Spain
Ph: 34 3 4393511

Fax: 34 3 4107921
Professional magazine covering the entertainment industry. **Founded:** 1975. **Freq:** Monthly. **Trim Size:** 240 x 340 mm. **Key Personnel:** Angel M. Estrago, Director. **Subscription Rates:** EUR55 individuals. **Remarks:** Accepts advertising. **URL:** http://www.showpress.net/. **Circ:** Non-paid 15,000

50699 ■ Siete Dias Medicos
Ediciones Mayo S.A.
Aribau, 185-187, 2 planta
E-08021 Barcelona, Spain
Ph: 34 932 090255
Fax: 34 932 020643
Publisher E-mail: edmayo@edicionesmayo.es
Professional journal covering medicine for primary care clinicians and specialists. **Freq:** 40/yr. **Print Method:** Offset. **Trim Size:** 205 x 270 mm. **Cols./Page:** 3. **Col. Width:** 45 millimeters. **Col. Depth:** 215 millimeters. **Key Personnel:** Antonio Vasconcellos Santiago, Editor; Dr. Ramon Planas Villa, Director. **ISSN:** 0214-3011. **Remarks:** Accepts advertising. **URL:** http://www.edicionesmayo.es; http://www.sietediasmedicos.com/. **Ad Rates:** BW: 2,600 Ptas. **Circ:** Controlled 25,000

50700 ■ Spanish Economic Review
Springer Netherlands
c/o Bruno Cassiman, Co-Ed.
Avda. Pearson, 21
08034 Barcelona, Spain
Publisher E-mail: permissions.dordrecht@springer.com
Journal covering articles in the field of economics and management. **Subtitle:** Revista Espanola de Economia. **Founded:** 1955. **Freq:** Quarterly. **Print Method:** Offset. **Trim Size:** 10 3/4 x 13. **Cols./Page:** 5. **Col. Width:** 10 3/4 picas. **Col. Depth:** 13 inches. **Key Personnel:** Claudio Michelacci, Co-Ed.; G. Fiorentini, Assoc. Ed.; M.D. Collado, Co-Ed.; L. Viceira, Assoc. Ed.; R. Casadesus-Masanell, Assoc. Ed.; Eduardo Ley, Editor, spanish.economic.review@gmail.com; A. Abadie, Assoc. Ed.; C. Amuedo-Dorantes, Assoc. Ed.; Sjaak Hurkens, Co-Ed.; Bruno Cassiman, Co-Ed. **ISSN:** 1435-5469. **Subscription Rates:** EUR287 institutions print incl. free access or e-only; EUR344.40 institutions print incl. enhanced access. **URL:** http://www.springer.com/economics/journal/10108.

50701 ■ Speak Up
Edipresse Publications S.A.
Perez Galdos 36
E-08012 Barcelona, Spain
Ph: 34 93 4157374
Fax: 34 93 2177378
Publisher E-mail: groupe@edipresse.com
Magazine focusing on the study of English language. **Freq:** Monthly. **Key Personnel:** Cati Miloro, Director; Jeronia Vidal, Ch. Ed. **URL:** http://www.edipresse.com/category/produits/magazines/various.

50702 ■ Tocado
Ediciones Cosmobelleza
c/o Muntaner
Entlo., 401
E-08021 Barcelona, Spain
Ph: 34 932 414690
Fax: 34 932 001544
Publication E-mail: contacto@cosmobelleza.com
Publisher E-mail: editocado@editocado.com
Trade magazine for hairdressers. **Founded:** 1956. **Freq:** Monthly. **Trim Size:** 215 x 287 mm. **ISSN:** 1139-4641. **Subscription Rates:** EUR45 individuals; EUR125 individuals; EUR150 individuals. **URL:** http://www.bellezapro.com/paginas/modelos/producto_belleza_39002_1620.asp. **Circ:** Paid 20,000

50703 ■ Trends in Transplantation
Permanyer Publications
Mallorca, 310
08037 Barcelona, Spain
Ph: 34 932 075920
Fax: 34 934 576642
Publisher E-mail: permanyer@permanyer.com
Journal covering progress in transplantation. **Freq:** Quarterly. **Key Personnel:** J.M. Campistol, Editor-in-Chief; K. Wood, Asst. Ed.; M. Sayegh, Asst. Ed.; D. Sutherland, Asst. Ed.; Fritz Diekmann, Asst. Ed.-in-Ch. **ISSN:** 1887-455X. **Subscription Rates:** EUR100 individuals print; EUR200 institutions print; EUR85 individuals electronic; EUR170 institutions electronic. **URL:** http://www.trendsintransplantation.com/.

50704 ■ Tu Bebe
RBA Edipresse

Perez Galdos 36
E-08012 Barcelona, Spain
Ph: 34 93 4157374
Fax: 34 93 2177378
Magazine providing information for future parents and parents of up to two years old babies. **Freq:** Monthly. **Key Personnel:** Lis Marce, Ch. Ed. **URL:** http://www.rbarevistas.com/revista.php?id=16. **Circ:** ‡95,092

50705 ■ Upgrade (English Edition)
Asociacion de Tecnicos de Informatica
Via Laietana, 46
E-08003 Barcelona, Spain
Ph: 34 93 4125235
Fax: 34 93 4127713
Publisher E-mail: secregen@ati.es
Online journal for the informatics professional. **Subtitle:** The European Journal for the Informatics Professional. **Freq:** Bimonthly. **Key Personnel:** Rafael Fernandez Calvo, Dep. Chief Ed., rfcalvo@ati.es; Roberto Carniel, Editorial Board; Llorenc Pages Casas, Editor-in-Chief, pages@ati.es; Francois Louis Nicolet, Editorial Board. **ISSN:** 1684-5285. **URL:** http://www.cepis.org/upgrade/index.jsp?p=2100&n=2109.

50706 ■ Viajes National Geographic
Edipresse Publications S.A.
Perez Galdos 36
E-08012 Barcelona, Spain
Publisher E-mail: groupe@edipresse.com
Magazine featuring travel ideas and destinations. **Freq:** Monthly. **Key Personnel:** Cati Miloro, Director; Anna Borras, Ch. Ed. **URL:** http://www.ngviajes.com/. **Circ:** ‡63,013

50707 ■ Contrabanda-FM - 91.4
Apartado de correos: 748
08080 Barcelona, Spain
Ph: 34 93 3177366
Fax: 34 93 4124710
E-mail: contrabandaradio@contrabanda.org
Format: Full Service. **URL:** http://www.contrabanda.org/contrabanda/.

50708 ■ Radio Estel-FM - 106.6
Comtes de Bell-lloc, 67-69
E-08014 Barcelona, Spain
Ph: 34 3 934092770
Fax: 34 3 934092775
Format: Ethnic; World Beat. **Operating Hours:** Continuous. **URL:** http://www.radioestel.com.

Benalmadena

50709 ■ The Euro Weekly News
The Euro Weekly News Group
Calle Moscatel
10 Poligono Industrial Arroyo dela Miel
E-29631 Benalmadena, Spain
Ph: 34 952 561245
Fax: 34 952 440887
Publisher E-mail: andalucia@euroweeklynews.com
English language newspaper for foreign residents of Spain. **Founded:** Apr. 1985. **Freq:** Weekly. **Print Method:** Offset. **Trim Size:** Tabloid. **ISSN:** 1882-2002. **Subscription Rates:** EUR70 individuals Spain; EUR148 individuals; EUR245 individuals America, Africa, Middle East; EUR245 individuals Asia, Australia. **Remarks:** Advertising accepted; rates available upon request. **URL:** http://www.euroweeklynews.com. **Formerly:** The Entertainer. **Circ:** Combined 65,000

Bilbao

50710 ■ Chemistry
Trade Science Inc.
c/o Prof. A. Orjales, Editorial Board
Research Dept., FAES
S.A. Aptdo 555
48080 Bilbao, Spain
Publisher E-mail: help@tsijournals.com
Journal covering research papers on all phases of chemistry. **Subtitle:** An Indian Journal. **Founded:** 1955. **Freq:** Monthly. **Print Method:** Offset. **Trim Size:** 8 x 10 3/4. **Key Personnel:** Prof. A. Orjales, Editorial Board; Prof. B. Lalljee, Editorial Board. **ISSN:** 0972-8376. **Subscription Rates:** Rs 3,000 institutions; US$180 institutions; Rs 2,400 individuals; US$160 individuals. **URL:** http://www.tsijournals.com/caij/.

Burjasot

50711 ■ Food Science and Technology International
Insituto de Agriquimica y Tecnologia de Alimentos
Consejo Superior de Investigaciones Cientificas
Apdo Correos, 73
E-46100 Burjasot, Spain
Ph: 34 9 63900022
Fax: 34 9 63636301
Publisher E-mail: info@iata.csis.es
Scientific journal covering food science and technology. **Founded:** 1961. **Freq:** Bimonthly. **Cols./Page:** 2. **Col. Width:** 8.5 centimeters. **Key Personnel:** Dr. Remedios Melero, Managing Editor, rmelero@iata.csic.es; Lorenzo Zacarmas, Editor-in-Chief; Gustavo V. Barbosa-Canovas, Assoc. Ed. **ISSN:** 1082-0132. **Subscription Rates:** 709 institutions print & e-access; 638 institutions e-access only; 695 institutions print only; 124 individuals print only. **Remarks:** Accepts advertising. **URL:** http://www.iata.csic.es/~bibrem/revfsti-eng.htm; http://www.uk.sagepub.com/journalsProdDesc.nav?prodId=Journal201579. **Former name:** Revista Espanola de Ciencia y Tecnologia de Alimentos. **Circ:** (Not Reported)

Ciudad Real

50712 ■ Nueva Onda Radio-FM - 88.1
I.E.S. Comendador Juan de Tavora
Puertollano
13500 Ciudad Real, Spain
Format: Contemporary Hit Radio (CHR). **URL:** http://www.nuevaondaradio.com/.

Cordoba

50713 ■ European Journal of Agronomy
Elsevier Science Inc.
c/o F. Villalobos, Ed.-in-Ch.
Instituto de Agricultura Sostenible
Consejo Superior de Investigaciones Cientificas
Codigo Postal Para Apartados Particulares Y Lista
14080 Cordoba, Spain
Publisher E-mail: usinfo-ehelp@elsevier.com
Journal covering original research papers reporting experimental and theoretical contributions. **Founded:** 1974. **Freq:** 8/yr. **Print Method:** Offset. **Trim Size:** 10 1/2 x 14. **Cols./Page:** 6. **Col. Width:** 18 nonpareils. **Col. Depth:** 224 agate lines. **Key Personnel:** M. Acutis, Editorial Board; O. Christen, Editorial Board; S. Asseng, Editorial Board; I. Cakmak, Editorial Board; M. Fuller, Editorial Board; M. Fotyma, Editorial Board; F. Villalobos, Editor-in-Chief. **ISSN:** 1161-0301. **Subscription Rates:** 121,100¥ institutions; US$1,019 institutions, other countries except Europe, Japan and Iran; EUR910 institutions for European countries and Iran; EUR175 individuals for European countries and Iran; US$236 other countries except Europe, Japan and Iran; 27,200¥ individuals. **URL:** http://www.elsevier.com/wps/find/journaldescription.cws_home/600108/descriptiondescription.

Esporles

50714 ■ Fisheries Research
Elsevier Science Inc.
c/o B. Morales-Nin, Assoc. Ed.
Natural Resources Dept.
Instituto Mediterraneo de Estudios Avanzados
carrer Miquel Marques, 21
07190 Esporles, Spain
Ph: 34 971 611721
Fax: 34 971 611761
Publisher E-mail: usinfo-ehelp@elsevier.com
Journal covering the areas of fisheries science, fishing technology, fisheries management and relevant socioeconomics. **Subtitle:** An International Journal on Fisheries Science, Fishing Technology and Fisheries Management. **Founded:** 1982. **Freq:** 18/yr. **Print Method:** Offset. **Trim Size:** 8 1/2 x 11. **Cols./Page:** 2. **Col. Width:** 2 1/2 inches. **Col. Depth:** 10 inches. **Key Personnel:** S. Holt, Editorial Advisory Board; R. Lae, Editorial Advisory Board; D. Mills, Editorial Advisory Board; E. Macpherson, Editorial Advisory Board; S. J. Hall, Editorial Advisory Board; S.J.M. Blaber, Editorial Advisory Board; A. Guerra, Editorial Advisory Board. **ISSN:** 0165-7836. **Subscription Rates:** US$2,766 institutions, other countries except Europe and Japan; EUR2,474 institutions for European countries and Iran; 328,700¥ institutions. **URL:** http://www.elsevier.com/

wps/find/journaldescription.cws_home/503309/
descriptiondescription.

Fuengirola

50715 ■ Kustradion-FM - 105
Calle Quemada 10
E-29640 Fuengirola, Spain
Ph: 34 95 1915043
Fax: 34 952 581851
Format: Ethnic; World Beat. **Operating Hours:** Continuous. **Ad Rates:** Advertising accepted; rates available upon request. **URL:** http://www.kustradion.nu.

Gijon

50716 ■ Abaco
CICEES
C/ La Muralla 3 entlo
E-33202 Gijon, Spain
Ph: 34 985 319385
Fax: 34 985 319385
Publication E-mail: redaccion@revista-abaco.com
Publisher E-mail: info@cicees.com
Magazine covering culture and social science. **Freq:** Quarterly. **Trim Size:** 21 x 21 cm. **Key Personnel:** M. A. Alvarez Areces, Director. **Subscription Rates:** EUR30 individuals Spain; EUR45 individuals libraries and institutions; EUR80 other countries. **URL:** http://www.revista-abaco.com.

Granada

50717 ■ International Journal of Business Environment
Inderscience Publishers
c/o Francisco Javier Llorens Montes, Editorial Board Member
University of Granada
Facultad de Ciencias Economicas y Empresariales
Campus de Cartuja s/n
E-18071 Granada, Spain
Publisher E-mail: editor@inderscience.com
Peer-reviewed journal addressing managerial issues in the social, political, economic, competitive, and technological environments of business. **Freq:** Quarterly. **Key Personnel:** Prof. Antonio J. Verdu, Editor, ajverdu@ umh.es; Dr. Kiran Jude Fernandes, Editorial Board Member; Dr. John C. Camillus, Assoc. Ed.; Prof. Paul Ireland, Editorial Board Member; Prof. Barry J. Babin, Editorial Board Member; Nir Ben-Aharon, Editorial Board Member; Dr. Francisco Javier Llorens Montes, Editorial Board Member; Dr. Anthony Bartzokas, Assoc. Ed.; Dr. Ernst Verwaal, Assoc. Ed. **ISSN:** 1740-0589. **Subscription Rates:** EUR494 individuals print only (surface mail); EUR840 individuals online only (2-3 users); EUR672 individuals print and online. **URL:** http://www.inderscience.com/browse/index.php?journalCODE=ijbe.

50718 ■ Pharmaceuticals Policy and Law
IOS Press, B.V.
c/o Prof. Jose Luis Valverde, Ed.-in-Ch.
University of Granada, Faculty of Pharmacy
Campus de la Cartuja sn
E-18071 Granada, Spain
Ph: 34 958 243898
Fax: 34 958 248908
Publisher E-mail: info@iospress.nl
Journal studying and evaluating the legal status of medicinal products in the European Union and its implications in other markets such as the USA and Japan, without neglecting the specific problems of developing countries. **Freq:** Quarterly. **Key Personnel:** Prof. Jose Luis Valverde, Editor-in-Chief, jlvalver@ugr. es; Dr. Lyle J. Bootman, Advisory Board; Ann P. Hoppe, Advisory Board; Alan G. Minsk, Advisory Board; Prof. Francis B. Palumbo, Advisory Board; Linda Horton, Advisory Board; Philippe Brunet, Advisory Board; Patrick Deboyser, Advisory Board; Prof. Tatsuo Kurokawa, Advisory Board; Dr. Rodica Badescu, Advisory Board. **ISSN:** 1389-2827. **Subscription Rates:** EUR358 institutions print and online; US$505 institutions print and online; EUR100 individuals online; US$115 individuals online. **URL:** http://www.iospress.nl/loadtop/load.php?isbn=13892827.

La Laguna

50719 ■ Journal for Nature Conservation
Elsevier Science Inc.
c/o Antonio Machado, Ed.-in-Ch.

Calle Chopin, 1
38208 La Laguna, Spain
Ph: 34 922 315888
Fax: 34 922 315696
Publisher E-mail: usinfo-ehelp@elsevier.com
Journal focused on methods and techniques used in nature conservation. **Founded:** 1992. **Freq:** 4/yr. **Print Method:** Offset. **Trim Size:** 8 x 10 1/8. **Cols./Page:** 3. **Col. Width:** 27 nonpareils. **Col. Depth:** 140 agate lines. **Key Personnel:** Keith Kirby, Editor, phone 44 1733 455245, fax 44 1733 568834, keith.kirby@english-nature.org.uk; Dirk Wascher, Editor, phone 31 317 485951, fax 31 317 419000, dirk.wascher@wur.nl; Gary Fry, Editorial Board; Andreas Troumbis, Editorial Board; Josef Langer, Editorial Board; Gordana Beltram, Editorial Board; Antonio Machado, Editor-in-Chief, antonio. machado@telefonica.net; Niamh Connolly, Editorial Board, nconnolly@esf.org; Giovanni Amori, Editorial Board; Manfred Niekisch, Editor, phone 49 69 21233727, fax 49 69 21237855, manfred.niekisch@stadt-frankfurt. de. **ISSN:** 1617-1381. **Subscription Rates:** EUR233 institutions European countries and Iran; 31,500¥ institutions; US$267 institutions, other countries except Europe, Japan and Iran; EUR85 individuals for European countries and Iran; 11,100¥ individuals; US$102 individuals all countries except Europe, Japan and Iran. **URL:** http://www.elsevier.com/wps/find/journaldescription.cws_home/701773/descriptiondescription.

Las Palmas de Gran Canaria

50720 ■ Atlantica Internacional
Centro Atlantico de Arte Moderno
Los Balcones, 11
E-35001 Las Palmas de Gran Canaria, Spain
Ph: 34 928 311800
Fax: 34 928 321629
Publisher E-mail: info@caam.net
Magazine covering research on plastic arts and other art forms and culture. **Freq:** Triennial. **Trim Size:** 24 x 30 cm. **Subscription Rates:** US$64 individuals Europe; US$72 individuals America/Africa; EUR15 individuals the general public; EUR16 individuals friends of the CAAM. **URL:** http://www.caam.net/en/atlantica/cont_atlantica. htm.

Macher

50721 ■ Atlantis-FM - 101.7
Camino de la Fabrica 14
35571 Macher, Spain
Ph: 34 620 393313
E-mail: info@atlantis-radio.com
Format: Ethnic; World Beat. **URL:** http://www.atlantisfm. de.

Madrid

50722 ■ Academia
Academia de las Artes y las Ciencias Cinematograficas de Espana
Sagasta, 20-3 Dcha
E-28004 Madrid, Spain
Ph: 34 910 014648
Fax: 34 915 931492
Magazine of the Spanish Academy of Cinematographic Arts and Science covering audiovisual culture in Spain. **Freq:** Semiannual. **Trim Size:** 21 x 29.5 cm. **URL:** http://www.academiadecine.com/.

50723 ■ Actualidad Economica
Recoletos Grupo de Comunicacion
P de la Castellana, No. 66
E-28046 Madrid, Spain
Ph: 34 913 373220
Publication E-mail: aeconomica@recoletos.es
Business publication. **Founded:** Mar. 1958. **Freq:** Weekly. **Print Method:** Offset. **Key Personnel:** Miguel Angel Belloso, Director, cartasdirectorae@ actualidadeconomica.com. **ISSN:** 0001-7655. **Subscription Rates:** EUR150 individuals Spain; EUR261 individuals; EUR350 individuals elsewhere; EUR75 individuals 6 months (Spain); EUR300 two years Spain; EUR522 two years; EUR699 two years elsewhere. **Remarks:** Accepts advertising. **URL:** http://www.actualidadeconomica.com/ suscripciones/. **Ad Rates:** 4C: EUR6,000. **Circ:** Combined 23,000

50724 ■ Ade-Teatro
Asociacion de Directores de Escena de Espana

Costanilla de los Angeles
13 Bajo Izq.
E-28013 Madrid, Spain
Ph: 34 915 591246
Fax: 34 915 483012
Publication E-mail: redaccion@adeteatro.com
Publisher E-mail: asociacion@adeteatro.com
Magazine of the Spanish Association of Theatre Directors. **Founded:** Apr. 1985. **Freq:** Quarterly. **Trim Size:** 22 x 31 cm. **Key Personnel:** Juan Antonio Hormigon, Director. **ISSN:** 1133-8792. **Subscription Rates:** EUR40 individuals for Spain; EUR55 individuals for Europe; EUR55 individuals for European countries; EUR55 other countries f. **Remarks:** Accepts advertising. **URL:** http://www.adeteatro.com/. **Ad Rates:** BW: EUR1,000. **Circ:** (Not Reported)

50725 ■ Agricultura
Editorial Agricola Espanola S.A.
Caballero de Gracia, 24
E-28013 Madrid, Spain
Ph: 34 91 5211633
Fax: 34 91 5224872
Scientific, agricultural periodical. **Founded:** 1928. **Freq:** Monthly. **Key Personnel:** Cristobal de la Puerta, Director. **ISSN:** 0002-1334. **URL:** http://www. editorialagricola.com/. **Circ:** Combined ‡6,426

50726 ■ Airline Ninety Two
Grupo Edefa S.A.
C/Puerto Principe No. 3-B 1A
E-28043 Madrid, Spain
Ph: 34 91 3821945
Fax: 34 91 7630021
Publication E-mail: airline@edefa.com
Publisher E-mail: edefa@edefa.com
Trade magazine covering the airline and airport business in Spanish and Latin American markets. **Subtitle:** Revista de Aviacion Comercial y Aeropuertos. **Founded:** 1989. **Freq:** Monthly. **Print Method:** Offset. **Trim Size:** 210 x 300 mm. **Cols./Page:** 2 and 3. **Key Personnel:** Eva Cervera, Director. **ISSN:** 0211-3732. **Subscription Rates:** EUR29.65 individuals Spain; EUR102 two years Spain. **Remarks:** Accepts advertising. **URL:** http://www. airline92.com; http://www.edefa.com. **Ad Rates:** GLR: US$175, BW: US$1,700, 4C: US$2,850. **Circ:** ‡15,000

50727 ■ Album
Album, Letras y Artes S.L.
Juan Alvarez Mendizabal, 58
E-28008 Madrid, Spain
Ph: 34 915 479742
Fax: 34 915 599027
Publication E-mail: album@albumletrasartes.com
Publisher E-mail: album@albumletrasartes.com
Magazine covering art, design, painting photography, architecture, and related fields. **Founded:** 1986. **Freq:** Bimonthly. **Trim Size:** 21 x 27.5 cm. **Key Personnel:** Jesus Tablate Miquis, Director. **ISSN:** 1131-6411. **Subscription Rates:** EUR27 individuals Spain; EUR87 individuals Europe; US$159 individuals U.S.; US$159 single issue rest of the world. **URL:** http://www. revistasculturales.com/revistas/4/album/.

50728 ■ ANIGP-TV
ANIGP—Asociacion Nacional de Informadores Graficos de Prensa y T.V.
Espronceda, 32
5a Planta
E-28003 Madrid, Spain
Ph: 34 914 413045
Fax: 34 914 420897
Publisher E-mail: anigp@anigp-tv.com
Professional magazine covering the television, photography, and photojournalism fields. **Key Personnel:** Cesar Lucas, Contact; Sonia Tercero, Contact; Jordi Lopez, Contact. **URL:** http://www.anigp-tv.com.

50729 ■ Arquitectura Viva
Arquitectura Viva S.L.
Calle de Aniceto Marinas, 32
E-28008 Madrid, Spain
Ph: 34 915 487317
Fax: 34 915 488191
Publisher E-mail: av@arquitecturaviva.com
Magazine covering architecture and related disciplines in Spanish with summaries in English. **Freq:** Bimonthly. **Trim Size:** 24 x 30 cm. **Key Personnel:** Luis Fernandez-Galiano, Director. **Subscription Rates:** EUR80 individuals Spain; EUR105 individuals Europe; EUR125 elsewhere. **URL:** http://www.arquitecturaviva.com. **Ad**

Circulation: ★ = ABC; △ = BPA; ♦ = CAC; • = CCAB; ❑ = VAC; ⊕ = PO Statement; ‡ = Publisher's Report; Boldface figures = sworn; Light figures = estimated.

Rates: BW: EUR2,103.54, 4C: EUR2,103.54. **Circ:** 11,000

50730 ■ Atletismo Espanol
Real Federacion Espanola de Atletismo
Avenida de Valladolid, 81, esc. Dcha. 1
E-28008 Madrid, Spain
Ph: 34 915 482423
Fax: 34 915 480638
Publication E-mail: publicaciones@rfea.es
Publisher E-mail: rfea@rfea.es
Consumer magazine covering track and field. **Subtitle:**
La Revista De La Real Federacion Espanola De
Atletismo. **Founded:** 1951. **Freq:** Monthly. **Print
Method:** Offset. **Trim Size:** 210 x 285 mm. **Cols./Page:**
4. **Col. Width:** 43 millimeters. **Col. Depth:** 240
millimeters. **Subscription Rates:** EUR42 individuals
ordinary Spain; EUR42 individuals ordinary Portugal;
EUR81 individuals ordinary Europe; EUR51 individuals
certificate Spain; EUR53 individuals certificate Portugal;
EUR81 individuals aerial Europe; EUR96 other countries
aerial. **Remarks:** Accepts advertising. **URL:** http://www.
rfea.es/revista/revista.htm. **Ad Rates:** 4C: EUR950. **Circ:**
Paid 15,000

50731 ■ AV Monografias
Arquitectura Viva S.L.
Calle de Aniceto Marinas, 32
E-28008 Madrid, Spain
Ph: 34 915 487317
Fax: 34 915 488191
Publisher E-mail: av@arquitecturaviva.com
Bilingual (English and Spanish) professional magazine
covering architecture. **Freq:** Bimonthly. **Trim Size:** 24 x
30 cm. **Key Personnel:** Luis Fernandez-Galiano,
Director. **Subscription Rates:** EUR115 individuals Spain;
EUR140 individuals Europe; EUR160 elsewhere. **URL:**
http://www.arquitecturaviva.es/Publicidad.asp. **Ad
Rates:** BW: EUR1,652.78, 4C: EUR1,652.78. **Circ:** 9,000

50732 ■ Car and Driver (Spain)
Hachette Filipacchi
Avda. Cardenal Herrera
Oria, 3
E-28034 Madrid, Spain
Ph: 34 917 287000
Fax: 34 917 289129
Consumer magazine covering automobiles and racing.
Founded: Oct. 1995. **Freq:** Monthly. **Key Personnel:**
Mark Gillies, Exec. Ed.; Eddie Alterman, Editor-in-Chief;
Jared Gall, Sen. Online Ed.; Scott L. Mosher, Produc-
tion Ed./Mgr. **Subscription Rates:** US$19.95 two years;
US$12 individuals. **URL:** http://www.caranddriverrevista.
com; http://www.caranddriver.com/.

50733 ■ Carreteras
c/o Marta Rodrigo, Exec. Mgr.
Goya, 23 4-Dcha
E-28001 Madrid, Spain
Ph: 34 915 779972
Fax: 34 915 766522
Publisher E-mail: mrodrigo@aecarretera.com
Trade magazine covering road and highway planning
and construction and the traffic and transportation
industry. **Founded:** 1951. **Freq:** Bimonthly. **Print
Method:** Offset. **Trim Size:** 210 x 297 mm. **Cols./Page:**
2. **Col. Depth:** 265 millimeters. **Key Personnel:** Re-
caredo Romero, Tech. Dir., recaredo@recaredoluz.
jazztel.com; Marta Rodrigo, Exec. Dir. **ISSN:** 0212-6389.
Subscription Rates: 59 Ptas individuals; EUR98 individuals; US$140 individuals. **Remarks:** Accepts
advertising. **URL:** http://www.aecarretera.com/rec_ing.
htm. **Ad Rates:** BW: EUR960, 4C: EUR1,114. **Circ:**
Controlled 16,000

50734 ■ Casa al Dia
RBA Edipresse
Lopez de Hoyos 141
E-28002 Madrid, Spain
Ph: 34 91 5106600
Fax: 34 91 5194813
Magazine featuring decorating style suggestions for
beginners in interior design. **Freq:** Monthly. **Key Person-
nel:** Aurea Diaz, Director; Susana de Vicente, Ch. Ed.
URL: http://www.rbarevistas.com/revista.php?id=53.
Circ: ‡87,531

50735 ■ Claves de Razon Practica
Progresa
Julian Camarillo, 29 B
1 planta
E-28037 Madrid, Spain
Ph: 34 91 5386104
Fax: 34 91 5229508

Publisher E-mail: publicidad@progresa.es
Magazine covering politics. **Founded:** 1990. **Freq:** 10/
yr. **Trim Size:** 23.6 x 33.9 cm. **Key Personnel:** Javier
Pradera, Director; Fernando Savater, Director. **Subscription Rates:** EUR70 individuals with Libro El Codigo; EUR70 individuals with Libro El Tercer Reich. **URL:**
http://www.progresa.es/pub/rev_kiosko_det.html?
idSeccion=23; http://claves.progresa.es/Claves.php.

50736 ■ Coches de Ocasion
Edipresse Publications S.A.
Hiedra No. 2-C
E-28036 Madrid, Spain
Ph: 34 91 7339713
Publication E-mail: web@moredi.com
Publisher E-mail: groupe@edipresse.com
Magazine featuring second-hand vehicles. **Freq:**
Monthly. **Key Personnel:** Ignacio de Lucas, Director;
Luis Miguel Domiguez, Ch. Ed. **URL:** http://www.
cochesdeocasion.es/. **Circ:** ‡17,108

50737 ■ Cognitiva
Fundacion Infancia y Aprendizaje
C/Naranjo de Bulnes 69
San Sebastian de los Reyes
E-28707 Madrid, Spain
Ph: 34 91 6589100
Fax: 34 91 6589100
Publisher E-mail: fundacionia@fia.es
Journal covering cognitive processes, including percep-
tion, attention, memory, language comprehension,
reasoning, problem solving and mental representation
for researchers and scholars in the field in Spanish and
English. **Founded:** 1989. **Freq:** Semiannual. **Key Per-
sonnel:** Manuel Carreiras, Editor. **ISSN:** 0214-3550.
Remarks: Accepts advertising scientific and cultural
contents only. **URL:** http://www.ingentaconnect.com/
content/fias/cog; jsessionid=af954fsfd57p2.victoria?.
Circ: (Not Reported)

50738 ■ ComputerWorld/Espana
IDG Communications S.A.
Claudio Coello 123, 5 Planta
E-28006 Madrid, Spain
Ph: 34 913 496600
Trade magazine covering computers for purchase deci-
sion makers in large corporations and information
system professionals. **Founded:** Mar. 1, 1983. **Freq:**
30/yr. **Print Method:** Offset. **Trim Size:** 277 x 365 mm.
Cols./Page: 5. **Key Personnel:** Daniel Comino, Director.
ISSN: 0212-2456. **Subscription Rates:** EUR139.50
individuals. **Remarks:** Advertising accepted; rates avail-
able upon request. **URL:** http://www.idg.es/
computerworld. **Circ:** Combined ‡10,000

50739 ■ Comunicaciones World
IDG Communications S.A.
Claudio Coello 123, 5 Planta
E-28006 Madrid, Spain
Ph: 34 913 496600
Trade magazine covering the telecommunications
industry for managers and industry professionals.
Founded: Nov. 1986. **Freq:** Monthly. **Print Method:**
Offset. **Trim Size:** 240 x 335 mm. **Cols./Page:** 4. **Col.
Width:** 51.25 millimeters. **Key Personnel:** Miguel Angel
Hermosell, Contact, mah@idg.es; Francisco Sanchez,
Editorial Dir., psanchez@idg.es; Juana Gandia, Contact,
jgandia@idg.es. **ISSN:** 1139-0867. **Subscription Rates:**
EUR57.42 individuals. **Remarks:** Accepts advertising.
URL: http://www.idg.es. **Formerly:** Comunicaciones
World. **Ad Rates:** BW: 6,230 Ptas. **Circ:** Combined
‡10,000

50740 ■ Cosas de Casa
RBA Edipresse
Lopez de Hoyos 141
E-28002 Madrid, Spain
Ph: 34 91 5106600
Fax: 34 91 5194813
Magazine featuring furniture and accessories for a small
living space. **Freq:** Monthly. **Key Personnel:** Aurea
Diaz, Director; Nuria San Frutos, Contact. **URL:** http://
www.rbarevistas.com/revista.php?id=52. **Circ:** ‡183,118

50741 ■ Cosmopolital (Spain)
G+J Espana
c/o Albasanz, 15 Edificio A
E-28037 Madrid, Spain
Ph: 34 914 369800
Fax: 34 915 767881
Publication E-mail: cosmopolitanweb@cosmohispano.
com

Publisher E-mail: publicidad@gyj.es
Consumer magazine for women. **Founded:** 1990. **Freq:**
Monthly. **Print Method:** Offset. **Subscription Rates:**
EUR31.20 individuals; EUR81.05 individuals UK;
EUR110.10 individuals rest of world; EUR24.95 individuals
for Spain only. **Remarks:** Accepts advertising. **URL:**
http://www.cosmohispano.com. **Circ:** Combined 140,000

50742 ■ Cronica Filatelica
Publiafinsa
Lagasca, 88 4o
E-28001 Madrid, Spain
Ph: 34 915 767007
Fax: 34 915 756117
Publisher E-mail: cronica@afinsa.com
Magazine covering stamps in Spain. **Founded:** 1984.
Freq: Monthly. **Print Method:** Offset. **Trim Size:** 1.50.
Cols./Page: 2. **ISSN:** 0214-7203. **URL:** http://www.
eltroc.org/butlletins/publicacions/comerciales/cronica.
htm. **Ad Rates:** BW: EUR511, 4C: EUR728. **Circ:** (Not
Reported)

50743 ■ Cuadernos de la Academia
Academia de las Artes y las Ciencias Cinematograficas
de Espana
Sagasta, 20-3 Dcha
E-28004 Madrid, Spain
Ph: 34 915 934648
Fax: 34 915 931492
Publication E-mail: academia@academiadecine.com
Magazine covering current and historical Spanish
cinema and its expression. **Freq:** Triennial. **Trim Size:**
14 x 22 cm. **Remarks:** Advertising not accepted. **URL:**
http://www.revistasculturales.com/noticias/140/
presentacion-cuadernos-dela-academia-13-14.html.
Circ: (Not Reported)

50744 ■ Cuadernos Hispanoamericanos
Agencia Espanola de Cooperacion Internacional
Avda. de los Reyes Catolicos, 4
E-28040 Madrid, Spain
Ph: 34 915 838100
Fax: 34 915 838310
Publication E-mail: cuadernos.hispanoamericanos@
aecid.es
Magazine covering Spanish culture, literature, arts,
politics, and related areas. **Founded:** 1948. **Freq:**
Monthly. **Trim Size:** 17 x 24 cm. **Key Personnel:**
Benjamin Prado, Director. **ISSN:** 0011-250X. **URL:** http://
www.revistasculturales.com/revistas/17/cuadernos-
hispanoamericanos.

50745 ■ Cuadernos de Jazz
Cuadernos de Jazz Editores S.L.
Hotraleze, 75
E-28004 Madrid, Spain
Ph: 34 913 080302
Fax: 34 913 080599
Publication E-mail: cuadernos@cuadernosdejazz.com
Publisher E-mail: cuardernos@cuadernosdejazz.com
Magazine covering jazz music and its relation to other
artistic disciplines. **Founded:** 1990. **Freq:** Bimonthly.
Trim Size: 21 x 29.7 cm. **Key Personnel:** Raul A. Mao,
Director; Ebbe Traberg, President; Maria Antoia Garcia,
Contact. **ISSN:** 1134-7457. **Subscription Rates:** EUR30
individuals Spain; EUR55 two years Spain; EUR60
individuals America; EUR110 two years America; EUR46
individuals Europe; EUR80 two years Europe. **URL:** http://
www.cuadernosdejazz.com/menuprincipal.html.

50746 ■ Cultura y Educacion
Fundacion Infancia y Aprendizaje
C/Naranjo de Bulnes 69
San Sebastian de los Reyes
E-28707 Madrid, Spain
Ph: 34 91 6589100
Fax: 34 91 6589100
Publisher E-mail: fundacionia@fia.es
Journal covering historical-cultural theory in education
for researchers and scholars in education, anthropology,
psychology, sociology, communication, teachers, coun-
selors, and social workers. In Spanish and English.
Founded: 1989. **Freq:** Quarterly. **Print Method:** Offset.
Trim Size: 150 x 240 cm. **Col. Width:** 125 millimeters.
Col. Depth: 200 millimeters. **Key Personnel:** Amelia Al-
varez, Editor; Javier Rosales, Editor; Donaldo Macedo,
Regional Ed. **ISSN:** 1135-6405. **Remarks:** Accepts
advertising scientific and cultural content only. **URL:**
http://www.fia.es/. **Ad Rates:** BW: 301 Ptas. **Circ:**
Combined 600

50747 ■ Current Sociology
Sage Publications Ltd.
Faculty of Political Sciences & Sociology
University Complutense
28223 Madrid, Spain
Ph: 34 913 527650
Fax: 34 913 524945
Peer-reviewed journal covering the theory, research and methodology of current international sociology. **Founded:** 1952. **Freq:** Bimonthly January - March - May - July - September - November. **Key Personnel:** Eloisa Martin, Editor; Sujata Patel, Editor. **ISSN:** 0011-3921. **Subscription Rates:** US$1,190 institutions print & e-access; US$1,309 institutions current volume print & all online content; US$1,071 institutions e-access; US$1,190 institutions e-access plus backfile (all online content); US$4,188 institutions e-access (content through 1998); US$1,166 institutions print only; US$117 individuals print only; US$214 institutions single print; US$25 individuals single print. **Remarks:** Accepts advertising. **URL:** http://www.sagepub.com/journalsProdDesc.nav?prodId=Journal200820&. **Circ:** (Not Reported)

50748 ■ Cybermetrics
Instituto de Estudios Documentales sobre Ciencia y Tecnologia
Consejo Superior de Investigaciones Cientificas
Joaquin Costa, 22
E-28002 Madrid, Spain
Ph: 34 915 635482
Fax: 34 915 642644
Journal dedicating to the study of quantitative analysis of scientific communications in the Internet. **Freq:** Annual. **Key Personnel:** Isidro F. Aguillo, Editor, isidro@cindoc.csic.es; Blaise Cronin, Contact, bcronin@indiana.edu; Stephen P. Harter, Contact, harter@indiana.edu; Moses A. Boudourides, Contact, mboudour@upatras.gr; Mari Davis, Contact, m.davis@unsw.edu.au; Judit Bar-Ilan, Contact, judit@cc.huji.ac.il; Elena Guardiola, Contact, elena.guardiola.eg@bayer.es; Jose L. Ortega, Dep. Ed., jortega@cindoc.csic.es. **Subscription Rates:** Free. **URL:** http://www.cindoc.csic.es/cybermetrics/.

50749 ■ Dealer World & Dealer World 15
IDG Communications S.A.
Claudio Coello 123, 5 Planta
E-28006 Madrid, Spain
Ph: 34 913 496600
Trade magazine for computer distributors, dealers and resellers. **Founded:** June 1995. **Freq:** Monthly. **Print Method:** Offset. **Trim Size:** 210 x 280 mm. **Cols./Page:** 3. **Col. Width:** 55 millimeters. **Key Personnel:** Juan Ramon Melara, Director; Miguel Angel Gomez, Editor-in-Chief; Silvia Hernandez, Contact. **ISSN:** 1135-3305. **Remarks:** Accepts advertising. **URL:** http://www.idg.es/dealer/. **Circ:** Controlled ‡13,826

50750 ■ Defensa
Grupo Edefa S.A.
C/Puerto Principe No. 3-B 1A
E-28043 Madrid, Spain
Ph: 34 91 3821945
Fax: 34 91 7630021
Publisher E-mail: edefa@edefa.com
Trade magazine covering defense. **Subtitle:** Revista Internacional de Ejercitos Armamento y Tecnologia. **Founded:** 1978. **Freq:** Monthly. **Print Method:** Offset. **Trim Size:** 210 x 300 mm. **Cols./Page:** 2 and 3. **Key Personnel:** Eva Cervera, Director. **Subscription Rates:** EUR6 individuals; EUR7 individuals; EUR8 individuals. **Remarks:** Accepts advertising. **URL:** http://www.defensa.com. **Ad Rates:** GLR: US$175, BW: US$1,950, 4C: US$3,950. **Circ:** Combined 21,000

50751 ■ Delibros
SL. Eloy Gonzalo, 27-3
E-28010 Madrid, Spain
Fax: 34 91 5943053
Publisher E-mail: info@delibros.com
Professional magazine covering the book and publishing industry. **Freq:** Monthly. **Trim Size:** 23 x 29.7 cm. **Key Personnel:** Jaime Brull, Editor; Rosa Melendo, Contact, publicidad@delibros.com; Gema Botica, Coord., suscripciones@delibros.com; Teresa M. Peces, Director, direccion@delibros.com. **ISSN:** 0214-2694. **Subscription Rates:** EUR155 individuals for Spain; EUR175 other countries. **Remarks:** Accepts advertising. **URL:** http://www.delibros.com/. **Circ:** (Not Reported)

50752 ■ Distribucion Actualidad
Enrique Larreta 9 1b A
E-28036 Madrid, Spain
Publisher E-mail: redaccion@distribucionactualidad.com
Trade magazine covering the consumer products and retail trade industry. **Founded:** 1974. **Freq:** Monthly. **Print Method:** Offset. **Trim Size:** 23 x 30 cm. **Cols./Page:** 3. **Key Personnel:** Miguel De Haro, Manager, phone 34 913159845, fax 34 913155628, miguel@ipmark.com. **Subscription Rates:** 150 individuals. **Remarks:** Accepts advertising. **Circ:** (Not Reported)

50753 ■ El Croquis
Avda. De los Reyes Catolicas, 9
E-28280 Madrid, Spain
Ph: 34 918 969410
Fax: 34 918 969411
Publication E-mail: elcroquis@elcroquis.es
Publisher E-mail: elcroquis@elcroquis.es
Bilingual (Spanish and English) architectural publication covering the work of architects worldwide. **Freq:** 5/yr. **Trim Size:** 24 x 34 cm. **Key Personnel:** Paloma Poveda, Editorial Board; Fernando Marquez, Publisher. **Subscription Rates:** EUR221 individuals Spain; EUR246.50 students for European union; EUR333 U.S. and Canada; EUR290 individuals non-European union; EUR355 other countries; EUR266.25 students rest of world. **Remarks:** Accepts advertising. **URL:** http://www.elcroquis.es/default.asp. **Circ:** Paid 35,000

50754 ■ El Ecologista
Ecologistas en Accion
Marques de Leganes, 12
E-28004 Madrid, Spain
Ph: 34 915 312739
Fax: 34 915 312611
Publisher E-mail: secretaria@ecologistasenaccion.org
Magazine covering environmental issues. **Founded:** 1993. **Freq:** Monthly. **Trim Size:** 21 x 29.6 cm. **ISSN:** 0211-6472. **Subscription Rates:** EUR30 individuals Spain; EUR45 individuals Europe; US$50 elsewhere America. **Remarks:** Accepts advertising. **URL:** http://www.ecologistasenaccion.org. **Circ:** (Not Reported)

50755 ■ El Extramundi y los papeles de Iria Flavia
Diputacion Provincial
Hortaleza, 75
E-15917 Madrid, Spain
Ph: 34 913086066
Fax: 34 913199267
Magazine covering cultural issues. **Freq:** Quarterly. **Key Personnel:** Ernesto Sanchez Pombo, Director. **ISSN:** 1134-9905. **Subscription Rates:** EUR40 individuals; EUR65 individuals; US$85 other countries by post. **Remarks:** Accepts advertising. **URL:** http://www.fundacioncela.com/asp/productos/productos_extramundi.asp. **Circ:** (Not Reported)

50756 ■ En Franquicia
Calle Alcala, 128
E-28009 Madrid, Spain
Ph: 34 913096515
Publisher E-mail: info@quefranquicia.com
Trade magazine covering business franchising. **Subtitle:** Sectores—Negocios—Oportunidades—Ideas. **Founded:** June 1998. **Freq:** Monthly. **Print Method:** Offset. **Trim Size:** 21 x 28 cm. **Cols./Page:** 3. **ISSN:** 1139-000X. **Subscription Rates:** EUR30 individuals annual; EUR3 single issue. **Remarks:** Accepts advertising. **URL:** http://www.quefranquicia.com. **Ad Rates:** 4C: EUR2,404. **Circ:** Paid 30,000

50757 ■ Estudios de Psicologia
Fundacion Infancia y Aprendizaje
C/Naranjo de Bulnes 69
San Sebastian de los Reyes
E-28707 Madrid, Spain
Ph: 34 91 6589100
Fax: 34 91 6589100
Publication E-mail: revista.estudios.psicologia@uam.es
Publisher E-mail: fundacionia@fia.es
Journal covering psychology and related disciplines for researchers, professionals, and scholars in the field in Spanish and English. **Founded:** 1980. **Freq:** Triennial. **Key Personnel:** Alberto Rosa, Editor; Ricardo Baquero, Editorial Board; Michael Cole, Editorial Board; Mario Carretero, Editorial Board; Antoni Gomila, Editorial Board; Juan Botella, Editorial Board; Jean Paul Bronckart, Editorial Board; Mercedes Cubero, Editorial Board; David Travieso, Editorial Assoc. **ISSN:** 0210-9395. **Subscription Rates:** EUR83 individuals; EUR165 individuals;

EUR275 individuals; EUR600 institutions; EUR390 institutions; EUR595 institutions. **Remarks:** Accepts advertising scientific and cultural content only. **URL:** http://www.uam.es/otros/web-ep/; http://www.fia.es/online/revistas.php?rev_selec=est. **Circ:** (Not Reported)

50758 ■ Eurocarne
Estrategias Alimentarias S.L.
Fermin Caballero, 64
E-28034 Madrid, Spain
Ph: 34 91 3780922
Fax: 34 91 3780711
Publication E-mail: info@eurocarne.com
Trade magazine for the meat industry. **Founded:** 1991. **Freq:** 10/yr. **Print Method:** Offset. **Trim Size:** 210 x 280 mm. **Cols./Page:** 3. **Key Personnel:** David Barreiro, Editor, dbarreiro@eurocarne.com. **ISSN:** 1132-2675. **URL:** http://www.eurocarne.com/index.php?/home/index.php. **Circ:** 6000

50759 ■ Foto Video
Omnicon
Seis de diciembre, s/n, local 25
E-28023 Madrid, Spain
Ph: 34 91 7402081
Fax: 34 91 3579295
Publisher E-mail: revistafv@omnicon.es
Magazine covering photography and video in Spain. **Founded:** 1988. **Freq:** Monthly. **Print Method:** Offset. **Trim Size:** 21 x 27.5 cm. **Key Personnel:** Juan M. Varela, Director, directorfv@omnicon.es. **Subscription Rates:** EUR44.30 individuals with covers; EUR39.50 individuals without covers; EUR60.75 individuals Portugal (surface mail, with covers); EUR84.60 individuals rest of Europe (airmail, without covers); EUR117.75 other countries airmail, without covers. **Remarks:** Accepts advertising. **URL:** http://www.omnicon.es; http://www.revistafv.es/. **Circ:** (Not Reported)

50760 ■ FV—Foto-Video Actualidad
Omnicon
Seis de diciembre, s/n, local 25
E-28023 Madrid, Spain
Ph: 34 91 7402081
Fax: 34 91 3579295
Publication E-mail: omnicon@skios.es
Publisher E-mail: revistafv@omnicon.es
Professional magazine covering photography and digital imaging. **Founded:** June 1988. **Freq:** Monthly. **Print Method:** Offset. **Trim Size:** 21 x 27.5 cm. **Cols./Page:** 5. **Key Personnel:** Juan M. Varela, Director, directorfv@omnicon.es. **ISSN:** 0219-2244. **Remarks:** Accepts advertising. **URL:** http://www.omnicon.es/fv.html. **Circ:** Paid 15,000

50761 ■ Geo
G+J Espana
c/o Albasanz, 15 Edificio A
E-28037 Madrid, Spain
Ph: 34 914 369800
Fax: 34 915 767881
Publisher E-mail: publicidad@gyj.es
Consumer magazine covering travel. **Founded:** 1986. **Freq:** Monthly. **Print Method:** Offset. **Trim Size:** 213 x 270 mm. **Key Personnel:** David Corral, Director. **ISSN:** 0213-7755. **Subscription Rates:** EUR33.60 individuals Spain; EUR60 individuals; EUR74.50 other countries. **Remarks:** Accepts advertising. **URL:** http://mundo-geo.es/. **Ad Rates:** 4C: EUR6,700. **Circ:** Combined 31,000

50762 ■ Gerokomos
Ediciones SPA S.L.
Antonio Lopez 249, 1
Edificio Vertice
E-28041 Madrid, Spain
Ph: 34 915 002077
Fax: 34 915 002075
Publisher E-mail: editorial6@drugfarma.es
Journal dedicated to nursing staff carrying out geriatrics tasks and other professionals involved both in the care of the aged and in the treatment of chronic injuries. **Founded:** June 20, 2006. **Freq:** Daily (eve.) and Sat. (morn.). **Print Method:** Web offset. **Trim Size:** 13 3/4 x 21 1/2. **Cols./Page:** 6. **Col. Width:** 25 nonpareils. **Col. Depth:** 301 agate lines. **Key Personnel:** Javier J. Soldevilla Agreda, Director; Azua M.D. Blanco, Editor; Vazquez A.M. Casares, Editor; Bartolome T. Salinero, Editor; Castanedo C. Pfeiffer, Editor. **ISSN:** 1134-928X. **URL:** http://scielo.isciii.es/scielo.php/script_sci_serial/pid_1134-928X/lng_es/nrm_iso.

Circulation: ★ = ABC; △ = BPA; ◆ = CAC; • = CCAB; ❑ = VAC; ⊕ = PO Statement; ‡ = Publisher's Report; Boldface figures = sworn; Light figures = estimated.

Gale Directory of Publications & Broadcast Media/147th Ed.   **5447**

50763 ■ Guia del Comprador de Casas
Edipresse Publications S.A.
Hiedra No. 2-C
E-28036 Madrid, Spain
Ph: 34 91 7339713
Fax: 34 91 7339673
Publication E-mail: guiacasas@moredi.com
Publisher E-mail: groupe@edipresse.com
Magazine featuring sales and lease of real estate properties in the Greater Madrid region. **Founded:** 1997. **Freq:** Monthly. **Key Personnel:** Ignacio de Lucas, Director; Marta Lopez, Ch. Ed. **URL:** http://www.edipresse.com/category/produits/magazines/home-design?page=1. **Circ:** ‡2,568

50764 ■ Guia del Comprador de Coches
Edipresse Publications S.A.
Hiedra No. 2-C
E-28036 Madrid, Spain
Ph: 34 91 7339713
Fax: 34 91 7339673
Publication E-mail: guiacoches@moredi.com
Publisher E-mail: groupe@edipresse.com
Magazine featuring car models with prices and technical specifications. **Freq:** Monthly. **Key Personnel:** Ignacio de Lucas, Director; Luis Miguel Domiguez, Ch. Ed. **URL:** http://www.edipresse.com/category/produits/magazines/automotive. **Circ:** ‡13,348

50765 ■ Guia del Comprador de Furgonetas y Autocaravanas
Edipresse Publications S.A.
Hiedra No. 2-C
E-28036 Madrid, Spain
Ph: 34 91 7339713
Fax: 34 91 7339673
Publication E-mail: guiafurgonetas@moredi.com
Publisher E-mail: groupe@edipresse.com
Magazine for people purchasing vans or four-wheel drive vehicles. **Founded:** 1988. **Freq:** Monthly. **Key Personnel:** Ignacio de Lucas, Director; Carlos Espinosa, Ch. Ed. **URL:** http://www.edipresse.com/automotive/gu%C3%AD-del-comprador-de-furgonetas-yautocaravanas. **Circ:** ‡2,524

50766 ■ Guia del Comprador de Ordenadores y Software
Edipresse Publications S.A.
Hiedra no. 2-C
E-28036 Madrid, Spain
Ph: 34 91 7339713
Fax: 34 91 7339673
Publication E-mail: guiaordenadores@moredi.com
Publisher E-mail: groupe@edipresse.com
Magazine featuring computer and software products. **Founded:** 1987. **Freq:** Monthly. **Key Personnel:** Rafael Marsal, Ch. Ed.; Ignacio de Lucas, Director. **URL:** http://www.edipresse.com/en/par_pays/espagne/rba_edipresse/magazines/guia_del_comprador_de_ordenadores_y_software. **Circ:** ‡4,054

50767 ■ Hot English Magazine
Hot English Publishing
Paseo del Rey 22,Planta 1, Oficina 1,
E-28008 Madrid, Spain
Ph: 34 915 498523
Publisher E-mail: business@hotenglishmagazine.com
Magazine covering information on English language including accents from all over the English-speaking world, English slang, useful English expressions, latest music and film, ways to learn phrasal verbs and idioms, and glossaries in easy-to-understand English. **Subscription Rates:** EUR54 individuals Spain; home elivery; EUR74 individuals Europe; home elivery; EUR84 other countries home elivery. **URL:** http://www.hotenglishmagazine.com/eng/HotEnglish.php.

50768 ■ IH Industria Hostelera
EPESA
Orense, 28-2C
E-28020 Madrid, Spain
Ph: 34 917 990080
Fax: 34 913 528882
Trade magazine covering the hospitality, travel and tourism industry. **Founded:** 1984. **Freq:** Biweekly. **Trim Size:** 27 x 35 cm. **Remarks:** Accepts advertising. **URL:** http://ih.eol.es/. **Ad Rates:** 4C: EUR1,985. **Circ:** Combined 7,000

50769 ■ Infancia y Aprendizaje/Journal for the Study of Education and Development
Fundacion Infancia y Aprendizaje

C/Naranjo de Bulnes 69
San Sebastian de los Reyes
E-28707 Madrid, Spain
Ph: 34 91 6589100
Fax: 34 91 6589100
Publication E-mail: infanciap@usal.es
Publisher E-mail: fundacionia@fia.es
Journal covering developmental and educational psychology for psychologists, counselors, and educators in Spanish and English. **Founded:** 1978. **Freq:** Quarterly. **Key Personnel:** Elena Marin, Gen. Ed.; Juan Ignacio Pozo, Gen. Ed. **ISSN:** 0210-3702. **Remarks:** Accepts advertising science and cultural contents only. **URL:** http://www.fia.es/online/. **Circ:** (Not Reported)

50770 ■ Informes de la Construccion
Instituto de Ciencias de la Construccion Eduardo Torroja
Serrano Galvache, s/n
Aptdo. 19002
E-28033 Madrid, Spain
Ph: 34 913 020440
Fax: 34 913 020700
Trade magazine covering the study of new buildings worldwide. **Freq:** Bimonthly. **Print Method:** Offset. **Trim Size:** 270 x 170. **Key Personnel:** Ignacio Oteiza, Editor-in-Chief. **ISSN:** 0020-0883. **Subscription Rates:** EUR65.61 individuals; EUR15.63 single issue. **Remarks:** Accepts advertising. **URL:** http://www.ietcc.csic.es/index.php?id=1437. **Circ:** (Not Reported)

50771 ■ Insula
Insula, Libreria
Via. of the Two Castillas
33 Atica Complex, Bldg. 4
Pozuelo de Alarcon
E-28224 Madrid, Spain
Publisher E-mail: insula@espasa.es
Magazine covering Hispanic literature. **Founded:** 1946. **Freq:** Monthly. **Trim Size:** 31.5 x 43.5 cm. **ISSN:** 0020-4536. **Subscription Rates:** EUR75 individuals Spain; EUR90 individuals; EUR115 individuals America, Africa; EUR130 other countries. **URL:** http://www.insula.es/.

50772 ■ Intercultural Pragmatics
Walter de Gruyter GmbH & Co. KG
c/o Jesus Romero-Trillo, Review Ed.
Departamento de Filologia Inglesa
Universidad Autonoma de Madridx
28049 Madrid, Spain
Publisher E-mail: info@degruyter.com
Peer-reviewed Journal covering the theoretical and applied pragmatics research in various culture and languages. **Freq:** Quarterly. **Key Personnel:** Istvan Kecskes, Editor-in-Chief, ikecskes@uamail.albany.edu. **ISSN:** 1612-295X. **Subscription Rates:** EUR229 individuals print and online; EUR199 individuals print or online; EUR55 single issue. **URL:** http://www.degruyter.de/journals/intcultpragm/detailEn.cfm.

50773 ■ International Journal of River Basin Management
International Association of Hydraulic Engineering and Research
Paseo Bajo Virgen del Puerto, 3
E-28005 Madrid, Spain
Ph: 34 91 3357908
Fax: 34 91 3357935
Publication E-mail: mail@jrbm.net
Publisher E-mail: iahr@iahr.org
Journal playing a specific role in promoting a cross-sectoral approach encompassing all aspects of river and floodplain management, with a truly global perspective. **Key Personnel:** Prof. Paul Bates, Ch. Ed., paul.bates@bristol.ac.uk; Dr. Jean-Antoine Faby, Ch. Ed., ja.faby@oieau.fr; Prof. Roger Falconer, Dep. Ed.-in-Ch., falconerra@cardiff.ac.uk. **Subscription Rates:** EUR53 members hard copy and electronic access; EUR14 members electronic access only; EUR135 nonmembers hard copy and electronic access; EUR35 nonmembers electronic access only; EUR350 institutions hard copy and electronic. **URL:** http://www.jrbm.net/pages.

50774 ■ Intramuros
Maria Sheila Cremaschi
Calle Ayala, N 7
2 Derecha
E-28001 Madrid, Spain
Ph: 34 915 779506
Fax: 34 917 811402
Magazine covering biographies and autobiographies of literary figures. **Subtitle:** Biografias, Autobiografias y

Memorias. **Founded:** 1995. **Freq:** Semiannual. **Print Method:** Offset. **Trim Size:** 27 x 40 cm. **Key Personnel:** Maria Sheila Cremaschi, Editor, editoramshc@grupointramuros.com. **ISSN:** 0329-3416. **URL:** http://www.grupointramuros.com. **Circ:** Combined 15,000

50775 ■ Ipmark
Ediciones y Estudios S.L.
S.L. Enrique Larreta No.5 Pi.1
E-28036 Madrid, Spain
Ph: 34 913 159845
Fax: 34 913 157419
Trade magazine covering advertising and marketing. **Founded:** 1965. **Freq:** Semimonthly. **Print Method:** Offset. **Trim Size:** 24 x 34 cm. **Key Personnel:** Miguel De Haro, Editor; Jaime De Haro, Director; Galician Raquel, Coordination; Fatima De Haro, Administration; Andres Navarro, Operations Mgr.; Alfonso Rodriguez, Design; Manuel G. Carbajo, Director. **Subscription Rates:** EUR150 individuals Spain; EUR275 other countries. **Remarks:** Accepts advertising. **URL:** http://www.ipmark.com/. **Circ:** (Not Reported)

50776 ■ iWorld
IDG Communications S.A.
Claudio Coello 123, 5 Planta
E-28006 Madrid, Spain
Ph: 34 913 496600
Trade magazine for professional, private Internet users. **Founded:** Jan. 1992. **Freq:** Monthly. **Print Method:** Offset. **Trim Size:** 210 x 280 mm. **Cols./Page:** 3. **Col. Width:** 54.3 millimeters. **Key Personnel:** Daniel Comino, Director, dcomino@idg.es; Marta Cabanillas, Contact, mcabanillas@idg.es. **ISSN:** 1139-0859. **Subscription Rates:** US$50 individuals Europe; US$75 elsewhere. **Remarks:** Accepts advertising. **URL:** http://www.idg.es/iworld. **Circ:** Paid 7,000

50777 ■ La Balsa de la Medusa
Visor Distribuciones
Tomas Breton, 66
E-28045 Madrid, Spain
Ph: 34 914681102
Fax: 34 914681098
Publication E-mail: visordis@infornet.es
Publisher E-mail: visordis@infornet.es
Magazine covering communication, arts theory, literary theory, philosophy, sociology, and related fields. **Freq:** Quarterly. **Trim Size:** 17 x 24 cm. **Key Personnel:** Carlos Piera, Director. **URL:** http://www.visordis.es.

50778 ■ Leviatan
Editorial Pablo Iglesias
Monte Esquinza, 30-2
E-28010 Madrid, Spain
Ph: 34 913 104313
Fax: 34 913 194585
Publisher E-mail: editorial@fpabloiglesias.es
Magazine covering Spanish culture and politics. **Freq:** Quarterly. **Trim Size:** 17 x 24 cm. **Key Personnel:** Amelia Valcarcel, Director. **Subscription Rates:** EUR60 individuals Spain. **URL:** http://www2.fpabloiglesias.es/shopalt/Magazines.aspx.

50779 ■ Macworld Espana
IDG Communications S.A.
Claudio Coello 123, 5 Planta
E-28006 Madrid, Spain
Ph: 34 913 496600
Trade magazine for highly qualified user of the Macintosh in Spain. **Founded:** Feb. 1992. **Freq:** 11/yr. **Print Method:** Offset. **Trim Size:** 210 x 280 mm. **Cols./Page:** 3. **Col. Width:** 54.6 millimeters. **Key Personnel:** Daniel de Blas, Editorial Dir., dblas@idg.es; Javier Rodriguez, Contact, javier@idg.es; Jose Carlos Daganzo, Contact, jcdaganzo@idg.es. **ISSN:** 1132-1156. **Subscription Rates:** EUR594 individuals. **Remarks:** Accepts advertising. **URL:** http://www.idg.com/www/IDGProducts.nsf/0/0B333FC4C23BD20A852577A0005879C8; http://www.idg.es/macworld. **Formerly:** Macworld Espana. **Ad Rates:** BW: EUR3,105. **Circ:** Combined ‡9,000

50780 ■ Marie Claire
G+J Espana
c/o Albasanz, 15 Edificio A
E-28037 Madrid, Spain
Ph: 34 914 369800
Fax: 34 915 767881
Publication E-mail: marieclaireweb@gyj.es
Publisher E-mail: publicidad@gyj.es
Consumer magazine for women. **Founded:** 1987. **Freq:**

Monthly. **Print Method:** Offset. **Key Personnel:** Elena Sanchez-Fabres, Advertising Dir.; Joanna Coles, Editor-in-Chief; Susan Plagemann, VP/Publisher. **Subscription Rates:** EUR36 individuals; EUR94.10 individuals for Europe; EUR127.95 individuals rest of the world; EUR28.80 individuals for Spain. **Remarks:** Accepts advertising. **URL:** http://www.marie-claire.es/. **Circ:** Combined ‡108,000

50781 ■ Matador
La Fabrica Gestion + Cultura
Alameda 9
Veronica 13
E-28014 Madrid, Spain
Ph: 34 913 601320
Publisher E-mail: info@lafabrica.com
Magazine covering culture, arts, ideas and trends in Spain and worldwide. **Founded:** 1995. **Trim Size:** 30 x 40 cm. **Key Personnel:** Raul Munoz, Contact, matador@lafabrica.com; Camino Brasa, Contact, camino@lafabrica.com; Chelo Lozano, Contact, chelo@lafabrica.com. **Subscription Rates:** EUR60 individuals. **URL:** http://www.revistamatador.com/.

50782 ■ Materiales de Construccion
Instituto de Ciencias de la Construccion Eduardo Torroja
Serrano Galvache, s/n
Aptdo. 19002
E-28033 Madrid, Spain
Ph: 34 913 020440
Fax: 34 913 020700
Trade magazine covering the study of new building materials for construction. **Founded:** 1951. **Freq:** Quarterly. **Print Method:** Offset. **Key Personnel:** Ma. del Mar Alonso Lopez, Sec.; Jose A. Coto, Contact; Manuel Fernandez Canovas, Contact; Demetrio Gaspar, Contact; Javier Martin de Eulate, Contact; Benita Silva, Contact; Nicanor Prendes, Contact; Francisca Puertas, Editor-in-Chief; Ma. Teresa Blanco, Contact. **ISSN:** 0465-2746. **Remarks:** Accepts advertising. **URL:** http://www.ietcc.csic.es/index.php?id=1365. **Circ:** (Not Reported)

50783 ■ Melomano
Orfeo Ediciones
Bloque 3 Oficina 2
Avda Espana 133
E-28231 Madrid, Spain
Ph: 34 913510253
Fax: 34 913510587
Publication E-mail: melomano@orfeoed.com
Publisher E-mail: redaccion@orfeoed.com
Magazine covering classical music. **Founded:** June 21, 1996. **Freq:** Monthly. **Trim Size:** 21 x 29.8 cm. **Key Personnel:** Alfonso Carrate, Director. **URL:** http://ecom.orfeoed.com/tienda.pl?action=ENTER&thispage=menu.html.

50784 ■ Mia
G+J Espana
c/o Albasanz, 15 Edificio A
E-28037 Madrid, Spain
Ph: 34 914 369800
Fax: 34 915 767881
Publisher E-mail: publicidad@gyj.es
Consumer magazine for women. **Founded:** 1986. **Freq:** Weekly. **Key Personnel:** Ketty Rico, Contact. **Subscription Rates:** EUR49.90 individuals for Spain only; EUR109 individuals for Europe; EUR148 individuals rest of Europe. **Remarks:** Accepts advertising. **URL:** http://www.miarevista.es/. **Circ:** Combined ‡140,000

50785 ■ Muy Interesante
G+J Espana
c/o Albasanz, 15 Edificio A
E-28037 Madrid, Spain
Ph: 34 914 369800
Fax: 34 915 767881
Publisher E-mail: publicidad@gyj.es
General interest magazine. **Founded:** Jan. 1, 1981. **Freq:** Monthly. **Print Method:** Offset. **Trim Size:** 224 x 285 mm. **Key Personnel:** Jose Pardina, Director. **ISSN:** 0213-7755. **Subscription Rates:** EUR76.80 individuals; EUR30.72 individuals in Spain; EUR73.30 individuals in Europe; EUR95.30 individuals rest of world. **Remarks:** Accepts advertising. **URL:** http://www.guj.de/index_en.php4?/en/produkte/zeitschrift/zeitschriftentitel/muy_Interesante.php4; http://www.muyinteresante.es. **Ad Rates:** 4C: EUR13,800. **Circ:** Combined ‡230,000

50786 ■ Nueva Revista
Diproedisa S.L.
Javier Ferrero, 2
E-28002 Madrid, Spain
Ph: 34 915 199756
Fax: 34 914 151254
Publisher E-mail: nuevarevista@tst.es
Magazine covering politics and the arts. **Founded:** 1990. **Freq:** Bimonthly. **Trim Size:** 15.5 x 21.5 cm. **Key Personnel:** Antonio Fontan, President; Alvaro Lucas, Director. **URL:** http://www.nuevarevista.net/.

50787 ■ Papeles de la FIM (Fundacion de Investigaciones Marxistas)
Fundacion de Investigaciones Marxistas
Calle Alameda
5 2o Izda
E-28014 Madrid, Spain
Ph: 34 91 4201388
Fax: 34 91 4202004
Publisher E-mail: info@fim.org.es
Magazine covering political issues. **Founded:** 1980. **Freq:** Semiannual. **Trim Size:** 17 x 24 cm. **Key Personnel:** Daniel Lacalle, Contact. **ISSN:** 1133-0562. **URL:** http://www.fim.org.es/.

50788 ■ PC World Espana
IDG Communications S.A.
Claudio Coello 123, 5 Planta
E-28006 Madrid, Spain
Ph: 34 913 496600
Trade magazine covering computers and computing for information technology professionals in medium and small companies. **Founded:** Mar. 1, 1985. **Freq:** Monthly. **Print Method:** Offset. **Trim Size:** 210 x 280 mm. **Cols./Page:** 4. **Col. Width:** 40.8 millimeters. **Key Personnel:** Arantxa G. Aguilera, Editor-in-Chief; Isabel Campo, Editorial Dir. **ISSN:** 0213-1307. **Subscription Rates:** EUR49.50 individuals; EUR100 two years. **Remarks:** Accepts advertising. **URL:** http://www.idg.es/pcworldtech/. **Formerly:** PC World Espana. **Ad Rates:** BW: 6,900 Ptas. **Circ:** Combined ‡62,450

50789 ■ Plasticulture Journal
International Committee of Plastics in Agriculture
Comite International des Plastiques en Agriculture
Coslada, 18
E-28028 Madrid, Spain
Ph: 34 902 281828
Fax: 34 913 565628
Publisher E-mail: cpacipa@club-internet.fr
Journal covering plastics in English, French and Spanish. **Freq:** Quarterly. **Subscription Rates:** EUR74 individuals; US$107 individuals; EUR35 individuals paper only; US$50 individuals paper only. **Remarks:** Accepts advertising. **URL:** http://www.plasticulture.com. **Ad Rates:** 4C: 1,500 Ptas. **Circ:** (Not Reported)

50790 ■ Politica Exterior
Estudios de Politica Exterior S.A.
Nunez de Balboa, 49
E-28001 Madrid, Spain
Ph: 34 91 4312628
Fax: 34 91 5777252
Publication E-mail: revista@politicaexteriro.com
Publisher E-mail: suscripciones@politicaexterior.com
Magazine covering political issues. **Founded:** 1987. **Freq:** Bimonthly. **Trim Size:** 17 x 24 cm. **Key Personnel:** Dario Valcarcel, CEO/Editorial Dir. **ISSN:** 0213-6856. **Subscription Rates:** EUR62 individuals Spain; EUR112 two years individual. **Remarks:** Accepts advertising. **URL:** http://www.politicaexterior.com/. **Ad Rates:** BW: EUR2,405, 4C: EUR2,925. **Circ:** (Not Reported)

50791 ■ Por la Danza
Asociacion Cultural por la Danza
Calle Antonio Vicent, 65
E-28019 Madrid, Spain
Ph: 34 915 695195
Fax: 34 914 698582
Publication E-mail: revista@porladanza.com
Publisher E-mail: danza@porladanza.com
Magazine covering Spanish dance and dancers, including Flamenco, ballet and contemporary dance. **Founded:** 1998. **Freq:** Quarterly. **Trim Size:** 20 x 30.5 cm. **ISSN:** 1134-6612. **Subscription Rates:** EUR24 individuals; EUR30 other countries; EUR41 other countries. **URL:** http://www.porladanza.com/.

50792 ■ Primer Acto
Ricardo de la Vega, 18

E-28028 Madrid, Spain
Ph: 34 917 258085
Fax: 34 917 263711
Publisher E-mail: primeracto@primeracto.com
Magazine covering theater worldwide, focusing on Latin American and Spanish theater. **Founded:** 1957. **Freq:** Bimonthly. **Trim Size:** 17 x 24 cm. **ISSN:** 0032-8367. **Subscription Rates:** EUR9.80 individuals; 43 Ptas individuals; EUR80.50 individuals. **URL:** http://www.primeracto.com/.

50793 ■ Psychology in Spain
Consejo General de Colegios Oficiales de Psicologos
Conde de Penalver
45 Planta 5
28006 Madrid, Spain
Ph: 34 91 4449020
Fax: 34 91 3095615
Publication E-mail: psyspain@cop.es
Publisher E-mail: secop@cop.es
Journal covering Spanish psychology. **Freq:** Annual. **Key Personnel:** Jose Ramon Fernandez Hermida, PhD, Editor; Manuel Berdullas Temes, Assoc. Ed. **ISSN:** 1137-9685. **Subscription Rates:** Free. **URL:** http://www.psychologyinspain.com/.

50794 ■ Quercus
Editorial America Iberica S.A.
Miguel Yuste, 33 bis
E-28037 Madrid, Spain
Ph: 34 913 277950
Fax: 34 913 044746
Publisher E-mail: direccion@eai.es
Magazine covering natural history and nature study. **Founded:** 1981. **Freq:** Monthly. **Key Personnel:** Jose Antonio Montero, Editor, jmontero@eai.es; Rafael Serra, Director, rafael.serra@eai.es; Pilar Perez, Contact, pilar.perez@eai.es. **URL:** http://www.eai.es/publi_quercus.html.

50795 ■ Reales Sitios
Patrimonio Nacional Palacio Real de Madrid
Real Palace
Palacio Real
E-28071 Madrid, Spain
Ph: 34 91 4548700
Publisher E-mail: info@patrimonionacional.es
Magazine covering news and analysis about the historical and artistic value of the assets of Spain's National Heritage. **Founded:** 1964. **Freq:** Quarterly. **Print Method:** Offset. **Trim Size:** 22.5 x 31.5 cm. **Key Personnel:** Rosario Diez del Corral, Director. **ISSN:** 0486-0993. **Subscription Rates:** EUR19 individuals Spain; EUR38 other countries. **URL:** http://www.patrimonionacional.es/Home/Programas-Culturales/Publicaciones/Otras-publicaciones/REVISTA-REALES-SITIOS.aspx. **Circ:** (Not Reported)

50796 ■ Revista del Calzado
Mundipress S.L.
San Ambrosio, 6 bajo
E-28011 Madrid, Spain
Ph: 34 91 3655700
Fax: 34 91 3662682
Publisher E-mail: mundipress@mundipress.com
Professional magazine covering the shoe industry. **Founded:** Jan. 1990. **Freq:** Bimonthly. **Print Method:** Offset. **Subscription Rates:** EUR50 individuals. **Remarks:** Accepts advertising. **URL:** http://www.mundipress.com/calzado.php. **Circ:** 4,500

50797 ■ Revista Espanola de Paleontologia
Spanish Paleontology Society
Sociedad Espanola de Paleontologia
Museo Nacional de Ciencias Naturales
Jose Gutierrez Abascal, 2
E-28006 Madrid, Spain
Publisher E-mail: sepaleontologia@gmail.com
Spanish, English and French language publication covering paleontology. **Freq:** Semiannual extraordinary volumes are occasionally published. **Key Personnel:** Rodolfo Gozalo, Editor, gozalo@uv.es. **ISSN:** 0213-6937. **Remarks:** Advertising not accepted. **URL:** http://www.sepaleontologia.es/publicaciones.html. **Circ:** 600

50798 ■ Revista Hispano Cubana HC
Fundacion Hispano Cubana
C/ Orfila, 8 1o A
E-28010 Madrid, Spain
Ph: 34 913 196313
Fax: 34 913 197008

Circulation: ★ = ABC; △ = BPA; ♦ = CAC; • = CCAB; ❑ = VAC; ⊕ = PO Statement; ‡ = Publisher's Report; Boldface figures = sworn; Light figures = estimated.

Gale Directory of Publications & Broadcast Media/147th Ed.										5449

Publisher E-mail: f.h.c@hispanocubana.org

Magazine covering politics, culture and the arts. **Founded:** 1998. **Freq:** Triennial. **Trim Size:** 16 x 22.5 cm. **Key Personnel:** Javier Martinez-Corbalan, Director. **ISSN:** 1139-0883. **Subscription Rates:** 24 individuals Spain; 60 other countries; 8 single issue; 60 individuals America. **Remarks:** Advertising accepted; rates available upon request. **URL:** http://www.revistasculturales.com/revistas/95/revista-hispano-cubana/. **Circ:** (Not Reported)

50799 ■ Revista de Occidente
Fundacion Jose Ortega y Gasset
Fortuny, 53
E-28010 Madrid, Spain
Ph: 34 917 004100
Fax: 34 917 003530
Publisher E-mail: comunicacion@fog.es
Scholarly journal covering literature, culture, communication, and the sciences. **Founded:** 1923. **Freq:** Monthly. **Trim Size:** 14.5 x 21 cm. **Key Personnel:** Alfredo Taberna, Editor; Jose Varela Ortega, Director; Begona Paredes, Coord. **ISSN:** 0034-8635. **Subscription Rates:** EUR123 individuals Europe; US$172 individuals U.S.; America, Africa & oriente.medio; mail aeria; US$195 individuals Asia and the Australian continent; mail aeria; 80 individuals Espana; 74 Ptas individuals mail ordinary; 94 Ptas individuals mail aerial; US$186 individuals America, Africa y oriente medio; US$210 individuals Asia y oceania; 132 individuals Europe; 102 individuals Espana. **URL:** http://www.ortegaygasset.edu/contenidos.asp?id_s=52.

50800 ■ Ritmo
Lira Editorial S.A.
Isabel Colbrand, 10
Oficina 87
E-28050 Madrid, Spain
Ph: 34 913 588774
Fax: 34 913 588944
Publisher E-mail: correo@ritmo.es
Magazine covering classical music and music publishing in Europe. **Founded:** 1929. **Freq:** Monthly 11/yr. **Trim Size:** 21 x 29.7 cm. **ISSN:** 0035-5658. **Subscription Rates:** EUR8,470 individuals Spain; EUR125 other countries airmail, terrestrial; EUR167 individuals Europe, airmail; EUR260 individuals rest of the world; EUR6,800 individuals surcharge for shipments. **Remarks:** Accepts advertising. **URL:** http://www.ritmo.es. **Circ:** (Not Reported)

50801 ■ Scherzo
Scherzo Editorial S.A.
C/Cartagena, 10-1 C
E-28028 Madrid, Spain
Ph: 34 913 567622
Fax: 34 917 261864
Publication E-mail: revista@scherzo.es
Publisher E-mail: revista@scherzo.es
Consumer magazine covering classical music. **Founded:** Dec. 1985. **Freq:** Monthly 11/yr. **Trim Size:** 170 x 250 mm. **Cols./Page:** 3. **Col. Width:** 5.2 millimeters. **Col. Depth:** 250 millimeters. **Key Personnel:** Luis Sunen, Director; Arantza Quintanilla, Publicity, arantza@scherzo.es; Enrique Martinez Miura, Editor-in-Chief. **ISSN:** 0213-4802. **Subscription Rates:** EUR70 individuals Spain; EUR105 individuals; EUR120 U.S. and Canada; EUR125 individuals Mexico, Central and South USA. **Remarks:** Accepts advertising. **URL:** http://www.scherzo.es. **Ad Rates:** BW: EUR1,250, 4C: EUR1,650. **Circ:** Combined 17,500

50802 ■ Ser Padres
GyJ Espana Ediciones
C/Albasanz, 15. Edif. A.
E-28037 Madrid, Spain
Ph: 91 4369800
Fax: 91 5767881
Hispanic magazine providing information on parenting. **Founded:** 1990. **Freq:** Bimonthly. **Print Method:** Offset. **Trim Size:** 7 7/8 x 10 1/2. **Cols./Page:** 4. **URL:** http://www.serpadres.es.

50803 ■ Ser Padres Bebe
G+J Espana
c/o Albasanz, 15 Edificio A
E-28037 Madrid, Spain
Ph: 34 914 369800
Fax: 34 915 767881
Publisher E-mail: publicidad@gyj.es
Consumer magazine covering pregnancy, childbirth and early parenting. **Freq:** Monthly. **Print Method:** Offset. **Subscription Rates:** EUR28.30 individuals for Spain

only; EUR63.20 individuals for Europe; EUR81.20 individuals rest of the world. **Remarks:** Accepts advertising. **URL:** http://www.serpadres.es/bebe. **Circ:** Combined ‡59,308

50804 ■ Ser Padres Hoy
G+J Espana
c/o Albasanz, 15 Edificio A
E-28037 Madrid, Spain
Ph: 34 914 369800
Fax: 34 915 767881
Publisher E-mail: publicidad@gyj.es
Consumer magazine covering parenting. **Founded:** 1974. **Freq:** Monthly. **Print Method:** Offset. **Remarks:** Accepts advertising. **URL:** http://www.guj.de/index_en.php4. **Circ:** Combined ‡35,000

50805 ■ SIC Seguridad en Informatica y Comunicaciones
Ediciones CODA S.L.
Goya 39
E-28001 Madrid, Spain
Ph: 34 915 758324
Fax: 34 915 777047
Publisher E-mail: info@revistasic.com
Professional magazine covering the security of computing and communication systems for large and medium Spanish companies. **Founded:** 1992. **Freq:** 5/yr (February, April, June, September & November). **Print Method:** Offset. **Trim Size:** 210 x 297 mm. **Cols./Page:** 4. **Key Personnel:** Virginia Moreno, Editor-in-Chief, vmoreno@codasic.com; Amparo Garcia, Contact, agarcia@codasic.com; Monica Marugan, Contact, mmarugan@codasic.com; Rafael Armisen, Contact, rarmisen@codasic.com; Luis Fernandez Delgado, Editor, lfernandez@codasic.com. **ISSN:** 1136-0623. **Subscription Rates:** EUR9.32 individuals Spain; EUR16.82 individuals Europe; EUR22.14 individuals U.S.; EUR46.63 individuals Spain; EUR84.14 individuals Europe; EUR110.70 individuals U.S.; EUR74.60 individuals Spain; EUR134.62 individuals Europe; EUR221.40 individuals U.S. **Remarks:** Accepts advertising. **URL:** http://www.revistasic.com. **Ad Rates:** BW: EUR1,125, 4C: EUR1,500. **Circ:** Paid 5,000

50806 ■ Sintesis
A.V. Sociedad Editorial Sintesis
Claudio Coello, 101
E-28006 Madrid, Spain
Ph: 34 915 770640
Fax: 34 915 763070
Publisher E-mail: info@aieti.es
Magazine covering political issues in Spain. **Founded:** 1987. **Freq:** Annual. **Trim Size:** 16 x 23.5 cm. **Key Personnel:** Guadalupe Ruiz-Gimenez, Director. **Subscription Rates:** EUR15.03 individuals; EUR40 other countries. **URL:** http://www.miramedios.com/cgi-bin/publico/ver_ficha.pl?ref=200310287193644&donde=medios.

50807 ■ Sistema
Fundacion Sistema
Fuencarral, 127-1
E-28010 Madrid, Spain
Ph: 34 914 487319
Fax: 34 914 487339
Publication E-mail: fsistema@teleline.es
Publisher E-mail: info@fundacionsistema.com
Magazine covering social science, including sociology, political science, philosophy, methodology, and social history. **Founded:** 1973. **Freq:** Bimonthly. **Trim Size:** 16 x 23 cm. **Key Personnel:** Jose Felix Tezanos, Editor; Elias Diaz, Director. **Subscription Rates:** EUR48 individuals Spain; EUR102 individuals; EUR88 individuals Europe; airmail; EUR70 individuals Europe and America. **URL:** http://www.fundacionsistema.com/Pubs/MagazineSumm.aspx?ID=2.

50808 ■ Spain Gourmetour
Instituto Espanol de Comercio Exterior
Paseo de la Castellana, 14-16
E-28046 Madrid, Spain
Ph: 34 913 496100
Publication E-mail: spaingourmetour@icex.es
Publisher E-mail: buzonicex@icex.es
Magazine covering food, wine and travel. **Subtitle:** Food, Wine and Travel Magazine. **Founded:** 1986. **Freq:** Quarterly. **Key Personnel:** Cathy Boirac, Editor-in-Chief. **ISSN:** 0214-2937. **Subscription Rates:** Free. **Remarks:** Accepts advertising. **URL:** http://www.spaingourmetour.com. **Circ:** Non-paid 25,000

50809 ■ Temas para el Debate
Iniciativas Editoriales Sistema S.A.

Fuencarral, 127 1
E-28010 Madrid, Spain
Ph: 34 914 487319
Fax: 34 914 487339
Publisher E-mail: info@fundacionsistema.com
Magazine covering current politics, economics and culture. **Founded:** 1994. **Freq:** Monthly. **Trim Size:** 20 x 28 cm. **Key Personnel:** Jose Felix Tezanos, Director; Alfonso Guerra, President; Carmen Barrios, Editor-in-Chief. **ISSN:** 1134-6574. **Subscription Rates:** EUR40 individuals to Spain; EUR85 individuals to Europe; EUR115 individuals. **URL:** http://www.fundacionsistema.com/Pubs/Magazine.aspx?ID=3.

50810 ■ Terra Incognita
Apartado de Correos 14401
E-28080 Madrid, Spain
Publisher E-mail: revistaterraincognita@yahoo.es
Literary review promoting bilingual intercultural exchange through the arts. **Freq:** Annual. **Key Personnel:** Robert J. Lavigna, Editor; Alexandra Van De Kamp, Editor; William Glenn, Editor; Fran G. Bobadilla Raton, Contact. **Subscription Rates:** EUR6 individuals Spain; EUR10 two years Spain; US$9 individuals U.S.; US$17 two years individual; US$11 other countries; US$19 other countries two issues. **URL:** http://www.terraincognita.50megs.com/index.html.

50811 ■ TEST
Society of Statistic and Operations Research Faculty of Mathematical Sciences
Facultad de Matematicas
Despacho 502
Plaza de Ciencias, 3
28040 Madrid, Spain
Ph: 34 91 5449102
Fax: 34 91 5449102
Publisher E-mail: oficina@seio.es
International journal dealing with all aspects of statistics and probability. **Freq:** 2/yr. **Key Personnel:** Ricardo Cao, Editor, rcao@udc.es; Domingo Morales, Editor. **URL:** http://www.seio.es/TEST.html.

50812 ■ Top Auto
Edipresse Publications S.A.
Cuesta de San Vicente 28
E-28008 Madrid, Spain
Ph: 34 91 5472300
Fax: 34 91 2043550
Publisher E-mail: groupe@edipresse.com
Magazine for car buyers and enthusiasts. **Founded:** 1989. **Freq:** Monthly. **Key Personnel:** Jose Luis Pader, Director; Norberto Fernandez, Chief Ed. **URL:** http://www.edipresse.com/e-versions-print-editions/topautonet. **Circ:** ‡24,234

50813 ■ Utopias/Nuestra Bandera
Partido Comunista de Espana
Mt. Olympus, 35
E-28043 Madrid, Spain
Ph: 34 91 3004969
Fax: 34 91 3004744
Publisher E-mail: comunistas@pce.es
Magazine covering social, political and cultural issues. **Freq:** Quarterly. **Trim Size:** 17 x 24 cm. **ISSN:** 1133-567X. **Subscription Rates:** EUR24 individuals Spain; EUR30 U.S. Europe; EUR48 other countries; EUR30 individuals America. **URL:** http://www.revistasculturales.com/revistas/31/utopias-nuestra-bandera/.

50814 ■ Via Libre
Fundacion de los Ferrocarriles Espanoles
Santa Isabel 44
E-28012 Madrid, Spain
Ph: 34 911 5110701
Publication E-mail: vialibre@ffe.es
Publisher E-mail: fugeu02@ffe.es
Technical magazine covering trains. **Founded:** 1964. **Freq:** Monthly. **Trim Size:** 28.5 x 21 cm. **ISSN:** 1134-1416. **Remarks:** Accepts advertising. **URL:** http://www.vialibre.org. **Circ:** Controlled 15,000

50815 ■ Visual
Blur Ediciones
Abtao 25
Interior Nave C.
E-28007 Madrid, Spain
Ph: 34 91434 8178
Magazine covering graphic design, photography, illustration, audiovisual, publicity, art and related elements of visual communication. **Freq:** Bimonthly. **Trim Size:** 22.5 x 29 cm. **Key Personnel:** Alvaro Sobrino, Director.

Subscription Rates: EUR39.50 individuals. URL: http://www.visual.gi/index2005.htm.

50816 ■ World Watch
Gobernador 3
E-28014 Madrid, Spain
Ph: 34 914 293774
Fax: 34 936 926675
Publisher E-mail: worldwatch@nodo50.org
Environmental magazine covering changes in climate, biodiversity, and related topics. Founded: 1996. Freq: Bimonthly. Key Personnel: Jose Santamaria, Editor. ISSN: 1136-8586. Subscription Rates: EUR17 individuals Europe, Spain; EUR32 institutions. Remarks: Accepts advertising. URL: http://www.terra.org/articulos/art00598.html. Ad Rates: BW: US$1,200, 4C: US$2,000. Circ: Paid 15,000

50817 ■ Zona Abierta
Editorial Pablo Iglesias
Monte Esquinza, 30-2
E-28010 Madrid, Spain
Ph: 34 913 104313
Fax: 34 913 194585
Publisher E-mail: editorial@fpabloiglesias.es
Magazine covering the theory of social science. Freq: Semiannual. Trim Size: 13.5 x 21 cm. Subscription Rates: EUR9.13 individuals; EUR9.50 individuals. URL: http://www.sigloxxieditores.com/116_117.html.

50818 ■ Radio Vallekas-FM - 107.5
Puerto del Milagro 6 posterior
28018 Madrid, Spain
Ph: 34 917 773928
Format: Full Service. Owner: Asociacion Cultural Taller de Comunicacion Radio Vallekas, at above address. Key Personnel: Mariano Sanchez, Director, ariano.sanchez@radiovallekas.org. URL: http://www.radiovallekas.org/spip/.

Mataro

50819 ■ El Viejo Topo
Ediciones de Intervencion Cultural S.L.
Sant Antoni, 86 local 9
E-08031 Mataro, Spain
Ph: 34 937 550832
Fax: 34 937 906795
Publisher E-mail: editor@edicionesdeintervenioncultural.com
Magazine covering politics, culture, and society. Freq: Monthly. Trim Size: 21 x 28 cm. Key Personnel: Miguel Riera, Editor. Subscription Rates: EUR58 individuals Spain; EUR100 individuals Europe; EUR112 individuals rest of world. URL: http://www.elviejotopo.com/web/index.php.

50820 ■ Quimera
Ediciones de Intervencion Cultural S.L.
Sant Antoni, 86 local 9
E-08031 Mataro, Spain
Ph: 34 937 550832
Fax: 34 937 906795
Publication E-mail: quimerarevista@gmail.com
Publisher E-mail: editor@edicionesdeintervenioncultural.com
Magazine covering literature, culture and current affairs. Freq: Monthly. Trim Size: 21 x 27.5 cm. Key Personnel: Llucia Ramis, Director; Antonio Garcia Vila, Director. ISSN: 0211-3325. Subscription Rates: EUR4 individuals Spain; EUR52 individuals Europe; EUR92 individuals America. URL: http://www.revistasculturales.com/revistas/43/quimera/.

Murcia

50821 ■ Anales de Psicologia
Universidad de Murcia, Servicio de Publicaciones
c/o Agustin Romero Medina, Ed.
University of Murcia
Campus de Espinardo
PO Box 4021
E-30080 Murcia, Spain
Peer-reviewed journal covering articles of investigation and theoretical revision in applied psychology. Founded: 1984. Freq: Biennial. Print Method: Offset. Uses mats. Trim Size: 6 x 9. Cols./Page: 1. Col. Width: 5 inches. Col. Depth: 7 1/2 inches. Key Personnel: Agustin Romero Medina, Editor; Francisco Roman Lapuente, Assoc. Ed. ISSN: 0212-9728. Subscription Rates: EUR18 individuals. URL: http://www.um.es/analesps/analesi.htm.

50822 ■ Phytochemistry
Phytochemical Society of Europe
Espinardo-Murcia
de Alimentos
E-30100 Murcia, Spain
Professional publication covering phytochemistry. Founded: 1962. Freq: 18/yr. Key Personnel: D. Strack, Editor; N.G. Lewis, Editor; G.P. Bolwell, Editor. ISSN: 0031-9422. Subscription Rates: 94,100¥ individuals; EUR708 individuals for European countries an Iran; US$797 other countries except Europe, Japan and Iran; 642,300¥ institutions; EUR4,840 institutions for European countries an Iran; US$5,414 institutions, other countries except Europe, Japan and Iran. Remarks: Advertising not accepted. URL: http://www.phytochemicalsociety.org/; http://www.elsevier.com/wps/find/journaldescription.cws_home/273/descriptiondescription. Circ: (Not Reported)

Oviedo

50823 ■ International Journal of Chinese Culture & Management
Inderscience Publishers
c/o Prof. Patricia Ordonez de Pablos, Ed.-in-Ch.
Universidad de Oviedo
Avd del Cristo
E-33071 Oviedo, Spain
Publisher E-mail: editor@inderscience.com
Peer-reviewed journal covering Chinese culture and business & management. Founded: 2007. Freq: 4/yr. Key Personnel: Prof. Patricia Ordonez de Pablos, Editor-in-Chief, patriop@uniovi.es; Prof. W.B. Lee, Assoc. Ed.; Prof. Zhongkai Xiong, Assoc. Ed.; Prof. Qingrui Xu, Assoc. Ed.; Zhiwei Wang, European Ed. ISSN: 1752-1270. Subscription Rates: EUR494 individuals includes surface mail, print only; EUR672 individuals print and online. URL: http://www.inderscience.com/browse/index.php?journalID=220.

50824 ■ International Journal of Learning and Intellectual Capital
Inderscience Publishers
c/o Prof. Patricia Ordonez de Pablos, Exec. Ed.
Universidad de Oviedo
Departamento de Administracion de Empresas y Contabilidad
Facultad de Ciencias Economicas, Avd del Cristo
E-33071 Oviedo, Spain
Publisher E-mail: editor@inderscience.com
Peer-reviewed journal providing a global forum for exchanging research findings and case studies which bridge the latest advances on organisational learning, knowledge management and intellectual capital measuring and reporting. Freq: Quarterly. Key Personnel: Prof. Patricia Ordonez de Pablos, Exec. Ed., patriop@uniovi.es; Prof. Pervaiz K. Ahmed, Editorial Board Member; Prof. Margaret Peteraf, Assoc. Ed.; Prof. Michael H. Zack, Assoc. Ed.; Prof. Eduardo Bueno Campos, Assoc. Ed.; Prof. Guy Ahonen, Editorial Board Member. ISSN: 1479-4853. Subscription Rates: EUR494 individuals print or online; EUR672 individuals print and online. URL: http://www.inderscience.com/browse/index.php?journalCODE=ijlic.

50825 ■ International Journal of Strategic Change Management
Inderscience Publishers
c/o Prof. Patricia Ordonez de Pablos, Ed.-in-Ch.
Universidad de Oviedo
Departamento de Administracion de Empresas y Contabilidad
Facultad de Ciencias Economicas, Avd del Cristo
E-33071 Oviedo, Spain
Publisher E-mail: editor@inderscience.com
Peer-reviewed journal proposing and fostering discussion on strategic change management implementation and follow-up and related topics, offering a wealth of valuable material on theories and practices which underpin successful strategic change. Freq: Quarterly. Key Personnel: Dr. Patricia Ordonez de Pablos, Editor-in-Chief, patriop@uniovi.es; Prof. Eduardo Bueno Campos, Assoc. Ed.; Prof. Margaret Peteraf, Exec. Ed., margaret.a.peteraf@dartmouth.edu; Prof. Anita M. McGahan, Consulting Ed.; Prof. Alok K. Chakrabarti, Assoc. Ed.; Prof. Joseph T. Mahoney, Assoc. Exec. Ed.; Prof. Oliver E. Williamson, Consulting Ed.; Prof. John R. Anchor, Editorial Board Member. ISSN: 1740-2859. Subscription Rates: EUR494 individuals print only (surface mail); EUR840 individuals online only (2-3 users); EUR534 individuals print only (airmail); EUR672 individuals print

and online. URL: http://www.inderscience.com/browse/index.php?journalCODE=ijscm.

Oviedo-Asturias

50826 ■ International Journal of Arab Culture, Management and Sustainable Development
Inderscience Enterprises Limited
c/o Prof. Patricia Ordonez de Pablos, Ed.-in-Chief
Universidad de Oviedo
Facultad de Ciencias Economicas
Avd del Cristo
E-33071 Oviedo-Asturias, Spain
Journal covering the Arab culture, management and sustainable development. Freq: 4/yr. Key Personnel: Prof. Patricia Ordonez de Pablos, Editor-in-Chief, patriop@uniovi.es. ISSN: 1753-9412. Subscription Rates: EUR494 individuals print or online; EUR672 individuals print and online. URL: http://www.inderscience.com/browse/index.php?journalID=256.

Pozuelo de Alarcon

50827 ■ Conectronica
Grupo Asesoramiento Comercial GM2 S.L.
Oslo, 1
Portal 1, 1
Oficina 1
28224 Pozuelo de Alarcon, Spain
Ph: 34 91 7150307
Fax: 34 91 7158421
Publisher E-mail: gm2pt@gm2pt.com
Professional magazine covering connection systems, connectors, cables, fiber optic, and connectivity in measurement systems and components. Subtitle: Technology and Devices in Connection and Connectivity. Founded: 1996. Freq: 10/yr. Print Method: Offset. Cols./Page: 3. Col. Width: 5.5 centimeters. Key Personnel: Atty. Andres Hennequet, Contact, redaccion@conectronica.com. ISSN: 1136-7539. Subscription Rates: EUR60 individuals; EUR90 other countries. Remarks: Accepts advertising. URL: http://www.conectronica.com. Ad Rates: BW: EUR842, 4C: EUR1,202. Circ: Controlled 4,000

Reus

50828 ■ The Cracker
International Nut Council
Consejo Internacional de los Frutos Secos
Calle Boule 2, 3
E-43201 Reus, Spain
Ph: 34 977 331416
Fax: 34 977 315028
Publisher E-mail: inc@nutfruit.org
Publication covering nuts. Freq: 3/yr. ISSN: 7497-1989. Subscription Rates: EUR170 nonmembers; Free to members. Remarks: Advertising accepted; rates available upon request. URL: http://www.nutfruit.org/cracker. Circ: 2,500

Santa Cruz de Tenerife

50829 ■ La Pagina
La Pagina Ediciones S.L.
Ramon y Cajal, 56
E-38006 Santa Cruz de Tenerife, Spain
Ph: 34 922 248559
Fax: 34 922 248559
Publisher E-mail: lapaginaed@telefonica.net
Literary magazine. Freq: Quarterly. Trim Size: 19.5 x 29.5. ISSN: 0214-8390. URL: http://www.telefonica.net/web2/lapaginaed/como_somos.html.

Santander

50830 ■ Arte y Parte
Arte y Parte S.L.
Three of November, 31
E-39010 Santander, Spain
Ph: 34 942 373131
Publisher E-mail: revista@arteyparte.com
Publication covering the field of art in Spain, Portugal, and Latin America. Founded: Feb. 1996. Freq: Bimonthly. Print Method: Offset. Trim Size: 16.5 x 23.5 cm. Key Personnel: Fernando Frances, Editor. ISSN: 1136-2006. Subscription Rates: 55 individuals Spain; 75 individuals Europe; 90 individuals America; EUR18 two years Spain; EUR225 two years Europe; EUR270 two years America. Remarks: Accepts advertising. URL: http://www.arteyparte.com/. Ad Rates: BW: EUR1,050,

4C: EUR1,955. **Circ:** Paid 40,000

Santiago de Compostela

50831 ■ Applied Econometrics and International Development
Euro-American Association of Economic Development Studies
Faculty of Economics, Rm. 119-B
University of Santiago de Compostela
15782 Santiago de Compostela, Spain
Ph: 34 981 563100
Publisher E-mail: eccgs@usc.es
Journal featuring information on international economics. **Freq:** Quarterly. **Key Personnel:** Carmen M. Guisan, Editor; Yu Hsing, Co-Ed.; Constantin Ogloblin, Advisory Board. **ISSN:** 1578-4487. **Subscription Rates:** EUR90 institutions online; EUR180 institutions print and online; EUR90 institutions print. **URL:** http://www.usc.es/economet/aeid.htm.

50832 ■ A Trabe de Ouro
Sotelo Blanco Edicions S.L.
San Marcos, 77
E-15820 Santiago de Compostela, Spain
Ph: 34 981 582571
Fax: 34 981 587290
Magazine covering socio-political analysis and thought. **Founded:** 1990. **Freq:** Quarterly. **Trim Size:** 19 x 25 cm. **Key Personnel:** X.L. Mendez Ferrin, Contact. **ISSN:** 1130-2674. **URL:** http://www.soteloblancoedicions.com/trabe.asp.

Seville

50833 ■ Cuadernos de Medicina Forense
Asociacion Andaluza de Medicos Forenses
Palacio de Justicia
Prado de San Sebastian S/N
E-41004 Seville, Spain
Publisher E-mail: aamefo@cica.es
Journal covering works specialized in medical legislation and jurisprudence related to the health. **Founded:** 1925. **Freq:** Daily. **Print Method:** Offset. **Cols./Page:** 5. **Col. Width:** 34 nonpareils. **Col. Depth:** 206 agate lines. **ISSN:** 1135-7606. **URL:** http://scielo.isciii.es/scielo.php?script=sci_serial&pid=1135-7606.

50834 ■ Integration, the VLSI Journal
Elsevier Science Inc.
c/o F.V. Fernandez, Ed.-in-Ch.
IMSE-CNM-CSIC, University of Seville
Avda. Americo Vespucio s/n
41092 Seville, Spain
Publisher E-mail: usinfo-ehelp@elsevier.com
Peer-reviewed journal covering all aspects of VLSI (very large scale integration) area. **Founded:** 1983. **Freq:** 4/yr. **Print Method:** Flexography. **Cols./Page:** 6. **Col. Width:** 25 nonpareils. **Col. Depth:** 294 agate lines. **Key Personnel:** R. Camposano, Subject Ed.; Y. Cai, Assoc. Ed.; G. Even, Assoc. Ed.; A: Acosta, Assoc. Ed.; M.A. Bayoumi, Subject Ed., mbayoumi@cacs.louisiana.edu; W. Rosenstiel, Subject Ed., rosenstiel@fzi.de; J.M. Delosme, Assoc. Ed.; F. V. Fernandez, Editor-in-Chief, integration@imse.cnm.es; R.H.J.M. Otten, Subject Ed., otten@ics.ele.tue.nl. **ISSN:** 0167-9260. **Subscription Rates:** EUR880 institutions for European countries and Iran; 116,500¥ institutions; US$982 institutions, other countries except Europe, Japan and Iran; US$145 other countries except Europe, Japan and Iran; 16,700¥ individuals; EUR109 individuals for European countries and Iran. **URL:** http://www.elsevier.com/wps/find/journaldescription.cws_home/505653/descriptiondescription.

50835 ■ International Journal of Vehicle Systems Modelling and Testing
Inderscience Publishers
c/o Dr. Johan P. Wideberg, Ed.-in-Ch.
Universidad de Sevilla, Escuela Superior de Ingenieros
Grupo de Ingenieria e Infraestructura de Transportes
Camino de los Descubrimientos s/n
E-41092 Seville, Spain
Publisher E-mail: editor@inderscience.com
Peer-reviewed journal aiming to highlight the theoretical background of research and development problems relating to numerical analysis, modelling and testing of vehicles and vehicle components. **Freq:** Quarterly. **Key Personnel:** Dr. Johan P. Wideberg, Editor-in-Chief, wideberg@us.es; Prof. John Ferris, Editorial Board Member; Dr. Bengt Jacobson, Editorial Board Member; Sergio M. Savaresi, Editorial Board Member; Dr. Erik

Dahlberg, Editorial Board Member; Dr. Avinash K. Agarwal, Editorial Board Member; Dr. Raul G. Longoria, Editorial Board Member; Thomas D. Gillespie, Editorial Board Member; Dr. Corina Sandu, Editorial Board Member. **ISSN:** 1745-6436. **Subscription Rates:** EUR494 individuals print only (surface mail); EUR840 individuals online only (2-3 users); EUR534 individuals print only (airmail); EUR672 individuals print and online. **URL:** http://www.inderscience.com/browse/index.php?journalCODE=ijvsmt.

Tenerife

50836 ■ Island Connections
IC News
c/o Island Connections
c/o Rodeo Aptos
Royal Palm, Local 236
Los Cristianos, Canary Islands
E-38650 Tenerife, Spain
Ph: 34 922750609
Fax: 34 922795810
Publisher E-mail: editorial@ic-news.com
English language community newspaper. **Founded:** 1984. **Freq:** Biweekly. **Print Method:** News print. **Trim Size:** 295 x 370 mm. **Cols./Page:** 6. **Col. Width:** 38 millimeters. **Subscription Rates:** EUR46. **Remarks:** Accepts advertising. **URL:** http://www.ic-web.com. **Former name:** Here and Now. **Ad Rates:** BW: 1,600 Ptas, 4C: 2,000 Ptas. **Circ:** Paid 6,000, Non-paid 19,000

50837 ■ The Paper
Oficina C, 2 Fase
Edif. Las Chafiras Golf
Las Chafiras, San Miguel de Abona
38639 Tenerife, Spain
Ph: 34 922 735659
Fax: 34 922 735659
Community newspaper. **Founded:** 1994. **Freq:** Weekly (Wed.). **Print Method:** Offset. **Trim Size:** 10 1/2 x 15 1/2. **Cols./Page:** 5. **Col. Width:** 1 3/4 inches. **Col. Depth:** 15 1/2 inches. **Key Personnel:** Sandie Laming-Powell, Editor and Publisher. **Subscription Rates:** 16 Ptas individuals; 20 Ptas out of state. **Remarks:** Accepts advertising. **URL:** http://www.thepaper.net/. **Ad Rates:** GLR: 4.50 Ptas, BW: 525 Ptas, 4C: 785 Ptas. **Circ:** ‡2,000

Terrassa

50838 ■ Tiempos Modernos
Sant Isidre, 83
08221 Terrassa, Spain
Magazine covering diverse historical disciplines such as History of the Art, History of Literature, History of Science, Political History, Socioeconomic History, with an aim to study the development of the human societies during centuries XVI, XVII and XVIII. **Subtitle:** Revista Electronica de Historia Moderna. **Freq:** Biennial. **Key Personnel:** Diego Tellez Alarcia, Director, diego.tellez@aurea.uniroja.es. **ISSN:** 1699-7778. **Subscription Rates:** Free. **URL:** http://www.tiemposmodernos.org/.

Teruel

50839 ■ Turia
Instituto de Estudios Turolenses
C/Amantes, 15
Planta 2
E-44001 Teruel, Spain
Ph: 34 978 617860
Fax: 34 978 617861
Publisher E-mail: ieturolenses@dpteruel.es
Magazine covering contemporary literature worldwide. **Founded:** 1983. **Freq:** Quarterly. **Trim Size:** 14.4 x 21.5 cm. **ISSN:** 0213-4373. **Subscription Rates:** EUR40 individuals America; EUR25 individuals Europe; EUR24 individuals Spain. **URL:** http://www.revistasculturales.com/revistas/46/turia/.

Toledo

50840 ■ Physical Chemistry
Trade Science Inc.
c/o Abderrazzak Douhal, Editorial Board
Departamento de Quimica Fisica, Seccion de Quimicas,
Faculta Ciencias del Medio Ambiente
Campus Tecnologico de Toledo, Avenida Carlos III
E-45071 Toledo, Spain

Publisher E-mail: help@tsijournals.com
Journal covering research on all phases of physical chemistry. **Subtitle:** An Indian Journal. **Founded:** 1969. **Freq:** 2/yr. **Print Method:** Offset. **Trim Size:** 8 1/2 x 11. **Cols./Page:** 2. **Col. Width:** 36 nonpareils. **Col. Depth:** 137 agate lines. **Key Personnel:** Abderrazzak Douhal, Editorial Board; Andreas Hirsch, Editorial Board; Alexander I. Boldyrev, Editorial Board; Baohui Li, Editorial Board; Bernd Giese, Editorial Board; Bernd Strehmel, Editorial Board. **ISSN:** 0974-7524. **Subscription Rates:** Rs 1,200 individuals; Rs 120 other countries. **URL:** http://www.tsijournals.com/pcaij/.

Torremoinos

50841 ■ Litoral
Revista Litoral
Urb. La Roca, 107 C
E-29630 Torremoinos, Spain
Ph: 34 952 388257
Fax: 34 952 380758
Publisher E-mail: litoral@edicioneslitoral.com
Magazine covering Spanish poetry. **Subtitle:** Revista de la poesia, el arte y el pensamiento. **Founded:** 1926. **Freq:** Semiannual. **Trim Size:** 16 x 24 cm. **Key Personnel:** Lorenzo Saval, Director. **Subscription Rates:** EUR56 individuals for Spain; EUR60 individuals for Europe; EUR95 other countries; EUR29 individuals back issues. **Remarks:** Accepts advertising. **URL:** http://www.edicioneslitoral.com. **Circ:** (Not Reported)

Valencia

50842 ■ Anglogermanica online
University of Valencia
Dept. of Filologia Espanola
Avda. Blasco Ibanez, 13
E-46010 Valencia, Spain
Ph: 34 963 864100
Publication E-mail: anglogermanica@uv.es
Journal focusing on linguistic and literary studies, both general and specific, within the fields of English and German studies. **Founded:** 1974. **Freq:** 8/yr. **Print Method:** Offset. **Trim Size:** 8 1/4 x 11. **Cols./Page:** 2 and 3. **Col. Width:** 42 and 14 picas. **Col. Depth:** 140 agate lines. **ISSN:** 1695-6168. **URL:** http://www.uv.es/anglogermanica/.

50843 ■ Bonsai Autoctono
Neagari Press
Plz. Fray Luis Colomer, 3-Entlo. B
E-46021 Valencia, Spain
Ph: 34 902 131331
Fax: 34 963 610673
Consumer magazine covering bonsai care, aesthetics and design for hobbyists. **Founded:** 1993. **Freq:** Bimonthly. **Print Method:** Offset. **Trim Size:** 215 x 287 mm. **Cols./Page:** 4. **ISSN:** 1138-3518. **Remarks:** Accepts advertising. **URL:** http://www.ngpress.com; http://www.ngpress.com/bonsai/bonsai.html. **Circ:** Combined 9,700

50844 ■ Celestinesca
University of Valencia
Dept. of Filologia Espanola
Avda. Blasco Ibanez, 13
E-46010 Valencia, Spain
Ph: 34 963 864100
Scholarly journal covering Spanish literature. **Founded:** 1977. **Freq:** Annual. **Print Method:** Web offset. **Trim Size:** 6 x 9. **Cols./Page:** 1. **Key Personnel:** Jose Luis Canet, Editor; Joseph T. Snow, Ed./Founder. **ISSN:** 0147-3085. **Subscription Rates:** EUR15 individuals; EUR25 institutions. **Remarks:** Advertising not accepted. **URL:** http://parnaseo.uv.es/Celestinesca/celestinesca.htm. **Circ:** Controlled 412

50845 ■ Historia Social
Fundacion Instituto de Historia Social UNED Valencia
Casa de la Misericordia, 34
E-46014 Valencia, Spain
Ph: 34 963 132621
Publication E-mail: fihs@valencia.uned.es
Publisher E-mail: fihs@uned-valencia.net
Research magazine covering history and historical criticism worldwide. **Founded:** 1988. **Freq:** Triennial. **Trim Size:** 19 x 24.5 cm. **Key Personnel:** Javier Paniagua, Director; Jose a. Piqueras, Director. **ISSN:** 0214-2570. **Subscription Rates:** EUR28 individuals Spain; EUR37 individuals Europe; US$50 individuals rest of world. **Remarks:** Advertising not accepted. **URL:** http://portal.

uned.es/portal/page?_pageid=93,1&_dad=portal&_ schema=PORTAL. **Circ:** (Not Reported)

50846 ■ Inorganic Chemistry
Trade Science Inc.
c/o Carlos Gomez, Editorial Board
Instituto de Ciencia Molecular (ICMol)
Edificio Institutos, Universidad de Valencia
E-46071 Valencia, Spain
Publisher E-mail: help@tsijournals.com
Peer-reviewed journal covering inorganic chemistry. Topics include synthetic and reaction chemistry, kinetics and mechanisms of reactions, bioinorganic chemistry and the use of metal and organometallic compounds in stoichiometric and catalytic synthesis of organic compounds. **Subtitle:** An Indian Journal. **Founded:** 1981. **Freq:** 4/yr. **Print Method:** Offset. **Trim Size:** 8 3/8 x 10 7/8. **Cols./Page:** 3. **Col. Width:** 28 nonpareils. **Col. Depth:** 140 agate lines. **Key Personnel:** Carlos Gomez, Editorial Board; Remi Chauvin, Editorial Board; H.C. Martin Jansen, Editorial Board; Michel Gruselle, Editorial Board; Manish K. Shah, Editorial Board; Roger Alberto, Editorial Board. **ISSN:** 0744-7612. **Subscription Rates:** Rs 2,400 individuals; US$240 other countries. **URL:** http://www.tsijournals.com/icaij/.

50847 ■ Valencia Maritima
Dr. J.J. Domine, 5 1-1a
E-46011 Valencia, Spain
Ph: 34 963 164515
Fax: 34 963 678555
Trade newspaper covering international transport and trade. **Founded:** 1968. **Freq:** Daily. **Print Method:** Offset. **Cols./Page:** 4. **Col. Width:** 36 millimeters. **Key Personnel:** Carlos Vicedo Alenda, Editor. **ISSN:** 1387-1982. **Remarks:** Accepts advertising. **URL:** http://www.veintepies.com/20/vm.php. **Ad Rates:** BW: EUR140, 4C: EUR300. **Circ:** (Not Reported)

Valladolid

50848 ■ Critical Approaches to Ethnic American Literature
Editions Rodopi B.V.
c/o Prof. Jesus Benito Sanchez, Ed.
Facultad de Filosofia y Letras
Departamento de Filologia Inglesa
Universidad de Valladolid
E-47011 Valladolid, Spain
Publisher E-mail: info@rodopi.nl
Journal covering the field of Ethnic American literature.

Key Personnel: Prof. Jesus Benito Sanchez, Editor, jbenito@uclm.es. **ISSN:** 1871-6067. **URL:** http://www.rodopi.nl/senj.asp?SerieId=CAEAL.

Vitoria-Gasteiz

50849 ■ a+t
a+t ediciones
General Alava, 15-2oA
E-01005 Vitoria-Gasteiz, Spain
Ph: 34 945 134276
Fax: 34 945 134901
Publication E-mail: aplust@aplust.net
Publisher E-mail: aplust@aplust.net
Architecture and technology magazine with thematic issues. **Founded:** 1992. **Freq:** Semiannual. **Print Method:** Offset. **Trim Size:** 23.5 x 32 cm. **Key Personnel:** Javier Arpa, Editor; Delia Argote, Contact; Idoia Esteban, Contact; Aurora Fernandez Per, Editor-in-Chief; Javier Mozas, Editor. **ISSN:** 1132-6409. **Subscription Rates:** EUR47 individuals Spain, registered mail; EUR70 individuals courier delivery; EUR80 individuals rest of the world; courier delivery; EUR57 individuals Spain, courier delivery. **Remarks:** Accepts advertising. **URL:** http://www.aplust.net. **Circ:** (Not Reported)

Circulation: ★ = ABC; △ = BPA; ◆ = CAC; • = CCAB; ❏ = VAC; ⊕ = PO Statement; ‡ = Publisher's Report; Boldface figures = sworn; Light figures = estimated.

Gale Directory of Publications & Broadcast Media/147th Ed.

5453

Battaramulla

Independent Television Network - See Deniyaya

Independent Television Network - See Naya-bedda

Colombo

50850 ■ Ceylon Journal of Medical Sciences
University of Colombo
c/o The Registrar
94, Cumaratunga Munidasa Mawatha
PO Box 1490
Colombo 00300, Sri Lanka
Ph: 94 158 1835
Fax: 94 158 3810
Publisher E-mail: postmast@admin.cmb.ac.lk
Journal covering all branches of medical, dental and veterinary sciences. **Founded:** 1949. **Freq:** Semiannual. **Key Personnel:** Senaka Rajapakse, Co-Ed., senaka. ucfm@gmail.com. **ISSN:** 0011-2232. **URL:** http://www. sljol.info/index.php/CJMS/about. **Circ:** Controlled 125

50851 ■ Chartered Accountants
Institute of Chartered Accountants of Sri Lanka
30A Malalasekera Mawatha
Colombo 00700, Sri Lanka
Ph: 94 11 2352000
Fax: 94 11 2352060
Publisher E-mail: secretariat@icasrilanka.com
Journal covering accounting. **Founded:** 1966. **Freq:** Semiannual. **Subscription Rates:** CRs 50 individuals. **Remarks:** Advertising accepted; rates available upon request. **URL:** http://www.icasrilanka.com/. **Circ:** Paid 1,000

50852 ■ Daily Mirror
Wijeya Newspapers Ltd.
8 Hunupitiya Cross Rd.
PO Box 1136
Colombo 2, Sri Lanka
Ph: 94 11 2436998
Fax: 94 11 5330811
Publication E-mail: mirror@dailymirror.wnl.lk
Newspaper. **Founded:** 1999. **Freq:** Daily. **ISSN:** 1391-4782. **Remarks:** Accepts advertising. **URL:** http://www. dailymirror.lk. **Circ:** 30,000

50853 ■ Daily News
The Associated Newspapers of Ceylon Ltd.
35 D.R. Wijewardene Mawatha
PO Box 1217
Colombo 10, Sri Lanka
Ph: 94 112 429231
Fax: 94 112 429230
Publication E-mail: editor@dailynews.lk
Publisher E-mail: editor@sundayobserver.lk
General newspaper. **Freq:** Daily. **Remarks:** Accepts advertising. **URL:** http://www.dailynews.lk. **Circ:** ‡88,000

50854 ■ Engineer
Institution of Engineers, Sri Lanka
120-15 Wijerama Mawatha
Colombo 7, Sri Lanka
Ph: 94 11 2698426

Fax: 94 11 2699202
Journal covering engineering. **Founded:** 1973. **Freq:** Quarterly. **Subscription Rates:** CRs 3,200 members; CRs 700 students under 35; CRs 2,000 students over 35. **Remarks:** Advertising accepted; rates available upon request. **URL:** http://www.iesl.lk. **Circ:** Paid 3,750

50855 ■ Journal of Development Administration
Sri Lanka Institute of Development Administration
28-10 Mallasekara Mawatha
Colombo 00700, Sri Lanka
Ph: 94 11 2582181
Fax: 94 11 2553215
Publisher E-mail: mail@slida.lk
Journal covering public administration. **Founded:** 1970. **Freq:** Semiannual. **ISSN:** 0047-2360. **URL:** http://www. slida.lk/. **Circ:** Paid 1,000

50856 ■ Journal of the National Aquatic Resources Research & Development Agency of Sri Lanka
National Aquatic Resources Research Development Agency
Crow Island
Colombo 01500, Sri Lanka
Ph: 94 112 521000
Fax: 94 112 521932
Publisher E-mail: postmaster@nara.ac.lk
Journal containing reports results of original research pertaining either directly or indirectly to living and non-living aquatic resources and their management in maritime zones of Sri Lanka. **Founded:** 1922. **Freq:** Annual. **Key Personnel:** N.Suresh Kumar, Editor-in-Chief, editor@nara.ac.lk. **ISSN:** 1391-6246. **Subscription Rates:** CRs 250 individuals; CRs 500 institutions; US$10 other countries. **URL:** http://www.nara.ac.lk/journals/narajournals.htm.

50857 ■ Journal of the National Science Foundation
National Science Foundation of Sri Lanka
47/5 Maitland Pl.
Colombo 00700, Sri Lanka
Ph: 94 112 696771
Fax: 94 112 694754
Publication E-mail: jnsf@nsf.ac.lk
Publisher E-mail: info@nsf.ac.lk
Journal covering natural science. **Founded:** 1973. **Freq:** Quarterly. **Key Personnel:** Rohini Wijayaratne, Asst. Ed.; Prof. A. Gunatilaka, Editorial Board; Prof. S. Atukorala, Editorial Board; Prof. Nalini Ratnasiri, Editor-in-Chief. **ISSN:** 1391-4558. **Subscription Rates:** CRs 1,200 individuals; CRs 350 single issue; US$50 individuals SAARC Countries; US$100 other countries. **URL:** http://www.nsf.ac.lk/jnsf.php.

50858 ■ Journal of Physics
Institute of Physics
Vidya Mandiraya
120/10 Wijerama Mawatha
Colombo 00700, Sri Lanka
Publication E-mail: jpcs@iop.org
Journal providing cost-effective and timely publication of international conferences of the highest quality. **Subtitle:** Conference Series. **Key Personnel:** Graham Douglas,

Sen. Publisher. **ISSN:** 1742-6588. **URL:** http://www.iop. org/ej/journal/1742-6596.

50859 ■ Journal of the Royal Asiatic Society of Sri Lanka
Royal Asiatic Society of Sri Lanka
Mahaweli Centre & Royal Asiatic Society Bldg., 1st Fl.
96 Ananda Coomaraswamy Mawatha
Colombo 7, Sri Lanka
Ph: 94 11 2699249
Publisher E-mail: info@royalasiaticsociety.lk
Sri Lankan journal covering the arts. **Founded:** 1845. **Freq:** Annual. **Trim Size:** 14 x 21 1/2 cm. **Key Personnel:** Prof. W.I. Siriweera, Editor. **ISSN:** 1391-720X. **Subscription Rates:** US$35 other countries plus postage; CRs 250 members; CRs 300 nonmembers. **Remarks:** Advertising not accepted. **URL:** http://www. royalasiaticsociety.lk/publications/journal/. **Circ:** (Not Reported)

50860 ■ Lanka Monthly Digest
Media Services (Private) Ltd.
59 Ward Pl.
Colombo 00700, Sri Lanka
Ph: 94 11 2672017
Fax: 94 11 2672019
Publisher E-mail: corporate@lmd.lk
Business magazine. **Founded:** 1994. **Freq:** Monthly. **Key Personnel:** Hiran Hewavisenti, Ed.-in-Ch./Mng. Dir. **ISSN:** 1391-135X. **Subscription Rates:** CRs 1,800 individuals; CRs 3,000 two years; CRs 18,000 individuals lifetime; CRs 50,000 individuals corporate perpetual; US$65 other countries; 40 other countries; $A 100 other countries; US$650 other countries lifetime; 400 other countries lifetime; $A 1,000 other countries lifetime. **Remarks:** Advertising accepted; rates available upon request. **URL:** http://www.lmd.lk/2009/March/index.asp. **Circ:** (Not Reported)

50861 ■ Lanka Woman
Wijeya Newspapers Ltd.
No. 8, Hunupitiya Cross Rd.
Colombo 02, Sri Lanka
Women's magazine. **Founded:** 1984. **Freq:** Weekly. **ISSN:** 1391-0493. **Subscription Rates:** US$17 individuals 6 months; US$33 individuals; CRs 1,800 individuals 6 months; CRs 3,600 individuals. **Remarks:** Accepts advertising. **URL:** http://www.wijeya.lk/About_Us.htm. **Circ:** (Not Reported)

50862 ■ Physical Biology
Institute of Physics
Vidya Mandiraya
120/10 Wijerama Mawatha
Colombo 00700, Sri Lanka
Peer-reviewed journal fostering the integration of biology with the traditionally more quantitative fields of physics, chemistry, computer science and other mathematics-based disciplines. **Key Personnel:** Terence Hwa, Editor-in-Chief. **Subscription Rates:** US$1,115 institutions North, Central and South America; 585 institutions, other countries. **URL:** http://www.iop.org/EJ/physbio.

50863 ■ Sri Lanka Engineering News
Institution of Engineers, Sri Lanka
120-15 Wijerama Mawatha

Colombo 7, Sri Lanka
Ph: 94 11 2698426
Fax: 94 11 2699202
Engineering newspaper. **Freq:** Monthly. **URL:** http://www.iesl.lk.

50864 ■ Sri Lanka Journal of Agrarian Studies
Hector Kobbekaduwa
Agrarian Research and Training Institute
114 Wijerama Mawatha
Colombo 7, Sri Lanka
Ph: 94 112 696981
Journal covering agrarian studies. **Founded:** 1980. **Freq:** Biennial. **Print Method:** Offset. **Trim Size:** 176 x 250 mm. **Key Personnel:** Dr. W.G. Jayasena, Contact. **ISSN:** 1391-0388. **Remarks:** Advertising not accepted. **URL:** http://www.harti.lk/en/Publications/ResearchReports/List/index.php. **Circ:** Paid 300

50865 ■ Sri Lanka Journal of Child Health
Sri Lanka College of Paediatricians
Wijerama House, No. 6
Wijerama Mawatha
Colombo 00700, Sri Lanka
Ph: 94 11 2683178
Fax: 94 11 2683178
Publication E-mail: slcp@sltnet.lk
Publisher E-mail: slcp@sltnet.lk
Journal covering child health. **Freq:** Quarterly. **Key Personnel:** Stella G. de Silva, Ed. Emeritus; G.N. Lucas, Editor; B.J.C. Perera, Editor. **ISSN:** 1391-5452. **URL:** http://www.slcp.slt.lk/index.htm.

50866 ■ Sri Lanka Journal of International Law
University of Colombo
Faculty of Law
94 Cumaratunga Munidasa Mawatha
Colombo 3, Sri Lanka
Ph: 94 1 581835
Fax: 94 1 583810
Publisher E-mail: postmast@admin.cmb.ac.lk
Journal discussing various aspects of international law, including how it applies to international relations. **Founded:** 1989. **Freq:** Annual. **Key Personnel:** Dr. Noel Dias, Editor-in-Chief, noeldias@isplanka.lk. **ISSN:** 1391-5568. **URL:** http://www.cmb.ac.lk/jilnew/node/2.

50867 ■ Sri Lanka Journal of Social Sciences
National Science Foundation of Sri Lanka
47/5 Maitland Pl.
Colombo 00700, Sri Lanka
Ph: 94 112 696771
Fax: 94 112 694754
Publication E-mail: sljss@nsf.ac.lk
Publisher E-mail: info@nsf.ac.lk
Peer-reviewed journal covering the social sciences. **Founded:** 1978. **Freq:** Semiannual. **Key Personnel:** Dr. Inoka Sandanayake, Scientific Off., jss@nsf.ac.lk. **ISSN:** 0258-9710. **Subscription Rates:** CRs 100 individuals including postage; US$8.50 other countries. **URL:** http://www.nsf.ac.lk/jss.php.

50868 ■ Sri Lankan Family Physician
College of General Practitioners of Sri Lanka
Wijerama House
6 Wijerama Mawatha
Colombo 00700, Sri Lanka
Publisher E-mail: cgpsl@sltnet.lk
Medical journal. **Key Personnel:** Dr. Dennis J. Aloysius, Editor. **URL:** http://www.cgpsl.org/?read_more=1.

50869 ■ Sri Lankan Journal of Management
Postgraduate Institute of Management
University of Sri Jayewardenepura
28 Lesley Ranagala Mawatha
Colombo 8, Sri Lanka
Ph: 94 11 2689639
Fax: 94 11 2689643
Journal covering management. **Founded:** 1996. **Freq:** Quarterly. **ISSN:** 1391-1503. **Subscription Rates:** CRs 1,000 individuals; US$80 out of country; CRs 300 single issue; US$30 out of country single copy. **URL:** http://www.pim.lk/?pg=journal.

50870 ■ Sri Lankan Journal of Physics
Institute of Physics
Vidya Mandiraya
120/10 Wijerama Mawatha
Colombo 00700, Sri Lanka
Journal covering physics. **Founded:** 2000. **Freq:** Annual. **Key Personnel:** Prof. T.R. Ariyaratne, Editor-in-

Chief; Prof. W.P. Siripala, Assoc. Ed.; Prof. W.L. Sumathipala, Assoc. Ed. **ISSN:** 1391-5800. **URL:** http://www.ip-sl.org/sljp/.

50871 ■ The Sunday Leader
Leader Publication Ltd.
1st Fl., Colombo Commercial Bldg.
121, Sir James Peiris Mawatha
Colombo 2, Sri Lanka
Ph: 94 753 65892
Fax: 94 753 65891
Publication E-mail: editor@thesundayleader.lk
Publisher E-mail: editor@thesundayleader.lk
Community newspaper. **Freq:** Weekly. **Subscription Rates:** US$2 individuals 1 month; US$4 individuals 3 months; US$6 individuals 6 months; US$10 individuals 12 months. **URL:** http://www.thesundayleader.lk/20030706/home.htm; http://www.thesundayleader.lk/20050313/home.htm.

50872 ■ Sunday Observer
The Associated Newspapers of Ceylon Ltd.
35 D.R. Wijewardene Mawatha
PO Box 1217
Colombo 10, Sri Lanka
Ph: 94 112 429231
Fax: 94 112 429230
Publication E-mail: editor@sundayobserver.lk
Publisher E-mail: editor@sundayobserver.lk
Newspaper. **Freq:** Weekly (Sun.). **Remarks:** Accepts advertising. **URL:** http://www.sundayobserver.lk. **Circ:** ‡175,000

50873 ■ The Sunday Times
Wijeya Newspapers Ltd.
8 Hunupitiya Cross Rd.
PO Box 1136
Colombo 2, Sri Lanka
Ph: 94 11 2326247
Fax: 94 11 2423922
Publication E-mail: subdesk@sundaytimes.wnl.lk
Newspaper covering news and current affairs of interest to Sri Lanka. **Founded:** 1987. **Freq:** Weekly (Sun.). **ISSN:** 1391-0531. **Remarks:** Accepts advertising. **URL:** http://www.sundaytimes.lk. **Circ:** Paid 80,000

50874 ■ Gold FM - 93.0 MHz
ABC Radio Network
Last Tower, 35th Fl.
Colombo 2346888, Sri Lanka
Owner: ABC Radio Network, at above address. **Founded:** 1998. **Key Personnel:** Sunil Sarath Perera, Chm. **URL:** http://www.slbc.lk.

50875 ■ Lakhanda Radio-FM - 88.5
PO Box 2124
Colombo, Sri Lanka
Ph: 94 11 2774725
Fax: 94 11 2774801
Format: Educational; Ethnic; Information; News; Sports; World Beat. **Founded:** Nov. 15, 1996. **Operating Hours:** 3 pm-8:30pm Sunday; 1 pm-11 pm Monday; 5 pm-9:30pm Wednesday. **Key Personnel:** Mr. Anura Siriwardena, Chm., phone 94 11 2775494, fax 94 11 2774591; Mr. W.P.A.M Wijesinghe, General Mgr., phone 94 11 2774595, fax 94 11 2774595; Mr. Anura Perera, Engr., phone 94 11 5552796, fax 94 11 5557882. **Ad Rates:** $15-1,000 for 10 seconds; $45-3,500 for 30 seconds. **URL:** http://www.lakhanda.lk.

MTV Channel (Pvt) Ltd - See Depanama

50876 ■ Neth-FM - 105.9
105/3 5th Ln.
Colombo 3, Sri Lanka
Ph: 94 11 5515433
Fax: 94 11 5515440
E-mail: info@nethfm.com
Format: Information; News; Sports. **Owner:** Asset Radio Broadcasting (Pvt.) Ltd., at above address. **Operating Hours:** Continuous. **URL:** http://www.nethfm.com.

Shakthi FM - See Gammaduwa

50877 ■ Sirasa FM - 106.5 MHz
PO Box 25
Araliya Uyana
Depanama
Pannipitiya, Sri Lanka
Ph: 94 11 2851371
Fax: 94 11 5340116

E-mail: sirasafm@maharaja.lk
Format: Sports; News. **Owner:** MBC Network Pvt. Ltd., No. 7, Braybrooke Pl., Colombo 2, Sri Lanka. **Operating Hours:** Continuous weekdays; 6 a.m.-12 p.m. Weekend. **Wattage:** 1000. **Ad Rates:** Advertising accepted; rates available upon request. **URL:** http://www.sirasa.com/.

50878 ■ Sooriyan FM - 103.2 MHz
World Trade Centre
Level 35, East Tower
Colombo 1, Sri Lanka
Ph: 94 11 2346744
Fax: 94 11 2346880
E-mail: sooriyanfm@abc-radio.com
Owner: ABC Radio Network, at above address. **Founded:** 1998. **URL:** http://www.sooriyanfmlive.com/site/listen.html.

Sooriyan FM - See Kandy

50879 ■ Sri Lanka Broadcasting Corporation - Colombo - 93.3 MHz
PO Box 574
Colombo 7, Sri Lanka
Ph: 94 11 2697491
Fax: 94 11 2691568
Format: News. **Owner:** Sri Lanka Broadcasting Corporation, at above address. **Operating Hours:** 5:45a.m.-11p.m. Daily. **Key Personnel:** Hudson Samarasingha, Chm., phone 94 11 2696439, fax 94 11 2695488, chairman@slbc.lk; Samantha Weliweriya, Dir. Gen., phone 94 11 2695248, fax 94 11 2697150, dg@slbc.lk. **Ad Rates:** $560-800 for 10 seconds; $1200-1600 for 15 seconds; $2000-2400 for 30 seconds; $3200-4000 for 60 seconds. **URL:** http://www.slbc.lk/.

50880 ■ Sri Lanka Broadcasting Corporation - Colombo - 105.6 MHz
PO Box 574
Colombo 7, Sri Lanka
Ph: 94 11 2697491
Fax: 94 11 2691568
Format: News; Public Radio; Adult Contemporary; Sports. **Owner:** Sri Lanka Broadcasting Corporation, at above address. **Operating Hours:** 11 p.m.-5:15 p.m. **Key Personnel:** Hudson Samarasingha, Chm., phone 94 11 2696439, fax 94 11 2695488, chairman@slbc.lk; Samantha Weliweriya, Dir. Gen., phone 94 11 2695248, fax 94 11 2697150, dg@slbc.lk. **Ad Rates:** Advertising accepted; rates available upon request. **URL:** http://www.slbc.lk.

50881 ■ Sri Lanka Broadcasting Corporation - Colombo - 95.6 MHz
PO Box 574
Colombo 7, Sri Lanka
Ph: 94 11 2697491
Fax: 94 11 2691568
Format: News. **Owner:** Sri Lanka Broadcasting Corporation, at above address. **Operating Hours:** 12 a.m.-5 p.m. **Key Personnel:** Hudson Samarasingha, Chm., phone 94 11 2696439, fax 94 11 2695488, chairman@slbc.lk; Samantha Weliweriya, Dir. Gen., phone 94 11 2695248, fax 94 11 2697150, dg@slbc.lk. **Ad Rates:** $450-640 for 10 seconds; $1000-1300 for 15 seconds; $1650-2000 for 30 seconds; $2650-3300 for 60 seconds. **URL:** http://www.slbc.lk/.

50882 ■ Sri Lanka Broadcasting Corporation - Colombo - 91.2 MHz
PO Box 574
Colombo 7, Sri Lanka
Ph: 94 11 2697491
Fax: 94 11 2691568
Format: News. **Owner:** Sri Lanka Broadcasting Corporation, at above address. **Operating Hours:** 5a.m.-11.15p.m. Mon.,Tue.,Thu.,Sun.; Continuous Fri.&Sun. **Key Personnel:** Hudson Samarasingha, Chm., phone 94 11 2696439, fax 94 11 2695488, chairman@slbc.lk; Samantha Weliweriya, Dir. Gen., phone 94 11 2695248, fax 94 11 2697150, dg@slbc.lk. **Ad Rates:** $560-800 for 10 seconds; $1200-1600 for 15 seconds; $2000-2400 for 30 seconds; $3200-4000 for 60 seconds. **URL:** http://www.slbc.lk/.

50883 ■ Sri Lanka Broadcasting Corporation - Colombo - 98.3 MHz
PO Box 574
Colombo 7, Sri Lanka
Ph: 94 11 2697491

Fax: 94 11 2691568
Format: Full Service; Public Radio. **Owner:** Sri Lanka Broadcasting Corporation, at above address. **Operating Hours:** 11 p.m.-4 p.m. **Key Personnel:** Hudson Samarasingha, Chm., phone 94 11 2696439, fax 94 11 2695488, chairman@slbc.lk; Samantha Weliweriya, Dir. Gen., phone 94 11 2695248, fax 94 11 2697150, dg@slbc.lk. **Ad Rates:** Advertising accepted; rates available upon request. **URL:** http://www.slbc.lk.

Sri Lanka Broadcasting Corporation - Deniyaya - See Deniyaya

Sri Lanka Broadcasting Corporation - Deniyaya - See Deniyaya

Sri Lanka Broadcasting Corporation - Deniyaya - See Deniyaya

Sri Lanka Broadcasting Corporation - Deniyaya - See Deniyaya

Sri Lanka Broadcasting Corporation - Deniyaya - See Deniyaya

Sri Lanka Broadcasting Corporation - Deniyaya - See Deniyaya

Sri Lanka Broadcasting Corporation - Haputale - See Haputale

Sri Lanka Broadcasting Corporation - Haputale - See Haputale

Sri Lanka Broadcasting Corporation - Haputale - See Haputale

Sri Lanka Broadcasting Corporation - Haputale - See Haputale

Sri Lanka Broadcasting Corporation - Hunasgir-iya - See Hunasgiriya

Sri Lanka Broadcasting Corporation - Hunasgir-iya - See Hunasgiriya

Sri Lanka Broadcasting Corporation - Hunasgir-iya - See Hunasgiriya

Sri Lanka Broadcasting Corporation - Hunasgir-iya - See Hunasgiriya

Sri Lanka Broadcasting Corporation - Hunasgir-iya - See Hunasgiriya

Sri Lanka Broadcasting Corporation - Hunasgir-iya - See Hunasgiriya

Sri Lanka Broadcasting Corporation - Karaga-hatenna - See Karagahatenna

Sri Lanka Broadcasting Corporation - Karaga-hatenna - See Karagahatenna

Sri Lanka Broadcasting Corporation - Karaga-hatenna - See Karagahatenna

Sri Lanka Broadcasting Corporation - Karaga-hatenna - See Karagahatenna

Sri Lanka Broadcasting Corporation - Karaga-hatenna - See Karagahatenna

Sri Lanka Broadcasting Corporation - Karaga-hatenna - See Karagahatenna

Sri Lanka Broadcasting Corporation - Palali (Jaffna) - See Palali (Jaffna)

Sri Lanka Broadcasting Corporation - Radella - See Radella

Sri Lanka Broadcasting Corporation - Radella - See Radella

Sri Lanka Broadcasting Corporation - Radella - See Radella

Sri Lanka Broadcasting Corporation - Radella - See Radella

Sri Lanka Broadcasting Corporation - Radella - See Radella

Sri Lanka Broadcasting Corporation - Radella - See Radella

Sri Lanka Broadcasting Corporation - Yatiyan-tota - See Yatiyantota

Sri Lanka Rupavahini Corporation - See Sooriya-kanda

50884 ■ TNL Rocks-FM - 101.7
52, 5th Ln.
Colombo 3, Sri Lanka
Ph: 94 2575000
Format: Alternative/New Music/Progressive; News. **Owner:** TNL Radio Network, at above address. **Founded:** 1993. **Ad Rates:** Advertising accepted; rates available upon request. **URL:** http://www.tnlrocks.com.

50885 ■ Yes FM - 89.5 MHz
36, Araliya Uyana
Depanama
Pannipitiya, Sri Lanka
Ph: 94 11 2851371
Fax: 94 11 2851373
Owner: MBC Network Pvt. Ltd., at above address. **Operating Hours:** Continuous. **Wattage:** 1000. **Ad Rates:** Advertising accepted; rates available upon request. **URL:** http://yesfmmusic.com; http://www.capitalmaharaja.com/mbcnetworks_content.html.

Deniyaya

50886 ■ Independent Television Network - 9
Wikramasinghepura
Battaramulla 10120, Sri Lanka
Ph: 94 11 2774424
Fax: 94 11 2774591
E-mail: itnch@slt.lk
Format: Educational; Commercial TV; Religious; News. **Owner:** Independent Television Network, at above address. **Key Personnel:** Mr. W.P.A.M Wijesinghe, General Mgr., phone 94 11 2774595, fax 94 11 2774595, itngm@slt.lk; Mr. Sudarman Radaliyagoda, Dep. Gen. Mgr. (News/Current Affairs), phone 94 11 4403975, fax 94 11 2774421, itnnews@slt.lk. **Wattage:** 1000. **Ad Rates:** Advertising accepted; rates available upon request. **URL:** http://www.itn.lk/.

50887 ■ Sri Lanka Broadcasting Corporation - Deniyaya - 107.2 MHz
PO Box 574
Colombo 7, Sri Lanka
Ph: 94 11 2697491
Fax: 94 11 2691568
Format: News; Public Radio; Adult Contemporary; Sports. **Owner:** Sri Lanka Broadcasting Corporation, at above address. **Operating Hours:** 11 p.m.-2:30 a.m.; 10 a.m.-3:30 p.m. **Key Personnel:** Hudson Samarasingha, Chm., phone 94 11 2696439, fax 94 11 2695488, chairman@slbc.lk; Samantha Weliweriya, Dir. Gen., phone 94 11 2695248, fax 94 11 2697150, dg@slbc.lk. **Ad Rates:** Advertising accepted; rates available upon request. **URL:** http://www.slbc.lk.

50888 ■ Sri Lanka Broadcasting Corporation - Deniyaya - 92.8 MHz
PO Box 574
Colombo 7, Sri Lanka
Ph: 94 11 2697491
Fax: 94 11 2691568
Format: News; Public Radio; Adult Contemporary; Sports. **Owner:** Sri Lanka Broadcasting Corporation, at above address. **Operating Hours:** Continuous. **Key Personnel:** Hudson Samarasingha, Chm., phone 94 11 2696439, fax 94 11 2695488, chairman@slbc.lk; Samantha Weliweriya, Dir. Gen., phone 94 11 2695248, fax 94 11 2697150, dg@slbc.lk. **Ad Rates:** $560-800 for 10 seconds; $1200-1600 for 15 seconds; $2000-2400 for 30 seconds; $3200-4000 for 60 seconds. **URL:** http://www.slbc.lk.

50889 ■ Sri Lanka Broadcasting Corporation - Deniyaya - 90.8 MHz
PO Box 574
Colombo 7, Sri Lanka
Ph: 94 11 2697491
Fax: 94 11 2691568
Format: News; Public Radio; Adult Contemporary; Sports. **Owner:** Sri Lanka Broadcasting Corporation, at above address. **Operating Hours:** 12 a.m.-5 p.m. **Key Personnel:** Hudson Samarasingha, Chm., phone 94 11 2696439, fax 94 11 2695488, chmnslbc@sltnet.lk; Samantha Weliweriya, Dir. Gen., phone 94 11 2695248, fax 94 11 2697150, dg@slbc.lk; Palitha Dissanayake, Dir., Mktg., phone 94 11 2696602, fax 94 11 2691977, palkume@dialogsl.net. **Ad Rates:** $450-650 for 10 seconds; $1000-1300 for 15 seconds; $1650-2000 for 30 seconds; $2650-3300 for 60 seconds. **URL:** http://www.slbc.lk.

50890 ■ Sri Lanka Broadcasting Corporation - Deniyaya - 104.8 MHz
PO Box 574
Colombo 7, Sri Lanka
Ph: 94 11 2697491
Fax: 94 11 2691568
Format: News; Public Radio; Adult Contemporary;

Sports. **Owner:** Sri Lanka Broadcasting Corporation, at above address. **Operating Hours:** 11 p.m.-5:15 p.m. **Key Personnel:** Hudson Samarasingha, Chm., phone 94 11 2696439, fax 94 11 2695488, chairman@slbc.lk; Samantha Weliweriya, Dir. Gen., phone 94 11 2695248, fax 94 11 2697150, dg@slbc.lk. **Ad Rates:** Advertising accepted; rates available upon request. **URL:** http://www.slbc.lk.

50891 ■ Sri Lanka Broadcasting Corporation - Deniyaya - 102.6 MHz
PO Box 574
Colombo 7, Sri Lanka
Ph: 94 11 2697491
Fax: 94 11 2691568
Format: News; Public Radio; Adult Contemporary; Sports. **Owner:** Sri Lanka Broadcasting Corporation, at above address. **Operating Hours:** Continuous. **Key Personnel:** Hudson Samarasingha, Chm., phone 94 11 2696439, fax 94 11 2695488, chairman@slbc.lk; Samantha Weliweriya, Dir. Gen., phone 94 11 2695248, fax 94 11 2697150, dg@slbc.lk. **Ad Rates:** $560-800 for 10 seconds; $1200-1600 for 15 seconds; $2000-2400 for 30 seconds; $3200-4000 for 60 seconds. **URL:** http://www.slbc.lk/.

50892 ■ Sri Lanka Broadcasting Corporation - Deniyaya - 99.6 MHz
PO Box 574
Colombo 7, Sri Lanka
Ph: 94 11 2697491
Fax: 94 11 2691568
Format: News; Public Radio; Adult Contemporary; Sports. **Owner:** Sri Lanka Broadcasting Corporation, at above address. **Operating Hours:** 11 p.m.-4 p.m. **Key Personnel:** Hudson Samarasingha, Chm., phone 94 11 2696439, fax 94 11 2695488, chairman@slbc.lk; Samantha Weliweriya, Dir. Gen., phone 94 11 2695248, fax 94 11 2697150, dg@slbc.lk. **Ad Rates:** Advertising accepted; rates available upon request. **URL:** http://www.slbc.lk.

Depanama

50893 ■ MTV Channel (Pvt) Ltd - 23
7 Braybrooke Pl.
Colombo 2, Sri Lanka
Ph: 94 115340112
Fax: 94 115340111
Format: News. **Owner:** MTV Channel (Pvt) Ltd., at above address. **Founded:** Sept. 1992. **Operating Hours:** Continuous. **Wattage:** 1000. **URL:** http://www.maharaja.lk/Activities/Companies/MTV01.html.

Ethul Kotte

50894 ■ Marga Journal
Marga Institute, Sri Lanka Centre for Development Studies
941/1 Jayanthi Mawatha, Kotte Rd.
Ethul Kotte, Sri Lanka
Ph: 94 112 888790
Fax: 94 112 888794
Publisher E-mail: egmarga@sltnet.lk
Journal covering community development in English, Sinhalese and Tamil. **Founded:** 1972. **Freq:** Semiannual. **Key Personnel:** Saman Amarasinghe, Contact. **Remarks:** Advertising not accepted. **URL:** http://www.margasrilanka.org. **Circ:** (Not Reported)

Gammaduwa

50895 ■ Shakthi FM - 105.1 MHz
45/3, Braybrooke Pl.
Colombo 2, Sri Lanka
Ph: 94 112 838540
Fax: 94 112 851373
E-mail: shakthifm@maharaja.lk
Format: Full Service. **Owner:** MBC Network (PVT) Ltd, at above address. **Founded:** 1998. **Operating Hours:** Continuous. **Wattage:** 1000. **Ad Rates:** Advertising accepted; rates available upon request. **URL:** http://www.shakthifm.com/.

Haputale

50896 ■ Sri Lanka Broadcasting Corporation - Haputale - 96.4 MHz
PO Box 574

Circulation: ★ = ABC; △ = BPA; ♦ = CAC; • = CCAB; ❑ = VAC; ⊕ = PO Statement; ‡ = Publisher's Report; Boldface figures = sworn; Light figures = estimated.

Gale Directory of Publications & Broadcast Media/147th Ed.   5457

Colombo 7, Sri Lanka
Ph: 94 11 2697491
Fax: 94 11 2691568
Format: News; Public Radio; Adult Contemporary; Sports. **Owner:** Sri Lanka Broadcasting Corporation, at above address. **Operating Hours:** Continuous. **Key Personnel:** Hudson Samarasingha, Chm., phone 94 11 2696439, fax 94 11 2695488, chairman@slbc.lk; Samantha Weliweriya, Dir. Gen., phone 94 11 2695248, fax 94 11 2697150, dg@slbc.lk. **Ad Rates:** $560-800 for 10 seconds; $1200-1600 for 15 seconds; $2000-2400 for 30 seconds; $3200-4000 for 60 seconds. **URL:** http://www.slbc.lk.

50897 ■ Sri Lanka Broadcasting Corporation - Haputale - 92.2 MHz
PO Box 574
Colombo 7, Sri Lanka
Ph: 94 11 2697491
Fax: 94 11 2691568
Format: News; Public Radio; Adult Contemporary; Sports. **Owner:** Sri Lanka Broadcasting Corporation, at above address. **Operating Hours:** Continuous. **Key Personnel:** Hudson Samarasingha, Chm., phone 94 11 2696439, fax 94 11 2695488, chairman@slbc.lk; Samantha Weliweriya, Dir. Gen., phone 94 11 2695248, fax 94 11 2697150, dg@slbc.lk. **Ad Rates:** Advertising accepted; rates available upon request. **URL:** http://www.slbc.lk/.

50898 ■ Sri Lanka Broadcasting Corporation - Haputale - 102.0 MHz
PO Box 574
Colombo 7, Sri Lanka
Ph: 94 11 2697491
Fax: 94 11 2691568
Format: News; Public Radio; Adult Contemporary; Sports. **Owner:** Sri Lanka Broadcasting Corp., at above address. **Operating Hours:** 11 p.m.-4 p.m. **Key Personnel:** Hudson Samarasingha, Chm., phone 94 11 2696439, fax 94 11 2695488, chairman@slbc.lk; Samantha Weliweriya, Dir. Gen., phone 94 11 2695248, fax 94 11 2697150, dg@slbc.lk. **Ad Rates:** Advertising accepted; rates available upon request. **URL:** http://www.slbc.lk/.

50899 ■ Sri Lanka Broadcasting Corporation - Haputale - 105.4 MHz
PO Box 574
Colombo 7, Sri Lanka
Ph: 94 11 2697491
Fax: 94 11 2691568
Format: News; Public Radio; Adult Contemporary; Sports. **Owner:** Sri Lanka Broadcasting Corporation, at above address. **Operating Hours:** 11 p.m.-2:30 a.m.; 10 a.m.-3:30 p.m. **Key Personnel:** Hudson Samarasingha, Chm., phone 94 11 2696439, fax 94 11 2695488, chairman@slbc.lk; Samantha Weliweriya, Dir. Gen., phone 94 11 2695248, fax 94 11 2697150, dg@slbc.lk. **Ad Rates:** Advertising accepted; rates available upon request. **URL:** http://www.slbc.lk.

Hunasgiriya

50900 ■ Sri Lanka Broadcasting Corporation - Hunasgiriya - 102.0 MHz
PO Box 574
Colombo 7, Sri Lanka
Ph: 94 11 2697491
Fax: 94 11 2691568
Format: News; Public Radio; Adult Contemporary; Sports. **Owner:** Sri Lanka Broadcasting Corporation, at above address. **Operating Hours:** 11 p.m.-4 p.m. **Key Personnel:** Hudson Samarasingha, Chm., phone 94 11 2696439, fax 94 11 2695488, chairman@slbc.lk; Samantha Weliweriya, Dir. Gen., phone 94 11 2695248, fax 94 11 2697150, dg@slbc.lk. **Ad Rates:** Advertising accepted; rates available upon request. **URL:** http://www.slbc.lk.

50901 ■ Sri Lanka Broadcasting Corporation - Hunasgiriya - 107.3 MHz
PO Box 574
Colombo 7, Sri Lanka
Ph: 94 11 2697491
Fax: 94 11 2691568
Format: News; Public Radio; Adult Contemporary; Sports. **Owner:** Sri Lanka Broadcasting Corporation, at above address. **Operating Hours:** 11 p.m.-2:30 a.m.; 10 a.m.-3:30 p.m. **Key Personnel:** Hudson Samaras-

ingha, Chm., phone 94 11 2696439, fax 94 11 2695488, chairman@slbc.lk; Samantha Weliweriya, Dir. Gen., phone 94 11 2695248, fax 94 11 2697150, dg@slbc.lk. **Ad Rates:** Advertising accepted; rates available upon request. **URL:** http://www.slbc.lk.

50902 ■ Sri Lanka Broadcasting Corporation - Hunasgiriya - 89.3 MHz
PO Box 574
Colombo 7, Sri Lanka
Ph: 94 11 2697491
Fax: 94 11 2691568
Format: News; Public Radio; Adult Contemporary; Sports. **Owner:** Sri Lanka Broadcasting Corporation, at above address. **Operating Hours:** 12 a.m.-5 p.m. **Key Personnel:** Hudson Samarasingha, Chm., phone 94 11 2696439, fax 94 11 2695488, chairman@slbc.lk; Samantha Weliweriya, Dir. Gen., phone 94 11 2695248, fax 94 11 2697150, dg@slbc.lk. **Ad Rates:** $450-650 for 10 seconds; $1000-1300 for 15 seconds; $1650-2000 for 30 seconds; $2650-3300 for 60 seconds. **URL:** http://www.slbc.lk/.

50903 ■ Sri Lanka Broadcasting Corporation - Hunasgiriya - 98.8 MHz
PO Box 574
Colombo 7, Sri Lanka
Ph: 94 11 2697491
Fax: 94 11 2691568
Format: News; Public Radio; Adult Contemporary; Sports. **Owner:** Sri Lanka Broadcasting Corporation, at above address. **Operating Hours:** 11 p.m.-5:15 p.m. **Key Personnel:** Hudson Samarasingha, Chm., phone 94 11 2696439, fax 94 11 2695488, chairman@slbc.lk; Samantha Weliweriya, Dir. Gen., phone 94 11 2695248, fax 94 11 2697150, dg@slbc.lk. **Ad Rates:** Advertising accepted; rates available upon request. **URL:** http://www.slbc.lk.

50904 ■ Sri Lanka Broadcasting Corporation - Hunasgiriya - 94.2 MHz
PO Box 574
Colombo 7, Sri Lanka
Ph: 94 11 2697491
Fax: 94 11 2691568
Format: News; Public Radio; Adult Contemporary; Sports. **Owner:** Sri Lanka Broadcasting Corporation, at above address. **Operating Hours:** 11 p.m.-5 p.m. **Key Personnel:** Hudson Samarasingha, Chm., phone 94 11 2696439, fax 94 11 2695488, chairman@slbc.lk; Samantha Weliweriya, Dir. Gen., phone 94 11 2695248, fax 94 11 2697150, dg@slbc.lk. **Ad Rates:** Advertising accepted; rates available upon request. **URL:** http://www.slbc.lk.

50905 ■ Sri Lanka Broadcasting Corporation - Hunasgiriya - 92.2 MHz
PO Box 574
Colombo 7, Sri Lanka
Ph: 94 11 2697491
Fax: 94 11 2691568
Format: Full Service; Public Radio. **Owner:** Sri Lanka Broadcasting Corporation, at above address. **Operating Hours:** 5 a.m.-11:15 p.m. Daily. **Key Personnel:** Hudson Samarasingha, Chm., phone 94 11 2696439, fax 94 11 2695488, chairman@slbc.lk; Samantha Weliweriya, Dir. Gen., phone 94 11 2695248, fax 94 11 2697150, dg@slbc.lk. **Ad Rates:** $560-800 for 10 seconds; $1200-1600 for 15 seconds; $2000-2400 for 30 seconds; $3200-4000 for 60 seconds. **URL:** http://www.slbc.lk/.

Kandy

50906 ■ Ethnic Studies Report
International Centre for Ethnic Studies
554/6A, Peradeniya Rd.
Kandy, Sri Lanka
Ph: 94 812 234892
Fax: 94 812 234892
Publication E-mail: icesky@sltnet.lk
Publisher E-mail: icesresch@sltnet.lk
Publication covering ethnic studies. **Founded:** Jan. 1983. **Freq:** Semiannual. **Print Method:** Offset. **Trim Size:** 21 x 14 cm. **ISSN:** 1010-5832. **Subscription Rates:** US$10 single issue sea mail; US$14 single issue air mail; CRs 250 single issue local. **Remarks:** Accepts advertising. **URL:** http://www.ices.lk/publications/esr.shtml. **Circ:** (Not Reported)

50907 ■ Identity Culture and Politics
International Centre for Ethnic Studies

554/6A, Peradeniya Rd.
Kandy, Sri Lanka
Ph: 94 812 234892
Fax: 94 812 234892
Publisher E-mail: icesresch@sltnet.lk
Journal covering the dissemination of knowledge and exchange of ideas and projections among African and Asian scholars and activists. **Subtitle:** An Afro-Asian Dialogue. **Freq:** Biennial. **Key Personnel:** Ousmane Kane, Editorial Advisory Board, ok2009@columbia.edu; Imtiaz Ahmed, Editor, imtiazalter@gmail.com; Partha Chatterjee, Editorial Advisory Board; Anna Tsing, Editorial Advisory Board; Abdelghani Abouhani, Editorial Advisory Board; Vinesh Y. Hookoomsing, Editorial Advisory Board; Tariq Banuri, Editorial Advisory Board; Ashis Nandy, Editorial Advisory Board; Radhika Coomaraswamy, Editorial Advisory Board. **ISSN:** 0851-2914. **Subscription Rates:** US$8 individuals Africa and South Asia; US$25 single issue elsewhere. **URL:** http://www.codesria.org/spip.php?rubrique50&lang=en.

50908 ■ Nethra
International Centre for Ethnic Studies
554/6A, Peradeniya Rd.
Kandy, Sri Lanka
Ph: 94 812 234892
Fax: 94 812 234892
Publisher E-mail: icesresch@sltnet.lk
Journal covering political science. **Freq:** Quarterly. **Key Personnel:** Chelva Kanaganayakam, Editor. **ISSN:** 1391-2380. **Subscription Rates:** US$10 individuals. **Remarks:** Advertising accepted; rates available upon request. **URL:** http://www.icescolombo.org. **Circ:** (Not Reported)

50909 ■ Sri Lanka Journal of Medicine
Kandy Society of Medicine
KSM Office
Postgraduate Medical Ctr.
General (Teaching) Hospital
Kandy, Sri Lanka
Ph: 94 820 1701
Fax: 94 820 1702
Medical journal. **Founded:** 1992. **Freq:** Semiannual. **ISSN:** 1021-2604. **URL:** http://kandysocmed.tripod.com.

50910 ■ Sirasa FM - 106.2 MHz
PO Box 25, Araliya Uyana
Depanama
Pannipitiya, Sri Lanka
Ph: 94 11 2851371
Fax: 94 11 5340116
E-mail: sirasafm@maharaja.lk
Format: Sports; News. **Owner:** MBC Network Pvy. Ltd., No. 7, Braybrooke Pl., Colombo 2, Sri Lanka. **Operating Hours:** Continuous Mon.-Fri.; 6 a.m.-10 p.m.,10.15 p.m.-12 p.m Sat. **Wattage:** 1000. **Ad Rates:** Advertising accepted; rates available upon request. **URL:** http://www.sirasa.com/.

50911 ■ Sooriyan FM - 97.3 MHz
World Trade Centre
Level 35, East Tower
Colombo 1, Sri Lanka
Ph: 94 11 2346744
Fax: 94 11 2346880
E-mail: sooriyanfm@abc-radio.com
Owner: ABC Radio Network, at above address. **Founded:** 1998. **URL:** http://www.sooriyanfmlive.com/site/listen.html.

50912 ■ Yes FM - 88.2 MHz
36, Araliya Uyana
Depanama
Pannipitiya, Sri Lanka
Ph: 94 11 2851371
Fax: 94 11 2851373
E-mail: info@media.maharaja.lk
Owner: MBC Network Pvt. Ltd., at above address. **Operating Hours:** Continuous. **Wattage:** 1000. **Ad Rates:** Advertising accepted; rates available upon request. **URL:** http://www.capitalmaharaja.com/mbcnetworks_content.html; http://yesfmmusic.com.

Karagahatenna

50913 ■ Sri Lanka Broadcasting Corporation - Karagahatenna - 102.4 MHz
PO Box 574
Colombo 7, Sri Lanka

Ph: 94 11 2697491
Fax: 94 11 2691568
Format: News; Public Radio; Adult Contemporary; Sports. **Owner:** Sri Lanka Broadcasting Corporation, at above address. **Operating Hours:** 11 p.m.-2:30 a.m.; 10 a.m.-3:30 p.m. **Key Personnel:** Hudson Samarasingha, Chm., phone 94 11 2696439, fax 94 11 2695488, chairman@slbc.lk; Samantha Weliweriya, Dir. Gen., phone 94 11 2695248, fax 94 11 2697150, dg@slbc.lk. **Ad Rates:** Advertising accepted; rates available upon request. **URL:** http://www.slbc.lk.

50914 ■ Sri Lanka Broadcasting Corporation - Karagahatenna - 87.9 MHz
PO Box 574
Colombo 7, Sri Lanka
Ph: 94 11 2697491
Fax: 94 11 2691568
Format: Sports; News; Public Radio; Adult Contemporary. **Owner:** Sri Lanka Broadcasting Corporation, at above address. **Operating Hours:** Continuous. **Key Personnel:** Hudson Samarasingha, Chm., phone 94 11 2696439, fax 94 11 2695488, chairman@slbc.lk; Samantha Weliweriya, Dir. Gen., phone 94 11 2695248, fax 94 11 2697150, dg@slbc.lk. **Ad Rates:** $560-800 for 10 seconds; $1200-1600 for 15 seconds; $2000-2400 for 30 seconds; $3200-4000 for 60 seconds. **URL:** http://www.slbc.lk/.

50915 ■ Sri Lanka Broadcasting Corporation - Karagahatenna - 99.6 MHz
PO Box 574
Colombo 7, Sri Lanka
Ph: 94 11 2697491
Fax: 94 11 2691568
Format: News; Public Radio; Adult Contemporary; Sports. **Owner:** Sri Lanka Broadcasting Corporation, at above address. **Operating Hours:** 12 a.m.-5 p.m. **Key Personnel:** Hudson Samarasingha, Chm., phone 94 11 2696439, fax 94 11 2695488, chairman@slbc.lk; Samantha Weliweriya, Dir. Gen., phone 94 11 2695248, fax 94 11 2697150, dg@slbc.lk. **Ad Rates:** $450-650 for 30 seconds; $1000-1300 for 15 seconds; $1650-2000 for 30 seconds; $2650-3300 for 60 seconds. URL: http://www.slbc.lk/.

50916 ■ Sri Lanka Broadcasting Corporation - Karagahatenna - 90.6 MHz
PO Box 574
Colombo 7, Sri Lanka
Ph: 94 11 2697491
Fax: 94 11 2691568
Format: News; Public Radio; Adult Contemporary; Sports. **Owner:** Sri Lanka Broadcasting Corporation, at above address. **Operating Hours:** 11 p.m.-5:15 p.m. **Key Personnel:** Hudson Samarasingha, Chm., phone 94 11 2696439, fax 94 11 2695488, chairman@slbc.lk; Samantha Weliweriya, Dir. Gen., phone 94 11 2695248, fax 94 11 2697150, dg@slbc.lk. **Ad Rates:** Advertising accepted; rates available upon request. **URL:** http://www.slbc.lk.

50917 ■ Sri Lanka Broadcasting Corporation - Karagahatenna - 104.5 MHz
PO Box 574
Colombo 7, Sri Lanka
Ph: 94 11 2697491
Fax: 04 11 2091568
Format: News; Public Radio; Adult Contemporary; Sports. **Owner:** Sri Lanka Broadcasting Corporation, at above address. **Operating Hours:** 11 p.m.-5 p.m. **Key Personnel:** Hudson Samarasingha, Chm., phone 94 11 2696439, fax 94 11 2695488, chairman@slbc.lk; Samantha Weliweriya, Dir. Gen., phone 94 11 2695248, fax 94 11 2697150, dg@slbc.lk. **Ad Rates:** Advertising accepted; rates available upon request. **URL:** http://www.slbc.lk.

50918 ■ Sri Lanka Broadcasting Corporation - Karagahatenna - 95.0 MHz
PO Box 574
Colombo 7, Sri Lanka
Ph: 94 11 2697491
Fax: 94 11 2691568
Format: Full Service; Public Radio. **Owner:** Sri Lanka Broadcasting Corporation, at above address. **Operating Hours:** Continuous. **Key Personnel:** Hudson Samarasingha, Chm., phone 94 11 2696439, fax 94 11 2695488, chairman@slbc.lk; Samantha Weliweriya, Dir. Gen.,

phone 94 11 2695248, fax 94 11 2697150, dg@slbc.lk. **Ad Rates:** $700-1000 for 10 seconds; $1500-2000 for 15 seconds; $2500-3000 for 30 seconds; $4200-5000 for 60 seconds. **URL:** http://www.slbc.lk/.

Nayabedda

50919 ■ Independent Television Network - 12
Wickramasinghepura
Battaramulla 10120, Sri Lanka
Ph: 94 11 2775494
Fax: 94 11 2774591
E-mail: itnch@slt.lk
Format: Full Service. **Owner:** Independent Television Network, at above address. **Founded:** Apr. 19, 1979. **Key Personnel:** Mr. W.P.A.M Wijesinghe, General Mgr., phone 94 11 2774595, itngm@slt.lk; Mr. Anura Siriwardana, Chm. **Wattage:** 100,000. **Ad Rates:** $60-16,000 for 20 seconds; $15-4,800 for 5 seconds. **URL:** http://www.itn.lk/.

Nuwara Eliya

50920 ■ MTV Channel (Pvt) Ltd - 25
PO Box 25, Araliya Uyana
Depanama
Pannipitiya, Sri Lanka
Ph: 94 115340112
Fax: 94 115340111
Format: News. **Owner:** MTV Channel (Pvt) Ltd., 7.Braybrooke Pl., Colombo 2, Sri Lanka. **Operating Hours:** Continuous. **Wattage:** 1000. **URL:** http://www.maharaja.lk/Activities/Companies/MTV01.html.

Palali (Jaffna)

50921 ■ Sri Lanka Broadcasting Corporation - Palali (Jaffna) - 102.0 MHz
PO Box 574
Colombo 7, Sri Lanka
Ph: 94 11 2697491
Fax: 94 11 2691568
Format: News; Public Radio; Adult Contemporary; Sports. **Owner:** Sri Lanka Broadcasting Corporation, at above address. **Operating Hours:** 11 p.m.-2.30 a.m.; 10 a.m.-3.30 p.m. **Key Personnel:** Hudson Samarasinghe, Chm., phone 94 11 2696417, fax 94 11 2695488, chairman@slbc.lk; Samantha Weliweriya, Dir. Gen., phone 94 11 2695248, fax 94 11 2697150, dg@slbc.lk. **Ad Rates:** Advertising accepted; rates available upon request. **URL:** http://www.slbc.lk.

Panadura

50922 ■ Losetha
United Nations Association of Sri Lanka
Sri Lanka Eksath Jatheenge Sangamaya
39/1 Cyril Jansz Mawatha
Panadura, Sri Lanka
Ph: 94 38 2243080
Fax: 94 38 2232123
Publisher E-mail: info@unasl.org
Newspaper covering the United Nations, in Sinhalese and Tamil. **Freq:** 3/yr. **Remarks:** Advertising accepted; rates available upon request. **URL:** http://www.unasl.org; http://www.unasl.org/index.php?option=com_content&task=view&id=21&Itemid=35. **Circ:** 2,000

Pannipitiya

MTV Channel (Pvt) Ltd - See Nuwara Eliya
50923 ■ Sirasa FM - 88.9 MHz
PO Box 25
Depanama
Pannipitiya, Sri Lanka
Ph: 94 77 2744943
Fax: 94 11 5340116
E-mail: sirasafm@maharaja.lk
Format: Sports; News. **Owner:** MBC Network (PVT) Ltd, Braybrooke Pl., No. 7, Colombo 2, Sri Lanka. **Operating Hours:** Continuous. **Wattage:** 1000. **Ad Rates:** Advertising accepted; rates available upon request. **URL:** http://www.sirasa.com/.

50924 ■ Sirasa-FM - 88.8
PO Box 25
Depanama
Pannipitiya, Sri Lanka

Ph: 94 11 2851371
Fax: 94 11 2838392
E-mail: radio@sirasafm.maharaja.lk
Format: Sports; News. **Owner:** MBC Network (PVT) Ltd., Braybrooke Pl., No. 7, Colombo 2, Sri Lanka. **Founded:** 1993. **Operating Hours:** Continuous. **URL:** http://www.sirasa.com.

50925 ■ Sirasa-FM - 101.7
PO Box 25
Depanama
Pannipitiya, Sri Lanka
Ph: 94 11 2851371
Fax: 94 11 2838392
E-mail: radio@sirasafm.maharaja.lk
Format: Sports; News. **Owner:** MBC Network (PVT) Ltd., Braybrooke Pl., No. 7, Colombo 2, Sri Lanka. **Operating Hours:** Continuous. **URL:** http://www.sirasa.com.

Sirasa FM - See Colombo
Sirasa FM - See Kandy
50926 ■ Yes FM - 101.0 MHz
36, Araliya Uyana
Depanama
Pannipitiya, Sri Lanka
Ph: 94 11 2851371
Fax: 94 11 2851373
E-mail: info@media.maharaja.lk
Owner: MBC Network Pvt. Ltd., at above address. **Operating Hours:** Continuous. **Wattage:** 1000. **Ad Rates:** Advertising accepted; rates available upon request. **URL:** http://yesfmmusic.com; http://www.capitalmaharaja.com/mbcnetworks_content.html.

Yes FM - See Colombo
Yes FM - See Kandy

Peradeniya

50927 ■ Ceylon Journal of Science, Biological Sciences
University of Peradeniya
PO Box 35
Peradeniya 20400, Sri Lanka
Ph: 94 812 388301
Fax: 94 812 388102
Journal covering biology. **Founded:** 1957. **Freq:** Biennial. **Key Personnel:** C.V.S. Gunatilleke, Editorial Board; J.P. Edirisinghe, Editor-in-Chief; R.S. Rajakaruna, Editorial Board; N.K.B. Adikaram, Editorial Board. **ISSN:** 0069-2379. **Subscription Rates:** CRs 250 individuals local; US$16 individuals foreign. **URL:** http://www.pdn.ac.lk/cjsbs/. **Circ:** Paid 500

50928 ■ Ceylon Journal of Science, Physical Sciences
University of Peradeniya
PO Box 35
Peradeniya 20400, Sri Lanka
Ph: 94 812 388301
Fax: 94 812 388102
Interdisciplinary journal in the physical sciences devoted to papers on original scientific research of high quality. **Founded:** 1995. **Freq:** Annual. **Key Personnel:** M.A. Careem, Editor-in-Chief. **ISSN:** 1391-1465. **Subscription Rates:** CRs 250 individuals; US$16 other countries. **URL:** http://www.pdn.ac.lk/cjsbs/cjsps/.

Radella

50929 ■ Sri Lanka Broadcasting Corporation - Radella - 89.7 MHz
PO Box 574
Colombo 7, Sri Lanka
Ph: 94 11 2697491
Fax: 94 11 2691568
Format: News; Public Radio; Adult Contemporary; Sports. **Owner:** Sri Lanka Broadcasting Corporation, at above address. **Operating Hours:** 11 p.m.-2:30 a.m.; 10 a.m.-3:30 p.m. **Key Personnel:** Hudson Samarasinghe, Chm., phone 94 11 2696417, fax 94 11 2695488, chairman@slbc.lk; Samantha Weliweriya, Dir. Gen., phone 94 11 2695248, fax 94 11 2697150, dg@slbc.lk. **Ad Rates:** Advertising accepted; rates available upon request. **URL:** http://www.slbc.lk.

Circulation: ★ = ABC; △ = BPA; ◆ = CAC; • = CCAB; ❑ = VAC; ⊕ = PO Statement; ‡ = Publisher's Report; Boldface figures = sworn; Light figures = estimated.

50930 ■ Sri Lanka Broadcasting Corporation - Radella - 106.9 MHz
PO Box 574
Colombo 7, Sri Lanka
Ph: 94 11 2697491
Fax: 94 11 2691568
Format: Sports; News; Public Radio; Adult Contemporary. **Owner:** Sri Lanka Broadcasting Corporation, at above address. **Operating Hours:** Continuous. **Key Personnel:** Hudson Samarasingha, Chm., phone 94 11 2696439, fax 94 11 2695488, chairman@slbc.lk; Samantha Weliweriya, Dir. Gen., phone 94 11 2695248, fax 94 11 2697150, dg@slbc.lk. **Ad Rates:** $560-800 for 10 seconds; $1200-1600 for 15 seconds; $2000-2400 for 30 seconds; $3200-4000 for 60 seconds. **URL:** http://www.slbc.lk.

50931 ■ Sri Lanka Broadcasting Corporation - Radella - 100.2 MHz
PO Box 574
Colombo 7, Sri Lanka
Ph: 94 11 2697491
Fax: 94 11 2691568
Format: News; Public Radio; Adult Contemporary; Sports. **Owner:** Sri Lanka Broadcasting Corporation, at above address. **Operating Hours:** 12 a.m.-5 p.m. **Key Personnel:** Hudson Samarasingha, Chm., phone 94 11 2696439, fax 94 11 2695488, chairman@slbc.lk; Samantha Weliweriya, Dir. Gen., phone 94 11 2695248, fax 94 11 2697150, dg@slbc.lk. **Ad Rates:** $450-650 for 10 seconds; $1000-1300 for 15 seconds; $1650-2000 for 30 seconds; $2650-3300 for 60 seconds. **URL:** http://www.slbc.lk.

50932 ■ Sri Lanka Broadcasting Corporation - Radella - 91.7 MHz
PO Box 574
Colombo 7, Sri Lanka
Ph: 94 112697491
Fax: 94 112691568
Format: News; Public Radio; Adult Contemporary; Sports. **Owner:** Sri Lanka Broadcasting Corporation, at

above address. **Operating Hours:** 11 p.m.-5 p.m. **Key Personnel:** Hudson Samarasingha, Chm., phone 94 11 2696439, fax 94 11 2695488, chairman@slbc.lk; Samantha Weliweriya, Dir. Gen., phone 94 11 2695248, fax 94 11 2697150, dg@slbc.lk. **Ad Rates:** Advertising accepted; rates available upon request. **URL:** http://www.slbc.lk/.

50933 ■ Sri Lanka Broadcasting Corporation - Radella - 94.4 MHz
PO Box 574
Colombo 7, Sri Lanka
Ph: 94 11 2697491
Fax: 94 11 2691568
Format: News; Public Radio; Adult Contemporary; Sports. **Owner:** Sri Lanka Broadcasting Corporation, at above address. **Operating Hours:** Continuous. **Key Personnel:** Hudson Samarasingha, Chm., phone 94 11 2696439, fax 94 11 2695488, chairman@slbc.lk; Samantha Weliweriya, Dir. Gen., phone 94 11 2695248, fax 94 11 2697150, dg@slbc.lk. **Ad Rates:** $560-800 for 10 seconds; $1200-1600 for 15 seconds; $2000-2400 for 30 seconds; $3200-4000 for 60 seconds. **URL:** http://www.slbc.lk/.

50934 ■ Sri Lanka Broadcasting Corporation - Radella - 97.0 MHz
PO Box 574
Colombo 7, Sri Lanka
Ph: 94 11 2697491
Fax: 94 11 2691568
Format: News; Public Radio; Adult Contemporary; Sports. **Owner:** Sri Lanka Broadcasting Corporation, at above address. **Operating Hours:** 11 p.m.-4 p.m. **Key Personnel:** Hudson Samarasingha, Chm., phone 94 11 2696439, fax 94 11 2695488, chairman@slbc.lk; Samantha Weliweriya, Dir. Gen., phone 94 11 2695248, fax 94 11 2697150, dg@slbc.lk. **Ad Rates:** Advertising accepted; rates available upon request. **URL:** http://www.slbc.lk.

Rajagiriya

50935 ■ Chemistry in Sri Lanka
Institute of Chemistry, Ceylon

341/22 Kotte Rd.
Welikada
Rajagiriya, Sri Lanka
Ph: 94 112 863154
Fax: 94 112 861231
Journal covering chemistry. **Founded:** 1984. **Freq:** 3/yr. **ISSN:** 1012-8999. **URL:** http://www.nsf.ac.lk.

Sooriyakanda

50936 ■ Sri Lanka Rupavahini Corporation - 11
Independence Sq.
Colombo 7, Sri Lanka
Ph: 94 11 2587352
Fax: 94 11 2580131
E-mail: webmaster@rupavahini.lk
Format: Full Service. **Operating Hours:** 0600-0100. **Key Personnel:** Mr. Rohan Perera, Dep. Dir. Gen. (Engg.), ddge@rupavahini.lk; Dr. Ariyaratne Athugala, Chm. & Dir. Gen. **Wattage:** 200. **Ad Rates:** Advertising accepted; rates available upon request. **URL:** http://www.rupavahini.lk.

Yatiyantota

50937 ■ Sri Lanka Broadcasting Corporation - Yatiyantota - 92.2 MHz
PO Box 574
Colombo 7, Sri Lanka
Ph: 94 11 2697491
Fax: 94 11 2691568
Format: Full Service; Public Radio. **Owner:** Sri Lanka Broadcasting Corporation, at above address. **Operating Hours:** Continuous. **Key Personnel:** Hudson Samarasingha, Chm., phone 94 11 2696439, fax 94 11 2695488, chairman@slbc.lk; Samantha Weliweriya, Dir. Gen., phone 94 11 2695248, fax 94 11 2697150, dg@slbc.lk. **Ad Rates:** Advertising accepted; rates available upon request. **URL:** http://www.slbc.lk/.

Khartoum

50938 ■ Agriculture and Development in the Arab World
Arab Organization for Agricultural Development
PO Box 474 S, No. 7
Al Amarat
Khartoum, Sudan
Ph: 24 911 472176
Fax: 24 911 471402
Publisher E-mail: info@aoad.org
Arab publication covering agriculture and development in Arabic and English. **Freq:** Quarterly. **Remarks:** Advertising accepted; rates available upon request. **URL:** http://www.aoad.org. **Circ:** (Not Reported)

50939 ■ Sudanese Journal of Dermatology
African Journals Online
PO Box 10486
Khartoum, Sudan
Publisher E-mail: info@ajol.info
Peer-reviewed journal providing research information for dermato-venereology. **Freq:** Quarterly. **Key Personnel:** Mahdi M.A. Shamad, MD, Editor-in-Chief, phone 249 912 350 864, mahdishamad@yahoo.co.uk; Mahmoud A. Abdullah, PhD, Editorial Board; Adel H. Basheir, MD, Editorial Board. **ISSN:** 1815-3941. **Subscription Rates:** US$40 individuals; US$10 single issue. **URL:** http://ajol. info/index.php/sjd.

Wad Medani

50940 ■ International Journal of Sudan Research, Policy and Sustainable Development
Inderscience Enterprises Limited
c/o Prof. Muddathir Ali Ahmed, Consulting Ed.
University of Gezira, Agricultural Economics Section
Faculty of Agricultural Sciences
PO Box 20
Wad Medani, Sudan
Peer-reviewed journal discussing integrated approaches and ways to achieve sustainable development in Sudan. **Freq:** 4/yr. **Key Personnel:** Prof. Muddathir Ali Ahmed, Consulting Ed. **ISSN:** 2040-4247. **Subscription Rates:** EUR494 individuals print or online; EUR672 individuals print and online. **URL:** http://www.inderscience.com/ browse/index.php?journalID=353.

Circulation: ★ = ABC; △ = BPA; ◆ = CAC; • = CCAB; ❑ = VAC; ⊕ = PO Statement; ‡ = Publisher's Report; Boldface figures = sworn; Light figures = estimated.

Gale Directory of Publications & Broadcast Media/147th Ed.   5461

Paramaribo

50941 ■ Radio 10-FM - 88.1
PO Box 110
Stadionlaan 3
Paramaribo, Suriname
Ph: 597 410881
Fax: 597 422294

E-mail: info@radio10.sr
Format: Adult Contemporary; Oldies. **Operating Hours:** Continuous. **Ad Rates:** Advertising accepted; rates available upon request. **URL:** http://www.radio10.sr.

50942 ■ Trishul-FM - 90.5
Flocislaan 4 Boven

Paramaribo, Suriname
Ph: 597 439500
E-mail: trishul@sr.net
Format: Ethnic; World Beat. **Ad Rates:** Advertising accepted; rates available upon request. **URL:** http://www.trishul.sr.

Circulation: ★ = ABC; △ = BPA; ◆ = CAC; • = CCAB; ❑ = VAC; ⊕ = PO Statement; ‡ = Publisher's Report; Boldface figures = sworn; Light figures = estimated.

Gale Directory of Publications & Broadcast Media/147th Ed.

5463

Kwaluseni

50943 ■ International Journal of Humanistic Studies
African Journals Online
U.S. Department of of African Languages & Literature
University of Swaziland
Kwaluseni, Swaziland
Publisher E-mail: info@ajol.info
Peer-reviewed journal covering the field of humanistic studies. **Freq:** Annual. **Key Personnel:** Dr. Foluke Ogunleye, Editor, editoruniswaijhs@yahoo.com; Prof. William D. Kamera, Editor; Prof. Donald R. Hill, Editor. **ISSN:** 1811-489X. **Subscription Rates:** US$50 institutions; US$35 individuals. **URL:** http://ajol.info/index.php/ijhs.

50944 ■ UNISWA Research Journal of Agriculture, Science and Technology
African Journals Online
UNISWA Research Journal of Agriculture
Private Bag 4
Luyengo Campus
Kwaluseni, Swaziland
Publisher E-mail: info@ajol.info
Peer-reviewed journal of agriculture, science and technology. **Freq:** Semiannual. **Key Personnel:** Prof. H.M. Mushala, Chm., Editorial Board, phone 268 5186126, fax 268 5185276, mushala@yahoo.com.

ISSN: 1029-9645. **Subscription Rates:** US$10 single issue. **URL:** http://ajol.info/index.php/uniswa-rjast.

Luyengo

50945 ■ UNISWA Journal of Agriculture
African Journals Online
Faculty of Agriculture
University of Swaziland
Luyengo, Swaziland
Publisher E-mail: info@ajol.info
Peer-reviewed journal based on agriculture. **Founded:** 1975. **Freq:** Annual. **Print Method:** Offset. **Trim Size:** 8 1/8 x 10 7/8. **Cols./Page:** 3. **Col. Width:** 26 nonpareils. **Col. Depth:** 140 agate lines. **Key Personnel:** Dr. M.P. Dlamini, Member of the Editorial Board; Dr. Emmanuel J. Mwendera, Editor-in-Chief, phone 268 5283021, fax 268 5283021, mwendera@agric.uniswa.sz; Dr. G.W. Ocen, Member of the Editorial Board; Dr. M.M. Shongwe, Member of the Editorial Board; Dr. M.K. Habedi, Member of the Editorial Board; Z.M.K. Phiri, Member of the Editorial Board; Dr. J.I. Rugambisa, Member of the Editorial Board. **ISSN:** 1021-0873. **Subscription Rates:** US$20 individuals; R 50 individuals. **URL:** http://ajol.info/index.php/uniswa.

Matsapha

50946 ■ Lwati
African Journals Online

A.1.10, Department of English Language & Literature
University of Swaziland
Private Bag 4
Kwaluseni
Matsapha, Swaziland
Ph: 268 5184011
Fax: 268 5185276
Publisher E-mail: info@ajol.info
Peer-reviewed journal covering humanities and the social sciences. **Subtitle:** A Journal of Contemporary Research. **Freq:** Annual. **Key Personnel:** Francis Ibe Mogu, Editor, lwatijo@yahoo.com. **ISSN:** 1813-2227. **Subscription Rates:** US$35 individuals; US$50 institutions. **URL:** http://ajol.info/index.php/lwati.

Mbabane

50947 ■ Y'ello
Swazi MTN Ltd.
Marketing and Sales Department
Public Relations
PO Box 5050
Mbabane, Swaziland
Ph: 268 4060000
Fax: 268 4046215
Magazine covering technology. **Freq:** Quarterly. **URL:** http://www.mtn.co.sz/.

Alvsjo

50948 ■ Djurens Ratt
Forbund Djurens Ratt
PO Box 2005
SE-125 02 Alvsjo, Sweden
Ph: 46 8 55591400
Fax: 46 8 55591450
Publisher E-mail: info@djurensratt.se
Journal covering animal rights in the Nordic countries.
URL: http://www.djurensratt.org. **Circ:** Combined 50,000

Bastad

50949 ■ Fackoversattaren
Swedish Association of Translators
PO Box 1091
S-269 21 Bastad, Sweden
Ph: 46 431 75500
Fax: 46 431 76990
Magazine containing articles, information about technological developments, and translation software tools.
Freq: Bimonthly. **Key Personnel:** Loole Hagberg, Editor-in-Chief, loole.hagberg@telia.com. **URL:** http://www.sfoe.se/omsfofackoversattaren.php.

Boras

50950 ■ Journal of Intercultural Communication
Immigrant-institutet
Katrinedalsgatan 43
504 51 Boras, Sweden
Ph: 46 331 36070
Fax: 46 331 36075
Publisher E-mail: info@immi.se
Peer-reviewed journal covering research, education and training in the field of intercultural communication. **Key Personnel:** Beatriz Dorriots, Managing Editor, beadorriots@yahoo.fr; Miguel Benito, Managing Editor, miguel.benito@immi.se; Prof. Jens Allwood, Editor-in-Chief, jens.allwood@ling.gu.se. **ISSN:** 1404-1634. **URL:** http://www.immi.se/intercultural/.

50951 ■ Svensk Biblioteksforskning/Swedish Library Research
University College of Boras
Swedish School of Library and Information Science
Swedish Library Research
SE-501 90 Boras, Sweden
Ph: 46 33 4354000
Publication E-mail: svensk.biblioteksforskning@hb.se
Publisher E-mail: registrator@hb.se
Journal covering research based articles in library and information science. **Key Personnel:** Lars Hoglund, Editor, lars.hoglund@hb.se. **ISSN:** 0284-4354. **URL:** http://www.hb.se/wps/portal/!ut/p/c0/04_SB8K8xLLM9MSSzPy8xBz9CP0os3hXX49QSydDRwMLfwMDAyNj_sxBHQy93D2dDY_3g4jL9gmxHRQDzU9.

Djursholm

50952 ■ Arkiv for Matematik
Springer Netherlands
Institute Mittag-Leffler
Auravagen 17
SE-182 60 Djursholm, Sweden
Publisher E-mail: permissions.dordrecht@springer.com
Journal on mathematics. **Freq:** Semiannual. **Key Personnel:** Anders Bjorner, Editor-in-Chief; Mikael Passare, Editorial Board. **ISSN:** 0004-2080. **Subscription Rates:** EUR123 institutions print incl. free access or e-only; EUR147.60 institutions print incl. enhanced access. **URL:** http://www.springer.com/math/journal/11512.

Eskilstuna

50953 ■ Husdjur
Svensk Mjolk
Kungsgatan 43
PO Box 1146
SE-631 80 Eskilstuna, Sweden
Ph: 46 771 191900
Fax: 46 162 1216
Agricultural magazine for dairy farmers. **Founded:** 1947. **Freq:** Monthly 11/yr. **Cols./Page:** 11. **Key Personnel:** Marie Louise Ankarsten, Contact, phone 46 161 63516, marielouise.ankarsten@svenskmjolk.se; Lennart Anderson, Publisher, phone 46 8 7905839, lennart.andersson@svenskmjolk.se; Eric Pettersson, Editor-in-Chief, phone 46 8 7905842, erik.pettersson@svenskmjolk.se. **ISSN:** 0046-8339. **Subscription Rates:** 572 SKr individuals. **Remarks:** Accepts advertising. **URL:** http://www.husdjur.se. **Ad Rates:** BW: 12,600 SKr, 4C: 15,000 SKr. **Circ:** Controlled 17,900

Farsta

50954 ■ Svensk Danssport
Swedish Dance Sport Federation
Svenska Danssportforbundet
Idrottshuset Farsta
Marbackagatan 19
S-123 43 Farsta, Sweden
Ph: 46 8 6996000
Fax: 46 8 6996531
Publication E-mail: kansli@danssport.co
Publisher E-mail: kansli@danssport.se
Swedish language publication covering dance. **Freq:** Quarterly. **Key Personnel:** Lars-Goran Goransson, Contact, dans@gmnorden.com. **Remarks:** Advertising accepted; rates available upon request. **URL:** http://www.danssport.se/. **Circ:** (Not Reported)

Goteborg

50955 ■ Acta Neurologica Scandanavica
John Wiley & Sons Inc.
Wiley-Blackwell
c/o Elinor Ben-Menachem, MD, Ed.-in-Ch.
Dept. of Neurology
Sahlgrenska University Hospital
S-413 45 Goteborg, Sweden
Ph: 46 313 423100
Fax: 46 318 27436
Journal focusing on original clinical, diagnostic or experimental work in neuroscience. **Freq:** Monthly. **Key Personnel:** Elinor Ben-Menachem, MD, Editor-in-Chief, acta@neuro.gu.se; Johan Aarli, Editorial Board; Anders Oldfors, Editorial Board. **ISSN:** 0001-6314. **Subscription Rates:** US$1,318 institutions print and online; US$1,198 institutions print or online; EUR907 institutions print or online; EUR998 institutions print and online; 786 institutions print and online; 714 institutions print or online; US$1,540 institutions, other countries print and online; US$1,400 institutions print or online. **Remarks:** Accepts advertising. **URL:** http://www.wiley.com/bw/journal.asp?ref=0001-6314&site=1. **Circ:** (Not Reported)

50956 ■ Africa & Asia
Dept of Oriental and African Languages
Goteborg University
PO Box 100
S-405 30 Goteborg, Sweden
Ph: 46 31 7731000
Publication E-mail: aa@oriental.gu.se
Journal devoted to the study of Asian and African languages and literatures. **Subtitle:** Goteborg Working Papers on Asian and African Languages. **Freq:** Annual. **ISSN:** 1650-2019. **URL:** http://www.african.gu.se/aa/index.html.

50957 ■ Blood Pressure
Taylor & Francis Ltd.
c/o Susanne Tullin, Editorial Asst.
Dept. of Clinical Trials & Entrepreneurship
Sahlgrenska Academy at Goteborg University
PO Box 418
S-405 30 Goteborg, Sweden
Ph: 46 313 422974
Fax: 46 314 19368
Publication E-mail: bloodpressure@pharm.gu.se
Journal providing a source for authoritative and timely information on all aspects of hypertension management, including: the physiology and pathophysiology of blood pressure regulation, essential and secondary hypertension, atherosclerotic cerebrocardiovascular disease, renal hypertensive diseases, non pharmacological and pharmacological management and methodology related to hypertension research. **Freq:** 6/yr. **Key Personnel:** Thomas Hedner, Editor-in-Chief; Krzysztof Narkiewicz, Editor; Sverre E. Kjeldsen, Editor; Susanne Tullin, Editorial Asst. **ISSN:** 0803 7051. **Subscription Rates:** 570 institutions print and online; US$570 institutions online; 570 individuals print and online; US$570 individuals online. **Remarks:** Advertising accepted; rates available upon request. **URL:** http://www.informaworld.com/smpp/title~content=t713699605. **Circ:** (Not Reported)

50958 ■ Current Genetics
Springer-Verlag Tokyo
Department of Cell & Molecular Biology
Goeteborg University
Box 462
S-40530 Goteborg, Sweden
Ph: 46 31 3608488
Fax: 49 31 7862599
Publisher E-mail: info@springer.jp
Journal providing a forum for publication of innovative research on eukaryotic organisms, focusing on the analysis of cellular and developmental systems using classical genetics, molecular genetics, genomics, functional genomics - and combinations thereof - in yeasts, fungi, algae, protists and cell organelles. **Freq:** Bimonthly. **Key Personnel:** Stefan Hohmann, Editor-in-Chief, editor@current-genetics.se; Ralph Bock, Editor; Katherine Borkovich, Editor. **ISSN:** 0172-8083. **Sub-**

Circulation: ★ = ABC; △ = BPA; ♦ = CAC; • = CCAB; ❑ = VAC; ⊕ = PO Statement; ‡ = Publisher's Report; Boldface figures = sworn; Light figures = estimated.

Gale Directory of Publications & Broadcast Media/147th Ed. 5467

scription Rates: EUR2,460 institutions print incl. free access or e-only; EUR2,952 institutions print incl. enhanced access. Remarks: Advertising accepted; rates available upon request. URL: http://www.springer.com/lifesci/genetics/journal/294. Circ: (Not Reported)

50959 ■ Molecular Genetics and Genomics
Springer-Verlag
c/o Stefan Hohmann, Ed.-in-Ch.
Dept. of Cell & Molecular Biology
Goteborg University
PO Box 462
S-405 30 Goteborg, Sweden
Ph: 46 31 3608488
Fax: 46 31 7862599
Journal dealing with all areas of genetics and genomics, including experimental and theoretical approaches in all organisms. Freq: 6/yr. Key Personnel: Andres Aguilera, Editor; Dan Andersson, Editor; Stefan Hohmann, Editor-in-Chief, editor@molecular-genetics-genomics.se; Martine Collart, Editor; Michel Georges, Editor; Reinhard Fischer, Editor; Thomas S. Becker, Editor; Christiane Gebhardt, Editor; Carol Dieckmann, Editor. ISSN: 1617-4615. Subscription Rates: EUR4,323 institutions print incl. free access; EUR5,187.60 institutions print incl. enhanced access. Remarks: Advertising accepted; rates available upon request. URL: http://www.springer.com/lifesci/cellbiology/journal/438. Circ: (Not Reported)

50960 ■ Montessori Tidningen
Drottninggatan 31
SE-411 14 Goteborg, Sweden
Professional magazine covering Montessori education in Sweden. Freq: Bimonthly. Print Method: Offset. Key Personnel: Peter Jormeau, Owner; Anders Carlsson, Editor-in-Chief, phone 46 31171110, anders@boxinformation.com; Gunnar Brissman, Art Dir. ISSN: 1103-8101. Remarks: Accepts advertising. URL: http://www.montessoriforbundet.se/. Circ: Paid 10,000, Non-paid 11,300

50961 ■ Nordicom Review
Nordic Information Center for Media and Communication Research (Nordicom)
Goteborgs University
PO Box 713
S-405 30 Goteborg, Sweden
Ph: 46 31 7860000
Fax: 46 31 7864655
Publisher E-mail: info@nordicom.gu.se
Peer-reviewed journal covering the media and communication research in the Nordic countries. Founded: 1980. Freq: Semiannual. Key Personnel: Ulla Carlsson, Editor, phone 46 31 7731219, fax 46 31 7734655, ulla.carlsson@nordicom.gu.se; Goran Bolin, Editorial Board, goran.bolin@sh.se; Lisbeth Clausen, Editorial Board, lc.ikl@cbs.dk. Subscription Rates: 250 SKr individuals. URL: http://www.nordicom.gu.se/?portal=publ&main=nordicom_review2.php&me=2.

50962 ■ Ord & Bild
Box 31120
SE-400 32 Goteborg, Sweden
Ph: 46 317439905
Fax: 46 317439906
Cultural review covering arts, politics, society and history. Founded: 1892. Freq: Bimonthly. Key Personnel: Cecilia Verdinelli Peralta, Editor, redaktion@tidskriftenordbild.se. Subscription Rates: 320 SKr individuals; 80 SKr single issue. Remarks: Accepts advertising. URL: http://www.tidskriftenordbild.se/?id=52. Circ: Paid 3,000

50963 ■ Restaurang Guiden
Stenklevsgatan 5
S-414 65 Goteborg, Sweden
Ph: 46 317 412545
Fax: 46 317 044810
Publisher E-mail: info@restaurangguiden.com
Trade magazine for restaurant owners, suppliers, and employees. Founded: 1993. Freq: Bimonthly. Print Method: Offset. Remarks: Accepts advertising. URL: http://www.restaurangguiden.se/. Circ: Controlled ⊕22,000

50964 ■ Scandinavian Economic History Review
Scandinavian Society for Economic and Social History
School of Business, Economics & Law
Goteborg University
PO Box 600
S-405 30 Goteborg, Sweden
Ph: 46 317 860000

Fax: 46 317 864970
Publisher E-mail: info@handels.gu.se
Scandinavian publication covering economic history. Founded: 1953. Freq: 3/yr. Key Personnel: Lars Magnusson, Editor; Mats Morell, Editor; Sverre Knutsen, Co-Ed. ISSN: 0358-5522. Subscription Rates: US$159 institutions print and online; US$143 institutions online; US$84 individuals; 88 institutions print and online; 79 institutions online only; 45 individuals; EUR124 institutions print & online; EUR112 institutions online only; EUR66 individuals. Remarks: Advertising not accepted. URL: http://www.tandf.co.uk/journals/journal.asp?issn=0358-5522&subcategory=EB050000&linktype=rates. Circ: 500

50965 ■ Scandinavian Journal of Information Systems
Information Systems Research in Scandinavia Association
Viktoria Research Institute
Box 620
SE-405 30 Goteborg, Sweden
Ph: 46 31 7735540
Fax: 46 31 7734754
Publisher E-mail: pan@cs.auc.dk
Journal covering studies of IT development and use. Founded: 1989. Freq: Semiannual. Key Personnel: Rikard Lindgren, Editor; Karlheinz Kautz, Advisory Board; Matti Rossi, Advisory Board. ISSN: 0905-0167. Subscription Rates: Free to all members. URL: http://iris.cs.aau.dk/index.php/welcome.html.

50966 ■ Swedish Journal of Musicology
Swedish Society for Musicology
c/o Musikhogskolan
PO Box 210
SE-405 30 Goteborg, Sweden
Ph: 46 31 7735220
Fax: 46 31 7735200
Publisher E-mail: stm@musik.gu.se
Swedish language journal covering music. Freq: Annual. Key Personnel: Anders Carlsson, Managing Editor; Jcob Derkert, President, jacob.derkert@musik.su.se; Tubias lund, Editor, tubias.lund@kultur.lu.se. ISSN: 0081-9816. Subscription Rates: Included in membership. Remarks: Advertising not accepted. URL: http://musikforskning.se/stm/index.php?menu=2. Circ: (Not Reported)

50967 ■ Telecommunications Policy
Elsevier Science
c/o E. Bohlin, Ed.-in-Ch.
Technology & Society
Chalmers University of Technology
Vera Sandbergs Alle 8
7701 Goteborg, Sweden
Ph: 46 317 721205
Fax: 46 317 723783
Publisher E-mail: nlinfo-f@elsevier.com
Journal on knowledge infrastructure development, management and regulation. Freq: 11/yr. Key Personnel: E. Bohlin, Editor-in-Chief, erik.bohlin@chalmers.se; C. Antonelli, International Editorial Board; Jason Whalley, Book Reviews Ed., jason.whalley@strath.ac.uk. ISSN: 0308-5961. Subscription Rates: 183,400¥ institutions; US$1,547 institutions for all countries except Europe, Japan & Iran; EUR1,382 institutions for European countries & Iran; US$363 individuals for all countries except Europe, Japan & Iran; EUR324 individuals for European countries & Iran; 43,200¥ individuals. Remarks: Accepts advertising. URL: http://www.elsevier.com/wps/find/journaldescription.cws_home/30471/description. Circ: (Not Reported)

Hamneda

50968 ■ Bindu
Scandinavian Yoga and Meditation School
Haa Course Center
S-340 13 Hamneda, Sweden
Ph: 46 372 55063
Fax: 46 372 55036
Publisher E-mail: haa@yogameditation.com
Consumer magazine covering the science and art of yoga and meditation in English, German, Danish and Swedish. Founded: 1973. Freq: Quarterly. Key Personnel: Daya Mullins, Editor. ISSN: 0107-4881. URL: http://www.yogameditation.com/articles/bindu_magazine. Circ: Combined 69,000

Huddinge

50969 ■ Acta Odontologica Scandinavica
Taylor & Francis Ltd.
Dept. of Cariology
Institute of Odontology
Karolinska Institutet
PO Box 4064
S-141 04 Huddinge, Sweden
Ph: 46 852 4881231
Fax: 46 871 18343
Peer-reviewed journal providing rapid publication of dental research in the areas of preventive and community dentistry, periodontal and oral mucus membrane diseases, oral implants, temporomandibular disorders, material science, and clinical and basic odontological sciences. Founded: 1939. Freq: 6/yr. Key Personnel: Peter Holbrook, Editor, phol@hi.is; Anette Oliveby, Asst. Ed., anette.oliveby@ki.se; Karin Heyeraas, Assoc. Ed.; Palle Holmstrup, Assoc. Ed.; Thomas Modeer, Assoc. Ed. ISSN: 0001-6357. Subscription Rates: 350 institutions; US$575 institutions; EUR460 institutions. Remarks: Advertising accepted; rates available upon request. URL: http://www.informaworld.com/smpp/title~content=t713394069; http://informahealthcare.com/ode. Circ: (Not Reported)

Jonkoping

50970 ■ Journal of Media Business Studies
Joenkoeping International Business School, Media Management and Transformation Centre
Jonkoping International Business School
Jonkoping University
PO Box 1026
SE-551 11 Jonkoping, Sweden
Peer-reviewed journal devoted to research on business aspects of media including strategic, organizational, financial, marketing, and entrepreneurial issues and practices. Freq: 3/yr. Key Personnel: Robert G. Picard, Editor, editor@jombs.com. ISSN: 1652-2354. Subscription Rates: 535 SKr individuals; EUR60 individuals; US$65 individuals; 1,735 SKr institutions; EUR195 institutions; US$225 institutions. URL: http://www.jombs.com.

Karlskrona

50971 ■ Planera Bygga Bo
Boverket
Box 534
SE-371 23 Karlskrona, Sweden
Publisher E-mail: registraturen@boverket.se
Trade magazine covering urban development, planning, building and housing. Founded: 1990. Freq: Bimonthly. Trim Size: 185 x 270 mm. Cols./Page: 3. Key Personnel: Birgitta Frejd, Editor; Barbro Larson Perez, Editor. ISSN: 1100-0678. Remarks: Accepts advertising. URL: http://www.boverket.se/Om-Boverket/Planera-Bygga-Bo/. Circ: Controlled 3,500

Knivsta

50972 ■ Scandinavian Journal of Forest Research
Taylor & Francis Group Journals
c/o Mats Hannerz, Ed.-in-Ch.
Silvinformation AB
Kolonivagen 6B
S-74144 Knivsta, Sweden
Ph: 46 18 188554
Publisher E-mail: customerservice@taylorandfrancis.com
Journal focusing on forests and forestry of boreal and temperate regions, including the forestry-to-wood production chain. Freq: Bimonthly. Key Personnel: Mats Hannerz, Editor-in-Chief, mats.hannerz@silvinformation.se; Lennart Norell, Editorial Board, norell@math.uu.se. ISSN: 0282-7581. Subscription Rates: 301 institutions print + online; US$500 institutions print + online; 286 institutions online; US$475 institutions online; 135 individuals; US$224 individuals; EUR178 individuals print; EUR379 institutions online; EUR398 institutions print & online. URL: http://www.tandf.co.uk/journals/titles/02827581.asp.

Linkoping

50973 ■ Cognitive Behaviour Therapy
Routledge
Taylor & Francis Group Ltd.
c/o Gerhard Andersson, Assoc. Ed.

Dept. of Behavioural Sciences
Linkoping University
S-581 83 Linkoping, Sweden
Publisher E-mail: webmaster.books@tandf.co.uk
Peer-reviewed journal focusing on the application of behavioral and cognitive sciences to clinical psychology and psychotherapy. **Freq:** Quarterly. **Key Personnel:** Gerhard Andersson, Assoc. Ed.; Gordon J.G. Asmundson, Editor-in-Chief, phone 306337-2415, fax 306337-3275, gordon.asmundson@uregina.ca; Martin M. Antony, Editorial Board; Ata Ghaderi, Assoc. Ed.; David Barlow, Editorial Board; Per Carlbring, Editor-in-Chief, perca@ibv.liu.se. **ISSN:** 1650-6073. **Subscription Rates:** US$164 individuals; US$263 institutions online; US$277 institutions print + online; 166 institutions print + online; 158 institutions online; EUR220 institutions print + online; EUR210 institutions online. **Remarks:** Advertising accepted; rates available upon request. **URL:** http://www.tandf.co.uk/journals/titles/16506073.asp. Formerly: Scandinavian Journal of Behaviour Therapy. **Circ:** (Not Reported)

50974 ■ Hygiea Internationalis
International Network for the History of Public Health
c/o Marie C. Nelson
Division of History/ISAK
Linkoping University
S-581 83 Linkoping, Sweden
Ph: 46 132 84465
Fax: 46 132 81843
Publisher E-mail: marne@isak.liu.se
Refereed electronic journal of the International Network for the History of Public Health, with limited paper copies. **Subtitle:** An Interdisciplinary Journal for the History of Public Health. **Key Personnel:** Jan Sundin, Editorial Board; Christopher Hamlin, Editorial Board; Giovanni Berlinguer, Editorial Board; Marie C. Nelson, Editorial Board; Linda Bryder, Editorial Board; Sam Willner, Editor, sam.willner@ihs.liu.se; Dorothy E. Porter, Editorial Board; Virginia Berridge, Editorial Board; Marcos Cueto, Editorial Board; Patrice Bourdelais, Editorial Board. **ISSN:** 1403-8668. **URL:** http://www.ep.liu.se/ej/hygiea/.

50975 ■ The International Journal of Ageing and Later Life (IJAL)
Linkoping University Electronic Press
Linkoping University/ISV
S-581 83 Linkoping, Sweden
Ph: 46 132 81000
Fax: 46 131 49403
Publication E-mail: ijal@isv.liu.se
Journal focusing on adult ageing and relations among generations in the social and cultural aspects of ageing and later life development. **Freq:** Semiannual. **Key Personnel:** Lars Anderson, Editor-in-Chief, lars.andersson@isv.liu.se; Sandra Torres, Assoc. Ed., sandra.torres@isv.liu.se; Sara Arber, Editorial Board; Peter Berkesand, Tech. Ed., petbe@ep.liu.se; Laura Machat-From, Editorial Asst., karlo@isv.liu.se; Peter Oberg, Assoc. Ed. **ISSN:** 1652-8670. **Subscription Rates:** Free online only. **URL:** http://www.ep.liu.se/ej/ijal/.

50976 ■ International Journal of Production Economics
Elsevier Science Inc.
c/o R.W. Grubbstrom, Ed.-in-Ch.
Dept. of Production Economics
Linkoping Institute of Technology
S-581 83 Linkoping, Sweden
Publisher E-mail: usinfo-ehelp@elsevier.com
Journal covering manufacturing and process industries, as well as production, including research, design, development, test, launch and disposal. **Founded:** 1976. **Freq:** Monthly. **Print Method:** Offset. **Trim Size:** 5 1/2 x 8 1/2. **Cols./Page:** 1. **Col. Width:** 50 nonpareils. **Col. Depth:** 100 agate lines. **Key Personnel:** L.E. Cardenas-Barron, Editorial Board; O. Tang, Asst. Ed.; P.J. Agrell, Editorial Board; W.L. Berry, Editorial Board; S.E. Elmaghraby, Editorial Board; P. Kelle, North-American Ed.; R.W. Grubbstrom, Editor-in-Chief, robert@grubbstrom.com; T. Durand, Editorial Board. **ISSN:** 0925-5273. **Subscription Rates:** US$2,939 institutions, other countries except Europe, Japan and Iran; EUR2,627 institutions for European countries and Iran; 349,000¥ institutions; EUR171 individuals for European countries and Iran; US$189 other countries except Europe, Japan and Iran; 23,100¥ individuals.

URL: http://www.elsevier.com/wps/find/journaldescription.cws_home/505647/descriptiondescription.

50977 ■ Reproduction in Domestic Animals
John Wiley & Sons Inc.
Wiley-Blackwell
c/o Dr. H. Rodriguez-Martinez, Ed.-in-Ch.
Linkoping University
Department of Clinical & Experimental Medicine
Faculty of Health Science
SE-581 85 Linkoping, Sweden
Ph: 46 101031522
Fax: 46 13132257
Journal covering physiology, pathology, and biotechnology of reproduction in domestic animals. **Freq:** Bimonthly. **Key Personnel:** Dr. H. Rodriguez-Martinez, Editor-in-Chief; Dr. W.A. King, Assoc. Ed.; Dr. E. Martinez-Garcia, Assoc. Ed. **ISSN:** 0936-6768. **Subscription Rates:** US$362 individuals Americas (print and online); 196 individuals non-Euro zone (print and online); EUR293 individuals Euro zone (print and online); US$216 other countries print and online; US$1,309 institutions Americas (print and online); 709 institutions UK (print and online); EUR900 institutions Europe (print and online); US$1,526 institutions, other countries print and online; US$1,190 institutions Americas (print or online only); 644 institutions UK (print or online only). **Remarks:** Accepts advertising. **URL:** http://www.wiley.com/bw/journal.asp?ref=0936-6768. **Circ:** (Not Reported)

50978 ■ Scandinavian Journal of Psychology
John Wiley & Sons Inc.
Wiley-Blackwell
c/o Jerker Ronnberg, Ed.-in-Ch.
Dept. of Behavioural Sciences
Linkoping University
S-581 83 Linkoping, Sweden
Ph: 46 132 82107
Fax: 46 132 82145
Peer-reviewed journal covering psychology with a focus on experimental psychology. **Freq:** Bimonthly. **Key Personnel:** Jerker Ronnberg, Editor-in-Chief; Stefan Gustafson, Editorial Asst., phone 46 13 285896; Magnus Lindgren, Section Ed., phone 46 46 2223062; Nils Inge Landro, Section Ed., phone 47 22 854278; Helen Johansson, Admin. Asst., phone 46 13 282163, fax 46 13 282142; Eric Lykke Mortensen, Section Ed., phone 35 32 7839. **ISSN:** 0036-5564. **Subscription Rates:** US$252 individuals print + online; US$89 members APS/RPA/NNS: print + online; US$1,157 institutions print + online; US$1,051 institutions print, online; US$1,349 institutions, other countries print + online; EUR143 individuals print + online; EUR78 members APS/RPA/NNS: print + online; 635 institutions print + online; 577 institutions print, online; EUR807 institutions print + online. **Remarks:** Advertising accepted; rates available upon request. **URL:** http://www.wiley.com/bw/journal.asp?ref=0036-5564&site=1. **Circ:** (Not Reported)

Ljusdal

50979 ■ Byggfakta Projektnytt
Byggfakta AB
Lojtnantsgatan 9
S-827 81 Ljusdal, Sweden
Ph: 46 651 552500
Fax: 46 651 552585
Publisher E-mail: kundtjanst@byggfakta.se
Trade magazine for construction professionals. **Founded:** 1987. **Freq:** Monthly 8/yr. **Print Method:** Offset. **Key Personnel:** Jan Nilsson, Contact; Karin Bergstrom, Contact; Hans Engblom, Contact; Jenny Marcuson, Contact; Mikael Sagstrom, Contact; Goran Cavallin, Contact; Nisse Olsson, Contact. **ISSN:** 1101-8437. **Remarks:** Accepts advertising. **URL:** http://www.byggfakta.se/. **Ad Rates:** BW: 20,400 SKr, 4C: 24,300 SKr. **Circ:** Controlled 23,000

Ludvika

50980 ■ pilotmagazinet
Pilotmagazinet
PO Box 301
S-77126 Ludvika, Sweden
Ph: 46 240 84890
Fax: 46 240 18015
Publisher E-mail: red@pilotmagazinet.com
Trade magazine covering aviation. **Freq:** Monthly. **Remarks:** Accepts advertising. **URL:** http://www.aeroflight.

co.uk/mags/sweden/swedmag.htm. **Ad Rates:** BW: 1,040 SKr. **Circ:** Paid 30,000

Lulea

50981 ■ Flow Measurement and Instrumentation
Elsevier Science
c/o Jerker Delsing, Ed.-in-Ch.
Dept. of Computer Science & Electrical Engineering
Lulea University of Technology
S-971-87 Lulea, Sweden
Publisher E-mail: nlinfo-f@elsevier.com
Peer-reviewed journal covering various aspects of flow measurement, in both closed conduits and open channels. **Freq:** Bimonthly. **Key Personnel:** J. Ningde, Editorial Advisory Board; M.L. Sanderson, Editorial Advisory Board, m.l.sanderson@cranfield.ac.uk; Jerker Delsing, Editor-in-Chief, jerker@sm.luth.se; C.J. Bates, Editorial Advisory Board; R.C. Baker, Editorial Advisory Board; N. Bignell, Editorial Advisory Board; S. Beck, Editorial Advisory Board; S. Dey, Editorial Advisory Board; M. Henry, Assoc. Ed. **ISSN:** 0955-5986. **Subscription Rates:** 132,900¥ institutions; US$1,119 institutions for all countries except Europe and Japan; EUR1,000 institutions for European countries; US$155 individuals; 17,800¥ individuals; EUR115 individuals. **Remarks:** Accepts advertising. **URL:** http://www.elsevier.com/wps/find/journaldescription.cws_home/30417/descript ion. **Circ:** (Not Reported)

50982 ■ Journal of Nonlinear Mathematical Physics
Lulea University of Technology
c/o Norbert Euler, Ed.-in-Ch.
Dept. of Mathematics
Lulea University of Technology
S-971 87 Lulea, Sweden
Ph: 46 920 492878
Fax: 46 920 491073
Publisher E-mail: webred@ltu.se
Mathematical journal dealing with research papers with description, solution, and applications of nonlinear problems in physics and mathematics. **Freq:** Quarterly. **Key Personnel:** Norbert Euler, Editor-in-Chief, norbert@sm.luth.se; Yuri Berest, Editorial Board, berest@math.cornell.edu; Maciej Blaszak, Editorial Board. **ISSN:** 1402-9251. **Subscription Rates:** EUR290 institutions; EUR95 individuals. **URL:** http://www.atlantis-press.com/publications/jnmp/.

Lund

50983 ■ Acta Orthopaedica
Informa Healthcare
Dept. of Orthopedics
Lund University Hospital
S-221 85 Lund, Sweden
Ph: 46 46 171596
Fax: 46 46 184454
Publication E-mail: acta.ort@ort.lu.se
Publisher E-mail: healthcare.enquiries@informa.com
Journal focusing on the field of orthopedics and related sub disciplines. **Freq:** Bimonthly. **Key Personnel:** Harald Steen, Co-Ed.; Anders Rydholm, Editor; Peter A. Frandsen, Dep. Ed., peter.frandsen@ouh.fyns-amt.dk; Per Aspenberg, Co-Ed.; Ivan Hvid, Co-Ed.; Marianne Arner, Co-Ed.; Rolf Onnerfalt, Co-Ed.; Bart A. Swierstra, Co-Ed.; Olle Svensson, Co-Ed. **ISSN:** 1745-3674. **Subscription Rates:** 365 institutions; US$595 institutions; EUR475 institutions; 720 institutions corporate; US$1,190 institutions corporate; EUR950 institutions corporate. **Remarks:** Accepts advertising. **URL:** http://informahealthcare.com/ort. **Circ:** (Not Reported)

50984 ■ Borrsavangen
Geotec
PO Box 1127
SE-221 04 Lund, Sweden
Ph: 46 75 7008820
Fax: 46 75 7008829
Trade magazine of the Swedish Water Well Drillers' Association. **Founded:** 1993. **Freq:** Quarterly. **Print Method:** Offset. **Cols./Page:** 3. **Col. Width:** 60 millimeters. **Key Personnel:** Henryk Rozenberg, Contact, redaktion@geotec.se. **ISSN:** 1103-7938. **Subscription Rates:** Free. **Remarks:** Accepts advertising. **URL:** http://www.geotec.se. **Circ:** (Not Reported)

50985 ■ Genes, Chromosomes & Cancer
John Wiley & Sons Inc.

c/o Felix Mitelman, Ed.-in-Ch.
U.S. Department of of Clinical Genetics
University Hospital
SE-221 85 Lund, Sweden
Ph: 46 46 173360
Fax: 46 46 131061
Publisher E-mail: info@wiley.com
Journal covering the study of neoplasia. **Freq:** Monthly. **Key Personnel:** Felix Mitelman, Editor-in-Chief; Janet D. Rowley, Editor-in-Chief; Thoas Fioretos, Assoc. Ed., gcc.fioretos@med.lu.se. **ISSN:** 1045-2257. **Subscription Rates:** US$375 U.S., Canada, and Mexico print only; US$459 other countries; US$2,703 institutions print and online; US$2,871 Canada and Mexico institution (print and online); US$2,955 institutions, other countries print and online; US$2,710 institutions print only; US$2,626 Canada and Mexico institution (print only); US$2,955 institutions, other countries print and online. **Remarks:** Accepts advertising. **URL:** http://www3.interscience.wiley.com/journal/38250/home. **Circ:** (Not Reported)

50986 ■ Graduate Journal of Social Science
c/o Mia Liinason, Managing Editor
Centre for Gender Studies
PO Box 117, Lund University
S-221 00 Lund, Sweden
Ph: 46 46 221000
Journal providing examples of and discussions over pluralism in methodology across the social sciences, thus building opportunities for progress through dialogue and reciprocal awareness. **Key Personnel:** Melissa Fernandez, Editor-in-Chief; Gwendolyn Beetham, Editor-in-Chief. **ISSN:** 1572-3763. **URL:** http://www.gjss.org/.

50987 ■ Microprocessors and Microsystems
Elsevier Science
c/o K. Kuchcinski, Ed.-in-Ch.
Dept. of Computer Science
Lund Institute
22100 Lund, Sweden
Publisher E-mail: nlinfo-f@elsevier.com
International covering design and implementation of microprocessor based systems. **Freq:** 8/yr. **Key Personnel:** K. Kuchcinski, Editor-in-Chief, krzysztof.kuchcinski@cs.lth.se; M. Berekovic, Editorial Board, berekovic@ida.ing.tu-bs.de; M. Chang, Editorial Board, morris@iastate.edu; P. Ellervee, Editorial Board, lrv@cc.ttu.ee; Simon W. Moore, Editorial Board; E. Maehle, Editorial Board, maehle@iti.uni-luebeck.de. **ISSN:** 0141-9331. **Subscription Rates:** 114,300¥ institutions; EUR861 institutions for Europe; US$963 institutions all countries except Europe and Japan; US$173 individuals; 19,900¥ individuals; EUR130 individuals. **Remarks:** Accepts advertising. **URL:** http://www.elsevier.com/wps/find/journaldescription.cws_home/525449/description. **Circ:** (Not Reported)

50988 ■ Oikos
John Wiley & Sons Inc.
Wiley-Blackwell
Lund University
Dept. of Ecology
Ecology Bldg.
S-223 62 Lund, Sweden
Publication E-mail: oikos@ekol.lu.se
Peer-reviewed journal covering the field of ecology. **Freq:** Monthly. **Key Personnel:** Tim Benton, Editor-in-Chief; Linus Svensson, Managing Editor. **ISSN:** 0030-1299. **Subscription Rates:** US$180 individuals Americas (print and online); EUR161 individuals Euro zone (print and online); 107 other countries print and online; US$1,525 institutions Americas (print and online); EUR1,154 institutions Europe; US$1,781 institutions, other countries print and online; 908 institutions UK (print and online); US$1,525 institutions Americas (print or online only); EUR1,049 institutions Europe (print or online only); US$1,619 institutions, other countries print or online only. **Remarks:** Accepts advertising. **URL:** http://www.wiley.com/bw/journal.asp?ref=0030-1299. **Circ:** (Not Reported)

50989 ■ Physiologia Plantarum
John Wiley & Sons Inc.
Wiley-Blackwell
St. Lars vag 44B (4 tr)
S-222 70 Lund, Sweden
Ph: 46 46 303229
Fax: 46 46 303246
Peer-reviewed journal dealing with physiological and molecular mechanisms governing plant development, growth and productivity. **Freq:** Monthly. **Key Personnel:**

Vaughan Hurry, Editor-in-Chief, vaughan.hurry@plantphys.umu.se; Karin Fredrikson, Subject Ed.; Ron Mittler, Subject Ed.; Dominique Van Der Straeten, Editorial Board; Leif Nord, Managing Editor. **ISSN:** 0031-9317. **Subscription Rates:** US$1,523 institutions print + online; US$1,384 institutions print, online; US$1,779 institutions, other countries print + online; US$38 members American Society for Plant Biologists (ASPB); EUR36 members American Society for Plant Biologists; 907 institutions print + online; 825 institutions print, online; EUR1,153 institutions print + online; EUR1,048 institutions print, online. **Remarks:** Advertising accepted; rates available upon request. **URL:** http://www.wiley.com/bw/journal.asp?ref=0031-9317&site=1. **Circ:** (Not Reported)

50990 ■ Scandinavian Journal of Food and Nutrition
Taylor & Francis Ltd.
SNF Swedish Nutrition Foundation
Ideon
S-223 70 Lund, Sweden
Journal presenting the latest research in the various fields within nutrition. **Freq:** 4/yr. **Key Personnel:** Sussanne Bryngelsson, Editorial Asst.; Inge Tetens, Editor; Prof. Nils-Georg Asp, Editor-in-Chief; Asim Duttaroy, Editor; Mikael Fogelholm, Editor. **ISSN:** 1748-2976. **Subscription Rates:** US$144 institutions online; US$64 individuals print only; US$152 institutions print and online; 92 institutions print and online; 87 institutions online; 38 individuals print only. **Remarks:** Accepts advertising. **URL:** http://www.informaworld.com/smpp/title~content=t713692040. **Formerly:** Scandinavian Journal of Nutrition. **Circ:** (Not Reported)

Malmo

50991 ■ Clinical Physiology and Functional Imaging
John Wiley & Sons Inc.
Wiley-Blackwell
c/o Prof. Per Wollmer, Ed.-in-Ch.
Dept. of Clinical Physiology
Malmo University Hospital
S-205 02 Malmo, Sweden
Ph: 46 403 31441
Fax: 46 403 36620
Journal focusing on clinical and experimental research pertinent to human physiology in health and disease. **Freq:** Bimonthly. **Key Personnel:** Prof. Per Wollmer, Editor-in-Chief, per.wollmer@med.lu.se; Jens Bulow, Assoc. Ed.; P. Friberg, Editorial Board. **ISSN:** 1475-0961. **Subscription Rates:** US$199 individuals print and online; US$1,938 institutions print and online; US$1,761 institutions print. or online; 1,047 institutions print and online; EUR161 individuals print and online (Euro zone); 108 institutions print and online (non Euro zone); US$2,259 institutions, other countries print and online; US$2,054 institutions, other countries print or online. **Remarks:** Accepts advertising. **URL:** http://www.wiley.com/bw/journal.asp?ref=1475-0961&site=1. **Circ:** (Not Reported)

50992 ■ World Maritime University Journal of Maritime Affairs
International Maritime Organization, World Maritime University
PO Box 500
S-201 24 Malmo, Sweden
Ph: 46 403 56300
Fax: 46 401 28442
Publisher E-mail: info@wmu.se
Journal presenting new ideas and current thinking on pertinent issues in these subject areas which are of interest to a wide range of professionals from maritime administration, industry and education world-wide. **Freq:** Semiannual. **Key Personnel:** Rosalie Balkin, Editorial Board; Janusz Mindykowski, Editorial Board; Edgar Gold, Editorial Board; Sam Bateman, Editorial Board; Michael Barnett, Editorial Board; Magnus Addico, Editorial Board; Aldo Chircop, Editorial Board; Zhengyiang Liu, Editorial Board. **ISSN:** 1651-436X. **Subscription Rates:** EUR80 individuals. **URL:** http://www.wmu.se/Library/Publications/WMUJournal/tabid/145/Default.aspx.

Molndal

50993 ■ Current Swedish Archaeology
Swedish Archaeological Society
Svenska Arkeologiska Samfundet
c/o Tore Artelius

Kvarnbygatan 12
S-431 34 Molndal, Sweden
Publisher E-mail: info@arkeologiskasamfundet.se
Publication covering current Swedish archaeology. **Freq:** Annual. **Key Personnel:** Asa Gillberg, Editor; Bjorn Nilsson, Editor. **Subscription Rates:** 150 SKr individuals postage extra. **Remarks:** Advertising not accepted. **URL:** http://www.arkeologiskasamfundet.se/aktuellt.html. **Circ:** (Not Reported)

Nora

50994 ■ Slojdforum
Pl. 6610 Mariedal 1
S-713 94 Nora, Sweden
Ph: 46 587 60015
Fax: 46 587 60032
Trade magazine covering fashion, design and crafts. **Freq:** Bimonthly. **Key Personnel:** Annie Grimlund, Editor and Publisher, phone 46 8 7376568, annica.grimlund@lararforbunddet.se; Mats Thoren, Editor, phone 46 70 3385676, mats.throne@lararforbundet.se. **ISSN:** 0346-0509. **Remarks:** Accepts advertising. **URL:** http://www.slojdforum.se/. **Circ:** (Not Reported)

Norrkoping

50995 ■ Hydrology Research
Nordic Association for Hydrology
Nordisk Hydrologisk Forening
c/o Hans Stjarnskog, Treas.
Swedish Meteorological & Hydrological Inst.
SE-601 76 Norrkoping, Sweden
Ph: 46 114958313
Fax: 46 114958573
Publication covering Nordic hydrology. **Freq:** Quarterly. **Key Personnel:** Dan Rosbjerg, Editor, phone 45 45251449, fax 45 45932850, dr@env.dtu.dk. **ISSN:** 0029-1277. **Subscription Rates:** US$666 institutions; EUR532 institutions; 355 institutions. **URL:** http://www2.er.dtu.dk/nordichydrology/. **Formerly:** Nordic Hydrology.

50996 ■ Tidskrift for Schack
Sveriges Schackforbund
Kabelvagen 19
S-602 20 Norrkoping, Sweden
Ph: 46 111 07420
Fax: 46 111 82341
Publisher E-mail: kansliet@schack.se
Official membership magazine of the Swedish Chess Federation. **Founded:** 1895. **Freq:** 10/yr. **Print Method:** Offset. **Key Personnel:** Niklas Sidmar, Editor, niklas.sidmar@schack.se. **ISSN:** 0040-6848. **Subscription Rates:** US$35 individuals. **Remarks:** Accepts advertising. **URL:** http://www.schack.se/tfs/. **Circ:** Non-paid 2,000

Ronneby

50997 ■ Information and Software Technology
Elsevier Science Inc.
c/o C. Wohlin, Ed.-in-Ch.
School of Engineering
Blekinge Institute of Technology
Box 520
S-372 25 Ronneby, Sweden
Ph: 46 457 385820
Publisher E-mail: usinfo-ehelp@elsevier.com
Peer-reviewed journal focusing on research and experience that contributes to the improvement of software development practices. **Founded:** June 1971. **Freq:** Monthly. **Print Method:** Web offset. **Trim Size:** 7 3/4 x 10 1/2. **Cols./Page:** 3. **Col. Depth:** 133 agate lines. **Key Personnel:** Claes Wohlin, Editor-in-Chief, claes.wohlin@bth.se; S. Elbaum, Editorial Board; G. Ruhe, Assoc. Ed., ruhe@ucalgary.ca; C. Seaman, Assoc. Ed., cseaman@umbc.edu; P. Grunbacher, Assoc. Ed., pg@sea.uni-linz.ac.at. **ISSN:** 0950-5849. **Subscription Rates:** US$1,288 institutions, other countries except Europe, Japan and Iran; 152,600¥ institutions; EUR1,149 institutions for European countries and Iran; 34,600¥ individuals; EUR224 individuals for European countries and Iran; US$299 other countries except Europe, Japan and Iran. **URL:** http://www.elsevier.com/wps/find/journaldescription.cws_home/525444/descriptiondescription.

Skillingaryd

50998 ■ SFF Filatelisten/Svensk Filatelistisk Tidskrift
Sveriges Filatelist-Forbund
Box 91
SE-568 22 Skillingaryd, Sweden
Ph: 46 370 70566
Publisher E-mail: kansli@sff.nu
Journal covering philately. **Founded:** 1899. **Freq:** Monthly 2nd of each month (except January and July). **Print Method:** Offset. **Subscription Rates:** US$395 individuals. **Remarks:** Accepts advertising. **URL:** http://sff.nu/. **Ad Rates:** 4C: 3,680 SKr. **Circ:** Paid 9,700

Solna

50999 ■ Acta Oncologica
Taylor & Francis Ltd.
Box 25
SE-171 11 Solna, Sweden
Ph: 46 8 54544150
Fax: 46 8 318204
Publication E-mail: lena.andreasson-haddad@karolinska.se
Journal accepting articles within all fields of clinical cancer research from applied basic research to cancer nursing and psychological aspects of cancer, including articles on tumour pathology, experimental oncology and biology, cancer epidemiology and medical radiophysics if they have a clinical aim or interest. **Freq:** 8/yr. **Key Personnel:** Bengt Glimelius, Editor-in-Chief; Olav Dahl, Editor; Timo Hakulinen, Editor; Roger Henriksson, Editor; Heikki Joensuu, Editor; Christoph Johansen, Editor; Jens Overgaard, Editor; Torsten Landberg, Book Review Ed.; Ludvig Paul Muren, Editor. **ISSN:** 0284-186X. **Subscription Rates:** 435 institutions; US$720 institutions; EUR575 institutions. **Remarks:** Advertising accepted; rates available upon request. **URL:** http://www.informaworld.com/smpp/title~content=t713690780~db=all. **Circ:** (Not Reported)

51000 ■ Skogssport
Swedish Orienteering Federation
Svenska Orienteringsforbundet
PO Box 22
S-171 18 Solna, Sweden
Ph: 46 8 58772000
Fax: 46 8 58772088
Publisher E-mail: info@orientering.se
Official magazine of the Swedish Orienteering Federation. **Freq:** 10/yr. **Key Personnel:** Ola Gustafsson, Editor, ola.gustafsson@orientering.se; Jan Eric Goth, Editor-in-Chief. **Remarks:** Accepts advertising. **URL:** http://www.orientering.se/. **Circ:** (Not Reported)

Stockholm

51001 ■ Acta Oto-Laryngologica
Taylor & Francis Ltd.
PO Box 3255
S-103 65 Stockholm, Sweden
Ph: 46 8 4408040
Fax: 46 8 4408050
Publication E-mail: actaoto@informa.com
Journal publishing original papers on basic research as well as clinical studies in the field of otolaryngology and head and neck surgery and related subdisciplines. **Freq:** 12/yr. **Key Personnel:** Prof. Matti Anniko, MD, Editor-in-Chief; Christer Lundberg, MD, Assoc. Ed. **ISSN:** 0001-6489. **Subscription Rates:** 605 institutions; US$995 institutions; EUR795 institutions. **Remarks:** Advertising accepted; rates available upon request. **URL:** http://www.informaworld.com/smpp/title~content=t713690940. **Circ:** (Not Reported)

51002 ■ Acta Paediatrica
John Wiley & Sons Inc.
Wiley-Blackwell
Building X5:01
Karolinska Hospital
SE-171 76 Stockholm, Sweden
Ph: 46 8 51772487
Fax: 46 8 51774034
Publication E-mail: mail@actapaediatrica.se
Peer-reviewed journal covering both clinical and experimental research, in all fields of pediatrics including developmental physiology. **Freq:** Monthly. **Key Personnel:** Hugo Lagercrantz, Editor-in-Chief, phone 46 8 51774700, hugo.lagercrantz@actapaediatrica.se. **ISSN:**

0803-5253. **Subscription Rates:** US$325 individuals print and online; US$963 institutions print and online; US$875 institutions online only; 197 individuals print and online; 562 institutions print and online; 511 institutions online only; EUR650 institutions online only; EUR715 institutions print and online; US$1,002 institutions, other countries online only; 1,123 institutions, other countries print and online. **Remarks:** Accepts advertising. **URL:** http://www.wiley.com/bw/journal.asp?ref=0803-5253. **Circ:** (Not Reported)

51003 ■ Advances in Physiotherapy
Taylor & Francis Ltd.
PO Box 3255
S-103 65 Stockholm, Sweden
Ph: 46 8 4408040
Fax: 46 8 4408050
Publication E-mail: advances@informa.com
Peer-reviewed and international journal covering all aspects of physiotherapy and analysing and debating research in the light of the consequences they have on physiotherapy, including contrasting different research perspectives on essential phenomena and questioning traditional paradigms, arousing lively discussions in both physiotherapy and related research communities, challenging and developing theoretical models, evaluating and criticizing interventions and discussing educational and professional issues of physiotherapy. **Freq:** Quarterly. **Key Personnel:** Barbara Richardson, Assoc. Ed.-in-Ch., b.richardson@uea.ac.uk; Chris Carpenter, Advisory Board; Hans Lund, Editorial Board; Gunnevi Sundelin, Editor-in-Chief, gunnevi.sundelin@physiother.umu.se; Birgitta Lindmark, Editorial Board; Sarianna Sipila, Editorial Board. **ISSN:** 1403-8196. **Subscription Rates:** 210 institutions; US$345 institutions; EUR275 institutions. **Remarks:** Advertising accepted; rates available upon request. **URL:** http://informahealthcare.com/loi/phy. **Circ:** (Not Reported)

51004 ■ Alcheringa
Taylor & Francis Group Journals
PO Box 50007
S-104 05 Stockholm, Sweden
Ph: 46 8 51954142
Fax: 46 8 51954221
Publisher E-mail: customerservice@taylorandfrancis.com
Peer-reviewed journal covering the study of Australasian paleontology. **Subtitle:** An Australasian Journal of Palaeontology. **Freq:** Quarterly. **Print Method:** Uses mats. Letterpress. **Cols./Page:** 6. **Col. Width:** 24 nonpareils. **Col. Depth:** 280 agate lines. **Key Personnel:** Dr. Stephen MaLoughlin, Honarary Ed.; Dr. Tony Wright, Asst. Ed. **ISSN:** 0311-5518. **Subscription Rates:** 126 institutions print and online; US$121 institutions print and online; 82 individuals; 211 institutions online; US$201 institutions, other countries online; US$135 individuals. **URL:** http://www.tandf.co.uk/journals/titles/03115518.asp.

51005 ■ Allergy
European Academy of Allergology and Clinical Immunology
Academie Europeenne d'Allergologie et d'Immunologie Clinique
c/o C. Ostrom, Exec. Mgr.
PO Box 24140
S-10451 Stockholm, Sweden
Ph: 46 8 4596623
Fax: 46 8 6633815
Publisher E-mail: executive.office@eaaci.org
European journal covering allergy. **Subtitle:** European Journal of Allergy and Clinical Immunology. **Freq:** Monthly. **Key Personnel:** Thomas Bieber, Editor. **ISSN:** 0105-4538. **Subscription Rates:** US$1,806 institutions America; print and online; US$2,106 institutions rest of the world; print and online; EUR1,367 institutions print and online; 1,831 institutions rest of the world; print only; US$1,570 institutions America; online only; US$1,831 institutions rest of the world; online only. **Remarks:** Advertising accepted; rates available upon request. **URL:** http://www3.interscience.wiley.com/journal/118519659/toc?func=showIssues&code=all; http://www.eaaci.net/site/content.php?l1=18. **Circ:** (Not Reported)

51006 ■ Ambio
Kungliga Vetenskapsakademien
Royal Swedish Academy of Sciences
PO Box 50005
SE-104 05 Stockholm, Sweden
Ph: 46 8 6739500

Fax: 46 8 155670
Publication E-mail: ambio@allenpress.com
Publisher E-mail: info@kva.se
Multidisciplinary, environmental journal. **Subtitle:** A Journal of the Human Environment. **Founded:** 1972. **Freq:** 8/yr. **Key Personnel:** Bo Soderstrom, Editor-in-Chief. **ISSN:** 0044-7447. **Subscription Rates:** US$93 individuals print only; US$85 individuals online only; US$105 individuals print and online; US$249 institutions print only; US$223 institutions online only; US$308 institutions print and online. **Remarks:** Accepts advertising. **URL:** http://www.kva.se/sv/kontakt/Tidskrifter/AMBIO/. **Circ:** (Not Reported)

51007 ■ Amyotrophic Lateral Sclerosis
Taylor & Francis Ltd.
PO Box 3255
S-103 65 Stockholm, Sweden
Ph: 46 844 08040
Fax: 46 844 08050
Journal providing coverage of research in a wide range of issues related to motor neuron diseases, especially ALS (Lou Gehrig's disease) and spinal muscular atrophies and related disorders of the motor system, when relevant to these core diseases, aiming to disseminate information on new developments in the pathogenesis and management of motor neuron disease, and enhance awareness of these devastating and often under-recognised disorders. **Freq:** 6/yr. **Key Personnel:** Michael Swash, Founding Ed.; Denise Figlewicz, Assoc. Ed.; Merit Cudkowicz, Editorial Advisory Board; Ettore Beghi, Editorial Advisory Board; Mamede de Carvalho, Editorial Advisory Board; M. Gouri-Devi, Editorial Advisory Board; Andrew A. Eisen, Editorial Advisory Board; Stanley H. Appel, Editorial Advisory Board; Reinhard Dengler, Assoc. Ed.; Ammar Al-Chalalbi, Editorial Advisory Board; Vincent Meininger, Editorial Advisory Board; John Ravitz, Editorial Advisory Board. **ISSN:** 1748-2968. **Subscription Rates:** 675 institutions; US$1,110 institutions; EUR895 institutions. **Remarks:** Accepts advertising. **URL:** http://www.informaworld.com/smpp/title~content=t713656198~db=all; http://informahealthcare.com/aml. **Formerly:** Amyotrophic Lateral Sclerosis and Other Motor Neuron Disorders. **Circ:** (Not Reported)

51008 ■ Annals of the ICRP
Elsevier Science
c/o Straalskyddinstitutet
International Commission on Radiological Protection
Solna Strandvaeg 122
S-17116 Stockholm, Sweden
Publisher E-mail: nlinfo-f@elsevier.com
Publication covering radiation. **Founded:** 1960. **Freq:** Bimonthly. **Key Personnel:** C.H. Clement, Editor-in-Chief; C. Cousins, Chm. **ISSN:** 0146-6453. **Subscription Rates:** 29,700¥ individuals; EUR221 individuals for European countries and Iran; US$251 individuals for all countries except Europe, Japan and Iran; 68,800¥ institutions; EUR518 institutions for European countries and Iran; US$579 institutions for all countries except Europe, Japan and Iran. **Remarks:** Advertising not accepted. **URL:** http://www.elsevier.com/wps/find/journaldescription.cws_home/442/descriptiondescription. **Circ:** Paid ‡1,800

51009 ■ Arkiv Samhalle och Forskning
Swedish Archival Association
Svenska Arkivsamfundet
c/o Stockholms stadsarkiv
PO Box 22063
S-104 22 Stockholm, Sweden
Swedish language publication covering archives. **Founded:** 1952. **Freq:** Semiannual. **Key Personnel:** Lars Lundqvist Dokonria, Editor. **ISSN:** 0349-0505. **Remarks:** Advertising not accepted. **URL:** http://www.arkivsamfundet.se/system/asf.html. **Circ:** (Not Reported)

51010 ■ Bulletin of the Brazilian Mathematical Society
Springer-Verlag Tokyo
Dept. of Mathematics
Institute of Technology
S-150 1004 Stockholm, Sweden
Publisher E-mail: info@springer.jp
Journal publishing high quality papers in mathematics. **Freq:** 4/yr. **Key Personnel:** Jacob Palis, Managing Editor, jpalis@impa.br; John Coates, Editorial Board, j.h.coates@dpmms.cam.ac.uk; Blaine Lawson, Editorial Board, blaine@math.sunysb.edu; Pierre-Louis Lions, Editorial Board, lions@ceremade.dauphine.fr; Djairo G.

De Figueiredo, Editorial Board, djairo@ime.unicamp.br; Steven L. Kleiman, Editorial Board, kleiman@math.mit. edu; John Milnor, Editorial Board, jack@math.sunysb. edu; Lennart Carleson, Editorial Board, carleson@math. kth.se; Manfredo P. Do Carmo, Editorial Board, manfredo@impa.br. **ISSN:** 1678-7544. **Subscription Rates:** EUR528 institutions print incl. free access or e-only; EUR633.60 institutions print incl. enhanced access. **Remarks:** Advertising accepted; rates available upon request. **URL:** http://www.springer.com/math/journal/574. **Circ:** (Not Reported)

51011 ■ Bygg & Teknik
PO Box 19099
S-104 32 Stockholm, Sweden
Ph: 46 861 21750
Fax: 46 861 25481
Trade magazine covering construction for architectural firms, consulting engineers, and contractors. **Subtitle:** Sveriges Aldsta Byggtidning Grundad 1909. **Founded:** Mar. 2, 1909. **Freq:** Monthly 8/yr. **Print Method:** Offset. **Cols./Page:** 3. **Col. Width:** 59 millimeters. **Key Personnel:** Stig Dahlin, Editor and Publisher; Roland Dahlin, Advertising Mgr.; Marcus Dahlin, Admin. **ISSN:** 0281-658X. **Remarks:** Accepts advertising. **URL:** http://www.byggteknikforlaget.se. **Former name:** Byggnadskonst. **Ad Rates:** BW: 11,000 SKr, 4C: 15,800 SKr. **Circ:** Controlled 6,800

51012 ■ CAP&Design
Karlbergsv 77
106 78 Stockholm, Sweden
Professional magazine providing information for professional graphic designers and illustrators. **Founded:** Feb. 15, 1989. **Freq:** Monthly. **Print Method:** Offset. **Trim Size:** 8 1/8 x 10 7/8. **Cols./Page:** 3. **ISSN:** 0036-8423. **Remarks:** Accepts advertising. **URL:** http://www.capdesign.idg.se. **Ad Rates:** 4C: 8,535 SKr. **Circ:** Paid 15,000

51013 ■ Contra
Stiftelsen Contra
PO Box 8052
SE-104 20 Stockholm, Sweden
Ph: 46 8 7200145
Fax: 46 8 7200195
Publisher E-mail: redax@contra.nu
Political journal. **Subtitle:** Frihetens rost. **Founded:** 1975. **Freq:** 6/yr. **Print Method:** Offset. **Cols./Page:** 3. **Key Personnel:** Geza Molnar, Publisher. **ISSN:** 0347-6472. **Subscription Rates:** 145 SKr local; 25 SKr single issue. **URL:** http://www.contra.nu. **Circ:** Paid 1,500

51014 ■ Damernas Varld
Bonnier Tidskrifter AB
Sveavagen 53
SE-105 44 Stockholm, Sweden
Ph: 46 87365300
Publisher E-mail: info@bt.bonnier.se
Consumer magazine covering fashion, beauty, food and other topics for women. **Founded:** 1940. **Freq:** 13/year. **Print Method:** Offset. **Trim Size:** 225 x 290 mm. **Cols./Page:** 4. **Key Personnel:** Linda Grahn, Editor-in-Chief. **Subscription Rates:** 449 SKr individuals; 39.50 SKr single issue. **Remarks:** Accepts advertising. **URL:** http://www.bonniermagazines.se/our-brands/damernas-varld/; http://damernasvarld.se/. **Alt. Formats:** CD-ROM. **Ad Rates:** 4C: 59,000 SKr. **Circ:** ‡87,700

51015 ■ EuroSurveillance
ECDC
S-171 83 Stockholm, Sweden
Ph: 46 85 8601000
Fax: 46 85 8601001
Publisher E-mail: eurosurveillance@ecdc.europa.eu
Journal covering communicable diseases from an European perspective. Featuring reports on specific diseases in individual countries, and on European-wide initiatives. **Founded:** Sept. 1971. **Freq:** Monthly. **Print Method:** Offset. **Trim Size:** 8 1/2 x 11. **Cols./Page:** 3. **Col. Width:** 2 1/4 inches. **Col. Depth:** 10 inches. **Key Personnel:** Karl Ekdahl, Editor-in-Chief; Ines Steffens, Managing Editor; Andrea Ammon, Assoc. Ed. **USPS:** 560-350. **URL:** http://www.eurosurveillance.org.

51016 ■ Fortattaren
Swedish Writers' Union
PO Box 3157
Drottninggatan 88 B
S-103 63 Stockholm, Sweden
Ph: 46 854 513200
Fax: 46 854 513210
Publisher E-mail: sff@sff.info
Magazine featuring topics and issues about the Union. **Freq:** 5/yr. **Key Personnel:** Henrik C. Enbohm, Contact, phone 46 8 54513208, forfattaren@sff.info. **Remarks:** Accepts advertising. **URL:** http://www.forfattarforbundet.se. **Circ:** (Not Reported)

51017 ■ Geografiska Annaler, Series A, Physical Geography
Swedish Society for Anthropology and Geography
Svenska Sallskapet for Antropologi och Geografi
Socialantropologiska institutionen Stockholms universitet
Villavagen 16
S-106 91 Stockholm, Sweden
Ph: 46 736466095
Publisher E-mail: ssagmail@yahoo.se
Publication covering physical geography and anthropology in English, French and German. **Freq:** Quarterly. **Key Personnel:** Prof. Wibjorn Karlen, Editor; Stig Jonsson, Editor; Nel Caine, Editorial Board. **ISSN:** 0435-3676. **Subscription Rates:** US$66 individuals Americas (print + online); EUR60 individuals Europe (print + online); 40 individuals UK (print + online); US$45 students Americas (print + online); EUR40 students Europe (print + online); 26 students UK (print + online); US$470 institutions Americas (print + online); EUR356 institutions Europe (print + online); 280 institutions UK (print + online). **Remarks:** Accepts advertising. **URL:** http://www.ssag.se/index.php?sida=gannalera; http://www.blackwellpublishing.com/journal.asp?ref=0435-3676&site=1. **Circ:** (Not Reported)

51018 ■ Geografiska Annaler, Series B, Social Geography
Swedish Society for Anthropology and Geography
Svenska Sallskapet for Antropologi och Geografi
Socialantropologiska institutionen Stockholms universitet
Villavagen 16
S-106 91 Stockholm, Sweden
Ph: 46 736466095
Publisher E-mail: ssagmail@yahoo.se
Publication covering anthropology and social geography in English, French and German. **Freq:** Quarterly. **Key Personnel:** Orjan Sjoberg, Editor-in-Chief, orjan.sjoberg@hhs.se; Jenny Appelblad, Editorial Coordinator, gab@humangeo.su.se; Guy Baeten, Review Ed., guy.baeten@keg.lu.se; Richard Ek, Review Ed., richard.ek@msm.lu.se. **ISSN:** 0435-3684. **Subscription Rates:** US$66 individuals America; print & online; US$45 students America; print & online; US$491 institutions America; print & premium online; US$446 institutions America; print or online only; 40 individuals UK; print and online; 40 other countries print & online; 26 students, other countries print & online; US$574 institutions, other countries print & premium online; US$521 institutions, other countries print or online only; EUR60 individuals Europe; print and online. **Remarks:** Accepts advertising. **URL:** http://www.ssag.se/index.php?sida=gannalerb; http://www.blackwellpublishing.com/journal.asp?ref=0435-3684&site=1. **Circ:** (Not Reported)

51019 ■ Grana
Taylor & Francis Group Journals
Dept. of Paleobotany
Swedish Museum of Natural History
PO Box 50007
S-104 05 Stockholm, Sweden
Publisher E-mail: customerservice@taylorandfrancis.com
Journal focusing on ontogony and aerobiology. **Founded:** 1954. **Freq:** Quarterly. **Key Personnel:** Else Marie Friis, Editor-in-Chief; R.H.W. Bradshaw, Editor; D. Cantrill, Editor. **ISSN:** 0017-3134. **Subscription Rates:** US$516 individuals online only; US$544 institutions print & online; US$184 individuals; 329 institutions print & online; 313 institutions online; 111 individuals; EUR432 institutions print and online; EUR411 institutions online only; EUR147 individuals. **URL:** http://www.tandf.co.uk/journals/journal.asp?issn=0017-3134&linktype=5.

51020 ■ International Journal of Entrepreneurial Venturing
Inderscience Enterprises Limited
c/o Dr. Terrence E. Brown, Ed.-in-Ch.
Industrial Engineering & Management
Royal Institute of Technology (Sweden)
Lindstedtsvagen 30
S-100 44 Stockholm, Sweden
Journal featuring business and management focusing on entrepreneurial venturing. **Freq:** Quarterly. **Key Per-** sonnel: Dr. Terrence E. Brown, Editor-in-Chief, terrence@kth.se; Dr. Sascha Kraus, Editor-in-Chief, sascha.kraus@uni-liechtenstein.de. **ISSN:** 1742-5360. **Subscription Rates:** EUR494 individuals print or online; EUR672 individuals print and online. **URL:** http://www.inderscience.com/browse/index.php?journalCODE=ijev.

51021 ■ International Journal of Social and Humanistic Computing
Inderscience Enterprises Limited
c/o Ambjorn Naeve, Ed.-in-Ch.
Royal Institute of Technology
School of Computer Science & Communication
S-100 44 Stockholm, Sweden
Journal covering the study of social and humanistic computing. **Freq:** 4/yr. **Key Personnel:** Ambjorn Naeve, Editor-in-Chief, amb@nada.kth.se; Konstantina N. Zefkili, Managing Editor, k.zefkili@ucl.ac.uk. **ISSN:** 1752-6124. **Subscription Rates:** EUR494 individuals print or online; EUR672 individuals print and online. **URL:** http://www.inderscience.com/browse/index.php?journalID=225.

51022 ■ International Journal of Technology Enhanced Learning
Inderscience Enterprises Limited
c/o Ambjorn Naeve, Ed.-in-Ch.
Royal Institute of Technology
School of Computer Science & Communication
S-100 Stockholm, Sweden
Journal covering research on technology enhanced learning. **Freq:** 4/yr. **Key Personnel:** Ambjorn Naeve, Editor-in-Chief, amb@nada.kth.se; Konstantina N. Zefkili, Managing Editor, k.zefkili@ucl.ac.uk. **ISSN:** 1753-5255. **Subscription Rates:** EUR494 individuals print or online; EUR672 individuals print and online. **URL:** http://www.inderscience.com/browse/index.php?journalID=246.

51023 ■ Jamsides
JamO—Jamstalldhetsombudsmannen
Box 3397
SE-103 68 Stockholm, Sweden
Ph: 46 84401060
Fax: 46 8210047
Publisher E-mail: info@jamombud.se
Trade magazine covering labor issues for men and women. **Freq:** Quarterly. **Key Personnel:** Eva Nikell, Editor. **Subscription Rates:** Free. **Remarks:** Advertising not accepted. **URL:** http://www.jamombud.se/jamsides/. **Circ:** Combined 30,000

51024 ■ Kvinnotryck
National Organization of Battered Women's Shelters in Sweden
Riksorganisationen foer Kvinnojourer i Sverige
Hornsgatan 66
S-118 21 Stockholm, Sweden
Ph: 46 8 4429930
Fax: 46 8 6127325
Publication E-mail: prenumeration@kvinnotryck.se
Publisher E-mail: info@roks.se
Swedish publication covering domestic violence. **Freq:** 8/yr. **Key Personnel:** Lina Ploug, Contact, lina.ploug@roks.se. **Remarks:** Advertising not accepted. **URL:** http://www.roks.se. **Circ:** (Not Reported)

51025 ■ MEDSOLS
Swedish Anti-Nuclear Movement
Tegelviksgatan 40
SE-116 41 Stockholm, Sweden
Ph: 46 884 1490
Fax: 46 884 5181
Publisher E-mail: info@folkkampanjen.se
Swedish language publication covering current information nuclear energy. **Freq:** Quarterly. **Remarks:** Advertising not accepted. **URL:** http://www.folkkampanjen.se/. **Circ:** Paid 2,000

51026 ■ Microbial Ecology in Health and Disease
Taylor & Francis Ltd.
PO Box 3255
S-103 65 Stockholm, Sweden
Ph: 46 844 08040
Fax: 46 844 08050
Journal drawing together research on different human microbial eco-systems to increase our understanding of their role in health and disease, including such topics as: the microbial populations of the mouth and skin, and in the respiratory, gastro-intestinal and genito-urinary tracts; investigative methods; animal and in vitro models; the effect of antibiotics or diet on the commensal flora or

its development; alterations in the host environment (e.g. the effect of foreign bodies or change in organs and tissues; the role of immunological and other mechanisms that help maintain a stable flora) and the clinical application of commensal flora in treatment and prevention of disease. **Freq:** Quarterly. **Key Personnel:** Patricia Conway, Editorial Board; Prof. Tore Midtvedt, Editor-in-Chief; Ian Rowland, Editorial Board; X. Guo, Editorial Board; M.J. Hudson, Editorial Board; Michel Fons, Editorial Board; T. Mitsuoka, Editorial Board; Joseph Beuth, Editorial Board; R.J. Carman, Editorial Board. **ISSN:** 0891-060X. **Remarks:** Advertising accepted; rates available upon request. **URL:** http://www.informaworld.com/smpp/. **Circ:** (Not Reported)

51027 ■ Nordic Journal of Building Physics
Div. of Building Technology
Department of Civil and Arcitecural Engineering
c/o Prof. Per Levin, Ed.
Royal Institute of Technology
Brinellvagen 34
SE-100 44 Stockholm, Sweden
Publication E-mail: bphys@byv.kth.se
Journal publishing research articles in the field of building physics. Covers heat, air and moisture transfer with regard to buildings, building constructions and building components. Includes development of new building design based on building physics knowledge. **Key Personnel:** Prof. Per Levin, Editor; Johan Claesson, PhD, Editorial Board; Knud Brodersen, PhD, Editorial Board; Kjartan Gudmundsson, PhD, Assoc. Ed.; Bengt Svennerstedt, Editorial Board; Tormod Aurlien, PhD, Editorial Board; Prof. Claes Bankvall, Editorial Board; Prof. Lars Jenssen, Editorial Board; David Etheridge, Editorial Board. **ISSN:** 1402-5728. **URL:** http://www.byv.kth.se/avd/byte/bphys/.

51028 ■ Nordisk Fysioterapi
Swedish Association of Registered Physical Therapists
Legitmerade Sjukgymnasters Riksforbund
Vasagatan 48
PO Box 3196
S-103 63 Stockholm, Sweden
Ph: 46 8 56706100
Fax: 46 8 56706199
Publication E-mail: kansli@lsr.se
Publisher E-mail: kansli@lsr.se
Publication covering health care. **Freq:** Quarterly. **ISSN:** 1402-3024. **Subscription Rates:** US$95 individuals full set. **URL:** http://www.lsr.se.

51029 ■ Ny Framtid
Kristdemokratiska Ungdomsforbundet
Munkbron 1
PO Box 2373
SE-10318 Stockholm, Sweden
Ph: 46 87232530
Fax: 46 87232510
Publication E-mail: info@nyframtid.com
Publisher E-mail: info@kdu.se
Political, Christian, Democratic youth magazine for members. **Freq:** Semiannual. **Subscription Rates:** 60 SKr individuals. **Remarks:** Accepts advertising. **URL:** http://www.nyframtid.com/. **Circ:** (Not Reported)

51030 ■ Popular Astronomi
SCFAB
AlbaNova University Ctr.
Dept. of Astronomy
Roslagstullsbacken 21
S-106 91 Stockholm, Sweden
Ph: 46 855 378500
Fax: 46 855 378510
Swedish language publication covering astronomy. **Freq:** Quarterly. **Remarks:** Advertising accepted; rates available upon request. **URL:** http://www.astro.su.se/sas/english/english.html; http://www.popast.nu/. **Formerly:** Astronomisk Tidskrift (July 1, 2001). **Circ:** 1,300

51031 ■ QX
QX Forlag AB
PO Box 17 218
SE-104 62 Stockholm, Sweden
Ph: 46 8 7203001
Publisher E-mail: webred@qx.se
Consumer gay and lesbian magazine. **Founded:** 1995. **Freq:** Monthly. **Print Method:** Offset. **Trim Size:** Tabloid. **ISSN:** 1401-1794. **Remarks:** Accepts advertising. **URL:** http://www.qx.se/english/. **Ad Rates:** BW: 21,000 SKr,

4C: 25,500 SKr. **Circ:** Controlled 32,000

51032 ■ Scandinavia Now
PO Box 26174
S-100 41 Stockholm, Sweden
Ph: 46 867 83230
Fax: 46 861 12358
Publication E-mail: newsdesk@scandinavianow.com
Magazine covering business, industry, travel, and trade news in Scandinavia. **Founded:** 1996. **Key Personnel:** Everett M. Ellestad, Editor-in-Chief; Tord Elfwendahl, Publisher, info@scandinavianow.com. **ISSN:** 1402-1897. **Subscription Rates:** Free. **Remarks:** Accepts advertising. **URL:** http://www.scandinavianow.com. **Circ:** (Not Reported)

51033 ■ Scandinavian Actuarial Journal
Taylor & Francis Group Journals
c/o Boualem Djehiche, Ed.-in-Ch.
Department of Mathematics
KTH-Royal Institute of Technology
S-100 44 Stockholm, Sweden
Fax: 46 8 7231788
Publisher E-mail: customerservice@taylorandfrancis.com
Journal covering actuarial sciences focusing on theory and application with mathematical methods. **Founded:** 1918. **Freq:** Quarterly. **Key Personnel:** Walter Neuhaus, Editorial Board; Lasse Koskinen, Editorial Board; Boualem Djehiche, Editor-in-Chief; Mogens Steffensen, Editorial Board. **ISSN:** 0346-1238. **Subscription Rates:** 237 institutions print + online; US$391 institutions print + online; 226 institutions online; US$372 institutions online; 90 individuals; US$150 individuals; EUR312 institutions print and online; EUR296 institutions online only; EUR120 individuals. **URL:** http://www.tandf.co.uk/journals/titles/03461238.asp.

51034 ■ Scandinavian Cardiovascular Journal
Taylor & Francis Ltd.
PO Box 3255
S-103 65 Stockholm, Sweden
Ph: 46 8 4408040
Fax: 46 8 4408050
Journal providing a forum for the entire field of cardiovascular research, basic and clinical such as: thoracic surgery, transplantation, interventional and non-invasive cardiology and cardiovascular epidemiology. **Freq:** 6/yr. **Key Personnel:** Rolf Ekroth, Ch. Ed., rolf.ekroth@informa.com; Elisabeth Stahle, Assoc. Ed.; Knut Gjesdal, Editor, knut.gjesdal@medisin.uio.no. **ISSN:** 1401-7431. **Subscription Rates:** 325 institutions; US$540 institutions; EUR430 institutions. **Remarks:** Advertising accepted; rates available upon request. **URL:** http://www.informaworld.com/smpp/title~content=t713683216. **Circ:** (Not Reported)

51035 ■ Scandinavian Journal of Occupational Therapy
Taylor & Francis Ltd.
c/o Sofie Wennstrom
PO Box 3255
S-103 65 Stockholm, Sweden
Ph: 46 8 4408040
Fax: 46 8 4408050
Peer-reviewed journal encouraging scientific inquiry, providing a forum for research results in the field of occupational therapy and publishing original research articles from all branches of occupational therapy, written in English, and examined by referees. **Freq:** Quarterly. **Key Personnel:** Birgitta Bernspang, Editor-in-Chief; Snaefridur Egilson, Editor; Tiina Lautamo, Editor; Louise Nygard, Editor; Tina Helle, Editor; Ingvild Kjeken, Editor. **ISSN:** 1103-8128. **Subscription Rates:** 230 institutions; US$375 institutions; EUR300 institutions. **Remarks:** Advertising accepted; rates available upon request. **URL:** http://informahealthcare.com/occ. **Circ:** (Not Reported)

51036 ■ Seminars in Cancer Biology
Elsevier Science Inc.
c/o Eva Klein, Ed.
MTC Karolinska Institutet
Box 280
17177 Stockholm, Sweden
Publisher E-mail: usinfo-ehelp@elsevier.com
Journal covering the field of molecular oncology. **Founded:** Apr. 9, 1880. **Freq:** 6/yr. **Print Method:** Offset. **Trim Size:** 11 1/2 x 12 5/8. **Cols./Page:** 6. **Col. Width:** 9 picas. **Col. Depth:** 78 picas. **Key Personnel:** Eva Klein, Editor. **ISSN:** 1044-579X. **Subscription**

Rates: EUR776 institutions for European countries and Iran; 83,700¥ institutions; US$690 institutions, other countries except Europe, Japan and Iran; EUR223 individuals for European countries and Iran; 24,000¥ individuals; US$226 other countries except Europe, Japan and Iran. **URL:** http://www.elsevier.com/wps/find/journaldescription.cws_home/622943/descriptiondescription.

51037 ■ Signal Processing
Elsevier Science Inc.
c/o B. Ottersten, Ed.-in-Ch.
Royal Institute of Technology
Stockholm, Sweden
Publisher E-mail: usinfo-ehelp@elsevier.com
Peer-reviewed journal covering all aspects of the theory and practice of signal processing. **Subtitle:** An International Journal. **Founded:** 1989. **Freq:** 12/yr. **Key Personnel:** B. Ottersten, Editor-in-Chief, bjorn.ottersten@ee.kth.se; P. Abry, Editorial Board; A.K. Barros, Editorial Board. **ISSN:** 0165-1684. **Subscription Rates:** 447,000¥ institutions; EUR3,366 institutions for European countries and Iran; US$3,766 institutions, other countries except Europe, Japan and Iran. **URL:** http://www.elsevier.com/wps/find/journaldescription.cws_home/505662/description.

51038 ■ Sjukgymnasten
Swedish Association of Registered Physical Therapists
Legitmerade Sjukgymnasters Riksforbund
Vasagatan 48
PO Box 3196
S-103 63 Stockholm, Sweden
Ph: 46 8 56706100
Fax: 46 8 56706199
Publisher E-mail: kansli@lsr.se
Swedish language publication covering health care. **Freq:** Monthly. **ISSN:** 0037-6019. **Remarks:** Advertising accepted; rates available upon request. **URL:** http://www.lsr.se/. **Circ:** (Not Reported)

51039 ■ Social Politics
Oxford University Press
c/o Barbara Hobson, Ed.
Dept. of Sociology
Stockholm University
S-106 91 Stockholm, Sweden
Fax: 46 861 25580
Publisher E-mail: webenquiry.uk@oup.com
Journal examining political systems and cultural institutions through the lens of gender, addressing changes in family, state, market, and civil society, employing several disciplines and drawing from a variety of cultures to illuminate these areas of research. **Subtitle:** International Studies in Gender, State & Society. **Freq:** 4/yr. **Key Personnel:** Barbara Hobson, Editor, social.politics@sociology.su.se; Rianne Mahon, Editor, rmahon@ccs.carleton.ca; Fiona Williams, Editor, j.f.williams@leeds.ac.uk; Ann Shola Orloff, Editor, a-orloff@northwestern.edu; Deborah Brennan, Assoc. Ed.; Kyle Schafer, Managing Editor, socialpolitics@gmail.com; Wendy Larner, Assoc. Ed.; Ito Peng, Assoc. Ed.; Monique Kremer, Assoc. Ed. **ISSN:** 1072-4745. **Subscription Rates:** 174 institutions corporate; print and online; 145 institutions corporate; online only; 160 institutions corporate; print only; 139 institutions print and online; 116 institutions online only; 128 institutions print only; 50 individuals print; 20 students print; 35 members print. **Remarks:** Advertising accepted; rates available upon request. **URL:** http://sp.oxfordjournals.org/. **Circ:** (Not Reported)

51040 ■ Socionomen
Akademikerforbundet SSR
PO Box 12800
S-112 96 Stockholm, Sweden
Ph: 46 861 74400
Swedish language publication covering government employees. **Founded:** 1987. **Freq:** Bimonthly. **ISSN:** 0283-1929. **Remarks:** Advertising accepted; rates available upon request. **URL:** http://www.socionomen.nu/. **Circ:** 9,000

51041 ■ STFI Kontakt
Swedish Pulp and Paper Research Institute
STFI-Packforsk AB
Drottning Kristinas vag 61
SE-114 86 Stockholm, Sweden
Ph: 46 867 67000
Fax: 46 841 15518
Publisher E-mail: info@stfi.se
Trade magazine covering the pulp and paper industry.

Circulation: ★ = ABC; △ = BPA; ◆ = CAC; • = CCAB; ❑ = VAC; ⊕ = PO Statement; ‡ = Publisher's Report; Boldface figures = sworn; Light figures = estimated.

Gale Directory of Publications & Broadcast Media/147th Ed.   5473

Founded: 1969. **Print Method:** Offset. **URL:** http://www.stfi-packforsk.se/.

51042 ■ Tellus
John Wiley & Sons Inc.
Wiley-Blackwell
Tellus
Arrhenius Laboratory
S-10691 Stockholm, Sweden
Publication E-mail: tellusa@misu.su.se
Journal dealing with all aspects of dynamic meteorology, climatology and oceanography, in connection with Swedish Geophysical Society. **Subtitle:** Series A, Dynamic Meteorology and Oceanography. **Freq:** Bimonthly. **Key Personnel:** H. Lejenas, Editor-in-Chief; Branko Grisogono, Advisory Board; Eugenia Kalnay, Advisory Board; Brian Hoskins, Advisory Board; Leo Donner, Advisory Board; T.N. Krishnamurti, Advisory Board; Nils Gustafsson, Advisory Board; Huw Davies, Advisory Board; Lennart Bengtsson, Advisory Board; Philip Rasch, Advisory Board; Joseph Tribbia, Advisory Board. **ISSN:** 0280-6495. **Subscription Rates:** US$190 individuals print + online; EUR170 individuals print + online; 113 individuals print + online; US$181 individuals online only; EUR162 individuals online only; 108 other countries online only; US$294 individuals print + online (with Tellus B); EUR262 individuals print + online (with Tellus B); 174 individuals print + online (with Tellus B); US$378 institutions print + online. **URL:** http://www.wiley.com/bw/journal.asp?ref=0280-6495&site=1.

51043 ■ Tellus
John Wiley & Sons Inc.
Wiley-Blackwell
Tellus
Arrhenius Laboratory
S-10691 Stockholm, Sweden
Publication E-mail: tellusb@misu.su.se
Journal dealing with air chemistry, surface exchange processes, long-range and global transport, aerosol science and cloud physics, in connection with Swedish Geophysical Society. **Subtitle:** Series B, Chemical and Physical Meteorology. **Freq:** Bimonthly. **Key Personnel:** Barry Huebert, Advisory Board; H. Rodhe, Editor-in-Chief; Greg Ayers, Advisory Board; Paul Crutzen, Advisory Board; David Fowler, Advisory Board; Robert Charlson, Advisory Board; Sandro Fuzzi, Advisory Board; Pieter Tans, Advisory Board; Xiao-Ye Zhang, Advisory Board. **ISSN:** 0280-6509. **Subscription Rates:** US$190 individuals print and online; US$181 individuals online only; US$378 institutions print and online; EUR286 institutions print and online; US$344 institutions print or online; EUR170 individuals print and online; 113 other countries print and online; EUR162 individuals online only; EUR286 institutions print or online; US$443 institutions, other countries print and online. **URL:** http://www.wiley.com/bw/journal.asp?ref=0280-6509&site=1.

51044 ■ Vinyl-FM - 107.1
Gjorwellsgatan 30 (DN-Huset)
PO Box 34108
S-100 26 Stockholm, Sweden
Ph: 46 8 4503300
Fax: 46 8 222107
E-mail: info@vinyl107.se
Format: Music of Your Life. **Owner:** SBS Radio, at above address. **Key Personnel:** Hakan Morland, Prog. Chef, hakan.morland@sbsradio.se. **Ad Rates:** Advertising accepted; rates available upon request. **URL:** http://www.vinyl107.se.

Umea

51045 ■ Hemslojden
National Association of Swedish Handicraft Societies
Tidskriffen Hemslojden
Kungsgatan 51
SE-903 26 Umea, Sweden
Ph: 46 90 718302
Fax: 46 90 718305
Publisher E-mail: redaktionen@hemslojden.org
Consumer magazine covering traditional Swedish crafts, including woodworking and textiles. **Founded:** 1933. **Freq:** Bimonthly. **Print Method:** Sheet Offset. **Trim Size:** A4. **Key Personnel:** Celia Dackenberg, Editor-in-Chief, celia.dackenberg@hemslojden.org; Marianne Sundell, Subscriptions, phone 46 854549453, fax 46 854549457, prenumerationer@hemsljden.org. **ISSN:** 0345-4649. **Subscription Rates:** 297 SKr individuals Sweden; 387 SKr individuals Nordic countries; 497 SKr individuals elsewhere. **Remarks:** Accepts advertising. **URL:** http://

www.hemslojden.org/startsida.dsp. **Ad Rates:** BW: 13,050 SKr, 4C: 14,300 SKr. **Circ:** Paid 14,800

51046 ■ Journal of Forest Economics
Elsevier Science
c/o P. Gong, Ed.-in-Ch.
Swedish University of Agricultural Sciences
S-901 83 Umea, Sweden
Ph: 46 907 868250
Publisher E-mail: nlinfo-f@elsevier.com
Journal dealing with all aspects of forest economics. **Freq:** Quarterly. **Key Personnel:** Ola Carlen, Managing Editor, phone 46 907 868423, fax 46 907 868164; P. Gong, Editor-in-Chief, jfe@sekon.slu.se; S. Wibe, Editor-in-Chief. **ISSN:** 1104-6899. **Subscription Rates:** US$245 institutions all countries except Europe and Japan; 31,000¥ institutions; EUR212 institutions for European countries; US$71 individuals all countries except Europe and Japan; EUR76 individuals for European countries; 9,900¥ individuals; EUR57 students; 7,500¥ students; US$54 students. **Remarks:** Accepts advertising. **URL:** http://www.elsevier.com/wps/find/journaldescription.cws_home/701775/descriptiondescription. **Circ:** (Not Reported)

51047 ■ Scandinavian Journal of Public Health
Sage Publications Ltd.
Epidemiology & Public Health Sciences
Dept. of Public Health & Clinical Medicine
Umea University
S-901 85 Umea, Sweden
International forum for Nordic as well as international public health research and policy, seeking to foster and disseminate valid results from public health endeavors; contribute to the conceptual and methodological developments of public health in terms of its: efficacy, cost effectiveness and social, ethical and political implications; influence the current health research imbalance and give more priority to global health issues. **Freq:** 8/yr. **Key Personnel:** Finn Kamper-Jorgensen, Editor-in-Chief; Mathilde Vinther-Larsen, Co-Ed.; Morten Gronbek, Co-Ed.; Krisela Steyn, Co-Ed.; Charli Eriksson, Co-Ed.; Elina Hemminki, Co-Ed. **ISSN:** 1403-4948. **Subscription Rates:** US$726 institutions online only; US$791 individuals print only; US$807 institutions print & online; US$241 individuals print & online; US$109 institutions single, print; US$39 individuals single, print. **Remarks:** Advertising accepted; rates available upon request. **URL:** http://www.sagepub.com/journalsProdDesc.nav?prodId=Journal201871. **Circ:** (Not Reported)

51048 ■ TumorBiology
S. Karger Publishers Inc.
c/o Prof. Torgny Stigbrand, Ed.-in-Ch.
Umea University
Dept. of Immunology
85 Umea
S-901 85 Umea, Sweden
Fax: 46 90 7852250
Publisher E-mail: karger@snet.net
Journal on the basic biology of tumor markers—the crucial indicators of the onset of cancer. **Subtitle:** The Journal of the International Society for Oncodevelopmental Biology and Medicine. **Founded:** 1980. **Freq:** 6/yr. **Print Method:** Offset. **Trim Size:** 210 x 280 mm. **Key Personnel:** Prof. Torgny Stigbrand, Editor-in-Chief, torgny.stigbrand@climi.umu.se; Prof. Timothy J. O'Brien, Assoc. Ed., obrientimothyj@exchange.uams.edu. **ISSN:** 1010-4283. **Subscription Rates:** US$1,344 institutions print or online; EUR1,059 institutions print or online; 1,482 SFr institutions print or online; US$1,478 institutions print and online; EUR1,164 institutions print and online; 1,630 SFr institutions print and online. **Remarks:** Accepts advertising. **URL:** http://content.karger.com/ProdukteDB/produkte.asp?Aktion=JournalHome&ProduktNr=224124. **Former name:** Oncodevelopmental Biology and Medicine. **Ad Rates:** BW: 1,600 SKr. **Circ:** 1,000

Uppsala

51049 ■ Acta Zoologica
John Wiley & Sons Inc.
Wiley-Blackwell
Dept. of Development & Genetics
Uppsala University
Norbyvagen 18A
S-752 36 Uppsala, Sweden
Journal focusing on the field of animal organization, development, structure and function. **Subtitle:** Morphology and Evolution. **Founded:** 1920. **Freq:** Quarterly.

Key Personnel: Dr. Graham Budd, Editor-in-Chief; Geof Boxshall, Editorial Board; James Hanken, Editorial Board; Bruce S. Heming, Editorial Board; Michael C. Thorndyke, Reviews Ed.; Nicholas D. Holland, Editorial Board; Danny Eibye-Jacobsen, Editorial Board; Dr. Lennart Olsson, Ed.-in-Ch./Book Reviews Ed.; Brian Hall, Editorial Board; Mark Wilkinson, Editorial Board. **ISSN:** 0001-7272. **Subscription Rates:** US$127 individuals print and online; EUR102 individuals print and online (Euro zone); 68 individuals print and online (U.K. and non Euro zone); 76 other countries print and online; US$92 members print and online; EUR84 members print and online (Euro Zone); 56 members print and online (U.K. and non Euro Zone); 61 members print and online, rest of the world; US$1,304 institutions print and online; EUR897 institutions print and online (Euro Zone). **Remarks:** Accepts advertising. **URL:** http://www.wiley.com/bw/journal.asp?ref=0001-7272&site=1. **Circ:** (Not Reported)

51050 ■ Computer Methods and Programs in Biomedicine
Mosby Inc.
c/o T. Groth, Ed.
Dept. of Medical Sciences
Biomedical Informatics & Engineering
University Hospital
S-751 85 Uppsala, Sweden
Ph: 46 18 4712843
Fax: 46 18 4716609
Publisher E-mail: custserv.ehs@elsevier.com
Journal reporting on formal computing methods and their application in biomedical research. **Founded:** 1970. **Freq:** Monthly. **Key Personnel:** T. Groth, Editor, torgny.groth@medsci.uu.se; J. Fox, Editorial Board; G. Chase, Editorial Board; J. Li, Asia-Pacific Assoc. Ed., jack@tmu.edu.tw; E.R. Carson, Special Receiving Ed., e.r.carson@soi.city.ac.uk; M. Van Gils, European Assoc. Ed., phone 358 20 7223342, fax 358 20 7223380, mark.vangils@vtt.fi; E. Bengtsson, Editorial Board; R. Engelbrecht, Editorial Board; D. D'Argenio, Editorial Board; D. Feng, Editorial Board; L. Peterson, Editorial Board. **ISSN:** 0169-2607. **Subscription Rates:** US$398 other countries except Europe, Japan and Iran; 47,200¥ individuals; EUR357 individuals European Countries and Iran; EUR1,992 institutions European Countries and Iran; 264,500¥ institutions; US$2,226 institutions, other countries except Europe, Japan and Iran. **URL:** http://www.elsevier.com/wps/find/journaldescription.cws_home/505960/descriptiondescription.

51051 ■ Development Dialogue
Dag Hammarskjold Foundation
Ovre Slottsgatan 2
S-753 10 Uppsala, Sweden
Ph: 46 184 101000
Fax: 46 181 22072
Publisher E-mail: secretariat@dhf.uu.se
Publication covering worldwide development. **Founded:** 1972. **Freq:** Semiannual. **ISSN:** 0345-2328. **Subscription Rates:** Free other. **Remarks:** Advertising not accepted. **URL:** http://www.dhf.uu.se/publications/development-dialogue/. **Circ:** (Not Reported)

51052 ■ Upsala Journal of Medical Sciences
Taylor & Francis Ltd.
Dept. of Medical Cell Biology
Biomedical Center
PO Box 751
S-751 23 Uppsala, Sweden
Journal publishing clinical and experimental original works in the medical field. **Freq:** Quarterly. **Key Personnel:** Dr. Gunnar Ronquist, Editor-in-Chief; Dr. Claes Hellerstrom, Editor-in-Chief; Ove Axelsson, Editorial Board; Christian Berne, Editorial Board; Pia Ek, Editorial Board; Birgitta Jonzen, Managing Editor. **ISSN:** 0300-9734. **Subscription Rates:** 100 institutions; US$165 institutions; EUR132 institutions. **Remarks:** Advertising accepted; rates available upon request. **URL:** http://informahealthcare.com/ups. **Circ:** (Not Reported)

51053 ■ Var Foda
Livsmedelsverket
PO Box 622
SE-751 26 Uppsala, Sweden
Ph: 46 181 75500
Fax: 46 181 05848
Publisher E-mail: livsmedelsverket@slv.se
Trade magazine covering the food industry. **Founded:** 1949. **Cols./Page:** 3. **Col. Width:** 55 centimeters. **ISSN:** 0042-2657. **URL:** http://www.slv.se/templates/SLV_Page.aspx?id=10171&epslanguage=SV. **Circ:** Combined 5,000

Aarau

51054 ■ Fit for Life
AZ Fachverlage AG
Neumattstrasse 1
CH-5001 Aarau, Switzerland
Ph: 41 58 2005858
Fax: 41 58 2005644
Publication E-mail: info@fitforlife.ch
Professional magazine covering fitness and sports. **Subtitle:** Schweizer Fachmagazin fur den Ausdauersport. **Founded:** 1997. **Freq:** 10/yr. **Print Method:** Offset. **Trim Size:** 210 x 280 mm. **Cols./Page:** 6. **Key Personnel:** Andreas Gonseth, Editor-in-Chief; Peter Jauch, Production Mgr.; Regina Senften, Contact. **Remarks:** Accepts advertising. **URL:** http://www.fitforlife.ch/. **Ad Rates:** 4C: 5,100 SFr. **Circ:** Combined ‡25,000

51055 ■ MegaLink
AZ Fachverlage AG
Neumattstrasse 1
CH-5001 Aarau, Switzerland
Ph: 41 58 2005858
Fax: 41 58 2005644
Professional magazine covering electronics, information technology, communication and automation. **Subtitle:** HK, Electroteclinik, Gebandeleduik, Installateus, Sport-Magastiu, Fit for Life, Masuite. **Founded:** Jan. 1994. **Freq:** Monthly. **Print Method:** Offset. **Trim Size:** A4. **Key Personnel:** Rudolf Bolliger, Editor-in-Chief, heinz.radde@azag.ch; Patrick Muller, Chief Ed., patrick.muller@megalink.ch. **ISSN:** 1420-5667. **Subscription Rates:** 85 SFr individuals plus postage. **Remarks:** Accepts advertising. **URL:** http://www.megalink.ch. **Formerly:** Vreni Muilles. **Ad Rates:** BW: 3,275 SFr, 4C: 4,475 SFr, PCI: 900 SFr. **Circ:** 12,500

51056 ■ Radio Argovia-FM - 90.3
Bahnhofstrasse 41
CH-5001 Aarau, Switzerland
Ph: 41 58 2004545
Fax: 41 58 2004590
E-mail: sekretariat@argovia.ch
Format: Contemporary Hit Radio (CHR); Classic Rock. **Operating Hours:** Continuous. **URL:** http://www.argovia.ch/.

Baden

51057 ■ Wasser Energie Luft/Eau Energie Air
Schweizerische Wasserwirtschaftsverband
Rutistr. 3A
CH-5401 Baden, Switzerland
Ph: 41 562225069
Fax: 41 562211083
Publisher E-mail: r.pfammatter@swv.ch
Technical journal covering hydropower, water resources management and hydraulic constructions. **Founded:** 1916. **Freq:** Bimonthly. **Cols./Page:** 3. **Col. Width:** 58 millimeters. **Key Personnel:** Dr. Walter Hauenstein, Editor, w.hauenstein@swv.ch. **Subscription Rates:** 100 SFr individuals. **Remarks:** Accepts advertising. **URL:** http://www.swv.ch/de/fachzeitschrift.cfm. **Former name:** Wasser und Energiewirtschaft. **Circ:** (Not Reported)

Basel

51058 ■ Antike Kunst
Association of Friends of Classical Art
Vereinigung der Freunde Antiker Kunst
Schoenbeinstrasse 20
CH-4056 Basel, Switzerland
Publication E-mail: editor@antikekunst.ch
Publisher E-mail: publisher@antikekunst.ch
Publication covering the arts in English, French, German and Italian. **Freq:** Annual. **ISSN:** 0003-5688. **Remarks:** Advertising not accepted. **URL:** http://www.antikekunst.ch/index.php?option=com_content&view=category&layout=blog&id=36&Itemid=55&lang=en. **Circ:** 1,100

51059 ■ Archives of Gynecology and Obstetrics
Springer-Verlag Tokyo
Wartenbergstrasse 9
CH-4052 Basel, Switzerland
Publisher E-mail: info@springer.jp
Peer-reviewed journal covering all sub-specialties in gynecology and obstetrics. **Founded:** 1870. **Freq:** Bimonthly. **Key Personnel:** Prof. K. Diedrich, Coord. Ed.; Dr. R. Felberbaum, Editorial Board; Dr. H. Ludwig, Honorary Ed.; Dr. E. Sheiner, Editorial Board; Dr. P. Husslein, Editorial Board; Dr. K. Vetter, Editorial Board; C. Kurzeder, Advisory Board; Dr. W. Jonat, Editorial Board; Prof. R. Kreienberg, Editorial Board. **ISSN:** 0932-0067. **Subscription Rates:** EUR2,160 institutions print incl. free access or e-only; EUR2,592 institutions enhanced access. **Remarks:** Advertising accepted; rates available upon request. **URL:** http://www.springer.com/medicine/gynecology/journal/404. **Circ:** (Not Reported)

51060 ■ Bookbird
International Board on Books for Young People
Union Internationale pour les livres de jeunesse
Nonnenweg 12
CH-4003 Basel, Switzerland
Ph: 41 61 272 29 17
Fax: 41 61 272 27 57
Publisher E-mail: ibby@ibby.org
Refereed journal devoted to international children's literature. **Subtitle:** A Journal of International Children's Literature. **Founded:** 1963. **Freq:** Quarterly. **Trim Size:** 190 x 254 mm. **Key Personnel:** Catherine Kurkjian, Contact, kurkjianc@comcast.net; Sylvia Vardell, Contact, svardell@twu.edu. **ISSN:** 0006-7377. **Subscription Rates:** US$100 institutions USA; US$110.20 institutions Mexico; US$115.20 institutions, Canada; US$113.80 institutions, other countries; US$50 individuals USA; US$60.20 individuals Mexico; US$62.70 Canada; US$64.60 other countries; US$30 single issue institutional buyers; US$15 single issue. **Remarks:** Accepts advertising rates negotiable. **URL:** http://www.ibby.org/index.php?id=276. **Circ:** 1,500

51061 ■ Chromosoma
Springer-Verlag Tokyo
Biozentrum
University of Basel
Klingelbergstrasse 50/70
CH-4056 Basel, Switzerland
Fax: 41 61 2672009
Publication E-mail: chromosoma@unibas.ch
Publisher E-mail: info@springer.jp
Journal publishing research and review articles on the functional organization of the eukaryotic cell nucleus, with a particular emphasis on the structure and dynamics of chromatin and chromosomes, the expression and replication of genomes, genome organization and evolution, the segregation of genomes during meiosis and mitosis, the function and dynamics of sub-nuclear compartments and the nuclear envelope and nucleocytoplasmic interactions. **Freq:** Bimonthly. **Key Personnel:** Erich A. Nigg, Editor-in-Chief; Robin Allshire, Assoc. Ed.; Genevieve Almouzni, Assoc. Ed. **ISSN:** 0009-5915. **Subscription Rates:** EUR2,125 institutions print incl. free access or e-only; EUR2,550 institutions print incl. enhanced access. **Remarks:** Advertising accepted; rates available upon request. **URL:** http://www.springer.com/lifesci/cellbiology/journal/412. **Circ:** (Not Reported)

51062 ■ International Journal of Molecular Sciences
Molecular Diversity Preservation International
MDPI AG, Postfach
CH-4005 Basel, Switzerland
Ph: 41 61 6837734
Fax: 41 61 3028918
Publication E-mail: ijms@mdpi.org
Publisher E-mail: lin@mdpi.org
Journal providing an advanced forum for chemistry, molecular physics (chemical physics and physical chemistry) and molecular biology, publishing reviews, regular research papers and short notes. **Freq:** Monthly. **Key Personnel:** Dr. Claude A. Daul, Editor-in-Chief, phone 41 26 3008741, claude.daul@unifr.ch. **ISSN:** 1422-0067. **URL:** http://www.mdpi.com/journal/ijms.

51063 ■ Marine Drugs
Molecular Diversity Preservation International
Kandererstrasse 25
CH-4057 Basel, Switzerland
Ph: 41 793 223379
Fax: 41 613 028918
Publication E-mail: marinedrugs@mdpi.org
Publisher E-mail: lin@mdpi.org
Journal publishing reviews, regular research papers and short notes on the research, development and production of drugs from the sea, with the aim of publishing as much as possible the experimental detail, particularly synthetic procedures and characterization information for bioactive compounds. **Freq:** Quarterly. **Key Personnel:** Dr. Hua-Shi Guan, Honorary Ed.-in-Ch.; Dr. Jordan K. Zjawiony, Assoc. Ed., jordan@olemiss.edu; Dr. Nobuhiro Fusetani, Assoc. Ed., anobu@fish.hokudai.ac.jp; Dr. Peter Proksch, Editor-in-Chief, proksch@uni-duesseldorf.de. **ISSN:** 1660-3397. **URL:** http://www.mdpi.com/journal/marinedrugs.

51064 ■ Merum
Merumpress AG
Verlag und Agentur fur italienische Lebensfreuden
Thiersteinerallee 17
Postfach
CH-4018 Basel, Switzerland
Publisher E-mail: redaktion@merum.info
Trade magazine covering food and wine. **Subtitle:** Die Zeitschrift fur Wein und Olivenol aus Italien. **Founded:** Oct. 1994. **Freq:** Bimonthly. **Print Method:** Offset. **Trim**

Size: 210 x 297. **Key Personnel:** Andreas Marz, Editor-in-Chief, am@merum.info; Jean Pierre Ritler, Manager, jpr@merum.info; Christina Dubbers, Contact, du@merum.info; Markus Blaser, Contact, mb@merum.info. **URL:** http://www.merum.info/. **Ad Rates:** BW: 2,700 SFr, 4C: 3,950 SFr. **Circ:** (Not Reported)

51065 ■ Progress in Histochemistry and Cytochemistry
Elsevier Science
c/o Dieter Sasse, Mng. Ed.
Institute of Anatomy, University of Basel
Pestalozzistrasse 20
CH-4056 Basel, Switzerland
Ph: 41 612 673921
Fax: 41 612 673959
Publisher E-mail: nlinfo-f@elsevier.com
Journal dealing with all aspects of histochemistry and cytochemistry. **Freq:** Quarterly. **Key Personnel:** Dieter Sasse, Managing Editor, dieter.sasse@unibas.ch; U. Schumacher, Managing Editor, phone 49 404 28033586, fax 49 404 28035427, uschumac@uke.uni-hamburg.de; M. Bendayan, Editor. **ISSN:** 0079-6336. **Subscription Rates:** US$520 institutions all countries except Europe and Japan; 70,500¥ institutions; EUR583 institutions for European countries; EUR97 individuals for European countries; 12,700¥ individuals; US$116 individuals all countries except Europe and Japan; EUR72 students for European countries; 9,600¥ students; US$87 students all countries except Europe and Japan. **URL:** http://www.elsevier.com/wps/find/journaldescription.cws_home/701795/description.

51066 ■ Radio X-FM - 94.5
Spitalstrasse 2
CH-4056 Basel, Switzerland
Ph: 41 61 2612122
Fax: 41 61 2612126
E-mail: rx@radiox.ch
Format: Eclectic. **Key Personnel:** Thomas Jenny, Contact. **URL:** http://www.radiox.ch.

Bassersdorf

51067 ■ Seed Science and Technology
International Seed Testing Association
Association Internationale d'Essais de Semences
Zurichstrasse 50
CH-8303 Bassersdorf, Switzerland
Ph: 41 183 86000
Fax: 41 183 86001
Publisher E-mail: ista.office@ista.ch
Publication covering seed technology. **Founded:** 1973. **Freq:** 3/yr. **Key Personnel:** Alison A. Powell, Ch. Ed. **ISSN:** 0251-0952. **Subscription Rates:** 442 SFr individuals print; 386 SFr individuals online; 1,349 SFr institutions online; 489 SFr individuals online and print; 1,710 SFr institutions online and print. **URL:** http://www.seedtest.org/en/home.html.

51068 ■ Radio LoRa-FM - 104.95 MHz
Militarstrasse 85a
8004 Zurich, Switzerland
Ph: 41 1 445672400
Fax: 41 1 445672417
E-mail: lora@lora.ch
Format: Full Service. **URL:** http://www.lora.ch/.

Bern

51069 ■ Amnestie
Amnesty International - AI Swiss Section
PO Box 3001
CH 3001 Bern, Switzerland
Ph: 41 313 072222
Fax: 41 313 072233
Publisher E-mail: info@amnesty.ch
German and French language publication covering human rights. **Subtitle:** Magazine for Human Rights. **Key Personnel:** Claudio Cordone, Senior Dir.; Irene Khan, Sec. Gen. **URL:** http://www.amnesty.ch. **Circ:** 22,000

51070 ■ Chimia
Swiss Chemical Society
Schweizerische Chemische Gesellschaft
c/o Philippe Renaud, Ed.-in-Ch.
Departement fur Chemie und Biochemie
Universitat Bern
Freiestrasse 3
CH-3000 Bern, Switzerland
Ph: 41 31 6314359

Fax: 41 31 6313426
Publisher E-mail: info@scg.ch
English and German publication covering chemistry. **Founded:** 1946. **Freq:** 10/yr. **Key Personnel:** Dr. Gillian Harvey, Tech. Ed., phone 41 442 626525, fax 41 442 626525, chimia.tr@bluewin.ch; Martin P. Brandle, Editorial Board, braendle@chem.ethz.ch; Martin Gadermann, Editorial Board, karl.gademann@epfl.ch; Dr. Roland W. Kunz, Asst. Ed., kunz@oci.uzh.ch; Philippe Renaud, Editor-in-Chief, philippe.renaud@chimia.ch. **ISSN:** 0009-4293. **Subscription Rates:** US$42 single issue electronic, via Ingenta; 220 SFr nonmembers Switzerland; 270 SFr nonmembers other Countries; 500 SFr institutions; US$35 single issue; US$35 single issue mail charge inclusive other Countries; US$25 single issue electronic, via Ingenta. **Remarks:** Advertising accepted; rates available upon request. **URL:** http://www.chimia.ch/. **Circ:** (Not Reported)

51071 ■ Die Alpen
Schweizer Alpen-Club
3000 Berne 23
Bern, Switzerland
Ph: 41 313 701818
Fax: 41 313 701800
Publisher E-mail: info@sac-cas.ch
Consumer magazine covering mountain climbing for club members. **Freq:** Monthly. **Key Personnel:** Gross Etienne, Editor-in-Chief. **ISSN:** 0002-6336. **Subscription Rates:** 24 Eg individuals for Germany. **Remarks:** Accepts advertising. **URL:** http://www.sac-cas.ch/. **Circ:** Controlled 83,000

51072 ■ Ernahrungs Info
Swiss Dietetic Association
Schweizerischer Verband Diplomierter Ernanrungsberaterinnen
Postgasse 17
Postfach 686
CH-3000 Bern, Switzerland
Ph: 41 31 3138870
Fax: 41 31 3138899
Publisher E-mail: service@svde-asdd.ch
Publication covering nutrition, in French, German and Italian. **Freq:** Bimonthly. **Remarks:** Advertising accepted; rates available upon request. **URL:** http://www.svde.ch/de/. **Circ:** (Not Reported)

51073 ■ Helvetica Chimica Acta
Swiss Chemical Society
Schweizerische Chemische Gesellschaft
Schwarztorstrasse 9
CH-3007 Bern, Switzerland
Ph: 41 313 104090
Fax: 41 313 104029
Publisher E-mail: info@scg.ch
English, French and German publication covering chemistry. **Freq:** Monthly. **ISSN:** 0018-019X. **Subscription Rates:** 2,990 SFr institutions print only (in SFR); 3,289 SFr institutions print & e-access (in SFR); 2,990 SFr institutions e-access only (in SFR). **Remarks:** Advertising accepted; rates available upon request. **URL:** http://www.vhca.ch/journals.htm. **Circ:** (Not Reported)

51074 ■ International Journal of Public Health
Springer Netherlands
Anke Berger, Mng. Ed.
Dept. of Social & Preventive Medicine
University of Bern
CH-3012 Bern, Switzerland
Ph: 41 31 6313512
Fax: 41 31 6313430
Publisher E-mail: permissions.dordrecht@springer.com
Journal focusing on health survey research. **Freq:** 6/yr. **Print Method:** Offset. Uses mats. **Cols./Page:** 6. **Col. Width:** 25 nonpareils. **Col. Depth:** 294 agate lines. **Key Personnel:** Petra Kolip, Assoc. Ed.; Louise Potvin, Assoc. Ed.; Salvatore Panico, Assoc. Ed.; Nino Kunzli, Assoc. Ed.; Thomas Kohlmann, Editor-in-Chief; David V. McQueen, Assoc. Ed.; Herman Van Oyen, Assoc. Ed.; Anke Berger, Managing Editor, ijph@ispm.unibe.ch; Thomas Abel, Editor-in-Chief. **ISSN:** 1661-8556. **Subscription Rates:** EUR525 institutions print incl. free access or e-only; EUR630 institutions print incl. enhanced access. **URL:** http://www.springer.com/birkhauser/biosciences/journal/38?detailsPage=description. **Formerly:** Sozial-und Praventivmedizin SPM.

51075 ■ Kunst & Architektur in der Schweiz
GSK

Pavillonweg 2
CH-3012 Bern, Switzerland
Ph: 41 31 3083838
Fax: 41 31 3016991
Publisher E-mail: gsk@gsk.ch
Professional journal covering art and architecture. **Freq:** Quarterly. **ISSN:** 1421-086X. **Remarks:** Accepts advertising. **URL:** http://www.gsk.ch/. **Circ:** 7,200

51076 ■ Multilingua
Mouton de Gruyter
c/o Prof. Richard J. Watts, Ed.
Englisches Seminar
Universitat Bern
Langgass-Strabe 49
CH-3000 Bern 0009, Switzerland
Publisher E-mail: info@degruyter.de
Peer-reviewed journal focusing on the development of cross-cultural understanding through the study of interlanguage communication. **Subtitle:** Journal of Cross-Cultural and Interlanguage Communication. **Freq:** Quarterly. **Key Personnel:** Prof. Richard J. Watts, Editor, watts@ens.unibe.ch. **ISSN:** 0167-8507. **Subscription Rates:** EUR237 individuals print or online; EUR273 individuals print + online. **URL:** http://www.degruyter.de/journals/multilin. **Ad Rates:** BW: 400 SFr. **Circ:** (Not Reported)

51077 ■ Space Research Today
Elsevier Science Inc.
c/o R.M. Bonnet, Pres. of COSPAR
International Space Science Institute
6 Hallerstrasse
03012 Bern, Switzerland
Publisher E-mail: usinfo-ehelp@elsevier.com
Journal featuring space research. **Founded:** 2007. **Freq:** 3/yr. **Print Method:** Offset. **Trim Size:** 13 3/4 x 21 1/2. **Cols./Page:** 6. **Col. Width:** 5 nonpareils. **Col. Depth:** 21 1/2 inches. **Key Personnel:** R.A. Harrison, Gen. Ed., r.harrison@rl.ac.uk; R.M. Bonnet, Pres. of COSPAR; C.R. Argent, Exec. Ed. **ISSN:** 1752-9298. **Subscription Rates:** EUR419 institutions European countries and Iran; 55,600¥ institutions; US$468 institutions all countries except Europe, Japan and Iran. **URL:** http://www.elsevier.com/wps/find/journaldescription.cws_home/712950/descrip tiondescription. **Formerly:** COSPAR's Information Bulletin.

51078 ■ SVPja
SVP Generalsekretariat
Bruckfeldstr. 18
Postfach 8252
CH-3001 Bern 26, Switzerland
Ph: 41 313 005858
Fax: 41 313 005859
Publication E-mail: klartext@svp.ch
Publisher E-mail: gs@svp.ch
Political periodical. **Freq:** Monthly. **Print Method:** Offset. **Trim Size:** 235 x 320 mm. **Cols./Page:** 4. **Col. Width:** 49 millimeters. **Remarks:** Accepts advertising. **URL:** http://www.svp.ch/. **Circ:** (Not Reported)

51079 ■ Radio BE1-FM - 101.7
Optingenstrasse 56
Postfach 7624
CH-7624 Bern, Switzerland
Ph: 41 31 3405050
Fax: 41 31 3405055
E-mail: kontakt@radiobe1.ch
Format: Ethnic; World Beat. **Operating Hours:** 13 hours Daily. **URL:** http://www.be1.ch.

51080 ■ Radio Swiss Classic-FM - 87.6
Giacomettistrasse 1
PO Box 3000
CH-3930 Bern, Switzerland
Ph: 41 31 3509333
Fax: 41 31 3509663
Format: Ethnic; World Beat. **Operating Hours:** Continuous. **Key Personnel:** Pietro Ribi, Mng. Dir.; Andre Scheurer, Music Dir. **URL:** http://www.swissclassic.ch.

Binz

51081 ■ CSI Magazine
Christian Solidarity International
Zelglistr 64
PO Box 70
CH-8122 Binz, Switzerland
Ph: 41 449 823333
Fax: 41 449 823334

Publisher E-mail: info@csi-int.org
Magazine covering religious freedom in Czech, English, French, German, Hungarian and Italian. **Freq:** Monthly. **URL:** http://csi-cr.cz.

Birmensdorf

51082 ■ Dendrochronologia
Elsevier Science Inc.
c/o Paolo Cherubini, Ed.-in-Ch.
WSL Swiss Federal Research Institute
Birmensdorf, Switzerland
Publisher E-mail: usinfo-ehelp@elsevier.com
Journal covering tree-ring research. **Founded:** 1983. **Freq:** 4/yr. **Print Method:** Offset. **Cols./Page:** 6. **Col. Width:** 24 nonpareils. **Col. Depth:** 126 agate lines. **Key Personnel:** Rosanne D'Arrigo, Assoc. Ed.; Leone Fasani, Founding Ed.; Hans Beeckman, Assoc. Ed.; Andre Billamboz, Assoc. Ed.; Keith Briffa, Assoc. Ed.; Henri D. Grissino-Mayer, Assoc. Ed.; Osamu Kobayashi, Assoc. Ed.; Cornelia Krause, Assoc. Ed.; Bernd Kromer, Assoc. Ed.; Paolo Cherubini, Editor-in-Chief. **ISSN:** 1125-7865. **Subscription Rates:** US$291 institutions, other countries except Europe, Japan and Iran; EUR233 institutions European countries and Iran; 33,400¥ institutions; US$161 other countries except Europe, Japan and Iran; 21,100¥ individuals; EUR159 individuals European countries and Iran. **URL:** http://www.elsevier.com/wps/find/journaldescription.cws_home/701757/descriptiondescription.

Buchs

51083 ■ Radio RI-FM - 99.1
Postfach 664
Bahnhofstrasse 14
CH-9471 Buchs, Switzerland
Ph: 41 81 7500302
Fax: 41 81 7500304
E-mail: redaktion@radiori.ch
Format: Sports. **Owner:** Radio Ri, at above address. **Operating Hours:** Continuous. **URL:** http://radiori-ch.site-preview.net.

Delemont

51084 ■ RFJ-FM - 96
Rue du 23 juin 20
CH-2800 Delemont, Switzerland
Ph: 41 32 4217040
Fax: 41 32 4217027
E-mail: redaction@rfj.ch
Format: Ethnic; Talk; World Beat. **Key Personnel:** Pierre Steulet, President; Stephane Duriez, Contact. **Ad Rates:** Advertising accepted; rates available upon request. **URL:** http://www.rfj.ch.

Dornach

51085 ■ Das Goetheanum
Wochenschrift fuer Anthroposophie
In den Zielbaumen 7
Postfach
CH-4143 Dornach 1, Switzerland
Ph: 41 617 064464
Fax: 41 617 064465
Publication E-mail: info@dasgoetheanum.ch
Publisher E-mail: info@dasgoetheanum.ch
Journal covering spirituality and topical events from an anthroposophical perspective. **Subtitle:** Wochenschrift fuer Anthroposophie. **Founded:** 1921. **Freq:** Weekly. **Print Method:** Offset. **Key Personnel:** Sebastian Jungel, Editor, sebastian.juengel@goetheanum.ch; Michaela Spaar, Editor, michaela.spaar@goetheanum.ch; Ursula Remund Fink, Editor; Axel Mannigel, Editor, axel.mannigel@goetheanum.ch. **ISSN:** 1422-7622. **Remarks:** Accepts advertising. **URL:** http://www.dasgoetheanum.ch. **Ad Rates:** BW: 2,050 SFr. **Circ:** Paid 10,246

Einsiedeln

51086 ■ Schweizer Jager
Verlag Schweizer Jager
Postfach 261
CH-8840 Einsiedeln, Switzerland
Ph: 41 55 4184343
Fax: 41 55 4184344

Publisher E-mail: kontakt@schweizerjaeger.ch
Trade magazine covering hunting. **Founded:** 1916. **Freq:** Monthly. **Print Method:** Offset. **Key Personnel:** Kurt Gansner, Contact, redaktion@schweizerjaeger.ch. **ISSN:** 0036-8016. **Remarks:** Accepts advertising. **URL:** http://www.schweizerjaeger.ch/. **Circ:** (Not Reported)

Fribourg

51087 ■ Universitas Friburgensis
Universite de Fribourg
Av. Europe 20
CH-1700 Fribourg, Switzerland
Ph: 41 26 3007111
Fax: 41 26 3009700
Publisher E-mail: webmaster@unifr.ch
College magazine for students. **Freq:** Quarterly. **Print Method:** Offset. **Trim Size:** 182 x 269 mm. **Cols./Page:** 3. **Col. Width:** 210 millimeters. **Col. Depth:** 297 millimeters. **Remarks:** Accepts advertising. **URL:** http://www.unifr.ch/alumni/fr/prestation/uf. **Circ:** 9,500

Geneva

51088 ■ The Botulinum Journal
Inderscience Enterprises Limited
World Trade Center Bldg. II
29, Rte. de Pre-Bois
Case Postale 896
CH-1215 Geneva 15, Switzerland
Ph: 41 1234 240515
Fax: 41 22 7910885
Journal covering the study on Botulinum neurotoxins and related fields. **Freq:** 4/yr. **Key Personnel:** Prof. Bal Ram Singh, Editor-in-Chief, tbj@umassd.edu; Michael Adler, Assoc. Ed. **ISSN:** 1754-7318. **Subscription Rates:** EUR494 individuals print or online; EUR672 individuals print and online. **URL:** http://www.inderscience.com/browse/index.php?journalID=262.

51089 ■ Bulletin of the World Health Organization
World Health Organization
20 Appia Ave.
CH-1211 Geneva 27, Switzerland
Ph: 41 22 7912111
Fax: 41 22 7913111
Publication E-mail: bulletin@who.int
Publisher E-mail: info@who.int
Health publication. **Subtitle:** International Journal of Public Health. **Founded:** 1948. **Freq:** Monthly. **Print Method:** Offset. **Trim Size:** A4. **Key Personnel:** Ian G. Neil, Editor; Hooman Momen, Editor; Melanie Lauckner, Production Asst.; Adetokunbo O. Lucas, Editorial Board; Peter G. Smith, Editorial Board; Laragh Gollogly, Managing Editor. **ISSN:** 0042-9686. **Subscription Rates:** 331 SFr individuals economy mail; 339 SFr individuals priority mail. **Remarks:** Advertising not accepted. **URL:** http://www.who.int/bulletin/en/; http://www.who.int/bookorders/anglais/subscription1.jsp?sesslan=1; http://www.scielosp.org. **Circ:** 6,000

51090 ■ Computer Graphics Forum Journal
EUROGRAPHICS Association
Ave. Frontenex 32
CH-1207 Geneva, Switzerland
Publisher E-mail: secretary@eg.org
Journal covering computer graphics. **Subtitle:** The International Journal of the Eurographics Association. **Founded:** 1981. **Freq:** 8/yr. **Print Method:** Print and Electronic. **Key Personnel:** Eduard Groller, Editor; Roberto Scopigno, Editor. **ISSN:** 0167-7055. **Subscription Rates:** US$1,632 institutions America online only; US$1906 institutions, other countries; 622 institutions online only; 789 institutions Europe, online only. **URL:** http://www.eg.org/EG/Publications/CGF. **Circ:** Paid ‡844

51091 ■ The Ecumenical Review
World Council of Churches
150 Rte. de Ferney
PO Box 2100
CH-1211 Geneva 2, Switzerland
Ph: 41 227 916111
Fax: 41 227 910361
Publisher E-mail: infowcc@wcc-coe.org
Publication covering philosophy and religion. **Founded:** 1948. **Freq:** Quarterly. **Print Method:** Offset. **Trim Size:** 16 x 24. **ISSN:** 0013-0796. **Subscription Rates:** 52 SFr individuals; US$38 individuals; 24 individuals; EUR38

individuals. **Remarks:** Accepts advertising. **URL:** http://www.wcc-coe.org/wcc/news/ec-rev.html. **Ad Rates:** BW: 395 SFr. **Circ:** Paid ‡2,000

51092 ■ Europa Star
VNU Business Media S.A.
Rte. des Acacias 25
PO Box 1355
CH-1211 Geneva 26, Switzerland
Ph: 41 22 3077837
Fax: 41 22 3003748
Trade magazine for watch professionals worldwide. **Subtitle:** The World's Leading Watch Magazine. **Founded:** 1927. **Freq:** Bimonthly. **Print Method:** Offset. **Trim Size:** 205 x 265 mm. **Key Personnel:** Sophie Furley, Managing Editor, sfurley@europastar.com; Catherine Giloux, Business Mgr., cgiloux@europastar.com; Alexandra Montandon, Credit Mgr., amontandon@europastar.com; Chris Casey, Gp. Publishing Dir., ccasey@couturejeweler.com; Pierre M. Maillard, Editor-in-Chief, pmaillard@europastar.com; Casey Bayandor, Contact, cbayandor@europastar.com; Philippe Maillard, Mng. Dir., phmaillard@europastar.com. **Subscription Rates:** 100 SFr individuals by surface mail; US$85 individuals by surface mail; EUR65 individuals by surface mail; 140 SFr out of country by airmail, international; US$115 out of country by airmail, international; EUR95 out of country by airmail, international; 180 SFr individuals by surface mail, for two year; US$150 two years by surface mail; EUR110 two years by surface mail; 270 SFr two years by airmail, international. **Remarks:** Accepts advertising. **URL:** http://www.europastar.com/europastar/index.jsp. **Ad Rates:** 4C: 7,500 SFr. **Circ:** Combined △10,000

51093 ■ Europa Star
Nielsen Business Media
25 route des Acacias
PO Box 1355
Geneva, Switzerland
Ph: 41 22 3077837
Fax: 41 22 3003748
Bimonthly magazine covering the European watch market, including production, distribution, marketing, communication, latest products and collections, brand development, and the state of the markets. **Founded:** 1927. **Freq:** 6/yr. **Key Personnel:** Philippe Maillard, Mng. Dir., phmaillard@europastar.com; Pierre M. Maillard, Editor-in-Chief, pmaillard@europastar.com. **Subscription Rates:** 100 SFr individuals by surface mail, Europe; US$180 two years by surface mail, Europe; 140 SFr individuals by airmail, outside Europe; 270 SFr individuals by airmail, outside Europe. **Remarks:** Accepts advertising. **URL:** http://www.europastar.com/europastar/index.jsp. **Circ:** (Not Reported)

51094 ■ Europa Star International
Nielsen Business Media
25 route des Acacias
PO Box 1355
Geneva, Switzerland
Ph: 41 22 3077837
Fax: 41 22 3003748
Magazine of the watch industry for distributors in the principal international markets and key retailers in each market. **Freq:** 6/yr. **Key Personnel:** Philippe Maillard, Mng. Dir., phmaillard@europastar.com; Pierre M. Maillard, Editor-in-Chief, pmaillard@europastar.com. **Subscription Rates:** 100 SFr individuals by surface mail, Europe; US$180 two years by surface mail, Europe; 140 SFr individuals by airmail, outside Europe; 270 SFr individuals by airmail, outside Europe. **Remarks:** Accepts advertising. **URL:** http://www.europastar.com/europastar/about_us/index.jsp. **Circ:** 10,000

51095 ■ European Journal of Pharmaceutics and Biopharmaceutics
Elsevier Science Inc.
c/o R. Gurny, Ed.-in-Ch.
School of Pharmaceutical Sciences
University of Geneva
30 Quai E.-Ansermet
CH-1211 Geneva, Switzerland
Publisher E-mail: usinfo-ehelp@elsevier.com
Peer-reviewed journal covering pharmaceutical technology and biopharmaceutical technology. **Founded:** 1997. **Freq:** 9/yr. **Print Method:** Offset. **Cols./Page:** 6. **Col. Width:** 24 nonpareils. **Col. Depth:** 294 agate lines. **Key Personnel:** R. Gurny, Editor-in-Chief, ejpb@unige.ch; A. Gopferich, Editor; K. Mader, Editor; G. Lee, Editor; C.M. Lehr, Editor; J.C. Leroux, Editor; J.W. McGinity,

Circulation: ★ = ABC; △ = BPA; ◆ = CAC; • = CCAB; ❑ = VAC; ⊕ = PO Statement; ‡ = Publisher's Report; Boldface figures = sworn; Light figures = estimated.

Gale Directory of Publications & Broadcast Media/147th Ed.

5477

Editor; M. Moller, Assoc. Ed.; E. Allemann, Editorial Board; J.M. Anderson, Editorial Board. **ISSN:** 0939-6411. **Subscription Rates:** US$1,141 institutions, other countries except Europe, Japan and Iran; EUR1,016 institutions for European countries & Iran; 135,000¥ institutions; 34,400¥ individuals; EUR223 individuals for European countries & Iran; US$300 individuals except Europe, Japan and Iran. **URL:** http://www.elsevier.com/wps/find/journaldescription.cws_home/600120/descriptiondescription.

51096 ■ Geneva Risk and Insurance Review
International Association for the Study of Insurance Economics
Association Internationale pour l'Etude de l'Economie de l'Assurance
53 Rte. de Malagnou
CH-1208 Geneva, Switzerland
Ph: 41 227 076600
Fax: 41 227 367536
Publisher E-mail: secretariat@genevaassociation.org
Insurance publication. **Freq:** Semiannual. **Key Personnel:** Mark J. Machina, Assoc. Ed.; Christian Gollier, Assoc. Ed.; Keith J. Crocker, Editor. **ISSN:** 1554-964X. **Subscription Rates:** EUR488 institutions print; 342 institutions, other countries print; US$579 institutions print. **URL:** http://www.genevaassociation.org. **Formerly:** Geneva Papers on Risk and Insurance Theory. **Circ:** 800

51097 ■ Geneve Home Informations
Edipresse Publications S.A.
22, Ave. du Mail
Case postale 167
CH-1211 Geneva 4, Switzerland
Ph: 41 22 8072211
Fax: 41 22 8072233
Publication E-mail: info@ghi.ch
Publisher E-mail: groupe@edipresse.com
Newspaper containing classified section and local news in Geneva. **Freq:** Weekly. **Key Personnel:** Jean-Marc Velleman, Director; Charles-Andre Aymon, Ch. Ed. **URL:** http://www.ghi.ch/live/1/home/.

51098 ■ IB World
International Baccalaureate Organization
Organisation du Baccalaureat International
Rte. des Morillons 15
CH-1218 Geneva, Switzerland
Ph: 41 22 791 7740
Fax: 41 22 791 0277
Publisher E-mail: ibhq@ibo.org
Publication covering higher education in English, French and Spanish. **Founded:** 1992. **Freq:** 3/yr. **Print Method:** Rotary. **Trim Size:** A4. **ISSN:** 1560-5795. **Subscription Rates:** US$29 payable by credit card. **URL:** http://www.ibo.org/ibworld/. **Circ:** 10,000

51099 ■ Interdisciplinary Environmental Review
Inderscience Enterprises Limited
World Trade Center Bldg. II
29, Rte. de Pre-Bois
Case Postale 896
CH-1215 Geneva 15, Switzerland
Ph: 41 1234 240515
Fax: 41 22 7910885
Journal covering the field of interdisciplinary environmental science. **Freq:** 4/yr. **Key Personnel:** Demetri Kantarelis, Interim Ed.-in-Ch. **ISSN:** 1521-0227. **Subscription Rates:** EUR494 individuals print or online; EUR672 individuals print and online. **URL:** http://www.inderscience.com/browse/index.php?journalID=363.

51100 ■ International Journal of Applied Decision Sciences
Inderscience Enterprises Limited
World Trade Center Bldg. II
29, Rte. de Pre-Bois
Case Postale 896
CH-1215 Geneva 15, Switzerland
Ph: 41 1234 240515
Fax: 41 22 7910885
Peer-reviewed journal focusing on the infusion of the functional and behavioral areas of business with the concepts and methodologies of the decision sciences and information systems. **Freq:** 4/yr. **Key Personnel:** Dr. Madjid Tavana, Editor-in-Chief, tavana@lasalle.edu. **ISSN:** 1755-8077. **Subscription Rates:** EUR494 individuals print or online; EUR672 individuals print and online. **URL:** http://www.inderscience.com/browse/index.php?journalID=283.

51101 ■ International Journal of Applied Management Science
Inderscience Enterprises Limited
World Trade Center Bldg. II
29, Rte. de Pre-Bois
Case Postale 896
CH-1215 Geneva 15, Switzerland
Ph: 41 1234 240515
Fax: 41 22 7910885
Journal covering the field of management science. **Freq:** 4/yr. **Key Personnel:** John Wang, Editor-in-Chief, j.john.wang@gmail.com. **ISSN:** 1755-8913. **Subscription Rates:** EUR494 individuals print or online; EUR672 individuals print and online. **URL:** http://www.inderscience.com/browse/index.php?journalID=286.

51102 ■ International Journal of Applied Nonlinear Science
Inderscience Enterprises Limited
World Trade Center Bldg. II
29, Rte. de Pre-Bois
Case Postale 896
CH-1215 Geneva 15, Switzerland
Ph: 41 1234 240515
Fax: 41 22 7910885
Peer-reviewed journal covering the research work on applied nonlinear science and numerical calculations. **Freq:** 4/yr. **ISSN:** 1752-2862. **Subscription Rates:** EUR494 individuals print or online; EUR672 individuals print and online. **URL:** http://www.inderscience.com/browse/index.php?journalID=221.

51103 ■ International Journal of Auditing Technology
Inderscience Enterprises Limited
World Trade Center Bldg. II
29, Rte. de Pre-Bois
Case Postale 896
CH-1215 Geneva 15, Switzerland
Ph: 41 1234 240515
Fax: 41 22 7910885
Journal focusing exclusively on the rapidly evolving area of auditing technology. **Freq:** Quarterly. **Key Personnel:** Dr. M.A. Dorgham, Editor-in-Chief, editorial@inderscience.com. **ISSN:** 1757-8752. **Subscription Rates:** EUR494 individuals print or online; EUR672 individuals print and online. **URL:** http://www.inderscience.com/browse/index.php?journalID=324.

51104 ■ International Journal of Biomedical Nanoscience and Nanotechnology
Inderscience Enterprises Limited
World Trade Center Bldg. II
29, Rte. de Pre-Bois
Case Postale 896
CH-1215 Geneva 15, Switzerland
Ph: 41 1234 240515
Fax: 41 22 7910885
Peer-reviewed journal covering the fields of biomedical nanoscience and nanotechnology in society. **Freq:** 4/yr. **Key Personnel:** Dr. Xudong Huang, Editor-in-Chief, xhuang3@partners.org. **ISSN:** 1756-0799. **Subscription Rates:** EUR494 individuals print or online; EUR672 individuals print and online. **URL:** http://www.inderscience.com/browse/index.php?journalCODE=ijbnn.

51105 ■ International Journal of Border Security and Immigration Policy
Inderscience Enterprises Limited
World Trade Center Bldg. II
29, Rte. de Pre-Bois
Case Postale 896
CH-1215 Geneva 15, Switzerland
Ph: 41 1234 240515
Fax: 41 22 7910885
Journal covering studies on new technologies, strategies, practices, methods, and research pertaining to border security and immigration policy. **Freq:** 4/yr. **Key Personnel:** Dr. Charles Keating, Editor-in-Chief, ckeating@odu.edu. **ISSN:** 1755-2419. **Subscription Rates:** EUR494 individuals print or online; EUR672 individuals print and online. **URL:** http://www.inderscience.com/browse/index.php?journalID=273.

51106 ■ International Journal of Business and Emerging Markets
Inderscience Enterprises Limited
World Trade Center Bldg. II
29, Rte. de Pre-Bois
Case Postale 896
CH-1215 Geneva 15, Switzerland
Ph: 41 1234 240515

Fax: 41 22 7910885
Peer-reviewed journal covering the study of business and emerging markets. **Freq:** 4/yr. **Key Personnel:** Dr. Satyendra Singh, Editor-in-Chief, ijbem@uwinnipeg.ca. **ISSN:** 1753-6219. **Subscription Rates:** EUR494 individuals print or online; EUR672 individuals print and online. **URL:** http://www.inderscience.com/browse/index.php?journalID=249.

51107 ■ International Journal of Business Excellence
Inderscience Enterprises Limited
World Trade Center Bldg. II
29, Rte. de Pre-Bois
Case Postale 896
CH-1215 Geneva 15, Switzerland
Ph: 41 1234 240515
Fax: 41 22 7910885
Journal covering the research and application of new developments in business performance measures, metrics, benchmarking, and best practices. **Freq:** 4/yr. **Key Personnel:** Prof. Angappa Gunasekaran, Editor-in-Chief, agunasekaran@umassd.edu. **ISSN:** 1756-0047. **Subscription Rates:** EUR494 individuals print or online; EUR672 individuals print and online. **URL:** http://www.inderscience.com/browse/index.php?journalID=291.

51108 ■ International Journal of Business Forecasting and Marketing Intelligence
Inderscience Enterprises Limited
World Trade Center Bldg. II
29, Rte. de Pre-Bois
Case Postale 896
CH-1215 Geneva 15, Switzerland
Ph: 41 1234 240515
Fax: 41 22 7910885
Journal covering the field of business forecasting and marketing intelligence as well as related disciplines. **Freq:** 4/yr. **Key Personnel:** Prof. Mazhar M. Islam, Managing Editor, mazhar.islam@famu.edu. **ISSN:** 1744-6635. **Subscription Rates:** EUR494 individuals print or online; EUR672 individuals print and online. **URL:** http://www.inderscience.com/browse/index.php?journalID=156.

51109 ■ International Journal of Business Innovation and Research (IJBIR)
Inderscience Enterprises Limited
World Trade Center Bldg. II
29, Rte. de Pre-Bois
Case Postale 896
CH-1215 Geneva 15, Switzerland
Ph: 41 1234 240515
Fax: 41 22 7910885
Peer-reviewed journal covering the developments in theory and applications of business and entrepreneurship innovation strategies, methods and tools to enhance organizational competitiveness. **Founded:** Mar. 3, 1905. **Freq:** 4/yr. **Print Method:** Offset. **Trim Size:** 14 x 22 3/4. **Cols./Page:** 6. **Col. Width:** 21 inches. **Col. Depth:** 301 agate lines. **Key Personnel:** Prof. Angappa Gunasekaran, Editor-in-Chief, agunasekaran@umassd.edu; Prof. Eric Abrahamson, Editorial Board Member; Prof. Constance E. Bagley, Editorial Board Member. **ISSN:** 1751-0252. **Subscription Rates:** EUR593 institutions online; EUR830 institutions print and online. **URL:** http://www.inderscience.com/browse/index.php?journalID=203.

51110 ■ International Journal of Complexity in Applied Science and Engineering
Inderscience Enterprises Limited
World Trade Center Bldg. II
29, Rte. de Pre-Bois
Case Postale 896
CH-1215 Geneva 15, Switzerland
Ph: 41 1234 240515
Fax: 41 22 7910885
Journal covering the study and design of technological and management systems in industrial companies. **Freq:** 4/yr. **Key Personnel:** Prof. Waguih H. El Maraghy, Editor-in-Chief, wem@uwindsor.ca. **ISSN:** 1740-0546. **Subscription Rates:** EUR494 individuals print or online; EUR672 individuals print and online. **URL:** http://www.inderscience.com/browse/index.php?journalID=71.

51111 ■ International Journal of Computational Biology and Drug Design
Inderscience Enterprises Limited
World Trade Center Bldg. II
29, Rte. de Pre-Bois
Case Postale 896
CH-1215 Geneva 15, Switzerland

Ph: 41 1234 240515
Fax: 41 22 7910885
Journal covering research and development in biomedical and pharmaceutical sciences. **Freq:** 4/yr. **Key Personnel:** Dr. Jack Y. Yang, Editor-in-Chief, dr.yang@jhu.edu; Dr. Dmitry Korkin, Managing Editor, korkined@missouri.edu; Dr. Zhongming Zhao, Managing Editor, zhongming.zhao@vanderbilt.edu. **ISSN:** 1756-0756. **Subscription Rates:** EUR494 individuals print or online; EUR672 individuals print and online. **URL:** http://www.inderscience.com/browse/index.php?journalID=294.

51112 ■ International Journal of Computational Medicine and Healthcare
Inderscience Enterprises Limited
World Trade Center Bldg. II
29, Rte. de Pre-Bois
Case Postale 896
CH-1215 Geneva 15, Switzerland
Ph: 41 1234 240515
Fax: 41 22 7910885
Journal covering medical and healthcare systems. **Freq:** 4/yr. **Key Personnel:** Prof. Jun Ni, Editor-in-Chief, jun-ni@uiowa.edu. **ISSN:** 1755-4500. **Subscription Rates:** EUR494 individuals print or online; EUR672 individuals print and online. **URL:** http://www.inderscience.com/browse/index.php?journalID=278.

51113 ■ International Journal of Corporate Governance
Inderscience Enterprises Limited
World Trade Center Bldg. II
29, Rte. de Pre-Bois
Case Postale 896
CH-1215 Geneva 15, Switzerland
Ph: 41 1234 240515
Fax: 41 22 7910885
Peer-reviewed journal covering issues related to corporate governance. **Freq:** 4/yr. **Key Personnel:** Han Donker, Editor-in-Chief, donker@unbc.ca; Saif Zahir, Editor-in-Chief, zahirs@unbc.ca. **ISSN:** 1754-3037. **Subscription Rates:** EUR494 individuals print or online; EUR672 individuals print and online. **URL:** http://www.inderscience.com/browse/index.php?journalID=260.

51114 ■ International Journal of Critical Accounting
Inderscience Enterprises Limited
World Trade Center Bldg. II
29, Rte. de Pre-Bois
Case Postale 896
CH-1215 Geneva 15, Switzerland
Ph: 41 1234 240515
Fax: 41 22 7910885
Peer-reviewed journal covering critical accounting. **Freq:** Quarterly. **Key Personnel:** Prof. Aida Sy, Co-Ed., aida.sy@manhattan.edu; Prof. Tony Tinker, Co-Ed., tony.tinker@baruch.cuny.edu. **ISSN:** 1757-9848. **Subscription Rates:** EUR494 individuals print or online; EUR672 individuals print and online. **URL:** http://www.inderscience.com/browse/index.php?journalCODE=ijca.

51115 ■ International Journal of Data Analysis Techniques and Strategies
Inderscience Enterprises Limited
World Trade Center Bldg. II
29, Rte. de Pre-Bois
Case Postale 896
CH-1215 Geneva 15, Switzerland
Ph: 41 1234 240515
Fax: 41 22 7910885
Journal covering all aspects of data analysis. **Freq:** 4/yr. **Key Personnel:** John Wang, Editor-in-Chief, j.john.wang@gmail.com; Hojjat Adeli, Assoc. Ed. **ISSN:** 1755-8050. **Subscription Rates:** EUR494 individuals print or online; EUR672 individuals print and online. **URL:** http://www.inderscience.com/browse/index.php?journalID=282.

51116 ■ International Journal of Economics and Business Research
Inderscience Enterprises Limited
World Trade Center Bldg. II
29, Rte. de Pre-Bois
Case Postale 896
CH-1215 Geneva 15, Switzerland
Ph: 41 1234 240515
Fax: 41 22 7910885
Peer-reviewed journal covering economics and business. **Freq:** 6/yr. **Key Personnel:** Demetri Kantarelis, Editor-in-Chief, dkan@besiweb.com; Vinko Belak, Assoc. Ed. **ISSN:** 1756-9850. **Subscription Rates:**

EUR593 individuals print or online; EUR830 individuals print and online. **URL:** http://www.inderscience.com/browse/index.php?journalID=310.

51117 ■ International Journal of Electronic Banking
Inderscience Enterprises Limited
World Trade Center Bldg. II
29, Rte. de Pre-Bois
Case Postale 896
CH-1215 Geneva 15, Switzerland
Ph: 41 1234 240515
Fax: 41 22 7910885
Journal covering the field of electronic banking. **Freq:** 4/yr. **Key Personnel:** M.A. Dorgham, Editor-in-Chief, editorial@inderscience.com; Peter Gomber, Assoc. Ed. **ISSN:** 1753-5239. **Subscription Rates:** EUR494 individuals print or online; EUR672 individuals print and online. **URL:** http://www.inderscience.com/browse/index.php?journalID=248.

51118 ■ International Journal of Environment and Pollution
Inderscience Enterprises Limited
c/o Dr. Bruce Cohen, Assoc. Ed.
16 rue Butini
1202 Geneva, Switzerland
Peer-reviewed journal covering the field of environment and pollution. **Freq:** 16/yr. **Key Personnel:** Dr. Bruce Cohen, Assoc. Ed.; Dr. M.A. Dorgham, Editor-in-Chief, editorial@inderscience.com. **ISSN:** 0957-4352. **Subscription Rates:** EUR1,386 individuals print or online; EUR1,917 individuals print and online. **URL:** http://www.inderscience.com/browse/index.php?journalID=9.

51119 ■ International Journal of Environmental Policy and Decision Making
Inderscience Enterprises Limited
World Trade Center Bldg. II
29, Rte. de Pre-Bois
Case Postale 896
CH-1215 Geneva 15, Switzerland
Ph: 41 1234 240515
Fax: 41 22 7910885
Journal focusing on environmental policy and decision making and the associated consequences at local, national, and global levels. **Freq:** 4/yr. **Key Personnel:** Dr. M.A. Dorgham, Editor-in-Chief, editorial@inderscience.com. **ISSN:** 1752-6906. **Subscription Rates:** EUR494 individuals print or online; EUR672 individuals print and online. **URL:** http://www.inderscience.com/browse/index.php?journalID=228.

51120 ■ International Journal of Exergy
Inderscience Enterprises Limited
World Trade Center Bldg. II
29, Rte. de Pre-Bois
Case Postale 896
CH-1215 Geneva 15, Switzerland
Ph: 41 1234 240515
Fax: 41 22 7910885
Journal covering the field of exergy and thermodynamic optimization. **Freq:** 6/yr. **Key Personnel:** Dr. Ibrahim Dincer, Editor-in-Chief, ibrahim.dincer@uoit.ca; Dr. Mark A. Rosen, Assoc. Ed. **ISSN:** 1742-8297. **Subscription Rates:** EUR593 individuals print or online; EUR830 individuals print and online. **URL:** http://www.inderscience.com/browse/index.php?journalID=135.

51121 ■ International Journal of Food Safety, Nutrition and Public Health
Inderscience Enterprises Limited
World Trade Center Bldg. II
29, Rte. de Pre-Bois
Case Postale 896
CH-1215 Geneva 15, Switzerland
Ph: 41 1234 240515
Fax: 41 22 7910885
Journal covering the fields of food science, nutrition, microbiology and diseases prevention, regulatory and quality assurance, health sector, primary production, and food processing. **Freq:** 4/yr. **Key Personnel:** Prof. Saundra Glover, Editor-in-Chief, sglover@mailbox.sc.edu; Gwendolyn Preston, Managing Editor, prestong@mailbox.sc.edu; Dr. Edith Williams, Assoc. Ed. **ISSN:** 1479-3911. **Subscription Rates:** EUR494 individuals print or online; EUR672 individuals print and online. **URL:** http://www.inderscience.com/browse/index.php?journalID=77.

51122 ■ International Journal of Functional Informatics and Personalised Medicine
Inderscience Enterprises Limited

World Trade Center Bldg. II
29, Rte. de Pre-Bois
Case Postale 896
CH-1215 Geneva 15, Switzerland
Ph: 41 1234 240515
Fax: 41 22 7910885
Journal focusing on developments in biomedical and pharmaceutical sciences. **Freq:** 4/yr. **Key Personnel:** Dr. Dong Xu, Editor-in-Chief, xudong@missouri.edu; Dr. Timothy B. Patrick, Managing Editor, tp5@uwm.edu. **ISSN:** 1756-2104. **Subscription Rates:** EUR494 individuals print or online; EUR672 individuals print and online. **URL:** http://www.inderscience.com/browse/index.php?journalID=295.

51123 ■ International Journal of Granular Computing, Rough Sets and Intelligent Systems
Inderscience Enterprises Limited
World Trade Center Bldg. II
29, Rte. de Pre-Bois
Case Postale 896
CH-1215 Geneva 15, Switzerland
Ph: 41 1234 240515
Fax: 41 22 7910885
Journal covering the areas of granular computing, rough sets, fuzzy sets, soft computing, and intelligent systems. **Freq:** 4/yr. **Key Personnel:** Prof. Xiaohua Hu, Editor-in-Chief, thu@cis.drexel.edu; Prof. T.Y. Lin, Editor-in-Chief, tylin@cs.sjsu.edu. **ISSN:** 1757-2703. **Subscription Rates:** EUR494 individuals print or online; EUR672 individuals print and online. **URL:** http://www.inderscience.com/browse/index.php?journalID=315.

51124 ■ International Journal of Heavy Vehicle Systems
Inderscience Enterprises Limited
World Trade Center Bldg. II
29, Rte. de Pre-Bois
Case Postale 896
CH-1215 Geneva 15, Switzerland
Ph: 41 1234 240515
Fax: 41 22 7910885
Journal covering the field of on/off road heavy vehicle systems. **Freq:** 4/yr. **Key Personnel:** Dr. Moustafa El-Gindy, Editor-in-Chief, moustafa.el-gindy@uoit.ca; Prof. Subhash Rakheja, Assoc. Ed. **ISSN:** 1744-232X. **Subscription Rates:** EUR494 individuals print or online; EUR672 individuals print and online. **URL:** http://www.inderscience.com/browse/index.php?journalID=17.

51125 ■ International Journal of Information and Decision Sciences
Inderscience Enterprises Limited
World Trade Center Bldg. II
29, Rte. de Pre-Bois
Case Postale 896
CH-1215 Geneva 15, Switzerland
Ph: 41 1234 240515
Fax: 41 22 7910885
Journal covering the field of information and decision sciences. **Freq:** 4/yr. **Key Personnel:** John Wang, Editor-in-Chief, j.john.wang@gmail.com; Francisco Javier Llorens Montes, Assoc. Ed. **ISSN:** 1756-7017. **Subscription Rates:** EUR494 individuals print or online; EUR672 individuals print and online. **URL:** http://www.inderscience.com/browse/index.php?journalID=306.

51126 ■ International Journal of Information Privacy, Security and Integrity
Inderscience Enterprises Limited
World Trade Center Bldg. II
29, Rte. de Pre-Bois
Case Postale 896
CH-1215 Geneva 15, Switzerland
Ph: 41 1234 240515
Fax: 41 22 7910885
Journal covering all aspects of information privacy, security, and integrity. **Freq:** 4/yr. **Key Personnel:** Justin Zhan, Editor-in-Chief, ijipsi@gmail.com. **ISSN:** 1741-8496. **Subscription Rates:** EUR494 individuals print or online; EUR672 individuals print and online. **URL:** http://www.inderscience.com/browse/index.php?journalID=114.

51127 ■ International Journal of Inventory Research
Inderscience Enterprises Limited
World Trade Center Bldg. II
29, Rte. de Pre-Bois
Case Postale 896
CH-1215 Geneva 15, Switzerland
Ph: 41 1234 240515

Circulation: ★ = ABC; △ = BPA; ◆ = CAC; ● = CCAB; ❑ = VAC; ⊕ = PO Statement; ‡ = Publisher's Report; Boldface figures = sworn; Light figures = estimated.

Gale Directory of Publications & Broadcast Media/147th Ed.

5479

Fax: 41 22 7910885

Journal covering all aspects of inventory theory. **Freq:** 4/yr. **Key Personnel:** Timothy L. Urban, Editor-in-Chief, timothy-urban@utulsa.edu. **ISSN:** 1746-6962. **Subscription Rates:** EUR494 individuals print or online; EUR672 individuals print and online. **URL:** http://www.inderscience.com/browse/index.php?journalID=178.

51128 ■ International Journal of Leisure and Tourism Marketing
Inderscience Enterprises Limited
World Trade Center Bldg. II
29, Rte. de Pre-Bois
Case Postale 896
CH-1215 Geneva 15, Switzerland
Ph: 41 1234 240515
Fax: 41 22 7910885
Journal covering the field of leisure, recreation and tourism. **Freq:** 4/yr. **Key Personnel:** Dr. Konstantinos Andriotis, Editorial Board Member. **ISSN:** 1757-5567. **Subscription Rates:** EUR494 individuals print or online; EUR672 individuals print and online. **URL:** http://www.inderscience.com/browse/index.php?journalID=318.

51129 ■ International Journal of Manufacturing Technology and Management
Inderscience Enterprises Limited
World Trade Center Bldg. II
29, Rte. de Pre-Bois
Case Postale 896
CH-1215 Geneva 15, Switzerland
Ph: 41 1234 240515
Fax: 41 22 7910885
Peer-reviewed journal covering engineering education. **Freq:** Monthly. **Key Personnel:** Dr. M.A. Dorgham, Editor-in-Chief, editorial@inderscience.com; Prof. David Wu, Fat East Ed. **ISSN:** 1368-2148. **Subscription Rates:** EUR1,025 institutions print; EUR1,434 institutions print and online. **URL:** http://www.inderscience.com/browse/index.php.

51130 ■ International Journal of Mechatronics and Manufacturing Systems
Inderscience Enterprises Limited
World Trade Center Bldg. II
29, Rte. de Pre-Bois
Case Postale 896
CH-1215 Geneva 15, Switzerland
Ph: 41 1234 240515
Fax: 41 22 7910885
Peer-reviewed journal covering the field of mechatronics and manufacturing systems. **Freq:** 6/yr. **Key Personnel:** Tugrul Ozel, Editor-in-Chief, ozel@rci.rutgers.edu. **ISSN:** 1753-1039. **Subscription Rates:** EUR593 individuals print or online; EUR830 individuals print and online. **URL:** http://www.inderscience.com/browse/index.php?journalID=239.

51131 ■ International Journal of Medical Engineering and Informatics
Inderscience Enterprises Limited
World Trade Center Bldg. II
29, Rte. de Pre-Bois
Case Postale 896
CH-1215 Geneva 15, Switzerland
Ph: 41 1234 240515
Fax: 41 22 7910885
Peer-reviewed journal covering the field of medical engineering and informatics. **Freq:** 4/yr. **Key Personnel:** Prof. Dinesh P. Mital, Editor-in-Chief, mitaldp@umdnj.edu. **ISSN:** 1755-0653. **Subscription Rates:** EUR494 individuals print or online; EUR672 individuals print and online. **URL:** http://www.inderscience.com/browse/index.php?journalID=268.

51132 ■ International Journal of Mining and Mineral Engineering
Inderscience Enterprises Limited
World Trade Center Bldg. II
29, Rte. de Pre-Bois
Case Postale 896
CH-1215 Geneva 15, Switzerland
Ph: 41 1234 240515
Fax: 41 22 7910885
Peer-reviewed journal focusing on the study of environmentally responsible exploration and extraction of mineral resources. **Freq:** 4/yr. **Key Personnel:** Dr. Vladislav Kecojevic, Editor-in-Chief, vlad.kecojevic@mail.wvu.edu. **ISSN:** 1754-890X. **Subscription Rates:** EUR494 individuals print or online; EUR672 individuals print and online. **URL:** http://www.inderscience.com/browse/index.php?journalID=265.

51133 ■ International Journal of Nano and Bio-materials
Inderscience Enterprises Limited
World Trade Center Bldg. II
29, Rte. de Pre-Bois
Case Postale 896
CH-1215 Geneva 15, Switzerland
Ph: 41 1234 240515
Fax: 41 22 7910885
Journal covering the study of nanomaterials. **Freq:** 4/yr. **Key Personnel:** Prof. D.Y. Li, Editor-in-Chief, dongyang.li@ualberta.ca; Prof. Mark J. Jackson, Assoc. Ed. **ISSN:** 1752-8933. **Subscription Rates:** EUR494 individuals print or online; EUR672 individuals print and online. **URL:** http://www.inderscience.com/browse/index.php?journalID=230.

51134 ■ International Journal of Petroleum Engineering
Inderscience Enterprises Limited
World Trade Center Bldg. II
29, Rte. de Pre-Bois
Case Postale 896
CH-1215 Geneva 15, Switzerland
Ph: 41 1234 240515
Fax: 41 22 7910885
Peer-reviewed journal covering the study of innovative solutions to design efficient petroleum operations. **Freq:** 4/yr. **Key Personnel:** Dr. M.A. Dorgham, Editor-in-Chief, editorial@inderscience.com. **ISSN:** 1754-8888. **Subscription Rates:** EUR494 individuals print or online; EUR672 individuals print and online. **URL:** http://www.inderscience.com/browse/index.php?journalID=266.

51135 ■ International Journal of Powertrain
Inderscience Enterprises Limited
World Trade Center Bldg. II
29, Rte. de Pre-Bois
Case Postale 896
CH-1215 Geneva 15, Switzerland
Ph: 41 1234 240515
Fax: 41 22 7910885
Journal covering the product lifecycle management. **Freq:** 4/yr. **Key Personnel:** Dr. Xubin Song, Editor-in-Chief, xubinsong@eaton.com; Dr. Hosam K. Fathy, Assoc. Ed. **ISSN:** 1742-4267. **Subscription Rates:** EUR494 individuals print or online; EUR672 individuals print and online. **URL:** http://www.inderscience.com/browse/index.php?journalID=122objectives.

51136 ■ International Journal of Quality Engineering and Technology
Inderscience Enterprises Limited
World Trade Center Bldg. II
29, Rte. de Pre-Bois
Case Postale 896
CH-1215 Geneva 15, Switzerland
Ph: 41 1234 240515
Fax: 41 22 7910885
Journal covering all areas of quality engineering. **Freq:** 4/yr. **Key Personnel:** Prof. Byung Rae Cho, Editor-in-Chief, bcho@clemson.edu. **ISSN:** 1757-2177. **Subscription Rates:** EUR494 individuals print or online; EUR672 individuals print and online. **URL:** http://www.inderscience.com/browse/index.php?journalID=339.

51137 ■ International Journal of Remanufacturing
Inderscience Enterprises Limited
World Trade Center Bldg. II
29, Rte. de Pre-Bois
Case Postale 896
CH-1215 Geneva 15, Switzerland
Ph: 41 1234 240515
Fax: 41 22 7910885
Journal covering the field of remanufacturing. **Freq:** 4/yr. **Key Personnel:** Dr. M.A. Dorgham, Editor-in-Chief, editorial@inderscience.com. **ISSN:** 1758-7964. **Subscription Rates:** EUR494 individuals print or online; EUR672 individuals print and online. **URL:** http://www.inderscience.com/browse/index.php?journalID=337.

51138 ■ International Journal of Security and Networks
Inderscience Enterprises Limited
World Trade Center Bldg. II
29, Rte. de Pre-Bois
Case Postale 896
CH-1215 Geneva 15, Switzerland
Ph: 41 1234 240515
Fax: 41 22 7910885
Journal covering the field of wireless/wired network security. **Freq:** 4/yr. **Key Personnel:** Prof. Yang Xiao,

Editor-in-Chief, yangxiao@cs.ua.edu. **ISSN:** 1747-8405. **Subscription Rates:** EUR494 individuals print or online; EUR672 individuals print and online. **URL:** http://www.inderscience.com/browse/index.php?journalID=183.

51139 ■ International Journal of Services Sciences
Inderscience Enterprises Limited
World Trade Center Bldg. II
29, Rte. de Pre-Bois
Case Postale 896
CH-1215 Geneva 15, Switzerland
Ph: 41 1234 240515
Fax: 41 22 7910885
Journal covering research and development in the area of services. **Freq:** 4/yr. **Key Personnel:** Desheng Wu, Editor-in-Chief, dash@risklab.ca; David L. Olson, Editor, dolson3@unl.edu. **ISSN:** 1753-1446. **Subscription Rates:** EUR494 individuals print or online; EUR672 individuals print and online. **URL:** http://www.inderscience.com/browse/index.php?journalID=238.

51140 ■ International Journal of Social Computing and Cyber-Physical Systems
Inderscience Enterprises Limited
World Trade Center Bldg. II
29, Rte. de Pre-Bois
Case Postale 896
CH-1215 Geneva 15, Switzerland
Ph: 41 1234 240515
Fax: 41 22 7910885
Journal containing articles and reports on various social computing and cyber-physical systems related issues. **Freq:** 4/yr. **Key Personnel:** Justin Zhan, Editor-in-Chief, justinzzhan@gmail.com. **ISSN:** 2040-0721. **Subscription Rates:** EUR494 individuals print or online; EUR672 individuals print and online. **URL:** http://www.inderscience.com/browse/index.php?journalID=349.

51141 ■ International Journal of Society Systems Science
Inderscience Enterprises Limited
World Trade Center Bldg. II
29, Rte. de Pre-Bois
Case Postale 896
CH-1215 Geneva 15, Switzerland
Ph: 41 1234 240515
Fax: 41 22 7910885
Journal covering the studies on society systems sciences. **Freq:** 4/yr. **Key Personnel:** John Wang, Editor-in-Chief, j.john.wang@gmail,com; Ardeshir Anjomani, Assoc. Ed. **ISSN:** 1756-2511. **Subscription Rates:** EUR494 individuals print or online; EUR672 individuals print and online. **URL:** http://www.inderscience.com/browse/index.php?journalID=296.

51142 ■ International Journal of Sustainable Manufacturing
Inderscience Enterprises Limited
World Trade Center Bldg. II
29, Rte. de Pre-Bois
Case Postale 896
CH-1215 Geneva 15, Switzerland
Ph: 41 1234 240515
Fax: 41 22 7910885
Journal covering all aspects of product sustainability. **Freq:** 4/yr. **Key Personnel:** Prof. I.S. Jawahir, Editor-in-Chief, jawahir@engr.uky.edu. **ISSN:** 1742-7223. **Subscription Rates:** EUR494 individuals print or online; EUR672 individuals print and online. **URL:** http://www.inderscience.com/browse/index.php?journalID=127.

51143 ■ International Journal of Sustainable Society
Inderscience Enterprises Limited
World Trade Center Bldg. II
29, Rte. de Pre-Bois
Case Postale 896
CH-1215 Geneva 15, Switzerland
Ph: 41 1234 240515
Fax: 41 22 7910885
Journal covering all aspects of our society. **Freq:** 4/yr. **Key Personnel:** John Wang, Editor-in-Chief, j.john.wang@gmail.com; Michael M. Bell, Assoc. Ed. **ISSN:** 1756-2538. **Subscription Rates:** EUR494 individuals print or online; EUR672 individuals print and online. **URL:** http://www.inderscience.com/browse/index.php?journalID=297.

51144 ■ International Journal of Sustainable Strategic Management
Inderscience Enterprises Limited
World Trade Center Bldg. II
29, Rte. de Pre-Bois

Case Postale 896
CH-1215 Geneva 15, Switzerland
Ph: 41 1234 240515
Fax: 41 22 7910885
Peer-reviewed journal covering the studies on economic sustainability. **Freq:** 4/yr. **Key Personnel:** John E. Spillan, Editor-in-Chief, john.spillan@uncp.edu. **ISSN:** 1753-3600. **Subscription Rates:** EUR494 individuals print or online; EUR672 individuals print and online. **URL:** http://www.inderscience.com/browse/index.php?journalID=244.

51145 ■ International Journal of Vehicle Design
Inderscience Enterprises Limited
World Trade Center Bldg. II
29, Rte. de Pre-Bois
Case Postale 896
CH-1215 Geneva 15, Switzerland
Ph: 41 1234 240515
Fax: 41 22 7910885
Journal covering the field of vehicle design and safety. **Freq:** 12/yr. **Key Personnel:** Dr. M.A. Dorgham, Editor-in-Chief, editorial@inderscience.com; Dr. Kevin Deng, Assoc. Ed. **ISSN:** 0143-3369. **Subscription Rates:** EUR1,025 individuals print or online; EUR1,434 individuals print and online. **URL:** http://www.inderscience.com/browse/index.php?journalID=31.

51146 ■ International Journal of Vehicle Performance
Inderscience Enterprises Limited
World Trade Center Bldg. II
29, Rte. de Pre-Bois
Case Postale 896
CH-1215 Geneva 15, Switzerland
Ph: 41 1234 240515
Fax: 41 22 7910885
Journal covering research on vehicle performance that contributes to engineers and scientists in the field. **Freq:** 4/yr. **Key Personnel:** Prof. Subhash Rakheja, Exec. Ed., rakheja@alcor.concordia.ca; Dr. Xiabo yang, Assoc. Ed. **ISSN:** 1745-3194. **Subscription Rates:** EUR494 individuals print or online; EUR672 individuals print and online. **URL:** http://www.inderscience.com/browse/index.php?journalID=164.

51147 ■ International Labour Review
International Labour Office
4, Rte. Des Morillons
CH1211 Geneva, Switzerland
Ph: 41 122 7996111
Fax: 44 122 79888685
Publisher E-mail: ilo@ilo.org
Publication covering human resources and labor relations. **Freq:** Quarterly. **Key Personnel:** Mark Lansky, Managing Editor; Luis Lazaro Martinez, Editor; Marie-Christine Nallet, Editorial Asst. **ISSN:** 0020-7780. **Subscription Rates:** 175 institutions print and online; US$323 institutions print and online; EUR223 institutions print and online; EUR90 individuals personal; 60 individuals personal; US$107 individuals personal; US$342 individuals rest of the world. **URL:** http://www.ilo.org/; http://www.ilo.org/public/english/revue/.

51148 ■ International Nursing Review
International Council of Nurses
Conseil International des Infirmieres
3, Pl. Jean Marteau
CH-1201 Geneva, Switzerland
Ph: 41 229 080100
Fax: 41 229 080101
Publisher E-mail: icn@icn.ch
Worldwide publication covering nursing. **Subtitle:** The Official Journal of the International Council of Nurses. **Freq:** Quarterly. **Key Personnel:** Jane Robinson, Editor; Marie Lomax, Coord., mlomax@wiley.com. **ISSN:** 0020-8132. **Subscription Rates:** US$118 individuals print and online, in the Americas; EUR95 individuals print and online; 63 individuals print and online, non Euro zone; 71 individuals print and online, elsewhere; US$66 individuals America & Canadian nurses asso. members; US$431 institutions print & online/the Americas; EUR295 institutions print & online/Europe; 503 institutions print & online/elsewhere. **Remarks:** Advertising accepted; rates available upon request. **URL:** http://www.wiley.com/bw/journal.asp?ref=0020-8132. **Circ:** (Not Reported)

51149 ■ International Review of Mission
World Council of Churches
150 Rte. de Ferney
PO Box 2100
CH-1211 Geneva 2, Switzerland
Ph: 41 227 916111

Fax: 41 227 910361
Publisher E-mail: infowcc@wcc-coe.org
Publication covering philosophy and religion. **Freq:** Quarterly. **Key Personnel:** Jacques Matthey, Editor. **ISSN:** 0020-8582. **Subscription Rates:** 38 SFr individuals; US$32 individuals; 18 individuals; EUR25 individuals. **URL:** http://www.oikoumene.org/en/programmes/unity-mission-evangelism-and-spirituality/mission-and-unity/.irm.html.

51150 ■ International Trade FORUM
International Trade Centre UNCTAD/WTO
Palais des Nations
CH-1211 Geneva 10, Switzerland
Publisher E-mail: itcreg@intracen.org
Publication covering international trade in English, French and Spanish. **Freq:** Quarterly. **Key Personnel:** Natalie Domeisen, Editor; Marilyn Langfeld, Design. **ISSN:** 0020-8957. **Subscription Rates:** US$45 Free to qualified subscribers in developing countries; US$45 out of country. **Remarks:** Advertising not accepted. **URL:** http://www.tradeforum.org/. **Circ:** (Not Reported)

51151 ■ ITU News
International Telecommunication Union
Union Internationale des Telecommunications
Palais des Nations
CH-1211 Geneva 20, Switzerland
Ph: 41 22 7305111
Fax: 41 22 7337256
Publication E-mail: itunews@itu.int
Publisher E-mail: itumail@itu.int
Publication covering telecommunications in English, French and Spanish. **Founded:** 1869. **Freq:** 10/yr. **Trim Size:** 210 x 297 mm. **Subscription Rates:** 100 SFr nonmembers; Included in membership. **Remarks:** Accepts advertising. **URL:** http://www.itu.int/net/itunews/about.aspx. **Circ:** (Not Reported)

51152 ■ The Journal of World Investment and Trade
Werner Publishing Company Ltd.
PO Box 5134
1211 Geneva 11, Switzerland
Ph: 41 22 3103422
Fax: 41 22 3114592
Publisher E-mail: wernerp@iprolink.ch
Law periodical. **Freq:** Bimonthly. **Key Personnel:** Jacques Werner, Editor; James Bacchus, Assoc. Ed.; Petros C. Mavroidis, Assoc. Ed. **ISSN:** 1011-6702. **Subscription Rates:** US$940 individuals including airmail postage; US$160 single issue. **URL:** http://www.wernerpubl.com/frame_inves.htm. **Formerly:** Journal of World Trade (Law-Economics-Public Policy).

51153 ■ Le Temps
Edipresse Publications S.A.
3, Pl. Cornavin
Case postale 2570
CH-1211 Geneva 2, Switzerland
Ph: 41 22 7995858
Fax: 41 22 7995859
Publication E-mail: info@letemps.ch
Publisher E-mail: groupe@edipresse.com
Newspaper reporting the economic, financial, political and cultural issues of the region. **Freq:** Daily. **Key Personnel:** Valerie Boagno, Director; Pierre Veya, Ch. Ed. **URL:** http://www.edipresse.com/dailies/le-temps; http://www.letemps.ch/. **Circ:** ‡45,506

51154 ■ Nutrition Information in Crisis Situations
UN System - Standing Committee on Nutrition
c/o World Health Organisation
20 Ave. Appia
CH-1211 Geneva 27, Switzerland
Ph: 41 227 910456
Fax: 41 227 988891
Publisher E-mail: scn@who.int
Publication covering hunger. **Founded:** Oct. 1993. **Freq:** Quarterly. **ISSN:** 1564-376X. **Subscription Rates:** Free. **Remarks:** Advertising not accepted. **URL:** http://www.unscn.org/en/publications/nics/. **Formerly:** Refugee Nutrition Information System (RNIS). **Circ:** 2,300

51155 ■ Pan American Journal of Public Health
World Health Organization
20 Appia Ave.
CH-1211 Geneva 27, Switzerland
Ph: 41 22 7912111

Fax: 41 22 7913111
Publisher E-mail: info@who.int
Journal providing information on the most recent advances in public health research in the Americas, including breakthroughs in combating disease, up-to-date health profiles, emerging health trends, and other public health news from the Americas. **Freq:** Monthly. **Key Personnel:** Celia Maria De Almeida, Editorial Board; Carlos Campbell, Editorial Board; Henry Fraser, Editorial Board. **Subscription Rates:** US$142 individuals print; US$113 individuals electronic; US$199 individuals print & electronic; US$233 institutions print; US$186 institutions electronic; US$328 institutions print & electronic; US$66 individuals Latin American and the Caribbean; online; US$108 institutions Latin American and the Caribbean; online. **URL:** http://publications.paho.org/home.php.

51156 ■ Prospects
International Bureau of Education
Bureau International d'Education
Case Postale 199
CH-1211 Geneva 20, Switzerland
Ph: 41 229177800
Fax: 41 229177801
Publication covering education in Arabic, Chinese, English, French, Russian and Spanish. **Founded:** 1971. **Freq:** Quarterly. **Key Personnel:** Simona Popa, Asst. Ed. **ISSN:** 0033-1538. **Subscription Rates:** US$107 institutions print or online only; US$128.40 institutions print and online. **Remarks:** Advertising accepted; rates available upon request. **URL:** http://www.ibe.unesco.org/en/services/online-materials/publications/prospects.html. **Circ:** (Not Reported)

51157 ■ Red Cross, Red Crescent
International Federation of Red Cross and Red Crescent Societies
PO Box 372
CH-1211 Geneva 19, Switzerland
Ph: 41 227 304222
Fax: 41 227 330395
Publication E-mail: rcrc@ifrc.org
Publication covering relief. **Freq:** Quarterly. **ISSN:** 1019-9349. **URL:** http://www.redcross.int/EN/mag/index.html.

51158 ■ Reformed World
World Alliance of Reformed Churches
150 rte. de Ferney
PO Box 2100
CH-1211 Geneva, Switzerland
Ph: 41 227 916240
Fax: 41 227 916505
Publisher E-mail: warc@warc.ch
Monothematic academic journal reflecting the diversity of the WARC community. **Founded:** 1971. **Freq:** Quarterly. **Print Method:** Offset. **Key Personnel:** Setri Nyomi, Contact. **ISSN:** 0034-3056. **Subscription Rates:** US$35 individuals; US$64 individuals 2 years; US$95 individuals 3 years; US$20 individuals; US$37 individuals 2 years; 54 individuals 3 years. **Remarks:** Advertising not accepted. **URL:** http://warc.jalb.de/warcajsp/side.jsp?news_id=886&navi=38&part_id=62. **Circ:** Combined 3,500

51159 ■ Refugee Survey Quarterly
UNHCR Library
Case Postale 2500
CH-1211 Geneva, Switzerland
Ph: 41 22 7398111
Peer-reviewed journal covering refugees in English and French. **Founded:** 1994. **Freq:** Quarterly. **Key Personnel:** Jeff Crisp, Editorial Board; Vincent Chetail, Editor-in-Chief, chetail5@hei.unige.ch; Gilles Giacca, Asst. Ed. **ISSN:** 1020-4067. **Subscription Rates:** US$396 institutions print and online; 198 institutions print and online; EUR298 individuals print and online; 68 individuals print; US$136 individuals print; EUR102 individuals print; US$363 institutions print; 182 institutions print; EUR273 institutions print. **Remarks:** Advertising accepted; rates available upon request. **URL:** http://rsq.oupjournals.org. **Formerly:** Refugee Abstracts. **Circ:** (Not Reported)

51160 ■ SCN News
UN System - Standing Committee on Nutrition
c/o World Health Organisation
20 Ave. Appia
CH-1211 Geneva 27, Switzerland
Ph: 41 227 910456
Fax: 41 227 988891

Circulation: ★ = ABC; △ = BPA; ♦ = CAC; • = CCAB; ❑ = VAC; ⊕ = PO Statement; ‡ = Publisher's Report; Boldface figures = sworn; Light figures = estimated.

Publication E-mail: scn@who.int
Publisher E-mail: scn@who.int
Publication covering hunger. **Freq:** Semiannual. **ISSN:** 1564-3751. **Subscription Rates:** Free. **Remarks:** Advertising not accepted. **URL:** http://www.unscn.org/en/publications/scn_news/. **Circ:** 8,000

51161 ■ Tribune des Arts
Edipresse Publications S.A.
Rue des Rois 11
CP 5320
CH-1211 Geneva 11, Switzerland
Ph: 44 22 3223461
Fax: 44 22 7813292
Publisher E-mail: groupe@edipresse.com
Magazine providing information for the arts and watchmaking. **Freq:** Monthly. **Key Personnel:** Marco Cattaneo, Ch. Ed. **URL:** http://www.tribunedesarts.ch; http://www.edipresse.com/category/produits/magazines/luxury. **Circ:** ‡72,000

51162 ■ Tribune de Geneve
Edipresse Publications S.A.
11, rue des Rois
Case postale 5115
CH-1211 Geneva 11, Switzerland
Ph: 41 22 3224000
Fax: 41 22 7810107
Publisher E-mail: groupe@edipresse.com
Newspaper covering the local, national and international events, sports, and culture. **Freq:** Daily. **Key Personnel:** Serge Reymond, Director; Pierre Ruetschi, Ch. Ed. **URL:** http://www.edipresse.com/dailies/tribune-de-gen%C3%A8ve. **Circ:** ‡56,333

51163 ■ UN Special
Palais des Nations
Bureau C507
CH-1211 Geneva, Switzerland
Ph: 41 22 9172501
Fax: 41 22 9170505
Publication E-mail: unspecial@unece.org
Publisher E-mail: unspecial@unece.org
Staff magazine. **Founded:** 1947. **Freq:** Monthly. **Key Personnel:** Christian David, Editor-in-Chief, cdavid@unog.ch. **Subscription Rates:** Free. **Remarks:** Accepts advertising. **URL:** http://www.unspecial.org. **Circ:** (Not Reported)

51164 ■ Union
ILO Staff Union
International Labour Office
4 rte. des Morillons
CH-1211 Geneva, Switzerland
Ph: 41 22 7996111
Fax: 41 22 7988685
Publisher E-mail: ilo@ilo.org
Publication covering organizations and staffing in English, French and Spanish. **Freq:** Monthly. **Key Personnel:** Catherine Comte-Tiberghien, Editor-in-Chief. **Remarks:** Advertising accepted; rates available upon request. **URL:** http://www.ilo.org/public/english/staffun/info/magazine/index.htm. **Circ:** (Not Reported)

51165 ■ Weekly Epidemiological Record
World Health Organization
20 Appia Ave.
CH-1211 Geneva 27, Switzerland
Ph: 41 22 7912111
Fax: 41 22 7913111
Publication E-mail: info@who.int
Publisher E-mail: info@who.int
Professional magazine covering epidemiological data for disease surveillance worldwide. **Founded:** 1927. **Freq:** Weekly. **Cols./Page:** 2. **ISSN:** 0049-8114. **Subscription Rates:** US$346 individuals economy mail; US$355 individuals priority mail. **Remarks:** Advertising not accepted. **URL:** http://www.who.int/wer/en/. **Circ:** Combined 6,500

51166 ■ WHO Drug Information
World Health Organization
20 Appia Ave.
CH-1211 Geneva 27, Switzerland
Ph: 41 22 7912111
Fax: 41 22 7913111
Publication E-mail: druginfo@who.int
Publisher E-mail: info@who.int
Publication covering the pharmaceutical and cosmetics industries. **Founded:** 1987. **Freq:** Quarterly. **ISSN:**

1010-9609. **Subscription Rates:** US$112 individuals economy mail; US$115 individuals priority mail. **URL:** http://www.who.int/druginformation/.

51167 ■ WMO Bulletin
World Meteorological Organization
7 Bis, Ave. de la Paix
Case postale No. 2300
12112 Geneva, Switzerland
Ph: 41 22 7308111
Fax: 41 22 7308181
Publisher E-mail: wmo@wmo.int
Official journal of the World Meteorological Organization. **Founded:** Apr. 1952. **Freq:** Quarterly January, April, July and October. **Print Method:** Offset. **Cols./Page:** 2. **Col. Width:** 137 millimeters. **Col. Depth:** 210 millimeters. **Subscription Rates:** 85 SFr; 30 SFr individuals surface mail; 55 SFr two years surface mail; 43 SFr individuals airmail; 75 SFr individuals airmail. **Remarks:** Accepts advertising. **URL:** http://www.wmo.ch/. **Ad Rates:** BW: 2,700 SFr, 4C: 4,950 SFr, CNU: 1,836 SFr. **Circ:** (Not Reported)

51168 ■ World Review of Intermodal Transportation Research
Inderscience Enterprises Limited
World Trade Center Bldg. II
29, Rte. de Pre-Bois
Case Postale 896
CH-1215 Geneva 15, Switzerland
Ph: 41 1234 240515
Fax: 41 22 7910885
Peer-reviewed journal covering the development and application of computer simulation in transportation studies. **Founded:** 1987. **Freq:** Quarterly. **Print Method:** Offset. **Cols./Page:** 5. **Col. Width:** 2 inches. **Col. Depth:** 11 1/2 inches. **Key Personnel:** Dr. Evanistu Irandu, Regional Ed., Africa; Prof. Dr. Dawna L. Rhoades, Editor-in-Chief, rhoadesd@erau.edu; Dr. Seock-Jin Hong, Regional Ed., Asia-Pacific. **ISSN:** 1749-4729. **Subscription Rates:** EUR494 institutions online; EUR672 institutions print and online. **URL:** http://www.inderscience.com/browse/index.php?journalID=194board.

51169 ■ World of Work
International Labour Organization - Switzerland
4, Rte. des Morillons
CH-1211 Geneva 22, Switzerland
Ph: 41 227 996111
Fax: 41 227 988685
Publisher E-mail: ilo@ilo.org
Publication covering the world of work in English, French and Spanish. **Founded:** 1993. **Freq:** Periodic. **Print Method:** Offset. **Trim Size:** A4 European. **Key Personnel:** Tom Netter, Contact. **ISSN:** 1020-0010. **Subscription Rates:** Free. **Remarks:** Advertising not accepted. **URL:** http://www.ilo.org/wow/PrintEditions/index.htm. **Circ:** (Not Reported)

51170 ■ WSCF Journal
World Student Christian Federation
Federation Universelle des Associations Chretiennes d'Etudiants
5 rte. des Morillons
PO Box 2100
CH-1211 Geneva, Switzerland
Ph: 41 22 7916358
Fax: 41 22 7916152
Publisher E-mail: wscf@wscf.ch
Journal covering Christianity. **Founded:** 1908. **Freq:** Irregular. **Key Personnel:** Michael Wallace, Sec. Gen.; Youhanna Kamal Shawky, Treas. **ISSN:** 1560-4861. **Subscription Rates:** Free. **Remarks:** Advertising not accepted. **URL:** http://www.wscfglobal.org/. **Circ:** (Not Reported)

51171 ■ OneFM-FM - 99.3
Rue des Bains 33
CH-1205 Geneva, Switzerland
Ph: 41 22 8071015
Fax: 41 22 8071001
E-mail: studio@onefm.ch
Format: World Beat. **Operating Hours:** Continuous. **Ad Rates:** Advertising accepted; rates available upon request. **URL:** http://www.onefm.com.

51172 ■ OneFM-FM - 107.2
Rue des Bains 33
CH-1205 Geneva, Switzerland
Ph: 41 22 8071015

Fax: 41 22 8071001
E-mail: studio@onefm.ch
Format: World Beat; Ethnic. **Operating Hours:** Continuous. **Ad Rates:** Advertising accepted; rates available upon request. **URL:** http://www.onefm.com.

51173 ■ WRS-FM - 88.4
2, Passage de la Radio
CH-1205 Geneva, Switzerland
Ph: 41 22 7087444
Fax: 41 22 7087454
E-mail: management@worldradio.ch
Format: Classic Rock; Contemporary Hit Radio (CHR); News. **Formerly:** WRG-FM (Nov. 1, 2007). **Key Personnel:** Philippe Mottaz, Director, phone 41 22 7087430, philippe.mottaz@worldradio.ch. **Ad Rates:** Advertising accepted; rates available upon request. **URL:** http://www.worldradio.ch.

Genolier

51174 ■ Critical Reviews in Oncology/Hematology
Elsevier Science
c/o M.S. Aapro, Ed.-in-Ch.
Institut Multidisciplinaire d'Oncologie
CH-1272 Genolier, Switzerland
Publisher E-mail: nlinfo-f@elsevier.com
Peer-reviewed journal publishing articles in the fields of oncology and hematology, in connection with the International Society for Geriatric Oncology (SIOG). **Founded:** 1991. **Freq:** Monthly. **Key Personnel:** M.S. Aapro, Editor-in-Chief, critical-reviews@genolier.net; R. Audisio, Editorial Board; T. Facon, Editorial Board. **ISSN:** 1040-8428. **Subscription Rates:** US$363 individuals for all countries except Europe, Japan & Iran; EUR326 individuals for European countries & Iran; 42,800¥ individuals; US$2,402 institutions for all countries except Europe, Japan & Iran; 285,100¥ institutions; EUR2,146 institutions for European countries & Iran. **Remarks:** Accepts advertising. **URL:** http://www.elsevier.com/wps/find/journaldescription.cws_home/522345/description. **Circ:** (Not Reported)

Gland

51175 ■ Parks
IUCN-The World Conservation Union
Programme On Protected Area
Rue Mauverney 28
CH 1196 Gland, Switzerland
Ph: 41 22 9990000
Fax: 41 22 9990002
Publication E-mail: parks@naturebureau.co.uk
Publisher E-mail: webmaster@iucn.org
Trade magazine covering environmental and management issues for managers of protected areas worldwide. **Founded:** 1994. **Freq:** 3/yr. **ISSN:** 0960-233X. **Subscription Rates:** 28.60 individuals U.K., 1-9 subscriptions; 31.15 individuals Europe, 1-9 subscriptions; 35.65 elsewhere rest of the world, 1-9 subscriptions; 21.30 individuals U.K., 10 above subscriptions; 25 individuals Europe, 10 above subscriptions; 29.30 individuals rest of the world, 10 above subscriptions. **Remarks:** Accepts advertising. **URL:** http://www.naturebureau.co.uk/parks/. **Circ:** 1,700

Glarus

51176 ■ Lebensmittel Industrie
Verlag Lebensmittelindustrie
Spielhof 14A
CH-8750 Glarus, Switzerland
Ph: 41 556 453750
Fax: 41 556 402171
Publisher E-mail: verlag@lebensmittelindustrie.com
Technical magazine for the food and beverage industry. **Founded:** 1992. **Freq:** Bimonthly. **Print Method:** Offset. **Trim Size:** 14. **ISSN:** 1420-5939. **Subscription Rates:** EUR80 individuals Abo Ausland; EUR92 individuals. **Remarks:** Accepts advertising. **URL:** http://www.lebensmittelindustrie.com/. **Ad Rates:** BW: 2,317 SFr, 4C: 2,997 SFr. **Circ:** Combined 4,300

Grand-Saconnex

51177 ■ Diffusion
EBU—European Broadcasting Union
L'Ancienne-Rte. 17A
CH-1218 Grand-Saconnex, Switzerland
Ph: 41 22 7172111

Fax: 41 22 7474000
Publisher E-mail: ebu@ebu.ch
Professional magazine covering radio and television broadcasting. **Freq:** Biennial weekly online articles. **Print Method:** Offset, Quadir & Pantone. **Subscription Rates:** Free. **Remarks:** Accepts advertising. **URL:** http://www.ebu.ch/union/publications/diffusion.php. **Ad Rates:** 4C: 2,500 SFr. **Circ:** Non-paid ⊕5,000

51178 ■ EBU Technical Review
EBU—European Broadcasting Union
L'Ancienne-Rte. 17A
CH-1218 Grand-Saconnex, Switzerland
Ph: 41 22 7172111
Fax: 41 22 7474000
Publication E-mail: techreview@ebu.ch
Publisher E-mail: ebu@ebu.ch
Trade journal covering broadcasting and production technologies. **Freq:** Quarterly. **Key Personnel:** Mike Meyer, Editor-in-Chief. **ISSN:** 1609-1469. **Remarks:** Advertising not accepted. **URL:** http://www.ebu.ch/en/technical/trev/trev_311_Jul-07.html. **Circ:** (Not Reported)

Hohtenn

51179 ■ Radio Rottu Oberwallis-FM - 101
Postfach
CH-3930 Visp, Switzerland
Ph: 41 27 9480948
Fax: 41 27 9480945
E-mail: info@rro.ch
Format: Ethnic; World Beat. **Operating Hours:** Continuous. **Key Personnel:** Michael Brunner, Prog. Master. **URL:** http://www.rro.ch.

Kastanienbaum

51180 ■ Aquatic Sciences
Springer-Verlag Tokyo
c/o Alfred Wuest, Co-Ed.
Swiss Federation Institute of Aquatic Science & Technology
Seestr. 79
CH-6047 Kastanienbaum, Switzerland
Publisher E-mail: info@springer.jp
Journal publishing original research, overviews and reviews dealing with aquatic (both freshwater and marine) systems and their boundaries, including the impact of human activities on these systems. **Subtitle:** Research Across Boundaries. **Founded:** 1920. **Freq:** Quarterly. **Trim Size:** 21 x 27.7 cm. **Key Personnel:** Klement Tockner, Editor-in-Chief, tockner@igb-berlin.de; Neil V. Blough, Editorial Board; Stuart E.G. Findlay, Co.-Ed.; Patricia J.S. Colberg, Editorial Board; Yu-Ping Chin, Editorial Board; Peter S. Liss, Editorial Board; Thomas Bernauer, Editorial Board; Eric Odada, Editorial Board. **ISSN:** 1015-1621. **Subscription Rates:** EUR631 institutions print incl. free access or e-only; EUR757.20 institutions print incl. enhanced access. **Remarks:** Advertising accepted; rates available upon request. **URL:** http://www.springer.com/birkhauser/biosciences/journal/27. **Circ:** (Not Reported)

Krattigen

51181 ■ Leben und Gesundheit (Life and Health)
Advent-Verlag
Leissigenstrasse 17
CH-3704 Krattigen, Switzerland
Ph: 41 336 541065
Fax: 41 336 544431
Publisher E-mail: info@adventverlag.ch
Magazine covering natural health, medicine, nutrition, the environment and related issues. **Founded:** 1929. **Freq:** Monthly. **Print Method:** Offset. **Trim Size:** 210 x 290 mm. **Cols./Page:** 4. **Col. Width:** 42.5 millimeters. **Col. Depth:** 252 millimeters. **Key Personnel:** Gunther Klenk, Editor-in-Chief. **Subscription Rates:** 117 SFr individuals. **Remarks:** Accepts advertising. **URL:** http://www.advent-verlag.ch/v2/praes.php?art=lug. **Ad Rates:** BW: 1,656 SFr, 4C: 2,867 SFr. **Circ:** Paid 15,200

Lausanne

51182 ■ Alcoholism
International Council on Alcohol and Addictions
Conseil International sur les Problemes de l'Alcoolisme et des
PO Box 189

CH-1001 Lausanne, Switzerland
Ph: 41 21 3209865
Fax: 41 21 3209868
Publisher E-mail: secretariat@icaa.ch
Publication covering substance abuse. **Freq:** Monthly. **URL:** http://www.icaa.ch/.

51183 ■ Bilan
Edipresse Publications S.A.
Av. de la Gare 33
CH-1001 Lausanne, Switzerland
Ph: 41 21 3494545
Fax: 41 21 3494110
Publication E-mail: bilan@bilan.ch
Publisher E-mail: groupe@edipresse.com
Swiss French magazine covering economics. **Founded:** June 1989. **Freq:** Bimonthly. **Print Method:** Offset Rotative. **Key Personnel:** Jean-Paul Schwindt, Contact; Serge Reymond, Director. **Subscription Rates:** 20 SFr individuals. **Remarks:** Accepts advertising. **URL:** http://www.bilan.ch/. **Ad Rates:** 4C: 10,250 SFr. **Circ:** 19,325

51184 ■ Cancer Immunity
Academy of Cancer Immunology
UNIL-Genopode
CH-1015 Lausanne, Switzerland
Ph: 41 21 6924064
Fax: 41 21 6924065
Publication E-mail: cancerimmunity@cancerimmunity.org
Publisher E-mail: info@academycancerimmunology.org
Journal on cancer immunology focusing on immunotherapies for cancer. **Key Personnel:** Victor Jongeneel, PhD, Managing Editor, victor.jongeneel@licr.org; Lloyd J. Old, MD, Editor-in-Chief, lold@licr.org; Garry I. Abelev, Contributing Ed., abelev@crc.umos.ru; Ronald Levy, Contributing Ed., levy@stanford.edu; Gert Riethmuller, Contributing Ed., riethmueller@med.uni-muenchen.de; Hiroshi Shiku, Contributing Ed., shiku@clin.medic.mie-u.ac.jp; Giorgio Parmiani, Contributing Ed., parmiani@istitutotumori.mi.it; Richmond T. Prehn, Contributing Ed., prehn@u.washington.edu; Rolf M. Zinkernagel, Contributing Ed., rolf.zinkernagel@pty.usz.ch; Eva Klein, Contributing Ed., eva.klein@mtc.ki.se. **ISSN:** 1424-9634. **URL:** http://www.cancerimmunity.org.

51185 ■ Cement and Concrete Research
Elsevier Science
c/o Karen Scrivener, Ed.-in-Ch.
Laboratory of Construction Materials (LMC)
Ecole Polytechnique Federale de Lausanne (EPFL)
CH-1015 Lausanne, Switzerland
Publisher E-mail: nlinfo-f@elsevier.com
Journal covering latest in research on cement, cement composites, concrete and other associated materials that use cement. **Founded:** 1971. **Freq:** Monthly. **Key Personnel:** Karen Scrivener, Editor-in-Chief, karen.scrivener@epfl.ch; Keith Baldie, Managing Editor, cacr@bluewin.ch; A. Bentur, Board of Ed.; Della M. Roy, Founding Ed.; C. Andrade, Board of Ed.; Hiroshi Uchikawa, Honorary Editorial Board. **ISSN:** 0008-8846. **Subscription Rates:** US$3,179 institutions for all countries except Europe, Japan & Iran; 377,400¥ institutions; EUR2,841 institutions for European countries & Iran; US$468 individuals for all countries except Europe, Japan & Iran; 55,400¥ individuals; EUR415 individuals for European countries & Iran. **Remarks:** Accepts advertising. **URL:** http://www.elsevier.com/wps/find/journaldescription.cws_home/352/description; http://www.elsevier.com/wps/find/journaldescription.cws_home/352/descriptio ndescription. **Circ:** (Not Reported)

51186 ■ Edelweiss
Ringier Publishing House Switzerland
7, Rue St.-Martin
Casa postale 6003
CH-1005 Lausanne, Switzerland
Ph: 41 21 3317500
Fax: 41 21 3317501
Publication E-mail: edelweiss@ringier.ch
Publisher E-mail: info@ringier.ch
Magazine for women. **Freq:** Monthly. **Key Personnel:** Laurence Desbordes, Editor-in-Chief, laurence.desbordes@ringier.ch; Anne Niederoest, Mktg. Mgr., anne.niederoest@ringier.ch. **Remarks:** Accepts advertising. **URL:** http://www.ringier.ch/index.cfm?&id=3788; http://home.edelweissmag.ch/. **Circ:** 24,185

51187 ■ Electrochimica Acta
International Society of Electrochemistry

Rue de Sebeillon 9b
CH-1004 Lausanne, Switzerland
Fax: 41 21 6483975
Publisher E-mail: info@ise-online.org
Publication covering chemistry. **Freq:** 28/yr. **Key Personnel:** S. Trasatti, Editor-in-Chief, electrochim.acta@unimi.it. **ISSN:** 0013-4686. **Subscription Rates:** EUR151 members print; EUR90 members electronic access. **Remarks:** Advertising accepted; rates available upon request. **URL:** http://www.ise-online.org. **Circ:** 1,400

51188 ■ European Journal of Cardio-Thoracic Surgery
Mosby Inc.
c/o Ludwig Karl von Segesser, MD, Ed.-in-Ch.
Rue du Bugnon 46
CH-1011 Lausanne, Switzerland
Publication E-mail: info@ejcts.ch
Publisher E-mail: custserv.ehs@elsevier.com
Peer-reviewed journal publishing scientific reports documenting progress in cardiac and thoracic surgery. **Freq:** Monthly. **Key Personnel:** Ludwig K. Von Segesser, MD, Editor-in-Chief, phone 41 21 3142280, fax 41 21 3142278, ludwig.von-segesser@chuv.hospvd.ch; Manuel J. Antunes, Assoc. Ed., phone 35 123 9400418, fax 35 123 9829674, antunes.cct.huc@sapo.pt; Jean E. Bachet, MD, Assoc. Ed., phone 97 1 509120454, jean.bachet@dms.mil.ae. **ISSN:** 1010-7940. **Subscription Rates:** US$394 other countries except Europe, Japan and Iran; 46,800¥ individuals; EUR353 individuals for European countries and Iran; US$885 institutions, other countries except Europe, Japan and Iran; 105¥ institutions; EUR791 institutions for European countries and Iran. **Remarks:** Accepts advertising. **URL:** http://ejcts.ctsnetjournals.org/; http://www.elsevier.com/wps/find/journaldescription.cws_home/600127/descriptiondescription; http://journals.elsevierhealth.com/periodicals/ejcts. **Circ:** (Not Reported)

51189 ■ Femina Fashion
Edipresse Publications S.A.
39, Ave. de la Gare
Case postale 615
CH-1001 Lausanne, Switzerland
Ph: 41 21 3494848
Fax: 41 21 3494859
Publication E-mail: femina@edipresse.ch
Publisher E-mail: groupe@edipresse.com
Magazine featuring latest trends in the world of fashion. **Freq:** Quarterly. **Key Personnel:** Serge Reymond, Director; Annick Chevillot, Ch. Ed. **URL:** http://www.edipresse.com/womens/femina-fashion; http://www.femina.ch/pages/home/mode. **Circ:** ‡25,000

51190 ■ L'Hebdo
Pont Bessieres 3
PO Box 6682
CH-1002 Lausanne, Switzerland
Ph: 41 213 317600
Fax: 41 213 317601
Publisher E-mail: hebdo@ringier.ch
Consumer news magazine. **Founded:** Sept. 1981. **Freq:** Weekly. **Print Method:** Offset. **Key Personnel:** Ringier Romandie, Editor, phone 41 213 317000, fax 41 213 317101, ringier.romandie@ringier.ch. **URL:** http://www.hebdo.ch. **Circ:** Controlled 72,000

51191 ■ L'illustre
Ringier Publishing House Switzerland
Pont Bessieres 3
CH-1002 Lausanne, Switzerland
Ph: 41 21 3317500
Fax: 41 21 3317501
Publication E-mail: illustre@ringier.ch
Publisher E-mail: info@ringier.ch
Illustrated magazine. **Freq:** Weekly. **Key Personnel:** Daniel Pillard, Editor-in-Chief, daniel.pillard@ringier.ch; Antoine Egger, Mktg. Mgr., antoine.egger@ringier.ch. **Remarks:** Accepts advertising. **URL:** http://www.illustre.ch/; http://www.ringier.ch/index.cfm?id=423&rub=159. **Circ:** 90,635

51192 ■ Insurance
Elsevier Science
c/o H.U. Gerber, Ed.
Ecole des Hautes Etudes Commerciales
CH-1015 Lausanne, Switzerland
Publisher E-mail: nlinfo-f@elsevier.com
Journal dealing with the theory of insurance mathematics and economics. **Subtitle:** Mathematics and Economics. **Founded:** 1982. **Freq:** Bimonthly. **Key Per-**

sonnel: R. Kaas, Managing Editor, insmathecon@gmail.com; M.J. Goovaerts, Editor; H.U. Gerber, Editor; E.S.W. Shiu, Editor; P.P. Boyle, Advisory Ed.; H. Albrecher, Editor; T. Hu, Assoc. Ed.; C. Hipp, Assoc. Ed.; P. Embrechts, Assoc. Ed. ISSN: 0167-6687. Subscription Rates: EUR100 individuals European countries; US$107 individuals all countries except Europe and Japan; 13,500¥ individuals; US$1,586 institutions for all countries except Europe and Japan; EUR1,419 institutions for European countries; 188,700¥ institutions. Remarks: Accepts advertising. URL: http://www.elsevier.com/wps/find/journaldescription.cws_home/505554/descrip tion. Circ: (Not Reported)

51193 ■ Lausanne-Cites
Edipresse Publications S.A.
17, Ave. d'Echallens
CH-1000 Lausanne 9, Switzerland
Ph: 41 21 6263939
Fax: 41 21 6263940
Publication E-mail: info@lausannecites.ch
Publisher E-mail: groupe@edipresse.com
Newspaper featuring the Lausanne region. Freq: Weekly. Key Personnel: Pascal Fleury, Director; Charles-Andre Aymon, Ch. Ed. URL: http://www.edipresse.com/weeklies/lausanne-cit%C3%A9s. Circ: ‡157,734

51194 ■ Le Matin
Edipresse Publications S.A.
Av. de la Gare 33
CH-1001 Lausanne, Switzerland
Ph: 41 21 3494545
Fax: 41 21 3494110
Publication E-mail: lematin@edipresse.ch
Publisher E-mail: groupe@edipresse.com
Newspaper reporting the sports, celebrities and latest events of the region. Freq: Daily. Key Personnel: Serge Reymond, Director; Sandra Jean, Ch. Ed. URL: http://www.edipresse.com/dailies/le-matin; http://www.lematin.ch/. Circ: ‡58,849

51195 ■ Le Matin
Edipresse Publications S.A.
Av. de la Gare 33
CH-1001 Lausanne, Switzerland
Ph: 41 21 3494545
Fax: 41 21 3494110
Publication E-mail: lematinbleu@edipresse.ch
Publisher E-mail: groupe@edipresse.com
Newspaper reporting the international, national and local current events. Founded: Oct. 2005. Freq: Daily. Key Personnel: Serge Reymond, Director; Sandra Jean, Ch. Ed. URL: http://www.edipresse.com/dailies/le-matin. Circ: ‡230,873

51196 ■ Le Matin Dimanche
Edipresse Publications S.A.
Av. de la Gare 33
CH-1001 Lausanne, Switzerland
Ph: 41 21 3494545
Fax: 41 21 3494110
Publisher E-mail: groupe@edipresse.com
Sunday newspaper covering Saturday's news. Freq: Weekly. Key Personnel: Serge Reymond, Director; Ariane Dayer, Ch. Ed. URL: http://www.edipresse.com/weeklies/le-matin-dimanche; http://www.lematin.ch/. Circ: ‡193,601

51197 ■ Montres Passion/Uhren Welt
Pont Bessieres 3
CH-1002 Lausanne, Switzerland
Ph: 41 21 331 7000
Fax: 41 21 331 7121
Publication E-mail: info.montres@ringier.ch
Publisher E-mail: ringier.romandie@ringier.ch
Consumer magazine covering watches. Freq: Semiannual March and November. Print Method: Offset. Trim Size: 210 x 280 mm. Cols./Page: 3. Key Personnel: Ringier Romandie, Editor; Tegin Kenan, Collaborator; Jean Philippe, Editor-in-Chief. Subscription Rates: 20 SFr individuals; 10 SFr single issue. Remarks: Accepts advertising. URL: http://www.montrespassion.ch/. Circ: Controlled 180,000

51198 ■ Optics and Lasers in Engineering
Elsevier Science
c/o P.K. Rastogi, Ed.
Swiss Federal Institute of Technology (EPFL)
Laboratory for Stress Analysis (IMAC, DGC)
CH-1015 Lausanne, Switzerland
Ph: 41 216 932445

Fax: 41 216 934748
Publisher E-mail: nlinfo-f@elsevier.com
Peer-reviewed journal providing a platform for exchange of information on the development and use of optical methods and laser technology in engineering. Founded: 1980. Freq: Monthly. Key Personnel: P.K. Rastogi, Editor, pramod.rastogi@epfl.ch; A.K. Asundi, Editor, phone 65 799 5936, fax 65 791 1859, anand.asundi@pmail.ntu.edu.sg; H.V. Tippur, Assoc. Ed.; D. Ambrosini, Editorial Board; P. Ferraro, Editorial Board; D. Inaudi, Editorial Board. ISSN: 0143-8166. Subscription Rates: 324,200¥ institutions; US$2,732 institutions for all countries except Europe, Japan & Iran; EUR2,444 institutions for European countries & Iran. Remarks: Advertising accepted; rates available upon request. URL: http://www.elsevier.com/wps/find/journaldescription.cws_home/405906/descriptiondescription. Circ: (Not Reported)

51199 ■ Revue Militaire Suisse
Association de la Revue Militaire Suisse
Av. Florimont 3
CH-1006 Lausanne, Switzerland
Ph: 41 213 114817
Publisher E-mail: administration@revuemilitairesuisse.ch
Swiss military publication. Founded: 1856. Freq: Monthly. Cols./Page: 3. Key Personnel: Herve de Weck, Editor, phone 41 324 665232, herve.deweck@bluewin.ch. ISSN: 0035-368X. Remarks: Accepts advertising. URL: http://www.revuemilitairesuisse.ch/. Circ: (Not Reported)

51200 ■ Tele top matin
Edipresse Publications S.A.
Av. de la Gare 33
CH-1001 Lausanne, Switzerland
Ph: 41 21 3494545
Fax: 41 21 3494110
Publication E-mail: teletop@edipresse.ch
Publisher E-mail: groupe@edipresse.com
Magazine featuring television programs in Switzerland. Freq: Weekly. Key Personnel: Serge Reymond, Director; Laurent Delaloye, Ch. Ed. URL: http://www.edipresse.com/tv/t%C3%A9l%C3%A9-top-matin. Circ: ‡193,316

51201 ■ TV8
Ringier Publishing House Switzerland
Pont Bessieres 3
Case Postale 7572
CH-1002 Lausanne, Switzerland
Ph: 41 21 3317700
Fax: 41 21 3317701
Publication E-mail: tv8@ringier.ch
Publisher E-mail: info@ringier.ch
Television program magazine. Freq: Weekly. Key Personnel: Christophe Passer, Editor-in-Chief, christophe.passer@ringier.ch; Antoine Egger, Mktg. Mgr., antoine.egger@ringier.ch. Remarks: Accepts advertising. URL: http://www.tv8.ch/; http://www.ringier.ch/index.cfm?&id=427. Circ: 84,087

51202 ■ 24 Heures
Edipresse Publications S.A.
Av. de la Gare 33
CH-1001 Lausanne, Switzerland
Ph: 41 21 3494545
Fax: 41 21 3494110
Publication E-mail: 24heures@edipresse.ch
Publisher E-mail: groupe@edipresse.com
Newspaper covering the whole canton of Vaud. Freq: Daily. Key Personnel: Serge Reymond, Director; Thierry Meyer, Ch. Ed. URL: http://www.24heures.ch/. Circ: ‡85,813

51203 ■ Radio Ndeke Luka-FM - 100.8
Ave. du Temple 19C
CH-1012 Lausanne, Switzerland
Ph: 41 21 6542020
Fax: 41 21 6542021
E-mail: info@hirondelle.org
Format: Ethnic; Information; News. Owner: Foundation Hirondelle, at above address. Operating Hours: Continuous. URL: http://www.hirondelle.org

51204 ■ Rouge-FM - 106.5
En Budron A6
CH-1052 Lausanne, Switzerland
Ph: 41 21 6546010

Fax: 41 21 6546003
Format: Ethnic; World Beat. Owner: Rouge FM SA, at above address. Operating Hours: 20 hours Daily. Key Personnel: Fradaric Piancastelli, Dir. Gen., frederic.piancastelli@rougefm.com. URL: http://www.rougefm.com.

Lausanne-Dorigny

51205 ■ Expositiones Mathematicae
Elsevier Science Inc.
c/o Robert C. Dalang, Mng. Ed.
Ecole Polytechnique Federale de Lausanne
Institut de Mathematiques (IMA)
SB-IMA-PROB, Sta. 8
CH-1015 Lausanne-Dorigny, Switzerland
Ph: 41 21 6932551
Fax: 41 21 6935380
Publisher E-mail: usinfo-ehelp@elsevier.com
Journal devoted to mathematicians. Founded: 1983. Freq: 4/yr. Print Method: Offset. Trim Size: 12 1/2 x 22. Cols./Page: 6. Col. Width: 11 nonpareils. Col. Depth: 301 agate lines. Key Personnel: Kristian Seip, Editorial Board; Nicolas H. Bingham, Editorial Board; Pierre Cartier, Editorial Board; Srishti D. Chatterji, Editorial Board; Bas Edixhoven, Editorial Board; John Friedlander, Editorial Board; Garth Gaudry, Editorial Board; Robert C. Dalang, Managing Editor, robert.dalang@epfl.ch. ISSN: 0723-0869. Subscription Rates: 55,500¥ institutions; EUR407 institutions for European countries and Iran; US$463 institutions except Europe, Japan and Iran. URL: http://www.elsevier.com/wps/find/journaldescription.cws_home/701763/descriptiondescription.

Leuk

51206 ■ Radio Rottu Oberwallis-FM - 97.8
Postfach
CH-3930 Visp, Switzerland
Ph: 41 27 9480948
Fax: 41 27 9480945
E-mail: info@rro.ch
Format: Ethnic; World Beat. Operating Hours: Continuous. URL: http://www.rro.ch.

Liestal

51207 ■ Organic Chemistry Highlights
Reto Muller
Oberer Burghaldenweg 22
CH-4410 Liestal, Switzerland
Publisher E-mail: contact@organic-chemistry.org
Journal dealing with organic, bioorganic, organometallic and microwave chemistry. Covers complete synthesis of natural products and multicomponent reactions. Key Personnel: Reto Muller, Publisher, contact@organic-chemistry.org. Remarks: Accepts advertising. URL: http://www.organic-chemistry.org/. Circ: (Not Reported)

51208 ■ Radio Basel 1-FM - 101.7
Rheinstrasse 16
CH-4410 Liestal, Switzerland
Ph: 41 61 9274949
Fax: 41 61 9274999
E-mail: feedback@basel1.ch
Format: Ethnic; News; World Beat. Operating Hours: Continuous. URL: http://www.basel1.ch.

Locarno

51209 ■ il caffe
Ringier Publishing House Switzerland
Via B. Luini 19
CH-6600 Locarno, Switzerland
Ph: 41 91 7562400
Fax: 41 91 7562439
Publication E-mail: caffe@caffe.ch
Publisher E-mail: info@ringier.ch
Sunday newspaper. Freq: Weekly. Key Personnel: Lillo Alaimo, Editor-in-Chief, alaimo@caffe.ch; Dr. Gio Rezzonico, Commercial Dir. Remarks: Accepts advertising. URL: http://www.ringier.ch/index.cfm?id=3937&rub=158; http://www.caffe.ch/mycaffe/index.php. Circ: Free 59,733

Lucerne

51210 ■ Schweizerische Kirchenzeitung
LZ Fachverlag AG

Maihofstrasse 76
CH-6002 Lucerne, Switzerland
Ph: 41 429 5252
Fax: 41 429 5367
Publication E-mail: skzredaktion@lzmedien.ch
Publisher E-mail: info@lzfachverlag.ch
Publication covering theology and Roman Catholic religion. **Founded:** 1832. **Freq:** Weekly. **Key Personnel:** Dr. Urban Fink-Wagner, Editor-in-Chief; Dr. Adrian Loretan, Editorial Commission; Prof. Heinz Angehrn, Editorial Commission; Dr. Berchtold Muller, Editorial Commission. **ISSN:** 1420-5041. **Subscription Rates:** US$156 individuals super saver shipping; US$3 single issue super saver shipping. **Remarks:** Accepts advertising. **URL:** http://www.kath.ch/skz/. **Circ:** Paid 3,000

Melide

51211 ■ Radio R3iii-FM - 106.8
Radio 3iii cp 372
CH-6815 Melide, Switzerland
Ph: 41 91 6401550
Fax: 41 91 6401559
E-mail: diretta@r3i.ch
Format: Ethnic; World Beat. **Ad Rates:** Advertising accepted; rates available upon request. **URL:** http://www.r3i.ch.

Mies

51212 ■ FIM Magazine
Federation Internationale de Motocyclisme
11 Rte. Suisse
CH-1295 Mies, Switzerland
Ph: 41 229 509500
Fax: 41 229 509501
Publication E-mail: press@fim.ch
Publisher E-mail: info@fim-live.com
Magazine covering motorcycles. **Founded:** 1992. **Freq:** Quarterly. **Key Personnel:** Vito Ippolito, President. **Subscription Rates:** Free. **Remarks:** Advertising accepted; rates available upon request. **URL:** http://www.fim.ch/en/default.asp?item=44. **Circ:** 2,600

Morges

51213 ■ Journal de Morges
Edipresse Publications S.A.
1, Grand-Rue
CH-1110 Morges 1, Switzerland
Ph: 41 21 8012138
Fax: 41 21 8012130
Publication E-mail: journal@morges.ch
Publisher E-mail: groupe@edipresse.com
Newspaper covering the current events in Morges region. **Freq:** Weekly. **Key Personnel:** Eric Hoesli, Director; Cedric Jotterand, Ch. Ed. **URL:** http://www.edipresse.com/weeklies/journal-de-morges. **Circ:** ‡7,052

Muttenz

51214 ■ Schweizerische Arztezeitung/Bulletin des Medecins Suisses
EMH Swiss Medical Publishers Ltd.
Farnsburgerstrasse 8
CH-4132 Muttenz, Switzerland
Ph: 41 614 678555
Fax: 41 614 678556
Publisher E-mail: verlag@emh.ch
Professional magazine of the Swiss Medical Association. **Founded:** 1920. **Freq:** Weekly. **Print Method:** Offset. **Trim Size:** 210 x 297 mm. **Key Personnel:** Thomas Heuer, Managing Editor. **ISSN:** 0036-7486. **Subscription Rates:** EUR277 individuals. **Remarks:** Accepts advertising. **URL:** http://www.saez.ch; http://www.bullmed.ch. **Circ:** Paid 29,599

51215 ■ Swiss Medical Weekly
EMH Swiss Medical Publishers Ltd.
Farnsburgerstrasse 8
CH-4132 Muttenz, Switzerland
Ph: 41 614 678555
Fax: 41 614 678556
Publisher E-mail: verlag@emh.ch
Professional medical journal. **Founded:** 1871. **Freq:** Semimonthly. **Print Method:** Offset. **Trim Size:** 210 x 297 mm. **Key Personnel:** Natalie Marty, MD, Managing

Editor, nmarty@emh.ch; Prof. Andre P. Perruchoud, Editorial Board; Prof. Jean Michel Dayer, Editorial Board; Prof. Peter Gehr, Editorial Board. **ISSN:** 1424-7860. **Subscription Rates:** 150 SFri individuals; EUR105 individuals excl. postage; 20 SFri individuals postage Switzerland; 37 SFri individuals Europe postage abroad; 52 SFri other countries postage abroad; 20 SFri single issue excl. postage. **Remarks:** Accepts advertising. **URL:** http://www.smw.ch. **Former name:** Schweizerische Medizinische Wochenschrift. **Circ:** Controlled 4,500

Neuhausen

51216 ■ Ars Medici
SAEH Verlag AG
Schaffhausersh 13
CH-8212 Neuhausen, Switzerland
Ph: 41 526 755060
Fax: 41 526 755061
Publisher E-mail: info@rosenfluh.ch
Professional, medical magazine for physicians. **Founded:** 1910. **Freq:** Semimonthly 26/yr. **Print Method:** Offset. **Cols./Page:** 3. **Key Personnel:** Halid Bas, Editor. **ISSN:** 0004-2897. **Remarks:** Accepts advertising. **URL:** http://www.rosenfluh.ch/rosenfluh/issues/view/96. **Ad Rates:** BW: 2,580 SFr, 4C: 4,180 SFr. **Circ:** (Not Reported)

51217 ■ Gynakologie
SAEH Verlag AG
Schaffhausersh 13
CH-8212 Neuhausen, Switzerland
Ph: 41 526 755060
Fax: 41 526 755061
Publisher E-mail: info@rosenfluh.ch
Professional, medical magazine for gynecologists and obstetricians. **Founded:** 1995. **Freq:** Bimonthly. **Print Method:** Offset. **Cols./Page:** 3. **ISSN:** 1420-6811. **Remarks:** Accepts advertising. **URL:** http://www.rosenfluh.ch/. **Ad Rates:** BW: 2,920 SFr, 4C: 4,520 SFr. **Circ:** (Not Reported)

51218 ■ Padiatrie
SAEH Verlag AG
Schaffhausersh 13
CH-8212 Neuhausen, Switzerland
Ph: 41 526 755060
Fax: 41 526 755061
Publisher E-mail: info@rosenfluh.ch
Professional magazine covering pediatric medicine. **Founded:** 1994. **Freq:** Bimonthly. **Print Method:** Offset. **Cols./Page:** 3. **ISSN:** 1424-8468. **Remarks:** Accepts advertising. **URL:** http://www.rosenfluh.ch/rosenfluh/publikationen/view/7. **Ad Rates:** BW: 2,920 SFr, 4C: 4,520 SFr. **Circ:** (Not Reported)

Niederonz

51219 ■ Forum Kleinwiederkaeuer
Verlagsgenossenschaft Caprovis
Industriestr. 9
Postfach 2
CH-3362 Niederonz, Switzerland
Ph: 41 62 9566874
Fax: 41 02 9500079
Publication E-mail: forum.kleinwiederkaeuer@caprovis.ch
Trade magazine covering agriculture. **Founded:** 1997. **Freq:** 10/yr. **Subscription Rates:** 46 SFr individuals; 63 SFr other countries. **Remarks:** Accepts advertising. **URL:** http://www.caprovis.ch. **Circ:** Controlled 14,569

Payerne

51220 ■ La Broye
Edipresse Publications S.A.
Rue d'Yverdon 19
Case postale 124
CH-1530 Payerne, Switzerland
Ph: 41 26 6624888
Fax: 41 26 6624899
Publisher E-mail: groupe@edipresse.com
Newspaper covering the latest events from Vaudois districts of Avenches, Moudon and Payerne, including the Fribourg district of La Broye. **Freq:** Weekly. **Key Personnel:** Serge Reymond, Director; Daniele Pittet, Ch. Ed. **URL:** http://www.edipresse.com/weeklies/labroye. **Circ:** ‡7,686

Posieux

51221 ■ Agrarforschung Schweiz
Bundesamt fur Landwirtschaft
c/o Andrea Leuenberger, Ed.
Agroscope Liebefeld (ALP)
CH-1725 Posieux, Switzerland
Ph: 41 264 077221
Fax: 41 264 077300
Publication E-mail: agrarforschung@alp.admin.ch
Publisher E-mail: psm@blw.admin.ch
Journal of the Swiss agricultural research stations. **Subtitle:** Journal of Swiss Agricultural Research. **Founded:** 1994. **Freq:** Monthly 11/yr. **Print Method:** Offset. **Cols./Page:** 4. **Col. Width:** 45 millimeters. **Key Personnel:** Nicole Boschung, Sec.; Andrea Leuenberger, Editor. **ISSN:** 1022-663X. **Subscription Rates:** 61 SFr individuals print-edition; 65 SFr other countries print-edition; 61 SFr individuals online-edition; 61 SFr out of country online-edition; 71 SFr individuals print + online; 75 SFr other countries print + online. **Remarks:** Accepts advertising. **URL:** http://www.agrarforschung.ch/. **Circ:** Paid 12,500

Pully

51222 ■ Le Cavalier Romand
Le Cavalier Romand—Pro Cheval
Rue du Port 24
CH-1009 Pully, Switzerland
Ph: 41 21 7298683
Fax: 41 21 7298761
Publisher E-mail: poudret@cavalier-romand.ch
Equestrian magazine. **Founded:** 1919. **Freq:** Monthly 11/yr. **Print Method:** Offset. **Trim Size:** 210 x 297 mm. **Key Personnel:** Alban Poudret, Editor, phone 44 21 7298683, fax 44 21 7298761, poudret@cavalier-romand.ch; Gaelle Kursner, Asst. of Drafting; Sophie Kasser-Deller, Writer; Nathalie Poudret, Collaborator; Laurence De Pescara, Contact; Helga Eppler, Contact, h.eppler@hispeed.ch; Pascal Mathieu, Contact, pascal.mathieu@bluewin.ch; Liliane Rochat, Contact, liliane@cheval-loisir.ch; Patricia Balsiger, Contact, patricia.balsiger@bluewin.ch. **Subscription Rates:** EUR98 individuals; EUR112 individuals French rider. **Remarks:** Accepts advertising. **URL:** http://www.cavalier-romand.ch/. **Ad Rates:** BW: 1,675 SFr, 4C: 3,100 SFr. **Circ:** Controlled 8,000

Saint Gallen

51223 ■ Coating
Verlag Coating Thomas & Co.
Schmiedgasse 5
Postfach 1762
CH-9001 Saint Gallen, Switzerland
Ph: 41 712 282011
Fax: 41 712 282014
Publisher E-mail: leser-service@coating.ch
Professional magazine covering chemical and technical coating worldwide. **Freq:** Monthly. **Print Method:** Offset. **Trim Size:** 213 x 303 mm. **Remarks:** Accepts advertising. **URL:** http://www.coating.ch. **Ad Rates:** BW: 2,170 SFr, 4C: 3,910 SFr. **Circ:** Combined 4,500

51224 ■ Thexis
Universitat St. Gallen
Swiss Research Institute for Marketing and Distribution
Dufourstrasse 50
CH-9000 Saint Gallen, Switzerland
Ph: 41 71 2242111
Fax: 41 71 2242816
Publisher E-mail: info@unisg.ch
Marketing journal of the University of St. Gallen in Switzerland. **Key Personnel:** Johannes Hattula, Contact. **ISSN:** 0254-9697. **URL:** http://thexis.imh.unisg.ch.

51225 ■ Viscom
Verlagsgemeinschaft Viscom/St. Galler Tagblatt AG
Furstenlandstr. 122
CH-9001 Saint Gallen, Switzerland
Ph: 41 71 2727248
Fax: 41 71 2727487
Publisher E-mail: office@viscom-press.ch
Trade magazine covering graphic design (German, French, and Italian). **Subtitle:** Print & Communication. **Founded:** Apr. 1998. **Freq:** Semimonthly. **Print Method:** Offset. **Trim Size:** 210 x 297 mm. **Cols./Page:** 4. Key

---

Circulation: ★ = ABC; △ = BPA; ♦ = CAC; • = CCAB; □ = VAC; ⊕ = PO Statement; ‡ = Publisher's Report; Boldface figures = sworn; Light figures = estimated.

Personnel: Imelda Sonderegger, Contact, office@viscom-press.ch. **Subscription Rates:** US$136 individuals; US$176 other countries. **URL:** http://www.viscom-press.ch. **Ad Rates:** BW: 2,930 SFr, 4C: 4,400 SFr. **Circ:** 14,595

51226 ■ Toxic-FM - 107.1
Engelaustrasse 15
CH-9010 Saint Gallen, Switzerland
Ph: 41 71 2450220
Fax: 41 71 2450221
E-mail: info@toxic.fm
Format: Eclectic. **Operating Hours:** Continuous. **URL:** http://www.toxic.fm.

Schaffhausen

51227 ■ Radio Munot-FM - 107.5
Bachstrasse 29a
Postfach 1226
CH-8201 Schaffhausen, Switzerland
Ph: 41 52 6247690
Fax: 41 52 6243008
Format: Ethnic; World Beat. **Operating Hours:** Continuous. **Key Personnel:** Thomas Spengler, President; Philipp Inauen, Editor-in-Chief, philippinauen@radiomunot.ch; Yves Keller, Editor, yveskeller@radiomunot.ch. **Ad Rates:** Advertising accepted; rates available upon request. **URL:** http://www.radiomunot.ch.

51228 ■ Radio Munot-FM - 101.85
PO Box 1226
Bachstrasse 29a
CH-8201 Schaffhausen, Switzerland
Ph: 41 52 6247690
Fax: 41 52 6243008
Format: Ethnic; World Beat. **Operating Hours:** Continuous. **Key Personnel:** Philipp Inauen, Editor-in-Chief, philippinauen@radiomunot.ch; Nora Winzeler, Editor, norawinzeler@radiomunot.ch; Severo Marchionne, Music Ed., musikredaktion@radiomunot.ch. **Ad Rates:** Advertising accepted; rates available upon request. **URL:** http://www.radiomunot.ch.

51229 ■ Radio Munot-FM - 103.1
Bachstrasse 29a
Postfach 1226
CH-8201 Schaffhausen, Switzerland
Ph: 41 52 6247690
Fax: 41 52 6243008
Format: Ethnic; World Beat. **Operating Hours:** Continuous. **Key Personnel:** Thomas Spengler, President; Philipp Inauen, Editor-in-Chief, philippinauen@radiomunot.ch; Yves Keller, Editor, yveskeller@radiomunot.ch. **Ad Rates:** Advertising accepted; rates available upon request. **URL:** http://www.radiomunot.ch.

Schlieren

51230 ■ Aktuelle Technik
B & L Verlags AG
Steinwiesenstr. 3
CH-8952 Schlieren, Switzerland
Ph: 41 44 7333999
Fax: 41 44 7333989
Trade magazine covering industrial electronics. **Founded:** 1977. **Freq:** Monthly. **Print Method:** Offset. **Trim Size:** 210 x 297 mm. **Key Personnel:** Marcus Back, Contact. **Subscription Rates:** 34 SFr individuals; 4 SFr single issue. **Remarks:** Accepts advertising. **URL:** http://www.blverlag.ch/web/internetblsw.nsf/Zeitschriften?ReadForm&magazin=AT&HR=01&nav=2.01&npreset=1. **Circ:** Combined 14,500

Sirnach

51231 ■ Professional Computing
UTK Media
Frauenfelderstr. 49
CH-8370 Sirnach, Switzerland
Ph: 41 719 666080
Fax: 41 719 666081
Publisher E-mail: info@utk.ch
Professional magazine covering information technology. **Founded:** Sept. 1996. **Freq:** Quarterly. **Trim Size:** A4. **Key Personnel:** Jorg Schelling, Editor-in-Chief, redaktion@utk.ch; Martin Hofer, Contact, martin.hofer@utk.ch; Pascal Tobler, Contact, pascal.tobler@utk.ch. **URL:** http://www.utk.ch.

Solothurn

51232 ■ Schweizer Waffen-Magazin
Vogt-Schild/Habegger Media
Zuchwilerstr. 21
PO Box 716
CH-4501 Solothurn, Switzerland
Ph: 41 326 247111
Fax: 41 326 247444
Consumer magazine covering guns, knives, and other weapons, self-defense and related topics. **Founded:** Nov. 1982. **Freq:** Monthly. **Print Method:** Offset. **Trim Size:** 21 x 28 cm. **Cols./Page:** 4. **Col. Width:** 4.2 centimeters. **Col. Depth:** 24.2 centimeters. **Key Personnel:** Laszlo Tolvaj, Editor-in-Chief. **ISSN:** 1017-5547. **Subscription Rates:** EUR94 individuals. **Remarks:** Accepts advertising. **URL:** http://www.waffenmagazin.ch/. **Former name:** Internationales Waffen Magazin. **Circ:** Paid 20,000, Non-paid 10,000

51233 ■ Radio 32-FM - 92.2
Niklaus-Konradstrasse 26
CH-4500 Solothurn, Switzerland
Ph: 41 32 6258220
Fax: 41 32 6258235
E-mail: radio32@radio32.ch
Format: Ethnic; Contemporary Hit Radio (CHR). **Ad Rates:** Advertising accepted; rates available upon request. **URL:** http://www.radio32.ch.

Thalwil

51234 ■ Infoweek.ch
Compress AG
Seestrasse 99
CH-8800 Thalwil, Switzerland
Ph: 41 44 7227700
Fax: 41 44 7227701
Publication E-mail: infoweek@compress.ch
Publisher E-mail: info@compress.ch
Trade magazine covering computing, the Internet, and electronic commerce. **Founded:** Sept. 14, 2000. **Freq:** Semiweekly. **Print Method:** Offset. **Trim Size:** 235 x 325 mm. **Key Personnel:** Marc von Ah, Contact, mva@compress.ch. **URL:** http://www.swissitmagazine.ch/. **Circ:** Combined 18,000

Torbel

51235 ■ Radio Rottu Oberwallis-FM - 102.9
Postfach
CH-3930 Visp, Switzerland
Ph: 41 27 9480948
Fax: 41 27 9480945
E-mail: info@rro.ch
Format: Ethnic; World Beat. **Owner:** Radio Rottu Oberwallis Ag., at above address. **Operating Hours:** Continuous. **URL:** http://www.rro.ch.

Uster

51236 ■ Rotary Suisse-Liechtenstein
Aathalstr. 34
8613 Uster, Switzerland
Ph: 41 44 9941666
Fax: 41 44 9941665
Publisher E-mail: schaffner@rotary.ch
Membership magazine of Rotary International covering current news about Rotary-related subjects in German, French, and Italian. **Key Personnel:** Oliver P. Schaffner, Editor, phone 41 19941666, fax 41 19941665, schaffner@rotary.ch. **URL:** http://www2.rotary.ch/; http://www.rotary.org/en/mediaandnews/morepublications/regionalmagazines/pages/ridefault.aspx. **Circ:** ‡12,000

Viganello-Lugano

51237 ■ Annals of Oncology
Oxford University Press
Via Luigi Taddei 4
CH-6962 Viganello-Lugano, Switzerland
Ph: 41 91 9731910
Publisher E-mail: webenquiry.uk@oup.com
Multidisciplinary journal publishing articles addressing medical oncology, surgery, radiotherapy, pediatric oncology, basic research and the comprehensive management of patients with malignant diseases including such topics as breast cancer, gastrointestinal tumors, lung cancer, urogenital tumors, hematologic malignancies, head and neck cancer, sarcomas, gynecologic cancer,

quality of life and supportive care, Phase I studies, Phase II studies, Phase III studies and translational science. **Freq:** 12/yr. **Key Personnel:** Prof. D.J. Kerr, Ed. Emeriti; Lewis Rowett, Exec. Ed., rowett.lewis@esmo.org; H. McLeod, Assoc. Ed. **ISSN:** 0923-7534. **Subscription Rates:** 1,106 institutions print and online; US$2,212 institutions print and online; EUR1,659 institutions print and online; 922 institutions print or online; US$1,844 institutions print or online; EUR1,383 institutions print or online; 598 members American society of clinical oncology; EUR897 members American society of clinical oncology; 959 individuals print; US$1,196 members American society of clinical oncology. **Remarks:** Advertising accepted; rates available upon request. **URL:** http://annonc.oxfordjournals.org. **Circ:** (Not Reported)

Visp

51238 ■ Radio Rottu Oberwallis-FM - 101.8
Postfach
CH-3930 Visp, Switzerland
Ph: 41 27 9480948
Fax: 41 27 9480945
E-mail: info@rro.ch
Format: Ethnic; World Beat. **Operating Hours:** Continuous. **URL:** http://www.rro.ch.

51239 ■ Radio Rottu Oberwallis-FM - 100
Postfach
CH-3930 Visp, Switzerland
Ph: 41 27 9480948
Fax: 41 27 9480945
E-mail: info@rro.ch
Format: Ethnic; World Beat. **Operating Hours:** Continuous. **Key Personnel:** Michael Brunner, Prog. Master. **URL:** http://www.rro.ch.

Radio Rottu Oberwallis-FM - See Hohtenn

Radio Rottu Oberwallis-FM - See Leuk

Radio Rottu Oberwallis-FM - See Torbel

Winterthur

51240 ■ European Vegetarian
European Vegetarian Union
Niederfeldstrasse 92
CH-8408 Winterthur, Switzerland
Ph: 41 71 4773377
Fax: 41 71 4773378
Publisher E-mail: evu.public01@euroveg.eu
Magazine featuring events, trends, developments, initiatives and activities of interest to vegetarians. **Freq:** Quarterly. **URL:** http://www.euroveg.eu/lang/en/news/magazine.php.

51241 ■ Filmbulletin/Kino in Augenhohe
Hard 4
Postfach 68
CH-8408 Winterthur, Switzerland
Ph: 41 52 2260555
Fax: 41 52 2260556
Publication E-mail: info@filmbulletin.ch
Publisher E-mail: info@filmbulletin.ch
Trade magazine covering film and film history. **Founded:** Jan. 1, 1959. **Freq:** 9/yr. **Key Personnel:** Josef Stutzer, Editorial Co-Worker; Walt R. Vian, Editor. **ISSN:** 0257-7852. **Subscription Rates:** 69 SFr individuals; 75 SFr individuals solidarity; 100 SFr individuals sponsor; 250 SFr individuals; 42 SFr individuals reduced; 38 SFr individuals schnupper; EUR45 individuals normally; EUR50 individuals solidarity; EUR75 individuals sponsor; EUR200 individuals. **Remarks:** Accepts advertising. **URL:** http://www.filmbulletin.ch. **Circ:** Combined 15,000

51242 ■ SAM-Focus
Swiss Alliance Mission
Schweizer Allianz Mission
Wolfensbergstrasse 47
CH-8400 Winterthur, Switzerland
Ph: 41 52 2690469
Fax: 41 52 2135681
Publisher E-mail: winterthur@sam-ame.org
German language publication covering evangelism. **Freq:** Quarterly. **Remarks:** Advertising not accepted. **URL:** http://www.sam-info.org/index.php. **Formerly:** SAM-Bote. **Circ:** 7,000

51243 ■ Spuren
Rudolfstrasse 13
CH-8400 Winterthur, Switzerland
Ph: 41 522 123361

Fax: 41 522 123371
Publisher E-mail: redaktion@spuren.ch
Magazine covering spirituality and psychology. **Subtitle:** Magazin fur neues Bewusstsein. **Founded:** 1986. **Freq:** Quarterly. **Print Method:** Offset. **Cols./Page:** 4. **Col. Width:** 42 millimeters. **Col. Depth:** 238 millimeters. **Key Personnel:** Sabina Ritzmann, Contact, anzeigen@spuren.ch. **ISSN:** 1424-0041. **Subscription Rates:** EUR30 individuals; EUR24 out of country. **Remarks:** Accepts advertising. **URL:** http://www.spuren.ch. **Ad Rates:** BW: 1,490 SFr. **Circ:** Controlled 10,000

51244 ■ Radio LoRa-FM - 102.35 MHz
Militarstrasse 85a
8004 Zurich, Switzerland
Ph: 41 1 445672400
Fax: 41 1 445672417
E-mail: lora@lora.ch
Format: Full Service. **URL:** http://www.lora.ch/.

Zug

51245 ■ Radio LoRa-FM - 98.9 MHz
Militarstrasse 85a
8004 Zurich, Switzerland
Ph: 41 1 445672400
Fax: 41 1 445672417
E-mail: lora@lora.ch
Format: Full Service. **URL:** http://www.lora.ch/.

Zurich

51246 ■ Acta Crystallographica Section A
John Wiley & Sons Inc.
Wiley-Blackwell
c/o Dr. Gernot Kostorz, Ed.-in-Ch.
ETH Zurich
Wolfgang-Pauli-Str. 16
CH-8093 Zurich, Switzerland
Fax: 41 446331105
Journal focusing on crystallography. **Subtitle:** Foundations of Crystallography. **Freq:** Bimonthly. **Key Personnel:** Prof. Charles W. Carter, Jr., Co-Ed., carter@med.unc.edu; Prof. Philip Coppens, Co-Ed., coppens@acsu.buffalo.edu; Prof. Dieter Schwarzenbach, Section Ed., dieter.schwarzenbach@epfl.ch; Dr. Paul Fewster, Co-Ed., paul.fewster@panalytical.com; Prof. Andre Authier, Co-Ed., aauthier@wanadoo.fr; Dr. Rick P. Millane, Co-Ed., rick@elec.canterbury.ac.nz; Dr. Vladimir E. Dmitrienko, Co-Ed., dmitrien@ns.crys.ras.ru; Dr. Gernot Kostorz, Editor-in-Chief, gk-iucr@ethz.ch. **ISSN:** 0108-7673. **Subscription Rates:** US$214 individuals print + online; US$196 individuals online; US$972 individuals with sections B and C; print + online; US$884 individuals with sections B and C; online; US$761 individuals with sections B and D; print + online; US$692 individuals combined with sections B and D; online; US$1,315 individuals with sections B, C and D; print + online; US$1,196 individuals with sections B, C and D; online; US$765 institutions print + online; US$695 institutions online. **Remarks:** Accepts advertising. **URL:** http://journals.iucr.org/a/journalhomepage.html; http://www.wiley.com/bw/journal.asp?ref=0108-7673&site=1. **Circ:** (Not Reported)

51247 ■ Acta Crystallographica Section B
John Wiley & Sons Inc.
Wiley-Blackwell
c/o Dr. Gernot Kostorz, Ed.-in-Ch.
ETH Zurich
Wolfgang-Pauli-Str. 16
CH-8093 Zurich, Switzerland
Fax: 41 446331105
Journal focusing on crystallography. **Subtitle:** Structural Science. **Freq:** Bimonthly. **Key Personnel:** Dr. Nadezhda B. Bolotina, Co-Ed., bolotina@ns.crys.ras.ru; Prof. Carolyn Pratt Brock, Section Ed.; Dr. Tim White, Co-Ed., tjwhite@ntu.edu.sg; Dr. Gernot Kostorz, Editor-in-Chief, gk-iucr@ethz.ch; Prof. Keiichiro Ogawa, Co-Ed., ogawa@ramie.c.u-tokyo.ac.jp; Prof. Gervais Chapuis, Co-Ed., gervais.chapuis@epfl.ch. **ISSN:** 0108-7681. **Subscription Rates:** US$226 individuals Americas (print and online); EUR202 individuals Euro zone (print and online); 135 other countries print and online; US$206 individuals Americas (print or online only); EUR185 individuals Euro zone (print or online only); 123 other countries print or online only; US$811 institutions, other countries print and online; EUR614 institutions Europe (print and online); 483 institutions UK (print and

online); US$737 institutions, other countries print or online only. **Remarks:** Accepts advertising. **URL:** http://journals.iucr.org/b/journalhomepage.html; http://www.wiley.com/bw/journal.asp?ref=0108-7681&site=1. **Circ:** (Not Reported)

51248 ■ Acta Crystallographica Section C
John Wiley & Sons Inc.
Wiley-Blackwell
c/o Dr. Gernot Kostorz, Ed.-in-Ch.
ETH Zurich
Wolfgang-Pauli-Str. 16
CH-8093 Zurich, Switzerland
Fax: 41 446331105
Journal focusing on crystallography. **Subtitle:** Crystal Structure Communications. **Freq:** Monthly. **Key Personnel:** Dr. Gernot Kostorz, Editor-in-Chief, gk-iucr@ethz.ch; Dr. John F. Gallagher, Co-Ed., john.gallagher@dcu.ie; Prof. George Ferguson, Co-Ed., actac@st-andrews.ac.uk; Christopher Glidewell, Co-Ed., cg@st-andrews.ac.uk; Dr. Ricardo Fortunato Baggio, Co-Ed., baggio@cnea.gov.ar; Prof. Alexander John Blake, Co-Ed., a.j.blake@nottingham.ac.uk; Dr. Ilia Guzei, Co-Ed., iguzei@chem.wisc.edu; Marcia Lorraine Scudder, Co-Ed., m.scudder@unsw.edu.au; Dr. Graeme John Gainsford, Co-Ed., g.gainsford@irl.cri.nz; Dr. Maciej Kubicki, Co-Ed., mkubicki@amu.edu.pl; Dr. Hidehiro Uekusa, Co-Ed., uekusa@cms.titech.ac.jp. **ISSN:** 0108-2701. **Subscription Rates:** US$583 individuals print and online; EUR521 individuals print and online; 347 other countries print and online; US$531 individuals print or online only; EUR474 individuals print or online only; 315 other countries print or online only; US$2,188 institutions, other countries print and online; 1,302 institutions UK (print and online); EUR1,653 institutions Europe (print and online); US$1,988 institutions, other countries print or online only. **Remarks:** Accepts advertising. **URL:** http://journals.iucr.org/c/journalhomepage.html; http://www.wiley.com/bw/journal.asp?ref=0108-2701&site=1. **Circ:** (Not Reported)

51249 ■ Acta Crystallographica Section D
John Wiley & Sons Inc.
Wiley-Blackwell
c/o Dr. Gernot Kostorz, Ed.-in-Ch.
ETH Zurich
Wolfgang-Pauli-Str. 16
CH-8093 Zurich, Switzerland
Fax: 41 446331105
Journal focusing on crystallography. **Subtitle:** Biological Crystallography. **Freq:** Monthly. **Key Personnel:** Dr. Gernot Kostorz, Editor-in-Chief, gk-iucr@ethz.ch; Prof. William N. Hunter, Section Ed., w.n.hunter@dundee.ac.uk; Jules Mitchell Guss, Co-Ed., m.guss@mmb.usyd.edu.au; Dr. Elspeth F. Garman, Co-Ed., elspeth.garman@bioch.ox.ac.uk; Prof. Hazel M. Holden, Co-Ed., hazel_holden@biochem.wisc.edu; Vladimir Lunin, Co-Ed., lunin@impb.psn.ru; Prof. Edward N. Baker, Section Ed., ted.baker@auckland.ac.nz; Dr. Steven Ealick, Co-Ed., see3@cornell.edu; Dr. Zbigniew Dauter, Section Ed., dauter@anl.gov; Peter Paufler, Book Review Ed., paufler@physik.tu-dresden.de; Naomi E. Chayen, Co-Ed., n.chayen@imperial.ac.uk. **ISSN:** 0907-4449. **Subscription Rates:** US$360 individuals Americas (print and online); EUR322 individuals Europe (print and online); 215 other countries print and online; US$329 individuals Americas (print or online only); EUR294 individuals Europe (print or online only); 196 other countries print or online only; US$1,306 institutions, other countries print and online; 776 institutions UK (print and online); EUR986 institutions Europe (print and online); US$1,186 institutions, other countries print or online only. **Remarks:** Accepts advertising. **URL:** http://journals.iucr.org/d/journalhomepage.html; http://www.wiley.com/bw/journal.asp?ref=0907-4449&site=1. **Circ:** (Not Reported)

51250 ■ Acta Crystallographica Section F
John Wiley & Sons Inc.
Wiley-Blackwell
c/o Dr. Gernot Kostorz, Ed.-in-Ch.
ETH Zurich
Wolfgang-Pauli-Str. 16
CH-8093 Zurich, Switzerland
Fax: 41 446331105
Journal focusing on crystallography. **Subtitle:** Structural Biology and Crystallization Communications. **Freq:** Monthly. **Key Personnel:** Dr. Gernot Kostorz, Editor-in-Chief, gk-iucr@ethz.ch; Prof. Jules Mitchell Guss, Co-Ed., m.guss@mmb.usyd.edu.au. **ISSN:** 1744-3091. **Subscription Rates:** US$1,104 institutions online; EUR834 institutions online; 657 institutions online;

US$279 individuals online; EUR248 individuals online; 165 other countries. **Remarks:** Accepts advertising. **URL:** http://journals.iucr.org/f/journalhomepage.html; http://www.wiley.com/bw/journal.asp?ref=1744-3091&site=1. **Circ:** (Not Reported)

51251 ■ Advances in Science and Technology
Trans Tech Publications Inc.
Laubrisrutistr. 24
CH-8712 Zurich, Switzerland
Fax: 41 44 9221033
Publisher E-mail: info@ttp.net
Journal covering science and technology. **Freq:** Irregular. **Key Personnel:** P. Vincenzini, Editor. **ISSN:** 1662-0356. **Subscription Rates:** EUR490 institutions. **URL:** http://www.scientific.net/AST/; http://www.ttp.net/1662-0356.html.

51252 ■ Approches
Evangelischer Frauenbund der Schweiz
Federation Suisse des Femmes Protestantes
Winterthurerstrasse 60
CH-8033 Zurich, Switzerland
Ph: 41 1 443630608
Fax: 41 1 443630760
Publisher E-mail: geschaeftsstelle@efs.ch
French language publication covering Christian interests. **Freq:** 5/yr. **Subscription Rates:** 30 SFr individuals. **URL:** http://www.efs.ch/.

51253 ■ Armada International
Hagenholzstrasse 65
CH-8050 Zurich, Switzerland
Ph: 41 1 3085050
Fax: 41 1 3085055
Publisher E-mail: mail@armada.ch
Military and naval science periodical. **Founded:** 1976. **Freq:** 6/yr. **Print Method:** Sheet offset. **Trim Size:** A4. **Key Personnel:** Caroline Schwegler, Publisher, caroline.schwegler@armada.ch; Eric H. Biass, Editor-in-Chief, ehb@bluewin.ch; John Keggler, Ed./Art Dir., johnny.keggler@armada.ch. **ISSN:** 0252-9793. **Subscription Rates:** 198 SFr individuals Europe; US$198 elsewhere. **Remarks:** Accepts advertising. **URL:** http://www.armada.ch. **Ad Rates:** BW: US$5,850, 4C: US$8,370. **Circ:** Controlled 25,088

51254 ■ Betty Bossi
Ringier Publishing House Switzerland
Burglistrasse 29
CH-8021 Zurich, Switzerland
Ph: 41 44 2091919
Fax: 41 44 2091920
Publication E-mail: bettybossi@ringier.ch
Publisher E-mail: info@ringier.ch
Cooking magazine. **Freq:** 10/yr. **Key Personnel:** Susanna Ries, Editor-in-Chief, susanna.ries@bettybossi.ch. **Remarks:** Accepts advertising. **URL:** http://www.ringier.ch/index.cfm?&id=420; http://www.bettybossi.ch. **Circ:** 850,000

51255 ■ Biometrical Journal
John Wiley & Sons Inc.
Institute of Social & Preventive Medicine
University of Zurich
Hirschengraben 84
CH-8001 Zurich, Switzerland
Ph: 41 44 6344641
Fax: 41 44 6344986
Publisher E-mail: info@wiley.com
Journal focusing on the development of statistical and related methodology and its applications to problems arising in all areas of the life sciences, particularly in medicine. **Freq:** Bimonthly. **Key Personnel:** Tim Friede, Editor; Leonhard Held, Editor; Todd A. Alonzo, Assoc. Ed. **ISSN:** 0323-3847. **Subscription Rates:** EUR1,673 institutions print only; 2,609 SFr institutions print only, Switzerland and Liechtenstein; EUR2,154 institutions, other countries print only; EUR225 individuals print; 356 SFr individuals print, Switzerland and Liechtenstein; US$315 other countries print. **URL:** http://www3.interscience.wiley.com/journal/117861849/grouphome.html.

51256 ■ Christliches Zeugnis
Campus fur Christus Schweiz
Josefstr. 206
CH-8005 Zurich, Switzerland
Ph: 41 1 2748434
Fax: 41 1 2748483
Publication E-mail: christlicheszeugnis@cfc.ch

Publisher E-mail: info@cfc.ch

Christian lifestyle magazine. **Freq:** Quarterly. **Subscription Rates:** 21 SFr individuals; 28 SFr out of country; 6 SFr single issue. **Remarks:** Advertising not accepted. **URL:** http://www.cfc.ch/. **Circ:** (Not Reported)

51257 ■ Defect and Diffusion Forum
Trans Tech Publications Inc.
Laubisrutistr. 24
CH-8712 Zurich, Switzerland
Fax: 41 44 9221033
Publisher E-mail: info@ttp.net
Journal covering developments in the general area of the defect solid state. **Freq:** 12/yr. **Key Personnel:** D.L. Beke, Co-Ed., dbeke@index.hu; D.J. Fisher, Editor, d.fisher@ttp.net; Graeme E. Murch, Editor, graeme. murch@newcastle.edu.au. **ISSN:** 1012-0386. **Subscription Rates:** EUR88 single issue; EUR1,056 individuals print + online. **URL:** http://www.scientific.net/DDF/; http://www.ttp.net/1012-0386.html.

51258 ■ European Joyce Studies
Editions Rodopi B.V.
c/o Dr. Fritz Senn, Ed.
Zurich James Joyce Foundation
Augustinergasse 9
CH-8001 Zurich, Switzerland
Fax: 41 1 2125128
Publication E-mail: joyce@es.unizh.ch
Publisher E-mail: info@rodopi.nl
Journal covering approaches and perspectives on the work, life and influence of James Joyce. **Key Personnel:** Dr. Fritz Senn, Editor. **ISSN:** 0923-9855. **URL:** http://www.rodopi.nl/senj.asp?SerieId=JOYCE.

51259 ■ FdH
Ringier Publishing House Switzerland
Hagenholzstrasse 83b
CH-8050 Zurich, Switzerland
Ph: 41 44 3085537
Fax: 41 44 3085540
Publication E-mail: fdh@ringier.ch
Publisher E-mail: info@ringier.ch
Health magazine. **Freq:** Monthly. **Key Personnel:** Ingrid Schindler, Editor-in-Chief. **Remarks:** Accepts advertising. **URL:** http://www.ringier.ch/index.cfm?id=4134&rub=159; http://www.gesundheitsprechstunde.ch/. **Circ:** 460,000

51260 ■ FLASH
International Philatelic Federation
Federation Internationale de Philatelie
Biberlinstrasse 6
CH-8032 Zurich, Switzerland
Ph: 41 1 4223839
Fax: 41 1 4223843
Publisher E-mail: heiri@f-i-p.ch
Philatelic publication, in English, French, German and Spanish. **Subtitle:** FIP Information Bulletin. **Founded:** 1980. **Freq:** Quarterly. **Print Method:** Offset. **Trim Size:** A4. **Key Personnel:** Marie-Louise Heiri, Sec. Gen. **Subscription Rates:** 30 SFr individuals CHF; EUR20 individuals. **URL:** http://www.f-i-p.ch/. **Ad Rates:** BW: 500 SFr, 4C: 1,000 SFr. **Circ:** 2,200

51261 ■ Gazzetta
ProLitteris
Postfach
CH-8033 Zurich, Switzerland
Ph: 41 433 006615
Fax: 41 433 006668
Publisher E-mail: mail@prolitteris.ch
Magazine containing a series of interesting articles and images on a specific theme by well-known and still unknown literary figures and artists. **Freq:** Semiannual. **URL:** http://www.prolitteris.ch/set.asp?go=/wis/gaz/gaz.asp.

51262 ■ Gesundheit Sprechstunde
Ringier Publishing House Switzerland
Hagenholzstrasse 83b
CH-8050 Zurich, Switzerland
Publisher E-mail: info@ringier.ch
Health magazine. **Freq:** Biweekly. **Key Personnel:** Regula Kach, Editor-in-Chief. **Remarks:** Accepts advertising. **URL:** http://www.gesundheitsprechstunde. ch/. **Circ:** 86,952

51263 ■ GlucksPost
Ringier Publishing House Switzerland
Dufourstrasse 49
CH-8008 Zurich, Switzerland

Ph: 41 44 2596912
Fax: 41 44 2596930
Publication E-mail: glueckspost@ringier.ch
Publisher E-mail: info@ringier.ch
Magazine for women. **Freq:** Weekly. **Key Personnel:** Beatrice Zollinger, Editor-in-Chief, beatrice.zollinger@ringier.ch. **Remarks:** Accepts advertising. **URL:** http://www.ringier.ch/index.cfm?id=421; http://www.glueckspost.ch/. **Circ:** 146,325

51264 ■ Heute
Ringier Publishing House Switzerland
Dufourstrasse 49
CH-8008 Zurich, Switzerland
Ph: 41 44 2596286
Fax: 41 44 2598601
Publication E-mail: redaktion@blickamabend.ch
Publisher E-mail: info@ringier.ch
Community newspaper. **Freq:** Daily. **Key Personnel:** Peter Rothlisberger, Editor-in-Chief, peter. roethlisberger@ringier.ch; Caroline Thoma, Commercial Dir., caroline.thoma.@ringier.ch. **Remarks:** Accepts advertising. **URL:** http://www.ringier.ch/index.cfm?id=2085&rub=158; http://www.blick.ch/. **Circ:** 225,226

51265 ■ Historic Motor Racing News
Historic Motor Racing News Ltd.
Grubenstrasse 34
CH-8702 Zurich, Switzerland
Ph: 41 44 4502370
Publication E-mail: carol@historicmotorracingnews.com
Publisher E-mail: contact@historicmotorracingnews.com
Consumer magazine covering historic automobile racing and rallying. **Founded:** 1994. **Freq:** 11/yr. **Trim Size:** A4. **ISSN:** 1472-2135. **Subscription Rates:** 50 individuals U.K. and Europe; 55 other countries; 100 two years U.K. and Europe; 110 two years U.S., Australia & rest of the world. **Remarks:** Accepts advertising. **URL:** http://www.historicmotorracingnews.com. **Ad Rates:** BW: EUR425, 4C: EUR525. **Circ:** Combined 1,000

51266 ■ International Journal of Legal Information Design
Inderscience Enterprises Limited
c/o Dr. Colette R. Brunschwig, Ed.-in-Ch.
University of Zurich, Dept. of Law
Centre for Legal History, Legal Visualisation Unit
Ramistrasse 74, PO Box 52
8001 Zurich, Switzerland
Journal focusing on the audio, visual, and audio-visual design of legal information. **Freq:** 4/yr. **Key Personnel:** Dr. Colette R. Brunschwig, Editor-in-Chief, colette. brunschwig@rwi.uzh.ch; Burkhard Schafer, Assoc. Ed. **ISSN:** 1750-8142. **Subscription Rates:** EUR494 individuals print or online; EUR672 individuals print and online. **URL:** http://www.inderscience.com/browse/index. php?journalID=202.

51267 ■ International Journal of Technology Policy and Management
Inderscience Publishers
Hochschule fur Wirtschaft und Verwaltung
Zurich University of Applied Sciences
Lagerstrasse 5
CH-8021 Zurich, Switzerland
Publisher E-mail: editor@inderscience.com
Peer-reviewed journal providing a professional and scholarly forum in the emerging field of decision making and problem solving in the integrated area of technology policy and management at the operational, organisational and public policy levels. **Freq:** 4/yr. **Key Personnel:** Prof. Simon French, Editorial Board Member; Prof. Jeryl L. Mumpower, Editorial Board Member; Prof. Kathleen Carley, Editorial Board Member; Prof. Kurt J. Engemann, Editor-in-Chief, kengemann@iona.edu; Prof. Giampiero E.G. Beroggi, Editorial Board Member; Prof. Richard De Neufville, Editorial Board Member; Prof. Manuel F. Heitor, Editorial Board Member; Prof. Donald E. Brown, Editorial Board Member; Prof. Jean L. Campl, Editorial Board Member. **ISSN:** 1498-4322. **Subscription Rates:** EUR170 individuals personal online; EUR494 individuals online only; EUR672 individuals print and online. **URL:** http://www.inderscience.com/browse/index. php?journalCODE=ijtpm.

51268 ■ IOS Bulletin
International Organization for Succulent Plant Study
Internationale Organisation fur Sukkulentenforschung
Sukkulenten-Sammlung Zurich
Mythenquai 88

CH-8002 Zurich, Switzerland
Publication covering botany. **Founded:** 1950. **Freq:** Annual. **Key Personnel:** Dr. Joachim Thiede, Editor, thiede@botanik.uni-hamburg.de. **ISSN:** 0141-2787. **Subscription Rates:** Included in membership. **Remarks:** Advertising not accepted. **URL:** http://www. iosweb.org/joinus.php. **Circ:** 300

51269 ■ Journal of Applied Mathematics and Physics (ZAMP)
Birkhauser Verlag AG
c/o Kaspar Nipp, Mng. Ed.
Angewandte Mathematik
ETH Zentrum
CH-8092 Zurich, Switzerland
Journal publishing articles in the areas of fluid mechanics, mechanics of solids and differential equations/ applied mathematics. **Founded:** 1950. **Freq:** 6/yr. **Trim Size:** 17 x 24 cm. **Key Personnel:** Kaspar Nipp, Managing Editor, nipp@sam.math.ethz.ch; Urs Kirchgraber, Co-Ed. **ISSN:** 0044-2275. **URL:** http://www.springer. com/journal/00033/. **Foreign language name:** Journal de Mathematiques et de Physique appliquees.

51270 ■ Journal of Inherited Metabolic Disease
Society for the Study of Inborn Errors of Metabolism
c/o Dr. Nenad Blau
University Children's Hospital
Division of Clinical Chemistry and Biochemistry
Steinwiesstrasse 75
8032 Zurich, Switzerland
Ph: 41 44 2667544
Fax: 41 44 2667169
Publication covering metabolic disorders. **Freq:** 6 to 8/yr. **Key Personnel:** Guy Besley, Communicating Ed.; Johannes Zschocke, Editor-in-Chief; Bruce A. Barshop, Communicating Ed.; Ivo Baric, Communicating Ed.; Michael K. Gibson, Editor; Michael J. Bennett, Communicating Ed.; Georg F. Hoffmann, Editor-in-Chief; Verena Peters, Managing Editor; Matthias Baumgartner, Communicating Ed.; Garry Brown, Editor. **ISSN:** 0141-8955. **Subscription Rates:** US$976 individuals. **Remarks:** Accepts advertising. **URL:** http://www.ssiem.org/membership/notesJournal.asp. **Circ:** (Not Reported)

51271 ■ Journal of Object Technology (JOT)
ETH Swiss Federal Institute of Technology
Department of Computer Science
ETH ZurichChair of Software Engineering, Meyer ETH Zentrum
RZ Bldg., Clausiusstrasse 59
CH-8092 Zurich,, Switzerland
Fax: 41 446 321435
Journal dealing with object technology under object oriented programming languages. **Freq:** Bimonthly. **Key Personnel:** Oscar Nierstrasz, Editor-in-Chief, jot-editor@jot.fm; Bertrand Meyer, Publisher, bertrand. meyer@inf.ethz.ch; Elisa Bertino, Editorial Board; Kent Beck, Editorial Board; Susan Eisenbach, Editorial Board; Doug Lea, Editorial Board. **ISSN:** 1660-1769. **Remarks:** Advertising accepted; rates available upon request. **URL:** http://www.jot.fm/general/about. **Circ:** (Not Reported)

51272 ■ Key Engineering Materials
Trans Tech Publications Inc.
Laubisrutistr. 24
CH-8712 Zurich, Switzerland
Publisher E-mail: info@ttp.net
Peer-reviewed Journal covering aspects of the synthesis and characterization, modelling, processing and application of advanced engineering materials. **Freq:** 30/yr. **Key Personnel:** E.A. Armanios, Editor; Y.W. Mai, Editor; G.M. Newaz, Editor; Dr. F.H. Wohlbier, Editor. **ISSN:** 1013-9826. **Subscription Rates:** EUR78 single issue; EUR2,340 individuals. **URL:** http://www.scientific.net/ KEM/; http://www.ttp.net/1013-9826.html.

51273 ■ Kunst Bulletin
Zeughausstr. 55
CH-8004 Zurich, Switzerland
Ph: 44 298 3030
Fax: 44 298 3038
Publisher E-mail: info@kunstbulletin.ch
Magazine covering contemporary art. **Founded:** 1968. **Col. Width:** 131 millimeters. **Col. Depth:** 190 millimeters. **ISSN:** 1013-6940. **Subscription Rates:** EUR40.50 individuals + postage outside of Switzerland; 116 SFr two years + postage outside of Switzerland; 68 SFr individuals + postage outside of Switzerland; EUR69 two years + postage outside of Switzerland. **URL:** http://

www.kunstbulletin.ch. **Circ:** Combined 30,544

51274 ■ LWT - Food Science and Technology
Elsevier Science Inc.
c/o Katrin Hecht, Ed.-in-Ch.
ETH Zurich
Institute of Food Science & Nutrition
Schmelzbergstrasse 9
8092 Zurich, Switzerland
Publisher E-mail: usinfo-ehelp@elsevier.com
Journal for food chemistry, biochemistry, microbiology, technology and nutrition. **Founded:** 1964. **Freq:** 10/yr. **Print Method:** Offset. **Trim Size:** 8 x 10 3/4. **Cols./Page:** 3. **Col. Width:** 2 3/16 inches. **Col. Depth:** 9 5/8 inches. **Key Personnel:** Shridhar K. Sathe, Review Ed.; Katrin Hecht, Editor-in-Chief; Rakesh K. Singh, Editor. **ISSN:** 0023-6438. **Subscription Rates:** US$892 institutions, other countries except Europe, Japan and Iran; EUR801 institutions for European countries and Iran; 96,600¥ institutions. **URL:** http://www.elsevier.com/wps/find/journaldescription.cws_home/622910/descriptiondescription.

51275 ■ Materials Science Forum
Trans Tech Publications Inc.
Laubisrutistr. 24
CH-8712 Zurich, Switzerland
Publisher E-mail: info@ttp.net
Peer-reviewed Journal covering all areas of materials science, solid state physics and solid state chemistry. **Freq:** 32/yr. **Key Personnel:** Y.W. Mai, Editor; G.E. Murch, Editor; F.H. Wohlbier, Editor. **ISSN:** 0255-5476. **Subscription Rates:** EUR78 single issue; EUR2,496 individuals. **URL:** http://www.scientific.net/MSF/; http://www.ttp.net/0255-5476.html.

51276 ■ Passages
Pro Helvetia Arts Council of Switzerland
Hirschengraben 22
CH-8024 Zurich, Switzerland
Ph: 41 1 4472677171
Fax: 41 1 442677106
Publisher E-mail: info@pro-helvetia.ch
Publication covering culture in Switzerland in English, French and German. **Founded:** Sept. 1985. **Freq:** Quarterly. **Key Personnel:** Pius Knusel, Director. **Remarks:** Advertising not accepted. **URL:** http://www.prohelvetia.in/. **Circ:** (Not Reported)

51277 ■ Schritte ins Offene
Evangelischer Frauenbund der Schweiz
Federation Suisse des Femmes Protestantes
Winterthurerstrasse 60
CH-8033 Zurich, Switzerland
Ph: 41 1 443630608
Fax: 41 1 443630760
Publisher E-mail: geschaeftsstelle@efs.ch
German language publication covering Christian interests. **Freq:** Bimonthly. **Key Personnel:** Ursula Stocker Glaettli, Writer, ursistocker@bluewin.ch. **ISSN:** 1422-0938. **Subscription Rates:** EUR28 individuals European Union; 42 Eg individuals Switzerland; US$48 other countries; US$10 single issue. **URL:** http://www.schritte-ins-offene.ch/; http://www.efs.ch/.

51278 ■ Schweizer Illustrierte
Ringier Publishing House Switzerland
Dufourstrasse 23
CH-8008 Zurich, Switzerland
Ph: 41 44 2596111
Publication E-mail: schweizer-illustrierte@ringier.ch
Publisher E-mail: info@ringier.ch
Lifestyle magazine. **Freq:** Weekly. **Key Personnel:** Nik Niethammer, Editor-in-Chief, nik.niethammer@ringier.ch; Urs Heller, Commercial Dir., urs.heller@ringier.ch. **Remarks:** Accepts advertising. **URL:** http://www.schweizer-illustrierte.ch/. **Circ:** 204,856

51279 ■ Schweizer Illustrierte Style
Ringier Publishing House Switzerland
Dufourstrasse 23
CH-8008 Zurich, Switzerland
Ph: 41 44 2596111
Publication E-mail: schweizer-illustrierte@ringier.ch
Publisher E-mail: info@ringier.ch
Celebrity and fashion magazine. **Freq:** Monthly. **Key Personnel:** Urs Heller, Commercial Dir., urs.heller@ringier.ch; Sabina Diethelm, Editor-in-Chief, sabina.diethelm@ringier.ch. **Remarks:** Accepts advertising. **URL:** http://www.ringier.ch/index.cfm?id=1577&rub=159;

http://www.schweizer-illustrierte.ch/. **Circ:** 109,983

51280 ■ Schweizer Lehrerinnen- und Lehrer-Zeitung
Swiss Teachers Federation
Dachverband Schweizer Lehrerinnen und Lehrer
Ringstrasse 54
Postfach 189
CH-8057 Zurich, Switzerland
Ph: 41 131 55454
Fax: 41 131 18315
Publisher E-mail: info@lch.ch
German language publication covering education. **Freq:** Monthly. **Remarks:** Advertising accepted; rates available upon request. **URL:** http://www.lch.ch/lch/bildung-schweiz/ausgaben-2009.html. **Circ:** (Not Reported)

51281 ■ Schweizer Monatshefte fur Politik, Wirtschaft und Kultur
Schweizer Monatshefte
Vogelsangstr. 52
CH-8006 Zurich, Switzerland
Ph: 41 443 612606
Fax: 41 443 637005
Publisher E-mail: info@schweizermonatshefte.ch
Consumer magazine covering politics, economics and culture. **Subtitle:** Fur Wirtschaft Politik Kulture. **Founded:** 1921. **Freq:** 10/yr. **Key Personnel:** Brigitte Kohler, Contact, brigitte.kohler@schweizermonatshefte.ch. **Remarks:** Accepts advertising. **URL:** http://www.schweizermonatshefte.ch. **Ad Rates:** 4C: 1,450 SFr. **Circ:** Combined 3,000

51282 ■ Schweizer Musikzeitung
SMZ
Bellariastr. 82
CH-8038 Zurich, Switzerland
Ph: 41 442 812321
Fax: 41 442 812353
Publisher E-mail: contact@musikzeitung.ch
Trade journal covering music and musicians for music teachers, musicians, scholars and amateurs. **Founded:** 1998. **Freq:** Monthly 11/yr. **Print Method:** Offset. **Trim Size:** 208 x 290 mm. **Cols./Page:** 4. **Key Personnel:** Katrin Spelinova, Contact. **ISSN:** 1422-4674. **Subscription Rates:** 55 SFr individuals; EUR45 out of country; 6 SFr single issue. **URL:** http://www.musikzeitung.ch/index.php?article_id=68&clang=0. **Ad Rates:** BW: 1,986 SFr, 4C: 2,979 SFr. **Circ:** Controlled 21,948

51283 ■ Solid State Phenomena
Trans Tech Publications Inc.
Laubisrutistr. 24
CH-8712 Zurich, Switzerland
Fax: 41 44 9221033
Publisher E-mail: info@ttp.net
Journal covering field of solid state materials, and its applications to materials science. **Freq:** 12/yr. **Key Personnel:** D.J. Fisher, Editor; G.E. Murch, Editor; F.H. Wohlbier, Editor. **ISSN:** 1012-0394. **Subscription Rates:** EUR88 single issue; EUR1,042 individuals print + online. **URL:** http://www.scientific.net/SSP/; http://www.ttp.net/1012-0394.html.

51284 ■ SonntagsBlick
Ringier Publishing House Switzerland
Dufourstrasse 23
CH-8008 Zurich, Switzerland
Ph: 41 44 2596111
Publication E-mail: sobli@ringier.ch
Publisher E-mail: info@ringier.ch
Sunday newspaper. **Freq:** Weekly. **Key Personnel:** Hannes Britschgi, Editor-in-Chief, hannes.britschgi@ringier.ch; Caroline Thoma, Commercial Dir., caroline.thoma.@ringier.ch. **Remarks:** Accepts advertising. **URL:** http://www.ringier.ch/index.cfm?id=3936&rub=158; http://www.blick.ch/sonntagsblick. **Circ:** 247,449

51285 ■ SonntagsBlick Magazin
Ringier Publishing House Switzerland
Dufourstrasse 23
CH-8008 Zurich, Switzerland
Ph: 41 44 2596111
Publication E-mail: sobli@ringier.ch
Publisher E-mail: info@ringier.ch
Lifestyle magazine. **Freq:** Weekly (Sun.). **Key Personnel:** Caroline Thoma, Commercial Dir., caroline.thoma.@ringier.ch; Karsten Witzmann, Editor-in-Chief, karsten.witzmann@ringier.ch. **Remarks:** Accepts advertising. **URL:** http://www.blick.ch/sonntagsblick; http://www.ringier.ch/index.cfm?id=3936&rub=158. **Circ:** 247,449

51286 ■ SPEEDUP Journal
SPEEDUP Society: Swiss forum for GRID and High Performance Computing
c/o Prof. Peter Arbenz
Chair of Computational Science
CAB G 69.3
Universitaetsstrasse 6
CH-8092 Zurich, Switzerland
Ph: 41 44 6327432
Journal containing articles on topics including molecular dynamics, environmental impacts, and industrial applications of high performance computers. **Freq:** Semiannual. **Key Personnel:** Peter Arbenz, Editor, arbenz@inf.ethz.ch. **URL:** http://www.speedup.ch/journal.html. **Circ:** ‡2,500

51287 ■ SPORTmagazin
Ringier Publishing House Switzerland
Dufourstrasse 23
CH-8008 Zurich, Switzerland
Ph: 41 44 2596111
Publisher E-mail: info@ringier.ch
Magazine featuring the world of sports. **Freq:** 10/yr. **Key Personnel:** Patrick Madder, Editor-in-Chief, patrick.maeder@ringier.ch; Caroline Thoma, Commercial Dir., caroline.thoma.@ringier.ch. **Remarks:** Accepts advertising. **URL:** http://www.ringier.ch/index.cfm?id=1241&rub=159. **Circ:** 25,000

51288 ■ Structural Engineering International
International Association for Bridge and Structural Engineering
ETH-Honggerberg
CH-8093 Zurich, Switzerland
Ph: 41 44 6332647
Fax: 41 44 6331241
Publisher E-mail: secretariat@iabse.org
Worldwide publication covering engineering. **Founded:** 1991. **Freq:** Quarterly. **Key Personnel:** Brindarica Bose, Manager, bose@iabse.org. **ISSN:** 1016-8664. **Subscription Rates:** 220 SFr individuals print and electronic; 630 SFr institutions print & site license for electronic version. **Remarks:** Accepts advertising. **URL:** http://www.iabse.ethz.ch/journalsei/index.php. **Ad Rates:** BW: 2,350 SFr, 4C: 3,500 SFr. **Circ:** 5,500

51289 ■ Swiss News
Swiss Businesspress SA
Koschenrutistrasse 109
8052 Zurich, Switzerland
Ph: 41 1 306 47 00
Fax: 41 1 306 47 11
Publisher E-mail: info@swissbusinesspress.ch
Travel, recreation and leisure publication. **Freq:** Monthly. **Key Personnel:** Remo Kuhn, Publisher, kuhn@swissnews.ch; Urs Huebscher, Mng. Dir., huebscher@swissnews.ch; Kati Clinton Robson, Editor, clinton@swissnews.ch. **ISSN:** 1420-1151. **Subscription Rates:** 75 SFr individuals; 95 SFr out of country; 135 SFr two years; 170 SFr out of country two years. **Remarks:** Accepts advertising. **URL:** http://www.swissnews.ch/. **Ad Rates:** BW: 3,600 SFr, 4C: 5,400 SFr. **Circ:** 12,000

51290 ■ Swisspack International
Postfach
CH-8048 Zurich, Switzerland
Ph: 41 44 4316445
Fax: 41 44 4316497
Publication E-mail: info@swisspack.ch
Publisher E-mail: info@swisspack.ch
Trade journal for the packaging, handling, storage and logistics industries worldwide. **Freq:** Continuous 5/yr. **Key Personnel:** Jules Kistler, Editor, jules.kistler@swisspack.ch; Peter Senecky, Editor-in-Chief, peter.senecky@swisspack.ch. **Subscription Rates:** 30 SFr individuals; EUR20 individuals Europe. **Remarks:** Accepts advertising. **URL:** http://www.swisspack.ch. **Ad Rates:** BW: 7,900 SFr, 4C: 3,000 SFr. **Circ:** Paid 3,800

51291 ■ Syna die Gewerkschaft
Zentralsekretariat Zurich
Josefstrasse 59
Postfach
CH-8031 Zurich, Switzerland
Ph: 41 44 2797171
Fax: 41 44 2797172
Publisher E-mail: info@syna.ch
Magazine for union members. **Founded:** Oct. 1999. **Freq:** Monthly. **URL:** http://www.syna.ch.

Circulation: ★ = ABC; △ = BPA; ♦ = CAC; • = CCAB; ❑ = VAC; ⊕ = PO Statement; ‡ = Publisher's Report; Boldface figures = sworn; Light figures = estimated.

51292 ■ Travel Inside
Primus Publishing Ltd.
Hammerstrasse 81
Postfach 1331
CH-8032 Zurich, Switzerland
Ph: 41 44 3875757
Fax: 41 44 3875707
Publication E-mail: info@travelinside.ch
Publisher E-mail: info@travelinside.ch
Switzerland's leading travel trade magazine in German.
Founded: 1985. **Freq:** Weekly. **Print Method:** Offset.
Trim Size: 210 x 290 mm. **Cols./Page:** 4. **Col. Width:**
49 millimeters. **Key Personnel:** Angelo Heuberger,
Publisher; Muriel Bassin, Publishing & Advertising Mgr.;
Simon Benz, Editor. **URL:** http://www.travelinside.ch/
travelinside/de/index.php. **Ad Rates:** BW: 4,850 SFr,
4C: 6,550 SFr. **Circ:** Paid 7,976

51293 ■ Travel Inside Francais
Primus Publishing Ltd.
Hammerstrasse 81
Postfach 1331
CH-8032 Zurich, Switzerland
Ph: 41 44 3875757
Fax: 41 44 3875707
Publication E-mail: info@travelinside.ch
Publisher E-mail: info@travelinside.ch
Switzerland's leading travel trade magazine in French.
Freq: Weekly. **Print Method:** Offset. **Trim Size:** 210 x
290 mm. **Cols./Page:** 4. **Col. Width:** 49 millimeters.
Key Personnel: Dominique Sudan, Editor; Muriel
Bassin, Advertising Mgr., info@travelmedia.ch; Angelo
Heuberger, Publisher. **URL:** http://www.travelinside.ch/
travelinside/fr/index.php. **Ad Rates:** BW: 3,500 SFr, 4C:
4,850 SFr. **Circ:** Paid 2,913

51294 ■ Travel Manager
Primus Publishing Ltd.
Hammerstrasse 81
Postfach 1331
CH-8032 Zurich, Switzerland
Ph: 41 44 3875757

Fax: 41 44 3875707
Publication E-mail: redaktion@travelmanager.ch
Publisher E-mail: info@travelinside.ch
Trade magazine covering issues for the travel industry.
Subtitle: Switzerland's Monthly Travel Industry
Magazine. **Founded:** 1999. **Freq:** Monthly 10/yr. **Print
Method:** Offset Litho. **Trim Size:** 210 x 297 mm. **Key
Personnel:** Muriel Bassin, Publishing & Advertising
Mgr.; Beat Eichenberger, Editor-in-Chief; Angelo Heu-
berger, Publisher. **Remarks:** Accepts advertising. **URL:**
http://www.travelmanager.ch/travelmanager/index.php.
Ad Rates: BW: 3,900 SFr, 4C: 5,250 SFr. **Circ:** Com-
bined 2,900

51295 ■ TVtaglich
Ringier Publishing House Switzerland
Werdstrasse 21
CH-8021 Zurich, Switzerland
Ph: 41 44 2486260
Fax: 41 44 2486316
Publication E-mail: tele@ringier.ch
Publisher E-mail: info@ringier.ch
Television program magazine. **Freq:** Weekly. **Key Per-
sonnel:** Ernst Seibold, Editor-in-Chief, ernst.seibold@
media-press.tv. **Remarks:** Accepts advertising. **URL:**
http://www.tvtaeglich.ch/j/home.html; http://www.ringier.
ch/index.cfm?&id=425. **Circ:** 1,221,000

51296 ■ Werk, Bauen und Wohnen
Talstrasse, 39
CH-8001 Zurich, Switzerland
Ph: 41 102 181430
Fax: 41 102 181434
Publication E-mail: redaktion@wbw.ch
Publisher E-mail: redaktion@wbw.ch
Architectural magazine. **Founded:** 1914. **Freq:** Monthly.
Print Method: Offset. **Trim Size:** 235 x 297 mm. **Key
Personnel:** Anna Schindler, Editor; Casper Scharer,
Editor; Tibor Joanelly, Editor; Nott Caviezel, Editor-in-
Chief. **ISSN:** 0257-9332. **Subscription Rates:** EUR135
individuals Europe and overseas, 10 issues; 220 SFr
single issue Europe and overseas, 10 issues; EUR95

students 10 issues; 145 SFr students 10 issues; EUR35
individuals Europe and overseas, 3 issues; 60 SFr
individuals Europe and overseas, 3 issues; EUR28
students 3 issues; 40 SFr students 3 issues; EUR16
individuals + shipping and handling; 25 SFr individuals
+ shipping and handling. **Remarks:** Accepts advertising.
URL: http://www.werkbauenundwohnen.ch. **Ad Rates:**
BW: 3,220 SFr, 4C: 5,140 SFr. **Circ:** Combined 8,500

51297 ■ Zeitlupe
Verlag Pro Senectute Schweiz
Lavaterstr. 60
CH-8027 Zurich, Switzerland
Ph: 49 44 2838989
Fax: 49 44 2838980
Publication E-mail: info@zeitlupe.ch
Consumer magazine for senior citizens. **Freq:** 10/yr.
Print Method: Offset. **Cols./Page:** 4. **Key Personnel:**
Marianne Noser, Editor-in-Chief, marianne.noser@
zeitlupe.ch. **ISSN:** 1420-8180. **Subscription Rates:** 42
SFr individuals; EUR50 individuals; 60 SFr other
countries. **Remarks:** Accepts advertising. **URL:** http://
www.zeitlupe.ch/. **Circ:** (Not Reported)

51298 ■ Radio LoRa-FM - 97.5 Mhz
Militarstrasse 85a
8004 Zurich, Switzerland
Ph: 41 1 445672400
Fax: 41 1 445672417
E-mail: lora@lora.ch
Format: Full Service. **URL:** http://www.lora.ch/.

Radio LoRa-FM - See Bassersdorf

Radio LoRa-FM - See Winterthur

Radio LoRa-FM - See Zug

51299 ■ Radio Tropic-FM - 93
Limmatstrasse 31
CH-8005 Zurich, Switzerland
Ph: 41 44 4407070
Fax: 41 44 4407071
E-mail: info@tropic93.com
Format: Eclectic. **Operating Hours:** 20 hours Daily.
URL: http://www.radio-tropic.ch.

Damascus

51300 ■ Syria Times
Teshreen Foundation for Press and Publication
PO Box 5452
Damascus, Syrian Arab Republic
Ph: 963 11 2131100
Fax: 963 11 2231374
Publication E-mail: syriatimes@teshreen.com
Publisher E-mail: syriatimes@teshreen.com
English language newspaper. **Freq:** Daily. **ISSN:** 1563-5880. **URL:** http://syriatimes.tishreen.info/.

51301 ■ Al Madina-FM - 100.5
PO Box 13275
Damascus, Syrian Arab Republic
Ph: 963 119443
Fax: 963 114470001
E-mail: info@almadinafm.com
Format: Educational; News. **Operating Hours:** Continuous. **Ad Rates:** $20-650 for 15 seconds; $30-850 for 25 seconds; $40-1,200 for 35 seconds; $50-1,400 for 45 seconds; $10-450 for 5 seconds; $60-1,600 for 55 seconds. **URL:** http://www.almadinafm.com.

51302 ■ Al Madina-FM - 101.5
PO Box 13275
Damascus, Syrian Arab Republic
Ph: 963 119443
Fax: 963 114470001
E-mail: info@almadinafm.com
Format: Educational; News. **Owner:** Al Madina FM, at above address. **Founded:** 2005. **Operating Hours:** Continuous. **Ad Rates:** $20-650 for 15 seconds; $30-850 for 25 seconds; $40-1,200 for 35 seconds; $50-1,400 for 45 seconds; $10-450 for 5 seconds; $60-1,600 for 55 seconds. **URL:** http://www.almadinafm.com.

Syrian Arab Republic Broadcasting Service - Deir El Zawr - See Deir El Zawr

Deir El Zawr

51303 ■ Syrian Arab Republic Broadcasting Service - Deir El Zawr - 954 KHz
Ommayad Sq.
Damascus, Syrian Arab Republic
Ph: 963 11 2452191
Fax: 963 11 2454085
Format: News. **Owner:** Syrian Arab Republic Broadcasting Service, at above address. **Operating Hours:** 3:15 a.m.-12:40 a.m. **Key Personnel:** Ma'oon Haydar, Dir. Gen.; Adnan Salhah, Dir., Engg.; Ghassan Shefiab, Dir., Public Relations. **Wattage:** 50,000. **URL:** http://www.rtv.gov.sy.

Circulation: ★ = ABC; △ = BPA; ◆ = CAC; • = CCAB; ❑ = VAC; ⊕ = PO Statement; ‡ = Publisher's Report; Boldface figures = sworn; Light figures = estimated.

Gale Directory of Publications & Broadcast Media/147th Ed. 5491

Chungli

51304 ■ Advances in Adaptive Data Analysis
World Scientific Publishing Company Inc.
c/o Norden E. Huang, Co-Ed.-in-Ch.
Research Center for Adaptive Data Analysis
National Central University
Chungli 32001, Taiwan
Ph: 886 3 4276884
Fax: 886 3 4269736
Publisher E-mail: wspc@wspc.com
Journal covering data analysis methodology developments and applications, with focus on adaptive approaches. **Key Personnel:** Norden E. Huang, Co-Ed.-in-Ch., norden@ncu.edu.tw; Thomas Yizhao Hou, Co-Ed.-in-Ch., phone 626395-4546, fax 626578-0124, hou@ama.caltech.edu; Jordan Camp, Editor, phone 301286-3528, jordan.b.camp@nasa.gov. **ISSN:** 1792-5369. **Subscription Rates:** US$334 institutions print + online; US$321 institutions online only. **URL:** http://www.worldscinet.com/aada/aada.shtml.

Fangliao

51305 ■ Radio Taiwan International- Fangliao - 585 KHz
55 Pei-An Rd.
Taipei 104, Taiwan
Ph: 886 2 28856168
Fax: 886 2 28867088
E-mail: rti@rti.org.tw
Format: Eclectic. **Owner:** Central Broadcasting System, at above address. **Founded:** Jan. 1, 1998. **Wattage:** 1,200,000. **URL:** http://english.rti.com.tw/.

Hsinchu

51306 ■ Journal of Micro/Nanolithography, MEMS, and MOEMS
International Society for Optical Engineering
TSMC, Ltd. Fab 12
Science-Based Industrial Pk.
Hsinchu 30077, Taiwan
Ph: 886 366 65858
Fax: 886 356 37386
Publisher E-mail: customerservice@spie.org
Scholarly journal that publishes peer-reviewed papers on the development of lithographic, fabrication, packaging, and integration technologies. **Freq:** Quarterly. **Key Personnel:** Thomas G. Bifano, Assoc. Ed.; Roxann Engelstad, Assoc. Ed.; Thomas J. Suleski, Sen. Ed.; Edward M. Motamedi, Sen. Ed.; William H. Arnold, Sen. Ed.; Jos Benschop, Assoc. Ed.; Will Conley, Assoc. Ed.; Hans Peter Herzig, Sen. Ed.; Burn J. Lin, Editor-in-Chief, burnlin@tsmc.com.tw. **Subscription Rates:** Included in membership; NTs 480 U.S. print and online; US$380 other countries online only. **URL:** http://spiedl.aip.org/journals/doc/SPIEDL-home/jrnls/jmm/JMMabout.jsp. **Formerly:** Microlithography, Microfabrication, and Microsystems.

51307 ■ The Taiwanese Journal of Mathematics
The Mathematical Society of the Republic of China
Dept. of Applied Mathematics
101, Sec. 2, Guangfu Rd.,

Hsinchu 300, Taiwan
Ph: 886 3 5713784
Fax: 886 3 5723888
Publisher E-mail: tjm@mail.nsysu.edu.tw
Publishes original research papers and survey articles in all areas of mathematics. **Founded:** 1997. **Freq:** Quarterly. **Key Personnel:** Liu Tai-Ping, Advisory Ed., tpliu@math.sinica.edu.tw; Hung-Lin Fu, Assoc. Ed., hlfu@math.nctu.edu.tw; Jen-Chih Yao, Editor-in-Chief, tjm@mail.nsysu.edu.tw; Bang-Yen Chen, Assoc. Ed., bychen@math.msu.edu; Sun-Yung Alice Chang, Assoc. Ed., chang@math.princeton.edu; Shu-Cheng Chang, Assoc. Ed., scchang@math.nthu.edu.tw; Der-Chen Chang, Assoc. Ed., chang@math.georgetown.edu. **Subscription Rates:** US$60 individuals surface mail. **URL:** http://www.math.nthu.edu.tw/~tjm/.

Jhongli City

51308 ■ International Journal of Internet Marketing and Advertising
Inderscience Publishers
c/o Dr. Rebecca H.J. Yen, Ed.-in-Ch.
National Central University
Graduate School of Management
No. 300, Jhongda Rd.
Jhongli City 32001, Taiwan
Publisher E-mail: editor@inderscience.com
Peer-reviewed journal is a professional and authoritative source of information in the field of internet and its applications in marketing and advertising, publishing theories and practices that are useful to executives in managing marketing and advertising activities over the internet. **Freq:** Quarterly. **Key Personnel:** Dr. Eldon Y. Li, Honorary Ed.; Dr. Veronica Liljander, Assoc. Ed.; Dr. George J. Avlonitis, Assoc. Ed.; Dr. Jef I. Richards, Assoc. Ed.; Dr. HsiuJu Rebecca Yen, Editor-in-Chief, hjyen@mx.nthu.edu.tw; Dr. C.K. Bennett Yim, Assoc. Ed. **ISSN:** 1477-5212. **Subscription Rates:** EUR494 individuals print only (surface mail); EUR840 individuals online only (2-3 users); EUR534 individuals print only (airmail); EUR672 individuals print and online. **URL:** http://www.inderscience.com/browse/index.php?journalCODE=ijima.

Jhubei City

51309 ■ PRS Programme 3-AM - 1116
No. 1-1, Jiansing Rd.
Hsinchu County 302
Jhubei City 302, Taiwan
Ph: 886 3 5500301
E-mail: prs@prs.gov.tw
Format: Information; Public Radio. **Ad Rates:** Noncommercial. **URL:** http://www.prs.gov.tw.

Kaohsiung

51310 ■ Kaohsiung Journal of Medical Sciences
Kaohsiung Medical University
100 Shih-Chuan 1st Rd.
Kaohsiung 80708, Taiwan
Ph: 886 7 3121101
Fax: 886 7 3212062

Publisher E-mail: service@kmu.edu.tw
Periodical containing scientific papers in all fields of medicine, review articles, original articles, and case reports. **Founded:** 1985. **Freq:** Monthly. **Key Personnel:** Wan-Long Chuang, Editor-in-Chief; Hsin-Su Yu, Publishing Supervisor. **ISSN:** 1607-551X. **Subscription Rates:** US$609 institutions except Europe, Japan and Iran; EUR465 institutions for European countries and Iran; 71,900¥ institutions. **URL:** http://www.elsevier.com/wps/find/journaldescription.cws_home/708701/descriptiondescription. **Circ:** Paid 1,500

51311 ■ BEM30 - 99.9 MHz
34th Fl., 2, 6 Minchuan 2nd Rd.
Kaohsiung 806, Taiwan
Ph: 886 7 3365888
Fax: 886 7 3380999
Format: Eclectic. **Owner:** Tachung Broadcasting Co., at above address. **Operating Hours:** Continuous. **Wattage:** 3000. **URL:** http://www.kiss.com.tw.

51312 ■ International Community Radio Taipei - 100.7 MHz
19-5F, No. 107, Sec. 1, Jhongshan Rd.
Sinjhuang City 24250, Taiwan
Ph: 886 2 85227766
Fax: 886 2 85227077
Format: News. **Operating Hours:** Continuous. **Wattage:** 30,000. **Ad Rates:** Advertising accepted; rates available upon request. **URL:** http://www.icrt.com.tw/.

51313 ■ Kiss Radio-FM - 97.1
34 F-2, No. 6
Min-Chaun Chen District
Kaohsiung, Taiwan
Ph: 886 7 3365888
Fax: 886 7 3380999
Format: Ethnic; World Beat. **URL:** http://www.kiss.com.tw.

51314 ■ Kiss Radio-FM - 98.3
34 F-2, No. 6
Min-Chaun Chen District
Kaohsiung, Taiwan
Ph: 886 7 3365888
Fax: 886 7 3380999
Format: Ethnic; World Beat. **URL:** http://www.kiss.com.tw.

51315 ■ Kiss Radio-FM - 99.9
34 F-2, No. 6
Min-Chaun Chen District
Kaohsiung, Taiwan
Ph: 886 7 3365888
Fax: 886 7 3380999
Format: Ethnic; World Beat. **URL:** http://www.kiss.com.tw.

Lukang

51316 ■ Radio Taiwan International- Lukang - 1008 KHz
55 Pei-An Rd.
Taipei 104, Taiwan
Ph: 886 2 28856168
Fax: 886 2 28867088

E-mail: rti@rti.org.tw
Format: News. **Owner:** Central Broadcasting System, at above address. **Founded:** 1998. **Wattage:** 600,000. **URL:** http://english.rti.com.tw/.

51317 ■ Radio Taiwan International- Lukang - 603 KHz
c/o Central Broadcasting System
55 Pei-An Rd.
Taipei 104, Taiwan
Ph: 886 2 28856168
Fax: 886 2 28867088
E-mail: rti@rti.org.tw
Format: News. **Owner:** Central Broadcasting System, at above address. **Founded:** 1998. **Wattage:** 1,000,000. **URL:** http://english.rti.com.tw/.

Minhsiung

51318 ■ Radio Taiwan International- Minhsiung - 1206 KHz
55 Pei-An Rd.
Taipei 104, Taiwan
Ph: 886 2 28856168
Fax: 886 2 28867088
E-mail: rti@rti.org.tw
Format: Eclectic. **Owner:** Central Broadcasting System, at above address. **Founded:** 1998. **Wattage:** 100,000. **URL:** http://english.rti.com.tw/.

51319 ■ Radio Taiwan International- Minhsiung - 747 KHz
55 Pei-An Rd.
Taipei 104, Taiwan
Ph: 886 2 28856168
Fax: 886 2 28867088
E-mail: rti@rti.org.tw
Format: Eclectic. **Owner:** Central Broadcasting System, at above address. **Founded:** 1998. **Wattage:** 250,000. **URL:** http://english.rti.com.tw/.

Sinjhuang City

International Community Radio Taipei - See Kaohsiung

International Community Radio Taipei - See Taichung

Taichung

51320 ■ International Journal of Electronic Customer Relationship Management
Inderscience Publishers
c/o Prof. Bruce Chien-Ta Ho, Ed.-in-Ch.
National Chung Hsing University
250 Kuokuang Rd.
Taichung 402, Taiwan
Publisher E-mail: editor@inderscience.com
Peer-reviewed journal covering electronic customer relationship management. **Founded:** 2007. **Freq:** 4/yr. **Key Personnel:** Prof. Bruce Chien-Ta Ho, Editor-in-Chief, bruceho@nchu.edu.tw; Prof. Tzong-Ru Lee, Editor, trlee@nchu.edu.tw; Prof. Jerome Dauw-Song Zhu, Assoc. Ed. **ISSN:** 1750-0664. **Subscription Rates:** EUR494 individuals includes surface mail, print only; EUR672 individuals print and online. **URL:** http://www.inderscience.com/browse/index.php?journalCODE=ijecrm.

51321 ■ International Journal of Value Chain Management
Inderscience Publishers
c/o Prof. Bruce Chien-Ta Ho, Ed.-in-Ch.
National Chung Hsing University, Institute of Electronic Commerce
Center for Electronic Commerce & Knowledge Economics Research
250, Kuokuang Rd.
Taichung 402, Taiwan
Publisher E-mail: editor@inderscience.com
Peer-reviewed journal aiming to establish an effective channel of communication between policy makers, corporate bodies, practitioners, academic, research institutions and government agencies, and to understand how enterprises harness new opportunities to create value, reinvent value chains and alter industry structures. **Freq:** Quarterly. **Key Personnel:** Prof. Bruce Chien-Ta Ho, Editor-in-Chief, bruceho@nchu.edu.tw; Prof. Siau Ching Lenny Koh, Editor-in-Chief, s.c.l.koh@sheffield.ac.uk; Dr. Simon Croom, Assoc. Ed. **ISSN:** 1741-5357. **Subscription Rates:** EUR494 individuals print only

(surface mail); EUR840 individuals online (2-3 users); EUR672 individuals print and online. **URL:** http://www.inderscience.com/browse/index.php?journalCODE=ijvcm.

51322 ■ Changhua FM Broadcasting Station - 98.7 MHz
No. 1-67 Wu Chuan Rd.
Taichung, Taiwan
Ph: 886 4 23712988
Fax: 886 4 23712999
E-mail: sakura.fm987@msa.hinet.net
Format: News. **Owner:** Changhua FM Broadcasting Station, at above address. **Founded:** Apr. 12, 1997. **Operating Hours:** Continuous. **Wattage:** 3000. **URL:** http://www.fm987.com.tw/.

51323 ■ Hao Chiating (Family) Broadcasting Co. - 97.7 MHz
37th Fl., 789 Chungming S Rd.
Taichung 402, Taiwan
Ph: 886 4 22603977
Fax: 886 4 22636433
Format: Eclectic. **Owner:** Hao Chiating (Family) Broadcasting Co., at above address. **Operating Hours:** Continuous. **Wattage:** 3000. **URL:** http://www.family977.com.tw.

51324 ■ International Community Radio Taipei - 100.1 MHz
19-5F, No. 107, Sec. 1, Jhongshan Rd.
Sinjhuang City 24250, Taiwan
Ph: 886 2 85227766
Fax: 886 2 85227077
Format: News. **Wattage:** 30,000. **Ad Rates:** Advertising accepted; rates available upon request. **URL:** http://www.icrt.com.tw/.

51325 ■ Ta chien Broadcasting Station - 99.1 MHz
9th Fl., 83 Hsuehshih Rd.
Taichung 404, Taiwan
Ph: 886 4 22025000
Fax: 886 4 22023000
E-mail: fm991@superfm99-1.com.tw
Format: Eclectic. **Owner:** Ta chien Broadcasting Station, at above address. **Wattage:** 3000. **URL:** http://www.superfm99-1.com.tw/.

Tainan

51326 ■ Centerpoint
Asian Vegetable Research and Development Center
Shanhua, PO Box 42
Tainan 74199, Taiwan
Ph: 886 65 837801
Fax: 886 65 830009
Publication E-mail: avrdcbox@netra.avrdc.org.tw
Publisher E-mail: info@worldveg.org
Periodical containing the latest news about the association and the vegetable research field. **Founded:** 1981. **Freq:** 3/yr. **Key Personnel:** Dr. S. Shanmugasundaram, Dep. Dir. **ISSN:** 0258-3070. **Remarks:** Accepts advertising. **URL:** http://www.avrdc.org. **Circ:** (Not Reported)

51327 ■ Materials Chemistry and Physics
Elsevier Science
c/o Prof. K.L. Lin, Ed.
Dept. of Materials Science & Engineering
National Cheng Kung University
Tainan 701, Taiwan
Publisher E-mail: nlinfo-f@elsevier.com
International journal focusing on structure, properties, processing and performance of materials covering thin films, surface and interface science, materials degradation and reliability, metallurgy, semiconductors and opto-electronic materials, fine ceramics, magnetics, superconductors, specialty polymers, nano-materials and composite materials in connection with the Chinese Society for Materials Science. **Founded:** 1976. **Freq:** 18/yr. **Key Personnel:** Prof. K.L. Lin, Editor, matkllin@mail.ncku.edu.tw; Prof. F.C. Hsu, Asst. Ed., fjshi@cubic.mat.ncku.edu.tw; W. Cao, Editorial Board. **ISSN:** 0254-0584. **Subscription Rates:** 530,600¥ institutions; US$4,497 institutions for all countries except Europe and Japan; EUR3,997 institutions for European countries. **Remarks:** Accepts advertising. **URL:** http://www.elsevier.com/wps/find/journaldescription.cws_home/504097/description. **Circ:** (Not Reported)

Taipei

51328 ■ Acta Oceanographica Taiwanica
National Taiwan University
College of Science
6th Fl., Shih-liang Hall
1, Sec. 4, Roosevelt Rd.
Taipei 106 ROC, Taiwan
Ph: 886 2 33664187
Fax: 886 2 23622005
Publisher E-mail: cos@ntu.edu.tw
Periodical containing original articles, notes, and letters on oceanographic research. **Founded:** 1971. **Freq:** Annual. **Key Personnel:** Prof. Liu Cho-Teng, Editor-in-Chief, ctliu@ccms.ntu.edu.tw. **ISSN:** 0379-7481. **Subscription Rates:** US$50 individuals. **URL:** http://sol.oc.ntu.edu.tw/. **Circ:** Paid 800

51329 ■ Acta Paediatrica Taiwanica
Taiwan Pediatric Association
10F/1 No. 69 Sec. 1 Hang Chow S Rd.
Taipei 100, Taiwan
Ph: 886 22 3516446
Fax: 886 22 3516448
Publisher E-mail: pediatr@pediatr.org.tw
Chinese and English language publication covering pediatrics. **Founded:** 1960. **Freq:** Bimonthly. **Key Personnel:** Huo-Yao Wei, President; Jing-Long Huang, Editor-in-Chief; Pen-Jung Wang, Editor. **ISSN:** 1608-8115. **Remarks:** Advertising not accepted. **URL:** http://www.pediatr.org.tw. **Formerly:** Acta Paediatrica Sinica. **Circ:** 3,000

51330 ■ Acta Zoologica Taiwanica
National Taiwan University
College of Science
Department of Zoology
No. 1, Sec. 4, Roosevelt Rd.
Taipei 107, Taiwan
Ph: 886 23 3664187
Fax: 886 22 3622005
Periodical containing original research on any aspects of zoological science from worldwide. **Founded:** 1988. **Freq:** Semiannual. **Key Personnel:** Yen Chen-Tung, Exec. Ed.; Tai-Sheng Chiu, Editor-in-Chief; Ju-Shey Ho, Editorial Board; Hong-Cheng Chen, Editorial Board; Shiu-Nan Chen, Editorial Board; Ching-Ming Kuo, Editorial Board. **ISSN:** 1019-5858. **URL:** http://zoologica.lifescience.ntu.edu.tw/index_e.htm. **Circ:** Controlled 500

51331 ■ Asian Air Transport
Tzeng Brothers Information Group
PO Box 43-345
7G-09 World Trade Ctr.
Taipei 105, Taiwan
Aviation magazine. **Founded:** 1988. **Freq:** Monthly. **Key Personnel:** Robert Tzeng, Editor. **ISSN:** 1021-3740. **Subscription Rates:** US$80. **Remarks:** Advertising accepted; rates available upon request. **Circ:** Paid 11,750

51332 ■ Asian Journal of Control
Chinese Automatic Control Society
c/o Li-Chen Fu, Society Pres.
Dept. of Electrical Engineering, EE II-524
National Taiwan University
Taipei, Taiwan
Ph: 886 223 622209
Journal of computers. **Founded:** 1999. **Freq:** Quarterly. **Key Personnel:** Li-Chen Fu, Editor-in-Chief, phone 886 2 23622209, lichen@ccms.ntu.edu.tw; Hidenori Kimura, Editor-in-Chief, hkimura@brain.riken.jp; Graham Goodwin, Editor, eegcg@cc.newcastle.edu.au. **ISSN:** 1561-8625. **Subscription Rates:** NTs 3,900 institutions; NTs 1,600 nonmembers individual; NTs 1,200 members; US$50 nonmembers; US$35 members; US$120 institutions, other countries. **URL:** http://www.ajc.org.tw/.

51333 ■ Botanical Studies
Institute of Plant and Microbial Biology
Academia Sinica
128 Sec. 2, Academia Rd.
Nankang
Taipei 11529, Taiwan
Ph: 886 2 27899590
Fax: 886 2 27827954
Publisher E-mail: ipmbmis@gate.sinica.edu.tw
Journal dealing with plant molecular biology. **Subtitle:** An International Journal. **Freq:** Quarterly January, April, July and October. **Key Personnel:** Yaw-Huei Lin, Editor-in-Chief, boyhlin@gate.sinica.edu.tw; Ching-I Peng,

Editor-in-Chief, bopeng@sinica.edu.tw; Anthony H.C. Huang, Publisher, ahuang@sinica.edu.tw. **ISSN:** 1817-406X. **Subscription Rates:** US$15 individuals; US$25 institutions. **URL:** http://ejournal.sinica.edu.tw/bbas/.

51334 ■ The China Post
8 Fu Shun St.
Taipei 104, Taiwan
Ph: 886 2 25969971
Fax: 886 2 25957962
Publisher E-mail: info@mail.chinapost.com.tw
General interest newspaper covering domestic and international news, investment, commerce, trade, health, science and technology, life and family. **Founded:** 1952. **Freq:** Daily. **Subscription Rates:** NTs 2,700 individuals 6 months; NTs 5,500 individuals. **Remarks:** Advertising accepted; rates available upon request. **URL:** http://www.chinapost.com.tw. **Circ:** Paid 180,000, 250,000

51335 ■ Chinese Journal of Physics
The Physical Society of the Republic of China
PO Box 23-30
Taipei 106, Taiwan
Ph: 886 2 23634923
Fax: 886 2 23626538
Publication E-mail: cjp@psroc.phys.ntu.edu.tw
Publisher E-mail: cjp@psroc.phys.ntu.edu.tw
Publishes reviews, regular articles, and refereed conference papers in various branches of physics. **Founded:** 1963. **Freq:** Quarterly. **Key Personnel:** Shin Nan Yang, Editor-in-Chief; Lin-Ni Hau, Assoc. Ed.-in-Ch.; Chen Chi-Ming, Editor; James M. Nester, Tech. Ed.; Pei-Chih Huang, Asst. Ed.; Ikai Lo, Editor. **ISSN:** 0577-9073. **Subscription Rates:** US$200 individuals airmail; US$150 individuals surface mail. **URL:** http://psroc.phys.ntu.edu.tw/cjp/index.php.

51336 ■ Contemporary Management Research
Academy of Taiwan Information Systems Research
PO Box 4-1
Taipei 23799, Taiwan
Publisher E-mail: chang@atisr.org
Journal covering all fields of management. **Freq:** Quarterly. **Trim Size:** A4. **Key Personnel:** Wenchang Fang, PhD, Editor, fang@mail.ntpu.edu.tw; Chih-Chien Wang, Editorial Board, wangson@mail.ntpu.edu.tw. **ISSN:** 1813-5498. **Subscription Rates:** US$200 institutions; US$150 individuals. **URL:** http://cmr-journal.org/; http://academic-journal.org/cmr/index2.htm.

51337 ■ Digitimes
DigiTimes Publication Inc.
12F, 133, Section 4, Mingsheng E Rd.
Songshan District
Taipei 105, Taiwan
Ph: 886 2 87128866
Fax: 886 2 87123366
Newspaper focusing on the IT industry. **Founded:** 1998. **Freq:** Daily. **Key Personnel:** Ken Tai, Publisher/Chm.; Colley Hwang, President; Morris Ko, COO/Ch. Ed.; Henry Chen, Editorial Dir.; Michael McManus, Managing Editor. **ISSN:** 1607-4114. **Remarks:** Advertising accepted; rates available upon request. **URL:** http://www.digitimes.com. **Circ:** ‡65,000

51338 ■ Dynasty
China Airlines Ltd.
131 Nanking E Rd., Sec. 3
Taipei, Taiwan
Ph: 886 22 7151212
Fax: 886 22 5146004
Airlines and aviation magazine. **Founded:** 1969. **Freq:** Bimonthly. **Subscription Rates:** Free. **URL:** http://www.china-airlines.com/en/index.htm. **Circ:** Paid 60,000

51339 ■ Environmental Policy Monthly
Environmental Protection Administration
No. 83 Section 1, Jhonghua Rd.
Taipei 10042, Taiwan
Ph: 886 22 3117722
Environmental policy journal. **Freq:** Monthly. **Key Personnel:** Chang Shao-Wen, Exec. Ed.; Dr. Stephen Shu-hung Shen, Publisher; Peter Morehead, Exec. Ed.; Dr. Y.F. Liang, Editor-in-Chief; Lee-Kuo Hsiao, Exec. Ed. **ISSN:** 1811-4008. **Subscription Rates:** Free. **URL:** http://www.epa.gov.tw/en/FileDownloadPage_EN.aspx?path=420.

51340 ■ Financial Statistics Monthly
Central Bank of the Republic of China

2 Roosevelt Rd., Section 1
Taipei 10006, Taiwan
Ph: 886 223 936161
Fax: 886 223 571974
Periodical containing financial statistical updates on Taiwan. **Founded:** 1951. **Freq:** Monthly. **URL:** http://www.cbc.gov.tw/ct.asp?xItem=1059&ctNode=535&mp=2. **Circ:** Paid 2,250

51341 ■ Industry Weekly
Trade Winds Inc.
No. 7, Ln. 75, Yung Kang St.
Taipei 106, Taiwan
Ph: 886 2 23913251
Fax: 886 2 23964022
Publisher E-mail: tradwind@ms2.hinet.net
Periodical covering Taiwan's export industries and products, especially hardware, autoparts, machinery and industrial supplies. **Founded:** 1975. **Freq:** Weekly. **Key Personnel:** Donald Shapiro, Editor. **ISSN:** 1024-9028. **Subscription Rates:** US$90; US$110 other countries. **Remarks:** Advertising accepted; rates available upon request. **Circ:** Paid 12,000

51342 ■ International Journal of Business and Information (IJBI)
Academy of Taiwan Information Systems Research
DaZhi St., No. 70
Taipei 10469, Taiwan
Ph: 886 2 25381111
Fax: 886 2 25333143
Publisher E-mail: chang@atisr.org
Journal covering all areas of business and information development around the world. **Key Personnel:** Kwei Tang, Editor-in-Chief, ktang@mgmt.purdue.edu; Chian-Son Yu, Managing Editor, csyu@mail.usc.edu.tw; Wenchang Fan, Managing Editor, fang@mail.ntpu.edu.tw. **ISSN:** 1728-8673. **URL:** http://ijbi.org/; http://www.knowledgetaiwan.org/ojs/index.php/ijbi.

51343 ■ International Journal of Cyber Society and Education
Academy of Taiwan Information Systems Research
PO Box 4-1
Taipei 23799, Taiwan
Publisher E-mail: chang@atisr.org
Journal covering all fields of cyber society and education. **Key Personnel:** Prof. Yih-Chearng Shiue, PhD, Editor-in-Chief, ijcse.journal@qmail.com; Chih-Chien Wang, Assoc. Ed. **ISSN:** 1995-6649. **URL:** http://www.academic-journals.org/ojs2/index.php/ijcse; http://atisr.org/journals.

51344 ■ International Journal of Design
Probability Surveys
43, Section 4, Keelung Rd.
College of Design, NTUST
Taipei 106, Taiwan
Ph: 886 227376432
Publisher E-mail: prsurvey@statslab.cam.ac.uk
Peer-reviewed journal covering all fields of design, including industrial design, visual communication design, interface design, animation and game design, architectural design and urban design. **Key Personnel:** Paul Hekkert, Editorial Board; Richard Buchanan, Editorial Board; Cheng Neng Kuan, Editorial Board; Lorraine Justice, Editorial Board; Ken Friedman, Editorial Board; Kuo-Hsiang Chen, Editorial Board; Lin-Lin Chen, Editor-in-Chief, llchen@mail.ntust.edu.tw; Uday Athavankar, Editorial Board; David Durling, Editorial Board; Soon-jong Lee, Editorial Board. **ISSN:** 1991-3761. **URL:** http://www.ijdesign.org/ojs/index.php/IJDesign/.

51345 ■ International Journal of Electronic Business
Inderscience Publishers
c/o Prof. Eldon Y. Li, Ed.-in-Ch.
National Chengchi University, Department of Management Information Systems
College of Commerce
No. 4, Sec. 2, Zhi-nan Rd., Wenshan
Taipei 11605, Taiwan
Publisher E-mail: editor@inderscience.com
Peer-reviewed journal aiming to develop, promote and coordinate the development and practice of electronic business methods. **Freq:** Bimonthly. **Key Personnel:** Prof. Eldon Y. Li, Editor-in-Chief, eli@calpoly.edu; Dr. Niclas Adler, Editorial Board Member; Dr. Jonathan A. Morell, American Ed.; Prof. Mitsuru Kodama, Assoc.

Ed.; Prof. Timon C. Du, Exec. Ed., timon@cuhk.edu.hk; Prof. Patrick Y.K. Chau, Asia-Pacific Ed.; Prof. Emilio Paolucci, Assoc. Ed.; Prof. Chaochang Chiu, Assoc. Ed.; Prof. Franz Josef Radermacher, Assoc. Ed. **ISSN:** 1470-6067. **Subscription Rates:** EUR593 individuals print only (surface mail); EUR1,010 individuals online only (2-3 users); EUR830 individuals print and online; EUR643 individuals print only (airmail). **URL:** http://www.inderscience.com/browse/index.php?journalCODE=ijeb.

51346 ■ International Journal of Information and Computer Security
Inderscience Publishers
c/o Dr. Eldon Y. Li, Ed.-in-Ch.
National Chengchi University
Department of Management Information System, College of Commerce
No. 64, Sec. 2, Zhi-nan Rd., Wenshan
Taipei 11605, Taiwan
Publisher E-mail: editor@inderscience.com
Journal covering developments of information & computer security. **Founded:** 2007. **Freq:** 4/yr. **Key Personnel:** Dr. Eldon Y. Li, Editor-in-Chief, eli@calpoly.edu; Prof. T.C. Ting, Editorial Board Member. **ISSN:** 1744-1765. **Subscription Rates:** EUR494 individuals print or online; EUR672 individuals print and online. **URL:** http://www.inderscience.com/browse/index.php?journalCODE=ijics.

51347 ■ Journal of Agricultural Research of China
Taiwan Agricultural Research Institute
189 Jhongjheng Rd., Wufeng
Taipei 41301, Taiwan
Ph: 886 4 23302301-5
Agricultural research journal. **Founded:** 1950. **Freq:** Quarterly. **ISSN:** 0376-477X. **Subscription Rates:** Free single issue. **URL:** http://www.tari.gov.tw/tarie/modules/icontent/index.php?op=explore&currentDir=50.

51348 ■ Journal of Banking and Finance
Asian Bankers Association
13F No. 3 Sung-shou Rd.
Taipei 00110, Taiwan
Ph: 886 2 27255663
Fax: 886 2 27255665
Publisher E-mail: cacci@ttn.net
Journal covering banking and finance. **Freq:** Semiannual. **Subscription Rates:** EUR165 individuals European countries and Iran; 22,500¥ individuals; US$178 individuals for all countries except Europe, Japan and Iran; EUR2,937 institutions for European countries and Iran; 390,300¥ institutions; US$3,289 institutions for all countries except Europe, Japan and Iran. **URL:** http://www.elsevier.com/wps/find/journaldescription.cws_home/505558/authorinstructions.

51349 ■ Journal of Chinese Chemical Society
PO Box 1-18
Nankang
Taipei 115, Taiwan
Ph: 886 2 33668206
Fax: 886 2 23648940
Publisher E-mail: jccs@chem.sinica.edu.tw
Periodical containing both experimental and theoretical research on fundamental aspects of chemistry. **Founded:** 1932. **Freq:** Bimonthly. **Key Personnel:** Yu Wang, Editor-in-Chief. **ISSN:** 0009-4536. **Subscription Rates:** NTs 650 members; NTs 1,400 nonmembers. **Remarks:** Advertising not accepted. **URL:** http://chemistry.org.tw/public_jour.php. **Circ:** Paid 2,000

51350 ■ Journal of Chinese Institute of Engineers
Chinese Institute of Engineers
3rd Fl., No. 1, Ren-ai Rd., Section 2
Taipei, Taiwan
Ph: 886 22 3925128
Fax: 886 22 3973003
Publication E-mail: jcie@mail.ntust.edu.tw
Publisher E-mail: secretariat@cie.org.tw
Periodical containing research and short commentary on issues and phenomena in many areas of engineering. **Founded:** 1978. **Freq:** 7/yr. **Key Personnel:** Shi-Shuenn Chen, Editor-in-Chief; John T. Yu, Publisher; Jinn P. Chu, Exec. Ed. **ISSN:** 0253-3839. **URL:** http://140.118.16.82/www/index.php/jcie. **Circ:** Paid 1,800

51351 ■ Journal of Commerce and Industry
Confederation of Asia-Pacific Chambers of Commerce and Industry
14 Fl., No. 11 Songgao Rd.
Xinyi District

Circulation: ★ = ABC; △ = BPA; ♦ = CAC; • = CCAB; ❑ = VAC; ⊕ = PO Statement; ‡ = Publisher's Report; Boldface figures = sworn; Light figures = estimated.

Gale Directory of Publications & Broadcast Media/147th Ed.

5495

Taipei 11073, Taiwan
Ph: 886 27 255663
Fax: 886 27 255665
Publisher E-mail: cacci@ttn.net
Journal covering commerce and industry. **Freq:** Semiannual. **URL:** http://www.cacci.org.tw/.

51352 ■ Journal of the Formosan Medical Association
Formosan Medical Association
No. 1 Chang-Te St.
Taipei 10016, Taiwan
Ph: 886 2 23810367
Fax: 886 2 23896716
Publisher E-mail: jfmaed@fma.org.tw
General medical journal for Taiwan. **Freq:** Monthly. **Key Personnel:** Kuo-Shyan Lu, Consultant Ed.; Tsu-Pei Hung, Consultant Ed.; Li-Min Huang, Editor-in-Chief. **ISSN:** 0929-6646. **Subscription Rates:** EUR499 individuals for European countries and Iran; 78,400¥ individuals for Japan; US$665 individuals for all countries except Europe, Japan and Iran. **URL:** http://www.elsevier.com/wps/find/journaldescription.cws_home/708700/authorinstructions; http://health.elsevier.com/ajws3/a260607.asp.

51353 ■ Journal of Geographical Science
National Taiwan University
Dept. of Geography
No. 1, Section 4, Roosevelt Rd.
Taipei 10617, Taiwan
Ph: 886 2 33663366
Fax: 886 2 23627651
Publisher E-mail: secretor@ntu.edu.tw
Geographic journal. **Founded:** 1962. **Freq:** Quarterly. **Key Personnel:** Mei-Hui Li, Editor-in-Chief; Tsung-yi Huang, English Ed. **ISSN:** 0494-5387. **Subscription Rates:** Free single issue. **URL:** http://www.geog.ntu.edu.tw/english/journal/journal.html. **Circ:** Paid 500

51354 ■ Journal of Microbiology, Immunology and Infection
Chinese Society of Microbiology
National Taiwan University Hospital
No. 7, Chung Shan S Rd.
Taipei 100, Taiwan
Ph: 886 22 3123456
Fax: 886 22 3955072
Publisher E-mail: editorialoffice@jmii.org
Periodical covering microbiology, immunology and various infections. **Founded:** 1968. **Freq:** Bimonthly. **Key Personnel:** Po Ren Hsueh, Managing Editor; Po-Ren Hsueh, Editor-in-Chief; Kwen Tay Luh, Chm.; Jin Town Wang, Editor-in-Chief. **ISSN:** 1684-1182. **Subscription Rates:** US$90 other countries; NTs 1,500 individuals Taiwan delivery. **Remarks:** Accepts advertising. **URL:** http://www.ejmii.com/about.php. **Circ:** Paid 4,000

51355 ■ Journal of Social Sciences and Philosophy
Academia Sinica Sun Yat-Sen Institute for Social Sciences and Philosophy
128 Academia Rd., Section 2
Nankang
Taipei 11529, Taiwan
Ph: 886 2 27822120
Publication E-mail: issppub@gate.sinica.edu.tw
Publisher E-mail: aspublic@gate.sinica.edu.tw
Publishes contributions in the fields of philosophy, political science, history, economics social studies and law. **Founded:** 1988. **Freq:** Quarterly. **Key Personnel:** Chiu Yeoung Kuo, Editor. **ISSN:** 1018-189X. **Subscription Rates:** Free single issue. **URL:** http://www.sinica.edu.tw/as/intro/issp.html. **Circ:** Paid 1,000

51356 ■ Let's Talk in English
Overseas Radio & Television Inc.
No. 10, Ln. 62, Dajhih St.
Jhongshan District
PO Box 104-127
Taipei 00104, Taiwan
Ph: 886 2 25338082
Fax: 886 2 25331009
Publisher E-mail: service@ortv.com
English-language magazine for junior high students. **Founded:** 1981. **Freq:** Monthly. **ISSN:** 1015-5899. **Subscription Rates:** NTs 120 single issue; NTs 1,440 individuals; NTs 1,200 individuals; NTs 220 individuals mp3 super CD-Rom, or audio CDPER set; NTs 2,640 individuals mp3 super CD-Rom, or audio CD set, 12. **URL:** http://studioclassroom.com/. **Circ:** 290,000

51357 ■ The Rotarian Monthly
3rd Fl., 18-1 Ln. 14
Chi Lin Rd.
Taipei 104, Taiwan
Ph: 886 2 25418580
Fax: 886 2 5418608
Publication E-mail: editor.rotapub@msa.hinet.net
Publisher E-mail: editor.rotapub@msa.hinet.net
Membership magazine of Rotary International covering current news about Rotary-related subjects. **Founded:** 1960. **Freq:** Monthly. **Key Personnel:** Robert T. Yin, Editor. **URL:** http://www.rotary.org. **Circ:** 11,300

51358 ■ Soochow Journal of History
Soochow University
Wai Shuang Hsi Campus
70, Lin-shi Rd., Shilin
Taipei 111, Taiwan
Ph: 86 228 819471
Fax: 86 223 890224
Publisher E-mail: secretary@scu.edu.tw
History journal. **Founded:** 1995. **Freq:** Annual. **ISSN:** 1025-0689. **URL:** http://www.scu.edu.tw/ENGLISH/history/publication/no.1.htm.

51359 ■ Soochow Journal of Political Science
Soochow University
Wai Shuang Hsi Campus
70, Lin-shi Rd., Shilin
Taipei 111, Taiwan
Ph: 86 228 819471
Fax: 86 223 890224
Publisher E-mail: secretary@scu.edu.tw
Political science journal. **Founded:** 1991. **Freq:** Semiannual. **ISSN:** 1019-8636. **URL:** http://www2.scu.edu.tw/politics/english/publication.asp.

51360 ■ Statistica Sinica
Academia Sinica
Institute of Statistical Science
128 Academia Rd., Section 2
Nankang
Taipei 115, Taiwan
Publication E-mail: ss@stat.sinica.edu.tw
Publisher E-mail: aspublic@gate.sinica.edu.tw
Journal publishing original work in all areas of statistics and probability, including theory, methods and applications. **Founded:** 1991. **Freq:** Quarterly. **Key Personnel:** P. Hall, Co-Ed.; J.S. Hwang, Co-Ed.; K.Y. Liang, Co-Ed. **ISSN:** 1017-0405. **Subscription Rates:** US$65 individuals surface; US$95 individuals airmail; US$225 institutions (surface or airmail). **URL:** http://www.stat.sinica.edu.tw/statistica.

51361 ■ Studio Classroom
Overseas Radio & Television Inc.
No. 10, Ln. 62, Dajhih St.
Jhongshan District
PO Box 104-127
Taipei 00104, Taiwan
Ph: 886 2 25338082
Fax: 886 2 25331009
Publisher E-mail: service@ortv.com
English-language teaching magazine. **Founded:** 1978. **Freq:** Monthly. **ISSN:** 1015-5902. **Subscription Rates:** NTs 120 single issue; NTs 1,440 individuals; NTs 2,400 other countries. **URL:** http://www.studioclassroom.com.tw/sc/. **Circ:** 210,000

51362 ■ Taipei Times
14th Fl., No. 399
Ruiguang Rd.
Taipei 11492, Taiwan
Ph: 886 226 561000
Fax: 886 226 561099
Publisher E-mail: ads@taipeitimes.com
General newspaper. **Founded:** June 15, 1999. **Freq:** Daily. **URL:** http://www.taipeitimes.com/News/. **Circ:** 285,130

51363 ■ The Taiwan Economic News
China Economic News Service
555 Chunghsiao E Rd., Sec. 4
Taipei 110, Taiwan
Ph: 886 2 2642 2629
Fax: 886 2 2642 7422
Publisher E-mail: news@cens.com
Economic newspaper. **Remarks:** Advertising accepted; rates available upon request. **URL:** http://cens.com/

cens/html/en/news/news_home.html. **Circ:** (Not Reported)

51364 ■ Taiwan International Trade
Importers & Exporters Association of Taipei
Information & Publications Dept.
350 Sung Chiang Rd.
Taipei 104, Taiwan
Ph: 886 2 25813521
Fax: 886 2 25238782
Publication E-mail: ieatmaga@ms24.hinet.net
Publisher E-mail: ieatpe@ieatpe.org.tw
International trade magazine. **Freq:** Quarterly. **Remarks:** Advertising accepted; rates available upon request. **URL:** http://www.ieatpe.org.tw/tit/tit4main.htm. **Circ:** (Not Reported)

51365 ■ Taiwan News
9th Fl., 290 Jhongsiao E Rd., Sec. 4
Taipei 10600, Taiwan
Ph: 886 22 3491500
Publisher E-mail: service@etaiwannews.com
English language newspaper for Taiwan. **Founded:** 1949. **Freq:** Daily. **ISSN:** 1607-2626. **Remarks:** Accepts advertising. **URL:** http://www.etaiwannews.com/. **Circ:** (Not Reported)

51366 ■ Taiwan Tatler
Edipresse Asia
8th Fl., 38 Fu Xing N Rd.
Taipei 104, Taiwan
Ph: 886 2 87711728
Fax: 886 2 87711724
Luxury magazine for the high society in Taiwan. **Freq:** Monthly. **Key Personnel:** Roddy Yu, Director; Celine Chang, Ch. Ed. **URL:** http://www.edipresse.com/lifestyle/taiwan-tatler. **Circ:** ‡20,000

51367 ■ Travel in Taiwan
Vision International Publishing Co.
10F-3/5, No. 2 Fuxing North Rd.
Taipei, Taiwan
Ph: 886 2 7115403
Fax: 886 2 7212790
Publisher E-mail: infor@tit.com.tw
Travel magazine. **Freq:** Monthly. **URL:** http://www.tit.com.tw/e_home.htm; http://www.sinica.edu.tw/tit/.

51368 ■ Zoological Studies
Institute of Zoology
Academia Sinica
Nankang
Taipei 115, Taiwan
Ph: 886 22 7899515
Fax: 886 22 7858059
Publication E-mail: zoolstud@gate.sinica.edu.tw
Publisher E-mail: zoinst@sinica.edu.tw
Journal on zoological studies. **Founded:** 1994. **Freq:** Bimonthly. **Key Personnel:** Kwang Tsao Shao, Editorial Board; Wen-Hsiung Li, Ch. Ed.; Sih-Che Lee, Managing Editor. **ISSN:** 1021-5506. **URL:** http://zoolstud.sinica.edu.tw/. **Formerly:** Bulletin of the Institute of Zoology, Academia Sinica.

51369 ■ BEG25 - 93.1 MHz
4th Fl., 62-2, Sec. 3, Chungshan N Rd.
Taipei 104, Taiwan
Ph: 886 2 25951233
Fax: 886 2 25962115
E-mail: web31000@mail.tcg.gov.tw
Format: News; Public Radio. **Owner:** Taipei Broadcasting Station, at above address. **Founded:** May 1995. **Operating Hours:** Continuous. **Wattage:** 13,000. **URL:** http://www.radio.taipei.gov.tw/.

51370 ■ BEG26 - 1134 KHz
4th Fl., 62-2, Sec. 3, Chungshan N Rd.
Taipei 104, Taiwan
Ph: 886 2 25951233
Fax: 886 2 25962115
E-mail: web31000@mail.tcg.gov.tw
Format: Eclectic. **Owner:** Taipei Broadcasting Station, at above address. **Founded:** May 5, 2005. **Operating Hours:** Continuous. **Wattage:** 10,000. **URL:** http://www.radio.taipei.gov.tw/.

51371 ■ Central Broadcasting System - 7445 KHz
55 Pei'an Rd.
Chungshan Ward
Taipei 104, Taiwan
Ph: 886 2 28856168

Fax: 886 2 28867088
E-mail: rti@rti.org.tw
Owner: Central Broadcasting System, at above address.
Founded: 1998. **Formerly:** Central Broadcasting System (July 1, 2003). **Wattage:** 100,000. **URL:** http://www.cbs.org.tw/.

Cheng Sheng Broadcasting Co. - See Taliao

51372 ■ GreenPeace Radio-FM - 97.3
Taipei County Rd. 97 to 14, 1st Fl.
Taipei, Taiwan
Ph: 886 2 29730409
Fax: 886 2 89732231
Format: Ethnic; World Beat. **Owner:** Greenpeace Broadcasting Station, at above address. **URL:** http://www.greenpeace.com.tw.

51373 ■ PRS Programme 5-FM - 94.5
No. 17, Guangjhou St.
Jhongjheng District
Taipei 100, Taiwan
Ph: 886 2 23888099
E-mail: prs@prs.gov.tw
Format: Information; Public Radio. **Owner:** Police Radio Station, at above address. **Ad Rates:** Noncommercial. **URL:** http://www.prs.gov.tw.

51374 ■ PRS Programme 4-AM - 1512
No. 17, Guangjhou St.
Jhongjheng District
Taipei 100, Taiwan
Ph: 886 2 23888099
E-mail: prs@prs.gov.tw
Format: Information; Public Radio. **Owner:** Police Radio Station, at above address. **Ad Rates:** Noncommercial. **URL:** http://www.prs.gov.tw.

51375 ■ PRS Programme 9-FM - 101.3
No. 17, Guangjhou St.
Jhongjheng District
Taipei 100, Taiwan
Ph: 886 2 23888099
E-mail: prs@prs.gov.tw
Format: Information; Public Radio. **Owner:** Police Radio Station, at above address. **Founded:** Jan. 3, 1954. **Ad Rates:** Noncommercial. **URL:** http://www.prs.gov.tw.

51376 ■ PRS Programme 7-FM - 93.1
No. 17, Guangjhou St.
Jhongjheng District
Taipei 100, Taiwan
Ph: 886 2 2388099
E-mail: prs@prs.gov.tw
Format: Information; Public Radio. **Owner:** Police Radio Station, at above address. **Ad Rates:** Noncommercial. **URL:** http://www.prs.gov.tw.

51377 ■ PRS Programme 6-AM - 1314
No. 17, Guangjhou St.
Jhongjheng District
Taipei 100, Taiwan
Ph: 886 2 23888099
E-mail: prs@prs.gov.tw
Format: Information; Public Radio. **Owner:** Police Radio Station, at above address. **Ad Rates:** Noncommercial. **URL:** http://www.prs.gov.tw.

51378 ■ PRS Programme 3-AM - 990
No.17, Guangjhou St.
Jhongjheng District
Taipei 100, Taiwan
Ph: 886 2 23888099
E-mail: prs@prs.gov.tw
Format: Information; Public Radio. **Owner:** Police Radio Station, at above address. **Ad Rates:** Noncommercial. **URL:** http://www.prs.gov.tw.

51379 ■ PRS Programme 3-AM - 1125
No. 17, Guangjhou St.
Jhongjheng District
Taipei 100, Taiwan
Ph: 886 2 23888099
E-mail: prs@prs.gov.tw
Format: Information; Public Radio. **Owner:** Police Radio Station, at above address. **Ad Rates:** Noncommercial. **URL:** http://www.prs.gov.tw.

51380 ■ PRS Programme 3-AM - 702
No.17, Guangjhou St.
Jhongjheng District
Taipei 100, Taiwan

Ph: 886 2 23888099
E-mail: prs@prs.gov.tw
Format: Information; Public Radio. **Owner:** Police Radio Station, at above address. **Ad Rates:** Noncommercial. **URL:** http://www.prs.gov.tw.

51381 ■ PRS Programme 3-AM - 1260
No.17, Guangjhou St.
Jhongjheng District
Taipei 100, Taiwan
Ph: 886 2 23888099
E-mail: prs@prs.gov.tw
Format: Information; Public Radio. **Owner:** Police Radio Station, at above address. **Ad Rates:** Noncommercial. **URL:** http://www.prs.gov.tw.

51382 ■ PRS Programme 2-FM - 94.3
Jhongjheng District
No. 17, Guangjhou St.
Taipei 100, Taiwan
Ph: 886 2 23888099
E-mail: prs@prs.gov.tw
Format: Information; Public Radio. **Owner:** Police Radio Station, at above address. **Ad Rates:** Noncommercial. **URL:** http://www.prs.gov.tw.

51383 ■ Radio Taiwan International - 11745 KHz
55 Pei-An Rd.
Taipei 104, Taiwan
Ph: 886 2 28856168
Fax: 886 2 28867088
E-mail: rti@rti.org.tw
Format: Eclectic. **Owner:** Central Broadcasting System, at above address. **Founded:** 1998. **Wattage:** 250,000. **URL:** http://english.rti.com.tw/.

51384 ■ Radio Taiwan International - 11550 KHz
55 Pei-An Rd.
Taipei 104, Taiwan
Ph: 886 2 28856168
Fax: 886 2 28867088
E-mail: rti@rti.org.tw
Format: News. **Owner:** Central Broadcasting System, at above address. **Founded:** 1998. **Formerly:** Central Broadcasting System (July 2003). **Wattage:** 100/250/300 KW. **URL:** http://english.rti.com.tw/.

51385 ■ Radio Taiwan International - 11725 KHz
55 Pei-An Rd.
Taipei 104, Taiwan
Ph: 886 2 28856168
Fax: 886 2 28867088
E-mail: rti@rti.org.tw
Format: News. **Owner:** Central Broadcasting System, at above address. **Founded:** 1998. **Wattage:** 100,000. **URL:** http://english.rti.com.tw/.

51386 ■ Radio Taiwan International - 9955 KHz
55 Pei-An Rd.
Taipei 104, Taiwan
Ph: 886 2 28856168
Fax: 886 2 28867088
E-mail: rti@rti.org.tw
Format: Eclectic. **Owner:** Central Broadcasting System, at above address. **Founded:** 1998. **Wattage:** 250,000. **URL:** http://english.rti.com.tw/.

51387 ■ Radio Taiwan International - 7130 KHz
55 Pei-An Rd.
Taipei 104, Taiwan
Ph: 886 2 28856168
Fax: 886 2 28867088
E-mail: rti@rti.org.tw
Format: News. **Owner:** Central Broadcasting System, at above address. **Founded:** 1998. **Formerly:** Central Broadcasting System (July 2003). **Wattage:** 50,000. **URL:** http://english.rti.com.tw/.

51388 ■ Radio Taiwan International - 7105 KHz
55 Pei-An Rd.
Taipei 104, Taiwan
Ph: 886 2 28856168
Fax: 886 2 28867088
E-mail: rti@rti.org.tw
Format: News. **Owner:** Central Broadcasting System, at above address. **Founded:** 1998. **Wattage:** 300,000. **URL:** http://english.rti.com.tw/.

Radio Taiwan International- Fangliao - See Fangliao

Radio Taiwan International- Lukang - See Lukang

Radio Taiwan International- Lukang - See Lukang

Radio Taiwan International- Minhsiung - See Minhsiung

Radio Taiwan International- Minhsiung - See Minhsiung

51389 ■ TURC-FM - 96.7
106 N 162, 7th Fl.
Chunghsiao E Rd.
Taipei 106, Taiwan
Ph: 886 2 7419396
Fax: 886 2 7786871
E-mail: uniradio@turc967.com.tw
Format: Ethnic; World Beat. **URL:** http://www.turc967.com.tw.

51390 ■ UFO Radio-FM - 92.1
102 Roosevelt Rd., Taipei bis, 25th Fl.
Taipei 10225, Taiwan
Ph: 886 2 23636600
Fax: 886 2 23688833
Format: Ethnic; World Beat. **URL:** http://www.uforadio.com.tw.

Taitung

51391 ■ BEV37 - 1269 KHz
21, Ln. 380
Hsinsheng Rd.
Taitung 950, Taiwan
Ph: 886 89 322644
Fax: 886 89 340871
E-mail: csbc_server@csbc.com.tw
Format: Eclectic. **Owner:** Cheng Sheng Broadcasting Co., 7th Fl., 66-1, Sec. 1, Chungching S Rd., Taipei 100, Taiwan, 886 2 23617231, Fax: 886 2 23113178. **Operating Hours:** Continuous (except 9:20 p.m. Sat.-3 p.m. Sun.). **Wattage:** 1000. **URL:** http://www.csbc.com.tw/.

Taliao

51392 ■ Cheng Sheng Broadcasting Co. - 819 KHz
7th Fl., 66-1, Sec. 1, Chungching S Rd.
Taipei 100, Taiwan
Ph: 886 2 23617231
Fax: 886 2 23113178
E-mail: csbc_server@csbc.com.tw
Format: Eclectic. **Owner:** Cheng Sheng Broadcasting Co., at above address. **Operating Hours:** Continuous. **Wattage:** 10,000. **Ad Rates:** Noncommercial. **URL:** http://www.csbc.com.tw.

Tamsui

51393 ■ International Journal of Information and Management Sciences
Tamkang University
Dept. of Management Sciences & Decision Making
151 Ying-Chuan Rd.
Republic of China
Tamsui 25137, Taiwan
Ph: 886 2 26215656
Fax: 886 2 26223204
Publishes original contributions on information systems, general systems, stochastic systems, transportation systems, industrial management, industrial engineering, management sciences, regional science, decision science, operations research, and applied science. **Founded:** 1990. **Freq:** Quarterly. **Key Personnel:** Dr. Shu-Hsien Liao, Managing Editor, ijims@staff.tku.edu.tw; Dr. Shigeichi Hirasawa, Editorial Board; Dr. Wen-Tao Huang, Editorial Board; Flora Chia-I Chang, Publisher; Dr. Dun-Ji Chen, Editor-in-Chief; Dr. Miao-Sheng Chen, Editorial Board; Dr. Saibal Chattopadhyay, Editorial Board; Dr. Jeffrey S. Pai, Editorial Board; Dr. Louis R. Chow, Editorial Board; Dr. Jinn-Tsair Teng, Editorial Board. **ISSN:** 1017-1819. **Subscription Rates:** NTs 1,500 individuals; US$100 other countries. **URL:** http://jims.ms.tku.edu.tw/. **Circ:** Paid 400

Circulation: ★ = ABC; △ = BPA; ◆ = CAC; • = CCAB; ❑ = VAC; ⊕ = PO Statement; ‡ = Publisher's Report; Boldface figures = sworn; Light figures = estimated.

51394 ■ Journal of Educational Media and Library Sciences
Tamkang University
Graduate Institute of Educational Media and Library Sciences
151 Ying-chuan Rd.
Tamsui 25137, Taiwan
Ph: 886 22 6215656
Fax: 886 22 6223204
Publication E-mail: emls@mail.dils.tku.edu.tw
Journal devoted to studies regarding the fields of library science, information science, audio-visual and educational technology. **Founded:** 1970. **Freq:** Quarterly. **Key Personnel:** Prof. Jeong-Yeou Chiu, Editor; Jianzhong Wu, Editorial Board; Sheue-Fang Song, Editorial Board; Ming-Yueh Tsay, Editorial Board; Hong-Chu Huang, Editorial Board; Shih-chung Lee, Editorial Board; Chaoyun Chaucer Liang, Editorial Board; Guchao Shen, Editorial Board; Zhiqiang Zhang, Regional Assoc. Ed. **ISSN:** 1013-090X. **Subscription Rates:** US$40 individuals outside Taiwan; US$55 individuals for America, Europe, Australia & Africa, airmail; US$48 individuals for Japan, Korea, Thailand & Philippines, airmail; US$46 individuals for Hong Kong & Macao, airmail. **URL:** http://joemls.tku.edu.tw/. **Circ:** Paid 1,200

51395 ■ Tamkang Journal of Futures Studies
Tamkang University
College of Education
Tamsui Campus

151 Ying-chuan Rd.
Tamsui 25137, Taiwan
Ph: 886 22 6215656
Fax: 886 22 6223204
Publication focusing on integrating sociology, technology, environment, economy, politics and other sciences, as well as on future trends forecasting. **Freq:** Quarterly. **Key Personnel:** Clement C.P. Chang, Editor, future@mail.tku.edu.tw; Flora C.I. Chang, Publisher; Shun-Jie Ji, Managing Editor, jishunji@mail.tku.edu.tw. **Subscription Rates:** US$30 individuals; US$10 students; US$40 institutions. **URL:** http://www.jfs.tku.edu.tw/.

51396 ■ Tamkang Journal of International Affairs
Tamkang University
College of International Studies
Taipei County Rd. 151, Taipei Hsien
Tamsui 25137, Taiwan
Ph: 886 22 6215656
Publisher E-mail: ficx@www2.tku.edu.tw
Publication providing an open forum for discussions on a wide range of topics related to a scholarly understanding of international relations in the contemporary world, as well as a historical approach in culture, economy and politics. **Founded:** 1997. **Freq:** Quarterly. **Key Personnel:** Edward I-hsin Chen, Editorial Board; Wan-Chin Tai, Editor. **ISSN:** 1027-4979. **URL:** http://www2.tku.edu.tw/~ti/future/Journal.htm.

51397 ■ Tamkang Journal of Mathematics
Tamkang University
Dept. of Mathematics
151 Ying-chuan Rd.
Taipei County
Tamsui 25137, Taiwan
Ph: 886 2 26215656
Fax: 886 2 26209916
Publishes in English research papers of broad interest in all fields of pure and applied mathematics. **Founded:** 1970. **Freq:** Quarterly. **ISSN:** 0049-2930. **Subscription Rates:** US$50 individuals. **Remarks:** Advertising not accepted. **URL:** http://www.math.tku.edu.tw/english/e_Journal.htm. **Circ:** (Not Reported)

51398 ■ Tamkang Journal of Tamkang Review
Tamkang University
151 Ying-chuan Rd.
Tamsui 25137, Taiwan
Ph: 886 2 26215656
Fax: 886 2 26223204
Publishes studies of Chinese Literature from a critical point of view that places the subject within the context of world literature and studies dealing with theoretical aspects of East-West comparative literature. **Founded:** 1970. **Freq:** Quarterly. **Key Personnel:** Flora Chia-I Chang, Publisher; Mei-Hwa Sung, Editor-in-Chief; Prof. Han-Ping Chiu, Assoc. Ed. **ISSN:** 0049-2949. **Remarks:** Advertising not accepted. **URL:** http://foreign.tku.edu.tw/TKUEnglish/libraryRes/Review.asp. **Circ:** (Not Reported)

Dar es Salaam

51399 ■ African Journal of Finance and Management
African Journals Online
PO Box 3918
Dar es Salaam, United Republic of Tanzania
Publisher E-mail: info@ajol.info
Peer-reviewed journal covering theoretical and empirical research, analysis of field experience and new developments in finance, management, banking, accountancy, insurance, social security, computers and related areas. **Founded:** 1870. **Freq:** Semiannual. **Print Method:** Offset. **Cols./Page:** 6. **Col. Width:** 24 nonpareils. **Col. Depth:** 294 agate lines. **Key Personnel:** Dr. S.R. Mohamed, Editor-in-Chief, fax 255 22 2112935, suleiman.mohamed@gmail.com; Simon S. Sekiete, Contact, phone 255 22 2123666, sekiete@hotmail.com. **ISSN:** 0856-6372. **Subscription Rates:** 48,000 TSh individuals; US$28 elsewhere. **URL:** http://ajol.info/index.php/ajfm.

51400 ■ East African Journal of Public Health
African Journals Online
PO Box 65015
Dar es Salaam, United Republic of Tanzania
Publisher E-mail: info@ajol.info
Peer-reviewed journal containing public health related information. **Freq:** Semiannual. **Key Personnel:** Kagoma S. Mnyika, Editor-in-Chief, kmnyika@muhas.ac.tz. **ISSN:** 0856-8960. **Subscription Rates:** US$25 individuals East Africa; US$120 individuals Europe; US$140 U.S.; US$50 institutions East Africa; US$200 institutions Europe; US$250 U.S. institution. **URL:** http://ajol.info/index.php/eajph.

51401 ■ Huria
African Journals Online
Open University of Tanzania
PO Box 23409
Dar es Salaam, United Republic of Tanzania
Ph: 255 22 2668820
Fax: 255 22 2668759
Publisher E-mail: info@ajol.info
Peer-reviewed journal containing information about the exchange of views and ideas between academicians and scholars in various fields. **Subtitle:** Journal of the Open University of Tanzania. **Freq:** Semiannual. **Key Personnel:** Dr. Modest Varisanga, Editor-in-Chief, deputyvc@out.ac.tz. **ISSN:** 0856-6739. **Subscription Rates:** US$10 individuals; US$20 other countries. **URL:** http://ajol.info/index.php/huria.

51402 ■ Journal of Building and Land Development
African Journals Online
PO Box 35176
Dar es Salaam, United Republic of Tanzania
Ph: 255 22 2771847
Fax: 255 22 2775479
Publisher E-mail: info@ajol.info
Peer-reviewed journal covering all fields of human settlements development and environmental management. **Freq:** Semiannual. **Key Personnel:** Mengiseny E. Kaseva, Editor-in-Chief, aru@aru.ac.tz; Prof. Gabriel R. Kasennga, Managing Editor, kassenga@aru.ac.tz. **ISSN:** 0856-0501. **URL:** http://ajol.info/index.php/jbld.

51403 ■ Tanzania Journal of Science
African Journals Online
University of Dar es Salaam
PO Box 35065
Dar es Salaam, United Republic of Tanzania
Ph: 255 22 2410129
Fax: 255 22 2410129
Publisher E-mail: info@ajol.info
Peer-reviewed journal covering all fields of science. **Founded:** 1975. **Freq:** Annual. **Key Personnel:** Prof. A.K. Kivaisi, Editor-in-Chief, tjs@science.udsm.ac.tz. **ISSN:** 0856-1761. **Subscription Rates:** US$30 individuals East Africa; US$50 other countries. **URL:** http://ajol.info/index.php/tjs.

51404 ■ Tanzania Medical Journal
African Journals Online
PO Box 701
Dar es Salaam, United Republic of Tanzania
Publisher E-mail: info@ajol.info
Peer-reviewed journal covering the field of biomedical science. **Freq:** Semiannual. **Key Personnel:** Dr. Yassin. M. Mgonda, Contact, ymgonda@muhas.ac.tz; Dr. Merina Njelekela, Contact, mnjelekela@muhas.ac.tz. **ISSN:** 0856-0719. **URL:** http://ajol.info/index.php/tmj.

51405 ■ Tanzanian Journal of Health Research
African Journals Online
c/o National Institute for Medical Research
PO Box 9653
Dar es Salaam, United Republic of Tanzania
Ph: 255 22 2130770
Fax: 255 22 2130660
Publisher F-mail: info@ajol.info
Peer-reviewed journal containing information on health research issues in Tanzania. **Freq:** Quarterly. **Key Personnel:** Dr. Leonard E.G. Mboera, Editor, lmboera@nimr.or.tz; V.P. Mvungi, Assoc. Ed.; M.A. Munga, Assoc. Ed. **ISSN:** 0856-6496. **Subscription Rates:** US$45 individuals; US$60 institutions; US$90 individuals developing countries; US$105 institutions developing countries; US$240 individuals developed countries; US$282 institutions developed countries. **URL:** http://ajol.info/index.php/thrb.

51406 ■ University of Dar es Salaam Library Journal
African Journals Online
PO Box 35092
Dar es Salaam, United Republic of Tanzania
Publisher E-mail: info@ajol.info
Peer-reviewed journal containing articles on all aspects of library and information science. **Freq:** Semiannual. **Key Personnel:** Dr. J. Msuya, Editor-in-Chief, director@libis.udsm.ac.tz. **ISSN:** 0856-1818. **Subscription Rates:** US$10 individuals Africa; US$20 other countries. **URL:** http://ajol.info/index.php/udslj.

Morogoro

51407 ■ Tanzania Journal of Forestry and Nature Conservation
African Journals Online
Faculty of Forestry & Nature Conservation
PO Box 3009
Morogoro, United Republic of Tanzania
Ph: 255 23 2604648
Fax: 255 23 2604648
Publisher E-mail: info@ajol.info
Peer-reviewed journal covering the management and conservation of tropical flora and fauna and other natural resources. **Freq:** Semiannual. **Key Personnel:** Prof. P.K. Munishi, Contact, pmunishi2001@yahoo.com; Prof. PR Gillah, Contact, forestry@suanet.ac.tz. **ISSN:** 1856-0315. **Subscription Rates:** US$50 single issue. **URL:** http://ajol.info/index.php/tjfnc.

51408 ■ Tanzania Veterinary Journal
African Journals Online
PO Box 3018
Chuo Kikuu
Morogoro, United Republic of Tanzania
Ph: 255 23 2604980
Fax: 255 23 2604647
Publisher E-mail: info@ajol.info
Peer-reviewed journal covering the field of veterinary and animal sciences. **Freq:** Semiannual. **Key Personnel:** Dr. Joshua J. Malago, Asst. Ed., jmalago@suanet.ac.tz; S.I. Kimera, Editor-in-Chief. **ISSN:** 0856-1451. **Subscription Rates:** US$500 individuals. **URL:** http://ajol.info/index.php/tvj.

Zanzibar

51409 ■ Western Indian Ocean Journal of Marine Science
Western Indian Ocean Marine Science Association
Mizingani St., House No. 13644/10
PO Box 3298
Zanzibar, United Republic of Tanzania
Ph: 255 24 2233472
Fax: 255 24 2233852
Journal featuring original research articles dealing with all aspects of marine sciences and coastal management. **Founded:** 2002. **Freq:** Semiannual. **Key Personnel:** Prof. Alan Whittick, Editor-in-Chief. **URL:** http://www.wiomsa.org/?id=718.

Circulation: ★ = ABC; △ = BPA; ◆ = CAC; • = CCAB; ❑ = VAC; ⊕ = PO Statement; ‡ = Publisher's Report; Boldface figures = sworn; Light figures = estimated.

Gale Directory of Publications & Broadcast Media/147th Ed.

5499

Bangkok

51410 ■ Asia Pacific Development Journal
United Nations Economic and Social Commission for
Asia and the Pacific
Trade amd Investment Division
United Nations Bldg.
Rajadamnern Nok Ave.
Bangkok 10200, Thailand
Ph: 66 228 81234
Fax: 66 228 81000
Publisher E-mail: unescap@unescap.org
Asia Pacific journal covering development. **Freq:**
Semiannual. **Key Personnel:** Prof. Syed Nawab Haider
Naqvi, Advisory Board; Dr. Chalongphob Sussangkarn,
Advisory Board; Prof. Jomo K. Sundaram, Advisory
Board; Prof. Karina Constantino-David, Advisory
Board; Aynul Hasan, Ch. Ed.; Prof. Suman K. Bery, Advisory
Board; Prof. Peter G. Warr, Advisory Board. **ISSN:** 1020-
1246. **URL:** http://www.unescap.org/pdd/publications/
index_apdj.asp.

51411 ■ Asia-Pacific Population Journal
United Nations Economic and Social Commission for
Asia and the Pacific
Trade amd Investment Division
United Nations Bldg.
Rajadamnern Nok Ave.
Bangkok 10200, Thailand
Ph: 66 228 81234
Fax: 66 228 81000
Publisher E-mail: unescap@unescap.org
Asia Pacific journal covering development. **Founded:**
1986. **Freq:** 3/yr. **Trim Size:** A5. **Key Personnel:** Dr.
Srinivas Tata, Editor-in-Chief; Wanphen Sreshthaputra,
Editor. **ISSN:** 0259-238X. **Remarks:** Advertising not
accepted. **URL:** http://www.unescap.org/esid/psis/
population/journal/index.asp. **Circ:** 2,000

51412 ■ Asia-Pacific Tropical Homes
Artasia Press Co., Ltd.
143/1-2 Soi Dumex
Charoen Nakorn Rd.
Klong Tonsai, Klongsarn
Bangkok 10600, Thailand
Ph: 66 2 8613360
Fax: 66 2 8613363
Publisher E-mail: info@aapress.net
Magazine exploring the unique and exotic blend of lif-
estyles and cultures from across a tropical belt stretch-
ing from Sri Lanka in the west, through the vast
archipelago of islands that forms Southeast Asia, to the
tropical North of Australia, then east into the Pacific
Islands. **Freq:** Quarterly. **Key Personnel:** Collin Piprell,
Managing Editor. **Subscription Rates:** US$40 individu-
als; US$75 individuals for 2 years. **Remarks:** Accepts
advertising. **URL:** http://www.trophomes.com/; http://
www.aapress.net/AA_Magazine_ATPH.html. **Ad Rates:**
BW: 4,800 Bht. **Circ:** (Not Reported)

51413 ■ BAMBI Magazine
Bangkok Babies & Mothers International
PO Box 1078
Suanphlu

Bangkok 10121, Thailand
Magazine providing support and information for pregnant
women and parents of babies and young children living
in Thailand. **Founded:** 1982. **Freq:** Monthly. **Remarks:**
Accepts advertising. **URL:** http://www.bambiweb.org/
services/bambi_magazines. **Circ:** (Not Reported)

51414 ■ Bangkok Post Student Weekly
The Post Publishing Public Company Ltd.
Bangkok Post Bldg.
136 Na Ranong Rd.
Klong Toey
Bangkok 10110, Thailand
Ph: 66 224 03700
Fax: 66 224 03790
News magazine for teenagers. **Founded:** 1969. **Freq:**
Weekly. **Key Personnel:** Anussorn Thavisin, Editor.
Subscription Rates: 490 Bht individuals; 980 Bht two
years. **Remarks:** Accepts advertising. **URL:** http://www.
student-weekly.com. **Circ:** 110,000

51415 ■ Buffalo Journal
Chulalongkorn University
Research Centre for Bioscience in Animal Production
254 Phyathai Rd.
Patumwan
Bangkok 10330, Thailand
Ph: 66 2 2150871
Fax: 66 2 2154804
Publication E-mail: kmaneewa@netserv.chula.ac.th
Publishes research papers, reviews and comments on
buffalo anatomy, breeding, diseases, genetics, manage-
ment, nutrition, physiology, reproduction, and socio-
economic problems. **Subtitle:** An International Journal
of Buffalo Science. **Founded:** 1985. **Freq:** Semiannual.
Key Personnel: Kamonpatana M. Kamonpatana, Editor.
ISSN: 0857-1554. **URL:** http://www.vet.chula.ac.th/.

51416 ■ Business Day
Business Day Company Ltd.
Olympia Tower, 22nd Fl.
444 Ratchadapisak Rd.
Bangkok 10320, Thailand
Ph: 66 251 23579
Fax: 66 251 235656
Publication E-mail: editor@biz-day.com
Publisher E-mail: info@bday.net
International business newspaper. **Subtitle:** Thailand's
First International Business Daily. **Remarks:** Accepts
advertising. **URL:** http://www.biz-day.com/. **Circ:** (Not
Reported)

51417 ■ Confluence
United Nations Economic and Social Commission for
Asia and the Pacific
United Nations Bldg.
Rajadamnern Nok Ave.
Bangkok 10200, Thailand
Ph: 66 2 2881234
Fax: 66 2 2881000
Publisher E-mail: unescap@unescap.org
Periodical covering the range of technological, manage-
rial and conceptual information related to water resource
developments. **Founded:** 1982. **Freq:** Semiannual.
ISSN: 0257-3520. **Subscription Rates:** Free. **URL:**

http://www.unescap.org. **Circ:** 600

**51418 ■ e-TISNET Monthly News/e-TISNET
Monthly Information Services**
United Nations Economic and Social Commission for
Asia and the Pacific
Trade amd Investment Division
United Nations Bldg.
Rajadamnern Nok Ave.
Bangkok 10200, Thailand
Ph: 66 228 81234
Fax: 66 228 81000
Publisher E-mail: unescap@unescap.org
Online publication covering economic development.
Founded: 1982. **Freq:** Monthly. **Subscription Rates:**
Free. **Remarks:** Advertising not accepted. **URL:** http://
www.unescap.org; http://www.unescap.org/tid/etisnet.
asp. **Formerly:** TISNET Trade and Investment Bulletin
(2004). **Circ:** (Not Reported)

51419 ■ EEAT Journal
Environmental Engineering Association of Thailand
122/4 Soi Rawadee, Rama VI Rd.
Samsen Nai, Phayathai
Bangkok 10400, Thailand
Ph: 66 2 6171530
Fax: 66 2 2799720
Publisher E-mail: info@eeat.or.th
English and Thai language journal covering pollution
control. **Freq:** Bimonthly. **Key Personnel:** Pranee Pan-
tumsinchai, President. **Remarks:** Advertising accepted;
rates available upon request. **URL:** http://www.eeat.or.
th. **Circ:** 1,500

51420 ■ Essential Guide to Home & Decor
Edipresse Asia
Bubhajit Bldg., 14 A Fl.
20 N Sathorn Rd.
Silom
Bangrak
Bangkok 10500, Thailand
Magazine featuring ideas for home decorations. **Freq:**
Annual. **Key Personnel:** Naphalai Areesorn, Ch. Ed.;
Nigel Oakins, Director. **URL:** http://www.edipresse.com/
home-design/essential-guide-home-decor. **Circ:** ‡63,350

51421 ■ Expat Society
Edipresse Asia
Bubhajit Bldg., 14 A Fl.
20 N Sathorn Rd.
Silom
Bangrak
Bangkok 10500, Thailand
Ph: 66 2 2379800
Fax: 66 2 2379810
Magazine featuring the top members of the Thailand's
expatriate society. **Freq:** Annual. **Key Personnel:** Nigel
Oakins, Director; Naphalai Areesorn, Ch. Ed. **URL:** http://
www.edipresse.com/lifestyle/expat-society.

51422 ■ Hobby Electronics
Se-Education Public Company Ltd.
1858/87-90 Nation Tower Bldg.
19th Fl., Bangna-Trad Rd., Km. 4.5
Bangkok 10260, Thailand
Ph: 66 2 7398000

Circulation: ★ = ABC; △ = BPA; ◆ = CAC; • = CCAB; ❑ = VAC; ⊕ = PO Statement; ‡ = Publisher's Report; Boldface figures = sworn; Light figures = estimated.

Publication E-mail: hobby@se-ed.com
Publisher E-mail: comment@se-ed.com
Publication providing information for fledgling electronics enthusiasts and interested readers. **Subtitle:** For inventors and experimenters. **Founded:** 1997. **Freq:** Monthly. **ISSN:** 0858-9976. **Subscription Rates:** 400 Bht. **Remarks:** Advertising accepted; rates available upon request. **URL:** http://electronics.se-ed.com/hobby/. **Circ:** (Not Reported)

51423 ■ Journal of the Medical Association of Thailand
Medical Association of Thailand
4th Royal Golden Jubilee Bldg., 2 Soi Soonvijai
New Pechburi Rd., Huaykwang
Bangkok 10310, Thailand
Ph: 66 231 44333
Fax: 66 231 46305
Medical sciences journal. **Founded:** 1929. **Freq:** Monthly. **ISSN:** 0125-2208. **Subscription Rates:** US$100 single issue single copies; 600¥ individuals local : 600 baht; US$180 other countries oversea (surfacemail); US$200 students medical. **URL:** http://www.mat.or.th/journal/index.php. **Circ:** 3,500

51424 ■ Journal of the Planetary Gemologists Association
Planetary Gemologists Association
131 Soi Asoke
Sukhumvit Rd.
Bangkok 10110, Thailand
Ph: 66 266 16479
Fax: 66 226 02833
Publisher E-mail: sec@p-g-a.org
Journal presenting findings and conclusions on planetary gemology. **Freq:** Annual. **URL:** http://www.p-g-a.org/membership.html.

51425 ■ Journal of Southeast Asian Education
SEAMEO Secretariat
Mom Luang Pin Malakul Bldg.
4th Fl., 920 Sukhumvit Rd.
Bangkok 10110, Thailand
Ph: 66 23910144
Fax: 66 23812587
Publisher E-mail: secretariat@seameo.org
Publication focusing on education. **Founded:** 2000. **Freq:** Semiannual. **ISSN:** 1513-4601. **URL:** http://www.seameo.org/vl/library/dlwelcome/publications/ejournal/seadex.htm.

51426 ■ LookEast
Advertising & Media Consultants Company Ltd.
18 Fl., Richmond Bldg., Klongtoey
75/65 Sukhumvit 26
Bangkok 10110, Thailand
Ph: 66 662 2042449
Fax: 66 662 2042984
Travel and tourism related magazine. **ISSN:** 0857-1139. **URL:** http://www.lookeastmagazine.com/index.html.

51427 ■ Microcomputer
Se-Education Public Company Ltd.
1858/87-90 Nation Tower Bldg.
19th Fl., Bangna-Trad Rd., Km. 4.5
Bangkok 10260, Thailand
Ph: 66 2 7398000
Publication E-mail: micro@se-ed.com
Publisher E-mail: comment@se-ed.com
Computer magazine. **Subtitle:** For General PC User. **Founded:** 1983. **Freq:** Monthly. **Key Personnel:** Thanong Chotisorayuth, Mng. Dir. **ISSN:** 0857-0140. **Subscription Rates:** 720 Bht. **Remarks:** Advertising accepted; rates available upon request. **URL:** http://micro.se-ed.com/; http://www.se-ed.com/default.aspx. **Circ:** (Not Reported)

51428 ■ The Nation
Nation Multimedia Group
1854 Bangna-Trat Rd.
Bangna
Bangkok 10260, Thailand
Ph: 66 233 83333
Fax: 66 233 83334
Publication E-mail: editor@nationgroup.com
Publisher E-mail: customer@nationgroup.com
Political science publication. **Freq:** Daily. **URL:** http://www.nationmultimedia.com.

51429 ■ Phuket Tatler
Edipresse Asia

Bubhajit Bldg., 14 A Fl.
20 N Sathorn Rd.
Silom
Bangrak
Bangkok 10500, Thailand
Ph: 66 2 2379800
Fax: 66 2 2379810
Publication E-mail: tatler@thailandtatler.com
Magazine covering the local high society lifestyle. **Freq:** Annual. **Key Personnel:** Nigel Oakins, Director; Naphalai Areesorn, Ch. Ed. **URL:** http://www.edipresseasia.com/magazines.php?MagID=HKTTATLER. **Circ:** ‡62,850

51430 ■ Pink Ink
MBE Surawong NO. 227
173/3 Surawong Rd.
Bangkok 10500, Thailand
Ph: 66 2 6613150
Publication E-mail: pinkink@khsnet.com
Publisher E-mail: pinkink@khsnet.com
Thailand's gay and lesbian magazine. **Freq:** Monthly. **Key Personnel:** Jennifer Bliss, Editor; Nick Wilde, Editor. **URL:** http://www.khsnet.net/pinkink/.

51431 ■ Population Headliners
United Nations Economic and Social Commission for Asia and the Pacific
United Nations Bldg.
Rajadamnern Nok Ave.
Bangkok 10200, Thailand
Ph: 66 2 2881234
Fax: 66 2 2881000
Publisher E-mail: unescap@unescap.org
Population studies journal. **Founded:** 1971. **Freq:** Bimonthly. **ISSN:** 0252-3639. **Subscription Rates:** Free. **URL:** http://www.unescap.org/esid/psis/population/popheadline/index.asp. **Circ:** 5,500

51432 ■ Property Report Thailand
Ensign Media Co. Ltd.
K Building, 4th Fl.
22 Sukhumvit Rd., Soi 35
Wattana
Bangkok 10110, Thailand
Ph: 66 2 2607643
Fax: 66 2 2607644
Publication E-mail: info@property-report.com
Publisher E-mail: duncan@ensign-media.com
Real estate newspaper featuring up-to-date information and coverage of industry trends and innovations. **Founded:** 2004. **Freq:** MON. **Subscription Rates:** US$50 individuals within Thailand; 90 Bht two years within Thailand; US$120 other countries within Asia; US$150 other countries Europe/Africa; US$165 individuals Americas. **Remarks:** Accepts advertising. **URL:** http://www.ensign-media.com/; http://www.property-report.com/. **Circ:** 25,000

51433 ■ The Rubber International
TRI Global Company Ltd.
72 PAV Bldg., 4A Fl.
Ladprao Rd., Soi 42
Huay Khwang
Bangkok 10310, Thailand
Ph: 66 2 5122128
Fax: 66 2 5122129
Rubber business magazine. **Freq:** Monthly. **Print Method:** Offset. **Subscription Rates:** US$250 two years; US$320 two years outside Asia; US$180 individuals outside Asia; US$250 two years in Asia except Thailand. **Remarks:** Accepts advertising front cover. **URL:** http://www.rubbmag.com. **Ad Rates:** BW: 500 Bht. **Circ:** (Not Reported)

51434 ■ Science Asia
Science Society of Thailand
c/o Prof. Worachart Sirawaraporn, Ed.
Dept. of Biochemistry
Faculty of Science, Mahidol University
272 Rama VI Rd.
Bangkok 10400, Thailand
Ph: 66 2 2015371
Fax: 66 2 2015103
Publication E-mail: scwsr@mahidol.ac.th
Science journal. **Freq:** Quarterly. **Key Personnel:** Prof. Jisnuson M.R. Svasti, Advisory Committee; Prof. Worachart Sirawaraporn, Editor. **ISSN:** 1513-1874. **Subscription Rates:** US$60 other countries; US$120 institutions, other countries; US$110 other countries 2 years;

US$220 institutions, other countries 2 years; 800 Bht individuals; 1,600 Bht institutions; 1,400 Bht two years; 2,800 Bht institutions; 200 Bht individuals back issues; 400 Bht institutions back issues. **URL:** http://www.scienceasia.org/index.php.

51435 ■ SEAMEO Journal of Southeast Asian Education
Southeast Asian Ministers of Education Organization
Mom Luang Pin Malakul Centenary Bldg., 4th Fl.
920 Sukhumvit Rd.
Bangkok 10110, Thailand
Ph: 66 2391 0144
Fax: 66 2381 2587
Publisher E-mail: secretariat@seameo.org
Publication covering education. **Founded:** 2000. **Freq:** Semiannual. **Key Personnel:** Alex Fung, Editor, alexfung@hkbu.edu.hk. **ISSN:** 1513-4601. **Remarks:** Advertising not accepted. **URL:** http://www.seameo.org. **Formerly:** SEAMEO Forum. **Circ:** (Not Reported)

51436 ■ Telcom Journal
Telcom Journal Company Ltd.
327/17-19 Soi Sri-Amporn (Phaholyothin 32)
Senanikom Rd., Ladyao
Chatuchak
Bangkok 10900, Thailand
Ph: 66 2 5614993
Fax: 66 2 5615033
Publisher E-mail: service@tj.co.th
Newspaper covering the telecom business. **Freq:** Weekly. **Key Personnel:** Yupayao Inthirat, Exec. Ed. **Subscription Rates:** 1,000 Bht individuals. **URL:** http://www.tj.co.th. **Ad Rates:** BW: 120,000 Bht, 4C: 150,000 Bht. **Circ:** 120,000

51437 ■ Thai-American Business
The American Chamber of Commerce in Thailand
7th Fl., GPF Witthayu A
93/1 Wireless Rd.
Lumphini
Pathumwan
Bangkok 10330, Thailand
Ph: 66 2254 1041
Fax: 66 2651 1605
Publisher E-mail: service@amchamthailand.com
Business and Economics journal. **Founded:** 1967. **Freq:** Bimonthly. **Key Personnel:** Thomas J. White, President; Judy Benn, Exec. Dir., execdirector@amchamthailand.com. **ISSN:** 0125-0191. **Remarks:** Advertising accepted; rates available upon request. **URL:** http://www.amchamthailand.com/acct/asp/general.asp?MenuItemID=97&SponsorID=236T-AB. **Circ:** Paid 3,000

51438 ■ Thai Journal of Anesthesiology
Royal College of Anesthesiologists of Thailand
Dept. of Anesthesiology
Faculty of Medicine
Chulalongkorn University
Rama 4 Rd., Pathumwan
Bangkok, Thailand
Publisher E-mail: fmedtwr@md2.chula.ac.th
Medical journal. **URL:** http://storm.prohosting.com/rcat/journal.htm.

51439 ■ Thai Journal of Development Administration
National Institute of Development Administration
Research Center
118 Moo3, Sereethai Rd.
Khwaeng Klong-Chan
Khet Bangkapi
Bangkok 10240, Thailand
Ph: 66 2 7273000
Fax: 66 2 3758798
Publisher E-mail: nisnida@nida.nida.ac.th
Periodical covering issues related to production of goods and services. **Founded:** 1960. **Freq:** Quarterly. **Print Method:** Printed by Publishing Company. **Trim Size:** 25 x 10.25. **ISSN:** 0125-3689. **Subscription Rates:** US$35. **URL:** http://www.nida.ac.th/en/epublishing/page2.html. **Ad Rates:** BW: 400 Bht, 4C: 800 Bht. **Circ:** Paid 1,500

51440 ■ Thai Spas
Edipresse Asia
Bubhajit Bldg., 14 A Fl.
20 N Sathorn Rd.
Silom
Bangrak
Bangkok 10500, Thailand

Ph: 66 2 2379800
Fax: 66 2 2379810
Publication E-mail: tatler@thailandtatler.com
Magazine featuring Thailand's luxurious spas, beauty and health centers. **Subtitle:** Inner and Outer Well-Being. **Freq:** Annual. **Key Personnel:** Nigel Oakins, Director; Naphalai Areesorn, Ch. Ed. **URL:** http://www.edipresseasia.com/magazines.php?MagID=THSPA.

51441 ■ Thailand Airline Timetable
Advertising & Media Consultants Company Ltd.
18 Fl., Richmond Bldg., Klongtoey
75/65 Sukhumvit 26
Bangkok 10110, Thailand
Ph: 66 662 2042449
Fax: 66 662 2042984
Air transport journal. **Founded:** 1976. **Freq:** Monthly. **ISSN:** 0125-1090. **Subscription Rates:** 1,000 Bht individuals; 1,800 Bht two years. **Remarks:** Accepts advertising. **URL:** http://www.thailandairlinetimetable.com. **Circ:** Paid 40,000

51442 ■ Thailand Society
Edipresse Asia
Bubhajit Bldg., 14 A Fl.
20 N Sathorn Rd.
Silom
Bangrak
Bangkok 10500, Thailand
Ph: 66 2 2379800
Fax: 66 2 2379810
Magazine featuring the top people in Thailand recognized for their outstanding achievements. **Freq:** Annual. **Key Personnel:** Nigel Oakins, Director; Naphalai Areesorn, Ch. Ed. **URL:** http://www.edipresse.com/lifestyle/thailand-society. **Circ:** ‡36,200

51443 ■ Thailand Tatler
Edipresse Asia
Bubhajit Bldg., 14 A Fl.
20 N Sathorn Rd.
Silom
Bangrak
Bangkok 10500, Thailand
Ph: 66 2 2379800
Fax: 66 2 2379810
Publication E-mail: tatler@thailandtatler.com
Magazine covering high society, business, cultural, social and sporting life of Thailand. **Freq:** Monthly. **Key Personnel:** Nigel Oakins, Director; Naphalai Areesorn, Ch. Ed. **URL:** http://www.edipresse.com/magazines.php?MagID=THTATLER. **Circ:** ‡54,850

51444 ■ Thailand's Best Restaurants
Edipresse Asia
Bubhajit Bldg., 14 A Fl.
20 N Sathorn Rd.
Silom
Bangrak
Bangkok 10500, Thailand
Ph: 66 2 2379800
Fax: 66 2 2379810
Magazine presenting the best fine dining restaurants and resorts in Thailand. **Freq:** Annual. **Key Personnel:** Nigel Oakins, Director; Naphalai Areesorn, Ch. Ed. **URL:** http://www.edipresse.com/en/par_pays/thailande/magazines/thailand_s_best_restaurants. **Circ:** ‡115,000

51445 ■ Tobacco Asia
Lockwood Publications
Vanit Bldg. II, Rm. 1403A
1126/2 New Petchburi Rd.
Bangkok 10400, Thailand
Ph: 66 225 56625
Fax: 66 265 52211
Publisher E-mail: info@tobaccoasia.com
Tobacco business magazine. **Founded:** 1997. **Freq:** Quarterly. **Key Personnel:** Heneage Mitchell, Managing Editor; Glenn A. John, Ed., Publisher. **Subscription Rates:** US$45 individuals; US$80 two years. **Remarks:** Accepts advertising. **URL:** http://www.tobaccoasia.com. **Ad Rates:** BW: 3,260 Bht, 4C: 4,790 Bht. **Circ:** 5,000

51446 ■ Travel Trade Report
Ross Publishing Ltd.
Baan Klang Muang, The Paris Patchavipha
55/96 Moo 2, Lad Yao
Chatuchak
Bangkok 10900, Thailand

Ph: 66 2 1581146
Fax: 66 2 1581152
Periodical containing information related to Thailand and Mekong Region's tourism industry. **Founded:** 1978. **Freq:** Weekly (Wed.). **Key Personnel:** Don Ross, Managing Editor. **Remarks:** Accepts advertising. **URL:** http://www.ttreport.com. **Circ:** Paid 15,000

51447 ■ Update Magazine
Se-Education Public Company Ltd.
1858/87-90 Nation Tower Bldg.
19th Fl., Bangna-Trad Rd., Km. 4.5
Bangkok 10260, Thailand
Ph: 66 2 7398000
Publication E-mail: update@se-ed.com
Publisher E-mail: comment@se-ed.com
Periodical covering the latest developments in the world of science and technology. **Subtitle:** Up to Date Reading Material for Modern People. **Founded:** 1978. **Freq:** Monthly. **Key Personnel:** Thanong Chotisorayuth, Mng. Dir. **ISSN:** 0858-6934. **Subscription Rates:** US$75 individuals. **URL:** http://update.se-ed.com/.

51448 ■ Water Resources Journal
United Nations Economic and Social Commission for Asia and the Pacific
Trade amd Investment Division
United Nations Bldg.
Rajadamnern Nok Ave.
Bangkok 10200, Thailand
Ph: 66 228 81234
Fax: 66 228 81000
Publisher E-mail: unescap@unescap.org
Journal covering development. **Founded:** 1949. **Freq:** Quarterly. **ISSN:** 0377-8053. **Remarks:** Advertising not accepted. **URL:** http://www.unescap.org/unis/pub/water.htm. **Circ:** (Not Reported)

51449 ■ Cool-FM - 93
160 Soi Mek Sawat
Khwaeng Thung Mahamek
Khet Yawana
Bangkok 10120, Thailand
Ph: 66 224 02461
Fax: 66 224 02460
Format: World Beat; Ethnic. **Wattage:** 5000. **Ad Rates:** Advertising accepted; rates available upon request. **URL:** http://www.asiawaves.net/thailand/bangkok-radio.htm.

51450 ■ Love-FM - 94.5
200 Soi Sukhumvit 49/12 Sukhumvit Rd.
North-Klongton Wattana
Bangkok 10110, Thailand
Ph: 66 271 28181
Fax: 66 271 22870
E-mail: lovefm@lovefm.co.th
Format: Jazz; Talk; Ethnic. **Ad Rates:** Advertising accepted; rates available upon request. **URL:** http://www.lyngsat-address.com/ln/Love-FM.html.

51451 ■ Peak-FM - 88
236 Viphavadee Rangsit Rd.
Khwaeng Din Daeng
Bangkok 10400, Thailand
Ph: 66 2 2765324
Fax: 66 2 2772809
Format: World Beat; Ethnic. **Wattage:** 10,000. **Ad Rates:** Advertising accepted; rates available upon request. **URL:** http://www.asiawaves.net/thailand/bangkok-radio.htm.

51452 ■ VOA Lao - 1575
PO Box 101
Rong Muang
Bangkok, Thailand
E-mail: lao@voanews.com
Format: News; Information; Educational. **Operating Hours:** 1230-1300. **URL:** http://www.voanews.com/lao/.

51453 ■ VOA Lao - 11930
PO Box 101
Rong Muang
Bangkok, Thailand
E-mail: lao@voanews.com
Format: News; Information; Educational. **Operating Hours:** 1230-1300. **URL:** http://www.voanews.com/lao/.

51454 ■ VOA Lao - 9510
PO Box 101
Rong Muang

Bangkok, Thailand
E-mail: lao@voanews.com
Format: News; Information; Educational. **Operating Hours:** 1230-1300. **URL:** http://www.voanews.com/lao/.

Chiang Mai

51455 ■ Bangkok Magazine
Infothai CM Company Ltd.
299/50 Moo 5
Tasala, Muang
Chiang Mai, Thailand
Ph: 66 53 248859
Fax: 66 53 248859
Publisher E-mail: sales@infothai.com
Magazine providing useful information about Bangkok, its people, and the many things to do and places to go in the City of Angels. **URL:** http://bangkokmag.infothai.com.

51456 ■ Chiangmai Mail
Chiangmai Mail Publishing Company Ltd.
209/5 Moo 6
T. Faham
A. Muang
Chiang Mai 50000, Thailand
Ph: 66 538 52557
Fax: 66 532 60738
Publisher E-mail: editor@chiangmai-mail.com
General newspaper. **Subtitle:** Serving the North of Thailand. **Freq:** Weekly. **Subscription Rates:** 1,560 Bht individuals Chiangmai; 2,520 Bht individuals Thailand (by mail); US$210 individuals overseas (airmail). **URL:** http://www.chiangmai-mail.com.

51457 ■ Citylife
Trisila Company Ltd.
3 Chom Doi Rd.
T. Suthep
A.Muang
Chiang Mai 50200, Thailand
Ph: 66 532 25201
Fax: 66 533 57491
Publisher E-mail: info@chiangmaicitylife.com
Online publication covering news and information on Chiang Mai and Thailand travel, entertainment, culture and related subjects in English. **URL:** http://www.chiangmainews.com. **Formerly:** Chiang Mai News Online.

51458 ■ Good Morning Chiangmai News Magazine
Good Morning Chiangmai News Magazine Company Ltd.
20/1 Ratchamanka Rd.
A. Muang
Chiang Mai 50200, Thailand
Ph: 66 53 278516
Fax: 66 53 278516
Publication E-mail: gmorning.david@gmail.com
Publisher E-mail: gmorning@loxinfo.co.th
News magazine covering Chiangmai and the North of Thailand. Includes features, pen pals and more. **Freq:** Monthly. **Remarks:** Accepts advertising. **URL:** http://www.gmorning.info/. **Circ:** (Not Reported)

Pathumthani

51459 ■ Geotechnical Engineering
Southeast Asian Geotechnical Society
c/o Asian Institute of Technology
Klong Luang
Pathumthani 12120, Thailand
Ph: 66 2 5245864
Fax: 66 2 5162126
Publisher E-mail: seags@ait.ac.th
Geotechnical engineering journal. **Founded:** 1970. **Freq:** Semiannual. **Key Personnel:** Dr. Noppadol Phienwej, Editor; W.H. Ting, Assoc. Ed.; Jian Chu, Editor. **ISSN:** 0046-5828. **Subscription Rates:** US$100 individuals including surface mail; plus airmail. **URL:** http://www.seags.ait.ac.th/ge%20journal.htm. **Circ:** 1,120

51460 ■ International Agricultural Engineering Journal
Asian Association for Agricultural Engineering
Agricultural Systems & Engineering
School of Environment, Resources & Development

Circulation: ★ = ABC; △ = BPA; ♦ = CAC; • = CCAB; ❑ = VAC; ⊕ = PO Statement; ‡ = Publisher's Report; Boldface figures = sworn; Light figures = estimated.

Gale Directory of Publications & Broadcast Media/147th Ed.   5503

Asian Institute of Technology
PO Box 4, Klong Luang
Pathumthani 12120, Thailand
Ph: 66 2 5245480
Fax: 66 2 5246200
Publication E-mail: aaae@ait.ac.th
Publisher E-mail: aaae@ait.ac.th
Periodical covering soil and water engineering, farm machinery, farm structures, post-harvest technology, and food processing and emerging technologies. **Founded:** 1992. **Freq:** Quarterly. **Key Personnel:** R.S. Kanwar, Editor. **ISSN:** 0858-2114. **Subscription Rates:** US$25 individuals; US$85 institutions. **URL:** http://www.aaae.ait.ac.th/journal.html. **Circ:** 300

51461 ■ International Agricultural Journal
Asian Association for Agricultural Engineering
PO Box 4
Klong Luang
Pathumthani 12120, Thailand
Ph: 66 252 45480
Fax: 66 252 46200
Publisher E-mail: aaae@ait.ac.th
Journal covering worldwide agricultural science. **Freq:** Quarterly. **Key Personnel:** Prof. R.S. Kanwar, Editor. **ISSN:** 0858-2114. **URL:** http://www.aaae.ait.ac.th/.

51462 ■ RERIC International Energy Journal
Regional Energy Resources Information Center

Asian Institute of Technology
Khlong Luang
PO Box 4
Pathumthani 12120, Thailand
Ph: 66 252 45866
Fax: 66 252 45439
Publisher E-mail: enreric@ait.ac.th
Journal covering worldwide energy. **Freq:** Quarterly March, June, September, and December. **Key Personnel:** Prof. S. Kumar, Editor. **ISSN:** 1513-718X. **Subscription Rates:** US$130 individuals Canada, Europe, Australia, New Zealand, Japan; US$85 elsewhere; US$275 institutions Canada, Europe, Australia, New Zealand, Japan; US$160 institutions, other countries; 1,500 Bht individuals; 5,000 Bht institutions. **URL:** http://www.rericjournal.ait.ac.th/index.php/reric. **Circ:** ‡4,247

Pattaya City

51463 ■ Pattaya Mail
Pattaya Mail Publishing Company Ltd.
370/7-8 Pattaya Second Rd.
Pattaya City 20260, Thailand
Ph: 66 384 11240
Fax: 66 384 27596
Publisher E-mail: ptymail@pattayamail.com
English language community newspaper. **Subtitle:** Pattaya's First English Language Newspaper. **Founded:** July 23, 1993. **Freq:** Weekly. **Subscription Rates:** 1,560 Bht individuals Pattaya; 2,520 Bht by mail Thailand; US$210 individuals overseas; airmail. **Remarks:** Accepts advertising. **URL:** http://www.pattayamail.com. **Ad Rates:** BW: 77,760 Bht. **Circ:** (Not Reported)

Phuket

51464 ■ Phuket Gazette
The Phuket Gazette Company Ltd.
79/94 Moo 4
Thepkrasattri Rd.
T. Koh Keaw, A. Muang
Phuket 83000, Thailand
Ph: 66 762 73555
Fax: 66 766 15240
Publication E-mail: info@phuketgazette.net
Publisher E-mail: info@phuketgazette.net
Community newspaper. **Founded:** May 1994. **Freq:** Semimonthly. **Trim Size:** 295 x 415 mm. **Key Personnel:** John F. Magee, Contact, john@phuketgazette.net; Kritchaya Kiattiwut, Asst. General Mgr., poo@phuketgazette.net; Kritchaya Kiattiwut, Contact. **Subscription Rates:** 2,800 Bht individuals domestic; 9,000 Bht other countries. **Remarks:** Accepts advertising. **URL:** http://www.phuketgazette.net/index.asp. **Feature Editors:** Alasdair Forbes, *Features*, alasdair@phuketgazette.net. **Ad Rates:** BW: 22,680 Bht, 4C: 30,618 Bht. **Circ:** Paid ‡15,000

Nuku'alofa

51465 ■ A3V-FM - 89.1
Kaipongipongi
13 Vaha'akolo Rd.
Nuku'alofa, Tonga
Ph: 676 25891
Fax: 676 25600

E-mail: a3v@tongaradio.com; magic@tongaradio.com
Format: Eclectic. **Founded:** 1996. **URL:** http://www.
tongaradio.com/.

51466 ■ Milennium Radio-FM - 89.1
PO Box 838
Tongatapu
Nuku'alofa, Tonga

Ph: 676 25891
Fax: 676 24195
E-mail: a3v@pobox.alaska.net
Format: Ethnio; World Beat; Top 40. **Owner:** Tonga Net,
at above address. **Key Personnel:** Sam Vea, Bus. Mgr.
Ad Rates: Advertising accepted; rates available upon
request. **URL:** http://www.tongatapu.net.to.

Circulation: ★ = ABC; △ = BPA; ♦ = CAC; • = CCAB; ❑ = VAC; ⊕ = PO Statement; ‡ = Publisher's Report; Boldface figures = sworn; Light figures = estimated.

Gale Directory of Publications & Broadcast Media/147th Ed.

5505

Port of Spain

51467 ■ The Trinidad Guardian
Trinidad Publishing & Trinidad Broadcasting Company Ltd.
22-24 St. Vincent St.
PO Box 122
Port of Spain, Trinidad and Tobago
Ph: (809)623-8871
Fax: (809)625-1782
General newspaper. **Subtitle:** The Guardian of Democracy. **Founded:** Sept. 9, 1917. **Freq:** Daily. **Cols./Page:** 7. **Col. Width:** 3.6 centimeters. **Key Personnel:** Cynthia Browne-Moore, Foreign Mktg. Rep., cbrownemoore@yahoo.com; Anthony Wilson, Editor-in-Chief, awilson@guardian.co.tt; Robert Alonzo, News Ed.; Valentino Singh, Sports Ed., vsingh@ttol.co.tt; Peter Ray Blood, Assoc. Ed., bloodline@ttol.co.tt; Keith Clement, Asst. Sports Ed., keithc@ttol.co.tt. **Remarks:** Accepts advertising. **URL:** http://www.guardian.co.tt. **Ad Rates:** 4C: US$2,510, 4C: US$3,030, PCI: US$22, PCI: US$25. **Circ:** Combined 45,000

51468 ■ Trinidad & Tobago Express
One Caribbean Media
Express House
35 Independence Sq.
Port of Spain, Trinidad and Tobago
Ph: (868)623-1711
Fax: (868)627-4886
Newspaper featuring national news in Trinidad and Tobago. **Founded:** 1967. **Key Personnel:** Michelle Lee, Advertising Mgr., denyse.lee@trinidadexpress.com; Brian Behny Persad, Circulation Mgr., brian.persad@trinidadexpress.com; Ailsa Simpson, Circulation Mgr., ailsa.simpson@trinidadexpress.com. **Remarks:** Accepts advertising. **URL:** http://www.trinidadexpress.com/; http://www.onecaribbeanmedia.net/index.pl/hnewspaper. **Circ:** (Not Reported)

51469 ■ I-FM - 95.5
20 Rust St., Saint Clair
Port of Spain, Trinidad and Tobago
Ph: (868)622-9292
Fax: (868)628-0251
Format: Religious; Contemporary Christian; Gospel; Sports; News. **Operating Hours:** Continuous. **Key Personnel:** Linda Besson, Sec. **Ad Rates:** Advertising accepted; rates available upon request. **URL:** http://www.i955fm.com.

Gafsa

51470 ■ Radio Gafsa-FM - 91.8 MHz
Av. Habib Bourguiba
2100 Gafsa, Tunisia
E-mail: info@radiotunis.com
Format: News; Music of Your Life. **Founded:** Nov. 7, 1991. **Operating Hours:** 18 hours Daily. **URL:** http://www.radiotunis.com/gafsa.html.

51471 ■ Radio Gafsa-FM - 93.5 MHz
Av. Habib Bourguiba
2100 Gafsa, Tunisia
E-mail: info@radiotunis.com
Format: News; Music of Your Life. **Founded:** Nov. 7, 1991. **Operating Hours:** 18 hours Daily. **URL:** http://www.radiotunis.com/gafsa.html.

51472 ■ Radio Gafsa-FM - 88.3 MHz
Av. Habib Bourguiba
2100 Gafsa, Tunisia
E-mail: info@radiotunis.com
Format: News; Music of Your Life. **Founded:** Nov. 7, 1991. **Operating Hours:** 18 hours Daily. **URL:** http://www.radiotunis.com/gafsa.html.

51473 ■ Radio Gafsa-FM - 89.2 MHz
Av. Habib Bourguiba
2100 Gafsa, Tunisia
E-mail: info@radiotunis.com
Format: News; Music of Your Life. **Founded:** Nov. 7, 1991. **Operating Hours:** 18 hours Daily. **URL:** http://www.radiotunis.com/gafsa.html.

Le Kef

51474 ■ Radio Kef-FM - 96.8 MHz
Rue Mongi Slim
7100 Le Kef, Tunisia
E-mail: info@radiotunis.com
Format: News; Music of Your Life. **Founded:** Nov. 7, 1991. **Operating Hours:** 18 hours Daily. **URL:** http://www.radiotunis.com/kef.html.

51475 ■ Radio Kef-FM - 88.2 MHz
Rue Mongi Slim
7100 Le Kef, Tunisia
E-mail: info@radiotunis.com
Format: News; Music of Your Life. **Operating Hours:** 18 hours Daily. **URL:** http://www.radiotunis.com/kef.html.

51476 ■ Radio Kef-FM - 92.2 MHz
Rue Mongi Slim
7100 Le Kef, Tunisia
E-mail: info@radiotunis.com
Format: News; Music of Your Life. **Founded:** Nov. 7, 1991. **Operating Hours:** 18 hours Daily. **URL:** http://www.radiotunis.com/kef.html.

51477 ■ Radio Kef-FM - 102.2 MHz
Rue Mongi Slim
7100 Le Kef, Tunisia
E-mail: info@radiotunis.com
Format: News; Music of Your Life. **Founded:** Nov. 7, 1991. **Operating Hours:** 18 hours Daily. **URL:** http://

www.radiotunis.com/kef.html.

Monastir

51478 ■ Radio Monastir-FM - 106.1 MHz
Rue Farhat Hached
5218 Monastir, Tunisia
E-mail: info@radiotunis.com
Format: News; Music of Your Life. **Operating Hours:** 19 1/2 hours Daily. **URL:** http://www.radiotunis.com/monastir.html.

51479 ■ Radio Monastir-FM - 99 MHz
Rue Farhat Hached
5218 Monastir, Tunisia
E-mail: info@radiotunis.com
Format: News; Music of Your Life. **Operating Hours:** 19 1/2 hours Daily. **URL:** http://www.radiotunis.com/monastir.html.

Sfax

51480 ■ Radio Sfax-AM - 720 KHz
Menzel Chaker Rd.
3058 Sfax, Tunisia
E-mail: info@radiotunis.com
Format: News. **Founded:** 1961. **Operating Hours:** 20 hours Daily. **URL:** http://www.radiotunis.com/gafsa.html.

51481 ■ Radio Sfax-FM - 105.21 MHz
Menzel Chaker Rd.
3058 Sfax, Tunisia
E-mail: info@radiotunis.com
Format: News. **Founded:** 1961. **Operating Hours:** 20 hours Daily. **URL:** http://www.radiotunis.com/sfax.html.

Sousse

51482 ■ Journal Tunisien d'ORL et de chirurgie cervico-faciale
African Journals Online
Service Orl Hopital Universitaire Farhat Hached
4000 Sousse, Tunisia
Ph: 216 3 98306989
Fax: 216 3 73226702
Publisher E-mail: info@ajol.info
Journal covering the field of otorhinolaryngology, and face and neck surgery. **Freq:** Semiannual. **Key Personnel:** Prof. Ch. Mbarek, Editor, chiraz.mbarek@lycos.com; H. Kooli, Editor, h.kooli@wanadoo.tn. **ISSN:** 1737-7803. **URL:** http://ajol.info/index.php/jtdorl.

Tataouine

51483 ■ Radio Tataouine-FM - 87.6 MHz
Cite 7 Novembre
3263 Tataouine, Tunisia
E-mail: info@radiotunis.com
Format: News; Music of Your Life. **Founded:** Nov. 7, 1993. **Operating Hours:** 18 hours Daily. **URL:** http://www.radiotunis.com/tataouine.html.

51484 ■ Radio Tataouine-FM - 89.5
Cite 7 Novembre

3263 Tataouine, Tunisia
E-mail: info@radiotunis.com
Format: News; Music of Your Life. **Founded:** Nov. 7, 1993. **URL:** http://www.radiotunis.com/tataouine.html.

51485 ■ Radio Tataouine-FM - 96.6 MHz
Cite 7 Novembre
3263 Tataouine, Tunisia
E-mail: info@radiotunis.com
Format: News; Music of Your Life. **Founded:** Nov. 7, 1993. **URL:** http://www.radiotunis.com/tataouine.html.

51486 ■ Radio Tataouine-FM - 92.2 MHz
Cite 7 Novembre
3263 Tataouine, Tunisia
E-mail: info@radiotunis.com
Format: News; Music of Your Life. **Founded:** Nov. 7, 1993. **Operating Hours:** 18 hours Daily. **URL:** http://www.radiotunis.com/tataouine.html.

51487 ■ Radio Tataouine-FM - 102.6 MHz
Cite 7 Novembre
3263 Tataouine, Tunisia
E-mail: info@radiotunis.com
Format: News; Music of Your Life. **Founded:** Nov. 7, 1993. **URL:** http://www.radiotunis.com/tataouine.html.

Tunis

51488 ■ Advances in Pure and Applied Mathematics
Walter de Gruyter Inc.
c/o Khalifa Trimeche, Ed.-in-Ch.
Dept. of Mathematics
Faculty of Mathematics
University Tunis El Manar
2092 Tunis, Tunisia
Publisher E-mail: info@degruyterny.com
Peer-reviewed Journal focusing on pure and applied mathematics. **Founded:** 2009. **Freq:** Semiannual. **Key Personnel:** Khalifa Trimeche, Editor-in-Chief, khlifa.trimeche@fst.rnu.tn. **ISSN:** 1867-1152. **Subscription Rates:** EUR134 individuals print or online; EUR155 individuals print + online; EUR50 single issue print only. **URL:** http://www.degruyter.com/journals/apam/detailEn.cfm.

51489 ■ Journal of the Arabization Bureau
Arab League Educational, Cultural and Scientific Organization
Organisation Arabe pour l'Education, la Culture et la Science
BP 1120
Mohamed V Ave.
TN-1120 Tunis, Tunisia
Ph: 216 71 785751
Publisher E-mail: alecso@email.ati.tn
Journal covering the Arabization bureau. **Subtitle:** Al Lissan Al Arari = The Arabic Language. **Freq:** Semiannual. **Print Method:** On Paper. **Trim Size:** 21/31. **ISSN:** 0258-3976. **Remarks:** Advertising not accepted. **URL:** http://www.alecso.org.tn. **Formerly:** Dar El Kitar (Casablanca). **Circ:** (Not Reported)

Circulation: ★ = ABC; △ = BPA; ♦ = CAC; • = CCAB; ❏ = VAC; ⊕ = PO Statement; ‡ = Publisher's Report; Boldface figures = sworn; Light figures = estimated.

Ankara

51490 ▪ Biyokimya Dergisi
Turkish Biochemical Society
Turk Biyokimya Dernegi
Hirfanli Sokak Banu Apt. 9/3
Gaziosmanpasa
TR-06700 Ankara, Turkey
Ph: 90 312 4470997
Fax: 90 312 4470963
Publisher E-mail: info@biyokimya.org
English and Turkish language publication covering
biochemistry. **Freq:** Quarterly March, June, September
and December. **Key Personnel:** Yahya Laleli, Editor-in-
Chief, editor@turkjbiochem.com. **ISSN:** 0250-4685. **Re-
marks:** Advertising accepted; rates available upon
request. **URL:** http://www.biyokimya.org/sayfa/english.
html; http://www.turkjbiochem.com/eng/index.html. **Circ:**
(Not Reported)

51491 ▪ Cooperation in Turkiye
Turkish Cooperative Association
Turk Kooperatifcilik Kurumu
Mithatpaba Caddesi 38-A
Kizilay
TR-06420 Ankara, Turkey
Ph: 90 312 4359899
Fax: 90 312 4304292
Publisher E-mail: admin@koopkur.org.tr
German and English language publication covering
cooperative education. **Founded:** 1984. **Freq:**
Semiannual. **Trim Size:** 19.5 x 27. **ISSN:** 1300-1477.
Subscription Rates: US$22 individuals. **Remarks:**
Advertising not accepted. **URL:** http://www.koopkur.org.
tr/coopin.htm. **Formerly:** Cooperation in Turkey. **Circ:**
500

51492 ▪ Diagnostic and Interventional Radiology
Turkish Society of Radiology
Hosdere Caddesi, Guzelkent Sokak
Cankaya Evlori, F Blok, No. 2
Cankaya
06540 Ankara, Turkey
Ph: 90 312 4423653
Fax: 90 312 4423654
Publication E-mail: info@dirjournal.org
Publisher E-mail: info@turkrad.org.tr
Journal publishing original contributions relating to all
fields of diagnostic and interventional radiology. **Freq:**
Quarterly. **Key Personnel:** Okan Akhan, MD, Editor-in-
Chief; Dr. Okan Akhan, MD, Ed. Emeritus; Fatih Boyvat,
MD, Editor; Kubilay Aydin, MD, Editor; Deniz Akata, MD,
Editor; Nevzat Karabulut, MD, Editor; Aype G. Erden,
MD, Editor; Suat Fitoz, MD, Editor. **ISSN:** 1305-3825.
URL: http://www.dirjournal.org/.

51493 ▪ Gazi Medical Journal
Gazi University
Faculty of Medicine, Dean's Office
Besevler
TR-06500 Ankara, Turkey
Ph: 90 312 2024444
Fax: 90 312 4444848
Publisher E-mail: hastane_halkla_iliskiler@gazi.edu.tr
Journal featuring articles on clinical or experimental
investigations and case histories reporting unusual clini-
cal syndromes or diseases. **Founded:** 1990. **Freq:**
Quarterly. **Key Personnel:** Russell Flaser, Language
Ed.; Dr. Hakan Ozdemir, Editor. **ISSN:** 1300-056X. **Sub-
scription Rates:** US$40 individuals. **URL:** http://www.
gmjournal.net/. **Circ:** Controlled 1,000

51494 ▪ Journal of American Studies of Turkey
American Studies Association of Turkey
c/o Gulriz Buken, Pres.
Bilkent University
Department of History
Faculty of Economic, Administrative & Social Sciences
Ankara, Turkey
Ph: 90 312 2902341
Publication E-mail: jast@egenet.com.tr
Publisher E-mail: buken@bilkent.edu.tr
Publishes work in English by scholars of any nationality
on American literature, history, art, music, film, popular
culture, institutions, politics, economics, geography and
related subjects. **Founded:** 1995. **Freq:** Semiannual
Spring & Fall. **Key Personnel:** Muammer Sanli, Manag-
ing Editor; Baris Gumusbas, Editorial Board,
gumusbas@yahoo.com; Ayse Lahur Kirtunc, Editor-in-
Chief, kirtunc@egenet.com.tr; Lawrence B. Goodheart,
Editorial Board, goodhear@uconnvm.uconn.edu; John
Grabowski, Editorial Board, jjg4@pop.cwru.edu; Clifford
Endres, Book Review Ed.; Matthew Gumpert, Editorial
Board, gumpert@bilkent.edu.tr; William Jones, Editorial
Board, cecbill@mindspring.com. **ISSN:** 1300-6606. **Re-
marks:** Advertising accepted; rates available upon
request. **URL:** http://www.theasa.net/journals/name/
journal_of_american_studies_of_turkey/. **Circ:** Paid 325

**51495 ▪ Journal of Modern Turkish Studies
(JMTS)**
Ankara University Rectorate
Dogol Caddesi
06100 Tandogan
Ankara, Turkey
Ph: 90 312 2126040
Fax: 90 312 2126049
Publisher E-mail: ankara@ankara.edu.tr
Journal dealing with Turkology and related fields. **Freq:**
Quarterly. **Key Personnel:** Prof. Sema F. Barutcu
Ozonder, Editor, phone 90 312 3103280, fax 90 312
3105713, barutcu@humanity.ankara.edu.tr; Selcan G.
Saglik-Sahin, Assoc. Ed.; Aynur Oz Ozcan, Editorial
Board; Melek Erdem, Editorial Board; Erkin Emet, Edito-
rial Board; Ufuk Tavkul, Editorial Board. **ISSN:** 1304-
8015. **Subscription Rates:** Free e-journal. **Remarks:**
Advertising accepted; rates available upon request.
URL: http://mtad.humanity.ankara.edu.tr/about.html.
Circ: (Not Reported)

51496 ▪ Karinca
Turkish Cooperative Association
Turk Kooperatifcilik Kurumu
Mithatpaba Caddesi 38-A
Kizilay
TR-06420 Ankara, Turkey
Ph: 90 312 4359899
Fax: 90 312 4304292
Publisher E-mail: admin@koopkur.org.tr
Turkish language publication covering cooperative
education. **Subtitle:** Kooperatif Postasi. **Founded:**
1934. **Freq:** Monthly. **Trim Size:** 19.5 x 27 cm. **ISSN:**
1300-1450. **Remarks:** Advertising not accepted. **URL:**
http://www.koopkur.org; http://www.koopkur.org.tr/
karinca.htm. **Formerly:** Karinca Kooperatif Postasi. **Circ:**
3,500

51497 ▪ METU Studies in Development
Middle East Technical University
Faculty of Economic and Administrative Sciences
Dept. of Economics
Balgat
TR-06531 Ankara, Turkey
Ph: 90 312 2102001
Fax: 90 312 2101107
Publisher E-mail: webadmin@feas.metu.edu.tr
Publishes research articles in the field of economics and
administrative sciences. **Founded:** 1970. **Freq:**
Semiannual. **Key Personnel:** A. Mert Yakut, Editorial
Asst. **ISSN:** 1010-9935. **Remarks:** Advertising accepted;
rates available upon request. **URL:** http://www.feas.
metu.edu.tr/metusd/ojs/index.php/metusd. **Circ:** Paid
1,500

51498 ▪ Neuroanatomy
M. Mustafa Aldur
Hacettepe University
Faculty of Medicine
Department of Anatomy
06100 Ankara, Turkey
Ph: 90 312 3052466
Fax: 90 312 4785200
Publisher E-mail: mmaldur@hacettepe.edu.tr
Journal publishing original articles related to the central
and peripheral nervous system morphology and
structure. **Freq:** Annual. **Key Personnel:** M. Mustafa Al-
dur, MD, Editor and Publisher; Ayberk Kurt, MD,
Language Ed.; Mustafa Aktekin, MD, Managing Editor.
ISSN: 1303-1783. **URL:** http://www.neuroanatomy.org.

51499 ▪ Photonics and Nanostructures
Eloovior (Singapore) Pte. Ltd
Nanotechnology Research Center
Bilkent University
06800 Ankara, Turkey
Ph: 90 312 2901966
Fax: 90 312 2901015
Publisher E-mail: asiabkinfo@elsevier.com
Journal establishing a dedicated channel for physicists,
material scientists, chemists, engineers and computer
scientists who are interested in photonic crystals and
photonic band gaps. **Subtitle:** Fundamentals and
Applications. **Founded:** 2003. **Freq:** Quarterly. **Key Per-
sonnel:** M. Notomi, Advisory Board, notomi@will.brl.ntt.
co.jp; J.D Joannopoulos, Advisory Board, joannop@mit.
edu; C.M. Soukoulis, Editor, soukoulis@ameslab.gov;
Kurt Busch, Advisory Board, kurt@tfp.uni-karlsruhe.de;
E. Ozbay, Editor, ozbay@bilkent.edu.tr; H. Benisty, Edi-
tor, hb@pmc.polytechnique.fr; Shanhui Fan, Advisory
Board, shanhui@stanford.edu; C.T. Chan, Advisory
Board, phchan@ust.hk; S. John, Advisory Board, john@
physics.utoronto.ca. **ISSN:** 1569-4410. **Subscription
Rates:** US$420 institutions all countries except Europe,
Japan and Iran; 44,200¥ institutions; EUR442 institutions
European countries and Iran; US$116 individuals all

Circulation: ★ = ABC; △ = BPA; ♦ = CAC; • = CCAB; ❑ = VAC; ⊕ = PO Statement; ‡ = Publisher's Report; Boldface figures = sworn; Light figures = estimated.

Gale Directory of Publications & Broadcast Media/147th Ed.   **5511**

countries except Europe, Japan and Iran; EUR86 individuals European countries and Iran; 13,400¥ individuals. **URL:** http://www.elsevier.com/wps/find/journaldescription.cws_home/658453/descriptiondescription.

51500 ■ Savunma Ve Havacilik
Monch Publishing Group
Halit Ziya Sok 26/9
TR-06540 Ankara, Turkey
Ph: 90 312 4419354
Fax: 90 312 4395724
Publisher E-mail: info@moench-group.com
Magazine featuring military issues in Turkey, and neighboring countries. **Founded:** 1987. **Freq:** Bimonthly. **Trim Size:** 210 x 297 mm. **Key Personnel:** Hakki Aris, Editor-in-Chief, aris@moench-group.com; Stephen Orr, Mktg. Mgr., phone 49 228 6483105, stephen.orr@moench-group.com. **Subscription Rates:** EUR60 individuals to Europe; EUR95 other countries; EUR10 single issue; US$80 individuals to Europe; US$140 other countries; US$22.50 single issue. **Remarks:** Accepts advertising. **URL:** http://www.moench-group.com/savunma.php. **Circ:** 15,000

51501 ■ TUBA-AR
Turkish Academy of Sciences
Piyade Sokak No. 27
Kavaklidere
TR-06550 Ankara, Turkey
Ph: 90 312 4422903
Fax: 90 312 4426491
Publisher E-mail: tubaulus@tuba.gov.tr
Publication covering studies on archaeology. **Subtitle:** Journal of Archaeology. **Founded:** 1998. **Freq:** Annual. **Key Personnel:** Sema Baykan, Editorial Board; Ufuk Esin, Chm. **ISSN:** 1301-8566. **Subscription Rates:** 7.50 single issue. **Remarks:** Advertising not accepted. **URL:** http://www.tuba.gov.tr/index_en.php?id=83. **Circ:** (Not Reported)

51502 ■ Turk Psikoloji Dergisi (Turkish Journal of Psychology)
Turkish Psychological Association
Mesrutiyet Cad. 22/12
Kizilay
TR-06640 Ankara, Turkey
Ph: 90 312 4256765
Publisher E-mail: bilgi@psikolog.org.tr
Journal including empirical articles, review papers, and articles concerning national policies for psychologists. **Subscription Rates:** 30 individuals. **URL:** http://www.turkpsikolojidergisi.com/.

51503 ■ Turkish Journal of Agriculture and Forestry
The Scientific and Technical Research Council of Turkey
Tunus Caddesi No. 80
Kavaklidere
TR-06100 Ankara, Turkey
Ph: 90 312 4272302
Fax: 90 312 4274024
Publication E-mail: agric@tubitak.gov.tr
Publisher E-mail: info@fp7.org.tr
Journal featuring research articles, short communications and review articles in various fields of agriculture and forestry at both national and international levels. **Founded:** 1976. **Freq:** Bimonthly. **Key Personnel:** Dr. Ali Inal, Editor-in-Chief; Dr. Abdurrahman Aliy, Hd. of the Department; Adnan Bahadir, Dep. Hd.; Seval Ozgul, Journal Admin. **ISSN:** 1300-011X. **Subscription Rates:** EUR60 individuals. **URL:** http://journals.tubitak.gov.tr/agriculture/.

51504 ■ Turkish Journal of Biology
The Scientific and Technical Research Council of Turkey
Tunus Caddesi No. 80
Kavaklidere
TR-06100 Ankara, Turkey
Ph: 90 312 4272302
Fax: 90 312 4274024
Publication E-mail: biol@tubitak.gov.tr
Publisher E-mail: info@fp7.org.tr
Journal covering the field of biological sciences. **Founded:** 1976. **Freq:** Quarterly. **Key Personnel:** Prof. Dr. Leyla Acik, Editor-in-Chief; Adnan Bahadir, Dep. Hd.; Dr. Ahmet Noyan, Honorary Ed.; Russell Fraser, English Ed. **ISSN:** 1300-0152. **Subscription Rates:** EUR40 individuals. **URL:** http://journals.tubitak.gov.tr/biology/.

51505 ■ Turkish Journal of Botany
The Scientific and Technical Research Council of Turkey
Tubitak, Akademik Yayinlar Mudurlugu
Ataturk Bulvary, No. 221
Kavaklydere
TR-06100 Ankara, Turkey
Publication E-mail: bot@tubitak.gov.tr
Publisher E-mail: info@fp7.org.tr
International journal covering all aspects relating to botany. **Founded:** 1976. **Freq:** 6/yr. **Key Personnel:** Russell Fraser, English Ed.; Harald Kurschner, Editorial Board; Zeki Kaya, Editorial Board; Dr. Ahmet Duran, Editor-in-Chief; Stephan Helfer, Advisory Board. **ISSN:** 1300-008X. **Subscription Rates:** EUR60 individuals. **URL:** http://journals.tubitak.gov.tr/botany/index.php.

51506 ■ Turkish Journal of Cancer
Turkish Association for Cancer Research and Control
Hacettepe University Institute of Oncology
Sihhiye
TR-06100 Ankara, Turkey
Ph: 90 312 3092904
Fax: 90 312 3092905
Publisher E-mail: editor@turkjcancer.org
Journal containing scientific research articles, reviews, editorials, and letters to the editor in the fields of basic and clinical oncology. **Founded:** 1967. **Freq:** Quarterly. **Key Personnel:** Ayse Kars, Editor; Dincer Firat, Editor-in-Chief; Meltem Sengelen, Asst. Ed. **ISSN:** 1019-3103. **Remarks:** Advertising accepted; rates available upon request. **URL:** http://www.turkjcancer.org/index.php3. **Circ:** (Not Reported)

51507 ■ Turkish Journal of Chemistry
The Scientific and Technical Research Council of Turkey
Tunus Caddesi No. 80
Kavaklidere
TR-06100 Ankara, Turkey
Ph: 90 312 4272302
Fax: 90 312 4274024
Publication E-mail: chem@tubitak.gov.tr
Publisher E-mail: info@fp7.org.tr
Journal featuring original articles and letters to the editor in various fields of research in chemistry and chemical engineering. **Founded:** 1976. **Freq:** 6/yr. **Key Personnel:** Adnan Bahadir, Dep. Hd.; Russell Fraser, English Ed.; Dr. Ayhan S. Demir, Editor-in-Chief. **ISSN:** 1300-0527. **Subscription Rates:** EUR60 other countries. **URL:** http://journals.tubitak.gov.tr/chem/.

51508 ■ Turkish Journal of Earth Sciences
The Scientific and Technical Research Council of Turkey
c/o Erdin Bozkurt, Ed.-in-Ch.
Middle East Technical University
Dept. of Geological Engineering
Tectonic Research Unit
TR-06531 Ankara, Turkey
Ph: 90 312 2105725
Fax: 90 312 2101263
Publication E-mail: earth@tubitak.gov.tr
Publisher E-mail: info@fp7.org.tr
Publishes significant original research and comprehensive reviews in all fields of the earth and planetary sciences, such as geology, geophysics, geochemistry, paleontology, oceanography, petrology, mineralogy, and mineral deposits research. **Founded:** 1976. **Freq:** 3/yr. **Key Personnel:** Erdin Bozkurt, Editor-in-Chief, erdin@metu.edu.tr; Xavier Le Pichon, Honorary Ed., lepichon@mailhost.geologie.ens.fr; Dan McKenzie, Honorary Ed. **ISSN:** 1300-0985. **Subscription Rates:** EUR60 individuals. **URL:** http://journals.tubitak.gov.tr/earth/.

51509 ■ Turkish Journal of Electrical Engineering and Computer Sciences
The Scientific and Technical Research Council of Turkey
Tubitak, Akademik Yayinlar Mudurlugu
Ataturk Bulvary, No. 221
Kavaklydere
TR-06100 Ankara, Turkey
Publication E-mail: elektrik@tubitak.gov.tr
Publisher E-mail: info@fp7.org.tr
Journal featuring articles related to electrical engineering and computer sciences. **Founded:** 1993. **Freq:** 3/yr. **Key Personnel:** Dale Allen Ross, English Ed.; Prof.Dr. Sadik Kara, Editor-in-Chief. **ISSN:** 1300-0632. **Subscription Rates:** EUR60 other countries. **URL:** http://journals.tubitak.gov.tr/elektrik/.

51510 ■ Turkish Journal of Engineering and Environmental Sciences
The Scientific and Technical Research Council of Turkey
Tubitak, Akademik Yayinlar Mudurlugu
Ataturk Bulvary, No. 221
Kavaklydere
TR-06100 Ankara, Turkey
Publication E-mail: engineering@tubitak.gov.tr
Publisher E-mail: info@fp7.org.tr
Publishes significant research results in all areas of engineering except earth sciences and electrical and electronics engineering. **Founded:** 1976. **Freq:** Quarterly. **Key Personnel:** Adnan Bahadir, Dep. Hd.; Dr. Vedat M. Akdeniz, Editor-in-Chief; Russell Fraser, English Ed. **ISSN:** 1300-0160. **Subscription Rates:** EUR40 other countries. **URL:** http://journals.tubitak.gov.tr/engineering/.

51511 ■ Turkish Journal of Gastroenterology
Turkish Society of Gastroenterology
Gaziler Sokak 22/1
Abidinpapa
TR-06620 Ankara, Turkey
Ph: 90 312 3622145
Fax: 90 312 3625948
Publisher E-mail: tjg@tgd.org.tr
Journal featuring articles pertaining to gastroenterology. **Founded:** 1990. **Freq:** Quarterly. **Key Personnel:** Cihan Yurdaydin, Editor-in-Chief; Ulku Dagli, Assoc. Ed.; Hakan Bozkaya, Assoc. Ed.; Ali Ozden, Advising Ed. **ISSN:** 1300-4948. **URL:** http://www.turkgastro.org/.

51512 ■ Turkish Journal of Mathematics
The Scientific and Technical Research Council of Turkey
Tubitak, Akademik Yayinlar Mudurlugu
Ataturk Bulvary, No. 221
Kavaklydere
TR-06100 Ankara, Turkey
Publication E-mail: math@tubitak.gov.tr
Publisher E-mail: info@fp7.org.tr
Journal featuring articles in all areas of mathematics. **Founded:** 1976. **Freq:** 4/yr. **Key Personnel:** Prof.Dr. Alp Eden, Editor-in-Chief; Dale Allen Ross, English Ed. **ISSN:** 1300-0098. **Subscription Rates:** EUR40 other countries. **URL:** http://journals.tubitak.gov.tr/math/.

51513 ■ Turkish Journal of Medical Sciences
The Scientific and Technical Research Council of Turkey
Tubitak, Akademik Yayinlar Mudurlugu
Ataturk Bulvary, No. 221
Kavaklydere
TR-06100 Ankara, Turkey
Publication E-mail: medsci@tubitak.gov.tr
Publisher E-mail: info@fp7.org.tr
Journal featuring papers in the field of medicine and related health sciences. **Founded:** 1976. **Freq:** 6/yr. **Key Personnel:** Russell Fraser, English Ed.; Sinasi Ozsoylu, Honorary Ed.; Erol Kilic, Journal Admin.; Ozcan Erel, Editor-in-Chief; Dr. Abdurrahman Aliy, Hd. of Department; Adnan Bahadir, Dep. Hd. **ISSN:** 1300-0144. **Subscription Rates:** EUR60 other countries. **URL:** http://journals.tubitak.gov.tr/medical/.

51514 ■ Turkish Journal of Pediatrics
International Children's Center
P.K. 36
Samanpazari
TR-06240 Ankara, Turkey
Fax: 90 312 3243284
Publisher E-mail: icc@icc.org.tr
Journal featuring articles related to the medical sciences and pediatrics. **Founded:** 1958. **Freq:** Quarterly. **Key Personnel:** Turgay Coskun, Editor; Corinne Can, Managing Editor; Guisev Kale, Production Mgr.; Murat Yurdakok, Assoc. Ed. **ISSN:** 0041-4301. **URL:** http://tjp.dergisi.org/index.php3. **Circ:** Paid 5,000

51515 ■ Turkish Journal of Physics
The Scientific and Technical Research Council of Turkey
Tubitak, Akademik Yayinlar Mudurlugu
Ataturk Bulvary, No. 221
Kavaklydere
TR-06100 Ankara, Turkey
Publication E-mail: phys@tubitak.gov.tr
Publisher E-mail: info@fp7.org.tr
Journal featuring original research articles and letters to the editor in various fields of research in physics and

astrophysics. **Freq:** 6/yr. **Key Personnel:** Dale Allen Ross, English Ed.; Prof. Dr. A. Nihat Berker, Editor-in-Chief. **ISSN:** 1300-0101. **Subscription Rates:** EUR30 other countries. **URL:** http://journals.tubitak.gov.tr/physics/.

51516 ■ Turkish Journal of Veterinary and Animal Sciences
The Scientific and Technical Research Council of Turkey
Tubitak, Akademik Yayinlar Mudurlugu
Ataturk Bulvary, No. 221
Kavaklydere
TR-06100 Ankara, Turkey
Publication E-mail: veterinary@tubitak.gov.tr
Publisher E-mail: info@fp7.org.tr
Publishes original papers, reviews, preliminary scientific reports and case reports on all aspects of veterinary medicine and animal sciences. **Founded:** 1976. **Freq:** 6/yr. **Key Personnel:** Russell Fraser, English Ed.; Dr. Omer Memduh Esendal, Editor-in-Chief, omer.esendal@veterinary.ankara.edu.tr; Adnan Bahadir, Dep. Hd. **ISSN:** 1300-0128. **Subscription Rates:** EUR60 individuals. **URL:** http://journals.tubitak.gov.tr/veterinary/.

51517 ■ Turkish Journal of Zoology
The Scientific and Technical Research Council of Turkey
Tubitak, Akademik Yayinlar Mudurlugu
Ataturk Bulvary, No. 221
Kavaklydere
TR-06100 Ankara, Turkey
Publication E-mail: zool@tubitak.gov.tr
Publisher E-mail: info@fp7.org.tr
Journal featuring research articles and research notes in English in the field of zoology. **Founded:** 1976. **Freq:** Quarterly. **Key Personnel:** Dr. Ercument Colak, Editor-in-Chief; H. Resit Akcakaya, Advisory Board; Nihat Aktac, Advisory Board; Ibrahim Baran, Advisory Board. **ISSN:** 1300-0179. **Subscription Rates:** EUR40 individuals. **URL:** http://journals.tubitak.gov.tr/zoology/index.php.

51518 ■ Ucuncu Sektor Kooperatifcilik
Turkish Cooperative Association
Turk Kooperatifcilik Kurumu
Mithatpaba Caddesi 38-A
Kizilay
TR-06420 Ankara, Turkey
Ph: 90 312 4359899
Fax: 90 312 4304292
Publisher E-mail: admin@koopkur.org.tr
Turkish language publication covering cooperative education. **Subtitle:** Ucuncu Sektor. **Founded:** 1931. **Freq:** Quarterly. **Trim Size:** 16 x 24. **Key Personnel:** Irfan Gundogdu, Member. **ISSN:** 1300-1469. **Remarks:** Advertising not accepted. **URL:** http://www.koopkur.org.tr. **Formerly:** Kooperatifcilik. **Circ:** 1,500

51519 ■ Capital Radio - Ankara - 99.5 MHz
Havuzlu Sok. 4/2
A. Ayrancy
TR-06540 Ankara, Turkey
Ph: 90 312 4199999
Fax: 90 312 4194555
Format: Music of Your Life. **Owner:** Capital Radio, at above address. **URL:** http://www.capitalradio.com.tr.

51520 ■ Hedef Radyo - Ankara - 91.8 MHz
Workplace Site 9
No. 20 Macunkoy
TR-06620 Ankara, Turkey
Ph: 312 3977837
Fax: 312 3977709
E-mail: hedef@hedefradyo.com
Owner: Hedef Radyo, Ziyabey Caddesi 3, Sokak No. 15/5, Bakgat, Ankara, Turkey. **URL:** http://www.wec-net.com.tr/Hedef/.

51521 ■ Radio Bilkent - Ankara - 96.6 MHz
Bilkent University, Main Campus
Student Union Bldg.
TR-06800 Ankara, Turkey
Ph: 90 312 2667833
Fax: 90 312 2664909
E-mail: odekan@bilkent.edu.tr
Format: Eclectic. **Owner:** Radio Bilkent, at above address. **Founded:** 1995. **Wattage:** 1000. **URL:** http://www.radyobilkent.com.

51522 ■ Radio Bilkent - Bilkent - 96.6 MHz
Bilkent University, Main Campus

Student Union Bldg.
TR-06800 Ankara, Turkey
Ph: 90 312 2667833
Fax: 90 312 2664909
E-mail: odekan@bilkent.edu.tr
Format: Eclectic. **Owner:** Radio Bilkent, at above address. **Founded:** 1995. **Wattage:** 1000. **URL:** http://www.radyobilkent.com.

51523 ■ RADYO ODTU-FM - 103.1
ODTU Kampusu
TR-06531 Ankara, Turkey
Ph: 90 312 2103030
Fax: 90 312 2101277
E-mail: radyo@radyoodtu.com.tr
Format: Ethnic; Contemporary Hit Radio (CHR). **Ad Rates:** Advertising accepted; rates available upon request. **URL:** http://www.radyoodtu.com.tr/.

51524 ■ Turkish Radio-Television Corporation - Adana - 92.5 MHz
TRT Sitesi Turan Gunes Bulvari
Or-an
TR-06540 Ankara, Turkey
Ph: 90 312 4634343
Fax: 90 312 4633174
E-mail: aktifhat@trt.net.tr; rdb@trt.net.tr
Format: News; Sports. **Owner:** Turkish Radio-Television Corporation, at above address. **Operating Hours:** Continuous. **Wattage:** 30,000. **URL:** http://www.trt.net.tr.

51525 ■ Turkish Radio-Television Corporation - Adana - 89.2 MHz
TRT Sitesi Turan Gunes Bulvari
Or-an
TR-06540 Ankara, Turkey
Ph: 90 312 4634343
Fax: 90 312 4633174
E-mail: aktifhat@trt.net.tr; rdb@trt.net.tr
Format: News; Sports. **Owner:** Turkish Radio-Television Corporation, at above address. **Operating Hours:** Continuous. **Wattage:** 30,000. **URL:** http://www.trt.net.tr.

51526 ■ Turkish Radio-Television Corporation - Ankara - 88.0 MHz
TRT Sitesi Turan Gunes Bulvari
Or-an
TR-06540 Ankara, Turkey
Ph: 90 312 4634343
Fax: 90 312 4633174
E-mail: aktifhat@trt.net.tr; rdb@trt.net.tr
Format: News; Sports. **Owner:** Turkish Radio-Television Corporation, at above address. **Operating Hours:** Continuous. **Wattage:** 30,000. **URL:** http://www.trt.net.tr.

51527 ■ Turkish Radio-Television Corporation - Ankara - 91.2 MHz
TRT Sitesi Turan Gunes Bulvari
Or-an
TR-06540 Ankara, Turkey
Ph: 90 312 4634343
Fax: 90 312 4633174
E-mail: aktifhat@trt.net.tr; rdb@trt.net.tr
Format: News; Sports. **Owner:** Turkish Radio-Television Corporation, at above address. **Operating Hours:** Continuous. **Wattage:** 30,000. **URL:** http://www.trt.net.tr.

51528 ■ Turkish Radio-Television Corporation - Bursa - 95.0 MHz
TRT Sitesi Turan Gunes Bulvari
Or-an
TR-06540 Ankara, Turkey
Ph: 90 312 4634343
Fax: 90 312 4633174
E-mail: aktifhat@trt.net.tr; rdb@trt.net.tr
Format: News; Sports. **Owner:** Turkish Radio-Television Corporation, at above address. **Operating Hours:** Continuous. **Wattage:** 30,000. **URL:** http://www.trt.net.tr.

51529 ■ Turkish Radio-Television Corporation - Bursa - 97.5 MHz
TRT Sitesi Turan Gunes Bulvari
Or-an
TR-06540 Ankara, Turkey
Ph: 90 312 4634343
Fax: 90 312 4633174
E-mail: aktifhat@trt.net.tr; rdb@trt.net.tr
Format: News; Sports. **Owner:** Turkish Radio-Television Corporation, at above address. **Operating Hours:** Continuous. **Wattage:** 30,000. **URL:** http://www.trt.net.tr.

51530 ■ Turkish Radio-Television Corporation - Diyarbakir - 88.4 MHz
TRT Sitesi Turan Gunes Bulvari
Or-an
TR-06540 Ankara, Turkey
Ph: 90 312 4634343
Fax: 90 312 4633174
E-mail: aktifhat@trt.net.tr; rdb@trt.net.tr
Format: News; Sports. **Owner:** Turkish Radio-Television Corporation, at above address. **Operating Hours:** Continuous. **Wattage:** 30,000. **URL:** http://www.trt.net.tr.

51531 ■ Turkish Radio-Television Corporation - Diyarbakir - 95.5 MHz
TRT Sitesi Turan Gunes Bulvari
Or-an
TR-06540 Ankara, Turkey
Ph: 90 312 4634343
Fax: 90 312 4633174
E-mail: aktifhat@trt.net.tr; rdb@trt.net.tr
Format: News; Sports. **Owner:** Turkish Radio-Television Corporation, at above address. **Operating Hours:** Continuous. **Wattage:** 30,000. **URL:** http://www.trt.net.tr.

51532 ■ Turkish Radio-Television Corporation - Eskisehir - 96.8 MHz
TRT Sitesi Turan Gunes Bulvari
Or-an
TR-06540 Ankara, Turkey
Ph: 90 312 4634343
Fax: 90 312 4633174
E-mail: aktifhat@trt.net.tr; rdb@trt.net.tr
Format: News; Sports. **Owner:** Turkish Radio-Television Corporation, at above address. **Operating Hours:** Continuous. **Wattage:** 30,000. **URL:** http://www.trt.net.tr.

51533 ■ Turkish Radio-Television Corporation - Eskisehir - 94.4 MHz
TRT Sitesi Turan Gunes Bulvari
Or-an
TR-06540 Ankara, Turkey
Ph: 90 312 4634343
Fax: 90 312 4633174
E-mail: aktifhat@trt.net.tr; rdb@trt.net.tr
Format: News; Sports. **Owner:** Turkish Radio-Television Corporation, at above address. **Operating Hours:** Continuous. **Wattage:** 30,000. **URL:** http://www.trt.net.tr.

51534 ■ Turkish Radio-Television Corporation - Gaziantep - 97.6 MHz
TRT Sitesi Turan Gunes Bulvari
Or-an
TR-06540 Ankara, Turkey
Ph: 90 312 4634343
Fax: 90 312 4633174
E-mail: aktifhat@trt.net.tr; rdb@trt.net.tr
Format: News; Sports. **Owner:** Turkish Radio-Television Corporation, at above address. **Operating Hours:** Continuous. **Wattage:** 30,000. **URL:** http://www.trt.net.tr.

51535 ■ Turkish Radio-Television Corporation - Gaziantep - 95.2 MHz
TRT Sitesi Turan Gunes Bulvari
Or-an
TR-06540 Ankara, Turkey
Ph: 90 312 4634343
Fax: 90 312 4633174
E-mail: aktifhat@trt.net.tr; rdb@trt.net.tr
Format: News; Sports. **Owner:** Turkish Radio-Television Corporation, at above address. **Operating Hours:** Continuous. **Wattage:** 30,000. **URL:** http://www.trt.net.tr.

51536 ■ Turkish Radio-Television Corporation - Istanbul - 91.4 MHz
TRT Sitesi Turan Gunes Bulvari
Or-an
TR-06540 Ankara, Turkey
Ph: 90 312 4634343
Fax: 90 312 4633174
E-mail: aktifhat@trt.net.tr; rdb@trt.net.tr
Format: News; Sports. **Owner:** Turkish Radio-Television Corporation, at above address. **Operating Hours:** Continuous. **Wattage:** 30,000. **URL:** http://www.trt.net.tr.

51537 ■ Turkish Radio-Television Corporation - Istanbul - 88.2 MHz
TRT Sitesi Turan Gunes Bulvari
Or-an
TR-06540 Ankara, Turkey
Ph: 90 312 4634343
Fax: 90 312 4633174

Circulation: ★ = ABC; △ = BPA; ♦ = CAC; ● = CCAB; ❑ = VAC; ⊕ = PO Statement; ‡ = Publisher's Report; Boldface figures = sworn; Light figures = estimated.

E-mail: aktifhat@trt.net.tr; rdb@trt.net.tr
Format: News; Sports. **Owner:** Turkish Radio-Television Corporation, at above address. **Operating Hours:** Continuous. **Wattage:** 30,000. **URL:** http://www.trt.net.tr.

51538 ■ Turkish Radio-Television Corporation - Izmir - 100.5 MHz
TRT Sitesi Turan Gunes Bulvari
Or-an
TR-06540 Ankara, Turkey
Ph: 90 312 4634343
Fax: 90 312 4633174
E-mail: aktifhat@trt.net.tr; rdb@trt.net.tr
Format: News; Sports. **Owner:** Turkish Radio-Television Corporation, at above address. **Operating Hours:** 4 a.m.- 11 p.m. **Wattage:** 30,000. **URL:** http://www.trt.net.tr.

51539 ■ Turkish Radio-Television Corporation - Izmir - 88.0 MHz
TRT Sitesi Turan Gunes Bulvari
Or-an
TR-06540 Ankara, Turkey
Ph: 90 312 4634343
Fax: 90 312 4633174
E-mail: aktifhat@trt.net.tr; rdb@trt.net.tr
Format: News; Sports. **Owner:** Turkish Radio-Television Corporation, at above address. **Operating Hours:** Continuous. **Wattage:** 30,000. **URL:** http://www.trt.net.tr.

51540 ■ Turkish Radio-Television Corporation - Izmir - 91.2 MHz
TRT Sitesi Turan Gunes Bulvari
Or-an
TR-06540 Ankara, Turkey
Ph: 90 312 4634343
Fax: 90 312 4633174
E-mail: aktifhat@trt.net.tr; rdb@trt.net.tr
Format: News; Sports. **Owner:** Turkish Radio-Television Corporation, at above address. **Operating Hours:** Continuous. **Wattage:** 30,000. **URL:** http://www.trt.net.tr.

51541 ■ Turkish Radio-Television Corporation - Izmir - 94.7 MHz
TRT Sitesi Turan Gunes Bulvari
Or-an
TR-06540 Ankara, Turkey
Ph: 90 312 4634343
Fax: 90 312 4633174
E-mail: aktifhat@trt.net.tr; rdb@trt.net.tr
Format: Sports. **Owner:** Turkish Radio-Television Corporation, at above address. **Operating Hours:** Continuous. **Wattage:** 30,000. **URL:** http://www.trt.net.tr.

51542 ■ Turkish Radio-Television Corporation - Kayseri - 99.2 MHz
TRT Sitesi Turan Gunes Bulvari
Or-an
TR-06540 Ankara, Turkey
Ph: 90 312 4634343
Fax: 90 312 4633174
E-mail: aktifhat@trt.net.tr; rdb@trt.net.tr
Format: News; Sports. **Owner:** Turkish Radio-Television Corporation, at above address. **Operating Hours:** Continuous. **Wattage:** 30,000. **URL:** http://www.trt.net.tr.

51543 ■ Turkish Radio-Television Corporation - Kayseri - 97.2 MHz
TRT Sitesi Turan Gunes Bulvari
Or-an
TR-06540 Ankara, Turkey
Ph: 90 312 4634343
Fax: 90 312 4633174
E-mail: aktifhat@trt.net.tr; rdb@trt.net.tr
Format: News; Sports. **Owner:** Turkish Radio-Television Corporation, at above address. **Operating Hours:** Continuous. **Wattage:** 30,000. **URL:** http://www.trt.net.tr.

51544 ■ Turkish Radio-Television Corporation - Konya - 92.4 MHz
TRT Sitesi Turan Gunes Bulvari
Or-an
TR-06540 Ankara, Turkey
Ph: 90 312 4634343
Fax: 90 312 4633174
E-mail: aktifhat@trt.net.tr; rdb@trt.net.tr
Format: News; Sports. **Owner:** Turkish Radio-Television Corporation, at above address. **Operating Hours:** Continuous. **Wattage:** 30,000. **URL:** http://www.trt.net.tr.

51545 ■ Turkish Radio-Television Corporation - Konya - 95.8 MHz
TRT Sitesi Turan Gunes Bulvari
Or-an
TR-06540 Ankara, Turkey
Ph: 90 312 4634343
Fax: 90 312 4633174
E-mail: aktifhat@trt.net.tr; rdb@trt.net.tr
Format: News; Sports. **Owner:** Turkish Radio-Television Corporation, at above address. **Operating Hours:** Continuous. **Wattage:** 30,000. **URL:** http://www.trt.net.tr.

51546 ■ Turkish Radio-Television Corporation - Marmaris - 101.0 MHz
TRT Sitesi Turan Gunes Bulvari
Or-an
TR-06540 Ankara, Turkey
Ph: 90 312 4632330
E-mail: genel.sekreterlik@trt.net.tr
Format: News. **Owner:** Turkish Radio-Television Corporation, at above address. **Operating Hours:** 5:30 a.m. - 10:45 a.m.; 4:30 p.m. - 8:00 p.m. **Key Personnel:** Bekir Erdem, President; Yucel Yener, Dir. Gen.; Haluk Buran, Dep. Dir. Gen. (Engg.). **Wattage:** 5000. **URL:** http://www.trt.net.tr.

Turkish Radio-Television Corporation - Trabzon - See Trabzon

51547 ■ Turkish Radio-Television Corporation - TV-4 - 4
TRT Sitesi Turan Gunes Bulvari
Or-an
TR-06540 Ankara, Turkey
Ph: 90 312 4632330
Fax: 90 312 4632406
E-mail: aktifhat@trt.net.tr; tvdb@trt.net.tr
Format: Sports. **Owner:** TRT-TV Department, at above address. **Operating Hours:** 1.30 p.m.-12.00 a.m. **URL:** http://www.trt.net.tr.

51548 ■ Turkish Radio-Television Corporation - TV-1 - 1
TRT Sitesi Turan Gunes Bulvari
Or-an
TR-06540 Ankara, Turkey
Ph: 90 312 4904300
E-mail: aktifhat@trt.net.tr
Owner: TRT-TV Department, at above address. **Operating Hours:** Continuous. **URL:** http://www.trt.net.tr.

51549 ■ Turkish Radio-Television Corporation - TV-3 - 3
TRT Sitesi Turan Gunes Bulvari
Or-an
TR-06540 Ankara, Turkey
Ph: 90 312 4634343
Fax: 90 312 4632406
E-mail: aktifhat@trt.net.tr; tvdb@trt.net.tr
Owner: TRT-TV Department, at above address. **Operating Hours:** 1.40 p.m.-12 a.m. Wed./Thu./Sat./Sun.; 5 p.m.-1 a.m. Mon./Tu. **URL:** http://www.trt.net.tr.

51550 ■ Turkish Radio-Television Corporation - TV-2 - 2
TRT Sitesi Turan Gunes Bulvari
Or-an
TR-06540 Ankara, Turkey
Ph: 90 312 4904300
E-mail: aktifhat@trt.net.tr
Format: Sports. **Owner:** TRT-TV Department, at above address. **Operating Hours:** 5 p.m.-1 a.m. Mon.-Fri.; 9.30 a.m.-3 p.m. Sat.; 9.30 a.m.-1. **URL:** http://www.trt.net.tr.

Bursa

51551 ■ Journal of Sports Science and Medicine (JSSM)
Department of Sports Medicine
Medical Faculty of Uludag University
Medical Faculty of Uludag University
16059 Bursa, Turkey
Ph: 90 224 4428200
Fax: 90 224 4428727
Publication E-mail: info@jssm.org
Publisher E-mail: hakan@uludag.edu.tr
Journal covering research and review articles on sports medicine and the exercise sciences. **Freq:** Quarterly. **Key Personnel:** Hakan Gur, MD, Editor, hakan@uludag.edu.tr. **ISSN:** 1303-2968. **URL:** http://www.jssm.org/contackform.php.

Cinarli-Izmir

51552 ■ Rotary Dergisi
1571 Sokak No. 16
TR-35110 Cinarli-Izmir, Turkey
Ph: 90 232 4619642
Fax: 90 232 4619646
Membership magazine of Rotary International covering current news about Rotary-related subjects. **Freq:** Bimonthly. **Key Personnel:** Ahmet S. Tukel, Editor, rotarydergisi@gmail.com. **URL:** http://www.rotary.org/en/mediaandnews/morepublications/regionalmagazines/pages/ridefault.aspx. **Circ:** 8,100

Elazig

51553 ■ Firat Tip Dergisi
Fyrat University
Faculty of Medicine
Firat Typ Dergisi
Firat Universitesi
Tip Fakultesi Dekanligi
TR-23119 Elazig, Turkey
Ph: 90 424 2122960
Fax: 90 424 2379138
Publisher E-mail: info@firattipdergisi.com
Peer-reviewed medical journal. **Founded:** 1897. **Freq:** Quarterly. **Print Method:** Offset. **Cols./Page:** 6. **Col. Width:** 19 nonpareils. **Col. Depth:** 210 agate lines. **Key Personnel:** Prof. Irfan Orhan, Editor-in-Chief; Prof. Yasar Dogan, Dep. Ed. **URL:** http://www.firattipdergisi.com/index.php3?14d5280773ffe0d6e0af085e6ae6f7ac.

Eskisehir

51554 ■ Anatolia
Yenisehir
School of Tourism & Hotel Management
Anadolu University
Yunusemre Kampusu
TR-26470 Eskisehir, Turkey
Publication E-mail: anatolia@tr.net
Publisher E-mail: anatolia@tr.net
Provides an outlet for innovative studies that will contribute to the understanding of tourism and hospitality. **Subtitle:** An International Journal of Tourism and Hospitality Research. **Founded:** 1990. **Freq:** Semiannual. **Key Personnel:** Nazmi Kozak, Editor-in-Chief, nkozak@anadolu.edu.tr; Metin Kozak, PhD, Editor-in-Chief, m.kozak@superonline.com; Seyhmus Baloglu, Regional Ed., baloglu@ccmail.nevada.edu. **ISSN:** 1300-4220. **Subscription Rates:** US$50 institutions; US$35 individuals professionals; US$25 students; US$90 institutions two years; US$60 two years professionals; US$45 students two years. **URL:** http://www.anatoliajournal.com. **Circ:** Paid 1,500

51555 ■ Turkish Online Journal of Distance Education
Andolu University
Yunusemre Campus
TR-26470 Eskisehir, Turkey
Ph: 90 222 3350580
Fax: 90 222 3353616
Publication E-mail: tojde@anadolu.edu.tr
Publisher E-mail: gensek@anadolu.edu.tr
Journal focusing on the issues and challenges of providing theory, research, and information services on open learning applications to students enrolled in any level of distance education. **Founded:** 2000. **Freq:** Quarterly. **Key Personnel:** Prof. Ugur Demiray, Editor-in-Chief, udemiray@anadolu.edu.tr; Antonis Lionarakis, Editor, alionar@eap.gr; Ferhan Odabasi, Editor, fodabasi@anadolu.edu.tr; Alan Smith, Editor, smith@usq.edu.au; Dr. Ali Ekrem Ozkul, Editor, aeozkul@anadolu.edu.tr; Betty Collis, Editor, collis@edte.utwente.nl. **ISSN:** 1302-6488. **URL:** http://tojde.anadolu.edu.tr/.

Istanbul

51556 ■ Acta Orthopaedica et Traumatologica Turcica
Turkish Association of Orthopaedics and Traumatology
Turk Ortopedi ve Travmatoloji Dernegi
Istanbul School of Medicine
Dept. of Orthopaedics & Traumatology
Topkapi
TR-34390 Istanbul, Turkey
Turkish language publication covering orthopedics.

Freq: 5/yr. **Key Personnel:** Mehmet S. Demirhan, Editor, demirhan@istanbul.edu.tr. **ISSN:** 1017-995X. **Subscription Rates:** Free to qualified subscribers. **URL:** http://www.aott.org.tr/index.php/aott. **Circ:** Paid ‡1,000

51557 ■ Bogazici Journal
Bogazici University
Southern Campus No:10
Bebek
TR-34342 Istanbul, Turkey
Ph: 90 212 3595400
Fax: 90 212 3597461
Publication E-mail: bjournal@boun.edu.tr
Publisher E-mail: emba@boun.edu.tr
Journal covering a variety of social science disciplines including economics, management studies, political science and international studies, social demography and sociology. Major attention is given to Turkey's domestic issues and international affairs. **Subtitle:** Review of Social, Economic and Administrative Studies. **Founded:** 1973. **Freq:** Semiannual. **Key Personnel:** Kadem Senkal, Executive Ed.; Fikret Adaman, Editor. **ISSN:** 1300-9583. **Subscription Rates:** US$10 other countries; US$20 institutions; TL 10 individuals. **Remarks:** Advertising accepted; rates available upon request. **URL:** http://www.mgmt.boun.edu.tr/content/view/367/247/lang,en/. **Formerly:** Journal of Economics and Administrative Studies. **Circ:** Paid 850

51558 ■ Journal of Turkish Ophthalmology
Journal Ophthalmological Society
Molla Gurani Cad. 22/2
Findikzade
34093 Istanbul, Turkey
Ph: 90 212 6219925
Fax: 90 212 6219927
Publication E-mail: iletisim@oftalmoloji.org
Publisher E-mail: eci@galenos.tr
Journal featuring articles related to ophthalmology. **Freq:** Bimonthly. **Key Personnel:** Nevbahar Tamcelik, Editor. **URL:** http://www.oftalmoloji.org/.

51559 ■ Konfeksiyon & Teknik
Ihlas Holding Mrk.
29 Ekim Cad
Yenibosna
TR-34197 Istanbul, Turkey
Ph: 90 212 4542000
Fax: 90 212 4542136
Publication E-mail: turkey@ihlas.net.tr
Publisher E-mail: turkey@ihlas.net.tr
Trade magazine covering the clothing industry. **Subtitle:** The Clothing Magazine. **Freq:** Monthly. **Print Method:** Offset. **Trim Size:** 218 x 300 mm. **ISSN:** 1300-9974. **Subscription Rates:** EUR100 individuals; US$130 individuals. **Remarks:** Accepts advertising. **URL:** http://www.img.com.tr/turkce/; http://www.img.com.tr/KonfeksiyonTeknik. **Ad Rates:** BW: US$1,500, 4C: US$2,950. **Circ:** 10,560

51560 ■ Marmara Journal of European Studies
Marmara University
European Community Institute
Goztepe Kampusu
Kadikoy
TR-81040 Istanbul, Turkey
Ph: 90 216 3384196
Fax: 90 216 3474543
Publication E-mail: mjes@marmara.edu.tr
Publisher E-mail: eci@marun.edu.tr
Peer-reviewed journal presenting studies pertinent to European integration and the position of Turkey in this context. **Founded:** 1991. **Freq:** Semiannual. **ISSN:** 1301-1359. **Remarks:** Accepts advertising. **URL:** http://avrupa.marmara.edu.tr/index.php?sayfa=12&dil=en. **Ad Rates:** BW: US$750, 4C: US$1,000. **Circ:** Paid 1,000

51561 ■ Matbaa & Teknik
Ihlas Holding Mrk.
29 Ekim Cad
Yenibosna
TR-34197 Istanbul, Turkey
Ph: 90 212 4542000
Fax: 90 212 4542136
Publication E-mail: info@ihlasfuar.com
Publisher E-mail: turkey@ihlas.net.tr
Trade magazine covering the printing and publishing industry. **Founded:** Dec. 1996. **Freq:** Monthly. **Print Method:** Offset. **Trim Size:** 218 x 300 mm. **Key Personnel:** Ahmet Kizil, Editor; Mehmet Oren, Editor. **ISSN:**

1300-4522. **Remarks:** Accepts advertising. **URL:** http://www.matbaateknik.com.tr/web/default.asp. **Ad Rates:** BW: US$1,500, 4C: US$2,950. **Circ:** 9,690

51562 ■ Medikal & Teknik
Ihlas Holding Mrk.
29 Ekim Cad
Yenibosna
TR-34197 Istanbul, Turkey
Ph: 90 212 4542000
Fax: 90 212 4542136
Publisher E-mail: turkey@ihlas.net.tr
Professional magazine covering medicine and health in Turkey. **Freq:** Monthly. **Print Method:** Offset. **Trim Size:** 218 x 300 mm. **Key Personnel:** Ahmet Erarslan, Contact; Ugur Dundar, Editor, ugur.dundar@ihlasdergigrubu.com. **ISSN:** 1301-0034. **Remarks:** Accepts advertising. **URL:** http://www.medikalteknik.com.tr/web/default.asp. **Ad Rates:** BW: US$1,500, 4C: US$2,950. **Circ:** 10,069

51563 ■ Tekstil & Teknik
Ihlas Holding Mrk.
29 Ekim Cad
Yenibosna
TR-34197 Istanbul, Turkey
Ph: 90 212 4542000
Fax: 90 212 4542136
Publisher E-mail: turkey@ihlas.net.tr
Trade magazine covering textiles and textile machinery. **Founded:** Nov. 1981. **Freq:** Monthly. **Print Method:** Offset. **Trim Size:** 218 x 300 mm. **Key Personnel:** Jack Soztutan, Editor-in-Chief, msoztutan@img.com.tr. **ISSN:** 1300-9982. **Subscription Rates:** TL 150 individuals. **Remarks:** Accepts advertising. **URL:** http://www.tekstilteknik.com.tr. **Ad Rates:** BW: US$2,500, 4C: US$1,250. **Circ:** 12,381

51564 ■ Acik Radyo - Istanbul - 94.9 MHz
Cumhuriyet Caddesi
Uftade Sokak, No. 1
ERN Han, Kat. 5-6
Elmadag
TR-34373 Istanbul, Turkey
Ph: 90 212 3434040
Fax: 90 212 2323219
E-mail: acikradyo@acikradyo.com.tr
Format: News. **Owner:** Acik Radyo, at above address. **Founded:** Nov. 13, 1995. **Ad Rates:** $1 per unit. **URL:** http://www.acikradyo.com.tr/.

51565 ■ Alem FM - Istanbul - 89.3 MHz
Davutpata Cad Sercekale Sok
No. 2 Topkapy
34020 Istanbul, Turkey
Ph: 90 212 4819600
Fax: 90 212 4819604
E-mail: info@alemfm.com
Owner: Alem FM, Ergenekon Cad, Se-tat Tic, Merkezi, No. 100, Ferikoy, Istanbul, Turkey. **URL:** http://www.medyatext.com/alemfm.

51566 ■ Dunya Radyo-FM - 90.2
Ferah Mah. Resatbey Sok. No. 12 34692
Buyukcamlica
Istanbul, Turkey
Ph: 90 216 5249494
Fax: 90 216 5218434
E-mail: dunya@dunya.com.tr
Format: Ethnic; World Beat; Folk. **Operating Hours:** Continuous. **Ad Rates:** Advertising accepted; rates available upon request. **URL:** http://www.dunya.com.tr.

51567 ■ I.T.U. Radyo-FM - 103.8
3308 Maslak
Istanbul, Turkey
Ph: 90 212 2853696
Format: Educational; Eclectic. **Founded:** 1998. **Operating Hours:** Continuous. **URL:** http://www.radyo.itu.edu.tr.

51568 ■ Power-FM - 100
Fahrettin Kerlm Gokay Cad. No. 13
Merter
TR-34173 Istanbul, Turkey
Ph: 90 216 5540400
Fax: 90 216 4741515
E-mail: kaynaklari:l.k@powerfm.com.tr
Format: Contemporary Hit Radio (CHR); Ethnic. **Owner:** Power Media Center, at above address. **Operating**

Hours: Continuous. **Ad Rates:** Advertising accepted; rates available upon request. **URL:** http://www.powerfm.com.tr.

51569 ■ Radio Bogazici - Bebek - 107.9 MHz
Bogazici Universitesi
Ucaksavar Kampus
Superdorm FB-007
TR-80815 Istanbul, Turkey
Ph: 90 212 2578900
E-mail: bodj@radyobogazici.net
Format: Eclectic. **Owner:** Radio Bogazici, at above address. **Wattage:** 250. **URL:** http://www.radyo.boun.edu.tr.

51570 ■ Radio Dunya - Bakanlyklar - 93.5 MHz
Ferah Mah. Resatbey Sok.
No. 12, 343692
Buyukcamlica
Istanbul, Turkey
Ph: 90 2165249494
Fax: 90 2165218434
E-mail: dunya@dunya.com.tr
Format: Eclectic. **Owner:** Radio Dunya, Ataturk Bulvary, No. 137/7, Bakanlyklar, Turkey. **URL:** http://www.dunya.com.tr/.

51571 ■ TGRT-FM - 104.4
29 Ekim Cad
No. 23, Ihlas Holding Plz., Zemin Kat.
Yenibosna
TR-34197 Istanbul, Turkey
Ph: 90 212 4545646
Fax: 90 212 4545626
Format: Ethnic; World Beat. **Operating Hours:** 16 hours Daily. **URL:** http://www.tgrt-fm.com.tr.

51572 ■ TGRT-FM - 93.1
29 Ekim Cad
No. 23, Ihlas Holding Plz., Zemin Kat.
Yenibosna
TR-34197 Istanbul, Turkey
Ph: 90 212 4545646
Fax: 90 212 4545626
Format: Ethnic; World Beat. **Operating Hours:** 16 hours Daily. **URL:** http://www.tgrt-fm.com.tr.

Izmir

51573 ■ Ekoloji
Murselpasa Bulvari 1265 Sokak No. 10/10
Basmane-Konak-Izmir, Pk. 63
TR-35230 Izmir, Turkey
Ph: 90 232 4459999
Fax: 90 232 4453131
Publication E-mail: abone@ekolojidergisi.com.tr
Publisher E-mail: editor@ekolojimagazin.com
Journal covering all aspects of environmental sciences such as air, water, solid waste, noise, recycling, natural resources, ecology, education, pollutants and environmental protection. **Founded:** 1991. **Freq:** Quarterly. **Key Personnel:** Ahmet Karacan, Production Mgr., ahmetkaracan@hotmail.com; Prof. Zafer Ayvaz, Editor, editor@ekolojidergisi.com.tr; Cevre Koruma Ve Araştirma Vakfi, Owner. **ISSN:** 1300 1361. **Subscription Rates:** EUR25 individuals. **URL:** http://www.ekolojimagazin.com/.

51574 ■ Journal of the Faculty of Science, Ege University, Series A
Ege University
Fen Fakultesi Dekanligi
Bornova
TR-35100 Izmir, Turkey
Ph: 90 232 3881092
Fax: 90 232 3881036
Publisher E-mail: fenfak@mail.ege.edu.tr
Journal featuring articles related to the sciences and comprehensive works. **Founded:** 1977. **Freq:** Semiannual. **Key Personnel:** Dr. Bekir Cetinkaya, Editor, ilknur.yalcin@ege.edu.tr. **ISSN:** 0254-5527. **Subscription Rates:** Free. **URL:** http://sci.ege.edu.tr/~jfs/.

51575 ■ Journal of Neurological Sciences
Aegean Neurological Society
Ege University Hospital
Dept. of Neurological Surgery
Bornova
TR-35100 Izmir, Turkey

Circulation: ★ = ABC; △ = BPA; ◆ = CAC; • = CCAB; ❑ = VAC; ⊕ = PO Statement; ‡ = Publisher's Report; Boldface figures = sworn; Light figures = estimated.

Fax: 90 232 3731330
Peer-reviewed journal covering experimental and clinical neuroscience articles. **Founded:** 1987. **Freq:** Quarterly. **Key Personnel:** Nezih Oktar, Editor-in-Chief; Irfan Palali, Co-Ed. **ISSN:** 1300-1817. **Subscription Rates:** Free. **URL:** http://www.jns.dergisi.org/.

Mersin

51576 ■ Anti-Inflammatory & Anti-Allergy Agents in Medicinal Chemistry
Bentham Science Publishers Ltd.
Mersin University
Dept. of Pharmacology
TR-33169 Mersin, Turkey
Publisher E-mail: subscriptions@bentham.org
Journal covering all the latest and outstanding developments in medicinal chemistry and rational drug design for the discovery of new anti-inflammatory & anti-allergy agents. **Freq:** Quarterly. **Key Personnel:** Bahar Tunctan, Editor-in-Chief, btunctan@yahoo.com; F. Apparailly, Editorial Advisory Board; M. Alfano, Editorial Advisory Board; K. Asadullah, Editorial Advisory Board; H. Akgun, Editorial Advisory Board; C.A. Akids, Editorial Advisory Board. **ISSN:** 1871-5230. **Subscription Rates:** US$1,310 institutions corporate, print; US$1,310 institutions corporate, print; US$1,570 institutions corporate, print and online; US$730 institutions academic, print; US$730 institutions academic, online; US$860 institutions academic, print and online; US$180 individuals print. **Remarks:** Accepts advertising. **URL:** http://www.bentham.org/cmcaiaa/. **Formerly:** Current Medicinal Chemistry. Anti-Inflammatory & Anti-Allergy Agents. **Circ:** (Not Reported)

51577 ■ Kadin/Woman 2000
Eastern Mediterranean University
Gazimagusa K.K.T.C.
Mersin, Turkey
Ph: 90 392 6301111

Fax: 90 392 3654479
Multi-disciplinary, refereed, bilingual journal (both Turkish and English) dedicated to the scholarly study of all aspects of women's issues. **Subtitle:** Kadin Arastirmalari Dergisi - Journal for Women Studies. **Freq:** Semiannual. **Key Personnel:** Dr. Netice Yildiz, Editor; Dr. Hanife Aliefendioglu, Asst. Ed.; Dr. Simel Esim, Asst. Ed.; Dr. Halil Guven, Contact; Dr. Hulya Argunsah, Asst. Ed. **ISSN:** 1302-9916. **URL:** http://kwj2000journal.emu.edu.tr/.

Trabzon

51578 ■ Turkish Journal of Fisheries and Aquatic Sciences
Central Fisheries Research Institute
Kasustu Beldesi
Yomra
TR-61250 Trabzon, Turkey
Ph: 90 462 3411056
Fax: 90 462 3411152
Publication E-mail: trjfas@sumae.gov.tr
Publisher E-mail: info@trjfas.org
Journal addressing research and needs of all working and studying within the many varied areas of fisheries and aquatic sciences. **Freq:** Semiannual. **Key Personnel:** Levent Bat, Editorial Board; Atilla Ozdemir, President; Orhan AK, Managing Editor. **URL:** http://www.trjfas.org/.

51579 ■ Turkish Radio-Television Corporation - Trabzon - 954 KHz
TRT Sitesi Turan Gunes Bulvari
Or-an
TR-06540 Ankara, Turkey
Ph: 90 312 4904300
E-mail: aktifhat@trt.net.tr
Format: News. **Owner:** Turkish Radio-Television Corporation, at above address. **Operating Hours:** Continuous. **Key Personnel:** Bekir Erdem, President; Yucel Yener, Dir. Gen.; Haluk Buran, Dep. Dir. Gen.

(Engg.). **Wattage:** 300,000. **URL:** http://www.trt.net.tr.

Van

51580 ■ Journal of Contemporary Mathematics
Serials Publications
c/o Prof. Cemil Tunc, Ed.-in-Ch.
Dept. of Mathematis
Faculty of Arts & Sciences
Yuzuncu Yil University
TR-65080 Van, Turkey
Publisher E-mail: serials@satyam.net.in
Journal covering research in the fields of algebra, analysis, applied mathematics, dynamical systems, geometry, mathematical physics, number theory, partial differential equations, and topology. **Freq:** Semiannual. **Key Personnel:** Prof. Cemil Tunc, Editor-in-Chief, cemtunc@yahoo.com; Hari M. Srivastava, Editorial Board; Ravi P. Agarwal, Editorial Board. **ISSN:** 0973-6298. **Subscription Rates:** US$150 institutions print. **URL:** http://www.serialspublications.com/journals1.asp?jid=310&jtype=1.

51581 ■ Journal of Pediatric Infectious Diseases
IOS Press, B.V.
c/o Huseyin Caksen, MD, Ed.-in-Ch.
Yuezuencue Yil University
Faculty of Medicine
Dept. of Pediatrics
Van, Turkey
Publisher E-mail: info@iospress.nl
Peer-reviewed journal covering articles on pediatric infectious diseases. **Freq:** Quarterly. **Key Personnel:** Huseyin Caksen, MD, Editor-in-Chief; Scott B. Halstead, MD, Assoc. Ed.; James William Gray, MD, Assoc. Ed.; Ravi Jhaveri, MD, Assoc. Ed.; Lisa M. Lee, PhD, Assoc. Ed.; Laura J. Podewils, PhD, Assoc. Ed. **ISSN:** 1305-7707. **Subscription Rates:** EUR298 individuals regular; US$420 individuals regular. **URL:** http://www.iospress.nl/loadtop/load.php?isbn=13057707; http://www.jpid.org/.

Jinja

51582 ■ African Journal of Tropical Hydrobiology and Fisheries
African Journals Online
PO Box 1625
Jinja, Uganda
Publisher E-mail: info@ajol.info
Peer-reviewed journal containing information for aquatic scientists, fishery economists and sociologists. **Freq:** Semiannual. **Key Personnel:** Dr. William M. Kudoja, Exec. Sec., lvfo@source.co.ug. **Subscription Rates:** US$50 individuals; US$25 students; US$75 institutions. **URL:** http://ajol.info/index.php/ajthf.

Kampala

51583 ■ African Crop Science Journal
African Crop Science Society
Makerere University
Department of Crop Science
PO Box 7062
Kampala, Uganda
Ph: 256 414 540464
Fax: 256 41 531641
Publisher E-mail: acss@starcom.co.ug
Journal reporting on all aspects of crop agronomy, production, genetics and breeding, germplasm, crop protection, post harvest systems and utilization, agroforestry, crop-animal interactions, information science, environmental science and soil science. **Freq:** Quarterly. **Key Personnel:** M.A. Bekunda, Assoc. Ed.; M.P. Nampala, Scientific Ed.; John S. Tenywa, Editor-in-Chief, acss@starcom.co.ug. **ISSN:** 1021-9730. **Subscription Rates:** US$80 individuals; US$50 individuals 2 years; US$180 institutions; US$340 institutions 2 years; US$140 individuals sales agent; US$260 two years sales agent. **URL:** http://www.bioline.org.br/cs.

51584 ■ African Health Sciences
African Journals Online
c/o Dr. James Tumwine, Ed.-in-Ch.
Makerere University Medical School
PO Box 7072
Kampala, Uganda
Ph: 256 415 30020
Publisher E-mail: info@ajol.info
Peer-reviewed journal publishing articles on research, clinical practice, public health, policy, planning, implementation and evaluation, in the health and related sciences relevant to Africa and the tropics. **Freq:** Quarterly. **Key Personnel:** Dr. James Tumwine, Editor-in-Chief, kabaleimc@gmail.com. **ISSN:** 1680-6905. **URL:** http://ajol.info/index.php/ahs.

51585 ■ African Journal of Ecology
John Wiley & Sons Inc.
Wiley-Blackwell
c/o F.I.B. Kayanja, Ed.-in-Ch.
Mbarara University
Liaison Office
PO Box 7062
Kampala, Uganda
Journal focusing on scientific research into the ecology of the animals and plants of Africa. **Freq:** Quarterly. **Key Personnel:** F.I.B. Kayanja, Editor-in-Chief, kayanjafib2001@yahoo.com; Hadley Becha, Editorial Board; Bryan Shorrocks, Assoc. Ed., bs529@york.ac.uk. **ISSN:** 0414-6707. **Subscription Rates:** US$187 members Americas; US$1,479 institutions print and online; US$1,345 institutions print; 800 institutions print and online; 727 institutions online; EUR1,016 institutions print and online; EUR924 institutions print; US$1,725 institutions, other countries print and online; US$1,568 institutions, other countries print; 113 members rest of the world. **Remarks:** Accepts advertising. **URL:** http://www.wiley.com/bw/journal.asp?ref=0141-6707&site=1. **Circ:** (Not Reported)

51586 ■ Eastern Africa Journal of Rural Development
African Journals Online
Dept. of Agricultural Economics & Agribusiness
Makerere University
PO Box 7062
Kampala, Uganda
Publisher E-mail: info@ajol.info
Peer-reviewed journal covering rural development of eastern America. **Freq:** Biennial. **Key Personnel:** Dr. Job Lagat, Board Member; Prof. Julius Mangisoni, Board Member; Dr. Imelda Nalukenge, Editor, phone 256 41 531152, fax 256 41 531641, nalukenge@agric.mak.ac.ug; Dr. Bernard Bashaasha, Board Member; Dr. Barnabas Kiiza, Board Member; Dr. Simeon Bamire, Board Member; Dr. Adam Mugume, Board Member. **ISSN:** 0377-7103. **Subscription Rates:** US$90 elsewhere; US$75 individuals outside Africa; US$50 members within Africa; US$30 members within Kenya and Tanzania; US$25 members within Uganda. **URL:** http://ajol.info/index.php/eajrd.

51587 ■ The Monitor
Monitor Publications Ltd.
PO Box 12141
Kampala, Uganda
Ph: 256 412 32367
Fax: 256 412 32369
Publication E-mail: editorial@ug.nationmedia.com
Publisher E-mail: info@monitor.co.ug
General newspaper. **Founded:** 1992. **Freq:** Daily. **URL:** http://www.monitor.co.ug. **Circ:** Combined 25,000

51588 ■ Mtafiti Mwafrika
African Journals Online
African Research & Documentation Ctr.
Uganda Martyrs University
PO Box 5498
Kampala, Uganda
Ph: 256 38 410635
Fax: 256 38 410100
Publisher E-mail: info@ajol.info
Peer-reviewed journal covering the socio-cultural, economic, political, and historical aspects of Africa. **Freq:** Quarterly. **Key Personnel:** Mugumya Levis, Editor, Imugumya@umu.ac.ug. **ISSN:** 1607-0011. **Subscription Rates:** 3,500 USh single issue; US$10 other countries. **URL:** http://ajol.info/index.php/mtafiti.

51589 ■ The Uganda Journal
The Uganda Society
PO Box 4980
Kampala, Uganda
Publisher E-mail: ncid@infocom.co.ug
Journal featuring information about Uganda. **Founded:** Jan. 1934. **Freq:** Semiannual. **Key Personnel:** Dent Ocaya-Lakidi, Editor. **Subscription Rates:** US$10 individuals; US$3 students; US$10 institutions. **URL:** http://www.africa.upenn.edu/ugandasoc/UgandaSociety.htm.

51590 ■ Mama-FM - 101.7
PO Box 7263
Kampala, Uganda
Ph: 256 41543996
Fax: 256 41543996
E-mail: umwa@africaonline.co.ug
Format: Educational. **Founded:** 1997. **URL:** http://www.interconnection.org/umwa/community_radio.html.

Circulation: ★ = ABC; △ = BPA; ♦ = CAC; • = CCAB; ❑ = VAC; ⊕ = PO Statement; ‡ = Publisher's Report; Boldface figures = sworn; Light figures = estimated.

Gale Directory of Publications & Broadcast Media/147th Ed.

5517

Donetsk

51591 ■ A Yidishe Mame
Federation of Jewish Communities
Darnitzkaya str. 4
83079 Donetsk, Ukraine
Ph: 380 62 3384586
Fax: 380 62 3829704
Magazine containing issues of literature and philosophic features of local Jewish women. **Founded:** 2000. **Key Personnel:** Olga Stein, Editor. **Subscription Rates:** Free. **URL:** http://www.fjc.ru/departments/DeptInst.asp?did=84076&aid=95401.

Kharkov

51592 ■ Fizika Nizkikh Temperatur
B.Verkin Institute for Low Temperature Physics and Engineering
47 Lenin Ave.
61103 Kharkov, Ukraine
Ph: 380 57 3402223
Fax: 380 57 3403370
Publisher E-mail: fnt@ilt.kharkov.ua
Journal covering quantum liquids and quantum crystals, superconductivity, low-temperature magnetism, electronic properties of metal and alloys, low-dimensional and disordered systems, quantum effects in semiconductors and dielectrics, physical properties of cryocrystals, lattice dynamics, low-temperature physics of plasticity and strength, ultra low temperature facilities, and new low-temperature experimental methods. **Founded:** 1975. **Freq:** Monthly. **Print Method:** Offset. **Trim Size:** 8 x 10 7/8. **Cols./Page:** 3. **Col. Width:** 26 nonpareils. **Col. Depth:** 142 agate lines. **Key Personnel:** V.V. Eremenko, Editor-in-Chief; A.S. Bakai, Editorial Board; K.M. Matsievskii, Managing Editor. **ISSN:** 0132-6414. **URL:** http://fnte.ilt.kharkov.ua/fnt_e.html.

Kiev

51593 ■ Afisha
KP Media
14-A Bazhana Ave., 7th Fl.
02140 Kiev, Ukraine
Ph: 380 44 4964563
Fax: 380 44 4964567
Magazine featuring cultural and entertainment listings including concerts, performances, movies and exhibitions, as well as a comprehensive guide to Kyiv's restaurants and bars, nightclubs, and casinos. **Founded:** Apr. 2001. **Freq:** Weekly. **Key Personnel:** Jed Sunden, Publisher, jed@kpmedia.ua. **Subscription Rates:** 169 Rb individuals. **Remarks:** Accepts advertising. **URL:** http://www.kpmedia.com.ua/. **Circ:** Combined 25,000

51594 ■ Edinstvennaya
Edipresse Publications S.A.
Dimitrova St. 5
Bldg. 10-a, 6th Fl.
03680 Kiev, Ukraine
Ph: 380 44 4907140
Fax: 380 44 4907141
Publication E-mail: edinstvennaya-editors@edipresse.com.ua

Publisher E-mail: groupe@edipresse.com
Magazine highlighting women. **Freq:** Monthly. **Key Personnel:** Inna Ryk, Director; Elena Skachko, Ch. Ed. **URL:** http://www.edipresse.com/womens/edinstvennaya. **Circ:** ‡265,000

51595 ■ Edinstvennaya - Tvoye Zdorovye
Edipresse Publications S.A.
Dimitrova St. 5
Bldg. 10-a, 6th Fl.
03680 Kiev, Ukraine
Ph: 380 44 4907140
Fax: 380 44 4907141
Publication E-mail: edinstvennaya-editors@edipresse.com.ua
Publisher E-mail: groupe@edipresse.com
Magazine focusing on women's health, diet, beauty, fashion and psychology. **Freq:** Monthly. **Key Personnel:** Inna Ryk, Director; Tatyana Petrasheva, Ch. Ed. **URL:** http://www.edipresse.com/womens/edinstvennaya. **Circ:** ‡265,000

51596 ■ Fizika Soznaniya i Zhyzni, Kosmologiya i Astrofizika (Physics of Consciousness and Life, Cosmology and Astrophysics)
Mezhdunarodnyi Institut Sotsioniki
a/s 23
2206 Kiev, Ukraine
Ph: 38 44 5580935
Publication E-mail: boukalov@gmail.com
Publisher E-mail: socion@ibc.com.ua
Journal concerned with the development of improved conceptions about the essence of the consciousness, mentality, and vital processes, not only within the Earth, but also in the space seale. **Freq:** Quarterly. **URL:** http://www.socionics.ibc.com.ua/physics

51597 ■ Haroshye Raditeli
Edipresse Publications S.A.
Dimitrova St. 5
Bldg. 10-a, 6th Fl.
03680 Kiev, Ukraine
Ph: 380 44 4907140
Fax: 380 44 4907141
Publisher E-mail: groupe@edipresse.com
Magazine focusing on parenting. **Freq:** Monthly. **Key Personnel:** Inna Ryk, Director; Vladislava Barsukova, Ch. Ed. **URL:** http://www.edipresse.com/parentschildren/haroshye-raditeli-good-parents. **Circ:** ‡45,000

51598 ■ Interior Magazine
KP Media
14-A Bazhana Ave., 7th Fl.
02140 Kiev, Ukraine
Ph: 380 44 4964563
Fax: 380 44 4964567
Magazine featuring retail catalogue for the home with information, prices, and addresses of retailers. **Founded:** Nov. 2004. **Freq:** Monthly. **Key Personnel:** Jed Sunden, Publisher, jed@kpmedia.ua. **Remarks:** Accepts advertising. **URL:** http://www.kpmedia.com.ua/eng/consumer/im/. **Circ:** Combined 17,500

51599 ■ Korrespondent
KP Media
14-A Bazhana Ave., 7th Fl.

02140 Kiev, Ukraine
Ph: 380 44 4964563
Fax: 380 44 4964567
Magazine featuring important events in Ukraine and around the world. **Founded:** Mar. 2002. **Freq:** Weekly. **Key Personnel:** Jed Sunden, Publisher, jed@kpmedia.ua. **Subscription Rates:** 299 Rb individuals; 149 Rb individuals 6 months. **URL:** http://www.kpmedia.com.ua/eng/newspr/kor/. **Circ:** Combined 50,000

51600 ■ Kyiv Post
KP Media
14-A Bazhana Ave., 7th Fl.
02140 Kiev, Ukraine
Ph: 380 44 4964563
Fax: 380 44 4964567
Newspaper featuring articles from the weekly English-language newspaper plus daily updates of events. **Founded:** 1995. **Freq:** Weekly. **Key Personnel:** Brian Bonner, Ch. Ed., bonner@kyivpost.com; Jed Sunden, Publisher, jed@kpmedia.ua. **Subscription Rates:** 95 Rb individuals; 220 Rb other countries. **Remarks:** Accepts advertising. **URL:** http://www.kyivpost.com/; http://www.kpmedia.com.ua/. **Circ:** Combined 25,000

51601 ■ Lyubimaya Datcha
Edipresse Publications S.A.
Dimitrova St. 5
Bldg. 10-a, 3rd Fl.
03680 Kiev, Ukraine
Ph: 380 44 4907140
Fax: 380 44 4907141
Publisher E-mail: groupe@edipresse.com
Magazine highlighting solutions for home renovation. **Freq:** Monthly. **Key Personnel:** Inna Ryk, Director; Aleksei Tatianchenko, Ch. Ed. **URL:** http://www.edipresse.com/en/par_pays/ukraine/magazines/lyubimaya_datcha_my_lovely_datcha. **Circ:** ‡20,000

51602 ■ Mama I ya
Edipresse Publications S.A.
Dimitrova St. 5
Bldg. 10-a, 3rd Fl.
03680 Kiev, Ukraine
Ph: 380 44 4907140
Fax: 380 44 4907143
Publisher E-mail: groupe@edipresse.com
Magazine covering health and care of a newborn. **Freq:** Monthly. **Key Personnel:** Inna Ryk, Director; Tatyana Petrasheva, Ch. Ed. **URL:** http://www.edipresse.com/parentschildren/mama-i-ya. **Circ:** ‡60,000

51603 ■ Novynar
KP Media
14-A Bazhana Ave., 7th Fl.
02140 Kiev, Ukraine
Ph: 380 44 4964563
Fax: 380 44 4964567
News magazine featuring Novynar's current events in politics, economics, and culture. **Founded:** 2007. **Freq:** Weekly. **Key Personnel:** Jed Sunden, Publisher, jed@kppublications.com. **URL:** http://www.kpmedia.com.ua/eng/inet/novynar/. **Circ:** Combined 150,000

51604 ■ Polina
Edipresse Publications S.A.

Circulation: ★ = ABC; △ = BPA; ♦ = CAC; • = CCAB; ❑ = VAC; ⊕ = PO Statement; ‡ = Publisher's Report; Boldface figures = sworn; Light figures = estimated.

Gale Directory of Publications & Broadcast Media/147th Ed.

5519

Dimitrova St. 5
Bldg. 10-a, 6th Fl.
03680 Kiev, Ukraine
Ph: 380 44 4907140
Fax: 380 44 4907141
Publication E-mail: readers@edipresse.com.ua
Publisher E-mail: groupe@edipresse.com
Magazine focusing on the needs of Ukrainian women.
Freq: Weekly. **Key Personnel:** Lusine Badalyan, Director; Anna Andryushchenko, Ch. Ed. **URL:** http://www.edipresse.com/womens/polina. **Circ:** ‡155,000

51605 ■ Privatnyi Dom
Edipresse Publications S.A.
Dimitrova St. 5
Bldg. 10-a, 3rd Fl.
03680 Kiev, Ukraine
Ph: 380 44 4907140
Fax: 380 44 4907142
Publisher E-mail: groupe@edipresse.com
Magazine featuring articles about home building, renovating, and improving. **Freq:** Monthly. **Key Personnel:** Oksana Nastenko, Ch. Ed.; Inna Ryk, Director. **URL:** http://www.edipresse.com/home-design/privatnyi-dom. **Circ:** ‡35,000

51606 ■ Problems of Aging & Longevity
Ukrainian Gerontological and Geriatric Society
Vyshgorodskaya St. 67
254114 Kiev, Ukraine
Ph: 380 44 4304068
Fax: 380 44 4329956
Publisher E-mail: tamur@carrier.kiev.ua
English and Russian language publication covering gerontology. **Founded:** 1990. **Freq:** Quarterly. **ISSN:** 0869-1703. **Subscription Rates:** US$153 individuals. **Remarks:** Advertising accepted; rates available upon request. **Circ:** (Not Reported)

51607 ■ Random Operators and Stochastic Equations
Walter de Gruyter GmbH & Co. KG
c/o V. Girko, Ed.-in-Ch.
Institute of Mathematics
Ukrainian National Academy of Sciences
Tereshchenkivska Str. 3
252601 Kiev, Ukraine
Publisher E-mail: info@degruyter.com
Peer-reviewed Journal containing articles on the theory of random operators and stochastic analysis. **Freq:** Quarterly. **Key Personnel:** V. Girko, Editor-in-Chief, agirko@i.com.ua; A. Skorokhod, Editor-in-Chief. **ISSN:** 0926-6364. **Subscription Rates:** EUR1,034 individuals print and online; EUR899 individuals print or online only; EUR248 single issue. **Remarks:** Accepts advertising. **URL:** http://www.degruyter.de/journals/rose/detailEn.cfm. **Ad Rates:** BW: 300 Rb. **Circ:** ‡140

51608 ■ Technical Diagnostics and Nondestructive Testing
The Paton Publishing House
E.O. Paton Welding Institute
11 Bozhenko St.
03680 Kiev, Ukraine
Ph: 380 44 2876302
Fax: 380 44 5280486
Publisher E-mail: journal@paton.kiev.ua
Magazine covering theoretical and practical articles on technical diagnosing and non-destructive testing, flaw detection, residual life of structures. **Founded:** 1989. **Freq:** Quarterly. **ISSN:** 0235-3474. **Subscription Rates:** US$52 individuals. **Remarks:** Accepts advertising. **URL:** http://www.nas.gov.ua/pwj/. **Foreign language name:** Tekhnicheskaya Diagnostika I Nerazrushayushchiy Kontrol. **Ad Rates:** BW: US$80, 4C: US$300. **Circ:** (Not Reported)

51609 ■ TV Ekran
Edipresse Publications S.A.
Dimitrova St. 5
Bldg. 10-a, 3rd Fl.
03680 Kiev, Ukraine
Ph: 380 44 4907140
Fax: 380 44 4907141
Publisher E-mail: groupe@edipresse.com
Magazine featuring TV schedules, articles about actors and behind the scenes of the shows. **Freq:** Weekly. **Key Personnel:** Irina Shtefan, Ch. Ed.; Inna Ryk, Director. **URL:** http://www.edipresse.com/tv/tv-ekran. **Circ:** ‡100,000

51610 ■ Tvoy Malysh
Edipresse Publications S.A.
Dimitrova St. 5
Bldg. 10-a, 6th Fl.
03680 Kiev, Ukraine
Ph: 380 44 4907140
Fax: 380 44 4907141
Publication E-mail: tvoymalysh-editors@edipresse.com.ua
Publisher E-mail: groupe@edipresse.com
Magazine containing information on health, care, beauty and fashion for parents. **Freq:** Monthly. **Key Personnel:** Vladislava Barsukova, Ch. Ed.; Inna Ryk, Director. **URL:** http://www.edipresse.com/parentschildren/tvoy-malish. **Circ:** ‡90,000

51611 ■ Uyutnaya Kvartira
Edipresse Publications S.A.
Dimitrova St. 5
Bldg. 10-a, 6th Fl.
03680 Kiev, Ukraine
Ph: 380 44 4907140
Fax: 380 44 4907141
Publication E-mail: readers@edipresse.com.ua
Publisher E-mail: groupe@edipresse.com
Magazine featuring information on interior decorating. **URL:** http://www.edipresse.com/home-design/uyutnaya-kvartira.

51612 ■ Veselye Ideiki
Edipresse Publications S.A.
Dimitrova St. 5
Bldg. 10-a, 3rd Fl.
03680 Kiev, Ukraine
Ph: 380 44 4907140
Fax: 380 44 4907141
Publisher E-mail: groupe@edipresse.com
Magazine featuring crafts and creative ideas for young children. **Freq:** Monthly. **Key Personnel:** Tatyana Petrasheva, Ch. Ed.; Inna Ryk, Director. **URL:** http://www.edipresse.com/entertainment/veselye-ideiki. **Circ:** ‡40,000

51613 ■ Viva! Beauty
Edipresse Publications S.A.
Dimitrova St. 5
Bldg. 10-a, 3rd Fl.
03680 Kiev, Ukraine
Ph: 380 44 4907140
Fax: 380 44 4907141
Publisher E-mail: groupe@edipresse.com
Magazine featuring the latest fashion and beauty trends. **Freq:** Monthly. **Key Personnel:** Ivanna Slaboshpitskaya, Ch. Ed.; Inna Ryk, Director. **URL:** http://www.edipresse.com/womens/viva-beauty; http://www.viva.ua/. **Circ:** ‡50,000

51614 ■ Viva! Biographia
Edipresse Publications S.A.
Dimitrova St. 5
Bldg. 10-a, 3rd Fl.
03680 Kiev, Ukraine
Ph: 380 44 4907140

Fax: 380 44 4907141
Publisher E-mail: groupe@edipresse.com
Magazine featuring the biography of famous personalities. **Freq:** Monthly. **Key Personnel:** Ivanna Slaboshpitskaya, Ch. Ed.; Inna Ryk, Director. **URL:** http://www.edipresse.com/celebrity-news/viva-biographia. **Circ:** ‡50,000

51615 ■ Young Lady
Edipresse Publications S.A.
Dimitrova St. 5
Bldg. 10-a, 6th Fl.
03680 Kiev, Ukraine
Ph: 380 44 4907140
Fax: 380 44 4907141
Publication E-mail: younglady@edipresse.com.ua
Publisher E-mail: groupe@edipresse.com
Magazine featuring information for young women. **Freq:** Monthly. **Key Personnel:** Inna Ryk, Director; Anna Andryushchenko, Ch. Ed. **URL:** http://www.edipresse.com/womens/young-lady. **Circ:** ‡65,000

Lugansk

51616 ■ World of Jewish Woman
Federation of Jewish Communities
Khersonskiy tupik 7a
91053 Lugansk, Ukraine
Ph: 380 642 501336
Magazine featuring articles about Jewish women. **Key Personnel:** Chana Gopin, Contact. **URL:** http://www.fjc.ru/departments/DeptInst.asp?did=84076&aid=95533.

Sumy

51617 ■ Investment Management & Financial Innovations
Business Perspectives
Dzerzhinsky Ln., 10
40022 Sumy, Ukraine
Ph: 380 542 775771
Fax: 380 542 775771
Publisher E-mail: head@businessperspectives.org
Journal exposing problems in investment management and financial innovations and finding the solutions of their improvement with the further dissemination of research results, by enabling both renowned and emerging researchers and scholars to present their findings to a global audience of peers. **Freq:** Quarterly. **Key Personnel:** Serhiy Kozmenko, Editor-in-Chief. **ISSN:** 1810-4967. **Subscription Rates:** EUR190 individuals online version; EUR260 individuals print version; EUR310 individuals print + online version; EUR180 individuals full back issues online; EUR560 institutions print version; EUR370 institutions online version; EUR720 institutions print + online version; EUR495 institutions full back issue online. **URL:** http://www.businessperspectives.org/component/option,com_journals/id,4.

51618 ■ Problems & Perspectives in Management
Business Perspectives
Dzerzhynsky Ln., 10
40022 Sumy, Ukraine
Ph: 380 542 775771
Fax: 380 542 775771
Publisher E-mail: head@businessperspectives.org
Journal devoted to the problems and perspectives in management of firms, companies, and organization with different forms of ownership, as well as the management of macroeconomic processes. **Freq:** Quarterly. **Key Personnel:** Serhiy Kozmenko, Editor-in-Chief. **ISSN:** 1727-7051. **Subscription Rates:** EUR260 individuals print; EUR560 institutions print; EUR190 individuals online; EUR370 institutions online; EUR310 individuals print and online; EUR720 institutions print and online. **URL:** http://www.businessperspectives.org/component/option,com_journals/id,3.

Abu Dhabi

51619 ■ Electronic Journal of Theoretical Physics
PO Box 48210
Abu Dhabi, United Arab Emirates
Publisher E-mail: info@ejtp.com
Open access journal for physics. **Key Personnel:** Amar Sakaji, Co-Ed., info@ejtp.com; Ignazio Licata, Editor-in-Chief, ignazio.licata@ejtp.info. **ISSN:** 1729-5254. **URL:** http://www.ejtp.com.

51620 ■ International Journal of Petroleum Science and Technology
Research India Publications
c/o Mohamed Aggour, Editorial Board Member
Petroleum Institute
PO Box 2533
Abu Dhabi, United Arab Emirates
Publisher E-mail: info@ripublication.com
Journal covering all branches of petroleum and topics in the fields of petroleum geology, exploration, and technology. **Founded:** 1961. **Freq:** Semiannual. **Print Method:** Web offset. **Trim Size:** 8 1/4 x 10 7/8. **Cols./Page:** 3. **Col. Width:** 27 nonpareils. **Col. Depth:** 140 agate lines. **Key Personnel:** Mohamed Aggour, Editorial Board Member; Meshal Algharaib, Editorial Board Member; Serhat Akin, Editorial Board Member; Faruk Civan, Editorial Board Member; Mingzhe Dong, Editorial Board Member. **ISSN:** 0973-6328. **Subscription Rates:** US$320 institutions and library; print + online; US$300 institutions and library; online only; US$220 individuals print only; US$200 individuals online only; Rs 1,800 individuals. **URL:** http://www.ripublication.com/ijpst.htm.

51621 ■ Radio of the United Arab Emirates - 88.6 MHz
4th St. Sector 18, Zone I
Abu Dhabi, United Arab Emirates
Ph: 971 2 4144000
Fax: 971 2 4144001
Format: Religious. **Owner:** Abu Dhabi Media Co., at above address. **Operating Hours:** Continuous. **Ad Rates:** Noncommercial. **URL:** http://www.admedia.ae.

51622 ■ Radio of the United Arab Emirates - 729 KHz
4th St. Sector 18, Zone I
Abu Dhabi, United Arab Emirates
Ph: 971 2 4144000
Fax: 971 2 4144001
Owner: Abu Dhabi Media Co., at above address. **Operating Hours:** 2 a.m.-10.10 p.m. **Wattage:** 750,000. **URL:** http://www.admedia.ae.

Radio of the United Arab Emirates - See Al Ain

Ajman

51623 ■ Channel 4 Ajman - 104.8 MHz
PO Box 442
Ajman, United Arab Emirates
Ph: 971 6 7461444
E-mail: info@channel4m.com
Format: Top 40. **Ad Rates:** Advertising accepted; rates available upon request. **URL:** http://www.channel4fm.com.

51624 ■ Radio 4 Ajman - 89.1 MHz
PO Box 442
Ajman, United Arab Emirates
Ph: 971 6 7460000
E-mail: info@radio4fm.com
Format: Eclectic. **Founded:** Oct. 1999. **Operating Hours:** Continuous. **Ad Rates:** Advertising accepted; rates available upon request. **URL:** http://www.radio4fm.com/index.htm.

51625 ■ Radio 4-FM - 89.1
PO Box 442
Ajman, United Arab Emirates
Ph: 971 6 7460000
E-mail: info@radio4fm.com
Format: Ethnic; Contemporary Hit Radio (CHR); World Beat. **Operating Hours:** Continuous. **Ad Rates:** Advertising accepted; rates available upon request. **URL:** http://www.radio4fm.com.

Al Ain

51626 ■ International Journal of Mathematics Manuscripts
Research India Publications
c/o Prof. Haydar Akca, Ed.-in-Ch.
United Arab Emirates University
Faculty of Sciences, Mathematical Sciences Dept.
PO Box 17551
Al Ain, United Arab Emirates
Publisher E-mail: info@ripublication.com
Journal covering ordinary and partial differential equations. **Freq:** 3/yr. **Key Personnel:** Prof. Haydar Akca, Editor-in-Chief, hakca@uaeu.ac.ae. **ISSN:** 0974-2883. **Subscription Rates:** US$380 institutions and library; print plus online free; US$360 institutions and library; online only; US$140 individuals print plus online free; US$120 individuals online only. **URL:** http://www.ripublication.com/ijmm.htm.

51627 ■ Radio of the United Arab Emirates - 828 KHz
4th St. Sector 18, Zone I
Abu Dhabi, United Arab Emirates
Ph: 971 2 4144000
Fax: 971 2 4144001
Owner: Abu Dhabi Media Co., at above address. **Operating Hours:** 0200-2210. **Wattage:** 1000. **Ad Rates:** Noncommercial. **URL:** http://www.admedia.ae.

Dubai

51628 ■ Ad-Vocate
Motivate Publishing
Al Wahaibi Bldg.
Al Garhoud Bridge Rd., Deira
PO Box 2331
Dubai, United Arab Emirates
Ph: 971 428 24060
Fax: 971 428 20428
Publisher E-mail: motivate@motivate.ae
Reports latest developments within the advertising association and the industry as a whole. **Freq:** Quarterly. **Remarks:** Accepts advertising. **URL:** http://www.motivatepublishing.com/library/default.asp?articlecode=art00441. **Circ:** 5,000

51629 ■ Al Shindagah
Al Habtoor Group L.L.C.
PO Box 25444
Dubai, United Arab Emirates
Ph: 971 4 3431111
Fax: 971 4 3431140
Publication E-mail: shindaga@alhabtoorgroup.com
Publisher E-mail: habtoor@emirates.net.ae
Periodical covering general news section. **Freq:** Bimonthly. **Key Personnel:** Shaima Alhassani, Editor-in-Chief; James Mowbray, Editor; Mohmed Al Habtoor, Ch. Executive; Jalal Khalil, Translator. **URL:** http://www.alshindagah.com/.

51630 ■ Arabian Business
The Information & Technology Publishing Company Ltd.
PO Box 500024
Dubai, United Arab Emirates
Ph: 971 4 21008000
Fax: 971 4 21008080
Publisher E-mail: info@itp.com
English-language business magazine for the Middle East. **Freq:** Weekly. **Trim Size:** 200 x 265. **Key Personnel:** Karam Awad, Dep. Mng. Dir., karam.awad@itp.com; Andy Sambidge, Editor, phone 971 4 2108542, andrew.sambidge@itp.com; Peter Conmy, General Mgr., peter.conmy@itp.com. **Remarks:** Accepts advertising. **URL:** http://www.arabianbusiness.com/. **Circ:** ‡22,995

51631 ■ Arabian Computer News
The Information & Technology Publishing Company Ltd.
PO Box 500024
Dubai, United Arab Emirates
Ph: 971 4 21008000
Fax: 971 4 21008080
Publisher E-mail: info@itp.com
Technology and business magazine for the Middle East. **Key Personnel:** Mark Sutton, Gp. Ed., phone 971 4 2108225, mark.sutton@itp.com; Imthishan Giado, Dep. Ed., imthishan.giado@itp.com. **Remarks:** Accepts advertising. **URL:** http://www.itp.com/magazine/7-Arabian_Computer_News. **Circ:** (Not Reported)

51632 ■ Arabian Woman
GoDubai.com
PO Box 112664
Dubai, United Arab Emirates
Ph: 971 4 2292675
Fax: 971 4 2292674
Periodical covering information related to Arabian women. **Subtitle:** Woman's Magazine in English. **Freq:** Monthly. **Remarks:** Accepts advertising. **URL:** http://www.godubai.com/arabianwoman. **Circ:** (Not Reported)

51633 ■ Business Traveller Middle East
Motivate Publishing
Al Wahaibi Bldg.
Al Garhoud Bridge Rd., Deira
PO Box 2331
Dubai, United Arab Emirates
Ph: 971 428 24060
Fax: 971 428 20428

Publisher E-mail: motivate@motivate.ae
Magazine covering business travel. **Founded:** 2003.
Freq: Bimonthly. **Trim Size:** 208 x 275 mm. **Key Personnel:** Abraham Koshy, Gp. Advertising Mgr. **Subscription Rates:** 88 Dh individuals; 185 Dh other countries; US$24 individuals; US$50 other countries. **Remarks:** Accepts advertising. **URL:** http://www.motivatepublishing.com/library/default.asp?ArticleCode=ART00558. **Circ:** △26,437

51634 ■ Channel Middle East
The Information & Technology Publishing Company Ltd.
PO Box 500024
Dubai, United Arab Emirates
Ph: 971 4 21008000
Fax: 971 4 21008080
Publisher E-mail: info@itp.com
Information technology channel magazine for the Middle East. **Freq:** Monthly. **Key Personnel:** Andrew Seymour, Editor, phone 971 4 2108320, andrew.seymour@itp.com; Natasha Pendleton, Publisher, phone 971 4 2108193, natasha.pendleton@itp.com. **Subscription Rates:** Free. **Remarks:** Accepts advertising. **URL:** http://www.itp.com/magazine/3-Channel_Middle_East. **Circ:** △7,485

51635 ■ Charged Middle East
The Information & Technology Publishing Company Ltd.
PO Box 500024
Dubai, United Arab Emirates
Ph: 971 4 21008000
Fax: 971 4 21008080
Publication E-mail: chgcontact@itp.com
Publisher E-mail: info@itp.com
Magazine covering latest technology from MP3 to DVD players. **Subtitle:** Where Life Meets Technology. **Freq:** Monthly. **Key Personnel:** James Francis, Editor, phone 971 4 2108000, james.francis@itp.com; Ranjith Kumar, Production Mgr., phone 971 4 1208266, ranjith.kumar@itp.com; Dustin Robertson, Sales Mgr., phone 971 4 2108278, dustin.robertson@itp.com. **Remarks:** Accepts advertising. **URL:** http://www.itp.com/magazine/5-Charged_Middle_East. **Circ:** 9,000

51636 ■ City Times
Galadari Printing and Publishing L.L.C.
PO Box 11243
Dubai, United Arab Emirates
Ph: 971 433 83535
Fax: 971 433 83345
Publisher E-mail: ktimes@emirates.net.ae
General newspaper. **Freq:** Daily. **Trim Size:** 27 1/2 x 34 cm. **Remarks:** Accepts advertising. **URL:** http://www.khaleejtimes.com/ratetariff/rt_ct.asp. **Ad Rates:** BW: 16,700 Dh. **Circ:** (Not Reported)

51637 ■ Communications Middle East & Africa
The Information & Technology Publishing Company Ltd.
PO Box 500024
Dubai, United Arab Emirates
Ph: 971 4 21008000
Fax: 971 4 21008080
Publication E-mail: cmeasales@itp.com
Publisher E-mail: info@itp.com
Communications magazine for the Middle East. **Key Personnel:** Roger Field, Editor, phone 971 4 4392750, roger.field@itp.com; Ali Fahmi, Dep. Production Mgr., phone 971 4 42108366. **Remarks:** Accepts advertising. **URL:** http://www.itp.com/magazine/8-Communications_Middle_East_&_Africa. **Circ:** 10,000

51638 ■ Digital Studio
The Information & Technology Publishing Company Ltd.
PO Box 500024
Dubai, United Arab Emirates
Ph: 971 4 21008000
Fax: 971 4 21008080
Publication E-mail: dscontact@itp.com
Publisher E-mail: info@itp.com
Magazine for broadcast professionals. **Freq:** Monthly. **Trim Size:** 205 x 275. **Key Personnel:** Vijaya Cherian, Editor, phone 971 4 4356296, vijaya.cherian@itp.com; Gavin Murphy, Sales Mgr., phone 971 4 4356369, gavin.murphy@itp.com. **Remarks:** Accepts advertising. **URL:** http://www.itp.com/magazine/9-Digital_Studio. **Ad Rates:** BW: 5,520 Dh. **Circ:** △6,023

51639 ■ Dubai Voyager
Motivate Publishing
Al Wahaibi Bldg.

Al Garhoud Bridge Rd., Deira
PO Box 2331
Dubai, United Arab Emirates
Ph: 971 428 24060
Fax: 971 428 20428
Publisher E-mail: motivate@motivate.ae
Magazine featuring travel guide in Dubai. **Founded:** 1987. **Freq:** Monthly. **Trim Size:** 210 x 297 mm. **Key Personnel:** Jaya Balakrishnan, Gp. Advertisement Mgr.; Alistair Crighton, Publisher, phone 971 4 2824060, fax 971 4 2824436, sales@motivate.ae. **Remarks:** Accepts advertising. **URL:** http://www.motivatepublishing.com/library/default.asp?ArticleCode=ART00559. **Circ:** △29,350

51640 ■ Emaar Properties Magazine
Motivate Publishing
Al Wahaibi Bldg.
Al Garhoud Bridge Rd., Deira
PO Box 2331
Dubai, United Arab Emirates
Ph: 971 428 24060
Fax: 971 428 20428
Publisher E-mail: motivate@motivate.ae
Magazine featuring the company of Emaar Properties lifestyle. **Founded:** 2003. **Freq:** Quarterly. **Trim Size:** 240 x 320 mm. **Key Personnel:** Catherine Belbin, Editor; Ashish Limaye, Gp. Advertisement Mgr. **Remarks:** Accepts advertising. **URL:** http://www.motivatepublishing.com/packages/default.asp?categorycode=Mag&packageid=ART00516; http://www.motivatepublishing.com/library/default.asp?ArticleCode=ART00563. **Also known as:** EP. **Circ:** 18,000

51641 ■ Emirates Bride
Motivate Publishing
Al Wahaibi Bldg.
Al Garhoud Bridge Rd., Deira
PO Box 2331
Dubai, United Arab Emirates
Ph: 971 428 24060
Fax: 971 428 20428
Publisher E-mail: motivate@motivate.ae
Magazine featuring wedding information for the brides in UAE. **Freq:** Bimonthly. **Trim Size:** 225 x 300 mm. **Key Personnel:** Seema Kausar, Gp. Advertisement Mgr. **Subscription Rates:** 60 Dh individuals; 150 Dh other countries; US$16 individuals; US$41 other countries. **Remarks:** Accepts advertising. **URL:** http://www.motivatepublishing.com/library/default.asp?ArticleCode=ART00560. **Ad Rates:** BW: 2,750 Dh. **Circ:** 15,000

51642 ■ Emirates Woman
Motivate Publishing
Al Wahaibi Bldg.
Al Garhoud Bridge Rd., Deira
PO Box 2331
Dubai, United Arab Emirates
Ph: 971 428 24060
Fax: 971 428 20428
Publisher E-mail: motivate@motivate.ae
Periodical covering information related to Emirates women. **Founded:** 1981. **Freq:** Monthly. **Print Method:** Offset. **Trim Size:** 300 x 225 mm. **Key Personnel:** Faye Marchant, Editor. **Subscription Rates:** US$33 individuals; US$71 other countries. **Remarks:** Accepts advertising. **URL:** http://www.motivatepublishing.com/mediakits/article.asp?categorycode=mag&articlecode=mag.emirates. **Ad Rates:** BW: US$4,500. **Circ:** Paid △20,324

51643 ■ Gulf Business
Motivate Publishing
Al Wahaibi Bldg.
Al Garhoud Bridge Rd., Deira
PO Box 2331
Dubai, United Arab Emirates
Ph: 971 428 24060
Fax: 971 428 20428
Publisher E-mail: motivate@motivate.ae
Consumer magazine covering business in the Middle East and worldwide. **Founded:** 1996. **Freq:** Monthly. **Print Method:** Offset. **Trim Size:** 206 x 270 mm. **Key Personnel:** Vicky Kapur, Editor. **Subscription Rates:** US$95 other countries. **Remarks:** Accepts advertising. **URL:** http://www.motivatepublishing.com/packages/default.asp?categorycode=Mag&packageid=ART00505. **Ad Rates:** BW: 5,000 Dh, 4C: 4,500 Dh. **Circ:** Paid 28,608

51644 ■ Gulf Industry Magazine
Al Hilal Publishing & Marketing Group
Hilal Al Khaleej
Al Moosa Business Ctr.
Umm Hurair Rd.
PO Box 6387
Dubai, United Arab Emirates
Ph: 971 4 3371366
Fax: 971 4 3371344
Publication E-mail: editor@gulfindustryworldwide.com
Publisher E-mail: hilaldxb@emirates.net.ae
Trade journal for the building and construction industries of Saudi Arabia and the Arabian Gulf. **Freq:** Monthly. **Trim Size:** 282 x 210. **Subscription Rates:** US$112 individuals; US$224 two years. **Remarks:** Accepts advertising. **URL:** http://www.gulfindustryworldwide.com/. **Ad Rates:** BW: US$3,730, 4C: US$9,260. **Circ:** 28,808

51645 ■ Jumeirah
Motivate Publishing
Al Wahaibi Bldg.
Al Garhoud Bridge Rd., Deira
PO Box 2331
Dubai, United Arab Emirates
Ph: 971 428 24060 .
Fax: 971 428 20428
Publisher E-mail: motivate@motivate.ae
Magazine featuring Jumeirah's hotels in Dubai. **Founded:** 2001. **Freq:** Bimonthly. **Trim Size:** 225 x 300 mm. **Key Personnel:** Ashish Limaye, Publisher, phone 971 4 2824060, fax 971 4 2824436, sales@motivate.ae. **Remarks:** Accepts advertising. **URL:** http://www.motivatepublishing.com/library/default.asp?ArticleCode=ART00569. **Ad Rates:** BW: 5,250 Dh. **Circ:** 17,500

51646 ■ Khaleej Times
Galadari Printing and Publishing L.L.C.
PO Box 11243
Dubai, United Arab Emirates
Ph: 971 433 83535
Fax: 971 433 83345
Publication E-mail: kteditor@emirates.net.ae
Publisher E-mail: ktimes@emirates.net.ae
General newspaper. **Freq:** Daily. **ISSN:** 1563-5856. **Subscription Rates:** 600 Dh individuals with global insurance cover; 400 Dh individuals without global insurance cover. **Remarks:** Accepts advertising. **URL:** http://www.khaleejtimes.com/Index00.asp. **Circ:** 72,000

51647 ■ Living in the Gulf
Motivate Publishing
Al Wahaibi Bldg.
Al Garhoud Bridge Rd., Deira
PO Box 2331
Dubai, United Arab Emirates
Ph: 971 428 24060
Fax: 971 428 20428
Publisher E-mail: motivate@motivate.ae
Magazine for Spinneys customers. **Freq:** Monthly. **Key Personnel:** Mev Khan, Editor; Liam Marshall, General Mgr. **Remarks:** Accepts advertising. **URL:** http://www.motivatepublishing.com/mediakits/article.asp?categorycode=mag&articlecode=art00509. **Ad Rates:** BW: 3,200 Dh. **Circ:** Controlled ‡25,000

51648 ■ MEED - The Middle East Business Weekly
MEED Communications
Dubai Media City
PO Box 25960
Al Thuraya Tower 1
Dubai, United Arab Emirates
Ph: 971 4 3900045
Fax: 971 4 3904560
Publisher E-mail: customerservice@meed-dubai.com
Periodical covering business and economic news in the Middle East. **Subtitle:** Middle East Economic Digest. **Founded:** 1957. **Freq:** Weekly. **Key Personnel:** Richard Thompson, Editorial Dir., richard.thompson@meed-dubai.com; Colin Foreman, News Ed., colin.foreman@meed-dubai.com. **Subscription Rates:** 2,603 Dh individuals; 426 individuals print only in U.K., Europe; 450 other countries. **Remarks:** Accepts advertising. **URL:** http://www.meed.com. **Circ:** 70,000

51649 ■ Middle East MICE & Events
Motivate Publishing
Al Wahaibi Bldg.
Al Garhoud Bridge Rd., Deira

PO Box 2331
Dubai, United Arab Emirates
Ph: 971 428 24060
Fax: 971 428 20428
Publisher E-mail: motivate@motivate.ae
Magazine covering meetings, incentive travel, conferences, exhibitions, and any events. **Founded:** 2006. **Freq:** Quarterly. **Trim Size:** 210 x 297 mm. **Key Personnel:** Abraham Koshy, Gp. Ad Mgr. **Subscription Rates:** 50 Dh individuals in UAE; 75 Dh individuals in GCC; 125 Dh other countries. **Remarks:** Accepts advertising. **URL:** http://www. motivatepublishing.com/library/default.asp?ArticleCode=ART00571. **Ad Rates:** BW: 4,000 Dh. **Circ:** 33,000

51650 ■ Network Middle East
The Information & Technology Publishing Company Ltd.
PO Box 500024
Dubai, United Arab Emirates
Ph: 971 4 21008000
Fax: 971 4 21008080
Publication E-mail: nmecontact@itp.com
Publisher E-mail: info@itp.com
Magazine for network professionals. **Key Personnel:** Mark Sutton, Gp. Ed, phone 971 4 2108225, mark.sutton@itp.com; Natasha Pendleton, Publisher, phone 971 4 4392708, natasha.pendleton@itp.com. **Remarks:** Accepts advertising. **URL:** http://www.itp.com/magazine/10-Network_Middle_East. **Circ:** 8,000

51651 ■ Open Skies
Motivate Publishing
Al Wahaibi Bldg.
Al Garhoud Bridge Rd., Deira
PO Box 2331
Dubai, United Arab Emirates
Ph: 971 428 24060
Fax: 971 428 20428
Publisher E-mail: motivate@motivate.ae
Travel and leisure magazine featuring flight services of Emirates airline. **Founded:** 1985. **Freq:** Monthly. **Trim Size:** 206 x 270 mm. **Key Personnel:** Guido Duken, Editor, guido@motivate.ae; Jaya Balakrishnan, Sen. Advertisement Mgr. **Remarks:** Accepts advertising. **URL:** http://www.motivatepublishing.com/library/default.asp?ArticleCode=ART00573. **Circ:** △73,178

51652 ■ PC Magazine Middle & Near East
Dabbagh Information Technology
PO Box 60934
Dubai, United Arab Emirates
Ph: 971 4 2240700
Fax: 971 4 2240750
Publisher E-mail: info@dit.net
Information technology and business publication. **Subtitle:** The Middle East's First Guide to Technology. **URL:** http://www.pcmag-mideast.com. **Ad Rates:** BW: US$5,100. **Circ:** 4,870

51653 ■ Souk
Motivate Publishing
Al Wahaibi Bldg.
Al Garhoud Bridge Rd., Deira
PO Box 2331
Dubai, United Arab Emirates
Ph: 971 428 24060
Fax: 971 428 20428
Publisher E-mail: motivate@motivate.ae
Magazine featuring shopping, dining, and entertainment establishments in Souk. **Founded:** 2005. **Freq:** Quarterly. **Trim Size:** 210 x 210 mm. **Key Personnel:** Leah Fielding, Editor; Jaya Balakrishnan, Gp. Ad Mgr., phone 971 4 2824060, fax 971 4 2824436, sales@motivate.ae. **Remarks:** Accepts advertising. **URL:** http://www.motivatepublishing.com/library/default.asp?ArticleCode=ART00576. **Ad Rates:** 4C: US$2,500. **Circ:** 30,000

51654 ■ Time Out Dubai
The Information & Technology Publishing Company Ltd.
PO Box 500024
Dubai, United Arab Emirates
Ph: 971 4 21008000
Fax: 971 4 21008080
Publisher E-mail: info@itp.com
General interest magazine. **Freq:** Monthly. **Key Personnel:** Gareth Jones, Gp. Advisory Mgr., phone 971 4 2108000, gareth.jones@itp.com. **Remarks:** Accepts advertising. **URL:** http://www.itp.com/magazine/13-

Timeout_Dubai; http://www.timeoutdubai.com/. **Circ:** △30,072

51655 ■ tv&radio
Motivate Publishing
Al Wahaibi Bldg.
Al Garhoud Bridge Rd., Deira
PO Box 2331
Dubai, United Arab Emirates
Ph: 971 428 24060
Fax: 971 428 20428
Publisher E-mail: motivate@motivate.ae
Magazine featuring audio visual channels, audio channels and external cameras. **Founded:** 1986. **Freq:** Bimonthly. **Trim Size:** 206 x 270 mm. **Key Personnel:** Jaya Balakrishnan, Gp. Ad Mgr., phone 971 4 2052402, fax 971 4 2822801, sales@motivate.ae. **Remarks:** Accepts advertising. **URL:** http://www.motivatepublishing.com/library/default.asp?ArticleCode=ART00578. **Circ:** △43,750

51656 ■ What's On
Motivate Publishing
Al Wahaibi Bldg.
Al Garhoud Bridge Rd., Deira
PO Box 2331
Dubai, United Arab Emirates
Ph: 971 428 24060
Fax: 971 428 20428
Publisher E-mail: motivate@motivate.ae
Leisure magazine for the Gulf. **Founded:** 1979. **Freq:** Monthly. **Trim Size:** 270 x 206 mm. **Key Personnel:** Mark Evans, Editor; Dale Isaac, Gp. Advertisement mgr. **Subscription Rates:** 33 Dh individuals; US$71 other countries. **Remarks:** Accepts advertising. **URL:** http://www.motivatepublishing.com/mediakits/article.asp?categorycode=mag&articlecode=whatson. **Ad Rates:** BW: 3,750 Dh. **Circ:** △31,055

51657 ■ Windows Middle East
The Information & Technology Publishing Company Ltd.
PO Box 500024
Dubai, United Arab Emirates
Ph: 971 4 21008000
Fax: 971 4 21008080
Publication E-mail: wmecontact@itp.com
Publisher E-mail: info@itp.com
English-language IT magazine for the Middle East. **Trim Size:** 205 x 275. **Key Personnel:** Mark Sutton, Sen. Group Ed., phone 971 4 2108225, mark.sutton@itp.com; Natasha Pendleton, Publisher, phone 971 4 2108193, natasha.pendleton@itp.com; Shadia Basravi, Circulation Mgr., phone 971 4 2108000. **Remarks:** Accepts advertising. **URL:** http://www.itp.com/magazine/2-Windows_Middle_East. **Circ:** (Not Reported)

51658 ■ Young Times
Galadari Printing and Publishing L.L.C.
PO Box 11243
Dubai, United Arab Emirates
Ph: 971 433 83535
Fax: 971 433 83345
Publication E-mail: feedback@youngtimes.com
Publisher E-mail: ktimes@emirates.net.ae
Magazine covering youth interests. **Freq:** Weekly (Tues.). **Remarks:** Accepts advertising. **URL:** http://www.youngtimes.co.ae/index.html. **Circ:** (Not Reported)

51659 ■ ARN Al Arabiya Info-FM - 99.0
PO Box 502012
Dubai, United Arab Emirates
Ph: 971 43912000
Fax: 971 43912007
E-mail: info@arnonline.com
Format: Ethnic; Information; News; Contemporary Hit Radio (CHR). **Operating Hours:** Continuous. **Ad Rates:** Advertising accepted; rates available upon request. **URL:** http://www.arnonline.com.

51660 ■ ARN Al Khaleejia Info-FM - 100.9
PO Box 502012
Dubai, United Arab Emirates
Ph: 971 43912000
Fax: 971 43912007
E-mail: info@arnonline.com
Format: Ethnic; Information; Talk; Sports. **Owner:** Arabian Radio Network, at above address. **Ad Rates:** Advertising accepted; rates available upon request. **URL:** http://www.arnonline.com.

51661 ■ ARN City Info-FM - 101.6
PO Box 502012
Dubai, United Arab Emirates
Ph: 971 43912000
Fax: 971 43912007
E-mail: info@arnonline.com
Format: Ethnic; News. **Owner:** Arabian Radio Network, at above address. **Founded:** May 12, 2002. **Ad Rates:** Advertising accepted; rates available upon request. **URL:** http://www.cityfm1016.com/.

51662 ■ ARN Eye-FM - 103.8
PO Box 502255
Dubai, United Arab Emirates
Ph: 971 44354700
Format: Ethnic; News; Sports; Talk. **Owner:** Arabian Radio Network, PO Box 502012, Dubai, United Arab Emirates, 971 43912000, Fax: 971 43912007. **Operating Hours:** Continuous. **Ad Rates:** Advertising accepted; rates available upon request. **URL:** http://www.dubaieye1038.com/.

51663 ■ ARN-FM - 92
PO Box 502012
Dubai, United Arab Emirates
Ph: 971 4 3912000
Fax: 971 4 3912007
E-mail: info@arnonline.com
Format: Ethnic; News. **Operating Hours:** Continuous. **Ad Rates:** Advertising accepted; rates available upon request. **URL:** http://www.arnonline.com.

51664 ■ ARN-FM - 100.9
PO Box 502012
Dubai, United Arab Emirates
Ph: 971 4 3912000
Fax: 971 4 3912007
E-mail: info@arnonline.com
Format: Information; Ethnic; News. **Owner:** Arabian Radio Network, at above address. **Founded:** Jan. 15, 2003. **Key Personnel:** Abdullatif Al Sayegh, CEO. **Ad Rates:** Advertising accepted; rates available upon request. **URL:** http://www.arnonline.com.

51665 ■ ARN Noor Dubai-FM - 93.9
PO Box 502012
Dubai, United Arab Emirates
Ph: 971 43912000
Fax: 971 43912007
E-mail: info@arnonline.com
Format: Ethnic; News. **Owner:** Arabian Radio Network, at above address. **Ad Rates:** Advertising accepted; rates available upon request. **URL:** http://www.arnonline.com; http://www.noordubai.com/Pages/default.aspx.

51666 ■ TVMAX - 93
Khalid Bin Walid St.
Dubai, United Arab Emirates
Ph: 971 4 4059999
Fax: 971 4 3966517
E-mail: tvmax@orbit.net
URL: http://www.orbit.net.

51667 ■ TVMAX - 92
Khalid Bin Walid St.
Dubai, United Arab Emirates
Ph: 971 4 4059999
Fax: 971 4 3966517
E-mail: tvmax@orbit.net
Owner: Orbit Satellite Television and Radio Network, c/o Panther Media Group, PO Box 502211, Dubai Media City, Dubai, United Arab Emirates. **URL:** http://www.orbit.net.

51668 ■ TVMAX - 91
Khalid Bin Walid St.
Dubai, United Arab Emirates
Ph: 971 4 4059999
Fax: 971 4 3966517
E-mail: tvmax@orbit.net
Owner: Orbit Satellite Television and Radio Network, c/o Panther Media Group, PO Box 502211, Dubai Media City, Dubai, United Arab Emirates. **URL:** http://www.orbit.net.

51669 ■ TVMAX - 90
Khalid Bin Walid St.
Dubai, United Arab Emirates

Circulation: ★ = ABC; △ = BPA; ◆ = CAC; • = CCAB; ▢ = VAC; ⊕ = PO Statement; ‡ = Publisher's Report; Boldface figures = sworn; Light figures = estimated.

Gale Directory of Publications & Broadcast Media/147th Ed. | 5523

Ph: 971 4 4059999
Fax: 971 4 3966517
E-mail: tvmax@orbit.net
Owner: Orbit Satellite Television and Radio Network, c/o Panther Media Group, PO Box 502211, Dubai Media City, Dubai, United Arab Emirates. **URL:** http://www.orbit.net.

51670 ■ Virgin Radio-FM - 104.4
PO Box 502255
Dubai, United Arab Emirates
Ph: 971 4 4231000
E-mail: virgin@virginradiodubai.com
Format: Ethnic; Sports; Information. **Formerly:** ARN Awaaz-FM. **Operating Hours:** Continuous. **Ad Rates:** Advertising accepted; rates available upon request. **URL:** http://www.virginradiodubai.com/Pages/Default.aspx.

Sharjah

51671 ■ Sharjah TV - 57
PO Box 111
Sharjah, United Arab Emirates
Ph: 971 6 5611111
Fax: 971 6 5669999
Format: News; Full Service; Religious. **Owner:** Sharjah TV, at above address. **Founded:** Feb. 11, 1989. **Operating Hours:** 1 p.m.-8 p.m. **URL:** http://www.sdci.gov.ae/english/rtv.html.

51672 ■ Sharjah TV - 28
PO Box 111
Sharjah, United Arab Emirates
Ph: 971 6 5611111
Fax: 971 6 5669999
Format: News; Full Service; Religious. **Owner:** Sharjah TV, at above address. **Founded:** Feb. 11, 1989. **Operating Hours:** 1 p.m.-8 p.m. **URL:** http://www.sdci.gov.ae/english/rtv.html.

51673 ■ Sharjah TV - 54
PO Box 111
Sharjah, United Arab Emirates
Ph: 971 6 5611111
Fax: 971 6 5669999
Owner: Sharjah TV, at above address. **Founded:** Feb. 11, 1989. **Operating Hours:** 1 p.m.-8 p.m. **URL:** http://www.sdci.gov.ae/english/rtv.html.

51674 ■ Sharjah TV - 22
PO Box 111
Sharjah, United Arab Emirates
Ph: 971 6 5611111
Fax: 971 6 5669999
Owner: Sharjah TV, at above address. **Founded:** Feb. 11, 1989. **Operating Hours:** 1 p.m.-8 p.m. **URL:** http://www.sdci.gov.ae/english/rtv.html.

Aberdeen

51675 ■ Current Diabetes Reviews
Bentham Science Publishers Ltd.
c/o Norman E. Cameron, Ed.-in-Ch.
Dept. of Biomedical Sciences
University of Aberdeen
Aberdeen AB24 3FX, United Kingdom
Publisher E-mail: subscriptions@bentham.org
Journal publishing frontier reviews on all the latest advances on diabetes and its related areas, e.g. pharmacology, pathogenesis, complications, epidemiology, clinical care, and therapy. **Freq:** Quarterly. **Key Personnel:** Norman E. Cameron, Editor-in-Chief; A. Ajayi, Editorial Advisory Board; L. Baier, Editorial Advisory Board. **ISSN:** 1573-3998. **Subscription Rates:** US$960 individuals corporate, print; US$960 individuals corporate, online; US$190 individuals print; US$460 individuals academic, print; US$460 individuals academic, online; US$1,150 individuals corporate, print & online; US$190 individuals print only. **Remarks:** Accepts advertising. **URL:** http://www.bentham.org/cdr/index.htm. **Circ:** (Not Reported)

51676 ■ Gaudie
Aberdeen University Students' Association
Butchart Centre
University Rd.
Aberdeen AB24 3UT, United Kingdom
Ph: 44 122 4272965
Publisher E-mail: ausa@abdn.ac.uk
College newspaper. **Founded:** 1934. **Freq:** Weekly. **Key Personnel:** Jenny Longden, Editor, gaudie.editor@abdn.ac.uk; Neil Murchison, Editor, gaudie.editor@abdn.ac.uk. **Subscription Rates:** Free. **Remarks:** Accepts advertising. **URL:** http://www.ausa.org.uk/9-99. **Ad Rates:** BW: 400, 4C: 660. **Circ:** Non-paid 4,000

51677 ■ Good Time Guide
Happy Publishing Limited
27 York Pl.
Aberdeen AB11 4DH, United Kingdom
Ph: 44 1224 594659
Publisher E-mail: info@happypublishing.co.uk
Entertainment guide magazine. **Freq:** Annual. **Key Personnel:** Danny Cowie, Mng. Dir. **Remarks:** Accepts advertising. **URL:** http://www.goodtimeguide.co.uk/; http://www.happypublishing.co.uk/goodtimeguide_magazine.htm. **Circ:** (Not Reported)

51678 ■ Journal of Private International Law
Hart Publishing Ltd.
c/o Prof. Paul Beaumont, Gen. Ed.
Taylor Bldg.
School of Law
University of Aberdeen
Aberdeen AB24 3UB, United Kingdom
Publisher E-mail: mail@hartpub.co.uk
Peer-reviewed Journal covering all aspects of private international law. **Founded:** 2005. **Freq:** 3/yr. **Key Personnel:** Prof. Paul Beaumont, Gen. Ed., p.beaumont@abdn.ac.uk; Prof. Jonathan Harris, Gen. Ed., j.m.harris.law@bham.ac.uk; Mary Keyes, Review Ed., m.keyes@griffith.edu.au. **ISSN:** 1744-1048. **Subscription Rates:** 150 individuals standard, United Kingdom and Europe;

160 other countries standard; 80 individuals reduced, United Kingdom and Europe; 90 other countries reduced; 135 individuals online, standard; 72 individuals online. **Remarks:** Accepts advertising. **URL:** http://www.hartjournals.co.uk/JPrivIntL/. **Circ:** (Not Reported)

51679 ■ Lady Biker Magazine
Happy Publishing Limited
27 York Pl.
Aberdeen AB11 4DH, United Kingdom
Ph: 44 1224 594659
Publication E-mail: info@ladybikermagazine.com
Publisher E-mail: info@happypublishing.co.uk
Motorcycle magazine for ladies. **Freq:** Semiannual. **Key Personnel:** Zoe Grice, Creative Dir., zoe@ladybikermagazine.com; Danny Cowie, Mng. Dir. **Remarks:** Accepts advertising. **URL:** http://www.ladybikermagazine.com/; http://www.happypublishing.co.uk/ladybiker_magazine.htm. **Circ:** (Not Reported)

51680 ■ Star Flyer Magazine
Happy Publishing Limited
27 York Pl.
Aberdeen AB11 4DH, United Kingdom
Ph: 44 1224 594659
Publisher E-mail: info@happypublishing.co.uk
Inflight magazine of City Star Airlines featuring news and entertainment. **Freq:** Quarterly. **Key Personnel:** Danny Cowie, Mng. Dir. **Remarks:** Accepts advertising. **URL:** http://www.happypublishing.co.uk/starflyer_magazine.htm. **Circ:** (Not Reported)

51681 ■ Me-FM - 87.7
15-17 Belmont St., 2nd-3rd Fl.
Aberdeen AB10 1JR, United Kingdom
Ph: 44 1224 641931
Format: Hip Hop; Album-Oriented Rock (AOR). **Key Personnel:** Daniel Christian, Contact, daniel@multiethnic.co.uk. **URL:** http://mefm.web0.co.uk/.

51682 ■ Northsound One-FM - 96.9
Abbotswell Rd.
W Tullos
Aberdeen AB12 3AJ, United Kingdom
Ph: 44 12 24400969
Format: Ethnic; Contemporary Hit Radio (CHR); Sports. **Key Personnel:** Luke McCullough, Mng. Dir., luke.mccullough@northsound.co.uk; Chris Thomson, Program Dir., chris.thomson@northsound.co.uk. **Ad Rates:** Advertising accepted; rates available upon request. **URL:** http://www.northsound1.com.

51683 ■ Northsound Two-AM - 1035
Abbotswell Rd.
Aberdeen AB12 3AJ, United Kingdom
Ph: 44 1224 337000
Fax: 44 1224 400003
Format: Adult Contemporary; Top 40; News; Sports. **Operating Hours:** Continuous. **Ad Rates:** Advertising accepted; rates available upon request. **URL:** http://www.northsound2.com.

51684 ■ Original-FM - 106.8
Original House
Craigshaw Rd.
West Tullos
Aberdeen AB12 3AR, United Kingdom

Ph: 44 1224 293800
E-mail: studio@originalfm.com
Format: Adult Album Alternative. **URL:** http://www.originalfm.com/.

51685 ■ Original-FM - 106.3
Original House
Craigshaw Rd.
West Tullos
Aberdeen AB12 3AR, United Kingdom
Ph: 44 1224 293800
E-mail: studio@originalfm.com
Format: Adult Album Alternative. **URL:** http://www.originalfm.com/.

Aberfeldy

51686 ■ FlyFishing and FlyTying
Rolling River Publications Ltd.
The Locus Ctr.
The Square
Perthshire
Aberfeldy PH15 2DD, United Kingdom
Ph: 44 1887 829868
Fax: 44 1887 829856
Magazine featuring articles about fly-fishing. **Founded:** 1990. **Freq:** Monthly 11/yr. **Key Personnel:** Mark Bowler, Publishing Ed., markb.ffft@btinternet.com. **Subscription Rates:** 36 individuals. **URL:** http://www.flyfishing-and-flytying.co.uk/.

Abergavenny

51687 ■ Descent
Wild Places Publishing
PO Box 100
Abergavenny NP7 9WY, United Kingdom
Publication E-mail: descent@wildplaces.co.uk
Consumer magazine covering sport caving and mine exploration. **Subtitle:** The Magazine of Underground Exploration. **Founded:** 1969. **Freq:** Bimonthly. **Print Method:** Offset litho. **Trim Size:** A4. **Cols./Page:** 4. **Key Personnel:** Chris Howes, Editor. **ISSN:** 0046-0036. **Subscription Rates:** 27 individuals; 52 two years; 78 individuals three years. **Remarks:** Accepts advertising. **URL:** http://www.wildplaces.co.uk/descent.html. **Circ:** (Not Reported)

Aberystwyth

51688 ■ Gender, Place and Culture
Routledge
Taylor & Francis Group Ltd.
c/o Deborah Dixon, Ed.
Institute of Geography & Earth Sciences
University of Wales-Aberystwyth
Aberystwyth SY23 3DB, United Kingdom
Publisher E-mail: webmaster.books@tandf.co.uk
Peer-reviewed journal discussing human geography and associated disciplines on theoretically-informed research concerned with gender issues. **Subtitle:** A Journal of Feminist Geography. **Freq:** Bimonthly. **Key Personnel:** Brenda Yeoh, Editor-in-Chief, geoysa@nus.edu.sg; Linda Peake, Editorial Board; Deborah Dixon, Editor, dxd@aber.ac.uk; Robyn Longhurst, Editor, robynl@

Circulation: ★ = ABC; △ = BPA; ♦ = CAC; • = CCAB; ❑ = VAC; ⊕ = PO Statement; ‡ = Publisher's Report; Boldface figures = sworn; Light figures = estimated.

Gale Directory of Publications & Broadcast Media/147th Ed. 5525

waikato.ac.nz; Claire Dwyer, Editorial Board; Patricia Noxolo, Book Review Ed., silvey@geog.utoronto.ca. **ISSN:** 0966-369X. **Subscription Rates:** US$354 individuals; US$1,083 institutions online only; US$1,140 institutions print & online; 214 individuals; 656 institutions online only; 690 institutions print & online; EUR908 institutions print and online; EUR863 institutions online only; EUR282 individuals. **Remarks:** Advertising accepted; rates available upon request. **URL:** http://www.tandf.co.uk/journals/journal.asp?issn=0966-369x&linktype=1. **Circ:** (Not Reported)

51689 ■ Y Ddolen
CILIP Cymru/Wales
Dept. of Information Studies
Llanbadarn Fawr
Aberystwyth SY23 3AS, United Kingdom
Ph: 44 1970 622174
Fax: 44 1970 622190
Publisher E-mail: cilip-wales@aber.ac.uk
Professional journal covering libraries and librarianship in Wales. **Subtitle:** Supplement to Update. **Freq:** 3/yr. **Trim Size:** A4. **ISSN:** 0261-3557. **Subscription Rates:** Free to qualified subscribers. **Remarks:** Accepts advertising. **URL:** http://www.dil.aber.ac.uk/cilip_w/English/Publications/index.htm. **Circ:** Non-paid ‡1,500

51690 ■ Radio Ceredigion-FM - 96.6
Yr Hen Ysgol Gymraeg
Fordd Alecsandra
Ceredigion
Aberystwyth SY23 1LF, United Kingdom
Ph: 44 1970 627999
Fax: 44 1970 627206
E-mail: admin@ceredigionfm.co.uk
Format: Eclectic; Public Radio; Agricultural; Information. **Operating Hours:** Continuous. **URL:** http://www.radioceredigion.net.

51691 ■ Radio Ceredigion-FM - 97.4
7 Aberystwyth Science Pk.
Ceredigion
Aberystwyth SY23 3AH, United Kingdom
Ph: 44 1970 229113
Fax: 44 1970 626992
E-mail: studio@radioceredigion.co.uk
Format: Ethnic. **URL:** http://www.radioceredigion.net/.

51692 ■ Radio Ceredigion-FM - 103.3
7 Aberystwyth Science Pk.
Ceredigion
Aberystwyth SY23 3AH, United Kingdom
Ph: 44 1970 229113
Fax: 44 1970 626992
E-mail: studio@radioceredigion.co.uk
Format: Ethnic. **URL:** http://www.radioceredigion.net/.

Abingdon

51693 ■ Accounting, Business & Financial History
Routledge
Taylor & Francis Group Ltd.
2 Park Sq.
Milton Pk.
Abingdon OX14 4RN, United Kingdom
Ph: 44 20 70176000
Fax: 44 20 70176699
Publisher E-mail: webmaster.books@tandf.co.uk
Peer-reviewed journal covering accounting practices, business and financial trends in the past. **Freq:** 3/yr. **Key Personnel:** Trevor Boyns, Editor, boyns@cardiff.ac.uk; John Richard Edwards, Editor, edwardsjr@cardiff.ac.uk; Geoffrey G. Jones, Editorial Advisor; Malcolm Anderson, Book Review Ed.; Josephine Maltby, Editorial Advisor; Richard Fleischman, Editorial Advisor; Roy A. Chandler, Editorial Advisor; Salvador Carmona, Editorial Advisor; Junichi Chiba, Editorial Advisor. **ISSN:** 0958-5206. **Subscription Rates:** US$207 individuals print only; US$574 individuals online only; US$604 individuals print & online; 364 institutions print & online; 346 institutions online; 122 individuals; EUR480 institutions print and online; EUR456 institutions online only; EUR165 individuals. **Remarks:** Advertising accepted; rates available upon request. **URL:** http://www.tandf.co.uk/journals/titles/09585206.asp. **Circ:** (Not Reported)

51694 ■ Acta Dermato-Venereologica
Taylor & Francis Ltd.
2 & 4 Park Sq.
Milton Pk.
Abingdon OX14 4RN, United Kingdom

Ph: 44 20 70176000
Fax: 44 20 70176336
Journal for clinical and experimental research in the field of dermatology and venereology, publishing manuscripts in English dealing with new observations on basic dermatological and venereological research, as well as clinical investigations, covering atopic dermatitis and contact allergy, skin immunology and lymphoma, psoriasis and genodermatoses, skin barrier and epidermal differentiation, sexually transmitted diseases and skin cancer and pigmentation. **Founded:** 1920. **Freq:** Bimonthly. **Key Personnel:** Prof. Anders Vahlquist, Editor-in-Chief; Torbjorn Egelrud, Editor; Jonathan Rees, Section Ed. **ISSN:** 0001-5555. **Subscription Rates:** EUR205 individuals paper and online; EUR120 individuals online; EUR462 institutions paper and online; EUR390 institutions online. **Remarks:** Advertising accepted; rates available upon request. **URL:** http://www.medicaljournals.se/adv/. **Circ:** (Not Reported)

51695 ■ Acta Radiologica
Taylor & Francis Ltd.
2 & 4 Park Sq.
Milton Pk.
Abingdon OX14 4RN, United Kingdom
Ph: 44 20 70176000
Fax: 44 20 70176336
Journal aiming for the prompt publication of original research articles on diagnostic and interventional radiology, clinical radiology, experimental investigations in animals, and all other research related to imaging procedures and providing complete updates on all radiological specialties and technical utilities, as well as physiology and physics related to imaging, including ultrasonography, computed tomography, radionuclide and magnetic resonance imaging. **Freq:** 10/yr. **Key Personnel:** Prof. Arnulf Skjennald, Editor-in-Chief; Andreas Abildgaard, Editor; Finn Rasmussen, Editor. **ISSN:** 0284-1851. **Subscription Rates:** 505 institutions; US$840 institutions; EUR670 institutions. **Remarks:** Accepts advertising. **URL:** http://www.informaworld.com/smpp/title~content=t713394674; http://informahealthcare.com/ard. **Circ:** (Not Reported)

51696 ■ Action Learning
Routledge
Taylor & Francis Group Ltd.
2 Park Sq.
Milton Pk.
Abingdon OX14 4RN, United Kingdom
Ph: 44 20 70176000
Fax: 44 20 70176699
Publisher E-mail: webmaster.books@tandf.co.uk
Peer-reviewed journal publishing articles on action learning that widens understanding of action learning and research in professional and organizational settings. **Subtitle:** Research and Practice. **Freq:** 3/yr. **Key Personnel:** Mike Pedler, Editor, mikepedler@phonecoop.coop; Joe Raelin, Assoc. Ed.; Kiran Trehan, Editor, k.trehan@lancaster.ac.uk. **ISSN:** 1476-7333. **Subscription Rates:** US$147 individuals print only; US$326 institutions online only; US$344 institutions print & online; 89 individuals print only; 196 institutions online; 206 institutions print & online; EUR274 institutions print and online; EUR261 institutions online only; EUR116 individuals. **Remarks:** Advertising accepted; rates available upon request. **URL:** http://www.tandf.co.uk/journals/titles/14767333.asp. **Circ:** (Not Reported)

51697 ■ Acute Cardiac Care
Taylor & Francis Ltd.
2 & 4 Park Sq.
Milton Pk.
Abingdon OX14 4RN, United Kingdom
Ph: 44 20 70176000
Fax: 44 20 70176336
Journal of interest and practical value to all those working in interventional cardiology, covering the frontiers of conventional and new device angioplasty modalities including: balloon angioplasty, stenting, atherectomy techniques, micro-technology innovations, imaging technologies, new drug therapies for restenosis, coronary physiology, and endothelial function. **Freq:** Quarterly. **Key Personnel:** Rafael Beyar, Ch. Ed.; Gad Keren, Section Ed.; F. Apple, Editorial Board; Hideo Tamai, Assoc. Ed.; G. Ambrosio, Editorial Board; Gerasimos Filippatos, Assoc. Ed.; A. Abzaid, Editorial Board; J. Alpert, Editorial Board; Mihai Gheorghiade, Assoc. Ed.; A. Battler, Editorial Board; A. Colombo, Editorial Board; M. Claeys, Editorial Board. **ISSN:** 1748-2941. **Subscription Rates:** 450 institutions; US$745 institutions; EUR595

institutions. **Remarks:** Accepts advertising. **URL:** http://informahealthcare.com/acc. **Formerly:** International Journal of Cardiovascular Interventions. **Circ:** (Not Reported)

51698 ■ Adelphi Series
Routledge
Taylor & Francis Group Ltd.
2 Park Sq.
Milton Pk.
Abingdon OX14 4RN, United Kingdom
Ph: 44 20 70176000
Fax: 44 20 70176699
Publisher E-mail: webmaster.books@tandf.co.uk
Journal providing rigorous analysis of strategic and defense topics for politicians and diplomats, as well as academic researchers, foreign-affairs analysts, defense commentators and journalists, including both thematic studies and papers on specific national and regional security problems. **Freq:** 8/yr. **Key Personnel:** Dr. Tim Huxley, Editor; Katharine Fletcher, Asst. Ed. **ISSN:** 1944-5571. **Subscription Rates:** US$391 individuals; US$763 institutions online; US$803 institutions print + online; 230 individuals; 433 institutions online; 457 institutions print + online; EUR673 institutions print and online; EUR640 institutions online only; EUR312 individuals. **URL:** http://www.tandf.co.uk/journals/titles/0567932x.asp. **Formerly:** Adelphi Papers (2009).

51699 ■ African Studies
Routledge
Taylor & Francis Group Ltd.
2 Park Sq.
Milton Pk.
Abingdon OX14 4RN, United Kingdom
Ph: 44 20 70176000
Fax: 44 20 70176699
Publisher E-mail: webmaster.books@tandf.co.uk
Peer-reviewed journal covering African studies. **Founded:** 1921. **Freq:** 3/yr. **Key Personnel:** Dr. Noor Nieftagodien, Editorial Committee, phone 27 11 7174281, fax 27 11 7174289, history-workshop@social.wits.ac.za; Prof. Shireen Hassim, Editorial Committee, phone 27 11 7174364, fax 27 11 4037482, hassims@social.wits.ac.za; Prof. Clive Glaser, Editorial Committee, phone 27 11 7174313, fax 27 11 7174329, glaserc@social.wits.ac.za; Prof. Charles Mather, Editorial Committee, phone 27 11 7176503, fax 27 11 4037281, matherc@geoarc.wits.ac.za. **ISSN:** 0002-0184. **Subscription Rates:** 336 institutions print + online; US$557 institutions print + online; EUR443 institutions print + online; 320 institutions online only; US$529 institutions online only; EUR421 institutions online only; 80 individuals; US$139 individuals; EUR111 individuals. **Remarks:** Accepts advertising. **URL:** http://www.tandf.co.uk/journals/titles/00020184.asp. **Former name:** Bantu Studies. **Circ:** (Not Reported)

51700 ■ Aging and Mental Health
Routledge
Taylor & Francis Group Ltd.
2 Park Sq.
Milton Pk.
Abingdon OX14 4RN, United Kingdom
Ph: 44 20 70176000
Fax: 44 20 70176699
Publisher E-mail: webmaster.books@tandf.co.uk
Peer-reviewed journal providing a forum for the rapidly expanding field which investigates the relationship between the aging process and mental health, addressing the mental changes associated with normal and abnormal or pathological aging, as well as the psychological and psychiatric problems of the aging population. **Freq:** 6/yr. **Key Personnel:** Prof. Dan G. Blazer, Assoc. Ed.; Prof. Martin W. Orrell, Editor; Donna Fick, Editorial Board; Louis Burgio, Editorial Board; Aartjan T.F. Beekman, Editorial Board; Knut Engedal, Editorial Board; Steven Zarit, Editor; Bob Woods, Assoc. Ed.; Bob Knight, Assoc. Ed. **ISSN:** 1360-7863. **Subscription Rates:** 1,226 institutions print and online; 1,165 institutions online; 309 individuals print only; US$2,017 institutions print and online; US$1,916 institutions online; US$510 individuals print only; EUR1,606 institutions print and online; EUR1,526 institutions online only; EUR406 individuals. **Remarks:** Accepts advertising. **URL:** http://www.tandf.co.uk/journals/titles/13607863.asp. **Circ:** (Not Reported)

51701 ■ AIDS Care
Routledge
Taylor & Francis Group Ltd.
2 Park Sq.

Milton Pk.
Abingdon OX14 4RN, United Kingdom
Ph: 44 20 70176000
Fax: 44 20 70176699
Publisher E-mail: webmaster.books@tandf.co.uk
Peer-reviewed journal focusing on research and reports from the many complementary disciplines involved in the HIV/AIDS field. **Freq:** 12/yr. **Key Personnel:** Jonathan Elford, International Editorial Board; Lorraine Sherr, Exec. Ed.; Richard Harding, Editorial Committee; Graham Hart, International Editorial Board; Michael Ross, Editorial Board. **ISSN:** 0954-0121. **Subscription Rates:** 1,684 institutions print + online; 1,600 institutions online; 432 individuals print only; US$2,793 institutions print + online; US$2,654 institutions online; US$715 individuals print only; US$40 individuals developing country; EUR2,226 institutions print and online; EUR2,115 institutions online only; EUR569 individuals. **Remarks:** Accepts advertising. **URL:** http://www.tandf.co.uk/journals/titles/09540121.asp. **Circ:** (Not Reported)

51702 ■ American Journal on Addictions
Taylor & Francis Ltd.
2 & 4 Park Sq.
Milton Pk.
Abingdon OX14 4RN, United Kingdom
Ph: 44 20 70176000
Fax: 44 20 70176336
Peer-reviewed journal encouraging research on the etiology, prevention, identification, and treatment of substance abuse and covering a wide variety of topics ranging from codependence to genetics, epidemiology to dual diagnostics, etiology to neuroscience. **Freq:** 6/yr. **Key Personnel:** Sheldon I. Miller, MD, Editor-in-Chief; Martha Bostick, Asst. Mng. Ed.; Ilana B. Crome, MD, International Ed.; Thomas R. Kosten, MD, Sen. Assoc. Ed.; Joseph J. Westermeyer, PhD, Editorial Board; Kathleen T. Brady, PhD, Editorial Board; Richard N. Rosenthal, MD, Editorial Board; Henry R. Kranzler, MD, Assoc. Ed.; Eric Strain, MD, Editorial Board. **ISSN:** 1055-0496. **Remarks:** Accepts advertising. **URL:** http://informahealthcare.com/loi/aja. **Circ:** (Not Reported)

51703 ■ Amyloid
Taylor & Francis Ltd.
2 & 4 Park Sq.
Milton Pk.
Abingdon OX14 4RN, United Kingdom
Ph: 44 20 70176000
Fax: 44 20 70176336
Peer-reviewed journal devoted entirely to amyloid research and clinical developments throughout the world. **Subtitle:** The Journal of Protein Folding Disorders. **Freq:** Quarterly. **Key Personnel:** Prof. Per Westermark, Editor-in-Chief, per.westermark@genpat.uu.se; Martha Skinner, MD, Assoc. Ed.; Carmela R. Abraham, PhD, Assoc. Ed.; Jean D. Sipe, PhD, Assoc. Ed. **ISSN:** 1350-6129. **Subscription Rates:** 640 institutions; US$1,210 institutions; EUR970 institutions. **Remarks:** Accepts advertising. **URL:** http://informahealthcare.com/loi/amy. **Circ:** (Not Reported)

51704 ■ Anthropological Forum
Routledge
Taylor & Francis Group Ltd.
2 Park Sq.
Milton Pk.
Abingdon OX14 4RN, United Kingdom
Ph: 44 20 70176000
Fax: 44 20 70176699
Publisher E-mail: webmaster.books@tandf.co.uk
Peer-reviewed journal focusing on social anthropology and comparative sociology. **Founded:** 1963. **Freq:** 3/yr. **Print Method:** Offset. **Trim Size:** 8 1/8 x 10 7/8. **Cols./Page:** 2. **Col. Width:** 13.5 picas. **Col. Depth:** 127 agate lines. **Key Personnel:** Greg Acciaioli, Editorial Board; Martin Forsey, Editorial Board; Robert Tonkinson, Editor; Michael Pinches, Editorial Board; David Trigger, Applied Forum Ed.; Victoria Burbank, Editorial Board; John Stanton, Editorial Board; Richard Davis, Editorial Board; Gillian Hutcherson, Book Review Ed. **ISSN:** 0066-4677. **Subscription Rates:** EUR305 institutions print + online; US$509 institutions print + online; $A 432 institutions print + online; EUR386 institutions online; US$484 institutions online; $A 410 institutions online; EUR120 individuals; US$150 individuals; $A 161 individuals. **URL:** http://www.tandf.co.uk/journals/titles/00664677.asp.

51705 ■ Applied Economics
Routledge
Taylor & Francis Group Ltd.
2 Park Sq.
Milton Pk.
Abingdon OX14 4RN, United Kingdom
Ph: 44 20 70176000
Fax: 44 20 70176699
Publisher E-mail: webmaster.books@tandf.co.uk
Peer-reviewed journal covering economics. **Freq:** 27/yr. **Trim Size:** 216 x 138. **Key Personnel:** Mark P. Taylor, Editor, appliedeconomics@warwick.ac.uk; Jerry Hausman, Advisory Ed.; Burton G. Malkiel, Advisory Ed.; William J. Baumol, Advisory Ed.; Richard E. Quandt, Advisory Ed.; Ron Smith, Advisory Ed. **ISSN:** 0003-6846. **Subscription Rates:** 5,755 institutions print and online; 5,467 institutions online; US$9,498 institutions print and online; US$9,023 institutions online. **Remarks:** Accepts advertising on request. **URL:** http://www.tandf.co.uk/journals/journal.asp?issn=0003-6846&linktype=rates. **Circ:** (Not Reported)

51706 ■ Asia Pacific Journal of Education
Routledge
Taylor & Francis Group Ltd.
2 Park Sq.
Milton Pk.
Abingdon OX14 4RN, United Kingdom
Ph: 44 20 70176000
Fax: 44 20 70176699
Publisher E-mail: webmaster.books@tandf.co.uk
Peer-reviewed journal focusing on major shifts in educational policy and governance, curriculum and pedagogy, and in the everyday lives and practices of students and teachers in the Asia-Pacific Rim. **Freq:** 4/yr. **Key Personnel:** David Hogan, Exec. Ed.; Jason Tan, Exec. Ed.; Philip Altbach, International Advisory Board; Mark Bray, International Advisory Board; Rui Yang, International Advisory Board; Dennis Kwek, Review Ed.; Robin Alexander, International Advisory Board; Ryuko Kubota, International Advisory Board; Yoonmi Lee, International Advisory Board. **ISSN:** 0218-8791. **Subscription Rates:** US$150 individuals print; US$712 institutions online only; US$749 institutions print & online; 495 institutions print & online; 470 institutions online; 97 individuals print; $A 1,319 institutions print & online; $A 1,252 institutions online; $A 266 individuals. **Remarks:** Accepts advertising. **URL:** http://www.tandf.co.uk/journals/titles/02188791.asp. **Circ:** (Not Reported)

51707 ■ Asian Philosophy
Routledge
Taylor & Francis Group Ltd.
2 Park Sq.
Milton Pk.
Abingdon OX14 4RN, United Kingdom
Ph: 44 20 70176000
Fax: 44 20 70176699
Publisher E-mail: webmaster.books@tandf.co.uk
Peer-reviewed journal covering philosophy and religion. **Freq:** 4/yr. **Key Personnel:** Dr. Brian Carr, Editor; Prof. Indira Mahalingam Carr, Editor; L.E. Goodman, Assoc. Ed.; F.J. Hoofman, Assoc. Ed.; Whalen Lai, Assoc. Ed. **ISSN:** 0955-2367. **Subscription Rates:** US$920 institutions print + online; US$874 institutions online only; US$258 individuals; 556 institutions print and online; 528 institutions online; 154 individuals. **URL:** http://www.tandf.co.uk/journals/titles/09552367.asp.

51708 ■ Asian Population Studies
Routledge
Taylor & Francis Group Ltd.
2 Park Sq.
Milton Pk.
Abingdon OX14 4RN, United Kingdom
Ph: 44 20 70176000
Fax: 44 20 70176699
Publisher E-mail: webmaster.books@tandf.co.uk
Peer-reviewed journal focusing exclusively on population issues in Asia including topics on all branches of population studies ranging from population dynamics such as the analysis of fertility, mortality and migration (from both technical and humanistic perspectives) to the consequences of population change from a variety of demographic perspectives. **Freq:** 3/yr. **Key Personnel:** Prof. Gavin Jones, Editor; Dr. Alaka Basu, International Advisory Board; Prof. Stephen Castles, International Advisory Board; Dr. Angelique Chan, Co-Ed.; Prof. Wolf-gang Lutz, Co-Ed.; Prof. Vipan Prachuabmoh, Co-Ed. **ISSN:** 1744-1730. **Subscription Rates:** US$86 individuals; US$305 institutions online only; US$321 institutions print & online; 181 institutions print & online; 172 institutions online; 49 individuals; EUR256 institutions print and online; EUR243 institutions online only; EUR68 individuals. **Remarks:** Accepts advertising. **URL:** http://www.tandf.co.uk/journals/titles/17441730.asp. **Circ:** (Not Reported)

51709 ■ Augmentative & Alternative Communication
Taylor & Francis Ltd.
2 & 4 Park Sq.
Milton Pk.
Abingdon OX14 4RN, United Kingdom
Ph: 44 20 70176000
Fax: 44 20 70176336
Journal publishing original articles with direct application to people with complex communication needs for whom augmentative and alternative communication techniques and systems may be appropriate. **Freq:** Quarterly. **Key Personnel:** Ann Sutton, Editor, ann.sutton@uottawa.ca; Erna Alant, Assoc. Ed.; Ann Beck, Assoc. Ed. **ISSN:** 0743-4618. **Subscription Rates:** 320 institutions print and online; US$480 institutions online only; EUR385 institutions print and online. **Remarks:** Accepts advertising. **URL:** http://www.informaworld.com/smpp/title~content=t713692248~db=all. **Circ:** (Not Reported)

51710 ■ Australasian Journal of Philosophy
Routledge
Taylor & Francis Group Ltd.
2 Park Sq.
Milton Pk.
Abingdon OX14 4RN, United Kingdom
Ph: 44 20 70176000
Fax: 44 20 70176699
Publisher E-mail: webmaster.books@tandf.co.uk
Peer-reviewed journal covering philosophy. **Founded:** 1923. **Freq:** 4/yr. **Trim Size:** 15.7 x 23.2 cm. **Key Personnel:** Stewart Candlish, Editor; David Braddon-Mitchell, Editorial Board; Chris Daly, Assoc. Ed.; Julian Dodd, Assoc. Ed.; David Liggins, Assoc. Ed. **ISSN:** 0004-8402. **Subscription Rates:** US$48 members AAP full/associate; US$45 members AAP full/associate, online only; US$24 members AAP student/senior; US$22 members AAP student/senior, online only; US$216 institutions print + online; 130 institutions print + online. **Remarks:** Advertising accepted; rates available upon request. **URL:** http://www.tandf.co.uk/journals/journal.asp?issn=0004-8402&linktype=1. **Circ:** Combined 1,200

51711 ■ Australian Feminist Studies
Routledge
Taylor & Francis Group Ltd.
2 Park Sq.
Milton Pk.
Abingdon OX14 4RN, United Kingdom
Ph: 44 20 70176000
Fax: 44 20 70176699
Publisher E-mail: webmaster.books@tandf.co.uk
Peer-reviewed journal covering feminist research and teaching. **Founded:** 1985. **Freq:** 4/yr. **Key Personnel:** Prof. Susan Magarey, Founding Ed.; Mary Spongberg, Editor-in-Chief, mspongbe@humn.mq.edu.au; Nicole Moore, Review Ed., nicole.moore@humn.mq.edu.au. **ISSN:** 0816-4649. **Subscription Rates:** US$209 individuals; US$796 institutions online; US$837 institutions print and online; 503 institutions print and online; $A 673 institutions print and online; EUR668 institutions print and online; 478 institutions online only; $A 640 institutions online only; EUR634 institutions online only; 126 individuals. **Remarks:** Accepts advertising. **URL:** http://www.tandf.co.uk/journals/titles/08164649.asp. **Circ:** (Not Reported)

51712 ■ Australian Geographer
Routledge
Taylor & Francis Group Ltd.
2 Park Sq.
Milton Pk.
Abingdon OX14 4RN, United Kingdom
Ph: 44 20 70176000
Fax: 44 20 70176699
Publisher E-mail: webmaster.books@tandf.co.uk
Peer-reviewed journal covering all aspects of geography, both human and physical. **Founded:** 1928. **Freq:** 4/yr. **Key Personnel:** Dr. Melissa Neave, Assoc. Ed.; Prof. Paul Bishop, Editorial Board; Prof. John Connell, Editor; Prof. Ruth Fincher, Editorial Board; Prof. Ron Johnston, Editorial Board; Prof. Edward Hickin, Editorial Board.

Circulation: ★ = ABC; △ = BPA; ◆ = CAC; • = CCAB; ❑ = VAC; ⊕ = PO Statement; ‡ = Publisher's Report; Boldface figures = sworn; Light figures = estimated.

Gale Directory of Publications & Broadcast Media/147th Ed.

5527

ISSN: 0004-9182. **Subscription Rates:** 343 institutions print + online; 326 institutions online; 175 individuals; US$567 institutions print + online; US$539 institutions online; US$295 individuals; $A 669 institutions print + online; $A 636 institutions online; $A 304 individuals. **Remarks:** Accepts advertising. **URL:** http://www.tandf.co.uk/journals/titles/00049182.asp. **Circ:** (Not Reported)

51713 ■ Australian Historical Studies
Routledge
Taylor & Francis Group Ltd.
2 Park Sq.
Milton Pk.
Abingdon OX14 4RN, United Kingdom
Ph: 44 20 70176000
Fax: 44 20 70176336
Publisher E-mail: webmaster.books@tandf.co.uk
Peer-reviewed journal covering Australian, New Zealand and Pacific regional issues. **Subtitle:** A Journal of Australian History. **Founded:** 1940. **Freq:** 3/yr. **Key Personnel:** Joy Damousi, Ch.; Andrew Brown-May, Business Mgr.; Prof. Richard Broome, Editor; Tiffany Shellam, Review Ed.; Christina Twomey, Editorial Board; Kate Darian-Smith, Review Ed.; Shurlee Swain, Editorial Board. **ISSN:** 1031-461X. **Subscription Rates:** US$86 individuals; $A 108 individuals; US$41 students unwaged; 145 institutions print and online; US$284 institutions print and online; $A 214 institutions print and online; EUR225 institutions print and online; 138 institutions online only; US$269 institutions online only; $A 204 institutions online only. **URL:** http://www.tandf.co.uk/journals/titles/1031461X.asp.

51714 ■ Australian Journal of International Affairs
Routledge
Taylor & Francis Group Ltd.
2 Park Sq.
Milton Pk.
Abingdon OX14 4RN, United Kingdom
Ph: 44 20 70176000
Fax: 44 20 70176699
Publisher E-mail: webmaster.books@tandf.co.uk
Peer-reviewed journal covering international affairs. **Founded:** 1946. **Freq:** Quarterly. **Key Personnel:** Andrew O'Neil, Editor; Tracey Arklay, Managing Editor; Yi-Chong Xu, Book Review Ed. **ISSN:** 1035-7718. **Subscription Rates:** US$600 institutions print and online; 361 institutions print and online; US$239 individuals; 143 individuals; US$270 institutions online; 344 institutions online; $A 545 institutions print and online; EUR479 institutions print and online; $A 518 institutions online only; EUR455 institutions online only. **Remarks:** Accepts advertising. **URL:** http://www.tandf.co.uk/journals/titles/10357718.asp. **Formerly:** Australian Outlook. **Circ:** (Not Reported)

51715 ■ Australian Journal of Political Science
Routledge
Taylor & Francis Group Ltd.
2 Park Sq.
Milton Pk.
Abingdon OX14 4RN, United Kingdom
Ph: 44 20 70176000
Fax: 44 20 70176699
Publisher E-mail: webmaster.books@tandf.co.uk
Peer-reviewed journal covering the field of political science. **Freq:** Quarterly. **Key Personnel:** Ian McAllister, Editor, phone 61 2 61255553, fax 61 2 61253051, ian.mcallister@anu.edu.au; Aaron Martin, Review Ed. **ISSN:** 1036-1146. **Subscription Rates:** US$245 individuals; US$636 institutions online only; US$670 institutions print and online; 404 institutions print and online; $A 670 institutions print and online; EUR533 institutions print and online; 384 institutions online only; $A 689 institutions online only; EUR507 institutions online only; 147 individuals. **Remarks:** Accepts advertising. **URL:** http://www.tandf.co.uk/journals/titles/10361146.asp. **Circ:** (Not Reported)

51716 ■ Australian & New Zealand Journal of Psychiatry
Taylor & Francis Ltd.
2 & 4 Park Sq.
Milton Pk.
Abingdon OX14 4RN, United Kingdom
Ph: 44 20 70176000
Fax: 44 20 70176336
Publication E-mail: anzjp@informa.com
Professional journal covering psychiatry. **Founded:** 1965. **Freq:** 12/yr. **Print Method:** Offset. **Trim Size:** A4. **Cols./Page:** 2. **Key Personnel:** Sue E. Luty, Assoc.

Ed.; Peter Joyce, Editor; Jan Scott, International Advisory Board Member; Anthony F. Jorm, Assoc. Ed.; Gavin Andrews, International Advisory Board Member; Philip B. Mitchell, Assoc. Ed. **ISSN:** 0004-8674. **Subscription Rates:** 585 institutions; US$1,020 institutions; 1,165 single issue corporate; US$2,035 single issue corporate. **Remarks:** Accepts advertising. **URL:** http://informahealthcare.com/anp. **Circ:** Paid 3,000

51717 ■ Behaviour and Information Technology
Taylor & Francis Ltd.
2 & 4 Park Sq.
Milton Pk.
Abingdon OX14 4RN, United Kingdom
Ph: 44 20 70176000
Fax: 44 20 70176336
Peer-reviewed journal publishing articles on topics including psychology, cognitive science, computer science, ergonomics, sociology, management education and training. **Freq:** 6/yr. **Key Personnel:** Tom Stewart, Founding Ed.; John Long, Editorial Board; Jennifer Preece, Editorial Board; Andrew Thatcher, Editorial Board, andrew.thatcher@wits.ac.za; Ahmet Cakir, Editor-in-Chief, bit.editor@ergonomic.de; Stuart Card, Editorial Board; Tomas Berns, Editorial Board; Jinwoo Kim, Editorial Board. **ISSN:** 0144-929X. **Subscription Rates:** US$578 individuals print only; US$1,359 institutions online only; US$1,431 institutions print & online; 861 institutions print & online; 819 institutions online only; 349 individuals print only. **Remarks:** Accepts advertising. **URL:** http://www.tandf.co.uk/journals/titles/0144929x.asp. **Circ:** (Not Reported)

51718 ■ British Journal of Guidance and Counselling
Routledge
Taylor & Francis Group Ltd.
2 Park Sq.
Milton Pk.
Abingdon OX14 4RN, United Kingdom
Ph: 44 20 70176000
Fax: 44 20 70176699
Publisher E-mail: webmaster.books@tandf.co.uk
Peer-reviewed journal dealing with the studies relating to the areas of guidance and counseling and their relationship to such associated fields as education, psychotherapy and social work. **Freq:** Quarterly. **Key Personnel:** Gillian Proctor, Co-Ed.; Jennifer M. Kidd, Co-Ed.; Helen Colley, Editorial Board. **ISSN:** 0306-9885. **Subscription Rates:** US$298 individuals print only; US$677 institutions online only; US$712 institutions print + online; 396 institutions print + online; 377 institutions online only; 164 individuals print only; 40 members; US$75 members; EUR567 institutions print and online; EUR539 institutions online only. **Remarks:** Advertising accepted; rates available upon request. **URL:** http://www.tandf.co.uk/journals/titles/03069885.asp. **Circ:** (Not Reported)

51719 ■ British Journal for the History of Philosophy
Routledge
Taylor & Francis Group Ltd.
2 Park Sq.
Milton Pk.
Abingdon OX14 4RN, United Kingdom
Ph: 44 20 70176000
Fax: 44 20 70176699
Publisher E-mail: webmaster.books@tandf.co.uk
Peer-reviewed journal publishing reviews on the history of philosophy, in connection with the British Society for the History of Philosophy. **Subtitle:** The Journal of the British Society for the History of Philosophy. **Freq:** 5/yr. **Key Personnel:** G.A.J. Rogers, Editor; Andrew Pyle, Editorial Board; Stuart Brown, Editorial Board; Sarah Hutton, Editorial Board; Nicholas Jolley, Editorial Board; John Cottingham, Editorial Board; John Valdimir Price, Editorial Board; Tom Sorell, Editorial Board. **ISSN:** 0960-8788. **Subscription Rates:** US$290 individuals print only; US$663 institutions online only; US$698 institutions print + online; 176 individuals print only; 401 institutions online only; 422 institutions print + online; EUR558 institutions print and online; EUR530 institutions online only; EUR232 individuals. **Remarks:** Advertising accepted; rates available upon request. **URL:** http://www.tandf.co.uk/journals/titles/09608788.asp. **Circ:** (Not Reported)

51720 ■ British Journal of Neurosurgery
Taylor & Francis Ltd.
2 & 4 Park Sq.

Milton Pk.
Abingdon OX14 4RN, United Kingdom
Ph: 44 20 70176000
Fax: 44 20 70176336
International forum for debate in the field of neurosurgery with coverage of all aspects of case assessment and surgical practice, as well as wide-ranging research, with an emphasis on clinical rather than experimental material. **Freq:** 6/yr. **Key Personnel:** Neil Kitchen, Assoc. Ed.; Paul Eldridge, Editor-in-Chief; Conor Mallucci, Dep. Ed. **ISSN:** 0268-8697. **Subscription Rates:** 955 individuals; US$1,720 institutions; EUR1,375 institutions. **Remarks:** Accepts advertising. **URL:** http://informahealthcare.com/bjn. **Circ:** (Not Reported)

51721 ■ The British Journal of Sociology
Routledge
Taylor & Francis Group Ltd.
2 Park Sq.
Milton Pk.
Abingdon OX14 4RN, United Kingdom
Ph: 44 20 70176000
Fax: 44 20 70176699
Publisher E-mail: webmaster.books@tandf.co.uk
Publication covering sociology and social work. **Freq:** Quarterly. **Key Personnel:** Fran Tonkiss, Editor; Richard Wright, Editor-in-Chief; Gillian Stevens, Editor. **ISSN:** 0007-1315. **Subscription Rates:** US$76 individuals print online; US$26 individuals print online (students & members); US$608 institutions print online; US$525 institutions online only; EUR53 individuals print online; EUR33 individuals print online (students & members); EUR426 institutions print online; EUR368 institutions online only; 42 other countries personal print online; 26 other countries print online (students & members). **Remarks:** Accepts advertising on request. **URL:** http://www.blackwellpublishing.com/journal.asp?ref=0007-1315&site=1. **Circ:** (Not Reported)

51722 ■ Bulletin of Spanish Studies
Routledge
Taylor & Francis Group Ltd.
2 Park Sq.
Milton Pk.
Abingdon OX14 4RN, United Kingdom
Ph: 44 20 70176000
Fax: 44 20 70176699
Publisher E-mail: webmaster.books@tandf.co.uk
Peer-reviewed journal covering the research into the languages, literatures, histories and civilizations of Spain, Portugal and Latin America. **Subtitle:** Hispanic Studies and Researches on Spain, Portugal and Latin America. **Founded:** 1923. **Freq:** 8/yr. **Key Personnel:** Ann L. MacKenzie, Gen. Ed.; Julia Biggane, Assoc. Ed.; Richard A. Cardwell, Editorial Advisory Committee; Patricia McDermott, Assoc. Ed.; James Whiston, Gen. Ed.; Jeremy Robbins, Gen. Ed.; Helder Macedo, Editorial Advisory Committee; Ceri Byrne, Asst. Ed. **ISSN:** 1475-3820. **Subscription Rates:** US$165 individuals print only; US$1,290 individuals online only; US$1,358 individuals print + online; 808 institutions print + online; 768 institutions online only; 98 institutions; EUR1,066 institutions print and online; EUR1,013 institutions online only; EUR130 individuals. **Remarks:** Advertising accepted; rates available upon request. **URL:** http://www.tandf.co.uk/journals/titles/14753820.html. **Circ:** (Not Reported)

51723 ■ Business History
Routledge
Taylor & Francis Group Ltd.
2 Park Sq.
Milton Pk.
Abingdon OX14 4RN, United Kingdom
Ph: 44 20 70176000
Fax: 44 20 70176699
Publisher E-mail: webmaster.books@tandf.co.uk
Business publication. **Freq:** 7/yr. **Key Personnel:** Steven Toms, Editor; William J. Hausman, Assoc. Ed.; John Wilson, Editor. **ISSN:** 0007-6791. **Subscription Rates:** 603 institutions print + online; 573 institutions online; 138 individuals; US$1,030 institutions print + online; US$978 institutions online; US$207 individuals; EUR820 institutions print + online; EUR779 institutions online; EUR165 individuals. **URL:** http://www.tandf.co.uk/journals/titles/00076791.asp.

51724 ■ Cambridge Journal of Education
Routledge
Taylor & Francis Group Ltd.
2 Park Sq.
Milton Pk.

Abingdon OX14 4RN, United Kingdom
Ph: 44 20 70176000
Fax: 44 20 70176699
Publisher E-mail: webmaster.books@tandf.co.uk
Peer-reviewed journal covering all aspects of education while integrating the various groups of people involved in education such as educationists, policy-makers and educational administrators. **Freq:** Quarterly. **Key Personnel:** Dr. Paul Andrews, Editor; Dr. Linda Hargreaves, Assoc. Ed.; Dr. Nalini Boodhoo, Editor; Dr. Terry Haydn, Editor; Dr. Esther Priyadharshini, Editor; Dr. Dominic Wyse, Assoc. Ed. **ISSN:** 0305-764X. **Subscription Rates:** US$277 individuals print only; US$945 institutions online only; US$995 institutions print + online; 159 individuals; 516 institutions online only; 543 institutions print + online; EUR792 institutions print and online; EUR752 institutions online only; EUR221 individuals. **Remarks:** Advertising accepted; rates available upon request. **URL:** http://www.tandf.co.uk/journals/titles/0305764x.asp. **Circ:** (Not Reported)

51725 ■ Cambridge Review of International Affairs
Routledge
Taylor & Francis Group Ltd.
2 Park Sq.
Milton Pk.
Abingdon OX14 4RN, United Kingdom
Ph: 44 20 70176000
Fax: 44 20 70176699
Publisher E-mail: webmaster.books@tandf.co.uk
Peer-reviewed journal promoting dialogue on developing issues and theoretical approaches in the study of international relations. **Freq:** Quarterly. **Key Personnel:** Lynn Kuok, Editorial Board; Josef Ansorge, Editorial Board; Jonathan Agensky, Managing Editor; Geoffrey Edwards, Editorial Board; Toni Erskine, Editorial Board; Ian Clark, Editorial Board; Stefan Halper, Editorial Board; David Armstrong, Book Review Ed.; George Joffe, Editorial Board. **ISSN:** 0955-7571. **Subscription Rates:** 332 institutions print + online; US$548 institutions print + online; 316 institutions online; US$521 institutions online; 69 individuals; US$118 individuals; EUR437 institutions print and online; EUR415 institutions online only; EUR94 individuals. **Remarks:** Advertising accepted; rates available upon request. **URL:** http://www.tandf.co.uk/journals/titles/09557571.asp. **Circ:** (Not Reported)

51726 ■ Central Asian Survey
Routledge
Taylor & Francis Group Ltd.
2 Park Sq.
Milton Pk.
Abingdon OX14 4RN, United Kingdom
Ph: 44 20 70176000
Fax: 44 20 70176699
Publisher E-mail: webmaster.books@tandf.co.uk
Peer-reviewed journal focusing on the history, religions, cultures, politics and economics of the Central Asian and Caucasian regions including a section on Mongolia and adjacent regions. **Freq:** Quarterly. **Key Personnel:** Deniz Kandiyoti, PhD, Editor, dk1@soas.ac.uk; Touraj Atabaki, Editorial Board; Olivier Roy, Editorial Board; Nick Megoran, Book Review Ed.; Bhavna Dave, Editorial Board; Sally Cummings, Editorial Board; Virginia Martin, Editorial Board; Cynthia Buckley, Editorial Board; Michael Reynolds, Editorial Board; Raphael Jacquet, Editorial Mgr.; Sergei Abashin, International Advisory Board; Peter Finke, International Advisory Board. **ISSN:** 0263-4937. **Subscription Rates:** 644 individuals print + online; US$1,166 institutions print + online; 612 institutions online; US$1,108 institutions online; 132 individuals; US$236 individuals; EUR928 institutions print and online; EUR882 institutions online only; EUR187 individuals. **Remarks:** Advertising accepted; rates available upon request. **URL:** http://www.tandf.co.uk/journals/carfax/02634937.html. **Circ:** (Not Reported)

51727 ■ Changing English
Routledge
Taylor & Francis Group Ltd.
2 Park Sq.
Milton Pk.
Abingdon OX14 4RN, United Kingdom
Ph: 44 20 70176000
Fax: 44 20 70176699
Publisher E-mail: webmaster.books@tandf.co.uk
Peer-reviewed journal providing a focal point for a dialogue between teachers and the researchers and other issues on literacy and language in English. **Sub-**
title: Studies in Culture and Education. **Freq:** Quarterly. **Key Personnel:** Jane Miller, Editor, jane@miller26.plus.com; John Hardcastle, Contributing Ed.; Ken Jones, Contributing Ed.; Tony Burgess, Co-Ed.; Anne Turvey, Contributing Ed.; Susan Alice Fischer, Co-Ed.; Andrew Burn, Contributing Ed.; Roxy Harris, Contributing Ed.; Suzanne Scafe, Contributing Ed. **ISSN:** 1358-684X. **Subscription Rates:** 445 institutions print + online; US$740 institutions print + online; 423 institutions online; US$703 institutions online; 126 individuals; US$223 individuals; EUR589 institutions print and online; EUR560 institutions online only; EUR178 individuals. **Remarks:** Advertising accepted; rates available upon request. **URL:** http://www.tandf.co.uk/journals/carfax/1358684x.html. **Circ:** (Not Reported)

51728 ■ Child Care in Practice
Routledge
Taylor & Francis Group Ltd.
2 Park Sq.
Milton Pk.
Abingdon OX14 4RN, United Kingdom
Ph: 44 20 70176000
Fax: 44 20 70176699
Publisher E-mail: webmaster.books@tandf.co.uk
Peer-reviewed journal focusing on all aspects of children's welfare right from social care to health care, medicine to psychology, education, the police and probationary services, to solicitors and barristers. **Freq:** Quarterly. **Key Personnel:** Margaret Fawcett, Book Review Ed.; Tracey Monson, Editorial Board; Dr. Peter Lyons, International Advisory Committee; Lynne Peyton, Editorial Board; Dr. Rosemary Kilpatrick, Editorial Board; Prof. Dorota Iwaniec, Editorial Board. **ISSN:** 1357-5279. **Subscription Rates:** US$102 individuals print only; US$269 institutions online only; US$284 institutions print + online; 171 institutions print + online; 162 institutions online only; 62 individuals; EUR226 institutions print and online; EUR214 institutions online only; EUR81 individuals. **Remarks:** Advertising accepted; rates available upon request. **URL:** http://www.tandf.co.uk/journals/titles/13575279.html. **Circ:** (Not Reported)

51729 ■ Children's Geographies
Routledge
Taylor & Francis Group Ltd.
2 Park Sq.
Milton Pk.
Abingdon OX14 4RN, United Kingdom
Ph: 44 20 70176000
Fax: 44 20 70176699
Publisher E-mail: webmaster.books@tandf.co.uk
Peer-reviewed journal discussing issues having impact upon the geographically scattered population of children, young people and of their families. **Subtitle:** Advancing Interdisciplinary Understanding of Younger People's Lives. **Freq:** Quarterly. **Key Personnel:** Hugh Matthews, PhD, Editor, hugh.matthews@northampton.ac.uk; Tracey Skelton, Viewpoints Ed.; Fiona Smith, Reviews Ed.; Stuart Aitken, Commissioning Ed.; Caitlin Cahill, Assoc. Ed.; Nicola Ansell, Assoc. Ed. **ISSN:** 1473-3285. **Subscription Rates:** US$118 individuals print; US$613 individuals print + online; US$582 individuals online only; 365 institutions print + online; 347 institutions online only; 70 individuals; EUR489 institutions print and online; EUR465 institutions online only; EUR94 individuals. **Remarks:** Advertising accepted; rates available upon request. **URL:** http://www.tandf.co.uk/journals/titles/14733285.html. **Circ:** (Not Reported)

51730 ■ Citizenship Studies
Routledge
Taylor & Francis Group Ltd.
2 Park Sq.
Milton Pk.
Abingdon OX14 4RN, United Kingdom
Ph: 44 20 70176000
Fax: 44 20 70176699
Publisher E-mail: webmaster.books@tandf.co.uk
Peer-reviewed journal dealing with citizenship, human rights issues with respect to the fields of politics, sociology, history and cultural studies. **Freq:** Bimonthly. **Key Personnel:** Prof. Engin F. Isin, Ch. Ed., e.f.isin@open.ac.uk; Prof. Peter Nyers, Assoc. Ed.; Prof. Bryan S. Turner, Ch. Ed., bturner@wellesley.edu; Stephen Kalberg, Editorial Board; Bonnie Honig, Editorial Board; Seyla Benhabib, Editorial Board. **ISSN:** 1362-1025. **Subscription Rates:** 492 institutions print + online; 467 institutions online; 127 individuals; US$812 institutions print + online; US$772 institutions online; US$207

individuals; $A 1,078 institutions print + online; $A 1,025 institutions online; EUR165 individuals; EUR165 institutions print + online. **Remarks:** Advertising accepted; rates available upon request. **URL:** http://www.tandf.co.uk/journals/titles/13621025.asp. **Circ:** (Not Reported)

51731 ■ Clinical Linguistics & Phonetics
Taylor & Francis Ltd.
2 & 4 Park Sq.
Milton Pk.
Abingdon OX14 4RN, United Kingdom
Ph: 44 20 70176000
Fax: 44 20 70176336
Journal covering research into multilingualism (including multidialectalism) and communication disorders and communication disorders or normal acquisition patterns in languages other than English. **Freq:** 3/yr. **Key Personnel:** Nicole Muller, Editor, nmueller@louisiana.edu; Martin J. Ball, Editor, mjball@louisiana.edu; Thomas W. Powell, Editor, tpowel@lsuhsc.edu. **ISSN:** 1476-9670. **URL:** http://informahealthcare.com/clp. **Formerly:** Journal of Multilingual Communication Disorders (Oct. 2020).

51732 ■ CoDesign
Taylor & Francis Ltd.
2 & 4 Park Sq.
Milton Pk.
Abingdon OX14 4RN, United Kingdom
Ph: 44 20 70176000
Fax: 44 20 70176336
Peer-reviewed journal with the goals of reporting new research and scholarship in principles, procedures and techniques relevant to collaboration in design; acting as an international forum for discussion of collaborative design issues; fostering communication between academic researchers and industry practitioners concerned with collaborative design; encouraging a flow of information across the boundaries of the disciplines contributing to collaborative design; stimulating ideas and provoke widespread discussion with a forward-looking perspective. **Freq:** Quarterly. **Key Personnel:** Stephen A.R. Scrivener, Founding Ed.-in-Ch.; Mary Lou Maher, Editorial Board; Janet McDonnell, Editor-in-Chief; Pele Ehn, Editorial Board; Linden Ball, Editorial Board; Omer Akin, Editorial Board; Uday Athavankar, Editorial Board; Richard Buchanan, Assoc. Ed.; Thomas Kvan, Assoc. Ed. **ISSN:** 1571-0882. **Subscription Rates:** 158 institutions print + online; 150 institutions online; 56 individuals personal; 40 individuals society; US$261 institutions print + online; US$247 institutions online; US$95 individuals personal; US$65 individuals society; EUR208 individuals print + online; EUR198 individuals online. **Remarks:** Accepts advertising. **URL:** http://www.tandf.co.uk/journals/titles/15710882.asp. **Circ:** (Not Reported)

51733 ■ Commonwealth & Comparative Politics
Routledge
Taylor & Francis Group Ltd.
2 Park Sq.
Milton Pk.
Abingdon OX14 4RN, United Kingdom
Ph: 44 20 70176000
Fax: 44 20 70176699
Publisher E-mail: webmaster.books@tandf.co.uk
Journal dealing with the politics of Commonwealth countries. **Freq:** Quarterly. **Key Personnel:** Vicky Randall, Editorial Advisor; Roger Charlton, Editor; E. Sridharan, Editorial Advisor; Richard Crook, Editorial Advisor; Bruce Baker, Reviews Ed.; David Potter, Editorial Advisor; Rob Jenkins, Editorial Advisor; John Warhurst, Editorial Advisor; Arnold Hughes, Editorial Advisor. **ISSN:** 1466-2043. **Subscription Rates:** US$124 individuals; US$711 institutions online; US$748 institutions print + online; 451 institutions print + online; 428 institutions online; 81 individuals; EUR596 institutions print + online; EUR566 institutions online; EUR98 individuals. **Remarks:** Advertising accepted; rates available upon request. **URL:** http://www.tandf.co.uk/journals/titles/14662043.asp. **Formerly:** The Journal of Commonwealth and Comparative Politics. **Circ:** (Not Reported)

51734 ■ Communication and Critical/Cultural Studies
Routledge
Taylor & Francis Group Ltd.
2 Park Sq.
Milton Pk.
Abingdon OX14 4RN, United Kingdom
Ph: 44 20 70176000
Fax: 44 20 70176699

Circulation: ★ = ABC; △ = BPA; ♦ = CAC; ● = CCAB; ❑ = VAC; ⊕ = PO Statement; ‡ = Publisher's Report; Boldface figures = sworn; Light figures = estimated.

Gale Directory of Publications & Broadcast Media/147th Ed.   5529

Publisher E-mail: webmaster.books@tandf.co.uk
Journal that publishes scholarship for an international readership on communication as a theory, practice, technology, and discipline of power. **Founded:** 2004. **Freq:** Quarterly. **Key Personnel:** John Sloop, Assoc. Ed.; J. Macgregor Wise, Editor; Tony Bennett, Assoc. Ed. **ISSN:** 1479-1420. **Subscription Rates:** 184 institutions print + online; US$281 institutions print + online; 175 institutions online; US$267 institutions online; 47 individuals; US$72 individuals; EUR224 institutions print and online; EUR213 institutions online only; EUR57 individuals. **Remarks:** Accepts advertising. **URL:** http://www.tandf.co.uk/journals/titles/14791420.asp; http://www.informaworld.com/smpp/title~db=all~content=t713684641. **Circ:** (Not Reported)

51735 ■ Communication Reports
Routledge
Taylor & Francis Group Ltd.
2 Park Sq.
Milton Pk.
Abingdon OX14 4RN, United Kingdom
Ph: 44 20 70176000
Fax: 44 20 70176699
Publisher E-mail: webmaster.books@tandf.co.uk
Journal publishing original manuscripts that are short, data/text-based, and related to the broadly defined field of human communication. **Founded:** 1988. **Freq:** Semiannual. **Key Personnel:** Dr. William F. Sharkey, Editor-in-Chief. **ISSN:** 0893-4215. **Subscription Rates:** US$340 institutions online; US$359 institutions print and online; 215 institutions print and online; EUR286 institutions print and online; 204 institutions online only; EUR271 institutions online only. **Remarks:** Accepts advertising. **URL:** http://www.tandf.co.uk/journals/titles/08934215.asp. **Circ:** (Not Reported)

51736 ■ Communication Research Reports
Routledge
Taylor & Francis Group Ltd.
2 Park Sq.
Milton Pk.
Abingdon OX14 4RN, United Kingdom
Ph: 44 20 70176000
Fax: 44 20 70176699
Publisher E-mail: webmaster.books@tandf.co.uk
Scholarly, academic journal publishing refereed manuscripts on a wide variety of topics pertaining to human communication. **Freq:** 4/yr (online issues). **Key Personnel:** Wendy Samter, Editor; Theodore A. Avtgis, Ed.-Elect; Scott Caplan, Assoc. Ed.; Amir Hetsroni, Assoc. Ed.; Timothy R. Levine, Assoc. Ed.; Kevin Pearce, Assoc. Ed. **ISSN:** 0882-4096. **Subscription Rates:** 28 individuals print; US$49 individuals print; EUR38 institutions print; 169 institutions print and online; US$278 institutions print and online; EUR221 institutions print and online. **Remarks:** Accepts advertising. **URL:** http://www.tandf.co.uk/journals/titles/08824096.asp. **Circ:** (Not Reported)

51737 ■ Communication Teacher
Routledge
Taylor & Francis Group Ltd.
2 Park Sq.
Milton Pk.
Abingdon OX14 4RN, United Kingdom
Ph: 44 20 70176000
Fax: 44 20 70176699
Publisher E-mail: webmaster.books@tandf.co.uk
Peer-reviewed journal focusing on research on quality teaching practices. **Freq:** Quarterly. **Key Personnel:** Deanna Sellnow, Editor; Cheri J. Simonds, Ed.-Elect. **ISSN:** 1740-4622. **Subscription Rates:** US$116 institutions online; EUR93 institutions online; 58 institutions online; EUR70 individuals; 58 institutions print and online; US$116 institutions print and online; EUR93 institutions print and online. **Remarks:** Advertising accepted; rates available upon request. **URL:** http://www.tandf.co.uk/journals/titles/17404622.asp. **Circ:** (Not Reported)

51738 ■ Community, Work & Family
Routledge
Taylor & Francis Group Ltd.
2 Park Sq.
Milton Pk.
Abingdon OX14 4RN, United Kingdom
Ph: 44 20 70176000
Fax: 44 20 70176699
Publisher E-mail: webmaster.books@tandf.co.uk
Peer-reviewed journal focusing on research in the areas of community, work and family and their interface. **Freq:** Quarterly. **Key Personnel:** Prof. Laura DenDulk, Editor; Prof. Judith Sixsmith, Editor; Asiya Siddiquee, Editor;

Prof. Cary L. Cooper, Editorial Advisory Board; Dr. Ian Roper, Book Review Ed.; Dr. Michele Moore, Voices Ed.; Dr. Peter M. Foster, Editorial Advisory Board; Ellen Galinsky, Editorial Advisory Board. **ISSN:** 1366-8803. **Subscription Rates:** US$204 individuals; US$793 institutions online; US$834 institutions print + online; 127 individuals; 475 institutions online; 500 institutions print + online; EUR664 institutions print and online; EUR631 institutions online only; EUR162 individuals. **Remarks:** Advertising accepted; rates available upon request. **URL:** http://www.tandf.co.uk/journals/titles/13668803.asp. **Circ:** (Not Reported)

51739 ■ Comparative Education
Routledge
Taylor & Francis Group Ltd.
2 Park Sq.
Milton Pk.
Abingdon OX14 4RN, United Kingdom
Ph: 44 20 70176000
Fax: 44 20 70176699
Publisher E-mail: webmaster.books@tandf.co.uk
Peer-reviewed journal focusing on analyses of theoretical and methodical issues and trends in the field of education. **Freq:** Quarterly. **Key Personnel:** Michael Crossley, Editorial Board; Julian Elliott, Editorial Board; Angela Little, Editorial Board; Robert Cowen, Editorial Board; David Phillips, Ch.; Michele Schweisfurth, Editor. **ISSN:** 0305-0068. **Subscription Rates:** 36 members; 300 individuals; 871 institutions online; 917 institutions print + online; US$1,781 institutions print + online; US$1,692 institutions online; US$498 individuals; EUR1,419 institutions print and online; EUR1,348 institutions online only; EUR397 individuals. **Remarks:** Advertising accepted; rates available upon request. **URL:** http://www.tandf.co.uk/journals/titles/03050068.asp. **Circ:** (Not Reported)

51740 ■ Computer Methods in Biomechanics and Biomedical Engineering
Taylor & Francis Ltd.
2 & 4 Park Sq.
Milton Pk.
Abingdon OX14 4RN, United Kingdom
Ph: 44 20 70176000
Fax: 44 20 70176336
Journal providing a means of communicating the advances being made in the areas of biomechanics and biomedical engineering, and to stimulate interest in the continually emerging computer-based technologies which are being applied in these multidisciplinary subjects, including the mechanical response of bone and bone/tissue/implant analysis, modelling of biomaterials, material identification, human body impact, computer assisted surgery, surgical simulation, computer animation, medical imaging, dental mechanics, biofluids, cardiovascular mechanics, soft-tissue modelling and joint/ligament mechanics. **Freq:** 6/yr. **Key Personnel:** John Middleton, Editor, middletonj2@cardiff.ac.uk; N. Shrive, Assoc. Ed.; L.E. Bilston, Editorial Board; Christopher R. Jacobs, Editor, christopher.jacobs@stanford.edu; T. David, Assoc. Ed.; P. Verdonck, Assoc. Ed.; J.M. Crolet, Editorial Board; R.T. Hart, Editorial Board; I. Knets, Editorial Board. **ISSN:** 1025-5842. **Subscription Rates:** 668 institutions print and online; 634 institutions online; 186 individuals print only; US$1,005 institutions print and online; US$955 institutions online; US$228 individuals print only. **Remarks:** Accepts advertising. **URL:** http://www.tandf.co.uk/journals/titles/10255842.asp. **Circ:** (Not Reported)

51741 ■ Connective Tissue Research
Taylor & Francis Ltd.
2 & 4 Park Sq.
Milton Pk.
Abingdon OX14 4RN, United Kingdom
Ph: 44 20 70176000
Fax: 44 20 70176336
Peer-reviewed journal presenting original and significant research in all basic areas of connective tissue and matrix biology, presenting a variety of perspectives from different disciplines, including biochemistry, cell and molecular biology, immunology, structural biology, biophysics and biomechanics, processes of growth, development, aging, tissue remodeling, wound healing, and biomineralization; the tissues of interest are bone, cartilage, dentin, skin, tooth and tendon, as well as the eyes, the vascular system, the kidneys and other connective tissue component-rich organs. **Freq:** 6/yr. **Key Personnel:** Arthur Veis, Editor-in-Chief; Gary J. Gibson,

Assoc. Ed.; Vincent C. Hascall, Assoc. Ed.; Gary Balian, Assoc. Ed.; Neil D. Broom, Assoc. Ed.; Yashpal S. Kanwar, Assoc. Ed. **ISSN:** 0300-8207. **Subscription Rates:** 2,240 institutions; US$3,365 institutions; EUR2,695 institutions. **Remarks:** Accepts advertising. **URL:** http://informahealthcare.com/cts. **Circ:** (Not Reported)

51742 ■ Counselling and Psychotherapy Research
Taylor & Francis Ltd.
2 & 4 Park Sq.
Milton Pk.
Abingdon OX14 4RN, United Kingdom
Ph: 44 20 70176000
Fax: 44 20 70176336
International peer-reviewed journal dedicated to connecting research with practice, recognizing the value of qualitative, quantitative and mixed method strategies of inquiry within psychotherapy and counseling research. **Freq:** Quarterly. **Key Personnel:** Dr. Andrew Reeves, Editor; Michael Barkham, Editor; Alison Brettle, Book Review Ed.; Mick Cooper, Editorial Board; Sarah Browne, Editorial Board; Robert Elliott, Editorial Board. **ISSN:** 1473-3145. **Subscription Rates:** US$131 individuals; US$475 institutions online; US$500 institutions print + online; 73 individuals; 264 institutions online; 278 institutions print + online; EUR400 institutions print + online; EUR380 institutions online; EUR105 individuals. **Remarks:** Accepts advertising. **URL:** http://www.tandf.co.uk/journals/titles/14733145.asp. **Circ:** (Not Reported)

51743 ■ Criminal Justice Studies
Routledge
Taylor & Francis Group Ltd.
2 Park Sq.
Milton Pk.
Abingdon OX14 4RN, United Kingdom
Ph: 44 20 70176000
Fax: 44 20 70176699
Publisher E-mail: webmaster.books@tandf.co.uk
Peer-reviewed journal dealing with criminal justice and criminological issues. **Subtitle:** A Critical Journal of Crime, Law and Society. **Freq:** Quarterly. **Key Personnel:** Roslyn Muraskin, Editor-in-Chief; David V. Baker, Assoc. Ed.; George E. Higgins, Assoc. Ed. **ISSN:** 1478-601X. **Subscription Rates:** US$118 individuals print only; US$368 institutions online only; US$388 institutions print + online; 235 institutions print + online; 224 institutions online only; 90 individuals; EUR309 institutions print and online; EUR294 institutions online only; EUR94 individuals. **Remarks:** Advertising accepted; rates available upon request. **URL:** http://www.tandf.co.uk/journals/titles/1478601x.html. **Formerly:** The Justice Professional. **Circ:** (Not Reported)

51744 ■ Critical Discourse Studies
Routledge
Taylor & Francis Group Ltd.
2 Park Sq.
Milton Pk.
Abingdon OX14 4RN, United Kingdom
Ph: 44 20 70176000
Fax: 44 20 70176699
Publisher E-mail: webmaster.books@tandf.co.uk
Peer-reviewed journal devoted to the study of role of discourse in social processes, social structures, and social change. **Freq:** 4/yr. **Key Personnel:** Jay Lemke, Editor; Norman Fairclough, Editor; Phil Graham, Editor; Ruth Wodak, Editor; Natalie Collie, Asst. Ed.; Dominic Boyer, International Advisory Board; Henrik Bang, International Advisory Board; David Boje, International Advisory Board; Dr. Bernard McKenna, Reviews Ed.; John Armitage, International Advisory Board; Michael Billig, International Advisory Board; Susan Gal, International Advisory Board. **ISSN:** 1740-5904. **Subscription Rates:** US$106 individuals print; US$544 institutions online; US$573 institutions print & online; 345 institutions print & online; 327 institutions online; 62 individuals; EUR456 institutions print and online; EUR434 institutions online only; EUR85 individuals. **Remarks:** Advertising accepted; rates available upon request. **URL:** http://www.tandf.co.uk/journals/titles/17405904.asp. **Circ:** (Not Reported)

51745 ■ Critical Review of International Social and Political Philosophy
Routledge
Taylor & Francis Group Ltd.
2 Park Sq.
Milton Pk.
Abingdon OX14 4RN, United Kingdom
Ph: 44 20 70176000

Fax: 44 20 70176699
Publisher E-mail: webmaster.books@tandf.co.uk
Peer-reviewed journal focusing on certain concepts, such as power, equality, sovereignty and liberty, and different schools of thought, such as republicanism, liberalism and nationalism. **Freq:** Quarterly. **Key Personnel:** Matt Matravers, Review Ed.; Preston King, Co-Ed.; Richard Bellamy, Co-Ed.; Samantha Ashenden, Review Ed.; Terence Ball, International Advisory Board; Chris Brown, International Advisory Board. **ISSN:** 1369-8230. **Subscription Rates:** 308 institutions print & online; US$486 institutions print & online; 293 institutions online; US$486 institutions online; 70 individuals; US$112 individuals; EUR408 institutions print and online; EUR387 institutions online only; EUR89 individuals. **Remarks:** Advertising accepted; rates available upon request. **URL:** http://www.tandf.co.uk/journals/titles/13698230.asp. **Circ:** (Not Reported)

51746 ■ Critical Studies in Education
Routledge
Taylor & Francis Group Ltd.
2 Park Sq.
Milton Pk.
Abingdon OX14 4RN, United Kingdom
Ph: 44 20 70176000
Fax: 44 20 70176699
Publisher E-mail: webmaster.books@tandf.co.uk
Peer-reviewed journal covering articles and contributing to theories and empirical research. **Freq:** 3/yr. **Key Personnel:** Trevor Gale, Editor; Stephen Ball, Editorial Board; Bob Lingard, Editorial Board. **ISSN:** 1750-8487. **Subscription Rates:** 161 institutions print + online; 153 institutions online; 43 individuals; US$269 institutions print + online; US$256 institutions online; US$73 individuals; $A 407 institutions print + online; $A 386 institutions online; $A 111 individuals; EUR214 institutions print and online. **URL:** http://www.tandf.co.uk/journals/titles/17508487.asp.

51747 ■ Cultural Studies
Routledge
Taylor & Francis Group Ltd.
2 Park Sq.
Milton Pk.
Abingdon OX14 4RN, United Kingdom
Ph: 44 20 70176000
Fax: 44 20 70176699
Publisher E-mail: webmaster.books@tandf.co.uk
Publication covering sociology and social work. **Freq:** 6/yr. **Key Personnel:** Della Pollock, Editor; Lawrence Grossberg, Editor; Mark Hayward, Assoc. Ed.; Rivker Eisner, Assoc. Ed.; Josh Smicker, Assoc. Ed.; Mark Davis, Book Review Ed. **ISSN:** 0950-2386. **Subscription Rates:** US$134 individuals; EUR107 individuals; 81 individuals; 477 institutions print + online; US$793 institutions print + online; EUR631 institutions print + online; 453 institutions online; US$753 institutions online; EUR600 institutions online. **Remarks:** Accepts advertising on request. **URL:** http://www.tandf.co.uk/journals/journal.asp?issn=0950-2386&linktype=44. **Circ:** (Not Reported)

51748 ■ Cultural Trends
Routledge
Taylor & Francis Group Ltd.
2 Park Sq.
Milton Pk.
Abingdon OX14 4RN, United Kingdom
Ph: 44 20 70176000
Fax: 44 20 70176699
Publisher E-mail: webmaster.books@tandf.co.uk
Peer-reviewed journal covering relatively important issues such as internet, poverty and access to the arts and funding. **Founded:** 1989. **Freq:** Quarterly. **Key Personnel:** Sara Selwood, Editor, sara@saraselwood.co.uk; Neil Churchill, Editorial Advisory Board; Paul Allin, Editorial Advisory Board. **ISSN:** 0954-8963. **Subscription Rates:** US$322 individuals print; US$425 institutions online; US$448 institutions print & online; 282 institutions print & online; 267 institutions online; 189 individuals; EUR358 institutions print and online; EUR341 institutions online only; EUR257 individuals. **Remarks:** Advertising accepted; rates available upon request. **URL:** http://www.tandf.co.uk/journals/titles/09548963.asp. **Circ:** (Not Reported)

51749 ■ Culture and Religion
Routledge
Taylor & Francis Group Ltd.
2 Park Sq.
Milton Pk.

Abingdon OX14 4RN, United Kingdom
Ph: 44 20 70176000
Fax: 44 20 70176699
Publisher E-mail: webmaster.books@tandf.co.uk
Peer-reviewed journal dealing with cultural studies and anthropology. **Freq:** Quarterly. **Key Personnel:** Steven Sutcliffe, Reviews Ed.; Malory Nye, Editor; Talal Asad, Editorial Board; Mary Keller, Editorial Board; Ananda Abeysekara, Editorial Board; Paul-Francois Tremlett, Asst. Ed. **ISSN:** 1475-5610. **Subscription Rates:** 273 institutions print + online; 260 institutions online; 84 individuals; US$452 institutions print + online; US$429 institutions online; US$135 individuals; EUR359 institutions print and online; EUR341 institutions online only; EUR108 individuals. **Remarks:** Advertising accepted; rates available upon request. **URL:** http://www.tandf.co.uk/journals/titles/01438301.html. **Circ:** (Not Reported)

51750 ■ Current Issues in Language Planning
Routledge
Taylor & Francis Group Ltd.
2 Park Sq.
Milton Pk.
Abingdon OX14 4RN, United Kingdom
Ph: 44 20 70176000
Fax: 44 20 70176699
Publisher E-mail: webmaster.books@tandf.co.uk
Peer-reviewed journal providing major summative and thematic review studies spanning and focusing the disparate language policy and language planning literature related to polities and language planning and issues in language planning. **Freq:** Quarterly. **Key Personnel:** Robert B. Kaplan, Editor, rkaplan@olypen.com; Nkonko Kamwangamalu, Editor, nkamwangamalu@howard.edu; Richard B. Baldauf, Jr., Editor, r.baldauf@uq.edu.au. **ISSN:** 1466-4208. **Subscription Rates:** 353 institutions print + online; US$708 institutions print + online; EUR531 institutions print + online; 75 individuals; US$149 individuals; EUR93 individuals; 331 institutions online; US$673 institutions online; EUR504 institutions online. **URL:** http://www.tandf.co.uk/journals/1466-4208.

51751 ■ Current Issues in Tourism
Routledge
Taylor & Francis Group Ltd.
2 Park Sq.
Milton Pk.
Abingdon OX14 4RN, United Kingdom
Ph: 44 20 70176000
Fax: 44 20 70176699
Publisher E-mail: webmaster.books@tandf.co.uk
Scholarly journal covering tourism. **Founded:** 1998. **Freq:** Bimonthly. **Key Personnel:** C. Michael Hall, Editor; Chris Cooper, Editor; John Jenkins, Reviews Ed. **ISSN:** 1368-3500. **Subscription Rates:** 372 institutions print and online; US$748 institutions print and online; EUR559 institutions print and online; 75 individuals print; US$135 individuals print; EUR108 individuals print; 353 institutions online; US$711 institutions online; EUR531 institutions online. **Remarks:** Accepts advertising. **URL:** http://www.tandf.co.uk/journals/journal.asp?issn=1368-3500&linktype=5. **Circ:** (Not Reported)

51752 ■ Curriculum Journal
Routledge
Taylor & Francis Group Ltd.
2 Park Sq.
Milton Pk.
Abingdon OX14 4RN, United Kingdom
Ph: 44 20 70176000
Fax: 44 20 70176699
Publisher E-mail: webmaster.books@tandf.co.uk
Peer-reviewed journal covering the developmental aspects of education in primary and secondary schools. **Subtitle:** The Official Journal of the British Curriculum Foundation. **Freq:** 4/yr. **Key Personnel:** Robert McCormick, Editor; Bob Moon, Editor; Elaine Wilson, Reviews Ed. **ISSN:** 0958-5176. **Subscription Rates:** 114 individuals; 355 institutions online; 374 institutions print + online; 626 institutions print + online; 595 institutions online; 194 individuals; EUR498 institutions print and online; EUR473 institutions online; EUR154 individuals. **Remarks:** Advertising accepted; rates available upon request. **URL:** http://www.tandf.co.uk/journals/titles/09585176.asp. **Circ:** (Not Reported)

51753 ■ Defence Studies
Routledge
Taylor & Francis Group Ltd.
2 Park Sq.
Milton Pk.

Abingdon OX14 4RN, United Kingdom
Ph: 44 20 70176000
Fax: 44 20 70176699
Publisher E-mail: webmaster.books@tandf.co.uk
Journal covering various aspects of defense mainly meant for staff colleges, military personnel, and academics interested in defense published in connection with British Joint Services Command and Staff College. **Subtitle:** Official Journal of the Joint Services Command and Staff College. **Freq:** 3/yr. **Key Personnel:** Geoffrey Till, Exec. Ed.; Warren Chin, Editor; Wyn Bowen, Founding Ed.; Tracey German, Editor; David P. Auerswald, Editorial Board; David Hall, Founding Ed. **ISSN:** 1470-2436. **Subscription Rates:** US$97 individuals; US$348 institutions online; US$366 institutions print + online; 2228 institutions print + online; 216 institutions online; 63 individuals; EUR292 institutions print and online; EUR277 institutions online only; EUR77 individuals. **Remarks:** Advertising accepted; rates available upon request. **URL:** http://www.tandf.co.uk/journals/titles/14702436.asp. **Circ:** (Not Reported)

51754 ■ Democratization
Routledge
Taylor & Francis Group Ltd.
2 Park Sq.
Milton Pk.
Abingdon OX14 4RN, United Kingdom
Ph: 44 20 70176000
Fax: 44 20 70176699
Publisher E-mail: webmaster.books@tandf.co.uk
Peer-reviewed journal covering various aspects of democratization as a process and analysis of democracy. **Freq:** 6/yr. **Key Personnel:** Peter Ferdinand, Editorial Board; Gordon Crawford, Editor; Mirjam Werner, Book Reviews; Jeffrey Haynes, Editor; Tom Gallagher, Editorial Board; Paul Lewis, Editorial Board. **ISSN:** 1351-0347. **Subscription Rates:** US$166 individuals print only; US$758 institutions online; US$797 institutions print + online; 482 institutions print + online; 459 institutions online; 113 individuals print only; EUR638 institutions print and online; EUR605 institutions online only; EUR132 individuals. **Remarks:** Advertising accepted; rates available upon request. **URL:** http://www.tandf.co.uk/journals/titles/13510347.asp. **Circ:** (Not Reported)

51755 ■ Development in Practice
Routledge
Taylor & Francis Group Ltd.
2 Park Sq.
Milton Pk.
Abingdon OX14 4RN, United Kingdom
Ph: 44 20 70176000
Fax: 44 20 70176699
Publisher E-mail: webmaster.books@tandf.co.uk
Peer-reviewed journal covering practice-based analysis and research concerning the social dimensions of development and humanitarianism. **Freq:** 8/yr. **Key Personnel:** Brian Pratt, Editor-in-Chief; Martha Thompson, Editorial Adviser; Frances Rubin, Dep. Review Ed.; Kate Critchley, Editorial Adviser; Pushpanath Krishnamurthy, Editorial Adviser; Stephen Commins, Editorial Adviser. **ISSN:** 0961-4524. **Subscription Rates:** US$234 individuals print only; US$885 institutions online; US$932 institutions print + online; 564 institutions print + online; 536 institutions online; 142 individuals; EUR746 institutions print and online; EUR709 institutions online only; EUR187 individuals. **Remarks:** Advertising accepted; rates available upon request. **URL:** http://www.tandf.co.uk/journals/titles/09614524.asp. **Circ:** (Not Reported)

51756 ■ Development Southern Africa
Routledge
Taylor & Francis Group Ltd.
2 Park Sq.
Milton Pk.
Abingdon OX14 4RN, United Kingdom
Ph: 44 20 70176000
Fax: 44 20 70176699
Publisher E-mail: webmaster.books@tandf.co.uk
Magazine covering developments challenges and policy issues in South Africa for development specialists, policy decision makers, scholar and students. **Freq:** 5/yr. **Key Personnel:** Marie Kirsten, Editor; Thomas Scott, Assoc. Ed.; Janine Thorne, Assoc. Ed.; Sarah Mosoetsa, Assoc. Ed.; Deryl Barlow-Weilbach, Assoc. Ed.; Paul Kibuuka, Assoc. Ed.; Norma Tsoti, Assoc. Ed.; Johann Kirsten, Editorial Advisory Board; Lyn Sumners, Coord. **ISSN:** 0376-835X. **Subscription Rates:** US$25 individuals

Circulation: ★ = ABC; △ = BPA; ◆ = CAC; • = CCAB; □ = VAC; ⊕ = PO Statement; ‡ = Publisher's Report; Boldface figures = sworn; Light figures = estimated.

Gale Directory of Publications & Broadcast Media/147th Ed.

5531

developing country; 290 institutions print + online; US$482 institutions print + online; 275 institutions online; US$458 institutions online; EUR482 institutions print + online; EUR364 institutions online. **Remarks:** Accepts advertising. **URL:** http://www.tandf.co.uk/journals/titles/0376835x.asp. **Circ:** (Not Reported)

51757 ■ Developmental Neurorehabilitation
Taylor & Francis Ltd.
2 & 4 Park Sq.
Milton Pk.
Abingdon OX14 4RN, United Kingdom
Ph: 44 20 70176000
Fax: 44 20 70176336
International vehicle for improving scientific awareness, communication and knowledge about recovery, development and outcome and childhood disorders. **Freq:** Quarterly. **Key Personnel:** Jeffrey Sigafoos, Editor, jeff. sigafoos@vuw.ac.nz; Walton O. Schalick, Editorial Board; Susan L. Andersen, Editorial Board; Russell Lang, Editorial Board; Mark F. O'Reilly, Editorial Board; David Rose, Editorial Board; Karen Barlow, Editorial Board; Charlene Robertson, Editorial Board. **ISSN:** 1751-8423. **Subscription Rates:** 405 institutions; US$645 institutions; EUR570 institutions. **Remarks:** Accepts advertising. **URL:** http://informahealthcare.com/pdr. **Formerly:** Pediatric Rehabilitation. **Circ:** (Not Reported)

51758 ■ Diplomacy & Statecraft
Routledge
Taylor & Francis Group Ltd.
2 Park Sq.
Milton Pk.
Abingdon OX14 4RN, United Kingdom
Ph: 44 20 70176000
Fax: 44 20 70176699
Publisher E-mail: webmaster.books@tandf.co.uk
Peer-reviewed journal covering international history and the current behavior of international affairs. Includes articles on diplomatic history. **Freq:** Quarterly. **Key Personnel:** Erik Goldstein, Editorial Exec. Committee; John Maurer, Editorial Exec. Committee; David Armstrong, Editorial Board; Thomas Otte, Editorial Exec. Committee; Ian Clark, Editorial Board; Peter Boyce, Editorial Board. **ISSN:** 0959-2296. **Subscription Rates:** US$115 individuals print; US$486 institutions online; US$512 institutions print & online; 309 institutions print & online; 294 institutions online; 77 individuals; EUR408 institutions print and online; EUR387 institutions online only; EUR91 individuals. **Remarks:** Advertising accepted; rates available upon request. **URL:** http://www.tandf.co.uk/journals/titles/09592296.asp. **Circ:** (Not Reported)

51759 ■ Distance Education
Routledge
Taylor & Francis Group Ltd.
2 Park Sq.
Milton Pk.
Abingdon OX14 4RN, United Kingdom
Ph: 44 20 70176000
Fax: 44 20 70176699
Publisher E-mail: webmaster.books@tandf.co.uk
Peer-reviewed journal covering research and other topics in distance education. **Freq:** 3/yr. **Key Personnel:** Dr. Som Naidu, Editor, distance-education@unimelb.edu.au; Alistair Inglis, Dep. Ed. **ISSN:** 0158-7919. **Subscription Rates:** US$392 institutions print and online; US$126 individuals; US$373 institutions online only; 255 institutions print and online; $A 373 institutions print and online; EUR313 institutions print and online; 242 institutions online only; $A 371 institutions online only; EUR297 institutions online only; 81 individuals. **URL:** http://www.tandf.co.uk/journals/carfax/01587919.html.

51760 ■ Drugs
Taylor & Francis Ltd.
2 & 4 Park Sq.
Milton Pk.
Abingdon OX14 4RN, United Kingdom
Ph: 44 20 70176000
Fax: 44 20 70176336
Refereed journal providing a forum for communication and debate between policy makers, practitioners and researchers concerned with social and health policy responses to legal and illicit drug use and drug-related harm. **Subtitle:** Education, Prevention and Policy. **Freq:** 6/yr. **Key Personnel:** Dr. Betsy Thom, Coord. Ed., b.thom@mdx.ac.uk; Shane Butler, Editor; Ilana Crome, Editor; Karen Duke, Editor; John Foster, Editor; Richard Ives, Editor. **ISSN:** 0968-7637. **Subscription Rates:** 865 institutions; US$1,560 institutions; US$1,245 institu-

tions print and online. **Remarks:** Accepts advertising. **URL:** http://informahealthcare.com/loi/dep. **Circ:** (Not Reported)

51761 ■ Early Child Development and Care
Routledge
Taylor & Francis Group Ltd.
2 Park Sq.
Milton Pk.
Abingdon OX14 4RN, United Kingdom
Ph: 44 20 70176000
Fax: 44 20 70176699
Publisher E-mail: webmaster.books@tandf.co.uk
Peer-reviewed multidisciplinary journal serving psychologists, educators, psychiatrists, pediatricians, social workers and other professionals who deal with research, planning, education and care of infants and young children on all aspects of early child development and care, containing descriptive and evaluative articles on social, educational and preventive medical programs for young children, experimental and observational studies, critical reviews and summary articles. **Freq:** 8/yr. **Key Personnel:** Roy Evans, Editor, roy.evans@brunel.ac.uk; Debo Akande, Editorial Board; Judith A. Chafel, Editorial Board; Deborah Jones, Assoc. Ed.; Kazuo Miyake, Assoc. Ed.; Wendy Schiller, Assoc. Ed.; Bettye Catdwell, Editorial Board; Zlatka Cugmas, Editorial Board; Alice Sterling Honig, Assoc. Ed.; Resia Pretorius, Editorial Board. **ISSN:** 0300-4430. **Subscription Rates:** 3,177 institutions print and online; US$3,997 institutions print and online; 3,018 institutions online; US$3,797 institutions online; 965 individuals print only; US$1,163 individuals print only. **Remarks:** Accepts advertising. **URL:** http://www.tandf.co.uk/journals/titles/03004430.asp. **Circ:** (Not Reported)

51762 ■ Early Popular Visual Culture
Routledge
Taylor & Francis Group Ltd.
2 Park Sq.
Milton Pk.
Abingdon OX14 4RN, United Kingdom
Ph: 44 20 70176000
Fax: 44 20 70176699
Publisher E-mail: webmaster.books@tandf.co.uk
Peer-reviewed, academic journal dedicated to stimulating research and interdisciplinary studies in relation to all forms of popular visual culture before 1930 by examining the use and exploitation of popular cultural forms such as (but not limited to) cinema, photography, magic lanterns and music hall within the fields of entertainment, education, science, advertising and the domestic environment; and is primarily concerned with the evolving social, technological and economic contexts which such popular cultural products inhabited and defined. **Freq:** 3/yr. **Key Personnel:** Simon Popple, Editor; Dr. Richard Crangle, Assoc. Ed.; Vanessa Toulmin, Editor; Richard Brown, Assoc. Ed.; Stephen Bottomore, Assoc. Ed.; Prof. Richard Abel, Assoc. Ed.; Elzbieta Ostrowska, Assoc. Ed.; Colin Harding, Assoc. Ed.; Prof. John Fullerton, Assoc. Ed.; Prof. Christopher Williams, Assoc. Ed. **ISSN:** 1746-0654. **Subscription Rates:** 269 institutions print + online; US$452 institutions print + online; 256 institutions online; US$429 institutions online; 63 individuals; US$105 individuals; EUR359 institutions print and online; EUR341 institutions online only; EUR84 individuals. **Remarks:** Accepts advertising. **URL:** http://www.tandf.co.uk/journals/titles/17460654.asp. **Circ:** (Not Reported)

51763 ■ Early Years
Routledge
Taylor & Francis Group Ltd.
2 Park Sq.
Milton Pk.
Abingdon OX14 4RN, United Kingdom
Ph: 44 20 70176000
Fax: 44 20 70176699
Publisher E-mail: webmaster.books@tandf.co.uk
Professional magazine covering early education. **Subtitle:** An International Journal of Research and Development. **Freq:** 3/yr. **Key Personnel:** David Whitebread, Reviews Ed.; Pamela Oberhuemer, Editor; Rod Parker-Rees, Editor; Malva Villalon Bravo, Editorial Board; Pat Broadhead, Editorial Board; Marian Whitehead, Editorial Board; Janet Moyles, Website Ed. **ISSN:** 0957-5146. **Subscription Rates:** 286 institutions print + online; US$463 institutions print + online; 271 institutions online; US$440 institutions online; 101 individuals;

US$168 individuals. **URL:** http://www.tandf.co.uk/journals/titles/09575146.asp.

51764 ■ East European Jewish Affairs
Routledge
Taylor & Francis Group Ltd.
2 Park Sq.
Milton Pk.
Abingdon OX14 4RN, United Kingdom
Ph: 44 20 70176000
Fax: 44 20 70176699
Publisher E-mail: webmaster.books@tandf.co.uk
Journal dealing with the position and prospects of Jews in the former Soviet Union and East-Central European countries. **Freq:** 3/yr. **Key Personnel:** Sam Johnson, Managing Editor, sam.johnson@ucl.ac.uk; Gennady Estraikh, Editor; Zvi Gitelman, Editor. **ISSN:** 1350-1674. **Subscription Rates:** US$136 individuals; US$318 institutions online only; US$334 institutions print & online; 80 individuals print only; 191 institutions online only; 202 institutions print & online; EUR266 institutions print and online; EUR253 institutions online only; EUR108 individuals. **Remarks:** Advertising accepted; rates available upon request. **URL:** http://www.tandf.co.uk/journals/titles/13501674.asp. **Formerly:** Soviet Jewish Affairs. **Circ:** (Not Reported)

51765 ■ Economic System Research
Routledge
Taylor & Francis Group Ltd.
2 Park Sq.
Milton Pk.
Abingdon OX14 4RN, United Kingdom
Ph: 44 20 70176000
Fax: 44 20 70176699
Publisher E-mail: webmaster.books@tandf.co.uk
Peer-reviewed journal covering economics and business. **Subtitle:** Journal of the International Input-Output Association. **Freq:** Quarterly. **Key Personnel:** Manfred Lenzen, Editor; Anne P. Carter, Editorial Board; Terry Barker, Editorial Board; Clopper Almon, Editorial Board; Jiemin Guo, Editorial Board; Faye Duchin, Editorial Board. **ISSN:** 0953-5314. **Subscription Rates:** US$407 individuals; US$1,352 institutions online only; US$1,423 institutions print and online; 858 institutions print and online; EUR1,133 institutions print and online; 816 institutions online only; EUR1,076 institutions online only; 242 individuals; EUR324 individuals. **URL:** http://www.tandf.co.uk/journals/journal.asp?issn=0953-5314&subcategory=eb050000.

51766 ■ Economy and Society
Routledge
Taylor & Francis Group Ltd.
2 Park Sq.
Milton Pk.
Abingdon OX14 4RN, United Kingdom
Ph: 44 20 70176000
Fax: 44 20 70176699
Publisher E-mail: webmaster.books@tandf.co.uk
Peer-reviewed journal covering social sciences. **Freq:** 4/yr. **Key Personnel:** Samantha Ashenden, Managing Editor, s.ashenden@bbk.ac.uk; Ali Rattansi, Editorial Advisory Board; Stuart Corbridge, Editorial Board; Sami Zubaida, Editorial Board; Andrew Barry, Editorial Board; Alain Pottage, Editorial Advisory Board; Maxine Molyneux, Editorial Board; Nikolas Rose, Editorial Board; Ian Hacking, Editorial Advisory Board; Sunil Khilnani, Editorial Advisory Board. **ISSN:** 0308-5147. **Subscription Rates:** 330 institutions print + online; US$545 institutions print + online; 313 institutions online; US$517 institutions online; 100 individuals; US$159 individuals. **Remarks:** Accepts advertising on request. **Online:** Gale. **URL:** http://www.tandf.co.uk/journals/titles/03085147.asp. **Circ:** (Not Reported)

51767 ■ Education Economics
Routledge
Taylor & Francis Group Ltd.
2 Park Sq.
Milton Pk.
Abingdon OX14 4RN, United Kingdom
Ph: 44 20 70176000
Fax: 44 20 70176699
Publisher E-mail: webmaster.books@tandf.co.uk
Peer-reviewed journal covering economics and education. **Freq:** Quarterly. **Key Personnel:** Steve Bradley, Editor, ecasb@exchange.lancs.ac.uk; Bruce Chapman, Assoc. Ed.; David Mitch, Assoc. Ed.; Peter Dolton, International Editorial Board; Martin Cave, International Editorial Board; Jere R. Behrman, Interna-

tional Editorial Board. **ISSN:** 0964-5292. **Subscription Rates:** US$1,440 institutions print and online; US$1,367 institutions online; US$363 individuals; 866 institutions print and online; EUR1,147 institutions print and online; 823 institutions online only; EUR1,090 institutions online only; 219 individuals; EUR290 individuals. **Remarks:** Accepts advertising. **URL:** http://www.tandf.co.uk/journals/routledge/09645292.html. **Circ:** (Not Reported)

51768 ■ Education, Knowledge & Economy
Routledge
Taylor & Francis Group Ltd.
2 Park Sq.
Milton Pk.
Abingdon OX14 4RN, United Kingdom
Ph: 44 20 70176000
Fax: 44 20 70176699
Publisher E-mail: webmaster.books@tandf.co.uk
Peer-reviewed journal focusing on education policy, social enterprise and entrepreneurship. **Subtitle:** A Journal for Education and Social Enterprise. **Freq:** 3/yr. **Print Method:** Offset. **Cols./Page:** 3 and 2. **Col. Width:** 27 and 41 nonpareils. **Col. Depth:** 130 agate lines. **Key Personnel:** Prof. Anthony Kelly, Editor; Prof. Gordon Boyce, Editorial Board; Dr. Paul Clarke, Editorial Board. **ISSN:** 1749-6896. **Subscription Rates:** 149 institutions print + online; US$278 institutions print + online; 142 institutions online; US$265 institutions online; 37 individuals; US$70 individuals; EUR221 institutions print and online; EUR210 institutions online only; EUR56 individuals. **URL:** http://www.tandf.co.uk/journals/titles/17496896.asp.

51769 ■ Education and the Law
Routledge
Taylor & Francis Group Ltd.
2 Park Sq.
Milton Pk.
Abingdon OX14 4RN, United Kingdom
Ph: 44 20 70176000
Fax: 44 20 70176699
Publisher E-mail: webmaster.books@tandf.co.uk
Peer-reviewed journal focusing on the law relating to primary, secondary, tertiary and higher education for principals, head teachers, governors, local authority officers and members, and practicing lawyers. **Freq:** Quarterly. **Key Personnel:** Prof. Geoffrey Bennett, Editor; Prof. Fernand N. Dutile, Editorial Board; Prof. Robert Bickel, Editorial Board; Catherine Barnard, Editorial Board; John Hall, Editorial Board; David Palfreyman, Co-Ed. **ISSN:** 0953-9964. **Subscription Rates:** US$235 individuals print only; US$428 institutions online version; US$450 institutions print and online version; 134 individuals print only; 257 institutions online version; 271 institutions print and online version; EUR358 institutions print and online; EUR340 institutions online only; EUR188 individuals. **Remarks:** Advertising accepted; rates available upon request. **URL:** http://www.tandf.co.uk/journals/titles/09539964.asp. **Circ:** (Not Reported)

51770 ■ Educational Action Research
Routledge
Taylor & Francis Group Ltd.
2 Park Sq.
Milton Pk.
Abingdon OX14 4RN, United Kingdom
Ph: 44 20 70176000
Fax: 44 20 70176699
Publisher E-mail: webmaster.books@tandf.co.uk
Peer-reviewed journal focusing on the research and practice in educational settings. **Freq:** Quarterly. **Print Method:** Offset. **Cols./Page:** 6. **Col. Width:** 19 nonpareils. **Col. Depth:** 210 agate lines. **Key Personnel:** Christopher Day, Editor; Julienne Meyer, Editor; Marie Brennan, Editor. **ISSN:** 0965-0792. **Subscription Rates:** US$594 institutions online only; 383 institutions online only; US$625 institutions print + online; 403 institutions print + online; US$96 individuals print only; 56 individuals print only; EUR498 institutions print and online; EUR473 institutions online only; EUR77 individuals. **URL:** http://www.tandf.co.uk/journals/titles/09650792.asp.

51771 ■ Environmental Politics
Taylor & Francis Group Ltd.
4 Park Sq.
Milton Pk.
Abingdon OX14 4RN, United Kingdom
Ph: 44 207 0176000
Fax: 44 207 0176336

Publisher E-mail: info@taylorandfrancis.com
Publication focusing on environmental issues. **Freq:** 6/yr. **Key Personnel:** Andrew Dobson, Editor; Neil Carter, Editor; John Barry, Editor; Christopher Rootes, Editor-in-Chief; Russell J. Dalton, Editorial Board; Elizabeth Bomberg, Editor; Graham Smith, Editorial Board; Riley E. Dunlap, Editorial Board; John S. Dryzek, Editorial Board. **ISSN:** 0964-4016. **Subscription Rates:** 365 institutions print online; US$602 institutions print online; 346 institutions online; US$571 institutions online; 76 individuals; US$109 individuals. **Remarks:** Accepts advertising. **URL:** http://www.tandf.co.uk/journals/titles/09644016.asp. **Circ:** (Not Reported)

51772 ■ Ethics and Education
Routledge
Taylor & Francis Group Ltd.
2 Park Sq.
Milton Pk.
Abingdon OX14 4RN, United Kingdom
Ph: 44 20 70176000
Fax: 44 20 70176699
Publisher E-mail: webmaster.books@tandf.co.uk
Peer-reviewed journal aiming to stimulate discussion and debate around the ethical dimensions of education by addressing issues in both formal and informal education and upbringing, and including within its scope relevant aspects of applied ethics, including: bioethics, medical ethics, management ethics, sex education, ethics of therapy and counseling and professional ethics. **Freq:** 3/yr. **Key Personnel:** Prof. Richard Smith, Editor, r.d.smith@durham.ac.uk; Michael Katz, Editorial Board; Jim Conroy, Editorial Board; Morwenna Griffiths, Editorial Board; Paul Smeyers, Editorial Board; Sharon Todd, Editorial Board. **ISSN:** 1744-9642. **Subscription Rates:** US$93 individuals print only; US$270 institutions online only; US$284 institutions print & online; 176 institutions print & online; 167 institutions online only; 57 individuals print only; EUR227 institutions print and online; EUR215 institutions online only; EUR74 individuals. **Remarks:** Accepts advertising. **URL:** http://www.tandf.co.uk/journals/titles/17449642.asp. **Circ:** (Not Reported)

51773 ■ Ethics and Social Welfare
Routledge
Taylor & Francis Group Ltd.
2 Park Sq.
Milton Pk.
Abingdon OX14 4RN, United Kingdom
Ph: 44 20 70176000
Fax: 44 20 70176699
Publisher E-mail: webmaster.books@tandf.co.uk
Peer-reviewed journal covering issues relating to professional interventions into social life. **Freq:** 3/yr. **Key Personnel:** Sarah Banks, Editor; Derek Clifford, Editor, ethicsandsocialwelfare@tandf.co.uk; Michael Preston-Shoot, Editor. **ISSN:** 1749-6535. **Subscription Rates:** 187 institutions print + online; 178 institutions online; 47 individuals; US$339 institutions print + online; US$323 institutions online; US$85 individuals; EUR270 institutions print and online; EUR257 institutions online only; EUR68 individuals. **URL:** http://www.tandf.co.uk/journals/titles/17496535.asp.

51774 ■ Ethnic and Racial Studies
Routledge
Taylor & Francis Group Ltd.
2 Park Sq.
Milton Pk.
Abingdon OX14 4RN, United Kingdom
Ph: 44 20 70176000
Fax: 44 20 70176699
Publisher E-mail: webmaster.books@tandf.co.uk
Publication covering ethnic, cultural, and racial issues and studies. **Freq:** 10/yr. **Key Personnel:** Martin Bulmer, Editor; Amanda Eastell-Bleakley, Managing Editor, ethnic@surrey.ac.uk; John Solomos, Editor. **ISSN:** 0141-9870. **Subscription Rates:** US$243 individuals print only; US$737 individuals online only; US$776 individuals print & online. **Remarks:** Accepts advertising on request. **Online:** Gale. **URL:** http://www.tandf.co.uk/journals/printview/?issn=0141-9870; http://www.informaworld.com/smpp/title~db=all~content=t713685087. **Circ:** (Not Reported)

51775 ■ Ethnography & Education
Routledge
Taylor & Francis Group Ltd.
2 Park Sq.
Milton Pk.

Abingdon OX14 4RN, United Kingdom
Ph: 44 20 70176000
Fax: 44 20 70176699
Publisher E-mail: webmaster.books@tandf.co.uk
International, peer-reviewed journal publishing articles illuminating educational practices through empirical methodologies, which prioritize the experiences and perspectives of those involved; supporting ethnographic research that involves long-term engagement with those studied in order to understand their cultures; using multiple methods of generating data, and recognizing the centrality of the researcher in the research process. **Freq:** 3/yr. **Key Personnel:** Prof. Geoff Troman, Dep. Ed., g.troman@roehampton.ac.uk; Bob Jeffrey, Dep. Ed., r.a.jeffrey@open.ac.uk; Prof. Tuula Gordon, Dep. Ed., tuula.gordon@helsinki.fi; Prof. Carl Bagley, Editorial Board; Prof. Geoffrey Walford, Dep. Ed., geoffrey.walford@edstud.ox.ac.uk; Dr. Ghazala Bhatti, Editorial Board. **ISSN:** 1745-7823. **Subscription Rates:** US$75 individuals print only; US$263 institutions online; US$276 institutions print + online; 43 individuals print only; 157 institutions online; 166 institutions print + online; EUR59 individuals; EUR209 institutions online only; EUR220 institutions print and online. **Remarks:** Accepts advertising. **URL:** http://www.tandf.co.uk/journals/titles/17457823.asp. **Circ:** (Not Reported)

51776 ■ Ethnomusicology Forum
Routledge
Taylor & Francis Group Ltd.
2 Park Sq.
Milton Pk.
Abingdon OX14 4RN, United Kingdom
Ph: 44 20 70176000
Fax: 44 20 70176699
Publisher E-mail: webmaster.books@tandf.co.uk
Peer-reviewed journal providing a focal point for the infusion of innovative ideas in the field of ethnomusicology, and encompasses the study of all music, including Western art music and popular music. **Subtitle:** Journal of the British Forum for Ethnomusicology. **Freq:** Semiannual. **Key Personnel:** Tina K. Ramnarine, Editorial Board; Rachel Harris, Editorial Board; Tan Hwee-San, Reviews Ed. **ISSN:** 1741-1912. **Subscription Rates:** 141 institutions print + online; US$234 institutions print + online; 134 institutions online; US$223 institutions online; 45 individuals; US$78 individuals; EUR186 institutions print and online; EUR177 institutions online only; EUR61 individuals. **Remarks:** Advertising accepted; rates available upon request. **URL:** http://www.tandf.co.uk/journals/titles/17411912.asp. **Former name:** British Journal of Ethnomusicology. **Circ:** (Not Reported)

51777 ■ Ethnopolitics
Routledge
Taylor & Francis Group Ltd.
2 Park Sq.
Milton Pk.
Abingdon OX14 4RN, United Kingdom
Ph: 44 20 70176000
Fax: 44 20 70176699
Publisher E-mail: webmaster.books@tandf.co.uk
Peer-reviewed journal focusing on the analysis, management, settlement, and prevention of ethnic conflicts, on minority rights, group identity, the intersection of identity group formations and politics, on minority and majority nationalisms in the context of transitions to democracy, and on the security and stability of states and regions as they are affected by of the above issues with particular attention devoted to the growing any importance of the international dimension of ethnopolitics, including diplomatic and military interventions, and the increasing impact of globalisation on ethnic identities and their political expressions. **Freq:** 4/yr. **Key Personnel:** Stefan Wolff, Editor, stefan@stefanwolff.com; Karl Cordell, Editor; Chris Gilligan, Review Ed. **ISSN:** 1744-9057. **Subscription Rates:** US$136 individuals; US$423 institutions online only; US$445 institutions print & online; EUR354 institutions print & online; US$30 members special; 267 institutions print & online; 254 institutions online; 81 individuals; EUR354 institutions online only; EUR108 individuals. **Remarks:** Accepts advertising. **URL:** http://www.tandf.co.uk/journals/titles/17449057.asp. **Circ:** (Not Reported)

51778 ■ Europe-Asia Studies
Routledge
Taylor & Francis Group Ltd.
2 Park Sq.
Milton Pk.

Circulation: ★ = ABC; △ = BPA; ◆ = CAC; • = CCAB; ❑ = VAC; ⊕ = PO Statement; ‡ = Publisher's Report; Boldface figures = sworn; Light figures = estimated.

Abingdon OX14 4RN, United Kingdom
Ph: 44 20 70176000
Fax: 44 20 70176699
Publisher E-mail: webmaster.books@tandf.co.uk
Peer-reviewed journal focusing on international relations. **Freq:** 10/yr. **Key Personnel:** Prof. Terry Cox, Editor, phone 44 141 3306687, fax 44 141 3305594, t.m.cox@lbss.gla.ac.uk; Dr. Sarah Badcock, National Advisory Board; Prof. Richard Berry, Editorial Board; Dr. Clare McManus-Czubinska, Book Review Ed.; Dr. Bhavna Dave, National Advisory Board; Dr. Robert Arnot, Editorial Board; Prof. Evan Mawdsley, Editorial Board; Dr. Sally Cummings, Editorial Board. **ISSN:** 0966-8136. **Subscription Rates:** 1,013 institutions print and online; US$1,684 institutions print and online; 963 institutions online; US$1,600 institutions online; 275 individuals; US$522 individuals; 52 individuals society; US$86 individuals society. **URL:** http://www.tandf.co.uk/journals/carfax/09668136.html.

51779 ■ European Journal of Contraception and Reproductive Health Care
Taylor & Francis Ltd.
2 & 4 Park Sq.
Milton Pk.
Abingdon OX14 4RN, United Kingdom
Ph: 44 20 70176000
Fax: 44 20 70176336
Peer-reviewed journal publishing original peer-reviewed research papers as well as review papers and other appropriate educational material. **Freq:** Bimonthly. **Key Personnel:** Prof. Jean-Jacques Amy, Editor-in-Chief; Prof. Medard Lech, Editor; Prof. Dan Apter, Editor; Dr. Dimitrios Lazaris, Editor; Dr. Anne Webb, Editor. **ISSN:** 1362-5187. **Subscription Rates:** US$910 individuals print only; US$910 institutions online only; US$910 institutions print only; US$910 individuals online only. **Remarks:** Accepts advertising. **URL:** http://www.escrh.eu/. **Circ:** (Not Reported)

51780 ■ European Journal of Engineering Education
Taylor & Francis Ltd.
2 & 4 Park Sq.
Milton Pk.
Abingdon OX14 4RN, United Kingdom
Ph: 44 20 70176000
Fax: 44 20 70176336
Peer-reviewed journal covering engineering education. **Freq:** 6/yr. **Key Personnel:** Jean Michel, Founding Ed.; E. de Graaff, Editor-in-Chief, ejee@tudelft.nl; S. Ihsen, Assoc. Ed.; J. Bernhard, Assoc. Ed.; A. Kolmos, Assoc. Ed.; M. F. Ramalhoto, Assoc. Ed. **ISSN:** 0304-3797. **Subscription Rates:** 1,395 institutions print + online; US$2,313 institutions print + online; 1,326 institutions online; US$2,197 institutions online; EUR39 individuals society. **Remarks:** Accepts advertising on request. **URL:** http://www.tandf.co.uk/journals/titles/03043797.asp. **Circ:** (Not Reported)

51781 ■ European Journal of Sport Science
Taylor & Francis Ltd.
2 & 4 Park Sq.
Milton Pk.
Abingdon OX14 4RN, United Kingdom
Ph: 44 20 70176000
Fax: 44 20 70176336
Peer-reviewed journal promoting the highest standards of scientific study and scholarship in respect of the following fields: (a) natural sciences of sport; (b) social and behavioural sciences and humanities (c) sports medicine; and (d) sport itself. **Freq:** 6/yr. **Key Personnel:** Dr. Asker E. Jeukendrup, Editor-in-Chief, a.e.jeukendrup@bham.ac.uk; Stephen D.R. Harridge, Assoc. Ed.; Paavo V. Komi, Assoc. Ed.; Anton Wagenmakers, Assoc. Ed.; Joan Duda, Assoc. Ed.; Hermann Schwameder, Motor Control and Learning. **ISSN:** 1746-1391. **Subscription Rates:** US$572 institutions online; US$543 institutions print & online; 380 institutions print & online; 362 institutions online; EUR455 institutions print & online; EUR432 institutions online. **Remarks:** Accepts advertising. **URL:** http://www.tandf.co.uk/journals/titles/17461391.asp. **Circ:** (Not Reported)

51782 ■ European Journal of Teacher Education (EJTE)
Routledge
Taylor & Francis Group Ltd.
2 Park Sq.
Milton Pk.
Abingdon OX14 4RN, United Kingdom

Ph: 44 20 70176000
Fax: 44 20 70176699
Publisher E-mail: webmaster.books@tandf.co.uk
Peer-reviewed journal focusing on policies, theories and practices related to the education and training of teachers at pre-service and in-service levels in European countries in connection with the Association for Teacher Education in Europe (ATEE). **Freq:** 4/yr. **Key Personnel:** James McCall, Editorial Board; Valerie Halstead, Editorial Board; Onno De Jong, Editorial Board; Kay Livingston, Editor; Geri Smith, Co-Ed. **ISSN:** 0261-9768. **Subscription Rates:** US$498 individuals print only; US$1,870 institutions online version; US$1,969 institutions print and online version; 327 individuals print only; 1,126 institutions online; 1,185 institutions print + online; EUR1,568 institutions print and online; EUR1,489 institutions online only; EUR397 individuals. **Remarks:** Advertising accepted; rates available upon request. **URL:** http://www.tandf.co.uk/journals/carfax/02619768.html. **Circ:** (Not Reported)

51783 ■ The European Legacy
Routledge
Taylor & Francis Group Ltd.
2 Park Sq.
Milton Pk.
Abingdon OX14 4RN, United Kingdom
Ph: 44 20 70176000
Fax: 44 20 70176699
Publisher E-mail: webmaster.books@tandf.co.uk
Peer-reviewed journal containing articles on European intellectual and cultural history. **Freq:** 7/yr. **Key Personnel:** Prof. Ezra Talmor, Editor; Richard Bellamy, Board of Advisory Ed.; Robert Mauzi, Board of Advisory Ed.; David W. Lovell, Editor; F.A.M. Alting Von Geusau, Board of Advisory Ed.; Stanley Hoffman, Board of Advisory Ed. **ISSN:** 1084-8770. **Subscription Rates:** US$79 individuals print only; US$714 institutions online only; US$752 institutions print & online; 47 individuals print only; 431 institutions online; 454 institutions print & online; EUR599 institutions print and online; EUR569 institutions online only; EUR63 individuals. **URL:** http://www.tandf.co.uk/journals/carfax/10848770.html.

51784 ■ European Security
Routledge
Taylor & Francis Group Ltd.
2 Park Sq.
Milton Pk.
Abingdon OX14 4RN, United Kingdom
Ph: 44 20 70176000
Fax: 44 20 70176699
Publisher E-mail: webmaster.books@tandf.co.uk
Peer-reviewed journal publishing critical analyses of policies of, and developments in, European institutions and member states, their relations within Europe and Europe in a global context, including regional and international organizations. **Freq:** Quarterly. **Key Personnel:** David J. Galbreath, Editor-in-Chief; Prof. Ian Manners, Editorial Board; Dr. Derek Averre, Editorial Board; Jacob Kipp, Founding Ed.; Anton Bebler, Editorial Board; Prof. Mark Webber, Editorial Board; Prof. James Sperling, Editorial Board; Prof. Edward Kolodziej, Editorial Board. **ISSN:** 0966-2839. **Subscription Rates:** 323 institutions print + online; 306 institutions online; 70 institutions print only; US$528 institutions print + online; US$502 institutions online; US$112 individuals print only; EUR420 institutions print and online; EUR400 institutions online only; EUR89 individuals. **Remarks:** Advertising accepted; rates available upon request. **URL:** http://www.tandf.co.uk/journals/titles/09662839.asp. **Circ:** (Not Reported)

51785 ■ European Societies
Routledge
Taylor & Francis Group Ltd.
2 Park Sq.
Milton Pk.
Abingdon OX14 4RN, United Kingdom
Ph: 44 20 70176000
Fax: 44 20 70176699
Publisher E-mail: webmaster.books@tandf.co.uk
Peer-reviewed journal covering social theory and analysis on European developments. **Freq:** 5/yr. **Key Personnel:** Karin Wall, Editorial Board; John Scott, Editor; Mary Daly, Editorial Advisory Board; Max Haller, Editorial Board; Agnes Skamballis, Editorial Asst.; Michele Lamb, Book Review Ed. **ISSN:** 1461-6696. **Subscription Rates:** US$305 individuals print only; US$868 institutions online; US$914 institutions print and online; 182 individuals print only; 523 institutions online; 551

institutions print & online; EUR728 institutions print and online; EUR691 institutions online only; EUR243 individuals. **Remarks:** Advertising accepted; rates available upon request. **URL:** http://www.tandf.co.uk/journals/titles/14616696.asp. **Circ:** (Not Reported)

51786 ■ European Sport Management Quarterly (ESMQ)
Routledge
Taylor & Francis Group Ltd.
2 Park Sq.
Milton Pk.
Abingdon OX14 4RN, United Kingdom
Ph: 44 20 70176000
Fax: 44 20 70176699
Publisher E-mail: webmaster.books@tandf.co.uk
Peer-reviewed journal focusing on the role of sport management and sport bodies in social life and covering the social forces and social practices affecting these organizations. **Freq:** 5/yr. **Key Personnel:** Trevor Slack, Editorial Board; Ian Henry, Editorial Board; Marijke Taks, Editor. **ISSN:** 1618-4742. **Subscription Rates:** 419 institutions print + online; 398 institutions online; 98 individuals print only; US$698 institutions print + online; US$663 institutions online; US$164 individuals print only; EUR555 institutions print and online; EUR528 institutions online only; EUR130 individuals. **Remarks:** Advertising accepted; rates available upon request. **URL:** http://www.tandf.co.uk/journals/titles/16184742.asp. **Circ:** (Not Reported)

51787 ■ Evaluation & Research in Education
Routledge
Taylor & Francis Group Ltd.
2 Park Sq.
Milton Pk.
Abingdon OX14 4RN, United Kingdom
Ph: 44 20 70176000
Fax: 44 20 70176699
Publisher E-mail: webmaster.books@tandf.co.uk
Peer-reviewed journal covering research and education. **Founded:** 1987. **Freq:** 4/yr. **Key Personnel:** Prof. Keith Morrison, Editor, kmorrison@must.edu.mo; Prof. Stephen Gorard, Assoc. Ed.; Dr. Emma Smith, Review Ed. **ISSN:** 0950-0790. **Subscription Rates:** 199 institutions print + online; US$397 institutions print + online; EUR298 institutions print + online; 75 individuals; US$149 individuals; EUR97 individuals; 188 institutions online access; US$378 institutions online access; EUR284 institutions online access. **Remarks:** Accepts advertising. **URL:** http://www.tandf.co.uk/journals/0950-0790. **Circ:** (Not Reported)

51788 ■ Feminist Economics
Routledge
Taylor & Francis Group Ltd.
2 Park Sq.
Milton Pk.
Abingdon OX14 4RN, United Kingdom
Ph: 44 20 70176000
Fax: 44 20 70176699
Publisher E-mail: webmaster.books@tandf.co.uk
Peer-reviewed scholarly journal providing a forum for exchange of views about feminist economic perspectives in connection with International Association for Feminist Economics (IAFFE). **Subtitle:** The International Scholarly Journal of the International Association for Feminist Economics (IAFFE). **Freq:** Quarterly. **Key Personnel:** Casey L. Fleming, Managing Editor; Diana Strassmann, Editor; Cheryl R. Doss, Book Review Ed. **ISSN:** 1354-5701. **Subscription Rates:** 322 institutions print + online; US$462 institutions print + online; 305 institutions online; US$439 institutions online; EUR367 institutions print and online; EUR349 institutions online only. **Remarks:** Advertising accepted; rates available upon request. **URL:** http://www.tandf.co.uk/journals/routledge/13545701.html. **Circ:** (Not Reported)

51789 ■ Fetal and Pediatric Pathology
Taylor & Francis Ltd.
2 & 4 Park Sq.
Milton Pk.
Abingdon OX14 4RN, United Kingdom
Ph: 44 20 70176000
Fax: 44 20 70176336
Peer-reviewed and International journal publishing data on diseases of the developing embryo, newborns, children, and adolescents, encompassing molecular basis of genetic disorders; molecular basis of diseases that lead to implantation failures; molecular basis of abnormal placentation; placentology and molecular basis of habitual abortion; intrauterine development and molecular basis of embryonic death; pathogenisis and

UNITED KINGDOM ▪ ABINGDON

etiologic factors involved in sudden infant death syndrome; the underlying molecular basis, and pathogenesis of diseases that lead to morbidity and mortality in newborns; prenatal, perinatal, and pediatric diseases and molecular basis of diseases of childhood including solid tumors and tumors of the hematopoietic system; and experimental and molecularpathology. **Freq:** Bimonthly. **Key Personnel:** Dr. Enid Gilbert-Barness, Editor-in-Chief; Dr. Atilano G. Lacson, Editorial Board; Daria M. Haust, MD, Assoc. Ed.; John M. Opitz, MD, Assoc. Ed.; Kathleen Lonkey, Managing Editor; Lewis A. Barness, MD, Editorial Board. **ISSN:** 1551-3815. **Subscription Rates:** 790 institutions; US$1,290 institutions; EUR1,035 institutions. **Remarks:** Accepts advertising. **URL:** http://informahealthcare.com/pdp. **Circ:** (Not Reported)

51790 ▪ Folklore
Routledge
Taylor & Francis Group Ltd.
2 Park Sq.
Milton Pk.
Abingdon OX14 4RN, United Kingdom
Ph: 44 20 70176000
Fax: 44 20 70176699
Publisher E-mail: webmaster.books@tandf.co.uk
Peer-reviewed journal covering anthropology and folklore. **Founded:** 1878. **Freq:** 3/yr. **Key Personnel:** Dr. Lizanne Henderson, Editorial Asst.; Dr. Jessica Hemming, Asst. Ed.; Prof. Patricia Lysaght, Editor; Jacqueline Simpson, Editorial Board; Galit Hasan-Rokem, International Advisory Board; Sandy Hobbs, Editorial Board; Dr. Caroline Oates, Assoc. Ed.; Robert McDowall, Editorial Board; Ulrika Wolf-Knuts, International Advisory Board. **ISSN:** 0015-587X. **Subscription Rates:** 296 institutions print + online; US$492 institutions print + online; 282 institutions online; US$467 institutions online. **Remarks:** Accepts advertising on request. **URL:** http://www.tandf.co.uk/journals/titles/0015587x.asp. **Circ:** (Not Reported)

51791 ▪ Free Radical Research
Taylor & Francis Ltd.
2 & 4 Park Sq.
Milton Pk.
Abingdon OX14 4RN, United Kingdom
Ph: 44 20 70176000
Fax: 44 20 70176336
Journal publishing articles on the chemistry of free radicals, the production of free radicals by xenobiotics and biological systems, free radical damage to cells and tissues, and defence mechanisms against free radical damage. **Freq:** Monthly. **Key Personnel:** Michael Davies, Editor-in-Chief, daviesm@hri.org.au; Prof. Helmut Sies, Editor-in-Chief, sies@uni-duesseldorf.de; Tilman Grune, Assoc. Ed., grune@uni-hohenheim.de. **ISSN:** 1071-5762. **Subscription Rates:** 2,415 institutions; US$3,770 institutions; EUR3,015 institutions. **Remarks:** Accepts advertising. **URL:** http://www.informaworld.com/smpp/title~content=t713642632~db=all; http://informahealthcare.com/fra. **Circ:** (Not Reported)

51792 ▪ Fyne Times
Linde Bldg.
7 Nuffield Way
Abingdon OX14 1RJ, United Kingdom
Ph: 44 1235 468428
Publisher E-mail: news@fyne.co.uk
Lifestyle magazine for gay and lesbian. **Founded:** 2001. **Freq:** Monthly. **URL:** http://www.fyne.co.uk.

51793 ▪ Gender and Education
Routledge
Taylor & Francis Group Ltd.
2 Park Sq.
Milton Pk.
Abingdon OX14 4RN, United Kingdom
Ph: 44 20 70176000
Fax: 44 20 70176699
Publisher E-mail: webmaster.books@tandf.co.uk
Peer-reviewed journal providing a platform for educational research and ideas that focus on gender as a category of analysis. **Freq:** Bimonthly. **Key Personnel:** Suki Ali, Editorial Board; Arwen Raddon, Reviews Ed.; Debbie Epstein, Editor; Tehmina Basit, Editorial Board; Shereen Benjamin, Editorial Board; Emma Renold, Editor; Mary Jane Kehily, Editor; Terri Kim, Editorial Board; Jackie Marsh, Editorial Board. **ISSN:** 0954-0253. **Subscription Rates:** US$376 individuals; US$1,975 institu-

tions online only; US$2,078 institutions print & online; 190 individuals; 1,053 institutions online only; 1,108 institutions print & online, EUR1,654 institutions print and online; EUR1,571 institutions online only; EUR299 individuals. **Remarks:** Advertising accepted; rates available upon request. **URL:** http://www.tandf.co.uk/journal.asp?issn=0954-0253&linktype=1. **Circ:** (Not Reported)

51794 ▪ Geopolitics
Routledge
Taylor & Francis Group Ltd.
2 Park Sq.
Milton Pk.
Abingdon OX14 4RN, United Kingdom
Ph: 44 20 70176000
Fax: 44 20 70176699
Publisher E-mail: webmaster.books@tandf.co.uk
Peer-reviewed journal covering all aspects of the social sciences. Emphasizes on political geography, international relations, the territorial aspects of political science and international law. **Freq:** Quarterly. **Key Personnel:** John Agnew, Ed. Emeritus, jagnew@geog.ucla.edu; David Newman, Editor, newman@bgumail.bgu.ac.il; Merje Kuus, Book Review Ed., kuus@geog.ubc.ca. **ISSN:** 1465-0045. **Subscription Rates:** US$122 individuals; US$474 institutions online only; US$499 institutions print + online; 300 institutions print & online; 286 institutions online only; 88 individuals; EUR397 institutions print and online; EUR378 institutions online only; EUR97 individuals. **Remarks:** Advertising accepted; rates available upon request. **URL:** http://www.tandf.co.uk/journals/titles/14650045.asp. **Circ:** (Not Reported)

51795 ▪ Global Change, Peace & Security
Routledge
Taylor & Francis Group Ltd.
2 Park Sq.
Milton Pk.
Abingdon OX14 4RN, United Kingdom
Ph: 44 20 70176000
Fax: 44 20 70176699
Publisher E-mail: webmaster.books@tandf.co.uk
Peer-reviewed journal focusing on competitive geopolitics and geoeconomics. **Freq:** 3/yr. **Key Personnel:** Michael O'Keefe, Editorial Committee; Stephen James, Editor; Luca Anceschi, Editorial Committee; Savitri Taylor, Dep. Ed.; Robin Cameron, Review Ed.; Lorraine Elliott, Editorial Committee. **ISSN:** 1478-1158. **Subscription Rates:** US$145 individuals print only; US$545 institutions online only; US$574 institutions print + online; 345 institutions print + online; 327 institutions online only; 101 individuals; $A 409 institutions print + online; $A 388 institutions online only; $A 172 individuals; EUR457 institutions print and online. **Remarks:** Advertising accepted; rates available upon request. **URL:** http://www.tandf.co.uk/journals/journal.asp?issn=1478-1158&linktype=1. **Formerly:** Pacifica Review: Peace, Security & Global Change. **Circ:** (Not Reported)

51796 ▪ Global Crime
Routledge
Taylor & Francis Group Ltd.
2 Park Sq.
Milton Pk.
Abingdon OX14 4RN, United Kingdom
Ph: 44 20 70176000
Fax: 44 20 70176699
Publisher E-mail: webmaster.books@tandf.co.uk
Peer-reviewed journal covering the whole range of criminal activities, from corruption and illegal market transactions to the shadowy corners where states, terrorist movements and similar actors engage in criminal conspiracy. **Freq:** 4/yr. **Key Personnel:** Mark Galeotti, Founding Ed.; Jay Albanese, Editorial Board; Federico Varese, Editor; Felia Allum, Assoc. Ed.; Fabio Armao, Editorial Board; Mike Levi, Editorial Board; Carlo Morselli, Assoc. Ed.; Liz David Barrett, Assoc. Ed.; Diego Gambetta, Editorial Board. **ISSN:** 1744-0572. **Subscription Rates:** 282 institutions print and online; 267 institutions online; 60 individuals print; US$463 institutions print and online; US$440 institutions online; US$98 individuals print; EUR368 institutions print and online; EUR350 institutions online; EUR78 individuals print. **Remarks:** Accepts advertising. **URL:** http://www.tandf.co.uk/journals/titles/17440572.asp. **Circ:** (Not Reported)

51797 ▪ Global Public Health
Taylor & Francis Ltd.
2 & 4 Park Sq.
Milton Pk.
Abingdon OX14 4RN, United Kingdom

Ph: 44 20 70176000
Fax: 44 20 70176336
Publication E-mail: gph-msph@columbia.edu
Peer-reviewed journal concerned with key public health issues that have come to the fore in the global environment: mounting inequalities between rich and poor; the globalization of trade; new patterns of travel and migration; epidemics of newly-emerging and re-emerging infectious diseases; the HIV/AIDS pandemic; the increase in chronic illnesses; escalating pressure on public health infrastructures around the world; and the growing range and scale of conflict situations, terrorist threats, environmental pressures, natural and human-made disasters. **Subtitle:** An International Journal for Research, Policy and Practice. **Freq:** Bimonthly. **Key Personnel:** Prof. Richard Parker, Editor-in-Chief; Paul Wilkinson, Assoc. Ed.; Anthony Zwi, Assoc. Ed.; Marni Sommer, Exec. Ed.; Marcia Inhorn, Assoc. Ed.; Sofia Gruskin, Assoc. Ed.; Ron Waldman, Assoc. Ed.; Maria Dulce F. Natividad, Managing Editor; Peter Aggleton, Sen. Ed. **ISSN:** 1744-1692. **Subscription Rates:** US$40 other countries developing country; 308 institutions print + online; US$551 institutions print + online; 292 institutions online; US$523 institutions online; 93 individuals print only; US$168 individuals print only; EUR441 institutions print + online; EUR419 institutions online; EUR135 individuals. **Remarks:** Accepts advertising. **URL:** http://www.tandf.co.uk/journals/titles/17441692.asp. **Circ:** (Not Reported)

51798 ▪ Global Society
Routledge
Taylor & Francis Group Ltd.
2 Park Sq.
Milton Pk.
Abingdon OX14 4RN, United Kingdom
Ph: 44 20 70176000
Fax: 44 20 70176699
Publisher E-mail: webmaster.books@tandf.co.uk
Peer-reviewed journal presenting new agenda in global and international relations. Promotes the analysis of multiple level international transactions. **Subtitle:** Journal of Interdisciplinary International Relations. **Freq:** Quarterly. **Key Personnel:** Dr. Doug Stokes, Editor-in-Chief; Chris Brown, International Editorial Board; Bertrand Badie, International Editorial Board; Gerald Chan, International Editorial Board; Anne Deighton, International Editorial Board; Fulvio Attina, International Editorial Board. **ISSN:** 1360-0826. **Subscription Rates:** US$134 individuals; US$718 institutions online only; US$757 institutions print + online; 455 institutions print + online; 433 institutions online only; 85 individuals; EUR602 institutions print and online; EUR572 institutions online only; EUR107 individuals. **Remarks:** Advertising accepted; rates available upon request. **URL:** http://www.tandf.co.uk/journals/journal.asp?issn=1360-0826&linktype=1. **Circ:** (Not Reported)

51799 ▪ Globalisation, Societies and Education
Routledge
Taylor & Francis Group Ltd.
2 Park Sq.
Milton Pk.
Abingdon OX14 4RN, United Kingdom
Ph: 44 20 70176000
Fax: 44 20 70176699
Publisher E-mail: webmaster.books@tandf.co.uk
Peer-reviewed journal analyzing the complexities of globalization. **Freq:** Quarterly. **Key Personnel:** Prof. Susan L. Robertson, Editor; Prof. Roger Dale, Editor; Prof. Andy Green, Editorial Board; Prof. Michael Apple, Consulting Ed.; Prof. Karen Mundy, Editorial Board; Jacky Brine, Consulting Ed. **ISSN:** 1476-7724. **Subscription Rates:** US$177 individuals print; US$508 institutions online; US$535 institutions print + online; 120 individuals; 305 institutions online only; 322 institutions print + online; EUR425 institutions print and online; EUR404 institutions online only; EUR142 individuals. **Remarks:** Advertising accepted; rates available upon request. **URL:** http://www.tandf.co.uk/journals/titles/14767724.asp. **Circ:** (Not Reported)

51800 ▪ Globalizations
Routledge
Taylor & Francis Group Ltd.
2 Park Sq.
Milton Pk.
Abingdon OX14 4RN, United Kingdom
Ph: 44 20 70176000
Fax: 44 20 70176699

Publisher E-mail: webmaster.books@tandf.co.uk
Peer-reviewed journal covering articles on globalization. **Freq:** Quarterly. **Key Personnel:** Barry Gills, PhD, Founding Ed., b.k.gills@ncl.ac.uk; Benjamin Barber, International Editorial Board; Saskia Sassen, International Editorial Board; Spike V. Peterson, International Editorial Board; Rebecca Harris, Editorial Asst.; Isidro Morales, International Editorial Board. **ISSN:** 1474-7731. **Subscription Rates:** US$119 individuals; US$499 institutions online only; US$525 institutions print + online; US$31 members; 19 members; 71 individuals; 300 institutions online only; 316 institutions print + online; EUR418 institutions print and online; EUR397 institutions online only. **Remarks:** Advertising accepted; rates available upon request. **URL:** http://www.tandf.co.uk/journals/titles/14747731.asp. **Circ:** (Not Reported)

51801 ■ Health, Risk and Society
Routledge
Taylor & Francis Group Ltd.
2 Park Sq.
Milton Pk.
Abingdon OX14 4RN, United Kingdom
Ph: 44 20 70176000
Fax: 44 20 70176699
Publisher E-mail: webmaster.books@tandf.co.uk
Peer-reviewed journal focusing on theoretical and empirical understanding of the social processes influencing communication, assessment and management of risks with regard to health. **Freq:** Bimonthly. **Key Personnel:** Andy Alaszewski, Editor, a.m.alaszewski@kent.ac.uk; John Brown, Editorial Board; Christopher Candlin, Editorial Board; Patrick Brown, Dep. Ed.; Joanne N. Warner, Book Review Ed.; Jens Zinn, Asia Pacific Ed. **ISSN:** 1369-8575. **Subscription Rates:** US$187 individuals; US$668 institutions online; US$703 institutions print + online; 130 individuals; 402 institutions online; 422 institutions print + online; EUR560 institutions print and online; EUR532 institutions online only; EUR149 individuals. **Remarks:** Accepts advertising. **URL:** http://www.tandf.co.uk/journals/carfax/13698575.html. **Circ:** (Not Reported)

51802 ■ High Ability Studies
Routledge
Taylor & Francis Group Ltd.
2 Park Sq.
Milton Pk.
Abingdon OX14 4RN, United Kingdom
Ph: 44 20 70176000
Fax: 44 20 70176699
Publisher E-mail: webmaster.books@tandf.co.uk
Peer-reviewed journal covering the study of the development of human abilities to their highest level. Official journal of the European Council for High Ability (ECHA). **Founded:** 1990. **Freq:** Semiannual. **Trim Size:** 17.4 x 24.8 cm. **Key Personnel:** Albert Ziegler, International Advisory Board; Jessie Ee, International Advisory Board; Heidrun Stoeger, Editor-in-Chief, heidrun.stoeger@paedagogik.uni-regensburg.de; Jean Cote, International Advisory Board; Ernst Hany, International Advisory Board; Joan Freeman, International Advisory Board; Hans Gruber, International Advisory Board; Judy L. Lupert, International Advisory Board; John Vincent, International Advisory Board. **ISSN:** 1359-8139. **Subscription Rates:** 260 institutions print + online; US$430 institutions print + online; 246 institutions online; US$408 institutions online; 73 individuals; US$116 individuals; EUR343 institutions print and online; EUR325 institutions online only; EUR92 individuals. **Remarks:** Advertising accepted; rates available upon request. **URL:** http://www.tandf.co.uk/journals/titles/13598139.asp. **Formerly:** European Journal for High Ability. **Circ:** 400

51803 ■ Historical Journal of Film, Radio and Television
Routledge
Taylor & Francis Group Ltd.
2 Park Sq.
Milton Pk.
Abingdon OX14 4RN, United Kingdom
Ph: 44 20 70176000
Fax: 44 20 70176699
Publisher E-mail: webmaster.books@tandf.co.uk
Peer-reviewed journal focusing on history. **Freq:** Quarterly. **Key Personnel:** David Culbert, Editor; Ian Jarvie, Assoc. Ed.; Philip M. Taylor, Assoc. Ed.; Brett Bowles, Review Ed.; Roel Vande Winkel, Review Ed. **ISSN:** 0143-9685. **Subscription Rates:** US$1,127 institutions print and online; US$1,071 institutions on-

line; US$392 individuals; 682 institutions print and online; 648 institutions online; 235 individuals. **URL:** http://www.tandf.co.uk/journals/carfax/01439685.html.

51804 ■ History and Anthropology
Routledge
Taylor & Francis Group Ltd.
2 Park Sq.
Milton Pk.
Abingdon OX14 4RN, United Kingdom
Ph: 44 20 70176000
Fax: 44 20 70176699
Publisher E-mail: webmaster.books@tandf.co.uk
Journal devoted to integration of history and social sciences, focusing on exchange between anthropologically-informed history, historically-informed anthropology and the history of ethnographic and anthropological representation. **Freq:** Quarterly. **Key Personnel:** Paul Sant Cassia, Editor; Jean Comaroff, Editorial Board; Stephen Bann, Editorial Board; James Clifford, Editorial Board; Michael Gilsenan, Editorial Board. **ISSN:** 0275-7206. **Subscription Rates:** US$1,114 institutions online; 718 institutions online; US$1,173 institutions print + online; 756 institutions print + online; US$239 individuals; 162 individuals; EUR934 institutions print + online; EUR887 institutions online only; EUR190 individuals. **Remarks:** Advertising accepted; rates available upon request. **URL:** http://www.tandf.co.uk/journals/titles/02757206.asp. **Circ:** (Not Reported)

51805 ■ History of Photography
Routledge
Taylor & Francis Group Ltd.
2 Park Sq.
Milton Pk.
Abingdon OX14 4RN, United Kingdom
Ph: 44 20 70176000
Fax: 44 20 70176699
Publisher E-mail: webmaster.books@tandf.co.uk
Peer-reviewed journal containing information on the history of photography. **Founded:** 1977. **Freq:** 4/yr. **Trim Size:** A4. **Key Personnel:** Graham Smith, Editor, jgrahamsmith@comcast.net; Peggy Ann Kusnerz, Contributing Ed.; John Mraz, Contributing Ed.; Natalie Adamson, Book Review Ed., na14@st-andrews.ac.uk; Jan Baetens, Contributing Ed.; Catherine De Lorenzo, Contributing Ed. **ISSN:** 0308-7298. **Subscription Rates:** 328 institutions print + online; US$548 institutions print + online; 172 individuals; US$289 individuals; EUR437 institutions print and online; EUR231 individuals. **Remarks:** Accepts advertising on request. **URL:** http://www.tandf.co.uk/journals/titles/03087298.asp. **Circ:** (Not Reported)

51806 ■ Housing Studies
Routledge
Taylor & Francis Group Ltd.
2 Park Sq.
Milton Pk.
Abingdon OX14 4RN, United Kingdom
Ph: 44 20 70176000
Fax: 44 20 70176699
Publisher E-mail: webmaster.books@tandf.co.uk
Journal initiating an academic dialogue in the housing field. **Freq:** Bimonthly. **Key Personnel:** Ray Forrest, Managing Editor; Charles E. Connerly, International Editorial Advisory Board; Alex Marsh, Management Board; Jeanet Kullberg, International Editorial Advisory Board; Ya Ping Wang, Management Board; Roger Andersson, Management Board. **ISSN:** 0267-3037. **Subscription Rates:** 492 institutions print + online; 467 institutions online; 154 individuals; US$817 institutions print + online; US$776 institutions online; US$258 individuals; EUR651 institutions print and online; EUR619 institutions online only; EUR205 individuals. **Remarks:** Advertising accepted; rates available upon request. **URL:** http://www.tandf.co.uk/journals/titles/02673037.asp. **Circ:** (Not Reported)

51807 ■ Housing, Theory & Society
Routledge
Taylor & Francis Group Ltd.
2 Park Sq.
Milton Pk.
Abingdon OX14 4RN, United Kingdom
Ph: 44 20 70176000
Fax: 44 20 70176699
Publisher E-mail: webmaster.books@tandf.co.uk
Journal applying social theory to the field of housing. **Freq:** Quarterly. **Key Personnel:** David Clapham, Editor; Keith Jacobs, Book Review Ed.; Chris Allen, Editorial Board; Sarah Blandy, Advisory Board; Rebecca Chiu,

Advisory Board; Craig Gurney, Advisory Board. **ISSN:** 1403-6096. **Subscription Rates:** US$374 institutions online; US$154 individuals; US$394 institutions print + online; 226 institutions online; 238 institutions print + online; 93 individuals; EUR314 institutions print and online; EUR2299 institutions online only; EUR123 individuals. **Remarks:** Advertising accepted; rates available upon request. **URL:** http://www.tandf.co.uk/journals/titles/14036096.asp. **Circ:** (Not Reported)

51808 ■ Human Fertility
Taylor & Francis Ltd.
2 & 4 Park Sq.
Milton Pk.
Abingdon OX14 4RN, United Kingdom
Ph: 44 20 70176000
Fax: 44 20 70176336
International, multidisciplinary journal dedicated to furthering research and promoting good practice in the areas of human fertility and infertility, including topics that span the range from molecular medicine to healthcare delivery, welcoming contributions from professionals and academics from the spectrum of disciplines concerned with human fertility. **Freq:** Quarterly. **Key Personnel:** Prof. Henry Leese, Editor-in-Chief; Dr. Daniel Brison, Editorial Board; Dr. Jane A. Stewart, Editorial Board; Dr. Mark Hamilton, Editorial Board; Dr. Alireza Fazeli, Editorial Board; Dr. Jim Monarch, Editorial Board; Prof. Debbie Barber, International Advisory Board. **ISSN:** 1464-7273. **Subscription Rates:** 400 institutions; US$680 institutions; EUR540 institutions. **Remarks:** Accepts advertising. **URL:** http://informahealthcare.com/huf. **Circ:** (Not Reported)

51809 ■ Human Resource Development International
Routledge
Taylor & Francis Group Ltd.
2 Park Sq.
Milton Pk.
Abingdon OX14 4RN, United Kingdom
Ph: 44 20 70176000
Fax: 44 20 70176699
Publisher E-mail: webmaster.books@tandf.co.uk
Peer-reviewed journal focusing on learning and performance by individuals, groups and organizations through out the world. **Freq:** 5/yr. **Key Personnel:** Peter K. Kuchinke, Editorial Board; Rob Poell, Editor, r.poell@uvt.nl; Jean Woodall, Editorial Board. **ISSN:** 1367-8868. **Subscription Rates:** US$193 individuals print only; US$783 institutions online only; US$825 institutions print + online; 142 individuals; 469 institutions online only; 494 institutions print + online; EUR656 institutions print and online; EUR623 institutions online only; EUR153 individuals. **Remarks:** Advertising accepted; rates available upon request. **URL:** http://www.tandf.co.uk/journals/routledge/13678868.html. **Circ:** (Not Reported)

51810 ■ Hypertension in Pregnancy
Taylor & Francis Ltd.
2 & 4 Park Sq.
Milton Pk.
Abingdon OX14 4RN, United Kingdom
Ph: 44 20 70176000
Fax: 44 20 70176336
Peer-reviewed journal publishing data that pertains to human and animal hypertension during gestation, such as physiology of circulatory control, pathophysiology, methodology, therapy or any other material relevant to the relationship between elevated blood pressure and pregnancy. **Freq:** Quarterly. **Key Personnel:** Dr. Peter von Dadelszen, Editor, pdadelszen@cw.bc.ca; Fiona Lyall, Editor; Marshall D. Lindheimer, Assoc. Ed. **ISSN:** 1064-1955. **Subscription Rates:** 1,065 institutions; US$1,750 institutions; EUR1,400 institutions. **Remarks:** Accepts advertising. **URL:** http://informahealthcare.com/loi/hip. **Circ:** (Not Reported)

51811 ■ Immigrants & Minorities
Routledge
Taylor & Francis Group Ltd.
2 Park Sq.
Milton Pk.
Abingdon OX14 4RN, United Kingdom
Ph: 44 20 70176000
Fax: 44 20 70176699
Publisher E-mail: webmaster.books@tandf.co.uk
Journal dedicated to the study of history of immigration and allied subjects, with emphasis ranging from construction of race, ethnic and minority relations in the past to current studies. **Founded:** 1981. **Freq:** 3/yr. **Key Personnel:** Colin Holmes, Editor; David Mayall, Editor;

Gavin Schaffer, Assoc. Ed. **ISSN:** 0261-9288. **Subscription Rates:** US$407 institutions print + online; US$386 institutions online only; US$97 individuals; 256 institutions print + online; 243 institutions online only; 62 individuals; EUR324 institutions print and online; EUR307 institutions online only; EUR77 individuals. **Remarks:** Advertising accepted; rates available upon request. **URL:** http://www.tandf.co.uk/journals/journal.asp?issn=0261-9288&linktype=5. **Circ:** (Not Reported)

51812 ■ India Review
Routledge
Taylor & Francis Group Ltd.
2 Park Sq.
Milton Pk.
Abingdon OX14 4RN, United Kingdom
Ph: 44 20 70176000
Fax: 44 20 70176699
Publisher E-mail: webmaster.books@tandf.co.uk
Peer-reviewed journal reporting recent issues of Indian politics, economics and society. **Freq:** Quarterly. **Key Personnel:** Sumit Ganguly, Founding Ed.; Christine Fair, Assoc. Ed.; Anthony Cerulli, Managing Editor; Paul Kapur, Assoc. Ed.; Jessica Seddon Wallack, Assoc. Ed.; Arthur Rubinoff, Contributing Ed. **ISSN:** 1473-6489. **Subscription Rates:** 228 institutions print + online; US$367 institutions print + online; 216 institutions online; US$349 institutions online; 63 individuals; US$97 individuals; EUR292 institutions print and online; EUR277 institutions online only; EUR77 individuals. **URL:** http://www.tandf.co.uk/journals/titles/14736489.asp.

51813 ■ Indonesia and the Malay World
Routledge
Taylor & Francis Group Ltd.
2 Park Sq.
Milton Pk.
Abingdon OX14 4RN, United Kingdom
Ph: 44 20 70176000
Fax: 44 20 70176699
Publisher E-mail: webmaster.books@tandf.co.uk
Peer-reviewed journal dealing with study of the entire region of Malaya. **Founded:** 1973. **Freq:** 3/yr. **Key Personnel:** Prof. Peter Austin, Editorial Board; Dr. Nigel Phillips, Honorary Ed.; Pauline Khng, Managing Editor, imw@soas.ac.uk. **ISSN:** 1363-9811. **Subscription Rates:** US$138 individuals; US$404 institutions online only; US$425 institutions print + online; 72 individuals; 246 institutions online only; 260 institutions print + online; EUR339 institutions print and online; EUR323 institutions online only; EUR110 individuals. **Remarks:** Advertising accepted; rates available upon request. **URL:** http://www.tandf.co.uk/journals/titles/13639811.asp. **Former name:** Indonesia Circle. **Circ:** (Not Reported)

51814 ■ Industry & Innovation
Routledge
Taylor & Francis Group Ltd.
2 Park Sq.
Milton Pk.
Abingdon OX14 4RN, United Kingdom
Ph: 44 20 70176000
Fax: 44 20 70176699
Publication E-mail: industryandinnovation@cbs.dk
Publisher E-mail: webmaster.books@tandf.co.uk
Journal dealing with dynamics of industries and innovation, focusing on emergence of new industries, restructuring of existing industries, rise of new institutional and organizational forms. **Freq:** 6/yr. **Key Personnel:** Jens F. Christensen, International Editorial Board; Keld Laursen, Assoc. Ed.; Mark Lorenzen, Editor-in-Chief. **ISSN:** 1366-2716. **Subscription Rates:** 528 institutions print + online; US$877 institutions print + online; $A 981 institutions print + online; 502 institutions online; US$833 institutions online; $A 933 institutions online; 205 individuals; US$328 individuals; $A 472 individuals; EUR698 institutions print + online. **Remarks:** Advertising accepted; rates available upon request. **URL:** http://www.tandf.co.uk/journals/titles/13662716.asp. **Circ:** (Not Reported)

51815 ■ Infant Observation
Routledge
Taylor & Francis Group Ltd.
2 Park Sq.
Milton Pk.
Abingdon OX14 4RN, United Kingdom
Ph: 44 20 70176000
Fax: 44 20 70176699
Publisher E-mail: webmaster.books@tandf.co.uk
Peer-reviewed journal comprising case studies on infant and young child observation, research papers, and articles focusing on wider applications of the psychoanalytic observational method, including its relevance to reflective professional practice in fields such as social work, teaching and nursing. **Freq:** 3/yr. **Key Personnel:** Lisa Miller, Editor; Maria Rhode, Editorial Committee; Michael Rustin, Editorial Committee; Margaret Rustin, Editorial Committee; Louise Allnut, Asst. Ed.; Judith Jackson, Editorial Committee; Anne Alvarez, UK Advisory Board; Maggie Turp, Editorial Committee. **ISSN:** 1369-8036. **Subscription Rates:** 171 institutions print + online; US$311 institutions print + online; 162 institutions online; US$295 institutions online; 52 individuals personal; US$75 individuals personal; 30 students; US$54 students. **Remarks:** Accepts advertising. **URL:** http://www.tandf.co.uk/journals/titles/13698036.asp. **Circ:** (Not Reported)

51816 ■ Informatics for Health and Social Care
Taylor & Francis Ltd.
2 & 4 Park Sq.
Milton Pk.
Abingdon OX14 4RN, United Kingdom
Ph: 44 20 70176000
Fax: 44 20 70176336
Journal promoting the application of analysis, inference and reasoning to medical information, including expert systems and the use of artificial intelligence techniques, hospital management information, patient records, clinical examinations, laboratory results, physiological measurements, medical images of all kinds, primary care information and epidemiology; it is also concerned with the gathering and organization of data and knowledge, and with applications to medical education. **Freq:** Quarterly. **Key Personnel:** Dr. Nicholas Hardiker, Editor; R. Badawi, Editorial Board; A.R. Bakker, Editorial Board; K. Atsumi, Editorial Board. **ISSN:** 1753-8157. **Subscription Rates:** 785 institutions; US$1,385 institutions; EUR1,110 institutions. **Remarks:** Accepts advertising. **URL:** http://www.informaworld.com/smpp/title~content=t713736879; http://informahealthcare.com/mif. **Formerly:** Medical Informatics and the Internet in Medicine. **Circ:** (Not Reported)

51817 ■ Information, Communication and Society
Routledge
Taylor & Francis Group Ltd.
2 Park Sq.
Milton Pk.
Abingdon OX14 4RN, United Kingdom
Ph: 44 20 70176000
Fax: 44 20 70176699
Publisher E-mail: webmaster.books@tandf.co.uk
Peer-reviewed journal dealing with the development and application of information and communications technologies. **Freq:** 8/yr. **Key Personnel:** Brian D. Loader, Editor, ics@tandf.co.uk; William H. Dutton, Editor; Beverly Geesin, Book Review Ed.; Stephen Coleman, Member of the Editorial Board; Abdul Alkalimat, Member of the Editorial Board; Michael Froomkin, Member of the Editorial Board. **ISSN:** 1369-118X. **Subscription Rates:** US$267 individuals print only; US$1,051 individuals online only; US$1,105 individuals print + online; 162 individuals; 631 institutions online; 664 institutions print + online; EUR880 institutions print and online; EUR836 institutions online only; EUR213 individuals. **Remarks:** Advertising accepted; rates available upon request. **URL:** http://www.tandf.co.uk/journals/titles/1369118x.asp. **Circ:** (Not Reported)

51818 ■ Information and Communications Technology Law
Routledge
Taylor & Francis Group Ltd.
2 Park Sq.
Milton Pk.
Abingdon OX14 4RN, United Kingdom
Ph: 44 20 70176000
Fax: 44 20 70176699
Publisher E-mail: webmaster.books@tandf.co.uk
Journal publishing the implications of information technology for legal processes and legal decision-making and related ethical and social issues. **Freq:** 3/yr. **Key Personnel:** Prof. Indira Carr, Exec. Ed., imcarr@btinternet.com; A. Adam, Editorial Board; D. Bainbridge, Editorial Board. **ISSN:** 1360-0834. **Subscription Rates:** US$240 individuals; US$778 institutions online only; US$820 institutions print + online; 480 institutions print + online; 456 institutions online; 132 individuals; 653 institutions print and online; EUR620 institutions online only; EUR190 individuals. **Remarks:** Advertising accepted; rates available upon request. **URL:** http://www.tandf.co.uk/journals/carfax/13600834.html. **Circ:** (Not Reported)

51819 ■ Innovations in Education & Teaching International
Routledge
Taylor & Francis Group Ltd.
2 Park Sq.
Milton Pk.
Abingdon OX14 4RN, United Kingdom
Ph: 44 20 70176000
Fax: 44 20 70176699
Publisher E-mail: webmaster.books@tandf.co.uk
Peer-reviewed journal publishing important contributions relating to the developments in educational technology, in connection with the Staff and Educational Development Association. **Freq:** Quarterly. **Key Personnel:** Gina Wisker, Editor, g.wisker@brighton.ac.uk; Philip Barker, Editor, barker_pg@yahoo.com; Graham Badley, Editorial Advisory Board. **ISSN:** 1470-3297. **Subscription Rates:** 329 institutions print and online; US$548 institutions print and online; 313 institutions online; US$521 institutions online; 87 individuals; US$152 individuals; EUR437 institutions print and online; EUR415 institutions online only; EUR121 individuals. **Remarks:** Advertising accepted; rates available upon request. **URL:** http://www.tandf.co.uk/journals/routledge/14703297.html. **Circ:** (Not Reported)

51820 ■ Intelligence & National Security
Routledge
Taylor & Francis Group Ltd.
2 Park Sq.
Milton Pk.
Abingdon OX14 4RN, United Kingdom
Ph: 44 20 70176000
Fax: 44 20 70176699
Publisher E-mail: webmaster.books@tandf.co.uk
Peer-reviewed journal covering articles on the historical background of intelligence. **Freq:** Bimonthly. **Key Personnel:** Loch K. Johnson, PhD, Editor, johnson@uga.edu; Peter Jackson, PhD, Editor, ptj@aber.ac.uk; David M. Barrett, Editorial Board; Desmond Ball, Editorial Board; Dr. Gerald R. Hughes, Asst. Ed.; Marie Milward, Asst. Ed. **ISSN:** 0268-4527. **Subscription Rates:** US$139 individuals print only; US$861 institutions online only; US$907 institutions print + online; 551 institutions print + online; 523 institutions online only; 92 individuals; 60 members; EUR721 institutions print and online; EUR685 institutions online only; EUR111 individuals. **Remarks:** Advertising accepted; rates available upon request. **URL:** http://www.tandf.co.uk/journals/titles/02684527.asp. **Circ:** (Not Reported)

51821 ■ Inter-Asia Cultural Studies
Routledge
Taylor & Francis Group Ltd.
2 Park Sq.
Milton Pk.
Abingdon OX14 4RN, United Kingdom
Ph: 44 20 70176000
Fax: 44 20 70176699
Publisher E-mail: webmaster.books@tandf.co.uk
Journal covering cultural studies practices in Asia, and focusing on improving communication and exchange between inter-Asia and other regions of the world. **Freq:** Quarterly. **Key Personnel:** Chua Beng Huat, Editorial Collective; Chen Kuan-Hsing, Editorial Collective; Malathi De Alwis, Editorial Collective; Colleen Lye, Editorial Collective; Dai Jinhua, Editorial Collective; Eric Ma, Editorial Collective; Melani Budianta, Editorial Collective; Hilmar Farid, Editorial Collective; Firdous Azim, Editorial Collective; Naifei Ding, Editorial Collective; Sun Ge, Editorial Collective; Rob Wilson, Editorial Collective. **ISSN:** 1464-9373. **Subscription Rates:** 410 institutions print + online; US$641 institutions print + online; 381 institutions online; US$609 institutions online; 80 individuals; US$123 individuals; EUR510 institutions print and online; EUR484 institutions online only; EUR98 individuals. **Remarks:** Advertising accepted; rates available upon request. **URL:** http://www.tandf.co.uk/journals/titles/14649373.asp. **Circ:** (Not Reported)

51822 ■ Intercultural Education
Routledge
Taylor & Francis Group Ltd.
2 Park Sq.
Milton Pk.
Abingdon OX14 4RN, United Kingdom

Ph: 44 20 70176000
Fax: 44 20 70176699
Publisher E-mail: webmaster.books@tandf.co.uk
Peer-reviewed journal covering education in plural societies and focusing on analysis and implementation of intercultural education. **Freq:** Bimonthly. **Key Personnel:** Barry van Driel, Editor; Nektaria Palaiologou, Assoc. Ed.; Agostino Portera, Book Review Ed. **ISSN:** 1476-5986. **Subscription Rates:** US$356 individuals print only; US$1,033 institutions online only; US$1,087 institutions print + online; 654 institutions print + online; 621 institutions online only; 240 individuals; EUR865 institutions print and online; EUR822 institutions online only; EUR283 individuals. **Remarks:** Advertising accepted; rates available upon request. **URL:** http://www.tandf.co.uk/journals/titles/14675986.asp. **Formerly:** European Journal of Intercultural Studies. **Circ:** (Not Reported)

51823 ■ International Economic Journal
Routledge
Taylor & Francis Group Ltd.
2 Park Sq.
Milton Pk.
Abingdon OX14 4RN, United Kingdom
Ph: 44 20 70176000
Fax: 44 20 70176699
Publisher E-mail: webmaster.books@tandf.co.uk
Peer-reviewed journal focusing on research in developmental and International economic areas. **Subtitle:** The International Scholarly Journal of the Korea International Economic Association (KIEA). **Freq:** Quarterly. **Key Personnel:** Jaymin Lee, Managing Editor; Koichi Hamada, Editorial Advisory Board; Robert J. Barro, Editorial Advisory Board; Sunwoong Kim, Co-Ed.; Gregory Chow, Editorial Advisory Board; Jagdish Bhagwati, Editorial Advisory Board; Jere R. Behrman, Editorial Advisory Board; Alan Dearforff, Editorial Advisory Board; Timothy J. Kehoe, Editorial Advisory Board. **ISSN:** 1016-8737. **Subscription Rates:** US$122 individuals; US$341 institutions online only; US$358 institutions print + online; 214 institutions print + online; 204 institutions online only; 72 individuals; EUR286 institutions print and online; EUR271 institutions online only; EUR97 individuals. **Remarks:** Advertising accepted; rates available upon request. **URL:** http://www.tandf.co.uk/journals/titles/10168737.asp. **Circ:** (Not Reported)

51824 ■ International Feminist Journal of Politics
Routledge
Taylor & Francis Group Ltd.
2 Park Sq.
Milton Pk.
Abingdon OX14 4RN, United Kingdom
Ph: 44 20 70176000
Fax: 44 20 70176699
Publisher E-mail: webmaster.books@tandf.co.uk
Peer-reviewed journal focusing on research on women in international relations, politics and women's studies. **Freq:** Quarterly. **Key Personnel:** Sandra Whitworth, Editor, sandraw@yorku.ca; Rekha Pande, Editorial Board; Catherine Eschle, Editor, catherine.eschle@strath.ac.uk. **ISSN:** 1461-6742. **Subscription Rates:** 389 institutions print + online; 369 institutions online; 92 individuals; US$645 institutions print + online; 613 institutions online; US$146 individuals; EUR513 institutions print and online; EUR487 institutions online only; EUR116 individuals. **Remarks:** Advertising accepted; rates available upon request. **URL:** http://www.tandf.co.uk/journals/titles/14616742.asp. **Circ:** (Not Reported)

51825 ■ International Gambling Studies
Routledge
Taylor & Francis Group Ltd.
2 Park Sq.
Milton Pk.
Abingdon OX14 4RN, United Kingdom
Ph: 44 20 70176000
Fax: 44 20 70176699
Publisher E-mail: webmaster.books@tandf.co.uk
Peer-reviewed journal covering analysis and research in gambling studies, focusing on the theory, methods, practice and history of gambling. **Freq:** 3/yr. **Key Personnel:** Jan McMillen, Co-Ed.; Maria Bellringer, International Editorial Board; John Wright, Book Review Ed.; Max Abbott, Co-Ed.; Alex Blaszczynski, PhD, Editor, alexb@psych.usyd.edu.au; David Miers, Co-Ed. **ISSN:** 1445-9795. **Subscription Rates:** 241 institutions print + online; 229 institutions online; 59 individuals; US$402 institutions print + online; US$382 institutions online; US$101 individuals; $A 474 institutions print + online;

$A 450 institutions online; $A 159 individuals; EUR319 institutions print and online. **Remarks:** Advertising accepted; rates available upon request. **URL:** http://www.tandf.co.uk/journals/titles/14459795.asp. **Circ:** (Not Reported)

51826 ■ International Journal for Academic Development
Routledge
Taylor & Francis Group Ltd.
2 Park Sq.
Milton Pk.
Abingdon OX14 4RN, United Kingdom
Ph: 44 20 70176000
Fax: 44 20 70176699
Publisher E-mail: webmaster.books@tandf.co.uk
Peer-reviewed journal covering educational change and focusing on improvements in teaching and learning theories. **Freq:** 3/yr. **Key Personnel:** Dr. Barbara Grant, Editor, bm.grant@auckland.ac.nz; Prof. Lynn K. Taylor, Editor, lynn.taylor@dal.ca; Prof. Mick Healey, Editor, mhealey@glos.ac.uk. **ISSN:** 1360-144X. **Subscription Rates:** 372 institutions print + online; US$615 institutions print + online; 353 institutions online; US$584 institutions online; 89 individuals; US$149 individuals; EUR490 institutions print and online; EUR465 institutions online only; EUR118 individuals. **Remarks:** Advertising accepted; rates available upon request. **URL:** http://www.tandf.co.uk/journals/titles/1360144x.asp. **Circ:** (Not Reported)

51827 ■ International Journal of Art Therapy
Routledge
Taylor & Francis Group Ltd.
2 Park Sq.
Milton Pk.
Abingdon OX14 4RN, United Kingdom
Ph: 44 20 70176000
Fax: 44 20 70176699
Publisher E-mail: webmaster.books@tandf.co.uk
Peer-reviewed journal covering the field of art therapy. **Subtitle:** Inscape. **Freq:** Semiannual. **Key Personnel:** Tim Wright, Editor. **ISSN:** 1745-4832. **Subscription Rates:** US$61 individuals; US$150 institutions online only; US$158 institutions print & online; 87 institutions print & online; 83 institutions online; 34 individuals; EUR49 individuals; EUR120 institutions online only; EUR126 institutions print and online. **Remarks:** Accepts advertising. **URL:** http://www.tandf.co.uk/journals/titles/17454832.asp. **Circ:** (Not Reported)

51828 ■ International Journal of Bilingual Education & Bilingualism
Routledge
Taylor & Francis Group Ltd.
2 Park Sq.
Milton Pk.
Abingdon OX14 4RN, United Kingdom
Ph: 44 20 70176000
Fax: 44 20 70176699
Publisher E-mail: webmaster.books@tandf.co.uk
Scholarly journal covering bilingual education. **Founded:** 1998. **Freq:** Bimonthly. **Key Personnel:** Jim Cummins, Editorial Board; Colin Baker, Editor; Aneta Pavlenko, Review Ed.; Hugo Baetens Beardsmore, Editorial Board; Donna Christian, Editorial Board; Mahmoud A. Al-Khatib, Editorial Board. **ISSN:** 1367-0050. **Subscription Rates:** US$774 institutions print + online; 409 institutions print + online; EUR619 institutions print + online; 75 individuals; US$149 individuals; EUR97 individuals; 388 institutions online only; US$736 institutions online only; EUR588 institutions online only. **Remarks:** Accepts advertising. **URL:** http://www.tandf.co.uk/journals/1367-0050. **Circ:** (Not Reported)

51829 ■ International Journal of Children's Spirituality
Routledge
Taylor & Francis Group Ltd.
2 Park Sq.
Milton Pk.
Abingdon OX14 4RN, United Kingdom
Ph: 44 20 70176000
Fax: 44 20 70176699
Publisher E-mail: webmaster.books@tandf.co.uk
Peer-reviewed journal focusing on research and development of spirituality in children and young people. **Freq:** Quarterly. **Key Personnel:** Cathy Ota, Editor; Karen-Marie Yust, Editor; Brendan Hyde, Editor; Gerard Pottesbaum, International Consulting Ed., gaphaus@earthlink.net; Jacqueline Watson, Book Reviews Ed., jacqueline.watson@uea.ac.uk; Robert Jackson, International Consulting Ed.; Yasim B. Rahim, International

Consulting Ed.; Elaine Champagne, International Consulting Ed.; Mary Petersen, International Consulting Ed. **ISSN:** 1364-436X. **Subscription Rates:** US$136 individuals print only; US$576 institutions online only; US$607 institutions print + online; 367 institutions print + online; 349 institutions online only; 83 individuals; EUR482 institutions print and online; EUR459 institutions online only; EUR108 individuals. **Remarks:** Advertising accepted; rates available upon request. **URL:** http://www.tandf.co.uk/journals/carfax/1364436x.html. **Circ:** (Not Reported)

51830 ■ International Journal of Construction Education and Research
Routledge
Taylor & Francis Group Ltd.
2 Park Sq.
Milton Pk.
Abingdon OX14 4RN, United Kingdom
Ph: 44 20 70176000
Fax: 44 20 70176699
Publisher E-mail: webmaster.books@tandf.co.uk
Peer-reviewed journal covering construction education and research. **Freq:** 4/yr. **Key Personnel:** Brian Moore, Editor, bcmoore@georgiasouthern.edu; Salman Azhar, Phd, Assoc. Ed., salman@auburn.edu; John Schaufelberger, Assoc. Ed., jesbcon@u.washington.edu. **ISSN:** 1557-8771. **Subscription Rates:** 334 institutions print + online; US$553 institutions print + online; 318 institutions online; US$528 institutions online; 87 individuals; US$142 individuals; EUR445 institutions print and online; EUR423 institutions online only; EUR113 individuals; 200 members. **URL:** http://www.tandf.co.uk/journals/titles/15578771.asp.

51831 ■ International Journal of Cultural Policy
Routledge
Taylor & Francis Group Ltd.
2 Park Sq.
Milton Pk.
Abingdon OX14 4RN, United Kingdom
Ph: 44 20 70176000
Fax: 44 20 70176699
Publisher E-mail: webmaster.books@tandf.co.uk
Peer-reviewed journal focusing on the study of the nature, function and impact of cultural policies. **Freq:** QRT. **Key Personnel:** Oliver Bennett, Editor, o.bennett@warwick.ac.uk; Jeremy Ahearne, Editorial Board, j.n.ahearne@warwick.ac.uk; Franco Bianchini, Editorial Board, fbianch@dmu.ac.uk. **ISSN:** 1028-6632. **Subscription Rates:** US$149 individuals print only; US$529 institutions online only; 421 institutions online only; US$557 institutions print + online; 443 institutions print + online; 117 individuals print only; EUR443 institutions print + online; EUR421 institutions online only; EUR118 individuals. **Remarks:** Advertising accepted; rates available upon request. **URL:** http://www.tandf.co.uk/journals/titles/10286632.asp. **Circ:** (Not Reported)

51832 ■ International Journal of Disability, Development and Education (IJDDE)
Routledge
Taylor & Francis Group Ltd.
2 Park Sq.
Milton Pk.
Abingdon OX14 4RN, United Kingdom
Ph: 44 20 70176000
Fax: 44 20 70176699
Publisher E-mail: webmaster.books@tandf.co.uk
Peer-reviewed journal focusing on education, development, and rehabilitation of persons with disabilities. **Founded:** 1954. **Freq:** Quarterly. **Key Personnel:** Christa Van Kraayenoord, Editor, ijdde@uq.edu.au; Annemaree Carroll, Book Review Ed.; Mary Beth Doyle, International Editorial Board; Monica Cuskelly, Assoc. Ed.; John Elkins, International Editorial Board; Dorothy Howie, International Editorial Board; Bob Conway, International Editorial Board. **ISSN:** 1034-912X. **Subscription Rates:** US$216 individuals; US$567 institutions online only; US$597 institutions print + online; 359 institutions print + online; 342 institutions online only; 130 individuals; $A 406 institutions print + online; $A 385 institutions online only; $A 211 individuals; EUR476 institutions print and online. **Remarks:** Advertising accepted; rates available upon request. **URL:** http://www.tandf.co.uk/journals/titles/1034912x.asp. **Circ:** (Not Reported)

51833 ■ International Journal of the Economics of Business
Routledge
Taylor & Francis Group Ltd.
2 Park Sq.

Milton Pk.
Abingdon OX14 4RN, United Kingdom
Ph: 44 20 70176000
Fax: 44 20 70176699
Publisher E-mail: webmaster.books@tandf.co.uk
Peer-reviewed journal covering economics and business. **Freq:** 3/yr. **Key Personnel:** Eleanor J. Morgan, Editor; H.E. Frech III, Editor, jbusecon@econ. ucsb.edu; Mick Silver, International Editorial Board; Roger Clarke, International Editorial Board; Mark Casson, International Editorial Board; Harry Bloch, International Editorial Board; Peter Zweifel, International Editorial Board; Peter Buckley, International Editorial Board; Harold Demsetz, International Editorial Board; Kenneth M. Lehn, International Editorial Board. **ISSN:** 1357-1516. **Subscription Rates:** 468 institutions print and online; US$757 institutions print and online; 444 institutions online; US$718 institutions online; 117 individuals; US$190 individuals; 26 individuals society; US$40 individuals society. **URL:** http://www.tandf.co.uk/journals/routledge/13571516.html.

51834 ■ International Journal of Environmental Health Research
Taylor & Francis Ltd.
2 & 4 Park Sq.
Milton Pk.
Abingdon OX14 4RN, United Kingdom
Ph: 44 20 70176000
Fax: 44 20 70176336
Peer-reviewed and International journal devoted to rapid publication of research in environmental health, acting as a link between the diverse research communities and practitioners in environmental health. **Freq:** 6/yr. **Key Personnel:** Dr. Don Bandaranayake, Editorial Advisory Board; Dr. Koos Engelbrecht, Regional Ed., engelbrechtjc@tut.ac.za; Prof. Chris Miller, Editor-in-Chief, ijehr-els@salford.ac.uk; Prof. Joan B. Rose, Regional Ed., rosejo@msu.edu; Prof. Angelo Carere, Editorial Advisory Board; Prof. Bertil Forsberg, Editorial Advisory Board. **ISSN:** 0960-3123. **Subscription Rates:** 718 institutions print and online; 682 institutions online; 286 individuals print only; US$1,191 institutions print + online; US$1,131 institutions online; US$473 individuals print only. **Remarks:** Accepts advertising. **URL:** http://www.tandf.co.uk/journals/titles/09603123.asp. **Circ:** (Not Reported)

51835 ■ International Journal of Food Sciences & Nutrition
Taylor & Francis Ltd.
2 & 4 Park Sq.
Milton Pk.
Abingdon OX14 4RN, United Kingdom
Ph: 44 20 70176000
Fax: 44 20 70176336
Journal integrating food science with nutrition, covering topics such as: impact of nutritional science on food product development, nutritional implications of food processing, bioavailibility of nutrients, nutritional quality of novel foods, food-nutrient interactions, use of biotechnology in food science/nutrition, tropical food processing and nutrition, food acceptibility and dietary selection, nutritional and physiological aspects of food and dietary requirements and nutritive value of food. **Freq:** 8/yr. **Key Personnel:** Prof. C.J.K. Henry, Editor, jhenry@brookes. ac.uk. **ISSN:** 0963-7486. **Subscription Rates:** 1,090 institutions; US$1,850 institutions; EUR1,475 institutions. **Remarks:** Accepts advertising. **URL:** http://informahealthcare.com/ijf. **Circ:** (Not Reported)

51836 ■ International Journal of Heritage Studies
Routledge
Taylor & Francis Group Ltd.
2 Park Sq.
Milton Pk.
Abingdon OX14 4RN, United Kingdom
Ph: 44 20 70176000
Fax: 44 20 70176699
Publisher E-mail: webmaster.books@tandf.co.uk
Peer-reviewed journal focusing on museum studies, tourism studies, heritage theory and history, conservation and restoration techniques and law, cultural studies, interpretation and design. **Freq:** Bimonthly. **Key Personnel:** Dr. Steve Watson, Reviews Ed., s.watson@yorksj. ac.uk; Dr. Laurajane Smith, Editor, laurajane.smith@ anu.edu.au; Dr. John Carman, Editorial Advisory Board.

ISSN: 1352-7258. **Subscription Rates:** US$245 individuals print only; US$709 institutions online only; US$746 institutions print + online; 448 institutions online only; 426 institutions print + online; 147 individuals print only; EUR595 institutions print and online; EUR565 institutions online only; EUR196 individuals. **Remarks:** Advertising accepted; rates available upon request. **URL:** http://www.tandf.co.uk/journals/routledge/13527258.html. **Circ:** (Not Reported)

51837 ■ International Journal of the History of Sport
Routledge
Taylor & Francis Group Ltd.
2 Park Sq.
Milton Pk.
Abingdon OX14 4RN, United Kingdom
Ph: 44 20 70176000
Fax: 44 20 70176699
Publisher E-mail: webmaster.books@tandf.co.uk
Peer-reviewed journal dealing with historical studies of sport in its political, social, cultural, economic, spiritual, educational, and aesthetic dimensions. **Freq:** 18/yr. **Key Personnel:** Boria Majumdar, Dep. Exec. Academic Ed.; Fan Hong, Assoc. Academic Ed.; Thierry Terret, Assoc. Academic Ed.; Mark Dyreson, Assoc. Academic Ed.; Projit Bihari Mukharji, Review/Monographs Ed.; J.A. Mangan, Exec. Academic/Reviews Ed.; Mike Huggins, Reviews Ed.; Douglas Booth, Reviews Ed.; Martin Crotty, Reviews Ed. **ISSN:** 0952-3367. **Subscription Rates:** 1,213 institutions print + online; US$1,152 institutions print + online; 1,823 institutions online; US$1,918 institutions online; 267 individuals personal; US$393 individuals personal; EUR1,536 institutions print and online; EUR1,459 institutions print and online; EUR314 individuals. **Remarks:** Advertising accepted; rates available upon request. **URL:** http://www.tandf.co.uk/journals/titles/09523367.asp. **Circ:** (Not Reported)

51838 ■ The International Journal of Human Rights
Routledge
Taylor & Francis Group Ltd.
2 Park Sq.
Milton Pk.
Abingdon OX14 4RN, United Kingdom
Ph: 44 20 70176000
Fax: 44 20 70176699
Publisher E-mail: webmaster.books@tandf.co.uk
Peer-reviewed journal focusing on human rights issues. **Freq:** 7/yr. **Key Personnel:** Frank Barnaby, PhD, Editor, frank.barnaby@btinternet.com; Jason Ralph, Assoc. Ed.; Lord Peter Archer, Editorial Board. **ISSN:** 1364-2987. **Subscription Rates:** 528 institutions print + online; US$876 institutions print + online; 501 institutions online only; US$833 institutions online only; 118 individuals; US$197 individuals; EUR697 institutions print and online; EUR662 institutions online only; EUR157 individuals. **Remarks:** Advertising accepted; rates available upon request. **URL:** http://www.tandf.co.uk/journals/titles/13642987.asp. **Circ:** (Not Reported)

51839 ■ International Journal of Language & Communication Disorders
Taylor & Francis Ltd.
2 & 4 Park Sq.
Milton Pk.
Abingdon OX14 4RN, United Kingdom
Ph: 44 20 70176000
Fax: 44 20 70176336
Journal covering speech, language, and swallowing disorders. **Founded:** 1966. **Freq:** 6/yr. **Trim Size:** B5. **Key Personnel:** Katerina Hilari, Editor, k.hilari@city.ac. uk; Nicola Botting, Editor, nbotting@lineone.net; Kate Cain, Assoc. Ed. **ISSN:** 1368-2822. **Subscription Rates:** 610 institutions; US$1,100 institutions; EUR880 institutions. **Remarks:** Accepts advertising on request. **URL:** http://www.informaworld.com/smpp/title~content= t713393930~db=all. **Circ:** (Not Reported)

51840 ■ International Journal of the Legal Profession
Routledge
Taylor & Francis Group Ltd.
2 Park Sq.
Milton Pk.
Abingdon OX14 4RN, United Kingdom
Ph: 44 20 70176000
Fax: 44 20 70176699
Publisher E-mail: webmaster.books@tandf.co.uk
Peer-reviewed journal dealing with the legal professions of the common law and civil law world. **Freq:** 3/yr. **Key**

Personnel: Prof. Avrom Sherr, Editor; Alan Paterson, Editorial Board; Richard Moorhead, Editorial Board; Richard Abel, Editorial Board; Lee Bridges, International Advisory Board; Jeremy Cooper, International Advisory Board. **ISSN:** 0969-5958. **Subscription Rates:** US$846 institutions print + online; US$803 institutions online; US$208 individuals; 511 institutions print + online; 485 institutions online; 130 individuals; EUR674 institutions print and online; EUR640 institutions online only; EUR166 individuals. **Remarks:** Advertising accepted; rates available upon request. **URL:** http://www.tandf.co.uk/journals/titles/09695958.asp; http://www.tandf.co.uk/journals/carfax/09695958.html. **Circ:** (Not Reported)

51841 ■ The International Journal of Multilingualism
Routledge
Taylor & Francis Group Ltd.
2 Park Sq.
Milton Pk.
Abingdon OX14 4RN, United Kingdom
Ph: 44 20 70176000
Fax: 44 20 70176699
Publisher E-mail: webmaster.books@tandf.co.uk
Peer-reviewed journal fostering, presenting and spreading research focused on psycholinguistic, sociolinguistic and educational aspects of multilingual acquisition and multilingualism. **Freq:** 4/yr. **Key Personnel:** Jasone Cenoz, Editor; Marilda C. Cavalcanti, Editorial Board; Tove Skutnabb-Kangas, Editorial Board; Colin Baker, Editorial Board; Prof. Anne Pakir, Editorial Board; Dr. Britta Hufeisen, Review Ed.; Prof. Michael Clyne, Editorial Board; Prof. Vivian Cook, Editorial Board; Dr. Ton Dijkstra, Editorial Board. **ISSN:** 1479-0718. **Subscription Rates:** 232 institutions print + online; US$464 institutions print + online; EUR349 institutions print + online; 73 institutions online; US$147 individuals; EUR92 individuals; 220 institutions online only; US$441 institutions online only; EUR331 institutions online only. **URL:** http://www.tandf.co.uk/journals/1479-0718.

51842 ■ International Journal of Neuroscience
Taylor & Francis Ltd.
2 & 4 Park Sq.
Milton Pk.
Abingdon OX14 4RN, United Kingdom
Ph: 44 20 70176000
Fax: 44 20 70176336
Peer-reviewed journal publishing papers, reviews, letters to the editor, comments and notes concerned with problems of nervous tissue, the nervous system, and behavior, dealing not only with the obvious areas of neuroanatomy, neurophysiology, neurochemistry, neuropharmacology, and neuroendocrinology, but all impinging and related areas of mathematics, physics, physical chemistry, biochemistry, biophysics, bioengineering, communication and information, learning, memory, conditioning, and higher behavioral considerations. **Freq:** Monthly. **Key Personnel:** Kelly E. Lyons, PhD, Editor-in-Chief, klyons@kumc.edu; Rajesh Pahwa, MD, Editor-in-Chief. **ISSN:** 0020-7454. **Subscription Rates:** 6,535 institutions; US$9,125 institutions; EUR7,300 institutions. **Remarks:** Accepts advertising. **URL:** http://informahealthcare.com/nes. **Circ:** (Not Reported)

51843 ■ International Journal of Philosophical Studies
Routledge
Taylor & Francis Group Ltd.
2 Park Sq.
Milton Pk.
Abingdon OX14 4RN, United Kingdom
Ph: 44 20 70176000
Fax: 44 20 70176699
Publisher E-mail: webmaster.books@tandf.co.uk
Peer-reviewed journal publishing articles of highest quality in all areas of philosophy. **Freq:** 5/yr. **Key Personnel:** Maria Baghramian, Editor; Dermot Moran, Founding Ed.; Margaret Brady, Editorial Asst. **ISSN:** 0967-2559. **Subscription Rates:** US$191 individuals print only; US$806 institutions online; US$848 institutions print + online; 509 institutions print + online; 484 institutions online only; 114 individuals; EUR675 institutions print and online; EUR641 institutions online only; EUR152 individuals. **Remarks:** Advertising accepted; rates available upon request. **URL:** http://www.tandf.co.uk/journals/routledge/09672559.html. **Circ:** (Not Reported)

51844 ■ International Journal of Prisoner Health
Taylor & Francis Ltd.
2 & 4 Park Sq.
Milton Pk.

Abingdon OX14 4RN, United Kingdom
Ph: 44 20 70176000
Fax: 44 20 70176336
Peer-reviewed journal providing a platform for an interdisciplinary approach to prisoners' health in order to facilitate an exchange of information and good practice among experts in the field from a range of different cultural interpretations and perspectives. **Freq:** 4/yr. **Key Personnel:** Dr. Morag MacDonald, Editor-in-Chief; Daniele Berto, International Advisory Board; Ralf Jurgens, Editorial Board; Aromaa Kauko, Editorial Board; Neo Lee Hong, Editorial Board; Heino Stover, Editorial Board; Dumitru Laticevschi, Editorial Board; Rick Lines, Editorial Board; Murdo L. Bijl, Editorial Board; Alexey Bobrik, International Advisory Board. **ISSN:** 1744-9200. **Subscription Rates:** US$40 institutions developing country; 199 institutions print + online; US$331 institutions print + online; 189 institutions online; US$314 institutions online; 70 individuals; US$118 individuals; 35 individuals society; US$55 individuals society; $A 50 individuals society. **Remarks:** Accepts advertising. **URL:** http://www.informaworld.com/smpp/title~content=t716100756~db=all. **Circ:** (Not Reported)

51845 ▪ International Journal of Research and Method in Education
Routledge
Taylor & Francis Group Ltd.
2 Park Sq.
Milton Pk.
Abingdon OX14 4RN, United Kingdom
Ph: 44 20 70176000
Fax: 44 20 70176699
Publisher E-mail: webmaster.books@tandf.co.uk
Peer-reviewed journal reporting new methods of educational research, discusses conceptual, theoretical and methodological issues in educational research. **Freq:** 3/yr. **Key Personnel:** Sarah Parsons, Book Review Ed.; Martyn Hammersley, Editorial Board; Maria Pampaka, Book Review Ed.; Kenneth Ruthven, Editorial Board; Geoffrey Walford, Editorial Board; Melanie Nind, Editor, m.a.nind@soton.ac.uk; Gary Thomas, Editorial Board. **ISSN:** 1743-727X. **Subscription Rates:** US$299 individuals print only; US$1,778 individuals online only; US$1,872 individuals print & online; 909 institutions print & online; 863 institutions online; 142 institutions; EUR1,498 institutions print and online; EUR1,422 institutions online only; EUR238 individuals. **Remarks:** Advertising accepted; rates available upon request. **URL:** http://www.tandf.co.uk/journals/titles/1743727x.asp. **Former name:** Westminster Studies in Education (Jan. 1, 2005). **Circ:** (Not Reported)

51846 ▪ International Journal of Speech-Language Pathology
Taylor & Francis Ltd.
2 & 4 Park Sq.
Milton Pk.
Abingdon OX14 4RN, United Kingdom
Ph: 44 20 70176000
Fax: 44 20 70176336
Journal containing articles relating to any area of child or adult communication or dysphagia, furthering knowledge on issues related to etiology, diagnosis, treatment, or theoretical frameworks. **Freq:** 6/yr. **Key Personnel:** Dr. Sharynne McLeod, Editor, ijslp@csu.edu.au; Chris Code, Exec. Board; Marc E. Fey, Exec. Board; Martin J. Ball, Editorial Consultant; David J. Ertmer, Editorial Consultant. **ISSN:** 1757-9507. **Subscription Rates:** US$545 individuals print only; US$545 institutions online; US$545 institutions print only; US$545 individuals online. **Remarks:** Accepts advertising. **URL:** http://www.informaworld.com/smpp/title~db=all~content=t713736271; http://informahealthcare.com/asl. **Formerly:** Advances in Speech Language Pathology. **Circ:** (Not Reported)

51847 ▪ International Journal of Water Resources Development
Routledge
Taylor & Francis Group Ltd.
2 Park Sq.
Milton Pk.
Abingdon OX14 4RN, United Kingdom
Ph: 44 20 70176000
Fax: 44 20 70176699
Publisher E-mail: webmaster.books@tandf.co.uk
Peer-reviewed journal covering all aspects of water development and management in both industrialized and Third World countries. **Freq:** Quarterly. **Key Person-**

nel: Cecilia Tortajada, Editor; Prof. Asit K. Biswas, Editor-in-Chief, akbiswas@att.net.mx; Dr. Mahmoud Abu-Zeid, International Editorial Board; Prof. Benedito P. F. Braga, International Editorial Board; Prof. M. Falkenmark, International Editorial Board; Dr. Alfredo Bone, International Editorial Board. **ISSN:** 0790-0627. **Subscription Rates:** US$1,275 institutions print + online; US$1,211 institutions online; US$220 individuals; 767 institutions print + online; 729 institutions online; 132 individuals; EUR1,016 institutions print and online; EUR966 institutions online only; EUR176 individuals. **Remarks:** Advertising accepted; rates available upon request. **URL:** http://www.tandf.co.uk/journals/titles/07900627.asp. **Circ:** (Not Reported)

51848 ▪ International Planning Studies
Routledge
Taylor & Francis Group Ltd.
2 Park Sq.
Milton Pk.
Abingdon OX14 4RN, United Kingdom
Ph: 44 20 70176000
Fax: 44 20 70176699
Publisher E-mail: webmaster.books@tandf.co.uk
Journal dealing with the globalization as both an objective socio-economic process and a shift in policy-maker perceptions and modes of analysis. **Freq:** Quarterly. **Key Personnel:** John Lovering, Managing Editor; Denise Phillips, Editorial Mgr.; Michael Batty, International Editorial Board. **ISSN:** 1356-3475. **Subscription Rates:** 364 institutions print + online; 346 institutions online; 94 individuals; US$608 institutions print + online; US$578 institutions online; US$155 individuals; EUR483 institutions print and online; EUR460 institutions online only; EUR124 individuals. **Remarks:** Advertising accepted; rates available upon request. **URL:** http://www.tandf.co.uk/journals/titles/13563475.asp. **Circ:** (Not Reported)

51849 ▪ International Public Management Journal
Routledge
Taylor & Francis Group Ltd.
2 Park Sq.
Milton Pk.
Abingdon OX14 4RN, United Kingdom
Ph: 44 20 70176000
Fax: 44 20 70176699
Publisher E-mail: webmaster.books@tandf.co.uk
Peer-reviewed journal covering research in the field of public management. **Founded:** 1971. **Freq:** Quarterly. **Print Method:** Offset. **Trim Size:** 6 7/8 x 9 15/16. **Cols./Page:** 2. **Col. Width:** 34 nonpareils. **Col. Depth:** 116 agate lines. **Key Personnel:** Lawrence R. Jones, Co-Ed.; Fred Thompson, Founding Ed.; Steven Kelman, Editor; Roderick Kramer, Consulting Ed.; David Marsden, Co-Ed.; Raquel Gallego Calderon, Editorial Board; Greg Dorchak, Managing Editor; Martha Feldman, Book Review Ed.; Sung Deuk Hahm, Co-Ed.; Kuno Schedler, Co-Ed.; Matthew Potoski, Co-Ed. **ISSN:** 1096-7494. **Subscription Rates:** 226 institutions print + online; 214 institutions online; 95 individuals; US$375 institutions print + online; US$356 institutions online; US$159 individuals; EUR298 institutions print and online; EUR284 institutions online only; EUR127 individuals. **URL:** http://www.tandf.co.uk/journals/titles/10967494.asp.

51850 ▪ International Research in Geography & Environment Education
Routledge
Taylor & Francis Group Ltd.
2 Park Sq.
Milton Pk.
Abingdon OX14 4RN, United Kingdom
Ph: 44 20 70176000
Fax: 44 20 70176699
Publisher E-mail: webmaster.books@tandf.co.uk
Scholarly journal covering education. **Founded:** 1992. **Freq:** Quarterly. **Key Personnel:** Prof. John Lidstone, Editor; Donna Bennett, Editorial Asst.; Dr. Gillian Kidman, Book Review Ed.; Dr. Sarah Witham Bednarz, Editorial Board; Prof. Joseph P. Stoltman, Editor. **ISSN:** 1038-2046. **Subscription Rates:** US$142 individuals print; US$543 individuals online; US$572 individuals print and online. **Remarks:** Accepts advertising. **URL:** http://www.informaworld.com/smpp/title~content=t794297793~db=all. **Circ:** (Not Reported)

51851 ▪ International Review of Applied Economics
Routledge
Taylor & Francis Group Ltd.
2 Park Sq.

Milton Pk.
Abingdon OX14 4RN, United Kingdom
Ph: 44 20 70176000
Fax: 44 20 70176699
Publisher E-mail: webmaster.books@tandf.co.uk
Peer-reviewed journal covering economics. **Freq:** 5/yr. **Key Personnel:** Malcolm Sawyer, Managing Editor; Philip Arestis, Editorial Board Member; Saziye Gazioglu, Assoc. Mng. Ed.; Keith Cowling, Editorial Board Member; Jonathan Michie, Book Review Ed.; R. Blecker, Editorial Advisory Board. **ISSN:** 0269-2171. **Subscription Rates:** 829 institutions print and online; US$1,457 institutions print and online; 788 institutions online; US$1,385 institutions online; 245 individuals; US$420 individuals. **URL:** http://www.tandf.co.uk/journals/journal.asp?issn=0269-2171&linktype=5.

51852 ▪ International Review of Law Computers & Technology
Routledge
Taylor & Francis Group Ltd.
2 Park Sq.
Milton Pk.
Abingdon OX14 4RN, United Kingdom
Ph: 44 20 70176000
Fax: 44 20 70176699
Publisher E-mail: webmaster.books@tandf.co.uk
Peer-reviewed journal covering law computing, business and management. **Freq:** 3/yr. **Key Personnel:** Andrew Charlesworth, International Advisory Board; Paul Maharg, Assoc. Ed.; Dr. Kenneth V. Russell, Editor; Euan Cameron, Assoc. Ed.; Martin Wasik, Assoc. Ed.; Richard P. Jones, Assoc. Ed.; David S. Wall, Assoc. Ed. **ISSN:** 1360-0869. **Subscription Rates:** US$1,062 institutions print + online; US$1,009 institutions online; US$149 individuals; 639 institutions print + online; 607 institutions online; 88 individuals; EUR845 institutions print + online; EUR802 institutions online; EUR118 individuals. **Remarks:** Accepts advertising. **URL:** http://www.tandf.co.uk/journals/titles/13600869.asp. **Circ:** (Not Reported)

51853 ▪ International Review of Psychiatry
Taylor & Francis Ltd.
2 & 4 Park Sq.
Milton Pk.
Abingdon OX14 4RN, United Kingdom
Ph: 44 20 70176000
Fax: 44 20 70176336
Peer-reviewed journal covering topics in the following areas: epidemiology, services and public health; psychiatric disorders and their etiologies; therapeutics and rehabilitation; clinical relevance of cognitive and basic neurosciences; psychiatric methodologies; and psychiatry in medicine. **Freq:** Bimonthly. **Key Personnel:** Prof. Constantine G. Lyketsos, Editor; Prof. Dinesh Bhugra, Editor; Laura Roberts, Assoc. Ed.; Christoph Lauber, Assoc. Ed.; Krishna Vaddadi, Assoc. Ed.; Oye Gureje, Assoc. Ed. **ISSN:** 0954-0261. **Subscription Rates:** 1,185 institutions; US$2,195 institutions; EUR1,755 institutions. **Remarks:** Accepts advertising. **URL:** http://informahealthcare.com/irp. **Circ:** (Not Reported)

51854 ▪ International Reviews of Immunology
Taylor & Francis Ltd.
2 & 4 Park Sq.
Milton Pk.
Abingdon OX14 4RN, United Kingdom
Ph: 44 20 70176000
Fax: 44 20 70176336
Journal relevant to immunologists, molecular biologists, microbiologists and physicians who are involved with autoimmune diseases, providing the most current information on research in immunology. **Freq:** 6/yr. **Key Personnel:** Adrian Bot, Editor-in-Chief, abot@mannkindcorp.com; Takeshi Sasaki, Editorial Board; Ronald Kennedy, Editorial Board; Thomas Kundig, Editorial Board; Maurizio Chiriva-Internati, Section Ed.; Yoram Reiter, Editorial Board. **ISSN:** 0883-0185. **Subscription Rates:** 1,635 institutions; US$2,525 institutions; EUR2,025 institutions. **Remarks:** Accepts advertising. **URL:** http://www.informaworld.com/smpp/title~content=t713643575; http://informahealthcare.com/iri. **Circ:** (Not Reported)

51855 ▪ The International Spectator
Routledge
Taylor & Francis Group Ltd.
2 Park Sq.
Milton Pk.
Abingdon OX14 4RN, United Kingdom
Ph: 44 20 70176000

Fax: 44 20 70176699
Publisher E-mail: webmaster.books@tandf.co.uk
Peer-reviewed journal focusing on the new realities of world politics. **Founded:** 1965. **Freq:** Quarterly. **Print Method:** Offset. **Trim Size:** 8 1/2 x 11. **Cols./Page:** 2. **Col. Width:** 20 picas. **Key Personnel:** Ettore Greco, Editor; Gabriele Tonne, Managing Editor; Nathalie Tocci, Assoc. Ed. **ISSN:** 0393-2729. **Subscription Rates:** 267 institutions print + online; US$443 institutions print + online; 48 individuals print only; US$80 individuals print only; EUR63 individuals print only; 254 institutions online; 421 institutions online; EUR353 institutions print and online; EUR335 institutions online only. **URL:** http://www.tandf.co.uk/journals/titles/03932729.asp.

51856 ■ International Studies in Sociology of Education
Routledge
Taylor & Francis Group Ltd.
2 Park Sq.
Milton Pk.
Abingdon OX14 4RN, United Kingdom
Ph: 44 20 70176000
Fax: 44 20 70176699
Publisher E-mail: webmaster.books@tandf.co.uk
Peer-reviewed journal covering articles on sociology from around the world. **Freq:** Quarterly. **Key Personnel:** Suzy Harris, Editor; Gill Crozier, Exec. Ed.; Len Barton, Founding Ed.; James Avis, Editorial Board; Hugh Lauder, Editorial Board; Madeleine Arnot, Editorial Board; Terri Kim, Book Review Ed.; Michael Apple, Editorial Board; Roger Dale, Editorial Board; Inge Bates, Editorial Board; Lynn Davies, Editorial Board; Kathleen Lynch, Editorial Board. **ISSN:** 0962-0214. **Subscription Rates:** 423 institutions print + online; 403 institutions online; 66 individuals; US$678 institutions print + online; US$644 institutions online; US$107 individuals; EUR522 institutions print and online; EUR496 institutions online only; EUR83 individuals. **URL:** http://www.tandf.co.uk/journals/titles/09620214.asp.

51857 ■ Interventions
Routledge
Taylor & Francis Group Ltd.
2 Park Sq.
Milton Pk.
Abingdon OX14 4RN, United Kingdom
Ph: 44 20 70176000
Fax: 44 20 70176699
Publisher E-mail: webmaster.books@tandf.co.uk
Peer-reviewed journal dealing with all aspects of post-colonial research. **Subtitle:** International Journal of Postcolonial Studies. **Freq:** 3/yr. **Key Personnel:** Robert Young, Gen. Ed.; Homi K. Bhabha, Consultant Ed.; Heather Zuber, Managing Editor. **ISSN:** 1369-801X. **Subscription Rates:** US$108 individuals print only; US$387 institutions online; US$408 institutions print + online; 66 individuals print only; 233 institutions online; 245 institutions print + online; EUR325 institutions print and online; EUR308 institutions online only; EUR86 individuals. **Remarks:** Advertising accepted; rates available upon request. **URL:** http://www.tandf.co.uk/journals/routledge/1369801x.html. **Circ:** (Not Reported)

51858 ■ Iranian Studies
Routledge
Taylor & Francis Group Ltd.
2 Park Sq.
Milton Pk.
Abingdon OX14 4RN, United Kingdom
Ph: 44 20 70176000
Fax: 44 20 70176699
Publisher E-mail: webmaster.books@tandf.co.uk
Peer-reviewed journal dealing with all aspects of Iranian and Persian history, literature, and society. **Freq:** 5/yr. **Key Personnel:** Homa Katouzian, Editor; Dominic Brookshaw, Asst. Ed.; Iraj Afshar, Advisory Council. **ISSN:** 0021-0862. **Subscription Rates:** US$424 individuals online; US$447 individuals print + online; 270 institutions print + online; 257 institutions online; EUR357 institutions print and online; EUR340 institutions online only. **Remarks:** Advertising accepted; rates available upon request. **URL:** http://www.tandf.co.uk/journals/titles/00210862.asp. **Circ:** (Not Reported)

51859 ■ Irish Political Studies
Routledge
Taylor & Francis Group Ltd.
2 Park Sq.
Milton Pk.
Abingdon OX14 4RN, United Kingdom

Ph: 44 20 70176000
Fax: 44 20 70176699
Publisher E-mail: webmaster.books@tandf.co.uk
Peer-reviewed journal covering academic articles on Irish politics. **Subtitle:** Official Journal of the Political Studies Association of Ireland (PSAI). **Founded:** 1986. **Freq:** Quarterly. **Key Personnel:** Euin O'Malley, Co-Ed.; Alan Greer, Editorial Board; Eamonn O'Kane, Assoc. Ed. **ISSN:** 0790-7184. **Subscription Rates:** US$125 individuals print only; US$333 institutions online only; US$351 institutions print + online; 212 institutions print + online; 202 institutions online only; 89 individuals print only; EUR278 institutions print and online; EUR265 institutions online only; EUR99 individuals; 35 members. **Remarks:** Advertising accepted; rates available upon request. **URL:** http://www.tandf.co.uk/journals/titles/07907184.asp. **Circ:** (Not Reported)

51860 ■ Irish Studies Review
Routledge
Taylor & Francis Group Ltd.
2 Park Sq.
Milton Pk.
Abingdon OX14 4RN, United Kingdom
Ph: 44 20 70176000
Fax: 44 20 70176699
Publisher E-mail: webmaster.books@tandf.co.uk
Peer-reviewed journal dealing with all aspects of Irish studies and related disciplines. **Founded:** 1992. **Freq:** Quarterly. **Key Personnel:** Paul Hyland, Editor, p.hyland@bathspa.ac.uk; Neil Sammells, Editor, n.sammells@bathspa.ac.uk; Aidan Arrowsmith, Editorial Advisory Board. **ISSN:** 0967-0882. **Subscription Rates:** US$109 individuals print only; US$420 institutions online; US$442 institutions print + online; 264 institutions print + online; 250 institutions online; 68 individuals print only; EUR352 institutions print and online; EUR334 institutions online only; EUR87 individuals. **Remarks:** Advertising accepted; rates available upon request. **URL:** http://www.tandf.co.uk/journals/carfax/09670882.html. **Circ:** (Not Reported)

51861 ■ Islam and Christian-Muslim Relations
Routledge
Taylor & Francis Group Ltd.
2 Park Sq.
Milton Pk.
Abingdon OX14 4RN, United Kingdom
Ph: 44 20 70176000
Fax: 44 20 70176699
Publisher E-mail: webmaster.books@tandf.co.uk
Peer-reviewed journal dealing with Christian-Muslim relations, published in connection with Center for the Study of Islam and Christian-Muslim Relations (CSIC), Center for Muslim-Christian Understanding. **Freq:** Quarterly. **Key Personnel:** Prof. David Thomas, Editor, d.r.thomas.1@bham.ac.uk; Dr. David Cheetham, Assoc. Ed.; Dr. Haifaa Jawad, Assoc. Ed. **ISSN:** 0959-6410. **Subscription Rates:** US$293 individuals; US$804 institutions online; US$847 institutions print + online; 159 individuals; 484 institutions print + online; 510 institutions print + online; EUR675 institutions print and online; EUR641 institutions online only; EUR234 individuals. **Remarks:** Advertising accepted; rates available upon request. **URL:** http://www.tandf.co.uk/journals/carfax/09596410.html. **Circ:** (Not Reported)

51862 ■ Isotopes in Environmental and Health Studies
Taylor & Francis Ltd.
2 & 4 Park Sq.
Milton Pk.
Abingdon OX14 4RN, United Kingdom
Ph: 44 20 70176000
Fax: 44 20 70176336
Peer-reviewed journal dealing with all aspects of non-radioactive isotope application in environmental and health studies, such as: investigations using variations in natural isotope abundance (isotope ecology, isotope hydrology, isotope geology), stable isotope tracer techniques to follow the fate of certain substances in soil, water, plants, animals and in the human body, isotope effects, tracer theory, and mathematical modelling of environmental cycles, isotope measurement methods and equipment with respect to environmental and health research, diagnostic (stable) isotope application in medicine and ionogenic radiation exposure and its effects on all living matter as well as radiation in protection. **Freq:** Quarterly. **Key Personnel:** Prof. Peter Krumbiegel, Editor; Dr. Gerhard Strauch, Co-Ed.; Dr.

Willi A. Brand, Editorial Board; Dr. Roland Bol, Editorial Board; Dr. Richard Robins, Editorial Board. **ISSN:** 1025-6016. **Subscription Rates:** 1,004 institutions print + online; 954 institutions online; 298 individuals print only; US$1,313 institutions print + online; US$1,247 institutions online; US$364 individuals print only. **Remarks:** Accepts advertising. **URL:** http://www.tandf.co.uk/journals/titles/10256016.asp. **Circ:** (Not Reported)

51863 ■ Israel Affairs
Routledge
Taylor & Francis Group Ltd.
2 Park Sq.
Milton Pk.
Abingdon OX14 4RN, United Kingdom
Ph: 44 20 70176000
Fax: 44 20 70176699
Publisher E-mail: webmaster.books@tandf.co.uk
Peer-reviewed journal covering Israeli history, politics, literature, art, strategic affairs and economics. **Freq:** Quarterly. **Key Personnel:** Efraim Karsh, PhD, Editor, efraim.karsh@kcl.ac.uk; Daniel Pipes, Editorial Board; Inari Rautsi, Assoc. Ed.; Shlomo Avineri, Editorial Board; Moshe Brawer, Editorial Board; Eliot Cohen, Editorial Board. **ISSN:** 1353-7121. **Subscription Rates:** US$583 institutions online; US$614 institutions print + online; US$130 individuals print; 371 institutions print + online; 352 institutions online; 92 individuals; EUR490 institutions print and online; EUR465 institutions online only; EUR104 individuals. **Remarks:** Advertising accepted; rates available upon request. **URL:** http://www.tandf.co.uk/journals/journal.asp?issn=1353-7121&linktype=5. **Circ:** (Not Reported)

51864 ■ IUBMB Life
Taylor & Francis Ltd.
2 & 4 Park Sq.
Milton Pk.
Abingdon OX14 4RN, United Kingdom
Ph: 44 20 70176000
Fax: 44 20 70176336
Journal devoted to the rapid publication of novel and significant short original research articles, short critical reviews, and hypotheses papers in the broadly defined fields of biochemistry, molecular biology, cell biology, and molecular medicine. **Freq:** Monthly. **Key Personnel:** Angelo Azzi, Editor-in-Chief, angelo.azzi@tufts.edu; William J. Whelan, Editor-in-Chief, wwhelan@miami.edu; Sidney Altman, Editor, sidney.altman@yale.edu; Pierre Chambon, Editor, igbmc@igbmc.u-strasbg.fr; Michael W. Gray, Editor, mwgray@is.dal.ca; Joan Guinovart, Editor, guinovart@pcb.ub.es; Ken-Ichi Arai, Editor, ken-ichi@ims.u-tokyo.ac.jp; Werner Arber, Editor, werner.arber@unibas.ch; Alan Roy Fersht, Editor, arf10@cam.ac.uk; Michael Karin, Editor, mkarin@ucsd.edu. **ISSN:** 1521-6543. **Remarks:** Accepts advertising. **URL:** http://www.informaworld.com/smpp/title~content=t713723531. **Circ:** (Not Reported)

51865 ■ Japan Forum
Routledge
Taylor & Francis Group Ltd.
2 Park Sq.
Milton Pk.
Abingdon OX14 4RN, United Kingdom
Ph: 44 20 70176000
Fax: 44 20 70176699
Publisher E-mail: webmaster.books@tandf.co.uk
Peer-reviewed journal dealing with the field of Japanese Studies. **Freq:** 4/yr. **Key Personnel:** Linda Flores, Assoc. Ed.; Hideko Mitsui, Assoc. Ed.; Koichi Nakano, Commissioning Ed.; Paul Midford, Assoc. Ed.; Richard Bowring, Editorial Advisory Board; Naoko Shimazu, Assoc. Ed.; Angus Lockyer, Sen. Ed., al21@soas.ac.uk; Chris Braddick, Commissioning Ed.; Dominic Kelly, Treas.; Rachael Hutchinson, Commissioning Ed.; Christopher Aldous, Book Reviews Ed.; Reinhard Drifte, Editorial Advisory Board. **ISSN:** 0955-5803. **Subscription Rates:** 461 institutions print + online; US$764 institutions print + online; 439 institutions online; US$725 institutions online; 135 individuals personal; US$223 individuals personal; EUR608 institutions print and online; EUR577 institutions online only; EUR176 individuals. **Remarks:** Accepts advertising. **URL:** http://www.tandf.co.uk/journals/routledge/09555803.html. **Circ:** (Not Reported)

51866 ■ Japanese Studies
Routledge
Taylor & Francis Group Ltd.

Circulation: ★ = ABC; △ = BPA; ◆ = CAC; • = CCAB; ❑ = VAC; ⊕ = PO Statement; ‡ = Publisher's Report; Boldface figures = sworn; Light figures = estimated.

Gale Directory of Publications & Broadcast Media/147th Ed. 5541

2 Park Sq.
Milton Pk.
Abingdon OX14 4RN, United Kingdom
Ph: 44 20 70176000
Fax: 44 20 70176699
Publisher E-mail: webmaster.books@tandf.co.uk
Peer-reviewed journal covering fields of professional interest in Japan. **Freq:** 3/yr. **Key Personnel:** Judith Snodgrass, Editor, japanese.studies@uws.edu.au; Tomoko Aoyama, Editorial Advisory Board; William Coaldrake, Editorial Advisory Board; Beatrice Bodart-Bailey, Editorial Advisory Board; Carolyn Stevens, Ed. for Contemporary Culture; Millie Creighton, Editorial Advisory Board. **ISSN:** 1037-1397. **Subscription Rates:** US$448 individuals online; 92 individuals; 270 institutions online; US$150 individuals; $A 396 institutions online; $A 166 individuals; 285 institutions print + online; US$472 institutions print + online; $A 417 institutions print + online; EUR376 institutions print and online. **Remarks:** Accepts advertising. **URL:** http://www.tandf.co.uk/journals/titles/10371397.asp. **Circ:** (Not Reported)

51867 ■ Jazz Perspectives
Routledge
Taylor & Francis Group Ltd.
2 Park Sq.
Milton Pk.
Abingdon OX14 4RN, United Kingdom
Ph: 44 20 70176000
Fax: 44 20 70176699
Publisher E-mail: webmaster.books@tandf.co.uk
Peer-reviewd journal promoting the cross-disciplinary scholarly dialogue across the academic jazz community. **Founded:** 1969. **Freq:** 3/yr. **Print Method:** Offset. **Trim Size:** 7 x 10. **Cols./Page:** 1. **Key Personnel:** Lewis Porter, Editorial Board; John Howland, Editor-in-Chief; Wolfram Knauer, Editorial Board. **ISSN:** 1749-4060. **Subscription Rates:** 182 institutions print + online; US$328 institutions print + online; 173 institutions online; US$312 institutions online; 31 individuals; US$57 individuals online only; EUR47 individuals. **URL:** http://www.tandf.co.uk/journals/titles/17494060.asp.

51868 ■ Journal of African Cultural Studies
Routledge
Taylor & Francis Group Ltd.
2 Park Sq.
Milton Pk.
Abingdon OX14 4RN, United Kingdom
Ph: 44 20 70176000
Fax: 44 20 70176699
Publisher E-mail: webmaster.books@tandf.co.uk
Peer-reviewd journal publishing articles on African culture. **Founded:** 1988. **Freq:** Semiannual. **Key Personnel:** Chege Githiora, Editor; Kwadwo Osei-Nyame, Editorial Committee; Alena Rettova, Editorial Committee; Graham Furniss, Editorial Committee; Lindiwe Dovey, Editorial Committee; Kai Easton, Editorial Committee; Philip Jaggar, Editorial Committee; Chege Githiora, Editorial Committee; Akin Oyetade, Editorial Committee. **ISSN:** 1369-6815. **Subscription Rates:** 178 institutions print + online; US$299 institutions print + online; 169 institutions online; US$285 institutions online; 41 individuals personal; US$78 individuals personal; EUR238 institutions print and online; EUR227 institutions online only; EUR61 individuals. **URL:** http://www.tandf.co.uk/journals/carfax/13696815.html.

51869 ■ Journal of Applied Statistics
Routledge
Taylor & Francis Group Ltd.
2 Park Sq.
Milton Pk.
Abingdon OX14 4RN, United Kingdom
Ph: 44 20 70176000
Fax: 44 20 70176699
Publisher E-mail: webmaster.books@tandf.co.uk
Peer-reviewed journal providing a platform for the discussion between applied statisticians and users of applied statistical techniques covering a wide range of fields. **Freq:** 12/yr. **Key Personnel:** Prof. Gopal K. Kanji, Founding Ed.; Dr. Robert G. Aykroyd, Editor; Julian Besag, Editorial Advisory Board. **ISSN:** 0266-4763. **Subscription Rates:** US$808 individuals print only; US$2,843 institutions online only; US$2,992 institutions print + online; 1,804 institutions print + online; 1,713 institutions online only; 487 institutions print only; EUR2,382 institutions print and online; EUR2,263 institutions online only; EUR644 individuals. **Remarks:** Advertis-

ing accepted; rates available upon request. **URL:** http://www.tandf.co.uk/journals/titles/02664763.asp. **Circ:** (Not Reported)

51870 ■ Journal of the Asia Pacific Economy
Routledge
Taylor & Francis Group Ltd.
2 Park Sq.
Milton Pk.
Abingdon OX14 4RN, United Kingdom
Ph: 44 20 70176000
Fax: 44 20 70176699
Publisher E-mail: webmaster.books@tandf.co.uk
Peer-reviewed journal on economic, historical, political, social and cultural factors of Asia Pacific region. **Freq:** Quarterly. **Key Personnel:** David Lim, Managing Editor; Yan Islam, Co-Ed.; Maureen Todhunter, Editorial Asst., m.todhunter@griffith.edu.au; Salim Rashid, Co-Ed.; Abuzar Asra, Editorial Board; Anis Chowdhury, Co-Ed. **ISSN:** 1354-7860. **Subscription Rates:** 502 institutions print + online; 477 institutions online; 107 individuals; US$832 institutions print + online; US$791 institutions online; US$160 individuals; EUR666 institutions print and online; EUR632 institutions online only; EUR128 individuals. **Remarks:** Advertising accepted; rates available upon request. **URL:** http://www.tandf.co.uk/journals/titles/13547860.asp. **Circ:** (Not Reported)

51871 ■ Journal of Balkan and Near Eastern Studies
Routledge
Taylor & Francis Group Ltd.
2 Park Sq.
Milton Pk.
Abingdon OX14 4RN, United Kingdom
Ph: 44 20 70176000
Fax: 44 20 70176699
Publisher E-mail: webmaster.books@tandf.co.uk
Peer-reviewed journal covering the geo-political and geo-economic issues of the Mediterranean, the Balkans and the Near East. **Freq:** Quarterly. **Key Personnel:** Vassilis K. Fouskas, Managing Editor, vfouskas@unipi.gr; Bulent Aras, Review Ed.; Maritsa Poros, Review Ed.; Ilaria Favretto, Editorial Committee; Christiana Papadopoulou, Asst. to the Ed.; Dejan Djokic, Reviews Ed. **ISSN:** 1944-8953. **Subscription Rates:** 401 institutions print + online; 381 institutions online; 101 individuals; US$663 institutions print + online; US$630 institutions online; US$169 individuals; EUR529 institutions print and online; EUR502 institutions online only; EUR114 individuals. **Remarks:** Advertising accepted; rates available upon request. **URL:** http://www.tandf.co.uk/journals/carfax/14613190.html. **Formerly:** Journal of Southern Europe and the Balkans (2009). **Circ:** (Not Reported)

51872 ■ Journal of Beliefs & Values
Routledge
Taylor & Francis Group Ltd.
2 Park Sq.
Milton Pk.
Abingdon OX14 4RN, United Kingdom
Ph: 44 20 70176000
Fax: 44 20 70176699
Publisher E-mail: webmaster.books@tandf.co.uk
Peer-reviewed journal covering issues in the areas of theology, religious studies, religious education, and values in education. **Subtitle:** Studies in Religion & Education. **Freq:** 3/yr. **Key Personnel:** Dr. William S. Campbell, Editor-in-Chief, ws.campbell@lamp.ac.uk; Dr. Marius C. Felderhof, Book Review Ed.; Dr. Mawil Izzi Dien, Editorial Advisory Board; Prof. Dan Cohn-Sherbok, Editorial Advisory Board; Prof. Brian Bocking, Editorial Advisory Board; Dr. George Chryssides, Editorial Advisory Board; Dr. Philip Barnes, Book Review Ed.; Prof. Leslie J. Francis, Assoc. Ed.; Prof. Kenneth Cracknell, Editorial Advisory Board; Prof. Denise Cush, Editorial Advisory Board; Prof. Ursula King, Editorial Advisory Board; Prof. Marilyn Nefsky, Editorial Advisory Board. **ISSN:** 1361-7672. **Subscription Rates:** 349 institutions print + online; US$647 institutions print + online; 331 institutions online only; US$615 institutions online only; 136 individuals print only; US$207 individuals print only; EUR515 institutions print and online; EUR490 institutions online only; EUR165 individuals. **Remarks:** Advertising accepted; rates available upon request. **URL:** http://www.tandf.co.uk/journals/carfax/13617672.html. **Circ:** (Not Reported)

51873 ■ Journal of Change Management
Routledge
Taylor & Francis Group Ltd.
2 Park Sq.

Milton Pk.
Abingdon OX14 4RN, United Kingdom
Ph: 44 20 70176000
Fax: 44 20 70176699
Publisher E-mail: webmaster.books@tandf.co.uk
Peer-reviewed journal identifying critical changes resulting in a better response from the various elements of a business organization such as structure, processes, resources, technology and its culture in the highly competitive environment of today. **Freq:** Quarterly. **Key Personnel:** Prof. Colin Carnall, Editorial Advisory Board; Rune Todnem By, Editor, r.t.by@staffs.ac.uk; Christine Teelken, Assoc. Ed.; Ingrid Nembhard, Assoc. Ed.; Ashley Braganza, Assoc. Ed.; Inger Stensaker, Assoc. Ed.; Stewart Clegg, Editorial Advisory Board; Karl E. Weick, Editorial Advisory Board; Andrew Pettigrew, Editorial Advisory Board. **ISSN:** 1469-7017. **Subscription Rates:** 260 institutions print + online; US$432 institutions print + online; 246 institutions online; US$410 institutions online; 95 individuals personal; US$158 individuals personal; EUR345 institutions print and online; EUR327 institutions online only; EUR126 individuals. **Remarks:** Advertising accepted; rates available upon request. **URL:** http://www.tandf.co.uk/journals/titles/14697017.asp. **Circ:** (Not Reported)

51874 ■ Journal of Children and Poverty
Routledge
Taylor & Francis Group Ltd.
2 Park Sq.
Milton Pk.
Abingdon OX14 4RN, United Kingdom
Ph: 44 20 70176000
Fax: 44 20 70176699
Publisher E-mail: webmaster.books@tandf.co.uk
Peer-reviewed journal focusing on policy issues affecting education, social services, public policy and welfare reform having a bearing on quality of life for children and families. **Freq:** Semiannual. **Key Personnel:** Ralph Da Costa Nunez, Editor; Kathleen M. Ziol-Guest, Managing Editor; Concha Mendoza, Editorial Asst. **ISSN:** 1079-6126. **Subscription Rates:** US$97 individuals print only; US$326 institutions online; US$344 institutions print + online; 207 institutions print + online; 197 institutions online; 60 institutions print only; EUR274 institutions print and online; EUR261 institutions online only; EUR77 individuals. **Remarks:** Advertising accepted; rates available upon request. **URL:** http://www.tandf.co.uk/journals/titles/10796126.asp. **Circ:** (Not Reported)

51875 ■ Journal of Civil Society
Routledge
Taylor & Francis Group Ltd.
2 Park Sq.
Milton Pk.
Abingdon OX14 4RN, United Kingdom
Ph: 44 20 70176000
Fax: 44 20 70176699
Publisher E-mail: webmaster.books@tandf.co.uk
Peer-reviewed journal providing an outlet for world-class scholarship and debate on civil society. **Freq:** 3/yr. **Key Personnel:** Helmut K. Anheier, Editor, anheier@spa.ucla.edu; Jocelyn Guihama, Managing Editor; Andreas Schoeer, Assoc. Ed. **ISSN:** 1744-8689. **Subscription Rates:** 244 institutions print + online; 234 institutions online; 45 individuals; US$407 institutions print + online; US$386 institutions online; US$76 individuals; EUR60 individuals; EUR307 institutions online only; EUR324 institutions print and online. **Remarks:** Accepts advertising. **URL:** http://www.tandf.co.uk/journals/titles/17448689.asp. **Circ:** (Not Reported)

51876 ■ Journal of Commonwealth Law and Legal Education
Routledge
Taylor & Francis Group Ltd.
2 Park Sq.
Milton Pk.
Abingdon OX14 4RN, United Kingdom
Ph: 44 20 70176000
Fax: 44 20 70176699
Publisher E-mail: webmaster.books@tandf.co.uk
Peer-reviewed journal of the Commonwealth Legal Education Association covering the legal profession, foreign, European, civil law systems, and education and law. **Freq:** Semiannual. **Key Personnel:** Vanessa Skelton, Managing Editor; Prof. Dawn Oliver, Editorial Board; Carol Howells, Book Review Ed.; Jane Goodey, Editor; Prof. John Hatchard, Editor; Prof. Peter Cane, Editorial Board; Marc Cornock, Lead Ed.; Prof. David Nelken, Editorial Board; Prof. Gary Slapper, Editor. **ISSN:** 1476-

0401. Subscription Rates: US$102 individuals; US$214 institutions online only; US$226 institutions print and online; 124 institutions print and online; 118 institutions online only; 56 individuals; EUR180 institutions print and online; EUR171 institutions online only; EUR81 individuals. **URL:** http://www.tandf.co.uk/journals/journal.asp?issn=1476-0401&linktype=1.

51877 ■ The Journal of Communist Studies and Transition Politics
Routledge
Taylor & Francis Group Ltd.
2 Park Sq.
Milton Pk.
Abingdon OX14 4RN, United Kingdom
Ph: 44 20 70176000
Fax: 44 20 70176699
Publisher E-mail: webmaster.books@tandf.co.uk
Peer-reviewed journal focusing on transformation brought about in the Eastern Europe due to the collapse of the communist regime as also revival of some of the communist parties, ruling and non-ruling, both in Europe outside. **Freq:** Quarterly. **Key Personnel:** Ronald J. Hill, Editor; Margot Light, Editor; Paul G. Lewis, Editor; Stephen White, Editor, s.white@socsci.gla.ac.uk; Richard Sakwa, Editorial Board; Michael Waller, Editor, michael_waller2000@yahoo.co.uk; Jane Duckett, Editorial Board; Rita di Leo, Editorial Board; Jeffrey W. Hahn, Editorial Board; Stanislaw Gebethner, Editorial Board; Graeme Gill, Editorial Board; Eugene Huskey, Editorial Board. **ISSN:** 1352-3279. **Subscription Rates:** 346 institutions print + online; US$573 institutions print + online; 328 institutions online; US$544 institutions online; 77 individuals personal; US$115 individuals personal; EUR456 institutions print and online; EUR434 institutions online only; EUR91 individuals. **Remarks:** Advertising accepted; rates available upon request. **URL:** http://www.tandf.co.uk/journals/titles/13523279.asp. **Circ:** (Not Reported)

51878 ■ Journal of Contemporary African Studies
Routledge
Taylor & Francis Group Ltd.
2 Park Sq.
Milton Pk.
Abingdon OX14 4RN, United Kingdom
Ph: 44 20 70176000
Fax: 44 20 70176699
Publisher E-mail: webmaster.books@tandf.co.uk
Peer-reviewed journal fostering a research based discussion on human sciences thereby helping in understanding of change and development in Africa. **Freq:** 4/yr. **Key Personnel:** Valerie Moller, Editorial Committee; Paul Maylam, Book Review Ed.; Roger Southall, Managing Editor; Greg Ruiters, Editorial Committee; Azwell Banda, Editorial Committee; Sola Akinrinade, Editorial Committee; Darlene Miller, Editorial Committee; William Beinart, Editorial Board; Bruce Baker, Editorial Board. **ISSN:** 0258-9001. **Subscription Rates:** US$208 individuals print only; US$948 institutions; US$998 institutions print + online; 600 institutions print + online; 570 institutions online; 127 individuals; EUR794 institutions print and online; EUR755 institutions online only; EUR166 individuals. **Remarks:** Advertising accepted; rates available upon request. **URL:** http://www.tandf.co.uk/journals/carfax/02589001.html. **Circ:** (Not Reported)

51879 ■ Journal of Contemporary China
Routledge
Taylor & Francis Group Ltd.
2 Park Sq.
Milton Pk.
Abingdon OX14 4RN, United Kingdom
Ph: 44 20 70176000
Fax: 44 20 70176699
Publisher E-mail: webmaster.books@tandf.co.uk
Peer-reviewed journal sharing information on contemporary Chinese affairs, of interest to wide ranging groups of people such as scholars, businessmen and government policy-makers. The areas of interest including economics, political science, law, culture, history, international relations, sociology and other social sciences and humanities. **Freq:** 5/yr. **Key Personnel:** Suisheng Zhao, Editor, szhao@du.edu; Richard Baum, Editorial Advisory Board; Chu-Yuan Cheng, Editorial Advisory Board; Yun-Han Chu, Editorial Advisory Board; Lowell Dittmer, Editorial Advisory Board; June Teufel Dreyer, Editorial Advisory Board. **ISSN:** 1067-0564. **Sub-**

scription **Rates:** US$135 individuals print only; US$757 institutions online; US$796 institutions print + online; 481 institutions print + online; 457 institutions online; 99 individuals; EUR637 institutions print and online; EUR604 institutions online only; EUR108 individuals. **Remarks:** Advertising accepted; rates available upon request. **URL:** http://www.tandf.co.uk/journals/titles/10670564.asp. **Circ:** (Not Reported)

51880 ■ Journal of Contemporary European Studies
Routledge
Taylor & Francis Group Ltd.
2 Park Sq.
Milton Pk.
Abingdon OX14 4RN, United Kingdom
Ph: 44 20 70176000
Fax: 44 20 70176699
Publisher E-mail: webmaster.books@tandf.co.uk
Peer-reviewed journal providing a platform for exchange of ideas on studies related to European societies, politics and cultures. **Freq:** 4/yr. **Key Personnel:** Spyros Sofos, Editorial Committee; Jeremy Leaman, Editor, j.leaman@lboro.ac.uk; Brian Jenkins, Editor, jenkins5063.freeserve.co.uk; Dave Berry, Editorial Committee; Martha Worsching, Editorial Committee; Martin Bull, Editorial Committee; Gill Allwood, Editorial Committee; Tony Chafer, Editorial Committee; Jonathan Beaverstock, Editorial Committee; Paul Flenley, Editorial Committee; Hans Kastendiek, International Advisory Board; Volker Kreibich, International Advisory Board. **ISSN:** 1478-2804. **Subscription Rates:** 425 institutions print + online; US$719 institutions print + online; 404 institutions online; US$683 institutions online; 137 individuals; US$223 individuals; $A 141 members; EUR572 institutions print and online; EUR544 institutions online only; EUR179 individuals. **Remarks:** Advertising accepted; rates available upon request. **URL:** http://www.tandf.co.uk/journals/titles/14782804.asp. **Circ:** (Not Reported)

51881 ■ Journal of Contemporary Religion
Routledge
Taylor & Francis Group Ltd.
2 Park Sq.
Milton Pk.
Abingdon OX14 4RN, United Kingdom
Ph: 44 20 70176000
Fax: 44 20 70176699
Publisher E-mail: webmaster.books@tandf.co.uk
Peer-reviewed journal covering contemporary religion. **Founded:** 1986. **Freq:** 3/yr. **Key Personnel:** Elisabeth Arweck, Editor; Prof. Peter B. Clarke, Editor; E. Barker, Editorial Advisory Board; I. Borowik, Editorial Advisory Board; S. Bruce, Editorial Advisory Board; M. Al-Rasheed, Editorial Advisory Board; M. Baumann, Editorial Advisory Board. **ISSN:** 1353-7903. **Subscription Rates:** US$146 individuals print only; US$666 institutions online only; US$701 institutions print and online; 422 institutions print and online; EUR557 institutions print and online; 401 institutions online only; EUR529 institutions online only; 87 individuals; EUR116 individuals. **Remarks:** Accepts advertising. **URL:** http://www.tandf.co.uk/journals/titles/13537903.asp. **Circ:** (Not Reported)

51882 ■ Journal of Cosmetic and Laser Therapy
Taylor & Francis Ltd.
2 & 4 Park Sq.
Milton Pk.
Abingdon OX14 4RN, United Kingdom
Ph: 44 20 70176000
Fax: 44 20 70176336
Journal aimed at dermatologists, cosmetic surgeons, plastic and facial plastic surgeons, oculoplastic surgeons and all those interested in the rapidly expanding field of cosmetic and laser therapy, focusing on the application of cosmetic laser and light therapies on the skin and providing a forum for up-to-date studies demonstrating the wide range of therapeutic options for clinicians and surgeons involved in cosmetic and dermatological treatment. **Freq:** Quarterly. **Key Personnel:** Gary P. Lask, Co-Ed.; David J. Goldberg, Editor-in-Chief; William H. Beeson, Editorial Board; Tina Alster, Assoc. Ed.; Rox R. Anderson, Editorial Board; Sterling S. Baker, Editorial Board; Zoe Draelos, Assoc. Ed.; Marc Avram, Assoc. Ed.; Richard Fitzpatrick, Assoc. Ed. **ISSN:** 1476-4172. **Subscription Rates:** 480 institutions; US$785 institutions; EUR630 institutions. **Remarks:** Accepts advertising. **URL:** http://www.informaworld.com/smpp/title~content=t713399564; http://informahealthcare.com/jcl. **Circ:** (Not Reported)

51883 ■ Journal for Cultural Research
Routledge
Taylor & Francis Group Ltd.
2 Park Sq.
Milton Pk.
Abingdon OX14 4RN, United Kingdom
Ph: 44 20 70176000
Fax: 44 20 70176699
Publisher E-mail: webmaster.books@tandf.co.uk
Peer-reviewed journal focusing on cultural research. **Freq:** Quarterly. **Key Personnel:** Michael Dillon, Managing Editor, m.dillon@lancaster.ac.uk; Scott Wilson, Managing Editor; Michael J. Shapiro, Corresponding Ed.; Fred Botting, International Advisory Board; Lauren Berlant, Corresponding Ed.; Ashis Nandy, International Advisory Board; George Lipsitz, Corresponding Ed.; Lu Dai, Asst. Ed.; Jeremy Valentine, International Advisory Board; Arthur Bradley, Book Review Ed.; Sam Weber, International Advisory Board; Andrew Quick, International Advisory Board. **ISSN:** 1479-7585. **Subscription Rates:** 255 institutions print + online; US$423 institutions print + online; 242 institutions online; US$403 institutions online; 63 individuals personal; US$83 individuals personal; EUR336 institutions print and online; EUR320 institutions online only; EUR66 individuals. **Remarks:** Accepts advertising. **URL:** http://www.tandf.co.uk/journals/titles/14797585.asp. **Circ:** (Not Reported)

51884 ■ Journal of Dermatological Treatment
Taylor & Francis Ltd.
2 & 4 Park Sq.
Milton Pk.
Abingdon OX14 4RN, United Kingdom
Ph: 44 20 70176000
Fax: 44 20 70176336
Journal covering all aspects of the treatment of skin disease, including the use of topically and systemically administered drugs and other forms of therapy. **Freq:** 6/yr. **Key Personnel:** Steven R. Feldman, Editor; Peter Van De Kerkhof, Editor; Ronald Marks, Founding Ed.; Enno Christophers, Editorial Board; John Berth-Jones, Assoc. Ed.; Ruggero Caputo, Editorial Board; Paul R Bergstresser, Editorial Board; David De Berker, Assoc. Ed. **ISSN:** 0954-6634. **Subscription Rates:** 520 institutions; US$860 institutions; EUR685 institutions. **Remarks:** Accepts advertising. **URL:** http://www.informaworld.com/smpp/title~content=t713889756; http://informahealthcare.com/jdt. **Circ:** (Not Reported)

51885 ■ Journal of Development Studies
Routledge
Taylor & Francis Group Ltd.
2 Park Sq.
Milton Pk.
Abingdon OX14 4RN, United Kingdom
Ph: 44 20 70176000
Fax: 44 20 70176699
Publisher E-mail: webmaster.books@tandf.co.uk
Publication covering economics. **Freq:** 10/yr. **Key Personnel:** John Harriss, Editorial Board; Chris Milner, Editorial Board. **ISSN:** 0022-0388. **Subscription Rates:** 820 institutions print + online; 778 institutions online; 157 individuals; US$1,320 institutions print + online; US$1,253 institutions online; US$253 individuals; EUR1,051 institutions print + online; EUR998 institutions online; EUR201 individuals. **Remarks:** Advertising accepted; rates available upon request. **URL:** http://www.tandf.co.uk/journals/titles/00220388.asp. **Circ:** (Not Reported)

51886 ■ Journal of Drug Targeting
Taylor & Francis Ltd.
2 & 4 Park Sq.
Milton Pk.
Abingdon OX14 4RN, United Kingdom
Ph: 44 20 70176000
Fax: 44 20 70176336
Journal publishing papers and reviews on all aspects of drug delivery and targeting for molecular and macromolecular drugs including the design and characterization of carrier systems (whether colloidal, protein or polymeric) for both vitro and/or in vivo applications of these drugs. **Freq:** 10/yr. **Key Personnel:** Saghir Akhtar, Editor-in-Chief, journaldrugtargeting@googlemail.com; Rudy Juliano, Editorial Board, hghandeh@rx.umaryland.edu; Yvonne Perrie, Assoc. Ed., y.perrie@aston.ac.uk; Oya Alpar, Editorial Board; David Begley, Editorial Board. **ISSN:** 1061-186X. **Subscription Rates:** 1,395 institutions; US$2,195 institutions; EUR1,755 institutions. **Remarks:** Accepts advertising. **URL:** http://www.

informaworld.com/smpp/title~content=t713640314;
http://informahealthcare.com/drt. **Circ:** (Not Reported)

51887 ■ Journal of Early Childhood Teacher Education
Taylor & Francis Ltd.
2 & 4 Park Sq.
Milton Pk.
Abingdon OX14 4RN, United Kingdom
Ph: 44 20 70176000
Fax: 44 20 70176336
Peer-reviewed journal providing a forum for consideration of issues and for exchange of information and ideas about research and practice in early childhood teacher education. **Freq:** Quarterly. **Key Personnel:** Amos Hatch, Editor; Aline Stomfay-Stitz, Assoc. Ed.; Amanda N. Branscombe, Editorial Board; Doris Bergen, Editorial Board; Roy Evans, Editorial Board; Vicki Fromberg, Editorial Board. **ISSN:** 1090-1027. **Subscription Rates:** US$499 individuals print + online; US$474 individuals online; US$122 individuals print. **Remarks:** Accepts advertising. **URL:** http://www.informaworld.com/smpp/title~content=t713872612~db=all. **Circ:** (Not Reported)

51888 ■ Journal of Economic Methodology
Routledge
Taylor & Francis Group Ltd.
2 Park Sq.
Milton Pk.
Abingdon OX14 4RN, United Kingdom
Ph: 44 20 70176000
Fax: 44 20 70176699
Publisher E-mail: webmaster.books@tandf.co.uk
Peer-reviewed journal focusing on the field of economic methodology. **Subtitle:** The International Scholarly Journal of the Journal Network for Economic Method (INEM). **Freq:** Quarterly. **Key Personnel:** John B. Davis, Editor; Wade D. Hands, Editor; Harold Kincaid, Assoc. Ed.; Roger Backhouse, Editorial Board; Marcel Boumans, Assoc. Ed.; Caterina Marchionni, Book Review Ed.; James Woodward, Editorial Board; Kevin Hoover, Editorial Board; Oliver Williamson, Editorial Board; Sheila Dow, Assoc. Ed.; Julian Reiss, Editorial Board; Philip Mirowski, Editorial Board. **ISSN:** 1350-178X. **Subscription Rates:** 344 institutions print + online; US$575 institutions print + online; 326 institutions online; US$546 institutions online; 114 individuals; US$181 individuals; EUR459 institutions print and online; EUR436 institutions online only; EUR144 individuals. **Remarks:** Advertising accepted; rates available upon request. **URL:** http://www.tandf.co.uk/journals/routledge/1350178x.html. **Circ:** (Not Reported)

51889 ■ Journal of Ecotourism
Routledge
Taylor & Francis Group Ltd.
2 Park Sq.
Milton Pk.
Abingdon OX14 4RN, United Kingdom
Ph: 44 20 70176000
Fax: 44 20 70176699
Publisher E-mail: webmaster.books@tandf.co.uk
Journal examining the social, economic, and ecological aspects of ecotourism at a number of scales, and including regions from around the world. **Freq:** 3/yr. **Key Personnel:** David Fennell, Editor; David Weaver, Reviews Ed. **ISSN:** 1472-4049. **Subscription Rates:** US$142 individuals print; US$395 individuals online; US$416 individuals print + online; 73 individuals; 197 institutions online; 207 institutions print + online; EUR109 individuals; EUR301 institutions online; EUR317 institutions print + online. **URL:** http://www.tandf.co.uk/journals/reco.

51890 ■ Journal of Education for Teaching
Routledge
Taylor & Francis Group Ltd.
2 Park Sq.
Milton Pk.
Abingdon OX14 4RN, United Kingdom
Ph: 44 20 70176000
Fax: 44 20 70176699
Publisher E-mail: webmaster.books@tandf.co.uk
Peer-reviewed journal focusing on the educating the teacher including initial training, in-service education and staff development in general. **Subtitle:** International Research and Pedagogy. **Freq:** Quarterly. **Key Personnel:** Peter Gilroy, Editor, j.m.gilroy@btinternet.com; Kirsi Tirri, International Editorial Board; Robert V. Bullough, Jr., International Editorial Board; Edgar Stones, Found-

ing Ed.; Allan Soares, Book Review Ed.; Kenneth Zeichner, Asst. Ed.; Noeline Alcorn, International Editorial Board; Richard Bates, International Editorial Board; Beno Csapo, International Editorial Board. **ISSN:** 0260-7476. **Subscription Rates:** 779 institutions print + online; US$1,383 institutions print + online; 288 individuals print only; US$472 individuals print only; 740 institutions online; US$1,313 institutions online; EUR1,100 institutions print and online; EUR1,045 institutions online only; EUR376 individuals. **Remarks:** Advertising accepted; rates available upon request. **URL:** http://www.tandf.co.uk/journals/titles/02607476.asp. **Circ:** (Not Reported)

51891 ■ Journal of Education and Work
Routledge
Taylor & Francis Group Ltd.
2 Park Sq.
Milton Pk.
Abingdon OX14 4RN, United Kingdom
Ph: 44 20 70176000
Fax: 44 20 70176699
Publisher E-mail: webmaster.books@tandf.co.uk
Peer-reviewed journal providing a platform for integrating education and economic systems by mainly studying how knowledge, skills, values and attitudes both about and for work and employment are developed within the education system. **Freq:** 5/yr. **Key Personnel:** Hugh Lauder, Editor-in-Chief, edshl@bath.ac.uk; Ian Jamieson, Assoc. Ed.; Phil Hodkinson, Assoc. Ed.; Michael Young, Assoc. Ed.; D. Ashton, Editorial Advisory Board; Philip Brown, Editorial Advisory Board. **ISSN:** 1363-9080. **Subscription Rates:** 544 institutions print + online; 518 institutions online; 199 individuals personal; US$904 institutions print + online; US$858 institutions online; US$331 individuals personal; EUR719 institutions print and online; EUR683 institutions online only; EUR263 individuals. **Remarks:** Advertising accepted; rates available upon request. **URL:** http://www.tandf.co.uk/journals/carfax/13639080.html. **Circ:** (Not Reported)

51892 ■ Journal of Educational Administration and History
Routledge
Taylor & Francis Group Ltd.
2 Park Sq.
Milton Pk.
Abingdon OX14 4RN, United Kingdom
Ph: 44 20 70176000
Fax: 44 20 70176699
Publisher E-mail: webmaster.books@tandf.co.uk
Peer-reviewed journal focusing on current issues in educational administration, leadership, management and policy in the period from immediate and distant past. **Freq:** 4/yr. **Key Personnel:** Prof. Roy Lowe, International Advisory Board; Prof. Richard Aldrich, International Advisory Board; Prof. Jane Martin, Editorial Board; Dr. Stephanie Spencer, Editorial Board; Prof. Tanya Fitzgerald, Editor, t.fitzgerald@latrobe.edu.au; Dr. David Crook, Editorial Board; Dr. Peter Cunningham, International Advisory Board; Dr. Paul Sharp, International Advisory Board; Dr. Terry Wrigley, Editorial Board. **ISSN:** 0022-0620. **Subscription Rates:** 288 institutions print + online; US$480 institutions print + online; 273 institutions online; US$456 institutions online; 81 individuals personal; US$137 individuals personal; EUR384 institutions print and online; EUR364 institutions online only; EUR109 individuals. **Remarks:** Advertising accepted; rates available upon request. **URL:** http://www.tandf.co.uk/journals/titles/00220620.asp. **Circ:** (Not Reported)

51893 ■ Journal of Elections, Public Opinion & Parties
Routledge
Taylor & Francis Group Ltd.
2 Park Sq.
Milton Pk.
Abingdon OX14 4RN, United Kingdom
Ph: 44 20 70176000
Fax: 44 20 70176699
Publisher E-mail: webmaster.books@tandf.co.uk
Peer-reviewed journal publishing research articles on elections, public opinion, participation and political parties. **Subtitle:** Official Journal of Elections, Public Opinion & Parties (EPOP). **Freq:** 4/yr. **Key Personnel:** Justin Fisher, PhD, Editor, justin.fisher@brunel.ac.uk; Christopher Wlezien, PhD, Editor, wlezien@temple.edu; Robert Andersen, Editorial Board; Ingrid Van Biezen, Editorial Board; Lynn Bennie, Editorial Board; David Denver, Editorial Board; Chrysa Lamprinakou, Editorial Asst.; John Bartle, Editorial Board; Shaun Bowler, Edito-

rial Board. **ISSN:** 1745-7289. **Subscription Rates:** 273 institutions print + online; US$454 institutions print + online; 260 institutions online; US$432 institutions online; 83 individuals; US$139 individuals; EUR362 institutions print and online; EUR345 institutions online only; EUR111 individuals. **Remarks:** Advertising accepted; rates available upon request. **URL:** http://www.tandf.co.uk/journals/titles/17457289.asp. **Formerly:** British Elections & Parties Review. **Circ:** (Not Reported)

51894 ■ Journal of Environmental Planning and Management
Routledge
Taylor & Francis Group Ltd.
2 Park Sq.
Milton Pk.
Abingdon OX14 4RN, United Kingdom
Ph: 44 20 70176000
Fax: 44 20 70176699
Publisher E-mail: webmaster.books@tandf.co.uk
Peer-reviewed journal covering all aspects of environmental planning and management. **Freq:** 8/yr. **Key Personnel:** Kenneth G. Willis, Managing Editor; Prof. Neil Ericksen, International Editorial Advisory Board; Lex Brown, Assoc. Ed.; Prof. Peter J. Clinch, International Editorial Advisory Board; William G. Page, Assoc. Ed.; Neil Powe, Book Reviews Ed. **ISSN:** 0964-0568. **Subscription Rates:** 1,202 institutions print + online; 1,142 institutions online; 288 individuals; US$1,980 institutions print + online; US$1,881 institutions online; US$480 individuals; EUR1,584 institutions print and online; EUR1,505 institutions online only; EUR384 individuals. **Remarks:** Advertising accepted; rates available upon request. **URL:** http://www.tandf.co.uk/journals/titles/09640568.asp. **Circ:** (Not Reported)

51895 ■ Journal of Environmental Policy & Planning
Routledge
Taylor & Francis Group Ltd.
2 Park Sq.
Milton Pk.
Abingdon OX14 4RN, United Kingdom
Ph: 44 20 70176000
Fax: 44 20 70176699
Publisher E-mail: webmaster.books@tandf.co.uk
Peer-reviewed journal providing a focal point for the critical analysis of environmental policy and planning. The journal explores on common policies such as transport, agriculture and fisheries, urban and rural policy, in the context of environment. **Freq:** Quarterly. **Key Personnel:** Denise Phillips, Managing Editor, jepp1@cardiff.ac.uk; Dr. Richard Cowell, Editor, cowellrj@cardiff.ac.uk; Dr. Andrew Flynn, Editor, flynnac@cardiff.ac.uk. **ISSN:** 1523-908X. **Subscription Rates:** US$177 individuals print only; US$422 institutions online; US$444 institutions print + online; 274 institutions print + online; 261 institutions online; 111 individuals; EUR353 institutions print and online; EUR335 institutions online only; EUR142 individuals. **Remarks:** Advertising accepted; rates available upon request. **URL:** http://www.tandf.co.uk/journals/titles/1523908x.asp. **Circ:** (Not Reported)

51896 ■ Journal of European Public Policy
Routledge
Taylor & Francis Group Ltd.
2 Park Sq.
Milton Pk.
Abingdon OX14 4RN, United Kingdom
Ph: 44 20 70176000
Fax: 44 20 70176699
Publisher E-mail: webmaster.books@tandf.co.uk
Peer-reviewed journal dealing with theoretical and methodological aspects of European public policy. **Freq:** 8/yr. **Key Personnel:** Jeremy Richardson, PhD, Editor, jeremy.richardson@nuffield.ox.ac.uk; David Levy, Editorial Board; Tanja Borzel, Editorial Board; Wyn Grant, Editorial Board; Berthold Rittberger, Editorial Board; Sabine Saurugger, Editorial Board; Frank Baumgartner, Editorial Board; Jon Pierre, Editorial Board; Walter Mattli, Editorial Board. **ISSN:** 1350-1763. **Subscription Rates:** 634 institutions print + online; US$1,052 institutions print + online; 602 institutions online; US$999 institutions online; 124 individuals personal; US$207 individuals personal; 45 individuals society; US$74 individuals society; EUR837 institutions print and online; EUR796 institutions online only. **Remarks:** Advertising accepted; rates available upon request. **URL:** http://www.tandf.co.uk/journals/titles/13501763.asp. **Circ:** (Not Reported)

51897 ■ Journal of Experimental Nanoscience
Taylor & Francis Ltd.
2 & 4 Park Sq.
Milton Pk.
Abingdon OX14 4RN, United Kingdom
Ph: 44 20 70176000
Fax: 44 20 70176336
Peer-reviewed journal providing a showcase for advances in the experimental sciences underlying nanotechnology and nanomaterials by bringing together the most significant papers making original contributions to nanoscience in a range of fields including biology and biochemistry, physics, chemistry, chemical electrical and mechanical engineering, materials, pharmaceuticals and medicine. **Freq:** 6/yr. **Key Personnel:** Prof. Kwong-Yu Chan, Editor; Dr. Molly Stevens, Editorial Board; P.M. Ajayan, Editorial Board; A.K.Y. Jen, Editorial Board; S.M. Kuebler, Editorial Board; Prof. Nick Quirke, Ch. of Ed. **ISSN:** 1745-8080. **Subscription Rates:** EUR389 institutions online; US$491 institutions online; US$516 institutions print + online; EUR410 institutions print and online; 305 institutions online; 321 institutions print + online. **Remarks:** Accepts advertising. **URL:** http://www.tandf.co.uk/journals/titles/17458080.asp. **Circ:** (Not Reported)

51898 ■ Journal of Further and Higher Education
Routledge
Taylor & Francis Group Ltd.
2 Park Sq.
Milton Pk.
Abingdon OX14 4RN, United Kingdom
Ph: 44 20 70176000
Fax: 44 20 70176699
Publisher E-mail: webmaster.books@tandf.co.uk
Peer-reviewed journal Education publication. **Freq:** Quarterly. **Key Personnel:** Jennifer Rowley, Editor-in-Chief, j.rowley@mmu.ac.uk; Ian McNay, Editorial Advisory Board; Patrick Ainley, Editorial Board; Tim Oates, Book Reviews Ed., info@cambridgeassessment.org.uk; Seb Schmoller, Editorial Board; Anne Jasman, Editorial Board; Dan Taubman, Editorial Board; Morag Gray, Editorial Board; Patrick Ainley, Editorial Board; Ann Hodgson, Editorial Board. **ISSN:** 0309-877X. **Subscription Rates:** 346 institutions print + online; US$580 institutions print + online; 328 institutions online; US$551 institutions online; 112 individuals personal; US$184 individuals personal. **Remarks:** Accepts advertising. **URL:** http://www.tandf.co.uk/journals/titles/0309877x.asp. **Circ:** (Not Reported)

51899 ■ Journal of Gender Studies
Routledge
Taylor & Francis Group Ltd.
2 Park Sq.
Milton Pk.
Abingdon OX14 4RN, United Kingdom
Ph: 44 20 70176000
Fax: 44 20 70176699
Publisher E-mail: webmaster.books@tandf.co.uk
Peer-reviewed journal focusing on women's issues and gender studies. **Freq:** Quarterly. **Key Personnel:** Alex Franklin, Editor; Blu Tirohl, Editor; Mark Llewellyn, Editor. **ISSN:** 0958-9236. **Subscription Rates:** US$762 institutions print and online; 452 institutions print and online; US$86 individuals; 51 individuals; US$723 institutions online; 430 institutions online. **URL:** http://www.tandf.co.uk/journals/journal.asp?issn=0958-9236&linktype=rates.

51900 ■ Journal of Genocide Research
Routledge
Taylor & Francis Group Ltd.
2 Park Sq.
Milton Pk.
Abingdon OX14 4RN, United Kingdom
Ph: 44 20 70176000
Fax: 44 20 70176699
Publisher E-mail: webmaster.books@tandf.co.uk
Peer-reviewed journal publishing articles related to the study of genocide. **Freq:** Quarterly. **Key Personnel:** Cathie Carmichael, Editor; Jurgen Zimmerer, Editor, j.zimmerer@sheffield.ac.uk; Simone Gigliotti, Editor; Sarah Danielsson, Assoc. Ed.; Dirk A. Moses, Editor; Omer Bartov, International Advisory Board; Christian Gerlach, Editor; Adam Jones, Book Review Ed.; Wolf Gruner, Book Review Ed.; Dan Stone, Editor; Doris L. Bergen, International Advisory Board; Frank Chalk, International Advisory Board. **ISSN:** 1462-3528. **Subscription Rates:** 328 institutions print + online; US$546

institutions print + online; 312 institutions online; US$520 institutions online; 68 individuals personal; US$107 individuals personal; EUR421 institutions print and online; EUR414 institutions online only; EUR86 individuals. **Remarks:** Advertising accepted; rates available upon request. **URL:** http://www.tandf.co.uk/journals/titles/14623528.asp. **Circ:** (Not Reported)

51901 ■ Journal of Geography in Higher Education
Routledge
Taylor & Francis Group Ltd.
2 Park Sq.
Milton Pk.
Abingdon OX14 4RN, United Kingdom
Ph: 44 20 70176000
Fax: 44 20 70176699
Publisher E-mail: webmaster.books@tandf.co.uk
Peer-reviewed journal covering teaching of geography in higher education. **Freq:** 4/yr. **Key Personnel:** David Higgitt, Editor; Tim Hall, Editorial Board; Derek France, Editor; Michael Bradford, Editorial Advisory Board; Nicola Ansell, Editorial Board; Sue Burkill, Editorial Board; Rita Gardner, Editorial Board; Debby Cotton, Editorial Board; Brian Chalkley, Editorial Board; Craig Jeffrey, Editorial Board; Pauline Kneale, Editorial Board. **ISSN:** 0309-8265. **Subscription Rates:** 1,135 institutions print + online; US$1,914 institutions print + online; 1,078 institutions online; US$1,818 institutions online; 76 individuals personal; US$121 individuals personal; $A 173 individuals personal; EUR1,524 institutions print and online; EUR1,448 institutions online only; EUR97 individuals. **Remarks:** Advertising accepted; rates available upon request. **URL:** http://www.tandf.co.uk/journals/carfax/03098265.html. **Circ:** (Not Reported)

51902 ■ Journal of Global Ethics
Routledge
Taylor & Francis Group Ltd.
2 Park Sq.
Milton Pk.
Abingdon OX14 4RN, United Kingdom
Ph: 44 20 70176000
Fax: 44 20 70176699
Publisher E-mail: webmaster.books@tandf.co.uk
Peer-reviewed journal covering the ethical issues that arise in the context of globalization and global relations. **Freq:** 3/yr. **Key Personnel:** Christien Van Den Anker, Editor; Hasna Bekum, Editorial Advisory Board; Simon Caney, Editorial Advisory Board; David Held, Editorial Advisory Board; Ruth Chadwick, Editorial Advisory Board; Keith Horton, Regional Ed.; Prof. Heather Widdows, Editor; Sirkku Hellsten, Editor; Pal Ahluwalia, Editorial Advisory Board. **ISSN:** 1744-9626. **Subscription Rates:** 240 institutions print + online; US$400 institutions print + online; 228 institutions online; US$380 institutions online; 70 individuals personal; US$114 individuals personal; EUR90 individuals; EUR302 institutions online only; EUR318 institutions print and online. **Remarks:** Accepts advertising. **URL:** http://www.tandf.co.uk/journals/titles/17449626.asp. **Circ:** (Not Reported)

51903 ■ Journal of Heritage Tourism
Routledge
Taylor & Francis Group Ltd.
2 Park Sq.
Milton Pk.
Abingdon OX14 4RN, United Kingdom
Ph: 44 20 70176000
Fax: 44 20 70176699
Publisher E-mail: webmaster.books@tandf.co.uk
Peer-reviewed journal focusing on many facets of tourism. **Freq:** Quarterly. **Key Personnel:** Dallen J. Timothy, Editor. **ISSN:** 1743-873X. **Subscription Rates:** 218 institutions print + online; 207 institutions online; 75 individuals; US$440 institutions print + online; US$418 institutions online; US$135 institutions; EUR328 institutions print + online; EUR312 institutions online; EUR108 individuals. **URL:** http://www.tandf.co.uk/journals/1743-873X.

51904 ■ Journal of Human Development and Capabilities
Routledge
Taylor & Francis Group Ltd.
2 Park Sq.
Milton Pk.
Abingdon OX14 4RN, United Kingdom
Ph: 44 20 70176000
Fax: 44 20 70176699

Publisher E-mail: webmaster.books@tandf.co.uk
Peer-reviewed journal dealing with human development, challenging the traditional views of economics. **Freq:** 4/yr. **Key Personnel:** Khadija Haq, Editor; Sakiko Fukuda-Parr, Co-Ed.; Sabina Alkire, Editorial Advisory Board; Nancy Birdsall, Editorial Advisory Board; Arunabha Ghosh, Book Review Ed.; Melanie Walker, Co-Ed.; Richard Jolly, Editorial Advisory Board; Bina Agarwal, Editorial Advisory Board; Kay Grigar, Admin. Ed.; David Clark, Book Review Ed.; Diane Elson, Editorial Advisory Board. **ISSN:** 1945-2829. **Subscription Rates:** 308 institutions print + online; US$513 institutions print + online; 293 institutions online; US$488 institutions online; 80 individuals personal; US$129 individuals personal. **Remarks:** Advertising accepted; rates available upon request. **URL:** http://www.tandf.co.uk/journals/titles/19452829.asp. **Formerly:** Journal of Human Development. **Circ:** (Not Reported)

51905 ■ Journal of Human Rights
Routledge
Taylor & Francis Group Ltd.
2 Park Sq.
Milton Pk.
Abingdon OX14 4RN, United Kingdom
Ph: 44 20 70176000
Fax: 44 20 70176699
Publisher E-mail: webmaster.books@tandf.co.uk
Peer-reviewed journal dealing with the study and practice of human rights. **Freq:** Quarterly. **Key Personnel:** Thomas Cushman, Founder/Ed.-at-Large; Thomas Brudholm, Editorial Board; Michael Davis, Editorial Board; Akbar Ahmed, Editorial Board; Aaron M. Paterson, Managing Editor; Serena Parekh, Book Review Ed. **ISSN:** 1475-4835. **Subscription Rates:** 270 institutions print + online; US$445 institutions print + online; 257 institutions online; US$423 institutions online; 60 individuals; US$99 individuals; EUR354 institutions print and online; EUR336 institutions online only; EUR79 individuals. **Remarks:** Advertising accepted; rates available upon request. **URL:** http://www.tandf.co.uk/journals/titles/14754835.html. **Circ:** (Not Reported)

51906 ■ Journal of Iberian & Latin American Studies
Routledge
Taylor & Francis Group Ltd.
2 Park Sq.
Milton Pk.
Abingdon OX14 4RN, United Kingdom
Ph: 44 20 70176000
Fax: 44 20 70176699
Publisher E-mail: webmaster.books@tandf.co.uk
Journal on the languages, literatures, history and cultures of the Iberian Peninsula and Latin America. **Freq:** 3/yr. **Key Personnel:** Montserrat Lunati, Editor; Jordi Larios, Editor; Jean Andrews, Asst. Ed.; Catherine Davies, Editorial Advisory Board; David Brookshaw, Editorial Advisory Board; Trevor J. Dadson, Editorial Advisory Board; Henry Ettinghausen, Editorial Advisory Board; John A. Gledson, Editorial Advisory Board; Albert Hauf, Editorial Advisory Board. **ISSN:** 1470-1847. **Subscription Rates:** 108 individuals; 385 institutions online; US$638 institutions online; US$203 individuals; 406 institutions print + online; US$671 institutions print + online; EUR533 institutions print and online; EUR506 institutions online only; EUR161 individuals. **Remarks:** Advertising accepted; rates available upon request. **URL:** http://www.tandf.co.uk/journals/titles/14701847.asp. **Formerly:** Tesserae. **Circ:** (Not Reported)

51907 ■ The Journal of Imperial & Commonwealth History
Routledge
Taylor & Francis Group Ltd.
2 Park Sq.
Milton Pk.
Abingdon OX14 4RN, United Kingdom
Ph: 44 20 70176000
Fax: 44 20 70176699
Publisher E-mail: webmaster.books@tandf.co.uk
Peer-reviewed journal dealing with the history of the British Empire and Commonwealth. **Freq:** Quarterly. **Key Personnel:** Prof. Stephen Howe, Editor; Prof. Philip Murphy, Editor; David Armitage, International Editorial Board. **ISSN:** 0308-6534. **Subscription Rates:** US$109 individuals print only; US$648 institutions online only; US$682 institutions print + online; 409 institutions print + online; 388 institutions online only; 72 individuals print

Circulation: ★ = ABC; △ = BPA; ◆ = CAC; • = CCAB; ❑ = VAC; ⊕ = PO Statement; ‡ = Publisher's Report; Boldface figures = sworn; Light figures = estimated.

Gale Directory of Publications & Broadcast Media/147th Ed.   5545

only; EUR543 institutions print and online; EUR516 institutions online only; EUR87 individuals. **Remarks:** Advertising accepted; rates available upon request. **URL:** http://www.tandf.co.uk/journals/titles/03086534.asp. **Circ:** (Not Reported)

51908 ■ Journal of Intellectual and Developmental Disability
Taylor & Francis Ltd.
2 & 4 Park Sq.
Milton Pk.
Abingdon OX14 4RN, United Kingdom
Ph: 44 20 70176000
Fax: 44 20 70176336
Journal of interest to researchers, academics and professionals concerned with people with disabilities, publishing original qualitative and quantitative research papers, literature reviews, conceptual articles, brief reports, case reports, data briefs, and opinions and perspectives in the field of intellectual and developmental disability. **Freq:** Quarterly. **Key Personnel:** Susan Balandin, Editor, susan.balandin@himolde.no; Ivan Brown, Editorial Consultant; Suzanne Bettison, Assoc. Ed.; Roy Brown, Assoc. Ed.; Ian Dempsey, Editor, ian.dempsey@newcastle.edu.au; Michael Aman, Editorial Consultant; Bruce Baker, Editorial Consultant. **ISSN:** 1366-8250. **Subscription Rates:** 380 institutions; US$690 institutions; EUR550 institutions. **Remarks:** Accepts advertising. **URL:** http://www.informaworld.com/smpp/title~content=t713432019; http://informahealthcare.com/jid. **Circ:** (Not Reported)

51909 ■ Journal of Intercultural Studies
Routledge
Taylor & Francis Group Ltd.
2 Park Sq.
Milton Pk.
Abingdon OX14 4RN, United Kingdom
Ph: 44 20 70176000
Fax: 44 20 70176699
Publisher E-mail: webmaster.books@tandf.co.uk
Peer-reviewed journal covering ethnic, cultural, and racial issues and studies. **Freq:** 5/yr. **Key Personnel:** Dr. Ajaya Sahoo, Book Review Ed.; Dr. Vince Marotta, Editor; Dr. Tseen Khoo, Editor; Paula Muraca, Assoc. Ed.; Melissa Phillips, Asst. Ed. **ISSN:** 0725-6868. **Subscription Rates:** US$321 individuals; US$841 institutions online only; US$885 institutions print and online; 533 institutions print and online; $A 1,084 institutions print and online; 194 individuals; $A 1,030 institutions online; $A 223 individuals; 506 institutions online. **URL:** http://www.tandf.co.uk/journals/titles/07256868.asp.

51910 ■ Journal of Interprofessional Care
Taylor & Francis Ltd.
2 & 4 Park Sq.
Milton Pk.
Abingdon OX14 4RN, United Kingdom
Ph: 44 20 70176000
Fax: 44 20 70176336
Peer-reviewed journal promoting collaboration within and between education, practice and research in health and social care and treating research as both a collaborative field in its own right and as a means to evaluate interprofessional education and practice. **Freq:** 6/yr. **Key Personnel:** Prof. Hugh Barr, Editor-in-Chief; Prof. Fiona Ross, Editor-in-Chief; Marion Jones, Editorial Board; Julianne Cheek, Editorial Board; Scott Reeves, Assoc. Ed.; Madeline Schmitt, Assoc. Ed.; Alan Bleakley, Editorial Board; John Gilbert, Editorial Board; Diane Lee, Editorial Board; Ester Mogensen, Assoc. Ed.; Marilyn Hammick, Assoc. Ed.; Della Freeth, Assoc. Ed. **ISSN:** 1356-1820. **Subscription Rates:** US$1,645 individuals print and online; US$1,645 institutions online only; US$1,645 institutions print and online; US$1,645 individuals online only. **Remarks:** Accepts advertising. **URL:** http://www.ingentaconnect.com/content/apl/cjic. **Circ:** (Not Reported)

51911 ■ Journal of Intervention and Statebuilding
Routledge
Taylor & Francis Group Ltd.
2 Park Sq.
Milton Pk.
Abingdon OX14 4RN, United Kingdom
Ph: 44 20 70176000
Fax: 44 20 70176699
Publisher E-mail: webmaster.books@tandf.co.uk
Journal covering intervention and statebuilding. **Founded:** Jan. 1975. **Freq:** Quarterly. **Print Method:**

Offset. **Trim Size:** 8 1/4 x 11. **Cols./Page:** 2. **Col. Width:** 46 nonpareils. **Col. Depth:** 126 agate lines. **Key Personnel:** Rita Abrahamsen, International Editorial Advisory Board; Adam Branch, Editorial Asst.; William Bain, International Editorial Advisory Board; Alex J. Bellamy, International Editorial Advisory Board; Liisa Laakso, Co-Ed.; John C. Alden, International Editorial Advisory Board; Philip Cunliffe, Reviews Ed.; Simon Chesterman, Co-Ed.; David Chandler, Editor; Giovanna Bono, International Editorial Advisory Board; Anne Orford, International Editorial Advisory Board. **ISSN:** 1750-2977. **Subscription Rates:** 272 institutions print + online; 259 institutions online; 67 individuals; US$451 institutions print + online; US$428 institutions online; US$109 individuals; EUR359 institutions print and online; EUR341 institutions online only; EUR88 individuals. **URL:** http://www.tandf.co.uk/journals/titles/17502977.asp.

51912 ■ Journal of Israeli History
Routledge
Taylor & Francis Group Ltd.
2 Park Sq.
Milton Pk.
Abingdon OX14 4RN, United Kingdom
Ph: 44 20 70176000
Fax: 44 20 70176699
Publisher E-mail: webmaster.books@tandf.co.uk
Peer-reviewed journal covering history of Israel. **Subtitle:** Politics, Society, Culture. **Freq:** Semiannual. **Key Personnel:** Derek J. Penslar, Editor; Anita Shapira, Editor; Menachem Mautner, Editorial Board; Philippa Shimrat, Asst. Ed.; Asher Susser, Editorial Board; Joseph Mali, Editorial Board; Dan Laor, Editorial Board; Meir Chazan, Editorial Asst.; Shalom Ratzabi, Editorial Board. **ISSN:** 1353-1042. **Subscription Rates:** 209 institutions print + online; US$347 institutions print + online; 199 institutions online; US$329 institutions online; 55 individuals; US$86 individuals; EUR276 institutions print and online; EUR263 institutions online only; EUR68 individuals. **Remarks:** Advertising accepted; rates available upon request. **URL:** http://www.tandf.co.uk/journals/titles/13531042.asp. **Circ:** (Not Reported)

51913 ■ Journal of Latin American Cultural Studies
Routledge
Taylor & Francis Group Ltd.
2 Park Sq.
Milton Pk.
Abingdon OX14 4RN, United Kingdom
Ph: 44 20 70176000
Fax: 44 20 70176699
Publisher E-mail: webmaster.books@tandf.co.uk
Peer-reviewed journal covering articles on the history and analysis of Latin American culture. **Freq:** 3/yr. **Key Personnel:** Ben Bollig, Editor; Lorraine Leu, Editor; Philip Derbyshire, Editor; Jens Andermann, Editor; Jean Franco, Editorial Advisory Board; Italia Boliver-Reynaud, Editorial Asst. **ISSN:** 1356-9325. **Subscription Rates:** 433 institutions print + online; 411 institutions online; 104 individuals; US$719 institutions print + online; US$683 institutions online; US$201 individuals; EUR572 institutions print and online; EUR543 institutions online only; EUR160 individuals. **Remarks:** Advertising accepted; rates available upon request. **URL:** http://www.tandf.co.uk/journals/carfax/13569325.html. **Circ:** (Not Reported)

51914 ■ Journal of Legal History
Routledge
Taylor & Francis Group Ltd.
2 Park Sq.
Milton Pk.
Abingdon OX14 4RN, United Kingdom
Ph: 44 20 70176000
Fax: 44 20 70176699
Publisher E-mail: webmaster.books@tandf.co.uk
Law periodical. **Freq:** 3/yr. **Key Personnel:** Dr. Neil Jones, Editor; Dr. Mark Godfrey, Editorial Committee; Prof. Patrick Polden, Editorial Committee; Sir John Baker, Honorary Editorial Board; Prof. David Ibbetson, Editorial Committee; Prof. Raymond Cocks, Editorial Committee; Dr. Thomas Gallanis, Editorial Committee. **ISSN:** 0144-0365. **Subscription Rates:** 293 institutions print + online; US$499 institutions print + online; 278 institutions online; US$474 institutions online; 70 individuals; US$115 individuals; EUR397 institutions print + online; EUR378 institutions online only; EUR91 individuals. **URL:** http://www.tandf.co.uk/journals/titles/01440365.asp.

51915 ■ Journal of Legal Medicine
Routledge
Taylor & Francis Group Ltd.
2 Park Sq.
Milton Pk.
Abingdon OX14 4RN, United Kingdom
Ph: 44 20 70176000
Fax: 44 20 70176699
Publisher E-mail: webmaster.books@tandf.co.uk
Law periodical. **Freq:** Quarterly. **Key Personnel:** Marshall B. Kapp, Ed. Emeriti; Marvin H. Firestone, MD, Editorial Board; Arnold J. Rosoff, Dep. Ed.; Dorothy Rasinski Gregory, MD, Editorial Board; Alan C. Hoffman, Editorial Board; Edward E. Hollowell, Editorial Board; Paul J. Connors, MD, Editorial Board; Dale H. Cowan, MD, Editorial Board; Alicejane Lippner, MD, Editorial Board; Theodore R. Leblang, Ed. Emeritus. **ISSN:** 0194-7648. **Subscription Rates:** 267 institutions print + online; US$445 institutions print + online; 254 institutions online; US$423 institutions online; 143 individuals personal; US$237 individuals personal. **Remarks:** Accepts advertising on request. **URL:** http://www.tandf.co.uk/journals/titles/01947648.asp. **Circ:** (Not Reported)

51916 ■ The Journal of Legislative Studies
Routledge
Taylor & Francis Group Ltd.
2 Park Sq.
Milton Pk.
Abingdon OX14 4RN, United Kingdom
Ph: 44 20 70176000
Fax: 44 20 70176699
Publisher E-mail: webmaster.books@tandf.co.uk
Peer-reviewed journal covering all aspects of legislative research and developments. **Freq:** Quarterly. **Key Personnel:** Philip Norton, Editor, p.norton@hull.ac.uk; Sally Clark, Editorial Asst.; Marvin L. Overby, Assoc. Ed.; Mark Shephard, Dep. Ed.; Cristina Leston-Bandeira, Dep. Ed.; Michael Rush, Assoc. Ed. **ISSN:** 1357-2334. **Subscription Rates:** US$115 individuals print only; US$508 institutions online only; US$535 institutions print + online; 70 individuals; 306 institutions online; 323 institutions print + online; EUR425 institutions print and online; EUR404 institutions online only; EUR91 individuals. **Remarks:** Advertising accepted; rates available upon request. **URL:** http://www.tandf.co.uk/journals/titles/13572334.asp. **Circ:** (Not Reported)

51917 ■ Journal of Marketing Communications
Routledge
Taylor & Francis Group Ltd.
2 Park Sq.
Milton Pk.
Abingdon OX14 4RN, United Kingdom
Ph: 44 20 70176000
Fax: 44 20 70176699
Publisher E-mail: webmaster.books@tandf.co.uk
Peer-reviewed journal covering marketing and corporate communication, branding and promotion management. **Freq:** 5/yr. **Key Personnel:** Philip J. Kitchen, Editor, pkitchen@brocku.ca; Prof. Charles H. Patti, Case Reviews Ed.; Patrick De Pelsmacker, Assoc. Ed.; Don E. Schultz, Assoc. Ed.; Pascale Quester, Assoc. Ed. **ISSN:** 1352-7266. **Subscription Rates:** 790 institutions print + online; 750 institutions online; 99 individuals; US$1,305 institutions print + online; US$1,204 institutions online; US$177 individuals; EUR1,039 institutions print and online; EUR987 institutions online only; EUR142 individuals. **Remarks:** Advertising accepted; rates available upon request. **URL:** http://www.tandf.co.uk/journals/titles/13527266.asp. **Circ:** (Not Reported)

51918 ■ Journal of Mental Health
Taylor & Francis Ltd.
2 & 4 Park Sq.
Milton Pk.
Abingdon OX14 4RN, United Kingdom
Ph: 44 20 70176000
Fax: 44 20 70176336
International forum for the latest research in the mental health field. **Freq:** 6/yr. **Key Personnel:** Til Wykes, Exec. Ed., jmh@iop.kcl.ac.uk; Tom Craig, Editor; Peter Beresford, Assoc. Ed.; Martin Knapp, Assoc. Ed.; Jan Scott, Assoc. Ed.; Trudie Chalder, Editor; Kim Mueser, Editor; David Penn, Editor; Diana Rose, Assoc. Ed. **ISSN:** 0963-8237. **Subscription Rates:** 935 institutions; US$1,675 institutions; EUR1,340 institutions. **Remarks:** Accepts advertising. **URL:** http://informahealthcare.com/jmh?cookieSet=1. **Circ:** (Not Reported)

51919 ■ Journal of Modern Italian Studies
Routledge
Taylor & Francis Group Ltd.
2 Park Sq.
Milton Pk.
Abingdon OX14 4RN, United Kingdom
Ph: 44 20 70176000
Fax: 44 20 70176699
Publisher E-mail: webmaster.books@tandf.co.uk
Peer-reviewed journal relating to the study of modern and contemporary Italy. **Freq:** 5/yr. **Key Personnel:** John A. Davis, Editor; Mary Gibson, Assoc. Ed.; Martha McCormick, Managing Editor; Maura Hametz, Book Review Ed.; David Ward, Book Review Ed.; Marzio Barbagli, Editorial Board. **ISSN:** 1354-571X. **Subscription Rates:** 368 institutions print + online; 349 institutions online; 63 individuals; US$595 institutions print + online; 571 institutions online; 98 individuals; EUR480 institutions print and online; EUR456 institutions online only; EUR76 individuals. **Remarks:** Advertising accepted; rates available upon request. **URL:** http://www.tandf.co.uk/journals/routledge/1354571x.html. **Circ:** (Not Reported)

51920 ■ Journal of Modern Jewish Studies
Routledge
Taylor & Francis Group Ltd.
2 Park Sq.
Milton Pk.
Abingdon OX14 4RN, United Kingdom
Ph: 44 20 70176000
Fax: 44 20 70176699
Publisher E-mail: webmaster.books@tandf.co.uk
Peer-reviewed journal covering literature, history, religion and social studies in relation to Jewish communities. **Freq:** 3/yr. **Key Personnel:** Glenda Abramson, Editor; Ronald Nettler, Assoc. Ed.; David Sorkin, Assoc. Ed. **ISSN:** 1472-5886. **Subscription Rates:** US$117 individuals; US$593 institutions online; US$624 institutions print + online; 375 institutions print + online; 356 institutions online; 69 individuals; EUR498 institutions print and online; EUR473 institutions online only; EUR92 individuals. **Remarks:** Advertising accepted; rates available upon request. **URL:** http://www.tandf.co.uk/journals/journal.asp?issn=1472-5886&linktype=1. **Circ:** (Not Reported)

51921 ■ Journal of Moral Education
Routledge
Taylor & Francis Group Ltd.
2 Park Sq.
Milton Pk.
Abingdon OX14 4RN, United Kingdom
Ph: 44 20 70176000
Fax: 44 20 70176699
Publisher E-mail: webmaster.books@tandf.co.uk
Peer-reviewed journal covering various features of moral education and development through the lifespan. **Freq:** Quarterly. **Key Personnel:** Monica J. Taylor, Editor-in-Chief, jmoraled@onetel.com; Barbara Applebaum, Editorial Advisory Board; James Conroy, Editorial Advisory Board. **ISSN:** 0305-7240. **Subscription Rates:** US$109 individuals print only; US$435 institutions online; US$457 institutions print + online; 221 institutions print + online; 210 institutions online; 54 individuals; EUR364 institutions print and online; EUR346 institutions online only; EUR07 individuals. **Remarks:** Advertising accepted; rates available upon request. **URL:** http://www.tandf.co.uk/journals/carfax/03057240.html. **Circ:** (Not Reported)

51922 ■ Journal of Multicultural Discourses
Routledge
Taylor & Francis Group Ltd.
2 Park Sq.
Milton Pk.
Abingdon OX14 4RN, United Kingdom
Ph: 44 20 70176000
Fax: 44 20 70176699
Publisher E-mail: webmaster.books@tandf.co.uk
Journal covering the existing assumptions about discourse analysis, understanding of the processes of language. **Freq:** 3/yr. **Key Personnel:** Doreen Wu, Editorial Board; Miguel Perez Milans, Review Ed. **ISSN:** 1744-7143. **Subscription Rates:** 156 institutions online only; EUR230 institutions online only; US$315 institutions online only; 165 institutions print + online; US$331 institutions print + online; EUR242 institutions print + online; US$149 individuals; 75 individuals; EUR93 individuals. **URL:** http://www.tandf.co.uk/journals/1744-7143.

51923 ■ Journal of Multilingual & Multicultural Development
Routledge
Taylor & Francis Group Ltd.
2 Park Sq.
Milton Pk.
Abingdon OX14 4RN, United Kingdom
Ph: 44 20 70176000
Fax: 44 20 70176699
Publisher E-mail: webmaster.books@tandf.co.uk
Scholarly journal covering multilingualism, language and cultural development. **Founded:** 1980. **Freq:** Bimonthly. **Key Personnel:** John Edwards, Editor, jedwards@stfx.ca. **ISSN:** 0143-4632. **Subscription Rates:** 353 institutions print + online; US$697 institutions print + online; EUR531 institutions print + online; 75 individuals; US$149 individuals; EUR93 individuals; 331 institutions online only; US$663 institutions online only; EUR504 institutions online only. **Remarks:** Accepts advertising. **URL:** http://www.tandf.co.uk/journals/0143-4632. **Circ:** (Not Reported)

51924 ■ Journal of Muslim Minority Affairs
Routledge
Taylor & Francis Group Ltd.
2 Park Sq.
Milton Pk.
Abingdon OX14 4RN, United Kingdom
Ph: 44 20 70176000
Fax: 44 20 70176699
Publisher E-mail: webmaster.books@tandf.co.uk
Peer-reviewed journal dealing with the issues of Muslim minorities in non-Muslim societies. **Founded:** 1979. **Freq:** 4/yr. **Key Personnel:** Saleha S. Mahmood, Editor-in-Chief, editorialoffice@imma.org.uk; Heba A. Khalid, Asst. Ed.; Zulekha Pirani, Asst. Ed. **ISSN:** 1360-2004. **Subscription Rates:** US$161 individuals; US$660 institutions online; US$695 institutions print + online; 98 individuals; 398 institutions online; 419 institutions print + online; EUR556 institutions print and online; EUR529 institutions online only; EUR128 individuals. **Remarks:** Advertising accepted; rates available upon request. **URL:** http://www.tandf.co.uk/journals/carfax/13602004.html. **Circ:** (Not Reported)

51925 ■ Journal of North African Studies
Routledge
Taylor & Francis Group Ltd.
2 Park Sq.
Milton Pk.
Abingdon OX14 4RN, United Kingdom
Ph: 44 20 70176000
Fax: 44 20 70176699
Publisher E-mail: webmaster.books@tandf.co.uk
Peer-reviewed journal reporting on subjects such as history, sociology, anthropology, economy and others emphasizing on regional coverage. **Freq:** Quarterly. **Key Personnel:** John P. Entelis, PhD, Editor, entelis@fordham.edu; Alison Pargeter, Assoc. Ed./Book Review Ed.; Greg White, Assoc. Ed./Book Review Ed.; George Joffe, Editor, gj235@cam.ac.uk; Maha Azzam, International Advisory Board; Eva Bellin, International Advisory Board. **ISSN:** 1362-9387. **Subscription Rates:** US$117 individuals print only; US$502 institutions online; US$528 institutions print + online; 321 institutions print + online; 305 institutions online; 77 individuals print only; EUR421 institutions print and online; EUR400 institutions online only; EUR94 individuals. **Remarks:** Advertising accepted; rates available upon request. **URL:** http://www.tandf.co.uk/journals/titles/13629387.asp. **Circ:** (Not Reported)

51926 ■ Journal of Nutritional & Environmental Medicine
Taylor & Francis Ltd.
2 & 4 Park Sq.
Milton Pk.
Abingdon OX14 4RN, United Kingdom
Ph: 44 20 70176000
Fax: 44 20 70176336
International journal publishing papers on toxicity/nutritional toxicology, nutritional and environmental factors and the immune system, chemical sensitivity, diagnosis and treatment techniques in allergy, nutrition and reproductive function, essential fatty acids in prevention and treatment, vitamins, minerals, amino acids and other dietary factors in prevention and treatment, human microflora in health and disease, nutritional/environmental medicine, antioxidants in health and disease, pesticides and modern farming techniques, laboratory methods in nutritional/environmental medicine, nutritional supplementation and dietary intervention and impact of food processing on nutrient availability. **Freq:** Quarterly. **Key Personnel:** Dr. Damien Downing, Sen. Ed., drd@naltd.co.uk; Derek Bryce-Smith, Editorial Advisory Board; Ian E. Brighthope, Editorial Advisory Board; John Bogden, Editorial Advisory Board; Dr. Stephen Davies, Consulting Ed.; Richard Anderson, Editorial Advisory Board; Jeffrey Bland, Editorial Advisory Board; W.A. Shrader, Jr., Editor; John Dickerson, Editorial Advisory Board; Stephen Cunnane, Editorial Advisory Board. **ISSN:** 1359-0847. **Remarks:** Accepts advertising. **URL:** http://informahealthcare.com/loi/cjne. **Circ:** (Not Reported)

51927 ■ Journal of Organ Dysfunctions
Taylor & Francis Ltd.
2 & 4 Park Sq.
Milton Pk.
Abingdon OX14 4RN, United Kingdom
Ph: 44 20 70176000
Fax: 44 20 70176336
Journal devoted to the publication of articles on significant work in pathophysiology as well as in clinical science and preclinical medicine related to multiple organ/system dysfunctions, providing a forum for exchange of ideas on potential molecular and cellular mechanisms of multiple organ/system dysfunctions. **Freq:** 4/yr. **Key Personnel:** Prof. Xiangdong Wang, MD, Editor-in-Chief; Keith J. Barrington, Editorial Board; Robert A. Balk, Editorial Board; Prof. Kenneth Adler, PhD, Editor; Prof. David Ray, PhD, Assoc. Ed.; Prof. Roland Andersson, Editor. **ISSN:** 1747-1060. **Subscription Rates:** US$360 institutions print + online; US$360 institutions online; US$360 individuals print + online; US$360 individuals print. **Remarks:** Accepts advertising. **URL:** http://www.informaworld.com/smpp/title~content=t716100745~db=jour. **Circ:** (Not Reported)

51928 ■ The Journal of Pacific History
Routledge
Taylor & Francis Group Ltd.
2 Park Sq.
Milton Pk.
Abingdon OX14 4RN, United Kingdom
Ph: 44 20 70176000
Fax: 44 20 70176699
Publisher E-mail: webmaster.books@tandf.co.uk
Peer-reviewed journal focusing on history. **Freq:** 3/yr. **Key Personnel:** Chris Ballard, Editor; Judith A. Bennett, Editor; Vicki Luker, Exec. Ed., vicki.luker@anu.edu.au. **ISSN:** 0022-3344. **Subscription Rates:** US$385 institutions print and online; 249 institutions print and online; US$64 individuals; 37 individuals; US$366 institutions online; 237 institutions online. **URL:** http://www.tandf.co.uk/journals/carfax/00223344.html.

51929 ■ Journal of Peace Education
Routledge
Taylor & Francis Group Ltd.
2 Park Sq.
Milton Pk.
Abingdon OX14 4RN, United Kingdom
Ph: 44 20 70176000
Fax: 44 20 70176699
Publisher E-mail: webmaster.books@tandf.co.uk
Peer-reviewed journal covering the study on peace education. **Freq:** Semiannual. **Key Personnel:** John P. Synott, Editorial Board; Candice C. Carter, Editorial Board; Alicia Cabezudo, Editorial Board; Sara Horowitz, Editorial Board; Ian Harris, Editorial Board; Kazuyo Yamane, Editorial Board. **ISSN:** 1740-0201. **Subscription Rates:** 151 institutions online; US$253 institutions online; 48 individuals; US$80 individuals; 159 institutions print + online; US$266 institutions print + online; EUR212 institutions print and online; EUR202 institutions online only; EUR63 individuals. **Remarks:** Advertising accepted; rates available upon request. **URL:** http://www.tandf.co.uk/journals/titles/17400201.asp. **Circ:** (Not Reported)

51930 ■ Journal of Peasant Studies
Routledge
Taylor & Francis Group Ltd.
2 Park Sq.
Milton Pk.
Abingdon OX14 4RN, United Kingdom
Ph: 44 20 70176000
Fax: 44 20 70176699

Circulation: ★ = ABC; △ = BPA; ♦ = CAC; • = CCAB; ❑ = VAC; ⊕ = PO Statement; ‡ = Publisher's Report; Boldface figures = sworn; Light figures = estimated.

Gale Directory of Publications & Broadcast Media/147th Ed. 5547

Publisher E-mail: webmaster.books@tandf.co.uk
Peer-reviewed journal dealing with the political economy of agrarian change. **Freq:** Quarterly. **Key Personnel:** Saturnino Borras, Jr., Editor; Elizabeth Fitting, Reviews Ed.; Ruth Hall, Reviews Ed. **ISSN:** 0306-6150. **Subscription Rates:** US$122 individuals; US$571 institutions online; US$601 institutions print + online; 77 individuals; 345 institutions online; 363 institutions print + online; EUR479 institutions print and online; EUR455 institutions online only; EUR97 individuals. **Remarks:** Advertising accepted; rates available upon request. **URL:** http://www.tandf.co.uk/journals/titles/03066150.asp. **Circ:** (Not Reported)

51931 ■ Journal of Plant Interactions
Taylor & Francis Ltd.
2 & 4 Park Sq.
Milton Pk.
Abingdon OX14 4RN, United Kingdom
Ph: 44 20 70176000
Fax: 44 20 70176336
Peer-reviewed journal of significance to plant biologists, plant physiologists, ecologists, mycologists, microbiologists, agronomists, landscape architects, environmental engineers, entomologists, students and all researchers interested in biological struggle and sustainable use of natural resources, covering most plant interactions with the surrounding environment. **Freq:** 4/yr. **Key Personnel:** Prof. Massimo Maffei, Editor-in-Chief, massimo.maffei@unito.it; Alan J.M. Baker, Editorial Board; Cinzia Bertea, Editorial Board. **ISSN:** 1742-9145. **Subscription Rates:** US$403 institutions online; US$320 institutions online; US$424 institutions print & online; 254 institutions print & online; 241 institutions online; EUR337 institutions print & online; **Remarks:** Accepts advertising. **URL:** http://www.tandf.co.uk/journals/titles/17429145.asp. **Circ:** (Not Reported)

51932 ■ Journal of Poetry Therapy
Routledge
Taylor & Francis Group Ltd.
2 Park Sq.
Milton Pk.
Abingdon OX14 4RN, United Kingdom
Ph: 44 20 70176000
Fax: 44 20 70176699
Publisher E-mail: webmaster.books@tandf.co.uk
Peer-reviewed journal covering the use of literary arts in therapeutic, educational, and community-building capacities. **Freq:** Quarterly. **Key Personnel:** Gillie Bolton, Editorial Board; Charles Rossiter, Book Review Ed.; Dahlia Lorenz, Editorial Board; Thomas Greening, Editorial Board; Dr. Nicholas Mazza, Editor; Raymond J. Corsini, Editorial Board. **ISSN:** 0889-3675. **Subscription Rates:** 455 institutions print + online; 433 institutions online; 63 individuals; US$686 institutions print + online; US$652 institutions online; US$97 individuals; EUR546 institutions print and online; EUR520 institutions online only; EUR77 individuals. **Remarks:** Advertising accepted; rates available upon request. **URL:** http://www.tandf.co.uk/journals/titles/08893675.asp. **Circ:** (Not Reported)

51933 ■ Journal of Political Ideologies
Routledge
Taylor & Francis Group Ltd.
2 Park Sq.
Milton Pk.
Abingdon OX14 4RN, United Kingdom
Ph: 44 20 70176000
Fax: 44 20 70176699
Publisher E-mail: webmaster.books@tandf.co.uk
Journal covering political studies and focusing on the analysis of political ideology both in its theoretical and conceptual aspects. **Freq:** 3/yr. **Key Personnel:** Michael Freeden, Editor; Terence Ball, Editorial Advisory Board; Andrew Vincent, Assoc. Ed.; Marc Stears, Assoc. Ed.; Ruth Levitas, Editorial Advisory Board; James Meadowcroft, Assoc. Ed. **ISSN:** 1356-9317. **Subscription Rates:** 275 institutions online; 69 individuals; US$459 institutions online; US$114 individuals; 290 institutions print + online; US$482 institutions print + online; EUR384 institutions print + online; EUR364 institutions online only; EUR90 individuals. **Remarks:** Advertising accepted; rates available upon request. **URL:** http://www.tandf.co.uk/journals/titles/13569317.asp. **Circ:** (Not Reported)

51934 ■ The Journal of Positive Psychology
Routledge
Taylor & Francis Group Ltd.
2 Park Sq.
Milton Pk.
Abingdon OX14 4RN, United Kingdom
Ph: 44 20 70176000
Fax: 44 20 70176699
Publisher E-mail: webmaster.books@tandf.co.uk
Peer-reviewed journal providing an interdisciplinary and international forum for the science and application of positive psychology, devoted to basic research and professional application on states of optimal human functioning and fulfillment, and the facilitation and promotion of well-being. **Freq:** 6/yr. **Key Personnel:** Robert A. Emmons, Editor-in-Chief, journalpospsych@ucdavis.edu; Jane Gillham, Assoc. Ed.; Felicia Huppert, Assoc. Ed.; Robert Biswas-Diener, Editorial Board; Ken Sheldon, PhD, Book Review Ed., sheldonk@missouri.edu; Jane Dutton, Editorial Board; Michael Eid, Assoc. Ed.; Dmitry Leontiev, Assoc. Ed.; Jeffrey Froh, Assoc. Ed. **ISSN:** 1743-9760. **Subscription Rates:** US$85 individuals print; US$490 institutions online; US$515 institutions print + online; 48 individuals print; 271 institutions online; 286 institutions print + online; EUR68 individuals; EUR392 institutions online only; EUR413 institutions print and online. **Remarks:** Accepts advertising. **URL:** http://www.tandf.co.uk/journals/titles/17439760.asp. **Circ:** (Not Reported)

51935 ■ Journal of Postcolonial Writing
Routledge
Taylor & Francis Group Ltd.
2 Park Sq.
Milton Pk.
Abingdon OX14 4RN, United Kingdom
Ph: 44 20 70176000
Fax: 44 20 70176699
Publisher E-mail: webmaster.books@tandf.co.uk
Journal devoted to the study of literature written in English, particularly aiming to explore the interface between the postcolonial writing of the modern global era and the economic forces of production which increasingly commodify culture. **Freq:** 5/yr. **Key Personnel:** Dr. Janet Wilson, Editor; Sarah Lawson Welsh, Assoc. Ed.; Fiona Tolan, Assoc. Ed. **ISSN:** 1744-9855. **Subscription Rates:** 255 institutions print + online; US$419 institutions print + online; 243 institutions online; US$398 institutions online; 71 individuals; US$119 individuals; EUR334 institutions print and online; EUR318 institutions online only; EUR94 individuals. **Remarks:** Accepts advertising. **URL:** http://www.tandf.co.uk/journals/titles/17449855.asp. **Circ:** (Not Reported)

51936 ■ Journal of Property Research
Routledge
Taylor & Francis Group Ltd.
2 Park Sq.
Milton Pk.
Abingdon OX14 4RN, United Kingdom
Ph: 44 20 70176000
Fax: 44 20 70176699
Publisher E-mail: webmaster.books@tandf.co.uk
Journal dealing with the property investment and finance, and land development. **Freq:** Quarterly. **Key Personnel:** Bryan D. MacGregor, Editor; Pat Hendershott, Dep. Ed.; Richard Barkham, Editorial Board; Alastair Adair, Dep. Ed.; Liow Kim Hiang, Dep. Ed.; Michael Ball, Editorial Board; Neil Crosby, Editorial Board; Paul Gallimore, Editorial Board. **ISSN:** 0959-9916. **Subscription Rates:** US$66 individuals society; US$288 individuals; US$890 institutions online; US$937 institutions print + online; 40 individuals society; 172 individuals; 536 institutions online; 564 institutions print + online; EUR746 institutions print and online; EUR709 institutions online only. **Remarks:** Advertising accepted; rates available upon request. **URL:** http://www.tandf.co.uk/journals/titles/09599916.asp. **Circ:** (Not Reported)

51937 ■ Journal of Psychosomatic Obstetrics and Gynecology
Taylor & Francis Ltd.
2 & 4 Park Sq.
Milton Pk.
Abingdon OX14 4RN, United Kingdom
Ph: 44 20 70176000
Fax: 44 20 70176336
Journal providing a scientific forum for gynecologists, psychiatrists and psychologists as well as for all those who are interested in the psychosocial and psychosomatic aspects of women's health, covering the many disciplines involved such as gynecology, gynecological oncology, nursing and nurse midwifery, obstetrics, perinatology, psychiatry, psychology and reproductive endocrinology. **Founded:** 1982. **Freq:** Quarterly. **Key Personnel:** Harry B.M. Van De Wiel, Editor-in-Chief; Willibrord C.M. Weijmar Schultz, Editor-in-Chief; Astrid

Pascal, Managing Editor; B. Alder, Editorial Board; F. Van Balen, Editorial Board; J. Bitzer, Editorial Board. **ISSN:** 0167-482X. **Subscription Rates:** 450 institutions; US$780 institutions. EUR625 institutions. **Remarks:** Accepts advertising. **URL:** http://www.informaworld.com/smpp/title~content=t713634100. **Circ:** (Not Reported)

51938 ■ Journal of Quantitative Linguistics
Routledge
Taylor & Francis Group Ltd.
2 Park Sq.
Milton Pk.
Abingdon OX14 4RN, United Kingdom
Ph: 44 20 70176000
Fax: 44 20 70176699
Publisher E-mail: webmaster.books@tandf.co.uk
Peer-reviewed journal covering research on the quantitative characteristics of language and text in an exact mathematical form. **Freq:** 4/yr. **Key Personnel:** Reinhard Kohler, Editor; Relja Vulanovic, Assoc. Ed.; Sheila Embleton, Assoc. Ed.; Gabriel Altmann, Assoc. Ed.; Raimund G. Piotrowski, Editorial Board; Ludek Hrebicek, Editorial Board. **ISSN:** 0929-6174. **Subscription Rates:** 348 institutions print + online; 330 institutions online; 136 individuals; US$596 institutions print + online; US$566 institutions online; US$232 individuals; EUR475 institutions print and online; EUR451 institutions online only; EUR184 individuals. **Remarks:** Advertising accepted; rates available upon request. **URL:** http://www.tandf.co.uk/journals/titles/09296174.asp. **Circ:** (Not Reported)

51939 ■ Journal of Rehabilitation Medicine
Taylor & Francis Ltd.
2 & 4 Park Sq.
Milton Pk.
Abingdon OX14 4RN, United Kingdom
Ph: 44 20 70176000
Fax: 44 20 70176336
International peer-reviewed journal providing a forum for different areas of research in rehabilitation medicine, including: functional assessment and intervention studies, clinical studies in various patient groups, papers on methodology in physical and rehabilitation medicine, epidemiological studies on disabling conditions and reports on vocational and sociomedical aspects of rehabilitation. **Freq:** Bimonthly. **Key Personnel:** Gunnar Grimby, Editor-in-Chief; Kristian Borg, Assoc. Ed.; Henk Stam, Assoc. Ed.; Gerold Stucki, Assoc. Ed.; Bengt H. Sjolund, Assoc. Ed.; Franco Franchignoni, Assoc. Ed. **ISSN:** 1650-1977. **Subscription Rates:** EUR175 individuals print + online; EUR145 individuals online; EUR430 institutions print + online; EUR370 institutions online. **Remarks:** Advertising accepted; rates available upon request. **URL:** http://www.ingentaconnect.com/content/16501977/; http://www.medicaljournals.se/jrm/. **Circ:** (Not Reported)

51940 ■ Journal of Reproductive and Infant Psychology
Routledge
Taylor & Francis Group Ltd.
2 Park Sq.
Milton Pk.
Abingdon OX14 4RN, United Kingdom
Ph: 44 20 70176000
Fax: 44 20 70176699
Publisher E-mail: webmaster.books@tandf.co.uk
Peer-reviewed journal reporting and reviewing outstanding research on psychological, behavioural, medical and social aspects of human reproduction, pregnancy and infancy. **Founded:** 1983. **Freq:** Quarterly. **Key Personnel:** Dr. Olga Van Den Akker, Editorial Board; John Worobey, Assoc. North American Ed.; Jo Green, Editorial Board; Michael O'Hara, Editorial Board; Jenny Hewison, International Advisory Board; Robert Edelmann, Editorial Board; Dr. Margaret Redshaw, Co-Ed.; Louise Bryant, Book Review Ed.; Rosemary Maunder, International Advisory Board. **ISSN:** 0264-6838. **Subscription Rates:** 465 institutions print + online; 442 institutions online; 140 individuals print only; US$773 institutions print + online; US$735 institutions online; US$235 individuals print only; EUR616 institutions print and online; EUR585 institutions online only; EUR190 individuals. **Remarks:** Accepts advertising. **URL:** http://www.tandf.co.uk/journals/titles/02646838.asp; http://www.srip.ac.uk/journal/. **Circ:** (Not Reported)

51941 ■ Journal of Sexual Aggression
Routledge
Taylor & Francis Group Ltd.
2 Park Sq.
Milton Pk.

Abingdon OX14 4RN, United Kingdom
Ph: 44 20 70176000
Fax: 44 20 70176699
Publication E-mail: adminjsa.hls@coventry.ac.uk
Publisher E-mail: webmaster.books@tandf.co.uk
Peer-reviewed journal for the dissemination of research findings and the development of theory, policy and practice regarding sexual aggression in all its forms, extending to the expression of sexual aggression across childhood and adulthood, with regard to abusers, victims and survivors, irrespective of gender, culture and sexual preference. **Subtitle:** An International, Interdisciplinary Forum for Research, Theory and Practice. **Freq:** 3/yr. **Key Personnel:** Simon Hackett, Editorial Board; Dr. Sarah Brown, Editor; Dr. Richard Laws, Editorial Board; Dr. Jeremy Tudway, Book Reviews Ed.; Dr. Ian Lambie, Editorial Board. **ISSN:** 1355-2600. **Subscription Rates:** US$165 individuals print only; US$459 institutions on-line only; US$482 institutions print & online; 321 institutions print & online; 305 institutions online only; 165 individuals print only. **Remarks:** Accepts advertising. **URL:** http://www.tandf.co.uk/journals/titles/13552600.asp. **Circ:** (Not Reported)

51942 ■ Journal of Social Welfare and Family Law
Routledge
Taylor & Francis Group Ltd.
2 Park Sq.
Milton Pk.
Abingdon OX14 4RN, United Kingdom
Ph: 44 20 70176000
Fax: 44 20 70176699
Publisher E-mail: webmaster.books@tandf.co.uk
Law periodical. **Freq:** Quarterly. **Key Personnel:** Jim Goddard, Editor, j.goddard@bradford.ac.uk; Christina M. Lyon, Advisory Ed.; Helen Stalford, Editor, stalford@liverpool.ac.uk. **ISSN:** 0964-9069. **Subscription Rates:** US$159 individuals print only; US$598 institutions on-line only; US$629 institutions print & online. **Remarks:** Accepts advertising on request. **URL:** http://www.informaworld.com/smpp/title~db=all~content=a781264566~tab=linking. **Circ:** (Not Reported)

51943 ■ Journal of Social Work Practice
Routledge
Taylor & Francis Group Ltd.
2 Park Sq.
Milton Pk.
Abingdon OX14 4RN, United Kingdom
Ph: 44 20 70176000
Fax: 44 20 70176699
Publisher E-mail: webmaster.books@tandf.co.uk
Peer-reviewed journal covering articles on analysis of practice in social welfare and allied health professions from psychodynamic and systemic perspectives. **Subtitle:** Psychotherapeutic Approaches in Health, Welfare and the Community. **Freq:** 4/yr. **Key Personnel:** Lynn Froggett, Editor, lfroggett@uclan.ac.uk; Stephen Briggs, Editor, sbriggs@tavi-port.nhs.uk; Liz Webb, Editorial Advisory Board; Martin Smith, Editor, msmith@buckscc.gov.uk; Jackie Sanders, Corresponding Ed.; Susan Bliss, Editor; Robyn Munford, Corresponding Ed.; Mechthild Bereswill, Corresponding Ed.; Gillian Ruch, Editorial Advisory Board. **ISSN:** 0265-0533. **Subscription Rates:** US$303 individuals; US$1,039 institutions print + online; US$987 institutions print + online; 626 institutions print + online; 595 institutions online; 182 individuals; EUR803 institutions print and online; EUR763 institutions online only; EUR234 individuals. **Remarks:** Advertising accepted; rates available upon request. **URL:** http://www.tandf.co.uk/journals/carfax/02650533.html; http://www.tandf.co.uk/journals/titles/02650533.asp. **Circ:** (Not Reported)

51944 ■ Journal of Southern African Studies
Routledge
Taylor & Francis Group Ltd.
2 Park Sq.
Milton Pk.
Abingdon OX14 4RN, United Kingdom
Ph: 44 20 70176000
Fax: 44 20 70176699
Publisher E-mail: webmaster.books@tandf.co.uk
Peer-reviewed journal covering Southern African history, economics, sociology, demography, social anthropology and related fields. **Freq:** Quarterly. **Key Personnel:** Lyn Schumaker, Editorial Board; Jo Beall, Editorial Board; Deborah Gaitskell, Editorial Board; David Simon, Editorial Board; Joann McGregor, Editor; Jocelyn Alexander, Editorial Board; Fareda Banda, Editorial Board; Colin Stoneman, Editorial Coord.; Josie Stadler, Editorial Asst.; Wayne Dooling, Editorial Board. **ISSN:** 0305-7070. **Subscription Rates:** 425 institutions print + online; US$761 institutions print + online; 404 institutions online; US$722 institutions online; 108 individuals; US$218 individuals; EUR605 institutions print and online; EUR575 institutions online only; EUR173 individuals. **URL:** http://www.tandf.co.uk/journals/titles/03057070.asp.

51945 ■ Journal of Spanish Cultural Studies
Routledge
Taylor & Francis Group Ltd.
2 Park Sq.
Milton Pk.
Abingdon OX14 4RN, United Kingdom
Ph: 44 20 70176000
Fax: 44 20 70176699
Publisher E-mail: webmaster.books@tandf.co.uk
Peer-reviewed journal on Spanish culture and Hispanism. **Freq:** 4/yr. **Key Personnel:** Georgina Dopico-Black, Editor; Chris Perriam, Reviews Ed.; Mari Paz Balibrea, Reviews Ed.; Jacques Lezra, Reviews Ed.; Jose Luis Villacanas, Reviews Ed.; Brad Epps, Editorial Advisory Board. **ISSN:** 1463-6204. **Subscription Rates:** US$154 individuals print only; US$609 institutions online; US$641 institutions print + online; 94 individuals print only; 366 institutions online; 386 institutions print + online; EUR510 institutions print and online; EUR484 institutions online only; EUR124 individuals. **Remarks:** Advertising accepted; rates available upon request. **URL:** http://www.tandf.co.uk/journals/carfax/14636204.html. **Circ:** (Not Reported)

51946 ■ Journal of Sport & Tourism
Routledge
Taylor & Francis Group Ltd.
2 Park Sq.
Milton Pk.
Abingdon OX14 4RN, United Kingdom
Ph: 44 20 70176000
Fax: 44 20 70176699
Publisher E-mail: webmaster.books@tandf.co.uk
Peer-reviewed journal covering aspects of sport tourism. **Freq:** Quarterly. **Key Personnel:** Paul Beedie, Advisory Board; Mike Weed, PhD, Editor, mike.weed@canterbury.ac.uk; Laurence Chalip, Assoc. Ed.; Liz Fredline, Book Reviews Ed.; Sean Gammon, Assoc. Ed.; Heather Gibson, Assoc. Ed. **ISSN:** 1477-5085. **Subscription Rates:** 245 institutions print + online; 233 institutions online; 58 individuals; US$411 institutions print + online; US$390 institutions online; US$98 individuals; EUR327 institutions print and online; EUR311 institutions online only; EUR78 individuals. **Remarks:** Advertising accepted; rates available upon request. **URL:** http://www.tandf.co.uk/journals/titles/14775085.asp. **Circ:** (Not Reported)

51947 ■ Journal of Strategic Marketing
Routledge
Taylor & Francis Group Ltd.
2 Park Sq.
Milton Pk.
Abingdon OX14 4RN, United Kingdom
Ph: 44 20 70176000
Fax: 44 20 70176699
Publisher E-mail: webmaster.books@tandf.co.uk
Journal containing articles on the relationship between marketing and management. **Freq:** 7/yr. **Key Personnel:** Nigel F. Piercy, Editor; Carolyn Strong, Editor; Gordon Greenley, Founding Ed. **ISSN:** 0965-254X. **Subscription Rates:** EUR1,322 institutions print and online; EUR1,255 institutions online only; 999 institutions print + online; 126 individuals; 949 institutions online; US$1,569 institutions online only; US$1,652 institutions print + online; US$224 individuals; 38 institutions society; US$65 institutions society. **Remarks:** Accepts advertising. **URL:** http://www.tandf.co.uk/journals/titles/0965254X.asp. **Circ:** (Not Reported)

51948 ■ Journal of Strategic Studies
Routledge
Taylor & Francis Group Ltd.
2 Park Sq.
Milton Pk.
Abingdon OX14 4RN, United Kingdom
Ph: 44 20 70176000
Fax: 44 20 70176699
Publisher E-mail: webmaster.books@tandf.co.uk
Peer-reviewed journal covering articles that explicitly combine the historical and theoretical approaches to the study of modern warfare, defense policy and modern strategy. **Founded:** 1978. **Freq:** Bimonthly. **Key Personnel:** Joe A. Maiolo, PhD, Editor, joe.maiolo@kcl.ac.uk; Thomas G. Mahnken, PhD, Editor, tmahnke1@jhu.edu; Alan James, Reviews Ed.; Timothy D. Hoyt, Dep. Ed.; Alan James, Reviews Ed.; Richard K. Betts, Editorial Board. **ISSN:** 0140-2390. **Subscription Rates:** 101 individuals print only; 511 institutions print + online; 485 institutions online; US$148 individuals; US$851 institutions print + online; US$808 institutions online; EUR678 institutions print and online; EUR644 institutions online only; EUR117 individuals. **Remarks:** Advertising accepted; rates available upon request. **URL:** http://www.tandf.co.uk/journals/titles/01402390.asp. **Circ:** (Not Reported)

51949 ■ Journal of Substance Use
Taylor & Francis Ltd.
2 & 4 Park Sq.
Milton Pk.
Abingdon OX14 4RN, United Kingdom
Ph: 44 20 70176000
Fax: 44 20 70176336
Peer-reviewed and international journal, publishing peer-reviewed, up-to-the-minute articles on a wide spectrum of issues relating to the use of legal and illegal substances, including issues of prevention, treatment and policy while ensuring that issues are examined from a variety of perspectives, for instance clinical, managerial, service development, problem use, service use, and family perspective. **Freq:** Bimonthly. **Key Personnel:** Richard Pates, Editor-in-Chief, phone 44 29 20460362, fax 44 29 20461768; Dr. Tina Alwin, Dep. Ed.; Prof. Ana Adan, Assoc. Ed. **ISSN:** 1465-9891. **Subscription Rates:** 435 institutions; US$780 institutions; EUR625 institutions. **Remarks:** Accepts advertising. **URL:** http://informahealthcare.com/jsu. **Circ:** (Not Reported)

51950 ■ Journal of Sustainable Tourism
Routledge
Taylor & Francis Group Ltd.
2 Park Sq.
Milton Pk.
Abingdon OX14 4RN, United Kingdom
Ph: 44 20 70176000
Fax: 44 20 70176699
Publisher E-mail: webmaster.books@tandf.co.uk
Scholarly journal covering tourism. **Founded:** 1993. **Freq:** 8/yr. **Key Personnel:** Bill Bramwell, Editor; Bernard Lane, Editor; Michael C. Hall, Book Review Ed. **ISSN:** 0966-9582. **Subscription Rates:** US$173 individuals print only; US$971 individuals online; US$1,021 institutions print and online. **Remarks:** Accepts advertising. **URL:** http://www.informaworld.com/smpp/title~content=t794297833~db=all. **Circ:** (Not Reported)

51951 ■ Journal of Systematic Palaeontology
Taylor and Francis Group Ltd
2 Park Sq., Milton Park
Abingdon OX14 4RN, United Kingdom
Ph: 44 20 70176000
Fax: 44 20 70176699
Publisher E-mail: orders@crcpress.com
Journal publishing major papers describing new or poorly understood faunas and floras, or which use systematics in ways that significantly advance our understanding of palaeogeography, palaeobiology, functional morphology, palaeoecology, biostratigraphy or phylogenetic relationships. **Freq:** Quarterly. **Key Personnel:** Dr. Chris Cleal, Editorial Board; Dr. Paul Barrett, Editorial Board; Dr. Greg Edgecombe, Assoc. Ed.; Prof. Doug Erwin, Editorial Board. **ISSN:** 1477-2019. **Subscription Rates:** 208 institutions online and print; 198 institutions online only; 75 individuals print only; US$343 institutions online and print; US$326 institutions online only; US$146 individuals print only; EUR275 institutions online and print; EUR261 institutions online only; EUR94 individuals print only. **Remarks:** Accepts advertising. **URL:** http://www.tandf.co.uk/journals/TJSP. **Circ:** ‡500

51952 ■ Journal of Tourism & Cultural Change
Routledge
Taylor & Francis Group Ltd.
2 Park Sq.
Milton Pk.
Abingdon OX14 4RN, United Kingdom
Ph: 44 20 70176000
Fax: 44 20 70176699
Publisher E-mail: webmaster.books@tandf.co.uk
Peer-reviewed journal focusing on critically examining the relationships, tensions, representations, conflicts

Circulation: ★ = ABC; △ = BPA; ♦ = CAC; • = CCAB; ❏ = VAC; ⊕ = PO Statement; ‡ = Publisher's Report; Boldface figures = sworn; Light figures = estimated.

Gale Directory of Publications & Broadcast Media/147th Ed. 5549

and possibilities that exist between tourism/travel and culture/cultures in an increasingly complex global context. **Freq:** Quarterly. **Key Personnel:** Prof. Mike Robinson, Editor; Dr. Alison Phipps, Editor. **ISSN:** 1476-6825. **Subscription Rates:** US$469 institutions print + online; US$445 institutions online; US$142 individuals; 233 institutions print + online; 221 institutions online; 73 individuals; EUR356 institutions print + online; EUR338 institutions online; EUR109 individuals. **URL:** http://www.tandf.co.uk/journals/rtcc.

51953 ■ Journal of Urban Design
Routledge
Taylor & Francis Group Ltd.
2 Park Sq.
Milton Pk.
Abingdon OX14 4RN, United Kingdom
Ph: 44 20 70176000
Fax: 44 20 70176699
Publisher E-mail: webmaster.books@tandf.co.uk
Peer-reviewed journal covering the field of urban design for a better urban environment including topics such as urban aesthetics and townscape; urban structure and form; sustainable development; urban history, preservation and conservation; urban regeneration; local and regional identity; design control and guidance; property development; practice and implementation. **Freq:** 4/yr. **Key Personnel:** Prof. Taner Oc, Editor; Ernesto Arias, International Advisory Board; Jonathan Barnett, International Advisory Board. **ISSN:** 1357-4809. **Subscription Rates:** US$134 individuals print only; US$596 institutions online; US$627 institutions print + online; 377 institutions print + online; 358 institutions online; 78 individuals print only; EUR500 institutions print and online; EUR475 institutions online only; EUR107 individuals. **Remarks:** Advertising accepted; rates available upon request. **URL:** http://www.tandf.co.uk/journals/carfax/13574809.html. **Circ:** (Not Reported)

51954 ■ Journal of Urban Technology
Routledge
Taylor & Francis Group Ltd.
2 Park Sq.
Milton Pk.
Abingdon OX14 4RN, United Kingdom
Ph: 44 20 70176000
Fax: 44 20 70176699
Publisher E-mail: webmaster.books@tandf.co.uk
Journal focusing on recent advances in the field of urban technologies including their impact on history and the political, economic, environmental, social, esthetic, and ethical issues. **Freq:** 3/yr. **Key Personnel:** Maryann Donato, Managing Editor; Richard E. Hanley, Editor; Bruce Posner, Assoc. Ed.; Siddartha Sen, Book Review Ed.; Randal Reed, Book Review Ed.; Hojjat Adeli, Editorial Board; Amy Glasmeier, Editorial Board. **ISSN:** 1063-0732. **Subscription Rates:** US$131 individuals; 272 institutions online; US$450 institutions online; 96 individuals; 287 institutions print + online; US$474 institutions print + online; EUR378 institutions print and online; EUR359 institutions online only; EUR105 individuals. **Remarks:** Advertising accepted; rates available upon request. **URL:** http://www.tandf.co.uk/journals/carfax/10630732.html. **Circ:** (Not Reported)

51955 ■ Journal of Victorian Culture
Routledge
Taylor & Francis Group Ltd.
2 Park Sq.
Milton Pk.
Abingdon OX14 4RN, United Kingdom
Ph: 44 20 70176000
Fax: 44 20 70176699
Publisher E-mail: webmaster.books@tandf.co.uk
Journal covering all aspects of Victorian history and culture. **Founded:** 1996. **Freq:** 3/yr. **Print Method:** Offset. **Cols./Page:** 9. **Col. Width:** 17 nonpareils. **Col. Depth:** 294 agate lines. **Key Personnel:** Dinah Birch, Editorial Board; Helen Rogers, Editor; Josephine McDonagh, Editorial Board; Rohan McWilliam, Review Ed.; Kate Newey, Editorial Board. **ISSN:** 1355-5502. **Subscription Rates:** 180 institutions print + online; 170 institutions online only; 40 individuals; 25 institutions society; US$324 institutions print + online; US$308 institutions online; US$72 individuals; US$45 institutions society; EUR259 institutions print + online; EUR246 institutions online. **Remarks:** Accepts advertising. **URL:** http://www.tandf.co.uk/journals/rjvc. **Ad Rates:** GLR: .85, BW: 200, BW: 400, 4C: 100, 4C: 200, PCI: 18. **Circ:** 5,700

51956 ■ Journal of Vocational Education & Training
Routledge
Taylor & Francis Group Ltd.
2 Park Sq.
Milton Pk.
Abingdon OX14 4RN, United Kingdom
Ph: 44 20 70176000
Fax: 44 20 70176699
Publisher E-mail: webmaster.books@tandf.co.uk
Peer-reviewed journal focusing on theoretical and practical aspects of employment oriented education. **Freq:** Quarterly. **Key Personnel:** Ann Harris, Editorial Board; James Avis, Editorial Board; Bill Bailey, Editorial Board. **ISSN:** 1363-6820. **Subscription Rates:** 56 individuals print; 380 institutions online; US$594 institutions online; US$96 individuals; 400 institutions print + online; US$625 institutions print + online; EUR498 institutions print and online; EUR473 institutions online only; EUR77 individuals. **Remarks:** Advertising accepted; rates available upon request. **URL:** http://www.tandf.co.uk/journals/titles/13636820.asp. **Formerly:** The Vocational Aspect of Education. **Circ:** (Not Reported)

51957 ■ Journal of Wine Research
Routledge
Taylor & Francis Group Ltd.
2 Park Sq.
Milton Pk.
Abingdon OX14 4RN, United Kingdom
Ph: 44 20 70176000
Fax: 44 20 70176699
Publisher E-mail: webmaster.books@tandf.co.uk
Peer-reviewed journal dealing with all aspects of viticulture, oenology and the international wine trade in connection with the Institute of Masters of Wine. **Freq:** 3/yr. **Key Personnel:** Jane Carr, Managing Editor; James Handford, Editorial Advisory Board; Prof. Tim Unwin, Founding Ed.; tim.unwin@rhul.ac.uk; Dr. Roberto Ferrarini, Editorial Advisory Board; Linda Bisson, Editorial Advisory Board; Stephen Charters, Editorial Advisory Board; Roger Bessis, Editorial Advisory Board; Prof. Larry Lockshin, Editorial Advisory Board; Prof. Terrance Leighton, Editorial Advisory Board. **ISSN:** 0957-1264. **Subscription Rates:** 717 institutions print + online; US$1,188 institutions print + online; 681 institutions online; US$1,129 institutions online; 218 individuals personal; US$362 individuals personal; EUR946 institutions print and online; EUR899 institutions online only; EUR289 individuals. **Remarks:** Advertising accepted; rates available upon request. **URL:** http://www.tandf.co.uk/journal.asp?issn=0957-1264&linktype=1. **Circ:** (Not Reported)

51958 ■ Journal of Youth Studies
Routledge
Taylor & Francis Group Ltd.
2 Park Sq.
Milton Pk.
Abingdon OX14 4RN, United Kingdom
Ph: 44 20 70176000
Fax: 44 20 70176699
Publisher E-mail: webmaster.books@tandf.co.uk
Peer-reviewed journal dealing with the life experiences of youth in a wide ranging contexts such as such as education, the labor market and the family, and highlights key research themes such as the construction of identity, the use of leisure time, involvement in crime, consumption and most significantly political behavior. **Freq:** 6/yr. **Key Personnel:** Andy Furlong, Editor-in-Chief; Rob White, Assoc. Ed.; Harvey Krahn, Assoc. Ed.; Jeffrey Arnett, International Advisory Board; John Bynner, International Advisory Board; Andy Biggart, International Advisory Board. **ISSN:** 1367-6261. **Subscription Rates:** 99 individuals; 380 institutions online; US$629 institutions online; US$164 individuals; 400 institutions print + online; US$662 institutions print + online; EUR528 institutions print and online; EUR502 institutions online only; EUR129 individuals. **Remarks:** Advertising accepted; rates available upon request. **URL:** http://www.tandf.co.uk/journals/titles/13676261.asp. **Circ:** (Not Reported)

51959 ■ Journalism Studies
Routledge
Taylor & Francis Group Ltd.
2 Park Sq.
Milton Pk.
Abingdon OX14 4RN, United Kingdom
Ph: 44 20 70176000
Fax: 44 20 70176699
Publisher E-mail: webmaster.books@tandf.co.uk
Peer-reviewed journal devoted to the study of journalism, both as a subject of academic inquiry and an arena of professional practice, in connection with the Journalism Studies Interest Group (JSIG) of the International Communication Association. **Freq:** Bimonthly. **Key Personnel:** Bob Franklin, Editor, franklinb1@cf.ac.uk; Ann Luce, Review Ed.; Kevin G. Barnhurst, Editorial Board; Bonnie Davis, Review Ed.; Anantha Babbili, Editorial Board; Beth Barnes, Editorial Board; Bonnie Brennan, Editorial Board; Elizabeth L. Toth, Assoc. Ed.; Gerd Kopper, Assoc. Ed., gerd.kopper@udo.edu; Kenichi Asano, Editorial Board; Judy Van Slyke Turk, Assoc. Ed., jvturk@vcu.edu; Jay Blumler, Editorial Board. **ISSN:** 1461-670X. **Subscription Rates:** 125 individuals personal; US$206 individuals personal; 59 elsewhere society; US$96 elsewhere society; EUR165 individuals personal. **Remarks:** Advertising accepted; rates available upon request. **URL:** http://www.tandf.co.uk/journals/titles/1461670x.asp. **Circ:** (Not Reported)

51960 ■ Justice Quarterly
Routledge
Taylor & Francis Group Ltd.
2 Park Sq.
Milton Pk.
Abingdon OX14 4RN, United Kingdom
Ph: 44 20 70176000
Fax: 44 20 70176699
Publisher E-mail: webmaster.books@tandf.co.uk
Peer-reviewed journal featuring articles on criminal justice and related issues. **Freq:** 6/yr. **Key Personnel:** Richard Tewlsbury, Editor, justice.quarterly@louisville.edu; Jennifer Cruze, Managing Editor; Gennaro F. Vito, Dep. Ed.; Elizabeth Mustaine, Dep. Ed.; Brandon Applegate, Assoc. Ed.; Heith Copes, Assoc. Ed. **ISSN:** 0741-8825. **Subscription Rates:** US$828 institutions print + online; US$786 institutions online; 498 institutions print + online; 473 institutions online; EUR659 institutions print and online; EUR626 institutions online only. **Remarks:** Accepts advertising. **URL:** http://www.tandf.co.uk/journals/titles/07418825.asp. **Circ:** (Not Reported)

51961 ■ Labor History
Routledge
Taylor & Francis Group Ltd.
2 Park Sq.
Milton Pk.
Abingdon OX14 4RN, United Kingdom
Ph: 44 20 70176000
Fax: 44 20 70176699
Publisher E-mail: webmaster.books@tandf.co.uk
Peer-reviewed journal covering human resources and labor relations. **Freq:** Quarterly. **Key Personnel:** Craig Phelan, Editor, c.l.phelan@swansea.ac.uk; Gerald Friedman, Editor, gfriedma@econs.umass.edu; Howard Stanger, Book Review Ed., stangerh@canisius.edu; Kevin Boyle, Editorial Board; Barry Bluestone, Editorial Board; Sakhela Buhlungu, Editorial Board. **ISSN:** 0023-656X. **Subscription Rates:** US$95 individuals; US$382 institutions online only; US$402 institutions print and online; 241 institutions print and online; 229 institutions online; 66 individuals online. **URL:** http://www.tandf.co.uk/journals/journal.asp?issn=0023-656x&linktype=5.

51962 ■ Language Awareness
Routledge
Taylor & Francis Group Ltd.
2 Park Sq.
Milton Pk.
Abingdon OX14 4RN, United Kingdom
Ph: 44 20 70176000
Fax: 44 20 70176699
Publisher E-mail: webmaster.books@tandf.co.uk
Peer-reviewed journal covering language. **Founded:** 1992. **Freq:** Quarterly. **Key Personnel:** Dr. Terry Shortall, Review Ed.; Michel Candelier, Editorial Board; Christopher N. Candlin, Editorial Board; Paolo Balboni, Editorial Board; Angie Williams, Editorial Board; Stephen Andrews, Editorial Board; Arthur Van Essen, Editorial Board; Leo Van Lier, Editorial Board; Suzanne Burley, Editor. **ISSN:** 0965-8416. **Subscription Rates:** 364 institutions print + online; US$730 institutions print + online; EUR553 institutions print + online; 72 individuals; US$145 individuals; EUR91 individuals; 331 institutions online only; US$693 institutions online only; EUR525 institutions online only. **Remarks:** Accepts advertising. **URL:** http://www.tandf.co.uk/journals/0965-8416. **Circ:** (Not Reported)

51963 ■ Language Culture & Curriculum
Routledge
Taylor & Francis Group Ltd.
2 Park Sq.
Milton Pk.
Abingdon OX14 4RN, United Kingdom
Ph: 44 20 70176000
Fax: 44 20 70176699
Publisher E-mail: webmaster.books@tandf.co.uk
Scholarly journal covering language. **Founded:** 1988.
Freq: 3/yr. **Key Personnel:** Dr. John Harris, Editor.
ISSN: 0790-8318. **Subscription Rates:** 277 institutions
print + online; US$555 institutions print + online; EUR416
institutions print + online; 75 individuals; US$149
individuals; EUR97 individuals; US$527 institutions on-
line; 263 institutions online; EUR395 institutions online.
Remarks: Accepts advertising. **URL:** http://www.tandf.
co.uk/journals/0790-8318. **Circ:** (Not Reported)

51964 ■ Language and Education
Routledge
Taylor & Francis Group Ltd.
2 Park Sq.
Milton Pk.
Abingdon OX14 4RN, United Kingdom
Ph: 44 20 70176000
Fax: 44 20 70176699
Publisher E-mail: webmaster.books@tandf.co.uk
Peer-reviewed journal covering language and education.
Founded: 1987. **Freq:** Bimonthly. **Key Personnel:** Viv
Edwards, Editor; Rita Elaine Silver, Review Ed. **ISSN:**
0950-0782. **Subscription Rates:** 442 institutions print
+ online; US$885 institutions print + online; EUR663
institutions print + online; 75 individuals; US$149
individuals; EUR97 individuals; 420 institutions online
only; US$840 institutions online only; EUR630 institutions
online only. **Remarks:** Accepts advertising. **URL:** http://
www.tandf.co.uk/journals/0950-0782. **Circ:** (Not Reported)

**51965 ■ Language and Intercultural Com-
munication**
Routledge
Taylor & Francis Group Ltd.
2 Park Sq.
Milton Pk.
Abingdon OX14 4RN, United Kingdom
Ph: 44 20 70176000
Fax: 44 20 70176699
Publisher E-mail: webmaster.books@tandf.co.uk
Journal promoting an interdisciplinary understanding of
the interplay between language and intercultural
communication. **Freq:** Quarterly. **Key Personnel:** Malcolm MacDonald, Editor; John O'Regan, Editor. **ISSN:**
1470-8477. **Subscription Rates:** 72 individuals;
US$145 individuals; EUR91 individuals; 232 institutions
print + online; US$464 institutions print + online; EUR349
institutions print + online; 220 institutions online only;
US$442 institutions online only; EUR331 institutions on-
line only. **URL:** http://www.tandf.co.uk/journals/1470-
8477.

**51966 ■ Latin American and Caribbean Ethnic
Studies**
Routledge
Taylor & Francis Group Ltd.
2 Park Sq.
Milton Pk.
Abingdon OX14 4RN, United Kingdom
Ph: 44 20 70176000
Fax: 44 20 70176699
Publisher E-mail: webmaster.books@tandf.co.uk
Peer-reviewed journal publishing quality research on
ethnicity, race relations, and indigenous peoples consist-
ing of case studies, comparative analysis and theoreti-
cal contributions that reflect innovative and critical
perspectives, focused on any country or countries in
Latin America and the Caribbean. **Freq:** 3/yr. **Key Personnel:** Prof. Leon Zamosc, Editor-in-Chief, laces@
weber.ucsd.edu; Tanya Korovkin, Editor; Moira McKinnon, Editorial Asst.; Wolfgang Gabbert, Editor; Jorge
Duany, Editor; Joanne Rappaport, Editor; Rhoda Red-
dock, Editor; Peter Wade, Editor; Nancy Postero, Editor.
ISSN: 1744-2222. **Subscription Rates:** 260 institutions
print + online; US$432 institutions print + online; 246
institutions online; US$410 institutions online; 47
individuals print only; US$78 individuals print only; 11
members society; US$20 members society; EUR345
institutions print and online; EUR327 institutions online
only. **Remarks:** Accepts advertising. **URL:** http://www.
tandf.co.uk/journals/titles/17442222.asp. **Circ:** (Not
Reported)

51967 ■ LeaFlet
Lea-Francis Owners Club
French's
Long Wittenham
Abingdon OX14 4QQ, United Kingdom
Publisher E-mail: secretary@lfoc.org
Club magazine covering automotive. **Subtitle:** The
Magazine of the Lea-Francis Owner's Club. **Founded:**
1953. **Freq:** Bimonthly. **Print Method:** Laser Printer.
Trim Size: 210 x 148 mm. **Subscription Rates:**
Included in membership. **Remarks:** Advertising ac-
cepted; rates available upon request. **URL:** http://www.
lfoc.co.uk. **Circ:** 350

51968 ■ Leukemia and Lymphoma
Taylor & Francis Ltd.
2 & 4 Park Sq.
Milton Pk.
Abingdon OX14 4RN, United Kingdom
Ph: 44 20 70176000
Fax: 44 20 70176336
International journal bringing together clinical and
laboratory data on lymphomas, leukemias and allied
disorders including myeloma and myelodysplastic
syndromes. **Freq:** Monthly. **Key Personnel:** Aaron Polli-
ack, Editor-in-Chief, apol@cc.huji.ac.il; John Seymour,
Editor-in-Chief, john.seymour@petermac.org; Jorge
Deeg, Editorial Board; John Anastasi, Editorial Board;
Morie A. Gertz, Editorial Board; Koen Van Besien,
Editor-in-Chief, kvbesien@medicine.bsd.uchicago.edu;
Rodney Hicks, Editorial Board; George Calin, Editorial
Board; Lucy Godley, Editorial Board. **ISSN:** 1042-8194.
Subscription Rates: 3,210 institutions; US$4,540
institutions; EUR3,630 institutions. **Remarks:** Accepts
advertising. **URL:** http://informahealthcare.com/lal. **Circ:**
(Not Reported)

51969 ■ Life Writing
Routledge
Taylor & Francis Group Ltd.
2 Park Sq.
Milton Pk.
Abingdon OX14 4RN, United Kingdom
Ph: 44 20 70176000
Fax: 44 20 70176699
Publisher E-mail: webmaster.books@tandf.co.uk
Peer-reviewed journal covering articles on anthropology,
cultural studies, history, literature, philosophy, psychol-
ogy and sociology. **Founded:** Mar. 2004. **Freq:** 3/yr.
Print Method: Web offset. **Trim Size:** 8 3/8 x 10 7/8.
Cols./Page: 2. **Col. Width:** 30 nonpareils. **Col. Depth:**
116 agate lines. **Key Personnel:** Sidonie Smith, Edito-
rial Board; Richard Freadman, Editorial Board; Eva Hoffmann, Editorial Board; Joy Hooton, Editorial Board; Susanna Egan, Editorial Board; Rosamund Dalziell,
Editorial Board; Lila Abu-Lughod, Editorial Board; Ruth
Behar, Editorial Board; Jerome Bruner, Editorial Board;
Maureen Perkins, Editor; Christina Houen, Assoc. Ed.;
Jackie Huggins, Editorial Board. **ISSN:** 1448-4528. **Subscription Rates:** 193 institutions print + online; 183
institutions online; 43 individuals; US$317 institutions
print + online; US$301 institutions online; US$65
individuals; EUR53 individuals; EUR254 institutions print
and online; EUR239 institutions online only. **URL:** http://
www.tandf.co.uk/journals/titles/14484528.asp.

51970 ■ Liquid Crystals
Taylor & Francis Ltd.
2 & 4 Park Sq.
Milton Pk.
Abingdon OX14 4RN, United Kingdom
Ph: 44 20 70176000
Fax: 44 20 70176336
Peer-reviewed journal publishes information on original
research concerned with all aspects of liquid crystal sci-
ence and technology. **Subtitle:** An International Journal
in the Field of Anisotropic Fluids. **Founded:** 1994. **Freq:**
12/yr. **Trim Size:** A4. **Key Personnel:** Prof. Noel Clark,
Editorial Board; Prof. C.T. Imrie, Editor, c.t.imrie@abdn.
ac.uk; G. Luckhurst, Editorial Board; H. Takezoe, Editorial Board; M.A. Osipov, Editorial Board; Y. Shimizu,
Editorial Board; G.W. Gray, Editorial Board; A. Bo-
brovsky, Editorial Board; S. Kumar, Editorial Board.
ISSN: 0267-8292. **Subscription Rates:** US$5,536
institutions online; US$5,828 institutions print and on-
line; 3,512 institutions print & online; 3,336 institutions
online; EUR4,641 institutions print & online; EUR4,409
institutions online. **Remarks:** Accepts advertising on
request. **URL:** http://www.iospress.nl/loadtop/load.php?

isbn=15732487. **Circ:** (Not Reported)

51971 ■ London Review of Education
Routledge
Taylor & Francis Group Ltd.
2 Park Sq.
Milton Pk.
Abingdon OX14 4RN, United Kingdom
Ph: 44 20 70176000
Fax: 44 20 70176699
Publisher E-mail: webmaster.books@tandf.co.uk
International peer-reviewed journal that aims to promote
and disseminate high-quality analysis of important is-
sues in contemporary education. **Freq:** 3/yr. **Key Per-
sonnel:** Norbert Pachler, Assoc. Ed.; Graeme Davies,
Advisory Board Member; Peter Aggleton, Advisory Board
Member; Paul Temple, Exec. Ed.; Ronald Barnett,
Advisory Board Member; Roger Slee, Editor, r.slee@
ioe.ac.uk. **ISSN:** 1474-8460. **Subscription Rates:**
US$114 individuals print only; US$326 institutions online
only; US$344 institutions print & online; 207 institutions
print & online; 197 institutions online; 77 individuals;
EUR274 institutions print and online; EUR261 institutions
online only; EUR90 individuals. **Remarks:** Accepts
advertising. **URL:** http://www.tandf.co.uk/journals/titles/
14748460.asp. **Circ:** (Not Reported)

51972 ■ Media History
Routledge
Taylor & Francis Group Ltd.
2 Park Sq.
Milton Pk.
Abingdon OX14 4RN, United Kingdom
Ph: 44 20 70176000
Fax: 44 20 70176699
Publisher E-mail: webmaster.books@tandf.co.uk
Peer-reviewed journal covering media and society from
the fifteenth century to the present. **Freq:** Quarterly.
Key Personnel: Amy Aronson, Editor; Tom O'Malley,
Editor; Michael Harris, Editor; Mark Hampton, Editor;
Megan Mullen, Editor; Mark Turner, Editor. **ISSN:** 1368-
8804. **Subscription Rates:** US$172 individuals print
only; US$552 institutions online only; US$581 institutions print + online; 350 institutions print + online; 332
institutions online only; 104 individuals; EUR466 institutions print and online; EUR443 institutions online only;
EUR138 individuals. **Remarks:** Advertising accepted;
rates available upon request. **URL:** http://www.tandf.co.
uk/journals/carfax/13688804.html. **Circ:** (Not Reported)

51973 ■ Medical Mycology
Taylor & Francis Ltd.
2 & 4 Park Sq.
Milton Pk.
Abingdon OX14 4RN, United Kingdom
Ph: 44 20 70176000
Fax: 44 20 70176336
International journal focusing on original and innovative
studies of all aspects of medical, veterinary and
environmental mycology, including mycological, biochemical and molecular investigations of etiological
agents of mycoses; aspects of pathogenesis, immunology, and epidemiology of mycotic diseases; case reports
of unusual medical or veterinary fungal infections;
laboratory approaches to the identification of fungal
pathogens, antifungal therapy and prophylaxis; mode of
action, pharmacokinetics and assessments of new antifungal agents; investigations of the mycological aspects
of the indoor environment, with a focus on human and
animal health. **Freq:** 8/yr. **Key Personnel:** Ira F. Salkin,
Ch. Ed.; Daniel Elad, Assoc. Ed.; R. Ashbee, Assoc. Ed.
ISSN: 1369-3786. **Subscription Rates:** 1,140 institutions; US$1,890 institutions; EUR1,510 institutions. **Re-
marks:** Accepts advertising. **URL:** http://
informahealthcare.com/loi/mmy. **Circ:** (Not Reported)

51974 ■ Medicine, Conflict & Survival
Routledge
Taylor & Francis Group Ltd.
2 Park Sq.
Milton Pk.
Abingdon OX14 4RN, United Kingdom
Ph: 44 20 70176000
Fax: 44 20 70176699
Publisher E-mail: webmaster.books@tandf.co.uk
Journal covering causes of war and group violence and
resolving violent conflicts. **Freq:** Quarterly. **Key Person-
nel:** Victor Sidel, Editorial Consultant; Simon Rushton,
Editor; Maria Kett, Editor. **ISSN:** 1362-3699. **Subscrip-
tion Rates:** US$428 institutions online; 259 institutions

Circulation: ★ = ABC; △ = BPA; ♦ = CAC; • = CCAB; ❑ = VAC; ⊕ = PO Statement; ‡ = Publisher's Report; Boldface figures = sworn; Light figures = estimated.

Gale Directory of Publications & Broadcast Media/147th Ed.   5551

online; US$451 institutions print + online; 272 institutions print + online; US$115 individuals; 69 individuals; EUR359 institutions print and online; EUR342 institutions online only; EUR91 individuals. **URL:** http://www.tandf.co.uk/journals/titles/13623699.asp.

51975 ■ Mediterranean Historical Review
Routledge
Taylor & Francis Group Ltd.
2 Park Sq.
Milton Pk.
Abingdon OX14 4RN, United Kingdom
Ph: 44 20 70176000
Fax: 44 20 70176699
Publisher E-mail: webmaster.books@tandf.co.uk
Peer-reviewed journal devoted to the study of issues whose significance is not confined to a particular area or period. It integrates various problems in the ancient, medieval, early modern and contemporary history of the Mediterranean region. **Freq:** Semiannual. **Key Personnel:** Elie Barnavi, Editor; Ron Barkai, Editor; Benjamin Arbel, Ch. Ed.; Shlomo Ben-Ami, Editor; Irad Malkin, Ch. Ed.; Amy Singer, Editor. **ISSN:** 0951-8967. **Subscription Rates:** 205 institutions print + online; US$341 institutions print + online; 195 institutions online; US$324 institutions online; 55 individuals; US$86 individuals; EUR271 institutions print and online; EUR258 institutions online only; EUR68 individuals. **Remarks:** Advertising accepted; rates available upon request. **URL:** http://www.tandf.co.uk/journals/titles/09518967.asp. **Circ:** (Not Reported)

51976 ■ Mediterranean Politics
Routledge
Taylor & Francis Group Ltd.
2 Park Sq.
Milton Pk.
Abingdon OX14 4RN, United Kingdom
Ph: 44 20 70176000
Fax: 44 20 70176699
Publisher E-mail: webmaster.books@tandf.co.uk
Academic journal focusing on the politics of the whole Mediterranean region and its implications in other parts of the world. **Freq:** 3/yr. **Key Personnel:** Thomas Diez, International Advisory Board; Richard Gillespie, PhD, Editor, richard.gillespie@liverpool.ac.uk; Bahgat Korany, International Advisory Board; Hakim Darbouche, Dep. Ed.; Alfred Tovias, International Advisory Board; Michael Willis, Editorial Board. **ISSN:** 1362-9395. **Subscription Rates:** US$423 institutions online; 254 institutions online; US$446 institutions print + online; 267 institutions print + online; US$107 individuals; 69 individuals; EUR355 institutions print and online; EUR337 institutions online only; EUR86 individuals. **Remarks:** Advertising accepted; rates available upon request. **URL:** http://www.tandf.co.uk/journals/titles/13629395.asp. **Circ:** (Not Reported)

51977 ■ Mental Health, Religion and Culture
Routledge
Taylor & Francis Group Ltd.
2 Park Sq.
Milton Pk.
Abingdon OX14 4RN, United Kingdom
Ph: 44 20 70176000
Fax: 44 20 70176699
Publisher E-mail: webmaster.books@tandf.co.uk
Peer-reviewed journal exploring the relationships between mental health and aspects of religion and culture, and discussing conceptual and philosophical aspects with contributions from a range of disciplines including psychiatry, psychology, anthropology, sociology and other social sciences, philosophy, theology and religious studies, community and social work, counselling and pastoral work. **Freq:** 8/yr. **Key Personnel:** Dr. Simon Deim, Editor; Prof. Kate Miriam Loewenthal, Editor; Dr. Christopher Alan Lewis, Editor; Prof. Kenneth Pargament, Editor. **ISSN:** 1367-4676. **Subscription Rates:** US$425 individuals print only; US$1,005 institutions online only; US$1,058 institutions print & online; US$80 members society; 638 institutions print & online; 605 institutions online only; 254 individuals print only; 48 members society; EUR842 institutions print and online; EUR800 institutions online only. **Remarks:** Accepts advertising. **URL:** http://www.tandf.co.uk/journals/titles/13674676.asp. **Circ:** (Not Reported)

51978 ■ Microcirculation
Taylor & Francis Ltd.
2 & 4 Park Sq.
Milton Pk.
Abingdon OX14 4RN, United Kingdom

Ph: 44 20 70176000
Fax: 44 20 70176336
Journal featuring original contributions that are the result of investigations contributing significant new information relating to the microcirculation addressed at the intact animal, organ, cellular, or molecular level. **Freq:** 8/yr. **Key Personnel:** Steven J. Alexander, Editorial Board; Prof. William F. Jackson, PhD, Editor-in-Chief, jacks783@msu.edu; Paul Kubes, Assoc. Ed.; Ann Baldwin, Editorial Board; Jefferson C. Frisbee, Assoc. Ed.; Joseph E. Brayden, Editorial Board; Susan K. Kovats, Managing Editor; Sarah Y. Yuan, Assoc. Ed.; Mark G. Clemens, Editorial Board; Michael J. Davis, Editorial Board; Julian Panes, Editorial Board; Maria Sanz, Editorial Board. **ISSN:** 1073-9688. **Subscription Rates:** 945 institutions; US$1,555 institutions; EUR1,250 institutions. **Remarks:** Accepts advertising. **URL:** http://www.informaworld.com/smpp/title~content=t713723262; http://informahealthcare.com/mic. **Circ:** (Not Reported)

51979 ■ Middle Eastern Literatures
Routledge
Taylor & Francis Group Ltd.
2 Park Sq.
Milton Pk.
Abingdon OX14 4RN, United Kingdom
Ph: 44 20 70176000
Fax: 44 20 70176699
Publisher E-mail: webmaster.books@tandf.co.uk
Journal on Middle Eastern literatures. Regional literatures of the area, such as the Arabic, French, and Tamazight ("Berber") literature from North Africa are also published. **Freq:** 3/yr. **Key Personnel:** Michael Beard, Editor; Roger Allen, Editor; Geert Jan Van Gelder, Editor. **ISSN:** 1475-262X. **Subscription Rates:** US$485 institutions online; 291 institutions online; US$511 institutions print + online; 306 institutions print + online; US$153 individuals; 92 individuals; EUR407 institutions print + online; EUR386 institutions online only; EUR122 individuals. **URL:** http://www.tandf.co.uk/journals/journal.asp?issn=1475-262x&linktype=5.

51980 ■ Middle Eastern Studies
Routledge
Taylor & Francis Group Ltd.
2 Park Sq.
Milton Pk.
Abingdon OX14 4RN, United Kingdom
Ph: 44 20 70176000
Fax: 44 20 70176699
Publisher E-mail: webmaster.books@tandf.co.uk
Journal focusing on academic research on the history and politics of the Arabic-speaking countries in the Middle East and North Africa as well as on Turkey, Iran and Israel, dating back to the nineteenth and twentieth centuries. **Founded:** 1964. **Freq:** Bimonthly. **Key Personnel:** Sylvia Kedourie, Editor; Elie Kedourie, Founding Ed.; H. Bowen-Jones, Editorial Advisory Board. **ISSN:** 0026-3206. **Subscription Rates:** US$803 institutions online; 496 institutions online; US$846 institutions print + online; 522 institutions print + online; US$158 individuals; 102 individuals; EUR674 institutions print and online; EUR640 institutions online only; EUR126 individuals. **URL:** http://www.tandf.co.uk/journals/titles/00263206.asp.

51981 ■ Military Balance
Routledge
Taylor & Francis Group Ltd.
2 Park Sq.
Milton Pk.
Abingdon OX14 4RN, United Kingdom
Ph: 44 20 70176000
Fax: 44 20 70176699
Publisher E-mail: webmaster.books@tandf.co.uk
Journal assessing the military capabilities and defense economics of nearly 170 countries world-wide with a region-by region analysis of the major military and economic trends and developments affecting security policy and the trade in weapons and other military equipment. **Freq:** Annual. **Key Personnel:** James Hackett, Editor; Jesse Simon, Contact; Dr. John Chipman, Director; Shirley Nicholls, Contact; Dr. Ayse Abdullah, Asst. Ed.; Nigel Adderley, Defence Anal. **ISSN:** 0459-7222. **Subscription Rates:** 248 institutions print + online; US$437 institutions print + online; 236 institutions online; US$414 institutions online; 121 individuals personal; US$202 individuals personal; EUR367 institutions print and online; EUR348 institutions online only; EUR160 individuals. **Remarks:** Accepts advertising. **URL:**

http://www.tandf.co.uk/journals/titles/04597222.asp. **Circ:** (Not Reported)

51982 ■ Minimally Invasive Therapy and Allied Technologies
Taylor & Francis Ltd.
2 & 4 Park Sq.
Milton Pk.
Abingdon OX14 4RN, United Kingdom
Ph: 44 20 70176000
Fax: 44 20 70176336
Journal dedicated to bringing details of the latest developments and innovations in minimally invasive therapy to its readers, and to promoting minimally invasive therapy across specialty boundaries. **Freq:** 6/yr. **Key Personnel:** Eiji Kanehira, Editor; Gerhard Buess, Editor; E. Hermann-Decker, Editorial Asst., elisabeth.hermann-decker@uni-tuebingen.de; G. Maddern, Asst. Ed.; D. Birkett, Asst. Ed.; A. Cuschieri, Asst. Ed.; J. Wickham, Founding Ed.; A. Melzer, Asst. Ed.; C. Russell, Asst. Ed.; M.O. Schurr, Asst. Ed. **ISSN:** 1364-5706. **Subscription Rates:** 500 institutions; US$830 institutions; EUR660 institutions. **Remarks:** Accepts advertising. **URL:** http://www.informaworld.com/smpp/title~content=t713683124; http://informahealthcare.com/mit. **Circ:** (Not Reported)

51983 ■ Mitochondrial DNA
Taylor & Francis Ltd.
2 & 4 Park Sq.
Milton Pk.
Abingdon OX14 4RN, United Kingdom
Ph: 44 20 70176000
Fax: 44 20 70176336
Journal accepting original high-quality reports based on mapping, sequencing and analysis of DNA and RNA, irrespective of supporting biological or functional data, include genes (including RNA genes), variation, promoters, epigenetic modifications and any features affecting DNA/RNA function, structure and evolution. **Subtitle:** The Journal of DNA Mapping, Sequencing, and Analysis. **Freq:** 6/yr. **Key Personnel:** Rob DeSalle, Editor-in-Chief, desalle@amnh.org. **ISSN:** 1940-1736. **Subscription Rates:** US$1,430 individuals print and online; US$1,430 institutions online only; US$1,430 institutions print and online; US$1,430 individuals online only. **Remarks:** Accepts advertising. **URL:** http://www.informaworld.com/smpp/title~content=t713640135~db=all; http://informahealthcare.com/mdn. **Formerly:** DNA Sequence. **Circ:** (Not Reported)

51984 ■ Mobilities
Routledge
Taylor & Francis Group Ltd.
2 Park Sq.
Milton Pk.
Abingdon OX14 4RN, United Kingdom
Ph: 44 20 70176000
Fax: 44 20 70176699
Publisher E-mail: webmaster.books@tandf.co.uk
Peer-reviewed journal encompassing both the large-scale movements of people, objects, capital, and information across the world, as well as more local processes of daily transportation, movement through public space, and the travel of material things within everyday life. **Freq:** 4/yr. **Key Personnel:** Allan Williams, Editorial Board; Prof. Kevin Hannam, Editor; Dr. Mimi Sheller, Editor; Ginette Verstraete, Editorial Board; Peter Burns, Editorial Board; Dallen Timothy, Editorial Board; Robin Cohen, Editorial Board; Tim Cresswell, Editorial Board; Soile Veijola, Editorial Board; Armando Montanari, Editorial Board; Prof. John Urry, Editor; Nigel Thrift, Editorial Board. **ISSN:** 1745-0101. **Subscription Rates:** US$103 individuals print only; US$512 institutions online; US$539 institutions print + online; 325 institutions print + online; 309 institutions online; 61 individuals print only; EUR428 institutions print and online; EUR407 institutions online only; EUR83 individuals. **Remarks:** Accepts advertising. **URL:** http://www.tandf.co.uk/journals/titles/17450101.asp. **Circ:** (Not Reported)

51985 ■ Modern & Contemporary France
Routledge
Taylor & Francis Group Ltd.
2 Park Sq.
Milton Pk.
Abingdon OX14 4RN, United Kingdom
Ph: 44 20 70176000
Fax: 44 20 70176699
Publisher E-mail: webmaster.books@tandf.co.uk
Peer-reviewed journal focusing on all aspects of France

from 1789 to the present day. **Subtitle:** The Journal of the Association for the Study of Modern & Contemporary France. **Founded:** 1980. **Freq:** Quarterly. **Key Personnel:** Brett Bowles, Co-Ed.; Jackie Clarke, Exec. Ed.; Raymond Kuhn, Editorial Board. **ISSN:** 0963-9489. **Subscription Rates:** 323 institutions print + online; 306 institutions online; 124 individuals; 44 members; 10 students; US$532 institutions print + online; US$505 institutions online; US$210 individuals; US$79 members; US$19 students. **Remarks:** Advertising accepted; rates available upon request. **URL:** http://www.tandf.co.uk/journals/titles/09639489.asp. **Circ:** (Not Reported)

51986 ■ Modern Italy
Routledge
Taylor & Francis Group Ltd.
2 Park Sq.
Milton Pk.
Abingdon OX14 4RN, United Kingdom
Ph: 44 20 70176000
Fax: 44 20 70176699
Publisher E-mail: webmaster.books@tandf.co.uk
Peer-reviewed journal covering the history, politics and social, economic and cultural studies of Italy, Italian affairs and the Italian people from the eighteenth to the present. **Founded:** 1995. **Freq:** Quarterly. **Key Personnel:** Martin Bull, Editorial Committee; Anna Cento Bull, Editorial Committee; Martin Brown, Editorial Committee; Philip Cooke, Editor; John Foot, Editor; Phil Edwards, Book Review Ed. **ISSN:** 1353-2944. **Subscription Rates:** US$236 individuals print only; US$602 institutions online; US$634 institutions print + online; 152 individuals; 365 institutions online; 385 institutions print + online; EUR506 institutions print and online; EUR481 institutions online only; EUR187 individuals. **Remarks:** Advertising accepted; rates available upon request. **URL:** http://www.tandf.co.uk/journals/carfax/13532944.html. **Circ:** (Not Reported)

51987 ■ Mortality
Routledge
Taylor & Francis Group Ltd.
2 Park Sq.
Milton Pk.
Abingdon OX14 4RN, United Kingdom
Ph: 44 20 70176000
Fax: 44 20 70176699
Publisher E-mail: webmaster.books@tandf.co.uk
Journal dealing with aspects of human mortality. **Subtitle:** Promoting the Interdisciplinary Study of Death and Dying. **Freq:** Quarterly. **Key Personnel:** Carol Komaromy, Editor; Prof. Allan Kellehear, Editor; Dr. Tony Walter, Book Review Ed. **ISSN:** 1357-6275. **Subscription Rates:** US$176 individuals print only; US$651 institutions online only; US$685 institutions print + online; 414 institutions print + online; 393 institutions online only; 108 institutions print only; 42 institutions society; US$69 institutions society; EUR546 institutions print and online; EUR520 institutions online only. **Remarks:** Advertising accepted; rates available upon request. **URL:** http://www.tandf.co.uk/journals/titles/13576275.html. **Circ:** (Not Reported)

51988 ■ National Identities
Routledge
Taylor & Francis Group Ltd.
2 Park Sq.
Milton Pk.
Abingdon OX14 4RN, United Kingdom
Ph: 44 20 70176000
Fax: 44 20 70176699
Publisher E-mail: webmaster.books@tandf.co.uk
Peer-reviewed journal covering all aspects of history. **Freq:** Quarterly. **Key Personnel:** Peter Catterall, Editor; Christopher Vernon, Editor; David Kaplan, Editor; Peter Carrier, Reviews Ed.; Elfie Rembold, Editor; John A. Agnew, Editorial Board. **ISSN:** 1460-8944. **Subscription Rates:** 286 institutions print + online; 271 institutions online; 91 individuals; US$473 institutions print + online; US$449 institutions online; US$160 individuals; EUR377 institutions print and online; EUR358 institutions online only; EUR128 individuals. **Remarks:** Advertising accepted; rates available upon request. **URL:** http://www.tandf.co.uk/journals/carfax/14608944.html. **Circ:** (Not Reported)

51989 ■ Nationalism & Ethnic Politics
Routledge
Taylor & Francis Group Ltd.
2 Park Sq.
Milton Pk.

Abingdon OX14 4RN, United Kingdom
Ph: 44 20 70176000
Fax: 44 20 70176699
Publisher E-mail: webmaster.books@tandf.co.uk
Peer-reviewed journal covering political aspects of nationalism and ethnicity. **Freq:** Quarterly. **Key Personnel:** Adrian Guelke, Editor-in-Chief; William Safran, Ed. Emeritus; Britt Cartrite, Reviews Ed.; Naomi Chazan, Editorial Board Member; Sam Samarasinghe, Editorial Board Member; Walker Connor, Editorial Board Member. **ISSN:** 1353-7113. **Subscription Rates:** 300 institutions print + online; 286 institutions online; 77 individuals; US$501 institutions print + online; US$476 institutions online; US$115 individuals; EUR398 institutions print and online; EUR379 institutions online only; EUR91 individuals. **Remarks:** Advertising accepted; rates available upon request. **URL:** http://www.tandf.co.uk/journals/titles/13537113.asp. **Circ:** (Not Reported)

51990 ■ Nationalities Papers
Routledge
Taylor & Francis Group Ltd.
2 Park Sq.
Milton Pk.
Abingdon OX14 4RN, United Kingdom
Ph: 44 20 70176000
Fax: 44 20 70176699
Publisher E-mail: webmaster.books@tandf.co.uk
Peer-reviewed journal dealing with all non-Russian nationalities of the former USSR and national minorities in Eastern and Central European countries in connection with Association for the Study of Nationalities. **Subtitle:** A Publication of the Association for the Study of Nationalities. **Freq:** 6/yr. **Key Personnel:** Florian Bieber, Editor-in-Chief; Carolin Roeder, Asst. Ed.; Roland Spickermann, Book Review Ed., spicker_r@utpb.edu; Zsuzsa Csergo, Assoc. Ed.; Troy McGrath, Assoc. Ed.; Marlene Laruelle, Assoc. Ed. **ISSN:** 0090-5992. **Subscription Rates:** 670 institutions print + online; 637 institutions online; 161 individuals; US$1,112 institutions print + online; US$1,056 institutions online; US$265 individuals; EUR889 institutions print and online; EUR845 institutions online only; EUR211 individuals. **Remarks:** Advertising accepted; rates available upon request. **URL:** http://www.tandf.co.uk/journals/titles/00905992.asp. **Circ:** (Not Reported)

51991 ■ Network
Taylor & Francis Ltd.
2 & 4 Park Sq.
Milton Pk.
Abingdon OX14 4RN, United Kingdom
Ph: 44 20 70176000
Fax: 44 20 70176336
Journal providing a forum for integrating theoretical and experimental findings in computational neuroscience across relevant interdisciplinary boundaries by making theoretical results and methods accessible to neurobiologists, psychologists and cognitive scientists. **Subtitle:** Computation in Neural Systems. **Freq:** 4/yr. **Key Personnel:** D.J. Willshaw, Previous Ed.; M. Riesenhuber, Editorial Board; L.F. Abbott, Editorial Board; W. Gerstner, Editorial Board; Prof. Geoffrey J. Goodhill, Editor-in-Chief, goodhill@uq.edu.au; P. Dayan, Editorial Board; C.D. Brody, Editorial Board; P.J.B. Hancock, Editorial Board; N. Brunel, Editorial Board; K. Doya, Editorial Board; M. Poo, Editorial Board; N. Swindale, Editorial Board. **ISSN:** 0954-898X. **Subscription Rates:** US$760 institutions print + online; US$760 institutions online; US$760 individuals print + online; US$760 individuals online. **Remarks:** Accepts advertising. **URL:** http://informahealthcare.com/net. **Circ:** (Not Reported)

51992 ■ New Genetics & Society
Routledge
Taylor & Francis Group Ltd.
2 Park Sq.
Milton Pk.
Abingdon OX14 4RN, United Kingdom
Ph: 44 20 70176000
Fax: 44 20 70176699
Publisher E-mail: webmaster.books@tandf.co.uk
Peer-reviewed journal covering business and management. **Freq:** 4/yr. **Key Personnel:** Prof. Harry Rothman, Editor; Prof. Peter Glasner, Editor; Flo Ticehurst, Book Review Ed. **ISSN:** 1463-6778. **Subscription Rates:** US$288 individuals; US$1,155 institutions online only; US$1,216 institutions print and online; 697 institutions print and online; EUR968 institutions print and

online; 661 institutions online only; EUR919 institutions online only; 151 individuals; EUR230 individuals. **URL:** http://www.tandf.co.uk/journals/titles/14636778.asp.

51993 ■ New Political Economy
Routledge
Taylor & Francis Group Ltd.
2 Park Sq.
Milton Pk.
Abingdon OX14 4RN, United Kingdom
Ph: 44 20 70176000
Fax: 44 20 70176699
Publisher E-mail: webmaster.books@tandf.co.uk
Peer-reviewed journal dealing with political economy. **Freq:** Quarterly. **Key Personnel:** Dr. Graham Harrison, Editor; Prof. Colin Hay, Editor; Prof. Nicola Phillips, Managing Editor; Dr. Tony Heron, Editor; Gail Birkett, Editorial Asst.; Prof. John O'Neill, Editor. **ISSN:** 1356-3467. **Subscription Rates:** US$145 individuals print only; US$676 individuals online; US$711 individuals print + online; 87 individuals print only; 409 institutions online; 431 institutions print + online; EUR566 institutions print and online; EUR538 institutions online only; EUR115 individuals. **Remarks:** Advertising accepted; rates available upon request. **URL:** http://www.tandf.co.uk/journals/titles/13563467.asp. **Circ:** (Not Reported)

51994 ■ New Political Science
Routledge
Taylor & Francis Group Ltd.
2 Park Sq.
Milton Pk.
Abingdon OX14 4RN, United Kingdom
Ph: 44 20 70176000
Fax: 44 20 70176699
Publisher E-mail: webmaster.books@tandf.co.uk
Peer-reviewed journal dealing with political science and cultural development, in connection with the Caucus for a New Political Science (CNPS), an Organized Section of the American Political Science Association. **Freq:** Quarterly. **Key Personnel:** Mark S. Mattern, Editor; Nancy S. Love, Editor; Elizabeth Kelly, Exec. Committee; Bradley MacDonald, Assoc. Ed.; Clyde W. Barrow, Assoc. Ed.; Claire R. Snyder, Assoc. Ed. **ISSN:** 0739-3148. **Subscription Rates:** 273 institutions print + online; 260 institutions online; 80 individuals personal; US$426 institutions print + online; US$405 institutions online; US$105 individuals; EUR341 institutions print and online; EUR324 institutions online only; EUR84 individuals. **Remarks:** Advertising accepted; rates available upon request. **URL:** http://www.tandf.co.uk/journals/titles/07393148.asp. **Circ:** (Not Reported)

51995 ■ New Review of Academic Librarianship
Routledge
Taylor & Francis Group Ltd.
2 Park Sq.
Milton Pk.
Abingdon OX14 4RN, United Kingdom
Ph: 44 20 70176000
Fax: 44 20 70176699
Publisher E-mail: webmaster.books@tandf.co.uk
Peer-reviewed journal covering wide range of topics concerning academic libraries. **Freq:** Semiannual. **Key Personnel:** Graham Walton, PhD, Editor, j.g.walton@lboro.ac.uk; Margaret Forrest, Assoc. Ed., margaret.forrest@ed.ac.uk; David Baker, Editorial Board; Ross Harvey, Editorial Board; Graham Bulpitt, Editorial Board; Sheila Corrall, Editorial Board. **ISSN:** 1361-4533. **Subscription Rates:** 164 institutions print + online; 155 institutions online; 36 individuals; US$290 institutions print + online; US$275 institutions online; US$58 individuals; EUR231 institutions print and online; EUR219 institutions online only; EUR47 individuals. **Remarks:** Advertising accepted; rates available upon request. **URL:** http://www.tandf.co.uk/journals/titles/13614533.asp. **Circ:** (Not Reported)

51996 ■ New Review of Children's Literature and Librarianship
Routledge
Taylor & Francis Group Ltd.
2 Park Sq.
Milton Pk.
Abingdon OX14 4RN, United Kingdom
Ph: 44 20 70176000
Fax: 44 20 70176699
Publisher E-mail: webmaster.books@tandf.co.uk
Peer-reviewed journal publishing information on managing library services to children and adolescents. **Freq:** Semiannual. **Key Personnel:** Dr. Sally Maynard, Editor,

Circulation: ★ = ABC; △ = BPA; ♦ = CAC; • = CCAB; ❑ = VAC; ⊕ = PO Statement; ‡ = Publisher's Report; Boldface figures = sworn; Light figures = estimated.

s.e.maynard@lboro.ac.uk; Robert Dunbar, Editorial Board; Adele Fasick, Editorial Board; John Dunne, Editorial Board; James Henri, Editorial Board; Dr. Dorothy McLelland, Editorial Board. **ISSN:** 1361-4541. **Subscription Rates:** 164 institutions print + online; US$290 institutions print + online; 155 institutions online; US$275 institutions online; 36 individuals; US$58 individuals; EUR231 institutions print and online; EUR219 institutions online only; EUR47 individuals. **Remarks:** Advertising accepted; rates available upon request. **URL:** http://www.tandf.co.uk/journals/titles/13614541. asp. **Circ:** (Not Reported)

51997 ■ New Review of Film & Television Studies
Routledge
Taylor & Francis Group Ltd.
2 Park Sq.
Milton Pk.
Abingdon OX14 4RN, United Kingdom
Ph: 44 20 70176000
Fax: 44 20 70176699
Publisher E-mail: webmaster.books@tandf.co.uk
Peer-reviewed journal covering the research on film and television studies. **Freq:** 4/yr. **Key Personnel:** Prof. Warren Buckland, Editor, wbuckland@brookes.ac.uk; Alison McMahan, Editorial Board; Jonathan Bignell, Editorial Board; Marshall Deutelbaum, Editorial Board; Peter Kramer, Editorial Board; Edward Branigan, Editorial Board; Glen Creeber, Editorial Board; Thomas Elsaesser, Editorial Board; Richard Allen, Editorial Board. **ISSN:** 1740-0309. **Subscription Rates:** 301 institutions print + online; US$528 institutions print + online; 286 institutions online; US$502 institutions online; 65 individuals personal; US$109 individuals personal; EUR422 institutions print and online; EUR402 institutions online only; EUR86 individuals. **Remarks:** Advertising accepted; rates available upon request. **URL:** http://www.tandf.co.uk/journals/titles/17400309.asp. **Circ:** (Not Reported)

51998 ■ New Review of Information Networking
Routledge
Taylor & Francis Group Ltd.
2 Park Sq.
Milton Pk.
Abingdon OX14 4RN, United Kingdom
Ph: 44 20 70176000
Fax: 44 20 70176699
Publisher E-mail: webmaster.books@tandf.co.uk
Peer-reviewed journal providing information on the role of networks in teaching, learning, research and scholarly communication, and the impact of networks on library and information services. **Freq:** Semiannual. **Key Personnel:** Theo Bothma, Editorial Board; Derek Law, Editor-in-Chief; Les Carr, Editorial Board; Beverly Lynch, Editorial Board; Sue McKnight, Editorial Board; Nicky Whitsed, Editorial Board; Elizabeth Winter, Editorial Board. **ISSN:** 1361-4576. **Subscription Rates:** US$56 individuals; US$266 institutions online; US$280 institutions print + online; 158 institutions print + online; 150 institutions online; 35 individuals; EUR223 institutions print and online; EUR212 institutions online only; EUR45 individuals. **Remarks:** Advertising accepted; rates available upon request. **URL:** http://www.tandf.co.uk/journals/titles/13614576.asp. **Circ:** (Not Reported)

51999 ■ New Writing
Routledge
Taylor & Francis Group Ltd.
2 Park Sq.
Milton Pk.
Abingdon OX14 4RN, United Kingdom
Ph: 44 20 70176000
Fax: 44 20 70176699
Publisher E-mail: webmaster.books@tandf.co.uk
Journal seeking to bridge the gap between creative writing on campus and the worlds of writing and publishing. **Subtitle:** The International Journal for the Practice and Theory of Creative Writing. **Freq:** 3/yr. **Key Personnel:** Graeme Harper, Ch. Ed./Book Review Ed.; Chad Davidson, Assoc. Ed.; Richard Kerridge, Assoc. Ed.; Donna Lee Brien, Peer Review Board; Stephanie Vanderslice, Assoc. Ed. **ISSN:** 1479-0726. **Subscription Rates:** 422 individuals; US$85 individuals; EUR53 individuals; 110 institutions print + online; US$220 institutions print + online; EUR165 institutions print + online; 108 institutions online; US$216 institutions online; EUR162 institutions online. **URL:** http://www.tandf.co.uk/journals/1479-0726.

52000 ■ Nonproliferation Review
Routledge

Taylor & Francis Group Ltd.
2 Park Sq.
Milton Pk.
Abingdon OX14 4RN, United Kingdom
Ph: 44 20 70176000
Fax: 44 20 70176699
Publisher E-mail: webmaster.books@tandf.co.uk
Peer-reviewed journal concerned with the causes, consequences, and control of the spread of weapons of mass destruction (WMD), featuring case studies, theoretical analyses, and policy debates on such issues as individual country programs, treaties and export controls, WMD terrorism, and economic and environmental effects of weapons proliferation. **Freq:** 3/yr. **Key Personnel:** Leonard S. Spector, Assoc. Ed.; Amy Smithson, Assoc. Ed.; Li Bin, Editorial Board; Ildar Akhtamzyzn, Editorial Board; Stephen Schwartz, Editor, stephen.schwartz@miis.edu; Catherine Auer, Managing Editor; Daniel Pinkston, Assoc. Ed.; Raymond Zilinskas, Assoc. Ed. **ISSN:** 1073-6700. **Subscription Rates:** 204 institutions print + online; 194 institutions online; 39 individuals; US$341 institutions print + online; US$324 institutions online; US$68 individuals; EUR271 institutions print and online; EUR258 institutions online only; EUR55 individuals. **Remarks:** Accepts advertising. **URL:** http://www.tandf.co.uk/journals/titles/10736700.asp. **Circ:** (Not Reported)

52001 ■ Ocean Development and International Law
Taylor & Francis Ltd.
2 & 4 Park Sq.
Milton Pk.
Abingdon OX14 4RN, United Kingdom
Ph: 44 20 70176000
Fax: 44 20 70176336
Peer-reviewed and law journal. **Freq:** Quarterly. **Key Personnel:** Ted L. McDorman, Editor-in-Chief, tlmcdorm@uvic.ca; Andrea G. Coffman, Editorial Board; David A. Colson, Editorial Board; Craig Allen, Editorial Board; Christopher C. Joyner, Editorial Board; William T. Burke, Founding Ed.; Lee A. Kimball, Editorial Board; Richard G. Hildreth, Editorial Board; John Duff, Editorial Board. **ISSN:** 0090-8320. **Subscription Rates:** 447 institutions print + online; US$743 institutions print + online; 424 institutions online; US$706 institutions online; 219 individuals personal; US$366 individuals personal. **Remarks:** Accepts advertising on request. **URL:** http://www.tandf.co.uk/journals/titles/00908320. asp. **Circ:** (Not Reported)

52002 ■ Open Learning
Routledge
Taylor & Francis Group Ltd.
2 Park Sq.
Milton Pk.
Abingdon OX14 4RN, United Kingdom
Ph: 44 20 70176000
Fax: 44 20 70176699
Publisher E-mail: webmaster.books@tandf.co.uk
Peer-reviewed journal covering advances in distance education and e-learning. **Subtitle:** The Journal of Open and Distance Learning. **Freq:** 3/yr. **Key Personnel:** Anne Gaskell, Editor, a.f.gaskell@open.ac.uk; Dr. Som Naidu, Editorial Board; Prof. Terry Evans, Editorial Board; Dr. Sally M. Johnstone, Editorial Board; Michael Moore, Editorial Board; Dr. Liz Burge, Editorial Board; Helen Lentell, Editorial Board; Prof. Ronnie Carr, Editorial Board; Dr. Fredric Litto, Editorial Board. **ISSN:** 0268-0513. **Subscription Rates:** 202 institutions print + online; US$341 institutions print + online; 191 institutions online; US$324 institutions online; 66 individuals personal; US$108 individuals personal; EUR271 institutions print and online; EUR258 institutions online only; EUR86 individuals. **Remarks:** Advertising accepted; rates available upon request. **URL:** http://www.tandf.co.uk/journals/titles/02680513.asp. **Circ:** (Not Reported)

52003 ■ The Pacific Review
Routledge
Taylor & Francis Group Ltd.
2 Park Sq.
Milton Pk.
Abingdon OX14 4RN, United Kingdom
Ph: 44 20 70176000
Fax: 44 20 70176699
Publisher E-mail: webmaster.books@tandf.co.uk
Journal providing a platform for the study of the Pacific Basin and swap of ideas on this region. **Freq:** 5/yr. **Key Personnel:** Prof. Shaun Breslin, Editor; Prof. Richard

Higgott, Editor; Amitav Acharya, Editorial Board; Dr. Christopher W. Hughes, Editor; Christopher Dent, Editorial Board. **ISSN:** 0951-2748. **Subscription Rates:** 425 institutions print + online; 404 institutions online; 97 individuals; US$707 institutions print + online; US$672 institutions online; US$160 individuals; EUR563 institutions print and online; EUR535 institutions online only; EUR128 individuals. **Remarks:** Advertising accepted; rates available upon request. **URL:** http://www.tandf.co.uk/journals/titles/09512748.asp. **Circ:** (Not Reported)

52004 ■ Peace Review
Routledge
Taylor & Francis Group Ltd.
2 Park Sq.
Milton Pk.
Abingdon OX14 4RN, United Kingdom
Ph: 44 20 70176000
Fax: 44 20 70176699
Publisher E-mail: webmaster.books@tandf.co.uk
Peer-reviewed journal focusing on the current issues and controversies that lie behind the promotion of a more peaceful world. **Subtitle:** A Journal for Social Justice. **Freq:** Quarterly. **Key Personnel:** Jennifer Turpin, Sen. Ed.; Robert Elias, PhD, Editor, eliasr@usfca.edu; Anne Barlett, Assoc. Ed.; Kerry Donoghue, Managing Editor; Susan Katz, Assoc. Ed.; Stephen Zunes, Assoc. Ed.; Stephen Zunes, Assoc. Ed.; Scott McElwain, Assoc. Ed.; Lois Ann Lorentzen, Assoc. Ed. **ISSN:** 1040-2659. **Subscription Rates:** 414 institutions print + online; US$686 institutions print + online; 393 institutions online; US$652 institutions online; 87 individuals personal; US$139 individuals personal; EUR546 institutions print and online; EUR520 institutions online only; EUR110 individuals. **Remarks:** Advertising accepted; rates available upon request. **URL:** http://www.tandf.co.uk/journals/titles/10402659.asp. **Circ:** (Not Reported)

52005 ■ Pedagogy, Culture and Society
Routledge
Taylor & Francis Group Ltd.
2 Park Sq.
Milton Pk.
Abingdon OX14 4RN, United Kingdom
Ph: 44 20 70176000
Fax: 44 20 70176699
Publisher E-mail: webmaster.books@tandf.co.uk
Peer-reviewed journal providing a platform for Pedagogy discussion and debate which has the features such as open and democratic, eclectic and interdisciplinary, concerned with the past, present and future, culturally diverse, and not restricted by geographical boundaries. **Freq:** 3/yr. **Key Personnel:** Richard Edwards, Editorial Board; Wilfred Carr, Editorial Board; Jo Frankham, Editorial Board; Naz Rassool, Editorial Board; Kari Dehli, Editorial Advisory Board; David Hamilton, Editorial Advisory Board; Carrie Paechter, Editorial Board; Mary Koutselini, Editorial Advisory Board; Becky Francis, Editorial Advisory Board. **ISSN:** 1468-1366. **Subscription Rates:** 324 institutions print + online; US$516 institutions print + online; 307 institutions online; US$491 institutions online; 52 individuals personal; US$82 individuals personal; EUR412 institutions print and online; EUR391 institutions online only; EUR65 individuals. **Remarks:** Advertising accepted; rates available upon request. **URL:** http://www.tandf.co.uk/journals/titles/14681366.asp. **Circ:** (Not Reported)

52006 ■ Pediatric Hematology & Oncology
Taylor & Francis Ltd.
2 & 4 Park Sq.
Milton Pk.
Abingdon OX14 4RN, United Kingdom
Ph: 44 20 70176000
Fax: 44 20 70176336
Peer-reviewed and Medical journal covering pediatric hematology and oncology. **Freq:** 8/yr. **Trim Size:** 6 3/4 x 10. **Cols./Page:** 1. **Key Personnel:** Claudia Rossig, Editor-in-Chief, rossig@uni-muenster.de; Catherine M. Bollard, Editor-in-Chief, cmbollar@txccc.org; Joergen Cohn, Founder/Ed. Emeritus. **ISSN:** 0888-0018. **Subscription Rates:** 1,810 single issue corporate; 1,495 institutions; US$1,195 institutions; US$2,990 single issue corporate. **Remarks:** Accepts advertising on request. **URL:** http://informahealthcare.com/pho. **Circ:** Combined 1,312

52007 ■ Performance Research
Routledge
Taylor & Francis Group Ltd.
2 Park Sq.

Milton Pk.
Abingdon OX14 4RN, United Kingdom
Ph: 44 20 70176000
Fax: 44 20 70176699
Publisher E-mail: webmaster.books@tandf.co.uk
Journal promoting dynamic interchange between scholarship and practice in an expanding field of performance. Focuses on research in contemporary performance arts within changing cultures. **Freq:** Quarterly. **Key Personnel:** Claire MacDonald, Consultant Ed.; Richard Gough, Editor; Ric Allsopp, Editor. **ISSN:** 1352-8165. **Subscription Rates:** 354 institutions print + online; 336 institutions online; 88 individuals; US$605 institutions print + online; US$575 institutions online; US$141 individuals; EUR481 institutions print and online; EUR457 institutions online only; EUR112 individuals. **Remarks:** Advertising accepted; rates available upon request. **URL:** http://www.tandf.co.uk/journals/titles/13528165.asp. **Circ:** (Not Reported)

52008 ■ Perspectives
Routledge
Taylor & Francis Group Ltd.
2 Park Sq.
Milton Pk.
Abingdon OX14 4RN, United Kingdom
Ph: 44 20 70176000
Fax: 44 20 70176699
Publisher E-mail: webmaster.books@tandf.co.uk
Languages and linguistics publication. **Subtitle:** Studies in Translatology. **Founded:** June 1, 1993. **Freq:** Quarterly. **Trim Size:** 15 x 21 cm. **Key Personnel:** Henrik Gottlieb, Editor-in-Chief; Hanne Jansen, Co-Ed.; Minako O'Hagan, Co-Ed.; Wang Ning, Co-Ed.; Roberto A. Valdeon, Co-Ed.; Vibeke Appel, Review Ed. **ISSN:** 0907-676X. **Subscription Rates:** 165 institutions print + online; US$331 institutions print + online; EUR242 institutions print + online; 75 individuals; US$149 individuals; EUR93 individuals. **Remarks:** Advertising not accepted. **URL:** http://www.tandf.co.uk/journals/0907-676X. **Circ:** Combined 4,500

52009 ■ Perspectives on European Politics and Society
Routledge
Taylor & Francis Group Ltd.
2 Park Sq.
Milton Pk.
Abingdon OX14 4RN, United Kingdom
Ph: 44 20 70176000
Fax: 44 20 70176699
Publisher E-mail: webmaster.books@tandf.co.uk
Journal covering articles on all aspects of European politics, including, comparative politics, political sociology, international relations, and modern history. **Freq:** 4/yr. **Key Personnel:** Dr. Norrie MacQueen, Assoc. Ed.; Prof. Paul Lewis, Editorial Board; Prof. Peter Mair, Editorial Board; Dr. Cameron Ross, Editor; Dr. Richard Dunphy, Assoc. Ed.; Prof. Mikhail Ilyin, Editorial Board; Prof. Stephen White, Editorial Board; Dr. David Lane, Editorial Board; Prof. Charlie Jeffery, Editorial Board; Prof. James Newell, Editorial Board; Prof. Ferran Requejo, Editorial Board; Prof. Richard Sakwa, Editorial Board. **ISSN:** 1570-5854. **Subscription Rates:** 235 institutions print + online; US$389 institutions print + online; 224 institutions online; US$369 institutions online; 63 individuals; US$106 individuals; EUR309 institutions print + online; EUR294 institutions online only; EUR85 individuals. **URL:** http://www.tandf.co.uk/journals/titles/15705854.asp.

52010 ■ Philosophical Explorations
Routledge
Taylor & Francis Group Ltd.
2 Park Sq.
Milton Pk.
Abingdon OX14 4RN, United Kingdom
Ph: 44 20 70176000
Fax: 44 20 70176699
Publisher E-mail: webmaster.books@tandf.co.uk
Peer-reviewed journal containing articles in the philosophy of mind and action, with an emphasis on issues concerning the interrelations between cognition and agency. **Subtitle:** An International Journal for the Philosophy of Mind and Action. **Freq:** 3/yr. **Key Personnel:** Anthonie Meijers, Editor; Stefaan Cuypers, Assoc. Ed.; Cynthia MacDonald, Board of Advisory; Marcus Willaschek, Assoc. Ed.; Jan Bransen, Assoc. Ed.; Jesse Prinz, Assoc. Ed.; Marc Slors, Assoc. Ed.; Bruno Verbeek, Assoc. Ed.; Joel Anderson, Assoc. Ed. **ISSN:**

1386-9795. **Subscription Rates:** 177 institutions print + online; US$294 institutions print + online; 168 institutions online; US$279 institutions online; 49 individuals personal; US$82 individuals personal; EUR235 institutions print and online; EUR223 institutions online only; EUR65 individuals. **Remarks:** Advertising accepted; rates available upon request. **URL:** http://www.tandf.co.uk/journals/13869795.asp. **Circ:** (Not Reported)

52011 ■ Philosophical Psychology
Routledge
Taylor & Francis Group Ltd.
2 Park Sq.
Milton Pk.
Abingdon OX14 4RN, United Kingdom
Ph: 44 20 70176000
Fax: 44 20 70176699
Publisher E-mail: webmaster.books@tandf.co.uk
Journal focusing on integrating developing and strengthening the links between psychological sciences and philosophy. **Freq:** Bimonthly. **Key Personnel:** Cees Van Leeuwen, Editor; William Bechtel, Editor; Jay Garfield, Editorial Board; Louise Anthony, Editorial Board; Mitchell Herschbach, Book Review Ed.; Dorrit Billman, Editorial Board; Lynne Rudder Baker, Editorial Board; Alan Costall, Editorial Board; David Chalmers, Editorial Board. **ISSN:** 0951-5089. **Subscription Rates:** US$367 individuals; US$1,461 institutions online; US$1,538 institutions print + online; 219 individuals print only; 881 institutions online; 927 institutions print + online; EUR1,224 institutions print and online; EUR1,163 institutions online only; EUR292 individuals. **Remarks:** Advertising accepted; rates available upon request. **URL:** http://www.tandf.co.uk/journals/titles/09515089.asp. **Circ:** (Not Reported)

52012 ■ Physical Education & Sport Pedagogy
Routledge
Taylor & Francis Group Ltd.
2 Park Sq.
Milton Pk.
Abingdon OX14 4RN, United Kingdom
Ph: 44 20 70176000
Fax: 44 20 70176699
Publisher E-mail: webmaster.books@tandf.co.uk
Peer-reviewed journal disseminating research in physical education youth sport teacher and coach education. **Freq:** Quarterly. **Key Personnel:** Prof. David Kirk, Editor, david.kirk@beds.ac.uk; Dr. David Brown, Editorial Board; Dr. Lorraine Cale, Advisory Board; Dr. Ang Chen, Editorial Board; Prof. Marc Cloes, Editorial Board; Dr. Tania Cassidy, Editorial Board. **ISSN:** 1740-8989. **Subscription Rates:** 235 institutions print + online; 224 institutions online; 85 individuals; US$357 institutions print + online; US$339 institutions online; US$128 individuals; EUR285 institutions print and online; EUR270 institutions online only; EUR102 individuals. **Remarks:** Advertising accepted; rates available upon request. **URL:** http://www.tandf.co.uk/journals/titles/17408989.asp. **Circ:** (Not Reported)

52013 ■ Physiotherapy Theory and Practice
Taylor & Francis Ltd.
2 & 4 Park Sq.
Milton Pk.
Abingdon OX14 4RN, United Kingdom
Ph: 44 20 70176000
Fax: 44 20 70176336
Journal providing an international, peer-reviewed forum for the publication, dissemination, and discussion of recent developments and current research in physiotherapy/physical therapy. **Freq:** 6/yr. **Key Personnel:** Scott Hasson, Editor, scott.hasson@angelo.edu; Karen McCulloch, Dep. Ed.; L. Brosseau, Assoc. Ed.; Darlene Sekerak, Assoc. Ed.; J. Balogun, Assoc. Ed.; Di Newham, Dep. Ed. **ISSN:** 0959-3985. **Subscription Rates:** 610 institutions; US$995 institutions; EUR795 institutions. **Remarks:** Accepts advertising. **URL:** http://informahealthcare.com/ptp. **Circ:** (Not Reported)

52014 ■ Planning Practice and Research
Routledge
Taylor & Francis Group Ltd.
2 Park Sq.
Milton Pk.
Abingdon OX14 4RN, United Kingdom
Ph: 44 20 70176000
Fax: 44 20 70176699
Publisher E-mail: webmaster.books@tandf.co.uk
Peer-reviewed journal providing information on current research in planning practice. **Freq:** 5/yr. **Key Person-

nel:** Vincent Nadin, Editor-in-Chief; Paul Butler, Editorial Board; Christine Booth, Editorial Board; Philip Allmendinger, Editorial Board; Robert Shipley, Assoc. Ed.; Simin Davoudi, Editorial Board. **ISSN:** 0269-7459. **Subscription Rates:** 525 institutions print + online; 499 institutions online; 100 individuals; US$871 institutions print + online; US$828 institutions online; US$161 individuals; EUR693 institutions print and online; EUR658 institutions online only; EUR129 individuals. **Remarks:** Advertising accepted; rates available upon request. **URL:** http://www.tandf.co.uk/journals/titles/02697459.asp. **Circ:** (Not Reported)

52015 ■ Police Practice and Research
Routledge
Taylor & Francis Group Ltd.
2 Park Sq.
Milton Pk.
Abingdon OX14 4RN, United Kingdom
Ph: 44 20 70176000
Fax: 44 20 70176699
Publisher E-mail: webmaster.books@tandf.co.uk
Journal devoted to latest innovative police research in addition to the operational and administrative practices in a global scenario. **Subtitle:** An International Journal. **Freq:** 6/yr. **Key Personnel:** Dilip K. Das, Editor-in-Chief, dilipkd@aol.com; Kam C. Wong, Advisory Board; Michael L. Birzer, Publicity Ed.; James M. Adcock, Assoc. Mng. Ed.; Darryl Plecas, Book Review Ed.; Lucia Dammert, Editorial Board. **ISSN:** 1561-4263. **Subscription Rates:** US$132 individuals; US$539 institutions online; US$567 institutions print + online; 91 individuals print only; 327 institutions online; 345 institutions print + online; EUR454 institutions print + online; EUR432 institutions online only; EUR107 individuals. **Remarks:** Advertising accepted; rates available upon request. **URL:** http://www.tandf.co.uk/journal.asp?issn=1561-4263&linktype=5. **Circ:** (Not Reported)

52016 ■ Policing and Society
Routledge
Taylor & Francis Group Ltd.
2 Park Sq.
Milton Pk.
Abingdon OX14 4RN, United Kingdom
Ph: 44 20 70176000
Fax: 44 20 70176699
Publisher E-mail: webmaster.books@tandf.co.uk
Peer-reviewed journal focusing on the activity of policing and factors impacting it. **Freq:** Quarterly. **Key Personnel:** Martin Innes, Editor, innesm@cardiff.ac.uk; David Bayley, Editorial Advisory Board; Jean-Paul Brodeur, Editorial Advisory Board; Benjamin Bowling, Editorial Advisory Board; Monica Den Boer, Editorial Advisory Board; Nigel Fielding, Editorial Advisory Board. **ISSN:** 1043-9463. **Subscription Rates:** US$760 institutions online; 569 institutions online; US$800 institutions print + online; 599 institutions print + online; US$210 individuals; 175 individuals; EUR638 institutions print and online; EUR605 institutions online only; EUR168 individuals. **Remarks:** Advertising accepted; rates available upon request. **URL:** http://www.tandf.co.uk/journals/journal.asp?issn=1043-9463&linktype=5. **Circ:** (Not Reported)

52017 ■ Policy Studies
Routledge
Taylor & Francis Group Ltd.
2 Park Sq.
Milton Pk.
Abingdon OX14 4RN, United Kingdom
Ph: 44 20 70176000
Fax: 44 20 70176699
Publisher E-mail: webmaster.books@tandf.co.uk
Peer-reviewed journal focusing on public policy. **Freq:** 6/yr. **Key Personnel:** Prof. Mark Evans, Editor; Lorna Evans, Editorial Coord.; David Bailey, Editorial Board; Paul Boreham, Editorial Board; Jim Buller, Editorial Board; Angela Coulter, Editorial Board. **ISSN:** 0144-2872. **Subscription Rates:** 637 institutions online; 671 institutions print + online; 161 individuals; US$1,109 institutions print + online; US$1,054 institutions online; US$268 individuals; EUR887 institutions print and online; EUR842 institutions online only; EUR214 individuals. **Remarks:** Advertising accepted; rates available upon request. **URL:** http://www.tandf.co.uk/journals/carfax/01442872.html. **Circ:** (Not Reported)

52018 ■ Political Communication
Routledge
Taylor & Francis Group Ltd.
2 Park Sq.

Circulation: ★ = ABC; △ = BPA; ◆ = CAC; ● = CCAB; ❏ = VAC; ⊕ = PO Statement; ‡ = Publisher's Report; Boldface figures = sworn; Light figures = estimated.

Gale Directory of Publications & Broadcast Media/147th Ed.   5555

Milton Pk.
Abingdon OX14 4RN, United Kingdom
Ph: 44 20 70176000
Fax: 44 20 70176699
Publisher E-mail: webmaster.books@tandf.co.uk
Peer-reviewed journal on intersection of politics and communication. **Freq:** Quarterly. **Key Personnel:** Shanto Iyengar, Editor; Ann N. Crigler, Editorial Board; Doris A. Graber, Founding Ed.; Scott L. Althaus, Editorial Board; Travis Dixon, Editorial Board; Roderick P. Hart, Editorial Board. **ISSN:** 1058-4609. **Subscription Rates:** US$219 individuals print; US$503 institutions online; US$530 institutions print & online; 319 institutions print & online; 303 institutions online; 131 individuals. **Remarks:** Accepts advertising on request. **URL:** http://www.tandf.co.uk/journals/titles/10584609.asp. **Circ:** (Not Reported)

52019 ■ Politikon
Routledge
Taylor & Francis Group Ltd.
2 Park Sq.
Milton Pk.
Abingdon OX14 4RN, United Kingdom
Ph: 44 20 70176000
Fax: 44 20 70176699
Publisher E-mail: webmaster.books@tandf.co.uk
Peer-reviewed journal covering South African politics and related issues. **Subtitle:** South African Journal of Political Studies. **Founded:** 1974. **Freq:** 3/yr. **Key Personnel:** Stephen Louw, Editorial Board; Dr. Pieter Fourie, Editor; Dr. Thomas Wilkins, Book Review Ed.; Gail Gerhart, Editorial Board; Susan Booysen, Editorial Board; Heribert Adam, Editorial Board; Adam Habib, Editorial Board; Manuel Hassassian, Editorial Board; Adrian Guelke, Editorial Board. **ISSN:** 0258-9346. **Subscription Rates:** 304 institutions print + online; US$507 institutions print + online; 289 institutions online; US$482 institutions online; EUR404 institutions print + online; EUR384 institutions online; 71 individuals; US$123 individuals; EUR98 individuals. **Remarks:** Accepts advertising. **URL:** http://www.tandf.co.uk/journals/titles/02589346.asp. **Circ:** (Not Reported)

52020 ■ Post-Communist Economies
Routledge
Taylor & Francis Group Ltd.
2 Park Sq.
Milton Pk.
Abingdon OX14 4RN, United Kingdom
Ph: 44 20 70176000
Fax: 44 20 70176699
Publisher E-mail: webmaster.books@tandf.co.uk
Peer-reviewed journal covering aspects of economic and political analysis. **Freq:** Quarterly. **Key Personnel:** Roger Clarke, Editor; Bruno Schonfelder, Editorial Board; Dr. Ljubo Sirc, Editorial Board; Morris Bornstein, Editorial Board; Philip Hanson, Editorial Board; William Tompson, Editorial Board. **ISSN:** 1463-1377. **Subscription Rates:** 607 institutions print + online; 576 institutions online; 176 individuals; US$1,151 institutions print + online; US$1,093 institutions online; US$324 individuals; EUR916 institutions print and online; EUR870 institutions online only; EUR258 individuals. **Remarks:** Advertising accepted; rates available upon request. **URL:** http://www.tandf.co.uk/journals/titles/14631377.asp. **Circ:** (Not Reported)

52021 ■ Postcolonial Studies
Routledge
Taylor & Francis Group Ltd.
2 Park Sq.
Milton Pk.
Abingdon OX14 4RN, United Kingdom
Ph: 44 20 70176000
Fax: 44 20 70176699
Publisher E-mail: webmaster.books@tandf.co.uk
Peer-reviewed journal focusing on work, which explores the various facets-textual, historical, figural, spatial, political, and economic-of the colonial encounter. **Freq:** Quarterly. **Key Personnel:** Dipesh Chakrabarty, International Editorial Board; Sanjay Seth, London Editorial; Michael Dutton, London Editorial; David L. Martin, Managing Editor; Vanita Seth, Santa Cruz Editorial; Karina Smith, Reviews Ed. **ISSN:** 1368-8790. **Subscription Rates:** 314 institutions online; 330 institutions print + online; 81 individuals; US$549 institutions print + online; US$522 institutions online; US$132 individuals; $A 727 institutions print + online; $A 690 institutions online; $A 180 individuals; EUR437 institutions print and online.

Remarks: Advertising accepted; rates available upon request. **URL:** http://www.tandf.co.uk/journals/titles/13688790.asp. **Circ:** (Not Reported)

52022 ■ Professional Development in Education
Routledge
Taylor & Francis Group Ltd.
2 Park Sq.
Milton Pk.
Abingdon OX14 4RN, United Kingdom
Ph: 44 20 70176000
Fax: 44 20 70176699
Publisher E-mail: webmaster.books@tandf.co.uk
Peer-reviewed journal publishing original contributions on the subject of teacher education. **Freq:** Quarterly. **Key Personnel:** Alex Alexandrou, Assoc. Ed.; Meryl Thompson, Assoc. Ed.; Malcolm Lee, Founding Ed.; Tony Bates, Assoc. Ed.; Bob Gough, Founding Ed.; Tom Bisschof, Editorial Advisory Board; Jim O'Brien, Assoc. Ed.; Anja Swennen, Assoc. Ed.; Kit Field, Book Reviews Ed.; Ken Jones, Editor; Danielle Zay, Editorial Advisory Board. **ISSN:** 1941-5257. **Subscription Rates:** 400 institutions print & online; 380 institutions online; 56 individuals; US$625 institutions print & online; US$594 institutions online; US$96 individuals; EUR498 institutions print and online; EUR473 institutions online only; EUR77 individuals. **URL:** http://www.tandf.co.uk/journals/titles/13674587.asp. **Former name:** Journal of In-Service Education.

52023 ■ Prometheus
Routledge
Taylor & Francis Group Ltd.
2 Park Sq.
Milton Pk.
Abingdon OX14 4RN, United Kingdom
Ph: 44 20 70176000
Fax: 44 20 70176699
Publisher E-mail: webmaster.books@tandf.co.uk
Peer-reviewed journal publishing research papers and contributions on national and international policy debate. Includes topics such as technological change, innovation, information economics, and telecommunications and science policy. **Freq:** Quarterly. **Key Personnel:** Stuart Macdonald, Gen. Ed., s.macdonald@sheffield.ac.uk; Dmimitris Assimakopoulos, Editor; Peter Armstrong, Book Review Ed., p.armstrong@le.ac.uk. **ISSN:** 0810-9028. **Subscription Rates:** US$181 individuals print only; US$538 institutions online; US$566 institutions print + online; $A 169 individuals print only; $A 455 institutions online; $A 479 institutions print + online; 108 individuals print only; 325 institutions online; 343 institutions print + online. **Remarks:** Advertising accepted; rates available upon request. **URL:** http://www.tandf.co.uk/journals/carfax/08109028.html. **Circ:** (Not Reported)

52024 ■ Prose Studies
Routledge
Taylor & Francis Group Ltd.
2 Park Sq.
Milton Pk.
Abingdon OX14 4RN, United Kingdom
Ph: 44 20 70176000
Fax: 44 20 70176699
Publisher E-mail: webmaster.books@tandf.co.uk
Peer-reviewed journal providing a platform for exchange of ideas on history, theory and criticism of non-fictional prose of all periods. **Subtitle:** History, Theory, Criticism. **Freq:** 3/yr. **Key Personnel:** Clare A. Simmons, Editor; Ronald Corthell, Editor; George Levine, Editorial Board; Jefferson D. Slagle, Editorial Asst.; Leo Braudy, Editorial Board; Thomas N. Corns, Editorial Board. **ISSN:** 0144-0357. **Subscription Rates:** 56 individuals; 199 institutions online; 209 institutions print + online; US$378 institutions print + online; US$359 institutions online; US$81 individuals; EUR300 institutions print and online; EUR286 institutions online only; EUR63 individuals. **Remarks:** Advertising accepted; rates available upon request. **URL:** http://www.tandf.co.uk/journals/titles/01440357.asp. **Circ:** (Not Reported)

52025 ■ Prosthetics & Orthotics International
Taylor & Francis Ltd.
2 & 4 Park Sq.
Milton Pk.
Abingdon OX14 4RN, United Kingdom
Ph: 44 20 70176000
Fax: 44 20 70176336
International, multidisciplinary journal for all professionals who have an interest in the medical, clinical, rehabilitation, technical, educational and research

aspects of prosthetics, orthotics and rehabilitation engineering, as well as their related topics. **Freq:** 4/yr. **Key Personnel:** Margrit R. Meier, Editor; Deirdre Desmond, Assoc. Ed.; Dick H. Plettenburgh, Assoc. Ed. **ISSN:** 0309-3646. **Remarks:** Accepts advertising. **URL:** http://informahealthcare.com/poi. **Circ:** (Not Reported)

52026 ■ Psychoanalytic Psychotherapy
Routledge
Taylor & Francis Group Ltd.
2 Park Sq.
Milton Pk.
Abingdon OX14 4RN, United Kingdom
Ph: 44 20 70176000
Fax: 44 20 70176699
Publisher E-mail: webmaster.books@tandf.co.uk
Peer-reviewed journal containing papers in the field of psychoanalysis and psychoanalytic psychotherapy, in connection with Association for Psychoanalytic Psychotherapy in the National Health Service. **Freq:** Quarterly. **Key Personnel:** Prof. Alessandra Lemma, Editor; Robin Anderson, Editorial Board; Dr. Thomas Pennybacker, Asst. Ed.; Geraldine Shipton, Book Reviews Ed.; Marco Chiesa, Editorial Board; Eric Karas, Editorial Board. **ISSN:** 0266-8734. **Subscription Rates:** 89 individuals; 157 institutions online; 166 institutions print + online; US$274 institutions print + online; US$261 institutions online; US$150 individuals; EUR218 institutions print and online; EUR207 institutions online only; EUR120 individuals. **Remarks:** Advertising accepted; rates available upon request. **URL:** http://www.tandf.co.uk/journals/titles/02668734.html. **Circ:** (Not Reported)

52027 ■ Psychodynamic Practice
Routledge
Taylor & Francis Group Ltd.
2 Park Sq.
Milton Pk.
Abingdon OX14 4RN, United Kingdom
Ph: 44 20 70176000
Fax: 44 20 70176699
Publisher E-mail: webmaster.books@tandf.co.uk
Peer-reviewed journal exploring the relevance of psychodynamic ideas to different occupational settings. **Subtitle:** Individuals, Groups and Organisations. **Freq:** Quarterly. **Key Personnel:** Jane Maitland, Editorial Board; Nick Barwick, Managing Editor; Jonathan Smith, Book Review Ed. **ISSN:** 1475-3634. **Subscription Rates:** US$114 individuals print only; US$527 institutions online; US$555 institutions print + online; 336 institutions print + online; 320 institutions online; 68 individuals print only; EUR441 institutions print and online; EUR419 institutions online only; EUR91 individuals. **Remarks:** Advertising accepted; rates available upon request. **URL:** http://www.tandf.co.uk/journals/titles/14753634.html. **Circ:** (Not Reported)

52028 ■ Psychology Crime and Law
Routledge
Taylor & Francis Group Ltd.
2 Park Sq.
Milton Pk.
Abingdon OX14 4RN, United Kingdom
Ph: 44 20 70176000
Fax: 44 20 70176699
Publisher E-mail: webmaster.books@tandf.co.uk
Peer-reviewed journal dealing with study and application of psychological methods to crime, criminal and civil law, and the effect of law on behavior. **Freq:** 8/yr. **Key Personnel:** Prof. Clive Hollin, Editor, crh9@leicester.ac.uk; Peter Van Koppen, Editor, peter.vankoppen@law.unimaas.nl; Hans F.M. Crombag, Editorial Board; David Farrington, Editorial Board; Emma J. Palmer, PhD, Managing Editor, ejp8@le.ac.uk; James H. Davis, Editorial Board; Paul Gendreau, Editorial Board; Brian H. Bornstein, Editor, pcl@unl.edu; Andreas Beelmann, Editorial Board. **ISSN:** 1068-316X. **Subscription Rates:** US$287 individuals print only; US$677 institutions online; US$712 institutions print + online; 533 institutions print + online; 506 institutions online; 227 individuals; EUR570 institutions print and online; EUR541 institutions online only; EUR229 individuals. **Remarks:** Advertising accepted; rates available upon request. **URL:** http://www.tandf.co.uk/journals/titles/1068316x.html. **Circ:** (Not Reported)

52029 ■ Psychology and Health
Routledge
Taylor & Francis Group Ltd.
2 Park Sq.
Milton Pk.
Abingdon OX14 4RN, United Kingdom

Ph: 44 20 70176000
Fax: 44 20 70176699
Publisher E-mail: webmaster.books@tandf.co.uk
Peer-reviewed journal promoting the study and application of psychological approaches to health and illness, including work on psychological aspects of physical illness, treatment processes and recovery; psychosocial factors in the etiology of physical illnesses; health attitudes and behavior, including prevention; the individual-health care system interface particularly communication and psychologically based interventions. **Freq:** 10/yr. **Key Personnel:** Lucy Yardley, Editor; Rona Moss-Morris, Editor; Mike Antoni, Assoc. Ed.; Crystal Park, Assoc. Ed.; Hein de Vries, Assoc. Ed.; David French, Assoc. Ed. **ISSN:** 0887-0446. **Subscription Rates:** US$206 individuals print only; US$1,436 institutions online only; US$1,511 institutions print & online; 1,145 institutions print & online; 1,086 institutions online only; 169 individuals print only; EUR1,204 institutions print and online; EUR1,144 institutions online only; EUR165 individuals. **Remarks:** Accepts advertising. **URL:** http://www.tandf.co.uk/journals/titles/08870446.asp. **Circ:** (Not Reported)

52030 ■ Psychology, Health and Medicine
Routledge
Taylor & Francis Group Ltd.
2 Park Sq.
Milton Pk.
Abingdon OX14 4RN, United Kingdom
Ph: 44 20 70176000
Fax: 44 20 70176699
Publisher E-mail: webmaster.books@tandf.co.uk
Peer-reviewed journal providing a forum to report on issues of psychology and health in practice, focusing on practical applications of theory, research and experience and providing a bridge between academic knowledge and health care practice. **Freq:** 6/yr. **Key Personnel:** Prof. Lorraine Sherr, Editor; Prof. Margaret Chesney, Assoc. Ed.; Prof. Paul Bennett, Book Review Ed.; Dr. Doug Drossman, International Editorial Board; Prof. Robert Bor, International Editorial Board; Dr. Martin Hagger, International Editorial Board. **ISSN:** 1354-8506. **Subscription Rates:** US$66 members society; US$308 individuals print only; US$1,067 institutions online; US$1,123 institutions print + online; 40 members society; 185 individuals print only; 653 institutions online; 687 institutions print + online; EUR55 members society. **Remarks:** Accepts advertising. **URL:** http://www.tandf.co.uk/journals/titles/13548506.asp. **Circ:** (Not Reported)

52031 ■ Public Management Review
Routledge
Taylor & Francis Group Ltd.
2 Park Sq.
Milton Pk.
Abingdon OX14 4RN, United Kingdom
Ph: 44 20 70176000
Fax: 44 20 70176699
Publisher E-mail: webmaster.books@tandf.co.uk
Peer-reviewed journal publishing articles relating to the strategic and operational management of public services. **Freq:** Quarterly. **Key Personnel:** Stephen P. Osborne, Editor-in-Chief, s.p.osborne@ed.ac.uk; Pete Alcock, Editorial Board; Alan Lawton, Editorial Board; David Hulme, Editor; Sue Dopson, Editorial Board; John Bryson, Editorial Board. **ISSN:** 1471-9037. **Subscription Rates:** 99 individuals; 559 institutions online; 588 institutions print + online; US$927 institutions print + online; US$881 institutions online; US$169 individuals; EUR738 institutions print and online; EUR701 institutions online only; EUR134 individuals. **Remarks:** Advertising accepted; rates available upon request. **URL:** http://www.tandf.co.uk/journals/journal.asp?issn=1471-9037&linktype=5. **Circ:** (Not Reported)

52032 ■ Quarterly Journal of Experimental Psychology
Taylor & Francis Ltd.
2 & 4 Park Sq.
Milton Pk.
Abingdon OX14 4RN, United Kingdom
Ph: 44 20 70176000
Fax: 44 20 70176336
Peer-reviewed and International journal publishing original articles on any topic within the field of experimental psychology, including the areas of learning, memory, motivation and cognitive processes in both non-human and human animals, and studies examining the acquisi-

tion and use of knowledge about the world, the nature of such knowledge, and the relationship between knowledge and behavior. **Freq:** 12/yr. **Key Personnel:** Steve Tipper, Editor; John Parkinson, Asst. Ed.; Andy Delamater, Assoc. Ed.; Marc Brysbaert, Assoc. Ed.; Chris Mitchell, Assoc. Ed.; Robin Murphy, Assoc. Ed. **ISSN:** 1747-0218. **Subscription Rates:** US$358 individuals print only; US$1,465 institutions online only; US$1,541 institutions print & online; 771 institutions print & online; 733 institutions online; 171 individuals print only. **Remarks:** Accepts advertising. **URL:** http://www.tandf.co.uk/journals/titles/17470218.asp. **Circ:** (Not Reported)

52033 ■ Race, Ethnicity and Education
Routledge
Taylor & Francis Group Ltd.
2 Park Sq.
Milton Pk.
Abingdon OX14 4RN, United Kingdom
Ph: 44 20 70176000
Fax: 44 20 70176699
Publisher E-mail: webmaster.books@tandf.co.uk
Peer-reviewed journal covering research exploring the dynamics of race, racism and ethnicity in education policy, theory and practice. **Freq:** Quarterly. **Key Personnel:** David Gillborn, Editor, d.gillborn@ioe.ac.uk; Annette Henry, Assoc. Ed.; James A. Banks, Editorial Board. **ISSN:** 1361-3324. **Subscription Rates:** 496 institutions print + online; US$816 institutions print + online; 144 individuals; US$236 individuals; 471 institutions online; US$775 institutions online; EUR649 institutions print and online; EUR617 institutions online only; EUR188 individuals. **Remarks:** Advertising accepted; rates available upon request. **URL:** http://www.tandf.co.uk/journals/titles/13613324.asp. **Circ:** (Not Reported)

52034 ■ Reading & Writing Quarterly
Taylor & Francis Ltd.
2 & 4 Park Sq.
Milton Pk.
Abingdon OX14 4RN, United Kingdom
Ph: 44 20 70176000
Fax: 44 20 70176336
Peer-reviewed journal covering learning disabilities and education. **Subtitle:** Overcoming Learning Disabilities. **Freq:** Quarterly. **Trim Size:** 6 x 9. **Key Personnel:** Dana L. Grisham, Editorial Review Board; Patrick P. McCabe, Assoc. Ed.; Stephanie Al Otaiba, Editorial Review Board; David J. Chard, Editorial Review Board; Rita Moore, Editorial Review Board; Katherine Stahl, Editorial Review Board; Elizabeth Dutro, Editorial Review Board; Jill Fitzgerald, Editorial Review Board; Rita M. Bean, Editorial Review Board; Howard Margolis, Editor, hm08043@yahoo.com. **ISSN:** 1057-3569. **Subscription Rates:** US$198 individuals print; US$502 individuals online; US$528 institutions print and online. **Remarks:** Accepts advertising ON request. **URL:** http://www.informaworld.com/smpp/title~content=t713775334. **Circ:** Combined 900

52035 ■ Reflective Practice
Routledge
Taylor & Francis Group Ltd.
2 Park Sq.
Milton Pk.
Abingdon OX14 4RN, United Kingdom
Ph: 44 20 70176000
Fax: 44 20 70176699
Publisher E-mail: webmaster.books@tandf.co.uk
Peer-reviewed journal containing papers that addresses the connections between reflection, knowledge generation, practice and policy. **Freq:** 5/yr. **Key Personnel:** Prof. Tony Ghaye, Editor; Liz Jones, International Editorial Board; Dennis Beach, International Editorial Board; Jean Clandinin, Editorial Board; John Loughran, Editorial Board; Charlene Tan, Editorial Board. **ISSN:** 1462-3943. **Subscription Rates:** US$238 individuals print only; US$732 institutions online only; US$770 institutions print & online; 467 institutions print & online; 443 institutions online only; 146 individuals print only; EUR616 institutions print and online; EUR585 institutions online only; EUR190 individuals. **Remarks:** Accepts advertising. **URL:** http://www.tandf.co.uk/journals/titles/14623943.asp. **Circ:** (Not Reported)

52036 ■ Regional Studies
Routledge
Taylor & Francis Group Ltd.
2 Park Sq.

Milton Pk.
Abingdon OX14 4RN, United Kingdom
Ph: 44 20 70176000
Fax: 44 20 70176699
Publisher E-mail: webmaster.books@tandf.co.uk
Peer-reviewed journal featuring the theoretical development, empirical analysis and policy debate in the multi- and inter-disciplinary field of regional studies. **Subtitle:** Journal of the Regional Studies Association. **Founded:** 1966. **Freq:** 10/yr. **Key Personnel:** Dr. Arnoud Lagendijk, Editor-in-Chief; Prof. Koen Frenken, Editor; Prof. Susan Christopherson, Editorial Board Member; Prof. Ron Martin, Editor; Prof. Barrie Needham, Editor; Prof. Attila Varga, Editor; Prof. David B. Audretsch, Editorial Board Member; Prof. Richard L. Florida, Editorial Board Member; Dr. Simona Iammarino, Editor; Dr. Andy Pike, Editor, phone 44 191 2228011, fax 44 191 2329259, andy.pike@ncl.ac.uk. **ISSN:** 0034-3404. **Subscription Rates:** 1,153 institutions print and online; US$1,937 institutions print and online; EUR1,544 institutions print and online; 1,153 institutions online only; US$2,039 institutions online only; EUR1,544 institutions online only; 315 individuals; US$569 individuals; EUR453 individuals. **URL:** http://www.tandf.co.uk/journals/titles/00343404.asp.

52037 ■ Research in Post-Compulsory Education
Routledge
Taylor & Francis Group Ltd.
2 Park Sq.
Milton Pk.
Abingdon OX14 4RN, United Kingdom
Ph: 44 20 70176000
Fax: 44 20 70176699
Publisher E-mail: webmaster.books@tandf.co.uk
Peer-reviewed journal covering research in the area of post-compulsory education. **Freq:** 4/yr. **Key Personnel:** Christopher Parkin, Editorial Board; Geoffrey Elliott, Editor; Dennis Ridley, Editorial Advisory Board; Chahid Fourali, Editorial Board; Nick Stratton, Editorial Board; Christine Ward, Editorial Board; Linda Miller, Editorial Board; Thomas Flint, Editorial Advisory Board; Tone Skinningsrud, Editorial Advisory Board; Sally Issler, Editorial Board; Miriam Conway, Editorial Advisory Board; Ian Finlay, Editorial Advisory Board. **ISSN:** 1359-6748. **Subscription Rates:** 406 institutions print + online; US$646 institutions print + online; 385 institutions online; US$614 institutions online; 65 individuals; US$101 individuals; EUR516 institutions print and online; EUR491 institutions online only; EUR81 individuals. **URL:** http://www.tandf.co.uk/journals/titles/13596748.asp.

52038 ■ Rethinking History
Routledge
Taylor & Francis Group Ltd.
2 Park Sq.
Milton Pk.
Abingdon OX14 4RN, United Kingdom
Ph: 44 20 70176000
Fax: 44 20 70176699
Publisher E-mail: webmaster.books@tandf.co.uk
Peer-reviewed journal focusing on history. **Subtitle:** The Journal of Theory and Practice. **Freq:** 4/yr. **Key Personnel:** Jonathan Walker, Reviews Ed.; Alun Munslow, Editor, amunslow@tiscali.co.uk; David Harlan, Editorial Board; Robert A. Rosenstone, Founding Ed.; James Goodman, Editor, goodmanj@andromeda.rutgers.edu; Allan Megill, Editorial Board. **ISSN:** 1364-2529. **Subscription Rates:** US$139 individuals; US$557 institutions online; US$586 institutions print & online; 353 institutions print & online; 335 institutions online; 83 individuals; EUR467 institutions print + online. **Remarks:** Accepts advertising. **URL:** http://www.tandf.co.uk/journals/titles/13642529.asp. **Circ:** (Not Reported)

52039 ■ Review
Routledge
Taylor & Francis Group Ltd.
2 Park Sq.
Milton Pk.
Abingdon OX14 4RN, United Kingdom
Ph: 44 20 70176000
Fax: 44 20 70176699
Publisher E-mail: webmaster.books@tandf.co.uk
Peer-reviewed journal providing a platform for current Latin American, Caribbean, and Canadian writing in English and English translation in the United States along with the coverage of arts in the Americas. **Subtitle:** Literature & Arts of the Americas. **Founded:** 1968. **Freq:**

Circulation: ★ = ABC; △ = BPA; ◆ = CAC; • = CCAB; ❏ = VAC; ⊕ = PO Statement; ‡ = Publisher's Report; Boldface figures = sworn; Light figures = estimated.

Semiannual. **Key Personnel:** Daniel Shapiro, Managing Editor; Mario Vargas Llosa, Advisory Board; Nelida Pinon, Advisory Board; Carmen Boullosa, Advisory Board; Ruben Gallo, Advisory Board; Gregory Rabassa, Advisory Board; Jose Negroni, Asst. to the Ed.; Jane Gregory Rubin, Advisory Board; Jason Weiss, Copy Ed. **ISSN:** 0890-5762. **Subscription Rates:** US$48 individuals print only; US$204 institutions online; US$215 institutions print + online; 129 institutions print + online; 122 institutions online; 26 individuals print only; EUR171 institutions print and online; EUR162 institutions online only; EUR37 individuals. **Remarks:** Advertising accepted; rates available upon request. **URL:** http://www.tandf.co.uk/journals/journal.asp?issn=0890-5762&linktype=5. **Former name:** Review: Latin American Literature and Arts. **Circ:** (Not Reported)

52040 ■ Review of African Political Economy
Routledge
Taylor & Francis Group Ltd.
2 Park Sq.
Milton Pk.
Abingdon OX14 4RN, United Kingdom
Ph: 44 20 70176000
Fax: 44 20 70176699
Publisher E-mail: webmaster.books@tandf.co.uk
Peer-reviewed journal on African political economy published in connection with ROAPE international collective covering radical analysis of trends and issues in Africa. **Freq:** Quarterly. **Key Personnel:** Ray Bush, Editorial Working Group; Giles Mohan, Editorial Working Group; Janet Bujra, Editorial Working Group; Tunde Zack Williams, Editorial Working Group. **ISSN:** 0305-6244. **Subscription Rates:** US$75 individuals; US$713 institutions online only; US$750 institutions print + online; 428 institutions print + online; 407 institutions online; 43 individuals; EUR598 institutions print and online; EUR568 institutions online only; EUR59 individuals. **Remarks:** Advertising accepted; rates available upon request. **URL:** http://www.tandf.co.uk/journals/journal.asp?issn=0305-6244&linktype=1. **Circ:** (Not Reported)

52041 ■ The Review of Communication
Routledge
Taylor & Francis Group Ltd.
2 Park Sq.
Milton Pk.
Abingdon OX14 4RN, United Kingdom
Ph: 44 20 70176000
Fax: 44 20 70176699
Publisher E-mail: webmaster.books@tandf.co.uk
Online journal that publishes review essays, book reviews, and other materials in the field of communication. **Freq:** 4/yr. **Key Personnel:** Jamese Chesebro, Advisory Board; Raymie McKerrow, Advisory Board; Julia Wood, Advisory Board. **ISSN:** 1535-8593. **Subscription Rates:** US$248 institutions print and online; 162 institutions print and online; EUR198 institutions print and online. **Remarks:** Accepts advertising. **URL:** http://www.tandf.co.uk/journals/titles/15358593.asp. **Circ:** (Not Reported)

52042 ■ Review of International Political Economy
Routledge
Taylor & Francis Group Ltd.
2 Park Sq.
Milton Pk.
Abingdon OX14 4RN, United Kingdom
Ph: 44 20 70176000
Fax: 44 20 70176699
Publisher E-mail: webmaster.books@tandf.co.uk
Peer-reviewed journal covering the topics on internationalization of governance, change of national to transnational economic system, study of developing trajectories. **Freq:** 5/yr. **Key Personnel:** Henry Wai-Chung Yeung, Editor; Cornelia Woll, Editor; Mark Blyth, Editor; Catherine Weaver, Editor; Catherine Corliss, Managing Editor; Leonard Seabrooke, Editor. **ISSN:** 0969-2290. **Subscription Rates:** 418 institutions print + online; 397 institutions online; 113 individuals personal; US$696 institutions print + online; US$660 institutions online; US$1172 individuals personal; EUR554 institutions print and online; EUR526 institutions online only; EUR138 individuals. **Remarks:** Advertising accepted; rates available upon request. **URL:** http://www.tandf.co.uk/journals/titles/09692290.asp. **Circ:** (Not Reported)

52043 ■ Review of Political Economy
Routledge
Taylor & Francis Group Ltd.
2 Park Sq.
Milton Pk.

Abingdon OX14 4RN, United Kingdom
Ph: 44 20 70176000
Fax: 44 20 70176699
Publisher E-mail: webmaster.books@tandf.co.uk
Peer-reviewed journal covering all areas of political economy, including the Post Keynesian, Sraffian, Marxian, Austrian and institutionalist traditions. **Freq:** Quarterly. **Key Personnel:** Gary Mongiovi, Editor; Steve Pressman, Editor; Marc Lavoie, Editorial Advisory Board; Mark Setterfield, Editorial Advisory Board; Roberto Ciccone, Editorial Advisory Board; E.J. Nell, Editorial Advisory Board; Deborah Figart, Editorial Advisory Board; J.E. King, Editorial Advisory Board; Geoff C. Harcourt, Editorial Advisory Board; Peter Earl, Editorial Advisory Board; Vivian Walsh, Editorial Advisory Board; Irene van Staveren, Editorial Advisory Board. **ISSN:** 0953-8259. **Subscription Rates:** US$214 individuals print only; US$876 institutions online; US$921 institutions print + online; 534 institutions print + online; 507 institutions online; 131 individuals print only; EUR734 institutions print and online; EUR698 institutions online only; EUR170 individuals. **Remarks:** Advertising accepted; rates available upon request. **URL:** http://www.tandf.co.uk/journals/journal.asp?issn=0953-8259&linktype=5. **Circ:** (Not Reported)

52044 ■ Review of Social Economy
Routledge
Taylor & Francis Group Ltd.
2 Park Sq.
Milton Pk.
Abingdon OX14 4RN, United Kingdom
Ph: 44 20 70176000
Fax: 44 20 70176699
Publisher E-mail: webmaster.books@tandf.co.uk
Peer-reviewed journal covering sociology and social work. **Freq:** 4/yr. **Key Personnel:** John B. Davis, Editorial Board; Deborah M. Figart, Co-Ed.; Wilfred Dolfsma, Co-Ed.; Robert McMaster, Co-Ed.; Martha Starr, Co-Ed.; Julie A. Nelson, Editorial Board. **ISSN:** 0034-6764. **Subscription Rates:** US$344 institutions print + online; 207 institutions print + online; US$326 institutions online only; 197 institutions online only; US$123 individuals; 85 individuals. **Remarks:** Accepts advertising on request. **Online:** Gale. **URL:** http://www.tandf.co.uk/journals/titles/00346764.asp. **Circ:** (Not Reported)

52045 ■ Revolutionary Russia
Routledge
Taylor & Francis Group Ltd.
2 Park Sq.
Milton Pk.
Abingdon OX14 4RN, United Kingdom
Ph: 44 20 70176000
Fax: 44 20 70176699
Publisher E-mail: webmaster.books@tandf.co.uk
Peer-reviewed journal focusing on the revolutionary period of Russian history, from c.1880-c.1932 published in connection with Study Group on the Russian Revolution. **Founded:** 1988. **Freq:** Semiannual. **Key Personnel:** Jonathan Smele, Editor; Peter Kenez, Editorial Board; Matthew Rendle, Reviews Ed.; Edward Acton, Editorial Board; Carter R. Elwood, Editorial Board; Paul Dukes, Editorial Board; Abraham Ascher, Editorial Board; Marc Ferro, Editorial Board; John Keep, Editorial Board. **ISSN:** 0954-6545. **Subscription Rates:** US$88 individuals print only; US$341 institutions online only; US$358 institutions print + online; 215 institutions print + online; 205 institutions online only; 55 individuals; EUR286 institutions print and online; EUR271 institutions online only; EUR70 individuals. **Remarks:** Advertising accepted; rates available upon request. **URL:** http://www.tandf.co.uk/journals/journal.asp?issn=0954-6545&linktype=5. **Circ:** (Not Reported)

52046 ■ Safety Fast!
MG Car Club
Kimber House
Cemetery Rd.
Abingdon OX14 1AS, United Kingdom
Ph: 44 12 35555552
Publisher E-mail: julianwhite@mgcc.co.uk
Trade publication covering automotive. **Freq:** Monthly. **Subscription Rates:** Free to members. **Remarks:** Advertising accepted; rates available upon request. **URL:** http://www.mgcc.co.uk/. **Circ:** 13,000

52047 ■ Scandinavian Journal of Clinical and Laboratory Investigation
Taylor & Francis Ltd.
2 & 4 Park Sq.

Milton Pk.
Abingdon OX14 4RN, United Kingdom
Ph: 44 20 70176000
Fax: 44 20 70176336
International scientific journal covering clinically-oriented biochemical and physiological research and containing peer-reviewed articles, editorials, invited reviews, and short technical notes. **Founded:** 1949. **Freq:** 8/yr. **Key Personnel:** Tor-Arne Hagve, Managing Editor; Johan Hultdin, Editor; Anders Kallner, Editor; Sverre Sandberg, Editor; Axel Brock, Editor; Jorgen Gram, Editor; Jens H. Henriksen, Editor; Elvar Theodorsson, Editor; Sverre Landaas, Editor; Sverre Sandberg, Editor; Ulf-Hakan Stenman, Editor; Ulf-Hakan Stenman, Editor. **ISSN:** 0036-5513. **Subscription Rates:** 440 institutions; US$725 institutions; EUR580 institutions. **Remarks:** Advertising accepted; rates available upon request. **URL:** http://informahealthcare.com/loi/clb. **Circ:** (Not Reported)

52048 ■ Scandinavian Journal of Gastroenterology
Taylor & Francis Ltd.
2 & 4 Park Sq.
Milton Pk.
Abingdon OX14 4RN, United Kingdom
Ph: 44 20 70176000
Fax: 44 20 70176336
Journal publishing research articles of high standard covering all aspects of digestive organs, not just within surgery and internal medicine, welcoming reports on all features of patient-oriented research and methodology, as well as cost-benefit evaluations, case reports, and biomedical basal research. **Founded:** 1966. **Freq:** Monthly. **Key Personnel:** Kristian Bjoro, Editor-in-Chief; Lars Aabakken, Exec. Ed.; Peter L.M. Jansen, Editor; Martti Farkkila, Editor; Gabriele Bianchi Porro, Editor; Rolf Hultcrantz, Editor. **ISSN:** 0036-5521. **Subscription Rates:** 850 institutions; US$1,400 institutions; 228 institutions. **Remarks:** Advertising accepted; rates available upon request. **URL:** http://www.informaworld.com/smpp/title~content=t713690387. **Circ:** (Not Reported)

52049 ■ Scandinavian Journal of Hospitality and Tourism
Routledge
Taylor & Francis Group Ltd.
2 Park Sq.
Milton Pk.
Abingdon OX14 4RN, United Kingdom
Ph: 44 20 70176000
Fax: 44 20 70176699
Publisher E-mail: webmaster.books@tandf.co.uk
Journal covering research of issues relevant to Scandinavian, North Sea and Baltic regions, and associated developments in the regional hospitality and tourism industry. **Freq:** Quarterly. **Key Personnel:** Reidar J. Mykletun, Ch. Ed.; Jan Vidar Haukeland, Ch. Ed.; Lena Mossberg, Assoc. Ed.; Ngaire Douglas, Review Board; Tommy Andersson, Assoc. Ed.; Trude Furunes, Managing Editor; Tor Busch, Review Board; Martin Dyer-Smith, Review Board; John Crotts, Review Board. **ISSN:** 1502-2250. **Subscription Rates:** US$406 institutions online; US$201 individuals; US$427 institutions print + online; 217 institutions online; 229 institutions print + online; 121 individuals; EUR341 institutions print + online; EUR324 institutions online; EUR160 individuals. **URL:** http://www.tandf.co.uk/journals/titles/15022250.asp.

52050 ■ Scandinavian Journal of Primary Health Care
Taylor & Francis Ltd.
2 & 4 Park Sq.
Milton Pk.
Abingdon OX14 4RN, United Kingdom
Ph: 44 20 70176000
Fax: 44 20 70176336
Journal publishing articles of relevance to primary health care, such as clinical scientific articles of importance to daily clinical work, including prevention in primary health care with special emphasis on general practice; articles on epidemiology and health service research; and articles that can contribute to the evolution and refinement of the scientific methods necessary for primary health care research. **Freq:** Quarterly. **Key Personnel:** Jakob Kragstrup, Editor-in-Chief; Anders Baerheim, Editorial Board; Lise Stark, Editorial Sec., phone 45 244 40934, fax 45 655 03980, sjphc@health.sdu.dk; Annelli Sandbaek, Editorial Board; Johann August-Sigurdsson, Editorial Board. **ISSN:** 0281-3432. **Subscription Rates:** 245 institutions; US$405 institutions; EUR325 institutions.

Remarks: Advertising accepted; rates available upon request. **URL:** http://informahealthcare.com/journal/pri. **Circ:** (Not Reported)

52051 ■ Scandinavian Journal of Rheumatology
Taylor & Francis Ltd.
2 & 4 Park Sq.
Milton Pk.
Abingdon OX14 4RN, United Kingdom
Ph: 44 20 70176000
Fax: 44 20 70176336
Publication E-mail: scandjrheumatol@editorialoffice.dk
International scientific journal for rheumatologists and also for general practitioners, orthopaedic surgeons, radiologists, pharmacologists, pathologists and health professionals with an interest in patients with rheumatic diseases, publishing original papers in the various fields of clinical and experimental rheumatology, such as: clinical aspects of rheumatic disorders including pharmacotherapy, prophylaxis, surgical and other treatments; laboratory investigations, including mainly biochemistry, immunology, immunopathology, microbiology, histopathology, pathophysiology and pharmacology; radiological, magnetic, and other forms of imaging; and epidemiological, genetic, and social aspects. **Freq:** 6/yr. **Key Personnel:** Kristian Stengaard-Pedersen, Editor; Ulrik Tarp, Assoc. Ed.; Dorit Sylvest, Managing Editor. **ISSN:** 0300-9742. **Subscription Rates:** 250 institutions; US$415 institutions; EUR330 institutions. **Remarks:** Advertising accepted; rates available upon request. **URL:** http://informahealthcare.com/rhe. **Circ:** (Not Reported)

52052 ■ Scandinavian Journal of Urology and Nephrology
Taylor & Francis Ltd.
2 & 4 Park Sq.
Milton Pk.
Abingdon OX14 4RN, United Kingdom
Ph: 44 20 70176000
Fax: 44 20 70176336
Journal publishing papers on urology and nephrology. **Freq:** 6/yr. **Key Personnel:** Jan Adolfsson, Editor-in-Chief; Rolf Lundgren, Managing Editor; Stefan H. Jacobson, Assoc. Ed.; Jens Thorup Andersen, Advisory Board; Lars Grenabo, Advisory Board; Bjarne Ivarsen, Advisory Board. **ISSN:** 0036-5599. **Subscription Rates:** 340 institutions; US$565 institutions; EUR450 institutions. **Remarks:** Advertising accepted; rates available upon request. **URL:** http://www.informaworld.com/smpp/title~content=t713692219; http://informahealthcare.com/uro. **Circ:** (Not Reported)

52053 ■ School Leadership & Management
Routledge
Taylor & Francis Group Ltd.
2 Park Sq.
Milton Pk.
Abingdon OX14 4RN, United Kingdom
Ph: 44 20 70176000
Fax: 44 20 70176699
Publisher E-mail: webmaster.books@tandf.co.uk
Peer-reviewed journal covering information on all aspects of the leadership and management practice in schools. **Freq:** 5/yr. **Key Personnel:** Mark Brundrett, Editorial Board; Clive Dimmock, International Advisory Board; Chris Chapman, Editor; Mark Hadfield, Dep. Ed.; David Hall, Book Review Ed., dave.hall@manchester.ac.uk; Brent Davies, Editorial Board. **ISSN:** 1363-2434. **Subscription Rates:** 751 institutions print + online; US$1,379 institutions print + online; 714 institutions online; US$1,309 institutions online; 154 individuals; US$258 individuals; EUR1,098 institutions print and online; EUR1,043 institutions online only; EUR205 individuals. **URL:** http://www.tandf.co.uk/journals/titles/13632434.asp. **Formerly:** School Organisation.

52054 ■ Science as Culture
Routledge
Taylor & Francis Group Ltd.
2 Park Sq.
Milton Pk.
Abingdon OX14 4RN, United Kingdom
Ph: 44 20 70176000
Fax: 44 20 70176699
Publisher E-mail: webmaster.books@tandf.co.uk
Journal on science and culture. **Freq:** Quarterly. **Key Personnel:** Les Levidow, Editor; Robert M. Young, Advisory Panel; Maureen McNeil, Advisory Panel. **ISSN:** 0950-5431. **Subscription Rates:** 273 institutions print & online; US$452 institutions print & online; 260 institu-

tions online only; US$430 institutions online only; 83 individuals; US$134 individuals; 44 institutions society; US$72 institutions society; EUR360 institutions print and online; EUR343 institutions online only. **URL:** http://www.tandf.co.uk/journals/journal.asp?issn=0950-5431&linktype=1.

52055 ■ The Service Industries Journal
Routledge
Taylor & Francis Group Ltd.
2 Park Sq.
Milton Pk.
Abingdon OX14 4RN, United Kingdom
Ph: 44 20 70176000
Fax: 44 20 70176699
Publisher E-mail: webmaster.books@tandf.co.uk
Business publication. **Freq:** 8/yr. **Key Personnel:** Eileen Bridges, Editorial Board; Ronald Goldsmith, Editor; Gary Akehurst, Editor; Len Berry, Editorial Board; John Bryson, Editorial Board; Peter Daniels, Editorial Board; Barry Howcroft, Editor; John Ashton, Editorial Board; Gonzales D'Alcantara, Editorial Board; Tom Baum, Editorial Board. **ISSN:** 0264-2069. **Subscription Rates:** 1,043 institutions print + online; US$1,689 institutions print + online; 991 institutions online; US$1,605 institutions online; 219 individuals; US$324 individuals; EUR1,352 institutions print + online; EUR1,285 institutions online; EUR260 individuals. **Remarks:** Advertising accepted; rates available upon request. **Online:** Gale. **URL:** http://www.tandf.co.uk/journals/titles/02642069.asp. **Circ:** (Not Reported)

52056 ■ Sexual Addiction & Compulsivity
Routledge
Taylor & Francis Group Ltd.
2 Park Sq.
Milton Pk.
Abingdon OX14 4RN, United Kingdom
Ph: 44 20 70176000
Fax: 44 20 70176699
Publisher E-mail: webmaster.books@tandf.co.uk
Peer-reviewed journal providing a forum for research and clinical practice of sexual addiction and compulsivity, which is understood to be a significant and widespread disorder and a complex problem requiring a multidisciplinary approach from psychiatrists, psychologists, social workers, family therapists, pastoral counselors and law enforcement personnel. **Freq:** Quarterly. **Key Personnel:** David L. Delmonico, Assoc. Ed.; Kenneth M. Adams, Editorial Board; Fred Berlin, Editorial Board; Charles Samenow, MD, Editor-in-Chief; Michael Alvarez, Editorial Board; Patrick Carnes, Assoc. Ed. **ISSN:** 1072-0162. **Subscription Rates:** 185 institutions print and online; 176 institutions online; 81 individuals print only; US$307 institutions print and online; US$292 institutions online; US$136 individuals print only; EUR244 institutions print and online; EUR232 institutions online only; EUR108 individuals. **Remarks:** Accepts advertising. **URL:** http://www.tandf.co.uk/journals/titles/10720162.asp. **Circ:** (Not Reported)

52057 ■ Shakespeare
Routledge
Taylor & Francis Group Ltd.
2 Park Sq.
Milton Pk.
Abingdon OX14 4RN, United Kingdom
Ph: 44 20 70176000
Fax: 44 20 70176699
Publisher E-mail: webmaster.books@tandf.co.uk
Peer-reviewed journal, publishing articles drawn from the best of current international scholarship on the most recent developments in Shakespearean criticism, aiming to bridge the gap between the disciplines of Shakespeare in Performance Studies and Shakespeare in English Literature and Language. **Freq:** 4/yr. **Key Personnel:** Brett Hirsch, Editor; Deborah Cartmell, Editor; Gabriel Egan, Editor; Catherine Belsey, Editorial Board; Linda Charnes, Editorial Board; Lisa Hopkins, Editor; Samuel Crowl, Editorial Board. **ISSN:** 1745-0918. **Subscription Rates:** 269 institutions print + online; US$446 institutions print + online; 256 institutions online; US$423 institutions online; 69 individuals; US$119 individuals; EUR355 institutions print and online; EUR337 institutions online only; EUR94 individuals. **Remarks:** Accepts advertising. **URL:** http://www.tandf.co.uk/journals/titles/17450918.asp. **Circ:** (Not Reported)

52058 ■ Sikh Formations
Routledge
Taylor & Francis Group Ltd.

2 Park Sq.
Milton Pk.
Abingdon OX14 4RN, United Kingdom
Ph: 44 20 70176000
Fax: 44 20 70176699
Publisher E-mail: webmaster.books@tandf.co.uk
Peer-reviewed journal covering the study of Sikhs, Sikhism, and Sikh identity within the context of a new and dynamic setting that embraces globalization, transnationalism, and other related processes. **Subtitle:** Religion, Culture, Theory. **Freq:** Semiannual. **Key Personnel:** Pal Ahluwalia, Editor; Dr. Arvind-Pal S. Mandair, Editor; Gurharpal Singh, Editor; Sukhdev Singh Deogon, Photographic Ed.; Nikky Singh, Editorial Collective; Harleen Singh, Assoc. Ed.; Navtej Kaur Purewal, Book Review Ed.; Christopher Shackle, Editorial Collective; Navdeep S. Mandair, Book Review Ed.; Virinder Kalra, Assoc. Ed. **ISSN:** 1744-8727. **Subscription Rates:** 206 institutions print + online; US$341 institutions print + online; 196 institutions online; US$324 institutions online; 34 individuals; US$51 individuals; EUR272 institutions print and online; EUR258 institutions online only; EUR40 individuals. **Remarks:** Accepts advertising. **URL:** http://www.tandf.co.uk/journals/titles/17448727.asp. **Circ:** (Not Reported)

52059 ■ Social History
Routledge
Taylor & Francis Group Ltd.
2 Park Sq.
Milton Pk.
Abingdon OX14 4RN, United Kingdom
Ph: 44 20 70176000
Fax: 44 20 70176699
Publisher E-mail: webmaster.books@tandf.co.uk
Peer-reviewed journal focusing on history. **Freq:** Quarterly. **Key Personnel:** Keith Nield, Editor; Janet Blackman, Editor; Gordon Johnston, Editorial Board; Geoff Eley, Editorial Board; Michael Anderson, Editorial Board; David Crew, Editorial Board; Larry Frohman, Review Ed.; Young-Sun Hong, Review Ed. **ISSN:** 0307-1022. **Subscription Rates:** 341 institutions online; 80 individuals; US$132 individuals; US$564 institutions online; 341 institutions print + online; US$594 institutions print + online. **Remarks:** Accepts advertising on request. **URL:** http://www.tandf.co.uk/journals/routledge/03071022.html. **Circ:** (Not Reported)

52060 ■ Social Influence
Taylor & Francis Ltd.
2 & 4 Park Sq.
Milton Pk.
Abingdon OX14 4RN, United Kingdom
Ph: 44 20 70176000
Fax: 44 20 70176336
Peer-reviewed journal providing an integrated focus for research into this dynamic, and multi-disciplinary field, containing such topics as: conformity, norms, social influence tactics such as norm of reciprocity, altercasting, and scarcity, interpersonal influence, persuasion, power, advertising, mass media effects, persuasion in democracy, propaganda, comparative influence, compliance, minority influence, influence in groups, cultic influence, social movements, social contagions, rumors, resistance to influence, influence across cultures, and the history of influence research. **Freq:** 4/yr. **Key Personnel:** Daniel J. Howard, Assoc. Ed.; Kipling D. Williams, Editor; Thomas E. Nelson, Assoc. Ed. **ISSN:** 1553-4510. **Subscription Rates:** US$124 individuals print only; US$265 institutions online only; US$278 institutions print & online; 158 institutions print & online; 150 institutions online only; 71 individuals print only. **Remarks:** Accepts advertising. **URL:** http://www.tandf.co.uk/journals/titles/15534510.asp. **Circ:** (Not Reported)

52061 ■ Socialism and Democracy
Routledge
Taylor & Francis Group Ltd.
2 Park Sq.
Milton Pk.
Abingdon OX14 4RN, United Kingdom
Ph: 44 20 70176000
Fax: 44 20 70176699
Publisher E-mail: webmaster.books@tandf.co.uk
Journal committed to showing the continuing relevance of socialist politics and vision with a broadly Marxist perspective, encouraging not only critique of the status quo, but also informed analysis of the many different ap-

---

Circulation: ★ = ABC; △ = BPA; ◆ = CAC; • = CCAB; ❑ = VAC; ⊕ = PO Statement; ‡ = Publisher's Report; Boldface figures = sworn; Light figures = estimated.

Gale Directory of Publications & Broadcast Media/147th Ed.   5559

proaches to bringing about fundamental change, and seeking to integrate issues of race, gender, sexuality, ethnicity and nationality with the traditional focus on class. **Freq:** 3/yr. **Key Personnel:** Victor Wallis, Editor, zendive@aol.com; Emelio Betances, Editorial Board; Eric Canepa, Editorial Board; Ludmila Melchior, Editorial Board; Ronald Hayduk, Editorial Board; Michael E. Brown, Editorial Board; Peter Roman, Editorial Board; Chris Agee, Editorial Board; Marcella Bencivenni, Editorial Board; Hester Eisenstein, Editorial Board. **ISSN:** 0885-4300. **Subscription Rates:** 272 institutions print + online; US$411 institutions print + online; 259 institutions online; US$390 institutions online; 68 individuals; US$113 individuals; EUR327 institutions print and online; EUR311 institutions online only; EUR90 individuals. **Remarks:** Accepts advertising. **URL:** http://www.tandf.co.uk/journals/titles/08854300.asp. **Circ:** (Not Reported)

52062 ■ Souvenir
Violet Needham Society
Blunsden, Faringdon Rd.
Abingdon OX14 1BQ, United Kingdom
Journal including a newsletter insert. **Freq:** 3/yr. **ISSN:** 0269-0160. **Subscription Rates:** Free to members; 7.50 individuals UK and Europe; 11 other countries. **Remarks:** Advertising not accepted. **URL:** http://violetneedhamsociety.org.uk/souvenir.html. **Circ:** (Not Reported)

52063 ■ Sport in History
Routledge
Taylor & Francis Group Ltd.
2 Park Sq.
Milton Pk.
Abingdon OX14 4RN, United Kingdom
Ph: 44 20 70176000
Fax: 44 20 70176699
Publisher E-mail: webmaster.books@tandf.co.uk
Peer-reviewed journal publishing original, archivally-based research on the history of sport, leisure and recreation, encouraging the study of sport to illuminate broader historical issues and debates. **Freq:** 4/yr. **Key Personnel:** Dr. Paul Dimeo, Co-Ed.; Dr. Martin Johnes, Co-Ed.; Dr. Neil Carter, Reviews Ed. **ISSN:** 1746-0263. **Subscription Rates:** US$490 institutions online only; US$465 institutions print & online; 294 institutions print & online; 279 institutions online; EUR389 institutions print & online; EUR369 institutions online. **Remarks:** Accepts advertising. **URL:** http://www.tandf.co.uk/journals/titles/17460263.asp. **Circ:** (Not Reported)

52064 ■ Sports Biomechanics
Routledge
Taylor & Francis Group Ltd.
2 Park Sq.
Milton Pk.
Abingdon OX14 4RN, United Kingdom
Ph: 44 20 70176000
Fax: 44 20 70176699
Publisher E-mail: webmaster.books@tandf.co.uk
Scientific journal of the International Society of Biomechanics in Sports (ISBS), aiming to generate knowledge to improve sports performance and reduce the incidence of injury and to communicate this knowledge to sports scientists, coaches, and sports participants. **Freq:** Quarterly. **Key Personnel:** Angus Burnett, Exec. Editorial Board; Young-Hoo Kwon, Editor; Bruce Elliott, Exec. Editorial Board; Michiyoshi Ae, Exec. Editorial Board; Joseph Hamill, Exec. Editorial Board; Elizabeth Bradshaw, Editorial Advisory Board; Glenn Fleisig, Editorial Advisory Board. **ISSN:** 1476-3141. **Subscription Rates:** 287 institutions print + online; 272 institutions online; 66 individuals; US$516 institutions print + online; US$491 institutions print + online; US$112 individuals; EUR413 institutions print + online; EUR392 institutions online; EUR89 individuals. **Remarks:** Accepts advertising. **URL:** http://www.tandf.co.uk/journals/titles/14763141.asp. **Circ:** (Not Reported)

52065 ■ Strategic Survey
Routledge
Taylor & Francis Group Ltd.
2 Park Sq.
Milton Pk.
Abingdon OX14 4RN, United Kingdom
Ph: 44 20 70176000
Fax: 44 20 70176699
Publisher E-mail: webmaster.books@tandf.co.uk
Journal publishing a one-volume analytical encapsulation of the year's key events in international relations for government policy-makers, journalists, business leaders and other leading think-tanks. **Freq:** Annual. **Key Personnel:** Dr. John Chipman, Director; Alex Nicoll, Editor; Jeffrey Mazo, Asst. Ed. **ISSN:** 0459-7230. **Subscription Rates:** US$204 institutions print + online; US$193 institutions online; US$86 individuals; 116 institutions print + online; 110 institutions online; 51 individuals; EUR170 institutions print and online; EUR162 institutions online only; EUR69 individuals. **Remarks:** Accepts advertising. **URL:** http://www.tandf.co.uk/journals/titles/04597230.asp. **Circ:** (Not Reported)

52066 ■ Studies in Conflict and Terrorism
Routledge
Taylor & Francis Group Ltd.
2 Park Sq.
Milton Pk.
Abingdon OX14 4RN, United Kingdom
Ph: 44 20 70176000
Fax: 44 20 70176699
Publisher E-mail: webmaster.books@tandf.co.uk
Peer-reviewed journal covering sociology and social work. **Freq:** 12/yr. **Key Personnel:** Dr. Bruce Hoffman, Editor-in-Chief; Ami Pedahzur, Assoc. Ed.; Michael L.R. Smith, Assoc. Ed.; George K. Tanham, Founding Ed.; Peter Bergen, Editorial Board Member; Rogelio Alonso, Editorial Board Member; Peter Chalk, Assoc. Ed,; Seth Jones, Editorial Board Member; David W. Brannan, Editorial Board Member; Gavin Cameron, Contributing Ed. **ISSN:** 1057-610X. **Subscription Rates:** 778 institutions print + online; US$1,291 institutions print + online; 739 institutions online; US$1,226 institutions online; 277 individuals personal; US$460 individuals personal. **Remarks:** Accepts advertising on request. **URL:** http://www.tandf.co.uk/journals/titles/1057610x.asp. **Circ:** (Not Reported)

52067 ■ Studying Teacher Education
Routledge
Taylor & Francis Group Ltd.
2 Park Sq.
Milton Pk.
Abingdon OX14 4RN, United Kingdom
Ph: 44 20 70176000
Fax: 44 20 70176699
Publisher E-mail: webmaster.books@tandf.co.uk
Peer-reviewed journal covering the research and dialogue in the study of teaching and teacher education practices. **Subtitle:** A Journal of Self-study of Teacher Education Practices. **Freq:** 3/yr. **Key Personnel:** Prof. Tom Russell, Editor, ste@post.queensu.ca; Prof. John Loughran, Editor; Ruth Kane, Editorial Board; Fred Korthagen, Editorial Board; Morwenna Griffiths, Editorial Board; Maria Ines Marcondes, Editorial Board. **ISSN:** 1742-5964. **Subscription Rates:** US$294 institutions print + online; US$279 institutions online; US$125 individuals print only; 192 institutions print + online; 183 institutions online; 81 individuals print only; EUR234 institutions print and online; EUR222 institutions online only; EUR99 individuals. **Remarks:** Accepts advertising. **URL:** http://www.tandf.co.uk/journals/titles/17425964.asp. **Circ:** (Not Reported)

52068 ■ Synthesis and Reactivity in Inorganic, Metal-Organic, and Nano-Metal Chemistry
Taylor & Francis Ltd.
2 & 4 Park Sq.
Milton Pk.
Abingdon OX14 4RN, United Kingdom
Ph: 44 20 70176000
Fax: 44 20 70176336
Peer-reviewed journal devoted to the rapid dissemination of original research papers of relevance to inorganic and metal-organic chemists and nano scientists engaged in synthesis, publishing syntheses and reactivity of new compounds, new methods for preparation of known compounds, and new experimental techniques and procedures. **Freq:** 10/yr. **Key Personnel:** Dr. Kattesh V. Katti, Exec. Ed., kattik@health.missouri.edu; J.J. Vittal, Assoc. Ed.; S. Liu, International Editorial Advisory Board; M. Yamashita, Assoc. Ed.; S. Gao, International Editorial Advisory Board; P.K. Das, Assoc. Ed.; R. Alberto, International Editorial Advisory Board; W. Linert, Assoc. Ed.; Maria-Isabelle Baraton, International Editorial Advisory Board. **ISSN:** 1553-3174. **Subscription Rates:** 1,803 institutions print + online; US$2,989 institutions print + online; 1,713 institutions online; US$2,840 institutions online; 406 individuals print only; US$673 individuals print only; EUR2,381 institutions print + online; EUR2,261 institutions online; EUR535 individuals. **Remarks:** Accepts advertising. **URL:** http://www.tandf.co.uk/journals/titles/15533174.asp. **Circ:** (Not Reported)

52069 ■ Teacher Development
Routledge
Taylor & Francis Group Ltd.
2 Park Sq.
Milton Pk.
Abingdon OX14 4RN, United Kingdom
Ph: 44 20 70176000
Fax: 44 20 70176699
Publisher E-mail: webmaster.books@tandf.co.uk
Peer-reviewed journal covering articles on all aspects of teachers' professional development. **Subtitle:** An International Journal of Teachers' Professional Development. **Freq:** 4/yr. **Key Personnel:** Anne Campbell, Editorial Board; Michelle Selinger, Editorial Board; Chris Husbands, Advisory Board; Norbert Pachler, Editorial Board; Michael Golby, Editorial Board; Jackie Manuel, Editorial Board; Carol Mullen, Editorial Board; Sue Brindley, Editor; Christopher Day, Advisory Board. **ISSN:** 1366-4530. **Subscription Rates:** 424 institutions print + online; 404 institutions online; 67 individuals; US$679 institutions print + online; US$645 institutions online; US$108 individuals; EUR541 institutions print and online; EUR514 institutions online only; EUR86 individuals. **URL:** http://www.tandf.co.uk/journals/titles/13664530.asp.

52070 ■ Teachers and Teaching
Routledge
Taylor & Francis Group Ltd.
2 Park Sq.
Milton Pk.
Abingdon OX14 4RN, United Kingdom
Ph: 44 20 70176000
Fax: 44 20 70176699
Publisher E-mail: webmaster.books@tandf.co.uk
Peer-reviewed journal dealing with research on teachers and teaching, in connection with International Study Association on Teachers and Teaching (ISATT). **Subtitle:** Theory and Practice. **Freq:** Bimonthly. **Key Personnel:** Douwe Beijaard, Exec. Ed.; John Loughran, Exec. Ed.; Prof. Christopher M. Clark, Assoc. Ed.; Prof. Christopher Day, Editor; Geert Kelchtermans, Exec. Ed.; Theo Bergen, Assoc. Ed. **ISSN:** 1354-0602. **Subscription Rates:** 667 institutions print + online; US$1,107 institutions print + online; 633 institutions online; US$1,053 institutions online; 200 individuals; US$332 individuals; EUR882 institutions print and online; EUR837 institutions online only; EUR264 individuals. **Remarks:** Advertising accepted; rates available upon request. **URL:** http://www.tandf.co.uk/journals/titles/13540602.asp. **Circ:** (Not Reported)

52071 ■ Teaching in Higher Education
Routledge
Taylor & Francis Group Ltd.
2 Park Sq.
Milton Pk.
Abingdon OX14 4RN, United Kingdom
Ph: 44 20 70176000
Fax: 44 20 70176699
Publisher E-mail: webmaster.books@tandf.co.uk
Peer-reviewed journal dealing with teaching, learning and the curriculum in higher education. **Freq:** Bimonthly. **Key Personnel:** Jan Parker, Exec. Ed.; Alan Skelton, Exec. Ed.; Stephen Rowland, Exec. Ed.; Cheryl Hunt, Exec. Ed.; Robert Cannon, Editorial Board; Louise Archer, Editorial Board. **ISSN:** 1356-2517. **Subscription Rates:** US$258 individuals print only; US$1,081 institutions online only; US$1,137 institutions print & online; 683 institutions print & online; 649 institutions online only; 156 individuals; EUR907 institutions print and online; EUR861 institutions online only; EUR205 individuals. **Remarks:** Advertising accepted; rates available upon request. **URL:** http://www.tandf.co.uk/journals/titles/13562517.asp. **Circ:** (Not Reported)

52072 ■ Technical Education & Training Abstracts
Routledge
Taylor & Francis Group Ltd.
2 Park Sq.
Milton Pk.
Abingdon OX14 4RN, United Kingdom
Ph: 44 20 70176000
Fax: 44 20 70176699
Publisher E-mail: webmaster.books@tandf.co.uk
Journal providing information needs of those engaged in technical or vocational education. **Freq:** Annual. **Key Personnel:** Dr. Stuart Trickey, Editor. **ISSN:** 1943-0272. **Subscription Rates:** 860 institutions print + online; US$1,507 institutions print + online; 817 institutions online; US$1,431 institutions online; 273 individuals;

US$463 individuals; EUR1,201 institutions print and on-line; EUR1,141 institutions online only; EUR368 individuals. **Remarks:** Advertising accepted; rates available upon request. **URL:** http://www.tandf.co.uk/journals/titles/0966162x.asp. **Circ:** (Not Reported)

52073 ■ Technology Analysis & Strategic Management
Routledge
Taylor & Francis Group Ltd.
2 Park Sq.
Milton Pk.
Abingdon OX14 4RN, United Kingdom
Ph: 44 20 70176000
Fax: 44 20 70176699
Publisher E-mail: webmaster.books@tandf.co.uk
Peer-reviewed journal covering business management. **Freq:** 8/yr. **Key Personnel:** Harry Rothman, Editor-in-Chief, rothman@biogenic.demon.co.uk; Sean Rothman, Managing Editor, sirothman@btinternet.com; Keith Dickson, International Editorial Board. **ISSN:** 0953-7325. **Subscription Rates:** US$2,337 institutions print and online; US$2,220 institutions online; US$135 individuals; 1,302 institutions print and online; EUR1,869 institutions print and online; 1,237 institutions online only; EUR1,776 institutions online only; 67 individuals; EUR108 individuals. **URL:** http://www.tandf.co.uk/journals/titles/09537325.asp.

52074 ■ Technology, Pedagogy and Education
Routledge
Taylor & Francis Group Ltd.
2 Park Sq.
Milton Pk.
Abingdon OX14 4RN, United Kingdom
Ph: 44 20 70176000
Fax: 44 20 70176699
Publisher E-mail: webmaster.books@tandf.co.uk
Peer-reviewed journal covering the international education community. **Freq:** 3/yr. **Key Personnel:** Tony Fisher, Editorial Board; Pedro Hepp, Editorial Board; Sue Brindley, Editorial Board; Avril Loveless, Editorial Board; Ian Gibson, Editorial Board; David Benzie, Editorial Board; Patrick Dillon, Editorial Board; Chris Higgins, Editorial Board; Niki Davis, Editorial Board; Solveig Jakobsdottir, Editorial Board; Richard Millwood, Editorial Board; Paul Resta, Editorial Board. **ISSN:** 1475-939X. **Subscription Rates:** 324 institutions print + online; US$516 institutions print + online; 307 institutions online; US$491 institutions online; 52 individuals; US$82 individuals; EUR412 institutions print and online; EUR391 institutions online only; EUR65 individuals. **URL:** http://www.tandf.co.uk/journals/titles/1475939X.asp.

52075 ■ Terrorism and Political Violence
Routledge
Taylor & Francis Group Ltd.
2 Park Sq.
Milton Pk.
Abingdon OX14 4RN, United Kingdom
Ph: 44 20 70176000
Fax: 44 20 70176699
Publisher E-mail: webmaster.books@tandf.co.uk
Peer-reviewed journal covering all aspects of political violence and organized crime, protest, rebellion, revolution, and human rights. **Freq:** Quarterly. **Key Personnel:** David C. Rapoport, Editor, phone 310825-4811, fax 310206-3555, rapoport@polisci.ucla.edu; Paul Wilkinson, Editorial Board; Max Taylor, Editor; Jeff Kaplan, Reviews Ed.; Kenneth Anderson, Editorial Board; Bruce Hoffman, Editorial Board. **ISSN:** 0954-6553. **Subscription Rates:** 432 institutions print + online; US$709 institutions print + online; 410 institutions online; US$674 institutions online; 85 individuals; US$125 individuals; EUR564 institutions print and online; EUR536 institutions online only; EUR99 individuals. **Remarks:** Advertising accepted; rates available upon request. **URL:** http://www.tandf.co.uk/journals/titles/09546553.asp. **Circ:** (Not Reported)

52076 ■ Textual Practice
Routledge
Taylor & Francis Group Ltd.
2 Park Sq.
Milton Pk.
Abingdon OX14 4RN, United Kingdom
Ph: 44 20 70176000
Fax: 44 20 70176699
Publisher E-mail: webmaster.books@tandf.co.uk
Peer-reviewed journal covering radical literary studies. **Founded:** 1987. **Freq:** Bimonthly. **Key Personnel:**

Peter Nicholls, Assoc. Ed.; Isobel Armstrong, Editorial Board; Peter Brooker, Editorial Board; Peter Boxall, Editor; Terry Castle, Editorial Board; Peter Nicholls, US Assoc. Ed. **ISSN:** 0950-236X. **Subscription Rates:** US$174 individuals print only; US$857 institutions online only; US$903 institutions print & online; 542 institutions print & online; 515 institutions online only; 101 individuals print only; EUR722 institutions print and online; EUR686 institutions online only; EUR140 individuals. **Remarks:** Advertising accepted; rates available upon request. **URL:** http://www.tandf.co.uk/journals/routledge/0950236x.html. **Circ:** (Not Reported)

52077 ■ Theology and Science
Routledge
Taylor & Francis Group Ltd.
2 Park Sq.
Milton Pk.
Abingdon OX14 4RN, United Kingdom
Ph: 44 20 70176000
Fax: 44 20 70176699
Publisher E-mail: webmaster.books@tandf.co.uk
Peer-reviewed journal publishing articles related to natural sciences and theology, dealing with research in philosophical and systematic theology, and scientific methodologies. **Subtitle:** The Journal of The Center for Theology and the Natural Sciences (CTNS). **Freq:** Quarterly. **Key Personnel:** Robert John Russell, Editor, rrussell@ctns.org; Ted Peters, Editor, tpeters2ct@aol.com; Joshua Moritz, Managing Editor, jmoritz@ctns.org. **ISSN:** 1474-6700. **Subscription Rates:** 367 institutions print + online; US$614 institutions print + online; 349 institutions online; US$583 institutions online; 51 individuals; US$85 individuals; EUR490 institutions print and online; EUR466 institutions online only; EUR68 individuals. **URL:** http://www.tandf.co.uk/journals/titles/14746700.htm.

52078 ■ Third World Quarterly
Routledge
Taylor & Francis Group Ltd.
2 Park Sq.
Milton Pk.
Abingdon OX14 4RN, United Kingdom
Ph: 44 20 70176000
Fax: 44 20 70176699
Publisher E-mail: webmaster.books@tandf.co.uk
Peer-reviewed journal focusing on international relations. **Freq:** 8/yr. **Key Personnel:** Reginald H. Green, International Editorial Board; Shahid Qadir, Editor, fax 44 20 89471243, editor@thirdworldquarterly.com; Mark T. Berger, International Editorial Board; Walden Bello, International Editorial Board; Nasser H. Aruri, International Editorial Board; Haleh Afshar, International Editorial Board; Noam Chomsky, International Editorial Board; Christopher Clapham, International Editorial Board; Robert Potter, International Editorial Board. **ISSN:** 0143-6597. **Subscription Rates:** 945 institutions print + online; US$1,556 institutions print + online; 897 institutions online; US$1,478 institutions online; 204 individuals; US$341 individuals. **URL:** http://www.tandf.co.uk/journals/boards/c-boards/twq-edb.html.

52079 ■ Total Quality Management & Business Excellence
Routledge
Taylor & Francis Group Ltd.
2 Park Sq.
Milton Pk.
Abingdon OX14 4RN, United Kingdom
Ph: 44 20 70176000
Fax: 44 20 70176699
Publisher E-mail: webmaster.books@tandf.co.uk
Peer-reviewed journal general business publication. **Freq:** Monthly. **Key Personnel:** Prof. Gopal K. Kanji, Founding Ed.; Kai Kristensen, Book Review Ed. **ISSN:** 1478-3363. **Subscription Rates:** 2,072 institutions print + online; US$2,181 institutions print + online; US$2,072 individuals print; US$712 individuals. **URL:** http://www.tandf.co.uk/journals/titles/14783363.asp. **Formerly:** Total Quality Management.

52080 ■ Totalitarian Movements and Political Religions
Routledge
Taylor & Francis Group Ltd.
2 Park Sq.
Milton Pk.
Abingdon OX14 4RN, United Kingdom
Ph: 44 20 70176000

Fax: 44 20 70176699
Publisher E-mail: webmaster.books@tandf.co.uk
Peer-reviewed journal providing a platform for exchange of views on politics and faith of salvation, with primary emphasis on authoritarian and totalitarian politics of the twentieth century. **Freq:** Quarterly. **Key Personnel:** Robert Mallet, Founding Ed.; Michael Burleigh, Founding Ed.; Naveed S. Sheikh, Editor; Erin Wilson, Review Ed.; Bassam Tibi, International Advisory Board. **ISSN:** 1469-0764. **Subscription Rates:** US$128 individuals print only; US$454 institutions online only; US$478 institutions print & online; 83 individuals; 278 institutions online only; 293 institutions print & online; EUR381 institutions print and online; EUR362 institutions online only; EUR102 individuals. **Remarks:** Advertising accepted; rates available upon request. **URL:** http://www.tandf.co.uk/journals/titles/14690764.asp. **Circ:** (Not Reported)

52081 ■ Tourism Geographies
Routledge
Taylor & Francis Group Ltd.
2 Park Sq.
Milton Pk.
Abingdon OX14 4RN, United Kingdom
Ph: 44 20 70176000
Fax: 44 20 70176699
Publisher E-mail: webmaster.books@tandf.co.uk
Peer-reviewed journal covering tourism and other related areas from a geographical perspective. **Subtitle:** An International Journal of Tourism Space, Place and Environment. **Freq:** Quarterly. **Key Personnel:** Alan A. Lew, Editor, alan.lew@nau.edu; Richard Butler, Resource Ed.; Michael C. Hall, Assoc. Ed.; Shaul Krakover, Assoc. Ed.; Allan M. Williams, Assoc. Ed.; Erlet Cater, Resource Ed.; Carolyn L. Cartier, Resource Ed.; Dimitri Ioannides, Resource Ed.; Alison Gill, Resource Ed. **ISSN:** 1461-6688. **Subscription Rates:** US$132 individuals; US$555 individuals online only; US$584 individuals print & online; 80 individuals; 331 institutions online only; 349 institutions print & online; EUR465 institutions print and online; EUR442 institutions online only; EUR106 individuals. **Remarks:** Advertising accepted; rates available upon request. **URL:** http://www.tandf.co.uk/journals/titles/14616688.asp. **Circ:** (Not Reported)

52082 ■ Tourism and Hospitality Planning & Development
Routledge
Taylor & Francis Group Ltd.
2 Park Sq.
Milton Pk.
Abingdon OX14 4RN, United Kingdom
Ph: 44 20 70176000
Fax: 44 20 70176699
Publisher E-mail: webmaster.books@tandf.co.uk
Journal for researchers and practitioners concerned with planning and development in tourism and hospitality industry. **Freq:** Quarterly. **Key Personnel:** Les Lumsdon, Co-Ed.; Peter Burns, Co-Ed.; Maria Alvarez, Editorial Board. **ISSN:** 1479-053X. **Subscription Rates:** 67 individuals; 281 institutions print + online; 267 institutions online only; US$467 institutions print + online; US$444 institutions online; US$111 individuals; EUR372 institutions print + online; EUR353 institutions online only; EUR88 individuals. **Remarks:** Advertising accepted; rates available upon request. **URL:** http://www.tandf.co.uk/journals/titles/1470053x.asp. **Circ:** (Not Reported)

52083 ■ Toxic Substance Mechanisms
Taylor & Francis Ltd.
2 & 4 Park Sq.
Milton Pk.
Abingdon OX14 4RN, United Kingdom
Ph: 44 20 70176000
Fax: 44 20 70176336
Publication for the chemical, plastics, and rubber industries. **Freq:** Quarterly. **Key Personnel:** Rakesh Dixit, Editor-in-Chief, rarakeshdixit2@gmail.com; Daniel Acosta, Editorial Board; Kulbir Bakshi, Editorial Board. **ISSN:** 1076-9188. **URL:** http://www.informaworld.com/smpp/title~content=t713394085~db=all; http://www.informaworld.com/smpp/title~content=t713394085.

52084 ■ Twenty-first Century Society
Routledge
Taylor & Francis Group Ltd.
2 Park Sq.
Milton Pk.
Abingdon OX14 4RN, United Kingdom
Ph: 44 20 70176000
Fax: 44 20 70176699

Circulation: ★ = ABC; △ = BPA; ♦ = CAC; • = CCAB; ❑ = VAC; ⊕ = PO Statement; ‡ = Publisher's Report; Boldface figures = sworn; Light figures = estimated.

Gale Directory of Publications & Broadcast Media/147th Ed.

5561

Publisher E-mail: webmaster.books@tandf.co.uk
Peer-reviewed journal focusing on interdisciplinary and multidisciplinary research across the social sciences. **Subtitle:** Journal of the Academy of Social Sciences. **Freq:** 3/yr. **Key Personnel:** Prof. David Canter, Editor; Prof. David Philips, Editorial Board; Jo Campling, Founding Consultant Ed.; Prof. Miriam David, Founding Ed.; Prof. Simin Davoudi, Editorial Board; Prof. Stephen Lea, Editorial Board; Prof. Robert Wright, Editorial Board; John Goddard, Editorial Board; Prof. John Holmwood, Editorial Board. **ISSN:** 1745-0144. **Subscription Rates:** 243 institutions print + online; US$406 institutions print + online; 231 institutions online; US$385 institutions online; 58 individuals; US$97 individuals; EUR323 institutions print and online; EUR306 institutions online only; EUR77 individuals. **URL:** http://www.tandf.co.uk/journals/titles/17450144.asp.

52085 ■ Virtual and Physical Prototyping
Taylor & Francis Ltd.
2 & 4 Park Sq.
Milton Pk.
Abingdon OX14 4RN, United Kingdom
Ph: 44 20 70176000
Fax: 44 20 70176336
Peer-reviewed journal providing an international forum for professionals and academics to exchange novel ideas and disseminate knowledge covering the full range of activities related to virtual and rapid prototyping, focusing on areas including, but not limited to: CAD and 3D data acquisition technologies: fast geometrical modeling schemes, 3D digitising, X-ray tomography, photogrammetry, image-based modeling systems, virtual environments: virtual engineering and manufacturing, virtual enterprise engineering, Internet-based product development, rapid prototyping simulation and optimisation, new methods for virtual prototyping. **Freq:** Quarterly. **Key Personnel:** Paulo Jorge Da Silva Bartolo, Editor-in-Chief, phone 351 244 820310, pbartolo@estg.ipleiria.pt; Chee Kai Chua, Editor-in-Chief, mckchua@ntu.edu.sg; Alain Bernard, Assoc. Ed. **ISSN:** 1745-2759. **Subscription Rates:** 454 institutions print + online; US$748 institutions print + online; 432 institutions online; US$711 institutions online; 98 individuals print only; US$150 individuals print only; 39 members society; US$69 members society. **Remarks:** Accepts advertising. **URL:** http://www.tandf.co.uk/journals/17452759.asp. **Circ:** (Not Reported)

52086 ■ Visual Culture in Britain
Routledge
Taylor & Francis Group Ltd.
2 Park Sq.
Milton Pk.
Abingdon OX14 4RN, United Kingdom
Ph: 44 20 70176000
Fax: 44 20 70176699
Publisher E-mail: webmaster.books@tandf.co.uk
Journal encouraging original material and introducing innovative work with the aim of placing visual culture — painting and sculpture, architecture and design, print, film, photography and the performing arts — in relation to the wider culture historically and geographically from the 18th century to the present. **Freq:** 3/yr. **Key Personnel:** Ysanne Holt, Editor; Elizabeth Kramer, Reviews Ed. **ISSN:** 1471-4787. **Subscription Rates:** 119 institutions print + online; US$113 institutions print + online; EUR190 institutions print + online; 41 individuals; US$83 individuals; EUR66 individuals; 113 institutions online; US$226 institutions online; EUR180 institutions online. **URL:** http://www.tandf.co.uk/journals/RVCB.

52087 ■ Vulnerable Children and Youth Studies
Routledge
Taylor & Francis Group Ltd.
2 Park Sq.
Milton Pk.
Abingdon OX14 4RN, United Kingdom
Ph: 44 20 70176000
Fax: 44 20 70176699
Publisher E-mail: webmaster.books@tandf.co.uk
Peer-reviewed journal focusing on psychological, sociological, health, cultural, economic, and educational aspects of children and adolescents in developed and developing countries. **Subtitle:** An International Interdisciplinary Journal for Research, Policy and Care. **Freq:** 4/yr. **Key Personnel:** Simon Davidson, International Editorial Board; Stefan Germann, Book Review Ed., stefan_germann@wvi.org; Leslie Snider, International Editorial Board; Rachel Baggaley, International Editorial

Board; Jacqueline Barnes, International Editorial Board; Geoff Foster, Exec. Ed.; Mary Jane Rotherham-Borus, Editorial Committee; Laurie Bauman, International Editorial Board; Hoosen Coovadia, International Editorial Board; Linda Richter, Editorial Committee; Sheila Eyberg, International Editorial Board; Ian Manion, International Editorial Board. **ISSN:** 1745-0128. **Subscription Rates:** US$90 elsewhere; 205 institutions print + online; US$371 institutions print + online; 195 institutions online; US$352 institutions online; 51 individuals; US$90 individuals; EUR296 institutions print and online; EUR282 institutions online only; EUR72 individuals. **URL:** http://www.tandf.co.uk/journals/titles/17450128.asp.

52088 ■ Wasafiri
Routledge
Taylor & Francis Group Ltd.
2 Park Sq.
Milton Pk.
Abingdon OX14 4RN, United Kingdom
Ph: 44 20 70176000
Fax: 44 20 70176699
Publisher E-mail: webmaster.books@tandf.co.uk
Journal focusing on new landscapes in contemporary international literature today. **Freq:** 4/yr. **Key Personnel:** Sharmilla Beezmohun, Deputy Ed.; Richard Dyer, Editorial Board; Sukhdev Sandhu, Advisory Board; Bernardine Evaristo, Reviews Ed.; Teresa Palmiero, Managing Editor; Aamer Hussein, Assoc. Ed.; Robert Fraser, Advisory Ed.; Lyn Innes, Assoc. Ed.; Susheila Nasta, Editor; Nisha Jones, Asst. Ed.; Minoli Salgado, Assoc. Ed. **ISSN:** 0269-0055. **Subscription Rates:** 206 institutions print + online; US$363 institutions print + online; 196 institutions online; US$345 institutions online; 42 individuals; US$75 individuals; EUR289 institutions print and online; EUR275 institutions online only; EUR59 individuals. **URL:** http://www.tandf.co.uk/journals/titles/02690055.asp.

52089 ■ Waves in Random and Complex Media
Taylor & Francis Ltd.
2 & 4 Park Sq.
Milton Pk.
Abingdon OX14 4RN, United Kingdom
Ph: 44 20 70176000
Fax: 44 20 70176336
Peer-reviewed and interdisciplinary journal reporting theoretical, applied and experimental research related to any wave phenomena, including studies of waves in random and/or complex media, such as tissue or metamaterials, nonlinear, chaotic or fractal media, as well as relevant inverse problems. **Freq:** 4/yr. **Key Personnel:** Prof. Michael A. Fiddy, Editor-in-Chief, mafiddy@uncc.edu; M. Saillard, Assoc. Ed., marc.saillard@lseet.univ-tln.fr; J.A. Desanto, Editorial Board; S. Broschat, Editorial Board; K.I. Hopcraft, Book Review Ed., keith.hopcraft@nottingham.ac.uk; W.C. Chew, Editorial Board; N.V. Movchan, Editorial Board; A. Ishimaru, Founding Ed. **ISSN:** 1745-5030. **Subscription Rates:** US$194 individuals print only; US$759 institutions online; US$799 institutions print + online; 117 individuals print only; 457 institutions online; 481 institutions print + online. **Remarks:** Accepts advertising. **URL:** http://www.tandf.co.uk/journals/titles/17455030.asp. **Circ:** (Not Reported)

52090 ■ West European Politics
Routledge
Taylor & Francis Group Ltd.
2 Park Sq.
Milton Pk.
Abingdon OX14 4RN, United Kingdom
Ph: 44 20 70176000
Fax: 44 20 70176699
Publisher E-mail: webmaster.books@tandf.co.uk
Political science publication. **Freq:** 5/yr. **Key Personnel:** Klaus Goetz, Editor; Peter Mair, Editor. **ISSN:** 0140-2382. **Subscription Rates:** US$955 institutions print + online; US$181 individuals; US$908 institutions online; 584 institutions print + online; 555 institutions online; 114 individuals; EUR762 institutions print + online; EUR723 institutions online; EUR144 individuals. **Remarks:** Advertising accepted; rates available upon request. **URL:** http://www.tandf.co.uk/journals/titles/01402382.asp. **Circ:** (Not Reported)

52091 ■ Women
Routledge
Taylor & Francis Group Ltd.
2 Park Sq.

Milton Pk.
Abingdon OX14 4RN, United Kingdom
Ph: 44 20 70176000
Fax: 44 20 70176699
Publisher E-mail: webmaster.books@tandf.co.uk
Publication focusing on women's issues and gender studies. **Subtitle:** A Cultural Review. **Freq:** 3/yr. **Key Personnel:** Laura Marcus, Editor; Helen Carr, Editor; Isobel Armstrong, Editor; Parveen Adams, Editorial Board; Lisa Tickner, Editorial Board; Alison Mark, Editor. **ISSN:** 0957-4042. **Subscription Rates:** 254 institutions print + online; 241 institutions online; 60 individuals; US$419 institutions print + online; US$398 institutions online; US$105 individuals. **Remarks:** Accepts advertising on request. **URL:** http://www.tandf.co.uk/journals/titles/09574042.asp; http://www.informaworld.com/smpp/title~db=all~content=t713689960. **Circ:** (Not Reported)

52092 ■ Women & Performance
Routledge
Taylor & Francis Group Ltd.
2 Park Sq.
Milton Pk.
Abingdon OX14 4RN, United Kingdom
Ph: 44 20 70176000
Fax: 44 20 70176699
Publisher E-mail: webmaster.books@tandf.co.uk
Peer-reviewed journal covering scholarly essays on performance, dance, film, new media and feminist perspectives. **Subtitle:** A Journal of Feminist Theory. **Founded:** 1983. **Freq:** 3/yr. **Key Personnel:** Kandice Chuh, Advisory Board; Pam Cobrin, Editorial Board; Robert Diaz, Contributing Ed.; Danielle Goldman, Editorial Board; Sianne Ngai, Advisory Board; Jeanne Vaccaro, Editorial Board; Joshua Chambers-Letson, Contributing Ed.; Alicia Arrizon, Advisory Board; Debra Levine, Editorial Board; Barbara Browning, Editorial Board; Jennifer Brody, Advisory Board; Rey Chow, Advisory Board. **ISSN:** 0740-770X. **Subscription Rates:** 107 institutions print + online; 101 institutions online; 23 individuals; US$194 institutions print + online; US$184 institutions online; US$43 individuals; EUR154 institutions print and online; EUR147 institutions online only; EUR34 individuals. **URL:** http://www.tandf.co.uk/journals/titles/0740770X.asp.

52093 ■ Women's Writing
Routledge
Taylor & Francis Group Ltd.
2 Park Sq.
Milton Pk.
Abingdon OX14 4RN, United Kingdom
Ph: 44 20 70176000
Fax: 44 20 70176699
Publisher E-mail: webmaster.books@tandf.co.uk
Journal focusing on women's writing up to the nineteenth century. **Freq:** 3/yr. **Key Personnel:** Germaine Greer, Advisory Board; Marie Mulvey-Roberts, Editor, marie.mulvey-roberts@uwe.ac.uk; Margaret J.M. Ezell, Advisory Board; Marilyn Butler, Advisory Board; Nancy Armstrong, Advisory Board; Lisa Vargo, Assoc. Ed.; Caroline Franklin, Assoc. Ed.; Jennie Batchelor, Reviews Ed. **ISSN:** 0969-9082. **Subscription Rates:** 324 institutions print + online; 307 institutions online; 52 individuals; US$516 institutions print + online; US$491 institutions online; US$82 individuals; EUR412 institutions print and online; EUR391 institutions online only; EUR65 individuals. **URL:** http://www.tandf.co.uk/journals/titles/09699082.asp.

52094 ■ World Archaeology
Routledge
Taylor & Francis Group Ltd.
2 Park Sq.
Milton Pk.
Abingdon OX14 4RN, United Kingdom
Ph: 44 20 70176000
Fax: 44 20 70176699
Publisher E-mail: webmaster.books@tandf.co.uk
Peer-reviewed journal covering anthropology, archeology, and folklore. **Freq:** Quarterly. **Key Personnel:** Prof. Chris Gosden, Advisory Board; Prof. N. David, Advisory Board; Nyree Finlay, Editorial Board; Michael Shott, Editorial Board; Alan K. Outram, Editorial Board; Prof. Richard Bradley, Advisory Board; Mark Lake, Editorial Board; Elizabeth DeMarrais, Editorial Board; Gabriel Cooney, Editorial Board; Robin Osborne, Exec. Ed., ro225@cam.ac.uk. **ISSN:** 0043-8243. **Subscription Rates:** 357 institutions print + online; US$590 institutions print + online; 339 institutions online; US$651

institutions online; 81 individuals; US$132 individuals print only. **Remarks:** Accepts advertising on request. **Online:** Gale. **URL:** http://www.tandf.co.uk/journals/titles/00438243.asp; http://www.informaworld.com/smpp/title~db=all~content=t713699333. **Circ:** (Not Reported)

Alcester

52095 ■ Rotary Magazine (GB & I)
Rotary International in Great Britain and Ireland
Kinwarton Rd.
Alcester B49 6PB, United Kingdom
Ph: 44 1789 765411
Fax: 44 1789 764916
Publisher E-mail: secretary@ribi.org
Membership magazine of Rotary International covering current news about Rotary-related subjects for Great Britain and Ireland. **Founded:** 1915. **Key Personnel:** John Pike, Editor, phone 44 1922 627227, john@russenpikemedia.co.uk. **URL:** http://www.rotary.org/en/MediaAndNews/MorePublications/RegionalMagazines/Pages/ridefault.aspx.

Alderney

52096 ■ Island-FM - 93.7
12 Westerbrook
St. Sampsons
Guernsey GY2 4QQ, United Kingdom
Ph: 44 14 81242000
Fax: 44 14 81241120
E-mail: studio@islandfm.com
Format: News. **Operating Hours:** Continuous. **Ad Rates:** Advertising accepted; rates available upon request. **URL:** http://www.islandfm.com.

Aldershot

52097 ■ The Business
National Caravan Council
Catherine House
Victoria Rd.
Aldershot GU11 1SS, United Kingdom
Ph: 44 12 52318251
Fax: 44 12 52322596
Publisher E-mail: info@nationalcaravan.co.uk
Publication covering recreational vehicles. **Founded:** 2002. **Freq:** Quarterly. **Key Personnel:** Louise Wood, Dir. of Communications. **Subscription Rates:** Free to members. **Remarks:** Advertising accepted; rates available upon request. **URL:** http://www.nationalcaravan.co.uk/home/index.asp?rid=70. **Formerly:** Caravan Business. **Circ:** (Not Reported)

52098 ■ Soldier Magazine
Ministry of Defence
Ordnance Rd.
Aldershot GU11 2DU, United Kingdom
Fax: 44 1252 347358
Journal of The British Army. **Founded:** May 1945. **Freq:** Monthly. **Trim Size:** 210 x 297 mm. **Cols./Page:** 4. **Col. Width:** 45 millimeters. **Col. Depth:** 297 millimeters. **Key Personnel:** Stephen Tyler, Editor, phone 44 1252 347356, styler@soldiermagazine.co.uk; Andrew Simms, Managing Editor, phone 44 1252 347355, asimms@soldiermagazine.co.uk; Joe Clapson, Asst. Ed., phone 44 1252 347154, jclapson@soldiermagazine.co.uk; Sharon Kean, Asst. Ed., phone 44 1252 340753, skean@soldiermagazine.co.uk. **Subscription Rates:** 23 individuals; 47 other countries. **Remarks:** Accepts advertising. **URL:** http://www.soldiermagazine.co.uk/. **Ad Rates:** BW: 995, 4C: 1,260, PCI: 12.75. **Circ:** Combined 88,000

Alfreton

52099 ■ Slimming World Magazine
Slimming World
PO Box 55
Alfreton DE55 4UE, United Kingdom
Ph: 44 844 8920400
Fax: 44 844 8920401
Consumer magazine covering dieting, healthy eating and lifestyle. **Founded:** Jan. 1998. **Freq:** 7/yr. **Print Method:** Web. **Trim Size:** 215 x 290 mm. **ISSN:** 1464-7826. **Subscription Rates:** 15 individuals. **Remarks:** Accepts advertising. **URL:** http://www.slimmingworld.com/magazine/magazine_home.asp. **Former name:**

SW-The Magazine. **Circ:** Controlled 248,862

52100 ■ Vintage Austin Magazine
Vintage Austin Register Ltd.
The Briars
Wingfield Rd.
Oakerthorpe
Alfreton DE55 7LH, United Kingdom
Ph: 44 173 3831646
Trade publication covering automotive. **Freq:** Quarterly. **Key Personnel:** Jim Stringer, Editor, phone 44 1795 880165. **Remarks:** Accepts advertising. **URL:** http://www.vintage-austin.co.uk/. **Circ:** (Not Reported)

Alnwick

52101 ■ Northumberland Gazette
Johnston Press PLC
32 Bondgate Without
Alnwick NE66 1PJ, United Kingdom
Ph: 44 1665 602234
Local community newspaper. **Freq:** Weekly (Thurs.). **Key Personnel:** Paul Larkin, Editor; Janet Hall, Asst. Ed. **Remarks:** Accepts advertising. **URL:** http://www.northumberlandgazette.co.uk/. **Circ:** (Not Reported)

52102 ■ Metro Radio-FM - 102.6
55 Degrees N
Pilgrim St.
Newcastle upon Tyne NE1 6BF, United Kingdom
Ph: 44 191 2306100
Fax: 44 191 2790288
E-mail: news@metroandmagic.com
Format: Contemporary Hit Radio (CHR). **URL:** http://www.metroradio.co.uk/.

Alston

52103 ■ In the Sticks
Market House
Market Pl.
Alston CA9 3HS, United Kingdom
Ph: 44 14 34382680
Consumer magazine covering property for sale in rural areas in the UK. **Subtitle:** Property, Architecture, Travel. **Founded:** 1989. **Freq:** Quarterly. **ISSN:** 1471-4280. **Subscription Rates:** 38 individuals. **Remarks:** Accepts advertising. **URL:** http://www.inthesticks.com. **Ad Rates:** 4C: 300. **Circ:** Combined 10,000

Altrincham

52104 ■ The Vegetarian
Vegetarian Society of the United Kingdom
Parkdale
Dunham Rd.
Altrincham WA14 4QG, United Kingdom
Ph: 44 161 9252000
Fax: 44 161 9269182
Publication E-mail: editor@vegsoc.org
Publisher E-mail: info@vegsoc.org
Publication covering vegetarianism. Membership magazine of the Vegetarian Society. **Freq:** Quarterly. **Key Personnel:** Jane Bowler, Editor. **Subscription Rates:** Included in membership. **Remarks:** Advertising accepted; rates available upon request. **URL:** http://www.vegsoc.org/vegmag/index.html. **Circ:** 15,000

Amersham

52105 ■ Aviation Modeller International
Model Activity Press Ltd.
5 Chiltern Business Ctr.
63-65 Woodside Rd.
Amersham HP6 6AA, United Kingdom
Ph: 44 1494 433453
Fax: 44 1494 433468
Magazine featuring aircraft modeling. **Freq:** Monthly. **Key Personnel:** Jackie Dunton, Contact, phone 44 1493 377267, jackie@modelactivitypress.com; Tony Dowdeswell, Publisher; Steve Dorling, Editor. **Subscription Rates:** 46 individuals; 59 individuals Europe; 63 other countries. **URL:** http://www.modelactivitypress.com/ami/.

52106 ■ Flying Scale Models
Model Activity Press Ltd.
5 Chiltern Business Ctr.
63-65 Woodside Rd.

Amersham HP6 6AA, United Kingdom
Ph: 44 1494 433453
Fax: 44 1494 433468
Magazine featuring flying scale model aircraft. **Freq:** Monthly. **Key Personnel:** Jackie Dunton, Contact, phone 44 1493 377267, jackie@modelactivitypress.com; Tony Dowdeswell, Publisher; Steve Dorling, Editor. **Subscription Rates:** 46 individuals; 60 individuals Europe; 64 other countries. **URL:** http://www.modelactivitypress.com/fsm/.

52107 ■ International Consultants' Guide
Prime Marketing Publications Ltd.
Cavendish House
Cavendish Ct.
44-47 Hill Ave.
Amersham HP6 5FA, United Kingdom
Ph: 44 870 9088767
Fax: 44 870 1340931
Publisher E-mail: info@pmp.co.uk
Professional magazine for information technology and business consultants in Europe. **Founded:** Nov. 1988. **Freq:** 6/yr. **Subscription Rates:** Free to qualified subscribers print and online. **Remarks:** Accepts advertising. **URL:** http://www.consultants-guide.com/; http://www.pmp.co.uk/content/publications/index.asp. **Circ:** Controlled 30,000

52108 ■ Military Machines International
Model Activity Press Ltd.
5 Chiltern Business Ctr.
63-65 Woodside Rd.
Amersham HP6 6AA, United Kingdom
Ph: 44 1494 433453
Fax: 44 1494 433468
Magazine for hobbyists of military service machines and vehicles. **Freq:** Monthly. **Key Personnel:** Jackie Dunton, Contact, phone 44 1493 377267, jackie@modelactivitypress.com; Tony Dowdeswell, Publisher; Steve Dorling, Editor. **Subscription Rates:** 44 individuals; 56 individuals Europe; 59 other countries. **URL:** http://www.modelactivitypress.com/mmi/.

52109 ■ Retreats
Retreat Association
Kerridge House
42 Woodside Close
Buckinghamshire
Amersham HP6 5EF, United Kingdom
Ph: 44 1494 433004
Fax: 44 871 7151917
Publisher E-mail: info@retreats.org.uk
Publication covering camping. **Freq:** Annual. **Key Personnel:** Paddy Lane, Exec. Off. **ISSN:** 1369-8702. **Subscription Rates:** 5.50 single issue; 8 individuals by post. **Remarks:** Advertising accepted; rates available upon request deadline for material 2nd Monday in September. **URL:** http://www.retreats.org.uk/retreatsjournal.html. **Circ:** 14,500

Andover

52110 ■ Andover Advertiser
Newsquest Media Group Ltd.
24-32 London St.
Andover SP10 2PE, United Kingdom
Ph: 44 1264 323456
Fax: 44 1264 338723
Publication E-mail: newsdesk@andoveradvertiser.co.uk
Newspaper featuring news and events in Andover. **Key Personnel:** Dick Bellringer, News Ed., phone 44 1264 321205, dick.bellringer@andoveradvertiser.co.uk; Sharon Dewey, Sales Mgr., sharon.dewey@andoveradvertiser.co.uk. **Remarks:** Accepts advertising. **URL:** http://www.andoveradvertiser.co.uk/. **Circ:** (Not Reported)

52111 ■ British Tax Review
Sweet & Maxwell Ltd.
PO Box 2000
North Way
Andover SP10 5BE, United Kingdom
Ph: 44 1264 332424
Fax: 44 207 3938074
Publisher E-mail: sweetandmaxwell.international@thomson.com
Law periodical. **Freq:** Bimonthly. **Key Personnel:** Judith Freedman, Editor, btr@work.ox.ac.uk; Ross Fraser, Editor; Gary Richards, Asst. Ed. **ISSN:** 0007-1870. **Sub-**

Circulation: ★ = ABC; △ = BPA; ◆ = CAC; ● = CCAB; ❑ = VAC; ⊕ = PO Statement; ‡ = Publisher's Report; Boldface figures = sworn; Light figures = estimated.

Gale Directory of Publications & Broadcast Media/147th Ed.   **5563**

scription Rates: 486 individuals. Remarks: Advertising not accepted. URL: http://www.sweetandmaxwell.co.uk/Catalogue/ProductDetails.aspx?recordid=338&productid=6614. Circ: (Not Reported)

52112 ■ Civil Justice Quarterly
Sweet & Maxwell Ltd.
PO Box 2000
North Way
Andover SP10 5BE, United Kingdom
Ph: 44 1264 332424
Fax: 44 207 3938074
Publisher E-mail: sweetandmaxwell.international@thomson.com
Law periodical. Freq: Quarterly. Key Personnel: Prof. Adrian Zuckerman, Gen. Ed.; John Sorabji, Asst. Ed.; Carla Crifo, Asst. Ed./Book Review Ed. ISSN: 0261-9261. Subscription Rates: 306 individuals. URL: http://www.sweetandmaxwell.co.uk/Catalogue/ProductDetails.aspx?recordid=447&productid=7028.

52113 ■ Construction Law Journal
Sweet & Maxwell Ltd.
PO Box 2000
North Way
Andover SP10 5BE, United Kingdom
Ph: 44 1264 332424
Fax: 44 207 3938074
Publisher E-mail: sweetandmaxwell.international@thomson.com
Law periodical. Freq: 8/yr. Key Personnel: Andrew Burr, Editor; Kim Franklin, Book Review Ed. ISSN: 0267-2359. Subscription Rates: 764 individuals. URL: http://www.sweetandmaxwell.co.uk/Catalogue/ProductDetails.aspx?recordid=438&productid=7003.

52114 ■ Conveyancer and Property Lawyer
Sweet & Maxwell Ltd.
PO Box 2000
North Way
Andover SP10 5BE, United Kingdom
Ph: 44 1264 332424
Fax: 44 207 3938074
Publisher E-mail: sweetandmaxwell.international@thomson.com
Law periodical. Freq: Bimonthly. Key Personnel: Dr. Martin Dixon, Gen. Ed. ISSN: 0010-8200. Subscription Rates: 301 individuals. Remarks: Advertising not accepted. URL: http://www.sweetandmaxwell.co.uk/Catalogue/ProductDetails.aspx?recordid=333&productid=6598. Circ: (Not Reported)

52115 ■ Criminal Law Review
Sweet & Maxwell Ltd.
PO Box 2000
North Way
Andover SP10 5BE, United Kingdom
Ph: 44 1264 332424
Fax: 44 207 3938074
Publisher E-mail: sweetandmaxwell.international@thomson.com
Law periodical. Freq: Monthly. Key Personnel: Prof. Ian Dennis, Editor; Prof. John Jackson, Book Review Ed.; Jon Hilton, House Ed. ISSN: 0011-135X. Subscription Rates: 346 individuals. Remarks: Advertising not accepted. URL: http://www.sweetandmaxwell.co.uk/Catalogue/ProductDetails.aspx?recordid=478&productid=7139. Circ: (Not Reported)

52116 ■ EIPR: European Intellectual Property Review
Sweet & Maxwell Ltd.
PO Box 2000
North Way
Andover SP10 5BE, United Kingdom
Ph: 44 1264 332424
Fax: 44 207 3938074
Publisher E-mail: sweetandmaxwell.international@thomson.com
Law periodical. Founded: 1978. Freq: Monthly. Key Personnel: Hugh Brett, Editor; Jo Slinn, Editor and Publisher; Rory Sullivan, News Ed. ISSN: 0142-0461. Subscription Rates: 1,026 individuals. Remarks: Advertising not accepted. URL: http://www.sweetandmaxwell.co.uk/Catalogue/ProductDetails.aspx?recordid=460&productid=7061. Circ: (Not Reported)

52117 ■ Intellectual Property Quarterly
Sweet & Maxwell Ltd.
PO Box 2000

North Way
Andover SP10 5BE, United Kingdom
Ph: 44 1264 332424
Fax: 44 207 3938074
Publisher E-mail: sweetandmaxwell.international@thomson.com
Law periodical. Freq: Quarterly. Key Personnel: Dr. Margaret Llewelyn, Editor, m.llewelyn@sheffield.ac.uk. ISSN: 1364-906X. Subscription Rates: 437 individuals. Remarks: Advertising not accepted. Online: Gale. URL: http://www.sweetandmaxwell.co.uk/Catalogue/ProductDetails.aspx?recordid=380&productid=6791. Circ: (Not Reported)

52118 ■ Journal of Business Law
Sweet & Maxwell Ltd.
PO Box 2000
North Way
Andover SP10 5BE, United Kingdom
Ph: 44 1264 332424
Fax: 44 207 3938074
Publisher E-mail: sweetandmaxwell.international@thomson.com
Law periodical. Freq: Bimonthly. Key Personnel: Prof. Robert Merkin, Gen. Ed.; Clive M. Schmitthoff, Founding Ed. ISSN: 0021-9460. Subscription Rates: 470 individuals UK. Remarks: Advertising not accepted. URL: http://www2.warwick.ac.uk/fac/soc/law/elj/directory/j/jbl/; http://www.sweetandmaxwell.co.uk/Catalogue/ProductDetails.aspx?recordid=476&productid=7128. Circ: (Not Reported)

52119 ■ Journal of Planning and Environment Law
Sweet & Maxwell Ltd.
PO Box 2000
North Way
Andover SP10 5BE, United Kingdom
Ph: 44 1264 332424
Fax: 44 207 3938074
Publisher E-mail: sweetandmaxwell.international@thomson.com
Law periodical. Freq: Monthly. Key Personnel: Prof. Michael Purdue, Editor; Martin Edwards, Editor; Richard Harwood, Editor. ISSN: 0307-4870. Subscription Rates: 434 individuals. Online: Gale. URL: http://www.sweetandmaxwell.co.uk/Catalogue/ProductDetails.aspx?recordid=428&productid=6972.

52120 ■ Law Quarterly Review
Sweet & Maxwell Ltd.
PO Box 2000
North Way
Andover SP10 5BE, United Kingdom
Ph: 44 1264 332424
Fax: 44 207 3938074
Publisher E-mail: sweetandmaxwell.international@thomson.com
Law periodical. Founded: Nov. 11, 1885. Freq: Quarterly. Key Personnel: Prof. Francis M.B. Reynolds, Editor; Sarah Mullins, House Ed.; Dan Prentice, Asst. Ed. ISSN: 0023-933X. Subscription Rates: 239 individuals. Remarks: Advertising not accepted. Online: Gale. URL: http://www.sweetandmaxwell.co.uk/Catalogue/ProductDetails.aspx?recordid=473&productid=7116. Circ: (Not Reported)

52121 ■ Public Law
Sweet & Maxwell Ltd.
PO Box 2000
North Way
Andover SP10 5BE, United Kingdom
Ph: 44 1264 332424
Fax: 44 207 3938074
Publisher E-mail: sweetandmaxwell.international@thomson.com
Law periodical. Founded: 1956. Freq: Quarterly. Key Personnel: Prof. Andrew Le Sueur, Editor, a.lesueur@qmul.ac.uk; Jo Eric Khushal Murkens, Book Review Ed.; Abigail Dyson, House Ed., abigail.dyson@thomsonreuters.com. ISSN: 0033-3565. Subscription Rates: 272 individuals. URL: http://www.sweetandmaxwell.co.uk/Catalogue/ProductDetails.aspx?recordid=469&productid=7106.

Annan

52122 ■ Annandale Herald
DNG Media
96 High St.

Annan DG12 6EJ, United Kingdom
Ph: 44 1461 202078
Publication E-mail: pre-press@dngonline.co.uk
Publisher E-mail: enquiries@dngonline.co.uk
Newspaper covering the local issues in Mid-Annandale. Freq: Weekly. Key Personnel: Bryan Armstrong, Editor, phone 44 1461 202417, ba@dngonline.co.uk; Brian Johnstone, Production Supvr. Remarks: Accepts advertising. URL: http://www.annandaleherald.co.uk/. Circ: (Not Reported)

52123 ■ Annandale Observer
DNG Media
96 High St.
Annan DG12 6EJ, United Kingdom
Ph: 44 1461 202078
Publisher E-mail: enquiries@dngonline.co.uk
Newspaper covering the local events in Lower Annandale. Founded: 1857. Freq: Weekly. Key Personnel: Bryan Armstrong, Editor, phone 44 1461 202417, ba@dngonline.co.uk. Remarks: Accepts advertising. URL: http://www.annandaleobserver.co.uk/. Circ: (Not Reported)

52124 ■ Dumfries Courier
DNG Media
96 High St.
Annan DG12 6EJ, United Kingdom
Ph: 44 1461 202078
Publisher E-mail: enquiries@dngonline.co.uk
Newspaper covering the local events in Dumfries. Founded: 1809. Freq: Weekly (Fri.). Key Personnel: Bryan Armstrong, Editor, phone 44 1461 202417, ba@dngonline.co.uk. Remarks: Accepts advertising. URL: http://www.dumfriescourier.co.uk/. Circ: (Not Reported)

52125 ■ Moffat News
DNG Media
96 High St.
Annan DG12 6EJ, United Kingdom
Ph: 44 1461 202078
Publisher E-mail: enquiries@dngonline.co.uk
Newspaper covering the local events in the town of Moffat. Freq: Weekly. Key Personnel: Bryan Armstrong, Editor, phone 44 1461 202417, ba@dngonline.co.uk. Remarks: Accepts advertising. URL: http://www.moffatnews.co.uk/. Circ: 1,000

Appleby-in-Westmorland

52126 ■ International Journal of Dairy Technology
Society of Dairy Technology
PO Box 12
Appleby-in-Westmorland CA16 6YJ, United Kingdom
Ph: 44 1768 354034
Publisher E-mail: execdirector@sdt.org
Journal covering worldwide dairy technology. Subtitle: IJDT. Founded: 1948. Freq: Quarterly. Key Personnel: Dr. Hugh Pinnock, Sci. Ed., phone 44 1869 345838, fax 44 1869 345838, editor@sdt.org; Andrew R. Wilbey, Chm., phone 44 1189 318722, fax 44 1189 316649, andrew@wilbey.demon.co.uk; Dr. A.Y. Tamime, Tech. Series Ed./Book Review Ed., phone 44 1292 265498, adnan@tamime.fsnet.co.uk; Maurice Walton, Exec. Dir. ISSN: 1364-727X. Subscription Rates: US$950 institutions America (print + online); US$8,663 institutions America (print only or online only); 512 institutions (print + online); EUR651 institutions Europe (print + online); EUR592 institutions Europe (print only or online only); US$1,110 institutions, other countries print + online; US$1,009 institutions, other countries print only or online only; 466 institutions (print only or online only). Remarks: Accepts advertising. URL: http://www.sdt.org/publications.htm. Formerly: Journal of the Society of Dairy Technology. Circ: 2,000

Arbroath

52127 ■ Arbroath Herald
Johnston Press PLC
21 Market Pl.
Arbroath DD11 1HR, United Kingdom
Ph: 44 1241 872274
Publication E-mail: arbroath.herald@jnscotland.co.uk
Local community newspaper. Remarks: Accepts advertising. URL: http://www.arbroathherald.co.uk/. Circ: (Not Reported)

52128 ■ Carnoustie Guide & Gazette
Johnston Press PLC

21 Market Pl.
Arbroath DD11 1NS, United Kingdom
Ph: 44 1241 872274
Local community newspaper. **Remarks:** Accepts advertising. **URL:** http://www.guideandgazette.co.uk/. **Circ:** (Not Reported)

Argyll

52129 ■ Journal of Customer Behaviour
Westburn Publishers Ltd.
23 Millig St.
Helensburgh
Argyll G84 9LD, United Kingdom
Ph: 44 1436 678699
Fax: 44 1436 670328
Publication E-mail: jcbeditorial@westburn.co.uk
Publisher E-mail: journals@westburn.co.uk
Peer-reviewed journal covering consumer behavior and organizational buyer behavior. **Founded:** 2001. **Freq:** 4/yr. **Key Personnel:** Prof. Michael J. Baker, Editor; Prof. Steve Baron, Dep. Ed.; Prof. Stephen Brown, Advisory Board. **ISSN:** 1475-3928. **Subscription Rates:** 90 individuals print; 70 individuals online; 310 institutions print; 285 institutions online; 370 institutions print and online; 940 institutions subs package. **URL:** http://www.westburnpublishers.com/journals/journal-of-customer-behaviour.aspx.

52130 ■ Journal of Marketing Management
Westburn Publishers Ltd.
23 Millig St.
Helensburgh
Argyll G84 9LD, United Kingdom
Ph: 44 1436 678699
Fax: 44 1436 670328
Publication E-mail: jmmeditorial@westburn.co.uk
Publisher E-mail: journals@westburn.co.uk
Journal covering all aspects of the management of marketing. **Freq:** 14/yr. **Key Personnel:** Prof. Susan Hart, Editor; Prof. Michael J. Baker, Founding Ed.; Prof. Gillian Hogg, Dep. Ed. **ISSN:** 0267-257X. **Subscription Rates:** US$326 individuals print; US$1,342 individuals online; US$1,413 institutions print and online. **URL:** http://www.westburnpublishers.com/journals/journal-of-marketing-managementaspx; http://www.informaworld.com/smpp/title~content=t914689377~db=all.

52131 ■ The Marketing Review
Westburn Publishers Ltd.
23 Millig St.
Helensburgh
Argyll G84 9LD, United Kingdom
Ph: 44 1436 678699
Fax: 44 1436 670328
Publisher E-mail: journals@westburn.co.uk
Journal covering field of marketing. **Founded:** 2000. **Key Personnel:** Dr. Jim Blythe, Editor; Prof. Caroline A. Tynan, Founding Ed.; Michael J. Baker, Advisory Board. **ISSN:** 1469-347X. **Subscription Rates:** 85 individuals print; 25 individuals online; 295 institutions print; 270 institutions online; 350 institutions print and online; 940 institutions subs package. **URL:** http://www.westburnpublishers.com/journals/the-marketing-review.aspx.

Argyll and Bute

52132 ■ The Muses Journal
International Institute of Peace Studies and Global Philosophy
Castle of the Muses
Craigard
Argyll and Bute PA24 6AH, United Kingdom
Publisher E-mail: iipsgp@educationaid.net
Journal containing information on issues of philosophy, education, peace, arts. **Freq:** Annual. **Subscription Rates:** US$25 individuals. **URL:** http://www.educationaid.net/homepage.html.

Arundel

52133 ■ Cat World
Ashdown Publishing
19 River Rd.
Partridge Green
Arundel BN18 9EY, United Kingdom
Ph: 44 19 3884988

Publisher E-mail: support@ashdown.co.uk
Magazine providing all the information about cats. **Key Personnel:** Laura Quiggan, Editor. **Subscription Rates:** 17 individuals for Europe; 27 individuals rest of the world; 33 individuals. **URL:** http://www.catworld.co.uk/.

52134 ■ Dolls House World
Ashdown Publishing
19 River Rd.
Partridge Green
Arundel BN18 9EY, United Kingdom
Ph: 44 19 3884988
Publication E-mail: kelly@ashdown.co.uk
Publisher E-mail: support@ashdown.co.uk
Magazine about doll houses. **Freq:** Weekly. **Subscription Rates:** 80 individuals; 158 two years. **Remarks:** Accepts advertising. **URL:** http://www.dollshouseworld.com. **Circ:** (Not Reported)

52135 ■ Toy Soldier & Model Figure
Ashdown Publishing
19 River Rd.
Partridge Green
Arundel BN18 9EY, United Kingdom
Ph: 44 19 3884988
Publication E-mail: jena@ashdown.co.uk
Publisher E-mail: support@ashdown.co.uk
Consumer magazine covering toy soldier collecting for hobbyists. **Founded:** July 31, 1995. **Freq:** Monthly. **Print Method:** Sheetfed Offset. **Trim Size:** 210 x 297 mm. **ISSN:** 1359-7426. **Subscription Rates:** US$69 individuals; US$135 two years. **Remarks:** Accepts advertising. **URL:** http://www.toy-soldier.com. **Former name:** Military Hobbies. **Ad Rates:** BW: US$837, 4C: US$1,444. **Circ:** Paid 10,000

Ascension Island

52136 ■ The Islander
Ascension Island ASCN 1ZZ, United Kingdom
Ph: 44 00 2476327
Fax: 44 00 2476327
Community newspaper. **Founded:** 1970. **Freq:** Bimonthly. **Trim Size:** A5. **Key Personnel:** Jacqui Ellick, Chp.; Gary Robinson, Internet Ed.; Helen Close, Editor. **Subscription Rates:** Free. **Remarks:** Accepts advertising. **URL:** http://www.the-islander.org.ac/. **Circ:** Non-paid 8,000

Ascot

52137 ■ Construction Information Quarterly
Chartered Institute of Building
Englemere
Kings Ride
Ascot SL5 7TB, United Kingdom
Ph: 44 13 44630700
Fax: 44 13 44630777
Publisher E-mail: reception@ciob.org.uk
Publication covering building industries. **Freq:** Quarterly. **ISSN:** 1469-4891. **Subscription Rates:** 41 members U.K.; 49 members rest of the world; 93 nonmembers. **URL:** http://www.ciob.org.uk/membership/benefits. **Circ:** 4,000

52138 ■ Construction Manager
Chartered Institute of Building
Englemere
Kings Ride
Ascot SL5 7TB, United Kingdom
Ph: 44 13 44630700
Fax: 44 13 44630777
Publisher E-mail: reception@ciob.org.uk
Publication covering building industries. **Freq:** Monthly. **Key Personnel:** Elaine Knutt, Editor, phone 44 20 74905636, elaine@atompublishing.co.uk; Stephen Quirke, Managing Editor, stephen@atompublishing.co.uk; Martin Sinclair, Advertising Mgr., phone 44 20 74905661, martin@atompublishing.co.uk. **Subscription Rates:** 73 individuals; 83 other countries. **Remarks:** Advertising accepted; rates available upon request. **URL:** http://www.ciob.org.uk/resources/constructionmanager; http://www.construction-manager.co.uk/. **Circ:** 33,000

52139 ■ Insect Conservation and Diversity
John Wiley & Sons Inc.
Wiley-Blackwell
c/o Simon R. Leather, Ed.

Division of Biology, Faculty of Life Sciences
Imperial College London
Silwood Pk. Campus
Ascot SL5 7PY, United Kingdom
Ph: 44 20759 42316
Fax: 44 20759 42339
Peer-reviewed journal covering the general area of insect. **Freq:** Quarterly. **Key Personnel:** Simon R. Leather, Editor, s.leather@imperial.ac.uk; Yves Basset, Editor, bassety@si.edu; Bradford A. Hawkins, Editor, bhawkins@uci.edu. **ISSN:** 1752-458X. **Subscription Rates:** US$222 individuals Americas (print and online); 119 individuals non-Euro zone (print and online); EUR180 institutions Euro zone (print and online); 132 other countries print and online; 613 institutions UK (print and online); US$1,132 institutions Americas (print and online); EUR777 institutions Europe (print and online); US$1,320 institutions, other countries print and online; 557 institutions UK (print or online only); US$1,029 institutions Americas (print or online only). **Remarks:** Accepts advertising. **URL:** http://www.wiley.com/bw/journal.asp?ref=1752-458X. **Circ:** (Not Reported)

Ashford

52140 ■ Food Policy
Elsevier Science Inc.
c/o C. Poulton, Mng. Ed.
School of Oriental & African Studies
Wye, Kent
Ashford, United Kingdom
Publisher E-mail: usinfo-ehelp@elsevier.com
Peer-reviewed journal covering formulation, implementation and analysis of policies for the food sector in developing, transition and advanced economies. **Freq:** 6/yr. **Print Method:** Offset. **Trim Size:** 13 3/4 x 22 3/4. **Cols./Page:** 6. **Col. Width:** 24 nonpareils. **Col. Depth:** 294 agate lines. **Key Personnel:** J. Kydd, Editor, j.kydd@imperial.ac.uk; A. Dorward, Editor, ad55@soas.ac.uk; N. Poole, Editor, np10@soas.ac.uk; C. Poulton, Editor; T. Cooper, Editorial Asst.; L.J. Hubbard, Editorial Board; H. Alderman, Editorial Board; M. Blackie, Editorial Board; J. Shaw, Editorial Board; E. Clay, Editorial Board. **ISSN:** 0306-9192. **Subscription Rates:** US$1,284 institutions, other countries except Europe, Japan and Iran; EUR1,147 institutions for European countries and Iran; 152,200¥ institutions; 26,500¥ individuals; EUR185 individuals for European countries and Iran; US$238 other countries except Europe, Japan and Iran. **URL:** http://www.elsevier.com/wps/find/journaldescription.cws_home/30419/descriptiondescription.

52141 ■ KM-FM - 96.4
34-36 North St.
Kent
Ashford TN24 8JR, United Kingdom
Ph: 44 1303 240402
E-mail: sfountain@thekmgroup.co.uk
Format: Adult Contemporary. **URL:** http://www.kmfm.co.uk/goto.php?sess=x183811lu183694lp111ln0lc)ll0lg6ld0.

52142 ■ KM-FM - 107.6
34-36 N St.
Ashford TN24 8JR, United Kingdom
Ph: 44 1233 623232
E-mail: sfountain@thekmgroup.co.uk
Format: Adult Contemporary. **URL:** http://www.kmfm.co.uk/goto.php?sess=x183812lu183694lp111ln0lc0ll0lg7ld0.

52143 ■ KM-FM - 106
34-36 North St.
Kent
Ashford TN24 8JR, United Kingdom
Ph: 44 1303 240402
E-mail: sfountain@thekmgroup.co.uk
Format: Adult Contemporary. **URL:** http://www.kmfm.co.uk/goto.php?sess=x183809lu183694lp111ln0lcQll0lg4ld0.

52144 ■ KM-FM - 106.8
34-36 North St.
Kent
Ashford TN24 8JR, United Kingdom
Ph: 44 1303 240402
E-mail: sfountain@thekmgroup.co.uk
Format: Adult Contemporary. **URL:** http://www.kmfm.co.uk/goto.php?sess=x183811u183694lp111ln0lc0ll0lg6ld0.

Circulation: ★ = ABC; △ = BPA; ♦ = CAC; • = CCAB; ❏ = VAC; ⊕ = PO Statement; ‡ = Publisher's Report; Boldface figures = sworn; Light figures = estimated.

Gale Directory of Publications & Broadcast Media/147th Ed.

5565

Ashurst

52145 ■ Engineering Analysis with Boundary Elements
Elsevier Science Inc.
c/o Carlos A. Brebbia, Ed.-in-Ch.
Wessex Institute of Technology
Ashurst Lodge
Ashurst SO40 7AA, United Kingdom
Fax: 44 238 0293223
Publisher E-mail: usinfo-ehelp@elsevier.com
Journal featuring engineering analysis techniques. **Founded:** 1984. **Freq:** 12/yr. **Key Personnel:** Henry Power, Editor, fax 44 115 9513800; Alexander H.-D. Cheng, Co-Ed., fax 662915-5523; H. Power, Editor, fax 44 115 9513800; D.E. Beskos, Editorial Board; A.J. Davies, Editorial Board; G. De Mey, Editorial Board; J. Dominguez, Editorial Board; E. Divo, Editorial Board; Carlos A. Brebbia, Editor-in-Chief, carlos@wessex.ac.uk. **ISSN:** 0955-7997. **Subscription Rates:** US$2,628 institutions, other countries all countries except Europe, Japan and Iran; EUR2,350 institutions European countries and Iran; 312,000¥ institutions. **URL:** http://www.elsevier.com/wps/find/journaldescription.cws_home/422920/descriptiondescription.

Aylesbury

52146 ■ Bucks Herald
Johnston Press PLC
The Gatehouse, Ground Fl.
Gatehouse Way
Aylesbury HP19 8DB, United Kingdom
Ph: 44 1296 619700
Local community newspaper. **Freq:** Weekly (Wed.). **Key Personnel:** Ellen Campbell, Editor, phone 44 1296 619760, fax 44 1296 399069, editorial@bucksherald.co.uk. **Remarks:** Accepts advertising. **URL:** http://www.bucksherald.co.uk/. **Circ:** (Not Reported)

52147 ■ English Bridge
English Bridge Union Ltd.
Broadfields, Bicester Rd.
Aylesbury HP19 8AZ, United Kingdom
Ph: 44 12 96317200
Fax: 44 12 96317220
Publisher E-mail: postmaster@ebu.co.uk
Consumer magazine covering bridge for card players. **Freq:** Bimonthly. **Print Method:** Web offset. **Cols./Page:** 3. **Col. Width:** 5.9 centimeters. **Col. Depth:** 27 centimeters. **Key Personnel:** Elena Jeronimidis, Editor, elena@ebu.co.uk. **Remarks:** Accepts advertising. **URL:** http://www.ebu.co.uk/. **Circ:** Non-paid 30,000

52148 ■ The Photographer
BIPP
1 Prebendal Ct.
Oxford Rd.
Bucks
Aylesbury HP19 8EY, United Kingdom
Ph: 44 1296 718530
Fax: 44 1296 336367
Publisher E-mail: info@bipp.com
Professional magazine covering photography. **Subtitle:** BIPP Journal of Professional Images and Imaging Technology. **Freq:** Monthly. **Key Personnel:** Chris Harper, Ch. Exec., chris@bipp.com. **Subscription Rates:** 30 individuals; 20 members; 65 other countries. **Remarks:** Accepts advertising. **URL:** http://www.bipp.com/. **Circ:** (Not Reported)

52149 ■ Point 3
TOCH
Wing House, 3rd Fl.
Britannia St.
Aylesbury HP20 1QS, United Kingdom
Ph: 44 1296 331099
Fax: 44 1296 331135
Publisher E-mail: info@toch.org.uk
Publication covering women. **Freq:** 5/yr. **Trim Size:** A5. **Key Personnel:** Christine Scippo, Editor, christines@toch.org.uk. **Remarks:** Advertising not accepted. **URL:** http://www.tochparticipation.co.uk/news/new-point-3-gets-thumbs-up.htm. **Circ:** 2,500

52150 ■ Mix 96-FM - 96.2
Friars Square Studios
11 Bourbon St.
Aylesbury HP20 2PZ, United Kingdom
Ph: 44 1296 399396
Format: Adult Contemporary; Talk; News. **Owner:** The Local Radio Company plc., Barncoose Industrial Estate, Cornwall, Redruth TR15 3RQ, United Kingdom, 44 1209 310435, Fax: 44 1209 310406. **Founded:** Apr. 1994. **Operating Hours:** Continuous. **Ad Rates:** Advertising accepted; rates available upon request. **URL:** http://www.mix96.co.uk/.

Ayr

52151 ■ West-FM - 96.7
Radio House
54a Holmston Rd.
Ayr KA7 3BE, United Kingdom
Ph: 44 1292 283662
Fax: 44 1292 283665
E-mail: info@westsound.co.uk
Format: Adult Contemporary. **Key Personnel:** Brenda Ritchie, Station Dir., brenda.ritchie@westsound.co.uk. **Ad Rates:** Advertising accepted; rates available upon request. **URL:** http://www.westfm.co.uk/.

52152 ■ West Sound-AM - 1035
Radio House
54a Holmston Rd.
Ayr KA7 3BE, United Kingdom
Ph: 44 1292 283662
Fax: 44 1292 283665
E-mail: info@westsound.co.uk
Format: Adult Contemporary; News; Information. **Key Personnel:** Brenda Ritchie, Station Dir., brenda.ritchie@westsound.co.uk. **Ad Rates:** Advertising accepted; rates available upon request. **URL:** http://www.westsound.co.uk/.

Bacton

52153 ■ Herefordshire Life
Archant Life
PO Box 229
Herefordshire
Bacton HR2 0WD, United Kingdom
Ph: 44 1527 831733
Fax: 44 1527 879646
Publisher E-mail: anne.basey-fisher@archant.co.uk
Magazine featuring social life in Herefordshire. **Freq:** Monthly. **Key Personnel:** Joanne Goodwin, Editor, phone 44 1782 850539, editorial@herefordshirelife.co.uk; Richard Drake, Circulation Mgr., richard.drake@archant.co.uk. **URL:** http://www.archantlife.co.uk/contact-us-regions-mid-west-and-midlands-herefordshire-life-contacts--10418.

Bailrigg

52154 ■ Bailrigg-FM - 87.7
Lancaster University
Fylde College
Bailrigg LA1 4YF, United Kingdom
Ph: 44 1524 593902
Format: Full Service. **Key Personnel:** James Kandel, Station Mgr., station.manager@bailriggfm.co.uk; Tony Chung, Chief Engineer, engineering@bailriggfm.co.uk. **URL:** http://radio.lancs.ac.uk.

Balfron

52155 ■ Artist Blacksmith
British Artist Blacksmiths Association
60 Buchanan St.
Balfron G63 0TW, United Kingdom
Fax: 44 1360 440830
Publisher E-mail: babatreasurer@baba.org.uk
British publication covering blacksmithing. **Founded:** 1980. **Freq:** Quarterly. **Subscription Rates:** 45 individuals Europe and offshore U.K.; 47 other countries. **URL:** http://www.baba.org.uk. **Formerly:** British Blacksmith. **Ad Rates:** BW: EUR150, 4C: EUR188. **Circ:** 600

Ballater

52156 ■ NECR-FM - 101.9
The Shed
School Rd.
Kintore
Aberdeenshire
Inverurie AB51 0UX, United Kingdom
Ph: 44 1467 632909
Fax: 44 1467 632969
E-mail: enquiries@necrfm.co.uk
Format: Oldies; Contemporary Hit Radio (CHR); News; Information. **Ad Rates:** Advertising accepted; rates available upon request. **URL:** http://www.necrfm.co.uk/.

Ballyclare

52157 ■ IA Journal
Ileostomy and Internal Pouch Support Group
Peverill House
1 - 5 Mill Rd.
Ballyclare BT39 9DR, United Kingdom
Ph: 44 28 93344043
Fax: 44 28 93324606
Publisher E-mail: info@iasupport.org
Professional journal covering ostomy. **Freq:** Quarterly. **Subscription Rates:** Free to members. **URL:** http://www.the-ia.org.uk/publications_journal.aspx. **Circ:** 12,000

Ballymena

52158 ■ Antrim Times
Johnston Press PLC
22-24 Ballymoney St.
Ballymena BT43 6AL, United Kingdom
Ph: 44 28 25653300
Community newspaper. **Print Method:** Offset. **Col. Depth:** 450 millimeters. **Key Personnel:** Stephanie Manson, Advertising Mgr., phone 44 28 25653300, fax 44 28 25641517. **Remarks:** Accepts advertising. **URL:** http://www.antrimtimes.co.uk/. **Circ:** (Not Reported)

52159 ■ Ballymena Guardian
Alpha Newspaper Group
83 Wellington St.
Ballymena BT43 6AD, United Kingdom
Ph: 44 28 25641221
Fax: 44 28 25653920
Publisher E-mail: editor@ballymenaguardian.co.uk
Newspaper featuring news and events. **Freq:** Weekly (Tues.). **Trim Size:** 265mm x 340mm. **Key Personnel:** Jim Flanagan, Editor, editor@ballymenaguardian.co.uk; Shaun O'Neill, Deputy & Sports Ed., sport@ballymenaguardian.co.uk. **Remarks:** Accepts advertising. **URL:** http://www.ballymenaguardian.co.uk/contact/. **Circ:** ‡17,261

52160 ■ Ballymena Times
Morton Newspapers
22 Ballymoney St.
Ballymena BT43 6AL, United Kingdom
Ph: 44 28 25653300
Community newspaper. **Freq:** Weekly (Wed.). **Print Method:** Offset. **Col. Depth:** 450 millimeters. **Key Personnel:** Desmond Blackadder, Editor, dessie.blackadder@jpress.co.uk; Stephanie Manson, Advertising Mgr., stephanie.manson@jpress.co.uk. **Remarks:** Accepts advertising. **URL:** http://www.ballymenatimes.com. **Circ:** Combined ‡7,981

52161 ■ Seven-FM - 107
Woodside Industrial Estate
Woodside Rd.
Ballymena BT42 4PT, United Kingdom
Ph: 44 28 25648777
E-mail: studio@sevenfm.co.uk
Format: Full Service. **URL:** http://www.sevenfm.co.uk/.

Ballymoney

52162 ■ Ballymoney Times
Morton Newspapers
6 Church St.
Ballymoney BT53 6DL, United Kingdom
Community newspaper. **Freq:** Weekly (Wed.). **Print Method:** Offset. **Col. Depth:** 450 millimeters. **Remarks:** Accepts advertising. **URL:** http://www.ballymoneytimes.co.uk/. **Circ:** Combined 6,744

Banbridge

52163 ■ Banbridge Chronicle
Banbridge Chronicle Press Ltd.
14 Bridge St.
Co. Down
Banbridge BT32 3JS, United Kingdom
Ph: 44 28 40662322
Fax: 44 284 0624397

Publisher E-mail: info@banbridgechronicle.com
Community newspaper. **Founded:** 1870. **Freq:** Weekly.
Print Method: Litho. **Cols./Page:** 7. **Col. Width:** 3.4
centimeters. **Col. Depth:** 40 centimeters. **Key Personnel:** Bryan Hooks, Editor, editor@banbridgechronicle.com. **Subscription Rates:** EUR1 individuals basic cover.
Remarks: Accepts advertising. **URL:** http://www.
banbridgechronicle.com. **Ad Rates:** GLR: 3.50, BW: 6,
4C: 10. **Circ:** 5,984

52164 ■ Banbridge Leader
Morton Newspapers
25 Bridge St.
Banbridge BT32 3JL, United Kingdom
Ph: 44 28 40662745
Community newspaper. **Freq:** Weekly (Wed.). **Print
Method:** Offset. **Col. Depth:** 450 millimeters. **Key Personnel:** John Hooks, Editor; Anita Murray, Advertising
Mgr., anita.murray@jpress.co.uk; Michael Scott, Sports
Ed. **Remarks:** Accepts advertising. **URL:** http://www.
banbridgeleader.co.uk/. **Circ:** (Not Reported)

Banbury

52165 ■ Banbury Cake
Newsquest Media Group Ltd.
13, Market Pl.
Oxfordshire
Banbury OX16 5LG, United Kingdom
Ph: 44 1295 256111
Fax: 44 1295 268544
Publication E-mail: banbury.cake@nqo.com
Newspaper containing Banbury news, sport and other
information. **Freq:** Weekly (Thurs.). **Key Personnel:** Simon O'Neill, Gp. Ed., phone 44 1865 425401, soneill@
nqo.com; Derek Holmes, Editor, dholmes@nqo.com;
David Duffy, Deputy Ed., dduffy@nqo.com. **Subscription Rates:** 52 individuals; 1 single issue. **Remarks:**
Accepts advertising. **URL:** http://www.banburycake.co.
uk/. **Circ:** (Not Reported)

52166 ■ Banbury Guardian
Johnston Press PLC
7 N Bar St.
Banbury OX16 0TQ, United Kingdom
Ph: 44 1295 227777
Local community newspaper. **Founded:** 1838. **Freq:**
Weekly. **Key Personnel:** Pauline Nicklin, Advertising
Mgr., phone 44 1295 227777, fax 44 1295 257689,
pauline.nicklin@banburyguardian.co.uk. **Remarks:** Accepts advertising. **URL:** http://www.banburyguardian.co.
uk/. **Circ:** (Not Reported)

52167 ■ Touch-FM - 107.6
Unit 9A, Manor Pk.
Banbury OX16 3TB, United Kingdom
Ph: 44 12 95661076
E-mail: news@banburysound.co.uk
Format: News; Contemporary Hit Radio (CHR). **Operating Hours:** Continuous. **Key Personnel:** John Crutch,
Mng. Dir.; Steve Hyden, Midlands Prog. Dir., steve.
hyden@cnradio.co.uk; Louise Hancock, Regional Ed.;
Michelle Ellis, Advertising Consultant; Dale Collins,
Program Dir.; Nick Jewers, Duty Ed. **Ad Rates:** Advertising accepted; rates available upon request. **URL:** http://
www.touchfm1076.co.uk.

Banchory

52168 ■ Deeside Piper & Herald
Johnston Press PLC
1 Scott Skinner Sq.
Banchory AB31 5SE, United Kingdom
Ph: 44 1330 824955
Local community newspaper. **Remarks:** Accepts
advertising. **URL:** http://www.deesidepiper.co.uk. **Circ:**
(Not Reported)

52169 ■ Donside Piper & Herald
Johnston Press PLC
1 Scott Skinner Sq.
Banchory AB31 5SE, United Kingdom
Ph: 44 1330 824955
Local community newspaper. **Remarks:** Accepts
advertising. **URL:** http://www.donsidepiper.co.uk/. **Circ:**
(Not Reported)

Bangor

52170 ■ Experimental Agriculture
Cambridge University Press
c/o Dr. Dave Harris, Ed.
CAZS Natural Resources
Bangor University
Gwynedd
Bangor LL57 2UW, United Kingdom
Publisher E-mail: customer_service@cup.org
Journal on research in the field of production of crops.
Freq: Quarterly. **Key Personnel:** Dr. Dave Harris, Editor; Dr. Lindsay N. Innes, Book Review Ed.,
minnes1960@aol.com; Dr. Sayed Azam-Ali, Editorial
Board. **ISSN:** 0014-4797. **Subscription Rates:** 364
institutions online and print; US$697 institutions online
and print; 287 institutions online; US$562 institutions
online. **Remarks:** Accepts display advertising. **URL:**
http://journals.cambridge.org/action/displayJournal?jid=
EAG. **Ad Rates:** BW: 885. **Circ:** 550

52171 ■ IAW!
Urdd Gobaith Cymru
Swyddfar Urdd
Uned 13 Llys Castan, Parc Menai
Bangor LL57 4FH, United Kingdom
Ph: 44 1248 672100
Fax: 44 1248 672101
Publication E-mail: iaw@urdd.org
Magazine for teenagers learning Welsh as a second
language. **Founded:** 1955. **Freq:** Monthly. **Key Personnel:** Sian Davies, Editor. **ISSN:** 1359-7396. **Subscription Rates:** 10 individuals; 1 single issue. **Remarks:**
Accepts advertising. **URL:** http://www.gwales.com/
magazine/; http://www.urdd.org/iaw/index.php?lng=en.
Formerly: Mynd (1995). **Ad Rates:** BW: 150, 4C: 200.
Circ: Combined 2,700

52172 ■ International Journal of Banking, Accounting and Finance
Inderscience Enterprises Limited
c/o Philip Molyneux, Ed.-in-Ch.
Bangor University
Bangor Business School
Hen Goleg, College Rd.
Bangor LL57 2DG, United Kingdom
Peer-reviewed journal covering all aspects of accounting, banking, and finance. **Freq:** 4/yr. **Key Personnel:**
Philip Molyneux, Editor-in-Chief, p.molyneux@bangor.
ac.uk. **ISSN:** 1755-3830. **Subscription Rates:** EUR494
individuals print or online; EUR672 individuals print and
online. **URL:** http://www.inderscience.com/browse/index.
php?journalID=277.

52173 ■ North Wales Chronicle
NWN Media Ltd.
302 High St.
Bangor LL57 1UL, United Kingdom
Ph: 44 1248 387400
Fax: 44 1248 354793
Publisher E-mail: internet@nwn.co.uk
Newspaper featuring news and events. **Founded:** 1808.
Key Personnel: Steve Rogers, Editor. **URL:** http://www.
northwaleschronicle.co.uk/.

52174 ■ Champion-FM - 103
Llys Y Dderwen
Parc Menai
Bangor LL57 4BN, United Kingdom
Ph: 44 12 48673400
Format: Contemporary Hit Radio (CHR); News. **Operating Hours:** Continuous. **Ad Rates:** Advertising accepted; rates available upon request. **URL:** http://www.
champion103.co.uk.

52175 ■ Heart-FM - 96.3
PO Box 963
Bangor LL57 4ZR, United Kingdom
Ph: 44 12 48673401
Format: Adult Contemporary; News. **Formerly:** Marcher
Coast-FM. **Operating Hours:** Continuous. **Ad Rates:**
Advertising accepted; rates available upon request.
URL: http://www.heartwalescoast.co.uk/.

52176 ■ Storm-FM - 87.7
Deiniol Rd.
Gwynedd
Bangor LL57 2TH, United Kingdom
Ph: 44 1248 388049

E-mail: enquiries@stormfm.com
Format: Eclectic. **Owner:** Bangor University Students'
Union, Bryn Haul, Victoria, Dr., Gwynedd, Bangor LL57
2EN, United Kingdom, 44 1248 388000, Fax: 44 1248
383939. **Key Personnel:** Cameron Ward, Station Mgr.,
stationmanager@stormfm.com. **Ad Rates:** Advertising
accepted; rates available upon request. **URL:** http://
www.stormfm.com/.

Barnsley

52177 ■ Assistive Technologies
Wharncliffe Publishing Ltd.
47 Church St.
South Yorkshire
Barnsley S70 2AS, United Kingdom
Ph: 44 1226 734639
Fax: 44 1226 734478
Publisher E-mail: editorial@wharncliffepublishing.co.uk
Magazine covering assistive technologies and mobility
improvement for healthcare professionals and business
associations. **Key Personnel:** Dominic Musgrave, Editor, phone 44 1226 734639, editorial@
assistivetechnologies.co.uk; Kelly Tarff, Circulation Mgr.,
phone 44 1226 734695, circulation@
wharncliffepublishing.co.uk; Judith Halkerston, Gp.
Production Ed., phone 44 1226 734458, jhalkerston@
whpl.net. **Subscription Rates:** 20 individuals; 30 other
countries. **Remarks:** Accepts advertising. **URL:** http://
www.assistivetechnologies.co.uk; http://www.
wharncliffepublishing.co.uk. **Circ:** (Not Reported)

52178 ■ Caring UK
Wharncliffe Publishing Ltd.
47 Church St.
South Yorkshire
Barnsley S70 2AS, United Kingdom
Ph: 44 1226 734639
Fax: 44 1226 734478
Publisher E-mail: editorial@wharncliffepublishing.co.uk
Magazine covering care for managers in the elderly
sector. **Freq:** Monthly. **Key Personnel:** Dominic Musgrave, Healthcare Ed., dm@whpl.net; Andrew Harrod,
Gp. Ed., ah@whpl.net; Kelly Tarff, Circulation Mgr., kt@
whpl.net. **Subscription Rates:** 40 individuals; 50 other
countries. **Remarks:** Accepts advertising. **URL:** http://
www.caring-uk.co.uk. **Circ:** (Not Reported)

52179 ■ Destination UK
Wharncliffe Publishing Ltd.
47 Church St.
South Yorkshire
Barnsley S70 2AS, United Kingdom
Ph: 44 1226 734639
Fax: 44 1226 734478
Publisher E-mail: editorial@wharncliffepublishing.co.uk
Magazine covering UK's travel and tourism industry.
Freq: Monthly. **Key Personnel:** Andrew Harrod, Gp.
Ed., ah@whpl.net; Judith Halkerston, Gp. Dep. Ed.,
phone 44 1226 734458, jhalkerston@whpl.net; Kelly
Tarff, Circulation Mgr., phone 44 1226 734695, kt@whpl.
net. **Subscription Rates:** 40 individuals; 50 other
countries. **Remarks:** Accepts advertising. **URL:** http://
www.destination.uk.com; http://www.
wharncliffepublishing.co.uk. **Circ:** 11,902

52180 ■ Future Fitness
Wharncliffe Publishing Ltd.
47 Church St.
South Yorkshire
Barnsley S70 2AS, United Kingdom
Ph: 44 1226 734639
Fax: 44 1226 734478
Publisher E-mail: editorial@wharncliffepublishing.co.uk
Magazine featuring sport and fitness for today's youth.
Key Personnel: Andrew Harrod, Gp. Ed., phone 44
1226 734639, ah@whpl.net; Rachel Collins, Asst. Sales
Mgr., phone 44 1226 734709, rc@astwhpl.net; Kelly
Tarff, Circulation Mgr., phone 44 1226 734695,
circulation@wharncliffepublishing.co.uk. **Subscription
Rates:** 35 individuals; 45 other countries. **Remarks:** Accepts advertising. **URL:** http://www.futurefitness.uk.net.
Circ: (Not Reported)

52181 ■ Horse Health Magazine
Wharncliffe Publishing Ltd.
47 Church St.
South Yorkshire
Barnsley S70 2AS, United Kingdom

Circulation: ★ = ABC; △ = BPA; ◆ = CAC; • = CCAB; ❑ = VAC; ⊕ = PO Statement; ‡ = Publisher's Report; Boldface figures = sworn; Light figures = estimated.

Gale Directory of Publications & Broadcast Media/147th Ed.   5567

Ph: 44 1226 734639
Fax: 44 1226 734478
Publisher E-mail: editorial@wharncliffepublishing.co.uk
Magazine covering horse health and well-being. **Key Personnel:** Andrew Harrod, Gp. Ed., phone 44 1226 734639, ah@whpl.net; Christine Keate, Editor, chris.keate@horsehealthmagazine.co.uk; Kelly Tarff, Circulation Mgr., phone 44 1226 734695, kt@whpl.net. **Subscription Rates:** 25 individuals; 40 other countries. **Remarks:** Accepts advertising. **URL:** http://www.horsehealthmagazine.co.uk. **Circ:** 10,000

52182 ■ The Main Event Magazine
Wharncliffe Publishing Ltd.
47 Church St.
Barnsley S70 2AS, United Kingdom
Ph: 44 1226 734639
Fax: 44 1226 734478
Publisher E-mail: editorial@wharncliffepublishing.co.uk
Magazine covering indoors and outdoors event. **Key Personnel:** Andrew Harrod, Gp. Ed., ah@whpl.net; Judith Halkerston, Gp. Deputy Ed., phone 44 1226 734458, jhalkerston@whpl.net; Kelly Tarff, Circulation Mgr., circulation@whpl.net. **Remarks:** Accepts advertising. **URL:** http://www.themaineventmagazine.co.uk; http://www.wharncliffepublishing.co.uk. **Circ:** 10,000

52183 ■ Out on a Limb
Wharncliffe Publishing Ltd.
47 Church St.
South Yorkshire
Barnsley S70 2AS, United Kingdom
Ph: 44 1226 734639
Fax: 44 1226 734478
Publisher E-mail: editorial@wharncliffepublishing.co.uk
Magazine featuring directional footwear and fashion accessories. **Key Personnel:** Louise Cordell, Editor, phone 44 1226 734694, lcordell@whpl.net; Andrew Harrod, Gp. Ed., phone 44 1226 734639, ah@whpl.net; Kelly Tarff, Circulation Mgr., phone 44 1226 734695, kt@whpl.net. **Subscription Rates:** 25 individuals; 40 other countries. **Remarks:** Accepts advertising. **URL:** http://www.ooalmagazine.co.uk. **Circ:** (Not Reported)

52184 ■ Wedding Professional
Wharncliffe Publishing Ltd.
47 Church St.
South Yorkshire
Barnsley S70 2AS, United Kingdom
Ph: 44 1226 734639
Fax: 44 1226 734478
Publisher E-mail: editorial@wharncliffepublishing.co.uk
Magazine covering professional wedding planning market. **Freq:** Bimonthly. **Key Personnel:** Andrew Harrod, Gp. Ed., ah@whpl.net; Kelly Tarff, Circulation Mgr., circulation@wharncliffepublishing.co.uk. **Subscription Rates:** 25 individuals; 40 other countries. **Remarks:** Accepts advertising. **URL:** http://www.weddingprofessional.co.uk. **Circ:** (Not Reported)

52185 ■ WorkOut Ireland
Wharncliffe Publishing Ltd.
47 Church St.
South Yorkshire
Barnsley S70 2AS, United Kingdom
Ph: 44 1226 734639
Fax: 44 1226 734478
Publisher E-mail: editorial@wharncliffepublishing.co.uk
Magazine covering health, leisure and fitness industry in Ireland. **Key Personnel:** Andrew Harrod, Gp. Ed., ah@whpl.net; Nicola Lambert, News Ed., nl@whpl.net; James Dickson, Publishing Mgr., jd@whpl.net. **Remarks:** Accepts advertising. **URL:** http://www.workout-ireland.com. **Circ:** (Not Reported)

52186 ■ WorkOut UK
Wharncliffe Publishing Ltd.
47 Church St.
South Yorkshire
Barnsley S70 2AS, United Kingdom
Ph: 44 1226 734639
Fax: 44 1226 734478
Publisher E-mail: editorial@wharncliffepublishing.co.uk
Magazine covering health, leisure and fitness industry in UK. **Freq:** Monthly. **Key Personnel:** Andrew Harrod, Gp. Ed., phone 44 1226 734639, ah@whpl.net; Tony Barry, Sales/Mktg. Dir., phone 44 1226 734333, tb@whpl.net; Emma Spencer, Editor, phone 44 1226 734712, emmas@whpl.net. **Subscription Rates:** 40 individuals; 50 other countries. **Remarks:** Accepts

advertising. **URL:** http://www.workout-uk.co.uk; http://www.wharncliffepublishing.co.uk. **Circ:** 8,000

52187 ■ Dearne-FM - 102
Unit 7, Network Ctr.
Zenith Pk.
Whaley Rd.
Barnsley S75 1HT, United Kingdom
Ph: 44 1226 321733
Fax: 44 1226 321755
E-mail: enquiries@dearnefm.co.uk
Format: Full Service. **Ad Rates:** Advertising accepted; rates available upon request. **URL:** http://www.dearnefm.co.uk/.

Dearne-FM - See Penistone

52188 ■ Hallam-FM - 102.9
900 Herries Rd.
Sheffield S6 1RH, United Kingdom
Ph: 44 114 2091000
Fax: 44 114 2855472
Format: Contemporary Hit Radio (CHR). **Key Personnel:** Simon Monk, Program Dir.; Lynn Dixon, News Ed. **URL:** http://www.hallamfm.co.uk/.

52189 ■ Ridings-FM - 106.8
Network Centre, Unit 7
Zenith Pk.
Whaley Rd.
Barnsley S75 1HT, United Kingdom
Ph: 44 1924 367177
Fax: 44 1924 367133
E-mail: studio@ridingsfm.co.uk
Format: Adult Contemporary; Information; News. **Key Personnel:** Jess Baines, Contact. **Ad Rates:** Advertising accepted; rates available upon request. **URL:** http://www.ridingsfm.co.uk/.

Barnstaple

52190 ■ Agricultural Trader
Archant Regional Ltd.
Unit 3, Old Sta. Rd.
Barnstaple EX32 8PB, United Kingdom
Ph: 44 1271 341650
Fax: 44 1271 341666
Publisher E-mail: sandra.roantree@archant.co.uk
Newspaper covering the agricultural industry. **Freq:** Monthly. **Key Personnel:** Tony Gussin, Editor, phone 44 1271 345056, tony.gussin@archant.co.uk; Lyn Brodie, Publishing Mgr., lyn.brodie@archant.co.uk. **Subscription Rates:** 17.50 individuals; 27.50 other countries. **Remarks:** Accepts advertising. **URL:** http://www.agriculturaltrader.co.uk/agritrader/content/. **Circ:** (Not Reported)

52191 ■ North Devon Gazette
Archant Regional Ltd.
Old Station Rd., Unit 3
Barnstaple EX32 8PB, United Kingdom
Ph: 44 1271 344303
Publisher E-mail: sandra.roantree@archant.co.uk
Local community newspaper. **Key Personnel:** Dave Tanner, Editor, phone 44 1271 345056, dave.tanner@archant.co.uk; Lyn Brodie, Publishing Mgr., lyn.brodie@archant.co.uk. **Remarks:** Accepts advertising. **URL:** http://www.northdevongazette.co.uk/home. **Circ:** (Not Reported)

Barry

52192 ■ Barry & District News
Newsquest Media Group Ltd.
156 Holton Rd.
Barry CF63 4TY, United Kingdom
Ph: 44 1446 733456
Newspaper providing news and events in Barry district. **Key Personnel:** Shira Valek, Editor, shira.valek@gwent-wales.co.uk; Andrea Hall, Advertising Mgr., andrea.hall@gwent-wales.co.uk. **Remarks:** Accepts advertising. **URL:** http://www.barryanddistrictnews.co.uk/. **Circ:** (Not Reported)

Basildon

52193 ■ Basildon and Wickford Recorder
Newsquest Media Group Ltd.
Chester Hall Ln.
Basildon SS14 3BL, United Kingdom
Ph: 44 844 4774512

Fax: 44 844 4774286
Newspaper providing up to date local news and sports. **Freq:** Weekly. **Key Personnel:** Martin McNeill, Editor, phone 44 844 4774463, echo.editor@nqe.com; Christina Ongley, News Ed., phone 44 844 4774393; Neil Reeve, Asst. Ed. **Remarks:** Accepts advertising. **URL:** http://www.basildonrecorder.co.uk/. **Circ:** (Not Reported)

Basingstoke

52194 ■ Asian Business & Management
Palgrave Macmillan
Houndsmills
Basingstoke RG21 6XS, United Kingdom
Ph: 44 1256 329242
Fax: 44 1256 479476
Publisher E-mail: booksellers@palgrave.com
Peer-reviewed journal covering the field of business and management. **Freq:** 4/yr. **Key Personnel:** Harukiyo Hasegawa, Gen. Ed. **ISSN:** 1472-4782. **Subscription Rates:** 498 institutions, other countries print; US$925 institutions print; 84 other countries print and online; US$156 individuals print and online. **URL:** http://www.palgrave-journals.com/abm/index.html.

52195 ■ Basingstoke Gazette
Newsquest Media Group Ltd.
Peltone Rd.
Basingstoke RG21 6YD, United Kingdom
Ph: 44 1256 461131
Newspaper featuring up to date information on local news and sports. **Key Personnel:** Kassey Chandler, Contact. **Subscription Rates:** 1 individuals Monday; 1.75 individuals Thursday. **Remarks:** Accepts advertising. **URL:** http://www.basingstokegazette.co.uk/. **Circ:** (Not Reported)

52196 ■ BioSocieties
Palgrave Macmillan
Houndsmills
Basingstoke RG21 6XS, United Kingdom
Ph: 44 1256 329242
Fax: 44 1256 479476
Publication E-mail: biosocieties@lse.ac.uk
Publisher E-mail: booksellers@palgrave.com
Journal featuring topics on life sciences and biomedicine focusing on issues affecting the society. **Freq:** Quarterly. **Key Personnel:** Prof. Adele Clarke, Editor, adele.clarke@ucsf.edu; Prof. Nikolas Rose, Editor, n.rose@lse.ac.uk; Dr. Ilina Singh, Editor, i.a.singh@lse.ac.uk. **ISSN:** 1745-8552. **Subscription Rates:** 28 other countries print + online; US$50 individuals print + online; 232 institutions, other countries print; US$418 institutions print. **URL:** http://www.palgrave-journals.com/biosoc.

52197 ■ British Politics
Palgrave Macmillan
Houndsmills
Basingstoke RG21 6XS, United Kingdom
Ph: 44 1256 329242
Fax: 44 1256 479476
Publisher E-mail: booksellers@palgrave.com
Journal devoted to British politics. **Freq:** 4/yr. **Key Personnel:** Steven Kettell, Editor, s.kettell@warwick.ac.uk; David Marsh, Editor; Colin Hay, Editor; Peter Kerr, Editor, p.kerr@bham.ac.uk. **ISSN:** 1746-918X. **Subscription Rates:** 395 institutions, other countries print; US$736 institutions print; 58 other countries print and online; US$108 individuals print and online. **URL:** http://www.palgrave-journals.com/bp/index.html.

52198 ■ Clinical Pharmacology and Therapeutics
Nature Publishing Group
Brunel Rd.
Houndsmills
Basingstoke RG21 6XS, United Kingdom
Ph: 44 12 56329242
Fax: 44 12 56842754
Peer-reviewed journal covering the study of the nature, action, efficacy, and total evaluation of drugs as they are used in humans. **Founded:** Oct. 1960. **Freq:** Monthly. **Print Method:** Offset. **Trim Size:** 8 1/4 x 10 7/8. **Cols./Page:** 2. **Col. Width:** 39 nonpareils. **Col. Depth:** 140 agate lines. **Key Personnel:** Scott Waldman, MD, Editor-in-Chief. **ISSN:** 0009-9236. **Subscription Rates:** US$304 individuals print and online; US$273 individuals online only; EUR264 individuals Europe (print and online); EUR238 individuals Europe (online only); 44,700¥

individuals Japan (print and online); 40,600¥ individuals Japan (online only); 169 other countries print and online; 153 other countries online only. **Remarks:** Accepts advertising. **URL:** http://www.nature.com/clpt/index.html. **Circ:** Combined ‡3,800

52199 ■ Economic & Labour Market Review
Palgrave Macmillan
Houndsmills
Basingstoke RG21 6XS, United Kingdom
Ph: 44 1256 329242
Fax: 44 1256 479476
Publisher E-mail: booksellers@palgrave.com
Journal describing more comprehensive picture of the UK economy and labor market. **Freq:** Monthly. **Key Personnel:** Graeme Chamberlin, Editor, phone 44 20 70142029, graeme.chamberlin@ons.gsi.gov.uk. **ISSN:** 1751-8326. **Subscription Rates:** 232 institutions, other countries print; US$440 institutions print. **URL:** http://www.palgrave-journals.com/elmr/index.html.

52200 ■ European Journal of Clinical Nutrition
Nature Publishing Group
Brunel Rd.
Houndmills
Basingstoke RG21 6XS, United Kingdom
Ph: 44 12 56329242
Fax: 44 12 56842754
Publication E-mail: ejcn@nature.com
Publication covering the theoretical aspects of nutrition, epidemiology of disease, community nutrition, and education. **Freq:** Monthly. **Key Personnel:** Prof. Prakash Shetty, Editor-in-Chief, shetty.ejcn@googlemail.com. **ISSN:** 0954-3007. **Subscription Rates:** US$522 individuals combined print and online; EUR414 individuals combined print and online; 71,000¥ individuals combined print and online; 267.54 individuals combined print and online; US$469 individuals online only; EUR373 individuals online only; 63,700¥ individuals online only; 240.45 individuals online only. **Remarks:** Accepts advertising. **URL:** http://www.nature.com/ejcn. **Ad Rates:** BW: 655, 4C: 1,340. **Circ:** (Not Reported)

52201 ■ European Management Review
Palgrave Macmillan
Houndsmills
Basingstoke RG21 6XS, United Kingdom
Ph: 44 1256 329242
Fax: 44 1256 479476
Publisher E-mail: booksellers@palgrave.com
Journal focusing on the International Management Research supported by the European Academy of Management. **Freq:** 4/yr. **Key Personnel:** Alfonso Gambardella, Editor, bruce.kogut@columbia.edu; Maurizio Zollo, Editor. **ISSN:** 1740-4754. **Subscription Rates:** 397 institutions, other countries print; EUR567 institutions print; US$753 institutions print; 98 other countries print and online; EUR142 other countries print and online; US$186 individuals print and online. **URL:** http://www.palgrave-journals.com/emr/index.html.

52202 ■ European Political Science
Palgrave Macmillan
Houndsmills
Basingstoke RG21 6XS, United Kingdom
Ph: 44 1256 329242
Fax: 44 1256 479476
Publisher E-mail: booksellers@palgrave.com
Journal of the European Consortium for Political Research. **Freq:** Quarterly. **Key Personnel:** Jonathan W. Moses, Editor; Martin Bull, Editor, m.j.bull@salford.ac.uk; Luis de Sousa, Editor. **ISSN:** 1680-4333. **Subscription Rates:** 273 institutions, other countries print; US$519 institutions print; EUR390 institutions print; 58 other countries print and online; US$108 individuals print and online; EUR83 individuals print and online. **URL:** http://www.palgrave-journals.com/eps/index.html.

52203 ■ EYE
Nature Publishing Group
Brunel Rd.
Houndmills
Basingstoke RG21 6XS, United Kingdom
Ph: 44 12 56329242
Fax: 44 12 56842754
Publication covering ophthalmology. **Freq:** Monthly. **Print Method:** Web. **Trim Size:** 210 x 280 mm. **Key Personnel:** Steve Beet, Editorial Asst.; Prof. Andrew Lotery, Editor-in-Chief, a.j.lotery@soton.ac.uk. **ISSN:** 0950-222X. **Subscription Rates:** US$297 individuals combined print and online; EUR277 individuals combined print and online; 47,400¥ individuals combined print and online; 179 other countries combined print and online;

US$270 individuals online only; EUR253 individuals online only; 43,300¥ individuals online only; 163.19 other countries online only. **Remarks:** Advertising accepted; rates available upon request. **URL:** http://www.nature.com/eye/index.html. **Circ:** 3,500

52204 ■ Family Spending
Palgrave Macmillan
Houndsmills
Basingstoke RG21 6XS, United Kingdom
Ph: 44 1256 329242
Fax: 44 1256 479476
Publisher E-mail: booksellers@palgrave.com
Journal focusing on the trends in household expenditures. **Freq:** Quarterly. **Key Personnel:** Rachel Skentelbery, Editor, efs@ons.gsi.gov.uk. **ISSN:** 0965-1403. **URL:** http://www.palgrave-journals.com/fsp/index.html.

52205 ■ Geneva Papers on Risk and Insurance Issues and Practice
Palgrave Macmillan
Houndsmills
Basingstoke RG21 6XS, United Kingdom
Ph: 44 1256 329242
Fax: 44 1256 479476
Publisher E-mail: booksellers@palgrave.com
Insurance publication. **Founded:** 1976. **Freq:** Quarterly. **Key Personnel:** Patrick M. Liedtke, Editor-in-Chief; Gerry Dickinson, Dep. Ed.; Christophe Courbage, Dep. Ed. **ISSN:** 1018-5895. **Subscription Rates:** 255 institutions, other countries print; EUR363 institutions print; US$433 institutions print; 72 other countries print and online; EUR102 individuals print and online; US$134 individuals print and online. **URL:** http://www.palgrave-journals.com/gpp/index.html. **Circ:** 950

52206 ■ Health Statistics Quarterly
Palgrave Macmillan
Houndsmills
Basingstoke RG21 6XS, United Kingdom
Ph: 44 1256 329242
Fax: 44 1256 479476
Publisher E-mail: booksellers@palgrave.com
Journal covering health statistics. **Freq:** Quarterly. **Key Personnel:** Myer Glickman, Editor. **ISSN:** 1465-1645. **Subscription Rates:** 126 institutions, other countries print; US$240 institutions print. **URL:** http://www.palgrave-journals.com/hsq/index.html.

52207 ■ Information Visualization
Palgrave Macmillan
Houndsmills
Basingstoke RG21 6XS, United Kingdom
Ph: 44 1256 329242
Fax: 44 1256 479476
Publisher E-mail: booksellers@palgrave.com
Peer-reviewed journal covering the theories, methodologies, techniques and evaluations of information visualization and its applications. **Freq:** 4/yr. **Key Personnel:** Chaomei Chen, Editor-in-Chief. **ISSN:** 1473-8716. **Subscription Rates:** 569 institutions, other countries print; US$1,058 institutions print; 200 other countries print and online; US$372 individuals print and online. **URL:** http://www.palgrave-journals.com/ivs/index.html. **Circ:** 350

52208 ■ International Abstracts in Operations Research
Palgrave Macmillan
Houndsmills
Basingstoke RG21 6XS, United Kingdom
Ph: 44 1256 329242
Fax: 44 1256 479476
Publisher E-mail: booksellers@palgrave.com
Journal focusing on comprehensive, unique and continually growing reference database. **Freq:** 8/yr. **Key Personnel:** Dr. David K. Smith, Editor, phone 44 1392 264478, d.k.smith@exeter.ac.uk. **ISSN:** 0020-580X. **Subscription Rates:** 952 institutions, other countries; US$1,618 institutions. **URL:** http://www.palgrave-journals.com/iaor/index.html.

52209 ■ International Journal of Disclosure and Governance
Palgrave Macmillan
Houndsmills
Basingstoke RG21 6XS, United Kingdom
Ph: 44 1256 329242
Fax: 44 1256 479476

Publisher E-mail: booksellers@palgrave.com
Journal publishing authoritative, refereed articles about the latest thinking, techniques and developments on all aspects of governance and disclosure. **Freq:** Quarterly. **Key Personnel:** Jeffrey Callen, Exec. Ed. Board; Prof. Dan Palmon, Exec. Ed. Board; Prof. Michael G. Alles, Editor; John Friedland, Exec. Ed. Board. **ISSN:** 1741-3591. **Subscription Rates:** 346. institutions, other countries print; 148 other countries print and online; US$266 individuals print and online; US$622 institutions print. **URL:** http://www.palgrave-journals.com/jdg/index.html.

52210 ■ International Journal of Educational Advancement
Palgrave Macmillan
Houndsmills
Basingstoke RG21 6XS, United Kingdom
Ph: 44 1256 329242
Fax: 44 1256 479476
Publisher E-mail: booksellers@palgrave.com
Journal publishing articles reflecting the integration of advancement into the strategic planning and mission statements of educational institutions with thought-provoking, topical articles from academic researchers and advancement professionals working in schools, colleges, and universities, providing a forum for the equally important aspects of alumni relations, fund raising, communications, public relations, and marketing. **Freq:** 4/yr. **Key Personnel:** Timothy C. Caboni, Editor; Chris Chapleo, Assoc. Ed.; David J. Weerts, Assoc. Ed. **ISSN:** 1744-6503. **Subscription Rates:** 214 institutions, other countries print; US$386 institutions print; 135 other countries print and online; US$244 individuals print and online. **URL:** http://www.palgrave-journals.com/ijea/index.html.

52211 ■ International Journal of Obesity
Nature Publishing Group
Brunel Rd.
Houndmills
Basingstoke RG21 6XS, United Kingdom
Ph: 44 12 56329242
Fax: 44 12 56842754
Journal covering obesity. **Freq:** Monthly. **Key Personnel:** Prof. Ian MacDonald, Editor, phone 44 115 8230119, ijo@nottingham.ac.uk; Richard Atkinson, Editor, vfschmidt@earthlink.net. **ISSN:** 0307-0565. **Subscription Rates:** US$625 institutions combined print and online; EUR497 institutions combined print and online; 84,900¥ institutions combined print and online; 320.59 institutions combined print and online; US$563 individuals online only; EUR448 individuals online only; 76,600¥ individuals online only; 288.99 individuals online only. **URL:** http://www.nature.com/ijo/index.html.

52212 ■ Journal of Banking Regulation
Palgrave Macmillan
Houndsmills
Basingstoke RG21 6XS, United Kingdom
Ph: 44 1256 329242
Fax: 44 1256 479476
Publisher E-mail: booksellers@palgrave.com
Journal providing a forum for analysis from leading representatives of regulation, practice and banking law. Covers banking regulation in its broadest sense, across the full field of financial services, from the protection of ordinary citizens' savings on the one hand to the regulation of multi-national financial institutions with a taste for huge risk and high profit on the other. **Freq:** Quarterly. **Key Personnel:** William Blair, Exec. Ed.; Mads Andenas, Exec. Ed.; Dr. Dalvinder Singh, Editor; Geoffrey Wood, Exec. Ed.; Rosa Maria Lastra, Exec. Ed. **ISSN:** 1745-6452. **Subscription Rates:** US$903 institutions print; US$235 individuals print and online; 485 institutions, other countries print; 126 other countries print and online. **URL:** http://www.palgrave-journals.com/jbr/index.html.

52213 ■ Journal of Building Appraisal
Palgrave Macmillan
Houndsmills
Basingstoke RG21 6XS, United Kingdom
Ph: 44 1256 329242
Fax: 44 1256 479476
Publisher E-mail: booksellers@palgrave.com
Journal dealing with building condition, defects, repair and maintenance. **Freq:** 4/yr. **Key Personnel:** Simon McLean, Managing Editor. **ISSN:** 1742-8262. **Subscrip-

tion **Rates:** US$447 institutions print; 240 institutions, other countries print. **URL:** http://www.palgrave-journals. com/jba/index.html.

52214 ■ Journal of Commercial Biotechnology
Palgrave Macmillan
Houndmills
Basingstoke RG21 6XS, United Kingdom
Ph: 44 1256 329242
Fax: 44 1256 479476
Publisher E-mail: booksellers@palgrave.com
International publication for bioscience business professionals, addressing topics such as: corporate strategy, financing, bioethics, public and investor relations, market analysis and legal and regulatory issues. **Freq:** Quarterly. **Key Personnel:** Dr. Yali Friedman, PhD, Managing Editor, jcbeditor@palgrave.com; Neil Henderson, Publishing Mgr., n.henderson@palgrave.com. **ISSN:** 1462-8732. **Subscription Rates:** 554 institutions print; 139 individuals print and online; US$1,031 institutions print; US$259 individuals print and online. **URL:** http://www.palgrave-journals.com/jcb/index.html. **Circ:** 400

52215 ■ Journal of Digital Asset Management
Palgrave Macmillan
Houndmills
Basingstoke RG21 6XS, United Kingdom
Ph: 44 1256 329242
Fax: 44 1256 479476
Publisher E-mail: booksellers@palgrave.com
Journal for business executives involved in developing and deploying DAM systems and those concerned with managing digital assets. Publishes peer-reviewed articles demonstrating how successful DAM systems have been defined, designed and implemented, as well as considering the ROI which can be generated by DAM projects, and how digital assets can be leveraged to open up new opportunities. **Freq:** Bimonthly. **Key Personnel:** Michael Moon, Editor-in-Chief; John Horodyski, Managing Editor. **ISSN:** 1743-6540. **Subscription Rates:** US$707 institutions print; 380 institutions, other countries print. **URL:** http://www.palgrave-journals.com/dam/index.html.

52216 ■ Journal of Financial Services Marketing
Palgrave Macmillan
Houndmills
Basingstoke RG21 6XS, United Kingdom
Ph: 44 1256 329242
Fax: 44 1256 479476
Publisher E-mail: booksellers@palgrave.com
International forum for financial services marketers. Journal publishing case studies from marketers worldwide, applied research from leading business schools, research institutes and universities, forum papers by expert practitioners and academics sharing thought-provoking and challenging papers, an authoritative series of legal papers which examine in detail the major changes in legislation and book reviews, providing a 'thumbnail' of best practice in marketing within the financial services field. **Freq:** 4/yr. **Key Personnel:** Tina Harrison, Editor; Cleopatra Veloutsou, Book Review Ed. **ISSN:** 1363-0539. **Subscription Rates:** 524 institutions, other countries print; US$1,025 institutions print. **URL:** http://www.palgrave-journals.com/fsm/index.html. **Circ:** 400

52217 ■ Journal of Generic Medicines
Palgrave Macmillan
Houndmills
Basingstoke RG21 6XS, United Kingdom
Ph: 44 1256 329242
Fax: 44 1256 479476
Publisher E-mail: booksellers@palgrave.com
Journal publishing analyses, briefings and updates which are of direct relevance to practitioners and that meet the highest intellectual standards and is essential for reading to everyone involved in the generic pharmaceuticals industry. **Freq:** Quarterly. **Key Personnel:** Greg Perry, Consulting Ed.; Fabiana M. Jorge, Managing Editor. **ISSN:** 1741-1343. **Subscription Rates:** 350 institutions, other countries print; US$626 institutions print. **URL:** http://www.palgrave-journals.com/jgm/index.html.

52218 ■ Journal of Medical Marketing
Palgrave Macmillan
Houndmills
Basingstoke RG21 6XS, United Kingdom

Ph: 44 1256 329242
Fax: 44 1256 479476
Publisher E-mail: booksellers@palgrave.com
Peer-reviewed journal publishing practice papers, research articles and professional briefings on competitive strategies of leading players in the global market place, the impact of emerging market segments, alternative strategies for new market entry and existing market share defense, and product strategies at all stages of the life cycle. **Freq:** Quarterly. **Key Personnel:** Dr. Brian D. Smith, Editor; Dr. Peter Dumovic, Editor; Dr. William Kilgallon, Editor. **ISSN:** 1745-7904. **Subscription Rates:** 399 institutions, other countries print; US$741 institutions print; 164 other countries print and online; US$305 individuals print and online. **URL:** http://www.palgrave-journals.com/jmm/index.html. **Circ:** 550

52219 ■ Journal of Public Health Policy
Palgrave Macmillan
Houndmills
Basingstoke RG21 6XS, United Kingdom
Ph: 44 1256 329242
Fax: 44 1256 479476
Publication E-mail: jphp@umb.edu
Publisher E-mail: booksellers@palgrave.com
Journal covering the epidemiologic and social foundations of public health policy. **Freq:** Quarterly. **Key Personnel:** Anthony Robbins, Editor; Phyllis Freeman, Editor. **ISSN:** 0197-5897. **Subscription Rates:** 205 institutions Europe; print; US$383 institutions print; 205 institutions rest of the world; print; 48 individuals Europe; print + online; US$82 individuals print + online; 48 individuals rest of the world; print + online. **URL:** http://www.palgrave-journals.com/jphp/index.html.

52220 ■ Journal of Retail and Leisure Property
Palgrave Macmillan
Houndmills
Basingstoke RG21 6XS, United Kingdom
Ph: 44 1256 329242
Fax: 44 1256 479476
Publisher E-mail: booksellers@palgrave.com
Journal for professionals responsible for managing or advising on retail and leisure property. **Freq:** 4/yr. **Key Personnel:** Prof. Michael Pitt, Managing Editor, phone 44 151 2312805, m.r.pitt@ljmu.ac.uk. **ISSN:** 1479-1110. **Subscription Rates:** US$497 institutions print; 267 institutions, other countries print; 118 other countries print and online; US$220 individuals print and online. **URL:** http://www.palgrave-journals.com/rlp/index.html.

52221 ■ Journal of Revenue and Pricing Management
Palgrave Macmillan
Houndmills
Basingstoke RG21 6XS, United Kingdom
Ph: 44 1256 329242
Fax: 44 1256 479476
Publisher E-mail: booksellers@palgrave.com
Peer-reviewed journal publishing articles and briefings on major developments, new strategic thinking and applied research in the fields of revenue management and pricing. **Freq:** Quarterly. **Key Personnel:** Dr. Ian Yeoman, Editor; Robert Shumsky, Editorial Board; Prof. Georgia Perakis, Editor. **ISSN:** 1476-6930. **Subscription Rates:** 515 institutions, other countries print; US$959 institutions print; 126 other countries print and online; US$234 individuals print and online. **URL:** http://www.palgrave-journals.com/rpm/index.html. **Circ:** 450

52222 ■ Latino Studies
Palgrave Macmillan
Houndmills
Basingstoke RG21 6XS, United Kingdom
Ph: 44 1256 329242
Fax: 44 1256 479476
Publisher E-mail: booksellers@palgrave.com
Peer-reviewed journal covering Latin American and Latino studies. **Founded:** 2003. **Freq:** Quarterly. **Key Personnel:** Suzanne Oboler, Editor, latstu@jjay.cuny.edu. **ISSN:** 1476-3435. **Subscription Rates:** 352 institutions, other countries print; US$654 institutions print; 48 other countries print and online; US$89 individuals print and online. **URL:** http://www.palgrave-journals.com/lst/index.html.

52223 ■ Maritime Economics and Logistics
Palgrave Macmillan
Houndmills
Basingstoke RG21 6XS, United Kingdom

Ph: 44 1256 329242
Fax: 44 1256 479476
Publisher E-mail: booksellers@palgrave.com
Peer-reviewed journal covering the field of maritime economics, maritime policy, transport economics and applied economics. **Freq:** Quarterly. **Key Personnel:** Prof. H.E. Haralambides, Editor; D. Kontou, Asst. Ed. **ISSN:** 1479-2931. **Subscription Rates:** 554 institutions, other countries print; US$1,031 institutions print; 220 other countries print and online; US$410 individuals print and online. **URL:** http://www.palgrave-journals.com/mel/index.html. **Formerly:** International Journal of Maritime Economics. **Circ:** 600

52224 ■ Molecular Therapy
Nature Publishing Group
Brunel Rd.
Houndmills
Basingstoke RG21 6XS, United Kingdom
Ph: 44 12 56329242
Fax: 44 12 56842754
Peer-reviewed journal covering genetics, gene transfer, gene regulation, gene discovery, cell therapy, experimental models, correction of genetic and acquired diseases, and clinical trials. **Freq:** Monthly. **Key Personnel:** Robert M. Frederickson, PhD, Editor, editor@molther.org; I.M. Verma, Founding Ed.; David Williams, Editor-in-Chief, dawilliams@childrens.harvard.edu. **ISSN:** 1525-0016. **Subscription Rates:** US$573 individuals print and online; EUR498 individuals print and online; 88,400¥ individuals print and online (Japan and Korea); US$516 individuals online only; 287 other countries online only; 75,900¥ individuals online only (Japan and Korea); EUR450 individuals online only; 319 other countries print and online. **URL:** http://www.nature.com/mt/index.html.

52225 ■ Monthly Digest of Statistics
Palgrave Macmillan
Houndmills
Basingstoke RG21 6XS, United Kingdom
Ph: 44 1256 329242
Fax: 44 1256 479476
Publisher E-mail: booksellers@palgrave.com
Digest of statistics providing the latest statistics for UK businesses, economy and society. **Freq:** Monthly. **Key Personnel:** Dilys Rosen, Editor, dilys.rosen@ons.gsi.gov.uk. **ISSN:** 0308-6666. **Subscription Rates:** 249 institutions, other countries print; US$4,730 institutions print. **URL:** http://www.palgrave-journals.com/mds/index.html.

52226 ■ Nature
Macmillan Publishers Ltd.
Houndmills
Basingstoke RG21 6XS, United Kingdom
Ph: 44 1256 329242
Fax: 44 1256 479476
Publisher E-mail: info@macmillan.com
Publication covering zoology and wildlife conservation. **Freq:** Weekly. **Key Personnel:** Nick Campbell, Managing Editor; Dr. Philip Campbell, Editor-in-Chief; Maxine Clarke, Publishing Exec. Ed. **ISSN:** 0028-0836. **Subscription Rates:** US$199 individuals print and online; US$338 two years print and online; 135 individuals print and online; 230 two years print and online. **URL:** http://international.macmillan.com/ContentDetails.aspx?id=1054; http://www.nature.com/nature/index.html. **Circ:** ‡65,955

52227 ■ Pensions
Palgrave Macmillan
Houndmills
Basingstoke RG21 6XS, United Kingdom
Ph: 44 1256 329242
Fax: 44 1256 479476
Publisher E-mail: booksellers@palgrave.com
Journal for all pension professionals concerned with the day to day practice of pensions administration, law, compliance and investment. **Subtitle:** An International Journal. **Freq:** Quarterly. **Key Personnel:** Robin Ellison, Editor; Ian Neale, Book Review Ed. **ISSN:** 1478-5315. **Subscription Rates:** US$650 institutions print; 352 institutions, other countries print. **URL:** http://www.palgrave-journals.com/pm/index.html.

52228 ■ Place Branding
Palgrave Macmillan
Houndmills
Basingstoke RG21 6XS, United Kingdom
Ph: 44 1256 329242

Fax: 44 1256 479476
Publisher E-mail: booksellers@palgrave.com
Peer-reviewed journal seeking to broaden the understanding of the nature, purposes and benefits of place branding, and to demonstrate how place branding strategies are implemented in practice. **Freq:** Quarterly. **Key Personnel:** Simon Anholt, Editor. **ISSN:** 1744-0696. **Subscription Rates:** US$553 institutions print only; 297 institutions, other countries print only; US$224 individuals print and online; 120 other countries print and online. **URL:** http://www.palgrave-journals.com/pb/index.html. **Circ:** 400

52229 ■ Regional Trends
Palgrave Macmillan
Houndsmills
Basingstoke RG21 6XS, United Kingdom
Ph: 44 1256 329242
Fax: 44 1256 479476
Publication E-mail: regional.trends@ons.gsi.gov.uk
Publisher E-mail: booksellers@palgrave.com
Journal featuring wide range of demographic, social, industrial and economic statistics, covering aspects of life in the regions. **Freq:** Annual. **Key Personnel:** Frances Sly, Editor, efs@ons.gsi.gov.uk. **ISSN:** 0261-1783. **URL:** http://www.palgrave-journals.com/rt/index.html.

52230 ■ Social Trends
Palgrave Macmillan
Houndsmills
Basingstoke RG21 6XS, United Kingdom
Ph: 44 1256 329242
Fax: 44 1256 479476
Publication E-mail: social.trends@ons.gsi.gov.uk
Publisher E-mail: booksellers@palgrave.com
Journal featuring social and economic statistical data. **Freq:** Annual. **Key Personnel:** Abigail Seif, Editor. **ISSN:** 0306-7742. **URL:** http://www.palgrave-journals.com/st/index.html.

52231 ■ Subjectivity
Palgrave Macmillan
Houndsmills
Basingstoke RG21 6XS, United Kingdom
Ph: 44 1256 329242
Fax: 44 1256 479476
Publication E-mail: subjectivity@palgrave.com
Publisher E-mail: booksellers@palgrave.com
Peer-reviewed journal featuring articles on social and political issues. **Freq:** Quarterly. **Key Personnel:** Lisa Blackman, Editor, l.blackman@gold.ac.uk; John Cromby, Editor, j.cromby@lboro.ac.uk; Derek Hook, Editor, d.w.hook@lse.ac.uk; Dimitris Papadopoulos, Editor, papadopoulosd@cardiff.ac.uk; Valerie Walkerdine, Editor, walkerdinev@cardiff.ac.uk. **ISSN:** 1755-6341. **Subscription Rates:** 331 institutions, other countries print; US$562 institutions print; 58 individuals print + online; US$108 other countries print + online. **URL:** http://www.palgrave-journals.com/sub/index.html. **Circ:** 400

52232 ■ Tourism and Hospitality Research
Palgrave Macmillan
Houndsmills
Basingstoke RG21 6XS, United Kingdom
Ph: 44 1256 329242
Fax: 44 1256 479476
Publisher E-mail: booksellers@palgrave.com
Journal publishing peer-reviewed, innovative, cross-disciplinary, international research papers, case-studies describing current attitudes and behavior, investigating the how and why of what is happening, identifying important new methodologies and approaches, defining the boundaries and landscape of tourism and hospitality, detecting significant and emerging trends and applying to day-to-day practice. **Freq:** 4/yr. **Key Personnel:** Prof. Andrew Lockwood, Managing Editor; Prof. Richard Butler, Ed. Emeritus. **ISSN:** 1467-3584. **Subscription Rates:** 298 institutions, other countries print; 136 other countries print and online; US$555 institutions print; US$253 individuals print and online. **URL:** http://www.palgrave-journals.com/thr/index.html.

52233 ■ United Kingdom Economic Accounts
Palgrave Macmillan
Houndsmills
Basingstoke RG21 6XS, United Kingdom
Ph: 44 1256 329242
Fax: 44 1256 479476

Publisher E-mail: booksellers@palgrave.com
Journal covering detailed estimates of national product, income and expenditure for the United Kingdom. **Freq:** Quarterly. **Key Personnel:** John Dye, Editor, phone 44 20 75336045, john.dye@ons.gsi.gov.uk. **ISSN:** 1350-4401. **Subscription Rates:** 114 institutions, other countries print; US$216 institutions print. **URL:** http://www.palgrave-journals.com/ukea/index.html.

52234 ■ Urban Design International
Palgrave Macmillan
Houndsmills
Basingstoke RG21 6XS, United Kingdom
Ph: 44 1256 329242
Fax: 44 1256 479476
Publisher E-mail: booksellers@palgrave.com
Peer-reviewed journal covering the field of urban design and management. **Freq:** Quarterly. **Key Personnel:** Vida Maliene, Editor; Michael Pitt, Editor. **ISSN:** 1357-5317. **Subscription Rates:** 497 institutions, other countries print; US$925 institutions print; 84 other countries print and online; US$156 individuals print and online. **URL:** http://www.palgrave-journals.com/udi/index.html.

52235 ■ Kestrel-FM - 107.6
Ste. 2, Paddington House
Festival Pl.
Hampshire
Basingstoke RG21 7LJ, United Kingdom
Ph: 44 1256 694040
Fax: 44 1256 694111
E-mail: studio@kestrelfm.com
Format: Contemporary Hit Radio (CHR). **Owner:** Tindle Radio, at above address. **URL:** http://www.kestrelfm.com/.

Bath

52236 ■ Airline Industry Information
M2 Communications Ltd.
1 Soulsbury View
The Normans
Bathampton
Bath BA2 6TF, United Kingdom
Ph: 44 20 70470200
Fax: 44 20 70570200
Publisher E-mail: info@m2.com
Publication covering the transportation industry. **Freq:** Daily. **Remarks:** Advertising not accepted. **URL:** http://www.m2.com/m2/web/publication.php/aii. **Circ:** (Not Reported)

52237 ■ Corporate IT Update
M2 Communications Ltd.
1 Soulsbury View
The Normans
Bathampton
Bath BA2 6TF, United Kingdom
Ph: 44 20 70470200
Fax: 44 20 70570200
Publisher E-mail: info@m2.com
Publication for the telecommunications industry. **Remarks:** Advertising not accepted. **URL:** http://www.m2.com/m2/web/publication.php/ciu. **Circ:** (Not Reported)

52238 ■ Digital Home
Future Publishing Ltd.
30 Monmouth St.
Bath BA1 2BW, United Kingdom
Publisher E-mail: future@subscription.co.uk
Magazine covering ultimate entertainment technology. **Key Personnel:** Nick Merritt, Editor-in-Chief, eic@techradar.com. **URL:** http://www.techradar.com/news/digital-home.

52239 ■ Flyer
Seager Publishing
9 Riverside Ct.
Lower Bristol Rd.
Bath BA2 3DZ, United Kingdom
Ph: 44 12 25481440
Fax: 44 12 25481262
Magazine covering aviation for pilots of light aircraft and airline pilots. **Freq:** Monthly 13/yr. **Key Personnel:** Ian Waller, Editor, ianw@flyermag.co.uk; Kate Munday, Production Mgr., katem@flyermag.co.uk; Ian Seager, Publisher, Mng. Dir., ians@flyermag.co.uk. **Subscription Rates:** 32.45 individuals U.K.; 53 individuals

Europe; 66 elsewhere; 63.45 two years U.K.; 104 two years Europe; 128 two years elsewhere. **Remarks:** Accepts advertising. **URL:** http://www.flyer.co.uk/. **Circ:** (Not Reported)

52240 ■ French Magazine
Merricks Media Ltd.
3-4 Riverside Ct.
Lower Bristol Rd.
Bath BA2 3DZ, United Kingdom
Ph: 44 12 25786800
Fax: 44 12 25786801
Lifestyle resource for people who love France or dream of owning a property there. **Freq:** Monthly. **Key Personnel:** Justin Postlethwaite, Editor. **Subscription Rates:** 49 individuals 24 issues; 28.50 individuals 12 issues; 23 individuals 6 issues; EUR51 individuals Europe; 12 issues; 71 other countries 12 issues. **Remarks:** Accepts advertising. **URL:** http://www.frenchentree.com/french-magazine/. **Circ:** (Not Reported)

52241 ■ Geochemistry
Geological Society Publishing House
Unit 7, Brassmill Enterprise Center
Brassmill Ln.
Bath BA1 3JN, United Kingdom
Ph: 44 12 25445046
Fax: 44 12 25442836
Publisher E-mail: sales@geolsoc.org.uk
Journal that covers geochemistry and the exploration and study of mineral resources, and related fields, including the geochemistry of the environment. **Subtitle:** Exploration, Environment, Analysis. **Freq:** Quarterly. **Key Personnel:** Gwendy Hall, Editor-in-Chief; R. Bowell, Assoc. Ed. **ISSN:** 1467-7873. **Subscription Rates:** 243.90 individuals print and online UK; 236 individuals print and online Europe; 236 individuals print and online rest of world; US$473 individuals print and online rest of world; 233.83 individuals online only UK; 225 individuals online only Europe; 225 individuals online only rest of the world; US$450 individuals online only rest of the world. **Remarks:** Accepts advertising. **URL:** http://geea.geoscienceworld.org/; http://www.geolsoc.org.uk/gsl/publications/journals/geea. **Ad Rates:** BW: 600. **Circ:** (Not Reported)

52242 ■ Good Woodworking
Future Publishing
Beauford Ct.
30 Monmouth St.
Bath BA1 2BW, United Kingdom
Ph: 44 12 25442244
Fax: 44 12 25822836
Publication E-mail: goodwood@futurenet.co.uk
Publisher E-mail: future@subscription.co.uk
Consumer magazine covering woodworking for professionals and hobbyists. **Founded:** Nov. 1992. **Freq:** 13/yr. **Subscription Rates:** 3.30 single issue; 45.50 individuals to UK; 59 individuals to Europe; 59 individuals rest of the world. **Remarks:** Accepts advertising. **URL:** http://www.futurelicensing.com/home/titles/GWW; http://www.subscription.co.uk/store/displayitem.asp?sid=3&id=5194. **Circ:** Paid 14,800

52243 ■ Gothic Studies
Manchester University Press
Newton Bldg.
Bath Spa University College
Bath BA2 9BN, United Kingdom
Publisher E-mail: m.frost@manchester.ac.uk
Journal on Gothic studies from the eighteenth century to the present day. It provides a platform for dialogue and cultural criticism. **Freq:** Semiannual May and November. **Key Personnel:** William Hughes, Editor, w.hughes@bathspa.ac.uk; Elisabeth Bronfen, Advisory Board; Glennis Byron, Advisory Board; Pierre Arnaud, Advisory Board; Ben Brabon, Advisory Board; Jodey Castricano, Advisory Board; Fred Botting, Advisory Board. **ISSN:** 1362-7937. **Subscription Rates:** EUR155 institutions; EUR50 individuals; 119 institutions; US$212 institutions; 40 individuals; US$74 individuals. **URL:** http://www.manchesteruniversitypress.co.uk/journals/journal.asp?id=2.

52244 ■ International Journal of Behavioural Accounting and Finance
Inderscience Enterprises Limited
c/o Richard Fairchild, Ed.-in-Ch,
University of Bath
School of Management

Circulation: ★ = ABC; △ = BPA; ♦ = CAC; • = CCAB; ❑ = VAC; ⊕ = PO Statement; ‡ = Publisher's Report; Boldface figures = sworn; Light figures = estimated.

Gale Directory of Publications & Broadcast Media/147th Ed.   5571

Claverton Down
Bath BA2 7AY, United Kingdom
Journal focusing on behavioral issues in accounting and finance across financial markets and in corporate or governmental contexts in different countries. **Freq:** 4/yr. **Key Personnel:** Richard Fairchild, Editor-in-Chief, mnsrf@bath.ac.uk. **ISSN:** 1753-1969. **Subscription Rates:** EUR494 individuals print or online; EUR672 individuals print and online. **URL:** http://www.inderscience.com/browse/index.php?journalID=237.

52245 ■ Internet Business News
M2 Communications Ltd.
1 Soulsbury View
The Normans
Bathampton
Bath BA2 6TF, United Kingdom
Ph: 44 20 70470200
Fax: 44 20 70570200
Publisher E-mail: info@m2.com
Online publication covering computers and the office automation industry. **Freq:** Weekly (Thurs.). **ISSN:** 1363-9919. **Remarks:** Advertising not accepted. **URL:** http://www.m2.com/m2/web/publication.php/ibn. **Circ:** (Not Reported)

52246 ■ Italia!
Anthem Publishing Limited
Piccadilly House, Ste. 6
London Rd.
Bath BA1 6PL, United Kingdom
Ph: 44 1225 489984
Fax: 44 1225 489980
Publisher E-mail: enquiries@anthem-publishing.com
Magazine for lovers of Italy. **Founded:** Nov. 2004. **Freq:** Monthly. **Key Personnel:** Amanda Robinson, Editor; Becky Ambury, Production Ed.; Jon Bickley, Publishing Dir. **Subscription Rates:** 17.70 individuals 6 issue; 37.90 individuals. **URL:** http://www.italia-magazine.com/.

52247 ■ Journal of Engineering Manufacture
Professional Engineering Publishing
Department Mechanical Engineering
University of Bath
Bath BA2 7AY, United Kingdom
Ph: 44 1225 385376
Fax: 44 1225 386928
Publisher E-mail: sales@portland-services.com
Journal covering developments in engineering manufacture. **Freq:** 12/yr. **Key Personnel:** Prof. P.G. Maropoulos, Editor, p.g.maropoulos@bath.ac.uk. **ISSN:** 0954-4054. **Subscription Rates:** US$3,172 individuals e-only; US$3,521 individuals print & online; 1,911 individuals print & online; 1,722 individuals e-only. **URL:** http://journals.pepublishing.com/content/119784.

52248 ■ Journal of the Geological Society
Geological Society Publishing House
Unit 7, Brassmill Enterprise Center
Brassmill Ln.
Bath BA1 3JN, United Kingdom
Ph: 44 12 25445046
Fax: 44 12 25442836
Publisher E-mail: sales@geolsoc.org.uk
Earth sciences periodical. **Founded:** 1845. **Freq:** Bimonthly. **Print Method:** Litho. **Trim Size:** 276 x 210 mm. **Key Personnel:** Richard England, Advisory Ed.; Duncan McIlroy, Specials Ed. **ISSN:** 0016-7649. **Subscription Rates:** 790 individuals; 879 other countries; US$1,758 other countries. **Remarks:** Advertising not accepted. **URL:** http://jgs.geoscienceworld.org. **Circ:** Paid 500

52249 ■ Journal of Micropalaeontology
Geological Society of London
Brassmill Enterprise Ctr., Unit 7
Brassmill Ln.
Bath BA1 3JN, United Kingdom
Journal covering all aspects of microfossils and their application both in applied studies and basic research. **Key Personnel:** Sarah Gibbs, Staff Ed., sarah.gibbs@geolsoc.org.uk; Prof. Alan Lord, Editor-in-Chief. **ISSN:** 0262-821X. **Subscription Rates:** 205.63 individuals online only; 175 other countries online only; US$350 other countries online only; 223.69 individuals online & print; 193 other countries online & print; US$385 other countries online & print. **URL:** http://www.geolsoc.org.uk/gsl/publications/journals/jm.

52250 ■ Journal of Transport Economics and Policy
University of Bath
School of Management
Claverton Down
Bath BA2 7AY, United Kingdom
Ph: 44 1225 386302
Fax: 44 1225 386767
Publisher E-mail: jtep@management.bath.uk.ac
Publication covering economics. **Founded:** 1967. **Freq:** 3/yr (January, May, September). **Key Personnel:** Mrs. Lachmi Bose, Manager; Prof. S.A. Morrison, Editor-in-Chief. **ISSN:** 0022-5258. **Subscription Rates:** 137 institutions print plus free online; US$267 institutions print plus free online; 25 individuals print only; US$50 individuals print only. **Remarks:** Advertising accepted; rates available upon request. **Online:** Gale. **URL:** http://www.bath.ac.uk/e-journals/jtep/. **Circ:** 1,000

52251 ■ Medical Engineering and Physics
Mosby Inc.
c/o Dr. Sally Clift, Ed.-in-Ch.
Dept. of Mechanical Engineering
University of Bath
Claverton Down
Bath BA2 7AY, United Kingdom
Publisher E-mail: custserv.ehs@elsevier.com
Journal providing a forum for the publication of the latest developments in biomedical engineering, and reflects the essential multidisciplinary nature of the subject. **Freq:** 10/yr. **Key Personnel:** Dr. Sally Clift, Editor-in-Chief, mep@elsevier.com; A. Miles, Assoc. Ed.; M. Viceconti, Assoc. Ed. **ISSN:** 1350-4533. **Subscription Rates:** EUR284 individuals European countries and Iran; US$315 other countries except Europe, Japan and Iran; 37,500¥ individuals; US$2,454 institutions, other countries except Europe, Japan and Iran; EUR2,193 institutions European countries and Iran; 291,400¥ institutions. **Remarks:** Accepts advertising. **URL:** http://www.elsevier.com/wps/find/journaldescription.cws_home/30456/descript iondescription. **Circ:** (Not Reported)

52252 ■ Music Tech Magazine
Anthem Publishing Limited
Piccadilly House, Ste. 6
London Rd.
Bath BA1 6PL, United Kingdom
Ph: 44 1225 489984
Fax: 44 1225 489980
Publisher E-mail: enquiries@anthem-publishing.com
Magazine for recording musicians, engineers, and producers. **Founded:** 2003. **Freq:** 8/yr. **Key Personnel:** Paul Pettengale, Editorial Dir., paul.pettengale@anthem-publishing.com; Simon Lewis, Advertising Dir., simon.lewis@anthem-publishing.com; Jon Bickley, Publishing Dir., jon.bickley@anthem-publishing.com. **Subscription Rates:** 43 individuals UK for credit & direct debit. **URL:** http://www.musictechmag.co.uk/.

52253 ■ PCPlus
Future Publishing Ltd.
30 Monmouth St.
Bath BA1 2BW, United Kingdom
Publication E-mail: pcplus@futurenet.co.uk
Publisher E-mail: future@subscription.co.uk
Magazine covering the personal computing industry. **Subtitle:** IT Enthusiasts, Developers, Professionals. **Founded:** 1983. **Freq:** Monthly. **Trim Size:** A4. **Key Personnel:** Martin Cooper, Editor. **Subscription Rates:** 13.69 individuals quarterly debit. **Remarks:** Accepts advertising. **URL:** http://www.pcplus.co.uk/. **Circ:** Paid ★72,698

52254 ■ Petroleum Geoscience
Geological Society Publishing House
Unit 7, Brassmill Enterprise Center
Brassmill Ln.
Bath BA1 3JN, United Kingdom
Ph: 44 12 25445046
Fax: 44 12 25442836
Publisher E-mail: sales@geolsoc.org.uk
Geoscience publication for those involved in the science and technology associated with rock-related petroleum disciplines. **Freq:** Quarterly. **Key Personnel:** Jean-Jacques Biteau, Editorial Board; Stuart Burley, Editorial Board; Mike Christie, Editorial Board; Mark Allen, Editorial Board; Stuart Buck, Editorial Board; Phil Christie, Editor-in-Chief; P.F. Worthington, Co-Ed. **ISSN:** 1354-0793. **Subscription Rates:** 305 individuals; US$610 individuals; 350 other countries; US$700 other countries.

Remarks: Accepts advertising. **URL:** http://www.geolsoc.org.uk/gsl/publications/journals/pg. **Ad Rates:** BW: EUR824, 4C: EUR1,648. **Circ:** 5,000

52255 ■ Quarterly Journal of Engineering Geology & Hydrogeology
Geological Society Publishing House
Unit 7, Brassmill Enterprise Center
Brassmill Ln.
Bath BA1 3JN, United Kingdom
Ph: 44 12 25445046
Fax: 44 12 25442836
Publisher E-mail: sales@geolsoc.org.uk
Journal covering papers on topics concerning geology as applied to civil engineering, mining practice and water resources. **Freq:** Quarterly. **Key Personnel:** N. Harries, Editorial Board; D. Norbury, Editorial Board; S. Jefferis, Editorial Board; D. Gooddy, Editorial Board; N. Dixon, Editorial Board; J.S. Griffiths, Editorial Board; M. Czerewko, Editorial Board; D. Gunn, Editorial Board; K. Hiscock, Editorial Board; Mike Winter, Editor-in-Chief, phone 44 131 4553230, fax 44 131 4553229, mwinter@trl.co.uk. **ISSN:** 1470-9236. **Subscription Rates:** 451.63 individuals online and print in UK; 434 other countries online and print; US$867 other countries online and print; 434 individuals European Union; 433.58 individuals online only UK; 413 individuals online only Europe; 413 individuals rest of the world online only; US$826 individuals rest of the world online only. **Remarks:** Accepts advertising. **URL:** http://www.geolsoc.org.uk/index.html; http://www.geolsoc.org.uk/gsl/publications/journals/qjegh. **Ad Rates:** BW: 900. **Circ:** 4,000

52256 ■ Quick & Easy Cross Stitch Magazine
Future Publishing
Beauford Ct.
30 Monmouth St.
Bath BA1 2BW, United Kingdom
Ph: 44 12 25442244
Fax: 44 12 25822836
Publisher E-mail: future@subscription.co.uk
Consumer magazine covering cross stitch designs and instruction for beginners and advanced stitchers. **Founded:** Nov. 1995. **Freq:** Monthly. **Key Personnel:** Joanne Weston, Educator; Ruth Spolton, Editor. **Subscription Rates:** 38.50 individuals UK; 76.40 two years Europe. **Remarks:** Accepts advertising. **URL:** http://www.myfavouritemagazines.co.uk. **Circ:** Controlled 27,304

52257 ■ RPS Journal
The Royal Photographic Society of Great Britain
Fenton House
122 Wells Rd.
Bath BA2 3AH, United Kingdom
Ph: 44 1225 325733
Publisher E-mail: reception@rps.org
Journal covering photography. **Freq:** 10/yr. **Key Personnel:** Dr. Rosemary Wilman, President. **Subscription Rates:** Included in membership. **Remarks:** Advertising accepted; rates available upon request. **URL:** http://www.rps.org. **Circ:** 10,500

52258 ■ Speculum
William Herschel Society
Herschel House
19 New King St.
Bath BA1 2BL, United Kingdom
Ph: 44 12 25446865
Publisher E-mail: efring@lineone.net
Journal containing lecture transcripts, news of research and astronomy/space research. **Freq:** Semiannual. **Key Personnel:** Prof. Francic Ring, Editor, phone 44 1225 864016. **Subscription Rates:** 10 individuals members; EUR15 individuals members; 13 other countries. **URL:** http://www.williamherschel.org.uk/publications.htm.

52259 ■ Sporting Legends
Anthem Publishing Limited
Piccadilly House, Ste. 6
London Rd.
Bath BA1 6PL, United Kingdom
Ph: 44 1225 489984
Fax: 44 1225 489980
Publisher E-mail: enquiries@anthem-publishing.com
Magazine featuring great sporting achievement of all kinds. **Freq:** Irregular. **Key Personnel:** Simon Lewis, Advertising Dir., simon.lewis@anthem-publishing.com; John Bickey, Contact, jon.bickley@anthem-publishing.com; Jon Palmer, Editor, jon.plamer@anthem-

publishing.com. **Subscription Rates:** 6.99 individuals UK; 9 individuals for Europe; 12 individuals rest of the world. **URL:** http://www.sportinglegendsmag.com/.

52260 ■ Taste Italia
Anthem Publishing Limited
Piccadilly House, Ste. 6
London Rd.
Bath BA1 6PL, United Kingdom
Ph: 44 1225 489984
Fax: 44 1225 489980
Publisher E-mail: enquiries@anthem-publishing.com
Magazine covering Italian recipes and features on Italian produce and producers. **Freq:** Monthly. **Key Personnel:** Becky Ambury, Editor, becky.ambury@anthem-publishing.com; Simon Lewis, Advertising Dir., simon.lewis@anthem-publishing.com; Sarah Hartley, Advertising Mgr., sarah.hartley@anthem-publishing.com. **Subscription Rates:** 16.65 individuals direct debit; 35.50 individuals credit card. **Remarks:** Accepts advertising. **URL:** http://www.tasteitaliamag.com/. **Circ:** 45,000

52261 ■ Total Vauxhall
Future Publishing
Beauford Ct.
30 Monmouth St.
Bath BA1 2BW, United Kingdom
Ph: 44 12 25442244
Fax: 44 12 25822836
Publisher E-mail: future@subscription.co.uk
Magazine that features topics about Vauxhall. **Subtitle:** The Performance Vauxhall Magazine. **Freq:** 13/yr. **Subscription Rates:** 10.39 individuals; 43.99 individuals per year; 82.99 two years. **Remarks:** Accepts advertising. **URL:** http://www.totalvauxhall.co.uk/page/totalvauxhall. **Circ:** (Not Reported)

52262 ■ Truckstop News
Future Publishing Ltd.
30 Monmouth St.
Bath BA1 2BW, United Kingdom
Publication E-mail: editorial@truckstopnews.co.uk
Publisher E-mail: future@subscription.co.uk
Newspaper for truckers in the UK. **Freq:** Monthly. **Print Method:** Web fed offset. **Key Personnel:** Steev Hayes, Editor. **Subscription Rates:** Free to qualified subscribers. **Remarks:** Accepts advertising. **URL:** http://www.truckstopnews.co.uk/. **Circ:** Combined ‡41,033

52263 ■ T3
Future Publishing
Beauford Ct.
30 Monmouth St.
Bath BA1 2BW, United Kingdom
Ph: 44 12 25442244
Fax: 44 12 25822836
Publisher E-mail: future@subscription.co.uk
Magazine covering technology and technological equipment, including phones, laptops, televisions, camcorders, and more. **Subtitle:** Tomorrow's Technology Today. **Founded:** Sept. 1996. **Freq:** 13/yr. **Key Personnel:** Luke Peters, Editor. **Subscription Rates:** 25.99 individuals; 51.99 two years; 6.49 single issue. **Remarks:** Accepts advertising. **URL:** http://www.myfavouritemagazines.co.uk. **Circ:** (Not Reported)

52264 ■ Worldwide Computer Products News
M2 Communications Ltd.
1 Soulsbury View
The Normans
Bathampton
Bath BA2 6TF, United Kingdom
Ph: 44 20 70470200
Fax: 44 20 70570200
Publisher E-mail: info@m2.com
Publication covering computers and the office automation industry. **Freq:** Weekly (Wed.). **Remarks:** Advertising not accepted. **URL:** http://www.m2.com/m2/web/publication.php/wcpn. **Circ:** (Not Reported)

52265 ■ Bath-FM - 107.9
Station House
Ashley Ave.
Lower Weston
Bath BA1 3DS, United Kingdom
Ph: 44 1225 471571
Format: News; Contemporary Hit Radio (CHR). **Owner:** The Local Radio Co. PLC, 11 Duke St., High Wycombe

HP13 6EE, United Kingdom, 44 49 4688200, Fax: 44 49 4688201. **Operating Hours:** Continuous. **Ad Rates:** Advertising accepted; rates available upon request. **URL:** http://www.bathfm.com.

52266 ■ URB-AM - 1449
University of Bath Students' Union
Claverton Down
Bath BA2 7AY, United Kingdom
Ph: 44 1225 386611
E-mail: studio@bath.ac.uk
Format: Contemporary Hit Radio (CHR). **Founded:** 1973. **Key Personnel:** Stephen Briscoe, Station Mgr., urb-eng@bath.ac.uk. **URL:** http://www.1449urb.co.uk/.

Batley

52267 ■ Batley News
Johnston Press PLC
11 Commercial St.
Batley WF17 5HL, United Kingdom
Ph: 44 1924 472121
Local community newspaper. **Freq:** Weekly. **Remarks:** Accepts advertising. **URL:** http://www.batleynews.co.uk/. **Circ:** (Not Reported)

52268 ■ Birstall News
Johnston Press PLC
11 Commercial St.
Batley WF14 5HL, United Kingdom
Ph: 44 1924 472121
A community newspaper. **Freq:** Weekly. **Remarks:** Accepts advertising. **URL:** http://www.batleynews.co.uk/. **Circ:** (Not Reported)

Battle

52269 ■ Furniture News
Nigel Gearing Ltd.
4 Red Barn Mews
High St.
Battle TN33 0AG, United Kingdom
Ph: 44 142 4774982
Fax: 44 142 4774321
Publisher E-mail: info@nigelgearing.com
Trade magazine covering furniture retailing and interior design in the UK. **Founded:** 2002. **Freq:** Monthly. **Print Method:** Litho. **Trim Size:** 297 x 420 mm. **Cols./Page:** 6. **Col. Width:** 45 millimeters. **Col. Depth:** 375 millimeters. **Key Personnel:** Paul Farley, Editor, phone 44 1424 776101, paul@gearingmediagroup.com; Nigel Gearing, Publisher, phone 44 142 4774211, fax 44 142 47743, nigel@furniturenews.net; James Ash, Production Mgr., phone 44 142 4775304, fax 44 142 4775077, james@furniturenews.net. **Subscription Rates:** 50 individuals U.K.; EUR60 individuals Europe; 70 other countries. **Remarks:** Accepts advertising. **URL:** http://www.furniturenews.net/. **Formerly:** Pine News International. **Ad Rates:** BW: 795, 4C: 1,295, PCI: 24. **Circ:** Non-paid 7,000

52270 ■ Furniture Production
Nigel Gearing Ltd.
4 Red Barn Mews
High St.
Battle TN33 0AG, United Kingdom
Ph: 44 142 4774902
Fax: 44 142 4774321
Publisher E-mail: info@nigelgearing.com
Trade magazine covering the furniture industry, including manufacturing, production machinery, materials, and components. **Founded:** 1991. **Freq:** Monthly. **Print Method:** Litho. **Trim Size:** 240 x 340 mm. **Cols./Page:** 4. **Col. Width:** 50 millimeters. **Col. Depth:** 297 millimeters. **Key Personnel:** James Ash, Studio Mgr., phone 44 1424 776102, james@gearingmediagroup.com; John Legg, Editor, phone 44 142 4776104, john@gearingmediagroup.com; Travis Posthumus, Contact, travis@gearingmediagroup.com. **ISSN:** 1364-9191. **Subscription Rates:** 134.10 individuals U.K.; 11.17 single issue Europe. **Remarks:** Accepts advertising. **URL:** http://www.furnitureproduction.net/. **Former name:** Furniture Production International. **Ad Rates:** BW: 655, 4C: 1,025. **Circ:** Non-paid 5,311

Bedford

52271 ■ Alert Magazine
Radio, Electrical and Television Retailers' Association
RETRA House, St. John's Ter.

1 Ampthill St.
Bedford MK42 9EY, United Kingdom
Ph: 44 1234 269110
Fax: 44 1234 269609
Publisher E-mail: retra@retra.co.uk
Magazine covering retailing. **Freq:** Monthly. **Subscription Rates:** Free to members. **Remarks:** Advertising accepted; rates available upon request. **URL:** http://www.retra.co.uk/. **Circ:** (Not Reported)

52272 ■ Applied Soft Computing
Elsevier (Singapore) Pte. Ltd.
c/o R. Roy, Ed.-in-Ch.
Cranfield University
Cranfield
Bedford MK43 0AL, United Kingdom
Ph: 44 1234 754062
Fax: 44 1234 750111
Publisher E-mail: asiabkinfo@elsevier.com
International journal promoting an integrated view of soft computing to solve real life problems. **Founded:** 2001. **Freq:** Quarterly. **Key Personnel:** R. Roy, Editor-in-Chief, fax 44 1234 754605, asoc@cranfield.ac.uk; L.A. Zadeh, Honorary Ed.; V. Bajic, Editorial Board; K. Deb, Assoc. Ed.; T.S. Dillon, Editorial Board; A. Bulsari, Editorial Board; H. Adeli, Editorial Board; D. Davis, Editorial Board; A. Tiwari, Book Review Ed. **ISSN:** 1568-4946. **Subscription Rates:** EUR625 institutions European countries and Iran; US$545 institutions all countries except Europe and Japan; 65,300 institutions. **URL:** http://www.elsevier.com/wps/find/journaldescription.cws_home/621920/descriptiondescription.

52273 ■ Journal of Applied Microbiology
Society for Applied Microbiology
Bedford Hts.
Brickhill Dr.
Bedford MK41 7PH, United Kingdom
Ph: 44 123 4326661
Fax: 44 123 4326678
Journal covering biology. **Freq:** Monthly. **Key Personnel:** Prof. Arthur Gilmour, Editor-in-Chief, arthur.gilmour@afbini.gov.uk. **Subscription Rates:** US$4,609 institutions print and online; EUR3,167 institutions print and online; 2,494 institutions print and online; US$5,367 institutions, other countries print and online. **URL:** http://www.sfam.org.uk; http://www.wiley.com/bw/editors.asp?ref=1364-5072&site=1; http://onlinelibrary.wiley.com/journal/10.1111/(ISSN)1365-2672.

52274 ■ Petcare
Pet Care Trust
Bedford Business Ctr.
170 Mile Rd.
Bedford MK42 9TW, United Kingdom
Ph: 44 1234 273933
Fax: 44 1234 273550
Publication covering pets. **Subtitle:** Review. **Founded:** Apr. 2002. **Freq:** Bimonthly. **Trim Size:** A4. **Key Personnel:** Steve Nowottny, Editor. **Remarks:** Accepts advertising. **URL:** http://www.petcare.org.uk/. **Ad Rates:** BW: 500. **Circ:** 1,600

52275 ■ The Power Engineer
Institution of Diesel and Gas Turbine Engineers
Bedford Hts.
Manton Ln.
Bedford MK41 7PH, United Kingdom
Ph: 44 1234 214340
Fax: 44 1234 355493
Publisher E-mail: enquiries@idgte.org
Publication covering engineering. **Founded:** Jan. 1997. **Freq:** 5/yr. **Trim Size:** 210 x 297 mm. **Cols./Page:** 2. **Col. Width:** 87 millimeters. **Col. Depth:** 244 millimeters. **Key Personnel:** Tom Woodford, President; Peter Tottman, Dir. Gen., dg@idgte.org; Anne Youngman, Office Mgr., anne@idgte.org. **ISSN:** 1367-191X. **Subscription Rates:** 15 individuals 1 copy; 12.75 individuals 2-5 copies; 11.25 individuals 6-10 copies; 10 individuals 11-20 copies; 7.50 individuals 21-30 copies; 5 individuals 30plus copies; 25 individuals print; 50 individuals floppy. **URL:** http://www.idgte.org; http://www.idgte.org/power_engineer.html. **Ad Rates:** BW: 400. **Circ:** 700

52276 ■ Radio Communication
Radio Society of Great Britain
3 Abbey Ct.
Fraser Rd.
Priory Business Park
Bedford MK44 3WH, United Kingdom
Ph: 44 1234 832700

Circulation: ★ = ABC; △ = BPA; ♦ = CAC; • = CCAB; ❏ = VAC; ⊕ = PO Statement; ‡ = Publisher's Report; Boldface figures = sworn; Light figures = estimated.

Fax: 44 1234 831496
Publication E-mail: subscriptions@rsgb.org.uk
Publisher E-mail: sales@rsgb.org.uk
Publication covering amateur radio. **Subtitle:** Radcom. **Founded:** 1912. **Freq:** Monthly. **Trim Size:** A4. **Subscription Rates:** Included in membership. **Remarks:** Accepts advertising. **URL:** http://www.rsgb.org/news/radcom/index.php. **Ad Rates:** BW: 1,090. **Circ:** 27,000

52277 ■ Heart-FM - 96.9
5 Abbey Ct., Fraser Rd.
Priory Business Pk.
Bedford MK44 3WH, United Kingdom
Format: Ethnic; Contemporary Hit Radio (CHR); Sports. **Owner:** Global Radio UK Ltd., 30 Leicester Sq., London WC2H 7LA, United Kingdom, 44 20 7666000, Fax: 44 20 7666111. **Formerly:** Chiltern-FM. **Key Personnel:** Tony Dibbin, Prog. Controller. **Ad Rates:** Advertising accepted; rates available upon request. **URL:** http://www.heartbedford.co.uk.

Bedfordshire

52278 ■ European Journal of Soil Science
British Society of Soil Science
Building 53
Cranfield University
Craigie Buckler
Bedfordshire MK43 0AL, United Kingdom
Ph: 44 12 34752983
Fax: 44 12 34752970
Publisher E-mail: admin@soils.org.uk
European journal covering soil science. **Freq:** Bimonthly. **Key Personnel:** Steve Jarvis, Editor-in-Chief, editor. ejss@ex.ac.uk; R.M. Lark, Assoc. Ed.; M. Deurer, Assoc. Ed.; G.J.D. Kirk, Assoc. Ed.; K. Smith, Dep. Ed.; N.J. Barrow, Assoc. Ed. **ISSN:** 1351-0754. **Subscription Rates:** US$77 members print and online; 42 members print and online; 42 members non Euro zone, print and online; EUR63 members print and online; 47 other countries print and online. **Remarks:** Accepts advertising. **URL:** http://www.soils.org.uk/ejss.htm; http://www.blackwellpublishing.com/journal.asp?ref=1351-0754. **Circ:** (Not Reported)

Belfast

52279 ■ The British Journal of Social Work
Oxford University Press
c/o Prof. John Pinkerton, Ed.
Queen's University of Belfast
6 College Park
Belfast BT7 1LP, United Kingdom
Publisher E-mail: webenquiry.uk@oup.com
Publication covering sociology and social work. **Freq:** 8/yr. **Key Personnel:** Prof. John Pinkerton, Editor; Dr. Jim Campbell, Editor; Penny Brown, Admin.; Rebecca L. Hegar, Assoc. Ed., rhegar@uta.edu; Dr. Carolyn Taylor, Book Review Ed., c.p.taylor@lancaster.ac.uk. **ISSN:** 0045-3102. **Subscription Rates:** US$1,076 institutions print and online; US$896 institutions online, print; 538 institutions print and online; US$172 institutions developing Countries - print only; EUR807 institutions print and online; 493 institutions print, online; EUR740 institutions print, online. **Remarks:** Accepts advertising. **URL:** http://bjsw.oxfordjournals.org/. **Circ:** (Not Reported)

52280 ■ Bulletin of the Irish Mathematical Society
Irish Mathematical Society Bulletin
Department of Pure Mathematics
Queen's University Belfast
Belfast, United Kingdom
Journal discussing mathematics in general, in addition to the activities of the society. **Freq:** Semiannual. **Key Personnel:** Dr. Martin Mathieu, Editor, ims.bulletin@qub.ac.uk. **Subscription Rates:** Free members; EUR30 libraries. **URL:** http://www.maths.tcd.ie/pub/ims/bulletin/index.php.

52281 ■ The Chronicle
International Association of Youth and Family Judges and Magistrates
175, Andersonstown Rd.
Belfast BT11 9EA, United Kingdom
Ph: 44 289 0615164
Fax: 44 289 0618374
Publication covering judicial issues in English, French and Spanish. **Freq:** Semiannual. **Key Personnel:** Avril Calder, Editor-in-Chief, avril.calder@btinternet.com. **Subscription Rates:** Included in membership. Re-

marks: Advertising accepted; rates available upon request. **URL:** http://www.judgesandmagistrates.org/chron.htm. **Circ:** (Not Reported)

52282 ■ Directory of Irish Family History Research
Ulster Historical Foundation
Unit 7, Cotton Ct.
30-42 Waring St.
Belfast BT1 2ED, United Kingdom
Ph: 44 28 90332288
Fax: 44 28 90661977
Publisher E-mail: enquiry@uhf.org.uk
Publication covering Irish family history research. **Founded:** 1976. **Freq:** Annual. **Print Method:** Softback. **Trim Size:** A4. **Key Personnel:** Fintan Mullan, Exec. Dir. **Remarks:** Advertising accepted; rates available upon request. **URL:** http://www.ancestryireland.com/. **Formerly:** Member's Interests List/Subscribers' Interest Lists. **Circ:** (Not Reported)

52283 ■ Garage Trader
Greer Publications
5B Edgewater Business Pk.
Belfast Harbour Estate
Belfast BT3 9JQ, United Kingdom
Ph: 353 28 90783200
Fax: 353 28 90783210
Publisher E-mail: info@greerpublications.com
Magazine featuring automotives. **Freq:** Quarterly. **Key Personnel:** Pat Burns, Editor, patburns@greerpublications.com; Jackie Stott, Advertising Mgr., jackiestott@greerpublications.com; James Greer, Publisher. **URL:** http://www.greerpublications.com/garage_trader.htm.

52284 ■ Glacial Geology and Geomorphology
Royal Geographical Society - The Institute of British Geographers
c/o Brian W. Whalley, Ed.
School of Geosciences
The Queen's University of Belfast
Belfast BT7 1NN, United Kingdom
Journal covering all aspects of glacial geology and geomorphology. **Key Personnel:** Jon Ove Hagen, Editorial Board, j.o.hagen@geografi.uio.no; Brian W. Whalley, Editor, b.whalley@qub.ac.uk; Michael J. Paul, Editorial Board, civmap@bonaly.heriot-watt.ac.uk; Martin J. Sharp, Editor, msharp@geog.ualberta.ca; Trevor Chinn, Editorial Board, t.chinn@gns.cri.nz; Dan E. Lawson, Editorial Board, dlawson@crrel.usace.army.mil; Edward Derbyshire, Editorial Board, 100666.1577@compuserve.com; David J.A. Evans, Editorial Board, devans@geog.glasgow.ac.uk; Brice R. Rea, Book Review Ed., reabr@cardiff.ac.uk. **ISSN:** 1085-0554. **URL:** http://ggg.qub.ac.uk/.

52285 ■ Hospitality Review
Federation of the Retail Licensed Trade
91 University St.
Belfast BT7 1HP, United Kingdom
Ph: 44 28 90327578
Fax: 44 28 90327578
Publisher E-mail: enquiries@pubsofulster.org
Publication covering catering and food licensing. **Freq:** 11/yr. **Key Personnel:** Louise Murphy, Editor, phone 353 28 90783221, louisemurphy@greerpublications.com; Karen Graham, Advertising Mgr., phone 353 28 90783235, karengraham@greerpublications.com. **Subscription Rates:** 27.50 individuals. **Remarks:** Advertising accepted; rates available upon request. **URL:** http://www.hospitalityreviewni.com/. **Formerly:** Catering and Licensing Review. **Circ:** (Not Reported)

52286 ■ Industrial & Manufacturing Engineer Magazine
Greer Publications
5B Edgewater Business Pk.
Belfast Harbour Estate
Belfast BT3 9JQ, United Kingdom
Ph: 353 28 90783200
Fax: 353 28 90783210
Publisher E-mail: info@greerpublications.com
Magazine featuring industrial manufacturing. **Subtitle:** The Only Magazine for Irelands Engineering Specialist. **Key Personnel:** David Elliot, Editor, davidelliot@greerpublications.com; Caroline McClean, Advertising Mgr., carolinemcclean@greerpublications.com; James Greer, Publisher. **URL:** http://www.greerpublications.com/industrial_manufacturing_engineer.htm.

52287 ■ Irish Pages
The Linen Hall Library
17 Donegall Sq. N
Belfast BT1 5GB, United Kingdom
Ph: 44 28 90434800
Publisher E-mail: editor@irishpages.org
Irish poetry magazine. **Subtitle:** A Journal of Contemporary Writing. **Founded:** 2002. **Freq:** Semiannual. **Key Personnel:** Chris Agee, Editor; Sean Mac Aindreasa, Managing Editor. **Subscription Rates:** 16 individuals; EUR26 individuals; US$24 individuals; 24 individuals 2 years; EUR39 individuals 2 years; US$36 individuals 2 years. **URL:** http://www.irishpages.org.

52288 ■ Journal of Pathology
John Wiley & Sons Ltd.
c/o Prof. Peter A. Hall, Ed.-in-Ch.
Institute of Pathology
School of Medicine
Queen's University of Belfast
Belfast BT12 6BL, United Kingdom
Publisher E-mail: customer@wiley.co.uk
Professional journal covering pathology. **Founded:** 1892. **Freq:** 13/yr. **Key Personnel:** Prof. Peter A. Hall, Editor-in-Chief; Prof. Ad Burt, Editorial Board; Prof. Andrew M. Hanby, Editorial Board. **ISSN:** 0022-3417. **Subscription Rates:** 748 individuals print only; US$1,475 other countries print only; 1,036 institutions print only; US$2,043 institutions, other countries print only; EUR1,318 institutions, other countries print only; EUR1,451 institutions combined print with online access; 1,140 institutions combined print with online access; US$2,248 institutions, other countries combined print with online access. **Remarks:** Accepts advertising. **URL:** http://www3.interscience.wiley.com/journal/117927941/grouphome; http://www3.interscience.wiley.com/. **Circ:** (Not Reported)

52289 ■ Keystone
Flagship Media Group Ltd.
48-50 York St.
Belfast BT15 1AS, United Kingdom
Ph: 44 28 90319008
Fax: 44 28 90727800
Trade newspaper for the construction industry. **Freq:** Monthly. **Subscription Rates:** Free. **Remarks:** Accepts advertising. **URL:** http://www.flagshipmedia.co.uk. **Ad Rates:** BW: 1,490. **Circ:** Controlled 15,000

52290 ■ Northern Woman
Greer Publications
5B Edgewater Business Pk.
Belfast Harbour Estate
Belfast BT3 9JQ, United Kingdom
Ph: 353 28 90783200
Fax: 353 28 90783210
Publisher E-mail: info@greerpublications.com
Fashion magazine for women. **Key Personnel:** Lyn Palmer, Editor, lynpalmer@greerpublications.com; Gabrielle Houston, Advertising Mgr., soniatohani@greerpublications.com; Gladys Greer, Publisher. **Remarks:** Accepts advertising. **URL:** http://www.greerpublications.com/northern_woman.htm. **Circ:** (Not Reported)

52291 ■ Offshore Investment
Lombard House
10-20 Lombard St.
Belfast BT1 1BW, United Kingdom
Ph: 44 28 90328777
Fax: 44 28 90328555
Publication E-mail: editorial@offshoreinvestment.com
Publisher E-mail: administration@offshoreinvestment.com
Magazine of interest for wealth management professionals. **Freq:** 10/yr. **Subscription Rates:** 336 individuals in Europe; 599 two years in Europe; 799 individuals in Europe, three years; US$830 individuals; US$1,490 two years; US$1,990 individuals 3 years; 460 other countries; 830 two years rest of the world; 1,100 other countries three years. **Remarks:** Accepts advertising. **URL:** http://www.offshoreinvestment.com. **Ad Rates:** BW: 3,400. **Circ:** (Not Reported)

52292 ■ The Presbyterian Herald
Presbyterian Church in Ireland
Church House
Belfast BT1 6DW, United Kingdom
Ph: 44 28 90322284
Publication E-mail: herald@presbyterianireland.org
Publisher E-mail: info@presbyterianireland.org
Magazine of the Presbyterian Church in Ireland.

Founded: 1956. **Freq:** 10/yr. **Key Personnel:** Arthur Clarke, Editor. **Subscription Rates:** 18 individuals for U.K.; 28 individuals Europe; 38 out of country surface. **Remarks:** Accepts advertising. **URL:** http://www. presbyterianireland.org/herald/. **Circ:** Paid 16,000

52293 ■ Specify
Greer Publications
5B Edgewater Business Pk.
Belfast Harbour Estate
Belfast BT3 9JQ, United Kingdom
Ph: 353 28 90783200
Fax: 353 28 90783210
Publisher E-mail: info@greerpublications.com
Magazine covering construction, building, and related trades. **Subtitle:** Northern Ireland's No.1 Construction Magazine. **Founded:** 1980. **Key Personnel:** Russell Campbell, Editor, russellcampbell@greerpublications. com; Caroline McClean, Advertising Mgr., carolinemcclean@greerpublications.com; Gladys Greer, Publisher, info@greerpublications.com. **Remarks:** Accepts advertising. **URL:** http://www.greerpublications. com/Specify.htm. **Circ:** (Not Reported)

52294 ■ Transactions of the Institute of Measurement and Control
Sage Publications Ltd.
Dept. of Mechanical & Manufacturing Engineering
Queen's University Ashby Bldg.
Stranmillis Rd.
Belfast BT9 5AH, United Kingdom
Peer-reviewed journal covering all areas of applications in instrumentation and control. **Freq:** 6/yr. **Key Personnel:** Steve Thompson, Editor; John O. Gray, Editor; Frank Lewis, Editor. **ISSN:** 0142-3312. **Subscription Rates:** 683 institutions print & e-access; 615 institutions e-access; 669 institutions print only; 178 individuals print & e-access; 123 institutions single print; 39 individuals single print. **Remarks:** Accepts advertising. **URL:** http:// www.sagepub.co.uk/journalsProdDesc.nav?prodId= Journal201831. **Circ:** (Not Reported)

52295 ■ Ulster Business
Greer Publications
5B Edgewater Business Pk.
Belfast Harbour Estate
Belfast BT3 9JQ, United Kingdom
Ph: 353 28 90783200
Fax: 353 28 90783210
Publisher E-mail: info@greerpublications.com
Magazine for business community in Northern Ireland. **Key Personnel:** David Elliot, Editor, davidelliott@ greerpublications.com; Louise Hunter, Advertising Mgr., louisehunter@greerpublications.com; James Greer, Publisher, info@greerpublications.com. **URL:** http:// www.greerpublications.com/ulster_business.htm.

52296 ■ Ulster Countrywoman
Federation of Women's Institutes of Northern Ireland
209-211 Upper Lisburn Rd.
Belfast BT10 0LL, United Kingdom
Ph: 44 28 90301506
Fax: 44 28 90431127
Publisher E-mail: wini@btconnect.com
Publication covering women. **Freq:** 10/yr. **Key Personnel:** Claire Douglas, Editor; Irene Sproule, Gen. Sec.; Kathleen Dickey, Office Admin. **Subscription Rates:** Free to members; 13 nonmembers including p&p. **URL:** http://www.wini.org.uk/?tabindex=37&tabid=1301. **Ad Rates:** BW: EUR100. **Circ:** 5,000

52297 ■ Ulster Grocer
Greer Publications
5B Edgewater Business Pk.
Belfast Harbour Estate
Belfast BT3 9JQ, United Kingdom
Ph: 353 28 90783200
Fax: 353 28 90783210
Publisher E-mail: info@greerpublications.com
Magazine featuring grocery trade in Northern Ireland. **Subtitle:** The voice of independent retailing. **Key Personnel:** Russell Campbell, Editor, russellcampbell@ greerpublications.com; Michelle Kearney, Advertising Mgr., michellekearney@greerpublications.com; James Greer, Publisher. **URL:** http://www.greerpublications. com/ulster_grocer.htm.

52298 ■ Citybeat-FM - 102.5
2 Fl., Arena Bldg.
85 Ormeau Rd.

Belfast BT7 1SH, United Kingdom
Ph: 44 28 90236967
Fax: 44 28 90890100
Format: Adult Contemporary. **URL:** http://www.citybeat. co.uk/.

52299 ■ Citybeat-FM - 96.7
85 Ormeau Rd.
Arena Bldg., 2nd Fl.
Belfast BT7 1SH, United Kingdom
Ph: 44 28 90234967
Fax: 44 28 90890100
Format: Adult Contemporary; Top 40; Talk; Oldies. **Operating Hours:** 2a.m.-7p.m. Mon.; 2a.m.-10p.m. Tue.-Sun. **Key Personnel:** Dorothy Nixon, Mng. Dir.; Stuart Robinson, Dep. Programme Controller/Hd. Of Music; Gordon Davidson, Gp. Prog. Controller. **URL:** http:// www.citybeat.co.uk/.

52300 ■ Cool-FM - 97.4
PO Box 974
Belfast BT1 1RT, United Kingdom
Ph: 44 28 91817181
Fax: 44 28 91814974
E-mail: music@coolfm.co.uk
Format: Adult Contemporary; Urban Contemporary; Sports; News; Top 40; Eclectic. **Operating Hours:** Continuous. **Key Personnel:** Mark Mahaffy, Mng. Dir., mark.mahaffy@coolfm.co.uk; Henry Owens, Program Dir., henry.owens@coolfm.co.uk; Richard Hoey, Chief Engr. & IT Mgr., richard.hoey@coolfm.co.uk. **Ad Rates:** Advertising accepted; rates available upon request. **URL:** http://www.coolfm.co.uk/.

52301 ■ Feile-FM - 103.2
1st Fl., Conway Mill
5-7 Conway St.
Belfast BT13 2DE, United Kingdom
Ph: 44 28 90242002
Fax: 44 28 90331247
Format: Full Service. **Founded:** 1996. **Key Personnel:** Rosemary Whelan, Admin., rosemary@feilefm.com. **URL:** http://www.feilefm.com/.

52302 ■ Magic-FM - 105.1
PO Box 105
Belfast BT66 7WA, United Kingdom
Ph: 44 28 38345555
E-mail: sales@magic105.net
Format: Adult Contemporary. **Operating Hours:** Continuous. **Ad Rates:** Advertising accepted; rates available upon request. **URL:** http://www.magic105.net.

52303 ■ NvTv - 62
23 Donegall St.
Belfast BT1 2FF, United Kingdom
Ph: 44 28 90245495
Fax: 44 28 90326608
E-mail: info@northernvisions.org
URL: http://www.nvtv.co.uk/.

52304 ■ U105-FM - 105.8
Havelock House
Ormeau Rd.
Belfast BT7 1EB, United Kingdom
Ph: 44 28 90332105
Fax: 44 28 90330105
Format: Adult Contemporary; Oldies; Easy Listening. **Key Personnel:** Peter McVerry, Station Mgr. **Ad Rates:** Advertising accepted; rates available upon request. **URL:** http://www1.u105.com/.

Bellshill

52305 ■ Bellshill Speaker
Johnston Press PLC
203-205 Main St.
Bellshill ML4 1AH, United Kingdom
Ph: 44 1698 748126
Local community newspaper. **URL:** http://www. bellshillspeaker.co.uk/.

52306 ■ Fast and Modified
Trader Media Group
Alexander Fleming House
Righead Industrial Estate
Innervations Pk., Melford Rd.
Bellshill ML4 3LR, United Kingdom
Ph: 44 845 2720077

Publication E-mail: info@fastandmodified.com
Magazine featuring the performance and modified car market in Scotland. **Founded:** Feb. 2003. **Freq:** Monthly. **Key Personnel:** John King, CEO. **Remarks:** Accepts advertising. **URL:** http://www.tradermediagroup.com/ companies/fast-and-modified.html. **Circ:** 14,000

Belmont

52307 ■ Sociology
British Sociological Association
Bailey Ste.
Palatine House
Belmont Business Pk.
Belmont DH1 1TW, United Kingdom
Ph: 44 19 13830839
Fax: 44 19 13830782
Publisher E-mail: enquiries@britsoc.org.uk
Publication covering sociology. **Founded:** 1967. **Freq:** Bimonthly February, April, June, August, October, December. **Key Personnel:** Amanda Coffey, Editor; Sally Power, Editor. **ISSN:** 0038-0385. **Subscription Rates:** 90 individuals print only; 417 institutions print only; 425 institutions print & e-access; 383 institutions e-access only. **Remarks:** Accepts advertising. **URL:** http://soc.sagepub.com/; http://www.britsoc.co.uk/ publications/soc. **Circ:** (Not Reported)

52308 ■ Work, Employment, and Society
British Sociological Association
Bailey Ste.
Palatine House
Belmont Business Pk.
Belmont DH1 1TW, United Kingdom
Ph: 44 19 13830839
Fax: 44 19 13830782
Publisher E-mail: enquiries@britsoc.org.uk
Publication covering sociology. **Founded:** 1985. **Freq:** Quarterly March, June, September and December. **Key Personnel:** Philip Taylor, Co-Ed.; Christopher Warhurst, Co-Ed. **ISSN:** 0950-0170. **Subscription Rates:** 72 individuals; 278 institutions. **Remarks:** Accepts advertising. **URL:** http://www.britsoc.co.uk/publications/ WES.htm. **Circ:** (Not Reported)

Belper

52309 ■ Belper News
Johnston Press PLC
8 Market Pl.
Belper DE56 1FZ, United Kingdom
Ph: 44 1773 881100
Publication E-mail: editor@belpernews.co.uk
Local community newspaper. **Remarks:** Accepts advertising. **URL:** http://www.belpernews.co.uk/. **Circ:** (Not Reported)

Berkhamsted

52310 ■ Guidelines
MGP Ltd.
Salter House
263-265 High St.
Berkhamsted HP4 1AB, United Kingdom
Ph: 44 1442 876100
Fax: 44 1442 877100
Journal highlighting guidelines for primary health care. **Freq:** 3/yr. **Subscription Rates:** 75 individuals; 30 single issue. **URL:** http://www.mgp.ltd.uk/publications_ guidelines.php.

52311 ■ Guidelines in Practice
MGP Ltd.
Salter House
263-265 High St.
Berkhamsted HP4 1AB, United Kingdom
Ph: 44 1442 876100
Fax: 44 1442 877100
Magazine featuring primary and shared care practice guidelines for health professionals. **Freq:** Monthly. **Key Personnel:** Guy Foord-Kelcey, Managing Editor. **Subscription Rates:** 90 individuals. **URL:** http://www.mgp. ltd.uk/publications_gip.php.

52312 ■ Lube
United Kingdom Lubricants Association
Berkhamstead House
121 High St.
Berkhamsted HP4 2DJ, United Kingdom

Circulation: ★ = ABC; △ = BPA; ♦ = CAC; • = CCAB; ❑ = VAC; ⊕ = PO Statement; ‡ = Publisher's Report; Boldface figures = sworn; Light figures = estimated.

Ph: 44 1442 230589
Fax: 44 1442 259232
Trade journal covering the lubricants industry in the UK. **Freq:** Bimonthly. **Print Method:** Litho. **Trim Size:** A4. **Key Personnel:** Rod Parker, Editor, lube@ukla.org.uk. **Subscription Rates:** Free to qualified subscribers. **Remarks:** Accepts advertising. **URL:** http://www.lube-media.com. **Circ:** 1,800

52313 ■ Medendium
MGP Ltd.
Salter House
263-265 High St.
Berkhamsted HP4 1AB, United Kingdom
Ph: 44 1442 876100
Fax: 44 1442 877100
Journal for primary care organizations. **Freq:** Semiannual. **Subscription Rates:** 100 individuals; 70 single issue. **URL:** http://www.mgp.ltd.uk/publications_medendium.php.

52314 ■ Steam Days
Redgauntlet Publications Ltd.
PO Box 464
Berkhamsted HP4 2UR, United Kingdom
Publisher E-mail: red.gauntlett@btconnect.com
Magazine for railway historians and steam railway enthusiasts. **Subtitle:** Steam Nostalgia and Railway History at its best!. **Freq:** Monthly. **Subscription Rates:** 42 individuals; 77 two years. **Remarks:** Accepts advertising. **URL:** http://www.steamdaysmag.co.uk/. **Circ:** (Not Reported)

Berkshire

52315 ■ Go Flying
Archant Specialist Ltd.
3 The Courtyard
Denmark St.
Berkshire RG40 2AZ, United Kingdom
Publisher E-mail: miller.hogg@atarchant.co.uk
Aviation magazine for pilots. **Freq:** Bimonthly. **Key Personnel:** Nick Bloom, Editor, nick.bloom@pilotweb.aero. **URL:** http://www.goflying24.aero/content/go_flying/article_list.aspx?type=11.

52316 ■ Plastiquarian
Plastics Historical Society
c/o Susan Lambert
Brick Hill
Burghclere
Berkshire RG20 9HJ, United Kingdom
Publisher E-mail: general@plastiquarian.com
Publication covering history and development of plastics and polymers. **Freq:** Semiannual. **Trim Size:** A-4. **Subscription Rates:** 5 individuals back issues. **URL:** http://www.plastiquarian.com/.

Berwick upon Tweed

52317 ■ Berwick Advertiser
Johnston Press PLC
90 Marygate
Berwick upon Tweed TD15 1BW, United Kingdom
Ph: 44 1289 306677
Local community newspaper. **Key Personnel:** Edith Scott, Gp. Advertising Mgr.; Jo Bell, Advertising Mgr. **Remarks:** Accepts advertising. **URL:** http://www.berwick-advertiser.co.uk/. **Circ:** (Not Reported)

52318 ■ Berwickshire News
Johnston Press PLC
90 Marygate
Berwick upon Tweed TD15 1BW, United Kingdom
Ph: 44 1289 306677
Local community newspaper. **Key Personnel:** Jo Bell, Advertising Mgr.; Sandra Brydon, Contact; Edith Scott, Gp. Advertising Mgr. **Remarks:** Accepts advertising. **URL:** http://www.berwickshire-news.co.uk/. **Circ:** (Not Reported)

Beverley

52319 ■ Association Magazine
British Association of Teachers of the Deaf
c/o Mrs. Ann Underwood, Ed.
41 The Orchard
Leven
E Yorkshire
Beverley HU17 5QA, United Kingdom

Publisher E-mail: secretary@batod.org.uk
Publication covering the education of hearing-impaired children. **Freq:** 5/yr. **Key Personnel:** Mrs. Ann Underwood, Editor, magazine@batod.org.uk. **ISSN:** 1366-0799. **Subscription Rates:** Included in membership. **URL:** http://www.batod.org.uk/index.php?id=/publications/magazine. **Ad Rates:** BW: 260, 4C: 440.. **Circ:** ‡1,800

Bexhill-on-Sea

52320 ■ Bexhill Observer
Johnston Press PLC
18 Sackville Rd.
Bexhill-on-Sea TN39 3JL, United Kingdom
Ph: 44 1424 730555
Local community newspaper. **Founded:** 1896. **Freq:** Weekly (Fri.). **Key Personnel:** Keith Ridley, Editor-in-Chief, phone 44 1424 856789, fax 44 1424 854284, keith.ridley@jpress.co.uk; Hayley Scott, Advertising Mgr., phone 44 1424 854242, fax 44 1424 852850, hayley.scott@trbeckett.co.uk; Julia Northcott, Dep. Ed., fax 44 1424 730832, julia.northcott@trbeckett.co.uk. **Remarks:** Accepts advertising. **URL:** http://www.bexhillobserver.net/. **Circ:** (Not Reported)

52321 ■ Fireworks
PO Box 40
Bexhill-on-Sea TN40 1GX, United Kingdom
Publication E-mail: editor@fireworks-mag.org
Publisher E-mail: editor@fireworks-mag.org
Magazine covering fireworks for professionals and enthusiasts. **Founded:** Feb. 1982. **Freq:** Semiannual. **Print Method:** Photo offset litho. **Cols./Page:** 2. **Key Personnel:** John Bennett, Editor. **ISSN:** 0264-9780. **Subscription Rates:** 10 individuals; 14 out of country; 1 individuals postage & packing. **Remarks:** Accepts advertising. **URL:** http://www.fireworks-mag.org/index.html. **Ad Rates:** BW: 140, 4C: 350. **Circ:** Paid 600

Bideford

52322 ■ Resurgence
Resurgence Ltd.
Ford House
Hartland
Bideford EX39 6EE, United Kingdom
Ph: 44 12 37441293
Publisher E-mail: info@resurgence.org
Consumer magazine covering ecology and environmental issues. **Founded:** 1966. **Freq:** Bimonthly. **Key Personnel:** June Mitchell, Assoc. Ed.; David Baker, Designer; Lorna Howarth, Co-Ed.; Lynn Batten, Office Mgr.; Gwyd Batten, Accounts Mgr.; Mandy Hodge, Subscriptions Asst.; Angela Burke, Website Ed.; Kate Hartgroves, Asst. Ed.; Jeanette Gill, Subscription Mgr.; Satish Kumar, Editor. **ISSN:** 0034-5970. **Subscription Rates:** 30 individuals; 55 two years; 80 individuals 3 years; 40 other countries airmail; 75 other countries airmail, 2 years; 110 other countries airmail, 3 years; 35 other countries surface mail; 65 other countries surface mail, 2 years; 96 other countries surface mail, 3 years. **Remarks:** Accepts advertising. **URL:** http://www.resurgence.org; http://www.resurgence.org/magazine/. **Ad Rates:** GLR: EUR80, BW: EUR960, 4C: EUR1,104. **Circ:** Combined 15,000

Biggleswade

52323 ■ Biggleswade Chronicle
Johnston Press PLC
7 High St.
Biggleswade SG18 0JB, United Kingdom
Ph: 44 1767 222333
Local community newspaper. **Founded:** Oct. 10, 1891. **Freq:** Weekly (Fri.). **Key Personnel:** Melissa Lynch, Contact, phone 44 1604 251195, melissa.lynch@jpress.co.uk. **Remarks:** Accepts advertising. **URL:** http://www.biggleswadetoday.co.uk/. **Circ:** (Not Reported)

52324 ■ Journal of Greek Linguistics
Brill Academic Publishers Inc.
c/o Turpin Distribution
Stratton Business Park
Pegasus Dr.
Bedfordshire
Biggleswade SG18 8TD, United Kingdom
Ph: 44 1767 604954
Fax: 44 1767 601640

Publisher E-mail: cs@brillusa.com
Peer-reviewed journal publishing high quality papers on any aspect of Greek linguistics phonetics, phonology, morphology, syntax, semantics, pragmatics, sociolinguistics, psycholinguistics, etc., whether from a synchronic or a diachronic perspective - with a preference for papers presenting a theoretically-informed description and/or analysis of data from any stage of the language, including the Koine and the Medieval periods, that can illuminate the more recent stages of the language, especially contemporary (Modern) Greek. **Freq:** Annual. **Key Personnel:** Gaberell Drachman, Editor; Geoffrey C. Horrocks, Editorial Board; Brian D. Joseph, Editor; Norway I. Tsimpli, Editorial Board; Anna Roussou, Editor. **ISSN:** 1566-5844. **Subscription Rates:** EUR178 individuals includes post and handling; EUR160 institutions online. **URL:** http://www.brill.nl/jgl; http://www.benjamins.com/cgi-bin/t_seriesview.cgi?series=jgl.

Bingham

52325 ■ Canoe Focus
British Canoe Union
18 Market Pl.
Nottingham
Bingham NG13 8AP, United Kingdom
Ph: 44 845 3709500
Fax: 44 845 3709501
Publisher E-mail: info@bcu.org.uk
Membership magazine of The British Canoe Union covering canoeing. **Freq:** Bimonthly. **Key Personnel:** Anne Egan, Contact; Peter Tranter, Contact. **Subscription Rates:** 19 nonmembers U.K.; 24 nonmembers rest of the world; Free to members. **Remarks:** Accepts advertising. **URL:** http://www.bcu.org.uk/; http://www.canoe-england.org.uk/membership/membership-benefits/canoe-focus/. **Ad Rates:** BW: 725. **Circ:** Paid 24,000

52326 ■ Transmit
Guild of Air Traffic Control Officers
4 St. Mary's Rd.
Bingham NG13 8DW, United Kingdom
Ph: 44 19 49876405
Fax: 44 19 49876405
Publisher E-mail: caf@gatco.org
In-house journal of the U.K. Guild of Air Traffic Patrol Officers. **Freq:** Quarterly. **Trim Size:** A4. **Cols./Page:** 3. **Key Personnel:** Steve Brindley, President, pcx@gatco.org. **Subscription Rates:** Included in membership. **URL:** http://www.gatco.org/benefits.html. **Circ:** Controlled 2,350

Bingley

52327 ■ International Turfgrass Bulletin
Sports Turf Research Institute
St. Ives Estate
Bingley BD16 1AU, United Kingdom
Ph: 44 12 74565131
Fax: 44 12 74561891
Publisher E-mail: info@stri.co.uk
Trade magazine covering developments in the golf and sports turf industries. **Subtitle:** Official Bulletin of The Sports Turf Research Organization - UK. **Founded:** 1929. **Freq:** Quarterly. **Print Method:** Web. **Trim Size:** 120 x 297 mm. **Key Personnel:** David M. Lawson, PhD, Contact; Emma Beggs, Contact; Steve Gingell, Contact. **ISSN:** 1362-9255. **Subscription Rates:** 65 individuals U.K & surface mail; 79 individuals airmail outside U.K; EUR105 individuals airmail outside U.K. **Remarks:** Accepts advertising. **URL:** http://www.stri.co.uk/277.asp?NewsID=390&SID=&CSID=3. **Formerly:** Sports Turf Bulletin (prior to April 1996). **Ad Rates:** BW: 895, 4C: 1,300. **Circ:** Controlled 5,000

52328 ■ Journal of Turfgrass Science (Incorporating the Journal of the Sports Turf Research Institute)
Sports Turf Research Institute
St. Ives Estate
Bingley BD16 1AU, United Kingdom
Ph: 44 1274 565131
Fax: 44 1274 561891
Journal of the Sports Turf Research Institute. **Freq:** Annual. **ISSN:** 1367-8361. **Subscription Rates:** 28 individuals. **URL:** http://www.stri.co.uk/107.asp?sid=&csid=14.

Birmingham

52329 ■ Bikersweb
Bikersweb.co.uk
PO Box 8341
Birmingham B33 8DA, United Kingdom
Ph: 44 21 7847018
Publisher E-mail: info@bikersweb.co.uk
Online magazine about motorcycles and motorcycling in the UK. **Founded:** Jan. 1, 2000. **Freq:** Daily. **Print Method:** Internet. **Key Personnel:** Matt Black, Contact. **Remarks:** Accepts advertising. **URL:** http://www.bikersweb.co.uk. **Circ:** (Not Reported)

52330 ■ Bird Study
British Trust for Ornithology
c/o Prof. Graham Martin, Ed.
School of Biosciences
University of Birmingham
Edgbaston
Birmingham B15 2TT, United Kingdom
Publisher E-mail: info@bto.org
Publication covering ornithology. **Subtitle:** The Science of Pure & Applied Ornithology. **Founded:** 1952. **Freq:** 3/yr. **Key Personnel:** Prof. Graham Martin, Editor; J. Gill, Editorial Board; R.W. Furness, Editorial Board; A.A. Dhondt, Editorial Board; W. Cresswell, Editorial Board. **ISSN:** 0006-3657. **Subscription Rates:** 95 individuals Europe; US$180 U.S. and Canada; 105 other countries; 18 members. **Remarks:** Accepts advertising. **URL:** http://www.bto.org; http://www.bto.org/membership/birdstudy.htm. **Circ:** 2,500

52331 ■ Black Theology
Equinox Publishing Ltd.
c/o Dr. Anthony G. Reddie, Ed.
The Queen's Foundation
Somerset Rd.
Edgbaston
Birmingham B15 2QH, United Kingdom
Journal covering issues of faith among Black people across the world. **Subtitle:** An International Journal. **Freq:** 3/yr (April, August and November). **Key Personnel:** Dr. Anthony G. Reddie, Editor, a.g.reddie@queens.ac.uk. **ISSN:** 1476-9948. **Subscription Rates:** 140 institutions, other countries print and online; US$280 institutions print and online; 53 individuals print; US$105 individuals print. **Remarks:** Accepts advertising. **URL:** http://www.equinoxjournals.com/ojs/index.php/BT. **Circ:** (Not Reported)

52332 ■ Boat Mart
Trinity Publications Ltd.
92-93 Edward House, Edward St.
Birmingham B1 2RA, United Kingdom
Ph: 44 12 12338712
Fax: 44 12 12338715
Consumer magazine covering small boats and leisure crafts and accessories. **Founded:** 1986. **Freq:** 13/yr. **Print Method:** Web Offset. **Trim Size:** 210 x 297 mm. **Cols./Page:** 4. **Col. Width:** 44 millimeters. **Col. Depth:** 270 millimeters. **Key Personnel:** Alex Smith, Editor, editorboatmart@boatmart.co.uk; Sam Broome, Advertising, phone 44 12 23460490, sam@boatmart.co.uk. **ISSN:** 0956-6589. **Subscription Rates:** 33 individuals UK; 43 other countries. **Remarks:** Accepts advertising. **URL:** http://www.boatmart.co.uk. **Former name:** Boat Mart International. **Circ:** (Not Reported)

52333 ■ The British Journal of Diabetes and Vascular Disease
MediNews (Diabetes) Ltd.
Edgbaston House
3 Duchess Pl.
Edgbaston
Birmingham B16 8NH, United Kingdom
Ph: 44 12 14544114
Fax: 44 121 4541190
Publisher E-mail: info@medinews.org
Peer-reviewed journal specifically focusing on the relationship between metabolic diseases (e.g. type 2 diabetes) and the vascular complications which cause fatal and non-fatal events in this high risk population. **Freq:** Bimonthly. **Key Personnel:** Dr. Clifford J. Bailey, Editor-in-Chief; Peter Andrews, Editorial Board; Prof. Ian Campbell, Editor-in-Chief; Christoph Schindler, Editor-in-Chief; Peter Andrews, Editorial Board; Caroline Day, Exec. Ed. **Subscription Rates:** US$475 institutions print & e-access; US$87 institutions single copy; US$364

individuals; 79 individuals single copy. **URL:** http://www.bjdvd.com/.

52334 ■ The British Journal of Religious Education
Christian Education Publications
1020 Bristol Rd.
Selly Oak
Birmingham B29 6LB, United Kingdom
Ph: 44 121 4724242
Fax: 44 121 4727575
Publisher E-mail: ceo@christianeducation.org.uk
Scholarly journal covering religious education. **Founded:** 1975. **Freq:** 3/yr. **Key Personnel:** Anstice Hughes, Editor, editorial@christianeducation.org.uk; Peter Fishpool, CEO, ceo@christianeducation.org.uk. **ISSN:** 0141-6200. **Subscription Rates:** US$307 individuals online only; US$323 individuals print + online. **Remarks:** Advertising not accepted. **URL:** http://www.retoday.org.uk/bjre.htm. **Circ:** Paid 2,000

52335 ■ Build It
Trinity Publications Ltd.
92-93 Edward House, Edward St.
Birmingham B1 2RA, United Kingdom
Ph: 44 12 12338712
Fax: 44 12 12338715
Magazine giving all the information needed to build a dream home, featuring a Land Update section, including the latest plots for sale around the country and advice from planning specialists. **Freq:** Monthly. **Key Personnel:** Phil Gibbs, Publisher; Anna-Marie DeSouza, Editor. **Subscription Rates:** 39.90 individuals UK; 51.90 individuals Europe; 75.90 other countries. **URL:** http://www.self-build.co.uk/.

52336 ■ Child and Family Social Work
John Wiley & Sons Inc.
Wiley-Blackwell
c/o Susan White, Ed.
The Institute of Applied Social Studies
The University of Birmingham
Muirhead Tower
Birmingham B15 2TT, United Kingdom
Publication E-mail: cfs_editor@oxon.blackwellpublishing.com
Journal focusing on the advanced the wellbeing and welfare of children and their families throughout the world. **Freq:** Quarterly. **Key Personnel:** Susan White, Editor; Ravi Kohli, Assoc. Ed., ravi.kohli@beds.ac.uk. **ISSN:** 1356-7500. **Subscription Rates:** US$163 individuals print and online; US$99 students print and online; US$828 institutions print and online; US$753 institutions print or online; US$965 institutions, other countries print and online; US$877 institutions, other countries print or online; EUR568 institutions print and online; EUR516 institutions print or online. **Remarks:** Accepts advertising. **URL:** http://www.wiley.com/bw/journal.asp?ref=1356-7500&site=1. **Circ:** (Not Reported)

52337 ■ Classic Car Mart
Trinity Publications Ltd.
92-93 Edward House, Edward St.
Birmingham B1 2RA, United Kingdom
Ph: 44 12 12338712
Fax: 44 12 12338715
Consumer magazine covering classic, vintage and veteran cars and related issues for enthusiasts. **Freq:** Monthly. **Print Method:** Web Offset. **Trim Size:** 210 x 303 mm. **Cols./Page:** 4. **Col. Width:** 44 millimeters. **Col. Depth:** 270 millimeters. **Key Personnel:** Mike Worthington Williams, Editor. **ISSN:** 1351-1203. **Remarks:** Accepts advertising. **URL:** http://www.trinitymirror.com/brands/magsexhibitions/tpl/. **Circ:** (Not Reported)

52338 ■ Contact Lens & Anterior Eye
Mosby Inc.
c/o Shehzad Naroo, Ed.-in-Ch.
Neurosciences Research Institute
Aston University
Birmingham B4 7ET, United Kingdom
Publisher E-mail: custserv.ehs@elsevier.com
Peer-reviewed journal covering all aspects of contact lens theory and practice. **Freq:** 5/yr. **Key Personnel:** Shehzad Naroo, Editor-in-Chief; P. Cho, Asia-Pacific Regional Ed. **ISSN:** 1367-0484. **Subscription Rates:** US$252 individuals; 29,800¥ individuals; EUR224 individuals for European countries and Iran; EUR378 institutions for European countries and Iran; 50,300¥ institutions; 423 institutions for all countries except

European, Japan, and Iran. **URL:** http://www.contactlensjournal.com/.

52339 ■ Diabetes and Vascular Disease Research
MediNews (Diabetes) Ltd.
Edgbaston House
3 Duchess Pl.
Edgbaston
Birmingham B16 8NH, United Kingdom
Ph: 44 12 14544114
Fax: 44 121 4541190
Publisher E-mail: info@medinews.org
Journal bridging diabetes and vascular disease, including information on related disorders, such as insulin resistance, dyslipidaemia, thrombosis, obesity, hypertension, and atherosclerosis. **Freq:** Quarterly. **Key Personnel:** Peter J. Grant, Editor-in-Chief; Darren K. McGuire, Clinical Trials Ed.; Clifford J. Bailey, Diabetes Ed. **Subscription Rates:** US$427 institutions print and online; US$265 individuals print and online; US$384 institutions online copy; US$86 individuals single copy; US$117 institutions single copy. **Remarks:** Accepts advertising. **URL:** http://www.dvdres.com. **Circ:** (Not Reported)

52340 ■ Diversity in Health and Social Care
Radcliffe Publishing Ltd.
c/o Prof. Paula McGee, Ed.
Faculty of Health Birmingham City University
Perry Barr
Birmingham B42 2SU, United Kingdom
Ph: 44 121 3315340
Fax: 44 121 3315498
Publisher E-mail: contact.us@radcliffemed.com
Journal dealing with all aspects of diversity in health and social care. **Freq:** Quarterly. **Key Personnel:** Prof. Mark Johnson, Editor, phone 44 116 2013906, mrdj@dmu.ac.uk; Prof. Paula McGee, Editor, paula.mcgee@uce.ac.uk. **ISSN:** 1743-1913. **Subscription Rates:** 445 individuals. **URL:** http://www.radcliffe-oxford.com/journals/J18_Diversity_in_Health_and_Social_Care/default.htm.

52341 ■ European Journal of Information Systems
Operational Research Society of the United Kingdom
Seymour House
12 Edward St.
Birmingham B1 2RX, United Kingdom
Ph: 44 12 12339300
Fax: 44 12 12330321
Publication E-mail: ejis@brunel.ac.uk
European journal covering operations research. **Freq:** Quarterly. **Key Personnel:** Richard Baskerville, Editor-in-Chief; Frantz Rowe, Editor. **URL:** http://www.theorsociety.com/publication/ejis.htm.

52342 ■ IMA Journal of Applied Mathematics
Oxford University Press
c/o Prof David J. Needham, Ed.
School of Mathematics
The University of Birmingham
Edgbaston
Birmingham B15 2TT, United Kingdom
Publisher E-mail: webenquiry.uk@oup.com
Journal providing research into physical and non-physical applied mathematical problems. **Founded:** 1965. **Freq:** 6/yr. **Key Personnel:** Prof. David J. Needham, Editor, needhamd@for.mat.bham.ac.uk; Prof. Alan Champneys, Editor, a.r.champneys@bristol.ac.uk; Prof. Demetrios T. Papageorgiou, Editor, d.papageorgiou@bristol.ac.uk; Prof. Yibin Fu, Editor, y.fu@maths.keele.ac.uk. **ISSN:** 0272-4960. **Subscription Rates:** 737 institutions corporate; print and online; 614 institutions corporate; online only; 675 institutions corporate; print only; 589 institutions print and online; 491 institutions online only; 540 institutions print only; 495 individuals print; 99 members print. **URL:** http://imamat.oxfordjournals.org/.

52343 ■ International Journal of Machine Tools and Manufacture
Elsevier Science
c/o T.A. Dean, Ed.-in-Ch.
The University of Birmingham
School of Manufacturing & Mechanical Engineering
Edgbaston
Birmingham B15 2TT, United Kingdom
Publisher E-mail: nlinfo-f@elsevier.com
Journal covering topics related to Machine Tools and

Circulation: ★ = ABC; △ = BPA; ◆ = CAC; • = CCAB; ❑ = VAC; ⊕ = PO Statement; ‡ = Publisher's Report; Boldface figures = sworn; Light figures = estimated.

Gale Directory of Publications & Broadcast Media/147th Ed.   5577

manufacture of engineering components. **Founded:** 1961. **Freq:** 12/yr. **Key Personnel:** T.A. Dean, Editor-in-Chief; T. Altan, Reviewing Committee; H. Hocheng, Regional Ed.; K. Cheng, Reviewing Committee; J. Lin, Reviewing Committee; W. Chen, Asst. Ed. **ISSN:** 0890-6955. **Subscription Rates:** US$3,928 institutions for all countries except Europe and Japan; 466,200¥ institutions; EUR3,511 institutions European countries. **Remarks:** Accepts advertising. **URL:** http://www.elsevier.com/wps/find/journaldescription.cws_home/264/descriptio ndescription. **Circ:** (Not Reported)

52344 ■ International Journal for Numerical Methods in Fluids
John Wiley & Sons Inc.
c/o Prof. Nigel P. Weatherill, Ed.
College of Engineering & Physical Sciences
University of Birmingham
Edgbaston
Birmingham B15 2TT, United Kingdom
Publisher E-mail: info@wiley.com
Journal containing articles related in computer-aided design, engineering analysis and research in computational fluid dynamics. **Freq:** 36/yr. **Key Personnel:** Prof. Nigel P. Weatherill, Editor; Dr. David K. Gartling, Editor. **ISSN:** 0271-2091. **Subscription Rates:** US$4,519 individuals print only; 3,336 institutions print; 3,670 institutions print and online; EUR4,218 institutions online. **Remarks:** Accepts advertising. **URL:** http://onlinelibrary.wiley.com/journal/10.1002/(ISSN)1097-0363. **Circ:** (Not Reported)

52345 ■ Journal of Antimicrobial Chemotherapy
British Society for Antimicrobial Chemotherapy
c/o A.P. Johnson, Ed.-in-Ch.
11 The Wharf
16 Bridge St.
Birmingham B1 2JS, United Kingdom
Ph: 44 12 16330415
Fax: 44 12 16439497
Publisher E-mail: enquiries@bsac.org.uk
Publication covering chemotherapy. **Freq:** Monthly. **Key Personnel:** D.S. Reeves, Editorial Board; M.B. Avison, Editorial Board; N.M. Brown, Editorial Board; A.P. Johnson, Editor-in-Chief, jac@bsac.org.uk. **ISSN:** 0305-7453. **Subscription Rates:** US$1,702 institutions print and online; US$1,375 institutions online only; US$1,560 institutions print only; US$782 individuals online only; US$846 individuals print; US$320 members print and online; US$166 members print; 851 institutions UK (print and online); 688 institutions IK (online only); 780 institutions print only. **Remarks:** Advertising accepted; rates available upon request. **URL:** http://www.bsac.org.uk/journal_of_antimicrobial_chemotherapy_jac.cfm; http://jac.oxfordjournals.org/content/current. **Circ:** (Not Reported)

52346 ■ Journal of Electrophysiological Technology
Electrophysiological Technologists' Association
Carbis
55 Tennal Rd.
Birmingham B32 2JD, United Kingdom
Publication E-mail: pat.leeson@btopenworld.com
Publisher E-mail: karene.taylor@rcht.swest.nhs.uk
Journal covering neurophysiology, a sub-speciality of neurology. **Founded:** 1950. **Freq:** 3/yr. **Print Method:** Litho. **Trim Size:** A4. **ISSN:** 0307-5095. **Subscription Rates:** Included in membership. **URL:** http://www.epta.50megs.com/jet.htmljetauth. **Ad Rates:** BW: 150, 4C: 500. **Circ:** (Not Reported)

52347 ■ Journal of Literary Semantics (JLS)
Walter de Gruyter GmbH & Co. KG
Dept. of English
University of Birmingham
Birmingham B15 2TT, United Kingdom
Publisher E-mail: info@degruyter.com
Peer-reviewed journal covering research in relations between linguistics and literature. **Founded:** 1972. **Freq:** Semiannual. **Print Method:** Offset. **Trim Size:** 14.8 X 22.5 cm. **Cols./Page:** 6. **Col. Width:** 26 nonpareils. **Col. Depth:** 280 agate lines. **Key Personnel:** Michael Toolan, Editor, m.toolan@bham.ac.uk. **ISSN:** 0341-7638. **Subscription Rates:** EUR127 individuals print or online only; EUR147 individuals print and online; EUR70 single issue. **URL:** http://www.degruyter.de/journals/jls/detailEn.cfm.

52348 ■ Journal of Manufacturing Technology Management
Emerald Group Publishing Ltd.

Aston Business School
Aston Triangle
Aston University
Birmingham B4 7ET, United Kingdom
Publisher E-mail: emerald@emeraldinsight.com
Journal aiming to give a broad international coverage of subjects relating to the management of manufacturing technology and the integration of the production, design, supply and marketing functions of manufacturing enterprises. **Freq:** 8/yr. **Key Personnel:** Prof. David Bennett, Editor, d.j.bennett@aston.ac.uk; Don G. Taylor, Assoc. Ed.; Bart L. MacCarthy, Editorial Review Board; Lucy Sootheran, Publisher, lsootheran@emeraldinsight.com; James D.T. Tannock, Reviews Ed., james.d.tannock@nottingham.ac.uk; Doug Love, Editorial Review Board; Afonso Fleury, Assoc. Ed.; Nourredine Boubekri, Editorial Review Board. **ISSN:** 1741-038X. **URL:** http://info.emeraldinsight.com/products/journals/journals.htm?id=jmtm.

52349 ■ Journal of Medical Microbiology
Society for General Microbiology
c/o Charles Penn, Ed.-in-Ch.
School of Biosciences
University of Birmingham
Birmingham B15 2TT, United Kingdom
Fax: 44 121 4145925
Publication E-mail: jmm@sgm.ac.uk
Journal covering medical microbiology. **Freq:** Monthly. **Key Personnel:** Charles Penn, Editor-in-Chief, c.w.penn@bham.ac.uk. **ISSN:** 0022-2615. **Subscription Rates:** 635 individuals print and online (UK); 600 individuals online (UK); US$1,110 U.S., Canada, and Mexico print and online; US$1,190 U.S., Canada, and Mexico online only; 715 other countries print and online; 670 other countries online. **Remarks:** Accepts advertising. **URL:** http://jmm.sgmjournals.org. **Ad Rates:** BW: 495, 4C: 945. **Circ:** Paid 700

52350 ■ Journal of the Operational Research Society
Palgrave Macmillan
Operational Research Society
Seymour House
12 Edward St.
Birmingham B1 2RX, United Kingdom
Ph: 44 121 2339300
Fax: 44 121 2330321
Publisher E-mail: booksellers@palgrave.com
Journal covering the Operational Research Society. **Freq:** Monthly. **Key Personnel:** John Wilson, Editor; Terry Williams, Editor. **ISSN:** 0160-5682. **Subscription Rates:** 1,107 institutions, other countries print; US$1,882 institutions print. **URL:** http://www.palgrave-journals.com/jors/index.html.

52351 ■ Journal of the Renin-Angiotensin-Aldosterone System
JRAAS Ltd.
Edgbaston House
3 Duchess Pl.
Edgbaston
Birmingham B16 8NH, United Kingdom
Ph: 44 121 4544114
Fax: 44 121 4541190
Publication E-mail: production@jraas.co.uk
Publisher E-mail: production@jraas.co.uk
Scientific journal devoted to original research on peptide systems, clinical research reports on the blockade of the RAAS as well as new developments such as vasopeptidase inhibition, results of clinical trials of drugs inhibiting the systems in the treatment of hypertension, renal disease, heart failure, post-myocardial infarction and diabetes as well as new areas of clinical research into the possible value of these agents in new indications such as maintenance of cognitive function. **Freq:** Quarterly. **Key Personnel:** Graham MacGregor, Editor-in-Chief. **Subscription Rates:** US$429 institutions; US$265 individuals; US$118 institutions single copy; US$86 individuals single copy. **Remarks:** Accepts advertising. **URL:** http://www.jraas.com/. **Ad Rates:** 4C: 1,200. **Circ:** (Not Reported)

52352 ■ Journal of Security Sector Management
Global Facilitation Network for Security Sector Reform
International Development Department
University of Birmingham
Birmingham B15 2TT, United Kingdom
Ph: 44 121 4145038

Fax: 44 121 4147995
Publisher E-mail: enquiries@ssrnetwork.net
Journal covering topics such as debates on security sector reform (SSR), SSR's contribution to international development, and management issues in SSR, and more. **Key Personnel:** Dr. Ann Fitz-Gerald, Editor. **ISSN:** 1740-2425. **URL:** http://www.ssronline.org/.

52353 ■ Journal of Simulation
Palgrave Macmillan
Seymour House
12 Edward St.
Birmingham B1 2RX, United Kingdom
Ph: 44 121 2339300
Fax: 44 121 2330321
Publication E-mail: parry@orsoc.org.uk
Publisher E-mail: booksellers@palgrave.com
Journal devoted to research and practice in the field of discrete-event simulation. **Founded:** 2006. **Freq:** 4/yr. **Key Personnel:** Simon J.E. Taylor, Editor; Stewart Robinson, Editor. **ISSN:** 1747-7778. **Subscription Rates:** 343 institutions, other countries print; US$583 institutions print; 94 other countries print and online; US$160 individuals print and online. **URL:** http://www.palgrave-journals.com/jos/index.html.

52354 ■ Journal of Small Business and Enterprise Development
Emerald Group Publishing Ltd.
c/o Dr. Harry Matlay, Ed.
Business School, Perry Barr
Birmingham City University, E131
Birmingham B42 2SU, United Kingdom
Publisher E-mail: emerald@emeraldinsight.com
Journal for leaders of SMEs and academics in the field of entrepreneurship, combining case studies with quality research, providing an authoritative discussion on the developments surrounding small businesses, seeking to explore best practice, investigate strategies for growth, and to assist and inform those responsible for the management of SMEs. **Freq:** 4/yr. **Key Personnel:** Andrew Smith, Publisher, agsmith@emeraldinsight.com; Dr. Harry Matlay, Editor, harry.matlay@bcu.ac.uk; Prof. Zoltan J. Acs, Editorial Advisory Board; Prof. Richard Lancioni, Editorial Advisory Board; Prof. Abdullah Al-Owaihan, Editorial Advisory Board; Prof. David A. Kirby, Editorial Advisory Board. **ISSN:** 1462-6004. **URL:** http://info.emeraldinsight.com/products/journals/journals.htm?id=jsbed.

52355 ■ Journal of Visual Communication in Medicine
Informa P.L.C.
Medical Illustration
Selly Oak Hospital
Birmingham B29 6JD, United Kingdom
Publisher E-mail: registrations@informa.com
International, peer-reviewed journal acting as a vehicle for the interchange of information and ideas in the production, manipulation, storage and transport of images for medical education, records and research. **Freq:** Quarterly. **Key Personnel:** Carly Betton, Editor, viscomm@imi.org.uk; Simon E. Brown, International Editorial Board; Amy Lake, Asst. Ed., amy.lake@cardiffandvale.wales.nhs.uk; Nicolas C. White, Book Review Ed., nick.white@bsuh.nhs.uk; Harold Ellis, International Editorial Board; Keith Duguid, International Editorial Board; Ronald M. Harden, International Editorial Board. **ISSN:** 1745-3054. **Subscription Rates:** US$725 individuals print and online; US$725 institutions online; US$725 institutions print and online; US$725 individuals online. **Remarks:** Accepts advertising. **URL:** http://informahealthcare.com/jau. **Circ:** (Not Reported)

52356 ■ Knowledge Management Research & Practice
Palgrave Macmillan
Seymour House
12 Edwards St.
Birmingham B1 2RX, United Kingdom
Ph: 44 121 2339300
Fax: 44 121 2330321
Publication E-mail: parry@orsoc.org.uk
Publisher E-mail: booksellers@palgrave.com
Peer-reviewed journal covering articles on all aspects of managing knowledge, organizational learning, intellectual capital and knowledge economics. **Freq:** Quarterly. **Key Personnel:** John S. Edwards, Editor. **ISSN:** 1477-8238. **Subscription Rates:** 290 institutions,

other countries print; US$492 institutions print; 110 other countries print and online; US$187 individuals print and online. **URL:** http://www.palgrave-journals.com/kmrp/index.html.

52357 ■ Language Issues
National Association for Teaching English and other Community Languages to Adults
South Birmingham College
Hall Green Campus
Cole Bank Rd.
Rm. HA205
Birmingham B28 8ES, United Kingdom
Ph: 44 12 16888121
Fax: 44 12 16945062
Publisher E-mail: co-ordinator@natecla.fsnet.co.uk
Publication covering languages. **Subtitle:** The Journal of NATECLA. **Freq:** 20/yr. **Key Personnel:** Rakesh Bhanot, Editor; Eva Illes, Editor. **ISSN:** 0263-5833. **Subscription Rates:** 15 individuals; 30 institutions; 5 single issue. **URL:** http://www.natecla.org.uk/content/483/language_issues:_the_journal_o/. **Ad Rates:** BW: 150. **Circ:** 450

52358 ■ Micro Mart
Trinity Publications Ltd.
92-93 Edward House, Edward St.
Birmingham B1 2RA, United Kingdom
Ph: 44 12 12338712
Fax: 44 12 12338715
Consumer magazine covering computer buying and selling for home and business use. **Freq:** Weekly. **Trim Size:** 190 x 270 mm. **Cols./Page:** 4. **Key Personnel:** Steve Playfoot, Sales Mgr.; Wendy Wood, Publisher; Simon Brew, Editor, editorial@micromart.co.uk. **ISSN:** 0956-3881. **Subscription Rates:** 1.52 single issue. **Remarks:** Accepts advertising. **URL:** http://www.micromart.co.uk. **Formerly:** Micro Computer Mart. **Circ:** Combined 27,090

52359 ■ Nursing Home News
Registered Nursing Home Association
John Hewitt House, Tunnel Ln.
Off Lifford Ln.
Kings Norton
Birmingham B30 3JN, United Kingdom
Ph: 44 121 4511088
Fax: 44 121 4863175
Publisher E-mail: frankursell@rnha.co.uk
Journal of the Registered Nursing Home Association. **Freq:** Monthly. **Remarks:** Accepts advertising. **URL:** http://www.rnha.co.uk/rnha_bulletins.php?r=STELUXY2AK. **Circ:** (Not Reported)

52360 ■ Occupational Safety & Health
Royal Society for the Prevention of Accidents
RoSPA House, Edgbaston Pk.
353 Bristol Rd.
Birmingham B5 7ST, United Kingdom
Ph: 44 12 12482000
Publisher E-mail: help@rospa.co.uk
Publication covering occupational safety and health. **Freq:** Monthly. **ISSN:** 0143-5353. **URL:** http://www.rospa.com/resources/journals.aspx.

52361 ■ Popular Astronomy
Society for Popular Astronomy
79 Chadwick Ave.
Rednal
Birmingham B45 8ED, United Kingdom
Publication E-mail: membership@popastro.com
Magazine of Britain's Society for Popular Astronomy. **Founded:** 1981. **Freq:** Quarterly January, April, July and October. **Trim Size:** A4. **Cols./Page:** 3. **Col. Width:** 5.5 centimeters. **Col. Depth:** 25 centimeters. **Key Personnel:** Peter Grego, Editor, editor@popastro.com; Guy Fennimore, Sec., secretary@popastro.com. **ISSN:** 0261-0892. **Subscription Rates:** 12 members; 24 two years. **URL:** http://www.popastro.com. **Circ:** Combined 3,000

52362 ■ Progress in Nuclear Energy
Elsevier Science
c/o T.D. Beynon, Ed.
School of Physics & Astronomy
University of Birmingham
Birmingham B15 2TT, United Kingdom
Ph: 44 12 14144694
Fax: 44 12 14144725
Publisher E-mail: nlinfo-f@elsevier.com
Journal dealing with all areas of nuclear science and

engineering. **Founded:** 1977. **Freq:** 8/yr. **Key Personnel:** D.J. Dudziak, Editor, dudziak@ncsu.edu; T.D. Beynon, Editor, t.d.beynon@bham.ac.uk; Y.Y. Azmy, Editorial Advisory Board. **ISSN:** 0149-1970. **Subscription Rates:** EUR2,482 institutions European countries; US$2,779 institutions all countries except Europe and Japan; 329,900¥ institutions. **Remarks:** Accepts advertising. **URL:** http://www.elsevier.com/wps/find/journaldescription.cws_home/478/description. **Circ:** (Not Reported)

52363 ■ REtoday
Christian Education Publications
1020 Bristol Rd.
Selly Oak
Birmingham B29 6LB, United Kingdom
Ph: 44 121 4724242
Fax: 44 121 4727575
Publication E-mail: retoday@retoday.org.uk
Publisher E-mail: ceo@christianeducation.org.uk
Professional magazine for teachers of religious education in the UK. **Founded:** 1984. **Freq:** Triennial. **Print Method:** Litho. **Trim Size:** A4. **Key Personnel:** Peter Fishpool, CEO, ceo@christianeducation.org.uk; Rosemary Rivett, Team Dir., rosemary@retoday.org.uk; Lat Blaylock, Editor. **ISSN:** 0266-7738. **Subscription Rates:** 27 individuals; 47 individuals primary teachers; 47 individuals secondary teachers; 70 individuals professional interest; 82 individuals academic interest; 41 institutions; 42 students; 110 individuals combined NATRE. **Remarks:** Accepts advertising. **URL:** http://www.retoday.org.uk/. **Ad Rates:** BW: 624, 4C: 686. **Circ:** Paid 7,000

52364 ■ Review
Pre-Raphaelite Society
c/o Barry Johnson
37 Larchmere Dr.
Hall Green
Birmingham B28 8JB, United Kingdom
Publisher E-mail: info@pre-raphaelitesociety.org
Publication covering art history. **Founded:** 1993. **Freq:** 3/yr. **Key Personnel:** Barry Johnson, Contact. **Subscription Rates:** Included in membership. **URL:** http://www.pre-raphaelitesociety.org/review/index.htm.

52365 ■ Safety Education
Royal Society for the Prevention of Accidents
RoSPA House, Edgbaston Pk.
353 Bristol Rd.
Birmingham B5 7ST, United Kingdom
Ph: 44 12 12482000
Publisher E-mail: help@rospa.co.uk
Publication covering safety education. **Freq:** Bimonthly. **URL:** http://www.rospa.com/resources/journals.aspx.

52366 ■ Safety Express
Royal Society for the Prevention of Accidents
RoSPA House, Edgbaston Pk.
353 Bristol Rd.
Birmingham B5 7ST, United Kingdom
Ph: 44 12 12482000
Publisher E-mail: help@rospa.co.uk
Newspaper covering safety. **Freq:** Bimonthly. **Remarks:** Accepts advertising. **URL:** http://www.rospa.com/resources/journals.aspx. **Circ:** (Not Reported)

52367 ■ Spaghetti Junction
University of Central England Union of Students
Franchise St.
Perry Barr
Birmingham B42 2SZ, United Kingdom
Ph: 44 121 3316801
Fax: 44 121 3316802
Publisher E-mail: union.comms@bcu.ac.uk
Student newspaper. **Founded:** Feb. 10, 2000. **Freq:** Monthly. **Trim Size:** 297 x 210 mm. **Subscription Rates:** Free. **Remarks:** Accepts advertising. **URL:** http://www.birminghamcitysu.com/media/spaghetti/. **Former name:** Deuce; Polygon. **Ad Rates:** 4C: 525. **Circ:** Controlled 4,000

52368 ■ Staying Alive
Royal Society for the Prevention of Accidents
RoSPA House, Edgbaston Pk.
353 Bristol Rd.
Birmingham B5 7ST, United Kingdom
Ph: 44 12 12482000
Publisher E-mail: help@rospa.co.uk
Publication covering home, water and leisure safety.

Freq: Quarterly. **ISSN:** 1354-2249. **Remarks:** Advertising accepted; rates available upon request. **URL:** http://www.rospa.com/resources/journals.aspx. **Circ:** Paid 2,000

52369 ■ Townswoman
Townswomen's Guilds
Tomlinson House, 1st Fl.
329 Tyburn Rd.
Erdington
Birmingham B24 8HJ, United Kingdom
Ph: 44 121 3260400
Fax: 44 121 3261976
Publisher E-mail: tghq@townswomen.org.uk
Publication covering social clubs. **Founded:** 1933. **Freq:** Quarterly. **Key Personnel:** Pauline Myers, Chm. **Remarks:** Advertising accepted; rates available upon request. **URL:** http://www.townswomen.org.uk/page.asp?node=34&sec=Magazine_Information. **Circ:** 34,000

52370 ■ Transactions of the Institute of Metal Finishing
Institute of Metal Finishing
Exeter House
48 Holloway Head
Birmingham B1 1NQ, United Kingdom
Ph: 44 121 6227387
Fax: 44 121 6666316
Publisher E-mail: exeterhouse@instituteofmetalfinishing.org
Publication covering metal finishing. **Freq:** Bimonthly. **ISSN:** 0020-2967. **Subscription Rates:** 342 institutions; US$634 institutions. **Remarks:** Advertising accepted; rates available upon request. **URL:** http://www.maney.co.uk/search?fwaction=show&fwid=631. **Circ:** 1,400

52371 ■ Transport Journal
Institute of Transport Management
14-20 George St.
Birmingham B12 9RG, United Kingdom
Ph: 44 12 14403003
Fax: 44 12 14404644
Publisher E-mail: marketing@itmworld.com
Trade journal covering all aspects of passenger and freight transportation by air, land and sea. **Subtitle:** Official Publication of the Institute of Transport Management. **Founded:** 1942. **Freq:** Bimonthly. **Key Personnel:** Caitriona Gavin, Managing Editor. **Remarks:** Accepts advertising. **URL:** http://www.itmworld.com. **Circ:** Controlled 17,500

52372 ■ The Vegan
Vegan Society - England
Donald Watson House
21 Hylton St.
Birmingham B18 6HJ, United Kingdom
Ph: 44 121 5231730
Fax: 44 121 5231749
Publisher E-mail: info@vegansociety.com
Publication promoting ways of living free from animal products. **Subtitle:** The Magazine of The Vegan Society. **Founded:** Nov. 1944. **Freq:** Quarterly. **Trim Size:** 297 x 210 mm. **Key Personnel:** George Rodger, Contact. **ISSN:** 0307-4811. **Subscription Rates:** 2.50 members. **Remarks:** Advertising accepted; rates available upon request. **URL:** http://www.vegansociety.com/about/publications/vegan-magazine/. **Circ:** 6,000

52373 ■ BBC Radio WM-FM - 95.6
The Mailbox
102-108 Wharfside St.
Birmingham B1 1AY, United Kingdom
Ph: 44 121 5676000
E-mail: birmingham@bbc.co.uk; bbcwm@bbc.co.uk
Format: Talk; News; Eclectic; Sports; Information. **Owner:** British Broadcasting Corporation, Broadcasting House, Portland Pl., London W1A 1AA, United Kingdom. **Founded:** Nov. 9, 1970. **Operating Hours:** Continuous weekdays; 6 a.m.-5 a.m. Weekend. **Key Personnel:** Keith Beech, Editor. **URL:** http://www.bbc.co.uk/birmingham/local_radio.

52374 ■ BRMB-FM - 96.4
9 Brindleyplace
4 Oozells Sq.
Birmingham B1 2DJ, United Kingdom
Ph: 44 121 5665200
Format: Eclectic; Adult Contemporary; Top 40; Talk. **Owner:** Orion Media Ltd., at above address. **Operating Hours:** Continuous. **URL:** http://www.brmb.co.uk.

Circulation: ★ = ABC; △ = BPA; ♦ = CAC; • = CCAB; ❑ = VAC; ⊕ = PO Statement; ‡ = Publisher's Report; Boldface figures = sworn; Light figures = estimated.

52375 ■ Heart-FM - 100.7
111 Broad St.
Birmingham B15 1AS, United Kingdom
Ph: 44 121 6950000
Format: Easy Listening; Adult Contemporary. **Operating Hours:** Continuous. **Ad Rates:** Advertising accepted; rates available upon request. **URL:** http://www.heartwestmids.co.uk/.

52376 ■ Radio XL-AM - 1296
KMS House
Bradford St.
Birmingham B12 0JD, United Kingdom
Ph: 44 121 7535353
Fax: 44 121 7533111
E-mail: info@radioxl.net
Format: Ethnic. **URL:** http://www.radioxl.net/.

52377 ■ Smooth-FM - 105.7
Crown House
123 Hagley Rd., 3rd Fl.
Birmingham B16 8LD, United Kingdom
Ph: 44 121 4521057
Fax: 44 121 4523222
Format: Full Service; Eclectic. **Owner:** Guardian Media Group Radio, 60 Farringdon Rd., London EC1R 3GA, United Kingdom, 44 20 72782332. **Founded:** Oct. 16, 2001. **Formerly:** SAGA 105.7-FM. **Operating Hours:** Continuous. **URL:** http://www.smoothradiowestmidlands.co.uk.

Bishop's Stortford

52378 ■ European Business Air News
Stansted News Ltd.
134 S St.
Bishop's Stortford CM23 3BQ, United Kingdom
Ph: 44 127 9714501
Fax: 44 127 9714519
Professional publication for business aircraft owners and operators in Europe. **Founded:** 1989. **Freq:** Monthly. **Print Method:** Sheetfed offset. **Trim Size:** A3. **Cols./Page:** 5. **Col. Width:** 51 millimeters. **Key Personnel:** Mark Ranger, Advertising Mgr., phone 44 127 9714509, mark@ebanmagazine.com; David Wright, Publisher, phone 44 127 9714502, david@ebanmagazine.com; Rod Smith, Ch. Reporter, phone 44 127 9714506, rod@ebanmagazine.com; Janet Bell, Circulation/Subscriptions, phone 44 127 9714515, janet@ebanmagazine.com. **ISSN:** 0959-1311. **Subscription Rates:** 15 individuals in the UK; 27 other countries. **Remarks:** Accepts advertising. **URL:** http://www.ebanmagazine.com/. **Ad Rates:** BW: 4,953, 4C: 7,347. **Circ:** Controlled △6,244

52379 ■ Global Business Jet
Stansted News Ltd.
134 S St.
Bishop's Stortford CM23 3BQ, United Kingdom
Ph: 44 127 9714501
Fax: 44 127 9714519
Professional magazine for owners and operators of long-range business jets worldwide. **Subtitle:** The News Magazine For Intercontinental Business Jet Owners. **Founded:** 1997. **Freq:** Monthly 8/yr. **Print Method:** Sheetfed offset. **Trim Size:** A3. **Cols./Page:** 5. **Col. Width:** 51 millimeters. **Key Personnel:** David Wright, Publisher, phone 44 127 9714502, david@gbjmagazine.com; Mark Ranger, Advertising Mgr., phone 44 127 9714509, mark@gbjyearbook.com; Janet Bell, Circulation/Subscriptions, phone 44 127 9714515, janet@gbjyearbook.com. **ISSN:** 1446-6510. **Remarks:** Accepts advertising. **URL:** http://www.gbjyearbook.com/yb_front.html. **Ad Rates:** BW: 4,953, 4C: 7,347. **Circ:** Controlled 6,244

52380 ■ Journal of Neonatal Nursing
Stansted News Ltd.
134 S St.
Bishop's Stortford CM23 3BQ, United Kingdom
Ph: 44 127 9714501
Fax: 44 127 9714519
Professional journal covering neonatal nursing. **Founded:** Sept. 1994. **Freq:** Bimonthly. **Print Method:** Sheetfed offset. **Trim Size:** 210 x 297 mm. **Key Personnel:** Christine Bishop, Publisher, phone 44 127 9714510, publishing@infantgrapevine.co.uk; Tricia Taylor, Subscription Mgr., phone 44 127 9714516, subscriptions@infantgrapevine.co.uk. **Subscription Rates:** 46 individuals UK; 130 institutions UK; 60 individuals overseas;

145 institutions overseas. **Remarks:** Accepts advertising. **URL:** http://www.neonatal-nursing.co.uk/. **Ad Rates:** BW: EUR920, 4C: EUR1,395. **Circ:** Combined 5,000

52381 ■ Monarchy
International Monarchist League
PO Box 5307
Bishop's Stortford CM23 3DZ, United Kingdom
Ph: 44 127 9465551
Publisher E-mail: enquiries@monarchy.net
Publication covering monarchy. **Freq:** Quarterly. **Subscription Rates:** 20 individuals; 10 students full-time; 27.50 other countries; 17.50 students, other countries. **Remarks:** Advertising accepted; rates available upon request. **URL:** http://www.monarchy.net. **Circ:** 4,000

52382 ■ Themescene
British Thematic Association
9 Oaklands Pk.
British Philatelic Centre
107 Charterhouse St.
Bishop's Stortford CM23 2BY, United Kingdom
Journal including thematic philately. **Freq:** Quarterly. **ISSN:** 0268-2508. **Subscription Rates:** Free to members. **Remarks:** Accepts advertising. **URL:** http://www.brit-thematic-assoc.com/themescene.htm. **Circ:** (Not Reported)

Blackburn

52383 ■ Edges Magazine
Thomas
St. Anne's House
France St.
Blackburn BB2 1LX, United Kingdom
Ph: 44 12 25459240
Fax: 44 12 25456884
Publisher E-mail: edges@globalnet.co.uk
Magazine on the socially excluded people. **Subtitle:** The Voice of THOMAS. **Freq:** Quarterly. **Key Personnel:** Fr. James McCartney, Director, james.mccartney@thomasonline.org.uk. **Subscription Rates:** Free. **URL:** http://www.users.globalnet.co.uk/~edges/online/.

52384 ■ BBC Radio Lancashire-FM - 103.9
20-26 Darwen St.
Blackburn BB2 2EA, United Kingdom
Ph: 44 1254 262411
Fax: 44 1254 680821
E-mail: lancashire@bbc.co.uk
Format: News; Talk; Sports; Oldies. **Owner:** British Broadcasting Corp., Broadcasting House, Portland Pl., London W1A 1AA, United Kingdom. **Operating Hours:** Continuous. **Key Personnel:** John Clayton, Editor. **URL:** http://www.bbc.co.uk/lancashire/local_radio.

Blackpool

52385 ■ Fylde Tramway News
Fylde Tramway Society
PO Box 1264
Blackpool FY1 9EG, United Kingdom
Publication covering tramway news. **Freq:** Monthly. **Subscription Rates:** Included in membership. **URL:** http://www.freewebs.com/fyldetramwaysociety-blackpool/aboutthefts.htm. **Circ:** 650

52386 ■ Radio Wave 96.5-FM - 96.5
965 Mowbray Dr.
Blackpool FY3 7JR, United Kingdom
Ph: 44 1253 650300
Fax: 44 1253 301965
Format: Eclectic; Top 40; Adult Contemporary; Easy Listening; News. **Operating Hours:** Continuous. **Key Personnel:** Helen Bowden, Station Dir., helen.bowden@thewavefm.co.uk; Roy Lynch, Program Mgr., roy.lynch@thewavefm.co.uk. **Ad Rates:** Advertising accepted; rates available upon request. **URL:** http://www.wave965.com/index.php.

Blaydon-on-Tyne

52387 ■ Classical Guitar
Ashley Mark Publishing Co.
1 Vance Ct.
Trans Britannia Enterprise Pk.
Blaydon-on-Tyne NE21 5NH, United Kingdom
Ph: 44 19 14149006
Fax: 44 19 14149001
Publication E-mail: classicalguitar@ashleymark.co.uk

Publisher E-mail: david@ashleymark.co.uk
Consumer magazine covering the classical guitar. **Founded:** 1982. **Freq:** Monthly. **Trim Size:** 297 x 210 mm. **Key Personnel:** David English, Advertising Mgr., david@ashleymark.co.uk. **ISSN:** 0950-429X. **Subscription Rates:** 54 individuals U.K.; 97.20 two years U.K.; 64.50 individuals Europe; 116 two years Europe; 72.60 other countries; 130.68 other countries 2 years. **Remarks:** Accepts advertising. **URL:** http://www.classicalguitarmagazine.com. **Circ:** Combined 8,000

Blechingley

52388 ■ Laudate Magazine
Guild of Church Musicians
Hillbrow
Godstone Rd.
Blechingley RH1 4PJ, United Kingdom
Ph: 44 18 83743168
Publisher E-mail: johnmusicsure@orbix.co.uk
Publication covering music. **Founded:** 1980. **Freq:** 3/yr. **Trim Size:** A5. **Key Personnel:** Dr. Micheal Walsh, PhD, Editor, phone 44 1243 788315, fax 44 1243 788315, michael@musicprint.org; Dr. Mary Archer, PhD, President; John Ewington, Contact, johnmusicsure@aol.com; Prof. Grenville Hancox, Academic Board; Prof. Bernard Lovell, Vice President; Jean Bannister, Academic Board; Prof. Peter Aston, Chm. **Remarks:** Advertising accepted; rates available upon request. **URL:** http://www.churchmusicians.org/publications.html. **Circ:** 600

Bletchley

52389 ■ Military Modelcraft International
Guideline Publications
Enigma Bldg., Unit 3
Bilton Rd.
Denbigh E
Bletchley MK1 1HW, United Kingdom
Ph: 44 1908 274433
Fax: 44 1908 270614
Magazine featuring information on the military modeling hobby. **Freq:** Monthly. **Subscription Rates:** 39.50 individuals; 58.65 individuals Europe; 79 other countries. **Remarks:** Accepts advertising. **URL:** http://mmi.guidelinepublications.co.uk/. **Circ:** (Not Reported)

52390 ■ Scale Aircraft Modelling
Guideline Publications
Enigma Bldg., Unit 3
Bilton Rd.
Denbigh E
Bletchley MK1 1HW, United Kingdom
Ph: 44 1908 274433
Fax: 44 1908 270614
Magazine featuring information on scale aircraft modeling hobby. **Freq:** Monthly. **Subscription Rates:** 43.45 individuals; 58.65 individuals Europe; 79 other countries. **Remarks:** Accepts advertising. **URL:** http://sam.guidelinepublications.co.uk/. **Circ:** (Not Reported)

52391 ■ Toy Soldier Collector
Guideline Publications
Enigma Bldg., Unit 3
Bilton Rd.
Denbigh E
Bletchley MK1 1HW, United Kingdom
Ph: 44 1908 274433
Fax: 44 1908 270614
Magazine for toy soldier collectors. **Freq:** Bimonthly. **Subscription Rates:** 27 individuals; 36.50 individuals Europe; 40 other countries. **Remarks:** Accepts advertising. **URL:** http://www.toysoldiercollector.com/. **Circ:** (Not Reported)

Bognor Regis

52392 ■ Bognor Regis Observer
Johnston Press PLC
14 Station Rd.
Bognor Regis PO21 1QE, United Kingdom
Ph: 44 1243 827111
Local community newspaper. **Key Personnel:** Colin Channon, Editor, phone 44 1243 534135, fax 44 1243 539386, colin.channon@chiobserver.co.uk; Kelly Brown, News Ed., phone 44 1243 534132, fax 44 1243 539386, news@chiobserver.co.uk. **Remarks:** Accepts advertising. **URL:** http://www.bognor.co.uk/. **Circ:** (Not Reported)

52393 ■ Briefings in Real Estate Finance
John Wiley & Sons Ltd.
1-7 Oldlands Way
Bognor Regis PO21 9FF, United Kingdom
Ph: 44 1865 778315
Publisher E-mail: cs-journals@wiley.co.uk
Journal increasing practical understanding of the processes and challenges associated with the funding of real estate, seeking to provide a peer-reviewed, international forum for the dissemination and evaluation of the current techniques, approaches and best practice in all aspects of the subject. **Freq:** Quarterly. **Key Personnel:** Elizabeth Edwards, Editorial Board; Howard Erbstein, Editorial Board; Sven Bienert, Editorial Board; Charles Follows, Editorial Board; Alastair Adair, Editorial Board; Fred Acker, Mng. Dir. **ISSN:** 1473-1894. **Subscription Rates:** 195 institutions print only; US$340 institutions, other countries print only; EUR220 institutions, other countries. **Remarks:** Accepts advertising. **URL:** http://www3.interscience.wiley.com/cgi-bin/jhome/110484210. **Circ:** (Not Reported)

52394 ■ Cochlear Implants International
John Wiley & Sons Ltd.
1-7 Oldlands Way
Bognor Regis PO21 9FF, United Kingdom
Ph: 44 1865 778315
Publisher E-mail: cs-journals@wiley.co.uk
Journal including scientific contributions from all the disciplines that are represented in cochlear implant teams: audiology, medicine and surgery, speech therapy and speech pathology, psychology, hearing therapy, radiology, pathology, engineering and acoustics, teaching, and communication. **Freq:** Quarterly. **Key Personnel:** John Graham, Editor; Huw Cooper, Dep. Ed.; Jonathan Osborne, Asst. Ed. **ISSN:** 1467-0100. **Subscription Rates:** 133 individuals print only; US$243 other countries print; US$526 institutions, other countries print only. **Remarks:** Accepts advertising. **URL:** http://www3.interscience.wiley.com/journal/112094302/home. **Circ:** (Not Reported)

52395 ■ European Diabetes Nursing
John Wiley & Sons Ltd.
1-7 Oldlands Way
Bognor Regis PO21 9FF, United Kingdom
Ph: 44 1865 778315
Publisher E-mail: cs-journals@wiley.co.uk
Official journal of the Federation of European Nurses in Diabetes, encompassing clinical practice, policy, research and systems of care specifically for nurses who work in diabetes across Europe. **Freq:** 3/yr. **Key Personnel:** Gillian Hood, Co-Ed., gillian.hood@bartsandthelondon.nhs.uk; Sofia Llahana, Editorial Board, s.llahana@warwick.ac.uk; Seyda Ozcan, Editorial Board, ozcanseyda@yahoo.com; Anne-Marie Felton, Editorial Board, anne.felton@fend.org; Marit Graue, Editorial Board, marit.graue@hib.no; Angelika Muenzinger, Editorial Board, angelica.muenzinger@klinikum-nuernberg.de. **ISSN:** 1551-7853. **Subscription Rates:** EUR53 other countries print only; EUR90 institutions, other countries print only; US$161 institutions, other countries print only. **Remarks:** Accepts advertising. **URL:** http://www3.interscience.wiley.com/cgi-bin/jhome/109710387. **Circ:** (Not Reported)

52396 ■ The International Journal of Applied Psychoanalytic Studies
John Wiley & Sons Ltd.
1-7 Oldlands Way
Bognor Regis PO21 9FF, United Kingdom
Ph: 44 1865 778315
Publisher E-mail: cs-journals@wiley.co.uk
Journal providing a forum for the publication of original work on the application of psychoanalysis to the entire range of human knowledge, offering a concentrated focus on the subjective and relational aspects of the human unconscious and its expression in human behavior in all its variety. **Freq:** Quarterly. **Key Personnel:** Nadia Ramzy, PhD, Editor-in-Chief; Salman Akhtar, MD, Assoc. Ed.; David Scharff, MD, Assoc. Ed.; Jonathan Cohen, PhD, Board of Consulting Ed.; Neil Altman, PhD, Board of Consulting Ed.; Douglas Kirsner, PhD, Assoc. Ed.; Henri Parens, MD, Assoc. Ed.; Stuart W. Twemlow, MD, Editor-in-Chief; John R. Suler, PhD, Assoc. Ed. **ISSN:** 1742-3341. **Subscription Rates:** 65 individuals print only; US$97 other countries print only; US$377 institutions, other countries print only; 192 institutions print only. **Remarks:** Accepts advertising. **URL:** http://www3.

interscience.wiley.com/cgi-bin/jhome/112094308. **Circ:** (Not Reported)

52397 ■ International Journal of Medical Robotics and Computer-Assisted Surgery
John Wiley & Sons Ltd.
1-7 Oldlands Way
Bognor Regis PO21 9FF, United Kingdom
Ph: 44 1865 778315
Publisher E-mail: cs-journals@wiley.co.uk
Journal presenting the latest developments in robotics and related technologies for medical applications, of interest to neurosurgeons, plastic surgeons, urologists, mcrosurgeons, surgeons in training, and engineers developing robotic surgery equipment. **Freq:** Quarterly. **Key Personnel:** Mehran Anvari, Editor-in-Chief; Joanne Pransky, Managing Editor; Clive Loughlin, Tech. Ed.; Monica Schofield, Founding Ed.; David Jayne, Founding Ed. **ISSN:** 1478-5951. **Subscription Rates:** 105 individuals print only; US$210 other countries print only; US$798 institutions, other countries print only; US$798 institutions print only. **Remarks:** Accepts advertising. **URL:** http://www3.interscience.wiley.com/cgi-bin/jhome/112094293. **Circ:** (Not Reported)

52398 ■ Journal of Consumer Behaviour
John Wiley & Sons Ltd.
1-7 Oldlands Way
Bognor Regis PO21 9FF, United Kingdom
Ph: 44 1865 778315
Publisher E-mail: cs-journals@wiley.co.uk
Journal offering an international forum for the latest thinking, new developments and cutting-edge techniques in all aspects of consumer behaviour, with a global focus which does not reflect the interests of any particular country. **Subtitle:** An International Research Review. **Freq:** Bimonthly. **Key Personnel:** Prof. James W. Gentry, North American Ed.; Prof. Alvin C. Burns, Editorial Board; Dr. Suraj Commuri, Editorial Board; Dr. Stacey M. Baker, Editorial Board; Dr. Geraldine Clarke, Editorial Board; Dr. Paul Copley, Editorial Board; Prof. Joseph A. Cote, Editorial Board. **ISSN:** 1472-0817. **Subscription Rates:** 114 individuals print only; US$196 other countries print only; 302 institutions print only; US$552 institutions, other countries print only. **Remarks:** Accepts advertising. **URL:** http://www3.interscience.wiley.com/cgi-bin/jhome/110483937. **Circ:** (Not Reported)

52399 ■ Journal of Public Affairs
John Wiley & Sons Ltd.
1-7 Oldlands Way
Bognor Regis PO21 9FF, United Kingdom
Ph: 44 1865 778315
Publisher E-mail: cs-journals@wiley.co.uk
International forum for public affairs professionals in private and public sector organizations and academic observers in universities and business schools, tackling themes such as government relations and lobbying, issues management, community relations, corporate social responsibility and political strategy and marketing. **Freq:** Quarterly. **Key Personnel:** Prof. Phil Harris, Editor-in-Chief; Geoffrey D. Allen, Regional Ed.; Dr. Ben Wooliscroft, Review Ed.; Leighton Andrews, Editorial Board; Prof. Craig S. Fleisher, Regional Ed.; Paul Baines, Editorial Board; Christian Scheucher, Regional Ed.; Dr. Danny Moss, Editor-in-Chief; Dr. Ruth Ashford, Editorial Board; Steven Atack, Editorial Board. **ISSN:** 1472-3891. **Subscription Rates:** 98 individuals print only; US$155 other countries print; 238 institutions print only; US$430 institutions, other countries print only; 262 institutions combined print with online; US$473 institutions, other countries combined print with online. **Remarks:** Accepts advertising. **URL:** http://www3.interscience.wiley.com/cgi-bin/jhome/110484432. **Circ:** (Not Reported)

52400 ■ Musculoskeletal Care
John Wiley & Sons Ltd.
1-7 Oldlands Way
Bognor Regis PO21 9FF, United Kingdom
Ph: 44 1865 778315
Publisher E-mail: cs-journals@wiley.co.uk
Journal providing allied health professionals with the clinical knowledge and skills required for the care management of musculoskeletal conditions, using the available evidence to promote best practice. **Freq:** Quarterly. **Key Personnel:** Sarah Ryan, Editor; Krysia

Dziedzic, Assoc. Ed.; Jackie Hill, Assoc. Ed. **ISSN:** 1478-2189. **Subscription Rates:** 54 individuals print only; US$99 other countries print; US$337 institutions, other countries print. **Remarks:** Accepts advertising. **URL:** http://onlinelibrary.wiley.com/journal/10.1002/(ISSN)1557-0681. **Circ:** (Not Reported)

52401 ■ Play Action
Fair Play for Children Association
32 Longford Rd.
Bognor Regis
Bognor Regis PO21 1AG, United Kingdom
Ph: 44 845 3307635
Publisher E-mail: administration@fairplayforchildren.net
Journal covering issues related to play. **Freq:** Quarterly. **Subscription Rates:** 15 individuals; Free to all members. **Remarks:** Accepts advertising. **URL:** http://www.fairplayforchildren.org/index.php?page=Playaction_Archives&section=Publications. **Circ:** (Not Reported)

52402 ■ Practice Development in Health Care
John Wiley & Sons Ltd.
1-7 Oldlands Way
Bognor Regis PO21 9FF, United Kingdom
Ph: 44 1865 778315
Publisher E-mail: cs-journals@wiley.co.uk
Journal aiming to promote and be a source of ideas, reflections and scholarly work in the field of clinical practice development. **Freq:** Quarterly. **Key Personnel:** Susan Hamer, Editor; Steve Page, Editor; Roger Cowell, Assoc. Ed. **ISSN:** 1475-9861. **Subscription Rates:** 79 individuals print only; US$142 other countries print only; US$420 institutions, other countries print only. **Remarks:** Accepts advertising. **URL:** http://www3.interscience.wiley.com/cgi-bin/jhome/112094320. **Circ:** (Not Reported)

52403 ■ Psychotherapy and Politics International
John Wiley & Sons Ltd.
1-7 Oldlands Way
Bognor Regis PO21 9FF, United Kingdom
Ph: 44 1865 778315
Publisher E-mail: cs-journals@wiley.co.uk
Journal exploring the manifold connections and interactions between politics and psychotherapy, both in theory and in practice, focusing on the application to political problematics of thinking that originates in the field of psychotherapy, and equally on the application within the field of psychotherapy of political concepts and values. **Freq:** 3/yr. **Key Personnel:** Nick Totton, Editor; Dr. Gottfried Heuer, Assoc. Ed.; Prof. Andrew Samuels, Consulting Ed. **ISSN:** 1476-9263. **Subscription Rates:** 63 individuals print; US$114 other countries print; US$258 institutions, other countries print; 132 institutions print. **Remarks:** Accepts advertising. **URL:** http://www3.interscience.wiley.com/cgi-bin/jhome/112094323. **Circ:** (Not Reported)

52404 ■ Teaching Mathematics and Its Applications
Oxford University Press
University College Chichester
Upper Bognor Rd.
West Sussex
Bognor Regis PO21 1HR, United Kingdom
Publisher E-mail: webenquiry.uk@oup.com
Journal for mathematics teachers, students, researchers and those concerned with curriculum development and assessment, providing a forum for the exchange of ideas and experiences which contribute to the improvement of mathematics teaching and learning for students from upper secondary/high school level through to university first-degree level, inclusive with an emphasis on the applications of mathematics and mathematical modelling within the context of mathematics education worldwide. **Freq:** 4/yr. **Key Personnel:** Prof. Adrian Oldknow, Editorial Board; Dr. Peter McPolin, Editorial Board; Prof. Richard Noss, Editorial Board; Duncan Lawson, Editor, tmajournal@aol.com; Dr. Peter Galbraith, Editorial Board; Prof. Afzal Ahmed, Editorial Board; Prof. John Berry, Editorial Board; Prof. Jerry Becker, Editorial Board; Honor Williams, Editor; Dr. Neil Challis, Editorial Board. **ISSN:** 0268-3679. **Subscription Rates:** 154 institutions corporate; print and online; 128 institutions corporate; online only; 141 institutions corporate; print only; 122 institutions print and online; 102 institutions online only; 112 institutions print only; 107 individuals

print; 50 members print. **Remarks:** Advertising accepted; rates available upon request. **URL:** http://teamat.oxfordjournals.org/. **Circ:** (Not Reported)

Bolton

52405 ■ The Bolton News
Newsquest Media Group Ltd.
1 Churchgate
Bolton BL1 1DE, United Kingdom
Ph: 44 1204 522345
Publication E-mail: newsdesk@theboltonnews.co.uk
Newspaper featuring local news and events. **Founded:** Mar. 19, 1867. **Freq:** Daily. **Key Personnel:** Helen Turnbull, Advertising Mgr., phone 44 1204 537372, fax 44 1204 537432, helen.turnbull@lancashire.newsquest.co.uk; Ian Savage, Editor-in-Chief, phone 44 1204 537257, fax 44 1204 537068, isavage@theboltonnews.co.uk. **URL:** http://www.theboltonnews.co.uk/. **Formerly:** The Bolton Evening News.

Bo'ness

52406 ■ Blastpipe
Scottish Railway Preservation Society
Bo'ness Sta.
Union St.
Bo'ness EH51 9AQ, United Kingdom
Ph: 44 1506 825855
Publisher E-mail: society@srps.org.uk
Magazine containing reports and articles of interest to members. **Freq:** Quarterly. **Subscription Rates:** Included in membership. **URL:** http://www.srps.org.uk/srps/membership.htm.

Bordon

52407 ■ Cracking Matters
Concrete Repair Association
Kingsley House
Ganders Business Park, Kingsley
Hampshire
Bordon GU35 9LU, United Kingdom
Ph: 44 1420 471615
Publisher E-mail: admin@cra.org.uk
Journal of the Concrete Repair Association. **Freq:** Semiannual. **URL:** http://concreterepair.org.uk/cracking_matters/cracking_matters.html.

Boston

52408 ■ Boston Standard
Johnston Press PLC
5/6 Church Ln.
Boston PE21 6ND, United Kingdom
Ph: 44 1205 311433
Local community newspaper. **Freq:** Weekly. **Key Personnel:** Karen Maw, Sales Mgr., fax 44 1205 352913, karen.maw@jpress.co.uk; Warren Moody, Dep. Ed., fax 44 1205 352913, warren.moody@jpress.co.uk. **Remarks:** Accepts advertising. **URL:** http://www.bostonstandard.co.uk/. **Circ:** (Not Reported)

Bourne

52409 ■ Caravan, Motorhome & Camping Mart
Warners Group Publications plc
The Maltings
West St.
Bourne PE10 9PH, United Kingdom
Ph: 44 1778 391000
Consumer magazine covering all aspects of caravanning, motorcaravanning, camping and trailers and accessories. **Freq:** Monthly. **Print Method:** Web Offset. **Trim Size:** 210 x 303 mm. **Cols./Page:** 4. **Col. Width:** 44 millimeters. **Col. Depth:** 270 millimeters. **Key Personnel:** Peter Sharpe, Editor, phone 44 1778 392059. **ISSN:** 0956-6562. **Subscription Rates:** 16.99 individuals. **Remarks:** Accepts advertising. **URL:** http://www.outandaboutlive.co.uk/magazines/Default.asp?magazine=1. **Formerly:** Caravan, Motorcaravan & Camping Mart. **Circ:** (Not Reported)

Bournemouth

52410 ■ Advanced Photoshop
Imagine Publishing Ltd.
Richmond House
33 Richmond Hill
Dorset
Bournemouth BH2 6EZ, United Kingdom
Ph: 44 1202 586200
Magazine featuring Adobe Photoshop. **Subtitle:** The magazine for Adobe "Photoshop" professionals. **Freq:** Monthly. **Key Personnel:** Julie Easton, Editor, phone 44 1202 586243, julie.easton@imagine-publishing.co.uk; Hang Deretz, Advertising Mgr., phone 44 1202 586442, hang.deretz@imagine-publishing.co.uk. **Subscription Rates:** 25.15 individuals 6 issues direct debit, United Kingdom; 62.30 individuals 13 issues by credit card, United Kingdom; 80 U.S. and Canada 13 issues by credit card; 80 other countries 13 issues by credit card; 70 individuals 13 issues by credit card, Europe. **Remarks:** Accepts advertising. **URL:** http://www.advancedphotoshop.co.uk. **Circ:** (Not Reported)

52411 ■ Corel Painter Official Magazine
Imagine Publishing Ltd.
Richmond House
33 Richmond Hill
Dorset
Bournemouth BH2 6EZ, United Kingdom
Ph: 44 1202 586200
Publication E-mail: corsite@imagine-publishing.co.uk
Magazine featuring Corel Painter. **Key Personnel:** Jo Cole, Editor-in-Chief, phone 44 1202 586224, jo.cole@imagine-publishing.co.uk; Hang Deretz, Advertising Mgr., phone 44 1202 586201, hang.deretz@imagine-publishing.co.uk; April Madden, Technology Ed., phone 44 1202 586442, april.madden@imagine-publishing.co.uk. **Subscription Rates:** 25.20 individuals 6 issues direct debit; 62.40 individuals 13 issues by credit card; 70 individuals 13 issues by credit card, Europe; 80 U.S. and Canada 13 issues by credit card; 80 other countries 13 issues by credit card. **Remarks:** Accepts advertising. **URL:** http://www.paintermagazine.co.uk. **Circ:** (Not Reported)

52412 ■ Digital Camera Buyer
Imagine Publishing Ltd.
Richmond House
33 Richmond Hill
Dorset
Bournemouth BH2 6EZ, United Kingdom
Ph: 44 1202 586200
Publication E-mail: dceteam@imagine-publishing.co.uk
Magazine on digital cameras. **Subtitle:** The UK's definitive digital camera buyers' guide. **Key Personnel:** Matt Tuffin, Dep. Ed., phone 44 1202 586210, matt.tuffin@imagine-publishing.co.uk; Debbi Allen, Editor-in-Chief, phone 44 1202 586218, debbi.allen@imagine-publishing.co.uk. **Subscription Rates:** 16.78 individuals 6 issues direct debit; 41.50 individuals 13 issues by credit card; 70 individuals 13 issues by credit card, Europe; 80 U.S. and Canada 13 issues by credit card; 80 other countries 13 issues by credit card. **Remarks:** Accepts advertising. **URL:** http://www.digicambuyer.co.uk. **Circ:** (Not Reported)

52413 ■ Digital Photographer
Imagine Publishing Ltd.
Richmond House
33 Richmond Hill
Dorset
Bournemouth BH2 6EZ, United Kingdom
Ph: 44 1202 586200
Publication E-mail: dphotographer@imagine-publishing.co.uk
Magazine for photography enthusiasts. **Subtitle:** The digital photography magazine for enthusiasts and pros. **Freq:** Monthly. **Key Personnel:** Debbi Allen, Editor-in-Chief, phone 44 1202 586218, debbi.allen@imagine-publishing.co.uk. **Subscription Rates:** 21 individuals 6 issues, UK; 52 individuals; 70 individuals in Europe; 80 other countries; 70 individuals in Eire. **Remarks:** Accepts advertising. **URL:** http://www.dphotographer.co.uk. **Circ:** (Not Reported)

52414 ■ gamesTM
Imagine Publishing Ltd.
Richmond House
33 Richmond Hill
Dorset
Bournemouth BH2 6EZ, United Kingdom
Ph: 44 1202 586200
Publication E-mail: gamestm@imagine-publishing.co.uk
Magazine for computer gamers. **Freq:** 13/yr. **Key Personnel:** Rick Porter, Editor-in-Chief, phone 44 1202 586256, rick.porter@imagine-publishing.co.uk. **Subscription Rates:** 46.80 individuals; 65 individuals Europe; 75 other countries. **Remarks:** Accepts advertising. **URL:** http://www.imagine-publishing.co.uk/GamesTM/. **Circ:** (Not Reported)

52415 ■ High Definition Review
Imagine Publishing Ltd.
Richmond House
33 Richmond Hill
Dorset
Bournemouth BH2 6EZ, United Kingdom
Ph: 44 1202 586200
Publication E-mail: hdreview@imagine-publishing.co.uk
Magazine providing information on high definition entertainment. **Freq:** 13/yr. **Key Personnel:** Keith Hennessey, Editor, phone 44 1202 586241, keith.hennessey@imagine-publishing.co.uk. **Subscription Rates:** 41.50 individuals; 60 individuals Europe; 70 other countries. **Remarks:** Accepts advertising. **URL:** http://www.imagine-publishing.co.uk/HDReview/. **Circ:** (Not Reported)

52416 ■ iCreate
Imagine Publishing Ltd.
Richmond House
33 Richmond Hill
Dorset
Bournemouth BH2 6EZ, United Kingdom
Ph: 44 1202 586200
Magazine for Apple computer users. **Subtitle:** The creative magazine for Mac users. **Freq:** Monthly. **Key Personnel:** Ben Harvell, Editor. **Subscription Rates:** 25.20 individuals 6 issues direct debit; 62.40 individuals 13 issues by credit card; 70 individuals 13 issues by credit card, Europe; 80 U.S. and Canada 13 issues by credit card; 80 other countries 13 issues by credit card. **Remarks:** Accepts advertising. **URL:** http://www.icreatemagazine.com. **Circ:** (Not Reported)

52417 ■ nRevolution
Imagine Publishing Ltd.
Richmond House
33 Richmond Hill
Dorset
Bournemouth BH2 6EZ, United Kingdom
Ph: 44 1202 586200
Gaming magazine featuring Nintendo Wii and DS. **Key Personnel:** James Hanslip, Hd. of Sales; Darren Pearce, Circulation Mgr.; Phil King, Editor. **Subscription Rates:** 21 individuals 6 issues direct debit; 51.90 individuals 13 issues by credit card; 65 individuals 13 issues by credit card, Europe; 75 other countries 13 issues by credit card, Eire. **Remarks:** Accepts advertising. **URL:** http://www.imagine-publishing.co.uk/nRevolution/. **Circ:** (Not Reported)

52418 ■ Paint Shop Pro Photo
Imagine Publishing Ltd.
Richmond House
33 Richmond Hill
Dorset
Bournemouth BH2 6EZ, United Kingdom
Ph: 44 1202 586200
Publication E-mail: paintermagazine@imagine-publishing.co.uk
Magazine providing information on Corel Paint Shop Pro Photo applications. **Key Personnel:** Duncan Evans, Editor, phone 44 1202 586282, duncan.evans@imagine-publishing.co.uk. **Remarks:** Accepts advertising. **URL:** http://www.imagine-publishing.co.uk/PaintShopProPhoto/. **Circ:** (Not Reported)

52419 ■ Photoshop Creative
Imagine Publishing Ltd.
Richmond House
33 Richmond Hill
Dorset
Bournemouth BH2 6EZ, United Kingdom
Ph: 44 1202 586200
Publication E-mail: photoshopcreative@imagine-publishing.co.uk
Magazine providing information on Adobe Photoshop application. **Freq:** 13/yr. **Key Personnel:** Rosie Tanner, Editor, phone 44 1202 586224, rosie.tanner@imagine-publishing.co.uk. **Subscription Rates:** 62.40 individuals; 70 individuals Europe; 80 other countries. **Remarks:** Accepts advertising. **URL:** http://www.imagine-

publishing.co.uk/PhotoshopCreative/. **Circ:** (Not Reported)

52420 ■ Play
Imagine Publishing Ltd.
Richmond House
33 Richmond Hill
Dorset
Bournemouth BH2 6EZ, United Kingdom
Ph: 44 1202 586200
Publication E-mail: play@imagine-publishing.co.uk
Magazine featuring PlayStation games. **Subtitle:** The UK's unofficial PlayStation Magazine. **Freq:** 13/yr. **Key Personnel:** Keith Hennessey, Editor, phone 44 1202 586241. **Subscription Rates:** 51.90 individuals; 70 individuals Europe; 80 other countries. **Remarks:** Accepts advertising. **URL:** http://www.imagine-publishing.co.uk/Play/. **Circ:** (Not Reported)

52421 ■ PowerStation
Imagine Publishing Ltd.
Richmond House
33 Richmond Hill
Dorset
Bournemouth BH2 6EZ, United Kingdom
Ph: 44 1202 586200
Publication E-mail: cheatmachine@imagine-publishing.co.uk
Magazine featuring tips in Playstation games. **Subtitle:** 100% Playstation 0% Fair. **Key Personnel:** Ryan Butt, Editor. **Subscription Rates:** 16.75 individuals 6 issues direct debit; 41.50 individuals 13 issues by credit card; 60 individuals 13 issues by credit card, Europe; 70 other countries 13 issues by credit card; 60 individuals 13 issues by credit card, Eire. **Remarks:** Accepts advertising. **URL:** http://www.cheatmachine.co.uk/. **Circ:** (Not Reported)

52422 ■ Practical Digital Video
Imagine Publishing Ltd.
Richmond House
33 Richmond Hill
Dorset
Bournemouth BH2 6EZ, United Kingdom
Ph: 44 1202 586200
Magazine for filmmakers. **Subtitle:** Creative guides for enthusiasts and pro's. **Key Personnel:** Stuart Tarrant, Editor; Scott Caisley, Advertising Dir. **Subscription Rates:** 5.99 single issue; 21.60 6 issues direct debit; 55 13 issues by credit card; 70 13 issues by credit card, Europe; 80 other countries 13 issues by credit card; 70 13 issues by credit card, Eire. **Remarks:** Accepts advertising. **URL:** http://dvtechniques.pgpartner.co.uk/. **Circ:** (Not Reported)

52423 ■ Retro Gamer
Imagine Publishing Ltd.
Richmond House
33 Richmond Hill
Dorset
Bournemouth BH2 6EZ, United Kingdom
Ph: 44 1202 586200
Publication E-mail: rgsite@imagine-publishing.co.uk
Gaming magazine for retro game enthusiasts. **Subtitle:** Breathing Life Into Classic Games. **Key Personnel:** Darran Jones, Editor, darran.jones@imagine-publishing.co.uk. **Subscription Rates:** 21 individuals 6 issues direct debit; 51.90 individuals 13 issues by credit card. **Remarks:** Accepts advertising. **URL:** http://www.retrogamer.net/. **Circ:** (Not Reported)

52424 ■ SciFiNow
Imagine Publishing Ltd.
Richmond House
33 Richmond Hill
Dorset
Bournemouth BH2 6EZ, United Kingdom
Ph: 44 1202 586200
Publication E-mail: scifinow@imagine-publishing.co.uk
Magazine featuring today's and retro SciFi television, movies, books and comics. **Subtitle:** The Premier Sci-Fi, Fantasy Horror & Cult TV Magazine. **Key Personnel:** Aaron Asadi, Editor-in-Chief. **Subscription Rates:** 18.50 individuals 6 issues direct debit; 45.80 individuals 13 issues by credit card; 65 individuals 13 issues by credit card, Europe; 75 other countries 13 issues by credit card; 75 U.S. and Canada 13 issues by credit card. **Remarks:** Accepts advertising. **URL:** http://www.scifinow.co.uk. **Circ:** (Not Reported)

52425 ■ Smartphone & PDA Essentials
Imagine Publishing Ltd.
Richmond House
33 Richmond Hill
Dorset
Bournemouth BH2 6EZ, United Kingdom
Ph: 44 1202 586200
Publication E-mail: pda@imagine-publishing.co.uk
Magazine covering areas of handheld computing. **Freq:** 13/yr. **Key Personnel:** Andrew Betts, Editor, phone 44 1202 586254. **Subscription Rates:** 62.30 individuals; 70 individuals Europe; 80 other countries. **Remarks:** Accepts advertising. **URL:** http://www.imagine-publishing.co.uk/PDA/. **Circ:** (Not Reported)

52426 ■ 360
Imagine Publishing Ltd.
Richmond House
33 Richmond Hill
Dorset
Bournemouth BH2 6EZ, United Kingdom
Ph: 44 1202 586200
Publication E-mail: 360@imagine-publishing.co.uk
Gaming magazine featuring Microsoft's Xbox 360 console. **Subtitle:** Xbox 360 Gaming & Lifestyle Magazine. **Key Personnel:** Sarah Slee, Dep.Ed.; James Haley, Advertising Mgr. **Subscription Rates:** 18.50 individuals 10 issues direct debit; 33 individuals 17 issues by credit card, United Kingdom; 75 U.S. and Canada 17 issues by credit card; 75 other countries 17 issues by credit card; 62 individuals 17 issues by credit card. **Remarks:** Accepts advertising. **URL:** http://www.imagine-publishing.co.uk/X360/index.html. **Circ:** (Not Reported)

52427 ■ Total 911
Imagine Publishing Ltd.
Richmond House
33 Richmond Hill
Dorset
Bournemouth BH2 6EZ, United Kingdom
Ph: 44 1202 586200
Magazine covering information on Porsche 911. **Freq:** 13/yr. **Key Personnel:** Phil Raby, Editor-in-Chief, phone 44 1202 586291, phil.raby@imagine-publishing.co.uk. **Subscription Rates:** 52.65 individuals; 60 individuals Europe; 70 other countries. **Remarks:** Accepts advertising. **URL:** http://www.imagine-publishing.co.uk/total911/; http://www.total911.com/. **Circ:** (Not Reported)

52428 ■ Total PC Gaming
Imagine Publishing Ltd.
Richmond House
33 Richmond Hill
Dorset
Bournemouth BH2 6EZ, United Kingdom
Ph: 44 1202 586200
Magazine for PC gamers. **Freq:** 13/yr. **Key Personnel:** Russell Barnes, Editor, phone 44 1202 586272. **Subscription Rates:** 50 individuals; 65 individuals Europe; 75 other countries. **Remarks:** Accepts advertising. **URL:** http://www.imagine-publishing.co.uk/TotalPCGaming/. **Circ:** (Not Reported)

52429 ■ Web Designer
Imagine Publishing Ltd.
Richmond House
33 Richmond Hill
Dorset
Bournemouth BH2 6EZ, United Kingdom
Ph: 44 1202 586200
Publication E-mail: webdesigner@imagine-publishing.co.uk
Magazine featuring web designing. **Subtitle:** The Ultimate Design Mag For The Web Professional. **Key Personnel:** Mark Billen, Editor. **Subscription Rates:** 25.15 individuals 6 issues direct debit; 62.30 individuals 13 issues by credit card; 80 U.S. and Canada 13 issues by credit card; 80 other countries 13 issues by credit card; 70 individuals 13 issues by credit card, Europe. **Remarks:** Accepts advertising. **URL:** http://www.webdesignermag.co.uk. **Circ:** (Not Reported)

52430 ■ Heart-FM - 102.3
5 Southcote Rd.
Bournemouth BH1 3LR, United Kingdom
Ph: 44 1202 234900
Fax: 44 1202 234909
Format: Full Service; Oldies. **Formerly:** 2CR-FM. Operating Hours: Continuous. **Ad Rates:** Advertising accepted; rates available upon request. **URL:** http://www.heartdorset.co.uk/.

52431 ■ Hope-FM - 90.1
Delta House
56 Westover Rd.
Dorset
Bournemouth BH1 2BS, United Kingdom
Ph: 44 1202 777321
E-mail: studio@hopefm.com
Format: Contemporary Christian. **Key Personnel:** Kevin Potter, Station Mgr., phone 44 1202 569239, kevinp@hopefm.com. **URL:** http://www.hopefm.com/.

Bracebridge Heath

52432 ■ Railwatch
Railfuture
12 Home Close
Bracebridge Heath LN4 2LP, United Kingdom
Publication E-mail: acc@freewire.co.uk
Publication covering railroads. **Freq:** Quarterly. **Trim Size:** A4. **Key Personnel:** Robert Stevens, Editor, editor@railwatch.org.uk. **ISSN:** 0267-5943. **Subscription Rates:** Included in membership. **Remarks:** Accepts advertising. **URL:** http://www.railwatch.org.uk. **Ad Rates:** GLR: .30, BW: 190. **Circ:** 4,500

Brackley

52433 ■ Popular Flying
Popular Flying Association
Turweston Aerodrome
Northants
Brackley NN13 5YD, United Kingdom
Ph: 44 12 80846786
Fax: 44 12 80846780
Publisher E-mail: office@laa.uk.com
Magazine containing news on members' projects, new designs and products. **Freq:** Bimonthly. **URL:** http://www.pfa.org.uk/whoswho.asp.

Bracknell

52434 ■ International Building Services Abstracts
Building Services Research and Information Association
Old Bracknell Ln. W
Bracknell RG12 7AH, United Kingdom
Ph: 44 1344 465600
Fax: 44 1344 465626
Publisher E-mail: bsria@bsria.co.uk
Publication covering construction. **Founded:** 1966. **Freq:** Bimonthly. **ISSN:** 0104-4237. **Remarks:** Advertising not accepted. **URL:** https://infonet.bsria.co.uk; http://www.bsria.co.uk. **Formerly:** Thermal Abstracts. **Circ:** (Not Reported)

Bradford

52435 ■ Accounting Research Journal
Emerald Group Publishing Ltd.
Howard House, Wagon Ln.
Bradford BD16 1WA, United Kingdom
Ph: 44 1274 777700
Fax: 44 1274 785201
Publisher E-mail: emerald@emeraldinsight.com
Journal providing a forum for communication between the professionals and academics in the accounting, finance, auditing, commercial law, and cognate disciplines. **Freq:** Semiannual. **Key Personnel:** Simon Linacre, Publisher, slinacre@emeraldinsight.com; Prof. Gerry Gallery, Editor, g.gallery@qut.edu.au; Prof. Natalie Gallery, Editor, n.gallery@qut.edu.au. **ISSN:** 1030-9616. **URL:** http://info.emeraldinsight.com/products/journals/journals.htm?id=arj.

52436 ■ Anti-Corrosion Methods & Materials
Emerald Group Publishing Ltd.
Howard House, Wagon Ln.
Bradford BD16 1WA, United Kingdom
Ph: 44 1274 777700
Fax: 44 1274 785201
Publisher E-mail: emerald@emeraldinsight.com
Journal examining and reporting on the latest advances in corrosion prevention and control. **Freq:** 6/yr. **Key Personnel:** Dr. William Cox, Editor, cox@corr-man.demon.co.uk; Harry Colson, Publisher, hcolson@

Circulation: ★ = ABC; △ = BPA; ♦ = CAC; • = CCAB; ❑ = VAC; ⊕ = PO Statement; ‡ = Publisher's Report; Boldface figures = sworn; Light figures = estimated.

Gale Directory of Publications & Broadcast Media/147th Ed.   5583

emeraldinsight.com; Dr. Kalliopi Aligizaki, Book Reviews Ed. **ISSN:** 0003-5599. **URL:** http://info.emeraldinsight. com/products/journals/journals.htm?id=acmm.

52437 ■ Baltic Journal of Management
Emerald Group Publishing Ltd.
Howard House, Wagon Ln.
Bradford BD16 1WA, United Kingdom
Ph: 44 1274 777700
Fax: 44 1274 785201
Publisher E-mail: emerald@emeraldinsight.com
Journal contributing to an understanding of different management cultures and provides readers with a fresh look at emerging management practices and research in the countries of the Baltic region and beyond. **Freq:** 3/yr. **Key Personnel:** Dr. Asta Pundziene, Editor, astpun@ism.lt; Martyn Lawrence, Publisher, mlawrence@emeraldinsight.com; Dr. Torger Reve, Editor-in-Chief, torger.reve@bi.no; Prof. Rolv Petter Amdam, Regional Ed.; Dr. Virginijus Kundrotas, Editorial Advisory Board. **ISSN:** 1746-5265. **URL:** http://info. emeraldinsight.com/products/journals/journals.htm?id= bjm.

52438 ■ British Food Journal
Emerald Group Publishing Ltd.
Howard House, Wagon Ln.
Bradford BD16 1WA, United Kingdom
Ph: 44 1274 777700
Fax: 44 1274 785201
Publisher E-mail: emerald@emeraldinsight.com
Journal publishing the latest food research from around the globe. **Freq:** 11/yr. **Key Personnel:** Prof. Christopher J. Griffith, Editor, cgriffith@uwic.ac.uk; Paul Allen, Editorial Advisory Board; Kate Snowden, Publisher, ksnowden@emeraldinsight.com; Howard Lyons, Editorial Advisory Board. **ISSN:** 0007-070X. **URL:** http://info. emeraldinsight.com/products/journals/journals.htm?id= bfj.

52439 ■ Business Strategy Series
Emerald Group Publishing Ltd.
Howard House, Wagon Ln.
Bradford BD16 1WA, United Kingdom
Ph: 44 1274 777700
Fax: 44 1274 785201
Publisher E-mail: emerald@emeraldinsight.com
Journal providing an immediate and ongoing resource to the most successful and enduring strategies in the market place today, covering all aspects of strategy development and implementation. **Freq:** 6/yr. **Key Personnel:** Dr. Alfred Lewis, Editor, alfred@alfredlewis. com; Andreas Hinterhuber, Assoc. Ed., andreas@hinterhuber.com; Ruth Young, Publisher, ryoung@emeraldinsight.com. **ISSN:** 1751-5637. **URL:** http://info. emeraldinsight.com/products/journals/journals.htm?id= bss. **Formerly:** Handbook of Business Strategy.

52440 ■ Career Development International
Emerald Group Publishing Ltd.
Howard House, Wagon Ln.
Bradford BD16 1WA, United Kingdom
Ph: 44 1274 777700
Fax: 44 1274 785201
Publisher E-mail: emerald@emeraldinsight.com
Journal providing an international forum for all those who wish to gain a greater understanding of career development and its associated issues, forming an arena for academics to share information and ideas, which will help them examine the links between individual career progression and organizational needs. **Freq:** 7/yr. **Key Personnel:** Prof. Jim Jawahar, Editor, jimoham@ilstu.edu; Dr. Nikos Bozionelos, Assoc. Ed., nikos.bozionelos@durham.ac.uk; Nancy Rolph, Publisher, nrolph@emeraldinsight.com; Dr. Samuel Rabinowitz, Editorial Advisory Board. **ISSN:** 1362-0436. **URL:** http://info.emeraldinsight.com/products/journals/ journals.htm?id=cdi.

52441 ■ Clinical Governance
Emerald Group Publishing Ltd.
Howard House, Wagon Ln.
Bradford BD16 1WA, United Kingdom
Ph: 44 1274 777700
Fax: 44 1274 785201
Publisher E-mail: emerald@emeraldinsight.com
Journal specifically produced for clinicians, audit managers and all those actively engaged in the pursuit of clinical excellence, publishing articles covering issues of practical importance in the areas of audit evidence

based practice, clinical guidelines, risk management and implementation of best practice health outcomes. **Subtitle:** An International Journal. **Freq:** Quarterly. **Key Personnel:** Prof. Alan Gillies, Editor, agillies@emeraldinsight.com; Nick Harrop, Editor; Nicola Codner, Publisher, ncodner@emeraldinsight.com. **ISSN:** 1477-7274. **URL:** http://info.emeraldinsight.com/products/ journals/journals.htm?id=cgij.

52442 ■ Collection Building
Emerald Group Publishing Ltd.
Howard House, Wagon Ln.
Bradford BD16 1WA, United Kingdom
Ph: 44 1274 777700
Fax: 44 1274 785201
Publisher E-mail: emerald@emeraldinsight.com
Journal aiming to provide well-researched and authoritative information on collection development for librarians in the academic, public, company and special libraries. **Freq:** 4/yr. **Key Personnel:** Kay Ann Cassell, Editor, kcassell@nyc.rr.com; Eileen Breen, Publisher, ebreen@emeraldinsight.com; Dr. Gary E. Gorman, Book Review Ed., gary.gorman@vuw.ac.nz. **ISSN:** 0160-4953. **URL:** http://info.emeraldinsight.com/products/journals/journals. htm?id=cb.

52443 ■ Coloration Technology
John Wiley & Sons Inc.
Wiley-Blackwell
c/o Carmel McNamara, Mng. Ed.
Society of Dyers & Colourists
PO Box 244
Perkin House
Bradford BD1 2JB, United Kingdom
Peer-reviewed journal covering reviews on topics related to coloration. **Founded:** 1918. **Freq:** Bimonthly. **Print Method:** Offset. **Trim Size:** 10 1/2 x 16. **Cols./Page:** 5. **Col. Width:** 2 inches. **Col. Depth:** 16 inches. **Key Personnel:** David Hinks, Academic Ed., david_hinks@ncsu.edu; Artur Cavaco-Paulo, Editorial Panel; Bob Christie, Editorial Panel; Geoff Collins, Editorial Panel; Peter Duffield, Editorial Panel; Carmel McNamara, Managing Editor, carmelmcn@sdc.org.uk. **ISSN:** 1472-3581. **Subscription Rates:** US$646 institutions print and online; US$518 institutions online; 324 institutions print and online; 259 institutions online; EUR411 institutions print and online; EUR329 institutions online; US$699 institutions, other countries print and online; US$557 institutions, other countries online. **URL:** http:// www.wiley.com/bw/journal.asp?ref=1472-3581&site=1.

52444 ■ COMPEL
Emerald Group Publishing Ltd.
Howard House, Wagon Ln.
Bradford BD16 1WA, United Kingdom
Ph: 44 1274 777700
Fax: 44 1274 785201
Publisher E-mail: emerald@emeraldinsight.com
Journal existing for the discussion and dissemination of computational and analytical methods in electrical and electronic engineering with the main emphasis of papers being on methods and new techniques, or the application of existing techniques in a novel way. **Subtitle:** The International Journal for Computation & Mathematics in Electrical & Electronic Engineering. **Founded:** 1982. **Freq:** 5/yr. **Key Personnel:** Prof. Jan K. Sykulski, Editor, jks@soton.ac.uk; Prof. David Lowther, Editorial Advisory Board; Prof. Osama Mohammed, Editorial Advisory Board; Prof. Oszkar Biro, Editorial Advisory Board; Harry Colson, Publisher, hcolson@emeraldinsight.com. **ISSN:** 0332-1649. **URL:** http://info. emeraldinsight.com/products/journals/journals.htm? PHPSESSID=peuptb654qql9uoh76jr25isu6&id=compel.

52445 ■ Construction Innovation
Emerald Group Publishing Ltd.
Howard House, Wagon Ln.
Bradford BD16 1WA, United Kingdom
Ph: 44 1274 777700
Fax: 44 1274 785201
Publisher E-mail: emerald@emeraldinsight.com
Journal covering topics relating to construction and information technology. **Key Personnel:** Prof. Mustafa Alshawi, Editor, m:a.alshawi@salford.ac.uk; Aimee Wood, Publisher, awood@emeraldinsight.com; Dr. Jack Goulding, Editor, j.s.goulding@salford.ac.uk. **ISSN:** 1471-4175. **URL:** http://www.emeraldinsight.com/info/ journals/ci/ci.jsp.

52446 ■ Corporate Communications
Emerald Group Publishing Ltd.

Howard House, Wagon Ln.
Bradford BD16 1WA, United Kingdom
Ph: 44 1274 777700
Fax: 44 1274 785201
Publisher E-mail: emerald@emeraldinsight.com
Scholarly journal covering strategic corporate communications and PR. **Subtitle:** An International Journal. **Founded:** 1996. **Freq:** Quarterly. **Key Personnel:** Dr. Sandra Oliver, Editorial Advisory Board; Shaun Powell, Editor; Dr. Wim J.L. Elving, Editor, w.j.l.elving@uva.nl; Martyn Lawrence, Publisher, mlawrence@emeraldinsight.com; Joep Cornelissen, Editor; Finn Frandsen, Editor. **ISSN:** 1356-3289. **Remarks:** Advertising not accepted. **URL:** http://www.emeraldinsight.com/products/journals/editorial_team.htm?id=ccij. **Circ:** (Not Reported)

52447 ■ Corporate Governance
Emerald Group Publishing Ltd.
Howard House, Wagon Ln.
Bradford BD16 1WA, United Kingdom
Ph: 44 1274 777700
Fax: 44 1274 785201
Publisher E-mail: emerald@emeraldinsight.com
Journal leading the international debate on board performance, corporate responsibility and CEO effectiveness through practical, real-world discussions and analysis of past, present and future concern, providing the most informed analysis, sound research, penetrating insights and practical case study experience available, while placing emphasis on practicality and application in real world organisations. **Subtitle:** The International Journal of Business in Society. **Freq:** 5/yr. **Key Personnel:** Prof. Nada K. Kakabadse, Editor, nada. kakabadse@northampton.ac.uk; Andrew Kakabadse, Editor; Andrew Smith, Publisher, agsmith@emeraldinsight.com. **ISSN:** 1472-0701. **URL:** http://info. emeraldinsight.com/products/journals/journals.htm?id= cg.

52448 ■ Critical Perspectives on International Business
Emerald Group Publishing Ltd.
Howard House, Wagon Ln.
Bradford BD16 1WA, United Kingdom
Ph: 44 1274 777700
Fax: 44 1274 785201
Publisher E-mail: emerald@emeraldinsight.com
Journal publishing material that engages critically with the broad field of international business, including but not restricted to, issues of globalization, production and consumption, economic change, societal change, politics and power of organizations and governments and environment. **Freq:** 4/yr. **Key Personnel:** Prof. George M. Cairns, Editor, george.cairns@rmit.edu.au; Dr. Martyna Sliwa, Reviews Ed., masliwa@essex.ac.uk; Martyn Lawrence, Publisher, mlawrence@emeraldinsight.com; Dr. Joanne Roberts, Editor, joanne. roberts@ncl.ac.uk. **ISSN:** 1742-2043. **URL:** http://info. emeraldinsight.com/products/journals/journals.htm?id= cpoib.

52449 ■ Development and Learning in Organizations
Emerald Group Publishing Ltd.
Howard House, Wagon Ln.
Bradford BD16 1WA, United Kingdom
Ph: 44 1274 777700
Fax: 44 1274 785201
Publisher E-mail: emerald@emeraldinsight.com
Journal written specifically for busy managers, consultants and researchers who need to know and understand more about the latest thinking in the fields of organizational learning and training. **Subtitle:** An International Journal. **Freq:** 6/yr. **Key Personnel:** Khalid Aziz, Editorial Advisory Board; Dr. Ian Cunningham, Editorial Advisory Board; Ben Bennett, Editorial Advisory Board; Moira Nangle, Editorial Advisory Board; Juliet Norton, Publisher; Prof. Miriam Y. Lacey, Editorial Advisory Board; Anne Gimson, Editor, anne@stratdevint.com; Prof. Harry Gray, Editorial Advisory Board; Dr. Binna Kandola, Editorial Advisory Board. **ISSN:** 1477-7282. **URL:** http://info.emeraldinsight.com/products/journals/ journals.htm?id=dlo.

52450 ■ Disaster Prevention and Management
Emerald Group Publishing Ltd.
Howard House, Wagon Ln.
Bradford BD16 1WA, United Kingdom

Ph: 44 1274 777700
Fax: 44 1274 785201
Publisher E-mail: emerald@emeraldinsight.com
Journal supporting the exchange of ideas, experience and practice between academics, practitioners and policy-makers, advancing the available knowledge in the fields of disaster prevention and management and acting as an integrative agent for extant methodologies and activities relating to disaster emergency and crisis management. **Subtitle:** An International Journal. **Freq:** 5/yr. **Key Personnel:** Dr. Harry C. Wilson, Ed. Emeritus, dpmeditor@netscape.net; Prof. David Weir, Editorial Advisory Board; Prof. David Alexander, Editorial Advisory Board; Nicola Codner, Publisher, ncodner@emeraldinsight.com; Eric E. Alley, Editorial Advisory Board; Keith Cassidy, Editorial Advisory Board. **ISSN:** 0965-3562. **URL:** http://info.emeraldinsight.com/products/journals/journals.htm?id=dpm.

52451 ■ Education, Business and Society
Emerald Group Publishing Ltd.
Howard House, Wagon Ln.
Bradford BD16 1WA, United Kingdom
Ph: 44 1274 777700
Fax: 44 1274 785201
Publisher E-mail: emerald@emeraldinsight.com
Journal providing theory-based research, and both quantitative and qualitative empirical studies on contemporary issues and debates in the Middle East. **Subtitle:** Contemporary Middle Eastern Issues. **Freq:** Semiannual. **Key Personnel:** Dr. Matthew Clarke, Editor, mclarke@hkucc.hku.hk; Prof. James S. Pounder, Editor, james.pounder@adu.ac.ae; Sharon Parkinson, Publisher, sparkinson@emeraldinsight.com. **ISSN:** 1753-7983. **URL:** http://info.emeraldinsight.com/products/journals/journals.htm?id=ebs.

52452 ■ Education Training
Emerald Group Publishing Ltd.
Howard House, Wagon Ln.
Bradford BD16 1WA, United Kingdom
Ph: 44 1274 777700
Fax: 44 1274 785201
Publisher E-mail: emerald@emeraldinsight.com
Journal focusing on the relationship between education and training, addressing vocationalism in learning and highlighting the changing nature of the partnership between the worlds of work and education. **Freq:** 9/yr. **Key Personnel:** Dr. Richard Holden, Editorial Advisory Board; Kate Snowden, Publisher, ksnowden@emeraldinsight.com; Dr. Erica Smith, Assoc. Ed., esmith@csu.edu.au. **ISSN:** 0040-0912. **URL:** http://info.emeraldinsight.com/products/journals/journals.htm?id=et.

52453 ■ Electronic Library
Emerald Group Publishing Ltd.
Howard House, Wagon Ln.
Bradford BD16 1WA, United Kingdom
Ph: 44 1274 777700
Fax: 44 1274 785201
Publisher E-mail: emerald@emeraldinsight.com
Journal aiming to be the definitive source of information for the application of technology in information environments, providing an independent and unbiased assessment of today's automated library and information center and offering practical advice, useful information and specific application recommendations. **Freq:** 6/yr. **Key Personnel:** Dr. David Raitt, Editor, david.raitt@esa.int; Eileen Breen, Publisher, ebreen@emeraldinsight.com; Philip James Calvert, Book Review Ed., philip.calvert@vuw.ac.nz. **ISSN:** 0264-0473. **URL:** http://info.emeraldinsight.com/products/journals/journals.htm?id=el.

52454 ■ Employee Relations
Emerald Group Publishing Ltd.
Howard House, Wagon Ln.
Bradford BD16 1WA, United Kingdom
Ph: 44 1274 777700
Fax: 44 1274 785201
Publisher E-mail: emerald@emeraldinsight.com
Publication covering human resources and labor relations. **Subtitle:** The International Journal. **Freq:** Bimonthly. **Key Personnel:** Prof. John Gennard, Editor; Nancy Rolph, Publisher, nrolph@emeraldinsight.com; Dr. Kirsty Newsome, Asst. Ed. **ISSN:** 0142-5455. **URL:**

http://www.emeraldinsight.com/products/journals/journals.htm?id=er.

52455 ■ Engineering, Construction and Architectural Management
Emerald Group Publishing Ltd.
Howard House, Wagon Ln.
Bradford BD16 1WA, United Kingdom
Ph: 44 1274 777700
Fax: 44 1274 785201
Publisher E-mail: emerald@emeraldinsight.com
International journal publishing research in all areas of construction: building, civil engineering, major infrastructure, maintenance, construction management, project management including design and construction processes, the management of construction companies and architectural practices, and industry developments from a national and international perspective. **Freq:** 6/yr. **Key Personnel:** Aimee Wood, Publisher, awood@emeraldinsight.com; Prof. Ronald McCaffer, Editor, ronald@mccaffer.com; Gemma Briggs, Asst. Publisher, gbriggs@emeraldinsight.com; Prof. Anthony Thorpe, Dep. Ed., a.thorpe@lboro.ac.uk. **ISSN:** 0969-9988. **URL:** http://www.emeraldinsight.com/products/journals/journals.htm?id=ecam.

52456 ■ Equality, Diversity and Inclusion
Emerald Group Publishing Ltd.
Howard House, Wagon Ln.
Bradford BD16 1WA, United Kingdom
Ph: 44 1274 777700
Fax: 44 1274 785201
Publisher E-mail: emerald@emeraldinsight.com
Journal covering equality of human and civil rights. **Founded:** 1982. **Freq:** 8/yr. **Key Personnel:** Mustafa F. Ozbilgin, Editor, eoi@ozbilgin.net; Nancy Rolph, Publisher, nrolph@emeraldinsight.com; Finola Kerrigan, Book Review Ed., finola.kerrigan@kcl.ac.uk. **ISSN:** 2040-7149. **URL:** http://info.emeraldinsight.com/products/journals/journals.htm?id=eoi. **Formerly:** Equal Opportunities International.

52457 ■ European Business Review
Emerald Group Publishing Ltd.
Howard House, Wagon Ln.
Bradford BD16 1WA, United Kingdom
Ph: 44 1274 777700
Fax: 44 1274 785201
Publisher E-mail: emerald@emeraldinsight.com
Journal providing up-to-date reviews and discussion, reflecting changing patterns in the European business environment, exploring the challenges of a growing and rapidly altering European market, exposing the real opportunities and threats to business in Europe, focusing on European economic integration as an ongoing process and offering insights into where Europe is really heading. **Freq:** 6/yr. **Key Personnel:** Prof. Goran Svensson, Editor, goran.svensson@hh.se; Martyn Lawrence, Publisher, mlawrence@emeraldinsight.com. **ISSN:** 0955-534X. **URL:** http://info.emeraldinsight.com/products/journals/journals.htm?id=ebr.

52458 ■ European Journal of Marketing
Emerald Group Publishing Ltd.
Howard House, Wagon Ln.
Bradford BD16 1WA, United Kingdom
Ph: 44 1274 777700
Fax: 44 1274 785201
Publisher E-mail: emerald@emeraldinsight.com
Publication covering advertising, marketing and public relations. **Freq:** 12/yr. **Key Personnel:** Richard Whitfield, Publisher, rwhitfield@emeraldinsight.com; Prof. Gordon E. Greenley, Editor, g.e.greenley@aston.ac.uk; Dr. Nick Lee, Editor, n.j.lee@aston.ac.uk; Prof. Nicholas Alexander, Editorial Review Board; Prof. George Avlonitis, Editorial Review Board; Dr. Ali Bin Al-Khalifa, Editorial Review Board. **ISSN:** 0309-0566. **URL:** http://www.emeraldinsight.com/products/journals/journals.htm?id=ejm.

52459 ■ Facilities
Emerald Group Publishing Ltd.
Howard House, Wagon Ln.
Bradford BD16 1WA, United Kingdom
Ph: 44 1274 777700
Fax: 44 1274 785201
Publisher E-mail: emerald@emeraldinsight.com
Journal offering discussion of key issues to help managers, architects and other interested parties maximise

building space resources. **Freq:** 14/yr. **Key Personnel:** Aimee Wood, Publisher, awood@emeraldinsight.com; Prof. Edward Frank Finch, Editor, e.finch@salford.ac.uk; Dr. Zehra Waheed, Book Review Ed., zehrawaheed@hotmail.com; Prof. Brian Sloan, Editorial Advisory Board. **ISSN:** 0263-2772. **URL:** http://info.emeraldinsight.com/products/journals/journals.htm?id=f.

52460 ■ Fashion Business International
World Textile Publications Ltd.
Perkin House
1 Longlands St.
Bradford BD1 2TP, United Kingdom
Ph: 44 1274 378800
Fax: 44 1274 378811
Publisher E-mail: info@world-textile.net
Trade magazine covering technical and business information for clothing manufacturers in Europe, Africa, Asia and Australasia. **Freq:** Bimonthly. **Print Method:** Sheetfed Offset Litho. **Trim Size:** 230 x 300 mm. **Key Personnel:** Jonathan Dyson, Managing Editor, phone 44 1274 378838, jdyson@world-textile.net. **ISSN:** 1473-0391. **Subscription Rates:** 235 individuals UK; 235 individuals Europe; 211 out of country. **Remarks:** Accepts advertising. **URL:** http://www.inteletex.com/bookstore/BookDetail.asp?id=m002&cat=Magazine; http://www.inteletex.com/Newsindex.asp?mode=filter&filter=publication&id=1. **Ad Rates:** BW: 975, 4C: 1,630, PCI: 25. **Circ:** Combined 7,500

52461 ■ Foresight
Emerald Group Publishing Ltd.
Howard House, Wagon Ln.
Bradford BD16 1WA, United Kingdom
Ph: 44 1274 777700
Fax: 44 1274 785201
Publisher E-mail: emerald@emeraldinsight.com
Journal for those in business, organization and government, providing a long-term perspective to better inform decisions and actions, publishing research, business analysis and policy thinking, providing a forum for debate on the important social, economic, political and technological issues, and is a source of information about future activities from around the world. **Subtitle:** The Journal of Future Studies, Strategic Thinking and Policy. **Freq:** Bimonthly. **Key Personnel:** Dr. Ozcan Saritas, Editor, osaritas@emeraldinsight.com; Tom P. Abeles, Editorial Advisory Board; Nicola Codner, Publisher, ncodner@emeraldinsight.com. **ISSN:** 1463-6689. **URL:** http://info.emeraldinsight.com/products/journals/journals.htm?id=fs.

52462 ■ Human Resource Management International Digest
Emerald Group Publishing Ltd.
Howard House, Wagon Ln.
Bradford BD16 1WA, United Kingdom
Ph: 44 1274 777700
Fax: 44 1274 785201
Publisher E-mail: emerald@emeraldinsight.com
Journal for human resource managers, scanning through 400 management journals and distilling the most topical human resource management issues and relevant implications for HR personnel out of the cutting-edge research, presenting case studies of the implementation of human resource strategies in organizations of varying sizes, ranging from SMEs to multinational corporations. **Subtitle:** International Digest. **Freq:** 7/yr. **Key Personnel:** David Pollitt, Editor, d.r.pollitt@bradford.ac.uk; Prof. Cary L. Cooper, Editorial Advisory Board; Prof. Yochanan Altman, Editorial Advisory Board; Prof. Russell Lansbury, Editorial Advisory Board; Prof. Warren Bennis, Editorial Advisory Board; Dr. Donald Cole, Editorial Advisory Board; Prof. Chris Argyris, Editorial Advisory Board; Prof. Richard N. Ottaway, Editorial Advisory Board. **ISSN:** 0967-0734. **URL:** http://info.emeraldinsight.com/products/journals/journals.htm?id=hrmid.

52463 ■ Humanomics
Emerald Group Publishing Ltd.
Howard House, Wagon Ln.
Bradford BD16 1WA, United Kingdom
Ph: 44 1274 777700
Fax: 44 1274 785201
Publisher E-mail: emerald@emeraldinsight.com
Journal focusing on the ethico-economic study of major socio-economic issues with a global perspective. **Sub-**

title: The international journal of systems and ethics. **Freq:** 4/yr. **Key Personnel:** Dr. Masudul Alam Choudhury, Editor; Kelly Dutton, Publisher, kdutton@emeraldinsight.com. **ISSN:** 0828-8666. **URL:** http://info.emeraldinsight.com/products/journals/journals.htm?id=h.

52464 ■ Industrial and Commercial Training
Emerald Group Publishing Ltd.
Howard House, Wagon Ln.
Bradford BD16 1WA, United Kingdom
Ph: 44 1274 777700
Fax: 44 1274 785201
Publisher E-mail: emerald@emeraldinsight.com
Journal aiming to provide all those involved in personnel training with current practice, ideas, news, etc. on major issues in the related areas, providing a balance between theory and practice and spell out implications for those involved in training. **Freq:** 7/yr. **Key Personnel:** Bryan Smith, Editor, bryan.smith@easynet.co.uk; Les Pickett, Editorial Advisory Board; Kay Baldwin-Evans, Editorial Advisory Board; David Pollitt, News Ed., david.pollitt@zoom.co.uk; Prof. Jyotsna Bhatnagar, Editorial Advisory Board; Prof. David Megginson, Editorial Advisory Board; Paul Loftus, Editorial Advisory Board; Alan H. Cattell, Book Reviews Ed.; Nancy Rolph, Publisher, nrolph@emeraldinsight.com; Mike Bagshaw, Editorial Advisory Board. **ISSN:** 0019-7858. **URL:** http://info.emeraldinsight.com/products/journals/journals.htm?id=ict.

52465 ■ Industrial Lubrication and Tribology
Emerald Group Publishing Ltd.
Howard House, Wagon Ln.
Bradford BD16 1WA, United Kingdom
Ph: 44 1274 777700
Fax: 44 1274 785201
Publisher E-mail: emerald@emeraldinsight.com
Journal blending international research papers with a comprehensive news section, providing broad coverage of the materials and techniques employed in tribology, promoting best practice in three disciplines: lubrication, wear and friction. **Freq:** 6/yr. **Key Personnel:** Harry Colson, Publisher, hcolson@emeraldinsight.com; John Taylor, Editor, john@cjtaylor.net. **ISSN:** 0036-8792. **URL:** http://info.emeraldinsight.com/products/journals/journals.htm?PHPSESSID=0onkd54o28l3c6rrkjhb05qm97&id=ilt.

52466 ■ Industrial Management and Data Systems
Emerald Group Publishing Ltd.
Howard House, Wagon Ln.
Bradford BD16 1WA, United Kingdom
Ph: 44 1274 777700
Fax: 44 1274 785201
Publisher E-mail: emerald@emeraldinsight.com
Business publication. **Freq:** 9/yr. **Key Personnel:** Dr. Binshan Lin, Editor-in-Chief, binshan.lin@lsus.edu; Lizzie Scott, Publisher, escott@emeraldinsight.com. **ISSN:** 0263-5577. **URL:** http://www.emeraldinsight.com/products/journals/journals.htm?id=imds.

52467 ■ Information Management & Computer Security
Emerald Group Publishing Ltd.
Howard House, Wagon Ln.
Bradford BD16 1WA, United Kingdom
Ph: 44 1274 777700
Fax: 44 1274 785201
Publisher E-mail: emerald@emeraldinsight.com
Journal contributing to the advance of knowledge directly related to the theory and practice of the management and security of information and information systems, publishing methodological developments, empirical studies and practical applications with emphasis placed on systematic studies that contribute to the general understanding of the power and usefulness of information and hence contribute to more effective management. **Freq:** 5/yr. **Key Personnel:** Prof. Steven M. Furnell, Editor, sfurnell@jack.see.plymouth.ac.uk; Lizzie Scott, Publisher, escott@emeraldinsight.com. **ISSN:** 0968-5227. **URL:** http://info.emeraldinsight.com/products/journals/journals.htm?id=imcs.

52468 ■ Information Technology & People
Emerald Group Publishing Ltd.
Howard House, Wagon Ln.
Bradford BD16 1WA, United Kingdom
Ph: 44 1274 777700
Fax: 44 1274 785201

Publisher E-mail: emerald@emeraldinsight.com
Journal covering the effectiveness of information technology to people's goals and practices. **Freq:** Quarterly. **Key Personnel:** Dr. Eleanor H. Wynn, Ed. Emeritus; Dr. Edgar A. Whitley, Co-Ed., e.a.whitley@lse.ac.uk; Lizzie Scott, Publisher, escott@emeraldinsight.com. **ISSN:** 0959-3845. **URL:** http://info.emeraldinsight.com/products/journals/journals.htm?id=itp.

52469 ■ Interactive Technology and Smart Education
Emerald Group Publishing Ltd.
Howard House, Wagon Ln.
Bradford BD16 1WA, United Kingdom
Ph: 44 1274 777700
Fax: 44 1274 785201
Publisher E-mail: emerald@emeraldinsight.com
Journal promoting innovation and human-/user-centred approaches. **Freq:** Quarterly. **Key Personnel:** Dr. Pedro Isaias, Editor, pisaias@univ-ab.pt; Dr. Maggie McPherson, Editor, m.mcpherson@education.leeds.ac.uk; Lizzie Scott, Publisher, escott@emeraldinsight.com. **ISSN:** 1741-5659. **URL:** http://info.emeraldinsight.com/products/journals/journals.htm?id=itse.

52470 ■ Interlending & Document Supply
Emerald Group Publishing Ltd.
Howard House, Wagon Ln.
Bradford BD16 1WA, United Kingdom
Ph: 44 1274 777700
Fax: 44 1274 785201
Publisher E-mail: emerald@emeraldinsight.com
Journal offering expert analysis and practical recommendations on all aspects of the supply of information through the library network, looking at new methods made possible by technological innovation both within and between countries worldwide and evaluating traditional methods and explores new ways of maximizing efficiency through better administration. **Freq:** 4/yr. **Key Personnel:** Eileen Breen, Publisher, ebreen@emeraldinsight.com; Mike McGrath, Editor, mike@mikemcgrath.org.uk; Dr. Heinz Fuchs, Editorial Advisory Board, fuchs@mail.sub.uni-goettingen.de; David Brown, Editorial Advisory Board, david.brown@bl.uk. **ISSN:** 0264-1615. **URL:** http://info.emeraldinsight.com/products/journals/journals.htm?id=ilds.

52471 ■ International Carpet Bulletin (ICB)
World Textile Publications Ltd.
Perkin House
1 Longlands St.
Bradford BD1 2TP, United Kingdom
Ph: 44 1274 378800
Fax: 44 1274 378811
Publisher E-mail: info@world-textile.net
Trade magazine covering the carpet manufacturing process for industry managers and technologists. **Freq:** Annual. **Print Method:** Sheetfed Offset Litho. **Trim Size:** 210 x 297 mm. **Key Personnel:** Jonathan Dyson, Managing Editor, phone 44 1274 378838, jdyson@world-textile.net; James Wilson, Sales Mgr., phone 44 1274 378825, jwilson@world-textile.net. **Subscription Rates:** 190 individuals UK; 190 individuals Europe; 190 other countries. **Remarks:** Accepts advertising. **URL:** http://www.inteletex.com/bookstore/BookDetail.asp?id=m004&cat=Magazine. **Ad Rates:** BW: EUR1,356. **Circ:** Combined 1,500

52472 ■ International Dyer
World Textile Publications Ltd.
Perkin House
1 Longlands St.
Bradford BD1 2TP, United Kingdom
Ph: 44 1274 378800
Fax: 44 1274 378811
Publisher E-mail: info@world-textile.net
Trade magazine for the textile dyeing, printing and finishing industry. **Freq:** 11/yr. **Print Method:** Sheetfed Offset Litho. **Trim Size:** 210 x 297 mm. **Key Personnel:** Jonathan Dyson, Managing Editor, phone 44 1274 378838, jdyson@world-textile.net; James Wilson, Sales Mgr., phone 44 1274 378825, jwilson@world-textile.net. **ISSN:** 0020-658X. **Subscription Rates:** EUR364 individuals. **Remarks:** Accepts advertising. **URL:** http://www.inteletex.com/Newsindex.asp?mode=filter&filter=publication&id=3. **Ad Rates:** BW: 1,310, 4C: 1,710, PCI: 25. **Circ:** (Not Reported)

52473 ■ International Journal of Accounting and Information Management
Emerald Group Publishing Ltd.

Howard House, Wagon Ln.
Bradford BD16 1WA, United Kingdom
Ph: 44 1274 777700
Fax: 44 1274 785201
Publisher E-mail: emerald@emeraldinsight.com
Journal featuring stimulating research in accounting, finance, information systems, and information management and discuss issues of significance to both the private and public sector. **Freq:** Annual. **Key Personnel:** Prof. Lee J. Yao, Editor, editor@ijaim.com; Simon Linacre, Publisher, slinacre@emeraldinsight.com. **ISSN:** 1834-7649. **URL:** http://info.emeraldinsight.com/products/journals/journals.htm?id=ijaim.

52474 ■ International Journal of Bank Marketing
Emerald Group Publishing Ltd.
Howard House, Wagon Ln.
Bradford BD16 1WA, United Kingdom
Ph: 44 1274 777700
Fax: 44 1274 785201
Publisher E-mail: emerald@emeraldinsight.com
Publication for the banking, finance, and accounting industries. **Freq:** 7/yr. **Key Personnel:** Richard Whitfield, Publisher, rwhitfield@emeraldinsight.com; Dr. Jillian Farquhar, Editor, jillian.farquhar@beds.ac.uk; Prof. Erdener Kaynak, Regional Ed. **ISSN:** 0265-2323. **URL:** http://www.emeraldinsight.com/products/journals/journals.htm?id=ijbm.

52475 ■ International Journal of Contemporary Hospitality Management
Emerald Group Publishing Ltd.
Howard House, Wagon Ln.
Bradford BD16 1WA, United Kingdom
Ph: 44 1274 777700
Fax: 44 1274 785201
Publisher E-mail: emerald@emeraldinsight.com
Journal communicating the latest developments and thinking on the management of hospitality operations worldwide, covering issues relevant to operations, marketing, finance and personnel and encouraging an interchange between hospitality managers, educators and researchers. **Freq:** 7/yr. **Key Personnel:** Dr. Richard E. Teare, Ed. Emeritus; Aimee Wood, Publisher, awood@emeraldinsight.com; Marianna Sigala, Book Review Ed., m.sigala@aegean.gr; Dr. Fevzi Okumus, Editor, fokumus@mail.ucf.edu. **ISSN:** 0959-6119. **URL:** http://info.emeraldinsight.com/products/journals/journals.htm?id=ijchm.

52476 ■ International Journal of Educational Management
Emerald Group Publishing Ltd.
Howard House, Wagon Ln.
Bradford BD16 1WA, United Kingdom
Ph: 44 1274 777700
Fax: 44 1274 785201
Publisher E-mail: emerald@emeraldinsight.com
Journal addressing the increasingly complex role of the educational manager against a backdrop of fundamental changes in structure and philosophy, and diminishing budgets and resources. Offers essential information to professionals dedicated to maximizing resources through intelligent management strategies which respond to national and international considerations, as well as specific concerns within individual communities and educational institutions. **Freq:** 7/yr. **Key Personnel:** Prof. Brian E. Roberts, Editor; Yin Cheong Cheng, Assoc. Ed.; Kate Snowden, Publisher, ksnowden@emeraldinsight.com. **ISSN:** 0951-354X. **URL:** http://info.emeraldinsight.com/products/journals/journals.htm?id=ijem.

52477 ■ International Journal of Emerging Markets
Emerald Group Publishing Ltd.
Howard House, Wagon Ln.
Bradford BD16 1WA, United Kingdom
Ph: 44 1274 777700
Fax: 44 1274 785201
Publisher E-mail: emerald@emeraldinsight.com
Journal bringing together the latest theoretical and empirical management research in emerging markets, offering both contributors and subscribers the opportunity to examine emerging markets from a comprehensive disciplinary and geographical perspective. **Freq:** 4/yr. **Key Personnel:** Yusaf H. Akbar, Editor, ijoemsubmit@googlemail.com; Martyn Lawrence, Publisher, mlawrence@emeraldinsight.com; Adam R. Cross,

Editorial Advisory Board; Hafiz Mirza, Editorial Advisory Board; Riad Ajami, Editorial Advisory Board; Kate Hutchings, Regional Ed. (Asia-Pacific), asiapacificijoem@gmail.com; Rangamohan V. Eunni, Regional Ed. (The Americas), rveunni@ysu.edu. **ISSN:** 1746-8809. **URL:** http://info.emeraldinsight.com/products/journals/journals.htm?id=ijoem.

52478 ■ International Journal of Entrepreneurial Behaviour & Research
Emerald Group Publishing Ltd.
Howard House, Wagon Ln.
Bradford BD16 1WA, United Kingdom
Ph: 44 1274 777700
Fax: 44 1274 785201
Publisher E-mail: emerald@emeraldinsight.com
Journal providing a wide ranging forum for the interdisciplinary discussion and information exchange on entrepreneurship-related topics, with the aim of advancing both conceptual development and application of empirical methodologies, leading to an improvement in our understanding of entrepreneurial behaviour in adverse cultural settings. **Freq:** Bimonthly. **Key Personnel:** Prof. Oswald Jones, Editor, o.jones@liverpool.ac.uk; Dr. Kevin Ibeh, Editorial Advisory Board; Dr. Dilani Jayawarna, Co-Ed.; Prof. Howard Aldrich, Editorial Advisory Board; Dr. Allan Macpherson, Editorial Advisory Board, a.macpherson@liverpool.ac.uk; Andrew Smith, Publisher, agsmith@emeraldinsight.com; Dr. Shawn Carraher, Editorial Advisory Board. **ISSN:** 1355-2554. **URL:** http://www.emeraldinsight.com/products/journals/journals.htm?id=ijebr.

52479 ■ International Journal of Health Care Quality Assurance
Emerald Group Publishing Ltd.
Howard House, Wagon Ln.
Bradford BD16 1WA, United Kingdom
Ph: 44 1274 777700
Fax: 44 1274 785201
Publisher E-mail: emerald@emeraldinsight.com
Journal providing a much needed resource for all those involved in developing, initiating and monitoring quality assurance programmes in the health care industry by providing a forum for the international exchange of theoretical and practical aspects of quality and management in health care and helping to develop knowledge about continuous improvement and its implementation in health care organizations. **Freq:** 7/yr. **Key Personnel:** Dr. Keith Hurst, Editor, k.hurst@leeds.ac.uk; Kay Downey-Ennis, Co-Ed., katieennis@eircom.net; Nicola Codner, Publisher, ncodner@emeraldinsight.com. **ISSN:** 0952-6862. **URL:** http://info.emeraldinsight.com/products/journals/journals.htm?id=ijhcqa.

52480 ■ International Journal of Managerial Finance
Emerald Group Publishing Ltd.
Howard House, Wagon Ln.
Bradford BD16 1WA, United Kingdom
Ph: 44 1274 777700
Fax: 44 1274 785201
Publisher E-mail: emerald@emeraldinsight.com
Journal providing a forum for the dialogue and discourse of research and new insight into the financing decision. **Key Personnel:** David Michayluk, Editor, david.michayluk@uts.edu.au; Ralf Zurbruegg, Editor, ralf.zurbrugg@adelaide.edu.au; Kelly Dutton, Publisher, kdutton@emeraldinsight.com. **ISSN:** 1743-9132. **URL:** http://info.emeraldinsight.com/products/journals/journals.htm?id=ijmf.

52481 ■ International Journal of Manpower
Emerald Group Publishing Ltd.
Howard House, Wagon Ln.
Bradford BD16 1WA, United Kingdom
Ph: 44 1274 777700
Fax: 44 1274 785201
Publisher E-mail: emerald@emeraldinsight.com
Publication covering human resources and labor relations. **Freq:** 8/yr. **Key Personnel:** Prof. Adrian Ziderman, Editor, zidera@mail.biu.ac.il; Nancy Rolph, Publisher, nrolph@emeraldinsight.com; Prof. Angeles Montoro-Sanchez, Assoc. Ed., mangeles@ccee.ucm.es. **ISSN:** 0143-7720. **URL:** http://www.emeraldinsight.com/products/journals/journals.htm?id=ijm.

52482 ■ International Journal of Operations and Production Management
Emerald Group Publishing Ltd.
Howard House, Wagon Ln.
Bradford BD16 1WA, United Kingdom
Ph: 44 1274 777700
Fax: 44 1274 785201
Publisher E-mail: emerald@emeraldinsight.com
International business publication. **Founded:** 1981. **Freq:** Monthly. **Key Personnel:** Prof. Margaret Taylor, Editorial Advisory Board; Prof. Andrew Taylor, Editorial Advisory Board, w.a.taylor@bradford.ac.uk; Dr. David Bamford, Book Review Ed., david.bamford@mbs.ac.uk; Prof. Jack R. Meredith, Editorial Advisory Board; Lucy Sootheran, Publisher, lsootheran@emeraldinsight.com; Prof. Will Bertrand, Editorial Advisory Board; Prof. Bart MacCarthy, Editorial Advisory Board; Prof. Kenneth K. Boyer, Editorial Advisory Board; Prof. Roger W. Schmenner, Regional Ed., rschmenn@iupui.edu; Prof. Ruth J. Boaden, Editorial Advisory Board. **ISSN:** 0144-3577. **Remarks:** Advertising not accepted. **Online:** Gale. **URL:** http://www.emeraldinsight.com/products/journals/journals.htm?id=ijopm. **Circ:** (Not Reported)

52483 ■ International Journal of Pervasive Computing and Communications
Emerald Group Publishing Ltd.
Howard House, Wagon Ln.
Bradford BD16 1WA, United Kingdom
Ph: 44 1274 777700
Fax: 44 1274 785201
Publisher E-mail: emerald@emeraldinsight.com
Journal disseminating innovative and important new work on pervasive computing and communications. **Freq:** Quarterly. **Key Personnel:** Prof. Laurence T. Yang, Editor-in-Chief, lyang@stfx.ca; Lizzie Scott, Publisher, escott@emeraldinsight.com. **ISSN:** 1742-7371. **URL:** http://info.emeraldinsight.com/products/journals/journals.htm?id=ijpcc.

52484 ■ International Journal of Physical Distribution and Logistics Management
Emerald Group Publishing Ltd.
Howard House, Wagon Ln.
Bradford BD16 1WA, United Kingdom
Ph: 44 1274 777700
Fax: 44 1274 785201
Publisher E-mail: emerald@emeraldinsight.com
Peer-reviewed journal covering international business. **Freq:** 10/yr. **Key Personnel:** Lucy Sootheran, Publisher, lsootheran@emeraldinsight.com; Prof. David J. Closs, Editorial Advisory Board; Dr. Richard R. Young, Reviews Ed., rry100@psu.edu; Prof. Ronald H. Ballou, Editorial Advisory Board; Dr. Arvinder Loomba, Editorial Advisory Board; Dr. Garland Chow, Editorial Advisory Board; Prof. Michael R. Crum, Editor, mcrum@iastate.edu; Prof. Joseph R. Carter, Editorial Advisory Board; Prof. Richard F. Poist, Jr., Editor, rpoist@iastate.edu. **ISSN:** 0960-0035. **URL:** http://www.emeraldinsight.com/products/journals/journals.htm?id=ijpdlm.

52485 ■ International Journal of Productivity and Performance Management
Emerald Group Publishing Ltd.
Howard House, Wagon Ln.
Bradford BD16 1WA, United Kingdom
Ph: 44 1274 777700
Fax: 44 1274 785201
Publisher E-mail: emerald@emeraldinsight.com
Journal addressing new developments and thinking in productivity science and performance management including new techniques, approaches and related reflective analysis designed to improve individual, group and organisational performance, seeking to develop an understanding in and across manufacturing, service and public sector organisations. **Freq:** 8/yr. **Key Personnel:** Dr. Zoe Radnor, Editorial Advisory Board; Prof. Umit S. Bititci, Editorial Advisory Board; Rabiul Ahasan, Editorial Advisory Board; Dr. Jacky Holloway, Editorial Advisory Board; Prof. Jiju Antony, Editorial Advisory Board; John Heap, Editor, johnheap@yahoo.com; Andrew Smith, Publisher, agsmith@emeraldinsight.com; Prof. Eileen Van Aken, Editorial Advisory Board. **ISSN:** 1741-0401. **URL:** http://info.emeraldinsight.com/products/journals/journals.htm?id=ijppm.

52486 ■ International Journal of Quality and Reliability Management
Emerald Group Publishing Ltd.
Howard House, Wagon Ln.
Bradford BD16 1WA, United Kingdom
Ph: 44 1274 777700
Fax: 44 1274 785201
Publisher E-mail: emerald@emeraldinsight.com
International business publication. **Founded:** 1984. **Freq:** 9/yr. **Key Personnel:** Prof. Christian N. Madu, Editor, chrismadu@aol.com; Prof. Barrie George Dale, Editorial Advisory Board; Prof. Ton Van Der Wiele, Editor, awiele@rsm.nl; Lucy Sootheran, Publisher, lsootheran@emeraldinsight.com; Dr. Jos Van Iwaarden, Assoc. Ed.; Prof. Amrik Sohal, Regional Ed. **ISSN:** 0265-671X. **Remarks:** Advertising not accepted. **URL:** http://www.emeraldinsight.com/products/journals/journals.htm?id=ijqrm. **Circ:** (Not Reported)

52487 ■ International Journal of Social Economics
Emerald Group Publishing Ltd.
Howard House, Wagon Ln.
Bradford BD16 1WA, United Kingdom
Ph: 44 1274 777700
Fax: 44 1274 785201
Publisher E-mail: emerald@emeraldinsight.com
Publication covering economics in relation to social and political changes throughout the world. **Freq:** Monthly. **Key Personnel:** Dr. Frank Peddle, Dep. Ed.; Dr. Peter Daniels, Book Review Ed., p.daniels@mailbox.gu.edu.au; Prof. Leslie Armour, Editor; Kelly Dutton, Publisher, kdutton@emeraldinsight.com. **ISSN:** 0306-8293. **URL:** http://www.emeraldinsight.com/products/journals/journals.htm?id=ijse&.

52488 ■ International Journal of Sustainability in Higher Education
Emerald Group Publishing Ltd.
Howard House, Wagon Ln.
Bradford BD16 1WA, United Kingdom
Ph: 44 1274 777700
Fax: 44 1274 785201
Publisher E-mail: emerald@emeraldinsight.com
Journal addressing environmental management systems (EMS), sustainable development and Agenda 21 issues at higher education institutions worldwide, acting as an outlet for papers dealing with curriculum greening and methodological approaches to sustainability, reporting on initiatives aimed at environmental improvements in universities, and the increased competitiveness of self-regulatory mechanisms such as environmental auditing and maintaining EMS. **Freq:** 4/yr. **Key Personnel:** Prof. Walter Leal Filho, PhD, Editor, walter.leal@ls.haw-hamburg.de; Dr. Ulisses Azeiteiro, Editorial Board; Nicola Codner, Publisher, ncodner@emeraldinsight.com; Elya Tagar, Regional Ed.; Dr. Wynn Calder, News Ed.; Dr. Paul Pace, Dep.-Ed.; Prof. Michael Narodoslawsky, Features Ed.; Dr. Sanjeev Chaudhari, Regional Ed.; Prof. David W. Orr, Editorial Board. **ISSN:** 1467-6370. **URL:** http://info.emeraldinsight.com/products/journals/journals.htm?id=ijshe.

52489 ■ International Journal of Web Information Systems
Emerald Group Publishing Ltd.
Howard House, Wagon Ln.
Bradford BD16 1WA, United Kingdom
Ph: 44 1274 777700
Fax: 44 1274 785201
Publisher E-mail: emerald@emeraldinsight.com
Journal focusing on providing a descriptive, analytical, and comprehensive assessment of factors, trends, and issues in the ever-changing field of web information systems. **Freq:** 3/yr. **Key Personnel:** Dr. Ismail Khalil, Editor, ismail.khalil@jku.at; Dr. David Taniar, Editor, david.taniar@infotech.monash.edu.au; Lizzie Scott, Publisher, escott@emeraldinsight.com. **ISSN:** 1744-0084. **URL:** http://info.emeraldinsight.com/products/journals/journals.htm?id=ijwis.

52490 ■ International Marketing Review
Emerald Group Publishing Ltd.
c/o Prof. Jeryl M. Whitelock, Ed.
School of Management
Emm Ln.
University of Bradford
Bradford BD9 4JL, United Kingdom

Circulation: ★ = ABC; △ = BPA; ♦ = CAC; • = CCAB; ❑ = VAC; ⊕ = PO Statement; ‡ = Publisher's Report; Boldface figures = sworn; Light figures = estimated.

Gale Directory of Publications & Broadcast Media/147th Ed.   5587

Publisher E-mail: emerald@emeraldinsight.com
Publication for the banking, finance, and accounting industries. **Freq:** Bimonthly. **Key Personnel:** Prof. Jeryl Whitelock, Editor, j.whitelock@bradford.ac.uk; Prof. John W. Cadogan, Editor, j.w.cadogan@lboro.ac.uk; Dr. David Ballantyne, Editorial Board; Martyn Lawrence, Publisher, mlawrence@emeraldinsight.com; Dr. Carlos M. Rodriguez, PhD, Reviews Ed., crodriguez@desu.edu. **ISSN:** 0265-1335. **URL:** http://www.emeraldinsight.com/products/journals/journals.htm?id=imr.

52491 ■ Internet Research
Emerald Group Publishing Ltd.
Howard House, Wagon Ln.
Bradford BD16 1WA, United Kingdom
Ph: 44 1274 777700
Fax: 44 1274 785201
Publisher E-mail: emerald@emeraldinsight.com
Journal fostering understanding of telecommunication networks in society and examining the social, ethical, economic and political implications which arises from mass public access to a wealth of information. **Freq:** 5/yr. **Key Personnel:** Dr. David G. Schwartz, Editor, dschwar@mail.biu.ac.il; Jerry Berman, Editorial Advisory Board; Lizzie Scott, Publisher, escott@emeraldinsight.com; David Bodoff, Editorial Advisory Board; Clare Brindley, Editorial Advisory Board. **ISSN:** 1066-2243. **URL:** http://info.emeraldinsight.com/products/journals/journals.htm?id=intr.

52492 ■ Journal of Accounting and Organisational Change
Emerald Group Publishing Ltd.
Howard House, Wagon Ln.
Bradford BD16 1WA, United Kingdom
Ph: 44 1274 777700
Fax: 44 1274 785201
Publisher E-mail: emerald@emeraldinsight.com
Journal providing a platform for researchers and practitioners from multiple disciplines to disseminate information on organizational and accounting systems change. **Key Personnel:** Prof. Zahirul Hoque, Editor, z.hoquel@latrobe.edu.au; Prof. Carol Adams, Assoc. Ed.; Prof. Jodie Moll, Assoc. Ed. **ISSN:** 1832-5912. **URL:** http://info.emeraldinsight.com/products/journals/journals.htm?id=jaoc.

52493 ■ Journal of Business Strategy
Emerald Group Publishing Ltd.
Howard House, Wagon Ln.
Bradford BD16 1WA, United Kingdom
Ph: 44 1274 777700
Fax: 44 1274 785201
Publisher E-mail: emerald@emeraldinsight.com
Business magazine. **Founded:** 1980. **Freq:** Bimonthly. **Print Method:** Offset. **Trim Size:** 8 1/2 x 11. **Cols./Page:** 2. **Col. Width:** 17 picas. **Col. Depth:** 50 picas. **Key Personnel:** Nanci Healy, Editor, nancihealy@comcast.net; Ruth Young, Publisher, ryoung@emeraldinsight.com; Ian Angell, Editorial Advisory Board, i.angell@lse.ac.uk; Jean-Daniel Clavel, Editorial Advisory Board, jdclavel@vtx.ch; Duane R. Ireland, Editorial Advisory Board; Dr. Yasar F. Jarrar, Editorial Advisory Board, yasar.jarrar@theexecutiveoffice.com. **ISSN:** 0275-6668. **Remarks:** Accepts advertising. **URL:** http://www.emeraldinsight.com/products/journals/journals.htm?id=jbs. **Circ:** (Not Reported)

52494 ■ Journal of Communication Management
Emerald Group Publishing Ltd.
Howard House, Wagon Ln.
Bradford BD16 1WA, United Kingdom
Ph: 44 1274 777700
Fax: 44 1274 785201
Publisher E-mail: emerald@emeraldinsight.com
International publication for communications and public relations professionals in private and public sector organizations as well as academics in universities and business schools. **Freq:** Quarterly. **Key Personnel:** Martyn Lawrence, Publisher, mlawrence@emeraldinsight.com; Prof. Anne Gregory, Editor-in-Chief, a.gregory@leedsmet.co.uk; Dr. Magda Pieczka, Editor, mpieczka@qmuc.ac.uk. **ISSN:** 1363-254X. **URL:** http://www.emeraldinsight.com/products/journals/journals.htm?PHPSESSID=gldgflc0g6tmq6fjjha1p6gq85&id=jcom.

52495 ■ Journal of Corporate Real Estate
Emerald Group Publishing Ltd.
Howard House, Wagon Ln.
Bradford BD16 1WA, United Kingdom

Ph: 44 1274 777700
Fax: 44 1274 785201
Publisher E-mail: emerald@emeraldinsight.com
Peer-reviewed journal dedicated to corporate real estate, a forum for authoritative, practical guidance not only on current best practice but also the key issues of tomorrow that the corporate real estate executive needs to be aware of. **Freq:** Quarterly. **Key Personnel:** Aimee Wood, Publisher, awood@emeraldinsight.com; Dr. Clare Eriksson, Editor, clare.eriksson@eu.jll.com. **ISSN:** 1463-001X. **URL:** http://www.emeraldinsight.com/info/journals/jcre/jcre.jsp.

52496 ■ Journal of Documentation
Emerald Group Publishing Ltd.
Howard House, Wagon Ln.
Bradford BD16 1WA, United Kingdom
Ph: 44 1274 777700
Fax: 44 1274 785201
Publisher E-mail: emerald@emeraldinsight.com
Journal covering information management. **Founded:** 1944. **Freq:** Bimonthly. **Key Personnel:** Lizzie Scott, Publisher, escott@emeraldinsight.com; Prof. David Bawden, Editor, db@soi.city.ac.uk. **ISSN:** 0022-0418. **Subscription Rates:** US$1,019 U.S. and Canada; 649 individuals plus tax; EUR899 individuals plus tax; $A 1,939 individuals. **Remarks:** Advertising not accepted. **URL:** http://ninetta.emeraldinsight.com; http://info.emeraldinsight.com/products/journals/journals.htm?id=jd. **Circ:** (Not Reported)

52497 ■ Journal of Educational Administration
Emerald Group Publishing Ltd.
Howard House, Wagon Ln.
Bradford BD16 1WA, United Kingdom
Ph: 44 1274 777700
Fax: 44 1274 785201
Publisher E-mail: emerald@emeraldinsight.com
Journal seeking to meet the needs of principals, inspectors, and directors of education interested in the practice and theory of educational administration. **Freq:** 6/yr. **Key Personnel:** Dr. A. Ross Thomas, Editor, rthomas@uow.edu.au; Dr. Narottam Bhindi, Assoc. Ed.; Kate Snowden, Publisher, ksnowden@emeraldinsight.com; Anthony H. Normore, Editorial Advisory Board, anormore@csudh.edu; Les Bell, Assoc. Ed. **ISSN:** 0957-8234. **URL:** http://info.emeraldinsight.com/products/journals/journals.htm?id=jea.

52498 ■ Journal of Enterprising Communities
Emerald Group Publishing Ltd.
Howard House, Wagon Ln.
Bradford BD16 1WA, United Kingdom
Ph: 44 1274 777700
Fax: 44 1274 785201
Publisher E-mail: emerald@emeraldinsight.com
Journal covering community enterprising. **Subtitle:** People and Places in the Global Economy. **Freq:** Quarterly. **Key Personnel:** Prof. Robert B. Anderson, Editor, robert.anderson@uregina.ca; Prof. Leo-Paul Dana, Editor, leo.dana@canterbury.ac.nz; Andrew Smith, Publisher, agsmith@emeraldinsight.com. **ISSN:** 1750-6204. **URL:** http://info.emeraldinsight.com/products/journals/journals.htm?id=jec.

52499 ■ Journal of European Industrial Training
Emerald Group Publishing Ltd.
Howard House, Wagon Ln.
Bradford BD16 1WA, United Kingdom
Ph: 44 1274 777700
Fax: 44 1274 785201
Publisher E-mail: emerald@emeraldinsight.com
Scholarly journal covering aspects of HRD and Training from European perspective. **Freq:** 9/yr. **Key Personnel:** Prof. Thomas N. Garavan, Editor, thomas.garavan@ul.ie; Dr. Ronan Carbery, Assoc. Ed.; Jeffrey Gold, Editorial Advisory Board; Nancy Rolph, Publisher, nrolph@emeraldinsight.com; Dr. Rob F. Poell, Editorial Advisory Board; Dr. Martin Mulder, Editorial Advisory Board; Dr. Michael Morley, Editorial Advisory Board; Prof. Rona Beattie, Editorial Advisory Board. **ISSN:** 0309-0590. **Remarks:** Advertising not accepted. **Online:** Gale. **URL:** http://www.emeraldinsight.com/products/journals/journals.htm?id=jeit. **Formerly:** MCB University Press Ltd. **Circ:** (Not Reported)

52500 ■ Journal of Facilities Management
Emerald Group Publishing Ltd.
Howard House, Wagon Ln.
Bradford BD16 1WA, United Kingdom
Ph: 44 1274 777700

Fax: 44 1274 785201
Publisher E-mail: emerald@emeraldinsight.com
Journal publishing high-quality, authoritative and detailed analysis, briefings and case studies on how facilities can and do play a vital part in helping deliver corporate strategy. **Freq:** Quarterly. **Key Personnel:** Dr. Michael Pitt, Editor, m.r.pitt@ljmu.ac.uk; Aimee W, Publisher, awood@emeraldinsight.com. **ISSN:** 1472-5967. **URL:** http://www.emeraldinsight.com/info/journals/jfm/jfm.jsp.

52501 ■ Journal of Fashion Marketing and Management
Emerald Group Publishing Ltd.
Howard House, Wagon Ln.
Bradford BD16 1WA, United Kingdom
Ph: 44 1274 777700
Fax: 44 1274 785201
Publisher E-mail: emerald@emeraldinsight.com
Journal examining the emerging trends and issues that impact on the fast-moving environment of the fashion and textile industry, blending high quality research with descriptive studies of current business practices and developments in marketing, employment, production, consumption and trade locally and globally. **Freq:** 4/yr. **Key Personnel:** Gaynor Lea-Greenwood, Editorial Advisory Board; Dr. Steven George Hayes, Editor, s.g.hayes@mmu.ac.uk; Richard Whitfield, Publisher, rwhitfield@emeraldinsight.com; Gail Taylor, Regional Ed. **ISSN:** 1361-2026. **URL:** http://info.emeraldinsight.com/products/journals/journals.htm?id=jfmm.

52502 ■ Journal of Health, Organization and Management
Emerald Group Publishing Ltd.
University of Bradford Management School
Emm Ln.
West Yorkshire
Bradford BD9 4JL, United Kingdom
Publisher E-mail: emerald@emeraldinsight.com
Journal providing a forum whereby academics and all those involved in managing and delivering health services throughout Europe and the wider world can explore, debate and analyse the latest leading-edge research in the field of health management and leadership and its relationship to the practice of health management with the objectives of: securing and publishing rigorous academic papers of the highest standard; securing and publishing applied papers that explore ways of applying the best management practices within health services, and initiating a debate between the theoretical and applied sections of the journal. **Freq:** 6/yr. **Key Personnel:** Dr. Nancy Harding, Editor, n.h.harding@bradford.ac.uk; Prof. Beverly Alimo-Metcalfe, Editorial Advisory Board; Dr. Ljuba Bacharova, Editorial Advisory Board; Nicola Codner, Publisher, ncodner@emeraldinsight.com; Dr. Mark Learmonth, Editorial Advisory Board; Dr. Jackie Ford, Sen. Editorial Advisory Board, j.m.ford@bradford.ac.uk; Prof. Annabelle Mark, Editorial Advisory Board; Dr. Hugh Lee, Co-Ed., hlee4@bradford.ac.uk. **ISSN:** 1477-7266. **URL:** http://info.emeraldinsight.com/products/journals/journals.htm?id=jhom.

52503 ■ Journal of Information, Communication & Ethics in Society
Emerald Group Publishing Ltd.
Howard House, Wagon Ln.
Bradford BD16 1WA, United Kingdom
Ph: 44 1274 777700
Fax: 44 1274 785201
Publisher E-mail: emerald@emeraldinsight.com
Journal focusing on the wider social and ethical issues related to the planning, development, implementation, and use of new media and information and communication technologies. **Freq:** 10/yr. **Key Personnel:** Dr. N. Ben Fairweather, Editor, nbf@dmu.ac.uk; Prof. Simon Rogerson, Editor, srog@dmu.ac.uk; Lizzie Scott, Publisher, escott@emeraldinsight.com. **ISSN:** 1477-996X. **URL:** http://info.emeraldinsight.com/products/journals/journals.htm?id=jices.

52504 ■ Journal of Intellectual Capital
Emerald Group Publishing Ltd.
Howard House, Wagon Ln.
Bradford BD16 1WA, United Kingdom
Ph: 44 1274 777700
Fax: 44 1274 785201
Publisher E-mail: emerald@emeraldinsight.com
Peer-reviewed journal covering intellectual capital and

business. **Freq:** Quarterly. **Key Personnel:** Rory L. Chase, Editor, jkm_jic@mac.com; James Guthrie, Regional Ed.; Jay Chatzkel, Regional Ed.; Jose Maria Viedma Marti, Editorial Advisory Board; Guy Ahonen, Editorial Advisory Board; Indra Abeyekera, Editorial Advisory Board; Nick Bontis, Assoc. Ed.; Jan Mouritsen, Editorial Advisory Board; Baruch Lev, Editorial Advisory Board. **ISSN:** 1469-1930. **URL:** http://www.emeraldinsight.com/products/journals/journals.htm?id=jic.

52505 ■ Journal of International Trade Law and Policy
Emerald Group Publishing Ltd.
Howard House, Wagon Ln.
Bradford BD16 1WA, United Kingdom
Ph: 44 1274 777700
Fax: 44 1274 785201
Publisher E-mail: emerald@emeraldinsight.com
Journal providing a forum for current issues in all aspects of international trade, including legal, economic, management and policy issues. **Freq:** Annual. **Key Personnel:** Dr. Moe Alramahi, Editor, m.alramahi@gmail.com; Adam Smith, Publisher, agsmith@emeraldinsight.com. **ISSN:** 1477-0024. **URL:** http://info.emeraldinsight.com/products/journals/journals.htm?id=jitlp.

52506 ■ The Journal of Investment Compliance
Emerald Group Publishing Ltd.
Howard House, Wagon Ln.
Bradford BD16 1WA, United Kingdom
Ph: 44 1274 777700
Fax: 44 1274 785201
Publisher E-mail: emerald@emeraldinsight.com
Professional journal covering the regulation of institutional investment funds as it relates to their management, trading, custody, transfers and investor rules. **Freq:** Quarterly. **Key Personnel:** Henry A. Davis, Editor, hdresearch@aol.com; Kelly Dutton, Publisher, kdutton@emeraldinsight.com. **ISSN:** 1528-5812. **Subscription Rates:** 649 individuals; EUR889 individuals; US$1079 individuals; $A 1609 individuals; US$1,350 individuals complete set; US$250 individuals per volume. **Remarks:** Accepts advertising. **URL:** http://www.emeraldinsight.com/products/journals/journals.htm?id=joic. **Ad Rates:** BW: 3,556, 4C: 5,138. **Circ:** (Not Reported)

52507 ■ Journal of Knowledge Management
Emerald Group Publishing Ltd.
Howard House, Wagon Ln.
Bradford BD16 1WA, United Kingdom
Ph: 44 1274 777700
Fax: 44 1274 785201
Publisher E-mail: emerald@emeraldinsight.com
Journal for executives, managers and academics who are struggling to understand and implement knowledge management strategies. **Freq:** 6/yr. **Key Personnel:** Rory L. Chase, Editor, jkm_jic@mac.com; Dr. Syed Z. Shariq, Assoc. Ed.; Ruth Young, Publisher, ryoung@emeraldinsight.com; Karl M. Wiig, Editorial Advisory Board. **ISSN:** 1367-3270. **URL:** http://info.emeraldinsight.com/products/journals/journals.htm?id=jkm.

52508 ■ Journal of Management History
Emerald Group Publishing Ltd.
Howard House, Wagon Ln.
Bradford BD16 1WA, United Kingdom
Ph: 44 1274 777700
Fax: 44 1274 785201
Publisher E-mail: emerald@emeraldinsight.com
Journal covering the historical development of management concepts and practices. **Key Personnel:** Prof. David Lamond, PhD, Editor-in-Chief, daplamond@bigpond.com; Ruth Young, Publisher, ryoung@emeraldinsight.com; Stan Glaser, Book Review Ed., stanglaser@ozemail.com.au; Dr. John Humphreys, Editorial Advisory Board; Bernard Batiz-Lazo, Editorial Advisory Board; Arthur G. Bedeian, Editorial Advisory Board. **ISSN:** 1751-1348. **URL:** http://www.emeraldinsight.com/info/journals/jmh/jmh.jsp.

52509 ■ Journal of Managerial Psychology
Emerald Group Publishing Ltd.
Howard House, Wagon Ln.
Bradford BD16 1WA, United Kingdom
Ph: 44 1274 777700
Fax: 44 1274 785201
Publisher E-mail: emerald@emeraldinsight.com
Publication covering human resources and labor

relations. **Freq:** 8/yr. **Key Personnel:** Dr. Diana Stone, Editor, diannastone@satx.rr.com; Nancy Rolph, Publisher, nrolph@emeraldinsight.com; Prof. Stuart Carr, Assoc. Ed. **ISSN:** 0268-3946. **URL:** http://info.emeraldinsight.com/products/journals/journals.htm?id=jmp.

52510 ■ Journal of Money Laundering Control
Emerald Group Publishing Ltd.
Howard House, Wagon Ln.
Bradford BD16 1WA, United Kingdom
Ph: 44 1274 777700
Fax: 44 1274 785201
Publisher E-mail: emerald@emeraldinsight.com
Journal designed to keep subscribers up to date with the latest law, regulation, techniques and best practice in the prevention, identification and prosecution of money laundering. **Freq:** Quarterly. **Key Personnel:** Prof. Barry A.K. Rider, Editor; Dr. Chizu Nakajima, Editorial Advisory Board; Kelly Dutton, Publisher, kdutton@emeraldinsight.com; Prof. Johan Henning, Editorial Advisory Board; Dr. Dayanath C. Jayasuriya, Editorial Advisory Board; Kris Hinterseer, Editorial Advisory Board; Alan Lambert, Editorial Advisory Board; Dr. Dayanath C. Jayasuriya, Editorial Advisory Board. **ISSN:** 1368-5201. **URL:** http://www.emeraldinsight.com/info/journals/jmlc/jmlc.jsp.

52511 ■ Journal of Organizational Change Management
Emerald Group Publishing Ltd.
Howard House, Wagon Ln.
Bradford BD16 1WA, United Kingdom
Ph: 44 1274 777700
Fax: 44 1274 785201
Publisher E-mail: emerald@emeraldinsight.com
Journal offering detailed analysis and discussion on the philosophies and practices which underpin successful organizational change, seeking to help build more promising futures for the societies and organizations of tomorrow. **Freq:** 6/yr. **Key Personnel:** Prof. Slawomir Magala, Editor, jocmmagala@fbk.eur.nl; Cliff Oswick, Regional Ed., clifford.oswick@kcl.ac.uk; Ruth Young, Publisher, ryoung@emeraldinsight.com; Dr. Adrian Carr, Regional Ed., a.carr@uws.edu.au; Prof. Hugo Letiche, Regional Ed., h.letiche@uvh.nl; Prof. Robert Kramer, Book Review Ed.; Tojo Joseph Thatchenkery, Book Review Ed.; Prof. James Barker, Editorial Advisory Board. **ISSN:** 0953-4814. **URL:** http://info.emeraldinsight.com/products/journals/journals.htm?id=jocm.

52512 ■ Journal of Product & Brand Management
Emerald Group Publishing Ltd.
Howard House, Wagon Ln.
Bradford BD16 1WA, United Kingdom
Ph: 44 1274 777700
Fax: 44 1274 785201
Publisher E-mail: emerald@emeraldinsight.com
Journal for academics and corporate practitioners, offering a direct route to worldwide research at the cutting edge of product and brand management and pricing, examining critical issues which need to be taken into consideration when determining brand and pricing strategies and policies, offering expert analysis and practical recommendations to aid decision making and stimulate further research activity. **Freq:** 7/yr. **Key Personnel:** Dr. Richard C. Leventhal, Editor, rcleventhal@hotmail.com; Richard Whitfield, Publisher, rwhitfield@emeraldinsight.com; Prof. Geoff P. Lantos, Books Review Ed., glantos@stonehill.edu. **ISSN:** 1061-0421. **URL:** http://info.emeraldinsight.com/products/journals/journals.htm?id=jpbm.

52513 ■ Journal of Property Investment & Finance
Emerald Group Publishing Ltd.
Howard House, Wagon Ln.
Bradford BD16 1WA, United Kingdom
Ph: 44 1274 777700
Fax: 44 1274 785201
Publisher E-mail: emerald@emeraldinsight.com
Journal providing a forum for discussion and debate relating to all areas of property investment and finance. **Freq:** 6/yr. **Key Personnel:** Nick French, Editor; Aimee Wood, Publisher, awood@emeraldinsight.com. **ISSN:** 1463-578X. **URL:** http://info.emeraldinsight.com/products/journals/journals.htm?id=jpif.

52514 ■ Journal of Quality in Maintenance Engineering
Emerald Group Publishing Ltd.
Howard House, Wagon Ln.
Bradford BD16 1WA, United Kingdom
Ph: 44 1274 777700
Fax: 44 1274 785201
Publisher E-mail: emerald@emeraldinsight.com
Journal showing how the maintenance function can be made more reliable, more cost-effective and more efficient by bringing the latest research findings to the notice of academics and practitioners and making a significant contribution to the achievement of total quality. **Freq:** 4/yr. **Key Personnel:** Prof. Salih O. Duffuaa, Editor, duffuaa@ccse.kfupm.edu.sa; Dr. Mohamed Ben-Daya, Assoc. Ed.; Lucy Sootheran, Publisher, lsootheran@emeraldinsight.com; Dr. Gerald M. Knapp, Internet Ed. **ISSN:** 1355-2511. **URL:** http://info.emeraldinsight.com/products/journals/journals.htm?id=jqme.

52515 ■ The Journal of Risk Finance
Emerald Group Publishing Ltd.
Howard House, Wagon Ln.
Bradford BD16 1WA, United Kingdom
Ph: 44 1274 777700
Fax: 44 1274 785201
Publisher E-mail: emerald@emeraldinsight.com
Professional journal covering risk finance and risk management. **Freq:** Quarterly. **Key Personnel:** Michael R. Powers, Editor, michael.powers@temple.edu; Adam Smith, Publisher, asmith@emeraldinsight.com; Leo M. Tilman, Contributing Ed. **ISSN:** 1526-5943. **Subscription Rates:** 899 individuals plus vat; EUR1,249 individuals plus vat; 1,549 U.S.; $A 2,279 other countries U.S.D. **Remarks:** Accepts advertising. **URL:** http://www.emeraldinsight.com/products/journals/journals.htm?id=jrf. **Ad Rates:** BW: 5,532, 4C: 9,133. **Circ:** (Not Reported)

52516 ■ Journal of Service Management
Emerald Group Publishing Ltd.
Howard House, Wagon Ln.
Bradford BD16 1WA, United Kingdom
Ph: 44 1274 777700
Fax: 44 1274 785201
Publisher E-mail: emerald@emeraldinsight.com
Journal bringing together specialist areas of research for the benefit of those working in the service sector focusing on both for-profit and non-profit areas of the sector and drawing on leading-edge contributions to help compare international developments and build up a broader understanding of key issues. **Freq:** 5/yr. **Key Personnel:** Jay Kandampully, Editor, kandampully.1@osu.edu; Kate Snowden, Publisher, ksnowden@emeraldinsight.com; Chris Voss, Editorial Advisory Board; Lester W. Johnson, Assoc. Ed.; Prof. Anders Gustafsson, Assoc. Ed.; Prof. Lerzan Aksoy, Editorial Advisory Board; Prof. Robert C. Ford, Editorial Advisory Board; Colin Armistead, Editorial Advisory Board; Javier Reynoso, Book Review Ed., jreynoso@itesm.mx. **ISSN:** 1757-5818. **URL:** http://info.emeraldinsight.com/products/journals/journals.htm?PHPSESSID=0onkd54o28l3c6rrkjhb05qm97&id=ijsim. **Formerly:** International Journal of Service Industry Management.

52517 ■ Journal of Strategy and Management
Emerald Group Publishing Ltd.
Howard House, Wagon Ln.
Bradford BD16 1WA, United Kingdom
Ph: 44 1274 777700
Fax: 44 1274 785201
Publisher E-mail: emerald@emeraldinsight.com
Journal focusing on improving the existing knowledge and understanding of strategy development and implementation globally in private and public organizations. **Freq:** Irregular. **Key Personnel:** Prof. Abby Ghobadian, Editor, abby.ghobadian@henleymc.ac.uk; Prof. Nicholas O'Reagan, Editor, nicholas.o'regan@uwe.ac.uk; Ruth Young, Publisher, ryoung@emeraldinsight.com. **ISSN:** 1755-425X. **URL:** http://info.emeraldinsight.com/products/journals/journals.htm?id=jsma.

52518 ■ Journal of Workplace Learning
Emerald Group Publishing Ltd.
Howard House, Wagon Ln.
Bradford BD16 1WA, United Kingdom
Ph: 44 1274 777700
Fax: 44 1274 785201

Circulation: ★ = ABC; △ = BPA; ◆ = CAC; • = CCAB; ❏ = VAC; ⊕ = PO Statement; ‡ = Publisher's Report; Boldface figures = sworn; Light figures = estimated.

Gale Directory of Publications & Broadcast Media/147th Ed.   5589

Publisher E-mail: emerald@emeraldinsight.com
Journal focusing on the growth of the individual within the enterprise and the interventions which can assist in the process with analysis of the key issues in this area set in the context of assisting the individual to maximize opportunities and performance within the working environment. **Freq:** 8/yr. **Key Personnel:** Dr. Sara Cervai, Editor, cervai@units.it; Nancy Rolph, Publisher, nrolph@emeraldinsight.com; Prof. Tauno Kekale, Editor, tauno.kekale@uwasa.fi. **ISSN:** 1366-5626. **URL:** http://info.emeraldinsight.com/products/journals/journals.htm?id=jwl.

52519 ■ Knitting International
World Textile Publications Ltd.
Perkin House
1 Longlands St.
Bradford BD1 2TP, United Kingdom
Ph: 44 1274 378800
Fax: 44 1274 378811
Publisher E-mail: info@world-textile.net
Trade magazine covering the knitting industry for manufacturers of knitwear, knitted fabric, hosiery and underwear worldwide. **Founded:** 1894. **Freq:** 11/yr. **Print Method:** Sheetfed Offset Litho. **Trim Size:** 210 x 279 mm. **Key Personnel:** Jonathan Dyson, Managing Editor, phone 44 1274 378838, jdyson@world-textile. net. **Subscription Rates:** EUR299 individuals. **Remarks:** Accepts advertising. **URL:** http://www.inteletex.com/bookstore/BookDetail.asp?id=m006&cat=Magazine. **Ad Rates:** BW: 1,905. **Circ:** 22,500

52520 ■ Leadership in Health Services
Emerald Group Publishing Ltd.
Howard House, Wagon Ln.
Bradford BD16 1WA, United Kingdom
Ph: 44 1274 777700
Fax: 44 1274 785201
Publisher E-mail: emerald@emeraldinsight.com
Journal aiming to broaden knowledge and understanding of quality assurance and its implementation in organizations, combining theoretical and practical considerations and drawing on contributions from worldwide sources and providing a much needed resource for all those involved in developing, initiating and monitoring quality assurance programmes in the health care industry. **Freq:** 4/yr. **Key Personnel:** Jennifer Bowerman, Editor, jbowerman@shaw.ca; Jo Lamb-White, Co-Ed.; Nicola Codner, Publisher, ncodner@emeraldinsight.com. **ISSN:** 1751-1879. **URL:** http://info.emeraldinsight.com/products/journals/journals.htm?id=lhs.

52521 ■ The Learning Organization
Emerald Group Publishing Ltd.
Howard House, Wagon Ln.
Bradford BD16 1WA, United Kingdom
Ph: 44 1274 777700
Fax: 44 1274 785201
Publisher E-mail: emerald@emeraldinsight.com
Journal for practitioners, consultants, researchers and students theory of the learning organization, aiming to bring ideas, debate issues and case studies on topics such as technology, the demands of an increasingly sophisticated workforce, independent thinking, global awareness and competition and out-working, showing how it works in practice, and the rich rewards that await the companies brave enough to adopt its strategies. **Subtitle:** The International Journal of Knowledge and Organizational Learning Management. **Freq:** 6/yr. **Key Personnel:** Prof. Colin Joseph Coulson-Thomas, Editorial Advisory Board; Dr. Nick Bontis, Editorial Advisory Board; Peter Smith, Consulting Ed., pasmith@tlainc.com; Nancy Rolph, Publisher, nrolph@emeraldinsight.com; Dr. Ivan Blanco, Editorial Advisory Board; Prof. Richard V. McCarthy, Editorial Advisory Board; Prof. Deborah Blackman, Editor, deborah.blackman@canberra.edu.au; Prof. David Megginson, Editorial Advisory Board. **ISSN:** 0969-6474. **URL:** http://ariel.emeraldinsight.com/info/journals/tlo/tlo.jsp.

52522 ■ Library Management
Emerald Group Publishing Ltd.
Howard House, Wagon Ln.
Bradford BD16 1WA, United Kingdom
Ph: 44 1274 777700
Fax: 44 1274 785201
Publisher E-mail: emerald@emeraldinsight.com
Journal offering international perspectives on the critical issues facing library management by publishing articles

which report contemporary thought while also exploring practical implications for those involved in teaching and practice, providing knowledge and practical perspectives on all aspects of the management of libraries and information services by drawing contributions from distinguished international figures. **Freq:** 9/yr. **Key Personnel:** Eileen Breen, Publisher, ebreen@emeraldinsight.com; Steve O'Connor, Editor, steve.oconnor@polyu.edu.hk; Dr. Judith Broady-Preston, Regional Ed., jbp@aber.ac.uk. **ISSN:** 0143-5124. **URL:** http://info.emeraldinsight.com/products/journals/journals.htm?id=lm.

52523 ■ Management of Environmental Quality
Emerald Group Publishing Ltd.
Howard House, Wagon Ln.
Bradford BD16 1WA, United Kingdom
Ph: 44 1274 777700
Fax: 44 1274 785201
Publisher E-mail: emerald@emeraldinsight.com
Journal examining in a deep and objective manner the various environmental factors and their impact on the overall quality of ecosystems and quality of life, suggesting possible remedies to environmental problems and adopting an inter-disciplinary approach to the problem of managing the environment and upkeeping good quality standards, with a view to reducing the deleterious effects of man's activities. **Subtitle:** An International Journal. **Freq:** 6/yr. **Key Personnel:** Dr. Munir Ozturk, Editorial Advisory Board; Prof. Walter Leal Filho, PhD, Editor, walter.leal@ls.haw-hamburg.de; Prof. Fernando O. Pereira, Regional Ed.; Prof. K.S. Murali, Regional Ed.; Prof. J.G. Llaurado, Dep. Ed.; Luca Bonomo, Editorial Advisory Board; Nicola Codner, Publisher, ncodner@emeraldinsight.com. **ISSN:** 1477-7835. **URL:** http://info.emeraldinsight.com/products/journals/journals.htm?id=meq.

52524 ■ Managerial Auditing Journal
Emerald Group Publishing Ltd.
Howard House, Wagon Ln.
Bradford BD16 1WA, United Kingdom
Ph: 44 1274 777700
Fax: 44 1274 785201
Publisher E-mail: emerald@emeraldinsight.com
Journal addressing the changing function of the auditor, examining the managerial as well as the professional aspects of the role, and exploring the positive impact of auditing on company policy, corporate governance and organizational progress, drawing together international, interdisciplinary contributions, offering a framework of explanation and guidance on the latest developments and research, and provides valuable insights into professional and career development. **Freq:** 9/yr. **Key Personnel:** Simon Linacre, Publisher, slinacre@emeraldinsight.com; Prof. Barry J. Cooper, Editor, barry.cooper@deakin.edu.au; Prof. Philomena Leung, Editor, philomena.leung@deakin.edu.au. **ISSN:** 0268-6902. **URL:** http://info.emeraldinsight.com/products/journals/journals.htm?id=maj.

52525 ■ Marketing Intelligence & Planning
Emerald Group Publishing Ltd.
Howard House, Wagon Ln.
Bradford BD16 1WA, United Kingdom
Ph: 44 1274 777700
Fax: 44 1274 785201
Publisher E-mail: emerald@emeraldinsight.com
Publication covering advertising, marketing and public relations. **Freq:** 7/yr. **Key Personnel:** Prof. Gillian H. Wright, Editor, g.wright@mmu.ac.uk; Richard Whitfield, Publisher, rwhitfield@emeraldinsight.com; Dr. Michael John Harker, Asst. Ed., michael.harker@strath.ac.uk. **ISSN:** 0263-4503. **URL:** http://info.emeraldinsight.com/products/journals/journals.htm?id=mip.

52526 ■ Measuring Business Excellence
Emerald Group Publishing Ltd.
Howard House, Wagon Ln.
Bradford BD16 1WA, United Kingdom
Ph: 44 1274 777700
Fax: 44 1274 785201
Publisher E-mail: emerald@emeraldinsight.com
Journal providing international insights into non-financial ways to measure business improvements, enabling business to apply best practice, implement innovative thinking and learn how to use difference practice. **Freq:** 4/yr. **Key Personnel:** Dr. Jos van Iwaarden, Editor, jiwaarden@rsm.nl; Bernard Marr, Editorial Advisory

Board, bernard.marr@ap-institute.com; Andrew Smith, Publisher, agsmith@emeraldinsight.com; Prof. Giovanni Schiuma, Co-Ed., giovanni.schiuma@unibas.it; K. Narasimhan, Book Reviewer Ed. **ISSN:** 1368-3047. **URL:** http://info.emeraldinsight.com/products/journals/journals.htm?id=mbe.

52527 ■ Microelectronics International
Emerald Group Publishing Ltd.
Howard House, Wagon Ln.
Bradford BD16 1WA, United Kingdom
Ph: 44 1274 777700
Fax: 44 1274 785201
Publisher E-mail: emerald@emeraldinsight.com
Journal providing an authoritative, international and independent forum for the critical evaluation and dissemination of research and development, applications, processes and current practices relating to advanced packaging, micro-circuit engineering, interconnection, semiconductor technology and systems engineering. **Freq:** 3/yr. **Key Personnel:** John Ling, Assoc. Ed.; Dr. John Karl Atkinson, Editor, jka@soton.ac.uk; Harry Colson, Publisher. **ISSN:** 1356-5362. **URL:** http://info.emeraldinsight.com/products/journals/journals.htm?id=mi.

52528 ■ Multidiscipline Modeling in Materials and Structures
Emerald Group Publishing Ltd.
Howard House, Wagon Ln.
Bradford BD16 1WA, United Kingdom
Ph: 44 1274 777700
Fax: 44 1274 785201
Publisher E-mail: emerald@emeraldinsight.com
Journal covering research contributions relating to multidiscipline modeling, design, and optimization in materials and structures. **Founded:** 1914. **Freq:** 4/yr. **Print Method:** Offset. **Trim Size:** 8 1/2 x 11. **Cols./Page:** 3. **Col. Width:** 28 nonpareils. **Col. Depth:** 130 agate lines. **Key Personnel:** Prof. Zhufeng Yue, Editor-in-Chief. **ISSN:** 1573-6105. **URL:** http://www.emeraldinsight.com/products/journals/journals.htm?id=mmms.

52529 ■ The Naturalist
Yorkshire Naturalists' Union
The University of Bradford
Bradford BD7 1DP, United Kingdom
Ph: 44 12 74234212
Publication E-mail: m.r.d.seaward@bradford.ac.uk
Journal covering natural history, biology and environmental science. **Founded:** 1875. **Freq:** Quarterly. **Col. Width:** 110 millimeters. **Col. Depth:** 173 millimeters. **Key Personnel:** Prof. M.R.D. Seaward, Editor. **ISSN:** 0028-0771. **Subscription Rates:** 4 nonmembers. **Remarks:** Accepts advertising. **URL:** http://www.ynu.org.uk/naturalistsindex.htm. **Ad Rates:** BW: US$120. **Circ:** Combined 5,800

52530 ■ New Library World
Emerald Group Publishing Ltd.
Howard House, Wagon Ln.
Bradford BD16 1WA, United Kingdom
Ph: 44 1274 777700
Fax: 44 1274 785201
Publisher E-mail: emerald@emeraldinsight.com
Journal providing an international appraisal of current library trends and emerging patterns for the future. **Freq:** 12/yr. **Key Personnel:** Linda Ashcroft, Editor, l.s.ashcroft@ljmu.ac.uk; Eileen Breen, Publisher, ebreen@emeraldinsight.com. **ISSN:** 0307-4803. **URL:** http://info.emeraldinsight.com/products/journals/journals.htm?id=nlw.

52531 ■ Nonwovens Report International
World Textile Publications Ltd.
Perkin House
1 Longlands St.
Bradford BD1 2TP, United Kingdom
Ph: 44 1274 378800
Fax: 44 1274 378811
Publication E-mail: info@worldtextile.com
Publisher E-mail: info@world-textile.net
Trade magazine covering the nonwoven textile industry worldwide. **Freq:** Bimonthly. **Print Method:** Sheetfed Offset Litho. **Trim Size:** 210 x 297 mm. **Key Personnel:** Jonathan Dyson, Managing Editor, phone 44 1274 378838, jdyson@world-textile.net; James Wilson, Sales Mgr., phone 44 1274 378825, jwilson@world-textile.net. **Subscription Rates:** EUR299 individuals. **Remarks:** Accepts advertising. **URL:** http://www.inteletex.com/

bookstore/BookDetail.asp?id=m007&cat=Magazine. **Ad Rates:** BW: EUR2,091. **Circ:** (Not Reported)

52532 ■ OCLC Systems & Services
Emerald Group Publishing Ltd.
Howard House, Wagon Ln.
Bradford BD16 1WA, United Kingdom
Ph: 44 1274 777700
Fax: 44 1274 785201
Publisher E-mail: emerald@emeraldinsight.com
Journal for information professionals, educators, students, and researchers around the world to share and exchange their ideas, applications, and research results concerning information education, management, technology, and dissemination and focusing on developments in OCLC system applications, services, and research. **Subtitle:** International Digital Library Perspectives. **Freq:** 4/yr. **Key Personnel:** Dr. Bradford Lee Eden, Editor, eden@library.ucsb.edu; Eileen Breen, Publisher, ebreen@emeraldinsight.com. **ISSN:** 1065-075X. **URL:** http://info.emeraldinsight.com/products/journals/journals.htm?id=oclc.

52533 ■ On the Horizon
Emerald Group Publishing Ltd.
Howard House, Wagon Ln.
Bradford BD16 1WA, United Kingdom
Ph: 44 1274 777700
Fax: 44 1274 785201
Publisher E-mail: emerald@emeraldinsight.com
International journal providing analysis and comment on the future of post-secondary education and "radar" service to key decision makers concerned with post secondary education in its many and emerging forms, from traditional institutions to corporate universities, from private/for-profits to non-profits around the world, informing educators about the challenges that they will face in a changing world and the steps they can take to meet these challenges. **Freq:** Quarterly. **Key Personnel:** Dr. Tom P. Abeles, Editor, tabeles@gmail.com; Jessica Davis, Asst. Publisher, jdavis@emeraldinsight.com; Kate Snowden, Publisher, ksnowden@emeraldinsight.com. **ISSN:** 1074-8121. **URL:** http://www.emeraldinsight.com/products/journals/journals.htm?id=oth.

52534 ■ Online Information Review
Emerald Group Publishing Ltd.
Howard House, Wagon Ln.
Bradford BD16 1WA, United Kingdom
Ph: 44 1274 777700
Fax: 44 1274 785201
Publisher E-mail: emerald@emeraldinsight.com
Journal covering information science worldwide. **Subtitle:** The International Journal of Digital Information Research and Use. **Founded:** 1977. **Freq:** Bimonthly. **Key Personnel:** Eileen Breen, Publisher, ebreen@emeraldinsight.com; Dr. Gary E. Gorman, Editor, gary.gorman@vuw.ac.nz; Louise Norton, Assoc. Ed., louise.norton@paradise.net.nz. **ISSN:** 1468-4527. **Remarks:** Advertising not accepted. **Online:** Ingenta; Emerald. **URL:** http://info.emeraldinsight.com/products/journals/journals.htm?id=oir. **Former name:** Online & CD ROM Review. **Circ:** (Not Reported)

52535 ■ Peace, Conflict & Development
Department of Peace Studies
Pemberton Bldg.
University of Bradford
Richmond Rd.
Bradford BD7 1DP, United Kingdom
Ph: 44 1274 232323
Publication E-mail: editor@peacestudiesjournal.org.uk
Publisher E-mail: ssisugadmissions@bradford.ac.uk
Journal publishing articles on contemporary issues in Conflict and Peace Studies. Covers topics such as human rights, democracy and democratization, conflict resolution, environment, security, war, culture, identity and community etc. **Freq:** Semiannual. **ISSN:** 1742-0601. **URL:** http://www.peacestudiesjournal.org.uk/.

52536 ■ Performance Measurements and Metrics
Emerald Group Publishing Ltd.
Howard House, Wagon Ln.
Bradford BD16 1WA, United Kingdom
Ph: 44 1274 777700
Fax: 44 1274 785201
Publisher E-mail: emerald@emeraldinsight.com
Journal aiming to cover both qualitative and quantitative performance measurement in the LIS field, containing authoritative articles; digests of information from the leading web discussion lists; news items from around the world; and reviews of books and other materials of interest, bringing together the research and experience of a world-wide team of experts. **Subtitle:** The International Journal for Library and Information Services. **Freq:** 3/yr. **Key Personnel:** Lizzie Scott, Publisher, escott@emeraldinsight.com; Pat Dixon, Editorial Advisory Board; Steve Thornton, Editor, stephen.thornton137@ntlworld.com; Dr. Roswitha Poll, Editorial Advisory Board; Dr. Colleen Cook, Editorial Advisory Board; Prof. Rowena Cullen, Editorial Advisory Board. **ISSN:** 1467-8047. **URL:** http://info.emeraldinsight.com/products/journals/journals.htm?id=pmm.

52537 ■ Pigment & Resin Technology
Emerald Group Publishing Ltd.
Howard House, Wagon Ln.
Bradford BD16 1WA, United Kingdom
Ph: 44 1274 777700
Fax: 44 1274 785201
Publisher E-mail: emerald@emeraldinsight.com
International journal publishing global research results and case studies which report on materials and techniques relevant to the formulation and manufacture of dyes, pigments, coatings, inks, adhesives, sealants and varnishes. **Freq:** 6/yr. **Key Personnel:** Dr. Long Lin, Editor, l.lin@leeds.ac.uk; Prof. Niki Kouloumbi, Editorial Advisory Board; Harry Colson, Publisher, hcolson@emeraldinsight.com; Andrea Watson Lee, Editorial Asst., awatsonlee@emeraldinsight.com; Prof. Abdullah Mohamed Asiri, Editorial Advisory Board; Dr. Abdul Iqbal, Editorial Advisory Board. **ISSN:** 0369-9420. **URL:** http://www.emeraldinsight.com/products/journals/journals.htm?id=prt.

52538 ■ Policing
Emerald Group Publishing Ltd.
Howard House, Wagon Ln.
Bradford BD16 1WA, United Kingdom
Ph: 44 1274 777700
Fax: 44 1274 785201
Publisher E-mail: emerald@emeraldinsight.com
Journal providing expert discussion, analysis and strategies to achieve greater effectiveness in police management and law enforcement, publishing peer-reviewed research articles and case studies and providing a truly global and comparative perspective on policing. **Subtitle:** An International Journal of Police Strategies & Management. **Freq:** 4/yr. **Key Personnel:** Prof. Lawrence F. Travis III, Editor, lawrence.travis@uc.edu; Nicola Codner, Publisher, ncodner@emeraldinsight.com; Dr. Stan K. Shernock, Book Review Ed. **ISSN:** 1363-951X. **URL:** http://info.emeraldinsight.com/products/journals/journals.htm?id=pijpsm.

52539 ■ Qualitative Market Research
Emerald Group Publishing Ltd.
Howard House, Wagon Ln.
Bradford BD16 1WA, United Kingdom
Ph: 44 1274 777700
Fax: 44 1274 785201
Publisher E-mail: emerald@emeraldinsight.com
Journal furthering the frontiers of knowledge and understanding of qualitative market research and its applications by exploring many contemporary issues and new developments in marketing, breaking new ground by raising awareness of the dichotomy of principles and practices in research, in an analytical and practical way, providing national, international and cross-cultural perspectives of principles and practices. **Subtitle:** An International Journal. **Freq:** 4/yr. **Key Personnel:** Richard Whitfield, Publisher, rwhitfield@emeraldinsight.com; Prof. Len Tiu Wright, Editor, lwright@dmu.ac.uk; Prof. Russell Abratt, Editorial Advisory Board; Prof. Gordon R. Foxall, Editorial Advisory Board; Prof. Audrey Gilmore, Editorial Advisory Board. **ISSN:** 1352-2752. **URL:** http://info.emeraldinsight.com/products/journals/journals.htm?id=qmr.

52540 ■ Qualitative Research in Accounting and Management
Emerald Group Publishing Ltd.
Howard House, Wagon Ln.
Bradford BD16 1WA, United Kingdom
Ph: 44 1274 777700
Fax: 44 1274 785201
Publisher E-mail: emerald@emeraldinsight.com
International research journal publishing qualitative and interdisciplinary studies of accounting, management and organizations. **Key Personnel:** Prof. Deryl Northcott, Editor, deryl.northcott@aut.ac.nz; Prof. Bill Doolin, Editorial Advisory Board; Prof. James Barker, Editorial Advisory Board; Simon Linacre, Publisher, slinacre@emeraldinsight.com; Prof. Sue Llewellyn, Editorial Advisory Board; Prof. Manzurul Alam, Editorial Advisory Board; Prof. David Levy, Editorial Advisory Board; Dr. Sharon C. Bolton, Editorial Advisory Board. **ISSN:** 1176-6093. **URL:** http://www.emeraldinsight.com/products/journals/journals.htm?id=qram.

52541 ■ Quality Assurance in Education
Emerald Group Publishing Ltd.
Howard House, Wagon Ln.
Bradford BD16 1WA, United Kingdom
Ph: 44 1274 777700
Fax: 44 1274 785201
Publisher E-mail: emerald@emeraldinsight.com
Journal focusing on the dissemination of best practice on the management of change and improvement in higher education, seeking to contribute to developing effective strategies to complex and uncertain environment in which education now operates, inviting insights into the perceptions and opinions of quality in education of a number of stakeholders to gain a balanced view. **Freq:** 4/yr. **Key Personnel:** Prof. John F. Dalrymple, Editor, jdalrymple@nd.edu.au; Kate Snowden, Publisher, ksnowden@emeraldinsight.com; Prof. Graham Badley, Editorial Advisory Board; Dr. G. Srikanthan, Editorial Advisory Board, jqae@rmit.edu.au; Prof. Alberto Amaral, Editorial Advisory Board; Philip Lewis, Editorial Advisory Board. **ISSN:** 0968-4883. **URL:** http://info.emeraldinsight.com/products/journals/journals.htm?id=qae.

52542 ■ Rapid Prototyping Journal
Emerald Group Publishing Ltd.
Howard House, Wagon Ln.
Bradford BD16 1WA, United Kingdom
Ph: 44 1274 777700
Fax: 44 1274 785201
Publisher E-mail: emerald@emeraldinsight.com
Journal publishing global research results and case studies, which report on the development and application of rapid prototyping, direct manufacturing and related technologies. **Freq:** 5/yr. **Key Personnel:** Dr. Ian Campbell, Editor, r.i.campbell@lboro.ac.uk; Prof. Deon De Beer, Editorial Advisory Board; Dr. Ian Gibson, Regional Ed., mpegi@nus.edu.sg; Dr. Brent Stucker, Editorial Advisory Board, brent.stucker@usu.edu; Harry Colson, Publisher, hcolson@emeraldinsight.com. **ISSN:** 1355-2546. **URL:** http://info.emeraldinsight.com/products/journals/journals.htm?id=rpj.

52543 ■ Sensor Review
Emerald Group Publishing Ltd.
Howard House, Wagon Ln.
Bradford BD16 1WA, United Kingdom
Ph: 44 1274 777700
Fax: 44 1274 785201
Publisher E-mail: emerald@emeraldinsight.com
Journal covering new sensor application and capabilities, meeting the needs of busy engineers, researchers and managers in a wide and growing range of user industries, offering essential information on fast-moving developments in sensor technology, as well as the latest news on technological innovation and industry application. **Subtitle:** The International Journal of Sensing for Industry. **Freq:** 4/yr. **Key Personnel:** Dr. Clive Loughlin, PhD, Editor, cliveloughlin@engineeringfirst.com; Richard Bloss, Assoc. Ed.; Harry Colson, Publisher, hcolson@emeraldinsight.com. **ISSN:** 0260-2288. **URL:** http://info.emeraldinsight.com/products/journals/journals.htm?id=sr.

52544 ■ Society and Business Review
Emerald Group Publishing Ltd.
Howard House, Wagon Ln.
Bradford BD16 1WA, United Kingdom
Ph: 44 1274 777700
Fax: 44 1274 785201
Publisher E-mail: emerald@emeraldinsight.com
Journal aiming to cultivate and share knowledge and ideas in order to assist businesses to enhance their commitment in societies, providing a platform for diverse

academic and practitioner communities to debate a broad spectrum of social issues and disciplinary perspectives. **Freq:** 3/yr. **Key Personnel:** Karim Ben Kahla, Editorial Advisory Board; Prof. Yvon Pesqueux, Editor, pesqueux@cnam.fr; Prof. Greg Bamber, Editorial Advisory Board; Ed Arrington, Editorial Advisory Board; Elena Antonocopoulou, Editorial Advisory Board; Andrew Smith, Publisher, agsmith@emeraldinsight.com; Gaetan Breton, Editorial Advisory Board; Eric Cornuel, Editorial Advisory Board. **ISSN:** 1746-5680. **URL:** http://info.emeraldinsight.com/products/journals/journals.htm?id=sbr.

52545 ■ Soldering & Surface Mount Technology
Emerald Group Publishing Ltd.
Howard House, Wagon Ln.
Bradford BD16 1WA, United Kingdom
Ph: 44 1274 777700
Fax: 44 1274 785201
Publisher E-mail: emerald@emeraldinsight.com
Journal providing an authoritative, international and independent forum for the critical evaluation and dissemination of research and development, applications, processes and current practices relating to all areas of soldering and surface mount technology, covering all aspects of SMT from alloys, pastes and fluxes, to reliability and environmental effects and providing an important dissemination route for new knowledge on lead-free solders and processes. **Freq:** 4/yr. **Key Personnel:** Prof. Martin Goosey, Editor, martingoosey@aol.com; Dr. Ning-Cheng Lee, Editorial Advisory Board; Prof. Ricky S.W. Lee, Editorial Advisory Board; Dr. Jennie S. Hwang, Editorial Advisory Board; Prof. Y.C. Chan, Editorial Advisory Board; Dr. Harry Colson, Publisher, hcolson@emeraldinsight.com. **ISSN:** 0954-0911. **URL:** http://info.emeraldinsight.com/products/journals/journals.htm?id=ssmt.

52546 ■ Strategic Direction
Emerald Group Publishing Ltd.
Howard House, Wagon Ln.
Bradford BD16 1WA, United Kingdom
Ph: 44 1274 777700
Fax: 44 1274 785201
Publisher E-mail: emerald@emeraldinsight.com
Professional journal covering strategic business management. **Freq:** 11/yr. **Key Personnel:** Martin Fojt, Editor-in-Chief, mfojt@emeraldinsight.com; Juliet Norton, Publisher, jnorton@emeraldinsight.com. **ISSN:** 0258-0543. **Remarks:** Advertising not accepted. **URL:** http://www.emeraldinsight.com/info/journals/sd/sd.jsp. **Circ:** (Not Reported)

52547 ■ Strategic HR Review
Emerald Group Publishing Ltd.
Howard House, Wagon Ln.
Bradford BD16 1WA, United Kingdom
Ph: 44 1274 777700
Fax: 44 1274 785201
Publisher E-mail: emerald@emeraldinsight.com
Journal featuring the latest ideas on how new technologies are impacting HR related processes. **Freq:** Bimonthly. **Key Personnel:** Sara Nolan, Editor, saranolanshr@emeraldinsight.com; Nancy Rolph, Publisher, nrolph@emeraldinsight.com. **ISSN:** 1475-4398. **URL:** http://info.emeraldinsight.com/products/journals/journals.htm?id=shr.

52548 ■ Strategic Outsourcing
Emerald Group Publishing Ltd.
Howard House, Wagon Ln.
Bradford BD16 1WA, United Kingdom
Ph: 44 1274 777700
Fax: 44 1274 785201
Publisher E-mail: emerald@emeraldinsight.com
Journal aiming to foster and lead the international debate on global sourcing and outsourcing. **Subtitle:** An International Journal. **Freq:** Irregular. **Key Personnel:** Dr. Marco Busi, Editor; Lucy Sootheran, Publisher, lsootheran@emeraldinsight.com. **ISSN:** 1753-8297. **URL:** http://info.emeraldinsight.com/products/journals/journals.htm?id=so.

52549 ■ Structural Survey
Emerald Group Publishing Ltd.
Howard House, Wagon Ln.
Bradford BD16 1WA, United Kingdom
Ph: 44 1274 777700
Fax: 44 1274 785201

Publisher E-mail: emerald@emeraldinsight.com
Journal offering access to expert comments and advice on all aspects of the inspection and appraisal of buildings, looking at the major issues facing the profession today and presents important case histories and research findings, highlighting topics such as building conservation and refurbishment and offering solutions to a wide range of building-related problems. **Freq:** 5/yr. **Key Personnel:** Aimee Wood, Publisher, awood@emeraldinsight.com; Prof. Michael Hoxley, Co-Ed., mike.hoxley@ntu.ac.uk; Dr. Shima Clarke, Editorial Advisory Board; Prof. Malcolm Hollis, Editorial Advisory Board; Prof. Malcolm Bell, Editorial Advisory Board; Prof. Michael Chew, Editorial Advisory Board; Paul Chynoweth, Legal Ed.; Peter Fall, Editorial Advisory Board; Stephen Brown, Editorial Advisory Board; Lawrence Hurst, Editorial Advisory Board. **ISSN:** 0263-080X. **URL:** http://info.emeraldinsight.com/products/journals.htm?id=ss.

52550 ■ Team Performance Management
Emerald Group Publishing Ltd.
Howard House, Wagon Ln.
Bradford BD16 1WA, United Kingdom
Ph: 44 1274 777700
Fax: 44 1274 785201
Publisher E-mail: emerald@emeraldinsight.com
Journal aiming to contribute to the successful implementation and development of work teams and team-based organisations by providing a forum for sharing experience and learning to stimulate thought and transfer of ideas, particularly aiming to bridge the gap between research and practice by publishing articles where the claims are evidence-based and the conclusions have practical value. **Freq:** 8/yr. **Key Personnel:** Nancy Rolph, Publisher, nrolph@emeraldinsight.com; Prof. Rebecca Gatlin-Watts, Editorial Advisory Board; Prof. Terry Desombre, Editorial Advisory Board; Dr. Diane Christopulus, Editorial Advisory Board; Dr. Fiona Lettice, Editor, fiona.lettice@uea.ac.uk. **ISSN:** 1352-7592. **URL:** http://info.emeraldinsight.com/products/journals/journals.htm?id=tpm.

52551 ■ Telegraph & Argus
Newsquest Media Group Ltd.
Hall Ings
Bradford BD1 1JR, United Kingdom
Ph: 44 1274 729511
Newspaper featuring sports, community news, motoring advice, and job hunting updates. **Freq:** Mon.-Sat. **Key Personnel:** Perry Austin-Clarke, Editor, newsdesk@telegraphandargus.co.uk; Peter Orme, Managing Editor, phone 44 1274 705346, peter.orme@bradford.newsquest.co.uk; Brian Nuttney, Dep. Ed., phone 44 1274 705226, brian.nuttney@telegraphandargus.co.uk. **Remarks:** Accepts advertising. **URL:** http://www.thetelegraphandargus.co.uk/. **Circ:** (Not Reported)

52552 ■ Textile Month (TM)
World Textile Publications Ltd.
Perkin House
1 Longlands St.
Bradford BD1 2TP, United Kingdom
Ph: 44 1274 378800
Fax: 44 1274 378811
Publisher E-mail: info@world-textile.net
Trade magazine covering the textile industry worldwide. **Freq:** Bimonthly. **Print Method:** Sheetfed Offset Litho. **Trim Size:** 210 x 297 mm. **Key Personnel:** Jonathan Dyson, Managing Editor, phone 44 1274 378838, jdyson@world-textile.net; James Wilson, Sales Mgr., phone 44 1274 378825, jwilson@world-textile.net. **Subscription Rates:** EUR364 individuals. **Remarks:** Accepts advertising. **URL:** http://www.inteletex.com/NewsIndex.asp?mode=filter&filter=publication&id=29. **Ad Rates:** BW: 1,565. **Circ:** (Not Reported)

52553 ■ Tourism Review
Emerald Group Publishing Ltd.
Howard House, Wagon Ln.
Bradford BD16 1WA, United Kingdom
Ph: 44 1274 777700
Fax: 44 1274 785201
Publisher E-mail: emerald@emeraldinsight.com
Journal aiming to contribute to a deeper understanding of tourism as an interdisciplinary phenomenon and providing insights into developments, issues and methods in tourism research. **Freq:** 4/yr. **Key Personnel:** Prof. Thomas Bieger, Editor, thomas.bieger@unisg.ch; Prof. Christian Laesser, Editor, christian.laesser@

unisg.ch; Nicola Codner, Publisher, ncodner@emeraldinsight.com. **ISSN:** 1660-5373. **URL:** http://info.emeraldinsight.com/products/journals/journals.htm?id=tr.

52554 ■ The TQM Journal
Emerald Group Publishing Ltd.
Howard House, Wagon Ln.
Bradford BD16 1WA, United Kingdom
Ph: 44 1274 777700
Fax: 44 1274 785201
Publisher E-mail: emerald@emeraldinsight.com
Magazine covering the implementation of Total Quality Management principles. **Freq:** 6/yr. **Key Personnel:** Dr. Alex Douglas, Editor; Lucy Sootheran, Publisher, lsootheran@emeraldinsight.com; Ruth Heppenstall, Asst. Publisher, rheppenstall@emeraldinsight.com. **ISSN:** 1754-2731. **URL:** http://www.emeraldinsight.com/products/journals/journals.htm?id=tqm.

52555 ■ Training & Management Development Methods
Emerald Group Publishing Ltd.
Howard House, Wagon Ln.
Bradford BD16 1WA, United Kingdom
Ph: 44 1274 777700
Fax: 44 1274 785201
Publisher E-mail: emerald@emeraldinsight.com
Journal aiming to provide an easy-to-use compendium of tested up-to-date training and development methods, incorporating new and interesting ideas and guidance on their use. **Freq:** 5/yr. **Key Personnel:** David Pollitt, Editor, d.r.pollitt@bradford.ac.uk; Nancy Rolph, Publisher, nrolph@emeraldinsight.com. **ISSN:** 0951-3507. **URL:** http://info.emeraldinsight.com/products/journals/journals.htm?id=tmdm.

52556 ■ VINE
Emerald Group Publishing Ltd.
Howard House, Wagon Ln.
Bradford BD16 1WA, United Kingdom
Ph: 44 1274 777700
Fax: 44 1274 785201
Publisher E-mail: emerald@emeraldinsight.com
Journal for those needing to keep abreast of the issues that really matter to information services, publishing material on all aspects of information services, knowledge management and library systems. **Subtitle:** The Journal of Information and Knowledge Management Systems. **Freq:** Quarterly. **Key Personnel:** Lizzie Scott, Publisher, escott@emeraldinsight.com; Prof. Michael A. Stankosky, Ed. Emeritus; Dr. Frada Burstein, Co-Ed., frada.burstein@infotech.monash.edu.au. **ISSN:** 0305-5728. **URL:** http://info.emeraldinsight.com/products/journals/journals.htm?id=vine.

52557 ■ Wool Record
World Textile Publications Ltd.
Perkin House
1 Longlands St.
Bradford BD1 2TP, United Kingdom
Ph: 44 1274 378800
Fax: 44 1274 378811
Publisher E-mail: info@world-textile.net
Trade magazine covering the wool industry for growers, processors, traders, spinners, weavers, knitters, carpet manufacturers, dyers, and fashion designers worldwide. **Freq:** Monthly. **Print Method:** Sheetfed Offset Litho. **Trim Size:** 210 x 297 mm. **Key Personnel:** Jonathan Dyson, Managing Editor, phone 44 1274 378838, jdyson@world-textile.net; James Wilson, Sales Mgr., phone 44 1274 378825, jwilson@world-textile.net. **Subscription Rates:** 190 individuals; 230 individuals; 255 other countries. **Remarks:** Accepts advertising. **URL:** http://www.inteletex.com/newsindex.asp?mode=filter&filter=publication&id=7. **Ad Rates:** BW: 1,448. **Circ:** (Not Reported)

52558 ■ BCB-FM - 106.6
11 Rawson Rd.
Bradford BD1 3SH, United Kingdom
Ph: 44 12 74771677
Fax: 44 12 74771680
E-mail: info@bcbradio.co.uk
Format: Eclectic; Public Radio. **Owner:** Bradford Community Broadcasting, at above address. **Operating Hours:** 17 hours Daily. **Key Personnel:** Mary Dowson, Director; Jonathan Pinfield, Manager. **Ad Rates:** Advertising accepted; rates available upon request. **URL:** http://www.bcbradio.co.uk.

52559 ■ Pulse-FM - 102.5
Forster Sq.
West Yorkshire
Bradford BD1 5NE, United Kingdom
Ph: 44 1274 203040
Fax: 44 1274 203120
E-mail: general@pulse.co.uk
Format: Contemporary Hit Radio (CHR); Top 40. **Key Personnel:** Mark Brow, Program Dir. **Ad Rates:** Advertising accepted; rates available upon request. **URL:** http://www.pulse.co.uk/.

52560 ■ Pulse-FM - 97.5
Forster Sq.
West Yorkshire
Bradford BD1 5NE, United Kingdom
Ph: 44 1274 203040
Fax: 44 1274 203120
E-mail: general@pulse.co.uk
Format: Top 40; News; Sports. **Operating Hours:** Continuous. **Key Personnel:** Mark Brow, Contact, mark.brow@pulse.co.uk; Bev Holmes, Station Dir., bev.holmes@pulse.co.uk; Danny Goodyear, Advertising Sales Mgr., daniel.goodyear@pulse.co.uk. **Ad Rates:** Advertising accepted; rates available upon request. **URL:** http://www.pulse.co.uk/.

Brasted

52561 ■ European Pharmaceutical Review
Russell Publishing Limited
Ct. Lodge
Hogtbough Hill
Brasted TN16 1NU, United Kingdom
Ph: 44 19 59563311
Fax: 44 19 59563123
Publisher E-mail: info@russellpublishing.com
Trade journal covering technological issues for the pharmaceutical industry in Europe. **Founded:** Sept. 1996. **Freq:** Bimonthly. **Trim Size:** 210 x 297 mm. **Key Personnel:** Carrie Lancaster, Commissioning Ed., clancaster@russellpublishing.com. **Subscription Rates:** 90 individuals; 145 two years. **Remarks:** Accepts advertising. **URL:** http://www.russellpublishing.com; http://www.europeanpharmaceuticalreview.com/. **Circ:** Controlled 14,000

52562 ■ International Airport Review
Russell Publishing Limited
Ct. Lodge
Hogtbough Hill
Brasted TN16 1NU, United Kingdom
Ph: 44 19 59563311
Fax: 44 19 59563123
Publication E-mail: airport@russellpublishing.com
Publisher E-mail: info@russellpublishing.com
Trade journal for the airport and supporting industries worldwide. **Freq:** Bimonthly. **Trim Size:** 210 x 297 mm. **Key Personnel:** Daren Quinn, Sales Dir., dquinn@russellpublishing.com. **ISSN:** 1366-6339. **Subscription Rates:** 90 individuals; 145 two years. **Remarks:** Accepts advertising. **URL:** http://www.russellpublishing.com; http://www.internationalairportreview.com/. **Circ:** Controlled 11,200

Brechin

52563 ■ Brechin Advertiser
Johnston Press PLC
13 Swan St.
Brechin DD9 6EE, United Kingdom
Ph: 44 1356 622767
Local community newspaper. **Remarks:** Accepts advertising. **URL:** http://www.brechinadvertiser.co.uk/. **Circ:** (Not Reported)

Brentwood

52564 ■ Acoustics Abstracts
Multi-Science Publishing Company Ltd.
5 Wates Way
Brentwood CM15 9TB, United Kingdom
Ph: 44 12 77224632
Fax: 44 12 77223453
Publisher E-mail: info@multi-science.co.uk
Journal covering current developments in acoustics worldwide. **Freq:** Monthly. **ISSN:** 0001-4974. **Subscription Rates:** 349 individuals. **Remarks:** Advertising not

accepted. **URL:** http://www.multi-science.co.uk; http://www.multi-science.co.uk/acous.htm. **Circ:** (Not Reported)

52565 ■ Adsorption Science & Technology
Multi-Science Publishing Company Ltd.
5 Wates Way
Brentwood CM15 9TB, United Kingdom
Ph: 44 12 77224632
Fax: 44 12 77223453
Publisher E-mail: info@multi-science.co.uk
Journal covering studies of adsorption and desorption phenomena, including studies of the pore structure and surface chemistry of active carbons, discussions of the application of the Dubinin-Radushkevich equation, the effect of cation-exchange on the sorption properties of zeolites, studies of the isosteric and differential heats of gas adsorption on microporous active carbons, and investigations of high-area manganese oxides by nitrogen adsorption. **Freq:** 10/yr. **Key Personnel:** Dr. Erich A. Muller, Editor; M. Anderson, Advisory Board; T.J. Bandosz, Advisory Board. **ISSN:** 0263-6174. **Subscription Rates:** 576 individuals print + on-line; 528 individuals print only; 509 individuals online only. **URL:** http://www.multi-science.co.uk/adsorpt.htm.

52566 ■ Advances in Structural Engineering
Multi-Science Publishing Company Ltd.
5 Wates Way
Brentwood CM15 9TB, United Kingdom
Ph: 44 12 77224632
Fax: 44 12 77223453
Publisher E-mail: info@multi-science.co.uk
Journal providing a publication channel for research in the general area of structural engineering, an international forum for the exchange of innovative ideas, and a conduit for the flow of information between the West and the East, particularly China. **Freq:** Bimonthly. **Key Personnel:** Prof. J.G. Teng, Editor-in-Chief, cejgteng@polyu.edu.hk; Dr. S.S. Law, Assoc. Ed.; Prof. K.F. Chung, Editor. **ISSN:** 1369-4332. **Subscription Rates:** 294 individuals print and online; 270 individuals print only; 262 individuals online only. **URL:** http://www.multi-science.co.uk/advstruc.htm.

52567 ■ Biomass Bulletin
Multi-Science Publishing Company Ltd.
5 Wates Way
Brentwood CM15 9TB, United Kingdom
Ph: 44 12 77224632
Fax: 44 12 77223453
Publisher E-mail: info@multi-science.co.uk
Publication covering summaries of research concerning biomass conversion and waste. **Founded:** 1982. **Freq:** Quarterly. **ISSN:** 0262-7183. **Subscription Rates:** 239 individuals print only. **Remarks:** Advertising not accepted. **URL:** http://www.multi-science.co.uk/biomass.htm. **Circ:** (Not Reported)

52568 ■ Brentwood Gazette Series
Brentwood Gazette
16 St. Thomas Rd.
Brontwood CM14 4DF, United Kingdom
Ph: 44 12 77219222
Fax: 44 12 77219172
Publication E-mail: editorial@gazettenews.co.uk
Community newspaper. **Founded:** 1919. **Freq:** Weekly. **URL:** http://www.thisistotalessex.co.uk/. **Circ:** Paid 22,819

52569 ■ Building Acoustics
Multi-Science Publishing Company Ltd.
5 Wates Way
Brentwood CM15 9TB, United Kingdom
Ph: 44 12 77224632
Fax: 44 12 77223453
Publisher E-mail: info@multi-science.co.uk
Journal covering acoustics in the built environment for architects, builders, engineers, and noise and acoustics practitioners and professionals. **Founded:** 1993. **Freq:** Quarterly. **Key Personnel:** Dr. George Dodd, Editor, g.dodd@auckland.ac.nz; Prof. R.J.M. Craik, Editor; Prof. R. Guy, Editorial Board. **ISSN:** 1351-010X. **Subscription Rates:** 233 individuals print + on-line; 213 individuals print only; 208 individuals online only. **Remarks:** Advertising not accepted. **URL:** http://www.multi-science.co.uk/buildaco.htm. **Circ:** (Not Reported)

52570 ■ Cephalalgia
John Wiley & Sons Inc.
Wiley-Blackwell
6 Ardleigh Gardens
Hutton
Brentwood CM13 1QR, United Kingdom
Ph: 44 1277 215940
Fax: 44 1865 714591
Peer-reviewed journal focusing on all aspects of headache. **Freq:** Monthly. **Key Personnel:** David Dodick, Editor-in-Chief; Rami Burstein, Assoc. Ed.; Richard Lipton, Assoc. Ed. **ISSN:** 0333-1024. **Remarks:** Accepts advertising. **URL:** http://www.wiley.com/bw/journal.asp?ref=0333-1024&site=1. **Circ:** (Not Reported)

52571 ■ Credit Control
House of Words Ltd.
7 Greding Walk
Hutton
Brentwood CM13 2UF, United Kingdom
Ph: 44 1277 225402
Professional journal covering credit control and accountancy. **Founded:** 1979. **Freq:** Monthly. **Key Personnel:** Gareth Price, Editor, gareth.price@creditcontrol.co.uk; Sally Halliday, Editorial Board Coord., sally.halliday@creditcontrol.co.uk; Sally Williams, Editorial Asst., sally.williams@creditcontrol.co.uk; Louise Hart, Accounts Department, louise.hart@creditcontrol.co.uk; Andrew McCormick, Tech. Advisor, andrew.mccormick@creditcontrol.co.uk; Robert Welham, Illustrator, robert.welham@creditcontrol.co.uk; Carol Baker, Editor, carol.baker@creditcontrol.co.uk. **ISSN:** 0143-5329. **Subscription Rates:** 635 individuals U.K. & Ireland; 685 individuals rest of Europe; 725 individuals rest of world; 495 individuals digital. **Remarks:** Accepts advertising. **URL:** http://www.creditcontrol.co.uk/resources/journal/index.htm. **Ad Rates:** 4C: EUR950. **Circ:** Paid 15,000

52572 ■ Energy and Environment
Multi-Science Publishing Company Ltd.
5 Wates Way
Brentwood CM15 9TB, United Kingdom
Ph: 44 12 77224632
Fax: 44 12 77223453
Publisher E-mail: info@multi-science.co.uk
Journal covering the direct and indirect environmental impacts of energy acquisition, transport, production and use for natural scientists, technologists and the social science and policy communities worldwide. **Founded:** 1989. **Freq:** 8/yr. **Key Personnel:** Dr. Sonja Boehmer-Christiansen, Editor, sonja.b-c@hull.ac.uk; Dr. Benny Peiser, Editor; Prof. B.W. Ang, Editorial Advisory Board. **ISSN:** 0958-305X. **Subscription Rates:** 455 individuals print + on-line; 421 individuals print only; 404 individuals online only. **Remarks:** Advertising not accepted. **URL:** http://www.multi-science.co.uk/ee.htm. **Circ:** (Not Reported)

52573 ■ Energy Exploration & Exploitation
Multi-Science Publishing Company Ltd.
5 Wates Way
Brentwood CM15 9TB, United Kingdom
Ph: 44 12 77224632
Fax: 44 12 77223453
Publisher E-mail: info@multi-science.co.uk
Peer-reviewed journal covering advances in events in all forms of energy and exploration worldwide. **Founded:** 1982. **Freq:** Bimonthly. **Key Personnel:** Prof. Yuzhuang Sun, Editor, sun-eee@hotmail.com. **ISSN:** 0144-5987. **Subscription Rates:** 350 individuals print + on-line; 323 individuals print only; 310 individuals online only. **Remarks:** Advertising not accepted. **URL:** http://www.multi-science.co.uk/eee.htm. **Circ:** (Not Reported)

52574 ■ High Spirit
105 High St., 1st Fl.
Brentwood CM14 4RR, United Kingdom
Ph: 44 01277 264284
Fax: 44 01277 264123
Publication E-mail: editor@highspiritmagazine.co.uk
Publisher E-mail: enquiries@highspiritmagazine.co.uk
Magazine for spiritual growth and self-improvement. **Freq:** Monthly. **Key Personnel:** Michelle Smith, Editor, michelle@highspiritmagazine.co.uk. **Remarks:** Accepts advertising. **URL:** http://www.highspiritmagazine.co.uk/home.php. **Circ:** ★40,000

Circulation: ★ = ABC; △ = BPA; ♦ = CAC; • = CCAB; □ = VAC; ⊕ = PO Statement; ‡ = Publisher's Report; Boldface figures = sworn; Light figures = estimated.

52575 ■ International Journal of Aeroacoustics
Multi-Science Publishing Company Ltd.
5 Wates Way
Brentwood CM15 9TB, United Kingdom
Ph: 44 12 77224632
Fax: 44 12 77223453
Publication E-mail: ijaeditor@aol.com
Publisher E-mail: info@multi-science.co.uk
Peer-reviewed journal publishing developments in all areas of fundamental and applied aeroacoustics. **Freq:** Bimonthly. **Key Personnel:** Dr. Ganesh Raman, Editor, raman@iit.edu; Dr. Thomas Brooks, Editorial Board; Dr. Edmane Envia, Editorial Board. **ISSN:** 1475-472X. **Subscription Rates:** 350 individuals print and online; 328 individuals print only; 308 individuals online only. **URL:** http://www.multi-science.co.uk/aeroacou.htm.

52576 ■ International Journal of Architectural Computing
Multi-Science Publishing Company Ltd.
5 Wates Way
Brentwood CM15 9TB, United Kingdom
Ph: 44 12 77224632
Fax: 44 12 77223453
Publisher E-mail: info@multi-science.co.uk
Peer-reviewed journal promoting collaborative research and development of computer-aided architectural design. **Freq:** Quarterly. **Key Personnel:** Prof. Andre Brown, Editor-in-Chief, andygpb@liv.ac.uk; Prof. Nancy Cheng, Editorial Board, nywc@darkwing.uoregon.edu; Prof. Wassim Jabi, Editorial Board, jabi@njit.edu. **ISSN:** 1478-0771. **Subscription Rates:** 260 individuals print + on-line; 245 individuals print only; 236 individuals online only. **URL:** http://www.multi-science.co.uk/ijac.htm.

52577 ■ International Journal of Innovation Science
Multi-Science Publishing Company Ltd.
5 Wates Way
Brentwood CM15 9TB, United Kingdom
Ph: 44 12 77224632
Fax: 44 12 77223453
Publisher E-mail: info@multi-science.co.uk
Journal covering research in innovation science. **Freq:** Quarterly. **Key Personnel:** Brett E. Trusko, PhD, Editor-in-Chief, brett.trusko@mssm.edu. **ISSN:** 1757-2223. **Subscription Rates:** 275 individuals print and online; 264 individuals print only; 231 individuals online only. **Remarks:** Accepts advertising. **URL:** http://www.multi-science.co.uk/ijis.htm. **Circ:** (Not Reported)

52578 ■ International Journal of Space Structures
Multi-Science Publishing Company Ltd.
5 Wates Way
Brentwood CM15 9TB, United Kingdom
Ph: 44 12 77224632
Fax: 44 12 77223453
Publisher E-mail: info@multi-science.co.uk
Journal providing an international forum for the interchange of information on all aspects of analysis, design and construction of space structures, encompassesing structures such as single-, double- and multi-layer grids, barrel vaults, domes, towers, folded plates, radar dishes, tensegrity structures, stressed skin assemblies, foldable structures, pneumatic systems and cable arrangements. **Freq:** Quarterly. **Key Personnel:** Prof. R. Motro, Editor, motro@lmgc.univ-montp2.fr. **ISSN:** 0266-3511. **Subscription Rates:** 281 individuals print + online; 259 individuals print only; 248 individuals online only. **URL:** http://www.multi-science.co.uk/space.htm.

52579 ■ The Journal of Computational Multiphase Flows
Multi-Science Publishing Company Ltd.
5 Wates Way
Brentwood CM15 9TB, United Kingdom
Ph: 44 12 77224632
Fax: 44 12 77223453
Publisher E-mail: info@multi-science.co.uk
Journal covering research on computational multiphase flows. **Key Personnel:** Dr. Guan Heng Yeoh, Editor, guan.yeoh@ansto.gov.au; Prof. Jiyuan Tu, Editor, jiyuan.tu@rmit.edu.au; Prof. Goodarz Ahmadi, Editor, gahmadi@clarkson.edu. **ISSN:** 1757-482X. **Subscription Rates:** 267 individuals print and online; 245 individuals print only; 223 individuals online only. **URL:** http://www.multi-science.co.uk/jcmf.htm.

52580 ■ Journal of Low Frequency Noise, Vibration & Active Control
Multi-Science Publishing Company Ltd.
5 Wates Way
Brentwood CM15 9TB, United Kingdom
Ph: 44 12 77224632
Fax: 44 12 77223453
Publisher E-mail: info@multi-science.co.uk
Journal covering low frequency noise and vibration and their effects for noise and acoustics practitioners and professionals. **Founded:** 1981. **Freq:** Quarterly. **Key Personnel:** Dr. W. Tempest, Editor; Dr. H.G. Leventhall, Assoc. Ed.; Dr. M.E. Bryan, Editorial Board. **ISSN:** 0263-0923. **Subscription Rates:** 281 individuals print + on-line; 248 individuals online only; 259 individuals print only. **Remarks:** Advertising not accepted. **URL:** http://www.multi-science.co.uk/lowfreq.htm. **Circ:** (Not Reported)

52581 ■ Low Frequency Noise, Vibration and Active Control
Multi-Science Publishing Company Ltd.
5 Wates Way
Brentwood CM15 9TB, United Kingdom
Ph: 44 12 77224632
Fax: 44 12 77223453
Publisher E-mail: info@multi-science.co.uk
Journal covering sources of infrasound and low frequency noise and vibration: detection, measurement and analysis; propagation of infrasound and low frequency noise in the atmosphere; propagation of vibration in the ground and in structures; perception of infrasound, low frequency noise and vibration by man and animals; effects on man and animals; interaction of low frequency noise and vibration: vibrations caused by noise, radiation of noise from vibrating structures; and low frequency noise and vibration control: problems and solutions. **Freq:** Quarterly. **Key Personnel:** Dr. W. Tempest, Editor; Dr. H.G. Leventhall, Assoc. Ed. **ISSN:** 0263-0923. **Subscription Rates:** 290 individuals print + online; 266 individuals print only; 255 individuals online only. **URL:** http://www.multi-science.co.uk/lowfreq.htm. **Formerly:** Low Frequency Noise & Vibration.

52582 ■ Noise Notes
Multi-Science Publishing Company Ltd.
5 Wates Way
Brentwood CM15 9TB, United Kingdom
Ph: 44 12 77224632
Fax: 44 12 77223453
Publisher E-mail: info@multi-science.co.uk
Journal covering all aspects of noise in the context of its being an environmental nuisance. **Freq:** Quarterly. **Key Personnel:** W.O. Hughes, Editor, bill@multi-science.co.uk. **ISSN:** 1475-4738. **Subscription Rates:** 192 individuals print + on-line; 181 individuals print only; 169 individuals online only. **URL:** http://www.multi-science.co.uk/noisenotes.htm.

52583 ■ Noise & Vibration Bulletin
Multi-Science Publishing Company Ltd.
5 Wates Way
Brentwood CM15 9TB, United Kingdom
Ph: 44 12 77224632
Fax: 44 12 77223453
Publisher E-mail: info@multi-science.co.uk
Journal covering all aspects of noise and vibration for noise and acoustics practitioners and professionals. **Founded:** 1968. **Freq:** Monthly. **Key Personnel:** H.G. Leventhall, Editor; B.R.V. Hughes, Editor. **ISSN:** 0029-0947. **Subscription Rates:** 259 individuals print only. **Remarks:** Advertising not accepted. **URL:** http://www.multi-science.co.uk/nvb.htm. **Circ:** (Not Reported)

52584 ■ Noise & Vibration in Industry
Multi-Science Publishing Company Ltd.
5 Wates Way
Brentwood CM15 9TB, United Kingdom
Ph: 44 12 77224632
Fax: 44 12 77223453
Publisher E-mail: info@multi-science.co.uk
Journal covering industrial noise and vibration for noise and acoustics practitioners and professionals. **Founded:** 1976. **Freq:** Quarterly. **Key Personnel:** B.R.V. Hughes, Editor. **ISSN:** 0950-8163. **Subscription Rates:** 246 individuals print only. **Remarks:** Advertising not accepted. **URL:** http://www.multi-science.co.uk/nvi.htm. **Circ:** (Not Reported)

52585 ■ Noise & Vibration Worldwide
Multi-Science Publishing Company Ltd.
5 Wates Way
Brentwood CM15 9TB, United Kingdom
Ph: 44 12 77224632
Fax: 44 12 77223453
Publisher E-mail: info@multi-science.co.uk
Professional magazine covering noise, vibration and condition monitoring. **Founded:** 1967. **Freq:** 11/yr. **Print Method:** Litho. **Trim Size:** 210 x 297 mm. **Col. Depth:** 205 millimeters. **Key Personnel:** W.O. Hughes, Editor, bill@multi-science.co.uk. **ISSN:** 0957-4565. **Subscription Rates:** 306 individuals print + online; 282 individuals print only; 270 individuals online only. **Remarks:** Accepts advertising. **URL:** http://www.multi-science.co.uk/nvw.htm. **Circ:** Paid 750

52586 ■ Parasite Immunology
John Wiley & Sons Inc.
Wiley-Blackwell
6 Ardleigh Gardens
Hutton
Essex
Brentwood CM13 1QR, United Kingdom
Journal covering research on all aspects of parasite immunology in human and animal hosts. Publishes original work on all parasites, mainly helminths, protozoa and ectoparasites. **Freq:** Monthly. **Key Personnel:** Eleanor Riley, Editor; Richard Grencis, Editor. **ISSN:** 0141-9838. **Subscription Rates:** US$204 individuals print and online; EUR166 individuals print and online; 111 individuals print and online; US$239 other countries print and online; US$2,286 institutions print and online; 1,240 institutions print and online; 1,126 institutions print or online; EUR1,574 institutions print and online; EUR1,430 institutions print or online; US$2,669 institutions, other countries print and online. **Remarks:** Advertising accepted; rates available upon request. **URL:** http://www.wiley.com/bw/journal.asp?ref=0141-9838&site=1. **Circ:** (Not Reported)

52587 ■ Rare Earth Bulletin
Multi-Science Publishing Company Ltd.
5 Wates Way
Brentwood CM15 9TB, United Kingdom
Ph: 44 12 77224632
Fax: 44 12 77223453
Publisher E-mail: info@multi-science.co.uk
Publication searching the world's journals for reported work on the lanthanides, yttrium and scandium; translating where necessary, summarizing and classifying. **Founded:** 1973. **Freq:** Bimonthly. **Key Personnel:** J.M.H. Wilson, Editor. **ISSN:** 0307-8531. **Subscription Rates:** 281 individuals print and online. **URL:** http://www.multi-science.co.uk/rareearth.htm.

52588 ■ Renewable Energy Bulletin
Multi-Science Publishing Company Ltd.
5 Wates Way
Brentwood CM15 9TB, United Kingdom
Ph: 44 12 77224632
Fax: 44 12 77223453
Publisher E-mail: info@multi-science.co.uk
Publication covering research in renewable energy, including solar, geothermal, hydropower, wind, ocean energy, biomass and waste conversion. **Founded:** 1973. **Freq:** Bimonthly. **ISSN:** 0306-364X. **Subscription Rates:** 365 individuals print only. **Remarks:** Advertising not accepted. **URL:** http://www.multi-science.co.uk; http://www.multi-science.co.uk/renew.htm. **Circ:** (Not Reported)

52589 ■ Step Forward
Limbless Association
Jubilee House; 3 The Dr.
Warley Hill
Brentwood CM13 3FR, United Kingdom
Ph: 44 1277 725182
Fax: 44 1277 725379
Publisher E-mail: enquiries@limbless-association.org
Publication covering the disabled. **Freq:** Quarterly. **Key Personnel:** Diana Morgan, Editor, phone 44 20 84873037, diana@limbless-association.org. **Subscription Rates:** 3 single issue elsewhere. **Remarks:** Advertising accepted; rates available upon request. **URL:** http://www.limbless-association.org. **Circ:** 2,000

52590 ■ Wind Engineering
Multi-Science Publishing Company Ltd.
5 Wates Way
Brentwood CM15 9TB, United Kingdom

Ph: 44 12 77224632
Fax: 44 12 77223453
Publisher E-mail: info@multi-science.co.uk
Journal covering the technology of wind energy. **Founded:** 1977. **Freq:** Bimonthly. **Key Personnel:** Prof. Jon McGowan, Editor, jgmcgowa@ecs.umass.edu; Ian Baring-Gould, Editorial Board; Tony Burton, Editorial Board. **ISSN:** 0309-524X. **Subscription Rates:** 367 individuals print + on-line; 345 individuals print only; 330 individuals online only. **Remarks:** Advertising not accepted. **URL:** http://www.multi-science.co.uk/windeng. htm. **Circ:** (Not Reported)

52591 ■ Wind Engineering Abstracts
Multi-Science Publishing Company Ltd.
5 Wates Way
Brentwood CM15 9TB, United Kingdom
Ph: 44 12 77224632
Fax: 44 12 77223453
Publisher E-mail: info@multi-science.co.uk
Publication featuring summaries of significant contributions to the advancement of wind energy drawn from journals, government agency reports, and conference proceedings. **Founded:** 1981. **Freq:** Quarterly. **Key Personnel:** P.K. Jones, Editor. **ISSN:** 0263-0915. **Subscription Rates:** 225 individuals print only. **Remarks:** Advertising not accepted. **URL:** http://www.multi-science.co.uk/windabs.htm. **Circ:** (Not Reported)

Brickendon

52592 ■ Motor Industry Magazine
Institute of the Motor Industry
Fanshaws
Hertford
Brickendon SG13 8PQ, United Kingdom
Ph: 44 1992 511521
Fax: 44 1992 511548
Publisher E-mail: imi@motor.org.uk
Publication covering automotive industries. **Freq:** Monthly. **Trim Size:** 216 x 291 mm. **Key Personnel:** Chris Phillips, Editor, phone 44 1992 511521, fax 44 1992 511548, chrisp@motor.org.uk; Steve Forsdick, Contact, phone 44 20 78782334, fax 44 20 73790811, steve.forsdick@tenalpspublishing.com. **Subscription Rates:** 45 individuals U.K. and Europe; 50 other countries surface mail; 60 other countries airmail. **Remarks:** Advertising accepted; rates available upon request. **URL:** http://www.motor.org.uk/magazine/index. html. **Circ:** 24,000

Bridgend

52593 ■ Bridge-FM - 106.3
PO Box 1063
Bridgend CF35 6WY, United Kingdom
Ph: 44 84 58904000
E-mail: studio@bridge.fm
Format: Contemporary Hit Radio (CHR); News. **Operating Hours:** Continuous. **Ad Rates:** Advertising accepted; rates available upon request. **URL:** http://www. bridge.fm/.

Bridgnorth

52594 ■ First Empire
First Empire Ltd.
59 Whitburn St.
Bridgnorth WV16 4QP, United Kingdom
Ph: 44 17 46765691
Fax: 44 87 09157965
Magazine covering Napoleonic war for historians, researchers, and war or reenactment enthusiasts. **Freq:** Bimonthly. **Subscription Rates:** 30 individuals BFPO; 54 two years BFPO; 36 other countries; 65 other countries two years. **Remarks:** Accepts advertising. **URL:** http://www.firstempire.net/indexmn.htm. **Ad Rates:** BW: 195, 4C: 250. **Circ:** (Not Reported)

Bridgwater

52595 ■ ABM Magazine
Association of Breastfeeding Mothers
PO Box 207
Bridgwater TA6 7YT, United Kingdom
Ph: 44 8444 122948
Publisher E-mail: chair@abm.me.uk
Magazine covering infant care. **Freq:** Quarterly. **Re-**

marks: Advertising accepted; rates available upon request. **URL:** http://www.abm.me.uk/ Magazinesandevents.htm. **Circ:** (Not Reported)

52596 ■ Journal of Holistic Healthcare
British Holistic Medical Association
PO Box 371
Somerset
Bridgwater TA6 9BG, United Kingdom
Ph: 44 1278 722000
Publisher E-mail: admin@bhma.org
Journal including detailed case examples of successful holistic practice and services, research findings and methodologies. **Freq:** Quarterly. **Key Personnel:** Dr. Michael Dixon, Advisory Board Member; Dr. Sarah Eagger, Advisory Board Member; Edwina Rowling, Editor; Jan Alcoe, Advisory Board Member; Dr. William House, Advisory Board Member; Dr. James Hawkins, Advisory Board Member; Prof. David Peters, Editor-in-Chief. **ISSN:** 1743-9493. **Remarks:** Accepts advertising. **URL:** http://bhma.org/journal. **Circ:** (Not Reported)

Bridlington

52597 ■ Bridlington Free Press
Johnston Press PLC
3 Prospect St.
Bridlington YO15 2AE, United Kingdom
Ph: 44 1262 606606
Local community newspaper. **Founded:** 1859. **Freq:** Weekly (Thurs.). **Key Personnel:** Nick Procter, Editor, phone 44 1262 677338, newsdesk@ bridlingtonfreepress.co.uk; Joanna Machin, Sales Mgr., joanna.machin@yrnltd.co.uk. **Remarks:** Accepts advertising. **URL:** http://www.bridlingtonfreepress.co.uk/. **Circ:** (Not Reported)

52598 ■ Yorkshire Coast Radio-FM - 102.4
PO Box 962
North Yorkshire
Scarborough YO11 3ZP, United Kingdom
Ph: 44 1723 581700
Fax: 44 1723 588990
E-mail: info@yorkshirecoastradio.com
Format: Adult Contemporary; News; Information. **Ad Rates:** Advertising accepted; rates available upon request. **URL:** http://www.yorkshirecoastradio.com/.

Bridport

52599 ■ Bridport & Lyme Regis News
Newsquest Media Group Ltd.
67 East St.
Bridport DT6 3LB, United Kingdom
Ph: 44 1308 422388
Newspaper featuring news and event for Lyme Regis and surrounding villages. **Key Personnel:** Toby Granville, Editor, toby.granville@dorsetecho.co.uk; Marie Burnett, Newspaper Sales Mgr., marie.burnett@ dorsetecho.co.uk; Rob Thomas, Advertising Mgr., rob. thomas@dorsetecho.co.uk. **Remarks:** Accepts advertising. **URL:** http://www.bridportnews.co.uk/. **Circ:** (Not Reported)

Brighouse

52600 ■ Brighouse Echo
Johnston Press PLC
1 W Park St.
Brighouse HD6 1JW, United Kingdom
Ph: 44 1484 721911
Local community newspaper. **Remarks:** Accepts advertising. **URL:** http://www.brighouseecho.co.uk/. **Circ:** (Not Reported)

52601 ■ Rugby League World
League Publications Ltd.
Wellington House
Briggate
Brighouse HD6 1DN, United Kingdom
Ph: 44 14 84401895
Fax: 44 14 84401995
Publisher E-mail: info@totalrl.com
Rugby league magazine. **Founded:** May 1976. **Freq:** Weekly. **Trim Size:** 210 x 297 mm. **ISSN:** 1466-0105. **Subscription Rates:** 39 individuals. **Remarks:** Accepts advertising. **URL:** http://www.totalrl.com; http://www.lpl-shop.co.uk. **Former name:** Open Rugby Magazine (1999). **Ad Rates:** BW: EUR900, 4C: EUR1,200, PCI: EUR.

60. **Circ:** Controlled ‡25,000

52602 ■ Rugby Leaguer & League Express
League Publications Ltd.
Wellington House
Briggate
Brighouse HD6 1DN, United Kingdom
Ph: 44 14 84401895
Fax: 44 14 84401995
Publisher E-mail: info@totalrl.com
Rugby league newspaper. **Founded:** Sept. 1990. **Freq:** Weekly (Mon.). **Key Personnel:** Tim Butcher, Mng. Dir., tim_butcher@totalrl.com; Honor James, Advertising & Sales, honor@totalrl.com; Martyn Sadler, Chm., martyn_ sadler@totalrl.com. **ISSN:** 0962-1547. **Remarks:** Accepts advertising. **URL:** http://www.totalrl.com/home/ index.php. **Ad Rates:** BW: EUR900, 4C: EUR900, PCI: EUR3. **Circ:** Paid 37,000

Brighton

52603 ■ ADI News
DSN Publishing
The Landsdowne Bldg.
Crowhurst Rd.
Hollingbury
Brighton BN1 8AF, United Kingdom
Ph: 44 1273 566058
Fax: 44 1273 566059
Publication E-mail: editorial@adinews.co.uk
Publisher E-mail: editorial@adinews.co.uk
Trade magazine for qualified and part-qualified driving instructors, and road safety professionals. **Founded:** 1993. **Freq:** Monthly. **Trim Size:** 210 x 297 mm. **Key Personnel:** Paul Caddick, Contributor; Jackie Violet, Contributor; Christie Rigg, Advertising Mgr., phone 44 1273 554102, advertising@adinews.co.uk. **ISSN:** 1471-8685. **Subscription Rates:** 30 individuals. **Remarks:** Accepts advertising. **URL:** http://www.adinews.co.uk/. **Former name:** DSN News. **Ad Rates:** 4C: EUR1,650. **Circ:** 16,000

52604 ■ Advances in Mental Health and Intellectual Disabilities
Pavilion Publishing
Richmond House
Richmond Rd.
Brighton BN2 3RL, United Kingdom
Ph: 44 1273 623222
Fax: 44 0844 8805062
Publisher E-mail: info@pavpub.com
Journal covering mental health needs of people with learning disabilities. **Founded:** Mar. 2007. **Freq:** Quarterly March, June, September and December. **Key Personnel:** Steven Hardy, Editor; Jane McCarthy, Editor. **ISSN:** 2044-1282. **Subscription Rates:** 299 institutions print and online; 319 institutions, other countries print and online; 75 individuals print and online; 95 individuals print and online; 45 students; 65 students, other countries. **URL:** http://www. pierprofessional.com/amhldflyer/. **Formerly:** Advances in Mental Health and Learning Disabilities.

52605 ■ The Argus Lite
Newsquest Media Group Ltd.
Crowhurst Rd.
Hollingbury
Brighton BN1 8AR, United Kingdom
Ph: 44 1273 544544
Fax: 44 1273 566114
Newspaper featuring local up to date news and events. **Freq:** Mon.-Sat. **Key Personnel:** Michael Beard, Editor, phone 44 1273 544501, editor@theargus.co.uk. **Remarks:** Accepts advertising. **URL:** http://www.arguslite. co.uk/. **Circ:** (Not Reported)

52606 ■ Batteries International
Batteries International Ltd.
17 Westmoston Ave.
Rottingdean
East Sussex
Brighton BN2 8AL, United Kingdom
Ph: 44 1798 839338
Trade magazine covering design, manufacture and application of battery technology. **Subtitle:** Technologies and Markets in Focus. **Founded:** 1989. **Freq:** Quarterly. **Key Personnel:** Mike Halls, Editor, editor@ batteriesinternational.com. **Subscription Rates:** US$200 individuals; 115 individuals, EUR170 individuals. **Remarks:** Accepts advertising. **URL:** http://www.

Circulation: ★ = ABC; △ = BPA; ◆ = CAC; • = CCAB; ❑ = VAC; ⊕ = PO Statement; ‡ = Publisher's Report; Boldface figures = sworn; Light figures = estimated.

Gale Directory of Publications & Broadcast Media/147th Ed.

5595

batteriesinternational.com/. **Circ:** Combined 5,800

52607 ■ The British Journal of Forensic Practice
Pavilion Publishing
Richmond House
Richmond Rd.
Brighton BN2 3RL, United Kingdom
Ph: 44 1273 623222
Fax: 44 0844 8805062
Publisher E-mail: info@pavpub.com
Journal covering forensic practice. **Subtitle:** For everyone involved in forensic services. **Freq:** Quarterly on February, May, August on November. **Key Personnel:** Carol Ireland, Editor; Neil Gredecki, Editor. **ISSN:** 1463-6646. **Subscription Rates:** 219 institutions; 239 institutions, other countries; 350 institutions 2 years; 59 individuals; 79 other countries corporate; 95 two years. **URL:** http://www.pierprofessional.com/bjfpflyer/index.html.

52608 ■ German Politics
International Association for the Study of German Politics
Department of Politics & Contemporary European Studies
University of Sussex
Falmer
Brighton BN1 9SN, United Kingdom
Ph: 44 1273 877648
Publisher E-mail: d.t.hough@sussex.ac.uk
Publication covering politics and political science. **Freq:** 4/yr. **Key Personnel:** Dan Hough, Editor; Wade Jacoby, Editor; Prof. Stephen Padgett, Editor; Prof. Thomas Poguntke, Editor. **ISSN:** 0964-4008. **Subscription Rates:** US$120 individuals; US$500 institutions online only; US$526 institutions print and online. **Remarks:** Accepts advertising. **URL:** http://www.iasgp.org/journal.asp. **Circ:** (Not Reported)

52609 ■ Golf Punk
JF Media Ltd.
GolfPunk Towers
Sussex Innovation Ctr., Unit 10-13
Science Pk. Sq.
Brighton BN1 9SB, United Kingdom
Publication E-mail: editorial@jf-media.co.uk
Magazine for golfers. **Freq:** 11/yr. **Key Personnel:** Vasu Mehra, Lifestyle Advertising Mgr., phone 44 1273 704536, vasu.mehra@jf-media.co.uk. **Subscription Rates:** 34.95 individuals; 49.10 individuals Europe; 56.37 other countries. **Remarks:** Accepts advertising. **URL:** http://www.golfpunkonline.com/. **Circ:** (Not Reported)

52610 ■ Government and Opposition
John Wiley & Sons Inc.
Wiley-Blackwell
c/o Prof. Paul Taggart, Ed.
Sussex European Institute
Dept. of Politics & Contemporary European Studies
University of Sussex
Brighton BN1 9RG, United Kingdom
Ph: 44 1273 678292
Fax: 44 1273 678571
Publication covering government and related issues. **Subtitle:** An International Journal of Comparative Politics. **Founded:** 1965. **Freq:** Quarterly. **Key Personnel:** Judith Squires, Review Ed., judith.squires@bristol.ac.uk; Prof. Paul Taggart, Editor, p.a.taggart@sussex.ac.uk; Helen Thompson, Editor, phone 44 1223 767264, het20@cam.ac.uk. **ISSN:** 0017-257X. **Subscription Rates:** US$54 individuals print & online (Americas); EUR47 individuals print & online (Europe); 32 other countries print & online; US$46 members print & online (Americas); EUR41 members print & online (Europe); 32 members print & online (other countries); US$302 institutions print + online (Americas); EUR214 institutions print + online (Europe); 329 institutions print + online (ROW). **Remarks:** Advertising accepted; rates available upon request. **URL:** http://www.wiley.com/bw/journal.asp?ref=0017-257X&site=1. **Circ:** (Not Reported)

52611 ■ Healthmatters
Pavilion Publishing
Richmond House
Richmond Rd.
Brighton BN2 3RL, United Kingdom
Ph: 44 1273 623222
Fax: 44 0844 8805062
Publisher E-mail: info@pavpub.com
Magazine focusing on public health care and well-being. **Founded:** 1988. **Freq:** Quarterly. **Key Personnel:** Paul

Walker, Editor, paulcrawfordwalker@googlemail.com. **ISSN:** 0954-903X. **Remarks:** Accepts advertising. **URL:** http://www.healthmatters.org.uk/. **Circ:** (Not Reported)

52612 ■ History of European Ideas
Elsevier Science
c/o Richard Whatmore, Ed.
School of English & American Studies
Arts Bldg., University of Sussex
Falmer
Brighton BN1 9QN, United Kingdom
Publisher E-mail: nlinfo-f@elsevier.com
Journal covering intellectual history of Europe from the origins of the Enlightenment onwards, focusing on political, philosophical, historiographical, theological, sociological, literary and cultural areas. **Founded:** 1980. **Freq:** Quarterly. **Key Personnel:** Richard Whatmore, Editor; Brian Young, International Advisory Board; M. Albertone, International Advisory Board; S. Avineri, International Advisory Board; F. Beiser, International Advisory Board; B. Fontana, International Advisory Board. **ISSN:** 0191-6599. **Subscription Rates:** US$100 individuals all countries except Europe and Japan; 11,900¥ individuals; EUR89 individuals for Europe; EUR726 institutions for Europe; US$811 institutions all countries except Europe and Japan; 96,300¥ institutions. **Remarks:** Accepts advertising. **URL:** http://www.elsevier.com/wps/find/journaldescription.cws_home/605/description. **Circ:** (Not Reported)

52613 ■ Housing, Care and Support
Pavilion Publishing
Richmond House
Richmond Rd.
Brighton BN2 3RL, United Kingdom
Ph: 44 1273 623222
Fax: 44 0844 8805062
Publisher E-mail: info@pavpub.com
Journal covering issues in supported housing policy and practice. **Freq:** Quarterly on February, May, August and November. **Key Personnel:** Gary Lashko, Editor; Lynn Vickery, Editor. **ISSN:** 1460-8790. **Subscription Rates:** 219 institutions; 239 institutions, other countries; 350 institutions 2 years; 59 individuals; 79 other countries; 95 two years. **URL:** http://www.pierprofessional.com/hcsflyer/index.html.

52614 ■ IDS Bulletin
Institute of Development Studies
c/o University of Sussex
Brighton BN1 9RE, United Kingdom
Ph: 44 1273 606261
Fax: 44 1273 621202
Publication E-mail: publications@ids.ac.uk
Publisher E-mail: ids@ids.ac.uk
Publication covering community development. **Founded:** 1966. **Freq:** Quarterly. **Print Method:** Litho. **Key Personnel:** Gary Edwards, Sales and Marketing Asst., g.edwards@ids.ac.uk. **ISSN:** 0265-5012. **URL:** http://www.ids.ac.uk/go/bookshop/ids-bulletin. **Circ:** 1,800

52615 ■ The Insight
Globe House, 1st Fl. E
3 Morley St.
Brighton BN2 9RA, United Kingdom
Ph: 44 1273 245956
Fax: 44 1273 245960
Publisher E-mail: info@theinsight.co.uk
Consumer magazine covering local entertainment and lifestyle. **Subtitle:** Under the skin of Brighton, Hove & Worthing. **Founded:** Apr. 1997. **Freq:** Monthly. **Print Method:** Web offset. **Cols./Page:** 4. **Key Personnel:** Nic Compton, Editor, nic@theinsight.co.uk; Jan Goodey, Commissioning Ed., jan@theinsight.co.uk; Melinda Saunders, Listings Ed., listings@theinsight.co.uk. **ISSN:** 1463-8142. **Subscription Rates:** 12.50 individuals in U.K.; incl. of p & p; 20 individuals Europe. **Remarks:** Accepts advertising. **URL:** http://www.nigelberman.co.uk/index_home.htm. **Formerly:** New Insight. **Ad Rates:** BW: 1,245, 4C: 1,725. **Circ:** Non-paid 20,000

52616 ■ The International Journal of Leadership in Public Services
Pavilion Publishing
Richmond House
Richmond Rd.
Brighton BN2 3RL, United Kingdom
Ph: 44 1273 623222
Fax: 44 0844 8805062
Publisher E-mail: info@pavpub.com
Journal covering leadership and improving public

services. **Subtitle:** Exploring partnerships and diversity. **Freq:** Quarterly on February, May, August and November. **Key Personnel:** Mark Davison, Editor; Steve Onyett, Editor. **ISSN:** 1747-9886. **Subscription Rates:** 299 institutions; 319 institutions, other countries; 480 institutions 2 years; 99 individuals; 119 other countries; 160 two years. **URL:** http://www.pierprofessional.com/ijlpsflyer/.

52617 ■ International Journal of Migration, Health and Social Care
Pavilion Publishing
Richmond House
Richmond Rd.
Brighton BN2 3RL, United Kingdom
Ph: 44 1273 623222
Fax: 44 0844 8805062
Publisher E-mail: info@pavpub.com
Journal covering labor migration, asylum seekers, refugees and undocumented migrants, with an emphasis on health and social care. **Freq:** 4/yr (February, May, August and November). **Key Personnel:** Dr. Charles Watters, Editor. **ISSN:** 1747-9894. **Subscription Rates:** 249 institutions; 269 institutions, other countries; 400 institutions 2 years; 59 individuals; 79 other countries; 95 two years. **URL:** http://www.pierprofessional.com/jcsflyer/index.html.

52618 ■ The Journal of Adult Protection
Pavilion Publishing
Richmond House
Richmond Rd.
Brighton BN2 3RL, United Kingdom
Ph: 44 1273 623222
Fax: 44 0844 8805062
Publisher E-mail: info@pavpub.com
Journal covering aspects of adult protection. **Freq:** 4/yr (February, May, August and November). **Key Personnel:** Margaret Flynn, Editor, margaret.flynn@tiscali.co.uk; Bridget Penhale, Editor, b.penhale@sheffield.ac.uk. **ISSN:** 1466-8203. **Subscription Rates:** 349 institutions; 369 institutions, other countries; 560 institutions 2 years; 75 individuals; 95 other countries; 75 two years. **URL:** http://www.pierprofessional.com/japflyer/.

52619 ■ Journal of Children's Services
Pavilion Publishing
Richmond House
Richmond Rd.
Brighton BN2 3RL, United Kingdom
Ph: 44 1273 623222
Fax: 44 0844 8805062
Publisher E-mail: info@pavpub.com
Journal covering the development of the services on children and their families. **Founded:** 2006. **Freq:** Quarterly. **Key Personnel:** Dr. Michael Little, Editor; Dr. Nick Axford, Editor. **ISSN:** 1746-6660. **Subscription Rates:** 299 institutions; 319 institutions, other countries; 480 institutions 2 years; 59 individuals; 79 other countries; 95 two years. **URL:** http://www.pavpub.com/pavpub/journals/JCS/index.asp.

52620 ■ Journal of Ethnic and Migration Studies (JEMS)
Routledge
Taylor & Francis Group Ltd.
Sussex Centre for Migration Research
University of Sussex
Falmer
Brighton BN1 9SJ, United Kingdom
Ph: 44 1273 877778
Fax: 44 1273 873158
Publication E-mail: jems@sussex.ac.uk
Publisher E-mail: webmaster.books@tandf.co.uk
Peer-reviewed journal covering the migration and ethnic studies. **Founded:** 1971. **Freq:** 10/yr. **Key Personnel:** Adrian Favell, Assoc. Ed.; Richard R.D. Bedford, Assoc. Ed.; Russell King, Editor-in-Chief; Jenny Money, Editorial Mgr.; Michael Collyer, Assoc. Ed. **ISSN:** 1369-183X. **Subscription Rates:** 987 institutions print + online; US$1,610 institutions print + online; EUR1,289 institutions print and online; 189 individuals; US$315 individuals; EUR252 individuals; 938 institutions online only; US$1,530 institutions online only; EUR1,224 institutions online only. **URL:** http://www.tandf.co.uk/journals/titles/1369183x.asp. **Former name:** New Community.

52621 ■ Journal of Integrated Care
Pavilion Publishing
Richmond House
Richmond Rd.

Brighton BN2 3RL, United Kingdom
Ph: 44 1273 623222
Fax: 44 0844 8805062
Publisher E-mail: info@pavpub.com
Journal covering integration of health, social care and other community services. **Subtitle:** Practical evidence for service improvement. **Founded:** 1992. **Freq:** 6/yr. **Key Personnel:** Peter Thistlethwaite, Editor. **ISSN:** 1476-9018. **Subscription Rates:** 295 institutions; 315 institutions, other countries; 475 institutions 2 years; 75 individuals; 95 other countries; 120 two years. **URL:** http://www.pierprofessional.com/jicflyer/index.html.

52622 ■ The Journal of Mental Health Training, Education and Practice
Pavilion Publishing
Richmond House
Richmond Rd.
Brighton BN2 3RL, United Kingdom
Ph: 44 1273 623222
Fax: 44 0844 8805062
Publisher E-mail: info@pavpub.com
Journal critical workforce issues in mental health services. **Freq:** Quarterly on March, June, September and December. **Key Personnel:** Di Bailey, Editor; Christina Pond, Editor; Peter Ryan, Editor. **ISSN:** 1755-6228. **Subscription Rates:** 219 institutions; 239 institutions, other countries; 350 institutions 2 years; 59 individuals; 79 other countries; 95 two years. **URL:** http://www.pierprofessional.com/jmhtepflyer/.

52623 ■ Journal of Public Mental Health
Pavilion Publishing
Richmond House
Richmond Rd.
Brighton BN2 3RL, United Kingdom
Ph: 44 1273 623222
Fax: 44 0844 8805062
Publisher E-mail: info@pavpub.com
Journal covering aspects of public mental health and mental health promotion. **Subtitle:** The art, science and politics of creating a mentally healthy society. **Freq:** Quarterly March, June, September and December. **Key Personnel:** Woody Caan, Editor, wody.caan@anglia.ac.uk. **ISSN:** 1746-5729. **Subscription Rates:** 219 institutions; 239 institutions, other countries; 350 institutions 2 years; 59 individuals; 79 other countries; 95 two years. **URL:** http://www.pierprofessional.com/jpmhflyer/index.html.

52624 ■ Learning Disability Review
Pavilion Publishing
Richmond House
Richmond Rd.
Brighton BN2 3RL, United Kingdom
Ph: 44 1273 623222
Fax: 44 0844 8805062
Publisher E-mail: info@pavpub.com
Journal for managers, practitioners and academics working in learning disability services. **Freq:** Quarterly on January, April, July and October. **Key Personnel:** Prof. Jim Mansell, Editor. **ISSN:** 1359-5474. **Subscription Rates:** 279 institutions; 450 institutions 2 years; 299 institutions, 69 individuals; 110 two years; 89 other countries. **URL:** http://pierprofessional.metapress.com/content/121408/.

52625 ■ Learning Disability Today
Pavilion Publishing
Richmond House
Richmond Rd.
Brighton BN2 3RL, United Kingdom
Ph: 44 1273 623222
Fax: 44 0844 8805062
Publisher E-mail: info@pavpub.com
Journal covering better quality lifestyle for people with learning disabilities. **Subtitle:** Promoting positive and inclusive lifestyles with people who have learning disabilities. **Freq:** Monthly. **Key Personnel:** Barbara McIntosh, Editor; Andrea Whittaker, Editor. **ISSN:** 1752-007X. **Subscription Rates:** 95 corporate; 45 individuals; 105 corporate, Europe; 55 individuals Europe; 115 other countries corporate; 65 individuals rest of the world. **URL:** http://www.learningdisabilities.org.uk/publications/learning-disability-today/.

52626 ■ Mental Health Review Journal
Pavilion Publishing
Richmond House

Richmond Rd.
Brighton BN2 3RL, United Kingdom
Ph: 44 1273 623222
Fax: 44 0844 8805062
Publisher E-mail: info@pavpub.com
Journal for managers and practitioners working in the mental health field. **Freq:** Quarterly on March, June, September and December. **Key Personnel:** Mark Freestone, Editor; Chiara Samele, Editor; Ian Shaw, Editor. **ISSN:** 1361-9322. **Subscription Rates:** 219 institutions; 239 institutions, other countries; 350 institutions 2 years; 59 individuals; 79 other countries; 95 two years. **URL:** http://www.pierprofessional.com/mhrjflyer/index.html.

52627 ■ Mental Health Today
Pavilion Publishing
Richmond House
Richmond Rd.
Brighton BN2 3RL, United Kingdom
Ph: 44 1273 623222
Fax: 44 0844 8805062
Publication E-mail: mhtoday@pavpub.com
Publisher E-mail: info@pavpub.com
Magazine focusing on mental health. **Freq:** Monthly. **Key Personnel:** Andy Bell, Editorial Advisory Board. **ISSN:** 1474-5186. **Subscription Rates:** EUR26 individuals digital; EUR36 individuals print. **Remarks:** Accepts advertising. **URL:** http://www.pavpub.com/c-31-mental-health-today.aspx?s=1. **Circ:** (Not Reported)

52628 ■ Polymer Degradation and Stability
Elsevier Science
c/o N.C. Billingham, Ed.-in-Ch.
The Dept. of Chemistry, Physics & Environmental Sciences
The University of Sussex
Brighton BN1 9QJ, United Kingdom
Publisher E-mail: nlinfo-f@elsevier.com
Journal dealing with all aspects of modern polymer technology. **Founded:** 1979. **Freq:** Monthly. **Key Personnel:** N.C. Billingham, Editor-in-Chief, n.billingham@sussex.ac.uk; N.S. Allen, Editorial Board; G. Camino, Editorial Board; T. Iwata, Regional Ed., atiwata@mail.ecc.u-tokyo.ac.jp; N. Grassie, Ed. Emeritus; S. Al-Malaika, Editorial Board; R.L. Clough, Editorial Board; M. Celina, New Regional Ed., mcelinaeditorpdst@netscape.com; A.C. Albertsson, Editorial Board; J. Wang, Editorial Board; G. Scott, Editorial Board; G. Montaudo, Editorial Board. **ISSN:** 0141-3910. **Subscription Rates:** 624,700¥ institutions; US$5,264 institutions for all countries except Europe, Japan & Iran; EUR4,704 institutions for European countries & Iran. **Remarks:** Advertising accepted; rates available upon request. **URL:** http://www.elsevier.com/wps/find/journaldescription.cws_home/405941/description. **Circ:** (Not Reported)

52629 ■ Quality in Ageing
Pavilion Publishing
Richmond House
Richmond Rd.
Brighton BN2 3RL, United Kingdom
Ph: 44 1273 623222
Fax: 44 0844 8805062
Publisher E-mail: info@pavpub.com
Journal covering quality of life in later years focusing on both the dependence and independence of older people. **Subtitle:** Policy, practice and research. **Freq:** Quarterly on March, June, September and December. **Key Personnel:** Dr. Ron Iphofen, Editor, r.iphofen@bangor.ac.uk. **ISSN:** 1471-7794. **Subscription Rates:** 219 institutions; 239 other countries; 350 institutions 2 years; 59 individuals; 79 other countries; 95 two years. **URL:** http://www.pierprofessional.com/qiaoaflyer/index.html.

52630 ■ Reformation
Ashgate Publishing Ltd.
c/o Prof. Andrew Hadfield
Department of English
University of Sussex
Falmer
Brighton BN1 9RH, United Kingdom
Scholarly journal covering the Reformation era. **Founded:** 1996. **Freq:** Annual. **Key Personnel:** Hannibal Hamlin, Editor, hamlin.22@osu.edu; Helen Parish, Book Review Ed. **ISSN:** 1357-4175. **Subscription Rates:** US$120 institutions print and online; 60 institutions print and online; 30 individuals; US$60 individuals; US$45 students; 22.50 students, other countries. **URL:**

http://www.equinoxjournals.com/ojs/index.php/reformation.

52631 ■ Research Policy
Elsevier Science Inc.
SPRU-Science & Technology Policy Research
The Freeman Centre
University of Sussex
Brighton BN1 9QE, United Kingdom
Publisher E-mail: usinfo-ehelp@elsevier.com
Journal devoted to the policy and management problems posed by innovation, R&D, technology and science, and related activities concerned with the acquisition of knowledge and its exploitation. **Founded:** 1972. **Freq:** 10/yr. **Print Method:** Offset. **Trim Size:** 8 x 10 7/8. **Cols./Page:** 3. **Col. Width:** 32 nonpareils. **Col. Depth:** 140 agate lines. **Key Personnel:** M. Bell, Editor, respol@sussex.ac.uk; M. Callon, Editor, callon@csi.ensmp.fr; F. Kodama, Advisory Ed., kodama_5@ga2.so-net.ne.jp; S. Kuhlmann, Editor, s.kuhlmann@utwente.nl; B. Martin, Editor; N. Von Tunzelmann, Advisory Ed.; W.W. Powell, Book Review Ed., woodyp@stanford.edu. **ISSN:** 0048-7333. **Subscription Rates:** 300,100¥ institutions; US$2,527 institutions, other countries except Europe, Japan and Iran; EUR2,260 institutions for European countries and Iran; 12,600¥ individuals; EUR94 individuals for European countries and Iran; US$97 other countries except Europe, Japan and Iran. **URL:** http://www.elsevier.com/wps/find/journaldescription.cws_home/505598/descriptiondescription.

52632 ■ Safer Communities
Pavilion Publishing
Richmond House
Richmond Rd.
Brighton BN2 3RL, United Kingdom
Ph: 44 1273 623222
Fax: 44 0844 8805062
Publisher E-mail: info@pavpub.com
Journal covering field of community safety. **Freq:** Quarterly on January, April, July, and October. **Key Personnel:** John Pitts, Editor; Chris Fox, Editor. **ISSN:** 1757-8043. **Subscription Rates:** 219 institutions; 239 institutions, other countries; 350 institutions 2 years; 59 individuals; 79 other countries; 95 two years. **Remarks:** Accepts advertising. **URL:** http://www.pierprofessional.com/scflyer/index.html. **Formerly:** Community Safety Journal. **Ad Rates:** BW: 350. **Circ:** (Not Reported)

52633 ■ Theatre Notebook
Society for Theatre Research
PO Box 3214
Brighton BN2 1LU, United Kingdom
Publication E-mail: theatrenotebook@str.org.uk
Publisher E-mail: contact@str.org.uk
Publication covering theater. **Founded:** 1945. **Freq:** 3/yr. **Key Personnel:** Trevor R. Griffiths, Contact. **ISSN:** 0040-5523. **Subscription Rates:** 20 individuals; 25 other countries; US$50 other countries. **Remarks:** Advertising accepted; rates available upon request. **URL:** http://www.str.org.uk/. **Circ:** (Not Reported)

52634 ■ Twentieth Century British History
Oxford University Press
c/o Dr. Claire Langhamer, Ed.
School of History
University of Sussex
Falmer
Brighton BN1 9QN, United Kingdom
Publisher E-mail: webenquiry.uk@oup.com
Journal covering the variety of British history in the twentieth century in all its aspects and linking the many different and specialized branches of historical scholarship with work in political science and related disciplines. **Freq:** 4/yr. **Key Personnel:** Prof. David Howell, International Board; Dr. Sian Nicholas, Advisory Board, shn@aber.ac.uk; Dr. Stephen Brooke, Editor, sjbrooke@yorku.ca; Pat Thane, International Board; Virginia Berridge, Advisory Board; Dr. Lawrence Black, Book Review Ed., lawrence.black@durham.ac.uk; Martin Francis, International Board. **ISSN:** 0955-2359. **Subscription Rates:** 251 institutions corporate; print and online; 209 institutions corporate; online only; 230 institutions corporate; print only; 200 institutions print and online; 167 institutions online only; 184 institutions print only; 53 individuals print; 32 students print. **Remarks:** Advertising accepted; rates available upon request. **URL:** http://tcbh.oxfordjournals.org/. **Circ:** (Not Reported)

52635 ■ Working with Older People
Pavilion Publishing
Richmond House
Richmond Rd.
Brighton BN2 3RL, United Kingdom
Ph: 44 1273 623222
Fax: 44 0844 8805062
Publisher E-mail: info@pavpub.com
Journal for people working in health, housing and social care services for older people. **Freq:** Quarterly on March, June, September and December. **ISSN:** 1366-3666. **Subscription Rates:** 219 institutions; 239 institutions, other countries; 350 institutions 2 years; 59 individuals; 79 other countries; 95 two years. **URL:** http://www.pierprofessional.com/wwopflyer/.

52636 ■ Heart-FM - 102.4
Franklin Rd.
Brighton BN41 1AF, United Kingdom
Ph: 44 1273 430111
Format: Adult Contemporary. **Owner:** Global Radio, 30 Leicester Sq., London WC2H 7LA, United Kingdom. **Formerly:** Southern-FM. **Operating Hours:** Continuous. **Ad Rates:** Advertising accepted; rates available upon request. **URL:** http://www.southernfm.co.uk/.

52637 ■ Juice-FM - 107.2
170 N St.
Brighton BN1 1EA, United Kingdom
Ph: 44 1273 323600
Format: Contemporary Hit Radio (CHR); Adult Contemporary. **Ad Rates:** Advertising accepted; rates available upon request. **URL:** http://www.juicebrighton.com/.

Bristol

52638 ■ Age and Ageing
Oxford University Press
The Hub
72 Prince St.
Bristol BS1 4QD, United Kingdom
Ph: 44 117 3700988
Fax: 44 117 3721875
Publisher E-mail: webenquiry.uk@oup.com
Publication focusing on seniors and related issues. **Freq:** 6/yr. **Key Personnel:** Prof. Roger Francis, Editor; Tom Robinson, Supplements Ed.; Cameron G. Swift, Editorial Board Chm.; Katy Ladbrook, Editorial Coord.; John Potter, Asst. Ed. **ISSN:** 0002-0729. **Subscription Rates:** 308 institutions print and online; US$616 institutions print and online; EUR462 institutions print and online; 249 institutions online, print; US$499 institutions online, print; EUR374 institutions online, print; 158 members print; US$316 members print; EUR237 members print. **Remarks:** Accepts advertising. **URL:** http://ageing.oupjournals.org/. **Circ:** (Not Reported)

52639 ■ Aircraft Engineering and Aerospace Technology
Emerald
c/o Dr. Askin Isikveren, Ed.
University of Bristol
Queen's Bldg.
University Walk
Bristol BS8 1TR, United Kingdom
Publisher E-mail: editorial@emeraldinsight.com
Journal covering technical facets of the manufacture and design of both civil and military aircraft, now including research articles that reflect the most interesting and strategically important research and development activities from around the world. **Freq:** Bimonthly 6/yr. **Key Personnel:** Dr. Askin Isikveren, Editor, askin.t.isikveren@bristol.ac.uk; Thomas Dark, Asst. Publisher, tdark@emeraldinsight.com; Harry Colson, Publisher, hcolson@emeraldinsight.com. **ISSN:** 0002-2667. **Subscription Rates:** US$4,729 individuals; 2,959 individuals; EUR4,099 individuals plus tax; $A 5,359 individuals. **URL:** http://www.emeraldinsight.com/products/journals/journals.htm?id=aeat.

52640 ■ Astrophysical Journal Supplement Series
IOP Publishing Ltd.
Dirac House
Temple Back
Bristol BS1 6BE, United Kingdom
Ph: 44 117 9297481
Fax: 44 117 9294318
Publication E-mail: apj@noao.edu
Publisher E-mail: custserv@iop.org
Astronomical research journal. **Founded:** 1953. **Freq:** Monthly. **Key Personnel:** Dr. Robert C. Kennicutt, Jr., Editor-in-Chief; Helmut A. Abt, Managing Editor. **ISSN:** 0067-0049. **Remarks:** Advertising not accepted. **URL:** http://iopscience.iop.org/0067-0049/. **Circ:** Paid ‡1,800

52641 ■ BBC Countryfile
BBC Worldwide Publishing Ltd.
Tower House, 9th Fl.
Fairfax St.
Bristol BS1 3BN, United Kingdom
Ph: 44 117 9279009
Magazine featuring rural Britain. **Founded:** Oct. 2007. **Freq:** 13/yr. **Key Personnel:** Cavan Scott, Editor, phone 44 117 3148849, cavanscott@bbcmagazinesbristol.com; Eleanor Godwin, Advertising Mgr., eleanorgodwin@bbcmagazines.co.uk. **Subscription Rates:** 3.40 single issue; 30.40 individuals. **Remarks:** Accepts advertising. **URL:** http://www.bbccountryfile.com; http://www.bbcmagazinesbristol.com/magazine.asp?id=32. **Circ:** ★33,839

52642 ■ BBC History
BBC Worldwide Publishing Ltd.
Tower House, 9th Fl.
Fairfax St.
Bristol BS1 3BN, United Kingdom
Ph: 44 117 9279009
Publication E-mail: historymagazine@bbcmagazinesbristol.com
Magazine with current news stories and events. **Freq:** Monthly. **Key Personnel:** Richard Gibson, Advertising Mgr., richardgibson@bbcmagazinesbristol.com; Dave Musgrove, Editor. **Subscription Rates:** 15.10 individuals 6 issues, direct debit. **Remarks:** Accepts advertising. **URL:** http://www.bbchistorymagazine.com; http://www.bbcworldwide.com/annualreviews/review2001/magazines2.html. **Circ:** 50,000

52643 ■ BBC Wildlife Magazine
BBC Worldwide Publishing Ltd.
Tower House, 14th Fl.
Fairfax St.
Bristol BS1 3BN, United Kingdom
Ph: 44 117 9279009
Fax: 44 117 9349008
Publication E-mail: wildlifemagazine@bbcmagazinesbristol.com
Magazine covering wildlife animals. **Founded:** 1963. **Freq:** 13/yr. **Key Personnel:** James Tawton, Gp. Advertising Mgr., phone 44 117 9338073, jamestawton@bbcmagazines.co.uk; Sophie Stafford, Editor. **Subscription Rates:** 3.60 single issue. **Remarks:** Accepts advertising. **URL:** http://www.bbcwildlifemagazine.com/Default.asp?bhcp=1; http://www.bbcmagazinesbristol.com/magazine.asp?id=19. **Circ:** ★44,564

52644 ■ Beautiful Cards
Origin Publishing Ltd.
Tower House
Fairfax St.
Bristol BS1 3BN, United Kingdom
Ph: 44 117 9279009
Fax: 44 117 9349008
Publisher E-mail: info@originpublishing.co.uk
Magazine featuring card design and ideas. **Founded:** 2005. **Freq:** 9/yr. **Key Personnel:** Melanie Harris, Advertising Mgr., phone 44 117 3148367, melanieharris@originpublishing.co.uk; Alison Zak-Collin, Gp. Ad Mgr. **Subscription Rates:** 44 individuals; 65 individuals Europe; US$99.95 individuals. **Remarks:** Accepts advertising. **URL:** http://www.originpublishing.co.uk/magazine.asp?id=24. **Circ:** 20,000

52645 ■ Biofabrication
IOP Publishing Ltd.
Dirac House
Temple Back
Bristol BS1 6BE, United Kingdom
Ph: 44 117 9297481
Fax: 44 117 9294318
Publication E-mail: bf@iop.org
Publisher E-mail: custserv@iop.org
Journal featuring the latest research and development in biofabrication. **Freq:** Quarterly. **Key Personnel:** Prof. Wei Sun, Editor-in-Chief. **ISSN:** 1758-5082. **URL:** http://www.iop.org/EJ/journal/bf.

52646 ■ Bioinspiration & Biomimetics
IOP Publishing Ltd.
Dirac House
Temple Back
Bristol BS1 6BE, United Kingdom
Ph: 44 117 9297481
Fax: 44 117 9294318
Publisher E-mail: custserv@iop.org
Journal covering research involving the study and distillation of principles and functions found in biological systems that have been developed through evolution, and application of this knowledge to produce basic technologies and new approaches to solving scientific problems. **Founded:** Dec. 11, 2006. **Freq:** Weekly (Thurs.). **Print Method:** Offset. **Cols./Page:** 6. **Col. Width:** 10.5 picas. **Col. Depth:** 15 inches. **Key Personnel:** R. Allen, Editor-in-Chief; T. Akamatsu, Editorial Board; Y. Bar-Cohen, Editorial Board; R.L. Clark, Editorial Board; L.P. Lee, Editorial Board; J.A. Simmons, Editorial Board; F.E. Fish, Editorial Board; R.J. Full, Editorial Board; S. Childress, Editorial Board; C. Melhuish, Editorial Board. **ISSN:** 1748-3182. **URL:** http://www.iop.org/EJ/journal/1748-3190.

52647 ■ Biomedical Materials
IOP Publishing Ltd.
Dirac House
Temple Back
Bristol BS1 6BE, United Kingdom
Ph: 44 117 9297481
Fax: 44 117 9294318
Publication E-mail: bmm@iop.org
Publisher E-mail: custserv@iop.org
Peer-reviewed journal covering studies of the preparation, performance, and evaluation of biomaterials, the chemical, physical, toxicological, and mechanical behavior of materials in physiological environments, and the response of blood and tissues to biomaterials. Topics include science and technology of alloys, polymers, ceramics, and reprocessed animal and human tissues in surgery, dentistry, artificial organs, and other medical devices. **Founded:** 1949. **Freq:** Quarterly. **Print Method:** Offset. **Trim Size:** 8 1/2 x 11. **Cols./Page:** 3. **Col. Width:** 27 nonpareils. **Col. Depth:** 140 agate lines. **Key Personnel:** F-Z Cui, Editor-in-Chief; M. Spector, Editor-in-Chief; I.S. Lee, Editor-in-Chief. **ISSN:** 1748-6041. **Subscription Rates:** US$1,110 institutions North, Central and South America; US$257 individuals North, Central and South America; 613 institutions, other countries; 133 individuals; 613 institutions European Union; 133 individuals European Union. **URL:** http://www.iop.org/ej/journal/bmm.

52648 ■ Blonde Hair
Origin Publishing Ltd.
Tower House
Fairfax St.
Bristol BS1 3BN, United Kingdom
Ph: 44 117 9279009
Fax: 44 117 9349008
Publisher E-mail: info@originpublishing.co.uk
Magazine featuring different hairstyles for blondes. **Founded:** 2004. **Freq:** Bimonthly. **Key Personnel:** Russ Cowley, Advertising Mgr., phone 44 117 3148369, russcowley@originpublishing.co.uk; Alison Zak-Collins, Gp. Advertising Mgr. **Subscription Rates:** 2.99 single issue. **Remarks:** Accepts advertising. **URL:** http://www.originpublishing.co.uk/magazine.asp?id=29. **Circ:** 11,264

52649 ■ The British Journal for the Philosophy of Science
Oxford University Press
c/o Prof. Alexander Bird, Ed.
Dept. of Philosophy
University of Bristol
9 Woodland Rd.
Bristol BS8 1TB, United Kingdom
Ph: 44 117 9287826
Fax: 44 117 9287825
Publisher E-mail: webenquiry.uk@oup.com
Publication covering science and technology. **Freq:** 4/yr. **Key Personnel:** Prof. Alexander Bird, Editor, bjps-editors@bristol.ac.uk; Dr. James Ladyman, Editor, phone 44 117 9287609, james.ladyman@bristol.ac.uk; Dr. Stuart Presnell, Asst. Ed. **ISSN:** 0007-0882. **Subscription Rates:** 140 institutions print and online; US$273 institutions print and online; EUR210 institutions print and online; 117 institutions online, print; US$228

institutions online, print; EUR176 institutions online, print; 129 institutions print only; US$252 institutions print only; EUR194 institutions print only. **Remarks:** Accepts advertising. **URL:** http://bjps.oxfordjournals.org. **Circ:** (Not Reported)

52650 ■ Card Making & Papercraft
Origin Publishing Ltd.
Tower House
Fairfax St.
Bristol BS1 3BN, United Kingdom
Ph: 44 117 9279009
Fax: 44 117 9349008
Publisher E-mail: info@originpublishing.co.uk
Magazine full of inspiring card making tips and ideas. **Freq:** 13/yr. **Subscription Rates:** 60 individuals by credit; 60 individuals by debit card. **Remarks:** Accepts advertising. **URL:** http://www.cardmakingandpapercraft. com. **Circ:** (Not Reported)

52651 ■ CERN Courier
IOP Publishing Ltd.
Dirac House
Temple Back
Bristol BS1 6BE, United Kingdom
Ph: 44 117 9297481
Fax: 44 117 9294318
Publisher E-mail: custserv@iop.org
Magazine covering current developments in high-energy physics and related fields worldwide. **Freq:** 10/yr. **Key Personnel:** Christine Sutton, Editor, cern.courier@cern. ch; Jesse Karjalainen, Web Site Ed., jesse.karjalainen@ iop.org. **Remarks:** Advertising accepted; rates available upon request. **URL:** http://cerncourier.com/cws/latest/ cern. **Circ:** (Not Reported)

52652 ■ Chinese Journal of Chemical Physics
IOP Publishing Ltd.
Dirac House
Temple Back
Bristol BS1 6BE, United Kingdom
Ph: 44 117 9297481
Fax: 44 117 9294318
Publication E-mail: cjcp@iop.org
Publisher E-mail: custserv@iop.org
Journal covering research in the areas of chemistry and physics. **Founded:** 1988. **Freq:** Bimonthly. **Key Personnel:** Xue-ming Yang, Editor-in-Chief; Hong-fei Wang, Exec. Assoc. Ed.; Xin-he Bao, Assoc. Ed. **ISSN:** 1674-0068. **URL:** http://www.iop.org/EJ/journal/cjcp.

52653 ■ Classical and Quantum Gravity
IOP Publishing Ltd.
Dirac House
Temple Back
Bristol BS1 6BE, United Kingdom
Ph: 44 117 9297481
Fax: 44 117 9294318
Publication E-mail: cqg@iop.org
Publisher E-mail: custserv@iop.org
Professional publication covering quantum gravity. **Founded:** 1984. **Freq:** 24/yr. **Key Personnel:** C.M. Will, Editor-in-Chief. **ISSN:** 0264-9381. **Subscription Rates:** 2,642 institutions, other countries. **URL:** http://www.iop. org/ej/cqg.

52654 ■ Compound Semiconductor
IOP Publishing Ltd.
Dirac House
Temple Back
Bristol BS1 6BE, United Kingdom
Ph: 44 117 9297481
Fax: 44 117 9294318
Publisher E-mail: custserv@iop.org
Magazine for compound semiconductor industry professionals. **Founded:** 1995. **Freq:** 11/yr. **Key Personnel:** David Ridsdale, Editor-in-Chief, phone 44 1923 690210, dr@angelbcl.co.uk; Jackie Cannon, Publisher, phone 44 1923 690205, jc@angelbcl.co.uk; Debbie Higham, Subscription Mgr., phone 44 1923 690220, dh@angelbcl.co.uk. **Subscription Rates:** 90 individuals; EUR135 individuals; US$165 individuals. **Remarks:** Accepts advertising. **URL:** http:// compoundsemiconductor.net/. **Circ:** △9,025

52655 ■ Computers and Law
Society for Computers and Law
10 Hurle Cres.
Clifton
Bristol BS8 2TA, United Kingdom
Ph: 44 11 79237393

Fax: 44 11 79239305
Publisher E-mail: enquires@scl.org
Publication covering computer science and law. **Freq:** Bimonthly. **Key Personnel:** Laurence Eastham, Editor, lseastham@aol.com. **ISSN:** 0140-3249. **Subscription Rates:** EUR50 members; EUR10 nonmembers. **URL:** http://www.scl.org/site.aspx?i=is9966. **Circ:** 2,700

52656 ■ Cross Stitch Card Shop
Origin Publishing Ltd.
Tower House
Fairfax St.
Bristol BS1 3BN, United Kingdom
Ph: 44 117 9279009
Fax: 44 117 9349008
Publisher E-mail: info@originpublishing.co.uk
Magazine featuring cross stitching designs for every occasion. **Founded:** 1998. **Freq:** Bimonthly. **Key Personnel:** Alison Zak-Collins, Gp. Advertising Mgr.; Melanie Harris, Advertising Mgr. **Subscription Rates:** 3.99 single issue. **Remarks:** Accepts advertising. **URL:** http:// www.originpublishing.co.uk/magazine.asp?id=3. **Circ:** 56,534

52657 ■ Cross Stitch Crazy
Origin Publishing Ltd.
Tower House
Fairfax St.
Bristol BS1 3BN, United Kingdom
Ph: 44 117 9279009
Fax: 44 117 9349008
Publisher E-mail: info@originpublishing.co.uk
Cross stitching magazine featuring designs and projects for all ages. **Founded:** 1997. **Freq:** 13/yr. **Key Personnel:** Emma Roberts, Editor, emmaroberts@ originpublishing.co.uk; Melanie Harris, Advertising Mgr., phone 44 117 3148367, melanieharris@originpublishing. co.uk; Ceara Ford, Contact, cearaford@originpublishing. co.uk. **Subscription Rates:** 3.75 single issue; 17.98 individuals for every 6 issues by UK direct debit. **Remarks:** Accepts advertising. **URL:** http://www.cross-stitching.com/; http://www.originpublishing.co.uk/ magazine.asp?id=2. **Circ:** ★19,225

52658 ■ Cross Stitch Gold
Origin Publishing Ltd.
Tower House
Fairfax St.
Bristol BS1 3BN, United Kingdom
Ph: 44 117 9279009
Fax: 44 117 9349008
Publisher E-mail: info@originpublishing.co.uk
Magazine full of cross stitch patterns. **Freq:** 9/yr. **Key Personnel:** Charlotte Lyon, Editor, charlottelyon@ originpublishing.co.uk; Alison Zak-Collins, Gp. Advertising Mgr., alisonzak-collins@originpublishing.co.uk. **Subscription Rates:** 28.35 individuals direct debit; 28.35 individuals credit card. **Remarks:** Accepts advertising. **URL:** http://www.cross-stitching.com/current.asp?mag_ id=5&mag_name=CrossStitchGOLD. **Circ:** (Not Reported)

52659 ■ Culture and Cosmos
PO Box 1071
Bristol BS99 1HE, United Kingdom
Publication E-mail: info@cultureandcosmos.com
Peer-reviewed journal covering the history of astrology and astronomy. **Subtitle:** A Journal of the History of Astrology and Cultural Astronomy. **Founded:** Jan. 1997. **Freq:** Semiannual. **Trim Size:** 230 x 150 mm. **Key Personnel:** Nicholas Campion, PhD, Editor, n.campion@lamp.ac.uk; Patrick Curry, PhD, Dep. Ed. **ISSN:** 1368-6534. **Subscription Rates:** 15 individuals U.K. & Europe; 17 other countries; 24 institutions U.K. & Europe; 26 institutions, other countries. **URL:** http:// www.cultureandcosmos.com/. **Circ:** Paid 300

52660 ■ Culture and Organization
Routledge
Taylor & Francis Group Ltd.
c/o Peter Case, Ed.
Bristol Business Scholarship
University of West of England, Frenchay Campus
Coldharbour Ln.
Bristol BS16 1QY, United Kingdom
Publisher E-mail: webmaster.books@tandf.co.uk
Peer-reviewed journal dealing with cultures and organizational phenomena, in connection with the Standing Conference on Organizational Symbolism. **Subtitle:** The

Official Journal of the Standing Conference on Organizational Symbolism. **Founded:** 1995. **Freq:** Quarterly. **Key Personnel:** Robert Westwood, Editorial Board; Heather Hopfl, Editorial Board; Steve Woolgar, Editorial Board. **ISSN:** 1475-9551. **Subscription Rates:** US$123 individuals print only; US$294 individuals online only; US$309 institutions print + online; 232 institutions print + online; 220 institutions online only; 104 individuals; EUR235 institutions online only; EUR98 individuals. **Remarks:** Advertising accepted; rates available upon request. **URL:** http://www. tandf.co.uk/journals/titles/14759551.asp. **Formerly:** Studies in Cultures, Organizations and Societies. **Circ:** (Not Reported)

52661 ■ DNJ
Matt Publishing
7 Unity St.
Bristol BS1 5HH, United Kingdom
Ph: 44 117 9300255
Fax: 44 117 9300245
Publication E-mail: dnj@mattmags.com
Publisher E-mail: dnj@mattmags.com
Online professional magazine for software developers working with the Windows platform. **Founded:** 1997. **Key Personnel:** Matt Nicholson, Editor and Publisher, phone 44 117 9300255, matt@mattmags.com. **Subscription Rates:** Free. **Remarks:** Accepts advertising. **URL:** http://dnjonline.com/dnjmedia/index. shtmldnjonline. **Former name:** Developer Network Journal. **Circ:** (Not Reported)

52662 ■ Endocrine Abstracts
BioScientifica Ltd.
Euro House
22 Apex Ct.
Woodlands
Bradley Stoke
Bristol BS32 4JT, United Kingdom
Ph: 44 14 54642220
Fax: 44 14 54642201
Journal covering issues of endocrinology. **Freq:** Semiannual. **ISSN:** 1470-3947. **Subscription Rates:** 159 individuals; EUR239 individuals; US$318 individuals; 53 single issue; EUR80 single issue; US$160 single issue. **URL:** http://www.portlandpress.com; http://www. endocrine-abstracts.org/index.aspx.

52663 ■ Endocrine-Related Cancer
Society for Endocrinology
22 Apex Ct.
Woodlands, Bradley Stoke
Bradley Stoke
Bristol BS32 4JT, United Kingdom
Ph: 44 1454 642200
Fax: 44 1454 642222
Publication covering endocrinology. **Freq:** Quarterly. **Trim Size:** 200 x 257 mm. **Key Personnel:** S.L. Asa, Editorial Board; J. Fagin, Editor-in-Chief; K. Knudsen, Assoc. Ed.; A.B. Grossman, Assoc. Ed.; V.H.T. James, Founding Ed.; C.L. Clarke, Assoc. Ed.; A. Heaney, Editorial Board. **ISSN:** 1351-0088. **Subscription Rates:** 1,058 institutions, other countries print & online; 881 institutions, other countries online only; EUR208 other countries print & online; US$1,935 institutions North and South America, print & online; US$1,520 institutions North and South America, online only; US$258 members North and South America, print & online; EUR1,564 institutions, other countries print & online only; EUR1,694 institutions, other countries online only. **Remarks:** Accepts advertising. **URL:** http://erc.endocrinology-journals.org/. **Ad Rates:** BW: 500, 4C: 1,300. **Circ:** 1,000

52664 ■ European Journal of Endocrinology
Society for Endocrinology
22 Apex Ct.
Woodlands, Bradley Stoke
Bradley Stoke
Bristol BS32 4JT, United Kingdom
Ph: 44 1454 642200
Fax: 44 1454 642222
European journal covering endocrinology. **Freq:** Monthly. **Trim Size:** 215 x 280 mm. **Key Personnel:** Maria Alevizaki, Dep. Ch. Ed.; Wiebke Arlt, Editorial Board; Hermann M. Behre, Editorial Board; Alla Vaag, Editorial Board; Christian J. Strasburger, Editor-in-Chief. **ISSN:** 0804-4643. **Subscription Rates:** 1,226 institutions print & online; EUR1,830 institutions print & online; 1,329 institutions online only; EUR1,983 institutions online only. **Remarks:** Accepts advertising. **URL:** http://www.eje-online.org/. **Ad Rates:** BW: 500, 4C: 995. **Circ:** 1,600

Circulation: ★ = ABC; △ = BPA; ◆ = CAC; • = CCAB; ❑ = VAC; ⊕ = PO Statement; ‡ = Publisher's Report; Boldface figures = sworn; Light figures = estimated.

Gale Directory of Publications & Broadcast Media/147th Ed. · · · 5599

52665 ■ European Journal of Physics
IOP Publishing Ltd.
Dirac House
Temple Back
Bristol BS1 6BE, United Kingdom
Ph: 44 117 9297481
Fax: 44 117 9294318
Publication E-mail: ejp@iop.org
Publisher E-mail: custserv@iop.org
Journal featuring papers on physics education at the university level. **Founded:** 1978. **Freq:** Bimonthly. **Print Method:** Litho. **Trim Size:** 171 x 248 mm. **Key Personnel:** D.L. Andrews, Editorial Board; A.I.M. Rae, Editor, a.i.m.rae@bham.ac.uk; M. Cepic, Editorial Board. **ISSN:** 0143-0807. **Remarks:** Advertising accepted; rates available upon request. **URL:** http://www.iop.org/EJ/journal/EJP. **Circ:** (Not Reported)

52666 ■ Europhysics Letters (EPL)
IOP Publishing Ltd.
Dirac House
Temple Back
Bristol BS1 6BE, United Kingdom
Ph: 44 117 9297481
Fax: 44 117 9294318
Publication E-mail: info@epljournal.org
Publisher E-mail: custserv@iop.org
Journal covering all aspects of research in physics. **Founded:** 1996. **Freq:** 24/yr. **Print Method:** Offset. **Trim Size:** 7 3/4 x 10 3/4. **Cols./Page:** 3. **Col. Width:** 28 nonpareils. **Col. Depth:** 138 agate lines. **Key Personnel:** Graeme Watt, Exec. Ed.; Frederic Burr, Editor; Barbara Ancarani, Production Ed.; Misha Khan, Production Ed. **ISSN:** 0002-2543. **URL:** http://www.iop.org/EJ/journal/EPL.

52667 ■ Evidence & Policy
The Policy Press
University of Bristol, Fourth Fl.
Beacon House, Queen's Rd.
Bristol BS8 1QU, United Kingdom
Ph: 44 117 3314054
Fax: 44 117 3314093
Publisher E-mail: tpp-info@bristol.ac.uk
Peer-reviewed journal focusing on criminal justice, providing evidence research for policy makers and practitioners. **Subtitle:** A Journal of Research, Debate and Practice. **Freq:** Quarterly. **Key Personnel:** Annette Boaz, Managing Editor. **ISSN:** 1744-2648. **Subscription Rates:** 73 individuals UK and European; print only; EUR103 individuals European Union; print only; US$142 individuals print only; 89 other countries print only; 415 institutions UK and European; print + online; EUR580 institutions European Union; print + online; US$723 institutions print + online; 450 institutions, other countries print + online. **URL:** http://www.policypress.co.uk/journals_eap.asp?.

52668 ■ Expo Times
The Expo Times
45 Constable Rd.
Bristol BS7 9YF, United Kingdom
Ph: 44 117 9081303
Publication E-mail: editor@expotimes.net
Publisher E-mail: info@expotimes.net
Independent online newspaper covering issues in Sierra Leone and Africa. **Founded:** Mar. 15, 2000. **Freq:** Bimonthly. **Key Personnel:** Wilson Appah, Web Site Devel. Mgr.; Kofi Akosah-Sarpong, Africa Ed.; Charles Abayomi Roberts, Dep. Ed.; Wilfred Leeroy Kabs-Kanu, Editor; Claudia A.R. Anthony, Germany Bureau Ed.; Michael N. Wundah, Political Anal.; Dr. Ibrahim Seaga Shaw, Publisher, i.shaw@expotimes.net; Abu Bakar Shaw, London Bureau Ed. **URL:** http://www.expotimes.net.

52669 ■ FibreSystems Europe
IOP Publishing Ltd.
Dirac House
Temple Back
Bristol BS1 6BE, United Kingdom
Ph: 44 117 9297481
Fax: 44 117 9294318
Publisher E-mail: custserv@iop.org
Magazine for the optical communications industry. **Founded:** 2000. **Freq:** Bimonthly. **Key Personnel:** Susan Curtis, Publisher, susan.curtis@iop.org; Pauline Rigby, Editor, pauline.rigby@iop.org. **Subscription Rates:** 75 individuals; EUR109 individuals; US$135 other countries. **Remarks:** Accepts advertising. **URL:** http://

fibresystems.org/cws/latest/magazine. **Circ:** (Not Reported)

52670 ■ Financial Planning
Institute of Financial Planning
Whitefriars Centre
Lewins Mead
Bristol BS1 2NT, United Kingdom
Ph: 44 117 9452470
Fax: 44 117 9292214
Publisher E-mail: enquiries@financialplanning.org.uk
Publication covering financial planning. **Freq:** Monthly. **Key Personnel:** John McCormick, Acting Ed.-in-Ch., john.mccormick@sourcemedia.com; Tim Whiting, Publisher; Douglas Manoni, CEO. **Remarks:** Accepts advertising. **URL:** http://www.financial-planning.com. **Ad Rates:** BW: 6,390, 4C: 7,090. **Circ:** 1,450

52671 ■ Food Quality and Preference
Elsevier Science Inc.
c/o H.J.H. MacFie, Ed.
43 Manor Rd.
Keynsham
Bristol, United Kingdom
Ph: 44 117 9863590
Publisher E-mail: usinfo-ehelp@elsevier.com
Journal covering nutrition and food choice, as well as food research, product development and sensory quality assurance. **Founded:** 1990. **Freq:** 8/yr. **Print Method:** Offset. **Trim Size:** 8 x 10 3/4. **Cols./Page:** 3. **Col. Width:** 26 nonpareils. **Col. Depth:** 140 agate lines. **Key Personnel:** G. Hough, Editorial Board; C. De Graaf, Assoc. Ed.; E.M. Qannari, Assoc. Ed.; H.L. Meiselman, Editor; J. Prescott, Editor, prescott18@googlemail.com; S. Issanchou, Editorial Board. **ISSN:** 0950-3293. **Subscription Rates:** 15,600¥ individuals; US$133 other countries except Europe, Japan and Iran; EUR119 individuals for European countries and Iran; US$1,290 institutions, other countries except Europe, Japan and Iran; EUR1,152 institutions for European countries and Iran; 153,000¥ institutions. **URL:** http://www.elsevier.com/wps/find/journaldescription.cws_home/405859/descriptiondescription.

52672 ■ Gardens Illustrated
BBC Worldwide Publishing Ltd.
Tower House, 14th Fl.
Fairfax St.
Bristol BS1 3BN, United Kingdom
Ph: 44 117 3148774
Publication E-mail: gardens@bbcmagazinesbristol.com
Magazine featuring inspiration, knowledge, and insight on gardening. **Founded:** 1993. **Freq:** Monthly. **Key Personnel:** Alison Zak-Collins, Gp. Advisory Mgr., alisonzak-collins@bbcmagazinesbristol.com; Kerry Pierson, Advertising Mgr., kerrypierson@bbcmagazinesbristol.com; Laura Stanley, Contact, phone 44 117 9338072. **Subscription Rates:** 3.85 single issue; 17.30 individuals every 6 issues; 34.65 individuals. **URL:** http://www.gardensillustrated.com/; http://www.bbcmagazinesbristol.com/magazine.asp?id=25. **Circ:** ⋆31,312

52673 ■ Hair Ideas
Origin Publishing Ltd.
Tower House
Fairfax St.
Bristol BS1 3BN, United Kingdom
Ph: 44 117 9279009
Fax: 44 117 9349008
Publisher E-mail: info@originpublishing.co.uk
Magazine featuring different hairstyles for ages 18 and above. **Founded:** 2003. **Freq:** Monthly. **Key Personnel:** Melanie Harris, Advertising Mgr., phone 44 117 3148367; Alison Zak-Collins, Gp. Ad. Mgr. **Subscription Rates:** 1.99 single issue. **Remarks:** Accepts advertising. **URL:** http://www.originpublishing.co.uk/magazine.asp?id=13. **Circ:** ⋆62,289

52674 ■ Hydrological Processes
John Wiley & Sons Inc.
c/o Prof. Malcolm G. Anderson, Ed.
University of Bristol
University Rd.
Bristol BS8 1SS, United Kingdom
Publisher E-mail: info@wiley.com
Journal of environmental hydrology. Emphasis is placed on how to model and forecast the effect of water on the earth's surface. **Subtitle:** An International Journal. **Founded:** 1986. **Freq:** 26/yr. **Key Personnel:** Dr. Norman E. Peters, Assoc. Ed., nepeters@usgs.gov; Prof.

Des Walling, Assoc. Ed., d.e.walling@exeter.ac.uk; Prof. Malcolm G. Anderson, Editor, hp-journal@bristol.ac.uk; Prof. Keith J. Beven, Assoc. Ed., k.beven@lancaster.ac.uk. **ISSN:** 0885-6087. **Subscription Rates:** US$3,681 other countries print; US$4,909 institutions, other countries print; EUR3,168 institutions, other countries print; 2,505 institutions print; EUR3,485 institutions, other countries print with online; 2,756 institutions print with online; US$5,401 institutions, other countries print with online. **Remarks:** Accepts advertising. **URL:** http://www3.interscience.wiley.com/journal/4125/home. **Circ:** (Not Reported)

52675 ■ Imagine Magazine
Wildfire Communications Ltd.
Unit 2.4 Paintworks
Arnos Vale
Totterdown
Bristol BS4 3EN, United Kingdom
Ph: 44 117 9029977
Fax: 44 117 9029978
Publication E-mail: editorial@imagineanimation.net
Publisher E-mail: webmaster@wildfirecomms.co.uk
Magazine featuring animation trends and culture. **Freq:** Bimonthly. **Subscription Rates:** 35.95 individuals in UK; 66.95 individuals in UK, 2 years; 44.12 individuals rest of the world; 67.90 individuals rest of the world, two years; EUR52 individuals rest of the world; EUR80 individuals rest of the world, two years. **Remarks:** Accepts advertising. **URL:** http://www.imagineanimation.net/?q=mag. **Circ:** 7,500

52676 ■ International Journal of Adhesion and Adhesives
Elsevier Science Inc.
c/o R.D. Adams, Ed.-in-Ch.
Department of Mechanical Engineering
University of Bristol
Queen's Bldg.
Bristol BS8 1TR, United Kingdom
Publisher E-mail: usinfo-ehelp@elsevier.com
Journal covering science and technology of adhesive materials and its work to industrial applications. **Freq:** 8/yr. **Print Method:** Offset. **Trim Size:** 8 1/2 x 11. **Cols./Page:** 3. **Col. Width:** 2 1/8 inches. **Col. Depth:** 12 3/4 inches. **Key Personnel:** A. Baker, Editorial Advisory Board; J.P. Bell, Editorial Advisory Board; M.R. Bowditch, Editorial Advisory Board; W. Brockmann, Editorial Advisory Board; G.W. Critchlow, Editorial Advisory Board; M. Barquins, Editorial Advisory Board; J.A. Bishopp, Editorial Advisory Board; L.S. Penn, Editor; K.B. Armstrong, Editorial Advisory Board; R.D. Adams, Editor-in-Chief; J. Comyn, Editor-in-Chief. **ISSN:** 0143-7496. **Subscription Rates:** US$1,406 institutions, other countries except Europe, Japan and Iran; EUR1,255 institutions for European countries and Iran; 166,800¥ institutions; EUR158 individuals for European countries and Iran; US$211 other countries except Europe, Japan and Iran; 24,300¥ individuals. **URL:** http://www.elsevier.com/wps/find/journaldescription.cws_home/30430/descriptiondescription.

52677 ■ International Journal of Computer Applications in Technology
Inderscience Enterprises Limited
c/o Prof. Quan Min Zhu, Ed.-in-Ch.
University of the West of England
Bristol Institute of Technology
Frenchay Campus, Coldharbour Ln.
Bristol BS16 1QY, United Kingdom
Journal covering the field of computer applications and related information technology. **Freq:** 12/yr. **Key Personnel:** Prof. Quan Min Zhu, Editor-in-Chief, quan.zhu@uwe.ac.uk. **ISSN:** 0952-8091. **Subscription Rates:** EUR1,025 individuals print or online; EUR1,434 individuals print and online. **URL:** http://www.inderscience.com/browse/index.php?journalID=5.

52678 ■ International Journal of Epidemiology
Oxford University Press
Dept. of Social Medicine
University of Bristol
Canynge Hall
39 Whatley Rd.
Bristol BS8 2PR, United Kingdom
Ph: 44 117 9287370
Fax: 44 117 9287222
Publisher E-mail: webenquiry.uk@oup.com
Journal encouraging communication among those engaged in the research, teaching, and application of epidemiology of both communicable and non-communicable disease, including research into health services and medical care, covering new methods,

epidemiological and statistical, for the analysis of data used by those who practice social and preventive medicine. **Freq:** Bimonthly. **Key Personnel:** Davey G. Smith, Editor; S. Ebrahim, Co-Ed., shah.ebrahim@lshtm.ac.uk; F. Binka, Assoc. Ed.; P. Garner, Assoc. Ed.; Y. Ben-Shlomo, Assoc. Ed.; N. Chaturvedi, Assoc. Ed.; F. Forastiere, Assoc. Ed.; P.S. Brachman, Assoc. Ed.; M. Egger, Assoc. Ed. **ISSN:** 0300-5771. **Subscription Rates:** 510 institutions corporate; print and online; 391 institutions corporate; online only; 468 institutions corporate; print only; 408 institutions print and online; 313 institutions online only; 374 institutions print only; 185 institutions developing countries; print; 376 individuals print; 255 members print. **Remarks:** Advertising accepted; rates available upon request. **URL:** http://ije.oxfordjournals.org. **Circ:** (Not Reported)

52679 ■ International Journal of Modelling, Identification and Control
Inderscience Publishers
c/o Prof. Quan Min Zhu, Ed.-in-Ch.
University of the West of England
Bristol Institute of Technology
Frenchay Campus, Coldharbour Ln.
Bristol BS16 1QY, United Kingdom
Publisher E-mail: editor@inderscience.com
Peer-reviewed journal for modeling, identification and control. **Freq:** Monthly. **Key Personnel:** Prof. Nabil Derbel, Regional Ed.; Prof. Khaled El Metwally, Regional Ed.; Dr. Dongbing Gu, Editorial Board Member; Prof. Hoon Heo, Editorial Board Member; Dr. Luis Antonio Aguirre, Regional Ed.; Prof. Boutaib Dahhou, Editorial Board Member; Prof. Yongji Wang, Regional Ed.; Prof. Tielong Shen, Regional Ed.; Prof. Quan Min Zhu, Editor-in-Chief, quan.zhu@uwe.ac.uk; Dr. Sabir Ghauri, Editorial Board Member; Prof. Giuseppe Fusco, Regional Ed. **ISSN:** 1746-6172. **Subscription Rates:** EUR1,025 individuals print only (surface mail); EUR1,730 individuals online only (2-3 users); EUR1,434 individuals print and online; EUR1,105 individuals print only (airmail). **URL:** http://www.inderscience.com/browse/index.php?journalCODE=ijmic.

52680 ■ International Review of Economics Education
The Economics Network
ILRT, University of Bristol
8-10 Berkeley Sq.
Bristol BS8 1HH, United Kingdom
Ph: 44 11 73314347
Fax: 44 11 73314396
Publisher E-mail: econ-network@bristol.ac.uk
Peer-reviewed journal dealing with the economics for higher education. **Freq:** Semiannual. **Key Personnel:** Prof. Ross Guest, Editor; Dr. Carol Johnston, Editorial Board; Prof. Peter Davies, Editor; Prof. Michael Watts, Editorial Board; Prof. Jan H.F. Meyer, Editorial Board; Prof. John Beath, Editorial Board; Prof. Ian MacDonald, Editorial Board; Prof. Tony Cockerill, Editorial Board; Prof. John Sloman, Editorial Board; Prof. Piet Coppieters, Editorial Board. **ISSN:** 1477-3880. **Subscription Rates:** Free UK/overseas educational; 15 individuals UK; 40 other countries. **Remarks:** Accepts advertising. **URL:** http://www.economicsnetwork.ac.uk/iree/. **Ad Rates:** BW: 325. **Circ:** (Not Reported)

52681 ■ Irish Dancing & Culture
Wildfire Communications Ltd.
Unit 2.4 Paintworks
Arnos Vale
Totterdown
Bristol BS4 3EN, United Kingdom
Ph: 44 117 9029977
Fax: 44 117 9029978
Publication E-mail: mail@irishdancing.com
Publisher E-mail: webmaster@wildfirecomms.co.uk
Magazine featuring competitions for teen girl Irish dancers. **Freq:** Monthly. **Key Personnel:** Tallulah Speed, Editor, tallulah@irishdancing.com. **Subscription Rates:** 29 individuals; EUR48 individuals; US$69.95 individuals; 40 individuals rest of the world; 4.25 single issue rest of the world; 3.25 single issue; EUR4.80 single issue; US$6.99 single issue. **Remarks:** Accepts advertising. **URL:** http://www.irishdancing.com. **Circ:** (Not Reported)

52682 ■ Journal of Breath Research
IOP Publishing Ltd.
Dirac House
Temple Back

Bristol BS1 6BE, United Kingdom
Ph: 44 117 9297481
Fax: 44 117 9294318
Publication E-mail: jbr@iop.org
Publisher E-mail: custserv@iop.org
Journal focusing on the research in breath science. **Key Personnel:** A. Amann, Editor-in-Chief; M. Rosenberg, Editor-in-Chief. **ISSN:** 1752-7155. **URL:** http://www.iop.org/EJ/journal/JBR.

52683 ■ Journal of Cellular Automata
Old City Publishing
c/o Andrew Adamatzky, Ed.-in-Ch.
University of the West of England
Bristol BS16 1QY, United Kingdom
Publisher E-mail: info@oldcitypublishing.com
Journal covering cellular automata, mathematical sciences, physical, chemical, biological, social and engineering systems. **Founded:** 1975. **Freq:** Quarterly. **Print Method:** Sheetfed offset. **Trim Size:** 8 1/2 x 11. **Cols./Page:** 2. **Col. Width:** 3 3/8 inches. **Col. Depth:** 10 inches. **Key Personnel:** Andrew Adamatzky, Editor-in-Chief, andrew.adamatzky@uwe.ac.uk; Stefania Bandini, Editorial Board, bandini@disco.unimib.it; Enrico Formenti, Editorial Board, enrico.formenti@unice.fr; Andrew Ilachinski, Editorial Board, ilachina@cna.org; Carter Bays, Editorial Board, bays@sc.edu; Bastien Chopard, Editorial Board, bastien.chopard@cui.unige.ch. **ISSN:** 1557-5969. **Subscription Rates:** US$1095 institutions; EUR910 institutions; 102,330¥ institutions; US$234 individuals; EUR220 individuals; 29,789¥ individuals. **URL:** http://www.oldcitypublishing.com/JCA/JCA.html.

52684 ■ Journal of Cosmology and Astroparticle Physics
IOP Publishing Ltd.
Dirac House
Temple Back
Bristol BS1 6BE, United Kingdom
Ph: 44 117 9297481
Fax: 44 117 9294318
Publication E-mail: jcap@iop.org
Publisher E-mail: custserv@iop.org
Peer-reviewed journal encompassing theoretical, observational and experimental areas as well as computation and simulation. Covers the latest development in the theory of all fundamental interactions and their cosmological implications (e.g. M-theory and cosmology, brane cosmology), formation, dynamics and clustering of galaxies, pre-galactic star formation, X-ray astronomy, radio astronomy, gravitational lensing, active galactic nuclei, intergalactic and interstellar matter. **Freq:** Monthly. **Key Personnel:** Carl W. Akerlof, Editorial Board; Asantha Cooray, Editorial Board; Robert Brandenberger, Editorial Board; Lars Bergstrom, Editorial Board; Ulf Danielsson, Editorial Board; Paolo de Bernardis, Editorial Board. **ISSN:** 1475-7516. **URL:** http://www.iop.org/ej/journal/jcap.

52685 ■ Journal of Endocrinology
Society for Endocrinology
22 Apex Ct.
Woodlands, Bradley Stoke
Bradley Stoke
Bristol BS32 4JT, United Kingdom
Ph: 44 1454 642200
Fax: 44 1454 642222
Journal covering endocrinology. **Freq:** Monthly. **Trim Size:** 200 x 257 mm. **Key Personnel:** Prof. A.J.L. Clark, Editor-in-Chief; D.W. Ray, Dep. Ed.; D.R. Brigstock, Editor. **ISSN:** 0022-0795. **Subscription Rates:** 1,329 institutions print & online only; 1,022 institutions online only; 1,594 individuals print and online; US$2,355 institutions North and South America, print & online only; US$1,963 institutions North and South America, online only; US$3,062 individuals North and South America, print and online; EUR1,490 institutions, other countries print & online only; EUR1,410 institutions, other countries online only; EUR380 individuals print and online; 165 members. **Remarks:** Accepts advertising. **URL:** http://joe.endocrinology-journals.org. **Ad Rates:** BW: 500, 4C: 1,300. **Circ:** 1,200

52686 ■ Journal of Geophysics and Engineering
IOP Publishing Ltd.
Dirac House
Temple Back
Bristol BS1 6BE, United Kingdom
Ph: 44 117 9297481
Fax: 44 117 9294318

Publication E-mail: jge@iop.org
Publisher E-mail: custserv@iop.org
Publication promoting research and developments in geophysics and related areas of engineering and all earth-physics disciplines from global geophysics to applied and engineering geophysics, including geodynamics, natural and controlled-source seismology, oil, gas and mineral exploration, petrophysics and reservoir geophysics. **Freq:** Quarterly. **Key Personnel:** Wang Yanghua, Editor-in-Chief; Qu Shouli, Editor-in-Chief; Guo Jian, Dep. Ed. **ISSN:** 1742-2132. **Subscription Rates:** US$1,670 institutions North, Central and South America; 818 institutions European Union. **URL:** http://www.iop.org/ej/journal/jge.

52687 ■ Journal of Instrumentation
IOP Publishing Ltd.
Dirac House
Temple Back
Bristol BS1 6BE, United Kingdom
Ph: 44 117 9297481
Fax: 44 117 9294318
Publication E-mail: jinst@iop.org
Publisher E-mail: custserv@iop.org
Peer-reviewed journal covering innovative instrument design and applications in chemistry, physics, biotechnology, and environmental science. Focuses on modern instrumental concepts including detectors, sensors, instrument control, chromatography, electrochemistry, spectroscopy of all types, electrophoresis, radiometry, relaxation methods, thermal analysis, physical property measurements, surface physics, membrane technology, microcomputer design, and chip-based processes. **Key Personnel:** Torsten Akesson, Editorial Board; Mike Albrow, Editorial Board; Elena Aprile, Editorial Board; Ronaldo Bellazzini, Editorial Board. **URL:** http://www.iop.org/EJ/journal/1748-0221.

52688 ■ Journal of the Kilvert Society
Kilvert Society
c/o Alan Brimson, Honorable Sec.
30, Bromley Heath Ave.
Downend
Bristol BS16 6JP, United Kingdom
Journal containing learned articles, news of forthcoming events, reports. **Freq:** Semiannual. **Subscription Rates:** Free free for members. **Remarks:** Advertising not accepted. **URL:** http://www.communigate.co.uk/here/kilvertsociety/index.phtml. **Circ:** (Not Reported)

52689 ■ Journal of Micromechanics and Microengineering
IOP Publishing Ltd.
Dirac House
Temple Back
Bristol BS1 6BE, United Kingdom
Ph: 44 117 9297481
Fax: 44 117 9294318
Publication E-mail: jmm@iop.org
Publisher E-mail: custserv@iop.org
Journal covering all aspects of microelectromechanical structures, devices and systems, as well as micromechanics and micromechatronics, aiming to highlight the link between fabrication technologies and their capacity to create novel devices and focusing on fundamental work in fabrication and process technologies, including bulk and surface micromachining, LIGA, EDM, bonding, lithography, and focused ion beam techniques. **Freq:** 12/yr. **Key Personnel:** R. Puers, Regional Ed.; M.G. Allen, Editor-in-Chief. **ISSN:** 0960-1317. **URL:** http://www.iop.org/ej/journal/jmm.

52690 ■ Journal of Molecular Catalysis A
Elsevier Science Inc.
c/o G.C. Lloyd-Jones, Ed.-in-Ch.
University of Bristol
School of Chemistry
Cantock's Close
Bristol BS8 1TS, United Kingdom
Ph: 44 117 9288165
Fax: 44 117 9298611
Publisher E-mail: usinfo-ehelp@elsevier.com
Journal focused on molecular and atomic aspects of catalytic activation. **Subtitle:** Chemical. **Founded:** 1976. **Freq:** 36/yr. **Key Personnel:** Y. Iwasawa, Editorial Board; G.C. Lloyd-Jones, Editor-in-Chief, guy.lloyd-jones@bristol.ac.uk; T. Tatsumi, Editor, ttatsumi@cat.res.titech.ac.jp; M. Barteau, Editorial Board; A. Corma,

---

Circulation: ★ = ABC; △ = BPA; ◆ = CAC; • = CCAB; ❑ = VAC; ⊕ = PO Statement; ‡ = Publisher's Report; Boldface figures = sworn; Light figures = estimated.

Editorial Board; I.P. Beletskaya, Editorial Board; B. Corain, Editorial Board; J.M. Basset, Editorial Board; R. Davis, Editorial Board; A. Sayari, Editor, abdel.sayari@science.uottawa.ca. **ISSN:** 1381-1169. **Subscription Rates:** 878,800¥ institutions; US$7,396 institutions, other countries except Europe, Japan and Iran; EUR6,613 institutions for European countries and Iran. **URL:** http://www.elsevier.com/wps/find/journaldescription.cws_home/504089/descrip tiondescription.

52691 ■ Journal of Molecular Endocrinology
Society for Endocrinology
22 Apex Ct.
Woodlands, Bradley Stoke
Bradley Stoke
Bristol BS32 4JT, United Kingdom
Ph: 44 1454 642200
Fax: 44 1454 642222
Publication covering endocrinology. **Freq:** Bimonthly. **Trim Size:** 200 x 257 mm. **Key Personnel:** C.V. Alvarez, Sen. Ed.; Prof. A. Spada, Editor-in-Chief; F. Beuschlein, Editorial Board; S. Farooqi, Sen. Ed.; B. Chow, Sen. Ed.; P. Maechler, Editorial Board; S. Ali, Sen. Ed.; P. Fuller, Editorial Board; G. Hammond, Editorial Board. **ISSN:** 0952-5041. **Subscription Rates:** 1,129 institutions Europe/rest of the world (print and online); EUR1,700 institutions Europe/rest of the world (print and online); US$2,139 institutions N&S America (print and online); 941 institutions Europe/rest of the world (online only); EUR1,417 institutions Europe/rest of the world (online only); US$1,782 institutions N&S America (online only). **Remarks:** Accepts advertising. **URL:** http://jme.endocrinology-journals.org/. **Ad Rates:** BW: 500, 4C: 1,300. **Circ:** 400

52692 ■ Journal of Neural Engineering
IOP Publishing Ltd.
Dirac House
Temple Back
Bristol BS1 6BE, United Kingdom
Ph: 44 117 9297481
Fax: 44 117 9294318
Publication E-mail: jne@iop.org
Publisher E-mail: custserv@iop.org
Journal publishing articles in the field of neural engineering at the molecular, cellular and systems levels, encompassing experimental, computational, theoretical, clinical and applied aspects of neural interfacing, brain-computer interfacing, neuroelectronics, neuromechanical systems, neural rehabilitation, neuroinformatics, neuroimaging, neural prostheses, neural circuits: artificial and biological, neural control, neural tissue regeneration, neural signal processing, neural modelling and neuro-computation and neural system analysis. **Freq:** Quarterly. **Key Personnel:** D.M. Durand, Editor-in-Chief; A.B. Schwartz, Editor-in-Chief. **ISSN:** 1741-2560. **URL:** http://www.iop.org/ej/journal/jne.

52693 ■ Journal of Optics
IOP Publishing Ltd.
Dirac House
Temple Back
Bristol BS1 6BE, United Kingdom
Ph: 44 117 9297481
Fax: 44 117 9294318
Publication E-mail: jopa@iop.org
Publisher E-mail: custserv@iop.org
Journal covering all aspects of classical optical phenomena, including (but not restricted to): metamaterials, nanophotonics, integrated optics, terahertz optics, photonics at the life science interface, singularities, light confinement, ultrafast optics, plasmonics, optical manipulation, adaptive optics, light assisted processing of materials, spatial solitons, information optics, structured photonic materials (including photonic crystals). **Freq:** Monthly. **Key Personnel:** Nikolay Zheludev, Editor-in-Chief. **ISSN:** 1464-4258. **URL:** http://iopscience.iop.org/2040-8986/. **Formerly:** Journal of Optics A.

52694 ■ Journal of Physics A
IOP Publishing Ltd.
Dirac House
Temple Back
Bristol BS1 6BE, United Kingdom
Ph: 44 117 9297481
Fax: 44 117 9294318
Publisher E-mail: custserv@iop.org
Journal covering research on the mathematical structures that describe fundamental processes of the physical world and on the analytical, computational and

numerical methods for exploring these structures. **Subtitle:** Mathematical and Theoretical. **Freq:** 50/yr. **Key Personnel:** M.T. Batchelor, Editor-in-Chief; M.V. Berry, Editorial Board; J. Feinberg, Reviews Ed. **ISSN:** 1751-8113. **URL:** http://www.iop.org/EJ/journal/1751-8121.

52695 ■ Journal of Physics D
IOP Publishing Ltd.
Dirac House
Temple Back
Bristol BS1 6BE, United Kingdom
Ph: 44 117 9297481
Fax: 44 117 9294318
Publisher E-mail: custserv@iop.org
International journal covering applied physics. **Subtitle:** Applied Physics. **Founded:** 1967. **Freq:** 50/yr. **Key Personnel:** U. Czarnetzki, Assoc. Ed.; G. Margaritondo, Assoc. Ed.; P. Bhattacharya, Editor-in-Chief; L.J. Balk, Editorial Board. **ISSN:** 0022-3727. **Subscription Rates:** US$4,422 institutions North, Central and South America; 2,246 institutions for European Union; 2,246 institutions, other countries. **URL:** http://iopscience.iop.org/0022-3727. **Former name:** British Journal of Applied Physics.

52696 ■ The Journal of Poverty and Social Justice
The Policy Press
University of Bristol, Fourth Fl.
Beacon House, Queen's Rd.
Bristol BS8 1QU, United Kingdom
Ph: 44 117 3314054
Fax: 44 117 3314093
Publisher E-mail: tpp-info@bristol.ac.uk
Journal focusing on the field related to all aspects of poverty and social exclusion. **Freq:** 3/yr. **Key Personnel:** Fran Bennett, Co-Ed., fran.bennett@socres.ox.ac.uk; Caroline Paskell, Co-Ed., c.a.paskell@lse.ac.uk. **ISSN:** 1759-8273. **Subscription Rates:** 52 individuals UK & Europe (print only); 73 other countries print only; 200 institutions UK & Europe (print and online); 225 institutions, other countries print and online; 180 institutions, other countries online only. **Remarks:** Accepts advertising. **URL:** http://www.portlandpress.com/pcs/journals/journal.cfm?product=BE; http://www.policypress.co.uk/journals_jpsj.asp. **Circ:** (Not Reported)

52697 ■ Journal of Radiological Protection
IOP Publishing Ltd.
Dirac House
Temple Back
Bristol BS1 6BE, United Kingdom
Ph: 44 117 9297481
Fax: 44 117 9294318
Publication E-mail: jrp@iop.org
Publisher E-mail: custserv@iop.org
Professional journal covering radiological protection. **Founded:** 1980. **Freq:** Quarterly. **Key Personnel:** J. Gray, Dep. Ed.; C. Hone, Editorial Board; M. Crick, Editorial Board; R. Wakeford, Editor-in-Chief; P. Allisy-Roberts, Editorial Board. **ISSN:** 0952-4746. **Subscription Rates:** US$700 institutions North, Central and South America; US$364 individuals North, Central and South America; 362 institutions for European Union; 183 individuals for European Union. **Remarks:** Accepts advertising. **URL:** http://www.iop.org/ej/journal/jrp. **Circ:** (Not Reported)

52698 ■ Journal of Semiconductors
IOP Publishing Ltd.
Dirac House
Temple Back
Bristol BS1 6BE, United Kingdom
Ph: 44 117 9297481
Fax: 44 117 9294318
Publication E-mail: jos@semi.ac.cn
Publisher E-mail: custserv@iop.org
Journal covering the latest in semiconductor physics, materials, devices, circuits and related technology. **Key Personnel:** Wang Shouwu, Editor-in-Chief. **ISSN:** 1674-4926. **URL:** http://www.iop.org/EJ/journal/jos.

52699 ■ Journal of Statistical Mechanics
IOP Publishing Ltd.
Dirac House
Temple Back
Bristol BS1 6BE, United Kingdom
Ph: 44 117 9297481
Fax: 44 117 9294318
Publication E-mail: jstat@iop.org

Publisher E-mail: custserv@iop.org
Peer-reviewed journal providing research in all aspects of statistical physics including exact results, low-dimensional quantum mechanics and quantum field theory, phase transitions and critical phenomena, non-equilibrium processes, granular matter, hydrodynamic instabilities, turbulence, complex fluids, mixing and chemical reactions, surfaces, interfaces, growth processes, disordered systems and glassy matter, soft condensed matter, statistical mechanics of complex materials, applications in biological physics, genomics, information theory, combinatorial optimization, graphs and networks, collective phenomena in economic and social systems and new applications of statistical mechanics. **Subtitle:** Theory and Experiment. **Freq:** Monthly. **Key Personnel:** John Chalker, Editorial Board; Damien Challet, Editorial Board; Francisco Alcaraz, Editorial Board; Mikko Alava, Editorial Board; Peter Arndt, Editorial Board; Denis Bernard, Editorial Board. **ISSN:** 1742-5468. **URL:** http://www.iop.org/ej/journal/jstat.

52700 ■ Knit Today
Origin Publishing Ltd.
Tower House
Fairfax St.
Bristol BS1 3BN, United Kingdom
Ph: 44 117 9279009
Fax: 44 117 9349008
Publication E-mail: knittoday@originpublishing.co.uk
Publisher E-mail: info@originpublishing.co.uk
Magazine featuring knitting and crocheting patterns and yarns. **Founded:** 2006. **Freq:** 13/yr. **Key Personnel:** Janice Broadstocks, Editor. **Subscription Rates:** 2.49 single issue; 32.44 individuals. **Remarks:** Accepts advertising. **URL:** http://www.originpublishing.co.uk/magazine.asp?id=37; http://www.knit-today.co.uk/. **Circ:** (Not Reported)

52701 ■ Koi
Origin Publishing Ltd.
Tower House
Fairfax St.
Bristol BS1 3BN, United Kingdom
Ph: 44 117 9279009
Fax: 44 117 9349008
Publisher E-mail: info@originpublishing.co.uk
Magazine for Koi keeping hobbyist. **Subtitle:** Britain's Best Practical Guide To Keeping Koi. **Founded:** 1999. **Freq:** 13/yr. **Key Personnel:** Tony Robinson, Contact, phone 44 117 3148811, tonyrobinson@originpublishing.co.uk; Rebecca Rodgers, Editor, phone 44 117 3148389. **Subscription Rates:** 3.95 single issue; 83.52 individuals; 30.81 individuals direct debit. **Remarks:** Accepts advertising. **URL:** http://www.koimag.co.uk; http://www.originpublishing.co.uk/magazine.asp?id=15. **Circ:** 15,000

52702 ■ Living Earth
Soil Association
South Plz.
Marlborough St.
Bristol BS1 3NX, United Kingdom
Ph: 44 117 3145000
Fax: 44 117 3145001
Magazine covering organic food issues for Soil Association members. **Founded:** 1950. **Freq:** Quarterly. **Key Personnel:** Patrick Holden, Director. **ISSN:** 1360-1741. **Subscription Rates:** Free to members. **Remarks:** Accepts advertising. **URL:** http://www.soilassociation.org/. **Ad Rates:** 4C: 1,950. **Circ:** 24,000

52703 ■ Mammal Review
John Wiley & Sons Inc.
Wiley-Blackwell
c/o Nancy Jennings, Mng. Ed.
Dotmoth, 1 Mendip Villas
Crabtree Ln.
Dundry
Bristol BS41 8LN, United Kingdom
Ph: 44 117 9780696
Journal covering all aspects of mammalian biology and ecology including analytical reviews of current theoretical and applied research on mammals in connection with the Mammal Society. **Freq:** Quarterly. **Key Personnel:** Klaus Hacklander, Editor, klaus.hacklaender@boku.ac.at; Nancy Jennings, Managing Editor, nancy@dotmoth.co.uk; John Durban, Editor, john.durban@noaa.gov. **ISSN:** 0305-1838. **Subscription Rates:** US$94

individuals print and online; EUR76 individuals print and online; 51 individuals print and online; 56 other countries print and online; US$90 individuals online only; US$824 institutions print and online; US$749 institutions online or print; EUR567 institutions print and online; EUR515 institutions print or online; US$961 institutions, other countries print and online. **Remarks:** Advertising accepted; rates available upon request. **URL:** http://www.wiley.com/bw/journal.asp?ref=0305-1838. **Circ:** (Not Reported)

52704 ■ Management & Organizational History
Sage Publications Inc.
c/o Charles Booth, Ed.
University of The West of England
Bristol BS16 1QY, United Kingdom
Publisher E-mail: info@sagepub.com
Journal covering academic research concerning historical approaches to the study of management, organizations, and organizing. **Founded:** 1974. **Freq:** Quarterly. **Print Method:** Offset. **Trim Size:** 5 1/2 x 8 1/2. **Cols./Page:** 1. **Col. Width:** 50 nonpareils. **Col. Depth:** 100 agate lines. **Key Personnel:** Roy Stager Jacques, Co-Ed.; Michael Rowlinson, Editor; Charles Booth, Editorial Board. **ISSN:** 1744-9359. **Subscription Rates:** US$609 institutions combined (print & e-access); US$548 institutions e-access; US$597 institutions print only; US$80 individuals print only; US$164 institutions single copy; US$26 single issue. **Remarks:** Accepts advertising. **URL:** http://moh.sagepub.com/. **Circ:** (Not Reported)

52705 ■ Measurement Science & Technology
IOP Publishing Ltd.
Dirac House
Temple Back
Bristol BS1 6BE, United Kingdom
Ph: 44 117 9297481
Fax: 44 117 9294318
Publication E-mail: mst@iop.org
Publisher E-mail: custserv@iop.org
Professional journal covering measurement science and technology for engineers and scientists. **Founded:** 1923. **Freq:** Monthly. **Key Personnel:** K. Fujii, Asian Regional Ed.; P. Hauptmann, Editor-in-Chief; R.J. Dewhurst, European Regional Ed.; J. Foss, North American Regional Ed.; D.J.S. Birch, Editorial Board; X. Chen, Editorial Board; R.S. Jachowicz, Editorial Board; U. Kaatze, Editorial Board; J. McGrath, Editorial Board; K. Okamoto, Editorial Board; P.P.L. Regtien, Editorial Board; K. Okamoto, Editorial Board. **ISSN:** 0957-0233. **Subscription Rates:** US$2,305 institutions North, Central and South America; 1,170 individuals European Union; 1,170 other countries. **Remarks:** Accepts advertising. **URL:** http://www.iop.org/EJ/journal/0957-0233. **Formerly:** Journal of Scientific Instruments; Journal of Physics E: Scientific Instruments. **Circ:** Combined 2,100

52706 ■ Metrologia
IOP Publishing Ltd.
Dirac House
Temple Back
Bristol BS1 6BE, United Kingdom
Ph: 44 117 9297481
Fax: 44 117 9294318
Publication E-mail: metrologia@iop.org
Publisher E-mail: custserv@iop.org
International journal dealing with the scientific aspects of metrology, publishing articles that report the results of original research directed towards the significant improvement of fundamental measurements and suggesting an improvement to the standards of the seven base units of the International System of Units (metre, kilogram, second, ampere, kelvin, candela, mole) or proposals to replace them with better ones. **Founded:** 1965. **Freq:** Quarterly plus technical supplement. **Key Personnel:** Ch J. Borde, Editorial Board; L.K. Issaev, Editorial Board; J.R. Miles, Editor; P. Gill, Editorial Board; B.N. Taylor, Editorial Board; L. Besley, Editorial Board; A. Ooiwa, Editorial Board; G. Moscati, Editorial Board. **ISSN:** 0026-1394. **Subscription Rates:** US$1,010 institutions North, Central and South America; 627 institutions, other countries. **URL:** http://www.iop.org/ej/journal/met.

52707 ■ Modelling and Simulation in Materials Science and Engineering
IOP Publishing Ltd.
Dirac House
Temple Back

Bristol BS1 6BE, United Kingdom
Ph: 44 117 9297481
Fax: 44 117 9294318
Publication E-mail: msmse@iop.org
Publisher E-mail: custserv@iop.org
Journal covering electronic structure, properties and behaviour of all classes of materials at scales from the atomic to the macroscopic. **Freq:** 8/yr. **Key Personnel:** M.I. Baskes, Exec. Editorial Board; W.A. Curtin, Editor-in-Chief; C. Beckermann, Exec. Editorial Board. **ISSN:** 0965-0393. **URL:** http://www.iop.org/ej/journal/msmse.

52708 ■ Nanotechnology
IOP Publishing Ltd.
Dirac House
Temple Back
Bristol BS1 6BE, United Kingdom
Ph: 44 117 9297481
Fax: 44 117 9294318
Publication E-mail: nano@iop.org
Publisher E-mail: custserv@iop.org
Journal publishing papers at the forefront of nanoscale science and technology and especially those of an interdisciplinary nature where nanotechnology is taken to include the ability to individually address, control, modify and fabricate materials, structures and devices with nanometre precision, and the synthesis of such structures into systems of micro- and macroscopic dimensions such as MEMS based devices, encompassing the understanding of the fundamental physics, chemistry, biology and technology of nanometre-scale objects and how such objects can be used in the areas of computation, sensors, nanostructured materials and nano-biotechnology. **Freq:** 50/yr. **Key Personnel:** M. Welland, Editorial Board; M. Reed, Editor-in-Chief; Y. Bando, Editorial Board. **ISSN:** 0957-4484. **URL:** http://www.iop.org/ej/journal/nano.

52709 ■ Neuropharmacology
Elsevier Science
c/o Graham L. Collingridge, Ed.-in-Ch.
University of Bristol
Bristol BS8 1TD, United Kingdom
Publisher E-mail: nlinfo-f@elsevier.com
Journal dealing with all aspects of neuropharmacology. **Founded:** 1962. **Freq:** 16/yr. **Key Personnel:** Graham L. Collingridge, Editor-in-Chief; Rachel Ince, Editorial Asst., rachel.incenp@googlemail.com; Stuart Allan, Editor; Roger Anwyl, Editorial Board; Nicholas M. Barnes, Editor; Angelique Bordey, Editor. **ISSN:** 0028-3908. **Subscription Rates:** EUR513 individuals for European countries & Iran; US$575 individuals for all countries except Europe, Japan & Iran; 68,100¥ individuals; EUR4,246 institutions for European countries & Iran; 462,100¥ institutions; US$4,749 institutions for all countries except Europe, Japan & Iran. **Remarks:** Accepts advertising. **URL:** http://www.elsevier.com/wps/find/journaldescription.cws_home/279/description. **Circ:** (Not Reported)

52710 ■ New Journal of Physics (NJP)
IOP Publishing Ltd.
Dirac House
Temple Back
Bristol BS1 6BE, United Kingdom
Ph: 44 117 9297481
Fax: 44 117 9294318
Publication E-mail: njp@iop.org
Publisher E-mail: custserv@iop.org
Journal publishing research on all areas of physics. **Founded:** 1998. **Key Personnel:** Eberhard Bodenschatz, Editor-in-Chief; Stephen J. Buckman, Editorial Board; Steve Cowley, Editorial Board; Yasuhiko Arakawa, Regional Ed.; Premala Chandra, Editorial Board; William P. Halperin, Regional Ed.; Antonio Ereditato, Editorial Board. **URL:** http://www.iop.org/ej/njp.

52711 ■ NOMINA
Society for Name Studies in Britain and Ireland
c/o Medical Library, School of Medical Science
University of Bristol
University Walk
Bristol BS8 1TD, United Kingdom
Publication E-mail: editor@snsbi.org.uk
Publisher E-mail: jiscmail@jiscmail.ac.uk
Publication covering language. **Freq:** Annual. **ISSN:** 0141-6340. **Subscription Rates:** Included in membership. **Remarks:** Advertising not accepted. **URL:** http://www.snsbi.org.uk/Nomina.html. **Circ:** (Not Reported)

52712 ■ Nonlinearity
IOP Publishing Ltd.
Dirac House
Temple Back
Bristol BS1 6BE, United Kingdom
Ph: 44 117 9297481
Fax: 44 117 9294318
Publication E-mail: non@iop.org
Publisher E-mail: custserv@iop.org
Professional publication covering physics and mathematics. **Founded:** 1987. **Freq:** 12/yr. **Key Personnel:** J.P. Keating, Editor-in-Chief; A.I. Neishtadt, Editor-in-Chief. **ISSN:** 0951-7715. **Subscription Rates:** US$2,125 institutions for North, Central and South America; 1,073 institutions for European Union. **Remarks:** Advertising accepted; rates available upon request. **URL:** http://www.iop.org/EJ/journal/Non. **Circ:** (Not Reported)

52713 ■ Optics & Laser Europe
IOP Publishing Ltd.
Dirac House
Temple Back
Bristol BS1 6BE, United Kingdom
Ph: 44 117 9297481
Fax: 44 117 9294318
Publisher E-mail: custserv@iop.org
Magazine covering research, technology, applications, products and patents in optoelectronics, lasers, fiber optics, advanced materials, optical techniques and imaging. **Founded:** 1992. **Freq:** 11/yr. **Key Personnel:** Susan Curtis, Publisher, susan.curtis@iop.org; Jacqueline Hewett, Editor, jacqueline.hewett@iop.org. **Subscription Rates:** Free individuals working in the industry; 125 individuals; EUR181 individuals; US$225 individuals. **Remarks:** Accepts advertising. **URL:** http://optics.org/cws/Ole/Welcome.do. **Circ:** (Not Reported)

52714 ■ Paediatric and Perinatal Epidemiology
John Wiley & Sons Inc.
Wiley-Blackwell
c/o Prof. Jean Golding, Ed.-in-Ch.
Centre for Child & Adolescent Health
Department of Community Based Medicine, University of Bristol
Barley House, Oakfield Grove
Bristol BS8 2BN, United Kingdom
Peer-reviewed journal covering the field of pediatric and perinatal studies. **Freq:** Bimonthly. **Key Personnel:** Prof. Tim J. Peters, Editor-in-Chief; Prof. Jean Golding, Editor-in-Chief; Dr. Peter Blair, Editor-in-Chief. **ISSN:** 0269-5022. **Subscription Rates:** US$343 individuals print + online; EUR277 individuals print + online; 185 individuals print + online; 204 other countries print + online; US$1,303 institutions print + online; US$1,184 institutions print, online; EUR898 institutions print + online; EUR816 institutions print, online; 707 institutions print + online; US$1,520 institutions, other countries print + online. **Remarks:** Advertising accepted; rates available upon request. **URL:** http://www.wiley.com/bw/journal.asp?ref=0269-5022&site=1. **Circ:** (Not Reported)

52715 ■ Perspectives
Association of University Administrators
School of Geographical Sciences
University of Bristol
University Rd.
Bristol BS8 1SS, United Kingdom
Ph: 44 117 9287875
Fax: 44 117 9287878
Publisher E-mail: aua@manchester.ac.uk
Quarterly international journal covering quality and practice in higher education. **Subtitle:** Policy and Practice in Higher Education. **Founded:** 1997. **Freq:** Quarterly. **Key Personnel:** Giles Brown, Editor-in-Chief, g.h.brown@bristol.ac.uk; Celia Whitchurch, Assoc. Ed.; Prof. John A. Douglas, Editorial Advisory Board, douglass@uclink4.berkeley.edu; Dr. Jim Franklin, Editorial Advisory Board, jim.franklin@luton.ac.uk; David Palfreyman, Book Ed.; Sheila Aynsley Smith, Editorial Advisory Board, sheilaaynsleysmith@btinternet.com; Allan Bolton, Assoc. Ed., phone 44 113 3434884, fax 44 113 3434885, arb@lubs.leeds.ac.uk; Sue Boswell, Asst. Ed., suejboswell@aol.com. **ISSN:** 1360-3108. **Subscription Rates:** Free to members; 86 nonmembers. **Remarks:** Accepts advertising. **URL:** http://www.aua.ac.uk/publications/perspectives/. **Circ:** Combined ‡4,000

52716 ■ Physica Scripta
IOP Publishing Ltd.

Circulation: ★ = ABC; △ = BPA; ◆ = CAC; ● = CCAB; ❑ = VAC; ⊕ = PO Statement; ‡ = Publisher's Report; Boldface figures = sworn; Light figures = estimated.

Gale Directory of Publications & Broadcast Media/147th Ed.   5603

Dirac House
Temple Back
Bristol BS1 6BE, United Kingdom
Ph: 44 117 9297481
Fax: 44 117 9294318
Publication E-mail: physscr@iop.org
Publisher E-mail: custserv@iop.org
Journal covering theoretical and experimental physics.
Freq: Monthly. **Key Personnel:** Roger Wappling,
Managing Editor. **ISSN:** 0031-8949. **URL:** http://www.
iop.org/EJ/journal/PhysScr.

52717 ■ Physics in Medicine and Biology
IOP Publishing Ltd.
Dirac House
Temple Back
Bristol BS1 6BE, United Kingdom
Ph: 44 117 9297481
Fax: 44 117 9294318
Publication E-mail: pmb@iop.org
Publisher E-mail: custserv@iop.org
Professional publication covering physics in medicine
and biology. **Founded:** 1955. **Freq:** 24/yr. **Trim Size:**
B5. **Key Personnel:** F.J. Beekman, Editorial Board; I.
Buvat, International Advisory Board; Steve Webb, Editor-
in-Chief, steve.webb@icr.ac.uk; S.R. Cherry, Editorial
Board. **ISSN:** 0031-9155. **Subscription Rates:** 1,893
institutions for European Union; US$3,660 institutions
for North, Central and South America. **Remarks:**
Advertising accepted; rates available upon request.
URL: http://www.iop.org/EJ/journal/PMB. **Circ:** (Not
Reported)

52718 ■ Physiological Measurement
IOP Publishing Ltd.
Dirac House
Temple Back
Bristol BS1 6BE, United Kingdom
Ph: 44 117 9297481
Fax: 44 117 9294318
Publication E-mail: pmea@iop.org
Publisher E-mail: custserv@iop.org
Professional publication covering physiological
measurement. **Founded:** 1980. **Freq:** Monthly. **Trim
Size:** B5. **Key Personnel:** S. Gao, Editorial Board; M.R.
Neuman, Editorial Board; P. Vadgama, Editorial Board;
W.M. Smith, Editorial Board; R. Bayford, Editor-in-Chief;
I.R. Chambers, Editorial Board; N. Lovell, Editorial
Board; R. Merletti, Editorial Board; M.E. Valentinuzzi,
Editorial Board; J. Crowe, Editorial Board. **ISSN:** 0967-
3334. **Subscription Rates:** US$1,300 institutions North,
Central and South America; 667 institutions European
Union. **Remarks:** Advertising accepted; rates available
upon request. **URL:** http://www.iop.org/ej/journal/pm.
Formerly: Clinical Physics and Physiological Measure-
ment (Jan. 1, 1993). **Circ:** (Not Reported)

52719 ■ Plant Biotechnology Journal
John Wiley & Sons Inc.
Wiley-Blackwell
School of Biological Sciences
University of Bristol
Woodland Rd.
Bristol BS8 1UG, United Kingdom
Ph: 44 117 9287883
Fax: 44 117 3317985
Publication E-mail: plant-biotechj@bristol.ac.uk
Peer-reviewed journal covering topics such as gene and
genome analysis, gene expression studies, biotech plant
breeding, transgenic technologies, functional genomics,
comparative genomics, and developmental studies.
Freq: 9/yr. **Key Personnel:** Keith Edwards, Editor-in-
Chief, phone 44 117 3317079, fax 44 117 3317985, k.j.
edwards@bristol.ac.uk; Malcolm Campbell, Editor,
malcolm.campbell@utoronto.ca; Robert Birch, Editor,
r.birch@botany.uq.edu.au. **ISSN:** 1467-7644. **Subscription Rates:** US$182 individuals print + online; EUR147
individuals print + online (Euro zone); 108 individuals
print + online; US$1,409 institutions, other countries
print, online; US$1,328 institutions print + online; 708
institutions print + online; 644 institutions print, online;
US$1,550 institutions, other countries print + online;
US$1,207 institutions print + online; EUR898 institutions
print + online. **URL:** http://www.wiley.com/bw/journal.
asp?ref=1467-7644&site=1.

52720 ■ Plasma Physics and Controlled Fusion
IOP Publishing Ltd.
Dirac House
Temple Back
Bristol BS1 6BE, United Kingdom

Ph: 44 117 9297481
Fax: 44 117 9294318
Publication E-mail: ppcf@iop.org
Publisher E-mail: custserv@iop.org
International journal covering plasma physics and
controlled fusion. **Founded:** 1958. **Freq:** Monthly. **Key
Personnel:** C. Hidalgo, Editorial Board; R. Bingham,
Editorial Board; K.A. Tanaka, Editorial Board; R.O.
Dendy, Editor-in-Chief; S. Atzeni, Editorial Board; M.
Koepke, Dep. Ed.; H.K. Park, Editorial Board; J.B. Lister,
International Advisory Panel; A. Becoulet, Editorial
Board; S. Coda, Editorial Board. **ISSN:** 0741-3335. **Sub-
scription Rates:** US$3,590 institutions North, Central
and South America; US$1,902 individuals North, Central
and South America; 1,782,413 institutions for European
Union; 958 individuals for European Union. **URL:** http://
www.iop.org/ej/journal/ppcf.

**52721 ■ Plasma Sources Science and Technol-
ogy**
IOP Publishing Ltd.
Dirac House
Temple Back
Bristol BS1 6BE, United Kingdom
Ph: 44 117 9297481
Fax: 44 117 9294318
Publication E-mail: psst@iop.org
Publisher E-mail: custserv@iop.org
Journal reporting on non-fusion plasma sources which
operate at all ranges of pressure and density including
neutral and non-neutral plasma sources; positive and
negative ion sources; free radical sources; microwave,
RF, direct current, laser and electron beam excited
sources; resonant sources; plasmas for etching, deposi-
tion, polymerization, sintering; plasma sources for accelerators; lighting applications; plasma sources for
medical physics; plasma sources for lasers; other applications, e.g. spacecraft thrusters, industrial arc melt-
ing; plasmas as sources of UV and x-ray radiation;
plasma source design, monitoring and control; source
stability and reproducibility; low-pressure plasma
sources: distribution functions; excitation-radiation
equilibria; vibrationalexcitation; mass, momentum and
energy transport; ion implantation; low-to-medium pressure plasma sources: plasma surface interactions; high
pressure sources, thermal plasmas; plasma diagnostic
techniques; plasma and plasma source modelling. **Freq:**
Quarterly. **Key Personnel:** N. Hershkowitz, Assoc. Ed.;
M.S. Benilov, Editorial Board; Y.P. Raizer, Editorial
Board; S. De Benedictis, Editorial Board; M.C.M. Van
De Sanden, Assoc. Ed.; M.J. Kushner, Editor-in-Chief.
ISSN: 0963-0252. **URL:** http://www.iop.org/ej/journal/
psst.

52722 ■ Policy and Politics
Policy Press
University of Bristol
Beacon House, 4th Fl.
Queen's Road
Bristol BS8 1QU UK, United Kingdom
Ph: 44 0117 331 4054
Fax: 44 0117 331 4093
Publisher E-mail: tpp-info@bristol.ac.uk
Peer-reviewed Journal focusing on human rights,
discrimination, globalization and internationalization.
Subtitle: An International Journal. **Key Personnel:** Tony
Fitzpatrick, Editor; Geetanjali Gangoli, Editor. **ISSN:**
0305-5736. **Subscription Rates:** 73 individuals; EUR103
individuals; 142 other countries; US$89 other countries.
URL: http://www.policypress.co.uk/journals_pap.asp?.

52723 ■ Primary Times
Brunel Press Ltd.
Temple Way
Bristol B599 7HD, United Kingdom
Ph: 44 117 9343733
Fax: 44 117 9343755
Publication E-mail: s.ackland@bepp.co.uk
Publisher E-mail: loaderni@bepp.co.uk
Magazine covering recreation, leisure, and issues for
parents and teachers. **Founded:** 1989. **Freq:** 7/yr. **Key
Personnel:** Harry Mottram, Editor. **Subscription Rates:**
10 individuals. **Remarks:** Accepts advertising. **URL:**
http://www.primarytimes.net/magazine.php. **Formerly:**
OSM (Avon) Our Schools Magazine. **Ad Rates:** 4C:
1,350. **Circ:** Free 72,000

52724 ■ Quick Cards Made Easy
Origin Publishing Ltd.
Tower House

Fairfax St.
Bristol BS1 3BN, United Kingdom
Ph: 44 117 9279009
Fax: 44 117 9349008
Publisher E-mail: info@originpublishing.co.uk
Magazine for card makers featuring card designs for
every occasion. **Founded:** 2004. **Freq:** 13/yr. **Key Per-
sonnel:** Melanie Harris, Advertising Mgr., phone 44 117
3148367, melanieharris@originpublishing.co.uk; Alison
Zak-Collin, Gp. Ad Mgr. **Subscription Rates:** 3.99 single
issue; 60 individuals. **Remarks:** Accepts advertising.
URL: http://www.originpublishing.co.uk/magazine.asp?
id=18. **Circ:** ★16,927

52725 ■ Reports on Progress in Physics
IOP Publishing Ltd.
Dirac House
Temple Back
Bristol BS1 6BE, United Kingdom
Ph: 44 117 9297481
Fax: 44 117 9294318
Publication E-mail: rop@iop.org
Publisher E-mail: custserv@iop.org
Journal publishing reviews covering all branches of
physics, containing articles surveying the development
of selected topics, typically over the previous decade,
within the wider context of physics. **Freq:** Monthly. **Key
Personnel:** Laura H. Greene, Editor-in-Chief,
lhgreene@illinois.edu; George T. Gillies, Dep. Ed., gtg@
virginia.edu. **ISSN:** 0034-4885. **URL:** http://www.iop.org/
ej/journal/ropp.

52726 ■ Reproduction
BioScientifica Ltd.
Euro House
22 Apex Ct.
Woodlands
Bradley Stoke
Bristol BS32 4JT, United Kingdom
Ph: 44 14 54642220
Fax: 44 14 54642201
Journal publishing original research and topical reviews
on the subject of reproductive biology. **Freq:** Monthly.
Key Personnel: Tom Fleming, Editor-in-Chief; Kevin
Sinclair, Review Ed. **ISSN:** 1741-7899. **Subscription
Rates:** US$2,629 institutions North America (print and
online); US$2,191 institutions North America (online
only); 1,337 institutions, other countries print and online;
EUR1,999 institutions print and online; EUR1,666 institu-
tions online only; 1,114 institutions, other countries online only. **URL:** http://www.reproduction-online.org.

**52727 ■ Research in Astronomy and Astrophys-
ics**
IOP Publishing Ltd.
Dirac House
Temple Back
Bristol BS1 6BE, United Kingdom
Ph: 44 117 9297481
Fax: 44 117 9294318
Publication E-mail: raa@raa-journal.org
Publisher E-mail: custserv@iop.org
Journal featuring research papers in astronomy and
astrophysics. **Freq:** Monthly. **Key Personnel:** Jingxiu
Wang, Editor-in-Chief, wangjx@ourstar.bao.ac.cn;
Yipeng Jing, Editor-in-Chief, ypjing@shao.ac.cn. **ISSN:**
1674-4527. **URL:** http://www.iop.org/EJ/journal/RAA.

52728 ■ Reviews in Gynaecological Practice
Mountain Association for Community Economic
Development
Southmead Hospital
Bristol, United Kingdom
Publisher E-mail: info@maced.org
Journal publishing addressing the practical, clinical is-
sues on key areas, following a problem oriented ap-
proach to include diagnosis, treatment and patient
management. **Freq:** Quarterly. **Key Personnel:** S. Vyas,
Editor-in-Chief; A. Cutner, Assoc. Ed.; S. Elneil, Assoc.
Ed. **ISSN:** 1471-7697. **Remarks:** Accepts advertising.
URL: http://www.elsevier.com/wps/find/
journaldescription.cws_home/631576/
descriptiondescription. **Circ:** (Not Reported)

**52729 ■ Science and Technology of Advanced
Materials**
Institute of Physics
Dirac House
Temple Back
Bristol BS1 6BE, United Kingdom

Ph: 44 117 9297481
Fax: 44 117 9294318
Publication E-mail: stam@iop.org
Publisher E-mail: custserv@iop.org
Journal dealing with design of materials. **Founded:** 2000. **Freq:** 8/yr. **Key Personnel:** Teruo Kishi, Editor-in-Chief; Lennart Bergstrom, Assoc. Ed.; Fatih Dogan, Assoc. Ed.; Tsuyoshi Masumoto, Honorary Ed.; Yoshio Sakka, Co-Ed., yoshida@plasma.t.u-tokyo.ac.jp. **ISSN:** 1468-6996. **URL:** http://www.iop.org/EJ/journal/stam.

52730 ■ Sky at Night Magazine
BBC Worldwide Publishing Ltd.
Tower House, 9th Fl.
Fairfax St.
Bristol BS1 3BN, United Kingdom
Publication E-mail: skyatnight@sevicehelpline.co.uk
Magazine for amateur astronomers and armchair space enthusiasts. **Founded:** 2005. **Freq:** Monthly. **Key Personnel:** Amie Price-Bates, Advertising Mgr., amieprice-bates@bbcmagazines.co.uk. **Subscription Rates:** 4.25 single issue; 19.10 individuals 6 issues; 40.80 individuals. **Remarks:** Accepts advertising. **URL:** http://www.skyatnightmagazine.com/; http://www.bbcmagazinesbristol.com/magazine.asp?id=22. **Circ:** (Not Reported)

52731 ■ Smart Materials and Structures
IOP Publishing Ltd.
Dirac House
Temple Back
Bristol BS1 6BE, United Kingdom
Ph: 44 117 9297481
Fax: 44 117 9294318
Publication E-mail: sms@iop.org
Publisher E-mail: custserv@iop.org
Journal covering technical areas concerned with smart materials and structures, such as materials science: composites, ceramics, processing science, interface science, sensor/actuator materials, chiral materials, conducting and chiral polymers, electrochromic materials, liquid crystals, molecular-level smart materials, biomaterials and sensing and actuation: electromagnetic, acoustic, chemical and mechanical sensing and actuation, single-measurand sensors, multiplexed multimeasurand distributed sensors and actuators, sensor/actuator signal processing, compatibility of sensors and actuators with conventional and advanced materials, smart sensors for materials and composites processing. **Freq:** Bimonthly. **Key Personnel:** E. Garcia, Editor-in-Chief; D. Abbott, Assoc. Ed.; Y. Matsuzaki, Assoc. Ed.; C. Boller, Assoc. Ed.; G. Akhras, Assoc. Ed. **ISSN:** 0964-1726. **URL:** http://www.iop.org/ej/journal/sms.

52732 ■ Survey Review
Commonwealth Association of Surveying and Land Economy
c/o Mrs. Susan Spedding
Faculty of Built Environment
University of W of England, Frenchay Campus
Coldharbour Ln.
Bristol BS16 1QY, United Kingdom
Ph: 44 17 3283036
Fax: 44 17 3283036
Publisher E-mail: susan.spedding@uwe.ac.uk
Technical journal covering land surveying and geomatics. **Founded:** 1931. **Freq:** Quarterly January, April, July and October. **Trim Size:** 170 x 245 mm. **Cols./Page:** 1. **Col. Depth:** 200 millimeters. **Key Personnel:** A.L. Allan, Editorial Board; S. Frank, Editorial Board; N. El-Sheimy, Editorial Board; C. Dann, Editorial Board; Mrs. Susan Spedding, Admin. Sec.; J.R. Smith, Editor, jim@smith1780.freeserve.co.uk. **ISSN:** 0039-6265. **Subscription Rates:** 98 individuals Europe; US$182 U.S., Canada, and Mexico; 229 institutions; US$435 U.S., Canada, and Mexico institution. **Remarks:** Accepts advertising. **URL:** http://www.surveyreview.org. **Ad Rates:** BW: 175. **Circ:** (Not Reported)

52733 ■ 220 Triathlon
Origin Publishing Ltd.
Tower House
Fairfax St.
Bristol BS1 3BN, United Kingdom
Ph: 44 117 9279009
Fax: 44 117 9349008
Publisher E-mail: info@originpublishing.co.uk
Magazine featuring the world of multisports. **Founded:**

1989. **Freq:** 13/yr. **Key Personnel:** Alison Zak-Collins, Gp. Ad Mgr.; Eleanor Godwin, Advertising Mgr., phone 44 117 9338013, eleanorgodwin@originpublishing.co.uk. **Subscription Rates:** 16.98 single issue; 39 individuals credit/debit card. **Remarks:** Accepts advertising. **URL:** http://www.220triathlon.com; http://www.originpublishing.co.uk/magazine.asp?id=16. **Circ:** 23,500

52734 ■ University Caterer
Wildfire Communications Ltd.
Unit 2.4 Paintworks
Arnos Vale
Totterdown
Bristol BS4 3EN, United Kingdom
Ph: 44 117 9029977
Fax: 44 117 9029978
Publisher E-mail: webmaster@wildfirecomms.co.uk
Magazine covering full spectrum of catering in the higher education. **Founded:** Sept. 2004. **Freq:** Monthly. **Key Personnel:** Duncan Wilde, Contact, duncan.wilde@wildfirecomms.co.uk. **Subscription Rates:** Free every university in UK. **Remarks:** Accepts advertising. **URL:** http://www.tuco.org/magazine. **Circ:** 2,500

52735 ■ Voluntary Sector Review
Policy Press
University of Bristol
Beacon House, 4th Fl.
Queen's Road
Bristol BS8 1QU UK, United Kingdom
Ph: 44 0117 331 4054
Fax: 44 0117 331 4093
Publisher E-mail: tpp-info@bristol.ac.uk
Peer-reviewed journal publishing articles on the voluntary sector studies. **Key Personnel:** Peter Halfpenny, Editor. **ISSN:** 2040-8056. **Subscription Rates:** 52 individuals UK & Europe (print only); 73 other countries print only; 305 institutions UK & Europe (print and online); 335 institutions, other countries print and online; 274 institutions UK & Europe (online only); 274 institutions, other countries online only. **URL:** http://www.policypress.co.uk/journals_vsr.asp.

52736 ■ Who Do You Think You Are?
BBC Worldwide Publishing Ltd.
Tower House, 9th Fl.
Fairfax St.
Bristol BS1 3BN, United Kingdom
Magazine covering the TV series Who Do You Think You Are?. **Founded:** 2007. **Freq:** 13/yr. **Key Personnel:** Richard Gibson, Advertising Mgr., richardgibson@bbcmagazinesbristol.com. **Subscription Rates:** 4.25 single issue. **Remarks:** Accepts advertising. **URL:** http://www.bbcwhodoyouthinkyouare.com; http://www.bbcmagazinesbristol.com/magazine.asp?id=34. **Circ:** ★20,266

52737 ■ The World of Cross Stitching
Origin Publishing Ltd.
Tower House
Fairfax St.
Bristol BS1 3BN, United Kingdom
Ph: 44 117 9279009
Fax: 44 117 9349008
Publisher E-mail: info@originpublishing.co.uk
Cross stitch magazine featuring designs, expert advice, product news. **Founded:** 1997. **Freq:** 13/yr. **Key Personnel:** Alison Zak-Collins, Gp. Ad Mgr.; Melanie Harris, Advertising Mgr., phone 44 117 3148367, melanieharris@originpublishing.co.uk; Michaela Montague, Account Mgr., phone 44 117 3148754, michaelamontague@originpublishing.co.uk. **Subscription Rates:** 3.99 single issue. **Remarks:** Accepts advertising. **URL:** http://www.originpublishing.co.uk/magazine.asp?id=1. **Circ:** ★40,116

52738 ■ Your Hair (Bristol)
Origin Publishing Ltd.
Tower House
Fairfax St.
Bristol BS1 3BN, United Kingdom
Ph: 44 117 9279009
Fax: 44 117 9349008
Publisher E-mail: info@originpublishing.co.uk
Magazines about hair styling, care, etc. **Founded:** 2000. **Freq:** Monthly. **Key Personnel:** Alison Zak-Collins, Gp. Ad Mgr.; Russ Cowley, Advertising Mgr., phone 44 117 3148369, russcowley@originpublishing.co.uk. **Sub-**

scription Rates: 2.99 single issue. **URL:** http://www.originpublishing.co.uk/magazine.asp?id=12. **Circ:** ★30,727

52739 ■ BBC Radio-AM - 1548
PO Box 194
Bristol BS99 7QT, United Kingdom
Ph: 44 117 9741111
Fax: 44 117 9238323
E-mail: radio.bristol@bbc.co.uk
Format: News; Sports; Talk. **Owner:** British Broadcasting Corp., Broadcasting House, Portland Pl., London W1A 1AA, United Kingdom. **Operating Hours:** Continuous. **URL:** http://www.bbc.co.uk/bristol/local_radio/index.shtml.

52740 ■ BBC Radio-FM - 94.9
PO Box 194
Bristol BS99 7QT, United Kingdom
Ph: 44 117 9741111
Fax: 44 117 9238323
E-mail: radio.bristol@bbc.co.uk
Format: News; Sports; Talk. **Owner:** British Broadcasting Corp., Broadcasting House, Portland Pl., London W1A 1AA, United Kingdom. **Operating Hours:** Continuous. **URL:** http://www.bbc.co.uk/bristol/local_radio.

52741 ■ BC-FM - 93.2
The Beacon Ctr.
Russell Town Ave.
Bristol BS5 9JH, United Kingdom
Ph: 44 117 9553721
E-mail: info@bcfm.org.uk
Format: Ethnic. **Key Personnel:** Phil Gibbons, Station Mgr., phil@bcfm.org.uk. **URL:** http://www.bcfm.org.uk/index.php?option=com_frontpage&Itemid=1-.

52742 ■ Kiss 101-FM - 101
26 Baldwin St.
Bristol BS1 1SE, United Kingdom
Ph: 44 117 9010101
Format: Urban Contemporary. **Formerly:** Vibe 101-FM. **Operating Hours:** Continuous. **Key Personnel:** Nathan Thomson, Contact, phone 44 117 9309143; Susannah Cole, Contact, phone 44 117 9309102. **Ad Rates:** Advertising accepted; rates available upon request. **URL:** http://www.totalkiss.com.

52743 ■ Original-FM - 106.5
County Gates
Ashton Rd.
Bristol BS3 2JH, United Kingdom
Ph: 44 117 9661106
Fax: 44 117 9531065
Format: Adult Album Alternative. **Ad Rates:** Advertising accepted; rates available upon request. **URL:** http://www.originalbristol.com/.

Broadstairs

52744 ■ Antiques Info
Antiques Information Services Ltd.
PO Box 93
Broadstairs CT10 3YR, United Kingdom
Ph: 44 1843 862069
Fax: 44 1843 862014
Publisher E-mail: webmaster@antiques-info.co.uk
Magazine listing antiques fairs and information on auctions. **Freq:** Bimonthly. **Subscription Rates:** 95.40 individuals U.K.; 122.40 individuals Europe; 140.40 individuals Rest of the World; 95.60 individuals Europe; 107.60 individuals world. **URL:** http://www.antiques-info.co.uk.

Bromley

52745 ■ FQ
3 Dimensional Media Ltd.
Seymour House
South St.
Bromley BR1 1RH, United Kingdom
Ph: 44 20 84606060
Fax: 44 20 84606050
Publication E-mail: contactus@fqmagazine.co.uk
Publisher E-mail: info@3dmediaworld.com
Magazine targeting today's modern man by celebrating parenthood and lifestyle changes that come along with it. **Subscription Rates:** 16 individuals U.K. customers only; 61 individuals international; 46 individuals in

Europe. **Remarks:** Accepts advertising. **URL:** http://www.fqmagazine.co.uk. **Circ:** (Not Reported)

Bromsgrove

52746 ■ Bromsgrove Standard
Observer Standard Newspapers Ltd.
44 High St.
Bromsgrove B61 8HQ, United Kingdom
Ph: 44 1527 588688
Publisher E-mail: hq@observerstandard.com
Local Community newspaper. **Freq:** Weekly. **Key Personnel:** Tristan Harris, Editor, editor@bromsgrovestandard.co.uk. **Remarks:** Accepts advertising. **URL:** http://www.bromsgrovestandard.co.uk/. **Circ:** (Not Reported)

52747 ■ Droitwich Standard
Observer Standard Newspapers Ltd.
44 High St.
Bromsgrove B61 8HQ, United Kingdom
Ph: 44 1527 574111
Publisher E-mail: hq@observerstandard.com
Local community newspaper. **Freq:** Weekly. **Key Personnel:** Tristan Harris, Editor, editor@bromsgrovestandard.co.uk. **Remarks:** Accepts advertising. **URL:** http://www.droitwichstandard.co.uk/. **Circ:** (Not Reported)

52748 ■ Homebuilding & Renovating
Ascent Publishing Ltd.
2 Sugar Brook Ct.
Aston Rd.
Bromsgrove B60 3EX, United Kingdom
Publisher E-mail: customerservice@centaur.com.uk
Magazine covering home building and renovating for the do-it-yourselfer. **Freq:** Monthly. **Key Personnel:** Jackie Smith, Online Commericial Dir., jackie.smith@centaur.co.uk; Michael Holmes, Editor-in-Chief, michael.holmes@centaur.co.uk; Gill Grimshaw, Group Advertising Dir., gill.grimshaw@centaur.co.uk; Peter Harris, Founder, peter.harris@centaur.co.uk. **Subscription Rates:** 18 individuals; 50 two years; 58 other countries. **Remarks:** Accepts advertising. **URL:** http://www.homebuilding.co.uk/; http://www.centaur.co.uk. **Circ:** ★41,602

Brookfield

52749 ■ The Scottish Beekeeper
Scottish Beekeepers' Association
c/o Ian Craig, Pres.
30 Burnside Ave.
Brookfield PA5 8UT, United Kingdom
Publisher E-mail: ian@iancraig.wanadoo.co.uk
Magazine containing general beekeeping subjects and technical services. **Freq:** Monthly. **Subscription Rates:** included in membership dues. **Remarks:** Accepts advertising. **URL:** http://www.scottishbeekeepers.org.uk/. **Circ:** (Not Reported)

Buckhurst Hill

52750 ■ Machinery World
Sheen Publishing Ltd.
50 Queens Rd.
Buckhurst Hill IG9 5DD, United Kingdom
Ph: 44 20 85041661
Fax: 44 20 85054336
Publication E-mail: machinery@sheenpublishing.co.uk
Publisher E-mail: sheenpublishing@sheenpublishing.co.uk
Magazine for machinery and production engineering market. **Founded:** 1982. **Freq:** Monthly. **Trim Size:** 210 x 297 mm. **Key Personnel:** Carole Titmuss, Publisher; Tony Prior, Editor and Publisher. **Subscription Rates:** 30 individuals; 50 individuals to Europe; 70 other countries. **Remarks:** Accepts advertising. **URL:** http://www.sheenpublishing.com/machinery_world/index.php. **Ad Rates:** BW: 420, BW: 420. **Circ:** ★9,000

52751 ■ Plant World
Sheen Publishing Ltd.
50 Queens Rd.
Buckhurst Hill IG9 5DD, United Kingdom
Ph: 44 20 85041661
Fax: 44 20 85054336
Publication E-mail: plant@sheenpublishing.co.uk

Publisher E-mail: sheenpublishing@sheenpublishing.co.uk
Magazine for construction plant and equipment market. **Founded:** 1981. **Freq:** Monthly. **Trim Size:** 190 x 123 mm. **Key Personnel:** Dannii Titmuss, Editor; Carole Titmuss, Mng. Dir.; Tony Titmuss, Co-Publisher. **Subscription Rates:** 45 individuals; 85 individuals to Europe; 95 other countries. **Remarks:** Accepts advertising. **URL:** http://www.sheenpublishing.com/plant_world/index.php. **Ad Rates:** 4C: 165. **Circ:** ★11,606

52752 ■ Refurbishment Projects
Sheen Publishing Ltd.
50 Queens Rd.
Buckhurst Hill IG9 5DD, United Kingdom
Ph: 44 20 85041661
Fax: 44 20 85054336
Publication E-mail: refurb@sheenpublishing.co.uk
Publisher E-mail: sheenpublishing@sheenpublishing.co.uk
Journal covering repair, maintenance, refurbishment, restoration and conservation sectors of the United Kingdom Building Industry. **Founded:** 1987. **Freq:** Monthly. **Trim Size:** 145 x 170 mm. **Key Personnel:** Tony Prior, Managing Editor; Peter Ashmore, Editor; Wendy Burnett, General Mgr. **Subscription Rates:** 18 individuals; 33 individuals to Europe; 36 other countries. **Remarks:** Accepts advertising. **URL:** http://www.sheenpublishing.com/refurb_projects/index.php. **Ad Rates:** BW: 800, 4C: 650. **Circ:** ★10,138

52753 ■ Secure Times
Sheen Publishing Ltd.
50 Queens Rd.
Buckhurst Hill IG9 5DD, United Kingdom
Ph: 44 20 85041661
Fax: 44 20 85054336
Publication E-mail: secure@sheenpublishing.co.uk
Publisher E-mail: sheenpublishing@sheenpublishing.co.uk
Magazine for professionals in security industry. **Subtitle:** The Journal for Fire, Safety, & Security Professionals. **Freq:** 3/yr. **Trim Size:** 210 x 296 mm. **Key Personnel:** Tony Prior, Editor and Publisher; Carole Titmuss, Publisher. **Subscription Rates:** 10 individuals; 20 individuals to Europe; 25 other countries. **Remarks:** Accepts advertising. **URL:** http://www.sheenpublishing.com/secure_times/index.php. **Ad Rates:** BW: 675, 4C: 750. **Circ:** ‡9,306

Buckingham

52754 ■ Biofouling
Taylor & Francis Group Journals
Yeomanry House
University of Buckingham
Hunter St.
Buckingham MK18 1EG, United Kingdom
Ph: 44 12 80820264
Fax: 44 12 80820267
Publisher E-mail: customerservice@taylorandfrancis.com
Peer-reviewed journal focusing on microbial, plant or animal fouling and its control, as well as studies of all kinds on bioadhesion and biofilms, including biofouling of medical and dental equipment and implants. **Subtitle:** The Journal of Bioadhesion & Biofilm Research. **Freq:** 8/yr. **Key Personnel:** Len Evans, Editor-in-Chief, mfbn@btinternet.com; Maureen Callow, Asst. Ed., m.e.callow@bham.ac.uk; Anne Meyer, Asst. Ed., aemeyer@acsu.buffalo.edu; R. Alberte, Editorial Board; Brenda Little, Editor, little@nrlssc.navy.mil; Paul Stoodley, Editor, pstoodle@epahs.org. **ISSN:** 0892-7014. **Subscription Rates:** US$690 individuals; US$3,073 institutions online only; 2,193 institutions online only; US$3,235 institutions print & online; 3,208 institutions print & online; 414 individuals; EUR551 individuals; EUR2,458 institutions online only; EUR2,587 institutions print & online. **URL:** http://www.tandf.co.uk/journals/journal.asp?issn=0892-7014& linktype=5.

52755 ■ Buckingham & Winslow Advertiser
Johnston Press PLC
61-62 Well St.
Buckingham MK18 1EN, United Kingdom
Ph: 44 1280 827940
Local community newspaper. **Key Personnel:** Clare Brennan, Editor, phone 44 1280 827970, fax 44 1280 823729, clare.brennan@jpress.co.uk; Vicky Key, Advertising Mgr., vicky.key@ccnltd.com. **Remarks:** Accepts

advertising. **URL:** http://www.buckinghamtoday.co.uk/. **Circ:** (Not Reported)

52756 ■ The Denning Law Journal
University of Buckingham Press
University of Buckingham
Buckingham MK18 1EG, United Kingdom
Ph: 44 1280 814080
Publisher E-mail: christopher.woodhead@buckingham.ac.uk
Peer-reviewed Journal covering values cherished by Lord Denning. **Key Personnel:** Prof. Susan Edwards, PhD, Editor, susan.edwards@buckingham.ac.uk; Christopher Woodhead, Publisher, christopher.woodhead@buckingham.ac.uk. **ISSN:** 0269-1922. **Subscription Rates:** 75 individuals. **URL:** http://www.ubpl.co.uk; http://www.denninglawjournal.com/.

52757 ■ The Journal of Gambling Business and Economics
University of Buckingham Press
University of Buckingham
Buckingham MK18 1EG, United Kingdom
Ph: 44 1280 814080
Publisher E-mail: christopher.woodhead@buckingham.ac.uk
Peer-reviewed Journal covering business and economic aspects of the study of gambling. **Key Personnel:** Prof. Leighton Vaughan Williams, Editor. **ISSN:** 1751-7990. **Subscription Rates:** 75 individuals paper and online; 50 individuals online only; 150 institutions paper and online; 99 institutions online only. **URL:** http://www.jgbe.com/.

52758 ■ The Journal of Prediction Markets
University of Buckingham Press
University of Buckingham
Buckingham MK18 1EG, United Kingdom
Ph: 44 1280 814080
Publisher E-mail: christopher.woodhead@buckingham.ac.uk
Peer-reviewed journal covering aspect of the study of prediction markets. **Key Personnel:** Prof. Leighton Vaughan Williams, Editor; Bruno Deschamps, Assoc. Ed. **ISSN:** 1750-6751. **Subscription Rates:** 75 individuals paper and online; 50 individuals online only; 150 institutions paper and online; 99 institutions online only. **URL:** http://www.predictionmarketjournal.com/.

Buntingford

52759 ■ Environmental Engineering
Society of Environmental Engineers
The Manor House, High St.
Buntingford SG9 9AB, United Kingdom
Ph: 44 17 63271209
Fax: 44 17 63273255
Publisher E-mail: office@environmental.org.uk
Publication covering environmental engineering. **Freq:** Quarterly. **Key Personnel:** Nigel Searle, Sales Mgr., phone 44 20 72223337, nigelse@pepublishing.com; Tristan Honeywill, Editor; John Pullin, Editorial Dir. **Remarks:** Accepts advertising. **URL:** http://www.environmental.org.uk/index.php?name=Content&pid=41. **Ad Rates:** BW: 2,000. **Circ:** 7,500

Burford

52760 ■ Journal of Society for Companion Animal Studies
SCAS
The Blue Cross
Shilton Rd.
Burford OX18 4PF, United Kingdom
Ph: 44 19 93825597
Fax: 44 19 93825598
Journal covering the Society for Companion Animal Studies. **Founded:** 1998. **Freq:** Quarterly. **Key Personnel:** Jo-an Fowler, Editor. **ISSN:** 1363-464X. **Subscription Rates:** 2.50 nonmembers. **Remarks:** Advertising accepted; rates available upon request. **URL:** http://www.scas.org.uk/; http://www.scas.org.uk/Publications/SCAS_Journal.aspx. **Circ:** 500

Burgess Hill

52761 ■ Teaching Business & Economics
Economics and Business Education Association
The Forum
277 London Rd.

Burgess Hill RH15 9QU, United Kingdom
Ph: 44 1444 240150
Fax: 44 1444 240101
Publisher E-mail: office@ebea.org.uk
Publication covering business education. **Freq:** October, February and May. **Key Personnel:** Nancy Wall, Gen. Ed., phone 44 1825 723267, enwall@aol.com. **ISSN:** 1367-3289. **Subscription Rates:** Included in membership. **Remarks:** Advertising accepted; rates available upon request. **URL:** http://www.ebea.org.uk/publications/. **Circ:** 3,200

52762 ■ Bright 106.4-FM - 106.4
Market Place Shopping Ctr., Unit 34
Burgess Hill RH15 9NP, United Kingdom
Ph: 44 144 4248899
E-mail: reception@bright1064.com
Format: Adult Contemporary; Top 40; Oldies. **Ad Rates:** Advertising accepted; rates available upon request. **URL:** http://www.bright1064.com/.

Burnham

52763 ■ Appropriate Technology
Research Information Ltd.
Grenville Ct.
Britwell Rd.
Burnham SL1 8DF, United Kingdom
Ph: 44 1628 600499
Fax: 44 1628 600488
Publisher E-mail: info@researchinformation.co.uk
Trade magazine covering practical technology, policies and issues for the elimination of poverty and hunger in third world countries and worldwide. **Subtitle:** Incorporating International Agricultural Development. **Founded:** 1974. **Freq:** Quarterly. **Trim Size:** 178 x 254 mm. **Key Personnel:** David Dixon, Editor, d.dixon@farmline.com. **ISSN:** 0305-0920. **Subscription Rates:** 158 individuals standard; US$316 individuals standard; 52 individuals; US$104 individuals. **Remarks:** Accepts advertising. **URL:** http://www.researchinformation.co.uk/apte.php. **Absorbed:** Agriculture & Equipment International. **Ad Rates:** BW: US$1,425, 4C: US$1,890. **Circ:** Controlled 3,000

52764 ■ Electronic Materials & Packaging
Research Information Ltd.
Grenville Ct.
Britwell Rd.
Burnham SL1 8DF, United Kingdom
Ph: 44 1628 600499
Fax: 44 1628 600488
Publisher E-mail: info@researchinformation.co.uk
Publication covering technical and business developments in electronic packaging. **Founded:** 1990. **Freq:** Bimonthly. **Key Personnel:** Keith Gurnett, Editor. **ISSN:** 1355-7599. **Remarks:** Advertising not accepted. **URL:** http://www.researchinformation.co.uk/. **Circ:** (Not Reported)

52765 ■ International Journal of Micrographics & Optical Technology
Research Information Ltd.
Grenville Ct.
Britwell Rd.
Burnham SL1 8DF, United Kingdom
Ph: 44 1628 600499
Fax: 44 1628 600488
Publisher E-mail: info@researchinformation.co.uk
Publication for workflow and document management professionals. **Founded:** 1982. **Freq:** Bimonthly. **Key Personnel:** Bob Yorke, Editor, bobyorke@researchinformation.co.uk. **ISSN:** 0958-9961. **Subscription Rates:** 310 individuals standard; US$620 individuals standard. **Remarks:** Advertising not accepted. **URL:** http://www.researchinformation.co.uk/mote.php. **Circ:** (Not Reported)

52766 ■ International Pest Control
Research Information Ltd.
Grenville Ct.
Britwell Rd.
Burnham SL1 8DF, United Kingdom
Ph: 44 1628 600499
Fax: 44 1628 600488
Publisher E-mail: info@researchinformation.co.uk
Trade magazine covering all aspects of pest prevention and eradication, including crop protection, food storage, forestry, animal welfare and public health. **Founded:**

1958. **Freq:** Bimonthly. **Trim Size:** A4. **Key Personnel:** Nigel Binns, Editor. **ISSN:** 0020-8256. **Subscription Rates:** 85 individuals; US$170 individuals; 156 institutions standard; US$312 institutions standard. **Remarks:** Accepts advertising. **URL:** http://www.researchinformation.co.uk/ipco.php. **Ad Rates:** BW: US$1,425, BW: US$750, 4C: US$1,645, 4C: US$995. **Circ:** (Not Reported)

52767 ■ Outlooks on Pest Management
Research Information Ltd.
Grenville Ct.
Britwell Rd.
Burnham SL1 8DF, United Kingdom
Ph: 44 1628 600499
Fax: 44 1628 600488
Publisher E-mail: info@researchinformation.co.uk
Journal providing a blend of international news and reviews covering all aspects of the management of weeds, pests and diseases through chemistry, biology and biotechnology. **Freq:** Bimonthly. **Key Personnel:** Graham Matthews, Editorial Board; Roger Turner, Editorial Board; Ken Pallett, Editorial Board; Nancy Ragsdale, Editorial Board; Phil Russell, Editorial Board; Len Copping, Ch. Ed. **ISSN:** 1743-1026. **Subscription Rates:** 575 individuals; US$1,150 individuals. **Remarks:** Advertising accepted; rates available upon request. **URL:** http://www.researchinformation.co.uk/pest.php. **Circ:** (Not Reported)

52768 ■ World Food Regulation Review
Research Information Ltd.
Grenville Ct.
Britwell Rd.
Burnham SL1 8DF, United Kingdom
Ph: 44 1628 600499
Fax: 44 1628 600488
Publisher E-mail: info@researchinformation.co.uk
Journal providing essential coverage of new laws, regulations, codes of practice, government actions worldwide, news and developments in the regulation and control of foodstuffs such as safety, agriculture, nutritional labeling regulations, food additives and pesticide residues. **Freq:** Monthly. **Key Personnel:** Bob Yorke, Managing Editor, bobyorke@researchinformation.co.uk. **ISSN:** 0963-4894. **Subscription Rates:** US$1,144 individuals standard; 572 individuals standard. **Remarks:** Advertising not accepted. **URL:** http://www.researchinformation.co.uk/wfrr.php. **Circ:** (Not Reported)

Burnham-on-Crouch

52769 ■ Saint-FM - 94.7
St. Peter's High School
Southminster Rd.
Burnham-on-Crouch CM0 8QB, United Kingdom
Ph: 44 1621 785689
E-mail: studio@saintfm.org.uk
Format: Eclectic. **Operating Hours:** Continuous. **URL:** http://www.saintfm.org.uk/.

Burton-on-Trent

52770 ■ Burton Mail
Burton Daily Mail Ltd.
65-68 High St.
Burton-on-Trent DE14 1LE, United Kingdom
Publication E-mail: editorial@burtonmail.co.uk
General newspaper. **Founded:** 1899. **Freq:** Daily. **Print Method:** Web offset. **Trim Size:** 29 x 40 cm. **Cols./Page:** 7. **Col. Width:** 8.6 picas. **Col. Depth:** 36 centimeters. **Remarks:** Accepts advertising. **URL:** http://www.burtonmail.co.uk. **Circ:** Paid ‡15,665

52771 ■ Ships Monthly
IPC Magazine Media Ltd.
222 Branston Rd.
Burton-on-Trent DE14 3BT, United Kingdom
Ph: 44 12 83542721
Trade magazine covering ships. **Founded:** 1966. **Freq:** Monthly. **Print Method:** Web offset. **Trim Size:** 210 x 297 mm. **Key Personnel:** Nick Hopkinson, Publishing Dir., phone 44 20 87268119, nick_hopkinson@ipcmedia.com; Iain Wakefield, Editor, phone 44 12 83542741, iain_wakefield@ipcmedia.com; Carol Storer, Subscriptions Mgr., ships_subs@ipcmedia.com; Nicholas Leach, Dep. Ed., nicholas_leach@ipcmedia.com. **ISSN:** 0037-394X. **Subscription Rates:** 45.60 individuals; 67.40 individuals Europe inc Eire; 78.50 other countries. **URL:**

http://www.shipsmonthly.com/ships/home.htm; http://www.ipcmedia.com. **Ad Rates:** BW: 361, 4C: 546. **Circ:** (Not Reported)

52772 ■ Singing
Association of Teachers of Singing
Weir House
108 Newton Rd.
Burton-on-Trent DE15 0TT, United Kingdom
Ph: 44 12 83542198
Fax: 44 12 83542198
Publication covering music specialty singing. **Subtitle:** Voice of the Association of Teachers of Singing. **Founded:** 1981. **Freq:** Semiannual Summer and Winter. **Print Method:** Lithography. **Trim Size:** A4. **Key Personnel:** Sue Anderson, Editor. **Subscription Rates:** Free to members. **Remarks:** Accepts advertising. **URL:** http://aotos.org.uk/magazine.php. **Ad Rates:** GLR: EUR40 to 50, BW: EUR100. **Circ:** (Not Reported)

Bury Saint Edmunds

52773 ■ Bury Free Press
Johnston Press PLC
King's Rd.
Bury Saint Edmunds IP33 3ET, United Kingdom
Ph: 44 1284 768911
Local community newspaper. **Freq:** Weekly. **Key Personnel:** Barry Peters, Editor, fax 44 1284 755619, barry.peters@buryfreepress.co.uk; Jamie Brodie, Advertising Mgr., phone 44 1284 757824, jamie.brodie@jpress.co.uk. **Remarks:** Accepts advertising. **URL:** http://www.buryfreepress.co.uk/. **Circ:** (Not Reported)

52774 ■ Journal of the Writing Equipment Society
Writing Equipment Society
c/o Mr. Martin Roberts
53 Horsecroft Rd.
Suffolk
Bury Saint Edmunds IP33 2DT, United Kingdom
Ph: 44 1284 750978
Publisher E-mail: membership@wesonline.org.uk
Journal for members of the Writing Equipment Society. News, views and relevant articles. **Founded:** 1980. **Freq:** 3/yr. **Trim Size:** A4. **Key Personnel:** Mike West, Advertising Mgr., advertise@wesonline.org.uk; Dr. David Shepherd, Editor, editor@wesonline.org.uk. **URL:** http://www.wesonline.org.uk/journal.html. **Ad Rates:** BW: 80, 4C: 350. **Circ:** 600

52775 ■ Kiss 105-FM - 105
Olding Rd.
Bury Saint Edmunds IP33 3TA, United Kingdom
Ph: 44 1284 715300
Format: Urban Contemporary; Sports; News; Eclectic. **Formerly:** Vibe 105-FM. **Operating Hours:** Continuous,Mon.-Sat.; 7 a.m.-4 a.m. Sun. **Key Personnel:** Glen White, Program Mgr., phone 44 1284 715311. **Ad Rates:** Advertising accepted; rates available upon request. **URL:** http://www.totalkiss.com/.

Bushey

52776 ■ The Landscaper
The Metropolis Group
Bournehall Rd.
Bushey WD23 3ZF, United Kingdom
Publisher E-mail: metropolis@metropolis.co.uk
Magazine for professional landscapers. **Founded:** 1998. **Freq:** Monthly. **Trim Size:** 150 x 219 mm. **Key Personnel:** David Curtis, Editor, phone 44 208 2538381, david.curtis@metropolis.co.uk. **Remarks:** Accepts advertising. **URL:** http://www.landscapermagazine.com/; http://www.metropolis.co.uk/landscaper.html. **Circ:** 7,000

Buxton

52777 ■ Buxton Advertiser
Johnston Press PLC
10 Scarsdale Pl.
Buxton SK17 6EG, United Kingdom
Ph: 44 1298 767070
Publication E-mail: news@buxtonadvertiser.co.uk
Local community newspaper. **Freq:** Weekly (Thurs.). **Remarks:** Accepts advertising. **URL:** http://www.buxtonadvertiser.co.uk/. **Circ:** (Not Reported)

52778 ■ Cave & Karst Science
British Cave Research Association

The Old Methodist Chapel
Great Hucklow
Buxton SK17 8RG, United Kingdom
Ph: 44 1298 873810
Fax: 44 1298 873801
Publisher E-mail: bcra-enquiries@bcra.org.uk
Journal covering research on caves in the U.K. and worldwide. **Subtitle:** The Transactions of the British Cave Research Association. **Founded:** 1974. **Freq:** 3/yr. **Trim Size:** A4. **Key Personnel:** John Gunn, Editor; David Lowe, Editor. **ISSN:** 1356-191X. **Subscription Rates:** 24 individuals print; 18 individuals online. **URL:** http://www.bcra.org.uk/pub/candks/index.html. **Circ:** Paid 1,000

52779 ■ Speleology
British Cave Research Association
The Old Methodist Chapel
Great Hucklow
Buxton SK17 8RG, United Kingdom
Ph: 44 1298 873810
Fax: 44 1298 873801
Publication E-mail: speleology@bcra.org.uk
Publisher E-mail: bcra-enquiries@bcra.org.uk
Publication covering cave exploration in the U.K. and worldwide. **Subtitle:** The Bulletin of the British Cave Research Association. **Founded:** 1976. **Freq:** 3/yr. **Trim Size:** A4. **Key Personnel:** Erin Lynch, Editor. **ISSN:** 1478-999X. **Subscription Rates:** 10 nonmembers; Included in membership. **Remarks:** Accepts advertising. **URL:** http://www.bcra.org.uk/pub/speleology/index.html. **Formerly:** Caves & Caving. **Circ:** Combined 1,200

52780 ■ High Peak Radio-FM - 106.4
PO Box 106
High Peak SK23 0DJ, United Kingdom
Ph: 44 1298 813377
Fax: 44 1298 813388
E-mail: info@highpeakradio.co.uk
Format: Adult Contemporary. **Operating Hours:** Continuous. **URL:** http://www.highpeakradio.co.uk/.

Caerfyrddin

52781 ■ Cambria
PO Box 22
Caerfyrddin SA32 7YH, United Kingdom
Ph: 44 845 1662147
Magazine covering Welsh culture, lifestyle, politics, and interviews and articles on leading figures in Wales. **Subscription Rates:** 18 individuals. **URL:** http://www.cambriamagazine.com/.

Camberley

52782 ■ BIIBUSINESS
British Institute of Innkeeping
Wessex House
80 Park St.
Camberley GU15 3PT, United Kingdom
Ph: 44 12 76684449
Fax: 44 12 7623045
Publisher E-mail: reception@bii.org
Magazine containing articles on licensing reform, smoking, qualifications and training. **Freq:** Monthly 10/yr. **Subscription Rates:** 50 individuals. **Remarks:** Advertising accepted; rates available upon request. **URL:** http://bii.org/news/biibusiness. **Circ:** (Not Reported)

52783 ■ CareerScope
ISCO Careerscope
St. George's House
Knoll Rd.
Surrey
Camberley GU15 3SY, United Kingdom
Ph: 44 1276 687525
Publication E-mail: careerscope@inspiringfutures.org.uk
Magazine containing current career information. **Freq:** 3/yr. **Remarks:** Accepts advertising. **URL:** http://www.isco.org.uk. **Circ:** (Not Reported)

52784 ■ Concrete
The Concrete Society
Riverside House, 4 Meadows Business Pk.
Sta. Approach, Blackwater
Camberley GU17 9AB, United Kingdom
Ph: 44 12 76607140
Fax: 44 12 76607141
Trade journal of The Concrete Society covering developments in concrete technology, materials, testing and

design. **Subtitle:** For the Construction Industry. **Founded:** 1967. **Freq:** 11/yr. **Print Method:** Litho. **Trim Size:** A4. **ISSN:** 0010-5317. **Subscription Rates:** 120 individuals; 142.50 individuals Europe; 157.50 other countries. **URL:** http://www.concrete.org.uk/products/mag_concrete.asp. **Ad Rates:** BW: 1,140, 4C: 1,650. **Circ:** Paid 5,500

Cambridge

52785 ■ Ageing and Society
Cambridge University Press
The Edinburgh Bldg.
Shaftesbury Rd.
Cambridge CB2 2RU, United Kingdom
Ph: 44 122 3312393
Fax: 44 122 3315052
Publisher E-mail: information@cambridge.org
Publication focusing on seniors and related issues. **Freq:** Bimonthly. **Key Personnel:** Prof. Tony Warnes, Editor; Dr. Mima Cattan, Assoc. Ed.; Dr. Caroline Holland, Book Review Ed. **ISSN:** 0144-686X. **Subscription Rates:** 70 individuals online and print; US$120 individuals print and online; 281 institutions online and print; US$499 institutions print and online; 241 institutions online only; US$411 institutions online only. **URL:** http://journals.cambridge.org/action/displayJournal?jid=ASO.

52786 ■ Analyst
Royal Society of Chemistry
Thomas Graham House
The Science Pk., Milton Rd.
Milton Rd.
Cambridge CB4 0WF, United Kingdom
Ph: 44 12 23420066
Fax: 44 12 23423623
Publisher E-mail: sales@rsc.org
Journal covering analytical sciences. **Freq:** Monthly. **Key Personnel:** May Copsey, Editor. **ISSN:** 0003-2654. **Subscription Rates:** 1,367 individuals print + online; US$2,552 individuals print + online; 1,231 individuals online only; US$2,297 individuals online only. **URL:** http://www.rsc.org/Publishing/Journals/an/index.asp.

52787 ■ Analytical Abstract
Royal Society of Chemistry
Thomas Graham House
The Science Pk., Milton Rd.
Milton Rd.
Cambridge CB4 0WF, United Kingdom
Ph: 44 12 23420066
Fax: 44 12 23423623
Publisher E-mail: sales@rsc.org
Journal featuring latest techniques and applications in the analytical sciences. **Freq:** Monthly. **Key Personnel:** Graham McCann, Publisher. **ISSN:** 0003-2689. **Subscription Rates:** 2,819 individuals print + online; US$5,263 individuals print + online; 2,538 individuals online only; US$4,737 individuals online only. **URL:** http://www.rsc.org/Publishing/CurrentAwareness/AA/index.asp.

52788 ■ Annals of Glaciology
International Glaciological Society - Scott Polar Research Institute
Lensfield Rd.
Cambridge CB2 1ER, United Kingdom
Ph: 44 12 23355974
Fax: 44 12 23354931
Publisher E-mail: igsoc@igsoc.org
Journal covering glaciology. **Founded:** 1980. **Freq:** 1-2/yr. **ISSN:** 0260-3055. **Subscription Rates:** Included in membership. **Remarks:** Advertising not accepted. **URL:** http://www.igsoc.org/annals/. **Circ:** Paid 500

52789 ■ Anthrozoos
Berg Publishers
University of Cambridge
Dept. of Veterinary Medicine
Cambridge CB3 0ES, United Kingdom
Peer-reviewed journal containing the latest scientific evidence about the ways animals influence our health, well-being and culture. **Subtitle:** A Multidisciplinary Journal on the Interactions of People and Animals. **Founded:** 1987. **Freq:** Quarterly. **Print Method:** Perfect bound. **Trim Size:** 6 x 9. **Cols./Page:** 2. **Col. Width:** 2 1/8 inches. **Col. Depth:** 8 inches. **Key Personnel:** Dr. Anthony Podberscek, Editor-in-Chief, alp18@cam.ac.uk. **ISSN:** 0892-7936. **Subscription Rates:** 169 institutions print and online; 144 institutions online only. **Remarks:**

Accepts advertising. **URL:** http://www.isaz.net/anthrozoos.html. **Ad Rates:** BW: 175. **Circ:** Paid 850, Non-paid 50

52790 ■ Applied Bionics and Biomechanics
Woodhead Publishing Ltd.
Abington Hall, Granta Park
Great Abington
Cambridge CB21 6AH, United Kingdom
Ph: 44 12 23891358
Fax: 44 12 23893694
Publisher E-mail: wp@woodheadpublishing.com
International, peer reviewed journal covering advanced technological developments based on the science of biological systems, including artificial body parts and related devices (both implantable and extracorporeal) and other applications of synthetic bionic systems, particularly those that is medically-oriented. **Freq:** Quarterly. **Key Personnel:** Andre Aubert, Editorial Board; Laurance Cheze, Editorial Board; Danilo De Rossi, Editorial Board; Dr. R. Mayorga, Editor-in-Chief. **ISSN:** 1176-2322. **Subscription Rates:** 510 individuals; US$645 individuals North and South America; 340 individuals rest of World. **URL:** http://www.woodheadpublishing.com/en/.

52791 ■ Behavioral and Brain Sciences
Cambridge University Press
The Edinburgh Bldg.
Shaftesbury Rd.
Cambridge CB2 2RU, United Kingdom
Ph: 44 122 3312393
Fax: 44 122 3315052
Publisher E-mail: information@cambridge.org
Publication covering psychology and mental health. **Subtitle:** An International Journal of Current Research and Theory with Open Peer Commentary. **Founded:** 1978. **Freq:** Quarterly. **Trim Size:** 278 X 210 mm. **Key Personnel:** Prof. Paul Bloom, Editor; Prof. Barbara L. Finlay, Editor; Dr. Shimon Edelman, Editorial Board, se37@cornell.edu; Dr. Wim E. Crusio, Editorial Board, wim_crusio@yahoo.com; Dr. Charles A. Catania, Editorial Board, catania@umbc.edu; Dr. Max Coltheart, Editorial Board, max@maccs.mq.edu.au; Prof. Robert Freidin, Editorial Board, bob@clarity.princeton.edu; Dr. Annette Karmiloff-Smith, Editorial Board, a.karmiloff-smith@bbk.ac.uk. **ISSN:** 0140-525X. **Subscription Rates:** 510 institutions online; 603 institutions print and online; 177 individuals print and online; US$302 institutions print and online. **Remarks:** Accepts advertising. **URL:** http://journals.cambridge.org/action/displayJournal?jid=BBS. **Ad Rates:** BW: US$1,035, 4C: US$2,875. **Circ:** Paid 2,100

52792 ■ Biological Reviews
John Wiley & Sons Inc.
Wiley-Blackwell
c/o Dr. William A. Foster, Ed.
Cambridge Philosophical Society
Bene't St.
Cambridge CB2 3PY, United Kingdom
Journal covering articles on biological sciences. **Founded:** 1951. **Freq:** Quarterly. **Print Method:** Offset. **Trim Size:** 8 1/8 x 10 3/8. **Cols./Page:** 3. **Col. Width:** 27 nonpareils. **Col. Depth:** 140 agate lines. **Key Personnel:** Tim Benton, Editorial Board; Mark Chase, Editorial Board; Dr. William A. Foster, Editor; Alison Cooper, Asst. Ed. **ISSN:** 1464-7931. **Subscription Rates:** 264 institutions print and online; US$489 institutions print and online; US$571 institutions, other countries online and print; US$445 institutions print. **URL:** http://www.wiley.com/bw/journal.asp?ref=1464-7931&site=1.

52793 ■ Bird Conservation International
BirdLife International
Wellbrook Ct.
Girton Rd.
Cambridge CB3 0NA, United Kingdom
Ph: 44 12 23277318
Fax: 44 12 23277200
Publisher E-mail: birdlife@birdlife.org
Journal focusing on major issues affecting birds and their habitats. **Freq:** Quarterly. **Key Personnel:** Dr. Thomas Brooks, Assoc. Ed.; Dr. Paul Donald, Assoc. Ed.; Prof. Stephen Garnett, Assoc. Ed.; Dr. Peter Ryan, Assoc. Ed.; Dr. Phil Atkinson, Editor-in-Chief, bcieditor@bto.org; Dr. Margaret Kinnaird, Assoc. Ed.; Prof. R.E. Green, Assoc. Ed.; Dr. Peter Jones, Assoc. Ed. **ISSN:** 0959-2709. **Subscription Rates:** 228 institutions online

and print; US$433 institutions online and print; 199 institutions online only; US$385 institutions online only. **URL:** http://journals.cambridge.org/action/displayJournal?jid=BCI; http://www.birdlife.org/publications/bci/index.html.

52794 ■ Boat and Yacht Buyer
CSL Publishing Ltd.
Alliance House
49 Sidney St.
Cambridge CB2 3HX, United Kingdom
Ph: 44 1223 460490
Fax: 44 1223 315960
Magazine featuring boats and boating accessories for sale. **Freq:** 13/yr. **Key Personnel:** Sam Broome, Contact, sam@boatmart.co.uk. **Subscription Rates:** 28.73 individuals; 38.73 other countries. **Remarks:** Accepts advertising. **URL:** http://www.boatandyachtbuyer.co.uk/. **Circ:** 20,000

52795 ■ British Journal of Nutrition
Cambridge University Press
The Edinburgh Bldg.
Shaftesbury Rd.
Cambridge CB2 2RU, United Kingdom
Ph: 44 122 3312393
Fax: 44 122 3315052
Publisher E-mail: information@cambridge.org
Peer-reviewed international journal publishing original papers, review articles, short communications and technical notes on human and clinical nutrition, general nutrition and animal nutrition. **Freq:** Bimonthly. **Key Personnel:** P. Yaqoob, Editorial Board; Prof. P.C. Calder, Editor-in-Chief; Prof. J.C. Mathers, Reviews Ed.; Dr. F. Bellisle, Dep. Ed.; Dr. A.E. Buyken, Editorial Board; Dr. D.R. Jacobs, Jr., Dep. Ed.; Prof. R.J. Wallace, Dep. Ed.; Dr. D. Attaix, Editorial Board. **ISSN:** 0007-1145. **Subscription Rates:** US$1,566 institutions online only; US$1,860 institutions print and online; EUR1,283 institutions online only; EUR1,528 institutions print and online; 803 institutions online only; 954 institutions print and online. **Remarks:** Accepts advertising. **URL:** http://journals.cambridge.org/action/displayJournal?jid=bjn. **Ad Rates:** BW: US$1,160. **Circ:** Combined 1,500

52796 ■ British Journal of Political Science
Cambridge University Press
The Edinburgh Bldg.
Shaftesbury Rd.
Cambridge CB2 2RU, United Kingdom
Ph: 44 122 3312393
Fax: 44 122 3315052
Publisher E-mail: information@cambridge.org
Political science publication. **Freq:** Quarterly. **Key Personnel:** Dr. Sarah Birch, Editor, bircsi@essex.ac.uk; Prof. David Sanders, Editorial Board, jayned@essex.ac.uk; Prof. Gary Cox, Editorial Board; Prof. Chris Brown, Editorial Board; Prof. James Alt, Editorial Board; Prof. Archie Brown, Editorial Board; Prof. Albert Weale, Editorial Board; Prof. H.B. Berrington, Editorial Board; Prof. Randall Calvert, Editorial Board. **ISSN:** 0007-1234. **Subscription Rates:** 224 institutions online; 257 institutions print and online; US$399 institutions online; US$449 institutions print and online. **URL:** http://journals.cambridge.org/action/displayJournal?jid=JPS. **Circ:** 1,350

52797 ■ British Yearbook of International Law
Oxford University Press
c/o Prof. James Crawford, Ed.
Lauterpacht Research Centre for International Law
University of Cambridge
5 Cranmer Rd.
Cambridge CB3 9BL, United Kingdom
Ph: 44 12 23335358
Fax: 44 12 23300406
Publisher E-mail: webenquiry.uk@oup.com
Law periodical. **Freq:** Annual. **Key Personnel:** Prof. James Crawford, Editor, jrc1000@hermes.cam.ac.uk; Prof. Vaughan Lowe, Editor; Prof. Craig J. Barker, Book Review Ed. **ISSN:** 0068-2691. **Subscription Rates:** 145 individuals. **URL:** http://ukcatalogue.oup.com/product/9780198181682.do.

52798 ■ The Cambridge Law Journal
Cambridge University Press
c/o Prof. John Bell, Ed.
Faculty of Law
University of Cambridge
10 West Rd.

Cambridge CB3 9DZ, United Kingdom
Publisher E-mail: information@cambridge.org
Law journal. **Freq:** Quarterly. **Key Personnel:** Mr. J. Rowbottom, Book Review Ed., clj.reviews@law.cam.ac.uk; Prof. John Bell, Editor, clj.editors@law.cam.ac.uk; Prof. C.F. Forsyth, Editorial Committee. **ISSN:** 0008-1973. **Subscription Rates:** 79 institutions online and print; 71 institutions online only; US$148 institutions online and print; US$131 institutions online only. **Remarks:** Accepts advertising. **URL:** http://journals.cambridge.org/action/displayJournal?jid=CLJ. **Circ:** 1,600

52799 ■ The Cambridge Quarterly
Oxford University Press
c/o Anne Newton, Mng. Ed.
Cambridge Quarterly
Clare College
Cambridge CB2 1TL, United Kingdom
Publisher E-mail: webenquiry.uk@oup.com
Publication covering literature and writing. **Freq:** Quarterly. **Key Personnel:** Ann Newton, Managing Editor, apn1000@cantab.net; R.D. Gooder, Editorial Board; F. Johnston, Editorial Board. **ISSN:** 0008-199X. **Subscription Rates:** 174 institutions print and online; US$339 institutions print and online; EUR261 institutions print and online; 145 institutions print only or online only; US$283 institutions print only or online only; EUR218 institutions print only or online only. **URL:** http://camqtly.oupjournals.org/.

52800 ■ Cambridgeshire Agenda
Archant Regional Ltd.
Alexander House, Ste. 3
Milton Rd.
Cambridge CB4 1UY, United Kingdom
Ph: 44 1223 365733
Fax: 44 1223 309226
Publication E-mail: agenda@archant.co.uk
Publisher E-mail: sandra.roantree@archant.co.uk
Magazine featuring the Cambridge county lifestyle. **Key Personnel:** Olivia Abbott, Editor, phone 44 1223 341908, olivia.abbott@archant.co.uk; Paul Richardson, Editorial Dir., paul.richardson@archant.co.uk. **Remarks:** Accepts advertising. **URL:** http://agenda.greatbritishlife.co.uk/. **Circ:** Combined 30,000

52801 ■ Cambridgeshire Property Plus
Archant Regional Ltd.
Alexander House, Ste. 3
Milton Rd.
Cambridge CB4 1UY, United Kingdom
Ph: 44 1223 309227
Fax: 44 1223 309226
Publisher E-mail: sandra.roantree@archant.co.uk
Magazine featuring the local property market in Cambridge. **Freq:** Weekly. **Key Personnel:** Stuart Mc-Creery, Mng. Dir. **Remarks:** Accepts advertising. **URL:** http://www.cambridgeshirepropertyplus.co.uk/content/propertyplus/default.aspx. **Circ:** (Not Reported)

52802 ■ Catalysts & Catalysed Reactions
Royal Society of Chemistry
Thomas Graham House
The Science Pk., Milton Rd.
Milton Rd.
Cambridge CB4 0WF, United Kingdom
Ph: 44 12 23420066
Fax: 44 12 23423623
Publisher E-mail: sales@rsc.org
Journal featuring graphical abstracts of new developments in catalysis. **Freq:** Monthly. **Key Personnel:** Graham McCann, Publisher. **ISSN:** 1474-9173. **Subscription Rates:** 785 individuals print + online; US$1,466 individuals print + online; 707 individuals online; US$1,319 individuals online. **URL:** http://www.rsc.org/Publishing/CurrentAwareness/CCR/index.asp.

52803 ■ Chemical Communications
Royal Society of Chemistry
Thomas Graham House
The Science Pk., Milton Rd.
Milton Rd.
Cambridge CB4 0WF, United Kingdom
Ph: 44 12 23420066
Fax: 44 12 23423623
Publisher E-mail: sales@rsc.org
Professional journal covering chemical communications. **Founded:** 1965. **Freq:** 48/yr. **Trim Size:** 210 x 297 mm. **Key Personnel:** Robert D. Eagling, Editor. **ISSN:** 1359-7345. **Subscription Rates:** 2,237 individuals print and

online; US$4,175 individuals print and online; 2,013 individuals online only; US$3,757 individuals online only. **Remarks:** Accepts advertising. **URL:** http://www.rsc.org/Publishing/Journals/cc/index.asp. **Former name:** Journal of the Chemical Society Chemical Communications. **Ad Rates:** BW: 755. **Circ:** Paid 3,000

52804 ■ Chemical Society Reviews
Royal Society of Chemistry
Thomas Graham House
The Science Pk., Milton Rd.
Milton Rd.
Cambridge CB4 0WF, United Kingdom
Ph: 44 12 23420066
Fax: 44 12 23423623
Publisher E-mail: sales@rsc.org
Professional publication covering chemistry. **Founded:** 1972. **Freq:** Monthly. **Key Personnel:** Dr. Robert D. Eagling, Editor. **ISSN:** 0306-0012. **Subscription Rates:** 586 individuals print + online; US$1,094 individuals print + online; 527 individuals online only; US$984 individuals online only. **Remarks:** Advertising accepted; rates available upon request. **URL:** http://www.rsc.org/Publishing/Journals/CS/article.asp?type=CurrentIssue. **Circ:** (Not Reported)

52805 ■ Chemistry Education Research and Practice
Royal Society of Chemistry
Thomas Graham House
The Science Pk., Milton Rd.
Milton Rd.
Cambridge CB4 0WF, United Kingdom
Ph: 44 12 23420066
Fax: 44 12 23423623
Publisher E-mail: sales@rsc.org
Journal for teachers, researchers, and other practitioners in chemistry education. **Freq:** 4/yr. **Key Personnel:** Stephen Breuer, Joint Ed.; Georgios Tsaparlis, Joint Ed. **Subscription Rates:** Free online. **URL:** http://www.rsc.org/Publishing/Journals/RP/index.asp.

52806 ■ Chinese Journal of Agricultural Biotechnology
Cambridge University Press
The Edinburgh Bldg.
Shaftesbury Rd.
Cambridge CB2 2RU, United Kingdom
Ph: 44 122 3312393
Fax: 44 122 3315052
Publisher E-mail: information@cambridge.org
Journal covering subjects such as biotechnology (cellular, chromosomal, enzymatic, genetic, and fermentation engineering) of agricultural plants, animals, and relevant microorganisms (including nitrogen fixing bacteria and pathogens), and related biochemistry and structural analysis. **Freq:** 3/yr. **Key Personnel:** Prof. R. Hull, Editor-in-Chief. **ISSN:** 1479-2362. **Subscription Rates:** 527 institutions online and print; US$1,005 institutions online and print; 418 institutions online only; US$798 institutions online only; 303 individuals online and print; US$583 individuals online and print; 100 individuals online only; US$195 individuals online only. **Remarks:** Accepts advertising. **URL:** http://journals.cambridge.org/action/displayJournal?jid=CJA. **Ad Rates:** BW: 245. **Circ:** (Not Reported)

52807 ■ Combinatorics, Probability and Computing
Cambridge University Press
c/o Prof. Bela Bollobas, Ed.-in-Ch.
Ctr. for Mathematical Sciences
University of Cambridge
Wilberforce Rd.
Cambridge CB3 0WB, United Kingdom
Publisher E-mail: customer_service@cup.org
Journal focusing on combinatorics, and related theoretical sciences. **Freq:** Bimonthly. **Key Personnel:** Dr. Imre Leader, Managing Editor, i.leader@dpmms.cam.ac.uk, ucl.ac.uk; Prof. Alex Scott, Editorial Board, scott@maths.ox.ac.uk; Prof. Graham Brightwell, Editorial Board, g.r.brightwell@lse.ac.uk; Prof. Bela Bollobas, Editor-in-Chief, b.bollobas@dpmms.cam.ac.uk. **ISSN:** 0963-5483. **Subscription Rates:** US$640 institutions print + online; US$576 institutions online. **Remarks:** Accepts advertising. **URL:** http://journals.cambridge.org/action/displayJournal?jid=CPC. **Ad Rates:** BW: 845. **Circ:** 300

Circulation: ★ = ABC; △ = BPA; ◆ = CAC; • = CCAB; ❑ = VAC; ⊕ = PO Statement; ‡ = Publisher's Report; Boldface figures = sworn; Light figures = estimated.

52808 ■ Comparative Exercise Physiology
Cambridge University Press
The Edinburgh Bldg.
Shaftesbury Rd.
Cambridge CB2 2RU, United Kingdom
Ph: 44 122 3312393
Fax: 44 122 3315052
Publisher E-mail: information@cambridge.org
Peer-reviewed journal dealing with the latest research in equine exercise physiology. **Freq:** Quarterly. **Key Personnel:** D. Marlin, Editor. **ISSN:** 1755-2540. **Subscription Rates:** 328 institutions print & online; US$635 institutions print & online; 260 institutions online; US$505 institutions online; 190 individuals print & online; US$365 individuals print & online; 108 individuals online; US$210 individuals online. **Remarks:** Accepts advertising. **URL:** http://journals.cambridge.org/action/displayJournal?jid=CEP. **Formerly:** Equine and Comparative Exercise Physiology. **Circ:** (Not Reported)

52809 ■ Comparative Studies in Society and History
Cambridge University Press
The Edinburgh Bldg.
Shaftesbury Rd.
Cambridge CB2 2RU, United Kingdom
Ph: 44 122 3312393
Fax: 44 122 3315052
Publisher E-mail: information@cambridge.org
Periodical focusing on history. **Freq:** Quarterly. **Key Personnel:** Thomas Trautmann, Editorial Committee, cssh@umich.edu; David Akin, Managing Editor, cssh@umich.edu; Diane Owen Hughes, Editorial Committee. **ISSN:** 0010-4175. **Subscription Rates:** 135 institutions online and print; US$181 institutions online only; 29 individuals print only; US$211 individuals online and print; 115 institutions online only; US$56 individuals print only. **Remarks:** Accepts advertising. **URL:** http://journals.cambridge.org/action/displayJournal?jid=CSS. **Circ:** 2,000

52810 ■ Connect
TWI Ltd.
Granta Pk.
Great Abington
Cambridge CB21 6AL, United Kingdom
Ph: 44 12 23899000
Fax: 44 12 23892588
Publisher E-mail: twi@twi.co.uk
Publication covering industrial equipment. **Freq:** Bimonthly. **Print Method:** Lithograph. **Trim Size:** A4. **Remarks:** Advertising not accepted. **URL:** http://www.twi.co.uk. **Circ:** (Not Reported)

52811 ■ Contemporary European History
Cambridge University Press
The Edinburgh Bldg.
Shaftesbury Rd.
Cambridge CB2 2RU, United Kingdom
Ph: 44 122 3312393
Fax: 44 122 3315052
Publisher E-mail: information@cambridge.org
Journal covering Eastern and Western European history from 1918 to the present. **Founded:** 1992. **Freq:** Quarterly. **Key Personnel:** Prof. Jonathan Morris, Editorial Board; Dr. Neville Wylie, Editor, neville.wylie@nottingham.ac.uk; Dr. Holger Nehring, Assoc. Ed., h.nehring@sheffield.ac.uk. **ISSN:** 0960-7773. **Subscription Rates:** US$272 institutions online and print; 156 institutions online and print; US$234 institutions online only; 135 institutions online only. **Remarks:** Accepts advertising. **URL:** http://journals.cambridge.org/action/displayJournal?jid=CEH. **Ad Rates:** BW: 835. **Circ:** 650

52812 ■ Contributions to Political Economy
Oxford University Press
c/o Murray Milgate, Ed.
Queens College
Cambridge CB3 9ET, United Kingdom
Publisher E-mail: webenquiry.uk@oup.com
Journal providing a forum for the academic discussion of original ideas and arguments drawn from important critical traditions in economic analysis. **Freq:** Annual. **Key Personnel:** Murray Milgate, Editor; John Eatwell, Editor; Giancarlo De Vivo, Editor. **ISSN:** 0277-5921. **Subscription Rates:** 86 institutions corporate; print and online; 72 institutions corporate; online only; 79 institutions corporate; print only; 70 institutions print and online; 58 institutions online only; 64 institutions print only;

25 individuals print. **Remarks:** Advertising accepted; rates available upon request. **URL:** http://cpe.oxfordjournals.org. **Circ:** (Not Reported)

52813 ■ CrystEngComm
Royal Society of Chemistry
Thomas Graham House
The Science Pk., Milton Rd.
Milton Rd.
Cambridge CB4 0WF, United Kingdom
Ph: 44 12 23420066
Fax: 44 12 23423623
Publisher E-mail: sales@rsc.org
Peer-reviewed journal dealing with aspects of crystal engineering. **Founded:** Oct. 1999. **Freq:** Monthly. **Key Personnel:** Jamie Humphrey, Editor. **ISSN:** 1466-8033. **Subscription Rates:** US$776 individuals online only; 416 individuals online only. **Remarks:** Advertising accepted; rates available upon request. **URL:** http://www.rsc.org/publishing/journals/ce/index.asp. **Circ:** (Not Reported)

52814 ■ Dalton Transactions
Royal Society of Chemistry
Thomas Graham House
The Science Pk., Milton Rd.
Milton Rd.
Cambridge CB4 0WF, United Kingdom
Ph: 44 12 23420066
Fax: 44 12 23423623
Publisher E-mail: sales@rsc.org
Journal dealing with inorganic and organometallic compounds, including biological inorganic chemistry and solid-state inorganic chemistry and to study their structure, properties and reactions. **Freq:** 48/yr. **Key Personnel:** Jamie Humphrey, Editor. **ISSN:** 1477-9226. **Subscription Rates:** 2,680 individuals print + online; US$5,002 individuals print + online; 2,412 individuals online only; US$4,502 individuals online only. **Remarks:** Advertising accepted; rates available upon request. **URL:** http://www.rsc.org/publishing/journals/dt/about.asp. **Circ:** (Not Reported)

52815 ■ Early Music
Oxford University Press
Faculty of Music
University of Cambridge
11 West Rd.
Cambridge CB3 9DP, United Kingdom
Ph: 44 1223 335178
Publisher E-mail: webenquiry.uk@oup.com
Publication covering early music. **Founded:** Feb. 1973. **Freq:** 4/yr. **Key Personnel:** Tess Knighton, Editorial Board; John Milsom, Editorial Board; Francis Knights, Editor; Ann Lewis, Editorial Asst.; Manuel Carlos De Brito, Consultant Ed.; Petr Danek, Consultant Ed. **ISSN:** 0306-1078. **Subscription Rates:** US$334 institutions print and online; US$278 institutions online, print; EUR251 institutions print and online; 209 institutions print and online; 139 institutions online, print; EUR209 institutions print, online; 62 individuals print; US$118 individuals print; EUR93 individuals print; 37 individuals print (senior). **Remarks:** Accepts advertising. **Online:** Gale. **URL:** http://em.oupjournals.org/. **Circ:** (Not Reported)

52816 ■ Eighteenth Century Music
Cambridge University Press
The Edinburgh Bldg.
Shaftesbury Rd.
Cambridge CB2 2RU, United Kingdom
Ph: 44 122 3312393
Fax: 44 122 3315052
Publisher E-mail: information@cambridge.org
Journal drawing together disparate areas of research, challenging accepted historical assumptions and adopting a broad and interdisciplinary approach which will serve the whole eighteenth-century music community. **Key Personnel:** Dr. Dean W. Sutcliffe, Editor, 18cmusic@kcl.ac.uk; Prof. Simon Keefe, Editorial Board; Dr. Keith Chapin, Editorial Board. **ISSN:** 1478-5706. **Subscription Rates:** 84 institutions online and print; US$147 institutions online and print; 77 institutions online only; US$134 institutions online only. **Remarks:** Accepts advertising. **URL:** http://journals.cambridge.org/action/displayJournal?jid=ECM. **Ad Rates:** BW: 415. **Circ:** (Not Reported)

52817 ■ Energy & Environmental Science
Royal Society of Chemistry
Thomas Graham House
The Science Pk., Milton Rd.

Milton Rd.
Cambridge CB4 0WF, United Kingdom
Ph: 44 12 23420066
Fax: 44 12 23423623
Publisher E-mail: sales@rsc.org
Journal focusing on energy conversion and storage, alternative fuel technologies, and environmental science. **Freq:** Monthly. **Key Personnel:** Mr. Philip Earis, Editor. **ISSN:** 1754-5692. **Subscription Rates:** 1,050 individuals print + online; US$2,000 individuals print + online; 945 individuals online; US$1,800 individuals online. **URL:** http://www.rsc.org/Publishing/Journals/EE/index.asp.

52818 ■ Environmental Practice
Cambridge University Press
The Edinburgh Bldg.
Shaftesbury Rd.
Cambridge CB2 2RU, United Kingdom
Ph: 44 122 3312393
Fax: 44 122 3315052
Publisher E-mail: information@cambridge.org
Journal covering environmental issues on behalf of the National Association of Environmental Professionals. **Freq:** Quarterly. **Key Personnel:** Kelly Tzoumis, Editor-in-Chief, kellytzoumis@ameritech.net. **ISSN:** 1466-0466. **Subscription Rates:** 172 institutions online & print; US$319 institutions online & print; 137 institutions online only; US$260 institutions online only. **Remarks:** Accepts advertising. **URL:** http://journals.cambridge.org/action/displayJournal?jid=ENP. **Ad Rates:** 4C: 870. **Circ:** (Not Reported)

52819 ■ Faraday Discussions
Royal Society of Chemistry
Thomas Graham House
The Science Pk., Milton Rd.
Milton Rd.
Cambridge CB4 0WF, United Kingdom
Ph: 44 12 23420066
Fax: 44 12 23423623
Publisher E-mail: sales@rsc.org
Professional journal covering physical chemistry and chemical physics papers presented at Faraday Discussion meetings. **Founded:** 1907. **Freq:** 4/yr. **Key Personnel:** Dr. Nicola Nugent, Sen. Publishing Ed.; Philip Earis, Editor; Jane Hordern, Deputy Ed. **ISSN:** 1359-6640. **Subscription Rates:** 622 individuals print + online; 560 individuals online only; US$1,160 individuals print + online; US$1,045 individuals online only. **Remarks:** Advertising not accepted. **URL:** http://pubs.rsc.org/en/Journals/JournalIssues/FD. **Circ:** (Not Reported)

52820 ■ FEBS Journal
John Wiley & Sons Inc.
Wiley-Blackwell
98 Regent St.
Cambridge CB2 1DP, United Kingdom
Ph: 44 12 23369020
Fax: 44 12 23369090
Publication E-mail: febsj@camfebs.co.uk
Journal focusing on molecular biosciences. **Key Personnel:** Richard Perham, Editor-in-Chief, perham@camfebs.co.uk; Ferdinand Hucho, Reviews Ed., hucho@chemie.fu-berlin.de; Rolf Apweiler, Editor, apweiler@ebi.ac.uk; Carmen Birchmeier, Editor, c.birch@mdc-berlin.de; Jan Johansson, Editor, jan.johansson@vmk.slu.se. **Subscription Rates:** US$5,567 institutions print + online; US$5,062 institutions print or online; 3,013 institutions print + online; 2,739 institutions print or online; EUR3,826 institutions print + online; EUR3,478 institutions print or online; US$6,495 institutions, other countries print + online; US$5,905 institutions, other countries print or online. **Remarks:** Accepts advertising. **URL:** http://www.febsjournal.org/default.asp. **Circ:** (Not Reported)

52821 ■ Focus on Catalysts
Elsevier Science Inc.
c/o J. Bingham, In-house Ed.
Elsevier Ltd.
Westbrook Ctr., Block 6
Milton Rd.
Cambridge CB4 1YG, United Kingdom
Ph: 44 1223 463160
Fax: 44 1223 463169
Publisher E-mail: usinfo-ehelp@elsevier.com
Journal covering monitoring technical and commercial developments in the manufacture and use of catalysts. **Freq:** Monthly. **Print Method:** Offset. **Cols./Page:** 6.

Col. Width: 24 nonpareils. **Col. Depth:** 303 agate lines. **Key Personnel:** A.E. Comyns, Editor; J. Bingham, In-house Ed., bingham_j@elsevier.com. **ISSN:** 1351-4180. **Subscription Rates:** US$1,230 institutions, other countries except Europe, Japan and Iran; 145,400¥ institutions; EUR1,090 institutions for European countries and Iran. **URL:** http://www.elsevier.com/wps/find/journaldescription.cws_home/622619/descriptiondescription.

52822 ■ GEO
GeoConnexion Ltd.
PO Box 594
Cambridge CB1 0FY, United Kingdom
Ph: 44 1223 279151
Fax: 44 1223 279148
Publisher E-mail: maiward@geoconnexion.com
Magazine devoted to users of spatial technologies in the British Isles, continental Europe, the Middle East, and Africa. **Subtitle:** Connexion. **Freq:** Monthly. **Key Personnel:** Maria Pellegrini, Editor, phone 44 7816 893097, maria@geoconnexion.com; Mai Ward, Publisher, maiward@geoconnexion.com; Micki Knight, Sales & Mktg. Contact, phone 44 114 2681133, mickiknight@geoconnexion.com; Eva Thompson, Events Mgr., phone 44 114 2681133, evethompson@geoconnexion.com. **Subscription Rates:** 45 individuals print only; 20 individuals online only; 50 individuals print and online; EUR85 individuals print only; EUR38 individuals online only; EUR95 individuals print and online. **Remarks:** Accepts advertising. **URL:** http://www.geoconnexion.com/geo.php; http://www.geoconnexion.com/. **Ad Rates:** BW: 1,305, 4C: 1,980. **Circ:** (Not Reported)

52823 ■ Geological Magazine
Cambridge University Press
The Edinburgh Bldg.
Shaftesbury Rd.
Cambridge CB2 2RU, United Kingdom
Ph: 44 122 3312393
Fax: 44 122 3315052
Publisher E-mail: information@cambridge.org
Earth sciences journal. **Founded:** 1864. **Freq:** Bimonthly. **Key Personnel:** Dr. G.E. Budd, Editor, graham.budd@pal.uu.se; Dr. D.M. Pyle, Editor, david.pyle@earth.ox.ac.uk; A.G. Whitham, Editor; Dr. M.B. Allen, Editor, m.b.allen@durham.ac.uk; Jane Holland, Asst. Ed. **ISSN:** 0016-7568. **Subscription Rates:** 426 institutions online; 515 institutions print and online; US$868 institutions print and online; US$823 institutions online. **Remarks:** Accepts advertising. **URL:** http://journals.cambridge.org/action/displayJournal?jid=GEO. **Circ:** 850

52824 ■ German as a Foreign Language
Dept. of Languages & Intercultural Communication
Anglia Ruskin University
East Rd.
Cambridge CB1 1PT, United Kingdom
Publisher E-mail: guido.rings@anglia.ac.uk
Academic journal promoting research and teaching in the field of German Language, publishing articles in English and German on all aspects of German language teaching and learning, including the intercultural aspects involved in this process and the specific perspectives on learning and teaching German outside the German-speaking countries. **Key Personnel:** Dr. Guido Rings, Editor. **ISSN:** 1470-9570. **URL:** http://www.gfl-journal.de/.

52825 ■ Green Chemistry
Royal Society of Chemistry
Thomas Graham House
The Science Pk., Milton Rd.
Milton Rd.
Cambridge CB4 0WF, United Kingdom
Ph: 44 12 23420066
Fax: 44 12 23423623
Publisher E-mail: sales@rsc.org
Journal covering research on the development of alternative sustainable technologies. **Freq:** Monthly. **Key Personnel:** Sarah Ruthven, Editor. **ISSN:** 1463-9262. **Subscription Rates:** 1,078 individuals print + online; US$2,013 individuals print + online; 970 individuals online; US$1,811 individuals online. **URL:** http://www.rsc.org/Publishing/Journals/gc/index.asp.

52826 ■ Highlights in Chemical Biology
Royal Society of Chemistry
Thomas Graham House

The Science Pk., Milton Rd.
Milton Rd.
Cambridge CB4 0WF, United Kingdom
Ph: 44 12 23420066
Fax: 44 12 23423623
Publisher E-mail: sales@rsc.org
Journal focusing on chemical biology. **Freq:** Monthly. **Key Personnel:** Sarah Dixon, Editor. **ISSN:** 2041-5842. **Subscription Rates:** Free online. **URL:** http://www.rsc.org/Publishing/Journals/cb/Index.asp. **Formerly:** Chemical Biology.

52827 ■ Highlights in Chemical Science
Royal Society of Chemistry
Thomas Graham House
The Science Pk., Milton Rd.
Milton Rd.
Cambridge CB4 0WF, United Kingdom
Ph: 44 12 23420066
Fax: 44 12 23423623
Publisher E-mail: sales@rsc.org
Journal focusing on chemical science. **Freq:** Monthly. **Key Personnel:** Sarah Dixon, Editor. **ISSN:** 2041-580X. **Subscription Rates:** Free online. **URL:** http://www.rsc.org/Publishing/ChemScience/index.asp. **Formerly:** Chemical Science.

52828 ■ The Historical Journal
Cambridge University Press
West Rd.
Cambridge CB3 9EF, United Kingdom
Publication E-mail: hj@hist.cam.ac.uk
Publisher E-mail: information@cambridge.org
Journal publishing papers on all aspects of British, European, and world history since the fifteenth century. **Founded:** 1957. **Freq:** Quarterly. **Key Personnel:** Prof. Julian Hoppit, Editor; Dr. Clare Jackson, Editor, hjeditcj@hermes.cam.ac.uk. **ISSN:** 0018-246X. **Subscription Rates:** 279 institutions online and print; US$484 institutions online and print; 241 institutions online only; US$416 institutions online only. **URL:** http://journals.cambridge.org/action/displayJournal?jid=HIS. **Ad Rates:** BW: 470. **Circ:** 1,300

52829 ■ Human Reproduction Update
Oxford University Press
5 Mill Yard
Childerley
Cambridge CB23 8BA, United Kingdom
Ph: 44 1954 212404
Fax: 44 1954 212359
Publisher E-mail: webenquiry.uk@oup.com
Journal offering reviews of research on various human reproductions related topics. **Founded:** 1995. **Freq:** 6/yr. **Key Personnel:** M.S. Bloom, Assoc. Ed.; J. Boivin, Assoc. Ed.; J. Collins, Editor-in-Chief; R. Homburg, Assoc. Ed.; A.C. Williams, Managing Editor. **ISSN:** 1355-4786. **Subscription Rates:** 877 institutions corporate; print and online; 585 institutions corporate; online only; 804 institutions corporate; print only; 702 institutions print and online; 468 institutions online only; 644 institutions print only; 143 individuals online only; 198 individuals print; 99 institutions online only; 116 members print. **URL:** http://humupd.oxfordjournals.org.

52830 ■ Industrial Law Journal
Oxford University Press
c/o Prof. Simon Deakin, Ed.-in-Ch.
Centre for Business Research, Top Fl.
The Judge Business School Bldg.
Trumpington St.
Cambridge CB2 1AG, United Kingdom
Publisher E-mail: webenquiry.uk@oup.com
Law periodical. **Freq:** 4/yr. **Key Personnel:** Prof. Simon Deakin, Editor-in-Chief, s.deakin@cbr.cam.ac.uk; William Brown, Editorial Committee; A.K. Asmal, Editorial Committee; S.D. Anderman, Editorial Committee. **ISSN:** 0305-9332. **Subscription Rates:** 112 institutions print and online; 93 institutions online, print; US$224 institutions print and online; EUR168 institutions print and online; 75 members print; US$204 institutions print, online; EUR153 institutions print, online; 91 individuals print; US$182 individuals print; EUR137 individuals print. **Remarks:** Accepts advertising. **URL:** http://ilj.oupjournals.org/. **Circ:** (Not Reported)

52831 ■ International and Comparative Law Quarterly
Cambridge University Press
The Edinburgh Bldg.

Shaftesbury Rd.
Cambridge CB2 2RU, United Kingdom
Ph: 44 122 3312393
Fax: 44 122 3315052
Publisher E-mail: information@cambridge.org
Journal offering coverage of comparative law as well as public and private international law. **Freq:** Quarterly. **Key Personnel:** Prof. Robert McCorquodale, Editor; Prof. Catherine Redgwell, Editor; Prof. James Fawcett, Board of Ed., james.fawcett@nottingham.ac.uk. **ISSN:** 0020-5893. **Subscription Rates:** 197 institutions online and print; US$394 institutions online and print; 181 institutions online only; US$364 institutions online only. **Remarks:** Accepts advertising. **URL:** http://journals.cambridge.org/action/displayJournal?jid=ILQ. **Ad Rates:** BW: 465. **Circ:** (Not Reported)

52832 ■ International Journal of Asian Studies
Cambridge University Press
The Edinburgh Bldg.
Shaftesbury Rd.
Cambridge CB2 2RU, United Kingdom
Ph: 44 122 3312393
Fax: 44 122 3315052
Publisher E-mail: information@cambridge.org
Journal examining Asia on a regional basis, emphasising patterns and tendencies that go beyond the borders of individual countries. **Key Personnel:** Prof. Takeshi Hamashita, Editor-in-Chief; Dr. Akinobu Kuroda, Managing Editor; Dr. Robert Chard, Managing Editor. **ISSN:** 1479-5914. **Subscription Rates:** 122 institutions print and online; US$189 institutions print and online; 113 institutions online; US$176 institutions online. **Remarks:** Accepts advertising. **URL:** http://journals.cambridge.org/action/displayJournal?jid=ASI. **Ad Rates:** BW: 425. **Circ:** (Not Reported)

52833 ■ International Journal of Astrobiology
Cambridge University Press
The Edinburgh Bldg.
Shaftesbury Rd.
Cambridge CB2 2RU, United Kingdom
Ph: 44 122 3312393
Fax: 44 122 3315052
Publisher E-mail: information@cambridge.org
Peer-reviewed journal covering cosmic prebiotic chemistry, planetary evolution, the search for planetary systems and habitable zones, extremophile biology and experimental simulation of extraterrestrial environments, life detection in our solar system and beyond, intelligent life and societal aspects of astrobiology. **Freq:** Quarterly. **Key Personnel:** Prof. Helga Stan-Lotter, Assoc. Ed.; Dr. Charles Cockell, Editorial Board; Dr. Frances Westall, Assoc. Ed.; Prof. Robert E. Blankenship, Editorial Board; Dr. Natalie Cabrol, Editorial Board; Dr. Rocco Mancinelli, Assoc. Ed. **ISSN:** 1473-5504. **Subscription Rates:** US$457 institutions print and online; US$374 institutions online only; US$123 individuals online; US$145 individuals print and online; 203 institutions online; 240 institutions print and online; 65 individuals online; 78 individuals print and online. **Remarks:** Accepts advertising. **URL:** http://journals.cambridge.org/action/displayJournal?jid=IJA. **Ad Rates:** BW: US$845. **Circ:** 450

52834 ■ International Journal of Cultural Property
Cambridge University Press
The Edinburgh Bldg.
Shaftesbury Rd.
Cambridge CB2 2RU, United Kingdom
Ph: 44 122 3312393
Fax: 44 122 3315052
Publisher E-mail: information@cambridge.org
Peer-reviewd Journal covering complexities, competing values, and other concerns about cultural property, cultural heritage and related issues. **Freq:** 3/yr. **Key Personnel:** Alexander A. Bauer, Editor, culturalproperty@cambridge.org; Robert K. Paterson, Case Notes Ed., paterson@law.ubc.ca; Kurt Siehr, Chronicles Ed., siehr@mpipriv-hh.mpg.de; Michael Brown, Assoc. Ed.; Stephanie Moser, Assoc. Ed.; Gregory J. Ashworth, Editorial Board. **ISSN:** 0940-7391. **Subscription Rates:** US$338 institutions online and print; US$276 institutions online only; US$70 individuals print only; 198 institutions print and online; 35 individuals print only; 163 institutions online only. **Remarks:** Accepts advertising. **URL:** http://journals.cambridge.org/

Circulation: ★ = ABC; △ = BPA; ◆ = CAC; • = CCAB; ❏ = VAC; ⊕ = PO Statement; ‡ = Publisher's Report; Boldface figures = sworn; Light figures = estimated.

Gale Directory of Publications & Broadcast Media/147th Ed.   5611

action/displayJournal?jid=JCP. **Ad Rates:** BW: 310. **Circ:** (Not Reported)

52835 ■ International Journal of Law in Context
Cambridge University Press
The Edinburgh Bldg.
Shaftesbury Rd.
Cambridge CB2 2RU, United Kingdom
Ph: 44 122 3312393
Fax: 44 122 3315052
Publisher E-mail: information@cambridge.org
Journal publishing contextual work about law and its relationship with other disciplines, including but not limited to science, literature, humanities, philosophy, sociology, psychology, ethics, history and geography. **Key Personnel:** Prof. Michael Freeman, Editor-in-Chief, uctlmdf@ucl.ac.uk; Prof. Carrie Menkel-Meadow, Editor-in-Chief, meadow@law.georgetown.edu; Alison Diduck, International Editorial Board, a.diduck@ucl.ac.uk. **ISSN:** 1744-5523. **Subscription Rates:** 201 institutions print and online; US$363 institutions print and online; 186 institutions online only; US$334 institutions online only. **Remarks:** Accepts advertising. **URL:** http://journals. cambridge.org/action/displayJournal?jid=IJC. **Ad Rates:** BW: 445. **Circ:** (Not Reported)

52836 ■ International Journal of Middle East Studies
Cambridge University Press
The Edinburgh Bldg.
Shaftesbury Rd.
Cambridge CB2 2RU, United Kingdom
Ph: 44 122 3312393
Fax: 44 122 3315052
Publisher E-mail: information@cambridge.org
Journal focusing on history. **Freq:** Quarterly. **Key Personnel:** Ellen Fleishmann, Book Review Ed.; Jeff Culang, Asst. Book Review Ed.; Jeffrey T. Kenney, Book Review Ed.; Mandana Limbert, Book Review Ed.; Beth Baron, Editor, ijmes@gc.cuny.edu. **ISSN:** 0020-7438. **Subscription Rates:** 250 institutions online and print; US$410 institutions online and print; 212 institutions online only; US$354 institutions online only; 175 individuals online and print; US$325 individuals online and print. **Remarks:** Accepts advertising. **URL:** http://journals. cambridge.org/action/displayJournal?jid=MES. **Circ:** 3,700

52837 ■ The International Journal of Neuropsychopharmacology
Cambridge University Press
The Edinburgh Bldg.
Shaftesbury Rd.
Cambridge CB2 2RU, United Kingdom
Ph: 44 122 3312393
Fax: 44 122 3315052
Publisher E-mail: information@cambridge.org
Journal covering research relating to neuropsychopharmacology. **Freq:** Annual. **Key Personnel:** Prof. Bernard Lerer, Founding Ed., lerer@cc.huji. ac.il; Jarmo Hietala, Field Ed.; Carlo Altamura, Editorial Board; Brian Dean, Editorial Board; Klaus Ebmeier, Editorial Board; Alan Frazer, Editor-in-Chief, frazer@ uthscsa.edu; Siegfried F. Kasper, Field Ed.; Dr. P. Albert, Editorial Board. **ISSN:** 1461-1457. **Subscription Rates:** 538 institutions online and print; US$936 institutions online and print; 370 institutions online only; US$655 institutions online only; 95 individuals online only; US$170 individuals online only; 160 individuals online and print; US$280 individuals online and print. **Remarks:** Accepts advertising. **URL:** http://journals.cambridge.org/ action/displayJournal?jid=PNP. **Ad Rates:** BW: 545, 4C: 1,395. **Circ:** 1,200

52838 ■ International Journal of Tropical Insect Science
Cambridge University Press
The Edinburgh Bldg.
Shaftesbury Rd.
Cambridge CB2 2RU, United Kingdom
Ph: 44 122 3312393
Fax: 44 122 3315052
Publisher E-mail: information@cambridge.org
International peer-reviewed journal serving as a forum for original research findings on tropical insects and related arthropods, with special emphasis on their environmentally benign and sustainable management, including biological diversity, ecology, systematics, and environmental issues. **Freq:** Quarterly. **Key Personnel:** C. Borgemeister, Editor. **ISSN:** 1742-7584. **Subscrip-**

tion **Rates:** US$550 institutions online & print; US$447 institutions online only; US$320 individuals online & print; US$212 individuals online only; 234 institutions online only; 286 institutions print & online. **Remarks:** Accepts advertising. **URL:** http://journals.cambridge.org/ action/displayJournal?jid=JTI. **Circ:** (Not Reported)

52839 ■ International Review of Social History
Cambridge University Press
The Edinburgh Bldg.
Shaftesbury Rd.
Cambridge CB2 2RU, United Kingdom
Ph: 44 122 3312393
Fax: 44 122 3315052
Publisher E-mail: information@cambridge.org
Journal covering labor and social history. **Freq:** Quarterly. **Key Personnel:** Mr. Aad Blok, Exec. Ed., irsh@iisg.nl; Prof. Marcel van Der Linden, Chm./Exec. Committee; Dennis Bos, Editorial Committee. **ISSN:** 0020-8590. **Subscription Rates:** 154 institutions online & print; US$263 institutions online & print; 131 institutions online; US$226 institutions online. **Remarks:** Accepts advertising. **URL:** http://journals.cambridge.org/ action/displayJournal?jid=ISH. **Ad Rates:** BW: 885. **Circ:** 1,200

52840 ■ Jet Skier & PW Magazine
CSL Publishing Ltd.
Alliance House
49 Sidney St.
Cambridge CB2 3HX, United Kingdom
Ph: 44 1223 460490
Fax: 44 1223 315960
Magazine for personal watercraft and jet skiing enthusiasts. **Freq:** 16/yr. **Key Personnel:** Sue Baggley, Editor, sue.baggaley@cslpublishing.com. **Subscription Rates:** 26.15 individuals; 37.90 other countries; 37.90 individuals; 31.80 individuals Europe. **Remarks:** Accepts advertising. **URL:** http://www.jetskier.co.uk/; http:// www.cslpublishingltd.co.uk/. **Circ:** (Not Reported)

52841 ■ Journal of Advanced Materials
Cambridge International Science Publishing
7 Meadow Walk
Great Abington
Cambridge CB1 6AZ, United Kingdom
Ph: 44 1223 893295
Fax: 44 1223 894539
Publisher E-mail: cisp@cisp-publishing.com
Journal covering development of materials. **Freq:** Bimonthly. **Key Personnel:** N.P. Lyakishev, Chm. of the Editorial Board; L.I. Ivanov, Ch. Ed.; S.V. Simakov, Exec. Ed. **Subscription Rates:** 400 individuals United Kingdom and Europe; 640 other countries. **URL:** http://www. cisp-publishing.com/.

52842 ■ The Journal of African History
Cambridge University Press
The Edinburgh Bldg.
Shaftesbury Rd.
Cambridge CB2 2RU, United Kingdom
Ph: 44 122 3312393
Fax: 44 122 3315052
Publisher E-mail: information@cambridge.org
Journal featuring articles and book reviews covering African history from the late Stone Age to the present. **Founded:** 1960. **Freq:** Quarterly. **Key Personnel:** Dr. Gareth Austin, Advisory Editorial Board, g.m.austin@lse. ac.uk; Prof. Michael Gomez, Advisory Editorial Board; Prof. Andreas Eckert, Editor; Prof. Mamadou Diouf, Advisory Editorial Board; Dr. Justin Willis, Editor, justin. willis@biea.ac.uk; Prof. Emmanuel K. Akyeampong, Editor, akyeamp@fas.harvard.edu; Prof. Teresa Barnes, Advisory Editorial Board. **ISSN:** 0021-8537. **Subscription Rates:** 205 institutions online and print; US$359 institutions online and print; 182 institutions online only; US$317 institutions online only; 48 individuals online and print; US$83 individuals online and print. **URL:** http://journals.cambridge.org/action/displayJournal?jid= AFH. **Ad Rates:** BW: 465. **Circ:** 1,600

52843 ■ Journal of African Law
Cambridge University Press
The Edinburgh Bldg.
Shaftesbury Rd.
Cambridge CB2 2RU, United Kingdom
Ph: 44 122 3312393
Fax: 44 122 3315052
Publisher E-mail: information@cambridge.org
Journal covering legal issues of sub-Saharan African

countries. **Key Personnel:** Prof. Nelson Enonchong, Editor, n.e.enonchong@bham.ac.uk; Dr. Fareda Banda, Editor, fb9@soas.ac.uk; Dr. Chaloka Beyani, Editor; Dr. Rachel Murray, Editor. **ISSN:** 0021-8553. **Subscription Rates:** 126 institutions print and online; US$216 institutions print and online; 114 institutions online only; US$197 institutions online only. **Remarks:** Accepts advertising. **URL:** http://journals.cambridge.org/action/ displayJournal?jid=JAL. **Ad Rates:** BW: 445. **Circ:** 500

52844 ■ Journal of Algebraic Geometry
University Press Inc.
c/o J. Coates, Ed.
Dept. of Pure Mathematics
University of Cambridge
16 Mill Ln.
Cambridge CB2 1SB, United Kingdom
Publication E-mail: jag-query@ams.org
Journal covering algebraic geometry and related fields. **Freq:** Quarterly. **Key Personnel:** M. Brion, Editor, michel.brion@ujf-grenoble.fr; J. Coates, Editor, j.h. coates@pmms.cam.ac.uk; S.S.T. Yau, Managing Editor, jagedit@uic.edu; F. Catanese, Editor, fabrizio. catanese@uni-bayreuth.de. **ISSN:** 1056-3911. **Subscription Rates:** US$368 individuals electronic; US$160 individuals print and electronic. **URL:** http://www.ams. org/bookstore-getitem/item=11JAG.

52845 ■ Journal of American Studies
Cambridge University Press
The Edinburgh Bldg.
Shaftesbury Rd.
Cambridge CB2 2RU, United Kingdom
Ph: 44 122 3312393
Fax: 44 122 3315052
Publisher E-mail: information@cambridge.org
Peer-reviewed journal publishing history, literature, politics & culture of United States. **Freq:** Quarterly. **Key Personnel:** Prof. Judith Newman, Editorial Board; Prof. Heidi MacPherson, Exec. Committee; Christina Matteotti, Editorial Asst.; Dr. Marina Moskowitz, Editorial Board; Prof. Susan Castillo, Editor, susan.castillo@kcl. ac.uk; Prof. Scott Lucas, Assoc. Ed., w.s.lucas@bham. ac.uk; Prof. Werner Sollors, Editorial Board. **ISSN:** 0021-8758. **Subscription Rates:** US$310 institutions online only; US$347 institutions print and online; 199 institutions print and online; 178 institutions online only. **Remarks:** Advertising accepted; rates available upon request. **URL:** http://journals.cambridge.org/action/ displayJournal?jid=AMS. **Circ:** (Not Reported)

52846 ■ Journal of Biosocial Science
Cambridge University Press
c/o Prof. C.G.N. Mascie-Taylor, Ed.
Dept. of Biological Anthropology
Downing St.
Cambridge CB2 3DZ, United Kingdom
Publisher E-mail: information@cambridge.org
Journal publishing research articles in the field of biosocial science. Covers social and biological aspects of reproduction and its control, gerontology, ecology, genetics, applied psychology, sociology, education, criminology, demography, health and epidemiology. **Freq:** Annual. **Key Personnel:** Prof. C.G.N. Mascie-Taylor, Editor; Caroline M. Gallimore, Assoc. Ed., cmg26@cam. ac.uk. **ISSN:** 0021-9320. **Subscription Rates:** 307 institutions online and print; US$556 institutions online and print; 260 institutions online only; US$454 institutions online only. **URL:** http://journals.cambridge.org/ action/displayJournal?jid=JBS. **Ad Rates:** BW: 405. **Circ:** 500

52847 ■ Journal of Cell Science
The Company of Biologists Ltd.
c/o Dr. Fiona M. Watt, Ed.-in-Ch.
CR-UK Cambridge Research Institute
Li Ka Shing Centre
Robinson Way
Cambridge CB2 0RE, United Kingdom
Journal devoted to cell biology primarily interesting to developmental biologists, molecular biologists and geneticists. **Freq:** Semimonthly. **Key Personnel:** Karen Vousden, Editor; John K. Heath, Editor; Dr. Fiona M. Watt, Editor-in-Chief; David M. Glover, Editor; Kathleen J. Green, Editor; Michael Way, Editor; Arnoud Sonnenberg, Editor; Francis Barr, Editor; Sharon Ahmad, Exec. Ed. **ISSN:** 0021-9533. **Subscription Rates:** 85 individuals U.K. and rest of World; online only; 440 individuals U.K. and rest of World; print + online; EUR130 individu-

als Europe; online only; EUR660 individuals Europe; print + online; US$635 individuals U.S., Canada & Mexico; print only; US$150 individuals U.S., Canada & Mexico; online only; US$770 individuals U.S., Canada & Mexico; print and online; EUR440 individuals U.K. and rest of the world; print only. URL: http://jcs.biologists.org/.

52848 ■ Journal of Cetacean Research and Management
International Whaling Commission
The Red House
135 Sta. Rd.
Impington
Cambridge CB24 9NP, United Kingdom
Ph: 44 122 3233971
Fax: 44 122 3232876
Publisher E-mail: secretariat@iwcoffice.org
Journal covering wildlife conservation. **Founded:** Apr. 1999. **Freq:** 3/yr. **Trim Size:** 295 x 210 mm. **Key Personnel:** G.P. Donovan, Editor. **ISSN:** 1561-0713. **Subscription Rates:** 110 institutions; US$220 institutions; EUR160 institutions; 75 individuals; US$150 individuals; EUR110 individuals. **Remarks:** Advertising not accepted. **URL:** http://www.iwcoffice.org/publications/jcrm.htm. **Circ:** (Not Reported)

52849 ■ The Journal of Ecclesiastical History
Cambridge University Press
Robinson College
Cambridge CB3 9AN, United Kingdom
Publisher E-mail: information@cambridge.org
Journal covering all aspects of the history of the Christian church. **Founded:** 1960. **Freq:** Quarterly. **Key Personnel:** Prof. Diarmaid MacCulloch, Editor, jeh@robinson.cam.ac.uk; Prof. Euan Cameron, Advisory Editorial Board; Prof. Eamon Duffy, Advisory Editorial Board; Dr. Martin Brett, Advisory Editorial Board; Prof. Patrick Collinson, Advisory Editorial Board; Prof. Judith Herrin, Advisory Editorial Board. **ISSN:** 0022-0469. **Subscription Rates:** 289 institutions print and online; US$498 institutions print and online; 244 institutions online only; US$421 institutions online only. **Remarks:** Accepts advertising. **URL:** http://journals.cambridge.org/action/displayJournal?jid=ECH. **Ad Rates:** BW: 465. **Circ:** 1,250

52850 ■ The Journal of Economic History
Cambridge University Press
The Edinburgh Bldg.
Shaftesbury Rd.
Cambridge CB2 2RU, United Kingdom
Ph: 44 122 3312393
Fax: 44 122 3315052
Publisher E-mail: information@cambridge.org
Journal covering economics. **Freq:** Quarterly. **Key Personnel:** Mr. Alan Miller, Book Review Ed.; Philip T. Hoffman, Co-Ed., jeh@hss.caltech.edu; Michael Haines, Editorial Board; Howard Bodenhorn, Editorial Board; Price V. Fishback, Co-Ed., jeh@eller.arizona.edu. **ISSN:** 0022-0507. **Subscription Rates:** 153 institutions print and online; US$249 institutions print and online; 131 institutions online only; US$211 institutions online only. **Remarks:** Accepts advertising. **URL:** http://journals.cambridge.org/action/displayJournal?jid=jeh. **Ad Rates:** BW: 600. **Circ:** 3,300

52851 ■ Journal of Environmental Monitoring
Royal Society of Chemistry
Thomas Graham House
The Science Pk., Milton Rd.
Milton Rd.
Cambridge CB4 0WF, United Kingdom
Ph: 44 12 23420066
Fax: 44 12 23423623
Publisher E-mail: sales@rsc.org
Journal covering environmental science in natural and anthropogenic environments. **Freq:** Monthly. **Key Personnel:** Harp Minhas, Editor. **ISSN:** 1464-0325. **Subscription Rates:** 1,431 individuals print + online; US$2,671 individuals print + online; 1,288 individuals online; US$2,405 individuals online. **URL:** http://www.rsc.org/Publishing/Journals/em/index.asp.

52852 ■ Journal of Experimental Biology
The Company of Biologists Ltd.
140 Cowley Rd.
Cambridge CB4 0DL, United Kingdom
Ph: 44 12 23426164
Fax: 44 12 23423353
Scholarly journal covering biology. **Freq:** 24/yr. **Print Method:** Litho. **Key Personnel:** Prof. Hans Hoppeler,

Editor-in-Chief; Prof. Michael H. Dickinson, Editor; Prof. Ken Lukowiak, Editor; Prof. Andrew A. Biewener, Dep. Ed. in Ch.; Prof. Julian A.T. Dow, Editor; Prof. William Harvey, Editorial Advisory Board. **ISSN:** 0022-0949. **Subscription Rates:** US$2,530 institutions U.S., Canada & Mexico, online; US$3,335 institutions U.S., Canada & Mexico, online & print; 1,460 institutions UK & rest of world, online; 1,930 institutions UK & rest of world, print & online; EUR2,190 institutions Europe, online; EUR2,900 institutions Europe, print & online; US$521 individuals U.S., Canada & Mexico, print; US$142 individuals U.S., Canada & Mexico, online; US$594 individuals U.S., Canada & Mexico, print & online; 296 individuals U.K. and rest of the world, print. **URL:** http://jeb.biologists.org/.

52853 ■ Journal of Glaciology
International Glaciological Society - Scott Polar Research Institute
Lensfield Rd.
Cambridge CB2 1ER, United Kingdom
Ph: 44 12 23355974
Fax: 44 12 23354931
Publisher E-mail: igsoc@igsoc.org
Journal covering glaciology. **Founded:** 1947. **Freq:** Quarterly. **Key Personnel:** Jo Jacka, Editor-in-Chief, jglac@bigpond.com; R. Hock, Sci. Ed., regine.hock@natgeo.su.se; N.F. Glasser, Sci. Ed.; M.A. Lange, Sci. Ed., m.a.lange@cyi.ac.uk; P. Bartelt, Sci. Ed., bartelt@slf.ch; J.W. Glen, Sci. Ed., john_glen@jgla.demon.co.uk; J. Hart, Sci. Ed., jhart@soton.ac.uk; R. Greve, Sci. Ed., greve@lowtem.hokudai.ac.jp. **ISSN:** 0022-1430. **Subscription Rates:** Included in membership. **Remarks:** Advertising not accepted. **URL:** http://www.igsoc.org/journal/. **Circ:** Paid 1,000

52854 ■ Journal of Helminthology
Cambridge University Press
The Edinburgh Bldg.
Shaftesbury Rd.
Cambridge CB2 2RU, United Kingdom
Ph: 44 122 3312393
Fax: 44 122 3315052
Publisher E-mail: information@cambridge.org
International vehicle for the publication of original papers and review articles on all aspects of pure and applied helminthology, particularly those helminth parasites of environmental health, medical or veterinary importance. **Freq:** Quarterly. **Key Personnel:** John Lewis, Editor. **ISSN:** 0022-149X. **Subscription Rates:** 115 individuals online only; 242 individuals print and online; 510 institutions print and online; US$232 individuals online only; US$460 individuals print and online; US$982 individuals print and online. **Remarks:** Accepts advertising. **URL:** http://journals.cambridge.org/action/displayJournal?jid=JHL. **Circ:** (Not Reported)

52855 ■ Journal of Institutional Economics
Cambridge University Press
The Edinburgh Bldg.
Shaftesbury Rd.
Cambridge CB2 2RU, United Kingdom
Ph: 44 122 3312393
Fax: 44 122 3315052
Publisher E-mail: information@cambridge.org
Journal devoted to the study of the nature, role and evolution of institutions in the economy, including firms, states, markets, money, households and other vital institutions and organizations. **Freq:** 3/yr. **Key Personnel:** Geoffrey M. Hodgson, Editor-in-Chief, g.m.hodgson@herts.ac.uk; Richard N. Langlois, Editor, richard.langlois@uconn.edu; Benito Arrunada, Editor; Prof. Esther-Mirjam Sent, Editor, e.m.sent@fm.ru.nl; Howard Aldrich, International Advisory Board. **ISSN:** 1744-1374. **Subscription Rates:** 185 institutions print and online; US$315 institutions print and online; 159 institutions online; US$299 institutions online. **Remarks:** Accepts advertising. **URL:** http://journals.cambridge.org/action/displayJournal?jid=JOI. **Circ:** (Not Reported)

52856 ■ Journal of Intellectual Disability Research (JIDR)
John Wiley & Sons Inc.
Wiley-Blackwell
c/o Prof. A.J. Holland, Ed.-in-Ch.
Developmental Psychology Section
Douglas House, 18B Trumpington Rd.
Cambridge CB2 2AH, United Kingdom
Publication covering mental disabilities. **Freq:** Monthly. **Trim Size:** 27 x 210 mm. **Key Personnel:** Prof. A.J.

Holland, Editor-in-Chief, ajh1008@cam.ac.uk; Prof. Sally-Ann Cooper, Editor, sacooper@clinmed.gla.ac.uk; B. Benson, Editorial Advisory Board; Prof. Chris Oliver, Assoc. Ed., c.oliver@bham.ac.uk; A. Alhamad, Editorial Advisory Board; Jan Blacher, Assoc. Ed., jan.blacher@ucr.edu; David Congdon, Editorial Advisory Board; T. Charman, Editorial Advisory Board; B. Baker, Editorial Advisory Board. **ISSN:** 0964-2633. **Subscription Rates:** US$238 individuals Americas; 129 individuals non-Euro zone; EUR193 individuals Euro zone; 141 other countries; US$1,358 institutions Americas (print and online); 737 institutions UK (print and online); EUR935 institutions Europe (print and online); US$1,584 institutions, other countries print and online; US$1,234 institutions Americas (online only); EUR850 institutions Europe (online only). **Remarks:** Advertising accepted; rates available upon request. **URL:** http://www.wiley.com/bw/journal.asp?ref=0964-2633. **Formerly:** Journal of Mental Deficiency. **Circ:** 1,400

52857 ■ Journal of International Farm Management
International Farm Management Association
38 W End
Whittlesford
Cambridge CB22 4LX, United Kingdom
Ph: 44 122 3832527
Publisher E-mail: honsecretary@ifmaonline.org
Worldwide agribusiness journal. **Freq:** Semiannual. **Key Personnel:** Nicola M. Shadbolt, Dep. Ed., n.m.shadbolt@massey.ac.nz; John W. Gardner, Managing Editor, journaleditor@ifmaonline.org. **ISSN:** 1816-2495. **Remarks:** Advertising not accepted. **URL:** http://www.ifmaonline.org. **Circ:** (Not Reported)

52858 ■ Journal of Linguistics
Cambridge University Press
The Edinburgh Bldg.
Shaftesbury Rd.
Cambridge CB2 2RU, United Kingdom
Ph: 44 122 3312393
Fax: 44 122 3315052
Publisher E-mail: information@cambridge.org
Languages and linguistics publication. **Freq:** 3/yr. **Key Personnel:** Dr. Ewa Jaworska, Managing Editor, ewa@ex.ac.uk; Prof. Caroline Heycock, Editor, c.heycock@ed.ac.uk; Prof. Robert D. Borsley, Editor, rborsley@essex.ac.uk. **ISSN:** 0022-2267. **Subscription Rates:** 136 institutions online; 167 institutions print and online; US$293 institutions print and online; US$242 institutions online. **Remarks:** Accepts advertising. **URL:** http://journals.cambridge.org/action/displayJournal?jid=LIN. **Circ:** 2,100

52859 ■ Journal of Materials Chemistry
Royal Society of Chemistry
Thomas Graham House
The Science Pk., Milton Rd.
Milton Rd.
Cambridge CB4 0WF, United Kingdom
Ph: 44 12 23420066
Fax: 44 12 23423623
Publisher E-mail: sales@rsc.org
Professional journal covering materials chemistry. **Founded:** 1990. **Freq:** Weekly. **Trim Size:** A4. **Key Personnel:** Jamie Humphrey, Editor. **ISSN:** 0959-9428. **Subscription Rates:** 2,502 individuals print + online; US$4,671 individuals print + online; 2,252 individuals online version; US$4,204 individuals online version. **Remarks:** Advertising accepted; rates available upon request. **URL:** http://www.rsc.org/Publishing/Journals/jm/index.asp. **Circ:** (Not Reported)

52860 ■ The Journal of Modern African Studies
Cambridge University Press
c/o Prof. Christopher Clapham, Ed.
Centre of African Studies
Free School Ln.
Cambridge CB2 3RQ, United Kingdom
Publisher E-mail: information@cambridge.org
Regional focus/area studies journal. **Freq:** Quarterly. **Key Personnel:** Prof. Christopher Clapham, Editor, csc34@cam.ac.uk; Prof. Michael Bratton, Editorial Advisory Board; Dr. Rosaleen Duffy, Book Review Ed., rosaleen.duffy@manchester.ac.uk; Prof. Jeffrey Herbst, Editorial Advisory Board; Dr. Melissa Leach, Editorial Advisory Board; Dr. Achille Mbembe, Editorial Advisory Board. **ISSN:** 0022-278X. **Subscription Rates:** US$378 institutions online and print; US$335 institutions online only; 191 institutions online only; 212 institutions print

Circulation: ★ = ABC; △ = BPA; ♦ = CAC; ● = CCAB; ❑ = VAC; ⊕ = PO Statement; ‡ = Publisher's Report; Boldface figures = sworn; Light figures = estimated.

Gale Directory of Publications & Broadcast Media/147th Ed.   5613

and online. **Remarks:** Accepts advertising. **URL:** http://journals.cambridge.org/action/displayJournal?jid=MOA. **Ad Rates:** BW: US$895. **Circ:** Combined 1,600

52861 ■ Journal of Public Policy
Cambridge University Press
The Edinburgh Bldg.
Shaftesbury Rd.
Cambridge CB2 2RU, United Kingdom
Ph: 44 122 3312393
Fax: 44 122 3315052
Publisher E-mail: information@cambridge.org
Peer-reviewed journal covering government and related issues. **Freq:** Quarterly. **Key Personnel:** Prof. Richard Rose, Editor, jpp@abdn.ac.uk; Prof. M.J. Artis, Assoc. Ed.; Prof. Edward C. Page, Editor. **ISSN:** 0143-814X. **Subscription Rates:** 153 institutions online only; US$265 institutions online only; US$310 institutions print and online; 177 institutions print and online. **URL:** http://journals.cambridge.org/action/displayJournal?jid=PUP. **Circ:** 800

52862 ■ Journal of Social Policy
Cambridge University Press
The Edinburgh Bldg.
Shaftesbury Rd.
Cambridge CB2 2RU, United Kingdom
Ph: 44 122 3312393
Fax: 44 122 3315052
Publisher E-mail: information@cambridge.org
Publication covering social policy in an international context. **Freq:** Quarterly. **Key Personnel:** Dr. Tania Burchadt, Editor, t.burchardt@lse.ac.uk; Prof. Hartley Dean, Editor, h.dean@lse.ac.uk; Dr. Brian Lund, Book Review Ed., brianlund26@aol.com. **ISSN:** 0047-2794. **Subscription Rates:** US$541 institutions online and print; US$465 institutions online only; 311 institutions print and online; 272 institutions online only. **Remarks:** Accepts advertising. **URL:** http://journals.cambridge.org/action/displayJournal?jid=JSP. **Circ:** 2,000

52863 ■ Journal of Southeast Asian Studies
Cambridge University Press
The Edinburgh Bldg.
Shaftesbury Rd.
Cambridge CB2 2RU, United Kingdom
Ph: 44 122 3312393
Fax: 44 122 3315052
Publisher E-mail: information@cambridge.org
Regional focus/area studies publication. **Freq:** Semiannual. **Key Personnel:** Bruce Lockhart, Editorial Board; Michael R. Feener, Editorial Board; Yong Mun Cheong, Editor; Peter Borschberg, Review Ed.; Maurizio Peleggi, Editor, hisjseas@nus.edu.sg; Maitrii Aung-Thwin, Editorial Board. **ISSN:** 0022-4634. **Subscription Rates:** 84 institutions online; US$155 institutions online; 93 institutions print and online; US$170 institutions print and online. **URL:** http://journals.cambridge.org/action/displayJournal?jid=SEA. **Circ:** 1,100

52864 ■ Journal of the United Reformed Church History Society
United Reformed Church History Society
Westminster College
Madingley Rd.
Cambridge CB3 0AA, United Kingdom
Ph: 44 1223 741300
Publisher E-mail: mt212@cam.ac.uk
Scholarly journal covering the history of religious denominations forming the United Reformed Church (URC). **Founded:** 1973. **Freq:** Semiannual. **Key Personnel:** M. Thompson, Membership Sec.; Prof. C. Binfield, Editor. **ISSN:** 0049-5433. **Subscription Rates:** 16.50 individuals. **Remarks:** Advertising not accepted. **URL:** http://www.urc.org.uk/about/history_society/history_soc/history_soc. **Circ:** (Not Reported)

52865 ■ Kiosk Europe
17 Sturton St.
Cambridge CB1 2SN, United Kingdom
Ph: 44 1223 350515
Fax: 44 1223 351725
Publication E-mail: editor@kioskeurope.com
Publisher E-mail: info@kioskeurope.com
Magazine featuring the industry of self-service solutions and technology. **Key Personnel:** Mr. Chris Thorpe, Project Mgr. **Remarks:** Accepts advertising. **URL:** http://www.kioskeurope.com/. **Circ:** (Not Reported)

52866 ■ Lab on a Chip
Royal Society of Chemistry
Thomas Graham House
The Science Pk., Milton Rd.
Milton Rd.
Cambridge CB4 0WF, United Kingdom
Ph: 44 12 23420066
Fax: 44 12 23423623
Publisher E-mail: sales@rsc.org
Journal providing information on miniaturisation. **Freq:** 24/yr. **Key Personnel:** Harp Minhas, Editor. **ISSN:** 1473-0197. **Subscription Rates:** 1,214 individuals print + online; US$2,266 individuals print + online; 1,092 individuals online; US$2,038 individuals online. **URL:** http://www.rsc.org/Publishing/Journals/lc/index.asp.

52867 ■ Magnetic Resonance in Chemistry
John Wiley & Sons Ltd.
c/o Dr. J. Keeler, Ed.-in-Ch.
Department of Chemistry
University of Cambridge
Lansfield Rd.
Cambridge CB2 1EW, United Kingdom
Ph: 44 1223 336913
Publisher E-mail: customer@wiley.co.uk
Journal covering research and development in magnetic resonance. **Freq:** 14/yr. **Trim Size:** 210 x 298 mm. **Cols./Page:** 2. **Col. Width:** 85 millimeters. **Col. Depth:** 250 millimeters. **Key Personnel:** Dr. J. Keeler, Editor-in-Chief, jhk10@cam.ac.uk; Dr. A.M. Gronenborn, Editorial Board, phone 412648-9959, amg100@pitt.edu; Dr. D. Massiot, Advisory Board, massiot@cnrs-orleans.fr; Prof. A.J. Shaka, Editorial Board, fax 949824-9920, ajshaka@uci.edu; Prof. S. Aime, Advisory Board; Prof. H. Duddeck, Editorial Board, fax 49 511 7624616, duddeck@mbox.oci.uni-hannover.de; Prof. B. Wrackmeyer, Editorial Board, fax 49 921 552157, b.wrack@uni-bayreuth.de; Prof. R.J. Abraham, Advisory Board; Prof. T. Cross, Advisory Board. **ISSN:** 0749-1581. **Subscription Rates:** US$7,709 institutions, other countries print only; 3,933 institutions print only; EUR4,973 institutions print only; EUR5,471 institutions, other countries combined print with online access; 4,326 institutions combined print with online access; US$8,480 institutions, other countries combined print with online access. **Remarks:** Accepts advertising. **URL:** http://www.interscience.wiley.com; http://www3.interscience.wiley.com/journal/117935720/grouphome/home.html. **Circ:** (Not Reported)

52868 ■ Metallomics
Royal Society of Chemistry
Thomas Graham House
The Science Pk., Milton Rd.
Milton Rd.
Cambridge CB4 0WF, United Kingdom
Ph: 44 12 23420066
Fax: 44 12 23423623
Publisher E-mail: sales@rsc.org
Journal covering the research fields related to biometals. **Freq:** 6/yr. **Key Personnel:** May Copsey, Editor. **ISSN:** 1756-5901. **Subscription Rates:** 1,575 individuals print and online; US$3,150 individuals print and online; 1,400 individuals online; US$2,800 individuals online. **URL:** http://www.rsc.org/Publishing/Journals/MT/index.asp.

52869 ■ Methods in Organic Synthesis
Royal Society of Chemistry
Thomas Graham House
The Science Pk., Milton Rd.
Milton Rd.
Cambridge CB4 0WF, United Kingdom
Ph: 44 12 23420 066
Fax: 44 12 23423623
Publisher E-mail: sales@rsc.org
Journal covering the most important current developments in organic synthesis. **Freq:** Monthly. **Key Personnel:** Graham McCann, Publisher. **ISSN:** 0265-4245. **Subscription Rates:** 785 individuals print + online; US$1,466 individuals print + online; 707 individuals online; US$1,319 individuals online. **URL:** http://www.rsc.org/Publishing/CurrentAwareness/MOS/index.asp.

52870 ■ Modern Asian Studies
Cambridge University Press
The Edinburgh Bldg.
Shaftesbury Rd.
Cambridge CB2 2RU, United Kingdom
Ph: 44 122 3312393
Fax: 44 122 3315052
Publisher E-mail: information@cambridge.org
Journal covering ethnic, cultural, and racial issues and studies. **Freq:** Bimonthly. **Key Personnel:** Dr. Joya Chatterji, Editor, modernasianstudies@cambridge.org; Dr. Norbert Peabody, Book Review Ed., np208@cam.ac.uk; Prof. Christopher Bayly, Editorial Board. **ISSN:** 0026-749X. **Subscription Rates:** US$515 institutions online and print; 286 institutions online and print; US$457 individuals online only; 255 institutions online only. **Remarks:** Accepts advertising. **URL:** http://journals.cambridge.org/action/displayJournal?jid=ASS. **Ad Rates:** BW: 885. **Circ:** 1,100

52871 ■ Molecular Biosystems
Royal Society of Chemistry
Thomas Graham House
The Science Pk., Milton Rd.
Milton Rd.
Cambridge CB4 0WF, United Kingdom
Ph: 44 12 23420066
Fax: 44 12 23423623
Publisher E-mail: sales@rsc.org
Journal on bridging the gap between chemistry and the -omic sciences and systems biology. **Freq:** Monthly. **Key Personnel:** Stephen Michnick, Editorial Board; Thomas Kodadek, Advisory Board; Benjamin F. Cravatt, Editorial Board; Harp Mintas, Editor; Michael Smith, Dep. Ed.; John Koh, Editorial Board. **ISSN:** 1742-206X. **Subscription Rates:** US$2,009 individuals print and online version; 1,076 individuals print and online version; US$1,809 individuals online only; 969 individuals online only. **Remarks:** Accepts advertising. **URL:** http://www.rsc.org/publishing/journals/mb/index.asp. **Ad Rates:** BW: 800. **Circ:** (Not Reported)

52872 ■ Mosaic
Association for the Study and Preservation of Roman Mosaics
61 Norwich St.
Cambridge CB2 1ND, United Kingdom
Publisher E-mail: honsec@asprom.org
Publication covering history. **Freq:** Annual In December. **Key Personnel:** Viscountess Hanworth, President; Prof. Roger Ling, Chm.; Stephen Cosh, Editor, editor@asprom.org. **ISSN:** 0286-9626. **Subscription Rates:** 3 single issue back issue; non members; 2.50 members back issue. **URL:** http://www.asprom.org/publications/.

52873 ■ Natural Product Reports
Royal Society of Chemistry
Thomas Graham House
The Science Pk., Milton Rd.
Milton Rd.
Cambridge CB4 0WF, United Kingdom
Ph: 44 12 23420066
Fax: 44 12 23423623
Publisher E-mail: sales@rsc.org
Journal covering all areas of natural products research including isolation, structural and stereochemical determination, biosynthesis, biological activity and synthesis. **Freq:** Monthly. **Key Personnel:** Dr. Richard Kelly, Editor. **ISSN:** 0265-0568. **Subscription Rates:** 882 individuals print and online; US$1,646 individuals print and online; 794 individuals online; 1,482 individuals online. **URL:** http://www.rsc.org/Publishing/Journals/NP/About.asp.

52874 ■ Neuron Glia Biology
Cambridge University Press
The Edinburgh Bldg.
Shaftesbury Rd.
Cambridge CB2 2RU, United Kingdom
Ph: 44 122 3312393
Fax: 44 122 3315052
Publisher E-mail: information@cambridge.org
Scientific journal recognizing that two-way communication between neurons and glia is essential for nervous system function, focusing on cell-cell interactions in the nervous system. **Key Personnel:** R. Douglas Fields, Editor-in-Chief; Dr. Bernard Zalc, Assoc. Ed., bernard.zalc@upmc.fr; Dr. Kazuhiro Ikenaka, Assoc. Ed.; Dr. Philip Haydon, Assoc. Ed. **ISSN:** 1740-925X. **Subscription Rates:** US$472 institutions online only; US$164 individuals online only; 276 institutions online only; 90 individuals online only. **Remarks:** Accepts advertising. **URL:** http://journals.cambridge.org/action/displayJournal?jid=NGB. **Ad Rates:** 4C: US$2,155. **Circ:** (Not Reported)

52875 ■ Neuropsychological Rehabilitation
Psychology Press
c/o Barbara A. Wilson, Ed.
MRC Cognition & Brain Sciences Unit
15 Chaucer Rd.
Cambridge CB2 7EF, United Kingdom
Journal publishing human experimental and clinical research related to rehabilitation, recovery of function, and brain plasticity. **Freq:** Bimonthly. **Key Personnel:** Ian Robertson, Dep. Ed., ian.robertson@tcd.ie; Barbara A. Wilson, Editor, barbara.wilson@mrc-apu.cam.ac.uk; Prof. Matt Lambon Ralph, Exec. Ed.; Catherine Mateer, Exec. Ed.; Guido Gainotti, Exec. Ed. **ISSN:** 0960-2011. **Subscription Rates:** EUR773 institutions print + online; EUR735 institutions print + online; US$971 institutions print + online; US$922 institutions online; US$463 individuals; 586 institutions print + online; 557 institutions online; 278 individuals. **Remarks:** Advertising accepted; rates available upon request. **URL:** http://www.tandf.co.uk/journals/titles/09602011.asp. **Circ:** (Not Reported)

52876 ■ New Journal of Chemistry
Royal Society of Chemistry
Thomas Graham House
The Science Pk., Milton Rd.
Milton Rd.
Cambridge CB4 0WF, United Kingdom
Ph: 44 12 23420066
Fax: 44 12 23423623
Publisher E-mail: sales@rsc.org
Journal covering multidisciplinary work in the chemical sciences. **Freq:** Monthly. **Key Personnel:** Sarah Ruthven, Editor; Denise Parent, Editor. **ISSN:** 1144-0546. **Subscription Rates:** 894 individuals print + online; US$1,668 individuals print + online; 804 individuals online; US$1,501 individuals online. **URL:** http://www.rsc.org/Publishing/Journals/nj/index.asp.

52877 ■ New Testament Studies
Cambridge University Press
The Edinburgh Bldg.
Shaftesbury Rd.
Cambridge CB2 2RU, United Kingdom
Ph: 44 122 3312393
Fax: 44 122 3315052
Publisher E-mail: information@cambridge.org
Peer-reviewed journal covering various issues related to the origins, history, and theology of the New Testament. **Freq:** Quarterly. **Key Personnel:** Prof. John Barclay, Editor. **ISSN:** 0028-6885. **Subscription Rates:** 135 institutions print and online; US$249 individuals print and online; 123 institutions online only; US$223 institutions online only. **Remarks:** Accepts advertising. **URL:** http://journals.cambridge.org/action/displayJournal?jid=NTS. **Ad Rates:** BW: 895. **Circ:** 2,400

52878 ■ New Theatre Quarterly
Cambridge University Press
The Edinburgh Bldg.
Shaftesbury Rd.
Cambridge CB2 2RU, United Kingdom
Ph: 44 122 3312393
Fax: 44 122 3315052
Publisher E-mail: information@cambridge.org
Journal providing an international forum discussing the various aspects of theatrical scholarship and practice and how they relate. **Founded:** 1985. **Freq:** Quarterly. **Key Personnel:** Maria Shevtsova, Editor, m.shevtsova@gold.ac.uk; Prof. Jamil Ahmed, Contributing Ed.; Eugenio Barba, Contributing Ed. **ISSN:** 0266-464X. **Subscription Rates:** 128 institutions online and print; US$213 institutions online and print; 115 institutions online only; US$191 institutions online only. **Remarks:** Accepts advertising. **URL:** http://journals.cambridge.org/action/displayJournal?jid=NTQ. **Formerly:** Theatre Quarterly. **Ad Rates:** BW: 835. **Circ:** 1,00

52879 ■ Nutrition Research Reviews
Cambridge University Press
The Edinburgh Bldg.
Shaftesbury Rd.
Cambridge CB2 2RU, United Kingdom
Ph: 44 122 3312393
Fax: 44 122 3315052
Publisher E-mail: information@cambridge.org
Journal presenting up-to-date, concise, critical reviews of key topics in nutrition science advancing new concepts and hypotheses that encourage the exchange of fundamental ideas on nutritional well-being in both humans and animals. **Freq:** Semiannual. **Key Personnel:** D.A. Bender, Editorial Advisory; Nino Binns, Editorial Board; Dominique Dardevet, Editorial Board. **ISSN:** 0954-4224. **Subscription Rates:** 186 institutions print and online; US$363 institutions print and online; EUR289 institutions print and online; 147 institutions online only; US$273 institutions online only; EUR221 institutions online only. **Remarks:** Accepts advertising. **URL:** http://journals.cambridge.org/action/displayJournal?jid=NRR. **Ad Rates:** BW: 610. **Circ:** (Not Reported)

52880 ■ Organic & Biomolecular Chemistry
Royal Society of Chemistry
Thomas Graham House
The Science Pk., Milton Rd.
Milton Rd.
Cambridge CB4 0WF, United Kingdom
Ph: 44 12 23420066
Fax: 44 12 23423623
Publisher E-mail: sales@rsc.org
Journal covering fundamental work on synthetic, physical, and biomolecular organic chemistry. **Freq:** 24/yr. **Key Personnel:** Dr. Richard Kelly, Editor. **ISSN:** 1477-0520. **Subscription Rates:** 3,105 individuals print + online; US$5,796 individuals print + online; 2,794 individuals online; US$5,216 individuals online. **URL:** http://www.rsc.org/Publishing/Journals/OB/index.asp.

52881 ■ Oryx
Fauna and Flora International
Jupiter House, 4th Fl.
Station Rd.
Cambridge CB1 2JD, United Kingdom
Ph: 44 122 3571000
Fax: 44 122 3461481
Publication E-mail: oryx@fauna-flora.org
Publisher E-mail: info@fauna-flora.org
Publication covering conservation. **Subtitle:** The International Journal of Conservation. **Founded:** 1903. **Freq:** Quarterly. **Key Personnel:** Martin Fisher, Editor, martin.fisher@fauna-flora.org. **ISSN:** 0030-6053. **Subscription Rates:** Included in membership. **Remarks:** Advertising accepted; rates available upon request. **URL:** http://www.journals.cambridge.org/action/displayJournal?jid=ORX; http://www.oryxthejournal.org/. **Alt. Formats:** CD-ROM. **Circ:** 2,800

52882 ■ Photochemical & Photobiological Science
Royal Society of Chemistry
Thomas Graham House
The Science Pk., Milton Rd.
Milton Rd.
Cambridge CB4 0WF, United Kingdom
Ph: 44 12 23420066
Fax: 44 12 23423623
Publisher E-mail: sales@rsc.org
Journal focusing on photochemical and photobiological sciences. **Freq:** Monthly. **Key Personnel:** Sarah Ruthven, Editor. **ISSN:** 1474-905X. **Subscription Rates:** US$1,367 individuals print + online; US$2,552 individuals print + online; 1,231 individuals online; US$2,297 individuals online. **URL:** http://www.rsc.org/Publishing/Journals/pp/index.asp.

52883 ■ Physical Chemistry, Chemical Physics
Royal Society of Chemistry
Thomas Graham House
The Science Pk., Milton Rd.
Milton Rd.
Cambridge CB4 0WF, United Kingdom
Ph: 44 12 23420066
Fax: 44 12 23423623
Publisher E-mail: sales@rsc.org
Professional journal covering physical chemistry and chemical physics worldwide. **Subtitle:** An International Journal. **Founded:** Jan. 1, 1999. **Freq:** 48/yr. **Trim Size:** A4. **Key Personnel:** Philip Earis, Editor; Dr. Nicola Nugent, Dep. Ed. **ISSN:** 1463-9076. **Subscription Rates:** 2,589 individuals print and online; US$4,833 individuals print and online; 2,330 individuals online only; US$4,349 individuals online only. **Remarks:** Accepts advertising. **URL:** http://www.rsc.org/Publishing/Journals/CP/index.asp. **Former name:** Faraday Transactions; Berichte der Bunsen-Gesellschaft. **Ad Rates:** BW: 755. **Circ:** (Not Reported)

52884 ■ Plant Genetic Resources
Cambridge University Press
The Edinburgh Bldg.
Shaftesbury Rd.
Cambridge CB2 2RU, United Kingdom
Ph: 44 122 3312393
Fax: 44 122 3315052
Publisher E-mail: information@cambridge.org
International peer-reviewed journal providing a forum for describing the application of novel genomic technologies, as well as their integration with established techniques, towards the understanding of the genetic variation captured in both in situ and ex situ collections of crop and non-crop plants. **Subtitle:** Characterization and Utilization. **Freq:** Triennial. **Key Personnel:** Robert Koebner, Editor-in-Chief, plantgeneticresources@googlemail.com. **ISSN:** 1479-2621. **Subscription Rates:** US$463 institutions online only; US$576 institutions print and online; 300 institutions print and online; 104 individuals online only; 144 individuals print and online; 240 institutions online only. **Remarks:** Accepts advertising. **URL:** http://journals.cambridge.org/action/displayJournal?jid=PGR. **Ad Rates:** BW: 625. **Circ:** (Not Reported)

52885 ■ Probability Surveys
c/o Geoffrey Grimmett, Mng. Ed.
Centre for Mathematical Sciences
University of Cambridge
Wilberforce Rd.
Cambridge CB3 0WB, United Kingdom
Ph: 44 1223 337957
Fax: 44 1223 337956
Publication E-mail: prsurvey@statslab.cam.ac.uk
Publisher E-mail: prsurvey@statslab.cam.ac.uk
Open access, peer-reviewed journal that publishes survey articles in theoretical and applied probability. **Founded:** 2004. **Freq:** Irregular. **Key Personnel:** David Aldous, Assoc. Ed. **ISSN:** 1549-5787. **Subscription Rates:** Free online. **Remarks:** Accepts advertising. **URL:** http://www.i-journals.org/ps/. **Circ:** (Not Reported)

52886 ■ Proceedings of the International Astronomical Union
Cambridge University Press
The Edinburgh Bldg.
Shaftesbury Rd.
Cambridge CB2 2RU, United Kingdom
Ph: 44 122 3312393
Fax: 44 122 3315052
Publisher E-mail: information@cambridge.org
Journal dealing with the astrophysical developments. **Freq:** Quarterly. **Key Personnel:** Dr. Thierry Montmerle, Ch. **ISSN:** 1743-9213. **Subscription Rates:** 723 institutions online and print; US$1,418 institutions online and print; 603 institutions online only; US$1,183 institutions online only. **Remarks:** Accepts advertising. **URL:** http://journals.cambridge.org/action/displayJournal?jid=IAU. **Circ:** (Not Reported)

52887 ■ Proceedings of the Nutrition Society
Cambridge University Press
The Edinburgh Bldg.
Shaftesbury Rd.
Cambridge CB2 2RU, United Kingdom
Ph: 44 122 3312393
Fax: 44 122 3315052
Publisher E-mail: information@cambridge.org
Journal publishing papers and abstracts presented by members and invited speakers at the scientific meetings of The Nutrition Society, including such topics as: cellular and molecular nutrition (including immunology), nutritional genomics, nutrition and the food chain, clinical nutrition and metabolism, obesity and body composition, infant nutrition and diet selection and control of intake. **Freq:** Quarterly. **Key Personnel:** C.J. Newbold, Deputy Ed., cjn@aber.ac.uk; C.N.M. Kelly, Editorial Board. **ISSN:** 0029-6651. **Subscription Rates:** 448 institutions print and online; US$874 institutions print and online; EUR715 institutions print and online; 373 institutions online only; US$727 institutions online only; EUR583 institutions online only. **Remarks:** Accepts advertising. **URL:** http://journals.cambridge.org/action/displayJournal?jid=PNS. **Ad Rates:** BW: 610. **Circ:** (Not Reported)

52888 ■ Public Health Nutrition
Cambridge University Press
The Edinburgh Bldg.
Shaftesbury Rd.
Cambridge CB2 2RU, United Kingdom

|

Ph: 44 122 3312393
Fax: 44 122 3315052
Publisher E-mail: information@cambridge.org
Peer-eviewed journal covering the studies and research in the nutrition-related public health achievements, situations and problems around the world. **Freq:** Monthly. **Key Personnel:** Agneta Yngve, Editor-in-Chief; M. Tseng, Dep. Ed.; A. Hodge, Dep. Ed. **ISSN:** 1368-9800. **Subscription Rates:** 589 institutions online only; 697 institutions print and online; EUR936 institutions online only; US$1,116 institutions online only; US$1,337 institutions print and online; EUR1,117 institutions print and online. **Remarks:** Accepts advertising. **URL:** http://journals.cambridge.org/action/displayJournal?jid=PHN. **Ad Rates:** BW: 1,160. **Circ:** (Not Reported)

52889 ■ Quarterly Reviews of Biophysics
Cambridge University Press
The Edinburgh Bldg.
Shaftesbury Rd.
Cambridge CB2 2RU, United Kingdom
Ph: 44 122 3312393
Fax: 44 122 3315052
Publisher E-mail: information@cambridge.org
Journal covering various topics from ion channels to DNA topology and from X-ray diffraction to NMR in the area of biophysics. **Key Personnel:** Wah Chiu, Editor; Dr. Andrew G.W. Leslie, Editor; David M.J. Lilley, Editor. **ISSN:** 0033-5835. **Subscription Rates:** 385 institutions print and online; US$707 institutions print and online; 322 institutions online only; US$588 institutions online only; 132 individuals print only; US$254 individuals print only. **Remarks:** Accepts advertising. **URL:** http://journals.cambridge.org/action/displayJournal?jid=QRB. **Ad Rates:** BW: 450. **Circ:** (Not Reported)

52890 ■ Renewable Agriculture and Food Systems
Cambridge University Press
The Edinburgh Bldg.
Shaftesbury Rd.
Cambridge CB2 2RU, United Kingdom
Ph: 44 122 3312393
Fax: 44 122 3315052
Publisher E-mail: information@cambridge.org
Journal publishing original research and review articles on the economic, ecological, and environmental impacts of agriculture; the effective use of renewable resources and biodiversity in agro-ecosystems; and the technological and sociological implications of sustainable food systems. **Freq:** Quarterly. **Key Personnel:** Prof. J.W. Doran, Editor-in-Chief; R. Welsh, Assoc. Ed.; R. Weil, Assoc. Ed. **ISSN:** 1742-1705. **Subscription Rates:** 190 institutions print and online; US$375 institutions print and online; 145 institutions online only; US$280 institutions online only; 109 individuals print and online; US$204 individuals print and online; 86 individuals online only; US$162 individuals online only. **Remarks:** Accepts advertising. **URL:** http://journals.cambridge.org/action/displayJournal?jid=RAF. **Ad Rates:** BW: 385. **Circ:** (Not Reported)

52891 ■ Repeat
Repeat Fanzine & Records
PO Box 438
Cambridge CB4 1FX, United Kingdom
Publisher E-mail: rosey@repeatfanzine.co.uk
Fan magazine covering the Manic Street Preachers. **Subtitle:** A Mess of Zeros and Ones. **Founded:** 1994. **Trim Size:** A4. **Subscription Rates:** 2 individuals; EUR88 individuals. **URL:** http://www.repeatfanzine.co.uk. **Circ:** 500

52892 ■ Scottish Journal of Theology
Cambridge University Press
The Edinburgh Bldg.
Shaftesbury Rd.
Cambridge CB2 2RU, United Kingdom
Ph: 44 122 3312393
Fax: 44 122 3315052
Publisher E-mail: information@cambridge.org
Scholarly journal covering historical and systematic theology and bible study. **Founded:** 1948. **Freq:** Quarterly. **Key Personnel:** Prof. Iain Torrance, Editor, sjt@ptsem.edu; Prof. Bryan Spinks, Editor, bryan.spinks@yale.edu; David Fergusson, Consulting Ed. **ISSN:** 0036-9306. **Subscription Rates:** 117 individuals online and print; US$218 individuals online and print; 109 institutions online; US$201 institutions online. **Remarks:** Advertising accepted; rates available upon request. **URL:** http://journals.cambridge.org/action/

displayJournal?jid=SJT. **Circ:** 1,200

52893 ■ Seed Science Research
Cambridge University Press
The Edinburgh Bldg.
Shaftesbury Rd.
Cambridge CB2 2RU, United Kingdom
Ph: 44 122 3312393
Fax: 44 122 3315052
Publisher E-mail: information@cambridge.org
International journal featuring high-quality original papers and review articles on the fundamental aspects of seed science, reviewed by internationally-distinguished editors with emphasis on the physiology, biochemistry, molecular biology and ecology of seeds. **Freq:** Quarterly. **Key Personnel:** M.A. Cohn, Editorial Board; H.W.M. Hilhorst, Editor-in-Chief; Dr. William Finch-Savage, Assoc. Ed. **ISSN:** 0960-2585. **Subscription Rates:** 378 institutions online only; 475 institutions print and online; US$552 individuals print and online; 109 individuals online only; 278 individuals print and online; US$218 individuals online only; US$752 institutions online only; US$945 institutions print and online. **Remarks:** Accepts advertising. **URL:** http://journals.cambridge.org/action/displayJournal?jid=SSR. **Ad Rates:** BW: 625. **Circ:** (Not Reported)

52894 ■ Shakespeare Survey
Cambridge University Press
The Edinburgh Bldg.
Shaftesbury Rd.
Cambridge CB2 2RU, United Kingdom
Ph: 44 122 3312393
Fax: 44 122 3315052
Publisher E-mail: information@cambridge.org
Publication covering literature and writing. **Founded:** 1948. **Freq:** Annual. **Key Personnel:** Peter Holland, Editor. **ISSN:** 0080-9152. **URL:** http://www.cambridge.org/features/literature/shakespearesurvey/.

52895 ■ Ships and Offshore Structures
Woodhead Publishing Ltd.
Abington Hall, Granta Park
Great Abington
Cambridge CB21 6AH, United Kingdom
Ph: 44 12 23891358
Fax: 44 12 23893694
Publisher E-mail: wp@woodheadpublishing.com
Peer-reviewed journal for academics and practitioners involved in maritime engineering, covering the entire range of issues and technologies related to both ships: tankers, LNG carriers, large container vessels, naval vessels, and offshore structures: floating, production, storage and off-loading units (FPSOs), with a strong emphasis on practical design, construction and operation. **Freq:** Quarterly. **Key Personnel:** Prof. Jeom Kee Paik, Editor-in-Chief. **ISSN:** 1744-5302. **Subscription Rates:** 202 individuals print only; US$744 individuals online only; EUR827 individuals print & online. **URL:** http://www.woodheadpublishing.com/en/; http://www.informaworld.com/smpp/title~content=t778188387~link=cover.

52896 ■ Social Policy and Society
Cambridge University Press
The Edinburgh Bldg.
Shaftesbury Rd.
Cambridge CB2 2RU, United Kingdom
Ph: 44 122 3312393
Fax: 44 122 3315052
Publisher E-mail: information@cambridge.org
Peer-reviewed journal containing articles that draw upon contemporary policy-related research, teaching and learning issues and wider developments in the social sciences. **Key Personnel:** Dr. Kim McKee, Editorial Board; Prof. Hugh Bochel, Editorial Board; Dr. Sharon Wright, Co-Ed., sharon.wright@stir.ac.uk; Prof. Hartley Dean, Editorial Board, h.dean@lse.ac.uk; Prof. Peter Dwyer, Co-Ed., peter.dwyer@ntu.ac.uk; Prof. Robert Hulme, Editorial Board; Dr. Philip Haynes, Editorial Board; Dr. John Hudson, Editorial Board; Dr. Graham Bowpitt, Editorial Board. **ISSN:** 1474-7464. **Subscription Rates:** 311 institutions online and print; US$541 institutions online and print; 272 institutions online only; US$465 institutions online only. **Remarks:** Accepts advertising. **URL:** http://journals.cambridge.org/action/displayJournal?jid=SPS. **Ad Rates:** BW: US$805, 4C: US$1,755. **Circ:** 1,000

52897 ■ Softmatter
Royal Society of Chemistry
Thomas Graham House
The Science Pk., Milton Rd.
Milton Rd.
Cambridge CB4 0WF, United Kingdom
Ph: 44 12 23420066
Fax: 44 12 23423623
Publisher E-mail: sales@rsc.org
Journal focusing on chemistry and biology. **Freq:** 24/yr. **Key Personnel:** Liz Davies, Editor. **ISSN:** 1744-683X. **Subscription Rates:** 1,131 individuals print + online; US$2,111 individuals print + online; 1,017 individuals online; US$1,899 individuals online. **URL:** http://www.rsc.org/Publishing/Journals/sm/index.asp.

52898 ■ Sportsboat
CSL Publishing Ltd.
Alliance House
49 Sidney St.
Cambridge CB2 3HX, United Kingdom
Ph: 44 1223 460490
Fax: 44 1223 315960
Magazine covering sports boats and sports boating. **Freq:** Monthly. **Key Personnel:** Alex Smith, Editor, editor@sportsboat.co.uk; Katie Hawksworth, Advertising Mgr., Katie.Hawksworth@cslpublishing.com. **Subscription Rates:** 63.50 individuals Europe; 52.20 individuals; 118.15 individuals. **Remarks:** Accepts advertising. **URL:** http://www.sportsboat.co.uk. **Circ:** Paid 10,000

52899 ■ Studies in History and Philosophy of Science Part A
Elsevier Science Inc.
Dept. of History & Philosophy of Science
University of Cambridge
Free School Ln.
Cambridge CB2 3RH, United Kingdom
Publisher E-mail: usinfo-ehelp@elsevier.com
Peer-reviewed journal covering history of the sciences and the philosophy of the sciences and in the topical areas of historiography of the sciences. **Founded:** 1970. **Freq:** 4/yr. **Key Personnel:** N. Jardine, Editor; M. Frasca-Spada, Editor; J. Whitelock, Asst. Ed.; R. Raphael, Book Review Ed.; K. Tybjerg, Book Review Ed.; G. Cantor, Consulting Ed. **ISSN:** 0039-3681. **Subscription Rates:** 9,700¥ individuals; EUR70 individuals for European countries and Iran; US$78 other countries except Europe, Japan and Iran; US$697 institutions except Europe, Japan and Iran; EUR623 institutions for European countries and Iran; 82,800¥ institutions. **URL:** http://www.elsevier.com/wps/find/journaldescription.cws_home/30586/descriptiondescription.

52900 ■ Studies in History and Philosophy of Science Part C
Elsevier Science Inc.
Dept. of History & Philosophy of Science
University of Cambridge
Free School Ln.
Cambridge CB2 3RH, United Kingdom
Publisher E-mail: usinfo-ehelp@elsevier.com
Peer-reviewed journal covering the historical, sociological, philosophical and ethical aspects and of the medical and biomedical sciences and technologies. **Subtitle:** Studies in History and Philosophy of Biological and Biomedical Sciences. **Founded:** Nov. 11, 1998. **Freq:** 4/yr. **Print Method:** Offset. **Trim Size:** 5 1/2 x 8 1/2. **Cols./Page:** 1. **Col. Width:** 50 nonpareils. **Col. Depth:** 100 agate lines. **Key Personnel:** J. Whitelock, Asst. Ed.; T. Lewens, Advisory Ed.; D.D. Turner, Consulting Ed.; N. Jardine, Editor; R. Raphael, Book Review Ed.; S. De Chadarevian, Advisory Ed.; R. Ashcroft, Consulting Ed.; M. Frasca-Spada, Editor; L. Darden, Consulting Ed.; M. Jackson, Consulting Ed. **ISSN:** 1369-8486. **Subscription Rates:** US$512 institutions, other countries except Europe, Japan and Iran; 60,800¥ institutions; EUR457 institutions for European countries and Iran; US$78 other countries except Europe, Japan and Iran; 9,700¥ individuals; EUR70 individuals for European countries and Iran. **URL:** http://www.elsevier.com/wps/find/journaldescription.cws_home/600658/descriptiondescription.

52901 ■ Theatre Research International
Cambridge University Press
The Edinburgh Bldg.
Shaftesbury Rd.
Cambridge CB2 2RU, United Kingdom
Ph: 44 122 3312393
Fax: 44 122 3315052

Publisher E-mail: information@cambridge.org
Journal covering the visual and performing arts. **Freq:** Quarterly. **Key Personnel:** Prof. Charlotte Canning, Assoc. Ed., rokem@post.tau.ac.il; Prof. Elaine Aston, Sen. Ed., e.aston@lancaster.ac.uk; Dr. Peter M. Boenisch, Book Review Ed., p.m.boenisch@kent.ac.uk. **ISSN:** 0307-8833. **Subscription Rates:** 144 institutions print and online; US$245 institutions print and online; 130 institutions online only; US$220 institutions online only. **Remarks:** Accepts advertising. **URL:** http://journals.cambridge.org/action/displayJournal?jid=TRI. **Ad Rates:** BW: US$835. **Circ:** Controlled 1,100

52902 ■ Theory and Practice of Logic Programming (TPLP)
Cambridge University Press
The Edinburgh Bldg.
Shaftesbury Rd.
Cambridge CB2 2RU, United Kingdom
Ph: 44 122 3312393
Fax: 44 122 3315052
Publisher E-mail: information@cambridge.org
Journal focusing on both the theory and the practice of logic programming. **Freq:** Bimonthly. **Key Personnel:** Maurice Bruynooghe, Editorial Advisor; Prof. I. Niemela, Editor-in-Chief; Peter J. Stuckey, Area Ed., pjs@cs.mu. oz.au. **ISSN:** 1471-0684. **Subscription Rates:** 305 institutions print and online; US$540 institutions print and online; 265 institutions online only; US$445 institutions online version; 75 individuals print and online; US$125 individuals print and online; 67 individuals online only; US$110 individuals online only. **Remarks:** Accepts advertising. **URL:** http://journals.cambridge.org/action/displayJournal?jid=TLP. **Ad Rates:** BW: 445. **Circ:** 300

52903 ■ Twentieth Century Music
Cambridge University Press
The Edinburgh Bldg.
Shaftesbury Rd.
Cambridge CB2 2RU, United Kingdom
Ph: 44 122 3312393
Fax: 44 122 3315052
Publication E-mail: tcm@cardiff.ac.uk
Publisher E-mail: information@cambridge.org
Journal dedicated to leading research on all aspects of the music of the twentieth century - a period which may be interpreted flexibly to encompass, where appropriate, music from the late-nineteenth century to the early years of the twenty-first. **Key Personnel:** Charles Wilson, Editor; Paul Attinello, Assoc. Ed.; Kenneth Gloag, Reviews Ed. **ISSN:** 1478-5722. **Subscription Rates:** 81 institutions print and online; 72 individuals online only; US$127 individuals online only. **Remarks:** Accepts advertising. **URL:** http://journals.cambridge.org/action/displayJournal?jid=TCM. **Ad Rates:** BW: 415. **Circ:** (Not Reported)

52904 ■ Ultramicroscopy
Elsevier Science Inc.
c/o P. Midgley, Ed.
University of Cambridge
Dept. of Materials Science & Metallurgy
Pembroke St.
Cambridge CB2 3QZ, United Kingdom
Publisher E-mail: usinfo-ehelp@elsevier.com
Peer-reviewed journal describing scientific knowledge in ultramicroscopy. **Founded:** 1975. **Freq:** Monthly. **Print Method:** Offset. **Trim Size:** 8 x 10 7/8. **Cols./Page:** 3. **Col. Width:** 13 picas. **Col. Depth:** 10 inches. **Key Personnel:** D.A. Muller, Editorial Board; U. Dahmen, Editorial Board; S.M. Lindsay, Assoc. Ed., stuart. lindsay@asu.edu; J.P. Chevalier, Editorial Board; R.F. Egerton, Editorial Board; K.H. Downing, Editorial Board; A.G. Cullis, Editorial Board; C. Durkan, Editorial Board; D.J.H. Cockayne, Editorial Board; W. Baumeister, Editorial Board; P. Midgley, Editor, ultram@msm.cam.ac.uk. **ISSN:** 0304-3991. **Subscription Rates:** US$3,160 institutions except Europe, Japan and Iran; 374,800¥ institutions except Europe, Japan and Iran; EUR 2,825 institutions for European countries and Iran. **URL:** http://www.elsevier.com/wps/find/journaldescription.cws_home/505679/descriptiondescription.

52905 ■ Workplace Law
Workplace Law Group
110 hills Rd.
Cambridge CB2 1LQ, United Kingdom
Ph: 44 871 7778881

Fax: 44 871 7778882
Publication E-mail: editorial@workplacelaw.net
Publisher E-mail: info@workplacelaw.net
Magazine covering employment law, health and safety, and premises management. **Founded:** Oct. 2004. **Freq:** 10/yr. **URL:** http://www.workplacelaw.net/magazine.

52906 ■ World Birdwatch
BirdLife International
Wellbrook Ct.
Girton Rd.
Cambridge CB3 0NA, United Kingdom
Ph: 44 12 23277318
Fax: 44 12 23277200
Publisher E-mail: birdlife@birdlife.org
Publication covering worldwide birdwatching. **Freq:** Quarterly. **Subscription Rates:** 30 individuals contributory; 15 individuals special; 60 individuals supporting; 170 individuals sustaining. **Remarks:** Advertising accepted; rates available upon request. **URL:** http://www.birdlife.org/. **Circ:** 6,000

52907 ■ BBC Radio-AM - 1026
104 Hills Rd.
Cambridge CB2 1LQ, United Kingdom
Ph: 44 12 23259696
E-mail: cambridgeshire@bbc.co.uk
Format: News; Sports; Talk. **Owner:** British Broadcasting Corp., Broadcasting House, Portland Pl., London W1A 1AA, United Kingdom. **Operating Hours:** Continuous. **URL:** http://www.bbc.co.uk/cambridgeshire/local_radio.

52908 ■ BBC Radio Cambridgeshire-FM - 96
Broadcasting House
Cambridge Business Pk.
Cowley Rd.
Cambridge CB4 0WZ, United Kingdom
Ph: 44 1223 259696
E-mail: cambridgeshire@bbc.co.uk
Format: Talk; News; Sports; Oldies. **Owner:** British Broadcasting Corp., Broadcasting House, Portland Pl., London W1A 1AA, United Kingdom. **Founded:** May 1, 1982. **Operating Hours:** Continuous. **URL:** http://www.bbc.co.uk/cambridgeshire/local_radio.

52909 ■ BBC Radio-FM - 95.7
104 Hills Rd.
Cambridge CB2 1LQ, United Kingdom
Ph: 44 12 23259696
E-mail: cambridgeshire@bbc.co.uk
Format: News; Information; Sports. **Owner:** British Broadcasting Corp., Broadcasting House, Portland Pl., London W1A 1AA, United Kingdom. **Operating Hours:** Continuous. **URL:** http://www.bbc.co.uk/cambridgeshire/local_radio/.

52910 ■ CUR-AM - 1350
Churchill College
Cambridge CB3 0DS, United Kingdom
Ph: 44 1223 852864
Fax: 44 1223 336180
Format: Eclectic; Full Service; Alternative/New Music/Progressive. **Founded:** 2002. **Operating Hours:** Continuous. **Key Personnel:** Martin Steers, Station Mgr.; Edmund Bolton, Finance Mgr. **Ad Rates:** Advertising accepted; rates available upon request. **URL:** http://www.cur1350.co.uk.

52911 ■ Star 107.9-FM - 107.9
20 Mercers Row
Cambridge CB5 8HY, United Kingdom
Ph: 44 1223 305107
Fax: 44 1223 309107
Format: Top 40; Adult Contemporary; News; Oldies; Blues. **Operating Hours:** Continuous. **Key Personnel:** Darren Taylor, Station Mgr., darren.taylor@star107.co. uk; Mark Peters, Contact, mark.peters@star107.co.uk. **Ad Rates:** Advertising accepted; rates available upon request. **URL:** http://www.star107.co.uk/.

Cambuskenneth

52912 ■ The Angry Corrie
3 Ferry Orchard
Cambuskenneth FK9 5ND, United Kingdom
Ph: 44 1786 450047
Publisher E-mail: theangrycorrie@googlemail.com
Magazine. **Subtitle:** Scotland's First and Finest Hillwalking Fanzine. **Founded:** 1991. **Freq:** Quarterly. **Trim**

Size: A4. **Key Personnel:** Perkin Warbeck, Editor; Craig Smillie, Artwork; Chris Tyler, Artwork; Dave Hewitt, Editor. **Subscription Rates:** 9 individuals 6 hot-off-the-press copies. **URL:** http://bubl.ac.uk/org/tacit/tac.

Campbeltown

52913 ■ Argyll FM - 107.7
27/29 Longrow
Campbeltown PA28 6ER, United Kingdom
E-mail: studio@argyllfm.co.uk
Format: News; Classical; Gospel; Alternative/New Music/Progressive. **Operating Hours:** Continuous. **Ad Rates:** Advertising accepted; rates available upon request. **URL:** http://www.argyllfm.co.uk/.

52914 ■ Argyll FM - 107.1
27/29 Longrow
Campbeltown PA28 6ER, United Kingdom
E-mail: studio@argyllfm.co.uk
Format: News; Classical; Gospel; Alternative/New Music/Progressive. **Operating Hours:** Continuous. **Ad Rates:** Advertising accepted; rates available upon request. **URL:** http://www.argyllfm.co.uk/.

52915 ■ Argyll FM - 106.5
27/29 Longrow
Campbeltown PA28 6ER, United Kingdom
E-mail: studio@argyllfm.co.uk
Format: News; Classical; Gospel; Alternative/New Music/Progressive. **Operating Hours:** Continuous. **Ad Rates:** Advertising accepted; rates available upon request. **URL:** http://www.argyllfm.co.uk/.

Cannock

52916 ■ The Vitreous Enameller
Institute of Vitreous Enamellers
39 Sweetbriar Way
Heath Hayes
Staffordshire
Cannock WS12 2US, United Kingdom
Ph: 44 15 43450596
Fax: 44 87 00941237
Publisher E-mail: admin@ive.org.uk
Journal of the Institute of Vitreous Enamellers. **Freq:** Quarterly. **ISSN:** 0042-7519. **Subscription Rates:** 57 individuals; 65 other countries. **Remarks:** Accepts advertising. **URL:** http://www.ive.org.uk/publications/publications-ve.html. **Circ:** (Not Reported)

Canterbury

52917 ■ Engineering Designer
Institution of Engineering Designers
c/o Clare Swaffer, Ed.
Engineering Designer
27 Castle St.
Canterbury CT1 2PX, United Kingdom
Ph: 44 1795 542435
Fax: 44 1795 535469
Publication covering engineering. **Freq:** Bimonthly. **Key Personnel:** Clare Swaffer, Editor, editorial@engineeringdesigner.co.uk. **ISSN:** 0013-7858. **Subscription Rates:** 39 individuals; US$88 U.S. and Canada; 7 other countries airmail; 7 single issue U.K. and Eire. **Remarks:** Advertising accepted; rates available upon request. **URL:** http://www.ied.org.uk/public/institution/eng-designer. **Circ:** 6,600

52918 ■ Family History
Institute of Heraldic and Genealogical Studies
79-82 Northgate
Canterbury CT1 1BA, United Kingdom
Ph: 44 1227 768664
Fax: 44 1227 765617
Publication covering genealogy. **Subtitle:** The Journal of IHGS. **Freq:** Quarterly. **Key Personnel:** Cecil R. Humphery-Smith, Editor. **ISSN:** 0014-7265. **Subscription Rates:** 15 individuals; 40 individuals 3 years; US$7.50 single issue back issue. **Remarks:** Advertising not accepted. **URL:** http://www.family-history.org/. **Circ:** (Not Reported)

52919 ■ Financial World
Institute of Financial Services - England
IFS House,4-9 Burgate Ln.
Canterbury CTI 2XJ, United Kingdom
Ph: 44 1227 818609

Fax: 44 1227 784331
Publisher E-mail: customerservices@ifslearning.ac.uk
Worldwide finance magazine. **Freq:** Monthly. **Key Personnel:** Jay Elwes, Editor, phone 44 20 74930173, jelwes@ifslearning.ac.uk. **Subscription Rates:** 75 individuals print (inc. free online access); 34.26 individuals online. **Remarks:** Advertising accepted; rates available upon request. **URL:** http://www.financialworld.co.uk/. **Formerly:** Chartered Banker. **Circ:** *22,080

52920 ■ From the Window
Hero Joy Nightingale
3 Sandbank Cottages
St. Stephen's Hill
Canterbury CT2 7AU, United Kingdom
Ph: 44 12 27456625
Fax: 44 12 27459963
Publisher E-mail: hojoy@rmplc.co.uk
Internet magazine featuring journalism, poetry, travelogues and experiential writing dealing with social issues and living with physical handicaps. **Key Personnel:** Hero Joy Nightingale, Editor, hojoy@rmplc.co.uk. **URL:** http://atschool.eduweb.co.uk/hojoy/.

52921 ■ inQuire
University of Kent Student's Union
Kent Union
Mandela Bldg.
University of Kent
Canterbury CT2 7NW, United Kingdom
Ph: 44 1227 824200
Fax: 44 1227 824204
Publisher E-mail: kentunion@kent.ac.uk
College magazine for students. **Founded:** Oct. 1986. **Freq:** 3/week. **Cols./Page:** 3. **Key Personnel:** Ed Atkins, Editor, newspaper.editor@inquiremedia.co.uk. **Subscription Rates:** Free. **Remarks:** Accepts advertising. **URL:** http://www.kentunion.co.uk/volunteeringcommunity/media/inquire/. **Formerly:** Kred. **Ad Rates:** BW: 250, 4C: 450. **Circ:** Non-paid 2,000

52922 ■ CSR-FM - 97.4
Mandela Bldg.
University of Kent
Canterbury CT2 7NW, United Kingdom
Ph: 44 1227 823301
E-mail: info@csrfm.com
Format: Educational; Contemporary Hit Radio (CHR). **Key Personnel:** Will Jones, Station Mgr., manager@csrfm.com. **URL:** http://www.csrfm.com/.

Cardiff

52923 ■ A470
Academi - Yr Academi Gymreig
3rd Fl., Mount Stuart House
Mount Stuart Sq.
Cardiff CF10 5FQ, United Kingdom
Ph: 44 29 20472266
Fax: 44 29 20492930
Publisher E-mail: post@academi.org
English and Welsh language publication covering literature. **Freq:** Bimonthly. **Trim Size:** 260 x 170. **Key Personnel:** Peter Finch, Editor. **Subscription Rates:** Free to members and associates. **Remarks:** Accepts advertising. **URL:** http://www.academi.org/introduction/. **Ad Rates:** BW: 170, 4C: 290. **Circ:** 6,000

52924 ■ Autonomic and Autacoid Pharmacology
John Wiley & Sons Inc.
Wiley-Blackwell
c/o Kenneth J. Broadley, Ed.
Dept. of Pharmacology
Welsh School of Pharmacy, Cardiff University
Cathays Pk.
Cardiff CF10 3XF, United Kingdom
Ph: 44 29 20874000
Fax: 44 29 20874149
Journal focusing on interactions of drugs and related substances with the central and peripheral divisions of the autonomic nervous system and its effector organs and tissues. **Freq:** Quarterly. **Key Personnel:** Kenneth J. Broadley, Editor; Prof. Francesco Amenta, Editorial Board; Prof. David J. Triggle, Editorial Board; Dr. Maria G. Belvisi, Editorial Board; Dr. Richard R. Eglen, Editorial Board; Dr. William R. Ford, Editor; Dr. Russell G. Chess-Williams, Editorial Board; Prof. James R. Docherty, Editorial Board; Dr. Michael D. Day, Editorial Board. **ISSN:** 1474-8665. **Subscription Rates:** US$307 individuals print and online; EUR250 individuals print and

online (Euro zone); 166 individuals print and online (non Euro zone); 183 other countries print and online; US$1,516 institutions print and online; EUR1,042 institutions print and online; EUR947 institutions print or online; US$1,769 institutions, other countries print and online; US$1,607 institutions, other countries print or online; US$1,378 institutions print or online. **Remarks:** Accepts advertising. **URL:** http://www.wiley.com/bw/journal.asp?ref=1474-8665&site=1. **Circ:** (Not Reported)

52925 ■ Building Research Capacity
Cardiff University School of Social Sciences
Research Capacity Building Network
Glamorgan Bldg.
King Edward VII Ave.
Cardiff CF10 3WT, United Kingdom
Ph: 44 29 20875345
Fax: 44 29 20874678
Publisher E-mail: rcbn@cardiff.ac.uk
Peer-reviewed journal devoted to capacity-building and methodological issues in the context of educational research. **Key Personnel:** Prof. Gareth Rees, Director; Prof. Huw Beynon, Chm. **Subscription Rates:** Free. **URL:** http://www.tlrp.org/rcbn/capacity/Journal.html.

52926 ■ Bulletin of Entomological Research
CAB International
School of Biosciences
University of Cardiff
PO Box 915
Cardiff CF10 3TL, United Kingdom
Publisher E-mail: enquiries@cabi.org
Journal publishing high quality and original research papers, review articles and short communications concerning insects, mites, ticks or other arthropods of economic importance in agriculture, forestry, stored products, biological control, medicine, animal health and natural resource management. **Freq:** Bimonthly. **Key Personnel:** Dr. William Symondson, Editor-in-Chief, symondson@cardiff.ac.uk; Dr. P.F. Billingsley, Subject Ed.; D.A. Bohan, Subject Ed.; D. Giga, Subject Ed.; D. Gillespie, Subject Ed. **ISSN:** 0007-4853. **Subscription Rates:** 455 individuals print and online; US$1,560 institutions print and online; 112 individuals online only; US$875 individuals print and online. **Remarks:** Accepts advertising. **URL:** http://journals.cambridge.org/action/displayJournal?jid=BER. **Circ:** (Not Reported)

52927 ■ Catholic Teachers Gazette
Cartref Communications
57 Lake Rd. W
Cardiff CF23 5PH, United Kingdom
Ph: 44 29 20766318
Fax: 44 29 20747929
Publication E-mail: info@e-ctg.co.uk
Publisher E-mail: info@e-ctg.co.uk
Magazine featuring teacher vacancies and articles of interest to Catholic school teachers. **Freq:** Weekly (Fri.). **Subscription Rates:** Free to Catholic schools in England and Wales; 5 individuals. **Remarks:** Accepts advertising. **URL:** http://www.e-ctg.co.uk/. **Circ:** (Not Reported)

52928 ■ CEBE Transactions
Cardiff University
Centre for Education in the Built Environment
Bute Bldg., King Edward VII Ave.
Cardiff CF10 3NB, United Kingdom
Ph: 44 29 20874600
Fax: 44 29 20874601
Peer-reviewed journal covering case studies, project reports, research findings, and reviews relating to teaching, learning, and scholarship. **Subtitle:** The Online Journal of the Centre for Education in the Built Environment. **Founded:** 1980. **Freq:** Monthly. **Trim Size:** 3/8 x 10 7/8. **Cols./Page:** 3. **Col. Width:** 27 nonpareils. **Col. Depth:** 134 agate lines. **Key Personnel:** Chris Webster, Editor; Ron Griffiths, Editorial Board; Martin Beck, Editorial Board; Robin Boyle, Editorial Board; Allan Ashworth, Editorial Board; Caroline Baillie, Editorial Board. **ISSN:** 1745-0322. **URL:** http://www.cebe.heacademy.ac.uk/transactions/index.php.

52929 ■ European Planning Studies
Taylor & Francis Group Journals
Centre for Advanced Studies
University of Wales
Cardiff, United Kingdom
Publisher E-mail: customerservice@taylorandfrancis.com
Peer-reviewed journal focusing on spatial development

planning. **Freq:** 12/yr. **Print Method:** Offset. **Cols./Page:** 6. **Col. Width:** 2 1/4 inches. **Col. Depth:** 21 1/2 inches. **Key Personnel:** Philip Cooke, Editor; Louis Albrechts, Editor; Guy Baeten, Book Review Ed. **ISSN:** 0965-4313. **Subscription Rates:** US$1,598 institutions print and online; US$1,518 institutions online; US$482 individuals; 2,637 institutions print and online; 2,506 institutions online; 801 individuals; EUR2,109 institutions print and online; EUR2,004 institutions online only; EUR639 individuals. **URL:** http://www.tandf.co.uk/journals/titles/09654313.asp.

52930 ■ International Journal of Human Resource Management
Routledge
Taylor & Francis Group Ltd.
c/o Prof. Michael Poole, Ed.
Cardiff Business School
Colum Dr.
Cardiff CF1 3EU, United Kingdom
Ph: 44 29 20874270
Fax: 44 29 20874419
Publisher E-mail: webmaster.books@tandf.co.uk
Peer-reviewed journal covering human resources and labor relations. **Freq:** 15/yr. **Key Personnel:** Prof. Michael Poole, Editor, poolem@cardiff.ac.uk; Chris Brewster, Editorial Board; Miguel Martinez Lucio, Editorial Board; Sandra Dawson, Editorial Board; John W. Hunt, Editorial Board; George Thomason, Editorial Board. **ISSN:** 0958-5192. **Subscription Rates:** 1,436 institutions online; 308 individuals online; US$445 individuals; 1,512 institutions print + online; US$2,445 institutions print + online; US$2,323 institutions online. **Remarks:** Accepts advertising on request. **URL:** http://www.tandf.co.uk/journals/titles/09585192.asp. **Circ:** (Not Reported)

52931 ■ International Journal of Metaheuristics
Inderscience Enterprises Limited
c/o Dr. C.L. Mumford, Ed.-in-Ch.
Cardiff University
School of Computer Science
5 The Parade
Cardiff CF24 3AA, United Kingdom
Journal covering all aspects of metaheuristic practice, including theoretical studies, empirical investigations, comparisons, and real-world applications. **Freq:** 4/yr. **Key Personnel:** Dr. C.L. Mumford, Editor-in-Chief, ijmheur@cf.ac.uk. **ISSN:** 1755-2176. **Subscription Rates:** EUR494 individuals print or online; EUR672 individuals print and online. **URL:** http://www.inderscience.com/browse/index.php?journalID=271.

52932 ■ International Journal of Mobile Network Design and Innovation
Inderscience Publishers
c/o Dr. Stuart Allen, Editorial Board Member
School of Computer Science, Cardiff University
Queens Bldg., 5 The Parade
PO Box 916
Cardiff CF24 3XF, United Kingdom
Publisher E-mail: editor@inderscience.com
Peer-reviewed journal addressing the state-of-the-art in computerisation for the deployment and operation of current and future wireless networks. **Freq:** Quarterly. **Key Personnel:** Dr. Stuart Allen, Editorial Board Member; Dr. Roger Whitaker, Editorial Board Member; Prof. Steve Hurley, Editorial Board Member; Dr. Michael R. Bartolacci, Editor, mrb24@psu.edu; Dr. Ken Craig, Editorial Board Member. **ISSN:** 1744-2869. **Subscription Rates:** EUR494 individuals print only (surface mail); EUR672 individuals hard copy and online; EUR840 individuals online only (2-3 users); EUR534 individuals print only (airmail). **URL:** http://www.inderscience.com/browse/index.php?journalcode=ijmndi.

52933 ■ Journal of Enzyme Inhibition and Medicinal Chemistry
Taylor & Francis Ltd.
c/o H.J. Smith, Ed.
The Welsh School of Pharmacy
U.W.C.C
King Edward VII Ave.
Cardiff CFI 3XF, United Kingdom
International and interdisciplinary vehicle publishing new knowledge and findings on enzyme inhibitors and inhibitory processes and agonist/antagonist receptor interactions in the development of medicinal and anti-cancer agents and an understanding of their action. **Freq:** 6/yr. **Key Personnel:** Prof. H. John Smith, Editor, jeimc@cardiff.ac.uk; D. Hadjipavlou-Litina, Editorial Board; M.

Le Borgne, Assoc. Ed.; J.C. Dearden, Editorial Board; R.W. Hartmann, Editorial Board; D. Poirier, Editorial Board. **ISSN:** 1475-6366. **Subscription Rates:** 1,665 individuals; US$2,360 institutions; EUR1,890 institutions. **Remarks:** Accepts advertising. **URL:** http://informahealthcare.com/enz. **Circ:** (Not Reported)

52934 ■ Journal of Medical Engineering and Technology
Taylor & Francis Ltd.
Dept. of Medical Physics & Bioengineering
University of Wales College of Medicine
Heath Pk.
Cardiff CF14 4XN, United Kingdom
International, independent, multidisciplinary journal promoting an understanding of the physiological processes underlying disease processes and the appropriate application of technology. **Freq:** Bimonthly. **Key Personnel:** Prof. J.P. Woodcock, Editor-in-Chief, john. woodcock@wales.nhs.uk; Prof. Peter N. Wells, Consulting Ed., wellspn@cardiff.ac.uk; Dr. Dimitri Parthimos, Editorial Board; Dr. Diane C. Crawford, Assoc. Ed., diane.crawford@uhbristol.nhs.uk; Prof. Anurag Srivastava, Editorial Board; Dr. John W. Fenner, Assoc. Ed., j.w.fenner@sheffield.ac.uk; Dr. Stuart J. Meldrum, Editorial Board. **ISSN:** 0309-1902. **Subscription Rates:** 1,050 institutions; US$1,870 institutions; EUR1,495 institutions. **Remarks:** Accepts advertising. **URL:** http://informahealthcare.com/loi/jmt. **Circ:** (Not Reported)

52935 ■ Journal of Neuroscience Methods
Elsevier Science
c/o Vincenzo Crunelli, Co-Ed.-in-Ch.
School of Biosciences, Preclinical Bldg.
Cardiff University, Museum Ave.
PO Box 911
Cardiff CF1 3US, United Kingdom
Ph: 44 29 20874764
Fax: 44 29 20874765
Publisher E-mail: nlinfo-f@elsevier.com
Journal devoted to new or innovations in existing methods of investigations, relating to all the aspects of the nervous system of humans, vertebrates and invertebrates. **Founded:** 1979. **Freq:** 18/yr. **Key Personnel:** Vincenzo Crunelli, Co-Ed.-in-Ch., crunelli@cardiff.ac.uk; Greg A. Gerhardt, Co-Ed.-in-Ch., naejnm@pop.uky.edu; J.S. Kelly, Founding Ed. **ISSN:** 0165-0270. **Subscription Rates:** EUR5,112 institutions for European Countries; 678,700¥ institutions; US$5,718 institutions for all countries except Europe and Japan; 67,500¥ individuals; EUR439 individuals; US$588 individuals. **Remarks:** Accepts advertising. **URL:** http://www.elsevier.com/wps/find/journaldescription.cws_home/506079/description. **Circ:** (Not Reported)

52936 ■ Marine Policy
Elsevier Science
c/o Prof. E.D. Brown, Ed.
Marine Policy
PO Box 5041
Cardiff CF5 6WT, United Kingdom
Publisher E-mail: nlinfo-f@elsevier.com
Peer-reviewed journal on ocean policy studies at regional, national and international levels with areas of interest on institutional arrangements for the management and regulation of marine activities, including fisheries and shipping, conflict resolution, marine pollution and environment, conservation and use of marine resources. **Freq:** Bimonthly. **Key Personnel:** Prof. E.D. Brown, Editor, member@duncan-brown.freeserve.co.uk; Prof. P. Birnie, Assoc. Ed.; Prof. H. D. Smith, Assoc. Ed.; E. Gold, Editorial Board; R. Goss, Editorial Board; V. Lowe, Editorial Board. **ISSN:** 0308-597X. **Subscription Rates:** EUR187 individuals European countries; US$242 individuals except Europe and Japan; 26,800¥ individuals; EUR1,205 institutions European countries; US$1,347 institutions except Europe and Japan; 160,000¥ institutions. **Remarks:** Accepts advertising. **URL:** http://www.elsevier.com/wps/find/journaldescription.cws_home/30453/descriptiondescription. **Circ:** (Not Reported)

52937 ■ Paediatrics & Child Health
Elsevier Science Inc.
c/o Patrick Cartlidge, Ed.-in-Ch.
Wales College of Medicine
Cardiff University
Cardiff, United Kingdom
Publisher E-mail: usinfo-ehelp@elsevier.com
Journal covering pediatrics and child health. **Freq:** Monthly. **Key Personnel:** Colin Powell, Assoc. Ed.; Allan Colver, MD, Assoc. Ed.; Nicholas Mann, MD, Assoc.

Ed.; Alistair Thomson, MD, Assoc. Ed.; Richard Wilson, Founding Ed.; R. Adelman, International Advisory Board; A. Bagga, International Advisory Board; Z. Bhutta, International Advisory Board; H. Buller, International Advisory Board; M.C. Chiu, International Advisory Board; Dr. Harish Vyas, Assoc. Ed.; Patrick Cartlidge, Editor-in-Chief. **ISSN:** 1751-7222. **Subscription Rates:** US$197 individuals all countries except Europe, Japan and Iran; 23,800¥ individuals; EUR221 individuals European countries and Iran; 107,000¥ institutions; EUR992 institutions European countries and Iran; US$884 institutions all countries except Europe, Japan and Iran. **URL:** http://www.elsevier.com/wps/find/journaldescription.cws_home/712422/descriptiondescription. **Formerly:** Current Paediatrics.

52938 ■ Qualitative Research
Sage Publications Ltd.
Cardiff School of Social Science
Cardiff University
Glamorgan Bldg., King Edward VII Ave.
Cardiff CF10 3WT, United Kingdom
Scholarly journal covering research methods. **Founded:** 2001. **Freq:** Bimonthly. **Trim Size:** 192 x 120 mm. **Key Personnel:** Paul A. Atkinson, Editor; Gregory Dimitriadis, Assoc. Ed.; Sara Delamont, Review Ed.; Anne Ryen, Regional Editorial Advisor; James Mienczakowski, Regional Editorial Advisor; Marc Berg, Editorial Board; Deborah Reed-Danahay, Regional Editorial Advisor; David Bloome, Editorial Board; Louisa Allen, Regional Editorial Advisor. **ISSN:** 1468-7941. **Subscription Rates:** US$955 institutions print & e-access; US$860 institutions e-access; US$936 institutions print only; US$87 individuals print only; US$172 institutions single print; US$19 individuals single print. **Remarks:** Accepts advertising. **URL:** http://www.sagepub.com/journalsProdDesc.nav?level1=200&currTree=Subjects&prodId=Journal201501. **Ad Rates:** BW: 200. **Circ:** (Not Reported)

52939 ■ South Wales Echo
Media Wales Ltd.
Six Park St.
Cardiff CF10 1XR, United Kingdom
Ph: 44 29 20223333
Publisher E-mail: newsdesk@mediawales.co.uk
Newspapers featuring news and events. **Key Personnel:** Mike Hill, Editor, mike.hill@mediawales.co.uk; Wayne Davies, Exec. Ed., wayne.davies@mediawales.co.uk. **Remarks:** Accepts advertising. **URL:** http://icwales.icnetwork.co.uk/news/cardiff-news/. **Circ:** (Not Reported)

52940 ■ Taliesin
Yr Academi Gymreig—The Welsh Academy
3rd Fl., Mount Stuart House
Mount Stuart Sq.
Cardiff CF10 5FQ, United Kingdom
Ph: 44 29 20472266
Fax: 44 29 20492930
Publication E-mail: post@academi.org
Publisher E-mail: post@academi.org
Welsh language literary journal. **Founded:** 1984. **Freq:** Triennial. **Print Method:** Offset. **Trim Size:** A5. **Key Personnel:** Christine James, Editor; Manon Rhys, Editor. **ISSN:** 0044-2884. **Subscription Rates:** 11 individuals; 19 two years; 13 other countries surface mail; 19 other countries airmail. **Remarks:** Accepts advertising. **URL:** http://www.academi.org. **Circ:** Paid 1,000

52941 ■ Western Mail
Media Wales Ltd.
Six Park St.
Cardiff CF10 1XR, United Kingdom
Ph: 44 29 20223333
Publisher E-mail: newsdesk@mediawales.co.uk
Newspapers featuring news and events. **Key Personnel:** Alan Edmunds, Editor, alan.edmunds@mediawales.co.uk; Wayne Davies, Exec. Ed., wayne.davies@mediawales.co.uk. **Remarks:** Accepts advertising. **URL:** http://icwales.icnetwork.co.uk/. **Circ:** (Not Reported)

52942 ■ Nation Radio-FM - 106.8
Newby House
Neath Abbey Business Pk.
Neath SA10 7DR, United Kingdom
Ph: 44 845 1062107
Fax: 44 845 0251001

E-mail: enquiries@nationwales.com; studio@nationwales.com
Format: Alternative/New Music/Progressive. **Owner:** Town & Country Broadcasting, at above address. **Ad Rates:** Advertising accepted; rates available upon request. **URL:** http://www.nationwales.com/.

52943 ■ Real Radio-FM - 105
1 Ty Nant Ct.
Morganstown
Cardiff CF15 8YF, United Kingdom
Ph: 44 29 20315100
Fax: 44 29 20315150
Format: Adult Contemporary. **Operating Hours:** Continuous. **Ad Rates:** Advertising accepted; rates available upon request. **URL:** http://www.realradiowales.co.uk/.

52944 ■ Red Dragon-FM - 103.2
The Red Dragon Ctr.
Cardiff Bay
Cardiff CF10 4DJ, United Kingdom
Ph: 44 2920 949494
Fax: 44 2920 942900
Format: Contemporary Hit Radio (CHR). **Owner:** Global Radio, 30 Leicester Sq., London WC2H 7LA, United Kingdom. **Operating Hours:** Continuous. **Ad Rates:** Advertising accepted; rates available upon request. **URL:** http://www.reddragonfm.co.uk/.

52945 ■ Rookwood Sound-AM - 945
The Jeff Lyons Ste.
Rookwood Hospital
Llandaff
Cardiff CF5 2YN, United Kingdom
Ph: 44 29 20313796
E-mail: info@rookwoodsound.co.uk
Format: Eclectic. **Founded:** Oct. 31, 1987. **Operating Hours:** Continuous. **Key Personnel:** Steve Allen, CEO, chief@rookwoodsound.co.uk; Lesley Jennings, Dep. Ch. Executive, deputychief@rookwoodsound.co.uk; Gavin Wilson, Prog. Controller, programmes@rookwoodsound.co.uk. **URL:** http://www.rookwoodsound.co.uk/.

Carlisle

52946 ■ Mastersinger
Association of British Choral Directors
Braelees, Kirkandrews on Eden
Carlisle CA5 6DU, United Kingdom
Publication E-mail: mastersinger@abcd.org.uk
Publisher E-mail: rachel.greaves@abcd.org.uk
Publication covering music. **Freq:** Quarterly. **Key Personnel:** Sir David Willcocks, President; Emma Disley, Editor. **Remarks:** Advertising accepted; rates available upon request. **URL:** http://www.abcd.org.uk/mswelcome.htm. **Circ:** (Not Reported)

52947 ■ BBC Radio Cumbria-FM - 95.6
Annetwell St.
Carlisle CA3 8BB, United Kingdom
Ph: 44 1228 592444
E-mail: radio.cumbria@bbc.co.uk
Format: News; Talk. **Owner:** British Broadcasting Corporation, Broadcasting House, Portland Pl., London W1A 1AA, United Kingdom. **Operating Hours:** Continuous. **Key Personnel:** Nigel Dyson, Managing Editor. **URL:** http://www.bbc.co.uk/cumbria/local_radio.

52948 ■ Carlisle-FM - 96.4
PO Box 964
Carlisle CA1 3NG, United Kingdom
Ph: 44 1228 818964
Format: News; Contemporary Hit Radio (CHR). **Owner:** Carlisle Radio Ltd., at above address. **Operating Hours:** Continuous. **Ad Rates:** Advertising accepted; rates available upon request. **URL:** http://www.cfmradio.

52949 ■ CFM Radio-FM - 96.4
PO Box 964
Carlisle CA1 3NG, United Kingdom
Ph: 44 1228 818964
Format: Contemporary Hit Radio (CHR). **URL:** http://www.cfmradio.com/.

Circulation: ★ = ABC; △ = BPA; ♦ = CAC; • = CCAB; ❏ = VAC; ⊕ = PO Statement; ‡ = Publisher's Report; Boldface figures = sworn; Light figures = estimated.

CFM Radio-FM - See Penrith

CFM Radio-FM - See Whitehaven

CFM Radio-FM - See Workington

Carluke

52950 ■ Carluke Gazette
Johnston Press PLC
3 High St.
Carluke ML8 4AL, United Kingdom
Ph: 44 1555 772226
Local community newspaper. **Remarks:** Accepts advertising. **URL:** http://www.carlukegazette.co.uk/. **Circ:** (Not Reported)

Carrickfergus

52951 ■ Carrick Times
Morton Newspapers
19 North St.
Carrickfergus BT38 7AQ, United Kingdom
Ph: 44 28 93351992
Community newspaper. **Freq:** Weekly. **Print Method:** Offset. **Col. Depth:** 450 millimeters. **Remarks:** Accepts advertising. **URL:** http://www.carrickfergustimes.co.uk. **Circ:** (Not Reported)

Castleford

52952 ■ Pontefract & Castleford Express
Johnston Press PLC
12 Bank St.
Castleford WF10 1HZ, United Kingdom
Ph: 44 1977 737200
Local community newspaper. **Key Personnel:** Dave Ward, Editor. **Remarks:** Accepts advertising. **URL:** http://www.pontefractandcastlefordexpress.co.uk/. **Circ:** (Not Reported)

52953 ■ Wood Protection
British Wood Preserving and Damp-Proofing Association
5C Flemming Ct.
Castleford WF10 5HW, United Kingdom
Publication covering property care. **Subtitle:** Preserve!. **Freq:** 3/yr. **Remarks:** Accepts advertising. **URL:** http://www.wood-protection.org/links.asp. **Former name:** Professional Treater. **Circ:** (Not Reported)

Ceredigion

52954 ■ Cylchgrawn Llyfrgell Genedlaethol Cymru
The National Library of Wales
Aberystwyth
Ceredigion SY23 3BU, United Kingdom
Ph: 44 19 70632800
Fax: 44 19 70615709
Publisher E-mail: nssaw-enquiries@llgc.org.uk
Scholarly journal covering the collections of the National Library of Wales. **Subtitle:** The National Library of Wales Journal. **Founded:** 1939. **Freq:** Semiannual. **Print Method:** Offset. **Trim Size:** 18 x 24.5 cm. **Cols./Page:** 1. **ISSN:** 0011-4421. **Subscription Rates:** US$8 single issue plus postage. **Remarks:** Advertising not accepted. **URL:** http://www.llgc.org.uk/lp/lp0066.htm. **Circ:** Combined 350

52955 ■ History of Science
Science History Publications Ltd.
c/o Iwan Rhys Morus, Ed.
Dept. of History & Welsh History
Hugh Owen Bldg.
Aberystwyth University
Ceredigion SY23 3DY, United Kingdom
Publisher E-mail: shp@shpltd.co.uk
Periodical focusing on history. **Founded:** 1962. **Freq:** Quarterly In March, June, September and December. **Trim Size:** 164 x 233 mm. **Key Personnel:** Iwan Rhys Morus, Editor, irm@aber.ac.uk. **ISSN:** 0073-2753. **Subscription Rates:** EUR130 institutions; US$265 institutions; US$42 individuals; US$84 individuals. **Remarks:** Advertising accepted; rates available upon request. **URL:** http://www.shpltd.co.uk/hs.html. **Circ:** Paid 600

Chapel-en-le-Frith

52956 ■ High Peak Radio-FM - 106.6
PO Box 106
Chapel-en-le-Frith SK23 0DJ, United Kingdom

Ph: 44 1298 813377
Fax: 44 1298 813388
E-mail: info@highpeakradio.co.uk
Format: Adult Contemporary. **Operating Hours:** Continuous. **URL:** http://www.highpeakradio.co.uk/.

Chard

52957 ■ Yeovil Express
Newsquest Media Group Ltd.
3a Fore St.
Somerset
Chard TA20 1PH, United Kingdom
Ph: 44 1460 238180
Fax: 44 1460 238188
Newspaper featuring local news and events. **Remarks:** Accepts advertising. **URL:** http://www.yeovilexpress.co.uk/. **Circ:** (Not Reported)

Charmouth

52958 ■ Tide Times
Nigel J. Clarke Publications
Befferlands Farm Workshops
Charmouth DT6 6RD, United Kingdom
Ph: 44 1297 561577
Fax: 44 1297 561577
Publication E-mail: nigel@njcpublications.co.uk
Publisher E-mail: nigel@njcpublications.co.uk
Trade magazine covering tidal predictions for the southwest coast of England. **Founded:** 1980. **Freq:** Annual in November. **Print Method:** Litho. **Key Personnel:** Nigel J. Clarke, Contact. **Subscription Rates:** 1.50 single issue; 4 other countries per item. **Remarks:** Accepts advertising. **URL:** http://www.njcpublications.co.uk. **Circ:** Paid 27,500

Chatham

52959 ■ Medical and Veterinary Entomology
John Wiley & Sons Inc.
Wiley-Blackwell
c/o Dr. Gabriella Gibson, Editorial Board
Natural Resources Institute
University of Greenwich, Medway Campus
Chatham ME4 4TB, United Kingdom
Journal reporting on biology and control of all kinds of insects with medical and veterinary significance, published in connection with the Royal Entomological Society. **Freq:** Quarterly. **Key Personnel:** Dr. Gabriella Gibson, Editorial Board, g.gibson@greenwich.ac.uk; Dr. Doug D. Colwell, Editor, colwelld@agr.gc.ca. **ISSN:** 0269-283X. **Subscription Rates:** US$171 individuals print and online; US$988 institutions print or online; US$1,087 institutions print and online; EUR680 institutions print or online; EUR748 institutions print and online; US$1,153 institutions, other countries print or online; US$1,268 institutions, other countries print and online; 534 institutions print or online; 102 other countries print and online; 92 individuals print and online. **Remarks:** Advertising accepted; rates available upon request. **URL:** http://www.wiley.com/bw/journal.asp?ref=0269-283x. **Circ:** (Not Reported)

Chelmsford

52960 ■ Blueprint
ETP Ltd.
Rosebery House
41 Springfield Rd.
Chelmsford CM2 6JJ, United Kingdom
Ph: 44 12 45491717
Fax: 44 12 45499110
Publisher E-mail: etpcirc@wilmington.co.uk
Professional magazine covering architecture, design and contemporary culture. **Freq:** Monthly. **Key Personnel:** Vicky Richardson, Editor, vrichardson@wilmington.co.uk; Peter Kelly, Asst. Ed., pkelly@blueprintmagazine.co.uk. **ISSN:** 0268-4926. **Subscription Rates:** 39.95 individuals UK; 49.95 Europe; 67.95 other countries; 74.95 individuals US subscription. **Remarks:** Accepts advertising. **URL:** https://www.wdis.co.uk/blueprint/. **Circ:** Combined 7,400

52961 ■ Gilbert & Sullivan News
Gilbert and Sullivan Society
7 Mace Walk
Essex
Chelmsford CM1 2GE, United Kingdom
Magazine featuring articles, reviews, information and

photos. **Freq:** 3/yr. **Subscription Rates:** Included in membership. **Remarks:** Accepts advertising. **URL:** http://www.gilbertandsullivansociety.org.uk/. **Circ:** (Not Reported)

52962 ■ BBC Radio Essex-FM - 103.5
PO Box 765
Chelmsford CM2 9XB, United Kingdom
Ph: 44 1245 616000
E-mail: essex.online@bbc.co.uk
Format: News; Talk; Sports; Oldies. **Owner:** British Broadcasting Corporation, Broadcasting House, Portland Pl., London W1A 1AA, United Kingdom. **Founded:** Nov. 11, 1986. **Operating Hours:** 4 a.m.-1 a.m. weekdays; 6 a.m.-1 a.m. Sat. & Sun. **Key Personnel:** Gerald Main, Editor, phone 44 1245 495050, gerald.main@bbc.co.uk. **URL:** http://www.bbc.co.uk/essex/local_radio.

Cheltenham

52963 ■ Arboricultural Journal
Arboricultural Association
Ullenwood Ct.
Hampshire
Gloucestershire
Cheltenham GL53 9QS, United Kingdom
Ph: 44 1242 522152
Fax: 44 1242 577766
Publisher E-mail: admin@trees.org.uk
Forestry journal. **Freq:** Quarterly. **ISSN:** 0307-1375. **Subscription Rates:** Free to members. **Remarks:** Advertising accepted; rates available upon request. **URL:** http://www.trees.org.uk/journal.php. **Circ:** 2,300

52964 ■ Birmingham Life
Archant Life
Archant Life Midlands
Archant House
Oriel Rd.
Cheltenham GL50 1BB, United Kingdom
Ph: 44 1242 216050
Publisher E-mail: anne.basey-fisher@archant.co.uk
Magazine featuring life in Birmingham. **Freq:** Monthly. **Key Personnel:** Jacquie Pond, Publisher, phone 44 7841 492687, jacquie.pond@archant.co.uk; Ceri McQueen, Contact, ceri.mcqueen@archant.co.uk; Suzanne Heaven, Publishing Dir., suzanne.heaven@archant.co.uk. **Subscription Rates:** 25 individuals. **Remarks:** Accepts advertising. **URL:** http://www.archantlife.co.uk/contact-us-regions-mid-west-and-midlands-birmingham-life-contacts--10417; http://leicestershire.greatbritishlife.co.uk. **Circ:** (Not Reported)

52965 ■ Cheltenham Oracle
Archant Life
Archant House
Oriel Rd.
Cheltenham GL50 1BB, United Kingdom
Ph: 44 1242 216050
Publisher E-mail: anne.basey-fisher@archant.co.uk
Magazine featuring life in Cheltenham. **Freq:** Bimonthly. **Key Personnel:** Charlie Griffin, Advertising Exec., phone 44 1242 265898, charlie.griffin@archant.co.uk; Richard Drake, Circulation Mgr., richard.drake@archant.co.uk. **Remarks:** Accepts advertising. **URL:** http://www.archantlife.co.uk/contact-us-regions-mid-west-and-midlands-cheltenham-oracle-contacts--10415; http://www.oraclemagazine.co.uk/. **Circ:** (Not Reported)

52966 ■ Croquet Gazette
Croquet Association
Old Bath Rd.
Cheltenham GL53 7DF, United Kingdom
Ph: 44 12 42242318
Publisher E-mail: caoffice@croquet.org.uk
Publication covering croquet. **Freq:** Bimonthly. **URL:** http://www.croquet.org.uk/tech/gazette.html.

52967 ■ The Drain Trader
Drain Trader Ltd.
Home Farm, Unit 6-8
Quat Goose Ln.
Swindon Village
Cheltenham GL51 9RP, United Kingdom
Ph: 44 1242 576777
Fax: 44 1242 577733
Publication E-mail: info@draintraderltd.com
Publisher E-mail: info@draintraderltd.com
Trade magazine covering drainage, sewage, and trenchless technology. **Subtitle:** The Magazine for the Drain-

age Industry. **Founded:** Apr. 1998. **Freq:** Monthly. **Trim Size:** 210 x 297 mm. **Key Personnel:** Lorraine Scale, Mng. Dir. **Subscription Rates:** 45 individuals U.K. and Channel; 55 individuals Eire & Europe; 85 other countries. **Remarks:** Accepts advertising. **URL:** http://www.draintraderltd.com/. **Ad Rates:** BW: 695, 4C: 995. **Circ:** Combined 4,500

52968 ■ Drugs in Context
CSF Medical Communications Ltd.
Ste. 119, Eagle Tower
Montpellier Dr.
Cheltenham GL50 1TA, United Kingdom
Ph: 44 1242 223890
Fax: 44 1242 243406
Publisher E-mail: enquiries@csfmedical.com
Independent, peer-reviewed and practice-orientated review of all the significant data on a specific drug, placed in the context of the disease or condition indicated and today's clinical practice. **Subtitle:** International Edition. **ISSN:** 1745-1981. **Subscription Rates:** 295 individuals; EUR525 individuals; US$600 individuals; 675 institutions; EUR995 institutions; US$1,150 institutions. **URL:** http://www.drugsincontext.com/. **Formed by the merger of:** Drugs in Context. General Medicine; Drugs in Context. Primary Care. Part A. Cardiovascular Medicine 1; Drugs in Context. Primary Care. Part B. Cardiovascular Medicine 2; Drugs in Context. Primary Care. Part C. Psychiatry and Neurology; Drugs in Context. Primary Care. Part D. Endocrinology and Gastroenterology; Drugs in Context. Primary Care. Part E. Respiratory Medicine and Infections.

52969 ■ The English Garden
Archant Specialist Ltd.
Archant House
Oriel Rd.
Cheltenham GL50 1BB, United Kingdom
Publisher E-mail: miller.hogg@atarchant.co.uk
Magazine devoted to gardening. **Founded:** 1929. **Freq:** Bimonthly. **Print Method:** Offset. **Trim Size:** 5 x 12 1/2. **Cols./Page:** 5. **Col. Width:** 11.5 picas. **Col. Depth:** 12 1/2 inches. **Key Personnel:** Janine Wookey, Editor. **Subscription Rates:** US$32.75 individuals; US$65.50 two years; US$39.95 Canada; US$79.90 two years Canada. **URL:** http://www.theenglishgarden.co.uk/. **Circ:** ★67,462

52970 ■ The English Home
Archant Specialist Ltd.
Archant House
Oriel Rd.
Cheltenham GL50 1BB, United Kingdom
Ph: 44 1242 211080
Publication E-mail: editorial@theenglishhome.co.uk
Publisher E-mail: miller.hogg@atarchant.co.uk
Magazine dedicated to home decor in traditional English style. **Founded:** 1941. **Freq:** Bimonthly. **Print Method:** Offset. **Trim Size:** 8 1/2 x 11. **Cols./Page:** 3. **Col. Width:** 2 1/8 inches. **Col. Depth:** 12 3/4 inches. **Key Personnel:** Kerryn Harper-Cuss, Editor, theenglishhome@archant.co.uk. **ISSN:** 0049-3821. **Subscription Rates:** 18.99 individuals direct debit; 37.98 individuals credit card, 16 issues; 36.98 two years direct debit; 19.99 individuals credit card, 8 issues. **Remarks:** Accepts advertising. **URL:** http://www.theenglishhome.co.uk/. **Ad Rates:** 4C: 3,750. **Circ:** ★61,355

52971 ■ Evergreen
This England Ltd.
PO Box 52
Cheltenham GL50 1YQ, United Kingdom
Ph: 44 1242 537900
Fax: 44 1242 537901
Publisher E-mail: sales@thisengland.co.uk
Pocket-size magazine covering the British Isles. **Founded:** 1985. **Freq:** Quarterly. **Subscription Rates:** 15 individuals U.K.; US$18 other countries by airspeed; US$3 single issue. **Remarks:** Accepts advertising. **URL:** http://www.evergreenmagazine.co.uk/single.htm?ipg=10666. **Ad Rates:** BW: 950, 4C: 1,200. **Circ:** Paid 48,000

52972 ■ Grafik
Archant Specialist Ltd.
Archant House
Oriel Rd.
Wendens Ambo
Cheltenham GL50 1BB, United Kingdom
Ph: 44 1242 216052

Publisher E-mail: miller.hogg@atarchant.co.uk
Professional magazine covering graphic design. **Freq:** Monthly. **Print Method:** Sheetfed offset. **Key Personnel:** Caroline Roberts, Editor-in-Chief, caroline@grafikmag.com; Angharad Lewis, Editor, angharad@grafikmag.com; Dan Rolfe Johnson, Dep. Web Ed., production@grafikmag.com. **Subscription Rates:** 84 individuals; 168 two years; 108 individuals Eire & Europe; 216 two years Eire & Europe; 120 individuals rest of world; 240 two years rest of world. **Remarks:** Accepts advertising. **URL:** http://www.grafikmagazine.co.uk/. **Formerly:** Graphics International. **Circ:** Paid 7,300

52973 ■ The Oracle Gloucester Life
Archant Life
Archant House
Oriel Rd.
Cheltenham GL50 1BB, United Kingdom
Ph: 44 1242 216050
Publisher E-mail: anne.basey-fisher@archant.co.uk
Magazine featuring life in Gloucester. **Freq:** Bimonthly. **Key Personnel:** Jan Allen, Advertising Exec., phone 44 1242 216065, jan.allen@archant.co.uk; Richard Drake, Circulation Mgr., richard.drake@archant.co.uk; Tim Thurston, Regional Mng. Dir., tim.thurston@archant.co.uk. **Subscription Rates:** Free. **URL:** http://cotswold.greatbritishlife.co.uk/; http://www.archantlife.co.uk/contact-us-regions-mid-west-and-midlands-glocester-oracle--10421.

52974 ■ Oxfordshire Life
Archant Life
Archant House
Oriel Rd.
Cheltenham GL50 1BB, United Kingdom
Ph: 44 1242 255116
Fax: 44 1242 216050
Publisher E-mail: johnny.hustler@archant.co.uk
Magazine focusing on the towns and villages in Oxfordshire, with comprehensive guides to enjoying life, including what's on, restaurant reviews and topical features on major events. **Freq:** Quarterly. **Key Personnel:** Karen Cross, Sales Mgr., phone 44 1242 216059, karen.cross2@archant.co.uk; Mike Lowe, Editor, mike.lowe@archant.co.uk. **Subscription Rates:** 25 individuals. **Remarks:** Accepts advertising. **URL:** http://www.oxfordshire-life.co.uk. **Circ:** (Not Reported)

52975 ■ Realm
Archant Specialist Ltd.
Archant House
Oriel Rd.
Wendens Ambo
Cheltenham GL50 1BB, United Kingdom
Ph: 44 1242 216052
Publication E-mail: editorial@realm-magazine.co.uk
Publisher E-mail: miller.hogg@atarchant.co.uk
Magazine covering Britain's history and countryside including features about British life, culture and heritage. **Founded:** 1984. **Freq:** Bimonthly. **Print Method:** Offset. Uses mats. **Trim Size:** 8 1/2 x 11. **Cols./Page:** 3. **Col. Width:** 28 nonpareils. **Col. Depth:** 133 agate lines. **Key Personnel:** Dan Robinson, Editor, dan.robinson@archant.co.uk. **ISSN:** 0008-1299. **Subscription Rates:** US$34.75 individuals; US$69.50 two years; US$39.95 Canada; US$79.90 two years Canada. **URL:** http://www.realm-magazine.co.uk/. **Circ:** ★48,874

52976 ■ Shropshire Life
Archant Life
Archant House
Oriel Rd.
Cheltenham GL50 1BB, United Kingdom
Ph: 44 1242 216050
Fax: 44 1242 255545
Publisher E-mail: anne.basey-fisher@archant.co.uk
Magazine featuring life in Shropshire County. **Freq:** Monthly. **Key Personnel:** Joanne Goodwin, Editor, joanne.goodwin@archant.co.uk; John Ford, Production Dir.; Suzanne Heaven, Publishing Dir., suzanne.heaven@archant.co.uk. **URL:** http://www.archantlife.co.uk/contact-us-regions-mid-west-and-midlands-shropshire-life-contacts--10419; http://shropshire.greatbritishlife.co.uk.

52977 ■ Staffordshire County
Archant Life
Archant House, Oriel Rd.

Cheltenham GL50 1BB, United Kingdom
Ph: 44 1242 216050
Fax: 44 1242 255545
Publisher E-mail: anne.basey-fisher@archant.co.uk
Magazine featuring life in Staffordshire County. **Freq:** Monthly. **Key Personnel:** Jacquie Pond, Publisher, jacquie.pond@archant.co.uk; Suzanne Heaven, Publishing Dir., suzanne.heaven@archant.co.uk; Ceri McQueen, Contact, ceri.mcqueen@archant.co.uk. **URL:** http://www.archantlife.co.uk/contact-us-regions-mid-west-and-midlands-staffordshire-county-contacts--10425; http://staffordshire.greatbritishlife.co.uk.

52978 ■ This England
This England Ltd.
PO Box 52
Cheltenham GL50 1YQ, United Kingdom
Ph: 44 1242 537900
Fax: 44 1242 537901
Publisher E-mail: sales@thisengland.co.uk
Magazine featuring articles on England's countryside, towns, villages, famous people, customs, and traditions. **Subtitle:** Britain's Loveliest Magazine. **Founded:** 1968. **Freq:** Quarterly. **Subscription Rates:** 22.25 individuals. **Remarks:** Accepts advertising. **URL:** http://www.thisengland.co.uk/index2.htm. **Circ:** 170,342

52979 ■ Warwickshire Life
Archant Life
Archant House, Oriel Rd.
Gloucestershire
Cheltenham GL50 1BB, United Kingdom
Ph: 44 1242 216050
Fax: 44 1527 558477
Publisher E-mail: anne.basey-fisher@archant.co.uk
Magazine featuring life in Warwickshire. **Freq:** Monthly. **Key Personnel:** Jane Sullivan, Editor, jane.sullivan@archant.co.uk; Richard Drake, Circulation Mgr., richard.drake@archant.co.uk. **URL:** http://www.archantlife.co.uk/contact-us-regions-mid-west-and-midlands-warwickshire-life-contacts--10426; http://warwickshire.greatbritishlife.co.uk.

52980 ■ Whisky
Archant Specialist Ltd.
Archant House
Oriel Rd.
Wendens Ambo
Cheltenham GL50 1BB, United Kingdom
Ph: 44 1242 216052
Publisher E-mail: miller.hogg@atarchant.co.uk
Magazine covering information on whisky. **Founded:** 1966. **Freq:** 8/yr. **Print Method:** Offset. **Trim Size:** 8 x 10 7/8. **Cols./Page:** 3. **Col. Width:** 27 nonpareils. **Col. Depth:** 142 agate lines. **Key Personnel:** Rob Allanson, Editor, rob@whiskymag.com; Jenna Leeds, Production Mgr., jenna@whiskymag.com; Damian Riley-Smith, Mng. Dir., damian@whiskymag.com. **ISSN:** 0890-0876. **Subscription Rates:** US$44.95 individuals; US$89.90 two years individual; EUR59.50 individuals Europe; EUR119 two years individual; 34 individuals UK; 68 two years individual. **URL:** http://www.whiskymag.com/.

52981 ■ Worcestershire Life
Archant Life
Archant House, Oriel Rd.
Cheltenham GL50 1BB, United Kingdom
Ph: 44 1527 831733
Fax: 44 1527 879646
Publisher E-mail: anne.basey-fisher@archant.co.uk
Magazine featuring life in Worcestershire. **Freq:** Monthly. **Key Personnel:** Jane Sullivan, Editor, jane.sullivan@archant.co.uk; Suzanne Heaven, Publishing Dir., suzanne.heaven@archant.co.uk; Richard Drake, Circulation Mgr., richard.drake@archant.co.uk. **URL:** http://www.archantlife.co.uk/contact-us-regions-mid-west-and-midlands-worcestershire-life-contacts--10420; http://worcestershire.greatbritishlife.co.uk.

Chepstow

52982 ■ Event Organiser
Event Services Association
Association House
18c Moor St.
Chepstow NP16 5DB, United Kingdom
Fax: 44 12 91630402
Trade publication covering conventions. **Freq:** Quarterly. **Key Personnel:** Kevin Minton, Manager, phone 44 12

Circulation: ★ = ABC; △ = BPA; ◆ = CAC; • = CCAB; ❑ = VAC; ⊕ = PO Statement; ‡ = Publisher's Report; Boldface figures = sworn; Light figures = estimated.

Gale Directory of Publications & Broadcast Media/147th Ed.   5621

91636335, kevin@jandmgroup.co.uk; Simon Ambrose, Editor, phone 44 1608 676151, editorial@papa.org.uk; Gina Mayo, Contact; Jim Winship, Director. **Subscription Rates:** Free for members. **Remarks:** Advertising accepted; rates available upon request. **URL:** http://www.tesa.org.uk/event_organiser_magazine/index.htm. **Circ:** 7,000

52983 ■ Sandwich and Snack News
British Sandwich Association
Association House
18c Moor St.
Chepstow NP16 5DB, United Kingdom
Fax: 44 1291 630402
Publisher E-mail: admin@sandwich.org.uk
Publication covering the snack industry. **Freq:** 8/yr. **Key Personnel:** Simon Ambrose, Editor, editorial@papa.org.uk. **Subscription Rates:** 55 individuals; 75 other countries. **Remarks:** Advertising accepted; rates available upon request. **URL:** http://www.sandwich.org.uk/magazine/index.shtml. **Circ:** 7,000

52984 ■ Travel Guide International
International Association of Air Travel Couriers - UK
The Old Cottage, Tidenham
Chepstow NP16 7JL, United Kingdom
Publisher E-mail: info@aircourier.co.uk
Magazine containing information on events, reviews of new books and travel stories. **Freq:** Bimonthly. **Subscription Rates:** 32 members. **URL:** http://www.aircourier.co.uk.

Chesham

52985 ■ Chesham Town Talk
Hawkes Design
c/o The White Hill Centre
White Hill
Chesham HP5 1AG, United Kingdom
Ph: 44 494 793000
Fax: 44 494 776331
Publisher E-mail: hawkestalk@aol.com
Magazine covering local heritage and local issues. **Founded:** 1994. **Freq:** Semiannual. **Print Method:** Litho. **Trim Size:** 210 x 297 mm. **Cols./Page:** 4. **Col. Width:** 44 millimeters. **Col. Depth:** 262 millimeters. **Key Personnel:** Peter Hawkes, Art Ed.; Anne Noakes, Editor. **ISSN:** 1465-0991. **Subscription Rates:** 1.50 single issue. **Remarks:** Accepts advertising. **URL:** http://www.cheshamtowntalk.org.uk/. **Circ:** Non-paid 4,500

52986 ■ Dental Trader
British Dental Trade Association
Mineral Ln.
Chesham HP5 1NL, United Kingdom
Ph: 44 1494 782873
Fax: 44 1494 786659
Publisher E-mail: admin@bdta.org.uk
Professional publication covering dentistry. **Freq:** Quarterly. **Key Personnel:** Simon Gambold, President; Edward Attenborough, Vice President. **Remarks:** Advertising accepted; rates available upon request. **URL:** http://www.bdta.org.uk/. **Circ:** 2,000

Cheshunt

52987 ■ Clematis International
International Clematis Society
c/o Ken Woolfenden, Ed.
3 Cuthberts Close
Cheshunt EN7 5RB, United Kingdom
Journal containing scientific research, conference papers, cultivating tips, book reviews, and news from other societies. **Freq:** Annual. **Key Personnel:** Ken Woolfenden, Editor, editor@clematisinternational.com. **Subscription Rates:** EUR30 individuals. **Remarks:** Accepts advertising. **URL:** http://www.clematisinternational.com/. **Circ:** (Not Reported)

Chessington

52988 ■ Asian Bride
Asian Interactive Media
Accessory House
Cox Ln.
Chessington KT9 1SD, United Kingdom
Ph: 44 8707 555502
Fax: 44 8707 555503
Publisher E-mail: production@asianwomanmag.com
Wedding magazine. **Key Personnel:** Sameera Mole-

dina, Editor, sameera@asianbridemags.com. **Subscription Rates:** 19.98 individuals. **Remarks:** Accepts advertising. **URL:** http://www.asianwomanmag.com/asianbride.php. **Circ:** *89,414

52989 ■ Asian Groom & Man
Asian Interactive Media
Accessory House
Cox Ln.
Chessington KT9 1SD, United Kingdom
Ph: 44 8707 555502
Fax: 44 8707 555503
Publisher E-mail: production@asianwomanmag.com
Magazine for grooms. **Freq:** Quarterly. **Key Personnel:** Sameera Moledina, Editor, sameera@asianbridemags.com. **Subscription Rates:** 23.95 individuals. **Remarks:** Accepts advertising. **URL:** http://www.asianwomanmag.com/asianman.php; http://www.amazon.com/ASIAN-GROOM-MAGAZINE-Asian-Groom/dp/B001E35QI8. **Circ:** (Not Reported)

52990 ■ Asian Woman
Asian Interactive Media
Accessory House
Cox Ln.
Chessington KT9 1SD, United Kingdom
Ph: 44 8707 555502
Fax: 44 8707 555503
Publisher E-mail: production@asianwomanmag.com
Fashion and lifestyle magazine for women. **Founded:** 1999. **Freq:** Monthly. **Key Personnel:** Brianna Ragel, Dep. Ed., brianna@asianwomanmag.com. **Subscription Rates:** 32.64 individuals 6 issues; 60 individuals 11 issues. **Remarks:** Accepts advertising. **URL:** http://www.asianwomanmag.com/asianwoman.php. **Circ:** *90,339

Chester

52991 ■ Acta Crystallographica Section A
International Union of Crystallography
Union Internationale de Cristallographie
5 Abbey Sq.
Chester CH1 2HU, United Kingdom
Ph: 44 12 44342878
Fax: 44 12 44344888
Publisher E-mail: execsec@iucr.org
Publication covering crystallogrphy in English, French, German and Russian. **Subtitle:** Foundations of Crystallography. **Freq:** Bimonthly. **Key Personnel:** Peter Strickland, Managing Editor, med@iucr.org; G. Kostorz, Editor-in-Chief, gk-iucr@ethz.ch. **ISSN:** 0108-7673. **Subscription Rates:** 505 institutions print and online; 439 institutions print only or online only; 141 individuals print and online; 123 individuals print only or online only. **Remarks:** Advertising accepted; rates available upon request. **URL:** http://www.iucr.org/. **Circ:** (Not Reported)

52992 ■ Chester Standard
NWN Media Ltd.
Linenhall House
Stanley St.
Chester CH1 2LR, United Kingdom
Ph: 44 1244 304500
Fax: 44 1244 351536
Publisher E-mail: internet@nwn.co.uk
Newspaper featuring news, views, sports, and features. **Key Personnel:** Christian Dunn, Digital Ed. **URL:** http://www.chesterfirst.co.uk/.

52993 ■ Ellesmere Port Standard
NWN Media Ltd.
Linenhall House
Stanley St.
Chester CH1 2LR, United Kingdom
Ph: 44 1244 304500
Fax: 44 1244 351536
Publisher E-mail: internet@nwn.co.uk
Newspaper featuring news, views, sports, and features. **Key Personnel:** Christian Dunn, Digital Ed. **URL:** http://www.ellesmereportstandard.co.uk/.

52994 ■ European Physical Education Review
Sage Publications Ltd.
c/o Ken Green, Ed.
Dept. of Sport & Exercise Sciences
University of Chester
Parkgate Rd.
Chester CH1 4BJ, United Kingdom
Scholarly journal covering physical education, including sport and leisure issues and research worldwide. **Sub-**

title: Published in Association with the North West Counties Physical Education Association. **Founded:** 1995. **Freq:** 3/yr. **Key Personnel:** Ken Green, Editor; Joe Marshall, Book Review Ed. **ISSN:** 1356-336X. **Subscription Rates:** US$622 institutions combined (print & e-access); US$684 institutions plus backfile (current volume print & all online); US$560 institutions e-access; US$622 individuals e-access plus backfile (all online content); US$560 institutions e-access (content through 1998); US$610 institutions print only; US$85 individuals print only; US$224 institutions single print; US$37 individuals single print. **Remarks:** Accepts advertising. **URL:** http://www.sagepub.com/journalsProdDesc.nav?prodId=Journal200962. **Circ:** (Not Reported)

52995 ■ Food and Agricultural Immunology
Taylor & Francis Group Journals
Dept. of Biological Sciences
Chester University College
Parkgate Rd.
Chester CH1 4BJ, United Kingdom
Publisher E-mail: customerservice@taylorandfrancis.com
Journal presenting original immunological research with food, agricultural, environmental and veterinary applications. **Freq:** Quarterly. **Key Personnel:** Prof. Chris Smith, Editor, fai@chester.ac.uk; D.L. Brandon, International Editorial Board; G. Banowetz, International Editorial Board; G. Bonwick, International Editorial Board; J. Banks, International Editorial Board; M. Morgan, International Editorial Board. **ISSN:** 0954-0105. **Subscription Rates:** US$1,499 individuals online only; US$1,577 individuals print & online; EUR1,256 individuals print & online; EUR1,193 institutions online; 954 institutions print & online; 907 institutions online; 312 individuals; US$515 individuals; EUR410 individuals. **URL:** http://www.tandf.co.uk/journals/journal.asp?issn=0954-0105& linktype=5.

52996 ■ LCGC Europe
Advanstar Communications (UK) Ltd.
Advanstar House
Park W
Sealand Rd.
Chester CH1 4RN, United Kingdom
Ph: 44 1244 378888
Fax: 44 1244 370011
Professional magazine for separation scientists and other analytical chemists. **Subtitle:** Solutions for Separation Scientists. **Founded:** 1987. **Freq:** Monthly. **Trim Size:** 203 x 273 mm. **Key Personnel:** Peter Houston, Editorial Dir.; Andrew Davies, Gp. Publisher. **ISSN:** 1471-6577. **Remarks:** Accepts advertising. **URL:** http://chromatographyonline.findanalytichem.com/lcgc/. **Former name:** LC-GC International. **Ad Rates:** BW: 6,205, 4C: 8,010. **Circ:** Controlled △26,000

52997 ■ Managed Healthcare Executive
Advanstar Communications
Advanstar House Park West
Sealand Rd.
Chester CH1 4RN, United Kingdom
Ph: 44 1244 378888
Fax: 44 1244 370011
Publisher E-mail: info@advanstar.com
Professional publication covering issues for the healthcare industry. **Freq:** Monthly. **Key Personnel:** Sheila M. Markes, Production Mgr., phone 218740-6509, jgrasha@advanstar.com; Julie Miller, Editor-in-Chief, phone 440891-2723, julie.miller@advanstar.com. **ISSN:** 1060-1392. **Subscription Rates:** US$89.25 individuals; US$131.25 two years; US$7.35 single issue; US$173.25 Canada and Mexico; US$267.25 two years Canada and Mexico; US$19.95 single issue Canada and Mexico. **Remarks:** Accepts advertising. **URL:** http://www.managedhealthcareexecutive.com/mhe/. **Ad Rates:** BW: 8,500. **Circ:** △41,800

52998 ■ Pharmaceutical Technology Europe
Advanstar Communications
Advanstar House Park West
Sealand Rd.
Chester CH1 4RN, United Kingdom
Ph: 44 1244 378888
Fax: 44 1244 370011
Publisher E-mail: info@advanstar.com
Trade publication covering the pharmaceutical manufacturing industry in Europe. **Freq:** Monthly. **Trim Size:** 8 x 10 3/4. **Key Personnel:** Andy Davies, Gp. Publisher, phone 44 1244 393408, adavies@advanstar.com;

Richard Hodson, Sales Mgr., phone 44 1244 393131, rhodson@advantar.com; Fedra Pavlou, Editor-in-Chief, phone 44 1244 393121, fpavlou@advantar.com. **ISSN:** 0164-6826. **Subscription Rates:** Free to qualified subscribers. **Remarks:** Accepts advertising. **URL:** http://www.ptemag.com/pharmtecheurope/. **Ad Rates:** BW: 5,440, 4C: 7,190. **Circ:** Controlled △18,000

52999 ■ Skin Deep
Jazz Publishing
The Old School
Main Rd.
Higher Kinerton
Chester CH4 9AJ, United Kingdom
Ph: 44 1244 663400
Publication E-mail: editor@skindeep.co.uk
Magazine featuring different styles of tattoo. **Subtitle:** The UK's Best Selling Tattoo Magazine. **Freq:** 13/yr. **Key Personnel:** Sion Smith, Editor. **Subscription Rates:** 43.45 individuals. **Remarks:** Accepts advertising. **URL:** http://www.jazzpublishing.co.uk/index.php?app=gbu0&ns=catshow&ref=skindeep. **Circ:** 38,764

53000 ■ Synchrotron Radiation
International Union of Crystallography
Union Internationale de Cristallographie
5 Abbey Sq.
Chester CH1 2HU, United Kingdom
Ph: 44 12 44342878
Fax: 44 12 44344888
Publisher E-mail: execsec@iucr.org
Publication covering crystallography. **Freq:** Bimonthly. **Key Personnel:** L.E. Berman, Co-Ed., berman@bnl.gov; A. Kvick, Editor, ake.kvick@maxlab.lu.se; T. Ohta, Editor, ohta@fc.ritsumei.ac.jp. **ISSN:** 0909-0495. **Subscription Rates:** US$401 individuals print + online; EUR206 individuals online only; US$1,389 institutions print + online; US$1,207 institutions online only; EUR237 individuals print + online; EUR1,048 institutions Europe; print + online; 236 out of country print + online; 206 out of country online only; EUR717 institutions online only; US$1,207 institutions online only rest of World. **Remarks:** Accepts advertising. **URL:** http://journals.iucr.org/s/journalhomepage.html. **Circ:** (Not Reported)

53001 ■ Dee-FM - 106.3
2 Chantry Ct.
Chester CH1 4QN, United Kingdom
Ph: 44 1244 391000
E-mail: studio@dee1063.com; info@dee1063.com
Format: Adult Contemporary; Talk; Sports. **Operating Hours:** 6 a.m.-12 a.m. Mon.-Sun. **Key Personnel:** Stef Roberts, Station Dir., stef.roberts@dee1063.com; Mike James, Program Mgr., mike.james@dee1063.com. **Ad Rates:** Advertising accepted; rates available upon request. **URL:** http://www.dee1063.com/.

Chesterfield

53002 ■ Derbyshire Times
Johnston Press PLC
37 Station Rd.
Chesterfield S41 7XD, United Kingdom
Ph: 44 1246 504500
Fax: 44 1246 504579
Publication E-mail: advertising@derbyshiretimes.co.uk
Local community newspaper. **Key Personnel:** Phil Bramley, Dep. Ed., phone 44 1246 504530, fax 44 1246 504579, phil.bramley@derbyshiretimes.co.uk. **Remarks:** Accepts advertising. **URL:** http://www.derbyshiretimes.co.uk/. **Circ:** (Not Reported)

53003 ■ Peak-FM - 107.4
Radio House
Foxwood Rd.
Chesterfield S41 9RF, United Kingdom
Ph: 44 1246 267138
Fax: 44 1246 267110
Format: Adult Contemporary; News; Sports; Top 40. **Operating Hours:** Continuous. **Key Personnel:** Chris Overend, Station Mgr., chris.overend@peak107.com; Bridget Ball, Sales Mgr., bridget.ball@peak107.com. **Ad Rates:** Advertising accepted; rates available upon request. **URL:** http://www.peakfm.net/.

Chichester

53004 ■ Applied Organometallic Chemistry
John Wiley & Sons Ltd.
The Atrium
Southern Gate
Chichester PO19 8SQ, United Kingdom
Ph: 44 1243 779777
Fax: 44 1243 775878
Publisher E-mail: customer@wiley.co.uk
Peer-reviewed journal covering applied work in the organometallic chemistry field. **Freq:** Monthly. **Cols./Page:** 2. **Key Personnel:** Cornelis J. Elsevier, Editor-in-Chief, elsevier@science.uva.nl; Peter J. Craig, Ed-in-Ch. Emeritus, pjcraig.@dmu.ac.uk; Richard Jenkins, Book Review Ed., roj@dmu.ac.uk. **ISSN:** 0268-2605. **Subscription Rates:** US$3,156 institutions, other countries print only; EUR2,036 institutions, other countries print only; 1,610 institutions print only; EUR2,028 institutions, other countries combined print with online access; 1,772 institutions combined print with online access; US$3,472 institutions, other countries combined print with online access. **Remarks:** Accepts advertising. **URL:** http://www.interscience.wiley.com; http://www3.interscience.wiley.com/journal/2676/home. **Circ:** (Not Reported)

53005 ■ Boat Trader
Trader Media Group
44a North St.
Chichester PO19 1NF, United Kingdom
Magazine featuring buying and selling of boats and other marine related items in United Kingdom. **Freq:** Monthly. **Key Personnel:** John King, CEO. **Subscription Rates:** 50 individuals. **Remarks:** Accepts advertising. **URL:** http://www.boatshop24.co.uk/. **Circ:** (Not Reported)

53006 ■ British Journal of Surgery
John Wiley & Sons Ltd.
The Atrium
Southern Gate
Chichester PO19 8SQ, United Kingdom
Ph: 44 1243 779777
Fax: 44 1243 775878
Publisher E-mail: customer@wiley.co.uk
British journal covering physicians and surgery. **Freq:** Monthly. **Key Personnel:** J.J. Earnshaw, Editor-in-Chief; D. Alderson, Editor-in-Chief; J. Beynon, Editor. **ISSN:** 0007-1323. **Subscription Rates:** EUR260 other countries print only; 164 individuals print only; US$247 other countries print only; EUR569 institutions, other countries print only; 390 institutions print only; US$582 institutions, other countries print only. **Remarks:** Accepts advertising. **URL:** http://www3.interscience.wiley.com/journal/99019821/home?CRETRY=1&SRETRY=0. **Circ:** (Not Reported)

53007 ■ Chichester Observer
Johnston Press PLC
Unicorn House
8 Eastgate Sq.
Chichester PO19 1JN, United Kingdom
Ph: 44 1243 539389
Fax: 44 1243 539386
Publication E-mail: news@chiobserver.co.uk
Local community newspaper. **Key Personnel:** Colin Channon, Editor, phone 44 1243 534135, fax 44 1243 539386, colin.channon@chiobserver.co.uk. **Remarks:** Accepts advertising. **URL:** http://www.chichester.co.uk/. **Circ:** (Not Reported)

53008 ■ ESL Magazine
Modern English Publishing
PO Box 100
Chichester PO18 8HD, United Kingdom
Ph: 44 1243 576444
Fax: 44 1243 576456
Publisher E-mail: info@keywayspublishing.com
Magazine covering the latest ESL/EFL products and services. Covers issues including instruction, testing, technology, professional life, cross cultural concerns, immigration trends and regulations, legislation pertaining to ESL/EFL, international student issues, refugee concerns, association news, ESL/EFL pioneer profiles, student life, and human interest stories. **Founded:** 1936. **Freq:** Bimonthly. **Print Method:** Offset. **Trim Size:** 6 3/4 x 9 7/8. **Cols./Page:** 2. **Col. Width:** 31 nonpareils. **Col. Depth:** 108 agate lines. **ISSN:** 1098-6553. **URL:** http://www.eslmag.com.

53009 ■ European Journal of Mass Spectrometry
IM Publications L.L.P.
6 Charlton Mill
Carlton
Chichester PO18 0HY, United Kingdom
Ph: 44 1243 811334
Fax: 44 1243 811711

Publisher E-mail: info@impublications.co.uk
Peer-reviewed journal focusing on mass spectrometry. **Key Personnel:** Prof. Peter J. Derrick, Editor-in-Chief, p.j.derrick@massey.ac.nz. **ISSN:** 1469-0667. **Subscription Rates:** 470 individuals in Europe (print and online); EUR705 individuals in Europe (print and online); US$895 other countries print and online; 430 individuals in Europe (online only); EUR645 individuals in Europe (online only); US$815 other countries online only. **Remarks:** Accepts advertising. **URL:** http://www.impublications.com/journal/ejms. **Circ:** (Not Reported)

53010 ■ European Journal of Social Psychology
John Wiley & Sons Ltd.
The Atrium
Southern Gate
Chichester PO19 8SQ, United Kingdom
Ph: 44 1243 779777
Fax: 44 1243 775878
Publisher E-mail: customer@wiley.co.uk
Peer-reviewed journal for social psychologists. **Founded:** 1971. **Freq:** 7/yr. **Key Personnel:** Andrea Abele, Consulting Ed., a.haslam@exeter.ac.uk; Anne Maass, Editor; Karen Douglas, Assoc. Ed. **ISSN:** 0046-2772. **Subscription Rates:** 217 individuals print only; US$361 other countries print only; US$1,170 institutions, other countries print only; 597 institutions print only; EUR755 institutions, other countries print only; EUR832 institutions, other countries combined print with online access; 658 institutions combined print with online access (UK); US$1,287 institutions, other countries combined print with online access. **Remarks:** Accepts advertising. **URL:** http://www.interscience.wiley.com; http://www3.interscience.wiley.com/journal/1823/home. **Circ:** (Not Reported)

53011 ■ Goodwood Magazine
Goodwood Estate Company Ltd.
Goodwood
Chichester PO18 0PX, United Kingdom
Ph: 44 124 3755000
Fax: 44 124 3755005
Consumer magazine covering sports for members and interested others. **Founded:** Apr. 1979. **Freq:** Annual. **Subscription Rates:** Free. **Remarks:** Accepts advertising. **URL:** http://www.goodwood.co.uk/. **Circ:** Controlled 20,000

53012 ■ International Journal of Robust & Nonlinear Control
John Wiley & Sons Ltd.
The Atrium
Southern Gate
Chichester PO19 8SQ, United Kingdom
Ph: 44 1243 779777
Fax: 44 1243 775878
Publisher E-mail: customer@wiley.co.uk
Journal covering engineering topics. **Freq:** 18/yr. **Key Personnel:** Mike J. Grimble, Managing Editor; Maria Di Benedetto, Editor; Andras Balogh, Editor; Wei Lin, Editor; Jeff Cook, Editor. **ISSN:** 1049-8923. **Subscription Rates:** US$3,345 other countries print only; US$4,439 institutions, other countries print only; 2,265 institutions print only; EUR2,864 institutions, other countries print only. **Remarks:** Accepts advertising. **URL:** http://www3.interscience.wiley.com/cgi-bin/jhome/5510. **Circ:** (Not Reported)

53013 ■ Journal of Analytical Atomic Spectrometry
John Wiley & Sons Ltd.
The Atrium
Southern Gate
Chichester PO19 8SQ, United Kingdom
Ph: 44 1243 779777
Fax: 44 1243 775878
Publisher E-mail: customer@wiley.co.uk
Professional journal covering analytical atomic spectrometry. **Freq:** Monthly. **Key Personnel:** Les Ebdon, Contact. **ISSN:** 0267-9477. **Subscription Rates:** US$100 individuals. **URL:** http://as.wiley.com/WileyCDA/WileyTitle/productCd-0471974188.html.

53014 ■ Microscopy and Analysis
John Wiley & Sons Inc.
The Atrium, Southern Gate
West Sussex
Chichester PO19 8SQ, United Kingdom
Ph: 44 1243 770351
Fax: 44 1243 770432
Publisher E-mail: info@wiley.com
Journal covering the field of microscopy. **Freq:**

Circulation: ★ = ABC; △ = BPA; ♦ = CAC; • = CCAB; ❑ = VAC; ⊕ = PO Statement; ‡ = Publisher's Report; Boldface figures = sworn; Light figures = estimated.

Gale Directory of Publications & Broadcast Media/147th Ed.

5623

Bimonthly. **Key Personnel:** Dr. Julian P. Heath, Editor, editor@microscopy-analysis.com; Roy Opie, Publisher, roy.opie@wiley.com; Liz Benson, Asst. Ed., lbenson@wiley.com. **Remarks:** Accepts advertising. **URL:** http://www.microscopy-analysis.com. **Circ:** ‡46,000

53015 ■ Optimal Control Applications & Methods
John Wiley & Sons Ltd.
The Atrium
Southern Gate
Chichester PO19 8SQ, United Kingdom
Ph: 44 1243 779777
Fax: 44 1243 775878
Publisher E-mail: customer@wiley.co.uk
Journal covering optimal control applications theory and applications. **Freq:** 6/yr. **Key Personnel:** Mike J. Grimble, Managing Editor, mgrimble@eee.strath.ac.uk; Michael Caputo, Subject Ed.; Ping Lu, Subject Ed. **ISSN:** 0143-2087. **Subscription Rates:** US$2,850 other countries print only; US$3,800 institutions, other countries print only; 1,939 institutions print only (UK); EUR2,451 institutions, other countries print only. **Remarks:** Accepts advertising. **URL:** http://www3.interscience.wiley.com/journal/2133/home. **Circ:** (Not Reported)

53016 ■ Quality & Reliability Engineering International
John Wiley & Sons Ltd.
The Atrium
Southern Gate
Chichester PO19 8SQ, United Kingdom
Ph: 44 1243 779777
Fax: 44 1243 775878
Publisher E-mail: customer@wiley.co.uk
Professional journal covering practical engineering aspects of quality and reliability. **Freq:** 8/yr. **Trim Size:** 200 x 260 mm. **Cols./Page:** 2. **Col. Width:** 75 millimeters. **Key Personnel:** Aarnout C. Brombacher, Editor-in-Chief, a.c.brombacher@tm.tue.nl; Dr. Douglas Montgomery, Editor-in-Chief, phone 480965-3836, fax 602965-8692, doug.montgomery@asu.edu; Dr. Richard K. Burdick, Editorial Board; John Andrews, Editorial Board; Dr. Christine M. Anderson-Cook, Editorial Board; Harriet Black-Nembhard, Editorial Board; Bo Bergman, Editorial Board; Aris Chirstou, Editorial Board; Frank P.A. Coolen, Editorial Board. **ISSN:** 0748-8017. **Subscription Rates:** US$2,603 other countries print only; 1,329 individuals print only; EUR1,680 other countries print only; EUR1,848 other countries combined print with online; 1,462 individuals combined print with online; US$2,864 other countries combined print with online. **Remarks:** Accepts advertising. **URL:** http://interscience.wiley.com/jpages/0748-8017/; http://www3.interscience.wiley.com/. **Circ:** (Not Reported)

53017 ■ Spectroscopy Asia
John Wiley & Sons Inc.
6 Charlton Mill
Charlton
Chichester PO18 0HY, United Kingdom
Ph: 44 1243 811334
Fax: 44 1243 811711
Publisher E-mail: info@wiley.com
Journal covering all areas of spectroscopy. **Founded:** 2005. **Freq:** Quarterly. **Key Personnel:** Ian Michael, Contact, ian@impublications.co.uk. **Subscription Rates:** Free to qualified subscribers for spectroscopists in the Asia-Pacific region. **Remarks:** Accepts advertising. **URL:** http://www.spectroscopyasia.com. **Circ:** ‡10,000

Childerley

53018 ■ Human Reproduction
Oxford University Press
5 Mill Yard
Cambs
Childerley CB23 8BA, United Kingdom
Ph: 44 1954 212404
Fax: 44 1954 212359
Publisher E-mail: webenquiry.uk@oup.com
Journal featuring full-length, peer-reviewed papers reporting original research, clinical case histories and opinions and debates on topical issues, containing papers covering the scientific and medical aspects of reproductive physiology and pathology, endocrinology, andrology, gonad function, gametogenesis, fertilization, embryo development, implantation, pregnancy, genetics, genetic diagnosis, oncology, infectious disease, surgery, contraception, infertility treatment, psychology, ethics

and social issues. **Freq:** Monthly. **Key Personnel:** A.C. Williams, Managing Editor; P.G. Crosignani, Dep. Ed.; A. Van Steirteghem, Editor-in-Chief. **ISSN:** 0268-1161. **Subscription Rates:** 1,253 institutions corporate; print and online; 981 institutions corporate; online only; 1,148 institutions corporate; print only; 1,002 institutions print and online; 785 institutions online only; 919 institutions print only; 401 individuals print; 127 members online only; 156 members print. **Remarks:** Advertising accepted; rates available upon request. **URL:** http://humrep.oupjournals.org/. **Circ:** (Not Reported)

53019 ■ Molecular Human Reproduction
Oxford University Press
5 Mill Yard
Childerley CB23 8BA, United Kingdom
Ph: 44 1954 212404
Fax: 44 1954 212359
Publisher E-mail: webenquiry.uk@oup.com
Peer-reviewed journal publishing articles on the molecular aspects of human reproductive physiology and pathology, endocrinology, andrology, gonadal function, gametogenesis, fertilization, embryo development, implantation, pregnancy and contraception. **Freq:** 6/yr. **Key Personnel:** Stephen G. Hillier, Editor-in-Chief; R. Apps, Assoc. Ed.; H.K. Beard, Managing Editor; D. Betts, Assoc. Ed.; C. Foresta, Assoc. Ed.; R. Canipari, Assoc. Ed. **ISSN:** 1360-9947. **Subscription Rates:** US$1,444 institutions print and online; US$975 institutions online only; US$1,324 institutions print only; US$298 individuals online only; US$408 individuals print; US$198 members human reproduction, online only; 116 members print; US$292 members reproductive medicine, print; US$292 members reproductive biology, print; US$292 members Canadian fertility and Andrology, print. **Remarks:** Advertising accepted; rates available upon request. **URL:** http://molehr.oxfordjournals.org/. **Circ:** (Not Reported)

Chippenham

53020 ■ Antiques & Art Independent
PO Box 3369
Wilts
Chippenham SN15 9DU, United Kingdom
Ph: 44 1225 742240
Publication E-mail: antiquesnews@hotmail.com
Publisher E-mail: mail@antiquesnews.co.uk
Newspaper for the British antiques and art trade. **Subtitle:** The Newspaper for the British Antiques and Art Trade. **Founded:** 1997. **Freq:** Weekly. **Print Method:** Web fed litho. **Trim Size:** 290 x 425 mm. **Cols./Page:** 6. **Col. Width:** 42 millimeters. **Key Personnel:** Gail Mcleod, Editor and Publisher. **ISSN:** 1460-9185. **Remarks:** Accepts advertising. **URL:** http://www.antiquesnews.co.uk/page_6.php. **Circ:** 21,000

Chorley

53021 ■ Chorley Guardian
Johnston Press PLC
32a Market St.
Chorley PR7 2RY, United Kingdom
Ph: 44 1257 264911
Local community newspaper. **Freq:** Weekly (Wed.). **Key Personnel:** Chris Maguire, Editor. **Remarks:** Accepts advertising. **URL:** http://www.chorley-guardian.co.uk/. **Circ:** (Not Reported)

53022 ■ The Glade
Withnell Farm
Bury Ln.
Chorley PR6 8SD, United Kingdom
Ph: 44 1254 832849
Fax: 44 1254 832849
Magazine covering archery. **Founded:** 1978. **Freq:** Quarterly. **Print Method:** Sheetfed. **Trim Size:** A4. **Subscription Rates:** 19 by mail U.K.; US$26 U.S. U.S.; 23 by mail Europe; 25 other countries. **Remarks:** Accepts advertising. **URL:** http://www.theglade.co.uk. **Circ:** (Not Reported)

53023 ■ Leyland Guardian
Johnston Press PLC
32a Market St.
Chorley PR7 2RY, United Kingdom
Ph: 44 1257 264911
Local community newspaper. **Key Personnel:** Chris Maguire, Editor. **Remarks:** Accepts advertising. **URL:**

http://www.leyland-guardian.co.uk/. **Circ:** (Not Reported)

Chorleywood

53024 ■ The Key Frame
Fair Organ Preservation Society
c/o Norman Rogers, Membership Sec.
Gaythorpe, Blacketts Wood Dr.
Chorleywood WD3 5QQ, United Kingdom
Publisher E-mail: memsec@fops.org
Publication covering music. **Founded:** 1961. **Freq:** Quarterly. **Print Method:** Lithographic. **Trim Size:** A5. **ISSN:** 0261-1546. **Subscription Rates:** Free members. **URL:** http://www.fops.org/journal/index.php. **Ad Rates:** BW: 50. **Circ:** 1,000

Cleckheaton

53025 ■ Spenborough Guardian
Johnston Press PLC
1 Market St.
Cleckheaton BD19 3RT, United Kingdom
Ph: 44 1274 874635
Local community newspaper. **Key Personnel:** Margaret Heward, Editor. **Remarks:** Accepts advertising. **URL:** http://www.spenboroughguardian.co.uk/. **Circ:** (Not Reported)

Clitheroe

53026 ■ Clitheroe Advertiser & Times
Johnston Press PLC
3a King St.
Clitheroe BB7 2EW, United Kingdom
Ph: 44 1200 422324
Local community newspaper. **Founded:** 1868. **Freq:** Weekly (Thurs.). **Remarks:** Accepts advertising. **URL:** http://www.clitheroeadvertiser.co.uk/. **Circ:** (Not Reported)

Cobham

53027 ■ Holiday-FM - 99
Cedar House
78 Portsmouth Rd.
Cobham KT11 1AN, United Kingdom
Ph: 44 780 2807777
Fax: 44 208 9520150
E-mail: info@holidayfm.com
Format: Contemporary Hit Radio (CHR); Top 40; Classic Rock. **Operating Hours:** Continuous. **Ad Rates:** Advertising accepted; rates available upon request. **URL:** http://www.holidayfm.com.

Colchester

53028 ■ Annals of The Royal College of Surgeons of England
Portland Press Ltd.
Commerce Way
Colchester C02 8HP, United Kingdom
Ph: 44 1206 796351
Fax: 44 1206 799331
Publisher E-mail: sales@portland-services.com
Peer-reviewed Journal focusing on surgical specialties. **Freq:** 8/yr (Jan., Mar., Apr., May, July, Sept., Oct., and Nov.). **Key Personnel:** Bruce Campbell, Editorial Board; Tom Dehn, Editorial Board; Colin Johnson, Editor; Robert Wheeler, Editorial Board; Mike Parker, Editorial Board. **ISSN:** 0035-8843. **Subscription Rates:** 195 institutions UK/Europe, online and print; 210 other countries online and print; US$355 institutions online and print; 172 institutions, other countries online only; US$320 institutions online only. **Remarks:** Accepts advertising. **URL:** http://www.rcseng.ac.uk/publications/annals/. **Ad Rates:** BW: 475, 4C: 1,250. **Circ:** (Not Reported)

53029 ■ Biochemical Society Symposia
Portland Press Ltd.
Commerce Way
Colchester C02 8HP, United Kingdom
Ph: 44 1206 796351
Fax: 44 1206 799331
Publisher E-mail: sales@portland-services.com
Journal covering cell biology and biochemical information. **ISSN:** 0067-8694. **URL:** http://symposia.biochemistry.org/.

53030 ■ Biochemical Society Transactions
Portland Press Ltd.
Commerce Way
Colchester C02 8HP, United Kingdom
Ph: 44 1206 796351
Fax: 44 1206 799331
Publisher E-mail: sales@portland-services.com
Journal giving information on latest advances across a wide spectrum of areas in the cellular and molecular life sciences fields and meant for undergraduate and postgraduate students, in connection with the Biochemical Society. **Freq:** 6/yr. **Key Personnel:** Colin Bingle, Advisory Panel. **ISSN:** 0300-5127. **Subscription Rates:** 175 institutions print only; EUR298 institutions print only; US$332 institutions print only; 175 institutions, other countries print only. **URL:** http://www.biochemsoctrans.org/.

53031 ■ Bulletin of Medical Ethics
Portland Press Ltd.
Commerce Way
Colchester C02 8HP, United Kingdom
Ph: 44 1206 796351
Fax: 44 1206 799331
Publisher E-mail: sales@portland-services.com
Journal focusing on health care ethics. **URL:** http://www.portlandpress.com/pcs/journals/journal.cfm?product=BME.

53032 ■ Craftbusiness
Aceville Publications Ltd.
Unit 21-23 Phoenix Ct.
Hawkins Rd.
Colchester CO2 8JY, United Kingdom
Ph: 44 12 06505900
Fax: 44 12 06505905
Publisher E-mail: elizabeth.sharp@aceville.co.uk
Magazine focusing on craft business. **Key Personnel:** Elizabeth Sharp, Editor, phone 44 1206 505983, elizabeth.sharp@aceville.co.uk; Sam Reubin, Advertising Mgr., sam.reubin@aceville.co.uk; Helen Tudor, Publishing Dir., phone 44 1206 505970, helen.tudor@aceville.co.uk. **Subscription Rates:** US$59.99 other countries. **URL:** http://craftbusiness.com/site/.

53033 ■ Crafts Beautiful
Aceville Publications Ltd.
Unit 21-23 Phoenix Ct.
Hawkins Rd.
Colchester CO2 8JY, United Kingdom
Ph: 44 12 06505900
Fax: 44 12 06505905
Publisher E-mail: elizabeth.sharp@aceville.co.uk
Magazine focusing on crafting. **Key Personnel:** Sarah Crosland, Editor, phone 44 1206 505974, sarah@aceville.co.uk. **Subscription Rates:** 44 individuals; US$99.95 individuals; 75 other countries. **URL:** http://www.crafts-beautiful.com/site/.

53034 ■ Disability Product News
Aceville Publications Ltd.
Unit 21-23 Phoenix Ct.
Hawkins Rd.
Colchester CO2 8JY, United Kingdom
Ph: 44 12 06505900
Fax: 44 12 06505905
Publisher E-mail: elizabeth.sharp@aceville.co.uk
Magazine for disabled persons. **Key Personnel:** Phil Curry, Editor, phone 44 1206 505115, fax 44 1206 500243, phillip.curry@aceville.co.uk. **Subscription Rates:** 25 individuals for 9 issues. **URL:** http://www.disabilityproductnews.co.uk/.

53035 ■ Essays in Biochemistry
Portland Press Ltd.
Commerce Way
Colchester C02 8HP, United Kingdom
Ph: 44 1206 796351
Fax: 44 1206 799331
Publisher E-mail: sales@portland-services.com
Journal focusing on latest research in rapidly moving areas of biochemistry and molecular biology. **Key Personnel:** Melanie Welham, Series Ed. **ISSN:** 0071-1365. **URL:** http://essays.biochemistry.org/.

53036 ■ Grow Your Own
Aceville Publications Ltd.
Unit 21-23 Phoenix Ct.
Hawkins Rd.
Colchester CO2 8JY, United Kingdom

Ph: 44 12 06505900
Fax: 44 12 06505905
Publisher E-mail: elizabeth.sharp@aceville.co.uk
Magazine focusing on kitchen gardening. **Key Personnel:** Lucy Halsall, Editor, phone 44 1206 505979, lucy.halsall@aceville.co.uk; Teresa Tudge, Advertising Mgr., phone 44 1206 505950, teresa.tudge@aceville.co.uk. **Subscription Rates:** 70 other countries; 38 individuals; EUR60 individuals. **URL:** http://www.growfruitandveg.co.uk/.

53037 ■ Gun Mart
Aceville Publications Ltd.
Unit 21-23 Phoenix Ct.
Hawkins Rd.
Colchester CO2 8JY, United Kingdom
Ph: 44 12 06505900
Fax: 44 12 06505905
Publisher E-mail: elizabeth.sharp@aceville.co.uk
Magazine covering sports shooting, gun collecting, and the militaria market. **Key Personnel:** Pat Farey, Editor, phone 44 1702 479884, patfarey@lineone.net. **Subscription Rates:** 37 individuals. **URL:** http://www.gunmart.net.

53038 ■ Hotel Business
Aceville Publications Ltd.
Unit 21-23 Phoenix Ct.
Hawkins Rd.
Colchester CO2 8JY, United Kingdom
Ph: 44 12 06505900
Fax: 44 12 06505905
Publisher E-mail: elizabeth.sharp@aceville.co.uk
Magazine covering front and back of house facilities and general hotel management. **Key Personnel:** Elizabeth Sharp, Editor, phone 44 1206 505983, fax 44 1206 505985, elizabeth.sharp@aceville.co.uk; Jenny O'Neill, Advertising Mgr., phone 44 1206 506227, fax 44 1206 500228, jenny@mspublications.co.uk. **Subscription Rates:** 35 individuals; 92 other countries; 62 two years. **URL:** http://www.hotel-magazine.co.uk/.

53039 ■ International Journal of Refugee Law
Oxford University Press
c/o Prof. Geoff Gilbert, Ed.-in-Ch.
University of Essex, Wivenhoe Pk.
Colchester CO4 3SQ, United Kingdom
Publisher E-mail: webenquiry@oup.com
Law periodical. **Freq:** 4/yr. **Key Personnel:** Prof. Geoff Gilbert, Editor-in-Chief, geoff@essex.ac.uk; Prof. Guy S. Goodwin-Gill, Founding Ed.; Prof. Ryszard Piotrowicz, Book Review Ed., ryp@aber.ac.uk. **ISSN:** 0953-8186. **Subscription Rates:** 529 institutions print and online, all 3 refugee titles; US$1,058 institutions print and online, all 3 refugee titles; EUR794 institutions print and online, all 3 refugee titles; 51 members print; US$102 members print; EUR77 members print; 75 individuals print; US$150 individuals print; EUR113 individuals print. **Remarks:** Accepts advertising. **URL:** http://ijrl.oupjournals.org/. **Circ:** (Not Reported)

53040 ■ Let's Knit!
Aceville Publications Ltd.
Unit 21-23 Phoenix Ct.
Hawkins Rd.
Colchester CO2 8JY, United Kingdom
Ph: 44 12 00505900
Fax: 44 12 06505905
Publisher E-mail: elizabeth.sharp@aceville.co.uk
Magazine featuring fashionable patterns and creations from some of the best contemporary designers. **Key Personnel:** Sarah Neal, Editor; Anna Blewett, Dep. Ed. **Subscription Rates:** 10.95 individuals for 3 issues paid by quarterly direct debit; 46.50 individuals for 12 issues by credit card; 93 individuals for 24 issues by credit card. **URL:** http://www.letsknit.co.uk/.

53041 ■ Let's Make Cards!
Aceville Publications Ltd.
Unit 21-23 Phoenix Ct.
Hawkins Rd.
Colchester CO2 8JY, United Kingdom
Ph: 44 12 06505900
Fax: 44 12 06505905
Publication E-mail: lmc@servicehelpline.co.uk
Publisher E-mail: elizabeth.sharp@aceville.co.uk
Magazine featuring card making. **Key Personnel:** Holly Markham, Editor, phone 44 1206 505994, holly.markham@aceville.co.uk. **Subscription Rates:** 60.95 individuals; 75 other countries; EUR70 individuals. **URL:**

http://www.crafts-beautiful.com/site/letsmakecards/.

53042 ■ Natural Health
Aceville Publications Ltd.
Unit 21-23 Phoenix Ct.
Hawkins Rd.
Colchester CO2 8JY, United Kingdom
Ph: 44 12 06505900
Fax: 44 12 06505905
Publisher E-mail: elizabeth.sharp@aceville.co.uk
Magazine focusing on natural health. **Key Personnel:** Emma Van Hinsbergh, Editor, phone 44 1206 508618, emma.vanhinsbergh@aceville.co.uk; Liz Alvis, Dep. Ed., phone 44 1206 508616, liz@atsaceville.co.uk. **Subscription Rates:** 50 other countries; 40 individuals Europe. **URL:** http://www.naturalhealthmagazine.co.uk/.

53043 ■ Natural Health & Well-Being
Aceville Publications Ltd.
Unit 21-23 Phoenix Ct.
Hawkins Rd.
Colchester CO2 8JY, United Kingdom
Ph: 44 12 06505900
Fax: 44 12 06505905
Publisher E-mail: elizabeth.sharp@aceville.co.uk
Magazine publishing articles on health. **Subtitle:** Complementary Therapies for you & yours. **Freq:** Monthly. **Key Personnel:** Emma Van Hinsberg, Editor, phone 44 1206 508618, emma.vanhinsbergh@aceville.co.uk; Liz Alvis, Dep. Ed., phone 44 1206 508616, liz@aceville.co.uk. **Subscription Rates:** 50 individuals outside United Kingdom; 40 individuals Europe. **Remarks:** Accepts advertising. **URL:** http://www.naturalhealthmagazine.co.uk. **Circ:** (Not Reported)

53044 ■ Oral History Journal
Oral History Society
c/o Dept. of History
Essex University
Colchester CO4 3SQ, United Kingdom
Ph: 44 20 74127405
Publisher E-mail: rob.perks@bl.uk
Journal covering history. **Founded:** 1969. **Freq:** Semiannual. **Key Personnel:** Rob Perks, Sec.; Joanna Bornat, Editor; Alan Ward, Vice President; Graham Smith, Chm. **ISSN:** 0143-0955. **Remarks:** Advertising accepted; rates available upon request. **URL:** http://www.ohs.org.uk. **Circ:** 795

53045 ■ Period House
Essential Publishing Ltd.
The Towes
Phoenix Sq.
Colchester CO4 9HU, United Kingdom
Ph: 44 12 06851117
Consumer magazine covering period homes. **Founded:** 1990. **Freq:** Monthly. **Key Personnel:** Toby Waltham, Advertising Sales Mgr., phone 44 206 851117, toby.waltham@essentialpublishing.co.uk. **Subscription Rates:** .32.50 individuals. **URL:** http://www.hubertburdamediauk.com/. **Ad Rates:** BW: 1,800, 4C: 2,000. **Circ:** 45,000

53046 ■ Period Ideas
Aceville Publications Ltd.
Unit 21-23 Phoenix Ct.
Hawkins Rd.
Colchester CO2 8JY, United Kingdom
Ph: 44 12 06505900
Fax: 44 12 06505905
Publisher E-mail: elizabeth.sharp@aceville.co.uk
Magazine covering home renovation, interior design, and style. **Key Personnel:** Jeannine McAndrew, Editor, phone 44 1206 505976, jeannine@aceville.co.uk. **Subscription Rates:** 29.99 individuals 12 issues by credit card; 29.99 individuals 12 issues by direct debit; 56 individuals 24 issues by credit card. **URL:** http://www.periodideas.com/.

53047 ■ Quick & Crafty!
Aceville Publications Ltd.
Unit 21-23 Phoenix Ct.
Hawkins Rd.
Colchester CO2 8JY, United Kingdom
Ph: 44 12 06505900
Fax: 44 12 06505905
Publisher E-mail: elizabeth.sharp@aceville.co.uk
Magazine featuring inspirational tips and ideas for all kinds of crafts. **Key Personnel:** Lynn Martin, Editor. **Subscription Rates:** 9.99 individuals for 3 issues by

---

Circulation: ★ = ABC; △ = BPA; ♦ = CAC; • = CCAB; ❑ = VAC; ⊕ = PO Statement; ‡ = Publisher's Report; Boldface figures = sworn; Light figures = estimated.

direct debit; 55.95 individuals for 9 issues by credit card. **URL:** http://www.crafts-beautiful.com/site/quickandcrafty/.

53048 ■ Seatrade Magazine
Seatrade Communications Ltd.
Seatrade House
42 N Station Rd.
Colchester CO1 1RB, United Kingdom
Ph: 44 12 06545121
Fax: 44 12 06545190
Publisher E-mail: mail@seatrade-global.com
International trade magazine presenting analyses of shipping business from cruise to tanker, as well as geographic focus reports. **Founded:** 1970. **Freq:** Bimonthly. **Print Method:** Heatset web. **Trim Size:** 8 1/4 x 11 3/4. **Key Personnel:** Bob Jaques, Editor; Namrata Nadkami, Asst. Ed.; Ian Middleton, Assoc. Ed. **ISSN:** 1476-3680. **Subscription Rates:** 100 individuals UK & Europe; EUR140 individuals; US$180 individuals USA and rest of world; 165 two years UK and Europe; EUR252 two years; US$324 two years USA and rest of world; 207 individuals 3 years, UK and Eurppe; EUR319 individuals 3 years; US$405 individuals 3 years, USA and rest of world. **Remarks:** Accepts advertising. **URL:** http://www.seatrade-global.com/. **Formerly:** Seatrade Business Review. **Ad Rates:** BW: US$3,630, 4C: US$4,775. **Circ:** ★6,426

53049 ■ Sexualities
Sage Publications Ltd.
c/o Ken Plummer, Ed.
Sociology Dept.
University of Essex
Wivenhoe Pk.
Colchester CO4 3SQ, United Kingdom
Scholarly journal covering the social organization of human sexual experience in the late modern world. **Subtitle:** Studies in Culture and Society. **Founded:** 1998. **Freq:** Bimonthly. **Key Personnel:** Shannon Bell, International Advisory Editorial Board; Henk Wilke, Book Reviews Ed.; Dennis Altman, International Advisory Editorial Board; Barry D. Adam, International Advisory Editorial Board; Ken Plummer, Editor; Gilbert Herdt, International Advisory Editorial Board; Lynne Segal, International Advisory Editorial Board; Henning Bech, International Advisory Editorial Board; Don Kulick, International Advisory Editorial Board; Steven Seidman, International Advisory Editorial Board. **ISSN:** 1363-4607. **Subscription Rates:** US$1,053 institutions print & e-access; US$1,158 institutions current volume print & all online content; US$948 institutions e-access; US$1,053 institutions e-access plus backfile (all online content); US$948 institutions content through 1998; US$1,032 institutions print only; US$105 individuals print only; US$189 institutions single print; US$24 individuals single print. **Remarks:** Accepts advertising. **URL:** http://www.sagepub.com/journalsProdDesc.nav?prodId=Journal200950. **Circ:** (Not Reported)

53050 ■ Shooting Sports
Aceville Publications Ltd.
Unit 21-23 Phoenix Ct.
Hawkins Rd.
Colchester CO2 8JY, United Kingdom
Ph: 44 12 06505900
Fax: 44 12 06505905
Publisher E-mail: elizabeth.sharp@aceville.co.uk
Magazine covering all aspects of shotguns, firearms, and airguns. **Key Personnel:** Peter Moore, Editor, phone 44 1206 525697, peter.moore403@ntlworld.com. **Subscription Rates:** 37 individuals. **URL:** http://www.shooting-sports.net/.

53051 ■ Slim at Home
Aceville Publications Ltd.
Unit 21-23 Phoenix Ct.
Hawkins Rd.
Colchester CO2 8JY, United Kingdom
Ph: 44 12 06505900
Fax: 44 12 06505905
Publication E-mail: slimathome@servicehelpline.co.uk
Publisher E-mail: elizabeth.sharp@aceville.co.uk
Slimming magazine for independent women who want to lose weight their own way. **Key Personnel:** Naomi Abeykoon, Editor, phone 44 1206 505960, naomi@aceville.co.uk; Jay Hurley, Advertising Mgr., phone 44 1206 505488, jay.hurley@bodyfitmagazine.co.uk; Laura Jones, Dep. Ed., phone 44 1206 505987, laura@aceville.co.uk. **Subscription Rates:** 3.20 individuals 3 issues. **URL:** http://www.slimmerrecipes.co.uk/.

53052 ■ Sound Vision Install
Aceville Publications Ltd.
Unit 21-23 Phoenix Ct.
Hawkins Rd.
Colchester CO2 8JY, United Kingdom
Ph: 44 12 06505900
Fax: 44 12 06505905
Publication E-mail: svimag@mspublications.co.uk
Publisher E-mail: elizabeth.sharp@aceville.co.uk
Magazine featuring finest home electronics. **Subtitle:** The Trade's Finest Home Electronics Resource. **Key Personnel:** Callum Fauser, Editor, phone 44 1206 505962, callum.fauser@aceville.co.uk. **Remarks:** Accepts advertising. **URL:** http://www.svimag.com/. **Circ:** (Not Reported)

53053 ■ Speciality Food
Aceville Publications Ltd.
Unit 21-23 Phoenix Ct.
Hawkins Rd.
Colchester CO2 8JY, United Kingdom
Ph: 44 12 06505900
Fax: 44 12 06505905
Publisher E-mail: elizabeth.sharp@aceville.co.uk
Magazine featuring fine food industry. **Key Personnel:** Louise Miles, Editor, phone 44 1206 505971, louise.miles@aceville.co.uk; Helen Tudor, Publisher, phone 44 1206 505970, helen.tudor@aceville.co.uk. **Subscription Rates:** 40 other countries; 70 two years rest of world. **Remarks:** Accepts advertising. **URL:** http://specialityfoodmagazine.com/site/. **Circ:** ★8,695

53054 ■ Wayfarer News
United Kingdom Wayfarer Association
c/o Sarah Burgess
49 Seaview Ave.
West Mersea
Colchester CO5 8BY, United Kingdom
Ph: 44 12 06384043
Magazine covering various topics of interest to wayfarers. **Freq:** 3/yr. **Key Personnel:** Ray Scragg, Editor. **URL:** http://www.wayfarer.org.uk/.

53055 ■ Dream 100-FM - 100.2
Northgate House
St. Peters St.
Colchester CO1 1HT, United Kingdom
Ph: 44 1206 764466
Fax: 44 1206 715102
E-mail: info@dream100.com; studio@dream100.com
Format: Public Radio; Easy Listening; Adult Contemporary; Sports; News; Information. **Founded:** Sept. 1998. **Operating Hours:** Continuous. **Key Personnel:** David Rees, Group Brand Dir. **Ad Rates:** Advertising accepted; rates available upon request. **URL:** http://www.dream100.com/.

53056 ■ Heart Colchester-FM - 96.1
Abbeygate Two
9 Whitewell Rd.
Colchester CO2 7DE, United Kingdom
Ph: 44 1206 577577
Format: Adult Contemporary. **Ad Rates:** Advertising accepted; rates available upon request. **URL:** http://www.heart.co.uk/colchester/contact-us.

Coleraine

53057 ■ Q97.2-FM - 97.2
24 Cloyfin Rd.
Co. Londonderry
Coleraine BT52 2NU, United Kingdom
Ph: 44 28 70344972
Fax: 44 28 70326666
Format: Adult Contemporary; News. **Key Personnel:** Robert Walshe, Ch. Exec./Prog. Dir. **URL:** http://www.q972.fm/.

Colwyn Bay

53058 ■ North Wales Pioneer
NWN Media Ltd.
22 Penrhyn Rd.
Colwyn Bay LL29 8HY, United Kingdom
Ph: 44 1492 531188
Fax: 44 1492 533564
Publisher E-mail: internet@nwn.co.uk
Newspaper featuring news coverage and human interest stories. **Key Personnel:** Steve Rogers, Editor; Claire Bryce, Advertising Mgr. **URL:** http://www.

northwalespioneer.co.uk/. **Circ:** Free 25,233

Congleton

53059 ■ Armourer
Beaumont Publishing
PO Box 161
Congleton CW12 3WJ, United Kingdom
Ph: 44 1260 278044
Fax: 44 1260 278044
Publication E-mail: editor.armourer@btinternet.com
Magazine covering military news and events. **Subtitle:** Militaria Magazine. **Freq:** Monthly. **Key Personnel:** Irene Moore, Editor; John Greenwood, Publisher. **Subscription Rates:** 24 individuals; 30 individuals Europe and Ireland; 35 other countries. **Remarks:** Accepts advertising. **URL:** http://www.armourer.co.uk/index.html. **Circ:** (Not Reported)

Cookstown

53060 ■ Mid-Ulster Mail
Morton Newspapers
52 Oldtown St.
Tyrone
Cookstown BT80 8EF, United Kingdom
Ph: 44 28 86762288
Community newspaper. **Freq:** Weekly (Thurs.). **Print Method:** Offset. **Remarks:** Accepts advertising. **URL:** http://www.midulstermail.co.uk/. **Circ:** Combined 12,038

53061 ■ Six-FM - 107.2
2C Park Ave.
Burn Rd.
Cookstown BT80 8AH, United Kingdom
Ph: 44 28 86758696
E-mail: studio@sixfm.co.uk
Format: Talk; Oldies; Contemporary Hit Radio (CHR). **Key Personnel:** Mr. Robert Walshe, CEO/Prog. Dir. **Ad Rates:** Advertising accepted; rates available upon request. **URL:** http://www.sixfm.co.uk/.

53062 ■ Six-FM - 106
2C Park Ave.
Burn Rd.
Cookstown BT80 8AH, United Kingdom
Ph: 44 28 86758696
E-mail: studio@sixfm.co.uk
Format: Talk; Oldies; Contemporary Hit Radio (CHR). **Key Personnel:** Mr. Robert Walshe, CEO/Prog. Dir.; Orla Ross, Brand Mgr., phone 44 28 25648777, fax 44 28 25648778, orla.ross@northernmediagroup.com. **Ad Rates:** Advertising accepted; rates available upon request. **URL:** http://www.sixfm.co.uk/.

Corby

53063 ■ Operations Management
Institute of Operations Management
Earlstrees Ct.
Earlstrees Rd.
Corby NN17 4AX, United Kingdom
Ph: 44 1536 740105
Fax: 44 1536 740101
Publisher E-mail: info@iomnet.org.uk
Technical professional journal covering operations management for managers in manufacturing, supply chain, materials production management, logistics, warehouse, inventory control, and more. Contains technical articles and information on Institute courses, activities, and events for members, news items, industry news, and book reviews. **Founded:** 1983. **Freq:** 6/yr. **Trim Size:** A4. **ISSN:** 0266-1713. **URL:** http://www.iomnet.org.uk/control-and-news/default.aspx. **Formerly:** Control. **Ad Rates:** BW: 900, 4C: 400. **Circ:** Paid 1,462

Cornwall

53064 ■ Adventure Cornwall
Coast Publishing Ltd.
St. Joseph's
St. Mawgan
Cornwall TR8 4ES, United Kingdom
Ph: 44 1637 860031
Publisher E-mail: info@coast-publishing.co.uk
Magazine featuring extreme sports and adventure destinations across the county. **Freq:** Quarterly. **Key Personnel:** Will Heathcote, Mktg. & Advertising Mgr., will@adventure-cornwall.co.uk. **URL:** http://www.adventure-cornwall.co.uk/.

53065 ■ The European Journal of Teleworking
Addico Cornix Ltd.
Tregannick Sancreed Penzance
Cornwall TR20 8QW, United Kingdom
Ph: 44 1736 332736
Fax: 44 1736 334702
Publisher E-mail: srs@cornix.co.uk
Journal covering teleworking. **Founded:** 1994. **Freq:** Quarterly. **Key Personnel:** Suze White, Contact, suze@cornix.co.uk; Stephen Simmons, Mng. Dir., srs@cornix.co.uk. **Remarks:** Accepts advertising. **URL:** http://www.ecoplan.org/assist/partners/addico.htm. **Circ:** (Not Reported)

Corsham

53066 ■ International Journal of Art & Design Education
National Society for Education in Art and Design
3 Masons Wharf
Potley Ln.
Wiltshire
Corsham SN13 9FY, United Kingdom
Ph: 44 12 25810134
Fax: 44 12 25812730
Publication E-mail: johnsteers@nsead.org
Publisher E-mail: info@nsead.org
Publication covering art and design education. **Freq:** 3/yr. **Key Personnel:** Dr. John Steers, Gen. Sec.; Dennis Atkinson, Publication Board; Jeff Adams, Editor. **ISSN:** 1476-8062. **Subscription Rates:** US$127 individuals print and online; 75 other countries print and online; 699 institutions, other countries print + online; EUR886 institutions, other countries print + online; 607 institutions, other countries print or online; US$1,410 individuals print + online; US$1,226 institutions print or online. **Remarks:** Advertising accepted; rates available upon request. **URL:** http://www.nsead.org/publications/ijade.aspx; http://www.blackwellpublishing.com/journal.asp?ref=1476-8062&site=1. **Formerly:** Journal of Arts and Design Education. **Circ:** 2,800

Coulsdon

53067 ■ Jane's Airport Review
Jane's Information Group Ltd.
Sentinel House
163 Brighton Rd.
Coulsdon CR5 2YH, United Kingdom
Ph: 44 20 87003700
Fax: 44 20 87003751
Publisher E-mail: customer.servicesuk@janes.com
Trade magazine covering the airport industry for senior management professionals. **Freq:** Monthly 10/yr. **ISSN:** 0954-7649. **Subscription Rates:** US$290 individuals; 180 individuals; US$1,440 individuals online. **URL:** http://catalog.janes.com/catalog/public/index.cfm?fuseaction=home.ProductInfoBrief&product_id=98981.

53068 ■ Jane's Defence Weekly
Jane's Information Group Ltd.
Sentinel House
163 Brighton Rd.
Coulsdon CR5 2YH, United Kingdom
Ph: 44 20 87003700
Fax: 44 20 87003751
Publisher E-mail: customer.servicesuk@janes.com
Publication covering news on defense issues, including technical and background data, worldwide. **Founded:** 1984. **Freq:** Weekly. **Key Personnel:** Peter Felstead, Editor. **ISSN:** 0265-3818. **Subscription Rates:** 280 individuals; US$1,795 individuals online; US$520 individuals. **Remarks:** Accepts advertising. **URL:** http://catalog.janes.com/catalog/public/index.cfm?fuseaction=home.ProductInfoBrief&product_id=96567. **Ad Rates:** BW: EUR4,505, 4C: EUR6,870. **Circ:** (Not Reported)

53069 ■ Jane's Intelligence Review
Jane's Information Group Ltd.
Sentinel House
163 Brighton Rd.
Coulsdon CR5 2YH, United Kingdom
Ph: 44 20 87003700
Fax: 44 20 87003751
Publisher E-mail: customer.servicesuk@janes.com
Journal covering threat analysis worldwide. **Freq:** Monthly. **Key Personnel:** Christian Le Miere, Editor. **ISSN:** 1350-6226. **Subscription Rates:** US$1,950 individuals online; 355 individuals; US$570 individuals.

URL: http://catalog.janes.com/catalog/public/index.cfm?fuseaction=home.ProductInfoBrief&product_id=98639.

53070 ■ Jane's International Defense Review
Jane's Information Group Ltd.
Sentinel House
163 Brighton Rd.
Coulsdon CR5 2YH, United Kingdom
Ph: 44 20 87003700
Fax: 44 20 87003751
Publisher E-mail: customer.servicesuk@janes.com
Publication covering defense technology. **Freq:** Monthly. **ISSN:** 0020-6512. **Subscription Rates:** 255 individuals; US$405 individuals; US$1,705 individuals online. **URL:** http://catalog.janes.com/catalog/public/index.cfm?fuseaction=home.ProductInfoBrief&product_id=97294.

53071 ■ Jane's Navy International
Jane's Information Group Ltd.
Sentinel House
163 Brighton Rd.
Coulsdon CR5 2YH, United Kingdom
Ph: 44 20 87003700
Fax: 44 20 87003751
Publisher E-mail: customer.servicesuk@janes.com
Magazine covering naval operations and technologies worldwide. **Founded:** 1894. **Freq:** Monthly 10/yr. **Key Personnel:** Nick Brown, Editor. **ISSN:** 0144-3194. **Subscription Rates:** 1,410 individuals online (U.K.); US$170 individuals; 265 individuals. **Remarks:** Accepts advertising. **URL:** http://catalog.janes.com/catalog/public/index.cfm?fuseaction=home.ProductInfoBrief&product_id=97750. **Circ:** Combined ‡3,606

53072 ■ Jane's Police Review
Jane's Information Group Ltd.
Sentinel House
163 Brighton Rd.
Coulsdon CR5 2YH, United Kingdom
Ph: 44 20 87003700
Fax: 44 20 87003751
Publisher E-mail: customer.servicesuk@janes.com
Trade magazine covering issues for police in the UK. **Freq:** Weekly. **Key Personnel:** Chris Herbert, Editor. **ISSN:** 0309-1410. **URL:** http://catalog.janes.com/catalog/public/index.cfm?fuseaction=home.ProductInfoBrief&product_id=101940.

53073 ■ Jane's Simulation & Training Systems
Jane's Information Group Ltd.
Sentinel House
163 Brighton Rd.
Coulsdon CR5 2YH, United Kingdom
Ph: 44 20 87003700
Fax: 44 20 87003751
Publisher E-mail: customer.servicesuk@janes.com
Trade magazine covering a survey of simulation and training equipment worldwide. **Freq:** Annual. **Key Personnel:** Giles Ebbutt, Editor; Huw R. Williams, Land Desk Researcher. **Subscription Rates:** US$2,695 individuals online; 440 individuals; US$725 individuals online. **URL:** http://jsts.janes.com/public/jsts/index.shtml.

53074 ■ Jane's Transport Finance
Jane's Information Group Ltd.
Sentinel House
163 Brighton Rd.
Coulsdon CR5 2YH, United Kingdom
Ph: 44 20 87003700
Fax: 44 20 87003751
Publisher E-mail: customer.servicesuk@janes.com
Journal covering news in the air, ship, and rail finance industries worldwide. **Freq:** Semimonthly. **Key Personnel:** Jim Smith, Editor. **ISSN:** 1351-1211. **Subscription Rates:** 4,660 individuals online; 1,390 individuals; US$2,100 individuals. **URL:** http://catalog.janes.com/catalog/public/index.cfm?fuseaction=home.ProductInfoBrief&product_id=99574.

County Antrim

53075 ■ Journal of European Real Estate Research
Emerald Group Publishing Ltd.
c/o Prof. Stanley McGreal, Editor
University of Ulster, School of the Built Environment
Shore Rd.
County Antrim BT37 0QB, United Kingdom

Publisher E-mail: emerald@emeraldinsight.com
Journal providing European forum for the interchange of information and ideas relating to commercial and residential property. **Freq:** Annual. **Key Personnel:** Prof. Stanley McGreal, Editor, ws.mcgreal@ulster.ac.uk; Aimee Wood, Publisher, awood@emeraldinsight.com. **ISSN:** 1753-9269. **URL:** http://info.emeraldinsight.com/products/journals/journals.htm?id=jerer.

Coventry

53076 ■ Abstracts and Reviews
Royal Institution of Chartered Surveyors - England
RICS Contact Ctr.
Surveyor Ct.
Westwood Way
Coventry CV4 8JE, United Kingdom
Ph: 44 870 3331600
Fax: 44 207 3343811
Publisher E-mail: contactrics@rics.org
Publication covering surveying. **Freq:** Annual. **URL:** http://www.rics.org/.

53077 ■ Applied Economics Letters
Taylor & Francis Group Journals
Dept. of Economics
Warwick University
Coventry CV4 7AL, United Kingdom
Publisher E-mail: customerservice@taylorandfrancis.com
Journal focusing on applied economics and applied financial economics. **Freq:** 18/yr. **Print Method:** Offset. **Cols./Page:** 6. **Col. Width:** 26 nonpareils. **Col. Depth:** 294 agate lines. **Key Personnel:** Mark P. Taylor, Editor, appliedeconomics@warwick.ac.uk; Philip Arestis, Assoc. Ed.; Jerry Coakley, Assoc. Ed. **ISSN:** 1350-4851. **Subscription Rates:** 967 institutions print and online; US$1,569 institutions print and online; 918 institutions online; US$1,490 institutions online; 135 individuals; US$221 individuals; EUR1,254 institutions print and online; EUR1,192 institutions online only; EUR177 individuals. **URL:** http://www.tandf.co.uk/journals/titles/13504851.asp.

53078 ■ Applied Financial Economics
Taylor & Francis Group Journals
Dept. of Economics
Warwick University
Coventry CV4 7AL, United Kingdom
Publisher E-mail: customerservice@taylorandfrancis.com
Peer-reviewed journal focusing research on financial markets. **Freq:** 24/yr. **Print Method:** Offset. **Trim Size:** 10 1/8 x 16. **Cols./Page:** 6. **Col. Width:** 10 picas. **Col. Depth:** 224 agate lines. **Key Personnel:** Richard H. Clarida, Co-Ed.; Jerry Coakley, Assoc. Ed.; Timo Terasvirta, Advisory Ed.; David F. Hendry, Advisory Ed.; David A. Peel, Assoc. Ed.; Andrei Shleifer, Advisory Ed.; Robert Faff, Assoc. Ed.; Paul McGuinness, Assoc. Ed.; Yin Wong Cheung, Assoc. Ed.; Mark P. Taylor, Editor, appliedeconomics@warwick.ac.uk. **ISSN:** 0960-3107. **Subscription Rates:** US$3,987 institutions print and online; US$3,787 institutions online only; 2,430 institutions print and online; 2,309 institutions online only; EUR3,190 institutions print and online; EUR3,030 institutions online. **URL:** http://www.tandf.co.uk/journals/titles/09603107.asp.

53079 ■ Camping and Caravanning
The Camping and Caravanning Club
Greenfields House
Westwood Way
Coventry CV4 8JH, United Kingdom
Ph: 44 845 1307632
Magazine containing useful tips, interesting articles, holiday ideas and road tests of new units, tents, and equipment. **Freq:** Monthly. **Remarks:** Accepts advertising. **URL:** http://www.campingandcaravanningclub.co.uk/publications. **Circ:** ★237,168

53080 ■ Community Development Journal
Oxford University Press
c/o Prof. Mick Carpenter, Ed.
Department of Sociology
University of Warwick
Coventry CV4 7AL, United Kingdom
Ph: 44 2476 523161
Fax: 44 2476 523497

Circulation: ★ = ABC; △ = BPA; ♦ = CAC; • = CCAB; ❑ = VAC; ⊕ = PO Statement; ‡ = Publisher's Report; Boldface figures = sworn; Light figures = estimated.

Gale Directory of Publications & Broadcast Media/147th Ed. 5627

Publisher E-mail: webenquiry.uk@oup.com
Journal providing an international forum for political, economic and social programs, linking the activities of people with institutions and government and dealing with the theory and practice of the policies, programs and methods employed, covering topics such as community action, village, town, and regional planning, community studies and rural development. **Freq:** 4/yr. **Key Personnel:** Prof. Mick Carpenter, Editor, m.j.carpenter@warwick.ac.uk. **ISSN:** 0010-3802. **Subscription Rates:** 246 institutions corporate; print and online; 205 institutions corporate; online only; 226 institutions corporate; print only; 197 institutions print and online; 164 institutions online only; 180 institutions print only; 40 individuals developing countries; print; 59 individuals print. **Remarks:** Advertising accepted; rates available upon request. **URL:** http://cdj.oxfordjournals.org. **Circ:** (Not Reported)

53081 ■ EurOhs Magazine
Angel Business Communications Ltd.
Unit 6, Bow Ct.
Fletchworth Gate
Burnsall Rd.
Coventry CV5 6SP, United Kingdom
Ph: 44 2476 718970
Fax: 44 2476 718971
Publisher E-mail: info@angelbc.co.uk
Business to business magazine covering occupational health, safety and environment. **Founded:** July 1997. **Freq:** 8/yr. **Key Personnel:** Sheila Pantry, Editor-in-Chief, sp@sheilapantry.com; Stephen Whitehurst, Commercial Dir./Advertising, stephen@angelbc.co.uk. **Subscription Rates:** Free. **Remarks:** Accepts advertising. **URL:** http://www.eurohs.eu.com. **Circ:** Controlled 10,000

53082 ■ European Journal of Operational Research
Elsevier Science Inc.
c/o Robert Dyson, Ed.
University of Warwick
Warwick Business School
Coventry CV4 7AL, United Kingdom
Ph: 44 247 6523775
Publisher E-mail: usinfo-ehelp@elsevier.com
Journal devoted to the methodology of operational research and to the practice of decision making. **Founded:** 1977. **Freq:** 24/yr. **Print Method:** Offset. **Key Personnel:** Robert Dyson, Editor, robert.dyson@wbs.ac.uk; E. Balas, Editorial Board; Y. Siskos, Editorial Board; J. Resing, Editorial Board; R.E. Burkard, Editorial Board; J. Carlier, Editorial Board; W.W. Cooper, Editorial Board; D. De Werra, Editorial Board. **ISSN:** 0377-2217. **Subscription Rates:** EUR5,674 institutions European countries and Iran; US$6,347 institutions, other countries except Europe, Japan and Iran; 753,500¥ institutions. **URL:** http://www.elsevier.com/wps/find/journaldescription.cws_home/505543/descriptiondescription.

53083 ■ Geometry & Topology
Geometry & Topology Publications
Mathematics Institute
University of Warwick
Coventry CV4 7AL, United Kingdom
Publisher E-mail: gt@msp.warwick.ac.uk
International journal covering various aspects of geometry and topology and their applications. **Key Personnel:** Martin Bridson, Board of Ed. Member; Joan Birman, Board of Ed. Member. **ISSN:** 1364-0380. **Subscription Rates:** US$520 individuals 3100 pages; US$340 individuals electronic. **URL:** http://www.msp.warwick.ac.uk/gt/2009/13-03/.

53084 ■ Housing
Chartered Institute of Housing
Octavia House
Westwood Way
Coventry CV4 8JP, United Kingdom
Ph: 44 24 76851700
Fax: 44 24 76695110
Publisher E-mail: customer.services@cih.org
Publication covering housing. **Freq:** Bimonthly. **Subscription Rates:** Free to members. **Remarks:** Advertising accepted; rates available upon request. **URL:** http://www.cih.org/join/benefits.htm. **Circ:** (Not Reported)

53085 ■ The International Journal of Ventilation
Veetech Ltd.
7A Barclays Venture Center

University of Warwick Science Pk.
Sir William Lyons Rd.
Coventry CV4 7EZ, United Kingdom
Ph: 44 24 1189477231
Fax: 44 24 1189477223
Publisher E-mail: mliddament@veetech.co.uk
Journal reporting all aspects related to ventilation of occupied buildings and other enclosed spaces. **Freq:** Quarterly. **Key Personnel:** Prof. Martin W. Liddament, Editor; Dr. Hazim Awbi, Editorial Board. **Subscription Rates:** 280 individuals online only; 315 individuals print only; 345 individuals print and online; plus vat. **URL:** http://www.ijovent.org.uk.

53086 ■ Journal of Information, Law & Technology (JILT)
University of Warwick
University of Warwick
Coventry CV4 7AL, United Kingdom
Ph: 44 24 76523523
Fax: 44 24 76461606
Publication E-mail: jilt@warwick.ac.uk
Publisher E-mail: wmg@warwick.ac.uk
Journal covering a range of topics relating to IT law and applications. **Founded:** Jan. 31, 1996. **Key Personnel:** Prof. Abdul Paliwala, Proj. Dir., a.paliwala@warwick.ac.uk; Mizanur Rahaman, Publication Ed.; Paul Trimmer, Production Ed., paul.trimmer@warwick.ac.uk. **ISSN:** 1361-4169. **URL:** http://www2.warwick.ac.uk/fac/soc/law/elj/jilt.

53087 ■ Journal of Research in Reading
John Wiley & Sons Inc.
Wiley-Blackwell
c/o Dr. Clare Wood, Ed.-in-Ch.
Psychology Department
Coventry University
Priory St.
Coventry CV1 5FB, United Kingdom
Peer-reviewed journal on literacy. **Freq:** Quarterly. **Key Personnel:** Dr. John Beech, Assoc. Ed.; Dr. Kate Cain, Assoc. Ed.; Dr. Ros Fisher, Assoc. Ed.; Dr. Clare Wood, Editor-in-Chief. **ISSN:** 0141-0423. **Subscription Rates:** US$118 individuals print and online; EUR107 individuals print and online; 71 other countries print and online; US$676 institutions print and online; 460 institutions print and online; US$961 institutions, other countries print and online; EUR583 institutions print and online; US$614 institutions print or online; 418 institutions print or online; US$873 institutions, other countries print or online. **Remarks:** Advertising accepted; rates available upon request. **URL:** http://www.wiley.com/bw/journal.asp?ref=0141-0423. **Circ:** (Not Reported)

53088 ■ Law and Humanities
Hart Publishing Ltd.
Warwick School of Law
University of Warwick
Coventry CV4 7AL, United Kingdom
Publisher E-mail: al@hartpub.co.uk
Peer-reviewed Journal covering arts and humanities around the subject of law. **Founded:** July 2007. **Freq:** Semiannual. **Key Personnel:** Paul Raffield, Gen. Ed., p.raffield@warwick.ac.uk; Gary Watt, Gen. Ed., g.watt@warwick.ac.uk. **Subscription Rates:** 85 individuals standard, United Kingdom and Europe; 95 other countries standard; 55 individuals reduced, United Kingdom and Europe; 60 other countries reduced; 76.50 individuals standard, online; 49.50 individuals online. **Remarks:** Accepts advertising. **URL:** http://www.hartjournals.co.uk/lh/. **Circ:** (Not Reported)

53089 ■ The Organic Way
HDRA
Garden Organic Ryton
Coventry CV8 3LG, United Kingdom
Ph: 44 247 6303517
Fax: 44 247 6639229
Publisher E-mail: enquiry@gardenorganic.org.uk
Members only journal covering organic farming, gardening, and food. **Freq:** Quarterly. **Print Method:** Web offset. **Trim Size:** 292 x 191 mm. **Key Personnel:** Bhupinder Ran, Advertising Sales, bhupinder@centuryonepublishing.ltd.uk. **Remarks:** Accepts advertising. **URL:** http://www.gardenorganic.org.uk/organic_way/index.php. **Formerly:** Growing Organically. **Ad Rates:** BW: 570, 4C: 825. **Circ:** 30,400

53090 ■ BBC Radio-FM - 94.8
Priory Pl.
Coventry CV1 5SQ, United Kingdom

Ph: 44 24 76551000
E-mail: coventry@bbc.co.uk
Format: Talk; Music of Your Life; Ethnic; Information. **Owner:** British Broadcasting Corp., Broadcasting House, Portland Pl., London W1A 1AA, United Kingdom. **Operating Hours:** Continuous. **URL:** http://www.bbc.co.uk/coventry/index.shtml.

53091 ■ BBC Radio-FM - 103.7
Priory Pl.
Coventry CV1 5SQ, United Kingdom
Ph: 44 24 76551000
E-mail: coventry@bbc.co.uk
Format: News; Ethnic; Information; Music of Your Life. **Owner:** British Broadcasting Corp., Broadcasting House, Portland Pl., London W1A 1AA, United Kingdom. **Operating Hours:** Continuous. **URL:** http://www.bbc.co.uk/coventry/local_radio/.

53092 ■ Mercia-FM - 97.0
Hertford Pl.
Coventry CV1 3TT, United Kingdom
Ph: 44 24 76868200
Format: Adult Contemporary; Contemporary Hit Radio (CHR). **Ad Rates:** Advertising accepted; rates available upon request. **URL:** http://www.mercia.co.uk/.

53093 ■ Mercia-FM - 102.9
Hertford Pl.
Coventry CV1 3TT, United Kingdom
Ph: 44 24 76868200
Format: Adult Contemporary; Contemporary Hit Radio (CHR). **Ad Rates:** Advertising accepted; rates available upon request. **URL:** http://www.mercia.co.uk/.

53094 ■ RaW-AM - 1251
Gibbet Hill Rd.
Coventry CV4 7AL, United Kingdom
Ph: 44 24 76573077
E-mail: studio@radio.warwick.ac.uk
Format: Full Service; Alternative/New Music/Progressive. **Owner:** University of Warwick, at above address. **Operating Hours:** Continuous. **Key Personnel:** Danny Fraser, Station Mgr., sm@radio.warwick.ac.uk; Jonathan Widdicombe, Chief Engineer, engineering@radio.warwick.ac.uk. **URL:** http://www.radio.warwick.ac.uk/.

Cowley

53095 ■ Heart-FM - 102.6
Radio House
Pony Rd.
Cowley OX4 2XR, United Kingdom
Ph: 44 1865 543315
Format: Adult Contemporary. **Owner:** Global Radio, 30 Leicester Sq., Pony Rd., London WC2 H7LA, United Kingdom. **Formerly:** Fox-FM. **Operating Hours:** Continuous. **URL:** http://www.heartoxfordshire.co.uk/.

Cranbrook

53096 ■ The New Writer
PO Box 60
Cranbrook TN17 2ZR, United Kingdom
Ph: 44 15 80212626
Fax: 44 15 80212041
Publisher E-mail: editor@thenewwriter.com
Consumer magazine covering literature, poetry and fiction. **Subtitle:** The Magazine You've Been Hoping To Find. **Founded:** 1996. **Freq:** 6/yr. **Cols./Page:** 3. **Key Personnel:** Merric Davidson, Publisher; Catherine Smith, Poetry Ed.; Suzanne Ruthven, Editor. **ISSN:** 1363-1667. **Subscription Rates:** 27 individuals; 33 individuals Europe, Ireland; 38 other countries airmail. **Remarks:** Accepts advertising. **URL:** http://www.thenewwriter.com; http://www.thenewwriter.com/subscribe.htm. **Circ:** (Not Reported)

Cranfield

53097 ■ Journal of Management Development
Emerald Group Publishing Ltd.
c/o Prof. Andrew K. Kakabadse, Ed.
International Management Development
Cranfield School of Management
Cranfield MK43 0AL, United Kingdom
Publisher E-mail: emerald@emeraldinsight.com
General business publication. **Freq:** 10/yr. **Print Method:** Double Bound issues. **Trim Size:** 2 x 5. **Key**

Personnel: Prof. Andrew K. Kakabadse, Editor; Prof. Nada K. Kakabadse, Editor, nada.kakabadse@ northampton.ac.uk; Nancy Rolph, Publisher, nrolph@ emeraldinsight.com; Rachel Gerlis, Asst. Publisher, rgerlis@emeraldinsight.com. **ISSN:** 0262-1711. **Remarks:** Advertising not accepted. **URL:** http://www. emeraldinsight.com/products/journals/journals.htm?id= jmd. **Circ:** (Not Reported)

Craven Arms

53098 ■ Commonwealth Forestry News
Commonwealth Forestry Association
Crib
Dinchope
Craven Arms SY7 9JJ, United Kingdom
Ph: 44 1588 672868
Fax: 44 870 0116645
Publisher E-mail: cfa@cfa-international.org
Forestry publication. **Freq:** Quarterly. **Key Personnel:** Philip Wardle, Editor, phone 44 1252 702204, philipwardle2@cs.com. **ISSN:** 1463-3868. **Subscription Rates:** Free hard copy to all members. **URL:** http://www. cfa-international.org/publications.html.

Crawley

53099 ■ British Baker
William Reed Publishing Ltd.
Broadfield Pk.
Crawley RH11 9RT, United Kingdom
Ph: 44 1293 613400
Magazine featuring British baking industry. **Founded:** 1885. **Freq:** Biweekly. **Key Personnel:** Sylvia Macdonald, Editor, phone 44 1293 846595, sylvia.macdonald@william-reed.co.uk; Helen Chater, Advertising Mgr., phone 44 1293 846571, helen.chater@william-reed.co.uk. **Subscription Rates:** 67 individuals; 120 two years. **Remarks:** Accepts advertising. **URL:** http:// bakeryinfo.co.uk/news/fullstory.php/aid/907. **Ad Rates:** 4C: 1,925. **Circ:** Combined ★6,074

53100 ■ Convenience Store
William Reed Publishing Ltd.
Broadfield Pk.
Crawley RH11 9RT, United Kingdom
Ph: 44 1293 613400
Trade magazine for independent, neighborhood and retail convenience stores. **Founded:** 1985. **Freq:** Semimonthly. **Print Method:** Sheetfed Litho test Web Offset. **Key Personnel:** David Rees, Editor, david.rees@william-reed.co.uk; Tony Hawkes, Commercial Dir., tony.hawkes@william-reed.co.uk; Toni Jenner, Internal Sales Mgr., toni.jenner@william-reed.co.uk. **ISSN:** 0267-9361. **Subscription Rates:** 65 individuals; 117 two years. **Remarks:** Accepts advertising. **URL:** http://www.william-reed.co.uk/default.aspx?page= products&ID=22. **Ad Rates:** BW: 2,210; 4C: 3,590. **Circ:** ★40,587

53101 ■ Crawley Observer
Johnston Press PLC
12 The Boulevard
Crawley RH10 1XY, United Kingdom
Ph: 44 1293 845076
Local community newspaper. **Freq:** Weekly (Wed.). **Key Personnel:** Richard Harmer, Contact, phone 44 1403 751263, fax 44 1403 751260, richard.harmer@ sussexnewspapers.co.uk; Kirk Ward, Ch. Reporter, phone 44 1293 845055, fax 44 1293 615589, kirk. ward@sussexnewspapers.co.uk. **Remarks:** Accepts advertising. **URL:** http://www.crawleyobserver.co.uk/. **Circ:** (Not Reported)

53102 ■ Drinks International
William Reed Publishing Ltd.
Broadfield Pk.
Crawley RH11 9RT, United Kingdom
Ph: 44 1293 613400
Magazine featuring wine and beer market. **Founded:** 1969. **Freq:** Monthly. **Trim Size:** 230 x 285 mm. **Key Personnel:** Christian Davis, Editor, phone 44 1293 590047, christian.davis@drinksint.com; Russell Dodd, Publisher, phone 44 1293 590052, russell.dodd@ drinksint.com; Justin Smith, Advertising Mgr., phone 44 1293 590041, justin.smith@drinksint.com. **Subscription Rates:** 105 individuals in UK; 151 individuals in Europe; 179 other countries. **Remarks:** Accepts advertising.

URL: http://www.drinksint.com. **Ad Rates:** 4C: 3,072. **Circ:** Controlled ★10,000

53103 ■ Food Manufacture
William Reed Publishing Ltd.
Broadfield Pk.
Crawley RH11 9RT, United Kingdom
Ph: 44 1293 613400
Trade magazine for managers of all levels in the food and beverage manufacturing industry. **Founded:** 1925. **Freq:** Monthly. **Print Method:** Web. **Key Personnel:** Rick Pendrous, Editor, rick.pendrous@william-reed.co. uk; Helen Darby, Advertising Mgr., helen.darby@william-reed.co.uk. **Subscription Rates:** 85 individuals; 153 two years. **Remarks:** Accepts advertising. **URL:** http:// www.william-reed.co.uk/default.aspx?page=products& ID=14. **Former name:** Inside Food and Drink. **Ad Rates:** BW: 2,168. **Circ:** Controlled 15,491

53104 ■ Forecourt Trader
William Reed Publishing Ltd.
Broadfield Pk.
Crawley RH11 9RT, United Kingdom
Ph: 44 1293 613400
Journal covering petrol retailing sector. **Founded:** 1987. **Freq:** Monthly. **Key Personnel:** Merril Boulton, Editor, phone 44 1293 610219, merril.boulton@william-reed.co. uk; James Bush, Advertising Mgr., phone 44 1293 610337, james.bush@william-reed.co.uk. **Subscription Rates:** 42 individuals in UK; 66 individuals in Europe; 108 individuals rest of the world. **Remarks:** Accepts advertising. **URL:** http://www.william-reed.co.uk/default. aspx?page=products&ID=25; http://www.forecourttrader. co.uk. **Ad Rates:** 4C: 2,650. **Circ:** ★10,922

53105 ■ Grocer
William Reed Publishing Ltd.
Broadfield Pk.
Crawley RH11 9RT, United Kingdom
Ph: 44 1293 613400
Business publication. **Founded:** 1862. **Freq:** Weekly. **Trim Size:** 297 mm x 210 mm. **Key Personnel:** Katherine Barrack, Editorial Admin Sec., phone 44 12 93610259, fax 44 12 93610340, katherine.barrack@ william-reed.co.uk; Jonathan Daniels, Commercial Dir., phone 44 12 93610216, fax 44 12 93610340, jonathan. daniels@william-reed.co.uk; Zoe Kray, Recruitment Advertising Mgr., zoe.cooper@william-reed.co.uk. **ISSN:** 0017-4351. **Subscription Rates:** 110 individuals. **Remarks:** Advertising accepted; rates available upon request. **URL:** http://www.william-reed.co.uk/default. aspx?page=products&ID=9; http://www.thegrocer.co. uk/?page=home&redir=true. **Circ:** (Not Reported)

53106 ■ H - The Hotel Magazine
William Reed Publishing Ltd.
Broadfield Pk.
Crawley RH11 9RT, United Kingdom
Ph: 44 1293 613400
Magazine featuring news and business analysis of the hotels in UK. **Freq:** Monthly. **Key Personnel:** Tim Brooke-Webb, Publisher, phone 44 1293 610236, fax 44 1293 610317, tim.brooke-webb@william-reed.co.uk; Lia Boccia, Advertising Mgr., phone 44 1293 610465, fax 44 1293 610317, lia.boccia@william-reed.co.uk. **Subscription Rates:** 50 individuals in UK; 60 individuals in Europe; 85 individuals rest of the world. **Remarks:** Accepts advertising. **URL:** http://www.william-reed.co.uk/ view_product.aspx?productid=243. **Circ:** ★8,602

53107 ■ Journal
Orchid Society of Great Britain
103 North Rd.
Three Bridges
Crawley RH10 1SQ, United Kingdom
Ph: 44 1293 528615
Publisher E-mail: val@micklewright.com
Journal covering gardening. **Freq:** Quarterly. **Key Personnel:** Dr. Eileen Watson, Editor, eileenrobin.watson@ virgin.net. **ISSN:** 0306-2996. **Remarks:** Advertising accepted; rates available upon request. **URL:** http://www. orchid-society-gb.org.uk/journal.html. **Circ:** (Not Reported)

53108 ■ Meat Trades Journal
William Reed Publishing Ltd.
Broadfield Pk.
Crawley RH11 9RT, United Kingdom
Ph: 44 1293 613400
Journal covering meat industry information, news and

views. **Founded:** 1888. **Freq:** Biweekly. **Key Personnel:** Ed Bedington, Editor, phone 44 1293 846567, ed. bedington@william-reed.co.uk; Martin Goult, Sales Mgr., phone 44 1293 846572, martin.goult@william-reed.co. uk. **Subscription Rates:** 70 individuals in UK; 82 individuals in Europe; 104 individuals rest of the world. **Remarks:** Accepts advertising. **URL:** http://www.william-reed.co.uk/default.aspx?page=products&ID=44; http:// www.meatinfo.co.uk. **Circ:** ★5,574

53109 ■ Morning Advertiser
William Reed Publishing Ltd.
Broadfield Pk.
Crawley RH11 9RT, United Kingdom
Ph: 44 1293 613400
Newspaper featuring on-trade industry in England and Wales. **Freq:** Weekly. **Key Personnel:** Paul Charity, Editor, phone 44 1293 610410, paul.charity@william-reed.co.uk; Tim Brooke-Webb, Publisher, phone 44 1293 610236, tim.brooke-webb@william-reed.co.uk. **Subscription Rates:** 78 individuals; 130 individuals in Europe; 200 other countries. **Remarks:** Accepts advertising. **URL:** http://www.morningadvertiser.co.uk. **Circ:** ★31,288

53110 ■ Off Licence News
William Reed Publishing Ltd.
Broadfield Pk.
Crawley RH11 9RT, United Kingdom
Ph: 44 1293 613400
Magazine featuring off-trade industry. **Subtitle:** The Voice of Drinks Retailing. **Freq:** Biweekly. **Key Personnel:** Rosie Davenport, Editor, phone 44 1293 610478, rosie.davenport@william-reed.co.uk; Lee Sharkey, Publisher, phone 44 1293 846511, lee.sharkey@william-reed.co.uk; Samantha Briney, Advertising Mgr., phone 44 1293 610494, samantha.briney@william-reed.co.uk. **Subscription Rates:** 65 individuals; 117 two years. **Remarks:** Accepts advertising. **URL:** http://www. offlicencenews.co.uk. **Circ:** ★18,440

53111 ■ PubChef
William Reed Publishing Ltd.
Broadfield Pk.
Crawley RH11 9RT, United Kingdom
Ph: 44 1293 613400
Magazine featuring pub food. **Freq:** Monthly. **Key Personnel:** Jo Bruce, Editor, phone 44 1293 610487, jo. bruce@william-reed.co.uk. **Remarks:** Accepts advertising. **URL:** http://www.william-reed.co.uk/. **Circ:** (Not Reported)

53112 ■ Restaurant Equipment
William Reed Publishing Ltd.
Broadfield Pk.
Crawley RH11 9RT, United Kingdom
Ph: 44 1293 613400
Magazine featuring kitchen equipment. **Founded:** 2002. **Freq:** Semiannual. **Key Personnel:** Stuart Ferguson, Editor, phone 44 8707 506107, stuart.ferguson@ restaurantmagazine.co.uk. **Remarks:** Accepts advertising. **URL:** http://www.william-reed.co.uk/view_ product.aspx?productid=178. **Circ:** 15,776

53113 ■ Shopping Centre
William Reed Publishing Ltd.
Broadfield Pk.
Crawley RH11 9RT, United Kingdom
Ph: 44 1293 613400
Magazine covering the shopping center industry. **Freq:** Monthly. **Key Personnel:** Graham Parker, Editor, graham.parker@jldmedia.com; Graham Harvey, Gp. Advertising Mgr., graham.harvey@jldmedia.com. **Subscription Rates:** 72 individuals; 120 other countries. **Remarks:** Accepts advertising. **URL:** http://www. shopping-centre.co.uk. **Circ:** Paid ★12,241

53114 ■ Shopping Centre Ireland
William Reed Publishing Ltd.
Broadfield Pk.
Crawley RH11 9RT, United Kingdom
Ph: 44 1293 613400
Magazine covering shopping center industry in Ireland. **Founded:** Nov. 2005. **Freq:** Quarterly. **Key Personnel:** Graham Harvey, Gp. Advertising Mgr., phone 44 2074 192755, graham.harvey@jldmedia.com; Graham Parker, Editor, phone 44 2074 192751, graham.parker@ jldmedia.com. **Subscription Rates:** 72 individuals; 120 other countries. **Remarks:** Accepts advertising. **URL:** http://www.shopping-centre.co.uk/. **Ad Rates:** BW:

Circulation: ★ = ABC; △ = BPA; ◆ = CAC; • = CCAB; ❑ = VAC; ⊕ = PO Statement; ‡ = Publisher's Report; Boldface figures = sworn; Light figures = estimated.

Gale Directory of Publications & Broadcast Media/147th Ed.

5629

1,500, 4C: 2,000. **Circ:** ★12,789

53115 ■ Wine & Spirit
William Reed Publishing Ltd.
Broadfield Pk.
Crawley RH11 9RT, United Kingdom
Ph: 44 1293 613400
Magazine covering wine, spirits, beers and cocktails.
Freq: Monthly. **Key Personnel:** Richard Siddle, Editor,
richard.siddle@william-reed.co.uk; Kathrin Leaver,
Advertising Mgr., phone 44 1293 846523, kathrin.
leaver@william-reed.co.uk. **Subscription Rates:** 161.20
individuals; 246.02 individuals; 260.96 other countries.
Remarks: Accepts advertising. **URL:** http://www.wine-
spirit.com. **Circ:** ★11,044

53116 ■ Mercury-FM - 102.7
Stanley Ctr.
Kelvin Way
Crawley RH10 9SE, United Kingdom
Ph: 44 1293 636000
Format: Adult Contemporary. **URL:** http://www.
mercuryfm.co.uk/.

Crediton

53117 ■ Crediton Country Courier
102 High St.
Crediton EX17 3LF, United Kingdom
Ph: 44 13 63774263
Fax: 44 13 63773545
Publisher E-mail: editor@creditoncouriernewspaper.
co.uk
Community newspaper. **Founded:** 1974. **Freq:**
Semimonthly. **Print Method:** Web Offset. **Trim Size:**
260 x 360 mm. **Cols./Page:** 7. **Col. Width:** 35
millimeters. **Col. Depth:** 360 millimeters. **Key Personnel:** Alan Quick, Editorial Mgr.; Kim Woods, Sales Exec.
Subscription Rates: 20 individuals. **Remarks:** Accepts
advertising. **URL:** http://www.creditoncouriernewspaper.
co.uk. **Ad Rates:** GLR: 1.40, BW: 353. **Circ:** Paid
10,000

Cromer

53118 ■ North Norfolk News
Archant Regional Ltd.
31 Church St.
Cromer NR27 9ES, United Kingdom
Ph: 44 1263 513232
Fax: 44 1263 515560
Publisher E-mail: sandra.roantree@archant.co.uk
Local community newspaper. **Key Personnel:** Terry
Redhead, Editor, phone 44 1603 772402, terry.
redhead@archant.co.uk; Steve Philp, Advertising Team
Leader, phone 44 1493 335007, steve.philp@archant.
co.uk; Tim Warner, Assoc. Ed., phone 44 1603 772409,
tim.warner@archant.co.uk. **Subscription Rates:** 14.95
individuals 13 weeks; 29.90 individuals 26 weeks. **Remarks:** Accepts advertising. **URL:** http://www.
northnorfolknews.co.uk/home. **Circ:** ★8,797

Cromhall

53119 ■ the HR Director
Brook Farm
Heathened
Cromhall GL12 8AT, United Kingdom
Ph: 44 1454 292060
Publication E-mail: editor@thehrdirector.com
Publisher E-mail: danielle@thehrdirector.com
Magazine focusing on human resource management
issues. **Freq:** Monthly. **Key Personnel:** Jason Spiller,
Editor, editor@hrdirector.com. **Subscription Rates:** 175
individuals platinum subscription; 200 individuals silver
subcription. **Remarks:** Accepts advertising. **URL:** http://
www.thehrdirector.com/. **Circ:** Controlled ★10,000

Crowborough

53120 ■ Dispensing Optics
Association of British Dispensing Opticians
PO Box 233
Crowborough TN6 9BD, United Kingdom
Ph: 44 18 92667626
Publisher E-mail: general@abdolondon.org.uk
Publication covering optics. **Founded:** 1985. **Freq:** 9/yr.
Key Personnel: Kevin Milsom, Pres.; Sheila Hope,
Production Ed., shope@abdo.uk.com; Sir Anthony Gar-
rett, Gen. Sec. **ISSN:** 0954-3201. **Remarks:** Accepts

advertising. **URL:** http://www.abdo.org.uk. **Ad Rates:**
BW: 840, 4C: 1,050. **Circ:** 7,502

Crowthorne

53121 ■ Communicator
The Institute of Scientific and Technical Communicators
c/o Felicity Davie
Tou-can Marketing, The Holy
42 Heath Hill Rd. S
Crowthorne RG45 7BW, United Kingdom
Publication E-mail: advertising@istc.org.uk
Publisher E-mail: istc@istc.org.uk
Publication for professional communicators. **Founded:**
1965. **Freq:** Quarterly. **Key Personnel:** Felicity Davie,
Contact, phone 44 1344 466600, fax 44 1344 466601.
ISSN: 0308-6925. **Subscription Rates:** 37 nonmembers
U.K.; 42 nonmembers Europe; 45 nonmembers rest of
the world; Free to members. **URL:** http://www.istc.org.
uk/Publications_&_Downloads/communicator.html. **Ad
Rates:** 4C: 400. **Circ:** 2,000

Croydon

53122 ■ Building Products
Quantum Business Media Ltd.
Quantum House
19 Scarbrook Rd.
Croydon CR9 1LX, United Kingdom
Ph: 44 20 85654200
Fax: 44 20 85654202
Trade magazine covering products for the building
industry. **Founded:** 1978. **Freq:** Monthly. **Trim Size:** A4.
Key Personnel: James Parker, Editor. **Remarks:** Ac-
cepts advertising. **URL:** http://www.buildingproducts.co.
uk/. **Circ:** Controlled 23,000

53123 ■ Caravan
Time Inc.
Leon House
233 High St.
Croydon CR9 1HZ, United Kingdom
Ph: 44 20 87268000
Publication E-mail: caravan@ipcmedia.com
Publisher E-mail: information@timeinc.com
British magazine devoted solely to the needs of touring
caravanners. **Freq:** Monthly. **Key Personnel:** Victoria
Health, Editor; Amy Hodge, Asst.Ed. **Remarks:** Accepts
advertising. **URL:** http://www.caravanmagazine.co.uk/.
Circ: (Not Reported)

53124 ■ Cycling Weekly
Time Inc.
IPC Focus Network
Leon House
233 High St.
Croydon CR9 1HZ, United Kingdom
Publisher E-mail: information@timeinc.com
British magazine focusing on bicycling. **Founded:** Jan.
1891. **Freq:** Weekly. **Key Personnel:** Kevin Attridge,
Group Ad Mgr., phone 44 20 87268409, kevin_attridge@
ipcmedia.com. **Subscription Rates:** 48.23 individuals 6
months; 96.46 individuals. **Remarks:** Accepts
advertising. **URL:** http://www.cyclingweekly.co.uk/. **Circ:**
(Not Reported)

53125 ■ Driving Instructor
Driving Instructors Association
Safety House
Beddington Farm Rd.
Croydon CR0 4XZ, United Kingdom
Ph: 44 20 86655151
Fax: 44 20 86655565
Publisher E-mail: dia@driving.org
Newspaper covering driver education. **Founded:** 1978.
Freq: Bimonthly. **Subscription Rates:** Free to
members. **Remarks:** Advertising accepted; rates avail-
able upon request. **URL:** http://www.driving.org/about.
html. **Circ:** 18,000

53126 ■ International Boat Industry
Time Inc.
IPC Country & Leisure Media Ltd.
Leon House, 233 High St.
Croydon CR9 1HZ, United Kingdom
Publisher E-mail: information@timeinc.com
British business magazine examining the international
boating market on a country-by-country basis. Investi-
gates, analyzes, and summarizes commercial develop-
ments in the key strategic markets such as the USA and

the major European markets in a program of detailed
business reports. Details opportunities in prospective
markets as they hove into view outside the mainstream
European and North American markets. Examine technical developments and market trends in specific product
sectors, be they mainstream areas such as marine
electronics, inboard and outboard engines or developing
ones such as onboard electrical power management or
environmental control. Reports on changes at the
distribution, retail, environmental, legislative and service
provision levelsof the market. **Freq:** 8/yr. **Key Personnel:** Belinda Snell, Journalist, phone 44 20 87268133,
fax 44 20 87268196, belinda_snell@ipcmedia.com; Ed
Slack, Editor, phone 44 20 87268134, fax 44 20
87268196, ed_slack@ipcmedia.com; Nick Hopkinson,
Publisher, phone 44 20 87268119, fax 44 20 87268196,
nick_hopkinson@ipcmedia.com. **Subscription Rates:**
Free to qualified subscribers. **URL:** http://www.ibinews.
com/ibinews/index.html.

53127 ■ IRS Employment Review
LexisNexis UK
2 Addiscombe Rd.
Croydon CR9 5AF, United Kingdom
Publisher E-mail: customer.services@lexisnexis.co.uk
Publication covering human resources and labor
relations. **Founded:** 1971. **Freq:** Semimonthly. **Key Personnel:** Mark Crail, Managing Editor, phone 44 20
86522247, mark.crail@rbi.co.uk. **ISSN:** 1358-2216. **Subscription Rates:** 767 individuals; 784 other countries.
Remarks: Advertising not accepted. **URL:** http://www.
xperthr.co.uk/. **Circ:** (Not Reported)

53128 ■ Laboratory News
The Metropolis Group
Davis House, 6th Fl.
2 Robert St.
Croydon CR0 1QQ, United Kingdom
Ph: 44 208 2538378
Fax: 44 208 2534609
Publisher E-mail: metropolis@metropolis.co.uk
Magazine providing the latest news and information for
the United Kingdom's laboratory sector. **Founded:** 1971.
Freq: Monthly. **Key Personnel:** Phil Prime, Editor,
phone 44 208 2534611, phil.prime@laboratorynews.co.
uk; Mark Wass, Advertising Mgr., phone 44 208
2534614, mark.wass@laboratorynews.co.uk; Kevin
Crook, Mng. Dir., phone 44 208 2534600, kevin.crook@
metropolis.co.uk. **Remarks:** Accepts advertising. **URL:**
http://www.labnews.co.uk/; http://www.metropolis.co.uk/
laboratory.html. **Circ:** Controlled ★11,095

53129 ■ MBR - Mountain Bike Rider
Time Inc.
IPC Media
Leon House, 233 High St.
Croydon CR9 1HZ, United Kingdom
Ph: 44 20 87268000
Publication E-mail: mbr@ipcmedia.com
Publisher E-mail: information@timeinc.com
British magazine focusing on mountain biking for begin-
ners and experts. Includes bike tests, bike and product
testing, workshop guides, route guides, product reviews,
and features. **Key Personnel:** Tom Hutton, Routes;
Danny Milner, Acting Ed.; Andy Waterman, Senior Staff
Writer; Alan Muldoon, Bike Test Ed.; Paul Burwell, Tech.
Ed.; Dan Thomas, Production Ch. **Subscription Rates:**
US$159.42 two years; US$90.83 individuals. **Remarks:**
Accepts advertising. **URL:** http://www.mbr.co.uk/. **Circ:**
(Not Reported)

53130 ■ Media Week
Quantum Business Media
Quantum House
19 Scarbrook Rd.
Croydon CR9 1LX, United Kingdom
Publisher E-mail: enquiries@quantumbusinessmedia.
com
Magazine for advertising agencies, media owners and
marketing personnel, a focal point for communication,
comment and social events across the industry. **Freq:**
Weekly. **Subscription Rates:** US$249 individuals;
US$299 Canada; US$419 other countries. **URL:** http://
www.mediaweek.co.uk/news/512373/.

53131 ■ Prediction
Time Inc.
IPC Focus Network
Leon House, 233 High St.
Croydon CR9 1HZ, United Kingdom

Publisher E-mail: information@timeinc.com

United Kingdom magazine focusing on mind, body, and spirit. Covers astrology, tarot, dreams, divination, psychic phenomena, holistic health, and all manner of mind, body, spirit topics. **Freq:** Monthly. **Key Personnel:** Marion Williamson, Editor; Clive Birch, Publisher; Joanne O'Brien, Advertising Mgr., phone 44 20 87268231; Jemma South, Asst. Ed. **Subscription Rates:** 29.99 individuals; 54.99 two years. **Remarks:** Accepts advertising. **URL:** http://www.predictionmagazine.com/; http://www.ipcmedia.com/brands/brands.php. **Circ:** (Not Reported)

53132 ∎ Selling Long Haul
BMI Publications Ltd.
Suffolk House
George St.
Croydon CR9 1SR, United Kingdom
Ph: 44 20 86497233
Fax: 44 20 86497234
Publisher E-mail: editorial@bmipublications.com
Trade magazine covering long-haul travel for travel agencies in the U.K. and Ireland. **Founded:** 1990. **Freq:** Monthly 11/yr. **Key Personnel:** Sally Parker, Contact, sally.parker@bmipublications.com; Steven Thompson, Contact, steven.thompson@bmipublications.com; Steve Hartridge, Editor, steve.hartridge@bmipublications.com. **Remarks:** Accepts advertising. **URL:** http://www.sellinglonghaul.com/. **Ad Rates:** BW: 5,895, 4C: 6,895. **Circ:** Non-paid 16,500

53133 ∎ Selling Short Breaks
BMI Publications Ltd.
Suffolk House
George St.
Croydon CR9 1SR, United Kingdom
Ph: 44 20 86497233
Fax: 44 20 86497234
Publisher E-mail: editorial@bmipublications.com
Trade magazine covering short break holidays for travel agencies in the U.K. and Ireland. **Founded:** 1993. **Freq:** 4/yr. **Key Personnel:** Steve Thompson, Sen. Advertisement. Mgr.; Steve Hartridge, Editor. **Remarks:** Accepts advertising. **URL:** http://www.bmipublications.com. **Ad Rates:** BW: 5,895, 4C: 6,895. **Circ:** Non-paid 16,500

53134 ∎ Stamp Magazine
Time Inc.
IPC Focus Network
Leon House, 233 High St.
Croydon CR9 1HZ, United Kingdom
Publisher E-mail: information@timeinc.com
Magazine focusing on stamps, postmarks, philatelic history, and collecting. **Freq:** Monthly. **Key Personnel:** Julia Lee, Asst. Ed., phone 44 20 87268242, julia_lee@ipcmedia.com; Guy Thomas, Editor, phone 44 20 87268243, guy_thomas@ipcmedia.com; Jay Jones, Gp. Advisory Mgr., jay.jones@myhobbystore.com. **Subscription Rates:** 28.08 individuals; 54.60 two years. **Remarks:** Accepts advertising. **URL:** http://www.stampmagazine.co.uk/. **Circ:** (Not Reported)

53135 ∎ Superbike
Time Inc.
Leon House
233 High St.
Croydon CR9 1HZ, United Kingdom
Ph: 44 20 87268000
Publication E-mail: superbike@ipcmedia.com
Publisher E-mail: information@timeinc.com
Magazine focusing on sportbike care and racing. **Freq:** Monthly. **Key Personnel:** Kenny Pryde, Editor, phone 44 20 87268445, kenny_pryde@ipcmedia.com; Huw Williams, Art Ed., huw_williams@ipcmedia.com; Jon Pearson, Real World Ed., phone 44 20 87268443, jon_pearson@ipcmedia.com; Neil Handley, Dep. Ad Mgr., neil_handley@ipcmedia.com; Alan Dowds, Dep. Ed., phone 44 20 87268444, alan_dowds@ipcmedia.com. **Subscription Rates:** 18.99 individuals direct debit; 39.99 individuals. **URL:** http://www.superbike.co.uk/.

53136 ∎ Taxation
LexisNexis UK
Tolley House
2 Addiscombe Rd.
Croydon CR9 5AF, United Kingdom
Publisher E-mail: customer.services@lexisnexis.co.uk
Business publication. **Founded:** 1927. **Freq:** Weekly.

Key Personnel: Mike Truman, Editor. **ISSN:** 0040-0149. **Subscription Rates:** 319 individuals. **Remarks:** Advertising accepted; rates available upon request. **URL:** http://www.taxation.co.uk/Home/Default.aspx. **Circ:** Paid ★7,464

53137 ∎ VolksWorld
Time Inc.
IPC Focus Network
Leon House, 233 High St.
Croydon CR9 1HZ, United Kingdom
Ph: 44 20 87268000
Fax: 44 20 87268296
Publication E-mail: volksworld@ipcmedia.com
Publisher E-mail: information@timeinc.com
European magazine featuring air-cooled Volkswagens. **Freq:** 13/yr. **Key Personnel:** Ivan McCutcheon, Editor, phone 44 20 87268347; Jon Gilbert, Web Ed.; Stephen Gosling, Art Ed.; Ian James, Gp. Ad Mgr., phone 44 20 87268333; Matt Keene, Tech. Ed.; Kara Goodwin, Dep. Ad Mgr., phone 44 20 87268334. **Subscription Rates:** 36.25 individuals; 70.50 two years. **Remarks:** Accepts advertising. **URL:** http://www.volksworld.co.uk/; http://www.ipcmedia.com/brands/brands.php. **Circ:** (Not Reported)

Cudham

53138 ∎ Classic Military Vehicle
Kelsey Publishing Ltd.
Cudham Tithe Barn
Berry's Hill
Cudham TN16 3AG, United Kingdom
Ph: 44 1959 541444
Fax: 44 1959 541400
Publication E-mail: cmv.info@kelsey.co.uk
Publisher E-mail: info@kelsey.co.uk
Magazine featuring modern and historic military vehicles. **Freq:** Monthly. **Key Personnel:** Matt Carson, Advertising Mgr., phone 44 1733 353362. **Subscription Rates:** 43.92 individuals; 49.44 individuals in Europe; 54.96 other countries. **Remarks:** Accepts display and classified advertising. **URL:** http://www.cmvmag.co.uk/. **Circ:** (Not Reported)

53139 ∎ Classic Plant & Machinery
Kelsey Publishing Ltd.
Cudham Tithe Barn
Berry's Hill
Cudham TN16 3AG, United Kingdom
Ph: 44 1959 541444
Fax: 44 1959 541400
Publication E-mail: cpm.info@kelsey.co.uk
Publisher E-mail: info@kelsey.co.uk
Magazine featuring vintage construction and mining plant as well as ancillary equipment. **Founded:** Sept. 2002. **Freq:** Monthly. **Key Personnel:** George Bowstead, Editor; Phil Weeden, Editorial Dir. **Subscription Rates:** 39.60 individuals; 45 individuals in Europe; 50.52 other countries. **Remarks:** Accepts advertising. **URL:** http://www.cpmmag.co.uk/. **Circ:** (Not Reported)

53140 ∎ Classic Van and Pick-up
Kelsey Publishing Ltd.
Cudham Tithe Barn
Berry's Hill
Cudham TN16 3AG, United Kingdom
Ph: 44 1959 541444
Fax: 44 1959 541400
Publisher E-mail: info@kelsey.co.uk
Magazine for vans, pick-ups and campers enthusiasts. **Subtitle:** For enthusiasts of vans, pick-ups and campers. **Founded:** Nov. 2000. **Freq:** Monthly. **Key Personnel:** Ted Connolly, Editor, van.ed@kelsey.co.uk; Adam Fergar, Advertising Mgr., adam.fergar@kelsey.co.uk. **Subscription Rates:** 36 individuals; 41.40 individuals in Europe; 47.28 other countries. **Remarks:** Accepts advertising. **URL:** http://www.classicvan.co.uk/. **Circ:** (Not Reported)

53141 ∎ Classic and Vintage Commercials
Kelsey Publishing Ltd.
Cudham Tithe Barn
Berry's Hill
Cudham TN16 3AG, United Kingdom
Ph: 44 1959 541444
Fax: 44 1959 541400
Publication E-mail: cvc.info@kelsey.co.uk

Publisher E-mail: info@kelsey.co.uk

Magazine featuring stories, news and views, along with tales of older lorries still running and a big dollop of nostalgia. **Subtitle:** Britain's Best Selling Classic Commercial Magazine. **Founded:** 1996. **Freq:** Monthly. **Key Personnel:** Ted Connolly, Editor; Matt Carson, Contact; Julia Johnston, Advertising Mgr. **Subscription Rates:** 43.92 individuals; 49.44 individuals to Europe; 54.96 other countries. **Remarks:** Accepts advertising. **URL:** http://www.cvcmag.co.uk/. **Circ:** (Not Reported)

53142 ∎ Farm and Horticultural Equipment
Kelsey Publishing Ltd.
Cudham Tithe Barn
Berry's Hill
Cudham TN16 3AG, United Kingdom
Ph: 44 1959 541444
Fax: 44 1959 541400
Publication E-mail: fhec.info@kelsey.co.uk
Publisher E-mail: info@kelsey.co.uk
Magazine featuring farm and horticultural equipment, including tractors, and lawn mowers. **Founded:** 1991. **Freq:** 6/yr. **Key Personnel:** Patrick Knight, Editor, fhec.ed@kelsey.co.uk. **Subscription Rates:** 18 individuals; 21 individuals to Europe and Ireland; 24 other countries. **Remarks:** Accepts advertising. **URL:** http://www.fhec.co.uk/. **Circ:** (Not Reported)

53143 ∎ Jaguar World Monthly
Kelsey Publishing Ltd.
Cudham Tithe Barn
Berry's Hill
Cudham TN16 3AG, United Kingdom
Ph: 44 1959 541444
Fax: 44 1959 541400
Publication E-mail: jwm.ed@kelsey.co.uk
Publisher E-mail: info@kelsey.co.uk
Magazine featuring Jaguar cars. **Subtitle:** The World's Best-Selling Independent Jaguar Magazine. **Freq:** Monthly. **Subscription Rates:** 49.20 individuals; 54.60 individuals Europe and Ireland; 60 other countries. **Remarks:** Accepts advertising. **URL:** http://www.jaguarworld.com/. **Circ:** (Not Reported)

53144 ∎ Modern MINI
Kelsey Publishing Ltd.
Cudham Tithe Barn
Berry's Hill
Cudham TN16 3AG, United Kingdom
Ph: 44 1959 541444
Fax: 44 1959 541400
Publisher E-mail: info@kelsey.co.uk
Magazine for Mini owners, featuring information about the car. **Freq:** Bimonthly. **Key Personnel:** Phil Weeden, Contact, phil.weeden@kelseypb.co.uk; Paul Wager, Editor, mm.ed@kelseypb.co.uk. **Subscription Rates:** 26.64 individuals; 28.80 individuals in Europe; 31.80 other countries. **Remarks:** Accepts advertising. **URL:** http://www.modernmini.co.uk/index.php. **Circ:** (Not Reported)

53145 ∎ Old Tractor
Kelsey Publishing Ltd.
Cudham Tithe Barn
Berry's Hill
Cudham TN16 3AG, United Kingdom
Ph. 44 1959 541444
Fax: 44 1959 541400
Publication E-mail: ot.mag@kelsey.co.uk
Publisher E-mail: info@kelsey.co.uk
Magazine featuring historical aspect of tractor development. **Subtitle:** The Number One Magazine for Historic Tractors. **Freq:** Monthly. **Key Personnel:** Scott Lambert, Editor. **Subscription Rates:** 39.60 individuals; 45 individuals in Europe; 40.52 other countries. **Remarks:** Accepts advertising. **URL:** http://www.oldtractor.co.uk/. **Circ:** (Not Reported)

53146 ∎ Practical Poultry
Kelsey Publishing Ltd.
Cudham Tithe Barn
Berry's Hill
Cudham TN16 3AG, United Kingdom
Ph: 44 1959 541444
Fax: 44 1959 541400
Publication E-mail: pp.ed@kelsey.co.uk
Publisher E-mail: info@kelsey.co.uk
Magazine for poultry enthusiasts. **Subtitle:** A magazine dedicated to keepers of chicken, waterfowl and exotic poultry. **Founded:** Mar. 2004. **Freq:** Monthly. **Key Per-**

sonnel: Andy Marshall, Editorial Team; Chris Graham, Editor; Stephen Curtis, Publisher. **Subscription Rates:** 37.92 individuals; 43.44 individuals in Europe and Eire; 48.96 other countries. **Remarks:** Accepts advertising. **URL:** http://www.practicalpoultry.co.uk/. **Circ:** (Not Reported)

53147 ■ Stationary Engine
Kelsey Publishing Ltd.
Cudham Tithe Barn
Berry's Hill
Cudham TN16 3AG, United Kingdom
Ph: 44 1959 541444
Fax: 44 1959 541400
Publication E-mail: se.info@kelsey.co.uk
Publisher E-mail: info@kelsey.co.uk
Magazine for stationary engine enthusiasts. **Freq:** Monthly. **Key Personnel:** Gordon Wright, Editor, phone 44 1959 541444, gordon.wright@kelsey.co.uk. **Subscription Rates:** 34.08 individuals; 38.40 individuals in Europe and Ireland; 45 other countries. **Remarks:** Accepts advertising. **URL:** http://www.stationary-engine-magazine.co.uk. **Circ:** (Not Reported)

53148 ■ Tractor & Machinery
Kelsey Publishing Ltd.
Cudham Tithe Barn
Berry's Hill
Cudham TN16 3AG, United Kingdom
Ph: 44 1959 541444
Fax: 44 1959 541400
Publication E-mail: tm.info@kelsey.co.uk
Publisher E-mail: info@kelsey.co.uk
Magazine featuring veteran, vintage, post vintage, classic and modern tractors. **Subtitle:** The World's Best Selling Tractor Magazine. **Founded:** Nov. 1994. **Freq:** Monthly. **Key Personnel:** Martin Oldaker, Editor. **Subscription Rates:** 42.84 individuals; 48.36 individuals in Europe; 53.88 other countries. **Remarks:** Accepts advertising. **URL:** http://www.tractor-and-machinery.com/. **Circ:** (Not Reported)

Cumbernauld

53149 ■ Cumbernauld News
Johnston Press PLC
Town Ctr.
10-12 Tay Walk
Cumbernauld G67 1BU, United Kingdom
Ph: 44 1236 725578
Fax: 44 1236 729931
Publication E-mail: editorial.cumbernauldnews@jnscotland.co.uk
Local community newspaper. **Remarks:** Accepts advertising. **URL:** http://www.cumbernauld-news.co.uk/. **Circ:** (Not Reported)

53150 ■ Kilsyth Chronicle
Johnston Press PLC
Town Ctr.
10-12 Tay Walk
Cumbernauld G67 1BU, United Kingdom
Ph: 44 1236 822116
Local community newspaper. **Remarks:** Accepts advertising. **URL:** http://www.kilsythchronicle.co.uk/. **Circ:** (Not Reported)

53151 ■ Revival-FM - 100.8
PO Box 106
Cumbernauld G67 1JX, United Kingdom
Ph: 44 12 36721110
Fax: 44 87 04868701
E-mail: admin@revival.fm
Format: Religious; Contemporary Christian. **Owner:** Revival Radio Ltd., at above address. **Operating Hours:** Continuous. **URL:** http://revival.fm.

Dalkeith

53152 ■ East Lothian News
Johnston Press PLC
12 High St.
Dalkeith EH22 1HR, United Kingdom
Ph: 44 131 5616617
Local community newspaper. **Key Personnel:** Jo Robinson, Editor. **Remarks:** Accepts advertising. **URL:** http://www.eastlothiannews.co.uk/. **Circ:** (Not Reported)

53153 ■ Midlothian Advertiser
Johnston Press PLC
12 High St.

Dalkeith EH22 1HR, United Kingdom
Ph: 44 131 5616617
Local community newspaper. **Key Personnel:** Jo Robinson, Editor; Edith Scott, Gp. Advertising Mgr. **Remarks:** Accepts advertising. **URL:** http://www.midlothianadvertiser.co.uk/. **Circ:** (Not Reported)

Darlington

53154 ■ Darlington & Stockton Times
Newsquest Media Group Ltd.
PO Box 25
Darlington DL1 1NF, United Kingdom
Ph: 44 1325 381313
Newspaper providing local news and events. **Freq:** Weekly. **Remarks:** Accepts advertising. **URL:** http://www.darlingtonandstocktontimes.co.uk/. **Circ:** (Not Reported)

53155 ■ Master Photographers
Master Photographers Association
Jubilee House
1 Chancery Ln.
Darlington DL1 5QP, United Kingdom
Ph: 44 13 25356555
Fax: 44 13 25357813
Publisher E-mail: general@mpauk.com
Publication covering photography. **Freq:** Monthly. **Key Personnel:** Colin Buck, Ch. Executive, colin@mpauk.com. **Remarks:** Advertising accepted; rates available upon request. **URL:** http://www.thempa.com/. **Circ:** (Not Reported)

53156 ■ Alpha-FM - 103.2
11 Woodland Rd.
Darlington DL3 7BJ, United Kingdom
Ph: 44 1325 255552
Format: Contemporary Hit Radio (CHR); Sports; Top 40; Information. **Owner:** The Local Radio Co. PLC, 11 Duke St., High Wycombe HP13 6EE, United Kingdom, 44 1494 688200, Fax: 44 1494 688201. **Operating Hours:** Continuous. **Ad Rates:** Advertising accepted; rates available upon request. **URL:** http://www.alpharadio.co.uk/.

Darwen

53157 ■ The Bee-FM - 107
8 Dalton Ct.
Darwen BB3 0DG, United Kingdom
Ph: 44 12 54778000
Fax: 44 12 54778001
Format: News; Sports; Contemporary Hit Radio (CHR); Classic Rock. **Operating Hours:** Continuous. **Key Personnel:** Simon Brierley, Station Mgr., simon.brierley@thebee.co.uk; Gina Millson, News Ed., gina.millson@thebee.co.uk. **Ad Rates:** Advertising accepted; rates available upon request. **URL:** http://thebee.co.uk/news.php.

Daventry

53158 ■ Advanced Carp Fishing
David Hall Publishing
2 Stephenson Close
Drayton Fields
Northamptonshire
Daventry NN11 8RF, United Kingdom
Ph: 44 1327 311999
Fax: 44 1327 311190
Publisher E-mail: info@dhpub.co.uk
Magazine featuring tips and instructional articles to the beginner and intermediate carp angler. **Freq:** Monthly. **Key Personnel:** Richard Stewart, Editor, richardstewart@dhpub.co.uk. **Subscription Rates:** 49.30 individuals. **URL:** http://www.advancedcarpfishing.com/About-Us/. **Circ:** 16,000

53159 ■ Daventry Express
Johnston Press PLC
63 High St.
Daventry NN11 4BQ, United Kingdom
Ph: 44 1327 703383
Local community newspaper. **Freq:** Weekly (Thurs.). **Key Personnel:** Chris Lillington, Editor; Melissa Lynch, Advertising Mgr., melissa.lynch@jpress.co.uk. **Remarks:** Accepts advertising. **URL:** http://www.daventrytoday.co.uk/. **Circ:** (Not Reported)

53160 ■ Match Fishing Magazine
David Hall Publishing
2 Stephenson Close
Drayton Fields
Northamptonshire
Daventry NN11 8RF, United Kingdom
Ph: 44 1327 311999
Fax: 44 1327 311190
Publisher E-mail: info@dhpub.co.uk
Consumer magazine covering competitive anglers in Europe. **Founded:** 1985. **Freq:** Monthly. **Print Method:** Web. **Trim Size:** 210 x 297 mm. **Cols./Page:** 4. **Key Personnel:** Mark Grafton, Creative Dir., phone 44 1327 315450; David Haynes, Ch. Sub Ed.; Cherry Hall, Administrative Dir., cherry@dhpub.co.uk; David Thomson, Production Mgr.; David Hall, Publisher, phone 44 1327 315402, david@dhpub.co.uk; Dave Harrell, Editor, phone 44 1327 315422, dave.harrell@dhpub.co.uk. **ISSN:** 0958-9023. **Subscription Rates:** 42 individuals; 3.15 single issue. **Remarks:** Accepts advertising. **URL:** http://www.matchfishingmagazine.com/Home/; http://www.davidhallpublishing.com/mags/mf/index.html. **Circ:** Paid 17,500

Deal

53161 ■ Tocatta
Leopold Stokowski Society
12 Market St.
Deal CT14 6HS, United Kingdom
Publisher E-mail: leopold.stokowski@yahoo.co.uk
Publication covering composers. **Freq:** 3/yr. **Subscription Rates:** 20 individuals; US$40 individuals; EUR35 individuals. **URL:** http://www.stokowskisociety.net.

Deeping Saint James

53162 ■ Best of British
Church Lane Publishing Ltd.
200 Eastgate
Deeping Saint James PE6 8RD, United Kingdom
Ph: 44 1778 342814
Fax: 44 1778 342814
Publisher E-mail: info@bestofbritishmag.co.uk
Magazine featuring all the best about Britain. **Freq:** Monthly. **Key Personnel:** Ian Beacham, Editor-in-Chief, ian@bestofbritishmag.co.uk; Linne Matthews, Editor, linne@bestofbritishmag.co.uk; Steve Windsor, Assoc. Ed. **Subscription Rates:** 39 individuals; 72 two years. **URL:** http://www.bestofbritishmag.co.uk/index.html.

Derby

53163 ■ Annals of Occupational Hygiene
British Occupational Hygiene Society
5/6 Melboune Business Ct.
Millenium Way
Pride Pk.
Derby DE24 8LZ, United Kingdom
Ph: 44 13 32298101
Fax: 44 13 32298099
Publisher E-mail: admin@bohs.org
Publication covering occupational medicine. **Freq:** 8/yr. **Key Personnel:** Dr. T.L. Ogden, Ch. Ed. **ISSN:** 0003-4878. **Subscription Rates:** 739 institutions print & online; 687 institutions online only; 702 institutions print only; 176 institutions discounted print only; 717 individuals print; 74 members print; 107 institutions print only; 112 individuals print. **URL:** http://annhyg.oxfordjournals.org/; http://www.bohs.org.

53164 ■ Ice Cream
Ice Cream Alliance
3 Melbourne Ct.
Pride Pk.
Derby DE24 8LZ, United Kingdom
Ph: 44 13 32203333
Fax: 44 13 32203420
Publisher E-mail: info@ice-cream.org
Publication covering ice cream. **Freq:** Monthly. **Remarks:** Advertising accepted; rates available upon request. **URL:** http://www.ice-cream.org. **Circ:** 1,000

53165 ■ Leicestershire Magazine
Archant Life
61 Friar Gate
Derby DE1 1DJ, United Kingdom
Ph: 44 1332 227850

Publisher E-mail: anne.basey-fisher@archant.co.uk
Magazine featuring life in Leicestershire County. **Freq:** Quarterly. **Key Personnel:** Carol Burns, Editor, carol. burns@archant.co.uk; Amanda Hamilton, Publisher, amanda.hamilton@archant.co.uk; Eileen Williams, Production Mgr., eileen.williams@archant.co.uk. **Remarks:** Accepts advertising. **URL:** http://www.archantlife. co.uk/contact-us-regions-mid-west-and-midlands-leicestershire-county-contacts--10422. **Ad Rates:** 4C: 750. **Circ:** 10,000

53166 ■ Materials & Design
Elsevier Science Inc.
c/o K.L. Edwards, Ed.-in-Ch.
School of Engineering
University of Derby
Kedleston Rd.
Derby DE22 1GB, United Kingdom
Publisher E-mail: usinfo-ehelp@elsevier.com
Journal promoting the attributes and capabilities of all types of modern engineering materials. **Freq:** 10/yr. **Key Personnel:** H.M. Loretto, International Editorial Board; C. Hepburn, International Editorial Board. **ISSN:** 0261-3069. **Subscription Rates:** US$1,558 institutions, other countries except Europe, Japan and Iran; 185,300¥ institutions; EUR1,395 institutions for European countries and Iran. **URL:** http://www.elsevier.com/wps/find/ journaldescription.cws_home/30454/ descriptiondescription.

53167 ■ Peak District Life
Archant Life
61 Friar Gate
Derby DE1 1DJ, United Kingdom
Ph: 44 1332 227850
Fax: 44 1332 227860
Publisher E-mail: johnny.hustler@archant.co.uk
Magazine featuring the Peak District. **Freq:** Bimonthly. **Key Personnel:** Joy Hales, Editor. **Subscription Rates:** 25 individuals. **Remarks:** Accepts advertising. **URL:** http://derbyshire.greatbritishlife.co.uk/. **Circ:** (Not Reported)

53168 ■ Professional Pest Controller
British Pest Control Association
Ground Fl.
1 Gleneagles House
Vernon Gate
South St.
Derby DE1 1UP, United Kingdom
Ph: 44 1332 294288
Publisher E-mail: enquiry@bpca.org.uk
Trade magazine covering pest control in the UK. **Founded:** 1993. **Freq:** Quarterly. **Trim Size:** 210 x 297 mm. **Remarks:** Accepts advertising. **URL:** http://www. bpca.org.uk/news.html. **Circ:** 3,000

53169 ■ BBC Radio-AM - 1116
56 St. Helen's St.
Derby DE1 3HY, United Kingdom
Ph: 44 13 32361111
E-mail: derby@bbc.co.uk
Format: Ethnic; News; Information; Sports. **Owner:** British Broadcasting Corp., Broadcasting House, Portland Pl., London W1A 1AA, United Kingdom. **Operating Hours:** Continuous. **URL:** http://www.bbc.co.uk/derby/ local_radio/index.shtml.

53170 ■ BBC Radio Derby-FM - 104.5
56 St. Helen's St.
Derby DE1 3HY, United Kingdom
Ph: 44 1332 361111
Fax: 44 1332 290794
E-mail: derby@bbc.co.uk
Format: Talk; News; Oldies. **Owner:** British Broadcasting Corporation, Broadcasting House, Portland Pl., London W1A 1AA, United Kingdom. **Operating Hours:** Continuous. **Key Personnel:** Simon Cornes, Editor, simon.cornes@bbc.co.uk. **URL:** http://www.bbc.co.uk/ derby/local_radio.

Dereham

53171 ■ Dereham Times
Archant Regional Ltd.
Bond House, High St.
Dereham NR19 1DZ, United Kingdom
Ph: 44 1362 854701
Fax: 44 1362 854710

Publisher E-mail: sandra.roantree@archant.co.uk
Local community newspaper. **Founded:** Feb. 7, 1880. **Key Personnel:** Terry Redhead, Dep. Ed., phone 44 1603 772402, terry.redhead@archant.co.uk; Tim Williams, News Ed., tim.williams@archant.co.uk. **Subscription Rates:** 14.95 individuals 13 weeks; 29.90 individuals 26 weeks. **Remarks:** Accepts advertising. **URL:** http://www.derehamtimes.co.uk/home. **Circ:** (Not Reported)

Derry

53172 ■ Derry Journal
Johnston Press PLC
22 Buncrana Rd.
Derry BT48 8AA, United Kingdom
Ph: 44 287 1272200
Community newspaper covering local news and events. **Key Personnel:** Sean McLaughlin, News Ed., phone 44 287 272254, sean.mclaughlin@derryjournal.com; Caroline Morris, Advertising Mgr., caroline.morris@ derryjournal.com; Martin McGinley, Editor, martin. mcginley@derryjournal.com. **URL:** http://www. derryjournal.com.

53173 ■ Q102.9-FM - 102.9
87 Rossdowney Rd.
Waterside
Derry BT47 5SU, United Kingdom
Ph: 44 28 71311980
Format: News; Contemporary Hit Radio (CHR). **Key Personnel:** Robert Walshe, Ch. Exec./Prog.Dir.; Gerard Twells, Advertising Mgr. **URL:** http://www.q102.fm/.

53174 ■ Radio Foyle-FM - 93.1
8 Northland Rd.
Derry BT48 7GD, United Kingdom
Ph: 44 28 71266522
Fax: 44 28 71378666
E-mail: radio.foyle@bbc.co.uk
Format: Sports; News. **Owner:** British Broadcasting Corporation, at above address. **Founded:** Sept. 11, 1979. **URL:** http://www.bbc.co.uk/northernireland/ radiofoyle/.

Desborough

53175 ■ The Powys Review
Beeches House
Harborough Rd.
Desborough NN14 2QX, United Kingdom
Literary journal covering the works of John C. Powys, T. F. Powys and Llewelyn Powys, and English literature from the 1890s to the 1960s. **Founded:** 1977. **Freq:** Annual. **Trim Size:** 9 x 25 cm. **Cols./Page:** 2. **Col. Width:** 7 centimeters. **Col. Depth:** 21.5 centimeters. **Key Personnel:** Belinda Humfrey, Editor, bhumfrey@ northamptonshire.gov.uk. **ISSN:** 0309-1619. **Subscription Rates:** 8 individuals inclusive of postage; 8.50 out of country. **Remarks:** Accepts advertising. **URL:** http:// www.powys-lannion.net. **Circ:** Controlled 620

Devon

63176 ■ IMCoS Journal
International Map Collectors' Society
c/o Rogues Roost
Poundsgate
Newton Abbot
Devon TQ13 7PS, United Kingdom
Fax: 44 1364 631042
Publisher E-mail: financialsecretariat@imcos.org
Trade journal covering collectors. **Freq:** Quarterly. **Key Personnel:** Valerie Newby, Editor. **Subscription Rates:** 10 individuals; US$17 individuals. **Remarks:** Advertising accepted; rates available upon request. **URL:** http:// www.intercol.co.uk/acatalog/IMCoS_Journal.html. **Circ:** (Not Reported)

53177 ■ Taqasim
Taqasim Magazine
PO Box 72
Devon EX39 1FA, United Kingdom
Magazine featuring Middle Eastern dance, music, and culture. **Freq:** Quarterly. **Key Personnel:** Afra al Kahira, Editor, afradancer@live.co.uk. **Subscription Rates:** 12 individuals print; 9 individuals electronic. **URL:** http:// taqasim.org.uk.

Dewsbury

53178 ■ Cook's Log
Captain Cook Society
13 Cowdry Close, Thornhill
West Yorkshire
Dewsbury WF12 0LW, United Kingdom
Publisher E-mail: secretary@captaincooksociety.com
Publication covering marine interests. **Founded:** 1975. **Freq:** Quarterly. **Trim Size:** A4. **ISSN:** 1358-0639. **Subscription Rates:** 10 individuals. **Remarks:** Advertising accepted; rates available upon request. **URL:** http:// www.captaincooksociety.com. **Circ:** (Not Reported)

53179 ■ Dewsbury Reporter
Johnston Press PLC
17 Wellington Rd.
Dewsbury WF13 1HQ, United Kingdom
Ph: 44 1924 468282
Local community newspaper. **Key Personnel:** Andy Bould, Contact, phone 44 1924 433032, andrewbould@ wakefieldexpress.co.uk. **Remarks:** Accepts advertising. **URL:** http://www.dewsburyreporter.co.uk/. **Circ:** (Not Reported)

53180 ■ Journal of the Society of Leather Technologists and Chemists
Society of Leather Technologists and Chemists
49 N Park St.
Dewsbury WF13 4LZ, United Kingdom
Ph: 44 19 24460864
Fax: 44 19 24460864
Publisher E-mail: office@sltc.org
Scientific journal covering research for the leather and allied industries. **Founded:** 1897. **Freq:** Bimonthly. **Print Method:** Sheetfed litho. **Trim Size:** 210 x 297 mm. **Cols./Page:** 2. **Key Personnel:** Malcolm K. Leafe, Editor, ed@sltc.org. **ISSN:** 0144-0322. **Remarks:** Accepts advertising. **URL:** http://www.sltc.org; http://www.sltc. org/jsltcexample.htm. **Former name:** Collegium/Journal of the International Society of Leather Technologists. **Ad Rates:** 4C: 1,900. **Circ:** Paid 900

53181 ■ Mirfield Reporter
Johnston Press PLC
17 Wellington Rd.
Dewsbury WF13 1HQ, United Kingdom
Ph: 44 1924 433038
Local community newspaper. **Key Personnel:** Lauren Chadwick, Contact. **Remarks:** Accepts advertising. **URL:** http://www.mirfieldreporter.co.uk/. **Circ:** (Not Reported)

53182 ■ Branch-FM - 101.8
17 Halifax Rd.
Dewsbury WF13 2JH, United Kingdom
Ph: 44 1924 465600
E-mail: studio@branchfm.co.uk
Format: Contemporary Christian. **Operating Hours:** Continuous. **Key Personnel:** Steve Hodgson, Station Mgr., steve.hodgson@branchfm.co.uk; Rob Ward, Tech. Dir., rob.ward@branchfm.co.uk. **URL:** http://www. branchfm.co.uk/index.htm.

Dinnington

53183 ■ Dinnington Guardian
Johnston Press PLC
64 Laughton Rd.
Dinnington S25 2PS, United Kingdom
Ph: 44 1909 550500
Local community newspaper. **Key Personnel:** George Robinson, Editor, fax 44 1909 474849, george. robinson@worksop-guardian.co.uk; James Mitchinson, Dep. Ed., phone 44 1909 543002, fax 44 1909 474849, james.mitchinson@worksop-guardian.co.uk. **Remarks:** Accepts advertising. **URL:** http://www.dinningtontoday. co.uk/. **Circ:** (Not Reported)

Diss

53184 ■ Diss Express
Johnston Press PLC
Norfolk & Suffolk House
Mere St.
Diss IP22 4AE, United Kingdom
Ph: 44 1379 642264
Local community newspaper. **Freq:** Weekly (Fri.). **Key Personnel:** Steven Penny, Editor, phone 44 1379

Circulation: ★ = ABC; △ = BPA; ◆ = CAC; • = CCAB; ❑ = VAC; ⊕ = PO Statement; ‡ = Publisher's Report; Boldface figures = sworn; Light figures = estimated.

Gale Directory of Publications & Broadcast Media/147th Ed.   5633

658002, fax 44 1379 650110, editorial@dissexpress.co.uk. **Remarks:** Accepts advertising. **URL:** http://www.dissexpress.co.uk/. **Circ:** (Not Reported)

53185 ■ Diss Mercury
Archant Regional Ltd.
26 Mere St.
Diss IP22 4AD, United Kingdom
Ph: 44 1379 644517
Fax: 44 1379 651221
Publisher E-mail: sandra.roantree@archant.co.uk
Local community newspaper. **Founded:** 1984. **Freq:** Weekly. **Subscription Rates:** 29.90 individuals 26 weeks; 14.95 individuals 13 weeks. **Remarks:** Accepts advertising. **URL:** http://www.dissmercury.co.uk/content/dissmercury/default.aspx. **Circ:** (Not Reported)

Doncaster

53186 ■ Doncaster Free Press
Johnston Press PLC
Sunny Bar
Doncaster DN1 1NB, United Kingdom
Ph: 44 1302 819111
Local community newspaper. **Freq:** Weekly. **Key Personnel:** Graeme Huston, Editor-in-Chief, fax 44 1302 348523, graeme.huston@doncastertoday.co.uk; Stuart Chandler, Asst. Ed., phone 44 1302 347256, stuart.chandler@doncastertoday.co.uk. **Remarks:** Accepts advertising. **URL:** http://www.doncasterfreepress.co.uk/. **Circ:** (Not Reported)

53187 ■ Hallam-FM - 103.4
900 Herries Rd.
Sheffield S6 1RH, United Kingdom
Ph: 44 114 2091000
Fax: 44 114 2855472
Format: Contemporary Hit Radio (CHR). **Key Personnel:** Simon Monk, Program Dir.; Lynn Dixon, News Ed. **URL:** http://www.hallamfm.co.uk/.

53188 ■ Trax-FM - 107.9
5 Sidings Ct.
White Rose Way
Doncaster DN4 5NU, United Kingdom
Ph: 44 1302 341166
Fax: 44 1302 326104
E-mail: studio@traxfm.co.uk
Format: Adult Contemporary. **URL:** http://www.traxfm.co.uk/.

53189 ■ Trax-FM - 107.1
5 Sidings Ct.
White Rose Way
Doncaster DN4 5NU, United Kingdom
Ph: 44 1302 341166
Fax: 44 1302 326104
E-mail: studio@traxfm.co.uk
Format: Adult Contemporary. **URL:** http://www.traxfm.co.uk/.

Dorchester

53190 ■ Thomas Hardy Journal
Thomas Hardy Society
PO Box 1438
High West St.
Dorchester DT1 1YH, United Kingdom
Ph: 44 1305 251501
Fax: 44 1305 251501
Publisher E-mail: info@hardysociety.org
Peer-reviewed journal covering authors. **Freq:** Annual. **Key Personnel:** Michael Irwin, Chm. **Subscription Rates:** Free. **Remarks:** Advertising accepted; rates available upon request. **URL:** http://www.hardysociety.org/. **Circ:** (Not Reported)

53191 ■ Wessex-FM - 96
Radio House
Trinity St.
Dorchester DT1 1DJ, United Kingdom
Ph: 44 1305 250333
Fax: 44 1305 250052
Format: Eclectic; Adult Contemporary; Top 40; News. **Owner:** The Local Radio Company plc., 11 Duke St., High Wycombe HP13 6EE, United Kingdom, Fax: 44 1494 688201. **Operating Hours:** Continuous. **Ad Rates:** Advertising accepted; rates available upon request. **URL:** http://www.wessexfm.com/.

Dorking

53192 ■ Call Centre Focus
Callcraft
The Loft
Dean House Farm
Church Rd.
Newdigate
Dorking RH5 5DL, United Kingdom
Ph: 44 13 06631661
Publisher E-mail: info@callcentre.co.uk
Trade magazine covering call centers. **Freq:** Monthly. **Key Personnel:** Marc Sales, Production Mgr., mark.sales@ubm.com; Mark Lewis, Editor, mark.lewis@ubm.com; Jonathan Collins, Publisher, jonathan.collins@ubm.com. **Subscription Rates:** Free. **Remarks:** Accepts advertising. **URL:** http://www.callcentre.co.uk/callcentrefocus. **Circ:** 47,000

53193 ■ Church Music Quarterly
Royal School of Church Music
19 The Close
Salisbury
Wiltshire
Dorking SP1 2EB, United Kingdom
Ph: 44 1722 424848
Fax: 44 1722 424849
Publisher E-mail: enquiries@rscm.com
Journal of the Royal School of Church Music. **Founded:** Jan. 1977. **Freq:** Quarterly March, June, September & December. **Key Personnel:** Esther Jones, Editor; Stephen Dutton, Advertising Mgr. **ISSN:** 0307-6334. **Remarks:** Accepts advertising. **URL:** http://www.rscm.com/publications/cmq.php. **Ad Rates:** BW: 825, 4C: 1,125. **Circ:** Paid ‡11,500

53194 ■ Company Profile & Financial Strength Update
AKG Actuaries & Consultants Ltd.
Anderton House
92 S St.
Dorking RH4 2EW, United Kingdom
Ph: 44 130 6876439
Fax: 44 130 6885325
Publisher E-mail: akg@akg.co.uk
Technical, trade journal covering insurance. **Founded:** 1998. **Freq:** Quarterly. **Key Personnel:** Guy Vonner, Editor. **Subscription Rates:** 795 individuals printed version U.K. only. **URL:** http://www.akg.co.uk/.

Dorset

53195 ■ Minor Monthly
Poundbury Publishing Ltd.
Middle Farm
Middle Farm Way
Poundbury
Dorset DT1 3RS, United Kingdom
Ph: 44 1305 266360
Fax: 44 1305 262760
Publisher E-mail: admin@poundbury.co.uk
Consumer magazine covering Morris Minor automobiles. **Subtitle:** The Only Monthly Magazine Dedicated to the Morris Minor. **Founded:** 1995. **Freq:** Monthly. **Key Personnel:** Russell Harvey, Editor, editor@minormonthly.co.uk; Kirsty Beach, Contact, info@minormonthly.co.uk. **Subscription Rates:** 20 individuals; 44 two years. **Remarks:** Accepts advertising. **URL:** http://www.minormonthly.co.uk/en. **Ad Rates:** BW: 755, 4C: 550. **Circ:** (Not Reported)

53196 ■ Point to Point and Hunter Chase Magazine
Poundbury Publishing Ltd.
Middle Farm
Middle Farm Way
Poundbury
Dorset DT1 3RS, United Kingdom
Ph: 44 1305 266360
Fax: 44 1305 262760
Publisher E-mail: admin@poundbury.co.uk
Consumer magazine covering point to point racing hunter-chasing. **Founded:** 1993. **Freq:** Bimonthly. **Trim Size:** 210 x 295 mm. **Cols./Page:** 4. **Key Personnel:** Brian Elliott, Advertising. **Subscription Rates:** 21 individuals U.K.; 30 individuals Europe; 35 other countries. **Remarks:** Accepts advertising. **URL:** http://www.mediauk.com/magazines/141989/point-to-point-&-hunter-chase. **Former name:** Between the Flags. **Ad**

Rates: BW: 640, 4C: 850. **Circ:** Controlled 23,000

Douglas

53197 ■ Statute Law Review
Oxford University Press
c/o Prof. John N. Bates, Ed.
24 Mona St.
Douglas, United Kingdom
Publisher E-mail: webenquiry.uk@oup.com
Law periodical. **Freq:** 3/yr. **Key Personnel:** Prof. John N. Bates, Editor, phone 44 16 24611522, bates@manx.net; G.R. Drewry, Dep. Ed. **ISSN:** 0144-3593. **Subscription Rates:** 222 institutions print and online; US$444 institutions print and online; EUR333 institutions print and online; 97 individuals print; US$194 individuals print; EUR146 individuals print; 67 members print (Statute Law Society); US$134 members print (Statute Law Society); EUR101 members print (Statute Law Society); US$370 institutions print, online. **Remarks:** Accepts advertising. **URL:** http://slr.oxfordjournals.org/. **Circ:** (Not Reported)

53198 ■ Manx Radio-AM - 1368 KHz
PO Box 1368
Douglas IM99 1SW, United Kingdom
Ph: 44 1624 682600
Fax: 44 1624 682604
E-mail: studio@manxradio.com
Format: News; Sports; Adult Contemporary; Religious; Country; Folk; Top 40; Talk. **Owner:** Radio Manx Ltd., at above address. **Founded:** Nov. 1979. **Operating Hours:** Continuous. **Key Personnel:** Anthony Pugh, Mng. Dir., anthonypugh@manxradio.com; John Marsom, Bus. Dir., johnmarsom@manxradio.com; Anna Martin, Contact, annamartin@manxradio.com. **Wattage:** 20,000. **Ad Rates:** Advertising accepted; rates available upon request. **URL:** http://www.manxradio.com/.

Driffield

53199 ■ Beverley Guardian
Johnston Press PLC
Times House
Driffield YO25 6TN, United Kingdom
Ph: 44 1377 241122
Local community newspaper. **Founded:** 1856. **Freq:** Weekly. **Key Personnel:** Jenny Harrison, Contact, jenny.harrison@ypn.co.uk; Nick Procter, Contact, phone 44 1377 241414, editorial@driffieldtoday.co.uk. **Remarks:** Accepts advertising. **URL:** http://www.beverleyguardian.co.uk/. **Circ:** (Not Reported)

53200 ■ craft&design
PSB Design & Print Consultants Ltd.
PO Box 5
Driffield YO25 8JD, United Kingdom
Ph: 44 13 77255213
Consumer magazine covering issues for craftspeople and artists in the UK. **Founded:** 1983. **Freq:** Monthly. **Print Method:** Web. **Trim Size:** 210 x 297 mm. **Cols./Page:** 3. **Col. Width:** 60 millimeters. **Col. Depth:** 272 millimeters. **Key Personnel:** Angie Boyer, Editor; Paul Boyer, Production and Design Dir. **Subscription Rates:** 35 individuals U.K.; free postage rate; 35 individuals Europe; plus 20 postage rate; 35 other countries plus 34 postage rate. **Remarks:** Accepts advertising. **URL:** http://www.craftanddesign.net/. **Formerly:** The Craftsman Magazine. **Circ:** (Not Reported)

53201 ■ Driffield Times
Johnston Press PLC
Times House
Mill St.
Driffield YO25 6TN, United Kingdom
Ph: 44 1377 241122
Local community newspaper. **Founded:** 1860. **Freq:** Weekly (Wed.). **Key Personnel:** Wendy Spalding, Web Admin., wendy.spalding@jpress.co.uk. **Remarks:** Accepts advertising. **URL:** http://www.driffieldtoday.co.uk/. **Circ:** (Not Reported)

53202 ■ International Dairy Topics
Positive Action Publications Ltd.
PO Box 4
Driffield YO25 9DJ, United Kingdom
Ph: 44 13 77241724
Fax: 44 13 77253640
Publisher E-mail: info@positiveaction.co.uk
Magazine for professional milk and dairy producers. **Founded:** 2001. **Freq:** Bimonthly. **Trim Size:** 297 X 420 mm. **Cols./Page:** 4. **Col. Width:** 42 millimeters. **Col.**

Depth: 255 millimeters. **Subscription Rates:** 50 individuals; 75 two years. **URL:** http://www. positiveaction.info/publications/magdetails.php?mag=4. **Ad Rates:** 4C: 3,100. **Circ:** Controlled ‡20,000

53203 ■ International Food Hygiene
Positive Action Publications Ltd.
PO Box 4
Driffield YO25 9DJ, United Kingdom
Ph: 44 13 77241724
Fax: 44 13 77253640
Publisher E-mail: info@positiveaction.co.uk
Technical publication covering food safety for food producers, caterers, retailers and laboratories. **Founded:** 1990. **Freq:** 8/yr. **Trim Size:** 297 x 420 mm. **Cols./Page:** 4. **Col. Width:** 42 millimeters. **Col. Depth:** 255 millimeters. **Key Personnel:** Nigel Horrox, Managing Editor. **ISSN:** 0961-2831. **Subscription Rates:** 50 individuals; 75 two years. **Remarks:** Accepts advertising. **URL:** http://www.positiveaction.info/publications/magdetails.php?mag=5. **Ad Rates:** BW: 3,029, 4C: 3,710, SAU: 4. **Circ:** Controlled 10,000

53204 ■ International Hatchery Practice
Positive Action Publications Ltd.
PO Box 4
Driffield YO25 9DJ, United Kingdom
Ph: 44 13 77241724
Fax: 44 13 77253640
Publisher E-mail: info@positiveaction.co.uk
Technical magazine for breeders and hatcherymen focusing on the key issues of breeder nutrition, environment, management, productivity and health. **Freq:** 8/yr. **Key Personnel:** Nigel Horrox, Managing Editor. **Subscription Rates:** 50 individuals; 75 two years. **URL:** http://www.positiveaction.info/publications/magdetails.php?mag=2.

53205 ■ International Pig Topics
Positive Action Publications Ltd.
PO Box 4
Driffield YO25 9DJ, United Kingdom
Ph: 44 13 77241724
Fax: 44 13 77253640
Publisher E-mail: info@positiveaction.co.uk
Technical magazine for professional pig producers that focuses on the key issues of nutrition, environment, management, and health. **Freq:** 8/yr. **Key Personnel:** Nigel Horrox, Managing Editor. **Subscription Rates:** 50 individuals; 75 two years. **URL:** http://www.positiveaction.info/publications/magdetails.php?mag=3.

53206 ■ International Poultry Production
Positive Action Publications Ltd.
PO Box 4
Driffield YO25 9DJ, United Kingdom
Ph: 44 13 77241724
Fax: 44 13 77253640
Publisher E-mail: info@positiveaction.co.uk
Technical magazine for producers of broilers, table eggs, turkeys and ducks focusing on the key issues of nutrition, environment, management and health. **Freq:** 8/yr. **Key Personnel:** Nigel Horrox, Managing Editor. **Subscription Rates:** 50 individuals; 75 two years. **URL:** http://www.positiveaction.info/publications/magdetails.php?mag=1.

Dromore

53207 ■ Dromore Leader
Morton Newspapers
30A Market St.
Dromore BT25 1AW, United Kingdom
Ph: 44 28 92692217
Community newspaper. **Freq:** Weekly (Wed.). **Print Method:** Offset. **Col. Depth:** 450 millimeters. **Key Personnel:** Mark Weir, Editor; Anita Grattan, Advertising Mgr., anita.murray@jpress.co.uk; Paul Wilkinson, Contact. **Remarks:** Accepts advertising. **URL:** http://www.dromoreleader.co.uk/. **Circ:** (Not Reported)

Duffield

53208 ■ Forge
Newton Mann Ltd.
Fourteen Business Centre
14 Town St.
Duffield DE56 4EH, United Kingdom
Ph: 44 1332 843107

Fax: 44 845 0098871
Publication E-mail: sales@forgemagazine.co.uk
Publisher E-mail: enquiries@newtonmann.co.uk
Official magazine of the National Association of Farriers, Blacksmiths and Agricultural Engineers. **Freq:** Bimonthly. **Key Personnel:** Gill Harris, Editor, editor@forgemagazine.co.uk; Charles Mann, Publisher. **ISSN:** 0955-5293. **Subscription Rates:** 42 individuals; 75 other countries. **Remarks:** Advertising accepted; rates available upon request. **URL:** http://www.forgemagazine.co.uk/. **Circ:** 3,400

Dulverton

53209 ■ Active Exmoor
7-9 Fore St.
Dulverton TA22 9EX, United Kingdom
Ph: 44 1398 324599
Publisher E-mail: info@activeexmoor.com
Sports tourism magazine focusing on supporting Exmoor's outdoor activity industry. **URL:** http://www.activeexmoor.com/site/about-us/publications.

Dumfries

53210 ■ West Sound-FM - 96.5
The Loreburne Ctr., Unit 40
High St.
Dumfries DG1 2BD, United Kingdom
Ph: 44 1387 250999
Fax: 44 1387 265629
Format: Contemporary Hit Radio (CHR). **Key Personnel:** Fiona Blackwood, Station Mgr.; James Pllu, Program Dir., news@southwestsound.co.uk. **URL:** http://www.westsoundradio.com; http://www.southwestsound.co.uk/.

53211 ■ West Sound-FM - 97
The Loreburne Ctr., Unit 40
High St.
Dumfries DG1 2BD, United Kingdom
Ph: 44 1387 250999
Fax: 44 1387 265629
Format: Contemporary Hit Radio (CHR). **Key Personnel:** Fiona Blackwood, Station Mgr.; James Pllu, Program Dir., news@atsouthwestsound.co.uk. **URL:** http://www.westsoundradio.com; http://www.southwestsound.co.uk/.

53212 ■ West Sound-FM - 103
The Loreburne Ctr., Unit 40
High St.
Dumfries DG1 2BD, United Kingdom
Ph: 44 1387 250999
Fax: 44 1387 265629
Format: Contemporary Hit Radio (CHR). **Key Personnel:** Fiona Blackwood, Station Mgr.; James Pllu, Program Dir., news@southwestsound.co.uk. **URL:** http://www.southwestsound.co.uk/; http://www.westsoundradio.com.

Dundee

53213 ■ Animals and You
D.C. Thomson & Company Ltd.
2 Albert Sq.
Dundee DD1 9QJ, United Kingdom
Ph: 44 1382 223131
Fax: 44 1382 322214
Consumer magazine covering animals for girls aged 7-10 years. **Subtitle:** For Cool Girls who Love Animals. **Founded:** 1998. **Freq:** Triweekly. **Trim Size:** 225 x 305 mm. **Col. Width:** 48 millimeters. **Col. Depth:** 276 millimeters. **Subscription Rates:** 9 single issue for U.K; 40 individuals for U.K; 60 other countries. **Remarks:** Accepts advertising. **URL:** http://www.dcthomson.co.uk/subscriptions/default.asp?pagename=productdetails&productid=51. **Ad Rates:** 4C: EUR1,500. **Circ:** Paid 60,000

53214 ■ International Journal of Energy Sector Management
Emerald Group Publishing Ltd.
c/o Dr. Subhes C. Bhattacharyya, Ed.
Centre for Energy, Petroleum & Mineral Law & Policy
University of Dundee
Dundee DD1 4HN, United Kingdom
Publisher E-mail: emerald@emeraldinsight.com
Journal covering management of the energy sector.

Freq: Quarterly. **Key Personnel:** Dr. Subhes C. Bhattacharyya, Editor, s.c.bhattacharyya@dundee.ac.uk; Nicola Codner, Publisher, ncodner@emeraldinsight.com; Dr. Prasanta Kumar Dey, Editor, p.k.dey@aston.ac.uk. **ISSN:** 1750-6220. **URL:** http://info.emeraldinsight.com/products/journals/journals.htm?id=ijesm

53215 ■ Medical Teacher
Association for Medical Education in Europe
Secretariat Office
Tay Pk. House
484 Perth Rd.
Dundee DD2 1LR, United Kingdom
Ph: 44 1382 381953
Fax: 44 1382 381987
Publisher E-mail: amee@dundee.ac.uk
Publication covering medical education. **Freq:** 10/yr. **Key Personnel:** Pat Lilley, Managing Editor, p.m.lilley@dundee.ac.uk; Ronald Harden, Editor, r.m.harden@dundee.ac.uk. **ISSN:** 0142-159X. **Subscription Rates:** US$2,635 institutions print and online; US$5,270 individuals corporate. **Remarks:** Advertising accepted; rates available upon request. **URL:** http://www.medicalteacher.org/. **Circ:** (Not Reported)

53216 ■ My Weekly
D.C. Thomson & Company Ltd.
Courier Bldg.
2 Albert Sq.
Dundee DD1 9QJ, United Kingdom
Ph: 44 20 74001030
Fax: 44 20 78319440
Publisher E-mail: mail@sundaypost.com
Consumer (Women's) magazine covering local lifestyle. **Freq:** Weekly. **Trim Size:** 295 x 225mm. **Key Personnel:** Sally Hampton, Editor. **Subscription Rates:** 31.62 individuals 6 month (inland UK); 39.65 other countries 6 month (Overseas/Europe); 54.61 other countries 6 month (airmail). **Remarks:** Accepts advertising. **URL:** http://www.dcthomson.co.uk/subscriptions/default.asp?pageName=productDetails&productID=46. **Ad Rates:** 4C: 5,980, SAU: 3,980. **Circ:** ‡198,980

53217 ■ Nicotine and Tobacco Research
Oxford University Press
University of Dundee Medical School
Ninewells Hospital
Dundee DD1 9SY, United Kingdom
Publisher E-mail: admin.in@oup.com
Peer-reviewed journal devoted exclusively to nicotine and tobacco research, providing a forum for empirical findings on the many aspects of nicotine and tobacco including research from the biobehavioral, neurophysiological, epidemiological, prevention, and treatment arenas. **Freq:** 12/yr. **Key Personnel:** Gary E. Swan, PhD, Founding Ed.-in-Ch.; David J.K. Balfour, PhD, Editor-in-Chief, d.j.k.balfour@dundee.ac.uk; Karl Fagerstrom, PhD, Dep. Ed. **ISSN:** 1462-2203. **Subscription Rates:** US$560 individuals print only; US$1,196 institutions online only; US$1,259 institutions print & online; 725 institutions print & online; 689 institutions online only; 280 individuals print only. **Remarks:** Accepts advertising. **URL:** http://ntr.oxfordjournals.org/. **Circ:** (Not Reported)

53218 ■ The Scots Magazine
D.C. Thomson & Company Ltd.
2 Albert Sq.
Dundee DD1 9QJ, United Kingdom
Ph: 44 1382 223131
Fax: 44 1382 322214
Publication E-mail: mail@scotsmagazine.com
Magazine covering Scotland's culture, heritage, and traditions. **Founded:** 1739. **Freq:** Monthly. **Key Personnel:** Paul Wilson, Online Advertising, pwilson@dcthomson.co.uk; Dorothy Hume, Print Advertising, dhoy@dcthomson.co.uk; Trish Blair, Contact. **Subscription Rates:** 25 individuals U.K; 40 individuals for overseas; 45 two years U.K; 72 two years overseas. **URL:** http://www.scotsmagazine.com/.

53219 ■ Tay-AM - 1584
PO Box 123
Dundee DD1 9UF, United Kingdom
Ph: 44 1382 200800
Format: Adult Contemporary; Oldies. **Key Personnel:** Ally Ballingall, Mng. Dir., ally.ballingall@radiotay.co.uk; Ian Reilly, Sales Dir., ian.reilly@radiotay.co.uk; Lorraine Stevenson, Program Dir., lorraine.stevenson@radiotay.

Circulation: ★ = ABC; △ = BPA; ◆ = CAC; ● = CCAB; ❑ = VAC; ⊕ = PO Statement; ‡ = Publisher's Report; Boldface figures = sworn; Light figures = estimated.

co.uk. **URL:** http://www.tayam.co.uk/.

53220 ■ Tay-AM - 1161
PO Box 123
Dundee DD1 9UF, United Kingdom
Ph: 44 1382 200800
Format: Adult Contemporary; Oldies. **Key Personnel:** Ally Ballingall, Mng. Dir., ally.ballingall@radiotay.co.uk; Ian Reilly, Sales Dir., ian.reilly@radiotay.co.uk; Lorraine Stevenson, Program Dir., lorraine.stevenson@radiotay.co.uk. **URL:** http://www.tayam.co.uk/.

53221 ■ Tay-FM - 96.4
PO Box 1028
Dundee DD3 7YH, United Kingdom
Ph: 44 1382 200800
Format: Top 40; Contemporary Hit Radio (CHR). **Key Personnel:** Ian Reilly, Sales Dir., ian.reilly@radiotay.co.uk; Gary Robinson, Hd. of Music/Station Dir., gary.robinson@radiotay.co.uk. **URL:** http://www.tayfm.co.uk/.

53222 ■ Tay-FM - 102.8
PO Box 1028
Dundee DD3 7YH, United Kingdom
Ph: 44 1382 200800
Format: Top 40; Contemporary Hit Radio (CHR). **Key Personnel:** Ian Reilly, Sales Dir., ian.reilly@radiotay.co.uk; Gary Robinson, Hd. of Music/Station Dir., gary.robinson@radiotay.co.uk. **URL:** http://www.tayfm.co.uk/.

53223 ■ Wave-FM - 102.0
8 S Tay St.
Dundee DD1 1PA, United Kingdom
Ph: 44 1382 901000
Fax: 44 1382 908035
Format: Adult Contemporary. **Key Personnel:** Adam Findlay, Mng. Dir., adam.findlay@wave102.co.uk. **Ad Rates:** Advertising accepted; rates available upon request. **URL:** http://www.wave102.co.uk/.

Dungannon

53224 ■ Tyrone Times
Johnston Press PLC
Unit B Buttermarket Ctr.
Thomas St.
Dungannon BT70 1HN, United Kingdom
Community newspaper. **Freq:** Weekly (Fri.). **Key Personnel:** Paul McCreary, Editor. **Remarks:** Accepts advertising. **URL:** http://www.tyronetimes.co.uk. **Circ:** Combined 3,626

Dunstable

53225 ■ OAG Rail Guide
OAG Worldwide
Church St.
Dunstable LU5 4HB, United Kingdom
Ph: 44 15 82600111
Fax: 44 15 82695230
Publisher E-mail: custsvc@oag.com
Railroad guide covering timetables for southeastern England. **Founded:** Oct. 1853. **Freq:** Monthly. **Print Method:** Web. **Trim Size:** 146 x 214 mm. **Cols./Page:** 3. **Col. Width:** 40 millimeters. **Col. Depth:** 195 millimeters. **ISSN:** 1365-6112. **Subscription Rates:** 196 individuals. **Remarks:** Accepts advertising. **URL:** http://www.oag.com; http://www2.oag.com/tt/catalog/travplan.html. **Circ:** Paid 5,000

53226 ■ Chiltern-FM - 97.6
Chiltern Rd.
Dunstable LU6 1HQ, United Kingdom
Ph: 44 15 82676200
Format: Top 40. **Operating Hours:** Continuous. **Key Personnel:** Kris Lingwood, Sales Mgr. **Ad Rates:** Advertising accepted; rates available upon request. **URL:** http://www.heartdunstable.co.uk/article.asp?id=386256.

Durham

53227 ■ Critical Horizons
Acumen Publishing Ltd.
4 Saddler St.
Durham DH1 3NP, United Kingdom
Ph: 44 191 3831889
Fax: 44 191 3862542
Publisher E-mail: enquiries@acumenpublishing.co.uk
Peer-reviewed journal covering a range of concerns such as forms of modernity and post modernity, chang-

ing social relations, politics, identities, feminisms, critical philosophy, aesthetics and visual culture. **Subtitle:** A Journal of Philosophy and Social Theory. **Founded:** Jan. 1953. **Freq:** 3/yr. **Print Method:** Offset. **Trim Size:** 6 x 9. **Cols./Page:** 2. **Col. Width:** 52 nonpareils. **Col. Depth:** 101 agate lines. **Key Personnel:** John Rundell, Editor; Danielle Petherbridge, Coord. Ed.; Robert Sinnerbrink, Review Ed. **ISSN:** 1440-9917. **Subscription Rates:** 110 institutions print and online; 30 individuals print only. **URL:** http://www.acumenpublishing.co.uk/journals.asp?TAG=&CID.

53228 ■ Durham Anthropology Journal
University of Durham
Department of Anthropology
Old Elvet
Durham DH1 3HP, United Kingdom
Ph: 44 191 3342000
Journal on anthropology. **Key Personnel:** Tom Callan, Guest Ed.; Beth Cullen, Guest Ed.; Claudia Merli, Gen. Ed. **ISSN:** 1742-2930. **URL:** http://www.dur.ac.uk/anthropology.journal/.

53229 ■ International Reviews in Physical Chemistry
Taylor & Francis Group Journals
c/o Prof. Jeremy M. Hutson, Ed.
Department of Chemistry
University of Durham
Durham DH1 3LE, United Kingdom
Publisher E-mail: customerservice@taylorandfrancis.com
Peer-reviewed journal containing information on frontier research areas in physical chemistry. **Founded:** 1994. **Freq:** Quarterly. **Key Personnel:** Prof. Jeremy M. Hutson, Editor, j.m.hutson@durham.ac.uk; Prof. Timothy S. Zwier, Consultant Ed.; Prof. F.F. Crim, Editorial Board; Prof. P.F. Barbara, Editorial Board; Prof. M.A. Collins, Editorial Board. **ISSN:** 0144-235X. **Subscription Rates:** US$1,576 institutions online; US$1,751 institutions print + online. **Remarks:** Accepts advertising. **URL:** http://www.informaworld.com/smpp/title~content=t713724383. **Circ:** (Not Reported)

53230 ■ Journal of Thermal Biology
Elsevier Science
c/o K. Bowler, Ed.
Dept. of Biological Sciences
University of Durham
Durham DH1 3LE, United Kingdom
Publisher E-mail: nlinfo-f@elsevier.com
Journal involved in the study of the effects of temperature on living organisms as well as their biochemical and physiological processes. **Founded:** 1976. **Freq:** 8/yr. **Key Personnel:** M. Sawka, Editorial Board; K. Bowler, Editor; M. Cabanac, Editorial Board; A.R. Cossins, Editorial Board; D. Atkinson, Editorial Board; G.S. Bakken, Editorial Board; C.J. Gordon, Editor; R.B. Huey, Editorial Board; M.E. Feder, Editorial Board; J. Roth, Editorial Board; L.R. Leon, Editorial Board. **ISSN:** 0306-4565. **Subscription Rates:** US$276 individuals for all countries except Europe, Japan & Iran; EUR245 individuals for European countries & Iran; 32,800¥ individuals; US$1,718 institutions for all countries except Europe, Japan & Iran; EUR1,536 institutions for European countries & Iran; 203,900¥ institutions. **Remarks:** Accepts advertising. **URL:** http://www.elsevier.com/wps/find/journaldescription.cws_home/383/description. **Circ:** (Not Reported)

53231 ■ The Seventeenth Century
Manchester University Press
Department of French
University of Durham
Elvet Riverside
New Elvet
Durham DH1 3JT, United Kingdom
Publisher E-mail: m.frost@manchester.ac.uk
Journal covering all aspects of the seventeenth century. **Freq:** Semiannual April and October. **Key Personnel:** Dr. Richard Maber, Gen. Ed., r.g.maber@durham.ac.uk; Christopher Brooks, Assoc. Ed.; Alan Ford, Assoc. Ed. **ISSN:** 0268-117X. **Subscription Rates:** 76 institutions; US$135 institutions; EUR98 institutions; 30 individuals; US$55 individuals; EUR40 individuals. **Remarks:** Accepts advertising. **URL:** http://www.manchesteruniversitypress.co.uk/journals/journal.asp?id=5. **Ad Rates:** BW: 145. **Circ:** (Not Reported)

53232 ■ Durham-FM - 106.8
3 Fram Well House
Framwelgate

Durham DH1 5SU, United Kingdom
Ph: 44 191 3835050
Fax: 44 191 3847880
E-mail: hello@durhamfm.com
Format: Full Service. **Ad Rates:** Advertising accepted; rates available upon request. **URL:** http://www.durhamfm.com/.

Durham City

53233 ■ The Wellsian
H.G. Wells Society
Societe H.G. Wells
c/o Dr. Simon James, Ed.
Hallgarth House
77 Hallgarth St.
Durham City DH1 3AY, United Kingdom
Publisher E-mail: secretaryhgwellssociety@hotmail.com
Publication covering the life, work and thought of H.G. Wells. **Subtitle:** The Journal of the H.G. Wells Society. **Founded:** 1976. **Freq:** Annual. **Print Method:** Camera-ready. **Trim Size:** A5. **Key Personnel:** Dr. Simon James, Editor, s.j.james@durham.ac.uk. **ISSN:** 0263-1176. **Subscription Rates:** 3 single issue; 4 single issue other countries. **Remarks:** Advertising not accepted. **URL:** http://www.hgwellsusa.50megs.com/UK/wellsian.html. **Circ:** (Not Reported)

East Budleigh

53234 ■ Tools and Trades
Tool and Trades History Society
Woodbine Cottage
Budleigh Hill
East Budleigh EX9 7DT, United Kingdom
Publisher E-mail: info@taths.org.uk
Publication covering tools and trades. **Founded:** 1984. **Freq:** Every 18 months. **Trim Size:** 200 x 250 cm. **Subscription Rates:** Included in membership. **Remarks:** Advertising not accepted. **URL:** http://www.taths.org.uk/. **Circ:** (Not Reported)

East Grinstead

53235 ■ The Caravan Club Magazine
The Caravan Club
East Grinstead House
East Grinstead RH19 1UA, United Kingdom
Ph: 44 1342 336804
Fax: 44 1342 410258
Publisher E-mail: enquiries@caravanclub.co.uk
Consumer magazine for members of The Caravan Club. **Freq:** Monthly. **Print Method:** Web offset. **Trim Size:** 210 x 297 mm. **Remarks:** Accepts advertising. **URL:** http://www.caravanclubmagazine.co.uk/. **Ad Rates:** BW: EUR3,460, 4C: EUR4,893. **Circ:** Controlled ★322,820, 383,396

East Horsley

53236 ■ International Journal of Project Management
Elsevier
c/o Rodney J. Turner, Ed.
EuroProjex, Wildwood, Manor Close
East Horsley KT24 6SA, United Kingdom
Peer-reviewed journal covering management. **Freq:** 8/yr. **Key Personnel:** Rodney J. Turner, Editor, ijpm@europrojex.co.uk. **ISSN:** 0263-7863. **Subscription Rates:** EUR264 individuals for European countries and Iran; 35,000¥ individuals; US$298 individuals except Europe, Japan and Iran; EUR1,295 institutions for European countries and Iran; US$1,449 institutions except Europe, Japan and Iran; 172,000¥ institutions, other countries. **Remarks:** Accepts advertising. **URL:** http://www.elsevier.com/wps/find/journaldescription.cws_home/30435/description. **Circ:** (Not Reported)

East London

53237 ■ South African Journal of Philosophy
African Journals Online
Department of Philosophy
University of Fort Hare
50 Church St.
East London 5201, United Kingdom
Publisher E-mail: info@ajol.info
Peer-reviewed journal covering the field of philosophy. **Freq:** Quarterly. **Key Personnel:** Abraham Olivier, Editor, aolivier@ufh.ac.za; Sharli Paphitis, Contact,

sharlipaphitis@gmail.com. **ISSN:** 0258-0136. **Subscription Rates:** R 200 individuals; US$60 other countries. **URL:** http://ajol.info/index.php/sajpem/

East Malling

53238 ■ Crop Protection
Elsevier Science Inc.
c/o J.V. Cross, Principal Ed.
East Malling Research
New Rd.
Kent
East Malling ME19 6BJ, United Kingdom
Publisher E-mail: usinfo-ehelp@elsevier.com
Journal covering all practical aspects of pest, disease and weed control. **Founded:** 1982. **Freq:** 12/yr. **Key Personnel:** L.N. Gatehouse, Editorial Board; C.A. Edwards, Editorial Board; Robert L. Gilbertson, Editorial Board; G.A. Matthews, Editorial Board; L. Godfrey, Editorial Board; Wade H. Elmer, Editorial Board; R.G. Turner, Editorial Board; D.P. Giga, Editorial Board; W.D. Hutchison, Principal Ed., hutch002@umn.edu. **ISSN:** 0261-2194. **Subscription Rates:** EUR1,823 institutions for European countries and Iran; 242,300¥ institutions; US$2,040 institutions, other countries except Europe, Japan and Iran; US$228 other countries except Europe, Japan and Iran; 27,100¥ individuals; EUR203 individuals for European countries and Iran. **URL:** http://www.elsevier.com/wps/find/journaldescription.cws_home/30406/descriptiondescription.

East Molesey

53239 ■ Ag Magazine
Picture-Box Media Ltd.
Dulwich Lodge
62 Pemberton Rd.
East Molesey KT8 9LH, United Kingdom
Ph: 44 20 89410249
Fax: 44 20 89411088
Publisher E-mail: info@ag-photo.co.uk
Journal containing photographs and articles and tips regarding photography. **Subtitle:** The International Journal of Photographic Art & Practice. **Founded:** 1991. **Freq:** Quarterly Jan., Apr., Jul., Oct. **Key Personnel:** Chris Dickie, Editor and Publisher, chris@picture-box.com. **Subscription Rates:** 37.50 individuals; 71 two years; EUR43.50 individuals; EUR83 two years; 53.50 individuals elsewhere; 102 two years elsewhere. **URL:** http://www.picture-box.com/about.html.

53240 ■ Stitch with the Embroiders' Guild
E.G. Enterprises Ltd.
c/o Kathy Troup, Ed.
PO Box 42B
East Molesey KT8 9BB, United Kingdom
Publisher E-mail: administrator@embroiderersguild.com
Magazine for all needlework enthusiasts. **Founded:** 1999. **Freq:** Bimonthly 6/yr. **Cols./Page:** 4. **Key Personnel:** Kathy Troup, Editor. **ISSN:** 1467-6648. **Subscription Rates:** 23.70 individuals; 28.80 individuals Europe; 35.70 individuals American countries; 38.10 other countries; 3.95 single issue; 4.80 single issue Europe; 5.95 single issue American countries; 6.35 other countries. **URL:** http://www.embroiderersguild.com/stitch/; http://www.embroiderersguild.com/stitch/subscribe/online/index.php. **Circ:** Combined 12,000

53241 ■ The World of Embroidery
Embroiderers' Guild
Embroidery
Apt. 41 Hampton Ct. Palace
East Molesey KT8 9AU, United Kingdom
Ph: 44 20 89431229
Fax: 44 20 89779822
Publication E-mail: embroiderersguild@mongoosemedia.com
Publisher E-mail: administrator@embroiderersguild.com
Magazine covering contemporary embroidery, ethnic embroidery, new techniques and developments for professionals and enthusiasts. **Founded:** 1934. **Freq:** Bimonthly. **Cols./Page:** 4. **Key Personnel:** Joanne Hall, Editor. **ISSN:** 1351-9603. **Subscription Rates:** 29.40 individuals incl. p&h; EUR36 elsewhere incl. p&h; 42.30 elsewhere the Americas; incl. p&h; 43.50 other countries incl. p&h; 4.90 single issue; 6 single issue Europe; 7.05 single issue The Americas; 7.25 single issue rest of the world. **Remarks:** Accepts advertising. **URL:** http://embroidery.embroiderersguild.com. **Circ:** Combined 12,500

East Sussex

53242 ■ Catchword
Association of Teachers of Lipreading to Adults
c/o Hearing Concern LINK
27-28 The Waterfront
Eastbourne
East Sussex BN23 5UZ, United Kingdom
Publisher E-mail: atla@lipreading.org.uk
Publication covering the hearing impaired. **Freq:** Semiannual. **Key Personnel:** Maggie Short, Editor. **Subscription Rates:** 3.50 individuals back copy. **URL:** http://www.lipreading.org.uk/about_atla/publicat.htm.

Eastbourne

53243 ■ Eastbourne Herald
Johnston Press PLC
11 Lismore Rd.
Eastbourne BN21 3BA, United Kingdom
Ph: 44 1323 437457
Local community newspaper. **Founded:** 1859. **Key Personnel:** Laura Sonier, Content Ed., laura.sonier@trbeckett.co.uk. **Remarks:** Accepts advertising. **URL:** http://www.eastbourneherald.co.uk/. **Circ:** (Not Reported)

53244 ■ Lighting & Sound International
Professional Lighting & Sound Association
Redoubt House
1 Edward Rd.
Eastbourne BN23 8AS, United Kingdom
Ph: 44 1323 524120
Fax: 44 1323 524121
Publication E-mail: info@lsionline.co.uk
Publisher E-mail: info@plasa.org
Trade magazine covering the entertainment technology industry. **Founded:** 1985. **Freq:** Monthly. **Print Method:** Litho. **Key Personnel:** Barry Howse, Advertising Mgr., barry@lsionline.co.uk; Sonja Walker, Production Mgr., sonja@lsionline.co.uk; Jane Cockburn, Sales Exec., jane@lsionline.co.uk; Oliver Kinne, IT Mgr., oliver@lsionline.co.uk; Lee Baldock, Editor, lee@lsionline.co.uk; Sheila Bartholomew, Circulation Mgr., sheila@lsionline.co.uk. **ISSN:** 0268-7429. **Subscription Rates:** 30 individuals U.K.; 40 other countries surface mail; 60 other countries airmail; 50 individuals Europe airmail; Free to qualified subscribers. **Remarks:** Accepts advertising. **URL:** http://www.lsionline.co.uk. **Ad Rates:** BW: 1,860. **Circ:** Combined ★10,000

Eastwood

53245 ■ Eastwood Advertiser
Johnston Press PLC
23 Nottingham Rd.
Eastwood NG16 3AH, United Kingdom
Ph: 44 1773 537850
Local community newspaper. **Key Personnel:** Peter Hemmett, Editor. **Remarks:** Accepts advertising. **URL:** http://www.eastwoodadvertiser.co.uk/. **Circ:** (Not Reported)

Ebbw Vale

53246 ■ Valleys Radio-AM - 1116
PO Box 1116
Ebbw Vale NP23 8XW, United Kingdom
Ph: 44 1495 300700
Fax: 44 1495 300710
E-mail: info@valleysradio.co.uk
Format: Contemporary Hit Radio (CHR). **Owner:** UTV Radio Ltd., 18 Hatfields, London SE1 8DJ, United Kingdom. **Operating Hours:** Continuous. **Key Personnel:** Carrie Mosley, Station Mgr., carrie.mosley@thewave.co.uk; Tony Peters, Program Mgr., tony.peters@valleysradio.co.uk; Jonathan Carter, Contact, jonathan.carter@valleysradio.co.uk. **Ad Rates:** Advertising accepted; rates available upon request. **URL:** http://www.valleysradio.co.uk.

53247 ■ Valleys Radio-AM - 999
PO Box 1116
Ebbw Vale NP23 8XW, United Kingdom
Ph: 44 14 95300700
Fax: 44 14 95300710
E-mail: info@valleysradio.co.uk
Format: Contemporary Hit Radio (CHR). **Owner:** UTV

PLC Group, 18 Hatfields, London SE1 8DJ, United Kingdom. **Operating Hours:** Continuous. **Key Personnel:** Carrie Mosley, Station Mgr., carrie.mosley@thewave.co.uk; Tony Peters, Program Mgr., tony.peters@valleysradio.co.uk; Jonathan Carter, Sales Dir., jonathan.carter@valleysradio.co.uk. **Ad Rates:** Advertising accepted; rates available upon request. **URL:** http://www.valleysradio.co.uk.

Edgbaston

53248 ■ Africa
Edinburgh University Press
c/o Prof. Karin Barber, Ed.
Centre of West African Studies
University of Birmingham
Edgbaston B15 2TT, United Kingdom
Publisher E-mail: marketing@eup.ed.ac.uk
Periodical focusing on African history and culture. **Subtitle:** Journal of the International African Institute. **Freq:** Quarterly. **Key Personnel:** Christine Obbo, Editorial Advisory Board; Prof. Karin Barber, Editor; Thomas J. Bassett, Editorial Advisory Board; Murray Last, Editorial Advisory Board. **ISSN:** 0001-9720. **Subscription Rates:** 75 individuals print and online; 84 other countries print and online; US$150 individuals print and online (North America); 365 institutions print and online; 404 institutions, other countries print and online; US$725 institutions print and online (North America). **Remarks:** Accepts advertising. **URL:** http://www.eupjournals.com/journal/afr. **Ad Rates:** BW: 200. **Circ:** Paid ‡1,000

Edinburgh

53249 ■ African Affairs
Oxford University Press
c/o Sara Rich Dorman, Joint Ed.
University of Edinburgh
Adam Ferguson Bldg.
George Sq.
Edinburgh EH8 9LL, United Kingdom
Ph: 44 131 6504239
Fax: 44 131 6506546
Publisher E-mail: webenquiry.uk@oup.com
Journal of the Royal African Society. **Freq:** Quarterly. **Key Personnel:** Sara Rich Dorman, Joint Ed., sara.dorman@ed.ac.uk. **ISSN:** 0001-9909. **Subscription Rates:** 338 institutions corporate; print and online; 282 institutions corporate; online only; 310 institutions corporate; print only; 271 institutions print and online; 226 institutions online only; 249 institutions print only; 60 individuals print; 15 individuals Africa; print. **Remarks:** Accepts advertising. **URL:** http://afraf.oupjournals.org/. **Circ:** (Not Reported)

53250 ■ Anon
67 Learmonth Grove
Edinburgh EH4 1BL, United Kingdom
Publisher E-mail: mike@volta1.fsworld.co.uk
Magazine featuring poems with anonymous authors. **Key Personnel:** Mike Stocks, Founding Ed.; Colin Fraser, Editor-in-Chief. **Subscription Rates:** 14.49 individuals. **URL:** http://www.blanko.org.uk/anon/.

53251 ■ Aquatic Conservation
John Wiley & Sons Inc.
c/o Prof. Philip J. Boon, Ch. Ed.
Scottish Natural Heritage
Silvan House, 3rd Fl. E
231 Corstorphine Rd.
Edinburgh EH12 7AT, United Kingdom
Publisher E-mail: info@wiley.com
Journal covering the study of marine and fresh water ecosystem. **Subtitle:** Marine and Freshwater Ecosystems. **Key Personnel:** Prof. Philip J. Boon, Ch. Ed.; Dr. John M. Baxter, Ch. Ed. **ISSN:** 1052-7613. **Subscription Rates:** EUR938 institutions, other countries print only; 938 institutions UK (print only); US$1,360 institutions, other countries print only; EUR966 institutions, other countries print and online; 765 institutions UK (print and online); US$1,497 institutions, other countries print and online; US$938 individuals. **URL:** http://onlinelibrary.wiley.com/journal/10.1002/(ISSN)1099-0755.

53252 ■ Architectural Heritage
Architectural Heritage Society of Scotland
The Glasite Meeting House
33 Barony St.
Edinburgh EH3 6NX, United Kingdom

Circulation: ★ = ABC; △ = BPA; ♦ = CAC; • = CCAB; ❑ = VAC; ⊕ = PO Statement; ‡ = Publisher's Report; Boldface figures = sworn; Light figures = estimated.

Gale Directory of Publications & Broadcast Media/147th Ed.   5637

Ph: 44 131 5570019
Fax: 44 131 5570049
Publisher E-mail: administrator@ahss.org.uk
Publication covering historical preservation. **Freq:** Annual. **Key Personnel:** Dawn Caswell Mcdowell, Editor. **Subscription Rates:** 20 single issue non members; 10 individuals back issue per volume; 100 individuals back issue; 12 volumes. **Remarks:** Advertising not accepted. **URL:** http://www.ahss.org.uk/pubjournal.html. **Circ:** (Not Reported)

53253 ■ Ashlar
Grand Lodge of Scotland
Freemasons Hall
96 George St.
Edinburgh EH2 3DH, United Kingdom
Ph: 44 131 2255577
Fax: 44 131 2253953
Publisher E-mail: curator@grandlodgescotland.org
Magazine covering the freemasonry in Scotland. **Founded:** 1997. **Freq:** 3/yr. **URL:** http://www.grandlodgescotland.com/index.php?option=com_content&task=view&id=245&Itemid=167.

53254 ■ ASTIN Bulletin
PEETERS - USA
c/o Andrew Cairns, Ed.-in-Ch.
Dept. of Actuarial Mathematics & Statistics
Heriot-Watt University
Edinburgh EH14 4AS, United Kingdom
Publisher E-mail: peeters@peeters-us.com
Journal covering mathematics of insurance and general insurance. **Subtitle:** Journal of the ASTIN and AFIR Sections of the International Actuarial Association. **Key Personnel:** Andrew Cairns, Editor-in-Chief, a.cairns@ma.hw.ac.uk; Samuel H. Cox, Editor. **ISSN:** 0515-0361. **Subscription Rates:** EUR80 individuals. **URL:** http://www.peeters-leuven.be/journoverz.asp?nr=63&number_of_volumes="0".

53255 ■ Ben Jonson Journal
Edinburgh University Press
22 George Sq.
Edinburgh EH8 9LF, United Kingdom
Ph: 44 131 6504218
Fax: 44 131 6503286
Publisher E-mail: marketing@eup.ed.ac.uk
Journal covering the study of Ben Jonson and the culture in which his manifold literary efforts thrived. **Freq:** 2/yr. **Key Personnel:** Richard Harp, Editor; Stanley Stewart, Editor; Robert C. Evans, Editor; Joyce Ahn, Managing Editor. **ISSN:** 1079-3453. **Subscription Rates:** 88 institutions print and online; US$186 institutions print and online (North America); 97 institutions, other countries print and online; 41 individuals print and online; US$85.50 individuals print and online (North America); 44.50 other countries print and online. **Remarks:** Accepts advertising. **URL:** http://www.eupjournals.com/journal/bjj. **Circ:** (Not Reported)

53256 ■ The Braille Sporting Record
Scottish Braille Press
Craigmillar Pk.
Edinburgh EH16 5NB, United Kingdom
Ph: 44 13 16624445
Fax: 44 13 16621968
Publisher E-mail: enquiries.sbp@royalblind.org
Community newspaper covering sports. **Freq:** Weekly (Wed.). **Subscription Rates:** 10.50 individuals. **Remarks:** Advertising not accepted. **URL:** http://www.royalblind.org/sbp/images/catalogue.doc. **Circ:** (Not Reported)

53257 ■ Britball
Britball.com
3-4 Madeira St.
Edinburgh EH6 64AJ, United Kingdom
Ph: 44 77 10509728
Publisher E-mail: magazine@britball.com
Magazine covering British and Irish basketball. **Founded:** 1996. **Key Personnel:** Mark Woods, Editor, mark@insidesport.co.uk. **Remarks:** Accepts advertising. **URL:** http://www.britball.com. **Circ:** 13,045

53258 ■ Business Citizen
Johnston Press PLC
c/o Richard Cooper
53 Manor Pl.
Edinburgh EH3 7EG, United Kingdom
Ph: 44 13 12253361
Business newspaper. **Founded:** 1993. **Freq:** Monthly.

Print Method: Web Offset. **Cols./Page:** 9. **Key Personnel:** Melissa Lynch, Contact, melissa.lynch@jpress.co.uk. **Subscription Rates:** Free. **Remarks:** Accepts advertising. **URL:** http://www.mysporttoday.co.uk/sportsmain.aspx?sitecode=mkc&sportcode=buscit. **Circ:** Non-paid ‡98,000

53259 ■ CA Magazine
Institute of Chartered Accountants of Scotland
CA House
21 Haymarket Yards
Edinburgh EH12 5BH, United Kingdom
Ph: 44 131 3470100
Fax: 44 131 3470105
Publisher E-mail: enquiries@icas.org.uk
Professional journal covering business, finance, management and accountancy of the Institute of Chartered Accountants of Scotland. **Subtitle:** Leading Figures in Business. **Founded:** 1897. **Freq:** Monthly. **Print Method:** Web litho. **Trim Size:** 210 x 297 mm. **Key Personnel:** Jennifer Whyte, Contact, phone 44 131 2714460, jenn@connectcommunications.co.uk. **ISSN:** 1352-9021. **Subscription Rates:** 45 individuals; 65 other countries; 20 students; 5 single issue back issues (subject to availability); 30 students, other countries. **Remarks:** Accepts advertising. **URL:** http://www.icas.org.uk/site/cms/contentChapterView.asp?chapter=74. **Former name:** The Accountants Magazine. **Ad Rates:** BW: 2,197, 4C: 2,977. **Circ:** ★22,362

53260 ■ Cardiology News
Pinpoint Scotland Ltd.
9 Gayfield Sq.
Edinburgh EH1 3NT, United Kingdom
Ph: 44 131 5574184
Fax: 44 131 4788405
Publisher E-mail: admin@pinpoint-scotland.com
Professional, medical magazine for the field of cardiology. **Founded:** Oct. 1997. **Freq:** 6/yr. **Print Method:** Web Offset. **Trim Size:** 210 x 297 mm. **Key Personnel:** Michael S. Norell, Editor. **Subscription Rates:** 17 individuals; 25 individuals Europe; 40 other countries; 34 two years. **Remarks:** Accepts advertising. **URL:** http://www.pinpointmedical.com/showPublication.php?publication=cardiologynews. **Ad Rates:** BW: 180. **Circ:** (Not Reported)

53261 ■ Chapman
Chapman Publishing
4 Broughton Pl.
Edinburgh EH1 3RX, United Kingdom
Ph: 44 13 15572207
Publisher E-mail: chapman-pub@blueyonder.co.uk
Journal covering literature. **Subtitle:** Scotland's Quality Literary Magazine. **Founded:** 1970. **Freq:** Quarterly. **Print Method:** Offset litho. **Trim Size:** 150 x 215 mm. **Cols./Page:** 1. **Col. Width:** 110 millimeters. **Col. Depth:** 180 millimeters. **Key Personnel:** Joy Hendry, Editor. **ISSN:** 0308-2695. **Subscription Rates:** 24 individuals; 30 other countries; 30 institutions, other countries; US$60 institutions. **Remarks:** Accepts advertising. **URL:** http://www.chapman-pub.co.uk. **Ad Rates:** BW: US$170, 4C: US$400. **Circ:** Combined 2,550

53262 ■ Classic Bus
Ian Allan Publishing Ltd.
18 Brunstane Rd.
Edinburgh EH15 2QJ, United Kingdom
Publication E-mail: subs@classicbusmag.co.uk
Publisher E-mail: info@ianallanpublishing.co.uk
Magazine featuring the history of classic buses and coaches. **Freq:** Bimonthly. **Subscription Rates:** 7.20 single issue. **Remarks:** Accepts advertising. **URL:** http://www.ianallanmagazines.com/classicbus. **Circ:** (Not Reported)

53263 ■ Cloning and Stem Cells
Mary Ann Liebert Incorporated Publishers
Centre for Regenerative Medicine
University of Edinburgh
GU. 426 Chancellor's Bldg.
49 Little France Cres.
Edinburgh EH16 4SB, United Kingdom
Ph: 44 13 12426630
Fax: 44 13 12426629
Publisher E-mail: info@liebertpub.com
Scientific journal covering all aspects of cloning research and applications. **Founded:** 2000. **Freq:** Quarterly. **Print Method:** Offset. **Trim Size:** 8 1/2 x 11. **Key Personnel:** Jane Taylor, PhD, Deputy Ed.; Ian Wilmut, PhD, Editor-

in-Chief. **ISSN:** 1536-2302. **Subscription Rates:** US$856 individuals print and online; US$1,018 other countries print and online; US$757 individuals online; US$1,442 institutions print and online; US$1,662 institutions, other countries print and online; US$1,173 institutions online; US$1,201 institutions, other countries print only; US$1,421 institutions, other countries print only. **Remarks:** Accepts advertising. **URL:** http://www.liebertpub.com/publication.aspx?pub_id=9; http://www.liebertonline.com. **Ad Rates:** BW: 1,270, 4C: 2,020. **Circ:** (Not Reported)

53264 ■ Coleraine Times
Morton Newspapers
108 Holyrood Rd.
Edinburgh EH8 8AS, United Kingdom
Ph: 44 131 2253361
Fax: 44 131 2254580
Community newspaper. **Freq:** Weekly (Wed.). **Print Method:** Offset. **Col. Depth:** 450 millimeters. **Key Personnel:** David Rankin, Editor, phone 44 28 70357610, david.rankin@colerainetimes.co.uk. **Remarks:** Accepts advertising. **URL:** http://www.colerainetimes.co.uk. **Circ:** Combined 6,744

53265 ■ Contemporary Music Review
Routledge
Taylor & Francis Group Ltd.
University of Edinburgh
12 Nicolson Sq.
Edinburgh EH8 9DF, United Kingdom
Publisher E-mail: webmaster.books@tandf.co.uk
Journal focusing on all aspects of music, covering techniques, aesthetics and technology. **Founded:** Jan. 1976. **Freq:** Bimonthly. **Print Method:** Offset. **Trim Size:** 8 1/8 x 10 7/8. **Cols./Page:** 3. **Col. Width:** 26 nonpareils. **Col. Depth:** 126 agate lines. **Key Personnel:** Peter Nelson, Editor; John Adams, Editorial Board; Bruce Adolphe, Editorial Board; Tod Machover, Editorial Board; Eduardo Miranda, Editorial Board; Peter Nelson, Editor, p.nelson@ed.ac.uk; Stephen Davismoon, Editorial Board; Oliver Knussen, Editorial Board. **ISSN:** 0749-4467. **Subscription Rates:** US$935 institutions online; 652 institutions online; US$984 institutions print & online; 686 institutions print & online; US$226 individuals print only; 149 individuals print only; EUR180 individuals print; EUR783 institutions print & online; EUR744 institutions online. **URL:** http://www.tandf.co.uk/journals/titles/07494467.asp.

53266 ■ Corpora
Edinburgh University Press
22 George Sq.
Edinburgh EH8 9LF, United Kingdom
Ph: 44 131 6504218
Fax: 44 131 6503286
Publisher E-mail: marketing@eup.ed.ac.uk
Journal of corpus linguistics focusing on the uses of corpora in linguistics and beyond. **Freq:** Semiannual. **Key Personnel:** Prof. Tony McEnery, Gen. Ed. **ISSN:** 1749-5032. **Subscription Rates:** 88 institutions print and online; 97 institutions, other countries print and online; 41 individuals print and online; 44.50 other countries print and online; 70 institutions print; 77.50 institutions, other countries print; 32 individuals print; 35 other countries print; US$185.50 institutions North America (print and online); US$85.50 individuals North America (print and online). **Remarks:** Accepts advertising. **URL:** http://www.eupjournals.com/journal/cor. **Circ:** (Not Reported)

53267 ■ Dance Research
Edinburgh University Press
22 George Sq.
Edinburgh EH8 9LF, United Kingdom
Ph: 44 131 6504218
Fax: 44 131 6503286
Publisher E-mail: marketing@eup.ed.ac.uk
Journal covering contemporary dance research. **Founded:** 1984. **Freq:** Semiannual. **Print Method:** Offset. **Cols./Page:** 6. **Col. Width:** 2 1/16 inches. **Col. Depth:** 21 1/2 inches. **Key Personnel:** Richard Ralph, Editor; Clement Crisp, Assoc. Ed.; Margaret McGowan, Assoc. Ed. **ISSN:** 0264-2875. **Subscription Rates:** 127 institutions print and online; 141 institutions, other countries print and online; US$268.50 institutions print and online (North America); 62 individuals print and online; 69 other countries print and online; US$132 individuals print and online (North America). **URL:** http://www.eupjournals.com/journal/drs.

53268 ■ Deleuze Studies
Edinburgh University Press
22 George Sq.
Edinburgh EH8 9LF, United Kingdom
Ph: 44 131 6504218
Fax: 44 131 6503286
Publisher E-mail: marketing@eup.ed.ac.uk
Journal covering the work of Gilles Deleuze. **Freq:** 3/yr.
Key Personnel: Ian Buchanan, Editor. **ISSN:** 1750-2241. **Subscription Rates:** 112.50 institutions print and online; US$237 institutions print and online (North America); 125 institutions, other countries print and online; 47 individuals print and online; US$102 individuals print and online (North America); 54 other countries print and online. **Remarks:** Accepts advertising. **URL:** http://www.eupjournals.com/journal/dls. **Circ:** (Not Reported)

53269 ■ Derrida Today
Edinburgh University Press
22 George Sq.
Edinburgh EH8 9LF, United Kingdom
Ph: 44 131 6504218
Fax: 44 131 6503286
Publisher E-mail: marketing@eup.ed.ac.uk
Journal on Derrida's thoughts in contemporary debates about politics, society and global affairs. **Freq:** Semiannual. **Key Personnel:** Nick Mansfield, Editor; Nicole Anderson, Editor. **ISSN:** 1754-8500. **Subscription Rates:** 99 institutions print and online; 101 institutions, other countries print and online; 38.50 individuals print and online; 40 other countries print and online; 79 institutions print; 81 institutions, other countries print; 30 individuals print; 32 other countries print; US$194 institutions North America (print and online); US$78 individuals North America (print and online). **Remarks:** Accepts advertising. **URL:** http://www.eupjournals.com/journal/drt. **Circ:** (Not Reported)

53270 ■ Double Tressure
Heraldry Society of Scotland
Societe Ecossaise d'Heraldique
25 Craigentinny Cres.
Edinburgh EH7 6QA, United Kingdom
Ph: 44 131 5532232
Publisher E-mail: info@heraldry-scotland.co.uk
Publication covering geneology. **Freq:** Annual. **Subscription Rates:** 7 individuals. **URL:** http://www.heraldry-scotland.co.uk/tressure.html.

53271 ■ The Edinburgh Law Review
Edinburgh University Press
22 George Sq.
Edinburgh EH8 9LF, United Kingdom
Ph: 44 131 6504218
Fax: 44 131 6503286
Publisher E-mail: marketing@eup.ed.ac.uk
Scholarly journal covering all aspects of law worldwide. **Freq:** 3/yr. **Key Personnel:** James Chalmers, Editor, james.chalmers@ed.ac.uk; Dr. Mark Godfrey, Book Review Ed., m.godfrey@law.gla.ac.uk; Prof. Hector L. MacQueen, Editorial Board. **ISSN:** 1364-9809. **Subscription Rates:** 95 individuals print and online; US$198.50 individuals print and online; 103.50 other countries print and online; 202 institutions print and online; US$422 institutions print and online; 222 institutions, other countries print and online; 22 students print and online; US$44.50 students print and online; 23 students print or online. **Remarks:** Accepts advertising. **URL:** http://www.eupjournals.com/journal/elr. **Ad Rates:** BW: 200. **Circ:** (Not Reported)

53272 ■ Episteme
Edinburgh University Press
22 George Sq.
Edinburgh EH8 9LF, United Kingdom
Ph: 44 131 6504218
Fax: 44 131 6503286
Publisher E-mail: marketing@eup.ed.ac.uk
Journal publishing articles on the social dimensions of knowledge from the perspective of philosophical epistemology and related social sciences (e.g., economics, political theory, information science), focusing on theoretical work. **Freq:** 3/yr. **Key Personnel:** Christian List, Assoc. Ed.; Leslie Marsh, Exec. Committee; Alvin I. Goldman, Editor; James Robert Brown, Assoc. Ed.; Chris Onof, Founding Ed./Exec. Committee; Jennifer Lackey, Assoc. Ed.; Frederick Schmitt, Assoc. Ed. **ISSN:** 1472-3600. **Subscription Rates:** 107 institutions print;

117 institutions, other countries print; 96 institutions online; 134 institutions print and online; 147 institutions, other countries print and online; 42 individuals print; 46 other countries print; 38 individuals online; 52 individuals print and online; 57 other countries print and online. **Remarks:** Accepts advertising. **URL:** http://www.eupjournals.com/journal/epi. **Circ:** (Not Reported)

53273 ■ European Journal of Archaeology
Sage Publications Ltd.
c/o Alan Saville, Ed.
Archaeology Dept.
National Museums of Scotland
Chambers St.
Edinburgh EH1 1JF, United Kingdom
Scholarly journal covering archaeology in Europe. **Subtitle:** Journal of the European Association of Archaeologists. **Founded:** 1998. **Freq:** 3/yr. **Key Personnel:** Alan Saville, Editor; Graeme Barker, Editorial Advisory Board; Ruth Tringham, Editorial Advisory Board; Robin Skeates, Incoming Ed. **ISSN:** 1461-9571. **Subscription Rates:** US$651 institutions combined (print & e-access); US$716 institutions (print & all online content); US$586 institutions e-access; US$651 institutions backfile lease, e-access; US$586 institutions content through 1998; US$638 institutions print only; US$234 institutions single print. **Remarks:** Accepts advertising. **URL:** http://www.sagepub.com/journalsProdDesc.nav?prodId=Journal200966. **Circ:** (Not Reported)

53274 ■ European Journal of Cancer
Mosby Inc.
c/o John Smyth, Ed.-in-Ch.
Cancer Research UK, Edinburgh Oncology Unit
Western General Hospital
Crewe Rd. S
Edinburgh EH4 2XR, United Kingdom
Publisher E-mail: custserv.ehs@elsevier.com
Journal for oncologists. **Freq:** 18/yr. **Key Personnel:** John Smyth, Editor-in-Chief; Maurizio D'Incalci, Editor; Jaap Verweij, Editor. **ISSN:** 0959-8049. **Subscription Rates:** EUR144 individuals for European countries and Iran; US$159 other countries except Europe, Japan and Iran; 18,900¥ individuals; EUR3,352 institutions for European countries and Iran; US$3,751 institutions, other countries except Europe, Japan and Iran; 445,300¥ institutions. **Remarks:** Accepts advertising. **URL:** http://www.ejcancer.info/; http://www.elsevier.com/wps/find/journaldescription.cws_home/104/descriptiondescription. **Circ:** (Not Reported)

53275 ■ Eye News
Pinpoint Scotland Ltd.
9 Gayfield Sq.
Edinburgh EH1 3NT, United Kingdom
Ph: 44 131 5574184
Fax: 44 131 4788405
Publisher E-mail: admin@pinpoint-scotland.com
Professional, medical magazine covering ophtalmology and updating its its practitioners of the latest developments in the field. **Founded:** 1995. **Freq:** Bimonthly. **Print Method:** Litho. **Trim Size:** 210 x 297 mm. **Cols./Page:** 3. **Key Personnel:** Winfried Amoaku, Editor. **ISSN:** 1368-8952. **Subscription Rates:** 19 individuals; 28 individuals Europe; 42 other countries; 38 two years. **Remarks:** Accepts advertising. **URL:** http://www.pinpointmedical.com/showPublication.php?publication=eye-news. **Ad Rates:** BW: 228, 4C: 1,385. **Circ:** 4,200

53276 ■ Fire Safety Journal
Elsevier Science
c/o Jose L. Torero, Ed.
University of Edinburgh
Scholarship of Engineering
Edinburgh EH9 3JL, United Kingdom
Ph: 44 131 6505723
Fax: 44 131 6506554
Publisher E-mail: nlinfo-f@elsevier.com
Journal dealing with all aspects of fire safety engineering in connection with international Association for Fire Safety Science. **Founded:** 1977. **Freq:** 8/yr. **Key Personnel:** Jose L. Torero, Editor, j.torero@ed.ac.uk; Colin Bailey, Assoc. Ed.; Richard Carvel, Assoc. Ed.; Bogdan Z. Dlugogorski, Assoc. Ed.; Andre Marshall, Assoc. Ed.; Bart Merci, Assoc. Ed. **ISSN:** 0379-7112. **Subscription Rates:** 36,900¥ individuals; US$312 individuals for all countries except Europe and Japan; EUR277 individuals for European countries; US$1,795 institutions for all countries except Europe and Japan; EUR1,605 institu-

tions for European countries; 212,800¥ institutions. **Remarks:** Accepts advertising. **URL:** http://www.elsevier.com/wps/find/journaldescription.cws_home/405896/description. **Circ:** (Not Reported)

53277 ■ Fish Farmer
Fish Farmer Magazine
Special Publications
Craigcrook Castle
Criagcrook Rd.
Edinburgh EH4 3PE, United Kingdom
Ph: 44 13 13124550
Fax: 44 13 13124551
Publisher E-mail: editor@fishfarmer-magazine.com
Trade magazine for the fish farming and aquaculture industry. **Founded:** 1977. **Freq:** Bimonthly. **Print Method:** Web Offset Litho. **Trim Size:** 210 x 296 mm. **Cols./Page:** 4. **Key Personnel:** Bob Kennedy, Sen. Ed.; William Dowds, Advertising, wdowds@fishupdate.com; Christina Reid, Journalist. **Subscription Rates:** 69 individuals; 87.50 elsewhere; 117.50 two years; 155 two years elsewhere. **Remarks:** Accepts advertising. **URL:** http://www.fishfarmer-magazine.com. **Circ:** Combined 6,500

53278 ■ Forestry Journal
Institute of Chartered Foresters
59 George St.
Edinburgh EH2 2JG, United Kingdom
Ph: 44 13 12401425
Fax: 44 13 12401424
Publisher E-mail: icf@charteredforesters.org
Journal covering forestry. **Subtitle:** An International Journal of Forestry Research. **Freq:** Quarterly. **Key Personnel:** Gary Kerr, Editor; Helen McKay, Editor; Jeffrey Go, Editor. **ISSN:** 0015-752X. **Subscription Rates:** 49 members print and online; Free member is free to view access. **Remarks:** Advertising accepted; rates available upon request. **URL:** http://www.charteredforesters.org/default.asp?page=8. **Circ:** 1,100

53279 ■ Fungal Biology Reviews
Elsevier Science Inc.
c/o Dr. N.D. Read, Sen. Ed.
University College Edinburgh
Edinburgh, United Kingdom
Publisher E-mail: usinfo-ehelp@elsevier.com
Journal covering all fields of fungal biology, whether fundamental or applied, including fungal diversity, ecology, evolution. **Founded:** 2006. **Freq:** 4/yr. **Print Method:** Offset. **Trim Size:** 7 7/8 x 10 1/2. **Cols./Page:** 3. **Key Personnel:** Dr. G. Robson, Sen. Ed., geoff.robson@manchester.ac.uk; Prof. K. Clay, Editorial Board; Dr. S. Avery, Editorial Board; Prof. N. Gow, Editorial Board; Prof. J. Colpaert, Editorial Board; Prof. G. Mueller, Editorial Board; Prof. R. Dean, Editorial Board; Dr. M. Fricker, Editorial Board; Prof. N.D. Read, Sen. Ed., nick.read@ed.ac.uk. **ISSN:** 1749-4613. **Subscription Rates:** US$131 institutions, other countries except Europe, Japan and Iran; 14,400¥ institutions; EUR104 institutions for European countries and Iran; US$59 other countries except Europe, Japan and Iran; EUR76 individuals for European countries and Iran; 6,400¥ individuals. **URL:** http://www.elsevier.com/wps/find/journaldescription.cws_home/709540/descriptiondescription.

53280 ■ Greens Business Law Bulletin
W. Green & Son Ltd.
21 Alva St.
Edinburgh EH2 4PS, United Kingdom
Ph: 44 13 12254879
Fax: 44 13 12252104
Publisher E-mail: wgreen.enquiries@thomson.com
Journal bringing the most recent information in a concise and user-friendly format, featuring such regulars columns as: Cases in Brief, Insolvency, Taxation, Editorial. **Founded:** Jan. 1, 2003. **Key Personnel:** David Bennett, Editor; Aidan O'Donnell, Editor. **ISSN:** 0967-2540. **Subscription Rates:** US$519 individuals rest of world, inclusive of VAT; 285 individuals rest of world, inclusive of VAT; 260 individuals UK/Europe, inclusive of VAT; EUR332 individuals UK/Europe, inclusive of VAT. **URL:** http://www.wgreen.co.uk.

53281 ■ Greens Criminal Law Bulletin
W. Green & Son Ltd.
21 Alva St.
Edinburgh EH2 4PS, United Kingdom
Ph: 44 13 12254879
Fax: 44 13 12252104

Circulation: ★ = ABC; △ = BPA; ♦ = CAC; ● = CCAB; ❑ = VAC; ⊕ = PO Statement; ‡ = Publisher's Report; Boldface figures = sworn; Light figures = estimated.

Gale Directory of Publications & Broadcast Media/147th Ed.   5639

Publisher E-mail: wgreen.enquiries@thomson.com
Journal covering issues across the field of substantive law and procedure, featuring comment, evidence, legal aid, sentencing cases, criminal roundup, human rights, misuse of drugs and current awareness.. **Founded:** Jan. 1, 2003. **Key Personnel:** Sheriff, Charles N. Stoddart, Editor. **ISSN:** 0967-2532. **Subscription Rates:** US$473 individuals rest of world, inclusive of VAT; 260 individuals rest of world, inclusive of VAT; 235 individuals UK/Europe, inclusive of VAT; EUR300 individuals UK/Europe, inclusive of VAT. **URL:** http://www.wgreen.co.uk.

53282 ■ Greens Property Law Bulletin
W. Green & Son Ltd.
21 Alva St.
Edinburgh EH2 4PS, United Kingdom
Ph: 44 13 12254879
Fax: 44 13 12252104
Publisher E-mail: wgreen.enquiries@thomson.com
Journal for solicitors engaged in property law, covering topics such as: enforcing commercial lease terms against successor landlords, rent-free periods and VAT and stamp duty group reliefs. **Key Personnel:** George B. Clark, Editor; Linda H. Urquhart, Editor. **ISSN:** 0967-2516. **Subscription Rates:** EUR270 individuals UK/Europe; 216 individuals UK/Europe; US$441 individuals rest of world; 240 individuals rest of world. **URL:** http://www.wgreen.co.uk/.

53283 ■ Greens Weekly Digest
W. Green & Son Ltd.
21 Alva St.
Edinburgh EH2 4PS, United Kingdom
Ph: 44 13 12254879
Fax: 44 13 12252104
Publisher E-mail: wgreen.enquiries@thomson.com
Professional journal covering case summaries of all decisions of the Scottish courts received by the publishers. **Subtitle:** Current Scottish Case Law. **Founded:** 1986. **Freq:** Weekly during court terms 40/yr. **Trim Size:** 185 x 270 mm. **Cols./Page:** 2. **Col. Width:** 70 millimeters. **Col. Depth:** 238 millimeters. **Key Personnel:** Peter Nicholson, Managing Editor. **ISSN:** 0955-4491. **Subscription Rates:** 455 individuals rest of world, inclusive of VAT; US$828 individuals rest of world, inclusive of VAT; 294 individuals UK/Europe; inclusive of VAT; EUR376 individuals UK/Europe; inclusive of VAT. **Remarks:** Advertising not accepted. **URL:** http://www.wgreen.co.uk; http://www.wgreen.co.uk/details?prodid=5887&unitid=5887. **Circ:** (Not Reported)

53284 ■ Home Help
Scottish Braille Press
Craigmillar Pk.
Edinburgh EH16 5NB, United Kingdom
Ph: 44 13 16624445
Fax: 44 13 16621968
Publisher E-mail: enquiries.sbp@royalblind.org
Magazine covering shopping, beauty, fashion, cooking and crafts. **Freq:** Weekly (Tues.). **Subscription Rates:** 10.50 individuals. **Remarks:** Advertising not accepted. **URL:** http://www.royalblind.org/shop/product-16175-0-1-Home_Help_.html. **Circ:** (Not Reported)

53285 ■ Human Reproduction & Genetic Ethics
European Bioethical Research
191 Leith Walk
Edinburgh EH6 8NX, United Kingdom
Publisher E-mail: bioethics@europe.com
Research journal covering medical ethics. **Subtitle:** An International Journal. **Founded:** Jan. 1995. **Freq:** Semiannual. **Cols./Page:** 2. **ISSN:** 1028-7825. **Subscription Rates:** 18.50 individuals; 37 two years individual; 57 individuals 3 years; EUR53 institutions; US$35 individuals; US$70 two years individual; US$55 institutions; US$105 institutions two years; EUR33 individuals personnel; EUR53 institutions. **Remarks:** Accepts advertising. **URL:** http://www.bioethics.org.uk/journal.htm. **Former name:** European Journal of Genetics in Society. **Circ:** (Not Reported)

53286 ■ Innes Review
Edinburgh University Press
22 George Sq.
Edinburgh EH8 9LF, United Kingdom
Ph: 44 131 6504218
Fax: 44 131 6503286
Publisher E-mail: marketing@eup.ed.ac.uk
Peer-reviewed journal covering Scottish history and the Catholic Church. **Subtitle:** Journal of the Scottish Catholic Historical Association. **Founded:** 1950. **Freq:** Semiannual. **Key Personnel:** Dr. Eila Williamson, Editor.

ISSN: 0020-157X. **Subscription Rates:** 71.50 institutions print; 76.50 institutions, other countries print; US$146 institutions print; 30 individuals print; 33 other countries; US$64 individuals. **URL:** http://www.euppublishing.com/journal/inr.

53287 ■ International Journal of Continuing Engineering Education and Life-Long Learning
Inderscience Enterprises Limited
c/o Dr. Paul Brna, Assoc. Ed.
University of Edinburgh
School of Informatics
10 Crighton St.
Edinburgh EH8 9LJ, United Kingdom
Journal covering the field of management, and government policies relating to continuing engineering education and lifelong learning. **Freq:** 6/yr. **Key Personnel:** Dr. Paul Brna, Assoc. Ed.; Dr. M.A. Dorgham, Editor-in-Chief. **ISSN:** 1560-4624. **Subscription Rates:** EUR593 individuals print or online; EUR830 individuals print and online. **URL:** http://www.inderscience.com/browse/index.php?journalID=6.

53288 ■ International Journal of Humanities and Arts Computing
Edinburgh University Press
22 George Sq.
Edinburgh EH8 9LF, United Kingdom
Ph: 44 131 6504218
Fax: 44 131 6503286
Publisher E-mail: marketing@eup.ed.ac.uk
Peer-reviewed journal covering all aspects of arts and humanities computing. **Freq:** 2/yr (March and October). **Key Personnel:** Dr. Paul Ell, Editor; Dr. David Bodenhamer, Editor. **ISSN:** 1753-8548. **Subscription Rates:** 92 institutions print and online; US$191 institutions print and online (North America); 100 institutions, other countries print and online; 40 individuals print and online; US$84 individuals print and online (North America); 44 other countries print and online. **URL:** http://www.eupjournals.com/journal/ijhac.

53289 ■ International Journal of Retail and Distribution Management
Emerald Group Publishing Ltd.
Prof. John Fernie
Heriot-Watt University
Riccarton
Edinburgh EH14 4HS, United Kingdom
Publisher E-mail: emerald@emeraldinsight.com
Retail industry publication. **Freq:** Monthly. **Key Personnel:** Prof. John Fernie, Editor, j.fernie@hw.ac.uk; Dr. Adelina Broadbridge, Retail Insights Ed., a.m.broadbridge@stir.ac.uk; Richard Whitfield, Publisher. **ISSN:** 0959-0552. **URL:** http://www.emeraldinsight.com/products/journals/journals.htm?id=ijrdm.

53290 ■ International Research in Children's Literature
Edinburgh University Press
22 George Sq.
Edinburgh EH8 9LF, United Kingdom
Ph: 44 131 6504218
Fax: 44 131 6503286
Publisher E-mail: marketing@eup.ed.ac.uk
Peer-reviewed journal covering children's literature for the literary scholar. **Freq:** Semiannual. **Key Personnel:** John Stephens, Sen. Ed. **ISSN:** 1755-6198. **Subscription Rates:** 92 institutions print and online; 100 institutions, other countries print and online; 38 individuals print and online; 44 other countries print and online; 20 members print; 73.50 institutions print; 80 institutions, other countries print; 31 individuals print; 35 other countries print; 28 individuals online. **Remarks:** Accepts advertising. **URL:** http://www.euppublishing.com/journal/ircl. **Circ:** (Not Reported)

53291 ■ Journal of Arabic and Islamic Studies
Edinburgh University Press
22 George Sq.
Edinburgh EH8 9LF, United Kingdom
Ph: 44 131 6504218
Fax: 44 131 6503286
Publisher E-mail: marketing@eup.ed.ac.uk
Journal covering the study of Arabic language and linguistic, medieval and modern Arabic literature, and Islamic civilization. **Key Personnel:** Joseph Norment Bell, Editorial Board; Alex Metcalfe, Editor. **ISSN:** 1748-3328. **URL:** http://www.uib.no/jais/.

53292 ■ Journal of British Cinema and Television
Edinburgh University Press
22 George Sq.
Edinburgh EH8 9LF, United Kingdom
Ph: 44 131 6504218
Fax: 44 131 6503286
Publisher E-mail: marketing@eup.ed.ac.uk
Journal for anyone interested in British cinema and television, and for those concerned with publishing cutting-edge work in these fields. **Freq:** 3/yr. **Key Personnel:** James Chapman, Principal Ed.; Prof. Julian Petley, Principal Ed.; Glen Creeber, Editorial Board; John Corner, Editorial Board; Jon Burrows, Editorial Board; John Caughie, Editorial Board; Alan Burton, Editorial Board; Sue Harper, Editorial Board; John Cook, Editorial Board. **ISSN:** 1743-4521. **Subscription Rates:** 118 institutions print and online; US$250 institutions print and online (North America); 131 institutions, other countries print and online; 59 individuals print and online; US$125 institutions print and online (North America); 65.50 other countries print and online. **Remarks:** Accepts advertising. **URL:** http://www.eupublishing.com/journal/jbctv. **Ad Rates:** BW: 200. **Circ:** (Not Reported)

53293 ■ Journal of Medical Education
Association for the Study of Medical Education
12 Queen St.
Edinburgh EH2 1JE, United Kingdom
Ph: 44 13 12259111
Fax: 44 13 12259444
Publisher E-mail: info@asme.org.uk
Journal covering medical education. **Founded:** 1966. **Freq:** Monthly. **Key Personnel:** Kevin W. Eva, Editor-in-Chief; Sue Symons, Acting Mng. Ed.; John Boulet, Dep. Ed.; Mark Albanese, Dep. Ed. **ISSN:** 0308-0110. **Subscription Rates:** US$2,198 institutions print + online; US$1,998 institutions print or online; 1,189 institutions print + online; 1,081 institutions print or online; EUR1,511 institutions print + online; EUR1,373 institutions print or online; US$2,564 institutions, other countries print + online; US$2,331 institutions, other countries print or online. **Remarks:** Advertising not accepted. **URL:** http://www.asme.org.uk/; http://www.wiley.com/bw/journal.asp?ref=0308-0110. **Circ:** (Not Reported)

53294 ■ Journal of Qur'anic Studies
Edinburgh University Press
22 George Sq.
Edinburgh EH8 9LF, United Kingdom
Ph: 44 131 6504218
Fax: 44 131 6503286
Publication E-mail: jqs@soas.ac.uk
Publisher E-mail: marketing@eup.ed.ac.uk
Peer-reviewed journal covering the study of Qur'an. **Freq:** Semiannual April and October. **Key Personnel:** Prof. M.A.S Abdel Haleem, Chm. **ISSN:** 1465-3591. **Subscription Rates:** 116 institutions print and online; US$243 institutions print and online (North America); 129 institutions, other countries print and online; 58 individuals print and online; US$121 individuals print and online (North America); 64.50 other countries print and online; 46 individuals print; US$97 individuals print (North America); 51 other countries print. **Remarks:** Accepts advertising. **URL:** http://www.euppublishing.com/journal/jqs. **Circ:** (Not Reported)

53295 ■ Journal of Scottish Philosophy
Edinburgh University Press
22 George Sq.
Edinburgh EH8 9LF, United Kingdom
Ph: 44 131 6504218
Fax: 44 131 6503286
Publisher E-mail: marketing@eup.ed.ac.uk
Journal aiming to provide a forum for philosophical discussion and historical scholarship on Scottish philosophy, philosophical theology, economic and political thought and related fields from any era of Scottish history. **Freq:** Semiannual. **Key Personnel:** Gordon Graham, Editor. **ISSN:** 1479-6651. **Subscription Rates:** 93 institutions print and online; 102 institutions, other countries print and online; 43 individuals print and online; 47 other countries print and online; US$91.50 individuals; US$196.50 institutions North America. **Remarks:** Accepts advertising. **URL:** http://www.eupjournals.com/journal/jsp. **Circ:** (Not Reported)

53296 ■ Juridical Review
W. Green & Son Ltd.

21 Alva St.
Edinburgh EH2 4PS, United Kingdom
Ph: 44 13 12254879
Fax: 44 13 12252104
Publisher E-mail: wgreen.enquiries@thomson.com
Law periodical. **Freq:** Quarterly. **Key Personnel:** Prof.
Joe M. Thomson, Editor. **ISSN:** 0022-6785. **Subscription Rates:** US$437 individuals rest of World; inclusive
of VAT; 240 individuals rest of World; inclusive of VAT;
220 individuals U.K./Europe; inclusive of VAT; EUR281
individuals U.K./Europe; inclusive of VAT. **URL:** http://
www.wgreen.co.uk/details?prodid=7122&unitid=7122.

53297 ■ Landwards
Institution of Agricultural Engineers
c/o Prof. Brian D. Witney, Ed.
Land Technology Ltd.
33 S Barnton Ave.
Edinburgh EH4 6AN, United Kingdom
Ph: 44 13 13363129
Publication E-mail: secretary@iagre.org
Publisher E-mail: secretary@iagre.org
Professional journal of the Institution of Agricultural
Engineers. **Freq:** Quarterly. **Key Personnel:** Peter L.
Redman, President; Prof. Brian D. Witney, Editor;
Christopher R. Whetnall, Ch. Exec. & Sec. **ISSN:** 1363-
8300. **Subscription Rates:** 52 nonmembers; 12 single
issue. **Remarks:** Accepts advertising. **URL:** http://www.
iagre.org/index.html. **Former name:** Agricultural
Engineer. **Circ:** 2,000

53298 ■ Legal Information Management
British and Irish Association of Law Librarians
c/o Elaine Bird, Hon. Sec.
12 S Bridge, Box 123
Edinburgh EH1 1DD, United Kingdom
Publisher E-mail: ebird@mail.com
Publication covering law libraries. **Freq:** Quarterly. **Key
Personnel:** Christine Miskin, Editor, c.miskin@
btinternet.com. **ISSN:** 1472-6696. **Subscription Rates:**
110 institutions online & print; 100 institutions online
only; US$179 institutions online & print; US$162 institutions online only. **URL:** http://www.biall.org.uk/pages/
legal-information-management.html; http://journals.
cambridge.org/action/displayJournal?jid=LIM. **Former
name:** Law Librarian. **Circ:** 1,200

53299 ■ Life and Work
Church of Scotland
121 George St.
Edinburgh EH2 4YN, United Kingdom
Ph: 44 131 2255722
Magazine of The Church of Scotland. **Founded:** 1879.
Freq: Monthly. **Key Personnel:** Lynne McNeil, Editor.
Subscription Rates: 24 surface; 33 airmail. **Remarks:**
Accepts advertising. **URL:** http://www.churchofscotland.
org.uk/lifework/index.htm. **Circ:** Paid 45,405

53300 ■ Luton News and Dunstable Gazette
Johnston Press PLC
108 Holyrood Rd.
Edinburgh EH8 8AS, United Kingdom
Ph: 44 131 2253361
Fax: 44 131 2254580
Community newspaper. **Freq:** Weekly. **Print Method:**
Web. **Trim Size:** 268 x 360 mm. **Cols./Page:** 9. **Key
Personnel:** Michael Johnston, Managing Dir.; John
Buckledee, Editor; Sally Twaite, Advertising Mgr. **Subscription Rates:** 52 individuals. **Remarks:** Accepts
advertising. **URL:** http://shop.lutontoday.co.uk/. **Circ:**
Controlled 14,716

53301 ■ Nanotoxicology
Taylor & Francis Ltd.
c/o Prof. Vicki Stone, Ed.
Biomedicine & Sport & Exercise Science Research
Group
School of Life Sciences, Napier University
Merchiston Campus
Edinburgh EH10 5DT, United Kingdom
Journal addressing research into the interactions
between nano-structured materials and living matter.
Freq: Annual. **Key Personnel:** Dr. Fanqing Frank Chen,
Editorial Board; Prof. Ken Donaldson, Editorial Board;
Prof. Paul Borm, Editorial Board; Prof. Marc Benedetti,
Editorial Board; Prof. Vicki Colvin, Editorial Board; Prof.
Vicki Stone, Editor. **ISSN:** 1743-5390. **Subscription
Rates:** 495 institutions; US$895 institutions; EUR715
institutions. **Remarks:** Accepts advertising. **URL:** http://
www.informaworld.com/smpp/title~content=

t716100760~db=all. **Circ:** (Not Reported)

53302 ■ Neuroendocrinology
S. Karger Publishers Inc.
c/o Dr. Robert Millar, Ed.-in-Ch.
Human Reproductive Sciences Unit
The Queen's Medical Research Center
47 Little France Cres.
Edinburgh EH16 4TJ, United Kingdom
Ph: 4 131 2426227
Publisher E-mail: karger@snet.net
Medical journal. **Subtitle:** International Journal for Basic
and Clinical Studies on Neuroendocrin Relationships.
Founded: 1965. **Freq:** 8/yr. **Print Method:** Offset. **Trim
Size:** 210 x 280 mm. **Cols./Page:** 1. **Col. Width:** 99
nonpareils. **Col. Depth:** 155 agate lines. **Key Personnel:** Dr. Robert Millar, Editor-in-Chief, nen@hrsu.mrc.ac.
uk; N. Oswald, Editorial Mgr.; M.J. Kelly, Editor; B.
Wiedenmann, Editor; A. Enjalbert, Editor; M.A. Cowley,
Editor; C. Coen, Editor; M. Tena-Sempere, Editor; P.A.
Kelly, Editor; I.J. Clarke, Editor. **ISSN:** 0028-3835. **Subscription Rates:** 3,022 SFr institutions print or online;
EUR2,158 institutions print or online; US$2,740 institutions print or online; 3,324 SFr institutions print and online; EUR2,374 institutions print and online; US$3,016
institutions print and online; 63.20 SFr institutions postage and handling; EUR44.80 institutions postage and
handling; 94.40 SFr institutions postage and handling,
overseas; US$89.60 institutions postage and handling,
overseas. **Remarks:** Accepts advertising. **URL:** http://
content.karger.com/ProdukteDB/produkte.asp?Aktion=
JournalHome&ProduktNr=223855. **Ad Rates:** BW:
1,195. **Circ:** 1,650

53303 ■ New Blackfriars
John Wiley & Sons Inc.
Wiley-Blackwell
c/o Fergus Kerr, Ed.
Blackfriars
24 George Sq.
Edinburgh EH8 9LD, United Kingdom
Peer-reviewed journal dealing with all aspects of preacherstheology, philosophy and cultural studies. **Subtitle:** A
Review: Edited by the Dominicans of the English
Province. **Founded:** 1920. **Freq:** Bimonthly. **Key Personnel:** Fergus Kerr, Editor, fergus.kerr@english.op.
org; Gregory Pearson, Reviews Ed., nb.reviews@
english.op.org; Vivian Boland, Reviews Ed. **ISSN:** 0028-
4289. **Subscription Rates:** US$47 individuals print and
online; US$39 students print and online; 22 students,
other countries print and online; US$244 institutions
print and online; US$222 institutions print, online;
US$334 institutions, other countries print and online;
EUR42 individuals print and online; EUR33 students print
and online; 171 institutions print and online; 155 institutions print, online. **Remarks:** Advertising accepted; rates
available upon request. **URL:** http://www.wiley.com/bw/
journal.asp?ref=0028-4289&site=1. **Circ:** (Not Reported)

53304 ■ Oxford Literary Review
Edinburgh University Press
22 George Sq.
Edinburgh EH8 9LF, United Kingdom
Ph: 44 131 6504218
Fax: 44 131 6503286
Publisher E-mail: marketing@eup.ed.ac.uk
Journal covering literary theory, concerned with the history and development of deconstructive thinking in all
areas of intellectual, cultural and political life. **Freq:**
Semiannual. **Key Personnel:** Prof. Geoffrey Bennington, Editor; Prof. Timothy Clark, Editor; Prof. Peggy Kamuf, Editor. **ISSN:** 0305-1498. **Subscription Rates:** 96
institutions print and online; 99 institutions, other
countries print and online; 39.50 individuals print and
online; 40 other countries print and online; US$193
institutions North America (print and online); US$80
individuals North America (print and online). **Remarks:**
Accepts advertising. **URL:** http://www.eupjournals.com/
journal/olr. **Circ:** (Not Reported)

53305 ■ Paragraph
Edinburgh University Press
22 George Sq.
Edinburgh EH8 9LF, United Kingdom
Ph: 44 131 6504218
Fax: 44 131 6503286
Publisher E-mail: marketing@eup.ed.ac.uk
Journal covering critical modern theory. **Founded:** 1983.
Freq: 3/yr (March, July and November). **Key Personnel:** Mairead Hanrahan, Editorial Committee; Terence
Cave, Advisory Ed.; Leslie Hill, Advisory Ed. **ISSN:** 0264-

8334. **Subscription Rates:** 124 institutions print; 155
institutions print and online; 59 individuals print; 73.50
individuals print and online; 111.50 institutions online;
170.50 institutions, other countries print and online;
53.50 individuals online; 80 other countries print and
online. **URL:** http://www.eupjournals.com/journal/para.
Circ: (Not Reported)

**53306 ■ Proceedings of the Edinburgh
Mathematical Society**
Cambridge University Press
14 India St.
Edinburgh EH3 6EZ, United Kingdom
Publisher E-mail: information@cambridge.org
Journal covering topics related to pure and applied
mathematics. **Founded:** 1984. **Freq:** 3/yr. **Key Personnel:** Dr. C. Athorne, Reviews Ed., c.athorne@maths.gla.
ac.uk; Prof. I. Gordon, Editorial Board, i.gordon@ed.ac.
uk; Prof. J.M. Rosenberg, Consulting Ed.; Dr. M.
Grinfeld, Editorial Board; Dr. C.J. Smyth, Editorial Board,
c.smyth@ed.ac.uk; Dr. M. Lawson, Editorial Board, m.v.
lawson@ma.hw.ac.uk; Prof. F. Kirwan, Consulting Ed.
ISSN: 0013-0915. **Subscription Rates:** 216 institutions
print and online; US$423 institutions print and online;
184 institutions online only; US$365 institutions online
only. **Remarks:** Accepts advertising. **URL:** http://
journals.cambridge.org/action/displayJournal?jid=PEM.
Ad Rates: BW: 445. **Circ:** 700

53307 ■ Psychoanalysis and History
Edinburgh University Press
22 George Sq.
Edinburgh EH8 9LF, United Kingdom
Ph: 44 131 6504218
Fax: 44 131 6503286
Publisher E-mail: marketing@eup.ed.ac.uk
Journal covering study of the history of psychoanalysis
and the application psychoanalytic ideas to
historiography. **Freq:** 2/yr (January and July). **Key Personnel:** John Forrester, Editor. **ISSN:** 1460-8235. **Subscription Rates:** 92 institutions print and online;
US$191 institutions print and online (North America);
100 institutions, other countries print and online; 42
individuals print and online; US$87.50 individuals print
and online (North America); 45.50 other countries print
and online. **Remarks:** Accepts advertising. **URL:** http://
www.eupjournals.com/journal/pah. **Circ:** (Not Reported)

53308 ■ Romanticism
Edinburgh University Press
22 George Sq.
Edinburgh EH8 9LF, United Kingdom
Ph: 44 131 6504218
Fax: 44 131 6503286
Publisher E-mail: marketing@eup.ed.ac.uk
Journal covering romantic studies. **Freq:** 3/yr. **Key Personnel:** Drummond Bone, Editor; Nicholas Roe, Editor;
Peter Vassallo, Sen. Advisory Ed. **ISSN:** 1354-991X.
Subscription Rates: 140 institutions print; 175 institutions print and online; 57 individuals print; 71.50 individuals print and online; 126.50 institutions online; 193
institutions, other countries print; 51.50 individuals online; 63.50 other countries print. **Remarks:** Accepts
advertising. **URL:** http://www.eupjournals.com/journal/
rom. **Circ:** (Not Reported)

53309 ■ Rutland & Stamford Mercury Series
Johnston Press PLC
108 Holyrood Rd.
Edinburgh EH8 8AS, United Kingdom
Ph: 44 131 2253361
Fax: 44 131 2254580
Community newspaper. **Founded:** 1695. **Freq:** Weekly
(Fri.). **Print Method:** Web offset. **Key Personnel:** Eileen Green, Editor, eileen.green@stamfordmercury.co.
uk. **Subscription Rates:** 6 individuals 1 month; 19
individuals 3 months; 37.18 individuals 6 months; 56
individuals 9 months; 74.36 individuals; 10 individuals
Europe; 1 month; 31.33 individuals Europe; 3 months;
63 individuals Europe; 6 months; 94 individuals Europe;
9 months; 125.32 individuals Europe. **Remarks:** Accepts advertising. **URL:** http://www.stamfordmercury.co.
uk. **Circ:** Paid 21,784

53310 ■ Scotland's New Homebuyer
Pinpoint Scotland Ltd.
9 Gayfield Sq.
Edinburgh EH1 3NT, United Kingdom
Ph: 44 131 5574184

Circulation: ★ = ABC; △ = BPA; ◆ = CAC; • = CCAB; ❑ = VAC; ⊕ = PO Statement; ‡ = Publisher's Report; Boldface figures = sworn; Light figures = estimated.

Gale Directory of Publications & Broadcast Media/147th Ed. 5641

Fax: 44 131 4788405
Publisher E-mail: admin@pinpoint-scotland.com
Consumer magazine covering new homes and apartments for sale in Scotland. **Founded:** 1985. **Freq:** Quarterly. **Print Method:** Web. **Cols./Page:** 2. **Key Personnel:** Helen Stuart, General Mgr., helen@pinpoint-scotland.com. **Subscription Rates:** 10 individuals; 2.50 single issue. **Remarks:** Accepts advertising. **URL:** http://www.snhb.co.uk/. **Circ:** Non-paid 18,000

53311 ■ The Scots Law Times
W. Green & Son Ltd.
21 Alva St.
Edinburgh EH2 4PS, United Kingdom
Ph: 44 13 12254879
Fax: 44 13 12252104
Publisher E-mail: wgreen.enquiries@thomson.com
Professional magazine covering decisions of all Scottish courts and other issues related to the legal profession. **Founded:** 1893. **Freq:** Weekly (Fri.) 40/yr. **Trim Size:** 185 x 270 mm. **Cols./Page:** 2. **Col. Width:** 70 millimeters. **Col. Depth:** 217 millimeters. **Key Personnel:** William Stewart, Contact; Peter Nicholson, Editor. **ISSN:** 0036-908X. **Subscription Rates:** 409 individuals; 18 single issue. **Remarks:** Accepts advertising. **URL:** http://www.wgreen.co.uk; http://www.wgreen.co.uk/scotslaw/index.html. **Circ:** (Not Reported)

53312 ■ Scottish Archaeological Journal
Edinburgh University Press
22 George Sq.
Edinburgh EH8 9LF, United Kingdom
Ph: 44 131 6504218
Fax: 44 131 6503286
Publisher E-mail: marketing@eup.ed.ac.uk
Journal covering perspective on Scottish archaeology. **Founded:** 1969. **Freq:** 2/yr (March and October). **Key Personnel:** Dr. Stephen T. Driscoll, Editor. **ISSN:** 1471-5767. **Subscription Rates:** 95 institutions print and online; US$204 institutions print and online (North America); 107 institutions, other countries print and online; 43.50 individuals print and online; US$91.50 individuals print and online (North America); 48.50 other countries print and online. **Remarks:** Accepts advertising. **URL:** http://www.eupjournals.com/journal/saj. **Circ:** (Not Reported)

53313 ■ Scottish Educational Journal
Educational Institute of Scotland, Edinburgh
46 Moray Pl.
Edinburgh EH3 6BH, United Kingdom
Ph: 44 13 12256244
Fax: 44 13 12203151
Publisher E-mail: enquiries@eis.org.uk
Journal covering education. **Freq:** 5/yr. **Key Personnel:** Kate Blackwell, Contact, kblackwell@els.org.uk. **Remarks:** Accepts advertising. **URL:** http://www.eis.org.uk/information/sej.htm. **Circ:** Paid 63,000

53314 ■ Scottish Field
Craigcrook Castle
Craigcrook Rd.
Edinburgh EH4 3PE, United Kingdom
Ph: 44 131 3124550
Fax: 44 131 3124551
Publisher E-mail: adverts@scottishfield.co.uk
Consumer magazine covering lifestyle. **Subtitle:** Scotland's Official Magazine of the Year. **Founded:** 1903. **Freq:** Monthly. **Print Method:** Web offset. **Trim Size:** 210 x 297 mm. **Cols./Page:** 4. **Col. Depth:** 267 millimeters. **Key Personnel:** Archie MacKenzie, Editor; Bill Donaldson, National Advertising Mgr.; Clare Cameron, Contact; Brian Cameron, Advertising Mgr. **ISSN:** 0036-9209. **Subscription Rates:** 124 other countries 3 years (worldwide delivery); 89 other countries 2 years (worldwide delivery); 49 other countries worldwide delivery; 97 individuals 3 years (U.K. delivery); 71 two years U.K. delivery; 40.80 individuals U.K. delivery. **URL:** http://www.scottishfield.co.uk/. **Ad Rates:** 4C: 1,875. **Circ:** Paid ★14,165

53315 ■ Scottish Genealogist
Scottish Genealogy Society
15 Victoria Ter.
Edinburgh EH1 2JL, United Kingdom
Ph: 44 13 12203677
Fax: 44 13 12203677
Publisher E-mail: enquiries@scotsgenealogy.com
Publication covering the Scottish genealogist. **Founded:** 1954. **Freq:** Quarterly. **Subscription Rates:** Free to all

members. **URL:** http://www.scotsgenealogy.com/.

53316 ■ Scottish Historical Review
Edinburgh University Press
22 George Sq.
Edinburgh EH8 9LF, United Kingdom
Ph: 44 131 6504218
Fax: 44 131 6503286
Publisher E-mail: marketing@eup.ed.ac.uk
Journal covering all periods of Scottish history from the early to the modern. **Freq:** 2/yr (April and October). **Trim Size:** 110 x 210 mm. **Key Personnel:** Dr. Catriona Mac-Donald, Editor; Dr. David Ditchburn, Editor. **ISSN:** 0036-9241. **Subscription Rates:** 115.50 institutions print and online; US$241.20 institutions print and online (North America); 127 institutions, other countries print and online; 55.50 individuals print and online; US$112.50 individuals print and online (North America); 59 other countries print and online; 28 students print and online; US$59.50 students print and online (North America); 32.50 students, other countries print and online. **Remarks:** Accepts advertising. **URL:** http://www.eupjournals.com/journal/shr. **Circ:** (Not Reported)

53317 ■ Scottish Home and Country
Scottish Women's Rural Institutes
42 Heriot Row
Edinburgh EH3 6ES, United Kingdom
Ph: 44 131 2251724
Fax: 44 131 2258129
Publisher E-mail: swri@swri.demon.co.uk
Scottish publication covering rural and women's issues. **Founded:** 1925. **Freq:** Monthly. **Trim Size:** 15 x 21 cm. **Subscription Rates:** 16.50 individuals U.K.; 20 other countries. **URL:** http://www.swri.org.uk/magazine/index.html. **Ad Rates:** BW: 174, 4C: 347. **Circ:** 11,000

53318 ■ Script-ed
Arts and Humanities Research Centre in Intellectual Property and Technology
School of Law
University of Edinburgh
Old College
Edinburgh EH8 9YL, United Kingdom
Ph: 44 131 6502014
Fax: 44 131 6506317
Publication E-mail: editors.scripted@ed.ac.uk
Publisher E-mail: itandip@ed.ac.uk
Online, international, interdisciplinary and multi-lingual journal featuring articles, reports, commentaries, analysis, case and legislation critiques, and book reviews pertaining to law and technologies in the broadest sense. **Subtitle:** A Journal of Law, Technology and Society. **Key Personnel:** Prof. Lionel Bently, Advisory Board; Prof. Lillian Edwards, Consulting Ed.; Prof. Graeme Laurie, Consulting Ed.; Shawn H.E. Harmon, Editor-in-Chief; Yolanda Stolte, Managing Editor; Prof. Margaret Brazier, Advisory Board; Prof. Ruth Chadwick, Advisory Board. **URL:** http://www.law.ed.ac.uk/ahrb/script-ed.

53319 ■ South Edinburgh Echo
South Edinburgh Community Newspaper Ltd.
64 Gilmerton Dykes St.
Edinburgh EH17 8PL, United Kingdom
Ph: 44 131 6217065
Fax: 44 131 6217064
Publication E-mail: news@southedinburgh.net
Publisher E-mail: echo@southedinburgh.net
Newspaper covering the latest events in the local areas of South Edinburgh. **Remarks:** Accepts advertising. **URL:** http://www.southedinburgh.net/echo. **Circ:** (Not Reported)

53320 ■ Spectrum Magazine Scotland on Sunday
The Scotsman Publications Ltd.
Barclay House
108 Holyrood Rd.
Edinburgh EH8 8AS, United Kingdom
Ph: 44 13 16208620
Consumer magazine covering lifestyle and arts. **Freq:** Weekly (Sun.). **URL:** http://scotlandonsunday.scotsman.com.

53321 ■ Studies in World Christianity
Edinburgh University Press
22 George Sq.
Edinburgh EH8 9LF, United Kingdom
Ph: 44 131 6504218
Fax: 44 131 6503286

Publisher E-mail: marketing@eup.ed.ac.uk
Journal covering the new forms of Christianity. **Freq:** 3/yr. **Key Personnel:** Alistair Kee, Editor; Marcella Maria Althaus-Reid, Assoc. Ed.; Afe Adogame, Assoc. Ed. **ISSN:** 1354-9901. **Subscription Rates:** 14.50 institutions print; 175.50 institutions print and online; 554 individuals print; 67.50 individuals print and online; 126.50 institutions online; 193 institutions, other countries print and online; 48.50 individuals online; 74.50 other countries print and online. **Remarks:** Accepts advertising. **URL:** http://www.eupjournals.com/journal/swc. **Circ:** (Not Reported)

53322 ■ Surgeons' News
Edinburgh University Press
22 George Sq.
Edinburgh EH8 9LF, United Kingdom
Ph: 44 131 6504218
Fax: 44 131 6503286
Publisher E-mail: marketing@eup.ed.ac.uk
Journal featuring opinions, reviews and reports on surgery. **Freq:** Quarterly. **Key Personnel:** David Tolley, Editor. **ISSN:** 1750-7995. **Subscription Rates:** 275 institutions; 121.50 individuals; 302 institutions, other countries; 132 other countries. **Remarks:** Accepts advertising. **URL:** http://www.eupjournals.com/journal/snws. **Circ:** (Not Reported)

53323 ■ Teaching Earth Sciences
Earth Science Teachers Association
ESTA Membership Secretary
PO Box 23672
Edinburgh EH3 9XQ, United Kingdom
Publisher E-mail: contact@esta.net
Publication covering science teacher education. **Freq:** Quarterly. **Key Personnel:** Hazel Clark, Contact. **ISSN:** 0957-8005. **Remarks:** Advertising accepted; rates available upon request. **URL:** http://www.esta-uk.net/magazine.html. **Circ:** (Not Reported)

53324 ■ World Structure
Edinburgh University Press
22 George Sq.
Edinburgh EH8 9LF, United Kingdom
Ph: 44 131 6504218
Fax: 44 131 6503286
Publisher E-mail: marketing@eup.ed.ac.uk
Journal covering linguistic morphology and all related disciplines. **Freq:** Semiannual. **Key Personnel:** Laurie Bauer, Editor, laurie.bauer@vuw.ac.nz; Heinz Giegerich, Editor, heinz.giegerich@ed.ac.uk; Greg Stump, Editor, gstump@uky.edu. **ISSN:** 1750-1245. **Subscription Rates:** 71.50 institutions print; 89.50 institutions print and online; 33.50 individuals print; 42 individuals print and online; 64.50 institutions online; 99.50 institutions, other countries print and online; 30 individuals online; 47.50 other countries print and online. **Remarks:** Accepts advertising. **URL:** http://www.eupjournals.com/journal/word. **Circ:** (Not Reported)

53325 ■ Forth One-FM - 97.3
Forth House
Forth St.
Edinburgh EH1 3LE, United Kingdom
Ph: 44 84 53454001
Format: Contemporary Hit Radio (CHR); News; Sports. **Owner:** Radio Forth Limited, at above address. **Operating Hours:** Continuous. **Key Personnel:** Katie Bruce, Contact; Joanna McCullough, Contact, joanna.mccullough@radioforth.com; Craig Lumsdaine, Sales Dir., craig.lumsdaine@radioforth.com. **Ad Rates:** Advertising accepted; rates available upon request. **URL:** http://www.forthone.com/.

53326 ■ Forth 2-AM - 1548
Forth House
Forth St.
Edinburgh EH1 3LE, United Kingdom
Ph: 44 84 53454002
Fax: 44 84 53454003
Format: Contemporary Hit Radio (CHR); News; Sports. **Owner:** Radio Forth Limited, at above address. **Operating Hours:** Continuous. **Key Personnel:** Craig Lumsdaine, Sales Dir. **Ad Rates:** Advertising accepted; rates available upon request. **URL:** http://www.forth2.com.

53327 ■ Leith-FM - 98.8
2nd Fl., 17 Academy St.
Edinburgh EH6 7EE, United Kingdom

Ph: 44 131 5550446
Format: Talk; Alternative/New Music/Progressive; Folk; Ethnic. **Ad Rates:** Advertising accepted; rates available upon request. **URL:** http://www.leithfm.co.uk/.

Egham

53328 ■ Dyslexia Review
Dyslexia Action
Park House
Wick Rd.
Egham TW20 0HH, United Kingdom
Ph: 44 17 84222300
Fax: 44 17 84222333
Publisher E-mail: info@dyslexiaaction.org.uk
Publication covering dyslexia. **Founded:** 1989. **Freq:** 3/yr. **Trim Size:** A4. **ISSN:** 0308-6275. **Remarks:** Accepts advertising. **URL:** http://www.dyslexia-teacher.com/t10d.html. **Ad Rates:** BW: 200. **Circ:** 1,200

53329 ■ Journal of Stored Products Research
Elsevier Science
c/o P.F. Credland, Ed.-in-Ch.
School of Biological Sciences
Royal Holloway, University of London
Egham TW20 0EX, United Kingdom
Publisher E-mail: nlinfo-f@elsevier.com
Journal in the field of stored products like food, foodstuffs and durable items, including materials such as timber and museum artifacts. **Freq:** Quarterly. **Key Personnel:** P.F. Credland, Editor-in-Chief; G.J. Daglish, Regional Ed.; C.H. Bell, Regional Ed. **ISSN:** 0022-474X. **Subscription Rates:** 176,000¥ institutions for Japan; EUR1,325 institutions for Europe; US$1,483 institutions, other countries; US$147 individuals for all countries except Europe, Japan and Iran; 16,800¥ individuals for Japan; EUR110 individuals for Europe. **Remarks:** Accepts advertising. **URL:** http://www.elsevier.com/wps/find/journaldescription.cws_home/306/description. **Circ:** (Not Reported)

Ellon

53330 ■ ArtWork
Famedram Publishers Ltd.
PO Box 3
Ellon AB41 9EA, United Kingdom
Ph: 44 16 51842429
Fax: 44 16 51842180
Publisher E-mail: info@famedram.com
Free newspaper covering the arts in Scotland and North England. **Freq:** Bimonthly. **Key Personnel:** Sandra Moore, Advertising Coord. **Subscription Rates:** 8 individuals; 13 two years. **Remarks:** Accepts advertising. **URL:** http://www.artwork.co.uk/. **Circ:** 100,000

Ely

53331 ■ Ely Standard
Archant Regional Ltd.
38 Market St.
Ely CB7 4LS, United Kingdom
Ph: 44 1353 667831
Fax: 44 1353 645689
Publication E-mail: editor@ely-standard.co.uk
Publisher E-mail: sandra.roantree@archant.co.uk
Local community newspaper. **Freq:** Weekly (Thurs.). **Key Personnel:** Debbie Davies, Editor. **Subscription Rates:** Free to Ely, Newmarket, Soham, Littleport; 19.50 individuals 13 weeks; 39 individuals 26 weeks; 78 individuals. **Remarks:** Accepts advertising. **URL:** http://www.elystandard.co.uk/. **Circ:** ★20,474

Enfield

53332 ■ LNG World Shipping
Riviera Maritime Media Limited
Mitre House
66 Abbey Rd.
Enfield EN1 2QN, United Kingdom
Ph: 44 208 3641551
Publisher E-mail: info@rivieramm.com
Journal of reference for companies throughout the LNG marine transport chain. **Freq:** 6/yr. **Trim Size:** 210 x 297 mm. **Key Personnel:** Mike Corkhill, Editor, phone 44 1252 721693, mike.corkhill@rivieramm.com. **ISSN:** 1746-0603. **Subscription Rates:** 299 individuals print and digital; 498 two years print and digital. **Remarks:** Accepts advertising. **URL:** http://www.rivieramm.com/

publications/LNG-World-Shipping-3. **Ad Rates:** 4C: 3,040. **Circ:** ‡3,637

53333 ■ LPG World Shipping
Riviera Maritime Media Limited
Mitre House
66 Abbey Rd.
Enfield EN1 2QN, United Kingdom
Ph: 44 208 3641551
Publisher E-mail: info@rivieramm.com
Magazine featuring comprehensive coverage of the LPG ship sector. **Founded:** 2007. **Freq:** every spring. **Trim Size:** 210 x 297 mm. **Key Personnel:** Mike Corkhill, Editor, phone 44 1252 721693, mike.corkhill@rivieramm.com. **Subscription Rates:** 199 individuals print, digital and web; 318 two years print, digital and web. **Remarks:** Accepts advertising. **URL:** http://www.rivieramm.com/publications/LPG-World-Shipping-5. **Ad Rates:** 4C: 2,950. **Circ:** Combined 2,586

53334 ■ Marine Electronics & Communications
Riviera Maritime Media Limited
Mitre House
66 Abbey Rd.
Enfield EN1 2QN, United Kingdom
Ph: 44 208 3641551
Publisher E-mail: info@rivieramm.com
Magazine featuring authoritative coverage of technological developments both on board and ashore. **Freq:** 6/yr. **Trim Size:** 210 x 297 mm. **Key Personnel:** Clare Nicholls, Dep. Ed., phone 44 20 83707797, clare.nicholls@rivieramm.com. **Subscription Rates:** 249 individuals print and digital; 398 two years print and digital. **Remarks:** Accepts advertising. **URL:** http://www.rivieramm.com/publications/Marine-Electronics-and-Communications-7. **Ad Rates:** 4C: 2,825. **Circ:** ★6,944

53335 ■ Marine Propulsion & Auxiliary Machinery
Riviera Maritime Media Limited
Mitre House
66 Abbey Rd.
Enfield EN1 2QN, United Kingdom
Ph: 44 208 3641551
Publisher E-mail: info@rivieramm.com
Magazine featuring the full spectrum of commercial tonnage, naval and paramilitary vessels, and yachts. **Freq:** 6/yr. **Trim Size:** 210 x 297 mm. **Key Personnel:** Duncan Payne, Editor, phone 44 20 83701745, duncan.payne@rivieramm.com. **Subscription Rates:** 299 individuals print and digital; 498 two years print and digital. **Remarks:** Accepts advertising. **URL:** http://www.rivieramm.com/publications/Marine-Propulsion-and-Auxiliary-Machinery-6. **Ad Rates:** 4C: 2,485. **Circ:** ★12,525

53336 ■ Offshore Support Journal
Riviera Maritime Media Limited
Mitre House
66 Abbey Rd.
Enfield EN1 2QN, United Kingdom
Ph: 44 208 3641551
Publisher E-mail: info@rivieramm.com
Journal covering information on the market of offshore support vessels. **Founded:** 1998. **Freq:** 6/yr. **Trim Size:** 210 x 297 mm. **Key Personnel:** David Foxwell, Editor, phone 44 1252 717898, david.foxwell@rivieramm.com. **Subscription Rates:** 249 individuals print and digital; 398 two years print and digital. **Remarks:** Accepts advertising. **URL:** http://www.rivieramm.com/publications/Offshore-Support-Journal-9. **Ad Rates:** 4C: 2,315. **Circ:** ‡4,800

53337 ■ Tanker Shipping & Trade
Riviera Maritime Media Limited
Mitre House
66 Abbey Rd.
Enfield EN1 2QN, United Kingdom
Ph: 44 208 3641551
Publisher E-mail: info@rivieramm.com
Magazine featuring articles about the design, construction, outfitting, operation, and maintenance of oil and chemical tankers. **Freq:** 6/yr. **Trim Size:** 210 x 297 mm. **Key Personnel:** Edwin Lampert, Editor, phone 44 20 83707077, edwin.lampert@rivieramm.com. **Subscription Rates:** 249 individuals print and digital; 398 two years print and digital. **Remarks:** Accepts advertising. **URL:** http://www.rivieramm.com/publications/Tanker-

Shipping-and-Trade-10. **Ad Rates:** 4C: 2,365. **Circ:** ★4,798

Esher

53338 ■ Pharmacy in Practice
Medicom Publishing Ltd.
Churston House
Portsmouth Rd.
Esher KT10 9AD, United Kingdom
Ph: 44 137 2471671
Fax: 44 137 2471672
Professional magazine covering issues for practicing pharmacists. **Freq:** Monthly. **Print Method:** Sheetfed offset litho. **Trim Size:** 210 x 280 mm. **Key Personnel:** Dr. Christine Knott, Editor, christine@medicomgroup.com. **Subscription Rates:** 220.30 individuals. **Remarks:** Accepts advertising. **URL:** http://www.medicomgroup.com. **Circ:** Controlled 6,000

Essex

53339 ■ The Jowetteer
Jowett Car Club
15 2nd Ave.
Chemsford
Essex CM1 4ET, United Kingdom
Ph: 44 1274 604455
Fax: 44 1274 604455
Trade publication covering automotive. **Freq:** Monthly. **URL:** http://jowett.org/.

53340 ■ LighterLife
LighterLife UK Ltd.
Cavendish House
Parkway
Harlow Business Park
Essex CM 19 5QF, United Kingdom
Publisher E-mail: Businessteam@lighterlife.com
Magazine covering weight loss program. **Freq:** Quarterly. **URL:** http://www.lighterlifefranchise.com/what_support_will_i_get/lighterlife_magazine.aspx. **Circ:** (Not Reported)

53341 ■ Newham Recorder
Archant Regional Ltd.
539 High Rd.
Ilford
Essex IG1 1UD, United Kingdom
Ph: 44 20 84784444
Publisher E-mail: sandra.roantree@archant.co.uk
Local community newspaper. **Founded:** 1968. **Key Personnel:** Colin Grainger, Editor, colin.grainger@newhamrecorder.co.uk; John Finn, Dep. Ed., phone 44 20 84773781, john.finn@newhamrecorder.co.uk. **Subscription Rates:** 10 individuals 1 month; 20 individuals 2 months. **Remarks:** Accepts advertising. **URL:** http://www.newhamrecorder.co.uk/home. **Circ:** (Not Reported)

53342 ■ Romford & Havering Post
Archant Regional Ltd.
539 High Rd.
Ilford
Essex IG1 1UD, United Kingdom
Ph: 44 20 84784444
Publisher E-mail: sandra.roantree@archant.co.uk
Local community newspaper. **Key Personnel:** Mark Sweetingham, Editor, phone 44 208 4784444, mark.sweetingham@archant.co.uk. **Remarks:** Accepts advertising. **URL:** http://www.romfordrecorder.co.uk/home. **Circ:** (Not Reported)

Evesham

53343 ■ Evesham Journal
Newsquest Media Group Ltd.
Sapphire House
Crab Apple Way
Vale Pk.
Evesham WR11 1GP, United Kingdom
Newspaper featuring local news and events. **Founded:** 1860. **Freq:** Weekly. **Key Personnel:** John Murphy, Editor; Mark Stanford, Sports Ed. **Remarks:** Accepts advertising. **URL:** http://www.eveshamjournal.co.uk/. **Circ:** (Not Reported)

53344 ■ Oldham & District Property News
Property Print Services
Banner House

Briar Close
Evesham WR11 4XA, United Kingdom
Ph: 44 1386 765832
Publication E-mail: nfo@oldhampropertynews.co.uk
Publisher E-mail: info@ppsprint.co.uk
Newspaper covering local real estate. **Founded:** Jan.
1994. **Freq:** Weekly (Thurs.). **Print Method:** Heatset
webfed Litho. **Cols./Page:** 8. **Key Personnel:** Alan
Kirkham, Contact, alan@alankirkham.co.uk. **Subscription Rates:** 5.60 individuals 8 issues; 9.10 individuals
13 issues; 18.20 individuals 26 issues. **Remarks:** Accepts advertising. **URL:** http://www.oldhampropertynews.
co.uk/. **Ad Rates:** GLR: 3.70, BW: 250, 4C: 390. **Circ:**
Combined 15,000

Exeter

53345 ▪ Africa Research Bulletin
John Wiley & Sons Inc.
Wiley-Blackwell
c/o Virginia Baily, Ed.
8 Jubilee Rd.
Exeter EX1 2HU, United Kingdom
Ph: 44 1392 214290
Journal focusing on political and economic developments throughout Africa. **Subtitle:** Economic, Financial
and Technical Series. **Freq:** Monthly. **Key Personnel:**
Virginia Baily, Editor, editors@africaresearch.co.uk.
ISSN: 0001-9852. **Subscription Rates:** US$166 members print and online; EUR1,205 institutions print and online; US$1,795 institutions print and online; US$1,632
institutions print; 947 institutions print and online; 99
members rest of world; print and online; 265 students,
other countries; US$2,096 institutions, other countries
print and online; US$1,905 institutions, other countries
print; 860 institutions online. **Remarks:** Accepts
advertising. **URL:** http://www.wiley.com/bw/journal.asp?
ref=0001-9852&site=1. **Circ:** (Not Reported)

53346 ▪ Africa Research Bulletin
John Wiley & Sons Inc.
Wiley-Blackwell
c/o Virginia Baily, Ed.
8 Jubilee Rd.
Exeter EX1 2HU, United Kingdom
Ph: 44 1392 214290
Journal focusing on political and economic developments throughout Africa. **Subtitle:** Political, Social and
Cultural Series. **Freq:** Monthly. **Key Personnel:** Pita Adams, Sub-Ed., pita@africaresearch.eclipse.co.uk;
Virginia Baily, Editor, editors@africaresearch.co.uk.
ISSN: 0001-9844. **Subscription Rates:** US$445 students print + online; 235 students print + online; EUR353
students print + online; 160 students Africa; print + online; 265 students, other countries print + online;
US$1,795 institutions Americas (print and online); 947
institutions UK (print and online); EUR1,201 institutions
Europe (print and online); US$1,205 institutions Africa
(print and online); US$2,096 institutions, other countries
print and online. **Remarks:** Accepts advertising. **URL:**
http://www.wiley.com/bw/journal.asp?ref=0001-9844&
site=1. **Circ:** (Not Reported)

53347 ▪ Atmospheric Science Letters
John Wiley & Sons Inc.
c/o Dr. Chris Jones, Assoc. Ed.
Hadley Centre, B2-W04
Met Office
Fitzroy Rd.
Exeter EX1 3PB, United Kingdom
Ph: 44 1392 884514
Fax: 44 1392 885681
Publisher E-mail: info@wiley.com
Peer-reviewed covering the field of atmospheric and
closely related sciences. **Freq:** Quarterly. **Key Personnel:** Prof. Paul Hardaker, Assoc. Ed., paul.hardaker@
virgin.net; Alan Gadian, Editor, phone 44 113 3436461,
fax 44 113 3436716, alan@env.leeds.ac.uk; Dr. Chris
Jones, Assoc. Ed., chris.d.jones@metoffice.gov.uk; Prof.
Geoff Austin, Assoc. Ed., phone 64 9 3737599, fax 64 9
3737445, gla@phy.auckland.ac.nz; Prof. Andreas Bott,
Assoc. Ed., phone 49 228 735189, fax 49 228 735188,
a.bott@uni-bonn.de; Prof. Keith Haines, Assoc. Ed.,
phone 44 118 9318742, fax 44 118 9316413, kh@mail.
nerc-essc.ac.uk. **ISSN:** 1530-261X. **Subscription
Rates:** US$286 individuals electronic only. **URL:** http://
www3.interscience.wiley.com/journal/106562719/home.

53348 ▪ Collingwood and British Idealism Studies
Imprint Academic
PO Box 200

Exeter EX5 5YX, United Kingdom
Ph: 44 13 92851550
Fax: 44 13 92851178
Publisher E-mail: keith@imprint.co.uk
Journal covering the study of British idealism. **Freq:**
Semiannual. **Key Personnel:** David Boucher, Exec. Ed.;
William Sweet, Editor, wsweet@stfx.ca; Andrew Vincent,
Editor; Bruce Haddock, Editor, haddockba@cardiff.ac.
uk; James Connely, Editor; Colin Tyler, Editor. **ISSN:**
1744-9413. **Subscription Rates:** US$120 institutions;
60 institutions; US$48 individuals; 24 individuals. **URL:**
http://www.imprint.co.uk/idealists/collingwoodstudies.
html.

53349 ▪ Complementary Therapies in Medicine
Elsevier
Stover Ct., Bampfylde St.
Exeter EX1 2AH, United Kingdom
Peer-reviewed and health journal. **Freq:** 6/yr. **Key Personnel:** Jon Adams, Assoc. Ed., j.adams@sph.uq.edu.
au; Robbert Van Haselen, Editor-in-Chief, vanhaselen@
compuserve.com; Max Pittler, Assoc. Ed.; Rainer
Luedtke, Assoc. Ed. **ISSN:** 0965-2299. **Subscription
Rates:** US$443 institutions, other countries all countries
except Europe, Iran and Japan; 52,000¥ institutions;
EUR485 institutions for European countries and Iran;
US$151 individuals for all countries except Europe and
Japan; EUR164 individuals for European countries and
Iran; 17,600¥ individuals. **URL:** http://www.elsevier.com/
wps/find/journaldescription.cws_home/623020/
descriptiondescription.

53350 ▪ Country Smallholding
Archant Regional Ltd.
Fair Oak Close
Exeter Airport Business Pk.
Clyst Honiton
Exeter EX5 2UL; United Kingdom
Publication E-mail: editorial.csh@archant.co.uk
Publisher E-mail: sandra.roantree@archant.co.uk
Magazine featuring small-scale farming. **Founded:**
1975. **Freq:** Monthly. **Key Personnel:** Simon McEwan,
Editor, phone 44 1392 888481, fax 44 1392 888499.
Remarks: Accepts advertising. **URL:** http://www.
countrysmallholding.com/. **Circ:** (Not Reported)

53351 ▪ Devon Link
Devon County Council
Social Services Directorate
County Hall
Topsham Rd.
Exeter EX2 4QR, United Kingdom
Ph: 44 845 1551000
Fax: 44 845 1551003
Publication E-mail: devonlink@devon.gov.uk
Magazine covering issues for people with physical and
sensory disabilities. **Subtitle:** The Quarterly Magazine
for People with Physical & Sensory Disabilities in Devon.
Founded: 1984. **Freq:** Quarterly. **Trim Size:** A4. **Key
Personnel:** Sarah Avery, Editor. **ISSN:** 0266-5964. **Remarks:** Accepts advertising. **URL:** http://www.devon.
gov.uk/index/socialcare/social_services/pic/devonlink.
htm. **Ad Rates:** BW: 550, 4C: 650. **Circ:** Non-paid 7,000

53352 ▪ Dynamical Systems
Taylor & Francis Group Journals
Mathematics Research Institute
Harrison Bldg.
University of Exeter
Exeter EX4 4QF, United Kingdom
Publisher E-mail: customerservice@taylorandfrancis.
com
Peer-reviewed journal focusing on all aspects of modern
dynamical systems. **Subtitle:** An International Journal.
Founded: Sept. 21, 1928. **Freq:** Quarterly. **Trim Size:** 8
1/2 x 11. **Key Personnel:** Peter Ashwin, Editor-in-Chief,
dynsys@maths.ex.ac.uk; Matthew Nicol, Editor-in-Chief,
nicol@math.uh.edu. **ISSN:** 1468-9367. **Subscription
Rates:** 808 institutions print and online; US$1,349
institutions print and online; 768 institutions online;
US$1,282 institutions online; 221 individuals; US$366
individuals; EUR1,074 institutions print and online;
EUR1,020 institutions online only; EUR291 individuals.
URL: http://www.tandf.co.uk/journals/titles/14689367.
asp. **Formerly:** Dynamics and Stability of Systems.

53353 ▪ European Journal of Herbal Medicine
National Institute of Medical Herbalists
Elm House
54 Mary Arches St.
Exeter EX4 3BA, United Kingdom

Ph: 44 13 92426022
Fax: 44 13 92498963
Publisher E-mail: info@nimh.org.uk
European journal covering herbal medicine. **Founded:**
1994. **ISSN:** 1352-4755. **URL:** http://www.gcwhite.co.uk/
nimh.htm.

53354 ▪ European Journal of Oncology Nursing
Mosby Inc.
Stover Ct.
Bampfylde St.
Devon
Exeter EX1 2AH, United Kingdom
Ph: 44 1392 285857
Fax: 44 1392 426436
Publisher E-mail: custserv.ehs@elsevier.com
Peer-reviewed journal for oncology nurses. **Freq:** 5/yr.
Key Personnel: Prof. A. Molassiotis, PhD, Editor-in-Chief; S. Aranda, PhD, Editorial Committee; F. Gibson,
PhD, Assoc. Ed.; Prof. A. Richardson, PhD, Founding
Ed.; S. O'Connor, Editorial Committee; M. Fitch,
International Advisory Board. **ISSN:** 1462-3889. **Subscription Rates:** US$126 other countries except
Europe, Japan and Iran; EUR126 individuals except
Europe, Japan and Iran; 14,200¥ individuals; EUR557
institutions European countries and Iran; 59,900¥ institutions; US$494 institutions, other countries except
Europe, Japan and Iran. **Remarks:** Accepts advertising.
URL: http://www.elsevier.com/wps/find/
journaldescription.cws_home/623031/
descriptiondescription. **Circ:** (Not Reported)

53355 ▪ European Journal of Special Needs Education
Taylor & Francis Group Journals
School of Education
Exeter University
Heavitree Rd.
Exeter EX1 2LU, United Kingdom
Publisher E-mail: customerservice@taylorandfrancis.
com
Peer-reviewed journal focusing on the theory and
practice of special needs education. **Founded:** Mar.
1985. **Freq:** Quarterly. **Print Method:** Offset. **Trim Size:**
10 3/4 x 13 11/16. **Cols./Page:** 5. **Col. Width:** 26
nonpareils. **Col. Depth:** 196 agate lines. **Key Personnel:** Mary Ruth Coleman, Editorial Board; Alan Dyson,
Editorial Board; Maurice Chazan, Editorial Board; Brahm
Norwich, Book Review Ed.; Julie Allan, Editorial Board;
Harry Daniels, Editorial Board; Dr. Seamus Hegarty,
Editor, seamus.hegarty@onetel.net; J.J. Detraux, Editorial Board; Judith Hollenweger, Editorial Board. **ISSN:**
0885-6257. **Subscription Rates:** 224 individuals print;
647 individuals online; 681 individuals print and online;
EUR477 institutions print and online. **URL:** http://www.
tandf.co.uk/journals/titles/08856257.asp; http://www.
informaworld.com.

53356 ▪ Exepose
University of Exeter
Student's Guild
Devonshire House
Stocker Rd.
Exeter EX4 4PZ, United Kingdom
Ph: 44 1392 723528
Fax: 44 1392 263546
Publication E-mail: exepose@ex.ac.uk
Publisher E-mail: devonshirehouse-guild-info@ex.ac.uk
College newspaper. **Freq:** every 2 weeks. **Key Personnel:** Tristan Barclay, Editor; Andrew Waller, Editor; Charlie Marchant, News Ed.; Eleanor Busby, News Ed.; Alexander Cook, Sports Ed. **Subscription Rates:** Free.
URL: http://xmedia.ex.ac.uk/newspaper/. **Feature Editors:** Anna-Marie Linnell, *Features*. **Circ:** Controlled
2,500

53357 ▪ Exmouth Herald
Archant Regional Ltd.
Fair Oak Close
Exeter Airport Business Pk.
Clyst Honiton
Exeter EX5 2UL, United Kingdom
Ph: 44 1392 888400
Publisher E-mail: sandra.roantree@archant.co.uk
Local community newspaper. **Subscription Rates:** .85
individuals per week; 1.85 individuals per week to
Europe; 2.40 individuals per week to Zone 1; 2.65
individuals per week to Zone 2. **Remarks:** Accepts
advertising. **URL:** http://www.exmouthherald.co.uk/
home. **Circ:** (Not Reported)

53358 ■ Filtration
Filtration Society
19 Clyst Valley Rd.
Clyst St Mary
Exeter EX5 1DD, United Kingdom
Ph: 44 1392 874398
Fax: 44 1392 874398
Publisher E-mail: richard.wakeman@lineone.net
Publication covering filtration. **Freq:** Quarterly. **Key Personnel:** Dr. Steve Tarleton, Editor, e.s.tarleton@lboro. ac.uk; Prof. Richard Wakeman, Editor, richard. wakeman@lineone.net. **URL:** http://www.filtsoc.org/ journal/about-the-journal/.

53359 ■ Geophysical & Astrophysical Fluid Dynamics
Taylor & Francis Group Journals
School of Mathematical Sciences
University of Exeter
Harrison Bldg.
N Park Rd.
Exeter EX4 4QE, United Kingdom
Publisher E-mail: customerservice@taylorandfrancis. com
Peer-reviewed journal focusing on the fluid mechanics of the earth and planets, including oceans, atmospheres and interiors, and the fluid mechanics of the sun, stars and other astrophysical objects. **Freq:** 6/yr. **Key Personnel:** A.M. Soward, Editor, a.m.soward@exeter.ac.uk; R.H.J. Grimshaw, Editorial Board; M. Kono, Editorial Board; S.M. Chitre, Editorial Board; J.M. Aurnou, Editorial Board; U. Frisch, Editorial Board; R. Hide, Editorial Board; J.A. Whitehead, Editorial Board; E.G Zweibel, Editorial Board. **ISSN:** 0309-1929. **Subscription Rates:** 2,627 institutions print + online; 2,495 institutions online; EUR3,142 institutions print + online; US$3,946 institutions print + online; US$3,749 institutions online; EUR2,985 institutions online; 467 individuals; US$566 individuals; EUR451 individuals. **URL:** http://www.tandf. co.uk/journals/journal.asp?issn=0309-1929& linktype=5.

53360 ■ History of Political Thought
Imprint Academic
PO Box 200
Exeter EX5 5YX, United Kingdom
Ph: 44 13 92851550
Fax: 44 13 92851178
Publication E-mail: sandra@imprint.co.uk
Publisher E-mail: keith@imprint.co.uk
Peer-reviewed journal covering the historical study of political ideas and associated methodological problems. **Founded:** 1980. **Freq:** Quarterly. **Key Personnel:** Prof. Janet Coleman, Exec. Ed.; Prof. Iain Hampsher-Monk, Exec. Ed.; Dr. Paul Cartledge, Consulting Ed. **Subscription Rates:** US$104 individuals; US$62 students; 31 students; US$230 institutions; 115 institutions. **URL:** http://www.imprint.co.uk/hpt.html.

53361 ■ Journal of Dentistry
Mosby Inc.
Stover Ct.
Bampfylde St.
Exeter EX1 2AH, United Kingdom
Ph: 44 1392 285809
Fax: 44 1865 853132
Publisher E-mail: custserv.ehs@elsevier.com
Journal publishing research and developments in the field of dental science with an emphasis on new knowledge and innovations pertinent to the contemporary practice of clinical dentistry. **Freq:** Monthly. **Key Personnel:** Prof. A.D. Walmsley, Editor-in-Chief, a.d. walmsley@bham.ac.uk; F.R. Tay, Assoc. Ed., franklintay@gmail.com; S. McHugh, Statistical Advisor; S. Ebisu, Editorial Board; G. Fleming, Statistical Advisor, garry.fleming@dental.tcd.ie; P. Brunton, Editorial Board; F. Garcia-Godoy, Statistical Advisor, godoy@nsu.nova. edu; K. Akca, Editorial Board; A. Fouad, Editorial Board. **ISSN:** 0300-5712. **Subscription Rates:** 171,400¥ institutions; EUR1,290 institutions for European countries and Iran; US$1,444 institutions, other countries except Europe, Japan and Iran; 27,700¥ individuals; EUR209 individuals for European countries and Iran; US$232 other countries except Europe, Japan and Iran; 147 individuals. **URL:** http://www.elsevier.com/wps/find/ journaldescription.cws_home/30441/ descriptiondescription.

53362 ■ Journal of Rural Studies
Elsevier
Paul J. Cloke
Amory Bldg.

University of Exeter
Rennes Dr.
Exeter EX4 4RJ, United Kingdom
Journal containing information on aspects of planning, policy and management in rural society. **Founded:** 1993. **Freq:** Quarterly. **Key Personnel:** Paul J. Cloke, Editor-in-Chief, jrs@exeter.ac.uk. **ISSN:** 0743-0167. **Subscription Rates:** EUR138 individuals Europe and Iran; 19,900¥ individuals Japan; US$179 other countries; EUR886 institutions Europe and Iran; 108,400¥ institutions Japan; US$986 institutions, other countries. **URL:** http://www.elsevier.com/wps/find/journaldescription.cws_ home/348/descriptiondescription.

53363 ■ Studies in French Cinema
Intellect
Film Studies Dept.
Queens Dr.
University of Exeter
Exeter EX4 4QH, United Kingdom
Ph: 44 1392 264342
Fax: 44 1392 264222
Publisher E-mail: info@intellectuk.org
Journal providing academics and students with a consistent quality of scholarly investigation across the full breadth of the subject, including a focus on largely underdeveloped areas of French Cinema in both English and French research. **Founded:** 2001. **Freq:** 3/yr. **Trim Size:** 174 x 244 mm. **Key Personnel:** Susan Hayward, Editor, s.hayward@ex.ac.uk; Phil Powrie, Editor, p.p. powrie@newcastle.ac.uk; Jeff Kline, Editorial Board; Julia Dobson, Editorial Board; Elizabeth Ezra, Editorial Board; Michael Witt, Editorial Board. **ISSN:** 1471-5880. **Subscription Rates:** 33 individuals print; 210 institutions print and online; 12 single issue print; 177 institutions online. **Remarks:** Accepts advertising. **URL:** http://www.intellectbooks.co.uk/journals/view-Journal,id=126/. **Ad Rates:** BW: 100. **Circ:** (Not Reported)

53364 ■ Studies in Theatre and Performance
Intellect
Dept. of Drama
University of Exeter
Thornlea, New North Rd.
Exeter EX4 4JZ, United Kingdom
Ph: 44 1392 264580
Fax: 44 1392 26459
Publisher E-mail: info@intellectuk.org
Academic journal for scholars, teachers and practitioners to share the methods and results of practical research, to discuss issues related to theatre practice and to examine experiments in teaching and performance. **Founded:** 1990. **Freq:** 3/yr. **Trim Size:** 174 x 244 mm. **Key Personnel:** Peter Thomson, Editor, p.w.thomson@ exeter.ac.uk; Christopher Balme, Editorial Board; Christie Carson, Editorial Board; David Bradby, Editorial Board; Kate Dorney, Editor, k.dorney@vam.ac.uk; Gerry Harris, Editorial Board. **ISSN:** 1468-2761. **Subscription Rates:** 33 individuals print; 210 institutions print; 12 single issue print; US$65 individuals print; US$330 institutions print; US$24 single issue print; 177 institutions online; US$220 institutions online. **Remarks:** Accepts advertising. **URL:** http://www.intellectbooks.co.uk/ journals/view-Journal,id=124/. **Circ:** (Not Reported)

53365 ■ Thinking Skills and Creativity
Elsevier Science Inc.
School of Education & Lifelong Learning
University of Exeter, & The Open University
Exeter, United Kingdom
Publisher E-mail: usinfo-ehelp@elsevier.com
Peer-reviewed journal focusing on the teaching for thinking and creativity. **Founded:** 2006. **Freq:** 3/yr. **Print Method:** Offset. **Cols./Page:** 3 and 2. **Col. Width:** 17 and 26 nonpareils. **Col. Depth:** 105 agate lines. **Key Personnel:** Robert Burden, Editorial Board; Philip Adey, Editorial Board; Pam Burnard, Editorial Board; Kieran Egan, Editorial Board; Guy Claxton, Editorial Board; Edward de Bono, Editorial Board; Anna Craft, Editor, a.r. craft@exeter.ac.uk; Beno Csapo, Editorial Board; Agnes Chang, Editorial Board; Nasser Mansour, Assoc. Ed.; Rupert Wegerif, Editor, r.b.wegerif@exeter.ac.uk. **ISSN:** 1871-1871. **Subscription Rates:** US$224 institutions, other countries except Europe, Japan and Iran; 26,600¥ institutions; EUR226 institutions for European countries and Iran; 4,200¥ individuals; EUR35 individuals for European countries and Iran; US$35 other countries. **URL:** http://www.elsevier.com/wps/find/

journaldescription.cws_home/706922/ descriptiondescription.

53366 ■ Young Consumers
Emerald Group Publishing Ltd.
University of Exeter
School of Psychology
Washington Singer Laboratories
Perry Rd.
Exeter EX4 4QG, United Kingdom
Publisher E-mail: emerald@emeraldinsight.com
Journal providing the latest thinking, research and new approaches in marketing to children and young people. **Subtitle:** Insight and Ideas for Responsible Marketers. **Founded:** 1985. **Freq:** Quarterly. **Print Method:** Offset. **Trim Size:** 10 1/4 x 14. **Cols./Page:** 4. **Col. Width:** 27 nonpareils. **Col. Depth:** 196 agate lines. **Key Personnel:** Dr. Brian Young, Editor, b.m.young@exeter.ac.uk; Martyn Lawrence, Publisher, mlawrence@ emeraldinsight.com; Barbie Clarke, Assoc. Ed., barbie@ kidsandyouth.com. **ISSN:** 1747-3616. **URL:** http://info. emeraldinsight.com/products/journals/journals.htm?id= yc.

53367 ■ Heart-FM - 97.0
Hawthorn House
Exeter Business Pk.
Exeter EX1 3QS, United Kingdom
Ph: 44 1392 444444
Format: Adult Contemporary. **Formerly:** Gemini-FM. **Ad Rates:** Advertising accepted; rates available upon request. **URL:** http://www.heart.co.uk/exeter/.

53368 ■ Heart-FM - 103.0
Hawthorn House
Exeter Business Pk.
Exeter EX1 3QS, United Kingdom
Ph: 44 1392 444444
Format: Adult Contemporary. **Formerly:** Gemini-FM. **Ad Rates:** Advertising accepted; rates available upon request. **URL:** http://www.heart.co.uk/exeter/.

53369 ■ Xpression-FM - 87.7
Devonshire House
Stocker Rd.
Exeter EX4 4PZ, United Kingdom
Ph: 44 1392 263568
Format: Alternative/New Music/Progressive. **Operating Hours:** Continuous. **Key Personnel:** Angharad Smith, Station Mgr.; Steve Stafford, Prog. Controller. **URL:** http://xmedia.ex.ac.uk/radio.

Exmouth

53370 ■ International Journal of Police Science and Management
Vathek Publishing
c/o Dr. Ian K. McKenzie, Mng. Ed.
PO Box 119
Exmouth EX8 4WZ, United Kingdom
Ph: 44 1395 273502
Publisher E-mail: mlw@valthek.com
Journal reporting information for practitioners as well as academics with a view to advancing knowledge, disseminating good practice and fostering the scientific study of the police and policing. **Freq:** Quarterly. **Key Personnel:** Dr. Ian K. McKenzie, Managing Editor, editor@ijpsm.com; Jennifer Brown, Assoc. Ed.; Nikki McKenzie, Book Review Ed., books@ijpsm.com. **ISSN:** 1461-3557. **Subscription Rates:** 274 institutions paper and online; US$492 institutions paper and online; 137 individuals paper and online; US$246 individuals paper and online; 205 institutions online only; US$367 institutions online only; 102 individuals online only; US$183 individuals online only; 227 institutions paper only; US$410 institutions paper only. **Remarks:** Advertising accepted; rates available upon request. **URL:** http:// www.vathek.com/ijpsm/index.shtml. **Circ:** (Not Reported)

Falkirk

53371 ■ Central-FM - 103.1
201-203 High St.
Falkirk FK1 1DU, United Kingdom
Fax: 44 1324 611168
E-mail: mail@centralfm.co.uk
Format: Talk; News; Sports; Eclectic. **Operating Hours:** 6 a.m.-12 a.m. weekdays; 7:15 a.m.-12 a.m. Sun. **Ad Rates:** Advertising accepted; rates available upon request. **URL:** http://www.centralfm.demon.co.uk/.

Circulation: ★ = ABC; △ = BPA; ♦ = CAC; • = CCAB; ❑ = VAC; ⊕ = PO Statement; ‡ = Publisher's Report; Boldface figures = sworn; Light figures = estimated.

Gale Directory of Publications & Broadcast Media/147th Ed.

5645

Falmouth

53372 ■ Minerals Engineering
Elsevier Science
c/o B.A. Wills, Ed.-in-Ch.
Minerals Engineering International
18 Dracaena Ave.
Falmouth TR11 2EQ, United Kingdom
Ph: 44 1326 318352
Fax: 44 1326 318352
Publisher E-mail: nlinfo-f@elsevier.com
Journal focusing on innovative methodologies in mineral processing and extractive metallurgy. **Founded:** 1988. **Freq:** 15/yr. **Key Personnel:** B.A. Wills, Editor-in-Chief, bwills@min-eng.com; M. Adams, Editorial Advisory Board; G.E. Agar, Editorial Advisory Board; E.G. Kelly, Editorial Advisory Board; T.J. Harvey, Editorial Advisory Board; D. Deglon, Editorial Advisory Board. **ISSN:** 0892-6875. **Subscription Rates:** 226,100¥ institutions for Japan; EUR1,703 institutions for Europe; US$1,905 institutions all countries except Europe and Japan; 15,900¥ individuals for Japan; EUR119 individuals for Europe; US$132 individuals all countries except Europe and Japan. **Remarks:** Accepts advertising. **URL:** http://www.elsevier.com/wps/find/journaldescription.cws_home/837/description. **Circ:** (Not Reported)

Fareham

53373 ■ Maritime Journal
Mercator Media Ltd.
The Old Mill
Lower Quay
Fareham PO16 0RA, United Kingdom
Ph: 44 1329 825335
Fax: 44 1329 825330
Publication E-mail: editor@maritimejournal.com
Publisher E-mail: corporate@mercatormedia.com
Professional magazine covering the commercial marine industry and workboats in Europe. **Founded:** 1987. **Freq:** Monthly. **Print Method:** Web Offset. **Trim Size:** 297 x 210 mm. **Cols./Page:** 4. **Col. Width:** 43 millimeters. **Col. Depth:** 276 millimeters. **ISSN:** 0957-7009. **Subscription Rates:** 70 nonmembers; 80 nonmembers Europe; 106.50 other countries non members. **Remarks:** Accepts advertising. **URL:** http://www.maritimejournal.com/. **Circ:** Controlled 6,000

53374 ■ Motor Ship
Mercator Media Ltd.
The Old Mill
Lower Quay
Fareham PO16 0RA, United Kingdom
Ph: 44 1329 825335
Fax: 44 1329 825330
Publisher E-mail: corporate@mercatormedia.com
Publication covering the transportation industry. **Freq:** Monthly. **Key Personnel:** Bill Thomson, Editor, phone 44 1329 825335, fax 44 1329 825330, bthomson@motorship.com. **ISSN:** 0027-2000. **Subscription Rates:** 127 individuals. **URL:** http://www.motorship.com/.

53375 ■ Heart-FM - 97.5
Radio House
Apple Industrial Estate
Whittle Ave.
Fareham PO15 5SX, United Kingdom
Ph: 44 1489 589911
Fax: 44 1489 587739
Format: Adult Contemporary. **Owner:** Global radio, 30 Leicester Sq., London WC2H 7LA, United Kingdom. **Formerly:** Ocean-FM. **Operating Hours:** Continuous. **Ad Rates:** Advertising accepted; rates available upon request. **URL:** http://www.hearthampshire.co.uk/.

53376 ■ Wave-FM - 105.8
PO Box 105
Fareham PO15 5YF, United Kingdom
Ph: 44 1489 481050
Fax: 44 1489 481060
E-mail: sales@wave105.com
Format: Adult Contemporary. **Ad Rates:** Advertising accepted; rates available upon request. **URL:** http://www.wave105.com/.

53377 ■ Wave-FM - 105.2
PO Box 105
Fareham PO15 5YF, United Kingdom
Ph: 44 1489 481050
Fax: 44 1489 481060

E-mail: sales@wave105.com
Format: Adult Contemporary. **Ad Rates:** Advertising accepted; rates available upon request. **URL:** http://www.wave105.com/.

Farnborough

53378 ■ Gamewise
Game & Wildlife Conservancy Trust
Fordingbridge
Farnborough SP6 1EF, United Kingdom
Ph: 44 14 25652381
Publication covering wildlife conservation. **Freq:** 3/yr. **Trim Size:** 210 x 297 mm. **Key Personnel:** Nick Sotherton, PhD, Contact; Teresa Dent, Ch. Exec. **Remarks:** Accepts advertising. **URL:** http://www.gct.org.uk/text01.asp?PageId=19. **Ad Rates:** BW: 1,300. **Circ:** (Not Reported)

Farnham

53379 ■ Animation
Sage Publications Inc.
c/o Suzanne Buchan, Ed.
Animation Research Centre
University College for the Creative Arts
Falkner Rd.
Farnham GU9 7DS, United Kingdom
Publisher E-mail: info@sagepub.com
Journal focusing on animation. **Subtitle:** An Interdisciplinary Journal. **Freq:** 3/yr. **Key Personnel:** Suzanne Buchan, Editor. **ISSN:** 1746-8477. **Subscription Rates:** US$598 institutions print and e-access; US$538 institutions e-access; US$586 institutions print only; US$80 individuals print only; US$215 institutions single copy; US$35 single issue. **Remarks:** Accepts advertising. **URL:** http://www.sagepub.com/journalsProdDesc.nav?prodId=Journal201763. **Ad Rates:** BW: 350. **Circ:** (Not Reported)

53380 ■ The British Journal of Cardiology
British Association for Cardiac Rehabilitation
Town Hall Exchange
Castle St.
Farnham GU9 7ND, United Kingdom
Ph: 44 1252 720640
Fax: 44 1252 720601
Publisher E-mail: info@bacrphaseiv.co.uk
Journal providing information on latest advances in the field of cardiology. **Freq:** Bimonthly. **Key Personnel:** Dr. Henry Purcell, Editor, hpurcell@bjcardio.co.uk; Prof. Kim Fox, Editor. **Subscription Rates:** 150 libraries U.K. and Europe; 215 elsewhere institutions and libraries; 100 individuals U.K. and Europe; 160 elsewhere individual. **Remarks:** Accepts advertising. **URL:** http://www.bjcardio.co.uk/default.asp. **Ad Rates:** BW: 1,920. **Circ:** (Not Reported)

53381 ■ Cakes & Sugarcraft
Squires Kitchen Magazine Publishing Ltd.
Squires House
3 Waverley Ln.
Farnham GU9 8BB, United Kingdom
Ph: 44 845 2255671
Fax: 44 845 2255673
Publication E-mail: editorial@squires-group.co.uk
Publisher E-mail: info@squires-group.co.uk
Consumer magazine covering cake decoration and sugar crafting. **Founded:** Nov. 1993. **Freq:** Quarterly. **Print Method:** Web. **Trim Size:** A4. **Key Personnel:** Sarah Richardson, Design & Art Dir.; Beverley Dutton, Editor and Publisher; Jenny Stewart, Copy Ed. **Subscription Rates:** US$11.99 individuals; 28 individuals Europe; 34 other countries. **Remarks:** Accepts advertising. **URL:** http://www.globalsugarart.com/cat.php?acid=1004&s=&name=SQUIRES%20KITCHEN. **Formerly:** Sugarcraft. **Ad Rates:** BW: 1,305, 4C: 1,750. **Circ:** Paid 18,000

Farnsfield

53382 ■ Shalom
Church's Ministry Among Jewish People
Eagle Lodge, Hexgreave Hall Business Pk.
Farnsfield NG22 8LS, United Kingdom
Ph: 44 1623 883960
Fax: 44 1623 884295
Publisher E-mail: enquiries@cmj.org.uk
Missionary magazine. **Founded:** 1809. **Freq:** Annual.

Subscription Rates: US$12 individuals; US$2 single issue; 10 individuals includes postage. **Remarks:** Advertising not accepted. **URL:** http://www.cmj.org.uk. **Former name:** CMJ Quarterly. **Formerly:** Jewish Intelligence. **Circ:** (Not Reported)

Faversham

53383 ■ Milk Industry
Dairy UK
c/o Mel Armstrong, Ed.
Ewell House
Graveney Rd.
Faversham ME13 8UP, United Kingdom
Ph: 44 1795 542435
Fax: 44 1795 535469
Publisher E-mail: info@dairyuk.org
Publication covering the worldwide milk industry. **Freq:** 10/yr. **Print Method:** Litho. **Trim Size:** A4. **Key Personnel:** Emma Abbott, Editor, editorial@milkindustrymag.co.uk. **Subscription Rates:** 80 individuals; 95 other countries; 8 single issue; 9.50 single issue overseas. **Remarks:** Accepts advertising. **URL:** http://www.milkindustry.com/. **Formerly:** Milk Industry International. **Ad Rates:** BW: 750, 4C: 950. **Circ:** 2,000

53384 ■ New Stitches
Creative Crafts Publishing Ltd.
Well Oast
Brenley Ln.
Faversham ME13 9LY, United Kingdom
Ph: 44 1227 750215
Fax: 44 1227 751813
Publisher E-mail: enquiries@ccpuk.co.uk
Magazine featuring cross stitch designs. **Founded:** Oct. 1992. **Freq:** Monthly. **Key Personnel:** Janice Broadstocks, Editor, janice@ccpuk.co.uk; David Jones, Advertising. **URL:** http://www.newstitches.co.uk/index.html.

Felixstowe

53385 ■ Ford & Fordson Tractors
Kelsey Publishing Ltd.
PO Box 123
Felixstowe IP11 7ZP, United Kingdom
Ph: 44 139 4275120
Fax: 44 781 1393537
Publisher E-mail: info@kelsey.co.uk
Magazine featuring tractors of Ford & Fordson Association. **Freq:** Bimonthly. **Key Personnel:** Steve Wright, Editor, ff.ed@kelsey.co.uk. **Remarks:** Accepts advertising. **URL:** http://www.kelsey.co.uk/magazines.php?mag=ff. **Circ:** (Not Reported)

Ferndown

53386 ■ Everyday Practical Electronics
Wimborne Publishing Ltd.
113 Lynwood Dr.
Ferndown BH21 1UU, United Kingdom
Ph: 44 12 02873872
Fax: 44 12 02874562
Publisher E-mail: adverts@epemag.wimborne.co.uk
Consumer magazine covering electronics for students, trainees and hobbyists. **Subtitle:** Incorporating Electronics Today International. **Founded:** 1971. **Freq:** Monthly. **Print Method:** Heatset web. **Trim Size:** 210 x 297 mm. **Cols./Page:** 3. **Key Personnel:** Mike Kenward, Editor. **ISSN:** 0262-3617. **Subscription Rates:** US$76 individuals; US$88 individuals standard mail; US$124 individuals airmail. **Remarks:** Accepts advertising. **URL:** http://www.epemag3.com/. **Ad Rates:** BW: EUR500, 4C: EUR475, PCI: EUR10. **Circ:** Paid 19,000

Fife

53387 ■ Fife Free Press
Johnston Press PLC
23 Kirkwynd
Kirkcaldy
Fife KY1 1EH, United Kingdom
Ph: 44 1592 598811
Local community newspaper. **Remarks:** Accepts advertising. **URL:** http://www.fifetoday.co.uk/sectionhome.aspx?sectionID=4924. **Circ:** (Not Reported)

53388 ■ Kingdom Magazine
Dalgety Bay Business Ctr.

Ridge Way
Dalgety Bay
Fife KY11 9JN, United Kingdom
Ph: 44 01383 823333
Fax: 44 01383 824444
Publisher E-mail: enquiries@kingdommagazine.com
Magazine covering aspects of living in Fife today. Featuring information on history, people, wildlife, fashion, visitor attractions, sporting activities, walks, hotels, and eating out. **Freq:** 4/yr. **Subscription Rates:** 15 individuals. **URL:** http://www.kingdommagazine.com.

Fleet

53389 ■ The Brooklands Society Gazette
The Brooklands Society Ltd.
Copse Heath
38 Coxheath Rd.
Church Crookham
Fleet GU52 6QG, United Kingdom
Ph: 44 12 52408877
Fax: 44 12 408878
Publisher E-mail: sales@brooklands.org.uk
Journal covering the history of Brooklands, early automobile racing, and aviation history. **Founded:** 1957. **Freq:** Quarterly. **Trim Size:** 5 4/5 x 8 3/10. **Cols./Page:** 1. **Key Personnel:** Chris Bass, Editor, chris.bass@brooklands.org.uk. **Subscription Rates:** 25 members national; 30 other countries add 5. **URL:** http://www.brooklands.org.uk. **Circ:** Controlled 1,300

Fleetwood

53390 ■ Fleetwood Weekly News
Johnston Press PLC
168 Lord St.
Fleetwood FY7 6SR, United Kingdom
Ph: 44 1253 772950
Local community newspaper. **Freq:** Weekly. **Key Personnel:** Claire Clark, Reporter. **Remarks:** Accepts advertising. **URL:** http://www.fleetwoodtoday.co.uk/. **Circ:** (Not Reported)

Flitwick

53391 ■ Plumbing, Heating & Air Movement News
Pinede Publishing
c/o Chris Jones
1B Station Sq.
Bedfordshire
Flitwick MK45 1DP, United Kingdom
Ph: 44 1525 716143
Fax: 44 1525 715316
Publication E-mail: info@phamnews.co.uk
Publisher E-mail: info@phamnews.co.uk
Trade magazine covering the plumbing, heating and air industry. **Founded:** 1964. **Freq:** Monthly. **Trim Size:** 293 x 390 mm. **Cols./Page:** 6. **Col. Width:** 42 millimeters. **Key Personnel:** Chris Jones, Contact; Chris Evans, Contact. **ISSN:** 1368-9061. **Remarks:** Accepts advertising. **URL:** http://www.phamnews.co.uk. **Ad Rates:** BW: 2,060, 4C: 2,535. **Circ:** Combined ★27,962

Folkestone

53392 ■ Journal and Report of Proceedings
Permanent Way Institution
4 Coombe Rd.
Folkestone CT19 4EG, United Kingdom
Ph: 44 130 3274534
Publisher E-mail: secretary@permanentwayinstitution.com
Journal covering railroads. **Freq:** Quarterly. **Key Personnel:** Ted Hamer, Editor, editor@permanentwayinstitution.com. **ISSN:** 0031-5521. **Subscription Rates:** Free to members. **Remarks:** Advertising accepted; rates available upon request. **URL:** http://www.permanentwayinstitution.com. **Circ:** 7,000

53393 ■ Saga
Saga Publishing Ltd.
The Saga Bldg.
Enbrook Pk.
Folkestone CT20 3SE, United Kingdom
Ph: 44 1303 771111
Publisher E-mail: subs.enquiries@saga.co.uk
Lifestyle magazine featuring articles from home to

health, people to places, gardening to games and culture to celebrity. **Freq:** Monthly. **Key Personnel:** Katy Bravery, Editor. **Remarks:** Accepts advertising. **URL:** http://www.saga.co.uk/saga-magazine/. **Circ:** (Not Reported)

53394 ■ BBC Radio Kent - 97.6
The Great Hall
Mt. Pleasant Rd.
Tunbridge Wells TN1 1QQ, United Kingdom
Ph: 44 1892 670000
Fax: 44 1892 549118
Format: Full Service. **URL:** http://www.bbc.co.uk/kent/local_radio/.

Fordingbridge

53395 ■ Game Conservancy Magazine
The Game Conservancy Trust
Game Conservancy
Fordingbridge SP6 1EF, United Kingdom
Ph: 44 1425 652381
Fax: 44 1245 655848
Publisher E-mail: info@gwct.org.uk
Membership magazine of the Game Conservancy Trust. **Subtitle:** Gamewise. **Freq:** 3/yr. **Print Method:** Offset litho. **Trim Size:** 210 x 298 mm. **Remarks:** Accepts advertising. **URL:** http://www.gct.org.uk. **Ad Rates:** BW: 1,300. **Circ:** Controlled ⊕25,000

Forest Row

53396 ■ Good Motoring Magazine
Guild of Experienced Motorists
Sta. Rd.
GEM Motoring Assist
Forest Row RH18 5EN, United Kingdom
Fax: 44 13 42824847
Magazine covering motor safety. **Freq:** Quarterly. **Key Personnel:** Sir Anthony Grant, Vice President; Maureen Emms, Chm.; David Williams, Ch. Exec. **Remarks:** Advertising accepted; rates available upon request. **URL:** http://www.motoringassist.com/Members-Area/Magazine. **Circ:** 53,000

53397 ■ North Wind
George MacDonald Society
9 Medway Dr.
Forest Row RH18 5NU, United Kingdom
Publisher E-mail: macdonaldsociety@britishlibrary.net
Publication covering author named George MacDonald. **Subtitle:** A Journal of George MacDonald Studies. **Founded:** 1981. **Freq:** Annual. **Trim Size:** A5. **Key Personnel:** Rachel Johnson, Contact. **ISSN:** 0265-7295. **Remarks:** Advertising accepted; rates available upon request. **URL:** http://www.george-macdonald.com/gmsociety/northwind.html. **Circ:** (Not Reported)

Forfar

53398 ■ Kirriemuir Herald
Johnston Press PLC
Craig O Loch Rd.
Forfar DD8 1BT, United Kingdom
Ph: 44 1307 464899
Local community newspaper. **Remarks:** Accepts advertising. **URL:** http://www.kirriemuirherald.co.uk/. **Circ:** (Not Reported)

Freeland

53399 ■ At the Interface/Probing the Boundaries
Editions Rodopi B.V.
c/o Dr. Robert Fisher, Ed.
Priory House
149B Wroslyn Rd.
Oxfordshire
Freeland OX29 8HR, United Kingdom
Publisher E-mail: info@rodopi.nl
Journal focusing on philosophy. **Key Personnel:** Dr. Robert Fisher, Editor, rf@inter-disciplinary.net. **ISSN:** 1570-7113. **URL:** http://www.rodopi.nl/senj.asp?SerieId=ATI/PTB.

Frome

53400 ■ Outposts Poetry Quarterly
Hippopotamus Press
Roland John, 22 Whitewell Rd.

Frome BA11 4EL, United Kingdom
Ph: 44 13 73466653
Fax: 44 13 73466653
Publication E-mail: rjhippopress@aol.com
Poetry magazine. **Founded:** 1944. **Freq:** Quarterly. **Print Method:** Litho. **Trim Size:** A5. **Key Personnel:** Roland John, Contact. **ISSN:** 0950-7264. **Subscription Rates:** 8 individuals. **Remarks:** Accepts advertising. **URL:** http://www.poetrycan.co.uk/listing_details.asp?id=55. **Circ:** Paid 2,000

Gainsborough

53401 ■ Gainsborough Standard
Johnston Press PLC
5-7 Market Pl.
Gainsborough DN21 2BP, United Kingdom
Ph: 44 1427 615323
Fax: 44 1427 613492
Publication E-mail: editorial@gainsboroughtoday.co.uk
Local community newspaper. **Key Personnel:** Dave Green, Contact, dgreen@gainsboroughtoday.co.uk. **Remarks:** Accepts advertising. **URL:** http://www.gainsboroughstandard.co.uk/. **Circ:** (Not Reported)

Gairloch

53402 ■ Two Lochs Radio-FM - 106
c/o Two Lochs Radio
Gairloch IV21 2LR, United Kingdom
Ph: 44 8707 414657
Fax: 44 1445 712857
E-mail: info@2lr.co.uk
Format: Country; Folk; Reggae. **Operating Hours:** Continuous. **Ad Rates:** Advertising accepted; rates available upon request. **URL:** http://www.twolochsradio.co.uk/.

Galashiels

53403 ■ International Journal of Clothing Science and Technology
Emerald Group Publishing Ltd.
Heriot-Watt University
The Scottish College of Textiles
Netherdale
Galashiels TD1 3HF, United Kingdom
Publisher E-mail: emerald@emeraldinsight.com
Journal serving the needs of researchers, industrialists and engineers in the clothing industry by publishing international research and case studies on innovative technology and novel applications in all branches of the clothing and allied industries. **Freq:** 6/yr. **Key Personnel:** Prof. George K. Stylios, Editor, g.stylios@hw.ac.uk; Harry Colson, Publisher, hcolson@emeraldinsight.com. **ISSN:** 0955-6222. **URL:** http://info.emeraldinsight.com/products/journals/journals.htm?id=ijcst.

Garstang

53404 ■ Garstang Courier
Johnston Press PLC
7 Pringle Ct.
Park Hill Rd.
Garstang PR3 1LN, United Kingdom
Ph: 44 1995 605910
Local community newspaper. **Founded:** 1963. **Freq:** Weekly (Fri.). **Remarks:** Accepts advertising. **URL:** http://www.garstangcourier.co.uk/. **Circ:** (Not Reported)

Gateshead

53405 ■ Smooth Radio-FM - 107.7
Marquis Ct.
Team Valley Trading Estate
Gateshead, United Kingdom
Ph: 44 191 4407500
Format: Adult Contemporary; Middle-of-the-Road (MOR). **URL:** http://www.smoothradionortheast.co.uk/.

53406 ■ Smooth Radio-FM - 97.5
Marquis Ct.
Team Valley Trading Estate
Gateshead NE11 0RU, United Kingdom
Ph: 44 191 4407500
Format: Adult Contemporary; Middle-of-the-Road (MOR). **URL:** http://www.smoothradionortheast.co.uk/.

Circulation: ★ = ABC; △ = BPA; ♦ = CAC; • = CCAB; □ = VAC; ⊕ = PO Statement; ‡ = Publisher's Report; Boldface figures = sworn; Light figures = estimated.

Gale Directory of Publications & Broadcast Media/147th Ed.

5647

Gerrards Cross

53407 ■ BFBS Brunei-FM - 101.7
Chalfont Grove
Narcot Ln.
Chalfont St. Peter
Gerrards Cross SL9 8TN, United Kingdom
Ph: 44 1494 874461
Fax: 44 1494 872982
E-mail: bfbsbrunei@bfbs.com
Format: Information; News; Contemporary Hit Radio (CHR). **Operating Hours:** Continuous. **URL:** http://www.bfbs-radio.com/pages/extranet/bfbs-brunei-i-1238.php.

Gillingham

53408 ■ The Irish Genealogist
Irish Genealogical Research Society
18 Stratford Ave.
Rainham
Gillingham ME8 OEP, United Kingdom
Publisher E-mail: info@igrsoc.org
Publication covering the Irish genealogist. **Freq:** Annual. **ISSN:** 0306-8358. **Remarks:** Advertising not accepted. **URL:** http://www.igrsoc.org. **Circ:** (Not Reported)

Glasgow

53409 ■ Addiction Research and Theory
Informa Healthcare
Centre for Applied Social Psychology
University of Strathclyde
Graham Hills Bldg.
40 George St.
Glasgow G1 1QE, United Kingdom
Publisher E-mail: healthcare.enquiries@informa.com
Journal examining the effects of context on the use and misuse of substances, and on the nature of intoxications. **Founded:** 1993. **Freq:** Bimonthly. **Print Method:** Offset. **Trim Size:** 11 1/2 x 17 1/2. **Cols./Page:** 5. **Col. Width:** 11 1/2 picas. **Col. Depth:** 16 inches. **Key Personnel:** Ruth Engs, Editorial Board; Richard Hammersley, Editorial Board; Ross Coomber, Editorial Board; Douglas Cameron, Founding Ed.; Lester Grinspoon, Editorial Board; Stanton Peele, Editorial Board; John Davies, Editor-in-Chief. **ISSN:** 1606-6359. **Subscription Rates:** 480 institutions; US$790 institutions; EUR630 institutions; 960 institutions; US$1,575 institutions; EUR1,260 institutions. **URL:** http://informahealthcare.com/art.

53410 ■ Brown's Nautical Almanac
Brown, Son & Ferguson Ltd.
4-10 Darnley St.
Glasgow G41 2SD, United Kingdom
Ph: 44 141 4291234
Fax: 44 141 4201694
Publication E-mail: info@skipper.co.uk
Publisher E-mail: info@skipper.co.uk
Nautical almanac covering tide tables, nautical tables, meteorology and related information. **Founded:** 1850. **Freq:** Annual. **Print Method:** Lithography. **Trim Size:** 117 x 190 mm. **Key Personnel:** Thomas Nigel Brown, Author. **ISSN:** 0068-290X. **Subscription Rates:** 60 individuals; 65.41 individuals by post; 71.98 other countries. **Remarks:** Accepts advertising. **URL:** http://www.skipper.co.uk. **Circ:** 13,000

53411 ■ Bunkered
PSP Publishing Ltd.
50 High Craighall Rd.
Glasgow G4 9UD, United Kingdom
Ph: 44 141 3532222
Fax: 44 141 3323839
Publisher E-mail: sales@psp.uk.net
Magazine featuring golf in Scotland. **Freq:** 8/yr. **Key Personnel:** Paul Grant, Director; Thomas Lovering, Director; Stephen McCann, Director. **Subscription Rates:** 25 individuals for printed copy. **Remarks:** Accepts advertising. **URL:** http://www.bunkered.co.uk/; http://www.psppublishing.com/bunkered.html. **Circ:** (Not Reported)

53412 ■ Cellular Signalling
Elsevier Science
c/o Miles D. Houslay, Ed.-in-Ch.
Molecular Pharmacology Group
Dept. of Biochemistry
University of Glasgow
Glasgow G12 8QQ, United Kingdom
Ph: 44 141 3305903

Fax: 44 141 3304365
Publisher E-mail: nlinfo-f@elsevier.com
Journal devoted to various mechanisms, actions and structural components of cellular signaling systems under normal as well as pathological conditions. **Founded:** 1989. **Freq:** Monthly. **Key Personnel:** Nigel Pyne, Editor, phone 44 14 15482659, fax 44 14 15522562, n.j.pyne@strath.ac.uk; Miles D. Houslay, Editor-in-Chief, m.houslay@bio.gla.ac.uk; George S. Baillie, Co-Ed., g.baillie@bio.gla.ac.uk; Susan Payne, Co-Ed., susan.pyne@strath.ac.uk; L. Birnbaumer, Editorial Board; J. Bockaert, Editorial Board. **ISSN:** 0898-6568. **Subscription Rates:** US$352 individuals all Countries except Europe and Japan; EUR311 individuals European Countries; 41,500¥ individuals; US$2,672 institutions for all countries except Europe, Japan & Iran; EUR2,388 institutions for European countries & Iran; 317,000¥ institutions. **Remarks:** Accepts advertising. **URL:** http://www.elsevier.com/wps/find/journaldescription.cws_home/525462/description. **Circ:** (Not Reported)

53413 ■ Dig BMX Magazine
Factory Media
Studio 153, 355 Byres Rd.
Glasgow G12 8QZ, United Kingdom
Ph: 44 141 9455019
Fax: 44 141 9455019
Publication E-mail: digbmx@servicehelpline.co.uk
Publisher E-mail: contact@factorymedia.com
Magazine featuring bicycling. **Founded:** Oct. 1993. **Freq:** Bimonthly. **Subscription Rates:** 17.99 individuals credit card; US$64 two years; US$32 individuals. **Remarks:** Accepts advertising. **URL:** http://digbmx.com/; http://factorymedia.com. **Circ:** (Not Reported)

53414 ■ The Drum
Carnyx Group Ltd.
Mercat Bldg., 4th Fl.
26 Gallowgate
Glasgow G1 5AB, United Kingdom
Ph: 44 141 5525858
Publisher E-mail: enquiry@carnyx.com
Magazine covering news, reviews and analysis across advertising, design, media, marketing, PR and online industries outside of London. **Trim Size:** 240 x 330 mm. **Key Personnel:** Gordon Young, Publisher; Richard Draycott, Editor; Gordon Laing, Dep. Ed. **Subscription Rates:** 172 individuals; 287 two years; 6.72 single issue. **Remarks:** Accepts advertising. **URL:** http://www.thedrum.co.uk/. **Circ:** (Not Reported)

53415 ■ English Club Golfer
PSP Publishing Ltd.
50 High Craighall Rd.
Glasgow G4 9UD, United Kingdom
Ph: 44 141 3532222
Fax: 44 141 3323839
Publisher E-mail: sales@psp.uk.net
Magazine for amateur golfers in England. **Subtitle:** England's No. 1 Amateur Golf Newspaper. **Founded:** 2005. **Freq:** 6/yr. **Key Personnel:** Paul Grant, Director; Thomas Lovering, Director; Stephen McCann, Director. **Subscription Rates:** 10 individuals; Free for golf clubs within England. **Remarks:** Accepts advertising. **URL:** http://www.englishclubgolfer.com/. **Circ:** 50,000

53416 ■ Envirotec
Peebles Media Group
Bergius House
Clifton St.
Glasgow G3 7LA, United Kingdom
Ph: 44 141 5676000
Fax: 44 141 3311395
Publication E-mail: envirotec@peeblesmedia.com
Publisher E-mail: info@peeblesmedia.com
Magazine covering environmental technology and service industry. **Freq:** Bimonthly. **Trim Size:** 210 x 297 mm. **Subscription Rates:** 37.50 individuals; 50 other countries. **Remarks:** Accepts advertising. **URL:** http://www.peeblesmedia.com/publications.html. **Circ:** ★8,958

53417 ■ eSharp
University of Glasgow
University Ave.
Glasgow G12 8QQ, United Kingdom
Ph: 44 141 3302000
Publication E-mail: esharp@gla.ac.uk
Peer-reviewed journal covering stuides for postgraduates enrolled in the arts, humanities and social sciences. **Founded:** 2003. **Key Personnel:** Kat Hughes, Co-Gen.-

Ed./Lead Ed.; Mark West, Co-Gen.-Ed./Lead Ed. **ISSN:** 1742-4542. **URL:** http://www.gla.ac.uk/departments/esharp/.

53418 ■ The Firm
Carnyx Group Ltd.
Mercat Bldg., 4th Fl.
26 Gallowgate
Glasgow G1 5AB, United Kingdom
Ph: 44 141 5525858
Publisher E-mail: enquiry@carnyx.com
Magazine covering legal issues. **Freq:** Monthly. **Key Personnel:** Steven Raeburn, Editor, steven.raeburn@carnyx.com. **Subscription Rates:** 39.50 individuals. **Remarks:** Accepts advertising. **URL:** http://www.firmmagazine.com/. **Circ:** (Not Reported)

53419 ■ First Five
Scottish Pre-School Play Association
21-23 Granville St.
Glasgow G3 7EE, United Kingdom
Ph: 44 14 12214148
Fax: 44 14 12216043
Publication covering childhood education. **Founded:** 1995. **Freq:** Quarterly. **Trim Size:** 210 x 297 mm. **ISSN:** 1364-8659. **Subscription Rates:** 12; 45 individuals single copy (includes p&p); 45 individuals five copies (includes p&p). **URL:** http://www.sppa.org.uk/publications/First%20Five/first_five_magazine.html. **Formerly:** Parent To Parent. **Ad Rates:** BW: 250, 4C: 360. **Circ:** 2,200

53420 ■ First Link 4 Parents
55 North Ltd.
Waterloo Chambers
19 Waterloo St.
Glasgow G2 6AY, United Kingdom
Ph: 44 141 2222100
Fax: 44 141 2222177
Publisher E-mail: info@55north.com
Magazine covering general parenting. **Freq:** 3/yr. **Key Personnel:** Antony Begley, Editor, phone 44 141 2225380, abegley@55north.com. **Subscription Rates:** Free. **Remarks:** Accepts advertising. **URL:** http://www.55north.com/FL4P_Home.asp. **Ad Rates:** BW: 665. **Circ:** Free 18,000

53421 ■ Glasgow Mathematical Journal
Cambridge University Press
c/o Dr. I.A.B. Strachan, Ed.-in-Ch.
Dept. of Mathematics
University Gardens
University of Glasgow
Glasgow S12 8QW, United Kingdom
Publisher E-mail: information@cambridge.org
International journal covering research in pure and applied mathematics in connection with Glasgow Mathematical Journal Trust. **Key Personnel:** Dr. I.A.B. Strachan, Editor-in-Chief; Prof. K.R. Goodearl, International Ed.; Prof. L.E. Payne, International Ed.; Dr. T. Bridgeland, International Ed.; Dr. A.J. Baker, Subject Ed.; Prof. W.G. Dwyer, International Ed. **ISSN:** 0017-0895. **Subscription Rates:** US$315 institutions online and print; US$269 institutions online; 176 institutions print and online; 148 institutions online. **Remarks:** Accepts advertising. **URL:** http://journals.cambridge.org/action/displayJournal?jid=GMJ. **Circ:** 600

53422 ■ Graefe's Archive for Clinical and Experimental Ophthalmology
Springer-Verlag
c/o Diana Epstein, Editorial Mgr.
Di-Ep Biomedical Editorial Services
10 Sandyford Pl.
Glasgow G3 7NB, United Kingdom
Ph: 44 141 6169095
Fax: 44 141 6169095
Peer-reviewed international journal publishing original clinical reports and clinically relevant experimental studies in the field of Ophthalmology. **Founded:** 1854. **Freq:** 12/yr. **Key Personnel:** Diana Epstein, Editorial Mgr., graefes_archive@di-ep.com; B. Kirchhof, Editor-in-Chief; J. Augsburger, Editorial Board; F. Kuhn, International Co-Ed.; I. Barbazetto, Editorial Board; Y. Tano, International Co-Ed.; M. Ohji, International Co-Ed.; S. Binder, Editorial Board; K.U. Bartz-Schmidt, Editorial Board; R.N. Weinreb, International Co-Ed.; D. Wong, International Co-Ed. **ISSN:** 0721-832X. **Subscription Rates:** US$2,298 institutions; US$2,757.60 institutions enhanced access. **Remarks:** Advertising accepted;

rates available upon request. **URL:** http://www.springer.com/medicine/ophthalmology/journal/417. **Circ:** (Not Reported)

53423 ■ Information Polity
IOS Press, B.V.
c/o Prof. J.A. Taylor, Ed.-in-Ch.
Caledonian Business School
Glasgow Caledonian University
Glasgow G4 OBA, United Kingdom
Ph: 44 141 3313128
Publisher E-mail: info@iospress.nl
Peer-reviewed journal publishing articles on political, economic, legal, managerial, organizational and wider social themes and issues as they relate to policy developments surrounding information and communications technologies (ICT) in government and democracy. **Freq:** Quarterly. **Key Personnel:** Prof. J.A. Taylor, Editor-in-Chief, jta@gcal.ac.uk; Dr. Miriam Lips, Assoc. Ed., miriam.lips@vuw.ac.nz. **ISSN:** 1570-1255. **Subscription Rates:** EUR348 individuals print and online; US$475 individuals print and online. **URL:** http://www.iospress.nl/loadtop/load.php?isbn=15701255.

53424 ■ Information Scotland
Information & Libraries Scotland
c/o Debby Raven, Ed.
74 Marlborough Ave.
Glasgow G11 7BH, United Kingdom
Publisher E-mail: cilips@slainte.org.uk
Trade magazine for the libraries in Scotland. **Subtitle:** The Journal of the Chartered Institute of Library and Information Professionals in Scotland. **Freq:** Bimonthly Feb., Apr., Jun., Aug., Oct., and Dec. **Key Personnel:** Debby Raven, Editor, debbyraven@btconnect.com. **ISSN:** 1743-5471. **Subscription Rates:** 37 individuals in sterling U.K.; 39 individuals outside U.K. **Remarks:** Advertising accepted; rates available upon request. **URL:** http://www.slainte.org.uk/publications/serials/infoscot/contents.html. **Formerly:** Scottish Libraries (2002). **Circ:** 2,500

53425 ■ International Journal of Adaptive Control & Signal Processing
John Wiley & Sons Ltd.
c/o Mike J. Grimble, Mng. Ed.
Industrial Control Centre
Dept. of Electronic & Electrical Engg.
University of Strathclyde, 50 George St.
Glasgow G1 1QE, United Kingdom
Publisher E-mail: customer@wiley.co.uk
Journal covering design, synthesis and application of estimators or controllers for uncertain systems. **Freq:** 10/yr. **Key Personnel:** Mike J. Grimble, Managing Editor; Brian D.O. Anderson, Editor; Suguru Arimoto, Editorial Board; Kartik Ariyur, Editor; Alessandro Astolfi, Editor; Angelo Alessandri, Editor. **ISSN:** 0890-6327. **Subscription Rates:** US$2,128 other countries print only; US$2,837 institutions, other countries print only; 1,447 institutions print only (UK); EUR1,830 institutions, other countries print only. **Remarks:** Accepts advertising. **URL:** http://www3.interscience.wiley.com/; http://www3.interscience.wiley.com/cgi-bin/jhome/4508. **Circ:** (Not Reported)

53426 ■ Journal of Baltic Studies
Routledge
Taylor & Francis Group Ltd.
Dept. of Central & East European Studies
University of Glasgow
Glasgow, United Kingdom
Publisher E-mail: webmaster.books@tandf.co.uk
Peer-reviewed journal for the advancement of Baltic studies. **Subtitle:** Journal of the Association for the Advancement of Baltic Studies. **Freq:** Quarterly. **Print Method:** Offset. **Trim Size:** 6 x 9. **Cols./Page:** 1. **Col. Width:** 5 inches. **Col. Depth:** 7 1/2 inches. **Key Personnel:** Matthew Kott, Book Review Ed., matthew.kott@valentin.uu.se; Leonidas Donskis, International Advisory Board; Terry Clark, Editor, jbs@creighton.edu; Inta Gale Carpenter, International Advisory Board; Birute Klass, International Advisory Board; Baiba Kangere, International Advisory Board; John Hiden, International Advisory Board; Trevor Fennell, International Advisory Board; Julija Sukys, Tech. Ed., julija.sukys@gmail.com; Andres Kasekamp, International Advisory Board; Thomas Salumets, International Advisory Board; Rein Taagepera, International Advisory Board. **ISSN:** 0162-9778. **Subscription Rates:** 272 institutions print + online; US$452 institutions print + online; 259 institutions online;

US$430 institutions online; 88 individuals; US$146 individuals; EUR361 institutions print and online; EUR344 institutions online only; EUR116 individuals. **URL:** http://www.tandf.co.uk/journals/titles/01629778.asp.

53427 ■ Journal of eLiteracy (JeLit)
University of Glasgow
IT Education Unit
Faculty of Education
University of Glasgow
St. Andrew's Bldg., 11 Eldon St.
Glasgow G3 6NH, United Kingdom
Fax: 44 141 3302602
Publication E-mail: queries@jelit.org
Journal focusing on eliteracy. **Key Personnel:** Allan Martin, Editor; Alix Hayden, Editorial Board; Nancy Becker, Editorial Board; Jan Brauer, Editorial Board; Alex Byrne, Editorial Board; Johannes Cronje, Editorial Board; Hilary Johnson, Editorial Board; Catherine Cardwell, Editorial Board; Philippa Levy, Editorial Board. **ISSN:** 1745-4360. **URL:** http://www.jelit.org/aboutus.html.

53428 ■ Justice and Peace
Justice and Peace Scotland
65 Bath St.
Glasgow G2 2BX, United Kingdom
Ph: 44 14 13330238
Fax: 44 14 13330238
Publisher E-mail: office@justiceandpeacescotland.org.uk
Publication covering human rights. **Freq:** Bimonthly. **Subscription Rates:** 12 individuals. **Remarks:** Advertising accepted; rates available upon request. **URL:** http://www.justiceandpeacescotland.org.uk. **Circ:** 800

53429 ■ Library Review
Emerald Group Publishing Ltd.
University of Strathclyde
Department of Computer & Information Sciences
Livingstone Tower
26 Richmond St.
Glasgow G72 8UT, United Kingdom
Publisher E-mail: emerald@emeraldinsight.com
Journal dedicated to providing a communication link between researchers, educators and library professionals with contributions from libraries from all over the world, submitting their experiences, views and reports, allowing information professionals to gain a wide perspective on developments in their profession and distil useful facts for their own use. **Freq:** 9/yr. **Key Personnel:** Eileen Breen, Publisher, ebreen@emeraldinsight.com; David McMenemy, Editor, david.mcmenemy@cis.strath.ac.uk; Briony Birdi, Assoc. Ed., b.birdi@sheffield.ac.uk. **ISSN:** 0024-2535. **URL:** http://info.emeraldinsight.com/products/journals/journals.htm?id=lr.

53430 ■ M8 Magazine
Music (Scotland) Ltd.
11 Lynedoch Pl.
Glasgow G3 6AB, United Kingdom
Ph: 44 14 13531118
Fax: 44 14 13531448
Magazine covering dance music and the club scene in UK and Ireland. **Founded:** Sept. 1088. **Freq:** Monthly. **Key Personnel:** Kevin McFarlane, Editor, kevin@m8magazine.com; Iain Thomson, Asst. Ed., iain@m8magazine.com; Jill Cram, Finance & Accounts Mgr., jill@m8magazine.com; Grant Ruxton, Account Mgr., grant.ruxton@mediaquarter.co.uk; David Faulds, Publisher, david@m8magazine.com. **Subscription Rates:** 35 individuals U.K.; 45 individuals Eire; 60 individuals to rest of the world; 45 individuals Europe. **URL:** http://www.m8magazine.com.

53431 ■ Multiagent and Grid Systems
IOS Press, B.V.
c/o Dr. Huaglory Tianfield, Exec. Ed.
School of Engineering & Computing
Glasgow Caledonian University
70 Cowcaddens Rd.
Glasgow G4 0BA, United Kingdom
Ph: 44 141 3318025
Fax: 44 151 3313690
Publisher E-mail: info@iospress.nl
International journal providing a focal research forum for academics and practitioners in the thematic areas of Multiagent Systems, Grid Computing and their

intersections. **Freq:** Quarterly. **Key Personnel:** Dr. Huaglory Tianfield, Exec. Ed., h.tianfield@gcal.ac.uk; M. Beer, Editorial Board; S. Ambroszkiewicz, Editorial Board; A. Andrzejak, Editorial Board; J. Koehler, Editorial Board; D. Laforenza, Editorial Board; Dr. Rainer Unland, Editor-in-Chief, rainer.unland@icb.uni-due.de; M. Baker, Editorial Board; M.B. Blake, Editorial Board. **ISSN:** 1574-1702. **Subscription Rates:** EUR522 individuals print and online; US$737 individuals print and online; EUR140 individuals online; US$165 individuals online. **URL:** http://www.iospress.nl/loadtop/load.php?isbn=15741702.

53432 ■ Nationwide Bowler
PSP Publishing Ltd.
50 High Craighall Rd.
Glasgow G4 9UD, United Kingdom
Ph: 44 141 3532222
Fax: 44 141 3323839
Publisher E-mail: sales@psp.uk.net
Magazine for bowlers in Great Britain. **Founded:** 2006. **Freq:** 4/yr. **Key Personnel:** Paul Grant, Director; Michael McEwan, Asst. Ed.; Stephen McCann, Director. **Subscription Rates:** 4 two years. **Remarks:** Accepts advertising. **URL:** http://www.psppublishing.com/nationwidebowler.html; http://www.nationwidebowler.co.uk/. **Circ:** (Not Reported)

53433 ■ The Nautical Magazine
Brown, Son & Ferguson Ltd.
4-10 Darnley St.
Glasgow G41 2SD, United Kingdom
Ph: 44 141 4291234
Fax: 44 141 4201694
Publication E-mail: info@skipper.co.uk
Publisher E-mail: info@skipper.co.uk
Trade magazine covering nautical and merchant naval information. **Founded:** Mar. 1832. **Freq:** Monthly. **Print Method:** Offset litho. **Trim Size:** 145 x 210 mm. **Key Personnel:** D.H. Provan, Advertising Sales, info@skipper.co.uk; L. Ingram-Brown, Editor, info@skipper.co.uk. **ISSN:** 0028-1336. **Subscription Rates:** 26.40 individuals; 34.20 individuals by post; 39.60 other countries. **Remarks:** Accepts advertising. **URL:** https://www.skipper.co.uk/BookStore/showpage.aspx?book=8. **Circ:** Combined 52,000

53434 ■ News and Views
National Association for Educational Guidance for Adults
c/o Meeting Makers Ltd.
Crawfurd Bldg.
Jordanhill Campus
76 Southbrae Dr.
Glasgow G13 1PP, United Kingdom
Ph: 44 141 4341500
Fax: 44 141 4341519
Publisher E-mail: admin@naega.org.uk
Journal containing information on adult guidance for lifelong learning. **Freq:** Quarterly. **Subscription Rates:** 50 individuals; 25 students. **URL:** http://www.naega.org.uk/publications/.

53435 ■ No.1
PSP Publishing Ltd.
50 High Craighall Rd.
Glasgow G4 9UD, United Kingdom
Ph: 44 141 3532222
Fax: 44 141 3323839
Publication E-mail: editor@no1magazine.co.uk
Publisher E-mail: sales@psp.uk.net
Entertainment and lifestyle magazine focusing on celebrity news and fashion. **Founded:** 2006. **Freq:** Triweekly. **Key Personnel:** Paul Grant, Director; Thomas Lovering, Director; Stephen McCann, Director. **Subscription Rates:** 15 individuals 17 issues. **Remarks:** Accepts advertising. **URL:** http://www.no1magazine.co.uk/; http://www.psppublishing.com/no1magazine.html. **Circ:** (Not Reported)

53436 ■ On-Trade Scotland
55 North Ltd.
Waterloo Chambers
19 Waterloo St.
Glasgow G2 6AY, United Kingdom
Ph: 44 141 2222100
Fax: 44 141 2222177
Publisher E-mail: info@55north.com
Magazine covering trade in Scotland. **Key Personnel:** Kevin Scott, Editor, phone 44 141 2225385, kscott@

Circulation: ★ = ABC; △ = BPA; ♦ = CAC; • = CCAB; ❏ = VAC; ⊕ = PO Statement; ‡ = Publisher's Report; Boldface figures = sworn; Light figures = estimated.

Gale Directory of Publications & Broadcast Media/147th Ed.   5649

55north.com; Antony Begley, Publishing Dir., phone 44 141 2225380, abegley@55north.com. **ISSN:** 1749-3838. **Subscription Rates:** 50 individuals. **Remarks:** Accepts advertising. **URL:** http://www.55north.com/OTS_Home. asp. **Circ:** 9,020.

53437 ■ OS
Peebles Media Group
Bergius House
Clifton St.
Glasgow G3 7LA, United Kingdom
Ph: 44 141 5676000
Fax: 44 141 3311395
Publisher E-mail: info@peeblesmedia.com
Magazine covering the secretarial industry. **Trim Size:** 102 x 297 mm. **Key Personnel:** Kim McAllister, Contact, phone 44 141 5676028, kim.mcallister@peeblesmedia. com. **Subscription Rates:** 37 individuals; 50 individuals. **Remarks:** Accepts advertising. **URL:** http://www. peeblesmedia.com/publications.html. **Circ:** ★25,520.

53438 ■ Packaging Scotland
Peebles Media Group
Bergius House
Clifton St.
Glasgow G3 7LA, United Kingdom
Ph: 44 141 5676000
Fax: 44 141 3311395
Publication E-mail: packagingscotland.sales@ peeblesmedia.com
Publisher E-mail: info@peeblesmedia.com
Magazine featuring the packaging industry in Scotland. **Freq:** Quarterly. **Trim Size:** 210 x 297 mm. **Key Personnel:** Kevin Scott, Editor, phone 44 141 5676068, kevin. scott@peeblesmedia.com. **Subscription Rates:** 32 individuals; 40 other countries. **Remarks:** Accepts advertising. **URL:** http://www.peeblesmedia.com/ publications.html. **Circ:** ★4,219.

53439 ■ Personality and Mental Health
John Wiley & Sons Inc.
c/o Kate Davidson, Ed.
Section of Psychological Medicine
Division of Community-Based Sciences, Gartnavel
Royal Hospital
1055 Great Western Rd.
Glasgow G12 0XH, United Kingdom
Publisher E-mail: info@wiley.com
Journal featuring information related in the field of personality and mental health. **Subtitle:** Multidisciplinary Studies from Personality Dysfunction to Criminal Behaviour. **Freq:** Quarterly. **Key Personnel:** Kate Davidson, Editor, k.davidson@clinmed.gla.ac.uk; Roger Mulder, Editor, roger.mulder@chmeds.ac.nz; Kenneth R. Silk, Editor, k.silk@med.umich.edu. **ISSN:** 1932-8621. **Subscription Rates:** 92 individuals print only; US$163 other countries print only. **Remarks:** Accepts advertising. **URL:** http://onlinelibrary.wiley.com/journal/10.1002/ (ISSN)1932-863X. **Circ:** (Not Reported)

53440 ■ Politics
John Wiley & Sons Inc.
Wiley-Blackwell
c/o Dr. Jane Duckett, Ed.
Department of Politics
Adam Smith Bldg.
University of Glasgow
Glasgow G12 8RT, United Kingdom
Ph: 44 14 13302871
Fax: 44 14 13305071
Journal publishing political analysis and providing information on conducting research and teaching politics. **Subtitle:** Surveys, Debates and Controversies in Politics. **Founded:** 1980. **Freq:** Quarterly. **Key Personnel:** James Bilsland, Editorial Asst., j.bilsland.1@ research.gla.ac.uk; Dr. Alasdair Young, Editor, phone 44 141 3304679, a.young@socsci.gla.ac.uk; Dr. Jane Duckett, Editor, j.duckett@socsci.gla.ac.uk; Dr. Paul Graham, Editor, phone 44 141 3304982, p.graham@ socsci.gla.ac.uk; Nigel Ashford, Editorial Board; Martin Bull, Editorial Board. **ISSN:** 0263-3957. **Subscription Rates:** US$429 institutions print and online; 176 institutions print and online; 201 institutions online; US$462 institutions, other countries print and online; US$415 institutions, other countries online; EUR223 institutions print and online; EUR201 institutions online; US$386 institutions online. **URL:** http://www.wiley.com/bw/ journal.asp?ref=0263-3957&site=1.

53441 ■ Project Plant
Peebles Media Group

Bergius House
Clifton St.
Glasgow G3 7LA, United Kingdom
Ph: 44 141 5676000
Fax: 44 141 3311395
Publication E-mail: projectplantsales@peeblesmedia. com
Publisher E-mail: info@peeblesmedia.com
Magazine featuring the construction plant equipment industry in Scotland. **Trim Size:** 210 x 227 mm. **Subscription Rates:** 32.50 individuals; 40 other countries. **Remarks:** Accepts advertising. **URL:** http://www. peeblesmedia.com/publications.html. **Circ:** ★5,330.

53442 ■ Project Scotland
Peebles Media Group
Bergius House
Clifton St.
Glasgow G3 7LA, United Kingdom
Ph: 44 141 5676000
Fax: 44 141 3311395
Publication E-mail: projectscotland@peeblesmedia.com
Publisher E-mail: info@peeblesmedia.com
Magazine focusing on Scotland's construction industry. **Freq:** Monthly. **Trim Size:** 302 x 406 mm. **Subscription Rates:** 64 individuals; 80 other countries. **Remarks:** Accepts advertising. **URL:** http://www.peeblesmedia.com/ publications.html. **Circ:** ★7,223.

53443 ■ The Property Executive
216 St. Vincent St.
Glasgow G2 5SG, United Kingdom
Ph: 44 1506 204913
Professional magazine covering commercial, industrial and residential property in the UK and Ireland. **Founded:** 1993. **Freq:** Bimonthly. **Trim Size:** A4. **Cols./Page:** 3. **Key Personnel:** Jane Ambrose, Editor, phone 44 131 4661103, jane@propertyexecutive.co.uk; Steve Georgiou, Advertising, phone 44 1506 204913, fax 44 1506 204913, sbeveg@propertyexecutive.co.uk. **Subscription Rates:** 60 individuals. **Remarks:** Accepts advertising. **URL:** http://www.propertyexecutive.co.uk. **Former name:** The Glasgow & Edinburgh Property Executive. **Ad Rates:** 4C: 1,600. **Circ:** Combined 9,600

53444 ■ The Radio Journal
Intellect
Division of Media, Language & Leisure Management
Glasgow Caledonian University
Cowcaddens Rd.
Glasgow G4 0BA, United Kingdom
Publisher E-mail: info@intellectuk.org
Journal designed for all those interested in research into the production, reception, texts and contexts of radio and audio media, including all structures, forms and genres of radio broadcasting and also embraces net distribution and audio streaming of radio services and texts, CD-ROMs, books-on-tape, and sound art. **Subtitle:** International Studies in Broadcast and Audio Media. **Founded:** 2003. **Freq:** 3/yr. **Trim Size:** 174 x 244 mm. **Key Personnel:** Ken Garner, Assoc. Ed., k.garner@gcal.ac.uk; Sean Street, Editorial Board; Caroline Mitchell, Editorial Board; Kate Lacey, Editorial Board; Hugh Chignell, Reviews Ed., hchignel@ bournemouth.ac.uk; Peter Lewis, Assoc. Ed.; Andrew Crisell, Editorial Board; Gail Phillips, Editorial Board; David Goodman, Editorial Board. **ISSN:** 1476-4504. **Subscription Rates:** 33 individuals print; 210 institutions print; 18 single issue print; 177 institutions online only. **Remarks:** Accepts advertising. **URL:** http://www. intellectbooks.co.uk/journals/view-Journal,id=123/. **Ad Rates:** BW: 100. **Circ:** (Not Reported)

53445 ■ Reformation and Renaissance Review
Equinox Publishing Ltd.
School of Divinity
University of Glasgow
Glasgow G12 8QQ, United Kingdom
Peer-reviewed journal covering aspects of religious thought and life, theology and spirituality, from the fifteenth to seventeenth centuries. **Freq:** 3/yr (April, August, December). **Key Personnel:** Ian Hazlett, Editor, i.hazlett@arts.gla.ac.uk. **ISSN:** 1462-2459. **Subscription Rates:** 140 institutions, other countries print and online; US$280 institutions print and online; 40 institutions developing countries; 45 individuals print; US$90 individuals print; 18 individuals developing counties; 33.75 students print; US$67.50 students print. **Remarks:** Accepts advertising. **URL:** http://www.equinoxjournals.

com/ojs/index.php/RRR. **Circ:** (Not Reported)

53446 ■ Scottish Club Golfer
PSP Publishing Ltd.
50 High Craighall Rd.
Glasgow G4 9UD, United Kingdom
Ph: 44 141 3532222
Fax: 44 141 3323839
Publisher E-mail: sales@psp.uk.net
Newspaper for amateur golfers in Scotland. **Subtitle:** Scotland's No. 1 Newspaper for Amateur Golf. **Founded:** 2003. **Freq:** 6/yr. **Key Personnel:** Paul Grant, Director; Thomas Lovering, Director; Stephen McCann, Director. **Subscription Rates:** 10 individuals; Free for golf clubs. **Remarks:** Accepts advertising. **URL:** http://www. scottishclubgolfer.com/; http://www.psppublishing.com/ golfingtitles.html. **Circ:** 25,000

53447 ■ scottish grocer
Peebles Media Group
Bergius House
Clifton St.
Glasgow G3 7LA, United Kingdom
Ph: 44 141 5676000
Fax: 44 141 3311395
Publisher E-mail: info@peeblesmedia.com
Magazine featuring Scotland's retailing industry. **Subtitle:** & convenience retailer. **Freq:** Monthly. **Trim Size:** 210 x 297 mm. **Subscription Rates:** 69 individuals; 80 other countries. **Remarks:** Accepts advertising. **URL:** http://www.peeblesmedia.com/publications.html. **Circ:** ★8,217

53448 ■ Scottish Hosteller
PSP Publishing Ltd.
50 High Craighall Rd.
Glasgow G4 9UD, United Kingdom
Ph: 44 141 3532222
Fax: 44 141 3323839
Publisher E-mail: sales@psp.uk.net
Magazine featuring Scotland. **Freq:** Semiannual. **Key Personnel:** Paul Grant, Director; Thomas Lovering, Director; Stephen McCann, Director. **Remarks:** Accepts advertising. **URL:** http://www.psppublishing.com/ hosteller.html. **Circ:** (Not Reported)

53449 ■ Scottish Local Retailer
55 North Ltd.
Waterloo Chambers
19 Waterloo St.
Glasgow G2 6AY, United Kingdom
Ph: 44 141 2222100
Fax: 44 141 2222177
Publisher E-mail: info@55north.com
Magazine covering small shop sector in Scotland. **Freq:** Monthly. **Key Personnel:** Antony Begley, Ed./Publishing Dir., phone 44 141 2225380, abegley@55north.com; Cara Thomson, Circulation Mgr., phone 44 141 2225381, cthomson@55north.com. **ISSN:** 1740-2409. **Subscription Rates:** 50 individuals. **Remarks:** Accepts advertising. **URL:** http://www.55north.com/slr_home.asp. **Circ:** 8,363

53450 ■ Scottish Planning and Environmental Law
i-documentsystems
Tontine House
8 Gordon St.
Glasgow G1 3PL, United Kingdom
Ph: 44 870 3337101
Fax: 44 870 3337131
Publication E-mail: marketing@i-documentsystems.com
Publisher E-mail: helpdesk@idoxplc.com
Journal covering environmental law. **Subtitle:** SPEL. **Founded:** 1981. **Freq:** Bimonthly. **ISSN:** 1350-2808. **Subscription Rates:** 145 individuals in sterling. **Remarks:** Accepts advertising. **URL:** http://www. periodicals.ru/import/good.phtml?id=447591&set_usr_ lang=eng. **Formerly:** Scottish Planning Law & Practice. **Ad Rates:** GLR: 6, BW: 500. **Circ:** Paid 500

53451 ■ SCROLL
Editions Rodopi B.V.
Dr. Rhona Brown, Ed.
Dept. of Scottish Literature
7 University Gardens
Glasgow G12 8QH, United Kingdom
Publisher E-mail: info@rodopi.nl
Journal featuring literature and languages of Scotland. **Subtitle:** Scottish Cultural Review of Language and

Literature. **Key Personnel:** Dr. Rhona Brown, Editor, r.brown@scotlit.arts.gla.ac.uk; Dr. John Corbett, Editor, j.corbett@englang.arts.gla.ac.uk. **ISSN:** 1571-0734. **URL:** http://www.rodopi.nl/senj.asp?SerieId=SCROLL.

53452 ■ Spatial Economic Analysis
Routledge
Taylor & Francis Group Ltd.
c/o Bernard Fingleton, Mng. Ed.
Strathclyde University
Glasgow G4 0GE, United Kingdom
Publisher E-mail: webmaster.books@tandf.co.uk
Peer-reviewed journal covering economic phenomena on the global scale. **Freq:** 4/yr. **Print Method:** Heatset web. **Trim Size:** 8 3/8 x 10 7/8. **Cols./Page:** 3 and 2. **Col. Width:** 28 and 42 nonpareils. **Col. Depth:** 134 agate lines. **Key Personnel:** Vassilis Monastiriotis, Co-Ed.; Steven Brakman, Editorial Board; John McCombie, Co-Ed.; Harry Garretsen, Co-Ed.; Johannes Brocker, Editorial Board; Barry Moore, Co-Ed.; Mark Roberts, Co-Ed.; Danilo Igliori, Co-Ed.; Philip McCann, Co-Ed. **ISSN:** 1742-1772. **Subscription Rates:** 293 institutions print + online; 278 institutions online; 77 individuals; US$500 institutions print + online; US$475 institutions online; US$129 individuals; EUR389 institutions print and online; EUR369 institutions online only; EUR104 individuals. **URL:** http://www.tandf.co.uk/journals/titles/17421772.asp.

53453 ■ Sunday Herald
200 Renfield St.
Glasgow G2 3QB, United Kingdom
Ph: 44 14 13027300
Newspaper. **Freq:** Weekly. **Key Personnel:** Ken Symon, Bus. Ed.; Andrew Jaspan, Editor; Kenny Kemp, Bus. Ed. **Subscription Rates:** 208 individuals 52 copies; 104 individuals 6 months (26 copies); 52 individuals 3 months (13 copies); 16 individuals 1 month (4 copies); 4 individuals 1 week; 4 individuals per copy (1.00p + 3.00 for postage). **Remarks:** Accepts advertising. **URL:** http://www.heraldscotland.com/; http://daol.newsquest.co.uk/glasgow/sundayherald/. **Circ:** 56,374

53454 ■ Toxicon
Elsevier Science
University of Strathclyde
Dept. of Physiology & Pharmacology
27 Taylor St.
Glasgow G4 0NR, United Kingdom
Publisher E-mail: nlinfo-f@elsevier.com
Journal publishing research articles on matters related to poisons resulting from animals, plants and microorganisms. **Subtitle:** An Interdisciplinary Journal on the Toxins Derived from Animals, Plants and Microorganisms. **Founded:** 1962. **Freq:** 16/yr. **Key Personnel:** Alan L. Harvey, Editor-in-Chief, toxicon@strath.ac.uk; Gerhard G. Habermehl, Honorary Ed.; Findlay E. Russell, Honorary Ed. **ISSN:** 0041-0101. **Subscription Rates:** EUR407 individuals for European countries & Iran; US$546 individuals for all countries except Europe, Japan & Iran; 62,700¥ individuals; US$3,341 institutions for all countries except Europe, Japan & Iran; 396,600¥ institutions; EUR2,988 institutions for European countries & Iran. **Remarks:** Accepts advertising. **URL:** http://www.elsevier.com/wps/find/journaldescription.cws_home/259/description. **Circ:** (Not Reported)

53455 ■ Translation & Literature
Edinburgh University Press
Dept. of English Literature
University of Glasgow
Glasgow G12 8QQ, United Kingdom
Publisher E-mail: marketing@eup.ed.ac.uk
Scholarly journal covering translation and literature. **Founded:** 1992. **Freq:** Biennial. **Key Personnel:** Umberto Eco, Editorial Board; Robert Cummings, Review Ed.; Peter France, Editorial Board; Dr. Stuart Gillespie, Editor; Gordon Braden, Editorial Board; Donald MacKenzie, Editorial Board; David Hopkins, Editorial Board; Edwin Morgan, Editorial Board; Adam Piette, Editorial Board. **ISSN:** 0968-1361. **Subscription Rates:** 130 institutions print and online; 144 institutions, other countries print and online; US$274.50 institutions print and online (North America); 52 individuals print and online; 57 other countries print and online; US$112 individuals print and online (North America). **Remarks:** Accepts advertising. **URL:** http://www.eupjournals.com/journal/tal. **Ad Rates:** BW: 200. **Circ:** Combined 450

53456 ■ Urban Realm
Carnyx Group Ltd.

Mercat Bldg., 4th Fl.
26 Gallowgate
Glasgow G1 5AB, United Kingdom
Ph: 44 141 5525858
Publication E-mail: prospect@carnyx.com
Publisher E-mail: enquiry@carnyx.com
Magazine covering architecture. **Founded:** 1922. **Freq:** Quarterly. **Trim Size:** 228 x 300 mm. **Subscription Rates:** 23.95 individuals. **Remarks:** Accepts advertising. **URL:** http://www.architecturescotland.co.uk/prospectmagazine. **Formerly:** Prospect. **Circ:** 7,000

53457 ■ Variant
1/2 189b Maryhill Rd.
Glasgow G20 7XJ, United Kingdom
Ph: 44 141 3339522
Publisher E-mail: variantmag@btinternet.com
Magazine covering international arts and culture. **Freq:** 3/yr. **Key Personnel:** Leigh French, Editor; Daniel Jewesbury, Editor. **Subscription Rates:** 15 institutions; EUR21.50 institutions; 20 institutions, other countries; 7.50 individuals; EUR13.50 individuals; 15 other countries. **Remarks:** Accepts advertising. **URL:** http://www.variant.randomstate.org/. **Circ:** (Not Reported)

53458 ■ Weir Bulletin
The Weir Group PLC
Clydesdale Bank Exchange
20 Waterloo St.
Glasgow G2 6DB, United Kingdom
Ph: 44 141 6377111
Fax: 44 141 2219789
Publisher E-mail: pr@weir.co.uk
Trade magazine covering engineering. **Freq:** Semiannual. **Key Personnel:** Helen Walker, Editor, phone 44 141 3083739, helen.walker@weir.co.uk. **Remarks:** Advertising not accepted. **URL:** http://www.weir.co.uk. **Circ:** Controlled 20,000

53459 ■ Welsh Club Golfer
PSP Publishing Ltd.
50 High Craighall Rd.
Glasgow G4 9UD, United Kingdom
Ph: 44 141 3532222
Fax: 44 141 3323839
Publisher E-mail: sales@psp.uk.net
Magazine for golfers in Wales. **Subtitle:** Welsh No. 1 Amateur Golf Newspaper. **Founded:** 2006. **Freq:** 4/yr. **Key Personnel:** Paul Grant, Director; Thomas Lovering, Director; Stephen McCann, Director. **Subscription Rates:** Free. **Remarks:** Accepts advertising. **URL:** http://www.welshclubgolfer.co.uk/; http://www.psppublishing.com/golfingtitles.html. **Circ:** 15,000

53460 ■ Awaz-FM - 107.2
Craig House
64 Darnley St., 1st Fl.
Pollokshields
Glasgow G41 2SE, United Kingdom
Ph: 44 141 4206666
E-mail: info@awazfm.co.uk
Format: Ethnic. **Owner:** Awaz FM, at above address. **Founded:** 1996. **Operating Hours:** Continuous. **Key Personnel:** Ali Malik, Sales Dir., ali@awazfm.co.uk; Shazia Akhtar, Business Mgr., shazia@awazfm.co.uk. **Ad Rates:** Advertising accepted; rates available upon request. **URL:** http://www.awazfm.co.uk.

53461 ■ BBC Radio Scotland-FM - 92
40 Pacific Quay
Glasgow G51 1DA, United Kingdom
Ph: 44 141 4226000
Format: Talk; News; Oldies; Sports; Information; Religious; Hip Hop; Agricultural; Jazz. **Owner:** British Broadcasting Corporation, Broadcasting House, Portland Pl., London W1A 1AA, United Kingdom. **Operating Hours:** Continuous. **URL:** http://www.bbc.co.uk/radioscotland

53462 ■ Celtic Music Radio-AM - 1530
Hunter Centre for Entrepreneurship
University of Strathclyde
Livingstone Tower
26 Richmond St.
Glasgow G1 1XH, United Kingdom
Ph: 44 141 5483397
Fax: 44 141 5484041

E-mail: studio@celticmusicradio.net; info@celticmusicradio.net
Format: Ethnic; Folk. **URL:** http://www.celticmusicradio.net/.

53463 ■ Clyde One-FM - 97.0
3 S Ave.
Clydebank Business Pk.
Glasgow G81 2RX, United Kingdom
Ph: 44 141 5652200
Format: Contemporary Hit Radio (CHR). **Key Personnel:** Tracey McNellan, Station Mgr. **Ad Rates:** Advertising accepted; rates available upon request. **URL:** http://www.clyde1.com/.

53464 ■ Clyde One-FM - 103.3
3 S Ave.
Clydebank Business Pk.
Glasgow G81 2RX, United Kingdom
Ph: 44 141 5652200
Format: Contemporary Hit Radio (CHR). **URL:** http://www.clyde1.com/.

53465 ■ Clyde 1-FM - 102.5
3 South Ave.
Clydebank Business Pk.
Glasgow G81 2RX, United Kingdom
Ph: 44 141 5652200
Format: Top 40; Sports; News. **Operating Hours:** Continuous. **URL:** http://www.clyde1.com/.

53466 ■ Clyde 2-AM - 1152
3 South Ave.
Clydebank Business Pk.
Glasgow G81 2RX, United Kingdom
Ph: 44 141 5652200
Format: Full Service; Oldies; Talk. **Owner:** Scottish Radio Holdings, at above address. **Operating Hours:** Continuous. **Ad Rates:** Advertising accepted; rates available upon request. **URL:** http://clyde2.com/.

53467 ■ Smooth Radio-FM - 105.2
PO Box 105
Glasgow G69 1AQ, United Kingdom
Ph: 44 141 7811011
Fax: 44 141 2711052
Format: Adult Contemporary. **URL:** http://www.smoothradioglasgow.co.uk/.

53468 ■ Subcity Radio-FM - 105.6
John McIntyre Bldg.
University Ave.
Glasgow G12 8QQ, United Kingdom
Ph: 44 141 3416219
Fax: 44 141 3373557
Format: Eclectic; Alternative/New Music/Progressive; Talk. **URL:** http://www.subcity.org/.

Glengormley

53469 ■ Newtonabbey Times
Johnston Press PLC
14 Portland Ave.
Newtownabbey
Glengormley BT36 8EY, United Kingdom
Ph: 44 2890 843621
Community newspaper. **Print Method:** Offset. **Col. Depth:** 450 millimeters. **Remarks:** Accepts advertising. **URL:** http://www.newtonabbeytoday.co.uk/newspaper.aspx. **Circ:** (Not Reported)

Gloucester

53470 ■ International Journal of Pressure Vessels and Piping
Elsevier Science
c/o R.A. Ainsworth, Ed.-in-Ch.
British Energy Generation Ltd.
Structural Integrity Br.
Barnett Way, Barnwood
Gloucester GL4 3RS, United Kingdom
Publisher E-mail: nlinfo-f@elsevier.com
Peer-reviewed journal for Pressure vessel design engineers, metallurgists, mechanical, civil, structural engineers, welding technologists, stress analysts and nuclear engineers. **Founded:** 1973. **Freq:** Monthly. **Key Personnel:** R.A. Ainsworth, Editor-in-Chief, bob.ainsworth@british-energy.com; H. Adeli, Editorial Board; G. Chell, Editorial Board; Prof. P. Dong, Editorial Board; M. Kikuchi, Editorial Board; J. Darlaston, Editorial Board.

Circulation: ★ = ABC; △ = BPA; ♦ = CAC; • = CCAB; ▢ = VAC; ⊕ = PO Statement; ‡ = Publisher's Report; Boldface figures = sworn; Light figures = estimated.

Gale Directory of Publications & Broadcast Media/147th Ed.   **5651**

ISSN: 0308-0161. **Subscription Rates:** EUR4,608 institutions for European countries; US$5,157 institutions for all countries except Europe and Japan; 612,100¥ institutions. **Remarks:** Accepts advertising. **URL:** http://www.elsevier.com/wps/find/ journaldescription.cws_home/405900/descrip tion. **Circ:** (Not Reported)

53471 ■ Journal—British Holiday & Home Parks Association
BH & HP Association
Chichester House
6 Pullman Ct.
Great Western Rd.
Gloucester GL1 3ND, United Kingdom
Ph: 44 1452 526911
Fax: 44 1452 508508
Publisher E-mail: enquiries@bhhpa.org.uk
Trade journal for member camping, caravan and residential park operators. **Founded:** 1950. **Freq:** Bimonthly. **Remarks:** Accepts advertising. **URL:** http://www.bhhpa. org.uk/. **Ad Rates:** BW: 541, 4C: 912. **Circ:** Controlled 2,600

53472 ■ Journal of Psychiatric Intensive Care
Cambridge University Press
c/o Roland Dix, Ed.-in-Ch.
Wotton Lawn Hospital
The Montpellier Unit
Horton Rd.
Gloucester GL1 3WL, United Kingdom
Publisher E-mail: information@cambridge.org
Journal for professionals concerned with all aspects of psychiatric intensive care. **Key Personnel:** Roland Dix, Editor-in-Chief, journal@napicu.org.uk; Jim Laidlaw, Dep. Ed.; Dr. Zerrin Atakan, Editorial Board. **ISSN:** 1742-6464. **Subscription Rates:** 127 institutions print and online; US$235 institutions print and online; 105 institutions online only; US$196 institutions online only; 49 individuals print and online; US$90 individuals print and online; 39 individuals online only; US$69 individuals online only. **Remarks:** Accepts advertising. **URL:** http:// journals.cambridge.org/action/displayJournal?jid=JPI. **Circ:** (Not Reported)

53473 ■ Heart-FM - 103
The Mall
Gloucester GL1 1SS, United Kingdom
Ph: 44 1452 331024
Format: Eclectic. **Formerly:** Severn Sound-FM. **Ad Rates:** Advertising accepted; rates available upon request. **URL:** http://www.heartgloucestershire.co.uk/.

53474 ■ Severn Sound-FM - 102.4
The Mall
Gloucester GL1 1SS, United Kingdom
Ph: 44 1452 331024
Format: Eclectic. **Ad Rates:** Advertising accepted; rates available upon request. **URL:** http://www.severnsound. co.uk/.

Godalming

53475 ■ Mollusc World
Conchological Society of Great Britain and Ireland
88 Peperharow Rd.
Godalming GU7 2PN, United Kingdom
Ph: 44 14 83417782
Publisher E-mail: president@conchsoc.org
Magazine of the Conchological Society, a means of staying in touch with the membership, communicating information to the conservation agencies, and promoting molluscs to the wider biological community. **Freq:** 3/yr. **Key Personnel:** Peter Topley, Honorary Ed., magazine@conchsoc.org; Bas Payne, President, president@conchsoc.org. **ISSN:** 1740-1070. **Subscription Rates:** 57 individuals in U.K; 60 other countries. **URL:** http://www.conchsoc.org/Frame_index.htm.

53476 ■ Monocle Magazine
Piton Publishing House Ltd.
79/81 High St.
Godalming GU7 1AW, United Kingdom
Ph: 44 1483425454
Consumer magazine covering society and lifestyle. **Freq:** Monthly. **Key Personnel:** Peter Tribe, Editor; Tony Usher, Managing Dir. **Subscription Rates:** 75 individuals. **URL:** http://www.monocle.com/Magazine/. **Circ:** Non-paid 12,000

Gowerton

53477 ■ Swansea Sound-AM - 1170
Radio House
Victoria Rd.
Gowerton SA4 3AB, United Kingdom
Ph: 44 17 92511964
Fax: 44 17 92511171
Format: Adult Contemporary. **Owner:** UTV Radio, 18 Hatfields, London SE1 8DJ, United Kingdom, 44 20 79597900, Fax: 44 20 79597808. **Operating Hours:** Continuous. **Key Personnel:** Carrie Mosley, Station Dir., carrie.mosley@thewave.co.uk; Steve Barnes, Program Dir., steve.barnes@thewave.co.uk; Richard Western, Sales Dir., richard.western@thewave.co.uk. **Ad Rates:** Advertising accepted; rates available upon request. **URL:** http://www.swanseasound.co.uk; http://www. thewirelessgroup.net/.

Gravesend

53478 ■ Casino World
The Maltings
50 Bath St.
Gravesend DA11 0DF, United Kingdom
Ph: 44 14 74335087
Publisher E-mail: info@casinoworld.co.uk
Trade magazine covering the global casino industry. **Founded:** Mar. 1994. **Freq:** 10/yr. **Print Method:** Sheet. **Trim Size:** 210 x 297 mm. **Key Personnel:** Roger Melling, Managing Editor; Peter Rubin, Amusement & Leisure Consultant; Sarah Lawrence, Sales & Mktg. Mgr. **ISSN:** 1365-4225. **Subscription Rates:** 85 individuals Europe and Middle East; 95 individuals North/South America and Africa; 110 individuals Australia and Pacific rim. **Remarks:** Accepts advertising. **URL:** http://www. casinoworld.co.uk. **Circ:** (Not Reported)

53479 ■ Gravesend Reporter
Archant Regional Ltd.
Unit 4, The Courtyard
7A Manor Rd.
Gravesend DA12 1AA, United Kingdom
Ph: 44 1474 320753
Publisher E-mail: sandra.roantree@archant.co.uk
Local community newspaper. **Freq:** Weekly (Thurs.). **Key Personnel:** Melody Foreman, Editor, melody. foreman@archant.co.uk. **Subscription Rates:** 10.60 individuals 4 weeks; 21.20 individuals 2 months; 31.80 individuals 3 months; 63.60 individuals 6 months; 137.80 individuals. **Remarks:** Accepts advertising. **URL:** http:// www.gravesendreporter.co.uk/home. **Circ:** (Not Reported)

Grayshott

53480 ■ Horse & Rider
D.J. Murphy (Publishers) Ltd.
Headley House
Headley Rd.
Grayshott GU26 6TU, United Kingdom
Ph: 44 14 28601020
Fax: 44 14 28601030
Publication E-mail: horseandrider@djmurphy.co.uk
Publisher E-mail: info@signaturepl.co.uk
Magazine covering horses, horse care, and riding for equestrians. **Subtitle:** A Real Passion for Horses. **Founded:** 1970. **Freq:** 13/yr. **Key Personnel:** Nicky Moffatt, Editor. **Subscription Rates:** 48.10 individuals; 69.90 individuals Europe; 86 individuals U.S., rest of the world. **URL:** http://www.horseandrideruk.com/. **Ad Rates:** 4C: 2,290. **Circ:** ‡42,184

53481 ■ Pony Magazine
D.J. Murphy (Publishers) Ltd.
Headley House
Headley Rd.
Grayshott GU26 6TU, United Kingdom
Ph: 44 14 28601020
Fax: 44 14 28601030
Publication E-mail: pony@djmurphy.co.uk
Publisher E-mail: info@signaturepl.co.uk
Consumer magazine for teenage and junior horse and pony enthusiasts covering riding and care. **Subtitle:** The Next Best Thing to Riding. **Founded:** 1949. **Freq:** 13/yr. **Print Method:** Web. **Trim Size:** 297 x 210 mm. **ISSN:** 0032-4256. **Subscription Rates:** 32.98 individuals U.K. **Remarks:** Accepts advertising. **URL:** http://

www.ponymag.com/. **Ad Rates:** GLR: 24, 4C: 2,000. **Circ:** Combined ‡34,132

Great Yarmouth

53482 ■ Great Yarmouth Advertiser
Archant Regional Ltd.
25 Regent St.
Great Yarmouth NR30 1RQ, United Kingdom
Publisher E-mail: sandra.roantree@archant.co.uk
Local community newspaper. **Key Personnel:** Anne Edwards, Editor, phone 44 1493 847958, anne.edwards@ archant.co.uk; Phil Beasley, Contact, phil.beasley@ archant.co.uk. **Subscription Rates:** 6 individuals 4 weeks; 18 individuals 12 weeks; 39 individuals 26 weeks. **Remarks:** Accepts advertising. **URL:** http://www. advertiser24.co.uk/content/advertiser24/. **Circ:** (Not Reported)

53483 ■ Great Yarmouth Mercury
Archant Regional Ltd.
169 King St.
Great Yarmouth NR30 2PA, United Kingdom
Ph: 44 1493 847940
Publisher E-mail: sandra.roantree@archant.co.uk
Community newspaper. **Founded:** 1880. **Freq:** Weekly. **Key Personnel:** Anne Edwards, Editor, phone 44 1493 847958, anne.edwards@archant.co.uk; Alan Thompson, Gen. Reporter, phone 44 1493 847961, alan. thompson2@archant.co.uk; Liz Coates, Ch. Reporter, liz.coates@archant.co.uk; Miles Jermy, Gen. Reporter, phone 44 1493 847953, miles.jermy@archant.co.uk. **Subscription Rates:** 36.40 individuals 26 weeks; 18.20 individuals 13 weeks. **Remarks:** Accepts advertising. **URL:** http://www.greatyarmouthmercury.co.uk/home. **Circ:** Paid 20,400

53484 ■ Waveney Advertiser
Archant Regional Ltd.
36 N Quay, 1st Fl.
Great Yarmouth NR30 1JE, United Kingdom
Ph: 44 1493 335042
Publisher E-mail: sandra.roantree@archant.co.uk
Local community newspaper. **Subscription Rates:** 6 individuals 4 weeks; 18 individuals 12 weeks; 39 individuals 26 weeks. **Remarks:** Accepts advertising. **URL:** http://www.waveneyadvertiser24.co.uk/home. **Circ:** (Not Reported)

Grimsby

53485 ■ Family History News and Digest
Federation of Family History Societies
PO Box 298
Grimsby DN36 5ZP, United Kingdom
Publisher E-mail: info@ffhs.org.uk
Publication covering geneology. **Founded:** 1978. **Freq:** Biennial. **Remarks:** Accepts advertising. **URL:** http:// www.ffhs.org.uk/about/communication.php. **Circ:** 5,000

53486 ■ Compass-FM - 96.4
26a Wellowgate
Grimsby DN32 0RA, United Kingdom
Ph: 44 1472 346666
Fax: 44 1472 508811
Format: Full Service. **URL:** http://www.compassfm.co. uk/.

Guernsey

53487 ■ Contact
Guernsey Chamber of Commerce
Ste. 1
16 Glategny Esplanande
St. Peter Port
Guernsey GY1 1WN, United Kingdom
Ph: 44 14 81727483
Fax: 44 14 81710755
Publisher E-mail: office@guernseychamber.com
Publication covering chambers of commerce. **Freq:** Monthly. **Subscription Rates:** Free to members. **Remarks:** Accepts advertising. **URL:** http://www. guernseychamber.com/index.php?page=94. **Circ:** 1,300

53488 ■ Island-FM - 104.7
12 Westerbrook
St. Sampsons
Guernsey GY2 4QQ, United Kingdom
Ph: 44 1481 248888
Fax: 44 1481 241120

E-mail: studio@islandfm.com
Format: News; Information; Adult Contemporary. **Operating Hours:** Continuous. **Ad Rates:** Advertising accepted; rates available upon request. **URL:** http://www.islandfm.com/.

Island-FM - See Aldemey

Guildford

53489 ■ Coat of Arms
The Heraldry Society
PO Box 772
Guildford GU3 3ZX, United Kingdom
Ph: 44 14 83237373
Fax: 44 14 83237373
Publisher E-mail: coatofarms@theheraldrysociety.com
Publication covering heraldry. **Founded:** 1950. **Freq:** Semiannual. **ISSN:** 0010-003X. **Remarks:** Advertising accepted; rates available upon request. **URL:** http://www.theheraldrysociety.com. **Circ:** (Not Reported)

53490 ■ International Journal of Oral & Maxillofacial Surgery
Mosby Inc.
Post Graduate Medical Studies
Stirling House
Surrey Research Park
Guildford GU1 2AP, United Kingdom
Ph: 44 1483 555936
Fax: 44 1483 569594
Publisher E-mail: custserv.ehs@elsevier.com
Journal publishing papers on work in oral and maxillofacial surgery and supporting specialties. **Freq:** 8/yr. **Key Personnel:** Ms. Jacqi Merrison, Admin. Ed., ijoms@elsevier.com; Piet Haers, Editor-in-Chief, editorialoffice.ijoms@surrey.ac.uk. **ISSN:** 0901-5027. **Subscription Rates:** US$318 U.S., Canada, and Mexico. **Remarks:** Accepts advertising. **URL:** http://www.ijoms.com/. **Circ:** (Not Reported)

53491 ■ International Journal of Satellite Communications and Networking
John Wiley & Sons Inc.
c/o Prof. Barry G. Evans, Ch. Ed.
Centre for Communication Systems Research
University of Surrey
Guildford GU2 7XH, United Kingdom
Fax: 44 1483 686011
Publisher E-mail: info@wiley.com
Journal covering all aspects of satellite systems, networks, components and services. **Freq:** Bimonthly. **Key Personnel:** Prof. Barry G. Evans, Ch. Ed., b.evans@ee.surrey.ac.uk. **ISSN:** 1542-0973. **Subscription Rates:** US$2,184 other countries print only; 1,479 institutions UK (print only); EUR1,869 institutions, other countries print only; US$2,898 institutions, other countries print only. **URL:** http://www3.interscience.wiley.com/journal/117946194/grouphome/home.html.

53492 ■ Journal of Chinese Economic and Business Studies
Routledge
Taylor & Francis Group Ltd.
c/o Xiaming Liu, Ed.-in-Ch.
School of Management
University of Surrey
Guildford GU2 7XH, United Kingdom
Publisher E-mail: webmaster.books@tandf.co.uk
Peer-reviewed journal providing a platform for sharing information on issues such as economics, business and the likes affecting Chinese economy. **Subtitle:** The International Scholarly Journal of the Chinese Economic Association UK (CEA-UK). **Freq:** 3/yr. **Key Personnel:** Xiaming Liu, Editor-in-Chief, phone 44 20 70790895, fax 44 20 76316769, xiaming.liu@bbk.ac.uk; Peter Nolan, Co-Ed.; Haiyan Song, Co-Ed.; Peter J. Buckley, Editorial Board Member; Charles Goodhart, Editorial Board Member; Ding Lu, Editorial Board Member; Wing Thye Woo, Co-Ed.; Guy Liu, Co-Ed.; Shujie Yao, Editorial Board Member; Eric Girardin, Editorial Board Member; Xinzhong Xu, Editorial Board Member; Yanrui Wu, Editorial Board Member. **ISSN:** 1476-5284. **Subscription Rates:** 342 institutions print + online; US$567 institutions print + online; 325 institutions online; US$539 institutions online; 105 individuals personal; US$173 individuals personal; EUR452 institutions print and online; EUR430 institutions online only; EUR139 individuals. **Remarks:** Advertising accepted; rates available upon request. **URL:** http://www.tandf.co.uk/journals/titles/

14765284.asp. **Circ:** (Not Reported)

53493 ■ Journal of Constructional Steel Research
Elsevier Science
c/o Patrick J. Dowling, Honorary Ed.
University of Surrey
Guildford GU2 5XH, United Kingdom
Publisher E-mail: nlinfo-f@elsevier.com
Journal devoted to latest developments in structural steel research and their applications. The areas of interest including theoretical and experimental approaches to elements, assemblages, connection and material properties are considered for publication. **Founded:** 1981. **Freq:** Monthly. **Key Personnel:** Patrick J. Dowling, Honorary Ed.; J.E. Harding, Editor, jeharding@onetel.net; Gerard A.R. Parke, Editor, g.parke@surrey.ac.uk. **ISSN:** 0143-974X. **Subscription Rates:** EUR2,733 institutions European countries; 362,800¥ institutions; US$3,058 institutions all countries except Europe and Japan. **Remarks:** Accepts advertising. **URL:** http://www.elsevier.com/wps/find/journaldescription.cws_home/405901/description. **Circ:** (Not Reported)

53494 ■ Plant Heritage
National Council for the Conservation of Plants and Gardens
12 Home Farm
Loseley Pk.
Guildford GU3 1HS, United Kingdom
Ph: 44 1483 447540
Fax: 44 1483 458933
Publisher E-mail: info@plantheritage.org.uk
Publication covering conservation. **Subtitle:** Journal of the National Council for the Conservation of Plants and Gardens. **Freq:** Semiannual. **Subscription Rates:** Free to all members. **Remarks:** Advertising accepted; rates available upon request. **URL:** http://www.nccpg.com/Page.aspx?page=178. **Circ:** (Not Reported)

53495 ■ BBC Radio Surrey-FM - 104
Broadcasting Ctr.
Surrey
Guildford GU2 7AP, United Kingdom
Ph: 44 370 4111046
E-mail: surrey@bbc.co.uk
Format: Talk; News; Sports. **Owner:** British Broadcasting Corporation, Broadcasting House, Portland Pl., London W1A 1AA, United Kingdom. **Founded:** 1968. **Formerly:** BBC Southern Counties-FM. **Operating Hours:** Continuous. **URL:** http://news.bbc.co.uk/local/surrey/hi/tv_and_radio/.

53496 ■ County Sound Radio-AM - 1566
Dolphin House
North St.
Guildford GU1 4AA, United Kingdom
Ph: 44 1483 300964
E-mail: studio@countysound.co.uk
Format: News; Full Service; Oldies; Religious. **Ad Rates:** Advertising accepted; rates available upon request. **URL:** http://www.countysound.co.uk/.

53497 ■ Eagle-FM - 96.4
Dolphin House, N St.
Guildford GU1 4AA, United Kingdom
Ph: 44 1483 300964
Format: Adult Contemporary. **Key Personnel:** Paul Marcus, Mng. Dir., paul.marcus@964eagle.co.uk; Peter Gordon, Program Dir., peter.gordon@964eagle.co.uk. **URL:** http://www.964eagle.co.uk/.

53498 ■ GU2 Radio-AM - 1350
Union House
University of Surrey
Guildford GU2 7XH, United Kingdom
Ph: 44 1483 689311
E-mail: studio@gu2.co.uk
Format: Contemporary Hit Radio (CHR). **Key Personnel:** John Bannister, Station Mgr., manager@gu2.co.uk. **URL:** http://www.gu2.co.uk/.

Guisborough

53499 ■ The Journal for Weavers, Spinners and Dyers
Association of Guilds of Weavers, Spinners and Dyers
51 Farmdale Dr.
Guisborough TS14 8JJ, United Kingdom
Ph: 44 12 87280469
Journal covering the craft of weaving. **Freq:** Quarterly

March, June, September, & December. **Key Personnel:** Dawn Willey, Book Reviews; Clive Rowlands, Treas.; Angela Pawlyn, Contact. **ISSN:** 0267-7806. **Subscription Rates:** 15 members; 22 other countries surface mail; 44 other countries two years, surface mail; 40.50 other countries 6 issues, airmail; 27 other countries airmail; 54 other countries two years, airmail. **Remarks:** Advertising accepted; rates available upon request. **URL:** http://www.wsd.org.uk/; http://www.thejournalforwsd.org.uk/home. **Circ:** (Not Reported)

Gwynedd

53500 ■ Ffestiniog Railway Magazine
Ffestiniog Railway Society
c/o Festiniog Railway Co.
Harbour Sta., Porthmadog
Gwynedd LL49 9NF, United Kingdom
Publisher E-mail: secretary@ffestiniograilway.org.uk
Journal covering railroads and transportation. **Subtitle:** Journal of the Ffestiniog Railway Society. **Founded:** 1958. **Freq:** Quarterly. **Print Method:** Offset. **Trim Size:** A5. **Cols./Page:** 2. **ISSN:** 0015-0355. **Subscription Rates:** 25 individuals single copy; Free to members; 75 individuals. **Remarks:** Accepts advertising. **URL:** http://www.festiniograilway.org.uk. **Ad Rates:** BW: 150. **Circ:** Paid 5,000

Hailsham

53501 ■ Mariner's Mirror
Society for Nautical Research
The Lodge
The Drive
Hellingly
East Sussex
Hailsham BN27 4EP, United Kingdom
Publisher E-mail: membership@snr.org.uk
English and French language publication covering marine interests. **Freq:** Quarterly. **Key Personnel:** Dr. Hugh Murphy, Editor, marinersmirroreditor@snr.org.uk. **ISSN:** 0025-3359. **Remarks:** Advertising accepted; rates available upon request. **URL:** http://www.snr.org.uk/mariners_mirror.htm. **Circ:** (Not Reported)

53502 ■ Sovereign Radio-FM - 107.5
14 St. Mary's Walk
East Sussex
Hailsham BN27 1AF, United Kingdom
Ph: 44 1323 442700
Fax: 44 1323 442866
E-mail: studio@sovereignfm.com
Format: Adult Contemporary. **Ad Rates:** Advertising accepted; rates available upon request. **URL:** http://www.sovereignfm.com/.

Hale

53503 ■ Living Edge
Archant Life
22A Victoria Rd.
Cheshire
Hale WA15 9AD, United Kingdom
Ph: 44 161 9280333
Fax: 44 161 9298656
Publication E-mail: editorial@livingedgemag.co.uk
Publisher E-mail: anne.basey-fisher@archant.co.uk
Magazine featuring interior companies in Cheshire. **Freq:** Monthly. **Key Personnel:** Claire Cooper, Sales Mgr., claire.cooper@archant.co.uk; Ian Henderson, Circulation Mgr., ian.henderson@archant.co.uk; Andy Phelan, Publisher, andy.phelan@archant.co.uk. **ISSN:** 1464-2034. **Subscription Rates:** Free. **Remarks:** Accepts advertising. **URL:** http://www.archantlife.co.uk/search-the-site-living-edge-magazine--12365. **Circ:** (Not Reported)

Halesworth

53504 ■ Deer
Perdix Publishing Ltd.
Bridge Farm
Chediston
Halesworth IP19 0AE, United Kingdom
Ph: 44 1986 873688
Publication covering wildlife conservation. Official publication of the British Deer Society. **Freq:** Quarterly. **Print Method:** Web Offset. **Trim Size:** A4. **Key Person-

nel: Graham Downing, Contact. **Subscription Rates:** 20 individuals; 5 single issue. **URL:** http://www.perdix-publishing.com/index.htm. **Ad Rates:** BW: 575, 4C: 625. **Circ:** Paid 6,000

Hampton

53505 ■ Coatings Comet
Paint Research Association
14 Castle Mews
High St.
Middlesex
Hampton TW12 2NP, United Kingdom
Ph: 44 20 84870800
Fax: 44 20 84870801
Journal containing companies, markets and economic trend information on Coatings Industry. **Freq:** Monthly. **Key Personnel:** Glenda Thisdell, PhD, Editor. **ISSN:** 0968-7149. **Subscription Rates:** 460 nonmembers print; 345 members print; 575 nonmembers print and pdf; 430 members print and pdf. **URL:** http://www.pra-world.com/business_services/journals/coatings_comet.

53506 ■ World Surface Coatings Abstracts
Paint Research Association
14 Castle Mews
High St.
Middlesex
Hampton TW12 2NP, United Kingdom
Ph: 44 20 84870800
Fax: 44 20 84870801
Publication covering paints and finishes. **Founded:** 1928. **Freq:** Monthly. **Key Personnel:** Dr. Norman Morgan, Editor. **ISSN:** 0043-9088. **Subscription Rates:** 980 members; 1,440 nonmembers. **Remarks:** Advertising not accepted. **URL:** http://www.pra-world.com/business_services/journals/wsca. **Circ:** 250

Harborough

53507 ■ Harborough Mail
Johnston Press PLC
9 Northampton Rd.
Harborough LE16 9HB, United Kingdom
Ph: 44 1858 436000
Local community newspaper. **Freq:** Weekly (Thurs.). **Key Personnel:** Brian Dodds, Editor, fax 44 1858 410097, brian.dodds@harboroughmail.co.uk; Alex Blackwell, Dep. Ed., alex.blackwell@harboroughmail.co.uk. **Remarks:** Accepts advertising. **URL:** http://www.harboroughmail.co.uk/. **Circ:** (Not Reported)

Harlescott

53508 ■ Veterinary Dermatology
John Wiley & Sons Inc.
Wiley-Blackwell
c/o Aiden Foster, Ed.-in-Ch.
VLA Shrewsbury
Kendal Rd.
Harlescott SY1 4HD, United Kingdom
Peer-reviewed journal covering all aspects of the skin of mammals, birds, reptiles, amphibians and fish. **Freq:** Bimonthly. **Key Personnel:** Peter Hill, Editorial Board; Rosanna Marsella, Editorial Board; Karen Moriello, Editor; Joan Rest, Editorial Board; Aiden Foster, Editor-in-Chief. **ISSN:** 0959-4493. **Subscription Rates:** US$1,427 institutions print and online; EUR982 institutions print and online; 773 institutions print and online; US$1,297 institutions print or online; EUR893 institutions print or online; US$1,663 institutions, other countries print and online; US$1,511 institutions, other countries print or online; US$265 individuals print and online; 145 individuals print and online; EUR218 individuals print and online. **Remarks:** Accepts advertising. **URL:** http://www.wiley.com/bw/journal.asp?ref=0959-4493. **Ad Rates:** BW: 525, 4C: 1,314. **Circ:** (Not Reported)

Harlesden

53509 ■ Life-FM - 103.6
2 Fl., 89-93 High St.
Harlesden NW10 4NX, United Kingdom
Ph: 44 208 9639560
E-mail: info@lifefm.org.uk
Format: Urban Contemporary. **Ad Rates:** Advertising accepted; rates available upon request. **URL:** http://www.lifefm.org.uk/.

Harleston

53510 ■ CARPology
Toffee Publications Ltd.
PO Box 28
Harleston IP20 0WT, United Kingdom
Fax: 44 1986 788655
Publication E-mail: editorial@carpology.net
Publisher E-mail: studio@carpology.net
Magazine featuring carp fishing. **Freq:** Monthly. **Key Personnel:** Joe Wright, Contact, phone 44 1986 788899. **Subscription Rates:** 34.65 individuals; 62 individuals Europe; 74 other countries. **Remarks:** Accepts advertising. **URL:** http://www.carpology.net/. **Circ:** (Not Reported)

Harlow

53511 ■ Harlow Edition Herald
Archant Regional Ltd.
Unit G6, Peartree Business Pk.
South Rd.
Templefields
Harlow CM20 2BD, United Kingdom
Ph: 44 1279 624351
Fax: 44 1279 624375
Publication E-mail: herald.news@archant.co.uk
Publisher E-mail: sandra.roantree@archant.co.uk
Local community newspaper. **Freq:** Weekly (Thurs.). **Key Personnel:** Barry Hunt, Editor; Phil White, Production Mgr. **Subscription Rates:** Free to homes across Harlow; 19.50 out of area 3 months; 39 out of area 6 months; 78 out of area. **Remarks:** Accepts advertising. **URL:** http://www.harlowherald.co.uk/content/hlwherald/default/default.aspx. **Circ:** 48,147

53512 ■ TEN 17-FM - 101.7
Latton Bush Ctr.
Southern Way
Harlow CM18 7BB, United Kingdom
Ph: 44 1279 441017
Format: Adult Contemporary. **Ad Rates:** Advertising accepted; rates available upon request. **URL:** http://www.ten17.co.uk/.

Harpenden

53513 ■ Agents News
Manufacturers' Agents' Association of Great Britain and Ireland
Unit 16, Thrales End
Harpenden AL5 3NS, United Kingdom
Ph: 44 15 82767618
Fax: 44 15 82766092
Publisher E-mail: info@themaa.co.uk
Magazine containing agency matters, linking agents with principals and legal aspects. **Freq:** Bimonthly January, March, May, July, September and November. **Remarks:** Accepts advertising. **URL:** http://www.themaa.co.uk/agents.htm. **Circ:** (Not Reported)

53514 ■ Gospel Standard
Gospel Standard Publications
12b Roundwood Ln.
Hertfordshire
Harpenden AL5 3DD, United Kingdom
Ph: 44 1582 765448
Publication E-mail: gospelm@3rivers.net
Journal of the Gospel Standard Baptists. **Founded:** 1835. **Freq:** Monthly. **Print Method:** Web offset. **Trim Size:** 5 x 8. **Cols./Page:** 1. **Col. Width:** 4 inches. **Key Personnel:** Benjamin Ashworth Ramsbottom, Editor. **Subscription Rates:** 18 individuals; US$43 individuals; $A 48 individuals; EUR29 individuals. **Remarks:** Accepts advertising. **URL:** http://www.gospelstandard.org. **Circ:** Paid 2,000

Harrogate

53515 ■ British Commercial Agents Review
British Agents Register
5A Cheltenham Mt.
North Yorkshire
Harrogate HG1 1DW, United Kingdom
Ph: 44 1423 560608
Publisher E-mail: info@agentsregister.com
Professional magazine for sales agents, sales agencies, and manufacturers. **Founded:** 1967. **Freq:** Monthly. **Subscription Rates:** 45 individuals; 35 members; 25 individuals; 17.50 members; 12 individuals; 10 members.

Remarks: Accepts advertising. **URL:** http://www.agentsregister.com/whyusebar.html. **Circ:** (Not Reported)

53516 ■ Harrogate Advertiser
Johnston Press PLC
Ackrill Media Group
1 Cardale Pk.
Harrogate HG3 1RZ, United Kingdom
Ph: 44 1423 564321
Local community newspaper. **Key Personnel:** Jean MacQuarrie, Editor. **Remarks:** Accepts advertising. **URL:** http://www.harrogateadvertiser.net/. **Circ:** (Not Reported)

53517 ■ Journal of Perioperative Practice
Association for Perioperative Practice
Daisy Ayris House
6 Grove Park Ct.
Harrogate HG1 4DP, United Kingdom
Ph: 44 14 23508079
Fax: 44 14 23531613
Publication E-mail: helen.holmes@afpp.org.uk
Publisher E-mail: hq@afpp.org.uk
British journal covering nursing. **Freq:** Monthly. **Key Personnel:** Helen Holmes, Contact. **ISSN:** 1467-1026. **Subscription Rates:** 65 nonmembers U.K.; 80 nonmembers overseas; 180 institutions U.K; 190 institutions overseas. **URL:** http://www.afpp.org.uk/books-journals/journals. **Formerly:** British Journal of Theatre Nurses; British Journal of Perioperitive Nurses. **Ad Rates:** BW: 260, 4C: 1,050. **Circ:** 8,000

53518 ■ Orthopaedic Product News
Pelican Magazines Ltd.
2 Cheltenham Mount
Harrogate HG1 1DL, United Kingdom
Ph: 44 1423 569676
Fax: 44 1423 569677
Publication E-mail: editor@opnews.com
Publisher E-mail: info@pelgrp.com
Professional magazine covering orthopaedic products for medical professionals in the UK. **Freq:** Bimonthly 6/yr. **Print Method:** Offset litho. **Trim Size:** 210 x 297 mm. **Subscription Rates:** 37.99 individuals U.K.; 47.99 individuals Europe; 61.99 other countries airmail. **Remarks:** Accepts advertising. **URL:** http://www.opnews.com/index.php. **Circ:** Combined ‡8,044

53519 ■ Pateley Bridge & Nidderdale Herald
Johnston Press PLC
1 Cardale Pk.
Beckwith Head Rd.
Harrogate HG3 1RZ, United Kingdom
Ph: 44 1423 564321
Local community newspaper. **Key Personnel:** Jean MacQuarrie, Editor. **Remarks:** Accepts advertising. **URL:** http://www.nidderdaleherald.co.uk/. **Circ:** (Not Reported)

53520 ■ Stray-FM - 97.2
The Hamlet
Hornbeam Park Ave.
Harrogate HG2 8RE, United Kingdom
Ph: 44 14 23522972
Format: Contemporary Hit Radio (CHR). **Operating Hours:** Continuous. **Ad Rates:** Advertising accepted; rates available upon request. **URL:** http://www.strayfm.com.

Harrow

53521 ■ Comparative Clinical Pathology
Springer-Verlag London Ltd.
c/o Paul Sibbons, Ed.
Dept. of Surgical Research
Northwick Park Institute of Medical Research
Harrow HA1 3UJ, United Kingdom
Journal publishing papers encompassing the total spectrum of comparative clinical pathology, including classical haematology and clinical chemistry, cellular and organ physiology and function, toxicology, immunology, cell kinetics, haemostasis, haematopoietic and other malignancies, immunodeficiency states, molecular biology, immunophenotyping, bone marrow transplantation, enzymology, endocrinology, cytokines, haematopoietic growth factors, evolutionary medicine, cellular lineage, rheology, functional identification and biomarkers, normal values, abnormal reactions, human, veterinary and zoological data, diagnostic and toxicological

changes, experimental studies (both in vivo and in vitro) and new technology and its impact on diagnosis and disease control. **Freq:** Quarterly. **Key Personnel:** Paul Sibbons, Editor, phone 44 20 88693266, fax 44 20 88693270, p.sibbons@imperial.ac.uk; Mike Hart, Editorial Board; Geoff Brown, Founding Ed. **ISSN:** 1618-5641. **Subscription Rates:** EUR737 institutions print and e-access; EUR884.40 institutions print and enhanced access. **Remarks:** Advertising accepted; rates available upon request. **URL:** http://www.springerlink.com/content/ 1618-5641; http://www.springer.com/medicine/ pathology/journal/580?detailsPage=description. **Circ:** (Not Reported)

53522 ■ Emergency Nurse
RCN Publishing Co.
The Heights
59-65 Lowlands Rd.
Harrow HA1 3AW, United Kingdom
Ph: 44 20 84231066
Publisher E-mail: advertising@rcnpublishing.co.uk
Professional journal covering emergency nursing. **Freq:** 10/yr. **Key Personnel:** Claire Picton, Editor; Helen Hyland, Editorial Admin.; Kate Ambrose, Editorial Advisory Board. **ISSN:** 1354-5752. **Subscription Rates:** 4.30 individuals. **Remarks:** Accepts advertising. **URL:** http:// emergencynurse.rcnpublishing.co.uk/. **Ad Rates:** BW: 950, 4C: 1,260. **Circ:** Paid ‡5,621

53523 ■ Evidence-Based Nursing
RCN Publishing Co.
The Heights
59-65 Lowlands Rd.
Harrow HA1 3AW, United Kingdom
Ph: 44 20 84231066
Publisher E-mail: advertising@rcnpublishing.co.uk
Professional journal covering research related to nursing. **Freq:** Quarterly. **Key Personnel:** Jane Brosnahan, Editorial Board; Richard Sands, Mgr., rsands@ bmjgroup.com; Caroline Carlisle, Editorial Board; Susan Marks, Contact, sumarks@mcmaster.ca; Carl Thompson, PhD, Editor, cat4@york.ac.uk; Andrew Jull, Editor, ajull@auckland.ac.nz. **ISSN:** 1367-6539. **URL:** http:// ebn.bmj.com/. **Circ:** ‡8,244

53524 ■ Inroads
Institute of Road Safety Officers
Pin Point, Rosslyn Cres.
Harrow HA1 2SU, United Kingdom
Ph: 44 870 0104442
Fax: 44 870 3337772
Publisher E-mail: irso@dbda.co.uk
Trade publication covering safety. **Freq:** Quarterly. **Key Personnel:** Steve Shannon, Chm. **Subscription Rates:** 15 individuals; Free MBS. **Remarks:** Advertising accepted; rates available upon request. **URL:** http://www. irso.org.uk/. **Circ:** 2,000

53525 ■ Mental Health Practice
RCN Publishing Co.
The Heights
59-65 Lowlands Rd.
Harrow HA1 3AW, United Kingdom
Ph: 44 20 84231066
Publisher E-mail: advertising@rcnpublishing.co.uk
Professional journal for mental health nurses. **Founded:** Sept. 1997. **Freq:** 10/yr. **Key Personnel:** Ian McMillan, Editor; Helen Hyland, Editorial Admin., helen.hyland@ rcnpublishing.co.uk; Cris Allen, Assoc. Ed. **ISSN:** 1351-5578. **Subscription Rates:** 4.30 individuals per month. **Remarks:** Accepts advertising. **URL:** http:// mentalhealthpractice.rcnpublishing.co.uk/. **Ad Rates:** BW: 1,190, 4C: 1,810. **Circ:** Paid 10,925

53526 ■ The Muslim News
Visitcrest Ltd.
PO Box 380
Harrow HA2 6LL, United Kingdom
Ph: 44 20 88638586
Fax: 44 20 88639370
Publication E-mail: info@muslimnews.co.uk
Publisher E-mail: info@muslimnews.co.uk
Community newspaper for Muslims and non-Muslims in the United Kingdom and worldwide. **Founded:** Feb. 1989. **Freq:** Monthly. **Cols./Page:** 5. **Col. Width:** 50 millimeters. **Key Personnel:** Ahmed Versi, Editor; Tahera Versi, Advertising Mgr. **ISSN:** 0956-5027. **Subscription Rates:** 12 individuals; 17 other countries overseas airmail; 20 two years; 30 two years overseas airmail. **Remarks:** Accepts advertising. **URL:** http://www.

muslimnews.co.uk. **Feature Editors:** Abdul Adil, *Book.* **Ad Rates:** BW: 2,420, 4C: 2,520. **Circ:** 26,000

53527 ■ Nurse Researcher
RCN Publishing Co.
The Heights
59-65 Lowlands Rd.
Harrow HA1 3AW, United Kingdom
Ph: 44 20 84231066
Publisher E-mail: advertising@rcnpublishing.co.uk
Professional journal covering nursing research. **Freq:** Quarterly. **Key Personnel:** Leslie Gelling, Editor, leslie. gelling@anglia.ac.uk. **ISSN:** 1351-5578. **Subscription Rates:** 3.80 individuals per month. **Remarks:** Advertising not accepted. **URL:** http://nurseresearcher. rcnpublishing.co.uk/. **Circ:** (Not Reported)

53528 ■ Nursing Management
RCN Publishing Co.
The Heights
59-65 Lowlands Rd.
Harrow HA1 3AW, United Kingdom
Ph: 44 20 84231066
Publisher E-mail: advertising@rcnpublishing.co.uk
Professional journal covering issues for the nursing field. **Freq:** 10/yr. **Key Personnel:** Helen Hyland, Editorial Admin.; Donna Kinnair, Consultant Ed.; Nick Lipley, Editor, nick.lipley@rcnpublishing.co.uk; David Benton, Editorial Advisory Board; Juliet Chambers, Editorial Advisory Board; Deborah Clatworthy, Editorial Advisory Board. **ISSN:** 1354-5760. **Subscription Rates:** 4.30 individuals. **URL:** http://nursingmanagement. rcnpublishing.co.uk/. **Circ:** ★4,564

53529 ■ Nursing Older People
RCN Publishing Co.
The Heights
59-65 Lowlands Rd.
Harrow HA1 3AW, United Kingdom
Ph: 44 20 84231066
Publisher E-mail: advertising@rcnpublishing.co.uk
Professional journal covering elderly care in hospitals, communities, or residential settings. **Freq:** 9/yr. **Key Personnel:** Sarah Harrison, Acting Ed.; Helen Hyland, Editorial Admin., helen.hyland@rcnpublishing.co.uk; Penny Lockwood, Mktg. Mgr. **ISSN:** 1472-0795. **Subscription Rates:** 4.30 individuals per month. **Remarks:** Accepts advertising. **URL:** http://nursingolderpeople. rcnpublishing.co.uk/. **Former name:** Elderly Care. **Ad Rates:** BW: 1,310, 4C: 1,990. **Circ:** Paid ★7,430

53530 ■ Nursing Standard
RCN Publishing Co.
The Heights
59-65 Lowlands Rd.
Harrow HA1 3AW, United Kingdom
Ph: 44 20 84231066
Publisher E-mail: advertising@rcnpublishing.co.uk
Professional journal covering research and issues in nursing. **Freq:** Weekly. **ISSN:** 0029-6570. **Subscription Rates:** 4.50 individuals per month. **URL:** http:// nursingstandard.rcnpublishing.co.uk/. **Circ:** ★67,272

53531 ■ Pediatric Nursing
RCN Publishing Co.
The Heights
59-65 Lowlands Rd.
Harrow HA1 3AW, United Kingdom
Ph: 44 20 84231066
Publisher E-mail: advertising@rcnpublishing.co.uk
Professional journal for child health nurses. **Freq:** 10/yr. **Key Personnel:** Anne Casey, Contact, anne.casey@ rcnpublishing.co.uk; Christine Walker, Editor, phone 44 20 84231066, chris.walker@rcnpublishing.co.uk. **ISSN:** 0962-9513. **Subscription Rates:** 4.30 individuals. **Remarks:** Accepts advertising. **URL:** http:// paediatricnursing.rcnpublishing.co.uk/. **Circ:** ★13,048

53532 ■ Primary Health Care
RCN Publishing Co.
The Heights
59-65 Lowlands Rd.
Harrow HA1 3AW, United Kingdom
Ph: 44 20 84231066
Publisher E-mail: advertising@rcnpublishing.co.uk
Professional journal of the RCN Community Nursing Groups for members. **Freq:** 10/yr. **Key Personnel:** Julie Sylvester, Editor; Helen Hyland, Editorial Admin., helen. hyland@rcnpublishing.co.uk; Sally Gauntlett, Advertise-

ment Production; Helen Sumner, Mktg. Mgr.; Yasser Hussain, Mktg. Exec. **ISSN:** 0269-9079. **Subscription Rates:** 4.30 individuals. **Remarks:** Accepts advertising. **URL:** http://primaryhealthcare.rcnpublishing.co.uk/. **Circ:** ★7,271

Hartlepool

53533 ■ Hartlepool Mail
Johnston Press PLC
New Clarence House
Wesley Sq.
Hartlepool TS24 8BX, United Kingdom
Ph: 44 1429 239333
Local community newspaper. **Freq:** Daily. **Key Personnel:** Gavin Foster, Dep. Ed.; Ian Willis, News Ed. **Remarks:** Accepts advertising. **URL:** http://www. hartlepoolmail.co.uk/. **Circ:** (Not Reported)

53534 ■ Peterlee Mail
Johnston Press PLC
New Clarence House
Wesley Sq.
Hartlepool TS24 8BX, United Kingdom
Ph: 44 1429 239333
Local community newspaper. **Freq:** Daily. **Key Personnel:** Gavin Foster, Dep. Ed.; Paul Foreman, Sales Mgr.; Elaine Simpson, Contact, elaine.simpson@northeast-press.co.uk. **Remarks:** Accepts advertising. **URL:** http:// www.peterleemail.co.uk/. **Circ:** (Not Reported)

53535 ■ Radio Hartlepool-FM - 102.4
Broadcasting House
79 York Rd.
Hartlepool TS26 8AH, United Kingdom
Format: Full Service. **Key Personnel:** Jason Anderson, Mng. Dir. **URL:** http://www.radiohartlepool.co.uk/.

Haslemere

53536 ■ Drug Delivery Systems and Sciences
Euromed Communications Ltd.
The Old Surgery Liphook Rd.
Lynchborough Rd.
Passfield
Hampshire
Haslemere GU27 1NL, United Kingdom
Ph: 44 14 28656665
Fax: 44 14 28656643
Publisher E-mail: info@euromed.uk.com
Journal containing primarily original work resulting from research and technological developments in the drug delivery field, emphasizing on applied research. **Freq:** Quarterly. **Subscription Rates:** 48 individuals inside Europe; 60 individuals outside Europe. **URL:** http://www. euromedscientific.co.uk/.

Hastings

53537 ■ Arrow-FM - 107.8
Priory Meadow Centre
Hastings TN34 1PJ, United Kingdom
Ph: 44 1424 461177
Format: Adult Contemporary. **Owner:** The Local Radio Co. PLC, 11 Duke St., High Wycombe HP13 6EE, United Kingdom, 44 1494 688200, Fax: 44 1494 688201. **Operating Hours:** Continuous. **Ad Rates:** Advertising accepted; rates available upon request. **URL:** http:// www.arrowfm.co.uk.

Hatfield

53538 ■ Body, Movement and Dance in Psychotherapy
Taylor & Francis Ltd.
School of Social, Community & Health Studies
University of Hertfordshire
Meridian House
32 The Common
Hatfield AL10 ONZ, United Kingdom
Ph: 44 17 07285861
Peer-reviewed and international journal exploring the relationship between body and mind and focusing on the significance of the body and movement in the therapeutic setting. **Subtitle:** An International Journal for Theory, Research and Practice. **Freq:** 3/yr. **Key Personnel:** Dr. Helen Payne, Editor-in-Chief, h.l.payne@herts. ac.uk; Yorai Sella, Assoc. Ed.; Gill Westland, Co-Ed.; Dr. Dita Federman, Assoc. Ed.; Dr. Vicky Karkou, Co-Ed.;

Michael Heller, Assoc. Ed.; Jeff Barlow, Assoc. Ed.; Dr. Bonnie Meekums, Assoc. Ed.; Jane Guthrie, Assoc. Ed. **ISSN:** 1743-2979. **Subscription Rates:** 164 institutions print + online; US$288 institutions print + online; 155 institutions online; US$273 institutions online; 37 individuals print only; US$65 individuals print only; 20 individuals society; US$40 individuals society; 20 students; US$40 students. **Remarks:** Accepts advertising. **URL:** http://www.tandf.co.uk/journals/titles/17432979.asp. **Circ:** (Not Reported)

53539 ■ Information Management & Technology
University of Hertfordshire
CIMTECH
Innovation Ctr.
College Ln.
Hatfield AL10 9AB, United Kingdom
Ph: 44 170 7281060
Fax: 44 170 7281061
Publisher E-mail: c.cimtech@herts.ac.uk
Professional journal covering information technology and electronic document management for information/records managers, archivists, consultants and systems vendors. **Subtitle:** The Journal of Cintech. **Freq:** 10/yr. **ISSN:** 0266-6960. **Subscription Rates:** 80 individuals U.K.; 80 other countries. **Remarks:** Advertising not accepted. **URL:** http://www.imat.cimtech.co.uk/Welcome.htm. **Former name:** Reprographics Quarterly. **Circ:** Controlled 700

53540 ■ Journal of Human Nutrition and Dietetics
John Wiley & Sons Inc.
Wiley-Blackwell
c/o Joan Gandy, Ed.
Health & Emergency Professions
University of Hertfordshire
College Ln.
Hatfield AL10 9AB, United Kingdom
Ph: 44 20 84290892
Peer-reviewed journal covering applied nutrition and dietetics in connection with the British Dietetic Association. **Freq:** Bimonthly. **Key Personnel:** A. Anderson, Editorial Board; Joan Gandy, Editor, jhnded@bda.uk.com; Ailsa Brotherton, CPD Ed., ambrotherton@uclan.ac.uk; Angela Madden, Book Review Ed., phone 44 1707 286494; a.madden@herts.ac.uk; Carrie Ruxton, Review Ed., carrie@nutrition-communications.com. **ISSN:** 0952-3871. **Subscription Rates:** US$215 individuals print + online; EUR175 individuals print + online; 116 individuals print + online (non Euro zone); 129 other countries print + online; US$1,007 institutions print + online; 545 institutions print + online; EUR693 institutions print + online; US$1,173 institutions, other countries print + online. **Remarks:** Advertising accepted; rates available upon request. **URL:** http://www.wiley.com/bw/journal.asp?ref=0952-3871. **Circ:** (Not Reported)

53541 ■ School Science Review
Association for Science Education
College Ln.
Hatfield AL10 9AA, United Kingdom
Ph: 44 1707 283000
Fax: 44 1707 266532
Publisher E-mail: info@ase.org.uk
Education publication. **Founded:** June 1919. **Freq:** Quarterly. **Print Method:** perfect bound. **Trim Size:** B5. **Key Personnel:** Geoff Auty, Editor. **ISSN:** 0036-6811. **Subscription Rates:** 116 individuals surface mail; 131 individuals airmail; Europe; 148 individuals airmail; non-Europe; 110 individuals agency; surface mail; 125 individuals agency (airmail Europe); 142 individuals agency (airmail Non-Europe). **URL:** http://www.ase.org.uk/journals/school-science-review/.

53542 ■ Science Education International
International Council of Associations for Science Education
Federacion Internacional de Asociaciones de Profesores de Ciencias
College Ln.
Hatfield AL10 9AA, United Kingdom
Ph: 44 1707 271034
Fax: 44 1707 270142
Publisher E-mail: icase@ase.org.uk
Publication covering worldwide science education. **Freq:** Quarterly. **ISSN:** 2077-2327. **Subscription Rates:** US$50 individuals; $A 50 individuals; EUR30 individuals; EUR60 institutions; US$100 institutions; $A 100 institutions. **Remarks:** Advertising accepted; rates avail-

able upon request. **URL:** http://www.icaseonline.net/seiweb/. **Circ:** 700

Havant

53543 ■ Business News (South East Hampshire)
Portsmouth & South East Hampshire Chamber of Commerce & Industry
The Regional Business Centre
Harts Farm Way
Havant PO9 1HR, United Kingdom
Ph: 44 23 92449449
Fax: 44 23 92449444
Publisher E-mail: sehants@chamber.org.uk
Professional magazine covering local business news. **Founded:** 1983. **Freq:** Monthly except January and August. **Cols./Page:** 3. **Key Personnel:** Maureen Frost, Ch. Exec., maureen.frost@chamber.org.uk; Max Breeze, International Trade Mgr., max.breeze@chamber.org.uk. **Subscription Rates:** Free to qualified subscribers. **URL:** http://www.chamber.org.uk. **Circ:** Controlled 1,100

Haverhill

53544 ■ Haverhill Echo
Johnston Press PLC
7 Queen's Sq.
Haverhill CB9 9EG, United Kingdom
Ph: 44 1440 703456
Local community newspaper. **Freq:** Weekly (Thurs.). **Key Personnel:** Barry Peters, Editor, phone 44 1440 764006, fax 44 1440 764013, barry.peters@jpress.co.uk; Karen Steel, Dep. Ed., phone 44 1440 764000, karen.steel@haverhillecho.com; Jamie Brodie, Advertising Mgr., phone 44 1440 764003, fax 44 1440 712684, jamie.brodie@jpress.co.uk. **Remarks:** Accepts advertising. **URL:** http://www.haverhillecho.co.uk/. **Circ:** (Not Reported)

Hawes

53545 ■ Fresh Radio-AM - 936
The Watermill
Broughton Hall
Skipton BD23 3AG, United Kingdom
Ph: 44 845 2242052
E-mail: info@freshradio.co.uk
Format: Contemporary Hit Radio (CHR). **Ad Rates:** Advertising accepted; rates available upon request. **URL:** http://www.freshradio.co.uk/.

Hawick

53546 ■ Hawick News
Johnston Press PLC
Crown Business Ctr.
Hawick TD9 9EH, United Kingdom
Ph: 44 1450 379690
Local community newspaper. **Key Personnel:** Jason Marshall, Editor; Edith Scott, Advertising Mgr. **Remarks:** Accepts advertising. **URL:** http://www.hawick-news.co.uk/. **Circ:** (Not Reported)

Haywards Heath

53547 ■ Autosport Magazine
Haymarket Publishing Ltd.
W Sussex
PO Box 568
Haywards Heath RH16 3XQ, United Kingdom
Publisher E-mail: info@haymarket.com
Magazine perceived by fans and industry alike as the bible for motorsport news analysis. **Freq:** Weekly. **Subscription Rates:** 122 individuals; EUR128 individuals; US$182 individuals. **URL:** http://www.autosport.com.

53548 ■ Furniture History
Furniture History Society
1 Mercedes Cottages
St. Johns Rd.
West Sussex
Haywards Heath RH16 4EH, United Kingdom
Ph: 44 1444 413845
Fax: 44 1444 413845
Publisher E-mail: furniturehistorysociety@hotmail.com
Journal covering the history of furniture and furnishings from all periods worldwide. Quarterly Newsletter. **Founded:** 1964. **Freq:** Annual. **Trim Size:** 188 x 240 mm. **Cols./Page:** 1. **Col. Width:** 135 millimeters. **Col. Depth:** 192 millimeters. **Key Personnel:** Dr. Brian Aus-

ten, Membership Sec. **ISSN:** 0016-3058. **Subscription Rates:** 30 individuals; 35 out of country. **Remarks:** Advertising not accepted. **URL:** http://www.furniturehistorysociety.org/journal.htm. **Circ:** Combined 1,750

53549 ■ Mid Sussex Times
Johnston Press PLC
7 South Rd.
Haywards Heath RH16 4LE, United Kingdom
Ph: 44 1444 452201
Local community newspaper. **Key Personnel:** John Hammond, Content Ed., phone 44 1403 751214, fax 44 1444 416611, john.hammond@westsussextoday.co.uk; Dianne Jones, Contact, phone 44 1444 419582, fax 44 1444 416611, dianne.jones@sussexnewspapers.co.uk. **Remarks:** Accepts advertising. **URL:** http://www.midsussextimes.co.uk/. **Circ:** (Not Reported)

53550 ■ Parking News
British Parking Association
Stuart House
41-43 Perrymount Rd.
Haywards Heath RH16 3BN, United Kingdom
Ph: 44 144 4447300
Fax: 44 144 4454105
Publisher E-mail: info@britishparking.co.uk
Information on the parking industry. **Subtitle:** Publication covering transportation. **Freq:** Monthly 10/yr. **Key Personnel:** Richard Langrish, Advertising Mgr., phone 44 1887 820533, richard.l@britishparking.co.uk. **Subscription Rates:** Free to members. **Remarks:** Advertising accepted; rates available upon request. **URL:** http://www.britishparking.co.uk/page.php?id=3. **Circ:** 1,600

Heathfield

53551 ■ Quarterly Journal
Dinosaur Society
PO Box 20
East Sussex
Heathfield TN21 8GY, United Kingdom
Ph: 44 14 35860881
Publisher E-mail: enquiries@dinosaursociety.com
Journal of the Dinosaur Society. **Freq:** Quarterly. **URL:** http://www.hmag.gla.ac.uk/dinosoc/quarterly.html.

Hebden Bridge

53552 ■ Hebden Bridge Times
Johnston Press PLC
19a Crown St.
Hebden Bridge HX7 8EH, United Kingdom
Ph: 44 1422 842106
Local community newspaper. **Key Personnel:** Norman Masters, Editor, norman.masters@halifaxcourier.co.uk; Gemma Kipping, Contact, phone 44 1706 815231, fax 44 1706 816671, gemma.kipping@halifaxcourier.co.uk; Luke Crawford, Contact, phone 44 1422 260244, fax 44 1422 330021, luke.crawford@halifaxcourier.co.uk. **Remarks:** Accepts advertising. **URL:** http://www.hebdenbridgetimes.co.uk/. **Circ:** (Not Reported)

53553 ■ Northern Earth
10 Jubilee St.
Mytholmroyd
West Yorkshire
Hebden Bridge HX7 5NP, United Kingdom
Publisher E-mail: editor@northernearth.co.uk
Journal covering archaeology and folklore. **Subtitle:** Earth Mysteries Archaeology Folklore. **Founded:** 1979. **Freq:** Quarterly. **Trim Size:** A5. **Cols./Page:** 2. **Col. Width:** 6 centimeters. **Col. Depth:** 18.5 centimeters. **Key Personnel:** Mike Haigh, Asst. Ed.; Andrew Riley, Web Ed.; John Billingsley, General Ed., editor@northernearth.co.uk. **ISSN:** 0268-8476. **Subscription Rates:** 1.95 single issue U.K. only; 2.30 single issue Europe; 3.20 elsewhere; 7.50 individuals; 11 individuals; 14.50 elsewhere. **Remarks:** Accepts advertising. **URL:** http://www.northernearth.co.uk. **Ad Rates:** BW: EUR32. **Circ:** Combined 450

Helston

53554 ■ Within Reach
Reach
PO Box 54
Helston TR13 8WD, United Kingdom
Ph: 44 845 1306225
Fax: 44 845 1300262

Publication E-mail: editor@reach.org.uk

Publisher E-mail: reach@reach.org.uk

Publication for Reach, The Association for Children With Hand or Arm Deficiency. **Subtitle:** The Official Magazine of the Association for Children with Hand or Arm. **Freq:** Quarterly. **Key Personnel:** Jane Tarrant, Editor. **Subscription Rates:** EUR20 members. **URL:** http://www.reach.org.uk/ReachCMS/view/Client/forms/Publication.aspx?ID=222. **Ad Rates:** BW: EUR450, 4C: EUR650. **Circ:** (Not Reported)

Hemel Hempstead

53555 ■ Boys' Brigade Gazette
Boys' Brigade
Felden Lodge
Hemel Hempstead HP3 0BL, United Kingdom
Ph: 44 14 42231681
Fax: 44 14 42235391
Publication E-mail: gazette@boys-brigade.org.uk
Publisher E-mail: enquiries@boys-brigade.org.uk
Publication covering boy scouts. **Freq:** Quarterly. **Subscription Rates:** 25 individuals. **URL:** http://www.boys-brigade.org.uk/. **Circ:** Paid 22,000

53556 ■ Demolition and Dismantling
National Federation of Demolition Contractors
Resurgam House
Paradise
Herts
Hemel Hempstead HP2 4TF, United Kingdom
Ph: 44 1442 217144
Fax: 44 1442 218268
Publisher E-mail: info@demolition.nfdc.com
Publication covering demolition and dismantling. **Freq:** Quarterly. **Subscription Rates:** Free. **Remarks:** Advertising accepted; rates available upon request. **URL:** http://www.demolition-nfdc.com/london/viewnews-autumn_2010_demolition_dismantling.php. **Circ:** 4,000

53557 ■ Hemel Gazette
Johnston Press PLC
Newspaper House
39 Marlowes
Hemel Hempstead HP1 1LH, United Kingdom
Ph: 44 1442 898488
Local community newspaper. **Freq:** Weekly. **Key Personnel:** Melissa Lynch, Contact, melissa.lynch@jpress.co.uk. **Remarks:** Accepts advertising. **URL:** http://www.hemeltoday.co.uk/. **Circ:** (Not Reported)

53558 ■ In Camera
Kodak Limited & Eastman Kodak Co.
Hemel One
Boundary Way
Hemel Hempstead HP2 7YU, United Kingdom
Ph: 44 1442 261122
Fax: 44 1442 240609
Trade magazine covering the motion picture industry for professionals worldwide. **Freq:** Quarterly. **Key Personnel:** Laura J. Watson, Admin. Ed., laura.watson@kodak.com; Fabien Fournillon, Bus. Ed., fabien.fournillon@kodak.com; Martin Pearce, Editor, martin.pearce@btconnect.com; Judith J. Doherty, Publisher, judith.doherty@kodak.com. **Subscription Rates:** Free. **URL:** http://motion.kodak.com/US/en/motion/Publications/In_Camera/index.htm. **Circ:** Controlled 65,000

53559 ■ CCHHR-AM - 1350
The Studio
Hemel Hempstead General Hospital
Hillfield Rd.
Hemel Hempstead HP2 4AD, United Kingdom
Ph: 44 1442 287018
Fax: 44 1442 249525
Format: Information; News; Oldies; Easy Listening; Talk; Eclectic. **Owner:** Hemel Hospital Radio, at above address. **Operating Hours:** Continuous. **URL:** http://www.hemelradio.org.uk/frameset.htm.

Henley-on-Thames

53560 ■ International Journal of Process Management and Benchmarking
Inderscience Publishers
c/o Prof. Abby Ghobadian, Exec. Ed.
Henley Management College
Greenlands
Oxfordshire
Henley-on-Thames RG9 3AU, United Kingdom

Publisher E-mail: editor@inderscience.com

Peer-reviewed journal aiming to disseminate original peer-reviewed theoretical or practical high-quality research in the field of process management, benchmarking and knowledge management, publishing both quantitative and qualitative research by academics and practitioners. **Freq:** Quarterly. **Key Personnel:** Prof. Abby Ghobadian, Exec. Ed., abby.ghobadian@henleymc.ac.uk; Dr. Mark Davis, North American Ed.; Prof. Harry Boer, Editorial Board Member. **ISSN:** 1460-6739. **Subscription Rates:** EUR494 individuals print only (surface mail); EUR840 individuals online only (2-3 users); EUR672 individuals print and online; EUR534 individuals print only (airmail). **URL:** http://www.inderscience.com/browse/index.php?journalCODE=ijpmb.

53561 ■ Journal of General Management
Braybrooke Press Ltd.
Remenham House
Remenham Hill
Henley-on-Thames RG9 3EP, United Kingdom
Ph: 44 14 91412061
Fax: 44 14 91411428
Publisher E-mail: braybrookehenley@btconnect.com
General business publication. **Freq:** Quarterly. **Key Personnel:** Prof. Ariane Berthoin Antal, Editorial Board; Prof. Malcolm Warner, Editorial Board; James Cross, Editor. **ISSN:** 0957-4212. **Subscription Rates:** 260 institutions print and online; 299 institutions, other countries print and online; 275 institutions online only; 225 institutions print only; 100 individuals print only; 130 other countries print only. **URL:** http://www.braybrooke.co.uk/jgm/.

53562 ■ Open Space
Open Spaces Society
25A Bell St.
Henley-on-Thames RG9 2BA, United Kingdom
Ph: 44 1491 573535
Fax: 44 1491 573051
Publisher E-mail: hq@oss.org.uk
Trade magazine covering the environment. **Freq:** 3/yr. **Subscription Rates:** 4 single issue non-members. **Remarks:** Accepts advertising. **URL:** http://www.oss.org.uk. **Circ:** (Not Reported)

Hereford

53563 ■ The Journal of Alternative & Complementary Medicine
Mary Ann Liebert Incorporated Publishers
c/o Kim A. Jobst, MA, Ed.-in-Ch.
Oxford Brookes University
Fern Lodge
5 Cotterell St.
Hereford HR4 0HH, United Kingdom
Ph: 44 1432 353656
Fax: 44 1432 354010
Publisher E-mail: info@liebertpub.com
Peer-reviewed journal containing information on research in alternative medicine. **Subtitle:** Research on Paradigm, Practice, and Policy. **Founded:** 1995. **Freq:** Monthly. **Print Method:** Offset. **Trim Size:** 8 1/2 x 11. **Cols./Page:** 2. **Col. Width:** 3 1/4 inches. **Col. Depth:** 9 1/2 inches. **Key Personnel:** Barbara Nell Perrin, Managing Editor, jacm-editorial@sbcglobal.net; Mitchell W. Krucoff, MD, Exec. Ed.; Kim A. Jobst, MA, Editor-in-Chief, admin@functionalshift.com. **ISSN:** 1075-5535. **Subscription Rates:** US$364 individuals print and online; US$395 other countries print and online; US$176 individuals online only; US$939 institutions print and online; US$1,088 institutions, other countries print and online; US$756 institutions online only; US$783 institutions print only; US$932 institutions, other countries print only. **Remarks:** Accepts advertising. **URL:** http://www.liebertpub.com/publication.aspx?pub_id=26; http://www.liebertonline.com. **Ad Rates:** BW: 1,200, 4C: 1,950. **Circ:** (Not Reported)

53564 ■ Wyvern-FM - 97.6
1st Fl., Kirkham House
John Comyn Dr.
Worcester WR3 7NS, United Kingdom
Ph: 44 1905 545510
Format: Contemporary Hit Radio (CHR). **Ad Rates:** Advertising accepted; rates available upon request. **URL:** http://www.wyvernfm.co.uk/.

Hertford

53565 ■ Rubber Developments
Tun Abdul Razak Research Centre
Brickendebberry
Hertford SG13 8NL, United Kingdom
Ph: 44 19 92584966
Fax: 44 19 92554837
Publisher E-mail: general@tarrc.co.uk
Publication covering rubber. **Freq:** Semiannual. **Remarks:** Advertising accepted; rates available upon request. **URL:** http://rubberdevelopments.com/. **Circ:** 10,000

Heslington

53566 ■ Discourse
Higher Education Academy
Innovation Way
York Science Pk.
Heslington YO10 5BR, United Kingdom
Ph: 44 19 04717500
Publisher E-mail: enquiries@heacademy.ac.uk
Peer-reviewed journal covering all aspects of developments in the scholarship of learning and teaching in all our subject areas. **Subtitle:** Learning and Teaching in Philosophical and Religious Studies. **Founded:** Aug. 2001. **Freq:** Semiannual. **ISSN:** 1741-4164. **URL:** http://www.prs.heacademy.ac.uk/publications/discourse.html.

53567 ■ Innovations in Teaching and Learning in Information and Computer Sciences
Higher Education Academy
Innovation Way
York Science Pk.
Heslington YO10 5BR, United Kingdom
Ph: 44 19 04717500
Publisher E-mail: enquiries@heacademy.ac.uk
Journal for information and computer sciences communities. **Freq:** 3/yr. **Key Personnel:** Alan Poulter, Editor-in-Chief, alan.poulter@cis.strath.ac.uk. **ISSN:** 1473-7507. **URL:** http://www.ics.heacademy.ac.uk/italics/.

53568 ■ Journal of Hospitality, Leisure, Sports & Tourism Education
Higher Education Academy
Innovation Way
York Science Pk.
Heslington YO10 5BR, United Kingdom
Ph: 44 19 04717500
Publication E-mail: johlste@brookes.ac.uk
Publisher E-mail: enquiries@heacademy.ac.uk
Online journal aiming to promote, enhance and disseminate research, good practice and innovation in all aspects of education in hospitality, leisure, sport and tourism to its prime audience including teachers, researchers, employers, and policy makers. **Freq:** Semiannual. **Key Personnel:** Prof. John Tribe, Editorial Board; Prof. David Litteljohn, Editorial Board; Dr. Fiona Jordan, Editorial Board. **ISSN:** 1473-8376. **URL:** http://www.heacademy.ac.uk/johlste/aimsandscope.

Hexham

53569 ■ North East Life
Archant Life
PO Box 199
Hexham NE46 9AG, United Kingdom
Publication E-mail: neleditor@archant.co.uk
Publisher E-mail: johnny.hustler@archant.co.uk
Magazine featuring lifestyle in the North East region. **Freq:** Monthly. **Trim Size:** 210 x 297 mm. **Key Personnel:** Andrew Smith, Editor, phone 44 7912 415334; Sue Campbell, Editor, phone 44 7973 367004, sue.campbell@archant.co.uk. **Subscription Rates:** 25 individuals. **Remarks:** Accepts advertising. **URL:** http://www.northeast-life.co.uk/. **Circ:** (Not Reported)

53570 ■ Metro Radio-FM - 103.2
55 Degrees N
Pilgrim St.
Newcastle upon Tyne NE1 6BF, United Kingdom
Ph: 44 191 2306100
Fax: 44 191 2790288
Format: Contemporary Hit Radio (CHR). **URL:** http://www.metroradio.co.uk/.

Circulation: ★ = ABC; △ = BPA; ♦ = CAC; • = CCAB; ❑ = VAC; ⊕ = PO Statement; ‡ = Publisher's Report; Boldface figures = sworn; Light figures = estimated.

High Peak

53571 ■ High Peak Radio-FM - 103.3
PO Box 106
High Peak SK23 0DJ, United Kingdom
Ph: 44 1298 813377
Fax: 44 1298 813388
E-mail: info@highpeakradio.co.uk
Format: Adult Contemporary. **Operating Hours:** Continuous. **URL:** http://www.highpeakradio.co.uk/.

High Peak Radio-FM - See Buxton

High Wycombe

53572 ■ Deafness and Education International
British Association of Teachers of the Deaf
175 Dashwood Ave.
High Wycombe HP12 3DB, United Kingdom
Ph: 44 14 94464190
Fax: 44 14 94464190
Publisher E-mail: secretary@batod.org.uk
Peer-reviewed British journal covering teachers of the deaf. **Subtitle:** Journal of BATOD. **Freq:** Quarterly. **Key Personnel:** Linda Watson, Editor, l.m.watson@bham.ac.uk; Margaret Brown, Editor, p.m.brown@unimelb.edu.au. **Remarks:** Accepts advertising. **URL:** http://www.batod.org.uk/index.php?id=/publications/journal/journal.htm. **Former name:** BATOD Journal. **Circ:** Paid 2,000

53573 ■ Double Reed News
British Double Reed Society
PO Box 713
High Wycombe HP13 5XE, United Kingdom
Publication E-mail: drn@bdrs.org.uk
Publisher E-mail: enquiries@bdrs.org.uk
Magazine featuring articles on oboe and bassoon. **Freq:** Quarterly. **Key Personnel:** Geoffrey Bridge, Advertising Mgr., advertising@bdrs.org.uk. **Subscription Rates:** Free members. **Remarks:** Accepts advertising. **URL:** http://www.bdrs.org.uk/drn/. **Circ:** (Not Reported)

53574 ■ Journal of Flood Risk Management
John Wiley & Sons Inc.
Wiley-Blackwell
c/o David Balmforth, Ed.-in-Ch.
Terriers House
201 Amersham Rd.
High Wycombe HP13 5AJ, United Kingdom
Ph: 44 1494 478450
Peer-reviewed journal covering all areas related to flood risk. **Key Personnel:** David Balmforth, Editor-in-Chief, david.balmforth@mwhglobal.com; Paul Samuels, Assoc. Ed., p.samuels@hrwallingford.co.uk; Jim Hall, Assoc. Ed., jim.hall@newcastle.ac.uk. **URL:** http://www.blackwellpublishing.com/jfrm_enhanced/.

Hindhead

53575 ■ Transport Engineer
Aztec Press Services
1 Bankside
Churt Rd.
Hindhead GU26 6NR, United Kingdom
Ph: 44 1428 605605
Fax: 44 1428 714278
Publisher E-mail: info@aztecxpress.com
Technical publication for road transport fleets. **Founded:** 1944. **Freq:** Monthly. **Print Method:** Sheet fed. **Trim Size:** 210 x 297 mm. **Key Personnel:** John Challen, Editor, jchallen@findlay.co.uk; Peter Knutton, Publisher, pknutton@findlay.co.uk. **ISSN:** 0020-3122. **Remarks:** Accepts advertising. **URL:** http://www.transportengineer.co.uk/. **Circ:** Combined 15,622

Hitchin

53576 ■ Attractions Management
The Leisure Media Company Ltd.
Portmill House
Portmill Ln.
Hitchin SG5 1DJ, United Kingdom
Ph: 44 14 62431385
Fax: 44 14 62433909
Magazine covering the international visitor attractions market, from theme parks and museums to science centres, zoos and corporate brandlands. **Freq:** Quarterly. **Key Personnel:** Kathleen Whyman, Editorial, phone 44 1462 471931. **Subscription Rates:** 34 individuals; 45

individuals in Europe; 17 students; 65 other countries. **URL:** http://www.attractions.co.uk/.

53577 ■ Dyspraxia Foundation Professional Journal
Dyspraxia Foundation
8 West Alley
Hitchin SG5 1EG, United Kingdom
Ph: 44 1462 454986
Fax: 44 1462 455052
Publisher E-mail: dyspraxia@dyspraxiafoundation.org.uk
Journal of the Dyspraxia Foundation, promoting awareness and understanding of dyspraxia, and supporting individuals and families affected be dyspraxia. **Freq:** Annual. **Subscription Rates:** Included in membership. **URL:** http://www.dyspraxiafoundation.org.uk/professionals/rs_intro.php.

53578 ■ Health Club Management
The Leisure Media Company Ltd.
Portmill House
Portmill Ln.
Hitchin SG5 1DJ, United Kingdom
Ph: 44 14 62431385
Fax: 44 14 62433909
Magazine helping improve the bottom line by keeping up to date with the leading title for the health & fitness industry. **Freq:** 11/yr. **Key Personnel:** Kate Cracknell, Contact, phone 44 14 62471906. **Subscription Rates:** 41 individuals; 52 individuals in Europe; 20 students; 73 other countries. **URL:** http://www.health-club.co.uk/.

53579 ■ Leisure Management
The Leisure Media Company Ltd.
Portmill House
Portmill Ln.
Hitchin SG5 1DJ, United Kingdom
Ph: 44 14 62431385
Fax: 44 14 62433909
Business publication covering the hospitality management industry. **Freq:** Bimonthly. **Key Personnel:** Tom Walker, News Ed.; Magali Robathan, Editorial, phone 44 117 9723101. **ISSN:** 0266-9102. **Subscription Rates:** 38 individuals; 49 individuals Europe; 69 elsewhere; 19 students. **Remarks:** Accepts advertising. **URL:** http://www.leisuremanagement.co.uk. **Ad Rates:** BW: 1,530, 4C: 3,827. **Circ:** (Not Reported)

53580 ■ Leisure Opportunities
The Leisure Media Company Ltd.
Portmill House
Portmill Ln.
Hitchin SG5 1DJ, United Kingdom
Ph: 44 14 62431385
Fax: 44 14 62433909
Business publication covering the hospitality management industry. **Subtitle:** Supplement to Leisure Management. **Freq:** Fortnightly. **Key Personnel:** Liz Terry, Editorial Dir., phone 44 14 6243185; Magali Robathan, Contact. **ISSN:** 0952-8210. **Subscription Rates:** 31 individuals; 41 individuals Europe; 62 elsewhere; 16 students. **Remarks:** Accepts advertising. **URL:** http://www.leisureopportunities.co.uk. **Circ:** (Not Reported)

53581 ■ Netball Magazine
All England Netball Association
Netball House
9 Paynes Pk.
Hitchin SG5 1EH, United Kingdom
Ph: 44 1462 442344
Fax: 44 1462 442343
Publication E-mail: editor@englandnetball.co.uk
Publisher E-mail: info@englandnetball.co.uk
Magazine covering netball. **Freq:** Bimonthly. **Key Personnel:** Dale Clarke, Dep. Ed.; Nikki Richardson, Editor. **Subscription Rates:** 15 individuals. **Remarks:** Advertising accepted; rates available upon request. **URL:** http://www.englandnetball.co.uk/media/Netball_Magazine/. **Circ:** 65,000

53582 ■ Sports Management
The Leisure Media Company Ltd.
Portmill House
Portmill Ln.
Hitchin SG5 1DJ, United Kingdom
Ph: 44 14 62431385
Fax: 44 14 62433909
Magazine for managers and policy makers in the sports and stadia industry who want to keep ahead of the

game. **Freq:** Quarterly. **Subscription Rates:** 27 individuals; 38 individuals in Europe; 37 individuals + Leisure Opportunities; 13 students. **URL:** http://www.leisuremedia.com; http://www.sportsmanagement.co.uk.

Holt

53583 ■ Birding World
Stonerunner, Coast Rd.
Holt NR25 7RZ, United Kingdom
Ph: 44 1263 741139
Fax: 44 1263 741173
Publication E-mail: sales@birdingworld.co.uk
Journal for birdwatchers in the UK and Europe. **Founded:** Jan. 1987. **Freq:** Monthly. **Trim Size:** B5. **Key Personnel:** Steve Gantlett, Editor. **Subscription Rates:** 47 individuals; 54 individuals Europe; 58 other countries. **Remarks:** Accepts advertising. **URL:** http://www.birdingworld.co.uk. **Circ:** Paid 6,000

Holywood

53584 ■ Ulster Folklife
Ulster Folk and Transport Museum
153 Bangor Rd.
Cultra
Holywood BT18 0EU, United Kingdom
Ph: 44 28 90428428
Fax: 44 28 90428728
Publisher E-mail: cedar.info@nmni.com
Journal featuring social history and popular culture. **Founded:** 1955. **Freq:** Annual. **Key Personnel:** Dr. Jonathan Bell, Editor. **ISSN:** 0082-7347. **Remarks:** Advertising not accepted. **URL:** http://www.uftm.org.uk/collections_and_research/publications_and_research/ulster_folklife/. **Circ:** (Not Reported)

Honiley

53585 ■ Rugby-FM - 107.1
Holly Farm Business Pk.
Honiley CV8 1NP, United Kingdom
Ph: 44 845 9493711
Format: Adult Contemporary. **Key Personnel:** Jason Moss, Contact. **URL:** http://www.rugbyfm.co.uk/.

Honiton

53586 ■ Coin News
Token Publishing Ltd.
Orchard House
Duchy Rd.
Heathpark
Honiton EX14 1YD, United Kingdom
Publisher E-mail: info@tokenpublishing.com
Magazine covering coin collecting and coin trade. **Founded:** 1983. **Freq:** Monthly. **Print Method:** Litho. **Trim Size:** A4. **Subscription Rates:** 34 individuals U.K.; 42 individuals Europe, rest of the world surface mail; 52 individuals rest of the world airmail; 60 two years U.K.; 80 two years Europe, rest of the world surface mail; 95 two years rest of the world airmail. **Remarks:** Accepts advertising. **URL:** http://www.tokenpublishing.com. **Ad Rates:** BW: 315. **Circ:** (Not Reported)

Hook

53587 ■ Project Manager Today
Larchdrift Projects Ltd.
Unit 12, Moor Pl. Farm
Plough Ln.
Bramshill
Hook RG27 0RF, United Kingdom
Ph: 44 11 89326665
Professional magazine for project and program managers in commerce and industry. **Founded:** 1989. **Freq:** Monthly. **Key Personnel:** Jim Potter, Conference Mgr.; Dave Singh, Advertising Mgr., phone 44 20 89799258; Ken Lane, Editorial Dir.; Steve Cotterell, Tech. Ed. **Subscription Rates:** 38 individuals; 48 individuals Europe; 58 other countries; 15 individuals digital. **Remarks:** Accepts advertising. **URL:** http://www.pmtoday.co.uk. **Ad Rates:** BW: 1,860. **Circ:** Controlled ★14,871

Horncastle

53588 ■ Classic and Motorcycle Mechanics
Mortons Motorcycle Media Ltd.
Media Ctr.

Morton Way
Horncastle LN9 6JR, United Kingdom
Ph: 44 15 07523456
Magazine covering classic motorcycles. **Freq:** Monthly third Wednesday of each month. **Key Personnel:** Ben Wilkins, Editor. **Subscription Rates:** 37 individuals U.K.; 44 individuals Europe; 54 individuals rest of the world. **Remarks:** Accepts advertising. **URL:** http://www. classicmechanics.com. **Circ:** 30,000

53589 ■ Classic Racer International
Mortons Motorcycle Media Ltd.
Media Ctr.
Morton Way
Horncastle LN9 6JR, United Kingdom
Ph: 44 15 07523456
Publication E-mail: info@classicmagazine.co.uk
Consumer magazine covering classic motorcycle sport worldwide. **Freq:** Bimonthly. **Key Personnel:** Malc Wheeler, Editor. **Subscription Rates:** 20 individuals U.K.; 44 individuals Europe; 54 individuals rest of world; 68 two years U.K.; 80 two years Europe; 100 two years rest of world; 3.85 single issue U.K.; 4.85 single issue Europe; 5.80 single issue rest of world. **Remarks:** Accepts classified advertising. **URL:** http://www. classicracer.com. **Circ:** (Not Reported)

53590 ■ Heritage Railway Magazine
Mortons Media Group
Media Ctr.
Morton Way
Horncastle LN9 6JR, United Kingdom
Ph: 44 1507 523456
Fax: 44 1507 529490
Publication E-mail: railway@ipcmedia.com
Magazine featuring steam, diesel and electric traction. Covers preserved lines and locations, in-depth features highlighting major issues on heritage lines, information on new restoration and reopening schemes, ordnance survey extracts to highlight featured railways, and special features on carriage and wagon restoration. **Founded:** 1916. **Freq:** 13/yr. **Print Method:** Offset. **Trim Size:** 10 7/8 x 14. **Cols./Page:** 5. **Col. Width:** 11 nonpareils. **Col. Depth:** 169 agate lines. **Key Personnel:** Robin Jones, Editor; Brian Sharpe, Asst. Ed.; Terry Clark, Managing Editor. **ISSN:** 1466-3562. **Subscription Rates:** 19.50 individuals 12 isssue. **URL:** http://mortons-secure.com/magviewer.asp?title=hr.

53591 ■ Horncastle News
Johnston Press PLC
Church Ln.
Horncastle LN9 5HW, United Kingdom
Ph: 44 1507 526868
Local community newspaper. **Key Personnel:** Sean Topham, News Ed., fax 44 1507 522025, sean.topham@jpress.co.uk; Tim Robinson, Managing Editor, phone 44 1476 562291, fax 44 1476 560564, tim.robinson@jpress.co.uk; Lisa Mitchell, Gp. Advertising Mgr., lisa.mitchell@jpress.co.uk. **Remarks:** Accepts advertising. **URL:** http://www.horncastlenews.co.uk/. **Circ:** (Not Reported)

53592 ■ Old Glory
Mortons Media Group
PO Box 43
Horncastle LN9 6JR, United Kingdom
Ph: 44 1507 529529
Magazine featuring restoration of machineries. **Subtitle:** Vintage Restoration Today. **Founded:** 1988. **Freq:** Monthly. **Key Personnel:** Colin Tyson, Editor, phone 44 1507 529306, fax 44 1507 529495, editor@oldglory.co.uk. **ISSN:** 0956-5922. **Subscription Rates:** 36 individuals; EUR20 individuals; EUR3.60 single issue. **Remarks:** Accepts advertising. **URL:** http://www.oldglory.co.uk/. **Circ:** (Not Reported)

53593 ■ Scootering
Mortons Media Group
Media Ctr.
Morton Way
Horncastle LN9 6JR, United Kingdom
Ph: 44 1507 523456
Fax: 44 1507 529490
Magazine for scootering enthusiasts. **Founded:** 1985. **Freq:** Monthly. **Key Personnel:** Andy Gillard, Editor, editorial@scootering.com. **ISSN:** 0268-7194. **Subscription Rates:** 37 individuals; EUR3.75 single issue. **Remarks:** Accepts advertising. **URL:** http://www.scootering. com/. **Circ:** (Not Reported)

Horsham

53594 ■ Animal Action
Royal Society for the Prevention of Cruelty to Animals
Wilberforce Way
Southwater
Horsham RH13 9RS, United Kingdom
Fax: 44 87 07530284
Publisher E-mail: engsen@rspca.org.uk
Publication covering animal welfare. **Freq:** Bimonthly. **Subscription Rates:** 9.10 individuals; 11.30 other countries. **Remarks:** Advertising accepted; rates available upon request. **Circ:** (Not Reported)

53595 ■ Animal Life
Royal Society for the Prevention of Cruelty to Animals
Wilberforce Way
Southwater
Horsham RH13 9RS, United Kingdom
Fax: 44 87 07530284
Publication E-mail: publications@rspca.org.uk
Publisher E-mail: engsen@rspca.org.uk
Publication covering animal welfare. **Freq:** Quarterly. **Subscription Rates:** 10 individuals; 12 other countries. **Remarks:** Advertising accepted; rates available upon request. **Circ:** Paid 45,000

53596 ■ Kennel and Cattery Management
Albatross Publications
PO Box 523
Horsham RH12 4WL, United Kingdom
Ph: 44 1293 871201
Fax: 44 1293 871301
Publication E-mail: kennelandcattery@aol.com
Trade magazine covering kennel and cattery management. **Founded:** 1983. **Freq:** Bimonthly. **Subscription Rates:** 20 individuals; 37 two years; 24 other countries Europe and surface; 45 other countries Europe and surface - two years; 28 other countries airmail; 53 other countries airmail - two years. **Remarks:** Accepts advertising. **URL:** http://www.kennelandcattery.com. **Ad Rates:** BW: 495, 4C: 650. **Circ:** Combined 3,100

53597 ■ Prestige Corporate Interiors
Albatross Publications
PO Box 523
Horsham RH12 4WL, United Kingdom
Ph: 44 1293 871201
Fax: 44 1293 871301
Trade magazine covering office interior design. **Freq:** Quarterly. **Subscription Rates:** 8 individuals. **Remarks:** Accepts advertising. **URL:** http://www.prestige-interiors. co.uk. **Ad Rates:** BW: 495, 4C: 650. **Circ:** Controlled 3,000

53598 ■ Prestige High Street Interiors
Albatross Publications
PO Box 523
Horsham RH12 4WL, United Kingdom
Ph: 44 1293 871201
Fax: 44 1293 871301
Trade magazine covering interior design for retail outlets, banks/building societies and leisure venues. **Freq:** Quarterly. **Subscription Rates:** 8 individuals. **Remarks:** Accepts advertising. **URL:** http://www.prestige-interiors.co.uk. **Ad Rates:** BW: 495, 4C: 650. **Circ:** Controlled 3,000

53599 ■ Prestige Hotel & Restaurant Interiors
Albatross Publications
PO Box 523
Horsham RH12 4WL, United Kingdom
Ph: 44 1293 871201
Fax: 44 1293 871301
Trade magazine covering interior design for hotels and restaurants. **Freq:** Quarterly. **Subscription Rates:** 8 single issue. **Remarks:** Accepts advertising. **URL:** http://www.prestige-interiors.co.uk. **Ad Rates:** BW: 495, 4C: 650. **Circ:** Controlled 3,000

53600 ■ Professional Landscaper & Groundsman
Albatross Publications
PO Box 523
Horsham RH12 4WL, United Kingdom
Ph: 44 1293 871201
Fax: 44 1293 871301
Trade magazine covering landscape architecture and groundskeeping for professionals. **Freq:** Semiannual. **Subscription Rates:** 6 individuals 2 issues. **Remarks:**

Accepts advertising. **URL:** http://professional-landscaper.co.uk. **Ad Rates:** BW: 495, 4C: 650. **Circ:** Combined 3,100

53601 ■ Science Review
Royal Society for the Prevention of Cruelty to Animals
Wilberforce Way
Southwater
Horsham RH13 9RS, United Kingdom
Fax: 44 87 07530284
Publisher E-mail: engsen@rspca.org.uk
Publication covering science. **Freq:** Annual. **Remarks:** Advertising accepted; rates available upon request. **URL:** http://www.rspca.org.uk. **Circ:** (Not Reported)

53602 ■ West Sussex County Times
Johnston Press PLC
14-16 Market Sq.
Horsham RH12 1HD, United Kingdom
Ph: 44 1403 751200
Local community newspaper. **Freq:** Weekly (Fri.). **Key Personnel:** Steve Payne, Hd. of Digital; Richard Harmer, Advertising Mgr., phone 44 1293 845071, richard.harmer@sussexnewspapers.co.uk. **Remarks:** Accepts advertising. **URL:** http://www.wscountytimes.co. uk/. **Circ:** (Not Reported)

Hove

53603 ■ Advances in Dual Diagnosis
Pier Professional
The Old Market, Ste. N4
Upper Market St.
Hove BN3 1AS, United Kingdom
Ph: 44 1273 783720
Fax: 44 1273 783723
Publisher E-mail: info@pierprofessional.com
Journal featuring articles on dual diagnosis of people with mental health problems. **Freq:** Quarterly. **ISSN:** 1757-0972. **Remarks:** Accepts advertising. **URL:** http:// pierprofessional.metapress.com/content/121394/?p= 3aac74a29b2f4c5a945fa6c487d9f85b&pi=1. **Circ:** (Not Reported)

53604 ■ Drugs and Alcohol Today
Pier Professional
The Old Market, Ste. N4
Upper Market St.
Hove BN3 1AS, United Kingdom
Ph: 44 1273 783720
Fax: 44 1273 783723
Publisher E-mail: info@pierprofessional.com
Peer-reviewed journal focusing on the latest in drug and alcohol policy, laws, and practices. **Freq:** Quarterly. **ISSN:** 1745-9265. **Remarks:** Accepts advertising. **URL:** http://pierprofessional.metapress.com/content/121399/? p=138a9846e423a8cd1afd603d2a0cb&pi=0. **Circ:** (Not Reported)

53605 ■ Ethnicity and Inequalities in Health and Social Care
Pier Professional
The Old Market, Ste. N4
Upper Market St.
Hove BN3 1AS, United Kingdom
Ph: 44 1273 783720
Fax: 44 1273 783723
Publisher E-mail: info@pierprofessional.com
Peer-reviewed journal focusing on health and social care inequalities. **Freq:** Quarterly. **ISSN:** 1757-0980. **Remarks:** Accepts advertising. **URL:** http:// pierprofessional.metapress.com/content/121400/?p= 1c41324356f04d5a8f7651a7b4e3ab2e&pi=0. **Circ:** (Not Reported)

53606 ■ Journal of Aggression, Conflict and Peace Research
Pier Professional
The Old Market, Ste. N4
Upper Market St.
Hove BN3 1AS, United Kingdom
Ph: 44 1273 783720
Fax: 44 1273 783723
Publisher E-mail: info@pierprofessional.com
Peer-reviewed journal featuring articles on conflict, aggression, and peace studies. **Freq:** Quarterly. **ISSN:** 1759-6599. **Remarks:** Accepts advertising. **URL:** http:// pierprofessional.metapress.com/content/121397/?p=

Circulation: ★ = ABC; △ = BPA; ◆ = CAC; • = CCAB; ❑ = VAC; ⊕ = PO Statement; ‡ = Publisher's Report; Boldface figures = sworn; Light figures = estimated.

Gale Directory of Publications & Broadcast Media/147th Ed.

5659

256acfe81a12400baea1c4405331f6e6&pi=10. **Circ:** (Not Reported)

53607 ■ Journal of Assistive Technologies
Pier Professional
The Old Market, Ste. N4
Upper Market St.
Hove BN3 1AS, United Kingdom
Ph: 44 1273 783720
Fax: 44 1273 783723
Publisher E-mail: info@pierprofessional.com
Peer-reviewed journal featuring the latest on assistive technologies. **Freq:** Quarterly. **ISSN:** 1754-9450. **Remarks:** Accepts advertising. **URL:** http://pierprofessional.metapress.com/content/121393/?p=256acfe81a12400baea1c4405331f6e6&pi=11. **Circ:** (Not Reported)

53608 ■ Journal of Clinical Pathology
Association of Clinical Pathologists
189 Dyke Rd.
Hove BN3 1TL, United Kingdom
Ph: 44 12 73775700
Fax: 44 12 73773303
Publisher E-mail: info@pathologists.org.uk
Peer-reviewed journal covering pathology. **Founded:** 1947. **Freq:** Monthly. **Key Personnel:** Cheok Soon Lee, Editor, soon.lee@uws.edu.au. **ISSN:** 0003-9888. **URL:** http://jcp.bmjjournals.com/.

53609 ■ Journal of Learning Disabilities and Offending Behaviour
Pier Professional
The Old Market, Ste. N4
Upper Market St.
Hove BN3 1AS, United Kingdom
Ph: 44 1273 783720
Fax: 44 1273 783723
Publisher E-mail: info@pierprofessional.com
Peer reviewed journal featuring articles on learning disabilites and offending behavior. **Freq:** Quarterly. **ISSN:** 2042-0927. **Remarks:** Accepts advertising. **URL:** http://pierprofessional.metapress.com/content/121645/?p=a25cb63fce7745bf800910915e1deddd&pi=5. **Circ:** (Not Reported)

53610 ■ A Life in the Day
Pier Professional
The Old Market, Ste. N4
Upper Market St.
Hove BN3 1AS, United Kingdom
Ph: 44 1273 783720
Fax: 44 1273 783723
Publisher E-mail: info@pierprofessional.com
Peer-reviewed journal focusing on mental health and social inclusion. **Freq:** Quarterly. **ISSN:** 1366-6282. **Remarks:** Accepts advertising. **URL:** http://pierprofessional.metapress.com/content/121413/?p=a9da0a05c66847ffa5c29e64e076bc72&pi=0. **Circ:** (Not Reported)

53611 ■ Musical Times
Musical Times Publications Ltd.
7 Brunswick Mews
Hove BN3 1HD, United Kingdom
Publisher E-mail: subs@webscribe.co.uk
Publication covering music. **Freq:** Quarterly. **Key Personnel:** Peter Phillips, Contact. **ISSN:** 0027-4666. **Subscription Rates:** 38 individuals; EUR78 individuals for Europe; US$88 U.S. and Canada; 68 other countries; 75 institutions; EUR155 institutions for Europe; US$174 institutions for U.S. & Canada; 141 institutions, other countries. **URL:** http://www.musicaltimes.co.uk/; http://www.ripm.org/journal_info.php5?ABB=MTI.

53612 ■ Safer Communities
Pier Professional
The Old Market, Ste. N4
Upper Market St.
Hove BN3 1AS, United Kingdom
Ph: 44 1273 783720
Fax: 44 1273 783723
Publisher E-mail: info@pierprofessional.com
Peer-reviewed journal on community safety. **Freq:** Quarterly. **ISSN:** 1757-8043. **Remarks:** Accepts advertising. **URL:** http://pierprofessional.metapress.com/home/aboutSC.mpx?p=6281dc48be3440f8a877bd4ace28cbe4&pi=0. **Circ:** (Not Reported)

53613 ■ Social Care and Neurodisability
Pier Professional

The Old Market, Ste. N4
Upper Market St.
Hove BN3 1AS, United Kingdom
Ph: 44 1273 783720
Fax: 44 1273 783723
Publisher E-mail: info@pierprofessional.com
Peer reviewed journal featuring articles on neurodisability and social care. **Freq:** Quarterly. **ISSN:** 2042-0919. **Remarks:** Accepts advertising. **URL:** http://pierprofessional.metapress.com/content/121646/?p=ca99040c8816401f9a5ecd91b397b3c9&pi=20. **Circ:** (Not Reported)

Hoylake

53614 ■ Candis
New Hall Publications Ltd.
New Hall Ln.
Wirral
Hoylake CH47 4BQ, United Kingdom
Ph: 44 870 7453004
Fax: 44 844 5458103
Lifestyle family magazine featuring parental advice, family health information, cooking, gardening, competitions, and celebrity interviews. **Freq:** Monthly. **Key Personnel:** Debbie Attewell, Editor. **URL:** http://www.candis.co.uk. **Circ:** Paid ★254,420

Hucknall

53615 ■ Hucknall Dispatch
Johnston Press PLC
1 Yorke St.
Hucknall NG15 7BT, United Kingdom
Ph: 44 115 9555577
Local community newspaper. **Freq:** Weekly. **Key Personnel:** Richard Silverwood, Editor, phone 44 115 9536551, newsdesk@hucknall-dispatch.co.uk; Margaret Fox, Contact, mags.fox@chad.co.uk. **Remarks:** Accepts advertising. **URL:** http://www.hucknalldispatch.co.uk/. **Circ:** (Not Reported)

Huddersfield

53616 ■ Bridal Buyer
RAS Publishing Ltd.
The Old Town Hall
Lewisham Rd.
Slaithwaite
Huddersfield HD7 5AL, United Kingdom
Ph: 44 14 84846069
Fax: 44 14 84846232
Publisher E-mail: mina@ras-publishing.com
Trade magazine covering the bridal industry in the U.K. **Freq:** 6/yr. **Print Method:** Web. **Trim Size:** 243 x 330 mm. **Cols./Page:** 5. **Col. Width:** 40 millimeters. **Col. Depth:** 312 millimeters. **Key Personnel:** Susi Rogol, Editor, phone 44 20 74312259, bridalbuyer@rogolgoodkind.co.uk; Nardene Smith, Advertising Mgr., phone 44 20 77728317, fax 44 20 77728599, nardene.smith@oceanmedia.co.uk. **Subscription Rates:** 96 individuals outside Europe. **Remarks:** Accepts advertising. **URL:** http://www.bridalbuyer.com/. **Circ:** (Not Reported)

53617 ■ Campus-Wide Information Systems
Emerald Group Publishing Ltd.
c/o Prof. Glenn Hardaker, Ed.
Innovation Management & National Teaching Fellow
Huddersfield University of Huddersfield
Huddersfield HD1 3DH, United Kingdom
Publisher E-mail: emerald@emeraldinsight.com
Journal publishing cutting-edge research and case studies relating to administrative, academic and library computing, as well as other educational technologies. The journal analyses the latest theories, applications and services relating to planning, developing, managing, using and evaluating information technologies in higher education. **Freq:** 5/yr. **Key Personnel:** Prof. Glenn Hardaker, Editor, g.hardaker@hud.ac.uk; Kate Snowden, Publisher, ksnowden@emeraldinsight.com. **ISSN:** 1065-0741. **URL:** http://info.emeraldinsight.com/products/journals/journals.htm?id=cwis.

53618 ■ Clinical Biomechanics
Mosby Inc.
c/o Kim Burton, Ed.
Spinal Research Unit
University of Huddersfield

30 Queen St.
Huddersfield HD1 2SP, United Kingdom
Ph: 44 14 84535200
Fax: 44 14 84435744
Publisher E-mail: custserv.ehs@elsevier.com
Peer-reviewed journal covering the field of biomechanics. **Freq:** 10/yr. **Key Personnel:** Kim Burton, Editor, kim@spineresearch.org.uk; G. Andersson, Assoc. Ed.; M. Adams, Editorial Board. **ISSN:** 0268-0033. **Subscription Rates:** US$1,379 institutions, other countries except Europe, Japan and Iran; EUR1,233 institutions for European countries and Iran; 163,600¥ institutions; EUR137 individuals for European countries and Iran; US$153 other countries except Europe, Japan and Iran; 17,900¥ individuals. **Remarks:** Accepts advertising. **URL:** http://www.elsevier.com/wps/find/journaldescription.cws_home/30397/descriptiondescription. **Circ:** (Not Reported)

53619 ■ CWB
RAS Publishing Ltd.
The Old Town Hall
Lewisham Rd.
Slaithwaite
Huddersfield HD7 5AL, United Kingdom
Ph: 44 14 84846069
Fax: 44 14 84846232
Publisher E-mail: mina@ras-publishing.com
Trade magazine covering the children's wear industry in the U.K. **Founded:** Apr. 1999. **Freq:** Bimonthly. **Print Method:** Web. **Trim Size:** 243 x 336 mm. **Cols./Page:** 5. **Col. Width:** 40 millimeters. **Col. Depth:** 312 millimeters. **Key Personnel:** Sam Chambers, Sales Mgr., sam.chambers@ras-publishing.com; Laura Kirkpatrick, Editor, laura@ras-publishing.com; Gill Brabham, Production Dir., gill@ras-publishing.com; Zabian Southwood, Writer, zabian@ras-publishing.com; Isabella Galuschka, Writer, isabella@ras-publishing.com; Martin Wanless, Managing Editor, martin@ras-publishing.com. **Subscription Rates:** 27 members Europe; 50 members outside Europe; 55 nonmembers Europe; 94 nonmembers outside Europe. **Remarks:** Accepts advertising. **URL:** http://www.ncwa.co.uk/cwb.html; http://www.ras-publishing.com/cwbintro.htm. **Ad Rates:** GLR: 4, BW: 1,400, 4C: 2,100. **Circ:** Combined 3,000

53620 ■ Free Press
Campaign for Press & Broadcasting Freedom
c/o Granville Williams, Ed.
University of Huddersfield, Division of Media
St. Peter's Bldg.
St. Peter's St.
Huddersfield HD1 1RA, United Kingdom
Publication E-mail: freepress@cpbf.org.uk
Publisher E-mail: freepress@cpbf.org.uk
Journal of the Campaign for Press & Broadcasting Freedom. **Founded:** 1979. **Freq:** Quarterly. **Print Method:** Offset. **Trim Size:** 210 x 297 mm. **Cols./Page:** 3. **Key Personnel:** Geoff Mason, Treas.; Tim Gopsill, Joint Ch.; Jonathan Hardy, Sec.; Barry White, National Organiser; Julian Petley, Joint Ch.; Granville Williams, Editor, phone 44 1484 478460, fax 44 1484 478407, g.williams@hud.ac.uk. **ISSN:** 1353-310X. **Remarks:** Advertising not accepted. **URL:** http://www.cpbf.org.uk/. **Circ:** Paid 5,250

53621 ■ Journal of Investigative Psychology and Offender Profiling
John Wiley & Sons Inc.
c/o David Canter, Ed.-in-Ch.
International Research Centre for Investigative Psychology
School of Human & Health Sciences
University of Huddersfield
Huddersfield HD1 3DH, United Kingdom
Ph: 44 1484 471637
Publisher E-mail: info@wiley.com
Journal for professionals in the field of investigative psychology. **Freq:** 3/yr. **Key Personnel:** David Canter, Editor-in-Chief, d.canter@hud.ac.uk; Robert Keppel, Editorial Board; Maria Ioanou, Asst. Ed., m.ioannou@hud.ac.uk; Donna Youngs, Assoc. Ed., d.youngs@hud.ac.uk; Gabrielle Salfati, Assoc. Ed., gsalfati@jjay.cuny.edu. **ISSN:** 1544-4759. **Subscription Rates:** 42 individuals print only; US$78 other countries print only; 118 institutions print only; US$220 institutions, other countries print only. **URL:** http://onlinelibrary.wiley.com/journal/10.1002/(ISSN)1544-4767.

53622 ■ Lingerie Buyer
RAS Publishing Ltd.

c/o Zabian Southwood, Ed.
RAS - Publishing
The Old Town Hall, Lewisham Rd.
Slaithwaite
Huddersfield HD7 5AL, United Kingdom
Ph: 44 14 84846069
Publisher E-mail: mina@ras-publishing.com
Trade magazine for the lingerie industry in the U.K. **Founded:** 1992. **Freq:** 8/yr. **Print Method:** Web. **Trim Size:** 243 x 336 mm. **Cols./Page:** 5. **Col. Width:** 40 millimeters. **Col. Depth:** 312 millimeters. **Key Personnel:** Emma Sabin, Publisher, phone 44 20 79734641, e.sabin@hgluk.com; Zabian Southwood, Editor, zabian@ras-publishing.com. **Subscription Rates:** 75 individuals; EUR130 individuals; US$200 individuals. **Remarks:** Accepts advertising. **URL:** http://www.lingerie-buyer.co.uk. **Circ:** Combined 3,000

53623 ■ Multicultural Education & Technology Journal
Emerald Group Publishing Ltd.
c/o Prof. Glenn Hardaker, Ed.
Huddersfield University Business School
University of Huddersfield
Brunswick Bldg.
Huddersfield HD1 3DH, United Kingdom
Publisher E-mail: emerald@emeraldinsight.com
Journal covering multicultural education and learning technologies. **Freq:** Quarterly. **Key Personnel:** Prof. Glenn Hardaker, Editor, g.hardaker@hud.ac.uk; Kate Snowden, Publisher, ksnowden@emeraldinsight.com. **ISSN:** 1750-497X. **URL:** http://info.emeraldinsight.com/products/journals/journals.htm?id=metj.

53624 ■ MWB
RAS Publishing Ltd.
The Old Town Hall
Lewisham Rd.
Slaithwaite
Huddersfield HD7 5AL, United Kingdom
Ph: 44 14 84846069
Fax: 44 14 84846232
Publisher E-mail: mina@ras-publishing.com
Trade magazine covering the menswear industry in the U.K. **Freq:** 11/yr. **Print Method:** Web. **Trim Size:** 243 x 330 mm. **Cols./Page:** 5. **Col. Width:** 40 millimeters. **Col. Depth:** 312 millimeters. **Key Personnel:** Nick Cook, Editor, nick@ras-publishing.com; Silvia Collins, Sales Mgr., silvia@ras-publishing.com; Martin Wanless, Managing Editor, martin@ras-publishing.com. **Subscription Rates:** 146 individuals outside Europe; 75 individuals. **Remarks:** Accepts advertising. **URL:** http://www.ras-publishing.com/mwbintro.htm. **Ad Rates:** BW: 1,680, 4C: 2,300. **Circ:** Combined 5,711

53625 ■ WWB
RAS Publishing Ltd.
The Old Town Hall
Lewisham Rd.
Slaithwaite
Huddersfield HD7 5AL, United Kingdom
Ph: 44 14 84846069
Fax: 44 14 84846232
Publisher E-mail: mina@ras-publishing.com
Trade magazine covering the womenswear industry in the U.K. **Freq:** Monthly. **Print Method:** Web. **Trim Size:** 243 x 330 mm. **Cols./Page:** 5. **Col. Width:** 40 millimeters. **Col. Depth:** 312 millimeters. **Key Personnel:** Isabella Galuschka, Editor, isabella@ras-publishing.com; Lindsay Hoyes, Gp. Sales Dir., lindsay@ras-publishing.com; Martin Wanless, Managing Editor, martin@ras-publishing.com. **Subscription Rates:** 146 individuals outside Europe; 75 individuals. **Remarks:** Accepts advertising. **URL:** http://www.ras-publishing.com/wwbintro.htm. **Formerly:** Fashion Buyer. **Ad Rates:** GLR: 6, BW: 1,680, 4C: 2,300, PCI: 16. **Circ:** Combined 7,259

Hull

53626 ■ International Journal of Agile Systems and Management
Inderscience Publishers
c/o Prof. Chandra Lalwani, Assoc. Ed.
Business School
University of Hull
Cottingham Rd.
Hull HU6 7RX, United Kingdom
Publisher E-mail: editor@inderscience.com
Peer-reviewed journal proposing and fostering discussion on business agility, responsiveness and competitiveness with the emphasis being on methodology, framework, tools and techniques, as well as operational performance, linkage between technology choice and product needs in the marketplace, extended enterprise, new forms of organisations, and contemporary management insights into better coordination of the organisation's internal and external supply chains. **Freq:** Quarterly. **Key Personnel:** Prof. Jim Wu, Assoc. Ed.; Prof. Surendra M. Gupta, Assoc. Ed.; Prof. Bok-Hyun Yoon, Assoc. Ed.; Prof. Sherali Zeadally, Assoc. Ed.; Prof. John Mo, Editor-in-Chief, john.mo@rmit.edu.au; Prof. Mark Goh, Editor-in-Chief, mark_goh@nus.edu.sg. **ISSN:** 1741-9174. **Subscription Rates:** EUR840 individuals online only (2-3 users); EUR494 individuals print only (surface mail); EUR534 individuals print only (airmail); EUR672 individuals print and online. **URL:** http://www.inderscience.com/browse/index.php?journalcode=ijasm.

53627 ■ Lobster
214 Westbourne Ave.
Hull HU5 3JB, United Kingdom
Ph: 44 1482 447558
Publisher E-mail: editor@lobster-magazine.co.uk
Journal investigating various political and governmental issues. **Subtitle:** The Journal of Parapolitics. **Founded:** 1983. **Freq:** Semiannual. **Key Personnel:** Robin Ramsay, Editor. **ISSN:** 0964-0436. **Subscription Rates:** 2 single issue issues no.9,10,13,and 17; 2.50 single issue other issues. **URL:** http://www.lobster-magazine.co.uk/index.php.

53628 ■ OR Insight
Operational Research Society of the United Kingdom
c/o Prof. Steve Clarke, Ed.
Business School
University of Hull
Cottingham Rd.
Hull HU6 7RX, United Kingdom
Publication covering operations research. **Freq:** Quarterly. **Key Personnel:** Prof. Steve Clarke, Editor, s.clarke@hull.ac.uk; Prof. Brian Lehaney, Editor, b.lehaney@coventry.ac.uk. **Subscription Rates:** 2.50 single issue members; 17.50 single issue non-members; 70 institutions. **URL:** http://www.theorsociety.com/publication/insight.htm.

53629 ■ BBC Radio Humberside-FM - 95.9
Queen's Ct.
Hull HU1 3RH, United Kingdom
Ph: 44 1482 323232
E-mail: humber.online@bbc.co.uk
Format: News; Talk; Sports. **Owner:** British Broadcasting Corporation, Broadcasting House, Portland Pl., London W1A 1AA, United Kingdom. **Founded:** 1971. **Operating Hours:** Continuous. **URL:** http://www.bbc.co.uk/humber/local_radio.

53630 ■ KCFM-FM - 99.8
Planet House
2 Woodhouse St.
Hedon Rd.
Hull HU9 1RJ, United Kingdom
Ph: 44 1482 333999
Format: Eclectic. **Key Personnel:** Ann Marie Pearcey, Contact, annmarie.pearcey@kcfm.co.uk. **URL:** http://www.kcfm.co.uk/.

53631 ■ Magic 1161-AM - 1161
The Boathouse
Commercial Rd.
Hull HU1 2SG, United Kingdom
Ph: 44 1482 325141
Fax: 44 1482 593067
Format: Easy Listening; Oldies; News; Talk. **Operating Hours:** Continuous. **Key Personnel:** Steve Allbones, Station Dir.; Jono Symonds, Program Dir.; Paul Dawson, News Ed. **URL:** http://www.magic1161.com.

53632 ■ Radio Humberside - 95.9
Queen's Ct.
Hull HU1 3RH, United Kingdom
Ph: 44 1482 323232
E-mail: humberside.news@bbc.co.uk
Format: Eclectic; News; Sports; Talk. **Owner:** British Broadcasting Corporation, Broadcasting House, Portland Pl., London W1A 1AA, United Kingdom. **Founded:** 1971. **Operating Hours:** Continuous. **URL:** http://news.bbc.co.uk/local/humberside/hi/tv_and_radio/.

53633 ■ Viking-FM - 96.9
The Boathouse
Commercial Rd.
Hull HU1 2SG, United Kingdom
Ph: 44 1482 325141
Fax: 44 1482 593067
Format: Adult Contemporary; Information. **Key Personnel:** Mark Lonsdale, Mktg. Exec.; Jono Symonds, Program Dir.; Caroline Leckenby, Sales Admin. **URL:** http://www.vikingfm.co.uk/.

Huntingdon

53634 ■ Durbar
Indian Military Historical Society
33 High St.
Tilbrook
Huntingdon PE18 0JP, United Kingdom
Ph: 44 14 80860437
Publisher E-mail: imhs@zetnet.co.uk
Journal containing articles, letters, queries. **Freq:** Quarterly. **Key Personnel:** Mr. A.N. McClenaghan, Editor. **Subscription Rates:** Included in membership. **Remarks:** Accepts advertising. **URL:** http://members.ozemail.com.au/~clday/imhs.htm. **Circ:** (Not Reported)

53635 ■ The Hunts Post
Archant Regional Ltd.
30 High St.
Huntingdon PE29 3TB, United Kingdom
Ph: 44 1480 411481
Publication E-mail: editor@huntspost.co.uk
Publisher E-mail: sandra.roantree@archant.co.uk
Local community newspaper. **Freq:** Weekly (Wed.). **Key Personnel:** Andy Veale, Editor; Angela Singer, Dep. Ed. **Subscription Rates:** Free to homes across Huntingdonshire; 26 out of area 13 weeks; 52 out of area 26 weeks; 104 out of area 52 weeks. **Remarks:** Accepts advertising. **URL:** http://www.huntspost.co.uk/home. **Circ:** ★45,579

53636 ■ Wound Care
Wound Care Society
PO Box 170
Huntingdon PE29 1PL, United Kingdom
Ph: 44 1480 434401
Journal containing case studies, literature review, and research studies. **Freq:** Quarterly. **Key Personnel:** Tracy Cowan, Editor. **Subscription Rates:** 91 individuals; EUR156 individuals; US$229 individuals. **URL:** http://www.journalofwoundcare.com/nav?page=jowc.linklist.linklist_uk.

Huntly

53637 ■ NECR-FM - 103.2
The Shed
School Rd.
Kintore
Aberdeenshire
Inverurie AB51 0UX, United Kingdom
Ph: 44 1467 632909
Fax: 44 1467 632969
E-mail: enquiries@necrfm.co.uk
Format: Oldies; Contemporary Hit Radio (CHR); News; Information. **Ad Rates:** Advertising accepted; rates available upon request. **URL:** http://www.necrfm.co.uk/.

Ilford

53638 ■ Christian Librarian
Librarians' Christian Fellowship
c/o Graham Hedges
34 Thurlestone Ave.
Seven Kings
Ilford IG3 9DU, United Kingdom
Ph: 44 20 85991310
Publisher E-mail: secretary@librarianscf.org.uk
Trade journal covering librarianship, publishing, communications and related topics from a Christian perspective. **Founded:** 1976. **Freq:** Quarterly. **Trim Size:** A5. **Cols./Page:** 1. **Key Personnel:** Gordon A. Harris, President, g.a.harris@bham.ac.uk; Louise Manners, Chm.; Graham Hedges, Sec.; John S. Andrews, Vice President. **ISSN:** 0309-4170. **Subscription Rates:** 3 nonmembers single issue. **Remarks:** Accepts

advertising. **URL:** http://www.librarianscf.org.uk. **Circ:** Paid 500

53639 ■ Ilford & Redbridge Post
Archant Regional Ltd.
539 High Rd.
Ilford IG1 1UD, United Kingdom
Ph: 44 20 84784444
Fax: 44 20 85927407
Publisher E-mail: sandra.roantree@archant.co.uk
Local community newspaper. **Freq:** Weekly (Wed.). **Key Personnel:** Chris Carter, Editor, phone 44 20 84784444, chris.carter@archant.co.uk. **Subscription Rates:** 8 individuals 4 weeks; 16 individuals 2 months; 24 individuals 3 months; 48 individuals 6 months. **Remarks:** Accepts advertising. **URL:** http://www.ilfordpost.co.uk/e-edition/ilfordandredbridgepost/. **Circ:** (Not Reported)

53640 ■ Stratford & Newham Express
Archant Regional Ltd.
539 High Rd.
Ilford IG1 1UD, United Kingdom
Ph: 44 20 84784444
Publisher E-mail: sandra.roantree@archant.co.uk
Local community newspaper. **Founded:** 1866. **Freq:** Weekly (Wed.). **Key Personnel:** Colin Grainger, Editor, colin.grainger@archant.co.uk. **Subscription Rates:** 9.20 individuals 4 weeks; 18.40 individuals 2 months; 27.60 individuals 3 months; 55.20 individuals 6 months. **Remarks:** Accepts advertising. **URL:** http://www.stratfordandnewhamexpress.co.uk/content/newham/express/default/default.aspx. **Circ:** (Not Reported)

Ilfracombe

53641 ■ Catalogue & E-business
Catalogue & e-business
151 High St.
Ilfracombe EX34 9EZ, United Kingdom
Ph: 44 1271 866221
Fax: 44 1271 866281
Publisher E-mail: info@catalog-biz.com
Trade magazine covering catalog, mail order, and electronic commerce. **Founded:** 1995. **Freq:** Monthly. **Key Personnel:** Jane Revell-Higgins, Publisher/Mng. Dir., jane@catalog-biz.com; Miri Thomas, Editor, miri@catalog-biz.com. **ISSN:** 1362-2315. **Subscription Rates:** 85 individuals; 95 other countries. **Remarks:** Accepts advertising. **URL:** http://www.catalog-biz.com. **Circ:** 8,500

Ilkeston

53642 ■ Ilkeston Advertiser
Johnston Press PLC
8 Heanor Rd.
Ilkeston DE7 8ER, United Kingdom
Ph: 44 1159 446160
Publication E-mail: advertising@ilkestonadvertiser.co.uk
Local community newspaper. **Key Personnel:** David Wade, Contact, phone 44 115 9446181; Peter Hemmett, Editor, phone 44 115 9446160, fax 44 115 9444990, news@ilkestonadvertiser.co.uk. **Remarks:** Accepts advertising. **URL:** http://www.ilkestonadvertiser.co.uk/. **Circ:** (Not Reported)

Ilkley

53643 ■ Armley & Wortley Advertiser
Newsquest Media Group Ltd.
8 Wells Rd.
Ilkley LS29 9JD, United Kingdom
Ph: 44 1943 603483
Newspaper providing up to date local news and sports. **Founded:** Nov. 2003. **Key Personnel:** John Lee, Hd. of Advertising, phone 44 274 705390, john.lee@bradford.newsquest.co.uk. **Remarks:** Accepts advertising. **URL:** http://www.advertiserseries.co.uk/. **Circ:** (Not Reported)

53644 ■ Assembly Automation
Emerald Group Publishing Ltd.
c/o Dr. Clive Loughlin, Ed.
17 Old Ln.
Low Mill Village
Addingham
Ilkley LS29 0SA, United Kingdom
Publisher E-mail: emerald@emeraldinsight.com
Journal keeping pace with international developments in both dedicated and programme assembly, especially the current trends towards flexible manufacturing, including

case histories about assembly technology in action. **Freq:** 4/yr. **Key Personnel:** Dr. Clive Loughlin, Editor, cliveloughlin@engineeringfirst.com; Harry Colson, Publisher, hcolson@emeraldinsight.com. **ISSN:** 0144-5154. **URL:** http://info.emeraldinsight.com/products/journals/journals.htm?id=aa.

53645 ■ Ilkley Gazette
Newsquest Media Group Ltd.
8 Wells Rd.
Ilkley LS29 9JD, United Kingdom
Ph: 44 1943 603483
Newspaper featuring Ilkley news, sports, and updates on local jobs. **Freq:** Weekly (Thurs.). **Key Personnel:** Sheena Stavert, Editor, phone 44 1943 607022, sheena.stavert@wharfedalenewspapers.co.uk; Alan Birkinshaw, Dep. Ed., phone 44 1943 607022, alan.b@ilkley.newsquest.co.uk. **Remarks:** Accepts advertising. **URL:** http://www.ilkleygazette.co.uk/. **Circ:** (Not Reported)

53646 ■ Industrial Robot
Emerald Group Publishing Ltd.
c/o Dr. Clive Loughlin, Ed.
17 Old Ln.
Low Mill Village
Addingham
Ilkley LS29 0SA, United Kingdom
Publisher E-mail: emerald@emeraldinsight.com
Peer-reviewed journal providing up to date coverage of international activities that relate to the design and application of industrial and service robot systems. **Subtitle:** An International Journal. **Founded:** 1973. **Freq:** Bimonthly. **Trim Size:** A4. **Key Personnel:** Harry Colson, Publisher, hcolson@emeraldinsight.com; Richard Bloss, Assoc. Ed.; Dr. Clive Loughlin, Editor, cliveloughlin@engineeringfirst.com. **ISSN:** 0143-991X. **Remarks:** Advertising not accepted. **URL:** http://www.emeraldinsight.com/products/journals/journals.htm?id=ir. **Circ:** (Not Reported)

Inverness

53647 ■ Scotland's Natural Heritage
Scottish Natural Heritage
Great Glen House
Leachkin Rd.
Inverness IV3 8NW, United Kingdom
Ph: 44 1463 725000
Fax: 44 1463 725067
Publisher E-mail: enquiries@snh.gov.uk
Publication covering conservation in Scotland. **Freq:** Quarterly. **Subscription Rates:** 10 individuals. **Remarks:** Advertising not accepted. **URL:** http://www.snh.org.uk/. **Circ:** (Not Reported)

53648 ■ MFR-AM - 1107
PO Box 271
Inverness IV3 8UJ, United Kingdom
Ph: 44 1463 224433
Format: Contemporary Hit Radio (CHR); Oldies. **Key Personnel:** Danny Gallagher, Mng. Dir. **URL:** http://www.mfr.co.uk/.

Inverurie

53649 ■ Inverurie Herald
Johnston Press PLC
15b High St.
Inverurie AB51 3QA, United Kingdom
Ph: 44 1467 625150
Local community newspaper. **Key Personnel:** David Duncan, Contact; Jenna Hall, Contact. **Remarks:** Accepts advertising. **URL:** http://www.inverurieherald.co.uk/. **Circ:** (Not Reported)

53650 ■ NECR-FM - 106.4
The Shed
School Rd.
Kintore
Aberdeenshire
Inverurie AB51 0UX, United Kingdom
Ph: 44 1467 632909
Fax: 44 1467 632969
E-mail: enquiries@necrfm.co.uk
Format: Oldies; Contemporary Hit Radio (CHR); News; Information. **Ad Rates:** Advertising accepted; rates available upon request. **URL:** http://www.necrfm.co.uk/.

53651 ■ NECR-FM - 102.6
The Shed
School Rd.

Kintore
Aberdeenshire
Inverurie AB51 0UX, United Kingdom
Ph: 44 1467 632909
Fax: 44 1467 632969
E-mail: enquiries@necrfm.co.uk
Format: Oldies; Contemporary Hit Radio (CHR); News; Information. **Ad Rates:** Advertising accepted; rates available upon request. **URL:** http://www.necrfm.co.uk/.

53652 ■ NECR-FM - 102.1
The Shed
School Rd.
Kintore
Aberdeenshire
Inverurie AB51 0UX, United Kingdom
Ph: 44 1467 632909
Fax: 44 1467 632969
E-mail: enquiries@necrfm.co.uk
Format: Oldies; Contemporary Hit Radio (CHR); News; Information. **Ad Rates:** Advertising accepted; rates available upon request. **URL:** http://www.necrfm.co.uk/.

NECR-FM - See Ballater

NECR-FM - See Huntly

NECR-FM - See Turriff

Ipswich

53653 ■ Coastal Advertiser
Archant Regional Ltd.
30 Lower Brook St.
Ipswich IP4 1AN, United Kingdom
Ph: 44 1473 230023
Publication E-mail: editor@ipswich-advertiser.co.uk
Publisher E-mail: sandra.roantree@archant.co.uk
Local community newspaper. **Remarks:** Accepts advertising. **URL:** http://www.coastaladvertiser.co.uk/content/coastal/default/. **Circ:** (Not Reported)

53654 ■ Disability and Rehabilitation
Taylor & Francis Group Journals
Suffolk College
Ipswich IP4 1LT, United Kingdom
Publisher E-mail: customerservice@taylorandfrancis.com
Peer-reviewed journal covering all aspects of disability; promotes the rehabilitation process. **Subtitle:** Assistive Technology. **Freq:** 18/yr. **Key Personnel:** Prof. Dave Muller, Editor, davemuller@suffolk.ac.uk; Magid Bakheit, Board Ed. **ISSN:** 0963-8288. **URL:** http://www.informaworld.com/smpp/title~db=all~content=t713723807~tab=issueslist.

53655 ■ East Anglian Daily Times
Archant Regional Ltd.
Press House
Lower Brook St.
Ipswich IP4 1AN, United Kingdom
Ph: 44 1473 230023
Publisher E-mail: sandra.roantree@archant.co.uk
Local community newspaper. **Founded:** Oct. 13, 1874. **Freq:** Mon.-Sat. **Remarks:** Accepts advertising. **URL:** http://www.eadt.co.uk/home. **Circ:** 37,338

53656 ■ East Anglian Daily Times Suffolk
Archant Regional Ltd.
30 Lower Brook St.
Ipswich IP4 1AN, United Kingdom
Ph: 44 1473 324762
Publisher E-mail: sandra.roantree@archant.co.uk
Magazine featuring the lifestyle and living in Suffolk county. **Freq:** Monthly. **Key Personnel:** Richard Bryson, Publisher, phone 44 1473 324763, richard.bryson@archant.co.uk; Chris Abbott, Advertising Mgr. **Subscription Rates:** 29.50 individuals. **Remarks:** Accepts advertising. **URL:** http://suffolk.greatbritishlife.co.uk. **Circ:** (Not Reported)

53657 ■ Green Un (Ipswich)
Archant Regional Ltd.
Press House
Lower Brook St.
Ipswich IP4 1AN, United Kingdom
Ph: 44 1473 230023
Publication E-mail: sport@greenun.co.uk
Publisher E-mail: sandra.roantree@archant.co.uk
Newspaper covering sports. **Founded:** 1923. **Freq:** Weekly. **Key Personnel:** Mike Bacon, Online Ed. **Subscription Rates:** EUR14 individuals Zone 1 incl. postage

cost; EUR15 individuals zone 2, incl. postage cost; EUR10 individuals incl. postage cost. **Remarks:** Accepts advertising. **URL:** http://www.greenun24.co.uk/home. **Circ:** Controlled 18,000

53658 ■ Heart Ipswich-FM - 96.4
Radio House
Alpha Business Pk.
White House Rd.
Ipswich IP1 5LT, United Kingdom
Ph: 44 1473 461000
Format: Adult Contemporary. **URL:** http://www. heartipswich.co.uk/.

53659 ■ Heart Ipswich-FM - 97.1
Radio House
Alpha Business Pk.
White House Rd.
Ipswich IP1 5LT, United Kingdom
Ph: 44 1473 461000
Format: Adult Contemporary. **URL:** http://www. heartipswich.co.uk/.

53660 ■ Town-FM - 102
1 Fl., Radio House
Orion Ct.
Great Blakenham
Ipswich IP6 0LW, United Kingdom
Ph: 44 845 3651102
Fax: 44 845 3652102
E-mail: info@town102.com
Format: Adult Contemporary. **Ad Rates:** Advertising accepted; rates available upon request. **URL:** http://www. town102.com/.

Isle of Arran

53661 ■ Arran Banner
The Arran Banner Printing & Publishing Co.
Brodick
Isle of Arran KA27 8AJ, United Kingdom
Community newspaper. **Founded:** 1974. **Freq:** Weekly (Sat.). **Cols./Page:** 4. **Col. Width:** 47.5 millimeters. **Col. Depth:** 260 millimeters. **Key Personnel:** John Millar, Editor; Jenni Turnbull, Admin. Asst. **Subscription Rates:** 32 individuals. **Remarks:** Accepts advertising. **URL:** http://www.arranbanner.co.uk/. **Circ:** Paid 3,600

53662 ■ Dalriada
Dalriada Celtic Heritage Trust
2 Brathwic Pl.
Brodick
Isle of Arran KA27 8BN, United Kingdom
Ph: 44 17 70302431
Fax: 44 17 70302431
Publisher E-mail: dalriada@dalriade.co.uk
Publication covering Celtic culture and music. **Freq:** Quarterly. **URL:** http://www.summerlands.com/ crossroads/celticlanguage/labara3.html.

Isle of Man

53663 ■ Common Law World Review
Vathek Publishing
Bridge House
Dalby
Isle of Man IM5 3BP, United Kingdom
Ph: 44 16 24844056
Fax: 44 16 24845043
Publication E-mail: mlw@vathek.com
Publisher E-mail: mlw@vathek.com
Professional journal covering common law issues worldwide. **Founded:** 1971. **Freq:** Quarterly. **Print Method:** Litho. **Trim Size:** 165 x 243 mm. **Cols./Page:** 1. **Key Personnel:** Prof. David Clarke, Editor; Prof. Keith Stanton, Editor; Prof. Paula Giliker, Editorial Committee; Dr. Charlotte Villiers, Editorial Committee; Dr. Oliver Quick, Editorial Committee; Dr. Eric Descheemaeker, Book Review Ed., eric.descheemaeker@bristol.ac.uk. **ISSN:** 1473-7795. **Subscription Rates:** 219 institutions paper and online; US$413 institutions paper and online; 110 individuals paper and online; US$206 individuals paper and online; 162 institutions online only; US$308 institutions online only; 81 individuals online only; US$154 individuals online only; 181 institutions paper only; US$341 institutions paper only. **URL:** http://www. vathek.com/clwr/home.php. **Former name:** Anglo-American Law Review. **Ad Rates:** BW: 100. **Circ:** Paid 400

53664 ■ The Police Journal
Vathek Publishing
Bridge House
Dalby
Isle of Man IM5 3BP, United Kingdom
Ph: 44 16 24844056
Fax: 44 16 24845043
Publisher E-mail: mlw@valthek.com
Police journal describing essential reading for all decision- and policy-makers, both within the police service and those working with the profession. **Freq:** Quarterly. **Key Personnel:** Barry Loveday, Editor; Zoe James, Book Review Ed. **ISSN:** 0032-258X. **Subscription Rates:** 171 institutions paper and online; US$320 institutions paper and online; 86 individuals paper and online; US$160 individuals paper and online; 126 institutions online only; US$238 institutions online only; 63 individuals online only; US$119 individuals online only; 141 institutions paper only; US$265 institutions paper only. **URL:** http://www.vathek.com/pj/index.shtml.

Jersey

53665 ■ Guernsey Press
Guiton Group Limited
Guiton House
Five Oaks, St. Saviour
Jersey JE4 8XQ, United Kingdom
Ph: 44 1534 611800
Fax: 44 1534 611825
Newspaper covering local news and sport, featuring daily business pages that focuses on the island's financial and commercial activities. **Freq:** Mon.-Sat. **Key Personnel:** Richard Digard, Editor; Nick Mann, News Ed., newseditor@guernsey-press.com. **Remarks:** Accepts advertising. **URL:** http://www.thisisguernsey.com/ guernsey-press/. **Circ:** ‡16,000

53666 ■ Jersey Evening Post
Guiton Group Limited
Guiton House
Five Oaks, St. Saviour
Jersey JE4 8XQ, United Kingdom
Ph: 44 1534 611800
Fax: 44 1534 611825
Newspaper providing comprehensive coverage of Jersey Island issues and events, as well as information and entertainment. **Founded:** 1890. **Freq:** Daily. **Key Personnel:** Chris Bright, Editor, phone 44 1534 611624, editorial@jerseyeveningpost.com; Carl Walker, News Ed., phone 44 1534 611640, fax 44 1534 611622, news@jerseyeveningpost.com. **Remarks:** Accepts advertising. **URL:** http://www.thisisjersey.com/jersey-evening-post/index/. **Circ:** (Not Reported)

53667 ■ Channel 103-FM - 103.7
6 Tunnell St.
St. Helier
Jersey JE2 4LU, United Kingdom
Ph: 44 1534 888103
Fax: 44 1534 877177
E-mail: info@channel103.com
Format: News; Top 40; Oldies. **Operating Hours:** Continuous. **Key Personnel:** Colin North, Sales Dir., colin.north@channel103.com. **Ad Rates:** Advertising accepted; rates available upon request. **URL:** http:// www.channel103.com.

Kempston

53668 ■ Investment Now
70 Singer Way
Kempston MK42 7PU, United Kingdom
Ph: 44 12 34843905
Fax: 44 12 34843901
Publisher E-mail: patw@investmentnow.co.uk
Journal covering economic development issues in the U.K. and worldwide. **Subscription Rates:** 50 individuals 12 issues. **Remarks:** Accepts advertising. **URL:** http:// www.investmentnow.co.uk/. **Ad Rates:** BW: 1,425, 4C: 1,825. **Circ:** Combined 70,000

53669 ■ Legal Executive Journal
Institute of Legal Executives
Kempston Manor
Bedfordshire
Kempston MK42 7AB, United Kingdom
Ph: 44 1234 841000

Fax: 44 1234 840373
Publisher E-mail: info@ilex.org.uk
Journal covering administrative services. **Freq:** Monthly. **Print Method:** Web. **Trim Size:** 210 x 298 mm. **Key Personnel:** Neil Rose, Editor. **Subscription Rates:** Included in membership. **URL:** http://www.ilex.org.uk/ membership/the_journal.aspx. **Ad Rates:** BW: 1,002, PCI: 25. **Circ:** 23,000

Kendal

53670 ■ The Barrow Browser
Newsquest Media Group Ltd.
1 Wainwright's Yard
Kendal LA9 4DP, United Kingdom
Fax: 44 1229 588634
Newspaper providing up to date information on local news and sports. **Freq:** Monthly. **Key Personnel:** Daniel Orr, Contact, phone 44 1229 588634, fax 44 1229 588637, daniel.orr@kendal.newsquest.co.uk. **Remarks:** Accepts advertising. **URL:** http://www.thebarrowbrowser. co.uk/. **Circ:** (Not Reported)

53671 ■ Lakeland Radio-FM - 100.8
Plumgarths
Cumbria
Kendal LA8 8QJ, United Kingdom
Ph: 44 1539 737380
E-mail: studio@lakelandradio.co.uk
Format: Adult Contemporary. **URL:** http://www. lakelandradio.co.uk/.

53672 ■ Lakeland Radio-FM - 100.1
Plumgarths
Cumbria
Kendal LA8 8QJ, United Kingdom
Ph: 44 1539 737380
E-mail: studio@lakelandradio.co.uk
Format: Adult Contemporary. **URL:** http://www. lakelandradio.co.uk/.

Kenilworth

53673 ■ Touch-FM - 102
Holly Farm Business Pk.
Honiley
Kenilworth CV8 1NP, United Kingdom
Ph: 44 1926 485600
Format: News; Contemporary Hit Radio (CHR). **Operating Hours:** Continuous. **Key Personnel:** Steve Hayden, Program Dir. **Ad Rates:** Advertising accepted; rates available upon request. **URL:** http://www.touchfm102. co.uk.

Kensington Village

53674 ■ Living Hadley
Archant Life
Avon House, 5th Fl.
Avonmore Rd.
Kensington Village W14 8TS, United Kingdom
Publisher E-mail: johnny.hustler@archant.co.uk
Magazine featuring lifestyle and living in the Hadley Wood area. **Key Personnel:** Mark Kebble, Editor, mark. kebble@archant.co.uk. **URL:** http://www.llvingnorthmag. co.uk/.

53675 ■ Living North
Archant Life
Avon House, 5th Fl.
Avonmore Rd.
Kensington Village W14 8TS, United Kingdom
Publisher E-mail: johnny.hustler@archant.co.uk
Magazine featuring lifestyle and living for people in the North. **Key Personnel:** Mark Kebble, Editor, mark. kebble@archant.co.uk. **URL:** http://www.livingnorthmag. co.uk/contact-us--67087.

Kent

53676 ■ Casino International
Datateam Publishing Ltd.
15A London Rd.
Maidstone
Kent ME16 8LY, United Kingdom
Ph: 44 16 22687031
Fax: 44 16 22757646
Publication E-mail: casino@datateam.co.uk

Circulation: ★ = ABC; △ = BPA; ◆ = CAC; • = CCAB; ❏ = VAC; ⊕ = PO Statement; ‡ = Publisher's Report; Boldface figures = sworn; Light figures = estimated.

Publisher E-mail: pkayani@datateam.co.uk
Magazine for industry casino professionals. **Freq:** 6/yr. **Trim Size:** 229 x 306 mm. **Key Personnel:** Jon Bruford, Managing Editor, phone 44.1584 877177, jonbruford@yahoo.co.uk; Ricki Chavez-Munoz, International Ed., phone 44 1202 425751, cwiberoamerica@yahoo.co.uk; Paul Ryder, Publisher, fax 44 1622 699105, pryder@datateam.co.uk. **Subscription Rates:** 55 individuals; EUR130 individuals to Europe; US$165 individuals to Americas and Middle East; US$195 individuals to Far East. **Remarks:** Accepts advertising. **URL:** http://www.casinointernational-online.com/. **Ad Rates:** 4C: 2,100. **Circ:** ★4,487

53677 ■ Footwear Today
Datateam Publishing Ltd.
15A London Rd.
Maidstone
Kent ME16 8LY, United Kingdom
Ph: 44 16 22687031
Fax: 44 16 22757646
Publisher E-mail: pkayani@datateam.co.uk
Magazine for the nation's retailers, featuring the latest industry news, developments and product information to help them run their business effectively, plus news and previews of forthcoming UK and European trade exhibitions. **Freq:** 10/yr. **Key Personnel:** John Andrews, Advertising Mgr., phone 44 1622 699135, jandrews@datateam.co.uk; Cheryl Taylor, Editor, phone 44 1622 862962, cherltayloreditor@googlemail.com; Paul Ryder, Publisher, phone 44 1622 699105, pryder@datateam.co.uk. **Subscription Rates:** 75 individuals Europe; 95 individuals rest of world. **Remarks:** Accepts advertising. **URL:** http://www.footweartoday.co.uk. **Circ:** (Not Reported)

53678 ■ The Independent Electrical Retailer
Datateam Publishing Ltd.
15A London Rd.
Maidstone
Kent ME16 8LY, United Kingdom
Ph: 44 16 22687031
Fax: 44 16 22757646
Publisher E-mail: pkayani@datateam.co.uk
Magazine for independent electrical retailers in United Kingdom. **Freq:** Monthly. **Trim Size:** 210 x 297 mm. **Key Personnel:** Anna Ryland, Editor, phone 44 1622 687031, aryland@datateam.co.uk; Mike Gammon, Advertising Mgr., phone 44 1622 699142, mgammont@datateam.co.uk; Hannah Dedman, Publisher, phone 44 1622 699175, hdedman@datateam.co.uk. **Remarks:** Accepts advertising. **URL:** http://www.independentelectricalretailer.co.uk/. **Ad Rates:** 4C: 3,200. **Circ:** Controlled ★6,895

53679 ■ Printwear & Promotion
Datateam Publishing Ltd.
15A London Rd.
Maidstone
Kent ME16 8LY, United Kingdom
Ph: 44 16 22687031
Fax: 44 16 22757646
Publisher E-mail: pkayani@datateam.co.uk
Journal for the decorated garment industry. **Subtitle:** The Total Promotion Package. **Freq:** Monthly. **Trim Size:** 210 x 297 mm. **Key Personnel:** Deborah Eales, Editor, phone 44 1622 699198, deales@datateam.co.uk; Tony Gardner, Advertising Mgr., phone 44 1622 699173, tgardner@datateam.co.uk. **Remarks:** Accepts advertising. **URL:** http://www.printwearandpromotion.co.uk/. **Ad Rates:** BW: 1,087, 4C: 1,549. **Circ:** ★5,536

53680 ■ Screen Process & Digital Imaging
Datateam Publishing Ltd.
15A London Rd.
Maidstone
Kent ME16 8LY, United Kingdom
Ph: 44 16 22687031
Fax: 44 16 22757646
Publisher E-mail: pkayani@datateam.co.uk
Magazine charting the industry's evolution for over five-decades, providing direct access to the new generation of digital equipment and consumable suppliers. **Freq:** Monthly. **Key Personnel:** Jon Barrett, Editor, phone 44 1622 850044, jbarrett@datateam.co.uk; Kathy Ambrose, Publisher, phone 44 1622 699129, kambrose@datateam.co.uk; Richard Smith, Advertising Mgr., phone 44 1622 699170, rsmith@datateam.co.uk. **Remarks:** Accepts advertising. **URL:** http://www.spdi-online.com. **Circ:** ★7,500

53681 ■ SGB Golf
Datateam Publishing Ltd.
15A London Rd.
Maidstone
Kent ME16 8LY, United Kingdom
Ph: 44 16 22687031
Fax: 44 16 22757646
Publisher E-mail: pkayani@datateam.co.uk
Magazine providing the latest product information, up-to-date industry & trade show news. **Subtitle:** The Trade Magazine. **Freq:** Monthly. **Key Personnel:** Jon Bruford, Editor, phone 44 1584 877177, jonbruford@datateam.co.uk; Paul Ryder, Publisher, phone 44 1622 699105, pryder@datateam.co.uk; Robin Barwick, Editor, robin@barwickmedia.com. **Remarks:** Accepts advertising. **URL:** http://www.sgb-sports.com. **Circ:** ★4,500

53682 ■ South East Business
Evegate Publishing Ltd.
South East Business
Spicer House
Lympne Business Park
Hythe
Kent CT21 4LR, United Kingdom
Ph: 44 1303 233880
Fax: 44 1303 239517
Publication E-mail: publish@dircon.co.uk
Professional magazine covering local business news. **Founded:** 1982. **Freq:** Monthly. **Key Personnel:** Michala Nason, Administration; Tom Philbrick, Advertising, tom@southeastbusiness.net; Nick Mercer, Editor; Maggie Wilkinson, Advertising; Cavan Furlong, Design; Clive Rabson, Publisher. **ISSN:** 0262-8597. **Subscription Rates:** 35 individuals; 57 elsewhere. **Remarks:** Accepts advertising. **URL:** http://www.southeastbusiness.net/. **Former name:** Business South East. **Ad Rates:** BW: 1,259, 4C: 1,469. **Circ:** Non-paid 13,000

53683 ■ South East Farmer
Evegate Publishing Ltd.
South East Business
Spicer House
Lympne Business Park
Hythe
Kent CT21 4LR, United Kingdom
Ph: 44 1303 233880
Fax: 44 1303 239517
Trade magazine covering farming news in South England. **Founded:** 1979. **Freq:** Monthly. **Key Personnel:** John Harvey, Editor, phone 44 1303 233880, newsdesk@southeastfarmer.net. **Subscription Rates:** 35 individuals; 57 other countries. **URL:** http://www.southeastfarmer.net/. **Circ:** Combined 12,500

Kettering

53684 ■ Kettering Evening Telegraph
Johnston Press PLC
Ise Pk.
Rothwell Rd.
Kettering NN16 8GA, United Kingdom
Ph: 44 1536 506100
Local community newspaper. **Key Personnel:** Jeremy Clifford, Editor, fax 44 1536 506195, jeremy.clifford@northantsnews.co.uk; Simon Kennedy, General Mgr., phone 44 1604 467011, simon.kennedy@northantsnews.co.uk. **Remarks:** Accepts advertising. **URL:** http://www.northantset.co.uk/. **Circ:** (Not Reported)

53685 ■ The Radio Magazine
Goldcrest Broadcasting Ltd.
Crown House
25 High St.
Rothwell
Kettering NN14 6AD, United Kingdom
Ph: 44 15 36418558
Fax: 44 15 36418539
Publication E-mail: editor@theradiomagazine.co.uk
Publisher E-mail: editor@theradiomagazine.co.uk
Trade magazine covering the radio industry. **Freq:** Weekly. **Print Method:** Litho. **Trim Size:** 125 x 187 mm. **Key Personnel:** Jacky Stevenson, Contact; Paul Boon, Managing Editor; Collette Hillier, Asst. Ed. **ISSN:** 0966-7105. **Subscription Rates:** 99 individuals; 110 individuals Europe; 130 other countries; 55 individuals 6 months; 33 individuals 3 months. **Remarks:** Accepts advertising. **URL:** http://www.theradiomagazine.co.uk/index.htm. **Ad Rates:** BW: 884, 4C: 1,235. **Circ:** Combined 4,000

Kidderminster

53686 ■ Wyre-FM - 107.2
Foley House
123 Stourport Rd.
Kidderminster DY11 7BW, United Kingdom
Ph: 44 1562 641072
E-mail: info@thewyre.com
Format: Oldies; Contemporary Hit Radio (CHR); Eighties. **Ad Rates:** Advertising accepted; rates available upon request. **URL:** http://www.thewyre.com/.

53687 ■ Wyvern-FM - 96.7
1st Fl., Kirkham House
John Comyn Dr.
Worcester WR3 7NS, United Kingdom
Ph: 44 1905 545510
Format: Contemporary Hit Radio (CHR). **Ad Rates:** Advertising accepted; rates available upon request. **URL:** http://www.wyvernfm.co.uk/.

Kidlington

53688 ■ Acta Ecologica Sinica
Elsevier
The Blvd., Langford Ln.
Kidlington OX5 1GB, United Kingdom
Ph: 44 1865 843000
Fax: 44 1865 843010
Journal covering ecological research, sustainable development and the revitalization of the nation through science and education. **Founded:** 1981. **Freq:** 6/yr. **Key Personnel:** Ru-Song Wang, Assoc. Ed.; Tian-Xing Liu, Managing Editor; Hong-Mei Kong, Managing Editor; Shao-Lin Peng, Assoc. Ed.; Zong-Wei Feng, Editor-in-Chief. **ISSN:** 1872-2032. **URL:** http://www.elsevier.com/wps/find/journaldescription.cws_home/709341/descriptiondescription.

53689 ■ Acta Mathematica Scientia
Elsevier
The Blvd., Langford Ln.
Kidlington OX5 1GB, United Kingdom
Ph: 44 1865 843000
Fax: 44 1865 843010
Scientific journal covering mathematical sciences for graduate student level and above. **Freq:** 6/yr. **Key Personnel:** Xiaqi Ding, Honorary Ed.-in-Ch., xqding@public.bta.net.cn; Wenjun Wu, Editor-in-Chief, wtwu@mmrc.iss.ac.cn. **ISSN:** 0252-9602. **Subscription Rates:** US$704 institutions, other countries except Europe, Japan and Iran; 103,200¥ institutions; EUR704 institutions for European countries and Iran. **URL:** http://www.elsevier.com/wps/find/journaldescription.cws_home/708310/descriptiondescription.

53690 ■ Computers in Human Behavior
Elsevier
The Blvd., Langford Ln.
Kidlington OX5 1GB, United Kingdom
Ph: 44 1865 843000
Fax: 44 1865 843010
Publication covering psychology and mental health. **Founded:** 1985. **Freq:** Bimonthly. **Key Personnel:** S. Randsell, Editorial Board; Robert D. Tennyson, Editor; M.J. Lee, Editorial Board; P. Kirschner, Assoc. Ed.; B. Nelson, Editorial Board; R. Whelan, Editorial Board. **ISSN:** 0747-5632. **Subscription Rates:** 192,300¥ institutions; EUR1,446 institutions for European countries and Iran; US$1,619 institutions other countries; 33,400¥ individuals; EUR233 individuals for European countries and Iran; US$302 individuals other countries except Europe, Japan and Iran. **Remarks:** Accepts advertising. **URL:** http://www.elsevier.com/wps/find/journaldescription.cws_home/759/descriptiondescription. **Circ:** (Not Reported)

53691 ■ Filtration Industry Analyst
Elsevier Science Inc.
c/o R. Reidy, Ed.
Elsevier Ltd.
The Blvd.
Langford Ln.
Kidlington OX5 1GB, United Kingdom
Ph: 44 186 5843695
Fax: 44 186 5843971
Publisher E-mail: usinfo-ehelp@elsevier.com
Journal covering trends and business developments in the filtration and separation industries. **Freq:** 12/yr. **Key Personnel:** R. Reidy, Editor, r.reidy@elsevier.com. **ISSN:** 1365-6937. **Subscription Rates:** EUR1,176 institutions European countries and Iran; US$1,319

institutions, other countries except Europe, Japan and Iran; 156,300¥ institutions. **URL:** http://www.elsevier.com/wps/find/journaldescription.cws_home/600705/descrip tiondescription.

53692 ■ Food and Chemical Toxicology
Elsevier
The Blvd., Langford Ln.
Kidlington OX5 1GB, United Kingdom
Ph: 44 1865 843000
Fax: 44 1865 843010
Peer-reviewed journal of BIBRA International. **Freq:** Monthly. **Key Personnel:** Joseph F. Borzelleca, Editor, josephfborzelleca@comcast.net; Alan R. Boobis, Editor, a.boobis@imperial.ac.uk; David J. Brusick, Assoc. Ed., brusick41@aol.com. **ISSN:** 0278-6915. **Subscription Rates:** EUR3,352 institutions European countries and Iran; 444,900¥ institutions; US$3,750 institutions, other countries except Europe, Japan and Iran; US$410 individuals except Europe, Japan and Iran; EUR363 individuals European counties and Iran; 48,100¥ individuals. **Remarks:** Accepts advertising. **URL:** http://www.elsevier.com/wps/find/journaldescription.cws_home/237/descriptiondescription. **Circ:** (Not Reported)

53693 ■ The History of the Family
Elsevier
The Blvd., Langford Ln.
Kidlington OX5 1GB, United Kingdom
Ph: 44 1865 843000
Fax: 44 1865 843010
Scholarly journal of research on historical family patterns, marriage, kinship, the life course, and demography. **Subtitle:** An International Quarterly. **Founded:** 1996. **Freq:** Quarterly. **Trim Size:** 7 x 10. **Cols./Page:** 1. **Col. Width:** 30 picas. **Col. Depth:** 46 picas. **Key Personnel:** T. Engelen, Editor; J. Kok, Editor. **ISSN:** 1081-602X. **Subscription Rates:** EUR157 individuals European countries and Iran; US$177 other countries except Europe and Japan; 20,900¥ individuals Japan; EUR414 institutions European countries and Iran; US$463 institutions, other countries except Europe, Iran and Japan; 55,000¥ institutions Japan. **Remarks:** Accepts advertising. **URL:** http://www.elsevier.com/wps/find/journaldescription.cws_home/620196/descriptiondescription. **Circ:** (Not Reported)

53694 ■ International Journal of Law, Crime and Justice
Elsevier
The Blvd., Langford Ln.
Kidlington OX5 1GB, United Kingdom
Ph: 44 1865 843000
Fax: 44 1865 843010
Refereed journal focusing on socio-legal studies. **Freq:** Quarterly. **Key Personnel:** J. Carrier, Editor, j.carrier@lse.ac.uk; Steve Savage, Editor, steve.savage@port.ac.uk. **ISSN:** 1756-0616. **Subscription Rates:** EUR119 individuals for European countries and Iran; US$105 individuals except Europe, Japan and Iran; 12,900¥ individuals; US$458 institutions except Europe, Japan and Iran; EUR514 institutions for European countries and Iran; 55,700¥ institutions. **Remarks:** Accepts advertising. **URL:** http://www.elsevier.com/wps/find/journaldescription.cws_home/716246/descriptiondescription. **Formerly:** International Journal of the Sociology of the Law. **Circ:** (Not Reported)

53695 ■ Journal of Adolescence
Elsevier
The Blvd., Langford Ln.
Kidlington OX5 1GB, United Kingdom
Ph: 44 1865 843000
Fax: 44 1865 843010
Publication covering adolescent psychology and mental health. **Founded:** 1978. **Freq:** Bimonthly. **Key Personnel:** Dr. A. Hagell, Editor, a.k.hagell@btinternet.com; Dr. N. Darling, Assoc. Ed.; Dr. W. Beyers, Asst. Ed. **ISSN:** 0140-1971. **Subscription Rates:** 15,200¥ individuals; EUR141 individuals for European countries and Iran; US$128 individuals for all countries except Europe, Iran and Japan; EUR696 institutions for European countries and Iran; US$622 institutions for all countries except Europe, Iran and Japan; 75,100¥ institutions. **Remarks:** Accepts advertising. **URL:** http://www.elsevier.com/wps/find/journaldescription.cws_home/622849/descriptiondescription. **Circ:** (Not Reported)

53696 ■ Journal of Cranio-Maxillofacial Surgery
Elsevier
The Blvd., Langford Ln.
Kidlington OX5 1GB, United Kingdom
Ph: 44 1865 843000
Fax: 44 1865 843010
Journal covering oral and maxillofacial surgery. **Freq:** 8/yr. **Key Personnel:** Prof. J. Wiltfang, Editor-in-Chief, phone 49 431 5972820, fax 49 431 5974084, wiltfang@mkg.uni-kiel.de; M.E. Foster, Asst. Ed., mef100@argonet.uk; B. Devauchelle, Section Ed. **ISSN:** 1010-5182. **Subscription Rates:** EUR297 individuals; EUR745 institutions; 172 individuals trainee; 31,900¥ individuals; 76,300¥ institutions; 18,500¥ individuals trainee; US$277 individuals; US$700 institutions; US$160 individuals trainee. **Remarks:** Advertising accepted; rates available upon request. **URL:** http://www.elsevier.com/wps/find/journaldescription.cws_home/623049/descriptiondescription. **Circ:** (Not Reported)

53697 ■ Journal of Environmental Management
Elsevier
The Blvd., Langford Ln.
Kidlington OX5 1GB, United Kingdom
Ph: 44 1865 843000
Fax: 44 1865 843010
Publication focusing on environmental issues. **Freq:** 12/yr. **Key Personnel:** A.L. Gill, Editor-in-Chief, jem@sfo.com; C. Allan, Editorial Board; G. Huang, Editorial Board; R. Cullen, Editorial Board; L. Firbank, Editorial Board. **ISSN:** 0301-4797. **Subscription Rates:** 46,000¥ individuals; EUR426 individuals for European countries and Iran; US$380 individuals for all countries except Europe, Japan and Iran; 182,400¥ institutions; US$1,502 institutions for all countries except Europe, Japan and Iran; EUR1,689 institutions for European countries and Iran. **Remarks:** Accepts advertising. **URL:** http://www.elsevier.com/wps/find/journaldescription.cws_home/622871/descriptiondescription. **Circ:** (Not Reported)

53698 ■ Journal of Environmental Sciences
Elsevier
The Blvd., Langford Ln.
Kidlington OX5 1GB, United Kingdom
Ph: 44 1865 843000
Fax: 44 1865 843010
Peer-reviewed journal introducing new research achievements, reporting research developments and advanced experience, strengthening academic exchanges, promoting cooperation in science and technology, and making contributions to the progress in environmental sciences, publishing original research papers on main aspects of environmental sciences, such as environmental chemistry, environmental biology, ecology geosciences and environmental physics. **Freq:** 12/yr. **Key Personnel:** Tang Hongxiao, Editor-in-Chief; Wong Po-Keung, Assoc. Ed.-in-Ch.; Nigel Bell, Assoc. Ed.-in-Ch.; Tao Shu, Assoc. Ed.-in-Ch.; Zhuang Yahui, Assoc. Ed.-in-Ch.; R.M. Atlas, Editorial Board; Alan Baker, Editorial Board. **ISSN:** 1001-0742. **Subscription Rates:** US$706 institutions, other countries except Europe, Japan and Iran; EUR902 institutions for European countries and Iran; 103,600¥ institutions. **Remarks:** Accepts advertising. **URL:** http://www.elsevier.com/wps/find/journaldescription.cws_home/709941/descriptiondescription. **Circ:** (Not Reported)

53699 ■ Journal of Historical Geography
Elsevier
The Blvd., Langford Ln.
Kidlington OX5 1GB, United Kingdom
Ph: 44 1865 843000
Fax: 44 1865 843010
Peer-reviewed journal focusing on historical geography. **Freq:** Quarterly. **Key Personnel:** M. Heffernan, Editorial Board; H. Clout, Editorial Board; A.R.H. Baker, Editorial Board; G. Wynn, Editor, wynn@geog.ubc.ca; S. Naylor, Book Review Ed., s.k.naylor@exeter.ac.uk; F. Driver, Editor, f.driver@rhul.ac.uk. **ISSN:** 0305-7488. **Subscription Rates:** EUR131 individuals for European countries and Iran; 14,000¥ individuals; US$118 individuals for all countries except Europe, Iran and Japan; US$539 institutions for all countries except Europe, Iran and Japan; 65,600¥ institutions; EUR608 institutions for European countries and Iran. **URL:** http://www.elsevier.com/wps/find/journaldescription.cws_home/622880/descriptiondescription.

53700 ■ Journal of Reproductive Immunology
Elsevier
The Blvd., Langford Ln.
Kidlington OX5 1GB, United Kingdom
Ph: 44 1865 843000
Fax: 44 1865 843010
Professional journal covering reproductive immunology. **Subtitle:** The International Journal for Experimental and Clinical Immunobiology. **Founded:** 1979. **Freq:** 8/yr. **Key Personnel:** Prof. S. Saito, Editor-in-Chief, phone 81 76 4347355, fax 81 76 4345036, jri@med.u-toyama.ac.jp; Prof. Ware D. Branch, Editor-in-Chief, phone 801581-7931, fax 801585-2594, wareb@aol.com; Sarah A. Robertson, Editor-in-Chief, phone 61 8 3034094, fax 61 8 3034099, sarah.robertson@adelaide.edu.au. **ISSN:** 0165-0378. **Subscription Rates:** EUR137 individuals Europe, Iran; US$153 other countries; 18,400¥ individuals; 185,100¥ institutions; EUR1,391 institutions Europe, Iran; US$1,557 institutions, other countries; 95 individuals. **Remarks:** Accepts advertising. **URL:** http://www.elsevier.com/wps/find/journaldescription.cws_home/506024/descriptiondescription. **Circ:** (Not Reported)

53701 ■ Journal of Rural Studies
Elsevier
The Blvd., Langford Ln.
Kidlington OX5 1GB, United Kingdom
Ph: 44 1865 843000
Fax: 44 1865 843010
Publication covering rural geography and rural studies. **Founded:** 1985. **Freq:** Quarterly. **Key Personnel:** Paul J. Cloke, Editor, p.cloke@exeter.ac.uk; T. Fuller, Editorial Board; M. Bunce, Editorial Board; B. Brandth, Editorial Board; I. Hodge, Editorial Board; J. Little, Editorial Board. **ISSN:** 0743-0167. **Subscription Rates:** 118,400¥ institutions; EUR876 institutions for European countries and Iran; US$986 institutions other countries; 19,900¥ individuals; EUR138 individuals for European countries and Iran; US$179 individuals other countries. **Remarks:** Advertising accepted; rates available upon request. **URL:** http://www.elsevier.com/wps/find/journaldescription.cws_home/348/descriptiondescription. **Circ:** (Not Reported)

53702 ■ Materials Today
Elsevier
The Blvd., Langford Ln.
Kidlington OX5 1GB, United Kingdom
Ph: 44 1865 843000
Fax: 44 1865 843010
Journal devoted to researchers in academia, industry, and government organizations. **Founded:** 1998. **Freq:** 12/yr. **Print Method:** Offset. **Trim Size:** 7 7/8 x 10 1/12. **Key Personnel:** J. Agbenyega, Editor, phone 44 1865 843784, j.agbenye@elsevier.com. **ISSN:** 1369-7021. **Subscription Rates:** EUR325 institutions for European countries and Iran; 43,300¥ institutions; US$364 institutions, other countries all countries except Europe, Japan and Iran; EUR79 individuals for European countries and Iran; 8,500¥ individuals; US$100 individuals all countries except Europe, Japan and Iran. **URL:** http://www.elsevier.com/wps/find/journaldescription.cws_home/601189/descriptiondescription.

53703 ■ Metal Powder Report
Elsevier Advanced Technology
The Blvd., Langford Ln.
Kidlington OX5 1GB, United Kingdom
Ph: 44 1865 843638
Fax: 44 1865 843973
Publisher E-mail: eatsales@elsevier.com
Trade and technical magazine for the powder metallurgy industry worldwide. **Founded:** 1965. **Freq:** Monthly 11/yr. **Key Personnel:** Greg Valero, Publisher, g.valero@elsevier.com; Richard Felton, Editor, phone 44 1865 843670, fax 44 1865 843971, r.felton@elsevier.com. **ISSN:** 0026-0657. **Subscription Rates:** US$582 individuals; 69,000¥ individuals; EUR520 individuals. **Remarks:** Accepts advertising. **URL:** http://www.metal-powder.net/. **Circ:** (Not Reported)

53704 ■ Physiotherapy
The Chartered Society of Physiotherapy
The Blvd.
Langford Ln.
Kidlington OX5 1GB, United Kingdom
Publisher E-mail: enquiries@csp.org.uk
Professional journal for physical therapists. **Founded:** 1915. **Freq:** Quarterly. **Print Method:** Web offset. **Trim Size:** A4. **Col. Depth:** 265 millimeters. **Key Personnel:** V. Pomeroy, Assoc. Ed.; M. Harms, Editor; C. Ballinger, Assoc. Ed.; T. Bury, Assoc. Ed.; V. Cross, Assoc. Ed.; M. Hurley, Assoc. Ed.; S. Lamb, Assoc. Ed.; J. Mantle, Assoc. Ed.; G. Noble, Assoc. Ed.; S. Payne, Assoc. Ed. **ISSN:** 0031-9406. **Subscription Rates:** US$86 individuals all countries except Europe and Japan; 10,300¥ individuals for Japan; EUR89 individuals for European countries; US$321 institutions all countries except Europe and Japan; 38,100¥ institutions for Japan; EUR344 institutions for European countries. **Remarks:** Accepts advertising. **URL:** http://www.csp.org.uk/director/members/practice/clinicalresources/physiotherapyjournal.cfm; http://www.csp.org.uk/; http://www.intl.elsevierhealth.com/. **Circ:** Controlled 35,000

Circulation: ★ = ABC; △ = BPA; ♦ = CAC; • = CCAB; ❑ = VAC; ⊕ = PO Statement; ‡ = Publisher's Report; Boldface figures = sworn; Light figures = estimated.

53705 ■ Reinforced Plastics
Elsevier Advanced Technology
The Boulevard
Langford Ln.
Kidlington OX5 1GB, United Kingdom
Publisher E-mail: eatsales@elsevier.com
Trade magazine covering business and technical developments in the fiber reinforced polymer industry. **Subtitle:** The Voice of the Composites Industry Worldwide. **Founded:** 1956. **Freq:** Monthly 11/yr. **Key Personnel:** Amanda Jacob, Editor, phone 44 1865 843638, a.jacob@elsevier.com; Mark Sherman, Key Accounts Mgr., phone 44 1865 843208, m.sherman@elseivier.com; Naomi Reeves, Sales Mgr., phone 44 1865 843271, fax 44 1865 843973, n.reeves@elsevier.com. **ISSN:** 0034-3617. **Subscription Rates:** US$408 individuals for all countries except Europe and Japan; 48,400¥ individuals for Japan; EUR364 individuals for all European countries and Iran. **Remarks:** Advertising accepted; rates available upon request. **URL:** http://www.reinforcedplastics.com. **Circ:** Controlled △15,000

53706 ■ Science & Justice
Elsevier
The Blvd., Langford Ln.
Kidlington OX5 1GB, United Kingdom
Ph: 44 1865 843000
Fax: 44 1865 843010
Journal covering forensic science. **Subtitle:** The Journal of the Forensic Science Society. **Founded:** 1959. **Freq:** Quarterly. **Key Personnel:** Niamh Nic Daeid, Editor-in-Chief. **ISSN:** 1355-0306. **Subscription Rates:** US$344 institutions, other countries except Europe, Japan and Iran; EUR260 institutions for European countries and Iran; 40,800¥ institutions. **Remarks:** Accepts advertising. **URL:** http://www.forensic-science-society.org.uk/publications/saj.html; http://www.elsevier.com/wps/find/journaldescription.cws_home/711629/descriptiondescription. **Circ:** (Not Reported)

53707 ■ The Surgeon
Elsevier
The Blvd., Langford Ln.
Kidlington OX5 1GB, United Kingdom
Ph: 44 1865 843000
Fax: 44 1865 843010
Journal published for the Fellows of the Royal College of Surgeons of Edinburgh and the Royal College of Surgeons in Ireland and the worldwide surgical community, publishing articles from all specialties and aiming to educate, entertain, give insight into new surgical techniques and technology, and provide a forum for debate and discussion. **Freq:** Bimonthly. **Key Personnel:** Prof. Austin L. Leahy, Editor-in-Chief; Prof. Jim McDonald, PhD, Editorial Advisory Board; Prof. Robert Steele, MD, Editor; Steve Nixon, Assoc. Ed. **ISSN:** 1479-666X. **Subscription Rates:** EUR149 individuals; 19,700¥ individuals; US$212 individuals; 131 individuals; EUR332 institutions; 44,000¥ institutions; US$474 institutions. **Remarks:** Accepts advertising. **URL:** http://www.elsevier.com/wps/find/journaldescription.cws_home/721359/descriptiondescription. **Circ:** (Not Reported)

53708 ■ Transportation Research Part E
Elsevier
The Blvd., Langford Ln.
Kidlington OX5 1GB, United Kingdom
Ph: 44 1865 843000
Fax: 44 1865 843010
Peer-reviewed journal covering the transportation industry. **Subtitle:** Logistic and Transportation Review. **Freq:** Bimonthly. **Key Personnel:** W.K. Talley, Editor-in-Chief; J.H. Bookbinder, Assoc. Ed.; S. Gudmundsson, Assoc. Ed. **ISSN:** 1366-5545. **Subscription Rates:** EUR1,179 institutions for European countries and Iran; US$1,321 institutions for all countries except Europe, Iran and Japan; 156,700¥ institutions; EUR189 individuals for European countries and Iran; US$245 individuals for all countries except Europe, Iran and Japan; 27,200¥ individuals. **URL:** http://www.elsevier.com/wps/find/journaldescription.cws_home/600244/descriptiondescription.

Kilmarnock

53709 ■ The Scottish Review
Standfirst
66 John Finnie St.
Kilmarnock KA1 1BS, United Kingdom
Ph: 44 15 63530830
Fax: 44 15 63549503
Publisher E-mail: enquiries@journalistshandbook.co.uk
Journal covering current events in Scotland. **Freq:** Semiweekly. **Trim Size:** 128 x 198 mm. **Cols./Page:** 1. **Key Personnel:** Fiona MacDonald, Contact; Kenneth Roy, Founding Ed. **Remarks:** Advertising not accepted. **URL:** http://www.scottishreview.net/. **Circ:** (Not Reported)

Kings Langley

53710 ■ The Grocery Trader
Flame Ltd.
12 Kings Pk.
Primrose Hill
Kings Langley WD4 8ST, United Kingdom
Ph: 44 19 23272920
Publication E-mail: grocery@flame1.com
Grocery trade magazine. **Freq:** Monthly. **Print Method:** Sheetfed Litho. **Cols./Page:** 5. **Key Personnel:** James Surridge, Contact; Trevor Surridge, Editor. **ISSN:** 1355-5928. **Subscription Rates:** 70 individuals 12 issues. **Remarks:** Accepts advertising. **URL:** http://grocerytrader.co.uk/. **Ad Rates:** 4C: 1,690. **Circ:** Combined 21,318

53711 ■ Warehouse & Logistics News
Flame Ltd.
12 Kings Pk.
Primrose Hill
Kings Langley WD4 8ST, United Kingdom
Ph: 44 19 23272920
Publication E-mail: warehouse@flame1.com
Trade magazine covering warehouse and logistics issues. **Freq:** Semimonthly. **Print Method:** Sheetfed Litho. **Key Personnel:** Charles Smith, Interviews; James Surridge, Publisher, phone 44 19 23272960; Graeme Walker, Advertising-Features; Adam Dillon, Website Ed.; John Chalkwright, Advertising Mgr.; Andy Page, Production Mgr. **ISSN:** 1368-5147. **Remarks:** Accepts advertising. **URL:** http://warehousenews.co.uk/. **Ad Rates:** 4C: 1,450. **Circ:** 27,822

King's Lynn

53712 ■ Ferrari Magazine
The Ferrari Owners Club Ltd.
Snettisham
PO Box 111
King's Lynn PE31 7TF, United Kingdom
Consumer magazine covering Ferrari automobiles, events, and news worldwide for club members. **Founded:** 1967. **Freq:** Quarterly. **Subscription Rates:** members not for public sale. **Remarks:** Accepts advertising. **URL:** http://www.ferrariownersclub.co.uk. **Circ:** Paid 2,848

53713 ■ Ferrari News
The Ferrari Owners Club Ltd.
Snettisham
PO Box 111
King's Lynn PE31 7TF, United Kingdom
Publication covering issues for Ferrari owners and enthusiasts for club members. **Founded:** 1967. **Freq:** Bimonthly. **Trim Size:** 188 x 265 mm. **Subscription Rates:** Free to qualified subscribers. **Remarks:** Accepts advertising. **URL:** http://www.ferrariownersclub.co.uk. **Circ:** Controlled 3,000

53714 ■ KL.FM - 96.7
18 Blackfriars St.
Norfolk
King's Lynn PE30 1NN, United Kingdom
Ph: 44 1553 772777
Fax: 44 1553 766453
E-mail: admin@klfm967.co.uk
Format: Adult Contemporary. **Key Personnel:** Pam Lawton, Mng. Dir., pam.lawton@klfm967.co.uk. **Ad Rates:** Advertising accepted; rates available upon request. **URL:** http://www.klfm967.co.uk/home.html.

Kingsbridge

53715 ■ Heart South Devon-FM - 101.2
South Hams Business Pk.
Churchstow
Kingsbridge TQ7 3QR, United Kingdom
Ph: 44 1548 854595
Fax: 44 1548 857345
Format: Adult Contemporary; Easy Listening. **Ad Rates:** Advertising accepted; rates available upon request. **URL:** http://www.heartsouthdevon.co.uk/.

53716 ■ Heart South Devon-FM - 101.9
South Hams Business Pk.
Churchstow
Kingsbridge TQ7 3QR, United Kingdom
Ph: 44 1548 854595
Fax: 44 1548 857345
Format: Adult Contemporary; Easy Listening. **Ad Rates:** Advertising accepted; rates available upon request. **URL:** http://www.heartsouthdevon.co.uk/.

53717 ■ Heart South Devon-FM - 100.5
South Hams Business Pk.
Churchstow
Kingsbridge TQ7 3QR, United Kingdom
Ph: 44 1548 854595
Fax: 44 1548 857345
Format: Adult Contemporary; Easy Listening. **Ad Rates:** Advertising accepted; rates available upon request. **URL:** http://www.heartsouthdevon.co.uk/.

53718 ■ Heart South Devon-FM - 100.8
South Hams Business Pk.
Churchstow
Kingsbridge TQ7 3QR, United Kingdom
Ph: 44 1548 854595
Fax: 44 1548 857345
Format: Adult Contemporary; Easy Listening. **Ad Rates:** Advertising accepted; rates available upon request. **URL:** http://www.heartsouthdevon.co.uk/.

Kingston upon Thames

53719 ■ Aircraft Illustrated
Ian Allan Publishing Ltd.
Riverdene Business Pk., Molesey Rd.
Hersham
Kingston upon Thames KT12 4RG, United Kingdom
Ph: 44 1932 266600
Fax: 44 1455 266601
Publisher E-mail: info@ianallanpublishing.co.uk
Magazine for modern aviation enthusiasts. **Freq:** Monthly. **Key Personnel:** Allan Burney, Managing Editor; David Lane, Advertising Mgr.; Ben Dunnell, Editor. **Remarks:** Accepts advertising. **URL:** http://www.ianallanmagazines.com/home.php?cat=1. **Circ:** (Not Reported)

53720 ■ Combat Aircraft
Ian Allan Publishing Ltd.
Riverdene Business Pk., Molesey Rd.
Hersham
Kingston upon Thames KT12 4RG, United Kingdom
Ph: 44 1932 266600
Fax: 44 1455 266601
Publisher E-mail: info@ianallanpublishing.co.uk
Magazine covering military aviation, modern and historic aircraft. **Subtitle:** The World's Top Military Aviation Magazine. **Freq:** Bimonthly. **Key Personnel:** Ben Dunnell, Dep. Ed., phone 44 1932 266636, fax 44 1932 266633, ben.dunnell@ianallanpublishing.co.uk; David Lane, Advertising Mgr., phone 44 1780 484632, fax 44 1780 763388, david.lane@ianallanpublishing.co.uk. **Subscription Rates:** EUR94 individuals; EUR188 two years. **Remarks:** Accepts advertising. **URL:** http://www.combataircraft.net/. **Circ:** (Not Reported)

53721 ■ Firefighter
Fire Brigades Union
Bradley House
68 Coombe Rd.
Kingston upon Thames KT2 7AE, United Kingdom
Ph: 44 20 85411765
Fax: 44 20 85465187
Publication E-mail: firefighter@fbu.org.uk
Publication covering fire fighting. **Freq:** Monthly. **URL:** http://www.fbu.org.uk/newspress/ffmag/2004/index.php.

53722 ■ Hornby Magazine
Ian Allan Publishing Ltd.
Riverdene Business Pk., Molesey Rd.
Hersham
Kingston upon Thames KT12 4RG, United Kingdom
Ph: 44 1932 266600
Fax: 44 1455 266601
Publisher E-mail: info@ianallanpublishing.co.uk
Magazine for railway enthusiasts. **Subtitle:** NEW hands-on magazine for modelers of all ages. **Founded:** Mar. 9, 2007. **Freq:** Bimonthly. **Key Personnel:** Mike Wild, Editor; David Lane, Advertising Mgr. **Remarks:** Accepts advertising. **URL:** http://www.

ianallanmagazines.com/home.php?cat=3. **Circ:** (Not Reported)

53723 ■ **Journal of Maps**
School of Geography, Geology & the Environment
Kingston University
Penrhyn Rd.
Kingston upon Thames KT1 2EE, United Kingdom
Ph: 44 20 70992817
Fax: 44 870 0633061
Publisher E-mail: editor.in.chief@journalofmaps.com
Multi-disciplinary journal drawing upon, and presenting, work from all geographic subject areas to build an increasing archive of mapped data for future researchers to draw upon. **Key Personnel:** Dr. Mike Smith, Editor-in-Chief, michael.smith@kingston.ac.uk; Dr. Dick Berg, Editor, berg@isgs.uiuc.edu; Dr. Ken, Field, Editor, ken.field@kingston.ac.uk. **ISSN:** 1744-5647. **URL:** http://www.journalofmaps.com.

53724 ■ **The Square**
Ian Allan Publishing Ltd.
Riverdene Business Pk., Molesey Rd.
Hersham
Kingston upon Thames KT12 4RG, United Kingdom
Ph: 44 1932 266600
Fax: 44 1455 266601
Publisher E-mail: info@ianallanpublishing.co.uk
Magazine featuring articles about freemasonry. **Subtitle:** The Independent Magazine for Freemasons. **Key Personnel:** Mike Porter, Editor, editorthesquare@hotmail.co.uk; Jenny Bell, Contact, jenny.bell@ianallanpublishing.co.uk; David Lane, Commercial Mgr., david.lane@ianallanpublishing.co.uk. **URL:** http://www.ianallanmagazines.com/thesquare/.

53725 ■ **Vintage Roadscene**
Ian Allan Publishing Ltd.
Riverdene Business Pk., Molesey Rd.
Hersham
Kingston upon Thames KT12 4RG, United Kingdom
Ph: 44 1932 266600
Fax: 44 1455 266601
Publisher E-mail: info@ianallanpublishing.co.uk
Magazine featuring the history of the transport network. **Subtitle:** The leading magazine for the historic road transport scene. **Freq:** Bimonthly. **Key Personnel:** Alan Earnshaw, Managing Editor. **Remarks:** Accepts advertising. **URL:** http://www.ianallanmagazines.com/home.php?cat=11. **Circ:** (Not Reported)

Kippen

53726 ■ **Fusion Flowers**
Hillcroft
Fore Rd.
Kippen FK8 3DT, United Kingdom
Ph: 44 01786 870204
Fax: 44 01786 201102
Magazine featuring floral designing and arranging. **Founded:** 2001. **Freq:** Bimonthly. **Key Personnel:** Alison Bradley, Editor, phone 44 1786 870204. **Subscription Rates:** 21 individuals; 31.30 individuals Europe; 39.60 other countries. **URL:** http://www.fusionflowers.com.

Kirkintilloch

53727 ■ **Kirkintilloch Herald**
Johnston Press PLC
11 Dalrymple Ct.
Kirkintilloch G66 3AA, United Kingdom
Ph: 44 141 7750040
Local community newspaper. **Remarks:** Accepts advertising. **URL:** http://www.kirkintilloch-herald.co.uk/. **Circ:** (Not Reported)

Knaresborough

53728 ■ **Knaresborough Post**
Johnston Press PLC
c/o Age Concern Knaresborough
Cliff House
Hilton Ln.
Knaresborough HG5 0FA, United Kingdom
Ph: 44 1423 869272
Local community newspaper. **Key Personnel:** Jean MacQuarrie, Editor. **Remarks:** Accepts advertising.

URL: http://www.knaresboroughpost.co.uk/. **Circ:** (Not Reported)

Knebworth

53729 ■ **Hertbeat-FM - 106.7**
The Pump House
Knebworth Pk.
Knebworth SG3 6HQ, United Kingdom
Ph: 44 1438 810900
Format: Adult Contemporary; News; Information. **Operating Hours:** Continuous. **URL:** http://www.hertbeat.com/.

Knutsford

53730 ■ **Downstream**
Federation of Petroleum Suppliers
6 Royal Ct.
Tatton St.
Knutsford WA16 6EN, United Kingdom
Ph: 44 15 65631313
Fax: 44 15 65631314
Publication E-mail: downstream@fpsonline.co.uk
Publisher E-mail: office@fpsonline.co.uk
Publication covering petroleum. **Founded:** 1998. **Freq:** Quarterly 5/yr. **ISSN:** 1473-5539. **Subscription Rates:** EUR60 out of country ROI; 30 individuals; EUR60 other countries; 42 other countries. **Remarks:** Advertising accepted; rates available upon request. **URL:** http://www.fpsonline.co.uk/downstream.asp. **Circ:** 750

Lanark

53731 ■ **Lanark Gazette**
Johnston Press PLC
5 Wellgate
Lanark ML11 9DS, United Kingdom
Ph: 44 1555 678792
Local community newspaper. **Remarks:** Accepts advertising. **URL:** http://www.lanarkgazette.co.uk/. **Circ:** (Not Reported)

Lancaster

53732 ■ **Defence and Security Analysis**
Routledge
Taylor & Francis Group Ltd.
c/o Martin Edmonds, Ed.-in-Ch.
Centre for Defence & International Security Studies
PO Box 801
Lancaster LA1 9DX, United Kingdom
Publisher E-mail: webmaster.books@tandf.co.uk
International journal on defense theory and analysis, covering quantitative, qualitative, and speculative methodological approaches to defense matters. **Freq:** Quarterly. **Key Personnel:** Julian Palmore, North American Ed.; Martin Edmonds, Editor-in-Chief, martin@haedmonds.freeserve.co.uk; Dr. Grant Hammond, Editorial Advisory Board; Pauline Elliott, Editorial Asst.; Dr. R. Beaumont, Editorial Advisory Board; Prof. A. Bebler, Editorial Advisory Board. **ISSN:** 1475-1798. **Subscription Rates:** US$728 institutions print + online; US$691 institutions online; US$122 individuals; 438 institutions print + online; 416 institutions online; 72 individuals; EUR580 institutions print and online; EUR551 institutions online only; EUR97 individuals. **Remarks:** Advertising accepted; rates available upon request. **URL:** http://www.tandf.co.uk/journals/titles/14751798.asp. **Formerly:** Defense Analysis. **Circ:** (Not Reported)

53733 ■ **Gynecological Endocrinology**
The Parthenon Publishing Group Ltd.
Richmond House, White Cross
South Rd.
Lancaster LA1 4XF, United Kingdom
Ph: 44 1524 585700
Fax: 44 1524 389659
Professional medical journal. **Freq:** Bimonthly. **ISSN:** 0951-3590. **Subscription Rates:** US$328 individuals; US$516 individuals; US$543 individuals. **Remarks:** Accepts advertising. **URL:** http://www.gynecologicalendocrinology.org/services/journal.htm. **Circ:** (Not Reported)

53734 ■ **Journal of Experimental Botany**
Society for Experimental Biology
Societe de Biologie Experimentale
Bailrigg House
Lancaster University

Lancaster LA1 4YE, United Kingdom
Ph: 44 1524 594690
Fax: 44 1524 594133
Publisher E-mail: c.trimmer@sebiology.org
Peer-reviewed journal covering botany. **Freq:** Monthly. **Key Personnel:** Prof. Jerry Roberts, Editor-in-Chief. **ISSN:** 0022-0957. **Subscription Rates:** 1,251 institutions print & online; US$2,502 institutions print & online; EUR1,877 institutions print & online; 1,167 institutions print only; US$2,332 institutions print only; EUR1,749 institutions print only; 118 members; US$235 members; EUR176 members. **URL:** http://jxb.oxfordjournals.org/.

53735 ■ **Journal of New Music Research**
Routledge
Taylor & Francis Group Ltd.
c/o Alan Marsden, Ed.
Music Dept.
Lancaster University
Bailrigg
Lancaster LA1 4YW, United Kingdom
Fax: 44 15 24593939
Publisher E-mail: webmaster.books@tandf.co.uk
Peer-reviewed journal reporting on both scientifically rigorous and musically relevant topics of interest from the wide spectrum of disciplines ranging from musicology (music theory, aesthetics, sociology), psychology (from psychoacoustics to cognitive psychology-with emphasis on modeling), acoustics (including sound engineering), computer science (from signal processing to artificial intelligence), philosophy (epistemology and methodology) to brain sciences. **Founded:** 1972. **Freq:** Quarterly. **Key Personnel:** Alan Marsden, Editor, a.marsden@lancaster.ac.uk; Robert Rowe, Assoc. Ed.; Roger Dannenberg, Assoc. Ed.; Xavier Serra, Assoc. Ed.; Antonio Camurri, Assoc. Ed.; Agostino Di Scipio, Book Review Ed., discipio@tin.it. **ISSN:** 0929-8215. **Subscription Rates:** 468 institutions print + online; US$801 institutions print + online; 444 institutions online; US$761 institutions online; 101 individuals; US$167 individuals; EUR639 institutions print and online; EUR607 institutions online only; EUR132 individuals. **Remarks:** Advertising accepted; rates available upon request. **URL:** http://www.tandf.co.uk/journals/titles/09298215.asp. **Former name:** Interface. **Circ:** (Not Reported)

53736 ■ **Spirituality and Health International**
John Wiley & Sons Ltd.
c/o Stephen G. Wright, Founding Ed.
St. Martin's College
Lancaster LA1 3JD, United Kingdom
Publisher E-mail: cs-journals@wiley.co.uk
Journal publishing high-quality material dealing with spirituality of concern to all those involved in health care. **Freq:** Quarterly. **Key Personnel:** Prof. Stephen G. Wright, Founding Ed.; Harald Walach, Editor-in-Chief; Lyren Chiu, Editorial Board; Thomas Heidenreich, Editorial Board; Tobias Esch, Editorial Board; Barbara Findlay, Editorial Board; Niko Kohls, Editorial Board; Michael Hyland, Book Review Ed. **ISSN:** 1743-1867. **Subscription Rates:** 181 individuals print only; US$354 other countries print only; EUR229 individuals print only. **Remarks:** Accepts advertising. **URL:** http://www3.interscience.wiley.com/cgi-bin/jhome/112094329. **Circ:** (Not Reported)

53737 ■ **The Bay-FM - 96.9**
St. Georges Quay
PO Box 969
Lancaster LA1 3LD, United Kingdom
Ph: 44 871 2000969
Format: Adult Contemporary. **Operating Hours:** Continuous. **Key Personnel:** Bill Johnston, Mng. Dir.; Tony Johnson, Sales Mgr.; Don Douglas, Group Prog. Dir. **Ad Rates:** Advertising accepted; rates available upon request. **URL:** http://www.thebay.co.uk.

53738 ■ **The Bay-FM - 103.2**
St. George's Quay
PO Box 969
Lancaster LA1 3LD, United Kingdom
Ph: 44 1524 848747
Format: Adult Contemporary. **Key Personnel:** Bill Johnston, Mng. Dir. **URL:** http://www.thebay.co.uk/.

53739 ■ **The Bay-FM - 102.3**
St. George's Quay
PO Box 969
Lancaster LA1 3LD, United Kingdom
Ph: 44 1524 848747
Format: Adult Contemporary. **Key Personnel:** Bill

Johnston, Mng. Dir. **URL:** http://www.thebay.co.uk/.

53740 ■ Diversity-FM - 103.5
Fleet Sq.
Lancaster LA1 1HA, United Kingdom
Ph: 44 1524 383394
Fax: 44 1524 389184
E-mail: studio@diversityfm.co.uk
Format: Eclectic. **Ad Rates:** Advertising accepted; rates available upon request. **URL:** http://www.diversityfm.co.uk/.

Larne

53741 ■ East Antrim Advertiser
Johnston Press PLC
8 Dunluce St.
Larne BT40 UG, United Kingdom
Ph: 44 28 28260605
Fax: 44 28 28260255
Community newspaper. **Freq:** Monthly. **Print Method:** Offset. **Col. Depth:** 450 millimeters. **Remarks:** Accepts advertising. **URL:** http://www.johnstonpress.co.uk/jpplc/ourbusiness/publishingdivision/division.jsp?ref=34. **Circ:** Combined ‡19,222

53742 ■ Larne Times
Morton Newspapers
8 Dunluce St.
Larne BT40 1JG, United Kingdom
Ph: 44 28 28272303
Community newspaper. **Freq:** Weekly. **Print Method:** Offset. **Col. Depth:** 450 millimeters. **Key Personnel:** Valerie Martin, Editor; Roy Sharpe, Advertising Mgr.; Dessie Houston, Contact. **Remarks:** Accepts advertising. **URL:** http://www.larnetimes.co.uk/. **Circ:** (Not Reported)

Laurencekirk

53743 ■ Speech & Language Therapy in Practice
33 Kinnear Sq.
Laurencekirk AB30 1UL, United Kingdom
Ph: 44 1561 377415
Professional magazine covering issues for speech and language therapists. **Founded:** May 1997. **Freq:** Quarterly. **Key Personnel:** Avril Nicoll, Editor and Publisher. **ISSN:** 1368-2105. **Subscription Rates:** 28 individuals; 24 individuals part time (5 or fewer sessions); 21 students; 33 individuals for Europe; 37 other countries; 28 students for Europe; 53 other countries single copy. **URL:** http://www.speechmag.com. **Ad Rates:** BW: 470. **Circ:** Paid 1,600

Leamington Spa

53744 ■ Bulletin
World War Two Railway Study Group
c/o Mike Christensen, Membership Sec.
25 Woodcote Rd.
Warwickshire
Leamington Spa CV32 6PZ, United Kingdom
Ph: 44 1926 429378
Journal containing articles on military railway topics. **Freq:** Bimonthly. **Subscription Rates:** Free to members; 13.50 individuals ordinary; 10 individuals pensioner. **Remarks:** Accepts advertising. **URL:** http://www.saxoncourtbooks.co.uk/ww2rsg/backissues.htm. **Circ:** (Not Reported)

53745 ■ Eurowire
Intras Ltd.
46 Holly Walk
Leamington Spa CV32 4HY, United Kingdom
Ph: 44 1926 334137
Fax: 44 1926 314755
Publication E-mail: eurowire@intras.co.uk
Publisher E-mail: intras@intras.co.uk
Trade magazine covering the cable, wire, and fiber optics industry. Published in five European languages. **Subtitle:** The International Magazine for the Wire and Cable Industries. **Founded:** 1998. **Freq:** Bimonthly. **Print Method:** Offset litho. **Trim Size:** 210 x 297 mm. **Cols./Page:** 3. **Col. Width:** 55 millimeters. **Col. Depth:** 260 millimeters. **Key Personnel:** Liz Hughes, Subscriptions Mgr., phone 44 1926 334137, liz@intras.co.uk; Julie Tomlin, Design & Production, julie@intras.co.uk; Caroline Sullens, Publisher, caroline@intras.co.uk; Paul Browne, Gp. Advertising Mgr., phone 44 1926 834684,

paul.b@intras.co.uk; David Bell, Editor, gill@intras.co.uk; Christian Bradley, Editorial Asst., christian@intras.co.uk. **ISSN:** 1463-2438. **Subscription Rates:** EUR140 individuals; 95 individuals; US$195 individuals; Rs 7,880 individuals. **Remarks:** Accepts advertising. **URL:** http://www.read-eurowire.com; http://www.eurowiremagazine.com/. **Ad Rates:** BW: 2,090, 4C: 2,805. **Circ:** Controlled ‡25,338

53746 ■ Kenilworth Weekly News
Johnston Press PLC
32 Hamilton Ter.
Leamington Spa CV32 4LY, United Kingdom
Ph: 44 1926 45725
Local community newspaper. **Founded:** 1946. **Freq:** Weekly (Fri.). **Key Personnel:** Martin Lawson, Editor; John Howes, Dep. Ed. **Remarks:** Accepts advertising. **URL:** http://www.kenilworthweeklynews.co.uk/. **Circ:** (Not Reported)

53747 ■ The Leamington Observer
Observer Standard Newspapers Ltd.
45 The Parade
Leamington Spa CV32 4BL, United Kingdom
Ph: 44 1926 451900
Fax: 44 1926 451754
Publication E-mail: editor@leamingtonobserver.co.uk
Publisher E-mail: hq@observerstandard.com
Local community newspaper. **Freq:** Weekly. **Key Personnel:** Chris Bullivant, Founder; Pat Bullivant, Founder. **Remarks:** Accepts advertising. **URL:** http://www.leamingtonobserver.co.uk/. **Circ:** (Not Reported)

53748 ■ Leamington Spa Courier
Johnston Press PLC
32 Hamilton Ter.
Leamington Spa CV32 4LY, United Kingdom
Ph: 44 1926 457777
Local community newspaper. **Founded:** 1828. **Freq:** Weekly (Fri.). **Key Personnel:** Chris Lillington, Editor, fax 44 1926 339960, editorial@leamingtoncourier.co.uk; Simon Steele, Dep. Ed., phone 44 1926 457737, simon.steele@leamingtoncourier.co.uk. **Remarks:** Accepts advertising. **URL:** http://www.leamingtoncourier.co.uk/. **Circ:** (Not Reported)

53749 ■ Tube & Pipe Technology
Intras Ltd.
46 Holly Walk
Warwickshire
Leamington Spa CV32 4HY, United Kingdom
Ph: 44 1926 334137
Fax: 44 1926 314755
Publication E-mail: intras@intras.co.uk
Publisher E-mail: intras@intras.co.uk
Trade magazine covering tube and pipe production and processing industries for users and producers of metal tubes and pipe and hollow products. **Founded:** 1987. **Freq:** Bimonthly. **Print Method:** Offset litho. **Trim Size:** 297 x 210 mm. **Cols./Page:** 3. **Col. Width:** 55 millimeters. **Key Personnel:** Rory McBride, Editor, phone 44 1926 334137, rory@intras.co.uk; Caroline Sullens, Publisher, caroline@intras.co.uk; Christian Bradley, Editorial Asst., christian@intras.co.uk. **ISSN:** 0953-2366. **Subscription Rates:** US$195 U.S.; EUR140 individuals; 120 individuals. **Remarks:** Accepts advertising. **URL:** http://www.read-tpt.com/. **Ad Rates:** BW: US$1,500, 4C: US$2,155. **Circ:** Combined 12,500

53750 ■ Warwick Courier
Johnston Press PLC
32 Hamilton Ter.
Leamington Spa CV32 4LY, United Kingdom
Ph: 44 1926 457777
Local community newspaper. **Freq:** Weekly (Fri.). **Key Personnel:** Martin Lawson, Editor; Simon Steele, Dep. Ed. **Remarks:** Accepts advertising. **URL:** http://www.warwickcourier.co.uk/. **Circ:** (Not Reported)

Leatherhead

53751 ■ Food Allergy and Intolerance Journal
Leatherhead Food International Ltd.
Randalls Rd.
Leatherhead KT22 7RY, United Kingdom
Ph: 44 1372 376761
Fax: 44 1372 386228
Publisher E-mail: help@leatherheadfood.com
Book covering the latest developments in the field of food allergy and intolerance, including the major allergens, foods commonly associated with intolerance, and technical considerations for the food industry. **Sub-**

title: A Journal for the World Food Industry. **Freq:** 3/yr. **Key Personnel:** Victoria Emerton, Editor, vemerton@leatherheadfood.com. **Subscription Rates:** EUR65 members; EUR70 nonmembers; US$75 members; US$85 nonmembers. **URL:** http://www.leatherheadfood.com/lfi/submenu.asp?item=3107&subsection=49&section=11.

53752 ■ Packaging Month
Pira International
Cleeve Rd.
Leatherhead KT22 7RU, United Kingdom
Ph: 44 1372 802000
Fax: 44 1372 802079
Publisher E-mail: info@pira-international.com
Publication covering packaging technology and business developments. **Subtitle:** Incorporating International Packaging Abstracts. **Founded:** 1980. **Freq:** Bimonthly. **Print Method:** Digital. **Trim Size:** A5. **Key Personnel:** Adam Page, Publisher. **ISSN:** 1475-598X. **Subscription Rates:** 950 individuals web. **Remarks:** Advertising not accepted. **URL:** http://www.pira-international.com/Packaging-Month.aspx. **Formerly:** International Packaging Abstracts. **Circ:** Paid 500

53753 ■ Police
Police Federation of England and Wales
Federation House
Highbury Dr.
Leatherhead KT22 7UY, United Kingdom
Ph: 44 1372 352000
Publication E-mail: corporateaffairs@jcc.polfed.org
Publisher E-mail: gensec@polfed.org
Professional journal covering police matters. **Subtitle:** The Voice of the Police Service. **Founded:** 1968. **Freq:** Monthly. **Print Method:** Web offset. **Trim Size:** A4. **Key Personnel:** Syreeta Lund, Editor, syreeta.lund@polfed.org; John Francis, Gen. Sec.; Ernie Hanrahan, Dep. Gen. Sec.; Sharon Davies, Advertising Agent, phone 44 20 76929292, fax 44 20 76929393; Brian Fenlon, Treas.; Alan Gordon, Vice-Chm.; Jan Berry, Chm.; Dave Moore, Dep. Treas.; Metin Enver, Editor. **Remarks:** Accepts advertising. **URL:** http://www.polfed.org/mediacenter/B88DCFD2C23541C8AF96AF80373256C3.asp. **Ad Rates:** BW: 1,250, 4C: 1,750. **Circ:** Controlled 42,000

Leeds

53754 ■ Artificial Intelligence
Elsevier Science Inc.
c/o A.G. Cohn, Ed.-in-Ch.
School of Computing
University of Leeds
Leeds LS2 9JT, United Kingdom
Publisher E-mail: usinfo-ehelp@elsevier.com
Peer-reviewed journal providing information on current research in computational accounts of aspects of intelligence. **Founded:** 1970. **Freq:** 18/yr. **Key Personnel:** R. Goebel, Review Ed.; F. Baader, Assoc. Ed.; C.R. Perrault, Editor-in-Chief; E. Sandewall, Editorial Board; M.A. Williams, Review Ed.; A. Chella, Review Ed.; T. Darrell, Assoc. Ed.; G. Brewka, Assoc. Ed.; E. Hansen, Assoc. Ed.; A. Galton, Assoc. Ed.; A.G. Cohn, Editor-in-Chief. **ISSN:** 0004-3702. **Subscription Rates:** US$2,890 institutions, other countries except Europe, Japan and Iran; 383,600¥ institutions; EUR2,868 institutions for European countries and Iran. **URL:** http://www.elsevier.com/wps/find/journaldescription.cws_home/505601/descriptiondescription.

53755 ■ ASDA Magazine
Publicis Blueprint
Asda House
Great Wilson St.
Leeds LS11 5AD, United Kingdom
Publication E-mail: asda.editor@asdamagazine.co.uk
Publisher E-mail: info@publicis-blueprint.co.uk
Magazine featuring women's lifestyle. **Founded:** 1999. **Freq:** Monthly. **Key Personnel:** Ali Carswell, Editor. **Remarks:** Accepts advertising. **URL:** http://www.asdamagazine.com/. **Circ:** 3,000,000

53756 ■ Astronomy and Geophysics
John Wiley & Sons Inc.
Wiley-Blackwell
c/o Sue Bowler, Ed.
Dept. of Physics & Astronomy
University of Leeds
Leeds LS2 9JT, United Kingdom
Ph: 44 113 3436672

Fax: 44 113 3433900

Journal focusing on cutting edge scientific research. **Freq:** Bimonthly. **Key Personnel:** Sue Bowler, Editor, s.bowler@leeds.ac.uk; Peter Bond, Editorial Board; Jacqueline Mitton, Editorial Board; Paul Murdin, Editorial Board; David Elliot, Editorial Board; Ian Howarth, Editorial Board. **ISSN:** 1366-8781. **Subscription Rates:** US$164 individuals print and online; US$58 members print and online; 38 members print and online (ROW); US$473 institutions print and online; US$430 institutions print or online; 252 institutions print and online; 114 other countries print and online; US$544 institutions, other countries print and online; US$494 institutions, other countries print or online; EUR136 individuals print and online. **Remarks:** Accepts advertising. **URL:** http://www.wiley.com/bw/journal.asp?ref=1366-8781&site=1. **Circ:** (Not Reported)

53757 ■ Bioscience Education E-journal
LTSN Centre for Bioscience
The Higher Education Academy
Rm. 9.15 Worsley Bldg.
University of Leeds
Leeds LS2 9JT, United Kingdom
Ph: 44 11 33433001
Fax: 44 11 33435894
Publisher E-mail: heabioscience@leeds.ac.uk
Journal facilitating knowledge to the community of teachers and high school students and thereby adding to the volume of knowledge in the biosciences disciplines. **Freq:** Semiannual. **Key Personnel:** Dr. Steve Maw, Acting Mng. Ed.; John Bryant, Editorial Board; Glenn Dickson, Editorial Board; Alan Cann, Editorial Board; Julian Park, Editorial Board; Jackie Wilson, Editorial Board. **ISSN:** 1479-7860. **URL:** http://www.bioscience.heacademy.ac.uk/journal/.

53758 ■ British Dragonfly Society Journal
British Dragonfly Society
8 Cookridge Grove
Leeds LS16 7LH, United Kingdom
Publisher E-mail: bdssecretary@dragonflysoc.org.uk
British journal covering entomology. **Freq:** Semiannual. **Trim Size:** A5. **Key Personnel:** Dr. Peter Mill, Editor, gpmill@supanet.com. **Remarks:** Advertising not accepted. **URL:** http://www.dragonflysoc.org.uk/home.html. **Circ:** (Not Reported)

53759 ■ British Journal of Middle Eastern Studies
British Society for Middle Eastern Studies
c/o Prof. Ian Netton, Ed.
Department of Arabic & Middle Eastern Studies
University of Leeds
Leeds LS2 9JT, United Kingdom
Publisher E-mail: a.l.haysey@durham.ac.uk
British journal covering Middle Eastern studies. **Freq:** 3/yr. **Key Personnel:** Dr. Lloyd Ridgeon, Assoc. Ed., l.ridgeon@arts.gla.ac.uk; Dr. David Shankland, Assoc. Ed., d.shankland1@yahoo.co.uk; Prof. A. Ehteshami, Editorial Advisory Board; Prof. Ian Netton, Editor, i.r. netton@leeds.ac.uk. **ISSN:** 1353-0194. **Subscription Rates:** US$184 individuals; US$556 individuals online; US$618 institutions print and online. **Remarks:** Accepts advertising. **URL:** http://www.dur.ac.uk/brismes/publications.htm; http://www.tandf.co.uk/journals/journal.asp?issn=1353-0194&linktype=5. **Circ:** (Not Reported)

53760 ■ Chapter&Verse
PopMatters Media, Inc.
c/o Simon Warner, Editor
School of Music
University of Leeds
Leeds LS2 9JT, United Kingdom
Publisher E-mail: books@popmatters.com
Journal on popular music and literature studies. **Key Personnel:** Simon Warner, Editor. **Remarks:** Accepts advertising. **URL:** http://www.popmatters.com/chapter/04Autumn/index.html; http://www.popmatters.com/chapter/Issue3/index.html. **Circ:** (Not Reported)

53761 ■ Coaching Edge
Sports Coach UK
114 Cardigan Rd.
Headingley
Leeds LS6 3BJ, United Kingdom
Ph: 44 11 32744802
Fax: 44 11 32755019
Publisher E-mail: coaching@sportscoachuk.org
Publication covering coaching. **Founded:** Sept. 1998.

Freq: Quarterly. **ISSN:** 1464-4495. **Subscription Rates:** 79 individuals full; 18 members; 70 students full; 13.75 students. **Remarks:** Advertising accepted; rates available upon request. **URL:** http://www.sportscoachuk.org. **Circ:** 4,000

53762 ■ Computational & Mathematical Methods in Medicine
Taylor & Francis Group Journals
Dept. of Applied Mathematics
School of Mathematics
University of Leeds
Leeds LS2 9JT, United Kingdom
Publisher E-mail: customerservice@taylorandfrancis.com
Peer-reviewed journal covering mathematical, theoretical and clinical aspects of medicine. **Founded:** Jan. 1946. **Freq:** Quarterly. **Print Method:** Offset. Uses mats. **Trim Size:** 6 x 9 1/4. **Cols./Page:** 1. **Col. Width:** 54 nonpareils. **Col. Depth:** 100 agate lines. **Key Personnel:** Brian Sleeman, Assoc. Ed., bds@maths.leeds.ac.uk; Pamela Jones, Editor, p.jones@leeds.ac.uk; Philip Maini, Assoc. Ed. **ISSN:** 1748-670X. **Subscription Rates:** US$696 institutions print + online; 464 institutions print + online; US$280 individuals; 188 individuals; EUR222 individuals; EUR556 institutions print + online; EUR528 institutions online; 440 institutions online; US$662 institutions online. **URL:** http://www.tandf.co.uk/journals/titles/10273662.asp.

53763 ■ Contemporary Hypnosis
British Society of Clinical and Academic Hypnosis
28 Dale Park Gardens
Cookridge
Leeds LS16 7PT, United Kingdom
Ph: 44 113 8843116
Fax: 44 113 8843116
Publisher E-mail: bscah@btinternet.com
Publication covering hypnosis. **Freq:** Quarterly. **Key Personnel:** John Gruzelier, Editor. **Subscription Rates:** Free. **URL:** http://www.bscah.com/Contemporary-Hypnosis.htm.

53764 ■ Epilepsy Today
Epilepsy Action
New Anstey House
Gate Way Dr.
Yeadon
Leeds LS19 7XY, United Kingdom
Ph: 44 11 32108800
Fax: 44 11 33910300
Publication E-mail: epilepsy@epilepsy.org.uk
Publisher E-mail: epilepsy@epilepsy.org.uk
Consumer magazine covering epilepsy for everyone with an interest in the condition. **Founded:** 1980. **Freq:** Bimonthly. **Print Method:** Sheetfed offset litho. **Trim Size:** A4. **Cols./Page:** 4. **ISSN:** 0958-496X. **Subscription Rates:** 17 individuals; Free to members. **Remarks:** Advertising not accepted. **URL:** http://www.epilepsy.org.uk/services/epilepsy-today-magazine. **Circ:** Combined 22,500

53765 ■ European Journal of Obstetrics & Gynecology
Mosby Inc.
c/o J.O. Drifc, Ed. in Ch.
University Dept. of Obstetrics & Gynaecology
Leeds LS1 3EK, United Kingdom
Publisher E-mail: custserv.ehs@elsevier.com
Peer-reviewed journal for obstetrics and gynecology. **Freq:** Monthly. **Key Personnel:** W. Kunzel, Editor-in-Chief; J.O. Drife, Editor-in-Chief; J.K. Gupta, Regional Receiving Ed.; D. Armanini, Editorial Board; S. Kehoe, Advisory Board Ed.; A.S. Arunkalaivanan, Advisory Board Ed.; T. Maggino, Regional Receiving Ed.; I. Cetin, Editorial Board; L.A.M. Stolte, Founding Ed. **ISSN:** 0301-2115. **Subscription Rates:** EUR312 individuals for European countries and Iran; US$3,829 institutions, other countries except Europe, Japan and Iran; 454,500¥ institutions; EUR3,421 institutions for European countries and Iran; US$350 other countries except Europe, Japan and Iran; 3,829¥ institutions. **Remarks:** Accepts advertising. **URL:** http://www.elsevier.com/wps/find/journaldescription.cws_home/505961/descriptiondescription. **Circ:** (Not Reported)

53766 ■ Fish Friers Review
National Federation of Fish Friers Ltd.
4 Greenwood Mount
Leeds LS6 4LQ, United Kingdom
Ph: 44 11 32307044

Fax: 44 11 32307010
Trade journal for the fish frying fast food establishments and take-away catering industry. **Freq:** Monthly. **Trim Size:** 210 x 297 mm. **Key Personnel:** Ann M. Kirk, Gen. Sec.; Douglas Roxburgh, President; Gregg Howard, Vice President. **Subscription Rates:** 55 nonmembers. **Remarks:** Accepts advertising. **URL:** http://www.federationoffishfriers.co.uk/pages/fish-friers-magazine-79.htm. **Ad Rates:** 4C: 1,200. **Circ:** (Not Reported)

53767 ■ History Scotland
31-32 Park Row
Leeds LS1 5JD, United Kingdom
Ph: 44 113 2002922
Publisher E-mail: info@historyscotland.com
Illustrated history and archaeology magazine for those with an interest in Scottish history. **Freq:** Bimonthly. **Key Personnel:** Dr. Alasdair Ross, Editor. **Subscription Rates:** 23 individuals; EUR39 individuals; US$52 other countries; 60 Canada. **URL:** http://www.historyscotland.com/.

53768 ■ Journal of Petrology
Oxford University Press
School of Earth & Environment
University of Leeds
Leeds LS2 9JT, United Kingdom
Ph: 44 1937 573595
Publisher E-mail: webenquiry.uk@oup.com
Journal providing an international forum for the publication of high quality research in the broad field of igneous and metamorphic petrology and petrogenesis. Papers published cover a vast range of topics in areas such as major element, trace element and isotope geochemistry and geochronology applied to petrogenesis; experimental petrology; processes of magma generation, differentiation and emplacement; quantitative studies of rock-forming minerals and their parageneisis; regional studies of igneous and meta morphic rocks which contribute to the solution of fundamental petrological problems; theoretical modelling of petrogenetic processes. **Freq:** Monthly. **Key Personnel:** Prof. Marjorie Wilson, Exec. Ed., m.wilson@earth.leeds.ac.uk; A. Lumsden, Editorial Mgr., j.petrology@earth.leeds.ac.uk; C. Devey, Editorial Board, cdevey@ifm-geomar.de; B.R. Frost, Editorial Board, rfrost@uwyo.edu; G. Clarke, Editorial Board, geoffc@mail.usyd.edu.au; W.A. Bohrson, Editorial Board, bohrson@geology.cwu.edu. **ISSN:** 0022-3530. **Subscription Rates:** 1,254 institutions corporate; print and online; 1,035 institutions corporate; online only; 1,150 institutions corporate; print only; 1,003 institutions print and online; 828 institutions online only; 920 institutions print only; 472 individuals print. **Remarks:** Advertising accepted; rates available upon request. **URL:** http://petrology.oxfordjournals.org/. **Circ:** (Not Reported)

53769 ■ Journal of Psychiatric and Mental Health Nursing
John Wiley & Sons Inc.
Wiley-Blackwell
c/o Dawn Freshwater, Ed.
School of Health & Social Care
Leeds University
Baines Wing
Leeds LS2 9JT, United Kingdom
Peer-reviewed journal focusing on the psychiatric and mental health nurses. **Freq:** 10/yr. **Key Personnel:** Dawn Freshwater, Editor, d.freshwater@leeds.ac.uk; Martin Ward, Practice Devel., mwoxford@aol.com; Cheryl Forchuk, Receiving Ed., cforchuk@uwo.ca; Eimear Muir Cochrane, Receiving Ed., eimear.muircochrane@flinders.edu.au; Christopher Barber, Editorial Board; Dr. Joy Bray, Editorial Board. **ISSN:** 1351-0126. **Subscription Rates:** US$236 individuals print and online; EUR195 individuals print + online; 130 individuals print + online; US$1,524 institutions print + online; US$1,385 institutions print or online; 826 institutions print + online; US$1,781 institutions, other countries print + online; EUR1,049 institutions, other countries print or online; US$1,619 institutions, other countries print or online. **Remarks:** Advertising accepted; rates available upon request. **URL:** http://www.wiley.com/bw/journal.asp?ref=1351-0126. **Circ:** (Not Reported)

53770 ■ Journal of the Royal Musical Association
Oxford University Press
c/o Dr. Rachel Cowgill, Ed.
University of Leeds

Circulation: ★ = ABC; △ = BPA; ♦ = CAC; • = CCAB; ❏ = VAC; ⊕ = PO Statement; ‡ = Publisher's Report; Boldface figures = sworn; Light figures = estimated.

Scholarship of Music
Leeds LS2 9JT, United Kingdom
Publisher E-mail: webenquiry.uk@oup.com
Publication covering music. **Freq:** Semiannual. **Key Personnel:** Katharine Ellis, Editorial Board; Mark Everist, Editorial Board; John Deathridge, Editorial Board; Jeffrey Dean, Editorial Board; Rachel Beckles Willson, Editorial Board; Patricia Thomas, Editorial Board; Ian Rumbold, Asst. Ed.; Dr. Rachel Cowgill, Editor, r.e. cowgill@leeds.ac.uk. **ISSN:** 0269-0403. **Subscription Rates:** US$207 institutions print and online; US$198 institutions online; US$198 institutions print; US$102 individuals print; US$64 single issue print. **Remarks:** Accepts advertising. **URL:** http://jrma.oupjournals.org. **Circ:** (Not Reported)

53771 ■ The Leeds Guide
Leeds Guide Ltd.
80 North St.
West Yorkshire
Leeds LS2 7PN, United Kingdom
Ph: 44 113 2441000
Fax: 44 113 2441002
Consumer magazine covering local entertainment. **Founded:** 1997. **Freq:** Bimonthly. **Print Method:** Web. **Trim Size:** 210 x 297 mm. **Key Personnel:** Bruce Hartley, Owner; Ian McDonald, Mng. Dir. **ISSN:** 1460-6429. **Subscription Rates:** 39 individuals. **Remarks:** Accepts advertising. **URL:** http://www.leedsguide.co.uk/. **Ad Rates:** BW: 400, 4C: 500. **Circ:** Paid 15,000

53772 ■ Leeds, Leeds, Leeds
Leeds United AFC Ltd.
Elland Rd.
Leeds LS11 0ES, United Kingdom
Publication E-mail: fans@lllmagazine.co.uk
Consumer magazine covering football. **Founded:** Sept. 1998. **Freq:** Monthly. **Print Method:** Sheetfed offset. **Trim Size:** 210 mm x 285 mm. **ISSN:** 1465-4660. **Subscription Rates:** Free to qualified subscribers. **Remarks:** Accepts advertising. **URL:** http://www.leedsunited.com. **Ad Rates:** GLR: 1,200, BW: 1,000. **Circ:** Paid 60,000

53773 ■ Review of Behavioral Finance
John Wiley & Sons Inc.
c/o Phil Holmes, Mng. Ed.
Leeds University Business School
The Maurice Keyworth Bldg.
Leeds LS2 9JT, United Kingdom
Publisher E-mail: info@wiley.com
Peer-reviewed journal covering the area of behavioral finance. **Founded:** 2009. **Key Personnel:** Phil Holmes, Managing Editor; Krishna Paudyal, Managing Editor; Chris Brooks, Editorial Board. **ISSN:** 1940-5979. **URL:** http://www3.interscience.wiley.com/journal/121355847/home.

53774 ■ Seminars in Fetal & Neonatal Medicine
Mosby Inc.
University of Leeds
School of Medicine
D Fl., Clarendon Wing
General Infirmary at Leeds
Leeds LS2 9NS, United Kingdom
Ph: 44 113 92432799
Publisher E-mail: custserv.ehs@elsevier.com
Journal publishing articles on topic-based issues, including the latest advances in fetal and neonatal medicine. **Freq:** Bimonthly. **Key Personnel:** M.I. Levene, Editor-in-Chief, m.i.levene@leeds.ac.uk; K. Marsal, Assoc. Ed.; I. Laing, Assoc. Ed. **ISSN:** 1744-165X. **Subscription Rates:** EUR195 individuals for European countries and Iran; US$175 other countries except Europe, Japan and Iran; 21,100¥ individuals; US$466 institutions, other countries except Europe, Japan and Iran; EUR523 institutions for European countries and Iran; 56,900¥ institutions. **URL:** http://www.sfnmjournal.com/; http://www.elsevier.com/wps/find/journaldescription.cws_home/703751/descrip tiondescription.

53775 ■ Tangentium
University of Leeds
The School of Computing
University of Leeds
The School of Computing
Leeds LS2 9JT, United Kingdom
Ph: 44 11 33435430
Fax: 44 11 33435468
Publisher E-mail: office@comp.leeds.ac.uk
Journal dedicating to IT, politics, education and society.

Freq: Monthly. **Key Personnel:** Drew Whitworth, Editor-in-Chief, phone 44 113 3435450, drew@comp.leeds.ac.uk. **URL:** http://personalpages.manchester.ac.uk/staff/andrew.whitworth/tangentium/intro.html.

53776 ■ Yorkshire Evening Post
Johnston Press PLC
PO Box 168
Leeds LS1 1RF, United Kingdom
Ph: 44 1132 432701
Local community newspaper. **Founded:** 1890. **Key Personnel:** Paul Napier, Editor. **Remarks:** Accepts advertising. **URL:** http://www.yorkshireeveningpost.co.uk/. **Circ:** (Not Reported)

53777 ■ Yorkshire Post
Yorkshire Post Newspapers Ltd.
Wellington St.
PO Box 168
Leeds LS1 1RF, United Kingdom
Ph: 44 11 32432701
Regional newspaper covering Yorkshire. **Founded:** July 2, 1754. **Freq:** Daily. **Subscription Rates:** 187.20 individuals 6 days; 49.40 individuals Saturday only. **Remarks:** Accepts advertising. **URL:** http://www.yorkshirepost.co.uk/. **Circ:** 225,000

53778 ■ Yorkshire Sport
Yorkshire Post Newspapers Ltd.
Wellington St.
PO Box 168
Leeds LS1 1RF, United Kingdom
Ph: 44 11 32432701
Newspaper covering sports. **Freq:** Weekly (Sun.). **Key Personnel:** Robin Barron, Chm.; Mel Welch, Sec.; David Oxley, President. **Remarks:** Accepts advertising. **URL:** http://www.yorkshirepost.co.uk. **Circ:** (Not Reported)

53779 ■ BBC Radio Leeds-FM - 92.4
Broadcasting Ctre.
2 St. Peter's Sq.
Leeds LS9 8AH, United Kingdom
Ph: 44 113 2442131
E-mail: leeds@bbc.co.uk
Format: News; Talk; Sports; Oldies. **Owner:** British Broadcasting Corporation, Broadcasting House, Portland Pl., London W1A 1AA, United Kingdom. **Founded:** 1968. **Operating Hours:** Continuous. **URL:** http://www.bbc.co.uk/leeds/local_radio.

53780 ■ Magic-AM - 828
51 Burley Rd.
Leeds LS3 1LR, United Kingdom
Ph: 44 113 2835500
Fax: 44 113 2835501
Format: Oldies. **URL:** http://www.magic828.co.uk/.

53781 ■ Radio Aire-FM - 96.3
51 Burley Rd.
Leeds LS3 1LR, United Kingdom
Ph: 44 113 2835500
Format: Eighties; Contemporary Hit Radio (CHR); Classic Rock. **Owner:** Radio Aire Ltd., 40 Bernard St., London WC1N 1LW, United Kingdom. **Operating Hours:** Continuous. **Ad Rates:** Advertising accepted; rates available upon request. **URL:** http://www.radioaire.co.uk.

Leicester

53782 ■ Adults Learning
National Institute of Adult Continuing Education
Renaissance House
20 Princess Rd. W
Leicester LE1 6TP, United Kingdom
Ph: 44 116 2044200
Fax: 44 116 2044201
Publisher E-mail: enquiries@niace.org.uk
Scholarly journal covering policy and practice developments in adult education for policymakers and practitioners. **Freq:** 10/yr. **Key Personnel:** Paul Stanistreet, Editor. **ISSN:** 0955-2308. **Subscription Rates:** 26 institutions; 13 individuals; 44 institutions, other countries; 16 individuals part time tutor/learner. **Remarks:** Accepts advertising. **URL:** http://www.niace.org.uk; http://shop.niace.org.uk/adults-learning.html. **Circ:** Paid 3,000

53783 ■ Advances in Computational Sciences and Technology
Research India Publications

c/o Marwan Al-Akaidi, Assoc. Ed.
De Montfort University
Engineering & Technology
Leicester LE1 9BH, United Kingdom
Publisher E-mail: info@ripublication.com
Journal covering areas computational sciences and technology. **Freq:** 4/yr. **Key Personnel:** Marwan Al-Akaidi, Assoc. Ed., mma@dmu.ac.uk. **ISSN:** 0973-6107. **Subscription Rates:** US$380 libraries and institution; print plus online free; US$360 libraries and institution; online only; US$360 individuals print plus online free; US$340 individuals online only. **URL:** http://www.ripublication.com/acst.htm.

53784 ■ Annals of Botany
Oxford University Press
c/o Dr. David Frost, Mng. Ed.
Annals of Botany Office
Department of Biology
University of Leicester, University Rd.
Leicester LE1 7RH, United Kingdom
Ph: 44 116 2523396
Publisher E-mail: webenquiry.uk@oup.com
Peer-reviewed journal providing articles related to the plant science field. **Freq:** 13/yr. **Key Personnel:** Prof. J.S. Heslop-Harrison, Editor-in-Chief, phone 44 116 2523381, phh4@le.ac.uk; Dr. David Frost, Managing Editor, annals-botany@le.ac.uk; Prof. J.W. Shipley, Regional Ed., bill.shipley@usherbrooke.ca; Prof. Margret Sauter, Editor, msauter@bot.uni-kiel.de; Dr. Karine Alix, Editor, alix@moulon.inra.fr; Prof. John R. Barnett, Editor, j.r.barnett@reading.ac.uk; Prof. Timothy D. Colmer, Regional Ed., tdcolmer@cyllene.uwa.edu.au; Prof. Hideyuki Takahashi, Regional Ed., hideyuki@ige.tohoku.ac.jp; Prof. Alex C. Buerkle, Editor, buerkle@uwyo.edu. **ISSN:** 0305-7364. **Subscription Rates:** 730 institutions print and online; US$1,460 institutions print and online; EUR1,095 institutions print and online; 602 institutions online only; US$1,204 institutions online only; EUR903 institutions online only; 669 institutions print only; US$1,338 institutions print only; EUR1,004 institutions print only. **URL:** http://aob.oxfordjournals.org.

53785 ■ Applied Cognitive Psychology
John Wiley & Sons Ltd.
School of Psychology
Henry Wellcome Bldg.
University of Leicester
Lancaster Rd.
Leicester LE1 9HN, United Kingdom
Publisher E-mail: customer@wiley.co.uk
Scientific journal covering applied aspects of memory and cognition. **Founded:** 1987. **Freq:** 9/yr. **Key Personnel:** Prof. Graham Davies, Editor-in-Chief, gmd@leicester.ac.uk; Martine Powell, Australasian Ed.; Andres Granhag, Dep. Ed.-in-Ch.; M.K. Johnson, Editorial Adviser; A.D. Baddeley, Editorial Adviser; E.F. Loftus, Editorial Adviser. **ISSN:** 0888-4080. **Subscription Rates:** 227 individuals print only; US$1,717 institutions, other countries print only; US$428 other countries print only; 876 institutions print only; EUR1,107 institutions, other countries print only; 964 institutions combined print with online access; US$1,888 institutions, other countries combined print with online access; EUR1,218 institutions, other countries combined print with online access. **Remarks:** Accepts advertising. **URL:** http://www.interscience.wiley.com; http://www3.interscience.wiley.com/cgi-bin/jhome/4438. **Circ:** (Not Reported)

53786 ■ British Journal of Clinical Psychology
The British Psychological Society
St. Andrews House
48 Princess Rd. E
Leicester LE1 7DR, United Kingdom
Ph: 44 116 2549568
Fax: 44 116 2271314
Publisher E-mail: enquiry@bps.org.uk
British journal covering the broad role of clinical psychologists. Features descriptive studies, including studies of the etiology, assessment, and amelioration of all types of disorders. **Freq:** Quarterly March, June, September, and November. **Trim Size:** 247 x 174 mm. **Key Personnel:** Gillian Hardy, Editor; Michael Barkham, Editor; Stephen Barton, Assoc. Ed.; Peter Bower, Assoc. Ed.; Chris Barker, Assoc. Ed.; Christine Barrowclough, Assoc. Ed.; Richard Bentall, Assoc. Ed. **ISSN:** 0144-6657. **Subscription Rates:** 52 nonmembers; US$102 other countries; EUR76 individuals; 227 institutions and libraries; US$414 institutions, other countries; EUR335 institutions; 24 members; 17 members student. **Remarks:** Accepts advertising. **URL:** http://www.

bpsjournals.co.uk/journals/bjcp/. **Ad Rates:** BW: 288. **Circ:** Combined 3,900.

53787 ■ British Journal of Developmental Psychology
The British Psychological Society
St. Andrews House
48 Princess Rd. E
Leicester LE1 7DR, United Kingdom
Ph: 44 116 2549568
Fax: 44 116 2271314
Publisher E-mail: enquiry@bps.org.uk
British journal covering all aspects of development from infancy to old age, including development during infancy, childhood and adolescence; abnormal development (handicaps, learning difficulties and childhood autism); educational implications of child development; parent-child interaction; social and moral development; and the effects of ageing. **Freq:** Quarterly March, June, September, and November. **Trim Size:** 247 x 174 mm. **Key Personnel:** Daisy Powell, Assoc. Ed.; Margaret Harris, Editor; Charles Helwig, Assoc. Ed.; Mark Bennett, Assoc. Ed.; Claire Hughes, Assoc. Ed.; Robin Banerjee, Assoc. Ed.; Mark Blades, Assoc. Ed. **ISSN:** 0261-510X. **Subscription Rates:** 24 members; 17 members student; 49 nonmembers; US$90 nonmembers rest of the world; EUR68 nonmembers; 218 institutions and libraries; US$399 institutions, other countries; EUR323 institutions. **Remarks:** Accepts advertising. **URL:** http://www.bpsjournals.co.uk/journals/bjdp/. **Ad Rates:** BW: 320. **Circ:** Combined 1,700

53788 ■ British Journal of Educational Psychology
The British Psychological Society
St. Andrews House
48 Princess Rd. E
Leicester LE1 7DR, United Kingdom
Ph: 44 116 2549568
Fax: 44 116 2271314
Publisher E-mail: enquiry@bps.org.uk
Journal publishing psychological research pertaining to education across all ages and educational levels, consisting of topics such as cognition, learning, motivation, literacy, numeracy and language, behaviour, social-emotional development and developmental difficulties linked to educational psychology or the psychology of education. **Freq:** Quarterly March, June, September and December. **Key Personnel:** Julie Dockrell, Advisory Ed.; Jim Boyle, Assoc. Ed.; Prof. Andrew Tolmie, Editor. **ISSN:** 0007-0998. **Subscription Rates:** EUR24 members; 17 members student; 49 nonmembers UK; US$90 nonmembers rest of the world; EUR68 nonmembers Europe; 172 institutions UK; US$300 institutions, other countries; EUR245 institutions Europe. **Remarks:** Advertising accepted; rates available upon request. **URL:** http://www.bpsjournals.co.uk/journals/bjep/. **Circ:** (Not Reported)

53789 ■ British Journal of Health Psychology
The British Psychological Society
St. Andrews House
48 Princess Rd. E
Leicester LE1 7DR, United Kingdom
Ph: 44 116 2549568
Fax: 44 116 2271314
Publisher E-mail: enquiry@bps.org.uk
British journal covering all aspects of psychology related to health and illness from birth to death. Covers experimental and clinical research on etiology and the management of acute and chronic illness, responses to ill-health, screening and medical procedures, research on health behavior, and psychological aspects of prevention. **Freq:** Quarterly February, May, September, and November. **Trim Size:** 247 x 174 mm. **Key Personnel:** Douglas Carroll, International Advisory Board; Paul Bennett, Editor; Kavita Vedhara, Editor. **ISSN:** 1359-107X. **Subscription Rates:** 24 members; 17 members student; 49 nonmembers; US$90 nonmembers rest of the world; EUR68 nonmembers; 190 institutions and libraries; US$345 institutions, other countries; EUR278 institutions. **Remarks:** Accepts advertising. **URL:** http://www.bpsjournals.co.uk/journals/bjhp/. **Ad Rates:** BW: 365. **Circ:** Combined 2,000

53790 ■ British Journal of Mathematical and Statistical Psychology
The British Psychological Society
St. Andrews House
48 Princess Rd. E
Leicester LE1 7DR, United Kingdom
Ph: 44 116 2549568

Fax: 44 116 2271314
Publisher E-mail: enquiry@bps.org.uk
British journal covering all aspects of quantitative psychology, including mathematical psychology, statistics, psychometrics, decision making, psychophysics, and relevant areas of mathematics, computing, and computer software. **Freq:** Semiannual May and November. **Trim Size:** 174 x 247 mm. **Key Personnel:** David Clark-Carter, Consultant Ed.; Dr. Thom Baguley, Editor; Prof. Mark Lansdale, Editor. **ISSN:** 0007-1102. **Subscription Rates:** 24 members; 17 members student; 49 nonmembers UK; US$90 nonmembers rest of the world; EUR68 nonmembers Europe; 199 institutions and libraries; US$368 institutions, other countries; EUR297 institutions. **Remarks:** Accepts advertising. **URL:** http://www.bpsjournals.co.uk/journals/bjmsp/. **Ad Rates:** BW: 250. **Circ:** Combined 700

53791 ■ British Journal of Psychology
The British Psychological Society
St. Andrews House
48 Princess Rd. E
Leicester LE1 7DR, United Kingdom
Ph: 44 116 2549568
Fax: 44 116 2271314
Publisher E-mail: enquiry@bps.org.uk
British journal featuring reports of empirical studies likely to further understanding of psychology, critical reviews of the literature, and theoretical papers. **Freq:** Quarterly February, May, August, and November. **Trim Size:** 174 x 247 mm. **Key Personnel:** Peter Mitchell, Editor; Alan Kingstone, Assoc. Ed.; Eamonn Ferguson, Dep. Ed. **ISSN:** 0007-1269. **Subscription Rates:** 24 members; 17 members student; 62 nonmembers; US$122 nonmembers rest of the world; EUR92 nonmembers; 292 institutions and libraries; US$542 institutions, other countries and libraries; EUR436 institutions and libraries. **Remarks:** Accepts advertising. **URL:** http://www.bpsjournals.co.uk/journals/bjp/. **Ad Rates:** BW: 375. **Circ:** Combined 2,800

53792 ■ British Journal of Social Psychology
The British Psychological Society
St. Andrews House
48 Princess Rd. E
Leicester LE1 7DR, United Kingdom
Ph: 44 116 2549568
Fax: 44 116 2271314
Publisher E-mail: enquiry@bps.org.uk
British journal of social psychology. **Freq:** Quarterly March, June, September, and December. **Trim Size:** 174 x 247 mm. **Key Personnel:** Jolanda Jetten, Editor. **ISSN:** 0144-6665. **Subscription Rates:** 24 members; 17 members student; 52 nonmembers UK; US$102 nonmembers rest of the world; EUR76 nonmembers; 218 institutions and libraries; US$399 institutions, other countries and libraries; EUR323 institutions and libraries. **Remarks:** Accepts advertising. **URL:** http://www.bpsjournals.co.uk/journals/bjsp/. **Ad Rates:** BW: 340. **Circ:** Combined 1,500

53793 ■ Clinical & Experimental Allergy
John Wiley & Sons Inc.
Wiley-Blackwell
c/o A.J. Wardlaw, Ed.
Institute for Lung Health
Leicester University & Medical School
Glenfield Hospital, Groby Rd.
Leicester LE3 9QP, United Kingdom
Journal focusing on allergic diseases and mechanisms. The Official Journal of the British Society for Allergy & Clinical Immunology. **Freq:** Monthly. **Key Personnel:** Qutayba Hamid, Editor; A.J. Wardlaw, Editor; Stephen R. Durham, Assoc. Ed. **ISSN:** 0954-7894. **Subscription Rates:** US$3,364 institutions print and online; US$3,058 institutions print or online; US$3,927 institutions, other countries print and online; US$3,570 institutions, other countries print or online; 1,819 institutions print and online; 1,654 institutions print or online. **Remarks:** Accepts advertising. **URL:** http://www.wiley.com/bw/journal.asp?ref=0954-7894&site=1. **Circ:** (Not Reported)

53794 ■ Clinical Focus
Rila Publications Ltd.
Consultant Gynaecologist
University Hospital of Leicester
Victoria Bldg.
Leicester Royal Infirmary
Leicester LE1 5WW, United Kingdom
Publisher E-mail: admin@rila.co.uk
Professional, medical magazine covering educational

materials for primary care physicians. **Subtitle:** Obstetrics & Gynaecology. **Freq:** Quarterly. **Cols./Page:** 2. **Key Personnel:** Nazar Amso, Co-Ed.; Justine Konje, Editorial Board; Marwan Habiba, Editorial Board; May Wahab, Editorial Board; Farook Al-Azzawi, Editor. **ISSN:** 1745-0837. **URL:** http://www.rila.co.uk/site/modules.php?name=Journals&file=journal2&func=showab&jid=055&aid=4982&iid=409. **Circ:** Controlled 15,000

53795 ■ Deutsch
Association for Language Learning
University of Leicester
University Rd.
Leicester LE1 7RH, United Kingdom
Ph: 44 116 2297600
Fax: 44 116 2231488
Publisher E-mail: info@all-languages.org.uk
Publication covering the teaching and learning of German. **Subtitle:** Lehren und Lernen. **Founded:** June 1990. **Freq:** Semiannual. **Key Personnel:** Uta Smail, Editor; Mandy Wight, Reviews Ed., info@all-languages.org.uk. **ISSN:** 0953-4822. **Subscription Rates:** 85 individuals European Union; 95 other countries; 70 individuals inside United Kingdom. **URL:** http://www.all-languages.org.uk/publications/journals/deutsch_lehren_und_lernen. **Ad Rates:** BW: 490. **Circ:** 2,500

53796 ■ The Edge
National Youth Agency
Eastgate House
19-23 Humberstone Rd.
Leicester LE5 3GJ, United Kingdom
Ph: 44 116 2427350
Fax: 44 116 2427444
Publisher E-mail: nya@nya.org.uk
Newspaper featuring youth affairs. **Freq:** Quarterly. **Key Personnel:** Andy Hopkinson, Editor; Helena Ferrao-Read, Contact. **URL:** http://www.nya.org.uk/catalogue/magazines/the-edge.

53797 ■ English Four to Eleven
English Association
University of Leicester
University Rd.
Leicester LE1 7RH, United Kingdom
Ph: 44 116 2297622
Fax: 44 116 2297623
Publisher E-mail: engassoc@leicester.ac.uk
Publication covering the English language. **Founded:** 1995. **Freq:** 3/yr. **Key Personnel:** Brenda Marshall, Board; Marion Hampton, Editor; Rob Sanderson, Board; Liz Connolly, Board; John Paine, Editor; Rebecca Kennedy, Board; Margaret Mallett, Board; Eve Bearne, Editorial Board; Gill Robins, Board. **Subscription Rates:** 23 individuals basic; US$46 individuals basic; 257 individuals YWES; 317 individuals YWCCT; 32 individuals essays & studies; US$523 individuals YWES; US$631 individuals YWCCT; US$67 individuals essays & studies. **Remarks:** Advertising not accepted. **URL:** http://www.le.ac.uk; http://www.le.ac.uk/engassoc/publications/411.html. **Formerly:** Primary English (1997). **Circ:** (Not Reported)

53798 ■ Equals
The Mathematical Association
259 London Rd.
Leicester LE2 3BE, United Kingdom
Ph: 44 116 2210013
Fax: 44 116 2122835
Publisher E-mail: office@m-a.org.uk
Professional journal covering mathematics education for special needs students. **Subtitle:** Mathematics and Special Educational Needs. **Freq:** Triennial. **Key Personnel:** Rachel Gibbons, Editor; Mundher Adhami, Editorial Team; Jane Gabb, Editorial Team; Dora Bowes, Editorial Team; Lynda Maple, Editorial Team; Nick Peacey, Editorial Team; Mary Clark, Editorial Team. **ISSN:** 1465-1254. **Subscription Rates:** 20.50 individuals. **Remarks:** Accepts advertising. **URL:** http://www.m-a.org.uk/jsp/index.jsp?lnk=650. **Circ:** (Not Reported)

53799 ■ European Foreign Affairs Review
Kluwer Academic/Plenum Publishing Corp.
Dept. of Politics
University of Leicester
University Rd.
Leicester LE1 7RH, United Kingdom
Ph: 44 11 62522643

Publisher E-mail: kluwer@wkap.com
Journal covering the position of the European Union in relation to the rest of the world. **Freq:** 4/yr. **Key Personnel:** Nanette A. Neuwahl, Editor; Jorg Monar, Editor. **ISSN:** 1384-6299. **Subscription Rates:** EUR349 individuals; US$465 individuals; 256 individuals print or online. **URL:** http://www.aspenpublishers.com/Product.asp?catalog_name=Aspen&product_id=SS13846299&cookie%5Ftest=1.

53800 ■ Finance on Windows
Tudor Rose
6 Friar Ln.
Leicester LE1 5RA, United Kingdom
Ph: 44 116 2229900
Publisher E-mail: contact@tudor-rose.co.uk
Magazine featuring information about the use of Microsoft Windows technology in Europe, Middle East, and Africa. **Founded:** 1999. **Freq:** Quarterly. **Key Personnel:** Jacqui Griffiths, Editor, jacqui.griffiths@tudor-rose.co.uk. **Subscription Rates:** Free. **Remarks:** Accepts advertising. **URL:** http://www.tudor-rose.co.uk/publishing/financeonwindows.html; http://www.onwindows.com/. **Circ:** (Not Reported)

53801 ■ Francophonie
Association for Language Learning
University of Leicester
University Rd.
Leicester LE1 7RH, United Kingdom
Ph: 44 116 2297600
Fax: 44 116 2231488
Publisher E-mail: info@all-languages.org.uk
Publication covering language, in French. **Founded:** June 1990. **Freq:** Semiannual. **Key Personnel:** Michael Wardle, Editor; Dianne Place, Reviews Ed. **ISSN:** 0957-1744. **Subscription Rates:** 70 individuals in UK; 85 individuals European Union; 95 other countries. **URL:** http://www.all-languages.org.uk/publications/journals/francophonie. **Ad Rates:** BW: 550. **Circ:** 5,500

53802 ■ Global Municipal Investor
Tudor Rose
6 Friar Ln.
Leicester LE1 5RA, United Kingdom
Ph: 44 116 2229900
Publication E-mail: subscribe@tudor-rose.co.uk
Publisher E-mail: contact@tudor-rose.co.uk
Magazine featuring municipalities with potential business area. **Founded:** 2003. **Remarks:** Accepts advertising. **URL:** http://www.tudor-rose.co.uk/publishing/globalmunicipalinvestor.html. **Circ:** (Not Reported)

53803 ■ Golf Course Architecture
Tudor Rose
6 Friar Ln.
Leicester LE1 5RA, United Kingdom
Ph: 44 116 2229900
Publisher E-mail: contact@tudor-rose.co.uk
Magazine featuring development of golf course architecture in America and the rest of the world. **Founded:** July 2005. **Freq:** Quarterly. **Trim Size:** 210 x 297 mm. **Key Personnel:** Adam Lawrence, Editor, phone 44 116 2229909, adam.lawrence@golfcoursearchitecture.net. **Remarks:** Accepts advertising. **URL:** http://www.tudor-rose.co.uk/publishing/golfcoursearchitecture.html; http://www.golfcoursearchitecture.net/. **Circ:** (Not Reported)

53804 ■ Immunobiology
Elsevier Science Inc.
University of Leicester
Medical Science Bldg.
University Rd.
Leicester LE1 9HN, United Kingdom
Ph: 44 116 2525674
Fax: 44 116 2525030
Publisher E-mail: usinfo-ehelp@elsevier.com
Journal covering serology, hematology, allergy, infectious diseases, transplantation, and nonspecific resistance. **Founded:** 1909. **Freq:** 12/yr. **Print Method:** Offset. **Cols./Page:** 6. **Col. Width:** 26 nonpareils. **Col. Depth:** 294 agate lines. **Key Personnel:** Brent W. Kiernan, Editorial Board; J.P. Atkinson, Section Ed.; M.J. Browning, Editorial Board; A. Ferreira, Section Ed.; T. Fujita, Section Ed.; S.H.E. Kaufmann, Section Ed.; P. Marche, Section Ed.; R.B. Sim, Section Ed.; Leyla Z. Al-Mansouri, Editorial Coord., zlam1@le.ac.uk; W.J. Schwaeble, Editor-in-Chief, ws5@le.ac.uk. **ISSN:** 0171-2985. **Subscription Rates:** 191,100¥ institutions; US$1,548 institutions, other countries except Europe,

Japan and Iran; EUR1,436 institutions for European countries and Iran; EUR562 individuals for European countries and Iran; 73,500¥ individuals; US$548 other countries except Europe, Japan and Iran. **URL:** http://www.elsevier.com/wps/find/journaldescription.cws_home/701769/descriptiondescription.

53805 ■ International Journal of Community Currency Research
University of Leicester
Management Centre
Ken Edwards Bldg.
Leicester LE1 7RH, United Kingdom
Ph: 44 11 62525520
Publisher E-mail: ulsm@le.ac.uk
Journal covering community currencies, both emerging and those being used at present and in the past. **Freq:** Annual. **Key Personnel:** Gill Seyfang, Editor, g.seyfang@uea.ac.uk; Colin Williams, Editor, c.c.williams@sheffield.ac.uk. **ISSN:** 1325-9547. **URL:** http://www.uea.ac.uk/env/ijccr/.

53806 ■ Journal of Applied Accounting Research
Emerald Group Publishing Ltd.
c/o Dr. Kumba Jallow, Founding Editor
Leicester Business School, De Montfort University
The Gateway
Leicester LE1 9BH, United Kingdom
Publisher E-mail: emerald@emeraldinsight.com
Journal focusing on issues relevant to the practice of accounting in a wide variety of contexts. **Freq:** 3/yr. **Key Personnel:** Prof. Elaine Harris, Managing Editor; Simon Linacre, Publisher, slinacre@emeraldinsight.com; Dr. Kumba, Jallow, Founding Ed., lhacc@dmu.ac.uk. **ISSN:** 0967-5426. **URL:** http://info.emeraldinsight.com/products/journals/journals.htm?id=jaar.

53807 ■ Journal of Occupational and Organizational Psychology
The British Psychological Society
St. Andrews House
48 Princess Rd. E
Leicester LE1 7DR, United Kingdom
Ph: 44 116 2549568
Fax: 44 116 2271314
Publisher E-mail: enquiry@bps.org.uk
British journal featuring conceptual and empirical papers which aim to increase understanding of people at work. Covers industrial, organizational, engineering, vocational and personnel psychology, as well as behavioral aspects of industrial relations, human resource management, ergonomics, and industrial sociology. **Freq:** Quarterly March, June, September, and December. **Trim Size:** 174 x 247 mm. **Key Personnel:** Jan de Jonge, Editor; Sharon Clarke, Assoc. Ed.; John Cordery, Consulting Ed.; Neil Anderson, Consulting Ed.; Kevin Daniels, Consulting Ed.; Doris Fay, Assoc. Ed.; Juan I. Sanchez, Assoc. Ed.; Cathy Cassell, Consulting Ed.; Marc van Veldhoven, Assoc. Ed. **ISSN:** 0963-1798. **Subscription Rates:** 24 members; 17 members student; 49 nonmembers; US$90 nonmembers rest of the world; EUR68 nonmembers; 210 institutions and libraries; US$387 institutions, other countries and libraries; EUR311 institutions and libraries. **Remarks:** Accepts advertising. **URL:** http://www.bpsjournals.co.uk/journals/joop/. **Ad Rates:** BW: 360. **Circ:** Combined 3,100

53808 ■ KFAT News
National Union of Knitwear, Footwear & Apparel Trades
55 New Walk
Leicester LE1 7EB, United Kingdom
Ph: 44 116 2556703
Publication E-mail: press@kfat.org.uk
Journal of the National Union of Knitwear, Footwear & Apparel Trades. **Founded:** 1991. **Freq:** Quarterly. **Key Personnel:** Baz Morris, Dep. Gen. Sec., bas.morris@kfat.org.uk; Paul Gates, Gen. Sec., paul.gates@kfat.org.uk; Tina Winslow, Finance Off., tina.winslow@kfat.org.uk. **URL:** http://www.poptel.org.uk/kfat/.

53809 ■ Language Learning Journal
Association for Language Learning
University of Leicester
University Rd.
Leicester LE1 7RH, United Kingdom
Ph: 44 116 2297600
Fax: 44 116 2231488
Publisher E-mail: info@all-languages.org.uk
Journal covering language study. **Founded:** Mar. 1990. **Freq:** Semiannual. **Key Personnel:** Dr. Norbert Pachler, Editor; Dr. Douglas Allford, Editor; Elspeth Broady,

Editor. **ISSN:** 0957-1736. **Subscription Rates:** US$416 institutions print and online; 213 institutions print and online; EUR332 institutions online only; 203 institutions online only; 68 individuals; US$146 individuals. **Remarks:** Accepts advertising. **URL:** http://www.all-languages.org.uk; http://www.tandf.co.uk/journals/titles/09571736.asp. **Ad Rates:** BW: 615. **Circ:** 3,500

53810 ■ Legal and Criminological Psychology
The British Psychological Society
St. Andrews House
48 Princess Rd. E
Leicester LE1 7DR, United Kingdom
Ph: 44 116 2549568
Fax: 44 116 2271314
Publisher E-mail: enquiry@bps.org.uk
Publication featuring reports of empirical research and theoretical papers that address applications of psychology to legal and criminological issues. Covers legal decision making, theories of criminal behavior, victimology, policing and crime detection, public attitudes to the law, mental health and the law, interrogation and testimony, and psychological interventions with offenders. **Freq:** Semiannual February and September. **Trim Size:** 247 x 174 mm. **Key Personnel:** Ron Blackburn, Editorial Board; Pekka Santilla, Editorial Board; Mary McMurran, Assoc. Ed.; Neil Brewer, Editorial Board; Aldert Vrij, Editor; Richard Laws, Editorial Board; Steve Penrod, Editorial Board; Tony Beech, Editorial Board; Ray Bull, Editorial Board; Par Anders Granhag, Assoc. Ed. **ISSN:** 1355-3259. **Subscription Rates:** 24 members; 17 members student; 41 nonmembers UK; US$78 nonmembers rest of the world; EUR56 nonmembers; 140 institutions and libraries; US$240 institutions, other countries and libraries; EUR194 institutions and libraries. **Remarks:** Accepts advertising. **URL:** http://www.bpsjournals.co.uk/journals/lcp/. **Ad Rates:** BW: 288. **Circ:** Combined 1,200

53811 ■ Leicester Link
Leicester City Council
New Walk Center
Welford Pl.
Leicester LE1 6ZG, United Kingdom
Ph: 44 116 2527000
Publication E-mail: customer.services@leicester.gov.uk; link@leicester.gov.uk
Publisher E-mail: customer.services@leicester.gov.uk
Civic newspaper covering local city council activities. **Founded:** 1987. **Freq:** Bimonthly. **URL:** http://www.leicester.gov.uk/your-council-services/council-and-democracy/council-news/our-news-service-/. **Circ:** Controlled 112,000

53812 ■ Marketing Theory
Sage Publications Ltd.
c/o Prof. Pauline Maclaran, Ed.-in-Ch.
De Montfort University
Bosworth House
The Gateway
Leicester LE1 9BH, United Kingdom
Peer-reviewed journal covering marketing theory. **Founded:** 2001. **Freq:** Quarterly. **Key Personnel:** Prof. Pauline MacLaran, Editor-in-Chief; Rod Brodie, Regional Ed.; Bernard Cova, Regional Ed.; Evert Gummesson, Advisory Board; Jaqueline Pels, Regional Ed.; Gordon R. Foxall, Advisory Board; Michael Saren, Regional Ed.; Les Carlson, Regional Ed.; Kristian K.E. Moller, Regional Ed. **ISSN:** 1470-5931. **Subscription Rates:** US$729 institutions print & e-access; US$656 institutions e-access; US$714 institutions print only; US$93 individuals print only; US$196 institutions single print; US$30 individuals single print. **Remarks:** Accepts advertising. **URL:** http://www.sagepub.com/journalsProdEditBoards.nav?prodId=Journal201550&curr Tree=Subjects&level1=600&level2=6C0. **Circ:** (Not Reported)

53813 ■ Mathematical Gazette
The Mathematical Association
259 London Rd.
Leicester LE2 3BE, United Kingdom
Ph: 44 116 2210013
Fax: 44 116 2122835
Publication E-mail: gazette@m-a.org.uk
Publisher E-mail: office@m-a.org.uk
Professional journal covering mathematics teaching, focusing on students aged 15-20. **Freq:** Triennial. **Key Personnel:** Bill Richardson, Production Ed., wpr3@tutor.open.ac.uk; Gerry Leversha, Editor. **ISSN:** 0025-5572. **Subscription Rates:** 77 individuals. **Remarks:** Accepts advertising. **URL:** http://www.m-a.org.uk/jsp/index.jsp?lnk=620. **Circ:** (Not Reported)

53814 ■ Mathematical Pie
The Mathematical Association
259 London Rd.
Leicester LE2 3BE, United Kingdom
Ph: 44 116 2210013
Fax: 44 116 2122835
Publisher E-mail: office@m-a.org.uk
Magazine featuring variety of problems and challenges, stimulating mathematical activity for pupils from 10 to 14 years of age. **Freq:** 3/yr. **Key Personnel:** Wil Ransome, Editor, pie@m-a.org.uk. **Subscription Rates:** Free members of Society of Young Mathematicians; 4 individuals. **URL:** http://www.m-a.org.uk/jsp/index.jsp?lnk=660.

53815 ■ Mathematics in School
The Mathematical Association
259 London Rd.
Leicester LE2 3BE, United Kingdom
Ph: 44 116 2210013
Fax: 44 116 2122835
Publisher E-mail: office@m-a.org.uk
Journal featuring contributions from mathematics practitioners at all levels. **Freq:** 5/yr. **Key Personnel:** Grant Macleod, Reviews Ed.; John Berry, Editor; Tina Webb, Production Ed.; Chris Pritchard, Editor; Paul Metcalf, Editor-in-Chief. **Subscription Rates:** 77 individuals in UK; 89.50 other countries air mail; 85 other countries surface mail. **Remarks:** Accepts advertising. **URL:** http://www.m-a.org.uk/jsp/index.jsp?lnk=610. **Circ:** (Not Reported)

53816 ■ Organised Sound
Cambridge University Press
c/o Prof. Leigh Landy, Ed.
De Montfort University
Music, Technology & Innovation Research Group
Clephan Bldg. 3.06c
Leicester LE1 9BH, United Kingdom
Publisher E-mail: information@cambridge.org
Peer-reviewed journal covering the techniques and issues stemming from the application of technology in music. **Subtitle:** An International Journal of Music and Technology. **Key Personnel:** Prof. Leigh Landy, Editor, llandy@dmu.ac.uk; Prof. Kenneth Fields, Regional Ed.; Joel Chadabe, Regional Ed.; Dr. Ross Kirk, Assoc. Ed.; Prof. Marc Battier, Editorial Board; Dr. Richard Orton, Assoc. Ed. **ISSN:** 1355-7718. **Subscription Rates:** US$272 institutions online and print; US$244 institutions online only; 136 institutions online only; 152 institutions print and online. **Remarks:** Accepts advertising. **URL:** http://journals.cambridge.org/action/displayJournal?jid=OSO. **Ad Rates:** BW: US$695. **Circ:** 400

53817 ■ Primary Mathematics
The Mathematical Association
259 London Rd.
Leicester LE2 3BE, United Kingdom
Ph: 44 116 2210013
Fax: 44 116 2122835
Publication E-mail: primarymaths@m-a.org.uk
Publisher E-mail: office@m-a.org.uk
Professional journal covering mathematics for primary mathematics teachers. **Freq:** 3/yr. **Key Personnel:** Lynne McClure, Editor. **ISSN:** 1465-0495. **Subscription Rates:** 41 individuals. **Remarks:** Accepts advertising. **URL:** http://www.m-a.org.uk/jsp/index.jsp?lnk=640. **Circ:** (Not Reported)

53818 ■ Prime
Tudor Rose
6 Friar Ln.
Leicester LE1 5RA, United Kingdom
Ph: 44 116 2229900
Publisher E-mail: contact@tudor-rose.co.uk
Magazine featuring processes and technologies on improving the manufacturing industry business. **Founded:** Apr. 2005. **Freq:** Quarterly. **Key Personnel:** Adam Lawrence, Editor, phone 44 116 2229900, adam.lawrence@tudor-rose.co.uk. **Subscription Rates:** Free. **Remarks:** Accepts advertising. **URL:** http://www.tudor-rose.co.uk/publishing/prime.html; http://www.primemagazine.net/home.htm. **Circ:** Combined 13,000

53819 ■ Psychologist Appointments
The British Psychological Society
St. Andrews House
48 Princess Rd. E
Leicester LE1 7DR, United Kingdom
Ph: 44 116 2549568
Fax: 44 116 2271314
Publication E-mail: enquiry@psychapp.co.uk
Publisher E-mail: enquiry@bps.org.uk
Professional magazine covering employment for psychology students in the UK and overseas. **Freq:** Monthly. **Trim Size:** 210 x 297 mm. **Key Personnel:** Dr. Jon Sutton, Managing Editor. **Remarks:** Accepts advertising. **URL:** http://www.appmemo.co.uk. **Formerly:** Appointments Memorandum. **Ad Rates:** BW: 2,191. **Circ:** (Not Reported)

53820 ■ Psychology and Psychotherapy
The British Psychological Society
St. Andrews House
48 Princess Rd. E
Leicester LE1 7DR, United Kingdom
Ph: 44 116 2549568
Fax: 44 116 2271314
Publisher E-mail: enquiry@bps.org.uk
British journal covering psychodynamic issues with the aim of bringing together the medical and psychological disciplines. Features original theoretical and research in the fields of psychodynamic and interpersonal psychology as they relate to recovery from medical and psychological disorders. **Subtitle:** Theory, Research and Practice. **Freq:** Quarterly March, June, September, and December. **Trim Size:** 174 x 247 mm. **Key Personnel:** Lyn Abramson, Editorial Board; Steven Jones, Editor; Lauren Alloy, Editorial Board. **ISSN:** 1476-0835. **Subscription Rates:** 24 members; 17 members student; 49 nonmembers; US$90 nonmembers rest of the world; EUR68 nonmembers; 218 institutions and libraries; US$410 institutions, other countries; EUR332 institutions and libraries. **Remarks:** Accepts advertising. **URL:** http://www.bpsjournals.co.uk/journals/paptrap/. **Formerly:** British Journal of Medical Psychology. **Ad Rates:** BW: 340. **Circ:** Combined 1,900

53821 ■ Retailspeak
Tudor Rose
6 Friar Ln.
Leicester LE1 5RA, United Kingdom
Ph: 44 116 2229900
Publisher E-mail: contact@tudor-rose.co.uk
Magazine featuring challenges in the retailing industry. **Founded:** Nov. 2006. **Freq:** Quarterly. **Key Personnel:** Mark Webb, Contact, phone 44 116 2229900, mark.webb@tudor-rose.co.uk. **Subscription Rates:** Free. **Remarks:** Accepts advertising. **URL:** http://www.tudor-rose.co.uk/publishing/RetailSpeak.html; http://www.retailspeak.com/. **Circ:** Combined 10,000

53822 ■ Ripple
Leicester University Students Union
University Rd.
Leicester LE1 7RH, United Kingdom
Ph: 44 11 62231148
Publication E-mail: ripple@le.ac.uk
Student newspaper. **Freq:** Semimonthly term time of the calendar year. **Key Personnel:** Emily Key, Editor, emk13@le.ac.uk; Anietie Isong, Sales & Public Relations Mgr., su-marketing@le.ac.uk. **Remarks:** Accepts advertising. **URL:** http://leicesterunion.com/ripple. **Circ:** (Not Reported)

53823 ■ Rusistika
Association for Language Learning
University of Leicester
University Rd.
Leicester LE1 7RH, United Kingdom
Ph: 44 116 2297600
Fax: 44 116 2231488
Publisher E-mail: info@all-languages.org.uk
Publication covering language. **Founded:** June 1990. **Freq:** Annual. **Key Personnel:** Dr. Daphne West, Editor; Andrew Jameson, Review Ed. **ISSN:** 0957-1760. **Subscription Rates:** 43 individuals European Union; 48 other countries. **Remarks:** Accepts advertising. **URL:** http://www.all-languages.org.uk/publications/journals/rusistika. **Ad Rates:** BW: 305. **Circ:** (Not Reported)

53824 ■ Sailplane & Gliding
British Gliding Association
8 Merus Ct.
Meridian Business Pk.
Leicester LE19 1RJ, United Kingdom
Ph: 44 116 2892956
Fax: 44 116 2895025
Publisher E-mail: office@gliding.co.uk
Publication covering aviation. **Freq:** Bimonthly. **Key Personnel:** Susan Newby, Editor, editor@sailplaneandgliding.co.uk. **Subscription Rates:** 22.75 individuals. **Remarks:** Accepts advertising. **URL:** http://www.gliding.co.uk/sailplaneandgliding/news.htm. **Circ:** (Not Reported)

53825 ■ Skydive Magazine
British Parachute Association
5 Wharf Way
Glen Parva
Leicester LE2 9TF, United Kingdom
Ph: 44 11 62785271
Fax: 44 11 62477662
Publisher E-mail: skydive@bpa.org.uk
Publication covering sport parachuting (skydiving). **Subtitle:** The British Parachute Association Magazine. **Founded:** 1964. **Freq:** Bimonthly. **Trim Size:** A4. **Key Personnel:** Louise Fordham, Contact, phone 44 1778 392445, louisef@warnersgroup.co.uk. **Subscription Rates:** 22 individuals United Kingdom & U.S.; EUR33 individuals other parts of Europe; 30 individuals rest of the world; US$36 individuals. **Remarks:** Accepts advertising. **URL:** http://www.skydivemag.com. **Ad Rates:** BW: 255, 4C: 670. **Circ:** 14,200

53826 ■ Skywings
British Hang Gliding and Paragliding Association
8 Merus Ct.
Meridian Business Pk.
Leicester LE19 1RJ, United Kingdom
Ph: 44 116 2894316
Fax: 44 116 2814949
Publication E-mail: skywings@bhpa.co.uk
Publisher E-mail: office@bhpa.co.uk
Publication covering aerospace. **Freq:** Monthly. **Subscription Rates:** Included in membership. **Remarks:** Accepts advertising. **URL:** http://www.bhpa.co.uk/bhpa/skywings/index.php. **Circ:** (Not Reported)

53827 ■ Social Responsibility Journal
Emerald Group Publishing Ltd.
c/o Prof. David Crowther
De Montforth University, Faculty of Business & Law
The Gateway
Leicester LE1 9BH, United Kingdom
Publisher E-mail: emerald@emeraldinsight.com
Journal publishing theoretical and empirical papers, speculative essays, and review articles in the field of social responsibility. **Freq:** Irregular. **Key Personnel:** Prof. David Crowther, Editor, davideacrowther@aol.com; Prof. Guler Aras, Editor, guleraras@aol.com; Andrew Smith, Publisher, agsmith@emeraldinsight.com. **ISSN:** 1747-1117. **URL:** http://info.emeraldinsight.com/products/journals/journals.htm?id=srj.

53828 ■ Studies in the Education of Adults
National Institute of Adult Continuing Education
Renaissance House
20 Princess Rd. W
Leicester LE1 6TP, United Kingdom
Ph: 44 116 2044200
Fax: 44 116 2044201
Publisher E-mail: enquiries@niace.org.uk
Scholarly journal covering the field of education and training for adults for academic specialists, practitioners, postgraduate students, and educational managers worldwide. **Freq:** Semiannual. **Key Personnel:** Prof. Miriam Zukas, Editorial Board, m.zukas@leeds.ac.uk; Lyn Tett, Reviews Ed.; Dr. Stephen Brookfield, Int'l Advisory Board; Dr. Kathryn Ecclestone, Editorial Board; Prof. Jim Crowther, Editor. **ISSN:** 0266-0830. **Subscription Rates:** 88 institutions; 33 other countries; 104 institutions Europe and North America; 33 individuals; 88 individuals Europe and North America; 22 other countries individual. **Remarks:** Accepts advertising. **URL:** http://www.niace.org.uk/publications/academic-journals/studies. **Circ:** Paid 750

53829 ■ Studies in Hispanic Cinemas
Intellect
Department of Media & Cultural Production
De Montfort University
The Gateway
Leicester LE1 9BH, United Kingdom
Publisher E-mail: info@intellectuk.org
Academic journal, written in English and aimed at scholars, teachers, students and devotees from all over the world whose focus is on Spanish-speaking cinemas.

Circulation: ★ = ABC; △ = BPA; ♦ = CAC; • = CCAB; ❑ = VAC; ⊕ = PO Statement; ‡ = Publisher's Report; Boldface figures = sworn; Light figures = estimated.

Gale Directory of Publications & Broadcast Media/147th Ed.

5673

Founded: 2004. Freq: 2/yr. Trim Size: 174 x 244 mm. Key Personnel: Barry Jordan, Editor, bjordan@dmu.ac. uk; Jo Labanyi, Editorial Board; Chris Perriam, Editorial Board. ISSN: 1478-0488. Subscription Rates: 33 individuals, print; 210 institutions print; 18 single issue print; US$65 individuals print; US$330 institutions print; US$36 single issue print. Remarks: Accepts advertising. URL: http://www.intellectbooks.co.uk/journals/view-Journal,id=125/. Ad Rates: BW: 100. Circ: (Not Reported)

53830 ■ Symmetry Plus
The Mathematical Association
259 London Rd.
Leicester LE2 3BE, United Kingdom
Ph: 44 116 2210013
Fax: 44 116 2122835
Publisher E-mail: office@m-a.org.uk
Magazine featuring puzzles, problems and competitions about mathematics for students from 10 to 18 years. Freq: 3/yr. Key Personnel: Martin Perkins, Editor, symmetryplus@m-a.org.uk. Subscription Rates: 19.50 individuals. URL: http://www.m-a.org.uk/jsp/index.jsp?lnk=670.

53831 ■ Tuttitalia
Association for Language Learning
University of Leicester
University Rd.
Leicester LE1 7RH, United Kingdom
Ph: 44 116 2297600
Fax: 44 116 2231488
Publisher E-mail: info@all-languages.org.uk
Publication covering language. Founded: June 1990. Freq: Semiannual. Key Personnel: Anna Constantino, Co-Ed.; Monica Boria, Review Ed.; Dr. Robin Price, Co-Ed. ISSN: 0957-1752. Subscription Rates: 95 other countries; 35 individuals in UK; 85 individuals Europe. Remarks: Accepts advertising. URL: http://www.all-languages.org.uk/publications_journals.asp. Ad Rates: BW: 305. Circ: 900

53832 ■ Use of English
English Association
University of Leicester
University Rd.
Leicester LE1 7RH, United Kingdom
Ph: 44 116 2297622
Fax: 44 116 2297623
Publisher E-mail: engassoc@leicester.ac.uk
Publication covering the English language and English literature. Founded: 1950. Freq: 3/yr. ISSN: 0042-1243. Subscription Rates: 29 individuals; US$60 individuals; 46 institutions; US$92 institutions. URL: http://www.le.ac.uk/engassoc/publications/use.html. Ad Rates: BW: 350. Circ: (Not Reported)

53833 ■ Vida Hispanica
Association for Language Learning
University of Leicester
University Rd.
Leicester LE1 7RH, United Kingdom
Ph: 44 116 2297600
Fax: 44 116 2231488
Publisher E-mail: info@all-languages.org.uk
Publication covering language. Founded: June 1990. Freq: Semiannual. Key Personnel: Jill Szutenberg, Editor; Nuria Lopez, Review Ed., info@all-languages.org. uk. ISSN: 0308-4957. Subscription Rates: 70 individuals inside United Kingdom; 95 other countries; 85 other countries. Remarks: Accepts advertising. URL: http://www.all-languages.org.uk/publications_journals.asp. Ad Rates: BW: 430. Circ: 2,000

53834 ■ Young People Now
National Youth Agency
Eastgate House
19-23 Humberstone Rd.
Leicester LE5 3GJ, United Kingdom
Ph: 44 116 2427350
Fax: 44 116 2427444
Publication E-mail: ypn.editorial@haymarket.com
Publisher E-mail: nya@nya.org.uk
Professional magazine for youth workers and related professionals. Founded: 1990. Freq: Weekly. Key Personnel: Ravi Chandiramani, Editor. ISSN: 0956-2843. Subscription Rates: 89 individuals; 160 two years. Remarks: Accepts advertising. URL: http://www.nya. org.uk/templates/system/journals.asp?nodeid=89074; http://www.cypnow.co.uk/News/ByDiscipline/Youth-

Work/. Ad Rates: BW: 595. Circ: Paid 4,000

53835 ■ Youth Policy Update
National Youth Agency
Eastgate House
19-23 Humberstone Rd.
Leicester LE5 3GJ, United Kingdom
Ph: 44 116 2427350
Fax: 44 116 2427444
Publisher E-mail: nya@nya.org.uk
Publication covering youth service, youth policy and youth affairs for managers of youth services. Subtitle: Policy Briefings and Commentaries for Managers of Youth Services. Founded: 1988. Freq: 10/yr. Print Method: Litho. Trim Size: 297 x 210 mm. Key Personnel: Kerry Williams, Consultant; Alex Stutz, Editor. Subscription Rates: 30 individuals; 3.50 single issue. Remarks: Accepts advertising. URL: http://www.nya. uk/. Circ: 1,250

53836 ■ BBC Radio Leicester-FM - 104.9
9 St. Nicholas Pl.
Leicester LE1 5LB, United Kingdom
Ph: 44 116 2516688
E-mail: leicester@bbc.co.uk
Format: Talk; News; Oldies; Sports. Owner: British Broadcasting Corporation, Broadcasting House, Portland Pl., London W1A 1AA, United Kingdom. Founded: Nov. 8, 1967. Operating Hours: Continuous. URL: http://www.bbc.co.uk/leicester/local_radio.

53837 ■ Demon-FM - 107.5
De Montfort University Students' Union
Campus Ctr., 1st Fl.
Mill Ln.
Leicester LE2 7DR, United Kingdom
Ph: 44 116 2506584
Format: Eclectic. Owner: De Montfort University, at above address. Operating Hours: Continuous. Key Personnel: Jeff Nunn, Station Mgr., manager@demonfm.co.uk. URL: http://www.demonfm.co.uk/.

Leigh

53838 ■ Leigh Journal
Newsquest Media Group Ltd.
44-46 Railway Rd.
Leigh WN7 4AT, United Kingdom
Ph: 44 1942 672241
Newspaper featuring local news and events. Key Personnel: Steve Leary, Editor, steve.leary@cheshire. newsquest.co.uk; Brian Gomm, News Ed., bgomm@leighjournal.co.uk. Remarks: Accepts advertising. URL: http://www.thisisleigh.co.uk/. Circ: (Not Reported)

Leighton Buzzard

53839 ■ Leighton Buzzard Observer
Johnston Press PLC
17 Bridge St.
Leighton Buzzard LU7 1AH, United Kingdom
Ph: 44 1525 858400
Community newspaper. Founded: 1861. Freq: Weekly (Tues.). Print Method: Web offset. Cols./Page: 9. Col. Depth: 360 millimeters. Key Personnel: Melissa Lynch, Contact; Lynn Hughes, Editor, phone 44 1582 798514, lynn.hughes@jpress.co.uk. Subscription Rates: 62.40 individuals. Remarks: Accepts advertising. URL: http://www.leightonbuzzardonline.co.uk/. Circ: Controlled 7,945

Leominster

53840 ■ Day One Diary
Lord's Day Observance Society
Day One Christian Ministries
Ryelands Rd.
Leominster HR6 8NZ, United Kingdom
Ph: 44 15 68613740
Fax: 44 15 68611473
Publisher E-mail: info@dayone.co.uk
Religious journal. Founded: 1926. Freq: Annual. Key Personnel: John Roberts, Director. Subscription Rates: 1,025 single issue. Remarks: Advertising not accepted. URL: http://www.docm.co.uk. Former name: Happy Day Diary. Circ: Combined 160,000

Lerwick

53841 ■ The New Shetlander
Shetland Council of Social Service
14 Market St.
Lerwick ZE1 0JP, United Kingdom
Ph: 44 1595743900
Fax: 44 1595696787
Publication E-mail: shetlander@zetnet.co.uk
Publisher E-mail: scss@shetland.org
Consumer magazine covering literature, poetry and fiction. Founded: 1959. Freq: Quarterly. Subscription Rates: 11 individuals; 12.50 out of country surface mail; 17 out of country airmail. Remarks: Accepts advertising. URL: http://www.shetlandcss.co.uk/. Circ: Combined 1,900

53842 ■ Shetland Fishing News
Shetland Seafood News Ltd.
Shetland Seafood Centre
Stewart Bldg.
Lerwick ZE1 0LL, United Kingdom
Publisher E-mail: sfa@zetnet.co.uk
Newspaper for the seafood industry. Subtitle: The Journal of Shetland's Fishing Industries. Freq: Monthly. Cols./Page: 6. Key Personnel: Karen Inkster, Editor. ISSN: 1471-1982. Subscription Rates: 8.40 individuals U.K.; 12 other countries surface mail; 18.72 by mail U.S., airmail; 20.16 by mail Australasia, airmail; 13.32 by mail Europe, airmail. Remarks: Accepts advertising. URL: http://www.users.zetnet.co.uk; http://www.users. zetnet.co.uk/sfn/old/index.htm. Ad Rates: BW: 515, 4C: 672. Circ: Combined 1,440

53843 ■ SIBC-FM - 96.2
Market St.
Lerwick ZE1 0JN, United Kingdom
Ph: 44 1595 695299
Fax: 44 1595 695696
Format: Adult Contemporary; Contemporary Hit Radio (CHR). Owner: Shetland Islands Broadcasting Company, at above address. Ad Rates: Advertising accepted; rates available upon request. URL: http://www.sibc.co.uk/index.html.

53844 ■ SIBC-FM - 102.2
Market St.
Lerwick ZE1 0JN, United Kingdom
Ph: 44 1595 695299
Fax: 44 1595 695696
Format: Adult Contemporary; Contemporary Hit Radio (CHR). Owner: Shetland Islands Broadcasting Company, at above address. Ad Rates: Advertising accepted; rates available upon request. URL: http://www.sibc.co.uk/index.html.

Leven

53845 ■ Buses
Ian Allan Publishing Ltd.
c/o Alan Millar, Ed.
PO Box 14644
Leven KY9 1WX, United Kingdom
Ph: 44 1333 340637
Fax: 44 1333 340608
Publisher E-mail: info@ianallanpublishing.co.uk
Magazine covering the bus and coach industries. Founded: 1949. Freq: Monthly. Key Personnel: Alan Millar, Editor, buseseditor@btconnect.com; David Lane, Commercial Mgr., phone 44 1780 484633, david.lane@ianallanpublishing.co.uk. Remarks: Accepts advertising. URL: http://www.busesmag.com/. Circ: (Not Reported)

Levenshulme

53846 ■ All-FM - 96.9
19 Albert Rd.
Levenshulme M19 2EQ, United Kingdom
Ph: 44 61 2486888
E-mail: info@allfm.org
Format: Hip Hop; Jazz; World Beat; Blues; Eclectic; Alternative/New Music/Progressive. Owner: Community Media Association, 15 Paternoster Row, Sheffield S1 2BX, United Kingdom, 44 114 2795219, Fax: 44 114 2798976. Operating Hours: Continuous. Key Personnel: Gina Hine, Bus. Devel. Mgr., phone 44 61 2489988, gina@allfm.org; Danielle Porter, Community Engagement Off., danielle@allfm.org. Ad Rates: Advertising accepted; rates available upon request. URL: http://www.allfm.org.

Lewes

53847 ■ Black and White Photography
Guild of Master Craftsmen Publications Ltd.
166 High St.
E Sussex
Lewes BN7 1XU, United Kingdom
Ph: 44 1273 477374
Magazine for monochrome photographers. **Freq:** Monthly. **Subscription Rates:** 43.09 individuals; 76.61 two years; 53.87 individuals Europe; 95.76 two years Europe; 60.33 individuals rest of world; 107.25 two years rest of world. **Remarks:** Accepts advertising. **URL:** http://www.thegmcgroup.com/item--black-and-white-photography--1003bw.htmlquicklink. **Circ:** (Not Reported)

53848 ■ The Chap
2 Mount Pl.
Lewes BN7 1YH, United Kingdom
Publisher E-mail: post@thechap.net
Magazine featuring the editors random musings. **Founded:** 1999. **Freq:** Quarterly. **Key Personnel:** Gustav Temple, Contact, gustav@thechap.net. **Subscription Rates:** 20 individuals U.K.; 36 other countries; 30 individuals Europe. **URL:** http://www.thechap.net.

53849 ■ Furniture and Cabinetmaking
Guild of Master Craftsmen Publications Ltd.
166 High St.
E Sussex
Lewes BN7 1XU, United Kingdom
Ph: 44 1273 477374
Woodworking magazine featuring furniture making. **Freq:** Monthly. **Key Personnel:** Sue Bennett, Contact, sueb@thegmcgroup.com. **Subscription Rates:** 40 individuals; 72 two years; 50 individuals Europe; 90 two years Europe; 56 other countries; 100 other countries 2 years. **Remarks:** Accepts advertising. **URL:** http://www.thegmcgroup.com/item--furniture-and-cabinet-making--1010fc.html. **Circ:** (Not Reported)

53850 ■ Organic Life
Guild of Master Craftsmen Publications Ltd.
166 High St.
E Sussex
Lewes BN7 1XU, United Kingdom
Ph: 44 1273 477374
Health magazine featuring organic diets. **Subtitle:** Helping you make a difference. **Founded:** Nov. 2005. **Freq:** Monthly. **Key Personnel:** Helen Vintner, Editor, phone 44 1273 402809, helenv@thegmcgroup.com; Sue Bennett, Contact, sueb@thegmcgroup.com. **Subscription Rates:** 32.25 12 issues; 57.25 24 issues; 40.25 other countries 12 issues; 71.75 other countries 24 issues. **Remarks:** Accepts advertising. **URL:** http://www.organic-life.net/; http://www.thegmcgroup.com/item--organic-life-magazine--1012ol.html. **Ad Rates:** 4C: 1,500. **Circ:** (Not Reported)

53851 ■ Wood Working Plans and Projects
Guild of Master Craftsmen Publications Ltd.
166 High St.
E Sussex
Lewes BN7 1XU, United Kingdom
Ph: 44 1273 477374
Magazine featuring woodworking tools and techniques. **Freq:** Monthly. **Subscription Rates:** 37.80 individuals; 67.20 two years; 47.25 other countries Europe; 84 two years Europe; 52.92 individuals rest of world; 94.80 two years rest of the world. **Remarks:** Accepts advertising. **URL:** http://www.thegmcgroup.com/item--woodworking-plans-projects--1013wp.html. **Circ:** (Not Reported)

53852 ■ Woodcarving
Guild of Master Craftsmen Publications Ltd.
166 High St.
E Sussex
Lewes BN7 1XU, United Kingdom
Ph: 44 1273 477374
Magazine featuring wood works. **Freq:** Monthly. **Key Personnel:** Stuart Lawson, Editor, Sue Bennett, Contact, sueb@thegmcgroup.com. **Subscription Rates:** 18.90 individuals six issues; 33.60 individuals; 23.63 individuals Europe, six issues; 42 individuals Europe; 26.46 other countries six issues; 47.04 other countries. **Remarks:** Accepts advertising. **URL:** http://www.thegmcgroup.com/item--woodcarving--1007wc.html;

http://www.woodworkersinstitute.com/page.asp?p=5. **Circ:** (Not Reported)

Lichfield

53853 ■ Management Services
Institute of Management Services
Brooke House
24 Dam St.
Staffordshire
Lichfield WS13 6AB, United Kingdom
Ph: 44 1543 266909
Fax: 44 1543 257848
Publication E-mail: editorial@msjournal.org.uk
Publisher E-mail: admin@ims-stowe.fsnet.co.uk
Trade publication covering management. **Founded:** 1946. **Freq:** Quarterly. **Print Method:** Sheetfed Offset Litho. **Trim Size:** 297 x 210 mm. **Key Personnel:** Melanie Armstrong, Editor, phone 44 1795 542436. **ISSN:** 0307-6768. **Subscription Rates:** 45 individuals; 3.80 single issue. **URL:** http://www.ims-productivity.com/; http://www.msjournal.org.uk/. **Ad Rates:** BW: 995, 4C: 1,395. **Circ:** 4,500

Limavady

53854 ■ Roe Valley Sentinel
Morton Newspapers
32A Market St.
Limavady BT49 0AA, United Kingdom
Ph: 44 28 77764090
Fax: 44 28 77722234
Community newspaper. **Freq:** Weekly (Wed.). **Print Method:** Offset. **Col. Depth:** 450 millimeters. **Remarks:** Accepts advertising. **URL:** http://www.roevalleytoday.co.uk/. **Circ:** Combined 5,321

Lincoln

53855 ■ Dream Catcher
4 Church St.
Market Rasen
Lincoln LN8 3ET, United Kingdom
Ph: 44 1673 844325
Magazine containing contemporary writing including poetry, prose, artwork and reviews. **Founded:** 1996. **Freq:** 3/yr. **Key Personnel:** Paul Sutherland, Editor. **Subscription Rates:** 15 individuals; 19 individuals Europe; 25 U.S. and Canada. **URL:** http://www.dreamcatchermagazine.co.uk/page132.aspx.

53856 ■ International Journal of Entrepreneurship and Innovation
IP Publishing Ltd.
c/o Gerard McElwee, Ed.
Lincoln Business School
University of Lincoln
Brayford Pool
Lincoln LN6 7TS, United Kingdom
Publisher E-mail: jedmondson@ippublishing.com
Peer-reviewed journal covering the development and application of entrepreneurship worldwide. **Subtitle:** 02002000. **Founded:** 2000. **Freq:** Quarterly. **Key Personnel:** Gerard McElwee, Editor, gmoelwee@lincoln.ac.uk, Prof. Leo Paul Dana, Editorial Advisory Board; Prof Alistair R. Anderson, Editorial Advisory Board; Clifford Conway, Internet Review Ed., c.conway@brighton.ac.uk. **ISSN:** 1465-7503. **Subscription Rates:** US$316 institutions; EUR303 institutions; 210 institutions, other countries in sterling. **Remarks:** Accepts advertising. **URL:** http://www.ippublishing.com/ei.htm. **Circ:** (Not Reported)

53857 ■ Lincs-FM - 102.2
Witham Pk.
Waterside S
Lincoln LN5 7JN, United Kingdom
Ph: 44 1522 549900
Fax: 44 1522 549911
E-mail: studio@lincsfm.co.uk
Format: Adult Contemporary; News; Talk; Sports; Oldies. **Operating Hours:** Continuous. **Ad Rates:** Advertising accepted; rates available upon request. **URL:** http://www.lincsfm.co.uk/.

Linlithgow

53858 ■ Bo'ness Journal
Johnston Press PLC

114 High St.
Linlithgow EH49 7AQ, United Kingdom
Ph: 44 1506 844592
Local community newspaper. **Remarks:** Accepts advertising. **URL:** http://www.bonessjournal.co.uk/. **Circ:** (Not Reported)

53859 ■ Linlithgow Gazette
Johnston Press PLC
114 High St.
Linlithgow EH49 7AQ, United Kingdom
Ph: 44 1506 844592
Local community newspaper. **Remarks:** Accepts advertising. **URL:** http://www.linlithgowgazette.co.uk/. **Circ:** (Not Reported)

53860 ■ Queensferry Gazette
Johnston Press PLC
114 High St.
Linlithgow EH49 7AQ, United Kingdom
Ph: 44 1506 844592
Local community newspaper. **Remarks:** Accepts advertising. **URL:** http://www.queensferrygazette.co.uk/. **Circ:** (Not Reported)

Liphook

53861 ■ Process Industry Informer
Process Products Ltd.
Passfield Business Center
Lynchborough Rd.
Passfield
Liphook GU30 7SB, United Kingdom
Ph: 44 1428 751188
Fax: 44 1428 751199
Publication E-mail: info@piimag.com
Publisher E-mail: info@piimag.com
Professional magazine covering process and chemical engineering equipment, products, applications and news. **Founded:** 1994. **Freq:** 6/yr. **Print Method:** Web. **Trim Size:** 290 x 365 mm. **Cols./Page:** 4. **Col. Width:** 62 centimeters. **Col. Depth:** 332 millimeters. **Key Personnel:** Peter Ullmann, Publisher/Advertisement Mgr., phone 44 142 8751188, fax 44 142 8751199, peterullmann@piimag.com; Phil Black, Editor, philblack@piimag.com. **Subscription Rates:** 25 individuals Europe; 50 single issue rest of the world. **Remarks:** Accepts advertising. **URL:** http://www.processpublications.co.uk. **Formerly:** Process Products (Sept. 2005). **Ad Rates:** BW: 3,150, 4C: 3,250. **Circ:** ‡4,000

Lisburn

53862 ■ Lisburn Echo
Morton Newspapers
12A Bow St.
Lisburn BT28 1BN, United Kingdom
Fax: 44 28 92609111
Community newspaper. **Freq:** Weekly (Wed.). **Print Method:** Offset. **Col. Depth:** 450 millimeters. **Key Personnel:** David Fletcher, Editor. **Subscription Rates:** Free. **Remarks:** Accepts advertising. **URL:** http://members.scotsman.com/terms-companies.cfm. **Circ:** Controlled ‡18,903

53863 ■ Ulster Star
Johnston Press PLC
12A Bow St.
Lisburn BT28 1BN, United Kingdom
Ph: 44 2892 679111
Fax: 44 2892 602904
Publication E-mail: news@ulsterstar.co.uk
Community newspaper. **Freq:** Weekly (Fri.). **Print Method:** Offset. **Col. Depth:** 450 millimeters. **Key Personnel:** Gary Ellis, Sports Ed., gary.ellis@jpress.co.uk; David Fletcher, Editor, david.fletcher@ulsterstar.co.uk. **Remarks:** Accepts advertising. **URL:** http://www.lisburntoday.co.uk/. **Circ:** Combined 12,684

Liskeard

53864 ■ Warship World
Maritime Books
Lodge Hill
Liskeard PL14 4EL, United Kingdom
Ph: 44 15 79343663
Fax: 44 15 79346747

Circulation: ★ = ABC; △ = BPA; ♦ = CAC; • = CCAB; ❏ = VAC; ⊕ = PO Statement; ‡ = Publisher's Report; Boldface figures = sworn; Light figures = estimated.

Gale Directory of Publications & Broadcast Media/147th Ed.

5675

Publisher E-mail: sales@navybooks.com
Journal covering current and historical naval matters. **Founded:** 1985. **Freq:** Bimonthly. **Trim Size:** 180 x 260 mm. **Cols./Page:** 3. **Key Personnel:** Mike Critchley, Publisher; Ben Warlow, Consultant Ed.; Steve Bush, Editor. **ISSN:** 1464-0511. **Subscription Rates:** 22 individuals U.K.; 26.50 individuals surface mail; 31 individuals airmail. **Remarks:** Accepts advertising. **URL:** http://www.navybooks.com/asps/Extra1.asp. **Circ:** Combined ‡4,000

Littlehampton

53865 ■ Littlehampton Gazette
Johnston Press PLC
34 Beach Rd.
Littlehampton BN17 5HT, United Kingdom
Ph: 44 1903 714135
Local community newspaper. **Founded:** 1896. **Freq:** Weekly (Thurs.). **Key Personnel:** Roger Green, Editor, fax 44 1903 739060, roger.green@littlehamptontoday.co.uk; Amanda Barrell, Reporter, amanda.barrell@littlehamptongazette.co.uk. **Remarks:** Accepts advertising. **URL:** http://www.littlehamptongazette.co.uk/. **Circ:** (Not Reported)

53866 ■ Smart Card News
Smart Card News Ltd.
Anchor Springs, Ste. 3
Duke St.
Littlehampton BN17 6BP, United Kingdom
Ph: 44 1903 734677
Fax: 44 1903 734318
Publication E-mail: info@smartcardgroup.com
Publisher E-mail: info@smartcard.co.uk
Professional magazine covering the smart card industry. **Founded:** 1992. **Freq:** Daily. **Key Personnel:** Patsy Everett, Mng. Dir., patsy.everett@smartcard.co.uk; Jack Smith, News Ed., Production Ed., jason.smith@smartcard.co.uk; Dr. David B. Everett, Tech. Ed. **Subscription Rates:** 495 individuals. **Remarks:** Accepts advertising. **URL:** http://www.smartcard.co.uk/aboutus.html. **Circ:** (Not Reported)

Littleport

53867 ■ Training Journal
Fenman Ltd.
Unit 2 e-space N
181 Wisbech Rd.
Cambridgeshire
Littleport CB6 1RA, United Kingdom
Ph: 44 13 53865350
Fax: 44 13 53865351
Publication E-mail: contact@trainingjournal.com
Publisher E-mail: service@fenman.co.uk
Journal covering management development training issues. **Founded:** 1965. **Freq:** Monthly. **Print Method:** Sheetfed litho. **Trim Size:** 210 x 297 mm. **Key Personnel:** Debbie Carter, Editor, debbiecarter@trainingjournal.com. **ISSN:** 1465-6523. **Subscription Rates:** 155 individuals; 248 two years; 172.50 individuals Europe; 276 two years Europe; 214 other countries; 342 two years other countries; 336.40 individuals 3 years, Europe. **Remarks:** Accepts advertising. **URL:** http://www.trainingjournal.com. **Ad Rates:** 4C: 1,095. **Circ:** Paid 3,500

Liverpool

53868 ■ Before Farming, the Archaeology and Anthropology of Hunter-Gatherers
Western Academic & Specialist Press Limited
PO Box 191
Liverpool L23 3WZ, United Kingdom
Ph: 44 15 19321312
Journal for archaeologists and anthropologists engaged in research on hunter-gatherers from past and present. **Founded:** 2002. **Freq:** Quarterly. **Key Personnel:** Larry Barham, Editor, l.s.barham@liverpool.ac.uk; Michael Alvard, Assoc. Ed., alvard@tamu.edu; Kenneth Ames, Assoc. Ed., amesk@pdx.edu. **ISSN:** 1476-4261. **Subscription Rates:** 36 individuals; 38 individuals Western Europe; 40 individuals rest of world; 110 institutions online & print; 85 institutions online only. **URL:** http://www.waspress.co.uk/journals/beforefarming/.

53869 ■ Biological Conservation
Elsevier Science

c/o R. Marrs, Editorial Board
Applied Vegetation Dynamics Lab.
School of Biological Sciences
Liverpool L69 7ZB, United Kingdom
Publisher E-mail: nlinfo-f@elsevier.com
Journal on protection of wildlife and its habitats, and judicious use of biological and allied natural resources. **Founded:** 1969. **Freq:** Monthly. **Key Personnel:** A.B. Gill, Editor, a.b.gill@cranfield.ac.uk; R. Marrs, Editorial Board; J.P. Metzger, Editor, jpm@b.usp.br; R.B. Primack, Editor-in-Chief, primack@bu.edu; R. Corlett, Editor, corlett@hkucc.hku.hk; Denis A. Saunders, Editorial Board. **ISSN:** 0006-3207. **Subscription Rates:** US$3,469 institutions for all countries except Europe, Japan & Iran; 411,300¥ institutions; EUR3,100 institutions for European countries & Iran. **Remarks:** Accepts advertising. **URL:** http://www.elsevier.com/wps/find/journaldescription.cws_home/405853/description; http://www.elsevier.com/wps/find/journaldescription.cws_home/405853/descrip tiondescription. **Circ:** (Not Reported)

53870 ■ Engineering Optimization
Taylor & Francis Group Journals
Dept. of Civil Engineering
University of Liverpool
PO Box 147
Liverpool L69 3GQ, United Kingdom
Publisher E-mail: customerservice@taylorandfrancis.com
Peer-reviewed journal aiming to serve all disciplines within the engineering community. **Freq:** 12/yr. **Key Personnel:** Prof. Andrew B. Templeman, Editor, a.b.templeman@liverpool.ac.uk; J.A. Bland, Editorial Advisory Board; J. Blachut, Editorial Advisory Board; C.A. Coello, Editorial Advisory Board; S.-K. Fan, Assoc. Ed.; Y. Kim, Assoc. Ed. **ISSN:** 0305-215X. **Subscription Rates:** US$5,034 institutions print and online; US$4,783 institutions online; US$623 individuals; 3,879 institutions print and online; 3,686 institutions online; 514 individuals; EUR3,808 institutions online only. **URL:** http://www.tandf.co.uk/journals/titles/0305215x.asp.

53871 ■ European Journal of Social Theory
Sage Publications Ltd.
c/o Gerard Delanty, Ed.
Dept. of Sociology
The University of Liverpool, Eleanor Rathbone Bldg.
Bedford St. S
Liverpool L69 7ZA, United Kingdom
Scholarly journal covering social theory. **Founded:** 1998. **Freq:** Quarterly. **Key Personnel:** Gerard Delanty, Editor; Heidrun Friese, Assoc. Ed.; Hans Joas, International Editorial Board; Thora Margareta Bertilsson, International Editorial Board; Peter Wagner, Assoc. Ed.; Piotr Sztompka, International Editorial Board. **ISSN:** 1368-4310. **Subscription Rates:** US$931 institutions combined (print & e-access); US$1,024 institutions plus backfile (current volume print & all online); US$838 institutions e-access; US$931 institutions e-access plus backfile (all online content); US$838 institutions e-access (content through 1998); US$912 institutions print only; US$100 individuals print only; US$251 institutions single print; US$33 individuals single print. **Remarks:** Accepts advertising. **URL:** http://www.sagepub.com/journalsProdDesc.nav?prodId=Journal200815. **Circ:** (Not Reported)

53872 ■ Fieldwork in Religion
Equinox Publishing Ltd.
c/o Ron Geaves, Ed.
Dept. of Theology & Religious Studies
Liverpool Hope University
Hope Pk.
Liverpool L16 9JD, United Kingdom
Peer-reviewed journal covering aspects of the empirical study of contemporary religion. **Freq:** Semiannual. **Key Personnel:** Andrew Dawson, Editor, andrew.dawson@lancaster.ac.uk; Ron Geaves, Editor, geavesr@hope.ac.uk. **ISSN:** 1743-0615. **Subscription Rates:** 95 institutions, other countries print and online; US$190 institutions print and online; 53 individuals print; US$105 individuals print; 35 students print; US$67.50 students print; 45 institutions developing countries. **Remarks:** Accepts advertising. **URL:** http://www.equinoxjournals.com/ojs/index.php/FIR. **Circ:** (Not Reported)

53873 ■ Fingerprint Whorld
Fingerprint Society
Fingerprint Bureau
2nd Fl., Norwich House

Water St.
Liverpool L2 9XR, United Kingdom
Peer-reviewed journal covering the study of fingerprints and the field of personal identification. **Freq:** Quarterly. **Key Personnel:** Phil Swindells, Subscription Sec.; Robert Doak, Chm. **ISSN:** 0951-1288. **URL:** http://www.fpsociety.org.uk/thejournal/index.html.

53874 ■ International Journal of Law and Management
Emerald Group Publishing Ltd.
Faculty of Business & Law
Liverpool John Moores University
John Foster Bldg.
98 Mt. Pleasant
Liverpool L3 5UZ, United Kingdom
Publisher E-mail: emerald@emeraldinsight.com
International journal for business managers. Looking at the law as one of the external environments of business with which managers should and must be familiar, considering how the law works and how it affects decision-making at all levels, aiming to: inform all areas of business through presenting the latest research and developments in managerial and business law and provide an independent and international research platform for academics, consultants and practitioners to share knowledge and experiences. **Subtitle:** The International Journal of Law and Management. **Freq:** 6/yr. **Key Personnel:** Prof. Clive Smallman, Editorial Advisory Board; Andrew Smith, Publisher, agsmith@emeraldinsight.com; Prof. David Milman, Editorial Advisory Board; Prof. Chris Gale, Book Review Ed.; Prof. James Kirkbride, Editor, j.kirkbride@livjm.ac.uk; Prof. John Birds, Editorial Advisory Board; Prof. Steve Letza, Editorial Advisory Board; Prof. Geraint Howells, Editor, geraint.howells@manchester.ac.uk. **ISSN:** 1754-243X. **URL:** http://www.emeraldinsight.com/products/journals/journals.htm?id=ijlma. **Formerly:** Managerial Law.

53875 ■ Journal of Latin American Studies
Cambridge University Press
c/o Dr. Rory Miller, Ed.
University of Liverpool
Management School
Chatham St.
Liverpool L69 7ZH, United Kingdom
Publisher E-mail: information@cambridge.org
Regional focus/area studies publication. **Freq:** Quarterly. **Key Personnel:** Prof. Paul Cammack, Editorial Board; Dr. Paulo Drinot, Editorial Board; Dr. Rory Miller, Editor; Dr. Gareth A. Jones, Editor; Dr. Fiona Macaulay, Editor; Prof. Nicola Phillips, Editorial Board. **ISSN:** 0022-216X. **Subscription Rates:** US$391 institutions online and print; US$352 institutions online only; 200 institutions online only; 220 institutions online and print. **Remarks:** Accepts advertising. **URL:** http://journals.cambridge.org/action/displayJournal?jid=LAS. **Ad Rates:** BW: US$895. **Circ:** 1,900

53876 ■ Modern Believing
Modern Churchpeople's Union
MCU Office
9 Westward View
Liverpool L17 7EE, United Kingdom
Ph: 44 15 17269730
Publication E-mail: a.hyde@lamp.ac.uk
Publisher E-mail: office@modchurchunion.org
Publication covering Liberal theology in the Anglican World. **Subtitle:** Church and Society. **Founded:** 1911. **Freq:** Quarterly. **Print Method:** Offset. **Trim Size:** 15 x 23 cm. **Key Personnel:** Prof. Paul Badham, Editor; Rev. Michael Brierley, Reviews Ed. **ISSN:** 1353-1425. **Subscription Rates:** 8.75 single issue; 10.50 single issue non-U.K. **Remarks:** Advertising accepted; rates available upon request. **URL:** http://www.modchurchunion.org; http://www.modchurchunion.org/publications/mb/index.htm. **Formerly:** Modern Churchman. **Circ:** 750

53877 ■ Open Government
c/o Steve Wood
School of Business Information
Liverpool John Moores University
Liverpool L3 5UZ, United Kingdom
Ph: 44 15 12313589
Fax: 44 15 17070423
Publisher E-mail: s.wood@livjm.ac.uk
Open access, peer-reviewed journal that covers open government and freedom of information. **Freq:** Biennial.

Key Personnel: Marc-Aurele Racicot, Editor, maracicot@gmail.com. **ISSN:** 1745-8293. **Subscription Rates:** Free online. **URL:** http://www.opengovjournal. org.

53878 ■ Social Enterprise Journal
Emerald Group Publishing Ltd.
c/o Dr. Bob Doherty, Editor
Liverpool Hope University, Hope Business School
Hope Pk.
Liverpool L16 9JD, United Kingdom
Publisher E-mail: emerald@emeraldinsight.com
Journal focusing on entrepreneurial activity. **Freq:** Irregular. **Key Personnel:** Dr. Bob Doherty, Editor, dohertb@hope.ac.uk; Andrew Smith, Publisher, agsmith@emeraldinsight.com. **ISSN:** 1750-8614. **URL:** http://info.emeraldinsight.com/products/journals/journals. htm?id=sej.

53879 ■ BBC Merseyside-FM - 95.8
PO Box 95.8
Liverpool L69 1ZJ, United Kingdom
Ph: 44 151 7085500
E-mail: liverpool@bbc.co.uk
Format: Talk; News; Oldies; Sports. **Owner:** British Broadcasting Corp., Broadcasting House, Portland Pl., London W1A 1AA, United Kingdom. **Founded:** Nov. 22, 1967. **Operating Hours:** Continuous. **URL:** http://www. bbc.co.uk/liverpool/local_radio.

53880 ■ Citytalk-FM - 105.9
St. Johns Beacon
1 Houghton St.
Liverpool L1 1RL, United Kingdom
Ph: 44 151 7081059
Fax: 44 151 4726821
Format: Talk; Sports; News. **Ad Rates:** Advertising accepted; rates available upon request. **URL:** http://www. citytalk.fm/.

53881 ■ Juice-FM - 107.6
27 Fleet St.
Liverpool L1 4AR, United Kingdom
Ph: 44 151 7073107
Fax: 44 151 7079702
E-mail: info@juiceliverpool.com
Format: Contemporary Hit Radio (CHR). **Key Personnel:** Graham Sarath, Station Dir., graham.sarath@ juiceliverpool.com; Sue Green, Promotions Mgr., sue@ juiceliverpool.com. **Ad Rates:** Advertising accepted; rates available upon request. **URL:** http://www.juicefm. com/.

53882 ■ Magic-AM - 1548
St. John's Beacon
1 Houghton St.
Liverpool L1 1RL, United Kingdom
Ph: 44 151 4726800
Fax: 44 151 4726801
Format: Oldies. **URL:** http://www.magic1548.com/.

53883 ■ Radio City-FM - 96.7 MHz
1 Houghton St.
Liverpool L1 1RL, United Kingdom
Ph: 44 151 4726800
E-mail: jonathan.breeze@radiocity.co.uk
Format: News; Contemporary Hit Radio (CHR). **Owner:** Emap PLC, 40 Bernard St., London WC1N 1LW, United Kingdom. **Operating Hours:** Continuous. **Key Personnel:** Richard Maddock, Station Dir.; Steve Hothersall, News Ed. **Ad Rates:** Advertising accepted; rates available upon request. **URL:** http://www.radiocity.co.uk.

Llandovery

53884 ■ The London Naturalist
London Natural History Society
c/o Keith H. Hyatt, Ed.
1 Tremcelynog
Rhandirmwyn
Carmarthenshire
Llandovery SA20 0NU, United Kingdom
Journal containing refereed articles. **Freq:** Annual. **Key Personnel:** Keith H. Hyatt, Editor. **ISSN:** 0076-0579. **URL:** http://www.lnhs.org.uk/publications.htm.

Llanelli

53885 ■ Welsh Music
Welsh Music Guild

Bronfelin
17 Penyrheol Dr.
Heol Felinfoel
Sir Gaerfyrddin
Llanelli SA15 3NX, United Kingdom
Publication E-mail: guild.info@ntlworld.com
Publisher E-mail: guild.info@ntlworld.com
Publication covering Welsh music. **Freq:** 3/yr. **Key Personnel:** Heward A.J. Rees, Editor. **Remarks:** Advertising accepted; rates available upon request. **URL:** http:// www.welshmusic.org.uk/welsh_music.htm. **Foreign language name:** Cerddoriaeth Cymru. **Circ:** (Not Reported)

53886 ■ Radio Carmarthenshire-FM - 97.1
PO Box 971
Carmarthenshire
Llanelli SA15 1YH, United Kingdom
Ph: 44 845 8907000
Fax: 44 845 8905000
E-mail: studio@radiocarmarthenshire.com
Format: Adult Contemporary. **Ad Rates:** Advertising accepted; rates available upon request. **URL:** http://www. radiocarmarthenshire.com/.

Lochgilphead

53887 ■ Argyllshire Advertiser
Wyvex Media Limited
Argyll St.
Argyll
Lochgilphead PA31 8NB, United Kingdom
Ph: 44 1546 602345
Fax: 44 1546 602661
Publisher E-mail: info@wyvexmedia.co.uk
Local newspaper covering Lochgilphead and the surrounding area. **Founded:** 1886. **Subscription Rates:** 57 individuals; 98 two years; 77 other countries; 138 other countries 2 years. **URL:** http://www. argyllshireadvertiser.co.uk/.

Lockerbie

53888 ■ Primary Care Respiratory Journal
Primary Care Respiratory Society UK
Smithy House
Waterbeck
Lockerbie 1G11 3EY, United Kingdom
Ph: 44 121 3514455
Fax: 44 121 3361914
Peer-reviewed journal covering all aspects of common respiratory conditions and allergy. **Subtitle:** Journal of the General Practice Airways Group and the Official Journal of the International Primary Care Respiratory Group. **Founded:** 2004. **Freq:** Bimonthly. **Key Personnel:** Mark Levy, MD, Editor-in-Chief; Paul Stephenson, Dep. Ed.; Peter Barnes, International Editorial Board; Chris Griffiths, Asst. Ed.; Aziz Sheikh, Asst. Ed.; Robert McKinley, Asst. Ed. **ISSN:** 1471-4418. **Remarks:** Accepts advertising. **URL:** http://www.thepcrj.org/. **Ad Rates:** BW: 525, 4C: 990. **Circ:** (Not Reported)

London

53889 ■ AB Europe
Centaur Communications Ltd.
St. Giles House
50 Poland St.
London W1V 4AX, United Kingdom
Ph: 44 20 79704000
Fax: 44 20 79704894
Trade magazine covering the amusement and leisure industry in Europe. **Founded:** 1994. **Freq:** Monthly. **Print Method:** Web. **Trim Size:** A4. **Cols./Page:** 4. **Remarks:** Accepts advertising. **URL:** http://randyfromm.com/ amusements/press.htm. **Former name:** Amusement Business. **Circ:** Controlled 8,300

53890 ■ Access All Areas
Ocean Media Events Ltd.
1 Canada Sq.
London E14 5AA, United Kingdom
Ph: 44 20 77728300
Fax: 44 20 77728599
Trade magazine covering the exhibitions and events industry. **Freq:** Monthly 10/yr. **Key Personnel:** Lisa Gudge, Dep. Ed., lisa.gudge@oceanmedia.co.uk; Nic Howden, Editor, nic.howden@oceanmedia.co.uk. Re-

marks: Accepts advertising. **URL:** http://www.access-aa.co.uk/. **Circ:** Controlled 5,000

53891 ■ Accountancy
Institute of Chartered Accountants in England & Wales
Chartered Accountants' Hall
PO Box 433
London EC2R 6EA, United Kingdom
Ph: 44 20 79208100
Fax: 44 20 79200547
Publication for the banking, finance, and accounting industries. **Freq:** Monthly. **Key Personnel:** Juliana Sancto, Editor; Jonathon Keymer, Editorial Team. **ISSN:** 0001-4664. **Subscription Rates:** 81 individuals; 96.60 other countries; 58 students retired, career break. **URL:** http://www.icaew.co.uk. **Circ:** ⋆150,952

53892 ■ Accountancy Age
Incisive Media Limited
Haymarket House
28-29 Haymarket
London SW1Y 4RX, United Kingdom
Ph: 44 870 2408859
Fax: 44 207 4849797
Publisher E-mail: customerservices@incisivemedia.com
Newspaper featuring news and information for accounting and finance professionals. **Freq:** Weekly. **Key Personnel:** Damian Wild, Editor and Publisher, damian. wild@incisivemedia.com; Gavin Hinks, Editor. **Remarks:** Accepts advertising. **URL:** http://www.incisivemedia. com/corporate/products/accountancyage; http://www. accountancyage.com/. **Circ:** (Not Reported)

53893 ■ Accounting and Business Research
Institute of Chartered Accountants in England & Wales
Chartered Accountants' Hall
PO Box 433
London EC2R 6EA, United Kingdom
Ph: 44 20 79208100
Fax: 44 20 79200547
Publication for the banking, finance, and accounting industries. **Freq:** Quarterly. **Key Personnel:** K.V. Peasnell, Editor. **ISSN:** 0001-4788. **Subscription Rates:** 176 institutions U.K.; 189 institutions; 60 individuals U.K.; 69 individuals. **URL:** http://www.icaew.co.uk/; http://www. periodicals.com/html/ihp_e.html?ea00091.

53894 ■ ACE Bulletin
Advisory Centre for Education
Ic Aberdeen Studios, 22 Highbury Grove
London N5 2DQ, United Kingdom
Ph: 44 20 77043370
Fax: 44 20 73549069
Publisher E-mail: enquiries@ace-ed.org.uk
Education publication. **Freq:** Bimonthly. **Key Personnel:** Katy Simmons, Ch.; Rob Honeybourne, Vice Ch. **ISSN:** 0266-6278. **Subscription Rates:** 33 individuals; EUR38 individuals; 48 elsewhere. **Remarks:** Advertising accepted; rates available upon request. **URL:** http:// www.ace-ed.org.uk/bulletin/index.html. **Circ:** (Not Reported)

53895 ■ Acta Pharmacologica Sinica
Nature Publishing Group
The Macmillan Bldg.
4 Crinan St.
London N1 9XW, United Kingdom
Ph: 44 20 78334000
Fax: 44 20 78434640
Journal publishing current original research on all aspects of life sciences, both experimental and clinical, from any part of the world, especially reviews based primarily on authors' own research of internationally-important topics. **Freq:** Monthly. **Key Personnel:** Kai-Xian Chen, Editorial Board; Guan-hua Du, Assoc. Ed.-in-Ch.; Jian Ding, Editor-in-Chief; Alex F. Chen, Editorial Board; Guo-yuan Hu, Assoc. Ed.-in-Ch. **ISSN:** 1671-4083. **Subscription Rates:** US$465 individuals print and online; EUR379 individuals print and online; 64,800¥ individuals print and online; 245 individuals print and online; US$419 individuals online only; EUR341 individuals online only; 58,400¥ individuals online only; 221 individuals online only. **Remarks:** Advertising accepted; rates available upon request. **URL:** http://www.nature. com/aps/index.html. **Circ:** (Not Reported)

53896 ■ ACU Bulletin
Association of Commonwealth Universities
20-24 Tavistock Sq.
London WC1H 9HF, United Kingdom
Ph: 44 20 73806700

Circulation: ⋆ = ABC; △ = BPA; ♦ = CAC; • = CCAB; ❏ = VAC; ⊕ = PO Statement; ‡ = Publisher's Report; Boldface figures = sworn; Light figures = estimated.

Gale Directory of Publications & Broadcast Media/147th Ed.   5677

Fax: 44 20 73872655
Publication E-mail: bulletin@acu.ac.uk
Publisher E-mail: info@acu.ac.uk
Professional magazine covering higher education. **Freq:** 4/yr. **ISSN:** 0044-9563. **Subscription Rates:** Free member university. **Remarks:** Accepts advertising. **URL:** http://www.acu.ac.uk/member_services/bulletin. **Ad Rates:** BW: 1,130, 4C: 1,620. **Circ:** Controlled 5,000

53897 ■ Acute Coronary Syndromes
Remedica Publishing Ltd
Commonwealth House
1 New Oxford St.
London WC1A 1NUN, United Kingdom
Ph: 44 20 77592999
Fax: 44 20 77592951
Publication E-mail: info@acute-coronary-syndromes.com
Publisher E-mail: info@remedica.com
Journal providing clinical solutions and approaches to the treatment of acute coronary syndrome. **Freq:** Quarterly. **Key Personnel:** Glenn N. Levine, Editor-in-Chief; Charles L. Campbell, Editor-in-Chief; Tracy Y. Wang, Editor; Kimberley Skelding, Editor. **ISSN:** 1369-5312. **Subscription Rates:** 70 Free online and print, for healthcare professionals; US$80 U.S. and Canada; EUR80 individuals for Germany; Free only online for non-healthcare professionals. **URL:** http://www.remedicajournals.com/Acute-Coronary-Syndromes/.

53898 ■ Acute Medicine
Rila Publications Ltd.
73 Newman St.
London W1A 4PG, United Kingdom
Ph: 44 20 76311299
Fax: 44 20 75807166
Publisher E-mail: admin@rila.co.uk
Journal covering perspective of acute medicine. **Freq:** 3/yr. **Key Personnel:** Dr. C.D. Roseveare, Editor; Dr. Nicola cooper, Editorial Board. **ISSN:** 1747-4884. **URL:** http://www.rila.co.uk/site/modules.php?name=Journals&func=journal&jid=030.

53899 ■ Ad Trader
Trader Media Group
41-47 Hartfield Rd., 3rd & 4th Fl.
Wimbledon
London SW19 3RQ, United Kingdom
Ph: 44 208 5447000
Fax: 44 208 8791879
Newspaper covering everything from pets to property. **Freq:** Weekly. **Key Personnel:** John King, CEO. **Remarks:** Accepts advertising. **URL:** http://www.adtrader.co.uk/; http://www.tradermediagroup.com/companies/ad-trader.html. **Circ:** 128,000

53900 ■ Addiction
John Wiley & Sons Inc.
Wiley-Blackwell
c/o Robert West, Ed.-in-Ch.
National Addiction Ctr.
4 Windsor Walk
London SE5 8AF, United Kingdom
Peer-reviewed publication covering substance abuse. **Freq:** Monthly. **Key Personnel:** Robert West, Editor-in-Chief; Molly Jarvis, Ed. Mgr., molly@addictionjournal.org; Thomas F. Babor, Assoc. Ed.-in-Ch.; Gill Rangel, Journal Mgr.; Editorial Ed., gill@addictionjournal.org. **ISSN:** 0965-2140. **Subscription Rates:** US$686 individuals print + online; US$2,745 institutions print + online; US$2,495 institutions print or online; EUR554 individuals print + online; EUR1,886 institutions print + online; EUR1,715 institutions print or online; 408 other countries print + online; US$3,203 institutions, other countries print + online; US$2,911 institutions, other countries print or online; 1,486 institutions print + online. **Remarks:** Advertising accepted; rates available upon request. **URL:** http://www.wiley.com/bw/journal.asp?ref=0965-2140&site=1; http://www.addictionjournal.org. **Circ:** Paid 1,200

53901 ■ Addiction Abstracts
Taylor & Francis Ltd.
c/o Michael Gossop, Ed.
National Addiction Centre
4 Windsor Walk
London SE5 8AF, United Kingdom
Focused, unbiased and international abstracting service, spanning all addictive substances as well as other compulsive behaviours, containing the most up-to-date literature in psychology, psychiatry, public health medicine, health behaviour, treatment and prevention.

Freq: Quarterly. **Key Personnel:** Michael Gossop, Editor; Duncan Stewart, Asst. Ed.; John Witton, Asst. Ed.; Robert West, Assoc. Ed.; Zheng Chengzheng, International Advisory Board; Eva Congreve, International Advisory Board; Michael Farrell, Assoc. Ed.; Marc Auriacombe, International Advisory Board; Sheila Lacroix, International Advisory Board; Griffith Edwards, International Advisory Board. **ISSN:** 0968-7610. **Subscription Rates:** 545 institutions print and online; US$980 institutions print and online; 518 institutions online; US$930 institutions online; 271 individuals print only; US$460 individuals print only. **Remarks:** Accepts advertising. **URL:** http://www.informaworld.com/smpp/title~tab=jdb_customer_feedback?content=a717271395. **Circ:** (Not Reported)

53902 ■ Admap
WARC Ltd.
85 Newman St.
London W1T 3EX, United Kingdom
Ph: 44 20 74678100
Publisher E-mail: enquiries@warc.com
Trade magazine covering advertising. **Founded:** 1970. **Freq:** Monthly. **Key Personnel:** Colin Grimshaw, Editor, colin.grimshaw@warc.com. **ISSN:** 0001-8295. **Subscription Rates:** 320 individuals. **Remarks:** Accepts advertising. **URL:** http://store.warc.com/DisplaySection.aspx?ProductID=3. **Ad Rates:** BW: 1,452, 4C: 2,328. **Circ:** Controlled 2,500

53903 ■ Adoption and Fostering
British Association for Adoption and Fostering
Saffron House
6-10 Kirby St.
London EC1N 8TS, United Kingdom
Ph: 44 20 74212600
Fax: 44 20 74212601
Publisher E-mail: mail@baaf.org.uk
Interdisciplinary journal covering developments in child care research, adoption and foster care. **Founded:** 1953. **Freq:** Quarterly. **Trim Size:** 152 x 210 mm. **Key Personnel:** Miranda Davies, Production Ed., phone 44 20 74212608, fax 44 20 74212001, miranda.davies@baaf.org.uk. **Subscription Rates:** 250 individuals student; 275 other countries student; 325 institutions; 350 other countries organisation; 300 other countries individual; 275 individuals. **Remarks:** Accepts advertising. **URL:** http://www.baaf.org.uk/; http://www.baaf.org.uk/bookshop/journal/about. **Ad Rates:** BW: 395. **Circ:** 4,800

53904 ■ Advanced Driving
Institute of Advanced Motorists
IAM House
510 Chiswick High Rd.
London W4 5RG, United Kingdom
Ph: 44 20 89969600
Fax: 44 20 89969601
Publication covering driver education. **Freq:** 3/yr. **Key Personnel:** John Maxwell, Chm.; Michael Robotham, Chm. **Subscription Rates:** Free to all members. **Remarks:** Advertising accepted; rates available upon request. **URL:** http://www.iam.org.uk. **Circ:** 110,000

53905 ■ Advances in Building Energy Research
James and James/Earthscan
Dunstan House
14a St., Cross St.
London EC1N 8XA, United Kingdom
Ph: 44 20 78411930
Fax: 44 20 72421474
Publisher E-mail: earthinfo@earthscan.co.uk
Journal covering energy research. **Freq:** Annual. **Key Personnel:** Prof. Mat Santamouris, Editor-in-Chief. **Subscription Rates:** 195 institutions online & print; EUR255 institutions online & print; US$390 institutions online & print; 195 institutions, other countries online & print; 185 individuals online; EUR240 individuals online; US$370 individuals online; 185 individuals online, rest of world. **URL:** http://www.earthscan.co.uk/JournalsHome/ABER/tabid/1503/Default.aspx; http://www.portlandpress.com/pcs/journals/journal.cfm?product=ABER.

53906 ■ Advances in Osteoporotic Fracture Management
Remedica Medical Education and Publishing
Commonwealth House
1 New Oxford St.
London WC1A 1NU, United Kingdom
Ph: 44 20 77592999
Fax: 44 20 77592951

Publication E-mail: info@fracturemanagement.com
Publisher E-mail: info@remedica.com
Journal serving the clinicians from around the world, by disseminating results of advances in the management of osteoporotic fractures. **Freq:** Quarterly. **Key Personnel:** Frank Phillips, Editor-in-Chief; Isador Lieberman, Editor-in-Chief; Manabu Ito, Editor; Sigurd Berven, Editor; Christian Kasperk, Editor-in-Chief; Tamara Vokes, Editor. **ISSN:** 1473-477X. **Subscription Rates:** EUR130 individuals Europe; US$170 individuals Canada and all other territories. **URL:** http://www.fracturemanagement.com/about.aspx?aid=80818.

53907 ■ Advances in Psychiatric Treatment
The Royal College of Psychiatrists
17 Belgrave Sq.
London SW1X 8PG, United Kingdom
Ph: 44 20 72352351
Fax: 44 20 72451231
Publisher E-mail: reception@rcpsych.ac.uk
Peer-reviewed journal containing articles dealing with physical and biological aspects of treatment, psychological and sociological interventions, management issues and treatments specific to the different psychiatric subspecialties. **Freq:** Bimonthly. **Key Personnel:** Joe Bouch, Editor. **ISSN:** 1355-5146. **Subscription Rates:** 62 members UK & Europe, print and online; 130 nonmembers UK & Europe, print and online; 141 institutions UK & Europe, print and online; US$110 members U.S. & Canada, print and online; US$205 nonmembers U.S. & Canada, print and online; US$243 institutions U.S. & Canada, print and online; 69 members elsewhere, print and online; 140 nonmembers elsewhere, print and online; 152 institutions elsewhere, print and online; 22 single issue print and online. **URL:** http://apt.rcpsych.org/misc/about.dtl.

53908 ■ Advances in Sepsis
Remedica Publishing Ltd
Commonwealth House
1 New Oxford St.
London WC1A 1NUN, United Kingdom
Ph: 44 20 77592999
Fax: 44 20 77592951
Publication E-mail: info@advancesinsepsis.com
Publisher E-mail: info@remedica.com
Journal reporting on advances in therapeutic techniques and emerging technologies in the area of sepsis. **Freq:** 3/yr. **Key Personnel:** Mitchell Levy, Editor-in-Chief; Daniel De Backer, Editor; Edward Abraham, Editorial Advisory Board; Benoit Vallet, Editor-in-Chief; Nicholas S. Ward, Editor; Eric Wiel, Editor. **ISSN:** 1472-2445. **Subscription Rates:** US$170 U.S. and Canada; EUR130 individuals; US$170 other countries. **URL:** http://www.advancesinsepsis.com/.

53909 ■ Advances in Solar Energy
James and James/Earthscan
Dunstan House
14a St., Cross St.
London EC1N 8XA, United Kingdom
Ph: 44 20 78411930
Fax: 44 20 72421474
Publisher E-mail: earthinfo@earthscan.co.uk
Journal on solar energy. **Key Personnel:** Yogi D. Goswani, Editor-in-Chief. **Subscription Rates:** 185 institutions print only. **URL:** http://www.earthscan.co.uk/?tabid=1097; http://www.portlandpress.com/pcs/journals/journal.cfm?product=ASE-P.

53910 ■ Advertising Forecast
World Advertising Research Center
85 Newman St.
London W1T 3EX, United Kingdom
Ph: 44 20 74678100
Fax: 44 20 74678101
Publisher E-mail: enquiries@warc.com
Magazine reporting the UK advertising expenditure. **Freq:** Quarterly. **Trim Size:** 210 x 297 mm. **Subscription Rates:** 660 members; 1,025 nonmembers. **URL:** http://store.warc.com/DisplaySection.aspx?Section=3&ProductID=58.

53911 ■ Aeronautical Journal
Royal Aeronautical Society
4 Hamilton Pl.
London W1J 7BQ, United Kingdom
Ph: 44 20 76704300
Fax: 44 20 76704309
Publisher E-mail: publications@aerosociety.com
Peer-reviewed journal covering aerospace. **Freq:**

Monthly. **Key Personnel:** Prof. Peter Bearman, Editor-in-Chief; Ben David, Contact, ben@pelusa.co.uk. **Remarks:** Accepts advertising. **URL:** http://www.raes.org.uk/cmspage.asp?cmsitemid=Publications_Journal. **Circ:** (Not Reported)

53912 ■ Aeroplane Monthly
IPC Media Ltd.
Blue Fin Bldg.
110 Southwark St.
London SE1 0SU, United Kingdom
Ph: 44 203 1485000
Publication E-mail: infoaero@ipcmedia.com
Magazine for historic aircraft enthusiasts. **Freq:** Monthly. **Key Personnel:** Michael Oakey, Editor, phone 44 20 31484100, editoraero@ipcmedia.com; Nick Stroud, Deputy Ed.; Tony Harmsworth, Asst. Ed., newsaero@ipcmedia.com. **Subscription Rates:** 41.48 individuals; 46.80 individuals european; 51.84 other countries. **Remarks:** Accepts advertising. **URL:** http://www.aeroplanemonthly.com/. **Circ:** (Not Reported)

53913 ■ Aerospace International
Royal Aeronautical Society
4 Hamilton Pl.
London W1J 7BQ, United Kingdom
Ph: 44 20 76704300
Fax: 44 20 76704309
Publication E-mail: publications@aerosociety.com
Publisher E-mail: publications@aerosociety.com
Journal covering worldwide aerospace. **Freq:** Monthly. **Key Personnel:** Chris Male, Publications Mgr./Ed. **Subscription Rates:** Free for members. **Remarks:** Accepts advertising. **URL:** http://www.raes.org.uk/cmspage.asp?cmsitemid=publications_international. **Circ:** △17,299

53914 ■ AES Bug Club Magazine
Amateur Entomologists' Society
PO Box 8774
London SW7 5ZG, United Kingdom
Children's magazine of the Amateur Entomologist Society. **Freq:** Bimonthly. **ISSN:** 1463-0494. **Remarks:** Accepts advertising. **URL:** http://www.amentsoc.org/publications/bcm/. **Circ:** (Not Reported)

53915 ■ Africa
International African Institute
Institut African International
School of Oriental and African Studies
Thornhaugh St.
Russell Sq.
London WC1H 0XG, United Kingdom
Ph: 44 20 78984420
Fax: 44 20 78984419
Publisher E-mail: iai@soas.ac.uk
Publication covering Africa. **Founded:** 1928. **Freq:** Quarterly. **Key Personnel:** Prof. Karin Barber, Editor; Prof. Thomas J. Bassett, Consultant Ed., rf@soas.ac.uk; Prof. Francesca Locatelli, Reviews Ed. **ISSN:** 0001-9720. **URL:** http://www.internationalafricaninstitute.org/journal.html.

53916 ■ Africa Confidential
John Wiley & Sons Inc.
Wiley Blackwell
c/o Patrick Smith, Ed.
73 Farringdon Rd.
London EC1M 3JQ, United Kingdom
Ph: 44 20 78313511
Fax: 44 20 78316778
Journal focusing on the latest developments in Africa and the forces that shape them. **Freq:** Semimonthly. **Key Personnel:** Clare Tauben, Managing Editor, clare@africa-confidential.com; Patrick Smith, Editor, patrick@africa-confidential.com. **ISSN:** 0044-6483. **Subscription Rates:** US$1,299 institutions North America; US$1,152 individuals North America; US$138 students North America; US$561 institutions U.K./Europe; 458 individuals U.K./Europe; EUR144 students U.K./Europe; 503 institutions Africa; 390 individuals Africa; 96 students Africa; 700 institutions rest of the World. **Remarks:** Accepts advertising. **URL:** http://www.blackwellpublishing.com/journal.asp?ref=0044-6483. **Circ:** (Not Reported)

53917 ■ Africa Monitor. West & Central Africa
Business Monitor International Ltd.
Mermaid House
2 Puddle Dock
London EC4V 3DS, United Kingdom
Ph: 44 20 72480468
Fax: 44 20 72480467
Publisher E-mail: subs@businessmonitor.com
Journal with country-by-country analyses, hard-to-find data, and authoritative 24-month forecasts covering government, economy, finance and the business environment. **Freq:** Monthly. **Subscription Rates:** US$765 individuals monitor, print & electronic; 480 individuals monitor, print & electronic; EUR570 individuals monitor, print & electronic; US$1,170 individuals for 2 months monitor, print & electronic; 690 individuals for 2 months monitor, print & electronic; EUR920 individuals for 2 months monitor, print & electronic; US$1,395 individuals for 3 months monitor, print & electronic; 870 individuals for 3 months monitor, print & electronic; EUR1,095 individuals for 3 months monitor, print & electronic. **URL:** http://www.meamonitor.com/file/36844/subscribe.html.

53918 ■ African Affairs
Royal African Society
36 Gordon Sq.
London WC1H 0PD, United Kingdom
Ph: 44 20 30738335
Fax: 44 20 30738340
Publisher E-mail: ras@soas.ac.uk
Journal covering recent political, social and economic developments in sub-Saharan countries. **Founded:** 1960. **Freq:** Quarterly. **Print Method:** Offset. **Trim Size:** 7 x 10. **Cols./Page:** 1. **Col. Width:** 6 inches. **Col. Depth:** 8 1/2 inches. **Key Personnel:** Rita Abrahamsen, Editor, rita.abrahamsen@googlemail.com; Stphen Ellis, Editorial Advisory Board; Sara Rich Dorman, Editor, phone 44 131 6504239, fax 44 131 6506546, sara.dorman@ed.ac.uk. **ISSN:** 0001-9909. **Subscription Rates:** 282 institutions print and online; US$564 institutions print and online; EUR424 institutions print and online; 259 institutions print only; US$517 institutions print only; EUR388 institutions print only; 62 individuals print; US$124 individuals print; EUR93 individuals print; US$22 individuals Africa print. **URL:** http://www.royalafricansociety.org/index.php?option=com_content&task=view&id=29&Itemid=63; http://afraf.oxfordjournals.org/content/current.

53919 ■ African Business
IC Publications Ltd.
7 Coldbath Sq.
London EC1R 4QL, United Kingdom
Ph: 44 20 78413210
Fax: 44 20 78413211
Business publication. **Founded:** 1966. **Freq:** Monthly. **Print Method:** Web. **Trim Size:** 270 x 210 mm. **Key Personnel:** Anver Versi, Editor, a.versi@africasia.com. **ISSN:** 0141-3929. **Subscription Rates:** 40 individuals U.K.; EUR80 individuals Europe; US$90 other countries; 70 two years U.K; EUR140 two years Europe; US$165 two years rest of the World. **Remarks:** Accepts advertising. **URL:** http://www.africasia.com/africanbusiness/. **Ad Rates:** BW: 3,000, 4C: 4,300. **Circ:** Paid ★21,332

53920 ■ African Farming and Food Processing
Alain Charles Publishing Ltd.
University House
11-13 Lower Grosvenor Pl.
London SW1W 0EX, United Kingdom
Ph: 44 20 78347676
Fax: 44 20 79730076
Publisher E-mail: post@alaincharles.com
Magazine covering farming and food processing in Africa. **Founded:** 1980. **Freq:** Bimonthly. **Print Method:** Sheetfed Offset. **Trim Size:** 208 x 292 mm. **ISSN:** 0266-8017. **Subscription Rates:** 54 individuals. **Remarks:** Accepts advertising. **URL:** http://www.alaincharles.com/index.php?option=com_content&view=article&id=46&Itemid=76. **Ad Rates:** BW: US$2,350, 4C: US$3,810. **Circ:** 10,755

53921 ■ African Journal of Business and Economic Research
Adonis & Abbey Publishers Ltd.
PO Box 43418
London SE11 4XZ, United Kingdom
Ph: 44 845 3887248
Publisher E-mail: editor@adonis-abbey.com
Peer-reviewed journal covering theoretical and empirical research of business and economy of Africa. **Key Personnel:** Dr. John O. Okpara, Editor-in-Chief. **URL:** http://www.adonisandabbey.com/about_journal.php?jid=2.

53922 ■ African Journal of Midwifery and Women's Health
MA Healthcare Ltd.
St. Jude's Church
Dulwich Rd.
Herne Hill
London SE24 0PB, United Kingdom
Ph: 44 20 77385454
Fax: 44 20 77332325
Peer-reviewed journal for midwives and nurses covering midwifery and women's health in Africa. **Freq:** Quarterly. **Key Personnel:** Dr. Helen Igobeko Lugina, Editor-in-Chief; Laura Dean-Osgood, Editor. **Subscription Rates:** 25 individuals UK, Eire & Europe; US$35 other countries; 19 students UK & Eire. **Remarks:** Accepts advertising. **URL:** http://www.africanjournalofmidwifery.com. **Circ:** (Not Reported)

53923 ■ African Performance Review
Adonis & Abbey Publishers Ltd.
PO Box 43418
London SE11 4XZ, United Kingdom
Ph: 44 845 3887248
Publisher E-mail: editor@adonis-abbey.com
Journal covering research and information on theatres and performance in Africa and the African Diaspora. **Freq:** Triennial. **Key Personnel:** Dr. Osita Okagbue, Editor; Dr. Jumai Ewu, Assoc. Ed.; Dr. Sam Kasule, Review Ed. **URL:** http://www.adonisandabbey.com/about_journal.php?jid=4.

53924 ■ African Renaissance
Adonis & Abbey Publishers Ltd.
PO Box 43418
London SE11 4XZ, United Kingdom
Ph: 44 845 3887248
Publisher E-mail: editor@adonis-abbey.com
Journal covering African economy, society, politics, and culture. **Founded:** June 2004. **Freq:** Quarterly. **Key Personnel:** Dr. Jideofor Adibe, Editor; Prof. Ali A. Mazrui, Contributing Ed.; Prof. Andrew Jamison, Contributing Ed. **Subscription Rates:** 250 institutions print; 200 institutions online; 100 individuals print; 80 individuals online. **URL:** http://www.adonisandabbey.com/about_journal.php?jid=1.

53925 ■ African Review of Business and Technology
Alain Charles Publishing Ltd.
University House
11-13 Lower Grosvenor Pl.
London SW1W 0EX, United Kingdom
Ph: 44 20 78347676
Fax: 44 20 79730076
Publisher E-mail: post@alaincharles.com
Magazine covering technology and business information about Africa. **Freq:** 11/yr. **Print Method:** Sheetfed Offset. **Trim Size:** 208 x 292 mm. **ISSN:** 0954-6782. **Remarks:** Accepts advertising. **URL:** http://www.alaincharles.com/index.php?option=com_content&view=article&id=47&Itemid=75. **Ad Rates:** BW: US$4,400, 4C: US$6,470. **Circ:** ★13,440

53926 ■ African Soccer Magazine
Unit F, Octagon Ct.
443-449 Holloway Rd.
London N7 6LJ, United Kingdom
Ph: 44 207 5610011
Fax: 44 207 2812377
Publisher E-mail: admin@africansoccermagazine.com
Magazine covering the Liberian national football team, scores and game highlights, player profiles, pictures, and interviews of players. **Key Personnel:** Emmanuel Maradas, Editor, emaradas@africansoccermagazine.com. **Subscription Rates:** 30 individuals; 36 other countries; US$65 other countries. **Remarks:** Accepts advertising. **URL:** http://www.africansoccermagazine.com/. **Circ:** (Not Reported)

53927 ■ Aging Health
Future Medicine Ltd.
Unitec House
2 Albert Pl.
London N3 1QB, United Kingdom
Ph: 44 20 83716080
Fax: 44 20 83432313
Publisher E-mail: info@futuremedicine.com
Peer-reviewed journal focusing on the most important advances in the mechanisms underlying disease and disability in the elderly and highlighting their relevance in the clinical setting. **Freq:** Bimonthly. **Key Personnel:** A. Barqawi, Editorial Advisory Board; C. Anderson,

Editorial Advisory Board; L. Balducci, Editorial Advisory Board. **ISSN:** 1745-509X. **Subscription Rates:** 605 institutions; US$1,160 institutions; EUR755 institutions; 126,000¥ institutions. **Remarks:** Accepts advertising. **URL:** http://www.futuremedicine.com/loi/ahe. **Circ:** (Not Reported)

53928 ■ AIDS Research and Therapy
BioMed Central Ltd.
236 Gray's Inn Rd., Fl. 6
34-42 Cleveland St.
London WC1X 8HL, United Kingdom
Ph: 44 20 31922000
Fax: 44 20 31922010
Publisher E-mail: info@biomedcentral.com
Online journal publishing peer-reviewed research articles from scientists working to prevent the spread of AIDS. **Key Personnel:** Kailash C. Gupta, Editor-in-Chief, kgupta@niaid.nih.gov. **ISSN:** 1742-6405. **Remarks:** Accepts advertising. **URL:** http://www.aidsrestherapy.com/home/. **Circ:** (Not Reported)

53929 ■ The AIM Guide
Vitesse Media
Octavia House
50 Banner St.
London EC1Y 8ST, United Kingdom
Ph: 44 20 72507010
Fax: 44 20 72507011
Publisher E-mail: info@vitessemedia.co.uk
Magazine featuring the young and fast-growing companies. **Freq:** Semiannual. **Key Personnel:** Rebecca Borrows, Sales Mgr., phone 44 20 72507028, rebecca.borrows@vitessemedia.co.uk. **Subscription Rates:** 79.95 individuals; 95.95 other countries. **Remarks:** Accepts advertising. **URL:** http://www.vitessemedia.co.uk/publications-and-research/entrepreneurs/259023/the-aim-guide.thtml. **Circ:** (Not Reported)

53930 ■ Aircraft Technology Engineering & Maintenance
Aviation Industry Press Ltd.
Ludgate House, 2nd Fl.
245 Blackfriars Rd.
London SE1 9UY, United Kingdom
Ph: 44 20 75794840
Fax: 44 20 75794848
Professional magazine covering commercial aviation manufacturing and maintenance issues. **Founded:** 1992. **Freq:** Bimonthly. **Print Method:** Offset litho. **Trim Size:** 8.27 x 10.95. **Cols./Page:** 3. **Key Personnel:** Simon Barker, Publisher, simonb@aviation-industry.com; Jason Holland, Editor, jason.holland@ubmaviation.com; Michael Gubisch, Staff Writer, michael.gubisch@ubmaviation.com; Phil Hine, Production Mgr., phil.hine@ubmaviation.com; Paul Canessa, Circulation Mgr., paul.canessa@ubmaviation.com. **ISSN:** 0967-439X. **Subscription Rates:** 150 individuals; 260 two years; US$300 individuals; US$520 two years; 170 other countries; 300 two years other countries; 350 individuals 3 years; US$700 individuals 3 years; 410 other countries 3 years. **Remarks:** Accepts advertising. **URL:** http://www.ubmaviationnews.com/Publications/Aircraft-Technology-Engineering-Maintenance. **Ad Rates:** BW: 4,969, 4C: 7,645. **Circ:** Controlled △11,500

53931 ■ Airfinance Journal
Euromoney Publications PLC
Nestor House
Playhouse Yard
London EC4V 5EX, United Kingdom
Ph: 44 20 77798888
Publisher E-mail: information@euromoneyplc.com
Magazine providing information on the financing of airline fleets and matters concerning commercial airlines, financiers, manufacturers, consultants and aviation law firms. **Freq:** 10/yr. **Key Personnel:** Sophie Segal, Editor, phone 44 20 77798853, ssegal@euromoneyplc.com. **Subscription Rates:** US$895 individuals. **URL:** http://www.airfinancejournal.com.

53932 ■ All About Animals
BBC Worldwide Publishing Ltd.
Media Centre
201 Wood Ln.
London W12 7TQ, United Kingdom
Ph: 44 20 84332000
Fax: 44 20 87490538
Magazine for 7-11 years old pet loving girls. **Subtitle:** Pets, wildlife, friendship. **Freq:** every 4 weeks. **Sub-**scription Rates: 1.99 single issue. **URL:** http://www.bbcmagazines.com/content/magazines/allaboutanimals/.

53933 ■ Aluminium International Today
DMG World Media
Northcliffe House
2 Derry St.
London W8 5TT, United Kingdom
Ph: 44 20 79386000
Publication for the metals, metalworking and machinery industries. **Freq:** 9/yr. **Trim Size:** 210 x 297 mm. **Key Personnel:** Tim Smith, Consultant Ed., phone 44 1737 855154, aluminium@quartzltd.co.uk; Annie Baker, Contact, phone 44 1737 855130, anniebaker@quartzltd.co.uk; Greg Morris, Editor, phone 44 1737 855132, gregmorris@quartzltd.co.uk. **ISSN:** 0955-8209. **Subscription Rates:** 201 individuals UK only; 219 other countries; US$337 individuals. **Remarks:** Accepts advertising. **Online:** Gale. **URL:** http://www.aluminiumtoday.com. **Formerly:** Aluminium Today. **Ad Rates:** BW: 1,670, 4C: 3,071. **Circ:** 5,500

53934 ■ Alumni News
London Business School Alumni Association
Regent's Pk.
London NW1 4SA, United Kingdom
Ph: 44 20 70007000
Fax: 44 20 70007001
Publisher E-mail: alumnirelations@london.edu
Publication covering alumni. **Freq:** Quarterly. **URL:** http://www.london.edu/publications/alumninews.html.

53935 ■ Amateur Gardening
IPC Media Ltd.
Blue Fin Bldg.
110 Southwark St.
London SE1 0SU, United Kingdom
Ph: 44 203 1485000
Magazine for new and experienced gardeners. **Founded:** 1884. **Freq:** Weekly. **Key Personnel:** Hazel Eccles, Publisher, phone 44 20 31484312, hazel_eccles@ipcmedia.com; Tim Rumball, Editor, phone 44 1202 440840, tim_rumball@ipcmedia.com; Lee Morris, Advertising Mgr., phone 44 20 31482517, lee_morris@ipcmedia.com. **Subscription Rates:** US$208.70 individuals; US$412 two years. **Remarks:** Accepts advertising. **URL:** http://www.ipcmedia.com/brands/amgarden/. **Circ:** ⋆42,691

53936 ■ Amateur Gardening
IPC Media Ltd.
Blue Fin Bldg.
110 Southwark St.
London SE1 0SU, United Kingdom
Ph: 44 203 1485000
Publication E-mail: amateurgardening@ipcmedia.com
British gardening magazine featuring practical tips from top gardening celebrities. **Freq:** Weekly. **Key Personnel:** Tim Rumball, Editor; Marc Rosenberg, News Ed. **Subscription Rates:** 69.99 individuals; 134.99 two years. **URL:** http://www.amateurgardening.co.uk.

53937 ■ Amateur Photographer
IPC Media Ltd.
Blue Fin Bldg.
110 Southwark St.
London SE1 0SU, United Kingdom
Ph: 44 203 1485000
Magazine featuring photography equipment. **Founded:** 1884. **Freq:** Weekly. **Key Personnel:** Damien Demolder, Editor, phone 44 20 31484133, damien_demolder@ipcmedia.com; Lee Morris, Advertising Mgr., phone 44 20 31482517, lee_morris@ipcmedia.com. **Subscription Rates:** 79.99 individuals; 152.99 two years. **Remarks:** Accepts advertising. **URL:** http://www.ipcmedia.com/brands/amphoto/. **Circ:** ⋆22,242

53938 ■ Ambit
17 Priory Gardens
Highgate
London N6 5QY, United Kingdom
Publication E-mail: info@ambitmagazine.co.uk
Journal covering poetry, fiction, art, literature and new and avant garde writing. **Founded:** 1959. **Freq:** Quarterly. **Key Personnel:** Kate Pemberton, Asst. Ed.; Gwen MacKeith, Editorial Asst.; Dr. Martin Bax, Editor; Carol Ann Duffy, Editor; Geoff Nicholson, Editor; Henry Graham, Editor; J.G. Ballard, Editor; Michael Foreman, Editor. **ISSN:** 0002-6972. **Subscription Rates:** 25 individuals for Europe; 30 individuals rest of Europe; 32 individuals rest of world; EUR44 individuals rest of Europe; EUR64 individuals rest of world. **Remarks:** Accepts advertising. **URL:** http://www.ambitmagazine.co.uk/. **Circ:** Paid 3,000

53939 ■ Amy
BBC Worldwide Publishing Ltd.
Media Centre
201 Wood Ln.
London W12 7TQ, United Kingdom
Ph: 44 20 84332000
Fax: 44 20 87490538
Lifestyle magazine for 5-8 years old girls. **Subtitle:** A girl's best friend. **Freq:** 3/week. **Subscription Rates:** 1.99 single issue. **URL:** http://www.bbcmagazines.com/content/magazines/amy/.

53940 ■ Anaesthesia
Association of Anaesthetists of Great Britain and Ireland
21 Portland Pl.
London W1B 1PY, United Kingdom
Ph: 44 20 76311650
Fax: 44 20 76314352
Publisher E-mail: info@aagbi.org
Professional publication covering anesthesiology. **Freq:** Monthly. **Key Personnel:** Dr. Steve Yenis, Editor-in-Chief, anaesthesia@nottingham.ac.uk. **ISSN:** 0003-2409. **Subscription Rates:** Free all members. **URL:** http://www.aagbi.org/publications/anaesthesia.htm.

53941 ■ Anatomical Science International
Springer-Verlag London Ltd.
236 Gray's Inn Rd., 6th Fl.
London WC1X 8HB, United Kingdom
Ph: 44 20 31922000
Official English journal of the Japanese Association of Anatomists covering the morphological sciences in animals and humans. **Freq:** Quarterly. **Key Personnel:** Kiyotaka Toshimori, Editor-in-Chief; Toshitaka Akisaka, Editorial Board; Tatsuo Sakai, Managing Editor; Osamu Ohtani, Managing Editor; Kiyotaka Toshimori, Managing Editor; Tetsuo Inokuchi, Editorial Board; Tatsuo Ushiki, Editorial Board; Hisatake Kondo, Editorial Board. **ISSN:** 1447-6959. **Subscription Rates:** US$380 institutions print plus premium online, America; US$345 institutions print plus standard; US$328 institutions premium online; 233 institutions print plus premium online, Europe; 212 institutions print plus standard, Europe; EUR201 institutions premium online only; 201 institutions premium online, Europe; 233 institutions print plus premium online, rest of World; 212 institutions print plus standard, rest of World. **URL:** http://www.springer.com/medicine/internal/journal/12565. **Formerly:** Anatomical Science.

53942 ■ Angler's Mail
IPC Media Ltd.
Blue Fin Bldg.
110 Southwark St.
London SE1 0SU, United Kingdom
Ph: 44 203 1485000
Magazine for anglers. **Founded:** 1965. **Freq:** Weekly. **Trim Size:** 297 x 420 mm. **Key Personnel:** Hazel Eccles, Publisher, phone 44 20 31484312, hazel_eccles@ipcmedia.com; Tim Knight, Editor, phone 44 20 31484150, tim_knight@ipcmedia.com; Lee Morris, Advertising Mgr., phone 44 20 31482517, lee_morris@ipcmedia.com. **Subscription Rates:** 64.99 individuals; 120.99 two years. **Remarks:** Accepts advertising. **URL:** http://www.ipcmedia.com/brands/anglers/. **Circ:** ⋆34,413

53943 ■ Anglican World
Anglican Communion Office
St. Andrew's House
16 Tavistock Cres.
London W11 1AP, United Kingdom
Ph: 44 20 73133900
Fax: 44 20 73133999
Publisher E-mail: aco@anglicancommunion.org
Publication covering Anglican Catholics. **Freq:** Quarterly. **Key Personnel:** Canon James M. Rosenthal, Editor; Suminder Duggal, Managing Editor. **ISSN:** 1367-238X. **URL:** http://www.aco.org/resources/aw/online/.

53944 ■ Angling Times
H. Bauer Publishing
Academic House
24-28 Oval Rd.
London NW1 7DT, United Kingdom
Ph: 44 20 72418000
Fax: 44 20 72418030
Magazine featuring regular news, tackle, tactics, and tips for today's angler. **Freq:** 51/yr. **Subscription Rates:**

83.20 individuals. **URL:** http://www.gofishing.co.uk/ Anglish-Times.

53945 ■ Animal Behaviour
Academic Press
Harcourt Pl.
32 Jamestown Rd.
London NW1 7BY, United Kingdom
Ph: 44 20 74244200
Fax: 44 20 74832293
Publication covering zoology. **Founded:** 1952. **Freq:** Monthly. **Key Personnel:** W.A. Searcy, Executive Ed.; Louise Barrett, Executive Ed.; S. Adamo, Editor; Kris Bruner, Managing Editor. **ISSN:** 0003-3472. **Subscription Rates:** US$1,249 institutions except Europe, Japan & Iran; EUR1,405 institutions European Countries & Iran; 151,800¥ institutions. **Remarks:** Advertising not accepted. **URL:** http://www.elsevier.com/wps/find/journaldescription.cws_home/622782/descriptiondescription. **Circ:** (Not Reported)

53946 ■ Animals and You
D C Thomson & Company Ltd.
185 Fleet St.
London EC4A 2HS, United Kingdom
Ph: 44 20 74001030
Fax: 44 20 78319440
Magazine containing articles, puzzles, stories, and games about animals designed for 7-11 year old girls. **Freq:** Monthly. **Subscription Rates:** 40 individuals inland U.K.; 60 individuals overseas. **URL:** http://www.dcthomsonshop.co.uk/Group-Animals_and_You.aspx.

53947 ■ Annals of Clinical Microbiology and Antimicrobials
BioMed Central Ltd.
236 Gray's Inn Rd., Fl. 6
34-42 Cleveland St.
London WC1X 8HL, United Kingdom
Ph: 44 20 31922000
Fax: 44 20 31922010
Publisher E-mail: info@biomedcentral.com
Online journal focusing on information concerning clinical microbiology, infectious diseases and antimicrobials. **Key Personnel:** Prof. Hakan Leblebicioglu, Editor-in-Chief, hakanomu@omu.edu.tr; Prof. Lionel Mandell, Editorial Board; Dr. Rudy Hartskeerl, Editorial Board; Niyaz Ahmed, Editorial Board; Prof. Murat Gunaydin, Editorial Board, muratomu@omu.edu.tr; George Lau, Editorial Board; Dr. Andreas Voss, Editorial Board, phone 31 24 3617575, fax 31 24 3540216, a.voss@mmb.azn.nl. **ISSN:** 1476-0711. **Remarks:** Accepts advertising. **URL:** http://www.ann-clinmicrob.com/home/. **Circ:** (Not Reported)

53948 ■ Annals of General Psychiatry
BioMed Central Ltd.
236 Gray's Inn Rd., Fl. 6
34-42 Cleveland St.
London WC1X 8HL, United Kingdom
Ph: 44 20 31922000
Fax: 44 20 31922010
Publisher E-mail: info@biomedcentral.com
Online journal covering the wider field of psychiatry, neurosciences and psychological medicine, publishing articles on all aspects of psychiatry. **Key Personnel:** Prof. Jules Angst, MD, Editorial Board; Dr. Konstantinos N. Fountoulakis, Editor-in-Chief, phone 30 2310 994622, fax 30 2310 266570, kfount@med.auth.gr; Prof. Hagop Akiskal, Editorial Board. **ISSN:** 1744-859X. **Remarks:** Accepts advertising. **URL:** http://www.annals-general-psychiatry.com/. **Circ:** (Not Reported)

53949 ■ Annals of the Rheumatic Disease
BMJ Publishing Group
BMA House
Tavistock Sq.
London WC1H 9JR, United Kingdom
Ph: 44 20 73834410
Fax: 44 20 73876400
Publisher E-mail: customerservice.group@bmjgroup.com
Peer-reviewed Journal for rheumatology specialists. **Subtitle:** The Eular Journal. **Founded:** 1939. **Freq:** Monthly. **Print Method:** Sheetfed Offset. **Trim Size:** 210 x 297 mm. **Key Personnel:** Tore K. Kvien, Editor, t.k. kvien@medisin.uio.no; Anthony Woolf, Advisory Committee, anthony.woolf@btopenworld.com; Prof. Leo Van De Putte, Advisory Committee; Frank Wollheim, Advisory Committee; Dimitrios Boumpas, Assoc. Ed.,

boumpasd@med.uoc.gr; Mary Crow, Assoc. Ed., crowm@hss.edu; Johannes Bijlsma, Assoc. Ed., j.w.j. bijlsma@azu.nl; Gerd Burmester, Assoc. Ed., gerd. burmester@charite.de. **ISSN:** 0003-4967. **Subscription Rates:** 250 individuals print & online; EUR338 individuals print & online; US$488 individuals print & online; 111 individuals online only; EUR150 individuals online only; US$216 individuals online only. **Remarks:** Accepts advertising. **URL:** http://ard.bmj.com/. **Circ:** Paid 9,500

53950 ■ Annals of Tropical Paediatrics
Maney Publishing
1 Carlton House Ter.
London SW1Y 5AF, United Kingdom
Ph: 44 20 74517300
Fax: 44 20 74517307
Publisher E-mail: maney@maney.co.uk
Peer-reviewed journal covering medical problems, achievements, and research in paediatrics and child health in the tropics and sub-tropics. **Subtitle:** International Child Health. **Founded:** 1981. **Freq:** Quarterly. **Key Personnel:** Bernard Brabin, Editor, b.j.brabin@liv. ac.uk; James Bunn, Editor, jegbunn@liv.ac.uk; Luis Cuevas, Editor, lcuevas@liv.ac.uk; Feiko ter Kuile, Editor, terkuile@liv.ac.uk. **ISSN:** 0272-4936. **Subscription Rates:** 157 other countries print or online; US$303 individuals print or online; 444 institutions, other countries print or online; US$820 institutions print or online. **Remarks:** Accepts advertising. **URL:** http://maney.co.uk/index.php/journals/atp/. **Circ:** (Not Reported)

53951 ■ Annual Bibliography of English Language & Literature
Modern Humanities Research Association
1 Carlton House Ter.
London SW1Y 5AF, United Kingdom
Publication E-mail: abell@bibl.org
Publisher E-mail: mail@mhra.org.uk
Bibliographical journal covering English studies. **Founded:** 1921. **ISSN:** 0066-3786. **Subscription Rates:** 212 institutions; US$493 institutions. **URL:** http://www.mhra.org.uk/Publications/Journals/abell.html.

53952 ■ Anomaly
Association for the Scientific Study of Anomalous Phenomena
27 Old Gloucester St.
London WC1N 3XX, United Kingdom
Ph: 44 845 6521648
Publication E-mail: assapjournal@assap.org
Publisher E-mail: assap@assap.org
Publication covering parapsychology. **Freq:** Semiannual. **Key Personnel:** Dave Wood, Editor; Matthew Hicks, Managing Editor. **ISSN:** 0969-7713. **Subscription Rates:** 2.50 single issue non members; Free members. **Remarks:** Advertising not accepted. **URL:** http://www. assap.org/newsite/htmlfiles/Anomaly.html. **Circ:** 500

53953 ■ Another Magazine
Another Publishing Ltd.
112 Old St.
London EC1V 9BG, United Kingdom
Ph: 44 20 73660766
Fax: 44 20 73660966
Magazine featuring fashion, people, arts, and literature. **Freq:** Semiannual. **Key Personnel:** Jefferson Hack, Editor-in-Chief; Nancy Waters, Editor, nancy@dazedgroup.com. **ISSN:** 1355-5901. **Subscription Rates:** 25 individuals; 50 two years. **Remarks:** Accepts advertising. **URL:** http://www.anothermag.com/. **Circ:** (Not Reported)

53954 ■ Anthropological Theory
Sage Publications Ltd.
1 Oliver's Yard
55 City Rd.
London EC1Y 1SP, United Kingdom
Ph: 44 20 73248500
Fax: 44 20 73248600
Scholarly journal covering anthropological theory and epistemology. **Founded:** 2001. **Freq:** Quarterly. **Key Personnel:** Joel Robbins, Editor; Jonathan Friedman, Editor; Steven Sampson, Book Review Ed.; Stephen P. Reyna, Assoc. Ed.; John Gledhill, Editorial Board; Jane Cowan, Assoc. Ed. **ISSN:** 1463-4996. **Subscription Rates:** US$409 institutions print & e-access; US$368 institutions e-access; US$401 institutions print; US$46 individuals print; US$110 institutions single print; US$15 individuals single print. **Remarks:** Accepts advertising.

URL: http://www.sagepub.co.uk/journalsProdDesc.nav? prodId=Journal200927. **Circ:** (Not Reported)

53955 ■ Anthropology Today
John Wiley & Sons Inc.
Wiley-Blackwell
c/o Gustaaf Houtman, Ed.
The Royal Anthropological Institute
50 Fitzroy St.
London W1T 5BT, United Kingdom
Publication E-mail: at@therai.org.uk
Journal focusing on interests with the discipline of anthropology. **Freq:** Bimonthly. **Key Personnel:** Gustaff Houtman, Editor. **ISSN:** 0268-540X. **Subscription Rates:** US$141 institutions print and online; US$135 institutions print or online; EUR106 institutions print and online; US$164 institutions, other countries print and online; EUR103 institutions print or online; US$158 institutions, other countries print or online. **Remarks:** Accepts advertising. **URL:** http://www.wiley.com/bw/journal.asp? ref=0268-540X&site=1. **Circ:** (Not Reported)

53956 ■ Antiquaries Journal
Society of Antiquaries of London
Burlington House
Piccadilly
London W1J 0BE, United Kingdom
Ph: 44 20 74797080
Fax: 44 20 72876967
Publisher E-mail: admin@sal.org.uk
Journal covering artifacts. **Founded:** 1920. **Freq:** Annual. **Trim Size:** 246 x 174 mm. **Key Personnel:** Kate Owen, Editor, kowen@sal.org.uk. **ISSN:** 0003-5815. **Subscription Rates:** 107 institutions; US$210 institutions. **Remarks:** Advertising not accepted. **URL:** http://www.sal.org.uk/books/theantiquariesjournal/; http:// journals.cambridge.org/action/displayJournal?jid=ANT. **Formerly:** Proceedings of the Society of Antiquaries. **Circ:** Paid 2,450

53957 ■ Antique Dealer & Collectors Guide
Statuscourt Ltd.
Greenwich
PO Box 805
London SE10 8TD, United Kingdom
Ph: 44 20 86914820
Consumer magazine covering antiques. **Founded:** 1946. **Freq:** Monthly. **Print Method:** Sheetfed offset. **Trim Size:** 229 x 296 mm. **Cols./Page:** 3. **Col. Width:** 61 millimeters. **Col. Depth:** 264 millimeters. **ISSN:** 0003-5866. **Subscription Rates:** 18 individuals; US$40 individuals air freight; 25 by mail overseas surface; 38 by mail air mail Australasia; 28 by mail air mail Europe; 36 by mail air mail middle East. **URL:** http://www. magazine-subscription-search.com/prd100478.php. **Circ:** Combined 12,000

53958 ■ The Antique Trade Calendar
GP London
32 Fredericks Pl.
London N12 8QE, United Kingdom
Ph: 44 20 84463604
Fax: 44 20 89228257
Trade magazine covering antiques and collectibles fairs and events. **Founded:** 1992. **Freq:** Quarterly. **Trim Size:** A5. **Subscription Rates:** 9 individuals; 15 individuals Europe; 20 elsewhere elsewhere; 2 single issue. **Remarks:** Accepts advertising. **URL:** http://www. antiquesnews.co.uk. **Circ:** Paid ‡12,000

53959 ■ Applied Earth Science
Maney Publishing
1 Carlton House Ter.
London SW1Y 5AF, United Kingdom
Ph: 44 20 74517300
Fax: 44 20 74517307
Publisher E-mail: maney@maney.co.uk
Journal covering all aspects of the application of the earth sciences in the discovery, exploration, development, and exploitation of all forms of mineral resources. **Freq:** Quarterly. **Key Personnel:** Prof. N. Phillips, Editor; Simon Dominy, Co-Ed., sdominy@snowdengroup. com. **ISSN:** 0371-7453. **Subscription Rates:** 245 institutions, other countries; US$411 institutions; 85 members other countries; US$135 members. **Remarks:** Accepts advertising. **URL:** http://maney.co.uk/index.php/journals/aes/. **Ad Rates:** BW: 300, 4C: 550. **Circ:** 500

53960 ■ Archaeological Reports
Society for the Promotion of Hellenic Studies

Senate House
Malet St.
London WC1E 7HU, United Kingdom
Ph: 44 20 78628730
Fax: 44 20 78628731
Publisher E-mail: office@hellenicsociety.org.uk
Publication covering archaeology. **Freq:** Annual. **Key Personnel:** Prof. Malcolm Schofield, President; Dr. Angus Bowie, Editor. **Remarks:** Advertising accepted; rates available upon request. **URL:** http://www.hellenicsociety.org.uk; http://www.hellenicsociety.org.uk/frame.htm. **Circ:** 3,100

53961 ■ Architectural Engineering and Design Management
James and James/Earthscan
Dunstan House
14a St., Cross St.
London EC1N 8XA, United Kingdom
Ph: 44 20 78411930
Fax: 44 20 72421474
Publication E-mail: sales@portland-services.com
Publisher E-mail: earthinfo@earthscan.co.uk
Journal covering developments and research of architectural engineering and building design management. **Key Personnel:** Prof. Dino Bouchlaghem, Editor-in-Chief, phone 44 1509 223775, n.m.bouchlaghem@lboro.aac.uk. **Subscription Rates:** 247 institutions online & print; EUR323 institutions online & print; US$494 institutions online & print; 247 institutions, other countries online & print; 99 individuals online; EUR130 individuals online; US$199 individuals online; 99 individuals online. **URL:** http://www.portlandpress.com/pcs/journals/journal.cfm?product=AEDM.

53962 ■ The Architectural Review
EMAP Construct
151 Rosebery Ave.
Hampstead Rd.
London EC1R 4GB, United Kingdom
Ph: 44 207 5056600
Publisher E-mail: ruth.merrian@emap.com
Publication for the architecture and design industries. **Founded:** 1896. **Freq:** Monthly. **Print Method:** Web Offset. **Trim Size:** 297 x 230 mm. **Key Personnel:** Kieran Long, Editor-in-Chief, phone 44 20 77284573, kieran.long@emap.com; Rob Gregory, Asst. Ed., phone 44 20 77284587, rob.gregory@emap.com; Cecilia Lindgren, Art Ed., phone 44 20 77284580, cecilia.lindgren@emap.com; Paul Finch, Ed. Emeritus; Catherine Slessor, Managing Editor, catherine.slessor@emap.com. **ISSN:** 0003-861X. **Subscription Rates:** 59 individuals; 45 students; 105 individuals; 85 individuals; 69 individuals International; 53 students International; 99 individuals airmail; 105 individuals 2 years; 82 students 2 years; 176 individuals 2 years. **URL:** http://www.arplus.com; http://www.emap.com/brands/architectural-review. **Ad Rates:** BW: 3,660. **Circ:** Paid ★22,700

53963 ■ Archives of Disease in Childhood. Education and Practice Edition
BMJ Publishing Group
BMA House
Tavistock Sq.
London WC1H 9JR, United Kingdom
Ph: 44 20 73834410
Fax: 44 20 73876400
Publisher E-mail: customerservice.group@bmjgroup.com
Peer-reviewed Journal focusing on all aspects of child health and disease from the perinatal period (in the Fetal and Neonatal edition) through to adolescence. **Founded:** 1926. **Freq:** Monthly. **Key Personnel:** Howard Bauchner, Editor-in-Chief, howard.bauchner@bmc.org. **Subscription Rates:** US$154 individuals print and online; US$127 individuals online only; EUR107 individuals print and online; 79 individuals print and online; EUR88 individuals online only; 65 individuals online only. **URL:** http://ep.bmj.com/current.dtl.

53964 ■ Arms & Armour
Maney Publishing
1 Carlton House Ter.
London SW1Y 5AF, United Kingdom
Ph: 44 20 74517300
Fax: 44 20 74517307
Publisher E-mail: maney@maney.co.uk
Peer-reviewed journal encouraging and publishing serious research in the field of arms and armour from scholars, both professional and amateur, around the

world, including, but are not limited to, the history, development, use, decoration and display of arms and armour throughout history. **Freq:** Semiannual. **Key Personnel:** Graeme Rimer, Editor, graeme.rimer@armouries.org.uk; Debbie Wurr, Managing Editor, debbie.wurr@armouries.org.uk. **ISSN:** 1741-6124. **Subscription Rates:** 146 institutions UK, Europe, rest of world; US$291 institutions in U.S.; 34 individuals UK, Europe, rest of world; US$60 individuals in U.S. **Remarks:** Accepts advertising. **URL:** http://maney.co.uk/index.php/journals/aaa/. **Ad Rates:** BW: 250. **Circ:** (Not Reported)

53965 ■ Arrowwords
H. Bauer Publishing
Academic House
24-28 Oval Rd.
London NW1 7DT, United Kingdom
Ph: 44 20 72418000
Fax: 44 20 72418030
Magazine featuring arrowwords puzzles. **Freq:** Monthly. **Key Personnel:** Clive Garsin, Gp. Ed.; Spike Figgett, Publishing Dir.; Helen Greenwood, Advertising Mgr. **Subscription Rates:** 15.47 individuals. **Remarks:** Accepts advertising. **URL:** http://www.puzzlemagazines.co.uk/arrowwords; http://www.bauer.co.uk/puzzle-magazines. **Circ:** (Not Reported)

53966 ■ Art Business Today
Fine Art Trade Guild
16-18 Empress Pl.
London SW6 1TT, United Kingdom
Ph: 44 20 73816616
Fax: 44 20 73812596
Publisher E-mail: info@fineart.co.uk
Trade magazine covering the art business in the UK. **Founded:** 1905. **Freq:** 5/yr. **Key Personnel:** Debra Doherty, Advertising; Annabelle Ruston, Managing Editor; Christrose Sumner, Publisher. **Subscription Rates:** 26 individuals; 31 individuals Europe; 38 elsewhere; 46 two years; 54 two years Europe; 66 elsewhere. **Remarks:** Accepts advertising. **URL:** http://www.fineart.co.uk/Public/Art_Business_Today/Art_Business_Today_public.aspx. **Circ:** Paid 5,500

53967 ■ Art, Design & Communication in Higher Education
Intellect
Russell Square House
10-12 Russell Sq.
London WC1B 5EE, United Kingdom
Ph: 44 20 73312000
Fax: 44 20 73312040
Publisher E-mail: info@intellectuk.org
Journal aiming to inform, stimulate and promote the development of research with a learning and teaching focus for art, design and communication within higher education. **Founded:** 2002. **Freq:** 2/yr. **Key Personnel:** Linda Drew, Editor, l.drew@chelsea.arts.ac.uk; Laura Lanceley, Editorial Asst., l.lanceley@chelsea.arts.ac.uk. **ISSN:** 1474-273X. **Subscription Rates:** 33 individuals; US$65 individuals; 210 institutions; US$330 institutions; 177 institutions online; US$265 institutions online. **URL:** http://www.intellectbooks.co.uk/journals/view-Journal,id=139/.

53968 ■ Art Monthly
Britannia Art Publications
28 Charing Cross Rd., 4th Fl.
London WC2H 0DB, United Kingdom
Ph: 44 20 72400389
Fax: 44 20 74970726
Publisher E-mail: info@artmonthly.co.uk
Journal covering contemporary visual arts. **Founded:** 1976. **Freq:** 10/yr. **Trim Size:** 297 x 210 cm. **Key Personnel:** Brendan Fan, Managing Editor; Patricia Bickers, Editor; Ian Hunt, Contact; Jack Wendler, Publisher; Chris McCormack, Contact; Matt Hale, Contact; Brendan Fan, Contact; Frederika Whitehead, Editorial Asst. **ISSN:** 0142-6702. **Subscription Rates:** 44 individuals U.K.; 55 individuals Europe; US$74 individuals North America; 72 other countries; 99 two years institutional U.K.; 128 two years institutional Europe; US$145 two years institutional North America; 164 two years rest of the world; 30 students U.K.; 41 students Europe. **Remarks:** Accepts advertising. **URL:** http://www.artmonthly.co.uk. **Ad Rates:** BW: 1,213. **Circ:** Combined 5,000

53969 ■ Art Review
1 Sekforde St.
London EC1R 0BE, United Kingdom
Ph: 44 20 72364880
Fax: 44 20 71072761
Publisher E-mail: info@art-review.co.uk
Magazine covering visual art, arts collecting, and arts buying. **Subtitle:** International Art & Style. **Founded:** 1949. **Freq:** Monthly. **Print Method:** Perfect bound. **Subscription Rates:** 39 individuals U.K.; 99 individuals U.S.D.; 99 Canada individual; 99 individuals Australia; 99 individuals India. **Remarks:** Accepts advertising. **URL:** http://www.art-review.com/. **Ad Rates:** GLR: 4,000, 4C: 1,201. **Circ:** Paid 25,000

53970 ■ Asharq Al-Awsat
Saudi Research & Publishing Co.
Arab Press House
184 High Holborn
London WC1V 7AP, United Kingdom
Ph: 44 207 831818
Newspaper carrying the latest local and international news and information. **Subtitle:** The leading Arabic international daily. **Founded:** 1978. **Freq:** Daily. **Key Personnel:** Tariq Alhomayed, Editor-in-Chief. **Subscription Rates:** 1,095 SRI; US$292 other countries. **Remarks:** Accepts advertising. **URL:** http://www.asharq-e.com/default.asp. **Ad Rates:** BW: 60,800, 4C: 105,600. **Circ:** Mon.-Fri. ★236,988

53971 ■ Asia Pacific Coatings Journal
DMG World Media
Northcliffe House
2 Derry St.
London W8 5TT, United Kingdom
Ph: 44 20 79386000
Publication for the chemical, plastics and rubber industries. **Freq:** Bimonthly. **Trim Size:** 210 x 297 mm. **Key Personnel:** Melanie Chiles, Production Mgr., phone 44 1737 855336, melaniechiles@quartzltd.co.uk; Ranjeet Sandhu, Advertising Mgr., phone 44 1737 855570, ranjeetsandhu@quartzltd.co.uk; Elit Kane, Editor, phone 44 1737 855328, elitkane@quartz.co.uk. **ISSN:** 1648-1412. **Remarks:** Accepts advertising. **URL:** http://www.asiapacificcoatingsjournal.com. **Formerly:** Paint and Ink International. **Ad Rates:** BW: 2,562, 4C: 4,952. **Circ:** 5,960

53972 ■ Asia Risk
Incisive Media Limited
Haymarket House
28-29 Haymarket
London SW1Y 4RX, United Kingdom
Ph: 44 870 2408859
Fax: 44 207 4849797
Publisher E-mail: customerservices@incisivemedia.com
Magazine featuring financial risk management in Asia-Pacific region. **Founded:** 1995. **Freq:** 11/yr. **Key Personnel:** Christopher Jeffery, Editor, phone 852 34114833, chris.jeffery@incisivemedia.com; Harjeet Singh, Publisher, phone 852 34114838, harjeet.singh@incisivemedia.com. **Subscription Rates:** 395 individuals; US$723 individuals; EUR593 individuals; 711 two years; US$1,301 two years; EUR1,067 two years; 1,007 individuals 3 years; US$1,844 individuals 3 years; EUR1,440 individuals 3 years. **Remarks:** Accepts advertising. **URL:** http://www.asiarisk.com.hk. **Circ:** (Not Reported)

53973 ■ Asian Affairs
Royal Society for Asian Affairs
2 Belgrave Sq.
London SW1X 8PJ, United Kingdom
Ph: 44 20 72355122
Publication E-mail: editor@rsaa.org.uk
Publisher E-mail: info@rsaa.org.uk
Publication covering Asian affairs. **Founded:** 1914. **Freq:** 3/yr. **Key Personnel:** Barney Smith, Editor. **ISSN:** 0306-8374. **Subscription Rates:** 59 individuals print only; US$100 individuals print only; 140 institutions print and online; US$232 institutions print and online. **Remarks:** Accepts advertising. **URL:** http://www.rsaa.org.uk/journal.htm. **Ad Rates:** BW: 150. **Circ:** Paid 1,500

53974 ■ Asian Art
Asian Art Newspaper
PO Box 22521
London W8 4GT, United Kingdom
Ph: 44 20 72296040
Fax: 44 20 75652913

Publisher E-mail: enquiries@asianartnewspaper.com Newspaper covering all the major international art events, auctions, and exhibits. **Freq:** Monthly. **Key Personnel:** Jane Grylls, Contact, phone 44 20 73005661, jane.grylls@royalacademy.org.uk; Kim Jenner, Contact, phone 44 20 73005658, fax 44 20 73008063, kim.jenner@royalacedemy.org.uk. **Subscription Rates:** 45 individuals print; 50 individuals rest of Europe; print; 55 other countries print; two years print; 60 individuals rest of Europe; print + digital; 65 other countries print + digital; 30 individuals digital. **URL:** http://www.asianartnewspaper.com/. **Circ:** 8,000

53975 ■ Asian Journal of Andrology
Nature Publishing Group
The Macmillan Bldg.
4 Crinan St.
London N1 9XW, United Kingdom
Ph: 44 20 78334000
Fax: 44 20 78434640
Peer-reviewed journal publishing new findings in basic and clinical (including modern, traditional and epidemiological) research on Andrology, especially regulation of spermatogenesis, gene expression in accessory sex organs and external genitalia, feedback regulation of gonadotropins, sperm capacitation, anatomical studies of the reproductive tract, prostate diseases and physiology of penile erectile tissue. **Freq:** Bimonthly. **Key Personnel:** David J. Handelsman, Dep. Ed.-in-Ch.; Sujoy K. Guha, Assoc. Ed.-in-Ch.; Yi-Fei Wang, Editor-in-Chief; Yuan-Cheng Xu, Corresponding Ed.; Shu-Jie Xia, Editorial Board; Bo Yang, Corresponding Ed.; Iwamoto Teruaki, Corresponding Ed. **ISSN:** 1008-682X. **Subscription Rates:** US$295 individuals print and online; EUR240 individuals print and online; 41,100¥ individuals print and online; 155 individuals print and online; US$266 individuals online only; EUR216 individuals online only; 37,000¥ individuals online only; 140 individuals online only. **Remarks:** Advertising accepted; rates available upon request. **URL:** http://www.nature.com/aja/index.html. **Circ:** (Not Reported)

53976 ■ Aslib Proceedings
Emerald Group Publishing Ltd.
c/o Prof. David Nicholas, Ed.
School of Library, Archive & Information Studies
University College London
Gower St.
London WC1E 6BT, United Kingdom
Publisher E-mail: emerald@emeraldinsight.com
Journal bringing currency, authority and accessibility to the reporting of current research, issues and debates in the broad area of information work. **Subtitle:** New Information Perspectives. **Freq:** 6/yr. **Key Personnel:** Prof. David Nicholas, Editor, david.nicholas@ucl.ac.uk; Dr. Ian Rowlands, Dep. Ed., i.rowlands@ucl.ac.uk; Lizzie Scott, Publisher, escott@emeraldinsight.com. **ISSN:** 0001-253X. **URL:** http://info.emeraldinsight.com/products/journals/journals.htm?id=ap.

53977 ■ Aspinalls
Luxury Publishing Limited
5 Jubilee Pl.
Chelsea
London SW3 3TD, United Kingdom
Ph: 44 20 75912900
Fax: 44 20 75912929
Publisher E-mail: info@luxurypublishing.com
Magazine covering all aspects of the high-net-worth lifestyle. **Freq:** Semiannual. **Trim Size:** 210 x 260 mm. **Key Personnel:** William Cash, Editor. **Remarks:** Accepts advertising. **URL:** http://www.luxurypublishing.co.uk/. **Ad Rates:** 4C: 2,950. **Circ:** (Not Reported)

53978 ■ Astrological Journal
Astrological Association of Great Britain
Unit 168, Lee Valley Technopark
Tottenham Hale
London N17 9LN, United Kingdom
Ph: 44 20 88804848
Fax: 44 20 88804849
Publisher E-mail: office@astrologicalassociation.com
Journal covering astrology. **Founded:** 1958. **Freq:** Bimonthly. **Key Personnel:** Gerasime Patilas, Editor, gerasime@patilas.freeserve.co.uk. **Remarks:** Advertising accepted; rates available upon request. **URL:** http://www.astrologer.com. **Circ:** 1,600

53979 ■ AT Magazine
Chartered Institute of Architectural Technologists

397 City Rd.
London EC1V 1NH, United Kingdom
Ph: 44 20 72782206
Fax: 44 20 78373194
Publisher E-mail: info@ciat.org.uk
Professional magazine covering issues for architectural technologists and related professionals. **Founded:** 1995. **Freq:** Bimonthly. **Key Personnel:** Hugh Morrison, Editor, phone 44 20 72782206, editorial@ciat.org.uk. **ISSN:** 1361-326X. **Subscription Rates:** 15 individuals. **Remarks:** Accepts advertising. **URL:** http://www.ciat.org.uk/en/media_centre/. **Former name:** Atrium, SAAT News (1991). **Formerly:** Architectural Technology. **Circ:** Non-paid 8,500, 11,000

53980 ■ Audience
Audience Media Ltd.
26 Dorset St.
London W1U 8AP, United Kingdom
Ph: 44 20 74867007
Fax: 44 20 74862002
Publisher E-mail: info@audience.uk.com
Magazine featuring business of contemporary live music. Also provides news, features and tour information to companies and individuals in more than 80 countries. **Key Personnel:** Stephen Parker, Managing Editor, steve@audience.uk.com; Fiona West, Subscriptions Mgr., fiona@audience.uk.com; James Drury, News Ed., james@audience.uk.com. **Subscription Rates:** 70 individuals; EUR80 individuals European Union; US$90 other countries. **URL:** http://www.audience.uk.com/.

53981 ■ Australian Religion Studies Review
Equinox Publishing Ltd.
1 Chelsea Manor Studios
Flood St.
London SW3 5SR, United Kingdom
Ph: 44 20 78233748
Fax: 44 20 78233748
Peer-reviewed journal covering aspects of the academic study of religion. **Subtitle:** The journal of the Australian Association for the Study of Religion. **Freq:** 3/yr (April, September and December). **Key Personnel:** Paul Hedges, Co-Ed., paul.hedges@winchester.ac.uk; Sarah Penicka-Smith, Reviews Ed., sarah.penicka-smith@sydney.edu.au. **ISSN:** 1031-2943. **Subscription Rates:** 140 institutions, other countries print and online; US$280 institutions print and online; 53 other countries print; US$105 individuals print. **Remarks:** Accepts advertising. **URL:** http://www.equinoxjournals.com/ojs/index.php/ARSR. **Circ:** (Not Reported)

53982 ■ Austrian Studies
Maney Publishing
1 Carlton House Ter.
London SW1Y 5AF, United Kingdom
Ph: 44 74517300
Fax: 44 20 74517307
Publisher E-mail: maney@maney.co.uk
Journal covering distinctive cultural traditions of the Habsburg Empire and the Austrian Republic. **Freq:** Annual. **Key Personnel:** Dr. Judith Beniston, Editor, j.beniston@ucl.ac.uk; Prof. Robert Vilain, Editor, r.vilain@rhul.ac.uk. **ISSN:** 1350-7532. **Subscription Rates:** 76 institutions, other countries; US$177 institutions. **URL:** http://maney.co.uk/index.php/journals/aus/.

53983 ■ Author
Society of Authors - England
84 Drayton Gardens
London SW10 9SB, United Kingdom
Ph: 44 20 73736642
Fax: 44 20 73735768
Publisher E-mail: info@societyofauthors.org
Publication covering writers. **Freq:** Quarterly. **Key Personnel:** Andrew Rosenheim, Editor. **ISSN:** 0005-0628. **Remarks:** Advertising accepted; rates available upon request. **URL:** http://www.societyofauthors.net/author. **Circ:** 9,200

53984 ■ Autism
Sage Publications Ltd.
1 Oliver's Yard
55 City Rd.
London EC1Y 1SP, United Kingdom
Ph: 44 20 73248500
Fax: 44 20 73248600
Scholarly journal covering research and practical relevance into the improvement of the quality of life for

individuals with autism and autism-related disorders. **Subtitle:** The International Journal of Research and Practice. **Founded:** 1997. **Freq:** 6/yr. **Trim Size:** 193 x 118 mm. **Key Personnel:** Rita Jordan, Editorial Board; Patricia Howlin, Editorial Board; Dermot M. Bowler, Editor; Prof. Tony Attwood, Assoc. Ed.; Elizabeth Hill, Book Review Ed.; Lorna Wing, Editorial Board; Dougal Julian Hare, Editor; Lonnie Zwaigenbaum, Editor; Gillian Baird, Assoc. Ed. **ISSN:** 1362-3613. **Subscription Rates:** 265 individuals school, print & electronic; 530 institutions electronic & print; 477 institutions electronic; 519 institutions print only; 62 individuals print only; 95 institutions single print; 13 individuals single print; 583 institutions current volume print & all online content; 477 institutions content through 1998. **Remarks:** Accepts advertising. **URL:** http://www.sagepub.co.uk/journalsProdDesc.nav?prodId=Journal200822. **Circ:** (Not Reported)

53985 ■ Auto Express
Dennis Publishing Ltd.
30 Cleveland St.
London W1T 4JD, United Kingdom
Ph: 44 20 79076000
Fax: 44 20 79076020
Publisher E-mail: reception@dennis.co.uk
Consumer magazine covering automobiles. **Founded:** Sept. 22, 1988. **Freq:** Weekly. **Print Method:** Heat set Web Offset. **Trim Size:** 226 x 300 mm. **Key Personnel:** David Johns, Editor-in-Chief, editor@autoexpress.co.uk; James Burnay, Publishing Dir., james_burnay@dennis.co.uk. **Subscription Rates:** 150 other countries; 90 individuals Europe; 60 individuals. **Remarks:** Accepts advertising. **URL:** http://www.autoexpress.co.uk. **Circ:** (Not Reported)

53986 ■ Auto Trader
Trader Media Group
41-47 Hartfield Rd., 3rd & 4th Fl.
Wimbledon
London SW19 3RQ, United Kingdom
Ph: 44 208 5447000
Fax: 44 208 8791879
Magazine featuring for sale cars, bikes, caravans, plant, trucks and caravans. **Freq:** Weekly. **Key Personnel:** John King, CEO. **Remarks:** Accepts advertising. **URL:** http://www.autotrader.co.uk/; http://www.tradermediagroup.com/companies/auto-trader.html. **Circ:** ★189,077

53987 ■ Automotive Engineer
Institution of Mechanical Engineers
1 Birdcage Walk
London SW1H 9JJ, United Kingdom
Ph: 44 20 72227899
Fax: 44 20 72224557
Publisher E-mail: international@imeche.org
Publication covering automotive engineering. **Founded:** 1975. **Freq:** Monthly 11/yr. **Key Personnel:** Christian Letessier Fenodot, Contact, phone 44 20 72223337; Sat Bains, Contact, advertising@pepublishing.com. **ISSN:** 0307-6490. **Subscription Rates:** EUR399 individuals. **Remarks:** Accepts advertising. **URL:** http://www.pepublishing.com/buspub/automotive.htm; http://www.ae-plus.com/. **Circ:** (Not Reported)

53988 ■ Automotive Logistics
Ultima Media Ltd.
Lamb House
Church St.
London W4 2PD, United Kingdom
Ph: 44 20 89870900
Fax: 44 20 89870948
Publisher E-mail: info@ultimamedia.com
Magazine featuring automotive industry. **Trim Size:** 210 x 297 mm. **Key Personnel:** Maxine Elkin, Editor, phone 44 20 89870962, fax 44 20 89955600, maxine.elkin@ultimamedia.com; Louis Yiakoumi, Publisher, louis.yiakoumi@ultimamedia.com. **Subscription Rates:** Free. **Remarks:** Accepts advertising. **URL:** http://www.automotivelogisticsmagazine.com/. **Circ:** △9,000

53989 ■ Automotive Manufacturing Solutions
Advanstar Communications (UK) Ltd.
Lamb House
Church St.
London W4 2PD, United Kingdom
Ph: 44 20 89870900
Fax: 44 20 89870948
Magazine offering an in-depth insight into the latest manufacturing technologies being employed by the

Circulation: ★ = ABC; △ = BPA; ♦ = CAC; • = CCAB; □ = VAC; ⊕ = PO Statement; ‡ = Publisher's Report; Boldface figures = sworn; Light figures = estimated.

Gale Directory of Publications & Broadcast Media/147th Ed.   **5683**

world's leading automakers and component suppliers. **Freq:** Bimonthly. **Key Personnel:** Julian Buckley, Editor, phone 44 20 89870979, julian.buckley@ultimamedia.com; Jim Ajayi, Sales Mgr., phone 44 20 89870957, jim.ajayi@ultimamedia.com; Andrew Fallon, Publisher, phone 44 20 89870931, andrew.fallon@ultimamedia.com; George Waga, Circulation Mgr., george.waga@ultimamedia.com. **URL:** http://www.automotivemanufacturingsolutions.com/.

53990 ■ Automotive Production China
Ultima Media Ltd.
Lamb House
Church St.
London W4 2PD, United Kingdom
Ph: 44 20 89870900
Fax: 44 20 89870948
Publication E-mail: apc@ultimamedia.com
Publisher E-mail: info@ultimamedia.com
Magazine for Chinese automotive industry. **Freq:** Semiannual. **Key Personnel:** Simon Timm, Chm., simon.timm@ultimamedia.com. **Subscription Rates:** Free. **Remarks:** Accepts advertising. **URL:** http://www.automotiveproductionchina.com/apc/. **Circ:** △5,000

53991 ■ Autonomic Neuroscience
Mosby Inc.
c/o G. Burnstock, Ed.-in-Ch.
Autonomic Neuroscience Institute
Royal Free & University College Medical School
Rowland Hill St.
London NW3 2PF, United Kingdom
Ph: 44 20 78302948
Fax: 44 20 78302949
Publisher E-mail: custserv.ehs@elsevier.com
Journal reporting on investigations on the nervous system. **Subtitle:** Basic and Clinical. **Freq:** 14/yr. **Key Personnel:** G. Burnstock, Editor-in-Chief, g.burnstock@ucl.ac.uk; R. Freeman, Editor, phone 617632-8454, fax 617632-0852, rfreeman@bidmc.harvard.edu; M.P. Gilbey, Editor, m.gilbey@ucl.ac.uk. **ISSN:** 1566-0702. **Subscription Rates:** EUR3,792 institutions European countries and Iran; 503,900¥ institutions; US$4,242 institutions, other countries. **URL:** http://www.elsevier.com/wps/find/journaldescription.cws_home/506089/descriptiondescription.

53992 ■ AV Magazine
Haymarket Business Magazines
174 Hammersmith Rd.
London W6 7JP, United Kingdom
Ph: 44 20 82674210
Publisher E-mail: info@haymarket.com
Magazine featuring information in audio-visual industry and technology. **Founded:** 1972. **Freq:** Monthly. **Key Personnel:** Bhavna Mistry, Editor, phone 44 20 82674128, bhavna.mistry@haymarket.com. **Subscription Rates:** 85 individuals; 153 two years. **Remarks:** Accepts advertising. **URL:** http://www.haymarket.com/av/av_magazine/default.aspx. **Circ:** ★11,731

53993 ■ Aviva
c/o Kate Burke, Ed.
41 Royal Cres.
London W11 4SN, United Kingdom
Ph: 44 20 76020140
Fax: 44 20 73716315
Publisher E-mail: kateb@aviva.org
Online feminist magazine for women worldwide. **Subtitle:** Women's World Wide Web. **Founded:** Jan. 10, 1996. **Key Personnel:** Farhat Bokhari, Asia Ed., farhatb@hrasia.org; Kate Burke, Editor, kateb@aviva.org. **Subscription Rates:** Free Online. **Remarks:** Accepts advertising. **URL:** http://www.womeninlondon.org.uk. **Circ:** Non-paid 20,000

53994 ■ Award World
Duke of Edinburgh's Award International Association
Award House
7-11 St. Matthew St.
London SW1P 2JT, United Kingdom
Ph: 44 20 72224242
Fax: 44 20 72224141
Publisher E-mail: sect@intaward.org
Publication covering youth interests. **Freq:** Semiannual. **Key Personnel:** Polly Underwood, Contact, phone 44 20 72224242, polly.underwood@intaward.org. **ISSN:** 1352-2574. **Remarks:** Advertising accepted; rates available upon request. **URL:** http://www.intaward.org; http://www.intaward.org/iaa/index_554.html. **Circ:** 22,000

53995 ■ AXIS
ROOM, the National Council for Housing and Planning
41 Botolph Ln.
London EC3R 8DL, United Kingdom
Ph: 44 20 79299494
Fax: 44 20 79299490
Publisher E-mail: room@rtpi.org.uk
Journal covering housing, planning and regeneration. **Subtitle:** The Journal of Housing, Planning and Regeneration. **Founded:** 1935. **Freq:** Bimonthly. **Print Method:** Offset. **Trim Size:** A4. **Key Personnel:** Chris Griffin, Editor, room@rtpi.org.uk. **ISSN:** 1467-9086. **Subscription Rates:** 42.50 individuals; 47.50 elsewhere. **Remarks:** Accepts advertising. **URL:** http://www.room.org.uk/archive/axis/index.htm. **Former name:** HPR—Housing & Planning Review. **Ad Rates:** BW: 650, 4C: 950. **Circ:** 6,000

53996 ■ axm
Millivres Prowler Group
Spectrum House, Unit M
32-34 Gordon House Rd.
London NW5 1LP, United Kingdom
Ph: 44 20 74247400
Fax: 44 20 74247401
Publisher E-mail: reception@millivres.co.uk
Magazine for young gays. **Freq:** Monthly. **Trim Size:** 225 x 300 mm. **Key Personnel:** Matt Miles, Editor; Gail Hackston, Advertising Mgr., phone 44 207 4247449, gail@axm-mag.com. **Remarks:** Accepts advertising. **URL:** http://www.axm-mag.com/axm/. **Circ:** (Not Reported)

53997 ■ AYGO Magazine
Publicis Blueprint
23 Howland St.
London W1A 1AQ, United Kingdom
Ph: 44 20 74627777
Publisher E-mail: info@publicis-blueprint.co.uk
Magazine featuring Toyota's small car model. **Freq:** Semiannual. **Key Personnel:** Jane Ditcham, Publisher, phone 44 20 78303863, jane.ditcham@publicis-blueprint.co.uk. **URL:** http://www.publicis-blueprint.co.uk. **Circ:** 250,000

53998 ■ Balamory
BBC Worldwide Publishing Ltd.
Media Centre
201 Wood Ln.
London W12 7TQ, United Kingdom
Ph: 44 20 84332000
Fax: 44 20 87490538
Magazine featuring coloring, drawing, puzzles and games for children. **Freq:** every 4 weeks. **Subscription Rates:** 1.99 single issue. **URL:** http://www.bbcmagazines.com/content/magazines/balamory/.

53999 ■ Balance
Diabetes UK
Macleod House
10 Pky.
London NW1 7AA, United Kingdom
Ph: 44 20 74241000
Fax: 44 20 74241001
Publisher E-mail: info@diabetes.org.ok
Publication covering Diabetes. **Freq:** Bimonthly. **Subscription Rates:** Free to members of Diabetes U.K. **Remarks:** Accepts advertising. **URL:** http://www.diabetes.org.uk/Professionals/Resources-for-patients/Balance-magazine/. **Circ:** Paid 200,000

54000 ■ Bank of England Quarterly Bulletin
Bank of England
Threadneedle St.
London EC2R 8AH, United Kingdom
Ph: 44 20 76014444
Fax: 44 20 76015460
Publication E-mail: ma_editor@bankofengland.co.uk
Publisher E-mail: enquiries@bankofengland.co.uk
Publication for the banking, finance, and accounting industries. **Founded:** 1960. **Freq:** Quarterly. **Print Method:** Litho Printing. **Trim Size:** A4. **ISSN:** 0005-5166. **Subscription Rates:** 21 individuals first class post; 6 individuals single first class post; 7 students; 2 students single; 14 academics; 4 academics, single; 25 individuals letter service; 7 individuals single, letter service; 25 other countries surface mail; 7 other countries single, surface mail. **Remarks:** Advertising not accepted. **URL:** http://www.bankofengland.co.uk; http://www.bankofengland.co.uk/publications/quarterlybulletin/

index.htm. **Circ:** (Not Reported)

54001 ■ The Banker
Financial Times Business Ltd.
One Southwark Bridge
London SE1 9HL, United Kingdom
Ph: 44 20 77756653
Fax: 44 20 77756413
Publisher E-mail: finance.event@ft.com
Publication for the banking, finance, and accounting industries. **Founded:** 1926. **Freq:** Monthly. **Print Method:** Perfect Bound. **Key Personnel:** Brian Caplen, Editor, phone 44 20 77756364, brian.caplen@ft.com; Stephen Timewell, Editor-in-Chief, phone 44 20 77756359, stephen.timewell@ft.com; Angus Cushley, Publishing Dir., phone 44 20 77756354, angus.cushley@ft.com. **ISSN:** 0005-5395. **Subscription Rates:** 289 individuals; EUR426 individuals; US$543 individuals. **Remarks:** Accepts advertising. **URL:** http://www.thebanker.com. **Ad Rates:** BW: 8,950, 4C: 11,950. **Circ:** ★28,771

54002 ■ Banking Technology
Informa Publishing Group
Informa House
30-32 Mortimer St.
London W1W 7RE, United Kingdom
Ph: 44 20 70175000
Publication E-mail: professional.enquiries@informa.com
Trade magazine covering financial systems worldwide. **Founded:** 1984. **Freq:** Monthly 10/yr. **Key Personnel:** David Bannister, Editor. **ISSN:** 0266-0865. **Subscription Rates:** 600 individuals; EUR749 individuals; 1,079 individuals. **Remarks:** Accepts advertising. **URL:** http://www.bankingtech.com. **Circ:** Combined 8,108

54003 ■ BBC Gardeners' World Magazine
BBC Magazines
Media Center
201 Wood Ln.
London W12 7TQ, United Kingdom
Ph: 44 20 84332000
Publication E-mail: gwletters@bbc.co.uk
Consumer magazine covering gardening worldwide. **Subtitle:** The Best Selling Gardening Magazine in the World. **Founded:** Mar. 1991. **Freq:** Monthly. **Trim Size:** 228 x 298 mm. **Key Personnel:** Tim Robinson, Contact, tim.robinson@bbc.co.uk; Adam Pasco, Editor. **Subscription Rates:** 16.20 individuals six issues (Direct Debit); 43.20 individuals basic; 36.70 individuals. **Remarks:** Accepts advertising. **URL:** http://www.gardenersworld.com. **Circ:** Paid 260,133

54004 ■ BBC Good Food
BBC Worldwide Publishing Ltd.
Media Centre
201 Wood Ln.
London W12 7TQ, United Kingdom
Ph: 44 20 84332000
Fax: 44 20 87490538
Consumer magazine covering cooking. **Founded:** 1989. **Freq:** Monthly. **Subscription Rates:** 16.99 individuals 6 issues; 32.50 individuals. **Remarks:** Accepts advertising. **URL:** http://www.bbcgoodfood.com/. **Circ:** Paid ★342,375

54005 ■ BBC Learning is Fun!
BBC Magazines
Media Center
201 Wood Ln.
London W12 7TQ, United Kingdom
Ph: 44 20 84332000
Educational magazine for children aged 5-7 years. **Founded:** Oct. 1996. **Freq:** every 4 weeks. **Subscription Rates:** 23.88 individuals. **Remarks:** Advertising not accepted. **URL:** http://www.bbcmagazines.com/magazinesubscriptions/learning.html. **Circ:** Controlled 60,000

54006 ■ BBC The Magic Key
BBC Worldwide Publishing Ltd.
Media Centre
201 Wood Ln.
London W12 7TQ, United Kingdom
Ph: 44 20 84332000
Fax: 44 20 87490538
Magazine devised specifically to help develop the literacy skills of young readers, with stories and activities designed to support the reading and writing skills of 5-7 year olds, encouraging children to develop an interest in words, an understanding of language and a love of reading. **Freq:** Monthly. **Subscription Rates:** 1.99

single issue. **URL:** http://www.bbc.co.uk/schools/magickey/.

54007 ■ BDJ British Dental Journal
Nature Publishing Group
The Macmillan Bldg.
4 Crinan St.
London N1 9XW, United Kingdom
Ph: 44 20 78334000
Fax: 44 20 78434640
Publication E-mail: bdj@nature.com
Peer-reviewed professional journal covering dentistry. **Subtitle:** The Journal of the British Dental Association. **Freq:** Semimonthly. **Print Method:** Offset Litho. **Trim Size:** A4. **Key Personnel:** Rowena Milan, Journal Ed., phone 44 20 78433678, r.milan@nature.com; Arveen Bajaj, News Ed., phone 44 20 78433679, a.bajaj@nature.com; Stephen Hancocks, Editor-in-Chief, phone 44 20 75355842, s.hancocks@bda.com; Kim Black-Totham, Publisher, phone 44 20 78434612, k.black-totham@nature.com. **ISSN:** 0007-0610. **Subscription Rates:** US$449 individuals print & online. **Remarks:** Accepts advertising. **URL:** http://www.nature.com/bdj/index.html. **Circ:** 20,562

54008 ■ Be My Parent
British Association for Adoption and Fostering
Saffron House
6-10 Kirby St.
London EC1N 8TS, United Kingdom
Ph: 44 20 74212600
Fax: 44 20 74212601
Publication E-mail: bmp@baaf.org.uk
Publisher E-mail: mail@baaf.org.uk
Newspaper covering adoption and fostering in the UK. **Founded:** 1980. **Freq:** Monthly. **Print Method:** Web. **Trim Size:** 11 x 18. **Key Personnel:** Patricia Oni, Manager. **Subscription Rates:** 42 individuals paper only; 28 individuals 6 months (paper only); 15 individuals 3 months (paper only); 5.50 individuals 1 month (paper only). **Remarks:** Advertising accepted; rates available upon request. **URL:** http://www.baaf.org.uk; http://www.bemyparent.org.uk/. **Circ:** Combined 22,000

54009 ■ Behavioral and Brain Functions
BioMed Central Ltd.
236 Gray's Inn Rd., Fl. 6
34-42 Cleveland St.
London WC1X 8HL, United Kingdom
Ph: 44 20 31922000
Fax: 44 20 31922010
Publisher E-mail: info@biomedcentral.com
Online journal encompassing all aspects of neurobiology, where the unifying theme is behavior or behavioral dysfunction. **Key Personnel:** Terje Sagvolden, Editor-in-Chief, terje.sagvolden@medisin.uio.no; Veronica Rodrigues, Editorial Board; Amy F.T. Arnsten, Assoc. Ed.; David G. Amaral, Editorial Board; Rosemary Tannock, Assoc. Ed.; Jan G. Bjaalie, Editorial Board; Charles A. Catania, Assoc. Ed.; Stephen V. Faraone, Assoc. Ed. **ISSN:** 1744-9081. **Remarks:** Accepts advertising. **URL:** http://www.behavioralandbrainfunctions.com/home. **Circ:** (Not Reported)

54010 ■ Bella
H. Bauer Publishing
Academic House
24-28 Oval Rd.
London NW1 7DT, United Kingdom
Ph: 44 20 72418000
Fax: 44 20 72418030
Magazine featuring celebrities, fashion and lifestyle. **Founded:** Oct. 1987. **Freq:** Weekly. **Trim Size:** 225 x 285 mm. **Key Personnel:** Lisa Carver, Advertising Mgr., phone 44 20 70750783, fax 44 20 70750786, lisa.carver@bauer.co.uk. **Subscription Rates:** 87 individuals. **Remarks:** Accepts advertising. **URL:** http://www.bauer.co.uk/magazineprofiles/42. **Circ:** ★246,446

54011 ■ Benefits & Compensation International
Pension Publications Ltd.
Hope House, E Wing, 4th Fl.
45 Great Peter St.
London SW1P 3LT, United Kingdom
Ph: 44 20 72220288
Fax: 44 20 77992163
Publisher E-mail: editorial@benecompintl.com
Global HR magazine specializing in employee benefits and compensation. **Subtitle:** Total Remuneration and

Pension Investment. **Founded:** 1971. **Freq:** 10/yr. **Print Method:** Offset Litho. **Trim Size:** A4. **Key Personnel:** Irena St. John Brooks, Editor; Belinda Devenish, Assoc. Ed.; Alexandra Hain-Cole, Production Ed. **ISSN:** 0268-764X. **Subscription Rates:** 395 individuals UK and CI; US$825 U.S.; 450 out of country; EUR610 Eurozone. **Remarks:** Accepts advertising. **URL:** http://www.benecompintl.com. **Ad Rates:** BW: 2,750, 4C: 3,560. **Circ:** Paid 1,007

54012 ■ Benelux unquote
Incisive Media Limited
Haymarket House
28-29 Haymarket
London SW1Y 4RX, United Kingdom
Ph: 44 870 2408859
Fax: 44 207 4849797
Publisher E-mail: customerservices@incisivemedia.com
Journal covering news from the venture capital and private equity market in Belgium, The Netherlands, and Luxembourg. **Founded:** 1992. **Freq:** Monthly. **Key Personnel:** Francinia Protti-Alvarez, Editor, phone 44 20 70047476, francinia.protti-alvarez@incisivemedia.com. **Remarks:** Accepts advertising. **URL:** http://www.incisivemedia.com/corporate/products/benunquote; http://www.beneluxunquote.com. **Circ:** (Not Reported)

54013 ■ Best Practice & Research Clinical Obstetrics & Gynecology
Elsevier Science
c/o Prof. S. Arulkumaran, Ed.-in-Ch.
Dept. of Obstetrics & Gynecology
St. George's Hospital
University of London, Cranmer Ter.
London SW17 0RE, United Kingdom
Ph: 44 20 87255956
Fax: 44 20 87255958
Publisher E-mail: nlinfo-f@elsevier.com
Journal providing solutions to the key clinical issues of diagnosis, treatment and patient management in the areas of clinical obstetrics & gynecology. **Freq:** Bimonthly. **Key Personnel:** Prof. S. Arulkumaran, Editor-in-Chief, sarulkum@sgul.ac.uk; K. Hayes, MCQ Ed.; T. Baskett, Editorial Board; I. Brosens, Editorial Board; J. Cain, Editorial Board; I. Fraser, Editorial Board. **ISSN:** 1521-6934. **Subscription Rates:** EUR271 individuals for European countries & Iran; 29,000¥ individuals; US$241 individuals for all countries except Europe, Japan & Iran; EUR681 institutions for European countries & Iran; US$818 institutions for all countries except Europe, Japan & Iran; 90,000¥ institutions. **Remarks:** Advertising accepted; rates available upon request. **URL:** http://www.elsevier.com/wps/find/journaldescription.cws_home/623004/descriptiondescription. **Circ:** (Not Reported)

54014 ■ Best Treatments
BMJ Publishing Group Ltd.
BMA House
Tavistock Sq.
London WC1H 9JR, United Kingdom
Ph: 44 20 73874410
Fax: 44 20 73836400
Journal covering latest health and medical treatments. **Key Personnel:** Rachel Armitage, Publishing Dir.; Rubin Minhas, Editorial Dir. **Subscription Rates:** 9.99 individuals online access, 1 month; 3 individuals online access, pay per view. **URL:** http://www.besttreatments.co.uk/btuk/home.jsp.

54015 ■ Big Cheese
Big Cheese Publishing
Unit 7, Clarendon Bldg.
25 Horsell Rd.
Highbury
London N5 1XL, United Kingdom
Ph: 44 20 76070303
Publisher E-mail: info@bigcheesemagazine.com
Consumer magazine covering music, sports, lifestyle and other issues for youth. **Freq:** Monthly. **Trim Size:** 210 x 280 mm. **Key Personnel:** Miles Hackett, Contact. **Subscription Rates:** 57.51 individuals Europe delivery; 29.99 individuals U.K. delivery; 88.32 individuals U.S., worldwide delivery. **Remarks:** Accepts advertising. **URL:** http://www.bigcheesemagazine.com. **Circ:** Paid 16,000

54016 ■ Big Issue Namibia
1-5 Wandsworth Rd.
London SW8 2LN, United Kingdom
Ph: 44 20 75263200

Publisher E-mail: info@bigissue.com
Magazine aiming to help homeless, long term unemployed and destitute people to regain their self esteem, to achieve economic independence and to socilitate their regeneration into mainstream society. **Freq:** Weekly. **Remarks:** Accepts advertising. **URL:** http://www.bigissue.com/. **Circ:** ★136,018

54017 ■ Big Value Codebreakers
H. Bauer Publishing
Academic House
24-28 Oval Rd.
London NW1 7DT, United Kingdom
Ph: 44 20 72418000
Fax: 44 20 72418030
Magazine featuring 70 coded crossword. **Freq:** Monthly. **Trim Size:** 185 x 255 mm. **Key Personnel:** Clive Garsin, Gp. Ed.; Spike Figgett, Publishing Dir.; Helen Greenwood, Advertising Mgr., heleng@tpc-manchester.com. **Subscription Rates:** 16.84 individuals. **Remarks:** Accepts advertising. **URL:** http://www.bauer.co.uk/our-magazines/big-value-codebreakers. **Circ:** ★41,000

54018 ■ Biocatalysis and Biotransformation
Taylor & Francis Group Journals
Division of Biology
Wolfson Biochemistry Bldg.
Faculty of Natural Sciences
Imperial College
London SW7 2AZ, United Kingdom
Publisher E-mail: customerservice@taylorandfrancis.com
Official journal of the Section on Applied Biocatalysis of the European Federation of Biotechnology. **Freq:** Bimonthly. **Key Personnel:** G. Carrea, Assoc. Ed.; M.N. Gupta, Review Ed.; David Leak, Editor-in-Chief, d.leak@imperial.ac.uk; Antonio Ballesteros, Exec. Ed., a.ballesteros@icp.csic.es; A. Bommarius, Assoc. Ed.; P. Adlercreutz, Review Ed.; J.M. Woodley, Assoc. Ed. **ISSN:** 1024-2422. **Subscription Rates:** US$1,460 institutions online only; US$1,460 individuals online only; US$1,460 individuals print & online. **URL:** http://www.informaworld.com/smpp/title~content=t713454445.

54019 ■ The Biochemist
The Biochemical Society
Charles Darwin House
12 Roger St.
London WC1N 2JU, United Kingdom
Ph: 44 20 76852400
Fax: 44 20 76852470
Publication E-mail: editorial@portlandpress.com; biochemist@portlandpress.com
Publisher E-mail: genadmin@biochemistry.org
Professional magazine covering biochemistry for members of The Biochemical Society. **Subtitle:** The Magazine for Life Scientists. **Freq:** Bimonthly. **Key Personnel:** Mark Burgess, Exec. Ed.; Richard Reece, Editor. **ISSN:** 1740-1194. **Subscription Rates:** 191 institutions U.K., rest of the world; US$362 institutions North America; EUR325 institutions Europe. **Remarks:** Accepts advertising. **URL:** http://www.biochemist.org. **Circ:** Controlled 9,000

54020 ■ Bioinformation
BioMed Central Ltd.
236 Gray's Inn Rd., Fl. 6
34-42 Cleveland St.
London WC1X 8HL, United Kingdom
Ph: 44 20 31922000
Fax: 44 20 31922010
Publisher E-mail: info@biomedcentral.com
Journal covering research articles in all aspects of biological knowledge discovery through mathematical and computational analysis of biological data. **Subtitle:** Discovery at the Interface of Physical and Biological Sciences. **Key Personnel:** Francesco Chiappelli, Editor, fchiappelli@dentistry.ucla.edu; Gad Yagil, Editor, gad.yagil@weizmann.ac.il; Nagarajan Pattabiraman, Editor, nagpat@gmail.com; Paul Shapshak, Editor, pshapsha@health.usf.edu; Subbiah Subramanian, Editor, subbiah@i-dns.net; William Perrizo, Editor, william.perrizo@ndsu.edu. **ISSN:** 0973-8894. **URL:** http://www.bioinformation.net/.

54021 ■ Biological Knowledge
BioMed Central Ltd.
236 Gray's Inn Rd., Fl. 6
34-42 Cleveland St.

London WC1X 8HL, United Kingdom
Ph: 44 20 31922000
Fax: 44 20 31922010
Publisher E-mail: info@biomedcentral.com
Journal emphasizing the importance of expansion of knowledge particularly in the fields of biological and biomedical research. **Key Personnel:** Robert P. Futrelle, Editor-in-Chief, biologicalknowledge@gmail.com; Dr. Jeff Shrager, Dep. Ed., jshrager@stanford.edu. **Remarks:** Advertising accepted; rates available upon request. **URL:** http://www.biologicalknowledge.com/info/about/. **Circ:** (Not Reported)

54022 ■ Biologicals
Academic Press
Harcourt Pl.
32 Jamestown Rd.
London NW1 7BY, United Kingdom
Ph: 44 20 74244200
Fax: 44 20 74832293
Journal covering biology. Publication of the International Association for Biologicals (IABS). **Freq:** 6 issues. **Key Personnel:** G. Vyas, Editor-in-Chief; Dr. Takao Hayakawa, Editorial Board; Dr. Anthony Lubiniecki, Editorial Board; Dr. Philip Minor, Editorial Board. **ISSN:** 1045-1056. **Subscription Rates:** US$553 institutions all countries except Europe, Japan & Iran; EUR620 institutions European countries; 67,100¥ institutions Japan. **Remarks:** Advertising not accepted. **URL:** http://www.elsevier.com; http://www.elsevier.com/wps/find/journaldescription.cws_home/622793/descriptiondescription. **Circ:** (Not Reported)

54023 ■ Biologist
Institute of Biology
9 Red Lion Ct.
London EC4A 3EF, United Kingdom
Ph: 44 20 79365900
Publication E-mail: biologist@iob.org
Publisher E-mail: info@iob.org
Scientific journal covering the biosciences for professionals in the field. **Subtitle:** Journal of the Institute of Biology. **Founded:** 1950. **Freq:** Bimonthly Feb., Apr., Jun., Aug., Oct., and Dec. **Print Method:** Full Color from PDF. **Trim Size:** A4. **Cols./Page:** 2. **Key Personnel:** Jacqui Lagrue, Production Ed.; Paul Merrifield, Book Review Ed.; Ian Clarke, Editorial Advisory Panel; Bill Parry, News Ed.; Prof. Dame Nancy Rothwell, President. **ISSN:** 0006-3347. **Subscription Rates:** Free. **URL:** http://www.iob.org/; http://www.iob.org/general.asp?section=publications&article=biologist.xml. **Ad Rates:** BW: 690, 4C: 845. **Circ:** 26,000

54024 ■ Biology Letters
Royal Society
6-9 Carlton House Ter.
London SW1Y 5AG, United Kingdom
Ph: 44 20 74512500
Fax: 44 20 79302170
Publisher E-mail: info@royalsoc.ac.uk
Journal focusing on biological sciences, evolution and ecology of organisms. **Freq:** Bimonthly. **Key Personnel:** Prof. Brian Charlesworth, Editor. **ISSN:** 1744-9651. **Subscription Rates:** 144 individuals; US$290 individuals; 155 other countries; US$294 other countries; 849 institutions Europe; US$1,588 institutions US/Canada; 924 institutions, other countries. **URL:** http://rsbl.royalsocietypublishing.org/.

54025 ■ Biomarkers
Taylor & Francis Group Journals
c/o Prof. Alan Paine, Ed.-in-Ch.
University of London
London, United Kingdom
Publisher E-mail: customerservice@taylorandfrancis.com
Journal focusing on the field of biomarker research. **Freq:** Bimonthly. **Key Personnel:** Jiin Chynan Luo, Editorial Board; Alfred Bernard, Editorial Board; P. Brandt-Rauf, Editorial Board; Catherine J. Waterfield, Assoc. Ed.; Paolo Boffetta, Editorial Board; Prof. Alan Paine, Editor-in-Chief, alanpaine@hotmail.com. **ISSN:** 1354-750X. **Subscription Rates:** US$1,385 individuals; EUR1,110 institutions; 1,710 institutions corporate; US$2,810 institutions corporate; EUR2,250 institutions corporate; 845 institutions. **URL:** http://informahealthcare.com/bmk.

54026 ■ Biomarkers in Medicine
Future Medicine Ltd.
Unitec House

2 Albert Pl.
London N3 1QB, United Kingdom
Ph: 44 20 83716080
Fax: 44 20 83432313
Publisher E-mail: info@futuremedicine.com
Peer-reviewed journal covering the applications of biomarkers in medicine. **Freq:** Bimonthly. **Key Personnel:** Elisa Manzotti, Editorial Dir., e.manzotti@futuremedicine.com. **ISSN:** 1752-0363. **Subscription Rates:** 605 institutions; EUR755 institutions; US$1,160 institutions; 126,000¥ institutions. **Remarks:** Accepts advertising. **URL:** http://www.futuremedicine.com/loi/bmm. **Circ:** (Not Reported)

54027 ■ BioMechanics
United Business Media
245 Blackfriars Rd.
London SE1 9UY, United Kingdom
Ph: 44 20 79215000
Cross-specialty magazine for healthcare practitioners covering technology trends and clinical developments in the areas of injury prevention and treatment, wound care, diabetes management, surgery, amputation, physical therapy, and other health concerns that impact patient mobility. **Founded:** 1994. **Freq:** Monthly. **Key Personnel:** Leo Robert, Editor, phone 203662-6720, leo.robert@cmpmedica.com. **Subscription Rates:** Free to qualified subscribers. **Remarks:** Accepts advertising. **URL:** http://www.biomech.com. **Ad Rates:** BW: 5,260, 4C: 1,145. **Circ:** Paid 32,000

54028 ■ Biomedical Digital Libraries
BioMed Central Ltd.
236 Gray's Inn Rd., Fl. 6
34-42 Cleveland St.
London WC1X 8HL, United Kingdom
Ph: 44 20 31922000
Fax: 44 20 31922010
Publisher E-mail: info@biomedcentral.com
Online journal covering all aspects of digital library content and usage in biomedical settings. **Key Personnel:** Charles J. Greenberg, Editorial Board; Wayne J. Peay, Editorial Board; Marcus A. Banks, Editor-in-Chief. **ISSN:** 1742-5581. **Remarks:** Accepts advertising. **URL:** http://www.bio-diglib.com/home/. **Circ:** (Not Reported)

54029 ■ BioMedical Engineering OnLine
BioMed Central Ltd.
236 Gray's Inn Rd., Fl. 6
34-42 Cleveland St.
London WC1X 8HL, United Kingdom
Ph: 44 20 31922000
Fax: 44 20 31922010
Publisher E-mail: info@biomedcentral.com
Online journal covering all aspects of biomedical engineering. **Key Personnel:** Dr. Alvin Wald, Editorial Board; Dr. Kenneth R. Foster, Editor-in-Chief; Dr. Monique Frize, Editorial Board; Dr. Alberto Diaspro, Editorial Board; Dr. Eduardo Abreu, Editorial Board; Dr. Edward J. Ciaccio, Editorial Board. **ISSN:** 1475-925X. **Remarks:** Accepts advertising. **URL:** http://www.biomedical-engineering-online.com. **Circ:** (Not Reported)

54030 ■ Biomedical Scientist
Institute of Biomedical Science
12 Coldbath Sq.
London EC1R 5HL, United Kingdom
Ph: 44 20 77130214
Fax: 44 20 78379658
Publisher E-mail: mail@ibms.org
Professional journal for biomedical scientists. **Freq:** Monthly. **Key Personnel:** Kate Phillips, Classified Advertisements, phone 44 18 92518877, katephillips@stepex.com; Brian Nation, Editor, phone 44 20 77130214, briannation@ibms.org. **Subscription Rates:** Free members. **Remarks:** Accepts advertising. **URL:** http://www.ibms.org; http://www.ibms.org/go/mediacentre:publications:the-biomedical-scientist. **Circ:** Paid 14,500

54031 ■ BioVenture View
PJB Publications Ltd.
Telephone House
69-77 Paul St.
London EC2A 4LQ, United Kingdom
Ph: 44 20 70175000
Fax: 44 20 70176792
Publisher E-mail: pjb.enquiries@informa.com
Journal covering analysis of companies, products, and

events in the biotechnology industry. **Founded:** 1986. **Freq:** Semimonthly. **Key Personnel:** Sarah Walkley, Publisher, phone 44 20 70174147, fax 44 20 70176905, sarah.walkley@informa.com; Vinita Chambore, Editor, phone 44 20 70176918, fax 44 20 70176905, vinita.chambore@informa.com. **ISSN:** 0892-1903. **Remarks:** Accepts advertising. **URL:** http://www.ovid.com/site/products/ovidguide/bvview.htm. **Circ:** Paid 327

54032 ■ Bizarre
John Brown Publishing
136-142 Bramley Rd.
London W10 6SR, United Kingdom
Ph: 44 17 15653000
Fax: 44 20 75653060
Publisher E-mail: andrew.hirsch@johnbrowngroup.co.uk
Consumer magazine covering alternative culture. **Freq:** Monthly. **Subscription Rates:** 14 individuals. **Remarks:** Accepts advertising. **URL:** http://www.bizarremag.com/. **Circ:** (Not Reported)

54033 ■ Black History Month
Talent Media
The Maltings, Studio 65/66
169 Tower Bridge Rd.
London SE1 3LJ, United Kingdom
Magazine featuring BME achievement, history, and culture. **Freq:** Annual. **Trim Size:** A4. **Remarks:** Accepts advertising. **URL:** http://www.blackhistorymonthuk.co.uk/. **Circ:** Free 100,000

54034 ■ BMA News
The British Medical Association
BMA House
Tavistock Sq.
London WC1H 9JP, United Kingdom
Ph: 44 20 73874499
Fax: 44 20 73836400
Professional magazine covering medicine and politics for doctors. **Founded:** Oct. 1966. **Freq:** Weekly 51/yr. **Trim Size:** 210 x 297 mm. **Remarks:** Accepts advertising. **URL:** http://www.bma.org.uk/news/bma_news_mag/index.jsp. **Formerly:** BMA News Review. **Ad Rates:** BW: 2,750, 4C: 4,400. **Circ:** Controlled 116,000

54035 ■ BMC Anesthesiology
BioMed Central Ltd.
236 Gray's Inn Rd., Fl. 6
34-42 Cleveland St.
London WC1X 8HL, United Kingdom
Ph: 44 20 31922000
Fax: 44 20 31922010
Publisher E-mail: info@biomedcentral.com
Online journal publishing original research articles in all aspects of anesthesiology. **Key Personnel:** Kesh Baboolal, Editorial Board; Dan Benhamou, Editorial Board; Paula M. Bokesch, Editorial Board; Melissa Norton, MD, Editor-in-Chief, bmcserieseditor@biomedcentral.com; Francis Bonnet, Assoc. Ed.; Vijay K. Chava, Editorial Board. **ISSN:** 1471-2253. **Remarks:** Accepts advertising. **URL:** http://www.biomedcentral.com/bmcanesthesiol/. **Circ:** (Not Reported)

54036 ■ BMC Biochemistry
BioMed Central Ltd.
236 Gray's Inn Rd., Fl. 6
34-42 Cleveland St.
London WC1X 8HL, United Kingdom
Ph: 44 20 31922000
Fax: 44 20 31922010
Publisher E-mail: info@biomedcentral.com
Online journal publishing original research articles in all aspects of biochemistry, including metabolic pathways, enzyme functions, and small molecular components of cells and tissues. **Key Personnel:** Alan Cooper, Editorial Board; David Atkinson, Assoc. Ed.; Christophe Ampe, Assoc. Ed.; Per Berglund, Editorial Board; Neil J. Bulleid, Editorial Board; Melissa Norton, MD, Editor-in-Chief, bmcserieseditor@biomedcentral.com. **ISSN:** 1471-2091. **Remarks:** Accepts advertising. **URL:** http://www.biomedcentral.com/bmcbiochem/. **Circ:** (Not Reported)

54037 ■ BMC Bioinformatics
BioMed Central Ltd.
236 Gray's Inn Rd., Fl. 6
34-42 Cleveland St.
London WC1X 8HL, United Kingdom
Ph: 44 20 31922000
Fax: 44 20 31922010

Publisher E-mail: info@biomedcentral.com
Online journal publishing original research articles in all aspects of computational methods used in the analysis and annotation of sequences and structures, as well as all other areas of computational biology. **Key Personnel:** Peer Bork, Editorial Board; Olivier Gascuel, Editorial Board; Richard Copley, Editorial Board; Rita Casadio, Assoc. Ed.; Adam Arkin, Editorial Board; Melissa Norton, MD, Editor-in-Chief, bmcserieseditor@biomedcentral.com. **ISSN:** 1471-2105. **Remarks:** Accepts advertising. **URL:** http://www.biomedcentral.com/bmcbioinformatics/. **Circ:** (Not Reported)

54038 ■ BMC Biology
BioMed Central Ltd.
236 Gray's Inn Rd., Fl. 6
34-42 Cleveland St.
London WC1X 8HL, United Kingdom
Ph: 44 20 31922000
Fax: 44 20 31922010
Publisher E-mail: info@biomedcentral.com
Online journal publishing original research articles and methodology articles in any area of biology but with a focus on the biomedical sciences. **Key Personnel:** David Baulcombe, Editorial Board; Stephen J. Benkovic, Editorial Board; Richard W. Aldrich, Editorial Board; James E. Cleaver, Editorial Board; Roland Contreras, Editorial Board. **ISSN:** 1741-7007. **Remarks:** Accepts advertising. **URL:** http://www.biomedcentral.com/bmcbiol/. **Circ:** (Not Reported)

54039 ■ BMC Biotechnology
BioMed Central Ltd.
236 Gray's Inn Rd., Fl. 6
34-42 Cleveland St.
London WC1X 8HL, United Kingdom
Ph: 44 20 31922000
Fax: 44 20 31922010
Publisher E-mail: info@biomedcentral.com
Online journal publishing original research articles in the manipulation of biological macromolecules or organisms for use in experimental procedures or in the pharmaceutical, agrobiological and allied industries. **Key Personnel:** Melissa Norton, MD, Editor-in-Chief, bmcserieseditor@biomedcentral.com; William Bentley, Editorial Board; Rup Lal, Editorial Board; Peter J. Halling, Editorial Board; Joaquim M. Cabral, Editorial Board; J. Ann Le Good, PhD, In-house Ed., editorial@biomedcentral.com. **ISSN:** 1472-6750. **Remarks:** Accepts advertising. **URL:** http://www.biomedcentral.com/bmcbiotechnol/. **Circ:** (Not Reported)

54040 ■ BMC Blood Disorders
BioMed Central Ltd.
236 Gray's Inn Rd., Fl. 6
34-42 Cleveland St.
London WC1X 8HL, United Kingdom
Ph: 44 20 31922000
Fax: 44 20 31922010
Publisher E-mail: info@biomedcentral.com
Online journal publishing original research articles in all aspects of the prevention, diagnosis and management of blood disorders, as well as related molecular genetics, pathophysiology, and epidemiology. **Key Personnel:** Dan Longo, Assoc. Ed.; Melissa Norton, MD, Editor-in-Chief, bmcserieseditor@biomedcentral.com; Alan Schechter, Editorial Board; Inderjeet Dokal, Editorial Board; Peter Browett, Editorial Board; Jeff Szer, Editorial Board. **ISSN:** 1471-2326. **Remarks:** Accepts advertising. **URL:** http://www.biomedcentral.com/bmcblooddisord/. **Circ:** (Not Reported)

54041 ■ BMC Cancer
BioMed Central Ltd.
236 Gray's Inn Rd., Fl. 6
34-42 Cleveland St.
London WC1X 8HL, United Kingdom
Ph: 44 20 31922000
Fax: 44 20 31922010
Publisher E-mail: info@biomedcentral.com
Online journal publishing original research articles in all aspects of research relating to cancer, including molecular biology, genetics, pathophysiology, epidemiology, clinical reports, and controlled trials. **Key Personnel:** Melissa Norton, MD, Editor-in-Chief, bmcserieseditor@biomedcentral.com; Maria Blasco, Editorial Board; Anton Berns, Editorial Board; Dario Alessi, Editorial Board; Mariano Barbacid, Editorial

Board; Rachel Neilan, In-house Ed., editorial@biomedcentral.com. **ISSN:** 1471-2407. **Remarks:** Accepts advertising. **URL:** http://www.biomedcentral.com/bmccancer/. **Circ:** (Not Reported)

54042 ■ BMC Cardiovascular Disorders
BioMed Central Ltd.
236 Gray's Inn Rd., Fl. 6
34-42 Cleveland St.
London WC1X 8HL, United Kingdom
Ph: 44 20 31922000
Fax: 44 20 31922010
Publisher E-mail: info@biomedcentral.com
Online journal publishing original research articles in all aspects of the prevention, diagnosis and management of cardiovascular disorders, as well as related molecular genetics, pathophysiology, and epidemiology. **Key Personnel:** Norman Briffa, Editorial Board; Morris J. Brown, Editorial Board; Peter Anderson, Editorial Board; Melissa Norton, MD, Editor-in-Chief, bmcserieseditor@biomedcentral.com; Timothy Shipley, PhD, In-house Ed., editorial@biomedcentral.com; Cathie Sudlow, Editorial Board. **ISSN:** 1471-2261. **Remarks:** Accepts advertising. **URL:** http://www.biomedcentral.com/bmccardiovascdisord/. **Circ:** (Not Reported)

54043 ■ BMC Cell Biology
BioMed Central Ltd.
236 Gray's Inn Rd., Fl. 6
34-42 Cleveland St.
London WC1X 8HL, United Kingdom
Ph: 44 20 31922000
Fax: 44 20 31922010
Publisher E-mail: info@biomedcentral.com
Online journal publishing original research articles in all aspects of cell biology including cellular compartments, traffic, signaling, motility, adhesion and division. **Key Personnel:** Penelope Webb, PhD, Biology Ed.; Ann J. Le Good, PhD, In-house Ed., editorial@biomedcentral.com; Matthias Falk, Editorial Board; Melissa Norton, MD, Editor-in-Chief, bmcserieseditor@biomedcentral.com; Richard G. Anderson, Editorial Board; Bruce Demple, Editorial Board. **ISSN:** 1471-2121. **Remarks:** Accepts advertising. **URL:** http://www.biomedcentral.com/bmccellbiol/. **Circ:** (Not Reported)

54044 ■ BMC Chemical Biology
BioMed Central Ltd.
236 Gray's Inn Rd., Fl. 6
34-42 Cleveland St.
London WC1X 8HL, United Kingdom
Ph: 44 20 31922000
Fax: 44 20 31922010
Publisher E-mail: info@biomedcentral.com
Online journal publishing original research articles in the application of chemistry to the investigation of biology and drug design. **Key Personnel:** Gerald Joyce, Editorial Board; Fred E. Cohen, Editorial Board; Sabato D'Auria, Editorial Board; Alan Fersht, Editorial Board; Harry Gray, Editorial Board; Philip A. Cole, Editorial Board; Melissa Norton, MD, Editor-in-Chief, bmcserieseditor@biomedcentral.com; Tim Sands, PhD, In-house Ed., editorial@biomedcentral.com. **ISSN:** 1472-6769. **Remarks:** Accepts advertising. **URL:** http://www.biomedcentral.com/bmcchembiol/. **Circ:** (Not Reported)

54045 ■ BMC Clinical Pathology
BioMed Central Ltd.
236 Gray's Inn Rd., Fl. 6
34-42 Cleveland St.
London WC1X 8HL, United Kingdom
Ph: 44 20 31922000
Fax: 44 20 31922010
Publisher E-mail: info@biomedcentral.com
Online journal publishing original research articles in all aspects of histopathology, haematology, clinical biochemistry, and medical microbiology (including virology, parasitology, and infection control). **Key Personnel:** Melissa Norton, MD, Editor-in-Chief, bmcserieseditor@biomedcentral.com; Dan Jones, Editorial Board; Philip R Cohen, Editorial Board; El Nasir Lalani, Editorial Board; Jagdish Butany, Assoc. Ed.; Hans Zauner, PhD, In-house Ed., editorial@biomedcentral.com. **ISSN:** 1472-6890. **Remarks:** Accepts advertising. **URL:** http://www.biomedcentral.com/bmcclinpathol/. **Circ:** (Not Reported)

54046 ■ BMC Clinical Pharmacology
BioMed Central Ltd.

236 Gray's Inn Rd., Fl. 6
34-42 Cleveland St.
London WC1X 8HL, United Kingdom
Ph: 44 20 31922000
Fax: 44 20 31922010
Publisher E-mail: info@biomedcentral.com
Online journal publishing original research articles in all aspects of clinical pharmacology. **Key Personnel:** Morris J. Brown, Editorial Board; Melissa Norton, MD, Editor-in-Chief, bmcserieseditor@biomedcentral.com; Tim Sands, PhD, In-house Ed., editorial@biomedcentral.com; Martin Duerden, Editorial Board; Herve Allain, Editorial Board; Douglas Ball, Assoc. Ed. **ISSN:** 1472-6904. **Remarks:** Accepts advertising. **URL:** http://www.biomedcentral.com/bmcclinpharmacol/. **Circ:** (Not Reported)

54047 ■ BMC Complementary and Alternative Medicine
BioMed Central Ltd.
236 Gray's Inn Rd., Fl. 6
34-42 Cleveland St.
London WC1X 8HL, United Kingdom
Ph: 44 20 31922000
Fax: 44 20 31922010
Publisher E-mail: info@biomedcentral.com
Online journal publishing original research articles in complementary and alternative healthcare interventions, with a specific emphasis on those that elucidate biological mechanisms of action. **Key Personnel:** George Lewith, Editorial Board; Edzard Ernst, Editorial Board; David Aldridge, Editorial Board; Brian M. Berman, Editorial Board; Daniel J. Benor, Editorial Board; Melissa Norton, MD, Editor-in-Chief, bmcserieseditor@biomedcentral.com; Natalie Pafitis, In-house Ed., editorial@biomedcentral.com; Adam Perlman, Editorial Board. **ISSN:** 1472-6882. **Remarks:** Accepts advertising. **URL:** http://www.biomedcentral.com/bmccomplementalternmed/. **Circ:** (Not Reported)

54048 ■ BMC Dermatology
BioMed Central Ltd.
236 Gray's Inn Rd., Fl. 6
34-42 Cleveland St.
London WC1X 8HL, United Kingdom
Ph: 44 20 31922000
Fax: 44 20 31922010
Publisher E-mail: info@biomedcentral.com
Online journal publishing original research articles in all aspects of the prevention, diagnosis and management of skin disorders, as well as related molecular genetics, pathophysiology, and epidemiology. **Key Personnel:** Michael Binder, Editorial Board; Veronique Bataille, Assoc. Ed.; Bruce Armstrong, Editorial Board; Melissa Norton, MD, Editor-in-Chief, bmcserieseditor@biomedcentral.com; Timothy Shipley, PhD, In-house Ed., editorial@biomedcentral.com; Luigi Naldi, Editorial Board. **ISSN:** 1471-5945. **Remarks:** Accepts advertising. **URL:** http://www.biomedcentral.com/bmcdermatol/. **Circ:** (Not Reported)

54049 ■ BMC Developmental Biology
BioMed Central Ltd.
236 Gray's Inn Rd., Fl. 6
34-42 Cleveland St.
London WC1X 8HL, United Kingdom
Ph: 44 20 31922000
Fax: 44 20 31922010
Publisher E-mail: info@biomedcentral.com
Online journal publishing original research articles in all aspects of cellular, tissue-level and organismal aspects of development. **Key Personnel:** Melissa Norton, MD, Editor-in-Chief, bmcserieseditor@biomedcentral.com; Paul N. Adler, Assoc. Ed.; J. Ann Le Good, In-house Ed., editorial@biomedcentral.com. **ISSN:** 1471-213X. **Remarks:** Accepts advertising. **URL:** http://www.biomedcentral.com/bmcdevbiol/. **Circ:** (Not Reported)

54050 ■ BMC Ear, Nose and Throat Disorders
BioMed Central Ltd.
236 Gray's Inn Rd., Fl. 6
34-42 Cleveland St.
London WC1X 8HL, United Kingdom
Ph: 44 20 31922000
Fax: 44 20 31922010
Publisher E-mail: info@biomedcentral.com
Online journal publishing original research articles in all aspects of the prevention, diagnosis and management

Circulation: ★ = ABC; △ = BPA; ◆ = CAC; • = CCAB; ❏ = VAC; ⊕ = PO Statement; ‡ = Publisher's Report; Boldface figures = sworn; Light figures = estimated.

Gale Directory of Publications & Broadcast Media/147th Ed.   5687

of ear, nose and throat disorders, as well as related molecular genetics, pathophysiology, and epidemiology. **Key Personnel:** Bolajoko O. Olusanya, Assoc. Ed.; Leslie Michaels, Editorial Board; Robert K. Jackler, Editorial Board; Thomas Lenarz, Editorial Board; Guy J. Petruzzelli, Editorial Board; Melissa Norton, MD, Editor-in-Chief, bmcserieseditor@biomedcentral.com; Timothy Shipley, PhD, In-house Ed., editorial@biomedcentral.com. **ISSN:** 1472-6815. **Remarks:** Accepts advertising. **URL:** http://www.biomedcentral.com/bmcearnosethroatdisord/. **Circ:** (Not Reported)

54051 ■ BMC Ecology
BioMed Central Ltd.
236 Gray's Inn Rd., Fl. 6
34-42 Cleveland St.
London WC1X 8HL, United Kingdom
Ph: 44 20 31922000
Fax: 44 20 31922010
Publisher E-mail: info@biomedcentral.com
Online journal publishing original research articles in environmental, behavioral and population ecology of plants, animals, and microbes. **Key Personnel:** David Eilam, Editorial Board; Concepcion L. Alados, Editorial Board; Jacques Baudry, Editorial Board; Jean-Marie Bouquegneau, Editorial Board; Steven L.L. Chown, Editorial Board; Sally Blower, Editorial Board; Melissa Norton, MD, Editor-in-Chief, bmcserieseditor@biomedcentral.com; Hans Zauner, PhD, In-house Ed., editorial@biomedcentral.com; Jan Komdeur, Editorial Board. **ISSN:** 1472-6785. **Remarks:** Accepts advertising. **URL:** http://www.biomedcentral.com/bmcecol/. **Circ:** (Not Reported)

54052 ■ BMC Emergency Medicine
BioMed Central Ltd.
236 Gray's Inn Rd., Fl. 6
34-42 Cleveland St.
London WC1X 8HL, United Kingdom
Ph: 44 20 31922000
Fax: 44 20 31922010
Publisher E-mail: info@biomedcentral.com
Online journal publishing original research articles in all aspects of emergency medicine, trauma, and pre-hospital care. **Key Personnel:** Ian Roberts, Editorial Board; Mark A. Davis, Editorial Board; John Heyworth, Editorial Board; Roger M. Barkin, Editorial Board; Richard Hardern, Editorial Board; Frank C. Day, Editorial Board; Grant Innes, Editorial Board; Melissa Norton, MD, Editor-in-Chief, bmcserieseditor@biomedcentral. com; Rachel Neilan, In-house Ed., editorial@biomedcentral.com. **ISSN:** 1471-227X. **Remarks:** Accepts advertising. **URL:** http://www.biomedcentral.com/bmcemergmed/. **Circ:** (Not Reported)

54053 ■ BMC Endocrine Disorders
BioMed Central Ltd.
236 Gray's Inn Rd., Fl. 6
34-42 Cleveland St.
London WC1X 8HL, United Kingdom
Ph: 44 20 31922000
Fax: 44 20 31922010
Publisher E-mail: info@biomedcentral.com
Online journal publishing original research articles in all aspects of the prevention, diagnosis and management of endocrine disorders, as well as related molecular genetics, pathophysiology, and epidemiology. **Key Personnel:** Melissa Norton, MD, Editor-in-Chief, bmcserieseditor@biomedcentral.com; Sabina Alam, PhD, In-house Ed., editorial@biomedcentral.com; Terry Davies, Editorial Board; Oreste Gualillo, Assoc. Ed.; Dereck Hunt, Editorial Board; Cheryl Watson, Assoc. Ed. **ISSN:** 1472-6823. **Remarks:** Accepts advertising. **URL:** http://www.biomedcentral.com/bmcendocrdisord/. **Circ:** (Not Reported)

54054 ■ BMC Evolutionary Biology
BioMed Central Ltd.
236 Gray's Inn Rd., Fl. 6
34-42 Cleveland St.
London WC1X 8HL, United Kingdom
Ph: 44 20 31922000
Fax: 44 20 31922010
Publisher E-mail: info@biomedcentral.com
Online journal publishing original research articles in all aspects of molecular and non-molecular evolution of all organisms, as well as phylogenetics and palaeontology. **Key Personnel:** Olivier Gascuel, Editorial Board; Chris Adami, Editorial Board; Lutz Bachmann, Assoc. Ed.; Al-

Ian Baker, Assoc. Ed.; Jacobus J. Boomsma, Editorial Board; Paul M. Brakefield, Assoc. Ed.; Nick H. Barton, Editorial Board; Melissa Norton, MD, Editor-in-Chief, bmcserieseditor@biomedcentral.com; Hans Zauner, PhD, In-house Ed., editorial@biomedcentral.com. **ISSN:** 1471-2148. **Remarks:** Accepts advertising. **URL:** http://www.biomedcentral.com/bmcevolbiol/. **Circ:** (Not Reported)

54055 ■ BMC Family Practice
BioMed Central Ltd.
236 Gray's Inn Rd., Fl. 6
34-42 Cleveland St.
London WC1X 8HL, United Kingdom
Ph: 44 20 31922000
Fax: 44 20 31922010
Publisher E-mail: info@biomedcentral.com
Online journal publishing original research articles in all aspects of primary health care, including clinical management of patients, professional training, shared decision making, and the organisation and evaluation of health care in the community. **Key Personnel:** Cindy L. Lam, Editorial Board; Melissa Norton, MD, Editor-in-Chief, bmcserieseditor@biomedcentral.com; Jigisha Patel, PhD, Medical Ed. **ISSN:** 1471-2296. **Remarks:** Accepts advertising. **URL:** http://www.biomedcentral.com/bmcfampract/. **Circ:** (Not Reported)

54056 ■ BMC Gastroenterology
BioMed Central Ltd.
236 Gray's Inn Rd., Fl. 6
34-42 Cleveland St.
London WC1X 8HL, United Kingdom
Ph: 44 20 31922000
Fax: 44 20 31922010
Publisher E-mail: info@biomedcentral.com
Online journal publishing original research articles in all aspects of the prevention, diagnosis and management of gastrointestinal and hepatobiliary disorders, as well as related molecular genetics, pathophysiology, and epidemiology. **Key Personnel:** Hubert Blum, Editorial Board; Pierre Alain Clavien, Editorial Board; Tsutomu Chiba, Editorial Board; Gianfranco Alpini, Assoc. Ed.; Matias A. Avila, Assoc. Ed.; Giuseppe Brisinda, Assoc. Ed.; Peter Devitt, Editorial Board; Melissa Norton, MD, Editor-in-Chief, bmcserieseditor@biomedcentral.com; Timothy Shipley, PhD, In-house Ed., editorial@biomedcentral.com. **ISSN:** 1471-230X. **Remarks:** Accepts advertising. **URL:** http://www.biomedcentral.com/bmcgastroenterol/. **Circ:** (Not Reported)

54057 ■ BMC Genetics
BioMed Central Ltd.
236 Gray's Inn Rd., Fl. 6
34-42 Cleveland St.
London WC1X 8HL, United Kingdom
Ph: 44 20 31922000
Fax: 44 20 31922010
Publisher E-mail: info@biomedcentral.com
Online journal publishing original research articles in all aspects of inheritance and variation in individuals and among populations. **Key Personnel:** Bertram Brenig, Editorial Board; Nancy Andrews, Editorial Board; William Dietrich, Editorial Board; John Brookfield, Assoc. Ed.; Brian Charlesworth, Editorial Board; Ernest Bailey, Editorial Board; Fred Ausubel, Editorial Board; Doug Forrest, Editorial Board; Melissa Norton, MD, Editor-in-Chief, bmcserieseditor@biomedcentral.com. **ISSN:** 1471-2156. **Remarks:** Accepts advertising. **URL:** http://www.biomedcentral.com/bmcgenet/. **Circ:** (Not Reported)

54058 ■ BMC Genomics
BioMed Central Ltd.
236 Gray's Inn Rd., Fl. 6
34-42 Cleveland St.
London WC1X 8HL, United Kingdom
Ph: 44 20 31922000
Fax: 44 20 31922010
Publisher E-mail: info@biomedcentral.com
Online journal publishing original research articles in all aspects of gene mapping, sequencing and analysis, functional genomics, and proteomics. **Key Personnel:** Melissa Norton, MD, Editor-in-Chief, bmcserieseditor@biomedcentral.com; Antoine Danchin, Editorial Board; Peer Bork, Editorial Board; Michael Boutros, Assoc. Ed.; Jean-Michel Claverie, Editorial Board; Roger Bumgarner, Editorial Board; Paul Denny, Assoc. Ed.; Jane Carlton, Assoc. Ed.; Joaquin Dopazo, Editorial Board; Edison Lui, Editorial Board; Scott Edmunds, PhD, In-house

Ed., editorial@biomedcentral.com; Adam Kuspa, Editorial Board. **ISSN:** 1471-2164. **Remarks:** Accepts advertising. **URL:** http://www.biomedcentral.com/bmcgenomics/. **Circ:** (Not Reported)

54059 ■ BMC Geriatrics
BioMed Central Ltd.
236 Gray's Inn Rd., Fl. 6
34-42 Cleveland St.
London WC1X 8HL, United Kingdom
Ph: 44 20 31922000
Fax: 44 20 31922010
Publisher E-mail: info@biomedcentral.com
Online journal publishing original research articles in all aspects of health care in elderly people. **Key Personnel:** Caleb E. Finch, Editorial Board; K. Hirokawa, Editorial Board; Tom Kirkwood, Editorial Board; Sataro Goto, Editorial Board Member; Tamas Fulop, Assoc. Ed.; Leon Flicker, Assoc. Ed.; Ian D. Cameron, Editorial Board Member; Melissa Norton, MD, Editor-in-Chief, bmcserieseditor@biomedcentral.com; Natalie Pafitis, In-house Ed., editorial@biomedcentral.com. **ISSN:** 1471-2318. **Remarks:** Accepts advertising. **URL:** http://www.biomedcentral.com/bmcgeriatr/. **Circ:** (Not Reported)

54060 ■ BMC Health Services Research
BioMed Central Ltd.
236 Gray's Inn Rd., Fl. 6
34-42 Cleveland St.
London WC1X 8HL, United Kingdom
Ph: 44 20 31922000
Fax: 44 20 31922010
Publisher E-mail: info@biomedcentral.com
Online journal publishing original research articles in all aspects of health services research, including delivery of care, management of health services, assessment of health care needs, evaluation of different health markets and health services organizations, health economics and the impact of health policies and regulations. **Key Personnel:** Melissa Norton, MD, Editor-in-Chief, bmcserieseditor@biomedcentral.com; Dan Berlowitz, Section Ed.; Nananda Col, Editorial Board; Amanda Burls, Editorial Board; Angela Coulter, Editorial Board; Glyn Elwyn, Editorial Board. **ISSN:** 1472-6963. **Remarks:** Accepts advertising. **URL:** http://www.biomedcentral.com/bmchealthservres/. **Circ:** (Not Reported)

54061 ■ BMC Immunology
BioMed Central Ltd.
236 Gray's Inn Rd., Fl. 6
34-42 Cleveland St.
London WC1X 8HL, United Kingdom
Ph: 44 20 31922000
Fax: 44 20 31922010
Publisher E-mail: info@biomedcentral.com
Online journal publishing original research articles in all aspects of cellular, tissue-level, organismal, functional, and developmental aspects of the immune system. **Key Personnel:** James Allison, Editorial Board; Terry Delovitch, Editorial Board; Jean Bousquet, Editorial Board; Sankar Ghosh, Editorial Board; Simon R. Carding, Assoc. Ed.; Shizuo Akira, Editorial Board; Douglas Green, Editorial Board; Melissa Norton, MD, Editor-in-Chief, bmcserieseditor@biomedcentral.com; Hans Zauner, PhD, In-house Ed., editorial@biomedcentral.com. **ISSN:** 1471-2172. **Remarks:** Accepts advertising. **URL:** http://www.biomedcentral.com/bmcimmunol/. **Circ:** (Not Reported)

54062 ■ BMC Infectious Diseases
BioMed Central Ltd.
236 Gray's Inn Rd., Fl. 6
34-42 Cleveland St.
London WC1X 8HL, United Kingdom
Ph: 44 20 31922000
Fax: 44 20 31922010
Publisher E-mail: info@biomedcentral.com
Online journal publishing original research articles in all aspects of the prevention, diagnosis and management of infectious and sexually transmitted diseases, as well as related molecular genetics, pathophysiology, and epidemiology. **Key Personnel:** Melissa Norton, MD, Editor-in-Chief, bmcserieseditor@biomedcentral.com; Diana Marshall, In-house Ed., editorial@biomedcentral.com; Sally Blower, Editorial Board; Jean Boyer, Editorial Board; Michael S. Bronze, Editorial Board; Itzhak Brook, Editorial Board. **ISSN:** 1471-2334. **Remarks:** Accepts advertising. **URL:** http://www.biomedcentral.com/

bmcinfectdis/. **Circ:** (Not Reported)

54063 ■ BMC International Health and Human Rights
BioMed Central Ltd.
236 Gray's Inn Rd., Fl. 6
34-42 Cleveland St.
London WC1X 8HL, United Kingdom
Ph: 44 20 31922000
Fax: 44 20 31922010
Publisher E-mail: info@biomedcentral.com
Online journal publishing original research articles in health care in developing and transitional countries, and all issues relating to health and human rights. **Key Personnel:** Richard Feachem, Editorial Board; Andrew Haines, Editorial Board; Alison Holmes, Editorial Board; Melissa Norton, MD, Editor-in-Chief, bmcserieseditor@biomedcentral.com; Diana Marshall, In-house Ed., editorial@biomedcentral.com; Godfrey Walker, Editorial Board. **ISSN:** 1472-698X. **Remarks:** Accepts advertising. **URL:** http://www.biomedcentral.com/bmcinthealthhumrights/. **Circ:** (Not Reported)

54064 ■ BMC Medical Education
BioMed Central Ltd.
236 Gray's Inn Rd., Fl. 6
34-42 Cleveland St.
London WC1X 8HL, United Kingdom
Ph: 44 20 31922000
Fax: 44 20 31922010
Publisher E-mail: info@biomedcentral.com
Online journal publishing original research articles in undergraduate, postgraduate, and continuing medical education. **Key Personnel:** P. Davies, Editorial Board; Amy Blue, Editorial Board; Brian Mavis, Editorial Board; Mark Albanese, Editorial Board; Peter Anderson, Assoc. Ed.; Chris Candler, Editorial Board; Khalid S. Khan, Assoc. Ed.; Melissa Norton, MD, Editor-in-Chief, bmcserieseditor@biomedcentral.com; Adrian Aldcroft, In-house Ed., editorial@biomedcentral.com. **ISSN:** 1472-6920. **Remarks:** Accepts advertising. **URL:** http://www.biomedcentral.com/bmcmededuc/. **Circ:** (Not Reported)

54065 ■ BMC Medical Ethics
BioMed Central Ltd.
236 Gray's Inn Rd., Fl. 6
34-42 Cleveland St.
London WC1X 8HL, United Kingdom
Ph: 44 20 31922000
Fax: 44 20 31922010
Publisher E-mail: info@biomedcentral.com
Online journal publishing original research articles in the ethics of medical research and practice. **Key Personnel:** Edmund G. Howe, Editorial Board; Solly Benatar, Editorial Board; Ezekiel Emanuel, Editorial Board; Lisa A. Bero, Editorial Board; Fernando Lolas, Assoc. Ed.; Bernard Dickens, Editorial Board; Melissa Norton, MD, Editor-in-Chief, bmcserieseditor@biomedcentral.com; Natalie Pafitis, In-house Ed., editorial@biomedcentral.com; James L. Nelson, Editorial Board. **ISSN:** 1472-6939. **Remarks:** Accepts advertising. **URL:** http://www.biomedcentral.com/bmcmedethics/. **Circ:** (Not Reported)

54066 ■ BMC Medical Genetics
BioMed Central Ltd.
236 Gray's Inn Rd., Fl. 6
34-42 Cleveland St.
London WC1X 8HL, United Kingdom
Ph: 44 20 31922000
Fax: 44 20 31922010
Publisher E-mail: info@biomedcentral.com
Online journal publishing original research articles in all aspects of medical genetics. **Key Personnel:** Arthur L. Beaudet, Editorial Board; Andrea Ballabio, Editorial Board; Bruno Dallapiccola, Editorial Board; Melissa Norton, MD, Editor-in-Chief, bmcserieseditor@biomedcentral.com; Scott Edmunds, PhD, In-house Ed., editorial@biomedcentral.com; Colin Palmer, Editorial Board. **ISSN:** 1471-2350. **Remarks:** Accepts advertising. **URL:** http://www.biomedcentral.com/bmcmedgenet/. **Circ:** (Not Reported)

54067 ■ BMC Medical Imaging
BioMed Central Ltd.
236 Gray's Inn Rd., Fl. 6
34-42 Cleveland St.
London WC1X 8HL, United Kingdom
Ph: 44 20 31922000

Fax: 44 20 31922010
Publisher E-mail: info@biomedcentral.com
Online journal publishing original research articles in the use, development, and evaluation of imaging techniques to diagnose and manage disease. **Key Personnel:** David Norris, Assoc. Ed.; Gabriel P. Krestin, Editorial Board; Kayvan Najarian, Assoc. Ed.; Peter Anderson, Editorial Board; Melissa Norton, MD, Editor-in-Chief, bmcserieseditor@biomedcentral.com; Rachel Neilan, In-house Ed., editorial@biomedcentral.com; Jigisha Patel, PhD, Medical Ed. **ISSN:** 1471-2342. **Remarks:** Accepts advertising. **URL:** http://www.biomedcentral.com/bmcmedimaging/. **Circ:** (Not Reported)

54068 ■ BMC Medical Informatics and Decision Making
BioMed Central Ltd.
236 Gray's Inn Rd., Fl. 6
34-42 Cleveland St.
London WC1X 8HL, United Kingdom
Ph: 44 20 31922000
Fax: 44 20 31922010
Publisher E-mail: info@biomedcentral.com
Online journal publishing original research articles in information management, systems and technology in healthcare and the study of medical decision making. **Key Personnel:** Vimla Patel, Editorial Board; Adrian Aldcroft, In-house Ed., editorial@biomedcentral.com; Jigisha Patel, PhD, Medical Ed.; Melissa Norton, MD, Editor-in-Chief, bmcserieseditor@biomedcentral.com; Blackford Middleton, Editorial Board; Takeo Nakayama, Editorial Board. **ISSN:** 1472-6947. **Remarks:** Accepts advertising. **URL:** http://www.biomedcentral.com/bmcmedinformdecismak/. **Circ:** (Not Reported)

54069 ■ BMC Medical Physics
BioMed Central Ltd.
236 Gray's Inn Rd., Fl. 6
34-42 Cleveland St.
London WC1X 8HL, United Kingdom
Ph: 44 20 31922000
Fax: 44 20 31922010
Publisher E-mail: info@biomedcentral.com
Online journal publishing original research articles in all aspects of nuclear medicine. **Key Personnel:** Melissa Norton, MD, Editor-in-Chief, bmcserieseditor@biomedcentral.com; Jigisha Patel, PhD, Med. Ed. **ISSN:** 1471-2385. **Remarks:** Accepts advertising. **URL:** http://www.biomedcentral.com/bmcnuclmed/. **Formerly:** BMC Nuclear Medicine. **Circ:** (Not Reported)

54070 ■ BMC Medical Research Methodology
BioMed Central Ltd.
236 Gray's Inn Rd., Fl. 6
34-42 Cleveland St.
London WC1X 8HL, United Kingdom
Ph: 44 20 31922000
Fax: 44 20 31922010
Publisher E-mail: info@biomedcentral.com
Online journal publishing original research articles in methodological approaches to healthcare research, encouraging articles on the methodology of epidemiological research, clinical trials, meta-analysis/systematic review, and empirical study of the associations between choice of methodology and study outcomes. **Key Personnel:** Marion Campbell, Editorial Board; Steven N. Goodman, Editorial Board; Charles Hoff, Editorial Board; Phil Alderson, Editorial Board; Paul Garner, Editorial Board; Doug Altman, Editorial Board; Harald Kittler, Editorial Board; Melissa Norton, MD, Editor-in-Chief, bmcserieseditor@biomedcentral.com; Adrian Aldcroft, PhD, In-house Ed., editorial@biomedcentral.com. **ISSN:** 1471-2288. **Remarks:** Accepts advertising. **URL:** http://www.biomedcentral.com/bmcmedresmethodol/. **Circ:** (Not Reported)

54071 ■ BMC Medicine
BioMed Central Ltd.
236 Gray's Inn Rd., Fl. 6
34-42 Cleveland St.
London WC1X 8HL, United Kingdom
Ph: 44 20 31922000
Fax: 44 20 31922010
Publisher E-mail: info@biomedcentral.com
Online journal publishing original research articles, technical advances and study protocols in any area of medical science or clinical practice. **Key Personnel:** Sally Blower, Editorial Board; Lelia Duley, Editorial

Board; Herve Allain, Editorial Board; Penny Asbell, Editorial Board; Roger M. Barkin, Editorial Board; Bruce Cronstein, Editorial Board; Melissa Norton, MD, Editor-in-Chief, bmcserieseditor@biomedcentral.com; Robin Cassady-Cain, Freelance Ed., bmcserieseditor@biomedcentral.com. **ISSN:** 1471-7015. **Remarks:** Accepts advertising. **URL:** http://www.biomedcentral.com/bmcmed/. **Circ:** (Not Reported)

54072 ■ BMC Microbiology
BioMed Central Ltd.
236 Gray's Inn Rd., Fl. 6
34-42 Cleveland St.
London WC1X 8HL, United Kingdom
Ph: 44 20 31922000
Fax: 44 20 31922010
Publisher E-mail: info@biomedcentral.com
Online journal publishing original research articles in analytical and functional studies of prokaryotic and eukaryotic microorganisms, viruses and small parasites, as well as host and therapeutic responses to them. **Key Personnel:** John Alderete, Editorial Board; Dlawer Ala'Aldeen, Editorial Board; Antoine Danchin, Editorial Board; Sailen Barik, Editorial Board; Peter Doherty, Editorial Board; Daniel Colley, Editorial Board; Jorge Galan, Editorial Board; Melissa Norton, MD, Editor-in-Chief, bmcserieseditor@biomedcentral.com; Philippa Harris, In-house Ed., editorial@biomedcentral.com. **ISSN:** 1471-2180. **Remarks:** Accepts advertising. **URL:** http://www.biomedcentral.com/bmcmicrobiol/. **Circ:** (Not Reported)

54073 ■ BMC Molecular Biology
BioMed Central Ltd.
236 Gray's Inn Rd., Fl. 6
34-42 Cleveland St.
London WC1X 8HL, United Kingdom
Ph: 44 20 31922000
Fax: 44 20 31922010
Publisher E-mail: info@biomedcentral.com
Online journal publishing original research articles in all aspects of DNA and RNA in a cellular context, encompassing investigations of transcription, mRNA processing, translation, replication, recombination, mutation, and repair. **Key Personnel:** Johan Auwerx, Editorial Board; Julian J. Blow, Editorial Board; Stefan Dimitrov, Editorial Board; Susan J. Baserga, Editorial Board; Sarah C. Elgin, Editorial Board; James E. Cleaver, Editorial Board; Robert J. Crouch, Assoc. Ed.; Melissa Norton, MD, Editor-in-Chief, bmcserieseditor@biomedcentral.com; Ann J. Le Good, PhD, In-house Ed., editorial@biomedcentral.com. **ISSN:** 1471-2199. **Remarks:** Accepts advertising. **URL:** http://www.biomedcentral.com/bmcmolbiol/. **Circ:** (Not Reported)

54074 ■ BMC Musculoskeletal Disorders
BioMed Central Ltd.
236 Gray's Inn Rd., Fl. 6
34-42 Cleveland St.
London WC1X 8HL, United Kingdom
Ph: 44 20 31922000
Fax: 44 20 31922010
Publisher E-mail: info@biomedcentral.com
Online journal publishing original research articles in all aspects of the prevention, diagnosis and management of musculoskeletal and associated disorders, as well as related molecular genetics, pathophysiology, and epidemiology. **Key Personnel:** Ronald Feise, Editorial Board; Jens Peter Bonde, Editorial Board; Nananda Col, Editorial Board; Graham R.V. Hughes, Editorial Board; Jonathan Adachi, Editorial Board; Nadine Foster, Editorial Board; Melissa Norton, MD, Editor-in-Chief, bmcserieseditor@biomedcentral.com; Gerard A. Malanga, Editorial Board; John Loughlin, Editorial Board. **ISSN:** 1471-2474. **Remarks:** Accepts advertising. **URL:** http://www.biomedcentral.com/bmcmusculoskeletdisord/. **Circ:** (Not Reported)

54075 ■ BMC Nephrology
BioMed Central Ltd.
236 Gray's Inn Rd., Fl. 6
34-42 Cleveland St.
London WC1X 8HL, United Kingdom
Ph: 44 20 31922000
Fax: 44 20 31922010
Publisher E-mail: info@biomedcentral.com
Online journal publishing original research articles in all aspects of the prevention, diagnosis and management

Circulation: ★ = ABC; △ = BPA; ♦ = CAC; • = CCAB; ❑ = VAC; ⊕ = PO Statement; ‡ = Publisher's Report; Boldface figures = sworn; Light figures = estimated.

Gale Directory of Publications & Broadcast Media/147th Ed.   5689

of kidney and associated disorders, as well as related molecular genetics, pathophysiology, and epidemiology. **Key Personnel:** Rachel Neilan, In-house Ed., editorial@biomedcentral.com; Melissa Norton, MD, Editor-in-Chief, bmcserieseditor@biomedcentral.com; Jigisha Patel, PhD, Medical Ed. **ISSN:** 1471-2369. **Remarks:** Accepts advertising. **URL:** http://www.biomedcentral.com/bmcnephrol/. **Circ:** (Not Reported)

54076 ■ BMC Neurology
BioMed Central Ltd.
236 Gray's Inn Rd., Fl. 6
34-42 Cleveland St.
London WC1X 8HL, United Kingdom
Ph: 44 20 31922000
Fax: 44 20 31922010
Publisher E-mail: info@biomedcentral.com
Online journal publishing original research articles in all aspects of the prevention, diagnosis and management of neurological disorders, as well as related molecular genetics, pathophysiology, and epidemiology. **Key Personnel:** Selim Benbadis, Editorial Board; Ludmila Belayev, Editorial Board; Wim Weber, Editorial Board; Marinos Dalakas, Section Board; Melissa Norton, MD, Editor-in-Chief, bmcserieseditor@biomedcentral.com; Sabina Alam, PhD, In-house Ed., editorial@biomedcentral.com. **ISSN:** 1471-2377. **Remarks:** Accepts advertising. **URL:** http://www.biomedcentral.com/bmcneurol/. **Circ:** (Not Reported)

54077 ■ BMC Neuroscience
BioMed Central Ltd.
236 Gray's Inn Rd., Fl. 6
34-42 Cleveland St.
London WC1X 8HL, United Kingdom
Ph: 44 20 31922000
Fax: 44 20 31922010
Publisher E-mail: info@biomedcentral.com
Online journal publishing original research articles in all aspects of cellular, tissue-level, organismal, functional and developmental aspects of the nervous system. **Key Personnel:** Susan G. Amara, Editorial Board; Cori Bargmann, Editorial Board; Richard T. Ambron, Editorial Board; Jonathan Ashmore, Editorial Board; Ben A. Barres, Editorial Board; Tim Bliss, Editorial Board; Heinrich Betz, Editorial Board; Edoardo Boncinelli, Editorial Board; Richard W. Aldrich, Editorial Board; Philippe Brulet, Editorial Board; Melissa Norton, MD, Editor-in-Chief, bmcserieseditor@biomedcentral.com; Sabina Alam, PhD, In-house Ed., editorial@biomedcentral.com. **ISSN:** 1471-2202. **Remarks:** Accepts advertising. **URL:** http://www.biomedcentral.com/bmcneurosci/. **Circ:** (Not Reported)

54078 ■ BMC Nursing
BioMed Central Ltd.
236 Gray's Inn Rd., Fl. 6
34-42 Cleveland St.
London WC1X 8HL, United Kingdom
Ph: 44 20 31922000
Fax: 44 20 31922010
Publisher E-mail: info@biomedcentral.com
Online journal publishing original research articles in all aspects of nursing research, training, education, and practice. **Key Personnel:** Rona McCandlish, Editorial Board; Karen A. Luker, Editorial Board; Elizabeth H. Anderson, Editorial Board; Nicky Cullum, Editorial Board; Sean Clarke, Editorial Board; Sabina De Geest, Editorial Board; Catherine Niven, Editorial Board; Donna K. Ciliska, Editorial Board; Christine Miaskowski, Editorial Board. **ISSN:** 1472-6955. **Remarks:** Accepts advertising. **URL:** http://www.biomedcentral.com/bmcnurs/. **Circ:** (Not Reported)

54079 ■ BMC Ophthalmology
BioMed Central Ltd.
236 Gray's Inn Rd., Fl. 6
34-42 Cleveland St.
London WC1X 8HL, United Kingdom
Ph: 44 20 31922000
Fax: 44 20 31922010
Publisher E-mail: info@biomedcentral.com
Online journal publishing original research articles in all aspects of the prevention, diagnosis and management of eye disorders, as well as related molecular genetics, pathophysiology, and epidemiology. **Key Personnel:** Melissa Norton, MD, Editor-in-Chief, bmcserieseditor@biomedcentral.com; Emilio C. Campos, Assoc. Ed.; Michael Marmor, Editorial Board; Jorge Alio, Editorial

Board; Penny Asbell, Editorial Board; Lalit Dandona, Editorial Board. **ISSN:** 1471-2415. **Remarks:** Accepts advertising. **URL:** http://www.biomedcentral.com/bmcophthalmol/. **Circ:** (Not Reported)

54080 ■ BMC Oral Health
BioMed Central Ltd.
236 Gray's Inn Rd., Fl. 6
34-42 Cleveland St.
London WC1X 8HL, United Kingdom
Ph: 44 20 31922000
Fax: 44 20 31922010
Publisher E-mail: info@biomedcentral.com
Online journal publishing original research articles in all aspects of the prevention, diagnosis and management of disorders of the mouth, teeth and gums, as well as related molecular genetics, pathophysiology, and epidemiology. **Key Personnel:** Melissa Norton, MD, Editor-in-Chief, bmcserieseditor@biomedcentral.com; Paul Batchelor, Editorial Board; Pentti Alanen, Editorial Board; Paul Allison, Editorial Board; Timothy Shipley, PhD, In-house Ed., editorial@biomedcentral.com; Derek Richards, Editorial Board. **ISSN:** 1472-6831. **Remarks:** Accepts advertising. **URL:** http://www.biomedcentral.com/bmcoralhealth/. **Circ:** (Not Reported)

54081 ■ BMC Palliative Care
BioMed Central Ltd.
236 Gray's Inn Rd., Fl. 6
34-42 Cleveland St.
London WC1X 8HL, United Kingdom
Ph: 44 20 31922000
Fax: 44 20 31922010
Publisher E-mail: info@biomedcentral.com
Online journal publishing original research articles in the clinical, scientific, ethical and policy issues, local and international, regarding all aspects of hospice and palliative care for the dying and for those with profound suffering related to chronic illness. **Key Personnel:** Melissa Norton, MD, Editor-in-Chief, bmcserieseditor@biomedcentral.com; Amy Abernethy, Editorial Board; Janet L. Abrahm, Editorial Board; Eduardo Bruera, Editorial Board; Diana Marshall, PhD, In-house Ed., editorial@biomedcentral.com; Diane Meier, Editorial Board. **ISSN:** 1472-684X. **Remarks:** Accepts advertising. **URL:** http://www.biomedcentral.com/bmcpalliatcare/. **Circ:** (Not Reported)

54082 ■ BMC Pediatrics
BioMed Central Ltd.
236 Gray's Inn Rd., Fl. 6
34-42 Cleveland St.
London WC1X 8HL, United Kingdom
Ph: 44 20 31922000
Fax: 44 20 31922010
Publisher E-mail: info@biomedcentral.com
Online journal publishing original research articles in all aspects of health care in neonates, children and adolescents, as well as related molecular genetics, pathophysiology, and epidemiology. **Key Personnel:** Melissa Norton, MD, Editor-in-Chief, bmcserieseditor@biomedcentral.com; Han C. Kemper, Editorial Board/Assoc. Ed.; Itzhak Brook, Editorial Board/Assoc. Ed.; Shally Awasthi, Editorial Board/Assoc. Ed.; Inge Axelsson, Editorial Board/Assoc. Ed.; Charles Hoff, Editorial Board; Adrian Aldcroft, In-house Ed., editorial@biomedcentral.com; Haluk Topaloglu, Editorial Board; Henri A. Verhaaren, Editorial Board. **ISSN:** 1471-2431. **Remarks:** Accepts advertising. **URL:** http://www.biomedcentral.com/bmcpediatr/. **Circ:** (Not Reported)

54083 ■ BMC Pharmacology
BioMed Central Ltd.
236 Gray's Inn Rd., Fl. 6
34-42 Cleveland St.
London WC1X 8HL, United Kingdom
Ph: 44 20 31922000
Fax: 44 20 31922010
Publisher E-mail: info@biomedcentral.com
Online journal publishing original research articles in aspects of the discovery, design, uses, effects, modes of action and metabolism of chemically defined therapeutic and toxic agents. **Key Personnel:** Paul Insel, Editorial Board; Maria Belvisi, Editorial Board; Norman G. Bowery, Editorial Board; Christian Bailly, Editorial Board; Jos H. Beijnen, Editorial Board; David A. Brown, Editorial Board; Melissa Norton, MD, Editor-in-Chief, bmcserieseditor@biomedcentral.com; Tim Sands, PhD, In-house Ed., editorial@biomedcentral.com; Clive Page,

Editorial Board. **ISSN:** 1471-2210. **Remarks:** Accepts advertising. **URL:** http://www.biomedcentral.com/bmcpharmacol/. **Circ:** (Not Reported)

54084 ■ BMC Physiology
BioMed Central Ltd.
236 Gray's Inn Rd., Fl. 6
34-42 Cleveland St.
London WC1X 8HL, United Kingdom
Ph: 44 20 31922000
Fax: 44 20 31922010
Publisher E-mail: info@biomedcentral.com
Online journal publishing original research articles in cellular, tissue-level, organismal, functional, and developmental aspects of physiological processes. **Key Personnel:** Qais Al-Awqati, Editorial Board; Jonathan Alexander, Editorial Board; Richard W. Aldrich, Editorial Board; Melissa Norton, MD, Editor-in-Chief, bmcserieseditor@biomedcentral.com; Philippa Harris, In-house Ed., editorial@biomedcentral.com; Paul M. Pilowsky, Editorial Board. **ISSN:** 1472-6793. **Remarks:** Accepts advertising. **URL:** http://www.biomedcentral.com/bmcphysiol/. **Circ:** (Not Reported)

54085 ■ BMC Plant Biology
BioMed Central Ltd.
236 Gray's Inn Rd., Fl. 6
34-42 Cleveland St.
London WC1X 8HL, United Kingdom
Ph: 44 20 31922000
Fax: 44 20 31922010
Publisher E-mail: info@biomedcentral.com
Online journal publishing original research articles in all aspects of cellular, tissue-level, organismal, functional and developmental aspects of plants. **Key Personnel:** Muhammad Ashraf, Editorial Board; Alison Baker, Editorial Board; Eva-mari Aro, Assoc. Ed.; Melissa Norton, MD, Editor-in-Chief, bmcserieseditor@biomedcentral.com; Philippa Harris, In-house Ed., editorial@biomedcentral.com; Edward Farmer, Editorial Board. **ISSN:** 1471-2229. **Remarks:** Accepts advertising. **URL:** http://www.biomedcentral.com/bmcplantbiol/. **Circ:** (Not Reported)

54086 ■ BMC Pregnancy and Childbirth
BioMed Central Ltd.
236 Gray's Inn Rd., Fl. 6
34-42 Cleveland St.
London WC1X 8HL, United Kingdom
Ph: 44 20 31922000
Fax: 44 20 31922010
Publisher E-mail: info@biomedcentral.com
Online journal publishing original research articles in all aspects of pregnancy and childbirth. **Key Personnel:** Ellen Hodnett, Editorial Board; Kirsten Duckitt, Editorial Board; Zarko Alfirevic, Editorial Board; Chris Kettle, Editorial Board; Phillip Hay, Editorial Board; Kavita Nanda, Editorial Board; Melissa Norton, MD, Editor-in-Chief, bmcserieseditor@biomedcentral.com; Adrian Aldcroft, In-house Ed., editorial@biomedcentral.com; Torvid Kiserud, Editorial Board. **ISSN:** 1471-2393. **Remarks:** Accepts advertising. **URL:** http://www.biomedcentral.com/bmcpregnancychildbirth/. **Circ:** (Not Reported)

54087 ■ BMC Psychiatry
BioMed Central Ltd.
236 Gray's Inn Rd., Fl. 6
34-42 Cleveland St.
London WC1X 8HL, United Kingdom
Ph: 44 20 31922000
Fax: 44 20 31922010
Publisher E-mail: info@biomedcentral.com
Online journal publishing original research articles in all aspects of the prevention, diagnosis and management of psychiatric disorders, as well as related molecular genetics, pathophysiology, and epidemiology. **Key Personnel:** Melissa Norton, MD, Editor-in-Chief, bmcserieseditor@biomedcentral.com; Paul S. Appelbaum, Editorial Board; Simon Baron-Cohen, Editorial Board; Jigisha Patel, PhD, Medical Ed.; Sabina Alam, PHD, In-house Ed. **ISSN:** 1471-244X. **Remarks:** Accepts advertising. **URL:** http://www.biomedcentral.com/bmcpsychiatr/. **Circ:** (Not Reported)

54088 ■ BMC Pulmonary Medicine
BioMed Central Ltd.
236 Gray's Inn Rd., Fl. 6
34-42 Cleveland St.
London WC1X 8HL, United Kingdom
Ph: 44 20 31922000

Fax: 44 20 31922010
Publisher E-mail: info@biomedcentral.com
Online journal publishing original research articles in all
aspects of the prevention, diagnosis and management
of pulmonary and associated disorders, as well as
related molecular genetics, pathophysiology, and
epidemiology. **Key Personnel:** Eric Bateman, Editorial
Board; Richard K. Albert, Editorial Board; Edwin R. Chil-
vers, Editorial Board; Rodolfo Dennis, Editorial Board;
Judith L. Black, Editorial Board; Melissa Norton, MD,
Editor-in-Chief, bmcserieseditor@biomedcentral.com.
ISSN: 1471-2466. **Remarks:** Accepts advertising. **URL:**
http://www.biomedcentral.com/bmcpulmmed/. **Circ:** (Not
Reported)

54089 ■ BMC Structural Biology
BioMed Central Ltd.
236 Gray's Inn Rd., Fl. 6
34-42 Cleveland St.
London WC1X 8HL, United Kingdom
Ph: 44 20 31922000
Fax: 44 20 31922010
Publisher E-mail: info@biomedcentral.com
Online journal publishing original research articles in
investigations into the structure and function of biologi-
cal macromolecules. **Key Personnel:** Yvonne E. Jones,
Editorial Board; Arthur Olson, Editorial Board; James
Hogle, Editorial Board; Christine A. Orengo, Editorial
Board; Fred E. Cohen, Editorial Board; Senyon Choe,
Assoc. Ed.; Alan Fersht, Editorial Board; Martino Bolog-
nesi, Editorial Board; Dino Moras, Editorial Board. **ISSN:**
1472-6807. **Remarks:** Accepts advertising. **URL:** http://
www.biomedcentral.com/bmcstructbiol/. **Circ:** (Not
Reported)

54090 ■ BMC Surgery
BioMed Central Ltd.
236 Gray's Inn Rd., Fl. 6
34-42 Cleveland St.
London WC1X 8HL, United Kingdom
Ph: 44 20 31922000
Fax: 44 20 31922010
Publisher E-mail: info@biomedcentral.com
Online journal publishing original research articles in
surgical research, training, and practice. **Key Person-
nel:** Michael Diamond, Editorial Board; Michael Dixon,
Editorial Board; Melissa Norton, MD, Editor-in-Chief,
bmcserieseditor@biomedcentral.com; Francis Seow-
Choen, Editorial Board; Andreas Tzakis, Editorial Board;
Jonathan A. Friedman, Editorial Board. **ISSN:** 1471-
2482. **Remarks:** Accepts advertising. **URL:** http://www.
biomedcentral.com/bmcsurg/. **Circ:** (Not Reported)

54091 ■ BMC Urology
BioMed Central Ltd.
236 Gray's Inn Rd., Fl. 6
34-42 Cleveland St.
London WC1X 8HL, United Kingdom
Ph: 44 20 31922000
Fax: 44 20 31922010
Publisher E-mail: info@biomedcentral.com
Online journal publishing original research articles in all
aspects of the prevention, diagnosis and management
of urological disorders, as well as related molecular
genetics, pathophysiology, and epidemiology. **Key Personnel:** Steven Brandes, Assoc. Ed.; Paul Abel, Editorial Board; Anthony Atala, Editorial Board; Paddy Dewan,
Editorial Board; John Gearhart, Assoc. Ed.; Melissa
Norton, MD, Editor-in-Chief, bmcserieseditor@
biomedcentral.com. **ISSN:** 1471-2490. **Remarks:** Accepts advertising. **URL:** http://www.biomedcentral.com/
bmcurol/. **Circ:** (Not Reported)

54092 ■ BMC Veterinary Research
BioMed Central Ltd.
236 Gray's Inn Rd., Fl. 6
34-42 Cleveland St.
London WC1X 8HL, United Kingdom
Ph: 44 20 31922000
Fax: 44 20 31922010
Publisher E-mail: info@biomedcentral.com
Online journal publishing original research articles in all
aspects of veterinary science and medicine, including
the epidemiology, diagnosis, prevention and treatment
of medical conditions of domestic, companion, farm and
wild animals, as well as the biomedical processes that
underlie their health. **Key Personnel:** Melissa Norton,
MD, Editor-in-Chief, bmcserieseditor@biomedcentral.

com; Zhen Fu, Assoc. Ed.; Birthe Avery, Editorial Board;
Michael Azain, Editorial Board; Peter J. Chenoweth,
Editorial Board; Bertram Brenig, Assoc. Ed. **ISSN:** 1746-
6148. **Remarks:** Accepts advertising. **URL:** http://www.
biomedcentral.com/bmcvetres. **Circ:** (Not Reported)

54093 ■ BMC Women's Health
BioMed Central Ltd.
236 Gray's Inn Rd., Fl. 6
34-42 Cleveland St.
London WC1X 8HL, United Kingdom
Ph: 44 20 31922000
Fax: 44 20 31922010
Publisher E-mail: info@biomedcentral.com
Online journal publishing original research articles in all
aspects of the prevention, diagnosis and management
of gynaecological, fertility, and breast disorders, as well
as related molecular genetics, pathophysiology, and
epidemiology. **Key Personnel:** Guillermo Carolli, Editorial Board; Donna K. Ciliska, Editorial Board; Melissa
Norton, MD, Editor-in-Chief, bmcserieseditor@
biomedcentral.com. **ISSN:** 1472-6874. **Remarks:** Accepts advertising. **URL:** http://www.biomedcentral.com/
bmcwomenshealth/. **Circ:** (Not Reported)

54094 ■ Boarding School
Boarding Schools Association
Grosvenor Gardens House
35-37, Grosvenor Gardens
London SW1W 0BS, United Kingdom
Ph: 44 20 77981580
Fax: 44 20 77981581
Publisher E-mail: bsa@iboarding.org.uk
Publication covering education. **Freq:** Semiannual. **Key
Personnel:** Dick Davison, Editor, phone 44 7725
754824, richardcdavison@gmail.com. **Remarks:** Ac-
cepts advertising. **URL:** http://www.boarding.org.uk/.
Circ: (Not Reported)

54095 ■ Bob the Builder
BBC Worldwide Publishing Ltd.
Media Centre
201 Wood Ln.
London W12 7TQ, United Kingdom
Ph: 44 20 84332000
Fax: 44 20 87490538
Magazine featuring educational information for children.
Subtitle: Reduce, reuse, recycle!. **Freq:** 3/week. **Sub-
scription Rates:** 1.99 single issue. **URL:** http://www.
bbcmagazines.com/content/magazines/bobthebuilder/.

54096 ■ Body & Society
Sage Publications Ltd.
1 Oliver's Yard
55 City Rd.
London EC1Y 1SP, United Kingdom
Ph: 44 20 73248500
Fax: 44 20 73248600
Peer-reviewed journal covering the social and cultural
analysis of the human body. **Founded:** 1995. **Freq:**
Quarterly. **Key Personnel:** Lisa Blackman, Editor; Mike
Featherstone, Editor-in-Chief; Tomoko Tamari, Managing Editor; Couze Venn, Review Ed. **ISSN:** 1357-034X.
Subscription Rates: 470 institutions print & e-access;
517 institutions current volume print & all online content;
423 institutions e-access; 470 institutions backfile lease,
e-access plus backfile; 423 institutions e-access (content
through 1998); 461 institutions print only; 50 individuals
print only; 127 single issue institutional; 16 single issue
individual. **Remarks:** Accepts advertising. **URL:** http://
www.sagepub.co.uk/journalsProdDesc.nav?prodId=
Journal200799. **Circ:** (Not Reported)

54097 ■ Book and Magazine Collector
The Metropolis Group
140 Wales Farm Rd.
London W3 6UG, United Kingdom
Ph: 44 20 87528181
Fax: 44 20 87528185
Publisher E-mail: metropolis@metropolis.co.uk
Magazine for lovers of rare books, magazines, comics
and related memorabilia. **Founded:** 1984. **Freq:** 13/yr.
Key Personnel: Kathryn Scott, Sales Exec.; Janet Davi-
son, Publisher; Chris Peachment, Editor. **Subscription
Rates:** 42 individuals UK, royal mail; 46 individuals to
Europe, airmail; 53 other countries; 79 two years UK; 87
two years to Europe; 100 two years rest of world; 112
individuals 39 issues; 123 individuals 39 issues to
Europe; 145 other countries 39 issues. **Remarks:** Ac-

cepts advertising. **URL:** http://www.
bookandmagazinecollector.com/site/sections/default.
asp; http://www.metropolis.co.uk/bookcollector.html. **Ad
Rates:** BW: 205, 4C: 265. **Circ:** (Not Reported)

54098 ■ Books for Keeps
1 Effingham Rd.
London SE12 8NZ, United Kingdom
Ph: 44 20 88524953
Fax: 44 20 83187580
Publisher E-mail: enquiries@booksforkeeps.co.uk
Magazine covering children's book reviews for consum-
ers and professionals. **Subtitle:** The Children's Book
Magazine. **Founded:** Mar. 1980. **Freq:** Bimonthly. **Trim
Size:** A4. **Key Personnel:** Richard Hill, Mng. Dir. **ISSN:**
0143-909X. **Subscription Rates:** 26.50 individuals; 16
students; 29.50 individuals Europe; 32.50 individuals
worldwide. **Remarks:** Accepts advertising. **URL:** http://
www.booksforkeeps.co.uk. **Circ:** Paid 9,000

54099 ■ Bookselling Essentials
Booksellers Association of The United Kingdom and
Ireland
Minster House
272 Vauxhall Bridge Rd.
London SW1V 1BA, United Kingdom
Ph: 44 20 78020802
Fax: 44 20 78020803
Publisher E-mail: mail@booksellers.org.uk
Professional journal of The Booksellers Association of
the United Kingdom and Ireland Ltd. **Freq:** Quarterly.
Key Personnel: Meryl Halls, Editor. **Remarks:** Advertis-
ing not accepted. **URL:** http://www.booksellers.org.uk/.
Former name: Bookselling News. **Formerly:**
Bookselling. **Circ:** Controlled 3,300

54100 ■ Bosnia Report
The Bosnian Institute
SAVO, 8th Fl.
Hannibal House
Elephant and Castle
London SE1 6TE, United Kingdom
Publisher E-mail: info@bosnia.org.uk
Magazine covering news and information on Bosnia-
Herzegovina and related issues. **Freq:** Bimonthly. **Key
Personnel:** Dr. Noel Malcolm, Chm.; Nermin Mulalic,
Assoc.; Quintin Hoare, Director. **Subscription Rates:**
20 individuals; 30 institutions; US$30 individuals; US$45
institutions. **URL:** http://www.bosnia.org.uk/about/
publicat.cfm.

54101 ■ The Bottle Street Gazette
Margery Allingham Society
c/o Barry Pike, Chm.
42 Scarborough Rd.
Leytonstone
London E11 4AL, United Kingdom
Ph: 44 20 85565243
Publisher E-mail: info@margeryallingham.org.uk
Journal featuring news items and regular articles regard-
ing the Allingham Oeuvre. **Freq:** Semiannual. **Key Per-
sonnel:** Barry Pike, Editor. **Subscription Rates:**
Included in membership. **URL:** http://www.
margeryallingham.org.uk/.

54102 ■ Boxing Monthly
Topwave Ltd.
40 Morpeth Rd.
London E9 7LD, United Kingdom
Ph: 44 20 89864141
Fax: 44 20 89864145
Publication E-mail: bmsubs@mmcltd.co.uk
Publisher E-mail: mail@boxing-monthly.demon.co.uk
Consumer magazine covering professional boxing
worldwide. **Founded:** May 1989. **Freq:** Monthly. **Trim
Size:** 297 x 210 mm. **Key Personnel:** Glyn Leach, Edi-
tor; Graham Houston, Editor. **Subscription Rates:** 44
individuals; 83 two years; 52 individuals Europe; 99 two
years Europe; 57 U.S. and Canada; 105 U.S. and
Canada 2 years; 75 other countries; 140 other countries
2 years. **Remarks:** Accepts advertising. **URL:** http://
www.boxing-monthly.co.uk. **Ad Rates:** BW: 800, 4C:
900. **Circ:** Paid 25,000

54103 ■ Brazil Business Brief
Brazilian Chamber of Commerce in Great Britain
32 Green St.
London W1K 7AT, United Kingdom
Ph: 44 20 73999281
Fax: 44 20 74990186

Circulation: ★ = ABC; △ = BPA; ◆ = CAC; • = CCAB; ❑ = VAC; ⊕ = PO Statement; ‡ = Publisher's Report; Boldface figures = sworn; Light figures = estimated;

Gale Directory of Publications & Broadcast Media/147th Ed.

5691

Publisher E-mail: brazilianchamber@brazilianchamber.org.uk

Publication covering Brazil business. **Freq:** Bimonthly. **ISSN:** 1351-4520. **Subscription Rates:** Free to members. **Remarks:** Advertising accepted; rates available upon request. **URL:** http://www.brazilianchamber.org.uk/. **Circ:** 500

54104 ■ Breathe
Maney Publishing
1 Carlton House Ter.
London SW1Y 5AF, United Kingdom
Ph: 44 20 74517300
Fax: 44 20 74517307
Publisher E-mail: maney@maney.co.uk

Peer-reviewed journal introducing basic concepts and state-of-the-art methods for those exploring continued education in respiratory medicine. **Subtitle:** Continuing Medical Education for Respiratory Professionals. **Freq:** Quarterly. **Key Personnel:** L. Bjermer, Editor-in-Chief, a.simonds@rbht.nhs.uk. **ISSN:** 1810-6838. **Subscription Rates:** 99 institutions UK; 99 institutions Europe; US$196 institutions in U.S.; 99 institutions rest of world. **URL:** http://dev.ersnet.org/101-about-breathe.htm; http://maney.co.uk/index.php/journals/bre/.

54105 ■ Bridge
Chess & Bridge Ltd.
44 Baker Rd.
London NW1 3AR, United Kingdom
Ph: 44 20 73882404
Fax: 44 20 73882407
Publication E-mail: info@bridgeshop.com
Publisher E-mail: info@chess.co.uk

Consumer magazine covering bridge. **Founded:** 1926. **Freq:** Monthly. **Trim Size:** A4. **Key Personnel:** Mark Horton, Editor. **Subscription Rates:** 4.50 single issue; 5 single issue Europe; 5.50 other countries single issue; 39.95 two years; 69.95 two years; 99.95 individuals 3 years; 50 U.S. and Canada 1; 85 U.S. and Canada 2 years; 110 U.S. and Canada 3 years; 49.95 individuals Europe. **URL:** http://www.bridgemagazine.co.uk.

54106 ■ Bridge Design & Engineering
Hemming Information Services
32 Vauxhall Bridge Rd.
London SW1V 2SS, United Kingdom
Ph: 44 207 79736400
Fax: 44 207 72335056
Publisher E-mail: info@hgluk.com

Trade magazine covering the bridge industry for bridge professionals worldwide. **Founded:** 1995. **Freq:** Quarterly. **Key Personnel:** Helena Russell, Editor, lisa@icehousemedia.com. **ISSN:** 1359-7493. **Subscription Rates:** 105 individuals; EUR168 individuals; US$216 individuals; 179 two years; EUR285 two years; US$298 two years; 236 individuals three years; EUR378 individuals three years; US$394 individuals three years. **Remarks:** Accepts advertising. **URL:** http://www.bridgeweb.com/; http://www.hemminginfo.co.uk/index.cfm?fuseaction=home.products&producttypeid=1. **Circ:** Combined 5,000

54107 ■ Britannia
Society for the Promotion of Roman Studies
Senate House
Malet St.
London WC1E 7HU, United Kingdom
Ph: 44 20 78628727
Fax: 44 20 78628728
Publisher E-mail: office@romansociety.org

Publication covering Roman Archaeological studies in Britain. **Founded:** 1970. **Freq:** Annual. **ISSN:** 0068-113X. **URL:** http://www.romansociety.org/publications/overview.html. **Ad Rates:** BW: US$330. **Circ:** 1,500

54108 ■ British Actuarial Journal
Faculty of Actuaries
Staple Inn Hall
High Holborn
London WC1V 7QJ, United Kingdom
Fax: 44 18 65268211
Publication E-mail: institute@actuaries.org.uk

British journal covering insurance. **Founded:** 1995. **Freq:** 3/yr (Dec., Feb., & June). **Subscription Rates:** Free to members. **Remarks:** Advertising not accepted. **URL:** http://www.actuaries.org.uk/knowledge/publications/baj. **Circ:** 13,400

54109 ■ British Chess Magazine
44 Baker St.
London W1U 7RT, United Kingdom

Ph: 44 20 73882404
Fax: 44 20 74863355
Publisher E-mail: info@chess.co.uk

Magazine for chess players and enthusiasts. **Founded:** 1881. **Freq:** Monthly. **Key Personnel:** John Saunders, Editor. **Subscription Rates:** 42 individuals U.K.; 79 two years U.K.; 45 individuals Europe; 85 two years Europe; 49 individuals rest of the world; 93 two years rest of the world; US$94 individuals rest of the world; US$17 two years rest of the world; 116 individuals U.K.(three years); 137 individuals rest of the world (three years). **Remarks:** Accepts advertising. **URL:** http://www.bcmchess.co.uk/. **Circ:** (Not Reported)

54110 ■ British Dental Journal
British Dental Association
The Macmillan Bldg.
4 Crinan St.
London N1 9XW, United Kingdom
Ph: 44 20 78434729
Fax: 44 20 78434996
Publisher E-mail: enquiries@bda.org

British journal covering dentistry. **Freq:** Bimonthly. **Key Personnel:** Kate Maynard, Asst. Ed., phone 44 20 78433680, k.maynard@nature.com; Kim Black-Totham, Publisher, phone 44 20 78434612, k.black-totham@nature.com; Ian Pope, Production Controller, phone 44 20 78434812, fax 44 20 78434838, i.pope@nature.com; Stephen Hancocks, Editor-in-Chief, phone 44 20 75355842, s.hancocks@bda.org; Rowena Milan, Managing Editor, phone 44 20 78433678, r.milan@nature.com; Arveen Bajaj, News Ed., phone 44 20 78433679, a.bajaj@nature.com; Anna Koumarianou, Sales and Mktg. Exec., phone 44 20 78434710, a.koumarianou@nature.com; James Richards, Advertising Exec., phone 44 20 78434716, j.richards@nature.com. **ISSN:** 0007-0610. **Subscription Rates:** US$412 individuals print and online. **Remarks:** Accepts advertising. **URL:** http://www.nature.com/bdj/index.html; http://www.bda-dentistry.org.uk/. **Circ:** 37,000

54111 ■ British Journal of Anaesthetic and Recovery Nursing
Cambridge University Press
c/o Jessica Inch, Ed.-in-Ch.
PACU S W London Elective Orthopaedic Centre
Epsom General Hospital
Dorking Rd.
London KT15 8PB, United Kingdom
Publisher E-mail: information@cambridge.org

Journal covering issues affecting clinical practice in the field of perianaesthetic nursing. **Freq:** Quarterly. **Key Personnel:** Jessica Inch, Editor-in-Chief. **ISSN:** 1742-6456. **Subscription Rates:** 172 institutions online and print; US$328 institutions online and print; 145 institutions online only; US$275 institutions online only; 46 individuals online and print; US$87 individuals online and print; 33 individuals online only; US$62 individuals online only. **Remarks:** Accepts advertising. **URL:** http://journals.cambridge.org/action/displayJournal?jid=ARN. **Ad Rates:** BW: 240, 4C: 610. **Circ:** (Not Reported)

54112 ■ British Journal of Biomedical Science
Institute of Biomedical Science
12 Coldbath Sq.
London EC1R 5HL, United Kingdom
Ph: 44 20 77130214
Fax: 44 20 78379658
Publisher E-mail: mail@ibms.org

British journal covering biomedical science. **Freq:** Quarterly. **Key Personnel:** Brian Nation, Editor, briannation@ibms.org; Joyce A. Overfield, Assoc. Ed. **Subscription Rates:** 169 nonmembers Europe; US$318 nonmembers; 184 nonmembers elsewhere. **Remarks:** Advertising accepted; rates available upon request. **URL:** http://www.ibms.org/index.cfm?method=publications.british_journal; http://www.bjbs-online.org/. **Circ:** (Not Reported)

54113 ■ British Journal of Cancer
British Association for Cancer Research
UCL Cancer Institute
Paul O'Gorman Bldg.
72 Huntley St.
London WC1E 6BT, United Kingdom
Publisher E-mail: bacr@leeds.ac.uk

British journal covering cancer. **Freq:** Bimonthly. **Key Personnel:** Adrian Harris, Editor-in-Chief; B. Leyland-Jones, Subject Ed.; J. Cassidy, Editorial Board; D.

Wynford-Thomas, Subject Ed. **ISSN:** 0007-0920. **Subscription Rates:** US$593 individuals Americas (print and online); US$539 individuals Americas (online only); EUR533 individuals Europe (print and online); EUR485 individuals Europe (online only); 82,700¥ individuals Japan (print and online); 62,300¥ individuals Japan (online only); 343.58 individuals U.K. (print and online); 312.24 individuals U.K. (online only). **Remarks:** Advertising accepted; rates available upon request. **URL:** http://www.nature.com/bjc/index.html. **Circ:** (Not Reported)

54114 ■ British Journal of Cancer Management
Hayward Medical Communications
Covent Garden
8-10 Dryden St.
London WC2E 9NA, United Kingdom
Publisher E-mail: admin@hayward.co.uk

Journal for all healthcare professionals involved in the treatment and management of cancer. **Founded:** 2004. **Freq:** 4/yr. **Key Personnel:** Graham H. Jackson, MD, Editor. **URL:** http://www.cancermanagement.co.uk/bjcm/.

54115 ■ British Journal of Cardiac Nursing
MA Healthcare Ltd.
St. Jude's Church
Dulwich Rd.
Herne Hill
London SE24 0PB, United Kingdom
Ph: 44 20 77385454
Fax: 44 20 77332325

Peer-reviewed journal covering all aspects of cardiovascular nursing. **Subtitle:** The leading clinical journal for cardiac nurses. **Founded:** Jan. 2006. **Freq:** Monthly. **Key Personnel:** Vicqui Stuart-Jones, Editor; Jenny Tagney, Consultant Ed.; Neil Angus, Editorial Board. **Subscription Rates:** 129 individuals Ireland; EUR211 individuals Europe; US$303 other countries personal; 92 students Ireland. **Remarks:** Accepts advertising. **URL:** http://www.cardiac-nursing.co.uk/. **Circ:** (Not Reported)

54116 ■ British Journal of Clinical Pharmacology
British Pharmacological Society
16 Angel Gate
City Rd.
London EC1V 2PT, United Kingdom
Ph: 44 20 74170110
Publisher E-mail: yn@bps.ac.uk

British journal covering clinical pharmacology. **Founded:** 1974. **Freq:** Monthly. **Key Personnel:** A. Cohen, Editor; James M. Ritter, Chm., james.ritter@kcl.ac.uk. **ISSN:** 0306-5251. **Subscription Rates:** US$299 individuals print & online, Americas; EUR242 individuals print & online, Europe; 161 individuals print & online, non-Euro zone; 178 other countries print & online; US$141 members print & online; EUR126 members print & online; 84 members print & online; US$2,543 institutions Americas (print and online); 1,376 institutions UK (print and online); 1,749 institutions Europe (print and online). **Remarks:** Advertising accepted; rates available upon request. **URL:** http://www.blackwellpublishing.com/journal.asp?ref=0306-5251. **Circ:** (Not Reported)

54117 ■ British Journal of Community Nursing
MA Healthcare Ltd.
St. Jude's Church
Dulwich Rd.
Herne Hill
London SE24 0PB, United Kingdom
Ph: 44 20 77385454
Fax: 44 20 77332325

Peer-reviewed journal covering primary care nursing. **Subtitle:** The monthly journal for community nursing professionals. **Freq:** Monthly. **Key Personnel:** Julie Smith, Editor; Alison While, Consultant Ed. **Subscription Rates:** 101 individuals Ireland; EUR175 individuals Europe; US$261 other countries personal; 68 students Ireland. **Remarks:** Accepts advertising. **URL:** http://www.bjcn.co.uk/. **Circ:** (Not Reported)

54118 ■ British Journal of Dermatology
British Association of Dermatologists
4 Fitzroy Sq.
Willan House
London W1T 5HQ, United Kingdom
Ph: 44 20 73830266
Fax: 44 20 73885263
Publisher E-mail: admin@bad.org.uk

British journal covering dermatology. **Subtitle:** An Official Journal of the British Association of Dermatologists. **Freq:** Monthly. **Key Personnel:** R. Murphy, Section Ed.; J. Caulfield, Editorial Mgr., john@bad.org.uk; E. Sprecher, Section Ed.; D.N. Slater, Section Ed.; T.O. Bleiker, Editor; Dr. H. Tsao, Section Ed.; J.S.C. English, Editorial Advisory Board. **ISSN:** 0007-0963. **Subscription Rates:** US$389 individuals print and online; US$369 individuals online only; US$290 members print + online; US$290 nonmembers print + online; US$2,458 institutions print + online; US$2,229 institutions print; US$2,229 institutions online; 1,325 institutions print & online in Europe; EUR1,530 institutions print; EUR1,530 institutions online. **Remarks:** Accepts advertising. **URL:** http://www.bad. org.uk//site/1156/default.aspx; http://onlinelibrary.wiley. com/journal/10.1111/(ISSN)1365-2133. **Circ:** (Not Reported)

54119 ■ British Journal of Dermatology Nursing
Hayward Medical Communications
Covent Garden
8-10 Dryden St.
London WC2E 9NA, United Kingdom
Publisher E-mail: admin@hayward.co.uk
Journal to nurses involved in the treatment and management of dermatological conditions. **Founded:** 1997. **Freq:** Quarterly. **Key Personnel:** Julie Bowman, Editor. **URL:** http://www.bjdn.co.uk/bjdn/.

54120 ■ British Journal of General Practice
Royal College of General Practitioners
1 Bow Churchyard
London EC4M 9DQ, United Kingdom
Ph: 44 20 31887400
Fax: 44 020 31887401
Publisher E-mail: info@rcgp.org.uk
British journal covering family medicine. **Freq:** Monthly. **Trim Size:** A4. **ISSN:** 0960-1643. **URL:** http://www.rcgp. org.uk/publications/bjgp.aspx. **Formerly:** Journal of the Royal College of General Practitioners. **Ad Rates:** BW: 1,000, 4C: 1,650. **Circ:** 23,000

54121 ■ British Journal of Health Care Management
MA Healthcare Ltd.
St. Jude's Church
Dulwich Rd.
Herne Hill
London SE24 0PB, United Kingdom
Ph: 44 20 77385454
Fax: 44 20 77332325
Peer-reviewed journal covering healthcare service management. **Founded:** 1995. **Freq:** Monthly. **Key Personnel:** Sarah David, Editor; Terry Bamford, Editorial Board; Kate Harmond, Editorial Board. **Subscription Rates:** 207 individuals Ireland; EUR323 individuals Europe, paper; US$456 other countries paper; 249 individuals Ireland, online and paper; EUR314 individuals Europe, online and paper; US$483 other countries online and paper. **Remarks:** Accepts advertising. **URL:** http://www.bjhcm.co.uk/. **Circ:** (Not Reported)

54122 ■ British Journal of Healthcare Assistants
MA Healthcare Ltd.
St. Jude's Church
Dulwich Rd.
Herne Hill
London SE24 0PB, United Kingdom
Ph: 44 20 77385454
Fax: 44 20 77332325
Peer-reviewed journal for healthcare assistants and assistant practitioners. **Subtitle:** The only clinical for HCAs and assistant practitioners. **Freq:** Monthly. **Key Personnel:** Polly Sullivan, Editor; Angela Grainger, Consultant Ed.; Menna Lloyd Jones, Consultant Ed. **Subscription Rates:** 73 individuals Ireland; EUR130 individuals Europe; US$193 other countries personal; 54 students Ireland. **Remarks:** Accepts advertising. **URL:** http:// www.healthcare-assistants.co.uk/. **Circ:** (Not Reported)

54123 ■ British Journal of Hospital Medicine
MA Healthcare Ltd.
St. Jude's Church
Dulwich Rd.
Herne Hill
London SE24 0PB, United Kingdom
Ph: 44 20 77385454
Fax: 44 20 77332325
Peer-reviewed journal covering developments in hospital medicine. **Founded:** 1966. **Freq:** Monthly. **Key Personnel:** Rob Miller, Editor-in-Chief; Rebecca Linssen, Editor. **Subscription Rates:** 140 individuals Ireland, print and online; EUR239 individuals Europe, print and online; US$358 other countries personal, print and online; 99 students Ireland, print and online. **Remarks:** Accepts

advertising. **URL:** http://www.bjhm.co.uk/. **Circ:** (Not Reported)

54124 ■ British Journal of Intensive Care
Greycoat Publishing Ltd.
148 Buckingham Palace Rd.
Kensington
London SW1W 9TR, United Kingdom
Ph: 44 20 77307995
Fax: 44 20 77303884
Publisher E-mail: mail@greycoatpublishing.co.uk
Journal covering intensive and critical care. **Freq:** Quarterly March, June, September and December. **Trim Size:** 210 x 297 mm. **Key Personnel:** Prof. Michael Rennie, PhD, Editor; Guy Wallis, Editorial Dir., g.wallis@ greycoatpublishing.co.uk. **ISSN:** 0961-7930. **Subscription Rates:** 40 individuals; 60 individuals Europe; 72 other countries; 84 institutions; 114 institutions Europe; 132 institutions, other countries. **Remarks:** Accepts advertising. **URL:** http://www.greycoatpublishing.co.uk/ content/Journals/BJIC.asp. **Circ:** (Not Reported)

54125 ■ British Journal of Midwifery
MA Healthcare Ltd.
St. Jude's Church
Dulwich Rd.
Herne Hill
London SE24 0PB, United Kingdom
Ph: 44 20 77385454
Fax: 44 20 77332325
Peer-reviewed journal covering all aspects of midwifery. **Subtitle:** The leading clinical journal for midwives. **Freq:** Monthly. **Key Personnel:** Prof. Tina Lavender, Editor-in-Chief; Yana Richens, Editor-in-Chief; Victoria Clift-Matthews, Editor. **Subscription Rates:** 125 individuals Ireland; EUR211 individuals Europe; US$312 other countries personal; 101 students Ireland. **Remarks:** Accepts advertising. **URL:** http://www. britishjournalofmidwifery.com/. **Circ:** ★4,051

54126 ■ British Journal of Music Therapy
British Society for Music Therapy
24-27 White Lion St.
London N1 9PD, United Kingdom
Ph: 44 20 78376100
Fax: 44 20 78376142
Publisher E-mail: info@bsmt.org
British journal covering music therapy. Published jointly with the Association of Professional Music Therapists. **Founded:** 1987. **Freq:** Semiannual. **Key Personnel:** Simon Procter, Editor. **Subscription Rates:** Free members. **Remarks:** Advertising accepted; rates available upon request. **URL:** http://www.bsmt.org/ publications.htm. **Circ:** 800

54127 ■ British Journal of Neuroscience Nursing
MA Healthcare Ltd.
St. Jude's Church
Dulwich Rd.
Herne Hill
London SE24 0PB, United Kingdom
Ph: 44 20 77385454
Fax: 44 20 77332325
Peer-reviewed professional journal for neuroscience nurses in the UK, keeping nurses up to date with clinical, professional and policy developments, as well as providing a forum for sharing research and innovation. **Freq:** Monthly. **Key Personnel:** Sue Woodward, Editor-in-Chief; Alice Hall, Editor. **Subscription Rates:** 289 individuals; EUR350 individuals Europe; US$520 other countries. **Remarks:** Accepts advertising. **URL:** http:// www.bjnn.co.uk/. **Circ:** (Not Reported)

54128 ■ British Journal of Occupational Therapy
British Association and College of Occupational Therapists
106-114 Borough High St.
Southwark
London SE1 1LB, United Kingdom
Ph: 44 20 73576480
Peer-reviewed British journal covering occupational therapy. **Freq:** Monthly. **Key Personnel:** Upma Barnett, Editor, upma.barnett@cot.co.uk; Katy Eggleton, Advertising Mgr., steve.meertens@cot.co.uk. **ISSN:** 0308-0226. **Remarks:** Accepts advertising. **URL:** http://www. cot.co.uk/Homepage/Library_and_Publications/British_ Journal_of_Occupational_Therapy_(BJOT)/. **Ad Rates:** BW: 3,600. **Circ:** 18,000

54129 ■ British Journal of Ophthalmology
BMJ Publishing Group
BMA House
Tavistock Sq.
London WC1H 9JR, United Kingdom
Ph: 44 20 73834410
Fax: 44 20 73876400
Publisher E-mail: customerservice.group@bmjgroup. com
Peer-reviewed Journal covering clinical ophthalmology and ophthalmic science. **Founded:** 1917. **Freq:** Monthly. **Print Method:** Offset. **Trim Size:** 8 1/2 x 10 7/8. **Cols./ Page:** 3. **Col. Width:** 15 picas. **Col. Depth:** 10 inches. **Key Personnel:** Dr. Arun Singh, Editor, singha@ccf.org; Prof. Harminder Dua, Editor, harminder.dua@ nottingham.ac.uk; Allison Lang, Publisher, alang@ bmjgroup.com. **ISSN:** 0007-1161. **Subscription Rates:** US$349 individuals print and online; 179 individuals print and online; EUR242 individuals print and online; US$224 individuals online only; EUR155 individuals online only; 115 individuals online only. **Remarks:** Accepts advertising. **URL:** http://bjo.bmj.com/. **Circ:** ‡2,370

54130 ■ British Journal of Pharmacology
British Pharmacological Society
16 Angel Gate
City Rd.
London EC1V 2PT, United Kingdom
Ph: 44 20 74170110
Publication E-mail: bjp@bps.ac.uk
Publisher E-mail: yn@bps.ac.uk
British journal covering pharmacology. **Founded:** 1946. **Freq:** Semimonthly. **Trim Size:** 210 x 280 mm. **Key Personnel:** Dr. R.A. Bond, Sen. Ed.; J.C. McGrath, Editor-in-Chief. **ISSN:** 0007-1188. **Subscription Rates:** 262 individuals print & online; EUR333 other countries print & online; US$515 other countries print & online; US$4,221 institutions print & online; US$3,670 institutions print or online. **Remarks:** Advertising accepted; rates available upon request. **URL:** http://www.bps.ac. uk/publications; http://onlinelibrary.wiley.com/journal/10. 1111/(ISSN)1476-5381. **Circ:** (Not Reported)

54131 ■ British Journal of Photography
Incisive Media Limited
Haymarket House
28-29 Haymarket
London SW1Y 4RX, United Kingdom
Ph: 44 870 2408859
Fax: 44 207 4849797
Publisher E-mail: customerservices@incisivemedia.com
Magazine about photography. **Founded:** 1854. **Freq:** Weekly. **Key Personnel:** Diane Smyth, Dep. Ed., phone 44 20 73169658, bjp.features@bjphoto.co.uk; Simon Baindridge, Editor, phone 44 20 73169416, simon. bainbridge@incisivemedia.com. **Subscription Rates:** 63 individuals. **URL:** http://www.incisivemedia.com/ corporate/products/britishjournalofphotography; http:// www.bjp-online.com. **Circ:** Paid ★8,015

54132 ■ British Journal of Psychiatry
The Royal College of Psychiatrists
17 Belgrave Sq.
London SW1X 8PG, United Kingdom
Ph: 44 20 72352351
Fax: 44 20 72451231
Publisher E-mail: reception@rcpsych.ac.uk
Peer-reviewed Journal covering information on clinical practice and research. **Founded:** 1920. **Freq:** Monthly. **Print Method:** Web. **Trim Size:** 8 1/8 x 10 7/8. **Cols./ Page:** 4. **Col. Width:** 10 picas. **Col. Depth:** 57 picas. **Key Personnel:** Simon Wessely, Dep. Ed.; Dinesh Bhugra, Assoc. Ed.; Prof. Peter Tyrer, Editor. **ISSN:** 0007-1250. **Subscription Rates:** 250 individuals UK & Europe, print + online; 304 institutions UK & Europe, print + online; US$399 U.S. and Canada U.S. & Canada, print and online; US$567 institutions U.S. & Canada, print and online; 277 individuals elsewhere, print and online; 355 institutions elsewhere, print and online; 26 single issue; US$45 single issue; 191.53 individuals worldwide, online only; 400 institutions worldwide, online only. **Remarks:** Accepts advertising. **URL:** http://bjp.rcpsych.org/misc/about.shtml. **Circ:** (Not Reported)

54133 ■ British Journal of Radiology
British Institute of Radiology
36 Portland Pl.
London W1B 1AT, United Kingdom
Ph: 44 20 73071400

Circulation: ★ = ABC; △ = BPA; ◆ = CAC; • = CCAB; ❏ = VAC; ⊕ = PO Statement; ‡ = Publisher's Report; Boldface figures = sworn; Light figures = estimated.

Gale Directory of Publications & Broadcast Media/147th Ed. 5693

Fax: 44 20 7307 1414
Publication E-mail: publications@bir.org.uk
Publisher E-mail: contact@bir.org.uk
Peer-reviewed British journal covering radiology. **Founded:** 1928. **Freq:** Monthly. **Trim Size:** A4. **Key Personnel:** D.W. Pilling, Honorary Ed.; R.G. Dale, Honorary Ed.; A. Munro, Dep. Ed.; A. Morgan, Assoc. Ed.; P. Mountford, Dep. Ed.; D. Birchall, Dep. Ed.; Z. Amin, Assoc. Ed. **ISSN:** 0007-1285. **Subscription Rates:** 705 institutions. **Remarks:** Advertising accepted; rates available upon request. **URL:** http://bjr.birjournals.org. **Circ:** 3,000

54134 ■ British Journal of Renal Medicine
Hayward Medical Communications
Covent Garden
8-10 Dryden St.
London WC2E 9NA, United Kingdom
Publisher E-mail: admin@hayward.co.uk
Journal covering renal care. **Founded:** 1995. **Freq:** Quarterly. **Key Personnel:** Dr. John Bradley, Editor. **URL:** http://www.bjrm.co.uk/bjrm/.

54135 ■ British Journal of School Nursing
MA Healthcare Ltd.
St. Jude's Church
Dulwich Rd.
Herne Hill
London SE24 0PB, United Kingdom
Ph: 44 20 77385454
Fax: 44 20 77332325
Peer-reviewed journal for school nurses and other professionals involved in the health and social care of the school aged population. **Subtitle:** The bi-monthly that promotes excellence in school health. **Founded:** Sept. 2006. **Freq:** 10/yr. **Key Personnel:** Caroline Voogd, Editor; Emma Croghan, Consultant Ed. **Subscription Rates:** 122 individuals Ireland; EUR196 individuals Europe; US$281 other countries personal; 101 students Ireland. **Remarks:** Accepts advertising. **URL:** http://www.school-nursing.co.uk/. **Circ:** (Not Reported)

54136 ■ British Journal of Sexual Medicine
Hayward Medical Communications
Covent Garden
8-10 Dryden St.
London WC2E 9NA, United Kingdom
Publisher E-mail: admin@hayward.co.uk
Journal covering all aspects of sexual health. **Founded:** 1973. **Key Personnel:** Paul Woolley, Editor. **URL:** http://www.bjsm.co.uk/bjsm/.

54137 ■ British Journal of Sports Medicine
BMJ Publishing Group Ltd.
BMA House
Tavistock Sq.
London WC1H 9JR, United Kingdom
Ph: 44 20 73874410
Fax: 44 20 73836400
Publication E-mail: bjsm@bmjgroup.com
Peer-reviewed journal covering latest advances in sport and exercise medicine. **Founded:** 1966. **Freq:** 12/yr. **Key Personnel:** Karim Khan, Editor, kkhan@interchange.ubc.ca; Susan White, Editorial Board. **ISSN:** 0306-3674. **Subscription Rates:** 163 individuals print and online; 106 institutions online only; EUR220 institutions print and online; US$318 institutions print and online; EUR143 institutions online only; US$207 institutions online only. **Remarks:** Advertising accepted; rates available upon request. **URL:** http://bjsm.bmj.com/. **Circ:** ‡1,650

54138 ■ British Journalism Review
Sage Publications Ltd.
1 Oliver's Yard
55 City Rd.
London EC1Y 1SP, United Kingdom
Ph: 44 20 73248500
Fax: 44 20 73248600
Journal covering the media and journalism. **Founded:** 1989. **Freq:** Quarterly March - June - September - December. **Key Personnel:** Bill Hagerty, Editor; Geoffrey Goodman, Chm. Emeritus; Brian Bass, Managing Editor. **ISSN:** 0956-4748. **Subscription Rates:** 341 institutions print and online; 341 institutions plus backfile (print and online); 307 institutions online only; 341 institutions e-access plus backfile (all online content); 307 institutions e-access (content through 1999); 334 institutions print only; 40 individuals print only; 92 institutions single copy; 13 individuals single copy. **Remarks:** Advertising not accepted. **URL:** http://www.bjr.org.uk;

http://www.sagepub.co.uk/journalsProdDesc.nav?prodId=Journal201658. **Circ:** (Not Reported)

54139 ■ British Medical Journal
BMJ Publishing Group Ltd.
BMA House
Tavistock Sq.
London WC1H 9JR, United Kingdom
Ph: 44 20 73874410
Fax: 44 20 73836400
British medical journal. **Founded:** 1840. **Freq:** Weekly. **Print Method:** Web Offset. **Trim Size:** A4. **Key Personnel:** Rajendra Kale, Editorials Ed.; Kamran Abbasi, Editor. **ISSN:** 0959-8138. **Subscription Rates:** 205 individuals print & online only, BMJ International; 45 students print & online only; EUR277 individuals print & online only, BMJ International; EUR61 students print & online only; US$400 individuals print & online only, BMJ International; US$88 students print & online only; EUR961 individuals print & online, BMJ; EUR277 individuals print & online, BMJ International; 492 individuals online only, BMJ clinical research; US$910 individuals online only, BMJ. **URL:** http://group.bmj.com/group/advertising/portfolio/bmj-editions. **Ad Rates:** BW: 780, 4C: 1,380. **Circ:** 28,241

54140 ■ British Medical Journal Clinical Evidence
BMJ Publishing Group
BMA House
Tavistock Sq.
London WC1H 9JR, United Kingdom
Ph: 44 20 73834410
Fax: 44 20 73876400
Publisher E-mail: customerservice.group@bmjgroup.com
Peer-reviewed Journal covering reviews of clinical conditions. **Founded:** 1999. **Key Personnel:** Rubin Minhas, Editor; Karen Pettersen, Dep. Ed. **Subscription Rates:** 213 individuals; EUR288 individuals; US$415 individuals; 107 students; EUR144 students; US$209 students. **URL:** http://clinicalevidence.bmj.com/ceweb/index.jsp.

54141 ■ British Museum Studies in Ancient Egypt and Sudan (BMSAES)
The British Museum
Great Russell St.
London WC1B 3DG, United Kingdom
Ph: 44 20 73238000
Fax: 44 20 73238616
Publication E-mail: bmsaes@britishmuseum.org
Publisher E-mail: information@britishmuseum.org
Journal dealing with all aspects of studies in ancient Egypt and Sudan. **Founded:** Jan. 2002. **URL:** http://www.thebritishmuseum.ac.uk/research/publications/bmsaes.aspx.

54142 ■ British National Formulary
Pharmaceutical Press
1 Lambeth High St.
London SE1 7JN, United Kingdom
Ph: 44 20 77359141
Fax: 44 20 75722509
Publisher E-mail: enquiries@rpharms.com
Professional magazine covering prescribing, dispensing and administering medicines for pharmacists. **Freq:** Annual. **Trim Size:** 130 x 215 mm. **Key Personnel:** Dinesh K. Mehta, Exec. Ed. **Subscription Rates:** 27.95 single issue. **Remarks:** Advertising not accepted. **URL:** http://www.pharmpress.com/shop/default.asp. **Circ:** (Not Reported)

54143 ■ British Numismatic Journal
British Numismatic Society
c/o Warburg Institute
Woburn Sq.
London WC1H 0AB, United Kingdom
Publisher E-mail: secretary@britnumsoc.org
British journal covering research papers concerned with British and Commonwealth coinages, including the United States. **Founded:** 1903. **Freq:** Annual. **Subscription Rates:** 11 members U.K.; 12 members Europe; 13 members rest of world. **Remarks:** Accepts advertising. **URL:** http://www.fitzmuseum.cam.ac.uk/dept/coins/britnumsoc/publications/bnj.html. **Circ:** (Not Reported)

54144 ■ British Orthoptic Journal
British Orthoptic Society
Tavistock House N
Tavistock Sq.
London WC1H 9HX, United Kingdom
Ph: 44 20 73877992

Fax: 44 20 73872584
British journal covering orthoptics. **Founded:** 1939. **Freq:** Annual. **Key Personnel:** Sarah Shea, Editor. **ISSN:** 0068-2314. **Subscription Rates:** 50 individuals plus postage and packing. **Remarks:** Advertising accepted; rates available upon request. **URL:** http://www.orthoptics.org.uk/journal/. **Circ:** 1,500

54145 ■ British Philatelic Bulletin
Royal Mail
148 Old St.
London EC1V 9HQ, United Kingdom
Consumer magazine covering stamp collecting and postal history. **Founded:** 1963. **Freq:** Monthly. **Trim Size:** A5. **Key Personnel:** John Holman, Editor, john.r.holman@royalmail.co.uk; Peter Stringham, General Mgr. **ISSN:** 0953-8119. **Subscription Rates:** 12.95 individuals UK & Europe; 17.95 elsewhere. **Remarks:** Advertising not accepted. **URL:** http://www.royalmail.com/portal/stamps/jump1?catId=32200669&mediaId=51000703. **Circ:** Paid 22,000

54146 ■ British Postmark Bulletin
Royal Mail
148 Old St.
London EC1V 9HQ, United Kingdom
Consumer magazine covering British postmarks and postmark collecting. **Founded:** 1971. **Freq:** Semimonthly. **Trim Size:** A5. **Key Personnel:** John Holman, Editor. **ISSN:** 0955-923X. **Subscription Rates:** 12.25 individuals 25 issues; 24.95 elsewhere outside the U.K. **Remarks:** Advertising not accepted. **URL:** http://www.royalmail.com/portal/stamps/content1?mediaId=32600683&catId=32300675. **Circ:** Paid 1,500

54147 ■ British Style
Scott Taylor Ltd.
Beacon House
2 Beacon Hill
London N7 9LY, United Kingdom
Ph: 44 20 76095100
Trade magazine covering fashion and style. **Freq:** Semiannual. **Print Method:** Digital Web. **Trim Size:** 210 x 297 mm. **Key Personnel:** John Taylor, Editor; Marie Scott, Publisher. **Subscription Rates:** 14 individuals; 20 out of country. **Remarks:** Accepts advertising. **URL:** http://www.savilerow-style.com/issue002/contact.htm. **Former name:** British Style. **Circ:** Non-paid 5,000

54148 ■ The British Theatre Directory
Richmond House Publishing Company Ltd.
70-76 Bell St.
Marylebone
London NW1 6SP, United Kingdom
Ph: 44 20 72249666
Fax: 44 20 72249688
Publisher E-mail: sales@rhpco.co.uk
Trade magazine covering theater suppliers and venues for the theatre and entertainment business in the UK. **Founded:** 1971. **Freq:** Annual. **Trim Size:** 135 x 210 mm. **ISSN:** 0306-4107. **Remarks:** Accepts advertising. **URL:** http://www.rhpco.co.uk. **Ad Rates:** BW: 775, 4C: 1,275. **Circ:** Paid 2,000

54149 ■ Brittle Star
PO Box 56108
London E17 0AY, United Kingdom
Publication E-mail: magazine@brittlestar.org.uk
Publisher E-mail: magazine@brittlestar.org.uk
Magazine containing unpublished and original poems, stories and articles. **Key Personnel:** Louisa Hooper, Editor; Jacqueline Gabbitas, Editor. **ISSN:** 1467-6230. **Subscription Rates:** 7 individuals 2 issues; 13 individuals 4 issues; 19 individuals 6 issues includes post and packing. **URL:** http://www.brittlestar.org.uk/.

54150 ■ Bronte Studies
Maney Publishing
1 Carlton House Ter.
London SW1Y 5AF, United Kingdom
Ph: 44 20 74517300
Fax: 44 20 74517307
Publisher E-mail: maney@maney.co.uk
Peer-reviewed journal covering Bronte family. **Subtitle:** Journal of the Bronte Society. **Founded:** 1895. **Freq:** 3/yr. **Trim Size:** 248 x 175 mm. **Key Personnel:** Robert Duckett, Editor, brontestudies@talk21.com; Amber Adams, Editor. **ISSN:** 1474-8932. **Subscription Rates:** 275 institutions UK, Europe, rest of world; US$452 institutions in U.S. **Remarks:** Accepts advertising. **URL:**

http://maney.co.uk/index.php/journals/bst/. **Formerly**: Bronte Society Transactions. **Ad Rates**: BW: 250. **Circ**: Paid 750

54151 ∎ Bubble Science, Engineering and Technology
Maney Publishing
1 Carlton House Ter.
London SW1Y 5AF, United Kingdom
Ph: 44 20 74517300
Fax: 44 20 74517307
Publisher E-mail: maney@maney.co.uk
Peer-reviewed journal covering the application of bubbles in various disciplines. **Freq**: Quarterly. **Key Personnel**: Prof. Mohan J. Edirisinghe, Editor, m.edirisinghe@ucl.ac.uk; Prof. Carlos Martinez, Co-Ed., cjmartinez@purdue.edu. **ISSN**: 1758-8960. **Subscription Rates**: 298 institutions, other countries; US$496 institutions in United States; 46 other countries; US$75 individuals in United States. **Remarks**: Accepts advertising. **URL**: http://maney.co.uk/index.php/journals/bub. **Circ**: (Not Reported)

54152 ∎ Building
The Builder Group PLC
Ludgate House
245 Blackfriars Rd.
London SE1 9UY, United Kingdom
Ph: 44 20 79215000
Publisher E-mail: building@cmpi.biz
Trade magazine covering the construction industry for architects, surveyors, contractors, engineers, and sub contractors. **Founded**: 1843. **Freq**: Weekly 49/yr. **Print Method**: Web Offset. **Trim Size**: 210 x 297 mm. **Key Personnel**: Denise Chevin, Editor, phone 44 20 75604150, denise.chevin@ubm.com; Alex Smith, Asst. Ed., alex.smith@ubm.com; Ed Sexton, Mktg. Mgr., phone 44 20 79553940, edward.sexton@ubm.com; Nina Wright, Dep. Ch. Exec., nina.wright@ubm.com. **Subscription Rates**: 139 individuals; 192 individuals Europe; airmail; 259 elsewhere airmail; 264 two years. **Remarks**: Advertising accepted; rates available upon request. **URL**: http://www.building.co.uk/. **Circ**: Combined ★23,961

54153 ∎ Building Research & Information
Routledge
Taylor & Francis Group Ltd.
c/o Richard Lorch, Ed.
43 St. George's Ave.
London N7 OAJ, United Kingdom
Publisher E-mail: webmaster.books@tandf.co.uk
Peer-reviewed journal publishing articles of the highest quality that are original, cutting-edge, well-detailed research and of significance to the international community. **Freq**: Bimonthly. **Key Personnel**: Richard Lorch, Editor; Sadi Assaf, Editorial Board; George Baird, Editorial Board. **ISSN**: 0961-3218. **Subscription Rates**: US$703 individuals; US$1,781 institutions online only; US$1,875 institutions print + online; 1,129 institutions print + online; 1,072 institutions online only; 428 individuals print only; EUR1,494 institutions print and online; EUR1,419 institutions online only; EUR560 individuals. **Remarks**: Advertising accepted; rates available upon request. **URL**: http://www.tandf.co.uk/journals/titles/09613218.asp. **Circ**: (Not Reported)

54154 ∎ Building Services Engineering Research and Technology
Sage Publications Ltd.
1 Oliver's Yard
55 City Rd.
London EC1Y 1SP, United Kingdom
Ph: 44 20 73248500
Fax: 44 20 73248600
Peer-reviewed journal covering engineering research and technology. **Founded**: July 1985. **Freq**: Quarterly. **Print Method**: Offset. **Trim Size**: 8.5 x 11. **Cols./Page**: 3. **Col. Width**: 14 picas. **Col. Depth**: 9 inches. **Key Personnel**: William H. Whalley, Managing Editor. **ISSN**: 0143-6244. **Subscription Rates**: 292 institutions print & e-access; 263 institutions e-access; 286 institutions print only; 78 individuals print & e-access; 79 institutions single print; 25 individuals single print. **Remarks**: Accepts advertising. **URL**: http://www.sagepub.co.uk/journalsProdDesc.nav?prodId=Journal201803. **Circ**: (Not Reported)

54155 ∎ Bulletin
Royal College of Speech and Language Therapists

2 White Hart Yard
London SE1 1NX, United Kingdom
Ph: 44 20 73781200
Publication E-mail: bulletin@rcslt.org
Publisher E-mail: info@rcslt.org
Publication covering speech and language. **Freq**: Monthly. **Key Personnel**: Kamini Gadhok, CEO. **ISSN**: 0953-6086. **URL**: http://www.rcslt.org/about/publications/overview. **Ad Rates**: 4C: 550. **Circ**: 11,500

54156 ∎ The Bulletin
Amateur Entomologists' Society
PO Box 8774
London SW7 5ZG, United Kingdom
Journal of the Amateur Entomologists Society. **Freq**: Bimonthly. **Key Personnel**: Dr. P. Wilkins, Editor; M. Hough, Editor. **ISSN**: 0266-836X. **Remarks**: Accepts advertising. **URL**: http://www.amentsoc.org/bulletin.htm. **Circ**: (Not Reported)

54157 ∎ Bulletin of the School of Oriental and African Studies
Cambridge University Press
c/o Elizabeth Gant, Editorial Off.
SOAS, University of London
Thornhaugh St., Russell Sq.
London WC1H 0XG, United Kingdom
Publication E-mail: bulletin@soas.ac.uk
Publisher E-mail: information@cambridge.org
Journal on Asia, Africa and the Near and Middle East, covering languages, cultures and civilizations of these regions from ancient times to the present, in connection with the School of Oriental and African Studies. **Key Personnel**: Elizabeth Gant, Editorial Off.; Dr. Theodore Proferes, Editor; Dr. M. Orwin, Editorial Board; Dr. Justin Watkins, Editorial Board. **ISSN**: 0041-977X. **Subscription Rates**: 172 institutions print and online; US$299 institutions print and online; 164 individuals online only; US$285 institutions online only. **Remarks**: Accepts display advertising. **URL**: http://journals.cambridge.org/action/displayJournal?jid=BSO. **Ad Rates**: BW: US$425. **Circ**: 900

54158 ∎ The Burlington Magazine
The Burlington Magazine Publication Ltd.
14-16 Duke's Rd.
London WC1H 9SZ, United Kingdom
Ph: 44 20 73881228
Fax: 44 20 73881229
Publisher E-mail: editorial@burlington.org.uk
Magazine featuring fine and decorative arts. **Founded**: 1903. **Freq**: Monthly. **Key Personnel**: Richard Shone, Editor, shone@burlington.org.uk; Kate Trevelyan, Mng. Dir., trevelyan@burlington.org.uk; Mark Scott, Advertising Dir., scott@burlington.org.uk. **Subscription Rates**: 229 individuals print and online; 366.40 two years; US$593 individuals; US$948.80 two years. **Remarks**: Accepts advertising. **URL**: http://www.burlington.org.uk/. **Circ**: (Not Reported)

54159 ∎ Business Strategy Review
John Wiley & Sons Inc.
Wiley-Blackwell
c/o Stuart Crainer, Ed.
London Business School
Regent's Park
London NW1 4SA, United Kingdom
Ph: 44 20 72625050
Fax: 44 20 77247875
General business publication. **Freq**: Quarterly. **Key Personnel**: Stuart Crainer, Editor, scrainer@london.edu; Len Waverman, Contributing Ed.; Rob Goffee, Contributing Ed.; George Yip, Contributing Ed.; Patrick Barwise, Contributing Ed.; Tim Ambler, Editorial Board; Julian Birkinshaw, Contributing Ed.; David Coen, Editorial Board; Chris Higson, Contributing Ed. **ISSN**: 0955-6419. **Subscription Rates**: US$70 individuals print + online; US$44 students; US$51 members AMBA/SPS; EUR70 individuals print + online; US$294 institutions print + online; US$256 institutions print, online; EUR325 institutions print + online; US$501 institutions, other countries print + online; EUR40 students; US$455 institutions, other countries print, online. **Remarks**: Accepts advertising. **URL**: http://www.wiley.com/bw/journal.asp?ref=0955-6419&site=1. **Circ**: (Not Reported)

54160 ∎ Business XL
Vitesse Media
Octavia House
50 Banner St.

London EC1Y 8ST, United Kingdom
Ph: 44 20 72507010
Fax: 44 20 72507011
Publisher E-mail: info@vitessemedia.co.uk
Magazine for entrepreneurs. **Key Personnel**: Rebecca Borrows, Sales Mgr., phone 44 20 72507028, rebecca.borrows@vitessemedia.co.uk; Marc Barber, Editor. **Remarks**: Accepts advertising. **URL**: http://www.vitessemedia.co.uk/publications-and-research/entrepreneurs/259327/business-xl-magazine.thtml; http://www.businessxl.co.uk/. **Circ**: (Not Reported)

54161 ∎ Buy-Side Technology
Incisive Media Limited
Haymarket House
28-29 Haymarket
London SW1Y 4RX, United Kingdom
Ph: 44 870 2408859
Fax: 44 207 4849797
Publisher E-mail: customerservices@incisivemedia.com
Business and Technology magazine. **Subtitle**: Trading technology for investment managers. **Freq**: Monthly. **Key Personnel**: Victor Anderson, Editor-in-Chief, phone 44 20 74849799, vanderson@riskwaters.com; Lee Hurt, Publisher. **Subscription Rates**: 595 individuals; EUR893 individuals; US$995 other countries. **Remarks**: Accepts advertising. **URL**: http://www.waterstechnology.com/buy-side-technology. **Circ**: (Not Reported)

54162 ∎ Byzantine and Modern Greek Studies
Maney Publishing
1 Carlton House Ter.
London SW1Y 5AF, United Kingdom
Ph: 44 20 74517300
Fax: 44 20 74517307
Publisher E-mail: maney@maney.co.uk
Peer-reviewed journal covering history, literature, and social anthropology of Byzantine and Modern Greek. **Founded**: 1975. **Freq**: Semiannual. **Key Personnel**: Peter Mackridge, Editor; Dr. Ruth Macrides, Editor. **ISSN**: 0307-0131. **Subscription Rates**: 46 other countries; US$84 individuals; 160 institutions, other countries; US$292 institutions. **Remarks**: Accepts advertising. **URL**: http://maney.co.uk/index.php/journals/byz/. **Ad Rates**: BW: 180. **Circ**: (Not Reported)

54163 ∎ Cabinet Maker
CMP Information Ltd.
Ludgate House
245 Blackfriars Rd.
London SE1 9UY, United Kingdom
Ph: 44 20 79215000
Publication E-mail: chris@cabinet-maker.co.uk
Trade magazine covering the domestic furniture and furnishings markets in the UK. **Founded**: 1880. **Freq**: 50/yr. **Print Method**: Offset Litho. **Trim Size**: 210 x 297 mm. **Key Personnel**: Edward Cook, Contaot, ed@cabinet-maker.co.uk; Adrian Sell, Gp. Sales Mgr., adrian@cabinet-maker.co.uk. **ISSN**: 0007-9278. **Subscription Rates**: 93.75 individuals; 165 other countries. **Remarks**: Accepts advertising. **URL**: http://www.cabinet-maker.co.uk/. **Circ**: Combined 4,634

54164 ∎ Cable & Satellite International
Perspective Publishing
3 London Wall Bldgs., 6th Fl.
London EC2M 5PD, United Kingdom
Ph: 44 20 75622400
Fax: 44 20 73742701
Magazine for cable, satellite and broadcast industries. **Founded**: 1999. **Freq**: Bimonthly. **Trim Size**: 210 x 297 mm. **Key Personnel**: Tiro Bestonso, Advertising Mgr., phone 44 20 75622427, fax 44 20 73742701, tiro.bestonso@csimagazine.com; Goran Nastic, Editor, phone 44 20 75622401, goran.nastic@csimagazine.com; Joel Whitefoot, Contact, joel.whitefoot@csimagazine.com. **Subscription Rates**: 68 individuals. **Remarks**: Accepts advertising. **URL**: http://www.cable-satellite.com. **Ad Rates**: 4C: 3,142. **Circ**: △10,000

54165 ∎ CAD User
Business and Technical Communications Ltd.
35 Station Sq.
Petts Wood
London BR5 1LZ, United Kingdom
Ph: 44 16 89616000
Fax: 44 16 89826622
Publication focusing on promotion and implementation of mechanical design products in areas ranging from

Circulation: ★ = ABC; △ = BPA; ♦ = CAC; • = CCAB; ❏ = VAC; ⊕ = PO Statement; ‡ = Publisher's Report; Boldface figures = sworn; Light figures = estimated.

Gale Directory of Publications & Broadcast Media/147th Ed.   5695

analysis, solid modeling, document management, visualizations, and rapid prototyping. **Freq:** 12/yr. **Trim Size:** 210 x 297 mm. **Key Personnel:** David Chadwick, Editor; Abby Penn, Production Mgr., abby.penn@btc.co.uk. **Subscription Rates:** 44 individuals U.K.; 60 individuals Europe; 60 other countries surface; 77 other countries airmail; 77 two years U.K.; 107 two years Europe & rest of world, surface; 143 two years rest of world, airmail; 109 individuals U.K., 3 years; 153 individuals Europe & rest of world, 3 years; 197 individuals rest of world; airmail, 3 years. **Remarks:** Accepts advertising. **URL:** http://www.caduser.com/. **Ad Rates:** 4C: 1,850. **Circ:** 13,000

54166 ■ Cage and Aviary Birds
IPC Media Ltd.
Blue Fin Bldg.
110 Southwark St.
London SE1 0SU, United Kingdom
Ph: 44 203 1485000
Magazine featuring aviculture. **Founded:** 1902. **Freq:** Weekly. **Key Personnel:** Hazel Eccles, Publisher, phone 44 20 31484312, hazel_eccles@ipcmedia.com; Kim Forrester, Editor, phone 44 20 31484171; kim_forrester@ipcmedia.com; Lee Morris, Advertising Mgr., phone 44 20 31482517, lee_morris@ipcmedia.com. **Subscription Rates:** US$143 individuals; US$281.20 two years; 54.99 individuals; 104.99 two years. **Remarks:** Accepts advertising. **URL:** http://www.ipcmedia.com/brands/cagebirds/. **Circ:** ★15,185

54167 ■ Call Center Magazine
United Business Media
245 Blackfriars Rd.
London SE1 9UY, United Kingdom
Ph: 44 20 79215000
Magazine featuring tools and techniques for customer service, help desk, sales, and support staff. **Founded:** 1988. **Freq:** Monthly. **Print Method:** Web offset. **Trim Size:** 7 3/4 x 10 1/2. **Key Personnel:** Max Steiger, Advertising Dir., msteiger@cmp.com; Keith Dawson, Editorial Dir., kdawson@cmp.com; Ruthann Fisher, Publisher, rfisher@cmp.com. **ISSN:** 1064-5543. **Remarks:** Accepts advertising. **URL:** http://www.callcentermagazine.com. **Ad Rates:** BW: 7,755. **Circ:** (Not Reported)

54168 ■ CallSign
Taxi Trade Promotions Ltd.
429-431 Caledonian Rd.
London N7 9BG, United Kingdom
Ph: 44 20 77005681
Fax: 44 20 77005684
Publisher E-mail: enquiries@knowledge-point.co.uk
Trade magazine for taxi drivers in London. **Founded:** 1963. **Trim Size:** A4. **Cols./Page:** 3. **Key Personnel:** Alan Fisher, Editor, callsignmag@aol.com. **Subscription Rates:** 12.95 individuals. **Remarks:** Accepts advertising. **URL:** http://www.dac-callsign.com/. **Circ:** Controlled 2,000

54169 ■ Camden Gazette
Archant Regional Ltd.
100A Avenue Rd.
London NW3 3HF, United Kingdom
Ph: 44 20 74336240
Publisher E-mail: sandra.roantree@archant.co.uk
Local community newspaper. **Founded:** May 4, 2005. **Freq:** Weekly (Wed.). **Key Personnel:** Rob Bleaney, Asst. Ed. **Remarks:** Accepts advertising. **URL:** http://www.camdengazette.co.uk/home. **Circ:** (Not Reported)

54170 ■ Campaign
Haymarket Publishing Ltd.
174 Hammersmith Rd.
London W6 7JP, United Kingdom
Ph: 44 20 82674210
Publisher E-mail: info@haymarket.com
Publication covering advertising, marketing and public relations. **Freq:** 49/yr. **Key Personnel:** Claire Beale, Editor, phone 44 20 82674893, claire.beale@haymarket.com; Ian Darby, Dep. Ed., ian.darby@haymaket.com; Suzzane Bidlake, Assoc. Ed., phone 44 20 82674744, john.tylee@haymarket.com. **ISSN:** 0008-2309. **Subscription Rates:** 159 individuals; 286 two years; 382 individuals three years. **URL:** http://www.brandrepublic.com/campaign/.

54171 ■ Cancer Cell International
BioMed Central Ltd.

236 Gray's Inn Rd., Fl. 6
34-42 Cleveland St.
London WC1X 8HL; United Kingdom
Ph: 44 20 31922000
Fax: 44 20 31922010
Publisher E-mail: info@biomedcentral.com
Online journal covering all aspects of cancer cell biology. **Key Personnel:** Denys Wheatley, Editor-in-Chief, phone 44 1467 670280, fax 44 1467 670280; Bruce Baguley, Assoc. Ed., b.baguley@auckland.ac.nz; Yoji Nagashima, Assoc. Ed., ynagas@med.yokohama-cu.ac.jp; Dr. Ivan Cameron, Assoc. Ed., cameron@uthscsa.edu; Dr. Michele Caraglia, Assoc. Ed., phone 39 81 5903595, fax 39 81 5903813; Dr. Ruy Tchao, Assoc. Ed., r.tchao@usip.edu; Tim Crook, Assoc. Ed.; Arthur Pardee, Assoc. Ed.; Bernard Perbal, Assoc. Ed. **ISSN:** 1475-2867. **Subscription Rates:** US$22 individuals. **Remarks:** Accepts advertising. **URL:** http://www.cancerci.com. **Circ:** (Not Reported)

54172 ■ Candid
Luxury Publishing Limited
5 Jubilee Pl.
Chelsea
London SW3 3TD, United Kingdom
Ph: 44 20 75912900
Fax: 44 20 75912929
Publisher E-mail: info@luxurypublishing.com
Lifestyle magazine featuring homes, furnitures, and interior designs. **Founded:** Mar. 2007. **Freq:** Semiannual. **Trim Size:** 280 x 280 mm. **Key Personnel:** Lucia Van Der Post, Editor. **Remarks:** Accepts advertising. **URL:** http://www.luxurypublishing.co.uk/. **Circ:** 8,000

54173 ■ CANS Digest of Social Legislation
Citizens Advice Notes Service Trust
89 Albert Embankment
London SE1 7TP, United Kingdom
Legal journal covering social legislation in England, Wales and Scotland. **Founded:** Sept. 1939. **Freq:** Monthly 8/yr. **Trim Size:** A5. **Cols./Page:** 2. **Key Personnel:** Robert Jack, Legal Ed.; Joanne Murray, Dep. Legal Ed.; Elizabeth Crampton, Editor; Flavia Wade, Consulting Ed.; Alison Morley, Editor; Mercedes Yasruddin, Editor. **ISSN:** 1747-6240. **Remarks:** Accepts advertising. **URL:** http://www.cans.org.uk/index.php?id=8295399; http://www.cans.org.uk/index.php?id=127. **Circ:** 1,831

54174 ■ Capital & Class
Conference of Socialist Economists
25 Horsell Rd.
London N5 1XL, United Kingdom
Publisher E-mail: cseoffice@gn.apc.org
Publication covering progressive economics and social sciences. **Founded:** 1977. **Freq:** 3/yr. **Print Method:** Perfect Bound. **Trim Size:** A5. **Key Personnel:** Owen North, Managing Editor; Adam Morton, Book Review Ed. **ISSN:** 0309-8168. **Subscription Rates:** US$52 other countries; US$28 other countries student/unwaged; US$210 institutions, other countries. **Remarks:** Accepts advertising. **URL:** http://www.cseweb.org.uk. **Ad Rates:** BW: EUR200. **Circ:** 1,100

54175 ■ Carbon Balance and Management
BioMed Central Ltd.
236 Gray's Inn Rd., Fl. 6
34-42 Cleveland St.
London WC1X 8HL, United Kingdom
Ph: 44 20 31922000
Fax: 44 20 31922010
Publication E-mail: editorialteam@cbmjournal.com
Publisher E-mail: info@biomedcentral.com
Journal focusing on the understanding of global carbon cycle. **Key Personnel:** Dr. Georgii Alexandrov, Editor-in-Chief, g.alexandrov@nies.go.jp; Prof. Robert Dickinson, Editor-in-Chief; Prof. Takehisa Oikawa, Editor-in-Chief. **ISSN:** 1750-0680. **URL:** http://www.cbmjournal.com/home.

54176 ■ Cardiology International
Greycoat Publishing Ltd.
148 Buckingham Palace Rd.
Kensington
London SW1W 9TR, United Kingdom
Ph: 44 20 77307995
Fax: 44 20 77303884
Publisher E-mail: mail@greycoatpublishing.co.uk
Journal covering research developments on cardiology.

Freq: Quarterly March, June, September and December. **Trim Size:** 210 x 297 mm. **Key Personnel:** Dr. Giuseppe Sangiorgi, Editor; Dr. Goran Stankovic, Editor. **ISSN:** 1468-8581. **Subscription Rates:** 40 individuals; 50 individuals Europe; 65 other countries; 84 institutions; 105 institutions Europe; 135 institutions, other countries. **Remarks:** Accepts advertising. **URL:** http://www.greycoatpublishing.co.uk/content/Journals/CI.asp. **Circ:** (Not Reported)

54177 ■ Cardiology in the Young
Cambridge University Press
c/o Prof. Robert H. Anderson, Emeritus Founding Ed.
60 Earlsfield Rd.
London SW18 3DN, United Kingdom
Publisher E-mail: information@cambridge.org
Journal covering cardiovascular issues affecting the young, and the older patient suffering the sequels of congenital heart disease, or other cardiac diseases acquired in childhood. **Key Personnel:** Prof. Robert H. Anderson, Emeritus Founding Ed.; Prof. Anton Becker, Founding Ed.; Dr. Maurice Beghetti, International Editorial Board; Prof. Lindsey Allan, Editorial Board; Dr. Giancarlo Crupi, Founding Ed.; Dr. Edward Baker, Editor-in-Chief, ctyeditor@cambridge.org; Dr. William G. Henry, International Ed.; Dr. Andrew Redington, International Editorial Board; Dr. Tom Karl, International Editorial Board. **ISSN:** 1047-9511. **Subscription Rates:** 658 institutions online and print; US$1,138 institutions online and print; 546 institutions online only; US$1,019 institutions online only; 338 individuals online and print; US$582 individuals online and print. **Remarks:** Accepts advertising. **URL:** http://journals.cambridge.org/action/displayJournal?jid=CTY. **Ad Rates:** BW: US$850, 4C: US$1,210. **Circ:** (Not Reported)

54178 ■ Cardiovascular Diabetology
BioMed Central Ltd.
236 Gray's Inn Rd., Fl. 6
34-42 Cleveland St.
London WC1X 8HL, United Kingdom
Ph: 44 20 31922000
Fax: 44 20 31922010
Publisher E-mail: info@biomedcentral.com
Online journal covering all aspects of the diabetes/cardiovascular interrelationship and the dysmetabolic syndrome; this includes genetic, experimental, clinical, pharmacological, epidemiological, molecular biology and laboratory research. **Key Personnel:** Prof. Enrique Z. Fisman, Editor-in-Chief, zfisman@post.tau.ac.il; Dr. Alexander Tenenbaum, Editor-in-Chief, altenen@post.tau.ac.il; Prof. Yehuda Adler, MD, Editorial Board. **ISSN:** 1475-2840. **Remarks:** Accepts advertising. **URL:** http://www.cardiab.com/. **Circ:** (Not Reported)

54179 ■ Cardiovascular Ultrasound
BioMed Central Ltd.
236 Gray's Inn Rd., Fl. 6
34-42 Cleveland St.
London WC1X 8HL, United Kingdom
Ph: 44 20 31922000
Fax: 44 20 31922010
Publisher E-mail: info@biomedcentral.com
Journal covering clinical, technological, experimental, biological, and molecular aspects of ultrasound applications in cardiovascular physiology and disease. **Key Personnel:** Dr. Eugenio Picano, Editor-in-Chief, picano@ifc.cnr.it; Dr. Rosa Sicari, Dep. Ed.; Dr. Lauro Cortigiani, Editorial Board. **ISSN:** 1476-7120. **URL:** http://www.cardiovascularultrasound.com.

54180 ■ CARF
BM PO Box 8784
London WC1N 3XX, United Kingdom
Ph: 44 20 78371450
Publisher E-mail: info@carf.org.uk
Magazine covering news and commentary on the issue of racism. **Subtitle:** Campaign Against Racism' & Fascism. **URL:** http://www.irr.org.uk/carf/about.html.

54181 ■ Caribbean Times
Ethnic Media Group
65 Whitechapel Rd., Unit 2
London E1 1DU, United Kingdom
Ph: 44 20 76502000
Fax: 44 20 76502001
Publisher E-mail: general@ethnicmedia.co.uk
Newspaper covering news and information for a Black and Asian audience in Britain. **Founded:** 1981. **Freq:** Weekly. **Cols./Page:** 8. **Col. Width:** 30 millimeters. **Key**

Personnel: Wayne Bower, Mng. Dir.; Mike Chinnery, Circulation Mgr. **Remarks:** Accepts advertising. **URL:** http://www.caribbeantimes.co.uk/. **Circ:** (Not Reported)

54182 ■ Caring Times
Hawker Publications
Culvert House
Culvert Rd.
London SW11 5DH, United Kingdom
Ph: 44 20 77202108
Fax: 44 20 74983023
Publisher E-mail: suec@hawkerpublications.com
Trade magazine for management in the long term care field. **Subtitle:** The Management Magazine for the Long Term Care Sector, **Founded:** 1988. **Freq:** Monthly. **Trim Size:** 238 x 330 mm. **Cols./Page:** 4. **Col. Width:** 49 millimeters. **Key Personnel:** Geoff Hodgson, Editor, caringtimes@oxpound.co.uk; Dr. Richard Hawkins, Editor-in-Chief; Caroline Bowern, Advertising Mgr., caroline@hawkerpublications.com. **Subscription Rates:** 70 individuals. **Remarks:** Advertising accepted; rates available upon request. **URL:** http://www.carehome.co.uk/supplier.cfm/searchazref/22531. **Circ:** Controlled *16,967

54183 ■ Carpet & Flooring Retail (CFR)
CMP Information Ltd.
Ludgate House
245 Blackfriars Rd.
London SE1 9UY, United Kingdom
Ph: 44 20 79215000
Publication E-mail: info@struktur.co.uk
Trade journal covering domestic and soft contract carpet and floorcoverings industry, including retail, manufacturing, wholesaling, and related fields. **Founded:** 1946. **Freq:** Monthly. **Print Method:** Sheetfed Offset Litho. **Trim Size:** 210 x 297 mm. **ISSN:** 1471-8162. **Subscription Rates:** US$75 individuals. **Remarks:** Accepts advertising. **URL:** http://www.struktur-design.com/magazines/cfr.html. **Formerly:** Carpet and Floorcoverings Review. **Ad Rates:** BW: 109, 4C: 1,507. **Circ:** Combined 4,045

54184 ■ Cartier International Polo @MAG
Luxury Publishing Limited
5 Jubilee Pl.
Chelsea
London SW3 3TD, United Kingdom
Ph: 44 20 75912900
Fax: 44 20 75912929
Publisher E-mail: info@luxurypublishing.com
Magazine featuring travel, luxury goods and fashion. **Freq:** Annual. **Trim Size:** 210 x 297 mm. **Key Personnel:** Martine Montgomery, Editor. **Remarks:** Accepts advertising. **URL:** http://www.luxurypublishing.co.uk/. **Circ:** 10,000

54185 ■ The Cartographic Journal
British Cartographic Society
c/o Royal Geographic Society
1 Kensington Gore
London SW9 2AR, United Kingdom
Ph: 44 115 9328684
Fax: 44 115 9328684
Publication E-mail: kon.field@kingcton.ac.uk
Publisher E-mail: admin@cartography.org.uk
Journal covering cartography. **Freq:** Quarterly June, September, and December. **Key Personnel:** Zhilin Li, Regional Commissioning Ed.; William Cartwright, Regional Commissioning Ed.; David Forrest, Editorial Board; Alexander Kent, Asst. Ed.; Giles Darkes, Editorial Board; Ute Dymon, Regional Commissioning Ed.; Elri Liebenberg, Regional Commissioning Ed.; Menno-Jan Kraak, Regional Commissioning Ed.; Kenneth Field, Editor. **ISSN:** 0008-7041. **Subscription Rates:** 348 institutions print and online; 328 institutions online only; US$634 institutions print and online; US$598 institutions online only; 158 institutions, other countries print and online; 148 institutions online only. **Remarks:** Advertising accepted; rates available upon request. **URL:** http://www.cartography.org.uk/default.asp?contentID=840; http://maney.co.uk/index.php/journals/caj/. **Circ:** 1,200

54186 ■ Cas London
Afro Universe Media
25B Admiral St.
London SE8 4HY, United Kingdom
Ph: 44 20 86946680

Fax: 44 20 86922454
Magazine offering a connection to the talent world, creativity and a place to connect with people with the same interests. **Freq:** Monthly. **Subscription Rates:** 18 individuals 6 issues; 36 individuals; 72 two years. **Remarks:** Accepts advertising. **URL:** http://www.caslondon.com/. **Circ:** (Not Reported)

54187 ■ CASEpapers
Suntory and Toyota International Centres for Economics and Related Disciplines
London School of Economics & Political Science
Houghton St.
London WC2A 2AE, United Kingdom
Ph: 44 20 79556699
Fax: 44 20 79556951
Publisher E-mail: sticerd@lse.ac.uk
Journal covering research by the members of Suntory and Toyota International Centers for Economics and Related Disciplines. **URL:** http://sticerd.lse.ac.uk/case/publications/papers.asp.

54188 ■ CBeebies Weekly Magazine
BBC Worldwide Publishing Ltd.
Media Centre
201 Wood Ln.
London W12 7TQ, United Kingdom
Ph: 44 20 84332000
Fax: 44 20 87490538
Publication E-mail: cbeebiesweekly@bbc.co.uk
Magazine featuring learning activities for pre-schoolers. **Subtitle:** Weekly fun for little learners!. **Freq:** Weekly. **Key Personnel:** Steph Cooper, Editor. **Subscription Rates:** 1.99 single issue; 17.75 individuals 3 months; 76 individuals 51 issues. **URL:** http://www.cbeebiesmagazine.com/; http://www.bbcmagazines.com/content/magazines/cbeebiesweeklymagazine/.

54189 ■ CCTV Today
United Business Media
245 Blackfriars Rd.
London SE1 9UY, United Kingdom
Ph: 44 20 79215000
Trade magazine covering security and non-security CCTV surveillance for installers and end-users. **Founded:** 1994. **Freq:** Bimonthly. **Key Personnel:** Anthony Hildebrand, Editor; Jonathan Collins, Publisher, jonathan.collins@ubm.com. **ISSN:** 1352-2272. **Subscription Rates:** 40 individuals; 48 other countries. **Remarks:** Accepts advertising. **URL:** http://www.info4security.com/sectionindex.asp?navcode=98. **Circ:** Paid ‡8,000

54190 ■ Cell Communication and Signaling
BioMed Central Ltd.
236 Gray's Inn Rd., Fl. 6
34-42 Cleveland St.
London WC1X 8HL, United Kingdom
Ph: 44 20 31922000
Fax: 44 20 31922010
Publisher E-mail: info@biomedcentral.com
Online journal covering all aspects of receptors, ligands, and other biomolecules participating in cellular signaling pathways. **Key Personnel:** Dr. Stephan Feller, PhD, Editor-in-Chief, cellsignal@imm.ox.ac.uk; Prof. Ralf Hass, PhD, Assoc. Ed.; Prof. Ottmar Janssen, PhD, Assoc. Ed.; Oresto Acuto, Editorial Board; Peter Angel, Editorial Board; Sebastian Arnold, Editorial Board. **ISSN:** 1478-811X. **Remarks:** Accepts advertising. **URL:** http://www.biosignaling.com/home/. **Circ:** (Not Reported)

54191 ■ Cell Death & Differentiation
Nature Publishing Group
The Macmillan Bldg.
4 Crinan St.
London N1 9XW, United Kingdom
Ph: 44 20 78334000
Fax: 44 20 78434640
Peer-review journal dealing with cell biology, molecular biology and biochemistry of cell death and disease in connection with Istituto Dermopatico dell'Immacolata. **Freq:** Monthly. **Key Personnel:** Gerry Melino, Editor-in-Chief, phone 39 6 72596976, fax 39 6 72596977, cell. death.differ@uniroma2.it. **ISSN:** 1350-9047. **Subscription Rates:** US$433 individuals combined print and online; EUR403 individuals combined print and online, Europe; 68,800¥ individuals combined print and online, Japan; 259 other countries combined print and online; US$395 individuals online only; EUR362 individuals online only, Europe; 62,300¥ individuals online only;

233.47 other countries online only. **Remarks:** Advertising accepted; rates available upon request. **URL:** http://www.nature.com/cdd/index.html. **Circ:** (Not Reported)

54192 ■ Cell Proliferation
John Wiley & Sons Inc.
Wiley-Blackwell
c/o Prof. C. Sarraf, Ed.
Dept. of Biomedical Sciences
University of Westminster, School of Biosciences
115 New Cavendish St.
London W1W 6UW, United Kingdom
Ph: 44 20 79115000
Fax: 44 20 79115087
Journal focusing on studies of all aspects of cell proliferation and differentiation in normal and abnormal states; control systems and mechanisms operating at inter- and intracellular, molecular and genetic levels; modification by and interactions with chemical and physical agents; mathematical modelling; and the development of new techniques. **Freq:** Bimonthly. **Key Personnel:** Prof. C. Sarraf, Editor; Z. Darzynkiewicz, North American Ed., phone 914347-2801, fax 914347-2804. **ISSN:** 0960-7722. **Subscription Rates:** US$353 individuals print + online; EUR279 individuals print + online (Euro zone); 185 individuals print + online (U.K. and non Euro zone); 210 other countries print + online; US$150 members print + online; EUR135 members print + online (Euro zone); 90 members print + online (U.K. and non Euro zone); US$2,223 institutions print + online; US$2,021 institutions print or online; US$2,595 institutions, other countries print + online. **Remarks:** Accepts advertising. **URL:** http://www.wiley.com/bw/journal.asp?ref=0960-7722&site=1. **Circ:** (Not Reported)

54193 ■ Central Europe
Maney Publishing
1 Carlton House Ter.
London SW1Y 5AF, United Kingdom
Ph: 44 20 74517300
Fax: 44 20 74517307
Publisher E-mail: maney@maney.co.uk
Peer-reviewed journal publishing original research articles on the history, languages, literature, political culture, music, arts and society of those lands once part of the Habsburg Monarchy and Poland-Lithuania from the Middle Ages to the present. **Freq:** Semiannual. **Key Personnel:** Prof. Richard Butterwick, Editor, r.butterwick@ssees.ucl.ac.uk; Angus Walker, Reviews Ed. **ISSN:** 1479-0963. **Subscription Rates:** 148 institutions, other countries; US$284 institutions; 38 other countries; US$76 individuals. **Remarks:** Accepts advertising. **URL:** http://maney.co.uk/index.php/journals/ceu/. **Circ:** (Not Reported)

54194 ■ Central Europe Monitor
Business Monitor International Ltd.
Mermaid House
2 Puddle Dock
London EC4V 3DS, United Kingdom
Ph: 44 20 72480468
Fax: 44 20 72480467
Publisher E-mail: subs@businessmonitor.com
Journal with country-by-country analyses, hard-to-find data, and authoritative 24-month forecasts covering government, economy, finance and the business environment. **Freq:** Monthly. **Subscription Rates:** US$765 individuals print & electronic; 480 individuals print & electronic; EUR570 individuals print & electronic; US$1,170 individuals print & electronic; 690 individuals print & electronic; EUR920 individuals print & electronic; US$1,395 individuals print & electronic; 870 individuals print & electronic; EUR1,195 individuals print & electronic. **URL:** http://www.emergingeuropemonitor.com/file/7537/centraleuropebalticstates.html.

54195 ■ Ceramic Review
Ceramic Review Publishing Ltd.
25 Fouberts Pl.
London W1F 7QF, United Kingdom
Ph: 44 20 74393377
Fax: 44 20 72879954
Trade magazine covering ceramics worldwide. **Subtitle:** The International Magazine of Ceramic Art and Craft. **Freq:** Bimonthly. **Print Method:** Offset. **Trim Size:** 300 x 220 mm. **Key Personnel:** Ben Eldridge, Production Ed., beneldridge@ceramicreview.com; Natasha Cawley, Dep. Ed., natashacawley@ceramicreview.com; Molly Davies, Contact, accounts@ceramicreview.com; Amelia Lawrence, Contact, subscriptions@ceramicreview.com; Paul Cuthill, Contact, advertising@ceramicreview.com; Bonnie Kemske, Editor, emmanuelcooper@

Circulation: ★ = ABC; △ = BPA; ◆ = CAC; • = CCAB; ❑ = VAC; ⊕ = PO Statement; ‡ = Publisher's Report; Boldface figures = sworn; Light figures = estimated.

Gale Directory of Publications & Broadcast Media/147th Ed.   5697

ceramicreview.com. **ISSN:** 0144-1825. **Subscription Rates:** 36 individuals; 42 out of country; 32 students; 32 members; 67 two years; 76 out of country two years. **Remarks:** Accepts advertising. **URL:** http://www. ceramicreview.com. **Ad Rates:** GLR: 15, BW: 775, 4C: 960. **Circ:** Paid 8,800

54196 ■ Cerebrospinal Fluid Research
BioMed Central Ltd.
236 Gray's Inn Rd., Fl. 6
34-42 Cleveland St.
London WC1X 8HL, United Kingdom
Ph: 44 20 31922000
Fax: 44 20 31922010
Publisher E-mail: info@biomedcentral.com
Online journal coveringall aspects of cerebrospinal fluid in health and disease. **Key Personnel:** Dr. Hazel C. Jones, Editor-in-Chief, hjones@ufl.edu; Ian Pople, Dep. Ed., ikpople@doctors.org.uk; Conrad E. Johnson, Assoc. Ed.; Prof. Miles Johnston, Dep. Ed.; Dr. Anthony M. Avellino, Edltorial Board; Dr. Peter Brown, Editorial Board. **ISSN:** 1743-8454. **Remarks:** Accepts advertising. **URL:** http://www.cerebrospinalfluidresearch.com/home/. **Circ:** (Not Reported)

54197 ■ Charity Times
Perspective Publishing
3 London Wall Bldgs., 6th Fl.
London EC2M 5PD, United Kingdom
Ph: 44 20 75622400
Fax: 44 20 73742701
Management and business magazine for United Kingdom non-profit professionals. **Freq:** 8/yr. **Trim Size:** 210 x 297 mm. **Key Personnel:** Andrew Holt, Editor, phone 44 20 75622411, andrew.holt@charitytimes.com; Cerys McLean, Advertising Mgr., phone 44 20 75622610, cerys.mclean@charitytimes.com. **Subscription Rates:** 119 individuals UK; 79 individuals; 132 elsewhere. **Remarks:** Accepts advertising. **URL:** http://www. charitytimes.com/. **Circ:** (Not Reported)

54198 ■ Charlie and Lola
BBC Worldwide Publishing Ltd.
Media Centre
201 Wood Ln.
London W12 7TQ, United Kingdom
Ph: 44 20 84332000
Fax: 44 20 87490538
Arts and crafts magazine for children. **Subtitle:** Lots to scribble, make and do!. **Freq:** every four weeks. **Subscription Rates:** 2.50 single issue. **URL:** http://www. bbcmagazines.com/content/magazines/charlieandlola/.

54199 ■ Chartered Secretary
Institute of Chartered Secretaries and Administrators
16 Park Cres.
London W1B 1AH, United Kingdom
Ph: 44 20 75804741
Fax: 44 20 73231132
Publisher E-mail: info@icsa.co.uk
Professional magazine covering management issues, corporate governance and best practices. **Freq:** Monthly. **Print Method:** Web. **Trim Size:** All. **Key Personnel:** Gareth Pearce, Asst. Ed., phone 44 20 76127038, gpearce@icsa.co.uk; Rachael Johnson, Editor, phone 44 20 76127094, rjohnson@icsa.co.uk. **ISSN:** 1363-5905. **Subscription Rates:** 80 nonmembers U.K.; 100 out of country; 140 two years; 185 two years other countries. **Remarks:** Accepts advertising. **URL:** http:// www.charteredsecretary.net/. **Circ:** Combined 20,057

54200 ■ Chat - It's Fate
IPC Media Ltd.
Blue Fin Bldg.
110 Southwark St.
London SE1 0SU, United Kingdom
Ph: 44 203 1485000
Psychic magazine for women. **Freq:** Monthly. **Key Personnel:** Angela O'Farrell, Publishing Dir., phone 44 20 31485711, angela_o'farrell@ipcmedia.com; Mary Bryce, Editor, phone 44 20 31486179, mary_bryce@ipcmedia. com; Richard Smith, Advertising Mgr., phone 44 20 31483678, richard_smith@ipcmedia.com. **Subscription Rates:** 34.99 two years; 19.99 individuals. **Remarks:** Accepts advertising. **URL:** http://www.ipcmedia.com/ brands/chatitsfate/. **Circ:** (Not Reported)

54201 ■ Chemistry & Industry
Society of Chemical Industry
Publications Dept.

14-15 Belgrave Sq.
London SW1X 8PS, United Kingdom
Ph: 44 20 75981500
Fax: 44 20 75981545
Publication E-mail: editor@soci.org
Publisher E-mail: secretariat@soci.org
Professional magazine covering science and business issues in the chemical biotech, pharma fine chemicals, life science and related industries worldwide. **Founded:** 1888. **Freq:** Semimonthly. **Print Method:** Sheetfed Offset. **Key Personnel:** Laura Murray, Contact, laura. murray@tenalpspublishing.com; Joseph Fernandes, Editorial Production, ciproduction@tenalpspublishing. com; Neil Eisberg, Editor, cieditor@tenalpspublishing. com. **ISSN:** 0009-3068. **Subscription Rates:** 1,000 institutions for US, Canada, Mexico; 515 institutions rest of the world; EUR700 institutions rest of the world; 220 individuals for US, Canada, Mexico; 110 individuals print; EUR150 individuals print. **Remarks:** Accepts advertising. **URL:** http://www.chemind.org/CI/index.jsp. **Ad Rates:** BW: 3,550, 4C: 3,040. **Circ:** Combined 9,824

54202 ■ Chess
Chess & Bridge Ltd.
369 Euston Rd.
London NW1 3AR, United Kingdom
Ph: 44 20 73882404
Fax: 44 20 73882407
Publication E-mail: info@chess.co.uk
Publisher E-mail: info@chess.co.uk
Consumer magazine covering chess. **Freq:** Monthly. **Trim Size:** A4. **Subscription Rates:** 39.95 individuals 1st time UK subscribers; 69.95 two years; 49.95 individuals Europe; 89.95 two years Europe; US$80 U.S. and Canada; US$150 U.S. and Canada two years; 60 elsewhere airmail; 110 elsewhere 2 years, airmail; 3.95 single issue; US$7 U.S. single issue. **URL:** http://www. chesscenter.com.

54203 ■ Child Language and Teaching Therapy
Sage Publications Ltd.
1 Oliver's Yard
55 City Rd.
London EC1Y 1SP, United Kingdom
Ph: 44 20 73248500
Fax: 44 20 73248600
Peer-reviewed journal covering the field of children's spoken and written language needs. **Freq:** 3/yr. **Key Personnel:** Judy Clegg, Editor; Maggie Vance, Editor; John Parrott, Book Review Ed. **ISSN:** 0265-6590. **Subscription Rates:** 498 institutions print & e-access; 448 institutions e-access; 488 institutions print only; 118 individuals print & e-access; 179 institutions single print; 51 individuals single print. **URL:** http://www.sagepub. com/journalsProdDesc.nav?prodId=Journal201804.

54204 ■ Childhood
Sage Publications Ltd.
1 Oliver's Yard
55 City Rd.
London EC1Y 1SP, United Kingdom
Ph: 44 20 73248500
Fax: 44 20 73248600
Peer-reviewed journal covering research related to children in contemporary society worldwide. **Founded:** 1994. **Freq:** Quarterly February - May - August - November. **Key Personnel:** Leena Alanen, Editor; Johanna Mierendorff, Review Ed.; Karin Ekberg, Managing Editor; Virginia Morrow, Editor; Olga Nieuwenhuys, Editor; Daniel Thomas Cook, Editor. **ISSN:** 0907-5682. **Subscription Rates:** 519 institutions print & e-access; 571 institutions current volume print & all online content; 467 institutions e-access; 519 institutions e-access plus backfile (all online content); 467 institutions e-access (content through 1998); 509 institutions print only; 54 individuals print only; 140 institutions single print; 18 individuals single print. **Remarks:** Accepts advertising. **URL:** http://www.sagepub.co.uk/journalsProdDesc.nav? prodId=Journal200979. **Circ:** (Not Reported)

54205 ■ Children & Society
John Wiley & Sons Inc.
Wiley-Blackwell
c/o Nicola Hilliard, Book Review Ed.
National Children's Bureau
8 Wakley St.
London EC1V 7QE, United Kingdom
Ph: 44 20 78436033
Fax: 44 20 72789512
Peer-reviewed journal covering research and debate on

all aspects of childhood and policies and services for children and young people. Includes academic research, policy and practice in relation to the health, education and welfare of children from infancy to adulthood. **Founded:** 1963. **Freq:** Bimonthly. **Print Method:** Offset. **Cols./Page:** 5. **Col. Width:** 24 nonpareils. **Col. Depth:** 224 agate lines. **Key Personnel:** Allison James, Editor; Nigel Thomas, Editor; Martin Woodhead, Editor. **ISSN:** 0951-0605. **Subscription Rates:** US$211 individuals print and online; US$761 institutions, other countries online; US$716 institutions print and online; US$651 institutions online; US$838 institutions, other countries print and online. **URL:** http://www.wiley.com/bw/journal. asp?ref=0951-0605&site=1.

54206 ■ China-Britain Business Review
China-Britain Business Council
Portland House, 3rd Fl.
Bressenden Pl.
London SW1E 5BH, United Kingdom
Ph: 44 20 78022000
Fax: 44 20 78022029
Publisher E-mail: enquiries@cbbc.org
Magazine featuring China-Britain trade and China economic news. **Freq:** 10/yr. **Key Personnel:** Fiona Huo, Contact, fiona.huo@cbbc.org. **Remarks:** Accepts advertising. **URL:** http://www.cbbc.org/the_review/index. html. **Circ:** Combined 7,000

54207 ■ China Economic Review
Alain Charles Publishing Ltd.
University House
11-13 Lower Grosvenor Pl.
London SW1W 0EX, United Kingdom
Ph: 44 20 78347676
Fax: 44 20 79730076
Publisher E-mail: post@alaincharles.com
Magazine covering economic and business information about China. **Founded:** 1990. **Freq:** Monthly. **Print Method:** Sheetfed Offset. **Trim Size:** 210 x 276 mm. **ISSN:** 1350-6390. **Subscription Rates:** US$150 individuals Hong Kong; US$225 two years Hong Kong; US$160 individuals China; US$270 two years China. **Remarks:** Accepts advertising. **URL:** http://www. chinaeconomicreview.com/. **Ad Rates:** BW: US$21,000, 4C: US$3,570. **Circ:** 9,537

54208 ■ The China Quarterly
Cambridge University Press
c/o Dr. Julia Strauss, Ed.
Dept. of Political Studies
School of Oriental & African Studies
Thornhaugh St.
London WC1H 0XG, United Kingdom
Publisher E-mail: information@cambridge.org
Journal focusing on history in China. **Freq:** Quarterly. **Key Personnel:** Raphaal Jacquet, Editorial Mgr.; Dr. Julia Strauss, Editor, chinaq@soas.ac.uk; Ms. Rowan Pease, Editorial Mgr. **ISSN:** 0305-7410. **Subscription Rates:** 40 individuals print only; US$69 individuals print only; 140 institutions online & print; US$235 institutions online & print; 128 institutions online only; US$216 institutions online only. **Remarks:** Accepts advertising. **URL:** http://journals.cambridge.org/action/ displayJournal?jid=cqy. **Ad Rates:** BW: US$885. **Circ:** 2,700

54209 ■ Christianity
CCP Ltd.
PO Box 17911
London SWIP 4YX, United Kingdom
Ph: 44 2073161472
Fax: 44 2073161453
Publisher E-mail: youthwork@premier.org.uk
Consumer magazine covering religious news. **Freq:** Monthly. **Trim Size:** 210 x 297 mm. **Key Personnel:** Candy O'Donovan, Contact; John Buckeridge, Sen. Ed. **Subscription Rates:** 26; 2.50 single issue. **Remarks:** Accepts advertising. **URL:** http://www. christianitymagazine.co.uk/about.aspx. **Absorbed:** Renewal. **Formerly:** Christianity & Renewal. **Ad Rates:** BW: 830, 4C: 895, PCI: 11.50. **Circ:** (Not Reported)

54210 ■ Chronic Respiratory Disease
Sage Publications Ltd.
1 Oliver's Yard
55 City Rd.
London EC1Y 1SP, United Kingdom
Ph: 44 20 73248500

Fax: 44 20 73248600
Peer-reviewed journal covering the rising incidence of chronic respiratory diseases worldwide, publishing research papers and original articles that have immediate relevance to clinical practice, and reflecting the nature of modern treatment. **Freq:** Quarterly. **Key Personnel:** Mike Morgan, Editor; Sally Singh, Editor; Carolyn Rochester, Editor. **ISSN:** 1479-9723. **Subscription Rates:** 292 institutions combined (print & e-access); 263 institutions e-access; 286 institutions print only; 90 individuals combined (print & e-access); 79 institutions single print; 29 individuals single print. **Remarks:** Accepts advertising. **URL:** http://www.sagepub.co.uk/journalsProdDesc.nav?prodId=Journal201805. **Circ:** (Not Reported)

54211 ■ The CIPA Journal
Chartered Institute of Patent Attorneys
95 Chancery Ln.
London WC2A 1DT, United Kingdom
Ph: 44 20 74059450
Fax: 44 20 74300471
Publication E-mail: publications@cipa.org.uk
Publisher E-mail: mail@cipa.org.uk
Publication covering patents, copyrights and trademarks. **Freq:** Monthly. **ISSN:** 0306-0314. **Subscription Rates:** 130 individuals. **Remarks:** Advertising accepted; rates available upon request. **URL:** http://www.cipa.org.uk/pages/journal/article?44564ED0-DBDA-407E-B8B3-A0DC5E6E3339. **Circ:** 3,600

54212 ■ Classic American
Trader Media Group
41-47 Hartfield Rd., 3rd & 4th Fl.
Wimbledon
London SW19 3RQ, United Kingdom
Ph: 44 208 5447000
Fax: 44 208 8791879
Publication E-mail: email@classic-american.com
Consumer magazine covering American cars for owners and enthusiasts in the UK. **Founded:** 1988. **Freq:** Monthly. **Print Method:** Web offset. **Trim Size:** A4. **Key Personnel:** Ben Klemenzson, Editor. **Subscription Rates:** 35 individuals; 44 individuals Europe; 54 elsewhere. **Remarks:** Accepts advertising. **URL:** http://www.classic-american.com. **Circ:** Combined 18,500

54213 ■ The Classic Marvel Figurine Collection
Eaglemoss Publications Ltd
Beaumont House, 1st Fl.
Kensington Village
Avonmore Rd.
London W14 8TS, United Kingdom
Ph: 44 20 76051200
Fax: 44 20 76051201
Publication E-mail: marvel@jacklinenterprises.com
Publisher E-mail: webenquiries@eaglemoss.co.uk
Magazine featuring character figurines, including detailed history and background. **Key Personnel:** Maggie Calmels, Editorial Dir., maggiecalmels@eaglemoss.co.uk; Andrew Jarvis, Ch. Exec. **Subscription Rates:** 5.99 single issue. **URL:** http://www.marvel-figurines.co.uk/.

54214 ■ Classic Record Collector
Newsquest Magazines
30 Cannon St.
London EC4M 6YJ, United Kingdom
Ph: 44 20 76183456
Publisher E-mail: info@newsquestspecialistmedia.com
Consumer magazine featuring classical music record reviews. **Freq:** Quarterly. **Key Personnel:** Tully Potter, Editor. **Subscription Rates:** 20 individuals UK; 24 individuals Europe; 28 individuals rest of world. **URL:** http://www.classicrecordcollector.com. **Formerly:** International Classic Record Collector (ICRC). **Circ:** Paid ‡6,000

54215 ■ Classical Music
Rhinegold Publishing
241 Shaftesbury Ave.
London WC2H 8TF, United Kingdom
Ph: 44 20 73331720
Fax: 44 20 73331765
Publication E-mail: classical.music@rhinegold.co.uk
Publisher E-mail: sales@rhinegold.co.uk
Magazine keeping those who are in the classical music industry abreast of the current news and information about the music and the industry. **Subtitle:** The magazine of the classical music profession. **Freq:** Biweekly. **Key Personnel:** Keith Clarke, Editor. **Subscription Rates:** 79 individuals; 142 two years. **Remarks:** Accepts advertising. **URL:** http://www.rhinegold.co.uk/magazines/classical_music/default.asp?css=1. **Circ:** (Not Reported)

54216 ■ Cleantech
Cleantech Investor Limited
PO Box 63865
London SE1 3SN, United Kingdom
Ph: 44 20 73947110
Fax: 44 20 72520910
Publisher E-mail: info@cleantechinvestor.co.uk
Magazine focusing on clean technology development. **Freq:** Bimonthly. **Key Personnel:** Anne McIvor, Editor. **Subscription Rates:** 285 individuals print and online; 135 individuals online only; 95 individuals print only; EUR349 individuals print and online; EUR165 individuals online only; EUR149 individuals print only; US$339 individuals print and online; US$165 individuals online only; US$185 individuals print only. **Remarks:** Accepts advertising. **URL:** http://cleantechinvestor.co.uk/. **Circ:** (Not Reported)

54217 ■ Climate Policy
James and James/Earthscan
Dunstan House
14a St., Cross St.
London EC1N 8XA, United Kingdom
Ph: 44 20 78411930
Fax: 44 20 72421474
Publication E-mail: climatepolicy@imperial.ac.uk
Publisher E-mail: earthinfo@earthscan.co.uk
Peer-reviewed journal addressing the broad spectrum of policy issues raised by the prospect of changes in the global climate, and by the need for mitigation of, and adaptation to, climate change. **Freq:** Bimonthly. **Key Personnel:** Prof. Michael Grubb, Editor-in-Chief; Dr. Frank J. Convery, Assoc. Ed.; Dr. Jonathan Pershing, Assoc. Ed.; Dr. Axel Michaelowa, Assoc. Ed.; Dr. Tom Downing, Assoc. Ed.; Prof. Roberto Schaeffer, Assoc. Ed. **ISSN:** 1469-3062. **Subscription Rates:** 427 institutions; US$850 institutions; EUR555 institutions; 125 individuals online; US$249 individuals online; EUR165 individuals online; 125 individuals print; US$249 individuals print. **URL:** http://www.earthscan.co.uk/Journals/ClimatePolicy/tabid/480/Default.aspx.

54218 ■ Clinica World Medical Device and Diagnostic News
PJB Publications Ltd.
Telephone House
69-77 Paul St.
London EC2A 4LQ, United Kingdom
Ph: 44 20 70175000
Fax: 44 20 70176792
Publisher E-mail: pjb.enquiries@informa.com
Professional journal covering news for the medical device and diagnostic industry. **Founded:** 1980. **Freq:** Weekly (Mon.). **Trim Size:** A4. **Key Personnel:** Jennifer Cheng, Sen. Sales Exec., phone 44 20 70174099, fax 44 20 70176787, jennifer.cheng@informa.com. **ISSN:** 0144-7777. **Remarks:** Accepts advertising. **Online:** DataStar (The Dialog Corporation); Dialog (The Dialog Corporation); Ovid Technologies, Inc.; STN; Profile; Newsedge. **URL:** http://www.pjbpubs.com/advertising/devices.htmClinica. **Circ:** Combined 2,373

54219 ■ Clinical Child Psychology and Psychiatry
Sage Publications Ltd.
1 Oliver's Yard
55 City Rd.
London EC1Y 1SP, United Kingdom
Ph: 44 20 73248500
Fax: 44 20 73248600
Peer-reviewed journal covering child and adolescent psychology and psychiatry. **Founded:** 1996. **Freq:** Quarterly. **Key Personnel:** Dr. Bernadette Wren, Assoc. Ed.; Arlene Verete, Editor; Rudi Dallos, Editor. **ISSN:** 1359-1045. **Subscription Rates:** US$1,053 institutions print & electronic; US$1,158 institutions current volume print & all online content; US$1,032 institutions print; US$42 individuals single print; US$284 single issue for institutions; US$948 institutions E-access; US$1,053 institutions all online content; US$948 institutions content through 1998; US$130 individuals print only. **Remarks:** Accepts advertising. **URL:** http://www.sagepub.com/journalsProdDesc.nav?prodId=Journal200869. **Circ:** (Not Reported)

54220 ■ Clinical Ethics
Royal Society of Medicine Press Ltd.
1 Wimpole St.
London W1G 0AE, United Kingdom
Ph: 44 20 72902921
Fax: 44 20 72902929
Publication E-mail: ceproduction@rsm.ac.uk
Publisher E-mail: publishing@rsm.ac.uk
Journal covering research and policy for clinical ethics. **Founded:** 2006. **Freq:** Quarterly. **Key Personnel:** Bobbie Farsides, Editor; Sue Eckstein, Editor. **ISSN:** 1477-7509. **Subscription Rates:** 168 institutions UK & Europe; EUR228 institutions Europe; US$335 institutions; 174 institutions, other countries; 99 individuals UK & Europe; EUR139 institutions Europe; US$208 individuals; 105 other countries; 151 individuals online only; EUR205 individuals online only. **URL:** http://ce.rsmjournals.com.

54221 ■ Clinical and Experimental Allergy Reviews
John Wiley & Sons Inc.
Wiley-Blackwell
c/o A.B. Kay, Ed.
Imperial College
Sir Alexander Fleming Bldg., Rm. 374
Leukocyte Biology, Division of Biomedical Sciences
London SW7 2AZ, United Kingdom
Supplementary publication to Clinical and Experimental Allergy. Supplements include sponsored symposia, position papers, guidelines, special reports, conference proceedings, and more. **Freq:** Semiannual. **Key Personnel:** A.B. Kay, Editor; S.T. Holgate, Editor; Anthony Frew, Treas. **ISSN:** 1472-9725. **Subscription Rates:** US$3,364 institutions print & online; US$3,058 institutions print; 1,654 institutions online only; 1,819 institutions print & online; 1,654 institutions print; 3,927 institutions, other countries print & online. **Remarks:** Accepts advertising. **URL:** http://www.wiley.com/bw/journal.asp?ref=1472-9725&site=1. **Circ:** (Not Reported)

54222 ■ Clinical & Experimental Dermatology
John Wiley & Sons Inc.
Wiley-Blackwell
c/o John Caulfield, Mng. Ed.
British Association of Dermatologists
4 Fitzroy Sq.
London W1P 5HQ, United Kingdom
Ph: 44 20 73916346
Fax: 44 20 73870240
Peer-reviewed journal covering the field of dermatological research. **Founded:** 1978. **Freq:** 8/yr. **Cols./Page:** 2. **Key Personnel:** Dr. John S.C. English, Editor; John Caulfield, Managing Editor; Robert Dawe, Co-Ed.; George Millington, Co-Ed.; Pam Todd, Co-Ed. **ISSN:** 0307-6938. **Subscription Rates:** US$301 individuals print + online; US$2,539 institutions print + online; US$2,308 institutions print; EUR1,743 institutions print and online; US$2,964 institutions, other countries print + online; US$2,694 institutions, other countries print; 179 other countries print + online; 162 individuals print + online; 1,372 institutions print + online; 1,247 institutions print. **Remarks:** Accepts advertising. **URL:** http://www.wiley.com/bw/journal.asp?ref=0307-6938&site=1. **Circ:** Combined 762

54223 ■ Clinical & Experimental Immunology
British Society for Immunology
Vintage House
37 Albert Embankment
London SE1 7TL, United Kingdom
Ph: 44 20 30319800
Fax: 44 20 75822882
Publisher E-mail: onlinecommunity@immunology.org
Publication covering immunology. **Freq:** Monthly. **Key Personnel:** Prof. M. Peakman, Editor-in-Chief; Dr. D.C. Douek, Assoc. Ed.; Prof. M. Botto, Assoc. Ed.; Prof. M. von Herrath, Assoc. Ed. **ISSN:** 0009-9104. **Subscription Rates:** US$124 members Americas (print and online); EUR109 members Europe (print and online); 72 members rest of the world (print and online); US$2,628 institutions Americas (print and online); EUR1,808 institutions Europe (print and online); US$3,065 institutions rest of the world (print and online); US$2,389 institutions Americas (online only); EUR1,643 institutions Europe (online only); US$2,786 institutions rest of the world (online only); 72 members print & online. **Remarks:** Advertising accepted; rates available upon request. **URL:** http://www.blackwellpublishing.com/journal.asp?ref=0009-9104& site=1/default.htm; http://www.

immunology.org/Page.aspx?pid=1473. **Circ:** (Not Reported)

54224 ■ Clinical Lipidology
Future Medicine Ltd.
Unitec House
2 Albert Pl.
London N3 1QB, United Kingdom
Ph: 44 20 83716080
Fax: 44 20 83432313
Publisher E-mail: info@futuremedicine.com
Journal covering all areas of lipids in health and disease. **Freq:** Bimonthly. **Key Personnel:** C.M. Ballantyne, Editorial Advisory Panel; A.M. Bargosi, Editorial Advisory Panel; P.J. Barter, Editorial Advisory Panel. **ISSN:** 1746-0875. **URL:** http://www.futuremedicine.com/loi/clp.

54225 ■ Clinical Medicine
Royal College of Physicians
11 St., Andrew's Pl.
Regents Pk.
London NW1 4LE, United Kingdom
Ph: 44 20 79351174
Fax: 44 20 74875218
Publisher E-mail: infocentre@rcplondon.ac.uk
Journal for consultant physicians. **Subtitle:** The Journal of the Royal College of Physicians of London. **Freq:** Bimonthly Feb., April, June, Aug., Oct., Dec. **Key Personnel:** Prof. Morris J. Brown, Editorial Board; Robert Allan, MD, Editor, robert.allan@rcplondon.ac.uk; Diana M. Beaven, Publications Mgr., diana.beaven@rcplondon.ac.uk; Johanna Webster, Asst. Ed., johanna.webster@rcplondon.ac.uk; Prof. Shirley Hodgson, Editorial Board; Dr. Rodger Charlton, Editorial Board; Prof. Humphrey Hodgson, Editorial Board; Prof. Brian Hurwitz, Editorial Board; Prof. Adam Zeman, Editorial Board; Prof. David Warrell, Editorial Board. **ISSN:** 1470-2118. **Subscription Rates:** 22 single issue; EUR27 single issue. **URL:** http://www.rcplondon.ac.uk/pubs/. **Formerly:** Journal of the Royal College of Physicians of London. **Circ:** Paid 14,000

54226 ■ Clinical Oncology
Royal College of Radiologists
38 Portland Pl.
London W1B 1JQ, United Kingdom
Ph: 44 20 76364432
Fax: 44 20 73233100
Publisher E-mail: enquiries@rcr.ac.uk
Publication covering radiology. **Freq:** Monthly 10/yr. **Key Personnel:** Dr. G.C.W. Howard, Asst. Ed.; Prof. P.J. Hoskin, Editor; Prof. R. Leonard, Board Member; J. Paul, Board Member; D. Jones, Board Member. **ISSN:** 0936-6555. **Subscription Rates:** US$700 individuals. **URL:** http://www.rcr.ac.uk/content.aspx?PageID=153.

54227 ■ Clinical Pharmacist
Pharmaceutical Press
1 Lambeth High St.
London SE1 7JN, United Kingdom
Ph: 44 20 77359141
Fax: 44 20 75722509
Publication E-mail: hospital.pharmacist@pharmj.org.uk
Publisher E-mail: enquiries@rpharms.com
Professional magazine for hospital pharmacists. **Freq:** 11/yr. **Key Personnel:** Matthew Wright, Editor, phone 44 20 75722425, matthew.wright@pharmj.org.uk; Kate Towers, Asst. Ed., phone 44 20 75722419, kate.towers@pharmj.org.uk. **ISSN:** 1352-7967. **Subscription Rates:** 135 individuals U.K. (print); 170 individuals overseas (print); 227 institutions U.K. (print); 286 institutions overseas (print). **Remarks:** Accepts advertising. **URL:** http://www.pjonline.com/about_clinical_pharmacist. **Merged with:** The Hospital Pharmacist. **Ad Rates:** BW: 1,540, 4C: 2,214. **Circ:** 7,500

54228 ■ Clinical Pharmacy Europe
Campden Publishing Ltd.
1 St. John's Sq.
London EC1M 4PN, United Kingdom
Ph: 44 20 72140500
Fax: 44 20 72140501
Publisher E-mail: enquiries@campden.com
Journal for European clinical pharmacists. **Key Personnel:** Stephen Taylor, Editor-in-Chief; Kelly Clarke, Supv. Ed. **Subscription Rates:** US$148 individuals; EUR111 individuals; 75 individuals; Free for clinical pharmacists. **URL:** http://www.pharmacyeurope.net/default.asp?page=issue.home&issue.id=91.

54229 ■ Clinical Radiology
Royal College of Radiologists

38 Portland Pl.
London W1B 1JQ, United Kingdom
Ph: 44 20 76364432
Fax: 44 20 73233100
Publisher E-mail: enquiries@rcr.ac.uk
Publication covering clinical radiology. **Freq:** Monthly. **Key Personnel:** G. Baxter, Dep. Ed.; N.R. Moore, Dep. Ed.; D.F. Martin, Editor. **ISSN:** 0009-9260. **Subscription Rates:** EUR175 individuals; EUR836 institutions; 18,900¥ individuals; 90,300¥ institutions; US$155 individuals; US$742 institutions. **Remarks:** Accepts advertising. **URL:** http://www.rcr.ac.uk; http://www.rcr.ac.uk/content.aspx?PageID=314. **Circ:** (Not Reported)

54230 ■ Clinical Rheumatology
Springer-Verlag London Ltd.
236 Gray's Inn Rd., 6th Fl.
London WC1X 8HB, United Kingdom
Ph: 44 20 31922000
Medical journal covering clinical research in rheumatology. **Freq:** Bimonthly. **Trim Size:** 210 x 277 mm. **Cols./Page:** 2. **Col. Width:** 84 millimeters. **Key Personnel:** Ade Adebajo, Assoc. Ed.; Paul Davis, Editor-in-Chief; N. Bellamy, Editorial Board; Wendy J. Pontefract, Managing Editor; Girish Mody, Assoc. Ed.; Hans Rasker, Assoc. Ed.; Cesar Ramos-Remus, Assoc. Ed.; I.C. Chikanza, Editorial Board. **ISSN:** 0770-3198. **Subscription Rates:** EUR1,198 institutions print & e-access; EUR1,437.60 institutions print & enhanced access. **Remarks:** Accepts advertising. **URL:** http://www.springer.com/medicine/rheumatology/journal/10067; http://www.springerlink.com/content/0770-3198. **Circ:** Paid 1,500

54231 ■ Clinical Risk
Royal Society of Medicine Press Ltd.
1 Wimpole St.
London W1G 0AE, United Kingdom
Ph: 44 20 72902921
Fax: 44 20 72902929
Publication E-mail: crproduction@rsm.ac.uk
Publisher E-mail: publishing@rsm.ac.uk
Journal focusing on patient safety, providing practice guidelines for doctors and managers. **Freq:** Bimonthly. **Key Personnel:** Roger V. Clements, Founding Ed.; Harvey Marcovitch, Editor-in-Chief. **ISSN:** 1356-2622. **Subscription Rates:** 262 individuals UK & Europe; EUR357 individuals Europe; US$517 U.S.; 268 other countries; 236 individuals online only; EUR321 individuals online only; US$465 individuals online only. **URL:** http://cr.rsmjournals.com/.

54232 ■ Clinical Trials
Sage Publications Ltd.
1 Oliver's Yard
55 City Rd.
London EC1Y 1SP, United Kingdom
Ph: 44 20 73248500
Fax: 44 20 73248600
Peer-reviewed journal focusing on the dissemination and development of knowledge about the design, conduct, analysis, synthesis, history, ethics, regulation and clinical or policy impact of all types of clinical trials and related medical research methodologies. **Freq:** 6/yr. **Key Personnel:** Constantine Frangakis, Dep. Ed.; Steven N. Goodman, Editor; Roberta Scheeler, Managing Editor. **ISSN:** 1740-7745. **Subscription Rates:** 595 institutions print & e-access; 536 institutions e-access; 583 institutions print only; 215 individuals print & e-access; 107 institutions single print; 47 individuals single print. **Remarks:** Accepts advertising. **URL:** http://www.sagepub.co.uk/journalsProdDesc.nav?prodId=Journal201807. **Circ:** (Not Reported)

54233 ■ Clio Medica
Rodopi
University College London
183 Euston Rd.
London NW1 2BE, United Kingdom
Ph: 44 20 76798195
Publisher E-mail: info@rodopi.nl
Journal covering the history of medicine and health care in various cultures and time periods. **Subtitle:** The Wellcome Series in the History of Medicine. **Founded:** Nov. 25, 1971. **Freq:** Weekly (Thurs.). **Print Method:** Offset. **Cols./Page:** 5. **Col. Width:** 25 nonpareils. **Col. Depth:** 224 agate lines. **Key Personnel:** R. Cooter, Editor; M. Neve; Editor; V. Nutton, Editor. **ISSN:** 0045-7183. **URL:** http://www.rodopi.nl/senj.asp?SerieId=CLIO.

54234 ■ Closer
EMAP Ltd.

Greater London House
Hampstead Rd.
London NW1 7EJ, United Kingdom
Ph: 44 20 77285000
Publisher E-mail: jon.ferro@emap.com
Magazine containing a mixture of celebrity news and real life stories. **Freq:** Weekly. **URL:** http://www.closeronline.co.uk/.

54235 ■ Codebreakers
H. Bauer Publishing
Academic House
24-28 Oval Rd.
London NW1 7DT, United Kingdom
Ph: 44 20 72418000
Fax: 44 20 72418030
Magazine containing crossword puzzles. **Freq:** Monthly. **Trim Size:** 185 X 255 mm. **Key Personnel:** Clive Garsin, Gp. Ed.; Spike Figgett, Publishing Dir.; Helen Greenwood, Advertising Mgr. **Subscription Rates:** 15.47 individuals. **Remarks:** Accepts advertising. **URL:** http://www.puzzlemagazines.co.uk/code-breakers. **Circ:** ★109,000

54236 ■ Cognition, Technology & Work
Springer-Verlag London Ltd.
236 Gray's Inn Rd., 6th Fl.
London WC1X 8HB, United Kingdom
Ph: 44 20 31922000
Journal bringing together people, technology and institutions, emphasizing the role of human cognition in the interdependent relationship, as work that is not with computers but through computers. **Freq:** Quarterly. **Key Personnel:** Erik Hollnagel, Editorial Board, erik.hollnagel@cindy.ensmp.fr; Pietro Carlo Cacciabue, Editor-in-Chief. **ISSN:** 1435-5558. **Subscription Rates:** EUR420 institutions print and e-access; EUR504 institutions print and enhanced access. **Remarks:** Advertising accepted; rates available upon request. **URL:** http://www.springerlink.com/content/1435-5558. **Circ:** (Not Reported)

54237 ■ Cognitive Neuropsychiatry
Taylor & Francis Ltd.
c/o Anthony S. David, Ed.
Institute of Psychiatry
King's College London
Denmark Hill
London SE5 8AF, United Kingdom
Peer-reviewed journal encouraging the exploration of new frontiers and the integration and application of theories, methods and research findings from related fields of clinical psychiatry, behavioural neurology and cognitive neuropsychology. **Freq:** 6/yr. **Key Personnel:** Peter W. Halligan, Editor, halliganpw@cardiff.ac.uk; Anthony S. David, Editor, a.david@iop.kcl.ac.uk; Ryan McKay, Book Review Ed.; Antonio Damasio, Editorial Board; Michael Green, Editorial Board; John Cutting, Editorial Board; Ray Dolan, Editorial Board; Terry Goldberg, Editorial Board; Alan Baddeley, Editorial Board; Max Coltheart, Editorial Board. **ISSN:** 1354-6805. **Subscription Rates:** US$392 individuals print only; US$761 institutions online only; US$801 institutions print & online; 482 institutions print & online; 459 institutions online only; 235 individuals print only. **Remarks:** Accepts advertising. **URL:** http://www.tandf.co.uk/journals/titles/13546805.asp. **Circ:** (Not Reported)

54238 ■ College Bulletin
Royal College of Pathologists
2 Carlton House Ter.
London SW1Y 5AF, United Kingdom
Ph: 44 20 74516700
Fax: 44 20 74516701
Publication E-mail: publications@rcpath.org
Publisher E-mail: info@rcpath.org
Publication covering pathology. **Subtitle:** Bulletin of the Royal College of Pathologists. **Founded:** 1960. **Freq:** Quarterly. **Trim Size:** A4. **Key Personnel:** Edward Hulme, Contact, phone 44 20 74516730. **ISSN:** 0959-972X. **Subscription Rates:** 95 nonmembers; Free to members. **URL:** http://www.rcpath.org; http://www.rcpath.org/index.asp?PageID=36. **Ad Rates:** 4C: 1,990. **Circ:** 7,500

54239 ■ Common Cause
ActionAid
33-39 Bowling Green Ln.
London EC1R 0BJ, United Kingdom
Ph: 44 20 31220561
Fax: 44 20 72785667

Publisher E-mail: mail@actionaid.org
Magazine for ActionAid sponsors. **Subtitle:** Young People, Sexuality and HIV/AIDS in three African Countries. **Founded:** 1989. **Freq:** Semiannual. **Trim Size:** A4. **ISSN:** 0967-0130. **Subscription Rates:** Free. **Remarks:** Accepts advertising. **URL:** http://www.actionaid.org.uk/index.asp?page_id=521. **Circ:** Nonpaid 140,000

54240 ■ Commonwealth Broadcaster
Commonwealth Broadcasting Association
17 Fleet St.
London EC4Y 1AA, United Kingdom
Ph: 44 207 5835550
Fax: 44 207 5835549
Publisher E-mail: cba@cba.org.uk
Broadcasting publication. **Freq:** Quarterly. **Subscription Rates:** 41 individuals; 49 other countries. **URL:** http://www.cba.org.uk. **Formerly:** Combroad. **Ad Rates:** 4C: US$2,195. **Circ:** 3,000

54241 ■ Commonwealth Judicial Journal
Commonwealth Magistrates and Judges' Association
Uganda House
58-59 Trafalgar Sq.
London WC2N 5DX, United Kingdom
Ph: 44 207 9761007
Fax: 44 207 9762394
Publisher E-mail: info@cmja.org
Journal covering Judicial issues. **Freq:** Semiannual. **Subscription Rates:** Free to members; 30 individuals. **URL:** http://www.cmja.org.

54242 ■ Commonwealth Law Bulletin
Commonwealth Secretariat
Marlborough House
Pall Mall
London SW1Y 5HX, United Kingdom
Ph: 44 20 77476500
Fax: 44 20 79300827
Publication E-mail: legaleditor@commonwealth.int
Publisher E-mail: info@commonwealth.int
Law periodical. **Founded:** 1974. **Freq:** 4/yr. **Trim Size:** A5. **Key Personnel:** Aldo Zammit-Borda, Editor; Gavin Murphy, Editorial Advisory Board. **ISSN:** 0305-0718. **Subscription Rates:** US$153 individuals print only; US$341 individuals online only; US$359 individuals print and online. **Remarks:** Accepts advertising. **URL:** http://www.thecommonwealth.org/Internal/140503/36809/law_bulletin/. **Ad Rates:** BW: EUR250. **Circ:** 1,500

54243 ■ Communicable Disease Report Weekly
Health Protection Agency
Holborn Gate
330 High Holborn, 7th Fl.
London WC1V 7PP, United Kingdom
Ph: 44 20 77592783
Fax: 44 20 77592789
Publisher E-mail: webteam@hpa.org.uk
Public health bulletin. **Freq:** Weekly (Thurs.). **Subscription Rates:** Free. **URL:** http://www.hpa.org.uk/cdr. **Also known as:** CDR Weekly.

54244 ■ Communicate
DMG World Media Ltd.
Equitable House Lyon Rd., Harrow
2 Derry St.
London HA1 2EW, United Kingdom
Ph: 44 20 85152000
Fax: 44 20 85152088
Publisher E-mail: careers@dmgworldmedia.com
Professional magazine for the communications industry, including telecommunication, datacommunications, wireless, and multimedia. **Founded:** 1980. **Freq:** Monthly. **Key Personnel:** Neil Gibbons, Editor; Andrew Thomas, Publisher. **Subscription Rates:** Free to qualified subscribers; 90 individuals; 135 other countries. **Remarks:** Accepts advertising. **URL:** http://www.communicatemagazine.co.uk/. **Circ:** 10,000

54245 ■ Communication
National Autistic Society
393 City Rd.
London EC1V 1NG, United Kingdom
Ph: 44 20 78332299
Fax: 44 20 78339666
Publication E-mail: communication@nas.org.uk
Publisher E-mail: nas@nas.org.uk
Publication covering issues relating to autistic spectrum disorders. **Subtitle:** The Magazine of the National

Autistic Society. **Founded:** 1962. **Freq:** 3/yr. **Print Method:** Offset Litho. **Trim Size:** A4. **Key Personnel:** Steve Forsdick, Contact, phone 44 20 78782334, fax 44 20 73797155, steve.forsdick@tenalpspublishing.com. **ISSN:** 0045-7663. **Remarks:** Advertising accepted; rates available upon request. **Circ:** 12,000

54246 ■ Communications Africa
Alain Charles Publishing Ltd.
University House
11-13 Lower Grosvenor Pl.
London SW1W 0EX, United Kingdom
Ph: 44 20 78347676
Fax: 44 20 79730076
Publisher E-mail: post@alaincharles.com
Magazine covering broadcast and telecommunications Africa. **Freq:** Bimonthly. **Print Method:** Sheetfed Offset. **Trim Size:** 208 x 292 mm. **ISSN:** 0962-3841. **Remarks:** Accepts advertising. **URL:** http://www.alaincharles.com/index.php?option=com_content&view=article&id=48&Itemid=74. **Ad Rates:** BW: US$3,650, 4C: US$5,370. **Circ:** *9,034

54247 ■ Community
Community Matters
12-20 Baron St.
London N1 9LL, United Kingdom
Ph: 44 20 78377887
Fax: 44 20 72789253
Publisher E-mail: info@communitymatters.org.uk
Publication covering community development. **Subtitle:** Community Magazine and Technical Briefing. **Founded:** Jan. 1979. **Freq:** Bimonthly. **Print Method:** Litho. **Trim Size:** A4. **Key Personnel:** David Tyler, Ch. Exec. **Subscription Rates:** 15 individuals. **URL:** http://www.communitymatters.org.uk. **Ad Rates:** GLR: EUR300, 4C: EUR300. **Circ:** 3,000

54248 ■ Comparative American Studies
Maney Publishing
1 Carlton House Ter.
London SW1Y 5AF, United Kingdom
Ph: 44 20 74517300
Fax: 44 20 74517307
Publisher E-mail: maney@maney.co.uk
Journal extending scholarly debates about American Studies beyond the geographical boundaries of the United States, repositioning discussions about American culture within an international, comparative framework. **Freq:** 4/yr. **Key Personnel:** Dr. Nick Selby, Editor; Jane Desmond, Editor; Hartwig Isernhagen, Editor. **ISSN:** 1477-5700. **Subscription Rates:** US$698 institutions; 386 institutions, other countries; US$96 individuals; 52 other countries; 35 members other countries; US$64 members. **Remarks:** Accepts advertising. **URL:** http://maney.co.uk/index.php/journals/cas/. **Circ:** (Not Reported)

54249 ■ Comparative Critical Studies
Edinburgh University Press
c/o Prof. Robert Weninger, Ed.
King's College London
London WC2R 2LS, United Kingdom
Publisher E-mail: marketing@eup.ed.ac.uk
Journal covering reception studies. **Freq:** 3/yr. **Key Personnel:** Prof. Robert Weninger, Editor. **ISSN:** 1744-1854. **Subscription Rates:** 107 institutions print and online; US$223 institutions print and online (North America); 117 institutions, other countries print and online; 41.50 individuals print and online; US$87 individuals print and online (North America); 46.50 other countries print and online. **Remarks:** Accepts advertising. **URL:** http://www.eupjournals.com/journal/ccs. **Circ:** (Not Reported)

54250 ■ Comparative Hepatology
BioMed Central Ltd.
236 Gray's Inn Rd., Fl. 6
34-42 Cleveland St.
London WC1X 8HL, United Kingdom
Ph: 44 20 31922000
Fax: 44 20 31922010
Publisher E-mail: info@biomedcentral.com
Online international journal for liver research, promoting and presenting basic and applied studies, in biology, veterinary and human medicine. **Key Personnel:** Prof. Eduardo Rocha, PhD, Editor-in-Chief, phone 351 22 2062254, fax 351 22 2062232, chepatol@icbas.up.pt; Prof. David E. Hinton, Dep. Ed., dhinton@duke.edu; Dr.

Charles Balabaud, Editorial Board, charles.balabaud@chu-bordeaux.fr; Dr. Michael J.P. Arthur, Editorial Board, m.j.arthur@soton.ac.uk; Dr. Eddie Wisse, Dep. Ed., eddie@wisse.be; Prof. Malcolm Alison, Editorial Board, m.alison@qmul.ac.uk; Dr. Rogerio Monteiro, Assoc. Ed., rafmonte@icbas.up.pt; Dr. Nazzareno Ballatori, Editorial Board, ned_ballatori@urmc.rochester.edu; Dr. Margaret F. Bassendine, Editorial Board, m.bassendine@ncl.ac.uk. **ISSN:** 1476-5926. **Remarks:** Accepts advertising. **URL:** http://www.comparative-hepatology.com. **Circ:** (Not Reported)

54251 ■ Competency & Emotional Intelligence
LexisNexis UK
Halsbury House
35 Chancery Ln.
London WC2A 1EL, United Kingdom
Ph: 44 20 74002500
Fax: 44 20 74002842
Publisher E-mail: customer.services@lexisnexis.co.uk
Professional magazine covering the theory and practice of competency and emotional intelligence in the workplace. **Founded:** 1993. **Freq:** Quarterly. **Key Personnel:** Neil Rankin, Editor; Jim Matthewman, Consulting Ed. **ISSN:** 1469-333X. **Subscription Rates:** 308 individuals; 316 other countries. **Remarks:** Advertising not accepted. **URL:** http://eiworld.org/docs/10_4pp_43-48.pdf. **Circ:** (Not Reported)

54252 ■ Competition & Change
Maney Publishing
1 Carlton House Ter.
London SW1Y 5AF, United Kingdom
Ph: 44 20 74517300
Fax: 44 20 74517307
Publisher E-mail: maney@maney.co.uk
Peer-reviewed journal covering global business and political economy. **Subtitle:** The Journal of Global Business and Political Economy. **Freq:** 4/yr. **Key Personnel:** Julie Froud, Editor, julie.froud@mbs.ac.uk; Sukhdev Johal, Editor, s.johal@rhul.ac.uk; Ismail Erturk, Assoc. Ed., ismail.erturk@mbs.ac.uk. **ISSN:** 1024-5294. **Subscription Rates:** 66 other countries; US$112 individuals; 244 institutions, other countries; US$474 institutions. **Remarks:** Accepts advertising. **URL:** http://maney.co.uk/index.php/journals/com/. **Ad Rates:** BW: 180. **Circ:** (Not Reported)

54253 ■ Competition Law Insight
Informa Professional Publishing
69-77 Paul St.
London EC2A 4LQ, United Kingdom
Ph: 44 20 70175532
Magazine containing analysis and expert comment on the latest news and developments in the law and economics of competition policy in Europe, America and around the world. **Subtitle:** Antitrust Law and Policy in a Global Market. **Freq:** Biweekly. **Key Personnel:** Max Findlay, Editor. **Subscription Rates:** 945 individuals. **URL:** http://www.informaprofessional.com/publications/newsletter/competition_law_insight.

54254 ■ The Computer Journal
Oxford University Press
c/o Prof. Erol Gelenbe, Ed.-in-Ch.
Dept. Electrical & Electronic Engineering
Imperial College London
S Kensington Campus
London SW7 2AZ, United Kingdom
Publisher E-mail: webenquiry.uk@oup.com
Journal providing a complete overview of developments in the field of Computer Science. **Freq:** 10/yr. **Key Personnel:** Prof. Erol Gelenbe, Editor-in-Chief; Prof. M. Dezani, Book Review Ed.; Prof. R. Meo, Book Review Ed. **ISSN:** 0010-4620. **Subscription Rates:** 1,114 institutions corporate; print and online; 928 institutions corporate; online only; 1,021 institutions corporate; print only; 890 institutions print and online; 742 institutions online only; 816 institutions print only; 742 individuals print; 80 members print. **Remarks:** Accepts advertising. **URL:** http://comjnl.oxfordjournals.org. **Circ:** (Not Reported)

54255 ■ Computeractive
Incisive Media Limited
Haymarket House
28-29 Haymarket
London SW1Y 4RX, United Kingdom
Ph: 44 870 2408859

Circulation: ★ = ABC; △ = BPA; ♦ = CAC; • = CCAB; ❏ = VAC; ⊕ = PO Statement; ‡ = Publisher's Report; Boldface figures = sworn; Light figures = estimated.

Fax: 44 207 4849797
Publisher E-mail: customerservices@incisivemedia.com
Magazine offering simple and clear computer advice.
Freq: Fortnightly. **Key Personnel:** Paul Allen, Editor, paul.allen@incisivemedia.com; Dylan Armbrust, Publishing Dir., dylan.armbrust@incisivemedia.com; Paul Harvey, Sales Mgr., paul.harvey@incisivemedia.com. **Subscription Rates:** 13.97 individuals. **URL:** http://www.incisivemedia.com/corporate/products/computeractive; http://www.computeractive.co.uk/. **Circ:** *159,210

54256 ■ Computing
Incisive Media Limited
Haymarket House
28-29 Haymarket
London SW1Y 4RX, United Kingdom
Ph: 44 870 2408859
Fax: 44 207 4849797
Publisher E-mail: customerservices@incisivemedia.com
Publication covering computers and the office automation industry. **Freq:** Weekly. **Key Personnel:** Abigail Waraker, Editor; Dave Bailey, Enterprise Ed., dave.bailey@incisivemedia.com. **ISSN:** 0267-4750. **Subscription Rates:** Free. **URL:** http://www.computing.co.uk/.

54257 ■ Concurrent Engineering
Sage Publications Ltd.
1 Oliver's Yard
55 City Rd.
London EC1Y 1SP, United Kingdom
Ph: 44 20 73248500
Fax: 44 20 73248600
Peer-reviewed journal for product managers, design engineers, and manufacturing engineers and managers covering a range of concurrent engineering topics such as theory, computer-aided applications, and integrated development. **Subtitle:** Research and Applications. **Freq:** Quarterly. **Trim Size:** 8 1/2 x 11. **Key Personnel:** A.M Agogino, Assoc. Ed.; M.S. Fox, Assoc. Ed. **ISSN:** 1063-293X. **Subscription Rates:** 672 institutions print & e-access; 739 institutions print & all online; 605 institutions e-access; 672 institutions e-access, all online content; 605 institutions content through 1998; 605 institutions print only; 181 institutions single print. **Remarks:** Accepts advertising. **URL:** http://www.sagepub.co.uk/journalsProdDesc.nav?prodId=Journal201578. **Circ:** 185

54258 ■ Confectionery Production
Specialised Publications Ltd.
57 Bath St.
Gravesend
London DA11 0DF, United Kingdom
Ph: 44 1474 532202
Fax: 44 1474 532203
Publication E-mail: con.prod@virgin.net
Publisher E-mail: katrine@bellpublishing.com
Trade magazine of the confectionery, baking, and ice cream industry. **Founded:** 1934. **Freq:** Monthly. **Print Method:** Disc. **Cols./Page:** 4. **Key Personnel:** Sarah McRitchie, Ed. Dir., phone 44 1474 532202, fax 44 1474 532203, sarah@bellpublishing.com; Katrine Kjoeller, Editor, katrine@bellpublishing.com. **ISSN:** 0010-5473. **Subscription Rates:** 125 individuals. **Remarks:** Accepts advertising. **URL:** http://confectioneryproduction.com. **Ad Rates:** BW: 875, 4C: 1,255. **Circ:** Controlled 3,500

54259 ■ Conference & Incentive Travel
Haymarket Marketing Publications
174 Hammersmith Rd.
London W6 7JP, United Kingdom
Ph: 44 20 82675000
Publication E-mail: cit@haynet.com
Publisher E-mail: info@haymarket.com
Trade magazine covering marketing and travel. **Freq:** Monthly. **Key Personnel:** Yasmin Arrigo, Editor, phone 44 20 82674362, yasmin.arrigo@haymarket.com; James Thornton, News Ed., phone 44 20 82674285, james.thornton@haynet.com; Parveen Samra, Sales Exec., phone 44 20 82674223, fax 44 20 82674272, parveen.samra@haymarket.com; Kunal Dutta, Junior Reporter, phone 44 20 82674307, kunal.dutta@haynet.com; Ian Porter, International Sales Mgr., phone 44 20 82674565, fax 44 20 82674272, ian.porter@haymarket.com. **Subscription Rates:** 85 individuals; 153 two years; 204 individuals 3 years; US$225 other countries; US$445 other countries 2 years; US$593 other countries 3 years;

EUR180 individuals Europe and Ireland; EUR324 individuals 2 years (Europe and Ireland); EUR432 individuals 3 years (Europe and Ireland). **Remarks:** Accepts advertising. **URL:** http://www.citmagazine.com/. **Ad Rates:** BW: 2,835, 4C: 3,845. **Circ:** Controlled *16,154

54260 ■ Constitutional and Parliamentary Information
Association of Secretaries General of Parliaments
Association des Secretaires Generaux des Parlements
Committee Office
House of Commons
London SW1A 0AA, United Kingdom
Publication covering constitutional and parliamentary information in English and French. **Freq:** Semiannual. **URL:** http://www.asgp.info/en/publications/constitutional.

54261 ■ Contact Dermatitis
John Wiley & Sons Inc.
Wiley-Blackwell
c/o Ian R. White, Ed.-in-Ch.
St. John's Institute of Dermatology
St. Thomas Hospital
London SE1 7EH, United Kingdom
Journal focusing on various aspects of environmental dermatitis. **Freq:** Monthly. **Key Personnel:** Ian R. White, Editor-in-Chief, ian.white@kcl.ac.uk; David Basketter, Section Ed.; Klaus E. Andersen, Editorial Board; Pieter-Jan Coenraads, Editorial Board; Ian White, Editor-in-Chief, ian.white@kcl.ac.uk. **ISSN:** 0105-1873. **Subscription Rates:** US$1,072 institutions print + online; US$1,254 institutions, other countries print + online; US$972 institutions print or online; US$1,140 institutions, other countries print or online; 640 institutions print + online; 581 institutions print or online; EUR812 institutions print + online; EUR738 institutions print or online. **Remarks:** Accepts advertising. **URL:** http://www.wiley.com/bw/journal.asp?ref=0105-1873&site=1. **Circ:** (Not Reported)

54262 ■ Container Intelligence Quarterly
Clarkson Research Studies
St. Magnus House
3 Lower Thames St.
London EC3R 6HE, United Kingdom
Ph: 44 20 73340000
Fax: 44 20 76264189
Publisher E-mail: crs@clarksons.com
Comprehensive source of information on the container shipping market. **Freq:** Quarterly. **ISSN:** 1478-9779. **Subscription Rates:** US$2,088 individuals. **URL:** http://www.bharatbook.com/detail.asp?id=4519.

54263 ■ Contemporary Physics
Taylor & Francis Ltd.
c/o Peter. L. Knight, Ed.
The Blackett Laboratory
Imperial College London
Prince Consort Rd.
London SW7 2AZ, United Kingdom
Peer-reviewed physics journal. **Freq:** 6/yr. **Key Personnel:** Peter L. Knight, Editor, p.knight@imperial.ac.uk; Martin Plenio, Assoc. Ed., martin.plenio@uni-ulm.de; J. Eberly, Editorial Board; P.W. Milonni, Editorial Board; Peter Torok, Book Review Ed., bookreviews-cph@imperial.ac.uk; P.T. Greenland, Editorial Board; A. Stefanovska, Editorial Board; R.C. Thompson, Editorial Board; D. Bailin, Editorial Board; R. Joseph, Editorial Board. **ISSN:** 0010-7514. **Subscription Rates:** 710 institutions print + online; US$1,182 institutions print + online; 675 institutions online; US$1,123 institutions online; 226 individuals; US$376 individuals; EUR941 institutions print + online; EUR894 institutions online; EUR299 individuals print. **Remarks:** Accepts advertising on request. **Online:** Gale. **URL:** http://www.tandf.co.uk/journals/tf/00107514.html. **Circ:** (Not Reported)

54264 ■ Continuity, Insurance & Risk
Perspective Publishing
3 London Wall Bldgs., 6th Fl.
London EC2M 5PD, United Kingdom
Ph: 44 20 75622400
Fax: 44 20 73742701
Magazine featuring topics in business insurance, risk management, and business continuity. **Founded:** 1996. **Freq:** Bimonthly. **Key Personnel:** Deborah Ritchie, Editor, phone 44 20 75622401, fax 44 20 73742701, deborah.ritchie@cirmagazine.com; Joel Whitefoot, Circulation Mgr., phone 44 20 7562 2419, joel.whitefoot@cirmagazine.com. **Subscription Rates:** 189 individuals. **Remarks:** Accepts advertising. **URL:** http://www.cirmagazine.com/. **Circ:** (Not Reported)

54265 ■ Cooler
Factory Media
1 W Smithfield
London EC1A 9JU, United Kingdom
Ph: 44 20 73329700
Publisher E-mail: contact@factorymedia.com
Magazine featuring women's action sports such as snowboarding and surfing. **Freq:** 6/yr. **Key Personnel:** Lalita Powell, Contact, lalita@coolermag.com. **Subscription Rates:** US$37.50 individuals credit card; 14.99 individuals direct debit; 15.99 individuals credit card. **Remarks:** Accepts advertising. **URL:** http://www.coolermag.com; http://factorymedia.com. **Circ:** (Not Reported)

54266 ■ Cooperation and Conflict
Sage Publications Ltd.
1 Oliver's Yard
55 City Rd.
London EC1Y 1SP, United Kingdom
Ph: 44 20 73248500
Fax: 44 20 73248600
Scholarly journal covering contemporary Scandinavian international relations research and world affairs. **Subtitle:** The Official Journal of the Nordic International Studies Association NISA. **Founded:** 1966. **Freq:** Quarterly. **Key Personnel:** Jan Angstrom, Editor; Eamonn McCallion, Editor; Lee Miles, Editor. **ISSN:** 0010-8367. **Subscription Rates:** US$673 institutions print & e-access; US$740 institutions backfile lease, current volume print & all online; US$606 institutions e-access; US$673 institutions backfile lease, e-access plus backfile; US$1,700 institutions backfile purchase, e-access (content through 1998); US$660 institutions print only; US$96 individuals print only; US$182 institutions single, print; US$31 individuals single, print. **Remarks:** Accepts advertising. **URL:** http://www.sagepub.com/journalsProdDesc.nav?prodId=Journal200863. **Circ:** (Not Reported)

54267 ■ Corporate Watch
Office 14, Unit 6
Wilmer Industrial Estate
Wilmer Pl.
London N16 0LW, United Kingdom
Ph: 44 20 79237082
Publication E-mail: mail@corporatewatch.org
Publisher E-mail: mail@corporatewatch.org
Consumer magazine covering the environment and politics. **Founded:** 1996. **Freq:** every two months. **URL:** http://www.corporatewatch.org/.

54268 ■ Correlation
Astrological Association of Great Britain
Unit 168, Lee Valley Technopark
Tottenham Hale
London N17 9LN, United Kingdom
Ph: 44 20 88804848
Fax: 44 20 88804849
Publisher E-mail: office@astrologicalassociation.com
Journal covering astrology. **Subtitle:** Journal of Research into Astrology. **Freq:** Semiannual. **Subscription Rates:** 13 members UK & Europe; 14 members overseas; 15 nonmembers UK & Europe; 17 nonmembers overseas. **URL:** http://www.astrologer.com/aanet/pub/correl/index.htm.

54269 ■ Corrosion Engineering, Science and Technology
Maney Publishing
1 Carlton House Ter.
London SW1Y 5AF, United Kingdom
Ph: 44 20 74517300
Fax: 44 20 74517307
Publisher E-mail: maney@maney.co.uk
Peer-reviewed journal covering of research and practice in corrosion processes and corrosion control. **Freq:** Bimonthly. **Key Personnel:** Prof. Stuart B. Lyon, Editor, stuart.lyon@manchester.ac.uk; Prof. Robert G. Kelly, North American Ed., rgkelly@virginia.edu. **ISSN:** 1478-422X. **Subscription Rates:** 817 institutions, other countries; US$1,440 institutions; 357 members other countries; US$626 members. **Remarks:** Accepts advertising. **URL:** http://maney.co.uk/index.php/journals/cst/. **Ad Rates:** BW: 500, 4C: 1,100. **Circ:** 900

54270 ■ Cosmetic Products Report
Communications International Group
Linen Hall
162/168 Regent St.

London W1R 5TB, United Kingdom
Ph: 44 20 7341530
Fax: 44 20 7370915
Publisher E-mail: cosmeticsint@1530.com
Publication covering the pharmaceutical and cosmetics industries. **Freq:** Monthly. **Trim Size:** 297 mm x 210 mm. **ISSN:** 1358-3387. **Subscription Rates:** 345 individuals print only; 820 individuals print & online; EUR380 individuals print only; EUR900 individuals print & online. **Remarks:** Accepts advertising. **URL:** http://www.cosmeticsinternational.net/ciproductrep.htm. **Ad Rates:** BW: 950, 4C: 1,290. **Circ:** Paid 2,000

54271 ■ Cosmetics International
Communications International Group
Linen Hall
162/168 Regent St.
London W1R 5TB, United Kingdom
Ph: 44 20 7341530
Fax: 44 20 7370915
Publisher E-mail: cosmeticsint@1530.com
International business publication. **Founded:** 1976. **Freq:** Semimonthly. **Trim Size:** 297 mm x 210 mm. **Key Personnel:** Vivienne Rudd, Editor, vivienne.rudd@1530.com; Suzi Richardson, Advertising Mgr., suzi@cormallen.com; Felim O'Brien, Publishing Dir., felim.obrien@1530.com. **ISSN:** 0963-6137. **Subscription Rates:** 410 individuals print only; EUR450 individuals print only; 820 individuals print & online; EUR900 individuals print & online. **Remarks:** Accepts advertising. **URL:** http://www.cosmeticsinternational.net. **Ad Rates:** BW: 950, 4C: 1,290. **Circ:** Paid 2,000

54272 ■ Cost Effectiveness and Resource Allocation
BioMed Central Ltd.
236 Gray's Inn Rd., Fl. 6
34-42 Cleveland St.
London WC1X 8HL, United Kingdom
Ph: 44 20 31922000
Fax: 44 20 31922010
Publisher E-mail: info@biomedcentral.com
Online journal covering all aspects of economic evaluation in health care and also encourages submissions on health policy issues relating to resource allocation and the trade-offs between economic, ethical and social criteria for decision-making. **Key Personnel:** Dr. David B. Evans, Editor-in-Chief; Dr. Dan Chisholm, Dep. Ed.; Dr. Rob Baltussen, Editor-in-Chief; Dr. Tessa Tan Torres, Dep. Ed.; Dr. Arnab Acharya, Dep. Ed., aacharya@rti.org; Prof. Stefano Bertozzi, Editorial Board. **ISSN:** 1478-7547. **Remarks:** Accepts advertising. **URL:** http://www.resource-allocation.com/home/. **Circ:** (Not Reported)

54273 ■ Counsel
Butterworths Tolley
A Division of Reed Elsevier (UK) Ltd.
Halsbury House
35 Chancery Ln.
London WC2A 1EL, United Kingdom
Ph: 44 20 74002500
Fax: 44 20 74002842
Professional magazine covering law in England and Wales. **Subtitle:** Incorporating Bar News. **Founded:** 1985. **Freq:** Monthly. **Subscription Rates:** 84 individuals. **Remarks:** Accepts advertising. **URL:** http://www.butterworths.com/. **Ad Rates:** BW: 1,210, 4C: 1,710. **Circ:** 23,000

54274 ■ The Country Bird Collection
Eaglemoss Publications Ltd
Beaumont House, 1st Fl.
Kensington Village
Avonmore Rd.
London W14 8TS, United Kingdom
Ph: 44 20 76051200
Fax: 44 20 76051201
Publisher E-mail: webenquiries@eaglemoss.co.uk
Magazine featuring collection of hand painted sculptures of bird. **URL:** http://www.eaglemoss.co.uk/curr-titles/birds.htm.

54275 ■ Country Life
IPC Media Ltd.
Blue Fin Bldg.
110 Southwark St.
London SE1 0SU, United Kingdom
Ph: 44 203 1485000
Magazine covering life, architecture, art, gardening and more on Britain's countryside. **Freq:** Weekly. **Key Per-**

sonnel: Mark Hedges, Editor, phone 44 20 31484435, mark_hedges@ipcmedia.com; Rosemary Archer, Gp. Advertising Mgr., phone 44 20 31484214; Jean Christie, Publishing Dir., jean_christie@ipcmedia.com. **Subscription Rates:** 254.99 two years; 129.99 individuals. **Remarks:** Accepts advertising. **URL:** http://www.countrylife.co.uk; http://www.ipcmedia.com/magazines/countrylife/. **Circ:** ★36,836

54276 ■ Country Music People
Music Farm Ltd.
1-3 Love Ln.
London SE18 6QT, United Kingdom
Ph: 44 20 88547217
Fax: 44 30 99666370
Publication E-mail: info@countrymusicpeople.com
Publisher E-mail: info@countrymusicpeople.com
Consumer magazine covering country music. **Freq:** Monthly. **Subscription Rates:** US$85 individuals; 33 individuals; 40 individuals Europe; 40 elsewhere; 64 two years; 42 individuals Europe, airmail. **Remarks:** Accepts advertising. **URL:** http://www.countrymusicpeople.com. **Circ:** Paid 20,000

54277 ■ Countryside Voice
Think Publishing
The Pall Mall Deposit
124-128 Barlby Rd.
London W10 6BL, United Kingdom
Ph: 44 20 89623020
Fax: 44 20 89628689
Magazine featuring beauty and diversity of English countryside. **Freq:** 3/yr. **Key Personnel:** Ian McAuliffe, Publishing Dir., ian.mcauliffe@thinkpublishing.co.uk; Tilly Boulter, Mng. Dir., tilly.boulter@thinkpublishing.co.uk; Polly Arnold, Mng. Dir., polly.arnold@thinkpublishing.co.uk. **Remarks:** Accepts advertising. **URL:** http://www.thinkpublishing.co.uk/mag_cvoice.html. **Circ:** 35,000

54278 ■ COVER
Incisive Media Limited
Haymarket House
28-29 Haymarket
London SW1Y 4RX, United Kingdom
Ph: 44 870 2408859
Fax: 44 207 4849797
Publisher E-mail: customerservices@incisivemedia.com
Magazine featuring information on the protection, health and life insurance industries. **Subtitle:** Putting protection and health insurance first. **Freq:** Monthly. **Key Personnel:** Paul Robertson, Editor, phone 44 20 70047428, paul.robertson@incisivemedia.com. **URL:** http://www.covermagazine.co.uk.

54279 ■ CPO Agenda
Redactive Media Group
17-18 Britton St.
London EC1M 5TP, United Kingdom
Ph: 44 20 78806200
Fax: 44 20 78807691
Publisher E-mail: info@redactive.co.uk
Magazine reporting on purchasing and supply management. **Freq:** Quarterly. **Key Personnel:** Aaron Nicholls, Contact. **Subscription Rates:** 90 institutions for members of CIPS; 110 individuals. **URL:** http://www.cpoagenda.com.

54280 ■ CPRE Voice
Council for the Protection of Rural England
128 Southwark St.
London SE1 0SW, United Kingdom
Ph: 44 20 79812800
Publisher E-mail: info@cpre.org.uk
Publication covering conservation. **Freq:** 3/yr. **Subscription Rates:** Free to members. **Remarks:** Advertising accepted; rates available upon request. **URL:** http://www.cpre.org.uk. **Circ:** (Not Reported)

54281 ■ Crafts
Crafts Council
44a Pentonville Rd.
Islington
London N1 9BY, United Kingdom
Ph: 44 20 78062500
Fax: 44 20 78376891
Publication covering crafts. **Freq:** Bimonthly. **Trim Size:** 237 x 297 mm. **Key Personnel:** Polly Benford, Contact, subscriptions@craftscouncil.org.uk. **Subscription Rates:** EUR34 individuals U.K. and Eire; 42 individuals Europe; US$48 other countries; 50 U.S. online; 30

students U.K. and Eire. **Remarks:** Accepts advertising. **URL:** http://www.craftscouncil.org.uk/crafts-magazine/. **Ad Rates:** GLR: .75, BW: 1,100, 4C: 1,385. **Circ:** 20,000

54282 ■ Creative Review
Centaur Publishing Ltd.
50 Poland St.
London W1F 7AX, United Kingdom
Ph: 44 20 79704000
Fax: 44 20 79704189
Publication for the arts and entertainment industries. **Freq:** Monthly. **Print Method:** Litho. **Trim Size:** 280 x 280 mm. **Key Personnel:** Jessica MacDermott, Publisher, phone 44 20 72923703, jessica.macdermot@centaur.co.uk; Patrick Burgoyne, Editor, phone 44 20 79706273, patrick.burgoyne@centaur.co.uk; Janice Hoyes-Thompson, Gp. Advisory Mgr., phone 44 20 79706262. **ISSN:** 0262-1037. **Subscription Rates:** 64 individuals; 108 two years; 151 individuals three years; 40 individuals online only. **Remarks:** Accepts advertising. **URL:** http://www.creativereview.co.uk. **Formerly:** Jessica Macdermott. **Ad Rates:** BW: 4,125, 4C: 4,125, PCI: 43. **Circ:** Paid ★19,032

54283 ■ Credit
Incisive Media Limited
Haymarket House
28-29 Haymarket
London SW1Y 4RX, United Kingdom
Ph: 44 870 2408859
Fax: 44 207 4849797
Publisher E-mail: customerservices@incisivemedia.com
Magazine featuring corporate bond markets. **Founded:** 2000. **Key Personnel:** Rob Davies, Editor; Rob Mannix, Publisher. **Subscription Rates:** 892 individuals; EUR2,408 two years; 2,275 individuals 3 years; EUR1,338 individuals; 2,275 two years; US$1,785 individuals; US$3,213 two years. **Remarks:** Accepts advertising. **URL:** http://www.risk.net/credit. **Circ:** (Not Reported)

54284 ■ Credit Today
Athene Publishing Ltd.
Axe & Bottle Ct.
70 Newcomen St.
London SE1 1YT, United Kingdom
Ph: 44 844 4774740
Fax: 44 20 79404843
Publication E-mail: online@credittoday.co.uk
Publisher E-mail: online@credittoday.co.uk
Magazine covering credit industry. **Subtitle:** The Magazine for the Commercial and Consumer Credit Industry. **Key Personnel:** Heather Greig-Smith, Editor, editorial@credittoday.co.uk; Ray Walsh, Production Mgr., ray@credittoday.co.uk. **Subscription Rates:** 195 individuals; 390 two years. **Remarks:** Accepts advertising. **URL:** http://www.credittoday.co.uk. **Circ:** ★13,670

54285 ■ Criminal Appeal Reports
Justis Publishing Ltd
Grand Union House
20 Kentish Town Rd.
London NW1 9NR, United Kingdom
Ph: 44 20 72848080
Fax: 44 20 72671133
Publisher E-mail: caloc@justic.com
Journal publishing all major criminal appeal cases. **Founded:** 1908. **Freq:** Quarterly. **URL:** http://www.justis.com/data-coverage/criminal-appeal-reports.aspx.

54286 ■ Criminology & Criminal Justice
Sage Publications Ltd.
1 Oliver's Yard
55 City Rd.
London EC1Y 1SP, United Kingdom
Ph: 44 20 73248500
Fax: 44 20 73248600
Peer-reviewed journal covering criminal justice worldwide. **Subtitle:** An International Journal. **Founded:** 2001. **Freq:** Quarterly. **Key Personnel:** Trevor Jones, Editor; Gordon Hughes, Editor; Matthew Williams, Editor. **ISSN:** 1748-8958. **Subscription Rates:** US$729 institutions print & E-access; US$665 institutions E-access; US$714 institutions print only; US$87 individuals print only; US$196 institutions single print; US$28 individuals single print. **Remarks:** Accepts advertising. **URL:** http://www.sagepub.com/journalsProdDesc.nav?prodId=Journal201382. **Formerly:** Criminal Justice. **Circ:** (Not Reported)

Circulation: ★ = ABC; △ = BPA; ◆ = CAC; • = CCAB; ❑ = VAC; ⊕ = PO Statement; ‡ = Publisher's Report; Boldface figures = sworn; Light figures = estimated.

Gale Directory of Publications & Broadcast Media/147th Ed.

5703

54287 ■ Criss Cross
H. Bauer Publishing
Academic House
24-28 Oval Rd.
London NW1 7DT, United Kingdom
Ph: 44 20 72418000
Fax: 44 20 72418030
Magazine containing criss cross puzzles. **Freq:** Monthly. **Trim Size:** 185 x 255 mm. **Key Personnel:** Clive Garsin, Gp. Ed.; Spike Figgett, Publishing Dir.; Helen Greenwood, Advertising Mgr. **Subscription Rates:** 17.29 individuals. **URL:** http://www.bauer.co.uk; http://www.puzzlemagazines.co.uk/criss-cross. **Circ: ★63,000**

54288 ■ Critical Care
BioMed Central Ltd.
236 Gray's Inn Rd., Fl. 6
34-42 Cleveland St.
London WC1X 8HL, United Kingdom
Ph: 44 20 31922000
Fax: 44 20 31922010
Publication E-mail: editorial@ccforum.com
Publisher E-mail: info@biomedcentral.com
Medical journal publishing commentaries, reviews, and research relating to intensive care and emergency medicine. **Key Personnel:** Prof. Jean-Louis Vincent, Editor-in-Chief. **ISSN:** 1364-8535. **Remarks:** Advertising accepted; rates available upon request. **URL:** http://ccforum.com/. **Circ:** (Not Reported)

54289 ■ Critical Social Policy
Sage Publications Ltd.
1 Oliver's Yard
55 City Rd.
London EC1Y 1SP, United Kingdom
Ph: 44 20 73248500
Fax: 44 20 73248600
Scholarly journal covering welfare from socialist, feminist, antiracist, and radical perspectives. **Subtitle:** A Journal of Theory and Practice in Social Welfare. **Founded:** 1981. **Freq:** Quarterly. **Key Personnel:** Alice Bloch, Editorial Collective; Norman Ginsburg, Editorial Collective. **ISSN:** 0261-0183. **Subscription Rates:** US$25 individuals single print; US$169 institutions single print; US$627 institutions print & e-access; US$690 institutions backfile lease, combined plus backfile; US$564 institutions e-access; US$627 institutions backfile lease, e-access plus backfile; US$863 institutions backfile purchase, e-access (content through 1998); US$614 institutions print only; US$76 individuals print. **Remarks:** Accepts advertising. **URL:** http://www.sagepub.com/journalsProdDesc.nav?prodId=Journal200748. **Ad Rates:** BW: 250. **Circ:** (Not Reported)

54290 ■ Critical Sociology
Sage Publications Ltd.
1 Oliver's Yard
55 City Rd.
London EC1Y 1SP, United Kingdom
Ph: 44 20 73248500
Fax: 44 20 73248600
Peer-reviewed journal covering sociology. **Founded:** 1969. **Freq:** Bimonthly. **Trim Size:** 6 x 9. **Cols./Page:** 1. **Key Personnel:** David Fasenfest, Editor; Denis Wall, Managing Editor; George Sanders, Book Review Ed. **ISSN:** 0896-9205. **Subscription Rates:** US$100 individuals print; US$808 institutions print and E-access; US$727 institutions E-access; US$792 institutions print; US$145 institutions single print; US$22 individuals single print. **Remarks:** Accepts advertising. **URL:** http://www.sagepub.com/journalsProdDesc.nav?prodId=Journal201869. **Former name:** Insurgent Sociologist. **Circ:** Paid 850

54291 ■ Critique of Anthropology
Sage Publications Ltd.
1 Oliver's Yard
55 City Rd.
London EC1Y 1SP, United Kingdom
Ph: 44 20 73248500
Fax: 44 20 73248600
Scholarly journal covering the development of anthropology as a discipline that subjects social reality to critical analysis. **Founded:** 1981. **Freq:** Quarterly March - June - September - December. **Key Personnel:** John Gledhill, Managing Editor; Stephen Nugent, Managing Editor; Nicola Frost, Book Review Ed. **ISSN:** 0308-275X. **Subscription Rates:** US$905 institutions print &

e-access; US$996 institutions current volume print & all online content; US$815 institutions e-access; US$906 institutions all online content; US$1,247 institutions e-access (content through 1998); US$887 institutions print only; US$93 individuals print only; US$244 institutions single, print; US$30 individuals single, print. **Remarks:** Accepts advertising. **URL:** http://www.sagepub.com/journalsProdDesc.nav?prodId=Journal200880. **Circ:** (Not Reported)

54292 ■ Cultural Dynamics
Sage Publications Ltd.
1 Oliver's Yard
55 City Rd.
London EC1Y 1SP, United Kingdom
Ph: 44 20 73248500
Fax: 44 20 73248600
Scholarly journal covering socio-cultural phenomena, including work from sociology, psychology, philosophy and other areas related to culture and society. **Founded:** 1989. **Freq:** 3/yr. **Key Personnel:** Dipesh Chakraborty, Editorial Board; Elvia Mendoza, Managing Editor; Rene Devisch, Editorial Board; Frank van Dun, Editorial Board; Aant Elzinga, Editorial Board; Johannes Fabian, Editorial Board; Barbara Frankel, Editorial Board; S.N. Balagangadhara, Editorial Board. **ISSN:** 0921-3740. **Subscription Rates:** US$1,006 institutions print & e-access; US$1,107 institutions current volume print & all online content; US$905 institutions e-access; US$1,006 institutions all online content; US$905 institutions e-access (content through 1998); US$986 institutions print only; US$87 individuals print only; US$362 institutions single print; US$38 individuals single print. **Remarks:** Accepts advertising. **URL:** http://www.sagepub.com/journalsProdDesc.nav?prodId=Journal200795. **Circ:** (Not Reported)

54293 ■ Cultural Geographies
Sage Publications Ltd.
1 Oliver's Yard
55 City Rd.
London EC1Y 1SP, United Kingdom
Ph: 44 20 73248500
Fax: 44 20 73248600
Journal covering all aspects of cultural geography. **Freq:** Quarterly. **Key Personnel:** Philip Crang, Editorial Board, p.crang@rhul.ac.uk; Tim J. Cresswell, Managing Editor. **ISSN:** 1474-4740. **Subscription Rates:** 405 institutions print & e-access; 365 institutions e-access; 397 institutions print only; 70 individuals print & e-access; 109 institutions single print; 23 individuals single print. **Remarks:** Accepts advertising. **URL:** http://www.sagepub.co.uk/journalsProdDesc.nav?prodId=Journal201809. **Circ:** (Not Reported)

54294 ■ Culture, Health and Sexuality
Routledge
Taylor & Francis Group Ltd.
Thomas Coram Research Unit
Institute of Education
University of London
27-28 Woburn Sq.
London WC1H 0AA, United Kingdom
Publisher E-mail: webmaster.books@tandf.co.uk
Peer-reviewed international environment journal for the publication of scholarly papers in the fields of culture, health and sexuality, publishing papers that deal with methodological concerns as well as those that are empirical and conceptual in nature. **Subtitle:** An International Journal for Research, Intervention and Care. **Freq:** 8/yr. **Key Personnel:** Peter Aggleton, Editor, p.aggleton@sussex.ac.uk; Susan Kippax, Founding Ed.; Shalini Bharat, Reviews Ed.; Gary Dowsett, Sen. Reviews Ed.; Purnima Mane, Founding Ed.; Paul Flowers, Review Ed. **ISSN:** 1369-1058. **Subscription Rates:** US$419 individuals print only; US$960 institutions online; US$1,011 institutions print + online; US$40 individuals developing country; 252 individuals print only; 580 institutions online; 610 institutions print + online. **Remarks:** Accepts advertising. **URL:** http://www.tandf.co.uk/journals/titles/13691058.asp. **Circ:** (Not Reported)

54295 ■ Culture & Psychology
Sage Publications Ltd.
1 Oliver's Yard
55 City Rd.
London EC1Y 1SP, United Kingdom
Ph: 44 20 73248500

Fax: 44 20 73248600
Peer-reviewed journal covering culture and human behavior, identity, emotions, development, language and experiences. **Founded:** 1995. **Freq:** Quarterly. **Key Personnel:** Margaret Luciano, Editorial Assoc.; Jaan Valsiner, Editor; Stuart McNaughton, Editorial Board; Mario Carretero, Editorial Board; Yasuko Minoura, Assoc. Ed.; Nandita Chaudhary, Assoc. Ed. **ISSN:** 1354-067X. **Subscription Rates:** US$919 institutions electronic & print; US$1,011 institutions current volume print & all online content; US$901 institutions print only; US$100 individuals print only; US$248 institutions single print; US$33 individuals single print; US$827 institutions E-access; US$901 institutions all online content; US$827 institutions content through 1998. **Remarks:** Accepts advertising. **URL:** http://www.sagepub.com/journalsProdDesc.nav?prodId=Journal200766. **Circ:** (Not Reported)

54296 ■ Current Neuropharmacology
Bentham Science Publishers Ltd.
Institute of Ophthalmology
University College London
London EC1V 9EL, United Kingdom
Publisher E-mail: subscriptions@bentham.org
Journal providing current, timely and comprehensive reviews of all areas of neuropharmacology and related matters of neuroscience. **Freq:** Quarterly. **Key Personnel:** Thomas E. Salt, Editor-in-Chief; Bernhard Bettler, Editorial Advisory Board; Nobuhisa Iwata, Regional Ed.; Jeffrey P. Conn, Regional Ed.; Paolo Calabresi, Editorial Advisory Board; Raymond G. Hill, Editorial Advisory Board. **ISSN:** 1570-159X. **Subscription Rates:** US$1,400 institutions corporate, print; US$1,400 institutions corporate, online; US$180 individuals personal, print; US$780 institutions academic, print; US$780 institutions academic, online. **Remarks:** Accepts advertising. **URL:** http://www.bentham.org/cn/. **Circ:** (Not Reported)

54297 ■ Current Opinion in Clinical Nutrition & Metabolic Care
Lippincott, Williams and Wilkins Ltd.
250 Waterloo Rd.
London SE1 8RD, United Kingdom
Ph: 44 20 79810500
Fax: 44 20 79810501
Journal covering specialist medical literature review. **Founded:** 1998. **Freq:** Bimonthly. **Key Personnel:** Ian Burgess, Publisher, ian.burgess@wolterskluwer.com; Yvon Carpentier, Editor-in-Chief; Luc A. Cynober, Editor-in-Chief. **ISSN:** 1363-1950. **Subscription Rates:** US$368 individuals; US$1,094 institutions; US$388 out of country individual; US$1,173 institutions, other countries. **Remarks:** Accepts classified advertising. **URL:** http://journals.lww.com/co-clinicalnutrition/pages/default.aspx. **Circ:** (Not Reported)

54298 ■ Current Opinion in Drug Discovery & Development
BioMed Central Ltd.
236 Gray's Inn Rd., Fl. 6
34-42 Cleveland St.
London WC1X 8HL, United Kingdom
Ph: 44 20 31922000
Fax: 44 20 31922010
Publisher E-mail: info@biomedcentral.com
Journal focusing on the chemical aspects of drug discovery and development. **Freq:** Bimonthly. **Key Personnel:** Suzanne Austin, Editor, suzanne.austin@thomsonreuters.com. **URL:** http://www.biomedcentral.com/curropindrugdiscovdevel/.

54299 ■ Current Opinion in Infectious Diseases
Lippincott, Williams and Wilkins Ltd.
250 Waterloo Rd.
London SE1 8RD, United Kingdom
Ph: 44 20 79810500
Fax: 44 20 79810501
Medical journal. **Founded:** 1987. **Freq:** Bimonthly. **Print Method:** Offset lithography. **Trim Size:** 8 1/2 x 11. **Cols./Page:** 2. **Key Personnel:** Thomas Patterson, Editor; Roger G. Finch, Editor. **ISSN:** 0951-7375. **Subscription Rates:** US$399.40 individuals; US$1,140.40 institutions U.S.; US$155.60 individuals in training; US$403.40 institutions, other countries; US$1,226.40 institutions International. **Remarks:** Accepts advertising. **URL:** http://journals.lww.com/co-infectiousdiseases/pages/

currenttoc.aspx. **Ad Rates:** BW: 820, 4C: 1,040. **Circ:** Paid ‡2,612

54300 ■ Current Opinion in Investigational Drugs
Current Drugs Ltd.
34-42 Cleveland St.
London W1T 4LB, United Kingdom
Ph: 44 20 73442800
Fax: 44 20 73442900
Journal delivering systematic and comprehensive coverage of the following therapeutic areas: anti-infectives; anti-inflammatory, immune-meditated and gastrointestinal; cardiovascular, renal and metabolic; central and peripheral nervous system; and oncological. **Freq:** Monthly. **Key Personnel:** Mike Williams, Editor-in-Chief. **Subscription Rates:** 2,140 institutions; US$3,896 institutions; 1,177 individuals. **URL:** http://www.biomedcentral.com/1472-4472.

54301 ■ Current Opinion in Molecular Therapeutics
BioMed Central Ltd.
236 Gray's Inn Rd., Fl. 6
34-42 Cleveland St.
London WC1X 8HL, United Kingdom
Ph: 44 20 31922000
Fax: 44 20 31922010
Publisher E-mail: info@biomedcentral.com
Journal covering the broad field of molecular medicine, including viral and non-viral gene therapy, oligonucleotides, peptide therapeutics, antibody approaches, molecular vaccines, and the technologies underlying genomics and proteomics. **Freq:** Bimonthly. **Key Personnel:** Barbara Chan, Managing Editor. **URL:** http://www.biomedcentral.com/curropinmolther/.

54302 ■ Current Opinion in Neurology
Lippincott, Williams and Wilkins Ltd.
250 Waterloo Rd.
London SE1 8RD, United Kingdom
Ph: 44 20 79810500
Fax: 44 20 79810501
Professional journal covering recent developments in neurology. **Founded:** 1988. **Freq:** Bimonthly. **Key Personnel:** Richard S.J. Frackowiak, Editor; John Mazziotta, Dep. Ed.; Ian Burgess, Publisher, ian.burgess@wolterskluwer.com. **ISSN:** 1350-7540. **Subscription Rates:** US$389.40 individuals; US$1,282.40 institutions; US$155.60 individuals in-training; US$400.40 individuals International; US$1,374.40 institutions, other countries; US$155.60 individuals in-training, International. **Remarks:** Accepts advertising. **URL:** http://journals.lww.com/co-neurology/pages/default.aspx. **Circ:** (Not Reported)

54303 ■ Current Pediatric Reviews
Bentham Science Publishers Ltd.
King's College Hospital
London SE5 9PJ, United Kingdom
Publisher E-mail: subscriptions@bentham.org
Journal publishing frontier reviews on all the latest advances in pediatric medicine. **Freq:** Quarterly. **Key Personnel:** Anne Greenough, Editor-in-Chief; G.P. Aylward, Editorial Advisory Board; J.B. Beckwith, Editorial Advisory Board; P. Adamson, Editorial Advisory Board; P.J. Ambrosini, Editorial Advisory Board; D.C. Aronson, Editorial Advisory Board; P.F. Ambros, Editorial Advisory Board; A. Aperia, Editorial Advisory Board; C. Agostoni, Editorial Advisory Board; P.E. Alvin, Editorial Advisory Board. **ISSN:** 1573-3963. **Subscription Rates:** US$960 institutions corporate, print; US$960 institutions corporate, online; US$190 individuals print; US$460 institutions academic, print; US$460 institutions academic, online. **Remarks:** Accepts advertising. **URL:** http://www.bentham.org/cpr/index.htm. **Circ:** (Not Reported)

54304 ■ Current Vascular Pharmacology
Bentham Science Publishers Ltd.
Dept. of Clinical Biochemistry
Royal Free & University College School of Medicine
Pond St.
London NW3 2QG, United Kingdom
Ph: 44 20 78302258
Fax: 44 20 78302235
Publisher E-mail: subscriptions@bentham.org
Journal publishing reviews to update all those concerned with the treatment of vascular disease, including reviews commenting on recently published trials or new drugs.

Freq: Quarterly. **Key Personnel:** Dimitri P. Mikhailidis, Editor-in-Chief, mikhailidis@hotmail.com; R. Wray, Co-Ed.; M.R. Dashwood, Co-Ed. **ISSN:** 1570-1611. **Subscription Rates:** US$1,400 individuals corporate print; US$1,400 individuals corporate online; US$1,680 individuals corporate print and online; US$780 individuals academic print; US$780 individuals academic online; US$860 individuals academic print and online; US$180 individuals print only. **Remarks:** Accepts advertising. **URL:** http://www.bentham.org/cvp/. **Circ:** (Not Reported)

54305 ■ Custom PC
Dennis Publishing Ltd.
30 Cleveland St.
London W1T 4JD, United Kingdom
Ph: 44 20 79076000
Fax: 44 20 79076020
Publisher E-mail: reception@dennis.co.uk
Magazine featuring news, product reviews, shopping, computer downloads, and more. **Freq:** Monthly. **Key Personnel:** Alex Watson, Group Ed., alex.watson@bit-tech.net. **Subscription Rates:** 15.99 individuals direct debit, every 6 issues; 31.99 individuals credit/debit card. **URL:** http://www.custompc.co.uk.

54306 ■ CWU Voice
Communication Workers Union - England
150 The Broadway
Wimbledon
London SW19 1RX, United Kingdom
Ph: 44 20 89717200
Fax: 44 20 89717300
Publisher E-mail: info@cwu.org
Publication covering communications. **Freq:** Bimonthly. **Key Personnel:** Howard Burns, Designer; Marcia Murray, Contact, mmurray@cwu.org; Kevin Slocombe, Contact, kslocombe@cwu.org; John Colbert, Communication/Campaigns Mgr., jcolbert@cwu.org; Simon Alford, Publications Ed.; Abigail Lawrence-Jones, Web Ed., alawrence-jones@cwu.org. **Remarks:** Advertising accepted; rates available upon request. **URL:** http://www.cwu.org. **Circ:** (Not Reported)

54307 ■ CytoJournal
BioMed Central Ltd.
236 Gray's Inn Rd., Fl. 6
34-42 Cleveland St.
London WC1X 8HL, United Kingdom
Ph: 44 20 31922000
Fax: 44 20 31922010
Publication E-mail: cytojournal@mcw.edu
Publisher E-mail: info@biomedcentral.com
Online journal covering all aspects of diagnostic cytopathology, including complementary topics such as molecular cytopathology. **Key Personnel:** Richard De-May, Editor-in-Chief; Dr. Vinod Shidham, Editor-in-Chief. **ISSN:** 1742-6413. **Remarks:** Accepts advertising. **URL:** http://www.cytojournal.com. **Circ:** (Not Reported)

54308 ■ Daisy
Egmont Magazines
184-192 Drummond St., 4th Fl.
London NW1 3HP, United Kingdom
Ph: 44 20 73806430
Magazine for little girls aged 4-7. **Freq:** Monthly. **Trim Size:** 220 x 300 mm. **Subscription Rates:** 2.99 individuals. **Remarks:** Accepts advertising. **URL:** http://www.egmont.co.uk/product.asp?prodid=1580&catid=. **Ad Rates:** 4C: 1,800. **Circ:** ★43,162

54309 ■ Dance Gazette
Royal Academy of Dancing
36 Battersea Sq.
London SW11 3RA, United Kingdom
Ph: 44 20 73268000
Publication E-mail: info@rad.org.uk
Publisher E-mail: info@rad.org.uk
Publication covering dance. **Freq:** 3/yr. **Key Personnel:** Olivia Swift, Editor, oswift@rad.org.uk. **Remarks:** Advertising accepted; rates available upon request. **URL:** http://www.rad.org.uk/article.asp?id=249. **Circ:** 12,000

54310 ■ Dance Today!
Dancing Times Ltd.
45-47 Clerkenwell Green
London EC1R 0EB, United Kingdom
Ph: 44 20 72503006
Fax: 44 20 72536679

Publication E-mail: dancetoday@dancing-times.co.uk
Publisher E-mail: dt@dancing-times.co.uk
Consumer magazine covering all forms of social dance. **Founded:** 1910. **Freq:** Monthly. **Trim Size:** 168 x 220 mm. **ISSN:** 1475-2336. **Subscription Rates:** 19.25 individuals; 22.50 individuals overseas. **Remarks:** Accepts advertising. **URL:** http://www.dancing-times.co.uk/dance-today. **Formerly:** Ballroom Dancing Times. **Circ:** (Not Reported)

54311 ■ Dancing Times
Dancing Times Ltd.
45-47 Clerkenwell Green
London EC1R 0EB, United Kingdom
Ph: 44 20 72503006
Fax: 44 20 72536679
Publication E-mail: dt@dancing-times.co.uk
Publisher E-mail: dt@dancing-times.co.uk
Consumer magazine covering all forms of social dance, including history, design, music, training and education. **Founded:** 1910. **Freq:** Monthly. **Print Method:** Web Offset. **Trim Size:** 210 x 297 mm. **Key Personnel:** Jonathan Gray, Editor. **ISSN:** 0011-605X. **Subscription Rates:** 32.45 individuals; 39.45 individuals overseas. **Remarks:** Accepts advertising. **URL:** http://www.dancing-times.co.uk. **Circ:** (Not Reported)

54312 ■ DARE
River Publishing Limited
Victory House
14 Leicester Pl.
London WC2H 7BZ, United Kingdom
Ph: 44 20 73060304
Publisher E-mail: nmurphy@riverltd.co.uk
Magazine featuring fashion, beauty and celebrity news. **Freq:** 7/yr. **Key Personnel:** Nathalie Gibbins, Editor. **Remarks:** Accepts advertising. **URL:** http://www.superdrug.com/scat/darecompetitions. **Circ:** (Not Reported)

54313 ■ DBI Review
Deafblind International
c/o 11-13 Clifton Ter.
Finsbury Pk.
London N4 3SR, United Kingdom
Ph: 44 20 72727881
Fax: 44 20 72726012
Publisher E-mail: secretariat@deafblindinternational.org
English and Spanish language publication covering the disabled. **Freq:** Semiannual. **Remarks:** Advertising accepted; rates available upon request. **URL:** http://www.deafblindinternational.org/; http://www.deafblindinternational.org/standard/review.html. **Circ:** 3,000

54314 ■ Decanter
Time Inc.
Blue Fin Bldg.
110 Southwark St.
London SE1 0SU, United Kingdom
Ph: 44 20 31485000
Fax: 44 20 31488524
Publisher E-mail: information@timeinc.com
British wine magazine geared toward those with an interest in wine - from connoisseurs to amateur enthusiasts. Experts recommend 4,000 wines a year. **Founded:** 1975. **Freq:** Monthly. **Key Personnel:** Guy Woodward, Editor, phone 44 20 31484488, guy_woodward@ipcmedia.com; Sarah Kemp, Publishing Dir., phone 44 20 31484480, sarah_kemp@ipcmedia.com; Sophia Dempsey, Publisher, phone 44 20 31484481, sophia_dempsey@ipcmedia.com; John Cullimore, Advertising Mgr., phone 44 20 31484502, john_cullimore@ipcmedia.com; Kerry MacDonald, Head of Mktg., phone 44 20 31484508, kerry_macdonald@ipcmedia.com. **Subscription Rates:** 29.99 individuals direct debit; 59.99 two years. **Remarks:** Accepts advertising. **URL:** http://www.decanter.com/; http://www.ipcmedia.com/brands/decanter/. **Circ:** 46,000

54315 ■ Dementia
Sage Publications Ltd.
1 Oliver's Yard
55 City Rd.
London EC1Y 1SP, United Kingdom
Ph: 44 20 73248500
Fax: 44 20 73248600
Scholarly journal covering the social experience of dementia worldwide. **Subtitle:** The International Journal of

Circulation: ★ = ABC; △ = BPA; ♦ = CAC; • = CCAB; ❑ = VAC; ⊕ = PO Statement; ‡ = Publisher's Report; Boldface figures = sworn; Light figures = estimated.

Gale Directory of Publications & Broadcast Media/147th Ed.   5705

Social Research and Practice. **Founded:** 2002. **Freq:** 5/yr. **Key Personnel:** John Keady, Editor; Phyllis Braudy Harris, Editor; Jaber F. Gubrium, Editorial Board; Jo Moriarty, Innovative Practice Ed.; Charlotte L. Clarke, Editorial Board; Heather Wilkinson, Book Review Ed. **ISSN:** 1471-3012. **Subscription Rates:** US$783 institutions print & e-access; US$705 institutions e-access; US$767 institutions print; US$89 individuals print; US$211 institutions single print; US$29 individuals single print. **Remarks:** Accepts advertising. **URL:** http://www.sagepub.com/journalsProdDesc.nav?prodId=Journal201266. **Ad Rates:** BW: 200. **Circ:** (Not Reported)

54316 ■ The Democrat
Campaign Against Euro-Federalism
PO Box 46295
London W5 2UG, United Kingdom
Ph: 44 845 3458902
Journal covering the campaign against the European Union including such issues as democracy, independence, jobs, peace, racism, single currency, military union and European Army, EU Constitution and other political/social issues. **Founded:** 1991. **Freq:** Bimonthly. **Print Method:** Digital Copy. **Trim Size:** A4. **ISSN:** 0967-3806. **Subscription Rates:** 6 individuals for ten issues. **URL:** http://www.caef.org.uk/democratindex.html. **Circ:** Paid 1,000

54317 ■ Dental Nursing
MA Healthcare Ltd.
St. Jude's Church
Dulwich Rd.
Herne Hill
London SE24 0PB, United Kingdom
Ph: 44 20 77385454
Fax: 44 20 77332325
Journal covering for all dental nurses. **Subtitle:** The essential resource for all dental nurses. **Founded:** Oct. 2005. **Freq:** Monthly. **Key Personnel:** Tessa Meese, Editor-in-Chief; Peter Black, Editor, peter.black@markallengroup.com; Kirsty Medlock, Advertising Mgr., kirsty.medlock@markallengroup.com. **Subscription Rates:** 80 individuals Ireland; 145 individuals Europe; 207 other countries paper; 64 students Ireland. **Remarks:** Accepts advertising. **URL:** http://www.dental-nursing.co.uk/. **Circ:** (Not Reported)

54318 ■ Depression
Remedica Medical Education and Publishing
Commonwealth House
1 New Oxford St.
London WC1A 1NU, United Kingdom
Ph: 44 20 77592999
Fax: 44 20 77592951
Publisher E-mail: info@remedica.com
Journal covering significant advances in the field of medicine. **Subtitle:** Mind and Body. **Freq:** Quarterly. **Key Personnel:** Alan F. Schatzberg, Editor-in-Chief; Christos Ballas, Editor; Po W. Wang, Editor. **ISSN:** 1479-5035. **Subscription Rates:** Free interested healthcare professionals; US$70 U.S. and Canada non-healthcare professionals; EUR70 individuals Europe, non-healthcare professionals; US$75 other countries non-healthcare professionals. **URL:** http://www.depressionmindbody.com/.

54319 ■ Derby Festival @MAG
Luxury Publishing Limited
5 Jubilee Pl.
Chelsea
London SW3 3TD, United Kingdom
Ph: 44 20 75912900
Fax: 44 20 75912929
Publisher E-mail: info@luxurypublishing.com
Magazine featuring the British sports festival. **Key Personnel:** Charlie Methven, Editor. **Remarks:** Accepts advertising. **URL:** http://www.luxurypublishing.co.uk/. **Circ:** (Not Reported)

54320 ■ Dermatology in Practice
Hayward Medical Communications
Covent Garden
8-10 Dryden St.
London WC2E 9NA, United Kingdom
Publisher E-mail: admin@hayward.co.uk
Journal covering all aspects of dermatology. **Founded:** 1989. **Key Personnel:** Neil H. Cox, Editor. **URL:** http://www.dermatologyinpractice.co.uk/dip/.

54321 ■ Design Week
Centaur Publishing Ltd.

50 Poland St.
London W1F 7AX, United Kingdom
Ph: 44 20 79704000
Fax: 44 20 79704189
Publication for the architecture and design industries. **Freq:** Weekly. **Trim Size:** 250 x 335 mm. **Key Personnel:** Lynda Relph-Knight, Editor, phone 44 20 79706408, lyndark@centaur.co.uk; Angus Montgomery, News Ed., phone 44 20 79706403, angus.montgomery@centaur.co.uk. **ISSN:** 0950-3676. **Subscription Rates:** 85 individuals UK residents; 162 two years UK residents; 223 individuals UK residents (three years); 138 individuals Europe residents; 260 two years Europe residents; 354 individuals Europe residents - three years; 160 individuals U.S. and Canada; 303 two years U.S. and Canada; 414 individuals three years, U.S. and Canada; 160 other countries. **Remarks:** Accepts advertising. **URL:** http://www.designweek.co.uk. **Circ:** (Not Reported)

54322 ■ Deutsche unquote
Incisive Media Limited
Haymarket House
28-29 Haymarket
London SW1Y 4RX, United Kingdom
Ph: 44 870 2408859
Fax: 44 207 4849797
Publisher E-mail: customerservices@incisivemedia.com
Journal covering news from the venture capital and private equity markets in Germany, Switzerland, and Austria. **Founded:** 1992. **Freq:** Monthly. **Key Personnel:** Helen Longhurst, Contact, phone 44 20 70047453, helen.longhurst@incisivemedia.com; Mareen Goebel, Editor, phone 44 20 70047462, mareen.goebel@incisivemedia.com. **Remarks:** Accepts advertising. **URL:** http://www.incisivemedia.com/corporate/products/deuunquote; http://www.deutscheunquote.com. **Circ:** (Not Reported)

54323 ■ Diabetes & Primary Care
SB Communications Group
3.05 Enterprise House
1-2 Hatfields
London SE1 9PG, United Kingdom
Ph: 44 20 76271510
Fax: 44 20 76271570
Publisher E-mail: info@sbcommunicationsgroup.co.uk
Journal containing news, articles and reviews on diabetes and its complications. **Subtitle:** The Official Journal of the PCDS. **Key Personnel:** Colin Kenny, Editor. **Remarks:** Accepts advertising. **URL:** http://www.diabetesandprimarycare.co.uk/index.php. **Circ:** (Not Reported)

54324 ■ Diabetes Update
Diabetes UK
Macleod House
10 Pky.
London NW1 7AA, United Kingdom
Ph: 44 20 74241000
Fax: 44 20 74241001
Publication E-mail: update@diabetes.org.uk
Publisher E-mail: info@diabetes.org.ok
Magazine of Diabetes UK. **Freq:** Quarterly. **Remarks:** Accepts advertising. **URL:** http://www.diabetes.org.uk/Professionals/Publications-reports-and-resources/Diabetes-Update/. **Circ:** (Not Reported)

54325 ■ Diagnostic Pathology
BioMed Central Ltd.
236 Gray's Inn Rd., Fl. 6
34-42 Cleveland St.
London WC1X 8HL, United Kingdom
Ph: 44 20 31922000
Fax: 44 20 31922010
Publisher E-mail: info@biomedcentral.com
Journal on various aspects of surgical and clinical pathology including classic diagnostic pathology, prognosis related diagnosis and therapy related findings. **Key Personnel:** Dr. G. Kayser, Dep. Ed., gian.kayser@niklinik-freiburg.de; Dr. Klaus Kayser, Editor-in-Chief, klaus.kayser@charite.de; Prof. N.J. Agnantis, Editorial Board, nagnanti@cc.uoi.gr; Dr. T. Goldman, Dep. Ed., tgoldmann@fz-borstel.de; Dr. R. An, Editorial Board; Dr. Y. Collan, Editorial Board. **ISSN:** 1746-1596. **URL:** http://www.diagnosticpathology.org/.

54326 ■ Dirt Mountain Bike Magazine
Factory Media
1 W Smithfield

London EC1A 9JU, United Kingdom
Ph: 44 20 73329700
Publisher E-mail: contact@factorymedia.com
Magazine featuring mountain biking. **Freq:** Monthly. **Subscription Rates:** 35.99 individuals credit card; 32.50 individuals direct debit; US$58 individuals. **URL:** http://www.dirtmag.co.uk; http://factorymedia.com.

54327 ■ Disability Now
Scope
6 Market Rd.
London N7 9PW, United Kingdom
Ph: 44 20 76197100
Publisher E-mail: response@scope.org.uk
Newspaper for disabled people, their families, carers and professionals in the field. Covers latest developments in motoring and equipment. **Freq:** Semimonthly fortnightly. **Key Personnel:** Patrick Durham-Matthews, Advertising Mgr., phone 44 20 76197336, patrick.durhammatthews@scope.org.uk; Jamie Trounce, Design, Production Ed., jamie.trounce@scope.org.uk; Elizabeth Choppin, Reporter, elizabeth.choppin@scope.org.uk; John Pring, Acting Ed. and Acting News Ed., john.pring@scope.org.uk; Lucy Howard, Editorial Asst., lucy.howard@scope.org.uk. **Subscription Rates:** 18 individuals U.K.; 35 two years U.K.; 33 individuals Europe; 35 other countries. **Remarks:** Accepts advertising. **URL:** http://www.disabilitynow.org.uk/. **Circ:** ★19,022

54328 ■ Disability and Society
Routledge
Taylor & Francis Group Ltd.
c/o Len Barton, Ed.-in-Ch.
Institute of Education
University of London
London WC1H 0AL, United Kingdom
Publisher E-mail: webmaster.books@tandf.co.uk
Peer-reviewed journal providing a focus for debate about such issues as human rights, discrimination, definitions, policy and practices. **Freq:** 7/yr. **Key Personnel:** Len Barton, Editor-in-Chief; Dora Bjarnason, Overseas Ed.; Michele Moore, Editor; Sally French, UK Ed.; Colin Barnes, Exec. Ed.; Julie Allan, UK Ed. **ISSN:** 0968-7599. **Subscription Rates:** 967 institutions print + online; 918 institutions online; 236 individuals print only; US$1,601 institutions print + online; US$1,521 institutions online; US$427 individuals print only; EUR1,275 institutions print and online; EUR1,211 institutions online only; EUR341 individuals. **Remarks:** Accepts advertising. **URL:** http://www.tandf.co.uk/journals/titles/09687599.asp. **Circ:** (Not Reported)

54329 ■ Disarmament Diplomacy
Acronym Institute for Disarmament Diplomacy
24 Colvestone Cres.
London E8 2LH, United Kingdom
Ph: 44 20 75038857
Fax: 44 20 75038857
Publication E-mail: rej@acronym.org.uk
Journal containing news, documentation and opinion pieces on disarmament and arms control negotiations. **Freq:** Monthly. **URL:** http://www.acronym.org.uk/dd/index.htm.

54330 ■ Discourse & Society
Sage Publications Ltd.
1 Oliver's Yard
55 City Rd.
London EC1Y 1SP, United Kingdom
Ph: 44 20 73248500
Fax: 44 20 73248600
Peer-reviewed journal covering the relevance of discourse analysis to the social sciences. **Subtitle:** An International Journal for the Study of Discourse and Communication in their Social, Political and Cultural Contexts. **Founded:** 1990. **Freq:** Bimonthly. **Key Personnel:** Teun A. Van Dijk, Editor; Doris Graber, Honorary Board; Deborah Cameron, Advisory Board; Ruth Wodak, Co-Ed.; Michael Billig, Co-Ed.; Jan Blommaert, Advisory Board. **ISSN:** 0957-9265. **Subscription Rates:** US$100 individuals print only; US$22 single issue print only. **Remarks:** Accepts advertising. **URL:** http://www.sagepub.com/journalsProdDesc.nav?prodId=Journal200873&. **Circ:** (Not Reported)

54331 ■ Discourse Studies
Sage Publications Ltd.
1 Oliver's Yard
55 City Rd.
London EC1Y 1SP, United Kingdom

Ph: 44 20 73248500
Fax: 44 20 73248600
Peer-reviewed journal covering the study of written and spoken discourse. **Subtitle:** An Interdisciplinary Journal for the Study of Text and Talk. **Founded:** 1999. **Freq:** Bimonthly. **Key Personnel:** Elaine Vine, Book Reviews Ed.; Teun A. Van Dijk, Editor. **ISSN:** 1461-4456. **Subscription Rates:** US$1,219 institutions print & e-access; US$1,097 institutions e-access; US$1,195 institutions print; US$93 individuals print; US$219 institutions single print; US$20 individuals single print. **Remarks:** Accepts advertising. **URL:** http://www.sagepub.com/journalsSubscribe.nav?prodId=Journal200865. **Circ:** (Not Reported)

54332 ■ Disney Fairies
Egmont Magazines
184-192 Drummond St., 4th Fl.
London NW1 3HP, United Kingdom
Ph: 44 20 73806430
Magazine featuring fairies and fairy world for 5-7 year old girls. **Freq:** Monthly. **Trim Size:** 220 x 300 mm. **Subscription Rates:** 7.99 individuals. **Remarks:** Accepts advertising. **URL:** http://www.egmont.co.uk/product.asp?prodid=1924&catid=. **Ad Rates:** 4C: 1,800. **Circ:** (Not Reported)

54333 ■ Disney and Me
Egmont Magazines
184-192 Drummond St., 4th Fl.
London NW1 3HP, United Kingdom
Ph: 44 20 73806430
Magazine for boys and girls aged 4-7. **Founded:** 1991. **Freq:** Semimonthly. **Trim Size:** 220 x 300 mm. **Key Personnel:** Anna Chacoliades, Contact; Sam Verno, Contact. **Subscription Rates:** 1.99 individuals. **Remarks:** Accepts advertising. **URL:** http://www.egmont.co.uk/product.asp?prodid=1520&catid=. **Ad Rates:** 4C: 1,800. **Circ:** ★49,002

54334 ■ Distance Running
Association of International Marathons and Distance Races
c/o Hugh Jones, AIMS Sec.
19 Kelly St.
London NW1 8PG, United Kingdom
Ph: 44 20 72093193
Publisher E-mail: aimssec@aol.com
Publication covering distance running. **Freq:** Quarterly. **Key Personnel:** Frank Baillie, Publisher. **Subscription Rates:** Free. **Remarks:** Advertising accepted; rates available upon request. **URL:** http://aimsworldrunning.org/distancerunning.htm. **Circ:** 400,000

54335 ■ Diva
Millivres Prowler Group
Spectrum House, Unit M
32-34 Gordon House Rd.
London NW5 1LP, United Kingdom
Ph: 44 20 74247400
Fax: 44 20 74247401
Publisher E-mail: reception@millivres.co.uk
Consumer magazine covering lesbian lifestyle. **Founded:** 1994. **Freq:** Monthly. **Trim Size:** 210 x 297 mm. **Key Personnel:** Kim Watson, Publisher; Jane Czyzselska, Editor; Louise Carolin, Dep. Ed.; Maggie Travers, Advertising & Customer Care; Bryony Weaver, Sub-Ed. **Subscription Rates:** 30 individuals; 45 other countries. **Remarks:** Accepts advertising. **URL:** http://www.divamag.co.uk/diva/. **Ad Rates:** BW: 1,250. **Circ:** Combined 55,643

54336 ■ DJ Magazine
DJ Magazine Ltd.
The Old Truman Brewery
London E1 6QL, United Kingdom
Ph: 44 20 72478855
Fax: 44 20 84170466
Publication E-mail: editors@djmag.com
Magazine featuring electronic music and DJs. **Freq:** Monthly. **Key Personnel:** Martin Carvell, Managing Editor; Ben Murphy, Editor; Martin Brown, Art Ed. **Subscription Rates:** 38.20 individuals; 62.50 individuals Europe; 76.80 other countries. **Remarks:** Accepts advertising. **URL:** http://www.djmag.com/. **Circ:** (Not Reported)

54337 ■ DM Magazine
Business and Technical Communications Ltd.
35 Station Sq.

Petts Wood
London BR5 1LZ, United Kingdom
Ph: 44 16 89616000
Fax: 44 16 89826622
Magazine dealing with document management, content management, workflows and e-business solutions. **Freq:** Bimonthly. **Trim Size:** 210 x 297 mm. **Key Personnel:** Dave Tyler, Editor, david.tyler@btc.co.uk; Abby Penn, Production Mgr., abby.penn@btc.co.uk; Liam Norval, Contact, liam.norval@btc.co.uk. **Subscription Rates:** Free. **Remarks:** Accepts advertising. **URL:** http://www.document-manager.com/default.asp. **Ad Rates:** BW: 1,850. **Circ:** 14,560

54338 ■ Doctor Who Adventures
BBC Worldwide Publishing Ltd.
Media Centre
201 Wood Ln.
London W12 7TQ, United Kingdom
Ph: 44 20 84332000
Fax: 44 20 87490538
Magazine for young boys and girls who love Doctor Who. **Subtitle:** Time-travel every two weeks!. **Freq:** Weekly. **Subscription Rates:** 2.10 single issue; 84 individuals. **URL:** http://www.bbcmagazines.com/content/magazines/doctorwhoadventures/.

54339 ■ Document Skateboard
Factory Media
1 W Smithfield
London EC1A 9JU, United Kingdom
Ph: 44 20 73329700
Publisher E-mail: contact@factorymedia.com
Magazine covering skateboarding. **Freq:** 9/yr. **Key Personnel:** Percy Dean, Ed./Sen. Photographer, percy@documentskateboard.com; Sam Ashley, Photo Ed./Sen. Photographer, sam@documentskateboard.com. **Subscription Rates:** 24.95 individuals credit card; 23.60 individuals direct debit; US$86 individuals credit card. **URL:** http://www.documentskateboard.com/; http://factorymedia.com.

54340 ■ Dora Dress Up and Go
GE Fabbri Ltd.
The Communications Bldg., 7th Fl.
48 Leicester Sq.
London WC2H 7LT, United Kingdom
Ph: 44 20 30317600
Fax: 44 20 30317601
Publication E-mail: dora@jacklinservice.com
Publisher E-mail: mailbox@gefabbri.co.uk
Magazine featuring Dora and her adventures. **Freq:** Semimonthly. **Key Personnel:** Peter Edwards, Mng. Dir.; Liz Glaze, Director; Katie Preston, Editor-in-Chief. **Subscription Rates:** 11.96 individuals; 2.99 single issue. **URL:** http://www.doradollcollection.com/.

54341 ■ Dora the Explorer
GE Fabbri Ltd.
The Communications Bldg., 7th Fl.
48 Leicester Sq.
London WC2H 7LT, United Kingdom
Ph: 44 20 30317600
Fax: 44 20 30317601
Publication E-mail: doradvd@dbfactory.co.uk
Publisher E-mail: mailbox@gefabbri.co.uk
Magazine featuring Dora and her friends adventures. **Freq:** Semimonthly. **Key Personnel:** Peter Edwards, Mng. Dir.; Liz Glaze, Director; Katie Preston, Editor-in-Chief. **Subscription Rates:** 1.99 single issue. **URL:** http://www.smallexplorers.com; http://www.gefabbri.co.uk/publication_doradvd.

54342 ■ Drama Magazine
National Drama Publications
Diorama Arts
34 Osnaburch St.
London NW1 3ND, United Kingdom
Publisher E-mail: asknd@nationaldrama.org.uk
Magazine for teachers of drama and theatre. **Founded:** Jan. 1991. **Freq:** 2/yr. **Key Personnel:** Marie Jeanne McNaughton, Editor, mariejeanne.mcnaughton@nationaldrama.co.uk; Peter Wild, Advertising Mgr., peter.wild@nationaldrama.co.uk; Peter Short, Contact, peter.short@nationaldrama.co.uk. **ISSN:** 0967-4454. **Subscription Rates:** 26 individuals Europe, airmail; 26 other countries surface mail; 32 other countries airmail; 22 individuals. **Remarks:** Accepts advertising. **URL:** http://nationaldrama.org.uk/nd/index.cfm/drama-

magazine/. **Ad Rates:** BW: 198. **Circ:** 1200

54343 ■ Drapers (London)
EMAP Ltd.
Greater London House
Hampstead Rd.
London NW1 7EJ, United Kingdom
Ph: 44 20 77285000
Publisher E-mail: jon.ferro@emap.com
Magazine covering the entire fashion market - womenswear, menswear, childrenswear, footwear, lingerie, and textiles. **Subtitle:** The Fashion Business Weekly. **Freq:** Weekly. **Key Personnel:** Jesica Brown, Editor, jessica.brown@emap.com; Katherine rushton, Dep. Ed., katherine.rushton@emap.com. **Subscription Rates:** 180 individuals direct debit; 225 individuals credit card. **Remarks:** Accepts advertising. **URL:** http://www.drapersonline.com/. **Circ:** (Not Reported)

54344 ■ Drug and Alcohol Findings
Alcohol Concern
64 Leman St.
London E1 8EU, United Kingdom
Ph: 44 20 72640510
Fax: 44 20 74889213
Publisher E-mail: contact@alcoholconcern.org.uk
Magazine of Alcohol Concern. **Key Personnel:** Mike Ashton, Editor, mike.ashton@blueyonder.co.uk. **URL:** http://www.findings.org.uk/.

54345 ■ Dutch Crossing
Maney Publishing
1 Carlton House Ter.
London SW1Y 5AF, United Kingdom
Ph: 44 20 74517300
Fax: 44 20 74517307
Publisher E-mail: maney@maney.co.uk
Peer-reviewed journal of the Association for Low Countries Studies in Great Britain and Ireland. **Subtitle:** Journal of Low Countries Studies. **Founded:** 1977. **Freq:** 3/yr. **Key Personnel:** Carol Fehringer, Editor; Jane Fenoulhet, Editor. **ISSN:** 0309-6564. **Subscription Rates:** 158 institutions, other countries; US$298 institutions; 148 institutions, other countries online only; US$288 institutions online only. **Remarks:** Accepts advertising. **URL:** http://maney.co.uk/index.php/journals/dtc. **Circ:** (Not Reported)

54346 ■ Early Medieval China
Maney Publishing
1 Carlton House Ter.
London SW1Y 5AF, United Kingdom
Ph: 44 20 74517300
Fax: 44 20 74517307
Publisher E-mail: maney@maney.co.uk
Peer-reviewed journal exploring medieval China's life, history and culture. **Founded:** 1994. **Freq:** Annual. **Key Personnel:** J. Michael Farmer, Editor, farmer@utdallas.edu. **ISSN:** 1529-9104. **Subscription Rates:** 98 institutions, other countries; US$178 institutions; 92 institutions, other countries online only; US$174 institutions online only. **Remarks:** Accepts advertising. **URL:** http://maney.co.uk/index.php/journals/emc. **Circ:** (Not Reported)

54347 ■ East London Advertiser
Archant Regional Ltd.
138 Cambridge Heath Rd.
London E1 5QJ, United Kingdom
Ph: 44 20 7791 7791
Publisher E-mail: sandra.roantree@archant.co.uk
Community newspaper. **Founded:** 1866. **Freq:** Weekly (Thurs.). **Key Personnel:** Malcolm Starbrook, Editor, malcolm.starbrook@archant.co.uk. **Subscription Rates:** 10 individuals 4 weeks; 20 individuals 2 months; 30 individuals 3 months; 60 individuals 6 months. **Remarks:** Accepts advertising. **URL:** http://www.eastlondonadvertiser.co.uk/. **Circ:** (Not Reported)

54348 ■ Easy Cook
BBC Worldwide Publishing Ltd.
Media Centre
201 Wood Ln.
London W12 7TQ, United Kingdom
Ph: 44 20 84332000
Fax: 44 20 87490538
Magazine featuring useful recipes for family meals, short cut tricks to save time and easy meals for the kids. **Subtitle:** Real food for real people. **Freq:** 7/yr. **Sub-**

scription Rates: 2.70 single issue; 16.99 individuals. URL: http://www.bbcmagazines.com/content/magazines/easycook/.

54349 ■ The Ecologist
Ecosystems Ltd.
102 D Lana House Studios
116-118 Commercial St.
Spitalfields
London E1 6NF, United Kingdom
Publication E-mail: editorial@theecologist.org
Publisher E-mail: ecosystems@theecologist.org
Magazine covering environmental, political, social, health and technology issues. Founded: July 1970. Freq: 10/yr. Print Method: Web offset. Trim Size: 279 x 215 mm. Key Personnel: Harry Ram, Managing Editor; Edward Goldsmith, Contact; Zac Goldsmith, Editor. ISSN: 0261-3131. Subscription Rates: 15 individuals; US$52 other countries. Remarks: Accepts advertising. URL: http://www.theecologist.org/index.asp?j=y. Ad Rates: GLR: EUR10, BW: EUR1,200, 4C: EUR1,500. Circ: Combined 25,000

54350 ■ Economic and Industrial Democracy
Sage Publications Ltd.
1 Oliver's Yard
55 City Rd.
London EC1Y 1SP, United Kingdom
Ph: 44 20 73248500
Fax: 44 20 73248600
Scholarly journal covering all aspects of industrial democracy. Subtitle: An International Journal. Founded: 1980. Freq: Quarterly. Key Personnel: Jan Ottosson, Editor; Lars Magnusson, Editor; Ann-Britt Hellmark, Assoc. Ed.; Elyce Rotella, Editorial Board; Joan Acker, Editorial Board; Jacques Freyssinet, Editorial Board. ISSN: 0143-831X. Subscription Rates: 960 institutions print & E-access; 864 institutions E-access; 941 institutions print; 122 individuals print; 259 institutions single print; 40 individuals single print; 1,056 institutions current volume print & all online content; 960 institutions all online content; 1,395 institutions content through 1998. Remarks: Accepts advertising. URL: http://www.sagepub.com/journalsProdDesc.nav?prodId=Journal200773. Circ: (Not Reported)

54351 ■ Economic Review (UK)
Philip Allan Updates
338 Euston Rd.
London NW1 3BH, United Kingdom
Ph: 44 20 78736000
Fax: 44 20 78736299
Business publication. Freq: Quarterly. Key Personnel: Peter Smith, Editor; Geoff Stewart, Editor; Jackline Wahba, Managing Editor. ISSN: 0265-0290. Subscription Rates: 14.50 students; 29.95 institutions. Remarks: Advertising not accepted. URL: http://www.philipallan.co.uk/economicreview/index.htm. Circ: (Not Reported)

54352 ■ The Economist
The Economist Group
25 St. James St.
London SW1A 1HG, United Kingdom
Ph: 44 20 78307000
Fax: 44 20 78392968
International magazine reporting on news, world affairs, business, and finance. Founded: Sept. 1843. Freq: Weekly (Fri.). Print Method: Offset. Trim Size: 10 5/8 x 8 1/16. Cols./Page: 3. Col. Width: 20 nonpareils. Col. Depth: 131 agate lines. Key Personnel: Marjorie Scardino, CEO; Willy Morgan, Publisher of Economist; Bill Emmott, Editor. ISSN: 0013-0613. Subscription Rates: $A 79 individuals 12 weeks; $A 365 individuals 51 weeks; $A 675 individuals 102 weeks; $A 915 individuals 153 weeks; US$79 individuals digital; with auto renewal; US$89 individuals digital; US$19.95 individuals digital; monthly with auto renewal; US$24.95 individuals digital; monthly. Remarks: Advertising not accepted. URL: http://www.economist.com. Circ: (Not Reported)

54353 ■ The Edge
Calligraphy and Lettering Arts Society
54 Boileau Rd.
London SW13 9BL, United Kingdom
Publisher E-mail: sue@clas.co.uk
Publication covering writing. Freq: Bimonthly. ISSN: 1358-6688. Remarks: Advertising accepted; rates available upon request. URL: http://www.clas.co.uk/the-edge-magazine.html. Circ: 2,000

54354 ■ Education Today
The College of Teachers
Institute of Education
20 Bedford Way
London WC1H 0AL, United Kingdom
Ph: 44 20 79115536
Fax: 44 20 76314865
Publication covering teachers. Founded: 1930. Freq: Quarterly. Trim Size: 210 x 297 mm. ISSN: 0013-1547. Subscription Rates: 140 individuals UK; 150 individuals Europe; 156 individuals rest of the world. Remarks: Advertising accepted; rates available upon request. URL: http://www.collegeofteachers.ac.uk/publications/education-today. Circ: Paid 2,000

54355 ■ Educational Management Administration and Leadership
Sage Publications Ltd.
1 Oliver's Yard
55 City Rd.
London EC1Y 1SP, United Kingdom
Ph: 44 20 73248500
Fax: 44 20 73248600
Peer-reviewed journal covering research and analysis on all aspects of leadership management, administration and policy in education. Founded: 1973. Freq: Bimonthly. Trim Size: 200 x 130 mm. Key Personnel: Tony Bush, Editor; Christopher Rhodes, Reviews Ed.; Helen Gunter, Assoc. Ed.; James Guthrie, International Editorial; Jacky Lumby, Assoc. Ed.; Philip A. Woods, Assoc. Ed.; Sneha Joshi, International Editorial; Paul Begley, International Editorial. ISSN: 1741-1432. Subscription Rates: 620 institutions combined (print & e-access); 682 institutions current volume print & all online; 558 institutions e-access; 620 institutions all online content; 1,233 institutions backfile purchase, e-access; 608 institutions print only; 310 individuals print & e-access; 59 individuals print only; 111 individuals single print; 13 individuals single print. Remarks: Accepts advertising. URL: http://www.sagepub.co.uk/journalsProdDesc.nav?prodId=Journal200888. Formerly: Educational Management & Administration. Circ: (Not Reported)

54356 ■ eFinancial News
Financial News Ltd.
Commodity Quay
East Smithfield
London E1W 1AZ, United Kingdom
Ph: 44 20 34261111
Fax: 44 20 77292910
Publisher E-mail: news@efinancialnews.com
Online publication covering investment banking , fund management and securities industries in Europe. Freq: Daily. Key Personnel: William Wright, Editor, william.wright@dowjones.com; Renee Schultes, Dep. Ed., renee.schultes@dowjones.com; Michael Foster, Assoc. Ed., mike.foster@dowjones.com; Phillipa Leighton-Jones, Online Ed., pjones@efinancialnews.com. Subscription Rates: 245 individuals. Remarks: Accepts advertising. URL: http://www.efinancialnews.com/. Circ: (Not Reported)

54357 ■ Ei Magazine
Ark Group Ltd.
266/276 Upper Richmond Rd.
Putney
London SW15 6TQ, United Kingdom
Ph: 44 20 87852700
Fax: 44 20 87859373
Publisher E-mail: info@ark-group.com
Magazine creating one resource for the information management professional. Freq: 10/yr. Key Personnel: Graeme Burton, Editor; Kate Clifton, Dep. Ed., kclifton@ark-group.com. Subscription Rates: US$540 individuals; EUR440 individuals; 295 individuals. URL: http://www.eimagazine.com/about.asp.

54358 ■ Ei8ht
Foto8 Ltd.
1-5 Honduras St.
London EC1Y 0TH, United Kingdom
Ph: 44 20 72538801
Fax: 44 20 72532752
Publisher E-mail: misc@foto8.com
Magazine providing an insight into the people, events and emotions that drive independent photographers to look beyond the surface to bring real-life stories to light. Subtitle: Photojournalism. Freq: Biennial. Subscription Rates: 42 individuals; 68 two years; 22 members. Re-

marks: Accepts advertising. URL: http://www.foto8.com/home/content/view/134/453/. Circ: (Not Reported)

54359 ■ Electrical/Mechanical Contractor
ECA Publications Ltd.
Ludgate House
245 Blackfriars Rd.
London SE1 9UY, United Kingdom
Ph: 44 20 79215000
Publication for the electrical and mechanical contracting industries. Founded: 1901. Freq: Monthly. Trim Size: 297 x 210 mm. Key Personnel: Andrew Brister, Editor, phone 44 20 75604122, abrister@cmpi.biz; Tracy Edwards, Asst. Ed., phone 44 20 75604125, tedwards@cmpi.biz; Socratis Socratous, Gp. Marketing Dir., phone 44 20 75604086, socratis.socratous@ubm.com; Sarah McGourty, Marketing Exec., phone 44 20 75604091, sarah.mcgourty@ubm.com. ISSN: 0308-7174. Subscription Rates: 25 individuals; 35 individuals Europe & rest of world. Online: Gale. URL: http://www.emconline.co.uk/Index.asp?pubCode=39. Former name: Electrical Contractor. Ad Rates: BW: 1,945, 4C: 2,975. Circ: Paid ★9,000

54360 ■ Elements
The Environment Council
212 High Holborn
London WC1V 7BF, United Kingdom
Ph: 44 20 78362626
Fax: 44 20 72421180
Publication E-mail: publications@envcouncil.org.uk
Publisher E-mail: winsomeg@envcouncil.org.uk
Publication covering environmental decision making. Subtitle: For Environmental Decisions. Founded: Oct. 2000. Freq: Quarterly. Key Personnel: Alison Bowman, Contact, alisonb@envcouncil.org.uk. ISSN: 1472-815X. Remarks: Accepts advertising. URL: http://www.the-environment-council.org.uk. Circ: Combined 2,200

54361 ■ ELLEgirl
Hachette Filipacchi (UK) Ltd.
64 North Row
London W1K 7LL, United Kingdom
Ph: 44 20 71507000
Fax: 44 20 71507001
Magazine about celebrities, shopping, etc., of interest to girls. Freq: Monthly 10/yr. URL: http://ellegirl.elle.com/.

54362 ■ EMBO Reports
Nature Publishing Group
The Macmillan Bldg.
4 Crinan St.
London N1 9XW, United Kingdom
Ph: 44 20 78334000
Fax: 44 20 78434640
Publication dedicated to providing a variety of sharply focused and rapidly published short papers and review articles in all areas of molecular biology. Freq: Monthly. Key Personnel: Esther Schnappv, Editor, esther.schnapp@embo.org; Nonia Pariente, Editor, pariente@embo.org; Barbara Pauly, Editor, pauly@embo.org. ISSN: 1469-221X. Subscription Rates: EUR163 individuals combined print & online; US$172 individuals combined print & online; 104.84 individuals U.K., rest of world combined print & online; 27,800¥ individuals combined print & online. Remarks: Accepts advertising. URL: http://www.nature.com/embor/index.html. Circ: (Not Reported)

54363 ■ Emel
Emel Media Ltd.
1 Canfield Pl.
London NW3 5HT, United Kingdom
Ph: 44 20 73287300
Publisher E-mail: info@emel.com
Magazine featuring the lifestyle of Muslims. Subtitle: The Muslim Lifestyle Magazine. Founded: 2003. Freq: Monthly. Key Personnel: Sarah Joseph, Editor. Subscription Rates: 35.95 individuals; 45 individuals Europe; 64 other countries. Remarks: Accepts advertising. URL: http://www.emelmagazine.com/index.php. Circ: (Not Reported)

54364 ■ Emerging Themes in Epidemiology
BioMed Central Ltd.
236 Gray's Inn Rd., Fl. 6
34-42 Cleveland St.
London WC1X 8HL, United Kingdom
Ph: 44 20 31922000
Fax: 44 20 31922010
Publication E-mail: ete@lshtm.ac.uk

Publisher E-mail: info@biomedcentral.com
Online journal promoting debate and discussion on theoretical and methodological aspects of epidemiology. **Key Personnel:** Prof. Peter G. Smith, Editor-in-Chief; Dr. Ben A. Lopman, Dep. Ed., ben.lopman@hpa.org.uk; Dr. Clarence C. Tam, Dep. Ed., clarence.tam@lshtm.ac. uk; Mauricio L. Barreto, Assoc. Ed.; Anne M. Johnson, Assoc. Ed.; Leland J. Yee, Assoc. Ed. **ISSN:** 1742-7622. **Remarks:** Accepts advertising. **URL:** http://www.ete-online.com/. **Circ:** (Not Reported)

54365 ■ Empire
EMAP Metro Ltd.
Greater London House
Hampstead Rd.
London NW1 7EJ, United Kingdom
Ph: 44 20 7728500
Consumer magazine covering film. **Founded:** 1989. **Freq:** Monthly. **Key Personnel:** Ian Freer, Asst. Ed., phone 44 20 72955596, ian.freer@ecm.emap.com. **Subscription Rates:** 9 individuals 4 issues; 30 individuals. **Remarks:** Accepts advertising. **URL:** http://www.empireonline.co.uk; http://www.greatmagazines.co.uk. **Circ:** Combined 173,000

54366 ■ Employee Benefits
Centaur Publishing Ltd.
50 Poland St.
London W1F 7AX, United Kingdom
Ph: 44 20 79704000
Fax: 44 20 79704189
Publication covering human resources and labor relations. **Founded:** Feb. 1997. **Freq:** Monthly. **Trim Size:** 225 x 297 mm. **Key Personnel:** Phil Hayne, Publisher, phil.hayne@centaur.co.uk; Debi O'Donovan, Editor, debi.odonovan@centaur.co.uk; Suzanne Saunders, Commercial Dir., suzanne.saunders@centaur.co. uk; Juliette Losardo, Sales Mgr., juliette.losardo@ centaur.co.uk. **ISSN:** 1366-8722. **Subscription Rates:** 67 individuals; 115 two years; 140 individuals three years. **Remarks:** Accepts advertising. **URL:** http://www. employeebenefits.co.uk/about/. **Ad Rates:** 4C: 2,770. **Circ:** 10,030

54367 ■ Employment Law Bulletin
LexisNexis UK
Halsbury House
35 Chancery Ln.
London WC2A 1EL, United Kingdom
Ph: 44 20 74002500
Fax: 44 20 74002842
Publisher E-mail: customer.services@lexisnexis.co.uk
Law periodical. **Freq:** 10/yr. **Key Personnel:** Douglas Leach, Editor. **ISSN:** 0969-3637. **Subscription Rates:** $A 653.40 individuals. **Remarks:** Advertising not accepted. **URL:** http://www.lexisnexis.com.au/aus/ default.asp. **Formerly:** Industrial Relations Law Bulletin. **Circ:** (Not Reported)

54368 ■ Employment Law Journal
Legalese Ltd.
Kensington Sq. House
12-14 Ansdell St.
London W8 5BN, United Kingdom
Ph: 44 20 73969292
Fax: 44 20 73969303
Professional journal covering developments in employment law. **Freq:** 10/yr. **Subscription Rates:** 160 individuals. **URL:** http://www.legalease.co.uk.

54369 ■ The Ends Report
Haymarket Business Magazines
174 Hammersmith Rd.
London W6 7JP, United Kingdom
Ph: 44 20 82674210
Publisher E-mail: info@haymarket.com
Magazine featuring information in environmental policy and legislation in the United Kingdom. **Founded:** 1978. **Freq:** Monthly. **Key Personnel:** Nick Schoon, Editor, phone 44 20 82678107, nick.schoon@haymarket.com; Tracy Awere, Sales Mgr., phone 44 20 82674607, tracy. awere@haymarket.com. **Subscription Rates:** 595 individuals; EUR774 individuals; US$1012 individuals. **URL:** http://www.haymarket.com/ends/multi/_the_ends_ report_magazine/default.aspx; http://www.endsreport. com/index.cfm.

54370 ■ Energy Risk
Incisive Media Limited
Haymarket House

28-29 Haymarket
London SW1Y 4RX, United Kingdom
Ph: 44 870 2408859
Fax: 44 207 4849797
Publisher E-mail: customerservices@incisivemedia.com
Magazine featuring oil, gas and electricity industry. **Freq:** Monthly. **Key Personnel:** Stella Farrington, Editor; Peter Petkov, Publisher. **Subscription Rates:** 899 individuals; US$1,891 individuals; EUR1,493 individuals; 1,618 two years; US$3,404 two years; EUR2,687 two years; 2,292 individuals 3 years; US$4,822 individuals 3 years; EUR3,807 individuals 3 years. **Remarks:** Accepts advertising. **URL:** http://www.energyrisk.com. **Circ:** (Not Reported)

54371 ■ Energy World
Energy Institute
61 New Cavendish St.
London W1G 7AR, United Kingdom
Ph: 44 20 74677100
Fax: 44 20 72551472
Publisher E-mail: info@energyinst.org.uk
Publication covering energy. **Freq:** Monthly. **Key Personnel:** Emma Parsons, Production Mgr., eparsons@ energyinst.org.uk; Steve Hodgson, Editor, stevehodgson@btinternet.com. **ISSN:** 0307-7942. **Subscription Rates:** 165 individuals; 270 individuals overseas (airmail). **URL:** http://www.energyinst.org/ information-centre/ei-publications/energy-world. **Ad Rates:** BW: 890, 4C: 1,190. **Circ:** Paid 4,500

54372 ■ The Engineer
Centaur Publishing Ltd.
50 Poland St.
London W1F 7AX, United Kingdom
Ph: 44 20 79704000
Fax: 44 20 79704189
Business publication. **Founded:** 1856. **Freq:** Weekly. **Key Personnel:** Jon Excell, Editor, phone 44 20 79704437, jon.excell@centaur.co.uk; Sean Marshall, Publisher, phone 44 20 79704151, sean.marshall@ centaur.co.uk. **ISSN:** 0013-7758. **Subscription Rates:** 75 individuals UK; 127 two years UK; 177 individuals three years, UK. **Remarks:** Accepts advertising. **URL:** http://www.theengineer.co.uk/Home/Default.aspx. **Ad Rates:** BW: 3,950. **Circ:** Non-paid ‡35,466

54373 ■ Environment & Planning A
Pion Ltd.
207 Brondesbury Pk.
London NW2 5JN, United Kingdom
Ph: 44 20 84590066
Fax: 44 20 84516454
Publication focusing on urban and regional research. **Founded:** 1969. **Freq:** Monthly. **Print Method:** Litho. **Trim Size:** 132 x 230 mm. **Key Personnel:** Noel Castree, Editorial Advisory Board, noel.castree@man.ac.uk; Trevor Barnes, Editor, tbarnes@geog.ubc.ca; Henry Yeung, Editor, geoywc@nus.edu.sg; Mike A. Crang, Editorial Advisory Board, m.a.crang@durham.ac.uk; Eric Sheppard, Editor, shepp001@umn.edu; Loretta Lees, Editorial Advisory Board, loretta.lees@kcl.ac.uk; Nigel Thrift, Editor, nigel.thrift@warwick.ac.uk; Sarah Whatmore, Editor, sarah.whatmore@ouce.ox.ac.uk; Neil Adger, Editorial Advisory Board, n.adger@uea.ac.uk; Jamie Peck, Editor, peck@geog.ubc.ca. **ISSN:** 0000-518X. **Subscription Rates:** US$1,755 individuals; US$166 single issue; 911 individuals; 91 single issue. **Remarks:** Accepts advertising. **URL:** http://www. envplan.com. **Circ:** (Not Reported)

54374 ■ Environment and Urbanization
International Institute for Environment and Development
3 Endsleigh St.
London WC1H 0DD, United Kingdom
Ph: 44 20 73882117
Fax: 44 20 73882826
Publication E-mail: subscription@sagepub.co.uk
Publisher E-mail: info@iied.org
Publication covering worldwide development. **Founded:** 1989. **Freq:** Semiannual. **Print Method:** Offset. **Key Personnel:** Jane Bicknell, Managing Editor; David Satterthwaite, Editor. **ISSN:** 0956-2478. **Subscription Rates:** 314 institutions high-income nations (print and online); 99 individuals charities, high-income nations (print and online); 40 individuals high-income nations (print only); 26 individuals high-income nations (single copy); 59 institutions low- and middle-income nations (print and online); 20 individuals low- and middle-income

nations (print only); 13 students low- and middle-income nations (print and online); 169 institutions high-income nations (single copy). **Remarks:** Advertising not accepted. **URL:** http://www.iied.org/human/eandu/ eandu_details.html. **Circ:** 3,100

54375 ■ Environmental Engineering
Institution of Mechanical Engineers
1 Birdcage Walk
London SW1H 9JJ, United Kingdom
Ph: 44 20 72227899
Fax: 44 20 72224557
Publisher E-mail: international@imeche.org
Publication covering engineering. **Freq:** Quarterly. **Key Personnel:** Nigel Searle, Contact, phone 44 20 72223337, nigels@pepublishing.com. **Subscription Rates:** 154 individuals. **URL:** http://www.pepublishing. com/buspub/enveng.htm. **Circ:** 7,000

54376 ■ Environmental Health
BioMed Central Ltd.
236 Gray's Inn Rd., Fl. 6
34-42 Cleveland St.
London WC1X 8HL, United Kingdom
Ph: 44 20 31922000
Fax: 44 20 31922010
Publisher E-mail: info@biomedcentral.com
Online journal covering all aspects of environmental and occupational medicine and related studies in toxicology and epidemiology. **Subtitle:** A Global Access Science Source. **Key Personnel:** Prof. Philippe Grandjean, Editor-in-Chief, phone 45 65503759, fax 45 65911458, pgrandjean@health.sdu.dk; Prof. David Christiani, Editorial Board, dchris@hohp.harvard.edu; Dr. Ake Bergman, Editorial Board, ake.bergman@mk.su.se; Prof. David Ozonoff, Editor-in-Chief, phone 617638-4620, fax 617638-4857, dozonoff@bu.edu; Prof. Klaus E. Andersen, Editorial Board, kea@dadlnet.dk; Lynn Goldman, Editorial Board, lgoldman@jhsph.edu. **ISSN:** 1476-069X. **Remarks:** Accepts advertising. **URL:** http://www. ehjournal.net. **Circ:** (Not Reported)

54377 ■ Environmental Health Practitioner
Chartered Institute of Environmental Health
Chadwick Ct.
15 Hatfields
London SE1 8DJ, United Kingdom
Ph: 44 20 79286006
Fax: 44 20 78275862
Publication E-mail: information@cieh.org
Publication covering environmental health. **Founded:** 1895. **Freq:** Monthly. **Key Personnel:** Stuart Spear, Editor. **Remarks:** Advertising accepted; rates available upon request. **URL:** http://www.cieh.org/ehp//. **Former name:** Environmental Health. **Circ:** 11,800

54378 ■ The Environmental Scientist
Institution of Environmental Sciences
Institut des Sciences de l'Environnement
2nd Fl., 34 Grosvenor Gardens
London SW1W 0DH, United Kingdom
Ph: 44 20 77305516
Fax: 44 20 77305519
Publisher E-mail: enquiries@ies-uk.org.uk
Publication covering environmental science. **Freq:** Bimonthly. **ISSN:** 0966-8411. **Subscription Rates:** 5 members; 8 nonmembers. **Remarks:** Advertising accepted; rates available upon request. **URL:** http://www. ies-uk.org.uk. **Circ:** (Not Reported)

54379 ■ Epidemiologic Perspectives & Innovations
BioMed Central Ltd.
236 Gray's Inn Rd., Fl. 6
34-42 Cleveland St.
London WC1X 8HL, United Kingdom
Ph: 44 20 31922000
Fax: 44 20 31922010
Publisher E-mail: info@biomedcentral.com
Online journal covering all aspects of epidemiologic research methods, applications, critical overviews, teaching tools, perspectives, and other analytic work. **Key Personnel:** Dr. Carl V. Phillips, Editor-in-Chief, epiperspectives@yahoo.com; Dr. Deborah J. Del Junco, Exec. Ed.; Dr. Charles Poole, Dep. Ed., cpoole@unc. edu; George Maldonado, Editor-in-Chief; Ulka B. Campbell, Assoc. Ed.; Ines Dourado, Assoc. Ed. **ISSN:** 1742-5573. **Remarks:** Accepts advertising. **URL:** http://www. epi-perspectives.com/home/. **Circ:** (Not Reported)

Circulation: ★ = ABC; △ = BPA; ♦ = CAC; • = CCAB; ❑ = VAC; ⊕ = PO Statement; ‡ = Publisher's Report; Boldface figures = sworn; Light figures = estimated.

Gale Directory of Publications & Broadcast Media/147th Ed.   **5709**

54380 ■ Epidemiology and Infection
Cambridge University Press
c/o Prof. Norman Noah, Ed.-in-Ch.
London School of Hygiene & Tropical Medicine
Keppel Street
London WC1E 7HT, United Kingdom
Publisher E-mail: customer_service@cup.org
Journal covering all aspects of infections in humans and animals. **Founded:** 1901. **Freq:** 2-3/yr. **Key Personnel:** Prof. Norman Noah, Editor-in-Chief, norman.noah@lshtm.ac.uk; Dr. Timothy Brewer, Editor; Prof. Anthony Fooks, Editor; Prof. Raina C. MacIntyre, Editor; Dr. Craig W. Hedberg, Editor. **ISSN:** 0950-2688. **Subscription Rates:** 588 institutions online; 728 institutions print and online; US$1,140 institutions online only; US$1,430 institutions online and print. **Remarks:** Accepts display advertising. **URL:** http://journals.cambridge.org/action/displayJournal?jid=HYG. **Ad Rates:** BW: US$845, 4C: US$1,825. **Circ:** 1,000

54381 ■ Equal Opportunities Review
LexisNexis UK
Halsbury House
35 Chancery Ln.
London WC2A 1EL, United Kingdom
Ph: 44 20 74002500
Fax: 44 20 74002842
Publisher E-mail: customer.services@lexisnexis.co.uk
Publication covering human resources and labor relations. **Freq:** Monthly. **Key Personnel:** Michael Rubenstein, Publisher, michael@rubensteinpublishing.com; Sue Johnstone, Editor, sue@rubensteinpublishing.com; Kate Godwin, Res. Off., kate@rubensteinpublishing.com. **ISSN:** 0268-7143. **Subscription Rates:** 380 individuals; 330 other countries; 760 two years; 722 two years. **URL:** http://www.eordirect.co.uk/.

54382 ■ Equity
British Actors' Equity Association
Guild House
Upper St. Martins Ln.
London WC2H 9EG, United Kingdom
Ph: 44 20 73796000
Fax: 44 20 73797001
Publisher E-mail: info@equity.org.uk
Publication covering performing arts. **Founded:** 1930. **Freq:** Quarterly. **Print Method:** Web. **Trim Size:** A4. **URL:** http://www.equity.org.uk. **Former name:** Equity Journal. **Ad Rates:** BW: 1,250, 4C: 1,500. **Circ:** Controlled 39,000

54383 ■ Esprit Magazine
Sandron Publishing Ltd.
Bouverie House
43a Effra Rd.
Wimbledon
London SW19 8PS, United Kingdom
Ph: 44 20 85439799
Fax: 44 20 85406519
Trade magazine for the perfume, cosmetics, skin care and toiletries markets in the U.K. and Southern Ireland. **Founded:** Apr. 1988. **Freq:** Monthly. **Key Personnel:** Jonathan Charles, Publisher/Dir., jon@esprit-magazine.co.uk; Lorraine Wilson-Morris, Ed./Dir., lorraine@esprit-magazine.co.uk. **Subscription Rates:** 95 individuals; 105 other countries. **URL:** http://www.esprit-magazine.co.uk/. **Circ:** 5,200

54384 ■ Essential Guide to Beauty
Eaglemoss Publications Ltd.
1st Fl., Beaumont House
Kensington Village
Avonmore Rd.
London W14 8TS, United Kingdom
Ph: 44 20 76051200
Fax: 44 20 76051201
Publication E-mail: beauty@jacklinenterprises.com
Magazine featuring beauty advice. **Freq:** Semimonthly. **Key Personnel:** Suzie Cullen, Marketing Dir.; Maggie Calmels, Editorial Dir. **URL:** http://www.essential-beauty-mag.com/magazine/mag-intro.htm.

54385 ■ Estates Gazette
Estates Gazette Ltd.
1 Procter St.
London WC1V 6EU, United Kingdom
Ph: 44 207 9111701
Real estate industry publication. **Freq:** Weekly. **Key Personnel:** Fiona Harnett, Contact, phone 44 20 79111800, fiona.harnett@rbi.co.uk; Peter Bill, Editor, phone 44 20 79111805, peter.bill@rbi.co.uk; Samantha McClary, News Ed., phone 44 20 79111811, samantha.mcclary@rbi.co.uk. **ISSN:** 0014-1240. **Subscription Rates:** 196 individuals; 371 two years. **Remarks:** Accepts advertising. **URL:** http://www.estatesgazettegroup.com. **Ad Rates:** BW: 1,960, 4C: 3,080. **Circ:** (Not Reported)

54386 ■ Ethnicities
Sage Publications Ltd.
1 Oliver's Yard
55 City Rd.
London EC1Y 1SP, United Kingdom
Ph: 44 20 73248500
Fax: 44 20 73248600
Peer-reviewed journal covering ethnicity, nationalism and related issues, including identity politics and minority rights. **Founded:** 2001. **Freq:** Quarterly. **Key Personnel:** Stephen May, Editor; Craig Calhoun, Corresponding Ed.; Tariq Modood, Editor; Thomas Hylland Eriksen, Editorial Board; Patricia Hill Collins, Editorial Board; Stuart Hall, Editorial Board; Troy Duster, Corresponding Ed. **ISSN:** 1468-7968. **Subscription Rates:** US$113 individuals print only; US$768 institutions print only; US$706 institutions e-access; US$784 institutions print & e-access; US$211 institutions single print; US$37 individuals single print. **Remarks:** Accepts advertising. **URL:** http://www.sagepub.com/journalsProdDesc.nav?prodId=Journal200776. **Circ:** (Not Reported)

54387 ■ Ethnography
Sage Publications Ltd.
1 Oliver's Yard
55 City Rd.
London EC1Y 1SP, United Kingdom
Ph: 44 20 73248500
Fax: 44 20 73248600
Scholarly journal covering ethnography. **Founded:** 2000. **Freq:** Quarterly. **Key Personnel:** Peter Geschiere, Editor; Paul Willis, Editor; Dorothy Holland, International Editorial Board; Michel Agier, International Editorial Board; Janice Radway, International Editorial Board; Elijah Anderson, International Editorial Board; Michael Burawoy, International Editorial Board. **ISSN:** 1466-1381. **Subscription Rates:** US$779 institutions combined (print & e-access); US$701 institutions e-access; US$763 institutions print; US$93 individuals print; US$210 institutions single print; US$30 individuals single print. **Remarks:** Accepts advertising. **URL:** http://www.sagepub.com/journalsProdDesc.nav?prodId=Journal200906. **Circ:** (Not Reported)

54388 ■ Etudes Episteme
Ecole Doctorale Des Etudes Anglophones
Drewry House 213 Marsh Wall
London E14 9FJ, United Kingdom
Journal covering science and literature. **Key Personnel:** Gisele Venet, Contact. **URL:** http://revue.etudes-episteme.org/.

54389 ■ Eukanuba
Axon Publishing
11 Plough Yard
London EC2A 3LP, United Kingdom
Ph: 44 20 76847111
Fax: 44 20 76847122
Publisher E-mail: mail@axonpublish.com
Magazine promoting dog food. **Key Personnel:** Ellen Brush, Managing Editor; Paul Keers, Editorial Dir. **URL:** http://www.axonpublish.com/.

54390 ■ Euromoney
Euromoney Publications PLC
Nestor House
Playhouse Yard
London EC4V 5EX, United Kingdom
Ph: 44 20 77798888
Publisher E-mail: information@euromoneyplc.com
Publication for the banking, finance, and accounting industries. **Freq:** Monthly. **ISSN:** 0014-2433. **Subscription Rates:** 389 individuals; US$750 individuals; EUR545 individuals. **URL:** http://www.euromoneyplc.com/product.asp?PositionID=3151&ProductID=949&pageid=343.

54391 ■ European BioPharmaceutical Review
Samedan Ltd.
16, Hampden Gurney St.
London W1H 5AL, United Kingdom
Ph: 44 20 77243456
Fax: 44 20 77242632
Publisher E-mail: info@samedanltd.com
Journal covering biopharmaceutical research and development. **Freq:** Quarterly January, April July, October. **Key Personnel:** Neil Clarke, Contact, neil@samedanltd.com. **Subscription Rates:** 125 individuals; US$230 other countries. **Remarks:** Accepts advertising. **URL:** http://www.samedanltd.com/magazine/12. **Circ:** (Not Reported)

54392 ■ European Competition Journal
Hart Publishing Ltd.
c/o Dr. Philip Marsden, Gen. Ed.
17 Russell Sq.
London WC1B 5JP, United Kingdom
Publisher E-mail: mail@hartpub.co.uk
Peer-reviewed Journal covering current developments in competition law. **Founded:** 2005. **Freq:** Semiannual. **Key Personnel:** Dr. Philip Marsden, Gen. Ed., p.marsden@biicl.org; Simon Bishop, Gen. ed., simon.bishop@rbbecon.com. **ISSN:** 1744-1056. **Subscription Rates:** 235 individuals standard, United Kingdom and Europe; 245 other countries standard; 125 individuals reduced, United Kingdom and Europe; 135 other countries reduced; 211.50 individuals online, standard; 112.50 individuals online. **Remarks:** Accepts advertising. **URL:** http://www.hartjournals.co.uk/ecj/. **Circ:** (Not Reported)

54393 ■ European Cosmetics Markets
Wilmington Media
6-14 Underwood St.
London N1 7JQ, United Kingdom
Ph: 44 20 75498626
Fax: 44 20 75498622
Publication E-mail: ecm@wilmington.co.uk
Publisher E-mail: ecm@wilmington.co.uk
Trade journal covering market analysis for the cosmetics and toiletries industry in Europe. **Founded:** 1984. **Freq:** Monthly. **Key Personnel:** Colin Bailey-Wood, Mng. Dir. **Subscription Rates:** 800 individuals UK; EUR1,270 individuals Europe; US$1,430 U.S. and Canada; 878 other countries; 1,440 two years UK; EUR2,300 two years Europe; US$2,574 U.S. and Canada 2 years; 1,580 other countries 2 years. **Remarks:** Accepts advertising. **URL:** http://www.cosmeticsbusiness.com/. **Ad Rates:** BW: 1,200. **Circ:** Paid 400

54394 ■ European History Quarterly
Sage Publications Ltd.
c/o Lucy Riall, Ed.
Birkbeck, University of London
London WC1E 7HX, United Kingdom
Peer-reviewed journal covering European history from the later Middle Ages to post-1945. **Founded:** 1971. **Freq:** Quarterly January, April, July, October. **Key Personnel:** Laurence Cole, Co-Ed.; Lucy Riall, Editor. **ISSN:** 0265-6914. **Subscription Rates:** US$725 institutions print & e-access; US$798 institutions current volume print & all online content; US$653 institutions e-access; US$726 institutions all online content; US$1,554 institutions e-access (content through 1998); US$711 institutions print only; US$109 individuals print only; US$196 institutions single print; US$35 individuals single print. **Remarks:** Accepts advertising. **URL:** http://www.sagepub.com/journalsProdDesc.nav?prodId=Journal200846. **Circ:** (Not Reported)

54395 ■ European Industrial Relations Review
LexisNexis UK
Halsbury House
35 Chancery Ln.
London WC2A 1EL, United Kingdom
Ph: 44 20 74002500
Fax: 44 20 74002842
Publisher E-mail: customer.services@lexisnexis.co.uk
Publication covering human resources and labor relations. **Freq:** Monthly. **Key Personnel:** Andrea Broughton, Editor. **ISSN:** 0309-7234. **Subscription Rates:** 349 individuals; 385 other countries. **Remarks:** Advertising not accepted. **URL:** http://194.203.155.143/pub_subjects/pub_pages/human_pub/european_ind_relati ons/european_ind_relations.htm. **Circ:** (Not Reported)

54396 ■ European Journal of American Culture
Intellect
Russell Square House
10-12 Russell Sq.
London WC1B 5EE, United Kingdom
Ph: 44 20 73312000
Fax: 44 20 73312040

Publisher E-mail: info@intellectuk.org

Journal facilitating the academic study of all aspects of American culture, both modern and historical, particularly in newer fields of academic enquiry such as film and new media. **Founded:** 2000. **Freq:** 3/yr. **Key Personnel:** Maeve Pearson, Editor, m.pearson@exeter.ac.uk; Dr. Mark Whalan, Assoc. Ed., m.whalan@exeter.ac.uk; Kathryn Napier-Gray, Reviews Ed., kathryn.gray@plymouth.ac.uk. **ISSN:** 1466-040X. **Subscription Rates:** 33 individuals print; 210 institutions print; 12 single issue print; 177 institutions online. **URL:** http://www.intellectbooks.co.uk/journals/view-Journal,id=138/.

54397 ■ European Journal of Cardiovascular Prevention & Rehabilitation
Mosby Inc.
LWW
3rd Fl., 241 Borough High St.
London SE1 1 GB, United Kingdom
Ph: 44 20 79407500
Fax: 44 20 79407575
Publisher E-mail: custserv.ehs@elsevier.com
Journal publishing articles that address the causes and prevention of cardiovascular disease. **Key Personnel:** Pantaleo Giannuzzi, Editor; Diederick E. Grobbee, Editor; Birna Bjarnason-Wehrens, Assoc. Ed. **ISSN:** 1741-8267. **Remarks:** Accepts advertising. **URL:** http://www.escardiocontent.org/periodicals/ejcpr. **Circ:** (Not Reported)

54398 ■ European Journal of Communication
Sage Publications Ltd.
1 Oliver's Yard
55 City Rd.
London EC1Y 1SP, United Kingdom
Ph: 44 20 73248500
Fax: 44 20 73248600
Peer-reviewed journal covering communication theory and research in Europe. **Founded:** 1986. **Freq:** Quarterly. **Key Personnel:** Peter Golding, Editor; Liesbet Van Zoonen, Editor; Denis McQuail, Editor; Michael Pickering, Book Review Ed. **ISSN:** 0267-3231. **Subscription Rates:** US$944 institutions print & e-access; US$850 institutions e-access; US$925 institutions print; US$109 individuals print; US$254 institutions single print; US$35 individuals single print; US$1,038 institutions current volume print & all online content; US$944 institutions all online content; US$939 institutions content through 1998. **Remarks:** Accepts advertising. **URL:** http://www.sagepub.com/journalsProdDesc.nav?prodId=Journal200857. **Circ:** (Not Reported)

54399 ■ European Journal of Cultural Studies
Sage Publications Ltd.
1 Oliver's Yard
55 City Rd.
London EC1Y 1SP, United Kingdom
Ph: 44 20 73248500
Fax: 44 20 73248600
Peer-reviewed journal covering cultural studies in Europe. **Founded:** 1998. **Freq:** Quarterly. **Key Personnel:** Jon Cruz, Editor; Joke Hermes, Editor; Ann Gray, Editor; Pertti Alasuutari, Editor; Ruth McElroy, Book Reviews Ed.; Jaap Kooijman, Assoc. Ed. **ISSN:** 1367-5494. **Subscription Rates:** US$807 institutions print & e-access; US$726 institutions e-access; US$791 institutions print; US$89 individuals print; US$218 institutions single print; US$29 individuals single print; US$888 institutions current volume print & all online content; US$807 institutions all online content; US$726 institutions content through 1998. **Remarks:** Accepts advertising. **URL:** http://www.sagepub.com/journalsSubscribe.nav?prodId=Journal200898. **Circ:** (Not Reported)

54400 ■ European Journal of Industrial Relations
Sage Publications Ltd.
1 Oliver's Yard
55 City Rd.
London EC1Y 1SP, United Kingdom
Ph: 44 20 73248500
Fax: 44 20 73248600
Scholarly journal covering key developments, and their theoretical and practical implications, in industrial relations in Europe. **Founded:** 1995. **Freq:** Quarterly. **Key Personnel:** Richard Hyman, Editor. **ISSN:** 0959-6801. **Subscription Rates:** US$964 institutions combined

(print & e-access); US$1,060 institutions backfile lease, combined plus backfile; US$868 institutions e-access; US$964 institutions backfile lease, e-access plus backfile; US$868 institutions backfile purchase, e-access (content through 1998); US$945 institutions print only; US$100 individuals print only; US$260 institutions single print; US$33 individuals single print. **Remarks:** Accepts advertising. **URL:** http://www.sagepub.com/journalsProdDesc.nav?prodId=Journal200877. **Circ:** (Not Reported)

54401 ■ European Journal of International Relations
Sage Publications Ltd.
1 Oliver's Yard
55 City Rd.
London EC1Y 1SP, United Kingdom
Ph: 44 20 73248500
Fax: 44 20 73248600
Peer-reviewed journal covering current research in international relations. **Founded:** 1995. **Freq:** Quarterly. **Key Personnel:** Tim Dunne, Editor; Lene Hansen, Editor; Colin Wight, Editor-in-Chief. **ISSN:** 1354-0661. **Subscription Rates:** US$1,143 institutions combined (print & e-access); US$1,257 institutions backfile lease, combined plus backfile; US$1,029 institutions e-access; US$1,143 institutions backfile lease, e-access plus backfile; US$1,029 institutions backfile purchase, e-access (content through 1998); US$1,120 institutions print only; US$100 individuals print only; US$308 institutions single print; US$33 individuals single print. **Remarks:** Accepts advertising. **URL:** http://www.sagepub.com/journalsProdDesc.nav?prodId=Journal200942. **Circ:** (Not Reported)

54402 ■ European Journal of Orthodontics
Oxford University Press
c/o Prof. Fraser McDonald, Ed.
Flat 20
49 Hallam St.
London, United Kingdom
Publisher E-mail: webenquiry.uk@oup.com
Journal providing a forum for orthodontists in Europe, publishing clinical papers covering all techniques as well as different approaches to treatment planning. **Freq:** 6/yr. **Key Personnel:** Prof. Fraser MacDonald, Editor; Dr. Susan Cunningham, Honorary Sec. **ISSN:** 0141-5387. **Subscription Rates:** 439 institutions corporate; print and online; 355 institutions corporate; online only; 403 institutions corporate; print only; 352 institutions print and online; 284 institutions online only; 322 institutions print only; 249 individuals print. **Remarks:** Advertising accepted; rates available upon request. **URL:** http://ejo.oxfordjournals.org. **Circ:** (Not Reported)

54403 ■ European Journal of Palliative Care
Hayward Medical Communications
Covent Garden
8-10 Dryden St.
London WC2E 9NA, United Kingdom
Ph: 44 20 72404493
Fax: 44 20 72404479
Publication E-mail: edit@hayward.co.uk
Publisher E-mail: admin@hayward.co.uk
Journal covering palliative care across Europe. **Subtitle:** The Journal of the European Association for Palliative Care. **Founded:** 1994. **Freq:** Bimonthly. **Key Personnel:** Keena McKillen, Publisher; Elaine Bennett, Editorial Dir. **Subscription Rates:** EUR45 individuals bronze (electronic); 75 members gold (print); 255 institutions gold (print); 135 other countries gold (print); 125 other countries member; 345 institutions, other countries gold (print). **URL:** http://www.ejpc.eu.com/ejpchome.asp?FR=1.

54404 ■ European Journal of Phycology
British Phycological Society
c/o Dr. Eileen J. Cox, Ed.-in-Ch.
Department of Botany, The Natural History Museum
Cromwell Rd.
London SW7 5BD, United Kingdom
Publisher E-mail: j.pottas@hull.ac.uk
Peer-reviewd European journal covering phycology. **Freq:** Quarterly. **Key Personnel:** Dr. J.G. Day, Editor-in-Chief, john.day@sams.ac.uk; Dr. Eileen J. Cox, Editor-in-Chief, e.j.cox@nhm.ac.uk; Dr. Jan Krokowski, Book Review Ed.; Dr. Michelle L. Tobin, Treas., phone 44 17 23357290, fax 44 17 23370815, m.l.tobin@hull.ac.uk; Prof. Michael D. Guiry, Director, michael.guiry@

nuigalway.ie; Jackie Parry, Sec., j.parry@lancaster.ac.uk. **ISSN:** 0967-0262. **Subscription Rates:** 27 members; 299 institutions; US$491 institutions. **Remarks:** Advertising not accepted. **URL:** http://www.brphycsoc.org/journal.lasso; http://www.tandf.co.uk/journals/titles/09670262.asp; http://www.taylorandfrancisgroup.com/. **Circ:** (Not Reported)

54405 ■ European Journal of Psychotherapy and Counselling
Taylor & Francis Group Journals
Roehampton University
Whitelands College
Holybourne Ave.
London SW15 4JD, United Kingdom
Publisher E-mail: customerservice@taylorandfrancis.com
Peer-reviewed journal covering psychotherapy for counseling practitioners and academics. **Founded:** May 2, 1982. **Freq:** Quarterly. **Print Method:** Offset. **Trim Size:** 10 3/4 x 14 1/2. **Cols./Page:** 4. **Col. Width:** 27 nonpareils. **Col. Depth:** 196 agate lines. **Key Personnel:** Richard House, Theory Ed.; Mikkel Bosch-Jacobsen, International Editorial Board; David Boadella, International Editorial Board; Prof. David Winter, Res. Ed.; Luis Botella, International Editorial Board; Mark Aveline, International Editorial Board; Tim Bond, International Editorial Board; Dr. Chris Mace, Practice Ed.; Robert Bor, International Editorial Board; Prof. Del Loewenthal, Editor, d.loewenthal@roehampton.ac.uk. **ISSN:** 1364-2537. **Subscription Rates:** US$551 institutions online; 332 institutions online; US$580 institutions print and online; 349 institutions print and online; US$128 individuals print; 77 institutions print and online; EUR462 institutions print and online; EUR439 institutions online only; EUR102 individuals. **URL:** http://www.tandf.co.uk/journals/titles/13642537.asp.

54406 ■ European Journal of Ultrasound
European Federation of Societies of Ultrasound in Medicine and Biology
36 Portland Pl.
London W1B 1LS, United Kingdom
Ph: 44 20 70997140
Fax: 44 20 74367934
Publisher E-mail: efsumb@efsumb.org
European journal covering ultrasound. **Freq:** Quarterly. **Key Personnel:** Gianna Stanford, Contact. **ISSN:** 0929-8266. **Remarks:** Advertising accepted; rates available upon request. **URL:** http://www.efsumb.org/; https://www.thieme-connect.com/ejournals/toc/ultraschall?locale=en&LgSwitch=1. **Circ:** (Not Reported)

54407 ■ The European Journal of Women's Studies
Sage Publications Ltd.
c/o Hazel Johnstone, Mng. Ed.
Gender Institute
London School of Economics
Houghton St.
London WC2A 2AE, United Kingdom
Scholarly, multidisciplinary feminist journal covering women in the context of Europe. **Subtitle:** Published with the Support of WISE the European Women's Studies Association. **Founded:** 1994. **Freq:** Quarterly. **Key Personnel:** Hazel Johnstone, Managing Editor; Kathy Davis, Editor; Gail Lewis, Editor. **ISSN:** 1350-5068. **Subscription Rates:** US$825 institutions combined (print & e-access); US$908 institutions backfile lease, combined plus backfile; US$743 institutions e-access; US$826 institutions backfile lease, e-access plus backfile; US$743 institutions backfile purchase, e-access (content through 1998); US$809 institutions print only; US$100 individuals print only; US$222 institutions single print; US$33 individuals single print. **Remarks:** Accepts advertising. **URL:** http://www.sagepub.com/journalsProdDesc.nav?prodId=Journal200932&. **Circ:** (Not Reported)

54408 ■ European Pensions
Perspective Publishing
3 London Wall Bldgs., 6th Fl.
London EC2M 5PD, United Kingdom
Ph: 44 20 75622400
Fax: 44 20 73742701
Magazine featuring European pensions industry. **Freq:** Bimonthly. **Trim Size:** 204 x 271 mm. **Key Personnel:** John Woods, Publisher, phone 44 20 75622421, john.woods@europeanpensions.net; Francesca Fabrizi, Edi-

Circulation: ★ = ABC; △ = BPA; ◆ = CAC; • = CCAB; ❑ = VAC; ⊕ = PO Statement; ‡ = Publisher's Report; Boldface figures = sworn; Light figures = estimated.

Gale Directory of Publications & Broadcast Media/147th Ed.   5711

tor, phone 44 20 75622409, francesca.fabrizi@europeanpensions.net. **Subscription Rates:** 198 individuals; EUR299 individuals. **Remarks:** Accepts advertising. **URL:** http://www.europeanpensions.net/. **Ad Rates:** 4C: 11,400. **Circ:** (Not Reported)

54409 ■ European Pharmaceutical Contractor
Samedan Ltd.
16, Hampden Gurney St.
London W1H 5AL, United Kingdom
Ph: 44 20 77243456
Fax: 44 20 77242632
Publisher E-mail: info@samedanltd.com
Journal for the international pharmaceutical contract market. **Freq:** Quarterly. **Key Personnel:** Dr. Graham Hughes, Editor. **Subscription Rates:** 125 individuals; US$230 other countries. **Remarks:** Accepts advertising. **URL:** http://www.samedanltd.com/magazine/11. **Circ:** (Not Reported)

54410 ■ European Research in Regional Science
Pion Ltd.
207 Brondesbury Pk.
London NW2 5JN, United Kingdom
Ph: 44 20 84590066
Fax: 44 20 84516454
Journal covering regional science. **Founded:** 1990. **Freq:** Annual. **Print Method:** Litho. **Key Personnel:** Prof. J.H.L. Dewhurst, Editor, j.h.l.dewhurst@dundee.ac.uk; J.B. Parr, Editorial Board; P. Batey, Editorial Board; R. Maggi, Editorial Board; B. Johansson, Editorial Board; S. Hill, Editorial Board. **ISSN:** 0960-6130. **Remarks:** Advertising not accepted. **URL:** http://www.envplan.com/ep/errs/inderrs.html. **Circ:** (Not Reported)

54411 ■ European Urban and Regional Studies
Sage Publications Ltd.
1 Oliver's Yard
55 City Rd.
London EC1Y 1SP, United Kingdom
Ph: 44 20 73248500
Fax: 44 20 73248600
Scholarly journal covering urban and regional development issues in Europe. **Founded:** 1994. **Freq:** Quarterly. **Key Personnel:** Diane Perrons, Managing Editor; Allan Williams, Editor; Judit Timar, Editor; Adrian Smith, Editor. **ISSN:** 0969-7764. **Subscription Rates:** US$840 institutions print & e-access; US$924 institutions current volume print & all online content; US$756 institutions e-access; US$840 individuals e-access plus backfile (all online content); US$756 institutions content through 1998; US$823 institutions print only; US$115 individuals print only; US$226 institutions single print; US$37 individuals single print. **Remarks:** Accepts advertising. **URL:** http://www.sagepub.com/journalsSubscribe.nav?prodId=Journal200838. **Circ:** (Not Reported)

54412 ■ Evaluation
Sage Publications Ltd.
The Tavistock Institute
30 Tabernacle St.
London EC2A 4DD, United Kingdom
Scholarly journal covering research and developments in evaluation policy and practice. **Subtitle:** The International Journal of Theory, Research and Practice. **Founded:** 1995. **Freq:** Quarterly. **Trim Size:** A5. **Key Personnel:** Elliot Stern, Editor; Murray Saunders, Assoc. Ed.; Nicoletta Stame, Assoc. Ed. **ISSN:** 1356-3890. **Subscription Rates:** 498 institutions combined (print & e-access); 548 institutions backfile lease, combined plus backfile; 448 institutions e-access; 498 institutions backfile lease, e-access plus backfile; 448 institutions backfile purchase, e-access (content through 1998); 488 institutions print only; 62 individuals print only; 134 institutions single print; 20 individuals single print. **Remarks:** Accepts advertising. **URL:** http://www.sagepub.co.uk/journalsProdDesc.nav?prodId=Journal200757. **Ad Rates:** BW: 250. **Circ:** 1,500

54413 ■ Event
Haymarket Business Magazines
174 Hammersmith Rd.
London W6 7JP, United Kingdom
Ph: 44 20 82674210
Publisher E-mail: info@haymarket.com
Magazine featuring news and stories on roadshow, exhibiting strategies, field marketing and live event production. **Founded:** 1997. **Freq:** 10/yr. **Key Personnel:** Jeremy King, Editor, phone 44 20 82674055, mike.

fletcher@haymarket.com; Vicky Chapman, Advertising Mgr., phone 44 20 82674511, victoria.kenney@haymarket.com; Tracy Awere, Sales Mgr., phone 44 20 82674607, tracy.awere@haymarket.com. **Subscription Rates:** 85 individuals; 153 two years; 204 individuals three years. **Remarks:** Accepts advertising. **URL:** http://www.haymarket.com/event/event__magazine/default.aspx; http://www.eventmagazine.co.uk. **Circ:** ★15,055

54414 ■ Evidence-Based Dentistry (EBD)
Nature Publishing Group
The Macmillan Bldg.
4 Crinan St.
London N1 9XW, United Kingdom
Ph: 44 20 78334000
Fax: 44 20 78434640
Journal dealing with oral health by evaluating the evidence available on the recent developments in oral health. **Freq:** 4/yr. **Key Personnel:** Derek Richards, Editor-in-Chief; Richard Niederman, Assoc. Ed.; Alan Lawrence, Founding Ed.; Asbjorn Jokstad, Assoc. Ed. **ISSN:** 1462-0049. **Subscription Rates:** US$117 individuals print and online version; EUR100 individuals for Europe; print and online version; 17,000¥ individuals print and online version; 64 individuals U.K. & rest of World; print and online version. **Remarks:** Advertising accepted; rates available upon request. **URL:** http://www.nature.com/ebd/index.html. **Circ:** (Not Reported)

54415 ■ Evidence-Based Mental Health (EBMH)
BMJ Publishing Group Ltd.
c/o Alan Lovell
Bazian Ltd.
85 Tottenham Court Rd.
London W1T 4TQ, United Kingdom
Ph: 44 20 78741593
Fax: 44 20 73883101
Journal covering studies of people developing psychiatric or psychological problems as a result of trauma including people with learning disabilities, head injuries, drug and alcohol problems and personality disorders. **Founded:** 1998. **Freq:** Quarterly. **Key Personnel:** Steve Reid, Editor, steve.reid@nhs.net; Corrado Barbui, Assoc. Ed.; Simon Hatcher, Assoc. Ed.; Kapil Sayal, Assoc. Ed.; David Taylor, Assoc. Ed.; Graham Towl, Assoc. Ed.; Alan Lovell, Contact, alan.lovell@bazian.com. **ISSN:** 1362-0347. **Subscription Rates:** 96 individuals print and online; 54 individuals online only; US$187 individuals print and online; EUR130 institutions print & online; US$105 institutions online only. **Remarks:** Advertising accepted; rates available upon request. **URL:** http://ebmh.bmj.com/. **Circ:** (Not Reported)

54416 ■ Exchange
National Eczema Society
Hill House
Highgate Hill
London N19 5NA, United Kingdom
Ph: 44 20 72813553
Publisher E-mail: info@eczema.org
Publication covering dermatology. **Founded:** 1975. **Freq:** Quarterly. **Print Method:** Offset. **Trim Size:** A4. **Subscription Rates:** EUR20 individuals U.K. & Republic of Ireland; EUR40 individuals EU & overseas. **Remarks:** Accepts advertising. **URL:** http://www.eczema.org/. **Ad Rates:** 4C: 840. **Circ:** Paid ‡11,500

54417 ■ Expert Opinion on Investigational Drugs
Ashley Publications Ltd.
Telephone House
69-77 Paul St.
London EC2A 4LQ, United Kingdom
Ph: 44 20 70175000
Fax: 44 20 70177667
Publisher E-mail: info@ashley-pub.com
Peer-reviewed journal covering developments in pharmaceutical research, from animal studies through to the launch of a new medicine. **Freq:** Monthly. **Key Personnel:** Dimitri Mikhailidis, Editor-in-Chief. **ISSN:** 1354-3784. **URL:** http://catalogue.informahealthcare.com/pjbp/product.htm?prd=20001537591; http://www.informapharmascience.com/loi/eid.

54418 ■ Expert Review of Anti-Infective Therapy
Expert Reviews
Unitec House
2 Albert Pl.
London N3 1QB, United Kingdom
Ph: 44 20 83716090
Fax: 44 20 83432313

Publisher E-mail: info@expert-reviews.com
Journal providing expert reviews on therapeutics and diagnostics in the treatment of infectious disease, including antibiotics, drug resistance, drug therapy, infectious disease medicine, antibacterial, antimicrobial, antifungal and antiviral approaches, and diagnostic tests. **Freq:** Bimonthly. **Key Personnel:** R. Burchmore, Editorial Advisory Panel; V.S. Chauhan, Editorial Advisory Panel; C.S. Crumpacker, Editorial Advisory Panel. **ISSN:** 1478-7210. **URL:** http://www.expert-reviews.com/loi/eri.

54419 ■ Expert Review of Anticancer Therapy
Expert Reviews
Unitec House
2 Albert Pl.
London N3 1QB, United Kingdom
Ph: 44 20 83716090
Fax: 44 20 83432313
Publisher E-mail: info@expert-reviews.com
Peer-reviewed journal providing expert appraisal and commentary on the major trends in cancer care and highlights the performance of new therapeutic and diagnostic approaches. **Subtitle:** An Essential Contribution to Decision Making in Cancer Care. **Freq:** 12/yr. **Key Personnel:** Ag Dalgleish, Editorial Board; M.B. Atkins, Editorial Board; L. Cheng, Editorial Board; J. Abraham, Editorial Board; K. Dhingra, Editorial Board; R.J. Ablin, Editorial Board; J. Bernier, Editorial Board; A. Ferlito, Editorial Board; A.A. Brandes, Editorial Board. **ISSN:** 1473-7140. **Subscription Rates:** 950 institutions; US$1,825 institutions; EUR1,190 institutions; 198,500¥ institutions. **Remarks:** Accepts advertising. **URL:** http://www.expert-reviews.com/loi/era. **Circ:** (Not Reported)

54420 ■ Expert Review of Cardiovascular Therapy
Expert Reviews
Unitec House
2 Albert Pl.
London N3 1QB, United Kingdom
Ph: 44 20 83716090
Fax: 44 20 83432313
Publisher E-mail: info@expert-reviews.com
Journal providing expert reviews on the clinical applications of new medicines, therapeutic agents and diagnostics in cardiovascular disease, including drug therapy, heart disease, vascular disorders, hypertension, cholesterol in cardiovascular disease, heart disease, stroke, heart failure and cardiovascular surgery. **Freq:** Monthly. **Key Personnel:** P.J. de Feyter, Editorial Advisory Panel; W.T. Abraham, Editorial Advisory Panel; A. Feldman, Editorial Advisory Panel. **ISSN:** 1477-9072. **URL:** http://www.expert-reviews.com/loi/erc.

54421 ■ Expert Review of Clinical Immunology
Expert Reviews
Unitec House
2 Albert Pl.
London N3 1QB, United Kingdom
Ph: 44 20 83716090
Fax: 44 20 83432313
Publisher E-mail: info@expert-reviews.com
Peer-reviewed journal covering topics on clinical immunology. **Freq:** Bimonthly. **Key Personnel:** Elisa Manzotti, Editorial Dir., e.manzotti@futuremedicine.com. **ISSN:** 1744-666X. **Subscription Rates:** 605 institutions; US$1,160 institutions; EUR755 institutions; 126,000¥ institutions. **Remarks:** Accepts advertising. **URL:** http://www.expert-reviews.com/loi/eci. **Circ:** (Not Reported)

54422 ■ Expert Review of Clinical Pharmacology
Expert Reviews
Unitec House
2 Albert Pl.
London N3 1QB, United Kingdom
Ph: 44 20 83716090
Fax: 44 20 83432313
Publisher E-mail: info@expert-reviews.com
Peer-reviewed journal covering various topics in pharmacology. **Freq:** Bimonthly. **Key Personnel:** Elisa Manzotti, Editorial Dir., e.manzotti@futuremedicine.com. **ISSN:** 1751-2433. **Subscription Rates:** 605 institutions; US$1,160 institutions; EUR755 institutions; 126,000¥ institutions. **Remarks:** Accepts advertising. **URL:** http://www.expert-reviews.com/loi/ecp. **Circ:** (Not Reported)

54423 ■ Expert Review of Endocrinology & Metabolism
Expert Reviews
Unitec House
2 Albert Pl.

London N3 1QB, United Kingdom
Ph: 44 20 83716090
Fax: 44 20 83432313
Publisher E-mail: info@expert-reviews.com
Peer-reviewed journal covering research and clinical advances in endocrinology and metabolism. **Freq:** Bimonthly. **Key Personnel:** Elisa Manzotti, Editorial Dir., e.manzotti@futuremedicine.com. **ISSN:** 1744-6651. **Subscription Rates:** 605 institutions; US$1,160 institutions; EUR755 institutions; 126,000¥ institutions. **Remarks:** Accepts advertising. **URL:** http://www.expert-reviews.com/loi/eem. **Circ:** (Not Reported)

54424 ■ Expert Review of Gastroenterology & Hepatology
Expert Reviews
Unitec House
2 Albert Pl.
London N3 1QB, United Kingdom
Ph: 44 20 83716090
Fax: 44 20 83432313
Publisher E-mail: info@expert-reviews.com
Peer-reviewed journal covering the latest research and clinical advances in gastroenterology and hepatology. **Freq:** Bimonthly. **Key Personnel:** Elisa Manzotti, Editorial Dir., e.manzotti@futuremedicine.com. **ISSN:** 1747-4124. **Subscription Rates:** 605 institutions; US$1,160 institutions; EUR755 institutions; 126,000¥ institutions. **Remarks:** Accepts advertising. **URL:** http://www.expert-reviews.com/loi/egh. **Circ:** (Not Reported)

54425 ■ Expert Review of Hematology
Expert Reviews
Unitec House
2 Albert Pl.
London N3 1QB, United Kingdom
Ph: 44 20 83716090
Fax: 44 20 83432313
Publisher E-mail: info@expert-reviews.com
Journal covering research on the treatment of hematologic diseases. **Freq:** Bimonthly. **Key Personnel:** L.M. Aledort, Editorial Advisory Board; P. Aplan, Editorial Advisory Board; K. Ataga, Editorial Advisory Board. **ISSN:** 1747-4086. **URL:** http://www.expert-reviews.com/loi/ehm.

54426 ■ Expert Review of Medical Devices
Expert Reviews
Unitec House
2 Albert Pl.
London N3 1QB, United Kingdom
Ph; 44 20 83716090
Fax: 44 20 83432313
Publisher E-mail: info@expert-reviews.com
Peer-reviewed journal providing commentary, analysis and debate for all professionals involved in research, development, testing and clinical use of devices. **Freq:** Bimonthly. **Key Personnel:** J. Birchall, Editorial Advisory Panel; P.S. Ayyaswamy, Editorial Advisory Panel; D. Bluestein, Editorial Advisory Panel. **ISSN:** 1743-4440. **Subscription Rates:** 605 institutions; US$1,160 institutions; EUR755 institutions; 126,000¥ institutions. **Remarks:** Accepts advertising. **URL:** http://www.expert-reviews.com/loi/erd. **Circ:** (Not Reported)

54427 ■ Expert Review of Molecular Diagnostics
Expert Reviews
Unitec House
2 Albert Pl.
London N3 1QB, United Kingdom
Ph: 44 20 83716090
Fax: 44 20 83432313
Publisher E-mail: info@expert-reviews.com
Journal providing expert reviews on molecular diagnostic technologies and applied pharmacogenomics in clinical medicine, including molecular diagnostics, biomarkers, diagnostic technologies, microarrays and biochips, proteomics, pharmacogenomics, pharmacogenetics and personalized medicine. **Freq:** Bimonthly. **Key Personnel:** W.C.S. Cho; K. Appasani, Editorial Panel; S. Hanash, Assoc. Ed. **ISSN:** 1473-7159. **URL:** http://www.expert-reviews.com/loi/erm?cookieSet=1.

54428 ■ Expert Review of Neurotherapeutics
Expert Reviews
Unitec House
2 Albert Pl.
London N3 1QB, United Kingdom
Ph: 44 20 83716090
Fax: 44 20 83432313

Publisher E-mail: info@expert-reviews.com
Journal providing expert reviews on the use of drugs and medicines in clinical neurology and neuropsychiatry, including disease management, new medicines and drugs in neurology, therapeutic indications, diagnostics, medical treatment guidelines and neurological diseases such as stroke, epilepsy, Alzheimer's and Parkinson's. **Subtitle:** A Key Contribution to Decision Making in the Treatment of Neurologic and Neuropsychiatric Disorders. **Freq:** Bimonthly. **Key Personnel:** M.J. Aminoff, Editorial Advisory Panel; S.R. Benbadis, Editorial Advisory Panel; J. Biller, Editorial Advisory Panel, e.manzotti@expert-reviews.com. **ISSN:** 1473-7175. **URL:** http://www.expert-reviews.com/loi/ern.

54429 ■ Expert Review of Obstetrics & Gynecology
Expert Reviews
Unitec House
2 Albert Pl.
London N3 1QB, United Kingdom
Ph: 44 20 83716090
Fax: 44 20 83432313
Publisher E-mail: info@expert-reviews.com
Peer-reviewed journal covering women's healthcare focusing on obstetrics and gynecology. **Freq:** Bimonthly. **Key Personnel:** Elisa Manzotti, Editorial Dir., e.manzotti@futuremedicine.com. **ISSN:** 1747-4108. **Subscription Rates:** 605 institutions; US$1,160 institutions; EUR755 institutions; 126,000¥ institutions. **Remarks:** Accepts advertising. **URL:** http://www.expert-reviews.com/loi/eog. **Circ:** (Not Reported)

54430 ■ Expert Review of Ophthalmology
Expert Reviews
Unitec House
2 Albert Pl.
London N3 1QB, United Kingdom
Ph: 44 20 83716090
Fax: 44 20 83432313
Publisher E-mail: info@expert-reviews.com
Peer-reviewed journal covering scientific advancements in ophthalmology. **Freq:** Bimonthly. **Key Personnel:** Elisa Manzotti, Editorial Dir., e.manzotti@futuremedicine.com. **ISSN:** 1746-9899. **Subscription Rates:** 605 institutions; US$1,160 institutions; EUR755 institutions; 126,000¥ institutions. **Remarks:** Accepts advertising. **URL:** http://www.expert-reviews.com/loi/eop. **Circ:** (Not Reported)

54431 ■ Expert Review of Pharmacoeconomics & Outcomes Research
Expert Reviews
Unitec House
2 Albert Pl.
London N3 1QB, United Kingdom
Ph: 44 20 83716090
Fax: 44 20 83432313
Publisher E-mail: info@expert-reviews.com
Peer-reviewed journal providing expert reviews on cost-benefit and pharmacoeconomic issues relating to the clinical use of drugs and therapeutic approaches. **Subtitle:** Informing Decision-Making in the Delivery of Cost-Effective Healthcare. **Freq:** Bimonthly. **Key Personnel:** D.M. Ashcroft, Editorial Advisory Panel; A. Bottomley, Sen. Ed.; C. Gotay, Assoc. Ed. **ISSN:** 1473-7167. **Subscription Rates:** 605 institutions; US$1,100 institutions; EUR755 institutions; 126,000¥ institutions. **Remarks:** Accepts advertising. **URL:** http://www.expert-reviews.com/loi/erp. **Circ:** (Not Reported)

54432 ■ Expert Review of Proteomics
Expert Reviews
Unitec House
2 Albert Pl.
London N3 1QB, United Kingdom
Ph: 44 20 83716090
Fax: 44 20 83432313
Publisher E-mail: info@expert-reviews.com
Journal collecting together technologies, methods and discoveries from the field of proteomics to advance scientific understanding of the many varied roles protein expression plays in human health and disease. **Freq:** Bimonthly. **Key Personnel:** J.S. Albala, Editorial Advisory Panel; R. Apweiler, Editorial Advisory Panel; J. Blackburn, Editorial Advisory Panel. **ISSN:** 1478-9450. **URL:** http://www.expert-reviews.com/loi/epr.

54433 ■ Expert Review of Respiratory Medicine
Expert Reviews
Unitec House

2 Albert Pl.
London N3 1QB, United Kingdom
Ph: 44 20 83716090
Fax: 44 20 83432313
Publisher E-mail: info@expert-reviews.com
Peer-reviewed journal covering the latest developments in pulmonary medicine. **Freq:** Bimonthly. **Key Personnel:** Elisa Manzotti, Editorial Dir., e.manzotti@futuremedicine.com. **ISSN:** 1747-6348. **Subscription Rates:** 605 institutions; US$1,160 institutions; EUR755 institutions; 126,000¥ institutions. **Remarks:** Accepts advertising. **URL:** http://www.expert-reviews.com/loi/ers. **Circ:** (Not Reported)

54434 ■ Expert Review of Vaccines
Expert Reviews
Unitec House
2 Albert Pl.
London N3 1QB, United Kingdom
Ph: 44 20 83716090
Fax: 44 20 83432313
Publisher E-mail: info@expert-reviews.com
Peer-reviewed journal providing expert reviews on the clinical effectiveness of new vaccines, including vaccine technology, vaccine adjuvants, prophylactic vaccines, therapeutic vaccines, AIDS vaccines and vaccines in bioterrorism. **Freq:** Bimonthly. **Key Personnel:** S. Abrignani, Editorial Advisory Panel; S. Adams, Editorial Advisory Panel; JK Andrus, Editorial Advisory Panel. **ISSN:** 1476-0584. **Subscription Rates:** 950 institutions; EUR1,190 institutions; US$1,825 institutions; 198,500¥ institutions. **Remarks:** Accepts advertising. **URL:** http://www.future-drugs.com/loi/erv. **Circ:** (Not Reported)

54435 ■ Expert Reviews of Dermatology
Expert Reviews
Unitec House
2 Albert Pl.
London N3 1QB, United Kingdom
Ph: 44 20 83716090
Fax: 44 20 83432313
Publisher E-mail: info@expert-reviews.com
Peer-reviewed journal covering the latest dermatological research and clinical advances. **Freq:** Bimonthly. **Key Personnel:** Elisa Manzotti, Editorial Dir., e.manzotti@futuremedicine.com. **ISSN:** 1746-9872. **Subscription Rates:** 605 institutions; US$1,160 institutions; EUR755 institutions; 126,000¥ institutions. **Remarks:** Accepts advertising. **URL:** http://www.expert-reviews.com/loi/edm. **Circ:** (Not Reported)

54436 ■ Exposure
Exposure Youth Enterprises
The Bigger Shoe Box
Muswell Hill Center
Hillfield Pk.
London N10 3QJ, United Kingdom
Ph: 44 20 88830260
Fax: 44 20 88832906
Publisher E-mail: manager@exposure.org.uk
Community magazine covering lifestyle and issues for young people in north London. **Founded:** Apr. 1996. **Freq:** Monthly. **Key Personnel:** Andreas Koumi, Manager; Ryan Alexander, Internet, ryan@exposure.org.uk. **ISSN:** 1362-8585. **Subscription Rates:** Free. **Remarks:** Accepts advertising. **URL:** http://www.exposure.org.uk. **Circ:** Non-paid 4,500

54437 ■ Faculty of 1000 Medicine
BioMed Central Ltd.
236 Gray's Inn Rd., Fl. 6
34-42 Cleveland St.
London WC1X 8HL, United Kingdom
Ph: 44 20 31922000
Fax: 44 20 31922010
Publication E-mail: info@f1000medicine.com
Publisher E-mail: info@biomedcentral.com
Online service drawing upon the authority and experience of a select faculty of the world's leading researchers and clinicians to select and evaluate the most relevant and important papers published in the medical sciences. **Key Personnel:** Steve Pogonowski, PR Mgr. **ISSN:** 1740-309X. **Subscription Rates:** 50 individuals. **Remarks:** Accepts advertising. **URL:** http://www.f1000medicine.com/. **Circ:** (Not Reported)

54438 ■ Fah Thai
Ink Publishing
141-143 Shoreditch High St.
London E1 6JE, United Kingdom
Ph: 44 20 7613 8777

Fax: 44 207 613 8776
Publication E-mail: bangkokairways.ed@ink-publishing.
com
Magazine of Bangkok Airways featuring travel, culture, and lifestyle. **Freq:** Bimonthly. **Remarks:** Accepts advertising. **URL:** http://www.fahthaimagazine.com/. **Circ:** (Not Reported)

54439 ■ Families in Business
Campden Publishing Ltd.
1 St. John's Sq.
London EC1M 4PN, United Kingdom
Ph: 44 20 72140500
Fax: 44 20 72140501
Publisher E-mail: enquiries@campden.com
Magazine featuring home-based family businesses. **Subtitle:** Making family business matter. **Freq:** 6/yr. **Key Personnel:** Bruce Love, Editor-in-Chief. **Subscription Rates:** US$415; EUR312; 210. **URL:** http://www.campdenfb.com/. **Circ:** 6,000

54440 ■ Family & Community History
Maney Publishing
1 Carlton House Ter.
London SW1Y 5AF, United Kingdom
Ph: 44 20 74517300
Fax: 44 20 74517307
Publisher E-mail: maney@maney.co.uk
Peer-reviewed journal covering research in family and community history. **Freq:** Semiannual. **Key Personnel:** Dr. Steve King, Editor; Dr. Steve King, Review Ed. **ISSN:** 1463-1180. **Subscription Rates:** 38 other countries; US$72 individuals; 138 institutions, other countries; US$264 institutions. **Remarks:** Accepts advertising. **URL:** http://maney.co.uk/index.php/journals/fch/. **Ad Rates:** BW: 180. **Circ:** (Not Reported)

54441 ■ Family History Monthly
The Metropolis Group
140 Wales Farm Rd.
London W3 6UG, United Kingdom
Ph: 44 20 87528181
Fax: 44 20 87528185
Publication E-mail: fhm@metropolis.co.uk
Publisher E-mail: metropolis@metropolis.co.uk
Magazine featuring genealogy. **Founded:** 1996. **Freq:** Monthly. **Key Personnel:** Penny Law, Editor, penny. law@metropolis.co.uk; Sue Maritz, Subscription Mgr., sue.maritz@metropolis.co.uk. **Subscription Rates:** 44 individuals; 52 individuals Europe; 65 other countries; 55 two years; 99 two years Europe; 124 two years rest of world; 120 individuals 3 years; 140 individuals Europe; 177 other countries 3 years. **Remarks:** Accepts advertising. **URL:** http://www.familyhistorymonthly.com. **Ad Rates:** BW: 530, 4C: 550. **Circ:** (Not Reported)

54442 ■ Family Law Journal
Legalese Ltd.
Kensington Sq. House
12-14 Ansdell St.
London W8 5BN, United Kingdom
Ph: 44 20 73969292
Fax: 44 20 73969303
Publication covering developments in family law. **Freq:** 10/yr. **Key Personnel:** Claire Bostock, Contact, claire. bostock@legalease.co.uk. **ISSN:** 0968-7009. **Subscription Rates:** 135 individuals. **URL:** http://www.legalease. co.uk.

54443 ■ Far Eastern Agriculture
Alain Charles Publishing Ltd.
University House
11-13 Lower Grosvenor Pl.
London SW1W 0EX, United Kingdom
Ph: 44 20 78347676
Fax: 44 20 79730076
Publisher E-mail: post@alaincharles.com
Magazine covering agricultural information about the Far East. **Founded:** 1983. **Freq:** Bimonthly. **Print Method:** Sheetfed offset. **Trim Size:** 210 x 276 mm. **ISSN:** 0266-8025. **Remarks:** Accepts advertising. **URL:** http://www.alaincharles.com/index.php?option=com_ content&view=article&id=49&Itemid=73. **Ad Rates:** BW: US$3,240, 4C: US$4,810. **Circ:** *7,050

54444 ■ Farmers Trader
Trader Media Group
41-47 Hartfield Rd., 3rd & 4th Fl.
Wimbledon
London SW19 3RQ, United Kingdom
Ph: 44 208 5447000

Fax: 44 208 8791879
Publication E-mail: private.sales@sw.autotrader.co.uk
Trade magazine featuring farming life. **Founded:** 1996. **Freq:** Monthly. **Key Personnel:** John King, CEO. **Remarks:** Accepts advertising. **URL:** http://www.autotrader. co.uk/FARMERS/; http://www.tradermediagroup.com/ companies/farmers-trader.html. **Circ:** 36,500

54445 ■ Fate & Fortune
H. Bauer Publishing
Academic House
24-28 Oval Rd.
London NW1 7DT, United Kingdom
Ph: 44 20 72418000
Fax: 44 20 72418030
Publication E-mail: fateandfortunefeedback@bauer. co.uk
Magazine featuring star gazer's look into the future. **Founded:** Nov. 2001. **Freq:** Monthly. **Trim Size:** 210 x 280 mm. **Key Personnel:** Sue Ricketts, Editor; Helen Lowe, Assoc. Publisher. **Subscription Rates:** 14.28 individuals. **Remarks:** Accepts advertising. **URL:** http:// www.fateandfortunemagazine.co.uk/. **Circ:** (Not Reported)

54446 ■ Feminism & Psychology
Sage Publications Ltd.
1 Oliver's Yard
55 City Rd.
London EC1Y 1SP, United Kingdom
Ph: 44 20 73248500
Fax: 44 20 73248600
Scholarly journal covering feminist theory and practice in psychology. **Subtitle:** An International Journal. **Founded:** 1991. **Freq:** Quarterly. **Key Personnel:** Nicola Gavey, Editor; Virginia Braun, Editor; Rosalind Gill, Assoc. Ed. **ISSN:** 0959-3535. **Subscription Rates:** 474 institutions combined (print & e-access); 521 institutions backfile lease, combined plus backfile; 427 institutions e-access; 474 institutions backfile lease, e-access plus backfile; 427 institutions backfile purchase, e-access (content through 1998); 465 institutions print only; 54 individuals print only; 128 institutions single print; 18 individuals single print. **Remarks:** Accepts advertising. **URL:** http://www.sagepub.co.uk/ journalsProdDesc.nav?prodId=Journal200868. **Circ:** (Not Reported)

54447 ■ Feminist Review
Palgrave Macmillan
Women's Studies
London Metropolitan University
166-220 Holloway Rd.
London N7 8DB, United Kingdom
Publication E-mail: feminist-review@londonmet.ac.uk
Publisher E-mail: booksellers@palgrave.com
Peer-reviewed journal offering informative resources to students and academics in higher education in various fields. **Founded:** 1979. **Freq:** 3/yr. **Key Personnel:** Amina Mama, Corresponding Ed. **ISSN:** 0141-7789. **Subscription Rates:** 312 institutions, other countries print; US$593 institutions print; 44 other countries print and online; US$82 individuals print and online. **URL:** http://www.palgrave-journals.com/fr/index.html. **Circ:** 1,300

54448 ■ Feminist Theory
Sage Publications Ltd.
1 Oliver's Yard
55 City Rd.
London EC1Y 1SP, United Kingdom
Ph: 44 20 73248500
Fax: 44 20 73248600
Scholarly journal covering critical analysis and debate within feminist theory worldwide. **Subtitle:** An International Interdisciplinary Journal. **Founded:** 2000. **Freq:** 3/yr. **Key Personnel:** Stevi Jackson, Honorary Founding Co-Ed.; Rosemary Hennessy, International Advisory Board; Sneja Gunew, Canadian/North American Ed.; Sarah Franklin, Assoc. Ed.; Jackie Stacey, Editor; Celia Roberts, Book Review Ed.; Stacy Gillis, Editor. **ISSN:** 1464-7001. **Subscription Rates:** 310 institutions print & e-access; 279 institutions e-access; 304 institutions print only; 44 individuals print only; 111 institutions single print; 19 individuals single print. **Remarks:** Accepts advertising. **URL:** http://www.sagepub.co.uk/ journalsProdDesc.nav?prodId=Journal200796. **Circ:** (Not Reported)

54449 ■ FHM
EMAP Metro Ltd.
Greater London House
Hampstead Rd.
London NW1 7EJ, United Kingdom
Ph: 44 20 7728500
Consumer magazine covering men's fashion and lifestyle. **Founded:** 1990. **Freq:** Monthly. **Print Method:** Web Offset. **Key Personnel:** Anthony Noguera, Editor-in-Chief; David Moynihan, Editor. **Subscription Rates:** 25 individuals direct debit; 8.50 individuals Quarterly direct debit; 35 individuals debit card; 60 other countries. **Remarks:** Accepts advertising. **URL:** http://www.fhm. com; http://www.greatmagazines.co.uk; http://www. isubscribe.co.uk/title_info.cfm?prodid=119. **Circ:** Paid 710,000

54450 ■ Fiction Feast
H. Bauer Publishing
Academic House
24-28 Oval Rd.
London NW1 7DT, United Kingdom
Ph: 44 20 72418000
Fax: 44 20 72418030
Magazine featuring fiction stories. **Founded:** Aug. 1988. **Freq:** Monthly. **Trim Size:** 210 x 280 mm. **Key Personnel:** Margaret Nichols, Editor; Andy Brooks, Publishing Dir.; Danielle Katz, Advertising Mgr. **Subscription Rates:** 16.32 individuals. **Remarks:** Accepts advertising. **URL:** http://www.bauer.co.uk/fiction-feast. **Circ:** (Not Reported)

54451 ■ The Field
IPC Media Ltd.
Blue Fin Bldg.
110 Southwark St.
London SE1 0SU, United Kingdom
Ph: 44 203 1485000
Consumer magazine covering field sports and local issues. **Founded:** Jan. 1853. **Freq:** Monthly. **Key Personnel:** Jonathan Young, Editor, phone 44 20 31484772, jonathan_young@ipcmedia.com; Fiona Mercer, Publisher, phone 44 20 31484311, fiona_mercer@ipcmedia. com; Rosemary Archer, Advertising Mgr., phone 44 20 31484214, rosemary_archer@ipcmedia.com. **Subscription Rates:** 34.99 individuals; 59.99 two years. **Remarks:** Accepts advertising. **URL:** http://www.ipcmedia. com/magazines/thefield/; http://www.thefield.co.uk. **Circ:** *30,428

54452 ■ Fifi and the Flowertots
BBC Worldwide Publishing Ltd.
Media Centre
201 Wood Ln.
London W12 7TQ, United Kingdom
Ph: 44 20 84332000
Fax: 44 20 87490538
Magazine featuring fun, friendship, and creativity for 3-5 years old. **Subtitle:** Flowertot fun in Fifi's world!. **Freq:** every 4 weeks. **Subscription Rates:** 1.99 single issue. **URL:** http://www.bbcmagazines.com/content/ magazines/fifiandtheflowertots/.

54453 ■ Fimbles Magazine
BBC Worldwide Publishing Ltd.
Media Centre
201 Wood Ln.
London W12 7TQ, United Kingdom
Ph: 44 20 84332000
Fax: 44 20 87490538
Magazine designed to take children aged 2-4 on a magical journey of discovery, finding all kinds of new and exciting objects to learn about. **Freq:** Monthly. **Subscription Rates:** 1.99 single issue. **URL:** http://www. bbcmagazines.com/content/magazines/fimbles/.

54454 ■ Financial Director
Incisive Media Limited
Haymarket House
28-29 Haymarket
London SW1Y 4RX, United Kingdom
Ph: 44 870 2408859
Fax: 44 207 4849797
Publisher E-mail: customerservices@incisivemedia.com
Magazine presenting topical and insightful articles which assists financial directors to manage their organizations. **Freq:** Monthly. **Key Personnel:** Damian Wild, Editor-in-Chief; Andrew Sawers, Editor. **Remarks:** Accepts advertising. **URL:** http://www.financialdirector.co.uk/. **Ad Rates:** BW: 4,669. **Circ:** *20,609

54455 ■ Financial Management
Chartered Institute of Management Accountants
26 Chapter St.
London SW1P 4NP, United Kingdom
Ph: 44 20 88492251
Fax: 44 20 88492450
Publisher E-mail: cima.contact@cimaglobal.com
Professional magazine covering finance, business, management and technology. **Founded:** Sept. 2000. **Freq:** Monthly. **ISSN:** 1471-9185. **Subscription Rates:** includes p&p. **Remarks:** Accepts advertising. **URL:** http://www.cimaglobal.com/cps/rde/xchg/live/root.xsl/1673.htm. **Former name:** Management Accounting. **Ad Rates:** BW: 3,300, 4C: 3,300. **Circ:** Paid 65,289

54456 ■ Financial Marketing
Incisive Media Limited
Haymarket House
28-29 Haymarket
London SW1Y 4RX, United Kingdom
Ph: 44 870 2408859
Fax: 44 207 4849797
Publisher E-mail: customerservices@incisivemedia.com
Marketing magazine focusing on financial services. **Founded:** 1992. **Key Personnel:** Jonathan Boyd, Editor, phone 44 20 74849769, jonathan.boyd@incisivemedia.com; Mike Jones, Publisher, phone 44 20 79684530, mike.jones@incisivemedia.com. **Remarks:** Accepts advertising. **URL:** http://www.financialmarketingonline.com. **Ad Rates:** 4C: 1,250. **Circ:** 2,103

54457 ■ Financial News
Financial News Ltd.
Commodity Quay
East Smithfield
London E1W 1AZ, United Kingdom
Ph: 44 20 34261111
Fax: 44 20 77292910
Publisher E-mail: news@efinancialnews.com
Professional magazine for the securities and investment banking industry in Europe. **Founded:** Apr. 1996. **Freq:** Weekly (Mon.). **Print Method:** Web Heatset Litho. **Trim Size:** 291 x 390 mm. **Key Personnel:** Phillips Leighton-Jones, Online Ed., phillipa.jones@dowjones.com; Mike Foster, Assoc. Ed., mike.foster@dowjones.com; William Wright, Editor, william.wright@dowjones.com; Renee Schultes, Dep. Ed., renee.schultes@dowjones.com. **ISSN:** 1461-1260. **Subscription Rates:** 576 two years excl vat; 320 individuals excl vat. **Remarks:** Accepts advertising. **URL:** http://www.efinancialnews.com. **Former name:** London Financial News. **Circ:** Controlled △21,089

54458 ■ Financial Sector Technology
Perspective Publishing
3 London Wall Bldgs., 6th Fl.
London EC2M 5PD, United Kingdom
Ph: 44 20 75622400
Fax: 44 20 73742701
Business magazine for information technology decision makers in the United Kingdom financial sector. **Freq:** Bimonthly. **Key Personnel:** Sophie Baker, Editor, phone 44 20 75622415, sophie.baker@fstech.co.uk; Marilou Tait, Contact, marilou.tait@fstech.co.uk. **Subscription Rates:** 149 individuals UK; 179 individuals airmail. **Remarks:** Accepts display and classified advertising. **URL:** http://www.fstech.co.uk/. **Circ:** ★12,776

54459 ■ The Financial Times
The Financial Times Ltd.
1 Southwark Bridge
London SE1 9HL, United Kingdom
Ph: 44 20 78733000
Banking, finance and accounting industries newspaper. **Freq:** Daily. **ISSN:** 0307-1766. **Subscription Rates:** US$109 individuals standard; US$299 individuals premium. **Remarks:** Accepts advertising. **URL:** http://www.ft.com. **Circ:** (Not Reported)

54460 ■ Fire International
DMG World Media Ltd.
Equitable House Lyon Rd., Harrow
2 Derry St.
London HA1 2EW, United Kingdom
Ph: 44 20 85152000
Fax: 44 20 85152088
Publisher E-mail: careers@dmgworldmedia.com
Trade magazine covering news, technology updates,

analysis and products for fire fighters. **Founded:** 1964. **Freq:** Monthly 10/yr. **Cols./Page:** 3. **Col. Width:** 60 millimeters. **Col. Depth:** 255 millimeters. **Key Personnel:** Andrew Lynch, Managing Editor. **ISSN:** 0015-2609. **Subscription Rates:** 84 individuals; 130 other countries. **Remarks:** Accepts advertising. **URL:** http://www.fire-magazine.com/index.aspx. **Ad Rates:** BW: 1,400, 4C: 2,230. **Circ:** (Not Reported)

54461 ■ Fireman Sam
Egmont Magazines
184-192 Drummond St., 4th Fl.
London NW1 3HP, United Kingdom
Ph: 44 20 73806430
Magazine featuring puzzles, colouring, stories and activities for children. **Freq:** 4/week. **Trim Size:** 220 x 300 mm. **Key Personnel:** Anna Chacoliades, Contact; Sam Verno, Contact. **Subscription Rates:** 2.25 individuals. **Remarks:** Accepts advertising. **URL:** http://www.egmont.co.uk/product.asp?prodid=1514&catid=30; http://www.firemansamonline.com/uk/. **Ad Rates:** 4C: 1,800. **Circ:** (Not Reported)

54462 ■ First
First Magazine Ltd.
56 Haymarket
London SW1Y 4RN, United Kingdom
Ph: 44 20 73899650
Fax: 44 20 73899644
Publisher E-mail: publisher@firstmagazine.com
Professional magazine enhancing communication between industry, finance and government for decision makers in those industries. **Founded:** 1986. **Freq:** Quarterly. **Print Method:** Offset. **Trim Size:** 220 x 297 mm. **Key Personnel:** Eamonn Daly, COO; Patrick Cormack, Consultant; Rupert Goodman, Chm., rupert.goodman@firstmagazine.com; Alastair Harris, Exec. Publisher. **Subscription Rates:** 145 individuals; 270 two years. **Remarks:** Accepts advertising. **URL:** http://www.firstmagazine.com/. **Ad Rates:** 4C: 15,200. **Circ:** Combined 157,000

54463 ■ Fiscal Studies
Institute for Fiscal Studies
7 Ridgmount St., 3rd Fl.
London WC1E 7AE, United Kingdom
Ph: 44 20 72914800
Fax: 44 20 73234780
Publisher E-mail: mailbox@ifs.org.uk
Publication covering taxation. **Freq:** Quarterly. **Key Personnel:** Samuel Berlinski, Editor, s.berlinski@ucl.ac.uk; Jerome Adda, Editor, j.adda@ucl.ac.uk. **ISSN:** 0143-5671. **Subscription Rates:** US$429 institutions print + premium online; US$140 institutions developing world, print + premium online; 84 institutions developing world, print + premium online; 225 institutions, other countries developing world, print + premium online; US$390 institutions print + standard online; US$127 institutions developing world, print + standard online; 76 institutions developing world, print + standard online; 232 other countries print + standard online; US$371 institutions premium online; US$121 institutions premium online, developing world. **Remarks:** Advertising accepted; rates available upon request. **URL:** http://www.ifs.org.uk/fiscalStudies. **Circ:** 1,500

54464 ■ Flagmaster
Flag Institute
38 Hill St.
London W1J 5NS, United Kingdom
Publication E-mail: editor@flaginstitute.org
Publisher E-mail: info@flaginstitute.org
Publication covering the study of flags. **Founded:** 1971. **Freq:** Quarterly. **Key Personnel:** Michael Faul, Editor. **Subscription Rates:** 2.50 members per back issue; 5 nonmembers per back issue. **URL:** http://www.flaginstitute.org/index.php?location=3.

54465 ■ Fleet News Europe
EMAP Automotive Ltd.
40 Bernard St.
London WC1N 1LW, United Kingdom
Source of news and expertise for decision-makers of the company car and van industry. **Freq:** Semiannual. **Key Personnel:** Adele Barry, Section Ed., phone 44 17 33468901, adele.burton@emap.com; Andrew Ryan, Dep. Production Ed., phone 44 17 33468310, andrew.ryan@emap.com; John Maslen, Supplements and Events Ed., phone 44 17 33468307, john.maslen@

emap.com; Martyn Moore, Editor, phone 44 17 33468024, martyn.moore@emap.com; Daniel Attwood, News Ed., phone 44 17 33468294, daniel.attwood@emap.com; Phill Tromans, Features Writer, phone 44 17 33468314, paul.clark@emap.com; Sandie Hurford, Production Ed., phone 44 17 33468312, sandie.hurford@emap.com; Julian Kirk, Motoring Ed., phone 44 17 33468308, julian.kirk@emap.com; Jeremy Bennett, Website Ed., phone 44 17 33468298, jeremy.bennett@emap.com. **URL:** http://www.fleetnews.co.uk/fn-europe-conference/.

54466 ■ Florist & Wholesale Buyer
Wordhouse Publishing Group
68 1st Ave.
Mortlake
London SW14 8SR, United Kingdom
Ph: 44 20 89396470
Fax: 44 20 88789983
Publisher E-mail: info@thewordhouse.co.uk
Trade magazine covering industry news, business, design, products, and other issues for the florist industry. **Founded:** 1949. **Freq:** Monthly. **Trim Size:** 267 x 190. **Key Personnel:** Chrissie Bestley, Sales & Mktg. Mgr., chrissie@thewordhouse.co.uk; Caroline Marshall-Foster, Editor; Marion Billett, Production Mgr., marion@thewordhouse.co.uk. **Subscription Rates:** 50 individuals; 65 other countries; 90 two years; 115 two years overseas. **Remarks:** Accepts advertising. **URL:** http://www.thewordhouse.co.uk/fwb.htm. **Formerly:** Florist Trade Magazine. **Ad Rates:** BW: 1,300, 4C: 1,700. **Circ:** Combined ★9,966

54467 ■ Flourish
Trinity College London
89 Albert Embankment
London SE1 7TP, United Kingdom
Ph: 44 20 78206100
Fax: 44 20 78206161
Publisher E-mail: info@trinitycollege.co.uk
Professional magazine covering music and education. **Subtitle:** Trinity Guildhall's Magazine for Music Examiners, Teachers and Students. **Freq:** Semiannual. **Print Method:** Offset litho. **Trim Size:** A4. **Key Personnel:** Keith Beniston, Ch. Examiner in Music. **Subscription Rates:** Free. **Remarks:** Accepts advertising. **URL:** http://www.trinitycollege.co.uk. **Circ:** Non-paid 20,000

54468 ■ The Flower Arranger
National Association of Flower Arrangement Societies
c/o Judith Blacklock, Ed.
52 Suffolk Rd.
London SW13 9NR, United Kingdom
Ph: 44 20 87482673
Publisher E-mail: flowers@nafas.org.uk
Publication covering flower arranging. **Freq:** Quarterly. **Key Personnel:** Judith Blacklock, Editor, editor@judithblacklock.com; Mo Duffill, Chm. **Subscription Rates:** 16 individuals; 22 individuals Europe (airmail); 26.50 individuals world zones 1 & 2 (airmail); 21.50 individuals overseas surface (not Europe). **Remarks:** Advertising accepted; rates available upon request. **URL:** http://www.nafas.org.uk/content/flower_arranger.html. **Circ:** 80,000

54469 ■ Flute
British Flute Society
c/o Robert Bigio, Editor
1 Doveridge Gardens
London N13 5BJ, United Kingdom
Ph: 44 20 88822627
Fax: 44 20 88822728
Publisher E-mail: secretary@bfs.org.uk
The journal of the British Flute Society. **Subtitle:** The Flute Magazine. **Founded:** 1984. **Freq:** Quarterly. **ISSN:** 1360-1563. **Remarks:** Advertising accepted; rates available upon request. **URL:** http://www.bfs.org.uk/pan.htm. **Circ:** Paid 1,700

54470 ■ The Fly
Fly Enterprises Ltd.
59-65 Worship St.
London EC2A 2DU, United Kingdom
Magazine covering British music and bands. **Founded:** 1999. **Freq:** Monthly. **Trim Size:** 210 x 143.5. **URL:** http://www.the-fly.co.uk/. **Ad Rates:** BW: 3,000. **Circ:** (Not Reported)

Circulation: ★ = ABC; △ = BPA; ♦ = CAC; • = CCAB; ❏ = VAC; ⊕ = PO Statement; ‡ = Publisher's Report; Boldface figures = sworn; Light figures = estimated.

54471 ■ Fly Navy
Fleet Air Arm Officers' Association
4 St. James's Sq.
London SW1Y 4JU, United Kingdom
Ph: 44 20 79307722
Fax: 44 20 79307728
Publisher E-mail: faaoa@fleetairarmoa.org
Journal including reports and professional articles together with historical material. **Freq:** Annual. **Subscription Rates:** Included in membership. **URL:** http://www.fleetairarmarchive.net/associations/FAAAssociations.html.

54472 ■ Flyfishers' Journal
Flyfishers Club
69 Brook St.
London W1K 4ER, United Kingdom
Ph: 44 20 76295958
Journal covering fly fishing for members. **Founded:** 1911. **Key Personnel:** K. Robson, Editor, phone 44 01942410531, kenneth.robson@ntlwnls.com. **Subscription Rates:** 18 individuals. **Remarks:** Accepts advertising. **URL:** http://flyfishersclub.org.uk/. **Ad Rates:** 4C: 150. **Circ:** Paid 650

54473 ■ Flying Angel News
The Mission to Seafarers
St. Michael Paternoster Royal
College Hill
London EC4R 2RL, United Kingdom
Ph: 44 20 72485202
Fax: 44 20 72484761
Publication E-mail: general@missiontoseafarers.org
Publisher E-mail: pr@missiontoseafarers.org
Newspaper covering seafarers. **Founded:** 1958. **Freq:** 3/yr. **Key Personnel:** Richard Rhydderch, Editor. **Subscription Rates:** 2 individuals; US$4 individuals. **Remarks:** Advertising not accepted. **URL:** http://www.missiontoseafarers.org/resources/flying-angel-news-uk. **Circ:** 18,800

54474 ■ FM World
Redactive Media Group
17-18 Britton St.
London EC1M 5TP, United Kingdom
Ph: 44 20 78806200
Fax: 44 20 78807691
Publisher E-mail: info@redactive.co.uk
Magazine featuring the latest in facilities management news and strategies. **Freq:** Biweekly. **Key Personnel:** Aaron Nicholls, Contact. **Subscription Rates:** 110 individuals for UK; 130 individuals outside UK. **URL:** http://www.fm-world.co.uk.

54475 ■ Focus Europe
Incisive Media Limited
Haymarket House
28-29 Haymarket
London SW1Y 4RX, United Kingdom
Ph: 44 870 2408859
Fax: 44 207 4849797
Publisher E-mail: customerservices@incisivemedia.com
Magazine featuring the interpretation of the European legal and business market for the American audience. **Key Personnel:** Stephen Lincoln, Contributing Ed. **Remarks:** Accepts advertising. **URL:** http://www.law.com/jsp/tal/focus_europe.jsp. **Circ:** (Not Reported)

54476 ■ Folk Music Journal
English Folk Dance and Song Society
Cecil Sharp House
2 Regents Park Rd.
London NW1 7AY, United Kingdom
Ph: 44 20 74852206
Fax: 44 20 72840534
Publisher E-mail: info@efdss.org
Scholarly journal covering research on folk music, song and dance. **Subtitle:** The Journal of Traditional Song, Music and Dance. **Freq:** Annual. **Key Personnel:** David Atkinson, Editor, fmj@efdss.org. **ISSN:** 0531-9684. **Subscription Rates:** US$7.50 single issue; Free to members. **Remarks:** Accepts advertising. **URL:** http://www.efdss.org/; http://www.efdss.org/front/folk-music-journal/about-the-journal/60. **Ad Rates:** BW: 225. **Circ:** Paid 4,000

54477 ■ Fonstret
Workers' Educational Association
Arbetarnas Bildningsforbund
96-100 Clifton St.

London EC2A 4TP, United Kingdom
Ph: 44 20 74263450
Fax: 44 20 74299821
Publication E-mail: fonstret@abf.se
Publisher E-mail: london@wea.org.uk
Swedish language publication covering workers. **Freq:** Bimonthly. **Key Personnel:** Jonas Helling, Editor, jonas.helling@abf.se. **Remarks:** Accepts advertising. **URL:** http://turture.abf.se/fonstret/. **Circ:** (Not Reported)

54478 ■ Food Science and Technology
Excel Publishing Company Ltd.
Institute of Food Science & Technology
5 Cambridge Ct.
210 Shepherds Bush Rd.
London W6 7NJ, United Kingdom
Ph: 44 20 76036316
Fax: 44 20 76029936
Publication E-mail: info@ifst.org
Professional journal covering technical information on food science and technology for industrial scientists and technologists, researchers and government scientists. **Subtitle:** The International Quarterly of the Institute of Food Science and Technology. **Freq:** Quarterly. **Key Personnel:** Paula English, Contact, paula.english@excelpublishing.co.uk. **ISSN:** 0950-9623. **Subscription Rates:** 101 individuals surface mail; 106 individuals airmail. **Remarks:** Accepts advertising. **URL:** http://www.ifst.org/publications/fsandt/. **Circ:** (Not Reported)

54479 ■ Foundation
Science Fiction Foundation
Middlesex University
White Hart Ln.
London N17 8HR, United Kingdom
Ph: 44 15 17943142
Fax: 44 15 17942681
Publisher E-mail: asawyer@liv.ac.uk
Publication covering science fiction. **Subtitle:** The International Review of Science Fiction. **Founded:** 1971. **Freq:** 3/yr. **Key Personnel:** Andy Sawyer, Reviews Ed.; Graham Sleight, Editor; Zara Baxter, Production Ed. **ISSN:** 0306-4964. **Subscription Rates:** 18 individuals U.K. & Ireland; 6 individuals outside Europe; 20 individuals Europe; 23 elsewhere other countries; 13 students anywhere; 39 elsewhere institutions; US$66 elsewhere institutions; US$12 individuals outside Europe, airmail surcharge. **Remarks:** Advertising accepted; rates available upon request. **URL:** http://www.sf-foundation.org/publications/foundation.html. **Circ:** 1,200

54480 ■ Freemasonry Today
Freemasonry Today Ltd.
Freemason's Hall
Great Queeen St.
London WC2B 5AZ, United Kingdom
Ph: 44 20 78319811
Fax: 44 20 78319811
Publisher E-mail: fmt@ugle.org.uk
Magazine covering freemasonry. **Founded:** July 1997. **Freq:** Quarterly. **Trim Size:** 210 x 297 mm. **Key Personnel:** Wesley Tatton, Advertising Dir., phone 44 20 73890823, fax 44 20 78396719, wesley.tatton@madisonbell.com. **ISSN:** 1369-040X. **Subscription Rates:** 14 individuals; 20 other countries. **Remarks:** Accepts advertising. **URL:** http://www.freemasonrytoday.com. **Ad Rates:** BW: 1,500. **Circ:** Paid ‡240,000

54481 ■ French Cultural Studies
Sage Publications Ltd.
1 Oliver's Yard
55 City Rd.
London EC1Y 1SP, United Kingdom
Ph: 44 20 73248500
Fax: 44 20 73248600
Publication covering literature and writing. **Founded:** 1990. **Freq:** Quarterly. **Trim Size:** 243 x 175 mm. **Key Personnel:** Nicholas Hewitt, Editor; Nicola Cooper, Assoc. Ed.; Susan Harris, Assoc. Ed. **ISSN:** 0957-1558. **Subscription Rates:** US$688 institutions print & e-access; US$757 institutions current volume print & all online content; US$619 institutions e-access; US$688 institutions e-access plus backfile (all online content); US$619 institutions e-access (content through 1998); US$674 institutions print only; US$76 individuals print only; US$185 institutions single print; US$25 individuals single print. **Remarks:** Accepts advertising. **URL:** http://www.sagepub.com/journalsProdDesc.nav?prodId=

Journal201664. **Ad Rates:** BW: 200. **Circ:** (Not Reported)

54482 ■ Fresh Produce Journal
Lockwood Press
1 Nine Elms Ln.
London SW8 5NN, United Kingdom
Ph: 44 20 75010300
Fax: 44 20 77202047
Publication E-mail: info@fpj.oc.uk
Publisher E-mail: info@fpj.co.uk
Trade magazine for the fresh produce industry. **Founded:** 1895. **Freq:** Weekly (Fri.). **Key Personnel:** Justin Hope-Mason, Mng. Dir., phone 44 20 75010309, justin@fpj.co.uk. **Subscription Rates:** 125 individuals; 148 other countries. **Remarks:** Accepts advertising. **URL:** http://www.freshinfo.com/index.php?s=p&ss=jn. **Ad Rates:** BW: 2,000, 4C: 2,600. **Circ:** Controlled 3,500

54483 ■ The Friend
Friend Publications Ltd.
173 Euston Rd.
London NW1 2BJ, United Kingdom
Ph: 44 20 76631010
Fax: 44 20 76631182
Journal covering news and articles of interest to members of the religious society of Friends (Quakers). **Founded:** 1843. **Freq:** Weekly. **Print Method:** Offset. **Trim Size:** 195 x 270 mm. **Cols./Page:** 3. **Key Personnel:** George Penaluna, Advertising Mgr., phone 44 15 35630230, fax 44 15 35630230; Roy Prockter, Finance Contractor; Clare-Marie White, Journalist & Production Mgr., clare@thefriend.org; Penny Dunn, Subscriptions Asst.; Trish Carn, Sub Ed., trishc@thefriend.org; Simon Risley, News Ed.; Judy Kirby, Editor. **Subscription Rates:** 74 individuals; 96 individuals rest of the world; 48 individuals online. **Remarks:** Accepts advertising. **URL:** http://www.thefriend.org; http://www.thefriend.org/subscribe.asp. **Ad Rates:** BW: 525. **Circ:** Paid 4,500

54484 ■ Frieze
81 Rivington St.
London EC2A 3AY, United Kingdom
Ph: 44 20 33726111
Magazine covering contemporary art and culture. **Founded:** 1991. **Freq:** 8/yr. **Subscription Rates:** 33.50 individuals; 43 institutions; 41 other countries; 47 institutions, other countries. **Remarks:** Accepts advertising. **URL:** http://www.frieze.com/. **Circ:** (Not Reported)

54485 ■ Frontier Brands
The Metropolis Group
140 Wales Farm Rd.
London W3 6UG, United Kingdom
Ph: 44 20 87528181
Fax: 44 20 87528185
Publisher E-mail: metropolis@metropolis.co.uk
Magazine containing product information, marketing, promotion and design. **Subtitle:** The Buyer'S Guide To Travel Retail. **Freq:** 3/yr. **Trim Size:** 210 x 297 mm. **Key Personnel:** Marek Kolasinski, Managing Editor, phone 44 20 82538393, marek.kolasinski@metropolis.co.uk. **Subscription Rates:** 385 individuals. **Remarks:** Accepts advertising. **URL:** http://www.frontiermagazine.co.uk/frontier_brands.html. **Ad Rates:** 4C: 2,800. **Circ:** 4,000

54486 ■ Frontiers in Zoology
BioMed Central Ltd.
236 Gray's Inn Rd., Fl. 6
34-42 Cleveland St.
London WC1X 8HL, United Kingdom
Ph: 44 20 31922000
Fax: 44 20 31922010
Publisher E-mail: info@biomedcentral.com
Online journal covering all aspects of animal life. **Key Personnel:** Dr. Jurgen Heinze, Editor-in-Chief, juergen.heinze@biologie.uni-regensburg.de; Prof. Diethard Tautz, Editor-in-Chief, tautz@evolbio.mpg.de; Prof. John N. Maina, Editorial Board, mainajn@anatomy.wits.ac.za. **ISSN:** 1742-9994. **Remarks:** Accepts advertising. **URL:** http://www.frontiersinzoology.com/. **Circ:** (Not Reported)

54487 ■ Future Cardiology
Future Medicine Ltd.
Unitec House
2 Albert Pl.
London N3 1QB, United Kingdom
Ph: 44 20 83716080
Fax: 44 20 83432313

Publisher E-mail: info@futuremedicine.com
Journal reflecting the new era of cardiology and highlighting the new molecular approach to advancing cardiovascular therapy, including the major technological advances in bioengineering in cardiology in terms of advanced and robust devices, miniaturization, imaging, system modeling and information management issues. **Freq:** Bimonthly. **Key Personnel:** R. Bonow, Editorial Advisory Board; A. Colombo, Editorial Advisory Board; A.M. Feldman, Editorial Advisory Board. **ISSN:** 1479-6678. **URL:** http://www.futuremedicine.com/loi/fca.

54488 ■ Future Microbiology
Future Medicine Ltd.
Unitec House
2 Albert Pl.
London N3 1QB, United Kingdom
Ph: 44 20 83716080
Fax: 44 20 83432313
Publisher E-mail: info@futuremeducine.com
Journal featuring articles on microbiology. **Freq:** 10/yr. **Key Personnel:** Peter W. Andrew, Editorial Advisory Board; Jozef Anne, Editorial Advisory Board; Glen D. Armstrong, Editorial Advisory Board. **ISSN:** 1746-0913. **URL:** http://www.futuremedicine.com/loi/fmb.

54489 ■ Future Neurology
Future Medicine Ltd.
Unitec House
2 Albert Pl.
London N3 1QB, United Kingdom
Ph: 44 20 83716080
Fax: 44 20 83432313
Publisher E-mail: info@futuremeducine.com
Journal featuring articles on neurology. **Freq:** Bimonthly. **Key Personnel:** A. Achiron, Editorial Board Member; C. Bernard, Editorial Board Member; A. Biegon, Editorial Board Member. **ISSN:** 1479-6708. **URL:** http://www.futuremedicine.com/loi/fnl.

54490 ■ Future Oncology
Future Medicine Ltd.
Unitec House
2 Albert Pl.
London N3 1QB, United Kingdom
Ph: 44 20 83716080
Fax: 44 20 83432313
Publisher E-mail: info@futuremeducine.com
Journal providing a forum for a new era of cancer care, focusing on the most important advances and highlighting their relevance in the clinical setting. **Freq:** Bimonthly. **Key Personnel:** R. Allison, Editorial Advisory Board; P. Arlen, Editorial Advisory Board; L.M. Berstein, Editorial Advisory Board. **ISSN:** 1479-6694. **URL:** http://www.futuremedicine.com/loi/fon.

54491 ■ Future Virology
Future Medicine Ltd.
Unitec House
2 Albert Pl.
London N3 1QB, United Kingdom
Ph: 44 20 83716080
Fax: 44 20 83432313
Publisher E-mail: info@futuremeducine.com
Journal covering research on virology and genomics. **Freq:** Bimonthly. **Key Personnel:** D.L. Barnard, Editorial Advisory Panel; R.W. Buckheit, Editorial Advisory Panel; R. Compans, Editorial Advisory Panel. **ISSN:** 1746-0794. **URL:** http://www.futuremedicine.com/loi/fvl.

54492 ■ Gaming Floor
Gamingfloor.com Ltd.
72 New Bond St.
London W1S 1RR, United Kingdom
Ph: 44 8700 113020
Online magazine featuring news and information about casino gaming. **Subtitle:** An Online Resource for Casino Trade and Industry News. **Founded:** May 1999. **Freq:** Daily updates. **Key Personnel:** Ian Sutton, Director, editorial@gamingfloor.com. **Remarks:** Accepts advertising. **URL:** http://www.gamingfloor.com/. **Circ:** (Not Reported)

54493 ■ Garden History
Garden History Society
70 Cowcross St.
London EC1M 6EJ, United Kingdom
Ph: 44 20 76082409
Fax: 44 20 74902974

Publication E-mail: journal@gardenhistorysociety.org
Publisher E-mail: enquiries@gardenhistorysociety.org
Publication covering gardening history. **Freq:** Semiannual. **Key Personnel:** Dr. Barbara Simms, Honorary Ed., gardenhistoryjoumal@gardentales.co.uk; Dr. Christopher Thacker, Founding Ed.; Dr. Andrew Eburne, Editorial Advisory Board; Cristiano Ratti, Asst. Ed. **Subscription Rates:** Included in membership; 15 single issue back issue. **Remarks:** Advertising accepted; rates available upon request. **URL:** http://www.gardenhistorysociety.org/publications/journal.html. **Circ:** 3,000

54494 ■ Gas Matters
35 New Bridge St.
London EC4V 6BW, United Kingdom
Ph: 44 20 73329900
Publisher E-mail: p.kolthammer@economatters.com
Trade magazine covering new, analysis and issues relating to natural gas worldwide. **Founded:** 1988. **Freq:** Monthly. **Key Personnel:** John Elkins, Editor; James Ball, Publisher. **ISSN:** 0964-8496. **Subscription Rates:** 1,163.25 individuals. **Remarks:** Advertising not accepted. **URL:** http://www.gasstrategies.com/publications/gas-matters. **Circ:** (Not Reported)

54495 ■ Gas Matters Today
Gas Matters
35 New Bridge St.
London EC4V 6BW, United Kingdom
Ph: 44 20 73329900
Publisher E-mail: p.kolthammer@economatters.com
Trade journal covering natural gas new and analysis in Europe. **Freq:** Daily. **Key Personnel:** Alex Forbes, Editor; John Elkins, Managing Editor; James Ball, Publisher. **ISSN:** 1464-3928. **Subscription Rates:** 495 individuals. **URL:** http://www.gasstrategies.com/publications/gas-matters-today/about-gas-matters-today. **Circ:** (Not Reported)

54496 ■ Gastrointestinal Nursing
MA Healthcare Ltd.
St. Jude's Church
Dulwich Rd.
Herne Hill
London SE24 0PB, United Kingdom
Ph: 44 20 77385454
Fax: 44 20 77332325
Journal covering all aspects of gastroenterology. **Subtitle:** For professionals working in gastroenterology and stoma care. **Founded:** Feb. 2003. **Freq:** 10/yr. **Key Personnel:** Alice Hall, Editor; Theresa Porret, Consultant Ed. **Subscription Rates:** 69 individuals Ireland; EUR120 individuals Europe; US$177 other countries personal; 50 students Ireland. **Remarks:** Accepts advertising. **URL:** http://www.gastrointestinalnursing.co.uk/. **Circ:** (Not Reported)

54497 ■ The GDP
The General Dental Practitioners' Association
61 Harley St., 2nd Fl.
London W1G 8QU, United Kingdom
Ph: 44 20 76361072
Fax: 44 20 76361086
Publication E-mail: info@uk-dentistry.org
Publisher E-mail: info@uk-dentistry.org
Trade magazine for general dental practitioners in the UK. **Founded:** Jan. 1, 1958. **Freq:** Bimonthly. **Trim Size:** 297 x 210 mm. **Key Personnel:** Dr. Joe Sullivan, Editor, sullijoe@googlemail.com. **Remarks:** Accepts advertising. **URL:** http://www.uk-dentistry.org/index.php?option=com_content&view=article&id=33&Itemid=21. **Circ:** 13,000

54498 ■ Gender and Language
Equinox Publishing Ltd.
1 Chelsea Manor Studios
Flood St.
London SW3 5SR, United Kingdom
Ph: 44 20 78233748
Fax: 44 20 78233748
Publication E-mail: genderandlanguage@utoronto.ca
Journal covering gender and language. **Freq:** 2/yr (January and June). **Key Personnel:** Bonnie McElhinny, Co-Ed., bonnie.mcelhinny@utoronto.ca; Ann Weatherall, Co-Ed., ann.weatherall@vuw.ac.nz. **ISSN:** 1747-6321. **Subscription Rates:** 95 institutions print & online; US$190 institutions print & online; 40 individuals; US$80 individuals; EUR35 members; 25 members; US$50 members. **Remarks:** Accepts advertising. **URL:** http://

www.equinoxjournals.com/ojs/index.php/GL. **Circ:** (Not Reported)

54499 ■ Gene Therapy
Nature Publishing Group
The Macmillan Bldg.
4 Crinan St.
London N1 9XW, United Kingdom
Ph: 44 20 78334000
Fax: 44 20 78434640
Journal publishing research and clinical applications of the new genetic therapy techniques. Provides various aspects of gene therapy as applied to human disease, including preclinical animal experiments, novel platform technologies for gene transfer, and gene expression analysis. **Freq:** 24/yr. **Key Personnel:** Joseph Glorioso, Editor; Nick Lemoine, Editor; Eric Alton, Editorial Board; Paul Robbins, Editorial Board; Hideaki Tahara, Editorial Board; David Curiel, Editorial Board; Dinko Valerio, Editorial Board. **ISSN:** 0969-7128. **Subscription Rates:** US$564 individuals online; US$626 individuals online only; EUR498 individuals print and online; EUR448 individuals online only; 85,100¥ individuals print and online; 76,600¥ individuals online only; 289 individuals online only, rest of world; 321 individuals print and online, rest of world. **Remarks:** Advertising accepted; rates available upon request. **URL:** http://www.nature.com/gt/index.html. **Circ:** (Not Reported)

54500 ■ Genealogists' Magazine
Society of Genealogists
14 Charterhouse Bldgs.
Goswell Rd.
London EC1M 7BA, United Kingdom
Ph: 44 20 7251 8799
Fax: 44 20 7250 1800
Trade magazine covering genealogy and family history for beginning through advanced researchers. **Founded:** 1920. **Freq:** Quarterly. **Trim Size:** 14 x 22. **Cols./Page:** 2. **Key Personnel:** Michael Gandy, Editor. **Remarks:** Accepts advertising. **URL:** http://www.sog.org.uk/genmag/genmag.shtml. **Ad Rates:** BW: 255, 4C: 300. **Circ:** Paid 15,500

54501 ■ Genetic Vaccines and Therapy
BioMed Central Ltd.
236 Gray's Inn Rd., Fl. 6
34-42 Cleveland St.
London WC1X 8HL, United Kingdom
Ph: 44 20 31922000
Fax: 44 20 31922010
Publisher E-mail: info@biomedcentral.com
Online journal covering all aspects of gene-based therapies for the prevention and control of disease. **Key Personnel:** Dr. Shyam S. Mohapatra, Editor-in-Chief; Dr. Gary Hellermann, Managing Editor, gellerm@hsc.usf.edu; Dr. Hinrich Abken, Editorial Board. **ISSN:** 1479-0556. **Remarks:** Accepts advertising. **URL:** http://www.gvt-journal.com/home/. **Circ:** (Not Reported)

54502 ■ Genome Biology (Online Edition)
BioMed Central Ltd.
236 Gray's Inn Rd., Fl. 6
34-42 Cleveland St.
London WC1X 8HL, United Kingdom
Ph: 44 20 31922000
Fax: 44 20 31922010
Publication E-mail: editorial@genomebiology.com
Publisher E-mail: info@biomedcentral.com
Online journal serving as an international forum for the dissemination, discussion and critical review of information about all areas of biology informed by genomic research. **Key Personnel:** Clare Garvey, Editor, clare.garvey@genomebiology.com; Elizabeth Gaskell, Sen. Asst. Ed., elizabeth.gaskell@genomebiology.com; Andrew Cosgrove, Asst. Ed., andrew.cosgrove@genomebiology.com. **ISSN:** 1465-6914. **Remarks:** Accepts advertising. **URL:** http://www.genomebiology.com. **Circ:** (Not Reported)

54503 ■ Geochemical Transactions
BioMed Central Ltd.
236 Gray's Inn Rd., Fl. 6
34-42 Cleveland St.
London WC1X 8HL, United Kingdom
Ph: 44 20 31922000
Fax: 44 20 31922010
Publication E-mail: editors@geochemicaltransactions.com

Circulation: ★ = ABC; △ = BPA; ◆ = CAC; • = CCAB; ❑ = VAC; ⊕ = PO Statement; ‡ = Publisher's Report; Boldface figures = sworn; Light figures = estimated.

Publisher E-mail: info@biomedcentral.com

Journal publishing research in all areas of chemistry related to materials and processes occurring in terrestrial and extraterrestrial systems in connection with Geochemistry Division of the American Chemical Society. **Founded:** 2000. **Key Personnel:** Dr. Martin Schoonen, Editor-in-Chief; Dr. Ken B. Anderson, Editor-in-Chief, kanderson@geo.siu.edu; Ken Koretsky, Editor-in-Chief. **ISSN:** 1467-4866. **URL:** http://www.geochemicaltransactions.com.

54504 ■ Geosynthetics International
Thomas Telford Ltd.
One Great George St.
London SW1P 3AA, United Kingdom
Ph: 44 20 79876999
Publisher E-mail: info@thomastelford.com
Peer-reviewed journal covering all topics relevant to geosynthetic materials. **Freq:** Bimonthly. **Key Personnel:** Prof. A.H. Aydilek, International Editorial Board Member; Maria Davis, Contact; Prof. R.J. Bathurst, Editor; Dr. N. Dixon, International Editorial Board Member; Prof. A. Fourie, International Editorial Board Member; Prof. A. Bouazza, International Editorial Board Member; Dr. J.P. Giroud, Ch. of the Editorial Board; Prof. P.J. Fox, International Editorial Board Member; Dr. R. Bonaparte, International Editorial Board Member. **ISSN:** 1072-6349. **Subscription Rates:** US$100 members; 421 institutions; 60 nonmembers. **Remarks:** Advertising accepted; rates available upon request. **URL:** http://www.geosyntheticssociety.org/journals_gi.htm. **Circ:** (Not Reported)

54505 ■ Geriatric Medicine
Ocean Media Events Ltd.
1 Canada Sq.
London E14 5AA, United Kingdom
Ph: 44 20 77728300
Fax: 44 20 77728599
Clinical medical journal covering geriatric medicine. **Subtitle:** The Pre Reviewed Journal of Midlife Medicine and Beyond. **Founded:** 1976. **Freq:** Monthly. **Print Method:** Saddlestitch. **Trim Size:** 400 mm. x 280 mm. **Key Personnel:** Peter Sayer, Publisher, phone 44 20 77728466, peter.sayer@oceanmedia.co.uk; Lynne Kidcaid, Editor, phone 44 20 77728461, lynne.kincaid@oceanmedia.co.uk; Allison Bloomer, Projects Ed., alison.bloomer@oceanmedia.co.uk; Dawn Powell, Dep. Ed., phone 44 20 77728463, dawn.powell@oceanmedia.co.uk. **ISSN:** 0268-201X. **Subscription Rates:** 90 individuals UK; EUR120 individuals Europe; EUR140 other countries. **Remarks:** Accepts advertising. **URL:** http://www.gerimed.co.uk/. **Formerly:** Incorporating Care of the Elderly. **Ad Rates:** BW: 1,200, 4C: 1,850. **Circ:** Controlled ‡23,000

54506 ■ Getting There
Redactive Media Group
17-18 Britton St.
London EC1M 5TP, United Kingdom
Ph: 44 20 78806200
Fax: 44 20 78807691
Publisher E-mail: info@redactive.co.uk
Magazine featuring transport services for the elderly and disabled population of London. **Key Personnel:** Aaron Nicholls, Contact, phone 44 20 78808547, aaron.nicholls@redactive.co.uk. **URL:** http://www.redactive.co.uk/our-clients/tfl/.

54507 ■ Girl Talk
BBC Worldwide Publishing Ltd.
Media Centre
201 Wood Ln.
London W12 7TQ, United Kingdom
Ph: 44 20 84332000
Fax: 44 20 87490538
Publication E-mail: girltalk.magazine@bbc.co.uk
Consumer magazine for girls aged 7-12 years. **Founded:** 1995. **Freq:** Biweekly. **Key Personnel:** Claire Stidwell, Advertising Mgr., phone 44 20 84332446, claire.stidwell@bbc.co.uk. **Subscription Rates:** 35 individuals. **Remarks:** Accepts advertising. **URL:** http://www.bbcgirltalk.com/. **Ad Rates:** BW: 3,025. **Circ:** ★1,161,019

54508 ■ Girl Talk Extra
BBC Worldwide Publishing Ltd.
Media Centre
201 Wood Ln.
London W12 7TQ, United Kingdom
Ph: 44 20 84332000

Fax: 44 20 87490538

Magazine featuring fashion, animals, puzzles and celebrities. **Freq:** Monthly. **Key Personnel:** Claire Stidwell, Gp. Advertising Mgr. **Subscription Rates:** 2.75 single issue. **URL:** http://www.bbcgirltalk.com/content/gtextra; http://www.bbcmagazines.com/content/magazines/girltalkextra/.

54509 ■ Glass
DMG World Media
Northcliffe House
2 Derry St.
London W8 5TT, United Kingdom
Ph: 44 20 79386000
Business magazine. **Freq:** 11/yr. **Trim Size:** 210 x 297 mm. **Key Personnel:** Ken Clark, Gp. Sales Mgr.; Leanne Dennehy, Editor; Martin Lawrence, Production Exec. **ISSN:** 0017-0984. **Remarks:** Accepts advertising. **URL:** http://www.glassmediaonline.com/. **Ad Rates:** BW: 1,296, 4C: 3,753. **Circ:** (Not Reported)

54510 ■ Glass International
DMG World Media
Northcliffe House
2 Derry St.
London W8 5TT, United Kingdom
Ph: 44 20 79386000
Business publication. **Freq:** Bimonthly. **Key Personnel:** Leanne Dennehy, Editor; Martin Lawrence, Production Exec.; Ken Clark, Gp. Sales Mgr. **ISSN:** 0143-7836. **Subscription Rates:** 147 individuals for UK; 207 individuals OTC; EUR250 individuals; US$319 individuals; 41 single issue; 265 two years for UK; 373 two years outside UK; EUR450 two years for Europe; US$574 two years. **Remarks:** Accepts advertising. **URL:** http://www.glassmediaonline.com/. **Ad Rates:** BW: 2,799, 4C: 4,861. **Circ:** 6,000

54511 ■ Global Investor
Euromoney Publications PLC
Nestor House
Playhouse Yard
London EC4V 5EX, United Kingdom
Ph: 44 20 77798888
Publisher E-mail: information@euromoneyplc.com
Professional journal covering international investing. **Subtitle:** The Journal of International Fund Management. **Founded:** 1987. **Freq:** Monthly. **Print Method:** Litho. **Trim Size:** 205 x 270 mm. **Key Personnel:** James Norris, Sen. Staff Writer, phone 44 20 77798004, jnorris@euromoneyplc.com; Craig MacDonald, Editor, phone 44 20 77798990, cmacdonald@euromoneyplc.com. **ISSN:** 0951-3604. **Remarks:** Accepts advertising. **URL:** http://www.globalinvestormagazine.com; http://www.euromoneyplc.com/. **Ad Rates:** BW: 6, 4C: 6,950. **Circ:** 8,100

54512 ■ Global Pensions
Incisive Media Limited
Haymarket House
28-29 Haymarket
London SW1Y 4RX, United Kingdom
Ph: 44 870 2408859
Fax: 44 207 4849797
Publisher E-mail: customerservices@incisivemedia.com
Magazine featuring information on pension schemes worldwide. **Founded:** 1999. **Freq:** Monthly. **Trim Size:** 250 x 350 mm. **Key Personnel:** Alex Beveridge, Editor-in-Chief, phone 44 20 79684572, alex.beveridge@incisivemedia.com; Raquel Pichardo-Allison, Editor, phone 44 20 79684576, raquel.pichardo-allison@incisivemedia.com. **Remarks:** Accepts advertising. **URL:** http://www.incisivemedia.com/corporate/products/globalpensions; http://www.globalpensions.com. **Circ:** (Not Reported)

54513 ■ Global Social Policy
Sage Publications Ltd.
1 Oliver's Yard
55 City Rd.
London EC1Y 1SP, United Kingdom
Ph: 44 20 73248500
Fax: 44 20 73248600
Scholarly journal covering the impact of globalization on social policy and social development. **Subtitle:** An Interdisciplinary Journal of Public Policy and Social Development. **Founded:** 2001. **Freq:** 3/yr. **Key Personnel:** Bob Deacon, Digest Ed.; Nicola Yeates, Editor; Rama V. Baru, South Asia Regional Ed.; Kara Vincent, Managing Editor; Meri Koivusalo, Editor; Robert O'Brien, Editor; Adebayo Olukoshi, Africa Regional Ed.; Rosalia

Cortes, Latin American Regional Ed. **ISSN:** 1468-0181. **Subscription Rates:** 309 institutions combined (print & e-access); 278 institutions e-access; 303 institutions print only; 45 individuals print only; 111 institutions single print; 20 individuals single print. **Remarks:** Accepts advertising. **URL:** http://www.sagepub.co.uk/journalsProdDesc.nav?prodId=Journal200964. **Ad Rates:** BW: 200. **Circ:** (Not Reported)

54514 ■ Globalization and Health
BioMed Central Ltd.
236 Gray's Inn Rd., Fl. 6
34-42 Cleveland St.
London WC1X 8HL, United Kingdom
Ph: 44 20 31922000
Fax: 44 20 31922010
Publication E-mail: globalizationandhealth@lse.ac.uk
Publisher E-mail: info@biomedcentral.com
Online journal considering the positive and negative influences of globalization on health. **Key Personnel:** Dr. Greg Martin, Editor-in-Chief, drgregmartin@gmail.com; Dr. Emma Pitchforth, Editor-in-Chief; Nick Drager, Editorial Board. **ISSN:** 1744-8603. **Remarks:** Accepts advertising. **URL:** http://www.globalizationandhealth.com/home. **Circ:** (Not Reported)

54515 ■ GO Girl
Egmont Magazines
184-192 Drummond St., 4th Fl.
London NW1 3HP, United Kingdom
Ph: 44 20 73806430
Magazine for girls aged 7-11. **Freq:** 3/week. **Key Personnel:** Anna Chacoliades, Contact; Sam Verno, Contact. **Subscription Rates:** 1.99 individuals. **Remarks:** Accepts advertising. **URL:** http://www.gogirlmag.co.uk/; http://www.egmont.co.uk/product.asp?prodid=1515&catid=reviews. **Ad Rates:** 4C: 2,400. **Circ:** ★43,163

54516 ■ Gold Bulletin
World Gold Council
55 Old Broad St.
London EC2M 1RX, United Kingdom
Ph: 44 20 78264700
Fax: 44 20 78264799
Publisher E-mail: info@gold.org
Peer-reviewed journal covering latest science, technology and applications of gold. **Freq:** Quarterly. **Key Personnel:** Dr. Richard J. Holliday, Editor, editor@goldbulletin.org; Patricia M. Harris, PhD, Tech. Ed., pm.harris@btopenworld.com. **ISSN:** 0017-1557. **URL:** http://www.goldbulletin.org/.

54517 ■ Goldsmiths Review
The Goldsmiths' Co.
Goldsmiths' Hall
Foster Ln.
London EC2V 6BN, United Kingdom
Ph: 44 20 76067010
Fax: 44 20 76061511
Publisher E-mail: the.clerk@thegoldsmiths.co.uk
Publication covering jewelry. **Freq:** Annual. **Key Personnel:** Malcolm Appleby, Contact; Jerry Wiggin, Craftsmen and Designers; Peter Crump, Contact; John Donald, Contact; Graham Stewart, Contact. **ISSN:** 0953-0355. **Subscription Rates:** 5 single issue UK; 7 single issue Europe; US$9 single issue worldwide. **Remarks:** Advertising not accepted. **URL:** http://www.thegoldsmiths.co.uk/thelibrary/publications.htm. **Circ:** 4,500

54518 ■ Golf Monthly
IPC Media Ltd.
Blue Fin Bldg.
110 Southwark St.
London SE1 0SU, United Kingdom
Ph: 44 203 1485000
Magazine featuring information in golfing. **Founded:** 1911. **Freq:** Monthly. **Key Personnel:** Michael Harris, Editor, phone 44 20 31484520, michael_harris@ipcmedia.com; Hamish Dawson, Publishing Dir., phone 44 20 31484310, hamish_dawson@ipcmedia.com; Andrew Boxer, Advertising Mgr., phone 44 20 31484251, andrew_boxer@ipcmedia.com. **Subscription Rates:** 34.99 individuals; 49.99 two years. **Remarks:** Accepts advertising. **URL:** http://www.ipcmedia.com/brands/golfmonthly; http://www.golf-monthly.co.uk/. **Circ:** ★61,408

54519 ■ Good Clinical Practice Journal (GCPj)
PJB Publications Ltd.
Telephone House
69-77 Paul St.
London EC2A 4LQ, United Kingdom
Ph: 44 20 70175000
Fax: 44 20 70176792
Publication E-mail: gcpj@informa.com
Publisher E-mail: pjb.enquiries@informa.com
Peer-reviewed journal covering good clinical practice in research on new drugs. **Founded:** 1994. **Freq:** Monthly. **Print Method:** Sheetfed Offset Litho. **Trim Size:** 210 x 297 mm. **Key Personnel:** Joanne Payne, Editor, joanne.payne@informa.com. **ISSN:** 1350-0961. **Subscription Rates:** EUR1,545 individuals print and online; US$1,990 individuals print and online; 995 individuals print and online. **Remarks:** Accepts advertising. **URL:** http://www.pjbpubs.com/gcpj/index.htm. **Ad Rates:** BW: 845, 4C: 1,200. **Circ:** ⊕1,300

54520 ■ Good Homes
BBC Worldwide Publishing Ltd.
Media Centre
201 Wood Ln.
London W12 7TQ, United Kingdom
Ph: 44 20 84332000
Fax: 44 20 87490538
Publication E-mail: deargoodhomes@bbc.co.uk
Magazine featuring home inspirational interiors, decorations, and practical consumer shopping guides. **Freq:** Monthly. **Subscription Rates:** 2.90 single issue. **URL:** http://www.bbcmagazines.com/ads/goodhomes/. **Circ:** ★127,202

54521 ■ Grazia
H. Bauer Publishing
Academic House
24-28 Oval Rd.
London NW1 7DT, United Kingdom
Ph: 44 20 72418000
Fax: 44 20 72418030
Publication E-mail: graziadaily@graziamagazine.co.uk
Magazine featuring fashion, beauty, and entertainment news. **Freq:** Weekly. **Subscription Rates:** 60 individuals direct debit; 60 individuals credit/debit card. **URL:** http://www.graziadaily.co.uk/.

54522 ■ Group Analysis
Sage Publications Ltd.
1 Oliver's Yard
55 City Rd.
London EC1Y 1SP, United Kingdom
Ph: 44 20 73248500
Fax: 44 20 73248600
Peer-reviewed journal covering the theory, practice and experience of analytic group psychotherapy. **Subtitle:** The International Journal of Group-Analytic Psychotherapy. **Founded:** 1967. **Freq:** Quarterly. **Key Personnel:** Malcolm Pines, Assoc. Ed.; Harold Behr, Editorial Committee; Morris Nitsun, Editorial Committee; Ben Davidson, Exec. Ed.; A.P. Ormay, Editor; Luisa Brunori, Editorial Committee; Dick Blackwell, Assoc. Ed.; Jason Maratos, Book Review Ed. **ISSN:** 0533-3164. **Subscription Rates:** 386 institutions print & e-access; 425 institutions current volume print & all online content; 347 institutions e-access; 386 institutions e-access plus backfile (all online content); 914 institutions e-access (content through 1998); 378 institutions print only; 67 individuals print only; 104 institutions single print; 22 individuals single print. **Remarks:** Accepts advertising. **URL:** http://www.sagepub.co.uk/journalsProdDesc.nav?prodId=Journal200871. **Circ:** (Not Reported)

54523 ■ Group Processes & Intergroup Relations
Sage Publications Ltd.
1 Oliver's Yard
55 City Rd.
London EC1Y 1SP, United Kingdom
Ph: 44 20 73248500
Fax: 44 20 73248600
Peer-reviewed journal covering group and intergroup phenomena. **Founded:** 1998. **Freq:** Bimonthly. **Key Personnel:** Dominic Abrams, Editor; Michael A. Hogg, Editor; Susan T. Fiske, Consulting Ed.; Richard Moreland, Consulting Ed.; Linda Tropp, Consulting Ed.; Scott R. Tindale, Assoc. Ed.; Deborah A. Prentice, Consulting Ed.; Craig D. Parks, Assoc. Ed.; Emanuele Castano, Consulting Ed. **ISSN:** 1368-4302. **Subscription Rates:** 549 individuals print & e-access; 604 institutions current volume print & all online content; 494 institutions e-access; 549 institutions e-access plus backfile (all online content); 494 institutions e-access (content through 1998); 538 institutions print only; 53 individuals print only; 99 institutions single print; 12 individuals single print. **Remarks:** Accepts advertising. **URL:** http://www.sagepub.co.uk/journalsProdDesc.nav?prodId=Journal200785. **Circ:** (Not Reported)

54524 ■ Growth Company Investor
Vitesse Media
Octavia House
50 Banner St.
London EC1Y 8ST, United Kingdom
Ph: 44 20 72507010
Fax: 44 20 72507011
Publisher E-mail: info@vitessemedia.co.uk
Magazine featuring small business companies in United Kingdom. **Freq:** 10/yr. **Key Personnel:** Rebecca Borrows, Sales Mgr., phone 44 20 72507028, rebecca.borrows@vitessemedia.co.uk; James Crux, Editor; Leslie Copeland, Editor-in-Chief. **Subscription Rates:** 59.50 individuals; 99.50 other countries. **Remarks:** Accepts advertising. **URL:** http://www.vitessemedia.co.uk/publications-and-research/investors/259372/growth-company-investor-magazine.thtml; http://www.growthcompany.co.uk/. **Circ:** (Not Reported)

54525 ■ The Guardian
Guardian Newspapers Ltd.
Kings Pl.
90 York Way
London N1 9GU, United Kingdom
Ph: 44 20 33532000
Newspaper featuring news, opinion and commentary. **Freq:** Daily. **Key Personnel:** Alan Rusbridger, Editor. **ISSN:** 0261-3077. **URL:** http://www.guardian.co.uk; http://www.gmgplc.co.uk/Ourbusinesses/GuardianNewsMedia/TheGuardian/tabid/136/Default.aspx.

54526 ■ The Guardian Weekend
Guardian Newspapers Ltd.
Kings Pl.
90 York Way
London N1 9GU, United Kingdom
Ph: 44 20 33532000
Publisher E-mail: letters@guardian.co.uk
Community newspaper. **Freq:** Monthly. **Trim Size:** 292 x 246 mm. **Key Personnel:** Guljeet Sandhu, Contact; Richard Harris, Contact; Ann Baker, Contact; Gina Walsh, Contact; Paul Smith, Contact; George Bainbridge, Contact; Matthew Walker, Contact; Merope Mills, Editor. **URL:** http://www.guardian.co.uk/theguardian/2010/sep/25/weekend.

54527 ■ Guiding Magazine
The Guide Association
17-19 Buckingham Palace Rd.
London SW1W 0PT, United Kingdom
Ph: 44 20 78346242
Fax: 44 20 78288317
Magazine for adult leaders of The Guide Association who work with girls and young women aged 5-25 years. **Freq:** Monthly. **ISSN:** 0265-2706. **Remarks:** Accepts advertising. **URL:** http://www.girlguiding.org.uk/. **Circ:** Controlled 28,000

54528 ■ Hackney Gazette
Archant Regional Ltd.
138 Cambridge Heath Rd.
London E1 5QJ, United Kingdom
Ph: 44 20 77908822
Publisher E-mail: sandra.roantree@archant.co.uk
Local community newspaper. **Founded:** 1864. **Freq:** Weekly (Thurs.). **Key Personnel:** Mick Ferris, Editor. **Subscription Rates:** 10 individuals 4 weeks; 20 individuals 2 months; 30 individuals 3 months; 60 individuals 6 months. **Remarks:** Accepts advertising. **URL:** http://www.hackneygazette.co.uk/home. **Circ:** (Not Reported)

54529 ■ Handbook of Practice Management
Royal Society of Medicine Press Ltd.
1 Wimpole St.
London W1G 0AE, United Kingdom
Ph: 44 20 72902921
Fax: 44 20 72902929
Publisher E-mail: publishing@rsm.ac.uk
Journal providing latest information on practice management issues for practice managers. **Freq:** Quarterly. **Key Personnel:** Junaid Bajwa, Contact. **ISSN:** 0962-144X. **Subscription Rates:** 94 individuals UK & Europe; EUR103 individuals Europe; US$134 individuals; 94 other countries. **URL:** http://hpm.rsmjournals.com/.

54530 ■ The Hardy Review
Maney Publishing
1 Carlton House Ter.
London SW1Y 5AF, United Kingdom
Ph: 44 20 74517300
Fax: 44 20 74517307
Publisher E-mail: maney@maney.co.uk
Journal covering the study of Thomas Hardy. **Founded:** 2007. **Freq:** Semiannual. **Key Personnel:** Prof. Rosemarie Morgan, Editor, rosemarie.morgan@yale.edu. **ISSN:** 1934-8908. **Subscription Rates:** 122 institutions, other countries; US$244 institutions. **Remarks:** Accepts advertising. **URL:** http://maney.co.uk/index.php/journals/hdy/. **Ad Rates:** BW: 180. **Circ:** (Not Reported)

54531 ■ Harm Reduction Journal
BioMed Central Ltd.
236 Gray's Inn Rd., Fl. 6
34-42 Cleveland St.
London WC1X 8HL, United Kingdom
Ph: 44 20 31922000
Fax: 44 20 31922010
Publisher E-mail: info@biomedcentral.com
Online journal covering all aspects of minimizing the adverse effects of psychoactive drugs. **Key Personnel:** Prof. Ernest Drucker, Editor-in-Chief, emdrucker@earthlink.net; Dr. Fabio Mesquita, Dep. Ed.; Dr. Nick Crofts, Dep. Ed. **ISSN:** 1477-7517. **Remarks:** Accepts advertising. **URL:** http://www.harmreductionjournal.com/home/. **Circ:** (Not Reported)

54532 ■ Harrods Estates @MAG
Luxury Publishing Limited
5 Jubilee Pl.
Chelsea
London SW3 3TD, United Kingdom
Ph: 44 20 75912900
Fax: 44 20 75912929
Publisher E-mail: info@luxurypublishing.com
Magazine covering issues on lifestyle. **Founded:** 1897. **Freq:** Semiannual. **Trim Size:** 220 x 300 mm. **Key Personnel:** Celestria Noel, Editor. **Remarks:** Accepts advertising. **URL:** http://www.luxurypublishing.co.uk/. **Circ:** 25,000

54533 ■ The HAT Magazine
The Hat Magazine Ltd.
170 Brick Ln.
London E1 6RU, United Kingdom
Ph: 44 20 72471120
Fax: 44 20 73752199
Publisher E-mail: info@thehatmagazine.com
Magazine covering the latest trends in hat industry. **Founded:** 1983. **Freq:** Quarterly. **Key Personnel:** Nigel Denford, Editor and Publisher; Carole Denford, Editor and Publisher. **Subscription Rates:** 52 individuals; 62 individuals Europe; 67 other countries. **URL:** http://www.thehatmagazine.com/.

54534 ■ Head & Face Medicine
BioMed Central Ltd.
236 Gray's Inn Rd., Fl. 6
34-42 Cleveland St.
London WC1X 8HL, United Kingdom
Ph: 44 20 31922000
Fax: 44 20 31922010
Publication E-mail: hfmed@me.com
Publisher E-mail: info@biomedcentral.com
Online journal covering all aspects of the prevention, diagnosis and management of cranial disorders. **Key Personnel:** Dr. Ulrich Meyer, Editor-in-Chief; Prof. Michael D Abramoff, Editorial Board; Dr. Johannes Kleinheinz, Dep. Ed.; Dr. Zafer C. Cehreli, Exec. Ed.; Prof. Heinrich Franz Arlinghaus, Editorial Board; Prof. Giuseppe Bonifazi, Editorial Board. **ISSN:** 1746-160X. **Remarks:** Accepts advertising. **URL:** http://www.head-face-med.com. **Circ:** (Not Reported)

54535 ■ Headache in Practice
Hayward Medical Communications
Covent Garden
8-10 Dryden St.

Circulation: ★ = ABC; △ = BPA; ◆ = CAC; • = CCAB; ❑ = VAC; ⊕ = PO Statement; ‡ = Publisher's Report; Boldface figures = sworn; Light figures = estimated.

Gale Directory of Publications & Broadcast Media/147th Ed. | 5719

London WC2E 9NA, United Kingdom
Publisher E-mail: admin@hayward.co.uk
Journal for primary and secondary health care professionals. **Key Personnel:** Timothy Steiner, PhD, Editor. **URL:** http://www.headacheip.co.uk/hip/.

54536 ■ Health
Sage Publications Ltd.
1 Oliver's Yard
55 City Rd.
London EC1Y 1SP, United Kingdom
Ph: 44 20 73248500
Fax: 44 20 73248600
Scholarly journal covering health and social science. **Subtitle:** An Interdisciplinary Journal for the Social Study of Health, Illness and Medicine. **Founded:** 1997. **Freq:** Bimonthly. **Key Personnel:** Alan Radley, Founding Ed.; Arthur Frank, Book Review Ed.; Julianne Cheek, Co-Ed.; Mildred Blaxter, Editorial Board; Michael Traynor, Editor; Nick Fox, Co-Ed.; David Armstrong, Editorial Board; Susan E. Bell, Editorial Board. **ISSN:** 1363-4593. **Subscription Rates:** 52 individuals print only; 568 institutions print only; 522 institutions electronic access only; 580 institutions print & electronic access; 104 institutions single print; 11 individuals single print; 638 institutions current volume print & all online content; 580 institutions all online content; 522 institutions content through 1998. **Remarks:** Accepts advertising. **URL:** http://www.sagepub.co.uk/journalsProdDesc.nav?prodId=Journal200904. **Circ:** (Not Reported)

54537 ■ Health Education Journal
Sage Publications Ltd.
1 Oliver's Yard
55 City Rd.
London EC1Y 1SP, United Kingdom
Ph: 44 20 73248500
Fax: 44 20 73248600
Peer-reviewed journal on health. **Freq:** Quarterly. **Key Personnel:** Maggie Palmer, Managing Editor; Prof. Anthony S. Blinkhorn, Editor; Peter Aggleton, Editorial Board. **ISSN:** 0017-8969. **Subscription Rates:** US$570 institutions print and e-access; US$513 institutions e-access; US$570 institutions print; US$104 individuals print; US$154 institutions single print; US$34 individuals single print; US$2,485 institutions e-access (content through 1998). **URL:** http://www.sagepub.com/journalsProdDesc.nav?prodId=Journal201777.

54538 ■ Health and Hygiene
Royal Society for Public Health
28 Portland Pl.
London W1B 1DE, United Kingdom
Ph: 44 20 75802731
Fax: 44 20 75806157
Publication E-mail: health.hygiene@riph.org.uk
Publisher E-mail: marketing@riph.org.uk
Quarterly journal covering public health and hygiene for members of the Royal Institute of Public Health and other public health professionals. **Freq:** 3/yr. **Key Personnel:** Nicole Seeff, Advertising Dir., phone 44 20 72918358. **Subscription Rates:** 50 individuals U.K., Europe & developing Countries; 70 other countries includes airmail delivery. **Remarks:** Accepts advertising. **URL:** http://www.riph.org.uk/index13.html. **Circ:** Paid 2,500

54539 ■ Health Insurance
Informa Publishing Group
Informa House
30-32 Mortimer St.
London W1W 7RE, United Kingdom
Ph: 44 20 70175000
Professional magazine covering health insurance. **Founded:** Dec. 1997. **Freq:** Monthly. **Key Personnel:** David Sawers, Editor, phone 44 20 70174154, david.sawers@informa.com; Madeleine Davies, Sen. Reporter, phone 44 20 70175581, madeleine.davies@informa.com; Matt Brookes, Sales Dir., phone 44 20 70176779, matthew.brookes@informa.com. **ISSN:** 1477-9781. **Subscription Rates:** 290 individuals; EUR341 individuals; US$505 individuals. **Remarks:** Accepts advertising. **URL:** http://www.hi-mag.com/healthinsurance/homepage.do. **Circ:** Combined 10,440

54540 ■ Health Policy and Planning
Oxford University Press
Dept. of Public
Health & Policy
London School of Hygiene & Tropical Medicine

Keppel Gower St.
London WC1E 7HT, United Kingdom
Peer-reviewed Journal covering epidemiology, health and development economics, management and social policy, planning and social anthropology. **Founded:** 1881. **Freq:** Bimonthly. **Print Method:** Offset. **Trim Size:** 8 5/16 x 11. **Cols./Page:** 3. **Col. Width:** 13 picas. **Col. Depth:** 58 picas. **Key Personnel:** Richard Coker, Editor; Kara Hanson, Editorial Board; Sara Bennett, Editor. **ISSN:** 0268-1080. **Subscription Rates:** 415 institutions print and online; US$830 institutions print and online; EUR623 institutions print and online; 284 institutions online; US$567 institutions online; EUR426 institutions online; 134 individuals; US$268 individuals; EUR201 individuals. **Remarks:** Accepts advertising. **URL:** http://www.oxfordjournals.org/heapol/access_purchase/price_list.html. **Ad Rates:** BW: 260. **Circ:** 720

54541 ■ Health Research Policy and Systems
BioMed Central Ltd.
236 Gray's Inn Rd., Fl. 6
34-42 Cleveland St.
London WC1X 8HL, United Kingdom
Ph: 44 20 31922000
Fax: 44 20 31922010
Publisher E-mail: info@biomedcentral.com
Online journal covering the use of electronic information and telecommunications technologies to support long distance clinical health care, patient and professional health-related education, public health and health administration. **Key Personnel:** Dr. Tikki Pang, Founding Ed.; Dr. Miguel Gonzalez Block, Editor-in-Chief; Dr. Metin Gulmezoglu, Assoc. Ed.; Dr. Stephen Hanney, Editor-in-Chief; Dr. Carlos Morel, Assoc. Ed.; Dr. Ritu Sadana, Assoc. Ed. **ISSN:** 1478-4505. **Remarks:** Accepts advertising. **URL:** http://www.health-policy-systems.com/start.asp. **Circ:** (Not Reported)

54542 ■ Health and Safety Bulletin
LexisNexis UK
Halsbury House
35 Chancery Ln.
London WC2A 1EL, United Kingdom
Ph: 44 20 74002500
Fax: 44 20 74002842
Publisher E-mail: customer.services@lexisnexis.co.uk
Law periodical. **Freq:** 10/yr. **Key Personnel:** Howard Fidderman, Editor. **ISSN:** 1358-2208. **Subscription Rates:** 379 individuals. **Remarks:** Advertising not accepted. **URL:** http://www1.lexisnexis.co.uk/campaigns/1107-011_composite/index.htm. **Circ:** (Not Reported)

54543 ■ Health & Safety at Work
LexisNexis UK
Halsbury House
35 Chancery Ln.
London WC2A 1EL, United Kingdom
Ph: 44 20 74002500
Fax: 44 20 74002842
Publisher E-mail: customer.services@lexisnexis.co.uk
Occupational health and safety publication. **Subtitle:** Journal of the Working Environment. **Founded:** Jan. 1978. **Freq:** Annual. **Trim Size:** 297 x 450 mm. **Key Personnel:** Louis Wustemann, Editor. **ISSN:** 0141-8246. **Subscription Rates:** 129 single issue. **Remarks:** Accepts advertising. **URL:** http://www.lnbconnect.co.uk/Compliance/Health-and-Safety-at-Work.html. **Ad Rates:** BW: 1,300, 4C: 1,515. **Circ:** ★23,051

54544 ■ Health Services Management Research
Royal Society of Medicine Press Ltd.
1 Wimpole St.
London W1G 0AE, United Kingdom
Ph: 44 20 72902921
Fax: 44 20 72902929
Publication E-mail: hsmrproduction@rsm.ac.uk
Publisher E-mail: publishing@rsm.ac.uk
Journal focusing on practical implementation of research activity in management of health services. **Freq:** Quarterly. **Key Personnel:** Peter Spurgeon, Editor. **ISSN:** 0951-4848. **Subscription Rates:** 199 individuals UK & Europe; EUR270 individuals Europe; US$394 individuals; 205 other countries; 179 individuals online only; EUR243 individuals online only; US$355 individuals online only. **URL:** http://hsmr.rsmjournals.com/.

54545 ■ Heart
BMJ Publishing Group Ltd.
BMA House
Tavistock Sq.

London WC1H 9JR, United Kingdom
Ph: 44 20 73874410
Fax: 44 20 73836400
Publication E-mail: heartjournal@bmjgroup.com
Peer-reviewed Journal covering the field of coronary disease, electrophysiology, valve disease, imaging techniques, congenital heart disease, heart failure, surgery, and basic science. **Founded:** 1939. **Freq:** Monthly. **Key Personnel:** Prof. Adam D. Timmis, Editor, adamtimmis@mac.com; John E. Sanderson, Dep. Ed., jesanderson@cuhk.edu.hk; Peter Mills, Educ. in Heart Ed., pmills@doctors.org.uk; Michael Burch, Correspondance Ed., burchm@gosh.nhs.uk; Keith Channon, Assoc. Ed., keith.channon@cardiol.ox.ac.uk; Iqbal Malik, Commissioning Ed., i.malik@imperial.ac.uk; Richard Schilling, Assoc. Ed.; Jeroen J. Bax, Assoc. Ed., heartbax@lumc.nl. **ISSN:** 1355-6037. **Subscription Rates:** EUR161 institutions online only; US$232 institutions online only; 119 institutions online only; 220 individuals print and online; US$729 individuals print and online version; EUR297 institutions print and online version. **Remarks:** Accepts advertising. **URL:** http://heart.bmj.com/. **Formerly:** British Heart Journal. **Circ:** (Not Reported)

54546 ■ Heart Failure Monitor
Remedica Publishing Ltd
Commonwealth House
1 New Oxford St.
London WC1A 1NUN, United Kingdom
Ph: 44 20 77592999
Fax: 44 20 77592951
Publisher E-mail: info@remedica.com
Journal analyzing literature on heart failure for providing better healthcare system and evolving better healthcare policies. **Freq:** Quarterly. **Key Personnel:** Karl Swedberg, Editorial Advisory Board; Josef Niebauer, Editor-in-Chief; Andrew L. Clark, Editor; Ceri Davies, Editor; Massimo Piepoli, Editor; Michael Bristow, Editorial Advisory Board. **ISSN:** 1470-8590. **Subscription Rates:** Free for healthcare professionals. **URL:** http://heartfailuremonitor.com/IssuePDF.aspx.

54547 ■ Hedge Funds Review
Incisive Media Limited
Haymarket House
28-29 Haymarket
London SW1Y 4RX, United Kingdom
Ph: 44 870 2408859
Fax: 44 207 4849797
Publisher E-mail: customerservices@incisivemedia.com
Magazine featuring the alternative investment industry. **Founded:** Sept. 2000. **Freq:** Monthly. **Key Personnel:** Margie Lindsay, Managing Editor, phone 44 20 74849889, margie.lindsay@incisivemedia.com; Jonathan Greene, Publisher, phone 44 20 74849867, jonathan.greene@incisivemedia.com; Claudia Barber, Mktg. Mgr., phone 44 20 74849773, claudia.barber@incisivemedia.com. **Subscription Rates:** 715 individuals; EUR199 individuals; US$150 individuals. **Remarks:** Accepts advertising. **URL:** http://www.hedgefundsreview.com/. **Circ:** (Not Reported)

54548 ■ Hematology
Maney Publishing
1 Carlton House Ter.
London SW1Y 5AF, United Kingdom
Ph: 44 20 74517300
Fax: 44 20 74517307
Publisher E-mail: maney@maney.co.uk
International journal publishing original and review articles in the field of general hematology, including oncology, pathology, biology, clinical research and epidemiology. **Freq:** 6/yr. **Key Personnel:** Prof. Adrian C. Newland, Editor-in-Chief; Jim Bussel, Assoc. Ed.; C. Chesterman, Editorial Board; Mark A. Popovsky, Assoc. Ed.; Hagop Kantarjian, Co-Ed.; J. Duguid, Editorial Board; Armand Keating, Co-Ed.; E. Ascari, Editorial Board. **ISSN:** 1024-5332. **Subscription Rates:** 605 institutions UK, Europe, rest of world; US$1,027 institutions in U.S.; 210 individuals UK, Europe, rest of world; US$398 individuals in U.S. **Remarks:** Accepts advertising. **URL:** http://maney.co.uk/index.php/journals/hem/. **Ad Rates:** BW: 320. **Circ:** (Not Reported)

54549 ■ Hi Fi News
IPC Media Ltd.
Blue Fin Bldg.
110 Southwark St.
London SE1 0SU, United Kingdom
Ph: 44 203 1485000

Publication E-mail: hi-finews@ipcmedia.com
Magazine featuring the latest trends in audio technology. **Founded:** 1956. **Freq:** Monthly. **Key Personnel:** Paul Miller, Editor; Patrick Fraser, Production Ed.; Clare Lordan, Production Mgr., phone 44 20 87268315. **Subscription Rates:** 34.99 individuals; 64.99 two years; US$99.90 individuals; US$194 two years. **Remarks:** Accepts advertising. **URL:** http://www.hifinews.co.uk/. **Circ:** (Not Reported)

54550 ■ Hide 'n' Seek Wordsearch
H. Bauer Publishing
Academic House
24-28 Oval Rd.
London NW1 7DT, United Kingdom
Ph: 44 20 72418000
Fax: 44 20 72418030
Magazine featuring word search puzzles. **Freq:** Monthly. **Trim Size:** 185 x 255 mm. **Key Personnel:** Clive Garsin, Gp. Ed.; Spike Figgett, Publishing Dir.; Helen Greenwood, Advertising Mgr. **Subscription Rates:** 15.93 individuals. **Remarks:** Accepts advertising. **URL:** http://www.puzzlemagazines.co.uk/hide-n-seek; http://www.bauer.co.uk/hidenseek-wordsearch. **Circ:** ★62,000

54551 ■ High Temperatures-High Pressures
Pion Ltd.
207 Brondesbury Pk.
London NW2 5JN, United Kingdom
Ph: 44 20 84590066
Fax: 44 20 84516454
Scholarly journal for physicists, chemists, and material scientists. **Founded:** 1969. **Freq:** Quarterly. **Print Method:** Litho. **Trim Size:** 132 x 230 mm. **Cols./Page:** 1. **Key Personnel:** Ivan Egry, Editor-in-Chief, ivan.egry@dlr.de; Bu-Xuan Wang, Advisory Editorial Board, bxwang@mail.tsinghua.edu.cn; Jean-Francois Sacadura, Editor-in-Chief, jfsaca@insa-lyon.fr; Boris Straumal, Regional Board, straumal@issp.ac.ru; Vladimir E. Fortov, Advisory Editorial Board, fortov@ficp.ac.ru; William A. Wakeham, Advisory Editorial Board, w.a.wakeham@soton.ac.uk; Akira Nagashima, Advisory Editorial Board, nag@cj9.so-net.ne.jp; Gunther Neuer, Advisory Editorial Board, guenther.neuer@ike.uni-stuttgart.de; Francesco Righini, Advisory Editorial Board, f.righini@inrim.it. **ISSN:** 0018-1544. **Subscription Rates:** US$157 individuals; EUR148 individuals; 19,859¥ individuals; US$766 institutions; EUR635 institutions; 76,372¥ institutions. **Remarks:** Advertising not accepted. **URL:** http://www.oldcitypublishing.com/HTHP/HTHP.html. **Circ:** (Not Reported)

54552 ■ Hildon Magazine
Axon Publishing
11 Plough Yard
London EC2A 3LP, United Kingdom
Ph: 44 20 76847111
Fax: 44 20 76847122
Publisher E-mail: mail@axonpublish.com
Magazine featuring Hildon natural mineral water. **Key Personnel:** Paul Keers, Editorial Dir. **URL:** http://www.axonpublish.com/.

54553 ■ Hispanic Research Journal
Maney Publishing
1 Carlton House Ter.
London SW1Y 5AF, United Kingdom
Ph: 44 20 74517300
Fax: 44 20 74517307
Publisher E-mail: maney@maney.co.uk
Journal promoting and disseminating research into the cultures of the Iberian Peninsula and Latin America, from the Middle Ages to the present day. **Subtitle:** Iberian and Latin American Studies. **Freq:** 5/yr. **Key Personnel:** Ralph Penny, Editor-in-Chief, r.j.penny@qmul.ac.uk; Else Vieira, Review Ed., e.vieira@qmul.ac.uk; Lola Badia, International Advisory Board. **ISSN:** 1468-2737. **Subscription Rates:** 76 other countries; US$132 individuals; 314 institutions, other countries; US$584 institutions. **URL:** http://maney.co.uk/index.php/journals/hrj/.

54554 ■ Historian
Historical Association
59 A Kennington Park Rd.
London SE11 4JH, United Kingdom
Ph: 44 20 77353901
Fax: 44 20 75824989
Publisher E-mail: enquiry@history.org.uk
Publication covering history. **Founded:** 1912. **Freq:**
Quarterly. **Key Personnel:** Ian Mason, Editor; Prof. Bill Speck, Editor. **ISSN:** 0265-1076. **Subscription Rates:** 26 individuals; 26 individuals concessionary; 29 members corporate. **URL:** http://www.history.org.uk/about/index.php?id=44. **Ad Rates:** 4C: 395. **Circ:** (Not Reported)

54555 ■ The Historic Environment
Maney Publishing
1 Carlton House Ter.
London SW1Y 5AF, United Kingdom
Ph: 44 20 74517300
Fax: 44 20 74517307
Publisher E-mail: maney@maney.co.uk
Journal covering the conservation, management, and investigation of historic environment. **Subtitle:** Policy & Practice. **Freq:** Semiannual. **Key Personnel:** Roger White, Editor, r.h.white@bham.ac.uk; Harriet Devlin, Co-Ed. **ISSN:** 1756-7505. **Subscription Rates:** 104 institutions, other countries; US$178 institutions; 28 other countries; US$62 individuals; 36 individuals in UK and European. **Remarks:** Accepts advertising. **URL:** http://maney.co.uk/index.php/journals/hen. **Circ:** (Not Reported)

54556 ■ Historic Scotland Magazine
Think Publishing
The Pal Mall Deposit
124-128 Barlby Rd.
London W10 6BL, United Kingdom
Ph: 44 20 89623020
Fax: 44 20 89628689
Publisher E-mail: watchdog@thinkpublishing.co.uk
Magazine covering Scotland's historical studies. **Freq:** Quarterly. **Key Personnel:** Ian McAuliffe, Director, ian@thinkpublishing.co.uk; Tilly Boulter, Ch. Exec., tilly@thinkpublishing.co.uk; Polly Arnold, Mng. Dir., pollya@thinkpublishing.co.uk. **Remarks:** Accepts advertising. **URL:** http://www.thinkpublishing.co.uk/mag_historic.html. **Circ:** 35,000

54557 ■ Historical Materialism
Brill Academic Publishers
Faculty of Law & Social Sciences
SOAS, University of London
Thornhaugh St., Russell Sq.
London WC1H 0XG, United Kingdom
Publication E-mail: historicalmaterialism@soas.ac.uk
Publisher E-mail: marketing@brill.nl
Journal identifying and developing the critical and explanatory potential of Marxist theory. **Subtitle:** Research in Critical Marxist Theory. **Freq:** 4/yr. **Key Personnel:** Sam Ashman, Editorial Board; Paul Blackledge, Editorial Board; Pablo Ghigliani, Corresponding Ed.; James Furner, Corresponding Ed.; Angela Dimitrakaki, Corresponding Ed. **ISSN:** 1465-4466. **Subscription Rates:** EUR65 individuals print only; US$88 individuals print only; EUR342 institutions print and electronic; US$466 institutions print and electronic; EUR285 institutions online only; US$388 institutions online only; EUR314 institutions print only; US$427 institutions print only. **URL:** http://www.brill.nl/m_catalogue_sub6_id17936.htm.

54558 ■ Historical Research
John Wiley & Sons Inc.
Wiley-Blackwell
c/o Prof. Miles Taylor, Ed.
Institute of Historical Research
London WC1E 7HU, United Kingdom
Ph: 44 20 78628756
Fax: 44 20 78628811
Periodical focusing on history. **Founded:** 1923. **Freq:** Quarterly. **Key Personnel:** Dr. Jane Winters, Exec. Ed., phone 44 20 78628780, ihrpub@sas.ac.uk; Prof. Miles Taylor, Editor; Dr. Julie Spraggon, Dep. Ed., fax 44 20 78628754. **ISSN:** 0950-3471. **Subscription Rates:** US$100 individuals print and online; US$476 institutions print and online; US$433 institutions print, online; 209 institutions print and online; EUR71 individuals print and online; 190 institutions print, online; EUR265 institutions print and online; US$556 institutions, other countries print and online; US$505 institutions, other countries print, online; EUR241 institutions print, online. **Remarks:** Accepts advertising. **URL:** http://www.wiley.com/bw/journal.asp?ref=0950-3471&site=1. **Circ:** (Not Reported)

54559 ■ History of the Human Sciences
Sage Publications Ltd.
1 Oliver's Yard
55 City Rd.
London EC1Y 1SP, United Kingdom
Ph: 44 20 73248500
Fax: 44 20 73248600
Scholarly journal covering social science research, history and interdisciplinary influences. **Founded:** 1998. **Freq:** 5/yr. **Key Personnel:** James Good, Editor; Hans Aarsleff, Advisory Board; Roger Smith, Assoc. Ed.; Thomas Osborne, Assoc. Ed.; Svetlana Alpers, Advisory Board; Rhodri Hayward, Review Ed.; Peter Lassman, Assoc. Ed.; Arthur Still, Assoc. Ed.; Stephen Bann, Advisory Board. **ISSN:** 0952-6951. **Subscription Rates:** 671 institutions print & e-access; 738 institutions current volume print & all online content; 604 institutions e-access; 671 institutions e-access plus backfile (all online content); 604 institutions e-access (content through 1998); 658 institutions print only; 57 individuals print only; 145 institutions single print; 15 individuals single print. **Remarks:** Accepts advertising. **URL:** http://www.sagepub.co.uk/journalsProdDesc.nav?prodId=Journal200813. **Circ:** (Not Reported)

54560 ■ History Review
History Today Ltd.
25 Bedford Ave.
London WC1B 3AT, United Kingdom
Ph: 44 20 32197810
Fax: 44 20 32197829
Periodical focusing on history. **Founded:** 1987. **Freq:** 3/yr (March, September, December). **Print Method:** Sheetfed. **Trim Size:** 210 x 297 mm. **ISSN:** 0962-9610. **Subscription Rates:** 29 individuals print. **Remarks:** Accepts advertising. **URL:** http://www.historytoday.com. **Ad Rates:** BW: 300, 4C: 500. **Circ:** 5,000

54561 ■ History Today
History Today Ltd.
25 Bedford Ave.
London WC1B 3AT, United Kingdom
Ph: 44 20 32197810
Fax: 44 20 32197829
Consumer magazine covering history for teachers, students and interested others. **Founded:** 1951. **Freq:** Monthly. **Print Method:** Web. **Trim Size:** 297 x 210 mm. **Cols./Page:** 4. **Col. Width:** 41 millimeters. **Col. Depth:** 267 millimeters. **Key Personnel:** Andy Patterson, Publisher. **ISSN:** 0018-2753. **Subscription Rates:** 85 individuals; US$150 individuals; EUR99 individuals; 96 other countries. **Remarks:** Accepts advertising. **URL:** http://www.historytoday.com. **Ad Rates:** BW: 1,700, 4C: 1,850. **Circ:** Paid 30,000

54562 ■ History Workshop Journal
Oxford University Press
c/o Carmen Mangion, Admin. Ed.
PO Box 60305
London WC1E 7WX, United Kingdom
Publisher E-mail: webenquiry.uk@oup.com
Journal with scholarship, accessible writing and lively engagement with contemporary concerns for both academic and general audiences. **Founded:** 1976. **Freq:** 2/yr. **Key Personnel:** Carmen Mangion, Admin. Ed., historyworkshopjournal@gmail.com; Anna Davin, Editor; Sally Alexander, Editor; Bernard Canavan, Editor; Felix Driver, Editor; David Feldman, Editor; Matt Cook, Editor; Jane Caplan, Editor; Laura Gowing, Editor. **ISSN:** 1363 3554. **Subscription Rates:** 154 institutions corporate; print and online; 128 institutions corporate; online only; 141 institutions corporate; print only; 122 institutions print and online; 102 institutions online only; 112 institutions print only; 50 individuals print; 20 students and senior; print; 37 members print. **Remarks:** Advertising accepted; rates available upon request. **URL:** http://hwj.oxfordjournals.org. **Circ:** (Not Reported)

54563 ■ HIV Therapy
Future Medicine Ltd.
Unitec House
2 Albert Pl.
London N3 1QB, United Kingdom
Ph: 44 20 83716080
Fax: 44 20 83432313
Publisher E-mail: info@futuremedicine.com
Journal covering research of HIV treatment and management. **Key Personnel:** W.S. Armstrong, International Editorial Advisory Board; M. Battegay, International Editorial Advisory Board; A. Boucher, International Editorial Advisory Board. **ISSN:** 1758-4310. **URL:** http://www.futuremedicine.com/loi/hiv.

54564 ■ The Holocene
Sage Publications Ltd.
1 Oliver's Yard
55 City Rd.
London EC1Y 1SP, United Kingdom
Ph: 44 20 73248500
Fax: 44 20 73248600
Journal focusing on fundamental scientific research at environmental change, on local, regional and global scales. **Subtitle:** A Major Interdisciplinary Journal Focusing on Recent Environmental Change. **Freq:** 8/yr. **Key Personnel:** John A. Matthews, Editor; C.E. Cordova, Book Review Ed. **ISSN:** 0959-6836. **Subscription Rates:** 1,023 institutions print & e-access; 1,023 institutions e-access; 1,003 institutions print only; 158 individuals print & e-access; 138 institutions single print; 26 individuals single print. **Remarks:** Accepts advertising. **URL:** http://www.hoddereducation.co.uk/; http://www.sagepub.co.uk/journalsProdDesc.nav?prodId=Journal201812. **Circ:** (Not Reported)

54565 ■ Home Cultures
Berg Publishers
University College London
Gower St.
London WC1E 6BT, United Kingdom
Peer-reviewed journal focusing on the critical understanding of the domestic sphere, its artifacts, spaces and relations, across timeframes and cultures. **Founded:** 2004. **Freq:** 3/yr. **Key Personnel:** Victor Buchli, Editor; Alison Clarke, Editor; Setha Low, Editor. **ISSN:** 1740-6315. **Subscription Rates:** 154 institutions online only; 181 institutions print and online; 49 individuals print only; 154 institutions online only. **Remarks:** Accepts advertising. **URL:** http://www.bergpublishers.com/JournalsHomepage/HomeCultures/tabid/3203/Default.aspx. **Ad Rates:** BW: 300. **Circ:** (Not Reported)

54566 ■ Home & Family
The Mothers' Union
Mary Sumner House
24 Tufton St.
London SW1P 3RB, United Kingdom
Ph: 44 20 72225533
Fax: 44 20 72279737
Publisher E-mail: mu@themothersunion.org
Consumer magazine covering family life and Christianity. **Freq:** Quarterly. **Subscription Rates:** 7 individuals; 8 individuals Europe; 10 other countries; 6 individuals subscribe through a U.K. Mother's Union branch. **Remarks:** Accepts advertising. **URL:** http://www.themothersunion.org/homeandfamily.aspx. **Circ:** Paid ★54,000

54567 ■ Homes & Antiques
BBC Worldwide Publishing Ltd.
Media Centre
201 Wood Ln.
London W12 7TQ, United Kingdom
Ph: 44 20 84332000
Fax: 44 20 87490538
Magazine for antiques and home interior lovers. **Founded:** 1993. **Freq:** Monthly. **Key Personnel:** Angela Linforth, Editor; Jan Waldron, Antiques Ed. **Subscription Rates:** 8.10 individuals every 3 issues; 31.90 individuals. **Remarks:** Accepts advertising. **URL:** http://www.homesandantiques.com/; http://www.bbcmagazinesbristol.com/magazine.asp?id=30. **Circ:** ★55,100

54568 ■ Hornsey & Crouch End Journal
Archant Regional Ltd.
100A Avenue Rd.
London NW3 3HF, United Kingdom
Ph: 44 20 74336240
Publisher E-mail: sandra.roantree@archant.co.uk
Local community newspaper. **Freq:** Weekly (Thurs.). **Key Personnel:** Stephen Moore, Asst. Ed. **Subscription Rates:** 11.60 individuals 1 month; 23.20 individuals 2 months; 34.80 individuals 3 months; 69.60 individuals 6 months; 150.80 individuals. **Remarks:** Accepts advertising. **URL:** http://www.hornseyjournal.co.uk/home. **Circ:** (Not Reported)

54569 ■ Horrible Science Collection
Eaglemoss Publications Ltd
Beaumont House, 1st Fl.
Kensington Village
Avonmore Rd.
London W14 8TS, United Kingdom

Ph: 44 20 76051200
Fax: 44 20 76051201
Publisher E-mail: webenquiries@eaglemoss.co.uk
Magazine featuring gadgets, gizmos and any science collection. **Freq:** 6/yr. **Key Personnel:** Nick Arnold, Contact. **Subscription Rates:** 11.94 individuals. **URL:** http://www.horrible-science-collection.co.uk/.

54570 ■ Horse
Time Inc.
9th Fl., IPC Media
Blue Fin Bldg.
110 Southwark St.
London SE1 0SU, United Kingdom
Publisher E-mail: information@timeinc.com
British magazine aiming to help readers get more out of their horses and riding. Geared toward hobby riders and aspiring competitors. Contains news and features from horse care to alternative therapies, and from veterinary advice to celebrity training masterclasses. Also features an extensive Q&A section. **Freq:** Monthly. **Key Personnel:** Jo Browne, Editor, joanna_browne@ipcmedia.com; Sarah Jenkins, Dep. Ed., sarah_jenkins@ipcmedia.com. **Remarks:** Accepts advertising. **URL:** http://www.horsemagazine.co.uk/. **Circ:** (Not Reported)

54571 ■ Horse & Hound
IPC Media Ltd.
Blue Fin Bldg.
110 Southwark St.
London SE1 0SU, United Kingdom
Ph: 44 203 1485000
British magazine for horse lovers and professionals. Provides reportage covering all disciplines, together with the latest news and views from around the country. **Freq:** Weekly. **Key Personnel:** Carol Phillips, Website Ed., carol_phillips@ipcmedia.com; Simon Hare, Publishing Dir., simon_hare@ipcmedia.com; Paula-Jayne Mitchell, Classified Sales Mgr., paula-jayne_mitchell@ipcmedia.com. **Subscription Rates:** 89.99 individuals; 174.99 two years individual. **Remarks:** Accepts advertising. **URL:** http://www.horseandhound.co.uk. **Circ:** (Not Reported)

54572 ■ Hospital Healthcare Europe
Campden Publishing Ltd.
1 St. John's Sq.
London EC1M 4PN, United Kingdom
Ph: 44 20 72140500
Fax: 44 20 72140501
Publisher E-mail: enquiries@campden.com
Magazine for hospitals and medical professionals. **Freq:** Annual. **Key Personnel:** Stephen Taylor, Publisher/Editorial Dir.; Kelly Clarke, Supv. Ed. **Subscription Rates:** 165 individuals; EUR245 individuals; US$326 individuals. **Remarks:** Accepts advertising. **URL:** http://www.campden.com/default.asp?ptid=3&pid=2&pgid=1; http://www.hospitalhealthcare.com/. **Circ:** (Not Reported)

54573 ■ Hospital Imaging and Radiology Europe
Campden Publishing Ltd.
1 St. John's Sq.
London EC1M 4PN, United Kingdom
Ph: 44 20 72140500
Fax: 44 20 72140501
Publisher E-mail: enquiries@campden.com
Magazine for radiologists. **Freq:** Quarterly. **Key Personnel:** Stephen Taylor, Publisher/Editorial Dir. **Remarks:** Accepts advertising. **URL:** http://www.hospitalradiologyeurope.com/. **Circ:** 8,750

54574 ■ Hospital Management International
SPG Media Group Plc.
Brunel House
55-57 N Wharf Rd.
London W2 1LA, United Kingdom
Ph: 44 20 79159660
Fax: 44 20 77242089
Publisher E-mail: info@spgmedia.com
Trade magazine covering hospital management worldwide. **Freq:** Annual. **Subscription Rates:** Free. **Remarks:** Accepts advertising. **URL:** http://www.hospitalmanagementinternational.com/. **Circ:** Non-paid ★10,039

54575 ■ House Builder
House Builders Federation
1st Fl.
7-9 St. James's St.
London SW1A 1DW, United Kingdom
Ph: 44 20 79601600

Fax: 44 20 79601601
Publisher E-mail: info@hbf.co.uk
Publication covering building industries. **Freq:** Monthly. **Key Personnel:** Chris Hart, Advertising Mgr., chris.hart@house-builder.co.uk. **Subscription Rates:** 80 individuals; 110 other countries. **Remarks:** Accepts advertising. **URL:** http://www.house-builder.co.uk/. **Circ:** (Not Reported)

54576 ■ HSJ
EMAP Healthcare Ltd.
Greater London House
Hampstead Rd.
London NW1 7EJ, United Kingdom
Ph: 44 20 77285000
Magazine covering news, analysis, and information for healthcare managers. **Subtitle:** Health Service Journal. **Freq:** Weekly (Thurs.). **Key Personnel:** Alastair McLellan, Editor, alastair.mclellan@emap.com; Alexis Nolan, Exec. Ed., alexis.nolan@emap.com; Anamika Rath, Online Ed., anamika.rath@emap.com. **Subscription Rates:** 105 individuals annual direct debit; 26.25 individuals quarterly direct debit; 8.75 individuals monthly direct debit; 170 institutions; 105 individuals. **Remarks:** Accepts advertising. **URL:** http://www.hsj.co.uk/. **Ad Rates:** 4C: 3,415. **Circ:** 105,000

54577 ■ Human Genomics
Henry Stewart Publications
Russell House
28-30 Little Russell St.
London WC1A 2HN, United Kingdom
Ph: 44 20 74043040
Fax: 44 20 74042081
Publisher E-mail: gweny@henrystewart.co.uk
Journal focusing on the application of genomic approaches to improve understanding of human disease, drug discovery and variable drug reaction. **Freq:** Quarterly. **Key Personnel:** David Ross, Editorial Board; Vasilis Vasiliou, Editor; Michael Stumpf, Book Review Ed. **ISSN:** 1473-9542. **Subscription Rates:** 120 institutions, other countries Europe and rest of the world, online; US$220 institutions online access, U.S./Canada; 60 individuals Europe and rest of the world, online access; US$110 U.S. and Canada online; 340 unlimited multi-user; US$625 unlimited multi-user. **URL:** http://www.henrystewart.com/human_genomics/.

54578 ■ Human Relations
Sage Publications Ltd.
1 Oliver's Yard
55 City Rd.
London EC1Y 1SP, United Kingdom
Ph: 44 20 73248500
Fax: 44 20 73248600
Scholarly journal covering multidisciplinary and action research in the social sciences. **Founded:** 1958. **Freq:** Monthly. **Key Personnel:** Stephen Deery, Editor-in-Chief; Mike A. Noon, Editorial Board; Sam Aryee, Assoc. Ed.; Kevin J. Daniels, Assoc. Ed.; Claire Castle, Managing Editor; Terry A. Beehr, Assoc. Ed. **ISSN:** 0018-7267. **Subscription Rates:** US$1,994 institutions print & e-access; US$2,193 institutions current volume print & all online content; US$1,795 institutions e-access; US$1,994 institutions all online content; US$7,781 institutions content through 1998; US$1,954 institutions print only; US$146 individuals print only; US$179 institutions single print; US$16 individuals single print. **Remarks:** Accepts advertising. **URL:** http://www.sagepub.com/journalsProdDesc.nav?prodId=Journal200870. **Circ:** (Not Reported)

54579 ■ Human Resources
Haymarket Business Magazines
174 Hammersmith Rd.
London W6 7JP, United Kingdom
Ph: 44 20 82674210
Publisher E-mail: info@haymarket.com
Professional magazine covering human resources for senior managers/directors. **Freq:** Monthly. **Key Personnel:** Sian Harrington, Editor, phone 44 20 82674632, sian.harrington@haymarket.com; Peter Crush, Dep. Ed., phone 44 20 82674325, peter.crush@haymarket.com; Rebecca Nolan, Asst. Advertising Mgr., phone 44 20 82674968, rebecca.nolan@haymarket.com. **Subscription Rates:** 89 individuals; 160 two years; 214 individuals three years. **Remarks:** Accepts advertising. **URL:** http://www.humanresourcesmagazine.com. **Circ:** 20,532

54580 ■ Human Resources for Health
BioMed Central Ltd.
236 Gray's Inn Rd., Fl. 6
34-42 Cleveland St.
London WC1X 8HL, United Kingdom
Ph: 44 20 31922000
Fax: 44 20 31922010
Publication E-mail: hrhjournal@who.int
Publisher E-mail: info@biomedcentral.com
Journal covering all aspects of planning, producing and managing the workforce involved in health services worldwide. **Key Personnel:** Dr. Orvill Adams, Editorial Board; Hugo Mercer, Dep. Ed., mercerh@who.int; Dr. Mario Dal Poz, Editor-in-Chief; Daniel Shaw, Managing Editor; Dr. Pedro Brito, Editorial Board; Dr. Stephen D. Bach, Editorial Board. **ISSN:** 1478-4491. **Subscription Rates:** Free. **URL:** http://www.human-resources-health.com/home/.

54581 ■ IBM Database Magazine
United Business Media
245 Blackfriars Rd.
London SE1 9UY, United Kingdom
Ph: 44 20 79215000
Solutions-oriented magazine for IT professionals, publishing strategic and technical information related to the IBM Data Management environment. **Freq:** Quarterly. **Key Personnel:** Kim Moutsos, Editor, phone 415947-6975, kmoutsos@cmp.com. **Subscription Rates:** Free. **Remarks:** Accepts advertising. **URL:** http://www.ibmdatabasemag.com/; http://www.ibmdatabasemag.com/showArticle.jhtml?articleID=206800435. **Formerly:** DB2 Magazine. **Circ:** (Not Reported)

54582 ■ Ideal Home
IPC Media Ltd.
Blue Fin Bldg.
110 Southwark St.
London SE1 0SU, United Kingdom
Ph: 44 203 1485000
Publication E-mail: ideal_home@ipcmedia.com
Magazine focusing on home interior decoration articles, news and advice. **Key Personnel:** Jess Smit, Editor, jessamy_smit@ipcmedia.com. **Subscription Rates:** 24.99 individuals. **Remarks:** Accepts advertising. **URL:** http://www.idealhomemagazine.co.uk/. **Circ:** (Not Reported)

54583 ■ IMAGE
Association of Photographers
81 Leonard St.
London EC2A 4QS, United Kingdom
Ph: 44 20 77396669
Fax: 44 20 77398707
Publisher E-mail: general@aophoto.co.uk
Publication covering photography for advertising and editorial photographers, art directors, photographers' agents, model agencies, art colleges, suppliers and manufacturers. **Freq:** Monthly. **Trim Size:** 297 x 210 mm. **Subscription Rates:** Free to all AOP members; 24 nonmembers; 36 nonmembers non UK. **URL:** http://www.the-aop.org/home.htm. **Ad Rates:** BW: 580, 4C: 980. **Circ:** 2,800

54584 ■ Immunity & Ageing
BioMed Central Ltd.
236 Gray's Inn Rd., Fl. 6
34-42 Cleveland St.
London WC1X 8HL, United Kingdom
Ph: 44 20 31922000
Fax: 44 20 31922010
Publication E-mail: immunity_ageing@unipa.it
Publisher E-mail: info@biomedcentral.com
Online journal covering all aspects of ageing examined from an immunological point of view. **Key Personnel:** Prof. Calogero Caruso, Editor-in-Chief, marcoc@unipa.it; Prof. Graham Pawelec, Dep. Ed., graham.pawelec@uni-tuebingen.de; Prof. Domenico Lio, Assoc. Ed., dolio@unipa.it; Sonya Vasto, Managing Editor, s.vasto@unipa.it; Arne Akbar, Section Ed., a.akbar@ucl.ac.uk; Emilio Jirillo, Section Ed. **ISSN:** 1742-4933. **Remarks:** Accepts advertising. **URL:** http://www.immunityageing.com/home/. **Circ:** (Not Reported)

54585 ■ Immunology
British Society for Immunology
Vintage House
37 Albert Embankment

London SE1 7TL, United Kingdom
Ph: 44 20 30319800
Fax: 44 20 75822882
Publisher E-mail: onlinecommunity@immunology.org
Peer-reviewed publication covering immunology. **Freq:** Monthly. **Key Personnel:** Frederica Sallusto, Assoc. Ed.; Stephen Anderton, Assoc. Ed.; Charles Surh, Assoc. Ed.; Steve Jameson, Assoc. Ed.; Danny Altmann, Editor-in-Chief; Klaus Heeg, Assoc. Ed. **ISSN:** 0019-2805. **Subscription Rates:** US$1,959 institutions Americas (online only); EUR1,347 institutions Europe (online only); US$2,285 institutions rest of the world (online only); US$170 members Americas (print and online); EUR150 members Europe (print and online); 100 members rest of the world (print and online); US$2,253 institutions Americas (print and online); EUR1,550 institutions Europe (print and online); US$2,628 institutions rest of the world (print and online); 100 members U.K., print & online. **Remarks:** Accepts advertising. **URL:** http://www.blackwellpublishing.com/subs.asp?ref=0019-2805. **Circ:** 4,500

54586 ■ Immunome Research
BioMed Central Ltd.
236 Gray's Inn Rd., Fl. 6
34-42 Cleveland St.
London WC1X 8HL, United Kingdom
Ph: 44 20 31922000
Fax: 44 20 31922010
Publisher E-mail: info@biomedcentral.com
Journal devoted to Immunomics, an emerging field in immunology, in connection with the International Immunities Society (IIMMS). **Key Personnel:** Prof. Nikolai Petrovsky, Editor-in-Chief, phone 61 8 82044572, fax 61 8 82045987, nikolai.petrovsky@flinders.edu.au; Prof. Vladimir Brusic, Dep. Ed., vladimir@i2r.a-star.edu.sg; Prof. Massimo Bernaschi, Section Ed., massimo@ac.cnr.it. **ISSN:** 1745-7580. **URL:** http://www.immunome-research.com/.

54587 ■ Immunotherapy
Future Medicine Ltd.
Unitec House
2 Albert Pl.
London N3 1QB, United Kingdom
Ph: 44 20 83716080
Fax: 44 20 83432313
Publisher E-mail: info@futuremeducine.com
Journal featuring articles on immunotherapeutics. **Freq:** Bimonthly. **Key Personnel:** Y. Kawakami, Sen. Ed.; F.M. Marincola, Sen. Ed.; D.C. Wraith, Sen. Ed. **ISSN:** 1750-743X. **URL:** http://www.futuremedicine.com/loi/imt.

54588 ■ Implicit Religion
Equinox Publishing Ltd.
CSIRCS
The Old School, Church Ln.
Yarnton
London OX5 1PY, United Kingdom
Journal reporting on theory and evidence in the study of religion and secularity, and those which explore the relationship between the context and dynamism of religious and secular phenomena. **Freq:** 3/yr (April, July & Nov.). **Key Personnel:** Edward Bailey, Editor, edward.bailey@implicitreligion.org; Roberto Cipriani, Council of Reference, rcipriani@equinoxpub.com; Meerten Ter Borg, Editorial Board, mterborg@equinoxpub.com; Eugene Bianchi, Editorial Board, ebianchi@equinoxpub.com; Jay N. Demerath III, Editorial Board, ndemerath@equinoxpub.com; Don Wiebe, Editorial Board; James Beckford, Council of Reference, dwiebe@equinoxpub.com; Eileen Barker, Council of Reference, e.barker@lse.ac.uk. **ISSN:** 1463-9955. **Subscription Rates:** 140 institutions, other countries print and online; US$280 institutions print and online; 53 individuals print; US$105 individuals print; 33.75 students print; US$67.50 students print. **Remarks:** Accepts advertising. **URL:** http://www.equinoxpub.com/journals/main.asp?jref=32. **Circ:** (Not Reported)

54589 ■ Improving Schools
Sage Publications Ltd.
1 Oliver's Yard
55 City Rd.
London EC1Y 1SP, United Kingdom
Ph: 44 20 73248500
Fax: 44 20 73248600
Professional magazine covering education. **Founded:** 1998. **Freq:** 3/yr. **Print Method:** Offset Litho. **Trim Size:** A4. **Col. Width:** 124 millimeters. **Col. Depth:** 202

millimeters. **Key Personnel:** Terry Wrigley, Editor; Hugh Busher, Editor. **ISSN:** 1365-4802. **Subscription Rates:** 322 institutions print & e-access; 354 institutions current volume print & all online content; 290 institutions e-access; 322 institutions all online content; 155 institutions print only; 155 institutions print & e-access; 47 individuals print only; 20 individuals single print; 116 institutions single print. **Remarks:** Accepts advertising. **URL:** http://www.sagepub.co.uk/journalsSubscribe.nav?prodId=Journal201678. **Ad Rates:** BW: 200. **Circ:** Paid 1,000

54590 ■ In Brief
Association of Qualitative Research
c/o Louella Miles, Ed.
45 Cornwall Grove
London W4 2LB, United Kingdom
Ph: 44 20 89958307
Fax: 44 20 85803909
Publisher E-mail: info@aqr.org.uk
Magazine keeping members informed on relevant issues and topics. **Freq:** Bimonthly. **Key Personnel:** Louella Miles, Editor, louella.miles@writers4management.com. **URL:** http://www.aqr.org.uk/about/inbrief.shtml.

54591 ■ The In-House Lawyer
Legalese Ltd.
Kensington Sq. House
12-14 Ansdell St.
London W8 5BN, United Kingdom
Ph: 44 20 73969292
Fax: 44 20 73969303
Professional magazine covering changes in the law affecting business. **Freq:** 10/yr. **Key Personnel:** Claire Bostock, Contact, claire.bostock@legalease.co.uk. **ISSN:** 0966-8012. **Subscription Rates:** 145 individuals. **URL:** http://www.legalease.co.uk; http://www.inhouselawyer.co.uk/. **Circ:** Combined ‡5,500

54592 ■ In the Night Garden
BBC Worldwide Publishing Ltd.
Media Centre
201 Wood Ln.
London W12 7TQ, United Kingdom
Ph: 44 20 84332000
Fax: 44 20 87490538
Magazine for children. **Subtitle:** Magical fun for little ones. **Freq:** every 2 weeks. **Subscription Rates:** 1.99 single issue. **URL:** http://www.bbcmagazines.com/content/magazines/inthenightgarden/.

54593 ■ In-Store Marketing
Centaur Communications Ltd.
50 Poland St.
London W1F 7AX, United Kingdom
Ph: 44 20 79704000
Trade magazine for retail marketers and brand managers. **Founded:** Apr. 1997. **Freq:** Monthly. **Print Method:** Sheetfed Offset. **Trim Size:** 235 x 285 mm. **Key Personnel:** Matthew Valentine, Editor, phone 44 20 79706535, matthew.valentine@centaur.co.uk; Kulsum Shaikh, Classified Sales Executive, phone 44 20 79706524, kulsum.shaikh@centaur.co.uk; Richard Marks, Sen. Account Mgr., phone 44 20 79706529, richard.marks@centaur.co.uk; John Hughes, Publisher, phone 44 20 79704000, jon.hughes@centaur.co.uk. **Subscription Rates:** 59 individuals; 85 two years; 114 U.S. and Canada; 194 U.S. and Canada 2 years. **Remarks:** Accepts advertising. **URL:** http://www.centaur.co.uk/communities/marketing/ism/. **Ad Rates:** 4C: 3,185. **Circ:** Combined 13,084, ★10,168

54594 ■ Index on Censorship
Writers and Scholars International Ltd.
Lancaster House
6-8 Anwell St.
London EC1R 3GA, United Kingdom
Ph: 44 20 73242522
Publication E-mail: enquiries@indexoncensorship.org
Publisher E-mail: contact@indexoncensorship.org
Journal covering censorship and freedom of expression worldwide. **Founded:** 1972. **Freq:** Quarterly. **Print Method:** Sheetfed offset. **Trim Size:** 151 x 200 mm. **Key Personnel:** Natasha Schmidt, Contact, natasha@indexoncensorship.org; Henderson Mullin, Mng. Dir., henderson@indexoncensorship.org; Judith Vidal-Hall, Editor, judith@indexoncensorship.org; Ursula Owen, Editor-in-Chief, ursula@indexoncensorship.org. **ISSN:**

0306-4220. **Subscription Rates:** 117 institutions online; US$194 institutions; 111 institutions online; US$184 institutions online; 39 individuals; US$64 individuals; 18 students; US$30 students. **Remarks:** Accepts advertising. **URL:** http://www.indexoncensorship.org. **Ad Rates:** BW: 600, 4C: 1,000. **Circ:** Combined 10,000

54595 ■ Index to Theses
Expert Information
Hamilton House
1 Temple Ave.
London EC4Y 0HA, United Kingdom
Publication E-mail: contact@theses.com
Journal covering bibliographic details on British theses. **Freq:** Semiannual. **Subscription Rates:** 370 institutions, other countries print; EUR470 institutions print; US$725 institutions print; 495 institutions, other countries print + online; EUR700 institutions print + online; US$970 institutions print + online; 480 other countries online; EUR630 institutions online; US$940 institutions online. **URL:** http://www.theses.com/.

54596 ■ Industrial Archaeology Review
Maney Publishing
1 Carlton House Ter.
London SW1Y 5AF, United Kingdom
Ph: 44 20 74517300
Fax: 44 20 74517307
Publisher E-mail: maney@maney.co.uk
Peer reviewed journal covering industrial archaeology. **Freq:** Semiannual. **Key Personnel:** David Gwyn, PhD, Editor, govannonconsult@hotmail.com; Marilyn Palmer, Book Review Ed., marilyn.palmer@tiscali.co.uk. **ISSN:** 0309-0728. **Subscription Rates:** 184 institutions, other countries; US$342 institutions; 30 members UK; 33 members rest of world; 35 members UK joint; 38 members rest of world joint; 18 members UK student; 21 members rest of world student; 39 members UK affiliated institution; 42 members rest of world affiliated institution. **Remarks:** Accepts advertising. **URL:** http://maney.co.uk/index.php/journals/iar/. **Ad Rates:** BW: 180. **Circ:** (Not Reported)

54597 ■ Industrial Cases Reports
The Incorporated Council of Law Reporting for England and Wales
Megarry House
119 Chancery Ln.
London WC2A 1PP, United Kingdom
Ph: 44 20 72426471
Fax: 44 20 78315247
Publisher E-mail: postmaster@iclr.co.uk
Legal journal covering case reports, specializing in employment and industrial law, in the UK. **Founded:** 1972. **Freq:** Monthly 14/yr (plus bound volume at year-end). **Key Personnel:** Margaret Froome, Contact, margaretf@iclr.co.uk; Julia Reed, Account Mgr., juliar@iclr.co.uk; Steve Mitchell, Binding Mgr., binding@iclr.co.uk; Clare Noon, Editor, claren@iclr.co.uk; Helen Yates, Agent's Subscriptions, heleny@iclr.co.uk. **ISSN:** 0306-2163. **Subscription Rates:** 395 other countries overseas; 380 other countries; 190 other countries; 76 other countries; 695 other countries U.K.; 740 other countries overseas; 905 other countries U.K.; 955 other countries overseas; 1,125 other countries U.K.; 1,190 other countries overseas. **Remarks:** Advertising not accepted. **URL:** http://www.lawreports.co.uk/Publications/general.htm. **Former name:** Industrial Court Reports (1975). **Circ:** (Not Reported)

54598 ■ Industrial Minerals (IM)
Industrial Minerals
16 Lower Marsh
Playhouse Yard
London SE1 7RJ, United Kingdom
Ph: 44 20 78279977
Fax: 44 20 78275292
Publisher E-mail: edit@indmin.com
Magazine dealing with non-metallic, non-fuel minerals which form critical raw materials for many manufacturing processes and industrial applications. **Freq:** Monthly. **Key Personnel:** Mike O'Driscoll, Editor, modriscoll@metalbulletin.com; Ismene Clarke, Advertising Mgr., iclarke@indmin.com; Simon Moores, Dep. Ed., smoores@indmin.com; Jessica Roberts, Asst. Ed., jroberts@indmin.com. **Subscription Rates:** 737 individuals; EUR1,217 individuals Europe; US$1,577 individuals. **URL:** http://www.indmin.com/Default.aspx.

54599 ■ Industry and Higher Education
IP Publishing Ltd.

258 Belsize Rd.
London NW6 4BT, United Kingdom
Ph: 44 20 73161870
Fax: 44 20 76249994
Publisher E-mail: jedmondson@ippublishing.com
Journal covering the relationship between business and higher education institutions worldwide, including technology transfers, academic entrepreneurship, and continuing education. **Founded:** 1987. **Freq:** Bimonthly. **Key Personnel:** John Edmondson, Editor, jedmondson@ippublishing.com. **ISSN:** 0950-4222. **Subscription Rates:** US$613 institutions; EUR604 institutions; 408 institutions, other countries in sterling. **Remarks:** Accepts advertising. **URL:** http://www.ippublishing.com/ihe.htm. **Circ:** (Not Reported)

54600 ■ Info
French Chamber of Commerce in Great Britain
Lincoln House, 4th Fl.
300 High Holborn
London WC1V 7JH, United Kingdom
Ph: 44 207 0926600
Fax: 44 207 0926601
Publisher E-mail: mail@ccfgb.co.uk
Trade magazine covering business in France and the UK. **Freq:** Bimonthly. **Trim Size:** 210 x 297 mm. **Cols./Page:** 2. **Col. Width:** 80 millimeters. **Col. Depth:** 230 millimeters. **Key Personnel:** Delphine de Wulf, Publications Mgr.; Capucine Oddo, Advertising Coord. **Remarks:** Accepts advertising. **URL:** http://www.ccfgb.co.uk. **Ad Rates:** 4C: 1,990, 4C: 1,490. **Circ:** Combined 12,100

54601 ■ InfoRM
Institute of Risk Management
Lloyds Ave. House
6 Lloyds Ave.
London EC3N 3AX, United Kingdom
Ph: 44 20 77099808
Fax: 44 20 77090716
Publisher E-mail: enquiries@theirm.org
Publication covering risk management. **Subtitle:** The Journal of the Institute of Risk Management. **Founded:** 1995. **Freq:** Bimonthly. **Trim Size:** A4. **Key Personnel:** Steve Fowler, CEO, steve.fowler@theirm.org; Rebecca Brueton, Devel. Asst. Mgr., rebecca.brueton@theirm.org; Sophie Williams, Operations Mgr., sophie.williams@theirm.org. **URL:** http://www.theirm.org. **Ad Rates:** BW: 1,025. **Circ:** 3,500

54602 ■ Information Bulletin
Age Concern England
207-221 Pentonville Rd.
London N1 9UZ, United Kingdom
Client awareness publication on aging. **Founded:** 1974. **Freq:** Monthly. **Subscription Rates:** 34 individuals. **Remarks:** Advertising not accepted. **URL:** http://www.ageconcern.org.uk/AgeConcern/CC665D0CE3874F91B6C53442A2814080. **Formerly:** Information Circular. **Circ:** (Not Reported)

54603 ■ Information Development
Sage Publications Ltd.
1 Oliver's Yard
55 City Rd.
London EC1Y 1SP, United Kingdom
Ph: 44 20 73248500
Fax: 44 20 73248600
Peer-reviewed journal covering current issues, problems and trends information science worldwide. **Freq:** Quarterly. **Print Method:** Litho. **Trim Size:** 276 x 210 mm. **Key Personnel:** Stephen J. Parker, Editor; Rashidah Begum Fazal, Editorial Advisory Board; Paul Sturges, Editorial Advisory Board; Barbara J. Ford, Editorial Advisory Board; Dominique Babini, Editorial Advisory Board; G.E. Gorman, Editorial Advisory Board. **ISSN:** 0266-6669. **Subscription Rates:** 350 institutions combined (print & e-access); 385 institutions current volume print & all online content; 315 institutions e-access; 350 institutions all online content; 375 institutions content through 1998; 343 institutions print only; 52 individuals print only; 94 institutions single print; 17 individuals single print. **Remarks:** Advertising not accepted. **URL:** http://www.sagepub.co.uk/journalsProdDesc.nav?prodId=Journal201674. **Circ:** (Not Reported)

54604 ■ Information World Review
Incisive Media Limited
Haymarket House

28-29 Haymarket
London SW1Y 4RX, United Kingdom
Ph: 44 870 2408859
Fax: 44 207 4849797
Publisher E-mail: customerservices@incisivemedia.com
Newspaper for the information industry. **Founded:** 1976. **Freq:** Monthly. **Key Personnel:** Peter Williams, Editor, phone 44 20 89959345, peterw@bizmedia.co.uk. **ISSN:** 0950-9879. **Remarks:** Accepts advertising. **URL:** http://www.iwr.co.uk. **Ad Rates:** 4C: 2,745. **Circ:** ‡15,000

54605 ■ Innate Immunity
Sage Publications Ltd.
1 Oliver's Yard
55 City Rd.
London EC1Y 1SP, United Kingdom
Ph: 44 20 73248500
Fax: 44 20 73248600
Peer-reviewed journal providing a common platform for sharing information on endotoxin and innate immunity to researchers from diverse scientific backgrounds. **Freq:** Bimonthly February, April, June, August, October, and December. **Trim Size:** 165 x 230 mm. **Key Personnel:** Dr. Otto Holst, Editor-in-Chief; Patricia M. Sanchez Carballo, Asst. Ed. **ISSN:** 1753-4259. **Subscription Rates:** 147 individuals print and online; 654 institutions print and online; 589 institutions online only; 641 institutions print only; US$118 institutions single copy, print; US$32 single issue print. **Remarks:** Accepts advertising. **URL:** http://www.sagepub.co.uk/journalsProdDesc.nav?prodId=Journal201861&. **Formerly:** Journal of Endotoxin Research. **Ad Rates:** BW: 180. **Circ:** (Not Reported)

54606 ■ Inside Housing
Ocean Media Events Ltd.
1 Canada Sq.
London E14 5AA, United Kingdom
Ph: 44 20 77728300
Fax: 44 20 77728599
Publication E-mail: editorial@insidehousing.co.uk
Trade magazine covering rental housing. **Founded:** 1984. **Freq:** Daily. **Print Method:** Web Offset. **Trim Size:** 230 x 300 mm. **Cols./Page:** 6. **Col. Width:** 69 millimeters. **Col. Depth:** 280 millimeters. **Key Personnel:** Stuart Macdonald, Editor, phone 44 20 77728434, fax 44 20 77728591, stuart.macdonald@insidehousing.co.uk; Martin Hilditch, News Ed., phone 44 20 77728430, martin.hilditch@insidehousing.co.uk. **Subscription Rates:** 119 individuals UK (50 issues); 147 individuals Europe (50 issues); 175 other countries 50 issues. **Remarks:** Accepts advertising. **URL:** http://www.insidehousing.co.uk. **Circ:** Combined ★26,343

54607 ■ Insight
Theosophical Society in England
50 Gloucester Pl.
London W1U 8EA, United Kingdom
Ph: 44 20 75639817
Fax: 44 20 79359543
Publisher E-mail: info@theosoc.org.uk
Journal exploring the field of spirituality. **Freq:** 4/yr. **Subscription Rates:** Free to members. **Remarks:** Accepts advertising. **URL:** http://www.theosophical-society.org.uk/ASP/insight.asp. **Circ:** (Not Reported)

54608 ■ Institutional Investor
Euromoney Publications PLC
Nestor House
Playhouse Yard
London EC4V 5EX, United Kingdom
Ph: 44 20 77798888
Publisher E-mail: information@euromoneyplc.com
Publication for the banking, finance, and accounting industries. **Freq:** Monthly. **ISSN:** 0020-3580. **Subscription Rates:** EUR1,667 individuals; 1,163 individuals; US$2,017 individuals. **URL:** http://www.euromoneyplc.com/product.asp?PositionID=3150&ProductID=5573&pageid=343.

54609 ■ Instrumenta
PJB Publications Ltd.
Telephone House
69-77 Paul St.
London EC2A 4LQ, United Kingdom
Ph: 44 20 70175000
Fax: 44 20 70176792
Publisher E-mail: pjb.enquiries@informa.com
Professional journal covering market and business information on the analytical instrument and lab equip-

ment industries. **Founded:** Feb. 1984. **Freq:** Monthly. **Key Personnel:** Dr. Stefan Fritsch, Editor, stefan. fritsch@informa.com; Robin Baker, Contact, robin. baker@informa.com. **ISSN:** 1474-0710. **Subscription Rates:** 680 individuals web daily alert, archive and monthly print; EUR1,052 individuals web daily alert, archive and monthly print; US$1,300 individuals web daily alert, archive and monthly print; 210,000¥ individuals web daily alert, archive and monthly print. **URL:** http://www.pjbpubs.com/instrumenta/index.htm. **Formerly:** Analytical Instrument Industry Report. **Circ:** Paid 7,000

54610 ■ Insurance Age
Incisive Media Limited
Haymarket House
28-29 Haymarket
London SW1Y 4RX, United Kingdom
Ph: 44 870 2408859
Fax: 44 207 4849797
Publisher E-mail: customerservices@incisivemedia.com
Magazine for insurance brokers. **Subtitle:** Serving the broker community for over 25 years. **Freq:** Monthly. **Key Personnel:** Martin Friel, Editor, phone 44 20 73169732, martin.friel@incisivemedia.com; Anthony Gould, Editor-in-Chief, phone 44 20 73169374, ant.gould@incisivemedia.com; Alex Broad, Publisher, phone 44 20 73169382, alex.broad@incisivemedia.com. **Remarks:** Accepts advertising. **URL:** http://www.insuranceage.com. **Ad Rates:** BW: 4,076, 4C: 5,244. **Circ:** Controlled ★15,880

54611 ■ Insurance Day
Informa Publishing Group
Informa House
30-32 Mortimer St.
London W1W 7RE, United Kingdom
Ph: 44 20 70175000
Online newspaper covering the international insurance, reinsurance and risk industry. **Founded:** Dec. 1999. **Freq:** Daily. **Key Personnel:** Graeme Cathie, Contact, phone 44 207 0174070, graeme.cathie@informa.com; Sarah Denton, Contact, phone 44 207 174122, sarah. denton@informa.com. **Subscription Rates:** 1,795 individuals. **Remarks:** Accepts advertising. **URL:** http://www.insuranceday.com/insday/news/home.htm; http://www.informaprofessional.com/publications/newspaper/insurance_day. **Former name:** Insurance Systems Bulletin; Insurance Technology. **Circ:** Controlled 7,000

54612 ■ Insurance & Technology
United Business Media
245 Blackfriars Rd.
London SE1 9UY, United Kingdom
Ph: 44 20 79215000
Publication for insurance professionals covering the role of the Internet in financial services organizations. **Freq:** Monthly. **Key Personnel:** Katherine Burger, Editorial Dir., phone 212600-3062, kburger@techweb.com; Anthony O'Donnell, Exec. Ed., phone 503465-4565, aodonell@techweb.com; Nathan Conz, Assoc. Mng. Ed., phone 212600-3105, nconz@techweb.com. **Subscription Rates:** US$65 individuals; 85 Canada; 295 other countries. **Remarks:** Accepts advertising. **URL:** http://www.insurancetech.com. **Circ:** Paid 18,100

54613 ■ Intellectual Asset Management
Globe White Page Ltd.
New Hibernia House
Winchester Walk
London Bridge
London SE1 9AG, United Kingdom
Ph: 44 20 72340606
Fax: 44 20 72340808
Publisher E-mail: tharriss@globewhitepage.com
Magazine designed to the inside track on how companies can ensure they extract the maximum value from the patents, trademarks, copyrights and trade secrets they own, as well as the know-how inside their employees' heads. **Freq:** Bimonthly. **Key Personnel:** Joff Wild, Editor, jwild@iam-magazine.com; Gavin Stewart, Publisher, gstewart@iam-magazine.com; Alan Mowat, Subscriptions and Mktg. Mgr., amowat@iam-magazine. com. **Subscription Rates:** 475 individuals. **URL:** http://www.iam-magazine.com/.

54614 ■ Intellectual History Review
Routledge
Taylor & Francis Group Ltd.
Birkbeck College
University of London

London, United Kingdom
Publisher E-mail: webmaster.books@tandf.co.uk
Peer-reviewed journal focusing on the Anglo-American and European intellectual history community, covering literature surveys, and essay reviews. **Freq:** 4/yr. **Print Method:** Offset. **Trim Size:** 8 1/4 x 10 3/4. **Cols./Page:** 2. **Col. Width:** 40 nonpareils. **Col. Depth:** 140 agate lines. **Key Personnel:** Richard Serjeantson, Editorial Board; Peter J. Forshaw, Book Reviews Ed.; Janet Browne, Editorial Board; Martin Mulsow, Editorial Board; Antonio Clericuzio, Editorial Board; Stephen Gaukroger, Editor; Lorraine Daston, Editorial Board; Catherine Wilson, Editorial Board; Roger Ariew, Editorial Board; Howard Hotson, Editorial Board; Constance Blackwell, Advisory Board; Cordula Grewe, Advisory Board. **ISSN:** 1749-6977. **Subscription Rates:** 173 institutions print + online; 165 institutions online; 40 elsewhere; US$313 institutions print + online; US$297 institutions online; US$70 elsewhere; EUR250 institutions print and online; EUR238 institutions online only. **URL:** http://www.tandf.co.uk/journals/titles/17496977.asp.

54615 ■ Interdisciplinary Science Reviews
Maney Publishing
1 Carlton House Ter.
London SW1Y 5AF, United Kingdom
Ph: 44 20 74517300
Fax: 44 20 74517307
Publisher E-mail: maney@maney.co.uk
Journal covering science and human affairs and focusing to set contemporary and historical developments in science and technology in their wider cultural context. **Freq:** Quarterly. **Key Personnel:** Howard Cattermole, Consultant Ed., howard.cattermole@dunelm.org.uk; Philip Ball, Editorial Board, p.ball@nature.com; Willard McCarty, Editor-in-Chief, willard.mccarty@kcl.ac.uk. **ISSN:** 0308-0188. **Subscription Rates:** 490 institutions, other countries; US$850 institutions; 40 other countries; US$64 individuals. **URL:** http://maney.co.uk/index.php/journals/isr/.

54616 ■ Interior Motives
Ultima Media Ltd.
Lamb House
Church St.
London W4 2PD, United Kingdom
Ph: 44 20 89870900
Fax: 44 20 89870948
Publisher E-mail: info@ultimamedia.com
Magazine featuring automotive design management. **Freq:** Quarterly. **Trim Size:** 230 x 297 mm. **Key Personnel:** Euan Sey, Editor, phone 44 20 89870980, euan. sey@ultimamedia.com; Abel Sampson, Publisher, phone 44 20 89870963, abel.sampson@ultimamedia.org. **Subscription Rates:** US$95 individuals; US$140 individuals; 80 individuals. **Remarks:** Accepts advertising. **URL:** http://www.interiormotivesmagazine.com/. **Circ:** (Not Reported)

54617 ■ Internal Auditing and Business Risk
Institute of Internal Auditors - U.K. and Ireland
13 Abbeville Mews
88 Clapham Pk. Rd.
London SW4 7BX, United Kingdom
Ph: 44 20 74980101
Fax: 44 20 79782492
Publication E-mail: publications@iia.org.uk
Publisher E-mail: membership@iia.org.uk
Publication covering internal auditing. **Freq:** Monthly. **Print Method:** Sheetfed Litho. **Trim Size:** A4. **Key Personnel:** Anne Marie Fox, Contact. **ISSN:** 1475-1984. **Subscription Rates:** 144 individuals; 164 individuals Europe; 174 other countries. **URL:** http://www.iia.org.uk. **Ad Rates:** BW: 2,088, 4C: 2,504. **Circ:** 8,000

54618 ■ Internal Comms Hub
Melcrum Publishing
The Glassmills
322B King St.
London W6 0AX, United Kingdom
Ph: 44 20 86004670
Fax: 44 20 87419975
Publisher E-mail: customerservice@melcrum.com
Magazine for business communication. **Freq:** Monthly 10/yr. **Key Personnel:** Robin Crumby, Mng. Dir. **Subscription Rates:** US$435 individuals; 275 individuals; EUR405 individuals. **URL:** http://www.internalcommshub.com/; http://www.melcrum.com/products/memberships/ich.shtml. **Formerly:** The Business Communicator.

54619 ■ International African Bibliography
Walter de Gruyter GmbH & Co. KG
c/o David Hall, Ed.
The Library of School of Oriental & African Studies
Thornhaugh St.
Russell Sq.
London WC1H 0XG, United Kingdom
Ph: 44 20 78984162
Publisher E-mail: info@degruyter.com
Journal focusing on African studies. **Freq:** Quarterly. **Key Personnel:** David Hall, Editor. **ISSN:** 0020-5877. **Subscription Rates:** EUR421 individuals print + online; EUR366 individuals print or online only; EUR101 single issue. **URL:** http://www.degruyter.de/journals/iab/detailEn.cfm.

54620 ■ International Breastfeeding Journal
BioMed Central Ltd.
236 Gray's Inn Rd., Fl. 6
34-42 Cleveland St.
London WC1X 8HL, United Kingdom
Ph: 44 20 31922000
Fax: 44 20 31922010
Publication E-mail: ibj-editor@unimelb.edu.au
Publisher E-mail: info@biomedcentral.com
Journal focusing on the management of and impediments to breastfeeding and also the effects of not breastfeeding. **Key Personnel:** Dr. Lisa Amir, Editor-in-Chief; Susan Donath, Dep. Ed.; James Akre, Editorial Board, akrej@yahoo.com. **ISSN:** 1746-4358. **URL:** http://www.internationalbreastfeedingjournal.com/.

54621 ■ International Business Lawyer
International Bar Association
1 Stephen St., 10th Fl.
London W1T 1AT, United Kingdom
Ph: 44 20 76916868
Fax: 44 20 76916544
Publication E-mail: editor@int-bar.org
Publisher E-mail: iba@int-bar.org
Law periodical. **Founded:** 1970. **Freq:** Bimonthly. **Print Method:** Offset litho. **Trim Size:** A4. **Key Personnel:** Paul Crick, Managing Editor. **ISSN:** 0309-7676. **Subscription Rates:** 275 individuals; US$495 individuals. **Remarks:** Accepts advertising. **URL:** http://www.ibanet.org. **Ad Rates:** BW: 1,200. **Circ:** 12,500

54622 ■ International Clinical Trials
Samedan Ltd.
16, Hampden Gurney St.
London W1H 5AL, United Kingdom
Ph: 44 20 77243456
Fax: 44 20 77242632
Publisher E-mail: info@samedanltd.com
Journal covering key topics pertinent to the clinical trials sector. **Freq:** Quarterly. **Key Personnel:** Dr. Graham Hughes, Editor. **Subscription Rates:** 125 individuals; US$230 other countries. **URL:** http://www.samedanltd.com/magazine/13.

54623 ■ International Communication Gazette
Sage Publications Ltd.
1 Oliver's Yard
55 City Rd.
London EC1Y 1SP, United Kingdom
Ph: 44 20 73248500
Fax: 44 20 73248600
Scholarly journal covering communication studies, including communication and international relations, communication and development and new information and communication technologies. **Founded:** 1939. **Freq:** 8/yr. **Key Personnel:** Cees J. Hamelink, Editor-in-Chief; Ester De Waal, Managing Editor; Ank Linden, Assoc. Ed.; Ed Hollander, Assoc. Ed.; Jean-Claude Burgelman, Editorial Advisory Board; Richard R. Cole, Editorial Advisory Board; Jan Wieten, Assoc. Ed.; Kwame S.T. Boafo, Editorial Advisory Board; Allerd Peeters, Assoc. Ed.; Leen d Haenens, Assoc. Ed. **ISSN:** 1748-0485. **Subscription Rates:** 707 institutions print & e-access; 778 institutions current volume print & all online content; 636 institutions e-access; 707 individuals e-access plus backfile (all online content); 3,244 institutions e-access (content through 1998); 693 institutions print only; 62 individuals print only; 95 institutions single print; 10 individuals single print. **Remarks:** Accepts advertising. **URL:** http://www.sagepub.co.uk/journalsProdDesc.nav?prodId=Journal200826. **Formerly:** Gazette. **Circ:** (Not Reported)

Circulation: ★ = ABC; △ = BPA; ♦ = CAC; • = CCAB; ❑ = VAC; ⊕ = PO Statement; ‡ = Publisher's Report; Boldface figures = sworn; Light figures = estimated.

54624 ■ International and Comparative Law Quarterly
British Institute of International & Comparative Law
Charles Clore House
17 Russell Sq.
London WC1B 5JP, United Kingdom
Ph: 44 2078 625151
Fax: 44 2078 625152
Publisher E-mail: contact@biicl.org
Law periodical. **Founded:** 1952. **Freq:** Quarterly. **Key Personnel:** Catherine Redgwell, Gen. Ed.; Robert Mc-Corquodale, Joint Gen. Ed. **ISSN:** 0020-5893. **Subscription Rates:** 197 nonmembers print & online; US$394 nonmembers print & online; Free to members. **URL:** http://www.biicl.org/; http://www.biicl.org/publications/iclq/.

54625 ■ The International Construction Law Review
Informa Publishing Group
Informa House
30-32 Mortimer St.
London W1W 7RE, United Kingdom
Ph: 44 20 70175000
Law periodical. **Freq:** Quarterly. **Key Personnel:** Humphrey Lloyd, Editor; David Wrightman, Editor. **ISSN:** 0265-1416. **Subscription Rates:** US$510 individuals rest of world; 200 individuals; 242 individuals bound volumes. **URL:** http://www2.warwick.ac.uk/fac/soc/law/elj/directory/i/iclr/.

54626 ■ International Custody & Fund Administration
Incisive Media Limited
Haymarket House
28-29 Haymarket
London SW1Y 4RX, United Kingdom
Ph: 44 870 2408859
Fax: 44 207 4849797
Publisher E-mail: customerservices@incisivemedia.com
Magazine focusing on financial services industry. **Freq:** Monthly. **Key Personnel:** Jonathan Greene, Publisher, phone 44 20 70342714, nicky.cooper@incisivemedia.com; Sophia Morrell, Editor, phone 44 20 70047535, sophia.morrell@incisivemedia.com. **Remarks:** Accepts advertising. **URL:** http://www.incisivemedia.com/corporate/products/icfamagazine; http://icfamagazine.com/. **Also known as:** ICFA. **Circ:** (Not Reported)

54627 ■ International Heat Treatment and Surface Engineering
Maney Publishing
1 Carlton House Ter.
London SW1Y 5AF, United Kingdom
Ph: 44 20 74517300
Fax: 44 20 74517307
Publisher E-mail: maney@maney.co.uk
Journal covering the understanding of existing and emerging heat treatment and surface engineering processes. **Subtitle:** Incorporating Heat Treatment of Metals. **Founded:** 2007. **Freq:** 4/yr. **Key Personnel:** Dr. Brian Birch, Editor; Prof. Shipu Chen, Editor, spchen@sjtu.edu.cn. **ISSN:** 1749-5148. **Subscription Rates:** 200 institutions, other countries; US$400 institutions; 155 members other countries; US$310 members. **Remarks:** Accepts advertising. **URL:** http://maney.co.uk/index.php/journals/iht/. **Circ:** (Not Reported)

54628 ■ International Investment
Incisive Media Limited
Haymarket House
28-29 Haymarket
London SW1Y 4RX, United Kingdom
Ph: 44 870 2408859
Fax: 44 207 4849797
Publisher E-mail: customerservices@incisivemedia.com
Magazine for financial professionals. **Freq:** Monthly. **Key Personnel:** Katrina Baugh, Editor, phone 44 20 74849783, katrina.baugh@incisivemedia.com. **Remarks:** Accepts advertising. **URL:** http://www.intinv.com. **Circ:** (Not Reported)

54629 ■ International Journal
Mensa International
15 The Ivories
6-8 Northampton St.
London N1 2HY, United Kingdom
Worldwide journal covering gifted people. **Freq:** 10/yr. **URL:** http://www.mensa.org/index0.php?page=11.

54630 ■ International Journal of Adipose Tissue
Greycoat Publishing Ltd.
148 Buckingham Palace Rd.
Kensington
London SW1W 9TR, United Kingdom
Ph: 44 20 77307995
Fax: 44 20 77303884
Publisher E-mail: mail@greycoatpublishing.co.uk
Journal covering the science and surgery of adipose tissue. **Freq:** Quarterly. **Key Personnel:** Guy Wallis, Editorial Dir., g.wallis@greycoatpublishng.co.uk; Ashley Wallis, Publishing Dir., a.wallis@greycoatpublishing.co.uk. **ISSN:** 1741-6582. **Remarks:** Accepts advertising. **URL:** http://www.greycoatpublishing.co.uk/content/Journals/IJAT.asp. **Circ:** (Not Reported)

54631 ■ International Journal of Advances in Rheumatology
Remedica Medical Education and Publishing
Commonwealth House
1 New Oxford St.
London WC1A 1NU, United Kingdom
Ph: 44 20 77592999
Fax: 44 20 77592951
Publication E-mail: info@advancesinrheumatology.com
Publisher E-mail: info@remedica.com
Journal publishing information on rheumatological medicine. **Key Personnel:** Steven B. Abramson, Editorial Advisory Board; Ferdinand C. Breedveld, Editor-in-Chief; Michael Weinblatt, Editor-in-Chief; Tom Huizinga, Editor; Maxime Dougados, Editorial Advisory Board; Paul Emery, Editorial Advisory Board; Hendrik Schulze-Koops, Editor; Eric Ruderman, Editorial Advisory Board; Gerd R. Burmester, Editorial Advisory Board; Daniel E. Furst, Editorial Advisory Board; Mark Genovese, Editorial Advisory Board; Carol M. Black, Editorial Advisory Board. **ISSN:** 1478-856X. **URL:** http://www.advancesinrheumatology.com.

54632 ■ International Journal of Advertising
WARC Ltd.
85 Newman St.
London W1T 3EX, United Kingdom
Ph: 44 20 74678100
Publisher E-mail: enquiries@warc.com
Journal covering advertising and marketing from both the academic and practitioner perspectives. **Freq:** 5/yr. **Key Personnel:** Prof. Douglas West, Editorial Advisory Board; T. Ambler, Editorial Advisory Board; Dr. Stephanie O'Donohoe, Book Review Ed.; Prof. S. Burgess, Editorial Advisory Board. **ISSN:** 0265-0487. **Subscription Rates:** 128 individuals; EUR256 institutions. **URL:** http://www.internationaljournalofadvertising.com/; http://store.warc.com/DisplaySection.aspx?Section=5&ProductID=30&TabID=1.

54633 ■ International Journal of Agricultural Sustainability
James and James/Earthscan
Dunstan House
14a St., Cross St.
London EC1N 8XA, United Kingdom
Ph: 44 20 78411930
Fax: 44 20 72421474
Publisher E-mail: earthinfo@earthscan.co.uk
Peer-reviewed journal covering study in the sustainability in agricultural and food systems. **Freq:** Quarterly. **Key Personnel:** Prof. Jules Pretty, Editor-in-Chief, jpretty@essex.ac.uk; Dr. Jacqueline Ashby, Assoc. Ed.; Prof. Michael M. Bell, Assoc. Ed. **ISSN:** 1473-5903. **Subscription Rates:** 195 institutions online and print; EUR255 institutions online and print (European Union); US$390 institutions online and print (Americas); 195 institutions online and print (Rest of World); 185 institutions online only, rest of the world; EUR240 institutions online; US$370 institutions online; 185 institutions online. **URL:** http://www.earthscan.co.uk/?tabid=503.

54634 ■ International Journal of Behavioral Nutrition and Physical Activity
BioMed Central Ltd.
236 Gray's Inn Rd., Fl. 6
34-42 Cleveland St.
London WC1X 8HL, United Kingdom
Ph: 44 20 31922000
Fax: 44 20 31922010
Publisher E-mail: info@biomedcentral.com
Journal that publishes articles on understanding the behavioral aspects of diet and physical activity. **Freq:** Irregular. **Key Personnel:** Dr. Simone A. French, Editorial Board; Prof. David Crawford, Editorial Board; Prof.

Robert Jeffery, Editor-in-Chief; Dr. Bente Wold, Editor-in-Chief; Dr. Elling Bere, Editorial Board; Dr. Stuart Biddle, Editorial Board. **ISSN:** 1479-5868. **Subscription Rates:** Free. **URL:** http://www.ijbnpa.org/.

54635 ■ International Journal of Biochemistry & Cell Biology
Elsevier Science Inc.
Centre for Respiratory Research
The Rayne Institute
University College London Medical School
5 University St.
London, United Kingdom
Publisher E-mail: usinfo-ehelp@elsevier.com
Peer-reviewed journal featuring research in the areas of contemporary biochemistry and cell biology. **Founded:** 1970. **Freq:** Monthly. **Print Method:** Offset. **Trim Size:** 5 1/2 x 8 1/2. **Cols./Page:** 1. **Col. Width:** 50 nonpareils. **Col. Depth:** 100 agate lines. **Key Personnel:** A. August, Editorial Board; D. Attaix, Editorial Board; S.G. Chen, Editorial Board; M. Gragunow, Editorial Board; H.R. Arias, Editorial Board; Lucia Altucci, Editor; S. Curry, Editorial Board; M. Bogoyevitch, Editorial Board; K.B. Adler, Editorial Board. **ISSN:** 1357-2725. **Subscription Rates:** US$4,481 institutions, other countries except Europe, Japan and Iran; EUR4,004 institutions for European countries and Iran; 531,700¥ institutions; 54,300¥ individuals; US$472 other countries except Europe, Japan and Iran; EUR352 individuals for European countries and Iran. **URL:** http://www.elsevier.com/wps/find/journaldescription.cws_home/395/descriptiondescription.

54636 ■ International Journal of Business Performance Management
Inderscience Enterprises Limited
c/o Prof. Jonathan Liu, Exec. Ed.
Regent's College
Regent's Business School
Inner Cir., Regent's Pk.
London NW1 4NS, United Kingdom
Journal covering both hard and soft perspectives in managing business performance, in both public and corporate organizations. **Freq:** 4/yr. **Key Personnel:** Prof. Jonathan Liu, Exec. Ed., liuj@regents.ac.uk. **ISSN:** 1368-4892. **Subscription Rates:** EUR494 individuals print or online; EUR672 individuals print and online. **URL:** http://www.inderscience.com/browse/index.php?journalID=3.

54637 ■ International Journal of Care Pathways
Royal Society of Medicine Press Ltd.
1 Wimpole St.
London W1G 0AE, United Kingdom
Ph: 44 20 72902921
Fax: 44 20 72902929
Publication E-mail: jicpproduction@rsm.ac.uk
Publisher E-mail: publishing@rsm.ac.uk
Peer-reviewed journal focusing on informatics, risk management and quality. **Freq:** Quarterly. **Key Personnel:** Massimiliano Panella, Editor; Kris Vanhaecht, Assoc. Ed. **ISSN:** 1473-2297. **Subscription Rates:** 225 institutions print only, UK & Europe; EUR307 institutions print only, Europe; US$446 institutions print only; 231 institutions, other countries print only; 109 individuals UK & Europe; EUR148 individuals Europe; US$222 individuals; 115 other countries. **URL:** http://ijcp.rsmjournals.com/. **Formerly:** Journal of Integrated Care Pathways.

54638 ■ International Journal of Cast Metals Research
Maney Publishing
1 Carlton House Ter.
London SW1Y 5AF, United Kingdom
Ph: 44 20 74517300
Fax: 44 20 74517307
Publisher E-mail: maney@maney.co.uk
Peer-reviewed journal reporting information on the science and engineering of cast metals, solidification and casting processes. **Freq:** Bimonthly. **Key Personnel:** Prof. D.M. Stefanescu, Editor, stefanescu.1@osu.edu; Prof. Hideyuki Yasuda, Editor, yasuda@ams.eng.osaka-u.ac.jp; Dr. N.R. Green, Editor, n.r.green@bham.ac.uk; Prof. D. Apelian, Editorial Board, dapelian@wpi.edu; Prof. C. Beckermann, Editorial Board, becker@engineering.uiowa.edu; Prof. J.T. Berry, Editorial Board, berry@me.msstate.edu; Prof. J. Campbell, Editorial Board, j.campbell.met@bham.ac.uk. **ISSN:** 1364-0461. **Subscription Rates:** 175 other countries; US$320 individuals; 360 institutions, other countries; US$581 institutions; 82 members other countries; US$150

members. **URL:** http://maney.co.uk/index.php/journals/ijc/.

54639 ■ International Journal of Clinical Rheumatology
Future Medicine Ltd.
Unitec House
2 Albert Pl.
London N3 1QB, United Kingdom
Ph: 44 20 83716080
Fax: 44 20 83432313
Publisher E-mail: info@futuremedicine.com
Peer-reviewed journal featuring articles on rheumatology. **Key Personnel:** Elisa Manzotti, Editorial Dir., e.manzotti@futuremedicine.com. **Subscription Rates:** 605 institutions; EUR755 institutions; US$1,160 institutions; 126¥ institutions. **Remarks:** Accepts advertising. **URL:** http://www.futuremedicine.com/loi/ijr. **Circ:** (Not Reported)

54640 ■ International Journal of Computer Mathematics
Taylor & Francis Group Journals
c/o George Loizou, Ed.-in-Ch.
School of Computer Science & Information System
Birkbeck Colorado
University of London
London WC1E 7HX, United Kingdom
Publisher E-mail: customerservice@taylorandfrancis.com
Peer-reviewed journal focusing on research and development in computer systems and the theory of programming languages, as well as mathematical techniques that are of interest to computer users in the fields of numerical analysis, mathematical software, discrete mathematics, computational geometry and graphics, image processing, pattern recognition, simulation and modelling; operations research and applied mathematics in general. **Freq:** 18/yr. **Key Personnel:** S. Grabowski, Editorial Review Board; J. Karhumaki, Editorial Review Board; A. Saito, Editorial Review Board; J. Pach, Editorial Review Board. **ISSN:** 0020-7160. **Subscription Rates:** US$7,284 individuals online only; US$8,094 individuals print & online; 6,237 institutions print & online; 5,613 institutions print & online; EUR6,447 institutions print & online; EUR5,803 institutions online. **URL:** http://www.tandf.co.uk/journals/journal.asp?issn=0020-7160& linktype=5.

54641 ■ International Journal of Cross Cultural Management
Sage Publications Ltd.
1 Oliver's Yard
55 City Rd.
London EC1Y 1SP, United Kingdom
Ph: 44 20 73248500
Fax: 44 20 73248600
Scholarly journal covering diversity management, organizational culture and international management issues. **Founded:** 2001. **Freq:** 3/yr. **Trim Size:** 190 x 137 mm. **Key Personnel:** Terence Jackson, Editor; Zeynep Aycan, Editor; Pawan Budhwar, Assoc. Ed. **ISSN:** 1470-5958. **Subscription Rates:** 301 institutions combined (print & e-access); 271 institutions e-access; 295 institutions print only; 45 individuals print only; 108 institutions single print; 20 individuals single print. **Remarks:** Accepts advertising. **URL:** http://www.sagepub.co.uk/journalsProdDesc.nav?prodId=Journal201498. **Ad Rates:** BW: 200. **Circ:** (Not Reported)

54642 ■ International Journal of Cultural Studies
Sage Publications Ltd.
1 Oliver's Yard
55 City Rd.
London EC1Y 1SP, United Kingdom
Ph: 44 20 73248500
Fax: 44 20 73248600
Scholarly, multidisciplinary journal covering culture and media worldwide. **Founded:** 1998. **Freq:** Bimonthly. **Key Personnel:** Graeme Turner, Assoc. Ed.; John Hartley, Editor; Jean Burgess, Reviews Ed.; William Uricchio, Assoc. Ed.; Sara Ahmed, Assoc. Ed.; Mizuko Ito, Assoc. Ed. **ISSN:** 1367-8779. **Subscription Rates:** US$1,038 individuals print & e-access; US$1,142 institutions print & all online; US$934 institutions e-access; US$1,038 institutions all online content; US$1,017 institutions print only; US$89 individuals print only; US$186 institutions single print; US$19 individuals single print; US$934 institutions content through 1998. **Remarks:** Accepts advertising. **URL:** http://www.sagepub.com/

journalsProdDesc.nav?prodId=Journal200946. **Circ:** (Not Reported)

54643 ■ International Journal of Damage Mechanics
Sage Publications Ltd.
1 Oliver's Yard
55 City Rd.
London EC1Y 1SP, United Kingdom
Ph: 44 20 73248500
Fax: 44 20 73248600
Peer-reviewed journal focusing on studies of the mechanics of fracture and damage in engineering materials and structures. **Founded:** Jan. 1992. **Freq:** 8/yr. **Trim Size:** 6 x 9. **Key Personnel:** Prof. J.L. Chaboche, Editor; Prof. Chi L. Chow, Editor; Prof. Yutaka Toi, Editor; Prof. J.W. Ju, Editor. **ISSN:** 1056-7895. **Subscription Rates:** 812 institutions print & e-access; 893 institutions print (all online content); 731 institutions e-access; 812 institutions all online content; 731 institutions backfile purchase, e-access; 796 institutions print only; 109 institutions single print. **Remarks:** Accepts advertising. **URL:** http://www.sagepub.co.uk/journalsProdDesc.nav?prodId=Journal201580. **Circ:** Controlled 160

54644 ■ International Journal of Economics and Accounting
Inderscience Enterprises Limited
c/o Prof. Charles Elad, Ed.
University of Westminster
Westminster Business School
35 Marylebone Rd.
London NW1 5LS, United Kingdom
Journal focusing on economics and accounting research. **Freq:** 4/yr. **Key Personnel:** Prof. Charles Elad, Editor, c.elad@westminster.ac.uk; Prof. Tony Tinker, Editor-in-Chief, anthony.tinker@baruch.cuny.edu. **ISSN:** 2041-868X. **Subscription Rates:** EUR494 individuals print or online; EUR672 individuals print and online. **URL:** http://www.inderscience.com/browse/index.php?journalID=357.

54645 ■ International Journal of Education through Art
Intellect
Russell Square House
10-12 Russell Sq.
London WC1B 5EE, United Kingdom
Ph: 44 20 73312000
Fax: 44 20 73312040
Publisher E-mail: info@intellectuk.org
Journal promoting relationships between art and education, providing a platform for those who wish to question and evaluate the ways in which art is produced, disseminated and interpreted across a diverse range of educational contexts. **Founded:** 2005. **Freq:** 3/yr. **Key Personnel:** Glen Coutss, Editor, editor1@insea.org; Teresa Eca, Editorial Asst., teresaeca@apecv.pt. **ISSN:** 1743-5234. **Subscription Rates:** 33 individuals print; 210 institutions print; 12 single issue print; 177 institutions online. **URL:** http://www.intellectbooks.co.uk/journals/view-Journal,id=121/.

54646 ■ International Journal of Electronic Democracy
Inderscience Enterprises Limited
c/o Konstantina N. Zefkili
University Colorado of London
London SW1V 1HU, United Kingdom
Journal covering the study of transformation in political systems by means of technology. **Freq:** 4/yr. **Key Personnel:** Konstantina N. Zefkili, Managing Editor, k.zefkili@ucl.ac.uk; Prof. Ernesto Damiani, Assoc. Ed. **ISSN:** 1742-4224. **Subscription Rates:** EUR494 individuals print or online; EUR672 individuals print and online. **URL:** http://www.inderscience.com/browse/index.php?journalID=120.

54647 ■ International Journal of Electronic Security and Digital Forensics
Inderscience Publishers
c/o Dr. Hamid Jahankhani, Ed.-in-Ch.
School of Computing Information Technology & Engineering
University Way
London E16 2RD, United Kingdom
Publisher E-mail: editor@inderscience.com
Peer-reviewed journal covering fields of electronic security and digital forensics. **Founded:** 2007. **Freq:** 4/yr. **Key Personnel:** Dr. Hamid Jahankhani, Editor-in-

Chief, hamid.jahankhani@uel.ac.uk; David Lilburn Watson, Assoc. Ed. **ISSN:** 1751-911X. **Subscription Rates:** EUR494 individuals includes surface mail, print only; EUR672 individuals print and online. **URL:** http://www.inderscience.com/browse/index.php?journalCODE=ijesdf.

54648 ■ International Journal for Equity in Health
BioMed Central Ltd.
236 Gray's Inn Rd., Fl. 6
34-42 Cleveland St.
London WC1X 8HL, United Kingdom
Ph: 44 20 31922000
Fax: 44 20 31922010
Publisher E-mail: info@biomedcentral.com
Online journal covering influences on and interventions and inequities in health. **Key Personnel:** Dr. Leiyu Shi, Dep. Ed.; Dr. Gerald Bloom, Section Ed.; Dr. Lars Borgquist, Section Ed.; Dr. Sally Guttmacher, Section Ed.; Prof. Barbara Starfield, Editor-in-Chief. **ISSN:** 1475-9276. **Remarks:** Accepts advertising. **URL:** http://www.equityhealthj.com/home/. **Circ:** (Not Reported)

54649 ■ International Journal of Health Geographics
BioMed Central Ltd.
236 Gray's Inn Rd., Fl. 6
34-42 Cleveland St.
London WC1X 8HL, United Kingdom
Ph: 44 20 31922000
Fax: 44 20 31922010
Publisher E-mail: info@biomedcentral.com
Online journal covering the application of geographic information systems and science in public health, healthcare, health services, and health resources. **Key Personnel:** Dr. Richard E. Hoskins, Editorial Board, richard.hoskins@doh.wa.gov; Dr. Maged N. Kamel Boulos, Editor-in-Chief, phone 44 175 2586530, mnkamelboulos@plymouth.ac.uk; Prof. Ewart R. Carson, Editorial Board, e.r.carson@city.ac.uk. **ISSN:** 1476-072X. **Remarks:** Accepts advertising. **URL:** http://www.ij-healthgeographics.com/home/. **Circ:** (Not Reported)

54650 ■ International Journal of Intensive Care
Greycoat Publishing Ltd.
148 Buckingham Palace Rd.
Kensington
London SW1W 9TR, United Kingdom
Ph: 44 20 77307995
Fax: 44 20 77303884
Publisher E-mail: mail@greycoatpublishing.co.uk
Journal covering emergency care and trauma medicine as well as all aspects of work in the intensive care unit. **Freq:** Quarterly March, June, September and December. **Trim Size:** 210 x 297 mm. **Key Personnel:** Dr. J. Denis Edwards, Editor; Guy Wallis, Editorial Dir., g.wallis@greycoatpublishing.co.uk. **ISSN:** 1350-2794. **Subscription Rates:** 50 individuals Europe; 65 other countries; 105 institutions Europe; 135 institutions, other countries. **Remarks:** Accepts advertising. **URL:** http://www.greycoatpublishing.co.uk/content/Journals/IJIC.asp. **Circ:** (Not Reported)

54651 ■ International Journal of Internet Technology & Secured Transactions
Inderscience Publishers
c/o Prof. Kazom Chaharbaghi, Assoc. Ed.
University of East London
Docklands Campus
University Way
London E16 2RD, United Kingdom
Publisher E-mail: editor@inderscience.com
Peer-reviewed journal covering information technology. **Founded:** 2007. **Freq:** 4/yr. **Key Personnel:** Dr. Charles A. Shoniregun, Editor-in-Chief, cshoniregun@infonomics-society.org; Prof. George A. Barnett, Assoc. Ed.; Prof. Elisa Bertino, Assoc. Ed.; Prof. Kazem Chaharbaghi, Assoc. Ed.; Prof. Panos K. Chrysanthis, Assoc. Ed.; Prof. Richard Connor, Assoc. Ed. **ISSN:** 1748-569X. **Subscription Rates:** EUR494 individuals print (includes surface mail); EUR672 individuals print and online. **URL:** http://www.inderscience.com/browse/index.php?journalCODE=ijitst.

54652 ■ International Journal of Islamic and Middle Eastern Finance and Management
Emerald Group Publishing Ltd.
c/o Dr. Kadom Shubber, Ed.
Westminster Business School
35 Marylebone Rd.

London NW1 5LS, United Kingdom
Publisher E-mail: emerald@emeraldinsight.com
Journal publishing research articles which provide in-depth insight and analysis into current issues within Islamic and Middle Eastern finance and management. **Freq:** Semiannual. **Key Personnel:** Dr. Kadom Shubber, Editor, kadom.shubber@btinternet.com; Kelly Dutton, Publisher, kdutton@emeraldinsight.com. **URL:** http://info.emeraldinsight.com/products/journals/journals.htm?id=imefm.

54653 ■ International Journal of Market Research
WARC Ltd.
85 Newman St.
London W1T 3EX, United Kingdom
Ph: 44 20 74678100
Publisher E-mail: enquiries@warc.com
Research journal. **Freq:** Bimonthly. **Key Personnel:** Peter Mouncey, Editor-in-Chief. **ISSN:** 0025-3618. **Subscription Rates:** 268 institutions academic; 102 members full (online); 134 members associate; 201 members affiliate. **Remarks:** Advertising not accepted. **URL:** http://www.ijmr.com/; http://store.warc.com. **Circ:** (Not Reported)

54654 ■ International Journal of Media and Cultural Politics
Intellect
Russell Square House
10-12 Russell Sq.
London WC1B 5EE, United Kingdom
Ph: 44 20 73312000
Fax: 44 20 73312040
Publisher E-mail: info@intellectuk.org
Journal committed to analyzing the politics of communications and cultural processes, addressing cultural politics in their local, international and global dimensions, recognizing equally the importance of issues defined by their specific cultural geography and those which run across cultures and nations. **Founded:** 2005. **Freq:** 3/yr. **Key Personnel:** Katharine Sarikakis, Editor, k.sarikakis@leeds.ac.uk; Neil Blain, Editor, klustyik@ithaca.edu. **ISSN:** 1740-8296. **Subscription Rates:** 33 individuals print; 225 institutions print; 12 single issue print; 192 institutions online. **URL:** http://www.intellectbooks.co.uk/journals/view-Journal,id=122/.

54655 ■ International Journal of Music Education
Sage Publications Ltd.
1 Oliver's Yard
55 City Rd.
London EC1Y 1SP, United Kingdom
Ph: 44 20 73248500
Fax: 44 20 73248600
Journal covering music education worldwide. Each issue has a special focus, including Research, Showcase and Practice. **Founded:** 1983. **Freq:** Quarterly. **Key Personnel:** Timothy Brophy, Co-Ed.; Christopher Johnson, Co-Ed.; Jane Cheung, Co-Ed. **ISSN:** 0255-7614. **Subscription Rates:** US$646 institutions print & e-access; US$711 institutions current volume print & all online content; US$581 institutions e-access; US$646 institutions all online content; US$790 institutions e-access (content through 1998); US$633 institutions print only; US$100 individuals print only; US$168 institutions single print; US$33 individuals single print. **Remarks:** Advertising accepted; rates available upon request. **URL:** http://www.sagepub.com/journalsProdDesc.nav?prodId=Journal201697. **Formerly:** Music Education International (2002). **Circ:** Paid ‡1,000

54656 ■ International Journal of Nursing Studies
Mosby Inc.
The Florence Nightingale School of Nursing & Midwifery
King's College London
James Clerk Maxwell Bldg.
57 Waterloo Rd.
London SE1 8WA, United Kingdom
Ph: 44 20 78483365
Fax: 44 20 78483069
Publication E-mail: ijns@kcl.ac.uk
Publisher E-mail: custserv.ehs@elsevier.com
Peer-reviewed journal featuring research findings and research-based reviews and analysis of interest to an international readership of nurses, midwives, educators, and researchers in all areas of nursing and caring

sciences. **Freq:** 12/yr. **Key Personnel:** Prof. Ian Norman, Editor-in-Chief, ijns@kcl.ac.uk; Prof. Mary Fitzgerald, Editor; Prof. Nancy Fugate Woods, Editor. **ISSN:** 0020-7489. **Subscription Rates:** US$215 other countries except Europe, Japan and Iran; 25,500¥ individuals; EUR195 individuals for European countries and Iran; EUR1,498 institutions for European countries and Iran; 188,600¥ institutions; US$1,676 institutions except Europe, Japan and Iran. **URL:** http://www.elsevier.com/wps/find/journaldescription.cws_home/266/descriptiondescription.

54657 ■ International Journal of Palliative Nursing
MA Healthcare Ltd.
St. Jude's Church
Dulwich Rd.
Herne Hill
London SE24 0PB, United Kingdom
Ph: 44 20 77385454
Fax: 44 20 77332325
Peer-reviewed journal covering palliative and hospice care for nurses. **Subtitle:** Promoting excellence across the palliative care team. **Founded:** 1995. **Freq:** 12/yr. **Key Personnel:** Laura Dean-Osgood, Editor; Robert Becker, Consultant Ed. **Subscription Rates:** 136 individuals Ireland; EUR223 individuals Europe; US$322 other countries personal; 104 students Ireland. **Remarks:** Accepts advertising. **URL:** http://www.ijpn.co.uk/. **Circ:** (Not Reported)

54658 ■ International Journal of Performance Arts and Digital Media
Intellect
Russell Square House
10-12 Russell Sq.
London WC1B 5EE, United Kingdom
Ph: 44 20 73312000
Fax: 44 20 73312040
Publisher E-mail: info@intellectuk.org
Journal acting as a forum to energize innovative and creative thinking and practice surrounding the combination of digital technologies with the performance arts (theatre, dance, music, live art). **Founded:** 2005. **Freq:** 3/yr. **Key Personnel:** David Collins, Editor, david.collins@don.ac.uk; Sita Popat, Assoc. Ed., s.popat@leeds.ac.uk; Steve Dixon, Assoc. Ed., steve.dixon@brunel.ac.uk; Philip Auslander, Editorial Board. **ISSN:** 1479-4713. **Subscription Rates:** 33 individuals print; 210 institutions print and online; 12 single issue print; 177 institutions online. **URL:** http://www.intellectbooks.co.uk/journals/view-Journal,id=120/.

54659 ■ International Journal of Respiratory Care
Greycoat Publishing Ltd.
148 Buckingham Palace Rd.
Kensington
London SW1W 9TR, United Kingdom
Ph: 44 20 77307995
Fax: 44 20 77303884
Publisher E-mail: mail@greycoatpublishing.co.uk
Journal for respiratory care physicians and sleep specialists. **Freq:** Semiannual. **Trim Size:** 210 x 297 mm. **Key Personnel:** Prof. Emiel Wouters, Editor; Guy Wallis, Editorial Dir., g.wallis@greycoatpublishing.co.uk. **ISSN:** 1747-1273. **Subscription Rates:** 25 individuals Europe; 30 other countries; 50 institutions Europe; 65 institutions, other countries. **Remarks:** Accepts advertising. **URL:** http://www.greycoatpublishing.co.uk/content/Journals/IJRC.asp. **Circ:** (Not Reported)

54660 ■ International Journal of Robotics Research
Sage Publications Ltd.
1 Oliver's Yard
55 City Rd.
London EC1Y 1SP, United Kingdom
Ph: 44 20 73248500
Fax: 44 20 73248600
Peer-reviewed journal containing original research papers and articles, perceptive reviews, and lively editorials on ground-breaking trends issues, technical developments, and theories in robotics by the outstanding scholars and practitioners in the field. **Founded:** 1982. **Freq:** 14/yr. **Print Method:** Offset. **Trim Size:** 8 1/2 x 11. **Cols./Page:** 2. **Col. Width:** 36 nonpareils. **Col. Depth:** 126 agate lines. **Key Personnel:** John M. Hollerbach, Editor; Peter Corke, Multimedia Ed.; Al Rizzi, Advisory Ed.; Paul M. Newman, Multimedia Ed.; Jennet Batten, Managing Editor; Nicholas Roy, Multimedia Ed.

ISSN: 0278-3649. **Subscription Rates:** US$1,917 institutions (print & e-access); US$2,109 institutions (current volume print & all online content); US$1,725 institutions e-access; US$1,917 institutions (all online content); US$2,493 institutions (content through 1998); US$1,879 institutions print only; US$204 individuals print only; US$148 institutions single print; US$19 individuals single print. **Remarks:** Accepts advertising. **URL:** http://www.sagepub.com/journalsProdDesc.nav?prodId=Journal201324. **Ad Rates:** GLR: 1.33, BW: 800. **Circ:** (Not Reported)

54661 ■ International Journal of Rock Mechanics and Mining Sciences
Elsevier Science Inc.
c/o R.W. Zimmerman, Ed.-in-Ch.
Dept. of Earth Science & Engineering
Imperial College
London SW7 2AZ, United Kingdom
Fax: 44 20 75947412
Publisher E-mail: usinfo-ehelp@elsevier.com
Journal covers original research, new developments, site measurements, case studies in rock mechanics and engineering. **Founded:** 1964. **Freq:** 8/yr. **Key Personnel:** R.W. Zimmerman, Editor-in-Chief, r.w.zimmerman@imperial.ac.uk; J.A. Hudson, Ed. Emeritus; E.T. Brown, Editorial Board; Xia-ting Feng, Editorial Board; C. Fairhurst, Editorial Board; A.K. Dhawan, Editorial Board; N. Barton, Editorial Board; C. Carranza-Torres, Editorial Board; B. Amadei, Editorial Board; B.H.G. Brady, Editorial Board. **ISSN:** 1365-1609. **Subscription Rates:** US$374 other countries except Europe, Japan and Iran; EUR333 individuals for European countries and Iran; 44,000¥ individuals for European countries and Iran; EUR3,144 institutions for European countries and Iran; US$3,515 institutions, other countries except Europe, Japan and Iran; 417,700¥ institutions. **URL:** http://www.elsevier.com/wps/find/journaldescription.cws_home/256/descriptiondescription.

54662 ■ International Journal of Speech, Language and the Law
Equinox Publishing Ltd.
1 Chelsea Manor Studios
Flood St.
London SW3 5SR, United Kingdom
Ph: 44 20·78233748
Fax: 44 20 78233748
Journal covering aspect of forensic language, speech and audio analysis. **Freq:** 2/yr (June and December). **Key Personnel:** Ronald R. Butters, Editorial Board, ronbutters@aol.com; Diana Eades, Editor, diana.eades@une.edu.au; Michael Jessen, Editor, michael.jessen@bka.bund.de; Peter French, Editor, jpf@jpfrench.com; Chris Heffer, Book Review Ed., hefferc2@cardiff.ac.uk. **ISSN:** 1748-8885. **Subscription Rates:** 150 institutions, other countries print and online; US$300 institutions print and online; 45 individuals print; US$90 individuals print; 33.75 students print; US$67.50 students print. **Remarks:** Accepts advertising. **URL:** http://www.equinoxjournals.com/ojs/index.php/IJSLL. **Circ:** (Not Reported)

54663 ■ International Journal of STD and AIDS
Royal Society of Medicine
1 Wimpole St.
London W1G 0AE, United Kingdom
Ph: 44 20 72902900
Fax: 44 20 72902989
Publication covering sexually transmitted diseases and aids. **Freq:** Monthly. **Key Personnel:** W.W. Dinsmore, Founding Ed., ijsaproduction@rsm.ac.uk; J.R.W. Harris, Founding Dep. Ed.; M.A. Waugh, Founding Dep. Ed.; J.S. Bingham, Asst. Ed.; S. Barton, Asst. Ed. **Subscription Rates:** 455 institutions U.K. and Europe; EUR619 institutions Europe; US$887 institutions America; 461 institutions other countries; 245 individuals U.K. and Europe; EUR333 individuals Europe; US$483 individuals America; US$251 other countries; 410 individuals online only; US$798 individuals online only. **Remarks:** Accepts advertising. **URL:** http://ijsa.rsmjournals.com/. **Circ:** (Not Reported)

54664 ■ International Journal of Technology Management & Sustainable Development
Intellect
Russell Square House
10-12 Russell Sq.
London WC1B 5EE, United Kingdom
Ph: 44 20 73312000
Fax: 44 20 73312040

Publisher E-mail: info@intellectuk.org

Journal dedicated to publishing high quality, original and research-based papers addressing policy issues arising from the relationship between technology and development, responding to the growing awareness of the need to understand sustainable development in terms of its underlying dynamics. **Founded:** 2002. **Freq:** 3/yr. **Key Personnel:** Mohammed Saad, Editor, mohammed.saad@uwe.ac.uk; Ajit S. Bhalla, Editorial Board; Kathryn Stokes, Reviews Ed.; John Bessant, Editorial Board; Girma Zawdie, Editor, g.zawdie@strath.ac.uk; Norman G. Clark, Assoc. Ed. **ISSN:** 1474-2748. **Subscription Rates:** 33 individuals print; 210 institutions print and online; 12 single issue print; 177 institutions online. **URL:** http://www.intellectbooks.co.uk/journals/view-Journal,id=133/.

54665 ■ International Journal of Therapy and Rehabilitation (IJTR)
MA Healthcare Ltd.
MA Healthcare Ltd.
St. Jude Church
Dulwich Rd.
London SE24 0PB, United Kingdom
Ph: 44 20 77385454
Peer-reviewed journal reporting issues related to pathology, education section covers many of the issues relevant to undergraduate and postgraduate education and continuing professional development. **Founded:** 1994. **Freq:** Monthly. **Key Personnel:** Joanna Bakewell, Consultant Ed.; Olivia Wood, Editor; Dr. Alison Rushton, Editor-in-Chief. **Subscription Rates:** 125 individuals paper; EUR211 individuals paper; US$312 individuals for personal (paper); 106 students paper; 157 individuals online and paper; EUR246 individuals online and paper; US$381 other countries; 123 students online and paper; EUR199 students online and paper; US$312 students online and paper. **Remarks:** Advertising accepted; rates available upon request. **URL:** http://www.ijtr.co.uk/. **Formerly:** British Journal of Therapy and Rehabilitation (BJTR). **Circ:** (Not Reported)

54666 ■ International Piano
Rhinegold Publishing
241 Shaftesbury Ave.
London WC2H 8TF, United Kingdom
Ph: 44 20 73331720
Fax: 44 20 73331765
Publication E-mail: internationalpiano@rhinegold.co.uk
Publisher E-mail: sales@rhinegold.co.uk
Professional magazine for professional and avid amateur pianists. **Founded:** 1993. **Freq:** Bimonthly. **Key Personnel:** Chloe Cutts, Editor. **Subscription Rates:** 33 individuals; 59 two years. **Remarks:** Accepts advertising. **URL:** http://www.rhinegold.co.uk/magazines/piano/default.asp?css=1. **Formerly:** Piano. **Circ:** Controlled ‡8,000

54667 ■ The International Political Science Review/Revue internationale de science politique
Sage Publications Ltd.
1 Oliver's Yard
55 City Rd.
London EC1Y 1SP, United Kingdom
Ph: 44 20 73248500
Fax: 44 20 73248600
Peer-reviewed journal covering research in political science. **Subtitle:** The Journal of the International Political Science Association IPSA. **Founded:** 1980. **Freq:** 5/yr. **Key Personnel:** Yvonne Galligan, Editor; Mark Kesselman, Editor. **ISSN:** 0192-5121. **Subscription Rates:** 349 institutions print & e-access; 384 institutions current volume print & all online content; 314 institutions e-access; 349 institutions all online content; 507 institutions content through 1998; 342 institutions print only; 62 individuals print; US$75 institutions single issue, print; US$16 single issue print. **Remarks:** Accepts advertising. **URL:** http://www.sagepub.co.uk/journalsProdDesc.nav?prodId=Journal200844&. **Circ:** (Not Reported)

54668 ■ International Review of Administrative Sciences
Sage Publications Ltd.
1 Oliver's Yard
55 City Rd.
London EC1Y 1SP, United Kingdom
Ph: 44 20 73248500
Fax: 44 20 73248600
Peer-reviewed journal covering comparative studies and

monographs on international administration, national civil services, government, administrative reform, public finance and related issues. **Subtitle:** An International Journal of Comparative Public Administration. **Founded:** 1935. **Freq:** Quarterly. **Key Personnel:** Isabella Proeller, Deputy Ed.; Kenneth Kernaghan, Editorial Committee; Christopher Pollitt, Editor. **ISSN:** 0020-8523. **Subscription Rates:** 66 individuals print only; 571 institutions print only; 525 institutions e-access only; 583 institutions print & e-access; 21 individuals single print; 157 institutions single print. **Remarks:** Accepts advertising. **URL:** http://www.sagepub.co.uk/journalsProdDesc.nav?prodId=Journal200833. **Circ:** (Not Reported)

54669 ■ International Review for the Sociology of Sport
Sage Publications Ltd.
1 Oliver's Yard
55 City Rd.
London EC1Y 1SP, United Kingdom
Ph: 44 20 73248500
Fax: 44 20 73248600
Peer-reviewed journal covering research on sport for the academic community worldwide. **Founded:** 1966. **Freq:** Quarterly. **Key Personnel:** Fabien Ohl, Corresponding Ed.; John Sugden, Editor; David L. Andrews, Corresponding Coord. **ISSN:** 1012-6902. **Subscription Rates:** US$813 institutions print & e-access; US$898 institutions plus backfile (current volume print & all online); US$734 institutions e-access; US$813 institutions e-access plus backfile (all online content); US$2,059 institutions e-access (content through 1998); US$800 institutions print only; US$220 institutions single print. **Remarks:** Accepts advertising. **URL:** http://www.sagepub.com/journalsProdDesc.nav?prodId=Journal200937. **Circ:** (Not Reported)

54670 ■ International Securities Finance
Euromoney Publications PLC
Nestor House
Playhouse Yard
London EC4V 5EX, United Kingdom
Ph: 44 20 77798888
Publication E-mail: hotline@euromoneyplc.com
Publisher E-mail: information@euromoneyplc.com
Professional journal covering international securities. **Subtitle:** The Journal of International Securities Financing. **Founded:** 1991. **Freq:** Quarterly. **Print Method:** Litho. **Trim Size:** 205 x 270 mm. **Key Personnel:** Craig MacDonald, Editor, phone 44 20 77798990, cmacdonald@euromoneyplc.com; Jonathan Hodder, Publisher, phone 44 20 77798216, jhodder@euromoneyplc.com. **Subscription Rates:** 360 individuals. **Remarks:** Accepts advertising. **URL:** http://www.euromoneyplc.com/. **Former name:** International Securities Lending. **Circ:** (Not Reported)

54671 ■ International Seminars in Surgical Oncology
BioMed Central Ltd.
236 Gray's Inn Rd., Fl. 6
34-42 Cleveland St.
London WC1X 8HL, United Kingdom
Ph: 44 20 31922000
Fax: 44 20 31922010
Publisher E-mail: info@biomedcentral.com
Online journal covering all aspects of surgical cancer care. **Key Personnel:** Prof. Mohamad Hussein, Editor-in-Chief; Gurpreet Singh-Ranger, Editor-in-Chief; Prof. Kefah Mokbel, Assoc. Ed.; Isador H. Lieberman, Section Ed.; Kwee Yong, Section Ed.; Andrew Jewell, Research Ed. **ISSN:** 1477-7800. **Remarks:** Accepts advertising. **URL:** http://www.issoonline.com/. **Circ:** (Not Reported)

54672 ■ International Social Work
Sage Publications Ltd.
1 Oliver's Yard
55 City Rd.
London EC1Y 1SP, United Kingdom
Ph: 44 20 73248500
Fax: 44 20 73248600
Scholarly journal covering social development, social welfare and human services. **Subtitle:** Exploring and Promoting Comparative and International Social Work in A Global Age. **Founded:** 1959. **Freq:** Bimonthly. **Key Personnel:** Dr. Karen H. Lyons, Editorial Board; Prof. Simon Hackett, Editor; Silvia Fargion, Book Review Ed. **ISSN:** 0020-8728. **Subscription Rates:** US$1,201 individuals print & e-access; US$1,321 institutions print

& all online; US$1,081 institutions e-access; US$1,201 institutions e-access (all online content); US$1,131 institutions print only; US$113 individuals print only; US$216 institutions single print only; US$24 individuals single print; US$3,767 institutions content through 1998. **Remarks:** Accepts advertising. **URL:** http://www.sagepub.com/journalsProdDesc.nav?prodId=Journal200781. **Ad Rates:** BW: 250. **Circ:** (Not Reported)

54673 ■ International Sociology
Sage Publications Ltd.
1 Oliver's Yard
55 City Rd.
London EC1Y 1SP, United Kingdom
Ph: 44 20 73248500
Fax: 44 20 73248600
Peer-reviewed journal covering the theory, method, and new directions in research in sociology worldwide. **Subtitle:** The Journal of the International Sociological Association. **Founded:** 1986. **Freq:** 6/yr. **Trim Size:** 175 x 113 mm. **Key Personnel:** Margaret Archer, Assoc. Ed.; Christine Inglis, Editor; Daniel Bertaux, Assoc. Ed.; Fabrizio Bernardi, Editorial Board. **ISSN:** 0268-5809. **Subscription Rates:** 515 individuals print & e-access; 567 institutions print & all online; 464 institutions e-access; 516 institutions e-access (all online content); 513 institutions e-access (content through 1998); 505 institutions print only; 56 individuals print only; 93 institutions single print; 12 individuals single print. **Remarks:** Accepts advertising. **URL:** http://www.sagepub.co.uk/journalsProdDesc.nav?prodId=Journal200944. **Ad Rates:** BW: 250. **Circ:** (Not Reported)

54674 ■ International Tax Review
Euromoney Publications PLC
Nestor House
Playhouse Yard
London EC4V 5EX, United Kingdom
Ph: 44 20 77798888
Publisher E-mail: information@euromoneyplc.com
Business publication. **Freq:** 10/yr. **Key Personnel:** Ralph Cunningham, Managing Editor; Joao Fernandes, Production Ed. **ISSN:** 0958-7594. **Subscription Rates:** 675 individuals; US$1,320 individuals; EUR900 individuals. **URL:** http://www.euromoneyplc.com; http://www.internationaltaxreview.com/.

54675 ■ International Wood Products Journal
Maney Publishing
1 Carlton House Ter.
London SW1Y 5AF, United Kingdom
Ph: 44 20 74517300
Fax: 44 20 74517307
Publisher E-mail: maney@maney.co.uk
Peer-reviewed journal covering wood processing and applications. **Freq:** Semiannual. **Key Personnel:** Gervais Sawyer, Editor, gervais.sawyer@blueyonder.co.uk. **ISSN:** 2042-6445. **Subscription Rates:** 136 institutions, other countries; US$220 institutions; 128 institutions, other countries online only; US$207 institutions online only. **Remarks:** Accepts advertising. **URL:** http://maney.co.uk/index.php/journals/iwp. **Circ:** (Not Reported)

54676 ■ Interreligious Insight
World Congress of Faiths
Congres Mondial des Religions
London Inter Faith Centre
125 Salusbury Rd.
London NW6 6RG, United Kingdom
Publication E-mail: information@interreligiousinsight.org
Publisher E-mail: enquires@worldfaith.org
Ecumenical publication. **Freq:** Quarterly. **Key Personnel:** Dr. K.L. Seshagiri Rao, Editor, srao@eh.sc.edu; Rev. Alan Race, Editor-in-Chief, alan.race@ntlworld.com; Jim Kenney, Editor, jim@seachanges.net; Ron Miller, Review Ed.; Elizabeth Harris, Review Ed. **ISSN:** 0968-7718. **Subscription Rates:** 24 individuals; 40 institutions; US$60 institutions; US$35 individuals; US$22 individuals developing countries; 15 individuals developing countries; US$45 institutions developing countries; 30 institutions developing countries. **Remarks:** Advertising accepted; rates available upon request. **URL:** http://www.worldfaiths.org/; http://www.interreligiousinsight.org/. **Former name:** World Faiths Encounter. **Circ:** 800

54677 ■ Inverse Problems
Institute of Physics

76 Portland Pl.
London W1B 1NT, United Kingdom
Ph: 44 20 74704800
Fax: 44 20 74704848
Publication E-mail: ip@iop.org
Publisher E-mail: physics@iop.org
Professional publication covering physics. **Founded:** 1985. **Freq:** Bimonthly. **Key Personnel:** A.K Louis, Editor-in-Chief. **ISSN:** 0266-5611. **Subscription Rates:** US$2,200 institutions North, Central and South America; 1,109 institutions European Union. **URL:** http://www.iop.org/ej/journal/0266-5611.

54678 ■ Investment & Pensions Europe (IPE)
IPE International Publishers Ltd.
320 Great Guildford House
30 Great Guildford St.
London SE1 0HS, United Kingdom
Ph: 44 20 72610666
Publisher E-mail: info@ipe.com
Journal dealing with pension funds in Europe and European institutional investor marketplace. **Founded:** Feb. 1997. **Freq:** Monthly. **Key Personnel:** Liam Kennedy, Editor, liam.kennedy@ipe.com; Eric Davis, Advertisement Dir., phone 44 20 72614607, eric.davis@ipe.com. **Remarks:** Accepts advertising. **URL:** http://www.ipe.com/products/magazine.php. **Ad Rates:** BW: 12,200. **Circ:** (Not Reported)

54679 ■ Investment Week
Incisive Media Limited
Haymarket House
28-29 Haymarket
London SW1Y 4RX, United Kingdom
Ph: 44 870 2408859
Fax: 44 207 4849797
Publisher E-mail: customerservices@incisivemedia.com
Newspaper covering aspects of the investment industry. **Subtitle:** The premier publication for the investment industry. **Freq:** Weekly. **Key Personnel:** Helen Varnava, Audience Development Mgr., helen.varnava@incisivemedia.com; Hysni Kaso, Investment News Ed., hysni.kaso@incisivemedia.com; Lawrence Gosling, Editorial Dir., lawrence.gosling@incisivemedia.com. **URL:** http://www.investmentweek.co.uk/.

54680 ■ Investors Chronicle
Financial Times Business Ltd.
One Southwark Bridge
London SE1 9HL, United Kingdom
Ph: 44 20 77756653
Fax: 44 20 77756413
Publication E-mail: ic.editor@ft.com
Publisher E-mail: finance.event@ft.com
Magazine presenting analysis and tips for UK stockmarket investors. **Founded:** 1860. **Freq:** Daily. **ISSN:** 0261-3115. **Subscription Rates:** EUR12.50 individuals monthly; EUR35 individuals quarterly; EUR115 individuals annually. **Remarks:** Accepts advertising. **URL:** http://www.investorschronicle.co.uk. **Circ:** (Not Reported)

54681 ■ IQ Magazine
Informed Publishing Ltd.
2nd Fl. Asia House
31-33 Lime St.
London EC3M 7HT, United Kingdom
Ph: 44 20 73970618
Publisher E-mail: info@insuranceinsider.com
Magazine targeted towards the senior decision makers and opinion formers within the global insurance and re-insurance industry. **Freq:** Quarterly. **Key Personnel:** Peter Hastie, Publisher/Ed., phone 44 207 3970615, peter@insuranceinsider.com; David Bull, Editor, david@insuranceinsider.com; Mark Geoghegan, Editor, mark@insuranceinsider.com. **URL:** http://www.insiderquarterly.com/insider_quarterly.html.

54682 ■ Irish Democrat
Connolly Publications Ltd.
244 Gray's Inn Rd.
London WC1X 8JR, United Kingdom
Consumer journal covering political issues in Ireland. **Founded:** 1939. **Freq:** Bimonthly. **Cols./Page:** 5. **Col. Width:** 55 millimeters. **Col. Depth:** 375 millimeters. **Key Personnel:** David Granville, On-line Ed.; Peter Mulligan, Editorial Board; Moya St Leger, Editorial Board. **ISSN:** 0021-1125. **Subscription Rates:** 7 individuals U.K.; 11 individuals airmail; Europe and republic of Ireland; 16 U.S. and Canada airmail; 17 individuals airmail; Australia and New Zealand. **Remarks:** Accepts

advertising. **URL:** http://www.irishdemocrat.co.uk/. **Circ:** Combined 2,100

54683 ■ Ironmaking & Steelmaking
Maney Publishing
1 Carlton House Ter.
London SW1Y 5AF, United Kingdom
Ph: 44 20 74517300
Fax: 44 20 74517307
Publisher E-mail: maney@maney.co.uk
Journal covering all aspects of iron and steel industry, published in connection with Institute of Materials, Minerals and Mining. **Subtitle:** Process, Products and Applications. **Freq:** 8/yr. **Trim Size:** 188 x 266 mm. **Key Personnel:** Dr. David J. Price, Exec. Ed., david.price123@btinternet.com; Dr. A. Chatterjee, Editorial Board, bob.alderdice@corusgroup.com; Dr. Peter C. Morgan, Chm. of the Editorial Board, petercmorgan@btinternet.com. **ISSN:** 0301-9233. **Subscription Rates:** 776 institutions, other countries; US$1,380 institutions; 287 members other countries; US$511 members. **Remarks:** Accepts advertising. **URL:** http://maney.co.uk/index.php/journals/irs/. **Ad Rates:** BW: 1,000, 4C: 1,600. **Circ:** (Not Reported)

54684 ■ Islington Gazette (EC1 Edition)
Archant Life
100A Ave., Rd.
London NW3 3HF, United Kingdom
Ph: 44 20 74336240
Publisher E-mail: johnny.hustler@archant.co.uk
Newspaper featuring news, sports, film and theatre reviews. **Founded:** Sept. 20, 1856. **Freq:** Weekly (Thurs.). **Key Personnel:** Keith Archer, Dep. Ed.; Tony Allcock, Editor, tony.allcock@archant.co.uk; Rob Bleaney, Asst. Ed., News Ed. **Subscription Rates:** 114.40 individuals. **Remarks:** Accepts advertising. **URL:** http://www.islingtongazette.co.uk/home. **Circ:** (Not Reported)

54685 ■ The Italianist
Maney Publishing
1 Carlton House Ter.
London SW1Y 5AF, United Kingdom
Ph: 44 20 74517300
Fax: 44 20 74517307
Publisher E-mail: maney@maney.co.uk
Journal covering all areas of Italian Studies. **Founded:** 1981. **Freq:** 3/yr. **Key Personnel:** Claire E. Honess, Editor, c.e.honess@leeds.ac.uk; Adam Ledgeway, Co-Ed., anl21@cam.ac.uk; Lisa Sampson, Co-Ed., l.m.sampson@reading.ac.uk; Shirley W. Vinall, Advisory Board, s.w.vinall@reading.ac.uk. **ISSN:** 0261-4340. **Subscription Rates:** 198 institutions, other countries; US$358 institutions; 48 other countries; US$94 individuals. **Remarks:** Accepts advertising. **URL:** http://maney.co.uk/index.php/journals/ita/. **Ad Rates:** BW: 180. **Circ:** (Not Reported)

54686 ■ ITF World
International Tennis Federation
Federation Internationale de Tennis
Bank Ln.
Roehampton
London SW15 5X2, United Kingdom
Ph: 44 20 88786464
Fax: 44 20 88787799
Magazine covering tennis. **Founded:** 1998. **Freq:** Quarterly. **Remarks:** Advertising accepted; rates available upon request. **URL:** http://www.itftennis.com. **Circ:** 7,000

54687 ■ Jackie Chan Adventures
Eaglemoss Publications Ltd.
1st Fl., Beaumont House
Kensington Village
Avonmore Rd.
London W14 8TS, United Kingdom
Ph: 44 20 76051200
Fax: 44 20 76051201
Collection magazine based on the TV show Jackie Chan Adventures. **Freq:** 8/yr. **Key Personnel:** Maggie Calmels, Editorial Dir.; Andrew Jarvis, Ch. Exec. **Subscription Rates:** 1.99 single issue. **URL:** http://www.eaglemoss.co.uk/curr-titles/jac-cha.htm.

54688 ■ Jazz Research Journal
Equinox Publishing Ltd.
1 Chelsea Manor Studios
Flood St.

London SW3 5SR, United Kingdom
Ph: 44 20 78233748
Fax: 44 20 78233748
Journal covering cultural and critical views on jazz. **Freq:** Semiannual. **Key Personnel:** Catherine Tackley, Editor, c.tackley@open.ac.uk; Tony Whyton, Editor, t.whyton@salford.ac.uk. **ISSN:** 1753-8637. **Subscription Rates:** 95 institutions, other countries print and online; US$190 institutions print and online; 45 individuals print; US$90 individuals print. **Remarks:** Accepts advertising. **URL:** http://www.equinoxjournals.com/ojs/index.php/JAZZ. **Circ:** (Not Reported)

54689 ■ Jazz UK
Jazz Newspapers Ltd.
1st Fl., 132 Southwark St.
Castle Arcade
London SE1 0SW, United Kingdom
Ph: 44 20 79289089
Fax: 44 20 74016870
Publication E-mail: jazzuk.cardiff@virgin.net
Publisher E-mail: info@jazzservices.org.uk
Magazine covering jazz. **Founded:** Jan. 1995. **Freq:** Bimonthly. **Print Method:** Web. **Trim Size:** 210 x 297 mm. **Cols./Page:** 4. **Key Personnel:** Chris Hodgkins, Director. **Subscription Rates:** 15 individuals; 25 two years. **Remarks:** Accepts advertising. **URL:** http://www.jazzservices.org.uk. **Ad Rates:** BW: 995, 4C: 1,450. **Circ:** Combined 30,000

54690 ■ Jazzwise Magazine
Jazzwise Publications Ltd.
2(b) Gleneagle Mews
London SW16 6AE, United Kingdom
Ph: 44 20 87697725
Fax: 44 20 86777128
Magazine covering information about Jazz. **Freq:** 11/yr. **Key Personnel:** Jon Newey, Editor and Publisher; Ros McRae, Advertising Mgr.; Stephen Graham, Co-Ed. **Subscription Rates:** 41 individuals; 55 individuals Europe; 62 other countries. **URL:** http://www.jazzwisemagazine.com/.

54691 ■ Jewish Quarterly
Jewish Literary Trust Ltd.
Haskell House
152 West End Ln.
London NW6 1SD, United Kingdom
Publication E-mail: admin@jewishquarterly.org
Publisher E-mail: editorial@jewishquarterly.org
Magazine featuring the Jewish contemporary writing, politics and culture. **Freq:** Quarterly. **Key Personnel:** Liz Oppedijk, Advertising. **Subscription Rates:** 25 individuals; 35 individuals Europe; 45 other countries. **URL:** http://www.jewishquarterly.org/index.asp.

54692 ■ Jewish Renaissance
Renaissance Publishing Ltd.
PO Box 28849
London SW13 0WA, United Kingdom
Ph: 44 20 88761891
Publication E-mail: editor@jewishrenaissance.org.uk
Publisher E-mail: advertising@jewishrenaissance.org.uk
Magazine featuring the Jewish culture. **Freq:** Quarterly. **Key Personnel:** Janet Levin, Editor. **Subscription Rates:** 19 individuals; 23 individuals Europe; 28 other countries. **URL:** http://www.jewishrenaissance.org.uk/.

54693 ■ The Journal
Chartered Institute of Journalists
2 Dock Offices
Surrey Quays Rd.
London SE16 2XU, United Kingdom
Ph: 44 20 72521187
Fax: 44 20 72322302
Publisher E-mail: memberservices@cioj.co.uk
Trade journal covering journalism for members and senior media personnel. **Founded:** 1912. **Freq:** Quarterly. **Key Personnel:** John Thorpe, President, president@cioj.co.uk; Macer Hall, Vice President; Andy Smith, Editor, editor@cioj.co.uk. **Subscription Rates:** 195 members; 133 other countries; 133 individuals affiliate; 98 individuals first year. **Remarks:** Advertising accepted; rates available upon request. **URL:** http://www.cioj.co.uk/the_journal.html. **Circ:** Controlled 2,000

54694 ■ Journal
Amateur Yacht Research Society
BCM, AYRS
London WC1N 3XX, United Kingdom

Ph: 44 1727 862268
Fax: 44 1727 862268
Publisher E-mail: office@ayrs.org
Journal covering boating. **Freq:** Quarterly. **ISSN:** 1469-6754. **Subscription Rates:** 4 nonmembers Nos. 1-17; 3.50 members; 5 nonmembers Nos. 18; 4.50 members. **URL:** http://www.ayrs.org. **Circ:** 800

54695 ■ The Journal
Chartered Insurance Institute
42-48 High Rd.
S Woodford
London E18 2JP, United Kingdom
Ph: 44 20 89898464
Fax: 44 20 85303052
Publisher E-mail: customer.serv@cii.co.uk
Publication covering insurance and financial services. **Freq:** Bimonthly. **Trim Size:** 210 x 297 mm. **Subscription Rates:** Free. **URL:** http://www.cii.co.uk/pages/membership/benefits/journal_info.aspx; http://www.cii.co.uk/cii/research/publications.aspx. **Formerly:** Journal of Insurance Practice; Society of Fellows Journal. **Ad Rates:** BW: 5,250. **Circ:** Non-paid 61,212

54696 ■ Journal of Adult Theological Education
Equinox Publishing Ltd.
1 Chelsea Manor Studios
Flood St.
London SW3 5SR, United Kingdom
Ph: 44 20 78233748
Fax: 44 20 78233748
Peer-reviewed journal covering adult theological education. **Subtitle:** Network of Adult Theological Educators. **Freq:** Semiannual. **Key Personnel:** Alison Le Cornu, Editor, alison.lecornu@ntlworld.com. **ISSN:** 1740-7141. **Subscription Rates:** 95 institutions, other countries print and online; US$190 institutions print and online; 40 individuals print; US$80 individuals print; 30 students print; US$60 students print; 40 institutions; 30 individuals developing countries. **Remarks:** Accepts advertising. **URL:** http://www.equinoxjournals.com/ojs/index.php/JATE. **Circ:** (Not Reported)

54697 ■ Journal of Animal Ecology
British Ecological Society
Charles Darwin House
12 Roger St.
Earley Gate
London WC1N 2JU, United Kingdom
Publisher E-mail: info@britishecologicalsociety.org
Publication covering animal ecology. **Freq:** Bimonthly. **Key Personnel:** Jenny Guthrie, Managing Editor; Graeme Hays, Editor; Ken Norris, Editor, k.norris@reading.ac.uk; Mike Boots, Editor. **ISSN:** 0021-8790. **Subscription Rates:** US$1,375 institutions print only or online only; 744 institutions print only or online only; EUR945 institutions print only or online only; Europe; US$1,603 institutions print only or online only; rest of world; 856 institutions print and online; US$1,582 institutions print and online; EUR1,087 institutions print and online; US$1,844 institutions print & online; rest of world. **URL:** http://www.britishecologicalsociety.org.

54698 ■ Journal of Applied Ecology
British Ecological Society
26 Blades Ct.
Putney
London SW16 2NU, United Kingdom
Ph: 44 20 88719797
Fax: 44 20 88719779
Publisher E-mail: info@britishecologicalsociety.org
Journal covering ecology. **Freq:** Bimonthly. **Key Personnel:** Prof. E.J. Milner-Gulland, Editor; Dr. Simon Thirgood, Editor; Dr. Gillian Kerby, Managing Editor; Jane Memmott, Exec. Ed. **Subscription Rates:** 856 institutions print and online; US$1,426 institutions print and online; EUR945 institutions Europe; US$1,844 institutions, other countries print and online. **URL:** http://www.britishecologicalsociety.org/journals_publications/journalofappliedecology/index.php; http://www.journalofappliedecology.org/view/0/index.html.

54699 ■ Journal of Applied Linguistics
Equinox Publishing Ltd.
1 Chelsea Manor Studios
Flood St.
London SW3 5SR, United Kingdom
Ph: 44 20 78233748
Fax: 44 20 78233748
Journal containing papers on a broad range of applied linguistic themes. **Freq:** 3/yr. **Key Personnel:** Ron Carter, Editorial Board, ronald.carter@nottingham.ac.uk; Kees De Bot, Editorial Board, cljde.bot@let.rug.nl; Vijay Bhatia, Editorial Board, enbhatia@cityu.edu.hk; Basil Hatim, Editorial Board, bhatim@aus.ac.ae; Christopher Candlin, Editor, ccandlin@ling.mq.edu.au; David Barton, Editorial Board, d.barton@lancaster.ac.uk; Guy Cook, Editorial Board, g.cook@open.ac.uk; Srikant Sarangi, Editor, sarangi@cardiff.ac.uk. **ISSN:** 1479-7887. **Subscription Rates:** 140 institutions, other countries print and online; US$280 institutions print and online; 53 individuals print; US$105 individuals print; 33.75 students print; US$67.50 students print. **Remarks:** Accepts advertising. **URL:** http://www.equinoxpub.com/journals/main.asp?jref=53. **Circ:** (Not Reported)

54700 ■ The Journal of Architecture
Routledge
Taylor & Francis Group Ltd.
c/o Murray Fraser, Ed.
University of Westminster
35 Marylebone Rd.
London NW1 5LS, United Kingdom
Publisher E-mail: webmaster.books@tandf.co.uk
Peer-reviewed journal covering theory, research and practice for design in the built environment, in connection with Royal Institute of British Architects. **Freq:** 6/yr. **Key Personnel:** Allen Cunningham, Editor; Murray Fraser, Editor; Ipek Akpinar, Regional Ed.; Barbara Penner, Book Reviews Ed.; Arie Sivan, Regional Ed.; Christoph Grafe, Commissioning Ed.; Charles Rice, Book Reviews Ed.; David Dunster, Commissioning Ed.; Peter Gibbs-Kennet, Editor, cunning@clara.net; Hilde Heynen, Commissioning Ed.; Stephen Fox, Regional Ed.; Zhang Qinnan, Regional Ed. **ISSN:** 1360-2365. **Subscription Rates:** 703 institutions print + online; US$1,165 institutions print + online; 668 institutions online; US$1,106 institutions online; 226 individuals personal; US$374 individuals personal; EUR928 institutions print and online; EUR882 institutions online only; EUR298 individuals. **Remarks:** Advertising accepted; rates available upon request. **URL:** http://www.tandf.co.uk/journals/titles/13602365.asp. **Circ:** (Not Reported)

54701 ■ Journal of Arms and Armour Society
Arms and Armour Society
Anthony Dove
PO Box 10232
London SW19 2ZD, United Kingdom
Publisher E-mail: armsandarmour.soc@fireflyuk.net
Journal covering arms and armor collectors. **Freq:** Semiannual. **ISSN:** 0004-2439. **Subscription Rates:** 15 individuals; 15 other countries surface mail; 20 other countries airmail. **Remarks:** Advertising accepted; rates available upon request. **URL:** http://www.armsandarmour.net/. **Circ:** (Not Reported)

54702 ■ Journal of Asset Management
Palgrave Macmillan
c/o Brenda Rouse, Publishing Ed.
The Macmillan Bldg.
4 Crinan St.
London N1 9XW, United Kingdom
Ph: 44 20 78434684
Publisher E-mail: booksellers@palgrave.com
Trade journal covering academic and commercial practices in asset management worldwide. **Founded:** July 2000. **Freq:** 6/yr. **Key Personnel:** Dr. Stephen Satchell, Editor. **ISSN:** 1470-8272. **Subscription Rates:** 474 institutions, other countries print; US$882 institutions print. **Remarks:** Accepts advertising. **URL:** http://www.palgrave-journals.com/jam/index.html. **Circ:** Combined 650

54703 ■ Journal of Autoimmune Diseases
BioMed Central Ltd.
236 Gray's Inn Rd., Fl. 6
34-42 Cleveland St.
London WC1X 8HL, United Kingdom
Ph: 44 20 31922000
Fax: 44 20 31922010
Publisher E-mail: info@biomedcentral.com
Online journal covering clinical and experimental research in autoimmunity. **Key Personnel:** Dr. David D'Cruz, Editor-in-Chief, david.d'cruz@kcl.ac.uk; Dr. Vitaly Ablamunits, Assoc. Ed., ablamunits@excite.com; Dr. Thomas Pap, Assoc. Ed., thomas.pap@medizin.uni-magdeburg.de. **ISSN:** 1740-2557. **Remarks:** Accepts advertising. **URL:** http://www.jautoimdis.com/home/. **Circ:** (Not Reported)

54704 ■ Journal of Bioactive and Compatible Polymers
Sage Publications Ltd.
1 Oliver's Yard
55 City Rd.
London EC1Y 1SP, United Kingdom
Ph: 44 20 73248500
Fax: 44 20 73248600
Peer-reviewed journal covering polymers and their human, animal, and botanical applications. **Founded:** Oct. 1, 1986. **Freq:** 6/yr. **Print Method:** Offset. **Trim Size:** 6 x 9. **Key Personnel:** Raphael M. Ottenbrite, Editor; Hamidreza Ghandehari, Editorial Board; Emo Chiellini, Editorial Advisory Board. **ISSN:** 0883-9115. **Subscription Rates:** 922 institutions print & e-access; 1,014 institutions print & all online; 830 institutions e-access; 922 institutions all online content; 917 institutions backfile purchase, e-access; 904 institutions print only; 166 institutions single print. **Remarks:** Accepts advertising. **URL:** http://www.sagepub.co.uk/journalsProdDesc.nav?prodId=Journal201575. **Circ:** 180

54705 ■ Journal of Bioinformatics and Computational Biology
Imperial College Press
57 Shelton St.
Covent Garden
London WC2H 9HE, United Kingdom
Ph: 44 20 78363954
Fax: 44 20 78362002
Publisher E-mail: sales@wspc.co.uk
Journal publishing original research articles, expository tutorial papers and review papers, as well as short, critical comments on technical issues associated with the analysis of cellular information. **Freq:** Bimonthly. **Key Personnel:** Limsoon Wong, Managing Editor, phone 65 65162902, fax 65 67794582, wongls@comp.nus.edu.sg; Vineet Bafna, Editorial Board. **ISSN:** 0219-7200. **Subscription Rates:** US$522 institutions electronic + print; US$501 institutions electronic only. **URL:** http://www.worldscinet.com/jbcb/jbcb.shtml.

54706 ■ Journal of Biological Education
Institute of Biology
9 Red Lion Ct.
London EC4A 3EF, United Kingdom
Ph: 44 20 79365900
Publication E-mail: jbe@iob.org
Publisher E-mail: info@iob.org
Publication covering biological education. **Founded:** 1967. **Freq:** Quarterly 4/yr (March, June, September, December). **Trim Size:** A4. **Key Personnel:** Simon Napper, Productions Ed.; David Slingsby, Editor. **ISSN:** 0021-9266. **Subscription Rates:** 40 members; 60 individuals for UK; 105 institutions; 75 individuals overseas; 135 institutions. **Remarks:** Advertising accepted; rates available upon request. **URL:** http://www.iob.org/general.asp?section=publications/jbe. **Circ:** Paid ‡1,800

54707 ■ Journal of Biomaterials Applications
Sage Publications Ltd.
1 Oliver's Yard
55 City Rd.
London EC1Y 1SP, United Kingdom
Ph: 44 20 73248500
Fax: 44 20 73248600
Peer-reviewed journal covering plastics and their medical applications. **Founded:** June 1986. **Freq:** 8/yr. **Print Method:** Offset. **Trim Size:** 6 x 9. **Key Personnel:** Jonathan Campbell Knowles, Editor; Traian Chirila, Reviews Ed. **ISSN:** 0885-3282. **Subscription Rates:** 962 institutions print & e-access; 1,058 institutions print (all online content); 866 institutions e-access; 962 institutions e-access (all online content); 883 institutions e-access (content through 1998); 943 institutions print only; 130 institutions single print. **Remarks:** Accepts advertising. **URL:** http://www.sagepub.co.uk/journalsProdDesc.nav?prodId=Journal201576. **Circ:** 160

54708 ■ Journal of Bodywork and Movement Therapies
Mosby Inc.
c/o Leon Chaitow, Ed.
School of Integrated Health
University of Westminster
115 New Cavendish St.
London W1M 8JS, United Kingdom

Publisher E-mail: custserv.ehs@elsevier.com

Journal publishing latest therapeutic techniques and current professional debate. **Freq:** Quarterly. **Key Personnel:** Leon Chaitow, Editor, jbmteditor@mac.com; Glenn M. Hymel, Assoc. Ed.; John Hannon, Assoc. Ed.; Craig Liebenson, Assoc. Ed., cldc@flash.net; Dimitrios Kostopoulos, Assoc. Ed. **ISSN:** 1360-8592. **Subscription Rates:** EUR119 individuals for European countries and Iran; EUR395 institutions for European countries and Iran; EUR60 students for European countries and Iran; 12,900¥ individuals; 42,500¥ institutions; 6,600¥ students; US$348 institutions, other countries except Europe, Japan and Iran; US$110 individuals except Europe, Japan and Iran. **Remarks:** Accepts advertising. **URL:** http://www.elsevier.com/wps/find/journaldescription.cws_home/623047/descriptiondescription. **Circ:** (Not Reported)

54709 ■ Journal of Bone & Joint Surgery (British Volume)
British Editorial Society of Bone and Joint Surgery
22 Buckingham St.
London WC2N 6ET, United Kingdom
Ph: 44 20 77820010
Fax: 44 20 77820995
Publisher E-mail: info@jbjs.org.uk
Medical journal covering orthopedics. **Founded:** 1948. **Freq:** Monthly. **Print Method:** Web. **Trim Size:** 213 x 275 mm. **Cols./Page:** 2. **Key Personnel:** Stephen Bishop, General Mgr.; James Scott, Editor. **ISSN:** 0301-620X. **Subscription Rates:** 193 individuals combined volume (36 issues + 5 supplements); 86 two years British volume (12 issues + 3 supplements); 114 institutions American volume (24 issues + 2 supplements). **Remarks:** Accepts advertising. **URL:** http://www.jbjs.org.uk. **Alt. Formats:** CD-ROM. **Ad Rates:** BW: 1,180, 4C: 2,030. **Circ:** Controlled 40,000

54710 ■ Journal of Brand Management
Palgrave Macmillan
c/o Brenda Rouse, Publishing Ed.
The Macmillan Bldg.
4 Crinan St.
London N1 9XW, United Kingdom
Ph: 44 20 78434684
Publisher E-mail: booksellers@palgrave.com
Peer-reviewed journal featuring analysis and latest thinking from leading figures in the world's foremost companies, consultancies and academic institutions in regards with marketing. **Freq:** 8/yr. **Key Personnel:** Brenda Rouse, Publishing Ed., submissions@palgrave.com; Prof. Dave Aaker, Editorial Board; Prof. Patrick Barwise, Editorial Board; T.C. Melewar, Editor-in-Chief; Temi Abimbola, Editor-in-Chief. **ISSN:** 1350-231X. **Subscription Rates:** US$420 individuals print and online; US$1,254 institutions print; 676 institutions, other countries print; 226 other countries print and online. **Remarks:** Advertising accepted; rates available upon request. **URL:** http://www.palgrave-journals.com/bm/index.html. **Circ:** 650

54711 ■ Journal of the British Archaeological Association
Maney Publishing
1 Carlton House Ter.
London SW1Y 5AF, United Kingdom
Ph: 44 20 74517300
Fax: 44 20 74517307
Publisher E-mail: maney@maney.co.uk
Journal covering the study of Britain's archaeology, art, and architecture. **Freq:** Annual. **Key Personnel:** Dr. Julian Luxford, Editor, jml5@st-andrews.ac.uk; Mellie Naydenova-Slade, Review Ed., mellie.naydenova-slade@courtauld.ac.uk. **ISSN:** 0068-1288. **Subscription Rates:** 32 other countries; US$65 individuals; 98 institutions, other countries; US$184 institutions. **Remarks:** Accepts advertising. **URL:** http://maney.co.uk/index.php/journals/jba/. **Circ:** (Not Reported)

54712 ■ Journal of the British Astronomical Association
British Astronomical Association
Burlington House
Piccadilly
London W1J 0DU, United Kingdom
Ph: 44 20 77344145
Fax: 44 20 74394629
Publisher E-mail: office@britastro.org
Journal covering astronomy. **Freq:** Bimonthly. **Key Personnel:** Hazel McGee, Editor, hazelmcgee@compuserve.com. **Remarks:** Accepts advertising. **URL:**

http://britastro.org/baa/content/view/74/109/. **Circ:** (Not Reported)

54713 ■ Journal of the British Interplanetary Society
British Interplanetary Society
27-29 S Lambeth Rd.
London SW8 1SZ, United Kingdom
Ph: 44 20 77353160
Fax: 44 20 78201504
Publisher E-mail: mail@bis-spaceflight.com
Journal covering astronomy. **Founded:** 1934. **Freq:** Monthly. **Key Personnel:** A.T. Lawton, Editor. **Subscription Rates:** 40 individuals; 25 members. **Remarks:** Advertising not accepted. **URL:** http://www.bis-spaceflight.com/JBIS.htm. **Circ:** (Not Reported)

54714 ■ The Journal of the British Tarantula Society
British Tarantula Society
3 Shepham Ln.
Polegate
East Sussex
London BN26 6LZ, United Kingdom
Ph: 44 95 6438187
Publisher E-mail: webmaster@thebts.co.uk
Journal covering tarantulas and associated invertebrates, husbandry, behavior and related topics. **Founded:** 1985. **Freq:** Quarterly. **Trim Size:** A5. **Key Personnel:** Richard Gallon, Editor, postmaster@zezz.demon.co.uk. **ISSN:** 0962-449X. **Subscription Rates:** 5 individuals; 10 other countries. **Remarks:** Accepts advertising. **URL:** http://www.thebts.co.uk/bts_study.htm; http://www.thebts.co.uk/framset2.htm. **Ad Rates:** BW: 20. **Circ:** (Not Reported)

54715 ■ Journal of Buddhist Ethics
c/o Prof. Damien Keown
Dept. of Historical & Cultural Studies
Univ. of London, Goldsmiths' College
London SE14 6NW, United Kingdom
Ph: 44 20 79197171
Journal covering Buddhist ethics. **Founded:** 1994. **Freq:** Annual. **Key Personnel:** Barbra Clayton, Editorial Board, bclayton@mta.ca; Prof. Charles S. Prebish, Founding Ed. Emeritus; Prof. Damien Keown, Founding Ed. Emeritus, d.keown@gold.ac.uk; Richard Gombrich, Editorial Board; Leslie Kawamura, Editorial Board; George Bond, Editorial Board; Ian Harris, Editorial Board; Sue Hamilton, Editorial Board. **ISSN:** 1076-9005. **Subscription Rates:** Free. **URL:** http://www.buddhistethics.org/.

54716 ■ Journal of Building Physics
Sage Publications Ltd.
1 Oliver's Yard
55 City Rd.
London EC1Y 1SP, United Kingdom
Ph: 44 20 73248500
Fax: 44 20 73248600
Peer-reviewed journal covering insulation for commercial and industrial use. **Founded:** 1978. **Freq:** Quarterly. **Print Method:** Offset. **Trim Size:** 6 x 9. **Cols./Page:** 1. **Col. Width:** 54 nonpareils. **Col. Depth:** 100 agate lines. **Key Personnel:** Mark T. Bomberg, Editor. **ISSN:** 1744-2591. **Subscription Rates:** US$1,200 institutions print & e-access; US$1,320 institutions print (all online content); US$1,080 institutions e-access; US$1,200 institutions e-access (all online content); US$1,928 institutions e-access (content through 1998); US$1,176 institutions print only; US$323 institutions single print. **Remarks:** Accepts advertising. **URL:** http://www.sagepub.com/journalsProdDesc.nav?prodId=Journal201633. **Formerly:** Journal of Thermal Insulation (1992); Journal of Thermal Envelope and Building Sciences. **Circ:** ‡200

54717 ■ Journal of Carcinogenesis
BioMed Central Ltd.
236 Gray's Inn Rd., Fl. 6
34-42 Cleveland St.
London WC1X 8HL, United Kingdom
Ph: 44 20 31922000
Fax: 44 20 31922010
Publisher E-mail: info@biomedcentral.com
Online journal covering all aspects of physical and chemical carcinogenesis and mutagenesis. **Key Personnel:** Dr. Gopala Kovvali, Exec. Ed., editor@carcinogenesis.com; Karam El-Bayoumy, Sen. Ed.; Maarten Bosland, Sen. Ed. **ISSN:** 1477-3163. **Subscrip-**

tion Rates: US$300 individuals; 150 individuals; EUR120 individuals. **Remarks:** Accepts advertising. **URL:** http://www.carcinogenesis.com/. **Circ:** (Not Reported)

54718 ■ Journal of Cardiovascular Magnetic Resonance
BioMed Central Ltd.
236 Gray's Inn Rd., Fl. 6
34-42 Cleveland St.
London WC1X 8HL, United Kingdom
Ph: 44 20 31922000
Fax: 44 20 31922010
Publisher E-mail: info@biomedcentral.com
Journal providing an international forum for the latest findings and state-of-the-art reviews on the burgeoning field of cardiovascular magnetic resonance (CMR) imaging and spectroscopy, helping cardiac professionals improve diagnostic capabilities, identify diseases more accurately, and assess the efficacy of therapeutic approaches. **Freq:** 6/yr. **Key Personnel:** Dr. Dudley Pennell, Editor-in-Chief, jcmr@ic.ac.uk; Warren J. Manning, Dep. Ed.; Fei Wang, Managing Editor. **ISSN:** 1097-6647. **URL:** http://jcmr-online.com/.

54719 ■ Journal of Cardiovascular Magnetic Resonance
BioMed Central Ltd.
236 Gray's Inn Rd., Fl. 6
34-42 Cleveland St.
London WC1X 8HL, United Kingdom
Ph: 44 20 31922000
Fax: 44 20 31922010
Publisher E-mail: info@biomedcentral.com
Journal providing concise critical evaluations of the newest concepts, methods, and data in the field of computed tomography. **Subtitle:** Offical Journal of the Society for Cardiovascular Magnetic Resonace. **Freq:** Bimonthly. **Key Personnel:** Dr. Dudley Pennell, Editor-in-Chief; Robert W. Biederman, MD, Editorial Board; Andrew Arai, Editorial Board; Albert De Roos, Editorial Board; Zahi Fayad, Editorial Board. **ISSN:** 1097-6647. **URL:** http://www.informaworld.com/smpp/title~db=all~content=t713597265; http://jcmr-online.com. **Former name:** Critical Reviews in Computed Tomography.

54720 ■ Journal of Cellular Plastics
Sage Publications Ltd.
1 Oliver's Yard
55 City Rd.
London EC1Y 1SP, United Kingdom
Ph: 44 20 73248500
Fax: 44 20 73248600
Peer-reviewed journal covering foamed plastics technology. **Founded:** 1964. **Freq:** 6/yr. **Print Method:** Offset. **Trim Size:** 6 x 9. **Cols./Page:** 2. **Col. Width:** 25 nonpareils. **Col. Depth:** 140 agate lines. **Key Personnel:** S.T Lee, Co-Ed.-in-Ch.; Chul B. Park, Editor-in-Chief. **ISSN:** 0021-955X. **Subscription Rates:** 729 institutions print & e-access; 802 institutions online; 656 institutions e-access; 729 institutions all online content; 1,896 institutions e-access (content through 1998); 714 institutions print only; 131 institutions single print. **Remarks:** Accepts advertising. **URL:** http://www.sagepub.co.uk/journalsProdDesc.nav?prodId=Journal201577. **Circ:** ‡340

54721 ■ Journal of Chemical Technology and Biotechnology
Society of Chemical Industry
Publications Dept.
Dept. of Biochemical Engineering
University College London
London WC1E 7JE, United Kingdom
Publisher E-mail: secretariat@soci.org
International research in process, environmental and sustainable technology. **Founded:** 1951. **Freq:** Monthly. **Trim Size:** A4. **Key Personnel:** John S. Smith, Tech. Ed.; Dionissios Mantzavinos, Assoc. Ed., mantzavi@mred.tuc.gr; Tajalli Keshavarz, Assoc. Ed., t.keshavarz@westminster.ac.uk; Peter Hambleton, Editor, peter.hambleton@ntlworld.com; Jack Melling, Editor-in-Chief, jmelling@ptd.net; Frank Baganz, Assoc. Ed., f.baganz@ucl.ac.uk; Eric Thwaites, Assoc. Ed.; Michael Cox, Editor, m.cox@herts.ac.uk. **ISSN:** 0268-2575. **Subscription Rates:** 965 individuals print only; US$1,911 individuals rest of world; US$2,548 institutions rest of world; 1,300 institutions print only; EUR1,645 institutions print only. **Remarks:** Accepts advertising. **URL:** http://www3.interscience.wiley.com/cgi-bin/home?CRETRY=1&SRETRY=0. **Circ:** (Not Reported)

54722 ■ Journal of Child Psychology and Psychiatry
Association for Child and Adolescent Mental Health
St. Saviours House
39-41 Union St.
London SE1 1SD, United Kingdom
Ph: 44 20 74037458
Fax: 44 20 74037081
Publisher E-mail: ingrid.king@acamh.org.uk
Professional publication covering child psychiatry. **Freq:** Monthly. **Key Personnel:** Daniel Pine, Editor; Thomas G. O'Connor, Editor; Edmund Sonuga-Barke, Editor-in-Chief; Jane Costello, Editor; Margaret Snowling, Editor. **ISSN:** 0021-9630. **Subscription Rates:** US$743 institutions; US$675 institutions; US$641 institutions; US$849 institutions; US$772 institutions; US$733 institutions; 463 institutions; 421 institutions; 400 institutions. **Remarks:** Advertising accepted; rates available upon request. **URL:** http://www.acamh.org.uk/bfora/systems/xmlviewer/default.asp?arg=DS_ACAMH_DOCART_43/_firsttitle.xsl/66. **Circ:** (Not Reported)

54723 ■ Journal of Child Psychotherapy
Association of Child Psychotherapists
120 W Heath Rd.
London NW3 7TU, United Kingdom
Ph: 44 20 84581609
Fax: 44 20 84581482
Publisher E-mail: admin@acp-uk.eu
Peer-reviewed journal covering child psychotherapy. **Freq:** 3/yr. **Key Personnel:** Viviane Green, Editor. **ISSN:** 0075-417X. **Subscription Rates:** US$130 individuals print only; US$412 individuals online only; US$434 individuals print and online. **Remarks:** Advertising accepted; rates available upon request. **URL:** http://www.childpsychotherapy.org.uk/content/journal; http://www.informaworld.com/smpp/title~db=all~content=t713735277. **Circ:** (Not Reported)

54724 ■ Journal of Circadian Rhythms
BioMed Central Ltd.
236 Gray's Inn Rd., Fl. 6
34-42 Cleveland St.
London WC1X 8HL, United Kingdom
Ph: 44 20 31922000
Fax: 44 20 31922010
Publisher E-mail: info@biomedcentral.com
Online journal covering all aspects of circadian and nycthemeral rhythms in living organisms. **Key Personnel:** Dr. Roberto Refinetti, Editor-in-Chief, phone 843549-6314, fax 843549-6007, editor@circadian.org; Dr. Helena Almirall, Editorial Board; Dr. John F. Araujo, Editorial Board. **ISSN:** 1740-3391. **Remarks:** Accepts advertising. **URL:** http://www.jcircadianrhythms.com/home/. **Circ:** (Not Reported)

54725 ■ Journal of Classical Sociology
Sage Publications Ltd.
1 Oliver's Yard
55 City Rd.
London EC1Y 1SP, United Kingdom
Ph: 44 20 73248500
Fax: 44 20 73248600
Scholarly journal covering classical sociology worldwide. **Founded:** 2001. **Freq:** Quarterly. **Key Personnel:** Bryan S. Turner, Editor; John O'Neill, Editor; Simon Susen, Editor. **ISSN:** 1468-795X. **Subscription Rates:** US$903 institutions combined (print & e-access); US$813 institutions e-access; US$885 institutions print only; US$87 individuals print only; US$243 institutions single print; US$28 individuals single print. **Remarks:** Accepts advertising. **URL:** http://www.sagepub.com/journalsProdDesc.nav?prodId=Journal201499. **Circ:** (Not Reported)

54726 ■ Journal of Clinical Research
PJB Publications Ltd.
Telephone House
69-77 Paul St.
London EC2A 4LQ, United Kingdom
Ph: 44 20 70175000
Fax: 44 20 70176792
Publisher E-mail: pjb.enquiries@informa.com
Journal covering research in the efficacy of new clinical interventions. **Freq:** Irregular. **Print Method:** Sheet fed offset litho. **Trim Size:** 170 x 245 mm. **Key Personnel:** Dr. J.H. Beijnen, Editorial Board. **ISSN:** 1369-5207. **Remarks:** Accepts advertising. **URL:** http://www.pjbpubs.

com/clinical_research/index.htm. **Formerly:** European Journal of Clinical Research; British Journal of Clinical Research. **Circ:** (Not Reported)

54727 ■ The Journal of Commonwealth Literature
Sage Publications Ltd.
1 Oliver's Yard
55 City Rd.
London EC1Y 1SP, United Kingdom
Ph: 44 20 73248500
Fax: 44 20 73248600
Publication covering postcolonial studies literature and writing. **Freq:** Quarterly. **Print Method:** Litho. **Trim Size:** 148 x 210 mm. **Key Personnel:** John Thieme, Editor; Vassilena Parashkevova, Bibliography Ed.; Maria-Sabina Alexandru, Editorial Asst. **ISSN:** 0021-9894. **Subscription Rates:** US$655 institutions print & e-access; US$721 institutions online; US$590 institutions e-access; US$656 institutions all online content; US$1,655 institutions e-access (content through 1998); US$642 institutions print only; US$139 individuals print only; US$177 institutions single print; US$45 individuals single print. **Remarks:** Advertising not accepted. **URL:** http://www.sagepub.com/journalsProdDesc.nav?prodId=Journal201677. **Circ:** (Not Reported)

54728 ■ Journal of Composite Materials
Sage Publications Ltd.
1 Oliver's Yard
55 City Rd.
London EC1Y 1SP, United Kingdom
Ph: 44 20 73248500
Fax: 44 20 73248600
Peer-reviewed journal covering engineering studies on composite materials. **Founded:** 1967. **Freq:** 26/yr. **Print Method:** Offset. **Trim Size:** 6 x 9. **Cols./Page:** 2. **Col. Width:** 33 nonpareils. **Col. Depth:** 113 agate lines. **Key Personnel:** Prof. Thomas H. Hahn, Editor-in-Chief; Prof. Stephen W. Tsai, Founding Ed.; Prof. Woo Il Lee, Editor; Prof. Mark Spearing, Editor. **ISSN:** 0021-9983. **Subscription Rates:** US$6,077 institutions print & e-access; US$6,685 institutions online; US$5,469 institutions e-access; US$6,077 institutions all online content; US$14,876 institutions e-access (content through 1998); US$5,955 institutions print only; US$252 institutions single print. **Remarks:** Accepts advertising. **URL:** http://www.sagepub.com/journalsProdDesc.nav?prodId=Journal201581. **Circ:** 800

54729 ■ The Journal of Computational Finance
Incisive Media Limited
Haymarket House
28-29 Haymarket
London SW1Y 4RX, United Kingdom
Ph: 44 870 2408859
Fax: 44 207 4849797
Publisher E-mail: customerservices@incisivemedia.com
Peer-reviewed journal covering advances in numerical and computational techniques in pricing, hedging and risk management of financial instruments. **Freq:** Quarterly. **Key Personnel:** Nick Carver, Publisher, nick.carver@incisivemedia.com. **Subscription Rates:** 479 institutions and practitioner; non-academic; 862 institutions and practitioner; non-academic (2 years); 1,221 institutions and practitioner; non-academic (3 years); 210 individuals academic; 378 two years academic; 536 individuals academic; 3 years. **Remarks:** Accepts advertising. **URL:** http://www.thejournalofcomputationalfinance.com/. **Circ:** (Not Reported)

54730 ■ Journal of Consumer Culture
Sage Publications Ltd.
1 Oliver's Yard
55 City Rd.
London EC1Y 1SP, United Kingdom
Ph: 44 20 73248500
Fax: 44 20 73248600
Scholarly journal covering modern consumer culture. **Founded:** 2001. **Freq:** 3/yr. **Key Personnel:** Prof. George Ritzer, Founding Ed.; Douglas B. Holt, Editor; Amanda Cowan, Managing Editor. **ISSN:** 1469-5405. **Subscription Rates:** US$622 institutions print & e-access; US$560 institutions e-access; US$610 institutions print only; US$83 individuals print only; US$224 institutions single print; US$36 individuals single print. **Remarks:** Accepts advertising. **URL:** http://www.

sagepub.com/journalsProdDesc.nav?prodId=Journal201468&. **Circ:** (Not Reported)

54731 ■ Journal of Contemporary History
Sage Publications Ltd.
1 Oliver's Yard
55 City Rd.
London EC1Y 1SP, United Kingdom
Ph: 44 20 73248500
Fax: 44 20 73248600
Scholarly journal covering analysis and discussion of 20th century history, including people, periods, places and issues. **Founded:** 1966. **Freq:** Quarterly. **Key Personnel:** Richard J. Evans, Editor; Stanley Payne, Editor; Walter Laqueur, Founding Ed.; George L. Mosse, Founding Ed.; Niall Ferguson, Editorial Board; Steven A. Aschheim, Editorial Board; Emilio Gentile, Editorial Board; Ute Frevert, Editorial Board; James Bjork, Review Ed. **ISSN:** 0022-0094. **Subscription Rates:** US$814 institutions print & e-access; US$895 institutions current volume print & all online content; US$733 institutions e-access; US$814 institutions e-access plus backfile (all online content); US$2,056 institutions e-access (content through 1998); US$798 institutions print only; US$109 individuals print only; US$219 institutions single print; US$35 individuals single print. **Remarks:** Accepts advertising. **URL:** http://www.sagepub.com/journalsProdDesc.nav?prodId=Journal200983. **Circ:** (Not Reported)

54732 ■ Journal of Credit Risk
Incisive Media Limited
Haymarket House
28-29 Haymarket
London SW1Y 4RX, United Kingdom
Ph: 44 870 2408859
Fax: 44 207 4849797
Publisher E-mail: customerservices@incisivemedia.com
Peer-reviewed journal covering the measurement and management of credit risk. **Key Personnel:** Ashish Dev, Editor-in-Chief; Edward Altman, Assoc. Ed.; Arthur Berd, Assoc. Ed. **Subscription Rates:** 479 institutions and practitioner; non-academic; 722 institutions and practitioner; non-academic; 909 institutions and practitioner; non-academic; 210 individuals academic; EUR317 individuals academic; 399 individuals academic. **Remarks:** Accepts advertising. **URL:** http://www.journalofcreditrisk.com. **Circ:** (Not Reported)

54733 ■ Journal of Critical Realism
Equinox Publishing Ltd.
Mervyn Hartwig
37 Stockwell Green
Stockwell
London SW9 9HZ, United Kingdom
Journal discussing on emancipatory philosophy, social theory and science with an interactive approach. **Founded:** 1997. **Freq:** Annual. **Key Personnel:** Mervyn Hartwig, Gen. Ed.; Karl Maton, Editor; Jamie Morgan, Book Review Ed.; Gideon Calder, Editorial Advisory Board. **ISSN:** 1476-7430. **Subscription Rates:** 140 institutions print & online; US$208 institutions print & online; 45 members print & online; US$80 members print & online; 139 members online only; US$68 members online only. **URL:** http://www.equinoxjournals.com/JCR.

54734 ■ Journal of Database Marketing & Customer Strategy Management
Palgrave Macmillan
c/o Brenda Rouse, Publishing Ed.
The Macmillan Bldg.
4 Crinan St.
London N1 9XW, United Kingdom
Ph: 44 20 78434684
Publisher E-mail: booksellers@palgrave.com
Journal covering the themes of customer management, including multichannel marketing, customer loyalty and experience, call-centre operations, e-business and account management; and marketing strategy, with analysis of results-based CRM, data sourcing, warehousing, lifestyle and psychographic data, database building and software and hardware selection. **Freq:** Quarterly. **Key Personnel:** Brenda Rouse, Publishing Ed., submissions@palgrave.com; John Ozimek, Managing Editor. **ISSN:** 1741-2439. **Subscription Rates:** US$672 institutions print; US$298 individuals print and online; 361 institutions, other countries print; 160 other countries print and online. **URL:** http://www.palgrave-journals.com/dbm/index.html.

Circulation: ★ = ABC; △ = BPA; ♦ = CAC; • = CCAB; ❑ = VAC; ⊕ = PO Statement; ‡ = Publisher's Report; Boldface figures = sworn; Light figures = estimated.

54735 ■ Journal of Derivatives & Hedge Funds
Palgrave Macmillan
The Macmillan Bldg.
4 Crinan St.
London N1 9XW, United Kingdom
Ph: 44 20 78434684
Publisher E-mail: booksellers@palgrave.com
Peer-reviewed journal for finance, securities and investment professionals worldwide. **Founded:** 1996. **Freq:** Quarterly. **Key Personnel:** Dr. Stephen Satchell, Editor; Dr. Greg N. Gregoriou, Editor. **ISSN:** 1753-9641. **Subscription Rates:** 474 institutions, other countries print; 194 other countries print and online; US$882 institutions print; US$361 individuals print and online. **Remarks:** Accepts advertising. **URL:** http://www.palgrave-journals.com/jdhf/index.html. **Formerly:** Derivatives Use, Trading and Regulation. **Circ:** Combined 1,400.

54736 ■ Journal of Dermatological Treatment
BioMed Central Ltd.
236 Gray's Inn Rd., Fl. 6
34-42 Cleveland St.
London WC1X 8HL, United Kingdom
Ph: 44 20 31922000
Fax: 44 20 31922010
Publisher E-mail: info@biomedcentral.com
Journal covering all aspects of the treatment of skin disease, including the use of topically and systemically administered drugs and other forms of therapy. **Freq:** Bimonthly. **Key Personnel:** Steven R. Feldman, Editor; Peter Van de Kerkhof, Editor; Ronald Marks, Founding Ed.; David De Berker, Assoc. Ed.; John Berth-Jones, Assoc. Ed.; Kenneth Gordon, Assoc. Ed. **ISSN:** 0954-6634. **Subscription Rates:** US$520 institutions; US$860 institutions; EUR685 institutions. **URL:** http://informahealthcare.com/journal/jdt.

54737 ■ Journal of Direct, Data and Digital Marketing Practice
Palgrave Macmillan
c/o Brenda Rouse; Publishing Ed.
The Macmillan Bldg.
4 Crinan St.
London N1 9XW, United Kingdom
Ph: 44 20 78434684
Publisher E-mail: booksellers@palgrave.com
Journal covering new marketing concepts, strategies and applications from around the world. **Freq:** Quarterly. **Key Personnel:** Derek Holder, Editor; Robin Fairlie, Editor; Brenda Rouse, Publishing Ed., submissions@palgrave.com. **ISSN:** 1746-0166. **Subscription Rates:** 233 institutions, other countries print; US$456 institutions print; 119 other countries print and online; US$234 individuals print and online. **URL:** http://www.palgrave-journals.com/dddmp/index.html.

54738 ■ Journal of Discrete Algorithms (Amsterdam)
Elsevier (Singapore) Pte. Ltd.
c/o D.M. Gabbay
Dept. of Computer Science
King's College London
Strand
London WC2R 2LS, United Kingdom
Publisher E-mail: asiabkinfo@elsevier.com
Journal aiming to facilitate communication between researchers in theoretical computer science who are concerned with the design and analysis of discrete algorithms. **Founded:** 2003. **Freq:** Quarterly. **Key Personnel:** D.M. Gabbay, Editor-in-Chief, dov.gabbay@kcl.ac.uk; C.S. Iliopoulos, Editor-in-Chief, csi@dcs.kcl.ac.uk; G.F Italiano, Editor-in-Chief, italiano@info.uniroma2.it; D. Wagner, Editor-in-Chief, dwagner@ira.uka.de; M. Smid, Editor-in-Chief, michiel@scs.carleton.ca; J. Abello, Editorial Board, abello@dimacs.rutgers.edu. **ISSN:** 1570-8667. **Subscription Rates:** US$682 institutions all countries except Europe, Japan and Iran; 76,000¥ institutions; EUR643 institutions European countries and Iran. **URL:** http://www.elsevier.com/wps/find/journaldescription.cws_home/672711/descriptiondescription.

54739 ■ Journal of Drug Assessment
PJB Publications Ltd.
Telephone House
69-77 Paul St.
London EC2A 4LQ, United Kingdom
Ph: 44 20 70175000
Fax: 44 20 70176792
Publisher E-mail: pjb.enquiries@informa.com
Peer-reviewed journal encompassing the Clinical Research, health Economics, and Outcomes on methods of drug assessment. **Founded:** 1998. **Freq:** Quarterly. **Print Method:** Digital Printing and Litho covers. **Trim Size:** 170 x 245 mm. **Key Personnel:** Dr. J.H. Beijnen, Editorial Board; Jay Magrann, Publisher. **ISSN:** 1369-9474. **Subscription Rates:** 166 institutions; EUR241 institutions; US$326 institutions; 118 individuals; EUR171 individuals; US$230 individuals. **Remarks:** Accepts advertising. **URL:** http://www.pjbpubs.com/drug_assessment/index.htm. **Circ:** Paid 100

54740 ■ Journal of Early Childhood Literacy
Sage Publications Ltd.
1 Oliver's Yard
55 City Rd.
London EC1Y 1SP, United Kingdom
Ph: 44 20 73248500
Fax: 44 20 73248600
Peer-reviewed journal covering literacy in children. **Founded:** Apr. 2001. **Freq:** Quarterly. **Key Personnel:** Stuart McNaughton, Editor; Julia Gillen, Editor; Deborah Wells Rowe, Editor; Jackie Marsh, Editor; Guy Merchant, Editor; Rosie Flewitt, Review Ed. **ISSN:** 1468-7984. **Subscription Rates:** US$614 institutions print & e-access; US$553 institutions e-access; US$602 institutions print only; US$307 institutions print & e-access; US$83 individuals print only; US$166 institutions single print; US$27 individuals single print. **Remarks:** Accepts advertising. **URL:** http://www.sagepub.com/journalsProdDesc.nav?prodId=Journal201285. **Circ:** (Not Reported)

54741 ■ The Journal of Ecology
John Wiley & Sons Inc.
Wiley-Blackwell
c/o Andrea Baier, Mng. Ed.
British Ecological Society
Charles Darwin House
12 Roger St.
London WC1N 2J, United Kingdom
Ph: 44 20 76852515
Fax: 44 20 76852501
Publication focusing on environmental issues. **Freq:** Bimonthly. **Key Personnel:** Michael J. Hutchings, Editor, m.j.hutchings@sussex.ac.ukdavid; Richard D. Bardgett, Editor, r.bardgett@lancaster.ac.uk; David J. Gibson, Editor, dgibson@plant.siu.edu. **ISSN:** 0022-0477. **Subscription Rates:** US$1,501 institutions print and online; 812 institutions print and online; US$1,752 institutions, other countries print and online; EUR939 institutions print and online; US$1,365 institutions print, online; 739 institutions print, online; EUR939 institutions print, online; US$1,593 institutions, other countries print, online. **Remarks:** Accepts advertising. **URL:** http://www.wiley.com/bw/journal.asp?ref=0022-0477&site=1. **Ad Rates:** BW: 900, 4C: 2,250. **Circ:** (Not Reported)

54742 ■ Journal of Elastomers and Plastics
Sage Publications Ltd.
1 Oliver's Yard
55 City Rd.
London EC1Y 1SP, United Kingdom
Ph: 44 20 73248500
Fax: 44 20 73248600
Peer-reviewed journal covering plastics science. **Founded:** 1969. **Freq:** Bimonthly. **Print Method:** Offset. **Trim Size:** 6 x 9. **Cols./Page:** 1. **Col. Width:** 54 nonpareils. **Col. Depth:** 100 agate lines. **Key Personnel:** Heshmat A. Aglan, Editor; M. El-Halwagi, Editorial Board; A.I. Isayev, Editorial Board; L.E. Brower, Editorial Board. **ISSN:** 0095-2443. **Subscription Rates:** US$1,399 institutions print & e-access; US$1,539 institutions print (all online content); US$1,259 institutions e-access; US$1,399 institutions e-access & online; US$3,210 institutions e-access (content through 1998); US$1,371 institutions print only; US$251 institutions single print. **Remarks:** Accepts advertising. **URL:** http://www.sagepub.com/journalsProdDesc.nav?prodId=Journal201556. **Circ:** ‡275

54743 ■ Journal of the Energy Institute
Maney Publishing
1 Carlton House Ter.
London SW1Y 5AF, United Kingdom
Ph: 44 20 74517300
Fax: 44 20 74517307
Publication E-mail: eni.ed@maney.co.uk
Publisher E-mail: maney@maney.co.uk
Peer-reviewed journal covering original high quality research on energy engineering and technology. **Freq:** 4/yr. **Key Personnel:** Prof. Alan Williams, Editor, a.williams@leeds.ac.uk. **ISSN:** 0144-2600. **Subscription Rates:** 281 institutions, other countries; US$566 institutions. **Remarks:** Accepts advertising. **URL:** http://maney.co.uk/index.php/journals/eni/. **Circ:** (Not Reported)

54744 ■ Journal of Environmental Health Research
Chartered Institute of Environmental Health
Chadwick Ct.
15 Hatfields
London SE1 8DJ, United Kingdom
Ph: 44 20 79286006
Fax: 44 20 78275862
Journal publishing original research papers, review articles, technical notes and professional evaluations covering the diverse range of topics which impinge on environmental health. **Key Personnel:** Dr. Marie Vaganay, Editor-in-Chief, hd.harvey@ulster.ac.uk; Martin Fitzpatrick, Assoc. Ed.; Dr. Gai Murphy, Assoc. Ed.; Dr. Ken M. Stewart, Assoc. Ed.; Dr. Paul Fleming, Editor. **URL:** http://www.cieh.org/jehr/.

54745 ■ Journal of Epidemiology and Community Health
BMJ Publishing Group Ltd.
BMA House
Tavistock Sq.
London WC1H 9JR, United Kingdom
Ph: 44 20 73874410
Fax: 44 20 73836400
Publication E-mail: jech@ua.es
Peer-reviewed Journal covering the field of epidemiology and public health. **Founded:** 1947. **Freq:** Monthly. **Key Personnel:** Mauricio L. Barreto, Editor, mauricio@ufba.br; Rosana Aquino, Assoc. Ed.; Martin Bobak, Dep. Ed., m.bobak@ucl.ac.uk. **ISSN:** 0143-005X. **Subscription Rates:** US$355 individuals print and online; US$207 individuals online only; 182 institutions print and online; EUR246 institutions print and online; 106 institutions online only; EUR143 institutions online only. **Remarks:** Advertising accepted; rates available upon request. **URL:** http://jech.bmj.com/. **Circ:** (Not Reported)

54746 ■ Journal of Ethnobiology and Ethnomedicine
BioMed Central Ltd.
236 Gray's Inn Rd., Fl. 6
34-42 Cleveland St.
London WC1X 8HL, United Kingdom
Ph: 44 20 31922000
Fax: 44 20 31922010
Publication E-mail: ethnobiomed@netcologne.de
Publisher E-mail: info@biomedcentral.com
Journal on ethnobiology and ethnomedicine dealing with interaction between human cultures and nature. **Key Personnel:** Dr. Andrea Pieroni, Editor-in-Chief, a.pieroni@unisg.it; Prof. Louis E. Grivetti, Assoc. Ed., legrivetti@ucdavis.edu; Prof. Berit Smestad Paulsen, Assoc. Ed., b.s.paulsen@farmasi.uio.no. **Remarks:** Advertising accepted; rates available upon request. **URL:** http://www.ethnobiomed.com/info/about/. **Circ:** (Not Reported)

54747 ■ Journal of European Social Policy
Sage Publications Ltd.
1 Oliver's Yard
55 City Rd.
London EC1Y 1SP, United Kingdom
Ph: 44 20 73248500
Fax: 44 20 73248600
Scholarly journal covering social policy issues in Europe. **Founded:** 1991. **Freq:** 5/yr. **Key Personnel:** Jochen Clasen, Editor; Traute Meyer, Editor; Daniel Clegg, Book Review Ed. **ISSN:** 0958-9287. **Subscription Rates:** US$971 institutions combined (print & e-access); US$1,068 institutions backfile lease, combined plus backfile; US$874 institutions e-access; US$971 institutions backfile lease, e-access plus backfile; US$874 institutions backfile purchase, e-access through 1998; US$952 institutions print only; US$115 institutions print only; US$209 institutions single print; US$30 individuals single print. **Remarks:** Accepts advertising. **URL:** http://www.sagepub.com/journalsProdDesc.nav?prodId=Journal200915&. **Circ:** (Not Reported)

54748 ■ Journal of European Studies
Sage Publications Ltd.
1 Oliver's Yard

55 City Rd.
London EC1Y 1SP, United Kingdom
Ph: 44 20 73248500
Fax: 44 20 73248600
Humanities publication. **Founded:** 1970. **Freq:** Quarterly. **Trim Size:** 233 x 153 mm. **Key Personnel:** Prof. John Flower, Gen. Ed.; A.G. Cross, Reviews Ed.; Tetsuo Arizai, Editorial Advisory Board. **ISSN:** 0047-2441. **Subscription Rates:** US$779 institutions print & e-access; US$857 institutions print (all online content); US$701 institutions e-access; US$779 institutions e-access & online; US$1,668 institutions e-access (content through 1998); US$763 institutions print only; US$80 individuals print only; US$210 institutions single print; US$26 individuals single print. **Remarks:** Accepts advertising. **URL:** http://www.sagepub.com/journalsProdDesc.nav?prodId=Journal201665. **Ad Rates:** BW: 200. **Circ:** (Not Reported)

54749 ■ Journal of Experimental & Clinical Assisted Reproduction
BioMed Central Ltd.
236 Gray's Inn Rd., Fl. 6
34-42 Cleveland St.
London WC1X 8HL, United Kingdom
Ph: 44 20 31922000
Fax: 44 20 31922010
Publisher E-mail: info@biomedcentral.com
Online journal publishing selected manuscripts on reproductive endocrinology, infertility, bioethics and the advanced reproductive technologies. **Key Personnel:** Prof. Gianpiero D. Palermo, PhD, Editor-in-Chief; Dr. Eric Scott Sills, Editor-in-Chief. **ISSN:** 1743-1050. **Remarks:** Accepts advertising. **URL:** http://www.jexpclinassistreprod.com/home/. **Circ:** (Not Reported)

54750 ■ Journal of Exposure Science and Environmental Epidemiology (JESEE)
Nature Publishing Group
The Macmillan Bldg.
4 Crinan St.
London N1 9XW, United Kingdom
Ph: 44 20 78334000
Fax: 44 20 78434640
Peer-reviewed journal focusing on evaluation of exposure to toxic substances and environmental epidemiology that includes a strong exposure analysis component and related disciplines that advance the exposure assessment process. **Freq:** Bimonthly. **Key Personnel:** Elaine A. Cohen-Hubal, Editorial Board; Richard Fenske, Editorial Board; Annie M. Jarabek, Editorial Board; Natalie C.G. Freeman, Editorial Board; Dana Barr, PhD, Editor; Junfeng Zhang, Editorial Board. **ISSN:** 1559-0631. **Subscription Rates:** US$207 individuals print and online; EUR178 individuals print and online; 26,718¥ individuals print and online; 114 other countries print and online. **Remarks:** Advertising accepted; rates available upon request. **URL:** http://www.nature.com/jea/index.html. **Circ:** (Not Reported)

54751 ■ Journal of Finance and Management in Public Services
Chartered Institute of Public Finance and Accountancy
3 Robert St.
London WC2N 6RL, United Kingdom
Ph: 44 20 75435600
Fax: 44 20 75435700
Publisher E-mail: corporate@cipfa.org
Journal disseminating research regarding public accounting practices, management, policy and governance. **Freq:** Semiannual. **Key Personnel:** Hugh Coombs, Managing Editor; Ellis Jenkins, Managing Editor. **ISSN:** 1475-1283. **URL:** http://www.cipfa.org.uk/thejournal/index.cfm; http://www.cipfa.org.uk/acipfal/journal_issues.cfm.

54752 ■ Journal of Financial Crime
Henry Stewart Publications
Russell House
28-30 Little Russell St.
London WC1A 2HN, United Kingdom
Ph: 44 20 74043040
Fax: 44 20 74042081
Publisher E-mail: gweny@henrystewart.co.uk
Journal covering authoritative and detailed information on understanding the methods used in economic crime and the steps that can be taken to avoid and combat it. **Freq:** Quarterly. **Key Personnel:** Prof. Barry A.K. Rider, Editor. **ISSN:** 1359-0790. **Subscription Rates:** US$400

individuals North America; 270 individuals Europe; 285 individuals rest of world. **URL:** http://www2.warwick.ac.uk/fac/soc/law/elj/directory/j/jfc/.

54753 ■ Journal of Financial Regulation and Compliance
Henry Stewart Publications
Russell House
28-30 Little Russell St.
London WC1A 2HN, United Kingdom
Ph: 44 20 74043040
Fax: 44 20 74042081
Publisher E-mail: gweny@henrystewart.co.uk
Journal covering the regulations and laws governing financial institutions. **Freq:** Quarterly. **Key Personnel:** Dr. Oonagh MacDonald, Managing Editor; Joanna Gray, Legal Ed. **ISSN:** 1358-1988. **Subscription Rates:** 295 individuals Europe; US$440 individuals North America; 310 individuals rest of world. **URL:** http://www2.warwick.ac.uk/fac/soc/law/elj/directory/j/jfrc/.

54754 ■ Journal of Fire Sciences
Sage Publications Ltd.
1 Oliver's Yard
55 City Rd.
London EC1Y 1SP, United Kingdom
Ph: 44 20 73248500
Fax: 44 20 73248600
Peer-reviewed journal covering fire technology. **Founded:** 1983. **Freq:** Bimonthly. **Print Method:** Offset. **Trim Size:** 6 x 9. **Cols./Page:** 1. **Col. Width:** 54 nonpareils. **Col. Depth:** 100 agate lines. **Key Personnel:** Gordon E. Hartzell, Editor; Clifford J. Jones, Editorial Advisory Board; Edward D. Weil, Assoc. Ed.; Sergei V. Levchik, Editorial Advisory Board; Michael J. Drews, Editorial Advisory Board; Yves C. Alarie, Editorial Advisory Board. **ISSN:** 0734-9041. **Subscription Rates:** US$1,567 institutions combined (print & e-access); US$1,724 institutions print (all online content); US$1,410 institutions e-access; US$1,567 institutions all online content; US$1,918 institutions backfile purchase, e-access; US$1,536 institutions print only; US$282 single issue institutional. **Remarks:** Accepts advertising. **URL:** http://www.sagepub.com/journalsProdDesc.nav?prodId=Journal201551. **Circ:** 350

54755 ■ Journal of Functional Ecology
British Ecological Society
26 Blades Ct.
Putney
London SW15 2NU, United Kingdom
Ph: 44 20 88719797
Fax: 44 20 88719779
Publisher E-mail: info@britishecologicalsociety.org
Journal covering functional ecology. **Founded:** 1987. **Freq:** Bimonthly. **Key Personnel:** Dr. Ken Thompson, Editor; Prof. Charles W. Fox, Editor. **Subscription Rates:** 896 institutions print and online; US$1,656 institutions print and online; EUR1,138 institutions print and online; US$1,934 institutions, other countries print and online. **URL:** http://www.britishecologicalsociety.org/journals_publications/functionalecology/index.php.

54756 ■ The Journal of Gemmology
Gemmological Association and Gem Testing Laboratory of Great Britain
27 Greville St.
London EC1N 8TN, United Kingdom
Ph: 44 20 74043334
Fax: 44 20 74048843
Publisher E-mail: information@gem-a.com
Journal covering gemmology. **Founded:** 1947. **Freq:** Semiannual. **Key Personnel:** Arianna Maccaferri, Contact, arianna.maccaferri@gem-a.com. **ISSN:** 1355-4565. **Subscription Rates:** Included in membership; 176 nonmembers. **URL:** http://www.gem-a.info/publications/journal-of-gemmology.aspx. **Ad Rates:** BW: 180, 4C: 230. **Circ:** 4,000

54757 ■ Journal of Global History
Cambridge University Press
c/o Prof. William Gervase Clarence-Smith, Ch. Ed.
Dept. of History
Thornhaugh St., Russell Sq.
London WC1H 0XG, United Kingdom
Publisher E-mail: information@cambridge.org
Journal addressing the main problems of global change over time, together with the diverse histories of globalization. **Key Personnel:** Prof. William Gervase Clarence-Smith, Ch. Ed., wc2@soas.ac.uk; Dr. Peer

Vries, Editor, peer.vries@univie.ac.at; Prof. Maxine Berg, Editorial Board; Dr. Ulrike Freitag, Editorial Board; Prof. Kenneth Pomeranz, Editor, klpomera@uci.edu; Dr. Gareth Austin, Editorial Board. **ISSN:** 1740-0228. **Subscription Rates:** 148 institutions online and print; US$267 institutions online and print; 140 institutions online only; US$254 institutions online only; 25 individuals print only; US$45 individuals print only. **Remarks:** Accepts advertising. **URL:** http://journals.cambridge.org/action/displayJournal?jid=JGH. **Ad Rates:** BW: 385. **Circ:** (Not Reported)

54758 ■ Journal of Hand Surgery (British & European Volume)
Mosby Inc.
c/o British Society for Surgery of the Hand
35-43 Lincoln's Inn Fields
London WC2A 3PE, United Kingdom
Ph: 44 20 78315162
Fax: 44 20 78314041
Publisher E-mail: custserv.ehs@elsevier.com
Journal publishing articles on restoring the function to the hand and upper limb. **Freq:** Bimonthly. **Key Personnel:** David Elliot, Editor, editor@journalofhandsurgery.com; Grey Giddens, Asst. Ed., greygiddins@thehandclinic.co.uk; Steven Hovius, Asst. Ed., stevenhovius@hotmail.com. **ISSN:** 0266-7681. **Subscription Rates:** EUR575 institutions; US$510 institutions all Countries except Europe and Japan; 62,100¥ institutions; EUR179 individuals; US$159 individuals all Countries except Europe and Japan; 19,200¥ individuals; EUR356 individuals; US$317 individuals for all Countries except Europe and Japan; 38,400¥ individuals. **Remarks:** Accepts advertising. **URL:** http://www.elsevier.com/wps/find/journaldescription.cws_home/623053/descriptiondescription. **Circ:** (Not Reported)

54759 ■ Journal of Health Psychology
Sage Publications Ltd.
1 Oliver's Yard
55 City Rd.
London EC1Y 1SP, United Kingdom
Ph: 44 20 73248500
Fax: 44 20 73248600
Peer-reviewed journal covering research in health psychology worldwide. **Subtitle:** An Interdisciplinary, International Journal. **Founded:** 1996. **Freq:** 8/yr. **Key Personnel:** David F. Marks, Editor; Michael Murray, Reviews Ed.; Chris McManus, Assoc. Ed.; Robert M. Kaplan, Assoc. Ed.; Catherine Campbell, Editorial Board; Kenneth A. Wallston, Assoc. Ed.; Suzanne Bennett Johnson, Editorial Board. **ISSN:** 1359-1053. **Subscription Rates:** US$1,695 individuals combined (print & e-access); US$1,865 institutions print & all online; US$1,526 institutions e-access; US$1,696 institutions all online content; US$1,526 institutions backfile purchase, e-access; US$1,661 institutions print only; US$100 individuals print only; US$228 single issue institutional; US$16 single issue individual. **Remarks:** Accepts advertising. **URL:** http://www.sagepub.com/journalsProdDesc.nav?prodId=Journal200899. **Circ:** (Not Reported)

54760 ■ Journal of Health Services Research & Policy
Royal Society of Medicine Press Ltd.
1 Wimpole St.
London W1G 0AE, United Kingdom
Ph: 44 20 72902921
Fax: 44 20 72902929
Publisher E-mail: publishing@rsm.ac.uk
Peer-reviewed journal covering scientific research in many areas of health and the relationship between health services research and health policy. **Founded:** Jan. 1996. **Freq:** Quarterly. **Trim Size:** 210 x 297 mm. **Cols./Page:** 2. **Key Personnel:** Nick Black, Editor; Nicholas Mays, Editor. **ISSN:** 1355-8196. **Subscription Rates:** 263 institutions UK & Europe; US$517 institutions for U.S.; 269 elsewhere; 136 individuals print & online; US$213 individuals print & online; 142 other countries print & online; EUR357 institutions; EUR185 individuals. **Remarks:** Accepts advertising. **URL:** http://jhsrp.rsmjournals.com/. **Circ:** (Not Reported)

54761 ■ Journal of Hellenic Studies
Society for the Promotion of Hellenic Studies
Senate House
Malet St.
London WC1E 7HU, United Kingdom
Ph: 44 20 78628730

Circulation: ★ = ABC; △ = BPA; ◆ = CAC; • = CCAB; ❏ = VAC; ⊕ = PO Statement; ‡ = Publisher's Report; Boldface figures = sworn; Light figures = estimated.

Gale Directory of Publications & Broadcast Media/147th Ed.   5735

Fax: 44 20 78628731
Publisher E-mail: office@hellenicsociety.org.uk
Publication covering Hellenic studies. **Freq:** Annual. **Key Personnel:** Dr. Riet van Bremen, Editorial Committee; Prof. M.M. McCabe, Editorial Committee; Prof. Robin Osborne, Editorial Committee; Prof. Malcolm Schofield, President; Dr. Poly Low, Book Review Ed.; Prof. Edith Hall, Editorial Committee; Dr. Angus Bowie, Editor. **Remarks:** Advertising accepted; rates available upon request. **URL:** http://www.hellenicsociety.org.uk. **Circ:** 3,100

54762 ■ Journal of High Energy Physics
Springer-Verlag London Ltd.
236 Gray's Inn Rd., 6th Fl.
London WC1X 8HB, United Kingdom
Ph: 44 20 31922000
Publication E-mail: jhep@iop.org
Journal encompassing the following areas of theoretical and experimental physics: Collider Physics, Underground and Large Array Physics, Astroparticles, Gauge Field Theories, General Relativity and Gravitation, Mathematical Methods of Physics, Solvable Models, Strong Interactions, Weak Interactions, Quantum Field Theory, Statistical Field Theories, String Theory, Supersymmetry, Duality, Branes. **Freq:** Monthly. **Key Personnel:** M. Albrow, Editorial Board; G. Altarelli, Editorial Board; J. Bagger, Editorial Board. **ISSN:** 1029-8479. **Subscription Rates:** EUR1,879 institutions print + online. **URL:** http://www.springer.com/physics/particleandnuclearphysics/journal/13130.

54763 ■ Journal of Human Hypertension
Nature Publishing Group
The Macmillan Bldg.
4 Crinan St.
London N1 9XW, United Kingdom
Ph: 44 20 78334000
Fax: 44 20 78434640
Peer-reviewed journal dealing with all clinical aspects of human hypertension. **Freq:** Monthly. **Key Personnel:** M. Stowasser, Assoc. Ed.; G.Y.H. Lip, Co-Ed. **ISSN:** 0950-9240. **Subscription Rates:** US$468 individuals online only; US$522 individuals print and online; EUR414 individuals print and online; EUR373 individuals online only; 70,900¥ individuals print and online; 63,700¥ individuals online only; 267.54 other countries print and online; 240 other countries online only. **Remarks:** Advertising accepted; rates available upon request. **URL:** http://www.nature.com/jhh/index.html. **Circ:** (Not Reported)

54764 ■ Journal of Hydroinformatics
IWA Publishing Ltd.
Alliance House
12 Caxton St.
London SW1H 0QS, United Kingdom
Ph: 44 20 76545500
Fax: 44 20 76545555
Peer-reviewed journal devoted to the application of information technology in the widest sense to problems of the aquatic environment. **Freq:** 4/yr. **Key Personnel:** Dragan Savic, Editor-in-Chief, d.savic@exeter.ac.uk. **ISSN:** 1464-7141. **Subscription Rates:** US$786 institutions; EUR692 institutions; 444 institutions. **URL:** http://www.iwaponline.com/jh/default.htm.

54765 ■ Journal of Immune Based Therapies and Vaccines
BioMed Central Ltd.
236 Gray's Inn Rd., Fl. 6
34-42 Cleveland St.
London WC1X 8HL, United Kingdom
Ph: 44 20 31922000
Fax: 44 20 31922010
Publisher E-mail: info@biomedcentral.com
Online journal covering all aspects of immune based therapies and vaccines. **Key Personnel:** Dr. Robert W. Malone, Editor-in-Chief, shotdoc92130@yahoo.com; Dr. Jonathan Angel, Editorial Board, jangel@ottawahospital.on.ca; Michele Harden, Assoc. Ed., phone 760519-8166, micheleharden@sbcglobal.net; Dr. Arthur Kavanaugh, Editorial Board, akavanaugh@ucsd.edu; Dr. Zvi Bentwich, Editorial Board, zbentwich@rosettagenomics.com; Prof. Frances Gotch, Editorial Board, f.gotch@ic.ac.uk. **ISSN:** 1476-8518. **Remarks:** Accepts advertising. **URL:** http://www.jibtherapies.com. **Circ:** (Not Reported)

54766 ■ Journal of Industrial Textiles
Sage Publications Ltd.
1 Oliver's Yard
55 City Rd.

London EC1Y 1SP, United Kingdom
Ph: 44 20 73248500
Fax: 44 20 73248600
Peer-reviewed journal for the coated fabrics and textiles industry. **Founded:** June 1972. **Freq:** Quarterly. **Print Method:** Offset. **Trim Size:** 6 x 9. **Cols./Page:** 1. **Col. Width:** 54 nonpareils. **Col. Depth:** 100 agate lines. **Key Personnel:** Dong Zhang, Editor; William C. Smith, Editor-in-Chief. **ISSN:** 1528-0837. **Subscription Rates:** US$1,112 institutions print & e-access; US$1,223 institutions print (all online content); US$1,001 institutions e-access; US$1,112 institutions e-access; US$2,297 institutions e-access (content through 1998); US$1,090 institutions print only; US$300 institutions single print. **Remarks:** Accepts advertising. **URL:** http://www.sagepub.com/journalsProdDesc.nav?prodId=Journal201552. **Formerly:** Journal of Coated Fabrics (July 1, 2000). **Circ:** ‡260

54767 ■ Journal of Inflammation
BioMed Central Ltd.
236 Gray's Inn Rd., Fl. 6
34-42 Cleveland St.
London WC1X 8HL, United Kingdom
Ph: 44 20 31922000
Fax: 44 20 31922010
Publication E-mail: editorial@journal-inflammation.com
Publisher E-mail: info@biomedcentral.com
Journal on inflammation. **Key Personnel:** Paul Kirkman, Editor-in-Chief, p.kirkham@imperial.ac.uk; Dennis Taub, Editor-in-Chief, taubd@grc.nia.nih.gov; Dr. Chris Bolton, Editorial Board, dr.chrisbolton@talk21.com. **ISSN:** 1476-9255. **URL:** http://www.journal-inflammation.com.

54768 ■ Journal of Information Science
Sage Publications Ltd.
1 Oliver's Yard
55 City Rd.
London EC1Y 1SP, United Kingdom
Ph: 44 20 73248500
Fax: 44 20 73248600
Publication covering library and information science. **Freq:** Bimonthly. **Print Method:** Litho. **Trim Size:** 276 x 210 mm. **Key Personnel:** Adrian Dale, Editor; Alan Gilchrist, Assoc. Ed.; Ronald N. Kostoff, Assoc. Ed. **ISSN:** 0165-5515. **Subscription Rates:** US$660 institutions print & e-access; US$726 institutions current volume print & all online content; US$594 institutions E-access; US$660 institutions all online content; US$1,212 institutions content through 1998; US$647 institutions print only; US$96 individuals print only; US$119 institutions single print; US$21 individuals single print. **Remarks:** Advertising not accepted. **Online:** Gale. **URL:** http://www.sagepub.com/journalsProdDesc.nav?prodId=Journal201676. **Circ:** (Not Reported)

54769 ■ Journal of Intellectual Disabilities
Sage Publications Ltd.
1 Oliver's Yard
55 City Rd.
London EC1Y 1SP, United Kingdom
Ph: 44 20 73248500
Fax: 44 20 73248600
Scholarly journal covering best practice, knowledge and research from the academic and professional disciplines of education and social and health care committed to the advancement of services for people with learning disabilities. **Founded:** 1997. **Freq:** Quarterly. **Key Personnel:** Dr. Owen Barr, Editor-in-Chief; Dr. Steve McNally, Forthcoming Events/Reports Ed.; Prof. Bob Gates, Founding Ed.; Mr. Derek Jones, Editorial Committee; Prof. Robert Newell, Statistical Reviewers; Jill Manthorpe, Editorial Committee; Prof. Chris Cullen, Editorial Committee. **ISSN:** 1744-6295. **Subscription Rates:** US$929 institutions combined (print & e-access); US$1,022 institutions current volume print & all online; US$836 institutions e-access; US$929 individuals all online content; US$836 institutions backfile purchase, e-access; US$910 institutions print only; US$89 individuals print only; US$250 single issue institutional; US$29 single issue individual. **Remarks:** Accepts advertising. **URL:** http://www.sagepub.com/journalsProdDesc.nav?prodId=Journal201355. **Formerly:** Journal of Learning Disabilities. **Circ:** (Not Reported)

54770 ■ Journal of Intelligent Material Systems and Structures
Sage Publications Ltd.
1 Oliver's Yard

55 City Rd.
London EC1Y 1SP, United Kingdom
Ph: 44 20 73248500
Fax: 44 20 73248600
Peer-reviewed journal reporting the results of experimental and theoretical work of intelligent materials systems and structures research. **Founded:** 1990. **Freq:** 18/yr. **Trim Size:** 8 1/2 x 11. **Key Personnel:** Daniel J. Inman, Editor-in-Chief; Norman M. Wereley, Editor; Ian Bond, Assoc. Ed. **ISSN:** 1045-389X. **Subscription Rates:** 1,664 institutions print & e-access; 1,830 institutions backfile current volume print & all online content; 1,498 institutions e-access; 1,664 institutions e-access plus backfile (all online content); 1,498 institutions backfile purchase, e-access; 1,631 institutions print only; 100 institutions single print. **Remarks:** Accepts advertising. **URL:** http://www.sagepub.co.uk/journalsProdDesc.nav?prodId=Journal201582. **Circ:** 300

54771 ■ Journal of International Marketing
Institute of International Marketing
PO Box 70
London E13 0UU, United Kingdom
Ph: 44 20 8700422072
Fax: 44 20 8700422062
Publication E-mail: info@journalofinternationalmarketing.com
Publisher E-mail: info@aim-org.com
Journal covering worldwide marketing. **Freq:** Periodic February, June and October. **ISSN:** 1069-031X. **Subscription Rates:** Free to IIM students or members; 20 nonmembers online read/downloads; 35 nonmembers online read/downloads; 20 nonmembers online only; 40.25 nonmembers hardcopy (UK/Europe); 43.75 nonmembers hardcopy (othre countries). **URL:** http://www.aim-org.com/; http://www.journalofinternationalmarketing.com/.

54772 ■ Journal of Location Based Services
Taylor & Francis Group Journals
School of Informatics
City University
London EC1V 0HB, United Kingdom
Publisher E-mail: customerservice@taylorandfrancis.com
Peer-reviewed journal focusing on network mobile devices. **Freq:** Quarterly. **Key Personnel:** Jonathan Raper, Editor-in-Chief, jlbs@tandf.co.uk; Georg Gartner, Assoc. Ed.; Hassan Karimi, Assoc. Ed. **ISSN:** 1748-9725. **Subscription Rates:** 211 institutions print and online; 201 institutions online; 53 individuals; US$347 institutions print and online; US$329 institutions online; US$88 individuals; EUR276 institutions print and online; EUR263 institutions online only; EUR70 individuals. **URL:** http://www.tandf.co.uk/journals/titles/17489725.asp.

54773 ■ Journal of Logic and Computation
Oxford University Press
c/o D.M. Gabbay, Ed.-in-Ch.
Dept. of Computer Science
Kings College London
Strand
London WC2R 2LS, United Kingdom
Publisher E-mail: webenquiry.uk@oup.com
Journal promoting the growth of logic and computing, including, among others, the following areas of interest: logical systems, such as classical and non-classical logic, constructive logic, categorical logic, modal logic, type theory, feasible maths, logical issues in logic programming, knowledge-based systems and automated reasoning; logical issues in knowledge representation, such as non-monotonic reasoning and systems of knowledge and belief; logics and semantics of programming; specification and verification of programs and systems; applications of logic in hardware and VLSI, natural language, concurrent computation, planning, and databases. **Freq:** 6/yr. **Key Personnel:** D.M. Gabbay, Editor-in-Chief; H. Barringer, Editorial Board; S. Abramsky, Editorial Board; H. Barendregt, Editorial Board; J. Van Benthem, Editorial Board; K.R. Apt, Editorial Board; H.D. Ehrich, Editorial Board; M. Fitting, Editorial Board; J. Halpern, Editorial Board. **ISSN:** 0955-792X. **Subscription Rates:** 931 institutions print and online; US$776 institutions print and online; EUR854 institutions print and online; 745 institutions print, online; US$621 institutions print, online; EUR683 institutions print, online; 323 individuals print; US$209 members print. **Remarks:** Advertising accepted; rates available upon request. **URL:** http://logcom.oxfordjournals.org. **Circ:** (Not Reported)

54774 ■ Journal of Manual & Manipulative Therapy
Maney Publishing
1 Carlton House Ter.
London SW1Y 5AF, United Kingdom
Ph: 44 20 74517300
Fax: 44 20 74517307
Publisher E-mail: maney@maney.co.uk
Peer-reviewed journal covering manual and manipulative therapy. **Freq:** Quarterly. **Key Personnel:** Chad Cook, Editor, jmmtcook@gmail.com. **ISSN:** 1066-9817. **Subscription Rates:** 190 institutions, other countries; US$319 institutions; 62 other countries; US$98 individuals; 74 individuals in UK and European. **Remarks:** Accepts advertising. **URL:** http://maney.co.uk/index.php/journals/jmt. **Circ:** (Not Reported)

54775 ■ Journal for Maritime Research
Friends of the National Maritime Museum
Greenwich
London SE10 9NF, United Kingdom
Ph: 44 20 83126632
Publication E-mail: jmr@nmm.ac.uk
Publisher E-mail: comments@nmm.ac.uk
Journal covering research in the field of maritime and naval history focusing on the political, social and economic aspects. **Founded:** 1999. **Key Personnel:** Dr. Robert Blyth, Editor; Dr. Martin Wilcox, Review Ed. **ISSN:** 1469-1957. **Subscription Rates:** 20 individuals; 95 institutions; 15 members; 10 students. **URL:** http://www.jmr.nmm.ac.uk/.

54776 ■ Journal of Material Culture
Sage Publications Ltd.
Dept. of Anthropology
University College London
Gower St.
London WC1E 6BT, United Kingdom
Scholarly journal covering the relationship between artifacts and social relations. **Founded:** 1996. **Freq:** Quarterly. **Key Personnel:** Danny Miller, Series Ed.; Susanne Kuechler, Series Ed.; Christopher Pinney, Series Ed.; Mike Rowlands, Series Ed.; Christopher Pinney, Managing Editor; James Clifford, Editorial Board; Nicholas J. Thomas, Editorial Board; Paul Basu, Managing Editor. **ISSN:** 1359-1835. **Subscription Rates:** US$831 institutions combined (print & e-access); US$914 institutions combined plus backfile current volume print & all; US$748 institutions e-access; US$831 institutions e-access plus backfile (all online content); US$748 institutions e-access (content through 1998); US$814 institutions print only; US$85 individuals print only; US$224 institutions single print; US$28 individuals single print. **Remarks:** Accepts advertising. **URL:** http://www.sagepub.com/journalsProdDesc.nav?prodId=Journal200859. **Circ:** (Not Reported)

54777 ■ Journal of Media Practice
Intellect
Russell Square House
10-12 Russell Sq.
London WC1B 5EE, United Kingdom
Ph: 44 20 73312000
Fax: 44 20 73312040
Publisher E-mail: info@intellectuk.org
Peer-reviewed journal covering the practical work in media teaching and research. **Founded:** 2000. **Freq:** 3/yr. **Key Personnel:** Lina Khatib, Editor, lina.khatib@rhul.ac.uk. **ISSN:** 1468-2753. **Subscription Rates:** 33 individuals print; 210 institutions print; 12 single issue print; US$65 individuals per volume; US$330 institutions print and online; US$265 institutions online; 177 institutions online; US$24 single issue. **URL:** http://www.intellectbooks.co.uk/journals/view-Journal,id=132/.

54778 ■ Journal of Medical Biography
Royal Society of Medicine
1 Wimpole St.
London W1G 0AE, United Kingdom
Ph: 44 20 72902900
Fax: 44 20 72902989
Journal covering medicine. **Freq:** Quarterly. **Key Personnel:** Dr. Christopher Gardner-Thorpe, Editor, jmbproduction@rsm.ac.uk; John M.T. Ford, Editorial Board; Harold Ellis, Editorial Board; Penelope Hunting, Editorial Board; Adrian Marston, Editorial Board. **ISSN:** 0967-7720. **Subscription Rates:** 155 institutions print only, UK and Europe; EUR210 institutions print only, Europe; US$309 institutions print only; 161 institutions,

other countries; US$79 individuals UK and Europe; EUR108 individuals; US$164 individuals; 85 individuals rest of the world. **URL:** http://jmb.rsmjournals.com.

54779 ■ Journal of Medical Ethics
BMJ Publishing Group
BMA House
Tavistock Sq.
London WC1H 9JR, United Kingdom
Ph: 44 20 73834410
Fax: 44 20 73876400
Publisher E-mail: customerservice.group@bmjgroup.com
Peer-reviewed Journal dealing with the entire field of medical ethics. **Founded:** 1975. **Freq:** Monthly. **Key Personnel:** John Harris, Editor, john.m.harris@manchester.ac.uk; Prof. Soren Holm, Editor, holms@cardiff.ac.uk; Lisa Bortolotti, Eletters Ed., l.bortolotti@bham.ac.uk; Dr. Steve Wilkinson, Board Member; Richard Ashcroft, Dep. Ed., r.ashcroft@qmul.ac.uk; Nikola Biller-Andorno, Dep. Ed., biller-andorno@ethik.unizh.ch; Allison Lang, Publisher, alang@bmjgroup.com; Kenneth Boyd, Dep. Ed., almq59@dial.pipex.com. **ISSN:** 0306-6800. **Subscription Rates:** EUR263 individuals print and online; 195 individuals print and online; US$380 individuals print and online; 115 individuals online only; EUR155 individuals online only; US$224 individuals online only. **Remarks:** Advertising accepted; rates available upon request. **URL:** http://jme.bmj.com/. **Circ:** ‡1,850

54780 ■ Journal of Medical Genetics
BMJ Publishing Group
BMA House
Tavistock Sq.
London WC1H 9JR, United Kingdom
Ph: 44 20 73834410
Fax: 44 20 73876400
Publication E-mail: jmg@bmjgroup.com
Publisher E-mail: customerservice.group@bmjgroup.com
Peer-reviewed journal covering original research in human genetics. **Founded:** 1964. **Freq:** Monthly. **Key Personnel:** Allison Lang, Publisher, alang@bmjgroup.com; Constantin Polychronakos, Editor, constantin.polychronakos@mcgill.ca; Andrew Griffith, Editorial Board; David T. Bonthron, Assoc. Ed., d.t.bonthron@leeds.ac.uk; Diana M. Eccles, Assoc. Ed., de1@soton.ac.uk; Nicola Ragge, Assoc. Ed., nicky.ragge@dpag.ox.ac.uk. **ISSN:** 0022-2593. **Subscription Rates:** US$419 individuals print and online; US$224 individuals online only; 215 individuals print and online; EUR290 individuals print and online; EUR155 individuals online only; 115 individuals online only. **URL:** http://jmg.bmj.com/. **Circ:** ‡1,495

54781 ■ Journal of Medical Screening
Royal Society of Medicine Press Ltd.
1 Wimpole St.
London W1G 0AE, United Kingdom
Ph: 44 20 72902921
Fax: 44 20 72902929
Publication E-mail: jmsproduction@rsm.ac.uk
Publisher E-mail: publishing@rsm.ac.uk
Journal concerned with all aspects of medical screening. **Freq:** Quarterly. **Key Personnel:** Prof. Nicholas Wald, Editor. **ISSN:** 0969-1413. **Subscription Rates:** 237 institutions UK & Europe; EUR322 institutions Europe; US$467 institutions, 243 institutions, other countries; 125 individuals UK & Europe; EUR169 individuals Europe; US$251 individuals; 131 other countries; 213 individuals online only; EUR290 individuals online only. **URL:** http://jms.rsmjournals.com.

54782 ■ Journal of Microencapsulation
Taylor & Francis Group Journals
c/o Prof. Oya Alpar, Ed.-in-Ch.
University of London, Centre for Drug Delivery Research
The School of Pharmacy
29-39 Brunswick Sq.
London WC1N 1AX, United Kingdom
Publisher E-mail: customerservice@taylorandfrancis.com
Peer-reviewed journal covering the preparation, properties and uses of individually encapsulated novel small particles, as well as significant improvements to tried-and-tested techniques relevant to micro and nano particles. **Founded:** 1994. **Freq:** 8/yr. **Key Personnel:** M. Alonso, Editorial Board; Hossain Zia, Regional Ed.; Yoshiaka Kawashima, Regional Ed.; Tony L. Whateley, Editorial Board; Prof. Oya Alpar, Editor-in-Chief, oya.

alpar@pharmacy.ac.uk; J.R. Nixon, Founding Ed. **ISSN:** 0265-2048. **Subscription Rates:** US$1,600 institutions print + online; US$1,600 institutions online; US$1,600 individuals online; US$1,600 individuals print + online. **Remarks:** Accepts advertising. **URL:** http://www.informaworld.com/smpp/title~db=all~content=g790330243~tab=linking. **Circ:** (Not Reported)

54783 ■ Journal of Nanobiotechnology
BioMed Central Ltd.
236 Gray's Inn Rd., Fl. 6
34-42 Cleveland St.
London WC1X 8HL, United Kingdom
Ph: 44 20 31922000
Fax: 44 20 31922010
Publisher E-mail: info@biomedcentral.com
Peer-reviewed journal disseminating investigations on scientific and technological advances in medical, biological and nanoscale sciences. **Key Personnel:** Dr. Mikhail Soloviev, Editor-in-Chief, mikhail.soloviev@rhul.ac.uk; Dr. Alan Bateson, Editorial Board, a.n.bateson@leeds.ac.uk; Dr. Michel.Bottlaender, Editorial Board, bottlaen@shfj.cea.fr. **ISSN:** 1477-3155. **Remarks:** Advertising accepted; rates available upon request. **URL:** http://www.jnanobiotechnology.com/info/about/. **Circ:** (Not Reported)

54784 ■ Journal of Negative Results in BioMedicine
BioMed Central Ltd.
236 Gray's Inn Rd., Fl. 6
34-42 Cleveland St.
London WC1X 8HL, United Kingdom
Ph: 44 20 31922000
Fax: 44 20 31922010
Publisher E-mail: info@biomedcentral.com
Online journal covering all aspects of unexpected, controversial, provocative and/or negative results/conclusions in the context of current tenets, providing scientists and physicians with responsible and balanced information to support informed experimental and clinical decisions. **Key Personnel:** Dr. Bjorn R. Olsen, Editor-in-Chief; Dr. Christian Pfeffer, Dep. Ed.; Dr. Alan Beggs, Editorial Board. **ISSN:** 1477-5751. **Remarks:** Accepts advertising. **URL:** http://www.jnrbm.com. **Circ:** (Not Reported)

54785 ■ Journal of NeuroEngineering and Rehabilitation (JNER)
BioMed Central Ltd.
236 Gray's Inn Rd., Fl. 6
34-42 Cleveland St.
London WC1X 8HL, United Kingdom
Ph: 44 20 31922000
Fax: 44 20 31922010
Publisher E-mail: info@biomedcentral.com
Journal concerned with research works in neuroscience and biomedical engineering that in fact are restructuring physical medicine & rehabilitation. **Key Personnel:** Dr. Paolo Bonato, Editor-in-Chief, pbonato@partners.org; Dr. Metin Akay, Assoc. Ed., phone 480965-7447, fax 480727-0789, metin.akay@asu.edu; Dr. Emilio Bizzi, Assoc. Ed., ebizzi@mit.edu. **ISSN:** 1743-0003. **Remarks:** Advertising accepted; rates available upon request. **URL:** http://www.jneuroengrehab.com/. **Circ:** (Not Reported)

54786 ■ Journal of Neuroinflammation
BioMed Central Ltd.
236 Gray's Inn Rd., Fl. 6
34-42 Cleveland St.
London WC1X 8HL, United Kingdom
Ph: 44 20 31922000
Fax: 44 20 31922010
Publication E-mail: editorial@jneuroinflammation.com
Publisher E-mail: info@biomedcentral.com
Online journal covering all aspects of innate immunological responses of the central nervous system. **Key Personnel:** Dr. Sue T. Griffin, Editor-in-Chief, griffinsuet@uams.edu; Dr. Steven W. Barger, Editorial Board; Dr. Robert E. Mrak, Editor-in-Chief, robert.mrak@utoledo.edu; Dr. Etty N. Benveniste, Editorial Board; Dr. Greg M. Cole, Editorial Board; Dr. David H. Cribbs, Editorial Board. **ISSN:** 1742-2094. **Remarks:** Accepts advertising. **URL:** http://www.jneuroinflammation.com/home/. **Circ:** (Not Reported)

Circulation: ★ = ABC; △ = BPA; ♦ = CAC; • = CCAB; ❏ = VAC; ⊕ = PO Statement; ‡ = Publisher's Report; Boldface figures = sworn; Light figures = estimated.

54787 ■ Journal of Neurology, Neurosurgery, and Psychiatry
BMJ Publishing Group
BMA House
Tavistock Sq.
London WC1H 9JR, United Kingdom
Ph: 44 20 73834410
Fax: 44 20 73876400
Publisher E-mail: customerservice.group@bmjgroup.com
Peer-reviewed Journal reporting results of investigations in the field of clinical neurological practice, neurosurgery & neuropsychiatry. **Freq:** 18/yr. **Key Personnel:** Prof. Martin Rossor, Ed. Emeritus; Prof. Mike G. Hanna, Dep. Ed., mhanna@ion.ucl.ac.uk. **ISSN:** 0022-3050. **Subscription Rates:** 255 individuals print and online; EUR344 individuals print and online; US$497 individuals print and online; 145 individuals online only; EUR196 individuals online only; US$283 individuals online only. **URL:** http://jnnp.bmj.com/.

54788 ■ Journal News
British Tarantula Society
3 Shepham Ln.
Polegate
East Sussex
London BN26 6LZ, United Kingdom
Ph: 44 95 6438187
Publisher E-mail: webmaster@thebts.co.uk
Journal containing articles about arachnoculture, particularly tarantula spiders. **ISSN:** 0962-449X. **Remarks:** Accepts advertising. **URL:** http://www.thebts.co.uk/framset.htm. **Circ:** (Not Reported)

54789 ■ The Journal of Operational Risk
Incisive Media Limited
Haymarket House
28-29 Haymarket
London SW1Y 4RX, United Kingdom
Ph: 44 870 2408859
Fax: 44 207 4849797
Publisher E-mail: customerservices@incisivemedia.com
Peer-reviewed journal focusing on the measurement and management of operational risk. **Freq:** Quarterly. **Key Personnel:** Marcelo Cruz, Editor-in-Chief. **Subscription Rates:** 479 institutions and practitioner; non-academic; EUR722 institutions and practitioner; non-academic; US$909 institutions and practitioner; non-academic; 210 individuals academic; EUR317 individuals academic; US$399 individuals academic. **Remarks:** Accepts advertising. **URL:** http://www.journalofoperationalrisk.com. **Circ:** (Not Reported)

54790 ■ Journal of Organisational Transformation and Social Change
Intellect
Russell Square House
10-12 Russell Sq.
London WC1B 5EE, United Kingdom
Ph: 44 20 73312000
Fax: 44 20 73312000
Publisher E-mail: info@intellectuk.org
Journal looking to research on the shaping of organizational theory through more traditional areas like human resource development and management systems - that has led to recent changes. **Founded:** 2004. **Freq:** 3/yr. **Key Personnel:** Maurice Yolles, Editor, m.yolles@livjm.ac.uk; Paul Iles, Editor, p.iles@leedsmet.ac.uk; Ann Mulhaney, Asst. Ed., a.mulhaney@livjm.ac.uk. **ISSN:** 1477-9633. **Subscription Rates:** 33 individuals print; 210 institutions print and online; 12 single issue print; 177 institutions online only. **URL:** http://www.intellectbooks.co.uk/journals/view-Journal,id=128/.

54791 ■ Journal of Outcomes Research
PJB Publications Ltd.
Telephone House
69-77 Paul St.
London EC2A 4LQ, United Kingdom
Ph: 44 20 70175000
Fax: 44 20 70176792
Publisher E-mail: pjb.enquiries@informa.com
Journal covering research on the effectiveness of normal medical practice, including measurements of therapeutic and/or preventative outcomes, including quality of life studies and patient-reported outcomes. **Founded:** 1997. **Freq:** Irregular. **Print Method:** Litho. **Trim Size:** 172 x 248 mm. **Key Personnel:** Prof. M. Hyland, Editorial Board; Prof. K. Lee, Editor-in-Chief; Dr. G. Hawthorne, Editorial Board. **ISSN:** 1369-698X. **Remarks:** Advertising not accepted. **URL:** http://www.pjbpubs.com/

outcomes_research/index.htm. **Circ:** (Not Reported)

54792 ■ Journal of Paramedic Practice
MA Healthcare Ltd.
St. Jude's Church
Dulwich Rd.
Herne Hill
London SE24 0PB, United Kingdom
Ph: 44 20 77385454
Fax: 44 20 77332325
Peer-reviewed journal for paramedic professionals. **Freq:** Monthly. **Key Personnel:** Sarah David, Editor, sarah.david@markallengroup.com; Kirsty Medlock, Advertising Mgr., kirsty.medlock@markallengroup.com. **Subscription Rates:** 106 individuals UK & Eire; EUR177 individuals Europe; US$258 other countries; 70 students UK & Eire. **Remarks:** Accepts advertising. **URL:** http://www.paramedicpractice.com. **Circ:** (Not Reported)

54793 ■ Journal of Peace Research
Sage Publications Ltd.
1 Oliver's Yard
55 City Rd.
London EC1Y 1SP, United Kingdom
Ph: 44 20 73248500
Fax: 44 20 73248600
Peer-reviewed journal covering peace research, including causes of violence, methods of conflict resolution and sustaining peace. **Subtitle:** Published Under the Auspices of IPRA. **Founded:** 1964. **Freq:** Bimonthly. **Key Personnel:** Henrik Urdal, Assoc. Ed.; Nils Petter Gleditsch, Editor; Bertrand Abadie, Managing Editor; Michael Brzoska, Assoc. Ed.; Patrick M. Regan, Assoc. Ed.; Scott Gates, Assoc. Ed.; Herbert Addo, International Advisory Board; Erik Allardt, International Advisory Board; Han Dorussen, Assoc. Ed. **ISSN:** 0022-3433. **Subscription Rates:** US$1,332 institutions print & e-access; US$1,465 institutions current volume print & all online content; US$1,199 institutions e-access; US$1,332 institutions e-access plus backfile (all online content); US$3,567 institutions e-access; US$1,305 institutions print only; US$130 individuals print only; US$239 institutions single print; US$28 individuals single print. **Remarks:** Accepts advertising. **URL:** http://www.sagepub.com/journalsProdDesc.nav?prodId=Journal200751. **Circ:** (Not Reported)

54794 ■ Journal of Pension Economics and Finance
Cambridge University Press
c/o Steven Haberman, Ed.
Cass Business School
City University
Northampton Sq.
London EC1V 0HB, United Kingdom
Publisher E-mail: information@cambridge.org
Journal focusing on the economics and finance of pensions and retirement income. **Key Personnel:** Prof. Jeffrey Brown, Editorial Board, brown@nber.org; Andre Laboul, Managing Editor, andre.laboul@oecd.org; Steven Haberman, Editor, s.haberman@city.ac.uk; Dr. Moshe Milevsky, Editorial Board, milevsky@yorku.ca; Dr. Michael J. Orszag, Sen. Ed., mike.orszag@watsonwyatt.com. **ISSN:** 1474-7472. **Subscription Rates:** 149 institutions online and print; US$249 institutions online and print; 139 institutions online only; US$229 institutions online only. **Remarks:** Accepts advertising. **URL:** http://journals.cambridge.org/action/displayJournal?jid=PEF. **Ad Rates:** BW: 445. **Circ:** 400

54795 ■ Journal of Petroleum Technology
Society of Petroleum Engineers
3rd Fl., Portland House
4 Great Portland St.
London W1W 8QJ, United Kingdom
Ph: 44 20 72993300
Fax: 44 20 72993309
Publisher E-mail: spelon@spe.org
Journal covering petroleum technology. **Freq:** Monthly. **Key Personnel:** John Donnelly, Editor, jdonnelly@spe.org; Dennis Denney, Sen. Tech. Ed. **Remarks:** Accepts advertising. **URL:** http://www.spe.org/; http://www.spe.org/spe-app/spe/jpt/index.htm. **Ad Rates:** BW: 5,120, 4C: 1,500. **Circ:** (Not Reported)

54796 ■ Journal of Pharmaceutical Medicine
Society of Pharmaceutical Medicine
9 Red Lion Ct.
London EC4A 3EF, United Kingdom
Ph: 44 20 79365903
Fax: 44 20 79365901

Publisher E-mail: spm@iob.org
Journal covering pharmaceutical medicine. **Freq:** Bimonthly. **Key Personnel:** Susan Pochon, Editor-in-Chief. **ISSN:** 1364-9027. **Subscription Rates:** US$799 institutions print & electronic; US$790 institutions electronic only; US$340 individuals print & electronic; US$335 individuals electronic only. **URL:** http://www.socpharmed.org/; http://adisonline.com/pharmaceuticalmedicine/pages/default.aspx.

54797 ■ Journal of Pharmacological and Toxicological Methods
Elsevier Science
c/o Michael J. Curtis, Ed.-in-Ch.
St. Thomas' Hospital
Rayne Institute, Dept. of Pharmacology
London SE1 7EH, United Kingdom
Ph: 44 20 71881095
Fax: 44 20.71883902
Publisher E-mail: nlinfo-f@elsevier.com
Journal focusing on latest methods of investigation used in pharmacology and toxicology. **Founded:** 1978. **Freq:** Bimonthly. **Key Personnel:** Michael J. Curtis, Editor-in-Chief, michael.curtis@kcl.ac.uk. **ISSN:** 1056-8719. **Subscription Rates:** 209,600¥ institutions; US$1,763 institutions for all countries except Europe and Japan; EUR1,579 institutions European countries; 23,300¥ individuals; EUR151 individuals; US$202 individuals. **Remarks:** Accepts advertising. **URL:** http://www.elsevier.com/wps/find/journaldescription.cws_home/505776/descriptiondescription. **Circ:** (Not Reported)

54798 ■ Journal of Philosophy of Education
John Wiley & Sons Inc.
Wiley-Blackwell
c/o Paul Standish, Ed.
Philosophy Section
Institute of Education
20 Bedford Way
London WC1H 0AL, United Kingdom
Journal covering philosophical issues related to education. **Freq:** Quarterly. **Key Personnel:** Paul Standish, Editor, p.standish@ioe.ac.uk; Bob Davis, Review Ed., r.davis@educ.gla.ac.uk; Richard Smith, Assoc. Ed., r.d.smith@durham.ac.uk. **ISSN:** 0309-8249. **Subscription Rates:** US$234 individuals print + online; US$204 members print + online; US$1,217 institutions print + online; US$1,106 institutions print or online; 651 institutions print + online; EUR176 individuals print + online; 118 individuals print + online; 591 institutions print or online; EUR825 institutions print + online; US$1,419 institutions, other countries print + online. **Remarks:** Advertising accepted; rates available upon request. **URL:** http://www.wiley.com/bw/journal.asp?ref=0309-8249. **Circ:** (Not Reported)

54799 ■ Journal of Physics B
Institute of Physics
76 Portland Pl.
London W1B 1NT, United Kingdom
Ph: 44 20 74704800
Fax: 44 20 74704848
Publication E-mail: jphysb@iop.org
Publisher E-mail: physics@iop.org
Journal of physics part B: atomic, molecular and optical. **Subtitle:** Atomic, Molecular and Optical Physics. **Freq:** Semimonthly. **Key Personnel:** Jan-Michael Rost, Editor-in-Chief; Paul Corkum, Dep. Ed. **ISSN:** 0953-4075. **Subscription Rates:** US$6,385 institutions North, Central and South America; 3,259 institutions, other countries. **URL:** http://www.iop.org/ej/journal/jphysb.

54800 ■ Journal of Physics C
Institute of Physics
76 Portland Pl.
London W1B 1NT, United Kingdom
Ph: 44 20 74704800
Fax: 44 20 74704848
Publisher E-mail: physics@iop.org
Journal of physics part C: condensed matter. **Subtitle:** Condensed Matter. **Founded:** 1989. **Freq:** Weekly. **Key Personnel:** David K. Ferry, Editor-in-Chief, ferry@asu.edu; John E. Inglesfield, Dep. Ed., inglesfield@cf.ac.uk; Hideaki Kasai, Dep. Ed., kasai@dyn.ap.eng.osaka-u.ac.jp. **ISSN:** 0953-8984. **Subscription Rates:** US$11,060 institutions North, Central and South America; 6,022 institutions, other countries. **URL:** http://www.iop.org/ej/journal/jphyscm.

54801 ■ Journal of Physics G
Institute of Physics
76 Portland Pl.

London W1B 1NT, United Kingdom
Ph: 44 20 74704800
Fax: 44 20 74704848
Publication E-mail: jphysg@iop.org
Publisher E-mail: physics@iop.org
Journal of physics G: nuclear and particle physics. **Subtitle:** Nuclear and Particle Physics. **Freq:** Monthly. **Key Personnel:** A.B. Balantekin, Editor-in-Chief; T. Motobayashi, Editorial Board; J.R. Fry, Editorial Board; G. McLaughlin, Editorial Board; B.R. Holstein, Editorial Board; A.D. Martin, Dep. Ed.; J. Cizewski, Editorial Board; N. Xu, Editorial Board. **ISSN:** 0954-3899. **Subscription Rates:** US$3,980 institutions North, Central and South America; 2,025 institutions, other countries. **URL:** http://www.iop.org/ej/journal/jphysg.

54802 ■ **The Journal of Physiology**
Physiological Society - England
Peer House
Verulam St.
London WC1X 8LZ, United Kingdom
Ph: 44 20 72695710
Fax: 44 20 72695720
Journal covering physiology. **Freq:** Semimonthly. **Key Personnel:** William A. Large, Editor-in-Chief. **ISSN:** 0022-3751. **Subscription Rates:** US$587 individuals print and online; EUR413 individuals print and online (Euro zone); 326 individuals print and online (non-Euro zone); 350 other countries print and online; US$5,597 institutions print and online; EUR3,846 institutions print and online; 3,029 institutions print and online; US$6,531 institutions, other countries print and online. **Remarks:** Advertising accepted; rates available upon request. **URL:** http://www.physoc.org; http://jp.physoc.org/. **Circ:** (Not Reported)

54803 ■ **Journal of Plastic Film and Sheeting**
Sage Publications Ltd.
1 Oliver's Yard
55 City Rd.
London EC1Y 1SP, United Kingdom
Ph: 44 20 73248500
Fax: 44 20 73248600
Journal covering plastics and packaging technology. **Founded:** 1985. **Freq:** Quarterly. **Print Method:** Offset. **Trim Size:** 6 x 9. **Cols./Page:** 1. **Col. Width:** 54 nonpareils. **Col. Depth:** 100 agate lines. **Key Personnel:** James P. Harrington, Editor; Syed S.H. Rizvi, Editorial Board; Raj Krishnaswamy, Editorial Board; John R. Wagner, Editor-in-Chief; A. Ajji, Editorial Board; Phillip T. DeLassus, Editorial Board; Douglas E. Hirt, Editorial Board; Ananda M. Chatterjee, Editorial Board; Gerard M. McNally, Editorial Board. **ISSN:** 8756-0879. **Subscription Rates:** US$1,052 institutions print & e-access; US$1,157 institutions print & all online content; US$947 institutions e-access; US$1,052 institutions all online content; US$1,127 institutions backfile purchase, e-access; US$1,031 institutions print only; US$284 institutions single print. **Remarks:** Accepts advertising. **URL:** http://www.sagepub.com/journalsProdDesc.nav?prodId=Journal201584. **Circ:** 300

54804 ■ **Journal of Portfolio Management**
Euromoney Publications PLC
Nestor House
Playhouse Yard
London EC4V 5EX, United Kingdom
Ph: 44 20 77798888
Publisher E-mail: information@euromoneyplc.com
Publication for the banking, finance, and accounting industries. **Founded:** 1974. **Freq:** Quarterly. **Key Personnel:** Frank J. Fabozzi, Editor; Peter L. Bernstein, Consulting Ed. **ISSN:** 0095-4918. **Subscription Rates:** 499 individuals; US$795 individuals; EUR542 individuals. **URL:** http://www.euromoneyplc.com/product.asp?PositionID=3147&ProductID=1927&PageID=342.

54805 ■ **Journal of Psychopharmacology**
Sage Publications Ltd.
1 Oliver's Yard
55 City Rd.
London EC1Y 1SP, United Kingdom
Ph: 44 20 73248500
Fax: 44 20 73248600
Peer-reviewed journal covering research and articles on psychopharmacology. **Subtitle:** The Official Journal of the British Association for Psychopharmacology. **Founded:** 1987. **Freq:** Monthly. **Key Personnel:** Prof. David J. Nutt, Editor; Prof. Pierre Blier, PhD, Editor. **ISSN:** 0269-8811. **Subscription Rates:** US$1,724

institutions print & e-access; US$1,896 institutions (current volume print & all online content); US$1,552 institutions e-access; US$1,724 institutions e-access plus backfile (all online content); US$1,583 institutions e-access (content through 1998); US$1,690 institutions print only; US$155 individuals print only; US$155 institutions single print; US$16 individuals single print. **Remarks:** Accepts advertising. **URL:** http://www.sagepub.com/journalsProdDesc.nav?prodId=Journal200774. **Circ:** (Not Reported)

54806 ■ **Journal of Public Health**
Faculty of Public Health
4 St. Andrew's Pl.
London NW1 4LB, United Kingdom
Ph: 44 20 79350243
Fax: 44 20 72246973
Publisher E-mail: enquiries@fph.org.uk
Journal covering public health medicine. **Freq:** Quarterly. **Key Personnel:** Prof. Selena Gray, Editor, selena.gray@uwe.ac.uk; Prof. Gabriel Leung, Editor, gmleung@hku.hk. **ISSN:** 1741-3842. **Subscription Rates:** 283 institutions print and online; 260 institutions print; 136 individuals print; US$566 institutions print and online; US$520 institutions print; US$326 individuals print; EUR425 institutions print and online; EUR390 institutions print; EUR245 individuals print. **URL:** http://jpubhealth.oupjournals.org/. **Formerly:** Journal of Public Health Medicine.

54807 ■ **Journal of Reinforced Plastics and Composites**
Sage Publications Ltd.
1 Oliver's Yard
55 City Rd.
London EC1Y 1SP, United Kingdom
Ph: 44 20 73248500
Fax: 44 20 73248600
Peer-reviewed journal covering materials, plastics, and composites. **Founded:** 1982. **Freq:** 24/yr. **Print Method:** Offset. **Trim Size:** 6 x 9. **Cols./Page:** 1. **Col. Width:** 54 nonpareils. **Col. Depth:** 100 agate lines. **Key Personnel:** George S. Springer, Editor-in-Chief. **ISSN:** 0731-6844. **Subscription Rates:** US$6,838 institutions print & e-access; US$7,522 institutions print (all online content); US$6,154 institutions e-access; US$6,838 institutions e-access (all online content); US$8,893 institutions e-access (content through 1998); US$6,701 institutions print only; US$307 institutions single print. **Remarks:** Accepts advertising. **URL:** http://www.sagepub.com/journalsProdDesc.nav?prodId=Journal201585. **Circ:** 320

54808 ■ **Journal of Renal Nursing**
MA Healthcare Ltd.
St. Jude's Church
Dulwich Rd.
Herne Hill
London SE24 0PB, United Kingdom
Ph: 44 20 77385454
Fax: 44 20 77332325
Peer-reviewed journal for renal nurses and other healthcare professionals. **Founded:** May 2009. **Freq:** Bimonthly. **Key Personnel:** Edda Hendry, Editor, edda.hendry@markallengroup.com. **Subscription Rates:** 66 individuals UK & Eire; EUR107 individuals Europe; US$154 other countries; 56 students UK & Eire. **Remarks:** Accepts advertising. **URL:** http://www.renalnursing.co.uk. **Circ:** (Not Reported)

54809 ■ **The Journal of Risk**
Incisive Media Limited
Haymarket House
28-29 Haymarket
London SW1Y 4RX, United Kingdom
Ph: 44 870 2408859
Fax: 44 207 4849797
Publisher E-mail: customerservices@incisivemedia.com
Journal covering the theoretical and empirical studies in financial risk management. **Freq:** Quarterly. **Key Personnel:** Stanislav Uryasev, Ed. Emeritus/Chm. of the Editorial Board; Farid AitSahlia, Editor-in-Chief; Carlo Acerbi, Assoc. Ed. **Subscription Rates:** 479 institutions and practitioner; non-academic; EUR722 institutions and practitioner; non-academic; US$909 institutions and practitioner; non-academic; 210 individuals academic; EUR317 individuals academic; US$399 individuals academic. **Remarks:** Accepts advertising. **URL:** http://www.journalofrisk.com/. **Circ:** (Not Reported)

54810 ■ **Journal of Risk Research**
Routledge
Taylor & Francis Group Ltd.
c/o Prof. Ragnar E. Lofstedt, Ed.-in-Ch.
Director, King Centre for Risk Management
School of Social Science & Public Policy
King College London, Strand Bldg.
London WC2R 2LS, United Kingdom
Publisher E-mail: webmaster.books@tandf.co.uk
Peer-reviewed journal publishing research articles in the field of risk management. **Freq:** 8/yr. **Key Personnel:** Prof. Ragnar E. Lofstedt, Editor-in-Chief, ragnar.lofstedt@kcl.ac.uk; Jamie K. Wardman, Managing Editor, jamie.wardman@kcl.ac.uk; Robin Cantor, Assoc. Ed.; Peter Simmons, Book Review Ed., p.simmons@uea.ac.uk; Ann Bostrom, Assoc. Ed.; Ortwin Renn, Assoc. Ed. **ISSN:** 1366-9877. **Subscription Rates:** 1,004 institutions print + online; 954 institutions online; 183 individuals; 38 individuals society; US$1,667 institutions print + online; US$1,584 institutions online; US$306 individuals; US$61 individuals society; EUR1,328 institutions print and online; EUR1,262 institutions online only. **Remarks:** Advertising accepted; rates available upon request. **URL:** http://www.tandf.co.uk/journals/titles/13669877.asp. **Circ:** (Not Reported)

54811 ■ **Journal of Roman Studies**
Society for the Promotion of Roman Studies
Senate House
Malet St.
London WC1E 7HU, United Kingdom
Ph: 44 20 78628727
Fax: 44 20 78628728
Publisher E-mail: office@romansociety.org
Journal covering Roman studies. **Founded:** 1911. **Freq:** Annual. **ISSN:** 0075-4358. **Subscription Rates:** 46 individuals; US$92 individuals; 60 institutions; US$120 institutions. **Remarks:** Accepts advertising. **URL:** http://www.romansociety.org/publications/journals/journal-of-roman-studieshtml. **Ad Rates:** BW: US$530. **Circ:** 3,200

54812 ■ **Journal of the Royal Anthropological Institute**
Royal Anthropological Institute of Great Britain and Ireland
50 Fitzroy St.
London W1T 5BT, United Kingdom
Ph: 44 20 73870455
Fax: 44 20 73888817
Publisher E-mail: admin@therai.org.uk
Journal covering the Royal Anthropological Institute. **Freq:** Quarterly. **Key Personnel:** Matthew Engelke, PhD, Editor, jrai@therai.org.uk. **ISSN:** 1359-0987. **Subscription Rates:** US$655 institutions Americas (print and premium online); US$389 institutions rest of the world (print and premium online); US$595 institutions Americas (print and standard online); 354 institutions rest of the world (print and standard online); US$565 institutions Americas (premium online only); 336 institutions rest of the world (premium online only). **Remarks:** Advertising accepted; rates available upon request. **URL:** http://www.therai.org.uk/publications/journal-of-the-royal-anthropologicalinstitute/; http://www.wiley.com/bw/journal.asp?ref=1359-0987. **Circ:** (Not Reported)

54813 ■ **Journal of the Royal Society Interface**
Royal Society
6-9 Carlton House Ter.
London SW1Y 5AG, United Kingdom
Ph: 44 20 74512500
Fax: 44 20 79302170
Publisher E-mail: info@royalsoc.ac.uk
Peer-reviewed journal highlighting research interface between the physical and life sciences. **Freq:** Monthly. **Key Personnel:** Prof. William Bonfield, Editor. **ISSN:** 1742-5689. **Subscription Rates:** 1,286 institutions online and print; US$2,391 U.S. and Canada online and print; 1,362 institutions, other countries online and print; 169 individuals; US$340 U.S. and Canada. **URL:** http://rsif.royalsocietypublishing.org/.

54814 ■ **Journal of the Royal Society of Medicine**
Royal Society of Medicine Press Ltd.
1 Wimpole St.
London W1G 0AE, United Kingdom
Ph: 44 20 72902921
Fax: 44 20 72902929

Publisher E-mail: publishing@rsm.ac.uk

General medical journal covering a range of specialities. **Freq:** Monthly. **Key Personnel:** Dr. Kamran Abbasi, Editor. **ISSN:** 0141-0768. **Subscription Rates:** 256 individuals UK & Europe, print & online; EUR349 individuals Europe; EUR505 individuals print & online; 262 other countries; 81 individuals UK & Europe; EUR111 individuals for Europe; US$168 individuals; 87 individuals rest of the world. **Remarks:** Accepts advertising. **URL:** http://jrsm.rsmjournals.com/. **Circ:** Combined 18,000

54815 ■ Journal of Sandwich Structures and Materials
Sage Publications Ltd.
1 Oliver's Yard
55 City Rd.
London EC1Y 1SP, United Kingdom
Ph: 44 20 73248500
Fax: 44 20 73248600
Peer-reviewed journal focusing on sandwich structure technology, materials, properties, design, manufacturing, applications, and performance. **Freq:** Bimonthly. **Key Personnel:** Jack R. Vinson, Editor. **ISSN:** 1099-6362. **Subscription Rates:** US$1,347 institutions print & e-access; US$1,212 institutions e-access; US$1,320 institutions print only; US$242 institutions single print. **Remarks:** Accepts advertising. **URL:** http://www.sagepub.com/journalsProdDesc.nav?prodId=Journal201586. **Circ:** (Not Reported)

54816 ■ Journal of the Science of Food and Agriculture
Society of Chemical Industry
Publications Dept.
14-15 Belgrave Sq.
London SW1X 8PS, United Kingdom
Ph: 44 20 75981500
Fax: 44 20 75981545
Publisher E-mail: secretariat@soci.org
Publication covering the science of food and agriculture. **Founded:** 1950. **Freq:** Continuous 15/yr. **Trim Size:** A4. **Key Personnel:** Prof. David Reid, Editor-in-Chief, dsreid@ucdavis.edu. **ISSN:** 0022-5142. **Subscription Rates:** 1,449 individuals print only, UK; US$3,827 individuals online; US$4,210 institutions print and online; US$2,869 individuals print only for USC; US$3,827 institutions for US, Canada and rest of the world; EUR2,468 institutions print only. **Remarks:** Accepts advertising. **URL:** http://www.soci.org/SCI/publications/jsfa.jsp. **Circ:** (Not Reported)

54817 ■ The Journal of Small Animal Practice
British Veterinary Association
7 Mansfield St.
London W1G 9NQ, United Kingdom
Ph: 44 20 76366541
Fax: 44 20 79086349
Publisher E-mail: bvahq@bva.co.uk
Official journal of the British Small Animal Veterinary Association covering clinical issues and case reports. **Founded:** 1959. **Freq:** Monthly. **Trim Size:** A4. **Cols./Page:** 3. **Col. Width:** 180 millimeters. **Col. Depth:** 250 millimeters. **Key Personnel:** Carmel T. Mooney, Editor. **ISSN:** 0022-4510. **Subscription Rates:** 236 individuals print + online; US$434 individuals print + online; EUR353 individuals print + online; 398 institutions print + online; US$736 institutions print + online; EUR505 institutions print + online. **Remarks:** Accepts advertising. **URL:** http://www.wiley.com/bw/journal.asp?ref=0022-4510. **Circ:** Paid 6,500

54818 ■ Journal of Social Archaeology
Sage Publications Ltd.
1 Oliver's Yard
55 City Rd.
London EC1Y 1SP, United Kingdom
Ph: 44 20 73248500
Fax: 44 20 73248600
Scholarly journal covering social archaeology. **Founded:** 2001. **Freq:** 3/yr. **Key Personnel:** Lynn Meskell, Editor; Joshua Pollard, Editor; Rosemary Joyce, Editorial Panel; Wendy Ashmore, Advisory Board; Gustavo Politis, Advisory Board; Robert Preucel, Editorial Panel; Arjun Appadurai, Advisory Board; Ian Hodder, Editorial Panel; Susan Alcock, Advisory Board. **ISSN:** 1469-6053. **Subscription Rates:** US$622 institutions print & e-access; US$560 institutions e-access; US$610 institutions print only; US$83 individuals print only; US$224 institutions single print; US$36 individuals single print. **Remarks:** Accepts advertising. **URL:** http://www.sagepub.com/journalsProdEditBoards.nav?prodId=Journal201500. **Circ:** (Not Reported)

54819 ■ Journal of Social and Personal Relationships
Sage Publications Ltd.
1 Oliver's Yard
55 City Rd.
London EC1Y 1SP, United Kingdom
Ph: 44 20 73248500
Fax: 44 20 73248600
Peer-reviewed journal covering social and personal relationships. **Founded:** 1984. **Freq:** 8/yr. **Key Personnel:** Dr. Paul A. Mongeau, Editor; April Trees, Advisory Board; Mark A. Fine, Former Ed.; Rebecca Cobb, Advisory Board; Duncan Cramer, Assoc. Ed.; Jacki Fitzpatrick, Assoc. Ed.; John P. Caughlin, Assoc. Ed.; Steve Duck, Founding Ed.; Larry A. Erbert, Assoc. Ed. **ISSN:** 0265-4075. **Subscription Rates:** US$1,585 institutions print & e-access; US$1,744 institutions current volume print & all online content; US$1,427 institutions e-access; US$1,586 institutions e-access plus backfile (all online content); US$1,819 institutions e-access (content through 1998); US$1,553 institutions print only; US$135 individuals print only; US$214 institutions single print; US$22 individuals single print. **Remarks:** Accepts advertising. **URL:** http://www.sagepub.com/journalsProdAdv.nav?prodId=Journal200790&currTree=Co urses&level1=K00&level2=KE0. **Circ:** (Not Reported)

54820 ■ Journal of Social Work
Sage Publications Ltd.
1 Oliver's Yard
55 City Rd.
London EC1Y 1SP, United Kingdom
Ph: 44 20 73248500
Fax: 44 20 73248600
Scholarly journal covering theory, policy and debate of key ideas in social work. **Founded:** 2001. **Freq:** Quarterly. **Key Personnel:** Shama Ahmed, Editorial Board; Jan Fook, Editorial Board; Gayla Rogers, Editorial Board; David Stanley, Editor; Robert Adams, Editorial Board; Christen Christensen, Editorial Board; Mel Gray, Editorial Board; Steven M. Shardlow, Editor-in-Chief; Stewart Collins, Review Ed.; Cherry Rowlings, Editorial Board. **ISSN:** 1468-0173. **Subscription Rates:** US$677 institutions print & e-access; US$609 institutions e-access; US$663 institutions print only; US$87 individuals print only; US$182 institutions single print; US$28 individuals single print. **Remarks:** Accepts advertising. **URL:** http://www.sagepub.com/journalsProdDesc.nav?prodId=Journal201477. **Ad Rates:** BW: 200. **Circ:** (Not Reported)

54821 ■ Journal of the Society of Archer-Antiquaries
Society of Archer-Antiquaries
29 Batley Ct. Oldland
S Gloustehire B
London BS30 8YZ, United Kingdom
Ph: 44 117 9323276
Publisher E-mail: bogaman@btinternet.com
Publication covering archer-antiquaries. **Founded:** 1965. **Freq:** Annual. **Remarks:** Advertising not accepted. **URL:** http://www.societyofarcher-antiquaries.org/publications.htm. **Circ:** 400

54822 ■ Journal of the Society of Archivists
Society of Archivists
c/o Dr. Andrew Flinn
School of Library
Archive & Information Studies
University College London, Gower St.
London WC1E 6BT, United Kingdom
Publisher E-mail: societyofarchivists@archives.org.uk
Journal covering the field of archives, conservation and records management. **Freq:** Semiannual April & October. **Key Personnel:** Elizabeth Shepherd, Editor; Alexandrina Buchanan, Editor; Dr. Andrew Flinn, Contact, a.flinn@btopenworld.com. **ISSN:** 0037-9816. **Subscription Rates:** US$154 individuals print only; 89 individuals print only; EUR123 individuals print only. **URL:** http://www.archives.org.uk/publications/journalofthesocietyofarchivists; http://www.tandf.co.uk/journals/boards/c-boards/jsa-edb.html.

54823 ■ Journal of Sociology
Sage Publications Ltd.
1 Oliver's Yard
55 City Rd.
London EC1Y 1SP, United Kingdom
Ph: 44 20 73248500

Fax: 44 20 73248600
Scholarly journal covering sociological research and theory of interest to Australian sociology. **Subtitle:** The Journal of the Australian Sociological Association. **Founded:** 1964. **Freq:** Quarterly. **Key Personnel:** Andrew Bennett, Editor-in-Chief; Malcolm Alexander, Editor; Sarah Baker, Editor; Russell Brennan, Book Review Ed.; Simone Fullagar, Editor; Ricardo Rivera, Managing Editor; Margaret Gibson, Editor; Suzanne Goopy, Editor. **ISSN:** 1440-7833. **Subscription Rates:** US$548 institutions combined (print & e-access); US$603 institutions plus backfile (current volume print & all online); US$493 institutions e-access; US$548 institutions e-access plus backfile (all online content); US$1,425 institutions e-access (content through 1998); US$537 institutions print only; US$83 individuals print only; US$148 institutions single print; US$27 individuals single print. **Remarks:** Accepts advertising. **URL:** http://www.sagepub.com/journalsSubscribe.nav?prodId=Journal201492. **Circ:** (Not Reported)

54824 ■ The Journal of Stained Glass
British Society of Master Glass Painters
6 Queen Sq.
London WC1N 3AR, United Kingdom
Ph: 44 16 43862807
Publication E-mail: journaled@bsmgp.org.uk
Publication covering stained glass of all periods. **Founded:** 1924. **Freq:** Annual. **Trim Size:** 245 x 173 mm. **Key Personnel:** Sandra Coley, MA, Editor. **Subscription Rates:** 22.50 individuals inland; 25 individuals Europe; 28.50 individuals rest of world. **Remarks:** Accepts advertising. **URL:** http://www.bsmgp.org.uk; http://www.bsmgp.org.uk/Publications/. **Ad Rates:** BW: 425, 4C: 850. **Circ:** (Not Reported)

54825 ■ Journal of Strain Analysis for Engineering Design
Institution of Mechanical Engineers
1 Birdcage Walk
London SW1H 9JJ, United Kingdom
Ph: 44 20 72227899
Fax: 44 20 72224557
Publisher E-mail: international@imeche.org
Publication covering engineering. **Freq:** 8/yr. **Key Personnel:** Prof. E.A. Patterson, Editor, phone 517353-9861, fax 517353-1750, eann@egr.msu.edu; T.N. Farris, Editorial Board; J. Dominguez, Editorial Board; P.J. Budden, Editorial Board; T.H. Hyde, Editorial Board; Z. Yao, Editorial Board; J. Komorowski, Editorial Board; G. Glinka, Editorial Board; Y. Lu, Editorial Board. **ISSN:** 0309-3247. **Subscription Rates:** 1,220 individuals print and online; US$2,263 individuals print and online; 1,099 individuals online; US$2,039 individuals online. **URL:** http://journals.pepublishing.com/content/119785. **Formerly:** Journal of Strain Analysis.

54826 ■ Journal of Targeting, Measurement and Analysis for Marketing
Palgrave Macmillan
The Macmillan Bldg.
4 Crinan St.
London N1 9XW, United Kingdom
Ph: 44 20 78434684
Publisher E-mail: booksellers@palgrave.com
Trade journal covering marketing worldwide. **Founded:** 1992. **Freq:** Quarterly. **Key Personnel:** Jonathan Reynolds, PhD, Editor; Prof. Sally Dibb, Book Review Ed. **ISSN:** 0967-3237. **Subscription Rates:** 401 institutions, other countries print; US$745 institutions print; 160 other countries print and online; US$297 individuals print and online. **Remarks:** Accepts advertising. **URL:** http://www.palgrave-journals.com/jt/index.html. **Circ:** 450

54827 ■ Journal of Telemedicine and Telecare
Royal Society of Medicine
1 Wimpole St.
London W1G 0AE, United Kingdom
Ph: 44 20 72902900
Fax: 44 20 72902989
Publication covering medicine. **Freq:** 8/yr. **Key Personnel:** Prof. Richard Wootton, Editor-in-Chief, jttproduction@rsm.ac.uk; Elizabeth Krupinski, Co-Ed.; David Hailey, Assoc. Ed.; Richard Scott, Assoc. Ed.; Adrian Barnett, Statistics Adviser; Victor Patterson, Assoc. Ed.; Sun Yoo, Assoc. Ed.; Trine Bergmo, Economics Adviser; Pamela Whitten, Assoc. Ed. **ISSN:** 1357-633X. **Subscription Rates:** 304 institutions U.K. and Europe includes free online access; EUR413 institutions Europe includes free online access; US$596

institutions U.S. includes free online access; 310 institutions, other countries includes free online access; 158 individuals U.K. and Europe includes free online access; EUR214 individuals Europe includes free online access; US$315 individuals U.S. includes free online access; 164 individuals rest of the World includes free online access; 274 individuals online only; EUR372 individuals online only. **Remarks:** Accepts advertising. **URL:** http://jtt.rsmjournals.com. **Circ:** (Not Reported)

54828 ■ Journal of Theoretical Politics
Sage Publications Ltd.
1 Oliver's Yard
55 City Rd.
London EC1Y 1SP, United Kingdom
Ph: 44 20 73248500
Fax: 44 20 73248600
Scholarly journal covering political process theory. **Founded:** 1989. **Freq:** Quarterly. **Key Personnel:** Gary W. Cox, Editorial Board; John Dryzek, Editorial Board; Kristen Monroe, Editorial Board; Keith Dowding, Co-Ed.; Nicholas R. Miller, Editorial Board; Kathleen Bawn, Editorial Board; Burt L. Monroe, Editorial Board; James R. Rogers, Co-Ed.; Jenna Bednar, Editorial Board; Josep M. Colomer, Editorial Board. **ISSN:** 0951-6298. **Subscription Rates:** US$990 institutions print & e-access; US$1,089 institutions current volume print & all online content; US$891 institutions e-access; US$990 institutions e-access plus backfile (all online content); US$891 institutions content through 1998; US$970 institutions print only; US$107 individuals print only; US$267 institutions single print; US$35 individuals single print. **Remarks:** Accepts advertising. **URL:** http://www.sagepub.com/journalsSubscribe.nav?prodId=Journal200984. **Circ:** (Not Reported)

54829 ■ Journal of Thermoplastic Composite Materials
Sage Publications Ltd.
1 Oliver's Yard
55 City Rd.
London EC1Y 1SP, United Kingdom
Ph: 44 20 73248500
Fax: 44 20 73248600
Peer-reviewed journal containing articles on plastics and composites. **Founded:** 1988. **Freq:** 6/yr. **Print Method:** Offset. **Trim Size:** 6 x 9. **Key Personnel:** Prof. John W. Gillespie, Jr., Editor; Mehrdad N. Ghasemi-Nejhad, Assoc. Ed. **ISSN:** 0892-7057. **Subscription Rates:** 973 institutions electronic & print; 1,070 institutions print (all online content); 876 institutions e-access; 973 institutions e-access (all online content); 954 institutions print only; 175 institutions single print; 876 institutions e-access, content through 1998. **Remarks:** Accepts advertising. **URL:** http://www.sagepub.co.uk/journalsProdDesc.nav?prodId=Journal201587. **Circ:** 200

54830 ■ Journal of Translational Medicine
BioMed Central Ltd.
236 Gray's Inn Rd., Fl. 6
34-42 Cleveland St.
London WC1X 8HL, United Kingdom
Ph: 44 20 31922000
Fax: 44 20 31922010
Publication E-mail: editorial@translational-medicine.com
Publisher E-mail: info@biomedcentral.com
Journal bridging the gap between basic and clinical science for better therapeutic insights and also in understanding the principles in biology from clinical studies. **Key Personnel:** Dr. Francesco Marincola, MD, Editor-in-Chief, fmarincola@cc.nih.gov. **ISSN:** 1479-5876. **URL:** http://www.translational-medicine.com.

54831 ■ Journal of Urban Health
Springer-Verlag London Ltd.
236 Gray's Inn Rd., 6th Fl.
London WC1X 8HB, United Kingdom
Ph: 44 20 31922000
Peer-reviewed journal covering the fields of urban health and epidemiology. **Freq:** Bimonthly. **Key Personnel:** David Vlahov, PhD, Editor-in-Chief; Kathleen O'Donnell, Managing Editor. **ISSN:** 1099-3460. **Subscription Rates:** EUR253 institutions print and e-access; EUR303.60 institutions print and enhanced access. **Remarks:** Advertising accepted; rates available upon request. **URL:** http://www.springer.com/public+health/journal/11524. **Circ:** (Not Reported)

54832 ■ Journal of Viral Hepatitis
John Wiley & Sons Inc.

Wiley-Blackwell
Imperial College Faculty of Medicine
Dept. of Medicine
St. Mary's Hospital Medical School
London W2 1PG, United Kingdom
Fax: 44 20 82207791
Peer-reviewed journal focusing on viral hepatitis. **Freq:** Monthly. **Key Personnel:** Howard C. Thomas, Editor-in-Chief; Dr. Peter Karayiannis, European Ed.; Prof. Graham R. Foster, European Ed. **ISSN:** 1352-0504. **Subscription Rates:** US$329 individuals print + online; US$249 members print + online; US$2,678 institutions print + online; US$3,123 institutions, other countries print + online; US$2,839 institutions print, online; 196 other countries print + online; 1,448 institutions print + online; 1,316 institutions print, online; EUR1,840 institutions print + online; EUR1,672 institutions print, online. **Remarks:** Advertising accepted; rates available upon request. **URL:** http://www.wiley.com/bw/journal.asp?ref=1352-0504&site=1. **Circ:** (Not Reported)

54833 ■ Journal of Virological Methods
Elsevier Science
c/o Prof. A.J. Zuckerman, Ed.-in-Ch.
Royal Free & University College Medical School
W.H.O. Center-Viral Diseases
Rowland Hill St.
London NW3 2PF, United Kingdom
Ph: 44 17 18302579
Fax: 44 17 18302070
Publisher E-mail: nlinfo-f@elsevier.com
Journal dealing with various techniques in virology. **Founded:** 1980. **Freq:** 16/yr. **Key Personnel:** Prof. A.J. Zuckerman, Editor-in-Chief, a.zuckerman@medsch.ucl.ac.uk; Tanya Shennan, Editorial Asst., j.v.meth@medsch.ucl.ac.uk; S. Alexandersen, Editorial Board; G. Klein, Editorial Board; J.J. Giambrone, Editorial Board; K. Sano, Editorial Board. **ISSN:** 0166-0934. **Subscription Rates:** EUR4,556 institutions for European countries & Iran; US$5,097 institutions for all countries except Europe, Japan & Iran; 604,400¥ institutions; EUR348 individuals for European countries & Iran; US$467 individuals for all countries except Europe, Japan & Iran; 53,700¥ individuals. **Remarks:** Accepts advertising. **URL:** http://www.elsevier.com/wps/find/journaldescription.cws_home/506080/description. **Circ:** (Not Reported)

54834 ■ Journal of Water and Health
IWA Publishing Ltd.
Alliance House
12 Caxton St.
London SW1H 0QS, United Kingdom
Ph: 44 20 76545500
Fax: 44 20 76545555
Journal representing a joint commitment to promote high quality research and practice across the full range of challenges to harnessing water for health in developing and developed countries alike. **Freq:** Quarterly. **Key Personnel:** Charles P. Gerba, Editor; In S. Kim, Editor; Paul Jagals, Editor; Paul R. Hunter, Editor. **ISSN:** 1477-8920. **Subscription Rates:** US$1,227 institutions online and print; EUR1,001 institutions online and print; 679 institutions online and print. **URL:** http://www.iwaponline.com/jwh/default.htm.

54835 ■ Journal of Water Supply
International Water Services Association
Association Internationale des Services d'Eau
Alliance House
12 Caxton St.
London SW1H 0QS, United Kingdom
Ph: 44 207 6545500
Fax: 44 207 6545555
Publisher E-mail: water@iwahq.org.uk
Journal covering water research and technology. **Subtitle:** Research and Technology - Aqua. **Freq:** 8/yr. **Key Personnel:** Rolf Gimbel, Editor; Graham A. Gagnon, Editor; Yoshimasa Watanabe, Editor. **ISSN:** 0003-7214. **Subscription Rates:** US$1,134 institutions print & free online access; EUR956 institutions print & free online access; 662 institutions print & free online access; 662 institutions, other countries print & free online access. **Remarks:** Advertising accepted; rates available upon request. **URL:** http://www.iwapublishing.com; http://www.iwaponline.com/jws/default.htm. **Circ:** (Not Reported)

54836 ■ Journal of Wide Bandgap Materials
Sage Publications Ltd.
1 Oliver's Yard
55 City Rd.
London EC1Y 1SP, United Kingdom

Ph: 44 20 73248500
Fax: 44 20 73248600
Journal focusing on wide bandgap materials: electronic, optical, thermal, mechanical, and structural. **Freq:** Quarterly. **Key Personnel:** Peter Gielisse, Editor; Andrzej R. Badzian, Assoc. Ed.; Kim L. Bigelow, Assoc. Ed. **ISSN:** 1524-511X. **Remarks:** Accepts advertising. **URL:** http://jwb.sagepub.com/. **Circ:** (Not Reported)

54837 ■ Journal of William Morris Studies
William Morris Society
Kelmscott House
26 Upper Mall
Hammersmith
London W6 9TA, United Kingdom
Ph: 44 20 87413735
Fax: 44 20 87485207
Publisher E-mail: uk@morrissociety.org
Publication covering authors. **Founded:** 1961. **Freq:** Biennial. **Key Personnel:** Patrick O'Sullivan, Editor, editor@morrissociety.org. **ISSN:** 0084-0254. **Subscription Rates:** Included in membership. **Remarks:** Advertising accepted; rates available upon request. **URL:** http://www.morrissociety.org. **Formerly:** Journal of William Morris Studies. **Circ:** (Not Reported)

54838 ■ Journal of Wound Care
EMAP Healthcare Ltd.
Greater London House
Hampstead Rd.
London NW1 7EJ, United Kingdom
Ph: 44 20 77285000
Journal covering all aspects of wound management. **Founded:** 1992. **Freq:** 10/yr. **Print Method:** Heat Set Web Offset. **Key Personnel:** Tracy Cowan, Editor; Anthony Kerr, Publisher, a.kerr@markallengroup.com. **Subscription Rates:** 91 individuals UK and Ireland; EUR156 individuals Europe; US$229 other countries. **Remarks:** Accepts advertising. **URL:** http://www.journalofwoundcare.com. **Circ:** Paid 6,000

54839 ■ Journalism
Sage Publications Ltd.
1 Oliver's Yard
55 City Rd.
London EC1Y 1SP, United Kingdom
Ph: 44 20 73248500
Fax: 44 20 73248600
Peer-reviewed journal covering the social, economic, political, cultural and practical understanding of journalism. **Subtitle:** Theory, Practice & Criticism. **Founded:** 2000. **Freq:** Bimonthly. **Key Personnel:** Michael Bromley, International Editorial Board; Carolyn Kitch, Reviews Ed.; Barbie Zelizer, Editor; Howard Tumber, Editor; Bonnie S. Brennen, International Editorial Board; Wendy Bacon, International Editorial Board; Chris Atton, International Editorial Board; Inta Brikse, International Editorial Board; Elizabeth S. Bird, International Editorial Board. **ISSN:** 1464-8849. **Subscription Rates:** US$881 institutions print & e-access; US$793 institutions e-access; US$863 institutions print only; US$89 individuals print; US$158 institutions single print; US$19 individuals single print. **Remarks:** Accepts advertising. **URL:** http://www.sagepub.com/journalsProdAims.nav?prodId=Journal200905. **Circ:** (Not Reported)

54840 ■ Journalist
National Union of Journalists - England
Headland House
308-312 Gray's Inn Rd.
London WC1X 8DP, United Kingdom
Ph: 44 20 72787916
Fax: 44 20 78378143
Publisher E-mail: info@nuj.org.uk
Publication covering the press. **Freq:** 10/yr. **Subscription Rates:** 20 individuals. **Remarks:** Accepts advertising. **URL:** http://www.nuj.org.uk/innerPagenuj.html?docid=871. **Ad Rates:** GLR: 5, PCI: 8. **Circ:** (Not Reported)

54841 ■ Justice Journal
Justice
59 Carter Ln.
London EC4V 5AQ, United Kingdom
Ph: 44 20 73295100
Fax: 44 20 73295055
Publisher E-mail: admin@justice.org.uk
Journal aiming to promote debate on topical issues relat-

ing to human rights and the rule of law. **Founded:** 2004. **Freq:** Semiannual. **ISSN:** 1743-2472. **Subscription Rates:** 60 individuals; US$120 individuals; EUR120 individuals. **URL:** http://www.justice.org.uk/publications/listofpublications/index.html.

54842 ■ Kerrang!
H. Bauer Publishing
Academic House
24-28 Oval Rd.
London NW1 7DT, United Kingdom
Ph: 44 20 72418000
Fax: 44 20 72418030
Magazine featuring rock music. **Freq:** Weekly. **Subscription Rates:** EUR123 individuals; EUR250 other countries. **URL:** http://www.kerrang.com.

54843 ■ Kids Alive!
The Salvation Army
2nd Fl., 33/35 Kings Exchange
Tileyard Rd.
London N7 9AH, United Kingdom
Ph: 44 20 76196100
Fax: 44 20 76196111
Publisher E-mail: londoncentral@salvationarmy.org.uk
Christian newspaper covering education and entertainment features for children. **Founded:** 1881. **Freq:** Weekly. **Key Personnel:** Ken Nesbitt, Editor. **ISSN:** 1363-5662. **Remarks:** Accepts advertising. **URL:** http://www2.salvationarmy.org.uk/uki/www_uki.nsf/vw-sublinks/6E8B1355593F14D0802572140032E892?openDocument. **Circ:** Non-paid 35,000

54844 ■ Kilburn Times
Archant Regional Ltd.
c/o North West London Newspapers
100A Avenue Rd.
London NW3 3HF, United Kingdom
Ph: 44 20 74330000
Publisher E-mail: sandra.roantree@archant.co.uk
Local community newspaper. **Freq:** Weekly (Wed.). **Key Personnel:** Geoff Martin, Editor, geoff.martin@archant.co.uk. **Subscription Rates:** 11.60 individuals 4 weeks; 23.20 individuals 2 months; 34.80 individuals 3 months; 69.60 individuals 6 months; 150.80 individuals. **Remarks:** Accepts advertising. **URL:** http://www.kilburntimes.co.uk/home. **Circ:** (Not Reported)

54845 ■ Kindred Spirit
Unit 101, The Perfume Factory
140 Wales Farm Rd.
London W3 6UG, United Kingdom
Ph: 44 208 7528172
Fax: 44 208 7528185
Consumer magazine covering spirituality, health and New Age topics. **Subtitle:** Leading the Way in Mind, Body and Spirit. **Founded:** 1987. **Freq:** Bimonthly. **Key Personnel:** Richard Beamont, Publisher; Patricia Yates, Publisher. **Subscription Rates:** 24 individuals; 28.50 individuals Europe and U.S.; 34.50 elsewhere; 45 two years; 54 two years Europe and U.S.; 66 two years rest of world; 64 individuals 3 years; 77.50 individuals 3 years, Europe and U.S.; 95.50 elsewhere 3 years. **Remarks:** Accepts advertising. **URL:** http://www.kindredspirit.co.uk/. **Ad Rates:** BW: 1,290, 4C: 1,235. **Circ:** Paid 160,000

54846 ■ Kingpin
Factory Media
1 W Smithfield
London EC1A 9JU, United Kingdom
Ph: 44 20 73329700
Publisher E-mail: contact@factorymedia.com
Magazine featuring skateboarding. **Subtitle:** Skateboarding Europa. **Founded:** Nov. 2002. **Freq:** Monthly. **Key Personnel:** Matt Fenton, Contact, advertising@onboardsnowboarding.com. **Subscription Rates:** 29.99 individuals credit card; 27.99 individuals direct debit; US$77 individuals credit card. **URL:** http://kingpinskateboarding.com/; http://factorymedia.com.

54847 ■ Laboratory Animals
Royal Society of Medicine Press Ltd.
1 Wimpole St.
London W1G 0AE, United Kingdom
Ph: 44 20 72902921
Fax: 44 20 72902929
Publisher E-mail: publishing@rsm.ac.uk
Peer-reviewed journal covering animal science and welfare publication. **Freq:** 4/yr. **Key Personnel:** Dr. Colin Dunn, Editor. **ISSN:** 0023-6772. **Subscription Rates:**

170 individuals UK & Europe; EUR231 individuals Europe; US$327 individuals; 176 other countries individual; 153 individuals online only; EUR208 individuals online only; US$294 individuals online only. **Remarks:** Accepts advertising. **URL:** http://www.portlandpress.com; http://la.rsmjournals.com. **Circ:** (Not Reported)

54848 ■ Labour History Review
Maney Publishing
1 Carlton House Ter.
London SW1Y 5AF, United Kingdom
Ph: 44 20 74517300
Fax: 44 20 74517307
Publication E-mail: subscriptions@maney.co.uk
Publisher E-mail: maney@maney.co.uk
Publication covering Labor party history. **Subtitle:** The Bulletin of the Society for the Study of Labour. **Freq:** 3/yr. **ISSN:** 0961-5652. **Remarks:** Advertising accepted; rates available upon request. **URL:** http://www.sslh.org.uk/. **Circ:** 1,000

54849 ■ Land & Liberty
Henry George Foundation of Great Britain Ltd.
212 Piccadilly
London W1J 9HG, United Kingdom
Ph: 44 20 79171899
Fax: 44 20 79171899
Journal covering politics and the economy. **Founded:** 1894. **Freq:** Quarterly. **Cols./Page:** 3. **Col. Width:** 6 centimeters. **Col. Depth:** 25 centimeters. **Key Personnel:** Peter Gibb, Editor. **ISSN:** 0023-7574. **Subscription Rates:** Free. **Remarks:** Accepts advertising. **URL:** http://www.henrygeorgefoundation.org/periodicals/land-a-liberty-magazine.html. **Circ:** Controlled 1,000

54850 ■ Landscape Design
Landscape Institute
Charles Darwin House
12 Roger St.
London WC1N 2JU, United Kingdom
Ph: 44 20 72994500
Fax: 44 20 72994501
Publisher E-mail: mail@landscapeinstitute.org
Publication covering landscaping. **Freq:** Quarterly. **Key Personnel:** Jim Riches, Contact, phone 44 20 76852650, jimr@landscapeinstitute.org; Peter Beecroft, Contact, phone 44 20 76852651, peterb@landscapeinstitute.org. **Subscription Rates:** 25 individuals UK; 45 individuals Europe; 55 other countries; Free members. **URL:** http://www.landscapeinstitute.org/.

54851 ■ Language & History
Maney Publishing
1 Carlton House Ter.
London SW1Y 5AF, United Kingdom
Ph: 44 20 74517300
Fax: 44 20 74517307
Publisher E-mail: maney@maney.co.uk
Journal of the Henry Sweet Society for the History of Linguistic Ideas, promoting the study of the history of linguistic thought and its application in technical and professional fields. **Freq:** Semiannual. **Key Personnel:** Nicola McLelland, Editor, nicola.mclelland@nottingham.ac.uk; David Cram, Editor, david.cram@jesus.ox.ac.uk. **ISSN:** 1759-7536. **Subscription Rates:** 143 institutions, other countries; US$241 institutions; 134 institutions, other countries online only; US$225 institutions online only. **Remarks:** Accepts advertising. **URL:** http://maney.co.uk/index.php/journals/lhi. **Circ:** (Not Reported)

54852 ■ Language and Literature
Sage Publications Ltd.
1 Oliver's Yard
55 City Rd.
London EC1Y 1SP, United Kingdom
Ph: 44 20 73248500
Fax: 44 20 73248600
Scholarly journal covering current developments in stylistic analysis, the linguistic analysis of literature and related areas. **Subtitle:** Journal of the Poetics and Linguistics Association. **Founded:** 1992. **Freq:** Quarterly. **Key Personnel:** Dan McIntyre, Reviews Ed.; Paul Simpson, Editorial Board; Derek Attridge, Editorial Board; Lesley E. Jeffries, Editorial Board; Monika Fludernik, Editorial Board; Ronald Carter, Editorial Board; David L. Hoover, Editorial Board; Geoffrey Leech, Editorial Board. **ISSN:** 0963-9470. **Subscription Rates:** US$816 institutions print & e-access; US$898 institutions current volume print & all online content; US$734 institutions e-access; US$816 institutions e-access plus

backfile (all online content); US$734 institutions content through 1998; US$800 institutions print only; US$100 individuals print only; US$220 institutions single print; US$33 individuals single print. **Remarks:** Accepts advertising. **URL:** http://www.sagepub.com/journalsProdDesc.nav?prodId=Journal200860. **Circ:** (Not Reported)

54853 ■ Language Teaching Research
Sage Publications Ltd.
1 Oliver's Yard
55 City Rd.
London EC1Y 1SP, United Kingdom
Ph: 44 20 73248500
Fax: 44 20 73248600
Peer-reviewed academic journal covering research in second or foreign language teaching. **Founded:** 1997. **Freq:** Quarterly. **Print Method:** Bound. **Trim Size:** 234 x 156. **Key Personnel:** Rod Ellis, Editor; John Norris, Book Review Ed. **ISSN:** 1362-1688. **Subscription Rates:** 292 institutions print & E-access; 263 institutions E-access; 292 institutions print only; 59 individuals print & E-access; 79 institutions single print; 19 individuals single print. **Remarks:** Accepts advertising. **URL:** http://www.sagepub.co.uk/journalsProdDesc.nav?prodId=Journal201815. **Ad Rates:** BW: 370. **Circ:** Paid 500

54854 ■ The Lantern
The British Housewives League
17 Osborne Rd.
London N13 5PT, United Kingdom
Publication covering women. **Freq:** Quarterly. **ISSN:** 1351-8623. **Subscription Rates:** 10 individuals; 10 other countries + 6 postage. **Remarks:** Advertising not accepted. **URL:** http://www.housewives.freeuk.com/membership.html. **Circ:** (Not Reported)

54855 ■ Lasers in Medical Science
Springer-Verlag London Ltd.
236 Gray's Inn Rd., 6th Fl.
London WC1X 8HB, United Kingdom
Ph: 44 20 31922000
Journal providing a forum for the publication of papers on the technical, experimental and clinical aspects of the use of medical lasers, including the use of lasers in surgery, endoscopy, angioplasty, hyperthermia of tumours, and photodynamic therapy. **Freq:** Quarterly. **Key Personnel:** Keyvan Nouri, Editor-in-Chief; P. Wright, Assoc. Ed.; G.S. Abela, Editorial Consultant; F.W. Cross, Editorial Board. **ISSN:** 0268-8921. **Subscription Rates:** EUR843 institutions print and e-access; EUR1,011.60 institutions print and enhanced access. **Remarks:** Advertising accepted; rates available upon request. **URL:** http://www.springerlink.com/content/0268-8921. **Circ:** (Not Reported)

54856 ■ LatinFinance
Euromoney Publications PLC
Nestor House
Playhouse Yard
London EC4V 5EX, United Kingdom
Ph: 44 20 77798888
Publisher E-mail: information@euromoneyplc.com
Publication for the banking, finance, and accounting industries. **Freq:** Monthly. **Key Personnel:** James Crombie, Editor, jcrombie@latinfinance.com. **ISSN:** 1048-535X. **Remarks:** Accepts advertising. **URL:** http://www.latinfinance.com/. **Ad Rates:** BW: 12,875, 4C: 15,500. **Circ:** △29,176

54857 ■ Law, Culture & the Humanities
Sage Publications Ltd.
1 Oliver's Yard
55 City Rd.
London EC1Y 1SP, United Kingdom
Ph: 44 20 73248500
Fax: 44 20 73248600
Peer-reviewed journal publishing a wide range of scholarship in legal history, legal theory and jurisprudence, law and cultural studies, law and literature, and legal hermeneutics. **Freq:** 3/yr. **Key Personnel:** Austin Sarat, Editor; Peter Fitzpatrick, Assoc. Ed.; William Macneil, Assoc. Ed. **ISSN:** 1743-8721. **Subscription Rates:** 294 institutions print & e-access; 265 institutions e-access; 288 institutions print only; 71 individuals print & e-access; 106 institutions single print; 31 individuals single print. **Remarks:** Accepts advertising. **URL:** http://www.sagepub.co.uk/journalsProdDesc.nav?prodId=Journal201817. **Circ:** (Not Reported)

54858 ■ LCR
National Association of Local Councils
109 Great Russell St.
London WC1B 3LD, United Kingdom
Ph: 44 20 76371865
Fax: 44 20 74367451
Publisher E-mail: nalc@nalc.gov.uk
Publication covering municipal government. **Founded:**
1943. **Freq:** Quarterly. **Key Personnel:** Alan Jones,
Contact, alan.jones@nalc.gov.uk; Marianne Webb,
Contact, marianne.webb@nalc.gov.uk. **Subscription
Rates:** 13.50 members up to 3 individuals; 12 members
4 or more individuals; 17 nonmembers up to 3 individu-
als; 15 nonmembers 4 or more individuals. **Remarks:**
Advertising accepted; rates available upon request.
URL: http://www.nalc.gov.uk/Publications/LCR/LCR.
aspx. **Formerly:** Local Council Review. **Circ:** ‡12,000

54859 ■ Leadership Focus
Redactive Media Group
17-18 Britton St.
London EC1M 5TP, United Kingdom
Ph: 44 20 78806200
Fax: 44 20 78807691
Publisher E-mail: info@redactive.co.uk
Magazine featuring articles about school leadership.
Freq: Bimonthly. **Key Personnel:** Aaron Nicholls,
Contact, phone 44 20 78808547, fax 44 20 78807691,
aaron.nicholls@redactive.co.uk. **URL:** http://www.
redactive.co.uk/about-us/careers/assistant-editor-legion-
leadership-focus/. **Circ:** ‡28,000

54860 ■ Learn with Bob the Builder
BBC Worldwide Publishing Ltd.
Media Centre
201 Wood Ln.
London W12 7TQ, United Kingdom
Ph: 44 20 84332000
Fax: 44 20 87490538
Magazine featuring educational activities for 3-5 years
old. **Freq:** every 4 weeks. **Key Personnel:** Peter Phip-
pen, Mng. Dir. **Subscription Rates:** $A 98.51 individu-
als 6 months; $A 176.58 individuals; $A 336.82 two
years. **URL:** http://www.bbcmagazines.com/content/
magazines/learnwithbobthebuilder/.

54861 ■ Leasing Life
VRL Publishing
The Colonnades
34 Porchester Rd.
London W2 6ES, United Kingdom
Ph: 44 20 75635600
Fax: 44 20 75635601
Trade magazine covering equipment and asset finance
news for the leasing industry. **Founded:** 1993. **Freq:**
Monthly. **Trim Size:** 297 x 215. **Key Personnel:** Liz
Bury, Editor, liz.bury@vrlfinancialnews.com. **Subscrip-
tion Rates:** 340 individuals plus VAT. **Remarks:** Ac-
cepts advertising. **URL:** http://www.vrl-financial-news.
com/asset-finance/leasing/leasing-life.aspx. **Ad Rates:** BW:
2,495, 4C: 2,100. **Circ:** Combined 1,000

54862 ■ Leaving School
Talent Media
The Maltings, Studio 65/66
169 Tower Bridge Rd.
London SE1 3LJ, United Kingdom
Magazine featuring information on career and educational opportunities available to all Britain's diverse
communities. **Freq:** Bimonthly. **Key Personnel:** Ian
Thomas, Publisher; Charlie Whitworth, Editor; Paul Coc-
ciadiferro, Managing Editor. **URL:** http://www.
sugarmedia.co.uk/; http://www.leavingschool.co.uk/.

**54863 ■ Lebensmittel-Wissenschaft und-
Technologie**
Academic Press
Harcourt Pl.
32 Jamestown Rd.
London NW1 7BY, United Kingdom
Ph: 44 20 74244200
Fax: 44 20 74832293
Scientific journal covering the areas of food science and
technology. **Subtitle:** Food Science & Technology.
Founded: 1967. **Freq:** 8/yr. **ISSN:** 0023-6438. **URL:**
http://www.ingentaconnect.com/content/ap/fs.

54864 ■ Legal Business
Legalese Ltd.
Kensington Sq. House
12-14 Ansdell St.
London W8 5BN, United Kingdom
Ph: 44 20 73969292
Fax: 44 20 73969303
Journal covering commercial law in Europe. **Founded:**
1990. **Freq:** Monthly. **Key Personnel:** Helen Berwick,
Advertising Mgr., phone 44 20 73965618, helen.
berwick@legalease.co.uk; Richard Lloyd, Editor, phone
44 20 73965674, richard.lloyd@legalease.co.uk. **ISSN:**
0958-4609. **Subscription Rates:** 495 individuals. **URL:**
http://www.legalbusiness.co.uk. **Circ:** Paid 9,000

54865 ■ Legal Week
Incisive Media Limited
Haymarket House
28-29 Haymarket
London SW1Y 4RX, United Kingdom
Ph: 44 870 2408859
Fax: 44 207 4849797
Publisher E-mail: customerservices@incisivemedia.com
Business magazine. **Freq:** Weekly. **Key Personnel:**
Alex Novarese, Editor, phone 44 20 73169847, alex.
novarese@incisivemedia.com. **Remarks:** Accepts
advertising. **URL:** http://www.legalweek.com/. **Ad Rates:**
BW: 7,324, 4C: 8,074. **Circ:** ★32,070

54866 ■ Lex
Legalese Ltd.
Kensington Sq. House
12-14 Ansdell St.
London W8 5BN, United Kingdom
Ph: 44 20 73969292
Fax: 44 20 73969303
Publication E-mail: lex100@legalease.co.uk
Magazine covering the legal profession for students in
the UK's leading law faculties. **Freq:** Triennial. **Key
Personnel:** Jo Thesiger, Editor; Teresa Sandon, Editor.
Subscription Rates: EUR10 single issue. **Remarks:** Ac-
cepts advertising. **URL:** http://www.legalease.co.uk.
Circ: (Not Reported)

54867 ■ Liberal Matters
Liberal International
Internationale Liberale
1 Whitehall Pl.
London SW1A 2HD, United Kingdom
Ph: 44 20 78395905
Fax: 44 20 79252685
Publisher E-mail: all@liberal-international.org
Publication covering political liberal parties. **Founded:**
Nov. 1996. **Freq:** Quarterly. **Key Personnel:** Jasper
Veen, Editor. **ISSN:** 0968-1884. **URL:** http://www.liberal-
international.org/thumbnails.asp?ia_id=515. **Former
name:** London Aerogramme. **Formerly:** Liberal
Aerogramme. **Circ:** 2,000

54868 ■ Liberator
Liberator Publications
Flat 1, 24 Alexandra Grove
London N4 2LF, United Kingdom
Publication E-mail: collective@liberator.org.uk
Publisher E-mail: collective@liberator.org.uk
Magazine that acts as a forum for debate among radical
liberals in all parties and none. **Founded:** 1970. **Freq:**
7-8/yr. **Subscription Rates:** 25 individuals U.K.; 30
individuals overseas. **Remarks:** Accepts advertising.
URL: http://www.liberator.org.uk. **Circ:** (Not Reported)

54869 ■ The Library
Bibliographical Society
c/o Dr. Nicolas Bell, Reviews Ed.
Music Collections
The British Library
96 Euston Rd.
London NW1 2DB, United Kingdom
Publisher E-mail: secretary@bibsoc.org.uk
Publication covering books. **Subtitle:** Transactions of
the Bibliographical Society. **Freq:** Quarterly. **Key Personnel:** Julianne Simpson, Reviews Ed., nicolas.bell@
bl.uk; Dr. Bill Bell, Editor, b.bell@ed.ac.uk. **ISSN:** 0024-
2160. **Subscription Rates:** 152 institutions print and
online; US$304 institutions print and online; EUR228
institutions print and online. **Remarks:** Advertising accepted; rates available upon request. **URL:** http://library.
oxfordjournals.org/; http://www.bibsoc.org.uk/library.htm.
Circ: (Not Reported)

54870 ■ Library and Information Research
Library and Information Research Group
c/o Colin S. Johnston, Review Ed.
Rutherford Information Services Bldg.
Goldsmiths College
New Cross
London SE14 6NW, United Kingdom
Publication covering library and information research.
Freq: 3/yr. **Key Personnel:** Colin S. Johnston, Review
Ed.; Miggie Pickton, Team Member. **ISSN:** 0141-6561.
Subscription Rates: 25 individuals; 50 institutions; 60
institutions overseas; 8 students. **Remarks:** Advertising
accepted; rates available upon request. **URL:** http://
www.cilip.org.uk/get-involved/special-interest-groups/
research/publications/journal/pages/default.aspx. **For-
merly:** Library and Information Research News. **Circ:**
(Not Reported)

54871 ■ Library + Information Update
Chartered Institute of Library and Information Profes-
sionals
7 Ridgmount St.
London WC1E 7AE, United Kingdom
Ph: 44 20 72550500
Fax: 44 20 72550501
Publication E-mail: update@cilip.org.uk
Publisher E-mail: info@cilip.org.uk
Magazine bringing industry news, comment and debate
on the big issues of the day where they impact on the
library and information scene. **Key Personnel:** Elspeth
Hyams, Editor, elspeth.hyams@cilip.org.uk; Christina
Brockhurst, Assoc. Ed., christina.brockhurst@cilip.org.
uk; Rachel Middleton, Managing Editor, rachel.
middleton@cilip.org.uk; Matthew Mezey, News Ed.,
matthew.mezey@cilip.org.uk; Diana Dixon, Hon Book
Review Ed., diana.dixon@cilip.org.uk. **Subscription
Rates:** 90 individuals U.K.; 98 other countries; US$195
individuals North America. **Remarks:** Accepts
advertising. **URL:** http://www.cilip.org.uk/publications/
updatemagazine. **Ad Rates:** BW: 3,000. **Circ:** (Not
Reported)

54872 ■ Life & Pensions
Incisive Media Limited
Haymarket House
28-29 Haymarket
London SW1Y 4RX, United Kingdom
Ph: 44 870 2408859
Fax: 44 207 4849797
Publisher E-mail: customerservices@incisivemedia.com
Magazine focusing on the risk and capital finance and
valuation for the life and pensions industry. **Freq:** 11/yr.
Key Personnel: Aaron Woolner, Editor, phone 44 20
74849927, aaron.woolner@incisivemedia.com; Rachel
White, Production Mgr., phone 44 20 73169666, rachel.
white@incisivemedia.com. **Subscription Rates:** 590
individuals; US$1,120 individuals; EUR885 individuals;
1,062 two years; US$2,016 two years; EUR1,593 two
years; 1,505 individuals 3 years; US$2,857 individuals 3
years; EUR2,256 individuals 3 years. **Remarks:** Accepts
advertising. **URL:** http://www.life-pensions.com. **Circ:**
(Not Reported)

54873 ■ Lighting Research and Technology
Sage Publications Ltd.
1 Oliver's Yard
55 City Rd.
London EC1Y 1SP, United Kingdom
Ph: 44 20 73248500
Fax: 44 20 73248600
Peer-reviewed journal covering the latest research in all
areas of illuminating engineering. **Freq:** Quarterly. **Key
Personnel:** David Carter, Ch.; Peter Boyce, PhD, Tech.
Ed. **ISSN:** 1477-1535. **Subscription Rates:** 292 institutions print & e-access; 263 institutions e-access; 286
institutions print only; 78 individuals print & e-access; 79
institutions single print; 25 individuals single print. **URL:**
http://www.sagepub.co.uk/journalsProdDesc.nav?
prodId=Journal201818.

54874 ■ Linguistics and the Human Sciences
Equinox Publishing Ltd.
1 Chelsea Manor Studios
Flood St.
London SW3 5SR, United Kingdom
Ph: 44 20 78233748
Fax: 44 20 78233748
Journal covering the understanding of language. **Freq:**
3/yr (April, August and December). **Key Personnel:** Dr.
Jonathan J. Webster, Editor, editorlhs@cityu.edu.hk.
ISSN: 1742-2906. **Subscription Rates:** 140 institutions,
other countries print and online; US$280 institutions
print and online; 53 individuals print; US$105 individuals

Circulation: ★ = ABC; △ = BPA; ♦ = CAC; • = CCAB; ❑ = VAC; ⊕ = PO Statement; ‡ = Publisher's Report; Boldface figures = sworn; Light figures = estimated.

Gale Directory of Publications & Broadcast Media/147th Ed.

5743

print; 33.75 students print; US$67.50 students print. **Remarks:** Accepts advertising. **URL:** http://www. equinoxjournals.com/ojs/index.php/LHS. **Circ:** (Not Reported)

54875 ■ Lipids in Health and Disease
BioMed Central Ltd.
236 Gray's Inn Rd., Fl. 6
34-42 Cleveland St.
London WC1X 8HL, United Kingdom
Ph: 44 20 31922000
Fax: 44 20 31922010
Publisher E-mail: info@biomedcentral.com
Online journal covering all aspects of lipids in health and disease. **Key Personnel:** Dr. Undurti N. Das, Editor-in-Chief, undurti@lipidworld.com; Dr. Kazuo Miyashita, Editorial Board, kmiya@fish.hokudai.ac.jp; Dr. Alvin Berger, Editorial Board, aberger@nc.rr.com; Prof. Asim K. Dutta-Roy, Editorial Board, a.k.dutta-roy@basalmed. uio.no; Lakshmi Das Undurti, Managing Editor, phone 928833-0316, lakshmi1957@hotmail.com; Dr. Aldo R. Eynard, Editorial Board, aeynard@cmefcm.uncor.edu. **ISSN:** 1476-511X. **Remarks:** Accepts advertising. **URL:** http://www.lipidworld.com. **Circ:** (Not Reported)

54876 ■ Literary and Linguistic Computing
Oxford University Press
c/o Marilyn Deegan, Ed.-in-Ch.
Ctr. for Computing in the Humanities
King's College London
The Strand
London WC2R 2LS, United Kingdom
Publisher E-mail: webenquiry.uk@oup.com
International journal publishing material on all aspects of computing and information technology applied to literature and language research and teaching, including results of research projects, description and evaluation of techniques and methodologies and reports on work in progress. **Freq:** 4/yr. **Key Personnel:** Marilyn Deegan, Editor-in-Chief, marilyn.deegan@kcl.ac.uk; Simon Horobin, Assoc. Ed., simon.horobin@magd.ox.ac.uk; Stefan Sinclair, Assoc. Ed., sgs@mcmaster.ca. **ISSN:** 0268-1145. **Subscription Rates:** 222 institutions print and online; US$389 institutions print and online; EUR333 institutions print and online; 185 institutions online; US$324 institutions online; EUR278 institutions online; 64 members print; US$128 members print; EUR96 members print. **Remarks:** Advertising accepted; rates available upon request. **URL:** http://llc.oxfordjournals. org. **Circ:** (Not Reported)

54877 ■ Live It
Axon Publishing
11 Plough Yard
London EC2A 3LP, United Kingdom
Ph: 44 20 76847111
Fax: 44 20 76847122
Publisher E-mail: mail@axonpublish.com
Magazine featuring the Conran brand. **Key Personnel:** Paul Keers, Editorial Dir. **URL:** http://www.axonpublish. com/.

54878 ■ Live & Kicking
BBC Magazines
Media Center
201 Wood Ln.
London W12 7TQ, United Kingdom
Ph: 44 20 84332000
Consumer magazine covering entertainment for teenagers. **Founded:** 1993. **Freq:** Monthly. **Key Personnel:** James Mannion, Editor. **Remarks:** Accepts advertising. **URL:** http://www.saturdaymornings.co.uk/ archive/archive-lkmagazines.shtml. **Circ:** (Not Reported)

54879 ■ Livingetc
IPC Media Ltd.
Blue Fin Bldg.
110 Southwark St.
London SE1 0SU, United Kingdom
Ph: 44 203 1485000
Consumer magazine covering lifestyle and home. **Founded:** 1995. **Freq:** Monthly. **Key Personnel:** Sharon Goode, Advertising Mgr., phone 44 20 31487631, sharon_goode@ipcmedia.com; Alex Russell, Group Ad Dir., phone 44 20 31487623, alex_russell@ipcmedia. com; Joanne O'Hara, Advertising Dir., phone 44 20 31487642, joanne_o'hara@ipcmedia.com. **Remarks:** Accepts advertising. **URL:** http://www.livingetc.com/; http://www.ipcadvertising.com/ipc-brands/2009/feb/03/ livingetc. **Circ:** ★92,685

54880 ■ LMS Journal of Computation and Mathematics
London Mathematical Society
De Morgan House
57-58 Russell Sq.
London WC1 B4HS, United Kingdom
Ph: 44 20 76373686
Fax: 44 20 73233655
Publisher E-mail: lms@lms.ac.uk
Peer-reviewed journal featuring high-quality research or expository papers in all areas where mathematics and computation meet. **Freq:** Bimonthly. **Key Personnel:** Prof. D.F. Holt, Editor-in-Chief; Prof. R.M. Thomas, Editor; Prof. A. Iserles, Editor. **ISSN:** 1461-1570. **URL:** http://www.cambridge.org/journals/journal_catalogue. asp?mnemonic=JCM.

54881 ■ Local Transport Today
Transport Planning Society
1 Great George St.
London SW1P 3AA, United Kingdom
Ph: 44 20 76652238
Fax: 44 20 77991325
Publisher E-mail: tps@ice.org.uk
Journal providing news coverage, analysis, and comments on UK Transport. **Subscription Rates:** 96 individuals; 173 two years; EUR153 individuals; EUR275 two years; 185 other countries. **Remarks:** Accepts advertising. **URL:** http://www.transportxtra.com/. **Circ:** (Not Reported)

54882 ■ Locomotive Journal
Associated Society of Locomotive Engineers and Firemen
9 Arkwright Rd.
Hampstead
London NW3 6AB, United Kingdom
Ph: 44 20 73178600
Fax: 44 20 77946406
Publisher E-mail: info@aslef.org.uk
Journal covering locomotives. **Freq:** Monthly. **Key Personnel:** Keith Norman, General Sec. **URL:** http://www. aslef.org.uk/.

54883 ■ Logical Methods in Computer Science
International Federation for Computational Logic
King's College Strand
London WC2R 2LS, United Kingdom
Publisher E-mail: office@ifcolog.org
Electronic journal publishing papers on all theoretical and practical areas in computer science involving logical methods. **Key Personnel:** Dana S. Scott, Editor-in-Chief, dana.scott@cs.cmu.edu; Bruno Courcelle, Editorial Board; Moshe Y. Vardi, Managing Editor; Rajeev Alur, Editorial Board; Franz Baader, Editorial Board; Samson Abramsky, Editorial Board; Gordon D. Plotkin, Managing Editor; Jiri Adamek, Executive Ed., adamek@ iti.cs.tu-bs.de; Henk Barendregt, Editorial Board. **ISSN:** 1860-5974. **URL:** http://www.lmcs-online.org/.

54884 ■ Logopedics Phoniatrics Vocology
Taylor & Francis Ltd.
c/o Informa Healthcare
Telephone House
69-77 Paul St.
London EC2A 4LQ, United Kingdom
Publication E-mail: lpv@informa.com
Journal covering topics related to speech, language and voice pathology as well as to normal voice function in its different aspects, including: phonation and laryngeal physiology, speech and language development, voice disorders, clinical measurements of speech, language and voice, professional voice including singing, bilingualism, cleft lip and palate, dyslexia, fluency disorders, neurolinguistics and psycholinguistics, aphasia, motor speech disorders, voice rehabilitation of laryngectomees, augmentative and alternative, communication, acoustics and dysphagia. **Freq:** Quarterly. **Key Personnel:** David Howard, Editor-in-Chief; Jan Svec, Dep. Ed.-in-Ch. **ISSN:** 1401-5439. **Subscription Rates:** US$265 institutions print + online; US$265 institutions online; US$265 institutions print + online; US$265 institutions online. **Remarks:** Advertising accepted; rates available upon request. **URL:** http://www.informaworld.com/smpp/ title~content=t713713058. **Circ:** (Not Reported)

54885 ■ The London Bird Report
London Natural History Society
c/o Andrew Self, Ed.
16 Harpisland Close
Neasden

London NW10 0DF, United Kingdom
Journal recording sightings and breeding behavior. **Freq:** Annual. **Key Personnel:** Andrew Self, Editor. **ISSN:** 0141-4348. **Subscription Rates:** 8 individuals. **URL:** http://www.lnhs.org.uk/publications.htm.

54886 ■ London Bulletin
London Councils
59 1/2 Southwark St.
London SE1 0AL, United Kingdom
Ph: 44 20 79349999
Publisher E-mail: info@londoncouncils.gov.uk
Corporate magazine covering municipal government. **Subtitle:** The Magazine for London Local Government. **Founded:** June 2000. **Freq:** Bimonthly. **Subscription Rates:** 40 individuals; 20 individuals voluntary organizations. **Remarks:** Advertising accepted; rates available upon request. **URL:** http://www.londoncouncils. gov.uk/publications/default.htm. **Circ:** Combined 6,000

54887 ■ The London Magazine
Premier Magazines
Haymarket House
1 Oxendon St.
London SW1Y 4EE, United Kingdom
Ph: 44 20 79252544
Consumer magazine covering lifestyle. **Subtitle:** A Review of Literature and the Arts. **Freq:** Bimonthly. **Key Personnel:** Karen Wheeler, Contact; Sebastian Barker, Editor; Nigel Evans, Editor; Christopher Arkell, Publisher. **Subscription Rates:** 45 individuals online; 60 individuals; 80 other countries surface mail; 135 other countries airmail printed paper; 260 other countries airmail letter 1st class. **Remarks:** Accepts advertising. **URL:** http:// www.thelondonmagazine.co.uk/. **Ad Rates:** BW: 200. **Circ:** (Not Reported)

54888 ■ The London Philatelist
The Royal Philatelic Society London
41 Devonshire Pl.
London W1G 6JY, United Kingdom
Ph: 44 20 74861044
Fax: 44 20 74860803
Publication E-mail: secretary@rpsl.org.uk
Magazine covering philately. **Founded:** 1892. **Freq:** Monthly 10/yr. **ISSN:** 0024-6131. **Subscription Rates:** Free to fellows and members. **URL:** http://www.rpsl.org. uk/philatelist.html.

54889 ■ The London Picture Book
The London Picture Book Ltd.
3rd Fl.
45 Albemarle St., Mayfair
London W1X 4FE, United Kingdom
Ph: 44 208 8744905
Publisher E-mail: info@londonstills.com
Consumer magazine covering local tourism and travel. **Founded:** 1996. **Print Method:** Web. **Trim Size:** 210 x 297 mm. **Key Personnel:** Ricky Leaver, Contact. **URL:** http://www.londonpicturebook.com. **Circ:** Combined 125,000

54890 ■ London Review of Books
LRB Ltd.
28 Little Russell St.
London WC1A 2HN, United Kingdom
Ph: 44 20 72091141
Fax: 44 20 72091151
Publication E-mail: subs@lrb.co.uk
Publisher E-mail: subs@lrb.co.uk
Journal offering critical reviews of books. **Founded:** 1979. **Freq:** Semimonthly. **Print Method:** Web offset. **Key Personnel:** Jean McNicol, Dep. Ed.; Daniel Soar, Sen. Ed.; Lidija Haas, Editorial Asst.; Thomas Jones, Contributing Ed.; John Lanchester, Contributing Ed.; John Sturrock, Consulting Ed.; Paul Myerscough, Sen. Ed.; Mary-Kay Wilmers, Editor; Nicholas Spice, Publisher. **ISSN:** 0260-9592. **Subscription Rates:** 33.97 individuals; 43.30 individuals Europe; US$35 U.S.; US$49.95 Canada; 43.30 other countries. **Remarks:** Advertising accepted; rates available upon request. **URL:** http://www.lrb.co.uk/. **Circ:** Paid ★42,721

54891 ■ The Lord of the Rings Collector's Models
Eaglemoss Publications Ltd
Beaumont House, 1st Fl.
Kensington Village
Avonmore Rd.
London W14 8TS, United Kingdom

Ph: 44 20 76051200
Fax: 44 20 76051201
Publication E-mail: lotr.enquiries@dbfactory.co.uk
Publisher E-mail: webenquiries@eaglemoss.co.uk
Magazine featuring The Lord of the Rings model character. **Key Personnel:** Maggie Calmels, Editorial Dir., maggiecalmels@eaglemoss.co.uk; Andrew Jarvis, Ch. Exec. **URL:** http://www.lotr-models.com/.

54892 ■ Lubrication Science
Leaf Coppin Publishing Ltd.
PO Box 46387
London SW17 8WF, United Kingdom
Ph: 44 20 86821001
Publication E-mail: cs-journals@wiley.co.uk
Publisher E-mail: landuse@leafcoppin.com
Scientific journal covering lubrication science. **Founded:** 1988. **Freq:** 10/yr. **Key Personnel:** W.J. Bartz, Editorial Board; H.A. Spikes, Editor; P.M. Cann, Editorial Board; S.K. Biswas, Editorial Board; E. Ciulli, Editorial Board; F. Franek, Editorial Board. **ISSN:** 0954-0075. **Subscription Rates:** US$2,108 individuals print only; US$2,810 institutions, other countries print only; EUR1,813 institutions, other countries print only; 1,434 institutions, other countries print only. **Remarks:** Advertising not accepted. **URL:** http://www3.interscience.wiley.com/journal/121576624/grouphome/home.html. **Circ:** (Not Reported)

54893 ■ Lung Cancer in Practice
Hayward Medical Communications
Covent Garden
8-10 Dryden St.
London WC2E 9NA, United Kingdom
Publisher E-mail: admin@hayward.co.uk
Journal covering issues on lung cancer. **Founded:** 2004. **Key Personnel:** Michael D. Peake, Editor. **URL:** http://www.lcip.co.uk/lcip/.

54894 ■ Magazine News
Periodical Publishers Association
Queens House
28 Kingsway
London WC2B 6JR, United Kingdom
Ph: 44 207 4044166
Fax: 44 207 4044167
Magazine covering publishing. **Freq:** 4/yr. **Key Personnel:** Jill Simmons, Contact, phone 44 2074007526; Kathy Crawford, Business Mgr., phone 44 1620 890800, kathy.crawford@ppascotland.co.uk. **Subscription Rates:** Included in membership. **Remarks:** Accepts advertising. **URL:** http://www.ppa.co.uk; http://www.ppa.co.uk/cgi-bin/wms.pl/325. **Formerly:** PPA Members' Handbook. **Ad Rates:** BW: 750, 4C: 1,000. **Circ:** Nonpaid ‡10,000

54895 ■ The Magic Circular Magazine
The Magic Circle
12 Stephenson Way
Euston
London NW1 2HD, United Kingdom
Publication E-mail: enquiries@themagiccircle.co.uk
Publisher E-mail: enquiries@themagiccircle.co.uk
Trade magazine for magicians covering tricks, illusions, history, news and book and video reviews. **Founded:** 1906. **Freq:** Monthly. **Print Method:** Web offset. **Trim Size:** A4. **Remarks:** Accepts advertising. **URL:** http://www.themagiccircle.co.uk. **Circ:** (Not Reported)

54896 ■ The Magical World of Roald Dahl
Eaglemoss Publications Ltd
Beaumont House, 1st Fl.
Kensington Village
Avonmore Rd.
London W14 8TS, United Kingdom
Ph: 44 20 76051200
Fax: 44 20 76051201
Publication E-mail: magical-world@dbfactory.co.uk
Publisher E-mail: webenquiries@eaglemoss.co.uk
Magazine featuring Roald Dahl's collections. **Freq:** Bimonthly. **Key Personnel:** Maggie Calmels, Editorial Dir., maggiecalmels@eaglemoss.co.uk. **URL:** http://www.magical-worldofrd.com/mag/mag.htm; http://www.magical-worldofrd.com/.

54897 ■ The Magistrate
Magistrates' Association of England and Wales
28 Fitzroy Sq.
London W1T 6DD, United Kingdom
Ph: 44 207 3872353
Fax: 44 207 3834020

Publisher E-mail: information@magistrates-association.org.uk
Professional publication covering judiciary issues. **Freq:** Monthly 10/yr. **Key Personnel:** Simon Hudson, Editor, phone 44 115 8462040; David Lancaster, Sales Mgr., phone 44 207 8782316, fax 44 207 3797155, david.lancaster@tenalpspublishing.com. **Subscription Rates:** Free to members. **Remarks:** Advertising accepted; rates available upon request. **URL:** http://www.magistrates-association.org.uk/about_us/communications/magistrate-magazine.htm. **Circ:** (Not Reported)

54898 ■ Majesty Magazine
Rex Publications Ltd.
64 Charlotte St.
Eltham
London W1T 4QD, United Kingdom
Ph: 44 20 74364006
Fax: 44 20 74363458
Consumer magazine covering features and photographs of royalty worldwide. **Subtitle:** The Quality Royal Magazine. **Founded:** 1980. **Freq:** Monthly. **Print Method:** Web offset. **Trim Size:** 210 x 297 mm. **Key Personnel:** Cliff Moulder, Mng. Dir.; Jeannie Pittard-Whitmarsh, Accounts & Administration Managing Editor, majestyads@aol.com; Joe Little, Managing Editor, joelittle@majestymagazine.com; Ingrid Seward, Editor-in-Chief. **Subscription Rates:** 30 individuals; 39 individuals Europe; US$70 individuals; US$75 Canada; 53 elsewhere. **Remarks:** Accepts advertising. **URL:** http://www.majestymagazine.com/links.php. **Circ:** (Not Reported)

54899 ■ Make the Grade
Redactive Media Group
17-18 Britton St.
London EC1M 5TP, United Kingdom
Ph: 44 20 78806200
Fax: 44 20 78807691
Publisher E-mail: info@redactive.co.uk
Magazine featuring information for the educational assessment. **Key Personnel:** Aaron Nicholls, Contact, phone 44 20 78808547, fax 44 20 78807691, aaron.nicholls@redactive.co.uk. **URL:** http://www.redactive.co.uk/clients/make-the-grade/.

54900 ■ Malaria Journal
BioMed Central Ltd.
236 Gray's Inn Rd., Fl. 6
34-42 Cleveland St.
London WC1X 8HL, United Kingdom
Ph: 44 20 31922000
Fax: 44 20 31922010
Publisher E-mail: info@biomedcentral.com
Online journal covering all aspects of malaria. **Key Personnel:** Prof. Marcel Hommel, Editor-in-Chief, phone 33 1 40613941, mhommel@pasteur.fr; Dr. Guy Barnish, Editorial Board, gbarnish@liv.ac.uk; Dr. Michel Cot, Editorial Board, phone 33 1 53739622, fax 33 1 53739617. **ISSN:** 1475-2875. **Remarks:** Accepts advertising. **URL:** http://www.malariajournal.com. **Circ:** (Not Reported)

54901 ■ Management Learning
Sage Publications Ltd.
1 Oliver's Yard
55 City Rd.
London EC1Y 1SP, United Kingdom
Ph: 44 20 73248500
Fax: 44 20 73248600
Peer-reviewed journal covering issues of learning, change and development in organizations for educators and practitioners in organizational behavior and allied fields. **Subtitle:** The Journal for Managerial and Organizational Learning. **Founded:** 1970. **Freq:** 5/yr. **Key Personnel:** Craig Prichard, Assoc. Ed.; Bente Elkjaer, Emeritus Ed.; Elena P. Antonacopoulou, International Editorial Board; Christopher Grey, International Editorial Board; Joseph Raelin, International Editorial Board; Russ Vince, Emeritus Ed.; Carole Elliott, Reviews Ed.; Ariane Berthoin Antal, International Editorial Board; Ann L. Cunliffe, Editor-in-Chief. **ISSN:** 1350-5076. **Subscription Rates:** US$1,023 institutions print & e-access; US$1,125 institutions current volume print & all online content; US$921 institutions e-access; US$1,023 institutions e-access plus backfile (all online content); US$221 institutions single print; US$1,003 institutions print only; US$117 individuals print only; 30 individuals single print;

US$2,270 institutions content through 1998. **Remarks:** Accepts advertising. **URL:** http://www.sagepub.com/journalsProdDesc.nav?prodId=Journal200957. **Circ:** (Not Reported)

54902 ■ Management Today
Haymarket Publishing Ltd.
174 Hammersmith Rd.
London W6 7JP, United Kingdom
Ph: 44 20 82674210
Publisher E-mail: info@haymarket.com
International business publication. **Founded:** 1966. **Freq:** Monthly. **Key Personnel:** Andrew Saunders, Dep. Ed., phone 44 20 82674958, andrew.saunders@haymarket.com; Matthew Gwyther, Editor, phone 44 20 82674967, matthew.gwyther@haymarket.com; Hannah Prevett, Section Ed., phone 44 20 82674959, hannah.prevett@haymarket.com. **ISSN:** 0025-1925. **Subscription Rates:** 79 individuals; 142 two years; 190 individuals three years. **Remarks:** Accepts advertising. **URL:** http://www.managementtoday.co.uk. **Circ:** ★100,184

54903 ■ Manager, British Journal of Administrative Management
Institute of Administrative Management
6 Graphite Sq.
Vauxhall Walk
London SE11 5EE, United Kingdom
Ph: 44 207 0912600
Publisher E-mail: info@instam.org
British journal covering management. **Freq:** Quarterly. **ISSN:** 1353-5188. **Remarks:** Advertising accepted; rates available upon request. **URL:** http://www.instam.org/products/manager.html. **Former name:** British Manager, Journal of Administrative Management. **Circ:** 12,500

54904 ■ Managing Information
The Association for Information Management
Howard House
Wagon Ln.
Bingley
London BD16 1WA, United Kingdom
Ph: 44 1274 777700
Fax: 44 1274 785201
Publisher E-mail: hshukla@aslib.com
Magazine covering information management. **Freq:** 10/yr. **Print Method:** Offset. **Key Personnel:** Graham Coult, Editor-in-Chief, gcoult@aslib.com; Diane Heath, Publisher, dheath@aslib.com. **ISSN:** 1352-0229. **Subscription Rates:** 181.68 individuals print + electronic; 189 individuals print + electronic (Europe); 199 other countries print + electronic; 16 single issue print. **Remarks:** Accepts advertising. **URL:** http://www.managinginformation.com/; http://www.aslib.co.uk/. **Ad Rates:** BW: 1,095, 4C: 1,570. **Circ:** 8,000

54905 ■ Managing Partner
Ark Group Ltd.
266/276 Upper Richmond Rd.
Putney
London SW15 6TQ, United Kingdom
Ph: 44 20 87852700
Fax: 44 20 87859373
Publisher E-mail: info@ark-group.com
Magazine providing information on strategic practice management for law firms. **Freq:** 10/yr. **Key Personnel:** Manju Manglani, Editor, mmanglani@ark-group.com; Brad Davison, Production Ed., bdavison@ark-group.com. **ISSN:** 1369-1368. **Subscription Rates:** 295 individuals print only; 295 individuals online only; 395 individuals standard. **Remarks:** Accepts advertising. **URL:** http://www.mpmagazine.com/. **Circ:** (Not Reported)

54906 ■ The Maritime Pilot
United Kingdom Maritime Pilots' Association
Transport House
128 Theobald's Rd.
London WC1X 8TN, United Kingdom
Ph: 44 20 76112568
Fax: 44 20 76112757
Publisher E-mail: ukmpa@tgwu.org.uk
Journal for members of the United Kingdom Pilots' Association (Marine). **Founded:** 1894. **Freq:** Quarterly. **Trim Size:** A4. **Cols./Page:** 3. **Key Personnel:** John Clandillon, Editor. **Remarks:** Accepts advertising. **URL:** http://www.pilotmag.co.uk. **Former name:** The Pilot. **Ad Rates:** BW: 200, PCI: 10. **Circ:** Controlled 1,250

Circulation: ★ = ABC; △ = BPA; ♦ = CAC; • = CCAB; ❑ = VAC; ⊕ = PO Statement; ‡ = Publisher's Report; Boldface figures = sworn; Light figures = estimated.

54907 ■ Market Leader
World Advertising Research Center
85 Newman St.
London W1T 3EX, United Kingdom
Ph: 44 20 74678100
Fax: 44 20 74678101
Publisher E-mail: enquiries@warc.com
Magazine featuring new approaches to marketing and business issues. **Freq:** Quarterly. **Trim Size:** 210 x 297 mm. **ISSN:** 1463-0877. **Subscription Rates:** 245 individuals. **URL:** http://store.warc.com/DisplaySection. aspx?Section=5&ProductID=75.

54908 ■ Marketing
Haymarket Publishing Ltd.
174 Hammersmith Rd.
London W6 7JP, United Kingdom
Ph: 44 20 82674210
Publisher E-mail: info@haymarket.com
Publication covering advertising, marketing and public relations. **Founded:** 1931. **Freq:** Weekly. **Key Personnel:** Lucy Barrett, Editor, phone 44 20 82674048; Tracy Awere, Sales Mgr., phone 44 208 2674607. **ISSN:** 0025-3650. **Subscription Rates:** 155 individuals; 279 two years; 372 individuals three years. **Remarks:** Accepts advertising. **URL:** http://www.haymarket.com/marketing/ marketing_magazine_magazine/default.aspx. **Ad Rates:** BW: 6,750. **Circ:** *35,615

54909 ■ Marketing Week
Centaur Communications Ltd.
50 Poland St.
London W1F 7AX, United Kingdom
Ph: 44 20 79704000
Publication E-mail: info@mad.co.uk
Magazine providing news and information for marketing, advertising, and media professionals. **Freq:** Weekly. **Key Personnel:** Sarah Gilchriest, Publisher, phone 44 20 79706300, sarah.gilchriest@centaur.co.uk; Mark Choueke, Editor, phone 44 20 79706335, mark. choueeke@centaur.co.uk. **Subscription Rates:** 150 individuals; 270 two years. **Remarks:** Accepts advertising. **URL:** http://www.marketingweek.co.uk. **Circ:** 40,000

54910 ■ Masonic Quarterly
United Grand Lodge of England
Freemason's Hall
60 Great Queen St.
London WC2B 5AZ, United Kingdom
Ph: 44 20 78319811
Fax: 44 20 78316021
Publication E-mail: editor@mqmagazine.co.uk; info@ mqmagazine.co.uk
Magazine featuring information about freemasonry in England. **Freq:** Quarterly. **Key Personnel:** John Jackson, Editor; John Hamill, Editorial Dir. **URL:** http://www. mqmagazine.co.uk/issue-23/index.php.

54911 ■ Massage World
PO Box 54879
London SW1P 9FW, United Kingdom
Ph: 44 20 73879111
Publisher E-mail: massageworld@btconnect.com
Magazine focusing on massage therapy and bodywork. **Freq:** Bimonthly. **Subscription Rates:** 25 individuals; 20 students; 45 other countries. **Remarks:** Accepts advertising. **URL:** http://www.massageworld.co.uk/. **Circ:** (Not Reported)

54912 ■ Master Builder
Federation of Master Builders
14-15 Great James St.
London WC1N 3DP, United Kingdom
Ph: 44 20 72427583
Fax: 44 20 74040296
Publication covering building industries. **Freq:** Monthly. **Key Personnel:** Nicky Rogers, Editor, phone 44 1778 391128, nickyr@warnersgroup.co.uk. **URL:** http://www. fmb.org.uk.

54913 ■ Materials Science and Technology
Maney Publishing
1 Carlton House Ter.
London SW1Y 5AF, United Kingdom
Ph: 44 20 74517300
Fax: 44 20 74517307
Publisher E-mail: maney@maney.co.uk
Peer-reviewed journal covering both fundamental and technological aspects of the properties, processing, and

fabrication of engineering materials in connection with the Institute of Materials, Minerals and Mining. **Founded:** 1900. **Freq:** Monthly. **Key Personnel:** Prof. J.F. Knott, Editor, j.f.knott@bham.ac.uk; Prof. A. Horsewell, Assoc. Ed.; Prof. V. Randle, Assoc. Ed., v.randle@swansea.ac. uk. **ISSN:** 0267-0836. **Subscription Rates:** 1,371 institutions, other countries; US$2,306 institutions; 459 other countries; US$690 individuals. **URL:** http://maney. co.uk/index.php/journals/mst/.

54914 ■ Materials World
Institute of Materials, Minerals & Mining
1 Carlton House Ter.
London SW1Y 5DB, United Kingdom
Ph: 44 20 74517300
Fax: 44 20 78391702
Publication E-mail: materials.world@iom3.org
Publication for the engineering materials industries, including metals, plastics, composites, ceramics and rubber. **Subtitle:** Incorporating International Mining and Minerals. **Founded:** 2002. **Freq:** Monthly. **Trim Size:** 255 x 180 mm. **Key Personnel:** Michael Forrest, Commisioning Ed., phone 44 20 74517334, katherine. williams@iom3.org; Martin Parley, Commisioning Ed., phone 44 20 74517319; Rupal Mehta, Dep. Ed., phone 44 20 74517334, rupal.mehta@iom3.org. **ISSN:** 0967-8638. **Subscription Rates:** 58 individuals Europe; US$110 other countries; 298 institutions; US$550 institutions, other countries. **Remarks:** Accepts advertising. **Online:** Gale. **URL:** http://www.iom3.org; http://www. iom3.org/content/materials-world. **Formerly:** Metals & Materials. **Ad Rates:** BW: 1,470, 4C: 2,120. **Circ:** 34,000

54915 ■ Mauritius News
583 Wandsworth Rd.
London SW8 3JD, United Kingdom
Ph: 44 20 74983066
Publication E-mail: editor@mauritiusnews.co.uk
Publisher E-mail: editor@mauritiusnews.co.uk
Newspaper for the Mauritian community in the UK. **Founded:** 1983. **Freq:** Monthly. **Key Personnel:** Peter Cheller, Editor. **Subscription Rates:** 20 individuals U.K. residents; 25 individuals Europe; 30 individuals rest of the world. **Remarks:** Accepts advertising. **URL:** http:// www.mauritius-news.co.uk. **Circ:** Combined 5,000

54916 ■ Maxim Fashion
Dennis Publishing Ltd.
30 Cleveland St.
London W1T 4JD, United Kingdom
Ph: 44 20 79076000
Fax: 44 20 79076020
Publisher E-mail: reception@dennis.co.uk
Magazine for men. **Key Personnel:** Ben Raworth, Editorial Dir., phone 44 20 79076458, ben_raworth@dennis. co.uk. **Subscription Rates:** 42.99 individuals Europe; 57 other countries; 19.95 individuals 6 months. **URL:** http://www.maxim.co.uk/fashion/. **Circ:** *43,542

54917 ■ Me Too!
BBC Worldwide Publishing Ltd.
Media Centre
201 Wood Ln.
London W12 7TQ, United Kingdom
Ph: 44 20 84332000
Fax: 44 20 87490538
Magazine featuring educational activities for children. **Freq:** every 4 weeks. **Subscription Rates:** 1.75 single issue. **URL:** http://www.bbc.co.uk/cbeebies/metoo/.

54918 ■ Measurement and Control
Institute of Measurement and Control
87 Gower St.
London WC1E 6AA, United Kingdom
Ph: 44 207 3874949
Fax: 44 207 3888431
Publication E-mail: publications@instmc.org.uk
Publication covering standards, instrumentalism, control, and matriculation. **Subtitle:** Measurement and Control— Journal of Inst MC. **Founded:** 1968. **Freq:** 10/yr. **Key Personnel:** Claudie Plen, Prod. Ed. **ISSN:** 0020-2940. **Subscription Rates:** EUR190 individuals; EUR250 individuals overseas; EUR42 single issue. **Remarks:** Accepts advertising. **URL:** http://www.instmc.org.uk/Menu-Items/publications.html. **Ad Rates:** BW: EUR700, 4C: EUR1,100. **Circ:** 4,500

54919 ■ Med Ad News
Euromoney Publications PLC
Nestor House

Playhouse Yard
London EC4V 5EX, United Kingdom
Ph: 44 20 77798888
Publisher E-mail: information@euromoneyplc.com
Publication covering advertising, marketing and public relations. **Freq:** Monthly. **Key Personnel:** Steven Niles, Managing Editor. **ISSN:** 1067-733X. **Remarks:** Accepts advertising. **URL:** http://www.medadnews.com/ magazines/medad/. **Ad Rates:** BW: 4,760, 4C: 6,260. **Circ:** 16,000

54920 ■ Media, Culture & Society
Sage Publications Ltd.
1 Oliver's Yard
55 City Rd.
London EC1Y 1SP, United Kingdom
Ph: 44 20 73248500
Fax: 44 20 73248600
Scholarly journal covering research and discussion concerning the media. **Founded:** 1979. **Freq:** Bimonthly. **Key Personnel:** Adigun Agbaje, Corresponding Ed.; John Corner, Editor; Colin Sparks, Editor; Andrew Goodwin, Corresponding Ed.; Paddy Scannell, Editor; Philip Schlesigner, Editor; Anna Reading, Editor; Raymond Boyle, Editor; Jorge A. Gonzalez, Corresponding Ed. **ISSN:** 0163-4437. **Subscription Rates:** US$1,406 institutions print & e-access; US$1,547 institutions current volume print & all online content; US$1,265 institutions e-access; US$2,151 institutions e-access plus backfile (all online content); US$1,406 institutions e-access, all online; US$1,378 institutions print only; US$117 individuals print only; US$253 institutions single print; US$25 individuals single print. **Remarks:** Accepts advertising. **URL:** http://www.sagepub.com/ journalsProdDesc.nav?level1=A00&currTree=Subjects< odId=Journal200958. **Circ:** (Not Reported)

54921 ■ Media Development
World Association for Christian Communication
71 Lambeth Walk
London SE11 6DX, United Kingdom
Ph: 44 20 77352877
English language publication covering global communications. **Freq:** Quarterly. **ISSN:** 0143-5558. **Remarks:** Advertising not accepted. **URL:** http://www. waccglobal.org/en/resources/media-development.html. **Circ:** (Not Reported)

54922 ■ Mediactive
Lawrence & Wishart Ltd.
99a Wallis Rd.
London E9 5LN, United Kingdom
Ph: 44 20 85332506
Fax: 44 20 85337369
Publisher E-mail: info@lwbooks.co.uk
Publication engaging with contemporary issues of culture and politics, aiming to be a fast and effective means of publishing ideas. **Subtitle:** Ideas, Knowledge and Culture. **Key Personnel:** Sally Davison, Managing Editor, sally@lwbooks.co.uk; Avis Greenaway, Finance Dir., avis@lwbooks.co.uk. **ISSN:** 9050-0714. **Subscription Rates:** 8 single issue. **Remarks:** Accepts advertising. **URL:** http://www.lwbooks.co.uk/journals/ mediactive/contents.html. **Circ:** (Not Reported)

54923 ■ Medical Humanities
BMJ Publishing Group
BMA House
Tavistock Sq.
London WC1H 9JR, United Kingdom
Ph: 44 20 73834410
Fax: 44 20 73876400
Publisher E-mail: customerservice.group@bmjgroup. com
Peer-reviewed and international journal for health professionals and researchers in medical humanities. **Founded:** 2000. **Freq:** Semiannual. **Key Personnel:** Deborah Kirklin, Editor, d.kirklin@pcps.ucl.ac.uk; Margaret Healy, Assoc. Ed., m.j.healy@sussex.ac.uk; Thomas Faunce, Assoc. Ed., thomas.faunce@anu.edu. au. **ISSN:** 1468-215X. **Subscription Rates:** 39 individuals print and online; EUR53 individuals print and online; US$76 individuals print and online; 35 individuals online only; EUR47 individuals online only; US$68 individuals online only. **URL:** http://mh.bmj.com/. **Circ:** ‡1,770

54924 ■ Medieval Sermon Studies
Maney Publishing
1 Carlton House Ter.
London SW1Y 5AF, United Kingdom

Ph: 44 20 74517300
Fax: 44 20 74517307
Publisher E-mail: maney@maney.co.uk
Journal featuring insightful articles on sermon studies and related areas. **Key Personnel:** Carolyn Muessig, Editor, c.a.muessig@bristol.ac.uk; Jonathan Adams, Review Ed. **ISSN:** 1366-0691. **Subscription Rates:** 85 institutions, other countries; US$148 institutions; US$138 institutions North America. **Remarks:** Accepts advertising. **URL:** http://maney.co.uk/index.php/journals/mss/. **Circ:** (Not Reported)

54925 ■ Mela UK
Talent Media
The Maltings, Studio 65/66
169 Tower Bridge Rd.
London SE1 3LJ, United Kingdom
Magazine featuring fashion, food, and culture. **Freq:** Annual. **URL:** http://www.sugarmedia.co.uk/; http://www.melauk.com/.

54926 ■ Menopause International
Royal Society of Medicine Press Ltd.
1 Wimpole St.
London W1G 0AE, United Kingdom
Ph: 44 20 72902921
Fax: 44 20 72902929
Publication E-mail: miproduction@rsm.ac.uk
Publisher E-mail: publishing@rsm.ac.uk
Journal covering news, research and opinion for study and treatment of menopausal conditions. **Freq:** Quarterly. **Key Personnel:** Edward Morris, Editor; Heather Currie, Editor. **ISSN:** 1754-0453. **Subscription Rates:** 173 institutions UK & Europe; EUR235 institutions Europe; US$345 institutions; 179 institutions, other countries; 75 individuals UK & Europe; EUR102 individuals Europe; US$156 individuals; US$311 individuals online only; 156 individuals online only; EUR212 individuals online only. **URL:** http://mi.rsmjournals.com. **Former name:** Journal of the British Menopause Society.

54927 ■ Metal Bulletin Monthly
Metal Bulletin
Nestor House
Playhouse Yard
London EC4V 5EX, United Kingdom
Ph: 44 20 78279977
Fax: 44 20 78276470
Publisher E-mail: editorial@metalbulletin.com
Magazine covering the latest information on the global non-ferrous metals and steel markets and professionals. **Founded:** 1913. **Freq:** Monthly. **Print Method:** Electronic CTP. **Trim Size:** 210 mm. x 297 mm. **ISSN:** 0373-4064. **Subscription Rates:** US$857 individuals; 397 individuals; EUR727 individuals. **Remarks:** Accepts advertising. **URL:** http://www1.metalbulletin.com. **Ad Rates:** BW: US$3,840, 4C: US$5,805. **Circ:** Paid ★5,554

54928 ■ Metallurgia
DMG World Media
Northcliffe House
2 Derry St.
London W8 5TT, United Kingdom
Ph: 44 20 79386000
Publication for the metals, metalforming and machinery industries. Thermal processing heat treatment. **Founded:** 1935. **Freq:** Bimonthly. **ISSN:** 0141-8602. **Subscription Rates:** Free online. **Remarks:** Accepts advertising. **URL:** http://journalseek.net/cgi-bin/journalseek/journalsearch.cgi?field=issn&query=0141-8602. **Circ:** (Not Reported)

54929 ■ Microbial Cell Factories
BioMed Central Ltd.
236 Gray's Inn Rd., Fl. 6
34-42 Cleveland St.
London WC1X 8HL, United Kingdom
Ph: 44 20 31922000
Fax: 44 20 31922010
Publisher E-mail: info@biomedcentral.com
Online journal covering all aspects of the development, use and investigation of microbial cells as factories for production of both natural products and recombinant proteins. **Key Personnel:** Prof. Antonio Villaverde, Editor-in-Chief, avillaverde@servet.uab.es; Dr. Pratul K. Agarwal, Editorial Board; Prof. Ricardo Amils, Editorial Board; Maurilio De Felice, Assoc. Ed.; Maria Papagianni, Assoc. Ed.; Grzegorz Wegrzyn, Assoc. Ed. **ISSN:** 1475-2859. **Remarks:** Accepts advertising. **URL:** http://www.microbialcellfactories.com. **Circ:** (Not Reported)

54930 ■ The Middle East
IC Publications Ltd.
7 Coldbath Sq.
London EC1R 4QL, United Kingdom
Ph: 44 20 78413210
Fax: 44 20 78413211
Business publication. **Founded:** 1974. **Freq:** Monthly. **Print Method:** Web. **Trim Size:** 270 x 210 mm. **ISSN:** 0305-0734. **Subscription Rates:** 40 individuals U.K; EUR80 individuals Europe; US$90 other countries; 70 two years U.K; EUR140 two years Europe; US$165 two years rest of the world. **Remarks:** Accepts advertising. **URL:** http://www.africasia.com/themiddleeast/. **Ad Rates:** BW: 3,100, 4C: 4,400. **Circ:** Combined ‡20,347

54931 ■ The Middle Way
Buddhist Society
58 Eccleston Sq.
London SW1V 1PH, United Kingdom
Ph: 44 20 78345858
Fax: 44 20 79765238
Publisher E-mail: info@thebuddhistsociety.org
Publication covering Buddhism. **Freq:** Quarterly in May, Aug., Nov., and Feb. **ISSN:** 0026-3214. **Subscription Rates:** 20 individuals; EUR30 individuals within Europe; 27 individuals outside Europe; airmail; 25 individuals outside Europe; surface; Free to members. **URL:** http://www.thebuddhistsociety.org/middleway/index.html.

54932 ■ Midland History
Maney Publishing
1 Carlton House Ter.
London SW1Y 5AF, United Kingdom
Ph: 44 20 74517300
Fax: 44 20 74517307
Publisher E-mail: maney@maney.co.uk
Peer-reviwed journal covering the history of the English midlands. **Founded:** 1971. **Freq:** Semiannual. **Key Personnel:** Dr. Richard Cust, Editor, r.p.cust@bham.ac.uk; Dr. Stephen K. Roberts, Editor, skennethroberts@yahoo.co.uk; Prof. John Beckett, Chm. of the Editorial Board. **ISSN:** 0047-729X. **Subscription Rates:** 20 other countries; US$38 individuals; 80 institutions, other countries; US$148 institutions. **Remarks:** Accepts advertising. **URL:** http://maney.co.uk/index.php/journals/mdh/. **Circ:** (Not Reported)

54933 ■ Midsomer Murders Magazine
GE Fabbri Ltd.
FreePost LON13490
London EC1B 1LP, United Kingdom
Ph: 44 845 6039711
Publication E-mail: order@midsomermurdersdvd.com
Publisher E-mail: mailbox@gefabbri.co.uk
Magazine featuring the television drama series Midsomer Murders. **Freq:** Semimonthly. **Key Personnel:** Peter Edwards, Mng. Dir.; Liz Glaze, Director; Katie Preston, Editor-in-Chief. **URL:** http://www.midsomermurdersdvd.com; http://www.gefabbri.co.uk/publication_midsomermurdersthedvdcollection.

54934 ■ Millennium
London School of Economics and Political Science
Houghton St.
London WC2A 2AE, United Kingdom
Ph: 44 20 74057686
Publication E-mail: millennium@lse.ac.uk
Scholarly journal covering international studies. **Subtitle:** Journal of International Studies. **Founded:** 1971. **Freq:** 3/yr. **Key Personnel:** Douglas Bulloch, Bus. Mgr.; Joe Hoover, Web Ed.; Jorge Lasmar, Dep. Ed.; Alex Edwards, Dep. Ed.; Jasmine Gani, Editor; Martha Iniguez de Heredia, Editor; Paul Kirby, Editor. **ISSN:** 0305-8298. **Subscription Rates:** 232 institutions print and online; 227 institutions print only; 209 institutions online only; 83 institutions single copy; 56 individuals print and online; US$24 single issue print. **Remarks:** Accepts advertising. **URL:** http://www.lse.ac.uk/Depts/intrel/millenn/. **Ad Rates:** BW: 250. **Circ:** Paid ‡1,000

54935 ■ MIMS
Haymarket Business Magazines
174 Hammersmith Rd.
London W6 7JP, United Kingdom
Ph: 44 20 82674210
Publisher E-mail: info@haymarket.com
Magazine featuring prescribing guide for doctors and pharmacists. **Founded:** 1959. **Freq:** Monthly. **Key Personnel:** Jenny Gowans, Editor, phone 44 20 82674614, jenny.gowans@haymarket.com; Robert Nuzzaci, Con-

tact, phone 44 20 82674884, robert.nuzzaci@haymarket.com; Tracy Awere, Sales Mgr., phone 44 20 82674607, tracy.awere@haymarket.com, **Subscription Rates:** 165 individuals; 297 two years; 396 individuals three years. **Remarks:** Accepts advertising. **URL:** http://www.haymarket.com/mims/multi/mims_magazine/default.aspx. **Circ:** Combined ★39,388

54936 ■ Mineral Processing and Extractive Metallurgy
Maney Publishing
1 Carlton House Ter.
London SW1Y 5AF, United Kingdom
Ph: 44 20 74517300
Fax: 44 20 74517307
Publisher E-mail: maney@maney.co.uk
Journal dealing with scientific, engineering, and economic aspects of the preparation, separation, extraction, and purification of ores, metals, and mineral products by both physical and chemical methods. **Subtitle:** IMM Transactions Section C. **Freq:** Quarterly. **Trim Size:** 188 x 266 mm. **Key Personnel:** Dr. R. Vasant Kumar, Editor, rvk10@cam.ac.uk; Dr. N. Subasinghe, Editorial Board, n.subasinghe@murdoch.edu.au; J.H. Canterford, Editorial Board, jcant@tassie.net.au; P.N. Benkendorff, Editorial Board, pbenken@bigpond.com; Prof. A. Jha, Editorial Board, a.jha@leeds.ac.uk. **ISSN:** 0371-9553. **Subscription Rates:** 245 institutions, other countries; US$411 institutions; 86 members; US$143 members. **Remarks:** Accepts advertising. **URL:** http://maney.co.uk/index.php/journals/mpm/. **Ad Rates:** BW: 300, 4C: 550. **Circ:** (Not Reported)

54937 ■ Mineralogical Magazine
Mineralogical Society of Great Britain and Ireland
c/o Dr. M.D. Welch, Ed.
Dept. of Mineralogy
The Natural History Museum
London SW7 5BD, United Kingdom
Publisher E-mail: info@minersoc.org
Journal dealing with mineralogy, crystallography, geochemistry, petrology, environmental geology and economic geology. **Founded:** 1876. **Freq:** 6/yr. **Key Personnel:** Dr. M.D. Welch, Editor, m.welch@nhm.ac.uk. **ISSN:** 0026-461X. **Subscription Rates:** 430 institutions print and online; 463 institutions, other countries print and online; 393 institutions online only; 393 institutions, other countries online only. **Remarks:** Accepts advertising. **URL:** http://www.minersoc.org/pages/e_journals/minmag.html. **Ad Rates:** BW: 220. **Circ:** (Not Reported)

54938 ■ Ming Studies
Maney Publishing
1 Carlton House Ter.
London SW1Y 5AF, United Kingdom
Ph: 44 20 74517300
Fax: 44 20 74517307
Publisher E-mail: maney@maney.co.uk
Peer-reviewed journal of the Society for Ming Studies, publishing articles and interpretations on the history and society of China's Ming period. **Freq:** Semiannual. **Key Personnel:** Dr. Kenneth J. Hammond, Editor, khammond@nmsu.edu; Dr. Philip A. Kafalas, Book Reviews Ed., kafalasp@georgetown.edu. **ISSN:** 0147-037X. **Subscription Rates:** 122 institutions, other countries; US$212 institutions; 114 institutions, other countries online only; US$198 institutions online only. **Remarks:** Accepts advertising. **URL:** http://maney.co.uk/index.php/journals/mng. **Circ:** (Not Reported)

54939 ■ Mining Environmental Management
Mining Journal Ltd.
Albert House
1 Singer St.
London EC2A 4BQ, United Kingdom
Ph: 44 20 72166060
Fax: 44 20 72166050
Publisher E-mail: lisa.huggins@aspermontuk.com
Trade magazine covering technical and social issues in mining and the environment worldwide. **Founded:** Mar. 1993. **Freq:** Quarterly. **Trim Size:** 297 mm x 210 mm. **Key Personnel:** Katherine Welch, Editor, katherine.welch@miningenvironmental.com; Richard Dolan, Advertising Mgr., phone 44 20 72166086, richard.dolan@miningmagazine.com. **Subscription Rates:** 95 individuals; EUR160 individuals; US$170 individuals. **Remarks:** Accepts advertising. **URL:** http://www.miningenvironmental.com. **Ad Rates:** BW: US$1,520,

4C: US$4,847. **Circ:** Combined 3,000

54940 ■ Mining Journal
Mining Journal Ltd.
Albert House
1 Singer St.
London EC2A 4BQ, United Kingdom
Ph: 44 20 72166060
Fax: 44 20 72166050
Publisher E-mail: lisa.huggins@aspermontuk.com
Newspaper covering the mining industry worldwide. **Founded:** 1835. **Freq:** Weekly. **Trim Size:** 297 x 210 mm. **Cols./Page:** 4. **Key Personnel:** Phil Halliday, Editor; Chris Hinde, Editorial Dir. **Subscription Rates:** 360 individuals; EUR580 individuals; US$650 individuals; 1,160 institutions; EUR1,870 institutions; US$2,090 institutions. **Remarks:** Accepts advertising. **URL:** http://www.mining-journal.com/breaking-news. **Ad Rates:** BW: US$2,277, 4C: US$4,847, PCI: US$40. **Circ:** Combined 3,600

54941 ■ Mining Magazine
Mining Journal Ltd.
Albert House
1 Singer St.
London EC2A 4BQ, United Kingdom
Ph: 44 20 72166060
Fax: 44 20 72166050
Publisher E-mail: lisa.huggins@aspermontuk.com
Trade magazine covering the mining industry worldwide. **Founded:** 1909. **Freq:** Monthly. **Trim Size:** 275 mm x 200 mm. **Key Personnel:** Paul Moore, Editor, paul.moore@miningjournal.com; Richard Dolan, Advertising Mgr., phone 44 20 72166086, richard.dolan@miningmagazine.com. **Subscription Rates:** EUR95 individuals UK and Europe; US$170 other countries; EUR160 two years UK and Europe; US$290 two years. **Remarks:** Accepts advertising. **URL:** http://www.miningmagazine.com/. **Ad Rates:** 4C: US$7,510. **Circ:** △19,900

54942 ■ Mining Technology
Maney Publishing
1 Carlton House Ter.
London SW1Y 5AF, United Kingdom
Ph: 44 20 74517300
Fax: 44 20 74517307
Publisher E-mail: maney@maney.co.uk
Journal focusing on all kinds of mining operations such as underground, opencast, and offshore as also other matters related to mining like finance, economics, management, law, and control among others. Covers technical aspects involved such as mine design and development, operational techniques, mining machinery, environmental issues, mine management and organization, production, education and training. **Freq:** Quarterly. **Key Personnel:** Prof. P.A. Dowd, Editor, peter.dowd@adelaide.edu.au; Robert Appleyard, Editorial Board, bappleyard@amcconsultants.com.au; Prof. Pierre Mousset-Jones, Editorial Board, mousset@mines.unr.edu; Dr. I.S. Lowndes, Editorial Board, ian.lowndes@nottingham.ac.uk; Prof. R.J. Pine, Editorial Board, r.j.pine@csm.ex.ac.uk; Dr. I. Clark, Editorial Board, geostokos@stokos.demon.co.uk; Dr. T. Szwedzicki, Editorial Board. **ISSN:** 0371-7844. **Subscription Rates:** 245 institutions, other countries; US$411 institutions; 86 members other countries; US$143 members. **URL:** http://maney.co.uk/index.php/journals/mnt/. **Ad Rates:** BW: 300, 4C: 550. **Circ:** (Not Reported)

54943 ■ Modern Language Review
Modern Humanities Research Association
1 Carlton House Ter.
London SW1Y 5AF, United Kingdom
Publication E-mail: mlr@mhra.org.uk
Publisher E-mail: mail@mhra.org.uk
Publication covering literature and writing. **Founded:** 1905. **Freq:** Quarterly. **ISSN:** 0026-7937. **Subscription Rates:** 132 institutions; 132 institutions; US$304 institutions North America; 157 institutions, other countries rest of World; 22 individuals U.K./Europe - MLR supplement; US$45 individuals North America - MLR supplement; 25 individuals rest of World - MLR supplement. **Remarks:** Advertising not accepted. **URL:** http://www.mhra.org.uk/Publications/Journals/mlr.html. **Circ:** (Not Reported)

54944 ■ Mojo
H. Bauer Publishing
Academic House
24-28 Oval Rd.
London NW1 7DT, United Kingdom

Ph: 44 20 72418000
Fax: 44 20 72418030
Magazine featuring classic rock music. **Key Personnel:** Phil Alexander, Editor. **Subscription Rates:** 59 individuals; 85 individuals rest of world. **URL:** http://www.mojo4music.com/blog/.

54945 ■ Molecular Cancer
BioMed Central Ltd.
236 Gray's Inn Rd., Fl. 6
34-42 Cleveland St.
London WC1X 8HL, United Kingdom
Ph: 44 20 31922000
Fax: 44 20 31922010
Publisher E-mail: info@biomedcentral.com
Online journal presenting original research and commentary in all areas of cancer-related science. **Key Personnel:** Dr. Alan Storey, Editor-in-Chief; Prof. Arunkumar B. Deora, Exec. Ed., adeora@med.cornell.edu; David Kelsell, Assoc. Ed.; Doris Mayer, Assoc. Ed.; Joe S. Mymryk, Assoc. Ed.; Lawrence Young, Assoc. Ed. **ISSN:** 1476-4598. **Remarks:** Accepts advertising. **URL:** http://www.molecular-cancer.com/. **Circ:** (Not Reported)

54946 ■ Molecular and Cellular Endocrinology
Elsevier Science
c/o I.T. Huhtaniemi, Ed.
Institute of Reproductive & Developmental Biology (IRDB)
Imperial College London
Du Cane Rd.
London W12 0NN, United Kingdom
Ph: 44 20 75942104
Fax: 44 20 75942184
Publisher E-mail: nlinfo-f@elsevier.com
Journal devoted to the study of hormones with regard to their biochemical effects, synthesis and secretions, as also the understanding of molecular mechanisms regulating hormone synthesis. **Founded:** 1974. **Freq:** 34/yr. **Key Personnel:** I.T. Huhtaniemi, Editor, ilpo.huhtaniemi@imperial.ac.uk; W.E. Rainey, Managing Editor, mce@mail.mcg.edu; R.J. Rodgers, Editor, phone 61 883 033932, fax 61 883 034099, ray.rodgers@adelaide.edu.au; M. Ascoli, Editorial Board; R. Baron, Editorial Board; J. Brosen, Editorial Board. **ISSN:** 0303-7207. **Subscription Rates:** EUR5,761 institutions for Japan; 765,100¥ institutions for Europe; US$6,444 institutions for all countries except Europe and Japan; EUR341 individuals; US$457 individuals; 52,500¥ individuals. **Remarks:** Accepts advertising. **URL:** http://www.elsevier.com/wps/find/journaldescription.cws_home/506028/description. **Circ:** (Not Reported)

54947 ■ Molecular Pain
BioMed Central Ltd.
236 Gray's Inn Rd., Fl. 6
34-42 Cleveland St.
London WC1X 8HL, United Kingdom
Ph: 44 20 31922000
Fax: 44 20 31922010
Publisher E-mail: info@biomedcentral.com
Online journal covering all aspects of pain research at the cellular, subcellular and molecular levels. **Key Personnel:** Dr. Jianguo Gu, Editor-in-Chief, phone 352392-5989, fax 352392-7609, jgu@dental.ufl.edu; Dr. Min Zhuo, Editor-in-Chief, min.zhuo@utoronto.ca; Prof. Michael Caterina, Dep. Ed., caterina@jhmi.edu; Emily England, Managing Editor. **ISSN:** 1744-8069. **Remarks:** Accepts advertising. **URL:** http://www.molecularpain.com/home/. **Circ:** (Not Reported)

54948 ■ Molecular Psychiatry
Nature Publishing Group
The Macmillan Bldg.
4 Crinan St.
London N1 9XW, United Kingdom
Ph: 44 20 78334000
Fax: 44 20 78434640
Journal dealing with the psychiatric disorders and their treatment. **Key Personnel:** Julio Licinio, MD, Editor; Ma-Li Wong, Assoc. Ed. **ISSN:** 1359-4184. **Subscription Rates:** US$578 individuals for America (print and online); EUR459 individuals for Europe (print and online); 78,500¥ individuals for Japan (print and online); 296 individuals for UK and rest of world (print and online); US$520 individuals online; EUR413 individuals for Europe; 70,600¥ individuals for Japan; 266 individuals for UK and rest of the world. **Remarks:** Advertising accepted; rates available upon request. **URL:** http://www.nature.com/mp/index.html. **Circ:** (Not Reported)

54949 ■ Molecular Systems Biology
Nature Publishing Group
The Macmillan Bldg.
4 Crinan St.
London N1 9XW, United Kingdom
Ph: 44 20 78334000
Fax: 44 20 78434640
Publication E-mail: msb@embo.org
Peer-reviewed journal covering all aspects of the rapidly growing and interdisciplinary field of systems biology at the molecular level, and attracting and helping shape the highest quality research in the evolving areas of genomics, proteomics, metabolomics, bioinformatics, microbial systems, and the integration of cell signaling and regulatory networks. **Key Personnel:** Ruedi Aebersold, Sen. Ed.; Peer Bork, Sen. Ed.; Leroy Hood, Sen. Ed.; Edison Liu, Sen. Ed.; Ewan Birney, Advisory Editorial Board; Thomas Lemberger, Ch. Ed.; Julie Ahringer, Advisory Editorial Board; George Church, Sen. Ed.; Charles Auffray, Advisory Editorial Board. **ISSN:** 1744-4292. **URL:** http://www.nature.com/msb/index.html.

54950 ■ Money Marketing
Centaur Publishing Ltd.
50 Poland St.
London W1F 7AX, United Kingdom
Ph: 44 20 79704000
Fax: 44 20 79704189
Publication E-mail: mmcirc@centaur.co.uk
Publication for the banking, finance, and accounting industries. **Freq:** Weekly. **Trim Size:** 266 x 360 mm. **Key Personnel:** Nita Patel, Dep. Production Mgr., nita.patel@centaur.co.uk; Paul McMillan, Editor, phone 44 20 79704776, paul.mcmillan@centaur.co.uk; David Cowan, Publisher, david.cowan@centaur.co.uk. **ISSN:** 0958-3769. **Remarks:** Accepts advertising. **URL:** http://www.moneymarketing.com/. **Ad Rates:** BW: 3,888, 4C: 5,004. **Circ:** (Not Reported)

54951 ■ Money Observer
Guardian Newspapers Ltd.
119 Farringdon Rd.
London EC1R 3ER, United Kingdom
Ph: 44 20 72782332
Publication E-mail: money.observer.news@guardian.co.uk
Publisher E-mail: letters@guardian.co.uk
Magazine featuring savings and investments. **Founded:** 1979. **Freq:** Monthly. **Key Personnel:** Andrew Pitts, Editor. **Remarks:** Accepts advertising. **URL:** http://www.moneyobserver.com/; http://www.guardian.co.uk/Money_Observer/0,5488,,00.html. **Circ:** (Not Reported)

54952 ■ Mood Food
Federation of Specialists Restaurant
PO Box 416
London KT1 9BJ, United Kingdom
Ph: 44 20 83994831
Publisher E-mail: enquiries@fedrest.com
Magazine featuring food, restaurant, recipes and nutrition. **Founded:** 1996. **Key Personnel:** Peter J. Grove, Editor, groveint@aol.com. **Remarks:** Accepts advertising. **URL:** http://www.menumagazine.co.uk/. **Circ:** (Not Reported)

54953 ■ Mortgage Edge
Incisive Media Limited
Haymarket House
28-29 Haymarket
London SW1Y 4RX, United Kingdom
Ph: 44 870 2408859
Fax: 44 207 4849797
Publisher E-mail: customerservices@incisivemedia.com
Magazine for mortgage brokers. **Founded:** 2000. **Freq:** Monthly. **Key Personnel:** Nick Rapley, Mng. Dir.; Lawrence Gosling, Editorial Dir.; Iain Cartlidge, Publishing Dir. **Remarks:** Accepts advertising. **URL:** http://www.incisivemedia.com/corporate/markets/mortgage. **Circ:** (Not Reported)

54954 ■ Mortgage Solutions
Incisive Media Limited
Haymarket House
28-29 Haymarket
London SW1Y 4RX, United Kingdom
Ph: 44 870 2408859
Fax: 44 207 4849797
Publisher E-mail: customerservices@incisivemedia.com
Magazine featuring mortgage market. **Subtitle:** Committed to mortgage intermediaries. **Founded:** May 1999.

Freq: Weekly. **Key Personnel:** Paula John, Editor-in-Chief, phone 44 20 70047491, paula.john@incisivemedia.com; Victoria Hartley, Editor, phone 44 20 70047506, vicky.hartley@incisivemedia.com. **Remarks:** Accepts advertising. **URL:** http://www.mortgagesolutions-online.com/. **Circ:** (Not Reported)

54955 ■ Mortgage Strategy
Centaur Media PLC
50 Poland St.
London W1F 7AX, United Kingdom
Ph: 44 20 79704000
Publisher E-mail: customerservices@centaur.co.uk
Magazine for mortgage intermediaries and other professionals. **Founded:** Sept. 2001. **Freq:** Weekly. **Key Personnel:** Robyn Thickett, Editor, robert.thickett@centaur.co.uk; Nick Wakeham, Commercial Mgr., phone 44 20 79438077, nick.wakeham@centaur.co.uk; Anna Ruddock, Publisher, phone 44 20 79438012, anna.ruddock@centaur.co.uk. **Remarks:** Accepts advertising. **URL:** http://www.mortgagestrategy.co.uk/. **Circ:** (Not Reported)

54956 ■ Moto Magazine
Factory Media
1 W Smithfield
London EC1A 9JU, United Kingdom
Ph: 44 20 73329700
Publisher E-mail: contact@factorymedia.com
Magazine featuring motocross. **Freq:** 12/yr. **Subscription Rates:** 31.99 individuals credit card; 28.99 individuals direct debit; US$86 individuals credit card. **URL:** http://motomagazine.co.uk/; http://factorymedia.com.

54957 ■ Motor Boat and Yachting
IPC Media Ltd.
Blue Fin Bldg.
110 Southwark St.
London SE1 0SU, United Kingdom
Ph: 44 203 1485000
Publication E-mail: mby@ipcmedia.com
Magazine featuring motor boat and yachting. **Freq:** Monthly. **Key Personnel:** Hugo Andreae, Editor, phone 44 20 31484640, hugo_andreae@ipcmedia.com; Rob Peake, Dep. Ed., phone 44 20 31484647, rob_peake@ipcmedia.com; David Marsh, Technical Ed., david_marsh@ipcmedia.com. **Subscription Rates:** US$189.16 two years; US$94.58 individuals. **URL:** http://www.mby.com/.

54958 ■ Motor Caravan
IPC Media Ltd.
Blue Fin Bldg.
110 Southwark St.
London SE1 0SU, United Kingdom
Ph: 44 203 1485000
British magazine focusing on motorhome travel. Provides buying advice, practical tips, touring ideas, and more. Provides information on model testing, a comprehensive buyer's guide, and hints and tips from motor caravaneers. **Freq:** Monthly. **Key Personnel:** Naomi Leach, Acting Ed., naomi_leach@ipcmedia.com. **URL:** http://www.motorcaravanmagazine.co.uk/.

54959 ■ MS Matters
Multiple Sclerosis Society of Great Britain and Northern Ireland
MS National Centre
372 Edgware Rd.
London NW2 6ND, United Kingdom
Ph: 44 20 84380700
Fax: 44 20 84380701
Publisher E-mail: info@mssociety.org.uk
Publication covering neurological disorders. **Freq:** Semiannual. **Subscription Rates:** Included in membership. **Remarks:** Advertising accepted; rates available upon request. **URL:** http://www.mssociety.org.uk/support_and_services/ms_books_journals/ms_journals.html. **Circ:** (Not Reported)

54960 ■ MSDN Magazine
United Business Media
245 Blackfriars Rd.
London SE1 9UY, United Kingdom
Ph: 44 20 79215000
Monthly magazine covering Microsoft tools, development environments, and technologies for Windows and the Web. **Freq:** Monthly. **Key Personnel:** Jill Thiry, Publisher; Howard Dierking, Editor-in-Chief. **Subscription Rates:** US$35 individuals; C$45 Canada. **Re-**

marks: Accepts advertising. **URL:** http://msdn.microsoft.com/en-au/magazine/default.aspx. **Circ:** Paid 75,378

54961 ■ Multiple Sclerosis
Sage Publications Ltd.
1 Oliver's Yard
55 City Rd.
London EC1Y 1SP, United Kingdom
Ph: 44 20 73248500
Fax: 44 20 73248600
Peer-reviewed journal covering inflammatory diseases of the central nervous system. **Subtitle:** Clinical and Laboratory Research. **Freq:** Monthly. **Trim Size:** 210 x 280 mm. **Cols./Page:** 2. **Col. Width:** 83 millimeters. **Col. Depth:** 231 millimeters. **Key Personnel:** Alan J. Thompson, Editor-in-Chief; Jack Antel, Co-Ed.; W. Carroll, Co-Ed. **ISSN:** 1352-4585. **Subscription Rates:** 925 institutions print & e-access; 1,018 institutions current volume print & all online content; 833 institutions e-access; 926 institutions all online content; 907 institutions print only; 190 individuals print & e-access; 21 individuals single print; 83 institutions single print. **Remarks:** Accepts advertising. **URL:** http://www.sagepub.co.uk/journalsProdDesc.nav?prodId=Journal201820. **Ad Rates:** BW: 730, 4C: 2,375. **Circ:** Paid 700

54962 ■ Municipal Engineer
Institution of Civil Engineers
1 Great George St.
Westminster
London SW1P 3AA, United Kingdom
Ph: 44 20 72227722
Publication covering engineering. **Freq:** Quarterly March, June, September, December. **Key Personnel:** Ian Jenkinson, Chm. **ISSN:** 0965-0903. **Subscription Rates:** 130 individuals. **Remarks:** Accepts advertising. **URL:** http://www.thomastelford.com/journals/Subscribe.asp. **Circ:** (Not Reported)

54963 ■ Music Journal
Incorporated Society of Musicians
10 Stratford Pl.
London W1C 1AA, United Kingdom
Ph: 44 20 76294413
Fax: 44 20 74081538
Publisher E-mail: membership@ism.org
Professional music magazine for association members. **Freq:** Monthly. **Key Personnel:** Deborah Annetts, Editor. **Subscription Rates:** 30 individuals; 3 single issue. **Remarks:** Accepts advertising. **URL:** http://www.ism.org/publications.html. **Circ:** Combined 5,100

54964 ■ Music & Letters
Oxford University Press
Department of Music
Kings College
Strand
London WC2R 2LS, United Kingdom
Ph: 44 20 78482384
Fax: 44 20 78482326
Publisher E-mail: webenquiry.uk@oup.com
Publication covering music. **Freq:** 4/yr. **Key Personnel:** Rebecca Herrisone, Editor; Michael Talbot, Editorial Board; Arnold Whittall, Assoc. Ed.; John Rink, Editorial Board; John Caldwell, Editorial Board; Sarah Hibberd, Editor; Jim Samson, Editorial Board; Dr. Daniel Grimley, Editor; Sam Barrat, Editor; John Whenham, Editorial Board. **ISSN:** 0027-4224. **Subscription Rates:** 160 institutions print and online; US$310 institutions print and online; EUR240 institutions print and online; 62 individuals print; US$123 individuals print; EUR93 individuals print; 146 institutions print, online; US$283 institutions print, online; EUR219 institutions print, online. **Remarks:** Accepts advertising. **URL:** http://ml.oxfordjournals.org. **Circ:** (Not Reported)

54965 ■ Musical Opinion
Musical Opinion Ltd.
1 Exford Rd.
London SE12 9HD, United Kingdom
Ph: 44 14 24855544
Fax: 44 14 24863686
Publisher E-mail: musicalopinion@hotmail.co.uk
Consumer magazine covering classical music, opera, and ballet. **Founded:** Oct. 8, 1877. **Freq:** Bimonthly. **Key Personnel:** Christopher Monk, Art Dir. & Production Ed., phone 44 14 24422105, fax 44 14 24202933; Robert Matthew-Walker, Editor. **ISSN:** 0027-4623. **Subscription Rates:** 28 individuals U.K.; US$75 individuals U.S.; 40 elsewhere rest of world. **Remarks:** Accepts

advertising. **URL:** http://www.musicalopinion.com. **Circ:** Paid ‡5,000, Non-paid ‡1,000

54966 ■ Musical Stages
Musical Stages Ltd.
PO Box 8365
London W14 0GL, United Kingdom
Ph: 44 20 76032227
Fax: 44 20 76032227
Publication E-mail: info@musicalstages.co.uk
Publisher E-mail: info@musicalstages.co.uk
Consumer magazine covering musical theatre. **Subtitle:** The World of Musical Theatre. **Founded:** 1995. **Freq:** Quarterly. **Trim Size:** A4. **Cols./Page:** 4. **Key Personnel:** Howard Sherwood, Production Ed., howard@howard-sherwood.co.uk; Lynda Trapnell, Editor, editor@musicalstages.co.uk; Michael Tornay, Advertising & Mktg., michael.tornay@virgin.net; Anne Highton, Administration. **ISSN:** 1361-3693. **Subscription Rates:** 20 individuals UK; 25 other countries. **Remarks:** Accepts advertising. **URL:** http://www.musicalstages.co.uk/. **Circ:** (Not Reported)

54967 ■ MWP
Centaur Publishing Ltd.
50 Poland St.
London W1F 7AX, United Kingdom
Ph: 44 20 79704000
Fax: 44 20 79704189
Publication for the metals, metalworking and machinery industries. **Founded:** 1900. **Freq:** Monthly. **Key Personnel:** Derek Rogers, Publishing Dir., phone 44 20 79704000, derek.rogers@centaur.co.uk; Mike Excell, Editor, mike.excell@centaur.co.uk. **ISSN:** 0026-1033. **Subscription Rates:** 58 individuals; 104.40 two years; 147.90 individuals. **Remarks:** Accepts advertising. **URL:** http://www.mwponline.com/; http://www.centaur.co.uk/. **Formerly:** Metalworking Production. **Ad Rates:** BW: 2,205. **Circ:** 16,861

54968 ■ Myeloproliferative Disorders in practice
Hayward Medical Communications
Covent Garden
8-10 Dryden St.
London WC2E 9NA, United Kingdom
Publisher E-mail: admin@hayward.co.uk
Journal covering myeloproliferative disorders. **Founded:** 2007. **Freq:** Quarterly. **Key Personnel:** John Reilly, MD, Editor. **URL:** http://www.mdip.co.uk/mdip/.

54969 ■ Names
Maney Publishing
1 Carlton House Ter.
London SW1Y 5AF, United Kingdom
Ph: 44 20 74517300
Fax: 44 20 74517307
Publisher E-mail: maney@maney.co.uk
Language journal. **Subtitle:** A Journal of Onomastics. **Founded:** 1951. **Freq:** Quarterly. **Print Method:** Letterpress. **Trim Size:** 6 x 9. **Cols./Page:** 1. **Col. Width:** 48 nonpareils. **Col. Depth:** 110 agate lines. **Key Personnel:** Frank Nuesel, Editor. **ISSN:** 0027-7738. **Subscription Rates:** US$198 individuals; 104 other countries. **Remarks:** Advertising not accepted. **URL:** http://maney.co.uk/index.php/journals/nam/. **Circ:** Paid 860

54970 ■ Nanomedicine
Future Medicine Ltd.
Unitec House
2 Albert Pl.
London N3 1QB, United Kingdom
Ph: 44 20 83716080
Fax: 44 20 83432313
Publisher E-mail: info@futuremedicine.com
Journal covering research and application of nanotechnology in medicine. **Freq:** 8/yr. **Key Personnel:** K. Kostarelos, Sen. Ed.; C.R. Martin, Sen. Ed.; W.C.W. Chan, Assoc. Ed. **ISSN:** 1743-5889. **URL:** http://www.futuremedicine.com/loi/nnm.

54971 ■ Nature Cell Biology
Nature Publishing Group
The Macmillan Bldg.
4 Crinan St.
London N1 9XW, United Kingdom
Ph: 44 20 78334000
Fax: 44 20 78434640
Journal publishing papers related to all areas of cell

Circulation: ★ = ABC; △ = BPA; ♦ = CAC; • = CCAB; ❑ = VAC; ⊕ = PO Statement; ‡ = Publisher's Report; Boldface figures = sworn; Light figures = estimated.

Gale Directory of Publications & Broadcast Media/147th Ed. 5749

biology. **Founded:** 1999. **Key Personnel:** Alison Schuldt, Sen. Ed., a.schuldt@nature.com; Sowmya Swaminathan, Ch. Ed., s.swaminathan@nature.com. **ISSN:** 1465-7392. **Subscription Rates:** US$225 individuals print and online; US$382 two years print and online. **Remarks:** Advertising accepted; rates available upon request. **URL:** http://www.nature.com/ncb/index.html. **Circ:** (Not Reported)

54972 ■ Nature Materials
Nature Publishing Group
The Macmillan Bldg.
4 Crinan St.
London N1 9XW, United Kingdom
Ph: 44 20 78334000
Fax: 44 20 78434640
Publication E-mail: materials@nature.com
Peer-reviewed multi-disciplinary journal aimed at bringing together cutting-edge research across the entire spectrum of materials science and engineering, providing a forum for the development of a common identity among materials scientists while encouraging researchers to cross established subdisciplinary divides. **Freq:** Monthly. **Key Personnel:** Vincent Dusastre, PhD, Editor; Alison Stoddart, Assoc. Ed.; Fabio Pulizzi, Assoc. Ed.; Joerg Heber, Sen. Ed. **ISSN:** 1476-1122. **Subscription Rates:** US$199 individuals print and online; US$351 two years print and online. **URL:** http://www.nature.com/nmat/.

54973 ■ Nature Methods
Nature Publishing Group
The Macmillan Bldg.
4 Crinan St.
London N1 9XW, United Kingdom
Ph: 44 20 78334000
Fax: 44 20 78434640
Publication E-mail: methods@natureny.com
Forum for the publication of novel methods and significant improvements to tried-and-tested techniques in the life sciences and related area of chemistry, publishing primary research papers as well as overviews of recent technical and methodological developments, and detailed descriptions of important established methods. **Freq:** Monthly. **Key Personnel:** Irene Kaganman, Sen. Copy Ed., i.kaganman@natureny.com; Natalie De Souza, Assoc. Ed., n.desouza@natureny.com; Nicole Rusk, Sen. Ed., n.rusk@natureny.com; Allison Doerr, Assoc. Ed., a.doerr@natureny.com; Brandy Moyer, Production Ed., b.moyer@natureny.com; Daniel Evanko, Ch. Ed., d.evanko@natureny.com; Ingrid McNamara, Sen. Production Ed., i.mcnamara@natureny.com. **ISSN:** 1548-7091. **Subscription Rates:** US$150 individuals print and online; US$225 two years print and online. **URL:** http://www.nature.com/nmeth/index.html.

54974 ■ Nature Physics
Nature Publishing Group
The Macmillan Bldg.
4 Crinan St.
London N1 9XW, United Kingdom
Ph: 44 20 78334000
Fax: 44 20 78434640
Publication E-mail: naturephysics@nature.com
Journal publishing papers of the highest quality and significance in all areas of physics, pure and applied, including core physics disciplines and theoretical physics. **Freq:** Monthly. **Key Personnel:** Alison Wright, Ch. Ed.; Edmund Gerstner, Sen. Ed. **ISSN:** 1745-2473. **Subscription Rates:** US$144 individuals print and online; US$209 two years. **URL:** http://www.nature.com/nphys/index.html.

54975 ■ Nature Reviews Cancer
Nature Publishing Group
The Macmillan Bldg.
4 Crinan St.
London N1 9XW, United Kingdom
Ph: 44 20 78334000
Fax: 44 20 78434640
Publication E-mail: naturereviews@nature.com
Journal proposing to be a gateway from which cancer researchers - from those investigating the molecular basis of cancer to those involved in translational research - access the information that they need to further the ability to diagnose, treat and ultimately prevent cancer. **Freq:** Monthly. **Key Personnel:** Nicola McCarthy, PhD, Ch. Ed.; Gemma Alderton, Sen. Ed.; Sarah Seton-Rogers, PhD, Sen. Ed. **ISSN:** 1474-175X.

Subscription Rates: US$265 individuals; US$450 two years. **URL:** http://www.nature.com/nrc/index.html.

54976 ■ Nature Reviews Cardiology
Nature Publishing Group
The Macmillan Bldg.
4 Crinan St.
London N1 9XW, United Kingdom
Ph: 44 20 78334000
Fax: 44 20 78434640
Journal delivering timely interpretations of key research developments, translating the latest findings into clinical practice. **Freq:** Monthly. **Key Personnel:** Valentin Fuster, MD, Editor-in-Chief, ncpcardio@nature.com; Bryony Mearns, Ch. Ed. **ISSN:** 1743-4297. **Subscription Rates:** US$175 individuals print and online; US$297 two years print and online. **URL:** http://www.nature.com/ncpcardio/. **Formerly:** Nature Clinical Practice Cardiovascular Medicine.

54977 ■ Nature Reviews Clinical Oncology
Nature Publishing Group
The Macmillan Bldg.
4 Crinan St.
London N1 9XW, United Kingdom
Ph: 44 20 78334000
Fax: 44 20 78434640
Peer-reviewed journal providing oncologists with authoritative and timely interpretations of key developments in oncology, translating the latest findings into clinical practice, with coverage including pathology, diagnosis, treatment (e.g. chemotherapy, radiotherapy, surgery), prevention, and palliative care of all types of human malignant disease. **Freq:** Monthly. **Key Personnel:** Lisa Hutchinson, Editor-in-Chief; Lisa Richards, Assoc. Ed.; James Butcher, Publisher. **ISSN:** 1743-4254. **Subscription Rates:** US$175 individuals print and online; US$297 two years print and online. **URL:** http://www.nature.com/nrclinonc/index.html. **Formerly:** Nature Clinical Practice Oncology.

54978 ■ Nature Reviews Drug Discovery
Nature Publishing Group
The Macmillan Bldg.
4 Crinan St.
London N1 9XW, United Kingdom
Ph: 44 20 78334000
Fax: 44 20 78434640
Publication E-mail: naturereviews@nature.com
Journal aimed at everyone working in the drug discovery and development arena, publishing the highest-quality reviews and perspectives highlighting the most important developments across the entire field, from chemistry to disease mechanisms and novel therapeutic approaches. **Freq:** Monthly. **Key Personnel:** Peter Kirkpatrick, PhD, Ch. Ed.; Judith Shadwell, Mng. Production Ed.; Charlotte Harrison, Sen. Ed.; Alexandra Flemming, Sen. Ed.; Natalie Smith, Production Controller; Sarah Crunkhorn, Sen. Ed.; Bethan Hughes, News Ed. **ISSN:** 1474-1776. **URL:** http://www.nature.com/nrd/.

54979 ■ Nature Reviews Gastroenterology & Hepatology
Nature Publishing Group
The Macmillan Bldg.
4 Crinan St.
London N1 9XW, United Kingdom
Ph: 44 20 78334000
Fax: 44 20 78434640
Journal containing articles on pathology, diagnosis, and treatment of diseases of the gastrointestinal tract, liver, pancreas, gall bladder, and biliary tract, such as functional gastrointestinal disorders, inflammatory diseases, cancer, infection, and nutritional disorders. **Freq:** Monthly. **Key Personnel:** Natalie Wood, Ch. Ed. **ISSN:** 1743-4378. **Subscription Rates:** US$175 individuals print and online; US$297 two years print and online. **URL:** http://www.nature.com/ncpgasthep/index.html. **Formerly:** Nature Clinical Practice Gastroenterology & Hepatology.

54980 ■ Nature Reviews Genetics
Nature Publishing Group
The Macmillan Bldg.
4 Crinan St.
London N1 9XW, United Kingdom
Ph: 44 20 78334000
Fax: 44 20 78434640
Publication E-mail: naturereviews@nature.com
Peer-reviewed journal covering the full scientific breadth

of modern genetics, capturing its excitement, diversity and implications. **Freq:** Monthly. **Key Personnel:** Louisa Flintoft, PhD, Ch. Ed.; Mary Muers, Assoc. Ed.; Tim Redding, Mktg. Mgr. **ISSN:** 1471-0056. **Subscription Rates:** US$265 individuals print and online; US$450 two years print and online. **URL:** http://www.nature.com/reviews/genetics.

54981 ■ Nature Reviews Immunology
Nature Publishing Group
The Macmillan Bldg.
4 Crinan St.
London N1 9XW, United Kingdom
Ph: 44 20 78334000
Fax: 44 20 78434640
Publication E-mail: naturereviews@nature.com
Peer-reviewed journal providing in-depth coverage of immunology, from fundamental mechanisms to applied aspects. **Freq:** Monthly. **Key Personnel:** Lucy Bird, Ch. Ed.; Olive Leavy, Sen. Ed.; Kirsty Minton, Sen. Ed. **ISSN:** 1474-1733. **Subscription Rates:** US$265 individuals print and online; US$450 two years print and online. **URL:** http://www.nature.com/nri/index.html.

54982 ■ Nature Reviews Microbiology
Nature Publishing Group
The Macmillan Bldg.
4 Crinan St.
London N1 9XW, United Kingdom
Ph: 44 20 78334000
Fax: 44 20 78434640
Publication E-mail: naturereviews@nature.com
Peer-reviewed journal focusing less on specific organisms and more on the processes and mechanisms that link them, bridging fundamental research and its clinical, industrial and environmental applications to create a single information resource for all who share an interest in microbial life. **Freq:** Monthly. **Key Personnel:** Christiaan van Ooij, Ch. Ed.; Andrew Jermy, Sen. Ed.; Sheilagh Molloy, PhD, Sen. Ed. **ISSN:** 1740-1526. **Subscription Rates:** US$265 individuals print and online; US$450 two years print and online. **URL:** http://www.nature.com/nrmicro/index.html.

54983 ■ Nature Reviews Molecular Cell Biology
Nature Publishing Group
The Macmillan Bldg.
4 Crinan St.
London N1 9XW, United Kingdom
Ph: 44 20 78334000
Fax: 44 20 78434640
Publication E-mail: naturereviews@nature.com
Peer-reviewed journal covering two distinct, yet complementary, disciplines: study of the macromolecules essential to life - nucleic acids and proteins - and cell biology, which is a natural extension of this, integrating what is known at the molecular level into an understanding of processes and interactions at the cellular level. **Key Personnel:** Alison Schuldt, Ch. Ed.; Katharine Wrighton, PhD, Assoc. Ed. **ISSN:** 1471-0072. **Subscription Rates:** US$265 individuals print and online; US$450 two years print and online. **URL:** http://www.nature.com/nrm/index.html.

54984 ■ Nature Reviews Neuroscience
Nature Publishing Group
The Macmillan Bldg.
4 Crinan St.
London N1 9XW, United Kingdom
Ph: 44 20 78334000
Fax: 44 20 78434640
Publication E-mail: naturereviews@nature.com
Journal covering the breadth and depth of modern neuroscience by providing an authoritative, accessible, topical, and engaging first port of call for scientists who are interested in all aspect of neuroscience — from molecules to the mind. **Freq:** Monthly. **Key Personnel:** Claudia Wiedemann, Ch. Ed.; Leonie Welberg, Sen. Ed.; Katherine Whalley, Sen. Ed.; Judith Shadwell, Mng. Production Ed.; Tim Redding, Mktg. Mng.; Leah Rodriguez, Mktg. Mng. **ISSN:** 1471-003X. **Subscription Rates:** US$265 individuals print and online + tax where applicable; US$450 two years print and online + tax where applicable. **URL:** http://www.nature.com/nrn/.

54985 ■ Nature Reviews Urology
Nature Publishing Group
The Macmillan Bldg.
4 Crinan St.
London N1 9XW, United Kingdom

Ph: 44 20 78334000
Fax: 44 20 78434640
Publication E-mail: ncpuro@nature.com
Peer-reviewed journal containing articles on urologic on-cology, sexual dysfunction, benign prostatic hyperplasia, urinary incontinence, endourology, trauma and recon-struction, male factor infertility, imaging and radiology, infection and inflammation, and pathology. **Freq:** Monthly. **Key Personnel:** Suzanne Farley, Ch. Ed.; An-nette Fenner, Assoc. Ed.; Sarah Payton, Assoc. Ed. **ISSN:** 1743-4270. **Subscription Rates:** US$175 indi-viduals print and online; US$297 two years print and online. **URL:** http://www.nature.com/ncpuro/index.html. **Formerly:** Nature Clinical Practice Urology.

54986 ■ The Naval Architect
RINA—The Royal Institute of Naval Architects
10 Upper Belgrave St.
London SW1X 8BQ, United Kingdom
Ph: 44 20 72354622
Fax: 44 20 72595912
Publisher E-mail: hq@rina.org.uk
Journal of The Royal Institution of Naval Architects covering the marine industry worldwide. **Freq:** 10/yr. **Print Method:** Offset Litho. **Trim Size:** 210 x 297 mm. **Key Personnel:** Nick Savvides, Editor. **ISSN:** 0306-0209. **Subscription Rates:** 150 individuals UK; 156 individuals Europe; 168 other countries rest of the world. **Remarks:** Accepts advertising. **URL:** http://www.rina.org.uk/tna.html. **Circ:** Combined ★11,650

54987 ■ Nephron Physiology
S. Karger Publishers Inc.
Royal Free & University College Medical School
Drayton House, University College London
Gower St.
London WC1E 6BT, United Kingdom
Ph: 44 20 76795486
Fax: 44 20 76795484
Publication E-mail: nephron@ucl.ac.uk
Publisher E-mail: karger@snet.net
Journal covers the broad field of cellular and integrative function of the kidney and urinary tract in health and disease. **Freq:** Monthly. **Trim Size:** 210 x 280 mm. **Key Personnel:** D. Bockenhauer, Dep. Ed.; R. Warth, Dep. Ed.; M. Bleich, Assoc. Ed.; G. Ciarimboli, Assoc. Ed.; S.M.R. Camargo, Assoc. Ed.; R. Kleta, Editor; H. Cas-trop, Assoc. Ed.; E. Klootwijk, Assoc. Ed.; R.J. Unwin, Editorial Board. **ISSN:** 1660-2137. **Remarks:** Accepts advertising. **URL:** http://content.karger.com/ProdukteDB/produkte.asp?Aktion=JournalHome&ProduktNr=228541. **Circ:** (Not Reported)

54988 ■ Network 21
Conservation Foundation
1 Kensington Gore
London SW7 2AR, United Kingdom
Ph: 44 20 75913111
Fax: 44 20 75913110
Publisher E-mail: info@conservationfoundation.co.uk
Trade magazine covering environmental news. **Founded:** 1993. **Freq:** Annual. **Trim Size:** A4. **Key Personnel:** David Shreeve, Contact; Prof. David Bel-lamy, PhD, Contact. **Remarks:** Accepts advertising. **URL:** http://www.n21corp.com/. **Ad Rates:** 4C: 1,500. **Circ:** 7,000

54989 ■ New Cinemas
Intellect
Russell Square House
10-12 Russell Sq.
London WC1B 5EE, United Kingdom
Ph: 44 20 73312000
Fax: 44 20 73312040
Publisher E-mail: info@intellectuk.org
Journal publishing articles about contemporary films and cinema in general. **Subtitle:** Journal of Contemporary Film. **Founded:** 2002. **Freq:** 3/yr. **Key Personnel:** Song Hwee Lim, Co-Ed.; Stephanie Dennison, Editor; Richard Tapper, Editorial Board; Dorota Ostrowska, Book Review Ed.; Nejat Ulusay, Editorial Board; Alberto Elena, Edito-rial Board. **ISSN:** 1474-2756. **Subscription Rates:** 33 individuals print; 210 institutions print and online; 12 single issue print; 177 institutions online. **URL:** http://www.intellectbooks.co.uk/journals/view-Journal,id=129/.

54990 ■ New Consumer
New Consumer Ltd.
1-5 Wandsworth Rd.

London SW8 2LN, United Kingdom
Ph: 44 20 75263314
Publisher E-mail: editorial@newconsumer.com
Magazine providing information about ethical living. **Founded:** 2002. **Freq:** Monthly. **Subscription Rates:** Free; 20 individuals; 30 individuals Europe; 35 other countries. **Remarks:** Accepts advertising. **URL:** http://www.newconsumer.com/. **Circ:** (Not Reported)

54991 ■ New Humanist
Rationalist Press Association Ltd.
One Gower St.
London WC1E 6HD, United Kingdom
Ph: 44 20 74361151
Fax: 44 20 70793588
Journal covering ideas from a humanist perspective. **Founded:** 1885. **Freq:** Bimonthly. **Print Method:** Litho. **Trim Size:** A4. **Key Personnel:** Caspar Nelville, Editor; Judith Walker, Business Mgr.; Paul Sims, News Ed. **ISSN:** 0306-512X. **Subscription Rates:** 21 individuals; 25 other countries. **Remarks:** Accepts advertising. **URL:** http://newhumanist.org.uk/. **Formerly:** Humanist. **Ad Rates:** BW: 400, 4C: 700. **Circ:** Combined 5,000

54992 ■ New Law Journal
LexisNexis UK
Halsbury House
35 Chancery Ln.
London WC2A 1EL, United Kingdom
Ph: 44 20 74002500
Fax: 44 20 74002842
Publication E-mail: newlaw.journal@lexisnexis.co.uk
Publisher E-mail: customer.services@lexisnexis.co.uk
Law periodical. **Freq:** Weekly. **Key Personnel:** Jan Miller, Editor, phone 44 20 74002582, jan.miller@lexisnexis.co.uk. **ISSN:** 0306-6479. **Subscription Rates:** 299 individuals. **Remarks:** Advertising accepted; rates available upon request. **URL:** http://www.new-law-journal.co.uk. **Circ:** (Not Reported)

54993 ■ New Left Review
6 Meard St.
London W1F 0EG, United Kingdom
Ph: 44 20 77348830
Fax: 44 20 74393869
Publication E-mail: mail@newleftreview.org
Publisher E-mail: mail@newleftreview.org
Scholarly journal covering the New Left philosophy, his-tory and sociology, and culture. **Founded:** 1960. **Freq:** Bimonthly. **Trim Size:** 105 x 180 mm. **Cols./Page:** 1. **Key Personnel:** Susan Watkins, Editor; Tony Wood, Dep. Ed.; Kheya Bag, Publishing Dir. **Subscription Rates:** 34 individuals; US$60 individuals; EUR315 individuals; 215 institutions print and online; US$400 institutions. **URL:** http://www.newleftreview.org/; http://newleftreview.org/?page=aboutnlr. **Circ:** Combined ‡7,500

54994 ■ New Media Age
Centaur Publishing Ltd.
50 Poland St.
London W1F 7AX, United Kingdom
Ph: 44 20 79704000
Fax: 44 20 79704189
Publication covering mass communications. **Founded:** June 1995. **Freq:** Weekly. **Print Method:** Web Offset. **Trim Size:** 210 x 280 mm. **Key Personnel:** Michael Nutley, Editor-In-Chief, phone 44 20 79704846, michael.nutley@centaur.co.uk; Andy Oakes, Publisher, phone 44 20 79704701, andy.oakes@centaur.co.uk; Justin Pearse, Editor, phone 44 20 79704851, justin.pearse@centaur.co.uk. **ISSN:** 1364-7776. **Subscription Rates:** 99 individuals in the UK; 178.20 two years; 252.45 individuals three years. **Remarks:** Accepts advertising. **URL:** http://www.nma.co.uk/. **Ad Rates:** BW: 1,610, 4C: 2,002. **Circ:** Controlled 12,255, Controlled ‡6,503

54995 ■ New Media & Society
Sage Publications Ltd.
1 Oliver's Yard
55 City Rd.
London EC1Y 1SP, United Kingdom
Ph: 44 20 73248500
Fax: 44 20 73248600
Scholarly journal covering the social dynamics of media and information change worldwide. **Founded:** 1999. **Freq:** 8/yr. **Key Personnel:** Keith Hampton, Previous Reviews Ed.; Nicholas Jankowski, Editor; Roger Silver-stone, Previous Ed.; Steve Jones, Editor. **ISSN:** 1461-4448. **Subscription Rates:** US$1,561 individuals print

& e-access; US$1,405 institutions e-access; US$1,530 institutions print only; US$89 individuals print only; US$210 institutions print; US$14 individuals print. **Re-marks:** Accepts advertising. **URL:** http://www.sagepub.com/journalsProdDesc.nav?prodId=Journal200834. **Circ:** (Not Reported)

54996 ■ The New Rambler
Johnson Society of London
16 Laurier Rd.
London NW5 1SG, United Kingdom
Publication covering authors. **Founded:** 1941. **Freq:** Annual. **Key Personnel:** Lord Harmsworth, President; Dr. Nicholas Cambridge, Chairman. **Subscription Rates:** 3 single issue back issue. **Remarks:** Advertising accepted; rates available upon request. **URL:** http://www.johnsonsocietyoflondon.org/newrambler.html. **Circ:** (Not Reported)

54997 ■ New Renaissance
Renaissance Universal
3a Cazenove Rd.
London N16 6PA, United Kingdom
Ph: 44 20 88064250
Magazine for social and spiritual awakening. **Founded:** 1990. **Freq:** Quarterly. **Key Personnel:** A.V. Avadhuta, Assoc. Ed.; Dada Jyotirupananda, Editor-in-Chief; So-hail Inayatullah, Assoc. Ed. **ISSN:** 0939-1657. **Subscrip-tion Rates:** US$15 individuals; US$26 two years; US$38 individuals three years. **Remarks:** Advertising accepted; rates available upon request. **URL:** http://www.ru.org/info/new-renaissance.html. **Circ:** Controlled 1,500

54998 ■ New Scientist
Reed Business Information Ltd.
Lacon House
84 Theobald's Rd.
London WC1X 8NS, United Kingdom
Publisher E-mail: enquiries@mardev.com
Magazine publishing latest science and technology news. **Founded:** 1956. **Key Personnel:** Henry Gomm, Office Mgr. **Subscription Rates:** US$137 individuals. **Remarks:** Advertising accepted; rates available upon request. **URL:** http://www.newscientist.com/home.ns. **Circ:** (Not Reported)

54999 ■ New Statesman
New Statesman Ltd.
Boundary House, 1st Fl.
91-93 Charterhouse St.
London EC1M 6HR, United Kingdom
Ph: 44 20 77303444
Fax: 44 20 72590181
Publisher E-mail: info@newstatesman.co.uk
Current affairs, letters, literary reviews, and politics from a British perspective. **Founded:** Apr. 12, 1913. **Freq:** Weekly. **Print Method:** Web offset. **Trim Size:** 177 x 210 mm. **Key Personnel:** Spencer Neal, Publisher, phone 44 20 79366454, spencer@newstatesman.co.uk; Jason Cowley, Editor. **ISSN:** 1364-7431. **Subscription Rates:** 82 individuals; 94 individuals for Europe; 119 individuals USA; 60 students and NUS members; 140 institutions; 155 institutions Europe; 220 institutions, other countries. **URL:** http://www.newstatesman.com. **Alt. Formats:** Audio tape; Microfilm. **Formerly:** New Statesman & Society. **Ad Rates:** BW: US$3,069, 4C: US$4,092. **Circ:** 25,000

55000 ■ New View
Anthroposophical Society in Great Britain
Rudolf Steiner House
35 Pk. Rd.
London NW1 6XT, United Kingdom
Ph: 44 20 77234400
Fax: 44 20 77244364
Publisher E-mail: rsh-office@anth.org.uk
Publication covering education. **Freq:** Quarterly. **Key Personnel:** Tom Raines, Editor. **ISSN:** 1365-3687. **Sub-scription Rates:** 22 individuals U.K.; 30 individuals rest of Europe; 30 other countries; 40 two years U.K.; 52 two years Europe, rest of the world; 52 two years North America. **Remarks:** Advertising accepted; rates avail-able upon request. **URL:** http://www.newview.org.uk/. **Circ:** Paid 350,000

55001 ■ New Woman
EMAP Ltd.
Greater London House

Circulation: ★ = ABC; △ = BPA; ♦ = CAC; • = CCAB; ❑ = VAC; ⊕ = PO Statement; ‡ = Publisher's Report; Boldface figures = sworn; Light figures = estimated.

Gale Directory of Publications & Broadcast Media/147th Ed.   5751

Hampstead Rd.
London NW1 7EJ, United Kingdom
Ph: 44 20 77285000
Publisher E-mail: jon.ferro@emap.com
Magazine for women. **Freq:** Monthly. **Print Method:** Offset Lithography. **Trim Size:** 275 x 210. **Key Personnel:** Kirsten Brearley, Contact. **Remarks:** Advertising accepted; rates available upon request. **URL:** http://www.emap.com/about-us/history-of-emap. **Circ:** (Not Reported)

55002 ■ News on the Block
Adrenaline Media
8 Canfield Pl.
London NW6 3BT, United Kingdom
Ph: 44 845 6187746
Fax: 44 845 6187749
Publisher E-mail: info@adrenalinemedia.plc.uk
Magazine addressing the needs of the apartment sector and a vital media channel for all the decision-makers involved in leasehold residential property. **Freq:** 6/yr. **Key Personnel:** Tony Gold, Contact, tony@newsontheblock.com. **Subscription Rates:** 49.99 individuals. **URL:** http://www.newsontheblock.com/. **Circ:** 10,000

55003 ■ News and Views
International Commission on Irrigation and Drainage - England
c/o Institution of Civil Engineers
1 Great George St.
Westminster
London SW1P 3AA, United Kingdom
Ph: 44 20 86652234
Fax: 44 20 87991325
Publisher E-mail: icid@ice.org.uk
Magazine of the International Commission on Irrigation and Drainage England. **Freq:** Semiannual. **Key Personnel:** R.A. Angier, Contact; C.L. Abernethy, Contact, abernethy@itmin.com; R.I. Alsop, Contact; S.J. Armitage, Contact, sarmitag@gibb.co.uk; M.J. Ashburn, Contact; D.G. Alsop, Contact; I.M. Anderson, Contact, ianmcanderson@cs.com; Adrian Laycock, Editor, enquiries@adrianlaycock.com. **URL:** http://www.icid.org.uk/newsandviews.htm.

55004 ■ NewsAfrica
Ste. 16 Canon Wharf Business Ctr.
35 Evelyn St.
London SE8 5RT, United Kingdom
Ph: 44 20 73944030
Fax: 44 20 73948600
Publication E-mail: editor@newsafrica.net
Publisher E-mail: publisher@newsafrica.net
Magazine serving the news and information needs of Africa and Africans in the Diaspora, also providing news and intelligence on the continent to the international business community. **Freq:** Fortnightly. **Key Personnel:** Jean Herskovits, Editorial Board. **Remarks:** Accepts advertising. **URL:** http://www.newsafrica.net. **Circ:** (Not Reported)

55005 ■ Nitrogen & Methanol
British Sulphur Publishing
31 Mount Pleasant
London WC1X 0AD, United Kingdom
Ph: 44 20 79032000
Fax: 44 20 78370976
Publication E-mail: bspservices@crugroup.com
Publisher E-mail: customer.services@crugroup.com
Professional magazine covering technical and market developments in the production of nitrogen fertilizer, methanol, ammonia, and downstream products. **Founded:** 1959. **Freq:** Bimonthly. **Key Personnel:** Richard Hands, Editor, phone 44 20 79032442, richard.hands@crugroup.com; John French, Contact, phone 44 20 79032435, fax 44 20 78374339, john.french@crugroup.com; Tina Firman, Contact, phone 44 20 79032437, fax 44 20 78374339, tina.firman@crugroup.com. **Subscription Rates:** US$780 individuals; 410 individuals; EUR635 individuals. **Remarks:** Accepts advertising. **URL:** http://www.britishsulphur.com. **Former name:** Nitrogen (1998). **Circ:** Combined ‡3,600

55006 ■ NMR in Biomedicine
John Wiley & Sons Inc.
c/o Stefanina Pelc
Department of Basic Medical Sciences
St. George's Hospital Medical School
University of London, Cranmer Ter.

London SW17 0RE, United Kingdom
Publisher E-mail: info@wiley.com
Scholarly journal investigating the use of nuclear magnetic resonance for solving biochemical and medical problems. **Subtitle:** An International Journal. **Freq:** 10/yr. **Key Personnel:** Joseph Helpern, Regional Ed., phone 212263-3970, fax 212263-7541, joseph.helpern@med.nyu.edu; John R. Griffiths, Editor-in-Chief, phone 44 1223 404460, john.griffiths@cancer.org.uk. **ISSN:** 0952-3480. **Subscription Rates:** EUR1,556 institutions, other countries print only; US$2,412 institutions, other countries print only; 1,231 institutions print only; EUR1,712 institutions, other countries print with online; 1,355 institutions print with online; US$2,654 institutions, other countries print with online. **Remarks:** Accepts advertising. **URL:** http://www3.interscience.wiley.com/journal/13087/home. **Circ:** (Not Reported)

55007 ■ Noddy
Egmont Magazines
184-192 Drummond St., 4th Fl.
London NW1 3HP, United Kingdom
Ph: 44 20 73806430
Magazine for children aged 6 and below featuring stories and activities. **Freq:** Monthly. **Trim Size:** 285 x 216 mm. **Subscription Rates:** 7.99 individuals. **Remarks:** Accepts advertising. **URL:** http://www.egmont.co.uk/product.asp?prodid=1937&catid=. **Ad Rates:** 4C: 1,800. **Circ:** *39,229

55008 ■ Noise and Health
Medknow Publications Pvt Ltd.
London Audiology
39 MacDonald Rd.
London N113JB, United Kingdom
Journal covering aspects of noise and its effects on human health. **Subtitle:** A Quarterly Inter-disciplinary International Journal. **Freq:** Quarterly. **Key Personnel:** Prof. Deepak Prasher, Editor-in-Chief, d.prasher@ucl.ac.uk. **Subscription Rates:** Rs 1,800 individuals; Rs 2,400 institutions; US$250 other countries; US$370 institutions, other countries. **Remarks:** Accepts advertising. **URL:** http://www.noiseandhealth.org/; http://www.medknow.com/journals.asp. **Ad Rates:** BW: 495, 4C: 995. **Circ:** (Not Reported)

55009 ■ Nordic unquote
Incisive Media Limited
Haymarket House
28-29 Haymarket
London SW1Y 4RX, United Kingdom
Ph: 44 870 2408859
Fax: 44 207 4849797
Publisher E-mail: customerservices@incisivemedia.com
Journal covering news from the venture capital and private equity markets in the Nordic and Baltic countries. **Founded:** 1992. **Freq:** Monthly. **Key Personnel:** Michael Wilkinson, Contact, phone 44 20 70047513, michael.wilkinson@incisivemedia.com; Rikke Lilla Eckhoff, Editor, phone 44 20 74849824, rikke.lilla-eckhoff@incisivemedia.com. **Remarks:** Accepts advertising. **URL:** http://www.incisivemedia.com/corporate/products/norunquote; http://www.nordicunquote.com. **Circ:** (Not Reported)

55010 ■ North
Archant Life
Avon House, 5th Fl.
Kensington Village
Avonmore Rd.
London W14 8TS, United Kingdom
Publisher E-mail: anne.basey-fisher@archant.co.uk
Magazine featuring lifestyle in North London. **Freq:** Monthly. **Trim Size:** 230 x 300 mm. **Key Personnel:** Danny Zahra-Lee, Commercial Mgr., phone 44 20 79783464, danny.zahra-lee@archant.co.uk; Mark Kebble, Editor, phone 44 20 7359 5500, mark.kebble@archant.co.uk. **Subscription Rates:** 40 individuals. **Remarks:** Accepts advertising. **URL:** http://www.archantlife.co.uk/contact-us-regions-london-north-contacts--10402; http://angel.greatbritishlife.co.uk/. **Circ:** (Not Reported)

55011 ■ Northern History
Maney Publishing
1 Carlton House Ter.
London SW1Y 5AF, United Kingdom
Ph: 44 20 74517300
Fax: 44 20 74517307
Publisher E-mail: maney@maney.co.uk
Peer-reviewed journal covering history of the seven historic Northern counties of England. **Founded:** 1966.

Freq: Semiannual. **Key Personnel:** G.C.F. Forster, Editor, c.cascarino@leeds.ac.uk; S.J.D. Green, Editor. **ISSN:** 0078-172X. **Subscription Rates:** 36 other countries; US$66 individuals; 142 institutions, other countries; US$232 institutions. **Remarks:** Accepts advertising. **URL:** http://maney.co.uk/index.php/journals/nhi/. **Circ:** (Not Reported)

55012 ■ Northwest
Archant Life
5th Fl., Avon House
Avonmore Rd.
London W14 8TS, United Kingdom
Publisher E-mail: anne.basey-fisher@archant.co.uk
Magazine featuring Northwest London. **Founded:** 1997. **Freq:** Monthly. **Key Personnel:** Natasha Paulini, Editor, phone 44 20 7605 2215, natasha.paulini@archant.co.uk. **Subscription Rates:** Free. **Remarks:** Accepts advertising. **URL:** http://northwest.greatbritishlife.co.uk/. **Circ:** *34,200

55013 ■ Notes & Records of the Royal Society
Royal Society
6-9 Carlton House Ter.
London SW1Y 5AG, United Kingdom
Ph: 44 20 74512500
Fax: 44 20 79302170
Publisher E-mail: info@royalsoc.ac.uk
Journal covering history of science, technology and medicine. **Freq:** Quarterly. **Key Personnel:** Prof. Robert Fox, Ed. **ISSN:** 0035-9149. **Subscription Rates:** 38 individuals; US$74 U.S. and Canada; EUR49 individuals; 124 institutions; US$226 institutions U.S./Canada; 130 institutions, other countries; US$233 institutions, other countries. **URL:** http://rsnr.royalsocietypublishing.org/.

55014 ■ Nurse Prescribing
MA Healthcare Ltd.
St. Jude's Church
Dulwich Rd.
Herne Hill
London SE24 0PB, United Kingdom
Ph: 44 20 77385454
Fax: 44 20 77332325
Peer-reviewed journal for nurses with prescribing rights. **Subtitle:** The only monthly journal for nurse prescribing. **Founded:** 2003. **Freq:** Monthly. **Key Personnel:** Omar Ali, Editorial Board; Christine Otway, Consultant Ed.; Sarah Hall, Editorial Board. **Subscription Rates:** 149 individuals Ireland, print and online; EUR299 individuals for practice subscription, print and online. **Remarks:** Accepts advertising. **URL:** http://www.nurseprescribing.com/. **Circ:** (Not Reported)

55015 ■ Nursing Ethics
Sage Publications Ltd.
1 Oliver's Yard
55 City Rd.
London EC1Y 1SP, United Kingdom
Ph: 44 20 73248500
Fax: 44 20 73248600
Academic journal covering ethical issues for health care professionals worldwide. **Subtitle:** An International Journal for Health Care Professionals. **Founded:** 1994. **Freq:** 6/yr. **Trim Size:** 246 x 189 mm. **Key Personnel:** Verena Tschudin, Founding Ed.; Douglas Olsen, Editorial Board; Elizabeth Niven, Regional Ed. **ISSN:** 0969-7330. **Subscription Rates:** 409 institutions print & E-access; 368 institutions E-access; 409 institutions print only; 75 individuals print & E-access; 74 institutions single print; 16 individuals single print. **Remarks:** Accepts advertising. **URL:** http://www.sagepub.co.uk/journalsProdDesc.nav?prodId=Journal201821. **Ad Rates:** BW: 340. **Circ:** Paid 1,000

55016 ■ Nursing in Practice
Campden Publishing Ltd.
1 St. John's Sq.
London EC1M 4PN, United Kingdom
Ph: 44 20 72140500
Fax: 44 20 72140501
Publisher E-mail: enquiries@campden.com
Journal featuring topical and accessible expert reviews summarising the latest thinking and developments in clinical practice in therapeutic areas related to practice nursing. **Subtitle:** The Journal for Today's Primary Care Nurse. **Freq:** Bimonthly. **Key Personnel:** Elaine Linnane, Editor-in-Chief; Polly Moffat, Supv. Ed. **Subscription Rates:** Free. **Remarks:** Accepts advertising. **URL:** http://www.nursinginpractice.com/. **Circ:** (Not Reported)

55017 ■ Nursing and Residential Care
MA Healthcare Ltd.
St. Jude's Church
Dulwich Rd.
Herne Hill
London SE24 0PB, United Kingdom
Ph: 44 20 77385454
Fax: 44 20 77332325
Peer-reviewed journal for nursing and residential care home professionals. **Subtitle:** The monthly journal for care assistants, nurses, and manager. **Freq:** Monthly. **Key Personnel:** Laura Dean-Osgood, Editor; Adrian M. Ashurst, Consultant Ed. **Subscription Rates:** 139 individuals Ireland; EUR225 individuals Europe; US$323 other countries personal; 101 students Ireland. **Remarks:** Accepts advertising. **URL:** http://www.nursingresidentialcare.com/. **Circ:** (Not Reported)

55018 ■ Nutraceuticals International
Marketletter (Publications) Ltd.
Appleton House
139 King St.
London W6 9JG, United Kingdom
Ph: 44 20 87356625
Fax: 44 20 87356688
Publisher E-mail: info@marketletter.com
Publication covering the pharmaceutical, vitamin and health food industries. **Founded:** 1996. **Freq:** Monthly. **Key Personnel:** Barbara Obstoj, Publisher/Mng. Ed.; Robin Cardwell, Contact, rcardwell@marketletter.com. **ISSN:** 1362-5411. **Subscription Rates:** 399 individuals print. **Online:** Gale. **URL:** http://www.marketletter.com.

55019 ■ Nutrition Journal
BioMed Central Ltd.
236 Gray's Inn Rd., Fl. 6
34-42 Cleveland St.
London WC1X 8HL, United Kingdom
Ph: 44 20 31922000
Fax: 44 20 31922010
Publisher E-mail: info@biomedcentral.com
Online journal covering all aspects of human and clinical nutrition, as well as research articles and animal studies in the field of nutrition. **Key Personnel:** Dr. Nehme Gabriel, Editor-in-Chief; Dr. Hiromichi Kumagai, Dep. Ed.; Dr. Catherine Chan, Editorial Board, cchan@upei.ca; Nagathihalli S. Nagaraj, Managing Editor; Sandeep Prabhu, Managing Editor. **ISSN:** 1475-2891. **Remarks:** Accepts advertising. **URL:** http://www.nutritionj.com. **Circ:** (Not Reported)

55020 ■ Nutrition & Metabolism
BioMed Central Ltd.
236 Gray's Inn Rd., Fl. 6
34-42 Cleveland St.
London WC1X 8HL, United Kingdom
Ph: 44 20 31922000
Fax: 44 20 31922010
Publisher E-mail: info@biomedcentral.com
Online journal covering all aspects of nutritional biochemistry and related clinical fields. **Key Personnel:** Dr. Richard D. Feinman, Editor-in-Chief, rfeinman@downstate.edu; Dr. M. Mahmood Hussain, Editor-in-Chief, mhussain@downstate.edu; Dr. Charles I. Abramson, Assoc. Ed., charles@okstate.edu; Salman Azhar, Assoc. Ed.; Ahmed Bakillah, Assoc. Ed. **ISSN:** 1743-7075. **Remarks:** Accepts advertising. **URL:** http://www.nutritionandmetabolism.com/. **Circ:** (Not Reported)

55021 ■ Nutritional Neuroscience
Maney Publishing
1 Carlton House Ter.
London SW1Y 5AF, United Kingdom
Ph: 44 20 74517300
Fax: 44 20 74517307
Publisher E-mail: maney@maney.co.uk
Journal for reporting both basic and clinical research in the field of nutrition that relates to the central and peripheral nervous system. **Subtitle:** An International Journal of Diet, Nutrition and the Nervous System. **Freq:** Bimonthly. **Key Personnel:** Chandan Prasad, Editor-in-Chief, cprasad@mail.twu.edu; Masatomo Mori, Editorial Advisory Board; Shlomo Yehuda, Editorial Advisory Board. **ISSN:** 1028-415X. **Subscription Rates:** US$293 individuals; US$200 individuals U.K. and Europe; 171 other countries; 639 institutions U.K. and Europe; US$778 institutions; 544 other countries. **URL:** http://maney.co.uk/index.php/journals/nns/.

55022 ■ Nuts
IPC ignite! Ltd.
Blue Fin Bldg.
110 Southwark St.
London SE1 0SU, United Kingdom
Ph: 44 203 1485000
Magazine delivering young British men a unique mix of sexy women, gritty real-life stories, sport, news and complete TV listings designed just for them. **Freq:** Weekly. **Key Personnel:** Clair Porteous, Publisher, phone 44 20 31486776, clair_porteous@ipcmedia.com; Jo Smalley, Publishing Dir., phone 44 20 31486751, jo_smalley@ipcmedia.com; Dominic Smith, Editor, phone 44 20 31486910, dominic_smith@ipcmedia.com. **Subscription Rates:** 13.67 individuals 3 monthly direct debit; 110.98 two years individual; 56.30 individuals. **Remarks:** Accepts advertising. **URL:** http://www.ipcmedia.com/brands/nuts/; http://www.nuts.co.uk/. **Circ:** (Not Reported)

55023 ■ The Observer
Guardian Newspapers Ltd.
Kings Pl.
90 York Way
London N1 9GU, United Kingdom
Ph: 44 20 33532000
Newspaper for the arts and entertainment industries. **Freq:** Weekly. **Key Personnel:** John Mulholland, Editor. **ISSN:** 0029-7712. **URL:** http://www.gmgplc.co.uk/Ourbusinesses/GuardianNewsMedia/TheObserver/tabid/137/Default.aspx; http://observer.guardian.co.uk.

55024 ■ Occupational Medicine Journal
Society of Occupational Medicine
6 St. Andrew's Pl.
Regent's Pk.
London NW1 4LB, United Kingdom
Ph: 44 20 74862641
Fax: 44 20 74860028
Publication E-mail: omjournal@som.org.uk
Publisher E-mail: admin@som.org.uk
Journal covering occupational medicine. **Freq:** 8/yr. **ISSN:** 0962-7480. **Subscription Rates:** 439 institutions print and online; 417 institutions print only or online only; 171 individuals print; 62 institutions single issue; 25 individuals single issue; US$790 institutions print and online; US$751 institutions print only or online only; US$308 individuals print; US$112 institutions single issue; US$46 individuals single issue. **URL:** https://www.som.org.uk/SOM-Publications.57.0.html.

55025 ■ Occupational Pensions
LexisNexis UK
Halsbury House
35 Chancery Ln.
London WC2A 1EL, United Kingdom
Ph: 44 20 74002500
Fax: 44 20 74002842
Publisher E-mail: customer.services@lexisnexis.co.uk
Trade magazine covering news and legislation affecting occupational pensions. **Founded:** Jan. 1987. **Freq:** Monthly. **Trim Size:** A4. **Cols./Page:** 4. **Key Personnel:** Colin Sherwood, Editor. **ISSN:** 0952-231X. **Subscription Rates:** 349 individuals; 355 individuals overseas. **Remarks:** Advertising not accepted. **URL:** http://www.lexisnexic.co.uk. **Circ:** (Not Reported)

55026 ■ Occupational Therapy News
The College of Occupational Therapists Ltd.
106-114 Borough High St.
London SE1 1LB, United Kingdom
Ph: 44 20 73576480
Professional magazine covering news and features for members of the College /British Association of Occupational Therapists. **Freq:** Monthly. **Print Method:** Web. **Trim Size:** 186 x 260 mm. **Cols./Page:** 4. **Col. Depth:** 260 millimeters. **Key Personnel:** Tracey Samuels, Editor, tracey.samuels@cot.co.uk; Katy Eggleton, Advertising Mgr., steve.meertens@cot.co.uk. **ISSN:** 0969-5095. **Remarks:** Accepts advertising. **URL:** http://www.cot.co.uk/Homepage/Library_and_Publications/Occupational_Therapy_News_(OTnews)/. **Ad Rates:** BW: 3,600, PCI: 31. **Circ:** Controlled 22,000

55027 ■ Oil Review Middle East
Alain Charles Publishing Ltd.
University House
11-13 Lower Grosvenor Pl.
London SW1W 0EX, United Kingdom
Ph: 44 20 78347676
Fax: 44 20 79730076
Publisher E-mail: post@alaincharles.com
Magazine covering developments and news in the oil, gas and petrochemical industry in the Middle East. **Founded:** 1997. **Freq:** Bimonthly. **Print Method:** Sheet-fed Offset. **Trim Size:** 210 x 276 mm. **ISSN:** 1464-9314. **Remarks:** Accepts advertising. **URL:** http://www.alaincharles.com/index.php?option=com_content&view=article&id=52&Itemid=77. **Ad Rates:** BW: US$3,650, 4C: US$5,370. **Circ:** ★9,034

55028 ■ The Old Lady
Bank of England
Threadneedle St.
London EC2R 8AH, United Kingdom
Ph: 44 20 76014444
Fax: 44 20 76015460
Publisher E-mail: enquiries@bankofengland.co.uk
Staff magazine of the Bank of England. **Founded:** 1921. **Freq:** Quarterly Spring, Summer, Autumn, and Winter. **Print Method:** 2 Color, Litho Printed. **Trim Size:** A3, four page. **ISSN:** 0030-199X. **Remarks:** Advertising not accepted. **URL:** http://www.bankofengland.co.uk/education/museum/walkthrough/did.htm. **Circ:** Paid 2,000

55029 ■ The Oldie
Oldie Publications Ltd.
65 Newman St.
London W1T 3EG, United Kingdom
Ph: 44 20 74368801
Fax: 44 20 74368804
Publisher E-mail: editorial@theoldie.co.uk
General interest magazine for mature persons providing "a haven for good sense and quality writing in a media obsessed with celebrity and yoof". **Freq:** Monthly. **Trim Size:** 297 x 210 mm. **Key Personnel:** Chris Mace, Advertising Mgr., phone 44 20 73060300, fax 44 20 73060301, theoldie@mongoosemedia.com; David Sturge, Contact, phone 44 20 83066292, fax 44 20 83315182, david.sturge@btopenworld.com. **ISSN:** 0965-2507. **Subscription Rates:** EUR35 individuals 12 issues, paid by credit card; EUR35 individuals 14 issues, paid by direct debit; EUR63 two years 24 issues, paid by credit card. **URL:** http://www.theoldie.co.uk/. **Circ:** ★26,151

55030 ■ Olive
BBC Worldwide Publishing Ltd.
Media Centre
201 Wood Ln.
London W12 7TQ, United Kingdom
Ph: 44 20 84332000
Fax: 44 20 87490538
Magazine featuring guide to recipes, restaurants and travel. **Subtitle:** Eat in, eat out, eat away. **Freq:** Monthly. **Subscription Rates:** 3.40 single issue; 15 individuals 6 issues; 34.50 individuals. **URL:** http://www.olivemagazine.co.uk/; http://www.bbcmagazines.com/content/magazines/olive/.

55031 ■ Onboard
Factory Media
1 W Smithfield
London EC1A 9JU, United Kingdom
Ph: 44 20 73329700
Publication E-mail: onboard@servicehelpline.co.uk
Publisher E-mail: contact@factorymedia.com
Magazine featuring snowboarding. **Freq:** 8/yr. **Subscription Rates:** 26.50 individuals credit card; 23.85 individuals direct debit; US$84 individuals credit card. **URL:** http://onboardsnowboarding.com; http://factorymedia.com.

55032 ■ Oncogene
Nature Publishing Group
The Macmillan Bldg.
4 Crinan St.
London N1 9XW, United Kingdom
Ph: 44 20 78334000
Fax: 44 20 78434640
Publication E-mail: oncogene@natureny.com
Journal dealing with all aspects of the structure and function of Oncogenes. **Freq:** 50/yr. **Key Personnel:** Douglas R. Green, Editor-in-Chief; Vishva Dixit, Dep. Ed.; James R. Downing, Editorial Board. **ISSN:** 0950-9232. **Subscription Rates:** US$1,990 individuals Americas (print and online); US$1,792 individuals Americas (online only); EUR1,583 individuals Europe

(print and online); EUR1,424 individuals Europe (online only); 270,500¥ individuals Japan (print and online); 243,600¥ individuals Japan (online only); 1,021 other countries print and online; 919 individuals online only. **Remarks:** Advertising accepted; rates available upon request. **URL:** http://www.nature.com/onc/index.html. **Circ:** (Not Reported)

55033 ■ One in Seven
Royal National Institute for Deaf People
19-23 Featherstone St.
London EC1Y 8SL, United Kingdom
Ph: 44 207 2968000
Fax: 44 207 2968001
Publisher E-mail: informationline@rnid.org.uk
Membership magazine of The Royal National Institute for Deaf People. **Freq:** Bimonthly. **ISSN:** 1460-0811. **Subscription Rates:** Included in membership. **Remarks:** Advertising accepted; rates available upon request. **URL:** http://www.rnid.org.uk; http://www.rnid.org.uk/howyoucanhelp/join_rnid/one_in_seven/. **Formerly:** See Hear! (Oct. 1997); Soundbarrier. **Circ:** 25,000

55034 ■ Openings
British Blind and Shutter Association
36 Broadway
London SW1H 0BH, United Kingdom
Ph: 44 20 7994050
Fax: 44 20 73406261
Publication E-mail: info@ta-publishing.co.uk
Publisher E-mail: info@bbsa.org.uk
Publication covering building industries. **Founded:** Oct. 1993. **Freq:** Quarterly. **Trim Size:** A4. **Remarks:** Accepts advertising. **URL:** http://www.bbsa.org.uk/openings/Default.aspx. **Ad Rates:** 4C: 1,540. **Circ:** 4,000

55035 ■ OpenMIND
MIND - Mental Health Charity
Granta House
15-19 Broadway
London E15 4BQ, United Kingdom
Ph: 44 20 85192122
Fax: 44 20 85221725
Publication E-mail: openmind@mind.org.uk
Publisher E-mail: contact@mind.org.uk
Publication covering mental health. **Subtitle:** The Mental Health Magazine. **Founded:** Feb. 1983. **Freq:** Bimonthly. **ISSN:** 0265-511X. **Subscription Rates:** 29 individuals; 17 members individual; 22 students unwaged; 55 individuals organizations; 50 individuals local; 38 individuals Europe; 45 other countries rest of world. **URL:** http://www.mind.org.uk/Shopping/Openmind/. **Ad Rates:** BW: EUR460, 4C: EUR700. **Circ:** Paid ‡5,500

55036 ■ Opera
Opera Magazine Ltd.
36 Black Lion Ln.
London W6 9BE, United Kingdom
Ph: 44 20 85638893
Fax: 44 20 85638635
Publisher E-mail: operasubs@opera.co.uk
Consumer magazine covering opera companies worldwide, including reviews of books, CD's, news, features and interviews. **Founded:** Feb. 1950. **Freq:** Monthly. **Key Personnel:** John Allison, Editor; Erica Jeal, Dep. Ed.; Megan Jackson, Subscription Mgr. **ISSN:** 0030-3526. **Subscription Rates:** 58.40 individuals; 75 by mail worldwide except U.S.; 97 individuals airmail; Europe; 75 individuals surface. **Remarks:** Accepts advertising. **URL:** http://www.opera.co.uk/magazine/home.htm. **Circ:** (Not Reported)

55037 ■ Opera Now
Rhinegold Publishing
241 Shaftesbury Ave.
London WC2H 8TF, United Kingdom
Ph: 44 20 73331720
Fax: 44 20 73331765
Publication E-mail: opera.now@rhinegold.co.uk
Publisher E-mail: sales@rhinegold.co.uk
Magazine covering aspects of opera. **Freq:** Bimonthly. **Key Personnel:** Ashutosh Khandekar, Editor. **Subscription Rates:** 32 individuals; 58 two years. **Remarks:** Accepts advertising. **URL:** http://www.rhinegold.co.uk/magazines/opera_now/. **Circ:** (Not Reported)

55038 ■ Operational Risk & Regulation
Incisive Media Limited
Haymarket House

28-29 Haymarket
London SW1Y 4RX, United Kingdom
Ph: 44 870 2408859
Fax: 44 207 4849797
Publisher E-mail: customerservices@incisivemedia.com
Magazine featuring news, analysis, commentary, and technical features on operational risk and compliance. **Freq:** Monthly. **Key Personnel:** Victoria Pennington, Editor, phone 44 20 70047508, victoria.pennington@incisivemedia.com; Nick Coles, Mktg. Mgr., phone 44 20 74849862, nick.coles@incisivemedia.com. **Subscription Rates:** 839 individuals; 1,510 two years; US$1,594 individuals; US$2,869 two years; EUR1,259 individuals; EUR2,266 two years. **Remarks:** Accepts advertising. **URL:** http://www.incisivemedia.com/corporate/products/opriskcomp; http://www.risk.net/operational-risk-and-regulation. **Formerly:** OpRisk & Compliance. **Circ:** (Not Reported)

55039 ■ Ophthalmic and Physiological Optics
College of Optometrists
42 Craven St.
London WC2N 5NG, United Kingdom
Ph: 44 20 78396000
Fax: 44 20 78396800
Publisher E-mail: optometry@college-optometrists.org
Journal of the College of Optometrists. **Founded:** 1925. **Freq:** Bimonthly. **URL:** http://www.college-optometrists.org/index.aspx/pcms/site.publication.Home.

55040 ■ Ophthalmology International
Greycoat Publishing Ltd.
148 Buckingham Palace Rd.
Kensington
London SW1W 9TR, United Kingdom
Ph: 44 20 77307995
Fax: 44 20 77303884
Publisher E-mail: mail@greycoatpublishing.co.uk
Journal covering fields of ophthalmology. **Founded:** Mar. 2006. **Freq:** Quarterly March, June, September and December. **Trim Size:** 210 x 297 mm. **Key Personnel:** Dot Watt, Commissioning Ed.; Guy Wallis, Editorial Dir., g.wallis@greycoatpublishing.co.uk. **ISSN:** 1750-1431. **Subscription Rates:** 50 individuals Europe; 65 other countries; 105 institutions Europe; 135 institutions, other countries. **Remarks:** Accepts advertising. **URL:** http://www.greycoatpublishing.co.uk/content/Journals/OI.asp. **Circ:** (Not Reported)

55041 ■ Optometry in Practice
College of Optometrists
42 Craven St.
London WC2N 5NG, United Kingdom
Ph: 44 20 78396000
Fax: 44 20 78396800
Publication E-mail: oip.editorial@gmail.com
Publisher E-mail: optometry@college-optometrists.org
Journal containing peer-reviewed articles. **Freq:** Quarterly. **Remarks:** Accepts advertising. **URL:** http://www.college-optometrists.org/index.aspx/pcms/site.publication.Home. **Circ:** (Not Reported)

55042 ■ Organization
Sage Publications Ltd.
1 Oliver's Yard
55 City Rd.
London EC1Y 1SP, United Kingdom
Ph: 44 20 73248500
Fax: 44 20 73248600
Scholarly journal covering theory and development in organization studies. **Subtitle:** The Critical Journal of Organization, Theory and Society. **Founded:** 1994. **Freq:** Bimonthly. **Key Personnel:** Gibson Burrell, Editorial Advisory Board; Linda Smircich, Editorial Advisory Board; Mike Reed, Editorial Advisory Board; Marta Calas, Editorial Advisory Board; Carl Rhodes, Assoc. Ed.; Paul S. Adler, Editorial Advisory Board; Rick Delbridge, Assoc. Ed.; George Cheney, Book Review Ed.; Mike Bresnen, Assoc. Ed.; Martin Parker, Editor. **ISSN:** 1350-5084. **Subscription Rates:** US$1,408 institutions print & e-access; US$1,549 institutions current volume print & all online content; US$1,267 institutions e-access; US$1,408 institutions e-access plus backfile (all online content); US$1,380 institutions print only; US$126 individuals print only; US$253 institutions single copy, print; US$27 single issue print. **Remarks:** Accepts advertising. **URL:** http://www.sagepub.com/journalsProdDesc.nav?prodId=Journal200981. **Circ:** (Not Reported)

55043 ■ Organization Studies
Sage Publications Ltd.
1 Oliver's Yard
55 City Rd.
London EC1Y 1SP, United Kingdom
Ph: 44 20 73248500
Fax: 44 20 73248600
Peer-reviewed business Journal covering study of organizations and their structures. **Subtitle:** An International Multidisciplinary Journal Devoted to the Study of Organizations, Organizing, and the Organized in and Between Societies. **Founded:** 1980. **Freq:** Monthly. **Key Personnel:** David Courpasson, Editor-in-Chief; David C. Wilson, Advisory Board; Kimberly B. Boal, Book Review Ed.; David Arellano Gault, Co-Ed.; Andrew D. Brown, Co-Ed.; Michael Lounsbury, Co-Ed. **ISSN:** 0170-8406. **Subscription Rates:** US$1,807 institutions print & e-access; US$1,807 institutions all online content; US$1,626 institutions e-access; US$1,988 institutions e-access & online; US$2,626 institutions e-access (content through 1998); US$1,771 institutions print only; US$183 individuals print only; US$162 institutions single print; US$20 individuals single print. **Remarks:** Accepts advertising. **URL:** http://www.sagepub.com/journalsProdDesc.nav?prodId=Journal201657. **Circ:** 1,000

55044 ■ The Osteopath
General Osteopathic Council
176 Tower Bridge Rd.
London SE1 3LU, United Kingdom
Ph: 44 70 3576655
Fax: 44 70 3570011
Publication E-mail: osteopath@wealdenad.co.uk
Publisher E-mail: pressoffice@osteopathy.org.uk
Journal including registrar's report, book reviews, letters, media reviews. **Freq:** Bimonthly. **Trim Size:** 210 x 297 mm. **Subscription Rates:** 24 individuals; 34 individuals including postage and handling; 47 individuals including worldwide postage and handling. **Remarks:** Accepts advertising. **URL:** http://www.osteopathy.org.uk/resources/publications/the-osteopath/. **Ad Rates:** BW: 275, 4C: 330. **Circ:** (Not Reported)

55045 ■ The Otorhinolaryngologist
Rila Publications Ltd.
73 Newman St.
London W1A 4PG, United Kingdom
Ph: 44 20 76311299
Fax: 44 20 75807166
Publisher E-mail: admin@rila.co.uk
Journal perspective of otorhinolaryngology, head & neck surgery. **Freq:** Annual. **Key Personnel:** Sanjai Sood, Editor-in-Chief; Francis Vaz, Editor-in-Chief; Simon Carney, International Ed. **ISSN:** 1752-9360. **URL:** http://www.rila.co.uk/site/modules.php?name=Journals&func=journal&jid=058.

55046 ■ Outlook on Agriculture
IP Publishing Ltd.
258 Belsize Rd.
London NW6 4BT, United Kingdom
Ph: 44 20 73161870
Fax: 44 20 76249994
Publisher E-mail: jedmondson@ippublishing.com
Journal covering scientific, political, and economic agricultural developments worldwide. **Founded:** 1971. **Freq:** Quarterly. **Key Personnel:** Dr. David Lister, Editor, outlookonagric@dsl.pipex.com; Prof. Deng Xi-Ping, Editorial Advisory Board; Dr. Loek Boonekamp, Editorial Advisory Board. **ISSN:** 0030-7270. **Subscription Rates:** US$462 institutions; EUR444 institutions in Europe zone; 299 institutions, other countries. **Remarks:** Accepts advertising. **URL:** http://www.ippublishing.com/oa.htm. **Circ:** (Not Reported)

55047 ■ Overseas
Royal Over-Seas League
Over-Seas House
Pk. Pl.
St. James's St.
London SW1A 1LR, United Kingdom
Ph: 44 207 4080214
Fax: 44 207 4996738
Publisher E-mail: info@rosl.org.uk
Arts publication. **Founded:** 1915. **Freq:** Quarterly. **Key Personnel:** Miranda Moore, Editor; Samantha Whitaker, Dep. Ed., phone 44 20 74080214, swhitaker@rosl.org.uk. **Subscription Rates:** Free. **URL:** http://www.rosl.org.uk/rosl/pages/rosl_overseas.php. **Formerly:** Over-

seas Journal. **Ad Rates:** BW: 690, 4C: 920. **Circ:** 25,000

55048 ■ Packaging News
Haymarket Business Magazines
174 Hammersmith Rd.
London W6 7JP, United Kingdom
Ph: 44 20 82674210
Publisher E-mail: info@haymarket.com
Magazine featuring reports industry news, marketing and brand design and new-product developments. **Founded:** 1947. **Freq:** Monthly. **Key Personnel:** Josh Brooks, Editor, phone 44 20 82678096, josh.brooks@ haymarket.com. **Subscription Rates:** 95 individuals. **Remarks:** Accepts advertising. **URL:** http://www. haymarket.com/packaging_news/default.aspx; http:// www.packagingnews.co.uk/. **Circ:** ★13,919

55049 ■ Packaging, Transport, Storage & Security of Radioactive Material
Maney Publishing
1 Carlton House Ter.
London SW1Y 5AF, United Kingdom
Ph: 44 20 74517300
Fax: 44 20 74517307
Publisher E-mail: maney@maney.co.uk
Peer-reviewed journal covering all aspects of the transport of radioactive materials, including regulations, package design, safety analysis, package testing, routine operations and experiences, storage and security, and accidents and emergency planning. **Freq:** 4/yr. **Key Personnel:** R.B. Pope, Editor, poper787@comcast.net; E.P. Goldfinch, Founding Ed., goldfinch@ramtrans.org.uk; Dr. R.E. Luna, Consultant Ed., lunar@asme.org. **ISSN:** 1746-5095. **Subscription Rates:** 328 institutions, other countries; US$620 institutions. **Remarks:** Accepts advertising. **URL:** http://maney.co.uk/index.php/journals/ prm/. **Circ:** (Not Reported)

55050 ■ Pact
Producers Alliance for Cinema and Television
3rd Fl. Fitzrovia House
153-157 Cleveland St.
London W1T 6QW, United Kingdom
Ph: 44 20 73808230
Publisher E-mail: davidalan@pact.co.uk
Publication for the UK independent production sector. **Freq:** Monthly. **URL:** http://www.pact.co.uk.

55051 ■ Palestine Exploration Quarterly
Maney Publishing
1 Carlton House Ter.
London SW1Y 5AF, United Kingdom
Ph: 44 20 74517300
Fax: 44 20 74517307
Publisher E-mail: maney@maney.co.uk
Peer-reviewd journal covering the study of Holy Land. **Freq:** 3/yr. **Key Personnel:** David Jacobson, Editor, jacobson.d.m@googlemail.com; Ashley Jones, Review Ed. **ISSN:** 0031-0328. **Subscription Rates:** 104 institutions, other countries; US$198 institutions. **Remarks:** Accepts advertising. **URL:** http://maney.co.uk/index.php/ journals/peq/. **Circ:** (Not Reported)

55052 ■ Palestine Times
PO Box 10355
London NW2 3WH, United Kingdom
Publisher E-mail: palestimes@ptimes.org
General interest newspaper. **Subtitle:** The Electronic Edition. **Freq:** Monthly. **Key Personnel:** Ahmad Karmawi, Editor-in-Chief. **URL:** http://www.ptimes.org/main/.

55053 ■ Paper Technology
Paper Industry Technical Association
c/o Margaret Marley, Ed.
Paper Industry Technical Association
2 St. Philip St.
London SW8 3SP, United Kingdom
Ph: 44 20 76229269
Fax: 44 20 76521632
Publisher E-mail: info@pita.co.uk
Official journal of the Paper Industry Technical Association covering technical information for the paper and allied industries. **Founded:** 1920. **Freq:** Monthly. **Trim Size:** 175 x 260 mm. **Key Personnel:** Barry Read, Tech. Dir.; Helen Dolan, Oper. Exec.; Margaret Marley, Editor, memarley@mac.com. **ISSN:** 0306-252X. **Subscription Rates:** 100 individuals; 10 single issue postage for Europe; 20 single issue postage(for rest of the world). **Remarks:** Accepts advertising. **URL:** http://www.pita.co.

uk; http://pita.co.uk/publications/journal.phpScene_1. **Former name:** Paper Technology and Industry. **Ad Rates:** BW: 1,100, 4C: 1,900. **Circ:** Combined 2,000

55054 ■ PaperCraft Inspirations
Future Publishing Ltd.
2 Balcombe St.
London NW1 6NW, United Kingdom
Ph: 44 20 70424000
Publisher E-mail: future@subscription.co.uk
Magazine for all papercrafters - from beginners to experts, with helpful tips to guide from the very first card to great scrapbooking pages. **Freq:** Monthly. **Key Personnel:** Alison Gibbins, Designer; Zoe Beer, Editor; Jo Chivers, Dep. Ed.; Lucille Thomas, Art Ed.; Jenny Dixon, Editor. **Remarks:** Accepts advertising. **URL:** http://www. papercraftinspirationsmagazine.co.uk/. **Circ:** (Not Reported)

55055 ■ Papers of the British School at Rome
The British School at Rome at British Academy
10 Carlton House Ter.
London SW1Y 5AH, United Kingdom
Ph: 44 20 79695202
Fax: 44 20 79695401
Publisher E-mail: bsr@britac.ac.uk
Scholarly journal covering archaeology, classics, history, and art history related to Italy and the western Mediterranean area. **Founded:** 1902. **Freq:** Annual. **Trim Size:** 170 x 242 mm. **Cols./Page:** 1. **Key Personnel:** Dr. Josephine Crawley Quinn, Editor, josephine.quinn@ classics.ox.ac.uk. **ISSN:** 0068-2462. **Subscription Rates:** 47.50 individuals. **Remarks:** Advertising not accepted. **URL:** http://www.bsr.ac.uk/BSR/sub_pub/ BSR_Pub_01Papers.htm. **Circ:** (Not Reported)

55056 ■ The Parkinson Magazine
Parkinson's Disease Society of the UK
215 Vauxhall Bridge Rd.
London SW1V 1EJ, United Kingdom
Ph: 44 20 79318080
Fax: 44 20 72339908
Publisher E-mail: hello@parkinsons.org.uk
Magazine for members of the Parkinson's Disease Society covering features, letters, news, and reviews about living with Parkinson's. **Founded:** 1969. **Freq:** Quarterly. **Trim Size:** A4. **Subscription Rates:** 4 members; 15 nonmembers. **Remarks:** Accepts advertising. **URL:** http://www.parkinsons.org.uk/default. aspx?page=7053. **Circ:** Combined 26,000

55057 ■ The Parliamentarian
Commonwealth Parliamentary Association
Association Parlementaire du Commonwealth
Westminster House, Ste. 700
7 Millbank
London SW1P 3JA, United Kingdom
Ph: 44 2077991460
Fax: 44 2072226073
Publisher E-mail: hq.sec@cpahq.org
Journal by and for members of Commonwealth Parliaments. **Freq:** Quarterly. **Key Personnel:** Andrew Imlach, Editor; Nicolas Bouchet, Asst. Ed. **ISSN:** 0031-2282. **Subscription Rates:** 36 individuals; 12 single issue; 44 out of country airmail; 38 out of country surface mail; 14 out of country single copy, airmail; 13 out of country single copy, surface mail. **Remarks:** Accepts advertising. **URL:** http://www.cpahq.org/. **Circ:** Combined 15,500

55058 ■ Parliamentary Brief
Lexington Press Ltd.
26 York St.
London W1U 6PZ, United Kingdom
Ph: 44 20 73811611
Publication E-mail: editor@parliamentarybrief.com
Publisher E-mail: bob@lexingtonpress.com
Journal covering political and social issues. **Subtitle:** Independent Commentary on Political Affairs. **Founded:** 1992. **Freq:** Monthly. **Trim Size:** 267 x 203 mm. **Key Personnel:** Roderick Crawford, Editor. **ISSN:** 1354-5507. **Subscription Rates:** 45 individuals print and online; EUR67 individuals print and online; US$101 Canada print and online; US$87 U.S. print and online; 55 individuals online. **Remarks:** Accepts advertising. **URL:** http://www.thepolitician.org. **Ad Rates:** BW: 3,750, 4C: 3,750. **Circ:** Controlled 2,500

55059 ■ Particle and Fibre Toxicology
BioMed Central Ltd.

236 Gray's Inn Rd., Fl. 6
34-42 Cleveland St.
London WC1X 8HL, United Kingdom
Ph: 44 20 31922000
Fax: 44 20 31922010
Publisher E-mail: info@biomedcentral.com
Online journal covering the toxicological effects of particles and fibres; it also advocates multi-disciplinary studies. **Key Personnel:** Prof. Ken Donaldson, Assoc. Ed., ken.donaldson@ed.ac.uk; Prof. Paul Born, Editor-in-Chief, phone 31 45 4006800, fax 31 45 4006749, p.borm@hszuyd.nl; Dr. Arnie Brody, Editorial Board, abrody@tmc.tulane.edu; Vince Castranova, Assoc. Ed.; Rodger Duffin, Editorial Board; Yuliang Zhao, Assoc. Ed. **ISSN:** 1743-8977. **Remarks:** Accepts advertising. **URL:** http://www.particleandfibretoxicology.com/home. **Circ:** (Not Reported)

55060 ■ Party Politics
Sage Publications Ltd.
1 Oliver's Yard
55 City Rd.
London EC1Y 1SP, United Kingdom
Ph: 44 20 73248500
Fax: 44 20 73248600
Peer-reviewed journal covering the character and organization of political parties and the various national political systems worldwide. **Subtitle:** An International Journal for the Study of Political Parties and Political Organizations. **Founded:** 1995. **Freq:** Bimonthly. **Key Personnel:** David M. Farrell, Editor; Paul D. Webb, Editor; Kenneth Janda, Editor; R.K. Carty, Editorial Board; David Denver, Editorial Board; Luciano Bardi, Editorial Board; Aleks Szczerbiac, Assoc. and Reviews Ed.; Michael Gallagher, Editorial Board; Richard S. Katz, Editorial Board; Shaun Bowler, Editorial Board. **ISSN:** 1354-0688. **Subscription Rates:** US$1,088 institutions print & e-access; US$1,197 institutions current volume print & all online content; US$979 institutions e-access; US$1,088 institutions e-access plus backfile (all online content); US$979 institutions content through 1998; US$1,066 institutions print only; US$100 individuals print only; US$195 institutions single print; US$22 individuals single print. **Remarks:** Accepts advertising. **URL:** http:// www.sagepub.com/journalsProdDesc.nav?prodId= Journal200772. **Circ:** (Not Reported)

55061 ■ The Pastoral Review
Tablet Publishing Company Ltd.
1 King St. Cloisters
Clifton Walk
London W6 0QZ, United Kingdom
Ph: 44 20 87488484
Fax: 44 20 87481550
Publisher E-mail: thetablet@thetablet.co.uk
Journal for clergy, religious and lay people active in the Christian ministry at any level. **Founded:** 1936. **Freq:** Bimonthly. **Cols./Page:** 2. **Col. Width:** 70 millimeters. **Col. Depth:** 210 millimeters. **Key Personnel:** Fr. Michael Hayes, Editor, hayesm@smuc.ac.uk; Clifford Longley, Editorial Consultant. **Subscription Rates:** 43.75 individuals. **Remarks:** Accepts advertising. **URL:** http://www.thepastoralreview.org. **Former name:** Clergy Review (1986). **Formerly:** Priests & People. **Circ:** Paid 3,800

55062 ■ Pathology
Informa Publishing Group
Informa House
30-32 Mortimer St.
London W1W 7RE, United Kingdom
Ph: 44 20 70175000
Journal featuring the Royal College of Pathologists of Australasia. **Freq:** 7/yr. **Print Method:** Offset. **Cols./ Page:** 6. **Col. Width:** 26 nonpareils. **Col. Depth:** 301 agate lines. **Key Personnel:** Prof. C.S. Lee, Editorial Board; H.K. Muller, Assoc. Ed.; P. Hickman, Assoc. Ed.; J.K.C. Chan, Assoc. Ed.; S.C.A. Chen, Assoc. Ed.; Prof. Brett Delahunt, Editor; W. Rawlinson, Assoc. Ed.; R. Trent, Assoc. Ed.; J. Rasko, Assoc. Ed. **ISSN:** 0031-3025. **Subscription Rates:** US$1,575 institutions; US$3,150 individuals corporate single site. **URL:** http:// informahealthcare.com/pat.

55063 ■ PC Magazine
Ziff-Davis UK Ltd.
International House
1 St. Katherine's Way

London E1 9UN, United Kingdom
Publication E-mail: pcmag@ziffdavis.com
Trade magazine covering product reviews of computers.
Founded: Apr. 1992. **Freq:** Monthly. **Key Personnel:**
Lance Ulanoff, Editor-in-Chief, lance_ulanoff@pcmag.
com; Stephanie Chang, Editor, stephanie_chang@
pcmag.com. **Subscription Rates:** US$24 individuals;
US$1 single issue. **Remarks:** Accepts advertising. **URL:**
http://www.pcmag.com/. **Circ:** Paid 218,000

55064 ■ Pediatric Health
Future Medicine Ltd.
Unitec House
2 Albert Pl.
London N3 1QB, United Kingdom
Ph: 44 20 83716080
Fax: 44 20 83432313
Publisher E-mail: info@futuremedicine.com
Peer-reviewed journal covering pediatric health and
healthcare. **Freq:** Bimonthly. **Key Personnel:** Elisa Man-
zotti, Editorial Dir., e.manzotti@futuremedicine.com.
ISSN: 1745-5111. **Subscription Rates:** 605 institutions;
US$1,160 institutions; EUR755 institutions; 126,000¥
institutions. **Remarks:** Accepts advertising. **URL:** http://
www.futuremedicine.com/loi/phe. **Circ:** (Not Reported)

55065 ■ Pensions Age
Perspective Publishing
3 London Wall Bldgs., 6th Fl.
London EC2M 5PD, United Kingdom
Ph: 44 20 75622400
Fax: 44 20 73742701
Magazine featuring pensions industry. **Subtitle:** The first
choice for people in pensions. **Freq:** Monthly. **Key Personnel:** John Woods, Publisher, phone 44 20 75622421,
john.woods@pensions-age.com; Marek Handzel, Editor,
phone 44 20 75622408, marek.handzel@pensionsage.
com; Ellie Bennett, Dep. Ed., phone 44 20 75622410,
ellie.bennett@pensionsage.com. **Subscription Rates:**
149 individuals UK; 197 individuals airmail; 298 two
years UK; 394 two years airmail. **Remarks:** Accepts
advertising. **URL:** http://www.pensionsage.com/. **Ad
Rates:** 4C: 3,950. **Circ:** ★14,000

55066 ■ People & Science
British Science Association
The Wellcome Wolfson Bldg.
165 Queens Gate
London SW7 5HE, United Kingdom
Ph: 44 870 7707101
Fax: 44 20 75816587
Professional publication covering science. **Founded:**
1991. **Freq:** Quarterly. **Trim Size:** A4. **Key Personnel:**
Wendy Barnaby, Editor. **ISSN:** 0268-490X. **Subscrip-
tion Rates:** 60 individuals; 70 individuals Europe; 80
other countries. **Remarks:** Accepts advertising. **URL:**
http://www.britishscienceassociation.org/web/News/
ReportsandPublications/Magazine/. **Formerly:** Science
and the Public Affairs (Aug. 12, 2000). **Ad Rates:** 4C:
1,000. **Circ:** 3,000

55067 ■ Performance Textiles
Performance Textiles Association
Priory Ct.
Pilgrim St.
London EC4V 6DR, United Kingdom
Ph: 44 207 6189196
Fax: 44 207 3297301
Publisher E-mail: info@muta.org.uk
Publication covering industrial textiles. **Freq:** Quarterly.
Key Personnel: David Ramus, President; Clive Moss,
CEO. **ISSN:** 0968-0861. **Subscription Rates:** Free in
U.K. **Remarks:** Advertising accepted; rates available
upon request. **URL:** http://www.performancetextiles.org.
uk/. **Formerly:** Industrial Textiles. **Circ:** (Not Reported)

55068 ■ Period Living
Centaur Media PLC
50 Poland St.
London W1F 7AX, United Kingdom
Ph: 44 20 79704000
Publication E-mail: period.living@centaur.co.uk
Publisher E-mail: customerservices@centaur.co.uk
Magazine featuring home restoration, renovations,
interior designs and gardens. **Freq:** Monthly. **Subscrip-
tion Rates:** EUR58 individuals; 44.40 two years. **Re-
marks:** Accepts advertising. **URL:** http://www.
periodliving.co.uk/. **Circ:** (Not Reported)

55069 ■ Personal Computer World
Incisive Media Limited

Haymarket House
28-29 Haymarket
London SW1Y 4RX, United Kingdom
Ph: 44 870 2408859
Fax: 44 207 4849797
Publisher E-mail: customerservices@incisivemedia.com
Computer periodical. **Founded:** Feb. 1978. **Freq:**
Monthly. **Print Method:** Web Offset. **Key Personnel:**
Will Stapley, Dep. Ed.; Kelvyn Taylor, Editor, kelvyn.
taylor@incisivemedia.com; Paul Harvey, Sales Mgr.,
paul.harvey@incisivemedia.com; Clive Akass, Assoc.
Ed. **ISSN:** 0142-0232. **Remarks:** Accepts advertising.
URL: http://www.pcw.co.uk/. **Ad Rates:** 4C: US$3,120.
Circ: ★54,069

55070 ■ Personal and Ubiquitous Computing
Springer-Verlag London Ltd.
236 Gray's Inn Rd., 6th Fl.
London WC1X 8HB, United Kingdom
Ph: 44 20 31922000
Publication E-mail: submissions@personal-ubicomp.
com
Peer-reviewed Journal focusing on issues surrounding
the innovation, design, use and evaluation of new
generations of innovative handheld and mobile informa-
tion appliances. Contains studies of end-user interface
issues in the design and use of personal technologies.
Freq: Bimonthly. **Key Personnel:** Dr. Stephen Brewster,
Editor, stephen@dcs.gla.ac.uk; Prof. Peter Thomas,
Editor-in-Chief, personalubicomp@gmail.com; Dr. Anind
Dey, Editor, anind@cms.edu; Prof. Hans W. Gellersen,
Editor, hwg@comp.lancs.ac.uk; David Frohlich, Editor,
d.frohlich@surrey.ac.uk; Steve Howard, Editor,
showard@unimelb.edu.au. **ISSN:** 1617-4909. **Subscription Rates:** EUR768 institutions print and e-access;
EUR921.60 institutions print and enhanced access. **Remarks:** Advertising accepted; rates available upon
request. **URL:** http://www.springerlink.com/content/
1617-4909. **Circ:** (Not Reported)

55071 ■ Personality and Individual Differences
Elsevier Science
c/o S.B.G. Eysenck, Ed.-in-Ch.
Dept. of Psychology
Institute of Psychiatry
De Crespigny Pk., Denmark Hill
London SE5 8AF, United Kingdom
Publisher E-mail: nlinfo-f@elsevier.com
Journal publishing articles which aim to integrate as far
as possible the major factors of personality with empiri-
cal paradigms from experimental, physiological, animal,
clinical, educational, criminological or industrial psychology or to seek an explanation for the causes and major
determinants of individual differences in concepts
derived from these disciplines. **Subtitle:** The Official
Journal of the International Society for the Study of
Individual Differences. **Founded:** 1980. **Freq:** 16/yr. **Key
Personnel:** P.A. Vernon, Editor-in-Chief, vernon@uwo.
ca; S.B.G. Eysenck, Editor-in-Chief, evans.eysenck@
virgin.net; E. Austin, Assoc. Ed. **ISSN:** 0191-8869. **Subscription Rates:** 352,400¥ institutions for Japan;
EUR2,656 institutions for European countries & Iran;
US$2,971 institutions for all countries except Europe,
Japan & Iran. **Remarks:** Advertising accepted; rates
available upon request. **URL:** http://www.elsevier.com/
wps/find/journaldescription.cws_home/603/
descriptiondescription. **Circ:** (Not Reported)

55072 ■ Personalized Medicine
Future Medicine Ltd.
Unitec House
2 Albert Pl.
London N3 1QB, United Kingdom
Ph: 44 20 83716080
Fax: 44 20 83432313
Publisher E-mail: info@futuremeducine.com
Peer-reviewed journal translating recent genomic,
genetic and proteomic advances into the clinical context,
addressing scientific, commercial and policy issues.
Freq: Bimonthly. **Key Personnel:** E. Abrahams, Sen.
Ed. **ISSN:** 1741-0541. **Subscription Rates:** 1,480
institutions; US$2,830 institutions; EUR1,845 institutions;
307,000¥ institutions. **Remarks:** Accepts advertising.
URL: http://www.futuremedicine.com/loi/pme. **Circ:** (Not
Reported)

55073 ■ Pet Product Marketing
H. Bauer Publishing
Academic House
24-28 Oval Rd.
London NW1 7DT, United Kingdom
Ph: 44 20 72418000

Fax: 44 20 72418030
Magazine featuring information about new products,
market news, business advice and analysis regarding
pet industry, as well as features written by leading
experts in the pet trade. **Freq:** Monthly. **Key Personnel:**
Sandra Pearce, Contact; Matt Clarke, Editor-in-Chief.
URL: http://www.petproductmarketing.co.uk/index.php.

55074 ■ Petroleum Economist
Euromoney Publications PLC
Nestor House
Playhouse Yard
London EC4V 5EX, United Kingdom
Ph: 44 20 77798888
Publisher E-mail: information@euromoneyplc.com
Publication for the petroleum, energy and mining
industries. **Freq:** Monthly. **Key Personnel:** Derek
Brower, Editor; Euan Soutar, Managing Editor. **ISSN:**
0306-395X. **Subscription Rates:** 1,728 individuals 3
years; 1,296 two years; 720 individuals. **URL:** http://
www.petroleum-economist.com/default.asp.

55075 ■ Petroleum Review
Energy Institute
61 New Cavendish St.
London W1G 7AR, United Kingdom
Ph: 44 20 74677100
Fax: 44 20 72551472
Publisher E-mail: pr@energyinst.org.uk
Publication covering petroleum. **Founded:** 1914. **Freq:**
Monthly. **Print Method:** Offset Litho. **Trim Size:** A4.
ISSN: 0020-3076. **Subscription Rates:** 250 nonmem-
bers; 420 nonmembers airmail. **URL:** http://www.
energyinst.org.uk/index.cfm?PageID=9. **Ad Rates:** 4C:
2,200. **Circ:** 10,000

**55076 ■ Pharmaceutical Manufacturing and
Packing Sourcer**
Samedan Ltd.
16, Hampden Gurney St.
London W1H 5AL, United Kingdom
Ph: 44 20 77243456
Fax: 44 20 77242632
Publisher E-mail: info@samedanltd.com
Journal covering topics relating to the pharmaceutical
manufacturing and packaging sector. **Freq:** Quarterly.
Key Personnel: Bruce Horton, Consultant Ed. **Sub-
scription Rates:** 125 individuals; US$230 other
countries. **URL:** http://www.samedanltd.com/magazine/
15.

55077 ■ Pharmacogenomics
Future Medicine Ltd.
Unitec House
2 Albert Pl.
London N3 1QB, United Kingdom
Ph: 44 20 83716080
Fax: 44 20 83432313
Publisher E-mail: info@futuremeducine.com
Peer-reviewd Journal presenting reviews and reports by
the researchers and decision-makers closely involved in
pharmacogenomics, providing the community with an
essential resource for keeping abreast of the latest
developments in all areas of this exciting field. **Freq:**
Bimonthly. **Key Personnel:** B. Boehm, Editorial Advisory
Board; T. Ishikawa, Editorial Advisory Board; D. Gurwitz,
Sen. Ed.; DA Campbell, Editorial Advisory Board; C.F.
Bennett, Editorial Advisory Board; D. Bailey, Editorial
Advisory Board; D. Altshuler, Editorial Advisory Board; T.
Freeman, Editorial Advisory Board; R. Judson, Editorial
Advisory Board. **ISSN:** 1462-2416. **Subscription Rates:**
1,480 institutions; US$2,830 institutions; EUR1,845
institutions; 307,000¥ institutions. **Remarks:** Accepts
advertising. **URL:** http://www.futuremedicine.com/loi/
pgs. **Circ:** (Not Reported)

55078 ■ The Pharmacogenomics Journal
Nature Publishing Group
The Macmillan Bldg.
4 Crinan St.
London N1 9XW, United Kingdom
Ph: 44 20 78334000
Fax: 44 20 78434640
Peer-reviewed journal dedicated to the rapid publication
of original research on basic pharmacogenomics
research and its clinical applications, providing coverage
concerning the effects of genetic variability on drug toxicity and efficacy, the characterization of polymorphisms
relevant to drug action, and the identification of novel
genomic targets for drug development. **Freq:** Bimonthly.

Key Personnel: Julio Licinio, MD, Editor. **ISSN:** 1470-269X. **Subscription Rates:** US$482 individuals print and online; EUR383 individuals print and online, 65,500¥ individuals print and online; 247 individuals print and online; US$434 individuals online; EUR345 individuals online; 59,000¥ individuals online; 223 individuals online. **URL:** http://www.nature.com/tpj/index.html.

55079 ■ Philosophical Transactions of the Royal Society A
Royal Society
6-9 Carlton House Ter.
London SW1Y 5AG, United Kingdom
Ph: 44 20 74512500
Fax: 44 20 79302170
Publisher E-mail: info@royalsoc.ac.uk
Journal covering topical scientific research. **Subtitle:** Mathematical, Physical & Engineering Sciences. **Freq:** Biweekly. **Key Personnel:** Michael Pepper, Editor; Prof. Celso Grebogi, Editorial Board. **ISSN:** 1364-503X. **Subscription Rates:** 1,801 institutions; US$3,412 U.S. and Canada; 1,950 institutions, other countries. **URL:** http://rsta.royalsocietypublishing.org/.

55080 ■ Philosophical Transactions of the Royal Society B
Royal Society
6-9 Carlton House Ter.
London SW1Y 5AG, United Kingdom
Ph: 44 20 74512500
Fax: 44 20 79302170
Publisher E-mail: info@royalsoc.ac.uk
Journal covering all areas of the biological sciences. **Subtitle:** Biological Sciences. **Freq:** Biweekly. **Key Personnel:** Prof. Georgina Mace, Editor. **ISSN:** 0962-8436. **Subscription Rates:** 2,145 institutions; US$4,058 U.S. and Canada; US$4,153 institutions, other countries. **URL:** http://rstb.royalsocietypublishing.org/.

55081 ■ Philosophy
Cambridge University Press
c/o Prof. Anthony O'Hear, Ed.
The Royal Institute of Philosophy
14 Gordon Sq.
London WC1H 0AR, United Kingdom
Publisher E-mail: information@cambridge.org
Journal covering philosophy and religion. **Founded:** 1925. **Freq:** Quarterly. **Key Personnel:** Prof. Anthony O'Hear, Editor, anthony@ohear.com; Prof. Brenda Almond, Editorial Board; Prof. Margaret Boden, Editorial Board. **ISSN:** 0031-8191. **Subscription Rates:** 311 institutions online and print; US$572 institutions online and print; 278 institutions online only; US$508 institutions online only. **Remarks:** Accepts advertising. **URL:** http://journals.cambridge.org/action/displayJournal?jid=PHI. **Ad Rates:** BW: 520, BW: 985. **Circ:** 2,000

55082 ■ Philosophy, Ethics, and Humanities in Medicine
BioMed Central Ltd.
236 Gray's Inn Rd., Fl. 6
34-42 Cleveland St.
London WC1X 8HL, United Kingdom
Ph: 44 20 31922000
Fax: 44 20 31922010
Publisher E-mail: info@biomedcentral.com
Journal covering all aspects of philosophy of medicine and biology in addition to ethical approach to clinical practice and research. **Key Personnel:** Prof. Dan J. Stein, Founding Ed., dan.stein@curie.uct.ac.za; Dr. Werdie Van Staden, Managing Editor, cwvanstaden@icon.co.za; Derek Bolton, Assoc. Ed.; Andrea Raballo, Managing Editor, d.denys@amc.nl; Dr. Jennifer Hansen, Assoc. Ed.; Dr. Michael Schwartz, Founding Ed., mas1@mas1.cnc.net. **ISSN:** 1747-5341. **URL:** http://www.peh-med.com/.

55083 ■ Philosophy & Social Criticism
Sage Publications Ltd.
1 Oliver's Yard
55 City Rd.
London EC1Y 1SP, United Kingdom
Ph: 44 20 73248500
Fax: 44 20 73248600
Peer-reviewed journal covering developments in social and political thought. **Subtitle:** An International, Interdisciplinary Journal. **Founded:** 1973. **Freq:** 9/yr. **Key Personnel:** David M. Rasmussen, Editor; James L. Taylor, Coord. **ISSN:** 0191-4537. **Subscription Rates:** 1,006 institutions combined (print & e-access); 1,107 institu-

tions plus backfile (current volume print & all online); 905 institutions e-access; 1,006 individuals e-access plus backfile (all online content); 1,846 institutions e-access (content through 1998); 986 institutions print only; 62 individuals print only; 121 institutions single print; 9 individuals single print. **Remarks:** Accepts advertising. **URL:** http://www.sagepub.co.uk/journalsProdDesc.nav?prodId=Journal201423. **Circ:** (Not Reported)

55084 ■ Phlebology
Royal Society of Medicine Press Ltd.
1 Wimpole St.
London W1G 0AE, United Kingdom
Ph: 44 20 72902921
Fax: 44 20 72902929
Publisher E-mail: publishing@rsm.ac.uk
Peer-reviewed journal covering study about venous disease. **Subtitle:** The journal of venous disease. **Freq:** 6/yr. **Key Personnel:** Alun Davies, MD, Editor; Steven Zimmet, North American Ed. **ISSN:** 0268-3555. **Subscription Rates:** 355 institutions UK & Europe; EUR483 institutions Europe; US$695 institutions; 361 institutions, other countries; 116 individuals UK & Europe; EUR158 individuals Europe; US$236 individuals; 122 other countries; 320 institutions online only; EUR435 individuals online only. **Remarks:** Accepts advertising. **URL:** http://www.portlandpress.com; http://phleb.rsmjournals.com. **Circ:** (Not Reported)

55085 ■ Physical Therapy Reviews
Maney Publishing
1 Carlton House Ter.
London SW1Y 5AF, United Kingdom
Ph: 44 20 74517300
Fax: 44 20 74517307
Publisher E-mail: maney@maney.co.uk
Journal focusing on diverse practices in physical therapy. **Freq:** Bimonthly. **Key Personnel:** Prof. David G. Baxter, Editor-in-Chief, physio.dean@otago.ac.nz. **ISSN:** 1083-3196. **Subscription Rates:** 118 other countries; US$198 individuals; 420 institutions, other countries; US$794 institutions, other countries; US$92 members. **Remarks:** Advertising accepted; rates available upon request. **URL:** http://maney.co.uk/index.php/journals/ptr/. **Circ:** (Not Reported)

55086 ■ Physics Education
Institute of Physics
76 Portland Pl.
London W1B 1NT, United Kingdom
Ph: 44 20 74704800
Fax: 44 20 74704848
Publication E-mail: ped@iop.org
Publisher E-mail: physics@iop.org
Professional publication covering physics. **Freq:** Bimonthly. **Key Personnel:** Gary Williams, Editor; Clare Thomson, Dep. Ed.; David Smith, Dep. Ed. **ISSN:** 0031-9120. **Subscription Rates:** US$560 institutions North, Central and South America; US$285 individuals North, Central and South America; 285 institutions European Union. **URL:** http://www.iop.org/ej/journal/physed.

55087 ■ Physics World
Institute of Physics
76 Portland Pl.
London W1B 1NT, United Kingdom
Ph: 44 20 74704800
Fax: 44 20 74704848
Publisher E-mail: physics@iop.org
Professional publication covering physics. **Freq:** Monthly. **Key Personnel:** Michael Banks, News Ed., michael.banks@iop.org; Dr. Matin Durrani, Editor, matin.durrani@iop.org; Dr. Hamish Johnston, Editor, hamish.johnston@iop.org; Dens Milne, Assoc. Ed., dens.milne@iop.org. **Subscription Rates:** 275 libraries corporate; US$520 libraries corporate; EUR405 libraries corporate. **Remarks:** Accepts advertising. **URL:** http://physicsworld.com/cws/home. **Ad Rates:** BW: 5,230. **Circ:** ★34,495

55088 ■ PIA (Papers from the Institute of Archaeology)
University College London
Gower St.
London WC1E 6BT, United Kingdom
Ph: 44 20 76792000
Publication E-mail: pia.journal@ucl.ac.uk
Journal publishing articles on archaeology and other related fields. **Founded:** 1989. **Freq:** Annual. **Key Personnel:** Louise Iles, Review Ed.; Iain Shearer, Sen. Ed. **ISSN:** 0965-9315. **Subscription Rates:** 35 individuals;

75 institutions. **URL:** http://www.ucl.ac.uk/archaeology/about/publications/pia.

55089 ■ Picture Arrowwords
H. Bauer Publishing
Academic House
24-28 Oval Rd.
London NW1 7DT, United Kingdom
Ph: 44 20 72418000
Fax: 44 20 72418030
Magazine featuring picture arrowwords. **Freq:** Bimonthly. **Trim Size:** 185 x 255 mm. **Key Personnel:** Clive Garsin, Gp. Ed.; Spike Figgett, Publishing Dir.; Helen Greenwood, Advertising Mgr. **Remarks:** Accepts advertising. **URL:** http://www.bauer.co.uk/node/103; http://www.puzzlemagazines.co.uk/picture-arrowwords. **Circ:** ★74,000

55090 ■ Pipeline World
Pipeline Industries Guild
14/15 Belgrave Sq.
London SW1X 8PS, United Kingdom
Ph: 44 20 72357938
Fax: 44 20 72350074
Publisher E-mail: enquiries@pipeguild.com
Publication covering petroleum. **Freq:** Bimonthly. **Key Personnel:** Samantha Cross, Operations Mgr., hqsec@pipeguild.co.uk. **Remarks:** Advertising accepted; rates available upon request. **URL:** http://www.pipeguild.co.uk. **Circ:** 2,500

55091 ■ Planning in London
Land Research Unit Ltd.
Studio Crown Reach
149a Grosvenor Rd.
London SW1V 3JY, United Kingdom
Ph: 44 20 78349471
Fax: 44 20 78349470
Publisher E-mail: planninginlondon@mac.com
Professional magazine of the London Planning and Development Forum. **Freq:** Quarterly. **Key Personnel:** Paul Finch, Editor; Brian Waters, MA, Exec. Ed., brian@bwcp.co.uk. **ISSN:** 1366-9672. **Subscription Rates:** 125 individuals 4 packs; 175 individuals 6 packs; 295 individuals 10 packs; 395 individuals 20 packs. **URL:** http://www.planninginlondon.com/. **Circ:** Combined 1,000

55092 ■ Planning (UK)
Royal Town Planning Institute
41 Botolph Ln.
London EC3R 8DL, United Kingdom
Ph: 44 20 79299494
Fax: 44 20 79299490
Publication E-mail: regeneration@haymarket.com
Business publication. **Freq:** Weekly. **Trim Size:** A4. **Key Personnel:** Domenic Donatantonio, Dep. News Ed., phone 44 20 82674364, domenic.donatantonio@haymarket.com; Huw Morris, Editor, phone 44 20 82674469, huw.morris@haymarket.com; Susanna Gillman, News Ed., phone 44 20 82674306, susanna.gillman@haymarket.com. **ISSN:** 1467-2073. **Subscription Rates:** 119 individuals. **Remarks:** Accepts advertising. **URL:** http://www.planningresource.co.uk/. **Ad Rates:** BW: 2,970. **Circ:** 21,413

55093 ■ Plant Methods
BioMed Central Ltd.
236 Gray's Inn Rd., Fl. 6
34-42 Cleveland St.
London WC1X 8HL, United Kingdom
Ph: 44 20 31922000
Fax: 44 20 31922010
Publisher E-mail: info@biomedcentral.com
Online journal covering all aspects of plant biology examined from a technological viewpoint. **Key Personnel:** Prof. Brian G. Forde, Editor-in-Chief, phone 44 1524 510207, b.g.forde@lancaster.ac.uk; Prof. Stanton Gelvin, Editorial Board; Dr. Mike R. Roberts, Dep. Ed., phone 44 1524 510210, fax 44 1524 525261, m.r.roberts@lancaster.ac.uk; Prof. Ton Bisseling, Editorial Board; Prof. Andrzej Jerzmanowski, Editorial Board; Prof. David W. Galbraith, Editorial Board; Dr. Anna Amtmann, Editorial Board; Dr. Tobias I. Baskin, Editorial Board; Dr. Claire Grierson, Editorial Board; Sidney L. Shaw, Editorial Board; Dr. Julia Kehr, Editorial Board; Dr. Mark Stitt, Editorial Board. **ISSN:** 1746-4811. **Remarks:** Accepts advertising. **URL:** http://www.plantmethods.com. **Circ:** (Not Reported)

Circulation: ★ = ABC; △ = BPA; ♦ = CAC; • = CCAB; ❑ = VAC; ⊕ = PO Statement; ‡ = Publisher's Report; Boldface figures = sworn; Light figures = estimated.

55094 ■ Plastics, Rubber and Composites
Maney Publishing
1 Carlton House Ter.
London SW1Y 5AF, United Kingdom
Ph: 44 20 74517300
Fax: 44 20 74517307
Publisher E-mail: maney@maney.co.uk
Peer-reviewed journal focusing on the macromolecular engineering of polymeric and related materials and polymer matrix composites. **Subtitle:** Macromolecular Engineering. **Freq:** 10/yr. **Key Personnel:** Prof. P.D. Coates, Editor, pdcoates@bradford.ac.uk; Prof. M.J. Bevis, Editorial Board, michael.bevis@brunel.ac.uk; Prof. Peter R. Hornsby, Assoc. Ed., peter.hornsby@qub.ac.uk; Prof. Clive B. Bucknall, Editorial Board, clivebucknall@aol.com; Prof. Klaus Friedrich, Editorial Board, klaus.friedrich@ivw.uni-kl.de; Prof. J.A. Covas, Editorial Board, jcovas@dep.uminho.pt; Prof. K. Funatsu, Editorial Board; Prof. A.J. Kelly, Editorial Board; Dr. J.J.C. Busfield, Editorial Board, j.busfield@qmul.ac.uk; Prof. A.G. Gibson, Assoc. Ed., a.g.gibson@ncl.ac.uk. **ISSN:** 1465-8011. **Subscription Rates:** 439 members other countries; US$693 members; 1,042 institutions, other countries; US$1,668 institutions. **Remarks:** Advertising accepted; rates available upon request. **URL:** http://maney.co.uk/index.php/journals/prc/. **Circ:** (Not Reported)

55095 ■ Platinum Metals Review
Johnson Matthey PLC
40-42 Hatton Garden
London EC1N 8EE, United Kingdom
Ph: 44 20 72698400
Fax: 44 20 72698433
Journal covering research on platinum metals and developments within the industry. **Founded:** 1957. **Freq:** Quarterly. **ISSN:** 0032-1400. **Subscription Rates:** Free to qualified subscribers. **Remarks:** Advertising not accepted. **URL:** http://www.platinummetalsreview.com/; http://www.platinum.matthey.com/publications/platinum-metals-review-scientific-research-journal/. **Circ:** Controlled 9,200

55096 ■ PNC
Community and District Nursing Association
367 Chiswick High Rd.
London W4 4AG, United Kingdom
Ph: 44 20 89714268
Publisher E-mail: info@cdnaonline.org
Journal containing an up-to-date view of the primary care environment. **Freq:** Quarterly. **Subscription Rates:** Included in membership. **Remarks:** Accepts advertising. **URL:** http://www.cdnaonline.org/index.php?option=com_content&task=category&sectionid=6&id=22&Itemid=69. **Circ:** (Not Reported)

55097 ■ Poetry Review
The Poetry Society
22 Betterton St.
London WC2H 9BX, United Kingdom
Ph: 44 20 74209880
Fax: 44 20 72404818
Publication E-mail: info@poetrysociety.org.uk
Publisher E-mail: info@poetrysociety.org.uk
Poetry magazine. **Founded:** 1912. **Freq:** Quarterly. **Print Method:** Offset litho. **Trim Size:** 240 x 170 mm. **Cols./Page:** 2. **Col. Width:** 67 millimeters. **Col. Depth:** 202 millimeters. **Key Personnel:** Fiona Sampson, Editor. **ISSN:** 0032-2156. **Subscription Rates:** 30 individuals; 50 institutions. **Remarks:** Accepts advertising. **URL:** http://www.poetrysociety.org.uk/content/publications/review. **Ad Rates:** BW: 370. **Circ:** Paid 4,000

55098 ■ PokerPlayer
Dennis Publishing Ltd.
30 Cleveland St.
London W1T 4JD, United Kingdom
Ph: 44 20 79076000
Fax: 44 20 79076020
Publisher E-mail: reception@dennis.co.uk
Gambling magazine. **Key Personnel:** Richard Downey, Publisher; Mark Stuart, Editor, mark_stuart@dennis.co.uk. **Subscription Rates:** 5.99 individuals direct debit, every 6 issues; 12 individuals credit card. **Remarks:** Accepts advertising. **URL:** http://www.pokerplayer.co.uk/. **Formerly:** InsidePoker. **Circ:** (Not Reported)

55099 ■ Political Theology
Equinox Publishing Ltd.
1 Chelsea Manor Studios
Flood St.
London SW3 5SR, United Kingdom
Ph: 44 20 78233748
Fax: 44 20 78233748
Journal covering religious and theological engagements with public and political life. **Freq:** Quarterly. **Key Personnel:** Graeme Smith, Exec. Ed., g.smith@chi.ac.uk; Julie Clague, Editor, j.clague@arts.gla.ac.uk; Timothy Simpson, Editor, tsimpson@christianalliance.org; David True, Editor, dtrue@wilson.edu. **ISSN:** 1462-317X. **Subscription Rates:** 260 institutions, other countries print and online; US$550 institutions print and online; 90 individuals print; US$180 individuals print; 230 institutions, other countries print; US$495 institutions print. **Remarks:** Accepts advertising. **URL:** http://www.equinoxjournals.com/ojs/index.php/PT. **Circ:** (Not Reported)

55100 ■ Politics, Philosophy & Economics
Sage Publications Ltd.
1 Oliver's Yard
55 City Rd.
London EC1Y 1SP, United Kingdom
Ph: 44 20 73248500
Fax: 44 20 73248600
Peer-reviewed journal covering political and economic institutions and practices. **Founded:** 2002. **Freq:** Quarterly. **Key Personnel:** Jonathan Riley, Editor; Gerald F. Gaus, Founding Ed.; Thomas Christiano, Editor; Jack Knight, Assoc. Ed.; Elizabeth Anderson, Editorial Board; Paula Casal, Assoc. Ed.; Peter Vanderschraaf, Assoc. Ed.; Andrew Williams, Assoc. Ed.; Gillian Brock, Assoc. Ed.; Jeremy Waldron, Editorial Board. **ISSN:** 1470-594X. **Subscription Rates:** US$744 institutions print & e-access; US$670 institutions e-access; US$729 institutions print only; US$83 individuals print only; US$200 institutions single print; US$27 individuals single print. **Remarks:** Accepts advertising. **URL:** http://www.sagepub.com/journalsProdAims.nav?prodId=Journal201490&currTree=Subjects&level1=B00. **Circ:** (Not Reported)

55101 ■ Popular Music History
Equinox Publishing Ltd.
1 Chelsea Manor Studios
Flood St.
London SW3 5SR, United Kingdom
Ph: 44 20 78233748
Fax: 44 20 78233748
Journal covering historical and historiographical issues on popular music. **Freq:** 3/yr (April, August and December). **Key Personnel:** Robert Strachan, Editor, bigmice@liverpool.ac.uk; Dave Laing, Exec. Ed., dave.laing@tinyonline.co.uk. **ISSN:** 1740-7133. **Subscription Rates:** 140 institutions, other countries print and online; US$280 institutions print and online; 53 individuals print; US$105 individuals print; 33.75 students print; US$67.50 students print. **Remarks:** Accepts advertising. **URL:** http://www.equinoxjournals.com/ojs/index.php/PMH. **Circ:** (Not Reported)

55102 ■ Population Health Metrics
BioMed Central Ltd.
236 Gray's Inn Rd., Fl. 6
34-42 Cleveland St.
London WC1X 8HL, United Kingdom
Ph: 44 20 31922000
Fax: 44 20 31922010
Publisher E-mail: info@biomedcentral.com
Online journal covering all aspects of the measurement of health at the population level. **Key Personnel:** Dr. Majid Ezzati, Assoc. Ed., mezzati@hsph.harvard.edu; Dr. Christopher J.L. Murray, Editor-in-Chief, cjlm@u.washington.edu; Dr. Alan D. Lopez, Editor-in-Chief, a.lopez@sph.uq.edu.au; Dr. Emmanuela Gakidou, Assoc. Ed., gakidou@u.washington.edu; Dr. Ali Mokdad, Assoc. Ed.; Dr. Joshua Salomon, Assoc. Ed., jsalomon@hsph.harvard.edu. **ISSN:** 1478-7954. **Remarks:** Accepts advertising. **URL:** http://www.pophealthmetrics.com/start.asp. **Circ:** (Not Reported)

55103 ■ Population Studies
Routledge
Taylor & Francis Group Ltd.
Population Investigation Committee
London School of Economics, Rm. PS201
Houghton St.
London WC2A 2AE, United Kingdom
Publisher E-mail: webmaster.books@tandf.co.uk
Publication covering demography and population studies. **Founded:** 1947. **Freq:** 3/yr. **Trim Size:** 210 x 276 mm. **Key Personnel:** John Simons, Managing Editor; John McDonald, Editor; Ian Timaeus, Editor; Alice Reid, Editor; John Cleland, Editor; Oystein Kravdal, Editor; Gigi Santow, Editor; Wendy Sigle-Rushton, Editor. **ISSN:** 0032-4728. **Subscription Rates:** 167 institutions print + online; 158 institutions online; 122 individuals; 54 members; US$274 institutions print + online; US$261 institutions online; US$208 individuals; US$90 members. **Remarks:** Accepts advertising on request. **URL:** http://www.tandf.co.uk/journals/titles/00324728.html. **Ad Rates:** BW: 250. **Circ:** Paid ‡1,300

55104 ■ Portuguese Journal of Social Science
Intellect
Russell Square House
10-12 Russell Sq.
London WC1B 5EE, United Kingdom
Ph: 44 20 73312000
Fax: 44 20 73312040
Publisher E-mail: info@intellectuk.org
Journal dedicated primarily to introducing an international readership to the work currently being produced by Portuguese scholarship in the social sciences of general interest to the social science community as well as of particular interest to specialists in Latin America and Southern Europe. **Founded:** 2002. **Freq:** 3/yr. **Trim Size:** 174 x 244 mm. **Key Personnel:** Onesimo T. Almeida, Editorial Board; Joao Ferreira de Almeida, Editor; Maurice Aymard, Editorial Board. **ISSN:** 1476-413X. **Subscription Rates:** 33 individuals print; 210 institutions print and online; 12 single issue print; 177 individuals online only. **Remarks:** Accepts advertising. **URL:** http://www.intellectbooks.co.uk/journals/view-Journal,id=141/. **Ad Rates:** BW: 100. **Circ:** (Not Reported)

55105 ■ Portuguese Studies
Modern Humanities Research Association
1 Carlton House Ter.
London SW1Y 5AF, United Kingdom
Publication E-mail: portuguese@mhra.org.uk
Publisher E-mail: mail@mhra.org.uk
Journal focusing on research on the cultures, societies, and history in the areas of Portugal, Brazil, and the Lusophone countries of Africa. **Freq:** Semiannual. **Subscription Rates:** 72 institutions; 72 institutions Europe; US$174 institutions North America; 89 institutions, other countries. **URL:** http://www.mhra.org.uk/Publications/Journals/Portuguese.html.

55106 ■ Positive Nation
Talent Media
Studio 37, Riverside Bldg.
Trinity Buoy Wharf
64 Ochard Pl.
London E14 0JW, United Kingdom
Ph: 44 20 70010754
Magazine featuring sexual health awareness. **Founded:** 1994. **Freq:** Quarterly. **Subscription Rates:** 15 individuals; 65 institutions; 35 institutions not-for-profit. **Remarks:** Accepts advertising. **URL:** http://www.positivenation.co.uk/. **Circ:** (Not Reported)

55107 ■ Post Magazine
Incisive Media Limited
Haymarket House
28-29 Haymarket
London SW1Y 4RX, United Kingdom
Ph: 44 870 2408859
Fax: 44 207 4849797
Publisher E-mail: customerservices@incisivemedia.com
Journal featuring the insurance industry. **Freq:** Weekly (Thurs.). **Key Personnel:** Anthony Gould, Editor-in-Chief, phone 44 20 73169374, anthony.gould@incisivemedia.com; Jonathan Swift, Editor, phone 44 20 73169321, jonathan.swift@incisivemedia.com; Lynn Rouse, Dep. Ed., phone 44 20 73169167, lynn.rouse@incisivemedia.com. **Subscription Rates:** 300 individuals print only; 345 individuals Europe; print only; 510 other countries. **Remarks:** Accepts advertising. **URL:** http://www.postonline.co.uk/. **Circ:** (Not Reported)

55108 ■ Post-Medieval Archaeology
Maney Publishing
1 Carlton House Ter.
London SW1Y 5AF, United Kingdom
Ph: 44 20 74517300
Fax: 44 20 74517307

Publisher E-mail: maney@maney.co.uk
Journal covering study of the material evidence of European society. **Freq:** Semiannual. **Key Personnel:** Jacqui Pearce, Editor, jpearce@museumoflondon.org.uk; Paul Courtney, Editor; Eleanor Conlin Casella, Review Board. **ISSN:** 0079-4236. **Subscription Rates:** 44 other countries; US$84 individuals; 158 institutions, other countries; US$310 institutions. **Remarks:** Accepts advertising. **URL:** http://maney.co.uk/index.php/journals/pma/. **Circ:** (Not Reported)

55109 ■ Postgraduate Medical Journal
BMJ Publishing Group
BMA House
Tavistock Sq.
London WC1H 9JR, United Kingdom
Ph: 44 20 73834410
Fax: 44 20 73876400
Publication E-mail: pmj@bmjgroup.com
Publisher E-mail: customerservice.group@bmjgroup.com
Peer-reviewed Journal for professional development of clinicians. **Founded:** 1925. **Freq:** Monthly. **Key Personnel:** Fiona Moss, Editor-in-Chief; Penny Fitzharris, Editor; Ana Grenfell, Editor. **ISSN:** 0032-5473. **Subscription Rates:** 165 individuals print and online; 115 institutions online only; EUR223 individuals print and online; US$322 individuals print and online; EUR155 individuals online only; US$224 individuals online only. **Remarks:** Advertising accepted; rates available upon request. **URL:** http://pmj.bmj.com/. **Circ:** ‡1,475

55110 ■ Powder Metallurgy
Maney Publishing
1 Carlton House Ter.
London SW1Y 5AF, United Kingdom
Ph: 44 20 74517300
Fax: 44 20 74517307
Publisher E-mail: maney@maney.co.uk
Peer-reviewed journal covering research on the science and practice of powder metallurgy. **Freq:** Quarterly. **Key Personnel:** J.J. Dunkley, Editor, jjd@atomising.co.uk. **ISSN:** 0032-5899. **Subscription Rates:** 484 institutions, other countries; US$848 institutions; 219 members other countries; US$357 members. **Remarks:** Advertising accepted; rates available upon request. **URL:** http://maney.co.uk/index.php/journals/pom/. **Circ:** (Not Reported)

55111 ■ POWDEReporter
Salisbury Sarum Ltd.
PO Box 1523
London N2 9HZ, United Kingdom
Ph: 44 20 84420654
Fax: 44 20 84421640
Publication E-mail: powderfax@aol.com
Trade magazine covering powder processing and handling in the chemical, pharmaceutical and process industries. **Founded:** May 1998. **Freq:** Bimonthly. **Print Method:** Web offset. **Cols./Page:** 4. **Col. Width:** 41 millimeters. **Key Personnel:** A. Davies, Publisher. **ISSN:** 1462-2025. **Subscription Rates:** 177 individuals; 29.50 single issue. **Remarks:** Accepts advertising. **URL:** http://www.powdereporter.co.uk/. **Circ:** (Not Reported)

55112 ■ Power Rangers
Egmont Magazines
184-192 Drummond St., 4th Fl.
London NW1 3HP, United Kingdom
Ph: 44 20 73806430
Magazine for Power Rangers fan. **Freq:** 3/week. **Trim Size:** 220 x 300 mm. **Key Personnel:** Anna Chacoliades, Contact; Sam Verno, Contact. **Subscription Rates:** 1.99 individuals. **Remarks:** Accepts advertising. **URL:** http://www.egmont.co.uk/product.asp?prodid=1521&catid=30. **Ad Rates:** 4C: 1,500. **Circ:** ★56,047

55113 ■ Practical Fishkeeping
H. Bauer Publishing
Academic House
24-28 Oval Rd.
London NW1 7DT, United Kingdom
Ph: 44 20 72418000
Fax: 44 20 72418030
Magazine covering all areas of fishkeeping hobby including tropical fish, marine fish, coldwater fish, pond fish, reefkeeping, and watergardening. **Freq:** 13/yr. **Key Personnel:** Matt Clarke, Editor-in-Chief, matt.clarke@bauermedia.co.uk; Jeremy Gay, Dep. Ed., jeremy.gay@bauermedia.co.uk. **Subscription Rates:** 48.94

individuals. **URL:** http://www.bauermedia.co.uk/Brands/Practical-Fishkeeping/.

55114 ■ The Practical Lawyer
Legalese Ltd.
Kensington Sq. House
12-14 Ansdell St.
London W8 5BN, United Kingdom
Ph: 44 20 73969292
Fax: 44 20 73969303
Digest covering legal developments in the UK. **Founded:** 1989. **Freq:** 10/yr. **Trim Size:** A5. **Key Personnel:** John Pritchard, Editor. **Subscription Rates:** 93 individuals. **Remarks:** Advertising not accepted. **URL:** http://www.practicallawyer.co.uk. **Circ:** Paid 6,000

55115 ■ Practical Neurology
BMJ Publishing Group Ltd.
BMA House
Tavistock Sq.
London WC1H 9JR, United Kingdom
Ph: 44 20 73874410
Fax: 44 20 73836400
Peer-reviewed journal covering all aspects of neurology. **Founded:** 2001. **Freq:** Bimonthly. **Key Personnel:** Prof. Charles Warlow, Editor-in-Chief, charles.warlow@ed.ac.uk. **ISSN:** 1474-7758. **Remarks:** Advertising accepted; rates available upon request. **URL:** http://pn.bmj.com/. **Circ:** (Not Reported)

55116 ■ Practical Parenting and Pregnancy
Magicalia Ltd.
15-18 White Lion St.
Islington
London N1 9PG, United Kingdom
Ph: 44 20 78438800
Fax: 44 20 78438999
Publisher E-mail: feedback@magicalia.com
Magazine containing advice and information about pregnancy, birth, babies and preschoolers. **Freq:** Monthly. **Remarks:** Accepts advertising. **URL:** http://www.practicalparenting.co.uk/default.asp?sp=&v=1. **Circ:** (Not Reported)

55117 ■ Precision Marketing
Centaur Publishing Ltd.
50 Poland St.
London W1F 7AX, United Kingdom
Ph: 44 20 79704000
Fax: 44 20 79704189
Publication covering advertising, marketing and public relations. **Freq:** Monthly. **Key Personnel:** Ed Tillotson, Assoc. Publisher; Charlie McKelvey, Editor; Annie Swift, Publishing Dir., annie.swift@centaur.co.uk. **ISSN:** 0957-4913. **Subscription Rates:** 75.90 individuals UK; 134 two years UK; 196 individuals 3 years; 141 U.S. and Canada; 229 U.S. and Canada 2 years; 318 U.S. and Canada 3 years. **Remarks:** Accepts advertising. **URL:** http://www.centaur.co.uk/section.asp?topNav=off?catid=59&docid=334. **Ad Rates:** BW: 3,095, 4C: 3,845. **Circ:** ★7,500

55118 ■ Print Buyer
Haymarket Business Magazines
174 Hammersmith Rd.
London W6 7JP, United Kingdom
Ph: 44 20 82674210
Publisher E-mail: info@haymarket.com
Magazine featuring advertising. **Founded:** 2004. **Freq:** Monthly. **Key Personnel:** Alison Carter, Editor; Steven Scaffardi, Advertising Mgr. **URL:** http://www.haymarket.com/pr_week/pr_week_magazine/default.aspx; http://www.haymarket.com/printbuyer/printbuyer_magazine/default.aspx. **Circ:** ★14,500

55119 ■ PrintWeek
Haymarket Business Publications Ltd.
174 Hammersmith Rd.
London W6 7JP, United Kingdom
Ph: 44 20 82675000
Fax: 44 20 82674268
Publication E-mail: printweek.editorial@haymarket.com
Publisher E-mail: hpg@haymarketgroup.com
Trade magazine covering the print industry. **Freq:** 51/yr. **Key Personnel:** Darryl Danielli, Editor, phone 44 20 82674473, darryl.danielli@haymarket.com. **Subscription Rates:** 119 individuals UK; 214.20 two years within UK; 285.60 individuals 3 years (UK). **Remarks:** Accepts advertising. **URL:** http://www.printweek.com; http://www.

haymarket.com/printweek/printweek_magazine/default.aspx. **Former name:** LithoWeek. **Circ:** Controlled ★16,536

55120 ■ PrivatAir
Luxury Publishing Limited
5 Jubilee Pl.
Chelsea
London SW3 3TD, United Kingdom
Ph: 44 20 75912900
Fax: 44 20 75912929
Publisher E-mail: info@luxurypublishing.com
Lifestyle magazine for clients and friends of PrivatAir airline. **Founded:** 2000. **Freq:** Quarterly. **Print Method:** Sheet Fed Lithography. **Trim Size:** 230 x 300 mm. **Key Personnel:** Celestria Noel, Editor. **Remarks:** Accepts advertising. **URL:** http://www.luxurypublishing.co.uk/. **Circ:** 7,000

55121 ■ Private Equity Europe
Incisive Media Limited
Haymarket House
28-29 Haymarket
London SW1Y 4RX, United Kingdom
Ph: 44 870 2408859
Fax: 44 207 4849797
Publisher E-mail: customerservices@incisivemedia.com
Magazine covering private equity industry. **Founded:** 1995. **Freq:** Monthly. **Key Personnel:** Emanuel Eftimiu, Editor. **Subscription Rates:** 1,196 individuals online; EUR1,794 individuals online; US$2,153 individuals online. **Remarks:** Accepts advertising. **URL:** http://www.incisivemedia.com/corporate/products/pee; http://www.unquote.com/private-equity-europe. **Circ:** (Not Reported)

55122 ■ Private Hospital Healthcare Europe
Campden Publishing Ltd.
1 St. John's Sq.
London EC1M 4PN, United Kingdom
Ph: 44 20 72140500
Fax: 44 20 72140501
Publisher E-mail: enquiries@campden.com
Magazine for private hospital sector. **Key Personnel:** Stephen Taylor, Publisher/Editorial Dir.; Kelly Clarke, Supv. Ed. **Subscription Rates:** US$326 individuals; 165 individuals; EUR245 individuals. **Remarks:** Accepts advertising. **URL:** http://www.campden.com/default.asp?ptid=3&pid=5&pgid=1; http://www.hospitalhealthcare.com/default.asp. **Circ:** (Not Reported)

55123 ■ PrivatSea
Luxury Publishing Limited
5 Jubilee Pl.
Chelsea
London SW3 3TD, United Kingdom
Ph: 44 20 75912900
Fax: 44 20 75912929
Publisher E-mail: info@luxurypublishing.com
Lifestyle magazine for PrivatSea club members and guests. **Freq:** Semiannual. **Remarks:** Accepts advertising. **URL:** http://www.luxurypublishing.co.uk/. **Circ:** 8,000

55124 ■ Proceedings
London Mathematical Society
De Morgan House
57-58 Russell Sq.
London WC1 D4I IG, United Kingdom
Ph: 44 20 76373686
Fax: 44 20 73233655
Publisher E-mail: lms@lms.ac.uk
Journal of the London Mathematical Society. **Founded:** 1865. **Freq:** Bimonthly. **Key Personnel:** S.P. Hezlet, Publisher. **Subscription Rates:** 119 institutions print only; US$214 institutions print only; EUR178 institutions print only; 570 institutions print only; US$1,026 institutions print only; EUR855 institutions print only; 698 institutions print and online; US$1,256 institutions print and online; EUR1,047 institutions print and online. **URL:** http://www.lms.ac.uk/.

55125 ■ Proceedings of the Aristotelian Society
John Wiley & Sons Inc.
Wiley-Blackwell
Stewart House, Rm. 281
Russell Sq.
London WC1B 5DN, United Kingdom
Ph: 44 20 78628685
Fax: 44 20 78628685
Publication E-mail: mail@aristoteliansociety.org.uk
Journal featuring articles related to philosophy. **Freq:**

Circulation: ★ = ABC; △ = BPA; ♦ = CAC; • = CCAB; ❑ = VAC; ⊕ = PO Statement; ‡ = Publisher's Report; Boldface figures = sworn; Light figures = estimated.

Gale Directory of Publications & Broadcast Media/147th Ed.   5759

Annual. **Key Personnel:** Mark Eli Kalderon, Editor, m.kalderon@ucl.ac.uk; David Harris, Asst. Ed. **ISSN:** 0066-7374. **Subscription Rates:** US$172 institutions Americas (print and online); EUR123 institutions Europe (print and online); 97 institutions UK (print and online); US$220 institutions, other countries print and online; US$156 institutions Americas (print or online only); EUR112 institutions Europe (print or online only); 88 institutions UK (print or online only); US$200 institutions, other countries print or online only. **URL:** http://www.wiley.com/bw/journal.asp?ref=0066-7374.

55126 ■ Process Engineering
Centaur Publishing Ltd.
50 Poland St.
London W1F 7AX, United Kingdom
Ph: 44 20 79704000
Fax: 44 20 79704189
Publication for the chemical, plastics and rubber industries. **Freq:** Monthly. **Trim Size:** 210 x 286 mm. **Key Personnel:** Matt Comley, Recruitment Ad Directory, phone 44 20 79704110, matt.comley@centaur.co.uk; Jon Excell, Editor, phone 44 20 79704437, jon.excell@centaur.co.uk; Sean Marshall, Publisher, phone 44 20 79704151, sean.marshall@certaur.co.uk. **ISSN:** 0370-1859. **Subscription Rates:** 75 individuals UK; 127 two years UK; 177 individuals three years, UK. **Remarks:** Accepts advertising. **URL:** http://www.processengineering.co.uk/Home/Default.aspx. **Circ:** Controlled 30,466

55127 ■ Professional Adviser
Incisive Media Limited
Haymarket House
28-29 Haymarket
London SW1Y 4RX, United Kingdom
Ph: 44 870 2408859
Fax: 44 207 4849797
Publisher E-mail: customerservices@incisivemedia.com
Magazine featuring investment news, financial planning, and vital analysis for advisers. **Freq:** Monthly. **Key Personnel:** Katrina Baugh, Editor, phone 44 20 74849783, katrina.baugh@incisivemedia.com; Scott Sinclair, phone 44 20 74849791, scott.sinclair@incisivemedia.com. **Remarks:** Accepts advertising. **URL:** http://www.incisivemedia.com/corporate/products/professionaladviser; http://www.ifaonline.co.uk/professional-adviser. **Circ:** (Not Reported)

55128 ■ Professional Beauty/LNE English Edition
Trades Exhibitions Ltd.
Professional Beauty
3rd Fl., Broadway House
2-6 Fulham Broadway
London SW6 1AA, United Kingdom
Ph: 44 20 76103001
Fax: 44 20 76103566
Publication E-mail: beauty@tradesexhibitions.com
Publisher E-mail: info@professionalbeauty.co.uk
Trade magazine covering the beauty industry in the UK. **Freq:** Monthly. **Key Personnel:** Jenni Middleton, Editor, phone 44 20 77283571, jenni.middleton@emap.com. **Subscription Rates:** 37 individuals. **Remarks:** Accepts advertising. **URL:** http://www.professionalbeauty.co.uk. **Circ:** Combined 11,867

55129 ■ Professional Broking
Incisive Media Limited
Haymarket House
28-29 Haymarket
London SW1Y 4RX, United Kingdom
Ph: 44 870 2408859
Fax: 44 207 4849797
Publisher E-mail: customerservices@incisivemedia.com
Magazine for insurance brokers. **Subtitle:** The management magazine for insurance brokers. **Key Personnel:** Andrew Tjaardstra, Editor, phone 44 20 73169316, andrew.tjaardstra@incisivemedia.com; Ant Gould, Editor-in-Chief, phone 44 20 73169374, anthony.gould@incisivemedia.com; Alex Broad, Publisher, phone 44 20 73169382, alex.broad@incisivemedia.com. **Remarks:** Accepts advertising. **URL:** http://www.professionalbroking.co.uk. **Circ:** (Not Reported)

55130 ■ Professional Engineering
Institution of Mechanical Engineers
1 Birdcage Walk
London SW1H 9JJ, United Kingdom
Ph: 44 20 72227899
Fax: 44 20 72224557

Publication E-mail: pe@pepublishing.com
Publisher E-mail: international@imeche.org
Publication covering engineering. **Freq:** Semimonthly 22/yr. **Key Personnel:** Sat Bains, Contact; Nigel Searle, Contact. **ISSN:** 0953-6639. **Subscription Rates:** 113 individuals; 579 libraries. **Remarks:** Advertising accepted; rates available upon request. **URL:** http://www.profeng.com/. **Circ:** Combined 90,000

55131 ■ Professional Marketing
Professional Marketing International
Warnford Ct.
29 Throgmorton St.
London EC2N 2AT, United Kingdom
Ph: 44 20 77869786
Fax: 44 20 77869799
Publication E-mail: pm@pmint.co.uk
Publisher E-mail: pmf@pmint.co.uk
Professional magazine covering marketing. **Founded:** 1993. **Freq:** 10/yr. **Trim Size:** A4. **Key Personnel:** Nadia Cristina, Managing Editor. **ISSN:** 0969-1847. **Remarks:** Accepts advertising. **URL:** http://www.pmint.co.uk; http://www.pmforum.co.uk/magazine/index.aspx. **Ad Rates:** BW: 950. **Circ:** (Not Reported)

55132 ■ Professional Pensions
Incisive Media Limited
Haymarket House
28-29 Haymarket
London SW1Y 4RX, United Kingdom
Ph: 44 870 2408859
Fax: 44 207 4849797
Publisher E-mail: customerservices@incisivemedia.com
Magazine covering news and features for the occupational pensions industry. **Freq:** Weekly. **Trim Size:** 250 x 350 mm. **Key Personnel:** Jonathan Stapleton, Editor, phone 44 20 70047530, jonathan.stapleton@incisivemedia.com. **Remarks:** Accepts advertising. **URL:** http://www.incisivemedia.com/corporate/products/professionalpensions; http://professionalpensions.com/. **Circ:** ★12,672

55133 ■ Profound (The Dialog Corporation) of the Royal Society A
Royal Society
6-9 Carlton House Ter.
London SW1Y 5AG, United Kingdom
Ph: 44 20 74512500
Fax: 44 20 79302170
Publisher E-mail: info@royalsoc.ac.uk
Journal describing research articles in the mathematical, physical and engineering sciences. **Subtitle:** Mathematical, Physical & Engineering Sciences. **Freq:** Monthly. **Key Personnel:** Prof. Michael Berry, Editor. **ISSN:** 1364-5021. **Subscription Rates:** 1,088 institutions Europe; 2,048 institutions US/Canada; 1,165 institutions, other countries. **URL:** http://rspa.royalsocietypublishing.org/.

55134 ■ Profound (The Dialog Corporation) of the Royal Society B
Royal Society
6-9 Carlton House Ter.
London SW1Y 5AG, United Kingdom
Ph: 44 20 74512500
Fax: 44 20 79302170
Publisher E-mail: info@royalsoc.ac.uk
Journal covering original research and articles from across the biological sciences. **Subtitle:** Biological Sciences. **Freq:** Biweekly. **Key Personnel:** Prof. Michael P. Hassell, Editor. **ISSN:** 0962-8452. **Subscription Rates:** 1,106 institutions Europe; US$2,128 institutions US/Canada; 1,231 institutions, other countries. **URL:** http://rspb.royalsocietypublishing.org/.

55135 ■ Progress in Development Studies
Sage Publications Ltd.
1 Oliver's Yard
55 City Rd.
London EC1Y 1SP, United Kingdom
Ph: 44 20 73248500
Fax: 44 20 73248600
Forum for the discussion of development issues, including poverty alleviation and international aid, the international debt crisis, economic development and industrialization, environmental degradation and sustainable development, political governance and civil society, gender relations, and the rights of the child. **Freq:** Quarterly. **Key Personnel:** Robert Potter, Editor-in-Chief. **ISSN:** 1464-9934. **Subscription Rates:** 292 institutions print & e-access; 263 institutions e-access;

286 institutions print only; 77 individuals print & e-access; 79 institutions single print; 25 individuals single print. **Remarks:** Accepts advertising. **URL:** http://www.sagepub.co.uk/journalsProdDesc.nav?prodId=Journal201836. **Circ:** (Not Reported)

55136 ■ Progress in Palliative Care
Maney Publishing
1 Carlton House Ter.
London SW1Y 5AF, United Kingdom
Ph: 44 20 74517300
Fax: 44 20 74517307
Publisher E-mail: maney@maney.co.uk
Peer-reviewed journal covering all aspects of the management of the problems of end-stage disease, with a focus on quick exchange of information amongst those engaged in palliative care. **Subtitle:** Science and the Art of Caring. **Freq:** Bimonthly Feb., Apr., Jun., Aug., Oct. and Dec. **Trim Size:** 180 x 265 mm. **Key Personnel:** Prof. Mellar Davis, Editor-in-Chief, davism6@ccf.org; Prof. Andreas Lubbe, Editorial Board; Patsy Yates, Editorial Board; Amy Abernethy, Editorial Board. **ISSN:** 0969-9260. **Subscription Rates:** 118 other countries; US$206 individuals; 340 institutions, other countries; US$556 institutions; 322 other countries online only. **Remarks:** Accepts advertising. **URL:** http://maney.co.uk/index.php/journals/ppc/. **Ad Rates:** BW: 275. **Circ:** (Not Reported)

55137 ■ Progressive Gifts and Home Worldwide
Max Publishing Ltd.
United House
North Rd.
London N7 9DP, United Kingdom
Ph: 44 20 77006740
Fax: 44 20 76076411
Publisher E-mail: maxubscriptions@blueyonder.co.uk
Magazine featuring gift industry. **Freq:** 8/yr. **Print Method:** 210 x 297 mm. **Key Personnel:** Sue Marks, Editor, sue@sjbassoc.freeserve.co.uk; Jacquelin Brown, Editor-in-Chief, jw@max-publishing.co.uk. **Subscription Rates:** 45 individuals; 75 two years; 110 individuals three years; 75 other countries; 125 other countries two years; 165 other countries three years. **Remarks:** Accepts advertising. **URL:** http://www.max-publishing.co.uk/progressive-gifts-home.html. **Ad Rates:** BW: 995, 4C: 1,395. **Circ:** 6,700

55138 ■ Progressive Greetings Worldwide
Max Publishing Ltd.
United House
North Rd.
London N7 9DP, United Kingdom
Ph: 44 20 77006740
Fax: 44 20 76076411
Publisher E-mail: maxubscriptions@blueyonder.co.uk
Magazine featuring worldwide greeting card industry. **Freq:** Monthly. **Trim Size:** 210 x 297 mm. **Key Personnel:** Jacquelin Brown, Editor, jw@max-publishing.co.uk; Warren Lomax, Advertisement Dir., warren@max-publishing.co.uk. **Subscription Rates:** 50 individuals; 85 two years; 110 individuals three years; 75 other countries; 125 other countries two years; 165 other countries three years. **Remarks:** Accepts advertising. **URL:** http://www.max-publishing.co.uk/progressive-greetings-home.html. **Ad Rates:** 4C: 1,500. **Circ:** 6,500

55139 ■ Progressive Housewares
Max Publishing Ltd.
United House
North Rd.
London N7 9DP, United Kingdom
Ph: 44 20 77006740
Fax: 44 20 76076411
Publisher E-mail: maxubscriptions@blueyonder.co.uk
Trade magazine for the housewares industry. **Freq:** 10/yr. **Trim Size:** 210 x 297 mm. **Key Personnel:** Ian Hyder, Publishing Dir., ianh@max-publishing.co.uk; Jakki Brown, Mng. Dir./Ed.-in-Ch., jw@max-publishing.co.uk. **Subscription Rates:** 50 individuals; 85 two years; 110 other countries; 75 other countries two years; 125 individuals three years; 165 other countries three years. **Remarks:** Accepts advertising. **URL:** http://www.progressivehousewares.co.uk/. **Ad Rates:** BW: 1,800. **Circ:** Controlled ‡3,500

55140 ■ Promotions & Incentives
Haymarket Business Magazines
174 Hammersmith Rd.
London W6 7JP, United Kingdom

Ph: 44 20 82674210
Publisher E-mail: info@haymarket.com
Magazine featuring promotional marketing. **Founded:** 1991. **Freq:** 10/yr. **Key Personnel:** Bhavna Mistry, Editor, phone 44 20 82674128, bhavna.mistry@haymarket.com; Daniel De'Ath, Advertising Mgr., phone 44 20 82674093, daniel.death@haymarket.com. **Subscription Rates:** 79 individuals; 142 two years. **URL:** http://www.haymarket.com/promotions_and_incentives/promotions_and_incentives_magazine/default.aspx. **Circ:** ★18,000

55141 ■ Property Law Journal
Legalese Ltd.
Kensington Sq. House
12-14 Ansdell St.
London W8 5BN, United Kingdom
Ph: 44 20 73969292
Fax: 44 20 73969303
Professional journal covering property law. **Freq:** 20/yr. **Subscription Rates:** 192 individuals. **URL:** http://www.legalease.co.uk.

55142 ■ Property Week
CMP Information Ltd.
Ludgate House
245 Blackfriars Rd.
London SE1 9UY, United Kingdom
Ph: 44 20 79215000
Publication E-mail: pwhelp@cmpi.biz
Professional magazine covering commercial property. **Founded:** 1982. **Freq:** 49/yr. **Print Method:** Web Offset. **Trim Size:** 302 x 230 mm. **Key Personnel:** Giles Barrie, Editor, phone 44 20 79218561, giles.barrie@ubm.com; James Whitmore, Dep. Ed., phone 44 20 79218565, james.whitmore@ubm.com; Chris Kilbee, Publisher, phone 44 20 79218350, fax 44 20 79218392, chris.kilbee@ubm.com. **ISSN:** 1354-1471. **Subscription Rates:** 175 individuals print and online; 125 individuals online only. **Remarks:** Accepts advertising. **URL:** http://www.propertyweek.com/. **Former name:** Chartered Surveyor Weekly. **Ad Rates:** BW: 3,225. **Circ:** ★27,520

55143 ■ Prospect
Prospect Publishing Ltd.
2 Bloomsbury Pl.
London WC1A 2QA, United Kingdom
Ph: 44 20 72551281
Fax: 44 20 72551279
Publication E-mail: info@prospect-magazine.co.uk; publishing@prospect-magazine.co.uk
Publisher E-mail: letters@prospect-magazine.co.uk
Consumer magazine covering politics and culture. **Subtitle:** Britain's Intelligent Conversation. **Founded:** 1995. **Freq:** Monthly. **Print Method:** Heat web offset. **Trim Size:** A4. **Key Personnel:** David Goodhart, Editor; David Hanger, Ch. Exec./Publisher; Hilly Janes, Managing Editor; Andy Hawkins, Subscription Mgr. **ISSN:** 1359-5024. **Subscription Rates:** US$24 U.S. and Canada online (paypal); 34.80 other countries online (credit card); US$86.28 U.S. and Canada print & online (credit card); 59.50 other countries print & online (paypal). **URL:** http://www.prospectmagazine.co.uk/. **Ad Rates:** BW: 2,000, 4C: 2,300. **Circ:** Controlled ★26,767

55144 ■ Prostate Cancer and Prostatic Diseases
Nature Publishing Group
c/o Nicola Bentham
The Prostate Ctr.
32 Wimpole St.
London W1G 8GT, United Kingdom
Ph: 44 20 74878186
Fax: 44 20 72245706
Publication E-mail: pcan@theprostatecentre.com
Journal dealing with all aspects of prostatic diseases, especially prostate cancer. **Freq:** Quarterly. **Key Personnel:** Stephen J. Freedland, Editor-in-Chief, steve.freedland@duke.edu. **ISSN:** 1365-7852. **Subscription Rates:** US$424 individuals combined print and online; US$383 individuals online only; EUR338 individuals combined print and online; EUR305 individuals online only; 57,700¥ individuals combined print and online; 52,000¥ individuals online only; 217.87 other countries combined print and online; 196.42 other countries online only. **Remarks:** Advertising accepted; rates available upon request. **URL:** http://www.nature.com/pcan/index.html. **Circ:** (Not Reported)

55145 ■ Proteome Science
BioMed Central Ltd.

236 Gray's Inn Rd., Fl. 6
34-42 Cleveland St.
London WC1X 8HL, United Kingdom
Ph: 44 20 31922000
Fax: 44 20 31922010
Publisher E-mail: info@biomedcentral.com
Online journal covering all aspects of functional and structural proteomics. **Key Personnel:** Dr. Martin Latterich, Editor-in-Chief; Dr. Shankar Subramaniam, Assoc. Ed.; Dr. Fred E. Indig, Managing Editor; Prof. Kazuyuki Nakamura, Assoc. Ed.; Dr. Mark Gerstein, Assoc. Ed.; Dr. Beth Baber, Editorial Board. **ISSN:** 1477-5956. **Remarks:** Accepts advertising. **URL:** http://www.proteomesci.com/home/. **Circ:** (Not Reported)

55146 ■ Protestant Truth
Protestant Truth Society Inc.
184 Fleet St.
London EC4A 2HJ, United Kingdom
Ph: 44 20 74054960
Publisher E-mail: info@protestant-truth.org
Official publication of The Protestant Truth Society. **Freq:** Bimonthly. **Subscription Rates:** 5 individuals; 11 out of country. **Remarks:** Advertising not accepted. **URL:** http://protestant-truth.org/magazine/. **Former name:** Churchman's Magazine. **Circ:** Combined 3,030

55147 ■ Prototype
Electronic Design Automation Ltd.
63-66 Hatton Garden
London EC1N 8SR, United Kingdom
Ph: 44 20 76811000
Fax: 44 20 72425124
Publisher E-mail: eda@edaltd.co.uk
Magazine providing productivity solutions for mechanical engineers and designers. **Key Personnel:** Al Dean, Editor, al@edaltd.co.uk. **URL:** http://www.edaltd.co.uk/magdownloads/; http://prototypemagazine.com/index.php?option=com_wrapper&Itemid=18.

55148 ■ PRWeek Magazine
Haymarket Publishing Ltd.
174 Hammersmith Rd.
London W6 7JP, United Kingdom
Ph: 44 20 82674210
Publisher E-mail: info@haymarket.com
Magazine publishing all the latest PR and marketing news. **Founded:** 1984. **Freq:** Weekly. **Key Personnel:** Danny Rogers, Editor, phone 44 20 82674370; Simon Lees, Publisher; Luke Burley, Advertising Dir., phone 44 20 82674607, luke.burley@haymarket.com. **Subscription Rates:** 145 individuals; 261 two years; 348 individuals three years. **URL:** http://www.haymarket.com/pr_week/pr_week_magazine/default.aspx. **Circ:** ★14,818

55149 ■ The Psychiatrist
The Royal College of Psychiatrists
17 Belgrave Sq.
London SW1X 8PG, United Kingdom
Ph: 44 20 72352351
Fax: 44 20 72451231
Publisher E-mail: reception@rcpsych.ac.uk
Peer-reviewed journal covering developments in psychiatric practice and service provision. **Subtitle:** Journal of Psychiatric Practice. **Founded:** 1955. **Freq:** Monthly. **Print Method:** Offset. **Cols./Page:** 5. **Col. Width:** 2 1/16 inches. **Col. Depth:** 13 1/4 inches. **Key Personnel:** Patricia Casey, Editor; David Cottrell, Editorial Board; Dominic Fannon, Editorial Board. **ISSN:** 1758-3209. **Subscription Rates:** 92 individuals U.K. & Europe; print and online; 92 institutions U.K. & Europe; print and online; US$148 individuals U.S. & Canada; print and online; US$148 institutions U.S. & Canada; print and online; 92 individuals elsewhere; print and online; 92 institutions elsewhere; print and online; 8 single issue; US$14 single issue; 79.35 individuals worldwide; online only; 87.40 institutions worldwide; online only. **URL:** http://pb.rcpsych.org/. **Formerly:** Psychiatric Bulletin.

55150 ■ Public Archaeology
Maney Publishing
1 Carlton House Ter.
London SW1Y 5AF, United Kingdom
Ph: 44 20 74517300
Fax: 44 20 74517307
Publisher E-mail: maney@maney.co.uk
Peer-reviewed journal covering archaeological issues relating to politics, ethics, government, social questions,

education, management, economics and philosophy. **Freq:** 4/yr. **Key Personnel:** Tim Schadla-Hall, Editor; Prof. Francis McMahamon, Editor. **ISSN:** 1465-5187. **Subscription Rates:** 54 other countries; US$97 individuals; 178 institutions, other countries; US$328 institutions. **URL:** http://maney.co.uk/index.php/journals/pua/.

55151 ■ Public Finance
Chartered Institute of Public Finance and Accountancy
17-18 Britton St.
London EC1M 5TP, United Kingdom
Ph: 44 20 78806200
Fax: 44 20 73242790
Publisher E-mail: corporate@cipfa.org
Publication covering government and related issues. **Freq:** Weekly. **Key Personnel:** Mike Thatcher, Editor, mike.thatcher@publicfinance.co.uk; Judy Hirst, Dep. Ed., judy.hirst@publicfinance.co.uk; Vivienne Russell, News Ed., vivienne.russell@publicfinance.co.uk. **ISSN:** 1352-9250. **Subscription Rates:** 100 individuals. **Remarks:** Accepts advertising. **URL:** http://www.publicfinance.co.uk/. **Ad Rates:** 4C: 3,465. **Circ:** (Not Reported)

55152 ■ Public Health
Royal Society for Public Health
28 Portland Pl.
London W1B 1DE, United Kingdom
Ph: 44 20 75802731
Fax: 44 20 75806157
Publisher E-mail: marketing@riph.org.uk
Publication covering public health. **Freq:** 12/yr. **Key Personnel:** PHil Mackie, Editor-in-Chief; Fiona Sim, Editor-in-Chief; Caitlyn Donaldson, Managing Editor. **ISSN:** 0033-3506. **Subscription Rates:** EUR522 institutions European countries; 69,600¥ institutions Japan; US$585 institutions, other countries; EUR138 individuals European countries; US$156 other countries; 18,500¥ individuals Japan. **URL:** http://www.rsph.org.uk/en/publications-and-bookshop/public-health/index.cfm.

55153 ■ Public Service Magazine (PSM)
FDA
8 Leake St.
London SE1 7NN, United Kingdom
Ph: 44 20 73431111
Publication E-mail: psm@fda.org.uk
Publisher E-mail: info@fda.org.uk
Trade magazine for those in civil and public service. **Subtitle:** For Decision Makers in Government. **Founded:** Mar. 1998. **Freq:** 5/yr. **Print Method:** Web offset litho. **Key Personnel:** Oliver Rowe, Editor, phone 44 20 74015588, oliver@fda.org.uk; Kay Hender, Staff Writer, phone 44 20 74015589. **Subscription Rates:** 20 individuals; 30 individuals European Union; 40 elsewhere 5 issues; 36 two years; 51 two years European union; 90 two years elsewhere. **Remarks:** Accepts advertising. **URL:** http://www.fda.org.uk/. **Circ:** Combined 10,364

55154 ■ Publications of the English Goethe Society
Maney Publishing
1 Carlton House Ter.
London SW1Y 5AF, United Kingdom
Ph: 44 20 74517300
Fax: 44 20 74517307
Publisher E-mail: maney@maney.co.uk
Journal covering German studies in the United Kingdom. **Freq:** 3/yr. **Key Personnel:** Prof. G.L. Fink, International Advisory Board; Prof. Jane Brown, International Advisory Board; Prof. Katharina Mommsen, International Advisory Board. **ISSN:** 0959-3683. **Subscription Rates:** 148 institutions, other countries; US$287 institutions. **Remarks:** Accepts advertising. **URL:** http://maney.co.uk/index.php/journals/peg/. **Circ:** (Not Reported)

55155 ■ Pulmonary Pharmacology and Therapeutics
Elsevier Science
c/o Prof. C.P. Page, Ed.-in-Ch.
GKT School of Biomedical Sciences
King's College
London WC2R 2LS, United Kingdom
Publisher E-mail: nlinfo-f@elsevier.com
Journal focusing on various aspects of lung pharmacology. Covers major diseases of the lung including asthma, cystic fibrosis, pulmonary circulation, ARDS, carcinoma, bronchitis, emphysema and drug delivery.

Freq: Bimonthly. **Key Personnel:** Prof. C.P. Page, Editor-in-Chief; Dr. M. Cazzola, Exec. Ed. **ISSN:** 1094-5539. **Subscription Rates:** US$265 individuals all countries except Europe and Japan; EUR255 individuals European countries; 27,600¥ individuals; US$858 institutions for all countries except Europe and Japan; EUR965 institutions for European countries; 104,100¥ institutions for European countries. **Remarks:** Accepts advertising. **URL:** http://www.elsevier.com/wps/find/journaldescription.cws_home/622936/description. **Formerly:** Pulmonary Pharmacology. **Circ:** (Not Reported)

55156 ■ Pulse
CMP Information Ltd.
Ludgate House
245 Blackfriars Rd.
London SE1 9UY, United Kingdom
Ph: 44 207 9215000
Publication E-mail: jrobinson@cmpmedica.com
Medical newspaper for general practitioners in the UK. **Founded:** 1959. **Freq:** Weekly. **Trim Size:** 287 x 400 mm. **Col. Width:** 42 millimeters. **Col. Depth:** 377 millimeters. **Key Personnel:** Sue Bound, Contact, phone 44 20 79218116, sbound@cmpmedica.com; Sanjay Chudasama, Contact, phone 44 20 79218128, schudasama@cmpmedica.com; Richard Hoey, Editor, phone 44 20 79218094, richard.hoey@ubm.com. **Subscription Rates:** 225 individuals. **Remarks:** Accepts advertising. **URL:** http://www.pulsetoday.co.uk/. **Ad Rates:** BW: 3,465, 4C: 2,925. **Circ:** Combined 40,269

55157 ■ Punishment & Society
Sage Publications Ltd.
1 Oliver's Yard
55 City Rd.
London EC1Y 1SP, United Kingdom
Ph: 44 20 73248500
Fax: 44 20 73248600
Peer-reviewed journal covering research in punishment, penal institutions and penal control. **Subtitle:** The International Journal of Penology. **Founded:** 1999. **Freq:** Quarterly. **Key Personnel:** Pat Carlen, International Assoc. Editorial Board; Prof. Malcolm M. Feeley, Co-Ed.; Keith A. Bottomley, International Assoc. Editorial Board; Kelly Hannah Moffat, Book Review Ed.; David Garland, Co-Ed.; Prof. Jonathan Simon, International Assoc. Editorial Board; Anthony Bottoms, International Assoc. Editorial Board; Alison Liebling, Editor-in-Chief; Shadd Maruna, Book Review Ed.; Arie Freiberg, International Assoc. Editorial Board. **ISSN:** 1462-4745. **Subscription Rates:** US$857 institutions print & e-access; US$771 institutions e-access; US$840 institutions print only; US$93 individuals print only; US$231 institutions single print; US$30 individuals single print. **Remarks:** Accepts advertising. **URL:** http://www.sagepub.com/journalsProdEditBoards.nav?prodId=Journal200845. **Circ:** (Not Reported)

55158 ■ Puzzle Selection
H. Bauer Publishing
Academic House
24-28 Oval Rd.
London NW1 7DT, United Kingdom
Ph: 44 20 72418000
Fax: 44 20 72418030
Magazine featuring over 100 colorful puzzles. **Freq:** Monthly. **Trim Size:** 185 x 255 mm. **Key Personnel:** Clive Garsin, Gp. Ed.; Spike Figgett, Publishing Dir.; Helen Greenwood, Advertising Mgr. **Subscription Rates:** 19.11 individuals direct debit. **Remarks:** Accepts advertising. **URL:** http://www.bauer.co.uk/puzzle-selection; http://www.puzzlemagazines.co.uk/puzzle-selection. **Circ:** ★93,434

55159 ■ Q News
Q News International
PO Box 4295
London W1A 7YH, United Kingdom
Consumer magazine covering news and issues for British Muslims. **Subtitle:** The Muslim Magazine. **Founded:** Mar. 1992. **Freq:** Monthly. **Trim Size:** 210 x 297 mm. **Cols./Page:** 4. **Col. Width:** 45 millimeters. **Col. Depth:** 245 millimeters. **Key Personnel:** Abdul-Rehman Malik, Contributing Ed., ar@q-news.com; Fuad Nahdi, Publisher, fuad@q-news.com; Fareena Alam, Editor, fareena@q-news.com. **Subscription Rates:** 24 individuals; 20 students; 30 individuals; 44 two years individual; 38 two years student; 55 two years organization. **Remarks:** Accepts advertising. **URL:** http://www.q-news.com/buy-UK.htm. **Circ:** Combined 15,000

55160 ■ Qualitative Research in Organizations and Management
Emerald Group Publishing Ltd.
c/o Dr. Gillian Symon, Ed.
Dept. of Organizational Psychology
Birkbeck College, University of London
Malet St., Bloomsbury
London WC1E 7HX, United Kingdom
Publisher E-mail: emerald@emeraldinsight.com
International journal committed to encouraging and publishing qualitative work from researchers and practitioners within the management and organisational field throughout the world, seeking to provide a forum for qualitative researchers through which they can share their work with others and discuss issues of research practice of particular pertinence to qualitative approaches. **Subtitle:** An International Journal. **Freq:** 3/yr. **Key Personnel:** Prof. Catherine Cassell, Editor, qrom@emeraldinsight.com; Ruth Young, Publisher, ryoung@emeraldinsight.com; Dr. Gillian Symon, Editor, qrom@emeraldinsight.com. **ISSN:** 1746-5648. **URL:** http://www.emeraldinsight.com/products/journals/journals.htm?id=qrom.

55161 ■ Qualitative Research in Psychology
Sage Publications Ltd.
1 Oliver's Yard
55 City Rd.
London EC1Y 1SP, United Kingdom
Ph: 44 20 73248500
Fax: 44 20 73248600
Forum for qualitative researchers in all areas of psychology - cognitive, social, developmental, educational, clinical, health, forensic - as well as for those conducting psychologically-relevant qualitative research in other disciplines. **Freq:** 4/yr. **Key Personnel:** David Giles, Editor; Brendan Gough, Editor; Martin Packer, Editor. **ISSN:** 1478-0887. **Subscription Rates:** 204 institutions print and online; 194 institutions online; 61 individuals print; US$338 institutions print and online; US$322 institutions online; US$101 individuals print; EUR270 institutions print and online; EUR257 institutions online; EUR81 individuals print. **Remarks:** Accepts advertising. **URL:** http://www.sagepub.co.uk/journalsProdDesc.nav?prodId=Journal201835. **Circ:** (Not Reported)

55162 ■ Quality and Safety in Health Care
BMJ Publishing Group
BMA House
Tavistock Sq.
London WC1H 9JR, United Kingdom
Ph: 44 20 73834410
Fax: 44 20 73876400
Publisher E-mail: customerservice.group@bmjgroup.com
Peer-reviewed Journal covering initiatives to improve quality of healthcare with an emphasis on patient safety. **Founded:** 1992. **Freq:** Bimonthly. **Key Personnel:** Christiane Notamarco, Publisher, cnotarmarco@bmjgroup.com; David P. Stevens, Editor-in-Chief, dstevens@aamc.org; Jim Battles, Assoc. Ed., jbattles@ahrq.gov. **ISSN:** 1475-3898. **Subscription Rates:** 179 individuals print and online; EUR242 individuals print and online; US$349 individuals print and online; 79 individuals online; EUR107 individuals online; US$154 individuals online. **URL:** http://qshc.bmj.com/. **Circ:** ‡6,000

55163 ■ Quality World
Chartered Quality Institute
12 Grosvenor Cres.
London SW1X 7EE, United Kingdom
Ph: 44 20 72456722
Fax: 44 20 72456788
Publication E-mail: editorial@thecqi.org
Publisher E-mail: info@thecqi.org
Trade magazine covering quality. **Freq:** Monthly. **Key Personnel:** Amy Holgate, Editor. **Subscription Rates:** 70 individuals; 126 two years; 89 individuals Europe; 158 two years Europe; 107 other countries; 200 two years rest of the world. **Remarks:** Accepts advertising. **URL:** http://www.thecqi.org//Knowledge-Hub/Qualityworld/. **Circ:** Combined 34,000

55164 ■ Quarterly Survey of Advertising Expenditure
World Advertising Research Center
85 Newman St.
London W1T 3EX, United Kingdom
Ph: 44 20 74678100
Fax: 44 20 74678101

Publisher E-mail: enquiries@warc.com
Magazine containing the advertising expenditure figures. **Freq:** Quarterly. **Trim Size:** 210 x 297 mm. **Subscription Rates:** 660 members; 800 nonmembers. **URL:** http://store.warc.com/PrintFormat.aspx?ProductID=48.

55165 ■ Quick-X-words
H. Bauer Publishing
Academic House
24-28 Oval Rd.
London NW1 7DT, United Kingdom
Ph: 44 20 72418000
Fax: 44 20 72418030
Magazine featuring straight, cryptic, and quiz style crosswords. **Freq:** Monthly. **Trim Size:** 185 X 255 mm. **Key Personnel:** Clive Garsin, Gp. Ed.; Spike Figgett, Publishing Dir.; Helen Greenwood, Advertising Mgr. **Remarks:** Accepts advertising. **URL:** http://www.puzzlemagazines.co.uk/quick-x-words. **Circ:** ★64,000

55166 ■ Quintessentially
Luxury Publishing Limited
5 Jubilee Pl.
Chelsea
London SW3 3TD, United Kingdom
Ph: 44 20 75912900
Fax: 44 20 75912929
Publisher E-mail: info@luxurypublishing.com
Magazine featuring arts, culture, academia, travel, fashion, leisure, and lifestyle. **Founded:** Feb. 2004. **Freq:** Quarterly. **Trim Size:** 240 x 355 mm. **Key Personnel:** James Brown, Editor. **Subscription Rates:** Free for members; 28 nonmembers; 35 nonmembers Europe; 48 other countries non-members. **Remarks:** Accepts advertising. **URL:** http://www.luxurypublishing.co.uk/. **Circ:** 25,000

55167 ■ RA Magazine
Royal Academy of Arts
Burlington House
Piccadilly
London W1J 0BD, United Kingdom
Ph: 44 20 73008000
Magazine covering features about exhibitions and current debates in the arts. **Founded:** 1974. **Freq:** Quarterly. **Key Personnel:** Kim Jenner, Contact, phone 44 20 73005658, kim.jenner@royalacademy.org.uk. **Subscription Rates:** 20 individuals UK; 28 other countries. **Remarks:** Accepts advertising. **URL:** http://www.ramagazine.org.uk. **Circ:** (Not Reported)

55168 ■ Race & Class
Sage Publications Ltd.
The Institute of Race Relations
2-6 Leeke St., King's Cross Rd.
London WC1X 9HS, United Kingdom
Scholarly journal covering racism and imperialism worldwide. **Subtitle:** A Journal on Racism, Empire and Globalisation. **Founded:** 1960. **Freq:** Quarterly January - April - July - October. **Trim Size:** 173 x 105 mm. **Key Personnel:** Hazel Waters, Advisory Ed.; A. Sivanandan, Advisory Ed.; Colin Prescod, Editorial Board; Bill Rolston, Editorial Board; Nancy Murray, Editorial Board; Manning Marable, Editorial Board; Jan Carew, Editorial Board; Neil Lazarus, Editorial Board; Victoria Brittain, Editorial Board. **ISSN:** 0306-3968. **Subscription Rates:** US$437 institutions combined (print & e-access); US$481 institutions current volume print & all online content; US$393 institutions e-access; US$437 institutions all online content; US$1,303 institutions e-access; US$428 institutions print only; US$54 individuals combined (print & e-access); US$118 institutions single print; US$18 individuals single print. **Remarks:** Accepts advertising. **URL:** http://www.sagepub.com/journalsProdDesc.nav?prodId=Journal200818. **Circ:** (Not Reported)

55169 ■ Radical Economics
New Economics Foundation
3 Jonathan St.
London SE11 5NH, United Kingdom
Ph: 44 20 78206300
Fax: 44 20 78206301
Publisher E-mail: info@neweconomics.org
Newspaper of the New Economics Foundation. **Freq:** Bimonthly. **URL:** http://www.neweconomics.org.

55170 ■ Radio Times
BBC Worldwide Publishing Ltd.
Media Centre

201 Wood Ln.
London W12 7TQ, United Kingdom
Ph: 44 20 84332000
Fax: 44 20 87490538
Consumer magazine covering radio and television listings in the UK. **Founded:** 1923. **Freq:** Weekly. **Subscription Rates:** 64 individuals; 28 individuals for every 6 months. **URL:** http://www.radiotimes.com. **Circ:** Paid 1,093,850

55171 ■ The Railway Magazine
IPC Media Ltd.
Blue Fin Bldg.
110 Southwark St.
London SE1 0SU, United Kingdom
Ph: 44 203 1485000
Consumer magazine covering railways and transportation. **Founded:** 1897. **Freq:** Monthly. **Key Personnel:** Nick Pigott, Editor, phone 44 20 31484680, nicholas_pigott@ipcmedia.com; Lee Morris, Advertising Mgr., phone 44 20 31482517, lee_morris@ipcmedia.com; Alex Robb, Publishing Dir., phone 44 20 31484320, alex_robb@ipcmedia.com. **Subscription Rates:** 14 individuals 6 monthly direct debit; 64.99 two years; 34.99 individuals. **Remarks:** Accepts advertising. **URL:** http://www.ipcmedia.com/brands/railway/. **Circ:** ★35,100

55172 ■ The Rambler
The Ramblers' Association
2nd Fl., Camelford House
87-90 Albert Embankment
London SE1 7TW, United Kingdom
Ph: 44 20 73398500
Fax: 44 20 73398501
Publication E-mail: ramblers@london.ramblers.org.uk
Publisher E-mail: ramblers@ramblers.org.uk
Membership magazine covering walking, outdoor leisure, and charities. **Freq:** Quarterly. **Print Method:** Web offset litho. **Trim Size:** A4. **Cols./Page:** 4. **Key Personnel:** Bruce Sparrow, Media Mgr., phone 44 20 73398531, bruces@ramblers.org.uk; Ruth Somerville, Contact, phone 44 20 73398532, ruths@ramblers.org.uk. **Subscription Rates:** 118 individuals; 176 individuals. **Remarks:** Accepts advertising. **URL:** http://ramblers.org.uk. **Circ:** Controlled 93,202

55173 ■ Rare Book Review
Countrywide Editions Ltd.
24 Maddox St.
London W1S 1PP, United Kingdom
Fax: 44 20 7409083
Publication E-mail: subs@rarebookreview.com
Trade magazine covering old and rare books. **Founded:** 1974. **Freq:** Monthly 10/yr. **Key Personnel:** Emma Lewis, Web Ed., phone 44 207 5294221, emma@rarebookreview.com; Jeff Hudson, Editor, phone 44 207 5294223, editor@rarebookreview.com. **ISSN:** 0306-1475. **Subscription Rates:** 34 individuals; 42 individuals in Europe; US$78 individuals; 52 other countries. **URL:** http://www.rarebookreview.com. **Former name:** Antiquarian Book Monthly; Antiquarian Book Review. **Ad Rates:** 4C: 950. **Circ:** (Not Reported)

55174 ■ Rationality and Society
Sage Publications Ltd.
1 Oliver's Yard
55 City Rd.
London EC1Y 1SP, United Kingdom
Ph: 44 20 73248500
Fax: 44 20 73248600
Scholarly journal covering rational-action based theory. **Founded:** 1989. **Freq:** Quarterly. **Key Personnel:** Douglas D. Heckathorn, Editor; Elissa Wolfson, Managing Editor; Mary C. Brinton, Assoc. Ed.; Phillip Bonacich, Editorial Board; Gary S. Becker, Assoc. Ed.; James S. Coleman, Founding Ed.; Robert H. Frank, Assoc. Ed.; James Fearon, Editorial Board; Peter Abell, Editorial Board; Raymond Boudon, Editorial Board. **ISSN:** 1043-4631. **Subscription Rates:** US$899 institutions print & e-access; US$989 institutions current volume print & all online content; US$809 institutions e-access; US$899 institutions e-access plus backfile (all online content); US$881 institutions print only; US$117 individuals print only; US$242 institutions print only; US$38 individuals single print. **Remarks:** Accepts advertising. **URL:** http://www.sagepub.com/journalsProdDesc.nav?prodId=Journal200827&. **Circ:** (Not Reported)

55175 ■ RCM Midwives' Journal
T.G. Scott & Son Ltd.
c/o Emma Godfrey, Ed.
Royal College of Midwives
15 Mansfield St.
London W1G 9NH, United Kingdom
Official journal for The Royal College of Midwives. **Freq:** Monthly. **Key Personnel:** Phillip Hemmings, Editor, phone 44 20 73123474; Emma Godfrey, Editor, emma@midwives.co.uk. **ISSN:** 1462-138X. **Remarks:** Accepts advertising. **URL:** http://www.rcm.org.uk; http://www.gamma-y.net/portfolio/midwives/aboutus.htm. **Former name:** Midwives Chronicle. **Circ:** Paid 36,350

55176 ■ Real Business
Caspian Publishing
198 King's Rd.
London SW3 5XP, United Kingdom
Ph: 44 20 73687100
Fax: 44 20 73687201
Publisher E-mail: info@caspianpublishing.co.uk
Professional magazine covering business. **Founded:** Mar. 1997. **Freq:** Monthly 10/yr. **Print Method:** Web. **Trim Size:** 220 x 285 mm. **Key Personnel:** Matthew Rock, Editor-in-Chief, mr1@caspianpublishing.co.uk; Kate Pritchard, Managing Editor, kate@realbusiness.co.uk; Carryn Dewing, Sub-Ed., cd3@caspianpublishing.co.uk. **ISSN:** 1462-3064. **Subscription Rates:** 40 individuals; 50 individuals Europe; 70 individuals zone 1 & 2. **Remarks:** Accepts advertising. **URL:** http://www.realbusiness.co.uk; http://www.caspianpublishing.co.uk/page/realbusiness. **Circ:** Combined 43,000

55177 ■ Record Collector
The Metropolis Group
140 Wales Farm Rd.
London W3 6UG, United Kingdom
Ph: 44 20 87528181
Fax: 44 20 87528185
Publisher E-mail: metropolis@metropolis.co.uk
Magazine featuring rare and collectible music records. **Founded:** 1979. **Freq:** Monthly. **Key Personnel:** Bill Edwards, Advertising Mgr. **Subscription Rates:** 46 individuals; 72 individuals Europe; 72 U.S. and Canada; 86 two years individual; 136 two years Europe; 140 two years U.S. & Canada; 121 individuals 39 issues; 192 individuals 39 issues to Europe; 200 U.S. and Canada for three years w/ 15% discount. **Remarks:** Accepts advertising. **URL:** http://www.recordcollectormag.com/; http://www.metropolis.co.uk/recordcollector.html. **Circ:** (Not Reported)

55178 ■ red pepper
Red Pepper
1B Waterlow Rd.
London N19 5NJ, United Kingdom
Ph: 44 20 72817024
Publisher E-mail: office@redpepper.org.uk
Magazine covering social and political issues. **Founded:** May 1995. **Freq:** Weekly. **Key Personnel:** Hilary Wainwright, Editor; Oscar Reyes, Editor. **Subscription Rates:** 20 individuals; 25 individuals in Europe; 30 individuals rest of the world. **Remarks:** Accepts advertising. **URL:** http://www.redpepper.org.uk/. **Circ:** (Not Reported)

55179 ■ Regeneration & Renewal
Haymarket Business Magazines
174 Hammersmith Rd.
London W6 7JP, United Kingdom
Ph: 44 20 82674210
Publisher E-mail: info@haymarket.com
Magazine featuring news sections on community renewal, economic development and physical regeneration. **Founded:** 2000. **Freq:** Weekly. **Key Personnel:** Richard Garlick, Editorial Dir., phone 44 20 82674440, richard.garlick@haymarket.com; Emily Mackenzie, Assoc. Publisher, phone 44 20 82674870, emily.mackenzie@haymarket.com; Tracy Awere, Sales Mgr., tracy.awere@haymarket.com. **Subscription Rates:** 119 individuals. **Remarks:** Accepts advertising. **URL:** http://www.haymarket.com/regeneration_and_renewal/regeneration_and_renewal_magazine/default.aspx. **Circ:** ★10,238

55180 ■ Regenerative Medicine
Future Medicine Ltd.
Unitec House
2 Albert Pl.
London N3 1QB, United Kingdom

Ph: 44 20 83716080
Fax: 44 20 83432313
Publisher E-mail: info@futuremedicine.com
Journal covering regenerative medicine and stem cell research. **Freq:** Bimonthly. **Key Personnel:** Chris Mason, Sen. Ed.; Robert Lanza, Assoc. Ed.; Phillipe Menasche, Assoc. Ed. **ISSN:** 1746-0751. **URL:** http://www.futuremedicine.com/loi/rme.

55181 ■ Regulatory Affairs Journal
PJB Publications Ltd.
Telephone House
69-77 Paul St.
London EC2A 4LQ, United Kingdom
Ph: 44 20 70175000
Fax: 44 20 70176792
Publisher E-mail: pjb.enquiries@informa.com
Journal covering the regulatory requirements of pharmaceuticals and cosmetics for governments and the pharmaceutical industry worldwide. **Founded:** 1990. **Freq:** Monthly. **Key Personnel:** Maureen Kenny, Editor, maureen.kenny@informa.com; Neena Brizmohun, Dep. Ed.; Karen Finn, Dep. Ed.; Dr. Brian Matthews, Board Member. **ISSN:** 0960-7889. **Subscription Rates:** EUR4,250 individuals; US$5,450 individuals; 4,250 individuals. **Remarks:** Accepts advertising. **URL:** http://www.pjbpubs.com; http://www.rajpharma.com/home/. **Ad Rates:** BW: 380, 4C: 320. **Circ:** Paid 810

55182 ■ Regulatory Affairs Journal (Devices)
PJB Publications Ltd.
Telephone House
69-77 Paul St.
London EC2A 4LQ, United Kingdom
Ph: 44 20 70175000
Fax: 44 20 70176792
Publisher E-mail: pjb.enquiries@informa.com
Journal covering the licensing of medical devices for governments and the device industry worldwide. **Founded:** 1993. **Freq:** Bimonthly. **Trim Size:** A4. **Key Personnel:** Dr. Karen Becker, Editor; Maureen Kenny, Editor. **ISSN:** 0969-4129. **Subscription Rates:** 1,045 individuals U.K. & Europe; US$2,040 U.S. and Canada; 1,045 elsewhere; EUR1,620 individuals. **Remarks:** Accepts advertising. **URL:** http://www.rajdevices.com/home/. **Circ:** (Not Reported)

55183 ■ Reinsurance
Incisive Media Limited
Haymarket House
28-29 Haymarket
London SW1Y 4RX, United Kingdom
Ph: 44 870 2408859
Fax: 44 207 4849797
Publisher E-mail: customerservices@incisivemedia.com
Trade magazine covering new and analysis of the reinsurance industry worldwide. **Founded:** 1969. **Freq:** Monthly. **Key Personnel:** Anthony Gould, Gp. Ed.-in-Ch., phone 44 20 73169374, anthony.gould@incisivemedia.com; Philip Harding, Publisher, phone 44 20 73169393, philip.harding@incisivemedia.com; Ro Osborne, Mktg. Mgr., ro.osborne@incisivemedia.com. **ISSN:** 0048-7171. **Remarks:** Accepts advertising. **URL:** http://www.reinsurancemagazine.com/; http://www.incisivemedia.com. **Ad Rates:** BW: EUR2,900, 4C: EUR4,170. **Circ:** Combined 8,996

55184 ■ Religion
Academic Press
Harcourt Pl.
32 Jamestown Rd.
London NW1 7BY, United Kingdom
Ph: 44 20 74244200
Fax: 44 20 74832293
Publication covering philosophy and religion. **Freq:** Quarterly. **Key Personnel:** M. Stausberg, Editor; S. Engler, Editor. **ISSN:** 0048-721X. **Subscription Rates:** EUR119 individuals European Countries and Iran; US$105 individuals all Countries except Europe and Japan; 12,900¥ individuals; US$395 institutions all Countries except Europe and Japan; 48,100¥ institutions; EUR444 institutions European Countries and Iran. **URL:** http://www.elsevier.com/wps/find/journaldescription.cws_home/622940/descriptiondescription.

55185 ■ Religions of South Asia
Equinox Publishing Ltd.
1 Chelsea Manor Studios
Flood St.
London SW3 5SR, United Kingdom
Ph: 44 20 78233748

Circulation: ★ = ABC; △ = BPA; ♦ = CAC; • = CCAB; ❑ = VAC; ⊕ = PO Statement; ‡ = Publisher's Report; Boldface figures = sworn; Light figures = estimated.

Gale Directory of Publications & Broadcast Media/147th Ed.

5763

Fax: 44 20 78233748
Peer-reviewed journal covering the studies of religions in South Asia. **Freq:** Semiannual. **Key Personnel:** Anna King, Editor, anna.king@winchester.ac.uk; Dermot Killingley, Editor, d.h.killingley@newcastle.ac.uk. **ISSN:** 1751-2689. **Subscription Rates:** 95 institutions, other countries print and online; US$190 institutions print and online; 40 individuals print; US$80 individuals print; 30 students print; US$60 students print. **Remarks:** Accepts advertising. **URL:** http://www.equinoxjournals.com/ojs/index.php/ROSA. **Circ:** (Not Reported)

55186 ■ Religious Studies
Cambridge University Press
c/o Christopher Hamilton, Book Review Ed.
Dept. of Theology & Religious Studies
King's College London Strand
Strand
London WC2R 2LS, United Kingdom
Publisher E-mail: information@cambridge.org
Journal covering philosophy and religion. **Freq:** Irregular. **Key Personnel:** Christopher Hamilton, Book Review Ed., christopher.hamilton@kcl.ac.uk; Prof. P.A. Byrne, Editor, peter.byrne@kcl.ac.uk; Prof. Robin Le Poidevin, Editorial Board; Dr. Jeffrey Jordan, Editorial Board; Prof. David Basinger, Editorial Board; Prof. Peter Forrest, Editorial Board. **ISSN:** 0034-4125. **Subscription Rates:** 213 institutions online and print; US$381 institutions online and print; 192 institutions online only; US$341 institutions online only. **Remarks:** Accepts advertising. **URL:** http://journals.cambridge.org/action/displayJournal?jid=RES. **Ad Rates:** BW: US$875. **Circ:** 1,200

55187 ■ Religious Studies and Theology
Equinox Publishing Ltd.
1 Chelsea Manor Studios
Flood St.
London SW3 5SR, United Kingdom
Ph: 44 20 78233748
Fax: 44 20 78233748
Peer-reviewed journal covering theology and religious studies. **Freq:** Semiannual. **Key Personnel:** Earle Waugh, Editor, earle.waugh@ualberta.ca. **ISSN:** 0829-2922. **Subscription Rates:** 95 institutions, other countries print and online; US$190 institutions print and online; 40 institutions print; 81 institutions, other countries online; 90 institutions, other countries print; 18 individuals print (developing countries); 30 students print; US$60 students print. **Remarks:** Accepts advertising. **URL:** http://www.equinoxjournals.com/ojs/index.php/RST. **Circ:** (Not Reported)

55188 ■ The Reparation Report
REDRESS
87 Vauxhall Walk
London SE11 5HJ, United Kingdom
Ph: 44 20 77931777
Fax: 44 20 77931719
Publisher E-mail: info@redress.org
Journal providing overview of the specialized work of the organization, and current developments in the area of reparation for torture. **Freq:** Semiannual. **URL:** http://www.redress.org/smartweb/home/home.

55189 ■ Report
Association of Teachers and Lecturers
7 Northumberland St.
London WC2N 5RD, United Kingdom
Ph: 44 20 79306441
Fax: 44 20 79301359
Publisher E-mail: info@atl.org.uk
Professional magazine covering education. **Founded:** 1978. **Freq:** Monthly 10/yr. **Key Personnel:** Vic Pocikett, Editor. **ISSN:** 0142-3134. **Subscription Rates:** 16 nonmembers; 19 nonmembers Europe; 28 nonmembers rest of the world. **Remarks:** Advertising accepted; rates available upon request. **URL:** http://www.atl.org.uk/publications-and-resources/report/latest-issue.asp. **Circ:** 160,000

55190 ■ Reproductive Health
BioMed Central Ltd.
236 Gray's Inn Rd., Fl. 6
34-42 Cleveland St.
London WC1X 8HL, United Kingdom
Ph: 44 20 31922000
Fax: 44 20 31922010
Publisher E-mail: info@biomedcentral.com
Online journal covering all aspects of human

reproduction. **Key Personnel:** Dr. Regina Kulier, Editor-in-Chief, regina.kulier@gfmer.ch; Prof. Aldo Campana, Editorial Board, aldo.campana@gfmer.ch; Dr. Jose Guilherme Cecatti, Editor-in-Chief; Prof. Giuseppe Benagiano, Editorial Board, pinoingeneva@freesurf.ch; Prof. Suneeta Mittal, Editorial Board, suneeta_mittal@yahoo.com; Prof. Mario Festin, Editorial Board, mfestinmd@yahoo.com. **ISSN:** 1742-4755. **Remarks:** Accepts advertising. **URL:** http://www.reproductive-health-journal.com/home/. **Circ:** (Not Reported)

55191 ■ The Resident (London)
Archant Life
5th Fl., Avon House
Kensington Village
Avonmore Rd.
London W14 8TS, United Kingdom
Publisher E-mail: anne.basey-fisher@archant.co.uk
Consumer magazine covering local lifestyle. **Freq:** Monthly. **Trim Size:** 210 x 297 mm. **Key Personnel:** Amanda Constance, Editor, phone 44 20 73515776, amanda.constance@archant.co.uk. **Remarks:** Accepts advertising. **URL:** http://theresident.greatbritishlife.co.uk. **Circ:** (Not Reported)

55192 ■ Resource Management & Recovery
Environmental Services Association
154 Buckingham Palace Rd.
London SW1W 9TR, United Kingdom
Ph: 44 20 78248882
Fax: 44 20 78248753
Publisher E-mail: info@esauk.org
Journal providing a commercial perspective on the rapidly developing environmental services in the U.K. **Freq:** Biweekly. **Key Personnel:** Fred Rayner, Contact, f-rayner@esauk.org. **Subscription Rates:** Free to all members. **Remarks:** Accepts advertising. **URL:** http://www.esauk.org/. **Circ:** (Not Reported)

55193 ■ Respiratory Disease in Practice
Hayward Medical Communications
Covent Garden
8-10 Dryden St.
London WC2E 9NA, United Kingdom
Publisher E-mail: admin@hayward.co.uk
Journal covering issues in respiratory disease. **Founded:** 1989. **Key Personnel:** Philip Ind, Editor. **URL:** http://www.rdip.co.uk/rdip/.

55194 ■ Respiratory Research
BioMed Central Ltd.
236 Gray's Inn Rd., Fl. 6
34-42 Cleveland St.
London WC1X 8HL, United Kingdom
Ph: 44 20 31922000
Fax: 44 20 31922010
Publisher E-mail: info@biomedcentral.com
Online journal covering all aspects of respiratory disease. **Key Personnel:** Dr. Jan Lotvall, Editor-in-Chief, jan.lotvall@mednet.gu.se; Dr. Reynold A. Panettieri, Editor-in-Chief; Dr. Kenneth Adler, Assoc. Ed., kenneth_adler@ncsu.edu; Francesco Blasi, Assoc. Ed.; Guy Joos, Assoc. Ed.; Peter J. Sterk, Assoc. Ed. **ISSN:** 1465-9921. **Remarks:** Accepts advertising. **URL:** http://respiratory-research.com/. **Circ:** (Not Reported)

55195 ■ Retail Newsagent
National Federation of Retail Newsagents
Yeoman House
Sekforde St.
London EC1R 0HF, United Kingdom
Ph: 44 20 72534225
Fax: 44 20 72500927
Publisher E-mail: service@nfrnonline.com
Publication covering retailing. **Freq:** Weekly. **Key Personnel:** Lindsay Sharman, Editor. **Remarks:** Advertising accepted; rates available upon request. **URL:** http://www.nfrnonline.com/. **Circ:** (Not Reported)

55196 ■ Retail Systems
Perspective Publishing
3 London Wall Bldgs., 6th Fl.
London EC2M 5PD, United Kingdom
Ph: 44 20 75622400
Fax: 44 20 73742701
Magazine featuring aspects of technology in retail operations in the United Kingdom. **Freq:** 6/yr. **Key Personnel:** Scott Thompson, Editor, scott.thompson@retail-systems.com; Lisa Gayle, Advertising Mgr., lisa.gayle@retail-systems.com; John Woods, Mng. Dir.

Subscription Rates: 98 individuals UK; 140 individuals airmail. **Remarks:** Accepts advertising. **URL:** http://www.retail-systems.com/. **Circ:** ∗13,000

55197 ■ Retirement Planner
Incisive Media Limited
Haymarket House
28-29 Haymarket
London SW1Y 4RX, United Kingdom
Ph: 44 870 2408859
Fax: 44 207 4849797
Publisher E-mail: customerservices@incisivemedia.com
Magazine for the advisers who specialize in retirement planning. **Subtitle:** Industry analysis for the professional adviser. **Freq:** Monthly. **Key Personnel:** Helen Morrissey, Editor, phone 44 20 70342665, helen.morrissey@incisivemedia.com. **URL:** http://www.incisivemedia.com/corporate/retirement-planner; http://www.retirement-planner.co.uk/. **Circ:** 12,000

55198 ■ Retrovirology
BioMed Central Ltd.
236 Gray's Inn Rd., Fl. 6
34-42 Cleveland St.
London WC1X 8HL, United Kingdom
Ph: 44 20 31922000
Fax: 44 20 31922010
Publisher E-mail: info@biomedcentral.com
Online journal covering all aspects of basic research in retrovirology, with special emphasis on human retroviruses. **Key Personnel:** Dr. Kuan-Teh Jeang, Editor-in-Chief, kjeang@niaid.nih.gov; Monsef Benkirane, Assoc. Ed.; Dr. Ben Berkhout, Assoc. Ed.; Andrew Lever, Assoc. Ed.; Mark Wainberg, Assoc. Ed. **ISSN:** 1742-4690. **Remarks:** Accepts advertising. **URL:** http://www.retrovirology.com/. **Circ:** (Not Reported)

55199 ■ Review of Nigeria Affairs
Adonis & Abbey Publishers Ltd.
PO Box 43418
London SE11 4XZ, United Kingdom
Ph: 44 845 3887248
Publisher E-mail: editor@adonis-abbey.com
Journal covering issues in Nigerian politics, economy, and society. **Freq:** Quarterly. **Key Personnel:** Dr. Jideofor Adibe, Editor. **URL:** http://www.adonisandabbey.com/about_journal.php?jid=3.

55200 ■ Reviews in History
Institute of Historical Research
University of London
Senate House
Malet St.
London WC1E 7HU, United Kingdom
Ph: 44 20 78628740
Fax: 44 20 78628745
Publisher E-mail: ihr.reception@sas.ac.uk
Journal publishing reviews and reappraisals of noteworthy work in all fields of historical interest. **Founded:** 1996. **Key Personnel:** Prof. Miles Taylor, Editor; Danny Millum, Dep. Ed., danny.millum@sas.ac.uk; Colin Lewis, Contact, danny.millum@sas.ac.uk; Ben Fortna, Contact; Serena Ferente, Contact; Stephen Baxter, Contact; Laura Gowing, Contact; Angus Lockyer, Contact; Dr. Richard Butterwick, Contact. **ISSN:** 1749-8155. **URL:** http://www.history.ac.uk/reviews/.

55201 ■ Revolution
Haymarket Business Publications Ltd.
174 Hammersmith Rd.
London W6 7JP, United Kingdom
Ph: 44 20 82675000
Fax: 44 20 82674268
Publisher E-mail: hpg@haymarketgroup.com
Professional magazine covering business and marketing in the digital economy for consumers and business professionals. **Founded:** June 1997. **Freq:** 11/yr. **Key Personnel:** Mark Gordon, Advertising Dir., phone 44 20 82674447, mark.gordon@haymarket.com; Gareth Jones, Editor, phone 44 20 82674705, gareth.jones@haymarket.com. **ISSN:** 1460-5953. **Subscription Rates:** 79 individuals; 142 two years; 190 individuals 3 years. **Remarks:** Accepts advertising. **URL:** http://www.brandrepublic.com/revolution; http://www.haymarketbusinesssubs.com. **Circ:** Combined 13,753

55202 ■ Rheumatology
British Society for Rheumatology
Bride House
18-20 Bride Ln.

London EC4Y 8EE, United Kingdom
Ph: 44 20 78420900
Fax: 44 20 78420901
Publication E-mail: editorial@rheumatology.org.uk
Publisher E-mail: bsr@rheumatology.org.uk
Peer-reviewed journal covering rheumatic diseases.
Freq: Monthly. **Key Personnel:** Prof. R.J. Moots, Editor;
S. Ahmed, Managing Editor; K. Wilson, Sen. Editorial
Off. **ISSN:** 1462-0324. **Subscription Rates:** 591 institutions print & online; 514 institutions online only; 561
institutions print only; 739 institutions corporate - print &
online; 643 institutions corporate - online; 702 institutions corporate - print; 591 individuals print only; 99
members European League against Rheumatism, online only; 171 members European League against
Rheumatism, print only. **URL:** http://www.rheumatology.
org.uk/; http://rheumatology.oxfordjournals.org/. **Formerly:** British Journal of Rheumatology. **Ad Rates:** BW:
475, 4C: 1,020. **Circ:** 3,500

55203 ■ Rise
Archant Life
Battersea Studios, Unit F3
80 Silverthorne Rd.
London SW8 3HE, United Kingdom
Ph: 44 20 79783499
Fax: 44 20 79783498
Publisher E-mail: anne.basey-fisher@archant.co.uk
Magazine featuring inspirational stories for the readers.
Freq: Monthly. **Key Personnel:** Grant Elgin, Advertising
Mgr., phone 44 20 79783476, grant.elgin@archant.co.
uk; Jon Watt, Editor, phone 44 20 79783488, jon.watt@
archant.co.uk. **URL:** http://www.archantlife.co.uk/
contact-us-regions-london-rise-contacts--10407; http://
www.risemagazine.co.uk. **Circ:** ★40,000

55204 ■ Risk
Incisive Media Limited
Haymarket House
28-29 Haymarket
London SW1Y 4RX, United Kingdom
Ph: 44 870 2408859
Fax: 44 207 4849797
Publisher E-mail: customerservices@incisivemedia.com
Magazine featuring financial risk management.
Founded: 1987. **Key Personnel:** Nick Sawyer, Editor,
nick.sawyer@incisivemedia.com. **Subscription Rates:**
899 individuals; US$1,891 individuals; EUR1,493 individuals; 1,618 two years; US$775 individuals 6 months;
EUR2,687 two years; 2,292 individuals 3 years; US$4,822
individuals 3 years; EUR3,807 individuals 3 years. **Remarks:** Accepts advertising. **URL:** http://www.risk.net/
risk-magazine. **Circ:** (Not Reported)

55205 ■ Risk and Regulation
London School of Economics and Political Science
Houghton St.
London WC2A 2AE, United Kingdom
Ph: 44 20 74057686
Publication E-mail: risk@lse.ac.uk
Magazine of the ESRC Centre for Analysis of Risk and
Regulation (CARR), including articles by leading
scholars and practitioners. **Freq:** Semiannual. **Key Personnel:** Will Jennings, Editor. **ISSN:** 1473-6004. **URL:**
http://www.lse.ac.uk/resources/
riskandregulationmagazine/.

55206 ■ RMT News
National Union of Rail, Maritime and Transport Workers
Unity House
39 Chalton St.
London NW1 1JD, United Kingdom
Ph: 44 20 73874771
Fax: 44 20 73874123
Publisher E-mail: info@rmt.org.uk
Magazine containing union news and information related
to the transport industry. **Freq:** Monthly. **Key Personnel:** Bob Crow, Gen. Ed.; Brian Denny, Managing Editor.
Remarks: Accepts advertising. **URL:** http://www.rmt.
org.uk/Templates/Internal.asp?NodeID=89783&
int2ndParentNodel. **Circ:** (Not Reported)

55207 ■ Robin Hood Adventures
BBC Worldwide Publishing Ltd.
Media Centre
201 Wood Ln.
London W12 7TQ, United Kingdom
Ph: 44 20 84332000
Fax: 44 20 87490538
Magazine featuring the adventures of Robin Hood. **Freq:**

Biweekly. **Subscription Rates:** 1.99 single issue. **URL:**
http://www.bbcmagazines.com/content/magazines/
robinhoodadventures/.

55208 ■ Roof
Shelter
88 Old St.
London EC1V 9HU, United Kingdom
Fax: 44 20 75052030
Publication E-mail: roof@shelter.org.uk
Publisher E-mail: info@shelter.org.uk
Independent housing policy and practice magazine.
Founded: 1975. **Freq:** Bimonthly. **Trim Size:** 210 x 297
mm. **Cols./Page:** 3. **Key Personnel:** Bill Rashleigh,
Editor, bill_rashleigh@shelter.org.uk; Emma Hawkey,
Managing Editor, emma_hawkey@shelter.org.uk; Kwun
Pang, Advertising Exec., kwun_pang@shelter.org.uk;
Sam Barber, Mktg. Mgr., sam_barber@shelter.org.uk.
ISSN: 0307-6911. **Subscription Rates:** 25 individuals;
69 institutions; 75 other countries. **Remarks:** Accepts
advertising. **URL:** http://www.roofmag.org.uk. **Ad Rates:**
BW: 1,000, 4C: 1,100. **Circ:** Paid 9,000

55209 ■ The Royal Society Yearbook
Royal Society
6-9 Carlton House Ter.
London SW1Y 5AG, United Kingdom
Ph: 44 20 74512500
Fax: 44 20 79302170
Publisher E-mail: info@royalsoc.ac.uk
Journal covering all the Royal Society's workings including valuable research grant schemes plus biographical
notes on every fellow. **Freq:** Annual. **ISSN:** 0080-4673.
Subscription Rates: 34 individuals print. **URL:** http://
royalsocietypublishing.org/site/othertitles/yearbook.
xhtml.

55210 ■ Rugby World
IPC Media Ltd.
Blue Fin Bldg.
110 Southwark St.
London SE1 0SU, United Kingdom
Ph: 44 203 1485000
Magazine focusing on news, views, and in-depth
interviews from all areas of the game rugby. **Subscription Rates:** 64.99 two years; 34.99 individuals. **Remarks:** Accepts advertising. **URL:** http://www.
rugbyworld.com/. **Circ:** (Not Reported)

55211 ■ Ryanair Magazine
Ink Publishing
141-143 Shoreditch High St.
London E1 6JE, United Kingdom
Ph: 44 20 7613 8777
Fax: 44 207 613 8776
In-flight magazine of Ryanair. **Founded:** Mar. 15, 2007.
Freq: Monthly. **Trim Size:** 200 x 260 mm. **Key Personnel:** Ramsay Short, Editor, ramsay.short@ink-publishing.
com; Jeffrey O'Rourke, Ch. Exec.; Dominique Afacan,
Dep. Ed. **Remarks:** Accepts advertising. **URL:** http://
www.ryanairmag.com/. **Circ:** (Not Reported)

55212 ■ SAA
Systematic and Applied Acarology Society
c/o Dr. Anne S Baker, Ed.
Dept. of Entomology
The Natural History Museum
Cromwell Rd.
London SW7 5BD, United Kingdom
Publisher E-mail: tingkui.qin@aqis.gov.au
Peer-reviewed journal containing short papers and
monographs about mites and tricks. **Subtitle:** Special
Publication. **Trim Size:** A4. **Key Personnel:** Dr. Anne S.
Baker, Editor, a.baker@nhm.ac.uk; Dr. Lance A. Durden, Editor, ldurden@gsvms2.cc.gasou.edu; Dr. Zhi-
Qiang Zhang, Editor, zhangz@landcare.cri.nz. **ISSN:**
1461-0183. **Subscription Rates:** US$12 individuals;
US$7.20 members. **URL:** http://www.nhm.ac.uk/hosted_
sites/acarology/saas/saasp.html.

55213 ■ Sabrina's Secrets
GE Fabbri Ltd.
The Communications Bldg., 7th Fl.
48 Leicester Sq.
London WC2H 7LT, United Kingdom
Ph: 44 20 30317600
Fax: 44 20 30317601
Publisher E-mail: mailbox@gefabbri.co.uk
Magazine for girls. **Key Personnel:** Peter Edwards,

Mng. Dir.; Liz Glaze, Director; Katie Preston, Editor-in-
Chief. **Remarks:** Accepts advertising. **URL:** http://www.
gefabbri.co.uk/publication_sabrinassecrets. **Circ:** (Not
Reported)

55214 ■ The Safety & Health Practitioner
CMP Information Ltd.
Ludgate House
245 Blackfriars Rd.
London SE1 9UY, United Kingdom
Ph: 44 20 79215000
Official magazine of the Institution of Occupational
Safety & Health. **Founded:** 1983. **Freq:** Monthly. **Key
Personnel:** Martina Weadick, Editor, phone 44 20
79218047, shpeditor@ubm.com; Andrew Sansom, Dep.
Ed., phone 44 20 79218046; Adrian Newton, Publisher,
phone 44 20 79218546, adrian.newton@ubm.com. **Subscription Rates:** 110 individuals; 132 other countries.
Remarks: Accepts advertising. **URL:** http://www.
shponline.co.uk. **Ad Rates:** BW: 1,500, 4C: 1,830. **Circ:**
Paid ★36,549

55215 ■ Safety Management
British Safety Council
70 Chancellors Rd.
London W6 9RS, United Kingdom
Ph: 44 20 87411231
Fax: 44 20 87414555
Publisher E-mail: mail@britsafe.org
Magazine containing health and safety advice and news.
Freq: Monthly. **Subscription Rates:** 60 nonmembers;
50 nonmembers 2-9 copies; 40 members 2-9 copies; 55
members. **URL:** http://www.britsafe.org/info-publications-
and-resources/publications/safety-management.aspx.

55216 ■ SAGE Race Relations Abstracts
Sage Publications Ltd.
1 Oliver's Yard
55 City Rd.
London EC1Y 1SP, United Kingdom
Ph: 44 20 73248500
Fax: 44 20 73248600
Scholarly journal covering race relations, including
discrimination, education, employment, health, politics,
law and legislation. **Founded:** 1976. **Freq:** Quarterly.
Key Personnel: Louis Kushnick, Editor-in-Chief; David
Gillborn, Editorial Board; James Frideres, Editorial
Board; Kusminder Chahal, Assoc. Ed.; Maxine Baca
Zinn, Editorial Board; Abdul Alkalimat, Editorial Board;
Evelyn Hu De Hart, Editorial Board; Manning Marable,
Editorial Board; Virinder Kalra, Assoc. Ed.; James Jennings, Editorial Board. **ISSN:** 0307-9201. **Remarks:** Accepts advertising. **URL:** http://www.sagepub.com/
journalsProdDesc.nav?prodId=Journal200806. **Circ:**
(Not Reported)

55217 ■ Saline Systems
BioMed Central Ltd.
236 Gray's Inn Rd., Fl. 6
34-42 Cleveland St.
London WC1X 8HL, United Kingdom
Ph: 44 20 31922000
Fax: 44 20 31922010
Publisher E-mail: info@biomedcentral.com
Online journal covering all aspects of basic and applied
research on halophilic organisms and saline
environments. **Key Personnel:** Dr. Shiladitya Dassarma,
Editor-in-Chief, dassarma@umbi.umd.edu; Dr. James S.
Clegg, Assoc. Ed., jsclegg@ucdavis.edu; Dr. Aharon
Oren, Assoc. Ed., orena@shum.cc.huji.ac.il; Dr. Yanhe
Ma, Assoc. Ed.; Dr. Robert Jellison, Assoc. Ed.; Dr. Terry
McGenity, Assoc. Ed. **ISSN:** 1746-1448. **Remarks:** Accepts advertising. **URL:** http://www.salinesystems.org.
Circ: (Not Reported)

55218 ■ Savile Row
Scott Taylor Ltd.
Beacon House
2 Beacon Hill
London N7 9LY, United Kingdom
Ph: 44 20 76095100
Publication E-mail: contact@savilerow-style.com
Consumer magazine covering men's fashion style and
general interest topics. **Freq:** Semiannual. **Print
Method:** Digital Web. **Trim Size:** 210 x 297 mm. **Key
Personnel:** John Taylor, Editor; Marie Scott, Publisher.
Subscription Rates: 14 individuals; 20 out of country.
Remarks: Accepts advertising. **URL:** http://www.

savilerow-style.com/. **Ad Rates:** BW: 2,155, 4C: 3,650. **Circ:** Non-paid 25,000

55219 ■ School Psychology International
Sage Publications Ltd.
1 Oliver's Yard
55 City Rd.
London EC1Y 1SP, United Kingdom
Ph: 44 20 73248500
Fax: 44 20 73248600
Scholarly journal covering issues for professionals in mental health, education, therapy and support services to schools and their communities worldwide. **Subtitle:** Published in Association with ISPA. **Founded:** 1980. **Freq:** Bimonthly. **Key Personnel:** Bruce A. Bracken, Assoc. Ed.; Robert L. Burden, Editor; Caven S. McLoughlin, Editor; Jo Groebel, Assoc. Ed.; Peg Dawson, Assoc. Ed.; H.C.M. Carroll, Assoc. Ed.; Herbert G.W. Bischoff, Assoc. Ed.; Scott E. Huebner, Assoc. Ed.; Thomas Fagan, Assoc. Ed. **ISSN:** 0143-0343. **Subscription Rates:** US$1,513 institutions print & e-access; US$1,664 institutions current volume print & all online content; US$1,362 institutions e-access; US$1,513 institutions e-access, all online content; US$2,200 institutions e-access, content through 1998; US$1,483 institutions print only; US$115 individuals print only; US$272 institutions single print; US$25 individuals single print. **Remarks:** Accepts advertising. **URL:** http://www.sagepub.com/journalsProdDesc.nav?prodId=Journal200800. **Circ:** (Not Reported)

55220 ■ Scouting Magazine
The Scout Association
Gilwell Pk.
Chingford
London E4 7QW, United Kingdom
Ph: 44 20 84337100
Fax: 44 20 84337103
Publisher E-mail: info.centre@scout.org.uk
Magazine covering scouting. **Founded:** 1909. **Freq:** Bimonthly. **Print Method:** Web Offset. **Key Personnel:** Chris James, Contact; Matthew Oakes, Editor; Hilary Galloway, Contact. **ISSN:** 0036-9489. **Remarks:** Advertising accepted; rates available upon request. **URL:** http://www.scouts.org.uk/magazine/. **Circ:** 22,000

55221 ■ Scrip Magazine
PJB Publications Ltd.
Telephone House
69-77 Paul St.
London EC2A 4LQ, United Kingdom
Ph: 44 20 70175000
Fax: 44 20 70176792
Publisher E-mail: pjb.enquiries@informa.com
Professional journal covering trends and analysis on the pharmaceutical industry. **Founded:** 1992. **Freq:** Monthly. **Key Personnel:** Alexandra Shimmings, Editor, phone 44 20701 796954, alex.shimmings@informa.com; John Davis, Managing Editor, john.davis@informa.com; Elizabeth Sukkar, World Ed., phone 44 20701 76945, elizabeth.sukkar@informa.com; Ian Haydock, Asia Ed., ian.haydock@informa.com. **ISSN:** 1353-6303. **Subscription Rates:** 2,415 individuals print and online; EUR3,750 individuals print and online; US$4,850 individuals print and online. **Remarks:** Accepts advertising. **URL:** http://www.scripnews.com/scripnews/home/. **Circ:** Combined 10,061

55222 ■ The Sculpture Journal
Public Monuments and Sculpture Association
70 Cowcross St.
London EC1M 6EJ, United Kingdom
Publisher E-mail: pmsa@btconnect.com
Scholarly journal devoted to sculpture from post-medieval to present day. **Founded:** Sept. 1997. **Freq:** Semiannual. **Key Personnel:** Katharine Eustace, Editor, katharine.eustace@btinternet.com. **ISSN:** 1366-2724. **Subscription Rates:** 85 U.S. and Canada institutions; 40 U.S. and Canada. **URL:** http://www.pmsa.org.uk/.

55223 ■ The Sea
The Mission to Seafarers
St. Michael Paternoster Royal
College Hill
London EC4R 2RL, United Kingdom
Ph: 44 20 72485202
Fax: 44 20 72484761
Publication E-mail: pr@missiontoseafarers.org
Publisher E-mail: pr@missiontoseafarers.org
Newspaper for seafarers. **Founded:** 1974. **Freq:**

Bimonthly. **Key Personnel:** Kathy Baldwin, Contact, phone 44 20 72485202. **Subscription Rates:** 3.50 individuals; US$5 individuals. **Remarks:** Advertising not accepted. **URL:** http://www.missiontoseafarers.org/resources/the-sea. **Circ:** Combined 25,000

55224 ■ Seafarer
Marine Society
202 Lambeth Rd.
London SE1 7JW, United Kingdom
Ph: 44 20 76547000
Fax: 44 20 79288914
Publication E-mail: seafarer@ms-sc.org
Publisher E-mail: info@ms-sc.org
Magazine containing news, articles and stories about seafaring matters. **Freq:** 3/yr. **Subscription Rates:** 8 individuals. **Remarks:** Accepts advertising. **URL:** http://www.ms-sc.org/seafarer-magazine.aspx. **Circ:** 8,500

55225 ■ Seaways
Nautical Institute
202 Lambeth Rd.
London SE1 7LQ, United Kingdom
Ph: 44 207 9281351
Fax: 44 207 4012817
Publisher E-mail: sec@nautinst.org
Publication covering marine interests. **Freq:** Monthly. **Key Personnel:** Claire Walsh, Editor, clairew@nildram.co.uk. **Subscription Rates:** Included in membership. **Remarks:** Accepts advertising. **URL:** http://www.nautinst.org/seaways/. **Ad Rates:** BW: 1,378, 4C: 1,678. **Circ:** 7,500

55226 ■ Security Dialogue
Sage Publications Ltd.
1 Oliver's Yard
55 City Rd.
London EC1Y 1SP, United Kingdom
Ph: 44 20 73248500
Fax: 44 20 73248600
Peer-reviewed journal covering issues in global security for researchers, journalists, the military, civil servants, politicians, and others. **Founded:** 1970. **Freq:** Bimonthly. **Key Personnel:** Mark B. Salter, Assoc. Ed.; Peter J. Burgess, Editor; James Der Derian, Editorial Board; Pinar Bilgin, Assoc. Ed.; Didier Bigo, Editorial Board; David Campbell, Editorial Board; Simon Chesterman, Editorial Board; Claudia Aradau, Assoc. Ed.; Marit Moe-Pryce, Managing Editor. **ISSN:** 0967-0106. **Subscription Rates:** US$1,053 institutions print & e-access; US$1,158 institutions current volume print & all online content; US$948 institutions e-access; US$1,053 institutions e-access plus backfile (all online content); US$2,337 institutions e-access; US$1,032 institutions print only; US$93 individuals print only; US$189 institutions single print; US$20 individuals single print. **Remarks:** Accepts advertising. **URL:** http://www.sagepub.com/journalsProdDesc.nav?prodId=Journal200769. **Circ:** (Not Reported)

55227 ■ Sell-Side Technology
Incisive Media Limited
Haymarket House
28-29 Haymarket
London SW1Y 4RX, United Kingdom
Ph: 44 870 2408859
Fax: 44 207 4849797
Publisher E-mail: customerservices@incisivemedia.com
Magazine featuring information technology. **Freq:** Weekly. **Key Personnel:** Rob Daly, Editor, phone 212457-7781, rob.daly@incisivemedia.com. **Subscription Rates:** 1,195 individuals print; EUR1,793 individuals print; US$1,995 individuals print. **Remarks:** Accepts advertising. **URL:** http://www.waterstechnology.com/sell-side-technology. **Formerly:** Dealing with Technology. **Circ:** (Not Reported)

55228 ■ Semiconductor Science and Technology
Institute of Physics
76 Portland Pl.
London W1B 1NT, United Kingdom
Ph: 44 20 74704800
Fax: 44 20 74704848
Publication E-mail: sst@iop.org
Publisher E-mail: physics@iop.org
Publication covering semiconductor science and technology. **Freq:** Monthly. **Key Personnel:** L. Molenkamp, Editor-in-Chief. **ISSN:** 0268-1242. **Subscription Rates:** US$3,360 institutions North, Central and South

America; 1,724 institutions European Union. **URL:** http://www.iop.org/ej/journal/sst.

55229 ■ Seventeenth-Century French Studies
Maney Publishing
1 Carlton House Ter.
London SW1Y 5AF, United Kingdom
Ph: 44 20 74517300
Fax: 44 20 74517307
Publisher E-mail: maney@maney.co.uk
Peer-reviewed journal covering literary, cultural, historical, and theoretical topics relating to early modern France. **Freq:** Semiannual. **Key Personnel:** Dr. Amy Wygant, Editor, a.wygant@french.arts.gla.ac.uk. **ISSN:** 0265-1068. **Subscription Rates:** 98 institutions, other countries; US$186 institutions. **Remarks:** Accepts advertising. **URL:** http://maney.co.uk/index.php/journals/sfs/. **Ad Rates:** BW: 180. **Circ:** (Not Reported)

55230 ■ Sex Education
Routledge
Taylor & Francis Group Ltd.
Institute of Education
University of London
20 Bedford Way
London WC1H 0AL, United Kingdom
Publisher E-mail: webmaster.books@tandf.co.uk
Peer-reviewed journal concerned both with the practice of sex education and with the thinking that underpins it, welcoming contributions from within a variety of academic disciplines: particularly health education, sociology philosophy and psychology. **Subtitle:** Sexuality, Society and Learning. **Freq:** 4/yr. **Key Personnel:** Michael Reiss, Editor, m.reiss@ioe.ac.uk; Ron Morris, Editorial Board; Peter Aggleton, Editorial Board; Simon Blake, Editorial Board; Juliette Goldman, Editorial Board; Gary Dowsett, Editorial Board; Ana Amuchastegui, Editorial Board; Mary Crewe, Editorial Board; Nicole Stone, Review Ed. **ISSN:** 1468-1811. **Subscription Rates:** 277 institutions print + online; US$456 institutions print + online; 264 institutions online; US$434 institutions online; 92 individuals print only; US$151 individuals print only; EUR363 institutions print and online; EUR345 institutions online only; EUR121 individuals. **Remarks:** Accepts advertising. **URL:** http://www.tandf.co.uk/journals/titles/14681811.asp. **Circ:** (Not Reported)

55231 ■ Sexually Transmitted Infections
BMJ Publishing Group Ltd.
BMA House
Tavistock Sq.
London WC1H 9JR, United Kingdom
Ph: 44 20 73874410
Fax: 44 20 73836400
Publication E-mail: sti@bmjgroup.com
Peer-reviewed Journal covering issues of sexual health and medicine. **Founded:** 1925. **Freq:** 7/yr. **Key Personnel:** Jackie A. Cassell, Editor, editor.sti@bmjgroup.com; David Lewis, Dep. Ed., davidl@nicd.ac.za. **ISSN:** 1368-4973. **Subscription Rates:** 148 institutions print and online; EUR200 institutions print and online; US$289 institutions print and online; 74 institutions online only; EUR100 institutions online only; US$144 institutions online only. **Remarks:** Accepts advertising. **URL:** http://sti.bmj.com/. **Circ:** 1,780

55232 ■ SHARES
MSM Media Ltd.
Thames House
18 Park St.
London SE1 9ER, United Kingdom
Ph: 44 20 73781605
Publisher E-mail: editorial@shares.msm.co.uk
Magazine covering information on private investments. **Founded:** 1999. **Freq:** Weekly (Thurs.). **Remarks:** Accepts advertising. **URL:** http://www.sharesmagazine.com/. **Circ:** (Not Reported)

55233 ■ Ship & Boat International
RINA—The Royal Institute of Naval Architects
10 Upper Belgrave St.
London SW1X 8BQ, United Kingdom
Ph: 44 20 72354622
Fax: 44 20 72595912
Publisher E-mail: hq@rina.org.uk
Professional journal covering the small crafts and fast ferry industry for designers, shipowners/operators and shipbuilders worldwide. **Freq:** Bimonthly. **Print Method:** Offset Litho. **Trim Size:** 210 x 297 mm. **Key Personnel:** Angela Velasco, Editor. **ISSN:** 0037-3834. **Subscription Rates:** 95 individuals UK; 100 individuals Europe; 115

other countries. **Remarks:** Accepts advertising. **URL:** http://www.rina.org.uk/sbi.html. **Circ:** Combined ★5,998

55234 ■ Ship Repair & Conversion Technology
RINA—The Royal Institute of Naval Architects
10 Upper Belgrave St.
London SW1X 8BQ, United Kingdom
Ph: 44 20 72354622
Fax: 44 20 72595912
Publisher E-mail: hq@rina.org.uk
Journal of The Royal Institution of Naval Architects covering ship repair and conversion technology. **Freq:** Quarterly. **Print Method:** Offset Litho. **Trim Size:** 210 x 297 mm. **Key Personnel:** Clive Woodbridge, Editor; Nick Savvides, Managing Editor. **ISSN:** 0969-0174. **Subscription Rates:** 52 individuals in UK; 58 individuals in Europe; 64 other countries; 92 two years; 100 two years; 110 two years. **Remarks:** Accepts advertising. **URL:** http://www.rina.org.uk/srct.html. **Circ:** Combined 6,096

55235 ■ Shout Magazine
D C Thomson & Company Ltd.
185 Fleet St.
London EC4A 2HS, United Kingdom
Ph: 44 20 74001030
Fax: 44 20 78319440
Magazine containing articles about fashion, beauty, celebrities, and growing up for girls between 12 and 16. **Freq:** Bimonthly. **Subscription Rates:** 55 individuals U.K.; 30 individuals 6 months. **URL:** http://www.shoutmag.co.uk/.

55236 ■ Shrek's Quests
GE Fabbri Ltd.
The Communications Bldg., 7th Fl.
48 Leicester Sq.
London WC2H 7LT, United Kingdom
Ph: 44 20 30317600
Fax: 44 20 30317601
Publisher E-mail: mailbox@gefabbri.co.uk
Magazine featuring Shrek and his friends adventures. **Freq:** Semimonthly. **Key Personnel:** Peter Edwards, Mng. Dir.; Liz Glaze, Director; Katie Preston, Editor-in-Chief. **Subscription Rates:** 2 single issue. **URL:** http://www.shreksquests.com/.

55237 ■ Sidewalk
Factory Media
1 W Smithfield
London EC1A 9JU, United Kingdom
Ph: 44 20 73329700
Publisher E-mail: contact@factorymedia.com
Magazine featuring skateboarding. **Freq:** Monthly. **Subscription Rates:** 35.99 individuals credit card; 29.99 individuals direct debit; US$86 individuals credit card. **URL:** http://sidewalkmag.com/; http://factorymedia.com.

55238 ■ Sightline
Association of British Theatre Technicians
55 Farringdon Rd.
London EC1M 3JB, United Kingdom
Ph: 44 20 72429200
Fax: 44 20 72429303
Publisher E-mail: info@abtt.org.uk
Publication covering theater. **Freq:** Quarterly. **Key Personnel:** Ken Bennett-Hunter, Editor. **Subscription Rates:** 590.75 individuals. **Remarks:** Accepts advertising through Entertainment Technology Press. **URL:** http://www.etnow.com/sightline/; http://www.abtt.org.uk/. **Former name:** ABTT Update. **Circ:** (Not Reported)

55239 ■ Significant Ships
RINA—The Royal Institute of Naval Architects
10 Upper Belgrave St.
London SW1X 8BQ, United Kingdom
Ph: 44 20 72354622
Fax: 44 20 72595912
Publisher E-mail: hq@rina.org.uk
Trade magazine covering commercial ship design and shipbuilding worldwide for the marine industry. **Freq:** Annual. **Print Method:** Offset Litho. **Trim Size:** 210 x 297 mm. **Key Personnel:** Nick Savvides, Editor. **Remarks:** Accepts advertising. **URL:** http://www.rina.org.uk/sigships.html. **Circ:** Combined 4,000

55240 ■ Simon Star
The Simon Community
129 Malden Rd.
89-93 Fonthill Rd.
London NW5 4HS, United Kingdom

Ph: 44 20 74856639
Publisher E-mail: info@simoncommunity.org.uk
Community newspaper. **Subtitle:** Living and Working with London's Street Homeless. **Freq:** Quarterly. **Key Personnel:** Joanna Pankhurst, Proj. Worker. **Subscription Rates:** Free. **Remarks:** Advertising not accepted. **URL:** http://www.simoncommunity.org.uk/documents/simon-star-winter-2006.pdf. **Circ:** Non-paid 5,600

55241 ■ Slavonic and East European Review
Modern Humanities Research Association
1 Carlton House Ter.
London SW1Y 5AF, United Kingdom
Publisher E-mail: mail@mhra.org.uk
Regional focus/area studies publication. **Founded:** 1922. **Freq:** Quarterly. **Key Personnel:** Dr. M. Rady, Contact, m.rady@ssees.ac.uk; Dr. Robin P. Aizlewood, Director, r.aizlewood@ssees.ucl.ac.uk. **ISSN:** 0037-6795. **URL:** http://www.ssees.ucl.ac.uk; http://www.ingentaconnect.com/content/mhra/see/.

55242 ■ Slavonica
Maney Publishing
1 Carlton House Ter.
London SW1Y 5AF, United Kingdom
Ph: 44 20 74517300
Fax: 44 20 74517307
Publisher E-mail: maney@maney.co.uk
Peer-reviewed journal covering fields of Russian, Central, and East European studies. **Founded:** 1983. **Freq:** Semiannual. **Key Personnel:** Jekaterina Young, Editor, katya.young@manchester.ac.uk. **ISSN:** 1361-7427. **Subscription Rates:** 34 other countries; US$62 individuals; 144 institutions, other countries; US$262 institutions. **Remarks:** Accepts advertising. **URL:** http://maney.co.uk/index.php/journals/sla/. **Ad Rates:** BW: 180. **Circ:** 200

55243 ■ Slovo
Maney Publishing
1 Carlton House Ter.
London SW1Y 5AF, United Kingdom
Ph: 44 20 74517300
Fax: 44 20 74517307
Publisher E-mail: maney@maney.co.uk
Peer-reviewed journal covering Russian, Eastern and Central European, and Eurasian affairs. **Freq:** Semiannual. **Key Personnel:** Yuliya Fruman, Gen. Ed.; Donna Boniface, Gen. Ed.; Henna Haavisto, Gen. Ed.; Juan Saucedo, Gen. Ed.; Luo Xi, Gen. Ed.; William Wheeler, Gen. Ed. **ISSN:** 0954-6839. **Subscription Rates:** 30 other countries; US$54 other countries; 116 other countries; US$220 institutions. **Remarks:** Accepts advertising. **URL:** http://maney.co.uk/index.php/journals/slv/. **Ad Rates:** BW: 120. **Circ:** (Not Reported)

55244 ■ Soaplife
IPC tx
Blue Fin Bldg.
110 Southwark St.
London SE1 0SU, United Kingdom
Ph: 44 20 31485000
Magazine targeting soap fans with gossip, interviews, story-lines, pull-out posters, puzzles and competitions giving everything needed to know about the nation's best loved TV programmes. **Freq:** Fortnightly. **Key Personnel:** Richard Smith, Advertising Mgr., richard_smith@ipcmedia.com; Sandy Gale, Publishing Dir., sandy_gale@ipcmedia.com; Hellen Gardner, Editor, phone 44 20 31485515, hellen_gardner@ipcmedia.com. **Subscription Rates:** 6.99 individuals 3 months; 54.99 two years; 29.99 individuals. **Remarks:** Accepts advertising. **URL:** http://www.ipcmedia.com/magazines/soaplife/. **Circ:** (Not Reported)

55245 ■ Social Compass
Sage Publications Ltd.
1 Oliver's Yard
55 City Rd.
London EC1Y 1SP, United Kingdom
Ph: 44 20 73248500
Fax: 44 20 73248600
Peer-reviewed journal covering sociology of religion for scholars I sociology, anthropology, religious studies and theology. **Subtitle:** Revue Internationale de Sociologie de la Religion/International Review of Sociology of Religion. **Founded:** 1954. **Freq:** Quarterly. **Key Personnel:** Kevin J. Christiano, Editorial Board; Eila Helander,

Editorial Board; Otto Maduro, Editorial Board; James A. Beckford, Editorial Board; Celine Polain, Editor; Irena Borowik, Editorial Board. **ISSN:** 0037-7686. **Subscription Rates:** US$579 institutions combined (print & e-access); US$521 institutions e-access; US$567 institutions print; US$93 individuals print; US$156 institutions single print; US$30 individuals single print; US$637 institutions current volume print & all online content; US$579 institutions all online content; US$1,993 institutions content through 1998. **Remarks:** Accepts advertising. **URL:** http://www.sagepub.com/journalsProdManSub.nav?prodId=Journal200920. **Circ:** (Not Reported)

55246 ■ Social & Legal Studies
Sage Publications Ltd.
1 Oliver's Yard
55 City Rd.
London EC1Y 1SP, United Kingdom
Ph: 44 20 73248500
Fax: 44 20 73248600
Scholarly journal covering socio-legal studies. **Subtitle:** An International Journal. **Founded:** 1992. **Freq:** Quarterly. **Trim Size:** 114 x 185 mm. **Key Personnel:** David Cowan, Editor; Linda Mulcahy, Assoc. Ed.; Sol Picciotto, Editor; Emilios Christodoulidis, Dialogue/Debate Ed.; David Campbell, Editor. **ISSN:** 0964-6639. **Subscription Rates:** 52 individuals print only; 471 institutions print & e-access; 518 institutions current volume print & all online content; 424 institutions e-access; 471 institutions online access; 408 institutions e-access; 462 institutions print only; 17 individuals single print; 127 institutions single print. **Remarks:** Accepts advertising. **URL:** http://www.sagepub.co.uk/journalsProdDesc.nav?prodId=Journal200832. **Circ:** Paid 800

55247 ■ Social Science Information
Sage Publications Ltd.
1 Oliver's Yard
55 City Rd.
London EC1Y 1SP, United Kingdom
Ph: 44 20 73248500
Fax: 44 20 73248600
Scholarly journal covering research in social anthropology, sociology of science, social psychology and sociological theory in English and French. **Subtitle:** Information sur les Sciences Sociales. **Founded:** 1962. **Freq:** Quarterly. **Key Personnel:** Clemens Heller, Founding Dir.; Maurice Aymard, International Advisory Committee; Maurice Godelier, International Advisory Committee; Roger D. Masters, International Advisory Committee; Terry Shinn, International Advisory Committee; Anne Rocha Perazzo, Editor-in-Chief; Nora Scott, Collaborating Ed.; Luc Boltanski, International Advisory Committee; Giovanni Gasparini, International Advisory Committee; Jean Copans, International Advisory Committee. **ISSN:** 0539-0184. **Subscription Rates:** US$853 institutions print & e-access; US$938 institutions current volume print & all online content; US$768 institutions e-access; US$853 institutions e-access plus backfile (all online content); US$2,415 institutions e-access; US$836 institutions print only; US$122 individuals print only; US$230 institutions single print; US$40 individuals single print. **Remarks:** Accepts advertising. **URL:** http://www.sagepub.com/journalsProdDesc.nav?prodId=Journal200955&currTree=Subjects&level1=200. **Circ:** (Not Reported)

55248 ■ Social Studies of Science
Sage Publications Ltd.
1 Oliver's Yard
55 City Rd.
London EC1Y 1SP, United Kingdom
Ph: 44 20 73248500
Fax: 44 20 73248600
Peer-reviewed journal covering the relationship between science and society. **Subtitle:** An International Review of Research in the Social Dimensions of Science and Technology. **Founded:** 1971. **Freq:** Bimonthly February - April - June - August - October - December. **Trim Size:** A5. **Key Personnel:** Aryn Martin, Reviews Ed.; Stephen Turner, Collaborating Ed.; Michael Lynch, Editor; Sergio Sismondo, Collaborating Ed.; Lucy Suchman, Collaborating Ed.; Roy MacLeod, Founding Ed.; Terry Shinn, Editorial Adviser; Steven Yearley, Editorial Adviser; Paul Wouters, Editorial Adviser. **ISSN:** 0306-3127. **Subscription Rates:** US$1,504 institutions print

Circulation: ★ = ABC; △ = BPA; ◆ = CAC; • = CCAB; ❑ = VAC; ⊕ = PO Statement; ‡ = Publisher's Report; Boldface figures = sworn; Light figures = estimated.

Gale Directory of Publications & Broadcast Media/147th Ed. 5767

& e-access; US$1,654 institutions current volume print & all online content; US$1,354 institutions e-access; US$1,504 institutions e-access, all online content; US$3,223 institutions e-access; US$1,474 institutions print only; US$122 individuals print only; US$270 institutions single print; US$26 individuals single print. **Remarks:** Accepts advertising. **URL:** http://www.sagepub.com/journalsProdDesc.nav?prodId=Journal200907. **Circ:** 1,100

55249 ■ Social Theory & Health
Palgrave Macmillan
Centre for Behavioral & Social Sciences in Medicine
Division of Medicine, University College London
Charles Bell House
67-73 Riding House St.
London W1W 7EJ, United Kingdom
Publication E-mail: rejusth@ucl.ac.uk
Publisher E-mail: booksellers@palgrave.com
Journal covering health issues. **Freq:** Quarterly. **Key Personnel:** Graham Scambler, Editor; Paul Higgs, Editor; Richard Levinson, Editor. **ISSN:** 1477-8211. **Subscription Rates:** 406 institutions, other countries print; US$755 institutions print; 58 other countries print and online; US$108 individuals print and online. **URL:** http://www.palgrave-journals.com/sth/index.html.

55250 ■ Socialist Review
Duke University Press
PO Box 42184
London SW8 2WD, United Kingdom
Ph: 44 207 8191176
Publication E-mail: editor@socialistreview.org.uk
Publisher E-mail: orders@dukeupress.edu
Political journal. **Freq:** Monthly. **Key Personnel:** Judith Orr, Editor. **Subscription Rates:** 30 individuals U.K.; 39 individuals Europe; 46 other countries. **URL:** http://www.socialistreview.org.uk/.

55251 ■ Socialist Standard
The Socialist Party of Great Britain
52 Clapham High St.
London SW4 7UN, United Kingdom
Ph: 44 20 76223811
Publisher E-mail: spgb@worldsocialism.org
Political journal. **Founded:** 1904. **Freq:** Monthly. **ISSN:** 0037-8259. **Subscription Rates:** 15 individuals; 10 individuals low income/unwaged; 20 other countries; 25 elsewhere rest of world. **Remarks:** Advertising not accepted. **URL:** http://www.worldsocialism.org/journals.php. **Circ:** (Not Reported)

55252 ■ Society of Fellows Journal
Chartered Insurance Institute
42-48 High Rd.
S Woodford
London E18 2JP, United Kingdom
Ph: 44 20 89898464
Fax: 44 20 85303052
Publisher E-mail: customer.serv@cii.co.uk
Journal of the Chartered Insurance Institute. **Freq:** Semiannual. **URL:** http://www.cii.co.uk/knowledge/jsof/.

55253 ■ Sociolinguistic Studies
Equinox Publishing Ltd.
1 Chelsea Manor Studios
Flood St.
London SW3 5SR, United Kingdom
Ph: 44 20 78233748
Fax: 44 20 78233748
Peer-reviewed journal covering sociolinguistic research and issues. **Founded:** 2000. **Freq:** 3/yr (April, August, December). **Key Personnel:** Fernando Ramallo, Editor, framallo@uvigo.es; Xoan Paulo Rodriguez-Yanez, Editor, xoanp@uvigo.es. **ISSN:** 1750-8649. **Subscription Rates:** 140 institutions, other countries print and online; US$280 institutions print and online; 40 institutions print (developing countries); 53 individuals print; US$90 individuals print; 119 institutions, other countries online; 33.75 students print; US$67.50 students print; US$266 institutions print. **Remarks:** Accepts advertising. **URL:** http://www.equinoxjournals.com/ojs/index.php/SS. **Circ:** (Not Reported)

55254 ■ Sociology Review
Philip Allan Updates
338 Euston Rd.
London NW1 3BH, United Kingdom
Ph: 44 20 78736000

Fax: 44 20 78736299
Publication covering sociology and social work. **Freq:** Quarterly. **Key Personnel:** Tony Lawson, Examinations Ed.; John Williams, Managing Editor; Joan Garrod, Editor. **ISSN:** 0959-8499. **Subscription Rates:** 15 students; 29.95 institutions. **Remarks:** Advertising not accepted. **URL:** http://www.philipallan.co.uk; http://www.philipallan.co.uk/sociologyreview/index.htm. **Circ:** (Not Reported)

55255 ■ Songlines
PO Box 54209
London W14 0WU, United Kingdom
Ph: 44 20 73712777
Fax: 44 20 73712220
Publisher E-mail: info@songlines.co.uk
Consumer magazine covering world music. **Subtitle:** The World Music Magazine. **Freq:** Bimonthly. **Key Personnel:** Ed Stocker, Asst. Ed.; Nasim Masoud, Subscription Mgr., subs@songlines.co.uk; Simon Broughton, Editor-in-Chief, editor@songlines.co.uk; Paul Geoghegan, Publisher, paul@songlines.co.uk. **Subscription Rates:** 29.75 individuals U.K. (8 issues); EUR39 individuals Europe and Ireland (8 issues); 44 other countries 8 issues; EUR65 individuals U.K (16 issues); 88 other countries 16 issues; 72 individuals Europe and Ireland (16 issues); US$141 other countries 16 issues; EUR79 individuals Europe and Ireland (16 issues); US$70 other countries 8 issues; US$58 individuals Europe and Ireland (8 issues). **Remarks:** Accepts advertising. **URL:** http://www.songlines.co.uk/. **Ad Rates:** BW: 1,118, 4C: 1,480. **Circ:** (Not Reported)

55256 ■ Sound Projector
The Sound Projector
c/o Ed Pinsent, Ed.
BM Bemused
London WC1N 3XX, United Kingdom
Publisher E-mail: ed@soundprojector.demon.co.uk
Consumer magazine covering music. **Key Personnel:** Jonathan Hellier, Contact; Harley Richardson, Contact; Rik Rawling, Contact; Ed Pinsent, Editor, ed@soundprojector.demon.co.uk; Chris Atton, Contact; Ian Nagoski, Contact. **Subscription Rates:** 1 individuals; 2 individuals; 4 other countries. **URL:** http://www.thesoundprojector.com. **Ad Rates:** BW: 190. **Circ:** (Not Reported)

55257 ■ South East Asia Research
IP Publishing Ltd.
c/o Dr. Rachel Harrison, Ed.
Dept. of Languages & Cultures of South East Asia
SOAS, Thornhaugh St.
Russell Sq.
London WC1H 0XG, United Kingdom
Publisher E-mail: jedmondson@ippublishing.com
Journal covering South East Asian studies, including archaeology, art history, economics, geography, history, language, literature, music, political science and religion. **Founded:** 1993. **Freq:** Quarterly. **Key Personnel:** Prof. Peter Boomgaard, Editorial Advisory Board; Dr. Rachel Harrison, Editor, rh6@soas.ac.uk; Prof. Anne Booth, Editorial Advisory Board; Prof. Benedict J. Kerkvliet, Editorial Advisory Board. **ISSN:** 0967-828X. **Subscription Rates:** US$261 institutions; EUR249 institutions; 169 institutions, other countries; EUR87 individuals; 59 individuals. **Remarks:** Accepts advertising. **URL:** http://www.ippublishing.com/sear.htm. **Circ:** (Not Reported)

55258 ■ South East Europe Monitor
Business Monitor International Ltd.
Mermaid House
2 Puddle Dock
London EC4V 3DS, United Kingdom
Ph: 44 20 72480468
Fax: 44 20 72480467
Publisher E-mail: subs@businessmonitor.com
Journal with country-by-country analyses, hard-to-find data, and authoritative 24-month forecasts covering government, economy, finance and the business environment. **Freq:** Monthly. **Subscription Rates:** US$765 individuals print and electronic; 480 individuals print and electronic; EUR570 individuals print and electronic; US$1,170 individuals for 2 months subscription; 690 individuals; EUR920 individuals; US$1,395 individuals; 870 individuals; EUR1,095 individuals. **URL:** http://www.emergingeuropemonitor.com/file/7560/southeasteurope.asp.

55259 ■ Spaceflight
British Interplanetary Society
27-29 S Lambeth Rd.
London SW8 1SZ, United Kingdom

Ph: 44 20 77353160
Fax: 44 20 78201504
Publisher E-mail: mail@bis-spaceflight.com
Technical publication covering events and developments in space exploration, astronauts, space technology, astronomy, current space events and space events worldwide. **Founded:** 1956. **Freq:** Monthly. **Print Method:** Offset litho. **Key Personnel:** C. Simpson, Editor. **Subscription Rates:** 48 individuals; 2.50 single issue. **Remarks:** Accepts advertising. **URL:** http://www.bis-spaceflight.com/sitesia.aspx/page/147/node/108/l/en-us. **Circ:** (Not Reported)

55260 ■ Span
London City Mission
175 Tower Bridge Rd.
London SE1 2AH, United Kingdom
Ph: 44 20 74077585
Fax: 44 20 74036711
Publication covering the work of the Mission in London. **Subtitle:** London City Mission Magazine. **Founded:** 1836. **Freq:** Bimonthly. **Trim Size:** A4. **Key Personnel:** David Linley, Contact; Debbie Breakspear, Editor. **Remarks:** Advertising not accepted. **URL:** http://www.lcm.org.uk/Groups/9969/London_City_Mission/About_Us/Magazine/Magazine.aspx. **Circ:** Non-paid 35,000

55261 ■ SPE Review
McQuillan Young Communications
1 Sekforde St.
Clerkenwell
London EC1R 0BE, United Kingdom
Ph: 44 20 72536450
Fax: 44 20 72536455
Publisher E-mail: info@mcquillanyoung.co.uk
Membership publication of the Society of Petroleum Engineers in London and Aberdeen. **Subtitle:** Magazine of the Aberdeen and London Sections of the Society of Petroleum Engineers. **Founded:** 1995. **Freq:** Monthly. **Print Method:** Litho. **Trim Size:** 210 x 297 mm. **Key Personnel:** Kate McMillan, Contact, katespe@aol.com. **Remarks:** Accepts advertising. **URL:** http://www.spe-uk.org. **Circ:** Controlled 8,500

55262 ■ Spirit & Destiny
H. Bauer Publishing
Academic House
24-28 Oval Rd.
London NW1 7DT, United Kingdom
Ph: 44 20 72418000
Fax: 44 20 72418030
Magazine for women featuring astrology and psychic matters and enlightening ideas on holistic therapies and alternative lifestyles. **Founded:** Sept. 2002. **Freq:** Monthly. **Print Method:** Heatset web offset. **Trim Size:** 225 x 285 mm. **Key Personnel:** Rhiannon Powell, Editor; Helen Greenwood, Regional Advisory; Helen Lowe, Assoc. Publisher. **Subscription Rates:** 24.78 individuals direct debit. **Remarks:** Accepts advertising. **URL:** http://www.bauer.co.uk/spirit-and-destiny; http://www.spiritanddestiny.co.uk. **Circ:** ★61,537

55263 ■ Sporting Gun
IPC Media Ltd.
Blue Fin Bldg.
110 Southwark St.
London SE1 0SU, United Kingdom
Ph: 44 203 1485000
Magazine focusing on clay, game and rough shooting. **Freq:** Monthly. **Key Personnel:** Andrew Horton, Syndication & Licensing; Jonathan Davitt, Advertising Mgr.; Fiona Mercer, Publisher; Hamish Dawson, Publishing Dir.; Robin Scott, Editor, robin_scott@ipcmedia.com. **Subscription Rates:** 13.99 individuals 6 monthly direct debit; 54.99 two years; 29.99 individuals. **URL:** http://www.ipcmedia.com/brands/sportinggun.

55264 ■ Statistical Modelling
Sage Publications Ltd.
1 Oliver's Yard
55 City Rd.
London EC1Y 1SP, United Kingdom
Ph: 44 20 73248500
Fax: 44 20 73248600
Journal containing articles from leading researchers and practitioners in fields as varied as economics, psychology, medicine and statistics. **Subtitle:** An International Journal. **Freq:** Quarterly. **Key Personnel:** John Hinde, Advisory Board; Herwig Friedl, Editor; Brian Marx, Editor; Jeffrey Simonoff, Editor. **ISSN:** 1471-082X. **Sub-**

scription **Rates:** 373 institutions combined (print & e-access); 336 institutions e-access; 366 institutions print only; 101 individuals combined (print & e-access); 101 institutions single print; 33 individuals single print. **Remarks:** Accepts advertising. **URL:** http://www.sagepub.co.uk/journalsProdDesc.nav?prodId=Journal201837. **Circ:** (Not Reported)

55265 ■ Strategy
Strategic Planning Society
Mayfair House
14-18 Heddon St.
London W1B 4DA, United Kingdom
Ph: 44 845 0563663
Fax: 44 845 0563663
Publisher E-mail: membership@sps.org.uk
Management publication. **Freq:** Quarterly. **Trim Size:** A4. **Subscription Rates:** Free single copy; Included in membership. **URL:** http://www.sps.org.uk/strategy_magazine.php. **Ad Rates:** 4C: EUR1,500. **Circ:** 15,000

55266 ■ Stroke News
Redactive Media Group
17-18 Britton St.
London EC1M 5TP, United Kingdom
Ph: 44 20 78806200
Fax: 44 20 78807691
Publisher E-mail: info@redactive.co.uk
Magazine focusing on stroke management. **Freq:** Quarterly. **Key Personnel:** Aaron Nicholls, Contact; Averil Mansfield, Vice President. **URL:** http://www.stroke.org.uk/information/stroke_news/index.html. **Circ:** ‡70,000

55267 ■ Structured Products
Incisive Media Limited
Haymarket House
28-29 Haymarket
London SW1Y 4RX, United Kingdom
Ph: 44 870 2408859
Fax: 44 207 4849797
Publisher E-mail: customerservices@incisivemedia.com
Magazine featuring wholesale marketing for derivatives-based investment products. **Subtitle:** Intelligence On Derivatives-Based Investments. **Freq:** 11/yr. **Key Personnel:** Richard Jory, Editor; Joanna Russell, Publisher. **Subscription Rates:** 755 individuals; US$1,435 individuals; EUR1,133 individuals; 1,359 two years; US$2,583 two years; EUR2,039 two years; 1,925 individuals 3 years; US$3,659 individuals 3 years; EUR2,889 individuals 3 years. **Remarks:** Accepts advertising. **URL:** http://www.structuredproductsonline.com. **Circ:** (Not Reported)

55268 ■ Student BMJ
BMJ Publishing Group Ltd.
BMA House
Tavistock Sq.
London WC1H 9JR, United Kingdom
Ph: 44 20 73874410
Fax: 44 20 73836400
British based, international student medical journal. **Founded:** 1995. **Freq:** Monthly. **Key Personnel:** Giselle Jones, Sen. Ed., phone 44 20 73836285, fax 44 20 73836418; Hugh Ip, Editor. **ISSN:** 0966-6494. **Subscription Rates:** 45 individuals; US$88 individuals; EUR61 individuals; 145 institutions; US$283 institutions; EUR196 institutions. **Remarks:** Accepts advertising. **URL:** http://student.bmj.com/student/student-bmj.html. **Circ:** (Not Reported)

55269 ■ Student Law Review
Cavendish Publishing Ltd.
The Glass House
Wharton St.
London WC1X 9PX, United Kingdom
Publication E-mail: info@pacecms.co.uk
Scholarly journal covering law for students. **Founded:** Apr. 7, 1994. **Freq:** 3/yr. **Trim Size:** 297 x 210 mm. **Key Personnel:** Fiona Kinnear, Gen. Ed. **ISSN:** 0961-0391. **Subscription Rates:** 16.50 individuals; 22 other countries overseas; 39.50 individuals 3 years; 49.50 other countries. **URL:** http://www.routledgelaw.com/journals/slr. **Circ:** Non-paid 37,000

55270 ■ Student Times
Talent Media
The Maltings, Studio 65/66
169 Tower Bridge Rd.
London SE1 3LJ, United Kingdom
Newspaper covering the main stories happening

amongst the student population as well as young people's awareness of wider national and global issues. **Freq:** Biweekly. **Key Personnel:** Ian Thomas, Publisher; Charles Whitworth, Editor; David Ruiz, International Ed. **Subscription Rates:** Free. **Remarks:** Accepts advertising. **URL:** http://www.studenttimes.org/. **Circ:** Free 200,000

55271 ■ Studies in Conservation
James and James/Earthscan
Dunstan House
14a St., Cross St.
London EC1N 8XA, United Kingdom
Ph: 44 20 78411930
Fax: 44 20 72421474
Publisher E-mail: earthinfo@earthscan.co.uk
Journal featuring the latest advances, techniques and practice in conservation and restoration from around the world. **Founded:** 1952. **Freq:** Quarterly. **Key Personnel:** Prof. Alan Phenix, Editor-in-Chief; Rene De La Rie, Editor. **ISSN:** 0039-3630. **Subscription Rates:** 170 institutions print; EUR225 institutions print; US$340 institutions print; 170 institutions, other countries print; 179 institutions UK & rest of the world; EUR225 institutions subcription Europe; US$340 institutions subcription North America. **URL:** http://www.earthscan.co.uk/?tabid=504.

55272 ■ Studies in Conservation
International Institute for Conservation of Historic and Artistic Works
6 Buckingham St.
London WC2N 6BA, United Kingdom
Ph: 44 20 78395975
Fax: 44 20 79761564
Publication E-mail: reviews@iiconservation.org
Publisher E-mail: iic@iiconservation.org
Journal devoted to the literature of conservation, with each article providing comprehensive coverage of the publications within a particular conservation discipline, including (but not limited to) conservation treatments, materials, scientific research, technical art history, analytical techniques, historiography of conservation, training and ethics. **Freq:** Annual. **Key Personnel:** Marika Spring, Editor; Fi Jordan, Editor. **URL:** http://www.iiconservation.org/publications/ric/ric.php. **Merged with:** Reviews in Conservation.

55273 ■ Studies in Ethnicity and Nationalism
Association for the Study of Ethnicity and Nationalism
Dept. of Government
London School of Economics
Houghton St.
London WC2A 2AE, United Kingdom
Ph: 44 20 79556801
Fax: 44 20 79556218
Publication E-mail: sen@lse.ac.uk
Publisher E-mail: asen@lse.ac.uk
Journal containing information on publications, conferences, public lectures and courses in the areas of ethnicity and nationalism, both in the UK and abroad. **Freq:** Semiannual. **Key Personnel:** Ulrike Ehret, Editor; Danielle Hemple, Editor; Carrie Heitmeyer, Editor. **URL:** http://www.lse.ac.uk/collections/ASEN.

55274 ■ Su-doku
H. Bauer Publishing
Academic House
24-28 Oval Rd.
London NW1 7DT, United Kingdom
Ph: 44 20 72418000
Fax: 44 20 72418030
Magazine containing su-doku puzzles. **Freq:** Monthly. **Subscription Rates:** 21.39 individuals. **URL:** http://www.bauer.co.uk/su-doku; http://www.puzzlemagazines.co.uk.

55275 ■ Su-doku Selection
H. Bauer Publishing
Academic House
24-28 Oval Rd.
London NW1 7DT, United Kingdom
Ph: 44 20 72418000
Fax: 44 20 72418030
Magazine featuring more than 80 su-doku puzzles. **Freq:** Monthly. **Trim Size:** 148 x 210 mm. **Key Personnel:** Clive Garsin, Gp. Ed.; Spike Figgett, Publishing Dir.; Helen Greenwood, Advertising Mgr. **Subscription Rates:** 20.93 individuals direct debit. **Remarks:** Accepts

advertising. **URL:** http://www.bauer.co.uk/su-doku-selection. **Circ:** *67,000

55276 ■ Summit
Think Publishing
The Pal Mall Deposit
124-128 Barlby Rd.
London W10 6BL, United Kingdom
Ph: 44 20 89623020
Fax: 44 20 89628689
Publisher E-mail: watchdog@thinkpublishing.co.uk
Magazine for business travellers. **Freq:** Semiannual. **Trim Size:** 225 x 297 mm. **Key Personnel:** Ian McAuliffe, Director, ian@thinkpublishing.co.uk; Tilly Boulter, Ch. Exec., tilly@thinkpublishing.co.uk; Polly Arnold, Mng. Dir., pollya@thinkpublishing.co.uk. **Subscription Rates:** Free Summit Hotels & Resorts guests. **Remarks:** Accepts advertising. **URL:** http://www.thinkpublishing.co.uk/mag_summit.html. **Circ:** Combined 29,949

55277 ■ The Sun Journal
The Sun Newspapers
1 Virginia St.
London E98 1SN, United Kingdom
Ph: 44 20 77824000
Publication E-mail: production@sunnews.org
Publisher E-mail: corporate.info@the-sun.co.uk
Community newspaper. **Founded:** 1966. **Freq:** Weekly (Thurs.). **Print Method:** Offset. **Cols./Page:** 5. **Col. Width:** 26 nonpareils. **Col. Depth:** 224 agate lines. **Key Personnel:** Randy Foster, Managing Editor; Scott Embry, Advertising Dir. **Subscription Rates:** 133.50 individuals home delivery; online print; 93 individuals weekend; home delivery; 300 by mail online; print edition. **Remarks:** Accepts advertising. **URL:** http://www.newbernsj.com/. **Formerly:** The Huntington Harbour Journal (1992). **Ad Rates:** GLR: 1.58, BW: 960, 4C: 1,300, PCI: 14.10. **Circ:** Free 32,000, Paid 50

55278 ■ Superconductor Science and Technology
Institute of Physics
76 Portland Pl.
London W1B 1NT, United Kingdom
Ph: 44 20 74704800
Fax: 44 20 74704848
Publication E-mail: subs@aip.org
Publisher E-mail: physics@iop.org
Publication covering superconductor science and technology. **Freq:** Monthly. **Key Personnel:** D.P. Hampshire, Editor-in-Chief; X. Xi, Advisory Board; K. Marken, Advisory Board; A. Ustinov, Advisory Board; W. Goldacker, Exec. Board; C. Park, Advisory Board; S. Awaji, Advisory Board; S.B. Roy, Advisory Board; K. Amm, Advisory Board. **ISSN:** 0953-2048. **Subscription Rates:** US$1,515 institutions North, Central and South America; US$766 individuals North, Central and South America; 772 institutions European Union; 389 individuals European Union. **URL:** http://www.iop.org/ej/journal/sust.

55279 ■ Supply Management
Redactive Media Group
17-18 Britton St.
London EC1M 5TP, United Kingdom
Ph: 44 20 78806200
Fax: 44 20 78807691
Publisher E-mail: info@redactive.co.uk
Magazine featuring articles for purchasing and supply professionals. **Freq:** Biweekly. **Key Personnel:** Steve Bagshaw, Editor; Rebecca Ellinor, Dep. Ed. **Subscription Rates:** 110 individuals. **Remarks:** Accepts advertising. **URL:** http://www.supplymanagement.com. **Circ:** ‡35,000

55280 ■ Surf Europe
Factory Media
1 W Smithfield
London EC1A 9JU, United Kingdom
Ph: 44 20 73329700
Publisher E-mail: contact@factorymedia.com
Magazine featuring surfing. **Founded:** 1999. **Freq:** 8/yr. **Key Personnel:** Georgina Sherman, Contact, georgina@surfeuropemag.com. **Subscription Rates:** 23.99 individuals credit card; 20.99 individuals direct debit; US$60 individuals credit card. **Remarks:** Accepts advertising. **URL:** http://surfeuropemag.com/; http://factorymedia.com. **Circ:** (Not Reported)

Circulation: ★ = ABC; △ = BPA; ♦ = CAC; • = CCAB; ❑ = VAC; ⊕ = PO Statement; ‡ = Publisher's Report; Boldface figures = sworn; Light figures = estimated.

55281 ■ Surface Engineering
Maney Publishing
1 Carlton House Ter.
London SW1Y 5AF, United Kingdom
Ph: 44 20 74517300
Fax: 44 20 74517307
Publisher E-mail: maney@maney.co.uk
Peer-reviewed journal covering any aspect of the use of surface engineering. **Freq:** 8/yr. **Key Personnel:** Dr. T.S. Sudarshan, Editor, sudarshan@matmod.com; Prof. Pei-Xin Qiao, China Ed. **ISSN:** 0267-0844. **Subscription Rates:** 1,015 institutions, other countries; US$1,770 institutions; 450 members other countries; 801 members. **Remarks:** Accepts advertising. **URL:** http://maney.co.uk/index.php/journals/sur/. **Ad Rates:** BW: 500, 4C: 1,100. **Circ:** (Not Reported)

55282 ■ The Surfer's Path
Factory Media
1 W Smithfield
London EC1A 9JU, United Kingdom
Ph: 44 20 73329700
Publisher E-mail: contact@factorymedia.com
Magazine featuring characters and stories in surfing and traveling. **Freq:** Bimonthly. **Key Personnel:** Alex Dick-Read, Founding Ed., phone 44 20 73329700, fax 44 20 73329799, alex@surferspath.com; Oli Tappin, Advertising Mgr., phone 44 20 78860680, fax 44 20 78860690, oliver.tappin@factorymedia.com. **Subscription Rates:** 23.99 individuals direct debit; 26.95 individuals credit card; US$45 individuals; US$90 two years. **URL:** http://surferspath.com/; http://factorymedia.com.

55283 ■ Survival
Routledge
Taylor & Francis Group Ltd.
IISS
Arundel House
13-15 Arundel St.
Temple Place
London WC2R 3DX, United Kingdom
Ph: 44 20 73797676
Fax: 44 20 78363108
Publisher E-mail: webmaster.books@tandf.co.uk
Journal covering strategic and international studies, including military and security issues worldwide. **Freq:** Bimonthly. **Key Personnel:** Dr. Dana Allin, Editor; Dr. Jeffrey Mazo, Asst. Ed.; Steven Simon, Contributing Ed. **ISSN:** 0039-6338. **Subscription Rates:** 314 institutions print + online; 298 institutions online only; 93 individuals print only; US$551 institutions print + online; US$524 institutions online only; US$159 individuals print only; EUR461 institutions print and online; EUR438 institutions online only; EUR127 individuals. **Remarks:** Accepts advertising. **URL:** http://www.tandf.co.uk/journals/titles/00396338.asp. **Ad Rates:** BW: 260. **Circ:** (Not Reported)

55284 ■ Systematic Parasitology
Springer Netherlands
Dept. of Zoology
The Natural History Museum
London, United Kingdom
Publisher E-mail: permissions.dordrecht@springer.com
Journal covering illustrated research papers, brief communications, and fully illustrated major revisions based on science, technology and medicine. **Founded:** Sept. 1947. **Freq:** 3/yr. **Print Method:** Offset. **Trim Size:** 8 1/2 x 11. **Cols./Page:** 3. **Col. Width:** 27 nonpareils. **Col. Depth:** 133 agate lines. **Key Personnel:** D.I. Gibson, Editor-in-Chief; G.A. Boxshall, Co-Ed.; D. Hunt, Co-Ed.; J. Caira, Co-Ed.; T.H. Cribb, Co-Ed.; A. Jones, Co-Ed.; G.C. Kearn, Co-Ed.; I. Beveridge, Co-Ed.; B.B. Georgiev, Co-Ed.; R.A. Bray, Co-Ed. **ISSN:** 0165-5752. **Subscription Rates:** EUR1,558 institutions print incl. free access or e-only; EUR1,869.60 institutions print incl. enhanced access. **URL:** http://www.springer.com/lifesci/zoology/journal/11230.

55285 ■ The Tablet
Tablet Publishing Company Ltd.
1 King St. Cloisters
Clifton Walk
London W6 0QZ, United Kingdom
Ph: 44 20 87488484
Fax: 44 20 87481550
Publication E-mail: thetablet@thetablet.co.uk
Publisher E-mail: thetablet@thetablet.co.uk
Consumer magazine covering religion, politics, social issues, literature and the arts from a Christian perspective. **Founded:** 1840. **Freq:** Weekly. **Print Method:** Web

Offset. **Trim Size:** 267 x 186 mm. **Cols./Page:** 3. **Col. Width:** 60 millimeters. **Col. Depth:** 267 millimeters. **Key Personnel:** Ignatius Kusiak, Publisher, ikusiak@thetablet.co.uk; Elena Curti, Dep. Ed., ecurti@thetablet.co.uk; Catherine Pepinster, Editor; Clifford Longley, Editorial Consultant; James Roberts, Asst. Ed. **ISSN:** 0039-8837. **Subscription Rates:** 75 individuals U.K.; 108 individuals ROI & Europe; EUR120 individuals ROI & Europe; 90 individuals airmail Worldwide; US$170 individuals airmail Worldwide; US$130.08 U.S. and Canada. **Remarks:** Accepts advertising. **URL:** http://www.thetablet.co.uk. **Ad Rates:** BW: US$1,094, 4C: US$1,370. **Circ:** Paid 22,738

55286 ■ Take a Break
H. Bauer Publishing
Academic House
24-28 Oval Rd.
London NW1 7DT, United Kingdom
Ph: 44 20 72418000
Fax: 44 20 72418030
Magazine for women featuring health, relationships, fashion, beauty and household tips, puzzles, and competitions offering cash prizes. **Founded:** Mar. 1990. **Freq:** Weekly. **Trim Size:** 225 x 285 mm. **Key Personnel:** John Dale, Editor; Andy Brooks, Publishing Dir.; Lisa Carver, Advertising Mgr., phone 44 20 70750783, fax 44 20 70750786, lisa.carver@bauer.co.uk. **Subscription Rates:** 80 individuals. **Remarks:** Accepts advertising. **URL:** http://www.bauer.co.uk/takeabreak. **Circ:** *855,372

55287 ■ Take a Break's Su-doku
H. Bauer Publishing
Academic House
24-28 Oval Rd.
London NW1 7DT, United Kingdom
Ph: 44 20 72418000
Fax: 44 20 72418030
Magazine containing su-doku puzzles. **Freq:** Monthly. **Trim Size:** 148 x 210 mm. **Key Personnel:** Clive Garsin, Gp. Ed.; Spike Figgett, Publishing Dir.; Helen Greenwood, Advertising Mgr. **Subscription Rates:** 1.70 single issue. **Remarks:** Accepts advertising. **URL:** http://www.bauer.co.uk/puzzle-magazines; http://www.puzzlemagazines.co.uk/Su-doku-Selection. **Circ:** *100,000

55288 ■ Take a Crossword
H. Bauer Publishing
Academic House
24-28 Oval Rd,
London NW1 7DT, United Kingdom
Ph: 44 20 72418000
Fax: 44 20 72418030
Magazine featuring crossword puzzles. **Freq:** Monthly. **Trim Size:** 220 x 290 mm. **Key Personnel:** Clive Garsin, Gp. Ed.; Spike Figgett, Publishing Dir.; Helen Greenwood, Advertising Mgr. **Subscription Rates:** 17.29 individuals direct debit. **Remarks:** Accepts advertising. **URL:** http://www.puzzlemagazines.co.uk/takeacrossword; http://www.bauer.co.uk/take-a-crossword. **Circ:** *133,604

55289 ■ Take a Puzzle
H. Bauer Publishing
Academic House
24-28 Oval Rd.
London NW1 7DT, United Kingdom
Ph: 44 20 72418000
Fax: 44 20 72418030
Magazine featuring crosswords, codebreakers and logic puzzles. **Freq:** Monthly. **Trim Size:** 220 x 290 mm. **Key Personnel:** Clive Garsin, Gp. Ed.; Spike Figgett, Publishing Dir.; Helen Greenwood, Advertising Mgr. **Subscription Rates:** 17.75 individuals direct debit. **Remarks:** Accepts advertising. **URL:** http://www.puzzlemagazines.co.uk/takeapuzzle; http://www.bauer.co.uk/take-a-puzzle. **Circ:** *107,264

55290 ■ Talk
National Deaf Children's Society
15 Dufferin St.
London EC1Y 8UR, United Kingdom
Ph: 44 20 74908656
Fax: 44 20 72515020
Publisher E-mail: ndcs@ndcs.org.uk
Magazine aiming to help families of deaf children and professionals working with them. **Freq:** Bimonthly. **ISSN:** 0049-2906. **Subscription Rates:** Included in membership. **Remarks:** Accepts advertising. **URL:** http://

www.ndcs.org.uk/. **Circ:** Paid 13,500

55291 ■ Talking Sense
Sense
101 Pentonville Rd.
London N1 9LG, United Kingdom
Ph: 44 845 1270060
Fax: 44 845 1270061
Publisher E-mail: info@sense.org.uk
Publication covering the hearing impaired. **Freq:** 3/yr. **Subscription Rates:** 12.50 members; 15 nonmembers. **Remarks:** Advertising accepted; rates available upon request. **URL:** http://www.sense.org.uk/publicationslibrary/allpubs/talking_sense/magazine. **Circ:** 5,000

55292 ■ T'ang Studies
Maney Publishing
1 Carlton House Ter.
London SW1Y 5AF, United Kingdom
Ph: 44 20 74517300
Fax: 44 20 74517307
Publisher E-mail: maney@maney.co.uk
Peer-reviewed journal of the T'ang Studies Society, publishing articles on all aspects of Tang China. **Founded:** 1982. **Freq:** Annual. **Key Personnel:** Ding Xiang Warner, Editor, dxw2@cornell.edu. **ISSN:** 0737-5034. **Subscription Rates:** 105 institutions, other countries; US$200 institutions; US$98 institutions, other countries online only; US$186 institutions online only. **Remarks:** Accepts advertising. **URL:** http://maney.co.uk/index.php/journals/tng. **Circ:** (Not Reported)

55293 ■ Teaching History
Historical Association
59 A Kennington Park Rd.
London SE11 4JH, United Kingdom
Ph: 44 20 77353901
Fax: 44 20 75824989
Publisher E-mail: enquiry@history.org.uk
Journal for teachers of secondary history. **Freq:** Quarterly. **Key Personnel:** Tony McConnell, Editor; Madeline Stiles, Publisher, mstiles@history.org.uk. **ISSN:** 0040-0610. **Subscription Rates:** 72 members corporate; 110 nonmembers corporate. **URL:** http://www.history.org.uk/about/index.php?id=43. **Ad Rates:** BW: 395, 4C: 495. **Circ:** (Not Reported)

55294 ■ Technical Review Middle East
Alain Charles Publishing Ltd.
University House
11-13 Lower Grosvenor Pl.
London SW1W 0EX, United Kingdom
Ph: 44 20 78347676
Fax: 44 20 79730076
Publication E-mail: post@alaincharles.com
Publisher E-mail: post@alaincharles.com
Magazine covering technical and business information about the Middle East. **Freq:** Bimonthly. **Print Method:** Sheetfed Offset. **Trim Size:** 210 x 276 mm. **ISSN:** 0267-5307. **Remarks:** Accepts advertising. **URL:** http://www.alaincharles.com/index.php?option=com_content&view=article&id=53&Itemid=70. **Ad Rates:** BW: US$4,400, 4C: US$6,470. **Circ:** *12,017

55295 ■ Technoetic Arts
Intellect
Russell Square House
10-12 Russell Sq.
London WC1B 5EE, United Kingdom
Ph: 44 20 73312000
Fax: 44 20 73312040
Publisher E-mail: info@intellectuk.org
Journal presenting the cutting edge of ideas, projects and practices arising from the confluence of art, science, technology and consciousness research. **Subtitle:** A Journal of Speculative Research. **Founded:** 2003. **Freq:** 3/yr. **Trim Size:** 174 x 244 mm. **Key Personnel:** Annick Bureaud, Editorial Advisory Board; Roy Ascott, Editor, roy.ascott@btinternet.com; James K. Gimzewski, Editorial Advisory Board; Oron Catts, Editorial Advisory Board; Marcos Novak, Editorial Advisory Board; Pierre Levy, Editorial Advisory Board. **ISSN:** 1477-965X. **Subscription Rates:** 33 individuals print; 210 institutions print and online; 12 single issue print; 177 institutions online. **Remarks:** Accepts advertising. **URL:** http://www.intellectbooks.co.uk/journals/view-Journal,id=142/. **Ad Rates:** BW: 100. **Circ:** (Not Reported)

55296 ■ Tel Aviv
Maney Publishing
1 Carlton House Ter.
London SW1Y 5AF, United Kingdom
Ph: 44 20 74517300
Fax: 44 20 74517307
Publisher E-mail: maney@maney.co.uk
Peer-reviewed journal covering archeological investigations including the history and culture of Near Eastern civilizations. **Subtitle:** Journal of the Institute of Archaeology of Tel Aviv University. **Freq:** Semiannual. **Key Personnel:** Prof. Israel Finkelstein, Editor, fink2@post.tau.ac.il; Prof. Benjamin Sass, Editor, sass@post.tau.ac.il. **ISSN:** 0334-4355. **Subscription Rates:** 136 institutions, other countries; US$222 institutions; 30 other countries; US$72 individuals; 38 individuals in UK and European. **Remarks:** Accepts advertising. **URL:** http://maney.co.uk/index.php/journals/tav. **Circ:** (Not Reported)

55297 ■ Telecommunications Heritage Group Journal
Telecommunications Heritage Group
Dalton House
60 Windsor Ave.
London SW19 2RR, United Kingdom
Ph: 44 20 80991699
Journal covering telecommunications history. **Founded:** Jan. 1987. **Freq:** Quarterly. **ISSN:** 0909-238X. **Subscription Rates:** Included in membership. **Remarks:** Advertising accepted; rates available upon request. **URL:** http://www.thg.org.uk/. **Circ:** 450

55298 ■ Teletubbies
BBC Worldwide Publishing Ltd.
Media Centre
201 Wood Ln.
London W12 7TQ, United Kingdom
Ph: 44 20 84332000
Fax: 44 20 87490538
Magazine featuring learning activities for children over 18 months. **Subtitle:** Look, play and do with the Teletubbies. **Freq:** Monthly. **Subscription Rates:** 2.50 single issue. **URL:** http://www.bbcmagazines.com/content/magazines/teletubbies/.

55299 ■ TenGoal
Luxury Publishing Limited
5 Jubilee Pl.
Chelsea
London SW3 3TD, United Kingdom
Ph: 44 20 75912900
Fax: 44 20 75912929
Publisher E-mail: info@luxurypublishing.com
Magazine covering sport of polo and the polo lifestyle. **Founded:** Mar. 2007. **Freq:** Semiannual. **Trim Size:** 204 x 275 mm. **Remarks:** Accepts advertising. **URL:** http://www.luxurypublishing.co.uk/. **Ad Rates:** 4C: 5,495. **Circ:** 7,000

55300 ■ Terrae Incognitae
Maney Publishing
1 Carlton House Ter.
London SW1Y 5AF, United Kingdom
Ph: 44 20 74517300
Fax: 44 20 74517307
Publisher E-mail: maney@maney.co.uk
Peer-reviewed journal covering the history of geographic exploration and cross-cultural interaction around the world and its effects. **Subtitle:** The Journal for the History of Discoveries. **Freq:** Annual. **Key Personnel:** Marguerite Ragnow, Editor, ragn0001@umn.edu; David Buisseret, Book Reviews Ed., buisser@uta.edu. **ISSN:** 0082-2884. **Subscription Rates:** 146 institutions, other countries; US$231 institutions; 136 institutions, other countries online only; US$216 institutions online only. **Remarks:** Accepts advertising. **URL:** http://maney.co.uk/index.php/journals/tin. **Circ:** (Not Reported)

55301 ■ Textile History
Maney Publishing
1 Carlton House Ter.
London SW1Y 5AF, United Kingdom
Ph: 44 20 74517300
Fax: 44 20 74517307
Publisher E-mail: maney@maney.co.uk
Peer-reviewed journal covering high-quality research and discussion in all aspects of scholarship in the field of history of textiles and dress, in connection with Pa-

sold Research Fund. **Freq:** Semiannual Spring and Autumn. **Trim Size:** 135 x 190 mm. **Key Personnel:** Mary M. Brooks, Editor, le.miller@vam.ac.uk; Dr. Katrina Honeyman, Editor, k.honeyman@leeds.ac.uk. **ISSN:** 0040-4969. **Subscription Rates:** 29 other countries; US$52 individuals; 104 institutions, other countries; US$198 institutions. **Remarks:** Accepts advertising. **URL:** http://maney.co.uk/index.php/journals/tex/. **Ad Rates:** BW: 180. **Circ:** (Not Reported)

55302 ■ that's life!
H. Bauer Publishing
Academic House
24-28 Oval Rd.
London NW1 7DT, United Kingdom
Ph: 44 20 72418000
Fax: 44 20 72418030
Magazine for young women featuring real life stories. **Founded:** June 1995. **Freq:** Weekly (Thurs.). **Trim Size:** 210 x 280 mm. **Key Personnel:** Jo Checkley, Editor; Andy Brooks, Publishing Dir.; Lisa Carver, Advertising Mgr., phone 44 20 70750787, lisa.carver@bauer.co.uk. **Subscription Rates:** 68 individuals. **Remarks:** Accepts advertising. **URL:** http://www.bauer.co.uk/thatslife. **Circ:** ★386,875

55303 ■ Theatre Record
131 Sherringham Ave.
London, United Kingdom
Ph: 44 20 88083656
Fax: 44 20 83500211
Publisher E-mail: editor@theatrerecord.com
Journal covering theatre. **Founded:** 1981. **Freq:** Semimonthly. **Trim Size:** A4. **Key Personnel:** Ian Shuttleworth, Editor and Publisher; Ian Herbert, Consulting Ed.; Ruth Keeley, Ed., Editorial Mgr., Subscriptions, ruth@trsubs.co.uk. **ISSN:** 0962-1792. **Subscription Rates:** 165 individuals; 190 individuals Europe (air mail); rest of world (airspeeded); 230 individuals rest of world (air mail); US$360 individuals Europe (air mail); rest of world (airspeeded); US$450 individuals rest of world (air mail); EUR300 individuals Europe (air mail); rest of world (airspeeded); EUR370 individuals rest of world (air mail). **Remarks:** Accepts advertising. **URL:** http://www.theatrerecord.org. **Formerly:** London Theatre Record (1981-90). **Circ:** (Not Reported)

55304 ■ Theatregoer Magazine
Axon Publishing
11 Plough Yard
London EC2A 3LP, United Kingdom
Ph: 44 20 76847111
Fax: 44 20 76847122
Publisher E-mail: mail@axonpublish.com
Magazine featuring information for theater audiences. **Key Personnel:** Paul Keers, Editorial Dir. **URL:** http://www.axonpublish.com/.

55305 ■ Theology
Society for Promoting Christian Knowledge
36 Causton St.
London SW1P 4ST, United Kingdom
Ph: 44 20 75923900
Fax: 44 20 75923939
Publication E-mail: theology@spck.org.uk
Publisher E-mail: spck@spck.org.uk
Publication covering theology. **Freq:** Bimonthly 1st of January, March, May, July, September and November. **Trim Size:** 5 3/4 x 9. **Key Personnel:** Dr. Stephen J. Plant, Editor. **ISSN:** 0040-571X. **Subscription Rates:** 29.50 individuals. **Remarks:** Accepts advertising. **URL:** http://www.spck.org.uk/cat/theology.php. **Ad Rates:** BW: 195. **Circ:** 3,400

55306 ■ Theoretical Biology and Medical Modelling
BioMed Central Ltd.
236 Gray's Inn Rd., Fl. 6
34-42 Cleveland St.
London WC1X 8HL, United Kingdom
Ph: 44 20 31922000
Fax: 44 20 31922010
Publisher E-mail: info@biomedcentral.com
Online journal covering all aspects of biology and the conceptual modelling required to understand its complexity. **Key Personnel:** Prof. Pier Paolo Delsanto, Assoc. Ed., pier.delsanto@polito.it; Dr. Paul S. Agutter, Editor-in-Chief, tbmm1234@btopenworld.com; Prof. Hans-Peter Meinzer, Assoc. Ed., h.p.meinzer@dkfz.de; Dr. Denys Wheatley, Founding Ed., phone 44 1467

670280, fax 44 1467 670280, pat028@abdn.ac.uk; Dr. Oleg Kvitko, Assoc. Ed.; David Phoenix, Assoc. Ed.; Tarynn Witten, Assoc. Ed.; Rongling Wu, Assoc. Ed. **ISSN:** 1742-4682. **Remarks:** Accepts advertising. **URL:** http://www.tbiomed.com/home/. **Circ:** (Not Reported)

55307 ■ Theoretical Criminology
Sage Publications Ltd.
1 Oliver's Yard
55 City Rd.
London EC1Y 1SP, United Kingdom
Ph: 44 20 73248500
Fax: 44 20 73248600
Scholarly journal covering the theory of criminology worldwide. **Subtitle:** An International Journal. **Founded:** 1997. **Freq:** Quarterly. **Key Personnel:** Lynn Chancer, Assoc. Ed.; Mary Bosworth, Editor; Eugene McLaughlin, Assoc. Ed.; Jock Young, Assoc. Ed.; Stanley Cohen, International Advisory Ed.; Stuart Henry, International Advisory Ed.; Christine Harrington, International Advisory Ed. **ISSN:** 1362-4806. **Subscription Rates:** US$873 institutions combined (print & e-access); US$960 institutions current volume print & all online content; US$786 institutions e-access; US$873 individuals all online content; US$786 institutions backfile purchase, e-access; US$856 institutions print only; US$89 individuals print only; US$235 single issue institutional; US$29 single issue individual. **Remarks:** Accepts advertising. **URL:** http://www.sagepub.com/journalsProdManSub.nav?prodId=Journal200923. **Circ:** (Not Reported)

55308 ■ Theory & Psychology
Sage Publications Ltd.
1 Oliver's Yard
55 City Rd.
London EC1Y 1SP, United Kingdom
Ph: 44 20 73248500
Fax: 44 20 73248600
Peer-reviewed journal covering theory and psychology. **Founded:** 1991. **Freq:** Bimonthly. **Key Personnel:** Kenneth Gergen, Advisory Ed.; Lorraine H. Radtke, Book Review Ed.; Henderikus J. Stam, Editor; Huib Looren De Jong, Assoc. Ed.; Peter Ayton, Editorial Board; Gerd Gigerenzer, Advisory Ed.; Jack Martin, Editorial Board; Amedeo Giorgi, Editorial Board; Alexa Hepburn, Editorial Board. **ISSN:** 0959-3543. **Subscription Rates:** US$1,067 institutions combined (print & e-access); US$1,174 institutions e-access; US$1,046 institutions print; US$107 individuals print; US$192 institutions single print; US$23 individuals single print; US$1,174 institutions current print and online content; US$1,067 institutions all online content; US$960 institutions content through 1998. **Remarks:** Accepts advertising. **URL:** http://www.sagepub.com/journalsProdDesc.nav?prodId=Journal200895. **Circ:** (Not Reported)

55309 ■ Therapy
Expert Reviews
Unitec House
2 Albert Pl.
London N3 1QB, United Kingdom
Ph: 44 20 83716090
Fax: 44 20 83432313
Publisher E-mail: info@expert-reviews.com
Forum for rapid publication of original research findings in medicine, augmented with commentary and analysis from international experts. **Subtitle:** Open Access in Clinical Medicine. **Freq:** 14/yr. **Key Personnel:** Gregory Y.H. Lip, Editor-in-Chief; S.I. McFarlane, Editor-in-Chief; RJ MacFadyen, Assoc. Ed. **ISSN:** 1475-0708. **Subscription Rates:** 400 institutions; EUR500 institutions; US$775 institutions; 84,000¥ institutions. **Remarks:** Accepts advertising. **URL:** http://www.futuremedicine.com/loi/thy?cookieSet=1. **Circ:** (Not Reported)

55310 ■ Thesis Eleven
Sage Publications Ltd.
1 Oliver's Yard
55 City Rd.
London EC1Y 1SP, United Kingdom
Ph: 44 20 73248500
Fax: 44 20 73248600
Scholarly journal covering social theory in the social sciences and liberal arts worldwide. **Subtitle:** Critical Theory and Historical Sociology. **Founded:** 1986. **Freq:** Quarterly. **Key Personnel:** Maria Pia Lara, Editorial Advisory Board; Peter Beilharz, Coord. Ed.; Johann Arnason, Editorial Advisory Board; Tessa Morris-Suzuki, Editorial Advisory Board; David Roberts, Commissioning

---

Circulation: ★ = ABC; △ = BPA; ◆ = CAC; • = CCAB; ❑ = VAC; ⊕ = PO Statement; ‡ = Publisher's Report; Boldface figures = sworn; Light figures = estimated.

Ed.; Trevor Hogan, Coord. Ed.; Margaret R. Somers, Editorial Advisory Board; Peter Murphy, Coord. Ed. **ISSN:** 0725-5136. **Subscription Rates:** 474 institutions combined (print & e-access); 521 institutions current volume print & all online content; 427 institutions e-access; 474 institutions all online content; 690 institutions content through 1998; 465 institutions print only; 56 individuals print only; 128 institutions single print; 18 individuals single print. **Remarks:** Accepts advertising. **URL:** http://www.sagepub.co.uk/journalsProdDesc.nav?prodId=Journal200952. **Circ:** (Not Reported)

55311 ■ Third Sector Magazine
Haymarket Publishing Ltd.
174 Hammersmith Rd.
London W6 7JP, United Kingdom
Ph: 44 20 82674210
Publisher E-mail: info@haymarket.com
Magazine offering the latest news, views and analysis on the key issues facing the not-for-profit sector. **Founded:** 1992. **Freq:** Weekly. **Key Personnel:** Stephen Cook, Editor, phone 44 20 82674858; Tracy Awere, Sales Mgr., phone 44 20 82674607. **Subscription Rates:** 116 individuals; 209 two years; 278 individuals three years. **URL:** http://www.haymarket.com/third_sector/third_sector_magazine/default.aspx. **Circ:** ★12,345

55312 ■ Third Text
Routledge
Taylor & Francis Group Ltd.
c/o Rasheed Araeen, Founding Ed.
2G Crusader House
289 Cricklewood Broadway
London NW2 6NX, United Kingdom
Ph: 44 20 88307803
Fax: 44 20 88307803
Publisher E-mail: webmaster.books@tandf.co.uk
Peer-reviewed journal covering contemporary art and culture, art criticism, art history and cultural studies. **Subtitle:** Critical Perspectives of Contemporary Art and Culture. **Founded:** 1987. **Freq:** Bimonthly. **Print Method:** Perfect Bound. **Trim Size:** 200 x 250 mm. **Cols./Page:** 2. **Key Personnel:** Richard Appignanesi, Editor; Rasheed Araeen, Founding Ed., thirdtext@btconnect.com; Ziauddin Sardar, Advisory Council; Raimi Gbadamosi, Editorial Board; Guy Brett, Advisory Council; Jorella Andrews, Editorial Board; Julian Stallabrass, Editorial Board; Annie Coombes, Editorial Board. **ISSN:** 0952-8822. **Subscription Rates:** 355 institutions print + online; US$540 institutions print + online; 337 institutions online; US$513 institutions online; 91 individuals; US$152 individuals print; 39 students; US$66 students; EUR409 institutions online; EUR431 institutions online. **Remarks:** Accepts advertising. **URL:** http://www.tandf.co.uk/journals/journal.asp?issn=0952-8822&subcategory=ah700000&linktype=rates. **Ad Rates:** BW: 450. **Circ:** Paid 3,000

55313 ■ Third Way Voice of the Radical Centre
Third Way Publications Ltd.
PO Box 1243
London SW7 3PB, United Kingdom
Publication E-mail: thirdwaycentre@aol.com
Consumer magazine covering politics. **Subtitle:** Voice of the Radical Centre. **Founded:** 1990. **Freq:** Quarterly. **Print Method:** Offset litho. **Cols./Page:** 3. **Col. Width:** 60 millimeters. **ISSN:** 0959-5031. **Subscription Rates:** 15 individuals U.K.; 18 individuals Europe; 20 other countries. **URL:** http://www.thirdway.org. **Circ:** Combined 1,000

55314 ■ Thomas & Friends
Egmont Magazines
184-192 Drummond St., 4th Fl.
London NW1 3HP, United Kingdom
Ph: 44 20 73806430
Magazine for children to read with their parents, grandparents, and guardians. **Founded:** 1999. **Freq:** Semimonthly. **Trim Size:** 220 x 300 mm. **Key Personnel:** Anna Chacoliades, Contact; Sam Verno, Contact. **Subscription Rates:** 1.99 individuals. **Remarks:** Accepts advertising. **URL:** http://www.egmont.co.uk/product.asp?prodid=1524&catid=30. **Ad Rates:** 4C: 1,800. **Circ:** ★50,002

55315 ■ Thorax
BMJ Publishing Group Ltd.
The British Thoracic Society
17 Doughty St.

London WC1N 2PL, United Kingdom
Peer-reviewed Journal publishing research papers on respiratory medicine, pediatrics, immunology, pharmacology, pathology, and surgery. **Subtitle:** An International Journal of Respiratory Medicine. **Founded:** 1946. **Freq:** Monthly. **Key Personnel:** Jeremy Brown, Assoc. Ed., jeremy.brown@ucl.ac.uk; Andy Bush, Editor, a.bush@rbht.nhs.uk. **ISSN:** 0040-6376. **Subscription Rates:** EUR143 institutions online only; 106 institutions online only; 198 institutions print & online; US$386 institutions print & online; EUR267 institutions print & online; US$207 institutions online only. **URL:** http://thorax.bmj.com/.

55316 ■ Thrombosis Journal
BioMed Central Ltd.
236 Gray's Inn Rd., Fl. 6
34-42 Cleveland St.
London WC1X 8HL, United Kingdom
Ph: 44 20 31922000
Fax: 44 20 31922010
Publisher E-mail: info@biomedcentral.com
Online journal covering all aspects of clinical and basic research in the different areas of thrombosis. **Key Personnel:** Prof. Raul Altman, Editor-in-Chief, thrombosisjournal@speedy.com.ar; Prof. Louis M. Aledort, Editorial Board, louis.aledort@mssm.edu; Dr. Alicia Blanco, Editorial Board, blanco@hematologia.anm.edu.ar; Juan Jose Badimon, Assoc. Ed.; Jaweed Fareed, Dep. Ed. **ISSN:** 1477-9560. **Remarks:** Accepts advertising. **URL:** http://www.thrombosisjournal.com/. **Circ:** (Not Reported)

55317 ■ Thrombus
Hayward Medical Communications
Covent Garden
8-10 Dryden St.
London WC2E 9NA, United Kingdom
Publisher E-mail: admin@hayward.co.uk
Journal covering treatment and management of deep vein thrombosis. **Founded:** 1997. **Freq:** Quarterly. **Key Personnel:** Peter Rose, Editor. **URL:** http://www.thrombus.co.uk/thrombus/.

55318 ■ Time Out Kids Out
Time Out Group Ltd.
Universal House
251 Tottenham Ct. Rd.
London W1T 7AB, United Kingdom
Ph: 44 20 78133000
Fax: 44 20 78136001
Consumer magazine covering parenting. **Founded:** 1983. **Freq:** Monthly. **Remarks:** Accepts advertising. **URL:** http://www.timeout.com. **Circ:** (Not Reported)

55319 ■ Time & Society
Sage Publications Ltd.
1 Oliver's Yard
55 City Rd.
London EC1Y 1SP, United Kingdom
Ph: 44 20 73248500
Fax: 44 20 73248600
Scholarly journal covering temporality and social and cultural behavior and action. **Founded:** 1992. **Freq:** 3/yr. **Key Personnel:** Robert Hassan, Editor; Hartmut Rosa, Editor; David Maines, Editorial Board; Joost Van Loon, Review Ed.; Patricia Allatt, Editorial Board; Ida Sabelis, Review Ed.; Hanns-Georg Brose, Editorial Board; Stuart Allan, Editorial Board; John Urry, Editorial Board. **ISSN:** 0961-463X. **Subscription Rates:** 549 institutions combined (print & e-access); 604 institutions current volume print & all online content; 494 institutions e-access; 549 institutions e-access plus backfile (all online content); 538 institutions print only; 43 individuals print only; 475 institutions content through 1998; 19 individuals single print; 197 institutions single print. **Remarks:** Accepts advertising. **URL:** http://www.sagepub.co.uk/journalsProdDesc.nav?prodId=Journal200801. **Circ:** (Not Reported)

55320 ■ Timeout.com
Time Out Group Ltd.
Universal House
251 Tottenham Ct. Rd.
London W1T 7AB, United Kingdom
Ph: 44 20 78133000
Fax: 44 20 78136001
Online magazine covering events, shopping, art, food, entertainment, news and more in cities around the world. **Key Personnel:** David Pepper, Mng. Dir., davidpepper@timeout.com; Alastair Lee, Dir. of Digital Dev. **Remarks:**

Accepts advertising. **URL:** http://www.timeout.com. **Ad Rates:** 4C: 4,197. **Circ:** (Not Reported)

55321 ■ The Times
Times Newspapers Ltd.
3 thomas More Sq.
London E98 1XY, United Kingdom
Ph: 44 20 78601133
Publisher E-mail: info@newsint.co.uk
Business newspaper. **Freq:** Daily. **ISSN:** 0140-0460. **Remarks:** Accepts classified advertising. **URL:** http://www.timesonline.co.uk/. **Circ:** (Not Reported)

55322 ■ Times Educational Supplement
TSL Education Ltd.
26 Red Lion Sq.
London WC1R 4HQ, United Kingdom
Ph: 44 20 31943000
Publication E-mail: editor@tes.co.uk
Publisher E-mail: info@tsleducation.com
Newspaper covering education. **Founded:** 1910. **Freq:** Weekly. **Print Method:** Coldset Lithograph. **Trim Size:** 280 mm. x 347 mm. **Key Personnel:** Matt Tillot, Contact, matt.tillott@tsleducation.com. **ISSN:** 0040-7887. **Subscription Rates:** 9 individuals cover; 45 individuals direct debit; 195 individuals overseas. **Remarks:** Accepts advertising. **URL:** http://www.tes.co.uk. **Ad Rates:** GLR: 3.85, BW: 4,579, 4C: 4,808. **Circ:** ★118,609

55323 ■ Times Higher Education Supplement
TSL Education Ltd.
26 Red Lion Sq.
London WC1R 4HQ, United Kingdom
Ph: 44 20 31943000
Publisher E-mail: info@tsleducation.com
Newspaper covering education. **Founded:** 1971. **Freq:** Weekly. **Print Method:** Coldset Lithograph. **Trim Size:** 230 mm. x 300 mm. **Key Personnel:** Ann Mroz, Editor, ann.mroz@tsleducation.com. **ISSN:** 0049-3929. **Subscription Rates:** 45 individuals U.K., direct debit; 55 individuals U.K.; 98 individuals Europe; 120 other countries. **Remarks:** Accepts advertising. **URL:** http://www.tsleducation.com/thes.asp; http://www.thes.co.uk. **Ad Rates:** BW: 4,725. **Circ:** ★31,140

55324 ■ The Times Law Reports
LexisNexis UK
Halsbury House
35 Chancery Ln.
London WC2A 1EL, United Kingdom
Ph: 44 207 4002500
Fax: 44 207 4002842
Publisher E-mail: scot.inquires@lexisnexis.co.uk
Legal reports publication. **Founded:** 1990. **Freq:** 22/yr. **Key Personnel:** Iain Sutherland, Editor. **ISSN:** 0958-0441. **Subscription Rates:** 285 individuals standard. **Remarks:** Advertising not accepted. **URL:** http://www.lexisnexis.co.uk/. **Circ:** (Not Reported)

55325 ■ Tobacco Control
BMJ Publishing Group Ltd.
BMA House
Tavistock Sq.
London WC1H 9JR, United Kingdom
Ph: 44 20 73874410
Fax: 44 20 73836400
Peer-reviewed Journal for health professionals and others involved in tobacco control. **Founded:** 1992. **Freq:** 6/yr. **Key Personnel:** Ruth E. Malone, Editor, ruth.malone@ucsf.edu; Melanie Wakefield, Editorial Advisory Board, phone 61 3 96355046, fax 61 3 96355380, melanie.wakefield@cancervic.org.au; Frank Chaloupka, Assoc. Ed. **ISSN:** 0964-4563. **Subscription Rates:** 133 institutions print & online; 74 institutions online only; US$259 institutions print & online; EUR180 institutions print & online; EUR100 institutions online only; US$144 institutions online only. **Remarks:** Advertising accepted; rates available upon request. **URL:** http://tobaccocontrol.bmj.com/. **Circ:** (Not Reported)

55326 ■ Top Gear Magazine
BBC Worldwide Ltd.
Woodlands
Media Ctr.
201 Wood Ln.
London W12 7TQ, United Kingdom
Ph: 44 20 84332000
Publication E-mail: tgweb@bbc.co.uk
Magazine on cars, providing guidance on buying, selling and owning a car. **Freq:** Monthly. **Subscription Rates:**

35.50 individuals UK, 13 issues; 92 individuals USA; 99.50 Canada. **Remarks:** Accepts advertising. **URL:** http://www.topgear.com. **Circ:** ★175,218

55327 ■ Top Marques
Trader Media Group
41-47 Hartfield Rd., 3rd & 4th Fl.
Wimbledon
London SW19 3RQ, United Kingdom
Ph: 44 208 5447000
Fax: 44 208 8791879
Magazine featuring prestige vehicles. **Founded:** 1994. **Freq:** every fortnightly. **Key Personnel:** John King, CEO. **Subscription Rates:** 60 individuals. **Remarks:** Accepts advertising. **URL:** http://www.topmarques.co.uk; http://www.tradermediagroup.com/companies/top-marques.html. **Circ:** ★24,118

55328 ■ Top of the Pops
BBC Worldwide Publishing Ltd.
Media Centre
201 Wood Ln.
London W12 7TQ, United Kingdom
Ph: 44 20 84332000
Fax: 44 20 87490538
Publication E-mail: totp.magazine@bbc.co.uk
Entertainment magazine featuring star gossip, hot fashion and beauty advice, sexy lads, and side-splitting cringes. **Subtitle:** More gossip! More scandal! More you!. **Freq:** Monthly. **Key Personnel:** Claire Stidwell, Contact, claire.stidwell@bbc.co.uk. **Subscription Rates:** 2.20 single issue. **URL:** http://www.totpmag.com/; http://www.bbcmagazines.com/content/magazines/topofthepops/.

55329 ■ Total TVguide
H. Bauer Publishing
Academic House
24-28 Oval Rd.
London NW1 7DT, United Kingdom
Ph: 44 20 72418000
Fax: 44 20 72418030
Guide magazine for digital television viewers. **Founded:** Sept. 2003. **Freq:** Weekly (Tues.). **Print Method:** Web offset Lithography. **Trim Size:** 225 x 300 mm. **Key Personnel:** Jon Peake, Editor; Liz Watkinson, Publishing Dir.; Danielle Katz, Advertising Mgr. **Subscription Rates:** 44.20 individuals. **Remarks:** Accepts advertising. **URL:** http://www.bauer.co.uk/total-tv-guide; http://www.tvchoicemagazine.co.uk. **Circ:** ★107,681

55330 ■ Totally Tracy Beaker
GE Fabbri Ltd.
FreePost LON13490
London EC1B 1LP, United Kingdom
Ph: 44 845 6039706
Publication E-mail: order@totallytracybeaker.com
Publisher E-mail: mailbox@gefabbri.co.uk
Magazine featuring Tracy Beaker. **Freq:** Semimonthly. **Key Personnel:** Peter Edwards, Mng. Dir.; Liz Glaze, Director; Katie Preston, Editor-in-Chief. **URL:** http://www.totallytracybeaker.com/; http://www.gefabbri.co.uk/publication_totallytracybeaker.

55331 ■ Tourism Economics
IP Publishing Ltd.
258 Belsize Rd.
London NW6 4BT, United Kingdom
Ph: 44 20 73161870
Fax: 44 20 76249994
Publisher E-mail: jedmondson@ippublishing.com
Journal covering the business and finance aspects of the tourism and recreation industry. **Subtitle:** The Business and Finance of Tourism and Recreation. **Founded:** 1995. **Freq:** Quarterly. **Key Personnel:** Prof. Stephen Wanhill, Editor, jedmondip@aol.com; Prof. Tom Baum, Editorial Advisory Board; Prof. Sang Mu Kim, Special Adviser; Prof. William C. Gartner, Special Adviser; Prof. John Fletcher, Special Adviser; Prof. Esteban Bardolet, Editorial Advisory Board. **ISSN:** 1354-8166. **Subscription Rates:** US$488 institutions; EUR471 institutions in Europe; 318 institutions, other countries. **Remarks:** Accepts advertising. **URL:** http://www.ippublishing.com/te.htm. **Circ:** (Not Reported)

55332 ■ Tourist Studies
Sage Publications Ltd.
1 Oliver's Yard
55 City Rd.
London EC1Y 1SP, United Kingdom

Ph: 44 20 73248500
Fax: 44 20 73248600
Scholarly journal covering the nature of tourism as a social phenomenon worldwide. **Subtitle:** An International Journal. **Founded:** 2001. **Freq:** 3/yr. **Key Personnel:** Andrian Franklin, Editor; Mike Crang, Editor; Felicity Picken, Book Review Ed.; Jennifer Craik, Editorial Board; Dean MacCannell, Editorial Board; Zygmunt Bauman, Editorial Board; Eric Cohen, Editorial Board; Greg Richards, Editorial Board. **ISSN:** 1468-7976. **Subscription Rates:** US$740 institutions electronic & print; US$666 institutions electronic; US$725 institutions print; US$83 individuals print; US$266 institutions single print; 36 individuals single print. **Remarks:** Accepts advertising. **URL:** http://www.sagepub.com/journalsProdDesc.nav?prodId=Journal201263. **Circ:** (Not Reported)

55333 ■ Toybox
BBC Worldwide Publishing Ltd.
Media Centre
201 Wood Ln.
London W12 7TQ, United Kingdom
Ph: 44 20 84332000
Fax: 44 20 87490538
Entertainment magazine for pre-schoolers. **Subtitle:** The UK's best-selling pre-school magazine. **Freq:** every 4 weeks. **Subscription Rates:** 2.99 single issue. **URL:** http://www.bbcmagazines.com/content/magazines/toybox/.

55334 ■ Transactions
Newcomen Society for the Study of the History of Engineering and Technology
The Science Museum
London SW7 2DD, United Kingdom
Ph: 44 20 73714445
Fax: 44 20 73714445
Publication E-mail: editor.trans@newcomen.com
Publisher E-mail: office@newcomen.com
Publication covering history. **Freq:** Semiannual. **ISSN:** 0372-0187. **Remarks:** Advertising not accepted. **URL:** http://www.newcomen.com/transactions.htm. **Circ:** 2,500

55335 ■ Transactions of the Royal Society of Tropical Medicine and Hygiene
Royal Society of Tropical Medicine and Hygiene
50 Bedford Sq.
London WC1B 3DP, United Kingdom
Ph: 44 20 75802127
Fax: 44 20 74361389
Publication E-mail: trans@rstmh.org
Publisher E-mail: mail@rstmh.org
Professional, scientific publication covering tropical medicine and international health issues. **Founded:** 1907. **Freq:** Monthly. **Trim Size:** 210 x 297 mm. **Key Personnel:** Bo Drasar, Editor-in-Chief; Geoffrey Pasvol, Assoc. Ed.; Brian Greenwood, Exec. Ed. **ISSN:** 0035-9203. **Subscription Rates:** US$691 institutions all countries except Europe, Japan and Iran; 82,000¥ institutions; EUR619 institutions European countries and Iran; 42¥ individuals; US$222 individuals all countries except Europe, Japan and Iran; EUR198 individuals European countries and Iran; 138 individuals. **Remarks:** Accepts advertising. **URL:** http://www.rstmh.org/transactions.asp; http://www.elsevier.com/wps/find/journaldescription.cws_home1061019/descriptiondescription. **Circ:** (Not Reported)

55336 ■ Transcultural Psychiatry
Sage Publications Ltd.
1 Oliver's Yard
55 City Rd.
London EC1Y 1SP, United Kingdom
Ph: 44 20 73248500
Fax: 44 20 73248600
Peer-reviewed journal covering psychopathology and psychosocial treatments of mental and behavioral problems for psychiatrists and other mental health professionals and social scientists. **Founded:** 1956. **Freq:** 5/yr. **Key Personnel:** Laurence J. Kirmayer, Editor-in-Chief; Sing Lee, Assoc. Ed.; Roland Littlewood, Assoc. Ed. **ISSN:** 1363-4615. **Subscription Rates:** US$454 institutions print & e-access; US$499 institutions current volume print & all online content; US$409 institutions e-access; US$454 institutions all online content; US$1,217 institutions content through 1998; US$445 institutions print only; US$524 individuals print only; US$98 single issue print; US$14 individuals single

print. **Remarks:** Accepts advertising. **URL:** http://www.sagepub.co.uk/journalsProdDesc.nav?prodId=Journal200977. **Circ:** (Not Reported)

55337 ■ Traveller
World Expeditionary Association
45-49 Brompton Rd.
Knightsbridge
London SW3 1DE, United Kingdom
Ph: 44 84 56436568
Fax: 44 20 78380837
Publisher E-mail: mship@wexas.com
Publication covering travel. **Founded:** 1970. **Freq:** Quarterly. **Remarks:** Advertising accepted; rates available upon request. **URL:** http://www.wexas.com/travel/traveller/. **Formerly:** Expedition. **Circ:** 35,000

55338 ■ The Treasurer
Association of Corporate Treasurers
51 Moorgate
London EC2R 6BH, United Kingdom
Ph: 44 20 78472540
Fax: 44 20 73748744
Publisher E-mail: enquiries@treasurers.org
Publication covering finance. **Freq:** Monthly. **Subscription Rates:** 195 nonmembers U.K. and European countries; 225 elsewhere rest of the world, nonmembers; 295 nonmembers U.K. and European countries, 2 years; 340 elsewhere rest of the world, nonmembers, 2 years; 400 nonmembers U.K. and European countries, 3 years; 470 elsewhere rest of the world, nonmembers, 3 years; 100 members ACT and students; 125 elsewhere ACT members and students; 100 nonmembers IGTA; 125 elsewhere IGTA. **Remarks:** Advertising accepted; rates available upon request. **URL:** http://www.treasurers.org/thetreasurer/. **Circ:** (Not Reported)

55339 ■ Trends in Endocrinology and Metabolism (TEM)
Elsevier Science
c/o Kevin J. Catt, PhD, Advisory Ed.
84 Theobald's Rd.
London WC1X 8RR, United Kingdom
Publisher E-mail: nlinfo-f@elsevier.com
Journal focusing on the field of endocrinology and metabolism. **Founded:** 1989. **Freq:** 12/yr. **Key Personnel:** Kevin J. Catt, PhD, Advisory Ed.; Jennifer Key, Editorial Asst.; Charlotte Wang, Exec. Ed. **ISSN:** 1043-2760. **Subscription Rates:** EUR223 individuals for European countries & Iran; 27,100¥ individuals; US$245 individuals for all countries except Europe, Japan & Iran; 253,400¥ institutions; US$2,043 institutions for all Countries except Europe and Japan; EUR1,827 institutions for European countries & Iran. **Remarks:** Advertising accepted; rates available upon request. **URL:** http://www.cell.com/trends/endocrinology-metabolism; http://www.elsevier.com/wps/find/journaldescription.cws_home/505783/descrip tiondescription. **Circ:** (Not Reported)

55340 ■ Trespass
32 Addison Grove
London W4 1ER, United Kingdom
Ph: 44 20 84005882
Fax: 44 20 89941713
Publisher E-mail: trespassmagazine@yahoo.co.uk
Magazine covering mysteries or mythical stories and poetry on sexuality. **Key Personnel:** Sara- Mae Tuson, Editor. **Subscription Rates:** 27.50 individuals; 36.45 individuals Europe; 39.50 other countries. **URL:** http://www.trespassmagazine.co.uk/.

55341 ■ Tribology International
Elsevier Science
c/o Philippa Cann, Ed.-in-Ch.
Dept. of Mechanical Engineering, Tribology Group
Imperial Colorado
London SW7 2BX, United Kingdom
Publisher E-mail: nlinfo-f@elsevier.com
Journal dealing with technology of lubrication, wear prevention and friction control. **Freq:** Monthly. **Key Personnel:** Philippa Cann, Editor-in-Chief, pmctribint@imperial.ac.uk; M.J. Adams, Editorial Board; S.K. Biswas, Editorial Board; A. Chateauminois, Editorial Board; K. Friedrich, Editorial Board; S. Hsu, Editorial Board. **ISSN:** 0301-679X. **Subscription Rates:** 27,300¥ individuals; US$229 individuals for all countries except Europe, Japan & Iran; EUR205 individuals for European countries & Iran; 262,000¥ institutions; EUR1,971 institutions for European countries & Iran; US$2,205 institu-

Circulation: ★ = ABC; △ = BPA; ◆ = CAC; • = CCAB; ❏ = VAC; ⊕ = PO Statement; ‡ = Publisher's Report; Boldface figures = sworn; Light figures = estimated.

Gale Directory of Publications & Broadcast Media/147th Ed.   5773

tions for all countries except Europe, Japan & Iran. **Remarks:** Accepts advertising. **URL:** http://www. elsevier.com/wps/find/journaldescription.cws_home/ 30474/descriptiondescription. **Circ:** (Not Reported)

55342 ■ Tropical Doctor
Royal Society of Medicine Press Ltd.
1 Wimpole St.
London W1G 0AE, United Kingdom
Ph: 44 20 72902921
Fax: 44 20 72902929
Publisher E-mail: publishing@rsm.ac.uk
Peer-reviewed journal establishing best practice, aiding communication between medical professionals in different environments. **Freq:** 4/yr. **Trim Size:** 200mm x 280mm. **Key Personnel:** Dr. Tom Doherty, Editor. **ISSN:** 0049-4755. **Subscription Rates:** 92 institutions UK & Europe; EUR123 institutions Europe; US$186 institutions; 98 institutions, other countries; 45 institutions developing countries; 83 individuals online only; EUR111 individuals online only; US$167 individuals online only. **Remarks:** Accepts advertising. **URL:** http://www. portlandpress.com; http://td.rsmjournals.com. **Circ:** (Not Reported)

55343 ■ Trust & Foundation News
Association of Charitable Foundations
Central House
14 Upper Woburn Pl.
London WC1H 0AE, United Kingdom
Ph: 44 20 72554499
Publisher E-mail: acf@acf.org.uk
Publication covering trusts and foundations. **Subtitle:** ACF's Quarterly Magazine. **Freq:** Quarterly. **Key Personnel:** Sue Benson, Editor. **ISSN:** 1354-2567. **Subscription Rates:** 50 individuals; 35 charities. **URL:** http:// www.acf.org.uk/publicationsandresources/?id=136.

55344 ■ Trusts and Estates Law & Tax Journal
Legalese Ltd.
Kensington Sq. House
12-14 Ansdell St.
London W8 5BN, United Kingdom
Ph: 44 20 73969292
Fax: 44 20 73969303
Professional journal covering trust and estates law. **Freq:** 10/yr. **Key Personnel:** Geoffrey Shindler, Consultant Ed. **Subscription Rates:** 179 individuals. **URL:** http:// www.legalease.co.uk.

55345 ■ TVChoice
H. Bauer Publishing
Academic House
24-28 Oval Rd.
London NW1 7DT, United Kingdom
Ph: 44 20 72418000
Fax: 44 20 72418030
Magazine featuring listings of television programs. **Founded:** Aug. 1999. **Freq:** Weekly (Tues.). **Print Method:** Web offset Lithography. **Trim Size:** 210 x 280 mm. **Key Personnel:** Jon Peake, Editor; Liz Watkinson, Publishing Dir.; Danielle Katz, Advertising Mgr. **Subscription Rates:** 42 individuals. **Remarks:** Accepts advertising. **URL:** http://www.bauer.co.uk/tv-choice. **Circ:** ★1,335,894

55346 ■ TVQuick
H. Bauer Publishing
Academic House
24-28 Oval Rd.
London NW1 7DT, United Kingdom
Ph: 44 20 72418000
Fax: 44 20 72418030
Magazine featuring the latest gossip on TV people in the news, in depth interviews, and the low down on the week's TV programmes. **Founded:** Mar. 1991. **Freq:** Weekly (Tues.). **Print Method:** Heatset web offset. **Trim Size:** 210 x 280 mm. **Key Personnel:** Jon Peake, Editor; Liz Watkinson, Publishing Dir.; Danielle Katz, Advertising Mgr., phone 44 20 70750788, danielle.katz@ bauer.co.uk. **Subscription Rates:** 78 individuals. **Remarks:** Accepts advertising. **URL:** http://www.bauer.co. uk/tv-quick. **Circ:** ★144,270

55347 ■ Tweenies
BBC Worldwide Publishing Ltd.
Media Centre
201 Wood Ln.
London W12 7TQ, United Kingdom
Ph: 44 20 84332000
Fax: 44 20 87490538
Magazine featuring creative play and learning for

children. **Freq:** every fortnightly. **Subscription Rates:** 1.85 single issue. **URL:** http://www.bbcmagazines.com/ content/magazines/tweenies/.

55348 ■ 25 Beautiful Homes
IPC Media Ltd.
Blue Fin Bldg.
110 Southwark St.
London SE1 0SU, United Kingdom
Ph: 44 203 1485000
Consumer magazine covering homes and interior design. **Founded:** Mar. 1998. **Freq:** Monthly. **Key Personnel:** Lynsey Bushell, Publisher, phone 44 20 31487665, lynsey_bushell@ipcmedia.com; Yvonne Ramsden, Publishing Dir., phone 44 20 31487663, yvonne_ramsden@ipcmedia.com; Deborah Barker, Editor, phone 44 20 31487311, deborah_barker@ipcmedia. com; Sharon Goode, Advertising Mgr., phone 44 20 31487631, sharon_goode@ipcmedia.com. **ISSN:** 1369-5290. **Subscription Rates:** 24.99 individuals; 49.99 two years. **Remarks:** Accepts advertising. **URL:** http://www. ipcmedia.com/brands/25homes/. **Circ:** ★102,868

55349 ■ 25 Beautiful Kitchens
IPC Media Ltd.
Blue Fin Bldg.
110 Southwark St.
London SE1 0SU, United Kingdom
Ph: 44 203 1485000
Magazine for women who are real home enthusiasts. **Founded:** 1999. **Freq:** 13/yr. **Key Personnel:** Lynsey Bushell, Publisher; John Smigielski, Editor; Sharon Goode, Advertising Mgr. **Subscription Rates:** 29.99 individuals; 54.99 two years. **Remarks:** Accepts advertising. **URL:** http://www.ipcmedia.com/southbank/ 25beautifulkitchens/. **Circ:** ★118,373

55350 ■ 20th Century History Review
Philip Allan Updates
338 Euston Rd.
London NW1 3BH, United Kingdom
Ph: 44 20 78736000
Fax: 44 20 78736299
Periodical focusing on history. **Freq:** 3/yr. **Key Personnel:** Gillian Staerck, Editor, gillian.staerck@sas.ac.uk; Robin Bunce, Editor; Laura Williams, Editor. **ISSN:** 0956-0726. **Subscription Rates:** 12.50 students; 29.95 institutions. **Remarks:** Advertising not accepted. **URL:** http://www.philipallan.co.uk/historyreview/index.htm. **Formerly:** Modern History Review. **Circ:** (Not Reported)

55351 ■ U Magazine
UNISON
1 Mabledon Pl.
London WC1H 9AJ, United Kingdom
Ph: 44 845 3550845
Journal for those working in public services. **Freq:** Quarterly. **Key Personnel:** Helen Barron, Communications Ed., phone 44 20 75511298. **Remarks:** Advertising accepted; rates available upon request. **URL:** http:// www.unison.co.uk/news/umagazine.asp. **Formerly:** Unison Journal. **Circ:** Non-paid 1,400,000

55352 ■ UCU
Redactive Media Group
17-18 Britton St.
London EC1M 5TP, United Kingdom
Ph: 44 20 78806200
Fax: 44 20 78807691
Publisher E-mail: info@redactive.co.uk
Magazine featuring academic related articles. **Key Personnel:** Aaron Nicholls, Contact, phone 44 20 78806200. **URL:** http://www.redactive.co.uk/clients/ucu/.

55353 ■ UK Baha'i Journal
National Spiritual Assembly of the Baha'is of the UK
27 Rutland Gate
London SW7 1PD, United Kingdom
Ph: 44 20 75842566
Fax: 44 20 75849402
Publisher E-mail: nsa@bahai.org.uk
Journal covering the Baha'i. **Freq:** Monthly. **Trim Size:** A4. **Key Personnel:** Anne Maund, Editor. **Subscription Rates:** Free. **Remarks:** Advertising not accepted. **URL:** http://www.bahai.org.uk/svic/svic.htm. **Former name:** Baha'i Journal UK. **Circ:** (Not Reported)

55354 ■ UK Excellence
Redactive Media Group
17-18 Britton St.
London EC1M 5TP, United Kingdom

Ph: 44 20 78806200
Fax: 44 20 78807691
Publisher E-mail: info@redactive.co.uk
Magazine highlighting business performance improvement and excellence. **Freq:** Bimonthly. **Key Personnel:** Aaron Nicholls, Contact, phone 44 20 78808547, fax 44 20 78807691, aaron.nicholls@redactive.co.uk. **Subscription Rates:** 30 members; 60 nonmembers. **URL:** http://www.redactive.co.uk/clients/uk-excellence/; http:// www.quality-foundation.co.uk/cgi-bin/pub_ excellencemagazine.cgi. **Circ:** ‡4,000

55355 ■ UK Unquote
Incisive Media Limited
Haymarket House
28-29 Haymarket
London SW1Y 4RX, United Kingdom
Ph: 44 870 2408859
Fax: 44 207 4849797
Publisher E-mail: customerservices@incisivemedia.com
Journal covering news from the venture capital and private equity markets in the United Kingdom and Ireland. **Freq:** Fortnightly. **Key Personnel:** Kimberly Romaine, Editor, phone 44 20 70047526, kimberly. romaine@incisivemedia.com. **Remarks:** Accepts advertising. **URL:** http://www.incisivemedia.com/ corporate/products/unquote; http://www.unquote.co.uk. **Circ:** 3,500

55356 ■ Ultra
Luxury Publishing Limited
5 Jubilee Pl.
Chelsea
London SW3 3TD, United Kingdom
Ph: 44 20 75912900
Fax: 44 20 75912929
Publisher E-mail: info@luxurypublishing.com
Magazine covering all aspects of wealth and financial management. **Freq:** Quarterly. **Key Personnel:** William Cash, Editor. **Remarks:** Accepts advertising. **URL:** http:// www.luxurypublishing.co.uk/. **Circ:** 54,450

55357 ■ Uncut
Time Inc.
IPC Media
4th Fl., Blue Fin Bldg.
Southwark St.
London SE1 0SU, United Kingdom
Ph: 44 20 31486970
Publisher E-mail: information@timeinc.com
Magazine focusing on movies and music. **Freq:** Monthly. **Key Personnel:** Allan Jones, Editor, allan_jones@ ipcmedia.com; John Mulvey, Dep. Ed., john_mulvey@ ipcmedia.com; Michael Bonner, Assoc. Ed., michael_ bonner@ipcmedia.com. **Subscription Rates:** 34.99 individuals; 64.99 two years. **Remarks:** Accepts advertising. **URL:** http://www.uncut.co.uk/; http://www. ipcmedia.com/brands/brands.php. **Circ:** (Not Reported)

55358 ■ Underground Ernie
BBC Worldwide Publishing Ltd.
Media Centre
201 Wood Ln.
London W12 7TQ, United Kingdom
Ph: 44 20 84332000
Fax: 44 20 87490538
Magazine featuring learning activities and stories for children. **Subtitle:** Big fun for tiny travelers. **Freq:** every 4 weeks. **Subscription Rates:** 1.75 single issue. **URL:** http://www.bbc.co.uk/cbeebies/undergroundernie/.

55359 ■ Underwater Technology
Society for Underwater Technology
80 Coleman St.
London EC2R 5BJ, United Kingdom
Ph: 44 20 7382 2601
Fax: 44 20 7382 2684
Publisher E-mail: info@sut.org
Publication covering underwater technology. **Freq:** Quarterly. **Key Personnel:** Dr. M.D.J. Sayer, Editor. **ISSN:** 0141-0814. **Subscription Rates:** 80 individuals UK; 86 individuals overseas; 20 single issue UK; 21.50 single issue overseas. **Remarks:** Accepts advertising. **URL:** http://www.sut.org.uk/. **Ad Rates:** BW: 400. **Circ:** 1,800

55360 ■ Urban Studies
Sage Publications Ltd.
1 Oliver's Yard
55 City Rd.

London EC1Y 1SP, United Kingdom
Ph: 44 20 73248500
Fax: 44 20 73248600
Publication covering sociology and social work. **Freq:** 14/yr. **Key Personnel:** Jon Bannister, Managing Editor; Kenneth Gibb, Managing Editor; Ronan Paddison, Managing Editor. **ISSN:** 0042-0980. **Subscription Rates:** US$2,911 institutions print only; US$512 individuals print only; US$2,970 institutions current volume print and all online content; US$2,673 institutions all online content; US$7,952 institutions content through 1998; US$48 individuals single print issue; US$229 institutions single, print. **URL:** http://www.sagepub.com/journalsProdDesc.nav?prodId=Journal201866.

55361 ■ Urban Water Journal
Taylor & Francis Group Journals
Dept. of Civil & Environmental Engineering
Skempton Bldg.
Imperial College London
London SW7 2AZ, United Kingdom
Publisher E-mail: customerservice@taylorandfrancis.com
Peer-reviewed journal covering articles in urban groundwater. **Freq:** 6/yr. **Print Method:** Offset. **Trim Size:** 13 x 21 1/4. **Cols./Page:** 6. **Col. Width:** 2 1/32 inches. **Col. Depth:** 297 agate lines. **Key Personnel:** Cedo Maksimovic, Editor-in-Chief, c.maksimovic@imperial.ac.uk; David Butler, Editor-in-Chief, d.butler@exeter.ac.uk; Jiri Marsalek, Assoc. Ed. **ISSN:** 1573-062X. **Subscription Rates:** 407 institutions print + online; US$675 institutions print + online; EUR534 institutions print + online; 387 institutions online; US$641 institutions online; EUR507 institutions online; 164 individuals; US$287 individuals; EUR230 individuals; 36 individuals society. **URL:** http://www.tandf.co.uk/journals/titles/1573062x.asp.

55362 ■ Urethanes Technology
Crain Communications Ltd.
3rd Fl., 21 St. Thomas St.
London SE1 9RY, United Kingdom
Ph: 44 20 74571400
Trade magazine covering issues for the polyurethane industry worldwide. **Founded:** Mar. 1984. **Freq:** Bimonthly. **Print Method:** Offset litho. **Trim Size:** A4. **Cols./Page:** 4. **Col. Width:** 10 centimeters. **Key Personnel:** Liz White, Editor; Paul Mitchell, Publisher, pmitchellcrain@compuserve.com. **ISSN:** 0265-637X. **Subscription Rates:** 75 individuals printed issues by post; 98 individuals electronic edition; 114 individuals issues by post and electronic edition. **Remarks:** Accepts advertising. **URL:** http://www.urethanes-technology.com/. **Alt. Formats:** CD-ROM. **Circ:** Controlled 5,381.

55363 ■ Urological Research
Springer-Verlag Tokyo
c/o Dr. William G. Robertson, Ed.
Centre for Nephrology
Royal Free & University College Medical School
Rowland Hill St.
London NW3 2PF, United Kingdom
Publisher E-mail: info@springer.jp
Journal publishing original articles in the fields of clinical and experimental investigation within the sphere of urolithiasis and its related areas of research, covering all aspects of urolithiasis research including the diagnosis, epidemiology, pathogenesis, genetics, clinical biochemistry, open and non-invasive surgical intervention, nephrological investigation, chemistry and prophylaxis of the disorder. **Freq:** Bimonthly. **Key Personnel:** Dr. William G. Robertson, Editor; Prof. Saeed R. Khan, Assoc. Ed.; P.H. Jaeger, Editorial Board; Prof. Koji Suzuki, Assoc. Ed.; G. Rumsby, Editorial Board. **ISSN:** 0300-5623. **Subscription Rates:** EUR1,250 institutions print incl. free access; EUR1,500 institutions print incl. enhanced access. **Remarks:** Advertising accepted; rates available upon request. **URL:** http://www.springer.com/medicine/urology/journal/240. **Circ:** (Not Reported)

55364 ■ Usus Antiquior
Maney Publishing
1 Carlton House Ter.
London SW1Y 5AF, United Kingdom
Ph: 44 20 74517300
Fax: 44 20 74517307
Publisher E-mail: maney@maney.co.uk
Journal covering the Roman rite tradition of the Christian worship. **Subtitle:** A Journal Dedicated to the Sacred Liturgy. **Freq:** Semiannual. **Key Personnel:** Rev. Dr.

Laurence Paul Hemming, Editor, laurence.hemming@ususantiquior.net; Ben Whitworth, Book Reviews Ed., reviewseditor@ususantiquior.net. **ISSN:** 1757-8949. **Subscription Rates:** 42 institutions, other countries for religious houses; US$68 institutions for religious houses; 16 students, other countries; US$23 students; 98 institutions, other countries; US$149 institutions; 27 individuals in UK and European; US$42 individuals. **Remarks:** Accepts advertising. **URL:** http://maney.co.uk/index.php/journals/usu. **Circ:** (Not Reported)

55365 ■ Vanguard
Publicis Blueprint
23 Howland St.
London W1A 1AQ, United Kingdom
Ph: 44 207 4627777
Publisher E-mail: info@publicis-blueprint.co.uk
Magazine featuring van models and accessories. **Freq:** Semiannual. **URL:** http://www.publicis-blueprint.co.uk. **Circ:** 80,000

55366 ■ Vascular Disease Prevention
Bentham Science Publishers Ltd.
Dept. of Clinical Biochemistry
Royal Free & University College School of Medicine
University of London, Pond St.
London NW3 2QG, United Kingdom
Publisher E-mail: subscriptions@bentham.org
Journal publishing reviews as well as original papers to update all those concerned with the topic of vascular disease prevention at the clinical or scientific level. **Freq:** Bimonthly. **Key Personnel:** D.P. Mikhailidis, Editor-in-Chief; M.R Dashwood, Section Ed.; M. Elisaf, Emerging Vascular Risk Factors; Anthony S. Wierzbicki, Dep. Ed.-in-Ch., anthony.wierzbicki@kcl.ac.uk; S. Goto, Editorial Advisory Board; C. Pitsavos, Editorial Advisory Board. **ISSN:** 1567-2700. **Remarks:** Accepts advertising. **URL:** http://www.bentham.org/open/vdp/. **Circ:** (Not Reported)

55367 ■ Vernacular Architecture
Maney Publishing
1 Carlton House Ter.
London SW1Y 5AF, United Kingdom
Ph: 44 20 74517300
Fax: 44 20 74517307
Publisher E-mail: maney@maney.co.uk
Peer-reviewed journal covering all aspects of vernacular architecture. **Freq:** Annual. **Key Personnel:** Dr. Martin Cherry, Editor, martincherry@btinternet.com; Kirsty Rodwell, Book Review Ed. **ISSN:** 0305-5477. **Subscription Rates:** 22 other countries; US$44 individuals; 102 institutions, other countries; US$198 institutions. **Remarks:** Accepts advertising. **URL:** http://maney.co.uk/index.php/journals/vea/. **Circ:** (Not Reported)

55368 ■ Via Inmarsat Magazine
Publicis Blueprint
23 Howland St.
London W1A 1AQ, United Kingdom
Ph: 44 20 74627777
Publisher E-mail: info@publicis-blueprint.co.uk
Magazine featuring the portable satellite technology. **Freq:** Quarterly. **Key Personnel:** Neal Anderson, Publisher, phone 44 20 74627619, neal.anderson@publicis-blueprint.co.uk; Martin Conway, Managing Editor, phone 44 20 74627947, martin.conway@publicis-blueprint.co.uk. **Remarks:** Accepts advertising. **URL:** http://www.publicis-blueprint.co.uk. **Ad Rates:** 4C: 3,750. **Circ:** 24,000

55369 ■ Victim Support
Hallam House
56-60 Hallam St.
London W1W 6JL, United Kingdom
Ph: 44 20 72680200
Fax: 44 20 72680210
Publisher E-mail: contact@victimsupport.org.uk
Publication covering crime victims support. **Freq:** Semiannual. **URL:** http://www.victimsupport.org/.

55370 ■ Viewfinder
British Universities Film and Video Council
77 Wells St.
London W1T 3QJ, United Kingdom
Ph: 44 20 73931500
Fax: 44 20 73931555
Publication E-mail: publications@bufvc.ac.uk
Publisher E-mail: ask@bufvc.ac.uk
Membership magazine covering instructional media.

Freq: Quarterly. **Print Method:** Plate. **Trim Size:** A4. **Key Personnel:** Prof. Michael Paris, Contact; Emily Fuller, Contact; Edward Lester, Contact; Andrew Logue, Contact. **ISSN:** 0952-4444. **Remarks:** Accepts advertising. **URL:** http://www.bufvc.ac.uk. **Ad Rates:** BW: 350. **Circ:** 5,500

55371 ■ Viewpoint
Royal Mencap Society
123 Golden Ln.
London EC1Y 0RT, United Kingdom
Ph: 44 20 74540454
Fax: 44 20 76083254
Publication E-mail: viewpoint@amencap.org.uk
Publisher E-mail: information@mencap.org.uk
Publication covering the mentally disabled. **Subtitle:** Learning Disability Magazine Published by Mencap. **Founded:** July 1995. **Freq:** Bimonthly. **Key Personnel:** Claire McMinn, Editor, phone 44 20 76965553, claire.hall@mencap.org.uk; Edd Fawcett, Asst. Ed., phone 44 42 076965509, edward.fawcett@mencap.org.uk. **ISSN:** 1358-6076. **Subscription Rates:** 18 individuals; 81 individuals 5-9 copies; 153 individuals 10-19 copies; 288 individuals 20 copies. **Remarks:** Accepts advertising. **URL:** http://www.mencap.org.uk/page.asp?id=526. **Ad Rates:** 4C: 700. **Circ:** Paid ‡6,300

55372 ■ Virology Journal
BioMed Central Ltd.
236 Gray's Inn Rd., Fl. 6
34-42 Cleveland St.
London WC1X 8HL, United Kingdom
Ph: 44 20 31922000
Fax: 44 20 31922010
Publisher E-mail: info@biomedcentral.com
Online journal covering all aspects of virology research. **Key Personnel:** Dr. Robert F. Garry, Editor-in-Chief, rfgarry@tulane.edu; Dr. William R. Gallaher, Dep. Ed., wgalla@lsuhsc.edu; Dr. Judith M. Ball, Editorial Board, jball@cvm.tamu.edu; Dr. David Sander, Managing Editor, dmsander@sanderassociates.com; Dr. Paul Digard, Editorial Board, pd1@mole.bio.cam.ac.uk; Dr. Donald L. Jarvis, Editorial Board, dljarvis@uwyo.edu. **ISSN:** 1743-422X. **Remarks:** Accepts advertising. **URL:** http://www.virologyj.com/. **Circ:** (Not Reported)

55373 ■ Visual Communication
Sage Publications Ltd.
c/o Carey Jewitt, Ed.
Institute of Education
University of London
23-29 Emerald St.
London WC1N 3QL, United Kingdom
Scholarly journal covering the role of the visual in society. **Founded:** 2000. **Freq:** Quarterly. **Key Personnel:** Theo Van Leeuwen, Editor; Carey Jewitt, Editor; Louise McWhinnie, Review Ed.; Teal Triggs, Editor; Kate Sweetapple, Review Ed.; Jay David Bolter, Honorary Board; Victor Burgin, Honorary Board; Paola Antonelli, Advisory Board. **ISSN:** 1470-3572. **Subscription Rates:** US$387 institutions print & e-access; US$348 institutions e-access; US$379 institutions print only; US$45 individuals print only; US$104 institutions single print; US$15 individuals single print. **Remarks:** Accepts advertising. **URL:** http://www.sagepub.co.uk/journalsProdDesc.nav?prodId=Journal201380. **Circ:** (Not Reported)

55374 ■ Vital
Nature Publishing Group
The Macmillan Bldg.
4 Crinan St.
London N1 9XW, United Kingdom
Ph: 44 20 78334000
Fax: 44 20 78434640
Publication E-mail: vitaleditorial@nature.com
Magazine containing features, news, views, advice and opinion. **Subtitle:** For the Whole Dental Team. **Freq:** Quarterly. **Key Personnel:** Stephen Hancocks, Editor-in-Chief; Kate Maynard, Editor, k.maynard@nature.com; Arveen Bajaj, News Ed., a.bajaj@nature.com. **ISSN:** 1741-7503. **Subscription Rates:** US$30 individuals online only. **Remarks:** Accepts advertising. **URL:** http://www.nature.com/vital/index.html. **Circ:** (Not Reported)

55375 ■ Voluntary Sector
National Council for Voluntary Organisations
Regent's Wharf
8 All Saints St.

London N1 9RL, United Kingdom
Ph: 44 20 77136161
Fax: 44 20 77136300
Publisher E-mail: ncvo@ncvo-vol.org.uk
Publication covering voluntarism. **Freq:** Monthly 10/yr.
Trim Size: A4. **Key Personnel:** Amanda Moss, Editor.
ISSN: 1672-2867. **URL:** http://www.ncvo-vol.org.uk. **Formerly:** NCVO News. **Ad Rates:** BW: 1,400. **Circ:** 5,000

55376 ■ Waitrose Food Illustrated
John Brown Citrus Publishing
136-142 Bramley Rd.
London W10 6SR, United Kingdom
Ph: 44 20 75653000
Fax: 44 20 75653060
Consumer magazine covering food and wine. **Founded:**
Apr. 1998. **Freq:** Monthly. **Print Method:** Web offset.
Trim Size: 222 x 300 mm. **Cols./Page:** 4. **Col. Width:**
45 millimeters. **Key Personnel:** William Sitwell, Editor.
Subscription Rates: 22 individuals for a partnership
card; 30 individuals; 35 U.S. **Remarks:** Accepts
advertising. **URL:** http://www.waitrose.com; http://www.
jbcp.co.uk. **Former name:** Food Illustrated. **Ad Rates:**
4C: 10,000, PCI: 85. **Circ:** (Not Reported)

55377 ■ Wallpaper*
IPC Media Ltd.
Blue Fin Bldg.
110 Southwark St.
London SE1 0SU, United Kingdom
Ph: 44 203 1485000
Publication E-mail: custsvc_wallpape@fulcoinc.com
Magazine focusing on interior design. Aimed at an
international, dual audience of urban modernists and
global navigators. Covers interiors, industrial design,
architecture, entertaining, fashion, and travel. **Freq:** 11/
yr. **Key Personnel:** Ben Giles, Publisher; Paula Cain,
Advertising Dir., paula_cain@wallpaper.com. **Remarks:**
Accepts advertising. **URL:** http://www.wallpaper.com/.
Circ: ★113,000

55378 ■ The War Cry
The Salvation Army
101 Newington Cswy.
London SE1 6BN, United Kingdom
Ph: 44 20 73674900
Fax: 44 20 73674710
Publication E-mail: warcry@salvationarmy.org.uk
Publisher E-mail: londoncentral@salvationarmy.org.uk
Religious newspaper covering the arts, sports, news,
and lifestyle. **Founded:** 1879. **Freq:** Weekly. **Print
Method:** Web Offset. **Trim Size:** 289 x 420 mm. **Cols./
Page:** 6. **Col. Width:** 44 millimeters. **Col. Depth:** 378
millimeters. **Key Personnel:** Philip Halcrow, Dep. Ed.;
Major Nigel Bovey, Editor; Claire Brine, Editorial Asst.;
Stephen Pearson, Prod. Ed.; Gill Cox, Ch. Designer.
Subscription Rates: 26 individuals; 41 other countries
surface mail; 44.50 other countries airmail. **Remarks:**
Accepts advertising. **URL:** http://www2.salvationarmy.
org.uk/warcry. **Circ:** Paid 17,000

55379 ■ War & Society
Maney Publishing
1 Carlton House Ter.
London SW1Y 5AF, United Kingdom
Ph: 44 20 74517300
Fax: 44 20 74517307
Publisher E-mail: maney@maney.co.uk
Journal covering war and its impact to society. **Founded:**
May 1983. **Freq:** 3/yr. **Key Personnel:** Jeffrey Grey,
Editor, j.grey@adfa.edu.au. **ISSN:** 0729-2473. **Subscription Rates:** 169 institutions, other countries;
US$275 institutions; 44 other countries; US$106 individuals; 44 individuals in UK and European. **Remarks:**
Accepts advertising. **URL:** http://maney.co.uk/index.php/
journals/war. **Circ:** (Not Reported)

55380 ■ Warship Technology
RINA—The Royal Institute of Naval Architects
10 Upper Belgrave St.
London SW1X 8BQ, United Kingdom
Ph: 44 20 72354622
Fax: 44 20 72595912
Publisher E-mail: hq@rina.org.uk
Journal of The Royal Institution of Naval Architects
covering technical information on design, construction
and outfitting of naval vessels worldwide. **Freq:** 5/yr.
Print Method: Offset Litho. **Trim Size:** 210 x 297 mm.
Key Personnel: David Foxwell, Editor. **Subscription
Rates:** 150 individuals; 156 individuals Europe; 168

other countries; 260 two years; 272 two years Europe;
292 two years OTC. **Remarks:** Accepts advertising.
URL: http://www.rina.org.uk/wt.html; http://www.rina.org.
uk/showarticle.pl?id=5974. **Circ:** Combined 11,650

55381 ■ Water Asset Management International
IWA Publishing Ltd.
Alliance House
12 Caxton St.
London SW1H 0QS, United Kingdom
Ph: 44 20 76545500
Fax: 44 20 76545555
Newsletter focusing on asset management in water and
wastewater utilities. **Freq:** 4/yr. **Key Personnel:** Dr. John
Bridgeman, Editor; Prof. Stewart Burn, Editor; Prof. Sunil
Sinha, Editor. **ISSN:** 1814-5434. **Subscription Rates:**
US$423 institutions; EUR320 institutions; 212 institutions.
URL: http://www.iwaponline.com/wami/default.htm.

55382 ■ Water and Environment Manager
Chartered Institution of Water and Environmental
Management
15 John St.
London WC1N 2EB, United Kingdom
Ph: 44 20 78313110
Fax: 44 20 74054967
Publisher E-mail: admin@ciwem.org.uk
Publication covering water and environment. **Freq:**
Quarterly. **Key Personnel:** David Butler, Editor-in-Chief.
ISSN: 1747-6585. **Subscription Rates:** 11 single issue;
16 single issue overseas; 103 individuals; 145 other
countries. **Remarks:** Advertising accepted; rates available upon request. **URL:** http://www.ciwem.org.uk/
information-resources/publications/water-and-
environment-journal.aspx. **Circ:** 12,000

55383 ■ Water Intelligence Online
IWA Publishing Ltd.
Alliance House
12 Caxton St.
London SW1H 0QS, United Kingdom
Ph: 44 20 76545500
Fax: 44 20 76545555
Peer-reviewed journal covering water and environmental
information service. **Freq:** 12/yr. **Key Personnel:** Maggie Smith, Editor, msmith@iwap.co.uk. **ISSN:** 1476-
1777. **Subscription Rates:** 2,217 institutions online
only; US$2,889 institutions online only; EUR1,526 institutions online only. **URL:** http://www.iwaponline.com/wio/
default.htm.

55384 ■ Water Policy
IWA Publishing Ltd.
Alliance House
12 Caxton St.
London SW1H 0QS, United Kingdom
Ph: 44 20 76545500
Fax: 44 20 76545555
Journal focused on water policy worldwide. **Founded:**
June 1, 1965. **Freq:** Monthly. **Print Method:** Offset. **Trim
Size:** 8 1/2 x 11. **Cols./Page:** 3. **Col. Width:** 26
nonpareils. **Col. Depth:** 140 agate lines. **Key Personnel:** J. Delli Priscoli, Editor-in-Chief. **ISSN:** 1366-7017.
Subscription Rates: US$1,304 institutions; EUR1,054
institutions; 671 institutions. **URL:** http://www.iwaponline.
com/wp/default.htm.

55385 ■ Water Practice and Technology
IWA Publishing Ltd.
Alliance House
12 Caxton St.
London SW1H 0QS, United Kingdom
Ph: 44 20 76545500
Fax: 44 20 76545555
Journal covering invaluable source of information for
water practitioners, including active in utilities, consultants and engineers. **Freq:** 4/yr. **Key Personnel:** Prof.
Helmut Kroiss, Editor-in-Chief. **ISSN:** 1751-231X. **Subscription Rates:** US$343 institutions online only;
EUR263 institutions online only; 181 institutions online
only. **URL:** http://www.iwaponline.com/wpt/default.htm.

55386 ■ Water Science & Technology
IWA Publishing Ltd.
Alliance House
12 Caxton St.
London SW1H 0QS, United Kingdom
Ph: 44 20 76545500
Fax: 44 20 76545555
Journal covering all aspects of water quality management and pollution control. **Subtitle:** Water Supply. **Freq:**
Bimonthly. **Key Personnel:** Prof. Helmut Kroiss, Editor-

in-Chief. **ISSN:** 1606-9749. **Subscription Rates:**
US$2,322 individuals online and print; EUR2,120 individuals online and print; 1,312 individuals online and print.
URL: http://www.iwaponline.com/ws/default.htm.

55387 ■ Water Science & Technology
IWA Publishing Ltd.
Alliance House
12 Caxton St.
London SW1H 0QS, United Kingdom
Ph: 44 20 76545500
Fax: 44 20 76545555
Journal covering water quality management and pollution control. **Freq:** Semimonthly. **Key Personnel:** Prof.
Helmut Kroiss, Editor-in-Chief. **ISSN:** 0273-1223. **Subscription Rates:** US$6,995 institutions print and free
online; EUR5,857 institutions print and free online; 3,803
institutions print and free online. **URL:** http://www.
iwaponline.com/wst/default.htm.

55388 ■ Water Supply
International Water Services Association
Association Internationale des Services d'Eau
Alliance House
12 Caxton St.
London SW1H 0QS, United Kingdom
Ph: 44 207 6545500
Fax: 44 207 6545555
Publisher E-mail: water@iwahq.org.uk
Publication covering water resources. **Freq:** Bimonthly.
Key Personnel: Gustaf Olsson, Editor-in-Chief. **ISSN:**
1606-9749. **Subscription Rates:** 99 nonmembers;
US$178.20 nonmembers; EUR133.65 nonmembers;
74.25 members; US$133.65 members; EUR100.24
members. **Remarks:** Accepts advertising. **URL:** http://
www.iwapublishing.com/template.cfm?name=
isbn0340720182. **Circ:** (Not Reported)

55389 ■ Water 21
IWA Publishing Ltd.
Alliance House
12 Caxton St.
London SW1H 0QS, United Kingdom
Ph: 44 20 76545500
Fax: 44 20 76545555
Worldwide publication covering water quality. **Subtitle:**
The Magazine of the International Water Association.
Freq: Bimonthly. **Trim Size:** 200 x 270 mm. **Key Personnel:** Keith Hayward, Editor, khayward@iwap.co.uk.
ISSN: 1561-9508. **Subscription Rates:** US$265 institutions print; EUR290 institutions; 175 institutions print.
Remarks: Accepts advertising. **URL:** http://www.
iwapublishing.com/template.cfm?name=w21. **Former
name:** Water Quality International. **Ad Rates:** 4C:
16,400. **Circ:** (Not Reported)

55390 ■ Water Utility Management International
IWA Publishing Ltd.
Alliance House
12 Caxton St.
London SW1H 0QS, United Kingdom
Ph: 44 20 76545500
Fax: 44 20 76545555
Journal focusing on the needs and interests of senior
water utility managers. **Freq:** 4/yr. **Key Personnel:** Dr.
Richard Franceys, Contact. **ISSN:** 1747-7751. **Subscription Rates:** US$397 institutions; EUR301 institutions; 199 institutions. **URL:** http://www.iwaponline.com/
wumi/default.htm.

55391 ■ Waterlife
Think Publishing
The Pall Mall Deposit
124-128 Barlby Rd.
London W10 6BL, United Kingdom
Ph: 44 20 89623020
Fax: 44 20 89628689
Magazine covering wetlands and waterbird conservation.
Subtitle: The Magazine for Members of the Wildfowl &
Wetlands Trust. **Freq:** Quarterly. **Key Personnel:** Ian
McAuliffe, Director, ian.mcauliffe@thinkpublishing.co.uk;
Tilly Boulter, Ch. Exec., tilly.boulter@thinkpublishing.co.
uk; Polly Arnold, Managing Editor, polly.arnold@
thinkpublishing.co.uk. **Remarks:** Accepts advertising.
URL: http://www.thinkpublishing.co.uk/magazine_
environment.aspx. **Circ:** 87,000

55392 ■ WDCS
Think Publishing
The Pall Mall Deposit
124-128 Barlby Rd.
London W10 6BL, United Kingdom
Ph: 44 20 89623020

Fax: 44 20 89628689

Magazine covering whale and dolphin conservation. **Freq:** Quarterly. **Trim Size:** 190 x 260 mm. **Key Personnel:** Ian McAuliffe, Director, ian.mcauliffe@thinkpublishing.co.uk; Tilly Boulter, Ch. Exec., tilly.boulter@thinkpublishing.co.uk; Polly Arnold, Managing Editor, polly.arnold@thinkpublishing.co.uk. **Remarks:** Accepts advertising. **URL:** http://www.thinkpublishing.co.uk/. **Circ:** 26,000

55393 ■ WDM in Action
World Development Movement
66 Offley Rd.
London SW9 0LS, United Kingdom
Ph: 44 207 8204900
Fax: 44 207 8204949
Publisher E-mail: wdm@wdm.org.uk
Magazine covering campaign news of the World Development Movement and information on current development issues. **Freq:** Quarterly. **Remarks:** Accepts advertising. **URL:** http://www.wdmscotland.org.uk/. **Circ:** (Not Reported)

55394 ■ Wealth
Incisive Media Limited
Haymarket House
28-29 Haymarket
London SW1Y 4RX, United Kingdom
Ph: 44 870 2408859
Fax: 44 207 4849797
Publisher E-mail: customerservices@incisivemedia.com
Business magazine for wealth professionals. **Subtitle:** For UK Professional Distributors of Wealth Management Solutions. **Freq:** Quarterly. **Key Personnel:** Toby Finden-Crofts, Publisher, phone 44 20 79684573, toby.finden-crofts@incisivemedia.com; Jenne Mannion, Editor, phone 44 20 79684563, jenne.mannion@incisivemedia.com; Lynsey Davis, Advertising Mgr., phone 44 20 79684524, lynsey.davis@incisivemedia.com. **Remarks:** Accepts advertising. **URL:** http://www.wealthmagazineonline.com. **Circ:** 4,000

55395 ■ Web User
IPC Country & Leisure Media Ltd.
Blue Fin Bldg.
110 Southwark St.
London SE1 0SU, United Kingdom
Ph: 44 20 31484327
Fax: 44 20 31488122
Magazine covering a wide range of topics, including how to build web pages, where to find the cheapest holidays, how to keep computers safe from hackers, reviews about the latest software and hardware and the latest websites. **Freq:** Fortnightly. **Key Personnel:** Claire Woffenden, Editor, phone 44 20 31484935. **Subscription Rates:** 38.29 individuals; 75.54 two years individual. **URL:** http://www.ipcmedia.com/brands/webuser/; http://www.web-user.co.uk/.

55396 ■ The Week
30 Cleveland St.
London W1T 4JT, United Kingdom
Ph: 44 20 79076180
Fax: 44 20 79850052
Publisher E-mail: theweek@servicehelpline.co.uk
Magazine featuring world news; reviews of books and arts; and leisure articles. **Founded:** 1995. **Freq:** Weekly. **Key Personnel:** Jonathan Kitchen, Advertising Dir., phone 44 20 79076616, jonathan_kitchen@dennis.co.uk; Caroline Law, Editor; Kerin O'Connor, Managing Editor, phone 44 20 79076452, kerin_oconnor@dennis.co.uk; Jeremi O'Grady, Editor-in-Chief, editorialadmin@theweek.co.uk; Jolyon Connel, Founder, Editorial Dir. **Subscription Rates:** 19.99 individuals U.K. (13 issues); 97 individuals Europe; 117 elsewhere. **Remarks:** Accepts advertising. **URL:** http://www.theweek.co.uk. **Circ:** (Not Reported)

55397 ■ Wembley & Kingsbury Times
Archant Regional Ltd.
c/o North West London Newspapers
100A Avenue Rd.
London NW3 3HF, United Kingdom
Ph: 44 20 74330000
Publisher E-mail: sandra.roantree@archant.co.uk
Local community newspaper. **Freq:** Weekly. **Key Personnel:** Geoff Martin, Editor, geoff.martin@archant.co.uk. **Subscription Rates:** 8.80 individuals 4 weeks; 17.60 individuals 2 months; 26.40 individuals 3 months;

52.80 individuals 6 months; 150.80 individuals. **Remarks:** Accepts advertising. **URL:** http://www.wktimes.co.uk/home. **Circ:** (Not Reported)

55398 ■ Westlife
Attic Futura (UK) Ltd.
17-18 Berners St.
London W1P 3DD, United Kingdom
Ph: 44 20 76646490
Fax: 44 20 76642250
Website for people interested in the musical group, Westlife. **Freq:** Bimonthly. **URL:** http://www.westlife.co.uk/; http://www.periodicals.ru/import/good.phtml?id=510574&set_usr_lang=eng.

55399 ■ Westside Magazine
Archant Life
Avon House, 5th Fl.
Kensington Village
Avonmore Rd.
London W14 8TS, United Kingdom
Publisher E-mail: anne.basey-fisher@archant.co.uk
Magazine featuring life in West London. **Founded:** 2003. **Freq:** Monthly. **Key Personnel:** Victoria White, Advertising Mgr., phone 44 20 76052228, victoria.white@archant.co.uk; Fiona Keating, Editor, fiona.keating@archant.co.uk. **URL:** http://westside.greatbritishlife.co.uk/; http://www.archantlife.co.uk/contact-us-regions-london-westside-contacts-10408. **Circ:** ★47,000

55400 ■ What Digital Camera
IPC Media Ltd.
Blue Fin Bldg.
110 Southwark St.
London SE1 0SU, United Kingdom
Ph: 44 203 1485000
British magazine focusing on digital photography. Includes product reviews, software tests, and tutorials and technique tips for programs, as well as other topics. **Freq:** Monthly. **Key Personnel:** Nigel Atherton, Editor; Jackie Porter, Production Ed. **Subscription Rates:** 39.99 two years; 64.99 two years. **Remarks:** Accepts advertising. **URL:** http://www.whatdigitalcamera.com; http://www.ipcmedia.com/contacts/index.php?lookuptype=MAGAZINE&lookup=657. **Circ:** (Not Reported)

55401 ■ What Mountain Bike?
Future Publishing Ltd.
2 Balcombe St.
London NW1 6NW, United Kingdom
Ph: 44 20 70424000
Publisher E-mail: future@subscription.co.uk
Magazine for mountain bike enthusiasts devoted to totally impartial testing to help find all the information needed to make the right choice on everything from tyres to complete full suspension bikes, with each issue including 3 free pullout route guides for beginners, enthusiasts or experts. **Freq:** Monthly. **Key Personnel:** Jeff Jones, Editor, jeff@bikeradar.com; John Stevenson, Editor, john@bikeradar.com. **Subscription Rates:** 11.60 individuals quarterly direct debit. **Remarks:** Accepts advertising. **URL:** http://www.bikeradar.com/mtb. **Circ:** (Not Reported)

55402 ■ What Van?
Wilmington Quest Magazines Ltd.
Global Trade Media
Progressive House
Maidstone Rd.
Foots Cray
London DA14 5HZ, United Kingdom
Ph: 44 20 82697741
Publication E-mail: whatvan@wilmington.co.uk
Publisher E-mail: pbarker@whatvan.co.uk
Magazine covering light commercial vehicles available in the UK for consumers and industry professionals. **Founded:** June 1985. **Freq:** Monthly. **Print Method:** Web offset litho. **Trim Size:** 210 x 297 mm. **Key Personnel:** Paul Barker, Editor, phone 44 20 82697741, pbarker@whatvan.co.uk; James Dallas, Deputy Ed., james.dallas@whatvan.co.uk; Jon Morton, Publishing Dir., jmorton@whatvan.co.uk. **ISSN:** 1350-6404. **Subscription Rates:** 3.95 single issue; US$75.22 individuals online only; US$135 U.S. and Canada; US$150 other countries. **Remarks:** Accepts advertising. **URL:** http://www.whatvan.co.uk. **Circ:** Combined ‡20,000

55403 ■ WHERE London
Miller Publishing Group L.L.C.
30 Little Russell St.
London WC1A 2HN, United Kingdom
Travel and tourism magazine focusing on London, England. **Key Personnel:** Chris Johnson, Editor; Chris Manning, Publisher. **Remarks:** Accepts advertising. **URL:** http://wheretraveler.com/classic/intl/uk/lon/. **Circ:** (Not Reported)

55404 ■ Whitelines Snowboard Magazine
Factory Media
1 W Smithfield
London EC1A 9JU, United Kingdom
Ph: 44 20 73329700
Publisher E-mail: contact@factorymedia.com
Magazine featuring snowboarding. **Freq:** 7/yr. **Key Personnel:** Ed Blomfield, Editor, ed@whitelines.com. **Subscription Rates:** 28.50 individuals direct debit; 34.65 individuals credit card; US$75 individuals. **URL:** http://whitelines.com; http://factorymedia.com.

55405 ■ Wildabout
Think Publishing
The Pall Mall Deposit
124-128 Barlby Rd.
London W10 6BL, United Kingdom
Ph: 44 20 89623020
Fax: 44 20 89628689
Magazine covering wildlife. **Freq:** 3/yr. **Trim Size:** 215 x 280 mm. **Key Personnel:** Ian McAuliffe, Director, ian.mcauliffe@thinkpublishing.co.uk; Tilly Boulter, Ch. Exec., tilly.boulter@thinkpublishing.co.uk; Polly Arnold, Managing Editor, polly.arnold@thinkpublishing.co.uk. **Remarks:** Accepts advertising. **URL:** http://www.thinkpublishing.co.uk/print_magazines.php. **Circ:** 30,000

55406 ■ Willesden & Brent Times
Archant Regional Ltd.
c/o North West London Newspapers
100A Avenue Rd.
London NW3 3HF, United Kingdom
Ph: 44 20 74330000
Publisher E-mail: sandra.roantree@archant.co.uk
Local community newspaper. **Freq:** Weekly (Wed.). **Key Personnel:** Geoff Martin, Editor, geoff.martin@archant.co.uk. **Subscription Rates:** 11.60 individuals 4 weeks; 23.20 individuals 2 months; 34.80 individuals 3 months; 69.60 individuals 6 months; 150.80 individuals. **Remarks:** Accepts advertising. **URL:** http://www.wbtimes.co.uk/home. **Circ:** (Not Reported)

55407 ■ Wills & Trusts Law Reports
Legalese Ltd.
Kensington Sq. House
12-14 Ansdell St.
London W8 5BN, United Kingdom
Ph: 44 20 73969292
Fax: 44 20 73969303
Set of law reports for trust, estates, and probate practitioners. **Freq:** 10/yr. **ISSN:** 1470-0638. **Subscription Rates:** 399 individuals. **URL:** http://www.legalease.co.uk.

55408 ■ The Wire
The Wire Magazine
23 Jack's Pl.
6 Corbet Pl.
London E1 6NN, United Kingdom
Ph: 44 20 74225010
Fax: 44 20 74225011
Consumer magazine covering experimental rock, jazz, electronic music, classical and world music. **Founded:** 1982. **Freq:** Monthly. **Print Method:** Web Offset. **Key Personnel:** Chris Bohn, Editor; Tony Herrington, Publisher; Anne Hilde Neset, Dep. Ed. **ISSN:** 0952-0686. **Subscription Rates:** US$78 individuals. **Remarks:** Accepts advertising. **URL:** http://www.thewire.co.uk/. **Ad Rates:** BW: 995, 4C: 1,450. **Circ:** (Not Reported)

55409 ■ W.I.T.C.H.
BBC Worldwide Publishing Ltd.
Media Centre
201 Wood Ln.
London W12 7TQ, United Kingdom
Ph: 44 20 84332000
Fax: 44 20 87490538
Magazine featuring five young teenage girls who have

Circulation: ★ = ABC; △ = BPA; ♦ = CAC; • = CCAB; ❑ = VAC; ⊕ = PO Statement; ‡ = Publisher's Report; Boldface figures = sworn; Light figures = estimated.

Gale Directory of Publications & Broadcast Media/147th Ed. 5777

special magical powers. **Freq:** Monthly. **Subscription Rates:** 1.99 single issue. **URL:** http://www.bbcmagazines.com/content/magazines/witch/.

55410 ■ WMS
Luxury Publishing Limited
5 Jubilee Pl.
Chelsea
London SW3 3TD, United Kingdom
Ph: 44 20 75912900
Fax: 44 20 75912929
Publisher E-mail: info@luxurypublishing.com
Magazine covering all aspects of wealth and financial management. **Freq:** Quarterly. **Key Personnel:** William Cash, Editor; Wendy Coumantaros, Advertising Dir. **Subscription Rates:** 100 individuals. **Remarks:** Accepts advertising. **URL:** http://www.luxurypublishing.co.uk/; http://www.wealthmanagementsurvey.com/. **Circ:** 54,450

55411 ■ The Wolf
3, Holly Mansions
Fortune Green Rd.
W Hampstead
London NW6 1UB, United Kingdom
Publication E-mail: editor@wolfmagazine.co.uk
Magazine containing contemporary poetry. **Founded:** Apr. 2002. **Freq:** 3/yr. **Key Personnel:** James Byrne, Editor. **ISSN:** 1755-3458. **Subscription Rates:** 15 individuals; US$12 single issue; US$35 individuals; 5 single issue. **URL:** http://www.wolfmagazine.co.uk/.

55412 ■ Woman
IPC Media Ltd.
Blue Fin Bldg.
110 Southwark St.
London SE1 0SU, United Kingdom
Ph: 44 203 1485000
Magazine focusing on women's interests. **Key Personnel:** Karen Livermore, Editor, phone 44 20 31486491; Adrian Booker, Publisher; Richard Smith, Advertising Mgr. **Subscription Rates:** 39.99 individuals; 74.99 two years. **URL:** http://www.ipcmedia.com/brands/woman/.

55413 ■ Woman & Home
IPC Media Ltd.
Blue Fin Bldg.
110 Southwark St.
London SE1 0SU, United Kingdom
Ph: 44 203 1485000
Publication E-mail: wandhmail@ipcmedia.com
Magazine focusing on fashion, beauty, well-being, food, wine, home, health, and other issues of interest to women. **Key Personnel:** Sue James, Editorial Dir.; Gaby Huddart, Dep. Ed.; David Dowding, Creative Dir. **Subscription Rates:** 49.99 two years; 49.99 individuals. **URL:** http://www.womanandhome.com/.

55414 ■ Women's Health
Future Medicine Ltd.
Unitec House
2 Albert Pl.
London N3 1QB, United Kingdom
Ph: 44 20 83716080
Fax: 44 20 83432313
Publisher E-mail: info@futuremedicine.com
Peer-reviewed journal covering the health and health care needs of women. **Freq:** Bimonthly. **Key Personnel:** Elisa Manzotti, Editorial Dir., e.manzotti@futuremedicine.com. **ISSN:** 1745-5057. **Subscription Rates:** 605 institutions; US$1,160 institutions; EUR755 institutions; 126,000¥ institutions. **Remarks:** Accepts advertising. **URL:** http://www.futuremedicine.com/loi/whe. **Circ:** (Not Reported)

55415 ■ W1 Magazine
26, York St.
London W1U 6PZ, United Kingdom
Ph: 44 207 7887547
Publisher E-mail: enquiries@w1magazine.co.uk
Magazine covering entertainment, food and culture in London. **Remarks:** Accepts advertising. **URL:** http://www.w1magazine.co.uk/Main.html. **Circ:** (Not Reported)

55416 ■ Wordsearches
H. Bauer Publishing
Academic House
24-28 Oval Rd.
London NW1 7DT, United Kingdom
Ph: 44 20 72418000
Fax: 44 20 72418030
Magazine featuring wordsearch puzzles. **Freq:** Monthly. **Trim Size:** 185 x 255 mm. **Key Personnel:** Clive Garsin,

Gp. Ed.; Spike Figgett, Publishing Dir.; Helen Greenwood, Advertising Mgr. **Subscription Rates:** 15.47 individuals. **Remarks:** Accepts advertising. **URL:** http://www.bauer.co.uk/wordsearch; http://www.puzzlemagazines.co.uk/word-searches. **Formerly:** Wordsearches. **Circ:** ★108,000

55417 ■ Wordsearches Collection
H. Bauer Publishing
Academic House
24-28 Oval Rd.
London NW1 7DT, United Kingdom
Ph: 44 20 72418000
Fax: 44 20 72418030
Magazine featuring over 100 wordsearches. **Freq:** Monthly. **Trim Size:** 185 x 255 mm. **Key Personnel:** Clive Garsin, Gp. Ed.; Spike Figgett, Publishing Dir.; Helen Greenwood, Advertising Mgr. **Subscription Rates:** 15.47 individuals direct debit. **Remarks:** Accepts advertising. **URL:** http://www.bauer.co.uk/wordsearches-collection; http://www.puzzlemagazines.co.uk/word-searches-collection. **Circ:** ★63,000

55418 ■ World Cruise Industry Review
SPG Media Group Plc.
Brunel House
55-57 N Wharf Rd.
London W2 1LA, United Kingdom
Ph: 44 20 79159660
Fax: 44 20 77242089
Publisher E-mail: info@spgmedia.com
Trade magazine covering yachts and the cruise industry worldwide. **Freq:** Annual. **Subscription Rates:** Free. **Remarks:** Accepts advertising. **URL:** http://www.worldcruiseindustryreview.com/. **Circ:** Non-paid 6,993

55419 ■ World Expro
SPG Media Group Plc.
Brunel House
55-57 N Wharf Rd.
London W2 1LA, United Kingdom
Ph: 44 20 79159660
Fax: 44 20 77242089
Publisher E-mail: info@spgmedia.com
Trade magazine covering energy, oil and gas industries worldwide. **Freq:** Annual. **Subscription Rates:** Free. **Remarks:** Accepts advertising. **URL:** http://www.worldexpro.com/. **Circ:** ‡12,500

55420 ■ World Gold Analyst
Mining Journal Ltd.
Albert House
1 Singer St.
London EC2A 4BQ, United Kingdom
Ph: 44 20 72166060
Fax: 44 20 72166050
Publisher E-mail: lisa.huggins@aspermontuk.com
Trade magazine covering the analysis of the top gold producing companies for the gold industry. **Freq:** Quarterly. **Key Personnel:** Paul Burton, Editor; Elena Patimova, Contact, elena.patimova@gfmsworldgold.com. **ISSN:** 1463-9327. **Subscription Rates:** US$400 individuals online. **URL:** http://www.gfmsworldgold.com/. **Former name:** Mining Journal Gold Service; International Gold Newsletter.

55421 ■ The World of Interiors
Conde Nast Publications Ltd.
Vogue House
Hanover Sq.
London W1S 1JU, United Kingdom
Ph: 44 20 74999080
Magazine covering decoration and home interiors. **Founded:** 1981. **Freq:** Monthly. **Key Personnel:** Rupert Thomas, Editor; Katherine Atkinson, Contact, woiadvertising@condenast.co.uk. **Subscription Rates:** US$93 individuals free with super saver shipping; US$60 individuals. **Remarks:** Accepts advertising. **URL:** http://www.worldofinteriors.co.uk/. **Circ:** Paid 65,000

55422 ■ World Mining Equipment
Metal Bulletin PLC
Nestor House
Playhouse Yard
London EC4V 5EX, United Kingdom
Ph: 44 20 78279977
Fax: 44 20 78276470
Trade magazine covering mining equipment worldwide. **Founded:** 1976. **Freq:** 10/yr. **Print Method:** Web offset. **Trim Size:** A4. **Key Personnel:** Peter Johnson, Pub-

lisher, pjohnson@mining-media.com. **ISSN:** 0746-729X. **Subscription Rates:** 120 individuals; Free to qualified subscribers. **Remarks:** Accepts advertising. **URL:** http://www.wme.com. **Ad Rates:** BW: US$5,060, 4C: US$5,200. **Circ:** Combined ★23,971

55423 ■ World Soccer
Time Inc.
Blue Fin Bldg.
110 Southwark St.
London SE1 0SU, United Kingdom
Ph: 44 20 31484817
Fax: 44 20 72617474
Publication E-mail: jamie_rainbow@ipcmedia.com
Publisher E-mail: information@timeinc.com
Magazine focusing on the British sport of football. Includes interviews with football stars. **Freq:** Monthly. **Key Personnel:** Gavin Hamilton, Editor, gavin_hamilton@ipcmedia.com; Lee Horris, Advertising Mgr., lee_morris@ipcmedia.com. **Subscription Rates:** 16.35 individuals direct debit (half-yearly); 65.50 two years; 33.70 individuals; US$148.40 two years; US$79.50 individuals. **Remarks:** Accepts advertising. **URL:** http://www.ipcmedia.com/brands/worldsoccer/; http://www.ipcmedia.com/brands/brands.php. **Circ:** (Not Reported)

55424 ■ World Superyacht Review
SPG Media Group Plc.
Brunel House
55-57 N Wharf Rd.
London W2 1LA, United Kingdom
Ph: 44 20 79159660
Fax: 44 20 77242089
Publisher E-mail: info@spgmedia.com
Trade magazine covering yachts. **Freq:** Semiannual. **Subscription Rates:** Free. **Remarks:** Accepts advertising. **URL:** http://www.worldsuperyacht.com. **Circ:** 10,000

55425 ■ World Tobacco
DMG World Media
Northcliffe House
2 Derry St.
London W8 5TT, United Kingdom
Ph: 44 20 79386000
Magazine covering the agricultural industry. **Founded:** 1963. **Freq:** Bimonthly. **Trim Size:** 210 x 297 mm. **Key Personnel:** Stefanie Rossel, Editor-in-Chief, phone 49 6131 484513, stefanie.rossel@konradin.de; Anja Helk, Editor, phone 49 6131 484514, anja.helk@konradin.de; William McEwen, Editor, phone 49 6131 484511, william.mcewen@konradin.de. **ISSN:** 0043-9126. **Remarks:** Accepts advertising. **URL:** http://www.worldtobacco.co.uk/. **Ad Rates:** BW: 2,160, 4C: 3,355. **Circ:** 4,256

55426 ■ The World Today
The Royal Institute of International Affairs
Chatham House
10 St. James's Sq.
London SW1Y 4LE, United Kingdom
Ph: 44 20 79575700
Fax: 44 20 79575710
Publisher E-mail: contact@chathamhouse.org.uk
International affairs publication. **Founded:** 1945. **Freq:** Monthly. **Trim Size:** A4. **Key Personnel:** Alison Couldridge, Contact, phone 44 20 7957 5712, wt@chathamhouse.org.uk. **ISSN:** 0043-9134. **Subscription Rates:** 35 individuals; US$65 U.S. and Canada; 28 students; US$50 students US & Canada; 112 institutions; US$195 institutions US & Canada; 38 individuals Europe & rest of world; 30 students Europe & rest of world; 130 institutions Europe & rest of world; Free to full members. **Remarks:** Accepts advertising. **URL:** http://www.chathamhouse.org.uk/publications/twt/. **Ad Rates:** BW: 500, 4C: 700. **Circ:** 7,500

55427 ■ World Tunnelling
Mining Journal Ltd.
Albert House
1 Singer St.
London EC2A 4BQ, United Kingdom
Ph: 44 20 72166060
Fax: 44 20 72166050
Publisher E-mail: lisa.huggins@aspermontuk.com
Journal covering tunneling methods and equipment worldwide. **Founded:** Mar. 1988. **Freq:** Monthly. **Print Method:** Sheetfed Offset. **Trim Size:** 8 1/4 x 11 3/8. **Cols./Page:** 4. **Col. Width:** 15 ems. **Col. Depth:** 61.5 ems. **ISSN:** 0956-8700. **Remarks:** Accepts advertising. **URL:** http://www.world-tunnelling.com. **Former name:**

World Tunnelling and Subsurface Excavation (1999). **Ad Rates:** BW: US$2,878, 4C: US$4,000, PCI: US$100. **Circ:** *7,000

55428 ■ WRVS Action
Think Publishing
The Pal Mall Deposit
124-128 Barlby Rd.
London W10 6BL, United Kingdom
Ph: 44 20 89623020
Fax: 44 20 89628689
Publisher E-mail: watchdog@thinkpublishing.co.uk
Magazine for supporters and volunteers of Women's Royal Voluntary Service. **Freq:** Semiannual. **Trim Size:** 190 x 260 mm. **Key Personnel:** Ian McAuliffe, Director, ian@thinkpublishing.co.uk; Tilly Boulter, Ch. Exec., tilly@thinkpublishing.co.uk; Polly Arnold, Mng. Dir., pollya@thinkpublishing.co.uk. **Remarks:** Accepts advertising. **URL:** http://www.thinkpublishing.co.uk/mag_action.html. **Circ:** 90,000

55429 ■ Yachting Monthly
Time Inc.
9th Fl., Blue Fin Bldg.
110 Southwark St.
London SE1 0SU, United Kingdom
Ph: 44 20 31484872
Fax: 44 20 31488128
Publisher E-mail: information@timeinc.com
Magazine focusing on boating and yachting. **Freq:** Monthly. **Key Personnel:** Paul Gelder, Editor, phone 44 20 31484867, paul_gelder@ipcmedia.com. **Subscription Rates:** 37.50 individuals; 75.50 two years; 112.50 individuals 3 years. **Remarks:** Accepts advertising. **URL:** http://www.yachtingmonthly.com/ym/home.htm; http://www.ipcmedia.com/brands/ym/. **Circ:** (Not Reported)

55430 ■ Yachting World
Time Inc.
Blue Fin Bldg., 9th Fl.
110 Southwark St.
London SE1 0SU, United Kingdom
Ph: 44 20 31484846
Fax: 44 20 31488127
Publisher E-mail: information@timeinc.com
Yachting news, competition information, etc. **Freq:** Monthly. **Key Personnel:** David Glen, Editor, phone 44 20 31484842, david_glenn@ipcmedia.com; Alan Warren, Advertising Mgr., alan_warren@ipcmedia.com. **Subscription Rates:** 39.99 individuals; 74.99 two years. **Remarks:** Accepts advertising. **URL:** http://www.yachting-world.com/yw/home.htm; http://www.ipcmedia.com/brands/yw/. **Circ:** (Not Reported)

55431 ■ Yoga and Health
Yoga Today Ltd.
c/o Jane Sill, Ed.
PO Box 16969
London E1W 1FY, United Kingdom
Ph: 44 20 74805456
Publisher E-mail: editor@yogaandhealthmag.co.uk
Journal covering yoga and health worldwide. **Founded:** 1975. **Freq:** Monthly. **Print Method:** Offset. **Trim Size:** 297 x 210 mm. **Col. Width:** 4.2 centimeters. **Key Personnel:** Jane Sill, Editor, editor@yogaandhealthmag.co.uk; Simon Briant, Contact, phone 44 1273 600073, fax 44 1273 600822, ads@yogaandhealthmag.co.uk. **Subscription Rates:** 25 individuals U.K.; 39 individuals Europe; 49 other countries airmail. **Remarks:** Accepts advertising. **URL:** http://www.yogaandhealthmag.co.uk. **Formerly:** Yoga Today. **Ad Rates:** BW: 950, 4C: 1,195. **Circ:** Paid 15,000

55432 ■ YOGA Magazine
YOGA Magazine Limited
26 York St.
London W1U 6PZ, United Kingdom
Ph: 44 20 77295454
Fax: 44 20 77390181
Publication E-mail: editor@yogamagazine.co.uk
Publisher E-mail: info@yogamagazine.co.uk
Magazine covering Yoga and lifestyle. **Freq:** Monthly. **Key Personnel:** Yogi Dr. Malik, Editor; Halima Malik, Dep. Ed./ Publisher, halima@yogamagazine.co.uk. **Subscription Rates:** 26.50 individuals; 50 individuals Europe; 70 other countries. **URL:** http://www.yogamagazine.co.uk/.

55433 ■ You & Your Wedding
National Magazine Company Ltd.
72 Broadwick St.
London W1F 9EP, United Kingdom
Ph: 44 20 74395000
Publication E-mail: yywinfo@natmags.co.uk
Magazine containing wedding fashion and preparations. **Key Personnel:** Colette Harris, Editor; Matt Salmon, Group Publishing Dir.; Helen Shepherd, Web Ed. **Remarks:** Accepts advertising. **URL:** http://www.youandyourwedding.co.uk/. **Circ:** (Not Reported)

55434 ■ Your Mortgage
Incisive Media Limited
Haymarket House
28-29 Haymarket
London SW1Y 4RX, United Kingdom
Ph: 44 870 2408859
Fax: 44 207 4849797
Publisher E-mail: customerservices@incisivemedia.com
Magazine covering mortgages in United Kingdom. **Founded:** 1986. **Freq:** Monthly. **Key Personnel:** Paula John, Editor, phone 44 20 70047491, paula.john@incisivemedia.com; Iain Cartlidge, Gp. Publisher, phone 44 20 70047482, iain.cartlidge@incisivemedia.com. **URL:** http://www.incisivemedia.com/corporate/products/yourmortgage; http://www.yourmortgage.co.uk. **Circ:** 15,000

55435 ■ Yours
Bauer Consumer Media Ltd.
21 Holborn Viaduct
London EC1A 2DY, United Kingdom
Publication E-mail: admin@yours.co.uk
Magazine featuring the lifestyle of people over-50. **Freq:** Biweekly. **Key Personnel:** Gareth Hargreaves, Web Ed., editor@yours.co.uk; Diane Pitts, Reader Advertising. **URL:** http://www.yours.co.uk. **Circ:** *344,438.

55436 ■ Youthwork
CCP Ltd.
PO Box 17911
London SWIP 4YX, United Kingdom
Ph: 44 2073161472
Fax: 44 2073161453
Publication E-mail: youthwork@premier.org.uk
Publisher E-mail: youthwork@premier.org.uk
Christian Youthwork magazine. **Freq:** Bimonthly. **Trim Size:** 210 x 297 mm. **Key Personnel:** Candy O'Donovan, Contact, phone 44 20 73161456, candy.odonovan@premier.org.uk. **Subscription Rates:** 29 individuals. **Remarks:** Accepts advertising. **URL:** http://www.youthwork.co.uk; http://www.youthwork.co.uk/magazine/. **Ad Rates:** BW: 645, 4C: 780, PCI: 7.50. **Circ:** ‡2,500

55437 ■ Zoo Weekly
EMAP Ltd.
Greater London House
Hampstead Rd.
London NW1 7EJ, United Kingdom
Ph: 44 20 77285000
Publisher E-mail: jon.ferro@emap.com
Magazine containing news interesting to young men. **Freq:** Weekly. **Remarks:** Accepts advertising. **URL:** http://www.zooweekly.com.au. **Circ:** (Not Reported)

55438 ■ BBC London-FM - 94.9
Marylebone High St.
PO Box 94.9
London W1A 6FL, United Kingdom
Ph: 44 20 72242424
E-mail: yourlondon@bbc.co.uk
Format: Full Service; Blues; Easy Listening; Urban Contemporary. **Owner:** British Broadcasting Corporation, Broadcasting House, Portland Pl., London W1A 1AA, United Kingdom. **Founded:** Oct. 6, 1970. **Operating Hours:** Continuous. **URL:** http://www.bbc.co.uk/london/.

55439 ■ BBC Radio 4-FM - 92
Broadcasting House
Portland Pl.
London W1A 1AA, United Kingdom
Format: News; Talk; Information; Religious. **Owner:** British Broadcasting Corp., at above address. **Operating Hours:** Continuous. **URL:** http://www.bbc.co.uk/radio4/.

55440 ■ BBC Radio 1-FM - 97
Radio 1
London W1W 6AJ, United Kingdom
Ph: 44 8700 100100
Format: Full Service; Adult Contemporary. **Owner:** British Broadcasting Corporation, Broadcasting House, Portland Pl., London W1A 1AA, United Kingdom. **Operating Hours:** Continuous. **URL:** http://www.bbc.co.uk/radio1/.

55441 ■ BBC Radio 3-FM - 90.2
Broadcasting House
Portland Pl.
London W1A 1AA, United Kingdom
Ph: 44 3700 100300
Format: Classical; Jazz; World Beat. **Owner:** British Broadcasting Corp., at above address. **Operating Hours:** Continuous. **URL:** http://www.bbc.co.uk/radio3/.

55442 ■ BBC Radio 2-FM - 88
Broadcasting House
Portland Pl.
London W1A 1AA, United Kingdom
Format: Full Service; Oldies; Eclectic. **Owner:** British Broadcasting Corp., at above address. **Founded:** Sept. 30, 1967. **URL:** http://www.bbc.co.uk/radio2/.

55443 ■ Capital-FM - 95.8
30 Leicester Sq.
London WC2H 7LA, United Kingdom
Ph: 44 20 70548145
Format: News; Sports; Information. **Owner:** Gcap Media plc, at above address. **Operating Hours:** Continuous. **URL:** http://www.capitalradio.co.uk.

55444 ■ Choice-FM - 96.9
30 Leicester Sq.
London WC2H 7LA, United Kingdom
Ph: 44 20 77666000
Format: Urban Contemporary. **Owner:** GCap Media plc, at above address. **Operating Hours:** 2a.m.-10p.m. weekdays; 2a.m.-12p.m. Sat; 3a.m.-11p.m. Sun. **Key Personnel:** Amber Lyseight, Contact, amber.lyseight@gcapmedia.com. **Ad Rates:** Advertising accepted; rates available upon request. **URL:** http://www.choice-fm.co.uk.

55445 ■ Choice-FM - 107.1
30 Leicester Sq.
London WC2H 7LA, United Kingdom
Ph: 44 87 00702969
E-mail: news@choicefm.com
Format: Urban Contemporary; Full Service. **Owner:** GCAP Media PLC, at above address. **Operating Hours:** Continuous. **Key Personnel:** Chris Hares, Contact, chris.hares@thisisglobal.com; Lisa Scarsbrook, Contact, lisa.scarsbrook@galaxyfm.co.uk. **Ad Rates:** Advertising accepted; rates available upon request. **URL:** http://www.choicefm.com.

55446 ■ Classic-FM - 100.4
30 Leicester Sq.
London WC2H 7LA, United Kingdom
Ph: 44 20 73439000
Format: Classical. **Owner:** GCAP Media PLC, at above address. **Operating Hours:** Continuous. **Ad Rates:** Advertising accepted; rates available upon request. **URL:** http://www.classicfm.co.uk.

55447 ■ Classic-FM - 100.5
30 Leicester Sq.
London WC2H 7LA, United Kingdom
Ph: 44 20 73439000
Format: Classical. **Owner:** GCAP Media PLC, at above address. **Operating Hours:** Continuous. **Ad Rates:** Advertising accepted; rates available upon request. **URL:** http://www.classicfm.com.

55448 ■ Classic-FM - 100.1
30 Leicester Sq.
London WC2H 7LA, United Kingdom
Ph: 44 20 73439000
Format: Classical. **Owner:** GCAP Media PLC, at above address. **Founded:** 1992. **Operating Hours:** Continuous. **Ad Rates:** Advertising accepted; rates available upon request. **URL:** http://www.classicfm.com.

55449 ■ Classic-FM - 101.5
30 Leicester Sq.
London WC2H 7LA, United Kingdom

Circulation: ★ = ABC; △ = BPA; ◆ = CAC; • = CCAB; ▢ = VAC; ⊕ = PO Statement; ‡ = Publisher's Report; Boldface figures = sworn; Light figures = estimated.

Ph: 44 20 73439000

Format: Classical. **Owner:** GCAP Media PLC, at above address. **Operating Hours:** Continuous. **Ad Rates:** Advertising accepted; rates available upon request. **URL:** http://www.classicfm.com.

55450 ■ Classic-FM - 100
30 Leicester Sq.
London WC2H 7LA, United Kingdom
Ph: 44 20 73439000

Format: Classical; Full Service; Oldies. **Owner:** GCap Media plc., at above address. **Ad Rates:** Advertising accepted; rates available upon request. **URL:** http://www.classicfm.co.uk.

55451 ■ Heart 106.2-FM - 106.2
30 Leicester Sq.
London WC2H 7LA, United Kingdom
E-mail: heartcreative@thisisglobal.com

Format: Adult Contemporary; Easy Listening; News. **Operating Hours:** Continuous. **Key Personnel:** Mark Burl, Contact, phone 44 20 70548770, mark.burl@thisisglobal.com. **Ad Rates:** Advertising accepted; rates available upon request. **URL:** http://www.heartlondon.co.uk.

55452 ■ LBC-AM - 1152
30 Leicester Sq.
London WC2H 7LA, United Kingdom
Ph: 44 20 70548770

Format: News; Talk; Sports. **Operating Hours:** Continuous. **Key Personnel:** Clare Patterson, Sponsorship & Promos Controller, clare.patterson@lbc.co.uk; Jonathan Richards, Editorial Dir./Prog. Dir., jonathan.richards@lbc.co.uk. **Ad Rates:** Advertising accepted; rates available upon request. **URL:** http://www.lbc.co.uk.

55453 ■ LBC-FM - 97.3
30 Leicester Sq.
London WC2H 7LA, United Kingdom
Ph: 44 845 6060973

Format: News; Sports; Talk. **Formerly:** ITN News Direct-FM. **Operating Hours:** Continuous. **Key Personnel:** Mark Burl, Contact, mark.burl@thisisglobal.com. **Ad Rates:** Advertising accepted; rates available upon request. **URL:** http://www.lbc.co.uk.

55454 ■ London Greek Radio-FM - 103.3
LGR House
437 High Rd.
London N12 0AP, United Kingdom
Ph: 44 20 83496969
Fax: 44 20 83496960
E-mail: live@lgr.co.uk

Format: Ethnic; News. **Founded:** 1983. **Operating Hours:** Continuous. **Key Personnel:** Vassoula Stavrides, Accounts Mgr., vassoula@lgr.co.uk; George Gregoriou, Program Dir., george@lgr.co.uk. **Ad Rates:** $8.25-9.75 for 10 seconds; $13.20-15.60 for 20 seconds; $16.50-19.50 for 30 seconds; $21.45-25.35 for 40 seconds; $27.23-32.18 for 50 seconds; $29.70-35.10 for 60 seconds. **URL:** http://www.lgr.co.uk/.

55455 ■ Magic-FM - 105.4
Mappin House
4 Winsley St.
London W1W 8HF, United Kingdom
Ph: 44 20 71828160
Fax: 44 20 71828165
E-mail: studio@magic.fm

Format: Adult Contemporary. **Operating Hours:** 5.30 a.m.-8 p.m. weekdays; 6 a.m.-8 p.m. Weekend. **Key Personnel:** Pete Simmons, Program Dir., phone 44 20 71828000; Steve Parkinson, Mng. Dir., phone 44 20 71828000; Jon Godel, News Ed., phone 44 20 74304090. **Ad Rates:** Advertising accepted; rates available upon request. **URL:** http://www.magic.co.uk.

55456 ■ MCR-FM - 101.4
3rd Fl., London Muslim Ctr.
38-44 Whitechapel Rd.
London E1 1JX, United Kingdom
Ph: 44 20 74561062
Fax: 44 20 74561063
E-mail: mcr101fm@hotmail.com

Format: Ethnic; Religious. **Owner:** Islamic Forum Europe, at above address. **Operating Hours:** Continuous. **URL:** http://www.islamicforumeurope.com/live/ife.php.

55457 ■ Premier-AM - 1413
PO Box 13000
London SW1P 4XP, United Kingdom
Ph: 44 20 73161300
E-mail: studio@premier.org.uk

Format: Contemporary Christian. **Ad Rates:** Advertising accepted; rates available upon request. **URL:** http://www.premierradio.org.uk/.

55458 ■ Premier Radio-AM - 1332
PO Box 13000
London SW1P 4XP, United Kingdom
Ph: 44 20 73161300
E-mail: studio@premier.org.uk

Format: Contemporary Christian; Gospel; Religious. **Owner:** Premier Media Group, at above address. **Operating Hours:** Continuous. **Ad Rates:** Advertising accepted; rates available upon request. **URL:** http://www.premier.org.uk.

55459 ■ Premier Radio-AM - 1305
PO Box 13000
London SW1P 4XP, United Kingdom
Ph: 44 8456 525252
E-mail: studio@premier.org.uk

Format: Religious; Gospel. **Owner:** Premier Media Group, at above address. **Operating Hours:** Continuous. **Ad Rates:** Advertising accepted; rates available upon request. **URL:** http://www.premier.org.uk/.

55460 ■ Radio Ulster-FM - 92.4
Broadcasting House
Portland Pl.
London W1A 1AA, United Kingdom
Format: Sports; News. **Owner:** British Broadcasting Corp., at above address. **URL:** http://www.bbc.co.uk/northernireland/radioulster.

55461 ■ Resonance-FM - 104.4
144 Borough High St.
London SE1 1LB, United Kingdom
Ph: 44 20 74071210
E-mail: info@resonancefm.com

Format: Ethnic. **Founded:** May 1, 2002. **Operating Hours:** Continuous. **Key Personnel:** Ed Baxter, Contact. **URL:** http://www.resonancefm.com/.

55462 ■ Smooth-FM - 102.2
26-27 Castlereagh St.
London W1H 5DL, United Kingdom
Ph: 44 20 77064100
Fax: 44 20 77239742

Format: Adult Contemporary. **Owner:** GMG Radio, Laser House, Manchester M50 3XW, United Kingdom, 44 161 8868800. **URL:** http://www.smoothradiolondon.co.uk; http://www.gmgradio.co.uk/.

55463 ■ South London Radio-FM - 107.3
2-6 Basildon Rd.
Abbey Wood
London SE2 0EW, United Kingdom
Ph: 44 20 83121669
E-mail: studio@south.fm

Format: Adult Contemporary. **Ad Rates:** Advertising accepted; rates available upon request. **URL:** http://www.south.fm/.

55464 ■ Spectrum Radio-AM - 558
4 Ingate Pl.
London SW8 3NS, United Kingdom
Ph: 44 20 76274433
Fax: 44 20 76273409

Format: Ethnic. **Key Personnel:** John Ogden, Station Dir., jogden@spectrumradio.net. **Ad Rates:** Advertising accepted; rates available upon request. **URL:** http://www.spectrumradio.net/.

55465 ■ Talk Sport UK-AM - 1089
18 Hatfields
London SE1 8DJ, United Kingdom
Ph: 44 87 17223344
E-mail: customerenquiries@firstprepay.com

Format: Sports; Talk. **Owner:** UTV PLC Group, Ormeau Rd., Belfast BT7 1EB, United Kingdom. **Ad Rates:** Advertising accepted; rates available upon request. **URL:** http://www2.talksport.net.

55466 ■ Talk Sport UK-AM - 1053
18 Hatlelds
London SE1 8DJ, United Kingdom

Ph: 44 87 17223344

Format: Sports; Talk. **Key Personnel:** Jon Don-Carolis, Sales Rep., phone 44 207 9597911, jon.don-carolis@talksport.co.uk; Lain Lecky, Sales Rep., phone 44 207 9597425, iain.lecky@talksport.co.uk. **Ad Rates:** Advertising accepted; rates available upon request. **URL:** http://new.talksport.net.

55467 ■ TalkSPORT-AM - 1089
18 Hatfields
London SE1 8DJ, United Kingdom
Ph: 44 8717 223344

Format: Sports; Talk; News. **Ad Rates:** Advertising accepted; rates available upon request. **URL:** http://www3.talksport.net/index.asp?.

55468 ■ TalkSPORT-AM - 1107
18 Hatfields
London SE1 8DJ, United Kingdom
Ph: 44 8717 223344

Format: Sports; Talk; News. **Ad Rates:** Advertising accepted; rates available upon request. **URL:** http://www3.talksport.net/index.asp?.

55469 ■ TalkSPORT-AM - 1071
18 Hatfields
London SE1 8DJ, United Kingdom
Ph: 44 8717 223344

Format: Sports; Talk; News. **Ad Rates:** Advertising accepted; rates available upon request. **URL:** http://www3.talksport.net/index.asp?.

55470 ■ TalkSPORT-AM - 1053
18 Hatfields
London SE1 8DJ, United Kingdom
Ph: 44 8717 223344

Format: Sports; Talk. **Operating Hours:** Continuous. **Key Personnel:** Kahlen Macaulay, Contact, kahlen.macaulay@talksport.co.uk; Laura Brown, Contact, laura.brown@talksport.co.uk. **Ad Rates:** Advertising accepted; rates available upon request. **URL:** http://www.talksport.net/.

55471 ■ X-FM - 104.9
30 Leicester Sq.
London WC2H 7LA, United Kingdom
Ph: 44 871 2221049

Format: Alternative/New Music/Progressive. **Owner:** GCap Media plc., at above address. **Operating Hours:** Continuous. **URL:** http://www.xfm.co.uk/.

55472 ■ Xfm-FM - 104.9
30 Leicester Sq.
London WC2H 7LA, United Kingdom
Ph: 44 20 70548000

Format: Alternative/New Music/Progressive; Contemporary Hit Radio (CHR); News. **Owner:** GCAP Media PLC, at above address. **Operating Hours:** Continuous. **Ad Rates:** Advertising accepted; rates available upon request. **URL:** http://www.xfm.co.uk.

Londonderry

55473 ■ Londonderry Sentinel
Johnston Press PLC
Spencer House, Unit 4 & 5
Spencer Rd.
Waterside
Londonderry BT47 6AA, United Kingdom
Ph: 44 2871 348889

Community newspaper. **Freq:** Weekly. **Print Method:** Offset. **Col. Depth:** 450 millimeters. **Remarks:** Accepts advertising. **URL:** http://www.londonderrysentinel.co.uk. **Circ:** Combined 5,321

55474 ■ BBC Radio-AM - 792
8 Northland Rd.
Londonderry BT48 7GD, United Kingdom
Ph: 44 28 71378600
Fax: 44 28 71378666
E-mail: radio.foyle@bbc.co.uk

Format: Eclectic; News; Talk. **Owner:** British Broadcasting Corp., Broadcasting House, Portland Pl., London W1A 1AA, United Kingdom. **Operating Hours:** Continuous. **URL:** http://www.bbc.co.uk/northernireland/radiofoyle/contact.shtml.

Longcot

55475 ■ The Richard Jefferies Society Journal
Richard Jefferies Society
Pear Tree Cottage

Longcot SN7 7SS, United Kingdom
Ph: 44 179 3783040
Publisher E-mail: info@richardjefferiessociety.co.uk
Journal covering authors. **Founded:** 1992. **Freq:** Annual. **Trim Size:** A5. **ISSN:** 0968-4247. **Subscription Rates:** 1 nonmembers; Included in membership. **Remarks:** Advertising accepted; rates available upon request. **URL:** http://www.richardjefferiessociety.co.uk/. **Circ:** (Not Reported)

Loughborough

55476 ■ Accounting Education
Routledge
Taylor & Francis Group Ltd.
c/o Richard M.S. Wilson, Ed.
Dept. of Information Science
Loughborough University Business School
Loughborough LE11 3TU, United Kingdom
Publisher E-mail: webmaster.books@tandf.co.uk
Peer-reviewed journal covering all aspects of accounting education. **Subtitle:** An International Journal. **Freq:** 5/yr. **Key Personnel:** Richard M.S. Wilson, Editor, r.m.wilson@lboro.ac.uk; Alan Sangster, Assoc. Ed.; Angus Duff, Assoc. Ed.; Hian Chye Koh, Sen. Assoc. Ed.; Ursula C. Lucas, Sen. Assoc. Ed.; Kim Watty, Assoc. Ed. **ISSN:** 0963-9284. **Subscription Rates:** US$169 individuals print only; US$1,272 institutions online only; US$1,339 institutions print & online; 822 institutions print & online; 781 institutions print + online; 109 individuals; EUR1,072 institutions print and online; EUR1,018 institutions online only; EUR136 individuals. **Remarks:** Advertising accepted; rates available upon request. **URL:** http://www.tandf.co.uk/journals/journal.asp?issn=0963-9284&linktype=5. **Circ:** (Not Reported)

55477 ■ Annals of Human Biology
Society for the Study of Human Biology
Department of Human Sciences
Loughborough University
Loughborough LE11 3TU, United Kingdom
Ph: 44 1509 223034
Fax: 44 1509 223940
Publication E-mail: annals@lists.lboro.ac.uk
Publisher E-mail: j.peters@sheffield.ac.uk
Publication covering biology. **Freq:** Bimonthly. **Key Personnel:** Noel Cameron, Editor, n.cameron@lboro.ac.uk; Stephen T. McGarvey, Editor; Olga Rickards, Editor. **ISSN:** 0301-4460. **Subscription Rates:** US$1,775 institutions print and online; Free online access for developing countries. **Remarks:** Advertising accepted; rates available upon request. **URL:** http://www.sshb.org/publications.htm; http://www.informaworld.com/smpp/title~content=t713723502~db=all. **Circ:** (Not Reported)

55478 ■ Circuit World
Emerald Group Publishing Ltd.
c/o Prof. Martin Goosey, Ed.
Wolfson School of Mechanical
& Manufacturing Engineering
Loughborough LE11 3TU, United Kingdom
Publisher E-mail: emerald@emeraldinsight.com
Journal providing a central, authoritative, international and independent forum for the exchange of information pertaining to the standard, design, analysis, materials, process, reliability and manufacturing of substrates for the first level packages such as ball grid array (BGA), chip scale package (CSP), flip chip, and multichip module (MCM) and printed circuit board (PCB) for the second-level assembly of the BGA modules, MCM and direct chip attach (DCA). **Freq:** 4/yr. **Key Personnel:** Prof. Martin Goosey, Editor, martingoosey@aol.com; Dr. David A. Hutt, Editorial Advisory Board; Paul Comer, Editorial Advisory Board; Dr. Raymond W.M. Kwok, Editorial Advisory Board; Harry Colson, Publisher, hcolson@emeraldinsight.com; Dr. Frank Cala, Editorial Advisory Board; Frank Bai, Editorial Advisory Board; John Ling, Assoc. Ed.; Dr. Alun Morgan, Editorial Advisory Board. **ISSN:** 0305-6120. **URL:** http://info.emeraldinsight.com/products/journals/journals.htm?id=cw.

55479 ■ Ergonomics
Taylor & Francis Ltd.
Dept. of Human Sciences
Loughborough University
Loughborough LE11 3TU, United Kingdom
Publication for the architecture and design industries. **Freq:** 12/yr. **Key Personnel:** Christine M. Haslegrave,

Editorial Board; Chris Baber, Book Review Ed., c.baber@bham.ac.uk; Neil Mansfield, Editor; Neville Stanton, Editor; Roger Haslam, Coord. Ed., ergonomics@tandf.co.uk; Sue Hignett, Editor; Leon Straker, Editor; Thurmon Lockhart, Editor; Wen-Ruey Chang, Editor. **ISSN:** 0014-0139. **Subscription Rates:** 2,446 institutions print + online; 2,324 institutions online; EUR3,230 institutions print + online; US$4,056 institutions print + online; US$3,853 institutions online; EUR3,069 institutions online; US$1,984 individuals print; EUR1,579 individuals print; 1,200 individuals print. **Remarks:** Accepts advertising on request. **URL:** http://www.tandf.co.uk/journals/titles/00140139.asp. **Circ:** (Not Reported)

55480 ■ Focus on International Library & Information Work
International Library & Information Group of CILIP
Scarsdale Cottage
Woodhouse
Loughborough LE12 8UA, United Kingdom
Ph: 44 15 09890050
Fax: 44 15 09890050
Publisher E-mail: ann.irving@britishlibrary.net
Academic journal covering library and information science. **Founded:** 1970. **Freq:** 3/yr. **Trim Size:** A5. **Key Personnel:** Dr. Ann Irving, Assoc. Ed./Book Review Ed., ann.irving@britishlibrary.net; Kathleen Ladizesky, Contact, phone 44 19 74282411, ladizesky@yahoo.com; Roger Stringer, Editor, roger@textpertise.co.zw. **ISSN:** 0305-8468. **Subscription Rates:** 25 individuals; EUR45 individuals; US$60 individuals. **Remarks:** Accepts advertising. **URL:** http://www.cilip.org.uk/get-involved/special-interest-groups/international/publications/pages/default.aspx. **Formerly:** Focus on International & Comparative Librarianship. **Circ:** Paid 1,500

55481 ■ Journal of Digital Information
Oxford University Press
Dept. of Information Science
Loughborough University
Loughborough LE11 3TU, United Kingdom
Ph: 44 15 09223061
Publisher E-mail: webenquiry.uk@oup.com
Peer-reviewed journal publishing papers on the management, presentation and uses of information in digital environments. **Founded:** 1997. **Key Personnel:** John Leggett, Editor-in-Chief; Scott Phillips, Managing Editor; Dion Goh, Theme Ed. **ISSN:** 1368-7506. **Remarks:** Advertising not accepted. **URL:** http://journals.tdl.org/jodi. **Circ:** (Not Reported)

55482 ■ Journal of Librarianship & Information Science
Sage Publications Ltd.
Dept. of Information Science
Loughborough University
Loughborough LE11 3TU, United Kingdom
Journal for librarians, information scientists, lecturers, and students in library and information science and related fields. **Freq:** Quarterly March - June - September - December. **Print Method:** Litho. **Trim Size:** 276 x 210 mm. **Key Personnel:** Anne Goulding, Editor; Dave Muddiman, Review Ed. **ISSN:** 0961-0006. **Subscription Rates:** 360 institutions print & e-access; 396 institutions current volume print & all online content; 324 institutions e-access; 360 institutions e-access plus backfile (all online content); 826 institutions e-access (content through 1998); 353 institutions print only; 52 individuals print only; 97 institutions single print; 17 individuals single print. **Remarks:** Advertising not accepted. **URL:** http://www.sagepub.co.uk/journalsProdDesc.nav?prodId=Journal201675. **Circ:** (Not Reported)

55483 ■ Journal of Politeness Research
Mouton de Gruyter
Dept. of English & Drama
Loughborough University
Loughborough LE11 3TU, United Kingdom
Publisher E-mail: info@degruyter.de
Peer-reviewed journal providing an international forum for the discussion of all aspects of politeness as a complex linguistic and non-linguistic phenomenon. **Subtitle:** Language, Behavior, Culture. **Freq:** Semiannual. **Key Personnel:** Chris Christie, Editor-in-Chief, c.christie@lboro.ac.ukbook; Helen Spencer Oatey, Advisory Board; Wendy Patterson, Editorial Asst., w.patterson@lboro.ac.uk; Maria Sifianou, Advisory Board; Arin Bayraktaroglu, Advisory Board; David Morand, Advisory Board; Miriam A. Locher, Advisory Board; Jonathan Culpeper, Advisory Board; Robert Arundale,

Advisory Board; Richard J. Watts, Ed. Team. **ISSN:** 1612-5681. **Subscription Rates:** EUR131 individuals print or online; EUR151 individuals print + online; US$73 single issue print only. **URL:** http://www.degruyter.com/journals/jpr/detailEn.cfm?sel=he.

55484 ■ Label
Loughborough Students' Union
Union Bldg.
Ashby Rd.
Loughborough LE11 3TT, United Kingdom
Ph: 44 1509 635000
Fax: 44 1509 635003
Publication E-mail: label@lborosu.org.uk
Publisher E-mail: union@lufbra.net
College magazine for students. **Founded:** Sept. 2000. **Freq:** Weekly. **Trim Size:** 170 x 245 mm. **Remarks:** Accepts advertising. **URL:** http://www.lufbra.net/; http://www.lborosu.org.uk/media/index.php?section=label. **Circ:** (Not Reported)

55485 ■ Meat Science
Elsevier Science
c/o D.A. Ledward, Ed.
School of Biosciences, Division of Food Sciences
University of Nottingham, Sutton Bonington Campus
Loughborough LE12 5RD, United Kingdom
Publisher E-mail: nlinfo-f@elsevier.com
Journal serving as a medium for spreading the knowledge on all the factors that influence the properties of meat. Journal published in connection with American Meat Science Association. **Founded:** 1977. **Freq:** Monthly. **Key Personnel:** D.A. Ledward, Editor, david.ledward@nottingham.ac.uk; H. Huff-Lonergan, Assoc. Ed., elonerga@iastate.edu; G.H. Zhou, Assoc. Ed., ghzhou@njau.edu.cn. **ISSN:** 0309-1740. **Subscription Rates:** 398,100¥ institutions; EUR2,997 institutions for Europe; US$3,353 institutions, other countries; 21,600¥ individuals; EUR164 individuals for Europe; US$184 individuals other countries. **Remarks:** Accepts advertising. **URL:** http://www.elsevier.com/wps/find/journaldescription.cws_home/405866/description. **Circ:** (Not Reported)

55486 ■ Pattern Analysis & Applications
Springer-Verlag London Ltd.
c/o Sameer Singh, Ed.-in-Ch.
Research School of Informatics
Loughborough University
Loughborough, United Kingdom
Medical journal covering research in intelligence pattern analysis and application in computer science and engineering. **Freq:** Annual. **Trim Size:** 210 x 277 mm. **Cols./Page:** 2. **Col. Width:** 85 millimeters. **Key Personnel:** David A. Stork, Book Review Ed., stork@rsv.ricoh.com; Sameer Singh, Editor-in-Chief, s.singh@lboro.ac.uk; Mike Fairhurst, Assoc. Ed., m.c.fairhurst@kent.ac.uk; Alberto Del Bimbo, Assoc. Ed., delbimbo@dsi.unifi.it. **ISSN:** 1433-7541. **Subscription Rates:** EUR610 institutions print & e-access; EUR732 institutions print & enhanced access. **Remarks:** Accepts advertising. **URL:** http://www.springer.com/computer/computerimaging/journal/10044; http://www.springerlink.com/content/1433-7541. **Ad Rates:** BW: 370, 4C: 990. **Circ:** Paid 950

55487 ■ Psychology of Sport and Exercise
Elsevier
c/o S. Diddle, Founding Ed.
School of Sport & Exercise Sciences
Sports Science & Recreation Management
Loughborough University
Loughborough LE11 3TU, United Kingdom
Journal publishing scholarly reports in the psychology of sport and exercise, broadly defined. **Freq:** Bimonthly. **Key Personnel:** D. Alfermann, Editor, alferman@rz.uni-leipzig.de; Nikos Ntoumanis, Assoc. Ed.; Martin Hagger, Editor, martin.hagger@nottingham.ac.uk. **ISSN:** 1469-0292. **Subscription Rates:** US$104 individuals all countries except Europe, Japan & Iran; 11,500¥ individuals; EUR81 individuals European countries & Iran; EUR504 institutions European countries & Iran; US$561 institutions all countries except Europe, Japan & Iran; 66,800¥ institutions. **URL:** http://www.elsevier.com/wps/find/journaldescription.cws_home/620792/descriptiondescription.

55488 ■ Thin-Walled Structures
Elsevier Science
c/o Joseph Loughlan, Ed.
Dept. of Aeronautical & Automotive Engineering
Loughborough University
Loughborough LE11 3TU, United Kingdom

Circulation: ★ = ABC; △ = BPA; ♦ = CAC; • = CCAB; ⬚ = VAC; ⊕ = PO Statement; ‡ = Publisher's Report; Boldface figures = sworn; Light figures = estimated.

Gale Directory of Publications & Broadcast Media/147th Ed.   5781

Fax: 44 15 09227221
Publisher E-mail: nlinfo-f@elsevier.com
Journal publishing articles on thin-walled structures.
Founded: 1983. **Freq:** Monthly. **Key Personnel:** Joseph
Loughlan, Editor, j.loughlan@lboro.ac.uk; J. Rhodes,
Founding Ed.; L. Gardner, Editorial Board; Ken P.
Chong, Editor, kchong@nist.gov; D.P. Billington, Edito-
rial Board. **ISSN:** 0263-8231. **Subscription Rates:**
EUR2,430 institutions for European countries & Iran;
322,900¥ institutions; US$2,723 institutions for all
countries except Europe, Japan & Iran. **Remarks:** Ac-
cepts advertising. **URL:** http://www.elsevier.com/wps/
find/journaldescription.cws_home/405910/description.
Circ: (Not Reported)

Loughton

55489 ■ Education Business
Public Sector Publishing Ltd.
226 High Rd.
Loughton IG10 1ET, United Kingdom
Ph: 44 20 85320055
Fax: 44 20 85320066
Publication E-mail: info@educationbusinessuk.com
Publisher E-mail: info@psi-media.co.uk
Magazine featuring administrative and commercial is-
sues affecting education. **Freq:** 6/yr. **Key Personnel:**
Sofie Lidefjard, Editor, editorial@psigroupltd.co.uk; Karl
O'Sullivan, Production Ed., karl.osullivan@psigroupltd.
co.uk; Carol Symons, Publisher, carol@
educationbusinessuk.com. **Remarks:** Accepts
advertising. **URL:** http://www.educationbusinessuk.net;
http://s212832884.websitehome.co.uk/education-
business. **Circ:** (Not Reported)

55490 ■ Government Business
Public Sector Publishing Ltd.
226 High Rd.
Loughton IG10 1ET, United Kingdom
Ph: 44 20 85320055
Fax: 44 20 85320066
Publication E-mail: info@governmentbusinessuk.com
Publisher E-mail: info@psi-media.co.uk
Magazine featuring news and case studies that explain
the commercial issues affecting local and central
government. **Freq:** Monthly. **Key Personnel:** Sofie
Lidefjard, Editor, phone 44 20 85325707, editorial@
psigroupltd.co.uk; Karl O'Sullivan, Production Ed., phone
44 20 85325708, karl.osullivan@psigroupltd.co.uk; John
O'Leary, Publisher, phone 44 20 85325731, john.
oleary@psigroupltd.co.uk. **URL:** http://www.
governmentbusiness.co.uk

55491 ■ Government Technology
Public Sector Publishing Ltd.
226 High Rd.
Loughton IG10 1ET, United Kingdom
Ph: 44 20 85320055
Fax: 44 20 85320066
Publication E-mail: info@governmenttechnologyuk.com
Publisher E-mail: info@psi-media.co.uk
Magazine featuring news and case studies that explain
the administrative and commercial issues affecting IT
and computing in central and local government.
Founded: 2003. **Freq:** Monthly. **Key Personnel:** Sofie
Lidefjard, Editor, phone 44 20 85325707, editorial@
psigroupltd.co.uk; Karl O'Sullivan, Production Ed., phone
44 20 85325708, karl.osullivan@psigroupltd.co.uk; Justine James, Publisher, phone 44 20 85325731, john.
oleary@psigroupltd.co.uk. **Remarks:** Accepts
advertising. **URL:** http://www.governmenttechnologyuk.
com. **Circ:** (Not Reported)

55492 ■ Health Business
Public Sector Publishing Ltd.
226 High Rd.
Loughton IG10 1ET, United Kingdom
Ph: 44 20 85320055
Fax: 44 20 85320066
Publication E-mail: info@healthbusinessuk.com
Publisher E-mail: info@psi-media.co.uk
Magazine featuring news and case studies that explain
the administrative and commercial issues affecting
healthcare and hospital management. **Founded:** 2003.
Freq: 6/yr. **Key Personnel:** Sofie Lidefjard, Editor,
phone 44 20 85325707, editorial@psigroupltd.co.uk;
Karl O'Sullivan, Production Ed., phone 44 20 85325708,
karl.osullivan@psigroupltd.co.uk; Karen Hopps, Publisher, phone 44 20 85325716, john.oleary@psigroupltd.
co.uk. **URL:** http://www.healthbusinessuk.net.

Lowestoft

55493 ■ Community Dental Health
FDI World Dental Press
5 Battery Green Rd.
Lowestoft NR32 IDE, United Kingdom
Ph: 44 15 02511522
Fax: 44 15 02583152
Publisher E-mail: office@fdipress.org
Publication covering dentistry. **Freq:** Quarterly. **Key Per-
sonnel:** Dennis Barber, Publishing Mgr. **ISSN:** 0265-
539X. **Subscription Rates:** 130 individuals print; 150
individuals print and online. **Remarks:** Accepts
advertising. **URL:** http://www.fdiworldental.org/content/
community-dental-health. **Ad Rates:** BW: 330, 4C: 440.
Circ: (Not Reported)

**55494 ■ The European Journal of Prosthodon-
tics and Restorative Dentistry**
FDI World Dental Press
5 Battery Green Rd.
Lowestoft NR32 IDE, United Kingdom
Ph: 44 15 02511522
Fax: 44 15 02583152
Publisher E-mail: office@fdipress.org
European journal covering restorative dentistry. **Freq:**
Quarterly. **Trim Size:** 210 x 297 mm. **ISSN:** 0965-7452.
Subscription Rates: 110 individuals print and online;
100 institutions print and online. **Remarks:** Accepts
advertising. **URL:** http://www.fdiworldental.org/content/
european-journal-prosthodontics-restorative-dentistry.
Ad Rates: BW: 330, 4C: 440. **Circ:** (Not Reported)

55495 ■ International Dental Journal
FDI World Dental Press
5 Battery Green Rd.
Lowestoft NR32 IDE, United Kingdom
Ph: 44 15 02511522
Fax: 44 15 02583152
Publisher E-mail: office@fdipress.org
Peer-reviewed journal covering worldwide dentistry.
Founded: 1950. **Freq:** Bimonthly. **Print Method:** Offset
Litho. **Trim Size:** A4. **Key Personnel:** Stephen Hancocks, OBE, Editor-in-Chief. **ISSN:** 0020-6539. **Subscription Rates:** EUR80 members print & online; EUR140
nonmembers print & online; EUR250 institutions print &
online; EUR70 members online only; EUR120 nonmembers online only; EUR200 institutions online only. **Remarks:** Advertising accepted; rates available upon
request. **URL:** http://www.fdiworldental.org; http://www.
fdiworldental.org/resources/4_1journal.html. **Circ:** Paid
2,000

55496 ■ Lowestoft Journal
Archant Regional Ltd.
147 London Rd. N
Lowestoft NR32 1NB, United Kingdom
Ph: 44 1502 525820
Publisher E-mail: sandra.roantree@archant.co.uk
Local community newspaper. **Founded:** July 26, 1873.
Freq: Weekly. **Key Personnel:** Russell Cook, Editor,
russell.cook@archant.co.uk. **Subscription Rates:** 18.20
individuals 13 weeks; 36.40 individuals 26 weeks. **Re-
marks:** Accepts advertising. **URL:** http://www.
lowestoftjournal.co.uk/home. **Circ:** (Not Reported)

55497 ■ The Beach-FM - 97.4
Radio House
10 Oulton Rd.
Suffolk
Lowestoft NR32 4QP, United Kingdom
Ph: 44 845 3451035
Fax: 44 845 3451036
E-mail: info@thebeach.co.uk
Format: Contemporary Hit Radio (CHR). **URL:** http://
www.thebeach.co.uk

55498 ■ The Beach-FM - 103.4
Radio House
10 Oulton Rd.
Suffolk
Lowestoft NR32 4QP, United Kingdom
Ph: 44 845 3451035
Fax: 44 845 3451036
E-mail: info@thebeach.co.uk
Format: Contemporary Hit Radio (CHR). **URL:** http://
www.thebeach.co.uk/.

Lurgan

55499 ■ Lurgan Mail
Morton Newspapers

4 High St.
Lurgan BT66 8AW, United Kingdom
Ph: 44 28 38327777
Community newspaper. **Freq:** Weekly (Thurs.). **Print
Method:** Offset. **Cols./Page:** 8. **Col. Depth:** 450
millimeters. **Key Personnel:** Clint Aiken, Editor. **Re-
marks:** Accepts advertising. **URL:** http://www.lurganmail.
co.uk. **Circ:** Combined 9,390

Luton

55500 ■ Computational Biology and Chemistry
Elsevier Science
c/o M.J.C. Crabbe, Ed.
Dean of Faculty of Creative Arts, Technologies & Sci-
ence
University of Bedfordshire
Park Sq.
Luton LU1 3JU, United Kingdom
Ph: 44 15 82489265
Fax: 44 15 82489212
Publisher E-mail: nlinfo-f@elsevier.com
Journal focusing in the field of computational life
sciences. **Founded:** 2003. **Freq:** Bimonthly. **Key Per-
sonnel:** M.J.C. Crabbe, Editor, james.crabbe@beds.ac.
uk; A.K. Konopka, Editor, akk@blingua.org; Philipp
Bucher, Editorial Board. **ISSN:** 1476-9271. **Subscrip-
tion Rates:** US$2,220 institutions for all countries except
Europe, Japan & Iran; 263,600¥ institutions; EUR1,989
institutions for European countries & Iran. **Remarks:** Accepts advertising. **URL:** http://www.elsevier.com/wps/
find/journaldescription.cws_home/627320/description.
Formerly: Computers & Chemistry. **Circ:** (Not Reported)

55501 ■ Convergence
University of Luton Press
75 Castle St.
Luton LU1 3AJ, United Kingdom
Ph: 44 1582 743297
Fax: 44 1582 743298
Publication E-mail: convergence@beds.ac.uk
Publisher E-mail: ulp@luton.ac.uk
Peer-reviwed journal covering media technology. **Sub-
title:** The Journal of Research into New Media
Technologies. **Founded:** Mar. 1995. **Freq:** Quarterly
February, May, August, November. **Print Method:**
Conventional. **Key Personnel:** Julia Knight, Editor, julia.
knight@sunderland.ac.uk; Alexis Weedon, Editor, alexis.
weedon@beds.ac.uk; Jeanette Steemers, Assoc. Ed.,
j.steemers@wmin.ac.uk; Rebecca Coyle, Assoc. Ed.,
rcoyle@scu.edu.au; Amy Bruckman, Assoc. Ed., asb@
cc.gatech.edu; Mark Deuze, Assoc. Ed., mdeuze@
indiana.edu; Jay David Bolter, Editorial Board, jay.
bolter@lcc.gatech.edu; Indrajit Banerjee, Editorial
Board, tibanerjee@ntu.edu.sg. **ISSN:** 1354-8565. **Subscription Rates:** 68 individuals; 327 institutions; 38.99
single issue. **Remarks:** Accepts advertising. **URL:** http://
convergence.beds.ac.uk/; http://www.uk.sagepub.com/
journalsProdDesc.nav?prodId=Journal201774. **Ad
Rates:** BW: EUR100. **Circ:** (Not Reported)

55502 ■ Database and Network Journal
AP Publications Ltd.
58 Ryecroft Way
Luton LU2 7TU, United Kingdom
Ph: 44 15 82722219
Trade magazine covering computer database technology software. **Founded:** 1971. **Freq:** Bimonthly. **Trim
Size:** A4. **Key Personnel:** Steve Patterson, Editor.
ISSN: 0265-4490. **Subscription Rates:** 135 individuals;
161 individuals Overseas; 122 individuals less agency
discount; 145 individuals less agency discount. **Remarks:** Advertising not accepted. **URL:** http://www.
softwareworldpublication.com/index.html. **Circ:** Paid 400

55503 ■ Overdrive
Rover P4 Drivers Guild
32 Arundel Rd.
Luton LU4 8DY, United Kingdom
Publication covering automobiles. **Freq:** Bimonthly. **Re-
marks:** Advertising accepted; rates available upon
request. **URL:** http://www.roverp4.com/. **Circ:** (Not
Reported)

55504 ■ The Pantaneto Forum
1st Fl., 3 Gordon St.
Luton LU1 2QP, United Kingdom
Journal stressing on improvement of communication of
scientists with the media, government and other sections of the public, and other scientists. **Freq:** Quarterly.
Key Personnel: Dr. Nigel Sanitt, Editor, nigel@

pantaneto.co.uk. **ISSN:** 1741-1572. **URL:** http://www. pantaneto.co.uk/.

55505 ■ Software World
AP Publications Ltd.
58 Ryecroft Way
Luton LU2 7TU, United Kingdom
Ph: 44 15 82722219
Trade magazine covering computer software. **Founded:** 1969. **Freq:** Bimonthly. **Trim Size:** A4. **Key Personnel:** E. Patterson, Editor, smpluton@ntlworld.com. **ISSN:** 0265-4490. **Subscription Rates:** 135 individuals; 161 other countries. **Remarks:** Advertising not accepted. **URL:** http://www.softwareworldpublication.com/index. html. **Circ:** Paid 400

55506 ■ BBC Three Counties Radio-AM - 1161
1 Hastings St.
Luton LU1 5XL, United Kingdom
Ph: 44 15 82637400
E-mail: bedfordshire@bbc.co.uk
Format: Information; Talk; Eclectic. **Owner:** British Broadcasting Corp., Broadcasting House, Portland Pl., London W1A 1AA, United Kingdom. **URL:** http://www. bbc.co.uk/threecounties/local_radio/.

55507 ■ BBC Three Counties Radio-FM - 103.8
1 Hastings St.
Luton LU1 5XL, United Kingdom
Ph: 44 15 82637400
Format: Information; Talk; Eclectic. **Owner:** British Broadcasting Corp., Broadcasting House, Portland Pl., London W1A 1AA, United Kingdom. **URL:** http://www. bbc.co.uk/threecounties/local_radio/.

55508 ■ BBC Three Counties Radio-FM - 104.5
1 Hastings St.
Luton LU1 5XL, United Kingdom
Ph: 44 15 82637400
Format: Talk; Eclectic; Information. **Owner:** British Broadcasting Corp., Broadcasting House, Portland Pl., London W1A 1AA, United Kingdom. **URL:** http://www. bbc.co.uk/threecounties/local_radio/.

55509 ■ BBC Three Counties Radio-FM - 95.5
1 Hastings St.
Luton LU1 5XL, United Kingdom
Ph: 44 15 82637400
E-mail: bedfordshire@bbc.co.uk
Format: Talk; Eclectic; Information. **Owner:** British Broadcasting Corp., Broadcasting House, Portland Pl., London W1A 1AA, United Kingdom. **URL:** http://www. bbc.co.uk/threecounties/local_radio/.

55510 ■ BBC 3CR-FM - 95.5
1 Hastings St.
Luton LU1 5XL, United Kingdom
Ph: 44 1582 637400
Fax: 44 1582 401467
E-mail: bedfordshire@bbc.co.uk
Format: Talk; News; Eclectic; Sports; Information; Classical. **Owner:** British Broadcasting Corporation, Broadcasting House, Portland Pl., London W1A 1AA, United Kingdom. **Operating Hours:** Continuous. **Key Personnel:** Mark Norman, Station Ed., mark.norman. 01@bbc.co.uk. **URL:** http://www.bbc.co.uk/ threecounties/local_radio/.

55511 ■ Diverse-FM - 102.8
Office 1-3
27 Brunswick St.
Luton LU2 0HG, United Kingdom
Ph: 44 1582 731400
E-mail: studio@diversefm.com
Format: Eclectic. **Ad Rates:** Advertising accepted; rates available upon request. **URL:** http://www.diversefm. com/.

Lutterworth

55512 ■ Healthcare Counselling and Psychotherapy Journal
British Association for Counselling and Psychotherapy
15 St. John's Business Pk.
Leicestershire
Lutterworth LE17 4HB, United Kingdom
Ph: 44 145 5883300
Fax: 44 145 5550243
Publisher E-mail: bacp@bacp.co.uk
Journal for counsellors and psychotherapists in healthcare settings, those working with them and for those

concerned with the needs of service users in this field. **Freq:** Quarterly. **Remarks:** Accepts advertising. **URL:** http://www.bacphealthcare.org.uk/journal.php. **Circ:** (Not Reported)

Lymington

55513 ■ Seahorse
5 Brittania Pl.
Station St.
Lymington SO41 3BA, United Kingdom
Ph: 44 1590 671899
Fax: 44 1590 671116
Publisher E-mail: info@seahorse.co.uk
Magazine of the Royal Ocean Racing Club. **Subtitle:** International Sailing. **Key Personnel:** Andrew Hurst, Editor; Graeme Beeson, Advertising Mgr., gb@ beesonstone.com. **Remarks:** Accepts advertising. **URL:** http://seahorsemagazine.com/. **Circ:** (Not Reported)

Macclesfield

55514 ■ Biologics
Dove Medical Press Ltd.
Beechfield House
Winterton Way
Macclesfield SK11 0JL, United Kingdom
Ph: 44 1625 509130
Fax: 44 1625 617 933
Journal focusing on the patho-physiological rationale for and clinical application of biologic agents in the management of autoimmune diseases, cancers or other pathologies. **Subtitle:** Targets & Therapy. **Freq:** 4/yr. **Key Personnel:** Prof. Doris Mangiaracina-Benbrook, Editor-in-Chief. **ISSN:** 1177-5475. **Subscription Rates:** 322 libraries print and online, UK and rest of world; 105 individuals print and online, UK and rest of world; 487 libraries print and online, Europe; 159 individuals print and online, Europe; 595 U.S. and Canada print and online; 192 U.S. and Canada print and online. **URL:** http:// dovepress.com/articles.php?journal_id=8.

55515 ■ Clinical Interventions in Aging
Dove Medical Press Ltd.
Beechfield House
Winterton Way
Macclesfield SK11 0JL, United Kingdom
Ph: 44 1625 509130
Fax: 44 1625 617 933
Journal focusing on evidence-based reports on the value or lack thereof of treatments intended to prevent or delay the onset of maladaptive correlates of aging in human beings. **Freq:** 4/yr. **Key Personnel:** Dr. Richard F. Walker, Editor-in-Chief. **ISSN:** 1176-9092. **Subscription Rates:** 322 libraries print and online, UK and rest of world; 105 individuals print and online, UK and rest of world; 487 libraries print and online, Europe; 159 individuals print and online, Europe; 595 U.S. and Canada print and online; 192 U.S. and Canada print and online. **URL:** http://dovepress.com/clinical-interventions-in-aging-journal.

55516 ■ Clinical Ophthalmology
Dove Medical Press Ltd.
Beechfield House
Winterton Way
Macclesfield SK11 0JL, United Kingdom
Ph: 44 1625 509130
Fax: 44 1625 617 933
Journal covering the field of ophthalmology. **Freq:** 4/yr. **Key Personnel:** Prof. Scott Fraser, Editor-in-Chief, editor-in-chief@dovepress.com. **ISSN:** 1177-5467. **Subscription Rates:** 322 libraries print and online, UK and rest of world; 105 individuals print and online, UK and rest of world; EUR487 libraries print and online, Europe; EUR159 individuals print and online, Europe; US$595 U.S. and Canada print and online; US$192 U.S. and Canada print and online. **URL:** http://dovepress.com/ articles.php?journal_id=9.

55517 ■ International Journal of Nanomedicine
Dove Medical Press Ltd.
Beechfield House
Winterton Way
Macclesfield SK11 0JL, United Kingdom
Ph: 44 1625 509130
Fax: 44 1625 617 933
Peer-reviewed Journal focusing on the application of nanotechnology in diagnostics, therapeutics, and drug

delivery systems. **Freq:** 4/yr. **Key Personnel:** Dr. Thomas J. Webster, Editor-in-Chief; Dr. J. Zach Hilt, Assoc. Ed.; Israel Rubinstein, Assoc. Ed. **ISSN:** 1176-9114. **URL:** http://dovepress.com/articles.php?pa= editor_profile&journal_id=5.

55518 ■ Neuropsychiatric Disease and Treatment
Dove Medical Press Ltd.
Beechfield House
Winterton Way
Macclesfield SK11 0JL, United Kingdom
Ph: 44 1625 509130
Fax: 44 1625 617 933
Peer-reviewed Journal focusing on clinical or pre-clinical studies on a range of neuropsychiatric and neurological disorders. **Freq:** Bimonthly. **Key Personnel:** Dr. Roger M. Pinder, PhD, Editor-in-Chief, editor-in-chief@ dovepress.com; Mike Briley, Editorial Board; Roger Bullock, Editorial Board; Joseph R. Calabrese, Editorial Board; Jeffrey Cummings, Editorial Board; Ray Chaudhuri, Editorial Board; Allan Young, Editorial Board; John Kane, Editorial Board; Giovanni Cassano, Editorial Board; Celso Arango, Editorial Board. **ISSN:** 1176-6328. **URL:** http://dovepress.com/articles.php?journal_id=3.

55519 ■ Therapeutics and Clinical Risk Management
Dove Medical Press Ltd.
Beechfield House
Winterton Way
Macclesfield SK11 0JL, United Kingdom
Ph: 44 1625 509130
Fax: 44 1625 617 933
International, peer-reviewed journal of clinical therapeutics and risk management, focusing on concise rapid reporting of clinical studies in all therapeutic areas, outcomes, safety, and programs for the effective, safe, and sustained use of medicines. **Key Personnel:** Prof. Garry Walsh, Editor-in-Chief, editor-in-chief@dovepress. com; Ruiwen Zhang, Assoc. Ed. **ISSN:** 1176-6336. **URL:** http://dovepress.com/articles.php?journal_id=1.

55520 ■ Vascular Health and Risk Management
Dove Medical Press Ltd.
Beechfield House
Winterton Way
Macclesfield SK11 0JL, United Kingdom
Ph: 44 1625 509130
Fax: 44 1625 617 933
International, peer-reviewed journal of therapeutics and risk management, focusing on concise rapid reporting of clinical studies on the processes involved in the maintenance of vascular health; the monitoring, prevention, and treatment of vascular disease and its sequelae; and the involvement of metabolic disorders, particularly diabetes. **Freq:** Quarterly. **Key Personnel:** Dr. Roland Asmar, Editor-in-Chief; Bian Jinsong, Assoc. Ed.; Jolanta Weaver, Assoc. Ed. **ISSN:** 1176-6344. **URL:** http:// dovepress.com/articles.php?journal_id=2.

55521 ■ Silk-FM - 106.9
140 Moss Ln.
Macclesfield SK11 7YT, United Kingdom
Ph: 44 1625 269000
Fax: 44 1625 268000
E-mail: hello@silkfm.com
Format: Adult Contemporary; Top 40; Easy Listening; Oldies. **Owner:** The Local Radio Company, 11 Duke St., High Wycombe HP13 6EE, United Kingdom, 44 1494 688200, Fax: 44 1494 688201. **Operating Hours:** Continuous. **Ad Rates:** Advertising accepted; rates available upon request. **URL:** http://www.silkfm.com/.

Machynlleth

55522 ■ Clean Slate
Centre for Alternative Technology
Powys
Machynlleth SY20 9AZ, United Kingdom
Ph: 44 165 4705950
Fax: 44 165 4702782
Publication covering appropriate technology. **Freq:** Quarterly. **Subscription Rates:** 2.50 individuals. **Remarks:** Advertising accepted; rates available upon request. **URL:** http://www.cat.org.uk/membership/cs. tmpl?subdir=membership. **Circ:** 8,500

Circulation: ★ = ABC; △ = BPA; ◆ = CAC; • = CCAB; ❑ = VAC; ⊕ = PO Statement; ‡ = Publisher's Report; Boldface figures = sworn; Light figures = estimated.

Maidenhead

55523 ■ Machine Knitting Monthly
RPA Publishing Ltd.
PO Box 1479
Maidenhead SL6 8DP, United Kingdom
Ph: 44 1628783080
Consumer magazine for machine knitters in the UK.
Founded: Apr. 1986. **Freq:** Monthly. **Print Method:**
Heatset web offset. **Trim Size:** 210 x 297 mm. **Cols./
Page:** 4. **Col. Width:** 42 millimeters. **Col. Depth:** 272
millimeters. **ISSN:** 0269-9761. **Subscription Rates:** 33
individuals; 55 out of country. **Remarks:** Accepts
advertising. **URL:** http://www.machineknittingmonthly.
net/. **Circ:** (Not Reported)

55524 ■ Pool
Through the Loop Consulting Ltd.
PO Box 2528
Maidenhead SL6 9WS, United Kingdom
Ph: 44 1628 898542
Fax: 44 1628 474836
Publisher E-mail: info@throughtheloop.com
Magazine covering business and marketing strategy.
Subtitle: Business and Marketing Strategy. **Founded:**
Jan. 1998. **Freq:** Quarterly. **Print Method:** Online. **Key
Personnel:** Martin Payne, Contact. **Subscription
Rates:** Free online. **Remarks:** Accepts advertising.
URL: http://www.throughtheloop.com/. **Circ:** (Not
Reported)

55525 ■ SOUTH Poetry
PO Box 3744
Cookham
Maidenhead SL6 9UY, United Kingdom
Publisher E-mail: south@southpoetry.org
Magazine featuring poems and profiles of southern
poets. **Freq:** Semiannual. **Subscription Rates:** 20
members; 10 nonmembers; 5.80 single issue. **URL:**
http://southpoetry.org/.

Maidens

55526 ■ Space Policy
Elsevier Science Inc.
c/o F. Brown, Ed.
Seabank
3 Turnberry Rd.
Ayrshire
Maidens KA26 9NN, United Kingdom
Publisher E-mail: usinfo-ehelp@elsevier.com
Peer-reviewed journal focusing on the relations, eco-
nomics, history, aerospace studies, security studies,
development studies, political science and ethics.
Founded: 1970. **Freq:** 4/yr. **Print Method:** Offset. **Cols./
Page:** 5. **Col. Width:** 24 nonpareils. **Col. Depth:** 175
agate lines. **Key Personnel:** X. Pasco, European Ed.;
O. Alifanov, International Editorial Board; C.Q. Christol,
International Editorial Board; J. Gabrynowicz, Interna-
tional Editorial Board; J.L. Culhane, International Edito-
rial Board; R. Boudreault, International Editorial Board;
F. Brown, Editor, fbrown.seabank@virgin.net; M.S.
Smith, North American Ed.; E.D. Gaggero, International
Editorial Board; R. Harris, International Editorial Board.
ISSN: 0265-9646. **Subscription Rates:** 206,000¥
institutions; US$1,737 institutions, other countries except
Europe, Japan and Iran; EUR1,552 institutions for
European countries and Iran; EUR260 individuals for
European countries and Iran; US$290 other countries
except Europe, Japan and Iran; 34,200¥ individuals.
URL: http://www.elsevier.com/wps/find/
journaldescription.cws_home/30469/
descriptiondescription.

Maidstone

55527 ■ Aerostat
British Balloon and Airship Club
1 Home Farm Cottages
Lenham Heath Rd.
Sandway
Maidstone ME17 2HX, United Kingdom
Ph: 44 16 22858956
Publisher E-mail: information@bbac.org
Magazine of the British Balloon and Airship Club. **Freq:**
Bimonthly. **Key Personnel:** Liz Meek, Editor, aerostat@
bbac.org. **Subscription Rates:** Included in membership.
URL: http://www.bbac.org/aerostat1.

55528 ■ The Drummer's Call
Corps of Drums Society

103 Clare Ln.
East Malling
Maidstone ME19 6JB, United Kingdom
Publication E-mail: info@corpsofdrums.com
Publisher E-mail: info@corpsofdrums.com
Publication covering music. **Freq:** Semiannual. **Key Per-
sonnel:** Peter Hart, Editor, peter_hart@ntlworld.com.
Remarks: Advertising accepted; rates available upon
request. **URL:** http://corpsofdrums.com/about/
drummers-call/. **Circ:** (Not Reported)

55529 ■ Education Today
Datateam Publishing Ltd.
15A London Rd.
Maidstone ME16 8LY, United Kingdom
Ph: 44 16 22687031
Fax: 44 16 22757646
Professional magazine covering education for students
aged 5 through adult. **Founded:** 1991. **Freq:** Annual.
Key Personnel: Becci Knowles, Editor, bknowles@
datateam.co.uk. **Subscription Rates:** 32.50 individuals;
75 individuals overseas; 100 individuals airmail. **Remarks:** Accepts advertising. **URL:** http://www.datateam.
co.uk/; http://www.education-today.co.uk/. **Ad Rates:**
GLR: 20, BW: 1,500, 4C: 1,900. **Circ:** Controlled
‡21,500

55530 ■ Pharos International
Cremation Society of Great Britain
Brecon House, 1st Fl.
16/16A Albion Pl.
Maidstone ME14 5DZ, United Kingdom
Ph: 44 16 22688292
Fax: 44 16 22686698
Publisher E-mail: info@cremation.org.uk
Publication for members of the death-care profession
interested in the cremation movement. **Founded:** 1934.
Freq: Quarterly. **Key Personnel:** R.N. Arber, Contact.
ISSN: 0048-3672. **Subscription Rates:** 31 individuals
UK; 36 individuals Europe; 42 individuals outside
Europe; 35 other countries. **Remarks:** Advertising ac-
cepted; rates available upon request. **URL:** http://www.
srgw.demon.co.uk/CremSoc/Publications.htmlpharos.
Circ: (Not Reported)

55531 ■ Stationery & Office Update
Datateam Publishing Ltd.
15A London Rd.
Maidstone ME16 8LY, United Kingdom
Ph: 44 16 22687031
Fax: 44 16 22757646
Trade magazine covering the stationery and office
product industry. **Founded:** 1989. **Freq:** Monthly. **Print
Method:** Sheetfed Offset. **Key Personnel:** Jon Barrett,
Editor, phone 44 1622 850044, jbarrett@datateam.co.
uk. **ISSN:** 1475-8644. **Subscription Rates:** 28 individuals; 50 individuals Europe; 70 individuals airmail. **Remarks:** Accepts advertising. **URL:** http://www.datateam.
co.uk//publications/4518616756. **Ad Rates:** BW: 750,
4C: 1,200. **Circ:** Combined ★5,586

Malton

55532 ■ Malton & Pickering Mercury
Johnston Press PLC
49 Market Pl.
Malton YO17 7LX, United Kingdom
Ph: 44 1653 600051
Local community newspaper. **Key Personnel:** Andrew
Pitt, Contact, andrew.pitt@yrnltd.co.uk. **Remarks:** Ac-
cepts advertising. **URL:** http://www.maltonmercury.co.
uk/. **Circ:** (Not Reported)

Malvern

55533 ■ Craft Stamper
Traplet Publications Ltd.
Traplet House
Pendragon Close
Malvern WR14 1GA, United Kingdom
Ph: 44 16 84588500
Fax: 44 16 84578558
Publisher E-mail: general@traplet.com
Magazine for all rubber stamping enthusiasts, full of
inspirational projects. **Freq:** Monthly. **Key Personnel:**
Katy Fox, Editor. **Subscription Rates:** 56.95 individuals
Europe; 107 two years; US$86 U.S. and Canada;
US$159 U.S. and Canada two years; 62.95 other
countries; 112.95 other countries two years; 42.95

individuals; 82.95 two years. **URL:** http://www.
craftstamper.com/.

55534 ■ Marine Modelling International
Traplet Publications Ltd.
Traplet House
Pendragon Close
Malvern WR14 1GA, United Kingdom
Ph: 44 16 84588500
Fax: 44 16 84578558
Publication E-mail: mmi@traplet.com
Publisher E-mail: general@traplet.com
Consumer magazine covering marine and boat model-
ing for hobbyists. **Freq:** Monthly. **Key Personnel:** Chris
Jackson, Editor. **ISSN:** 0268-3326. **Subscription Rates:**
56.95 individuals; 107 two years; US$86 U.S. and
Canada; US$159 U.S. and Canada two years; 59.95
other countries; 109.95 other countries two years; 39.95
individuals; 74.95 two years. **Remarks:** Accepts
advertising. **URL:** http://www.marinemodelmagazine.
com/. **Former name:** Marine Modeling Monthly. **Circ:**
(Not Reported)

55535 ■ QFI Quiet Flight International
Traplet Publications Ltd.
Traplet House
Pendragon Close
Malvern WR14 1GA, United Kingdom
Ph: 44 16 84588500
Fax: 44 16 84578558
Publisher E-mail: general@traplet.com
Consumer magazine covering radio controlled gliding
and soaring. **Freq:** Monthly. **Key Personnel:** Mike Knott,
Editor. **Subscription Rates:** 53 individuals; US$86
individuals. **Remarks:** Accepts advertising. **URL:** http://
www.traplet.com/. **Circ:** (Not Reported)

55536 ■ Quiet & Electric Flight International
Traplet Publications Ltd.
Traplet House
Pendragon Close
Malvern WR14 1GA, United Kingdom
Ph: 44 16 84588500
Fax: 44 16 84578558
Publication E-mail: qef@traplet.com
Publisher E-mail: general@traplet.com
Magazine for enthusiasts of electric and gliding model
airplanes. **Freq:** Monthly. **Key Personnel:** Mike Nott,
Editor. **Subscription Rates:** 56.95 individuals Europe;
107 two years Europe; US$86 U.S. and Canada;
US$159 U.S. and Canada two years; 62.95 other
countries; 109.95 other countries two years; 42.95
individuals; 74.95 two years. **URL:** http://www.
qefimagazine.com/issue/issue.aspx?cid=4258.

55537 ■ R/C Jet International
Traplet Publications Ltd.
Traplet House
Pendragon Close
Malvern WR14 1GA, United Kingdom
Ph: 44 16 84588500
Fax: 44 16 84578558
Publication E-mail: rcj@traplet.com
Publisher E-mail: general@traplet.com
Original radio control 'Jet' magazine for all jet fanatics.
Freq: Bimonthly. **Subscription Rates:** 31.95 individuals
Europe; 58 two years; US$49 U.S. and Canada; US$89
U.S. and Canada two years; 32.95 other countries;
59.95 other countries two years; 21.95 individuals; 41.95
two years. **URL:** http://www.rcjetinternational.com/issue/
issue.aspx?cid=4266.

55538 ■ Radio Control Model World
Traplet Publications Ltd.
Traplet House
Pendragon Close
Malvern WR14 1GA, United Kingdom
Ph: 44 16 84588500
Fax: 44 16 84578558
Publisher E-mail: general@traplet.com
Consumer magazine covering radio control model
aircraft for hobbyists. **Founded:** 1984. **Freq:** Monthly
second from the last Thursday. **Key Personnel:** Tony
Van Geffen, Editor. **ISSN:** 0268-3334. **Subscription
Rates:** 56.95 individuals Europe; 42.95 individuals;
74.95 two years; US$86 U.S. and Canada; US$159 U.S.
and Canada two years; 109.95 other countries two
years; 107 two years Europe; 62.95 other countries.
Remarks: Accepts advertising. **URL:** http://www.
rcmodelworld.com/. **Circ:** (Not Reported)

55539 ■ Radio Race Car International
Traplet Publications Ltd.
Traplet House
Pendragon Close
Malvern WR14 1GA, United Kingdom
Ph: 44 16 84588500
Fax: 44 16 84578558
Publisher E-mail: general@traplet.com
Consumer magazine covering radio controlled cars.
Freq: Monthly. **Key Personnel:** Claire Alley, Advertising Exec.; Peter Gray, Editor. **Subscription Rates:** 54.95 individuals; 105 two years; US$86 U.S. and Canada; US$159 U.S. and Canada two years; 39.95 individuals; 74.95 two years; 59.95 other countries; 109.95 other countries two years. **Remarks:** Accepts advertising. **URL:** http://www.radioracecar.com/; http://shop.traplet.com/product.aspx?c=2770. **Circ:** (Not Reported)

55540 ■ The Sheep Farmer
National Sheep Association
The Sheep Centre
Malvern WR13 6PH, United Kingdom
Ph: 44 16 84892661
Fax: 44 16 84892663
Publisher E-mail: enquiries@nationalsheep.org.uk
Publication covering the sheep industry. **Freq:** Bimonthly. **Remarks:** Advertising accepted; rates available upon request. **URL:** http://www.nationalsheep.org.uk/index.php?option=com_content&task=blogsection&id=5&Itemid=58. **Circ:** (Not Reported)

Manchester

55541 ■ Ancient Egypt
Empire Publications Ltd.
1 Newton St.
Manchester M1 1HW, United Kingdom
Ph: 44 16 18723319
Fax: 44 16 18724721
Publisher E-mail: empire@globalnet.co.uk
Magazine covering the people, history, and culture of the Nile Valley. **Subtitle:** The History, People and Culture of the Nile Valley. **Freq:** Bimonthly. **Key Personnel:** Bob Partridge, Editor. **Subscription Rates:** 24 individuals in U.K.; 42 two years in U.K.; 28.50 individuals Europe (airmail); 52 two years Europe (airmail); 37.50 other countries airmail; 71 two years rest of the world (airmail). **Remarks:** Accepts advertising. **URL:** http://www.ancientegyptmagazine.co.uk/. **Circ:** (Not Reported)

55542 ■ Auto Freeway
Trader Media Group
Optimum House
Clippers Quay, Salford Quays
Manchester M50 3XP, United Kingdom
Magazine featuring cars for sale, together with motoring accessories, parts, car related products and services, and caravans and vans. **Founded:** 1997. **Freq:** Weekly. **Key Personnel:** John King, CEO. **Subscription Rates:** Free. **Remarks:** Accepts advertising. **URL:** http://www.autotrader.co.uk/AUTOFREEWAY/; http://www.tradermediagroup.com/companies/auto-freeway.html. **Circ:** 143,000

55543 ■ Bike Trader
Trader Media Group
Optimum House
Clippers Quay, Salfords Quay
Salfords
Manchester M50 3XP, United Kingdom
Publication E-mail: biket@tradermedia.co.uk
Magazine featuring motorbikes, motor scooters, and all related accessories and products. **Founded:** 1996. **Freq:** every fortnightly. **Key Personnel:** John King, CEO. **Remarks:** Accepts advertising. **URL:** http://www.autotrader.co.uk/BIKES/bikes.jsp; http://www.tradermediagroup.com/companies/bike-trader.html. **Circ:** ★17,876

55544 ■ Biochemical Engineering Journal
Elsevier Science
c/o Colin Webb, Ed.
The University of Manchester
Dept. of Chemical Engineering
PO Box 88
Manchester M60 1QD, United Kingdom
Ph: 44 161 2004379
Fax: 44 161 2004399

Publisher E-mail: nlinfo-f@elsevier.com
Journal devoted to the critical chemical engineering aspects of the development of biological processes right from raw materials preparation to product recovery, relevant to industries as diverse as medical/healthcare, food and environmental protection. **Freq:** 15/yr. **Key Personnel:** Colin Webb, Editor, colin.webb@umist.ac.uk; H. Unno, Advisory Board; M. Diaz, Assoc. Editor. **ISSN:** 1369-703X. **Subscription Rates:** US$1,758 institutions for all countries except Europe, Japan & Iran; 205,500¥ institutions for European countries & Iran. **Remarks:** Accepts advertising. **URL:** http://www.elsevier.com/wps/find/journaldescription.cws_home/600804/description. **Circ:** (Not Reported)

55545 ■ Bulletin of the Malacological Society of London
The Malacological Society of London
School of Biological Sciences
University of Manchester
Manchester M13 9PL, United Kingdom
Ph: 44 16 12753861
Fax: 44 16 12753938
Publisher E-mail: webmanager@malacsoc.org.uk
Bulletin dedicated to all aspects of malacology. **Freq:** Semiannual Feb. & Aug. **Key Personnel:** Stuart Bailey, PhD, Editor, bbailey@fs1.scg.man.ac.uk; Tony Cook, Editor, a.cook@ulster.ac.uk. **ISSN:** 1365-3725. **Subscription Rates:** 45 individuals ordinary members; 25 individuals student members; 225 institutions print edition and online; 392 institutions print. **URL:** http://www.malacsoc.org.uk/Publications.htm.

55546 ■ Cell Calcium
Mosby Inc.
University of Manchester
School of Biological Sciences
1-124 Stopford Bldg.
Oxford Rd.
Manchester M13 9PT, United Kingdom
Ph: 44 161 2755414
Fax: 44 161 2755363
Publisher E-mail: custserv.ehs@elsevier.com
Journal reporting on all fields of calcium metabolism and signaling in living systems, publishing works from all branches of life science and medicine. **Freq:** Monthly. **Key Personnel:** A. Scarpa, Editorial Board; A. Verkhratsky, Editor-in-Chief, alex.verkhratsky@man.ac.uk; S. Muallem, Editor-in-Chief, phone 214645-6008, fax 214645-6054, shmuel.muallem@utsouthwestern.edu. **ISSN:** 0143-4160. **Subscription Rates:** 208,100¥ institutions; US$1,758 institutions, other countries except Europe, Japan and Iran; EUR1,926 institutions for European Countries and Iran. **Remarks:** Accepts advertising. **URL:** http://www.elsevier.com/wps/find/journaldescription.cws_home/623014/descriptiondescription. **Circ:** (Not Reported)

55547 ■ The Classical Review
Cambridge University Press
c/o Prof. Roy Gibson, Ed.
Dept. of Classics & Ancient History
University of Manchester
Oxford Rd.
Manchester M13 9PL, United Kingdom
Publisher E-mail: information@cambridge.org
Periodical focusing on history. **Freq:** Semiannual. **Key Personnel:** Prof. Roy Gibson, Editor; Prof. Neil Hopkinson, Editor. **ISSN:** 0009-840X. **Subscription Rates:** 119 institutions online and print; US$217 institutions online and print; 113 institutions online only; US$206 institutions online only. **Remarks:** Accepts advertising. **URL:** http://journals.cambridge.org/action/displayJournal?jid=CAR. **Circ:** (Not Reported)

55548 ■ Comparative and Functional Genomics
John Wiley & Sons Inc.
School of Biological Sciences
University of Manchester
The Michael Smith Bldg.
Oxford Rd.
Manchester M13 9PT, United Kingdom
Publisher E-mail: info@wiley.com
Journal focusing on the post-sequencing phases of genome analysis. **Freq:** Annual. **Key Personnel:** Dr. Jo Wixon, Managing Editor, cfg@wiley.co.uk; Prof. Steve Oliver, Editor-in-Chief, steve.oliver@man.ac.uk; T. Altman, Editorial Board. **ISSN:** 1531-6912. **Subscription Rates:** US$350 individuals online only access; US$350 institutions print only; US$368 institutions print and on-

line access; US$75 individuals online only access; US$110 individuals print only; US$115 individuals print and online access. **Remarks:** Accepts advertising. **URL:** http://www3.interscience.wiley.com/cgi-bin/jhome/77002016. **Circ:** (Not Reported)

55549 ■ Constitutional Political Economy
Springer Netherlands
University of Manchester
Manchester, United Kingdom
Publisher E-mail: permissions.dordrecht@springer.com
Journal covering research of constitutional analysis. **Freq:** Quarterly. **Print Method:** Offset. **Trim Size:** 8 1/2 x 11. **Cols./Page:** 2. **Col. Width:** 3 3/8 inches. **Key Personnel:** Douglas Heckathorn, Editorial Board; Jose Casas Pardo, Editorial Board; Peter C. Ordeshook, Editor; Alan Hamlin, Editor-in-Chief; Peter Bernholz, Editorial Board; Albert Breton, Editorial Board; Ronald Heiner, Editorial Board; Robert Cooter, Editorial Board; Dennis C. Mueller, Editor; Geoffrey Brennan, Editorial Board. **ISSN:** 1043-4062. **Subscription Rates:** EUR533 institutions print incl. free access or e-only; EUR639.60 institutions print incl. enhanced access. **URL:** http://www.springer.com/socialsciences/politicalscience/journal/10602.

55550 ■ Credit Union News
Association of British Credit Unions Limited
Holyoake House, Hanover St.
Manchester M60 0AS, United Kingdom
Ph: 44 16 18323694
Fax: 44 16 18323706
Publisher E-mail: info@abcul.org
Journal containing news in the credit union movement. **Freq:** Quarterly. **URL:** http://www.abcul.coop.

55551 ■ Critical Studies in Television
Manchester University Press
Oxford Rd.
Manchester M13 9NR, United Kingdom
Ph: 44 161 2752310
Fax: 44 161 2743346
Publisher E-mail: m.frost@manchester.ac.uk
Journal covering research and sustained intellectual discussion on television. **Subtitle:** Scholarly Studies in Small Screen Fictions. **Freq:** Semiannual May and November. **Key Personnel:** Kim Akass, Editor; Stephen Lacey, Editor; David Lavery, Editor; Janet McCabe, Editor; Robin Nelson, Editor; Rhonda W. Wilcox, Editor. **ISSN:** 1749-6020. **Subscription Rates:** 119 institutions; US$212 institutions; EUR155 institutions; 30 individuals; US$55 individuals; EUR40 individuals. **Remarks:** Accepts advertising. **URL:** http://www.manchesteruniversitypress.co.uk/journals/journal.asp?id=16. **Circ:** (Not Reported)

55552 ■ Crystallography Reviews
Taylor & Francis Group Journals
c/o Prof. John R. Helliwell, Ed.
School of Chemistry
The University of Manchester
Oxford Rd.
Manchester M13 9PL, United Kingdom
Ph: 44 161 2754970
Fax: 44 161 2754598
Publisher E-mail: customerservice@taylorandfrancis.com
Journal focusing on crystallography and crystal growth, covering all theoretical and applied aspects of biological, chemical, industrial, mineralogical and physical crystallography. **Freq:** Quarterly. **Key Personnel:** Prof. John Helliwell, Editor, john.helliwell@manchester.ac.uk; Prof. Moreton Moore, Editor, m.moore@rhul.ac.uk; Dr. Frank H. Allen, Assoc. Ed., allen@ccdc.cam.ac.uk; Prof. Frank H. Herbstein, Assoc. Ed., chr03fh@tx.technion.ac.il; Prof. Yuji Ohashi, Assoc. Ed., yohashi@chem.titech.ac.jp; Dr. H. Einspahr, Assoc. Ed., hmeinspahr@yahoo.com. **ISSN:** 0889-311X. **Subscription Rates:** US$1,327 institutions print and online; US$1,261 institutions online; US$209 individuals. **URL:** http://www.informaworld.com/smpp/title~content=t713456298.

55553 ■ Dental Materials
Mosby Inc.
c/o David C. Watts, Ed.-in-Ch.
University of Manchester Dental School
Higher Cambridge St.
Manchester M15 6FH, United Kingdom
Fax: 44 161 2756748
Publisher E-mail: custserv.ehs@elsevier.com
Journal publishing original research and review articles

Circulation: ★ = ABC; △ = BPA; ◆ = CAC; • = CCAB; ❑ = VAC; ⊕ = PO Statement; ‡ = Publisher's Report; Boldface figures = sworn; Light figures = estimated.

Gale Directory of Publications & Broadcast Media/147th Ed.   5785

for dentists. **Founded:** 1998. **Freq:** Monthly. **Key Personnel:** David C. Watts, PhD, Editor-in-Chief, dentistry. dentmatj@man.ac.uk; Ronald L. Sakaguchi, Editor; Joseph Antonucci, Editorial Board. **ISSN:** 0109-5641. **Subscription Rates:** US$402 other countries except Europe, Japan and Iran; EUR360 individuals European Countries and Iran; 47,700¥ individuals; US$817 institutions, other countries except Europe, Japan and Iran; EUR729 institutions European Countries and Iran; 84,400¥ institutions. **URL:** http://www.elsevier.com/wps/find/journaldescription.cws_home/601024/descriptiondescription.

55554 ■ Education for Information
IOS Press, B.V.
c/o Dick Hartley, Ed.
Manchester Metropolitan University
Dept. of Information & Communications
Humanities Bldg., Rosamund St.
Manchester M15 6LL, United Kingdom
Ph: 44 161 247 6144
Fax: 44 161 247 6351
Publisher E-mail: info@iospress.nl
Journal providing a forum for debate and discussion on education and training issues in the sphere of information handling, which is in great demand in all sectors, including government, business and commerce. **Freq:** Quarterly. **Key Personnel:** Dick Hartley, Editor, r.j. hartley@mmu.ac.uk; Andrew Large, Editor, phone 514398-3360, fax 514398-7193, andrew.large@mcgill.ca. **ISSN:** 0167-8329. **Subscription Rates:** EUR398 institutions print and online; US$565 institutions print and online. **URL:** http://www.iospress.nl/loadtop/load.php?isbn=01678329.

55555 ■ Emotional and Behavioral Difficulties
Social, Emotional and Behavioural Difficulties Association
The Triangle, Rm. 211
Exchange Sq.
Manchester M4 3TR, United Kingdom
Ph: 44 161 2402418
Fax: 44 161 8385601
Publisher E-mail: admin@sebda.org
Multidisciplinary practitioners journal of Social, Emotional and Behavioural Difficulties Association. **Freq:** 4/yr. **Key Personnel:** Harry Daniels, Editor; Ted Cole, Editor; Paul Cooper, Hon. Assoc. Ed. **ISSN:** 1363-2752. **Subscription Rates:** US$124 individuals print only; US$634 institutions online only; US$704 institutions print + online. **URL:** http://www.sebda.org/resources/journal.asp.

55556 ■ Gender in Management
Emerald Group Publishing Ltd.
Manchester Business School
The University of Manchester
Booth St. E
Manchester M15 6PB, United Kingdom
Publisher E-mail: emerald@emeraldinsight.com
Journal seeking to provide current research, practice, ideas, developments and news of major issues in the field of women in management by publishing papers considering the sociological, the psychological and the political as well as the vocational aspects. **Subtitle:** An International Journal. **Freq:** 8/yr. **Key Personnel:** Nancy Rolph, Publisher, nrolph@emeraldinsight.com; Dr. Sandra L. Fielden, Editor, sandra.fielden@mbs.ac.uk; Dr. Barbara Poggio, Regional Ed.; Dr. Sonia Liff, Editorial Advisory Board; Dr. Ariane Berthoin Antal, Editorial Advisory Board; Prof. Suzan Lewis, Editorial Advisory Board; Dr. Judith Helen McGregor, Regional Ed.; Marianne Tremaine, Book Review Ed.; Prof. Beverly Alimo-Metcalfe, Editorial Advisory Board. **ISSN:** 1754-2413. **URL:** http://info.emeraldinsight.com/products/journals/journals.htm?id=gm. **Formerly:** Women in Management Review.

55557 ■ Grip
UMIST Students Association
Oxford Rd.
Manchester M13 9PL, United Kingdom
Ph: 44 161 3066000
Student lifestyle magazine. **Founded:** 1981. **Freq:** Monthly. **Trim Size:** 24 x 34 cm. **Subscription Rates:** Free. **Remarks:** Accepts advertising. **URL:** http://www.manchester.ac.uk/. **Ad Rates:** GLR: 530. **Circ:** Combined 6,000

55558 ■ International Journal of Electrical Engineering Education
Manchester University Press

School of Electrical & Electronic Engineering
The University of Manchester
Sackville St.
PO Box 88
Manchester M60 1QD, United Kingdom
Publisher E-mail: m.frost@manchester.ac.uk
Peer-reviewed journal covering developments in the teaching of electrical engineering and electronics. **Founded:** 1963. **Freq:** Quarterly January, April, July and October. **Key Personnel:** Julie Johnson, Editor; Prof. A.M. Song, Consultant Ed.; Prof. J.V. Milanovic, Consultant Ed. **ISSN:** 0020-7209. **Subscription Rates:** 245 institutions; US$436 institutions; EUR319 institutions; 76 individuals; US$136 individuals; EUR98 individuals. **Remarks:** Accepts advertising. **URL:** http://www.eee.manchester.ac.uk/ijeee/. **Ad Rates:** BW: 145. **Circ:** (Not Reported)

55559 ■ International Journal of Health Promotion and Education
Institute of Health Promotion and Education
c/o Helen Draper, Sec.
School of Dentistry
University of Manchester
Coupland 3, Oxford Rd.
Manchester M13 9PL, United Kingdom
Publisher E-mail: honsec@ihpe.org.uk
Journal covering health education. **Freq:** Quarterly. **Key Personnel:** Prof. Stephen Palmer, Editor. **ISSN:** 1463-5240. **Remarks:** Advertising accepted; rates available upon request. **URL:** http://www.ihpe.org.uk/jour/index.htm. **Circ:** (Not Reported)

55560 ■ International Journal of Mechanical Engineering Education
Manchester University Press
Oxford Rd.
Manchester M13 9NR, United Kingdom
Ph: 44 161 2752310
Fax: 44 161 2743346
Publisher E-mail: m.frost@manchester.ac.uk
Journal covering developments in the teaching of mechanical engineering. **Freq:** Quarterly January, April, July and October. **Key Personnel:** Dr. Bin Wang, Editor, ijmee@abdn.ac.uk. **ISSN:** 0306-4190. **Subscription Rates:** 245 institutions; US$436 institutions; EUR319 institutions; 76 individuals; US$136 individuals; EUR98 individuals. **Remarks:** Accepts advertising. **URL:** http://www.manchesteruniversitypress.co.uk/journals/journal.asp?id=12. **Ad Rates:** BW: 145. **Circ:** (Not Reported)

55561 ■ Interpreter and Translator Trainer
St. Jerome Publishing
2 Maple Rd. W
Brooklands
Manchester M23 9HH, United Kingdom
Ph: 44 161 9739856
Fax: 44 161 9053498
Publisher E-mail: ken@stjeromepublishing.com
Peer-reviewed journal focusing on the education and training of language interpreters and translators. **Freq:** Semiannual. **Key Personnel:** Catherine Way, Editor. **ISSN:** 1750-399X. **Subscription Rates:** 45 individuals; 85 institutions. **URL:** http://www.stjerome.co.uk/page.php?id=454.

55562 ■ Italian Studies
Society for Italian Studies
c/o Spencer Pearce, Treas.
School of Languages Linguistics and Cultures
University of Manchester
Oxford Rd.
Manchester M13 9PL, United Kingdom
Ph: 44 161 2753125
Publisher E-mail: spencer.pearce@manchester.ac.uk
Scholarly journal covering Italian studies. **Founded:** 1937. **Freq:** Semiannual. **Key Personnel:** Dr. Robert Gordon, Editor, rscg1@cam.ac.uk. **ISSN:** 0075-1634. **Subscription Rates:** 25 individuals members living in the U.K. and Ireland; 30 individuals members living elsewhere; 12.50 students full-time postgraduate (U.K. and Ireland). **Remarks:** Accepts advertising. **URL:** http://www.sis.ac.uk/cgi-bin/safeperl/sisinfo/sistine.pl?is. **Circ:** Paid 500

55563 ■ Jobs North West
Diverse Media Ltd.
164 Deansgate
Manchester M60 2RD, United Kingdom
Ph: 44 845 0508040
Fax: 44 161 8320870

Publication E-mail: jnw@menmediasales.co.uk
Publication covering local employment and job listings. **Freq:** Weekly (Fri.). **Cols./Page:** 8. **Col. Width:** 33 millimeters. **Subscription Rates:** 3 single issue; 32.63 individuals 3 months; 61.62 individuals 6 months; 110.76 individuals. **Remarks:** Accepts advertising. **URL:** http://www.jobs-nw.co.uk. **Circ:** Paid 27,000

55564 ■ Journal of Place Management and Development
Emerald Group Publishing Ltd.
c/o Prof. Cathy Parker, Editor
Industry of Place Management, Manchester Metropolitan
University Business School
Aytoun St.
Manchester M1 3GH, United Kingdom
Publisher E-mail: emerald@emeraldinsight.com
Journal providing a central repository for research into this expanding topic, pulling together theory and practice in the field. **Founded:** 2008. **Freq:** Semiannual. **Key Personnel:** Prof. Cathy Parker, Editor, cathy@placemanagement.org; Aimee Wood, Publisher, awood@emeraldinsight.com. **ISSN:** 1753-8335. **URL:** http://info.emeraldinsight.com/products/journals/journals.htm?id=jpmd.

55565 ■ Journal of Psychosomatic Research
Mosby Inc.
Psychiatry Research Group, School of Community Based Medicine
The University of Manchester
University Pl., 3rd F. E, Rm. 3.312
Oxford Rd.
Manchester M13 9PL, United Kingdom
Publisher E-mail: custserv.ehs@elsevier.com
Peer-reviewed journal covering all aspects of the relationships between psychology and medicine. **Founded:** 1956. **Freq:** Monthly. **Key Personnel:** Dr. Colin Shapiro, Editor; Prof. Francis Creed, Editor; M. Sharpe, Assoc. Ed.; W. Katon, Assoc. Ed.; G.M. Devins, Assoc. Ed.; J. Weinmann, Assoc. Ed. **ISSN:** 0022-3999. **Subscription Rates:** US$3,057 institutions, other countries; US$462 individuals; US$2,689 institutions; US$529 other countries. **URL:** http://www.elsevier.com/wps/find/journaldescription.cws_home/525474/descriptiondescription.

55566 ■ Journal of Semitic Studies
Oxford University Press
Dept. of Middle Eastern Studies
University of Manchester
Oxford Rd.
Manchester M13 9PL, United Kingdom
Ph: 44 16 12753551
Fax: 44 16 12753551
Publisher E-mail: webenquiry.uk@oup.com
International academic journal of Semitic studies, including the modern as well as the ancient Near (Middle) East, with special emphasis on research into the languages and literatures of the area. **Freq:** 2/yr. **Key Personnel:** P.S. Alexander, Editorial Committee; A. Christmann, Editorial Committee; G.J. Brooke, Editorial Committee. **ISSN:** 0022-4480. **Subscription Rates:** 166 institutions print and online; US$315 institutions print and online; EUR249 institutions print and online; 60 institutions developing Countries - print only; 54 individuals print only; US$103 individuals print only; EUR81 individuals print only; EUR228 institutions print; EUR207 institutions online; US$289 institutions print. **Remarks:** Advertising accepted; rates available upon request. **URL:** http://jss.oxfordjournals.org/. **Circ:** (Not Reported)

55567 ■ Journal of the Textile Institute
The Textile Institute
1st Fl., St. James's Bldg., Oxford St.
Manchester M1 6FQ, United Kingdom
Ph: 44 161 2371188
Fax: 44 161 2361991
Publisher E-mail: tiihq@tileinst.org.uk
Journal covering textile clothing and footwear technology and management for industry professionals. **Freq:** 8/yr. **Trim Size:** 6 x 9. **Cols./Page:** 1. **Key Personnel:** David R. Buchanan, Editor-in-Chief, david_buchanan@ncsu.edu. **ISSN:** 0400-5000. **Subscription Rates:** US$423 institutions print only; US$1,025 individuals online only; US$1,079 individuals print + online. **Remarks:** Advertising not accepted. **URL:** http://www.tandf.co.uk/journals/titles/00405000.asp. **Circ:** Combined 700

55568 ■ Journal of Transport Geography
Elsevier Science
c/o Prof. Richard D. Knowles, Ed.
Peel Bldg. 309
School of Environment & Life Sciences-Geography
University of Salford
Manchester M5 4WT, United Kingdom
Ph: 44 16 12954994
Fax: 44 16 12955015
Publisher E-mail: nlinfo-f@elsevier.com
Peer-reviewed journal devoted to transport and spatial change. **Freq:** Bimonthly. **Key Personnel:** Prof. Richard D. Knowles, Editor; Andrew Goetz, Assoc. Ed., agoetz@du.edu; Jon Shaw, Assoc. Ed., jon.shaw@plymouth.ac.uk; A.M. Abane, International Editorial Board; Y. Boquet, International Editorial Board; I. Docherty, International Editorial Board. **ISSN:** 0966-6923. **Subscription Rates:** US$110 individuals for all countries except Europe, Japan & Iran; 12,100¥ individuals; EUR85 individuals for European countries & Iran; US$556 institutions for all countries except Europe, Japan & Iran; 73,800¥ institutions; EUR623 institutions for European countries & Iran. **Remarks:** Accepts advertising. **URL:** http://www.elsevier.com/wps/find/journaldescription.cws_home/30448/description. **Circ:** (Not Reported)

55569 ■ The Journal of Transport History
Manchester University Press
Oxford Rd.
Manchester M13 9NR, United Kingdom
Ph: 44 161 2752310
Fax: 44 161 2743346
Publication E-mail: jth.editorial@gmail.com
Publisher E-mail: m.frost@manchester.ac.uk
Peer-reviewed journal analyzing the history of transportation in the context of economy and society. **Freq:** Semiannual. **Key Personnel:** Dr. Hans-Ludger Dienel, Book Review Ed.; Dorian Gerhold, Editorial Board; Prof. John Armstrong, Editorial Board; Dr. Jeff Schramm, Book Review Ed.; Prof. Gordon Boyce, Editorial Board; Mathieu Flonneau, Editorial Board; Prof. Bruce Pietrykowski, Dep. Ed. **ISSN:** 0022-5266. **Subscription Rates:** 128 institutions and individuals; US$128 institutions and individuals; EUR167 institutions and individuals. **Remarks:** Advertising accepted; rates available upon request. **URL:** http://www.manchesteruniversitypress.co.uk/journals/journal.asp?id=4. **Circ:** (Not Reported)

55570 ■ Literature & History
Manchester University Press
Oxford Rd.
Manchester M13 9NR, United Kingdom
Ph: 44 161 2752310
Fax: 44 161 2743346
Publisher E-mail: m.frost@manchester.ac.uk
Journal covering the investigation of the relations between writing, history, and ideology. **Founded:** 1975. **Freq:** Semiannual April and October. **Key Personnel:** Jeremy Gregory, Editor, jeremy.gregory@manchester.ac.uk; Andrew Thacker, Editor, athacker@dmu.ac.uk; Christopher Highley, Editor, highly.1@osu.edu. **ISSN:** 0306-1973. **Subscription Rates:** 91 institutions; US$163 institutions; EUR119 institutions; 38 individuals; US$68 individuals; EUR48 individuals. **Remarks:** Accepts advertising. **URL:** http://www.manchesteruniversitypress.co.uk/journals/journal.asp?id=1. **Ad Rates:** BW: 145. **Circ:** (Not Reported)

55571 ■ Manchester Living
Accent Magazines Ltd.
33 Whitworth St. W
Manchester M1 5ND, United Kingdom
Ph: 44 161 2373500
Fax: 44 161 2373501
Publication E-mail: editorial@manchester-living.com
Magazine featuring exclusive properties for the whole of Greater Manchester. **Founded:** July 2005. **Freq:** Weekly. **Trim Size:** 230 x 297 mm. **Key Personnel:** Camilla Crockett, Contact, camilla.crockett@manchester-living.com/. **URL:** http://www.manchester-living.com/. **Circ:** Paid 12,000

55572 ■ Motorhome and Caravan Trader
Trader Media Group
Optimum House
Clippers Quay, Salfords Quay
Salfords
Manchester M50 3XP, United Kingdom
Publication E-mail: caravan@tradermedia.co.uk
Magazine featuring buying and selling caravans and motor homes. **Freq:** Biweekly. **Key Personnel:** John King, CEO. **Remarks:** Accepts advertising. **URL:** http://www.autotrader.co.uk/CARAVANS/caravans.jsp; http://www.tradermediagroup.com/companies/motorhome-and-caravan-trader.html. **Circ:** 10,028

55573 ■ New Start
Centre for Local Economic Strategies
Express Networks
One George Leigh St.
Manchester M4 5DL, United Kingdom
Ph: 44 114 2816130
Publisher E-mail: ad@newstartmag.co.uk
Magazine featuring news, comment, analysis and more on community regeneration. **Founded:** 1999. **Freq:** Weekly. **Key Personnel:** Julian Dobson, Editorial Dir.; Austin Macauley, Editor; Susan Downer, Asst. Ed.; Tim Mawdsley, Production Ed.; Rosie Niven, Reporter; Chloe Stothart, Special Reporter; Ryan May, Advertising Adviser; Chloe Gray, Advertising and Events consultant; Chris Dowson, Advertising Production; Jamie Veitch, Sales Dir.; Kath Acres, Mng. Dir. **Subscription Rates:** 95 individuals U.K.; 75 individuals digital; 105 individuals Europe; 145 individuals rest of the world. **Remarks:** Accepts advertising. **URL:** http://www.newstartmag.co.uk/magazine. **Circ:** (Not Reported)

55574 ■ Nineteenth Century Theatre and Film
Manchester University Press
Oxford Rd.
Manchester M13 9NR, United Kingdom
Ph: 44 161 2752310
Fax: 44 161 2743346
Publisher E-mail: m.frost@manchester.ac.uk
Journal covering narrative or variety entertainments. **Freq:** Semiannual June and December. **Key Personnel:** Viv Gardner, Editor; David Mayer, Editor; Kate Newey, Editor. **ISSN:** 1748-3727. **Subscription Rates:** 99 institutions; US$176 institutions; EUR129 institutions; 36 individuals; US$65 individuals; EUR46 individuals. **Remarks:** Accepts advertising. **URL:** http://www.manchesteruniversitypress.co.uk/journals/journal.asp?id=6. **Ad Rates:** BW: 145. **Circ:** (Not Reported)

55575 ■ Progress in Planning
Elsevier Science
c/o Michael J. Hebbert, International Editorial Board
School of Environment & Development
University of Manchester
Oxford Rd.
Manchester M13 9PL, United Kingdom
Publisher E-mail: nlinfo-f@elsevier.com
Peer-reviewed journal publishing research papers on matters pertaining to urban planning, city design, spatial strategy, regional development and environmental management. **Founded:** 1973. **Freq:** 8/yr. **Key Personnel:** Michael J. Hebbert, International Editorial Board, michael.hebbert@man.ac.uk; M. Hibbard, Editor, mhibbard@uoregon.edu; Derek R. Diamond, Founding Ed. **ISSN:** 0305-9006. **Subscription Rates:** EUR160 individuals for European Countries; US$207 individuals for all Countries except Europe and Japan; 23,100¥ individuals; EUR994 institutions for European Countries; US$1,114 institutions for all Countries except Europe and Japan; 132,100¥ institutions. **URL:** http://www.elsevier.com/wps/find/journaldescription.cws_home/409/description

55576 ■ Reactive and Functional Polymers
Elsevier Science Inc.
c/o N. Tirelli, Ed.-in-Ch.
School of Pharmacy & Pharmaceutical Science
University of Manchester
Oxford Rd.
Manchester M13 9PL, United Kingdom
Publisher E-mail: usinfo-ehelp@elsevier.com
Journal dealing with science and technology of polymers with functional groups providing chemical or physical reactivity. **Founded:** 1983. **Freq:** Monthly. **Print Method:** Offset. **Trim Size:** 8 x 10 3/4. **Cols./Page:** 3. **Col. Width:** 28 nonpareils. **Col. Depth:** 140 agate lines. **Key Personnel:** A. SenGupta, Editorial Board; D. Clifford, Editorial Board; V.A. Davankov, Editorial Board; R.J. Eldridge, Editorial Board; M.L. Turner, Editorial Board, michael.turner@man.ac.uk; W.T. Ford, Editorial Board; S. Rimmer, Editorial Board; S.D. Alexandratos, Editorial Board; S. Itsuno, Editorial Board; Y. Tezuka, Editor, rfp-editor@op.titech.ac.jp; N. Tirelli, Editor-in-Chief, nicola.tirelli@manchester.ac.uk. **ISSN:** 1381-5148. **Subscription Rates:** 307,100¥ institutions; EUR2,310 institutions for European countries and Japan; US$2,596 institutions, other countries except Europe, Japan and Iran. **URL:** http://www.elsevier.com/wps/find/journaldescription.cws_home/502694/descriptiondescription.

55577 ■ Sign Language Translator & Interpreter
St. Jerome Publishing
2 Maple Rd. W
Brooklands
Manchester M23 9HH, United Kingdom
Ph: 44 161 9739856
Fax: 44 161 9053498
Publisher E-mail: ken@stjeromepublishing.com
Peer-reviewed journal focusing on sign language interpretation, translation, and analysis. **Freq:** Semiannual. **Key Personnel:** Lorraine Leeson, Editor. **ISSN:** 1750-3981. **Subscription Rates:** 45 individuals; 85 institutions. **URL:** http://www.stjerome.co.uk/page.php?id=457.

55578 ■ Student Direct
University of Manchester
Student Union
Steve Biko Bldg.
Oxford Rd.
Manchester M13 9PR, United Kingdom
Ph: 44 16 12752930
Fax: 44 16 12752936
Student newspaper. **Founded:** Sept. 20, 2001. **Freq:** Weekly. **Print Method:** Web offset. **Key Personnel:** Robyn McKeown, Editor, phone 44 16 12752943. **Subscription Rates:** Free. **Remarks:** Accepts advertising. **URL:** http://www.umu.man.ac.uk/activities/studentdirect.shtml; http://www.student-direct.co.uk/. **Circ:** Non-paid 60,000

55579 ■ Textile Progress
The Textile Institute
1st Fl., St. James's Bldg., Oxford St.
Manchester M1 6FQ, United Kingdom
Ph: 44 161 2371188
Fax: 44 161 2361991
Publisher E-mail: tiihq@tileinst.org.uk
Trade magazine covering textile technology for industry professionals. **Founded:** 1969. **Freq:** Quarterly. **Trim Size:** 6 x 9. **Cols./Page:** 1. **Key Personnel:** D. Buchanan, Editorial Board; Xiao-Ming Tao, Editor-in-Chief, tctaoxm@inet.polyu.edu.hk. **ISSN:** 0040-5167. **Subscription Rates:** 170 institutions print + online; US$324 institutions print + online; EUR258 institutions print + online. **URL:** http://www.texi.org/PublicationsProgress.asp; http://www.tandf.co.uk/journals/ttpr.

55580 ■ The Translator
St. Jerome Publishing
2 Maple Rd. W
Brooklands
Manchester M23 9HH, United Kingdom
Ph: 44 161 9739856
Fax: 44 161 9053498
Publisher E-mail: ken@stjeromepublishing.com
Journal focusing on language translation and interpretation focusing on intercultural communication. **Subtitle:** Studies in Intercultural Communication. **Freq:** Semiannual. **Key Personnel:** Mona Baker, Editor. **ISSN:** 1355-6509. **Subscription Rates:** 32 individuals Europe; 73 institutions Europe; 30 individuals UK; 69 institutions UK; 34 other countries; 76 institutions, other countries. **URL:** http://www.stjerome.co.uk/page.php?id=27.

55581 ■ Truck and Plant Trader
Trader Media Group
Optimum House
Clippers Quay, Salfords Quay
Manchester M50 3XP, United Kingdom
Ph: 44 161 8777467
Fax: 44 161 8364433
Publication E-mail: trucktrader@tradermedia.co.uk
Magazine featuring selection of trucks, large goods vehicles, trailers and plant vehicles in the United Kingdom and Ireland. **Founded:** 1996. **Freq:** Weekly. **Key Personnel:** John King, CEO. **Remarks:** Accepts advertising. **URL:** http://www.autotrader.co.uk/TRUCKS/trucks.jsp; http://www.autotrader.co.uk/PLANT/; http://www.tradermediagroup.com/companies/truck-and-plant-trader.html. **Circ:** ★14,383

55582 ■ Asian Sound Radio-AM - 963
42 Southall St.
Manchester M3 1LG, United Kingdom
Ph: 44 161 2881000
Fax: 44 161 2889000

Circulation: ★ = ABC; △ = BPA; ♦ = CAC; • = CCAB; ❏ = VAC; ⊕ = PO Statement; ‡ = Publisher's Report; Boldface figures = sworn; Light figures = estimated.

E-mail: info@asiansoundradio.co.uk
Format: News; Information; Religious. **URL:** http://www.
asiansoundradio.co.uk/.

55583 ■ Asian Sound Radio-AM - 1377
42 Southall St.
Manchester M3 1LG, United Kingdom
Ph: 44 161 2881000
Fax: 44 161 2889000
E-mail: info@asiansoundradio.co.uk
Format: News; Information; Religious. **URL:** http://www.
asiansoundradio.co.uk/.

55584 ■ BBC Radio Manchester-FM - 95.1
PO Box 27
Oxford Rd.
Manchester M60 1SJ, United Kingdom
Ph: 44 161 2002020
E-mail: manchester.online@bbc.co.uk
Format: Talk; Information; News; Sports; Folk; Country;
Eclectic. **Owner:** British Broadcasting Corp., Broadcast-
ing House, Portland Pl., London W1A 1AA, United
Kingdom. **Founded:** 1970. **Former name:** Radio
Manchester. **Formerly:** BBC GMR-FM. **URL:** http://www.
bbc.co.uk/manchester/index.shtml.

55585 ■ Century Radio - 105.4
Laser House
Waterfront Quay
Salford Quays
Manchester M50 3XW, United Kingdom
Ph: 44 161 8868800
Fax: 44 161 8868811
Format: Adult Contemporary. **Owner:** GMG Radio, at
above address. **URL:** http://www.centuryradionorthwest.
co.uk/.

55586 ■ Key 103-FM - 103
Castle Quay
Castlefield
Manchester M15 4PR, United Kingdom
Ph: 44 161 2885000
E-mail: news@key103.co.uk
Format: Top 40; Adult Contemporary; Sports; News;
Eclectic; Talk; Information. **Operating Hours:**
Continuous. **Key Personnel;** Michelle Surrell, Contact;
Gary Stein, Program Dir. **Ad Rates:** Advertising ac-
cepted; rates available upon request. **URL:** http://www.
key103.co.uk/.

55587 ■ Real Radio-FM - 105.4
Laser House
Waterfront Quay
Salford Quays
Manchester M50 3XW, United Kingdom
Ph: 44 161 8868800
Fax: 44 161 8868811
Format: Adult Contemporary; Sports; Top 40; Oldies.
Owner: GMG Radio, at above address. **Formerly:**
Century-FM. **Operating Hours:** Continuous. **Ad Rates:**
Advertising accepted; rates available upon request.
URL: http://www.realradionorthwest.co.uk/.

55588 ■ Smooth-FM - 100.4
Laser House
Waterfront Quay
Salford Quays
Manchester M50 3XW, United Kingdom
Ph: 44 845 501004
Fax: 44 845 541005
Format: Easy Listening. **Owner:** GMG Radio, Laser
House, Manchester M50 3XW, United Kingdom, 44 161
8868800. **Operating Hours:** Continuous. **Ad Rates:**
Advertising accepted; rates available upon request.
URL: http://www.smoothradionorthwest.co.uk; http://
www.gmgradio.co.uk/.

55589 ■ XFM-FM - 97.7
4 Exchange Quay, Ste. 1.1
Manchester M5 3EE, United Kingdom
Ph: 44 161 6624700
Fax: 44 161 6624799
Format: Alternative/New Music/Progressive. **URL:** http://
www.xfm.co.uk/.

Mansfield

55590 ■ Mansfield Chad
Johnston Press PLC
121 Newgate Ln.
Mansfield NG18 2PA, United Kingdom

Ph: 44 1623 456789
Local community newspaper. **Freq:** Weekly. **Key Personnel:** Tracy Powell, Editor, fax 44 1623 464647, tracy.
powell@chad.co.uk; Emma Angell, Promotions Mgr.,
emma.angell@sheffieldnewspapers.co.uk; Tim Morriss,
Dep. Ed., tim.morriss@chad.co.uk. **Remarks:** Accepts
advertising. **URL:** http://www.chad.co.uk/. **Circ:** (Not
Reported)

55591 ■ Transport Ticket Society Journal
Transport Ticket Society
6 Breckbank, Forest Town
Notts
Mansfield NG19 0PZ, United Kingdom
Journal covering collectors. **Freq:** Monthly. **ISSN:** 0144-
347X. **Subscription Rates:** 25 individuals; 32 individuals Europe, airmail; 32 other countries surface mail; 50
other countries airmail. **Remarks:** Advertising accepted;
rates available upon request. **URL:** http://www.transport-
ticket.org.uk. **Circ:** 480

March

55592 ■ Cambs Times
Archant Regional Ltd.
51 High St.
March PE15 9JJ, United Kingdom
Ph: 44 1354 652621
Publication E-mail: editor@cambs-times.co.uk; news@
cambs-times.co.uk
Publisher E-mail: sandra.roantree@archant.co.uk
Local community newspaper. **Freq:** Weekly (Fri.). **Key
Personnel:** John Elworthy, Editor; Phil White, Produc-
tion Mgr.; Paul Richardson, Editorial Dir. **Subscription
Rates:** Free to homes across March, Chatteris, Whittle-
sey; 21.61 out of area 13 weeks; 45.50 out of area 26
weeks; 70.20 out of area; 91 individuals. **Remarks:** Accepts advertising. **URL:** http://www.cambstimes.co.uk/
home. **Circ:** 60,957

55593 ■ Wisbech Standard
Archant Regional Ltd.
51 High St.
March PE15 9JJ, United Kingdom
Ph: 44 1354 652621
Fax: 44 1354 652751
Publication E-mail: editor@cambs-times.co.uk; news@
cambs-times.co.uk
Publisher E-mail: sandra.roantree@archant.co.uk
Local community newspaper. **Freq:** Weekly (Fri.). **Key
Personnel:** John Elworthy, Editor. **Subscription Rates:**
1.75 individuals latest issue only; 22.75 individuals 13
weeks; 45.50 individuals 26 weeks; 91 individuals. **Re-
marks:** Accepts advertising. **URL:** http://www.
wisbechstandard.co.uk/home. **Circ:** *17,538

Margate

55594 ■ KM-FM - 107.2
183 Northdown Rd.
Cliftonville
Margate CT9 2PA, United Kingdom
Ph: 44 1843 296969
E-mail: sfountain@thekmgroup.co.uk
Format: Adult Contemporary. **URL:** http://www.kmfm.co.
uk/goto.php?sess=x183810|u183694|p111|n0|c0|I0|g5|
d0.

Market Rasen

55595 ■ Market Rasen Mail
Johnston Press PLC
Waverley Ct.
Market Rasen LN8 3EH, United Kingdom
Ph: 44 1673 844644
Local community newspaper. **Freq:** Weekly. **Key Per-
sonnel:** Lisa Mitchell, Gp. Advertising Mgr., phone 44
1507 353200, jason.hippisley@jpress.co.uk; Tim Robin-
son, Managing Editor, phone 44 1205 311433, fax 44
1205 318751, tim.robinson@jpress.co.uk. **Remarks:**
Accepts advertising. **URL:** http://www.marketrasenmail.
co.uk/. **Circ:** (Not Reported)

Markinch

55596 ■ Kingdom-FM - 96.1
Haig House
Haig Business Pk.
Fife
Markinch KY7 6AQ, United Kingdom

Ph: 44 15 92753753
Fax: 44 15 92612022
E-mail: info@kingdomfm.co.uk
Format: Easy Listening; Contemporary Hit Radio
(CHR); Adult Contemporary. **Owner:** Kingdom FM, at
above address. **Operating Hours:** Continuous. **Key
Personnel:** Kevin Brady, Mng. Dir.; Linda McCrabbe,
Sales Mgr.; Blair Crofts, Financial Controller. **Ad Rates:**
Advertising accepted; rates available upon request.
URL: http://www.kingdomfm.co.uk.

55597 ■ Kingdom-FM - 105.4
Haig House
Haig Business Pk.
Fife
Markinch KY7 6AQ, United Kingdom
Ph: 44 1592 753753
Fax: 44 1592 612022
Format: Adult Contemporary; Contemporary Hit Radio
(CHR); Easy Listening. **Owner:** Kingdom FM, at above
address. **Operating Hours:** Continuous. **Ad Rates:**
Advertising accepted; rates available upon request.
URL: http://www.kingdomfm.co.uk.

55598 ■ Kingdom-FM - 95.2
Haig House
Haig Business Pk.
Fife
Markinch KY7 6AQ, United Kingdom
Ph: 44 1592 757757
Fax: 44 1592 612022
Format: Easy Listening; Contemporary Hit Radio
(CHR); Adult Contemporary. **Owner:** Kingdom FM, at
above address. **Operating Hours:** Continuous. **Key
Personnel:** Kevin Brady, Mng. Dir.; Linda McCrabbe,
Sales Mgr.; Darren Stenhouse, Prog. Controller. **Ad
Rates:** Advertising accepted; rates available upon
request. **URL:** http://www.kingdomfm.co.uk.

Marlborough

55599 ■ Arab Horse Society News
Arab Horse Society
Windsor House
The Sq.
Marlborough SN8 2PE, United Kingdom
Ph: 44 16 72521411
Publication covering horses. **Freq:** Bimonthly. **Key Per-
sonnel:** Val Cridge, Editor. **URL:** http://www.
arabhorsesociety.com/index.php?section=2. **Ad Rates:**
4C: 175. **Circ:** 3,000

Marlow

55600 ■ Menopause International
British Menopause Society
4-6 Eton Pl.
Marlow SL7 2QA, United Kingdom
Ph: 44 162 8890199
Fax: 44 162 8474042
Publisher E-mail: admin@thebms.org.uk
Peer-reviewed journal covering issues in the study and
treatment of menopausal conditions, including the
controversies surrounding postmenopausal health in an
ageing and expanding female population. **Founded:**
1890. **Freq:** Weekly Mon.-Fri. in Fall and Spring, Weekly
in Summer. **Print Method:** Offset. **Trim Size:** 10 5/16 x
16. **Cols./Page:** 6. **Col. Width:** 19 nonpareils. **Col.
Depth:** 224 agate lines. **Key Personnel:** Dr. Heather
Currie, Editor; Edward Morris, Editor; Mary Ann Lumsden, Chm. **ISSN:** 1754-0453. **Subscription Rates:** 147
individuals U.K. and Europe; EUR220 individuals;
US$271 individuals; EUR151 individuals rest of the world.
URL: http://www.thebms.org.uk/journals.php. **Formerly:**
Journal of the British Menopause Society.

55601 ■ Seventh Wave
Marine Connection
322 Marlow Bottom
Buckinghamshire
Marlow SL7 3QH, United Kingdom
Publisher E-mail: info@marineconnection.org
Magazine featuring news and information about the
projects and developments of the organization. **Freq:**
Quarterly. **URL:** http://www.seventhwave.co.uk/.

Martlesham Heath

55602 ■ KlubKat Music Magazine
KlubKat

15 Saddlers Pl.
Martlesham Heath IP5 3SS, United Kingdom
Publication E-mail: news@klubkat.com
Publisher E-mail: katharine@klubkat.com
Internet magazine covering local music and musicians.
Freq: Weekly. **Key Personnel:** Simon Burford, Editor, simon@klubkat.com; Katharine Webb, Editor, katharine@klubkat.com. **Remarks:** Accepts advertising. **URL:** http://www.klubkat.com/. **Circ:** (Not Reported)

Matlock

55603 ■ Iota Magazine
Templar Poetry
PO Box 7721
Matlock DE4 9DD, United Kingdom
Publication E-mail: info@iotamagazine.co.uk
Publisher E-mail: info@templarpoetry.co.uk
Magazine featuring contemporary poetry. **Founded:** 1987. **Key Personnel:** Nigel McLoughlin, Editor. **Subscription Rates:** 6 single issue for U.K; 50 institutions; 8 other countries single copy; 15 individuals 4 issues; 25 other countries 4 issues; 70 other countries institutional. **URL:** http://www.iotamagazine.co.uk/Home.html.

55604 ■ Matlock Mercury
Johnston Press PLC
4 Firs Parade
Matlock DE4 3AS, United Kingdom
Ph: 44 1629 762120
Local community newspaper. **Key Personnel:** Amanda Hatfield, Editor, phone 44 1629 762130, fax 44 1629 584270, amanda.hatfield@jpress.co.uk; Lindsey Bowers, Contact, phone 44 1773 514151, lindsey.bowers@jpress.co.uk; Susannah Shields, Contact, newmedia@sheffieldnewspapers.co.uk. **Remarks:** Accepts advertising. **URL:** http://www.matlockmercury.co.uk/. **Circ:** (Not Reported)

Melksham

55605 ■ The Ptolemaic Terrascope Magazine
The Ptolemaic Terrascope
PO Box 2152
Melksham SN12 7UQ, United Kingdom
Ph: 44 12 25706134
Publication E-mail: editor@terrascope.co.uk
Publisher E-mail: editor@terrascope.org
Magazine covering music and musicians. **Founded:** May 1989. **Freq:** Semiannual. **Print Method:** Offset. **Trim Size:** A4. **Key Personnel:** Pat Thomas, Editor, normalsf@earthlink.net. **ISSN:** 1472-9639. **Remarks:** Advertising accepted; rates available upon request. **URL:** http://www.terrascope.co.uk/Home/FAQ.htm. **Circ:** 4,000

Melton Mowbray

55606 ■ Melton Times
Johnston Press PLC
49 Nottingham St.
Melton Mowbray LE13 1NT, United Kingdom
Ph: 44 1664 410041
Local community newspaper. **Key Personnel:** Michael Cooke, Editor, phone 44 1664 412516, fax 44 1664 412515, michael.cooke@meltontoday.co.uk; Lisa Williams, Advertising Mgr., lisa.williams@jpress.co.uk. **Remarks:** Accepts advertising. **URL:** http://www.meltontimes.co.uk/. **Circ:** (Not Reported)

55607 ■ The Eye-FM - 103
PO Box 103
Melton Mowbray LE13 9AW, United Kingdom
Ph: 44 16 64481103
E-mail: studio@103theeye.co.uk
Format: Contemporary Hit Radio (CHR); News; Information. **Owner:** The Eye FM Ltd., at above address. **URL:** http://www.103theeye.co.uk.

Meopham

55608 ■ Swedish Book Review
Swedish-English Literary Translators' Association
c/o Sarah Death, Ed.
85 Ediva Rd.
Meopham DA13 0ND, United Kingdom
Publisher E-mail: peter@lintononline.co.uk
Publication introducing Swedish literature in English.

Features translations, books reviews and rights information. **Founded:** 1983. **Freq:** Semiannual. **Key Personnel:** Sarah Death, Editor; Tom Geddes, Editorial Board; Neil Smith, Dep. Ed. **ISSN:** 0265-8119. **Subscription Rates:** 15 individuals; US$25 individuals; 200 SKr individuals; 18 individuals airmail; US$30 individuals airmail; 230 SKr individuals airmail. **Remarks:** Advertising accepted; rates available upon request. **URL:** http://www.swedishbookreview.com. **Circ:** 800

Mere

55609 ■ Advances in Clinical Neuroscience & Rehabilitation
Whitehouse Publishing
1 The Lynch
Mere BA12 6DQ, United Kingdom
Ph: 44 1747 860168
Fax: 44 1747 860168
Publisher E-mail: rachael@acnr.co.uk
Journal covering neuroscience includes current therapeutic controversies, summary of a neuroscientific topics relevant to future clinical arena, conference reports and product updates, and book reviews. **Freq:** Bimonthly. **Key Personnel:** Rachael Hansford, Publisher, rachael@acnr.co.uk; Roger Barker, Editor, editor@acnr.co.uk; Alasdair Coles, Editor. **Subscription Rates:** 75 individuals. **URL:** http://www.acnr.co.uk/aboutus.htm.

Mexborough

55610 ■ South Yorkshire Times
Johnston Press PLC
27-29 High St.
Mexborough S64 9AF, United Kingdom
Ph: 44 1709 303030
Local community newspaper. **Key Personnel:** Jim Oldfield, Editor, phone 44 1709 303055, fax 44 1709 303099, jim.oldfield@dearnetoday.co.uk; Kevin Rogers, Reporter, phone 44 1709 303060, fax 44 1709 303098, kevin.rogers@dearnetoday.co.uk. **Remarks:** Accepts advertising. **URL:** http://www.southyorkshiretimes.co.uk/. **Circ:** (Not Reported)

Middlesbrough

55611 ■ Critical Public Health
Routledge
Taylor & Francis Group Ltd.
School of Social Sciences & Law
University of Teesside
Middlesbrough TS1 3BA, United Kingdom
Publisher E-mail: webmaster.books@tandf.co.uk
Peer-reviewed journal for researchers and practitioners working in public health, health promotion and related fields, exploring and debating issues of equity and social justice, in particular, issues of sexism, racism and other forms of oppression. **Freq:** Quarterly. **Key Personnel:** David Evans, Editorial Board; Jane Wills, Editorial Board; Paul Crawshaw, Assoc. Ed.; John Coveney, Assoc. Ed.; Ronald Labonte, Assoc. Ed.; Judith Green, Editor; Chris Bonell, Book Review Ed., chris.bonell@lshtm.ac.uk. **ISSN:** 0958-1596. **Subscription Rates:** 342 institutions print + online; US$564 institutions print + online; 325 institutions online; US$536 institutions online; 108 individuals print only; US$181 individuals print only; 50 members society; US$83 members society; $A 112 members society. **Remarks:** Accepts advertising. **URL:** http://www.tandf.co.uk/journals/titles/09581596.asp. **Circ:** (Not Reported)

55612 ■ Spatial Practices
Editions Rodopi B.V.
c/o Dr. Robert Burden, Ed.
School of Arts & Media
University of Teesside
Borough Rd.
Middlesbrough TS1 3BA, United Kingdom
Publisher E-mail: info@rodopi.nl
Journal covering the study of culture and identity. **Subtitle:** An Interdisciplinary Series in Cultural History, Geography and Literature. **Key Personnel:** Dr. Robert Burden, Editor, r.burden@tees.ac.uk; Stephan Kohl, Editor, stephan.kohl@mail.uni-wuerzburg.de. **ISSN:** 1871-689X. **URL:** http://www.rodopi.nl/senj.asp?SerieId=SPATIAL.

55613 ■ BBC Tees-FM - 95
Broadcasting House
Newport Rd.
Middlesbrough TS1 5DG, United Kingdom
Ph: 44 1642 225211
E-mail: tees@bbc.co.uk
Format: News; Talk; Sports. **Owner:** British Broadcasting Corporation, Broadcasting House, Portland St., London W1A 1AA, United Kingdom. **Formerly:** BBC Radio Cleveland-FM. **Operating Hours:** Continuous. **URL:** http://www.bbc.co.uk/england/radiocleveland/.

Middlesex

55614 ■ Aeromilitaria
Air-Britain Historians
5 Walnut Tree Rd.
Shepperton
Middlesex TW17 0RW, United Kingdom
Publisher E-mail: pete.webber@air-britain.co.uk
Publication covering the history British military aviation. **Founded:** 1975. **Freq:** Quarterly. **Key Personnel:** James J. Halley, Editor; Phil Butler, Editor. **Subscription Rates:** 6.50 single issue. **Remarks:** Advertising not accepted. **URL:** http://www.air-britain.com/aeromil.html. **Circ:** (Not Reported)

55615 ■ Autocar
Haymarket Magazines Ltd.
Teddington Studios
Broom Rd.
Teddington
Middlesex TW11 9BE, United Kingdom
Ph: 44 20 82675630
Fax: 44 20 82675759
Publication E-mail: autocar@haymarket.com
Publisher E-mail: info@haymarket.com
Publication covering automobiles. **Freq:** Weekly. **Key Personnel:** Chas Hallett, Editor, phone 44 20 82675000, charles.hallett@haymarket.com. **ISSN:** 1355-8293. **Subscription Rates:** 2.13 single issue. **URL:** http://www.haymarket.com/autocar/autocar_magazine/default.aspx; http://www.autocar.co.uk/. **Circ:** ★47,646

55616 ■ Environmental Hazards
James and James/Earthscan
c/o Edmund Penning-Rowsell, Ed.-in-Ch.
Flood Hazard Research Centre
Middlesex University
Queensway
Middlesex EN3 4SA, United Kingdom
Publisher E-mail: earthinfo@earthscan.co.uk
Journal devoted to environmental hazards. **Freq:** Quarterly. **Print Method:** Offset. **Trim Size:** 13 3/4 x 22 3/4. **Cols./Page:** 6. **Col. Width:** 2 1/16 inches. **Col. Depth:** 21 1/2 inches. **Key Personnel:** Stephen Bender, Editorial Board; Dr. Niel Britton, Editorial Board; Prof. Ian Davis, Editorial Board; Dr. Kenneth Hewitt, Editorial Board; Dr. Allan Lavell, Editorial Board; Prof. Peter J. May, Editorial Board; Edmund Penning-Rowsell, Editor-in-Chief, edmund2@nw.mdx.ac.uk. **ISSN:** 1747-7891. **Subscription Rates:** 99 institutions print only; EUR130 institutions print only; US$199 institutions print only; 99 institutions, other countries print only; 260 institutions print & online; EUR340 institutions print & online; US$520 institutions Americas; 260 institutions print & online. **Remarks:** Accepts advertising. **URL:** http://www.earthscan.co.uk/Journals/EHAZ/tabid/37213/Default.aspx. **Circ:** (Not Reported)

55617 ■ Interacting with Computers
Elsevier Science Inc.
c/o Dianne Murray, Gen. Ed.
59 Cambridge Rd.
Teddington
Middlesex TW11 8DT, United Kingdom
Publisher E-mail: usinfo-ehelp@elsevier.com
Peer-reviewed journal focusing on the research of human-computer interaction. **Freq:** 6/yr. **Key Personnel:** J. Noyes, Ed. Emeritus; G. Cockton, Ed. Emeritus; I. Oakley, Editorial Board; J. Pierce, Editorial Board; J. Earthy, Editorial Board; D.L. Day, Ed. Emeritus; R. Brooks, Editorial Board; G. Lindgaard, Dep. Ed., glindgaa@connect.carleton.ca; Dianne Murray, Gen. Ed., dianne@city.ac.uk. **ISSN:** 0953-5438. **Subscription Rates:** 131,700¥ institutions; EUR989 institutions for European countries and Iran; US$1,110 institutions, other countries except Europe, Japan and Iran; US$124 other countries except Europe, Japan and Iran; 14,600¥ individuals; EUR111 other countries for European

Circulation: ★ = ABC; △ = BPA; ◆ = CAC; • = CCAB; ❑ = VAC; ⊕ = PO Statement; ‡ = Publisher's Report; Boldface figures = sworn; Light figures = estimated.

Gale Directory of Publications & Broadcast Media/147th Ed.

5789

countries and Iran. **URL:** http://www.elsevier.com/wps/find/journaldescription.cws_home/525445/descriptiondescription.

55618 ■ International Journal of Dynamics of Fluids (IJDF)
Research India Publications
c/o Wrobel, Editorial Board
U.S. Department of of Mechanical Engineering
Brunel University
Uxbridge
Middlesex UB8 3PH, United Kingdom
Publisher E-mail: info@ripublication.com
Journal focusing on investigative techniques and analytical methods in fluid mechanics. **Freq:** Semiannual. **Key Personnel:** Luiz C. Wrobel, Editorial Board, leo@unimb.si; Shaaban A. Abdallah, Editorial Board Member; Sumanta Acharya, Editorial Board Member; Ramesh K. Agarwal, Editorial Board Member; Yiannis Andreopoulos, Editorial Board Member; Li Cheng, Editorial Board Member. **ISSN:** 0973-1784. **Subscription Rates:** US$180 individuals print plus online free; US$160 individuals online only; US$280 institutions and library; print plus online free; US$260 institutions and library; online only; Rs 2,200 individuals. **URL:** http://www.ripublication.com/ijdf.htm.

55619 ■ Journal of 3-D Imaging
Stereoscopic Society
6 Sheppards Ct., Horsenden Ln., N
Greenford
Middlesex UB6 7QJ, United Kingdom
Publisher E-mail: info@stereoscopy.net
Photographic journal. Members only. **Subtitle:** Journal of 3D Imagery. **Freq:** Quarterly. **Trim Size:** B5. **Key Personnel:** B. Makinson, Editor. **Subscription Rates:** Included in membership. **Remarks:** Advertising accepted; rates available upon request. **URL:** http://www.stereoscopicsociety.org.uk/. **Circ:** 750

55620 ■ The Squash Player
McKenzie Publishing Ltd.
Longhouse, 460 Bath Rd.
Longford
Middlesex UB7 0EB, United Kingdom
Ph: 44 17 53775511
Fax: 44 17 53775512
Magazine providing news, reports, photos, and results on the game of squash and its players. **Key Personnel:** Stephen Line, Photos, steve@squashpics.com; Martin Bronstein, Writers; Malcolm Willstrop, Writers; Richard Eaton, Writers; Tim Garner, Writers, tgsquash@aol.com; Ozkan Mustafa, Web Site, ossie_mustafa@hotmail.com; Joe Laredo, Advertising, spadverts@aol.com; Ian McKenzie, Editor, editor@squashplayer.co.uk; Ray Ball, Art Dir. **Remarks:** Accepts advertising. **URL:** http://www.squashplayer.co.uk/; http://www.squashplayer.co.uk/index.asp. **Circ:** (Not Reported)

55621 ■ Sunrise Radio-AM - 1458
Sunrise House
Southall
Middlesex UB2 4AT, United Kingdom
Ph: 44 208 5746666
Fax: 44 208 8139700
E-mail: reception@sunriseradio.com
Format: Ethnic; Oldies; Folk; Talk; Easy Listening. **Founded:** Jan. 1, 1994. **Operating Hours:** Continuous. **Ad Rates:** Advertising accepted; rates available upon request. **URL:** http://www.sunriseradio.com/.

Middleton

55622 ■ SOFHT Focus
Society of Food Hygiene Technology
Middleton House Farm
Tamworth Rd.
Middleton B78 2BD, United Kingdom
Ph: 44 1827 872500
Fax: 44 1827 875800
Publisher E-mail: adrnin@sofht.co.uk
Publication covering food, hygiene and food supply. **Freq:** Quarterly. **Key Personnel:** Ian Booth, Editor. **ISSN:** 1477-7401. **Subscription Rates:** Included in membership. **Remarks:** Advertising accepted; rates available upon request. **URL:** http://www.sofht.co.uk/publications/index.asp. **Circ:** 3,000

Middleton Cheney

55623 ■ Rapport
Nationwide Group Staff Union
Middleton Farmhouse
37 Main Rd.
Oxfordshire
Middleton Cheney OX17 2QT, United Kingdom
Ph: 44 12 95710767
Fax: 44 12 95712580
Publisher E-mail: ngsu@ngsu.org.uk
Trade union magazine covering employment issues. **Founded:** 1990. **Freq:** Quarterly. **Print Method:** Offset litho. **Trim Size:** A4. **Cols./Page:** 2. **Col. Width:** 77 millimeters. **Col. Depth:** 252 millimeters. **ISSN:** 0961-3935. **Remarks:** Accepts advertising. **URL:** http://www.ngsu.org.uk. **Circ:** Non-paid 11,000

Middlewich

55624 ■ Journal of Bryology
British Bryological Society
Wheelock St.
Middlewich CW10 9AB, United Kingdom
Publisher E-mail: walton@ivyhouse.u-net.com
Publication covering botany. **Freq:** Quarterly. **Key Personnel:** Dr. Jeff W. Bates, Scientific Ed., j.bates@imperial.ac.uk; Howard Matcham, Managing Editor, hwlgmatch@yahoo.co.uk. **ISSN:** 0373-6687. **Subscription Rates:** 101 individuals; US$194 individuals; 348 institutions; US$619 institutions. **URL:** http://www.britishbryologicalsociety.org.uk/; http://rbg-web2.rbge.org.uk/bbs/Activities/Journal.htm.

Midhurst

55625 ■ Midhurst & Petworth Observer
Johnston Press PLC
Capron House
North St.
Midhurst GU29 9DT, United Kingdom
Ph: 44 7801 195419
Local community newspaper. **Key Personnel:** Bharat Lukka, Mktg. Mgr., phone 44 1403 751200, fax 44 1403 751291, bharat.lukka@sussexnewspapers.co.uk; Colin Channon, Editor, phone 44 1243 534135, fax 44 1243 539386, colin.channon@chiobserver.co.uk; Jenny Mouland, Contact, jenny.mouland@chiobserver.co.uk. **Remarks:** Accepts advertising. **URL:** http://www.midhurstandpetworth.co.uk/. **Circ:** (Not Reported)

Midlothian

55626 ■ Agricultural and Forest Entomology
John Wiley & Sons Inc.
Wiley-Blackwell
c/o Dr. A.D. Watt, Ed.
Centre for Ecology & Hydrology
Bush Estate
Penicuik
Midlothian EH26 0QB, United Kingdom
Ph: 44 131 4454343
Fax: 44 131 4453943
Journal covering all aspects of agricultural and forest entomology. **Freq:** Quarterly. **Key Personnel:** Allan D. Watt, Editor, adw@ceh.ac.uk; Barbara Ekbom, Editor, barbara.ekbom@ekol.slu.se; Hefin Jones, Editor, jonesth@cardiff.ac.uk. **ISSN:** 1461-9555. **Subscription Rates:** US$212 individuals Americas (print and online); US$1,029 institutions Americas (online only); US$1,132 institutions Americas (print and online); 117 individuals UK (print and online); 557 institutions UK (online only); 613 institutions UK (print and online); 127 other countries print and online; US$1,200 institutions, other countries online only; US$1,320 institutions, other countries print and online; EUR173 individuals Euro zone (print and online). **URL:** http://www.wiley.com/bw/journal.asp?ref=1461-9555.

55627 ■ Cabletalk
SELECT
The Walled Garden
Bush Estate
Midlothian EH26 0SB, United Kingdom
Ph: 44 131 4455577
Fax: 44 131 4455548
Publisher E-mail: admin@select.org.uk
Publication covering electrical engineering industry. **Subtitle:** Magazine of Scotland's Electrotechnical Industry.

Founded: 1976. **Freq:** Monthly. **Key Personnel:** Georgia Love, Editor. **ISSN:** 1365-3288. **Subscription Rates:** Free to qualified subscribers. **Remarks:** Advertising accepted; rates available upon request. **URL:** http://www.select.org.uk. **Circ:** 5,000

55628 ■ Taste of Scotland
Taste of Scotland Scheme Ltd.
c/o Expresss Media
Bush House
Bush State
Midlothian EH26 0BB, United Kingdom
Ph: 44 13 68865444
Fax: 44 13 68865777
Publication E-mail: info@taste-of-scotland.com
Publisher E-mail: info@taste-of-scotland.com
Consumer magazine covering restaurants in Scotland. **Remarks:** Advertising not accepted. **URL:** http://www.taste-of-scotland.com. **Circ:** (Not Reported)

Milngavie

55629 ■ Milngavie Herald
Johnston Press PLC
27 Stewart St.
Milngavie G62 6BW, United Kingdom
Ph: 44 141 9562314
Local community newspaper. **Remarks:** Accepts advertising. **URL:** http://www.milngavieherald.co.uk/. **Circ:** (Not Reported)

Milton Keynes

55630 ■ Badminton
Badminton Association of England
National Badminton Ctr.
Milton Keynes MK8 9LA, United Kingdom
Ph: 44 19 08268400
Publisher E-mail: enquiries@badmintonengland.co.uk
Publication covering badminton. **Freq:** Quarterly. **Subscription Rates:** Included in membership; 42 individuals society/direct affiliate; 15 individuals senior oncourt; 7 individuals junior oncourt; 36 individuals oncourt platinum. **Remarks:** Advertising accepted; rates available upon request. **URL:** http://www.badmintonengland.co.uk/. **Circ:** 8,000

55631 ■ Closer to God
Scripture Union Publishing
207-209 Queensway
Bletchley
Milton Keynes MK2 2EB, United Kingdom
Ph: 44 1908 856000
Publication E-mail: closertogod@scriptureunion.org.uk
Publisher E-mail: info@scriptureunion.org.uk
Consumer magazine covering the Bible for adults. **Founded:** 1996. **Freq:** Quarterly. **Key Personnel:** Phil Andrews, Editor. **Subscription Rates:** 14 individuals; 18 individuals Europe; 20 individuals outside Europe & UK. **Remarks:** Advertising not accepted. **URL:** http://www.closertogod.org.uk/. **Former name:** Closer to God Incorporating Alive to God. **Circ:** (Not Reported)

55632 ■ Daily Bread
Scripture Union Publishing
207-209 Queensway
Bletchley
Milton Keynes MK2 2EB, United Kingdom
Ph: 44 1908 856000
Publisher E-mail: info@scriptureunion.org.uk
Consumer magazine covering the Bible for adults. **Freq:** Quarterly. **Key Personnel:** Andrew Clark, Editor. **Subscription Rates:** 14 individuals for delivery to UK; 18 individuals for Europe; 20 individuals for outside Europe & UK. **Remarks:** Advertising not accepted. **URL:** http://www.scriptureunion.org.uk/SU_Core/41809.id. **Circ:** (Not Reported)

55633 ■ Design Studies
Elsevier Science
c/o N. Cross, Ed.-in-Ch.
Dept. of Design & Innovation
Faculty of Technology
The Open University Walton Hall
Milton Keynes MK7 6AA, United Kingdom
Publisher E-mail: nlinfo-f@elsevier.com
Peer-reviewed journal covering advanced techniques, knowledge and applications in the practice and education of design, published in connection with Design Research Society. Includes design management, design

methods, participation in planning and design, design education, AI and computer aids in design, design in engineering, theoretical aspects of design, design in architecture, design and manufacturing, innovation in industry and design and society. **Subtitle:** The International Journal for Design Research in Engineering, Architecture, Products and Systems. **Freq:** Bimonthly. **Key Personnel:** N. Cross, Editor-in-Chief, n.g.cross@ open.ac.uk; C. Atman, Editorial Board; D. Durling, Editorial Board; Prof. L. Drew, Editorial Board; K. Friedman, Editorial Board; P. Galle, Editorial Board. **ISSN:** 0142-694X. **Subscription Rates:** 144,000¥ institutions; EUR1,033 institutions for European countries; US$1,215 institutions for all countries except Europe and Japan; EUR263 individuals for European countries; US$293 individuals for all countries except Europe and Japan; 34,600¥ individuals. **Remarks:** Accepts advertising. **URL:** http://www.elsevier.com/wps/find/ journaldescription.cws_home/30409/ descriptiondescription. **Circ:** (Not Reported)

55634 ■ Encounter with God
Scripture Union Publishing
207-209 Queensway
Bletchley
Milton Keynes MK2 2EB, United Kingdom
Ph: 44 1908 856000
Publisher E-mail: info@scriptureunion.org.uk
Consumer magazine covering Bible reading notes. **Subtitle:** Hearing God Speak Today. **Freq:** Quarterly. **Key Personnel:** Andrew Clark, Editor. **Subscription Rates:** 15.80 individuals; 20 individuals Europe; 23 other countries. **Remarks:** Advertising not accepted. **URL:** http://www.scriptureunion.org.uk/1019.id. **Formerly:** Daily Notes. **Circ:** (Not Reported)

55635 ■ Food Marketing & Manufacturing
Yandell Publishing Ltd.
PO Box 5116
Milton Keynes MK15 8ZQ, United Kingdom
Ph: 44 190 8613323
Fax: 44 190 8210656
Publisher E-mail: editorial@yandellmedia.com
Trade magazine for executives in the food industry. **Founded:** 1997. **Freq:** 11/yr. **ISSN:** 1368-5732. **Remarks:** Accepts advertising. **URL:** http://www. magazinesubscriptionsearch.com/prd113912.php. **Circ:** Controlled 10,219

55636 ■ Geostandards & Geoanalytical Research
John Wiley & Sons Inc.
Wiley-Blackwell
c/o Philip J. Potts, Ed.-in-Ch.
The Open University
Faculty of Science
Walton Hall
Milton Keynes MK7 6AA, United Kingdom
Peer-reviewed journal covering the field of geology. **Freq:** Quarterly. **Key Personnel:** Philip J. Potts, Editor-in-Chief, p.j.potts@open.ac.uk; William F. McDonough, Editor-in-Chief, mcdonoug@geol.umd.edu. **ISSN:** 1639-4488. **Subscription Rates:** US$174 individuals Americas (print and online); 98 other countries print and online; EUR147 individuals Euro zone (print and online); US$782 institutions Americas (print and online); 429 institutions UK (print and online); EUR545 institutions Europe (print and online); US$843 institutions, other countries print and online; US$677 institutions Americas (online only); 371 institutions UK (online only); EUR472 institutions Europe (online only). **Remarks:** Accepts advertising. **URL:** http://www.wiley.com/bw/journal.asp? ref=1639-4488. **Circ:** (Not Reported)

55637 ■ Group Leisure
Yandell Publishing Ltd.
PO Box 5122
Milton Keynes MK15 8ZP, United Kingdom
Ph: 44 1908 613323
Fax: 44 1908 210656
Publication E-mail: info@groupleisure.com
Publisher E-mail: editorial@yandellmedia.com
Magazine featuring information for group travel and tourism. **Freq:** Monthly. **Subscription Rates:** 45 individuals. **Remarks:** Accepts advertising. **URL:** http:// www.groupleisure.com/home/. **Circ:** (Not Reported)

55638 ■ International Journal of Forensic Engineering
Inderscience Publishers
c/o Dr. Peter R. Lewis, Ed.
Open University

Materials Engineering
Walton Hall
Milton Keynes MK7 6AA, United Kingdom
Publisher E-mail: editor@inderscience.com
Peer-reviewed journal seeking original contributions of analysis of product or process failure which result in personal injury or loss of property. **Freq:** Quarterly. **Key Personnel:** Dr. Peter R. Lewis, Editor, p.r.lewis@open. ac.uk; Prof. Roy Crawford, Editorial Board Member; Dr. Donald Duvall, Editorial Board Member; Dr. Mike Fitzpatrick, Editorial Board Member; Colin Gagg, Editorial Board Member; Dr. Colin Goodchild, Editorial Board Member; Dr. Myer Ezrin, Editorial Board Member; Dr. Mike R. Edwards, Editorial Board Member; Prof. Alex Chudnovsky, Editorial Board Member. **ISSN:** 1744-9944. **Subscription Rates:** EUR494 individuals print only (surface mail); EUR840 individuals online only (2-3 users); EUR672 individuals print and online; EUR534 individuals print only (airmail). **URL:** http://www. inderscience.com/browse/index.php?journalCODE=ijfe.

55639 ■ Journal of Interactive Media in Education
Institute of Educational Technology
Walton Hall
The Open University
Milton Keynes MK7 6AA, United Kingdom
Ph: 44 1908 274066
Publication E-mail: jime@open.ac.uk
Journal dealing with practical and theoretical aspects of interactive media in education. **Founded:** Sept. 1996. **Freq:** Semiannual. **Key Personnel:** Doug Clow, Editor, d.j.clow@open.ac.uk; Patrick McAndrew, Editor, p.mcandrew@open.ac.uk. **ISSN:** 1365-893X. **URL:** http://www-jime.open.ac.uk.

55640 ■ NEWSLI
Association of Sign Language Interpreters
Fortuna House
S 5th St.
Milton Keynes MK9 2EU, United Kingdom
Ph: 44 87 14740522
Fax: 44 19 08325259
Publisher E-mail: office@asli.org.uk
Magazine containing issues on practicing interpreters. **Freq:** Quarterly. **URL:** http://www.asli.org.uk/about-asli-p2.aspx.

Mold

55641 ■ Denbighshire Free Press
NWN Media Ltd.
Mold Business Pk.
Mold CH7 1XY, United Kingdom
Ph: 44 1352 707707
Fax: 44 1352 752180
Publisher E-mail: internet@nwn.co.uk
Newspaper featuring news, views, sports, and features. **Key Personnel:** Nic Outterside, Editor. **URL:** http://www. denbighshirefreepress.co.uk/.

55642 ■ European Information
European Information Association
PO Box 28
Flintshire
Mold CH7 6FE, United Kingdom
Journal of the European Information Association. **Freq:** Quarterly. **ISSN:** 1461-5428. **Subscription Rates:** EUR10 members. **Remarks:** Accepts advertising. **URL:** http://www.eia.org.uk/publications.php. **Circ:** (Not Reported)

55643 ■ Focus
European Information Association
PO Box 28
Flintshire
Mold CH7 6FE, United Kingdom
Journal covering issues related to information about and from the European Union. **Subtitle:** News and Views from the EIA. **Founded:** Jan. 2003. **Freq:** Monthly 11/yr. **Trim Size:** A4. **ISSN:** 1479-5450. **Subscription Rates:** Included in membership. **URL:** http://www.eia.org.uk/. **Former name:** European Information. **Ad Rates:** BW: 90. **Circ:** (Not Reported)

Monmouth

55644 ■ Bees for Development Journal
Bees for Development
PO Box 105

Monmouth NP25 9AA, United Kingdom
Ph: 44 1600 713648
Publisher E-mail: info@beesfordevelopment.org
Magazine covering beekeeping news. **Subtitle:** The Journal for Sustainable Beekeeping. **Founded:** 1983. **Freq:** Quarterly. **Print Method:** Offset. **Trim Size:** A4. **Key Personnel:** Nicola Bradbear, PhD, Editor. **ISSN:** 1477-6588. **Subscription Rates:** 20 individuals. **Remarks:** Accepts advertising. **URL:** http://www.planbee. org.uk/journal. **Former name:** Bookeeping & Development. **Ad Rates:** BW: 200, 4C: 250. **Circ:** Paid 4,000

Montrose

55645 ■ Kincardineshire Observer
Johnston Press PLC
63 Murray St.
Montrose DD10 8JZ, United Kingdom
Ph: 44 1674 672605
Local community newspaper. **Remarks:** Accepts advertising. **URL:** http://www.kincardineshireobserver. co.uk/. **Circ:** (Not Reported)

55646 ■ Montrose Review
Johnston Press PLC
63 Murray St.
Montrose DD10 8JZ, United Kingdom
Publication E-mail: reviewnews@montrosereview.com
Local community newspaper. **Remarks:** Accepts advertising. **URL:** http://www.montrosereview.co.uk/. **Circ:** (Not Reported)

Morecambe

55647 ■ Dirt Bike Rider
Lancaster & Morecambe Newspapers
12 Victoria St.
Morecambe LA4 4AG, United Kingdom
Ph: 44 15 24833111
Fax: 44 15 24420939
Consumer magazine covering off-road motorcycling and motocross. **Founded:** 1978. **Freq:** Monthly. **Key Personnel:** Sean Lawless, Editor, sean.lawless@ dirtbikerider.co.uk; Anne Pardula, Subscriptions, subs. dbr@lmnews.co.uk; Anthony Sutty Sutton, Dep. Ed., anthony.sutton@dirtbikerider.co.uk. **Subscription Rates:** 30 individuals U.K.; 49.50 individuals Europe; 65 other countries. **Remarks:** Accepts advertising. **URL:** http://www.dirtbikerider.co.uk/. **Ad Rates:** GLR: 9.66, BW: 630, 4C: 1,213. **Circ:** Paid ‡25,000

55648 ■ Lakeland Echo
Johnston Press PLC
Lakeland Echo
Victoria St.
Morecambe LA4 4AG, United Kingdom
Ph: 44 1524 833111
Local community newspaper. **Key Personnel:** David Waddington, Editor. **Remarks:** Accepts advertising. **URL:** http://www.lakelandecho.co.uk/. **Circ:** (Not Reported)

55649 ■ Trials & Motocross News
Lancaster & Morecambe Newspapers
12 Victoria St.
Morecambe LA4 4AG, United Kingdom
Ph: 44 15 24833111
Fax: 44 15 24420939
Consumer magazine covering off-road bikes and motocross. **Founded:** 1977. **Freq:** Weekly. **Print Method:** Web Offset. **Cols./Page:** 7. **Col. Depth:** 34 centimeters. **Key Personnel:** John Dickinson, News Ed., john.dickinson@tmxnews.co.uk; Mannix Devlin, Production Ed., mannix.devlin@tmxnews.co.uk. **ISSN:** 0958-4226. **Subscription Rates:** 130 individuals Europe; 169 other countries; 79.95 individuals U.K.; 34.99 individuals Europe; 13 weeks; 45 other countries 13 weeks; 42 individuals U.K.; 26 weeks; 65 individuals Europe; 26 weeks; 85 other countries 26 weeks; 19.99 individuals U.K.; 13 weeks. **Remarks:** Accepts advertising. **URL:** http://www.tmxnews.co.uk/. **Ad Rates:** GLR: 3.18, BW: 757. **Circ:** Paid ‡24,000

Moreton-in-Marsh

55650 ■ Fire Prevention
The Fire Protection Association
London Rd.

Circulation: ★ = ABC; △ = BPA; ◆ = CAC; • = CCAB; ❑ = VAC; ⊕ = PO Statement; ‡ = Publisher's Report; Boldface figures = sworn; Light figures = estimated.

Gale Directory of Publications & Broadcast Media/147th Ed.   5791

Moreton-in-Marsh GL56 0RH, United Kingdom
Ph: 44 16 08812500
Fax: 44 16 08812501
Publication E-mail: fpa@thefpa.co.uk
Publisher E-mail: fpa@thefpa.co.uk
Trade magazine covering fire prevention and safety. **Founded:** 1946. **Freq:** Monthly. **Print Method:** Sheet-fed litho. **Trim Size:** 297 x 210 mm. **Cols./Page:** 4. **Col. Width:** 40 centimeters. **Col. Depth:** 260 millimeters. **Key Personnel:** Jane Thurgood, Assoc. Dir.; Glenn Tomkins, Tech. Ed.; Anna Hayes, Gp. Publisher; Howard Passey, Educ. & Training Dir. **ISSN:** 0309-6866. **Remarks:** Accepts advertising. **URL:** http://www.thefpa.co.uk/Resources/MemberLibrary/Books/FirePrevention/. **Ad Rates:** BW: 1,020, 4C: 1,485. **Circ:** 15,000

55651 ■ Fire Risk Management
Institution of Fire Engineers - England
London Rd.
Gloucestershire
Moreton-in-Marsh GL56 0RH, United Kingdom
Ph: 44 1608 812580
Fax: 44 1608 812581
Publisher E-mail: info@ife.org.uk
Official journal of the Institution of Fire Engineers and the Fire Protection Association. **Founded:** Jan. 2002. **Freq:** Monthly. **Trim Size:** 260 x 184 mm. **Key Personnel:** Rupert Gilbey, Editor, rgilbey@thefpa.co.uk. **Remarks:** Accepts advertising. **URL:** http://www.frmjournal.com/; http://www.fp-fej.com/. **Formerly:** Fire Prevention and Fire Engineers Journal. **Ad Rates:** 4C: 1,485. **Circ:** 15,000

Morley

55652 ■ Morley Observer & Advertiser
Johnston Press PLC
40 Queen St.
Morley LS27 9BR, United Kingdom
Ph: 44 1132 523456
Local community newspaper. **Freq:** Weekly (Wed.). **Key Personnel:** Bob Evans, Editor; Sarah Hall, Dep. Ed. **Remarks:** Accepts advertising. **URL:** http://www.morleyobserver.co.uk/. **Circ:** (Not Reported)

Morpeth

55653 ■ Morpeth Herald
Northeast Press Ltd.
17 Newgate St.
Morpeth NE61 1AW, United Kingdom
Ph: 44 1670 516066
Community newspaper. **Founded:** Apr. 1, 1854. **Freq:** Weekly. **Key Personnel:** Terry Hackett, Editor; Alastair Craig, News Reporter; Anna Smith, Ch. Reporter; Neil MacFarlane, News Reporter. **Subscription Rates:** .45 individuals 1 week; 5.85 individuals 13 weeks (1 quarter). **Remarks:** Accepts advertising. **URL:** http://www.morpethherald.co.uk/. **Ad Rates:** BW: 5,500. **Circ:** Paid *3,122

Munster

55654 ■ Solid State Nuclear Magnetic Resonance
Elsevier Science Inc.
c/o H. Eckert, Ed.-in-Ch.
Inst. fur Physikalische Chemie
Westfalische Wilhelms-Universitat Munster
Corrensstrasse 28-30
Munster D-48149, United Kingdom
Ph: 49 251 8329161
Fax: 49 251 8329159
Publisher E-mail: usinfo-ehelp@elsevier.com
Journal covering experimental, theoretical aspects of solid state nuclear magnetic resonance. **Freq:** 8/yr. **Print Method:** Offset. **Trim Size:** 13 3/4 x 22 3/4. **Cols./Page:** 6. **Col. Width:** 24 nonpareils. **Col. Depth:** 294 agate lines. **Key Personnel:** F. Babonneau, Editorial Board; C. Dybowski, Editorial Board; R. Botto, Editorial Board, phone 202872-6186, nikabob1@verizon.net; H. Eckert, Editor-in-Chief, eckerth@uni-muenster.de; L. Emsley, Editorial Board; D.E. Demco, Editorial Board; G. Bodenhausen, Editorial Board; M. Duer, Editorial Board; J. Klinowski, Consulting Ed. **ISSN:** 0926-2040. **Subscription Rates:** 168,700¥ institutions; EUR1,614 institutions for European countries and Iran; US$1,405 institutions, other countries except Europe, Japan and Iran; EUR704 individuals for European countries and Iran; US$618

other countries except Europe, Japan and Iran; 73,500¥ individuals; EUR354 students for European countries and Iran; US$309 students, other countries except Europe, Japan and Iran; 37,000¥ students. **URL:** http://www.elsevier.com/wps/find/journaldescription.cws_home/622947/descriptiondescription.

Narberth

55655 ■ Radio Pembrokeshire-FM - 102.5
Old School Estate, Unit 14
Station Rd.
Narberth SA67 7DU, United Kingdom
Ph: 44 1834 869292
Fax: 44 1834 861524
E-mail: studio@radiopembrokeshire.com
Format: Adult Contemporary. **Ad Rates:** Advertising accepted; rates available upon request. **URL:** http://www.radiopembrokeshire.com/.

Neath

Nation Radio-FM - See Cardiff

Nation Radio-FM - See Swansea

55656 ■ Swansea Bay Radio-FM - 102.1
Newby House
Neath Abbey Business Pk.
Neath SA10 7DR, United Kingdom
Ph: 44 1792 323900
Format: Adult Contemporary. **Ad Rates:** Advertising accepted; rates available upon request. **URL:** http://www.swanseabayradio.co.uk/.

Nelson

55657 ■ 2BR-FM - 99.8
Lomeshaye Business Village
Nelson BB9 7DR, United Kingdom
Ph: 44 1282 690000
E-mail: news@2br.co.uk
Format: Eclectic; Top 40; Adult Contemporary; Sports; News. **Owner:** The Local Radio Company, 11 Duke St., High Wycombe HP13 6EE, United Kingdom, 44 1494 688200, Fax: 44 1494 688201. **Operating Hours:** Continuous. **Ad Rates:** Advertising accepted; rates available upon request. **URL:** http://www.2br.co.uk/.

New Malden

55658 ■ Dalton's Weekly
United Advertising Publications Ltd.
C.I. Twr.
St. George's Sq.
New Malden KT3 4JA, United Kingdom
Ph: 44 208 3290100
Fax: 44 208 3290101
Publication covering businesses and property for sale. **Founded:** 1870. **Freq:** Weekly (Thurs.). **Print Method:** Web offset. **Cols./Page:** 6. **Col. Width:** 44 millimeters. **Subscription Rates:** 48 individuals; 128 other countries; 1.95 single issue. **Remarks:** Accepts advertising. **URL:** http://www.daltons.co.uk. **Ad Rates:** BW: 3,000, 4C: 3,400. **Circ:** Paid *32,124

Newark

55659 ■ Horological Journal
British Horological Institute
Upton Hall
Upton
Newark NG23 5TE, United Kingdom
Ph: 44 16 36813795
Fax: 44 16 36812258
Publisher E-mail: info@bhi.co.uk
Trade journal covering technical articles on clocks and watches, workshop equipment, trade news, and book reviews. **Founded:** 1858. **Freq:** Monthly. **Print Method:** Offset. **Trim Size:** A4. **Cols./Page:** 3. **Col. Width:** 58 millimeters. **Col. Depth:** 26 millimeters. **Key Personnel:** Jayne Hall, Editor, jayne@bhi.co.uk. **ISSN:** 0018-5108. **Subscription Rates:** 88 individuals 24 months; 132 individuals 36 months. **Remarks:** Accepts advertising. **URL:** http://www.bhi.co.uk/hj.html. **Ad Rates:** BW: 435, 4C: 870. **Circ:** Controlled 3,800

55660 ■ Members Journal
Commemorative Collectors Society
Lumless House
77 Gainsborough Rd.
Winthorpe

Newark NG24 2NR, United Kingdom
Ph: 44 1636 671377
Publisher E-mail: commemorativecollectorssociety@hotmail.com
Trade journal covering collectors. **Founded:** 1972. **Freq:** Quarterly. **Print Method:** Offset Litho. **Trim Size:** A4. **Key Personnel:** S.N. Jackson, Contact, steven_n_jackson@hotmail.com. **Subscription Rates:** Included in membership; US$30 U.S. **Remarks:** Advertising not accepted. **URL:** http://www.commemorativescollecting.co.uk/index.php. **Circ:** 4,311

Newbury

55661 ■ Avian Pathology
Taylor & Francis Ltd.
Institute for Animal Health
Compton
Newbury RG20 7NN, United Kingdom
Publication covering the diseases of domesticated poultry and other birds in English. Abstracts in French, German, and Spanish. **Freq:** 6/yr. **Key Personnel:** J.M. Bradbury, Editor-in-Chief; D. Alexander, Editor; S. Sharif, Editor; J.J. de Wit, Editor; H. Christensen, Editor; T. Ito, Advisory Board; A. Noormohammadi, Editor; J.K.A. Cook, Editor; H.J. Barnes, Advisory Board; A. Wood, Editor; M. Hess, Editor. **ISSN:** 0307-9457. **Subscription Rates:** US$244 individuals; US$585 institutions online only; US$616 institutions print & online; 368 institutions print & online; 350 institutions online; 129 individuals; EUR493 institutions print and online; EUR468 institutions online; EUR196 individuals. **Remarks:** Accepts advertising on request. **URL:** http://www.tandf.co.uk/journals/tf/03079457.html. **Circ:** (Not Reported)

55662 ■ Soldiers of the Queen
Victorian Military Society
PO Box 5837
Newbury RG14 7FJ, United Kingdom
Journal covering worldwide military history from 1837-1914. **Founded:** 1974. **Freq:** Quarterly. **Print Method:** Litho. **Remarks:** Accepts advertising. **URL:** http://www.victorianmilitarysociety.org.uk/. **Circ:** Controlled 1,250

55663 ■ Kick-FM - 107.4
42 Bone Ln.
Berkshire
Newbury RG14 5SD, United Kingdom
Ph: 44 1635 841000
Fax: 44 1635 841010
E-mail: studio@newburysound.co.uk
Format: Contemporary Hit Radio (CHR). **URL:** http://www.kickfm.co.uk/.

55664 ■ Kick-FM - 105.6
42 Bone Ln.
Berkshire
Newbury RG14 5SD, United Kingdom
Ph: 44 1635 841600
Fax: 44 1635 841010
E-mail: studio@newburysound.co.uk
Format: Contemporary Hit Radio (CHR). **URL:** http://www.kickfm.co.uk/.

Newcastle

55665 ■ Mourne Observer
Mourne Observer Ltd.
Castlewellan Rd.
County Down
Newcastle BT33 0JX, United Kingdom
Ph: 44 284 3722666
Fax: 44 284 3724566
Publication E-mail: news@mourneobserver.com
Publisher E-mail: info@mourneobserver.com
Community newspaper. **Subtitle:** Co-Down News. **Founded:** Oct. 1949. **Freq:** Weekly. **Print Method:** Web offset. **Cols./Page:** 8. **Col. Width:** 33 millimeters. **Col. Depth:** 450 millimeters. **Remarks:** Accepts advertising. **URL:** http://www.mourneobserver.com/. **Ad Rates:** GLR: 4, BW: 1,000, 4C: 1,350. **Circ:** Paid 11,988

Newcastle upon Tyne

55666 ■ Accent
Accent Magazines Ltd.
11 Causey St.
Tyne & Wear
Newcastle upon Tyne NE3 4DJ, United Kingdom

Ph: 44 191 2849994

Magazine covering local news, entertainment, and business. **Trim Size:** 230 x 297 mm. **Key Personnel:** Mike Grahamslaw, Sales Dir., mike.grahamslaw@ accentmagazines.co.uk; Kevin Wright, Editor, kevin. wright@accentmagazines.co.uk. **Subscription Rates:** 43.45 individuals. **URL:** http://accentmagazine.co.uk/. **Circ:** 18,000

55667 ■ Archaeologia Aeliana
Society of Antiquaries of Newcastle-upon-Tyne
Great North Museum
Hancock, Barras Bridge
Newcastle upon Tyne NE2 4PT, United Kingdom
Ph: 44 19 12312700
Publisher E-mail: admin@newcastle-antiquaries.org.uk
Journal containing articles on history and archeology of NE England. **Founded:** 1822. **Freq:** Annual. **Key Personnel:** Humphrey Welfare, Editor. **Subscription Rates:** 32 members hardback; 27 members paperback; 32 institutions paperback; 37 institutions hardback. **URL:** http://www.newcastle-antiquaries.org.uk/index.php? pageId=86.

55668 ■ Crime Prevention & Community Safety
Palgrave Macmillan
c/o Elaine Campbell, Reviews Ed.
School of Geography, Politics & Sociology
Bridge Bldg.
University of Newcastle upon Tyne
Newcastle upon Tyne NE1 7RU, United Kingdom
Ph: 44 191 2225030
Publisher E-mail: booksellers@palgrave.com
Journal devoted to crime reduction and community safety practitioners. **Freq:** 4/yr. **Key Personnel:** Prof. Rob Mawby, Editor, professorrobmawby@hotmail.com; Elaine Campbell, Reviews Ed., elaine.campbell@ncl.ac. uk. **ISSN:** 1460-3780. **Subscription Rates:** 290 institutions, other countries print; US$539 institutions print; 98 other countries print and online; US$182 individuals print and online. **URL:** http://www.palgrave-journals.com/ cpcs/index.html.

55669 ■ Environmental Law Review
Vathek Publishing
c/o Prof. Christopher P. Rodgers, Ed.-in-Ch.
Newcastle Law School
The University of Newcastle upon Tyne
21-24 Windsor Ter.
Newcastle upon Tyne NE1 7RU, United Kingdom
Ph: 44 1912 227624
Fax: 44 1912 120064
Publisher E-mail: mlw@valthek.com
Journal focusing on environmental law, environmental management and business. **Freq:** Quarterly. **Key Personnel:** Prof. Lynda M. Warren, Editor-in-Chief, phone 44 16 54781344, fax 44 19 70622729, lm.warren@ btopenworld.com; Prof. Christopher P. Rodgers, Editor-in-Chief, cpr@ncl.ac.uk; Paul Davies, Update Ed.; Prof. Maria Lee, Legislation Ed., maria.lee@ucl.ac.uk; Prof. Peter Kunzlik, Editorial Board; Prof. Karen Morrow, Case Note Ed., k.morrow@swansea.ac.uk; Dr. Ramon Ojeda Mestre, Editorial Board; Brian Jack, Case Note Ed., phone 44 28 90273451, fax 44 28 90325590, b.jack@ qub.ac.uk. **ISSN:** 1461-4529. **Subscription Rates:** 303 institutions paper and online; US$542 institutions paper and online; 152 individuals paper and online; US$271 individuals paper and online; 226 institutions online only; US$407 institutions online only; 113 individuals online only; US$203 individuals online only; 253 institutions paper only; US$451 institutions paper only. **Remarks:** Advertising accepted; rates available upon request. **URL:** http://www.vathek.com/elr/index.shtml. **Circ:** (Not Reported)

55670 ■ Formal Aspects of Computing
Springer-Verlag London Ltd.
c/o Prof. Cliff B. Jones, Founding Ed.
Department of Computing Science
University of Newcastle Upon Tyne
Newcastle upon Tyne NE1 7RU, United Kingdom
Journal of formal methods containing notations, theories and tools and practical applications of computing. **Subtitle:** Applicable Formal Methods. **Key Personnel:** Prof. J.M. Wing, North American Ed., wing@cs.cmu.edu; Prof. Cliff B. Jones, Founding Ed., cliff.jones@ncl.ac.uk; Prof. R. Backhouse, Editorial Board, rcb@cs.nott.ac.uk; Dr. D.J. Cooke; Assoc. Ed., d.j.cooke@lboro.ac.uk; Prof.

J.C.P Woodcock, Editor-in-Chief, jim@cs.york.ac.uk; Prof. E. Astesiano, Editorial Board, astes@disi.unige.it. **ISSN:** 0934-5043. **Remarks:** Advertising accepted; rates available upon request. **URL:** http://www.springer.com/ computer/mathematics/journal/165. **Circ:** (Not Reported)

55671 ■ Fuel
Elsevier Science Inc.
c/o K.M. Thomas, Ed.
School of Chemical Engineering & Advanced Materials
Northern Carbon Research Labs
Newcastle University, Bedson Bldg.
Newcastle upon Tyne NE1 7RU, United Kingdom
Publisher E-mail: usinfo-ehelp@elsevier.com
Peer-reviewed journal featuring research work in fuel science. **Subtitle:** The Science and Technology of Fuel and Energy. **Founded:** 1973. **Freq:** 12/yr. **Print Method:** Offset. Uses mats. **Trim Size:** 8 x 10 3/4. **Cols./Page:** 3. **Col. Width:** 26 nonpareils. **Col. Depth:** 140 agate lines. **Key Personnel:** K.M. Thomas, Editor, phone 44 191 2226835, fax 44 191 2226929, mark.thomas@ newcastle.ac.uk; R.M. Davidson, International Editorial Board; A. Tomita, Editor, fax 81 22 2175626, yatomita@ dj8.so-net.ne.jp; J.W. Patrick, Editor, john.patrick@ nottingham.ac.uk; E. Suuberg, Editor, fax 401863-1157, eric_suuberg@brown.edu; K. Miura, Editor, phone 81 753 862663, fax 81 753 862663, miura@cheme.kyoto-u-ac.jp; C.S. Lee, International Editorial Board; C.Z. Li, International Editorial Board. **ISSN:** 0016-2361. **Subscription Rates:** 16,100¥ individuals; US$135 other countries except Europe, Japan and Iran; EUR123 individuals for European countries and Iran; EUR3,537 institutions for European countries and Iran; 469,500¥ institutions. **URL:** http://www.elsevier.com/wps/find/ journaldescription.cws_home/30420/ descriptiondescription.

55672 ■ International Journal of Clinical Legal Education
Northumbria Law Press
Northumbria University
Sutherland Bldg.
Northumberland Rd.
Newcastle upon Tyne NE1 8ST, United Kingdom
Ph: 44 19 12437587
Fax: 44 19 12437506
Publisher E-mail: ann.conway@northumbria.ac.uk
Journal featuring articles, discussion and news about the ever-expanding area of clinical legal education, providing a forum for exchange of ideas between clinical programs throughout the world, as well as a basis for academic development of this field. **Key Personnel:** Mary Anne Noone, Editorial Board; Judith Dickson, Editorial Board. **ISSN:** 1467-1069. **Subscription Rates:** 50 individuals; 25 individuals. **URL:** http://www. northumbria.ac.uk/sd/academic/law/entunit/norlawpress/ jour/IJCLE_2/?t=1290638878609.

55673 ■ Interspectives
Children's International Summer Villages International
MEA House
Ellison Pl.
Newcastle upon Tyne NE1 8XS, United Kingdom
Ph: 44 191 2324998
Fax: 44 191 2614710
Publisher E-mail: international@cisv.org
Peer-reviewed publication covering exchange students. **Freq:** Annual. **URL:** http://www.cisv.org/educators/ interspectives.html.

55674 ■ Journal of Obligations & Remedies
Northumbria Law Press
Northumbria University
Sutherland Bldg.
Northumberland Rd.
Newcastle upon Tyne NE1 8ST, United Kingdom
Ph: 44 19 12437587
Fax: 44 19 12437506
Publisher E-mail: ann.conway@northumbria.ac.uk
Journal featuring articles and comments which will focus on ideas and developments within the areas of contract, tort and restitution. **ISSN:** 1470-8086. **Subscription Rates:** 50 institutions; 20 individuals. **URL:** http:// northumbria.ac.uk.

55675 ■ North East Househunter
Accent Magazines Ltd.
11 Causey St.
Tyne & Wear
Newcastle upon Tyne NE3 4DJ, United Kingdom

Ph: 44 191 2849994
Magazine featuring exclusive properties for the whole of the North East. **Founded:** Jan. 2001. **Freq:** Weekly. **Trim Size:** 265 x 375 mm. **Key Personnel:** Jacqui Lyon, Sales & Mktg. Dir., jacqui.lyon@accentmagazines.co.uk; Richard Holmes, Editor, richard.holmes@ accentmagazines.co.uk. **URL:** http://www. accentmagazines.co.uk/ourpublications.html. **Circ:** 14,500

55676 ■ North East Times
Accent Magazines Ltd.
11 Causey St.
Tyne & Wear
Newcastle upon Tyne NE3 4DJ, United Kingdom
Ph: 44 191 2849994
Magazine featuring business in North East England. **Founded:** Sept. 1981. **Freq:** Monthly. **Trim Size:** 210 x 297 mm. **Key Personnel:** Richard Holmes, Editor, richard.holmes@accentmagazines.co.uk; Karen Southern, Dep. Ed., karen.southern@accentmagazines.co.uk; Martin Stout, Sales Exec., martin.stout@ accentmagazines.co.uk. **Subscription Rates:** 50 individuals including postage. **Remarks:** Accepts advertising. **URL:** http://northeasttimes.co.uk/. **Ad Rates:** BW: 895. **Circ:** (Not Reported)

55677 ■ Personnel Review
Emerald Group Publishing Ltd.
c/o Prof. John Leopold, Ed.
Newcastle University Business School
Citywall, City Gate
St. James Blvd.
Newcastle upon Tyne NE1 4JH, United Kingdom
Publisher E-mail: emerald@emeraldinsight.com
Journal covering human resources and labor relations. **Freq:** Bimonthly. **Trim Size:** Quarto. **Key Personnel:** Prof. Tom Redman, Editorial Advisory Board; Dr. Mark Saunders, Editorial Advisory Board; Prof. Julian Teicher, Editorial Advisory Board; Nancy Rolph, Publisher, nrolph@emeraldinsight.com; Prof. Stephen Procter, Ch. of Editorial Board; Prof. John Leopold, Editor, john. leopold@ncl.ac.uk; Dr. Paul Boselie, Regional Ed.; Dr. Simon Down, Editorial Advisory Board; Dr. John Blenkinsopp, Editorial Advisory Board. **ISSN:** 0048-3486. **Remarks:** Advertising not accepted. **Online:** Gale. **URL:** http://info.emeraldinsight.com/products/journals/journals. htm?id=pr. **Circ:** (Not Reported)

55678 ■ Records Management Journal
Emerald Group Publishing Ltd.
c/o Prof. Julie McLeod, Ed.
School of Computer Engineering & Information Sciences
Pandon Bldg.
Northumbria University
Newcastle upon Tyne NE1 8ST, United Kingdom
Publisher E-mail: emerald@emeraldinsight.com
Scholarly journal covering records management worldwide. **Founded:** 1989. **Freq:** 3/yr. **Cols./Page:** 1. **Key Personnel:** Prof. Julie McLeod, Editor, julie. mcleod@northumbria.ac.uk; Catherine Hare, Professional Insights Ed., catherinehare46@yahoo.co.uk; Lizzie Scott, Publisher, escott@emeraldinsight.com. **ISSN:** 0956-5698. **Remarks:** Advertising not accepted. **URL:** http://www.emeraldinsight.com/products/journals/ journals.htm?id=rmj. **Circ:** (Not Reported)

55679 ■ South Tyne & Wear HouseHunter
Accent Magazines Ltd.
11 Causey St.
Tyne & Wear
Newcastle upon Tyne NE3 4DJ, United Kingdom
Ph: 44 191 2849994
Magazine featuring exclusive properties for the whole of South Tyneside and Sunderland. **Founded:** July 2005. **Freq:** Weekly. **Key Personnel:** June Davies, Contact, june.davies@accentmagazines.co.uk. **URL:** http://www. stw-househunter.com/. **Circ:** 17,000

55680 ■ BBC Radio Newcastle-FM - 95.4
Broadcasting Ctr.
Barrack Rd.
Newcastle upon Tyne NE99 1RN, United Kingdom
Ph: 44 191 2324141
E-mail: tyne@bbc.co.uk
Format: Talk; News; Oldies; Sports; Eclectic; Folk; Easy Listening. **Owner:** British Broadcasting Corp., Broadcasting House, Portland Pl., London W1A 1AA, United

Circulation: ★ = ABC; △ = BPA; ◆ = CAC; • = CCAB; ❑ = VAC; ⊕ = PO Statement; ‡ = Publisher's Report; Boldface figures = sworn; Light figures = estimated.

Gale Directory of Publications & Broadcast Media/147th Ed.

5793

Kingdom. **Operating Hours:** Continuous. **URL:** http://news.bbc.co.uk/local/tyne/hi/tv_and_radio/.

55681 ■ Magic-AM - 1152
55 Degrees N
Pilgrim St.
Newcastle upon.Tyne NE1 6BF, United Kingdom
Ph: 44 191 2306100
Format: Oldies. **Operating Hours:** Continuous. **Key Personnel:** Esther Morton, Station Mgr.; Simon Monk, Program Dir.; Lynn Dixon, News Ed. **Ad Rates:** Advertising accepted; rates available upon request. **URL:** http://www.magic1152.co.uk/.

55682 ■ Magic 1152-AM - 1152 KHz
55 Degrees N
Pilgrim St.
Newcastle upon Tyne NE1 6BF, United Kingdom
Ph: 44 191 2306100
Fax: 44 191 2790288
Format: Easy Listening; News; Talk; Oldies. **Operating Hours:** Continuous. **Key Personnel:** Sally Aitchison, Mng. Dir.; Trevor James, Program Dir.; Kim Miljus, Sales Dir. **URL:** http://www.magic1152.co.uk/.

55683 ■ Metro Radio-FM - 97.1
55 Degrees N
Pilgrim St.
Newcastle upon Tyne NE1 6BF, United Kingdom
Ph: 44 191 2306100
Format: Eclectic; Talk; Sports; News. **Operating Hours:** Continuous. **Key Personnel:** Kim Miljus, Sales Dir.; Sally Aitchison, Mng. Dir. **Ad Rates:** Advertising accepted; rates available upon request. **URL:** http://www.metroradio.co.uk/.

55684 ■ Metro Radio-FM - 103.0
55 Degrees N
Pilgrim St.
Newcastle upon Tyne NE1 6BF, United Kingdom
Ph: 44 191 2306100
Fax: 44 191 2790288
E-mail: news@metroandmagic.com
Format: Contemporary Hit Radio (CHR). **URL:** http://www.metroradio.co.uk/.

Metro Radio-FM - See Alnwick

Metro Radio-FM - See Hexham

55685 ■ NE1-FM - 102.5
1 Clarence St.
Newcastle upon Tyne NE2 1YH, United Kingdom
Ph: 44 191 2401025
E-mail: studio@ne1fm.com
Format: Full Service. **URL:** http://www.ne1fm.com/.

Newmarket

55686 ■ Newmarket Journal
Johnston Press PLC
Rookery House
40 The Guineas
Newmarket CB8 8SY, United Kingdom
Ph: 44 1638 668441
Community newspaper. **Freq:** Weekly (Thurs.). **Print Method:** Web Offset. **Cols./Page:** 9. **Col. Width:** 26 millimeters. **Col. Depth:** 355 millimeters. **Key Personnel:** Phil Minett, Editor, phone 44 1638 564107, fax 44 1638 665547, philip.minett@newmarketjournal.co.uk. **Remarks:** Accepts advertising. **URL:** http://www.newmarketjournal.co.uk. **Ad Rates:** BW: 1,955. **Circ:** Paid 12,600

Newport

55687 ■ AI & Society
Springer-Verlag Tokyo
c/o Karamjit S. Gill, Ed.
Newport School of Art, Media & Design
University of Wales, Newport
PO Box 179
Newport NP18 3YG, United Kingdom
Publisher E-mail: info@springer.jp
Peer-reviewed journal focusing on the issues associated with the policy, design and management of information, communications and media technologies, and their broader social, economic, cultural and philosophical implications. **Freq:** Quarterly. **Key Personnel:** Karamjit S. Gill, Editor, kgillbton@yahoo.co.uk; Victoria Vesna, Editor, vesna@arts.ucla.edu; Richard Ennals, Review Ed., ennals@kingston.ac.uk. **ISSN:** 0951-5666. **Sub-**

scription **Rates:** EUR638 institutions print incl. free access or e-only; EUR765.60 institutions print incl. enhanced access. **Remarks:** Advertising accepted; rates available upon request. **URL:** http://www.springer.com/computer/artificial/journal/146. **Circ:** (Not Reported)

55688 ■ Archery UK
Grand National Archery Society
Lilles Hall National Sports Ctr.
Newport TF10 9AT, United Kingdom
Ph: 44 1952 677888
Fax: 44 1952 606019
Publisher E-mail: enquiries@archerygb.org
British publication covering archery. **Freq:** Quarterly. **Key Personnel:** Ann Shepherd, Editor. **Remarks:** Advertising accepted; rates available upon request. **URL:** http://www.gnas.org/development/dyncat.cfm?catid=30311. **Circ:** 12,500

55689 ■ Res Publica
Springer Netherlands
c/o Gideon Calder, Ed.
University of Wales
School of Health & Social Sciences
Lodge Rd., Caerleon
Newport NP18 3QT, United Kingdom
Publisher E-mail: permissions.dordrecht@springer.com
Scholarly journal covering philosophical analysis of moral, political, social and legal issues. **Subtitle:** A Journal of Moral, Legal and Social Philosophy. **Freq:** Quarterly. **Key Personnel:** Gideon Calder, Editor, gideon.calder@newport.ac.uk; Daniel Bell, Editorial Board; Jonathan Seglow, Editor, j.seglow@rhul.ac.uk. **ISSN:** 1356-4765. **Subscription Rates:** EUR359 institutions print incl. free access or e-only; EUR430 institutions print incl. enhanced access. **Remarks:** Accepts advertising. **URL:** http://www.springer.com/philosophy/philosophyoflaw/journal/11158. **Circ:** (Not Reported)

55690 ■ South Wales Argus
Newsquest Media Group Ltd.
Cardiff Rd.
Maesglas
Newport NP20 3QN, United Kingdom
Ph: 44 1633 810000
Fax: 44 1633 777202
Publication E-mail: letters@gwent-wales.co.uk
Newspaper featuring business, community, sports and community news. **Founded:** 1892. **Freq:** Mon.-Sat. **Key Personnel:** Gerry Keighley, Editor, phone 44 1633 777201; Nicole Garnon, Dep. Ed., phone 44 1633 777203, nicole.garnon@gwent-wales.co.uk; Mark Templeton, Asst. Ed., phone 44 1633 777008, mark.templeton@gwent-wales.co.uk. **Remarks:** Accepts advertising. **URL:** http://www.southwalesargus.co.uk/. **Circ:** (Not Reported)

55691 ■ Isle of Wight Radio-FM - 107
Dodnor Pk.
Isle of Wight
Newport PO30 5XE, United Kingdom
Ph: 44 1983 822002
E-mail: hello@iwradio.co.uk
Format: Adult Contemporary. **Ad Rates:** Advertising accepted; rates available upon request. **URL:** http://www.iwradio.co.uk/.

55692 ■ Isle of Wight Radio-FM - 102
Dodnor Pk.
Newport PO30 5XE, United Kingdom
Ph: 44 1983 822557
E-mail: hello@iwradio.co.uk
Format: Adult Contemporary; Oldies; News; Easy Listening. **Owner:** The Local Radio Company, 11 Duke St., High Wycombe, United Kingdom. **Founded:** 1998. **Operating Hours:** Continuous. **Ad Rates:** Advertising accepted; rates available upon request. **URL:** http://www.iwradio.co.uk/.

Newquay

55693 ■ Carve
Orca Publications
Berry Rd. Studios
Newquay TR7 1AT, United Kingdom
Ph: 44 16 37878074
Fax: 44 16 37850226
Publication E-mail: carve@carvemag.com
Publisher E-mail: shop@orcasurf.co.uk
Surfing magazine. **Freq:** Monthly 9/yr. **Subscription Rates:** 29.99 individuals surfgirl; 36.99 individuals Europe and Ireland; 53.99 elsewhere rest of the world;

52.99 two years U.K.; 69.99 two years Europe and Ireland; 99.99 two years rest of the world. **URL:** http://www.orcasurf.co.uk.

Newry

55694 ■ Five-FM - 101.1
Win Business Pk.
Canal Quay
Newry BT35 6PH, United Kingdom
Ph: 44 28 30269655
E-mail: studio@fivefm.co.uk
Format: Full Service. **Key Personnel:** Robert Walshe, Ch. Exec./Prog. Dir. **Ad Rates:** Advertising accepted; rates available upon request. **URL:** http://www.fivefm.co.uk/.

55695 ■ Five-FM - 100.5
Win Business Pk.
Canal Quay
Newry BT35 6PH, United Kingdom
Ph: 44 28 30269655
E-mail: studio@fivefm.co.uk
Format: Full Service. **Key Personnel:** Robert Walshe, Ch. Exec./Prog. Dir. **Ad Rates:** Advertising accepted; rates available upon request. **URL:** http://www.fivefm.co.uk/.

55696 ■ Five-FM - 100.5
Win Business Pk.
Canal Quay
County Down
Newry BT35 6PH, United Kingdom
Ph: 44 28 30269655
E-mail: studio@fivefm.co.uk
Format: Adult Contemporary. **Key Personnel:** Mr. Robert Walshe, Ch. Exec./Prog. Dir.; Orla Ross, Brand Dir.; Damien McGinley, Operations Mgr. **Ad Rates:** Advertising accepted; rates available upon request. **URL:** http://www.fivefm.co.uk.

55697 ■ IUR-FM - 101.4
RDC House
WIN Business Pk.
Canal Quay, County Down
Newry BT35 6PH, United Kingdom
E-mail: info@mediaireland.org
Format: Full Service. **URL:** http://www.iurfm.com/.

Newton Stewart

55698 ■ Galloway Gazette
Johnston Press PLC
71 Victoria St.
Newton Stewart DG8 6NL, United Kingdom
Ph: 44 1671 402503
Local community newspaper. **Key Personnel:** Robin Young, Editor, phone 44 1671 404768, robin.young@carrickgazette.com; Julie Hamilton, Advertising Mgr., phone 44 1671 404762, fax 44 1671 404843, julie.hamilton@gallowaygazette.com. **Remarks:** Accepts advertising. **URL:** http://www.gallowaygazette.co.uk/. **Circ:** (Not Reported)

55699 ■ Scottish Forestry
Royal Scottish Forestry Society
c/o Richard Kay, Dir.
4 Doonhill Way
Newton Stewart DG8 6JF, United Kingdom
Ph: 44 1671 401591
Publication E-mail: editor@rsfs.org.uk
Publisher E-mail: director@rsfs.org.uk
Publication covering Scottish forestry. **Freq:** Quarterly. **ISSN:** 0036-9217. **Remarks:** Advertising accepted; rates available upon request. **URL:** http://www.rsfs.org/. **Circ:** 1,500

Newtown

55700 ■ Radio Maldwyn-AM - 756
The Park
Newtown SY16 2NZ, United Kingdom
Ph: 44 1686 623555
Fax: 44 1686 623666
E-mail: radio@magic756.net
Format: Adult Contemporary; News; Oldies. **Operating Hours:** Continuous. **URL:** http://www.magic756.net/.

Newtownabbey

55701 ■ Five Foot Three
Railway Preservation Society of Ireland
PO Box 461
County Antrim
Newtownabbey BT36 9BT, United Kingdom
Ph: 44 28 93373968
Publisher E-mail: rpsitrains@hotmail.com
Publication covering historic preservation. **Founded:** 1964. **Freq:** Annual. **Key Personnel:** Johnny Glendinning, Chm.; Paul McCann, Sec.; David Houston, Vice-Chm. **Subscription Rates:** Included in membership. **Remarks:** Advertising accepted; rates available upon request. **URL:** http://www.rpsi-online.org/5ft3/. **Circ:** (Not Reported)

55702 ■ Leadership and Organization Development Journal
Emerald Group Publishing Ltd.
c/o Prof. Marie McHugh, Ed.
School of Business Organization & Management
University of Ulster
Shore Rd.
Newtownabbey BT37 0QB, United Kingdom
Publisher E-mail: emerald@emeraldinsight.com
General business publication. **Freq:** 8/yr. **Key Personnel:** Prof. Andrew Kakabadse, Assoc. Ed.; Prof. Marie McHugh, Editor; Ruth Young, Publisher, ryoung@emeraldinsight.com; Dr. Rune Lines, Editorial Review Board; Dr. Sandi Mann, Book Review Ed.; Prof. Fred E. Fiedler, Editorial Advisory Board; Dr. Cliff Cheng, Editorial Review Board. **ISSN:** 0143-7739. **Online:** Gale. **URL:** http://www.emeraldinsight.com/products/journals/journals.htm?id=lodj.

Norfolk

55703 ■ The Review
Naval Historical Collectors and Research Association
9 Lyngate Gardens
Lyngate Rd.
N Walsham
Norfolk NR28 0NE, United Kingdom
Publication covering collectors. **Founded:** 1988. **Freq:** Quarterly. **Trim Size:** 5 3/4 x 8 1/4. **Key Personnel:** Robert Mullock-Morgans, Editor, phone 44 1492 641254, mullockmorgans@yahoo.co.uk. **Subscription Rates:** Included in membership. **Remarks:** Advertising accepted; rates available upon request. **URL:** http://www.nhcra-online.org/the_review.htm. **Circ:** (Not Reported)

North Berwick

55704 ■ Alcohol and Alcoholism
Oxford University Press
c/o Prof. Jonathan D. Chick, Ch. Ed.
May View
Canty Bay
North Berwick EH39 5PJ, United Kingdom
Ph: 44 131 5376557
Fax: 44 131 5376866
Publisher E-mail: webenquiry.uk@oup.com
Journal covering various aspects of alcoholism-related research published on the behalf of the Medical Council on Alcohol. **Freq:** 6/yr. **Key Personnel:** Prof. Jonathan D. Chick, Ch. Ed., jonathan.chick@gmail.com; P. Buckland, Assoc. Ed.; C. Diclemente, Assoc. Ed.; A. Romelsjo, Assoc. Ed.; E. Albano, Assoc. Ed.; A. Helander, Assoc. Ed.; Prof. P. De Witte, Editor-in-Chief, phone 32 10 474384, fax 32 10 474094, dewitte@bani.ucl.ac.be; O. Lesch, Assoc. Ed. **ISSN:** 0735-0414. **Subscription Rates:** 805 institutions corporate; print and online; 651 institutions corporate; online only; 738 institutions corporate; print only; 644 institutions print and online; 521 institutions online only; 591 institutions print only; 564 individuals print; 50 members print. **URL:** http://alcalc.oxfordjournals.org.

North Tyneside

55705 ■ SISTERS (Sisterhood and International Solidarity to End Racism and Sexism)
National Assembly of Women
92 Wansbeck Ave.
Cullercoats
Tyne and Wear
North Tyneside NE30 3DJ, United Kingdom
Ph: 44 191 2520961
Publisher E-mail: naw@sisters.org.uk
Publication covering feminism. **Freq:** Quarterly. **Remarks:** Advertising accepted; rates available upon request. **URL:** http://www.sisters.org.uk/. **Circ:** (Not Reported)

Northampton

55706 ■ Building Engineer
Association of Building Engineers
Lutyens House
Billing Brook Rd.
Weston Favell
Northampton NN3 8NW, United Kingdom
Ph: 44 84 51261058
Fax: 44 16 04784220
Publication E-mail: subscriptions@abe.org.uk
Publisher E-mail: building.engineers@abe.org.uk
Association journal covering building and construction for members. **Founded:** 1993. **Freq:** Monthly. **Trim Size:** 210 x 297 mm. **Cols./Page:** 3. **Col. Width:** 57 millimeters. **ISSN:** 0969-8213. **Subscription Rates:** 40 individuals online inland or overseas; 40 individuals hard copy inland; 50 individuals hard copy overseas. **Remarks:** Accepts advertising. **URL:** http://www.abe.org.uk/publications/buildingengineer. **Former name:** Architect and Surveyor. **Ad Rates:** BW: 670, 4C: 1,050. **Circ:** Combined 6,500

55707 ■ Country Doctor
5 Manor Farm Close
Gate Ln.
Broughton
Kettering
Northampton NN14 1ND, United Kingdom
Ph: 44 15 36791515
Fax: 44 15 36791175
Online, professional magazine covering news, education, entertainment and other issues for physicians, especially rural doctors, in the UK. **Founded:** May 2000. **Freq:** Daily. **Print Method:** Online. **Key Personnel:** Dr. David Roberts, Editor, davidroberts@doctors.org.uk. **Remarks:** Accepts advertising. **URL:** http://www.countrydoctor.co.uk. **Ad Rates:** 4C: 100. **Circ:** (Not Reported)

55708 ■ Herbs
The Herb Society
Sulgrave Manor
PO Box 946
Northampton NN3 0BN, United Kingdom
Ph: 44 1295768899
Publisher E-mail: info@herbsociety.org.uk
Consumer magazine covering herbs. **Founded:** 1980. **Freq:** Quarterly. **Key Personnel:** Barbara Segall, Editor; Sue Minter, Editorial Board. **Subscription Rates:** 2.50 single issue. **Remarks:** Accepts advertising. **URL:** http://www.herbsociety.co.uk/journal.htm. **Circ:** Combined 3,000

55709 ■ The Homeopath Journal
Society of Homeopaths
11 Brookfield, Duncan Close
Moulton Pk.
Northampton NN3 6WL, United Kingdom
Ph: 44 84 54506611
Fax: 44 84 54506622
Publisher E-mail: info@homeopathy-soh.org
Journal covering homeopathic medicine. **Founded:** 1983. **Freq:** Quarterly. **Key Personnel:** Francis Treuherz, Editor. **Subscription Rates:** 42 individuals UK; 63 individuals overseas. **URL:** http://www.homeopathy-soh.org/for-homeopaths/Journal.aspx. **Ad Rates:** BW: 295. **Circ:** 3,000

55710 ■ Insight
British Institute of Non-Destructive Testing
Newton Bldg.
St. George's Ave.
Northampton NN2 6JB, United Kingdom
Ph: 44 1604 893811
Fax: 44 1604 893861
Publication E-mail: insight@bindt.org
Publisher E-mail: info@bindt.org
British journal covering testing. **Subtitle:** The Journal of the British Institute of Non-Destructive Testing. **Founded:** Sept. 1994. **Freq:** Monthly with quarterly European issues. **Print Method:** Litho Offset. **Trim Size:** 210 x 297 mm. **ISSN:** 1354-2575. **Subscription Rates:** 130 individuals; 165 by mail Europe, Republic of Ireland (airmail); 165 other countries surface; 255 other countries airmail; 69 individuals members of participating societies of ECNDT; 99 nonmembers European issues (airmail); 130 other countries airmail(European issues only). **URL:** http://www.bindt.org/Publications/Insight_Journal. **Formerly:** The British Journal of NonDestructive Testing. **Ad Rates:** BW: 540, 4C: 1,150. **Circ:** 2,500

55711 ■ Journal for Critical Education Policy Studies
Institute for Education Policy Studies
University of Northampton
Boughton Green Rd.
Northampton NN2 7AL, United Kingdom
Publisher E-mail: dave.hill@northampton.ac.uk
Journal publishing articles that critique global, national, neo-liberal, neo-conservative, New Labour, Third Way, and postmodernist analyses and policy, together with articles that attempt to report on, analyse and develop socialist/Marxist transformative policy for schooling and education. **Key Personnel:** Prof. Dave Hill, Editor, dave.hill@northampton.ac.uk. **ISSN:** 1740-2743. **URL:** http://www.jceps.com.

55712 ■ The Journal of Research in Special Educational Needs
John Wiley & Sons Inc.
Wiley-Blackwell
c/o Sue Ralph, Ed.
University of Northampton
Park Campus
Boughton Green Rd.
Northampton NN2 7AL, United Kingdom
Online forum for the dissemination of research on special educational needs, publishing original research, literature reviews and theoretical papers on meeting special educational needs. **Freq:** 3/yr. **Key Personnel:** Sue Ralph, Editor, jorsen@nasen.org.uk; Prof. Richard Rose, Editorial Board; Dr. Helen Fisher, Editorial Board. **ISSN:** 1471-3802. **Remarks:** Accepts advertising. **URL:** http://www.wiley.com/bw/journal.asp?ref=1471-3802&site=1. **Circ:** (Not Reported)

55713 ■ Northampton Chronicle & Echo
Johnston Press PLC
Upper Mounts
Northampton NN1 3HR, United Kingdom
Ph: 44 1604 467000
Local community newspaper. **Freq:** Daily. **Key Personnel:** David Summers, General Mgr., david.summers@northantsnews.co.uk; Graham Tebbutt, Dep. Ed., graham.tebbutt@northantsnews.co.uk. **Remarks:** Accepts advertising. **URL:** http://www.northamptonchron.co.uk/. **Circ:** (Not Reported)

55714 ■ Support for Learning
National Association of Special Educational Needs
c/o Philip Garner, Ed.
School of Education
Park Campus
Boughton Green Rd.
Northampton NN2 7AL, United Kingdom
Publisher E-mail: welcome@nasen.org.uk
Journal covering special education issues. **Subtitle:** British Journal of Learning Support. **Founded:** 1986. **Freq:** Quarterly. **Trim Size:** A4. **Key Personnel:** Richard Gerrish, Editorial Board; Prof. Richard Rose, Ch. of Editorial Board; Sue Pearson, Reviews Ed.; Andrea Bennington, Editorial Board; Philip Garner, Editor. **ISSN:** 0268-2141. **Subscription Rates:** US$91 individuals print + online; EUR81 individuals print + online; 54 individuals print + online; US$74 members print + online; EUR66 members print + online; 44 members print + online; US$537 institutions print + online; EUR356 institutions print + online; 281 institutions print + online. **Remarks:** Accepts advertising. **URL:** http://www.wiley.com/bw/editors.asp?ref=0268-2141&site=1; http://www.nasen.org.uk. **Circ:** 11,500

55715 ■ Thumbprint
Motor Neurone Disease Association
PO Box 246
Northampton NN1 2PR, United Kingdom
Ph: 44 160 4250505
Fax: 44 160 4624726
Publisher E-mail: enquiries@mndassociation.org
Publication covering neurological disorders. **Subtitle:** The Magazine of the Motor Neurone Disease

---

Circulation: ★ = ABC; △ = BPA; ♦ = CAC; • = CCAB; ▢ = VAC; ⊕ = PO Statement; ‡ = Publisher's Report; Boldface figures = sworn; Light figures = estimated.

Association. **Founded:** 1979. **Freq:** Quarterly. **Trim Size:** 8 1/4 x 11 3/5. **Subscription Rates:** Included in membership. **Remarks:** Advertising accepted; rates available upon request. **URL:** http://www.mndassociation.org. **Circ:** 9,000

55716 ■ BBC Northampton-FM - 104.2
Broadcasting House
Abngton St.
Northampton NN1 2BH, United Kingdom
Ph: 44 1604 239100
Fax: 44 1604 230709
E-mail: northamptonshire@bbc.co.uk
Format: Talk; News; Sports; Eclectic; Religious. **Owner:** British Broadcasting Corporation, Broadcasting House, Portland Pl., London W1A 1AA, United Kingdom. **Founded:** June 16, 1982. **Operating Hours:** 5 a.m.-10 p.m. weekdays; 6 a.m.-9 p.m. Sat. & Sun. **Key Personnel:** Laura Moss, Editor. **URL:** http://news.bbc.co.uk/local/northampton/hi/tv_and_radio/.

Northill

55717 ■ Historical Metallurgy
Historical Metallurgy Society
17A Thorncote Rd.
Bedfordshire
Northill SG18 9AQ, United Kingdom
Publication E-mail: justine.bayley@english-heritage.org.uk
Journal covering metallurgy and related topics. **Freq:** Annual. **Key Personnel:** Justine Bayley, Editor, editor@hist-met.org. **ISSN:** 0142-3304. **Subscription Rates:** 20 individuals; 20 institutions; 6 students. **Remarks:** Advertising not accepted. **URL:** http://hist-met.org/journal.html. **Circ:** (Not Reported)

Northwich

55718 ■ Acupuncture in Medicine
British Medical Acupuncture Society
BMAS House
3 Winnington Ct.
Northwich CW8 1AQ, United Kingdom
Ph: 44 16 06786782
Fax: 44 16 06786783
Publisher E-mail: admin@medical-acupuncture.org.uk
Publication covering alternative medicine and acupuncture. **Subtitle:** Journal of the British Medical Acupuncture Society. **Freq:** Quarterly. **Trim Size:** A4. **Key Personnel:** Dr. Mike Cummings, Editor; Joy Ogden, Managing Editor; Dr. Jacqueline Filshie, Editorial Board; Adrian White, Editor-in-Chief; Dr. Susan Ashley, Editorial Board; Dr. Peter Baldry, Editorial Board. **ISSN:** 0964-5284. **Subscription Rates:** 60 individuals U.K. & West Europe/incl. p& h; 150 individuals U.K. & West Europe/incl. p& h; 12 issues; 195 individuals non-European subscribers/incl; 12 issues; 75 individuals non-European subscribers/incl. p& h. **Remarks:** Accepts advertising. **URL:** http://aim.bmj.com/; http://www.medical-acupuncture.co.uk/Default.aspx?tabid=76. **Ad Rates:** BW: 395, 4C: 555. **Circ:** Combined 6,225

55719 ■ International Journal of Cosmetic Science
Society of Cosmetic Scientists
c/o Anthony Rawlings, Ed.-in-Ch.
AVR Consulting Ltd.
26 Shavington Way
Kingsmead, Cheshire
Northwich CW9 8FH, United Kingdom
Publisher E-mail: ifscc.scs@btconnect.com
Peer-reviewed journal covering worldwide cosmetic science. **Freq:** Bimonthly. **Key Personnel:** Christine Lafforgue, Assoc. Ed., christine.lafforgue@u-psud.fr; Anthony Rawlings, Editor-in-Chief, tonyrawlings@aol.com. **ISSN:** 0142-5463. **Subscription Rates:** US$2,297 institutions Americas (print and online); 1,241 institutions UK (print and online); EUR1,575 institutions Euro (print and online); US$2,679 institutions, other countries print and online; US$416 members Americas (print and online); 225 members non-Euro (print and online); EUR321 members Euro zone (print and online); 336 members other countries (print and online); US$1,997 institutions Americas (print or online only); 1,080 institutions UK (online only). **Remarks:** Advertising accepted; rates available upon request. **URL:** http://www.scs.org.uk/publications; http://www.blackwellpublishing.com/journal.asp?ref=0142-5463&site=1. **Circ:** (Not Reported)

Northwood

55720 ■ The Ephemerist
Ephemera Society
PO Box 112
Northwood HA6 2WT, United Kingdom
Ph: 44 19 23829079
Fax: 44 19 23825207
Publisher E-mail: info@ephemera-society.org.uk
Publication covering collectors. **Founded:** Nov. 1975. **Freq:** Quarterly. **Key Personnel:** Robert Banham, Editor; Lord Briggs, President. **ISSN:** 0309-4383. **Subscription Rates:** Free to all members. **Remarks:** Advertising accepted; rates available upon request. **URL:** http://www.ephemera-society.org.uk/membership.html. **Circ:** (Not Reported)

55721 ■ Journal of Heart Valve Disease
ICR Publishers Ltd.
Crispin House
12A S Approach
Moor Pk.
Northwood HA6 2ET, United Kingdom
Ph: 44 1923 836871
Fax: 44 1923 836872
Publisher E-mail: icrfinance@aol.com
Journal dealing with heart valve disease, in connection with the Society for Heart Valve Disease. **Freq:** Bimonthly. **ISSN:** 0966-8519. **Subscription Rates:** US$200 individuals online only; US$350 institutions online only; US$250 individuals hard copy only; US$400 institutions hard copy only; US$300 individuals hard copy & online; US$500 institutions hard copy & online. **Remarks:** Accepts advertising. **URL:** http://www.icr-heart.com/journal/gen_info.htm. **Circ:** (Not Reported)

Norwich

55722 ■ Anglia Afloat
Archant Regional Ltd.
Prospect House
Rouen Rd.
Norwich NR1 1RE, United Kingdom
Ph: 44 1603 772772
Publication E-mail: angliaafloat@atssubscription.co.uk
Publisher E-mail: sandra.roantree@archant.co.uk
Magazine featuring boating in East Anglian region. **Freq:** Bimonthly. **Key Personnel:** Paul Thomas, Editor, phone 44 7768 392800, angliaafloat@paulgwynthomas.co.uk. **Subscription Rates:** 15 individuals 6 issues. **URL:** http://www.angliaafloat.co.uk/

55723 ■ Atmospheric Environment
Elsevier Science Inc.
School of Environmental Sciences
University of E Anglia
Earlham Rd.
Norwich NR4 7TJ, United Kingdom
Ph: 44 1603 593003
Fax: 44 1603 507719
Publisher E-mail: usinfo-ehelp@elsevier.com
Journal providing information on air pollution its effects on environments and remedial measures. **Founded:** 1967. **Freq:** 40/yr. **Print Method:** Web offset. **Trim Size:** 11 3/8 x 14. **Cols./Page:** 5. **Col. Width:** 22 nonpareils. **Col. Depth:** 196 agate lines. **Key Personnel:** M. Raychaudhuri, Sen. Editorial Asst.; C.K. Chan, Editor-in-Chief; N.T. Lau, Sen. Editorial Asst.; P. Brimblecombe, Editor-in-Chief, atmos_env@uea.ac.uk; H.B. Singh, Editor-in-Chief, hanwant.b.singh@nasa.gov. **ISSN:** 1352-2310. **Subscription Rates:** EUR6,750 institutions for European countries and Iran; US$7,552 institutions, other countries except Europe, Japan and Iran; 896,500¥ institutions; EUR506 individuals for European countries and Iran; 67,300¥ individuals; US$506 other countries except Europe, Japan and Iran. **URL:** http://www.elsevier.com/wps/find/journaldescription.cws_home/246/descriptiondescription.

55724 ■ Beccles & Bungay Journal
Archant Regional Ltd.
Prospect House
Rouen Rd.
Norwich NR1 1RE, United Kingdom
Ph: 44 1603 772772
Publisher E-mail: sandra.roantree@archant.co.uk
Local community newspaper. **Founded:** 1933. **Freq:** Weekly. **Key Personnel:** Tim Williams, Editor, tim.williams@archant.co.uk. **Subscription Rates:** 29.90 individuals 26 weeks; 14.95 individuals 13 weeks. **Remarks:** Accepts advertising. **URL:** http://www.

becclesandbungayjournal.co.uk/home. **Circ:** 7,445

55725 ■ Beers of the World
Paragraph Publishing Limited
St. Faiths House
Mountergate
Norwich NR1 1PY, United Kingdom
Ph: 44 1603 633808
Fax: 44 1603 632808
Publisher E-mail: publishing@paragraph.co.uk
Magazine featuring beer. **Subtitle:** Celebrating the beers of the world. **Freq:** 6/yr. **Key Personnel:** Jenna Leeds, Production Mgr., jenna@paragraphpublishing.com; Damian Riley-Smith, Contact. **URL:** http://www.tastingbeers.com/:

55726 ■ Brighton & Hove Life
Archant Life
Prospect House
Rouen Rd.
Norwich NR1 1RE, United Kingdom
Ph: 44 1603 772101
Publisher E-mail: anne.basey-fisher@archant.co.uk
Consumer magazine covering local lifestyle. **Founded:** 1998. **Freq:** Monthly. **Print Method:** Sheetfed offset. **Trim Size:** 210 x 297 mm. **Key Personnel:** Jonathan Hustler, Advertising Mgr. **Subscription Rates:** 1 individuals 3 issue; 30 individuals. **Remarks:** Accepts advertising. **URL:** http://www.archant.co.uk/business_life.aspx. **Ad Rates:** GLR: 15, 4C: 1,650. **Circ:** Controlled 22,000

55727 ■ British Journal for the History of Science
British Society for the History of Science
PO Box 3401
Norwich NR7 7JF, United Kingdom
Ph: 44 1603 516236
Fax: 44 1603 208563
Publisher E-mail: media@bshs.org
Peer-reviewed journal covering the history of science, technology and medicine. **Founded:** 1962. **Freq:** Quarterly. **Print Method:** Letterpress. **Trim Size:** 174 x 247 mm. **Key Personnel:** Dr. Jon Agar, Editor; Dr. Gregory Radick, Book Review Ed.; Prof. Hasok Chang, Assoc. Ed. **ISSN:** 0007-0874. **Subscription Rates:** 135 institutions online; 147 institutions print and online; US$259 institutions online; US$287 institutions print and online. **URL:** http://www.bshs.org.uk/publications/bjhs. **Ad Rates:** BW: 410. **Circ:** ‡1,500

55728 ■ Cigar Buyer Magazine
Paragraph Publishing Limited
St. Faiths House
Mountergate
Norwich NR1 1PY, United Kingdom
Ph: 44 1603 633808
Fax: 44 1603 632808
Publication E-mail: info@cigarbuyer.co.uk
Publisher E-mail: publishing@paragraph.co.uk
Magazine for cigar enthusiasts. **Subtitle:** Exclusively for cigar trade professionals. **Freq:** 4/yr. **Key Personnel:** Rob Allanson, Editor. **URL:** http://www.cigarbuyer.co.uk/online/.

55729 ■ Compass South
Archant Life
Prospect House
Rouen Rd.
Norwich NR1 1RE, United Kingdom
Ph: 44 1603 772101
Publisher E-mail: johnny.hustler@archant.co.uk
Magazine featuring lifestyle and entertainment for people in the South. **Freq:** Monthly. **Trim Size:** 210 x 297 mm. **Key Personnel:** Guy Hanson, Publisher, phone 44 7977 054861, guy.hanson@archant.co.uk. **Subscription Rates:** Free. **Remarks:** Accepts advertising. **URL:** http://www.compassmags.com/; http://www.archantlife.co.uk/contact-us-regions-south-east-and-east-contact-compass-south--31875. **Circ:** ‡40,000

55730 ■ Compass Wessex
Archant Life
Prospect House
Rouen Rd.
Norwich NR1 1RE, United Kingdom
Ph: 44 1603 772101
Publisher E-mail: johnny.hustler@archant.co.uk
Magazine featuring lifestyle and entertainment in Wessex. **Freq:** Monthly. **Trim Size:** 210 x 297 mm. **Key**

Personnel: Guy Hanson, Publisher, phone 44 7977 054861, guy.hanson@archant.co.uk. **Subscription Rates:** Free. **Remarks:** Accepts advertising. **URL:** http://www.compassmags.com/; http://www.archantlife.co.uk/contact-us-regions-south-east-and-east-compass-wessex-contacts--31876. **Circ:** ‡40,000

55731 ■ French Property News
Archant Life
Prospect House
Rouen Rd.
Norwich NR1 1RE, United Kingdom
Ph: 44 1603 772101
Publisher E-mail: johnny.hustler@archant.co.uk
Magazine for buyers of properties in France. **Founded:** June 1989. **Freq:** Monthly. **Key Personnel:** Karen Tait, Editor, karen.tait@archant.co.uk; Debbie Macleod, Advertising Mgr., debbie.macleod@archant.co.uk. **Subscription Rates:** 5 individuals 5 issues, direct debit. **Remarks:** Accepts advertising. **URL:** http://www.french-property-news.com/. **Ad Rates:** BW: 1,275, 4C: 1,750. **Circ:** Controlled 50,000

55732 ■ health24
Archant Regional Ltd.
Prospect House
Rouen Rd.
Norwich NR1 1RE, United Kingdom
Ph: 44 1603 772772
Publisher E-mail: sandra.roantree@archant.co.uk
Magazine providing information on women's health and fitness. **Key Personnel:** Olivia Abbott, Editor, phone 44 1763 250232, olivia.abbott@archant.co.uk. **Subscription Rates:** Free. **Remarks:** Accepts advertising. **URL:** http://www.health24.co.uk/. **Circ:** (Not Reported)

55733 ■ Let's Talk!
Archant Regional Ltd.
Prospect House
Rouen Rd.
Norwich NR1 1RE, United Kingdom
Ph: 44 1603 772772
Publication E-mail: letstalk@archant.co.uk
Publisher E-mail: sandra.roantree@archant.co.uk
Magazine featuring the lifestyle and entertainment in Norfolk, Suffolk and Essex. **Freq:** Monthly. **Key Personnel:** Anne Gould, Editor, anne.gould@archant.co.uk. **Subscription Rates:** 17.99 individuals. **Remarks:** Accepts advertising. **URL:** http://www.letstalk24.co.uk/. **Circ:** ★27,205

55734 ■ Midweek Herald
Archant Regional Ltd.
Prospect House
Rouen Rd.
Norwich NR1 1RE, United Kingdom
Ph: 44 1603 772772
Publisher E-mail: sandra.roantree@archant.co.uk
Local community newspaper. **Key Personnel:** Belinda Bennett, Editor, phone 44 1392 888486, belinda.bennett@archant.co.uk; Lee Glanville, Sports Ed., sport.devon@archant.co.uk. **Subscription Rates:** 1 single issue. **Remarks:** Accepts advertising. **URL:** http://www.midweekherald.co.uk/home. **Circ:** (Not Reported)

55735 ■ Moneyfacts
Moneyfacts Group PLC
66-70 Thorpe Rd.
Norwich NR1 1BJ, United Kingdom
Publisher E-mail: subscriptions@moneyfacts.co.uk
Magazine for financial professionals. **Subscription Rates:** 134.50 individuals. **URL:** http://www.moneyfacts.co.uk/default.aspx.

55736 ■ North Norfolk Advertiser
Archant Regional Ltd.
Prospect House
Rouen Rd.
Norwich NR1 1RE, United Kingdom
Publisher E-mail: sandra.roantree@archant.co.uk
Local community newspaper. **Key Personnel:** Tim Williams, Editor, phone 44 1603 772493, tim.williams@archant.co.uk. **Subscription Rates:** 6 individuals 4 weeks; 18 individuals 12 weeks; 39 individuals 26 weeks. **Remarks:** Accepts advertising. **URL:** http://www.advertiser24.co.uk/content/advertiser24/default.aspx. **Circ:** (Not Reported)

55737 ■ Norwich Advertiser
Archant Regional Ltd.

Prospect House
Rouen Rd.
Norwich NR1 1RE, United Kingdom
Ph: 44 1603 772443
Publisher E-mail: sandra.roantree@archant.co.uk
Local community newspaper. **Key Personnel:** Tim Williams, Editor, phone 44 1603 772493, tim.williams@archant.co.uk. **Subscription Rates:** 6 individuals 4 weeks; 18 individuals 12 weeks; 39 individuals 26 weeks. **Remarks:** Accepts advertising. **URL:** http://www.norwichadvertiser24.co.uk/home. **Circ:** (Not Reported)

55738 ■ The Pink 'Un
Archant Regional Ltd.
Prospect House
Rouen Rd.
Norwich NR1 1RE, United Kingdom
Ph: 44 1603 772772
Publisher E-mail: sandra.roantree@archant.co.uk
Newspaper covering the latest events in Norwich City and the non-league football in Norfolk. **Freq:** Weekly (Tues.). **Subscription Rates:** 43.50 individuals; 68.50 individuals Europe; 89.50 other countries. **Remarks:** Accepts advertising. **URL:** http://www.pinkun.com/home. **Circ:** (Not Reported)

55739 ■ Popular Music
Cambridge University Press
c/o John Street, Coord. Ed.
School of Political, Social & International Studies
University of East Anglia
Norwich NR4 7TJ, United Kingdom
Publisher E-mail: information@cambridge.org
Journal covering the workings of the global music industry. **Freq:** 3/yr. **Key Personnel:** Dr. Keith Negus, Coord. Ed., cos01kn@gold.ac.uk; John Street, Coord. Ed., j.street@uea.ac.uk; Prof. Christopher Ballantine, International Advisory Board; Prof. Allan Moore, Editorial Gp.; Dr. Jan Fairley, Book Review Ed.; Dr. Jill Halstead, International Advisory Board. **ISSN:** 0261-1430. **Subscription Rates:** 163 institutions online and print; US$286 institutions online and print; 147 institutions online only; US$257 institutions online only. **Remarks:** Accepts advertising. **URL:** http://journals.cambridge.org/action/displayJournal?jid=PMU. **Ad Rates:** BW: 470. **Circ:** 800

55740 ■ Pure Weddings North
Archant Life
Prospect House
Rouen Rd.
Norwich NR1 1RE, United Kingdom
Ph: 44 1603 772101
Publisher E-mail: johnny.hustler@archant.co.uk
Bridal magazine. **Freq:** Quarterly. **Trim Size:** 220 x 300 mm. **Key Personnel:** Jan Robinson, Advertisement Mgr., jan.robinson@archant.co.uk; Amanda Griffiths, Editor, amanda.griffiths@archant.co.uk. **Remarks:** Accepts advertising. **URL:** http://www.pureweddingsnorth.co.uk/. **Circ:** (Not Reported)

55741 ■ Scotland Magazine
Paragraph Publishing Limited
St. Faiths House
Mountergate
Norwich NR1 1PY, United Kingdom
Ph: 44 1603 633808
Fax: 44 1603 632808
Publication E-mail: info@scotlandmag.com
Publisher E-mail: publishing@paragraph.co.uk
Magazine featuring Scotland. **Subtitle:** Celebrating Scotland across the world. **Freq:** 6/yr. **Key Personnel:** Sally Toms, Editor, sally@scotlandmag.com; Damian Riley-Smith, Publisher, damian@scotlandmag.com; Jenna Leeds, Production Mgr., jenna@scotlandmag.com. **Subscription Rates:** 23.95 individuals; 47.90 two years plus 1 free issue; 29.04 individuals Europe; 58.09 two years plus 1 free issue, Europe; 32.75 other countries; 65.50 other countries 2 years. **Remarks:** Accepts advertising. **URL:** http://www.scotlandmag.com/. **Circ:** (Not Reported)

55742 ■ Thetford & Brandon Times
Archant Regional Ltd.
Prospect House
Rouen Rd.
Norwich NR1 1RE, United Kingdom
Ph: 44 1603 628311

Publisher E-mail: sandra.roantree@archant.co.uk
Local community newspaper. **Freq:** Weekly. **Key Personnel:** Tim Williams, News Ed. **Subscription Rates:** 14.95 individuals 13 weeks; 29.90 individuals 26 weeks. **Remarks:** Accepts advertising. **URL:** http://www.thetfordandbrandontimes.co.uk/home. **Circ:** (Not Reported)

55743 ■ Whisky Magazine
Paragraph Publishing Limited
St. Faiths House
Mountergate
Norwich NR1 1PY, United Kingdom
Ph: 44 1603 633808
Fax: 44 1603 632808
Publication E-mail: office@whiskymag.com
Publisher E-mail: publishing@paragraph.co.uk
Magazine featuring whisky. **Subtitle:** Celebrating whiskies of the world. **Freq:** 8/yr. **Key Personnel:** Rob Allanson, Editor, rob@whiskymag.com; Damian Riley-Smith, Mng. Dir., damian@whiskymag.com; Jenna Leeds, Production Mgr., jenna@whiskymag.com. **Subscription Rates:** 34 individuals; 68 two years plus 2 issues free; 45.60 individuals Europe; 91.20 two years Europe; US$44.95 individuals; US$89.90 two years; US$45.95 individuals Canada; US$99.90 two years Canada. **Remarks:** Accepts advertising. **URL:** http://www.whiskymag.com/. **Circ:** (Not Reported)

55744 ■ Wood & Vale Express
Archant Life
Prospect House
Rouen Rd.
Norwich NR1 1RE, United Kingdom
Ph: 44 1603 772101
Publication E-mail: editorial@hamhigh.co.uk
Publisher E-mail: johnny.hustler@archant.co.uk
Newspaper featuring news, sports, film and theatre reviews. **Freq:** Weekly. **Key Personnel:** Geoff Martin, Editor, geoff.martin@archant.co.uk; John Dunne, Dep. Ed. **Remarks:** Accepts advertising. **URL:** http://www.hamhigh.co.uk/home. **Circ:** (Not Reported)

55745 ■ Wymondham & Attleborough Mercury
Archant Regional Ltd.
Prospect House
Rouen Rd.
Norwich NR1 1RE, United Kingdom
Ph: 44 1379 644517
Publisher E-mail: sandra.roantree@archant.co.uk
Local community newspaper. **Founded:** 1984. **Key Personnel:** Richard Willner, Sports Ed. **Subscription Rates:** 14.95 individuals 13 weeks; 29.90 individuals 26 weeks. **Remarks:** Accepts advertising. **URL:** http://www.wymondhamandattleboroughmercury.co.uk/home. **Circ:** (Not Reported)

55746 ■ BBC Radio Norfolk-FM - 95.1
The Forum
Millennium Plain
Norwich NR2 1BH, United Kingdom
Ph: 44 1603 617411
Fax: 44 1603 284488
E-mail: norfolk@bbc.co.uk
Format: Full Service; Oldies. **Owner:** British Broadcasting Corporation, Broadcasting House, Portland Pl., London W1A 1AA, United Kingdom. **Operating Hours:** Continuous. **URL:** http://news.bbc.co.uk/local/norfolk/hi/tv_and_radio.

55747 ■ Heart-FM - 102.4
47-49 Colegate
Norwich NR3 1DB, United Kingdom
Ph: 44 16 03630621
Format: Contemporary Hit Radio (CHR); News; Sports. **Owner:** Global Radio UK Ltd., 30 Leicester Sq., London WC2H 7LA, United Kingdom, 44 20 7666000, Fax: 44 20 7666111. **Formerly:** Boadland-FM. **Operating Hours:** Continuous. **Key Personnel:** Sophie Hind, Mng. Dir., sophie.hind@thisisglobal.com; Jane Nash, Admin. Mgr., jane.nash@thisisglobal.com. **Ad Rates:** Advertising accepted; rates available upon request. **URL:** http://www.heartnorwich.co.uk.

55748 ■ Radio Norwich-FM - 99.9
PO Box 999
Norwich, United Kingdom
Ph: 44 845 3656999

Circulation: ★ = ABC; △ = BPA; ◆ = CAC; • = CCAB; ❑ = VAC; ⊕ = PO Statement; ‡ = Publisher's Report; Boldface figures = sworn; Light figures = estimated.

E-mail: sales@999radionorwich.com
Format: Adult Contemporary; News; Information. **URL:** http://www.999radionorwich.com/.

Nottingham

55749 ■ Breast Cancer Online
Cambridge University Press
c/o Prof. John F.R. Robertson, Ed.-in-Ch.
Prof. of Surgery
Professorial Unit of Surgery
City Hospital, Hucknall Rd.
Nottingham NG5 1PB, United Kingdom
Publisher E-mail: information@cambridge.org
Peer-reviewed journal featuring studies for healthcare professionals working in the numerous fields of breast cancer research and treatment. **Key Personnel:** Prof. John F.R. Robertson, Editor-in-Chief; Prof. Anthony Howell, Editorial Board; Dr. Beryl McCormick, Editorial Board; Dr. Barbara Rabinowitz, Editorial Board; Dr. Wolfgang Eiermann, Editorial Board; Dr. E.J. Th. Rutgers, Editorial Board. **ISSN:** 1470-9031. **Subscription Rates:** Free professionals in breast cancer field. **URL:** http://www.bco.org; http://journals.cambridge.org/action/displayJournal?jid=BCO.

55750 ■ The British Journal of Politics and International Relations
Political Studies Association of the UK
School of Politics
University of Nottingham
Nottingham NG7 2RD, United Kingdom
Ph: 44 115 8467529
Fax: 44 115 9514859
Publisher E-mail: psa@ncl.ac.uk
British journal covering political science. **Freq:** Quarterly. **Key Personnel:** Philip Cowley, Editor, phone 44 115 8466230, philip.cowley@nottingham.ac.uk; Prof. Chris Pierson, Managing Editor, phone 44 115 9514865, chris.pierson@nottingham.ac.uk; Andreas Bieler, Editor, andreas.bieler@nottingham.ac.uk; Sharon Craig, Editorial Asst., sharon.craig@nottingham.ac.uk; Dr. Lucy Sargisson, Editor, phone 44 115 9514870, lucy.sargisson@nottingham.ac.uk; Dr. Lauren McLaren, Editor, lauren.mclaren@nottingham.ac.uk; Dr. Wyn Rees, Editor, phone 44 115 9567510, wyn.rees@nottingham.ac.uk; Dr. Catherine Fieschi, Editor, phone 44 115 9514857, catherine.fieschi@nottingham.ac.uk. **ISSN:** 1369-1481. **Subscription Rates:** US$114 individuals America (print and online); EUR63 individuals Europe (print and online); 63 other countries print and online; US$599 institutions America (print and premium online); EUR329 institutions Europe (print and premium online); US$644 institutions, other countries print + online; US$538 institutions online, U.S.; EUR377 institutions online, Europe; US$580 institutions, other countries online. **Remarks:** Accepts advertising. **URL:** http://www.blackwellpublishing.com/society.asp?ref=1369-1481. **Circ:** (Not Reported)

55751 ■ Dental Laboratory
Dental Laboratories Association Ltd.
44-46 Wollaton Rd.
Beeston
Nottingham NG9 2NR, United Kingdom
Ph: 44 115 9254888
Fax: 44 115 9254800
Publisher E-mail: info@dla.org.uk
Trade journal for dental technicians. **Freq:** 10/yr. **Trim Size:** 210 x 297 mm. **Key Personnel:** Richard Daniels, Ch. Exec.; Christine Statham, Membership Admin., christine@dla.org.uk; Kim O'Connor, Contact, kim@dla.org.uk. **ISSN:** 0957-5318. **Subscription Rates:** 40 individuals; 28 individuals; 21 students trainees; 80 individuals. **Remarks:** Accepts advertising. **URL:** http://www.dla.org.uk/?q=content/dental-lab-journal. **Ad Rates:** GLR: EUR5, 4C: EUR550. **Circ:** Combined 3,500

55752 ■ Digressus
Department of Classics, University of Nottingham
University Pk.
Nottingham NG7 2RD, United Kingdom
Ph: 44 115 9515151
Fax: 44 115 9513666
Publication E-mail: info@digressus.org
Publisher E-mail: classics@nottingham.ac.uk
Journal on classical studies. **Subtitle:** The Internet Journal for the Classical World. **Key Personnel:** Ulrike Roth, Editor; Thomas Talboy, Editor. **ISSN:** 1475-9578. **URL:** http://www.digressus.org/.

55753 ■ Direction
New Life Publishing Co.
PO Box 777
Nottingham NG11 6ZZ, United Kingdom
Ph: 44 115 8240777
Publisher E-mail: editor@newlife.co.uk
Magazine covering issues for Christians. **Freq:** Monthly. **Print Method:** Offset Litho. **Trim Size:** 210 x 297 mm. **Cols./Page:** 4. **Col. Width:** 44 millimeters. **Key Personnel:** Peter Wreford, Editor; John Glass, Editor-in-Chief. **Subscription Rates:** 24 individuals; 44 two years; 31.95 individuals Europe, by airmail; 41.95 other countries by airmail; 62 individuals 3 years. **Remarks:** Accepts advertising. **URL:** http://www.newlifepublishing.co.uk/direction/. **Circ:** Paid 10,000

55754 ■ Earthwise
British Geological Survey
Kingsley Dunham Center
Keyworth
Nottingham NG12 5GG, United Kingdom
Ph: 44 11 59363143
Fax: 44 11 59363276
Publisher E-mail: enquiries@bgs.ac.uk
Professional magazine covering earth science. **Founded:** 1991. **Freq:** Semiannual. **Print Method:** Litho. **Trim Size:** A4. **Cols./Page:** 3. **Col. Width:** 58 millimeters. **Col. Depth:** 240 millimeters. **Key Personnel:** Adrian Minks, Designer. **ISSN:** 0967-9669. **Subscription Rates:** Free. **Remarks:** Advertising not accepted. **URL:** http://www.bgs.ac.uk/earthwise. **Circ:** Non-paid 5,000

55755 ■ EPNS Journal
English Place-Name Society
School of English Studies
University of Nottingham
Nottingham NG7 2RD, United Kingdom
Ph: 44 11 59515919
Fax: 44 11 58467526
Publication E-mail: name-studies@nottingham.ac.uk
Publisher E-mail: name-studies@nottingham.ac.uk
Journal covering English, places, and names. **Freq:** Annual. **ISSN:** 1351-3095. **Subscription Rates:** 12 members; 15 nonmembers. **Remarks:** Advertising not accepted. **URL:** http://www.nottingham.ac.uk/english/ins/epns/publications/pub12. **Circ:** 650

55756 ■ Geomechanics and Geoengineering
Taylor & Francis Group Journals
c/o Prof. Hai-Sui Yu, Ed.-in-Ch.
Nottingham Centre for Geomechanics
School of Civil Engineering
University of Nottingham
Nottingham NG7 2RD, United Kingdom
Publisher E-mail: customerservice@taylorandfrancis.com
Peer-reviewed journal covering the application of the principle of mechanics to geo-materials and wide range of engineering disciplines related to geo-materials. **Freq:** Quarterly. **Key Personnel:** Prof. Michele Jamiolkowski, Editor-in-Chief, michele.jamiolkowski@polito.it; Prof. Hai-Sui Yu, Editor-in-Chief, hai-sui.yu@nottingham.ac.uk; Prof. James K. Mitchell, Honorary Ed. **ISSN:** 1748-6025. **Subscription Rates:** US$411 institutions print + online; US$370 institutions online; US$135 individuals; 249 institutions print + online; 224 institutions online; 81 individuals; EUR327 institutions print + online; EUR294 institutions online; EUR107 individuals. **Remarks:** Advertising accepted; rates available upon request. **URL:** http://www.tandf.co.uk/journals/titles/17486025.asp. **Circ:** (Not Reported)

55757 ■ Gut
BMJ Publishing Group Ltd.
c/o Prof. Robin C. Spiller, Ed.
University Hospital Nottingham
Nottingham NG7 2UH, United Kingdom
Publication E-mail: guteditorial@bmjgroup.com
Peer-reviewed Journal covering clinical research of the alimentary tract, liver, biliary tree and pancreas. **Subtitle:** International Journal in Gastroenterology. **Founded:** 1960. **Freq:** Monthly. **Key Personnel:** Emad El-Omar, Editor, e.el-omar@abdn.ac.uk; Alexander Gerbes, Dep. Ed., gerbes@med.uni-muenchen.de; Magnus Simren, Dep. Ed., magnus.simren@medicine.gu.se; Markus M. Lerch, Board Member; William Grady, Assoc. Ed., wgrady@fhcrc.org; Herbert Tilg, Assoc. Ed., herbert.tilg@i-med.ac.at. **ISSN:** 0017-5749. **Subscription Rates:** 194 individuals print and online; 106 individuals

online only; US$207 institutions online; US$378 individuals print and online; EUR143 individuals online only; EUR262 individuals print and online. **URL:** http://gut.bmj.com/.

55758 ■ Headway News
Headway - The Brain Injury Association
Bradbury House.
190 Bagnall Rd.
Nottingham NG6 8SF, United Kingdom
Ph: 44 11 59240800
Fax: 44 11 59584446
Publisher E-mail: enquiries@headway.org.uk
Publication covering both Headways activities and those of the Headway Groups and branches throughout Britain. **Freq:** Quarterly. **URL:** http://www.headway.org.uk/sitepages.asp?step=4&contentID=1347&navid=149.

55759 ■ International Journal of Design Engineering
Inderscience Publishers
c/o Prof. Daizhong Su, Ed.-in-Ch.
The Nottingham Trent University
Maudslay Bldg., Rm. M243
Burton St.
Nottingham NG1 4BU, United Kingdom
Publisher E-mail: editor@inderscience.com
Peer-reviewed journal covering research and development in design engineering. **Founded:** 2007. **Freq:** 4/yr. **Key Personnel:** Prof. Daizhong Su, Editor-in-Chief, daizhong.su@ntu.ac.uk. **ISSN:** 1751-5874. **Subscription Rates:** EUR494 individuals includes surface mail, print only; EUR672 individuals print and online. **URL:** http://www.inderscience.com/browse/index.php?journalCODE=ijde.

55760 ■ International Journal of Educational Development
Elsevier Science Inc.
c/o Simon McGrath, Ed.-in-Ch.
UNESCO Centre for Comparative Education Research
Jubilee Campus Wollaton Rd.
Nottingham NG8 1BB, United Kingdom
Publisher E-mail: usinfo-ehelp@elsevier.com
Journal brings all developments to the attention of professionals in the field of education. **Founded:** 1981. **Freq:** 6/yr. **Key Personnel:** Joel Samoff, Regional Ed., joel.samoff@stanford.edu; M. Schweisfurth, Exec. Ed.; L. Tikly, Exec. Ed.; K. Watson, Exec. Ed.; A. Rogers, Exec. Ed.; M. Crossley, Exec. Ed.; G. Vulliamy, Exec. Ed.; Qing Gu, Review Ed.; C. Harber, Exec. Ed.; C. Dyer, Exec. Ed.; Simon McGrath, Editor-in-Chief, simon.mcgrath@nottingham.ac.uk. **ISSN:** 0738-0593. **Subscription Rates:** 145,900¥ institutions; EUR1,100 institutions for European countries and Iran; US$1,231 institutions, other countries except Europe, Japan and Iran; EUR175 individuals for European countries and Iran; 25,300¥ individuals; US$228 other countries except Europe, Japan and Iran. **URL:** http://www.elsevier.com/wps/find/journaldescription.cws_home/719/descriptiondescription.

55761 ■ International Journal of Evidence and Proof
Vathek Publishing
c/o Jenny McEwan, Ed.
School of Law
University of Exeter
Amory Bldg., Rennes Dr.
Nottingham EX4 4RJ, United Kingdom
Ph: 44 139 2263365
Fax: 44 139 2263196
Publisher E-mail: mlw@valthek.com
Peer-reviewed journal reporting latest developments in the law of evidence and the process of proof. **Freq:** Quarterly. **Key Personnel:** Jenny McEwan, Editor, j.a.mcewan@exeter.ac.uk; Roderick Bagshaw, Book Review Ed., roderick.bagshaw@law.ox.ac.uk. **ISSN:** 1365-7127. **Subscription Rates:** 274 institutions paper and online; US$511 institutions paper and online; 137 individuals paper and online; US$256 individuals paper and online; 204 institutions online only; US$386 institutions online only; 102 individuals online only; US$193 individuals online only; 226 institutions paper only; US$427 institutions paper only. **Remarks:** Accepts advertising. **URL:** http://www.vathek.com/ijep/index.shtml. **Circ:** (Not Reported)

55762 ■ International Journal of Public Sector Management
Emerald Group Publishing Ltd.
c/o Prof. Joyce Liddle, Ed.
Nottingham Trent University

Chaucer Bldg., Rm. 555
Goldsmith St.
Nottingham NG1 4BU, United Kingdom
Publisher E-mail: emerald@emeraldinsight.com
Journal focusing on the common issues which public sector managers face the world over: improving efficiency and effectiveness in situations of scarce resources and rising public expectations, drawing on theory, concepts, methods and practical experience. **Freq:** 7/yr. **Key Personnel:** Prof. Joyce Liddle, Editor, joyce.liddle@ntu.ac.uk; Dr. Arto Haveri, Editorial Advisory Board; Nicola Codner, Publisher, ncodner@emeraldinsight.com; Prof. Stephen Ackroyd, Editorial Advisory Board; Dr. Jon Coaffee, Book Review Ed., jon.coaffee@manchester.ac.uk; Prof. Ricardo C. Gomes, Editorial Advisory Board; Dr. Jamal Daoud Abu-Doleh, Editorial Advisory Board. **ISSN:** 0951-3558. **URL:** http://info.emeraldinsight.com/products/journals/journals.htm?id=ijpsm.

55763 ■ International Journal of Remote Sensing
Remote Sensing and Photogrammetry Society
U.S. Department of of Geography
University of Nottingham
University Pk.
Nottingham NG7 2RD, United Kingdom
Ph: 44 11 59515435
Fax: 44 11 59515249
Publisher E-mail: rspsoc@rspsoc.org
Journal covering the science and technology of remote sensing and the applications of remotely sensed data in all major disciplines. **Freq:** Semimonthly. **Subscription Rates:** 5,205 institutions print & online; US$9,108 institutions print & online; EUR7,287 institutions print & online; 4,944 institutions online only; US$8,652 institutions online only; EUR6,923 institutions online only. **Remarks:** Accepts advertising. **URL:** http://www.tandf.co.uk/journals/journal.asp?issn=0143-1161&linktype=rates; http://www.rspsoc.org/publications/. **Circ:** (Not Reported)

55764 ■ Journal of Molecular Graphics and Modeling
Elsevier Science
c/o Prof. J.D. Hirst, Ed.
School of Chemistry
University of Nottingham
University Pk.
Nottingham NG7 2RD, United Kingdom
Ph: 44 115 9513478
Fax: 44 115 9513562
Publisher E-mail: nlinfo-f@elsevier.com
Journal providing a platform for discussion of research works on molecular modeling in the study of molecular structure, function, interactions and design in computational chemistry, protein and polymer engineering, pharmaceutical design, structural biology and materials design. Journal published connection with the Molecular Graphics and Modeling Society and the ACS Division of Computers in Chemistry. **Freq:** 8/yr. **Key Personnel:** A.J. Holder, International Editorial Board; Prof. J.D. Hirst, Editor, jonathan.hirst@nottingham.ac.uk; Dr. J.D. Madura, Editor, jdmadura@me.com. **ISSN:** 1093-3263. **Subscription Rates:** 51,100¥ individuals; US$432 individuals for all countries except Europe and Japan; EUR385 individuals for European countries; EUR1,379 institutions for European countries; US$1,541 institutions for all countries except Europe and Japan; 183,100¥ institutions. **Remarks:** Accepts advertising. **URL:** http://www.elsevier.com/wps/find/journaldescription.cws_home/525012/description. **Circ:** (Not Reported)

55765 ■ The Law Teacher
Association of Law Teachers
Nottingham Law School
Burton St.
Nottingham NG1 4BU, United Kingdom
Ph: 44 1158482550
Fax: 44 1159486569
Publisher E-mail: john.hodgson@ntu.ac.uk
Peer-reviewed journal covering legal education. **Subtitle:** The International Journal of Legal Education. **Freq:** 3/yr. **Key Personnel:** Nigel Duncan, Gen. Ed., phone 44 20 74003629, fax 44 20 78314188, n.j.duncan@city.ac.uk. **ISSN:** 0303-9400. **Subscription Rates:** Free to members. **Remarks:** Advertising accepted; rates available upon request. **URL:** http://www.lawteacher.ac.uk/. **Circ:** (Not Reported)

55766 ■ Mathematical Medicine and Biology
Oxford University Press
School of Mathematical Sciences
University of Nottingham
University Pk.
Nottingham NG7 2RD, United Kingdom
Publisher E-mail: webenquiry.uk@oup.com
Journal publishing original articles with a significant mathematical content, such as biomechanics, biophysics, cell biology, developmental biology, ecology and the environment, epidemiology, immunology, infectious diseases, neuroscience, pharmacology, physiology and population biology. **Subtitle:** A Journal of the IMA. **Freq:** 4/yr. **Key Personnel:** A. Deutsch, Assoc. Ed.; P. Bressloff, Assoc. Ed.; M. Chaplain, Assoc. Ed.; S. Cox, Assoc. Ed.; F. Ball, Assoc. Ed.; V. Capasso, Assoc. Ed.; H. Byrne, Assoc. Ed. **ISSN:** 1477-8599. **Subscription Rates:** 431 institutions corporate; print and online; 359 institutions corporate; online only; 395 institutions corporate; print only; 344 institutions print and online; 287 institutions online only; 316 institutions print only; 298 individuals print; 100 members print; 122 members others. **Remarks:** Advertising accepted; rates available upon request. **URL:** http://imammb.oxfordjournals.org/. **Circ:** (Not Reported)

55767 ■ Miniature Wargames
Pireme Publishing Ltd.
c/o Andrew Hubback
Strelley Hall
Nottingham NG8 6PE, United Kingdom
Ph: 44 115 9061200
Fax: 44 115 9061251
Publisher E-mail: andrew@miniwargames.com
Consumer magazine covering war games in all periods of history worldwide. **Founded:** 1983. **Freq:** Monthly. **Print Method:** Offset litho. **Trim Size:** 210 x 297 mm. **Cols./Page:** 3. **Col. Width:** 58 millimeters. **Col. Depth:** 185 millimeters. **Key Personnel:** Andrew Hubback, Editor; Gareth Mcfarlane, Advertising Sales Mgr., gareth@efmedia.co.uk. **ISSN:** 0266-3228. **Subscription Rates:** 43 individuals; 67 individuals airmail; 53 out of country. **Remarks:** Accepts advertising. **URL:** http://www.miniwargames.com. **Ad Rates:** GLR: 1.26, BW: 302, 4C: 393. **Circ:** Paid 9,000

55768 ■ Optical and Quantum Electronics
Springer Netherlands
c/o Trevor M. Benson, Ed.-in-Ch.
University of Nottingham
School of Electrical & Electronic Engineering
University Pk.
Nottingham NG7 2RD, United Kingdom
Publisher E-mail: permissions.dordrecht@springer.com
Journal dealing with optical physics, optical engineering and optoelectronics. **Freq:** 15/yr. **Key Personnel:** Trevor M. Benson, Editor-in-Chief; John Dudley, Editor-in-Chief. **ISSN:** 0306-8919. **Subscription Rates:** EUR2,404 institutions print incl. free access or e-only; EUR2,884.80 institutions print incl. enhanced access. **Remarks:** Advertising accepted; rates available upon request. **URL:** http://www.springerlink.com/content/0306-8919. **Circ:** (Not Reported)

55769 ■ Planning Perspectives
Routledge
Taylor & Francis Group Ltd.
c/o Prof. Helen Meller, Ed.
University of Nottingham
University Park
Nottingham NG7 2RD, United Kingdom
Ph: 44 115 9254354
Fax: 44 115 9135128
Publisher E-mail: webmaster.books@tandf.co.uk
Peer-reviewed journal covering all aspects of plan-making and implementation. **Subtitle:** An International Journal of history, Planning and the Environment. **Freq:** Quarterly. **Key Personnel:** Prof. Stephen V. Ward, Editorial Board; Prof. Robert B. Fairbanks, Editor, phone 817272-2862, fax 817272-2852, fairbank@uta.edu; Prof. John R. Gold, Review Ed., jrgold@brookes.ac.uk; Prof. John F. Bauman, Editorial Board; Nora Lafi, Review Ed., nora.lafi@rz.hu-berlin.de; Prof. Helen Meller, Editor, helen.meller@nottingham.ac.uk. **ISSN:** 0266-5433. **Subscription Rates:** US$1,422 institutions print + online; US$1,350 institutions online; EUR1,075 institutions online; US$50 students; 847 institutions print + online; 805 institutions online; EUR1,132 institutions print + online; EUR40 students; 25 students. **Remarks:** Advertising accepted; rates available upon request. **URL:** http://www.tandf.co.uk/journals/titles/02665433.html. **Circ:** (Not Reported)

55770 ■ Platelets
Taylor & Francis Ltd.
Cardiovascular Medicine
University Hospital
Queen's Medical Centre
Nottingham NG7 2UH, United Kingdom
Ph: 44 11 58231013
Fax: 44 11 58231017
International, fully peer-reviewed journal covering all aspects of platelet-related research. **Freq:** 8/yr. **Key Personnel:** S. Heptinstall, Editor-in-Chief, s.heptinstall@nottingham.ac.uk; B. Ashby, Editorial Board; P. Harrison, Editorial Board; A. Weber, Editorial Board; S. Goto, Editorial Board; G. De Gaetano, Principal Ed., gdegaetano@rm.unicatt.it; K.J. Clemetson, Editorial Board; A.W. Poole, Review Ed., a.poole@bristol.ac.uk; Michael C. Berndt, Principal Ed., michael.berndt@med.monash.edu.au. **ISSN:** 0953-7104. **Subscription Rates:** 1,130 institutions; US$2,040 institutions; EUR1,625 institutions. **Remarks:** Accepts advertising. **URL:** http://informahealthcare.com/loi/plt. **Circ:** (Not Reported)

55771 ■ Public Policy and Administration
Joint University Council
College of Business, Law & Social Science
Victoria House, Rm. 517
Nottingham Trent University
Nottingham NG1 4BU, United Kingdom
Ph: 44 11 58488117
Fax: 44 11 58486808
Publisher E-mail: sandra.odell@ntu.ac.uk
Publication covering colleges and universities. **Freq:** Quarterly. **Key Personnel:** Karen Johnston Miller, Editor; Duncan McTavish, Editor. **ISSN:** 0952-0767. **Subscription Rates:** 370 institutions print & e-access; 333 institutions e-access; 363 institutions print only; 45 individuals print only; 100 single issue institutional, print; 15 single issue individual, print. **Remarks:** Advertising accepted; rates available upon request. **URL:** http://www.juc.ac.uk/juc-journals.aspx; http://www.uk.sagepub.com/journalsProdDesc.nav?prodId=Journal201778. **Circ:** 600

55772 ■ Theory, Culture & Society
Sage Publications Ltd.
c/o Mike Featherstone, Ed.
School of Arts, Communication & Culture
Nottingham Trent University Clifton Ln.
Nottingham NG11 8NS, United Kingdom
Peer-reviewed journal covering culture and contemporary social science. **Subtitle:** Explorations in Critical Social Science. **Founded:** 1982. **Freq:** 8/yr. **Key Personnel:** Nicholas Gane, Annual Review Ed.; Vikki Bell, Editorial Board; Roy Boyne, Notes and Commentary Ed.; Couze Venn, Managing Editor; Mike Featherstone, Editor; Scott Lash, Notes and Commentary Ed. **ISSN:** 0263-2764. **Subscription Rates:** US$1,449 institutions electronic & print; US$1,594 institutions backfile lease, combined plus backfile; US$1,304 institutions e-access; US$1,449 institutions backfile lease, e-access plus backfile; US$1,663 institutions backfile purchase, e-access; US$1,420 institutions print only; US$117 individuals print only; US$195 institutions single print; US$19 individuals single print. **Remarks:** Accepts advertising. **URL:** http://www.sagepub.com/journalsProdDesc.nav?prodId=Journal200853. **Circ:** (Not Reported)

55773 ■ Today's Technician
National Pest Technicians Association
NPTA House, Hall Ln., Kinoulton
Nottingham NG12 3EF, United Kingdom
Ph: 44 115 194981133
Fax: 44 115 1949823905
Publisher E-mail: officenpta@aol.com
Magazine containing news, articles, new products, and reports relevant to members. **Freq:** Quarterly. **Remarks:** Accepts advertising. **URL:** http://www.npta.org.uk/assets/pages/todaystechnician.html. **Ad Rates:** BW: 377, 4C: 200. **Circ:** (Not Reported)

55774 ■ BBC Radio Nottingham-FM - 95.5
London Rd.
Nottingham NG2 4UU, United Kingdom
Ph: 44 115 9550500

Circulation: ★ = ABC; △ = BPA; ◆ = CAC; ● = CCAB; ❑ = VAC; ⊕ = PO Statement; ‡ = Publisher's Report; Boldface figures = sworn; Light figures = estimated.

E-mail: nottingham@bbc.co.uk
Format: Talk; News; Oldies; Sports; Eclectic; Folk; Jazz; Country. **Owner:** British Broadcasting Corporation, Broadcasting House, Portland Pl., London W1A 1AA, United Kingdom. **Founded:** Jan. 31, 1968. **Operating Hours:** Continuous. **URL:** http://www.bbc.co.uk/nottingham/local_radio.

55775 ■ Trent-FM - 96.5
Chapel Quarter
Maid Marian Way
Nottingham NG1 6JR, United Kingdom
Ph: 44 115 8731500
Fax: 44 115 8731569
Format: Contemporary Hit Radio (CHR). **Ad Rates:** Advertising accepted; rates available upon request. **URL:** http://www.trentfm.co.uk/.

55776 ■ Trent-FM - 96.2
The Top Fl.
Chapel Quarter
Maid Marian Way
Nottingham NG1 6JR, United Kingdom
Ph: 44 115 8731500
Fax: 44 115 8731569
Format: Contemporary Hit Radio (CHR). **Ad Rates:** Advertising accepted; rates available upon request. **URL:** http://www.trentfm.co.uk/.

Nuneaton

55777 ■ Pastoral Care in Education
National Association for Pastoral Care in Education
PO Box 6005
Nuneaton CV11 9GY, United Kingdom
Ph: 44 24 76765639
Fax: 44 24 76765639
Publisher E-mail: base@napce.org.uk
Publication covering pastoral care in education. **Freq:** Quarterly. **Key Personnel:** Colleen McLaughlin, Executive Ed. **ISSN:** 0264-3944. **Subscription Rates:** 42 individuals U.K and Europe; 59 individuals elsewhere; 42 institutions U.K. and Europe; 59 institutions elsewhere; 65 institutions U.K. and Europe; 75 institutions elsewhere; 21 students U.K. and Europe; 21 individuals retired members U.K. and Europe. **Remarks:** Advertising accepted; rates available upon request. **URL:** http://napce.org.uk/journal/. **Circ:** 2,000

Nutley

55778 ■ American in Britain
American in Britain Ltd.
Yewlands House
Millbrook House
East Sussex
Nutley TN22 3PH, United Kingdom
Ph: 44 18 25713676
Fax: 44 18 25713687
Consumer magazine for Americans living and working in the UK. **Freq:** Quarterly. **Print Method:** Litho. **Trim Size:** A4. **Cols./Page:** 3. **Key Personnel:** Helen Elliott, Publisher, phone 44 20 86610186, helen@theamericanhour.com. **Subscription Rates:** 20 individuals. **Remarks:** Accepts advertising. **URL:** http://www.americaninbritain.co.uk/. **Ad Rates:** BW: 2,200; 4C: 2,800. **Circ:** Controlled ‡20,000

55779 ■ Homeopathy in Practice
Alliance of Registered Homeopaths
Millbrook
Millbrook Hill
Nutley TN22 3PJ, United Kingdom
Ph: 44 1825 714506
Fax: 44 1825 714506
Publication E-mail: editor@a-r-h.org
Publisher E-mail: info@a-r-h.org
Journal of the Alliance of Registered Homeopaths. **Freq:** Quarterly. **Subscription Rates:** 32 individuals U.K.; 40 other countries; 8 individuals U.K. (single copy); 10 other countries single copy; Included in membership. **Remarks:** Accepts advertising. **URL:** http://www.a-r-h.org/Publications/Journal.htm. **Ad Rates:** BW: 150, 4C: 225. **Circ:** (Not Reported)

Oakham

55780 ■ Credit Management
Institute of Credit Management
The Water Mill

Station Rd.
South Luffenham
Oakham LE15 8NB, United Kingdom
Ph: 44 17 80722900
Fax: 44 17 80721333
Publisher E-mail: info@icm.org.uk
Publication covering credit management. **Freq:** Monthly. **Key Personnel:** Angela Cooper, Contact; Sean Feast, Editor, editorial@icm.org.uk; Rob Beddington, Advertising Mgr., rob.beddington@icm.org.uk. **Subscription Rates:** 5 individuals per issue; 55 individuals; 75 individuals overseas. **Remarks:** Advertising accepted; rates available upon request Display advertising. **URL:** http://www.icm.org.uk/default.asp?edit_id=568-69. **Ad Rates:** BW: 1095, 4C: 1470. **Circ:** 8,791

55781 ■ Rutland Radio-FM - 107.2
40 Melton Rd.
Oakham LE15 6AY, United Kingdom
Ph: 44 1572 757868
Fax: 44 1572 757744
E-mail: enquiries@rutlandradio.co.uk
Format: Oldies; Contemporary Hit Radio (CHR). **Operating Hours:** Continuous. **Ad Rates:** Advertising accepted; rates available upon request. **URL:** http://www.rutlandradio.co.uk/.

Rutland Radio-FM - See Stamford

Oban

55782 ■ Oban-FM - 103.3
132 George St.
Argyll
Oban PA34 5NT, United Kingdom
Format: Full Service. **Key Personnel:** Laura Johnston, Contact, laura@obanfm.org.uk. **URL:** http://www.obanfm.org.uk/.

Oldham

55783 ■ Glazed Expressions
Tiles and Architectural Ceramics Society
27 Spurn Ln.
Holden Smithy, Diggle
Oldham OL3 5QP, United Kingdom
Publisher E-mail: membership@tilesoc.org.uk
Magazine containing a wide range of national and international articles dealing with tiles and architectural ceramics. **Freq:** Semiannual. **URL:** http://www.tilesoc.org.uk/glazed_expressions.htm.

55784 ■ Journal of the Tiles and Architectural Ceramic Society
Tiles and Architectural Ceramics Society
27 Spurn Ln.
Holden Smithy, Diggle
Oldham OL3 5QP, United Kingdom
Publisher E-mail: membership@tilesoc.org.uk
Journal containing illustrated articles of original research, many covering subjects being studied for the first time. **Freq:** Annual. **Subscription Rates:** 20 members individual; 28 members family; 35 members institutional; 30 members European/overseas (sterling only accepted); 40 members institutional European/overseas. **URL:** http://www.tilesoc.org.uk/tacs_journal.htm.

55785 ■ The Revolution-FM - 96.2
Sarah Moor Studios
PO Box 962
Oldham OL1 3JF, United Kingdom
Ph: 44 16 16216500
Fax: 44 16 16216521
E-mail: info@therevolution962.com
Format: Alternative/New Music/Progressive; Classic Rock. **Operating Hours:** Continuous. **Key Personnel:** John Evington, Station Dir., john.evington@therevolution962.com. **URL:** http://www.therevolution962.com.

Olney

55786 ■ International Journal of Ad Hoc and Ubiquitous Computing
Inderscience Publishers
PO Box 735
Olney MK46 5WB, United Kingdom
Fax: 44 12 34240515
Publisher E-mail: editor@inderscience.com
Peer-reviewed journal publishing papers that address networking or computing problems in the context of

mobile and wireless ad hoc networks, wireless sensor networks, ad hoc computing systems, and ubiquitous computing systems. **Freq:** Quarterly. **Key Personnel:** Prof. Han-Chieh Chao, Editor-in-Chief, hcc@mail.niu.edu.tw; Prof. Dharma P. Agrawal, Editorial Board Member; Dr. Xiuzhen Cheng, Editorial Board Member; Prof. Yuh-Shyan Chen, Editor-in-Chief, yschen@mail.ntpu.edu.tw; Prof. Schahram Dustdar, Editorial Board Member; Prof. Pingyi Fan, Editorial Board Member. **ISSN:** 1743-8225. **Subscription Rates:** EUR735 individuals hardcopy only (surface mail); EUR1,025 individuals hardcopy and online; EUR1,240 individuals online only (2-3 users). **URL:** http://www.inderscience.com/browse/index.php?journalCODE=ijahuc.

55787 ■ International Journal of Advanced Media and Communication
Inderscience Publishers
PO Box 735
Olney MK46 5WB, United Kingdom
Fax: 44 12 34240515
Publisher E-mail: editor@inderscience.com
Peer-reviewed journal describing and explaining communication technology and information in the knowledge economy, focusing on the role of communication technologies as the knowledge infrastructure and the effect of information in various forms on the economy. **Freq:** Quarterly. **Key Personnel:** Dr. Shervin Shirmohammadi, Editorial Board Member, shervin@site.uottawa.ca; Prof. Ziad Sakr, Editorial Board Member; Dr. Rosa Iglesias, Editorial Board Member. **ISSN:** 1462-4613. **Subscription Rates:** EUR494 individuals print only (surface mail); EUR534 individuals print only (airmail); EUR672 individuals print and online; EUR840 individuals online only (2-3 users). **URL:** http://www.inderscience.com/browse/index.php?journalCODE=ijamc.

55788 ■ International Journal of Aerodynamics
Inderscience Publishers
PO Box 735
Olney MK46 5WB, United Kingdom
Fax: 44 12 34240515
Publisher E-mail: editor@inderscience.com
Peer-reviewed journal aiming to promote the advancement of science and technology of aerodynamics by disseminating original technical information of permanent interest in the field of aerodynamics. **Freq:** Quarterly. **Key Personnel:** Dr. M.A. Dorgham, Editor-in-Chief, editorial@inderscience.com; Dr. Zhigang Yang, Editor, zhigang_yang@yahoo.com; Dr. Bahram Khalighi, Editorial Board Member. **ISSN:** 1743-5447. **Subscription Rates:** EUR494 individuals print only (surface mail); EUR840 individuals online only (2-3 users); EUR672 individuals print and online. **URL:** http://www.inderscience.com/browse/index.php?journalID=140.

55789 ■ International Journal of Alternative Propulsion
Inderscience Publishers
PO Box 735
Olney MK46 5WB, United Kingdom
Fax: 44 12 34240515
Publisher E-mail: editor@inderscience.com
Peer-reviewed journal aiming to establish an effective channel of communication between policy makers, government agencies academics and research institutions and persons concerned with the issues of alternative propulsion, and to provide a forum for them to disseminate information and to learn from each other's work. **Freq:** Quarterly. **Key Personnel:** Dr. M.A. Dorgham, Editor-in-Chief, editorial@inderscience.com; Prof. Jorge Estevesjo, Editorial Board Member; Dr. Giuseppe Giulio Calabrese, Editorial Board Member; Prof. Jean-Jacques Chanaron, Editorial Board Member; Dr. Dimitrios C. Kyritsis, Editorial Board Member; Jie Chen, Editorial Board Member; Prof. Andrew Alfonso Frank, Editorial Board Member; Prof. Yaobin Chen, Editorial Board Member; Francois Badin, Editorial Board Member. **ISSN:** 1741-0234. **Subscription Rates:** EUR494 individuals print only (surface mail); EUR840 individuals online only (2-3 users); EUR672 individuals print and online; EUR534 individuals print only (airmail). **URL:** http://www.inderscience.com/browse/index.php?journalCODE=ijap.

55790 ■ International Journal of Automotive Technology and Management
Inderscience Publishers
PO Box 735
Olney MK46 5WB, United Kingdom
Fax: 44 12 34240515
Publisher E-mail: editor@inderscience.com
Peer-reviewed journal aiming to establish channels of

communication between policy makers, executives in the automotive industry, both OEM and suppliers, and related business and academic experts in the field. **Freq:** Quarterly. **Key Personnel:** Dr. Giuseppe Giulio Calabrese, Co-Ed.; Prof. Jean-Jacques Chanaron, Co-Ed. **ISSN:** 1740-9511. **Subscription Rates:** EUR494 individuals print only (surface mail); EUR534 individuals print only (airmail); EUR840 individuals online only (2-3 users); EUR672 individuals print and online. **URL:** http://www.inderscience.com/browse/index.php?journalCODE=ijatm.

55791 ■ International Journal of Autonomic Computing
Inderscience Publishers
PO Box 735
Olney MK46 5WB, United Kingdom
Fax: 44 12 34240515
Publisher E-mail: editor@inderscience.com
Peer-reviewed journal aiming to establish an effective channel of communication between autonomic computing researchers, engineers, and policy makers. **Freq:** Quarterly. **Key Personnel:** Ajith Abraham, Editor-in-Chief, ajith.abraham@ieee.org; Vaclav Snasel, Editor-in-Chief, vaclav.snasel@vsb.cz; Jan Kozusznik, Managing Editor, jan.kozusznik@vsb.cz. **ISSN:** 1741-8569. **Subscription Rates:** EUR494 individuals hardcopy (surface mail); EUR840 individuals online only for 2-3 users; EUR672 individuals print and online; EUR1,230 individuals online only for 4-5 users; EUR1,600 individuals online only for 6-7 users; EUR1,950 individuals online only for 8-9 users; EUR2,275 individuals online only for 10-14 users; EUR2,580 individuals online only for 15-19 users; EUR3,020 individuals online only for 20 users. **URL:** http://www.inderscience.com/browse/index.php?journalCODE=ijac.

55792 ■ International Journal of Biomedical Engineering and Technology
Inderscience Publishers
PO Box 735
Olney MK46 5WB, United Kingdom
Fax: 44 12 34240515
Publication E-mail: ijbet@inderscience.com
Publisher E-mail: editor@inderscience.com
Journal covering multi-disciplinary area of biomedical engineering & technology. **Founded:** 2007. **Freq:** 8/yr. **Key Personnel:** Dr. Nilmini Wickramasinghe, Editor-in-Chief, nilmini@stuart.iit.edu. **ISSN:** 1752-6418. **Subscription Rates:** EUR735 individuals online only for 1 user; EUR1,240 individuals online only for 2-3 users; EUR1,025 individuals print and online; EUR1,815 individuals online only for 4-5 users; EUR2,360 individuals online only for 6-7 users; EUR2,870 individuals online only for 8-9 users; EUR3,350 individuals online only for 10-14 users; EUR3,800 individuals online only for 15-19 users; EUR4,440 individuals online only for 20 users. **URL:** http://www.inderscience.com/browse/index.php?journalCODE=ijbet.

55793 ■ International Journal of Cognitive Performance Support (IJCPS)
Inderscience Publishers
PO Box 735
Olney MK46 5WB, United Kingdom
Fax: 44 12 34240515
Publisher E-mail: editor@inderscience.com
Peer-reviewed journal acting as a scientific cross fertilisation between disciplines such as cognitive science, ergonomics, system design and task performance analysis. **Freq:** Quarterly. **Key Personnel:** Dr. Kenneth Revett, Editor, k.revett@westminster.ac.uk. **ISSN:** 1742-7207. **Subscription Rates:** EUR494 individuals print only (surface mail); EUR840 individuals online only (2-3 users); EUR672 individuals print and online. **URL:** http://www.inderscience.com/browse/index.php?journalCODE=ijcps.

55794 ■ International Journal of Collaborative Enterprise
Inderscience Publishers
PO Box 735
Olney MK46 5WB, United Kingdom
Fax: 44 12 34240515
Publisher E-mail: editor@inderscience.com
Peer-reviewed journal providing a global forum for exchanging research findings on new concepts for the systematic integration of methods dealing with people, process and technology that can lead to the development of capability for the design of enterprise. **Freq:** Quarterly. **Key Personnel:** Prof. Ali K. Kamrani, Editorin-Chief, akamrani@uh.edu; Dr. Charu Chandra, Editorial Board Membership; Dr. Manfredi Bruccoleri, Editorial Board Membership. **ISSN:** 1740-2085. **Subscription**

Rates: EUR494 individuals print (surface mail); EUR840 individuals online only (2-3 users); EUR672 individuals print and online. **URL:** http://www.inderscience.com/browse/index.php?journalCODE=ijcent. **Formerly:** International Journal of Intelligent Collaborative Enterprise.

55795 ■ International Journal of Complexity
Inderscience Publishers
PO Box 735
Olney MK46 5WB, United Kingdom
Fax: 44 12 34240515
Publisher E-mail: editor@inderscience.com
Peer-reviewed journal providing a platform to network the various pure and applied science disciplines that underpin the study and design of technological and management systems in industrial companies. **Freq:** Quarterly. **Key Personnel:** Prof. Waguih H. ElMaraghy, Editor-in-Chief, wem@uwindsor.ca. **ISSN:** 1740-0546. **Subscription Rates:** EUR494 individuals print only (surface mail); EUR840 individuals online only (2-3 users); EUR672 individuals print and online; EUR534 individuals print only (airmail). **URL:** http://www.inderscience.com/browse/index.php?journalID=71.

55796 ■ International Journal of Computational Materials Science & Surface Engineering
Inderscience Publishers
PO Box 735
Olney MK46 5WB, United Kingdom
Fax: 44 12 34240515
Publisher E-mail: editor@inderscience.com
Peer-reviewed journal covering computational materials science & surface engineering. **Founded:** 2007. **Freq:** 6/yr. **Key Personnel:** Prof. Qingyou Han, Editor-in-Chief, hanq@purdue.edu; Prof. Xiaozhu Liu, Assoc. Ed. **ISSN:** 1753-3465. **Subscription Rates:** EUR494 individuals includes surface mail, print only; EUR672 individuals print and online. **URL:** http://www.inderscience.com/browse/index.php?journalCODE=ijcmsse.

55797 ■ International Journal of Critical Infrastructures
Inderscience Publishers
PO Box 735
Olney MK46 5WB, United Kingdom
Fax: 44 12 34240515
Publisher E-mail: editor@inderscience.com
Peer-reviewed journal providing a professional and scholarly forum for cross-learning between different scientific and technological disciplines, between business and economic, as well as between societal and managerial disciplines in the area of critical infrastructures. **Freq:** Quarterly. **Key Personnel:** Dr. Adrian V. Gheorghe, Editor, agheorgh@odu.edu; Dr. Margot P.C. Weijnen, European Ed.; Prof. Erhan Erkut, Editorial Board Member; Dr. Richard Little, Editorial Board Member; Prof. Florin Filip, Editorial Board Member; Prof. Lamine Mili, North American Ed.; Prof. Hideyuki Horii, Editorial Board Member; Dr. Samuel G. Varnado, Editorial Board Member; Dr. Wolfgang Kroger, Ed. at Large. **ISSN:** 1475-3219. **Subscription Rates:** EUR494 individuals print only (surface mail); EUR840 individuals online only (2-3 users); EUR534 individuals print only (airmail); EUR672 individuals print and online. **URL:** http://www.inderscience.com/browse/index.php?journalCODE=ijcis.

55798 ■ International Journal of Embedded Systems
Inderscience Publishers
PO Box 735
Olney MK46 5WB, United Kingdom
Fax: 44 12 34240515
Publication E-mail: ijes@inderscience.com
Publisher E-mail: editor@inderscience.com
Journal covering all aspects of embedded computing systems. **Founded:** 2005. **Freq:** 4/yr. **Key Personnel:** Dr. M.A. Dorgham, Editor-in-Chief; Prof. K.H. Kim, Advisory Board. **ISSN:** 1741-1068. **Subscription Rates:** EUR494 individuals online only for 1 user; EUR840 individuals online only for 2-3 users; EUR672 individuals print and online; EUR1,230 individuals online only for 4-5 users; EUR1,600 individuals online only for 6-7 users; EUR1,950 individuals online only for 8-9 users; EUR2,275 individuals online only for 10-14 users; EUR2,580 individuals online only for 15-19 users; EUR3,020 individuals online only for 20 users. **URL:** http://www.inderscience.com/browse/index.php?journalCODE=ijes.

55799 ■ International Journal of Emergency Management
Inderscience Publishers

PO Box 735
Olney MK46 5WB, United Kingdom
Fax: 44 12 34240515
Publisher E-mail: editor@inderscience.com
Peer-reviewed journal published to address contingencies and emergencies as well as crisis and disaster management, including the issues associated with storms and flooding; nuclear power accidents; ferry, air and rail accidents; computer viruses; and earthquakes. **Freq:** Quarterly. **Key Personnel:** Dr. William A. Anderson, Honorary Advisory Board; Prof. Berndt Brehmer, Honorary Advisory Board; Prof. Ahmet Mete Isikara, Honorary Advisory Board; Michail I. Faleev, Honorary Advisory Board; Dr. John Clizbe, Honorary Advisory Board; Dr. Sandro Bologna, Honorary Advisory Board. **ISSN:** 1471-4825. **Subscription Rates:** EUR494 individuals print only (surface mail); EUR840 individuals online only (2-3 users); EUR672 individuals print and online. **URL:** http://www.inderscience.com/browse/index.php?journalCODE=ijem.

55800 ■ International Journal of Energy Technology and Policy
Inderscience Publishers
PO Box 735
Olney MK46 5WB, United Kingdom
Fax: 44 12 34240515
Publisher E-mail: editor@inderscience.com
Peer-reviewed journal aiming to further the development of energy technology and policy and to disseminate knowledge and provide a global forum for professionals in the field to learn from each other's work. **Freq:** Bimonthly. **Key Personnel:** Dr. Nasr Alkadi, Editor-in-Chief, nasr1.alkadi@gmail.com; Mr. P. Bacher, Editorial Board Member; Dr. Thierry Alleau, Editorial Board Member; Prof. Lars Bergman, Editorial Board Member; Prof. A.C. Benim, Assoc. Ed.; Prof. Henrik Lund, Assoc. Ed.; Dr. Ahmed F. Zobaa, Assoc. Ed.; Jim McConnach, Assoc. Ed.; Prof. Bryan M. Jenkins, Assoc. Ed.; Dr. Per Dannemand Andersen, Editorial Board Member. **ISSN:** 1472-8923. **Subscription Rates:** EUR593 individuals print (surface mail); EUR830 individuals print and online; EUR1,010 individuals online only (2-3 users); EUR830 individuals print and online. **URL:** http://www.inderscience.com/browse/index.php?journalCODE=ijetp.

55801 ■ International Journal of Entrepreneurial Venturing
Inderscience Publishers
PO Box 735
Olney MK46 5WB, United Kingdom
Fax: 44 12 34240515
Publisher E-mail: editor@inderscience.com
Journal proposing and fostering discussion on the organisational processes surrounding the concepts of opportunity, growth and value creation. **Freq:** Quarterly. **Key Personnel:** Dr. Terrence E. Brown, Editor-in-Chief, terrence@kth.se; Dr. Sascha Kraus, Editor-in-Chief, sascha.kraus@fh-salzburg.ac.at. **ISSN:** 1742-5360. **Subscription Rates:** EUR494 individuals print or online; EUR672 individuals print and online. **URL:** http://www.inderscience.com/browse/index.php?journalCODE=ijev. **Formerly:** International Journal of Opportunity, Growth and Value Creation.

55802 ■ International Journal of Entrepreneurship and Innovation Management
Inderscience Publishers
PO Box 735
Olney MK46 5WB, United Kingdom
Fax: 44 12 34240515
Publisher E-mail: editor@inderscience.com
Peer-reviewed journal providing a refereed and authoritative source of information and international forum in the field of entrepreneurship and innovation management and related topics, offering an interface between entrepreneurship and innovation, as well as business corporate strategy and government economic policy. **Freq:** Bimonthly. **Key Personnel:** Dr. M.A. Dorgham, Editor-in-Chief, editorial@inderscience.com; Prof. Benjamin Yuan, Far East Ed.; Prof. Moreno Muffatto, Regional Ed.; Iain Bitran, Assoc. Ed.; Dr. Max Von Zedtwitz, Assoc. Ed.; Prof. Pier A. Abetti, Assoc. Ed.; Dr. Christoph F. Buechtemann, Editorial Board Member; Prof. David Bennett, Editorial Board Member; Prof. Klaus K. Brockhoff, Editorial Board Member. **ISSN:** 1368-275X. **Subscription Rates:** EUR735 individuals print only (surface mail); EUR1,025 individuals print and online; EUR1,240 individuals online only (2-3 users); EUR1,025 individuals print and online. **URL:** http://www.

Circulation: ★ = ABC; △ = BPA; ♦ = CAC; • = CCAB; ❏ = VAC; ⊕ = PO Statement; ‡ = Publisher's Report; Boldface figures = sworn; Light figures = estimated.

Gale Directory of Publications & Broadcast Media/147th Ed.

5801

inderscience.com/browse/index.php?journalCODE=ijeim.

55803 ■ International Journal of Environment and Sustainable Development
Inderscience Publishers
PO Box 735
Olney MK46 5WB, United Kingdom
Fax: 44 12 34240515
Publisher E-mail: editor@inderscience.com
Peer-reviewed journal addressing matters related to environment and sustainable development, paying special attention to relevant issues in developing countries while reporting on the latest environmental trends in industrialised nations. **Freq:** Quarterly. **Key Personnel:** Prof. Desheng Wu, Editor-in-Chief, dash@risklab.ca; Prof. Michel Installe, Editorial Board Member; Dr. Rishi Basak, Editorial Board Member; Prof. Nikolaj Ivanov, Book Ed.; Dr. Jo Blakeley, Editorial Board Member; Dr. Sanjeev Chaudhari, Editorial Board Member; Dr. Antonella Bachiorri, Editorial Board Member; Prof. Nicholas Ashford, Editorial Board Member. **ISSN:** 1474-6778. **Subscription Rates:** EUR494 individuals print (surface mail); EUR840 individuals online (2-3 users); EUR672 individuals print and online. **URL:** http://www.inderscience.com/browse/index.php?journalCODE=ijesd.

55804 ■ International Journal of Environmental Technology and Management
Inderscience Publishers
PO Box 735
Olney MK46 5WB, United Kingdom
Fax: 44 12 34240515
Publisher E-mail: editor@inderscience.com
Peer-reviewed journal aiming to establish an effective channel of communication between policy-makers, government agencies, academics and research institutions, and professionals working in the field, and to provide a forum for them to disseminate information and to learn from each other's work. **Freq:** 8/yr. **Key Personnel:** Dr. M.A. Dorgham, Editor-in-Chief; Prof. Kingsley E. Haynes, Assoc. Ed.; Prof. Ravi Jain, Assoc. Ed.; Prof. Per Christensen, Assoc. Ed.; Dr. Mustafa Dinc, Assoc. Ed. **ISSN:** 1466-2132. **Subscription Rates:** EUR735 individuals print or online; EUR1,025 individuals print and online. **URL:** http://www.inderscience.com/browse/index.php?journalCODE=ijetm.

55805 ■ International Journal of Financial Services Management
Inderscience Publishers
PO Box 735
Olney MK46 5WB, United Kingdom
Fax: 44 12 34240515
Publisher E-mail: editor@inderscience.com
Peer-reviewed journal covering all aspects of financial services management worldwide, dealing with current practices as well as future prospects and developments. **Freq:** Quarterly. **Key Personnel:** Prof. Desheng Wu, Editor-in-Chief, dash@risklab.ca; Dr. Hsien-Chang Kuo, Regional Ed.; Dr. Ziqi Liao, Regional Ed.; Prof. Jose Maria Barrutia, Regional Ed.; Prof. George Agiomirgianakis, Editorial Board Member; Prof. Violeta Ciurel, Editorial Board Member; David R. Koenig, Editorial Board Member, david.koenig@ductilibility.com. **ISSN:** 1460-6712. **Subscription Rates:** EUR494 individuals print or online; EUR672 individuals print and online. **URL:** http://www.inderscience.com/browse/index.php?journalCODE=ijfsm.

55806 ■ International Journal of Forensic Engineering and Management
Inderscience Publishers
PO Box 735
Olney MK46 5WB, United Kingdom
Fax: 44 12 34240515
Publisher E-mail: editor@inderscience.com
Peer-reviewed journal providing a refereed source of information on failure in technical and societal systems, specifically recognizing the interplay of engineering and management in the causation and prevention of failures. **Freq:** Quarterly. **Key Personnel:** Dr. M.A. Dorgham, Editor-in-Chief, editorial@inderscience.com. **ISSN:** 1478-1476. **Subscription Rates:** EUR494 individuals print only (surface mail); EUR840 individuals online only (2-3 users); EUR672 individuals print and online; EUR534 individuals print only (airmail). **URL:** http://www.inderscience.com/browse/index.php?journalCODE=ijfem.

55807 ■ International Journal of Foresight and Innovation Policy
Inderscience Publishers

PO Box 735
Olney MK46 5WB, United Kingdom
Fax: 44 12 34240515
Publisher E-mail: editor@inderscience.com
Peer-reviewed journal publishing academic articles dealing with knowledge creation, diffusion and utilization in innovation policy. **Freq:** Quarterly. **Key Personnel:** Dr. M.A. Dorgham, Editor-in-Chief, editorial@inderscience.com; Dr. Ruud E. Smits, Assoc. Ed.; Prof. Terutaka Kuwahara, Assoc. Ed.; Prof. Philip Shapira, Assoc. Ed.; Dr. Yi-Ming Wei, Regional Ed.; Dr. Attila Havas, Regional Ed.; Prof. Remi Barre, Assoc. Ed.; Dr. Stefan Kuhlmann, Assoc. Ed. **ISSN:** 1740-2816. **Subscription Rates:** EUR494 individuals print only (surface mail); EUR840 individuals online only (2-3 users); EUR534 individuals print only (airmail); EUR672 individuals print and online. **URL:** http://www.inderscience.com/browse/index.php?journalCODE=ijfip.

55808 ■ International Journal of Global Environmental Issues
Inderscience Publishers
PO Box 735
Olney MK46 5WB, United Kingdom
Fax: 44 12 34240515
Publisher E-mail: editor@inderscience.com
Peer-reviewed journal offering a comprehensive view of the key issues in the environmental debate. **Freq:** Quarterly. **Key Personnel:** Dr. M.A. Dorgham, Editor-in-Chief; Prof. Roger R. Stough, Assoc. Ed.; Dr. Gerald Geernaert, Assoc. Ed.; Prof. Detlev Moller, Assoc. Ed.; Dr. Saeed M. Ordoubadi, Assoc. Ed.; Prof. William C.G. Burns, Assoc. Ed. **ISSN:** 1466-6650. **Subscription Rates:** EUR494 individuals print only (surface mail); EUR840 individuals online only (2-3 users); EUR672 individuals print and online. **URL:** http://www.inderscience.com/browse/index.php?journalCODE=ijgenvi.

55809 ■ International Journal of High Performance Computing and Networking
Inderscience Publishers
PO Box 735
Olney MK46 5WB, United Kingdom
Fax: 44 12 34240515
Publication E-mail: ijhpcn@inderscience.com
Publisher E-mail: editor@inderscience.com
Journal addressing the most innovative developments in high-performance computing and networking such as information and system architectures, grid and web based information management and infrastructures, data storage, management, analysis and visualisation, advanced networking with applications, scalable parallel computing, cluster and grid computing, distributed systems, and high performance scientific and engineering computing with applications. **Freq:** 4/yr. **Key Personnel:** Dr. M.A. Dorgham, Editor-in-Chief, editorial@inderscience.com. **ISSN:** 1740-0562. **Subscription Rates:** EUR494 individuals online only for 1 user; EUR840 individuals online only for 2-3 users; EUR672 individuals print and online; EUR1,230 individuals online only for 4-5 users; EUR1,600 individuals online only for 6-7 users; EUR1,950 individuals online only for 8-9 users; EUR2,275 individuals online only for 10-14 users; EUR2,580 individuals online only for 15-19 users; EUR3,020 individuals online only for 20 users. **URL:** http://www.inderscience.com/browse/index.php?journalCODE=ijhpcn.

55810 ■ International Journal of Human Resources Development and Management
Inderscience Publishers
PO Box 735
Olney MK46 5WB, United Kingdom
Fax: 44 12 34240515
Publisher E-mail: editor@inderscience.com
Peer-reviewed journal aiming to enrich the quality of human life at work by serving as a forum for exchanging experiences and disseminating information in human resources development and management originating in diverse disciplines such as engineering, business and commerce, politics, health and biological sciences, law enforcement and defence, management, and education, among others. **Freq:** Quarterly. **Key Personnel:** Dr. M.A. Dorgham, Editor-in-Chief, editorial@inderscience.com; Prof. Soon Beng Chew, Assoc. Ed.; Prof. Rosalind Chew, Assoc. Ed.; Prof. Shihab S. Asfour, Editorial Board Member; Prof. Dominique Jolly, Assoc. Ed.; Dr. Jan N. Streumer, Assoc. Ed.; Prof. Martin Carnoy, Editorial Board Member; Prof. Robert D. Dryden, Editorial Board Member; Prof. Kamal Fatehi, Editorial Board Member. **ISSN:** 1465-6612. **Subscription Rates:**

EUR494 individuals print only (surface mail); EUR840 individuals online only (2-3 users); EUR534 individuals print only (airmail); EUR672 individuals print and online. **URL:** http://www.inderscience.com/browse/index.php?journalCODE=ijhrdm.

55811 ■ International Journal of Information Technology and Management
Inderscience Publishers
PO Box 735
Olney MK46 5WB, United Kingdom
Fax: 44 12 34240515
Publisher E-mail: editor@inderscience.com
Peer-reviewed journal covering information technology, its evolution and future prospects, addressing technological, managerial, political, economic and organisational aspects of the application of IT. **Freq:** Quarterly. **Key Personnel:** Dr. M.A. Dorgham, Editor-in-Chief, editorial@inderscience.com; Prof. Dimitris Assimakopoulos, Co-Ed., dimitris.assimakopoulos@grenoble-em.com; Prof. B. Bowonder, Co-Ed., bowonder@tata.com; Dr. Dimitri Corpakis, Editorial Board Member; Dr. Petter Gottschalk, Editorial Board Member; Prof. Wendy L. Currie, Editorial Board Member; Dr. Detlef Schoder, Assoc. Ed.; Prof. Luis M. Camarinha-Matos, Editorial Board Member; Dr. Xavier Boucher, Editorial Board Member. **ISSN:** 1461-4111. **Subscription Rates:** EUR494 individuals print only (surface mail); EUR840 individuals online only (2-3 users); EUR672 individuals print and online; EUR534 individuals print only (airmail). **URL:** http://www.inderscience.com/browse/index.php?journalCODE=ijitm.

55812 ■ International Journal of Innovation and Sustainable Development
Inderscience Publishers
PO Box 735
Olney MK46 5WB, United Kingdom
Fax: 44 12 34240515
Publisher E-mail: editor@inderscience.com
Peer-reviewed journal focusing on broad aspects of innovation and sustainable development, fostering discussion not only on technological innovation but on new ways of thinking about the complex and contested issues of sustainable development. **Freq:** Quarterly. **Key Personnel:** Prof. Desheng Wu, Editor-in-Chief, dash@risklad.ca; Prof. Robyn Eckersley, Editorial Board Member; Dr. Frank Den Hond, Editorial Board Member; Dr. Derick De Jongh, Editorial Board Member; Prof. David Gibbs, Editorial Board Member; Prof. John Fien, Editorial Board Member. **ISSN:** 1740-8822. **Subscription Rates:** EUR494 individuals print only (surface mail); EUR840 individuals online only (2-3 users); EUR672 individuals print and online; EUR534 individuals print only (airmail). **URL:** http://www.inderscience.com/browse/index.php?journalCODE=ijisd.

55813 ■ International Journal of Intellectual Property Management
Inderscience Publishers
PO Box 735
Olney MK46 5WB, United Kingdom
Fax: 44 12 34240515
Publisher E-mail: editor@inderscience.com
Peer-reviewed journal welcoming research papers across a wide range of topics embracing the studies of intellectual property from the perspectives of business management, organisational principles, and government policies. **Freq:** Quarterly. **Key Personnel:** Dr. M.A. Dorgham, Editor-in-Chief, editorial@inderscience.com; Dr. Knut Blind, Assoc. Ed. **ISSN:** 1478-9647. **Subscription Rates:** EUR494 individuals print only (surface mail); EUR672 individuals print and online; EUR840 individuals online only (2-3 users); EUR672 individuals print and online. **URL:** http://www.inderscience.com/browse/index.php?journalCODE=ijipm.

55814 ■ International Journal of Intelligent Systems Technologies and Applications
Inderscience Publishers
PO Box 735
Olney MK46 5WB, United Kingdom
Fax: 44 12 34240515
Publisher E-mail: editor@inderscience.com
Peer-reviewed journal publishing original papers featuring innovative and practical technologies related to the design and development of intelligent systems. **Freq:** 8/yr. **Key Personnel:** Dr. M.A. Dorgham, Editor-in-Chief, editorial@inderscience.com; Prof. Serge N. Demidenko, Editorial Board Member; Prof. Clara Fang, Editorial Board Member; Prof. Wisama Khalil, Editorial Board Member; Prof. Seung-Bok Choi, Editorial Board Member; Prof. Yongtae Do, Editorial Board Member; Prof. Shyi-

Ming Chen, Editorial Board Member; Prof. Peter Xu, Editor, w.l.xu@massey.ac.nz. **ISSN:** 1740-8865. **Subscription Rates:** EUR735 individuals print only (surface mail); EUR1,240 individuals online only (2-3 users); EUR795 individuals print only (airmail); EUR1,025 individuals print and online. **URL:** http://www.inderscience.com/browse/index.php?journalCODE=ijista.

55815 ■ International Journal of Internet and Enterprise Management
Inderscience Publishers
PO Box 735
Olney MK46 5WB, United Kingdom
Fax: 44 12 34240515
Publisher E-mail: editor@inderscience.com
Peer-reviewed journal is a professional and authoritative source of information in the field of the internet and its applications in enterprise management, publishing theories and practices that are useful to executives in managing enterprises. **Freq:** Quarterly. **Key Personnel:** Dr. Eldon Y. Li, Honorary Ed.; Dr. Hiroshi Katayama, Assoc. Ed.; Dr. David Walters; Dr. Michael McGrath, Assoc. Ed.; Dr. Wayne Huang, Exec. Ed., huangw@ohio.edu; Dr. Chwen Sheu, Assoc. Ed. **ISSN:** 1476-1300. **Subscription Rates:** EUR494 individuals print only (surface mail); EUR840 individuals online only (2-3 users); EUR534 individuals print only (airmail); EUR672 individuals print and online. **URL:** http://www.inderscience.com/browse/index.php?journalCODE=ijiem.

55816 ■ International Journal of Internet Protocol Technology
Inderscience Publishers
PO Box 735
Olney MK46 5WB, United Kingdom
Fax: 44 12 34240515
Publisher E-mail: editor@inderscience.com
Peer-reviewed journal providing an open forum for researchers, academics, engineers, network managers, and service providers in internet protocol technology with extensive exchange of information provided on new protocols, standards, services, and various applications in this area. **Freq:** Quarterly. **Key Personnel:** Prof. Han-Chieh Chao, Editor-in-Chief, hcc@mail.niu.edu.tw; Prof. Hojjat Adeli, Consulting Ed.; Dr. Sherali Zeadally, Editor-in-Chief, szeadally@udc.edu; Prof. Jiann-Liang Chen, Editor-in-Chief, lchen@mail.ntust.edu.tw; Prof. Yuh-Shyan Chen, Editorial Board Member; Prof. Ruay-Shiung Chang, Editorial Board Member. **ISSN:** 1743-8209. **Subscription Rates:** EUR494 individuals print only (surface mail); EUR672 individuals online only (2-3 users); EUR840 individuals online only (2-3 users); EUR672 individuals online and print. **URL:** http://www.inderscience.com/browse/index.php?journalCODE=ijipt.

55817 ■ International Journal of Knowledge Management Studies
Inderscience Publishers
PO Box 735
Olney MK46 5WB, United Kingdom
Fax: 44 12 34240515
Publisher E-mail: editor@inderscience.com
Peer-reviewed journal providing information in the field of knowledge management and related aspects. **Freq:** Quarterly. **Key Personnel:** Dr. M.A. Dorgham, Editor-in-Chief, editorial@inderscience.com; Dr. Kuan Yew Wong, Regional Ed.; Prof. Vittal S. Anantatmula, Editorial Board Member; Dr. Yukika Awazu, Editorial Board Member; Dr. Wolfgang H. Guettel, Assoc. Ed. **ISSN:** 1743-8268. **Subscription Rates:** EUR494 individuals print only (surface mail); EUR840 individuals online only (2-3 users); EUR534 individuals print only (airmail); EUR672 individuals print and online. **URL:** http://www.inderscience.com/browse/index.php?journalCODE=ijkms.

55818 ■ International Journal of Liability and Scientific Enquiry
Inderscience Publishers
PO Box 735
Olney MK46 5WB, United Kingdom
Fax: 44 12 34240515
Publisher E-mail: editor@inderscience.com
Journal covering application of scientific knowledge. **Founded:** 2007. **Freq:** 4/yr. **Key Personnel:** Dr. M.A. Dorgham, Editor-in-Chief, editorial@inderscience.com; Prof. Sylvia Mercado Kierkegaard, Editorial Board Member. **ISSN:** 1741-6426. **Subscription Rates:** EUR494 individuals print or online; EUR672 individuals print and online. **URL:** http://www.inderscience.com/browse/index.php?journalCODE=ijlse.

55819 ■ International Journal of Low Radiation
Inderscience Publishers
PO Box 735
Olney MK46 5WB, United Kingdom
Fax: 44 12 34240515
Publisher E-mail: editor@inderscience.com
Peer-reviewed journal dedicated to the publication of research articles, review papers and technical notes in all domains related to low-dose radiation, among which are the biological and health effects in humans and the biota, in vitro and in vivo research on low radiation effects, regulatory and policy aspects, risk estimation and public perception. **Freq:** 6/yr. **Key Personnel:** Prof. Leonid Ilyin, Honorary Advisory Board; Prof. Ludwig E. Feinendegen, Honorary Advisory Board; Dr. Zbigniew Jaworowski, Honorary Advisory Board; Prof. Andre Maisseu, Editor-in-Chief, a.maisseu@wonuc.org; Prof. Kaushala Prasad Mishra, Co-Ed.; Dr. Nicolas Foray, Co-Ed.-in-Ch. **ISSN:** 1477-6545. **Subscription Rates:** EUR593 individuals print only (surface mail); EUR1,010 individuals online only (2-3 users); EUR830 individuals print and online. **URL:** http://www.inderscience.com/browse/index.php?journalCODE=ijlr.

55820 ■ International Journal of Management Concepts and Philosophy
Inderscience Publishers
PO Box 735
Olney MK46 5WB, United Kingdom
Fax: 44 12 34240515
Publisher E-mail: editor@inderscience.com
Peer-reviewed journal aiming to encourage and support development of new management thinking, concepts and paradigms for business management practice and philosophy, particularly fresh solutions to critical management problems. **Freq:** Quarterly. **Key Personnel:** Prof. Pervaiz K. Ahmed, Editor, pervaiz@buseco.monash.edu.my; Dr. Michael J. Haynes, Assoc. Ed.; Dr. Catherine L. Wang, Assoc. Ed. **ISSN:** 1478-1484. **Subscription Rates:** EUR494 individuals print only (surface mail); EUR840 individuals online only (2-3 users); EUR534 individuals print only (airmail); EUR672 individuals print and online. **URL:** http://www.inderscience.com/browse/index.php?journalCODE=ijmcp.

55821 ■ International Journal of Management and Decision Making
Inderscience Publishers
PO Box 735
Olney MK46 5WB, United Kingdom
Fax: 44 12 34240515
Publisher E-mail: editor@inderscience.com
Peer-reviewed journal providing a new venue for high-quality papers focusing on the analytical and empirical study of management processes in private and public sector organisations - including cases and action research. **Freq:** Bimonthly. **Key Personnel:** Dr. M.A. Dorgham, Editor-in-Chief, editorial@inderscience.com; Prof. John Bryson, Editorial Board Member; Prof. John Milton-Smith, Asst. Ed.; Prof. Robert Allinson, Editorial Board Member; Prof. Houn-Gee Chen, Editorial Board Member; Prof. Michael Connolly, Editorial Board Member. **ISSN:** 1462-4621. **Subscription Rates:** EUR593 individuals print only (surface mail); EUR830 individuals hardcopy and online; EUR643 individuals print only (airmail); EUR1,010 individuals online only (2-3 users). **URL:** http://www.inderscience.com/browse/index.php?journalCODE=ijmdm.

55822 ■ International Journal of Manufacturing Research
Inderscience Publishers
PO Box 735
Olney MK46 5WB, United Kingdom
Fax: 44 12 34240515
Publisher E-mail: editor@inderscience.com
Journal covering new developments in modern manufacturing research. **Founded:** 2006. **Freq:** 4/yr. **Key Personnel:** Dr. Lihui Wang, Editor-in-Chief, lihui.wang@his.se. **ISSN:** 1750-0591. **Subscription Rates:** EUR494 individuals includes surface mail, print only; EUR672 individuals print & online. **URL:** http://www.inderscience.com/browse/index.php?journalCODE=ijmr.

55823 ■ International Journal of Materials & Structural Integrity
Inderscience Publishers
PO Box 735
Olney MK46 5WB, United Kingdom
Fax: 44 12 34240515
Publisher E-mail: editor@inderscience.com
Peer-reviewed journal covering materials and structural integrity. **Founded:** 2007. **Freq:** 4/yr. **Key Personnel:** Dr. M.A. Dorgham, Editor-in-Chief, editorial@inderscience.com; Prof. Yang Ping, Assoc. Ed.-in-Ch.; Dr. Cemal Basaran, Regional Ed. **ISSN:** 1745-0055. **Subscription Rates:** EUR494 individuals includes surface mail, print only; EUR672 individuals print and online. **URL:** http://www.inderscience.com/browse/index.php?journalCODE=ijmsi.

55824 ■ International Journal of Metadata, Semantics and Ontologies
Inderscience Publishers
PO Box 735
Olney MK46 5WB, United Kingdom
Fax: 44 12 34240515
Publisher E-mail: editor@inderscience.com
Peer-reviewed journal publishing research advances and discussions about meta-data in a broad sense, and about their associated semantics and ontological structures, from a multi-disciplinary perspective, and with an emphasis on domain-specific ontologies and organisational, human interaction and social issues regarding metadata annotation, use and assessment. **Freq:** Quarterly. **Key Personnel:** Dr. Miguel-Angel Sicilia, Editor-in-Chief, msicilia@uah.es; Prof. Tharam Dillon, Assoc. Ed.; Prof. Asuman Dogac, Assoc. Ed. **ISSN:** 1744-2621. **Subscription Rates:** EUR494 individuals print only (surface mail); EUR840 individuals online only (2-3 users); EUR672 individuals print and online. **URL:** http://www.inderscience.com/browse/index.php?journalCODE=ijmso.

55825 ■ International Journal of Nanomanufacturing
Inderscience Publishers
PO Box 735
Olney MK46 5WB, United Kingdom
Fax: 44 12 34240515
Publisher E-mail: editor@inderscience.com
Peer-reviewed journal covering new micro and nanomanufacturing technologies. **Founded:** 2006. **Freq:** 8/yr. **Key Personnel:** Prof. Fengzhou Fang, Editor-in-Chief, fzfang@gmail.com; Prof. Jack Luo, Editor-in-Chief, j.luo@bolton.ac.uk; Prof. Wei Gao, Regional Ed. **ISSN:** 1746-9392. **Subscription Rates:** EUR735 individuals includes surface mail, print only; EUR1,025 individuals print and online. **URL:** http://www.inderscience.com/browse/index.php?journalCODE=ijnm.

55826 ■ International Journal of Networking and Virtual Organisations
Inderscience Publishers
PO Box 735
Olney MK46 5WB, United Kingdom
Fax: 44 12 34240515
Publisher E-mail: editor@inderscience.com
Peer-reviewed journal aiming to further the development of networking and virtual organisations. **Freq:** Quarterly. **Key Personnel:** Nilmini Wickramasinghe, Editor-in-Chief, nilmini.work@gmail.com; Latif Al-Hakim, Assoc. Ed.; Rajeev Bali, Assoc. Ed. **ISSN:** 1470-9503. **Subscription Rates:** EUR593 individuals online only (1 user); EUR1,010 individuals online only (2 or 3 users); EUR1,480 individuals online only (4 to 5 users); EUR1,920 individuals online only (6 to 7 users); EUR2,335 individuals online only (8 to 9 users); EUR2,725 individuals online only (10 to 14 users); EUR3,090 individuals online only (15 to 19 users); EUR3,610 individuals online only (20 or more users); EUR830 individuals print and online; EUR643 individuals print only (airmail). **URL:** http://www.inderscience.com/browse/index.php?journalCODE=ijnvo.

55827 ■ International Journal of Product Development
Inderscience Publishers
PO Box 735
Olney MK46 5WB, United Kingdom
Fax: 44 12 34240515
Publisher E-mail: editor@inderscience.com
Peer-reviewed journal providing an authoritative source of information in the field of product development and innovation, devoted to the development, promotion and coordination of the science and practice of this field. **Freq:** 8/yr. **Key Personnel:** Dr. M.A. Dorgham, Editor-in-Chief, editorial@inderscience.com; Prof. Abdelaziz Bouras, Assoc. Ed.; Dr. Harri Jouni Olavi Haapasalo, Assoc. Ed. **ISSN:** 1477-9056. **Subscription Rates:** EUR1,025 individuals print only (surface mail); EUR1,730 individuals online only (2-3 users); EUR1,105 individuals print only (airmail); EUR1,434 individuals print and online. **URL:** http://www.inderscience.com/browse/index.php?journalCODE=ijpd.

55828 ■ International Journal of Product Sound Quality
Inderscience Publishers
PO Box 735
Olney MK46 5WB, United Kingdom
Fax: 44 12 34240515
Publisher E-mail: editor@inderscience.com
Peer-reviewed journal aiming to provide an international forum for researchers and practitioners across the many relevant disciplines and industries to disseminate information and learn from each other's work. **Freq:** Quarterly. **Key Personnel:** Dr. M.A. Dorgham, Editor-in-Chief, editorial@inderscience.com. **ISSN:** 1742-6758. **Subscription Rates:** EUR494 individuals print only (surface mail); EUR534 individuals print only (airmail); EUR840 individuals online only (2-3 users); EUR672 individuals online and print. **URL:** http://www.inderscience.com/browse/index.php?journalCODE=ijpsq.

55829 ■ International Journal of Project Organisation and Management
Inderscience Publishers
PO Box 735
Olney MK46 5WB, United Kingdom
Fax: 44 12 34240515
Publisher E-mail: editor@inderscience.com
Peer-reviewed journal fostering active dialogue about successful practice and theoretical research concerned with project management, providing an inter-disciplinary vehicle for reporting and debating new developments related to the application and execution of project management and for addressing the organisational, political and strategic implications of adopting a project culture. **Freq:** Quarterly. **Key Personnel:** John Wang, Editor-in-Chief, j.john.wang@gmail.com; Mike Bresnen, Assoc. Ed.; Martin Loosemore, Assoc. Ed.; Denis Felix Cioffi, Assoc. Ed.; Li-Yin Shen, Assoc. Ed.; Gad Vitner, Assoc. Ed. **ISSN:** 1740-2891. **Subscription Rates:** EUR494 individuals print only (surface mail); EUR840 individuals online only (2-3 users); EUR534 individuals print only (airmail); EUR672 individuals online and print. **URL:** http://www.inderscience.com/browse/index.php?journalCODE=ijpom.

55830 ■ International Journal of Public Policy
Inderscience Publishers
PO Box 735
Olney MK46 5WB, United Kingdom
Fax: 44 12 34240515
Publisher E-mail: editor@inderscience.com
Peer-reviewed journal proposing and fostering discussion on public policy issues facing nation states and national and supranational organisations, including governments, and how these diverse groups approach and solve common public policy problems. **Freq:** 8/yr. **Key Personnel:** Dr. M.A. Dorgham, Editor-in-Chief, editorial@inderscience.com; Dr. Ulrich Fritsche, Editorial Board Member; Prof. Carol Adams, Editorial Board Member; Prof. Noel Hyndman, Editorial Board Member; Prof. Philip Arestis, Editorial Board Member; Prof. Arne Heise, Regional Ed.; Prof. Graeme Hodge, Editorial Board Member; Prof. Wolfram Elsner, Editorial Board Member; Prof. Mark B. Arvin, Regional Ed.; Prof. Tony Bovaird, Editorial Board Member; Prof. Kingsley E. Haynes, Editorial Board Member; Prof. Hansjorg Herr, Editorial Board Member. **ISSN:** 1740-0600. **Subscription Rates:** EUR735 individuals print only (surface mail); EUR1,240 individuals online only (2-3 users); EUR1,025 individuals print and online; EUR795 individuals print only (airmail). **URL:** http://www.inderscience.com/browse/index.php?journalCODE=ijpp.

55831 ■ International Journal of Risk Assessment and Management
Inderscience Publishers
PO Box 735
Olney MK46 5WB, United Kingdom
Fax: 44 12 34240515
Publisher E-mail: editor@inderscience.com
Peer-reviewed journal providing cross learning between different business and economics, as well as scientific and technological, disciplines; energy industries, environmental and ecological systems; safety, public health and medical services; and software services, reliability and safety. **Freq:** 12/yr. **Key Personnel:** Dr. M.A. Dorgham, Editor-in-Chief, editorial@inderscience.com; Dr. Jerry Busby, Assoc. Ed.; Prof. Robert G. Batson, Editorial Board Member. **ISSN:** 1466-8297. **Subscription Rates:** EUR593 individuals hardcopy only (surface mail); EUR643 individuals hardcopy only (airmail); EUR1,010 individuals online only (2-3 users); EUR830

individuals online and hardcopy. **URL:** http://www.inderscience.com/browse/index.php?journalCODE=ijram.

55832 ■ International Journal of Six Sigma and Competitive Advantage
Inderscience Publishers
PO Box 735
Olney MK46 5WB, United Kingdom
Fax: 44 12 34240515
Publisher E-mail: editor@inderscience.com
Peer-reviewed journal publishing papers that address Six Sigma issues from the perspectives of customers, industrial engineers, business managers, management consultants, industrial statisticians and Six Sigma practitioners. **Freq:** Quarterly. **Key Personnel:** Prof. Nanua Singh, Editor-in-Chief, ijssca@gmail.com; Prof. Lawrence Fredendall, Editorial Board Member; Prof. Ken Black, Editorial Board Member; Dr. Roger Hoerl, Editorial Board Member; Prof. V.K. Jain, Assoc. Ed.; Dr. Parveen S. Goel, Assoc. Ed. **ISSN:** 1479-2494. **Subscription Rates:** EUR494 individuals print only (surface mail); EUR534 individuals print only (airmail); EUR840 individuals online only (2-3 users); EUR672 individuals print and online. **URL:** http://www.inderscience.com/browse/index.php?journalCODE=ijssca.

55833 ■ International Journal of Sport Management and Marketing
Inderscience Publishers
PO Box 735
Olney MK46 5WB, United Kingdom
Fax: 44 12 34240515
Publisher E-mail: editor@inderscience.com
Peer-reviewed multidisciplinary journal aiming to provide a unique focus on a wide range of sport management and sport technology topics, covering advances in theory, new concepts, methods and applications and case studies. **Freq:** 8/yr. **Key Personnel:** Dr. M.A. Dorgham, Editor-in-Chief, editorial@inderscience.com; Terri Byers, Editorial Board Member; Dr. Simon Chadwick, Editorial Board Member; Dr. John Beech, Editorial Board Member; Prof. Wladimir Andreff, Editorial Board Member; Prof. Carlos Pestana Barros, Editorial Board Member; Prof. Peter Chen, Editorial Board Member; Prof. Fred Coalter, Editorial Board Member. **ISSN:** 1475-8962. **Subscription Rates:** EUR735 individuals print only (surface mail); EUR795 individuals print only (airmail); EUR1,240 individuals online only (2-3 users); EUR1,025 individuals online and print. **URL:** http://www.inderscience.com/browse/index.php?journalCODE=ijsmm.

55834 ■ International Journal of Teaching & Case Studies
Inderscience Publishers
PO Box 735
Olney MK46 5WB, United Kingdom
Fax: 44 12 34240515
Publisher E-mail: editor@inderscience.com
Journal covering management, management science, computer engineering, computer science, information systems, information technology and software engineering. **Founded:** 2007. **Freq:** 4/yr. **Key Personnel:** M.A. Dorgham, Editor-in-Chief; Konstantina N. Zefkili, Managing Editor, k.zefkili@ucl.ac.uk. **ISSN:** 1749-9151. **Subscription Rates:** EUR494 individuals print or online; EUR672 individuals print and online. **URL:** http://www.inderscience.com/browse/index.php?journalCODE=ijtcs.

55835 ■ International Journal of Technology Intelligence and Planning
Inderscience Publishers
PO Box 735
Olney MK46 5WB, United Kingdom
Fax: 44 12 34240515
Publisher E-mail: editor@inderscience.com
Peer-reviewed journal providing an authoritative source of information in the field of technology intelligence, technology planning, R&D resource allocation, technology controlling, technology decision-making processes and related disciplines. **Freq:** Quarterly. **Key Personnel:** Dr. M.A. Dorgham, Editor-in-Chief, editorial@inderscience.com; Prof. Kumiko Miyazaki, Assoc. Ed.; Prof. Barrett S. Caldwell, Editorial Board Member; Prof. Michael Radnor, Assoc. Ed.; Dr. Eckhard Lichtenthaler, Assoc. Ed.; Dr. Ariane Berthoin Antal, Editorial Board Member. **ISSN:** 1740-2832. **Subscription Rates:** EUR494 individuals print only (surface mail); EUR840 individuals online only (2-3 users); EUR534 individuals print only (airmail); EUR672 individuals print and online.

URL: http://www.inderscience.com/browse/index.php?journalCODE=ijtip.

55836 ■ International Journal of Technology Transfer and Commercialisation
Inderscience Publishers
PO Box 735
Olney MK46 5WB, United Kingdom
Fax: 44 12 34240515
Publisher E-mail: editor@inderscience.com
Peer-reviewed journal providing an authoritative source of information in the field of knowledge and technology transfer and diffusion, as well as commercialisation and related disciplines. **Freq:** Quarterly. **Key Personnel:** Dr. M.A. Dorgham, Editor-in-Chief, editorial@inderscience.com; Prof. Ravi Jain, Assoc. Ed.; Prof. Jeremy Howells, Assoc. Ed.; Prof. Daniel Rouach, Editor; Prof. David B. Audretsch, Editorial Board Member; Prof. Calestous Juma, Assoc. Ed.; Prof. David Bennett, Editorial Board Member; Prof. Francis Bidault, Editorial Board Member. **ISSN:** 1470-6075. **Subscription Rates:** EUR494 individuals print only (surface mail); EUR534 individuals print only (airmail); EUR840 individuals online only (2-3 users); EUR672 individuals print and online. **URL:** http://www.inderscience.com/browse/index.php?journalCODE=ijttc.

55837 ■ International Journal of Vehicle Autonomous Systems
Inderscience Publishers
PO Box 735
Olney MK46 5WB, United Kingdom
Fax: 44 12 34240515
Publisher E-mail: editor@inderscience.com
Peer-reviewed journal aiming to investigate how vehicle autonomous systems contribute to the high and safe performance, as well as the reliability and cost effectiveness of vehicles in an ecologically friendly environment; how the systems contribute to the driver comfort and reduce his/her working load during driving; and how the systems are designed and accepted by the driver (the customer). **Freq:** Quarterly. **Key Personnel:** Dr. Annie Zhao, Assoc. Ed.; Dr. Kevin Deng, Editor-in-Chief, kvdeng@gmail.com; Dr. Matt Best, Editorial Board Member; Prof. Lotfi Beji, Editorial Board Member; Prof. David M. Bevly, Editorial Board Member; Prof. Zhengdong Dai, Editorial Board Member. **ISSN:** 1471-0226. **Subscription Rates:** EUR494 individuals print only (surface mail); EUR840 individuals online (2-3 users); EUR672 individuals print and online. **URL:** http://www.inderscience.com/browse/index.php?journalCODE=ijvas.

55838 ■ International Journal of Vehicle Information & Communication System
Inderscience Publishers
PO Box 735
Olney MK46 5WB, United Kingdom
Fax: 44 12 34240515
Publisher E-mail: editor@inderscience.com
Peer-reviewed journal covering field of vehicle networking, information, and communication systems. **Founded:** 2005. **Freq:** 4/yr. **Key Personnel:** Dr. M.A. Dorgham, Editor-in-Chief, editorial@inderscience.com; Prof. Hongchao Liu, Assoc. Ed.; Prof. Radu Popescu-Zeletin, Assoc. Ed. **ISSN:** 1471-0242. **Subscription Rates:** EUR494 individuals print or online; EUR672 individuals print and online. **URL:** http://www.inderscience.com/browse/index.php?journalCODE=ijvics.

55839 ■ International Journal of Virtual Technology and Multimedia
Inderscience Publishers
PO Box 735
Olney MK46 5WB, United Kingdom
Fax: 44 12 34240515
Publisher E-mail: editor@inderscience.com
Peer-reviewed international journal devoted to original papers employing virtual technology and multimedia systems in science and engineering. **Freq:** Quarterly. **Key Personnel:** Prof. Abdel Magid Hamouda, Editor-in-Chief, hamouda@qu.edu.qa; Prof. Nick Avis, Assoc. Ed.; Prof. Sebastiano Bagnara, Editorial Board Member. **ISSN:** 1741-1874. **Subscription Rates:** EUR840 individuals online only (2-3 users); EUR494 individuals print only (surface mail); EUR534 individuals print only (airmail); EUR672 individuals print and online. **URL:** http://www.inderscience.com/browse/index.php?journalCODE=ijvtm.

55840 ■ International Journal of Water
Inderscience Publishers
PO Box 735
Olney MK46 5WB, United Kingdom

Fax: 44 12 34240515

Publisher E-mail: editor@inderscience.com

Peer-reviewed journal providing a high profile international outlet for analyses and discussions of all aspects of water, environment and society. **Freq:** Quarterly. **Key Personnel:** Dr. Delilah Al-Khudhairy, Editorial Board Member; Dr. Steve Bloomfield, Editorial Board Member; Prof. Andrew K. Dragun, Editor-in-Chief, @ flairwood.net; Dr. Federico Aguilera-Klink, Editorial Board Member; Prof. Kristin Jakobsson, Editor-in-Chief, ijweditor@flairwood.net. **ISSN:** 1465-6620. **Subscription Rates:** EUR494 individuals print only (surface mail); EUR672 individuals print and online; EUR840 individuals online only (2-3 users); EUR534 individuals print only (airmail). **URL:** http://www.inderscience.com/browse/index.php?journalCODE=ijw.

55841 ■ International Journal of Wireless and Mobile Computing
Inderscience Publishers
PO Box 735
Olney MK46 5WB, United Kingdom
Fax: 44 12 34240515
Publication E-mail: ijwmc@inderscience.com
Publisher E-mail: editor@inderscience.com
Journal addressing the state-of-the-art of all aspects of wireless communications and mobile computing including devices, hardware, software, architectures, networks, systems, support services, algorithm/protocol design and analysis, mobile environments, wireless communications and networks, applications, implementation issues, and emerging technologies. **Freq:** Quarterly. **Key Personnel:** Dr. M.A. Dorgham, Editor-in-Chief. **ISSN:** 1741-1084. **Subscription Rates:** EUR494 individuals online only for 1 user; EUR840 individuals online only for 2-3 users; EUR672 individuals print and online; EUR1,230 individuals online only for 4-5 users; EUR1,600 individuals online only for 6-7 users; EUR1,950 individuals online only for 8-9 users; EUR2,275 individuals online only for 10-14 users; EUR2,580 individuals online only for 15-19 users; EUR3,020 individuals online only for 20 users. **URL:** http://www.inderscience.com/browse/index.php?journalCODE=ijwmc.

55842 ■ Journal of Design Research
Inderscience Publishers
PO Box 735
Olney MK46 5WB, United Kingdom
Fax: 44 12 34240515
Publisher E-mail: editor@inderscience.com
Peer-reviewed journal emphasising human aspects as a central issue of design through integrative studies of social sciences and design disciplines. **Freq:** Quarterly. **Key Personnel:** Dr. Henri Christiaans, Editor-in-Chief, h.h.c.m.christiaans@tudelft.nl; Dr. Tiiu Poldma, Regional Ed.; Dr. Paulien M. Herder, Editor-in-Chief, p.m.herder@tudelft.nl; Prof. Mark R. Henderson, Regional Ed.; Prof. Chris McMahon, Regional Ed.; Dr. Ina T. Klaasen, Editor-in-Chief, i.t.klaasen@tudelft.nl; Prof. Ken Friedman, Regional Ed.; Prof. Nigel Cross, Editorial Board Member; Prof. Louis Bucciarelli, Editorial Board Member. **ISSN:** 1748-3050. **Subscription Rates:** EUR494 individuals print only (surface mail); EUR840 individuals online only (2-3 users); EUR672 individuals print and online. **URL:** http://www.inderscience.com/browse/index.php?journalcode=jdr.

55843 ■ Journal for Global Business Advancement
Inderscience Publishers
PO Box 735
Olney MK46 5WB, United Kingdom
Fax: 44 12 34240515
Publication E-mail: jgba@inderscience.com
Publisher E-mail: editor@inderscience.com
Journal aiming to provide a global platform to facilitate communication between policy makers, government officials, academics, scholars, consultants, professionals working for multinational corporations, international civil servants, and entrepreneurs by providing a global platform to overcome cultural, national, ethnic, religious, economic barriers, and national boundaries, and meet the needs of accelerated economic and social change occurring in variety of countries participating in the global economy. **Freq:** Quarterly. **Key Personnel:** Prof. Zafar U. Ahmed, Editor-in-Chief, zahmed@fnm.psu.edu.sa; Ahmad Jamal, Managing Editor, jamala@cardiff.ac.uk. **ISSN:** 1746-966X. **Subscription Rates:** EUR494 individuals online only for 1 user; EUR840 individuals online only for 2-3 users; EUR672 individuals print and online; EUR1,230 individuals online only for 4-5 users; EUR1,600 individuals online only for 6-7 users; EUR1,950 individuals

als online only for 8-9 users; EUR2,275 individuals online only for 10-14 users; EUR2,580 individuals online only for 15-19 users; EUR3,020 individuals online only for 20 users. **URL:** http://www.inderscience.com/browse/index.php?journalCODE=jgba.

55844 ■ Journal for International Business and Entrepreneurship Development
Inderscience Publishers
PO Box 735
Olney MK46 5WB, United Kingdom
Fax: 44 12 34240515
Publication E-mail: jibed@inderscience.com
Publisher E-mail: editor@inderscience.com
Journal dedicated to the advancement of practice and theory of international business, international entrepreneurship and international franchising with an emphasis on developing countries attempting to assert themselves on the global stage. **Freq:** Quarterly. **Key Personnel:** Prof. Zafar U. Ahmed, Editor-in-Chief, zahmed@fnm.psu.edu.sa; Mohammad Sadiq Sohail, Managing Editor. **ISSN:** 1549-9324. **Subscription Rates:** EUR494 individuals online only for 1 user; EUR840 individuals online only for 2-3 users; EUR672 individuals print and online; EUR1,230 individuals online only for 4-5 users; EUR1,600 individuals online only for 6-7 users; EUR1,950 individuals online only for 8-9 users; EUR2,275 individuals online only for 10-14 users; EUR2,580 individuals online only for 15-19 users; EUR3,020 individuals online only for 20 users. **URL:** http://www.inderscience.com/browse/index.php?journalCODE=jibed.

55845 ■ PBWnews
6 The Rickyard
Clifton Reynes
Olney MK46 5LQ, United Kingdom
Ph: 44 12 34714644
Fax: 44 12 34714633
Publisher E-mail: info@pbwnews.com
Trade journal for all pet trade professionals, including retailers, wholesalers, manufacturers, breeders, groomers, vets, and others. **Subtitle:** The Original Magazine for the Pet Industry. **Founded:** 1951. **Freq:** Monthly. **Trim Size:** 210 x 297 mm. **Key Personnel:** Mark Lightfoot, Sales Mgr., phone 44 12 34714404, sales@pbwnews.com; Karen Pickwick, Editor, editor@pbwnews.com. **ISSN:** 1472-0531. **Subscription Rates:** 18 individuals U.K.; 35 individuals Europe; 45 individuals airmail (outside Europe). **Remarks:** Accepts advertising. **URL:** http://www.petbusinessworld.co.uk/pbw-news. **Former name:** Pet Business World. **Ad Rates:** 4C: EUR850, PCI: EUR12. **Circ:** Combined 5,100

55846 ■ World Review of Entrepreneurship, Management and Sustainable Development
Inderscience Publishers
PO Box 735
Olney MK46 5WB, United Kingdom
Fax: 44 12 34240515
Publisher E-mail: editor@inderscience.com
Peer-reviewed journal aiming to consider new perspectives in the field of business and entrepreneurship management. **Freq:** Quarterly. **Key Personnel:** Sabine Urban, Editor-in-Chief; Bernd Britzelmaier, Assoc. Ed.; Frank Hoy, Assoc. Ed. **ISSN:** 1746-0573. **Subscription Rates:** EUR494 individuals print only (surface mail); EUR840 individuals online only (2-3 users); EUR672 individuals print and online; EUR534 individuals print only (airmail). **URL:** http://www.inderscience.com/browse/index.php?journalCODE=wremsd.

55847 ■ World Review of Science, Technology and Sustainable Development
Inderscience Publishers
PO Box 735
Olney MK46 5WB, United Kingdom
Fax: 44 12 34240515
Publisher E-mail: editor@inderscience.com
Peer-reviewed journal discussing integrated approaches to the problems of technology transfer within an urban and rural development context. **Freq:** Quarterly. **Key Personnel:** Dr. Farhad Memarzadeh, Editor-in-Chief; Dr. Giovanni Cerulli, Assoc. Ed.; Prof. Hojjat Adeli, Editorial Board Member. **ISSN:** 1741-2242. **Subscription Rates:** EUR494 individuals print or online; EUR672 individuals print and online. **URL:** http://www.inderscience.com/browse/index.php?journalCODE=wrstsd.

Omagh

55848 ■ Q101.2-FM - 101.2
42 Market St.

Omagh, United Kingdom
Ph: 44 28 82245777
Format: Adult Contemporary; News. **Key Personnel:** Robert Walshe, Ch. Exec./Prog. Dir.; Pauric Hilferty, Advertising Mgr. **URL:** http://www.q101west.fm/portal/.

Ormskirk

55849 ■ Card Times
Magpie Publications
70 Winifred Ln.
Aughton
Ormskirk L39 5DL, United Kingdom
Ph: 44 16 95423470
Fax: 44 16 54200185
Publisher E-mail: mail@cardtimes.co.uk
Consumer magazine covering cigarette cards, trading cards, gum cards and related items for hobbyists. **Founded:** May 1989. **Freq:** Monthly. **Print Method:** DTP. **Key Personnel:** Joan Stuckey, Ed., Admin. & Advertising; David Stuckey, Ed., Admin. and Advertising. **ISSN:** 0956-5124. **Subscription Rates:** 17.50 individuals; 26 other countries surface mail; 35 other countries airmail. **Remarks:** Accepts advertising. **URL:** http://www.cardtimes.co.uk/ct2/ctadvertising.htm. **Ad Rates:** BW: 160, 4C: 260. **Circ:** Paid 2,800

55850 ■ Midwifery Matters
Association of Radical Midwives
c/o Ishbel Kargar, Membership Sec.
62 Greetby Hill
Lancashire
Ormskirk L39 2DT, United Kingdom
Ph: 44 1695 571748
Publisher E-mail: ikargar@tiscali.co.uk
Publication covering obstetrics and gynecology. **Founded:** June 1978. **Freq:** Quarterly. **Key Personnel:** Margaret Jowitt, Coord., margaret.jowitt@talktalk.net. **ISSN:** 0961-1479. **Subscription Rates:** Free to members. **Remarks:** Advertising accepted; rates available upon request. **URL:** http://www.midwifery.org.uk/. **Circ:** 1,750

Orpington

55851 ■ Gardens Monthly
MyHobbyStore Ltd.
Hadlow House
9 High St.
Orpington BR6 6BG, United Kingdom
Ph: 44 844 4122262
Publisher E-mail: info@myhobbystore.com
Magazine featuring information on plants and gardening. **Founded:** Jan. 2002. **Freq:** Monthly. **Key Personnel:** Liz Dobbs, Editor, phone 44 1689 899297, liz.dobbs@myhobbystore.com; Sui Kee Lee, Promotions Exec., suikee.lee@myhobbystore.com; Conrad Cornelius, Circulation Mgr., conrad.cornelius@seymour.co.uk. **URL:** http://www.gardensmonthly.co.uk/.

55852 ■ IMIS Journal
Institute for the Management of Information Systems
5 Kingfisher House
New Mill Rd.
Orpington BR5 3QG, United Kingdom
Ph: 44 70 00023456
Fax: 44 70 00023023
Publisher E-mail: central@imis.org.uk
Publication covering information management. **Freq:** Bimonthly. **ISSN:** 1369-4189. **Remarks:** Advertising accepted; rates available upon request. **URL:** http://www.imis.org.uk/services/imis_journal. **Circ:** 11,000

55853 ■ Journal of Automated Methods and Management in Chemistry
Hindawi Publishing Corp.
c/o Peter B. Stockwell, Editorial Board
P.S. Analytical Ltd., Arthur House
Unit 3, Crayfields Industrial Estate, Main Rd.
St. Pauls Cray
Orpington BR5 3HP, United Kingdom
Publisher E-mail: hindawi@hindawi.com
Journal publishing research articles relating to automation and mechanization in analytical, clinical and industrial environments. **Key Personnel:** Peter B. Stockwell, Editorial Board; Christin Collombel, Editorial Board; Pierangelo Bonini, Editorial Board; A.C. Brown, Editorial Board; Joe Liscouski, Editorial Board; R.W. Arndt, Edito-

Circulation: ★ = ABC; △ = BPA; ◆ = CAC; • = CCAB; ❏ = VAC; ⊕ = PO Statement; ‡ = Publisher's Report; Boldface figures = sworn; Light figures = estimated.

Gale Directory of Publications & Broadcast Media/147th Ed.   5805

rial Board; R. Haeckel, Editorial Board; Bonner M. Denton, Editorial Board. **ISSN:** 1463-9246. **Subscription Rates:** US$495 individuals worldwide. **URL:** http://www.hindawi.com/journals/jammc/.

55854 ■ Karting
Lodgemark Press
15 Moorfield Rd.
Orpington BR6 OXD, United Kingdom
Ph: 44 1689 897123
Fax: 44 1689 890998
Publication E-mail: support@kartingmagazine.com
Publisher E-mail: support@kartingmagazine.com
Consumer magazine covering automobile racing. **Founded:** Mar. 1960. **Freq:** Monthly. **Trim Size:** 210 x 280 mm. **ISSN:** 0022-913X. **Subscription Rates:** 38 individuals U.K.; 21 individuals 6 issues U.K.; 47 individuals Europe; 56 other countries. **Remarks:** Accepts advertising. **URL:** http://www.kartingmagazine.com. **Ad Rates:** BW: EUR600, 4C: EUR800. **Circ:** Paid 12,800

55855 ■ Popular Patchwork
MyHobbyStore Ltd.
Hadlow House
9 High St.
Orpington BR6 6BG, United Kingdom
Ph: 44 844 4122262
Publisher E-mail: info@myhobbystore.com
Magazine covering patchwork and quilting. **URL:** http://www.popularpatchwork.com.

Oswestry

55856 ■ Border Counties Advertizer
NWN Media Ltd.
16-18 Oswald Rd.
Oswestry SY111RE, United Kingdom
Ph: 44 1691 655321
Fax: 44 1691 626530
Publisher E-mail: internet@nwn.co.uk
Newspaper featuring local news, sport, advertising, and information. **Founded:** 1849. **Freq:** Weekly. **Key Personnel:** Sue Perry, Editor, news@bordercountiesadvertizer.co.uk. **URL:** http://www.bordercountiesadvertizer.co.uk/.

Oxford

55857 ■ Abacus
John Wiley & Sons Inc.
Wiley-Blackwell
9600 Garsington Rd.
Oxford OX4 2DQ, United Kingdom
Ph: 44 1865 776868
Fax: 44 1865 714591
Journal covering academic and professional aspects of accounting, finance and business. **Subtitle:** A Journal of Accounting, Finance and Business Studies. **Freq:** Quarterly. **Key Personnel:** G.W. Dean, Editor; J. Baxter, Editorial Board; A. Charitou, Editorial Board. **ISSN:** 0001-3072. **Subscription Rates:** US$449 institutions Australia & New Zealand, print and online; US$580 institutions print and online; 405 institutions print and online; EUR464 institutions print and online; US$795 institutions, other countries print and online; US$527 institutions print or online; EUR421 institutions print or online; 368 institutions print or online; US$722 institutions, other countries print or online; US$136 individuals print and online. **Remarks:** Accepts advertising. **URL:** http://www.wiley.com/bw/journal.asp?ref=0001-3072&site=1. **Ad Rates:** BW: 260. **Circ:** (Not Reported)

55858 ■ Accounting and Finance
John Wiley & Sons Inc.
Wiley-Blackwell
9600 Garsington Rd.
Oxford OX4 2DQ, United Kingdom
Ph: 44 1865 776868
Fax: 44 1865 714591
Publication for the banking, finance, and accounting industries. **Freq:** Quarterly. **Key Personnel:** Robert Faff, Editor; Philip Brown, Editorial Board; Steve Cahan, Editorial Board; Frank Finn, Editorial Board; Tim Brailsford, Editorial Board; Gary Moore, Dep. Ed.; Maggie Abernethy, Editorial Board; Michael Bradbury, Deputy Ed.; Peter Booth, Editorial Board. **ISSN:** 0810-5391. **Subscription Rates:** $A 399 institutions Australia/NZ (print and online); US$539 institutions Americas (print and online); 374 institutions UK (print and online); EUR475 institutions Europe (print and online); US$733 institu-

tions, other countries print and online; $A 362 institutions Australia/NZ (print or online only); US$489 institutions Americas (print or online only); 340 institutions UK (print or online only); EUR432 institutions Europe (print or online only); US$666 institutions, other countries print or online only. **URL:** http://www.wiley.com/bw/editors.asp?ref=0810-5391.

55859 ■ Acta Biochimica et Biophysica Sinica
John Wiley & Sons Inc.
Wiley-Blackwell
9600 Garsington Rd.
Oxford OX4 2DQ, United Kingdom
Ph: 44 1865 776868
Fax: 44 1865 714591
Scientific journal publishing research papers, short communications and minireviews in biochemistry, molecular biology and biophysics. **Freq:** Monthly. **Key Personnel:** You-Shang Zhang, Editor-in-Chief, yszhang@sibs.ac.cn; Li Boliang, Editor-in-Chief, blli@sibs.ac.cn; Xu Minghua, Dep. Ed.-in-Ch., mhxu@sibs.ac.cn; Guan Junlin, Editor; H.E. Fuchu, Editorial Board Membership; Chang Tayuan, Editor; Chen Changzheng, Editor; Zhu Dahai, Editor, dhzhu@pumc.edu.cn. **ISSN:** 1672-9145. **Remarks:** Advertising accepted; rates available upon request. **URL:** http://www.abbs.info/. **Circ:** (Not Reported)

55860 ■ Acta Histochemica
Elsevier Science
c/o Susan A. Brooks, Editorial Board
School of Life Sciences
Oxford Brookes University
Gipsy Ln., Headington
Oxford OX3 OBP, United Kingdom
Ph: 44 20 664970
Fax: 44 20 974156
Publisher E-mail: nlinfo-f@elsevier.com
Journal devoted to current advances in research in cytochemistry and histochemistry, discussing on structural biochemistry of cells and tissues. **Founded:** 1954. **Freq:** Bimonthly. **Key Personnel:** Raymond Coleman, Editor-in-Chief, coleman@techunix.technion.ac.il; Susan A. Brooks, Editorial Board, sbrooks@brookes.ac.uk; Steven B. Oppenheimer, Editor, steven.oppenheimer@csun.edu. **ISSN:** 0065-1281. **Subscription Rates:** EUR930 institutions for European countries and Iran; US$275 individuals for all countries except Europe, Japan and Iran; 37,900¥ individuals; US$290 individuals all countries except Europe, Japan and Iran; US$275 institutions for European countries and Iran; 122,800¥ institutions. **URL:** http://www.elsevier.com/wps/find/journaldescription.cws_home/701749/description.

55861 ■ Agricultural Economics
John Wiley & Sons Inc.
Wiley-Blackwell
9600 Garsington Rd.
Oxford OX4 2DQ, United Kingdom
Ph: 44 1865 776868
Fax: 44 1865 714591
Journal publishing articles covering the range of work done on agricultural economics, divided into three categories: disciplinary work, multi-disciplinary subject matter areas and problem solving. **Freq:** Bimonthly. **Key Personnel:** Willis Oluoch-Kosura, Advisory Board; Gerald Shively, Editor-in-Chief; Heidi Albers, Assoc. Ed.; Jikun Huang, Advisory Board; Prahbu Pingali, Advisory Board; William Masters, Editor-in-Chief; Peter Matlon, Advisory Board; Rachael Goodhue, Assoc. Ed. **ISSN:** 0169-5150. **Subscription Rates:** US$105 institutions print + online; US$863 institutions print + online; US$784 institutions print or online; US$941 institutions, other countries print + online; EUR88 individuals print + online; 480 institutions print + online; 436 institutions print or online; EUR610 institutions print + online; 59 individuals print + online. **Remarks:** Accepts advertising. **URL:** http://www.wiley.com/bw/journal.asp?ref=0169-5150&site=1. **Circ:** (Not Reported)

55862 ■ Allergy
John Wiley & Sons Inc.
Wiley-Blackwell
9600 Garsington Rd.
Oxford OX4 2DQ, United Kingdom
Ph: 44 1865 776868
Fax: 44 1865 714591
Publication E-mail: allergy@wanadoo.fr
Journal focusing on allergology and immunology. **Freq:** Monthly. **Key Personnel:** B. Niggemann, Assoc. Ed.; W. Fokkens, Assoc. Ed.; H.U. Simon, Editor-in-Chief; T. Bieber, Editor-in-Chief; C. Akdis, Editorial Board. **ISSN:** 0105-4538. **Subscription Rates:** US$1,630 institutions

print and online; US$1,481 institutions print or online; 881 institutions print or online; US$1,900 institutions, other countries print and online; US$1,727 institutions, other countries print or online; 970 institutions print and online; EUR1,232 institutions print and online; EUR1,120 institutions print or online. **Remarks:** Accepts advertising. **URL:** http://www.wiley.com/bw/journal.asp?ref=0105-4538&site=1. **Circ:** (Not Reported)

55863 ■ ALT-J
Association for Learning Technology
Gipsy Ln.
Headington
Oxford OX3 0BP, United Kingdom
Ph: 44 18 65484125
Fax: 44 18 65484165
Publisher E-mail: admin@alt.ac.uk
Journal devoted to research and good practice in the use of learning technologies in higher education. **Freq:** 3/yr. **Key Personnel:** Rhona Sharpe, Editor; Frances Bell, Editor. **ISSN:** 0968-7769. **Subscription Rates:** US$315 institutions print and online; US$299 institutions online; US$142 individuals; 209 institutions print and online; 199 institutions online; 94 individuals. **Remarks:** Accepts advertising. **URL:** http://www.tandf.co.uk/journals/titles/09687769.asp; http://www.alt.ac.uk/alt_j.html. **Circ:** (Not Reported)

55864 ■ American Business Law Journal
John Wiley & Sons Inc.
Wiley-Blackwell
9600 Garsington Rd.
Oxford OX4 2DQ, United Kingdom
Ph: 44 1865 776868
Fax: 44 1865 714591
Law review journal exploring the whole range of topics related to business law. **Freq:** Quarterly. **Key Personnel:** Daniel R. Cahoy, Editor-in-Chief; Ann Morales Olazabal, Managing Editor; Robert C. Bird, Editor. **ISSN:** 0002-7766. **Subscription Rates:** US$579 institutions print and online; US$526 institutions print, online; EUR499 institutions print and online; 499 institutions print and online; 357 institutions print, online; EUR453 institutions print, online; US$769 institutions, other countries print and online; US$699 institutions, other countries print, online. **Remarks:** Accepts advertising. **URL:** http://www.wiley.com/bw/journal.asp?ref=0002-7766&site=1. **Circ:** (Not Reported)

55865 ■ American Law and Economics Review
Oxford University Press
Great Clarendon St.
Oxford OX2 6DP, United Kingdom
Ph: 44 1865 556767
Fax: 44 1865 353485
Publisher E-mail: webenquiry.uk@oup.com
Peer-reviewed journal publishing international work that is accessible to practicing lawyers, consulting economics, academic lawyers, and academic economists, featuring book reviews and review essays. **Freq:** Semiannual. **Key Personnel:** Karen Crocco, Managing Editor, alea@pantheon.yale.edu; Gary S. Becker, Editorial Board; Prof. Steven Shavell, Editor, shavell@law.harvard.edu; Christine Jolls, Editorial Board; Richard Craswell, Editorial Board; Lisa Bernstein, Editorial Board; Prof. John J. Donohue, Editor, j.donohue@yale.edu; Robert C. Ellickson, Editorial Board; Theodore Eisenberg, Editorial Board. **ISSN:** 1465-7252. **Subscription Rates:** 156 institutions print and online; US$234 institutions print and online; 130 institutions print; US$215 institutions print. **Remarks:** Advertising accepted; rates available upon request. **URL:** http://aler.oxfordjournals.org/. **Circ:** (Not Reported)

55866 ■ Anaesthesia
John Wiley & Sons Inc.
Wiley-Blackwell
9600 Garsington Rd.
Oxford OX4 2DQ, United Kingdom
Ph: 44 1865 776868
Fax: 44 1865 714591
Publication E-mail: anaesthesia@aagbi.org
Peer-reviewed journal focusing on all aspects of general and regional anaesthesia, intensive care and pain therapy, including research on equipment. **Freq:** Monthly. **Key Personnel:** Dr. S.M. Yentis, Editor-in-Chief; Dr. N.M. Bedforth, Editor; Dr. A. Klein, Editor; Susan Jarvis, Editorial Asst.; Dr. D.R. Goldhill, Editor; Dr. S. Malhotra, Editor; Dr. M.H. Nathanson, Editor; Dr. S.M. Yentis, Editor; Dr. P.A. Clyburn, Editor. **ISSN:** 0003-2409. **Subscription Rates:** US$273 individuals print +

online; EUR221 individuals print + online; 148 individuals non Euro, print + online; 163 individuals rest of World, print + online; US$273 members print + online; 148 members print + online; 148 individuals non Euro, print + online; US$1,457 institutions, other countries print + online; US$1,324 institutions, other countries print; US$1,324 institutions online. **Remarks:** Accepts advertising. **URL:** http://www.wiley.com/bw/journal.asp?ref=0003-2409&site=1. **Circ:** (Not Reported)

55867 ■ Animal Science Journal
John Wiley & Sons Inc.
Wiley-Blackwell
9600 Garsington Rd.
Oxford OX4 2DQ, United Kingdom
Ph: 44 1865 776868
Fax: 44 1865 714591
Peer-reviewed journal covering all fields of animal and poultry science. **Freq:** Bimonthly. **Key Personnel:** Kunihiko Naito, Editor-in-Chief. **ISSN:** 1344-3941. **Subscription Rates:** US$483 individuals print and online; EUR447 individuals print and online; 299 individuals print and online; US$895 institutions print and online; 554 institutions print and online; EUR703 institutions print and online; US$1,085 institutions, other countries print and online; US$814 institutions print, online; 503 institutions print, online; US$986 institutions, other countries print, online. **Remarks:** Accepts advertising. **URL:** http://www.wiley.com/bw/journal.asp?ref=1344-3941&site=1. **Circ:** (Not Reported)

55868 ■ Annals of Anatomy
Anatomical Society
Anatomische Gesellschaft
U.S. Department of of Human Anatomy & Genetics
University of Oxford
South Parks Rd.
Oxford OX1 3QX, United Kingdom
Professional publication covering anatomy. **Founded:** 1886. **Freq:** Bimonthly. **Key Personnel:** Friedrich Paulsen, Editor-in-Chief, friedrich.paulsen@medizin.uni-halle.de. **ISSN:** 0940-9602. **Subscription Rates:** 828 institutions Germany, Austria, Switzerland, Liechtenstein; 465 Rb individuals Germany, Austria, Switzerland, Liechtenstein; 880 USh institutions rest of Europe; 465 USh individuals rest of Europe; US$971 institutions, other countries; US$468 other countries; 115,200¥ institutions; 60,800¥ individuals. **URL:** http://www.uni-luebeck.de; http://www.elsevier.de/aanat.

55869 ■ Annals of Public and Cooperative Economics
John Wiley & Sons Inc.
Wiley-Blackwell
9600 Garsington Rd.
Oxford OX4 2DQ, United Kingdom
Ph: 44 1865 776868
Fax: 44 1865 714591
French and English language publication covering economics. **Founded:** 1908. **Freq:** Quarterly. **Key Personnel:** Christine Dussart, Editorial Asst., apce.ciriec@guest.ulg.ac.be; Bernard Thiry, Director, b.thiry@ulg.ac.be; Fabienne Fecher, Editor, ffecher@ulg.ac.be. **ISSN:** 1370-4788. **Subscription Rates:** EUR133 individuals print + online; 79 other countries print + online; 68 members AEA, ISTR, ARNOVA, IAFEP; US$115 members AEA, ISTR, ARNOVA, IAFEP; US$603 institutions print + online; US$457 institutions print, online; US$588 institutions, other countries print + online; US$535 institutions, other countries print. **Remarks:** Advertising accepted; rates available upon request. **URL:** http://www.wiley.com/bw/journal.asp?ref=1370-4788&site=1. **Circ:** (Not Reported)

55870 ■ Applied Mathematics Research eXpress
Oxford University Press
Great Clarendon St.
Oxford OX2 6DP, United Kingdom
Ph: 44 1865 556767
Fax: 44 1865 353485
Publisher E-mail: webenquiry.uk@oup.com
Peer-reviewed journal that publishes research articles of high current interest dealing with the use of mathematics in all other areas of knowledge usually in the form of mathematical/computational models and algorithms. **Freq:** Semiannual. **Key Personnel:** Andrea L. Bertozzi, Editor, bertozzi@math.ucla.edu; Claude Le Bris, Editor-in-Chief, lebris@cermics.enpc.fr; David Cai, Editor, cai@cims.nyu.edu; Rene Carmona, Editor, rcarmona@princeton.edu; Jean-Michel Coron, Editor, coron@ann.jussieu.fr; Jean-Francois Delmas, Editor, delmas@cermics.enpc.fr. **ISSN:** 1687-1200. **Subscription Rates:** 128 institutions print and online; US$256 institutions

print and online; EUR192 institutions print and online; 107 institutions print, online; US$214 institutions print, online; EUR161 institutions print, online. **URL:** http://amrx.oxfordjournals.org/.

55871 ■ Archaeometry
John Wiley & Sons Inc.
Wiley-Blackwell
c/o Mark Pollard, Mng. Ed.
Research Laboratory for Archaeology & the History of Art
Dyson Perrins Bldg.
South Parks Rd.
Oxford OX1 3QY, United Kingdom
Peer-reviewed journal focusing on the physical and biological sciences with archaeology and art history. **Freq:** Bimonthly. **Key Personnel:** Mark Pollard, Managing Editor; Ernst Pernicka, Managing Editor; James Burton, Managing Editor. **ISSN:** 0003-813X. **Subscription Rates:** US$446 institutions print and online; US$404 institutions print and online; 226 institutions print and online; 205 institutions print; EUR287 institutions print and online; EUR260 institutions print; US$441 institutions, other countries print and online; US$401 institutions, other countries print. **Remarks:** Accepts advertising. **URL:** http://www.wiley.com/bw/journal.asp?ref=0003-813X&site=1. **Circ:** (Not Reported)

55872 ■ Archive for Rational Mechanics and Analysis
Springer-Verlag Tokyo
Mathematical Institute
24-29 St. Giles
Oxford OX1 3LB, United Kingdom
Publisher E-mail: info@springer.jp
Journal nourishing the discipline of mechanics as a deductive, mathematical science in the classical tradition and promoting analysis, particularly in the context of application. **Freq:** 3/yr. **Key Personnel:** J.M. Ball, Editor, arma@maths.ox.ac.uk; R.D. James, Editor, arma@aem.umn.edu; K. Bhattacharya, Editorial Board, arma@caltech.edu; L. Ambrosio, Editorial Board, luigi@ambrosio.sns.it; A. Bressan, Editorial Board, bressan@math.psu.edu. **ISSN:** 0003-9527. **Subscription Rates:** EUR3,228 institutions print incl. free access or e-only; EUR3,873.60 institutions print incl. enhanced access. **Remarks:** Advertising accepted; rates available upon request. **URL:** http://www.springer.com/physics/mechanics/journal/205. **Circ:** (Not Reported)

55873 ■ Area
John Wiley & Sons Inc.
Wiley-Blackwell
9600 Garsington Rd.
Oxford OX4 2DQ, United Kingdom
Ph: 44 1865 776868
Fax: 44 1865 714591
Publication covering geography. **Founded:** 1933. **Freq:** Quarterly. **Key Personnel:** Kevin Ward, Editor; Louise Bracken, Co-Ed.; Helen Jarvis, Book Review Ed. **ISSN:** 0004-0894. **Subscription Rates:** US$359 institutions Americas (print and online); 214 institutions UK (print and online); EUR271 institutions Europe (print and online); US$417 institutions, other countries print and online; US$326 institutions Americas (print or online only); 193 institutions UK (print or online only); EUR245 institutions Europe (print or online only); US$379 institutions, other countries print or online only. **Remarks:** Advertising accepted; rates available upon request. **URL:** http://www.wiley.com/bw/journal.asp?ref=0004-0894. **Circ:** (Not Reported)

55874 ■ Art History
John Wiley & Sons Inc.
Wiley-Blackwell
9600 Garsington Rd.
Oxford OX4 2DQ, United Kingdom
Ph: 44 1865 776868
Fax: 44 1865 714591
Peer-reviewed journal covering the visual and performing arts. **Founded:** 1978. **Freq:** 5/yr. **Key Personnel:** David Peters Corbett, Editor; Christine Riding, Dep. Ed.; Cordelia Warr, Reviews Ed. **ISSN:** 0141-6790. **Subscription Rates:** US$248 nonmembers Americas; 117 nonmembers non-Euro zone; EUR176 nonmembers Euro zone; US$149 nonmembers other countries; US$211 members Americas; 100 members non-Euro zone; EUR150 members Euro zone; US$126 members other countries; US$1,064 institutions Americas; 553 institutions UK. **Remarks:** Accepts advertising. **URL:** http://www.wiley.com/bw/journal.asp?ref=0141-6790. **Circ:** (Not Reported)

55875 ■ Asia-Pacific Journal of Clinical Oncology
John Wiley & Sons Inc.
Wiley-Blackwell
9600 Garsington Rd.
Oxford OX4 2DQ, United Kingdom
Ph: 44 1865 776868
Fax: 44 1865 714591
Peer-reviewed journal publishing pre-clinical studies, translational research, clinical trials and epidemiological studies. **Freq:** Quarterly. **Key Personnel:** Da-Tong Chu, Editor; Atsushi Ohtsu, Editor; Stephen Ackland, Editor-in-Chief; Alex Chang, Editor; Takeshi Sano, Consulting Ed.; Yasuaki Arai, Assoc. Ed. **ISSN:** 1743-7555. **Subscription Rates:** US$117 individuals print + online; EUR119 individuals print + online; 80 individuals print + online; US$592 institutions print + online; US$538 institutions print, online; 366 institutions print + online; 332 institutions print, online; EUR465 institutions print + online; US$717 institutions, other countries print + online; US$651 institutions, other countries print, online. **Remarks:** Accepts advertising from members only. **URL:** http://www.wiley.com/bw/journal.asp?ref=1743-7555&site=1. **Circ:** (Not Reported)

55876 ■ Australian Economic Review
John Wiley & Sons Inc.
Wiley-Blackwell
9600 Garsington Rd.
Oxford OX4 2DQ, United Kingdom
Ph: 44 1865 776868
Fax: 44 1865 714591
Peer-reviewed journal covering economics. **Freq:** Quarterly. **Key Personnel:** Prof. Ross Williams, Editor, phone 61 3 83442125, fax 61 3 83442111, rossaw@unimelb.edu.au; Prof. Ian McDonald, Editor, phone 61 3 83445266, fax 61 3 83446899, i.mcdonald@unimelb.edu.au; Prof. Mark Wooden, Editor, phone 61 3 83442089, m.wooden@unimelb.edu.au. **ISSN:** 0004-9018. **Subscription Rates:** US$108 individuals print and online; 75 other countries print and online; EUR33 students print and online; US$525 institutions print and online; US$721 institutions, other countries print and online; US$477 institutions, online; US$656 institutions, other countries online. **Remarks:** Accepts advertising. **Online:** Gale. **URL:** http://www.wiley.com/bw/journal.asp?ref=0004-9018&site=1. **Circ:** (Not Reported)

55877 ■ Australian Endodontic Journal
John Wiley & Sons Inc.
Wiley-Blackwell
9600 Garsington Rd.
Oxford OX4 2DQ, United Kingdom
Ph: 44 1865 776868
Fax: 44 1865 714591
Journal covering dentistry. **Founded:** Jan. 1936. **Freq:** 3/yr. **Print Method:** Offset. **Trim Size:** 8 x 10 3/4. **Cols./Page:** 3. **Col. Width:** 26 nonpareils. **Col. Depth:** 96 agate lines. **Key Personnel:** Dr. Ralph Reid, Editor; Dr. Christine Yu, Sub Ed. **ISSN:** 1329-1947. **Subscription Rates:** US$201 institutions print + online; US$174 institutions online; 118 institutions print + online; 102 institutions online; EUR150 institutions print + online; 130 institutions online; US$232 institutions, other countries print + online; US$201 institutions, other countries online. **Remarks:** Accepts advertising. **URL:** http://www.wiley.com/bw/journal.asp?ref=1329-1947&site=1. **Circ:** (Not Reported)

55878 ■ The Australian Journal of Agricultural and Resource Economics
John Wiley & Sons Inc.
Wiley-Blackwell
9600 Garsington Rd.
Oxford OX4 2DQ, United Kingdom
Ph: 44 1865 776868
Fax: 44 1865 714591
Publication E-mail: ajare@blackwellpublishing.com
Scholarly journal covering agriculture and resource economics. **Founded:** 1997. **Freq:** Quarterly. **Key Personnel:** Tom Kompas, Editor; Jeff Bennett, Editor; Quentin R. Grafton, Editor; John Rolfe, Book Review Ed.; Colin Brown, Assoc. Ed.; Dianne Dupont, Assoc. Ed. **ISSN:** 1364-985X. **Subscription Rates:** US$500 institutions print and online; 324 institutions print and online; US$454 institutions print, online; 277 institutions print; EUR412 institutions print and online; EUR374 institutions print; US$422 institutions print and online (Australia and NZ); US$383 institutions print; US$634 institutions, other countries print and online; US$576 institutions, other countries print. **Remarks:** Accepts advertising. **URL:** http://www.wiley.com/bw/journal.asp?ref=1364-

Circulation: ★ = ABC; △ = BPA; ♦ = CAC; • = CCAB; ❑ = VAC; ⊕ = PO Statement; ‡ = Publisher's Report; Boldface figures = sworn; Light figures = estimated.

Gale Directory of Publications & Broadcast Media/147th Ed.

5807

985X&site=1. **Circ:** (Not Reported)

55879 ■ Behavioral Ecology
Oxford University Press
Great Clarendon St.
Oxford OX2 6DP, United Kingdom
Ph: 44 1865 556767
Fax: 44 1865 353485
Publisher E-mail: webenquiry.uk@oup.com
Journal of International Society for Behavioral Ecology. **Founded:** 1990. **Freq:** Bimonthly. **Print Method:** Offset. **Trim Size:** 8 1/2 x 11. **Cols./Page:** 2. **Col. Width:** 2 3/4 inches. **Col. Depth:** 9 1/2 inches. **Key Personnel:** Dr. Mark Elgar, Editor-in-Chief; Dr. Will Cresswell, Editor; Dr. Ben Hatchwell, Editor; Dr. Hans Hofmann, Editor; Dr. Candy Rowe, Editor; Dr. Daiqin Li, Editor; Dr. Gil Rosenthal, Editor; Dr. Rob Brooks, Editor; Dr. Sue Healy, Editor; Sigal Balshin, Editorial Board. **ISSN:** 1045-2249. **Subscription Rates:** 589 institutions corporate; print and online; 486 institutions corporate; online only; 540 institutions corporate; print only; 472 institutions print and online; 389 institutions online only; 432 institutions print only; 32 members online only; 63 members print; 16 members student; online only; 35 members student; print. **Remarks:** Accepts advertising. **URL:** http://beheco.oxfordjournals.org/. **Ad Rates:** BW: 565. **Circ:** Paid 1,300, Non-paid 35

55880 ■ Bioethics
John Wiley & Sons Inc.
Wiley-Blackwell
9600 Garsington Rd.
Oxford OX4 2DQ, United Kingdom
Ph: 44 1865 776868
Fax: 44 1865 714591
Publication covering biological sciences. **Freq:** 9/yr. **Key Personnel:** Ruth Chadwick, Editor, chadwickr1@cardiff.ac.uk; Margaret Pabst Battin, Editorial Board; John D. Arras, Editorial Board; Dr. Anne Donchin, Assoc. Ed.; Erica Haimes, Editorial Board; Prof. Udo Schuklenk, Editor, udo.schuklenk@gmail.com; Atsushi Asai, Editorial Board; Arthur L. Caplan, Editorial Board; Robert Baker, Editorial Board. **ISSN:** 0269-9702. **Subscription Rates:** US$225 individuals print + online; EUR167 individuals print + online (Euro zone); 111 individuals print + online (non Euro zone); US$71 individuals print + online, developing World; 32 individuals print + online, developing World; 134 other countries print + online; US$1,720 institutions print + online; US$1,563 institutions print, online; US$2,005 institutions, other countries print + online; US$1,823 institutions, other countries print, online. **Remarks:** Accepts advertising. **URL:** http://www.wiley.com/bw/journal.asp?ref=0269-9702&site=1. **Circ:** (Not Reported)

55881 ■ Bioinformatics
Oxford University Press
Great Clarendon St.
Oxford OX2 6DP, United Kingdom
Ph: 44 1865 556767
Fax: 44 1865 353485
Publisher E-mail: webenquiry.uk@oup.com
Journal publishing scientific papers and review articles of interest to academic and industrial researchers, mainly focusing on new developments in genome bioinformatics and computational biology. **Freq:** 24/yr. **Key Personnel:** B. Rost, Assoc. Ed.; Alex Bateman, Exec. Ed.; Alfonso Valencia, Exec. Ed.; K.A. Crandall, Editorial Board; W. Huber, Editorial Board; Joaquin Dopazo, Assoc. Ed.; Trey Ideker, Assoc. Ed.; Dmitrij Frishman, Assoc. Ed. **ISSN:** 1367-4803. **Subscription Rates:** 2,033 institutions corporate; print and online; 1,220 institutions corporate; online only; 1,863 institutions corporate; print only; 1,626 institutions print and online; 976 institutions online only; 1,491 institutions print only; 474 individuals print; 106 members online only; 185 members print. **Remarks:** Advertising accepted; rates available upon request. **URL:** http://bioinformatics.oupjournals.org/. **Circ:** (Not Reported)

55882 ■ Biometrika
Oxford University Press
Great Clarendon St.
Oxford OX2 6DP, United Kingdom
Ph: 44 1865 556767
Fax: 44 1865 353485
Publisher E-mail: webenquiry.uk@oup.com
Journal of statistics emphasizing papers containing original theoretical contributions of direct or potential value in applications. **Freq:** 4/yr. **Key Personnel:** X. Lin, Assoc. Ed.; A.C. Davison, Editor, biometrika@epfl.ch;

O. Papaspiliopoulos, Assoc. Ed.; N.P. Jewell, Assoc. Ed.; J.T. Kent, Assoc. Ed.; G.P. Nason, Assoc. Ed. **ISSN:** 0006-3444. **Subscription Rates:** 143 institutions corporate; print and online; 119 institutions corporate; online only; 131 institutions corporate; print only; 114 institutions print and online; 95 institutions online only; 105 institutions print only; 34 individuals print. **Remarks:** Advertising accepted; rates available upon request. **URL:** http://biomet.oxfordjournals.org. **Circ:** (Not Reported)

55883 ■ Biostatistics
Oxford University Press
Great Clarendon St.
Oxford OX2 6DP, United Kingdom
Ph: 44 1865 556767
Fax: 44 1865 353485
Publisher E-mail: webenquiry.uk@oup.com
Journal focusing on statistics related to human health. **Freq:** 4/yr. **Key Personnel:** Scott L. Zeger, Founding Ed., fax 410955-3067, szeger@jhsph.edu; Peter J. Diggle, Founding Ed., fax 44 1524 593747, p.diggle@lancaster.ac.uk; Rebecca Betensky, Assoc. Ed., betensky@hsph.harvard.edu. **ISSN:** 1465-4644. **Subscription Rates:** 497 institutions corporate; print and online; 381 institutions corporate; online only; 455 institutions corporate; print only; 397 institutions print and online; 305 institutions online only; 364 institutions print only; 184 individuals print; 118 members print. **URL:** http://biostatistics.oxfordjournals.org.

55884 ■ BJIR: British Journal of Industrial Relations
John Wiley & Sons Inc.
Wiley-Blackwell
9600 Garsington Rd.
Oxford OX4 2DQ, United Kingdom
Ph: 44 1865 776868
Fax: 44 1865 714591
Publication covering industrial relations. **Freq:** Quarterly. **Key Personnel:** Simon Deakin, International Advisory Board; William Roche, International Advisory Board; Virginia Doellgast, Reviews Ed., v.l.doellgast@lse.ac.uk; Christopher L. Erickson, Editorial Board, phone 310825-1697, fax 310825-0218, chris.erickson@anderson.ucla.edu; Sylvia Roesch, Managing Editor, phone 44 20 79557931, bjir@lse.ac.uk; Carola Frege, Editor-in-Chief, phone 44 12 22874000, fax 44 12 22874419, c.m.frege@lse.ac.uk; Morris M. Kleiner, Editorial Board, phone 612625-2089, fax 612625-6351, mkleiner@hhh.umn.edu; Erling Barth, International Advisory Board. **ISSN:** 0007-1080. **Subscription Rates:** US$187 individuals print + online; EUR100 individuals print + online; 79 individuals print + online (non Euro zone); 109 other countries print + online; US$78 members BUIRA: print + online; 34 students, other countries print + online; 27 students print + online; US$995 institutions, other countries print + online; US$55 students print + online; US$861 institutions, other countries print. **Remarks:** Accepts advertising. **URL:** http://www.wiley.com/bw/journal.asp?ref=0007-1080&site=1. **Circ:** (Not Reported)

55885 ■ BJOG
John Wiley & Sons Inc.
Wiley-Blackwell
9600 Garsington Rd.
Oxford OX4 2DQ, United Kingdom
Ph: 44 1865 776868
Fax: 44 1865 714591
Peer-reviewed journal covering obstetrics and gynecology. **Subtitle:** An International Journal of Obstetrics and Gynaecology. **Founded:** 1904. **Freq:** 13/yr. **Print Method:** Offset Litho. **Trim Size:** 274 x 228 mm. **Key Personnel:** Michael Marsh, Dep. Ed.-in-Ch.; Philip J. Steer, Editor-in-Chief; P. Bennett, Editorial Board. **ISSN:** 1470-0328. **Subscription Rates:** US$250 individuals print + online; EUR223 individuals print + online; 149 individuals print + online (non Euro zone); 164 other countries print + online; US$105 members the Americas; EUR101 members; 67 members non Euro zone; 74 members rest of World; US$662 institutions print and online; US$602 institutions print, online. **Remarks:** Advertising accepted; rates available upon request. **URL:** http://www.wiley.com/bw/journal.asp?ref=1470-0328&site=1. **Formerly:** British Journal of Obstetrics and Gynaecology. **Circ:** (Not Reported)

55886 ■ BloodMed
John Wiley & Sons Inc.
Wiley-Blackwell
9600 Garsington Rd.
Oxford OX4 2DQ, United Kingdom

Ph: 44 1865 776868
Fax: 44 1865 714591
Online resource for hematology research, practice and education. **Freq:** Monthly. **Key Personnel:** Finbarr Cotter, Editor-in-Chief; Cheryl Willman, Editor-in-Chief. **ISSN:** 1478-1247. **Remarks:** Accepts advertising. **URL:** http://www.bloodmed.com. **Circ:** (Not Reported)

55887 ■ Brain
Oxford University Press
Great Clarendon St.
Oxford OX2 6DP, United Kingdom
Ph: 44 1865 556767
Fax: 44 1865 353485
Publisher E-mail: webenquiry.uk@oup.com
Journal providing researchers and clinicians with original contributions in neurology in which leading studies in neurological science are balanced with practical clinical articles. **Subtitle:** A Journal of Neurology. **Freq:** Monthly. **Key Personnel:** Alastair Compston, Editor; Patrick Chinnery, Assoc. Ed.; Angela Vincent, Assoc. Ed.; Dimitri M. Kullmann, Assoc. Ed.; Mark Hallett, Assoc. Ed.; Geraint Rees, Assoc. Ed. **ISSN:** 0006-8950. **Subscription Rates:** 794 institutions corporate; print and online; 536 institutions corporate; online only; 728 institutions corporate; print only; 636 institutions print and online; 429 institutions online only; 583 institutions print only; 244 individuals print and online; 72 individuals print. **Remarks:** Advertising accepted; rates available upon request. **URL:** http://brain.oxfordjournals.org. **Circ:** (Not Reported)

55888 ■ Brief Treatment and Crisis Intervention
Oxford University Press
Great Clarendon St.
Oxford OX2 6DP, United Kingdom
Ph: 44 1865 556767
Fax: 44 1865 353485
Publisher E-mail: webenquiry.uk@oup.com
Journal dedicated to advancing clinical practice, public policy, and knowledge-building related to behavioral health, health care, and forensic studies with objective being to expand research, theory-building, treatment plans, and practice developments in mental health assessment and treatment, crisis intervention, time-limited psychotherapy, cognitive therapy, coping efficacy, critical incident stress management, psychopharmacology, violence and violence prevention, psychological trauma, forensic risk assessment, suicide prevention and emergency services. **Freq:** Quarterly. **Key Personnel:** Albert R. Roberts, PhD, Editor-in-Chief; James Barber, PhD, Editorial Board; Cheryl Regehr, PhD, Assoc. Ed.; Bernard Bloom, PhD, Editorial Board; Gunnar Almgren, PhD, Editorial Board; Elizabeth Plionis, PhD, Book Review Ed. **ISSN:** 1474-3310. **Remarks:** Advertising accepted; rates available upon request. **URL:** http://www.oxfordjournals.org/our_journals/btcint/editorial_board.html. **Circ:** (Not Reported)

55889 ■ Briefings in Bioinformatics
Oxford University Press
Great Clarendon St.
Oxford OX2 6DP, United Kingdom
Ph: 44 1865 556767
Fax: 44 1865 353485
Publisher E-mail: webenquiry.uk@oup.com
International forum for researchers and educators in the life sciences covering topics such as: DNA sequencing, expression profiling, alignment methods, gene expression studies, protein profiles and HMMs, metabolic and signaling pathways, structure and function prediction, mapping and microarrays. **Freq:** 6/yr. **Key Personnel:** Martin Bishop, Editor; Russ B. Altman, Assoc. Ed.; Sean Mooney, Book Reviews Ed. **ISSN:** 1467-5463. **Subscription Rates:** 454 institutions print and online; US$908 institutions print and online; EUR681 institutions print and online; 378 institutions online; US$756 institutions online; EUR567 institutions online; 220 individuals print; US$440 individuals print; EUR330 individuals print. **URL:** http://bib.oxfordjournals.org/.

55890 ■ Briefings in Functional Genomics & Proteomics
Oxford University Press
Great Clarendon St.
Oxford OX2 6DP, United Kingdom
Ph: 44 1865 556767
Fax: 44 1865 353485
Publisher E-mail: webenquiry.uk@oup.com
International forum for researchers and educators in the

life sciences, reviewing the techniques, protocols and approaches in genome and proteome research with papers ranging in scope and depth from the introductory level to specific details of protocols and analyses encompassing bacterial, plant, animal and human data. **Freq:** 6/yr. **Key Personnel:** Greg Elgar, Managing Editor; Joel G. Pounds, Book Review Ed. **ISSN:** 1473-9550. **Subscription Rates:** 454 institutions print and online; US$908 institutions print and online; EUR681 institutions print and online; 378 institutions online; US$756 institutions online; EUR567 institutions online; 220 individuals print; US$440 individuals print; EUR330 individuals print. **URL:** http://bfgp.oxfordjournals.org/.

55891 ■ The British Journal of Aesthetics
Oxford University Press
Great Clarendon St.
Oxford OX2 6DP, United Kingdom
Ph: 44 1865 556767
Fax: 44 1865 353485
Publisher E-mail: webenquiry.uk@oup.com
Publication covering the visual and performing arts. **Founded:** Jan. 1960. **Freq:** Quarterly. **Key Personnel:** John Hyman, Editor, bja@queens.ox.ac.uk; Terry Diffey, Editorial Board; Paisley Livingston, Editorial Consultant; Robert Hopkins, Editorial Consultant; Elisabeth Schellekens, Assoc. Ed., bja.1@durham.ac.uk; Arthur Danto, Editorial Board; Gregory Currie, Editorial Consultant; David Davies, Editorial Consultant; Roger Scruton, Editorial Board; Malcolm Budd, Editorial Board. **ISSN:** 0007-0904. **Subscription Rates:** 174 institutions print and online; US$348 institutions print and online; EUR261 institutions print and online; 145 institutions online, print; US$290 institutions online, print; EUR218 institutions online, print; 34 members print only; US$68 members print only; EUR51 members print only. **Remarks:** Accepts advertising. **URL:** http://bjaesthetics.oxfordjournals.org. **Circ:** (Not Reported)

55892 ■ British Journal of Anaesthesia
Oxford University Press
Great Clarendon St.
Oxford OX2 6DP, United Kingdom
Ph: 44 1865 556767
Fax: 44 1865 353485
Publisher E-mail: webenquiry.uk@oup.com
Journal presenting anesthesia-related papers on a variety of topics. **Founded:** 1923. **Freq:** Monthly. **Key Personnel:** J.M. Hunter, Board Member; Charles S. Reilly, Editor-in-Chief; M.M.R.F. Struys, Editor; H.C. Hemmings, Editor; S.J. Howell, Editor; D.G. Lambert, Board Member; R.P. Mahajan, Editor; J.P. Thompson, Editor; J.G. Hardman, Editor. **ISSN:** 0007-0912. **Subscription Rates:** 527 institutions corporate; print and online; 435 institutions corporate; online only; 483 institutions corporate; print only; 421 institutions print and online; 347 institutions online only; 386 institutions print only; 379 individuals print; 186 individuals trainee; print; 186 members print. **URL:** http://bja.oxfordjournals.org. **Also known as:** BJA.

55893 ■ The British Journal of Criminology
Oxford University Press
Great Clarendon St.
Oxford OX2 6DP, United Kingdom
Ph: 44 1865 556767
Fax: 44 1865 353485
Publisher E-mail: webenquiry.uk@oup.com
Law periodical. **Freq:** 6/yr. **Key Personnel:** Barbara Hudson, Editor; Chris Hale, Editor; Pat Carlen, Editor-in-Chief, pat.carlen@editorialoffice.co.uk. **ISSN:** 0007-0955. **Subscription Rates:** 388 institutions print and online; 323 institutions online, print; US$757 institutions print and online; EUR582 institutions print and online; US$692 institutions print; EUR533 institutions print; 28 members of Centre for Crime and Justice Studies. **Remarks:** Accepts advertising. **URL:** http://bjc.oxfordjournals.org/. **Circ:** (Not Reported)

55894 ■ British Journal of Management
John Wiley & Sons Inc.
Wiley-Blackwell
9600 Garsington Rd.
Oxford OX4 2DQ, United Kingdom
Ph: 44 1865 776868
Fax: 44 1865 714591
General business publication. **Freq:** 5/yr. **Key Personnel:** Celeste Wilderom, Assoc. Ed.; Matthew Robson, Assoc. Ed.; Pawan S. Budhwar, Assoc. Ed.; Mustafa Ozbilgin, Editor-in-Chief, m.ozbilgin@uea.ac.uk; Mark Wouters, Assoc. Ed.; Susan Cartwright, Editorial Board; Emma Missen, Managing Editor, phone 44 1277 215940, bjm@bam.ac.uk; Steffen Giessner, Editorial Board; Veronique Ambrosini, Assoc. Ed.; Catherine Cassell, Assoc. Ed.; Astrid Homan, Editorial Board; Robert Ford, Editorial Board. **ISSN:** 1045-3172. **Subscription Rates:** US$150 individuals print + online; EUR180 individuals print + online; 121 individuals print + online; EUR148 members print + online; 99 members print online; US$1,662 institutions Americas (print and online); EUR1,256 institutions Europe (print and online); 989 institutions UK (print and online); US$1,939 institutions, other countries print and online; US$1,511 institutions Americas (print or online only). **Remarks:** Accepts advertising. **URL:** http://www.wiley.com/bw/journal.asp?ref=1045-3172&site=1. **Circ:** (Not Reported)

55895 ■ British Medical Bulletin
Oxford University Press
Great Clarendon St.
Oxford OX2 6DP, United Kingdom
Ph: 44 1865 556767
Fax: 44 1865 353485
Publisher E-mail: webenquiry.uk@oup.com
Journal for generalist physicians, junior doctors and medical students in both developed and developing countries, providing interpretations of growing points in medicine by trusted experts in the field, and assisting practitioners in incorporating not just evidence but new conceptual ways of thinking into their practice. **Freq:** Quarterly. **Key Personnel:** Prof. D. Coggon, Editorial Advisory Board; Dr. Norman J. Vetter, Editor-in-Chief, vetter@cardiff.ac.uk; Prof. S.K. Smith, Editorial Advisory Board; Prof. A-L Kinmonth, Editorial Advisory Board; Prof. S. Ghosh, Commissioning Ed.; G. Watts, Editorial Advisory Board; Prof. P.J. Guillou, Commissioning Ed.; Prof. D. Stott, Commissioning Ed. **ISSN:** 0007-1420. **Subscription Rates:** 408 institutions corporate; print and online; 340 institutions corporate; online only; 374 institutions corporate; print only; 326 institutions print and online; 272 institutions online only; 299 institutions print only; 104 individuals print; 104 institutions developing countries; print only; 284 individuals print. **Remarks:** Advertising not accepted. **URL:** http://bmb.oxfordjournals.org. **Circ:** (Not Reported)

55896 ■ BSHM Bulletin
Taylor & Francis Group Journals
The Queen's College
Oxford OX1 4AW, United Kingdom
Publisher E-mail: customerservice@taylorandfrancis.com
Journal aiming to promote research into the history of mathematics. **Subtitle:** Journal of the British Society for the History of Mathematics. **Founded:** 1973. **Freq:** 3/yr. **Print Method:** Web offset. **Trim Size:** 8 1/8 x 10 7/8. **Cols./Page:** 2. **Col. Width:** 3 1/4 inches. **Col. Depth:** 10 inches. **Key Personnel:** Jackie Stedall, Editor, jackie.stedall@queens.ox.ac.uk; June Barrow-Green, Editor; Snezana Lawrence, Editor. **ISSN:** 1749-8430. **Subscription Rates:** US$227 institutions online only; 138 institutions online only; US$239 institutions print & online; 145 institutions print & online; US$60 individuals print only; 35 individuals print only; EUR190 institutions print and online; EUR181 institutions online only; EUR48 individuals. **URL:** http://www.tandf.co.uk/journals/titles/17498430.asp.

55897 ■ Bulletin of Economic Research
John Wiley & Sons Inc.
Wiley-Blackwell
9600 Garsington Rd.
Oxford OX4 2DQ, United Kingdom
Ph: 44 1865 776868
Fax: 44 1865 714591
Peer-reviewed journal covering economics. **Freq:** Quarterly. **Key Personnel:** Gianni De Fraja, Board of Trustee; Gabriel Talmain, Editor; Giacomo Bonanno, Assoc. Ed.; Gulcin Ozkan, Assoc. Ed.; Hassan Molana, Assoc. Ed.; George Norman, Assoc. Ed.; Christina Atanasova, Assoc. Ed.; Klaus G. Zauner, Editor; David Newbery, Assoc. Ed. **ISSN:** 0307-3378. **Subscription Rates:** US$81 individuals print + online; EUR72 individuals print + online; 48 individuals print + online; US$980 institutions print + online; US$891 institutions print, online; EUR558 institutions print + online; EUR507 institutions print, online; 439 institutions print + online; US$1,143 institutions, other countries print + online; US$1,039 institutions, other countries print, online. **Remarks:** Accepts advertising. **URL:** http://www.wiley.com/bw/journal.asp?ref=0307-3378&site=1. **Circ:** (Not Reported)

55898 ■ Business Ethics
John Wiley & Sons Inc.
Wiley-Blackwell
9600 Garsington Rd.
Oxford OX4 2DQ, United Kingdom
Ph: 44 1865 776868
Fax: 44 1865 714591
Publication covering economics. **Subtitle:** A European Review. **Freq:** Quarterly. **Key Personnel:** Prof. Christopher Cowton, Editor, phone 44 1484 473063, fax 44 1484 472753, beer@hud.ac.uk; Prof. Antonio Argandona, Editorial Board; Dr. David Campbell, Editorial Board. **ISSN:** 0962-8770. **Subscription Rates:** US$173 individuals Americas; 103 other countries; EUR155 individuals Euro zone; US$1,466 institutions Americas (print and online); 873 institutions UK (print and online); EUR1,108 institutions Europe (print and online); US$1,710 institutions, other countries print and online; US$1,333 institutions Americas (print or online only); 793 institutions UK (print or online only); EUR1,007 institutions Europe (print or online only). **Remarks:** Accepts advertising. **URL:** http://www.wiley.com/bw/journal.asp?ref=0962-8770. **Circ:** (Not Reported)

55899 ■ Business and Society Review
John Wiley & Sons Inc.
Wiley-Blackwell
9600 Garsington Rd.
Oxford OX4 2DQ, United Kingdom
Ph: 44 1865 776868
Fax: 44 1865 714591
Law periodical. **Freq:** Quarterly. **Key Personnel:** Michael W. Hoffman, Exec. Dir.; Robert E. Frederick, Editor, phone 781891-2747, fax 781891-2988, rfrederick@bentley.edu; John R. Boatright, Editorial Board. **ISSN:** 0045-3609. **Subscription Rates:** US$88 individuals print + online; EUR120 individuals print + online; 80 other countries print + online; US$311 institutions print + online; 244 institutions print + online; US$479 institutions, other countries print + online; US$282 institutions print, online; 222 institutions print, online; EUR281 institutions print, online; US$435 institutions, other countries print, online. **Remarks:** Accepts advertising. **URL:** http://www.wiley.com/bw/journal.asp?ref=0045-3609&site=1. **Circ:** (Not Reported)

55900 ■ Cambridge Journal of Economics
Oxford University Press
Great Clarendon St.
Oxford OX2 6DP, United Kingdom
Ph: 44 1865 556767
Fax: 44 1865 353485
Publisher E-mail: webenquiry.uk@oup.com
Journal providing research into social and economic issues. **Founded:** 1977. **Freq:** 6/yr. **Key Personnel:** Jacqui Lagrue, Managing Editor, phone 44 12 23335266, fax 44 12 23335299, cje@econ.cam.ac.uk; Stephanie Blankenburg, Editor; Brendan Burchell, Editor; Geoff Harcourt, Editor; Geoff Hodgson, Assoc. Ed.; Simon Deakin, Editor; Ha-Joon Chang, Editor; Alan Hughes, Editor; Michael Landesmann, Assoc. Ed.; Ken Coutts, Editor. **ISSN:** 0309-166X. **Subscription Rates:** 491 institutions corporate; print and online; 409 institutions corporate; online only; 450 institutions corporate; print only; 392 institutions print and online; 327 institutions online only; 360 institutions print only; 65 individuals print; 51 members print. **URL:** http://cje.oxfordjournals.org.

55901 ■ Canadian Journal of Agricultural Economics
John Wiley & Sons Inc.
Wiley-Blackwell
9600 Garsington Rd.
Oxford OX4 2DQ, United Kingdom
Ph: 44 1865 776868
Fax: 44 1865 714591
Peer reviewed Journal providing a forum for scholarship in agricultural economics and farm management including agri-food-related topics concerning agribusiness, the environment and resource use. **Freq:** Quarterly. **Key Personnel:** Cornelis G. van Kooten, Editor; James F. Nolan, Editor; Elwin G. Smith, Editor. **ISSN:** 0008-3976. **Subscription Rates:** US$273 institutions print + online; US$247 institutions print, online; 162 institutions print + online; 147 institutions print, online; US$242 institutions, Canada and Mexico print + online; EUR205 institutions print + online; EUR186 institutions print, online; US$315 institutions, other countries print + online; US$220 institutions, Canada and Mexico print, online. **Remarks:** Advertising not accepted. **URL:** http://www.wiley.com/

Circulation: ★ = ABC; △ = BPA; ♦ = CAC; • = CCAB; ❑ = VAC; ⊕ = PO Statement; ‡ = Publisher's Report; Boldface figures = sworn; Light figures = estimated.

Gale Directory of Publications & Broadcast Media/147th Ed. 5809

bw/journal.asp?ref=0008-3976&site=1. **Circ:** (Not Reported)

55902 ■ Cancer Letters
Mosby Inc.
The Blvd. Langford Ln.
Kidlington
Oxford OX5 1GB, United Kingdom
Ph: 44 18 65843203
Fax: 44 18 65843992
Publication E-mail: cancerletters@elsevier.com
Publisher E-mail: custserv.ehs@elsevier.com
Peer-reviewed Journal providing rapid publication of brief articles in the broad area of cancer research. **Founded:** 1975. **Freq:** 28/yr. **Key Personnel:** B.B. Aggarwal, Editorial Board; C.J. Der, Editorial Board; D. Bagchi, Editorial Board; R.J. Duhe, Editorial Board; A. Nakagawara, Assoc. Ed.; Jo Hodgkison, Admin. Ed.; H. Li, Editorial Board; M. Schwab, Editor-in-Chief; J. Gu, Editorial Board. **ISSN:** 0304-3835. **Subscription Rates:** US$7,087 institutions, other countries except Europe, Japan and Iran; 841,700¥ institutions; EUR6,337 institutions for European countries and Iran. **URL:** http://www.elsevier.com/wps/find/journaldescription.cws_home/506050/descriptiondescription.

55903 ■ Cancer Science
John Wiley & Sons Inc.
Wiley-Blackwell
9600 Garsington Rd.
Oxford OX4 2DQ, United Kingdom
Ph: 44 1865 776868
Fax: 44 1865 714591
Peer-reviewed journal covering the fields of basic, translational and clinical cancer. **Freq:** Monthly. **Key Personnel:** Takashi Nishimura, Assoc. Ed.; Kohei Miyazono, Editor; Richard J. Ablin, Assoc. Ed.; Yusuke Nakamura, Editor-in-Chief; Takashi Sugimura, Ed. Emeritus; Setsuo Hirohashi, Editor; Ryuzo Ueda, Editor; Takao Yamori, Assoc. Ed. **ISSN:** 1347-9032. **Subscription Rates:** US$339 individuals print + online; US$1,311 institutions print + online; US$1,192 institutions print, online; US$1,527 institutions, other countries print + online; EUR301 individuals print + online; 779 institutions print + online; 709 institutions print, online; EUR992 institutions print + online; 201 individuals print + online; US$1,389 institutions, other countries print + online. **Remarks:** Advertising not accepted. **URL:** http://www.wiley.com/bw/journal.asp?ref=1347-9032&site=1. **Circ:** (Not Reported)

55904 ■ Carcinogenesis
Oxford University Press
Great Clarendon St.
Oxford OX2 6DP, United Kingdom
Ph: 44 1865 556767
Fax: 44 1865 353485
Publisher E-mail: webenquiry.uk@oup.com
Multi-disciplinary journal bringing together all the varied aspects of research that will ultimately lead to the prevention of cancer in man in the areas of Cancer Biology (including the processes of promotion, progression, signal transduction, apoptosis, genomic instability, growth factors, cell and molecular biology, mutation, DNA repair, genetics etc.), Molecular Epidemiology and Cancer Prevention (including molecular dosimetry, epidemiology, genetic predisposition to cancer, chemoprevention, nutrition and cancer, etc.) and Carcinogenesis (including viral, chemical and physical carcinogenesis, metabolism of carcinogens, and the formation, detection, identification and quantification of environmental carcinogens). **Freq:** Monthly. **Key Personnel:** Dr. Curtis C. Harris, Exec. Ed.; A. Dipple, Founding Ed.; Takashi Takahashi, Editorial Board; Alan Clarke, Editorial Board; C. Garner, Founding Ed.; Thomas Kensler, Editorial Board. **ISSN:** 0143-3334. **Subscription Rates:** US$2,590 institutions print and online; US$1,942 institutions online only; US$2,374 institutions print only; US$942 individuals print only; 1,295 institutions print and online; 971 institutions online only; 1,187 institutions print only; EUR1,943 institutions print and online; EUR1,457 institutions online only; EUR1,781 institutions print only. **Remarks:** Advertising accepted; rates available upon request. **URL:** http://carcin.oxfordjournals.org. **Circ:** (Not Reported)

55905 ■ CESifo Economic Studies
Oxford University Press
Great Clarendon St.
Oxford OX2 6DP, United Kingdom
Ph: 44 1865 556767
Fax: 44 1865 353485

Publisher E-mail: webenquiry.uk@oup.com
Journal covering economics. **Freq:** Quarterly. **Key Personnel:** Prof. Gerhard Illing, Assoc. Ed., illing@lmu.de; Rick van der Ploeg, Editor, rick.vanderploeg@economics.ox.ac.uk; John Whalley, Editor; Prof. Efraim Sadka, Assoc. Ed.; Prof. Richard Arnott, Assoc. Ed.; Prof. Roel Beetsma, Assoc. Ed. **ISSN:** 1610-241X. **Subscription Rates:** 223 institutions corporate; print and online; 186 institutions corporate; online only; 205 institutions corporate; print only; 179 institutions print and online; 149 institutions online only; 164 institutions print only; 49 individuals print. **URL:** http://www.cesifo-group.de/portal/page?_pageid=36,34689&_dad=portal&_schema=PORTAL; http://cesifo.oxfordjournals.org/.

55906 ■ Chemical Physics Letters
Elsevier Science
c/o D.C. Clary, Ed.
Physical & Theoretical Chemistry Laboratory
University of Oxford
S Parks Rd.
Oxford OX1 3QZ, United Kingdom
Publisher E-mail: nlinfo-f@elsevier.com
Journal covering latest in research in the field of chemical physics including structures, properties and dynamics of molecules, solid surfaces, interfaces, condensed phases, polymers, nanostructures and biomolecular systems. **Founded:** 1967. **Freq:** 102/yr. **Key Personnel:** V. Sundstrom, Editor; D.C. Clary, Editor; A.H. Zewail, Honorary Advisory Ed.; M. Okumura, Editor; V. Aquilanti, Advisory Editorial Board; C. Bai, Advisory Editorial Board. **ISSN:** 0009-2614. **Subscription Rates:** 1,934,600¥ institutions; US$16,284 institutions for all countries except Europe, Japan & Iran; EUR14,558 institutions for European Countries and Iran; 89,600¥ individuals; US$764 individuals for all countries except Europe, Japan & Iran; EUR681 individuals for European countries & Iran. **Remarks:** Accepts advertising. **URL:** http://www.elsevier.com/wps/find/journaldescription.cws_home/505707/description. **Circ:** (Not Reported)

55907 ■ Child
John Wiley & Sons Inc.
Wiley-Blackwell
9600 Garsington Rd.
Oxford OX4 2DQ, United Kingdom
Ph: 44 1865 776868
Fax: 44 1865 714591
Publication E-mail: gwatkins@wiley.com
Peer-reviewed journal focusing on all aspects of the health and development of children and young people. **Subtitle:** Care, Health and Development. **Freq:** Bimonthly. **Key Personnel:** Stuart Logan, Editor; Helen McConachie, Assoc. Ed.; Dr. Paul Bouvier, Editorial Board. **ISSN:** 0305-1862. **Subscription Rates:** US$1,393 institutions print and online; US$1,266 institutions print; 755 institutions print and online; 686 institutions print; US$1,627 institutions, other countries print and online; US$1,478 institutions, other countries online. **Remarks:** Accepts advertising. **URL:** http://www.wiley.com/bw/journal.asp?ref=0305-1862&site=1. **Circ:** (Not Reported)

55908 ■ Chinese Journal of International Law
Oxford University Press
Great Clarendon St.
Oxford OX2 6DP, United Kingdom
Ph: 44 1865 556767
Fax: 44 1865 353485
Publisher E-mail: webenquiry.uk@oup.com
Journal providing a forum for articles on international law by Chinese scholars and on international law issues relating to China, edited primarily by scholars from Mainland China, focusing on materials and viewpoints from and/or about China, other parts of Asia and the broader developing world. **Freq:** 4/yr. **Key Personnel:** Prof. Antony Anghie, Editor; Mr. Liu Zhenmin, Dep. Ed.-in-Ch.; Prof. Sienho Yee, Editor-in-Chief. **ISSN:** 1540-1650. **Subscription Rates:** 303 institutions corporate; print and online; 252 institutions corporate; online only; 277 institutions corporate; print only; 241 institutions print and online; 201 institutions online only; 221 institutions print only; 77 individuals print. **Remarks:** Advertising accepted; rates available upon request. **URL:** http://chinesejil.oxfordjournals.org. **Circ:** (Not Reported)

55909 ■ Citizenship, Social and Economics Education
Symposium Journals Ltd.
PO Box 204

Oxford OX11 9ZQ, United Kingdom
Ph: 44 1235 818062
Fax: 44 1235 817275
Publisher E-mail: info@symposium-journals.co.uk
Journal including refereed articles on innovations and research, analysis of curriculum practice, and reviews. **Subtitle:** An International Journal. **Freq:** 3/yr. **ISSN:** 1478-8047. **Subscription Rates:** US$490 libraries; US$50 individuals. **URL:** http://www.iacsee.org/JournalSubscribe.aspx. **Formerly:** Children's Social and Economics Education.

55910 ■ The Classical Quarterly
Cambridge University Press
c/o Dr. Rhiannon Ash, Ed.
Merton College
Merton St.
Oxford OX1 4JD, United Kingdom
Publisher E-mail: information@cambridge.org
Publication covering languages and linguistics. **Freq:** Quarterly. **Key Personnel:** Prof. John Wilkins, Editor; Dr. Rhiannon Ash, Editor, cqeditor@classics.ox.ac.uk. **ISSN:** 0009-8388. **Subscription Rates:** 111 institutions print and online; 103 institutions online; US$205 institutions print and online; US$190 institutions online. **Remarks:** Accepts advertising. **URL:** http://journals.cambridge.org/action/displayJournal?jid=CAQ. **Circ:** (Not Reported)

55911 ■ Clinical and Experimental Optometry
John Wiley & Sons Inc.
Wiley-Blackwell
9600 Garsington Rd.
Oxford OX4 2DQ, United Kingdom
Ph: 44 1865 776868
Fax: 44 1865 714591
Peer-reviewed journal covering the field of clinical optometry and vision science. **Freq:** Bimonthly. **Key Personnel:** Prof. Barry H. Collin, Editor; Prof. Raymond Applegate, Editorial Board; Prof. Robert F. Hess, Editorial Board; Prof. David Atchison, Editorial Board; Prof. Nathan Efron, Editorial Board; Dr. Erica Fletcher, Assoc. Ed. **ISSN:** 0816-4622. **Subscription Rates:** 78 individuals print and online; 110 other countries print and online; 212 institutions print and online; 192 institutions online only; US$184 individuals print and online; EUR164 individuals print and online; US$415 institutions print and online.(Australia and New Zealand); US$377 institutions online only (Australia and New Zealand); US$415 institutions print and online; US$322 institutions online. **Remarks:** Advertising accepted; rates available upon request. **URL:** http://www.wiley.com/bw/journal.asp?ref=0816-4622&site=1. **Circ:** (Not Reported)

55912 ■ The Clinical Teacher
John Wiley & Sons Inc.
Wiley-Blackwell
9600 Garsington Rd.
Oxford OX4 2DQ, United Kingdom
Ph: 44 1865 776868
Fax: 44 1865 714591
Journal providing a digest of current research, practice and thinking in medical education presented in a readable, stimulating and practical style. **Freq:** Quarterly. **Key Personnel:** Sue Symons, Editorial Mgr.; Steve Trumble, Editor-in-Chief; Jane Dacre, Editorial Advisory Board; Elizabeth Spencer, Editorial Advisory Board; Denis Wilkins, Editorial Advisory Board. **ISSN:** 1743-4971. **Subscription Rates:** US$180 individuals print + online; US$517 institutions print + online; US$469 institutions print or online; EUR357 institutions print + online; EUR324 institutions print or online; US$603 institutions, other countries print + online; 108 other countries print + online; US$547 institutions, other countries print or online; EUR146 individuals print + online; 280 institutions print + online. **Remarks:** Accepts advertising. **URL:** http://www.wiley.com/bw/journal.asp?ref=1743-4971&site=1. **Circ:** (Not Reported)

55913 ■ Communication Theory
John Wiley & Sons Inc.
Wiley-Blackwell
9600 Garsington Rd.
Oxford OX4 2DQ, United Kingdom
Ph: 44 1865 776868
Fax: 44 1865 714591
Publication covering languages and linguistics. **Freq:** Quarterly. **Key Personnel:** Angharad Valdivia, Editor; Sharon Mazzarella, Assoc. Ed.; Donnalyn Pompper, Assoc. Ed. **ISSN:** 1050-3293. **Subscription Rates:** US$70 individuals Americas (print & online); EUR64 individuals Europe (print & online); 43 other countries

print & online. **Remarks:** Accepts advertising. **URL:** http://www.wiley.com/bw/journal.asp?ref=1050-3293. **Circ:** (Not Reported)

55914 ■ Comparative Strategy
Taylor & Francis Group Ltd.
2 & 4 Park Sq.
Milton Pk.
Oxford OX14 4RN, United Kingdom
Ph: 44 20 70176000
Fax: 44 20 70176699
Publisher E-mail: international@tandf.co.uk
Publication focusing on international relations. **Freq:** 5/yr. **Key Personnel:** Keith B. Payne, Editor-in-Chief, keith.payne@nipp.org. **ISSN:** 0149-5933. **Subscription Rates:** 131 individuals print only; US$218 individuals print only; EUR175 individuals print only. **Remarks:** Accepts advertising. **URL:** http://www.taylorandfrancisgroup.com/; http://www.informaworld.com/smpp/title~db=all~content=t713769613~tab=editorialboard. **Circ:** (Not Reported)

55915 ■ Contemporary Issues in Early Childhood
wwwords Ltd.
Didcot
PO Box 204
Oxford OX11 9ZQ, United Kingdom
Ph: 44 1235 818062
Fax: 44 1235 817275
Publisher E-mail: info@wwwords.co.uk
Journal considering issues related to the lives of young children and their families. **Print Method:** Offset. **Cols./Page:** 5. **Col. Width:** 34 nonpareils. **Col. Depth:** 206 agate lines. **Key Personnel:** Michelle Knobel, Editorial Board; Gaile Cannella, Editorial Board; Nicola J. Yelland, Editor; Elizabeth Jones, Editorial Board; Judith Bernard, Editorial Board; Liz Brooker, Editorial Board; Debbie Epstein, Editorial Board; Celia Genishi, Editorial Board; Susan J. Grieshaber, Editor. **ISSN:** 1463-9491. **Subscription Rates:** US$50 individuals; 660 individuals library. **URL:** http://www.wwwords.co.uk/ciec.

55916 ■ Contemporary Review
Contemporary Review Company Ltd.
PO Box 1242
Oxford OX1 4FJ, United Kingdom
Publisher E-mail: editorial@contemporaryreview.co.uk
Scholarly journal covering current politics, international affairs, literature and the arts. **Founded:** 1866. **Freq:** Quarterly. **Cols./Page:** 1. **Key Personnel:** Dr. Richard Mullen, Editor; Dr. Alex Kerr, Managing Editor; Dr. James Munson, Literary Ed.; James LoGerfo, Editorial Advisor; Robin Findlay, Editorial Advisor; Charles Foster, Editorial Advisor; Anselma Bruce, Assoc. Ed. **ISSN:** 0010-7565. **Subscription Rates:** US$215 institutions U.S. and Canada; 55 institutions; 44 individuals; US$172 individuals U.S. and Canada; 61 institutions Europe; 48.80 individuals Europe; 65 institutions rest of the world; 52 individuals rest of the world. **Remarks:** Advertising not accepted. **Online:** Gale. **URL:** http://www.contemporaryreview.co.uk/. **Circ:** (Not Reported)

55917 ■ Continuing Education in Anaesthesia, Critical Care & Pain
Oxford University Press
Great Clarendon St.
Oxford OX2 6DP, United Kingdom
Ph: 44 1865 556767
Fax: 44 1865 353485
Publisher E-mail: webenquiry.uk@oup.com
Journal containing articles for the education and development of specialist's anesthesia, critical care medicine, and pain management. **Freq:** Bimonthly. **Key Personnel:** Jeremy A. Langton, Editor-in-Chief, ceaccp@pcmd.ac.uk. **ISSN:** 1743-1816. **Subscription Rates:** 204 institutions corporate; print and online; 170 institutions corporate; online only; 187 institutions corporate; print only; 163 institutions print and online; 136 institutions online only; 150 institutions print only; 73 individuals print; 32 members print. **URL:** http://ceaccp.oxfordjournals.org.

55918 ■ Critical Quarterly
John Wiley & Sons Inc.
Wiley-Blackwell
9600 Garsington Rd.
Oxford OX4 2DQ, United Kingdom
Ph: 44 1865 776868

Fax: 44 1865 714591
Publication featuring news, opinion, and commentary. **Freq:** Quarterly. **Key Personnel:** Colin MacCabe, Editor, phone 412624-6531, fax 412624-6639; Joanna Jellinek, Publishing Ed.; Shalini Puri, Assoc. Ed. **ISSN:** 0011-1562. **Subscription Rates:** US$52 individuals print + online; EUR46 individuals print + online; 30 individuals print + online; US$457 institutions print + online; 243 institutions print + online; 280 institutions print, online; US$415 institutions print, online; 221 institutions print, online; US$534 institutions, other countries print + online; US$485 institutions, other countries print, online. **Remarks:** Accepts advertising. **URL:** http://www.wiley.com/bw/journal.asp?ref=0011-1562&site=1. **Circ:** (Not Reported)

55919 ■ Critical Survey
Oxford University Press
Great Clarendon St.
Oxford OX2 6DP, United Kingdom
Ph: 44 1865 556767
Fax: 44 1865 353485
Publisher E-mail: webenquiry.uk@oup.com
Publication covering literature and writing. **Freq:** 3/yr. **Key Personnel:** Roger Ebbatson, Editor, alasdair@pinpoint-scotland.com; Graham Holderness, PhD, Gen. Ed.; Catherine Belsey, Editorial Board; Richard H. King, Editorial Board; Peter Brooker, Editorial Board; Daniel Cordle, Editorial Board. **ISSN:** 0011-1570. **Subscription Rates:** US$194 institutions print & online; US$176 institutions online; US$55 individuals; 118 institutions print & online; 107 institutions online; 32 individuals. **URL:** http://journals.berghahnbooks.com/cs/index.php.

55920 ■ Cultural Politics
Berg Publishers
1st Fl., Angel Ct.
81 St. Clements St.
Oxford OX4 1AW, United Kingdom
Ph: 44 18 65245104
Fax: 44 18 65791165
International, refereed journal exploring the global character and effects of contemporary culture and politics. **Subtitle:** Exploring Cultural and Political Power Across the Globe. **Freq:** 3/yr. **Key Personnel:** John Armitage, Editor; Douglas Kellner, Editor; Tom Conley, Editorial Advisory Board; Ryan Bishop, Editorial Advisory Board; Joy Garnett, Editorial Advisory Board; Mark Featherstone, Editorial Advisory Board. **ISSN:** 1743-2197. **Subscription Rates:** 49 individuals print only; 201 institutions online only; 236 institutions print and online; 201 individuals online only. **Remarks:** Accepts advertising. **URL:** http://www.bergpublishers.com/BergJournals/CulturalPolitics/tabid/520/Default.aspx. **Ad Rates:** BW: 550. **Circ:** (Not Reported)

55921 ■ Cultural & Social History
Berg Publishers
1st Fl., Angel Ct.
81 St. Clements St.
Oxford OX4 1AW, United Kingdom
Ph: 44 18 65245104
Fax: 44 18 65791165
Peer-reviewed Journal covering disciplinary shifts between social and cultural historians. **Subtitle:** The Journal of the Social History Society. **Founded:** 2000. **Freq:** 4/yr. **Key Personnel:** David Hopkin, Editor; Padma Anagol, Editor; John Arnold, Editor. **ISSN:** 1478-0038. **Subscription Rates:** 187 institutions print and online; 159 institutions online only. **Remarks:** Accepts advertising. **URL:** http://www.bergpublishers.com/JournalsHomepage/CulturalandSocialHistory/tabid/522/Default.aspx. **Circ:** (Not Reported)

55922 ■ Current Legal Problems
Oxford University Press
Great Clarendon St.
Oxford OX2 6DP, United Kingdom
Ph: 44 1865 556767
Fax: 44 1865 353485
Publisher E-mail: webenquiry.uk@oup.com
Law periodical. **Freq:** Semiannual. **Key Personnel:** Dr. Jane Holder, Editor; Colm O'Cinneide, Editor. **ISSN:** 0070-1998. **Subscription Rates:** US$225 individuals. **URL:** http://www.oup.com/us/catalog/general/subject/Law/LawSociety/?view=usa&ci= 9780199237999.

55923 ■ Decision Sciences Journal of Innovative Education
John Wiley & Sons Inc.

Wiley-Blackwell
9600 Garsington Rd.
Oxford OX4 2DQ, United Kingdom
Ph: 44 1865 776868
Fax: 44 1865 714591
Peer-reviewed journal covering the field of decision sciences. **Freq:** Semiannual. **Key Personnel:** Chetan S. Sankar, Editor-in-Chief; Hope M. Baker, Review Board; Stephen Bushardt, Review Board. **ISSN:** 1540-4595. **Subscription Rates:** US$420 institutions Americas (print and online); 314 institutions UK (print and online); EUR400 institutions Europe (print and online); US$615 institutions, other countries print and online; US$400 institutions Americas (print or online only); 314 institutions UK (print or online only); EUR342 institutions Europe (print or online only); US$559 institutions, other countries print or online only. **Remarks:** Advertising not accepted. **URL:** http://www.wiley.com/bw/journal.asp?ref=1540-4595&site=1. **Circ:** (Not Reported)

55924 ■ The Design Journal
Berg Publishers
1st Fl., Angel Ct.
81 St. Clements St.
Oxford OX4 1AW, United Kingdom
Ph: 44 18 65245104
Fax: 44 18 65791165
Peer-reviewed journal covering all aspects of design practice, theory, management and education for all design professionals worldwide. **Founded:** 1998. **Freq:** 3/yr. **Key Personnel:** Jack Ingram, Co-Founder; Rachel Cooper, Editor. **ISSN:** 1460-6925. **Subscription Rates:** 99 individuals print only; 695 individuals online only; 817 institutions print and online; 695 institutions online only. **URL:** http://www.bergpublishers.com/BergJournals/TheDesignJournal/tabid/3650/Default.aspx.

55925 ■ Diabetes Research and Clinical Practice
Mosby Inc.
The Blvd.
Langford Ln.
Kidlington
Oxford OX5 1GB, United Kingdom
Ph: 44 1865 843753
Fax: 44 1865 843997
Publisher E-mail: custserv.ehs@elsevier.com
Journal publishing original research articles and reviews in diabetology and related fields. **Freq:** Monthly. **Key Personnel:** S. Colagiuri, MD, Editor-in-Chief; M. Massi-Benedetti, MD, Assoc. Ed.; J. Gerich, MD, Assoc. Ed. **ISSN:** 0168-8227. **Subscription Rates:** US$284 other countries except Europe, Japan and Iran; EUR252 individuals for European countries and Iran; 34,000¥ individuals; EUR2,794 institutions for European countries and Iran; US$3,125 institutions, other countries except Europe, Japan and Iran; 370,000¥ institutions. **URL:** http://www.elsevier.com/wps/find/journaldescription.cws_home/505949/descriptiondescription.

55926 ■ Diabetic Medicine
John Wiley & Sons Inc.
Wiley-Blackwell
9600 Garsington Rd.
Oxford OX4 2DQ, United Kingdom
Ph: 44 1865 776868
Fax: 44 1865 714591
Peer-reviewed journal covering the field of clinical research and practice in diabetes. **Subtitle:** Journal of Diabetes UK. **Freq:** Monthly. **Key Personnel:** Prof. Graham A. Hitman, Editor; S.R. Heller, Editorial Board; A. Gray, Assoc. Ed. **ISSN:** 0742-3071. **Subscription Rates:** US$428 individuals print + online; 256 individuals print + online; US$2,324 institutions print + online; US$2,712 institutions, other countries print + online; 1,258 institutions print + online; EUR1,598 institutions print and online; EUR428 individuals print + online; 1,143 institutions print, online; EUR1,453 institutions print, online; US$2,465 institutions, other countries print, online. **URL:** http://www.wiley.com/bw/journal.asp?ref=0742-3071&site=1.

55927 ■ Dialectica
John Wiley & Sons Inc.
Wiley-Blackwell
9600 Garsington Rd.
Oxford OX4 2DQ, United Kingdom
Ph: 44 1865 776868
Fax: 44 1865 714591
Journal publishing articles predominantly in theoretical and systematic philosophy with a focus on analytical philosophy. **Freq:** Quarterly. **Key Personnel:** Philipp Keller, Managing Editor, philipp.keller@lettres.unige.ch;

Gianfranco Soldati, Editorial Board; Francois Recanati, Editorial Board; Peter Simons, Editorial Board; Carlos Moya, Editorial Board; Pascal Engel, Editor; Kevin Mulligan, Reviews Ed.; Diego Marconi, Editorial Board; Manuel Garcia-Carpintero, Editorial Board. **ISSN:** 0012-2017. **Subscription Rates:** US$72 individuals print and online; EUR59 individuals print and online; 39 individuals print and online; US$454 institutions print and online; 42 other countries print and online; US$56 students print and online; EUR43 students print and online; 28 students print and online; 30 students, other countries print and online; US$528 institutions, other countries print and online. **Remarks:** Advertising not accepted. **URL:** http://www.wiley.com/bw/journal.asp?ref=0012-2017&site=1. **Circ:** (Not Reported)

55928 ■ The Economic History Review
John Wiley & Sons Inc.
Wiley-Blackwell
9600 Garsington Rd.
Oxford OX4 2DQ, United Kingdom
Ph: 44 1865 776868
Fax: 44 1865 714591
Journal covering economics. **Freq:** Quarterly. **Key Personnel:** Steve Hindle, Managing Editor; Roger Middleton, Review Ed.; David Pratt, Periodical Reviewers; Peter Kirby, Periodical Reviewers. **ISSN:** 0013-0117. **Subscription Rates:** US$427 institutions print or online; US$470 institutions print + online; US$59 students print + online; 214 institutions print or online; 236 institutions print + online; 34 students, other countries print + online; EUR272 institutions print or online; 300 institutions print + online; US$170 institutions developing countries; print or online; US$187 institutions developing countries; print + online. **Remarks:** Accepts advertising. **URL:** http://www.wiley.com/bw/journal.asp?ref=0013-0117&site=1. **Circ:** (Not Reported)

55929 ■ Economic Inquiry
John Wiley & Sons Inc.
Wiley-Blackwell
9600 Garsington Rd.
Oxford OX4 2DQ, United Kingdom
Ph: 44 1865 776868
Fax: 44 1865 714591
Journal presenting articles on a variety of economic-related topics. **Freq:** Quarterly. **Key Personnel:** Prof. R. Preston McAfee, Editor; Peter Arcidiacono, Co-Ed. **ISSN:** 0095-2583. **Subscription Rates:** US$397 institutions print and online; US$474 institutions, other countries print and online; EUR308 institutions print and online; 242 institutions, other countries print and online; US$378 institutions online only; EUR291 institutions online only; US$449 institutions, other countries online only; 229 institutions online only. **URL:** http://www.wiley.com/bw/journal.asp?ref=0095-2583&site=1.

55930 ■ The Economic Journal
John Wiley & Sons Inc.
Wiley-Blackwell
9600 Garsington Rd.
Oxford OX4 2DQ, United Kingdom
Ph: 44 1865 776868
Fax: 44 1865 714591
Publication covering economics. **Freq:** 8/yr. **Key Personnel:** David Myatt, Editor; Antonio Ciccone, Editor; Steve Machin, Editor, fax 44 171 9162775, s.machin@ucl.ac.uk; Heather Daly, Publisher; David G. Mayes, Production Ed., david.mayes@bof.fi; Andrew Scott, Managing Editor, econjournal@london.edu. **ISSN:** 0013-0133. **Subscription Rates:** US$743 institutions print and online; US$675 institutions print, online; EUR552 institutions print and online; EUR501 institutions print, online; 435 institutions print and online; 395 institutions print, online; US$273 institutions print and online (developing world, Americas); US$332 institutions print and online (developing world, ROW); US$877 institutions, other countries print and online; US$798 institutions, other countries print, online. **Remarks:** Accepts advertising. **URL:** http://www.wiley.com/bw/journal.asp?ref=0013-0133&site=1. **Circ:** (Not Reported)

55931 ■ The Economic Record
John Wiley & Sons Inc.
Wiley-Blackwell
9600 Garsington Rd.
Oxford OX4 2DQ, United Kingdom
Ph: 44 1865 776868
Fax: 44 1865 714591
Publication covering economics. **Freq:** Quarterly. **Key Personnel:** Prof. Harry Bloch, Editorial Board; Prof. Paul Miller, Editor; Dr. Mardi Dungey, Editorial Board; Prof. Denise Doiron, Editorial Board; Prof. John Lodewijks, Survey Ed.; Prof. Michael Kidd, Editorial

Board; Dr. Robert Breunig, Book Review Ed.; Prof. Denzil Fiebig, Editorial Board; Prof. Jeff Borland, Editorial Board; Prof. Jeffrey Sheen, Co-Ed.; Dr. Timo Henckel, Book Review Ed.; Prof. Don Wright, Co-Ed. **ISSN:** 0013-0249. **Subscription Rates:** US$291 institutions print and online; US$264 institutions print, online; US$348 institutions print + online (Australia and NZ); US$443 institutions, other countries print + online; EUR288 institutions print + online; 205 institutions print, online; US$316 institutions print, online (Australia and NZ); EUR262 institutions print, online; US$403 institutions, other countries print, online. **Remarks:** Accepts advertising. **URL:** http://www.wiley.com/bw/journal.asp?ref=0013-0249&site=1. **Circ:** (Not Reported)

55932 ■ Economica
John Wiley & Sons Inc.
Wiley-Blackwell
9600 Garsington Rd.
Oxford OX4 2DQ, United Kingdom
Ph: 44 1865 776868
Fax: 44 1865 714591
Publication covering economics. **Freq:** Quarterly. **Key Personnel:** Peter Norman Sorensen, Editor; Frank Cowell, Editor; Alex Michaelides, Editor; Francesco Caselli, Editor; Prof. Amos Witztum, Review Ed.; Lena Edlund, Assoc. Ed. **ISSN:** 0013-0427. **Subscription Rates:** US$70 individuals print + online; US$49 students print + online; US$447 institutions print + online; US$406 institutions print; US$387 institutions online; 46 individuals print + online; 31 students print + online; EUR328 institutions print + online; US$506 institutions, other countries print + online; US$460 institutions, other countries print. **Remarks:** Accepts advertising. **URL:** http://www.wiley.com/bw/journal.asp?ref=0013-0427&site=1. **Circ:** (Not Reported)

55933 ■ Educational Measurement
John Wiley & Sons Inc.
Wiley-Blackwell
9600 Garsington Rd.
Oxford OX4 2DQ, United Kingdom
Ph: 44 1865 776868
Fax: 44 1865 714591
Journal for practitioners and users of tests containing information about proven practices in testing, news of interest to the educational measurement community, and organizational news of the National Council on Measurement in Education. **Subtitle:** Issues and Practice. **Freq:** Quarterly. **Key Personnel:** Steve Ferrara, Advisory Board; Jacqueline Leighton, Editor; Susan M. Brookhart, Advisory Board. **ISSN:** 0731-1745. **Subscription Rates:** US$389 institutions print or online; US$428 institutions print + online; 239 institutions print or online; 263 institutions print PLS online; EUR304 institutions print or online; EUR334 institutions print + online; US$468 institutions, other countries print or online; US$516 institutions, other countries print + online. **Remarks:** Accepts advertising. **URL:** http://www.wiley.com/bw/journal.asp?ref=0731-1745&site=1. **Circ:** (Not Reported)

55934 ■ EJVES Extra
Mosby Inc.
The Blvd., Langford Ln.
Kidlington
Oxford OX5 1GB, United Kingdom
Ph: 44 18 65843672
Fax: 44 18 65843992
Publication E-mail: ejves@elsevier.com
Publisher E-mail: custserv.ehs@elsevier.com
Journal for vascular and endovascular surgeons. **Freq:** Monthly. **Key Personnel:** P.G. Cao, Editor-in-Chief; A.R. Naylor, Assoc. Ed.; J. Powell, Assoc. Ed. **ISSN:** 1078-5884. **URL:** http://ejvesextra.com/.

55935 ■ Electrochemistry Communications
Elsevier Science Inc.
c/o R.G. Compton, Ed.-in-Ch.
Observatory St.
Oxford OX2 6HU, United Kingdom
Ph: 44 1865 275413
Fax: 44 1865 275410
Publisher E-mail: usinfo-ehelp@elsevier.com
Journal covering electrochemistry. **Founded:** 1999. **Freq:** 12/yr. **Print Method:** Offset. **Trim Size:** 11 1/2 x 13. **Cols./Page:** 6. **Col. Width:** 1 5/8 inches. **Col. Depth:** 12 inches. **Key Personnel:** R.G. Compton, Editor-in-Chief, elchem@physchem.ox.ac.uk; C. Amatore, Editorial Board; R.J. Forster, Editorial Board; Kohei Uosaki, Regional Ed., uosaki@pcl.sci.hokudai.ac.jp; A. Aldaz, Editorial Board; Y. Wu, Editorial Board; S. Daniele, Edito-

rial Board; J.F. Rusling, Regional Ed., jrusling@nucleus.chem.uconn.edu; E.J. Calvo, Editorial Board. **ISSN:** 1388-2481. **Subscription Rates:** EUR835 institutions for European countries and Iran; 110,900¥ institutions; US$932 institutions, other countries except Europe, Japan and Iran. **URL:** http://www.elsevier.com/wps/find/journaldescription.cws_home/601449/descriptiondescription.

55936 ■ Emotional and Behavioral Difficulties
Taylor & Francis Group Ltd.
2 & 4 Park Sq.
Milton Pk.
Oxford OX14 4RN, United Kingdom
Ph: 44 20 70176000
Fax: 44 20 70176699
Publisher E-mail: international@tandf.co.uk
Scholarly journal covering research to improve the quality of life for individuals with emotional and behavioral disorders for professionals worldwide. **Subtitle:** The Journal of the Association of Workers for Children with Emotional and Behavioral Difficulties. **Founded:** 2001. **Freq:** Quarterly. **Trim Size:** 202 x 117 mm. **Key Personnel:** Harry Daniels, Editor; Lyndal Bullock, Assoc. Ed.; Joan Pritchard, Reviews Ed.; Egide Royer, Assoc. Ed.; Alison Brice, Editorial Asst.; Carmel Cefai, Assoc. Ed. **ISSN:** 1363-2752. **Subscription Rates:** US$124 individuals print only; US$634 institutions online only; US$704 institutions print & online; 369 institutions print & online; 332 institutions online; 66 individuals print. **Remarks:** Accepts advertising. **URL:** http://www.tandf.co.uk/journals/journal.asp?issn=1363-2752&linktype=5. **Circ:** (Not Reported)

55937 ■ Enterprise & Society
Oxford University Press
Great Clarendon St.
Oxford OX2 6DP, United Kingdom
Ph: 44 1865 556767
Fax: 44 1865 353485
Publisher E-mail: webenquiry.uk@oup.com
Journal offering a forum for research on the historical relations between businesses and their larger political, cultural, institutional, social and economic contexts. **Freq:** Quarterly. **Key Personnel:** Philip Scranton, Editor, scranton@camden.rutgers.edu; Francesca Carnevali, Assoc. Ed.; Andrea Lluch, Assoc. Ed.; Lisa Jacobson, Assoc. Ed.; Mark Rose, Assoc. Ed.; Marcelo Bucheli, Assoc. Ed. for Reviews, mbucheli@uiuc.edu. **ISSN:** 1467-2227. **Subscription Rates:** 217 institutions corporate; print and online; 181 institutions corporate; online only; 199 institutions corporate; print only; 149 institutions print and online; 124 institutions online only; 137 institutions print only; 58 individuals print; 47 members print. **Remarks:** Advertising accepted; rates available upon request. **URL:** http://es.oxfordjournals.org. **Circ:** (Not Reported)

55938 ■ Environmental Science & Policy
Elsevier Science Inc.
Environmental Change Institute
Oxford University Centre for the Environment
Dyson Perrins Bldg.
S Parks Rd.
Oxford OX1 3QY, United Kingdom
Publisher E-mail: usinfo-ehelp@elsevier.com
Journal covering the solution of environmental problems. **Freq:** 8/yr. **Print Method:** Offset. **Cols./Page:** 6. **Col. Depth:** 21 inches. **Key Personnel:** J.C. Briden, Editor-in-Chief, esp@eci.ox.ac.uk; J. Curtis, Asst. Ed.-in-Ch.; S. Dovers, Assoc. Ed., stephen.dovers@anu.edu.au; H.P. Hanson, Assoc. Ed., hph@hphanson.com; J. Alcamo, Editorial Board; D.J. Baker, Editorial Board; A. Comrie, Editorial Board; T. Bernauer, Editorial Board; J. Boardman, Editorial Board; K. Brown, Editorial Board. **ISSN:** 1462-9011. **Subscription Rates:** 119,200¥ institutions; EUR897 institutions European countries and Iran; US$1,007 institutions, other countries except Europe, Japan and Iran; EUR159 individuals European countries and Iran; US$212 other countries except Europe, Japan and Iran; 24,500¥ individuals. **URL:** http://www.elsevier.com/wps/find/journaldescription.cws_home/601264/descriptiondescription.

55939 ■ Epidemiologic Reviews
Oxford University Press
Great Clarendon St.
Oxford OX2 6DP, United Kingdom
Ph: 44 1865 556767
Fax: 44 1865 353485

Publisher E-mail: webenquiry.uk@oup.com

Journal in public health recently focusing on prostate cancer, cohort study, vaccines, genetic epidemiology, injury prevention and social epidemiology. **Freq:** Annual. **Key Personnel:** Michel A. Ibrahim, MD, Editor-in-Chief; Nancy Adler, Editorial Committee; Shirley A.A. Beresford, Editorial Committee; Jean G. Ford, Editorial Committee; Luisa Franzini, Editorial Committee; Charles N. Rotimi, Editorial Committee; Lovell A. Jones, Editorial Committee; Nancy Krieger, Editorial Committee; Jay S. Kaufman, Editorial Committee; Carol R. Hogue, Editorial Committee. **ISSN:** 0193-936X. **Subscription Rates:** 56 institutions corporate; print and online; 47 institutions corporate; online only; 51 institutions corporate; print only; 45 institutions print and online; 37 institutions online only; 41 institutions and individual; print only. **Remarks:** Advertising not accepted. **URL:** http://epirev.oxfordjournals.org. **Circ:** (Not Reported)

55940 ■ ESHRE Monographs
Oxford University Press
Great Clarendon St.
Oxford OX2 6DP, United Kingdom
Ph: 44 1865 556767
Fax: 44 1865 353485
Publisher E-mail: webenquiry.uk@oup.com
Journal covering the proceedings of various scientific meetings including reproductive science and reproduction medicine. **Freq:** Quarterly. **ISSN:** 1477-741X. **Subscription Rates:** Included in membership. **URL:** http://eshremonographs.oxfordjournals.org.

55941 ■ Essays in Criticism
Oxford University Press
c/o Stephen Wall, Ed.
6A Rawlinson Rd.
Oxford OX2 6UE, United Kingdom
Publisher E-mail: webenquiry.uk@oup.com
Publication covering literature and writing. **Founded:** 1951. **Freq:** 4/yr. **Key Personnel:** Stephen Wall, Editor; Seamus Perry, Editor, seamus.perry@balliol.ox.ac.uk; Christopher Ricks, Book Review Ed. **ISSN:** 0014-0856. **Subscription Rates:** 156 institutions print and online; US$312 institutions print and online; EUR234 institutions print and online; 57 individuals print; US$114 individuals print; EUR86 individuals print; 43 members print; US$86 members print; EUR65 members print; 33 individuals print (senior, student). **Remarks:** Accepts advertising. **URL:** http://eic.oupjournals.org/. **Circ:** (Not Reported)

55942 ■ European Biophysics Journal
Springer-Verlag Tokyo
Oxford Biomembrane Structure Unit, Biochemistry Dept.
University of Oxford
South Parks Rd.
Oxford OX1 3QU, United Kingdom
Publication E-mail: ebj@bioch.ox.ac.uk
Publisher E-mail: info@springer.jp
Journal publishing papers in the field of biophysics, where biophysics is defined as the study of biological phenomena by using physical methods and concepts. **Freq:** Monthly. **Key Personnel:** A. Watts, Managing Editor; D. Andelman, Advisory Ed.; P.M. Bayley, Advisory Board; K. Berndt, Advisory Ed.; P. Schwille, Advisory Board; P.W. Kuchel, Editor; P. Janmey, Editor; W. Stuhmer, Editor. **ISSN:** 0175-7571. **Subscription Rates:** EUR1,530 institutions print incl. free online or e-access only; EUR1,836 institutions print incl. enhanced access. **Remarks:** Advertising accepted; rates available upon request. **URL:** http://www.springer.com/physics/biophysics/journal/249. **Circ:** (Not Reported)

55943 ■ European Educational Research Journal
wwwords Ltd.
Didcot
PO Box 204
Oxford OX11 9ZQ, United Kingdom
Ph: 44 1235 818062
Fax: 44 1235 817275
Publisher E-mail: info@wwwords.co.uk
Journal covering research intelligence, general announcements and conference news. **Freq:** Quarterly. **Print Method:** Typeset. **Key Personnel:** Martin Lawn, Editor, m.lawn@btinternet.com; Jan van den Akker, Editorial Board; Nafsika Alexiadou, Editorial Board. **ISSN:** 1474-9041. **Subscription Rates:** US$50 individuals; US$660 libraries. **URL:** http://www.wwwords.co.uk/eerj/.

55944 ■ European Heart Journal
Oxford University Press
Great Clarendon St.
Oxford OX2 6DP, United Kingdom
Ph: 44 1865 556767
Fax: 44 1865 353485
Publisher E-mail: webenquiry.uk@oup.com
Peer-reviewed journal publishing material, both clinical and scientific, on all aspects of Cardiovascular Medicine, including articles related to research findings, technical evaluations and reviews, providing a forum for the exchange of information on all aspects of Cardiovascular Medicine, including education issues. **Freq:** 24/yr. **Key Personnel:** Frank Rademakers, International Editorial Board; Stefan Janssens, International Editorial Board; Frans Van De Werf, Consulting Ed.; Thomas F. Luscher, Editor-in-Chief; J.T. Willerson, International Editorial Board; J. Vanhaecke, International Editorial Board. **ISSN:** 0195-668X. **Subscription Rates:** EUR1,476 institutions print and online; EUR1,107 institutions online only; EUR1,353 institutions print only; US$1,726 institutions print and online; US$1,968 institutions online only; US$1,804 institutions print only; 984 institutions print and online; 738 institutions online only; 920 institutions print only; 266 individuals print only. **Remarks:** Accepts advertising. **URL:** http://eurheartj.oxfordjournals.org/. **Circ:** (Not Reported)

55945 ■ European Journal of Applied Mathematics
Cambridge University Press
c/o Dr. S.D. Howison, Ed.-in-Ch.
Mathematical Institute
24-29 St. Giles
University of Oxford
Oxford OX1 3LB, United Kingdom
Publisher E-mail: customer_service@cup.org
Journal of applied and theoretical mathematical analysis. **Founded:** 1990. **Freq:** Bimonthly. **Key Personnel:** Prof. A.A. Lacey, Editor-in-Chief, a.a.lacey@ma.hw.ac.uk; Prof. M.J. Ward, Editor-in-Chief, ward@math.ubc.ca; Dr. S.D. Howison, Editor-in-Chief, ejam@maths.ox.ac.uk. **ISSN:** 0956-7925. **Subscription Rates:** 90 individuals online; 105 individuals print and online; 399 institutions online only; US$160 individuals online; US$200 individuals print and online; US$750 institutions online only; 445 institutions print and online; US$840 institutions print and online. **Remarks:** Accepts advertising. **URL:** http://journals.cambridge.org/action/displayJournal?jid=EJM. **Ad Rates:** BW: 590. **Circ:** 350

55946 ■ European Journal of Echocardiography
Oxford University Press
Great Clarendon St.
Oxford OX2 6DP, United Kingdom
Ph: 44 1865 556767
Fax: 44 1865 353485
Publisher E-mail: webenquiry.uk@oup.com
Journal for echocardiologists. **Freq:** 8/yr. **Key Personnel:** Jos Roelandt, Editor-in-Chief; P. Nihoyannopoulos, Assoc. Ed.; D. Poldermans, Assoc. Ed. **ISSN:** 1525-2167. **Subscription Rates:** 540 institutions corporate; print and online; 450 institutions corporate; online only; 495 institutions corporate; print only; 432 institutions print and online; 360 institutions online only; 396 institutions print only; 114 individuals print. **Remarks:** Accepts advertising. **URL:** http://ejechocard.oxfordjournals.org/. **Circ:** (Not Reported)

55947 ■ European Journal of Public Health
Oxford University Press
Great Clarendon St.
Oxford OX2 6DP, United Kingdom
Ph: 44 1865 556767
Fax: 44 1865 353485
Publisher E-mail: webenquiry.uk@oup.com
Multidisciplinary journal in the field of public health, publishing contributions from social medicine, epidemiology, health services research, management, ethics and law, health economics, social sciences and environmental health, providing a forum for discussion and debate of current international public health issues with a focus on the European region. **Freq:** 6/yr. **Key Personnel:** Peter Allebeck, Editor-in-Chief; Edison Manrique, Managing Editor; Sara Sjolund, Managing Editor; Johan P. Mackenbach, Editor; Martin McKee, Assoc. Ed.; Walter Ricciardi, Editor. **ISSN:** 1101-1262. **Subscription Rates:** 401 institutions print and online; US$802 institutions print and online; EUR602 institutions print and on-

line; 367 institutions print only; US$734 institutions print only; EUR551 institutions print only; 352 individuals print; US$704 individuals print; EUR528 individuals print; US$45 members European public health association. **Remarks:** Advertising accepted; rates available upon request. **URL:** http://eurpub.oxfordjournals.org. **Circ:** (Not Reported)

55948 ■ European Law Reports
Hart Publishing Ltd.
16C Worcester Pl.
Oxford OX1 2JW, United Kingdom
Ph: 44 1865 517530
Fax: 44 1865 510710
Publisher E-mail: mail@hartpub.co.uk
Journal covering judgments involving issues of European Community law decided by national courts and tribunals in the UK and Ireland. **Key Personnel:** David Vaughan, Editorial Board; Nicholas Green, Editorial Board; Mark Hoskins, Editorial Board. **ISSN:** 1091-3297. **Subscription Rates:** 310 individuals United Kingdom and Europe; 335 other countries; 279 individuals online. **Remarks:** Accepts advertising. **URL:** http://www.hartjournals.co.uk/eulr/. **Circ:** (Not Reported)

55949 ■ European Sociological Review
Oxford University Press
Great Clarendon St.
Oxford OX2 6DP, United Kingdom
Ph: 44 1865 556767
Fax: 44 1865 353485
Publisher E-mail: webenquiry.uk@oup.com
Journal presenting a wide variety of articles on the field of sociology. **Freq:** 6/yr. **Key Personnel:** Dr. Hans-Peter Blossfeld, Editor, phone 49 951 8632595, fax 49 951 8632597, soziologie1@sowi.uni-bamberg.de; Louis-Andre Vallet, Assoc. Ed.; Richard Breen, Editorial Board; Michelle Jackson, Assoc. Ed.; Robert Erikson, Editorial Board; Merike Darmody, Assoc. Ed. **ISSN:** 0266-7215. **Subscription Rates:** 442 institutions corporate; print and online; 361 institutions corporate; online only; 405 institutions corporate; print only; 353 institutions print and online; 288 institutions online only; 323 institutions print only; 77 individuals developing countries; print; 69 individuals print. **URL:** http://esr.oxfordjournals.org/.

55950 ■ Evidence-based Complementary and Alternative Medicine
Oxford University Press
Great Clarendon St.
Oxford OX2 6DP, United Kingdom
Ph: 44 1865 556767
Fax: 44 1865 353485
Publisher E-mail: webenquiry.uk@oup.com
International, peer-reviewed journal seeking to understand the sources and to encourage rigorous research in this new, yet ancient world of complementary and alternative medicine and to apply scientific rigor to the study of complementary and alternative medicine (CAM) modalities, particularly traditional Asian healing systems; the journal is devoted to the advancement of science in the field of basic research, clinical studies, methodology or scientific theory in diverse areas of Biomedical Sciences. **Freq:** 4/yr. **Key Personnel:** Prof. Edwin L. Cooper, Founding Ed.-in-Ch.; Susumu Kawashima, Mng. Ed./Pres.; Catherine Carpenter, Editorial Board; Piu Chan, Editorial Board; Elaine Elisabetsky, Editorial Board; Paolo Bellavite, Editorial Board; Peter Houghton, Editorial Board; Prof. Nobuo Yamaguchi, Founding Mng. Ed.; Edzard Ernst, Editorial Board. **ISSN:** 1741-427X. **Subscription Rates:** 228 institutions print and online; US$456 institutions print and online; EUR342 institutions print and online; 209 institutions print; US$418 institutions print; EUR314 institutions print; 190 institutions online; US$380 institutions online; EUR285 institutions online; 80 individuals print. **Remarks:** Advertising accepted; rates available upon request. **URL:** http://ecam.oxfordjournals.org. **Circ:** (Not Reported)

55951 ■ Family Court Review
John Wiley & Sons Inc.
Wiley-Blackwell
9600 Garsington Rd.
Oxford OX4 2DQ, United Kingdom
Ph: 44 1865 776868
Fax: 44 1865 714591
Journal for judges, attorneys, mediators and professionals in mental health and human services, covering topics such as family court practice, theory, research, and legal opinion. **Freq:** Quarterly. **Key Personnel:** Andrew I. Schepard, Editor-in-Chief; Glenda Rothberg, Editorial

Board, gmrlaw@aol.com; Philip Stahl, Editorial Board, pstahl@earthlink.net; Jack Arbuthnot, Editorial Board, arbuthno@ohiou.edu; Naomi Adler, Editorial Board, nadler@nshs.edu; Janet Walker, Editorial Board, j.a. walker@ncl.ac.uk; Janet R. Johnston, PhD, Assoc. Ed.; Barbara A. Babb, Editorial Board, bbabb@ubalt.edu; Karen Blaisure, Editorial Board, blaisure@wmich.edu. **ISSN:** 1531-2445. **Subscription Rates:** US$84 individuals print and online; US$668 institutions print or online; US$735 institutions print and online; 56 other countries print and online; 381 institutions print or online; 419 institutions print and online; EUR484 institutions print or online; EUR533 institutions print and online; EUR84 individuals. **Remarks:** Accepts advertising. **URL:** http://www.wiley.com/bw/journal.asp?ref=1531-2445&site=1. **Circ:** (Not Reported)

55952 ■ Family Practice
Oxford University Press
Great Clarendon St.
Oxford OX2 6DP, United Kingdom
Ph: 44 1865 556767
Fax: 44 1865 353485
Publisher E-mail: webenquiry.uk@oup.com
Journal discussing a wide variety of health topics for practitioners, teachers, and researchers. **Subtitle:** An International Journal. **Freq:** 6/yr. **Key Personnel:** Prof. Tom Fahey, Assoc. Ed.; Prof. Victoria Neale, Editor; Dr. Sandra Eldridge, Assoc. Ed.; Dr. William Hamilton, Assoc. Ed. **ISSN:** 0263-2136. **Subscription Rates:** 467 institutions corporate; print and online; 373 institutions corporate; online only; 428 institutions corporate; print only; 373 institutions print and online; 299 institutions online only; 342 institutions print only; 321 individuals print; 83 members print. **URL:** http://fampra. oxfordjournals.org.

55953 ■ Fashion Theory
Berg Publishers
1st Fl., Angel Ct.
81 St. Clements St.
Oxford OX4 1AW, United Kingdom
Ph: 44 18 65245104
Fax: 44 18 65791165
Academic journal covering fashion and dress. **Subtitle:** The Journal of Dress, Body & Culture. **Founded:** Mar. 1997. **Freq:** Quarterly. **Print Method:** Offset. **Trim Size:** 6 3/4 x 9. **Cols./Page:** 1. **Col. Depth:** 230 millimeters. **Key Personnel:** Valerie Steele, Editor; Alexandra Palmer, Exhibition Review; Christopher Breward, Editorial Advisory Board; Patrizia Calefato, Editorial Advisory Board; Pamela Golbin, Editorial Advisory Board; John S. Major, Editorial Advisory Board; Harold Koda, Editorial Advisory Board; Caroline Evans, Editorial Advisory Board. **ISSN:** 1362-704X. **Subscription Rates:** 313 institutions print and online; 266 institutions online only; 49 individuals print only. **Remarks:** Accepts advertising. **URL:** http://www.bergpublishers.com/ JournalsHomepage/FashionTheory/tabid/524/Default. aspx. **Ad Rates:** 4C: 210. **Circ:** Combined ‡716

55954 ■ FEMS Immunology and Medical Microbiology
John Wiley & Sons Inc.
Wiley-Blackwell
9600 Garsington Rd.
Oxford OX4 2DQ, United Kingdom
Ph: 44 1865 776868
Fax: 44 1865 714591
Journal covering various aspects of immunology and medical microbiology in connection with the Federation of European Microbiological Societies. **Freq:** 9/yr. **Key Personnel:** Patrik M. Bavoil, Editor, pbavoil@umaryland. edu; Willem Van Eden, Editor, w.eden@vet.uu.nl; Artur J. Ulmer, Editor, ajulmer@fz-borstel.de; Stephan Ehlers, Editorial Board Members, sehlers@fz-borstel.de; Patrick J. Brennan, Editor, patrick.brennan@colostate.edu; R. Mark, Editorial Board Members; Kai Man Kam, Editor, kmkam@dh.gov.hk. **ISSN:** 0928-8244. **Subscription Rates:** EUR1,145 institutions print or online; US$1,946 institutions, other countries print or online; US$1,834 institutions Americas (print and online); 992 institutions UK (print and online); EUR1,260 institutions Europe (print and online); US$2,141 institutions, other countries print and online; US$1,667 institutions Americas (print or online only); 901 institutions UK (print or online only). **URL:** http://www.fems-microbiology.org/website/nl/page23. asp; http://www.wiley.com/bw/journal.asp?ref=0928-8244.

55955 ■ FEMS Microbiology Reviews
John Wiley & Sons Inc.

Wiley-Blackwell
9600 Garsington Rd.
Oxford OX4 2DQ, United Kingdom
Ph: 44 1865 776868
Fax: 44 1865 714591
Journal dealing with microbiology surveyed. **Freq:** Bimonthly. **Print Method:** Offset. **Trim Size:** 13 x 21. **Cols./Page:** 6. **Col. Width:** 12 picas. **Col. Depth:** 294 agate lines. **Key Personnel:** Dieter Hass, Editor-in-Chief; Cecilia Arraiano, Editor; Colin Berry, Editor. **ISSN:** 0168-6445. **Subscription Rates:** US$9170 institutions print and online; US$881 institutions print or online; 525 institutions print and online; EUR668 institutions print and online; US$1,136 institutions, other countries print and online. **URL:** http://www.wiley.com/bw/editors.asp?ref= 0168-6445&site=1.

55956 ■ FEMS Yeast Research
John Wiley & Sons Inc.
Wiley-Blackwell
9600 Garsington Rd.
Oxford OX4 2DQ, United Kingdom
Ph: 44 1865 776868
Fax: 44 1865 714591
Journal publishing original research papers and mini-reviews that cover both yeast and yeast-like organisms, covering the entire field of yeast research in its broadest sense. **Freq:** 8/yr. **Key Personnel:** Monique Bolotin-Fukuhara, Editor; Teun Boekhout, Ch. Ed.; Richard Calderone, Editor. **ISSN:** 1567-1356. **Subscription Rates:** US$1,088 institutions print or online; US$1,197 institutions print + online; 589 institutions print or online; 648 institutions print + online; EUR748 institutions print or online; EUR823 institutions print + online; US$1,268 institutions, other countries print or online; US$1,395 institutions, other countries print + online. **URL:** http:// www.wiley.com/bw/journal.asp?ref=1567-1356&site=1.

55957 ■ Financial Accountability and Management
John Wiley & Sons Inc.
Wiley-Blackwell
9600 Garsington Rd.
Oxford OX4 2DQ, United Kingdom
Ph: 44 1865 776868
Fax: 44 1865 714591
Journal for the banking, finance, and accounting industries. **Freq:** Quarterly. **Key Personnel:** Prof. Irvine Lapsley, Editor, phone 44 131 6503790, fax 44 131 6503790, i.lapsley@ed.ac.uk; Willie Seal, Academic Editorial Board; Regina Herzlinger, Academic Editorial Board; Audrey Marsh, Asst. Ed., phone 44 1203 223480, fax 44 1203 222435, audrey@mhl4u.demon.co.uk; Mahmoud Ezzamel, Academic Editorial Board; Rowan Jones, Academic Editorial Board; Gwyn Bevan, Academic Editorial Board; Norvald Monsen, Academic Editorial Board. **ISSN:** 0267-4424. **Subscription Rates:** US$177 individuals print + online; EUR135 individuals print + online; 106 other countries print + online; US$987 institutions print + online; EUR590 institutions print + online; 422 institutions print or online; EUR536 institutions print or online; US$987 institutions, other countries print + online; US$897 institutions, other countries print or online. **Remarks:** Accepts advertising. **URL:** http://www.wiley.com/bw/journal.asp?ref=0267-4424&site=1. **Circ:** (Not Reported)

55958 ■ Fiscal Studies
John Wiley & Sons Inc.
Wiley-Blackwell
9600 Garsington Rd.
Oxford OX4 2DQ, United Kingdom
Ph: 44 1865 776868
Fax: 44 1865 714591
Journal for policy makers, public finance practitioners and academic researchers offering a perspective on the whole spectrum of ways in which government action affects the private sector and covering a broad range of topical issues of worldwide concern including studies into educational inequality, debt in low-income families and welfare-to-work programmes. **Freq:** Quarterly. **Key Personnel:** Gareth D. Myles, Editor, gdmyles@exeter. ac.uk; Samuel Berlinski, Editor, s.berlinski@ucl.ac.uk; Stephen Bond, Editorial Board; David Miles, Editorial Board; Ian Walker, Editorial Board; Richard Cornes, Editorial Board; Joel Slemrod, Editorial Board; Judith Payne, Production Ed.; Richard Blundell, Advisory Board; Michael Keen, Editorial Board. **ISSN:** 0143-5671. **Subscription Rates:** US$533 institutions print and online; US$484 institutions print or online; 318 institutions print and online; 288 institutions print or online; US$565 institutions, other countries print and online; US$622

institutions, other countries print, online. **Remarks:** Advertising not accepted. **URL:** http://www.wiley.com/ bw/journal.asp?ref=0143-5671&site=1. **Circ:** (Not Reported)

55959 ■ Foreign Policy Analysis
John Wiley & Sons Inc.
Wiley-Blackwell
9600 Garsington Rd.
Oxford OX4 2DQ, United Kingdom
Ph: 44 1865 776868
Fax: 44 1865 714591
Journal publishing academic research relating to the processes, outcomes and theories of foreign policy. **Freq:** Quarterly. **Key Personnel:** Douglas A. Van Belle, Editorial Board; Marijke Breuning, Editorial Board; Valerie Hudson, Editorial Board; Charles Hermann, Editorial Board; Alex Mintz, Editorial Board; Juliet B. Kaarbo, Editorial Board; Cooper A. Drury, Editor-in-Chief; Philip Nel, Editor. **ISSN:** 1743-8586. **Subscription Rates:** US$1,579 institutions print or online; US$1,737 institutions print + online; 1,206 institutions print or online; 1,327 institutions print + online; EUR1,532 institutions print or online; EUR1,686 institutions print + online; US$2,364 institutions, other countries print or online; US$2,601 institutions, other countries print + online. **Remarks:** Accepts advertising. **URL:** http://www.wiley. com/bw/journal.asp?ref=1743-8586&site=1. **Circ:** (Not Reported)

55960 ■ Forestry
Oxford University Press
Great Clarendon St.
Oxford OX2 6DP, United Kingdom
Ph: 44 1865 556767
Fax: 44 1865 353485
Publisher E-mail: webenquiry.uk@oup.com
Journal publishing refereed papers on all aspects of research, practice and policy that promote the sustainable development of forests, woodlands and trees. **Subtitle:** An International Journal of Forest Research. **Freq:** 5/yr. **Key Personnel:** Christine Cahalan, Editor; Gary Kerr, Editor; Marcos Barrio Anta, Editorial Board; Mark J. Ducey, Editorial Board; Jeffrey Gove, Editor; Helen McKay, Editor; Catherine Collet, Editor; Steve Mitchell, Editor. **ISSN:** 0015-752X. **Subscription Rates:** 473 institutions corporate; print and online; 366 institutions corporate; online only; 433 institutions corporate; print only; 378 institutions print and online; 293 institutions online only; 347 institutions print only; 79 members print. **Remarks:** Advertising accepted; rates available upon request. **URL:** http://forestry.oxfordjournals.org. **Circ:** (Not Reported)

55961 ■ French History
Oxford University Press
Great Clarendon St.
Oxford OX2 6DP, United Kingdom
Ph: 44 1865 556767
Fax: 44 1865 353485
Publisher E-mail: webenquiry.uk@oup.com
Journal presenting research related to the history of France. **Freq:** 4/yr. **Key Personnel:** Dr. Julian Wright, Editor, julian.wright@durham.ac.uk; Dr. Timothy Baycroft, Review Ed., t.baycroft@sheffield.ac.uk. **ISSN:** 0269-1191. **Subscription Rates:** 254 institutions corporate; print and online; 212 institutions corporate; online only; 233 institutions corporate; print only; 204 institutions print and online; 170 institutions online only; 187 institutions print only; 28 members online only; 39 members print; 22 members senior, student; print; 12 members senior, student; online only. **URL:** http://fh. oxfordjournals.org.

55962 ■ Gender & Development
Oxfam GB
Oxfam House
John Smith Dr.
Oxford OX4 2JY, United Kingdom
Scholarly journal covering gender development for policy makers, researchers, practitioners, students and activists. **Founded:** 1993. **Freq:** 3/yr. **Print Method:** Offset litho. **Trim Size:** 189 x 246 mm. **Cols./Page:** 2. **Col. Width:** 65 millimeters. **Col. Depth:** 200 millimeters. **Key Personnel:** Caroline Sweetman, Editor. **ISSN:** 1355-2074. **Subscription Rates:** 236 institutions print and online access; US$398 institutions print and online access; 212 institutions online only; US$358 institutions online only; 78 individuals print and online access; US$129 individuals print and online access. **Remarks:**

Accepts advertising. **URL:** http://www. genderanddevelopment.org/; http://www.oxfam.org.uk. **Circ:** (Not Reported)

55963 ■ Geographical Journal
John Wiley & Sons Inc.
Wiley-Blackwell
9600 Garsington Rd.
Oxford OX4 2DQ, United Kingdom
Ph: 44 1865 776868
Fax: 44 1865 714591
Peer-reviewed journal covering geography. **Freq:** Quarterly. **Key Personnel:** Klaus Dodds, Editor; Madeleine Hatfield, Managing Editor; Prof. Maano Ramutsindela, Editorial Board; Dr. Emma Mawdsley, Editorial Board; Dr. Frances Harris, Editorial Board; Prof. Mark Maslin, Editorial Board. **ISSN:** 0016-7398. **Subscription Rates:** US$324 institutions print + online; 192 institutions print + online; US$294 institutions print, online; 174 institutions print, online; US$376 institutions, other countries print + online; EUR243 institutions print + online; EUR221 institutions print, online; 341 institutions, other countries print, online. **Remarks:** Accepts advertising. **URL:** http://www.wiley.com/bw/journal.asp?ref=0016-7398&site=1. **Circ:** (Not Reported)

55964 ■ Geriatrics & Gerontology International
John Wiley & Sons Inc.
Wiley-Blackwell
9600 Garsington Rd.
Oxford OX4 2DQ, United Kingdom
Ph: 44 1865 776868
Fax: 44 1865 714591
Official journal of the Japanese Geriatrics Society, reflecting the growing importance of the subject area in developed economies and its particular significance to a country like Japan with a large aging population. **Freq:** Quarterly. **Key Personnel:** Hidetada Sasaki, Editor-in-Chief; Tsutomu Chiba, Editorial Board; Toru Kita, Assoc. Ed.; Yoshinori Doi, Editorial Board; Yasuyoshi Ouchi, Assoc. Ed.; Hidetoshi Endo, Editorial Board; Fumio Eto, Editorial Board; Takashi Inamatsu, Editorial Board; Toshio Ogihara, Assoc. Ed. **ISSN:** 1444-1586. **Subscription Rates:** US$391 institutions print + online; 241 institutions print + online; US$472 institutions, other countries print + online; EUR307 institutions print + online; US$355 institutions print or online; 219 institutions print or online; EUR278 institutions print or online; US$429 institutions, other countries print or online. **Remarks:** Accepts advertising. **URL:** http://www.wiley.com/bw/journal.asp?ref=1444-1586. **Circ:** (Not Reported)

55965 ■ German History
Oxford University Press
Great Clarendon St.
Oxford OX2 6DP, United Kingdom
Ph: 44 1865 556767
Fax: 44 1865 353485
Publisher E-mail: webenquiry.uk@oup.com
Academic journal for the history of the German-speaking world. **Founded:** 1984. **Freq:** Quarterly. **Key Personnel:** Neil Gregor, Editor, ng1@soton.ac.uk; Maiken Umbach, Editor, maiken.umbach@manchester.ac.uk; Moritz Foellmer, Review Ed. **ISSN:** 0266-3554. **Subscription Rates:** US$388 institutions print and online; US$323 institutions online, print; US$98 individuals print only; US$32 members print only; 204 institutions print and online; 170 institutions online, print; 49 individuals print only; 16 members print only; EUR281 individuals print; EUR255 institutions online. **Remarks:** Accepts advertising. **URL:** http://gh.oxfordjournals.org/. **Circ:** (Not Reported)

55966 ■ Global Networks (Oxford)
John Wiley & Sons Inc.
Wiley-Blackwell
Keble College
Oxford University
Oxford OX1 3PG, United Kingdom
Publication E-mail: global.networks@keble.ox.ac.uk
Journal publishing peer-reviewed research on global networks, transnational affairs and practices, and their relation to wider theories of globalization. **Subtitle:** A Journal of Transnational Affairs. **Freq:** Quarterly. **Key Personnel:** Dr. Alisdair Rogers, Editor, ali.rogers@geog.ox.ac.uk; Prof. Steve Vertovec, Co-Ed., vertovec@mmg.mpg.de; Prof. Robin Cohen, Co-Ed., robin.cohen@qeh.ox.ac.uk. **ISSN:** 1470-2266. **Subscription Rates:** US$80 individuals print and online; EUR71 individuals print and online; 47 other countries print and online; US$49 students print and online; US$613 institutions

print and online; US$557 institutions print or online; 366 institutions print and online; EUR464 institutions print and online; US$716 institutions, other countries print and online; 332 institutions print or online. **Remarks:** Accepts advertising. **URL:** http://www.blackwellpublishing.com/glob_enhanced/default.asp. **Circ:** (Not Reported)

55967 ■ Glycobiology
Oxford University Press
Great Clarendon St.
Oxford OX2 6DP, United Kingdom
Ph: 44 1865 556767
Fax: 44 1865 353485
Publisher E-mail: webenquiry.uk@oup.com
Journal for researchers in biomedicine, basic science, and the biotechnology industries, providing a forum dedicated to research into the structure and function of glycoconjugates (including glycoproteins, glycolipids, proteoglycans or free complex saccharides) or on any aspect of proteins that specifically interacts with glycoconjugates (e.g. lectins, glycotransferases, glycosidases). **Freq:** Monthly. **Key Personnel:** Ronald L. Schnaar, Editor-in-Chief; Anthony Bacic, Assoc. Ed.; Reiji Kannagi, Assoc. Ed.; Ulf Lindahl, Assoc. Ed.; Sam Turco, Assoc. Ed.; Gerald W. Hart, Founding Ed. **ISSN:** 0959-6658. **Subscription Rates:** 1,303 institutions corporate; print and online; 955 institutions corporate; online only; 1,194 institutions corporate; print only; 1,041 institutions print and online; 764 institutions online only; 955 institutions print only; 329 individuals print; 227 members print. **Remarks:** Advertising accepted; rates available upon request. **URL:** http://glycob.oxfordjournals.org. **Circ:** (Not Reported)

55968 ■ Grassland Science
John Wiley & Sons Inc.
Wiley-Blackwell
9600 Garsington Rd.
Oxford OX4 2DQ, United Kingdom
Ph: 44 1865 776868
Fax: 44 1865 714591
Journal publishing original research papers, review articles and short reports in all aspects of grassland science including topics on better management and use of grasslands, forage crops and turf plants for both agricultural and non-agricultural purposes across the world. **Freq:** Quarterly. **Key Personnel:** Hitoshi Nakagawa, Editorial Board; Masahiko Hirata, Editor-in-Chief; Shuichi Sugiyama, Editorial Board; Shinro Yamamoto, Editorial Board; Makoto Kobayashi, Managing Editor; Suguru Saiga, President; Masakazu Goto, Vice President; David Chapman, Editorial Board. **ISSN:** 1744-6961. **Subscription Rates:** US$407 institutions print and online; US$370 institutions print or online; 209 institutions print and online; 190 institutions print or online; EUR242 institutions print or online; EUR266 institutions print and online; US$370 institutions, other countries print or online; US$407 institutions, other countries print and online. **Remarks:** Advertising accepted; rates available upon request. **URL:** http://www.wiley.com/bw/journal.asp?ref=1744-6961&site=1. **Circ:** (Not Reported)

55969 ■ Ground Water
John Wiley & Sons Inc.
Wiley-Blackwell
9600 Garsington Rd.
Oxford OX4 2DQ, United Kingdom
Ph: 44 1865 776868
Fax: 44 1865 714591
Journal publishing papers on topics related to ground water including ground water flow and well hydraulics, hydrogeochemistry and contaminant hydrogeology, application of geophysics, groundwater management and policy, and history of ground water hydrology with emphasis on articles that includes presentation of theory with practical application. **Freq:** Bimonthly. **Key Personnel:** Mary P. Anderson, Editor; Christopher Neuzil, PhD, Advisors to the Ed.-in-Ch.; Chunmiao Zheng, Software Ed.; Robert J. Sterrett, PhD, Advisor to the Ed.-in-Ch.; Kenneth R. Bradbury, PhD, Advisor to the Ed.-in-Ch.; Keith J. Halford, PhD, Assoc. Ed.; Laura Sander, PhD, Book Ed. **ISSN:** 0017-467X. **Subscription Rates:** US$558 institutions print or online; US$592 institutions print + online; US$696 institutions, other countries print + online; 356 institutions print + online; 323 institutions print or online; EUR451 institutions print + online; EUR410 institutions print or online; US$632 institutions, other countries print or online. **Remarks:** Advertising not accepted. **URL:** http://www.wiley.com/bw/journal.asp?

ref=0017-467X&site=1. **Circ:** (Not Reported)

55970 ■ Ground Water Monitoring & Remediation
John Wiley & Sons Inc.
Wiley-Blackwell
9600 Garsington Rd.
Oxford OX4 2DQ, United Kingdom
Ph: 44 1865 776868
Fax: 44 1865 714591
Peer-reviewed journal containing information on ground water treatment technology, EPA updates, news briefs, industry announcements, equipment news, professional services, annual directories and buyer's guides. **Freq:** Quarterly. **Key Personnel:** Paul C. Johnson, Editor; Richard L. Johnson, Assoc. Ed.; David Huntley, Assoc. Ed.; David W. Major, Assoc. Ed.; William G. Rixey, Assoc. Ed.; Michael J. Barcelona, Assoc. Ed. **ISSN:** 1069-3629. **Subscription Rates:** US$294 institutions print and online; US$267 institutions print, online; 243 institutions print and online; US$476 institutions, other countries print and online; EUR309 institutions print and online; US$433 institutions, other countries print, online. **Remarks:** Advertising not accepted. **URL:** http://www.wiley.com/bw/journal.asp?ref=1069-3629&site=1. **Circ:** (Not Reported)

55971 ■ Health Education Research
Oxford University Press
Great Clarendon St.
Oxford OX2 6DP, United Kingdom
Ph: 44 1865 556767
Fax: 44 1865 353485
Publisher E-mail: webenquiry.uk@oup.com
Peer-reviewed journal presenting health education related papers. **Freq:** 6/yr. **Key Personnel:** D.S. Leathar, Founding Ed.; Dr. Michael P. Eriksen, Editor-in-Chief; P. Aggleton, Assoc. Ed. **ISSN:** 0268-1153. **Subscription Rates:** 592 institutions print and online; 473 institutions online only; 542 institutions print only; US$1,184 institutions print and online; US$947 institutions online only; US$1,084 institutions print only; EUR888 institutions print and online; EUR710 institutions online only; EUR813 institutions print only. **URL:** http://her.oxfordjournals.org.

55972 ■ Health Promotion International
Oxford University Press
Great Clarendon St.
Oxford OX2 6DP, United Kingdom
Ph: 44 1865 556767
Fax: 44 1865 353485
Publisher E-mail: webenquiry.uk@oup.com
Peer-reviewed journal providing health-related innovations in various fields. **Freq:** Quarterly. **Key Personnel:** J. Catford, Editor-in-Chief; L. Levin, Editorial Board; Evelyne De Leeuw, Assoc. Ed.; A. Lee, Editorial Board; H. Ling, Editorial Board; H. Madi, Editorial Board; H. Arroyo, Editorial Board; L. Aaro, Editorial Board; D. Nutbeam, Editorial Board; D. Nyamwaya, Editorial Board. **ISSN:** 0957-4824. **Subscription Rates:** 425 institutions print and online; US$850 institutions print and online; EUR638 institutions print and online; 164 individuals print; US$328 individuals print; EUR246 individuals print; 389 institutions print; US$778 institutions print; EUR584 institutions print; 312 institutions online. **URL:** http://heapro.oxfordjournals.org.

55973 ■ History
John Wiley & Sons Inc.
Wiley-Blackwell
9600 Garsington Rd.
Oxford OX4 2DQ, United Kingdom
Ph: 44 1865 776868
Fax: 44 1865 714591
Periodical focusing on history. **Subtitle:** The Journal of the Historical Association. **Founded:** 1912. **Freq:** Quarterly. **Key Personnel:** Joseph Smith, Editor, phone 44 1392 264297, fax 44 1392 263305, jha@exeter.ac.uk; Sarah Hamilton, Review Ed.; Alex Walsham, Review Ed. **ISSN:** 0018-2648. **Subscription Rates:** US$132 individuals print and online; US$588 institutions print and online; EUR420 institutions print and online; US$688 institutions, other countries print and online. **URL:** http://www.wiley.com/bw/journal.asp?ref=0018-2648&site=1.

55974 ■ History Compass
John Wiley & Sons Inc.
Wiley-Blackwell
9600 Garsington Rd.
Oxford OX4 2DQ, United Kingdom
Ph: 44 1865 776868

Circulation: ★ = ABC; △ = BPA; ♦ = CAC; ● = CCAB; ❑ = VAC; ⊕ = PO Statement; ‡ = Publisher's Report; Boldface figures = sworn; Light figures = estimated.

Gale Directory of Publications & Broadcast Media/147th Ed.   5815

Fax: 44 1865 714591
Peer-reviewed journal covering research from across all branches of historical scholarship. **Freq:** Monthly. **Key Personnel:** Felice Lifshitz, Editor-in-Chief; Charles Armstrong, Editorial Board; Chris Saunders, Section Ed.; Jocelyn Alexander, Editorial Board; Toyin Falola, Section Ed.; Laura J. Mitchell, Editorial Board; Christopher Ehret, Editorial Board; Richard Rathbone, Editorial Board; Sara Berry, Editorial Board. **ISSN:** 1478-0542. **Subscription Rates:** US$878 institutions online; US$978 institutions, other countries online; US$69 individuals online; 35 other countries online; EUR45 individuals online; EUR634 institutions online. **Remarks:** Advertising accepted; rates available upon request. **URL:** http://www.wiley.com/bw/journal.asp?ref=1478-0542. **Circ:** (Not Reported)

55975 ■ History and Theory
John Wiley & Sons Inc.
Wiley-Blackwell
9600 Garsington Rd.
Oxford OX4 2DQ, United Kingdom
Ph: 44 1865 776868
Fax: 44 1865 714591
Periodical focusing on history. **Subtitle:** Studies in the Philosophy of History. **Freq:** Quarterly. **Key Personnel:** Richard T. Vann, Sen. Ed.; Brian C. Fay, Exec. Ed., phone 860685-3648, fax 860685-2491, bfay@wesleyan.edu; Julia Perkins, Admin. Ed., phone 860685-3292, jperkins@wesleyan.edu; Philip Pomper, Assoc. Ed.; David Gary Shaw, Assoc. Ed.; Ethan Kleinberg, Assoc. Ed. **ISSN:** 0018-2656. **Subscription Rates:** US$48 individuals print and online; EUR61 individuals print and online; 41 individuals print and online; US$40 members print and online; EUR46 members print and online; 30 members print and online; US$285 institutions print and online; 220 institutions print and online; US$430 institutions, other countries print and online; 23 students print and online. **Remarks:** Accepts advertising. **URL:** http://www.wiley.com/bw/journal.asp?ref=0018-2656&site=1. **Circ:** (Not Reported)

55976 ■ Holocaust and Genocide Studies
Oxford University Press
Great Clarendon St.
Oxford OX2 6DP, United Kingdom
Ph: 44 1865 556767
Fax: 44 1865 353485
Publisher E-mail: webenquiry.uk@oup.com
International journal featuring research articles, interpretive essays, and book reviews in the social sciences and humanities, the purpose being to address the issue of how insights into the Holocaust apply to other genocides and to provide a forum for scholarship on the Holocaust and other genocides with articles that compel readers to confront many aspects of human behavior, to contemplate major moral issues, to consider the role of science and technology in human affairs and to reconsider significant political and social factors. **Freq:** 3/yr. **Key Personnel:** Richard D. Breitman, Editor-in-Chief; David Bankier, Assoc. Ed.; Hubert G. Locke, Assoc. Ed. **ISSN:** 8756-6583. **Subscription Rates:** 143 institutions print and online; 131 institutions print or online; 33 institutions developing Countries - print only; US$215 institutions print and online; US$179 institutions print or online; US$50 institutions developing Countries - print only; EUR49 individuals print; EUR35 students print; 33 individuals print. **Remarks:** Advertising accepted; rates available upon request. **URL:** http://hgs.oxfordjournals.org. **Circ:** (Not Reported)

55977 ■ The Howard Journal of Criminal Justice
John Wiley & Sons Inc.
Wiley-Blackwell
9600 Garsington Rd.
Oxford OX4 2DQ, United Kingdom
Ph: 44 1865 776868
Fax: 44 1865 714591
Law periodical. **Freq:** 5/yr. **Key Personnel:** Tony Fowles, Editor; David Wilson, Editor, david.wilson@uce.ac.uk; Frances Crook, Managing Editor; Loraine Gelsthorpe, Book Review Ed.; Brenda McWilliams, Publishing Ed., phone 44 1223 511810, fax 44 1223 510912, nq69@dial.pipex.com; Richard Abel, Editorial Advisor. **ISSN:** 0265-5527. **Subscription Rates:** US$173 individuals Americas; 65 individuals non-Euro zone; EUR98 individuals Euro zone; 103 other countries; US$974 institutions Americas (print and online); 477 institutions UK (print and online); EUR606 institutions Europe (print and online); US$1,137 institutions, other countries print and online); US$43 students Americas; EUR25 students non-Euro zone. **Remarks:** Accepts advertising. **URL:** http://www.wiley.com/bw/journal.asp?ref=0265-5527&site=1. **Circ:** (Not Reported)

55978 ■ HPB
Wiley InterScience
c/o Michael Willis
Wiley-Blackwell
9600 Garsington Rd.
Oxford 5042, United Kingdom
Ph: 44 1865 476387
Fax: 44 1865 471387
Publisher E-mail: info@wiley.com
International forum for surgeons, physicians, radiologists and basic scientists, publishing original research, reviews, HPB images, editorials, case reports and reader correspondence connected with the various scientific and clinical interests involved in hepatic, pancreatic and biliary disease, along with the latest news from the IHPBA. **Founded:** 1999. **Freq:** 6/yr. **Key Personnel:** James Garden, Editor-in-Chief; Mark Callery, Assoc. Ed.; Saxon Connor, Assoc. Ed. **ISSN:** 1365-182X. **Remarks:** Accepts advertising. **URL:** http://www3.interscience.wiley.com/journal/122196895/home?CRETRY=1&SRETRY=0. **Circ:** (Not Reported)

55979 ■ Human Molecular Genetics
Oxford University Press
Department of Physiology, Anatomy & Genetics
University of Oxford
South Parks Rd.
Oxford OX1 3QX, United Kingdom
Publisher E-mail: webenquiry.uk@oup.com
Peer-reviewed journal concentrating on full-length research papers covering a wide range of topics in all aspects of human molecular genetics, including the molecular basis of human genetic disease, developmental genetics, cancer genetics, neurogenetics, chromosome and genome structure and function, gene therapy, mouse and other models of human diseases, functional genomics and computational genomics. **Freq:** 26/yr. **Key Personnel:** Prof. Kay Davies, Exec. Ed.; Dr. Anthony Wynshaw-Boris, Exec. Ed.; Chris Amos, Editorial Board; Alexis Brice, Editorial Board; Marisa Bartolomei, Editorial Board; David Chan, Editorial Board. **ISSN:** 0964-6906. **Subscription Rates:** 1,668 institutions print and online; US$3,336 institutions print and online; EUR2,502 institutions print and online; 1,168 institutions online only; US$2,335 institutions online only; EUR1,751 institutions online only; 403 individuals print; US$806 individuals print; EUR605 individuals print. **Remarks:** Advertising accepted; rates available upon request. **URL:** http://hmg.oxfordjournals.org. **Circ:** (Not Reported)

55980 ■ Human Resource Management Journal
John Wiley & Sons Inc.
Wiley-Blackwell
9600 Garsington Rd.
Oxford OX4 2DQ, United Kingdom
Ph: 44 1865 776868
Fax: 44 1865 714591
Peer-reviewed journal focusing on people management in the areas of economics, politics and sociology. **Freq:** Quarterly. **Key Personnel:** Adrian Wilkinson, Assoc. Ed.; Mick Marchington, Editor; Frank Bournois, Editorial Advisory; David Collings, Editor; Scott A. Snell, Assoc. Ed.; Jaap Paauwe, Assoc. Ed. **ISSN:** 0954-5395. **Subscription Rates:** US$271 individuals print + online; US$436 institutions print + online; US$259 institutions online only; US$524 institutions, other countries print + online; US$462 institutions, other countries online only; EUR329 individuals print + online; 259 institutions print + online; 268 institutions online only; EUR329 institutions print + online; EUR340 institutions online only. **URL:** http://www.wiley.com/bw/journal.asp?ref=0954-5395&site=1.

55981 ■ Human Rights Law Review
Oxford University Press
Great Clarendon St.
Oxford OX2 6DP, United Kingdom
Ph: 44 1865 556767
Fax: 44 1865 353485
Publisher E-mail: webenquiry.uk@oup.com
Journal for those involved in human rights in governmental, intergovernmental and non-governmental spheres and those involved in human rights work, promoting knowledge, awareness and debate of human rights law and policy. **Founded:** 2001. **Freq:** 4/yr. **Key Personnel:** Prof. David Harris, Editor. **ISSN:** 1461-7781. **Subscription Rates:** 247 institutions corporate; print and online; 206 institutions corporate; online only; 227 institutions corporate; print only; 198 institutions print and online; 165 institutions online only; 182 institutions print only;

75 individuals print. **URL:** http://hrlr.oxfordjournals.org.

55982 ■ HyperScale
Osprey Publishing
Midland House
West Way
Botley
Oxford OX2 0PH, United Kingdom
Ph: 44 1865 727022
Fax: 44 1865 242009
Publication E-mail: editor@hyperscale.com
Online resource for aircraft and armour modellers. **Subtitle:** A Virtual Magazine for Aircraft and Armour Modellers. **Key Personnel:** Brett Green, Editor, btgreen@optusnet.com.au. **URL:** http://www.hyperscale.com.

55983 ■ ICES Journal of Marine Science
Oxford University Press
Great Clarendon St.
Oxford OX2 6DP, United Kingdom
Ph: 44 1865 556767
Fax: 44 1865 353485
Publisher E-mail: webenquiry.uk@oup.com
Scholarly journal covering marine science. **Freq:** 9/yr. **Key Personnel:** Dr. Andrew I.L. Payne, Editor-in-Chief, andy.payne@cefas.co.uk; Pierre Pepin, Editor, pierre.pepin@dfo-mpo.gc.ca; Audrey J. Geffen, Editor, audrey.geffen@bio.uib.no; Sarah B.M. Kraak, Editor, sarah.kraak@marine.ie; John W. Ramster, Editor, jramster@lineone.net; Rochelle Seitz, Editor, seitz@vims.edu. **ISSN:** 1054-3139. **Subscription Rates:** 755 institutions print and online; US$1,306 institutions print and online; EUR1,133 institutions print and online; 604 institutions online; US$1,044 institutions online; EUR906 institutions online; 692 institutions print; US$1,187 institutions print; EUR1,038 institutions print; 174 individuals print. **URL:** http://icesjms.oxfordjournals.org.

55984 ■ IMA Journal of Management Mathematics
Oxford University Press
Great Clarendon St.
Oxford OX2 6DP, United Kingdom
Ph: 44 1865 556767
Fax: 44 1865 353485
Publisher E-mail: webenquiry.uk@oup.com
Peer-reviewed journal covering management-related mathematics studies and papers. **Freq:** Quarterly. **Key Personnel:** Prof. K. Darby-Dowman, Assoc. Ed.; Prof. R.D. Baker, Assoc. Ed.; Prof. Russell Barton, Assoc. Ed.; Prof. Ton De-Kok, Assoc. Ed.; Prof. P. Scarf, Editor, p.a.scarf@salford.ac.uk; Prof. Sydney Chu, Assoc. Ed.; Prof. Zvi Drezner, Assoc. Ed. **ISSN:** 1471-678X. **Subscription Rates:** US$688 institutions print and online; US$574 institutions online only; US$632 institutions print only; 344 institutions print and online; 287 institutions online only; 316 institutions print only; EUR516 institutions print and online; EUR431 institutions online only; EUR474 institutions print only; US$596 individuals print. **URL:** http://imaman.oxfordjournals.org/.

55985 ■ IMA Journal of Mathematical Control and Information
Oxford University Press
Great Clarendon St.
Oxford OX2 6DP, United Kingdom
Ph: 44 1865 556767
Fax: 44 1865 353485
Publisher E-mail: webenquiry.uk@oup.com
Journal providing solution-driven research in control and information theories. **Freq:** 4/yr. **Key Personnel:** E. Fridman, Assoc. Ed.; C. Moog, Assoc. Ed.; A. Astolfi, Assoc. Ed.; N. Koussoulas, Assoc. Ed.; G. Conte, Assoc. Ed.; Sarah Spurgeon, Editor; P. Caines, Assoc. Ed.; Nick Karcanias, Editor; G. Halikas, Assoc. Ed. **ISSN:** 0265-0754. **Subscription Rates:** 451 institutions corporate; print and online; 376 institutions corporate; online only; 414 institutions corporate; print only; 361 institutions print and online; 301 institutions online only; 331 institutions print only; 316 individuals print; 99 members print. **URL:** http://imamci.oxfordjournals.org.

55986 ■ IMA Journal of Numerical Analysis
Oxford University Press
Great Clarendon St.
Oxford OX2 6DP, United Kingdom
Ph: 44 1865 556767
Fax: 44 1865 353485
Publisher E-mail: webenquiry.uk@oup.com
Journal presenting original research in the area of

numerical analysis. **Freq:** 4/yr. **Key Personnel:** I.S. Duff, Assoc. Ed.; E. Suli, Editor; J.W. Barrett, Assoc. Ed.; A. Iserles, Editor; M. Ainsworth, Assoc. Ed.; M.L. Overton, Assoc. Ed. **ISSN:** 0272-4979. **Subscription Rates:** 505 institutions corporate; print and online; 421 institutions corporate; online only; 463 institutions corporate; print only; 404 institutions print and online; 337 institutions online only; 371 institutions print only; 349 individuals print; 99 members print. **URL:** http://imajna.oxfordjournals.org/.

55987 ■ IMRN
Oxford University Press
Great Clarendon St.
Oxford OX2 6DP, United Kingdom
Ph: 44 1865 556767
Fax: 44 1865 353485
Publisher E-mail: webenquiry.uk@oup.com
Scholarly journal for mathematicians and research libraries. **Subtitle:** International Mathematics Research Notices. **Founded:** 1991. **Freq:** 24/yr. **Key Personnel:** Morris Weisfeld, Editor-in-Chief, mw@math.duke.edu; Anton Yu Alekseev, Editor; Enrico Arbarello, Editor. **ISSN:** 1073-7928. **Subscription Rates:** 1,042 institutions print and online; US$4,084 institutions print and online; EUR3,063 institutions print and online; 1,702 institutions print, online; US$3,404 institutions print, online; EUR2,553 institutions print, online. **Remarks:** Advertising not accepted. **URL:** http://imrn.oxfordjournals.org/. **Circ:** (Not Reported)

55988 ■ Industrial Relations Journal
John Wiley & Sons Inc.
Wiley-Blackwell
9600 Garsington Rd.
Oxford OX4 2DQ, United Kingdom
Ph: 44 1865 776868
Fax: 44 1865 714591
Peer-reviewed journal covering human resources and labor relations. **Freq:** Bimonthly. **Key Personnel:** Peter Nolan, Editor; Peter Prowse, Book Review Ed.; Linda Dickens, Editorial Board; John Benson, Editorial Board; Kim Hoque, Editorial Board; Bob Hepple, Editorial Board. **ISSN:** 0019-8692. **Subscription Rates:** US$211 individuals print and online; US$81 students print and online; US$107 members BUIRA: print online; US$1,578 institutions print and online; US$1,434 institutions print, online; US$1,841 institutions, other countries print and online; EUR143 individuals print and online; EUR72 students print and online; EUR949 institutions print and online; US$1,673 institutions, other countries print, online. **Remarks:** Accepts advertising. **URL:** http://www.wiley.com/bw/journal.asp?ref=0019-8692&site=1. **Circ:** (Not Reported)

55989 ■ infocus Magazine
John Wiley & Sons Inc.
Wiley-Blackwell
9600 Garsington Rd.
Oxford OX4 2DQ, United Kingdom
Ph: 44 1865 776868
Fax: 44 1865 714591
Journal providing a platform for scientists and technologists from all fields which use any type of microscope, with a focus on optical, mechanical and electronic features of design of all types of light, electron, X-ray and ion microscopes and microanalysers. **Freq:** Quarterly. **Key Personnel:** Timothy F. Watson, Scientific Ed.; Adrian P. Burden, Scientific Ed.; Laura Kingsbury, Editor, phone 44 1865 254767, editor@infocus.org.uk; Allison Winton, Contact, phone 44 1865 254764, advertising@infocus.org.uk. **ISSN:** 1750-4740. **Subscription Rates:** US$626 institutions print only; 335 institutions print only; US$730 institutions, other countries print only; EUR426 institutions print only. **Remarks:** Advertising accepted; rates available upon request. **URL:** http://www.wiley.com/bw/journal.asp?ref=1750-4740. **Formerly:** Proceedings of the Royal Microscopical Society. **Circ:** (Not Reported)

55990 ■ Insect Science
John Wiley & Sons Inc.
Wiley-Blackwell
9600 Garsington Rd.
Oxford OX4 2DQ, United Kingdom
Ph: 44 1865 776868
Fax: 44 1865 714591
Peer-reviewed journal covering the entomological discipline including in the adaptation and evolutionary biology of insects from their molecules to the ecosystems3. **Freq:** Bimonthly. **Key Personnel:** Le Kang, Editor-in-Chief; D. Ren, Editorial Board; K.Y. Zhu, Editorial Board; Yun Xian Zhao, Managing Editor; D. Denlinger, Editorial Board; S.J. Simpson, Editorial Board; Mu Mu Wang, Managing Editor; A. Ayali, Editorial Board; J.A. Cheng, Editorial Board. **ISSN:** 1672-9609. **Subscription Rates:** US$218 individuals print + online; US$568 institutions print + online; US$516 institutions print, online; 338 institutions print + online; EUR196 individuals print + online; US$602 institutions print; 307 institutions print, online; EUR430 institutions print + online; 131 individuals print + online; US$662 institutions, other countries print + online. **Remarks:** Advertising accepted; rates available upon request. **URL:** http://www.wiley.com/bw/journal.asp?ref=1672-9609&site=1. **Circ:** (Not Reported)

55991 ■ International Immunology
Oxford University Press
Great Clarendon St.
Oxford OX2 6DP, United Kingdom
Ph: 44 1865 556767
Fax: 44 1865 353485
Publisher E-mail: webenquiry.uk@oup.com
Journal providing wide-ranging studies into immunology. **Freq:** Monthly. **Key Personnel:** T. Kishimoto, Editor-in-Chief; T. Honjo, Editorial Board; T. Tada, Founding Ed.; M.D. Cooper, Editorial Board; P. Marrack, Editorial Board; S. Akira, Assoc. Ed.; H. Kikutani, Assoc. Ed.; K. Takatsu, Assoc. Ed.; A. Fischer, Editorial Board. **ISSN:** 0953-8178. **Subscription Rates:** 1,140 institutions corporate; print and online; 893 institutions corporate; online only; 1,045 institutions corporate; print only; 912 institutions print and online; 714 institutions online only; 836 institutions print only; 319 individuals print; 111 members print; 59 members senior, graduate student; print. **URL:** http://intimm.oxfordjournals.org.

55992 ■ International Journal of Constitutional Law
Oxford University Press
Great Clarendon St.
Oxford OX2 6DP, United Kingdom
Ph: 44 1865 556767
Fax: 44 1865 353485
Publisher E-mail: webenquiry.uk@oup.com
Journal of international and comparative constitutional law, examining an array of theoretical and practical issues and offering critical analysis of current issues and debates, featuring articles by international legal scholars, judges and people from related fields, such as economics, philosophy and political science. **Freq:** 4/yr. **Key Personnel:** Michel Rosenfeld, Co-Ed.-in-Ch.; Norman Dorsen, Founder. **ISSN:** 1474-2640. **Subscription Rates:** 257 institutions corporate; print and online; 214 institutions corporate; online only; 235 institutions corporate; print only; 205 institutions print and online; 171 institutions online only; 188 institutions print only; 48 institutions developing countries; print; 29 individuals print; 37 students print; 45 members print. **Remarks:** Advertising accepted; rates available upon request. **URL:** http://icon.oxfordjournals.org/. **Circ:** (Not Reported)

55993 ■ International Journal of Dental Hygiene
Blackwell Munksgaard
9600 Garsington Rd.
Oxford OX4 2DQ, United Kingdom
Ph: 44 1865 476511
Fax: 44 1865 714591
Official, scientific, peer-reviewed journal of the International Federation of Dental Hygienists (IFDH), bringing the latest scientific news, high-quality commissioned reviews and clinical, professional and educational developmental and legislative news to the profession world-wide. **Freq:** Quarterly. **Key Personnel:** Marjolijn Hovius, Editor-in-Chief, intjdenhyg@inholland.acta.nl; M. Darby, Assoc. Ed.; C. Nielsen, Assoc. Ed. **ISSN:** 1601-5029. **Subscription Rates:** 83 individuals print and online; US$140 individuals (print and online); EUR125 individuals Europe (print and online); 83 other countries online only; US$132 individuals (online only); 50 members UK (print and online); US$94 members (print and online); EUR74 members Europe (print and online); 40 members rest of the world (print and online); 29 members rest of the world (online only). **Remarks:** Accepts advertising. **URL:** http://www3.interscience.wiley.com/journal/118537311/home. **Circ:** (Not Reported)

55994 ■ International Journal of Economic Theory
John Wiley & Sons Inc.
Wiley-Blackwell
9600 Garsington Rd.
Oxford OX4 2DQ, United Kingdom
Ph: 44 1865 776868
Fax: 44 1865 714591
International journal for all fields of economic theory. **Freq:** Quarterly. **Key Personnel:** Makoto Yano, Managing Editor; Kazuo Nishimura, Managing Editor; Robert Becker, Assoc. Ed. **ISSN:** 1742-7355. **Subscription Rates:** US$164 individuals print and online; US$504 institutions print and online; US$458 institutions print, online; US$609 institutions, other countries print and online; EUR127 individuals print and online; 310 institutions print and online; 282 institutions print, online; EUR395 institutions print and online; 101 individuals print and online; US$553 institutions, other countries print, online. **Remarks:** Advertising accepted; rates available upon request. **URL:** http://www.wiley.com/bw/journal.asp?ref=1742-7355&site=1. **Circ:** (Not Reported)

55995 ■ International Journal of Evidence-based Healthcare
John Wiley & Sons Inc.
Wiley-Blackwell
9600 Garsington Rd.
Oxford OX4 2DQ, United Kingdom
Ph: 44 1865 776868
Fax: 44 1865 714591
Peer-reviewed journal publishing original scholarly work from the international Joanna Briggs Institute and Collaboration, which aims to advance the international understanding and development of evidence-based practice in nursing, midwifery, nutrition and dietetics, physiotherapy, occupational therapy, medical radiation, complimentary therapy, medicine and podiatry. **Freq:** Quarterly. **Key Personnel:** Prof. Derek Frewin, Editor-in-Chief. **ISSN:** 1744-1595. **Subscription Rates:** US$122 individuals print and online; $A 207 individuals print and online; EUR113 individuals print and online; 75 other countries print and online; US$648 institutions print and online; US$753 institutions print and online (Australia); 400 institutions print and online; US$784 institutions, other countries print and online; EUR509 institutions print and online; US$589 institutions print or online. **Remarks:** Accepts advertising. **URL:** http://www.wiley.com/bw/journal.asp?ref=1744-1595. **Circ:** (Not Reported)

55996 ■ International Journal of Law and Information Technology
Oxford University Press
Great Clarendon St.
Oxford OX2 6DP, United Kingdom
Ph: 44 1865 556767
Fax: 44 1865 353485
Publisher E-mail: webenquiry.uk@oup.com
Law periodical. **Freq:** 3/yr. **Key Personnel:** Christopher Millard, Gen. Ed., c.millard@qmul.ac.uk; B. Amory, Editorial Board; Dr. Julia Hornle, Managing Editor, j.hornle@qmul.ac.uk; M. Lauritsen, Editorial Board; Prof. Lilian Edwards, Editorial Board; Anne Cheung, Editorial Board; Prof. Jon Bing, Editorial Board; Ian C. Kyer, Editorial Board; Dr. Ian J. Lloyd, Editor, i.j.lloyd@strath.ac.uk; Richard Sussking, Editor. **ISSN:** 0967-0769. **Subscription Rates:** 239 institutions print and online; US$478 institutions print and online; EUR359 institutions print and online; 199 institutions print, online; US$398 institutions print, online; EUR299 institutions print, online; 58 members Society for computers and law; US$110 members Society for computers and law; EUR87 members Society for computers and law; 219 individuals print. **Remarks:** Accepts advertising. **URL:** http://ijlit.oxfordjournals.org. **Circ:** (Not Reported)

55997 ■ International Journal of Law, Policy and the Family
Oxford University Press
c/o Mr. John Eekelaar, Ed.
Pembroke College
Oxford OX1 1DW, United Kingdom
Ph: 44 18 65276429
Fax: 44 18 65276418
Publisher E-mail: webenquiry.uk@oup.com
Law periodical. **Freq:** 3/yr. **Key Personnel:** Mr. John Eekelaar, Editor, john.eekelaar@law.ox.ac.uk; Prof. Robert Dingwall, Editor; Dr. Jonathan Herring, Book Review Ed. **ISSN:** 1360-9939. **Subscription Rates:** 214 institutions print and online; 178 institutions online, print; 91 individuals print only; US$428 institutions print and online; US$356 institutions online, print; US$182 individuals print only; EUR321 institutions print and online; EUR267 institutions online, print; EUR137 individuals

Circulation: ★ = ABC; △ = BPA; ♦ = CAC; • = CCAB; ❑ = VAC; ⊕ = PO Statement; ‡ = Publisher's Report; Boldface figures = sworn; Light figures = estimated.

Gale Directory of Publications & Broadcast Media/147th Ed.
5817

print only. **Remarks:** Accepts advertising. **URL:** http://lawfam.oupjournals.org/. **Circ:** (Not Reported)

55998 ■ International Journal of Lexicography
Oxford University Press
Great Clarendon St.
Oxford OX2 6DP, United Kingdom
Ph: 44 1865 556767
Fax: 44 1865 353485
Publisher E-mail: webenquiry.uk@oup.com
Journal addressing various elements in the field of lexicography. **Founded:** 1988. **Freq:** 4/yr. **Key Personnel:** Dr. Paul Bogaards, Editor, p.bogaards@hum.leidenuniv.nl; T. Fontenelle, Assoc. Ed.; C. Marello, Assoc. Ed. **ISSN:** 0950-3846. **Subscription Rates:** 247 institutions corporate; print and online; 206 institutions corporate; online only; 227 institutions corporate; print only; 198 institutions print and online; 165 institutions online only; 182 institutions print only; 163 individuals print; 87 members print; 82 members institution; print; 45 members individual; print. **URL:** http://ijl.oxfordjournals.org.

55999 ■ International Journal of Nursing Terminologies and Classifications
John Wiley & Sons Inc.
Wiley-Blackwell
9600 Garsington Rd.
Oxford OX4 2DQ, United Kingdom
Ph: 44 1865 776868
Fax: 44 1865 714591
International journal seeking manuscripts, articles and commentaries that reflects knowledge development related to nursing terminology and classification for diagnoses, interventions and outcomes; use of nursing language in practice and education; the processes of clinical judgment and knowledge presentation; and the use of nursing language and classification in research, practice, and education. **Freq:** Quarterly. **Key Personnel:** Jane Flanagan, Editor; Takako Egawa, PhD, Editorial Board; Alba Leite De Barros, PhD, Editorial Board. **ISSN:** 1541-5147. **Subscription Rates:** US$79 individuals print and online; US$209 institutions print and online; US$190 institutions print, online; EUR174 institutions print and online; US$268 institutions, other countries print and online; US$243 institutions, other countries print, online; 137 institutions print and online; EUR54 individuals print and online; 125 institutions print, online; EUR158 institutions print, online. **Remarks:** Advertising accepted; rates available upon request. **URL:** http://www.wiley.com/bw/journal.asp?ref=1541-5147&site=1. **Circ:** (Not Reported)

56000 ■ International Journal of Older People Nursing
John Wiley & Sons Inc.
Wiley-Blackwell
9600 Garsington Rd.
Oxford OX4 2DQ, United Kingdom
Ph: 44 1865 776868
Fax: 44 1865 714591
Journal covering gerontological nursing. **Founded:** 1895. **Freq:** Quarterly. **Print Method:** Offset. **Cols./Page:** 4. **Col. Width:** 2 1/4 inches. **Col. Depth:** 16 inches. **Key Personnel:** Jan Reed, Editor; Jackie Bridges, Editorial Board; Brendan McCormack, Editor-in-Chief; Tanya McCance, Editorial Board; Jan Dewing, Editorial Board. **ISSN:** 1748-3735. **Subscription Rates:** US$145 individuals print and online; US$430 institutions print and online; US$499 institutions, other countries print and online; US$391 institutions print; US$453 institutions, other countries print. **Remarks:** Accepts advertising. **URL:** http://www.wiley.com/bw/journal.asp?ref=1748-3735&site=1. **Circ:** (Not Reported)

56001 ■ International Journal of Public Opinion Research
Oxford University Press
Great Clarendon St.
Oxford OX2 6DP, United Kingdom
Ph: 44 1865 556767
Fax: 44 1865 353485
Publisher E-mail: webenquiry.uk@oup.com
Publication covering sociology and social work. **Freq:** 4/yr. **Key Personnel:** Michael W. Traugott, Editor; Peter Neijens, Managing Editor, ijpor@uva.nl; Connie de Boer, Book Review Ed., c.deboer@uva.nl; Allen Barton, Editorial Board; Albert C. Gunther, Editorial Board; Ottar Hellevik, Editorial Board; Marta Lagos, World Opinion Ed.; Jonathan Kelley, Editorial Asst.; Norman M. Bradburn, Editorial Board; Lotte Willemsen, Asst. Ed. **ISSN:**

0954-2892. **Subscription Rates:** 269 institutions print and online; US$525 institutions print and online; EUR404 institutions print and online; 224 institutions online, print; US$437 institutions online, print; EUR336 institutions online, print; 227 individuals print only; US$443 individuals print only; EUR341 individuals print only; 102 members print. **Remarks:** Accepts advertising. **URL:** http://ijpor.oxfordjournals.org: **Circ:** (Not Reported)

56002 ■ International Journal for Quality in Health Care
Oxford University Press
Great Clarendon St.
Oxford OX2 6DP, United Kingdom
Ph: 44 1865 556767
Fax: 44 1865 353485
Publisher E-mail: webenquiry.uk@oup.com
Peer-reviewed journal focusing on health care related quality-driven activities and research. **Freq:** 6/yr. **Key Personnel:** Eric Schneider, Editor-in-Chief, eschneid@rand.org; Rosa Sunol, Dep. Ed., rsunol@fadq.org; Anthony Staines, Dep. Ed., anthony.staines@bluewin.ch; R. Alvarez, Editorial Committee; Saul Weingart, Dep. Ed., saul_weingart@dfci.harvard.edu; Jerod Leob, Dep. Ed. **ISSN:** 1353-4505. **Subscription Rates:** US$1,152 institutions print and online; US$931 institutions online only; US$1,056 institutions print only; 576 institutions print and online; 466 institutions online only; 528 institutions print only; EUR864 institutions print and online; EUR698 institutions online only; EUR792 institutions print only; 91 individuals print only. **URL:** http://intqhc.oxfordjournals.org.

56003 ■ International Journal of Rheumatic Diseases
John Wiley & Sons Inc.
Wiley-Blackwell
9600 Garsington Rd.
Oxford OX4 2DQ, United Kingdom
Ph: 44 1865 776868
Fax: 44 1865 714591
Peer-reviewed journal covering the clinical or experimental research pertinent to the rheumatic diseases. **Freq:** Quarterly. **Key Personnel:** C.S. Lau, Editor-in-Chief; D. Danda, Sen. Ed.; K. Torralba, Assoc. Ed. **ISSN:** 1756-1841. **Subscription Rates:** US$331 institutions print and online; 204 institutions print and online; US$300 institutions print, online; US$122 individuals print and online; EUR113 individuals print and online; 185 institutions print, online; EUR259 institutions print and online; EUR235 institutions print, online; US$400 institutions, other countries print and online; US$363 institutions, other countries print, online. **Remarks:** Accepts advertising. **URL:** http://www.wiley.com/bw/journal.asp?ref=1756-1841&site=1. **Formerly:** APLAR Journal of Rheumatology. **Circ:** (Not Reported)

56004 ■ International Journal of Urban and Regional Research
John Wiley & Sons Inc.
Wiley-Blackwell
9600 Garsington Rd.
Oxford OX4 2DQ, United Kingdom
Ph: 44 1865 776868
Fax: 44 1865 714591
Peer-reviewed journal covering government and related issues. **Freq:** Quarterly. **Key Personnel:** Simon Parker, Editorial Board; Terry McBride, Managing Editor, tmcbride@mistral.co.uk; Roger Keil, Editor, rkeil@yorku.ca; Talja Blokland, Book Review Ed., talja.blokland@sowi.hu-berlin.de; Marisol Garcia, Corresponding Ed.; Jeremy Seekings, Editor, jeremy.seekings@uct.ac.za; Julie-Anne Boudreau, Editor; Neil Brenner, Editorial Board; Takashi Machimura, Corresponding Ed. **ISSN:** 0309-1317. **Subscription Rates:** US$83 individuals print + online; US$71 members print + online; US$792 institutions print + online; US$720 institutions print, online; 423 institutions print and online; EUR38 students print + online; EUR117 individuals print + online; EUR537 institutions print + online; 384 institutions print, online; US$925 institutions, other countries print + online. **Remarks:** Accepts advertising. **URL:** http://www.wiley.com/bw/journal.asp?ref=0309-1317&site=1. **Circ:** (Not Reported)

56005 ■ International Mathematics Research Papers
Oxford University Press
Great Clarendon St.
Oxford OX2 6DP, United Kingdom
Ph: 44 1865 556767
Fax: 44 1865 353485
Publisher E-mail: webenquiry.uk@oup.com
Peer-reviewed journal that publishes research articles of

high current interest in all areas of mathematics. **Freq:** Quarterly. **Key Personnel:** Enrico Arbarello, Editor, ea@mat.uniromal.it; Morris Weisfeld, Editor-in-Chief, mw@math.duke.edu; Joseph Bernstein, Editor, bernstei@post.tau.ac.il. **ISSN:** 1687-3017. **URL:** http://imrp.oxfordjournals.org/.

56006 ■ International Relations of the Asia-Pacific
Oxford University Press
Great Clarendon St.
Oxford OX2 6DP, United Kingdom
Ph: 44 1865 556767
Fax: 44 1865 353485
Publisher E-mail: webenquiry.uk@oup.com
Journal addressing the major issues and developments taking place in the Asia-Pacific, providing frontier knowledge of and fresh insights into the Asia-Pacific and a meeting place where various issues are debated from refreshingly diverging angles, backed up by rigorous scholarship, welcoming contributions on all important developments in the Asia-Pacific, ranging from China's accession to the WTO; America's antiterrorist war and regional power reconfiguration; the poverty of institutions and the challenge of regional governance; Japan's belated entry into regional politics; Asian NGOs Crossing Borders; China's increasing economic importance; deepening globalization; and changing national identities. **Freq:** 3/yr. **Key Personnel:** John G. Ikenberry, Editor-in-Chief; Masayuki Tadokoro, Exec. Ed.; Tsuneo Akaha, Editorial Board; Garren Mulloy, Exec. Ed.; Hayward Alker, Editorial Board; Thomas Biersteker, Editorial Board; Kaoru Kurusu, Exec. Ed.; Atsushi Tago, Exec. Ed.; Yoshihide Soeya, Editor-in-Chief; Akio Takahara, Exec. Ed. **ISSN:** 1470-482X. **Subscription Rates:** 298 institutions corporate; print and online; 248 institutions corporate; online only; 273 institutions corporate; print only; 238 institutions print and online; 198 institutions online only; 218 institutions print only; 54 institutions developing countries; print; 54 individuals print. **Remarks:** Advertising accepted; rates available upon request. **URL:** http://irap.oxfordjournals.org/. **Circ:** (Not Reported)

56007 ■ International Studies Quarterly
John Wiley & Sons Inc.
Wiley-Blackwell
9600 Garsington Rd.
Oxford OX4 2DQ, United Kingdom
Ph: 44 1865 776868
Fax: 44 1865 714591
Political science journal. **Freq:** Quarterly. **Key Personnel:** William R. Thompson, Managing Editor; David Fidler, Assoc. Ed.; Sumit Ganguly, Assoc. Ed.; Jeffrey Hart, Assoc. Ed.; Karen Rasler, Co-Ed. **ISSN:** 0020-8833. **Subscription Rates:** US$1,737 institutions print and online; US$1,579 institutions print, online; 1,327 institutions print and online; 1,206 institutions print, online; EUR1,686 institutions print and online; EUR1,532 institutions print, online; US$2,601 institutions, other countries print and online; US$2,364 institutions, other countries print, online. **Remarks:** Accepts advertising. **URL:** http://www.wiley.com/bw/journal.asp?ref=0020-8833&site=1. **Circ:** (Not Reported)

56008 ■ The Japanese Economic Review
John Wiley & Sons Inc.
Wiley-Blackwell
9600 Garsington Rd.
Oxford OX4 2DQ, United Kingdom
Ph: 44 1865 776868
Fax: 44 1865 714591
Professional journal of the Japanese Economic Association. **Founded:** 1950. **Freq:** Quarterly. **Key Personnel:** Kazou Mino, Co-Ed.; Kazuhiro Ohtani, Editor; Nobuhiro Kiyotaki, Assoc. Ed.; Kazuo Ogawa, Co-Ed.; John Sutton, Assoc. Ed.; Kazuya Kamiya, Assoc. Ed. **ISSN:** 1352-4739. **Subscription Rates:** US$98 individuals print and online; EUR86 individuals print and online; US$299 institutions print and online; 208 institutions print and online; US$272 U.S. print, online; EUR68 individuals print and online; US$180 institutions, other countries print, online; EUR242 institutions print, online; 190 institutions print, online. **Remarks:** Accepts advertising. **URL:** http://www.wiley.com/bw/journal.asp?ref=1352-4739&site=1. **Former name:** The Economic Studies Quarterly. **Ad Rates:** BW: 260. **Circ:** (Not Reported)

56009 ■ Japanese Journal of Clinical Oncology
Oxford University Press
Great Clarendon St.

Oxford OX2 6DP, United Kingdom
Ph: 44 1865 556767
Fax: 44 1865 353485
Publisher E-mail: webenquiry.uk@oup.com
Journal from Japan publishing clinical research on cancer in English. **Founded:** 1971. **Freq:** Monthly. **Key Personnel:** Tadao Kakizoe, Editor-in-Chief; Teruhiko Yoshida, Editor; Hideyuki Akaza, Assoc. Ed.; Daisuke Aoki, Assoc. Ed.; Hideo Kunitoh, Editor; Teruhiko Yoshida, Editor; Hisao Asamura, Assoc. Ed.; Kenji Eguchi, Assoc. Ed.; Yasuhiro Fujiwara, Assoc. Ed. **ISSN:** 0368-2811. **Subscription Rates:** 239 institutions corporate; print and online; 187 institutions corporate; online only; 219 institutions corporate; print only; 191 institutions print and online; 149 institutions online only; 175 institutions print only; 124 individuals print. **Remarks:** Advertising not accepted. **URL:** http://jjco.oupjournals.org/. **Circ:** (Not Reported)

56010 ■ JCMS: Journal of Common Market Studies
John Wiley & Sons Inc.
Wiley-Blackwell
9600 Garsington Rd.
Oxford OX4 2DQ, United Kingdom
Ph: 44 1865 776868
Fax: 44 1865 714591
International business publication covering integration issues related to the politics and economics of the European Union. Annual subscription includes The European Union: Annual Review. **Founded:** 1962. **Freq:** 5/yr. **Key Personnel:** Michelle Cini, Editor; Iain Begg, Editorial Board; Charles Lees, Managing Editor; Amy Verdun, Editor; Brian Ardy, Book Review Ed.; Jackie Gower, Book Review Ed. **ISSN:** 0021-9886. **Subscription Rates:** 731 institutions print + online; EUR257 individuals print + online; US$1,477 institutions print + online; US$1,342 institutions print, online; EUR928 institutions print + online; US$66 members print + online; EUR56 members print + online; US$1,724 institutions, other countries print + online; US$1,567 institutions, other countries print + online; EUR843 institutions print, online. **Remarks:** Accepts advertising. **URL:** http://www.wiley.com/bw/journal.asp?ref=0021-9886&site=1. **Ad Rates:** BW: 275. **Circ:** (Not Reported)

56011 ■ Journal of Advanced Transportation
John Wiley & Sons Inc.
Wiley-Blackwell
9600 Garsington Rd.
Oxford OX4 2DQ, United Kingdom
Ph: 44 1865 776868
Fax: 44 1865 714591
Peer-reviewed Journal covering transportation technology and engineering. **Founded:** 1967. **Freq:** 4/yr. **Key Personnel:** S.C. Wirasinghe, Editor-in-Chief; Paul Schonfeld, Editor; William H.K. Lam, Editor-in-Chief. **ISSN:** 0197-6729. **Remarks:** Advertising not accepted. **URL:** http://www3.interscience.wiley.com/journal/123197986/home. **Circ:** Combined 355

56012 ■ Journal of African Economies
Oxford University Press
Ctr. for the Study of African Economies
Dept. of Economics
University of Oxford
Manor Road Bldg., Manor Rd.
Oxford OX1 3UQ, United Kingdom
Publisher E-mail: webenquiry.uk@oup.com
Journal for consultants, policymakers, academics, traders, financiers, development agents or aid workers, publishing economic analysis, focused entirely on Africa, for Africans and anyone interested in the continent. **Freq:** 5/yr. **Key Personnel:** Marcel Fafchamps, Managing Editor; S. Appleton, Assoc. Ed.; J. Aron, Assoc. Ed.; C. Barrett, Assoc. Ed.; J. Fedderke, Assoc. Ed.; Michael Bleaney, Managing Editor; Augustin Fosu, Managing Editor; John Hoddinott, Managing Editor. **ISSN:** 0963-8024. **Subscription Rates:** 479 institutions corporate; print and online; 399 institutions corporate; online only; 439 institutions corporate; print only; 383 institutions print and online; 319 institutions online only; 351 institutions print only; 70 individuals print; 48 individuals Africa; print. **Remarks:** Advertising accepted; rates available upon request. **URL:** http://jae.oupjournals.org/. **Circ:** (Not Reported)

56013 ■ Journal of the American Ceramic Society
John Wiley & Sons Inc.

Wiley-Blackwell
9600 Garsington Rd.
Oxford OX4 2DQ, United Kingdom
Ph: 44 1865 776868
Fax: 44 1865 714591
Journal containing records of original research that provide or lead to fundamental principles in the science of ceramics and ceramic-based composites including reports of the discovery of new phases, phase relationships, processing approaches and microstructures that relate to ceramic materials and processes and establishing the links between processing, structure characterization and properties of ceramics, including modeling approaches that are founded on basic mechanisms. **Freq:** Monthly. **Key Personnel:** David J. Green, Sen. Journal Ed.; David W. Johnson, Jr., Journal Ed.; Lisa Klein, Journal Ed. **ISSN:** 0002-7820. **Subscription Rates:** US$1,862 institutions print and online; 1,142 institutions print and online; US$2,236 institutions, other countries print and online; US$1,861 institutions print or online; 1,037 institutions print or online; US$2,033 institutions, other countries print or online; EUR1,450 institutions print and online; EUR1,318 institutions print or online. **Remarks:** Accepts advertising. **URL:** http://www.wiley.com/bw/journal.asp?ref=0002-7820&site=1. **Circ:** (Not Reported)

56014 ■ Journal of Antimicrobial Chemotherapy
Oxford University Press
Great Clarendon St.
Oxford OX2 6DP, United Kingdom
Ph: 44 1865 556767
Fax: 44 1865 353485
Publisher E-mail: webenquiry.uk@oup.com
Journal focusing on antimicrobial research and its use in chemotherapy. **Freq:** Monthly. **Key Personnel:** D.S. Reeves, Editorial Board; J. Campos, Editorial Board; S. Simjee, Editorial Board; A.P. Johnson, Editor-in-Chief, jac@bsac.org.uk; D. Honeybourne, Editorial Board; A. Tsakris, Editorial Board. **ISSN:** 0305-7453. **Subscription Rates:** 1,063 institutions corporate; print and online; 859 institutions corporate; online only; 975 institutions corporate; print only; 851 institutions print and online; 688 institutions online only; 780 institutions print only; 391 individuals online only; 423 individuals print; 160 members print and online; 111 members print. **URL:** http://jac.oxfordjournals.org.

56015 ■ Journal of Applied Corporate Finance
John Wiley & Sons Inc.
Wiley-Blackwell
9600 Garsington Rd.
Oxford OX4 2DQ, United Kingdom
Ph: 44 1865 776868
Fax: 44 1865 714591
Journal covering a range of topics including risk management, corporate strategy, corporate governance and capital structure and featuring roundtable discussions among corporate executives and academics on topics such as integrity in financial reporting. **Freq:** Quarterly. **Key Personnel:** Donald H. Chew, Jr., Editor-in-Chief; Jason Draho, Assoc. Ed.; Yakov Amihud, Advisory Board. **ISSN:** 1078-1196. **Subscription Rates:** US$105 individuals print and online; US$37 students print and online; US$84 individuals for Journal author's club; 21 students print and online; US$416 institutions print and online; US$378 institutions print or online; US$499 institutions, other countries print and online; EUR323 institutions print and online; 255 institutions print and online; US$453 institutions, other countries print or online. **Remarks:** Advertising not accepted. **URL:** http://www.wiley.com/bw/journal.asp?ref=1078-1196&site=1. **Circ:** (Not Reported)

56016 ■ Journal of Architectural Education
John Wiley & Sons Inc.
Wiley-Blackwell
9600 Garsington Rd.
Oxford OX4 2DQ, United Kingdom
Ph: 44 1865 776868
Fax: 44 1865 714591
Refereed journal addressing significant questions in architectural thought and practice in order to examine and question, in a scholarly way, institutions that have an impact on the many facets of architecture and the education of architects. **Founded:** 1947. **Freq:** Quarterly. **Key Personnel:** George Dodds, Exec. Ed.; Jerry Portwood, Managing Editor; Sharon Haar, Reviews Ed. **ISSN:** 1046-4883. **Subscription Rates:** US$67

individuals print + online; US$368 institutions print + online; US$334 institutions print, online; 237 institutions print + online; EUR67 individuals print + online; EUR300 institutions print + online; EUR273 institutions print, online; US$463 institutions, other countries print + online; 43 individuals print + online; US$420 institutions, other countries print, online. **Remarks:** Accepts advertising. **URL:** http://www.wiley.com/bw/journal.asp?ref=1046-4883&site=1. **Circ:** (Not Reported)

56017 ■ The Journal of Biochemistry
Oxford University Press
Great Clarendon St.
Oxford OX2 6DP, United Kingdom
Ph: 44 1865 556767
Fax: 44 1865 353485
Publisher E-mail: webenquiry.uk@oup.com
Journal publishing articles on topics such as biochemistry, biotechnology and molecular biology. **Founded:** 1922. **Freq:** Monthly. **Key Personnel:** Kazumitsu Ueda, Managing Editor; Kohei Miyazono, Editor-in-Chief; Keiji Miyazawa, Editor; Kensaku Mizuno, Managing Editor; Koichi Honke, Editor; Katsuyuki Tanizawa, Editor. **ISSN:** 0021-924X. **Subscription Rates:** 361 institutions corporate; print and online; 301 institutions corporate; online only; 331 institutions corporate; print only; 289 institutions print and online; 241 institutions online only; 265 institutions print only. **Remarks:** Advertising not accepted. **URL:** http://jb.oxfordjournals.org. **Circ:** (Not Reported)

56018 ■ Journal of the BIOS
Positif Press
130 Southfield Rd.
Oxford OX4 1PA, United Kingdom
Ph: 44 1865 243220
Fax: 44 1865 243272
Publication covering music and all aspects relating to organs. **Founded:** 1977. **Freq:** Annual In November. **ISSN:** 0141-4992. **Subscription Rates:** 10 members + postage; 16 nonmembers + postage. **URL:** http://www.positifpress.com/journals.html; http://www.bios.org.uk/jbios.htm.

56019 ■ Journal of Business Finance and Accounting
John Wiley & Sons Inc.
Wiley-Blackwell
9600 Garsington Rd.
Oxford OX4 2DQ, United Kingdom
Ph: 44 1865 776868
Fax: 44 1865 714591
Publication for the banking, finance, and accounting industries. **Freq:** 10/yr. **Key Personnel:** A.W. Stark, Editor; P.F. Pope, Editor; D.J. Ashton, Editorial Board; M. Walker, Editor; P. Andre, Assoc. Ed. **ISSN:** 0306-686X. **Subscription Rates:** US$239 individuals print + online; US$2,019 institutions print + online; US$1,834 institutions print, online; EUR1,342 institutions print + online; EUR175 individuals print + online; EUR1,220 institutions print, online; US$2,357 institutions, other countries print + online; US$2,142 institutions, other countries print, online; 116 individuals print + online; 143 other countries print + online. **Remarks:** Accepts advertising. **URL:** http://www.wiley.com/bw/journal.asp?ref=0306-686X. **Circ:** (Not Reported)

56020 ■ Journal of Child and Adolescent Psychiatric Nursing
John Wiley & Sons Inc.
Wiley-Blackwell
9600 Garsington Rd.
Oxford OX4 2DQ, United Kingdom
Ph: 44 1865 776868
Fax: 44 1865 714591
Peer-reviewed journal focusing on the issues of child and adolescent mental health around the world. **Freq:** Quarterly. **Key Personnel:** Elizabeth C. Poster, PhD, Editor, phone 817272-2776, fax 817272-5006, poster@uta.edu; Linda M. Finke, PhD, Assoc. Ed., phone 260481-6564, fax 260481-5767, finkel@ipfw.edu; John S. Carlson, PhD, Editorial Board, phone 517432-4856, fax 517353-6393, carlsoj@msu.edu; Carol T. Bush, PhD, Editorial Board, phone 404373-4140, fax 404373-4150; Carol J. Dashiff, PhD, Editorial Board, phone 205996-6110, dashiffc@uab.edu; Steven Pryjmachuk, PhD, Editorial Board, phone 44 161 3067859, fax 44 161 3067707, steven.pryjmachuk@manchester.ac.uk. **ISSN:** 1073-6077. **Subscription Rates:** US$83 individuals print + online; US$238 institutions print + online; US$216 institutions print, online; US$306 institutions,

Circulation: ★ = ABC; △ = BPA; ♦ = CAC; ▪ = CCAB; ❑ = VAC; ⊕ = PO Statement; ‡ = Publisher's Report; Boldface figures = sworn; Light figures = estimated.

Gale Directory of Publications & Broadcast Media/147th Ed.   **5819**

other countries print + online; EUR57 individuals print + online; 156 institutions print + online; 141 institutions print, online; EUR180 institutions print, online. **Remarks:** Advertising accepted; rates available upon request. **URL:** http://www.wiley.com/bw/journal.asp?ref=1073-6077&site=1. **Circ:** (Not Reported)

56021 ■ Journal of Communication
John Wiley & Sons Inc.
Wiley-Blackwell
9600 Garsington Rd.
Oxford OX4 2DQ, United Kingdom
Ph: 44 1865 776868
Fax: 44 1865 714591
Scholarly journal focusing on the communications field. **Founded:** 1952. **Freq:** Quarterly. **Print Method:** Offset. **Trim Size:** 6 7/8 x 9 3/4. **Cols./Page:** 1. **Col. Width:** 5 inches. **Col. Depth:** 7 3/4 inches. **Key Personnel:** Daniel Berkowitz, Editorial Board; William Benoit, Editorial Board; Kevin Barnhurst, Editorial Board; Joseph Cappella, Editorial Board; Elisia L. Cohen, Review and Criticism Ed.; Michael Cody, Editor; Travis Dixon, Editorial Board; Carl Botan, Editorial Board. **ISSN:** 0021-9916. **Subscription Rates:** US$75 individuals print + online; US$49 students print + online; US$1,138 institutions print + online; US$1,034 institutions online; EUR74 individuals print + online; EUR49 students print + online; EUR881 institutions print + online; 631 institutions online; 694 institutions print + online; US$1,359 institutions, other countries print + online. **Remarks:** Color advertising not accepted. **URL:** http://www.wiley.com/bw/journal.asp?ref=0021-9916. **Ad Rates:** BW: 350. **Circ:** Paid ‡5,000

56022 ■ Journal of Competition Law and Economics
Oxford University Press
Great Clarendon St.
Oxford OX2 6DP, United Kingdom
Ph: 44 1865 556767
Fax: 44 1865 353485
Publisher E-mail: webenquiry.uk@oup.com
Peer-reviewed journal for academics, practitioners (law firms, economic consultancies), graduate and postgraduate students, policy-makers, and competition authorities, publishing articles providing in-depth analysis of developments in competition law and economic papers relevant to legal theory and practice, including developments in the U.S. and Europe, but also covering other regional and national developments. **Founded:** 2004. **Freq:** 4/yr. **Key Personnel:** Prof. Damien Geradin, Editorial Board, geradind@howrey.com; Prof. J. Gregory Sidak, Editorial Board, jcle@criterioneconomics.com. **ISSN:** 1744-6414. **Subscription Rates:** 356 institutions corporate; print and online; 273 institutions corporate; online only; 327 institutions corporate; print only; 284 institutions print and online; 218 institutions online only; 261 institutions print only; 92 individuals print. **URL:** http://jcle.oxfordjournals.org/.

56023 ■ Journal of Computer-Mediated Communication
John Wiley & Sons Inc.
Wiley-Blackwell
9600 Garsington Rd.
Oxford OX4 2DQ, United Kingdom
Ph: 44 1865 776868
Fax: 44 1865 714591
Peer-reviewed journal focusing on computer mediated research on social science via the Internet. **Freq:** Quarterly. **Key Personnel:** Kevin B. Wright, Editor; Naomi Baron, Editorial Board; David Crystal, Editorial Board. **ISSN:** 1083-6101. **Subscription Rates:** US$63 individuals print and online; for the Americas; EUR62 individuals print and online; Europe; 41 individuals print and online; rest of World; US$42 students print and online; for the Americas; EUR41 students print and online; Europe; 27 students, Canada print and online; rest of World; US$893 institutions print and premium online, Americas; 545 institutions print and premium online, Europe; 545 institutions print and premium online, rest of World. **Remarks:** Advertising not accepted. **URL:** http://www.wiley.com/bw/journal.asp?ref=1083-6101. **Circ:** (Not Reported)

56024 ■ Journal of Conflict and Security Law
Oxford University Press
Great Clarendon St.
Oxford OX2 6DP, United Kingdom
Ph: 44 1865 556767
Fax: 44 1865 353485
Publisher E-mail: webenquiry.uk@oup.com
Peer-reviewed journal aimed at academics, government officials, military lawyers, and lawyers working in the area, as well as people interested in the areas of arms control law, of armed conflict law and collective security law, covering the whole spectrum of international law relating to armed conflict from the pre-conflict stage when the issues include those of arms control, disarmament and conflict prevention, through to the outbreak of armed conflict and discussions of the legality of resort to force, to the coverage of the conduct of military operations and the protection of non-combatants by international humanitarian law. **Freq:** 3/yr. **Key Personnel:** Prof. Nigel White, Editor, nigel.white@nottingham.ac.uk; Robert Cryer, Editor; Prof. Masahiko Asada, Editorial Board; Ige Dekker, Editorial Board; Prof. Eric Myjer, Editor; Terry Gill, Editorial Board. **ISSN:** 1467-7954. **Subscription Rates:** 200 institutions print and online; 167 institutions online, print; 53 individuals print only; US$400 institutions print and online; US$334 institutions online, print; US$106 individuals print only; EUR300 institutions print and online; EUR251 institutions online, print; EUR80 individuals print only; EUR80 individuals print only. **Remarks:** Advertising accepted; rates available upon request. **URL:** http://jcsl.oxfordjournals.org/. **Circ:** (Not Reported)

56025 ■ The Journal of Corporate Law Studies
Hart Publishing Ltd.
16C Worcester Pl.
Oxford OX1 2JW, United Kingdom
Ph: 44 1865 517530
Fax: 44 1865 510710
Publisher E-mail: mail@hartpub.co.uk
Journal providing a forum for scholarship on corporate, securities and financial law. **Freq:** Semiannual. **Key Personnel:** John Armour, Editor; Eilis Ferran, Editor. **ISSN:** 1473-5970. **Subscription Rates:** 140 individuals U.K. and Europe; 155 individuals overseas; 75 individuals U.K. and Europe (personal); 80 individuals overseas (personal); 126 individuals standard; online; 67.50 individuals online. **Remarks:** Accepts advertising. **URL:** http://www.hartjournals.co.uk/jcls/. **Circ:** (Not Reported)

56026 ■ Journal of Design History
Oxford University Press
Great Clarendon St.
Oxford OX2 6DP, United Kingdom
Ph: 44 1865 556767
Fax: 44 1865 353485
Publisher E-mail: webenquiry.uk@oup.com
Journal playing an active role in the development of design history (including the history of the crafts and applied arts), as well as contributing to the broader field of studies of visual and material culture. **Freq:** 4/yr. **Key Personnel:** Dipti Bhagat, Editorial Board; Artemis Yagou, Editorial Board; Tim Putnam, Editorial Board; Regina Lee Blaszczyk, Editorial Board; Cheryl Buckley, Editorial Board; Javier Gimeno Martinez, Editorial Board. **ISSN:** 0952-4649. **Subscription Rates:** 222 institutions corporate; print and online; 185 institutions corporate; online only; 204 institutions corporate; print only; 178 institutions print and online; 148 institutions online only; 163 institutions print only; 54 individuals print; 46 members print; 164 members corporate; print; 25 members senior, student; print. **Remarks:** Advertising accepted; rates available upon request. **URL:** http://jdh.oupjournals.org/. **Circ:** (Not Reported)

56027 ■ Journal of Educational Measurement
John Wiley & Sons Inc.
Wiley-Blackwell
9600 Garsington Rd.
Oxford OX4 2DQ, United Kingdom
Ph: 44 1865 776868
Fax: 44 1865 714591
Journal publishing original measurement research and reports of applications of measurement in an educational context. **Freq:** Quarterly. **Key Personnel:** James E. Carlson, Editor; Barbara G. Dodd, Advisory Ed.; James Algina, Advisory Ed.; Dan Eignor, Advisory Ed.; Brian Clauser, Review Ed.; Robert Brennan, Advisory Ed.; Patricia Busk, Advisory Ed.; Jimmy dela Torre, Advisory Ed. **ISSN:** 0022-0655. **Subscription Rates:** US$428 institutions print and online; US$389 institutions print or online; 263 institutions print and online; 239 institutions print or online; EUR334 institutions print and online; EUR304 institutions print or online; US$516 institutions, other countries print and online; US$468 institutions, other countries print or online. **Remarks:** Accepts advertising. **URL:** http://www.wiley.com/bw/journal.asp?ref=0022-0655&site=1. **Circ:** (Not Reported)

56028 ■ Journal of Electron Microscopy
Oxford University Press
Great Clarendon St.
Oxford OX2 6DP, United Kingdom
Ph: 44 1865 556767
Fax: 44 1865 353485
Publisher E-mail: webenquiry.uk@oup.com
International journal, open to all scientists in the field, publishing research in advanced electron microscopy and new scanning probe microscopy with articles covering theories, methods, techniques and instrumentation, as well as their applications to life and material sciences. **Freq:** 6/yr. **Key Personnel:** Jiro Usukura, Managing Editor; Yoshio Bando, Editor-in-Chief; Akio Kikuta, Exec. Ed. **ISSN:** 0022-0744. **Subscription Rates:** 409 institutions print and online; 341 institutions online, print; 170 individuals print only; 117 members print; US$818 institutions print and online; US$682 institutions online, print; US$340 individuals print only; US$234 members print; EUR614 institutions print and online; EUR512 institutions online, print. **Remarks:** Advertising not accepted. **URL:** http://jmicro.oxfordjournals.org. **Circ:** (Not Reported)

56029 ■ Journal of Environmental Law
Oxford University Press
Great Clarendon St.
Oxford OX2 6DP, United Kingdom
Ph: 44 1865 556767
Fax: 44 1865 353485
Publisher E-mail: webenquiry.uk@oup.com
Law periodical. **Freq:** 3/yr. **Key Personnel:** Prof. Chris Hilson, Editor-in-Chief, c.j.hilson@reading.ac.uk; Ben Boer, Advisory Board; Mark Stallworthy, Review Ed.; Gerd Winter, Advisory Board. **ISSN:** 0952-8873. **Subscription Rates:** 217 institutions print and online; US$434 institutions print and online; EUR326 institutions print and online; 80 individuals print; US$160 individuals print; EUR120 individuals print; 56 members print; US$112 members print; EUR84 members print. **Remarks:** Accepts advertising. **URL:** http://jel.oupjournals.org/. **Circ:** (Not Reported)

56030 ■ Journal of Eukaryotic Microbiology
John Wiley & Sons Inc.
Wiley-Blackwell
9600 Garsington Rd.
Oxford OX4 2DQ, United Kingdom
Ph: 44 1865 776868
Fax: 44 1865 714591
Journal publishing original research on protists, including lower algae and fungi, covering all aspects of these organisms, including their behavior, biochemistry, cell biology, chemotherapy, development, ecology, evolution, genetics, molecular biology, morphogenetics, parasitology, systematics and ultrastructure. **Freq:** Bimonthly. **Key Personnel:** Denis H. Lynn, Editor-in-Chief; Portia A. Holt, Managing Editor; David J. Asai, Assoc. Ed.; James D. Berger, Assoc. Ed.; Janet S. Keithly, Assoc. Ed.; Melanie T. Cushion, Assoc. Ed.; Francine Marciano-Cabral, Assoc. Ed. **ISSN:** 1066-5234. **Subscription Rates:** US$379 institutions print + online; US$417 institutions print or online; 232 institutions print + online; 255 institutions print or online; EUR294 institutions print + online; EUR324 institutions print or online; US$453 institutions, other countries print + online; US$499 institutions, other countries print or online. **Remarks:** Accepts display advertising. **URL:** http://www.wiley.com/bw/journal.asp?ref=1066-5234&site=1. **Circ:** (Not Reported)

56031 ■ Journal of the European Ceramic Society
Elsevier Science
c/o R.J. Brook, Ed.
Dept. of Materials
University of Oxford
16 Parks Rd.
Oxford OX1 3PH, United Kingdom
Publisher E-mail: nlinfo-f@elsevier.com
Peer-reviewed journal concerned with the structure, properties and processing of ceramic materials in connection with the European Ceramic Society. **Founded:** 1989. **Freq:** 16/yr. **Key Personnel:** R.J. Brook, Editor; L. Berzina, Editorial Board; F. Cambier, Editorial Board; R. Freer, Editorial Board; J.G. Heinrich, Editorial Board; R. Pompe, Editorial Board. **ISSN:** 0955-2219. **Subscription Rates:** 517,900¥ institutions; US$4,362 institutions for all countries except Europe, Japan & Iran; EUR3,899 institutions for European countries & Iran. **Remarks:** Accepts advertising. **URL:** http://www.elsevier.com/wps/

find/journaldescription.cws_home/405935/description.
Circ: (Not Reported)

56032 ■ Journal of Experimental Botany
Oxford University Press
Great Clarendon St.
Oxford OX2 6DP, United Kingdom
Ph: 44 1865 556767
Fax: 44 1865 353485
Publisher E-mail: webenquiry.uk@oup.com
Journal publishing primary research papers in the plant
sciences covering a range of disciplines from molecular
and cellular physiology and biochemistry through whole
plant physiology to community physiology. **Freq:** 15/yr.
Key Personnel: Prof. Jerry Roberts, Editor; Mary
Traynor, Managing Editor; Erwin Dreyer, Assoc. Ed.;
Neil Baker, Advisory Board; Eliot Herman, Assoc. Ed.;
Karl-Josef Dietz, Assoc. Ed.; Mike Emes, Assoc. Ed.;
Bill Davies, Assoc. Ed.; Donald Briskin, Advisory Board;
Chris Atkinson, Advisory Board. **ISSN:** 0022-0957. **Sub-
scription Rates:** 1,461 institutions corporate; print and
online; 1,388 institutions corporate; print or online; 1,169
institutions print and online; 1,111 institutions print or on-
line; 112 members print; 165 members others. **Remarks:**
Advertising accepted; rates available upon request.
URL: http://jxb.oxfordjournals.org/. **Circ:** (Not Reported)

56033 ■ Journal of Finance
John Wiley & Sons Inc.
Wiley-Blackwell
9600 Garsington Rd.
Oxford OX4 2DQ, United Kingdom
Ph: 44 1865 776868
Fax: 44 1865 714591
Publication for the banking, finance, and accounting
industries. **Freq:** Bimonthly. **Key Personnel:** Campbell
R. Harvey, Editor; Kerry Back, Assoc. Ed.; Anat R. Ad-
mati, Assoc. Ed.; David A. Chapman, Assoc. Ed.; Paul
A. Gompers, Assoc. Ed.; Michael Lemmon, Assoc. Ed.
ISSN: 0022-1082. **Subscription Rates:** US$487 institu-
tions Americas (print and online); US$574 institutions,
Canada and Mexico print and online; 377 institutions UK
(print and online); EUR478 institutions Europe (print and
online); US$737 institutions, other countries print and
online; US$442 institutions Americas (print or online
only); US$495 institutions, Canada and Mexico print or
online only; 342 institutions UK (print or online only);
EUR434 institutions Europe (print or online only); US$670
institutions, other countries print or online only. **Remarks:** Accepts advertising. **URL:** http://www.wiley.com/
bw/journal.asp?ref=0022-1082. **Circ:** (Not Reported)

56034 ■ Journal of Financial Econometrics
Oxford University Press
Great Clarendon St.
Oxford OX2 6DP, United Kingdom
Ph: 44 1865 556767
Fax: 44 1865 353485
Publisher E-mail: webenquiry.uk@oup.com
Journal presenting statistical issues related to the
financial industry. **Freq:** 4/yr. **Key Personnel:** Rene Gar-
cia, Editor; Eric Renault, Editor; Eric Ghysels, Co-Ed.
ISSN: 1479-8409. **Subscription Rates:** 534 institutions
corporate; print and online; 401 institutions corporate;
online only; 490 institutions corporate; print only; 355
institutions print and online; 266 institutions online only;
326 institutions print only; 55 individuals print. **URL:**
http://jfec.oxfordjournals.org.

**56035 ■ Journal of Food Processing and
Preservation**
John Wiley & Sons Inc.
Wiley-Blackwell
9600 Garsington Rd.
Oxford OX4 2DQ, United Kingdom
Ph: 44 1865 776868
Fax: 44 1865 714591
Peer-reviewed Journal covering the latest information
and advances in food processing and preservation
technologies. **Freq:** Bimonthly. **Key Personnel:** Y.
Martin Lo, PhD, Editor-in-Chief; Charles Onwulata,
Assoc. Ed., charles.onwulata@ars.usda.gov; Kostadin
Fikiin, Assoc. Ed., agf@tu-sofia.bg. **ISSN:** 0145-8892.
Subscription Rates: EUR381 institutions print and on-
line; US$441 institutions print and online; 300 institu-
tions print and online; US$401 institutions online. **Re-
marks:** Advertising accepted; rates available upon
request. **URL:** http://www.wiley.com/bw/journal.asp?ref=
0145-8892&site=1. **Circ:** (Not Reported)

56036 ■ Journal of Group Theory
Walter de Gruyter GmbH & Co. KG

Mathematical Institute
University of Oxford
24-29 St. Giles
Oxford OX1 3LB, United Kingdom
Publisher E-mail: info@degruyter.com
Journal covering publication of research articles in
aspects of group theory. **Freq:** Bimonthly. **Print Method:**
Offset. **Trim Size:** 17 x 24 cm. **Cols./Page:** 5. **Col.
Width:** 2 inches. **Col. Depth:** 16 inches. **Key Personnel:** Robert Guralnick, Editor, guralnic@usc.edu; Gunter
Malle, Editor, malle@mathematik.uni-kl.de; Martin R.
Bridson, Editor, bridson@maths.ox.ac.uk; Michel Broue,
Editor, broue@ihp.jussieu.fr; William M. Kantor, Editor,
kantor@math.uoregon.edu; E.I. Khukhro, Editor,
khukhro@yahoo.co.uk; Francesco De Giovanni, Editor,
degiovan@unina.it; Alexandre V. Borovik, Editor,
borovik@manchester.ac.uk; Linus Kramer, Editor, linus.
kramer@math.uni-muenster.de. **ISSN:** 1433-5883. **Subscription Rates:** EUR2,499 individuals print or online
only; EUR2,874 individuals print + online; EUR229 single
issue. **URL:** http://www.degruyter.de/journals/jgt/
detailEn.cfm. **Circ:** 250

56037 ■ Journal of Heredity
Oxford University Press
Great Clarendon St.
Oxford OX2 6DP, United Kingdom
Ph: 44 1865 556767
Fax: 44 1865 353485
Publisher E-mail: webenquiry.uk@oup.com
Publication covering biological sciences. **Freq:** 6/yr. **Key
Personnel:** Anjanette Baker, Managing Editor; Stephen
J. O'Brien, Advisory Ed.; Rob Desalle, Editorial Board;
John M. Burke, Editorial Board; Ernest Bailey, Editorial
Board; Warren E. Johnson, Editorial Board; Scott C.
Baker, Editor-in-Chief; Jerry Dodgson, Editorial Board;
Brian Bowen, Editorial Board; James L. Hamrick, Edito-
rial Board. **ISSN:** 0022-1503. **Subscription Rates:** 307
institutions print and online; US$460 institutions print
and online; 281 institutions print, online; US$421 institu-
tions print, online; 41 members print; US$67 members
print; EUR60 members print; 13 members print (student);
US$20 members print (student); EUR18 members print
(student). **Remarks:** Accepts advertising. **URL:** http://
jhered.oxfordjournals.org. **Circ:** (Not Reported)

56038 ■ Journal of Historical Sociology
John Wiley & Sons Inc.
Wiley-Blackwell
9600 Garsington Rd.
Oxford OX4 2DQ, United Kingdom
Ph: 44 1865 776868
Fax: 44 1865 714591
Periodical focusing on history. **Founded:** 1988. **Freq:**
Quarterly. **Key Personnel:** Derek Sayer, Managing Edi-
tor, d.sayer@lancaster.ac.uk; Wong Yoke-Sum, Manag-
ing Editor, y.wong@lancaster.ac.uk; Rod Bantjes, Editor;
Richard Biernacki, Editor; Bruce Curtis, Editor; Claude
Denis, Editor. **ISSN:** 0952-1909. **Subscription Rates:**
US$152 individuals print and online; EUR136 individuals
print and online; 91 individuals print and online; US$78
students print and online; EUR71 students print and online; 47 students, other countries print and online;
US$894 institutions print and online; US$812 institutions
print, online; US$1,041 institutions, other countries print
and online; US$946 institutions, other countries print,
online. **Remarks:** Accepts advertising. **URL:** http://www.
wiley.com/bw/journal.asp?ref=0952-1909&site=1. **Circ:**
(Not Reported)

56039 ■ Journal of the History of Collections
Oxford University Press
c/o Dr. Arthur MacGregor, Ed.
Ashmolean Museum
Oxford OX1 2PH, United Kingdom
Ph: 44 1865 278000
Fax: 44 18 65278018
Publisher E-mail: webenquiry.uk@oup.com
Journal providing the clearest insight into all aspects of
collecting activity. **Freq:** Semiannual. **Key Personnel:**
Dr. Arthur MacGregor, Editor; Dr. Kate Heard, Dep. Ed.,
kate.heard@hotmail.co.uk; Prof. John Boardman, Editorial Board; Prof. Gerard Turner, Editorial Board; Prof.
Hugh Torrens, Editorial Board. **ISSN:** 0954-6650. **Subscription Rates:** 221 institutions corporate; print and
online; 184 institutions corporate; online only; 202 institutions corporate; print only; 176 institutions print and online; 147 institutions online only; 162 institutions print
only; 53 individuals print; 34 students senior; print; 43
members print. **Remarks:** Advertising accepted; rates

available upon request. **URL:** http://jhc.oupjournals.org/.
Circ: (Not Reported)

56040 ■ Journal of the ICRU
Oxford University Press
Great Clarendon St.
Oxford OX2 6DP, United Kingdom
Ph: 44 1865 556767
Fax: 44 1865 353485
Publisher E-mail: webenquiry.uk@oup.com
Journal of interest to radiation protection practitioners,
dosimetrists and scientists in medicine, research,
industry (including nuclear power) and universities radiation oncologists, radiotherapists, diagnostic radiologists,
nuclear medicine physicians, medical physicists, regula-
tors, radiobiologists, epidemiologists, emergency
preparedness engineers, environmentalists and instrument designers, publishing reports on important and
topical subjects within the field of radiation science and
measurement and is the successor to the series of
reports published by or on behalf of the International
Commission on Radiation Units and Measurements
since 1927. **Freq:** Semiannual. **Key Personnel:** R.A.
Gahbauer, Chm,; D.T.L. Jones, Sec.; P.M. DeLuca,
Commission Membership. **ISSN:** 1473-6691. **Subscription Rates:** 307 institutions corporate; print and online;
256 institutions corporate; online only; 282 institutions
corporate; print only; 246 institutions print and online;
205 institutions online only; 226 institutions print only;
117 individuals print. **Remarks:** Advertising accepted;
rates available upon request. **URL:** http://jicru.
oxfordjournals.org/. **Circ:** (Not Reported)

56041 ■ Journal of Industrial Economics
John Wiley & Sons Inc.
Wiley-Blackwell
9600 Garsington Rd.
Oxford OX4 2DQ, United Kingdom
Ph: 44 1865 776868
Fax: 44 1865 714591
Publication covering economics. **Freq:** Quarterly. **Key
Personnel:** Saul Lach, Editor; Kai-Uwe Kuhn, Editor;
Thomas Hubbard, Editorial Board; Patrick Legros, Edi-
tor; Kenneth Corts, Editor; Steven T. Berry, Editorial
Board; Aviv Nevo, Editor; Jan Stevenson, Editorial Asst.
ISSN: 0022-1821. **Subscription Rates:** US$85 individu-
als print + online; US$33 students print + online;
US$304 institutions print + online; US$275 institutions
print, online; EUR253 institutions print and online; EUR229
institutions print, online; US$423 institutions, other
countries print + online; US$384 institutions, other
countries print, online; 199 institutions print + online;
181 institutions print, online. **Remarks:** Accepts
advertising. **URL:** http://www.wiley.com/bw/journal.asp?
ref=0022-1821&site=1. **Circ:** (Not Reported)

56042 ■ Journal of Information Technology
Palgrave Macmillan
Said Business School
Oxford University
Egrove Pk.
Oxford OX1 5NY, United Kingdom
Ph: 44 1865 422755
Fax: 44 1865 422501
Publication E-mail: jitedoffice@lse.ac.uk
Publisher E-mail: booksellers@palgrave.com
Journal covering topics in management science, infor-
mation systems and computer science disciplines. **Freq:**
4/yr. **Key Personnel:** Leslie Willcocks, Editor-in-Chief,
l.p.willcocks@lse.ac.uk; Chris Sauer, Editor-in-Chief,
chris.saucer@sbs.ox.ac.uk. **ISSN:** 0268-3962. **Sub-
scription Rates:** 569 institutions, other countries print;
US$1,063 institutions print; 52 other countries print and
online; US$97 individuals print and online. **URL:** http://
www.palgrave-journals.com/jit/index.html.

56043 ■ Journal of Integrative Plant Biology
John Wiley & Sons Inc.
Wiley-Blackwell
9600 Garsington Rd.
Oxford OX4 2DQ, United Kingdom
Ph: 44 1865 776868
Fax: 44 1865 714591
Peer-reviewed journal publishing original research
articles, rapid communications and reviews dealing with
all aspects of plant science. **Freq:** Monthly. **Key Person-
nel:** Dr. Leon V. Kochian, Assoc. Ed., lvk1@cornell.edu;
Hong Ma, Co-Ed.; Prof. William J. Lucas, Assoc. Ed.,
wjlucas@ucdavis.edu; Prof. Chun-Ming Liu, Editor-in-

Circulation: ★ = ABC; △ = BPA; ◆ = CAC; ● = CCAB; ❑ = VAC; ⊕ = PO Statement; ‡ = Publisher's Report; Boldface figures = sworn; Light figures = estimated.

Chief, cmliu@ibcas.ac.cn; Xiao-Ya Chen, Co-Ed.; Prof. Clive Lloyd, Assoc. Ed., clive.lloyd@bbsrc.ac.uk; Kang Chong, Co-Ed.; Prof. Rowan Sage, Assoc. Ed., rsage@ botany.utoronto.ca. **ISSN:** 1672-9072. **Subscription Rates:** US$229 individuals print + online; EUR205 individuals print + online; 137 other countries print + online; US$871 institutions print + online; 518 institutions print + online; 470 institutions print or online; US$1,013 institutions, other countries print + online; EUR658 institutions print + online; US$791 institutions print or online; EUR597 institutions print or online. **Remarks:** Advertising accepted; rates available upon request. **URL:** http://www.wiley.com/bw/journal.asp?ref= 1672-9072&site=1. **Circ:** (Not Reported)

56044 ■ Journal of International Criminal Justice
Oxford University Press
Great Clarendon St.
Oxford OX2 6DP, United Kingdom
Ph: 44 1865 556767
Fax: 44 1865 353485
Publisher E-mail: webenquiry.uk@oup.com
Journal for graduate and post-graduate students, practitioners, academics and government officials, promoting a collective reflection on the new problems facing international law and addressing the major problems of justice from the angle of law, jurisprudence, criminology, penal philosophy and the history of international judicial institutions. **Freq:** 5/yr. **Key Personnel:** Antonio Cassese, Editor-in-Chief; Mireille Delmas-Marty, Advisory Board; Bert Swart, Board of Ed.; Salvatore Zappala, Managing Editor; George P. Fletcher, Board of Ed.; Jia Bing Bing, Board of Ed.; Francoise Tulkens, Board of Ed.; Bert Swart, Board of Ed.; Thomas Weigend, Board of Ed. **ISSN:** 1478-1387. **Subscription Rates:** 482 institutions corporate; print and online; 402 institutions corporate; online only; 442 institutions corporate; print only; 386 institutions print and online; 322 institutions online only; 354 institutions print only; 98 individuals print; 47 students print; 68 members print. **Remarks:** Advertising accepted; rates available upon request. **URL:** http://jicj.oxfordjournals.org/. **Circ:** (Not Reported)

56045 ■ Journal of International Financial Management & Accounting
John Wiley & Sons Inc.
Wiley-Blackwell
9600 Garsington Rd.
Oxford OX4 2DQ, United Kingdom
Ph: 44 1865 776868
Fax: 44 1865 714591
Journal covering research focusing on international aspects of financial management and reporting, banking and financial services, auditing and taxation. **Freq:** 3/yr. **Key Personnel:** Prof. Frederick Choi, Editor, phone 212998-0047, fax 212995-4221, fchoi@stern.nyu.edu; Prof. Richard Levich, Editor, phone 212998-0422, fax 212995-4220, rlevich@stern.nyu.edu; Sidney Gray, Assoc. Ed. **ISSN:** 0954-1314. **Subscription Rates:** US$177 individuals print and online; EUR149 individuals print and online; 99 other countries print and online; 74 members print and online; US$124 members print and online; US$894 institutions print and online; US$812 institutions print or online; EUR603 institutions print and online; 474 institutions print and online; US$1,041 institutions, other countries print and online. **Remarks:** Advertising accepted; rates available upon request. **URL:** http://www.wiley.com/bw/journal.asp?ref=0954-1314. **Circ:** (Not Reported)

56046 ■ Journal of Islamic Studies
Oxford University Press
George St.
Oxford OX1 2AR, United Kingdom
Ph: 44 1865 278730
Fax: 44 1865 248942
Publisher E-mail: webenquiry.uk@oup.com
Multi-disciplinary publication dedicated to the scholarly study of all aspects of Islam and of the Islamic world, containing works dealing with history, geography, political science, economics, anthropology, sociology, law, literature, religion, philosophy, international relations, environmental and developmental issues, as well as ethical questions related to scientific research. **Freq:** 3/yr. **Key Personnel:** Dr. Farhan Ahmad Nizami, Editor; Prof. Zafar Ishaq Ansari, Consultant Ed. **ISSN:** 0955-2340. **Subscription Rates:** 228 institutions print and online; US$388 institutions print and online; EUR342 institutions print and online; 209 institutions print online; US$355 institutions print, online; EUR314 institutions print, online; 59 individuals print; US$113 individuals

print; EUR89 individuals print; 45 members print. **Remarks:** Advertising accepted; rates available upon request. **URL:** http://jis.oxfordjournals.org/. **Circ:** (Not Reported)

56047 ■ Journal of Law, Economics, and Organization
Oxford University Press
Great Clarendon St.
Oxford OX2 6DP, United Kingdom
Ph: 44 1865 556767
Fax: 44 1865 353485
Publisher E-mail: webenquiry.uk@oup.com
Law periodical. **Freq:** 3/yr. **Key Personnel:** Al Klevorick, Co-Ed.; Guido Calabresi, Editorial Board; Pablo Spiller, Editor, jleo@pantheon.yale.edu; Cathy Orcutt, Editorial Asst.; Gary Cox, Editorial Board; Henry Hansmann, Editorial Board; Francine Lafontaine, Co-Ed.; Robert Kagan, Editorial Board; Aaron Edlin, Editorial Board. **ISSN:** 8756-6222. **Subscription Rates:** 104 institutions print and online; 87 institutions online, print; 50 individuals print only; US$198 institutions print and online; US$165 institutions online, print; US$95 individuals print only; EUR156 institutions print and online; EUR131 institutions online, print; EUR75 individuals print only. **Remarks:** Accepts advertising. **URL:** http://jleo.oupjournals.org/. **Circ:** (Not Reported)

56048 ■ Journal of Law and Society
John Wiley & Sons Inc.
Wiley-Blackwell
9600 Garsington Rd.
Oxford OX4 2DQ, United Kingdom
Ph: 44 1865 776868
Fax: 44 1865 714591
Law periodical. **Freq:** Quarterly. **Key Personnel:** Prof. Philip A. Thomas, Editor, phone 44 29 20874368, fax 44 29 20874354, thomaspa@cardiff.ac.uk; Peter Alldridge, Advisory Board; Robert Lee, Asst. Ed.; Stewart Field, Asst. Ed.; Richard K. Lewis, Asst. Ed.; Reza Banakar, Assoc. Ed. **ISSN:** 0263-323X. **Subscription Rates:** US$68 individuals print and online; EUR62 individuals print and online; 42 individuals print and online; US$47 members print and online; 27 students print and online; US$982 institutions print and online; US$892 institutions print, online; EUR611 institutions print and online; EUR555 institutions print, online; US$1,143 institutions, other countries print and online. **Remarks:** Accepts advertising. **URL:** http://www.wiley.com/bw/journal.asp?ref=0263-323X&site=1. **Circ:** (Not Reported)

56049 ■ Journal of Legal Studies Education
John Wiley & Sons Inc.
Wiley-Blackwell
9600 Garsington Rd.
Oxford OX4 2DQ, United Kingdom
Ph: 44 1865 776868
Fax: 44 1865 714591
Peer-reviewed journal covering the issues on business legal studies. **Freq:** Biennial. **Key Personnel:** Lucien J. Dhooge, Advisory Ed.; Tonia Hap Murphy, Editor-in-Chief; Roger Reinsch, Staff Ed.; Robert C. Bird, Staff Ed.; Richard Coffinberger, Staff Ed.; Ronnie Cohen, Staff Ed.; Vincent A. Carrafiello, Staff Ed.; Mark S. Blodgett, Staff Ed.; Konrad S. Lee, Staff Ed. **ISSN:** 0896-5811. **Subscription Rates:** US$579 institutions print and online; US$526 individuals print; US$526 institutions online; 357 institutions online; 393 institutions print and online; EUR453 institutions online; EUR499 institutions print and online; US$699 institutions, other countries online; US$769 institutions, other countries print and online; US$699 institutions print. **Remarks:** Advertising accepted; rates available upon request. **URL:** http://www.wiley.com/bw/journal.asp?ref=0896-5811&site=1. **Circ:** (Not Reported)

56050 ■ Journal of Management Studies
John Wiley & Sons Inc.
Wiley-Blackwell
9600 Garsington Rd.
Oxford OX4 2DQ, United Kingdom
Ph: 44 1865 776868
Fax: 44 1865 714591
General business publication. **Freq:** 8/yr. **Key Personnel:** Steven W. Floyd, Gen. Ed., steven.floyd@unisg.ch; Mike Wright, Editorial Board; Timothy Clark, Editorial Board; Jo Brudenell, Managing Editor, j.m.brudenell@ durham.ac.uk; Andrew Delios, Gen. Ed., bizakd@nus. edu.sg; Joep Cornelissen, Gen. Ed., j.cornelissen@ leeds.ac.uk; Jay Anand, Editorial Board; Margaret Turner, Editorial Asst. **ISSN:** 0022-2380. **Subscription Rates:** US$205 nonmembers print and online, America; EUR124 nonmembers print and online, Europe; 124

nonmembers print and online, rest of World; US$129 members print and online, America; EUR115 members print and online, Europe; 76 members print and online, rest of World; US$2,065 institutions print and online, America; EUR1,245 institutions print and online, Europe; 980 institutions print and online, UK; 2,409 institutions, other countries print and online. **Remarks:** Accepts advertising. **URL:** http://www.wiley.com/bw/journal.asp? ref=0022-2380. **Circ:** (Not Reported)

56051 ■ The Journal of Medicine and Philosophy
Oxford University Press
Great Clarendon St.
Oxford OX2 6DP, United Kingdom
Ph: 44 1865 556767
Fax: 44 1865 353485
Publisher E-mail: webenquiry.uk@oup.com
Health publication. **Freq:** Bimonthly. **Key Personnel:** Edmund D. Pellegrino, Founding Ed.; H. Tristram Engelhardt, Jr., Sen. Ed.; Mark J. Cherry, Editor. **ISSN:** 0360-5310. **Subscription Rates:** 310 institutions print & online; 258 institutions online or print only; US$513 institutions print & online; US$427 institutions online or print only; EUR465 institutions print & online; EUR387 institutions online or print only; 44 individuals print; US$73 individuals print; EUR66 individuals print. **Remarks:** Accepts advertising. **URL:** http://jmp. oxfordjournals.org/. **Circ:** (Not Reported)

56052 ■ Journal of Molluscan Studies
Oxford University Press
Great Clarendon St.
Oxford OX2 6DP, United Kingdom
Ph: 44 1865 556767
Fax: 44 1865 353485
Publisher E-mail: webenquiry.uk@oup.com
International journal covering the biology of mollusks, featuring the newly developing subjects of molecular genetics, cladistic phylogenetics and ecophysiology, but also maintaining coverage of ecological, behavioural and systematic malacology. **Freq:** 4/yr. **Key Personnel:** Dr. D.G. Reid, Editor; Prof. T. Backeljau, Assoc. Ed.; Dr. J.R. Voight, Assoc. Ed.; Dr. J.D. Taylor, Assoc. Ed.; Prof. J. Davenport, Assoc. Ed.; Dr. S. Cragg, Assoc. Ed. **ISSN:** 0260-1230. **Subscription Rates:** 372 institutions print and online; US$744 institutions print and online; EUR558 institutions print and online; 310 institutions online; US$620 institutions online; EUR465 institutions online; 301 individuals print; US$602 individuals print; EUR452 individuals print. **Remarks:** Advertising accepted; rates available upon request. **URL:** http://mollus. oxfordjournals.org/. **Circ:** (Not Reported)

56053 ■ Journal of the National Cancer Institute
Oxford University Press
Great Clarendon St.
Oxford OX2 6DP, United Kingdom
Ph: 44 1865 556767
Fax: 44 1865 353485
Publisher E-mail: webenquiry.uk@oup.com
Journal publishing peer-reviewed original research from around the world and is a source for up-to-date news and information from the rapidly changing fields of cancer research and treatment. **Freq:** 24/yr. **Key Personnel:** Barnett S. Kramer, Editor-in-Chief; Frederic J. Kaye, Reviews Ed.; Douglas L. Weed, Reviews Ed.; Adriana Albini, Assoc. Ed.; William J. Blot, Assoc. Ed.; George P. Browman, Assoc. Ed. **ISSN:** 0027-8874. **Subscription Rates:** 745 institutions corporate; print and online; 522 institutions corporate; online only; 683 institutions corporate; print only; 597 institutions print and online; 417 institutions online only; 547 institutions print only; 291 individuals online only; 385 individuals print; 237 members online only; 313 members print. **Remarks:** Accepts advertising. **URL:** http://jnci.oxfordjournals.org/. **Circ:** (Not Reported)

56054 ■ Journal of Nursing and Healthcare of Chronic Illness
John Wiley & Sons Inc.
Wiley-Blackwell
9600 Garsington Rd.
Oxford OX4 2DQ, United Kingdom
Ph: 44 1865 476489
Publication E-mail: jci@wiley.com
Peer-reviewed journal containing articles for nurses and health care professionals who care for people with chronic illness. **Freq:** Quarterly. **Key Personnel:** Debbie Kralik, Editor; Vivien Coates, Regional Ed.; Diana Lee, Regional Ed. **ISSN:** 1752-9816. **Subscription Rates:** US$632 institutions Americas (print and online); 323 institutions UK (print and online); EUR409 institutions

Europe (print and online); US$801 institutions, other countries print and online; US$575 institutions Americas (print or online only); 293 institutions UK (print or online only); EUR372 institutions Europe (print or online only); US$729 institutions, other countries print or online only. **URL:** http://www.wiley.com/bw/journal.asp?ref=1752-9816.

56055 ■ Journal of Nursing Management
John Wiley & Sons Inc.
Wiley-Blackwell
9600 Garsington Rd.
Oxford OX4 2DQ, United Kingdom
Ph: 44 1865 776868
Fax: 44 1865 714591
Journal dealing with issues on the management of nurses and nursing. **Founded:** 1993. **Freq:** 8/yr. **Key Personnel:** Melanie Jasper, Editor-in-Chief; Dr. Alistair Hewison, Editor. **ISSN:** 0966-0429. **Subscription Rates:** US$172 individuals print + online; EUR139 individuals print + online; 93 individuals print + online; 102 other countries print + online; US$1,042 institutions print + online; 564 institutions print + online; EUR716 institutions print + online; US$1,215 institutions, other countries print + online; US$947 institutions print or online; 512 institutions print or online. **Remarks:** Advertising accepted; rates available upon request. **URL:** http://www.wiley.com/bw/journal.asp?ref=0966-0429. **Circ:** (Not Reported)

56056 ■ Journal of Paediatrics and Child Health
John Wiley & Sons Inc.
Wiley-Blackwell
9600 Garsington Rd.
Oxford OX4 2DQ, United Kingdom
Ph: 44 1865 776868
Fax: 44 1865 714591
Peer-reviewed journal covering research in pediatrics and child health. **Freq:** 12/yr. **Key Personnel:** David Isaacs, Editor-in-Chief; Spencer W. Beasley, Editor; Mike South, Editor; David Tudehope, Editor; Catherine Skellern, Editor; Polly Hardy, Editorial Panel. **ISSN:** 1034-4810. **Subscription Rates:** US$233 individuals print and online; $A 261 individuals print and online (Australia and New Zealand); EUR215 individuals print and online; 142 individuals print and online; US$1,271 institutions print and online; 787 institutions print and online; US$698 institutions print and online (Australia and New Zealand); EUR999 institutions print and online; US$1,543 institutions, other countries print and online; US$1,156 institutions print or online. **Remarks:** Advertising accepted; rates available upon request. **URL:** http://www.wiley.com/bw/journal.asp?ref=1034-4810. **Circ:** (Not Reported)

56057 ■ Journal of Personality
John Wiley & Sons Inc.
Wiley-Blackwell
9600 Garsington Rd.
Oxford OX4 2DQ, United Kingdom
Ph: 44 1865 776868
Fax: 44 1865 714591
Publication covering psychology and mental health. **Freq:** Bimonthly. **Key Personnel:** Howard Tennen, Editor, tennen@nso1.uchc.edu; Chi-Yue Chiu, Assoc. Ed.; Samuel A. Ball, Assoc. Ed. **ISSN:** 0022-3506. **Subscription Rates:** US$130 individuals Americas; 112 other countries; EUR169 individuals Euro zone; US$1,141 institutions Americas (print and online); 974 institutions UK (print and online); EUR1,236 institutions Europe (print and online); US$1,909 institutions, other countries; US$1,037 institutions Americas (print or online only); 885 institutions UK (print or online only); EUR1,236 institutions Europe (print or online only). **Remarks:** Accepts advertising. **URL:** http://www.wiley.com/bw/journal.asp?ref=0022-3506. **Circ:** (Not Reported)

56058 ■ Journal of Phytopathology
John Wiley & Sons Inc.
Wiley-Blackwell
9600 Garsington Rd.
Oxford OX4 2DQ, United Kingdom
Ph: 44 1865 776868
Fax: 44 1865 714591
Journal focusing on the population, organism, physiological, biochemical and molecular genetic level of Phytopathology. **Freq:** Monthly. **Key Personnel:** Prof. Alan A. Brunt, Editor-in-Chief, brunt@hriab.u-net.com; Prof. Robert C. Seem, Editor-in-Chief, rcs4@nysaes.cornell.edu; Prof. Andreas Von Tiedemann, Editor-in-Chief, atiedem@gwdg.de; Prof. Brigitte Mauch-Mani, Editor-in-Chief, brigitte.mauch@unine.ch; Dr. Sabine Von Tiedemann, Editorial Asst., stiedem@gwdg.de; B. Barna, Editorial Board. **ISSN:** 0931-1785. **Subscription Rates:** US$351 individuals print and online; EUR325 individuals print and online; 217 individuals print and online (non-Euro zone); US$2,162 institutions print and online; US$1,965 institutions print or online; 1,287 institutions print and online; 1,170 institutions print or online; EUR1,635 institutions print and online; EUR1,486 institutions print or online; US$2,773 institutions, other countries print and online. **Remarks:** Advertising accepted; rates available upon request. **URL:** http://www.wiley.com/bw/journal.asp?ref=0931-1785. **Foreign language name**: Phytopathologische Zeitschrift. **Circ:** (Not Reported)

56059 ■ Journal of Plankton Research
Oxford University Press
Great Clarendon St.
Oxford OX2 6DP, United Kingdom
Ph: 44 1865 556767
Fax: 44 1865 353485
Publisher E-mail: webenquiry.uk@oup.com
Journal publishing innovative papers that advance the field of plankton research, covering all kinds of marine, brackish and freshwater plankton: viruses, bacteria, fungi, phytoplankton, and zooplankton, including meroplankton and ichthyoplankton, including topics such as: plankton ecology and behaviour, including model studies; plankton physiology, including experimental results; genetics and taxonomy of planktonic organisms; biological properties and content of natural waters as they impinge directly on plankton physiology and ecology; development and testing of new methods for plankton research. **Freq:** 13/yr. **Key Personnel:** Kevin J. Flynn, Editorial Board and Interests; Christophe Brunet, Editorial Board and Interests; David Cushing, Founding Ed.; Albert Calbet, Editorial Board and Interests; Tom Anderson, Editorial Board and Interests; Bopaiah Biddanda, Editorial Board and Interests; Roger Harris, Editor-in-Chief; Heather Bouman, Editorial Board and Interests; Lulu Stader, Managing Editor; Miguel Alcaraz, Editorial Board and Interests. **ISSN:** 0142-7873. **Subscription Rates:** 887 institutions corporate; print and online; 739 institutions corporate; online only; 813 institutions corporate; print only; 709 institutions print and online; 591 institutions online only; 650 institutions print only; 298 individuals print. **Remarks:** Advertising accepted; rates available upon request. **URL:** http://plankt.oxfordjournals.org/. **Circ:** (Not Reported)

56060 ■ Journal of Policy and Practice in Intellectual Disabilities
John Wiley & Sons Inc.
Wiley-Blackwell
9600 Garsington Rd.
Oxford OX4 2DQ, United Kingdom
Ph: 44 1865 776868
Fax: 44 1865 714591
Journal is a forum for description of evidence-based policy and practice related to people with intellectual and developmental disabilities. **Freq:** Quarterly. **Key Personnel:** Matthew P. Janicki, PhD, Editor. **ISSN:** 1741-1122. **Subscription Rates:** US$113 individuals print + online; US$419 institutions print + online; US$381 institutions print or online; 321 institutions print + online; US$68 individuals ASSID member; 87 individuals print + online; 291 institutions print, online; EUR406 institutions print + online, EUR360 institutions print or online; EUR130 individuals print + online. **Remarks:** Advertising not accepted. **URL:** http://www.wiley.com/bw/journal.asp?ref=1741-1122&site=1. **Circ:** (Not Reported)

56061 ■ The Journal of Political Philosophy
John Wiley & Sons Inc.
Wiley-Blackwell
9600 Garsington Rd.
Oxford OX4 2DQ, United Kingdom
Ph: 44 1865 776868
Fax: 44 1865 714591
Journal focusing on political philosophy. **Freq:** Quarterly. **Key Personnel:** Robert E. Goodin, Editor, phone 61 261 252156, fax 61 261 253294, goodinb@coombs.anu.edu.au; Geoffrey Brennan, Assoc. Ed.; Claus Offe, Assoc. Ed.; Philip Pettit, Assoc. Ed.; Jeremy Waldron, Assoc. Ed.; Carole Pateman, Assoc. Ed.; Chandran Kukathas, Assoc. Ed.; John Dryzek, Assoc. Ed.; Anne Phillips, Editorial Board. **ISSN:** 0963-8016. **Subscription Rates:** US$60 individuals print + online; EUR56 individuals print + online; 38 individuals print + online; US$42 students print + online; EUR37 students print + online; 24 students, other countries print + online; US$798 institutions print + online; 577 institutions print + online; US$1,129 institutions, other countries print + online; EUR732 institutions print + online. **Remarks:** Advertising accepted; rates available upon request. **URL:** http://www.wiley.com/bw/journal.asp?ref=0963-8016. **Circ:** (Not Reported)

56062 ■ Journal of Public Administration Research and Theory
Oxford University Press
Great Clarendon St.
Oxford OX2 6DP, United Kingdom
Ph: 44 1865 556767
Fax: 44 1865 353485
Publisher E-mail: webenquiry.uk@oup.com
Journal providing in-depth analysis of developments in the organizational, administrative and policy sciences as they apply to government and governance. **Freq:** 4/yr. **Key Personnel:** George H. Frederickson, Editor-in-Chief; Craig Thomas, Editor; Keith Provan, Co-Ed.; Jodi Sandfort, Co-Ed.; Andrew Whitford, Co-Ed.; Anne M. Khademian, Co-Ed.; George Boyne, Co-Ed.; Don Moyhihan, Co-Ed. **ISSN:** 1053-1858. **Subscription Rates:** 384 institutions corporate; print and online; 320 institutions corporate; online only; 352 institutions corporate; print only; 308 institutions print and online; 256 institutions online only; 282 institutions print only; 68 individuals print; 59 members print; 33 members student; print. **Remarks:** Advertising accepted; rates available upon request. **URL:** http://jpart.oxfordjournals.org/. **Circ:** (Not Reported)

56063 ■ Journal of Public Economic Theory
John Wiley & Sons Inc.
Wiley-Blackwell
9600 Garsington Rd.
Oxford OX4 2DQ, United Kingdom
Ph: 44 1865 776868
Fax: 44 1865 714591
Peer-reviewed journal focusing on research in the field of public economics. **Freq:** Bimonthly. **Key Personnel:** Myrna Holtz Wooders, Editor, phone 615343-0462, fax 615343-8495, myrna.wooders@vanderbilt.edu; John P. Conley, Editor, phone 615322-2920, j.p.conley@vanderbilt.edu; Reinhard Selten, Advisory Ed.; Martin Shubik, Advisory Ed.; John Ledyard, Advisory Ed.; Rod Garrat, Assoc. Ed.; James Mirrlees, Advisory Ed.; Roger Guesnerie, Advisory Ed.; Alessandra Casella, Assoc. Ed. **ISSN:** 1097-3923. **Subscription Rates:** US$949 institutions print + online; 700 institutions print + online; 636 institutions print or online; US$8862 institutions print or online; EUR890 institutions print + online; EUR808 institutions print or online; US$1,372 institutions, other countries print + online; US$1,247 institutions, other countries print or online. **Remarks:** Accepts advertising. **URL:** http://www.wiley.com/bw/journal.asp?ref=1097-3923. **Circ:** (Not Reported)

56064 ■ Journal of Public Health
Oxford University Press
Great Clarendon St.
Oxford OX2 6DP, United Kingdom
Ph: 44 1865 556767
Fax: 44 1865 353485
Publication E-mail: jph.editorialoffice@oxfordjournals.org
Publisher E-mail: webenquiry.uk@oup.com
Journal focusing on current theory and practice within the whole spectrum of public health, promoting high standards of public health practice by publishing readable papers of high scientific quality and looking in depth at the causes of disease, how to prevent ill-health and promote good health and planning, provision and evaluation of health services; disease trends are also monitored, as are outbreaks of environmental hazards. **Freq:** 4/yr. **Key Personnel:** Prof. Gabriel Leung, Editor, gmleung@hku.hk; Dr. Hilary Burton, Scientific Editorial Board; Prof. Rona Campbell, Scientific Editorial Board; Dr. Davis Evans, Scientific Editorial Board; Prof. Sian Griffiths, Scientific Editorial Board; Prof. Phil Hanlon, Scientific Editorial Board; Prof. Selena Gray, Editor, selena.gray@uwe.ac.uk. **ISSN:** 1741-3842. **Subscription Rates:** 354 institutions corporate; print and online; 280 institutions corporate; online only; 325 institutions corporate; print only; 283 institutions print and online; 224 institutions online only; 260 institutions print only; 163 individuals print. **Remarks:** Advertising accepted; rates available upon request. **URL:** http://jpubhealth.oxfordjournals.org/. **Circ:** (Not Reported)

56065 ■ Journal of Refugee Studies
Oxford University Press

Circulation: ★ = ABC; △ = BPA; ♦ = CAC; • = CCAB; ❑ = VAC; ⊕ = PO Statement; ‡ = Publisher's Report; Boldface figures = sworn; Light figures = estimated.

Great Clarendon St.
Oxford OX2 6DP, United Kingdom
Ph: 44 1865 556767
Fax: 44 1865 353485
Publisher E-mail: webenquiry.uk@oup.com
Journal providing a forum for exploration of the complex problems of forced migration and national, regional and international responses, covering all categories of forcibly displaced people. **Freq:** 4/yr. **Key Personnel:** Khalid Koser, Co-Ed., k.koser@gcsp.ch; Dr. Joanne van Selm, Co-Ed., jvanselm@gmail.com; Margaret Okole, Asst. Ed.; Michael Cernea, International Editorial Advisory Board; Roberta Cohen, International Editorial Advisory Board; Alistair Ager, International Editorial Advisory Board; Stephen Castles, International Editorial Advisory Board; Wolfgang Bosswick, International Editorial Advisory Board; Jacqueline Bhabha, International Editorial Advisory Board. **ISSN:** 0951-6328. **Subscription Rates:** 322 institutions corporate; print and online; 268 institutions corporate; online only; 295 institutions corporate; print only; 257 institutions print and online; 214 institutions online only; 235 institutions print only; 64 individuals print. **Remarks:** Advertising accepted; rates available upon request. **URL:** http://jrs.oxfordjournals.org/. **Circ:** (Not Reported)

56066 ■ Journal of Regional Science
John Wiley & Sons Inc.
Wiley-Blackwell
9600 Garsington Rd.
Oxford OX4 2DQ, United Kingdom
Ph: 44 1865 776868
Fax: 44 1865 714591
Publication covering social sciences. **Founded:** 1958. **Freq:** 5/yr. **Key Personnel:** Marlon G. Boarnet, Editor; Walter Isard, Advisory Board; Prof. Roger E. Bolton, Assoc. Ed.; Casey Wagner, Asst. Ed.; Gilles Duranton, Assoc. Ed.; Mark D. Partridge, Editor. **ISSN:** 0022-4146. **Subscription Rates:** US$124 individuals print and online; EUR151 individuals print and online; US$63 members print and online; EUR72 members print and online; US$44 students print and online; US$489 institutions print and online; US$445 institutions print, online; EUR466 institutions print and online; US$718 institutions, other countries print and online; US$652 institutions, other countries print, online. **Remarks:** Accepts advertising. **URL:** http://www.wiley.com/bw/journal.asp?ref=0022-4146&site=1. **Ad Rates:** BW: 325. **Circ:** (Not Reported)

56067 ■ Journal of the Royal Statistical Society
John Wiley & Sons Inc.
Wiley-Blackwell
9600 Garsington Rd.
Oxford OX4 2DQ, United Kingdom
Ph: 44 1865 776868
Fax: 44 1865 714591
Publication E-mail: journal@rss.org.uk
Peer-reviewed journal focusing on statisticians both inside and outside the academic world. **Subtitle:** Series C, Applied Statistics. **Freq:** 5/yr. **Key Personnel:** M.S. Ridout, Editor; C.J. Skinner, Editor. **ISSN:** 0035-9254. **Subscription Rates:** US$509 institutions print and online; US$463 institutions print, online; 243 institutions print and online; 221 institutions print, online; EUR309 institutions print and online; EUR280 institutions print, online; US$543 institutions, other countries print and online; US$493 institutions, other countries print, online. **Remarks:** Advertising accepted; rates available upon request. **URL:** http://www.wiley.com/bw/journal.asp?ref=0035-9254&site=1. **Circ:** (Not Reported)

56068 ■ Journal of the Royal Statistical Society
John Wiley & Sons Inc.
Wiley-Blackwell
9600 Garsington Rd.
Oxford OX4 2DQ, United Kingdom
Ph: 44 1865 776868
Fax: 44 1865 714591
Peer-reviewed journal focusing on the significant role of statistics in life and in the society. **Subtitle:** Series A, Statistics in Society. **Freq:** Quarterly. **Key Personnel:** M. Cortina Borja, Book Review Ed., phone 44 20 76388998, fax 44 20 76143905; A. Fielding, Editor; A. Vignoles, Editorial Panel; S. Pudney, Editorial Panel; A. Chevalier, Editorial Panel; R. Gueorguieva, Editorial Panel; W. Browne, Editorial Panel. **ISSN:** 0964-1998. **Subscription Rates:** 325 institutions print + online; US$667 institutions print + online; US$605 institutions print, online; EUR403 institutions print + online; EUR375 institutions print, online; US$709 institutions, other countries print + online; US$644 institutions print, online; 296 institutions print, online. **Remarks:** Advertising accepted; rates available upon request. **URL:** http://www.wiley.com/bw/journal.asp?ref=0964-1998&site=1. **Circ:** (Not Reported)

56069 ■ Journal of the Royal Statistical Society
John Wiley & Sons Inc.
Wiley-Blackwell
9600 Garsington Rd.
Oxford OX4 2DQ, United Kingdom
Ph: 44 1865 776868
Fax: 44 1865 714591
Publication E-mail: rss@rss.org.uk
Peer-reviewed journal dealing with the methodological aspects of statistics. **Subtitle:** Series B, Statistical Methodology. **Freq:** 5/yr. **Key Personnel:** C.P. Robert, Editor; G. Casella, Editor. **ISSN:** 1369-7412. **Subscription Rates:** US$509 institutions print and online; US$463 institutions print, online; 243 institutions print and online; 221 institutions print, online; EUR309 institutions print and online; EUR280 institutions print, online; US$543 institutions, other countries print and online; US$493 institutions, other countries print, online. **Remarks:** Advertising accepted; rates available upon request. **URL:** http://www.wiley.com/bw/journal.asp?ref=1369-7412&site=1. **Circ:** (Not Reported)

56070 ■ Journal of School Health
John Wiley & Sons Inc.
Wiley-Blackwell
9600 Garsington Rd.
Oxford OX4 2DQ, United Kingdom
Ph: 44 1865 776868
Fax: 44 1865 714591
Journal addressing practice, theory and research related to the health and well-being of school-aged youth. **Freq:** Monthly. **Key Personnel:** Robert F. Valois, PhD, Editorial Board; Thomas M. Reed, Managing Editor; Kelli McCormack Brown, Editor-in-Chief; Sherry Everett Jones, PhD, Assoc. Ed.; Mark D. Weist, PhD, Editorial Board; Suzanne Sneed, Asst. to the Ed.-in-Ch. **ISSN:** 0022-4391. **Subscription Rates:** US$417 institutions print + online; US$378 institutions print or online; EUR337 institutions print + online; EUR306 institutions print or online; 265 institutions print + online; US$520 institutions, other countries print + online. **Remarks:** Accepts advertising. **URL:** http://www.wiley.com/bw/journal.asp?ref=0022-4391&site=1. **Circ:** (Not Reported)

56071 ■ Journal of Semantics
Oxford University Press
Great Clarendon St.
Oxford OX2 6DP, United Kingdom
Ph: 44 1865 556767
Fax: 44 1865 353485
Publisher E-mail: webenquiry.uk@oup.com
Journal publishing articles, notes, discussions and book reviews in the area of academic research into the semantics of natural language, aiming at an integration of philosophical, psychological and linguistic semantics as well as semantic work done in logic, artificial intelligence and anthropology. **Freq:** 4/yr. **Key Personnel:** Danny Fox, Assoc. Ed.; Philippe Schlenker, Managing Editor, managing.editor.atsjs@gmail.com; Rick Nouwen, Assoc. Ed.; Yael Sharvit, Assoc. Ed.; Regine Eckardt, Assoc. Ed.; Nicholas Asher, Editorial Board; Peter Bosch, Editorial Board. **ISSN:** 0167-5133. **Subscription Rates:** 253 institutions corporate; print and online; 211 institutions corporate; online only; 232 institutions corporate; print only; 203 institutions print and online; 169 institutions online only; 186 institutions print only; 77 individuals print; 58 members print. **Remarks:** Advertising accepted; rates available upon request. **URL:** http://jos.oxfordjournals.org/. **Circ:** (Not Reported)

56072 ■ Journal of Sexual Medicine
John Wiley & Sons Inc.
Wiley-Blackwell
9600 Garsington Rd.
Oxford OX4 2DQ, United Kingdom
Ph: 44 1865 776868
Fax: 44 1865 714591
Peer-reviewed Journal covering the latest research in basic science and clinical research in both male and female sexual function and dysfunction. **Subtitle:** Basic Research and Clinical Studies in Male and Female Sexual Function and Dysfunction. **Freq:** Monthly. **Key Personnel:** Irwin Goldstein, MD, Editor-in-Chief; Jason Roberts, PhD, Managing Editor; Sue W. Goldstein, Editorial Asst.; Ira Sharlip, MD, Assoc. Ed.; Wayne Hellstrom, MD, Assoc. Ed.; Annamaria Giraldi, MD, Assoc. Ed. **ISSN:** 1743-6095. **Subscription Rates:** US$441 individuals print and online; US$961 institutions print and online; US$873 institutions print, online; EUR745 institutions print and online; US$1,148 institutions, other countries print and online; US$1,044 institutions, other countries print, online; 587 institutions print and online; EUR366 individuals print and online; 244 other countries print and online. **Remarks:** Accepts advertising. **URL:** http://www.wiley.com/bw/journal.asp?ref=1743-6095&site=1. **Circ:** (Not Reported)

56073 ■ Journal of Sleep Research
John Wiley & Sons Inc.
Wiley-Blackwell
9600 Garsington Rd.
Oxford OX4 2DQ, United Kingdom
Ph: 44 1865 776868
Fax: 44 1865 714591
Peer-reviewed journal covering the field of sleep and wakefulness. **Freq:** Quarterly. **Key Personnel:** Derk-Jan Dijk, Editor, d.j.dijk@surrey.ac.uk; Claudio Bassetti, Assoc. Ed.; Tom de Boer, Assoc. Ed. **ISSN:** 0962-1105. **Subscription Rates:** US$193 members print + online (National societies); EUR158 members print + online (National societies); 105 members print + online (National societies); 114 members print + online (National societies, rest of wo; US$760 institutions print + online; 414 institutions print + online; EUR526 institutions print + online; US$886 institutions, other countries print + online; US$690 institutions print or online; US$805 institutions, other countries print or online. **Remarks:** Advertising accepted; rates available upon request. **URL:** http://www.wiley.com/bw/journal.asp?ref=0962-1105. **Circ:** (Not Reported)

56074 ■ Journal of Supply Chain Management
John Wiley & Sons Inc.
Wiley-Blackwell
9600 Garsington Rd.
Oxford OX4 2DQ, United Kingdom
Ph: 44 1865 776868
Fax: 44 1865 714591
Journal for and by supply management professionals and academicians publishing in-depth coverage and analysis of management issues, leading-edge research, long-term strategic developments, supplier relationships and applications, containing articles dealing with concepts from business, supply chain management, economics, operations management, logistics, information systems, the behavioral sciences and other disciplines which contribute to the advancement of knowledge in the various areas of purchasing, materials and supply management, supply chain management, and related fields. **Subtitle:** A Global Review of Purchasing and Supply. **Freq:** Quarterly. **Key Personnel:** Alvin J. Williams, Advisory Board; W.C. Benton, Reviewer; Harold E. Fearon, Advisory Board; Craig R. Carter, Co-Ed.-in-Ch.; Thomas Choi, Assoc. Ed.; Joseph L. Cavinato, Advisory Board; Larry Giunipero, Assoc. Ed.; Donald W. Dobler, Advisory Board; Phillip L. Carter, Advisory Board. **ISSN:** 1523-2409. **Subscription Rates:** US$109 individuals print + online; EUR103 individuals print + online; 68 other countries print + online; US$290 institutions print + online; EUR229 institutions print + online; 181 institutions print + online; US$353 institutions, other countries print + online; EUR208 institutions print or online; 164 institutions print or online; US$321 institutions, other countries print or online. **Remarks:** Accepts display advertising. **URL:** http://www.wiley.com/bw/journal.asp?ref=1523-2409&site=1. **Circ:** (Not Reported)

56075 ■ The Journal of Theological Studies
Oxford University Press
St. Stephen's House
16 Marston St.
Oxford OX4 1JX, United Kingdom
Ph: 44 1865 432301
Publisher E-mail: webenquiry.uk@oup.com
Publication covering philosophy and religion. **Founded:** Apr. 1899. **Freq:** Semiannual. **Key Personnel:** Prof. John Barton, Editor; Dr. Graham Gould, Editor. **ISSN:** 0022-5185. **Subscription Rates:** 240 institutions print and online; US$431 institutions print and online; EUR360 institutions print and online; US$144 institutions developing Countries - print only; 52 individuals print; US$104 individuals print; EUR78 individuals print. **Remarks:** Accepts advertising. **URL:** http://jts.oxfordjournals.org/. **Circ:** (Not Reported)

56076 ■ Journal of Tropical Pediatrics
Oxford University Press
Great Clarendon St.
Oxford OX2 6DP, United Kingdom
Ph: 44 1865 556767
Fax: 44 1865 353485

Publisher E-mail: webenquiry.uk@oup.com

Journal providing a link between theory and practice in the field containing papers that report key results of clinical and community research and considerations of programme development. **Freq:** 6/yr. **Key Personnel:** Prof. G.J. Ebrahim, Editor; Dr. D. Simkiss, Editor; Dr. A.J.R. Waterston, Editor. **ISSN:** 0142-6338. **Subscription Rates:** 451 institutions corporate; print and online; 376 institutions corporate; online only; 414 institutions corporate; print only; 361 institutions print and online; 301 institutions online only; 331 institutions print only; 133 institutions developing countries; print; 108 individuals print; 60 individuals developing countries; print; 70 members print. **Remarks:** Advertising accepted; rates available upon request. **URL:** http://tropej.oxfordjournals. org/. **Circ:** (Not Reported)

56077 ■ Journal of Urban Affairs
John Wiley & Sons Inc.
Wiley-Blackwell
9600 Garsington Rd.
Oxford OX4 2DQ, United Kingdom
Ph: 44 1865 776868
Fax: 44 1865 714591

Journal covering sociology and social work. **Freq:** 5/yr. **Key Personnel:** Katherine Tate, Assoc. Ed.; Cheryl Maxson, Assoc. Ed.; David Smith, Assoc. Ed.; Laura Reese, Editor, jua@msu.edu; Scott Bollens, Assoc. Ed. **ISSN:** 0735-2166. **Subscription Rates:** US$847 institutions print & online; EUR870 institutions print & online; US$1,344 institutions, other countries print & online; 685 institutions print & online; 623 institutions print or online; US$726 institutions print or online; EUR745 institutions print or online; US$1,151 institutions, other countries print or online. **Remarks:** Accepts advertising. **URL:** http://www.wiley.com/bw/journal.asp?ref=0735-2166; http://ordering.onlinelibrary.wiley.com/subs.asp? ref=1467-9906&site=1. **Circ:** (Not Reported)

56078 ■ Journal of Veterinary Emergency and Critical Care
John Wiley & Sons Inc.
Wiley-Blackwell
9600 Garsington Rd.
Oxford OX4 2DQ, United Kingdom
Ph: 44 1865 776868
Fax: 44 1865 714591

Peer-reviewed journal publishing basic, applied and clinical Research articles that address the emergency treatment and critical management of veterinary patients. **Subtitle:** The Official Journal of the Veterinary Emergency and Critical Care Society. **Freq:** Bimonthly. **Key Personnel:** Dr. Shane Bateman, Editorial Board, jvecc@mac.com; Gary Stamp, Business Mgr., stamp@veccs.org; Laura Brashear, Managing Editor, jvecc@veccs.org. **ISSN:** 1479-3261. **Subscription Rates:** US$147 individuals print & online; Canada + GST; EUR172 individuals print & online; plus VAT; 114 individuals Europe-non-Euro zone; print & online; plus VAT; 114 individuals rest of world; print & online; US$563 institutions print & online; Canada plus GST; EUR522 institutions print & online; plus VAT; US$563 institutions The Americas; print & online; Canada + GST; EUR474 institutions print & online; plus VAT; US$511 institutions online; Canada + GST; EUR474 institutions online; plus VAT. **Remarks:** Advertising accepted; rates available upon request. **URL:** http://www.wiley.com/bw/journal.asp?ref=1479-3261&site=1; http://ordering.onlinelibrary.wiley.com/subs.asp?ref=1476-4431&site=1. **Circ:** (Not Reported)

56079 ■ The Journal of World Intellectual Property
John Wiley & Sons Inc.
Wiley-Blackwell
9600 Garsington Rd.
Oxford OX4 2DQ, United Kingdom
Ph: 44 1865 776868
Fax: 44 1865 714591

Peer-reviewed journal dedicated to intellectual property issues in the context of trade and investment as per World Trade Organization and the Agreement on Trade-Related Aspects of Intellectual Property Rights. **Freq:** Bimonthly. **Key Personnel:** Prof. Daniel Gervais, Editor; Casey Fiesler, Assoc. Ed.; Prof. Paul Torremans, Editorial Board. **ISSN:** 1422-2213. **Subscription Rates:** US$786 institutions print and online; 467 institutions print and online; 424 institutions print or online; US$715 institutions print or online; EUR593 institutions print or online; US$914 institutions, other countries print and online; US$832 institutions, other countries print or online; EUR539 institutions print or online. **Remarks:** Advertising

accepted; rates available upon request. **URL:** http://www.wiley.com/bw/journal.asp?ref=1422-2213&site=1. **Circ:** (Not Reported)

56080 ■ Judicial Review
Hart Publishing Ltd.
16C Worcester Pl.
Oxford OX1 2JW, United Kingdom
Ph: 44 1865 517530
Fax: 44 1865 510710
Publisher E-mail: mail@hartpub.co.uk

Journal for lawyers engaged in judicial review, catering for both practitioners and academics. **Freq:** 4/yr. **Key Personnel:** Michael Fordham, Editor; James Maurici, Editor; Michael J. Beloff, Consultant Ed. **ISSN:** 1085-4681. **Subscription Rates:** 195 institutions United Kingdom and Europe; 215 institutions, other countries; 90 individuals United Kingdom and Europe; 100 other countries; 175 individuals online, standard; 81 individuals online. **Remarks:** Accepts advertising. **URL:** http://www.hartjournals.co.uk/jr/. **Circ:** (Not Reported)

56081 ■ King's Law Journal
Hart Publishing Ltd.
16C Worcester Pl.
Oxford OX1 2JW, United Kingdom
Ph: 44 1865 517530
Fax: 44 1865 510710
Publisher E-mail: mail@hartpub.co.uk

Peer-reviewed journal covering legal issues of current importance to both academic research and legal practice. **Founded:** 1990. **Freq:** 3/yr. **Key Personnel:** Satvinder Juss, Gen. Ed., satvinder.juss@kcl.ac.uk; Leslie Turano, Review Ed., leslie.turano@kcl.ac.uk. **ISSN:** 0961-5768. **Subscription Rates:** 115 individuals standard, United Kingdom and Europe; 130 other countries standard; 62 individuals United Kingdom and Europe; 68 other countries; 103.50 individuals standard, online; 55.80 individuals online. **Remarks:** Accepts advertising. **URL:** http://www.hartjournals.co.uk/klj/. **Circ:** (Not Reported)

56082 ■ KYKLOS
John Wiley & Sons Inc.
Wiley-Blackwell
9600 Garsington Rd.
Oxford OX4 2DQ, United Kingdom
Ph: 44 1865 776868
Fax: 44 1865 714591

Journal covering social sciences. **Subtitle:** International Review for Social Sciences. **Freq:** Quarterly. **Key Personnel:** Rene L. Frey, Ed./Mng. Ed., kyklos@crema-research.ch; Bruno S. Frey, Managing Editor; Reiner Eichenberger, Managing Editor. **ISSN:** 0023-5962. **Subscription Rates:** US$668 institutions print or online; US$736 institutions print + online; US$53 students print + online; 399 institutions print or online; 439 institutions print + online; 31 students print + online; EUR506 institutions print or online; 557 institutions print + online; EUR48 students print + online; US$781 institutions, other countries print or online. **Remarks:** Accepts advertising. **URL:** http://www.wiley.com/bw/journal.asp?ref=0023-5962&site=1. **Circ:** (Not Reported)

56083 ■ Landscape Research
Landscape Research Group
PO Box 1482
Oxford OX4 9DN, United Kingdom
Publisher E-mail: admin@landscaperesearch.org

Landscaping publication. **Freq:** 5/yr. **Key Personnel:** Dr. Ian Thompson, Editor. **ISSN:** 0142-6397. **Subscription Rates:** 658 institutions print and online; US$1,089 institutions print and online; EUR868 institutions print and online; 229 individuals print only; US$372 individuals print only; EUR295 individuals print only. **Remarks:** Advertising accepted; rates available upon request. **URL:** http://www.landscaperesearch.org/journal.htm. **Circ:** (Not Reported)

56084 ■ Language & Communication
Elsevier Science Inc.
c/o Elsevier Ltd.
The Blvd.
Langford Ln.
Oxford OX5 1GB, United Kingdom
Publisher E-mail: usinfo-ehelp@elsevier.com

Journal covering verbal and non-verbal communication. **Founded:** 1981. **Freq:** 4/yr. **Print Method:** Offset. **Trim Size:** 11 x 17. **Cols./Page:** 6. **Col. Width:** 1 3/4 inches. **Col. Depth:** 16 inches. **Key Personnel:** Roy Harris, Editor; S. Auroux, Editorial Board; E. Francis, Editorial

Board; H. Giles, Editorial Board; H. Gardner, Editorial Board; R.P. Botha, Editorial Board; L. Formigari, Editorial Board; J.N. Bailey, Editorial Board; Talbot Taylor, Editor, txtayl@mail.wm.edu; J.S. Bruner, Editorial Board. **ISSN:** 0271-5309. **Subscription Rates:** US$755 institutions, other countries except Europe, Japan and Iran; 89,600¥ institutions; EUR674 institutions for European countries and Iran; US$110 other countries except Europe, Japan and Iran; 15,900¥ individuals; EUR144 individuals for European countries and Iran. **URL:** http://www.elsevier.com/wps/find/journaldescription.cws_home/616/descriptiondescription.

56085 ■ Law and Financial Markets Review
Hart Publishing Ltd.
16C Worcester Pl.
Oxford OX1 2JW, United Kingdom
Ph: 44 1865 517530
Fax: 44 1865 510710
Publisher E-mail: mail@hartpub.co.uk

Peer-reviewed Journal covering banking and financial market issues, legal and regulatory developments affecting the financial markets. **Freq:** Bimonthly. **Key Personnel:** Roger McCormick, Gen. Ed., roger.mccormick@ukonline.co.uk. **Subscription Rates:** 725 individuals United Kingdom and Europe; 750 other countries; 652.50 individuals online. **Remarks:** Accepts advertising. **URL:** http://www.hartjournals.co.uk/lfmr/. **Circ:** (Not Reported)

56086 ■ Law & Policy
John Wiley & Sons Inc.
Wiley-Blackwell
9600 Garsington Rd.
Oxford OX4 2DQ, United Kingdom
Ph: 44 1865 776868
Fax: 44 1865 714591

Peer-reviewed journal publishing articles on law & policy. **Freq:** Quarterly. **Key Personnel:** Keith Hawkins, Editorial Board; Murray Levine, Editorial Board; Fiona Haines, Editor; Jennie MacDonald Lewis, Managing Editor; Nancy Reichman, Editor; Colin Scott, Editor. **ISSN:** 0265-8240. **Subscription Rates:** US$ other countries; US$51 individuals Americas; EUR54 individuals Euro zone; 417 institutions UK (print and online); US$521 institutions Americas (print and online); EUR529 institutions Europe (print and online); US$817 institutions, other countries; 379 institutions UK (print or online only); US$473 institutions Americas (print or online only); EUR481 institutions Europe (print or online only). **Remarks:** Accepts advertising. **URL:** http://www.blackwellpublishing.com/journal.asp?ref=0265-8240&site=1. **Circ:** (Not Reported)

56087 ■ Law, Probability and Risk
Oxford University Press
Great Clarendon St.
Oxford OX2 6DP, United Kingdom
Ph: 44 1865 556767
Fax: 44 1865 353485
Publisher E-mail: webenquiry.uk@oup.com

Journal academic lawyers, mathematicians, statisticians and social scientists with interests in quantitative reasoning, publishing papers that deal with topics on the interface of law and probabilistic reasoning, including communications law, computers and the law, environmental law, law and medicine, regulatory law for science and technology, identification problems (such as DNA but including other materials), sampling issues (drugs, computer pornography, fraud), offender profiling, credit scoring, risk assessment, the role of statistics and probability in drafting legislation, the assessment of competing theories of evidence (possibly with a view to forming an optimal combination of them). **Freq:** 4/yr. **Key Personnel:** M. Redmayne, Editorial Board; Prof. J. Gastwirth, Editor-in-Chief; D. Bourcier, Editorial Board; S. Brewer, Editorial Board; G. Van Calster, Editorial Board; Dr. D. Lucy, Book Review Ed., d.lucy@ed.ac.uk; R. Baldwin, Editorial Board; Prof. Jonathan Koehler, Editor, koehler@mail.utexas.edu; Prof. Peter Tillers, Editor, peter@tillers.net. **ISSN:** 1470-8396. **Subscription Rates:** 382 institutions corporate; print and online; 318 institutions corporate; online only; 350 institutions corporate; print only; 305 institutions print and online; 254 institutions online only; 279 institutions print only; 205 individuals print. **Remarks:** Advertising accepted; rates available upon request. **URL:** http://lpr.oxfordjournals.org/. **Circ:** (Not Reported)

56088 ■ Learning in Health and Social Care
John Wiley & Sons Inc.

Wiley-Blackwell
9600 Garsington Rd.
Oxford OX4 2DQ, United Kingdom
Ph: 44 1865 776868
Fax: 44 1865 714591
Peer-reviewed journal contributing to the growth and development of knowledge about approaches to the facilitation of individual, team and organisational learning in a variety of professional environments. **Freq:** Quarterly. **Key Personnel:** Michael Eraut, Founding Ed., phone 44 1273 877794, fax 44 1273 678568, m.eraut@ sussex.ac.uk; Anne Adams, Book Review Ed., phone 44 1908 858430, a.adams@open.ac.uk; Collette Clifford, Editorial Board; Pam Shakespeare, Editor, lhs@wiley. com; Auldeen Alsop, Editorial Board. **ISSN:** 1473-6853. **Remarks:** Accepts advertising. **URL:** http://www.wiley. com/bw/journal.asp?ref=1473-6853. **Circ:** (Not Reported)

56089 ■ Legal Ethics
Hart Publishing Ltd.
16C Worcester Pl.
Oxford OX1 2JW, United Kingdom
Ph: 44 1865 517530
Fax: 44 1865 510710
Publisher E-mail: mail@hartpub.co.uk
Journal covering field of legal ethics. **Freq:** Semiannual. **Key Personnel:** Prof. Kim Economides, Advisory Board; Christine Parker, Gen. Ed., legalethics@hartpub.co.uk; Bradley W. Wendel, Book Review Ed. **Subscription Rates:** 100 individuals standard, United Kingdom and Europe; 110 other countries standard; 60 individuals reduced, United Kingdom and Europe; 65 other countries reduced; 90 individuals standard, online; 54 individuals online. **Remarks:** Accepts advertising. **URL:** http://www. hartjournals.co.uk/le/. **Circ:** (Not Reported)

56090 ■ Literature Compass
John Wiley & Sons Inc.
Wiley-Blackwell
9600 Garsington Rd.
Oxford OX4 2DQ, United Kingdom
Ph: 44 1865 776868
Fax: 44 1865 714591
Online resource publishing original survey articles within nine online journals, combined with a range of useful reference resources. **Freq:** Monthly. **Key Personnel:** Regenia Gagnier, Editor-in-Chief; Antony Hasler, Sec. Ed.; Elaine Treharne, Section Ed.; Larry Scanlon, Section Ed.; Ruth Evans, Editorial Board; Pascale Aebischer, Editorial Board. **ISSN:** 1741-4113. **Subscription Rates:** US$69 individuals Americas (online only); EUR45 individuals Europe (online only); 35 other countries online only; US$878 institutions Americas (online only); 499 institutions UK (online only); EUR634 institutions Europe (online only); US$978 institutions, other countries online only; US$439 institutions developing countries (online only). **URL:** http://www.wiley.com/bw/journal.asp?ref=1741-4113.

56091 ■ Logic Journal of the IGPL
Oxford University Press
Great Clarendon St.
Oxford OX2 6DP, United Kingdom
Ph: 44 1865 556767
Fax: 44 1865 353485
Publisher E-mail: webenquiry.uk@oup.com
Journal publishing papers in all areas of pure and applied logic, including pure logical systems, proof theory, model theory, recursion theory, type theory, non-classical logics, non-monotonic logic, numerical and uncertainty reasoning, logic and AI, foundations of logic programming, logic and computation, logic and language, and logic engineering. **Freq:** 6/yr. **Key Personnel:** Ruy De Queiroz, Editor-in-Chief; Dov Gabbay, Editor-in-Chief; Hans Kamp, Editorial Board; Wilfrid Hodges, Editorial Board; Amir Pnueli, Editorial Board. **ISSN:** 1367-0751. **Subscription Rates:** 809 institutions corporate; print and online; 674 institutions corporate; online only; 741 institutions corporate; print only; 647 institutions print and online; 539 institutions online only; 593 institutions print only; 312 individuals print; 113 members print. **Remarks:** Advertising not accepted. **URL:** http://jigpal. oxfordjournals.org/. **Circ:** (Not Reported)

56092 ■ Management and Organization Review
John Wiley & Sons Inc.
Wiley-Blackwell
9600 Garsington Rd.
Oxford OX4 2DQ, United Kingdom

Ph: 44 1865 776868
Fax: 44 1865 714591
Journal publishing innovative research contributing to management knowledge in three domains: fundamental research in management, international and comparative management and Chinese management, including research on the management and organization of Chinese companies and multinational companies operating in China. **Freq:** 3/yr. **Key Personnel:** Anne S. Tsui, Editor-in-Chief; Doug Guthrie, Sen. Ed.; John Child, Sen. Ed.; Michael Morris, Sen. Ed.; Yanjie Bian, Sen. Ed.; Marshall Meyer, Sen. Ed.; Kwok Leung, Sen. Ed.; Oded Shenkar, Sen. Ed. **ISSN:** 1740-8776. **Subscription Rates:** US$90 individuals print + online; EUR78 individuals print + online; 62 other countries print + online; US$600 institutions print + online; 329 institutions print + online; EUR417 institutions print + online; US$644 institutions, other countries print + online; US$545 institutions print or online; 298 individuals print or online; 379 institutions print or online. **Remarks:** Advertising not accepted. **URL:** http://www.wiley.com/bw/journal.asp?ref=1740-8776& site=1. **Circ:** (Not Reported)

56093 ■ The Manchester School
John Wiley & Sons Inc.
Wiley-Blackwell
9600 Garsington Rd.
Oxford OX4 2DQ, United Kingdom
Ph: 44 1865 776868
Fax: 44 1865 714591
Journal covering all areas of economics discipline. **Freq:** Bimonthly. **Key Personnel:** Eyal Winter, Editor, man. school@man.ac.uk; Martyn Andrews, Editor; Keith Blackburn, Editor; Rabah Amir, Editor; Chris Orme, Managing Editor; Mike Artis, Assoc. Ed.; Richard Cornes, Assoc. Ed.; Hans Haller, Assoc. Ed.; Paul Madden, Assoc. Ed. **ISSN:** 1463-6786. **Subscription Rates:** US$824 institutions print or online; US$906 institutions print + online; US$130 individuals print + online; 395 institutions print or online; 436 institutions print + online; 68 individuals print + online; EUR502 institutions print or online; 553 institutions print + online; EUR68 individuals print + online; US$961 institutions, other countries print or online. **Remarks:** Accepts advertising. **Online:** Gale. **URL:** http://www.wiley.com/bw/journal.asp?ref=1463-6786&site=1. **Circ:** (Not Reported)

56094 ■ Material Religion
Berg Publishers
1st Fl., Angel Ct.
81 St. Clements St.
Oxford OX4 1AW, United Kingdom
Ph: 44 18 65245104
Fax: 44 18 65791165
Peer-reviewed journal exploring how religion happens in material culture, images, devotional and liturgical objects, architecture and sacred space, works of art and mass-produced artifacts. **Subtitle:** The Journal of Objects, Art & Belief. **Founded:** 2005. **Freq:** 3/yr. **Key Personnel:** S. Brent Plate, Editor; Birgit Meyer, Editor; David Morgan, Editor. **ISSN:** 1743-2200. **Subscription Rates:** 181 individuals online only; 213 institutions print and online; 49 individuals print only; 181 institutions online only. **Remarks:** Accepts advertising. **URL:** http:// www.bergpublishers.com/BergJournals/MaterialReligion/ tabid/517/Default.aspx. **Circ:** (Not Reported)

56095 ■ Medical Law Review
Oxford University Press
Great Clarendon St.
Oxford OX2 6DP, United Kingdom
Ph: 44 1865 556767
Fax: 44 1865 353485
Publisher E-mail: webenquiry.uk@oup.com
Journal for academics, lawyers, legal and medical practitioners, law students and anyone interested in health care and the law, presenting articles of international interest which provide thorough analyses and comment on the wide range of topical issues that are fundamental to this expanding area of law. **Freq:** 4/yr. **Key Personnel:** Prof. Margot Brazier, Editor, margaret.r. brazier@man.ac.uk. **ISSN:** 0967-0742. **Subscription Rates:** 305 institutions corporate; print and online; 254 institutions corporate; online only; 279 institutions corporate; print only; 220 institutions print and online; 183 institutions online only; 201 institutions print only; 82 individuals print; 66 members print. **Remarks:** Advertising accepted; rates available upon request. **URL:** http://medlaw.oxfordjournals.org/. **Circ:** (Not Reported)

56096 ■ Membrane Technology
Elsevier Science
c/o S. Barrett, In-house Ed.
Elsevier Advanced Technology
The Blvd. Langford Ln.
Kidlington
Oxford OX5 1GB, United Kingdom
Ph: 44 18 65843239
Fax: 44 18 65843971
Publisher E-mail: nlinfo-f@elsevier.com
Journal throwing light on the latest happenings in international membrane industry, highlighting emerging markets. Also covers chemicals, pharmaceuticals, biotechnology, food and beverage, brewing and wine, drinking water treatment, desalination, sewage treatment, oil and gas, mineral extraction, power generation, pulp and paper, and electronics. **Freq:** Monthly. **Key Personnel:** S. Atkinson, Editor, xnp43@dial.pipex.com; S. Barrett, In-house. Ed., s.barrett@elsevier.com; P. Ball, Editorial Advisory Board. **ISSN:** 0958-2118. **Subscription Rates:** EUR1,215 institutions for European countries; US$1,362 institutions for all countries except Europe and Japan; 161,400¥ institutions. **Remarks:** Accepts advertising. **URL:** http://www.elsevier.com/wps/find/ journaldescription.cws_home/422864/description. **Circ:** (Not Reported)

56097 ■ Metaphilosophy
John Wiley & Sons Inc.
Wiley-Blackwell
9600 Garsington Rd.
Oxford OX4 2DQ, United Kingdom
Ph: 44 1865 776868
Fax: 44 1865 714591
Broad base journal on philosophy, philosophical schools, methods, and so on. **Freq:** 5/yr. **Key Personnel:** Otto Bohlmann, Managing Editor, metaphil@southernct.edu; Armen T. Marsoobian, Editor-in-Chief, phone 203392-6792, fax 203392-6338, marsoobian@southernct.edu; Terrell Ward Bynum, Advisory Ed.; Kathleen Wallace, Book Review Ed., phone 516463-5613, fax 516463-2201, phikaw@hofstra.edu; Bernard Baumrin, Consulting Ed.; Eric Cavallero, Assoc. Ed.; Tom Rockmore, Consulting Ed.; Brian J. Huschle, Assoc. Ed.; Jane Duran, Consulting Ed.; Judith Genova, Consulting Ed.; Richard Kearney, Consulting Ed.; David Weissman, Consulting Ed. **ISSN:** 0026-1068. **Subscription Rates:** US$116 individuals print + online; EUR112 individuals print + online; 74 individuals print + online (non Euro zone); 93 other countries print + online; US$918 institutions print + online; EUR562 institutions print + online; US$1,072 institutions, other countries print + online; 442 institutions print + online; US$834 institutions print or online; EUR510 institutions print or online. **Remarks:** Advertising accepted; rates available upon request. **URL:** http://www.wiley.com/bw/journal.asp?ref=0026-1068. **Circ:** (Not Reported)

56098 ■ Microlight Flying
British Microlight Aircraft Association
The Bullring, Deddington
Banbury
Oxford OX15 0TT, United Kingdom
Ph: 44 18 69338888
Fax: 44 18 69337116
Publisher E-mail: general@bmaa.org
Consumer magazine covering aviation. **Founded:** 1980. **Freq:** Bimonthly. **Print Method:** Litho. **Trim Size:** 297 x 210 mm. **Key Personnel:** David Bremner, Editor, phone 44 17 06824909. **ISSN:** 0968-3100. **Subscription Rates:** Free members. **URL:** http://www.pagefast.co.uk/ mf/home.html. **Former name:** Flightline. **Ad Rates:** BW: 215, 4C: 376. **Circ:** Paid 4,200

56099 ■ Midwest Studies in Philosophy
John Wiley & Sons Inc.
Wiley-Blackwell
9600 Garsington Rd.
Oxford OX4 2DQ, United Kingdom
Ph: 44 1865 776868
Fax: 44 1865 714591
Journal dealing with philosophy. **Freq:** Annual. **Key Personnel:** Peter A. French, Editor; Howard K. Wettstein, Editor. **ISSN:** 0363-6550. **Subscription Rates:** US$541 institutions print + online; US$491 institutions print or online; 428 institutions print + online; 388 institutions print or online; EUR543 institutions print + online; EUR493 institutions print or online; US$837 institutions, other countries print + online; US$761 institutions print or online. **Remarks:** Advertising accepted; rates available upon request. **URL:** http://www.wiley.com/bw/journal. asp?ref=0363-6550. **Circ:** (Not Reported)

56100 ■ The Milbank Quarterly
John Wiley & Sons Inc.
Wiley-Blackwell
9600 Garsington Rd.
Oxford OX4 2DQ, United Kingdom
Ph: 44 1865 776868
Fax: 44 1865 714591
Health care industry journal. **Freq:** Quarterly. **Key Personnel:** Bradford H. Gray, Editor, phone 202261-5342, bgray@ui.urban.org; Ruth R. Faden, Editorial Board; Judith Feder, Editorial Board; Ronald Bayer, Editorial Board; Sherry A. Glied, Editorial Board; Lawrence O. Gostin, Editorial Board; Mark R. Chassin, Editorial Board; Mark A. Hall, Editorial Board; Vanessa Northington Gamble, Editorial Board; David Mechanic, Editorial Board; Carmen Hooker Odom, Publisher; David Wilsford, Editorial Board. **ISSN:** 0887-378X. **Subscription Rates:** US$76 individuals print + online; EUR91 individuals print + online; 61 individuals print + online; US$43 students print + online; EUR52 students print + online; 35 students print + online; US$229 institutions print + online; EUR209 institutions print + online; 168 institutions print + online; US$329 institutions, other countries print + online. **Remarks:** Accepts advertising. **Online:** Gale. **URL:** http://www.wiley.com/bw/journal.asp?ref=0887-378X&site=1. **Circ:** (Not Reported)

56101 ■ Mind & Language
John Wiley & Sons Inc.
Wiley-Blackwell
9600 Garsington Rd.
Oxford OX4 2DQ, United Kingdom
Ph: 44 1865 776868
Fax: 44 1865 714591
Journal dealing with linguistics, philosophy, psychology, artificial intelligence, and cognitive anthropology. **Freq:** 5/yr. **Key Personnel:** Tony Stone, Editor; Tim Crane, Editor; Ruth Campbell, Editor; Robyn Carston, Editor; Michael Martin, Editor; Deirdre Wilson, Editor; Samuel Guttenplan, Exec. Ed. **ISSN:** 0268-1064. **Subscription Rates:** US$192 individuals print + online; EUR143 individuals print + online; 94 individuals print + online (non Euro zone); 115 other countries print + online; US$154 members print + online; EUR113 members print + online; 92 members print + online (rest of World); US$1,134 institutions print + online; EUR703 institutions print + online. **Remarks:** Advertising accepted; rates available upon request. **URL:** http://www.wiley.com/bw/journal.asp?ref=0268-1064. **Circ:** (Not Reported)

56102 ■ The Modern Language Journal
John Wiley & Sons Inc.
Wiley-Blackwell
9600 Garsington Rd.
Oxford OX4 2DQ, United Kingdom
Ph: 44 1865 776868
Fax: 44 1865 714591
Magazine devoted to research and discussion about the learning and teaching of foreign and second languages. **Founded:** 1916. **Freq:** Quarterly. **Print Method:** Letterpress and offset. **Cols./Page:** 2. **Col. Width:** 33 nonpareils. **Col. Depth:** 117 agate lines. **Key Personnel:** Leo van Lier, Editor, mlj@miis.edu; Judith Liskin-Gasparro, Assoc. Ed., mljrev@uiowa.ed; Gabriel Appel, Assoc. Ed., gxa9@psu.edu. **ISSN:** 0026-7902. **Subscription Rates:** US$42 individuals (print & online); EUR56 individuals (print & online) for Europe. **Remarks:** Advertising accepted; rates available upon request. **URL:** http://mlj.miis.edu//index.htm. **Circ:** Paid 4,000, Controlled ‡74

56103 ■ The Modern Law Review
John Wiley & Sons Inc.
Wiley-Blackwell
9600 Garsington Rd.
Oxford OX4 2DQ, United Kingdom
Ph: 44 1865 776868
Fax: 44 1865 714591
Peer-reviewed journal publishing articles relating to common law jurisdictions. **Founded:** 1937. **Freq:** Bimonthly. **Key Personnel:** Martin Loughlin, Editorial Committee; Julia Black, Editorial Committee; W.R. Cornish, Editorial Board; J.S. Anderson, Editorial Board; M.R. Chesterman, Editorial Board; Stephen Weatherill, Editorial Committee. **ISSN:** 0026-7961. **Subscription Rates:** US$73 students print + online Americas; US$95 individuals print + online; 58 individuals print + online; 31 students print + online; EUR47 students print + online; EUR17 students the Americas, print + online; EUR87 individuals print + online; 58 individuals print + online. **Remarks:** Accepts advertising. **URL:** http://www.wiley.com/bw/journal.asp?ref=0026-7961&site=1. **Circ:** (Not Reported)

56104 ■ Modern Theology
John Wiley & Sons Inc.
Wiley-Blackwell
9600 Garsington Rd.
Oxford OX4 2DQ, United Kingdom
Ph: 44 1865 776868
Fax: 44 1865 714591
Peer-reviewed journal covering philosophy and religion. **Freq:** Quarterly. **Key Personnel:** Jim Fodor, Editor, jfodor@sbu.edu; Nicholas Lash, Editorial Board; Lewis Ayres, Editorial Board; Sarah Coakley, Editorial Board; Catherine Pickstock, Assoc. Ed.; Gregory L. Jones, Assoc. Ed.; William T. Cavanaugh, Editor, phone 651962-5315, wtcavanaugh@stthomas.edu; David Ford, Editorial Board; James J. Buckley, Assoc. Ed. **ISSN:** 0266-7177. **Subscription Rates:** US$918 institutions, other countries print, online; US$55 members APA/AAR: print + online; US$742 institutions print + online; US$675 institutions print, online; US$742 institutions print + online; EUR518 institutions print, online; 449 institutions print + online; 408 institutions print, online; 38 members APA/AAR: print + online; US$1,011 institutions, other countries print + online. **Remarks:** Accepts advertising. **Online:** Gale. **URL:** http://www.wiley.com/bw/journal.asp?ref=0266-7177&site=1. **Circ:** (Not Reported)

56105 ■ Molecular Biology and Evolution
Oxford University Press
Great Clarendon St.
Oxford OX2 6DP, United Kingdom
Ph: 44 1865 556767
Fax: 44 1865 353485
Publisher E-mail: webenquiry.uk@oup.com
Journal publishing investigations of molecular evolutionary patterns and processes, tests of evolutionary hypotheses that use molecular data and studies that use molecular evolutionary information to address questions about biological function at all levels of organization. **Freq:** Monthly. **Key Personnel:** Marcy Uyenoyama, Editor, marcy@duke.edu; Walter Fitch, Founding Ed.; Masatoshi Nei, Founding Ed.; Patricia Beldade, Assoc. Ed., p.beldade@biology.leidenuniv.nl; Adriana Briscoe, Assoc. Ed., abriscoe@uci.edu. **ISSN:** 0737-4038. **Subscription Rates:** 587 institutions corporate; print and online; 425 institutions corporate; online only; 538 institutions corporate; print only; 469 institutions print and online; 340 institutions online only; 430 institutions print only; 97 members print and online; 87 members online only; 92 members print. **Remarks:** Advertising accepted; rates available upon request. **URL:** http://mbe.oxfordjournals.org/. **Circ:** (Not Reported)

56106 ■ Molecular Ecology
John Wiley & Sons Inc.
Wiley-Blackwell
9600 Garsington Rd.
Oxford OX4 2DQ, United Kingdom
Ph: 44 1865 776868
Fax: 44 1865 714591
Journal bringing out contributions that employs molecular genetic techniques to address significant questions in ecology, evolution, behavior and conservation. **Freq:** Semimonthly. **Key Personnel:** Godfrey Hewitt, Editor; Loren Rieseberg, Editor-in-Chief, phone 604827-4540, lriesebe@interchange.ubc.ca; Prof. John Benzie, Assoc. Ed.; Pierre Taberlet, Editor; Tim Vines, Managing Editor, managing.editor@molecol.com; Louis Bernatchez, Review Ed. **ISSN:** 0962-1083. **Subscription Rates:** US$335 individuals print + online; EUR273 individuals print + online; 182 individuals print + online; 200 other countries print + online; US$304 individuals online; EUR247 individuals online; 165 individuals online; 181 other countries online; US$196 students print + online; EUR159 students print + online. **Remarks:** Advertising accepted; rates available upon request. **URL:** http://www.wiley.com/bw/journal.asp?ref=0962-1083. **Circ:** (Not Reported)

56107 ■ Molecular Ecology Resources
John Wiley & Sons Inc.
Wiley-Blackwell
9600 Garsington Rd.
Oxford OX4 2DQ, United Kingdom
Ph: 44 1865 776868
Fax: 44 1865 714591
Peer-reviewed journal vehicle for the rapid dissemination of technical advances in molecular ecology, such as new computer programs, methodological innovations, and molecular marker development. **Freq:** Bimonthly. **Key Personnel:** Kevin Livingstone, Editor-in-Chief, phone 210999-7236, klivings@trinity.edu; Alex Buerkle, Editor; Albano Beja-Pereira, Editor; Corey Davis, Editor; Vincent Castric, Editor; Carolyne Bardeleben, Editor; Tim Vines, Managing Editor, managing.editor@molecol.com; Brian G. Golding, Editor. **ISSN:** 1755-098X. **Subscription Rates:** US$196 students print and online; 106 students print and online; EUR159 students print and online; US$335 individuals print and online; 182 individuals print and online; EUR273 individuals print and online; US$304 individuals online; 165 individuals online; EUR247 individuals online; US$8,556 institutions online. **Remarks:** Accepts advertising. **URL:** http://www.wiley.com/bw/journal.asp?ref=1755-098X. **Formerly**: Molecular Ecology Notes. **Circ:** (Not Reported)

56108 ■ Molecular Oral Microbiology
John Wiley & Sons Inc.
Wiley-Blackwell
9600 Garsington Rd.
Oxford OX4 2DQ, United Kingdom
Ph: 44 1865 776868
Fax: 44 1865 714591
Journal covering the fundamental and applied aspects of oral infections. **Freq:** Bimonthly. **Key Personnel:** Howard F. Jenkinson, Editor-in-Chief; Richard J. Lamont, Co-Ed. **ISSN:** 0902-0055. **Subscription Rates:** US$346 individuals print and online; in the U.S.; EUR308 individuals print and online; in Europe; 205 other countries print and online; US$920 institutions print and online; in the U.S.; EUR696 institutions print and online; in Europe; US$836 institutions print or online; in the U.S.; 498 institutions, other countries print or online. **Remarks:** Advertising accepted; rates available upon request. **URL:** http://www.wiley.com/bw/journal.asp?ref=2041-1006&site=1. **Former name**: Oral Microbiology and Immunology. **Circ:** (Not Reported)

56109 ■ Monthly Notices of the Royal Astronomical Society
John Wiley & Sons Inc.
Wiley-Blackwell
9600 Garsington Rd.
Oxford OX4 2DQ, United Kingdom
Ph: 44 1865 776868
Fax: 44 1865 714591
Journal focusing on astronomy and astrophysics. Journal covering outcomes of original research in positional and dynamical astronomy, astrophysics, cosmology, space research, radio astronomy, and the design of astronomical instruments, in connection with Royal Astronomical Society. **Freq:** 36/yr. **Key Personnel:** R.F. Carswell, Editor-in-Chief; A.R. King, Dep. Ed.-in-Ch.; Collier A. Cameron, Board of Ed.; M.J. Barlow, Board of Ed.; M.W. Feast, Board of Ed.; A.R. Liddle, Board of Ed. **ISSN:** 0035-8711. **Subscription Rates:** US$902 individuals print + online; US$7,094 institutions print or online; US$7,094 institutions print + online; 534 individuals print + online; 3,839 institutions print or online; 4,224 institutions print + online; EUR801 individuals print + online; EUR4,876 institutions print or online; EUR5,364 institutions print + online; US$9,105 institutions, other countries print + online. **Remarks:** Advertising not accepted. **URL:** http://www.wiley.com/bw/journal.asp?ref=0035 8711. **Circ:** (Not Reported)

56110 ■ Museum International
John Wiley & Sons Inc.
Wiley-Blackwell
9600 Garsington Rd.
Oxford OX4 2DQ, United Kingdom
Ph: 44 1865 776868
Fax: 44 1865 714591
Journal covering different topics related to museum and heritage. **Freq:** Quarterly. **Key Personnel:** Isabelle Vinson, Ed.-in-Ch./Review Ed., phone 33 1 45684353, fax 33 1 45685823; Atieh Asghazardeh, Editorial Asst.; Sandra Acao, Editorial Asst. **ISSN:** 1350-0775. **Subscription Rates:** US$107 individuals print and online; EUR96 individuals print and online; 64 individuals print and online; US$376 institutions print and online; US$341 institutions print or online; EUR286 institutions print and online; EUR259 institutions print or online; US$439 institutions, other countries print and online; 225 institutions print and online; 204 institutions print or online. **Remarks:** Advertising accepted; rates available upon request. **URL:** http://www.wiley.com/bw/journal.asp?ref=1350-0775. **Circ:** (Not Reported)

56111 ■ Music Analysis
John Wiley & Sons Inc.

Circulation: ★ = ABC; △ = BPA; ♦ = CAC; • = CCAB; ❑ = VAC; ⊕ = PO Statement; ‡ = Publisher's Report; Boldface figures = sworn; Light figures = estimated.

Gale Directory of Publications & Broadcast Media/147th Ed. 5827

Wiley-Blackwell
9600 Garsington Rd.
Oxford OX4 2DQ, United Kingdom
Ph: 44 1865 776868
Fax: 44 1865 714591
Journal publishing articles on musical works and repertoires, in connection with the society of music analysis. **Freq:** 3/yr. **Key Personnel:** Alan Street, Editor, d.a.street@exeter.ac.uk; Julian Horton, Critical Forum Ed., julian.horton@ucd.ie; Michael Spitzer, Assoc. Ed., michael.spitzer@durham.ac.uk; Nicholas Marston, Advisory Panel; Craig Ayrey, Advisory Panel. **ISSN:** 0262-5245. **Subscription Rates:** US$84 individuals print and online; EUR67 individuals print and online; 45 individuals for non-Euro zone (print and online); 50 students, other countries print and online; US$923 institutions print and online; EUR42 students print and online; 27 students U.K. and non-Euro zone (print and online); EUR569 institutions print and online; US$1,075 institutions, other countries print and online. **Remarks:** Advertising accepted; rates available upon request. **URL:** http://www.wiley.com/bw/journal.asp?ref=0262-5245. **Circ:** (Not Reported)

56112 ■ Natural Resources Forum
John Wiley & Sons Inc.
Wiley-Blackwell
9600 Garsington Rd.
Oxford OX4 2DQ, United Kingdom
Ph: 44 1865 776868
Fax: 44 1865 714591
Publication E-mail: nrforum@un.org
Peer-reviewed journal focusing on the issues related to sustainable development and management of natural resources. **Founded:** 1976. **Freq:** Quarterly. **Key Personnel:** David Le Blanc, Editor; Kathleen Abdalla, Editorial Board; Diane Quarless, Editorial Board. **ISSN:** 0165-0203. **Subscription Rates:** US$183 individuals print and online; US$132 members print and online; US$1,073 institutions print and online; US$976 institutions print, online; EUR165 individuals print and online; EUR812 institutions print and online; 640 institutions print and online; 581 institutions print, online; 110 individuals print and online; US$1,253 institutions, other countries print and online. **Remarks:** Advertising not accepted. **URL:** http://www.wiley.com/bw/journal.asp?ref=0165-0203&site=1. **Circ:** (Not Reported)

56113 ■ Network Security
Elsevier Science Inc.
c/o S. Barrett, In-house Ed.
Elsevier Ltd.
The Blvd.
Langford Ln., Kidlington
Oxford OX5 1GB, United Kingdom
Ph: 44 186 5843239
Fax: 44 186 5843971
Publisher E-mail: usinfo-ehelp@elsevier.com
Journal devoted to network security problems. **Founded:** 1968. **Freq:** Monthly. **Print Method:** Offset. **Trim Size:** 5 1/2 x 8 1/2. **Cols./Page:** 1. **Col. Width:** 50 nonpareils. **Col. Depth:** 100 agate lines. **Key Personnel:** S. Barrett, In-house Ed., s.barrett@elsevier.com; M. Marietta, Editorial Board; K. Lindup, Editorial Board; T. Mulhall, Editorial Board; D. Longley, Editorial Board; J. David, Editorial Board; D. Forte, Editorial Board; B. Hancock, Editorial Board; E. Amoroso, Editorial Board. **ISSN:** 1353-4858. **Subscription Rates:** EUR1,112 institutions for European countries and Iran; US$1,244 institutions, other countries except Europe, Japan and Iran; 147,500¥ institutions. **URL:** http://www.elsevier.com/wps/find/journaldescription.cws_home/30358/descriptiondescription.

56114 ■ Neuromodulation
John Wiley & Sons Inc.
Wiley-Blackwell
9600 Garsington Rd.
Oxford OX4 2DQ, United Kingdom
Ph: 44 1865 776868
Fax: 44 1865 714591
Journal publishing scientific and clinical information focusing on neuromodulation, in connection with the International Neuromodulation Society and the International Functional Electrical Stimulation Society (IFESS). **Freq:** Quarterly. **Key Personnel:** Robert Levy, MD, Editor-in-Chief; Tia Sofatzis, Managing Editor. **ISSN:** 1094-7159. **Subscription Rates:** US$210 individuals print & online; US$437 institutions print & online; 335 institutions print & online; US$397 institutions online only; EUR264 individuals print & online; EUR426 institutions print & online; EUR386 institutions online only. **Remarks:** Advertising accepted; rates available upon

request. **URL:** http://www.wiley.com/bw/journal.asp?ref=1094-7159. **Circ:** (Not Reported)

56115 ■ Neuropathology
John Wiley & Sons Inc.
Wiley-Blackwell
9600 Garsington Rd.
Oxford OX4 2DQ, United Kingdom
Ph: 44 1865 776868
Fax: 44 1865 714591
Peer-reviewed journal dealing with all aspects of human and experimental neuropathology. **Freq:** Bimonthly. **Key Personnel:** Hitoshi Takahashi, Editor-in-Chief; Hitoshi Takahashi, President; Haruhiko Akiyama, Editorial Board. **ISSN:** 0919-6544. **Subscription Rates:** US$200 individuals print and online; US$987 institutions print and online; US$897 institutions print, online; US$1,190 institutions print and online; EUR186 individuals print and online; 607 institutions print and online; 552 institutions print, online; 125 individuals print and online; EUR772 institutions print and online; EUR701 institutions print, online. **Remarks:** Advertising accepted; rates available upon request. **URL:** http://www.wiley.com/bw/journal.asp?ref=0919-6544&site=1. **Circ:** (Not Reported)

56116 ■ Neuropathology and Applied Neurobiology
John Wiley & Sons Inc.
Wiley-Blackwell
9600 Garsington Rd.
Oxford OX4 2DQ, United Kingdom
Ph: 44 1865 776868
Fax: 44 1865 714591
Peer-reviewed journal covering the field of neuropathology and muscle disease. **Founded:** 1974. **Freq:** 7/yr. **Key Personnel:** D. Louis, Editor; J.S. Lowe, Consulting Ed.; R.O. Weller, Book Review Ed.; Dr. Stephen B. Wharton, Editor-in-Chief; R. De Silva, Editorial Advisory Board. **ISSN:** 0305-1846. **Subscription Rates:** US$232 members print and online; US$2,631 institutions print and online; US$2,393 institutions print, online; US$3,067 institutions, other countries print and online; 1,423 institutions print and online; 1,294 institutions print, online; EUR1,808 institutions print and online; EUR1,643 institutions print, online; US$2,789 institutions, other countries print, online. **Remarks:** Advertising accepted; rates available upon request. **URL:** http://www.wiley.com/bw/journal.asp?ref=0305-1846&site=1. **Circ:** (Not Reported)

56117 ■ New Internationalist
55 Rectory Rd.
Oxford OX4 1BW, United Kingdom
Ph: 44 1865 728181
Fax: 44 1865 793152
Publisher E-mail: subscriptions@newint.org
Magazine covering major issues on justice and equality. **Freq:** Monthly Jan/Feb combined bumper issue. **Key Personnel:** Katharine Ainger, Editor, katharinea@newint.org; Vanessa Baird, Editor, vanessab@newint.org; David Ransom, Editor, davidr@newint.org; Dinyar Godrej, Editor, dinyarg@newint.org. **Subscription Rates:** 24.95 individuals. **Remarks:** Accepts advertising. **URL:** http://www.newint.org/. **Circ:** 75,000

56118 ■ New Perspectives Quarterly
John Wiley & Sons Inc.
Wiley-Blackwell
9600 Garsington Rd.
Oxford OX4 2DQ, United Kingdom
Ph: 44 1865 776868
Fax: 44 1865 714591
Political science publication. **Freq:** Quarterly. **Key Personnel:** Nathan Gardels, Editor, phone 310474-0011, fax 310474-8061, npq@pacificnet.net; Emma Cherniavsky, Assoc. Ed.; Sidney Drell, Board of Advisors. **ISSN:** 0893-7850. **Subscription Rates:** US$53 individuals print and online; EUR69 individuals print and online; 46 individuals print and online; US$44 members print and online; EUR57 members print and online; 38 members print and online; US$424 institutions print and online; EUR430 institutions print and online; US$663 institutions, other countries print and online; US$603 institutions, other countries print. **Remarks:** Accepts advertising. **URL:** http://www.wiley.com/bw/journal.asp?ref=0893-7850&site=1. **Circ:** (Not Reported)

56119 ■ New Zealand Geographer
John Wiley & Sons Inc.
Wiley-Blackwell
9600 Garsington Rd.
Oxford OX4 2DQ, United Kingdom
Ph: 44 1865 776868

Fax: 44 1865 714591
Peer-reviewed journal publishing academic papers on aspects of the physical, human and environmental geographies and landscapes of its region; commentaries and debates; discussions of educational questions and scholarship of concern to geographers; short interventions and assessments of topical matters of interest to university and high school teachers and book reviews. **Freq:** 3/yr. **Key Personnel:** Prof. Michael Roche, Editorial Board; Dr. David Kennedy, Editorial Board; Dr. Janine Wiles, Editorial Board; Prof. Eric Pawson, Editorial Board. **ISSN:** 0028-8144. **Subscription Rates:** US$294 institutions print + online; 164 institutions print + online; 149 institutions print or online; US$267 institutions print or online; EUR208 institutions print + online; EUR189 institutions print or online; US$322 institutions, other countries print + online; US$292 institutions, other countries print or online; US$218 institutions print + online (New Zealand). **Remarks:** Advertising not accepted. **URL:** http://www.wiley.com/bw/journal.asp?ref=0028-8144&site=1. **Circ:** (Not Reported)

56120 ■ Notes and Queries
Oxford University Press
Great Clarendon St.
Oxford OX2 6DP, United Kingdom
Ph: 44 1865 556767
Fax: 44 1865 353485
Publisher E-mail: webenquiry.uk@oup.com
Publication covering literature and writing. **Freq:** 4/yr. **Key Personnel:** Bernard J. O'Donoghue, Editor; Glenn L. Black, Editor; E.G. Stanley, Advisory Ed.; Andy Orchard, Editor; Duncan Wu, Editor. **ISSN:** 0029-3970. **Subscription Rates:** 184 institutions print and online; US$368 institutions print and online; EUR276 institutions print and online; 52 individuals print; US$104 individuals print; EUR78 individuals print; 34 students print; US$68 students print; EUR51 students print. **Remarks:** Accepts advertising. **URL:** http://nq.oxfordjournals.org. **Circ:** (Not Reported)

56121 ■ Nucleic Acids Research
Oxford University Press
Great Clarendon St.
Oxford OX2 6DP, United Kingdom
Ph: 44 1865 556767
Fax: 44 1865 353485
Publisher E-mail: webenquiry.uk@oup.com
Journal publishing the results of leading edge research into physical, chemical, biochemical and biological aspects of nucleic acids and proteins involved in nucleic acid metabolism and/or interactions, including chemistry, computational biology, genomics, molecular biology, RNA and structural biology. **Freq:** 22/yr. **Key Personnel:** Keith Fox, Sen. Exec. Ed.; M.J. Gait, Exec. Ed., mgait@mrc-lmb.cam.ac.uk; M. Churchill, Exec. Ed., mair.churchill@uchsc.edu; W. Dynan, Exec. Ed., nar@mcg.edu; B. Stoddard, Sen. Exec. Ed., stoddnar@fhcrc.org. **ISSN:** 0305-1048. **Subscription Rates:** 2,511 institutions corporate; print only; 2,009 institutions print only; 2,305 institutions online only; 504 individuals print. **Remarks:** Advertising accepted; rates available upon request. **URL:** http://nar.oxfordjournals.org/. **Circ:** (Not Reported)

56122 ■ Nursing and Health Sciences
John Wiley & Sons Inc.
Wiley-Blackwell
9600 Garsington Rd.
Oxford OX4 2DQ, United Kingdom
Ph: 44 1865 776868
Fax: 44 1865 714591
Peer-reviewed journal covering the field of nursing and health sciences. **Freq:** Quarterly. **Key Personnel:** Susumu Tomonaga, PhD, Founder; Carolyn S. Melby, Assoc. Ed.; Sue Turale, Editor-in-Chief; Patricia R. Underwood, Founding Ed.-in-Ch.; Masato Tsukahara, Founding Ed.-in-Ch.; David Arthur, Assoc. Ed. **ISSN:** 1441-0745. **Subscription Rates:** US$176 individuals print and online; EUR161 individuals print and online; 108 individuals print and online; US$719 institutions print and online; 446 institutions print and online; US$653 institutions print, online; EUR514 institutions print and online; EUR565 institutions print, online; US$872 institutions, other countries print and online; US$792 institutions, other countries print, online. **Remarks:** Advertising accepted; rates available upon request. **URL:** http://www.wiley.com/bw/journal.asp?ref=1441-0745&site=1. **Circ:** (Not Reported)

56123 ■ Nursing Philosophy
John Wiley & Sons Inc.

Wiley-Blackwell
9600 Garsington Rd.
Oxford OX4 2DQ, United Kingdom
Ph: 44 1865 776868
Fax: 44 1865 714591
Peer-reviewed journal providing theoritical information and ideas for nurses and healthcare professionals. **Subtitle:** The Official Journal of the International Philosophy of Nursing Society. **Freq:** Quarterly. **Key Personnel:** Steven Edwards, Founding Ed.; Patricia Rodney, Editorial Board; Beverly Whelton, Book Review Ed., phone 304281-2005, bwhelton@wju.edu. **ISSN:** 1466-7681. **Subscription Rates:** US$113 individuals print + online; US$540 institutions print + online; US$490 institutions print, online; 291 institutions print + online; EUR90 individuals print + online; 264 institutions print, online; EUR369 institutions print + online; EUR335 institutions print, online; 68 other countries print + online; US$629 institutions, other countries print + online. **Remarks:** Accepts advertising. **URL:** http://www.wiley.com/bw/journal.asp?ref=1466-7681&site=1. **Circ:** (Not Reported)

56124 ■ Nutrition Bulletin
John Wiley & Sons Inc.
Wiley-Blackwell
9600 Garsington Rd.
Oxford OX4 2DQ, United Kingdom
Ph: 44 1865 776868
Fax: 44 1865 714591
Journal covering various aspects of nutrition science, in connection with British Nutrition Foundation. **Freq:** Quarterly. **Key Personnel:** Sara Stanner, Editor, s.stanner@nutrition.org.uk; Judith Buttriss, Editor; I. Darnton-Hill, Editorial Advisory Board; R. Johnson, Editorial Advisory Board; Claire Williamson, Editor, c.williamson@nutrition.org.uk; M. Howie, Editorial Advisory Board; T. Hutton, Editorial Advisory Board; C. Leonard, Editorial Advisory Board; E. Diaz, Editorial Advisory Board; J. Gray, Editorial Advisory Board; V. Parry, Editorial Advisory Board. **ISSN:** 1471-9827. **Subscription Rates:** US$159 individuals print + online; US$52 students print + online; US$758 institutions print + online; EUR130 individuals print + online; EUR42 students print + online; 410 institutions print + online; 87 individuals print + online; US$688 institutions print or online; EUR520 institutions print + online; US$884 institutions, other countries print + online. **Remarks:** Advertising accepted; rates available upon request. **URL:** http://www.wiley.com/bw/journal.asp?ref=1471-9827&site=1. **Circ:** (Not Reported)

56125 ■ Obesity Reviews
John Wiley & Sons Inc.
Wiley-Blackwell
9600 Garsington Rd.
Oxford OX4 2DQ, United Kingdom
Ph: 44 1865 776868
Fax: 44 1865 714591
Journal publishing papers from all disciplines related to obesity. **Freq:** Bimonthly. **Key Personnel:** Arne Astrup, Editor, phone 45 353 32507, fax 45 353 32483, ast@life.ku.dk; Claude Mona, Editorial Asst., clmo@life.ku.dk; Dr. David B. Allison, Editorial Board. **ISSN:** 1467-7881. **Subscription Rates:** US$198 individuals print and online; US$883 institutions print and online; US$802 institutions print or online; EUR609 institutions print and online; EUR557 institutions print, online; EUR159 individuals print and online; 479 institutions print and online; US$938 institutions, other countries print and online; US$938 institutions, other countries print or online; 438 institutions print or online. **Remarks:** Accepts advertising. **URL:** http://www.wiley.com/bw/journal.asp?ref=1467-7881&site=1. **Circ:** (Not Reported)

56126 ■ Oil and Energy Trends
John Wiley & Sons Inc.
Wiley-Blackwell
9600 Garsington Rd.
Oxford OX4 2DQ, United Kingdom
Ph: 44 1865 776868
Fax: 44 1865 714591
Magazine providing latest information on all major energy statistics. **Subtitle:** A Monthly Publication of International Energy Statistics and Analysis. **Freq:** Monthly. **Key Personnel:** Anna Kachkova, Editor, phone 44 18 65476218, fax 44 18 65471218, akachkova@wiley.com; Francisco R. Parra, Founding Ed.; Paul McDonald, Consulting Ed. **ISSN:** 0950-1045. **Subscription Rates:** 2,455 institutions print and online; US$4,811 institutions, other countries print and online; 2,232 institutions print, online; US$4,373 institutions, other

countries print, online; EUR3,111 institutions print and online; EUR2,834 institutions print, online; US$4,151 institutions print and online; US$3,774 institutions print, online. **Remarks:** Advertising not accepted. **URL:** http://www.wiley.com/bw/journal.asp?ref=0950-1045&site=1. **Circ:** (Not Reported)

56127 ■ OPEC Energy Review
John Wiley & Sons Inc.
Wiley-Blackwell
9600 Garsington Rd.
Oxford OX4 2DQ, United Kingdom
Ph: 44 1865 776868
Fax: 44 1865 714591
Magazine focusing on energy economics and related issues, such as economic development and the environment. **Subtitle:** Energy Economics and Related Issues. **Freq:** Quarterly. **Key Personnel:** Omar Farouk Ibrahim, Editor-in-Chief; Angela U. Agowike, Exec. Ed. **ISSN:** 1753-0229. **Subscription Rates:** US$173 individuals print + online; EUR465 individuals print + online (Euro zone); 103 individuals print + online (non-Euro zone); US$677 institutions print + online; 403 institutions print + online (UK); EUR511 institutions print + online (Europe); 366 institutions print or online (UK); US$615 institutions print or online; US$789 institutions, other countries print + online. **Remarks:** Advertising accepted; rates available upon request. **URL:** http://www.wiley.com/bw/journal.asp?ref=1753-0229&site=1. **Formerly:** OPEC Review. **Circ:** (Not Reported)

56128 ■ Oral History Review
Oxford University Press
Great Clarendon St.
Oxford OX2 6DP, United Kingdom
Ph: 44 1865 556767
Fax: 44 1865 353485
Publisher E-mail: webenquiry.uk@oup.com
Scholarly journal of the Oral History Association covering oral history of people who have participated in important political, cultural, and economic social developments in modern times. **Founded:** 1973. **Freq:** 2/yr. **Trim Size:** 6 x 9. **Key Personnel:** Mary Stromme, Editorial Asst., mary.stromme@und.nodak.edu; John Wolford, Book Review Ed., wolford.john@gmail.com; Doug Boyd, Media Review Ed., doug.boyd@uky.edu; Kimberly Porter, Editor, kimberly.porter@und.nodak.edu. **ISSN:** 0094-0798. **Subscription Rates:** 104 institutions print and online; US$156 institutions print and online; 156 institutions print, online; US$143 institutions print, online; 60 individuals print; US$90 individuals print; 23 students print; US$35 students print. **Remarks:** Accepts advertising. **URL:** http://ohr.oxfordjournals.org/. **Ad Rates:** BW: 325. **Circ:** 1,065

56129 ■ Oral Oncology
Mosby Inc.
The Blvd.
Langford Ln.
Kidlington
Oxford OX5 1GB, United Kingdom
Ph: 44 1865 843203
Fax: 44 1865 843992
Publisher E-mail: custserv.ehs@elsevier.com
Peer-reviewed journal covering the issues related to the study of aetiopathogenesis, epidemiology, prevention and management of oral and perioral tumors and of oral disease in patients with malignancies. **Freq:** 12/yr. **Key Personnel:** Crispian Scully, Editor; Dr. Paul Allison, Editorial Board; Prof. Ahmad Awada, Editorial Board. **ISSN:** 1368-8375. **Subscription Rates:** EUR174 individuals for European countries and Iran; US$196 other countries except Europe, Japan and Iran; 23,200¥ individuals; EUR1,438 institutions for European countries and Iran; 190,600¥ institutions; US$1,606 institutions for all countries except Europe, Japan and Iran. **URL:** http://www.elsevier.com/wps/find/journaldescription.cws_home/105/descriptiondescription.

56130 ■ Oxford Art Journal
Oxford University Press
Great Clarendon St.
Oxford OX2 6DP, United Kingdom
Ph: 44 1865 556767
Fax: 44 1865 353485
Publisher E-mail: webenquiry.uk@oup.com
Journal publishing innovative critical work in art history, committed to the political analysis of visual art and material representation from a variety of theoretical perspectives and carrying work addressing themes from Antiquity to contemporary art practice. **Freq:** 3/yr. **Key Personnel:** Simon Baker, Editor; Andrew Hemingway, Editor;

Hanneke Grootenboer, Editor; Alastair Wright, Editor; Steve Edwards, Editor; Mark Godfrey, Editor. **ISSN:** 0142-6540. **Subscription Rates:** 222 institutions corporate; print and online; 185 institutions corporate; online only; 204 institutions corporate; print only; 178 institutions print and online; 148 institutions online only; 163 institutions print only; 50 individuals print; 38 students print; 40 members print. **Remarks:** Advertising accepted; rates available upon request. **URL:** http://oaj.oxfordjournals.org/. **Circ:** (Not Reported)

56131 ■ Oxford Bulletin of Economics & Statistics
John Wiley & Sons Inc.
Wiley-Blackwell
9600 Garsington Rd.
Oxford OX4 2DQ, United Kingdom
Ph: 44 1865 776868
Fax: 44 1865 714591
Publication covering economics. **Freq:** 5/yr. **Key Personnel:** Christopher Adam, Editor; Victoria Prowse, Editor; David Hendry, Editor; Anindya Banerjee, Editor; John Knight, Editor; Jonathan Temple, Editor. **ISSN:** 0305-9049. **Subscription Rates:** US$130 individuals print + online; US$1,011 institutions print + online; US$918 institutions print or online; EUR116 individuals print + online; EUR627 institutions print + online; EUR570 institutions print or online; 78 other countries print + online; US$1,180 institutions, other countries print + online; US$1,072 institutions, other countries print or online; 494 institutions print + online. **Remarks:** Accepts advertising. **URL:** http://www.wiley.com/bw/journal.asp?ref=0305-9049&site=1. **Circ:** (Not Reported)

56132 ■ Oxford Development Studies
Routledge
Taylor & Francis Group Ltd.
c/o Frances Stewart, Mng. Ed.
Dept. of International Development
Queen Elizabeth House
University of Oxford
Oxford OX1 3TB, United Kingdom
Publisher E-mail: webmaster.books@tandf.co.uk
Journal providing a platform for thorough analysis of traditional theories and policy matters in all areas of development. covers various subjects such as economics, history, politics, anthropology and sociology, for the student, research and policy-making community in the field of development. **Freq:** Quarterly. **Key Personnel:** John Toye, Editorial Board, john.toye@economics.ox.ac.uk; Raufu Mustapha, Editor; Nandini Gooptu, Editor; Barbara Harriss-White, Editorial Board; Judith Heyer, Editorial Board; Matthew Gibney, Editorial Board; Adrian Wood, Editor; Frances Stewart, Managing Editor; Valpy Fitzgerald, Editorial Board; Christopher Adam, Editorial Board; Gavin Williams, Editorial Board. **ISSN:** 1360-0818. **Subscription Rates:** 653 institutions print + online; US$1,089 institutions print + online; 620 institutions online; US$1,034 institutions online; 77 individuals personal; US$128 individuals personal; EUR866 institutions print and online; EUR823 institutions online only; EUR102 individuals; US$43 institutions developing country. **Remarks:** Advertising accepted; rates available upon request. **URL:** http://www.tandf.co.uk/journals/titles/13600818.asp. **Circ:** (Not Reported)

56133 ■ Oxford Economic Papers
Oxford University Press
Manor Road Bldg.
Manor Rd.
Oxford OX1 3UQ, United Kingdom
Ph: 44 1865 271083
Publisher E-mail: webenquiry.uk@oup.com
Peer-reviewed journal covering economics. **Freq:** 4/yr. **Key Personnel:** S. Anand, Editorial Board; Anindya Banerjee, Managing Editor; C.J.E. Bliss, Editorial Board; Simon Cowan, Assoc. Ed.; C.S. Adam, Editorial Board; Liz Skalka, Editorial Sec., oep@economics.ox.ac.uk; James Forder, Managing Editor; Ken Mayhew, Assoc. Ed.; Mark Rogers, Assoc. Ed.; D.L. Bevan, Editorial Board. **ISSN:** 0030-7653. **Subscription Rates:** 294 institutions print and online; US$559 institutions print and online; EUR441 institutions print and online; 58 individuals print; US$110 individuals print; EUR87 individuals print; 270 institutions print, online; US$513 institutions print, online; EUR405 institutions print, online. **Remarks:** Accepts advertising. **URL:** http://oep.oxfordjournals.org. **Circ:** (Not Reported)

56134 ■ Oxford Journal of Archaeology
John Wiley & Sons Inc.
Wiley-Blackwell

Circulation: ★ = ABC; △ = BPA; ◆ = CAC; • = CCAB; ❑ = VAC; ⊕ = PO Statement; ‡ = Publisher's Report; Boldface figures = sworn; Light figures = estimated.

Gale Directory of Publications & Broadcast Media/147th Ed. 5829

c/o Barry Cunliffe, Ed.
University of Oxford
Oxford, United Kingdom
Ph: 44 1865 278240
Fax: 44 1865 278254
Journal covering the European and Mediterranean archaeology. **Freq:** Quarterly. **Key Personnel:** Barry Cunliffe, Editor; Chris Gosden, Editor; Helena Hamerow, Editor, phone 44 1865 278245, fax 44 1865 278254, helena.hamerow@history.oxford.ac.uk. **ISSN:** 0262-5253. **Subscription Rates:** US$68 individuals Americas (print and online); EUR62 individuals Europe (print and online); US$42 other countries print and online; US$1,070 institutions Americas (print and online); EUR632 institutions Europe (print and online); US$1,248 institutions, other countries print and online; 498 institutions UK (print and online); US$973 institutions Americas (print or online only); EUR574 institutions Europe (print or online only); 452 institutions UK (print or online only). **Remarks:** Accepts advertising. **URL:** http://www.wiley.com/bw/journal.asp?ref=0262-5253. **Circ:** (Not Reported)

56135 ■ Oxford Journal of Legal Studies
Oxford University Press
Great Clarendon St.
Oxford OX2 6DP, United Kingdom
Ph: 44 1865 556767
Fax: 44 1865 353485
Publisher E-mail: webenquiry.uk@oup.com
Law periodical. **Freq:** 4/yr. **Key Personnel:** Prof. Andrew Burrows, Editorial Committee; Prof. Timothy Endicott, Editorial Committee; Dr. A.C.L. Davies, Gen. Ed.; Dr. J. Dickson, Editorial Committee; Prof. John Gardner, Editorial Committee; Dr. Bettina Lange, Editorial Committee. **ISSN:** 0143-6503. **Subscription Rates:** 259 institutions print and online; US$518 institutions print and online; EUR389 institutions print and online; 91 individuals print; US$182 individuals print; EUR137 individuals print; 238 institutions print, online; US$476 institutions print, online; EUR357 institutions print, online. **Remarks:** Accepts advertising. **URL:** http://ojls.oxfordjournals.org. **Circ:** (Not Reported)

56136 ■ Oxford Review of Economic Policy
Oxford University Press
c/o Alison Gomm, Production Ed.
Park Central
40-41 Park End St.
Oxford OX1 1JD, United Kingdom
Publisher E-mail: webenquiry.uk@oup.com
Peer-reviewed journal covering economics. **Freq:** 4/yr. **Key Personnel:** Christopher Allsopp, Editor; Tim Jenkinson, Managing Editor; Christopher Adam, Assoc. Ed. **ISSN:** 0266-903X. **Subscription Rates:** 302 institutions print and online; US$604 institutions print and online; EUR453 institutions print and online; 57 individuals print; US$114 individuals print; EUR86 individuals print. **Remarks:** Accepts advertising. **URL:** http://oxrep.oxfordjournals.org. **Circ:** (Not Reported)

56137 ■ Oxford Today
John Wiley & Sons Inc.
Wiley-Blackwell
Public Affairs Directorate University Offices
Wellington Sq.
Oxford OX1 2JD, United Kingdom
Ph: 44 1865 280545
Fax: 44 1865 270178
Publication E-mail: oxford.today@admin.ox.ac.uk
University magazine, featuring news of Oxford's achievements and its future plans. **Subtitle:** The University Magazine. **Founded:** 1988. **Freq:** 3/yr. **Key Personnel:** Greg Neale, Editor, ot.editor@admin.ox.ac.uk. **ISSN:** 0954-1306. **Subscription Rates:** US$23 individuals Americas (print only); 11 individuals UK (print only); EUR14 individuals Europe (print only); US$31 other countries print only. **Remarks:** Accepts advertising. **URL:** http://www.oxfordtoday.ox.ac.uk/; http://www.wiley.com/bw/journal.asp?ref=0954-1306. **Circ:** (Not Reported)

56138 ■ Oxford University Commonwealth Law Journal
Hart Publishing Ltd.
St. Cross Bldg.
Faculty of Law
St. Cross Rd.
Oxford OX1 3UR, United Kingdom
Ph: 44 1865 271095
Fax: 44 1865 271493
Publication E-mail: ouclj@law.ox.ac.uk

Publisher E-mail: mail@hartpub.co.uk
Journal covering legal topics of interest throughout the Commonwealth. **Freq:** Semiannual. **Key Personnel:** Helen Dale, Editorial Board; Rabeea Assy, Editorial Board. **Subscription Rates:** 80 individuals standard, United Kingdom and Europe; 85 other countries standard; 45 individuals reduced, United Kingdom and Europe; 50 other countries reduced; 72 individuals online, standard; 40.50 individuals online. **Remarks:** Accepts advertising. **URL:** http://www.hartjournals.co.uk/ouclj/. **Circ:** (Not Reported)

56139 ■ Pacific Philosophical Quarterly
John Wiley & Sons Inc.
Wiley-Blackwell
9600 Garsington Rd.
Oxford OX4 2DQ, United Kingdom
Ph: 44 1865 776868
Fax: 44 1865 714591
Publication covering philosophy and religion. **Freq:** Quarterly. **Key Personnel:** Geoff Georgi, Managing Editor; Ernest W. Adams, Advisory Board; Virgil C. Aldrich, Advisory Board. **ISSN:** 0279-0750. **Subscription Rates:** US$91 individuals print + online; EUR72 individuals print + online; US$73 members print + online; EUR59 members print + online; US$393 institutions print + online; 270 institutions print + online; US$357 institutions print, online; 245 institutions print, online; US$603 institutions, other countries print and online; US$548 institutions, other countries print, online. **Remarks:** Accepts advertising. **URL:** http://www.wiley.com/bw/journal.asp?ref=0279-0750&site=1. **Circ:** (Not Reported)

56140 ■ Palaeontology
John Wiley & Sons Inc.
Wiley-Blackwell
9600 Garsington Rd.
Oxford OX4 2DQ, United Kingdom
Ph: 44 1865 776868
Fax: 44 1865 714591
Journal covering various paleontological topics such as paleozoology, paleobotany, systematic studies, paleoecology, micropaleontology, paleobiogeography, functional morphology, stratigraphy, taxonomy, taphonomy, paleoenvironmental reconstruction, paleoclimate analysis, and biomineralisation studies published in connection with paleontological association. **Freq:** Bimonthly. **Key Personnel:** M.P. Smith, Editor; S. Stouge, Editor-in-Chief; P.C.J. Donoghue, Editor; P.J. Orr, Editor. **ISSN:** 0031-0239. **Subscription Rates:** US$1,183 institutions print + online; 640 institutions print + online; 582 institutions print or online; US$1,075 institutions print or online; EUR815 institutions print + online; EUR740 institutions print or online; US$1,382 institutions, other countries print + online; US$1,256 institutions, other countries print or online. **Remarks:** Advertising accepted; rates available upon request. **URL:** http://www.wiley.com/bw/journal.asp?ref=0031-0239&site=1. **Circ:** (Not Reported)

56141 ■ Parliamentary Affairs
Oxford University Press
Great Clarendon St.
Oxford OX2 6DP, United Kingdom
Ph: 44 1865 556767
Fax: 44 1865 353485
Publisher E-mail: webenquiry.uk@oup.com
Peer-reviewed journal covering government and related issues. **Freq:** Quarterly. **Key Personnel:** Prof. Martin Bull, Assoc. Ed.; Prof. James Newell, Assoc. Ed.; Dr. Gideon Baker, Assoc. Ed.; Prof. Steven Fielding, Editor; Dr. Stephen Ward, Assoc. Ed.; Prof. Rachel Gibson, Assoc. Ed.; Prof. Jocelyn Evans, Editor; Prof. Jonathan Tonge, Assoc. Ed.; Dr. Cristina Chiva, Assoc. Ed. **ISSN:** 0031-2290. **Subscription Rates:** 270 institutions print and online; US$540 institutions print and online; EUR405 institutions print and online; 34 institutions schools - print only; US$68 institutions schools - print only; EUR51 institutions schools - print only; 248 institutions print, online; US$496 institutions print, online; EUR372 institutions print, online. **Remarks:** Accepts advertising. **URL:** http://pa.oxfordjournals.org. **Circ:** (Not Reported)

56142 ■ Past & Present
Oxford University Press
175 Banbury Rd.
Oxford OX2 7AW, United Kingdom
Publisher E-mail: webenquiry.uk@oup.com
Periodical focusing on history. **Founded:** Feb. 1952. **Freq:** 4/yr. **Key Personnel:** Eric J. Hobsbawm, President; David Cannadine, Editorial Board; Judith Herrin, Editorial Board; C.A. Bayly, Editorial Board; Charles H.E. Philpin, Assoc. Ed.; Joanna Innes, Editorial Board;

Alison E. Grant, Sub-Ed.; Paul Slack, Editorial Board; Eric Foner, Editorial Board; Lyndal Roper, Editor. **ISSN:** 0031-2746. **Subscription Rates:** 174 institutions print and online; US$348 institutions print and online; EUR261 institutions print and online; 145 individuals online, print; US$290 institutions online, print; EUR218 institutions online, print; 39 individuals print only; US$74 individuals print only; EUR59 individuals print only; 24 students print. **Remarks:** Accepts advertising. **URL:** http://past.oxfordjournals.org. **Circ:** (Not Reported)

56143 ■ Pathology International
John Wiley & Sons Inc.
Wiley-Blackwell
9600 Garsington Rd.
Oxford OX4 2DQ, United Kingdom
Ph: 44 1865 776868
Fax: 44 1865 714591
Peer-reviewed journal containing articles of scientific excellence in human and experimental pathology. **Freq:** Monthly. **Key Personnel:** Masahide Takahashi, Editor; Junichiro Fujimoto, Assoc. Ed.; Koichi Ohshima, Assoc. Ed. **ISSN:** 1320-5463. **Subscription Rates:** US$361 individuals print + online; EUR337 individuals print + online; 224 individuals print + online; US$1,469 institutions print + online; EUR1,049 institutions print + online; EUR1,154 institutions print + online; US$1,779 institutions, other countries print + online; US$1,617 institutions, other countries print + online; EUR1,617 institutions print, online. **Remarks:** Advertising accepted; rates available upon request. **URL:** http://www.wiley.com/bw/journal.asp?ref=1320-5463&site=1. **Circ:** (Not Reported)

56144 ■ Peace & Change
John Wiley & Sons Inc.
Wiley-Blackwell
9600 Garsington Rd.
Oxford OX4 2DQ, United Kingdom
Ph: 44 1865 776868
Fax: 44 1865 714591
Magazine publishing articles on peace-related topics such as peace movements and activism, conflict resolution, nonviolence, internationalism, race and gender issues, cross-cultural studies, economic development, the legacy of imperialism, and the post-Cold War upheaval. **Subtitle:** A Journal of Peace Research. **Freq:** Quarterly. **Key Personnel:** Cynthia Boaz, Co-Exec. Ed.; Kevin Clements, Board of Ed.; Sandi E. Cooper, Board of Ed.; Cris Toffolo, Board Exec. Committee; Mohammed Abu-Nimer, Board Exec. Committee; Elavie Ndura-Ouedraogo, Board of Ed.; Christina Bearden-White, Managing Editor; Robbie Lieberman, Co-Exec. Ed.; Lee Smithey, Board of Ed. **ISSN:** 0149-0508. **Subscription Rates:** US$509 institutions print + online; US$441 institutions print, online; US$109 nonmembers print + online; 374 institutions print + online; US$87 members of AHA/APSA; print + online; EUR101 members of AHA/APSA; Europe; print + online; EUR474 institutions print + online; US$733 institutions, other countries print + online; EUR130 nonmembers print + online; 85 nonmembers print + online. **Remarks:** Advertising accepted; rates available upon request. **URL:** http://www.wiley.com/bw/journal.asp?ref=0149-0508&site=1. **Circ:** (Not Reported)

56145 ■ Pediatric Allergy and Immunology
John Wiley & Sons Inc.
Wiley-Blackwell
9600 Garsington Rd.
Oxford OX4 2DQ, United Kingdom
Ph: 44 1865 776868
Fax: 44 1865 714591
Publication E-mail: paieditorial@imperial.ac.uk
Journal publishing original articles related to the understanding and treatment of immune deficiency, allergic inflammatory, and infectious diseases in children. **Freq:** 8/yr. **Key Personnel:** Ulrich Wahn, Editor-in-Chief; Paolo Matricardi, Managing Editor. **ISSN:** 0905-6157. **Subscription Rates:** US$292 individuals print + online; US$278 individuals online only; US$1,288 institutions print + online; US$1,171 institutions print, online; US$1,503 institutions, other countries print + online; 175 individuals print + online; 166 individuals online only; 767 institutions print + online; 697 institutions print or online; EUR975 institutions print + online. **Remarks:** Advertising accepted; rates available upon request. **URL:** http://www.wiley.com/bw/journal.asp?ref=0905-6157&site=1. **Circ:** (Not Reported)

56146 ■ Pediatric Anesthesia
John Wiley & Sons Inc.
Wiley-Blackwell
9600 Garsington Rd.
Oxford OX4 2DQ, United Kingdom

Ph: 44 1865 776868
Fax: 44 1865 714591
Peer-reviewed journal covering all areas relevant to anesthesia and intensive care in new-borns, infants and children. **Freq:** Monthly. **Key Personnel:** B. Anderson, Section Ed.; N.S. Morton, Editor; G.H. Bush, Founding Ed. **ISSN:** 1155-5645. **Subscription Rates:** US$443 individuals print + online; EUR358 individuals print + online, Europe (Euro zone); 239 individuals print + online, Europe (non Euro zone); 263 other countries print + online; US$1,776 institutions print + online; US$1,614 institutions print, online; 961 institutions print + online; 873 institutions print, online; US$2,072 institutions, other countries print + online; US$1,883 institutions, other countries print, online. **Remarks:** Advertising accepted; rates available upon request. **URL:** http://www.wiley.com/bw/journal.asp?ref=1155-5645&site=1. **Circ:** (Not Reported)

56147 ■ Pediatric Dermatology
John Wiley & Sons Inc.
Wiley-Blackwell
9600 Garsington Rd.
Oxford OX4 2DQ, United Kingdom
Ph: 44 1865 776868
Fax: 44 1865 714591
Journal providing information on pediatric dermatology, with a particular emphasis on diagnosis and treatment. **Freq:** Bimonthly. **Key Personnel:** Prof. Nancy B. Esterly, MD, Ed. Emeritus; Ilona J. Frieden, MD, Editor-in-Chief; Nigel Burrows, MD, Editorial Board; Bernard A. Cohen, MD, Assoc. Ed.; Eulalia Baselga, MD, Editorial Board; Arnold Oranje, PhD, International Assoc. Ed.; Walter Burgdorf, Editorial Board; Gayle O. Fischer, MD, Editorial Board. **ISSN:** 0736-8046. **Subscription Rates:** US$413 individuals print + online; US$392 individuals online only; US$128 students print + online; US$1,110 Canada and Mexico print + online; US$1,016 Canada and Mexico print or online; EUR481 individuals print + online; EUR457 individuals online; EUR129 students print + online; 802 institutions print + online; US$1,571 institutions, other countries print + online. **Remarks:** Advertising accepted; rates available upon request. **URL:** http://www.wiley.com/bw/journal.asp?ref=0736-8046&site=1. **Circ:** (Not Reported)

56148 ■ Pediatrics International
John Wiley & Sons Inc.
Wiley-Blackwell
9600 Garsington Rd.
Oxford OX4 2DQ, United Kingdom
Ph: 44 1865 776868
Fax: 44 1865 714591
Journal publishing articles of scientific research in pediatrics and child health delivery. **Freq:** Bimonthly. **Key Personnel:** Yukishige Yanagawa, Editorial Board; Hiroaki Tsutsumi, Editorial Board; Yasuhiko Itoh, Asst. Ed.; Norikazu Shimizu, Editor-in-Chief; Yoshiyuki Ohtomo, Asst. Ed.; Junko Takita, Asst. Ed.; Yoshihiro Takeuchi, Editorial Board; Hiroshi Mochizuki, Asst. Ed.; Susumu Kanzaki, Editorial Board. **ISSN:** 1328-8067. **Subscription Rates:** US$277 individuals print + online; EUR258 individuals print + online; 172 individuals print + online; US$880 institutions print + online; 543 institutions print + online; 493 institutions print or online; US$800 institutions print or online; EUR691 institutions print + online; EUR627 institutions print or online; US$1,065 institutions, other countries print + online. **Remarks:** Advertising accepted; rates available upon request. **URL:** http://www.wiley.com/bw/journal.asp?ref=1328-8067&site=1. **Formerly:** Acta Paediatrica Japonica. **Circ:** (Not Reported)

56149 ■ Periodontology 2000
John Wiley & Sons Inc.
Wiley-Blackwell
9600 Garsington Rd.
Oxford OX4 2DQ, United Kingdom
Ph: 44 1865 776868
Fax: 44 1865 714591
Journal comprising monographs useful for periodontists and general practitioners with interest in periodontics. **Freq:** 3/yr. **Key Personnel:** Jorgan Slots, Editor-in-Chief; Mark P. Bartold, Editorial Board; Ian L.C. Chapple, Editorial Board. **ISSN:** 0906-6713. **Subscription Rates:** US$377 individuals print + online; EUR338 individuals print + online; 225 individuals print + online; US$734 institutions print + online; US$667 institutions print or online; EUR555 institutions print + online; US$856 institutions, other countries print + online; US$777 institutions, other countries print or online; 437 institutions print + online; 397 institutions print or online. **Remarks:** Advertising accepted; rates available upon request. **URL:** http://www.wiley.com/bw/journal.asp?ref=0906-6713&site=1. **Circ:** (Not Reported)

56150 ■ Personnel Psychology
John Wiley & Sons Inc.
Wiley-Blackwell
9600 Garsington Rd.
Oxford OX4 2DQ, United Kingdom
Ph: 44 1865 776868
Fax: 44 1865 714591
Journal publishing applied psychological research on personnel problems facing public and private sector organizations with articles dealing with all human resource topics, including selection and recruitment, training and development, performance and career management, diversity, rewards and recognition, work attitudes and motivation and leadership. **Subtitle:** A Journal of Applied Research. **Freq:** Quarterly. **Key Personnel:** Michael J. Burke, Editorial Board; Jeff Johnson, Assoc. Ed.; Lilian Eby, Editorial Board. **ISSN:** 0031-5826. **Subscription Rates:** US$89 individuals print + online; EUR77 individuals print + online; 49 individuals print + online; US$448 institutions print + online; US$406 institutions print or online; US$448 institutions print + online; EUR330 institutions print or online; US$560 institutions, other countries print + online; US$509 institutions, other countries print or online; 287 institutions print + online. **Remarks:** Accepts display advertising. **URL:** http://www.wiley.com/bw/journal.asp?ref=0031-5826&site=1. **Circ:** (Not Reported)

56151 ■ Perspectives in Psychiatric Care
John Wiley & Sons Inc.
Wiley-Blackwell
9600 Garsington Rd.
Oxford OX4 2DQ, United Kingdom
Ph: 44 1865 776868
Fax: 44 1865 714591
Peer-reviewed journal focusing on International interdisciplinary resource for advanced practice psychiatric nurses and for nurse psychotherapists. **Freq:** Quarterly. **Key Personnel:** Geraldine S. Pearson, Editor; Kristen Overstreet, Managing Editor, kristin.overstreet@mac.com. **ISSN:** 0031-5990. **Subscription Rates:** US$83 individuals print & online; US$245 institutions print & online; EUR210 institutions print & online; US$223 institutions online only; US$223 institutions print only. **Remarks:** Advertising accepted; rates available upon request. **URL:** http://www.wiley.com/bw/submit.asp?ref=0031-5990&site=1; http://ordering.onlinelibrary.wiley.com/subs.asp?ref=1744-6163&site=1. **Circ:** (Not Reported)

56152 ■ Perspectives on Psychological Science
John Wiley & Sons Inc.
Wiley-Blackwell
9600 Garsington Rd.
Oxford OX4 2DQ, United Kingdom
Ph: 44 1865 776868
Fax: 44 1865 714591
Journal publishing articles on latest advances in the entire field of psychology. Includes articles on related areas in other behavioral and social sciences and neuroscience. **Freq:** Bimonthly. **Key Personnel:** Torrance Gloss, Managing Editor; Ed Diener, Founding Ed.; Arthur Shimamura, Consulting Ed.; Alice Moon, Asst. to the Ed.; Lisa Feldman Barrett, Consulting Ed. **ISSN:** 1745-6916. **Remarks:** Advertising accepted; rates available upon request. **URL:** http://www.wiley.com/bw/journal.asp?ref=1745-6916&site=1. **Circ:** (Not Reported)

56153 ■ Philosophia Mathematica
Oxford University Press
Great Clarendon St.
Oxford OX2 6DP, United Kingdom
Ph: 44 1865 556767
Fax: 44 1865 353485
Publisher E-mail: webenquiry.uk@oup.com
Journal publishing peer-reviewed new work in philosophy of mathematics, the application of mathematics, and computing. **Freq:** 3/yr. **Key Personnel:** Robert S.D. Thomas, Editor, thomas@cc.umanitoba.ca; John L. Bell, Editorial Board; John P. Burgess, Editorial Board; Stephen E. Fienberg, Editorial Board; Douglas S. Bridges, Editorial Board; Neil Tennant, Editorial Board; Paul Ernest, Editorial Board; J. Fang, Founding Ed.; Richard Tieszen, Editorial Board. **ISSN:** 0031-8019. **Subscription Rates:** 133 institutions corporate; print and online; 111 institutions corporate; online only; 122 institutions corporate; print only; 107 institutions print and online; 89 institutions online only; 98 institutions print only; 50 individuals print; 27 members print. **Remarks:** Advertising accepted; rates available upon request. **URL:** http://philmat.oxfordjournals.org. **Circ:** (Not Reported)

56154 ■ The Philosophical Forum
John Wiley & Sons Inc.
Wiley-Blackwell
9600 Garsington Rd.
Oxford OX4 2DQ, United Kingdom
Ph: 44 1865 776868
Fax: 44 1865 714591
Journal reporting on contemporary philosophical inquiry. **Founded:** 1970. **Freq:** Quarterly. **Key Personnel:** Douglas Lackey, Editor; Alan W. Grose, Managing Editor; Marx Wartofsky, Founder; Sandeep Sreekumar, Asst. Ed.; Anita Allen, Board of Editorial Advisor; Hans Albert, Board of Editorial Advisor; Thomas Teufel, Assoc. Ed. **ISSN:** 0031-806X. **Subscription Rates:** US$53 other countries print + online; EUR83 individuals print + online; 257 institutions print or online; US$347 institutions print + online; US$315 institutions print or online; EUR359 institutions print + online; EUR326 institutions print or online; US$554 institutions, other countries print + online; US$503 institutions, other countries print or online; 284 institutions print + online. **Remarks:** Advertising accepted; rates available upon request. **URL:** http://www.wiley.com/bw/journal.asp?ref=0031-806x. **Circ:** (Not Reported)

56155 ■ The Philosophical Quarterly
John Wiley & Sons Inc.
Wiley-Blackwell
9600 Garsington Rd.
Oxford OX4 2DQ, United Kingdom
Ph: 44 1865 776868
Fax: 44 1865 714591
Journal covering philosophy and religion. **Freq:** Quarterly. **Key Personnel:** Katherine Hawley, Editorial Ch.; Moira Gilruth, Editorial Asst., pq@st-andrews.ac.uk; Sarah Broadie, Exec. Ed. **ISSN:** 0031-8094. **Subscription Rates:** US$455 institutions print only; 201 institutions print only; EUR254 institutions print only; US$531 institutions, other countries print only; US$501 institutions print + online; 221 institutions print + online; EUR280 institutions print + online; US$585 institutions, other countries print + online; US$84 individuals print + online; 35 individuals print + online. **Remarks:** Accepts advertising. **URL:** http://www.wiley.com/bw/journal.asp?ref=0031-8094&site=1. **Circ:** (Not Reported)

56156 ■ Photodermatology, Photoimmunology and Photomedicine
John Wiley & Sons Inc.
Wiley-Blackwell
9600 Garsington Rd.
Oxford OX4 2DQ, United Kingdom
Ph: 44 1865 776868
Fax: 44 1865 714591
Journal providing a focal point for dissemination of investigations on direct and indirect effects of electromagnetic radiation (ultraviolet, visible and infrared) entering through skin. The thrust areas include aging, carcinogenesis, immunology, instrumentation and optics, lasers, photodynamic therapy, photosensitivity, pigmentation and therapy. **Freq:** Bimonthly. **Key Personnel:** James Ferguson, Co-Ed.; Warwick L. Morison, Editor-in-Chief; Ryoichi Kamide, Editorial Board; Craig Elmets, Editorial Board; Thomas M. Ruenger, Assoc. Ed.; Ponciano Cruz, Editorial Board; Rik Roelandts, Assoc. Ed.; Goren Wennersten, Founding Ed. **ISSN:** 0905-4383. **Subscription Rates:** US$617 institutions print and online; US$721 institutions, other countries print and online; US$561 institutions print or online; US$656 institutions, other countries print or online; EUR469 institutions print and online; EUR426 institutions print or online; 36 institutions print and online; 334 institutions print or online. **Remarks:** Advertising accepted; rates available upon request. **URL:** http://www.wiley.com/bw/journal.asp?ref=0905-4383&site=1. **Circ:** (Not Reported)

56157 ■ Physiological Entomology
John Wiley & Sons Inc.
Wiley-Blackwell
9600 Garsington Rd.
Oxford OX4 2DQ, United Kingdom
Ph: 44 1865 776868
Fax: 44 1865 714591
Peer-reviewed journal on physiology insects and other arthropods. **Freq:** Quarterly. **Key Personnel:** Jim Hardie, Editor, j.hardie@imperial.ac.uk; Graham Goldsworthy, Editorial Advisor; H. Numata, Editorial Advisor; J.S.

Circulation: ★ = ABC; △ = BPA; ♦ = CAC; • = CCAB; ❑ = VAC; ⊕ = PO Statement; ‡ = Publisher's Report; Boldface figures = sworn; Light figures = estimated.

Bale, Editorial Advisor; T.C. Baker, Editorial Advisor; S.B. Vinson, Editorial Advisor; R. Galun, Editorial Advisor; G. Powell, Editorial Advisor; A.E. Douglas, Editorial Advisor. **ISSN:** 0307-6962. **Subscription Rates:** US$174 individuals print + online; EUR142 individuals print + online, (Euro zone); 97 individuals print + online, (non Euro zone); 104 other countries print + online; US$1,001 institutions print + online; US$1,168 institutions, other countries print + online; 542 institutions print + online; 492 institutions print, online; US$1,062 institutions, other countries print, online; US$910 institutions print, online. **Remarks:** Advertising accepted; rates available upon request. **URL:** http://www.wiley.com/bw/journal.asp?ref=0307-6962&site=1. **Circ:** (Not Reported)

56158 ■ Pigment Cell and Melanoma Research
John Wiley & Sons Inc.
Wiley-Blackwell
9600 Garsington Rd.
Oxford OX4 2DQ, United Kingdom
Ph: 44 1865 776868
Fax: 44 1865 714591
Peer-reviewed journal dealing with all aspects of pigment cells or melanocytes including development, cell and molecular biology, genetics and melanoma. **Freq:** Bimonthly. **Key Personnel:** Zeev Ronai, Editor-in-Chief, pcmreditor@burnham.org; Richard A. Spritz, Editorial Board; Heinz Arnheiter, Exec. Ed.; Vincent J. Hearing, Editorial Board; Mickey Marks, Editorial Board; David Parichy, Editorial Board. **ISSN:** 1755-1471. **Subscription Rates:** US$907 institutions print and online; US$1,059 institutions, other countries print and online; US$824 institutions print, online; US$963 institutions, other countries print, online; EUR687 institutions print and online; 541 institutions print and online; 491 institutions print, online; EUR625 institutions print, online. **Remarks:** Advertising accepted; rates available upon request. **URL:** http://www.wiley.com/bw/journal.asp?ref=1755-1471&site=1. **Formerly:** Pigment Cell Research. **Circ:** (Not Reported)

56159 ■ Plant Breeding
John Wiley & Sons Inc.
Wiley-Blackwell
9600 Garsington Rd.
Oxford OX4 2DQ, United Kingdom
Ph: 44 1865 776868
Fax: 44 1865 714591
Peer-reviewed journal covering all aspects of plant breeding especially in crop plants. **Freq:** Bimonthly. **Key Personnel:** Prof. Christian Jung, Subject Ed., c.jung@plantbreeding.uni-kiel.de; Dr. W.E. Weber, Subject Ed., weber@landw.uni-halle.de; Dr. Jens Leon, Editor-in-Chief, phone 49 228 732877, fax 49 228 732045, j.leon@uni-bonn.de. **ISSN:** 0179-9541. **Subscription Rates:** US$181 individuals print and online; EUR168 individuals Euro zone, print and online; 112 other countries print and online; US$2,190 institutions print and online; 1,185 institutions print and online; US$2,807 institutions, other countries print and online; US$1,991 institutions print, online; 1,185 institutions print, online; EUR1,655 institutions, other countries print and online; EUR1,505 institutions print, online. **Remarks:** Advertising accepted; rates available upon request. **URL:** http://www.wiley.com/bw/journal.asp?ref=0179-9541&site=1. **Circ:** (Not Reported)

56160 ■ Plant and Cell Physiology
Oxford University Press
Great Clarendon St.
Oxford OX2 6DP, United Kingdom
Ph: 44 1865 556767
Fax: 44 1865 353485
Publisher E-mail: webenquiry.uk@oup.com
International journal publishing original papers pertaining to physiology, biochemistry, biophysics, chemistry, genetics, molecular biology, gene engineering and cell engineering of plants and microorganisms. **Freq:** Monthly. **Key Personnel:** Amane Makino, Editor, phone 81 22 7178769, fax 81 22 7178765, makino@biochem.tohoku.ac.jp; Makoto Matsuoka, Editor-in-Chief, phone 81 52 7895218, fax 81 52 7895226, makoto@agr.nagoya-u.ac.jp; Manuel Echeverria, Editor, phone 33 4 68662119, fax 33 4 68668499, manuel@univ-perp.fr; Frank Gubler, Editor, phone 61 2 62465269, fax 61 2 62465000, frank.gubler@csiro.au; Toru Fujiwara, Editor, phone 81 3 58412407, fax 81 3 58412408, atorufu@mail.ecc.u-tokyo.ac.jp; Ilha Lee, Editor, ilhalee@snu.ac.kr; Akira Nagatani, Editor, nagatani@physiol.bot.kyoto-u.ac.jp; Takashi Hashimoto, Editor, phone 81 743 725520, fax 81 743 725529, hasimoto@bs.naist.jp. **ISSN:** 0032-0781. **Subscription Rates:** 611 institutions print and online; US$1,222 institutions print and online; EUR917 institutions print and online; 247 individuals print; US$494 individuals print; EUR371 individuals print; 560 institutions print; US$1,120 institutions print; EUR840 institutions print. **Remarks:** Advertising accepted; rates available upon request. **URL:** http://pcp.oxfordjournals.org/. **Circ:** (Not Reported)

56161 ■ Plant Species Biology
John Wiley & Sons Inc.
Wiley-Blackwell
9600 Garsington Rd.
Oxford OX4 2DQ, United Kingdom
Ph: 44 1865 776868
Fax: 44 1865 714591
Peer-reviewed journal covering the study of plant species and their biological aspects. **Founded:** 1986. **Freq:** 3/yr. **Key Personnel:** William F. Grant, Honorary Ed.-in-Ch.; Masashi Ohara, Editor-in-Chief; Shoichi Kawano, Honorary Ed.-in-Ch.; Shu-Miaw Chaw, Editorial Board; Teruyoshi Nagamitsu, Assoc. Ed.; Makoto Kato, Assoc. Ed.; E.R. Alvarez-Buylla, Editorial Board; David W. Inouye, Editorial Board; Hong-Ya Gu, Editorial Board; Michael J. Hutchings, Editorial Board; Nobumitsu Kawakubo, Assoc. Ed. **ISSN:** 0913-557X. **Subscription Rates:** US$204 individuals print; EUR188 individuals print; 125 individuals print; US$514 institutions print + online; 315 institutions print + online; 315 institutions print, online; US$467 institutions print, online; EUR401 institutions print + online; EUR364 institutions print, online; US$618 institutions, other countries print + online. **Remarks:** Advertising accepted; rates available upon request. **URL:** http://www.wiley.com/bw/journal.asp?ref=0913-557X&site=1. **Circ:** (Not Reported)

56162 ■ Plastics, Additives and Compounding
Elsevier Science
c/o Mark Holmes, Ed.
Elsevier Advanced Technology
The Blvd. Langford Ln.
Kidlington
Oxford OX5 1GB, United Kingdom
Publisher E-mail: nlinfo-f@elsevier.com
Magazine dealing with technical additives and pigments and their incorporation into compounds and master batches. **Founded:** 1999. **Freq:** Bimonthly. **Key Personnel:** Mark Holmes, Editor, phone 44 18 65843441, fax 44 18 65843971, m.holmes@elsevier.com; J. Kummer, Advertisement Mgr., phone 212633-3199, fax 212633-3140, j.kummer@elsevier.com; K. Simpson, Dep. Ed., phone 44 1865 843730, fax 44 1865 843971, k.simpson@elsevier.com. **ISSN:** 1464-391X. **Subscription Rates:** EUR548 institutions for European countries & Iran; US$613 institutions for all countries except Europe, Japan & Iran; 72,500¥ institutions. **Remarks:** Advertising accepted; rates available upon request. **URL:** http://www.elsevier.com/wps/find/journaldescription.cws_home/601441/description. **Circ:** (Not Reported)

56163 ■ Poe Studies/Dark Romanticism
John Wiley & Sons Inc.
Wiley-Blackwell
9600 Garsington Rd.
Oxford OX4 2DQ, United Kingdom
Ph: 44 1865 776868
Fax: 44 1865 714591
Literature & Modern Language. **Founded:** 1968. **Freq:** Annual. **Trim Size:** 8 1/2 x 11. **Key Personnel:** Jana L. Argersinger, Editor; Scott Peeples, Editor. **ISSN:** 1543-1789. **Subscription Rates:** US$133 institutions online only; EUR108 institutions online only; US$167 institutions, other countries online only; 85 institutions online only. **Remarks:** Advertising accepted; rates available upon request. **URL:** http://www.wiley.com/bw/journal.asp?ref=1543-1789. **Formerly:** Poe Newsletter. **Circ:** Combined 500

56164 ■ Political Analysis
Oxford University Press
Great Clarendon St.
Oxford OX2 6DP, United Kingdom
Ph: 44 1865 556767
Fax: 44 1865 353485
Publisher E-mail: webenquiry.uk@oup.com
Journal advancing the field of political methodology, broadly defined, containing articles that cover the entire range of interests and problems centering upon how political enquiry can be conducted and encouraging submissions dealing with the logic of inquiry, measurement, estimation, specification and theory development. **Freq:** Quarterly. **Key Personnel:** R. Michael Alvarez, Editor-in-Chief; Jonathan N. Katz, Editor-in-Chief; Andrew Gelman, Assoc. Ed.; Simon Jackman, Assoc. Ed.; Vera Troeger, Assoc. Ed. **ISSN:** 1047-1987. **Subscription Rates:** 359 institutions corporate; print and online; 299 institutions corporate; online only; 329 institutions corporate; print only; 287 institutions print and online; 239 institutions online only; 263 institutions print only; 57 individuals print. **Remarks:** Advertising accepted; rates available upon request. **URL:** http://pan.oupjournals.org/. **Circ:** (Not Reported)

56165 ■ The Political Quarterly
John Wiley & Sons Inc.
Wiley-Blackwell
9600 Garsington Rd.
Oxford OX4 2DQ, United Kingdom
Ph: 44 1865 776868
Fax: 44 1865 714591
Journal focusing on Political Science. **Founded:** 1930. **Freq:** Quarterly. **Key Personnel:** Prof. Andrew Gamble, Editor, phone 44 1223 767255, amg59@cam.ac.uk; Tony M.P. Wright, Editor, wrightt@parliament.uk; Colin Crouch, Editorial Board. **ISSN:** 0032-3179. **Subscription Rates:** US$387 institutions online only; US$448 institutions print + online; US$408 students print only; US$47 individuals print + online; US$41 members print + online; 197 institutions online only; 228 institutions print + online; 207 individuals print only; 27 individuals print + online; 24 members print PLS online. **Remarks:** Accepts advertising. **URL:** http://www.wiley.com/bw/journal.asp?ref=0032-3179&site=1. **Circ:** (Not Reported)

56166 ■ Political Studies
John Wiley & Sons Inc.
Wiley-Blackwell
9600 Garsington Rd.
Oxford OX4 2DQ, United Kingdom
Ph: 44 1865 776868
Fax: 44 1865 714591
Journal publishing work in all fields of politics and international relations. **Freq:** Quarterly. **Key Personnel:** Matthew Festenstein, Editor, mf517@york.ac.uk; Martin Smith, Editor; Katherine Adeney, Assoc. Ed., k.adeney@sheffield.ac.uk. **ISSN:** 0032-3217. **Subscription Rates:** US$1,477 institutions print + online; 697 institutions print + online; EUR884 institutions print + online; US$1,592 institutions, other countries print + online; US$1,331 institutions online only; 628 institutions online only; EUR797 institutions online only; US$1,431 institutions, other countries online only. **Remarks:** Accepts advertising. **Online:** Gale. **URL:** http://www.wiley.com/bw/journal.asp?ref=0032-3217&site=1. **Circ:** (Not Reported)

56167 ■ Political Studies Review
John Wiley & Sons Inc.
Wiley-Blackwell
9600 Garsington Rd.
Oxford OX4 2DQ, United Kingdom
Ph: 44 1865 776868
Fax: 44 1865 714591
Journal providing review coverage of new books and literature on political science and international relations. **Freq:** 3/yr. **Key Personnel:** Matthew Festenstein, Assoc. Ed., mf517@york.ac.uk; Linda Weiss, International Advisory Board; Rene Bailey, Managing Editor, politicalstudies@sheffield.ac.uk; Rhiannon Vickers, Assoc. Ed., phone 44 114 2221694, fax 44 114 2221717, r.m.vickers@sheffield.ac.uk; Martin Smith, Assoc. Ed., phone 44 114 2221667, m.j.smith@sheffield.ac.uk; Katharine Adeney, Assoc. Ed., phone 44 114 2221704, k.adeney@sheffield.ac.uk; Amitav Acharya, International Advisory Board; Suzanne Berger, International Advisory Board. **ISSN:** 1478-9299. **Subscription Rates:** US$33 individuals print and online; EUR28 individuals print and online, Euro zone; 19 other countries print and online. **Remarks:** Accepts advertising. **URL:** http://www.wiley.com/bw/journal.asp?ref=1478-9299&site=1. **Circ:** (Not Reported)

56168 ■ Proceedings of the London Mathematical Society
Oxford University Press
Great Clarendon St.
Oxford OX2 6DP, United Kingdom
Ph: 44 1865 556767
Fax: 44 1865 353485
Publisher E-mail: webenquiry.uk@oup.com
Journal on mathematics. **Founded:** 1865. **Freq:** 3/yr. **Key Personnel:** John E. Cremona, Editor; David Preiss, Editor. **ISSN:** 0024-6115. **Subscription Rates:** 976 institutions corporate; print and online; 884 institutions corporate; online only; 976 institutions corporate; print

only; 781 institutions print and online; 707 institutions print and online; 781 institutions print and online. **Remarks:** Advertising accepted; rates available upon request. **URL:** http://www.lms.ac.uk/publications/proceedings/. **Circ:** (Not Reported)

56169 ■ The Professional Geographer
John Wiley & Sons Inc.
Wiley-Blackwell
9600 Garsington Rd.
Oxford OX4 2DQ, United Kingdom
Ph: 44 1865 776868
Fax: 44 1865 714591
Peer-reviewed journal on geography. **Freq:** Quarterly. **Key Personnel:** Sharmistha Bagchi-Sen, Editor; Robin Friedman, Managing Editor; Jay D. Gatrell, Book Review Ed., jgatrell@isugw.indstate.edu. **ISSN:** 0033-0124. **Subscription Rates:** US$1,184 individuals print; US$1,124 individuals online; US$1,184 individuals print and online. **Remarks:** Accepts advertising. **Online:** OARE. **URL:** http://www.informaworld.com/smpp/1236482088-89875929/title~content=t7883 52615~db=all. **Ad Rates:** BW: 600. **Circ:** (Not Reported)

56170 ■ Progress in Biophysics & Molecular Biology
Elsevier Science
c/o Denis Noble, Ed.
Laboratory of Physiology, University of Oxford
Park Rd.
Oxford OX1 3PT, United Kingdom
Ph: 44 1865 272533
Fax: 44 1865 272554
Publisher E-mail: nlinfo-f@elsevier.com
Journal covering structural and functional problems of the living organism. **Subtitle:** An International Review Journal. **Founded:** 1950. **Freq:** 9/yr. **Key Personnel:** Tom L. Blundell, Editor, phone 44 12 23333628, fax 44 12 23766082, tom@cryst.bioc.cam.ac.uk; Denis Noble, Editor; A. Bax, Editorial Board. **ISSN:** 0079-6107. **Subscription Rates:** US$2,486 institutions for all countries except Europe, Japan & Iran; 330,300¥ institutions; EUR2,782 institutions for European countries & Iran; EUR213 individuals for European countries & Iran; US$286 individuals for all countries except Europe, Japan & Iran; 32,900¥ individuals. **Remarks:** Advertising accepted; rates available upon request. **URL:** http://www.elsevier.com/wps/find/journaldescription.cws_home/408/description. **Circ:** (Not Reported)

56171 ■ Progress in Retinal and Eye Research
Elsevier Science
c/o Neville N. Osborne, Ed.
Nuffield Laboratory of Ophthalmology
University of Oxford
Walton St.
Oxford OX2 6AW, United Kingdom
Publisher E-mail: nlinfo-f@elsevier.com
Journal dealing with basic and clinical aspects of eye research, intended for molecular biologists, neuroscientists, physiologists, vision researchers and ophthalmologists. **Founded:** 1982. **Freq:** Bimonthly. **Key Personnel:** Gerald J. Chader, Editor, gchader@doheny.org; Neville N. Osborne, Editor, neville.osborne@eye.ox.ac.uk. **ISSN:** 1350-9462. **Subscription Rates:** EUR1,217 institutions for European countries; US$1,361 institutions for all countries except Europe and Japan; 161,400¥ institutions; US$184 individuals; 21,300¥ individuals; EUR138 individuals. **URL:** http://www.elsevier.com/wps/find/journaldescription.cws_home/664/description.

56172 ■ Protein Engineering, Design and Selection
Oxford University Press
Great Clarendon St.
Oxford OX2 6DP, United Kingdom
Ph: 44 1865 556767
Fax: 44 1865 353485
Publisher E-mail: webenquiry.uk@oup.com
Journal publish research papers and review articles relevant to the engineering, design and selection of proteins for use in biotechnology and therapy, and for understanding fundamental properties of activity, stability, folding, misfolding and disease. **Freq:** Bimonthly. **Key Personnel:** Greg Winter, Consulting Ed.; Alan Fersht, Sen. Ed.; Valerie Daggett, Sen. Ed. **ISSN:** 1741-0126. **Subscription Rates:** 1,235 institutions corporate; print and online; 885 institutions corporate; online only; 1,132 institutions corporate; print only; 988 institutions print and online; 708 institutions online only; 905 institu-

tions print only; 268 individuals print; 58 members online only; 128 members print. **Remarks:** Advertising accepted; rates available upon request. **URL:** http://peds.oxfordjournals.org/. **Circ:** (Not Reported)

56173 ■ Psychogeriatrics
John Wiley & Sons Inc.
Wiley-Blackwell
9600 Garsington Rd.
Oxford OX4 2DQ, United Kingdom
Ph: 44 1865 776868
Fax: 44 1865 714591
Journal aiming to exchange information concerning research results and clinical experiences in the field of psychogeriatrics between Japan and other countries, and to promote worldwide research activity in psychogeriatrics. **Freq:** Quarterly. **Key Personnel:** Masatoshi Takeda, Editor-in-Chief; Naoji Amano, Editorial Board; Toshihisa Tanaka, Managing Editor. **ISSN:** 1346-3500. **Subscription Rates:** US$438 institutions print + online; US$398 institutions print or online; US$529 institutions, other countries print + online; US$481 institutions, other countries print or online; 271 institutions print + online; EUR344 institutions print + online; 245 institutions print or online; EUR312 institutions print or online. **Remarks:** Accepts advertising. **URL:** http://www.wiley.com/bw/journal.asp?ref=1346-3500. **Circ:** (Not Reported)

56174 ■ Psychological Science in the Public Interest
John Wiley & Sons Inc.
Wiley-Blackwell
9600 Garsington Rd.
Oxford OX4 2DQ, United Kingdom
Ph: 44 1865 776868
Fax: 44 1865 714591
Journal providing definitive assessments of topics where psychological science may have the potential to inform and improve the lives of individuals and the well-being of society. **Freq:** 3/yr. **Key Personnel:** Elaine Walker, Editor; Richard J. Klimoski, Editorial Board; Robert A. Bjork, Editorial Board; Ludy T. Benjamin, Jr., Editorial Board; Wendy M. Williams, Editorial Board; Elizabeth F. Loftus, Editorial Board; Eric Wargo, Managing Editor; Elliot Aronson, Editorial Board; Susan Mineka, Editorial Board. **ISSN:** 1529-1006. **Remarks:** Accepts advertising. **URL:** http://www.wiley.com/bw/journal.asp?ref=1529-1006&site=1. **Circ:** (Not Reported)

56175 ■ Psychology of Women Quarterly
John Wiley & Sons Inc.
Wiley-Blackwell
9600 Garsington Rd.
Oxford OX4 2DQ, United Kingdom
Ph: 44 1865 776868
Fax: 44 1865 714591
Journal covering psychology and mental health. **Freq:** Quarterly. **Key Personnel:** Janice D. Yoder, Editor; Sarah Buday, Student Advisory Board; Chana K. Akins, Assoc. Ed. **ISSN:** 0361-6843. **Subscription Rates:** US$335 institutions print or online; US$369 institutions print + online; US$85 individuals print + online; 263 institutions print or online; 290 institutions print + online; 60 individuals print + online; EUR334 institutions print or online; 368 institutions print + online; EUR90 individuals print + online; US$515 institutions, other countries print or online. **Remarks:** Accepts advertising. **URL:** http://www.wiley.com/bw/journal.asp?ref=0361-6843&site=1. **Ad Rates:** BW: 650. **Circ:** (Not Reported)

56176 ■ Public Administration
John Wiley & Sons Inc.
Wiley-Blackwell
9600 Garsington Rd.
Oxford OX4 2DQ, United Kingdom
Ph: 44 1865 776868
Fax: 44 1865 714591
Peer-reviewed journal publishing articles on public administration, public policy and public management. **Freq:** Quarterly. **Key Personnel:** Prof. R.A.W. Rhodes, Managing Editor, rhodes@coombs.anu.edu.au; Prof. Walter Kickert, Dep. Ed., kickert@fsw.eur.nl; Geert Bouckaert, Editorial Advisory Board. **ISSN:** 0033-3298. **Subscription Rates:** US$1,174 institutions print or online; US$1,292 institutions print + online; US$94 individuals print + online; 589 institutions print or online; 648 institutions print + online; 56 individuals print + online; EUR748 institutions print or online; 823 institutions print + online; EUR83 individuals print + online; US$1,372 institutions, other countries print or online.

Online: Gale. **URL:** http://www.wiley.com/bw/journal.asp?ref=0033-3298&site=1.

56177 ■ Public Health Nursing
John Wiley & Sons Inc.
Wiley-Blackwell
9600 Garsington Rd.
Oxford OX4 2DQ, United Kingdom
Ph: 44 1865 776868
Fax: 44 1865 714591
Journal publishing contributions on public health, with a particular emphasis on matters relating to public health professionals. **Freq:** Bimonthly. **Key Personnel:** Sarah E. Abrams, PhD, Editor; Judith C. Hays, PhD, Editor; Patricia J. Bradley, Editorial Advisory Board; Jan Carney, MD, Editorial Advisory Board; Bobbie Berkowitz, PhD, Editorial Advisory Board; Joan Magilvy, Editorial Advisory Board. **ISSN:** 0737-1209. **Subscription Rates:** US$179 individuals print + online (excl. Canada & Mexico); US$683 institutions print + online; EUR304 individuals print + online; 202 individuals print + online; US$129 students print + online (excl. Canada & Mexico); US$621 institutions print or online; EUR152 students print + online; 101 students print + online; 523 institutions print + online; EUR664 institutions print + online. **Remarks:** Advertising accepted; rates available upon request. **URL:** http://www.wiley.com/bw/journal.asp?ref=0737-1209&site=1. **Circ:** (Not Reported)

56178 ■ Public Opinion Quarterly
Oxford University Press
Great Clarendon St.
Oxford OX2 6DP, United Kingdom
Ph: 44 1865 556767
Fax: 44 1865 353485
Publisher E-mail: webenquiry.uk@oup.com
Journal for academicians and all social science researchers, publishing important theoretical contributions to opinion and communication research, analyses of current public opinion, and investigations of methodological issues involved in survey validity including questionnaire construction, interviewing and interviewers, sampling strategy and mode of administration. **Founded:** 1937. **Freq:** 4/yr. **Key Personnel:** Phyllis Silverstein, Managing Editor; Dan Merkle, Assoc. Ed.; Christopher Wlezien, Section Ed.; Mark Schulman, Section Ed.; James N. Druckman, Editor-in-Chief; Patricia Moy, Assoc. Ed. **ISSN:** 0033-362X. **Subscription Rates:** 201 institutions corporate; print and online; 168 institutions corporate; online only; 185 institutions corporate; print only; 161 institutions print and online; 135 institutions online only; 148 institutions print only; 28 individuals print; 18 students print. **Remarks:** Advertising accepted; rates available upon request. **URL:** http://poq.oxfordjournals.org/. **Circ:** (Not Reported)

56179 ■ Publius
Oxford University Press
Great Clarendon St.
Oxford OX2 6DP, United Kingdom
Ph: 44 1865 556767
Fax: 44 1865 353485
Publisher E-mail: webenquiry.uk@oup.com
Research on federalism, intergovernmental relations, and state and local government in the United States and internationally. **Subtitle:** The Journal of Federalism. **Founded:** 1971. **Freq:** Quarterly. **Print Method:** Letterpress and offset. **Trim Size:** 6 x 9. **Cols./Page:** 1. **Col. Width:** 54 nonpareils. **Col. Depth:** 104 agate lines. **Key Personnel:** Dr. Frank J. Thompson, Book Review Ed.; Carol S. Weissert, Editor, phone 850645-2940, fax 850645-2938, publius@fsu.edu. **ISSN:** 0048-5950. **Subscription Rates:** 257 institutions print and online; US$385 institutions print and online; 214 institutions print, online; US$321 institutions print, online; 33 individuals print only; US$50 individuals print only. **Remarks:** Color advertising not accepted. **URL:** http://publius.oxfordjournals.org/. **Ad Rates:** BW: 100. **Circ:** Paid ‡1,200, Non-paid ‡100

56180 ■ Pump Industry Analyst
Elsevier Science
c/o R. Reidy, Ed.
Elsevier Advanced Technology
The Blvd. Langford Ln.
Kidlington
Oxford OX5 1GB, United Kingdom
Ph: 44 18 65843695
Fax: 44 18 65843971

Circulation: ★ = ABC; △ = BPA; ♦ = CAC; • = CCAB; ❑ = VAC; ⊕ = PO Statement; ‡ = Publisher's Report; Boldface figures = sworn; Light figures = estimated.

Gale Directory of Publications & Broadcast Media/147th Ed. 5833

Publisher E-mail: nlinfo-f@elsevier.com
Magazine publishing international business news for those engaged in the business of pumps. Includes industry news, market prospects, company profile, and company watch. **Founded:** 1995. **Freq:** Monthly. **Key Personnel:** R. Reidy, Editor, r.reidy@elsevier.com. **ISSN:** 1359-6128. **Subscription Rates:** EUR1,176 institutions European countries; US$1,319 institutions all countries except Europe and Japan; 156,300¥ institutions. **Remarks:** Accepts advertising. **URL:** http://www.elsevier.com/wps/find/journaldescription.cws_home/31020/description. **Circ:** (Not Reported)

56181 ■ QJM
Oxford University Press
Great Clarendon St.
Oxford OX2 6DP, United Kingdom
Ph: 44 1865 556767
Fax: 44 1865 353485
Publisher E-mail: webenquiry.uk@oup.com
Journal focusing on internal medicine and publishing peer-reviewed articles, which promote medical science and practice. **Subtitle:** An International Journal of Medicine. **Freq:** Monthly. **Key Personnel:** Prof. Michael Bannon, Editor; J. Alcolado, Editorial Board; G. Currie, Editorial Board; P. Dargan, Editorial Board; A. Schattner, Editorial Board; T. Cox, Editorial Board; M. Halperin, Editorial Board; S. Song, Editorial Board; R. Unwin, Editorial Board; J. Wass, Editorial Board. **ISSN:** 1460-2725. **Subscription Rates:** 661 institutions corporate; print and online; 540 institutions corporate; online only; 606 institutions corporate; print only; 529 institutions print and online; 432 institutions online only; 485 institutions print only; 207 individuals print. **Remarks:** Advertising accepted; rates available upon request. **URL:** http://qjmed.oxfordjournals.org/. **Circ:** (Not Reported)

56182 ■ The Quarterly Journal of Mathematics
Oxford University Press
Mathematical Institute
Oxford OX1 3LB, United Kingdom
Publisher E-mail: webenquiry.uk@oup.com
Journal publishing original contributions to pure mathematics in areas such as algebra, differential geometry and global analysis receive particular emphasis. **Freq:** Quarterly. **Key Personnel:** R. Heath-Brown, Exec. Ed., rhb@maths.ox.ac.uk; A.S. Dancer, Exec. Ed., dancer@math.ox.ac.uk; S.K. Donaldson, Consulting Ed.; A. MacIntyre, Consulting Ed.; M.J. Hopkins, Consulting Ed., mjh@math.mit.edu. **ISSN:** 0033-5606. **Subscription Rates:** 426 institutions corporate; print and online; 355 institutions corporate; online only; 391 institutions corporate; print only; 341 institutions print and online; 284 institutions online only; 312 institutions print only; 294 individuals print; 188 members print. **Remarks:** Advertising accepted; rates available upon request. **URL:** http://qjmath.oxfordjournals.org/. **Circ:** (Not Reported)

56183 ■ The Quarterly Journal of Mechanics and Applied Mathematics
Oxford University Press
Great Clarendon St.
Oxford OX2 6DP, United Kingdom
Ph: 44 1865 556767
Fax: 44 1865 353485
Publisher E-mail: webenquiry.uk@oup.com
Journal publishing original research articles on the application of mathematics to the field of mechanics interpreted in its widest sense ranging from traditional areas, such as fluid and solid mechanics to modern and emerging areas of applied mathematics. **Freq:** Quarterly. **Key Personnel:** R. Craster, Exec. Ed., craster@ualberta.ca; P.W. Duck, Exec. Ed., duck@ma.man.ac.uk; P.A. Martin, Exec. Ed., pamartin@mines.edu. **ISSN:** 0033-5614. **Subscription Rates:** 540 institutions corporate; print and online; 450 institutions corporate; online only; 495 institutions corporate; print only; 432 institutions print and online; 360 institutions online only; 396 institutions print only; 391 individuals print; 248 members print. **Remarks:** Advertising accepted; rates available upon request. **URL:** http://qjmam.oxfordjournals.org/. **Circ:** (Not Reported)

56184 ■ R & D Management
John Wiley & Sons Inc.
Wiley-Blackwell
9600 Garsington Rd.
Oxford OX4 2DQ, United Kingdom
Ph: 44 1865 776868
Fax: 44 1865 714591
General business publication. **Freq:** 5/yr. **Key Personnel:** Alan W. Pearson, Founding Ed.; Jeff Butler, Managing Editor, phone 44 161 2755859, fax 44 870 4200401, rndmanagement@mbs.ac.uk; Dr. K. Brockhoff, Editorial Advisory Board; Prof. A. Piccaluga, Editorial Advisory Board; Khaleel Malik, Book Review Ed., khaleel.malik@mbs.ac.uk; Prof. O. Gassmann, Editorial Advisory Board; Prof. K. Debackere, Editorial Advisory Board; Dr. D. Wilemon, Editorial Advisory Board; Prof. M. von Zedtwitz, Editorial Advisory Board. **ISSN:** 0033-6807. **Subscription Rates:** US$177 individuals Americas (print + online); EUR158 individuals Euro zone (print + online); 106 other countries print + online; US$1,877 institutions Americas (print + online); US$1,706 institutions Americas; 921 institutions UK (print + online); 837 institutions UK (print or online only); EUR1,170 institutions Europe (print + online); EUR1,063 institutions Europe (print or online only); US$2,188 institutions, other countries print + online. **Remarks:** Accepts advertising. **Online:** Gale. **URL:** http://www.wiley.com/bw/journal.asp?ref=0033-6807&site=1. **Circ:** (Not Reported)

56185 ■ Radiation Protection Dosimetry
Oxford University Press
Great Clarendon St.
Oxford OX2 6DP, United Kingdom
Ph: 44 1865 556767
Fax: 44 1865 353485
Publication E-mail: rpd.editorialoffice@oxfordjournals.org
Publisher E-mail: webenquiry.uk@oup.com
Journal publishing peer-reviewed papers covering all aspects of personal and environmental dosimetry and monitoring for both ionizing and non-ionizing radiations, including biological aspects, physical concepts, biophysical dosimetry, external and internal personal dosimetry and monitoring, environmental and workplace monitoring and accident dosimetry and dosimetry related to the protection of patients. **Freq:** 20/yr. **Key Personnel:** Dr. J.C. McDonald, Editor-in-Chief; Dr. J. Stather, Consultant Ed.; Prof. Y. Horowitz, Consultant Ed.; E.P. Goldfinch, Founder; Dr. D.T. Bartlett, Consultant Ed.; Dr. J. Zoetelief, Consultant Ed. **ISSN:** 0144-8420. **Subscription Rates:** 2,114 institutions corporate; print and online; 1,727 institutions corporate; online only; 1,938 institutions corporate; print only; 1,692 institutions print and online; 1,382 institutions online only; 1,551 institutions print only; 778 individuals print; 241 members print. **Remarks:** Advertising accepted; rates available upon request. **URL:** http://rpd.oxfordjournals.org/. **Circ:** (Not Reported)

56186 ■ Ratio Juris
John Wiley & Sons Inc.
Wiley-Blackwell
9600 Garsington Rd.
Oxford OX4 2DQ, United Kingdom
Ph: 44 1865 776868
Fax: 44 1865 714591
Journal providing international and trans-cultural forum for the communication of philosophical ideas about law and legal questions. **Freq:** Quarterly. **Key Personnel:** Enrico Pattaro, Founding Ed., pattaro@cirfid.unibo.it; Chiara Valentini, Editorial Asst., phone 39 51 277261, rjuris@cirfid.unibo.it; Carla Faralli, Editor-in-Chief, carla.faralli@unibo.it. **ISSN:** 0952-1917. **Subscription Rates:** US$1,090 institutions print or online; US$1,199 institutions print + online; US$64 individuals print + online; 568 institutions print or online; 625 institutions print + online; 40 other countries print + online; EUR720 institutions print or online; 792 institutions print + online; EUR59 individuals print + online; US$1,272 institutions, other countries print or online. **Remarks:** Accepts advertising. **URL:** http://www.wiley.com/bw/journal.asp?ref=0952-1917&site=1. **Circ:** (Not Reported)

56187 ■ Research in Comparative and International Education
wwwords Ltd.
Didcot
PO Box 204
Oxford OX11 9ZQ, United Kingdom
Ph: 44 1235 818062
Fax: 44 1235 817275
Publisher E-mail: info@wwwords.co.uk
Journal covering topics on international advisory board. **Freq:** Quarterly. **Key Personnel:** David Phillips, Editor, david.phillips@edstud.ox.ac.uk; Laura Day Ashley, International Advisory Committee Member; Nafsika Alexiadou, International Advisory Committee Member; Erwin Beck, International Advisory Committee Member; Indra Dedze, International Advisory Committee Member; Hubert Ertl, Editor; Sheila Aikman, International Advisory Committee Member; Ingrid Gogolin, International Advisory Committee Member; David Johnson, Editor. **ISSN:** 1745-4999. **Subscription Rates:** US$50 individuals; US$660 libraries. **URL:** http://www.wwwords.co.uk/rcie.

56188 ■ Restoration Ecology
John Wiley & Sons Inc.
Wiley-Blackwell
9600 Garsington Rd.
Oxford OX4 2DQ, United Kingdom
Ph: 44 1865 776868
Fax: 44 1865 714591
Journal publishing research articles concerned with the halting and reversing of ecological damage. **Freq:** Bimonthly. **Key Personnel:** Richard Hobbs, Editor-in-Chief; Peter Friederici, Book Review Ed.; Mark Briggs, Editorial Board; Stuart Allison, Editorial Board; Brandon Bestelmeyer, Editorial Board; Susan Galatowitsch, Editorial Board; Susan A. Yates, Managing Editor; James Aronson, Editorial Board; Roger Anderson, Editorial Board; Darren Ryder, Editorial Board; John Scullion, Editorial Board. **ISSN:** 1061-2971. **Subscription Rates:** US$232 individuals print + online; US$245 Canada and Mexico print + online; EUR286 individuals print + online; 190 other countries print + online; 180 individuals online; US$233 Canada and Mexico online; EUR2770 individuals online; 530 institutions print + online; EUR674 institutions print + online; US$1,038 institutions, other countries print + online. **URL:** http://www.wiley.com/bw/journal.asp?ref=1061-2971&site=1. **Ad Rates:** BW: 568, 4C: 850. **Circ:** (Not Reported)

56189 ■ Review of Development Economics
John Wiley & Sons Inc.
Wiley-Blackwell
9600 Garsington Rd.
Oxford OX4 2DQ, United Kingdom
Ph: 44 1865 776868
Fax: 44 1865 714591
Journal publishing articles on current growth problems of developing countries, including the transition economies. **Subtitle:** An Essential Resource for any Development Economist. **Freq:** Quarterly. **Key Personnel:** Kaushik Basu, Editorial Board; Kwan E. Choi, Editor, phone 515294-5999, fax 515294-9913, kchoi@iastate.edu; Joseph Francois, Assoc. Ed.; Sajal Lahiri, Assoc. Ed.; Timothy Besley, Editorial Board; William Darity, Jr., Assoc. Ed.; Abhijit Banerjee, Editorial Board; Jeffrey B. Nugent, Editorial Board; Hossein Farzin, Assoc. Ed.; Elias Dinopoulos, Assoc. Ed.; Martin Ravallion, Editorial Board; Jorge Braga, Editorial Board. **ISSN:** 1363-6669. **Subscription Rates:** US$107 individuals print + online; US$907 institutions print + online; US$824 institutions print, online; US$1,204 institutions, other countries print + online; US$1,093 institutions, other countries print or online; 614 institutions print + online; EUR133 individuals print + online; 89 individuals print + online; 558 institutions print, online; EUR780 institutions print + online. **Remarks:** Advertising accepted; rates available upon request. **URL:** http://www.wiley.com/bw/journal.asp?ref=1363-6669&site=1. **Circ:** (Not Reported)

56190 ■ The Review of Economic Studies
John Wiley & Sons Inc.
Wiley-Blackwell
9600 Garsington Rd.
Oxford OX4 2DQ, United Kingdom
Ph: 44 1865 776868
Fax: 44 1865 714591
Publication covering economics. **Founded:** 1933. **Freq:** Quarterly. **Key Personnel:** Bruno Biais, Editor; Kjetil Storesletten, Editor; Imran Rasul, Editor. **ISSN:** 0034-6527. **Subscription Rates:** 55 other countries print and online; EUR79 individuals Euro zone (print and online); US$89 individuals Americas (print and online); US$568 institutions, other countries print and online; EUR42 students Euro zone (print and online); 27 students, other countries print and online; US$47 students Americas (print and online); EUR367 institutions Europe (print and online); US$568 institutions, other countries print and online; US$488 institutions Americas (print and online). **Remarks:** Accepts advertising. **URL:** http://www.wiley.com/bw/journal.asp?ref=0034-6527&site=1. **Circ:** (Not Reported)

56191 ■ The Review of English Studies
Oxford University Press
Great Clarendon St.

Oxford OX2 6DP, United Kingdom
Ph: 44 1865 556767
Fax: 44 1865 353485
Publisher E-mail: webenquiry.uk@oup.com
Publication covering literature and writing. **Freq:** 5/yr.
Key Personnel: Colin Burrow, Editor; Elaine Treharne, Editor; Thomas Keymer, Editor; Michael Whitworth, Editor. **ISSN:** 0034-6551. **Subscription Rates:** 244 institutions print and online; US$464 institutions print and online; EUR366 institutions print and online; 223 institutions print, online; US$424 individuals print, online; EUR335 institutions print, online; 59 individuals print; US$118 individuals print; US$89 individuals print. **Remarks:** Accepts advertising. **URL:** http://res.oxfordjournals.org/. **Circ:** (Not Reported)

56192 ■ The Review of Income and Wealth
John Wiley & Sons Inc.
Wiley-Blackwell
9600 Garsington Rd.
Oxford OX4 2DQ, United Kingdom
Ph: 44 1865 776868
Fax: 44 1865 714591
Association journal covering research on national and economic and social accounting as related to the measurement and analysis of income and wealth. **Founded:** 1966. **Freq:** Quarterly. **Key Personnel:** Robert J. Hill, Managing Editor; David Johnson, Editorial Board; Stephan Klasen, Managing Editor. **ISSN:** 0034-6586. **Subscription Rates:** 187 institutions print & online; US$299 institutions print & online; US$271 institutions print or online; 169 institutions print or online; US$365 institutions, other countries print & online; US$365 institutions, other countries online. **Remarks:** Advertising accepted; rates available upon request. **URL:** http://www.wiley.com/bw/journal.asp?ref=0034-6586&site=1. **Circ:** ‡1,400

56193 ■ Review of International Economics
John Wiley & Sons Inc.
Wiley-Blackwell
9600 Garsington Rd.
Oxford OX4 2DQ, United Kingdom
Ph: 44 1865 776868
Fax: 44 1865 714591
Journal containing articles on international economics including novel and controversial ideas. **Freq:** 5/yr. **Key Personnel:** Kwan E. Choi, Editor, phone 515294-5999, fax 515294-9913, kchoi@iastate.edu; Gene M. Grossman, Assoc. Ed. **ISSN:** 0965-7576. **Subscription Rates:** US$85 individuals print + online; US$1,272 institutions, other countries print or online; US$1,047 institutions print + online; US$951 institutions print or online; US$1,400 institutions, other countries print + online; EUR101 individuals print + online; EUR824 institutions print or online; 715 institutions print + online; 649 institutions print or online; EUR907 institutions print + online. **Remarks:** Accepts advertising. **URL:** http://www.wiley.com/bw/journal.asp?ref=0965-7576&site=1. **Circ:** (Not Reported)

56194 ■ Review of Policy Research
John Wiley & Sons Inc.
Wiley-Blackwell
9600 Garsington Rd.
Oxford OX4 2DQ, United Kingdom
Ph: 44 1865 776868
Fax: 44 1865 714591
Peer-reviewed journal focusing on the research outcomes and consequences of policy change in domestic and comparative contexts. **Freq:** Bimonthly. **Key Personnel:** Paul Rich, Interim Ed., rich@hoover.stanford.edu; Gary C. Bryner, Editorial Board; Christopher J. Bosso, Editorial Board; Sandra Braman, Editorial Board; David H. Guston, Editorial Board; Thomas Bernauer, Editorial Board. **ISSN:** 1541-132X. **Subscription Rates:** US$1,471 institutions print + online; 1,081 institutions print + online; US$1,336 institutions print, online; 982 institutions print, online; EUR1,373 institutions print + online; EUR1,248 institutions print, online; US$2,119 institutions, other countries print + online; US$1,925 institutions, other countries print + online. **Remarks:** Advertising accepted; rates available upon request. **URL:** http://www.wiley.com/bw/journal.asp?ref=1541-132X&site=1. **Circ:** (Not Reported)

56195 ■ Review of Urban & Regional Development Studies
John Wiley & Sons Inc.
Wiley-Blackwell
9600 Garsington Rd.

Oxford OX4 2DQ, United Kingdom
Ph: 44 1865 776868
Fax: 44 1865 714591
Publication E-mail: rurds@sk.tsukuba.ac.jp
Journal containing thorough empirical analysis, stressing theoretical and methodological issues, others policy relevance and the operational aspects of the academic disciplines. **Subtitle:** Journal of the Applied Regional Science Conference. **Freq:** 3/yr. **Key Personnel:** Tatsuaki Kuroda, Editor; Phillip McCann, Editor; Ryohei Nakamura, Editor. **ISSN:** 0917-0553. **Subscription Rates:** US$44 students print + online; EUR101 individuals print + online; 67 other countries print + online; US$343 institutions print + online; US$311 institutions print or online; 29 students print + online; US$472 institutions, other countries print + online; US$429 institutions, other countries print or online; 219 institutions print + online; EUR278 institutions print + online. **Remarks:** Advertising accepted; rates available upon request. **URL:** http://www.wiley.com/bw/journal.asp?ref=0917-0553&site=1. **Circ:** (Not Reported)

56196 ■ Risk Management & Insurance Review
John Wiley & Sons Inc.
Wiley-Blackwell
9600 Garsington Rd.
Oxford OX4 2DQ, United Kingdom
Ph: 44 1865 776868
Fax: 44 1865 714591
Journal covering articles in the field of risk and insurance. It contains original research involving applications and applied techniques, research literature, business practice, and public policy along with articles discussing and evaluating instructional techniques. **Freq:** Biennial. **Key Personnel:** Mary A. Weiss, Editor; Martin Shubik, Assoc. Ed.; Lawrence Berger, Assoc. Ed. **ISSN:** 1098-1616. **Subscription Rates:** US$183 institutions print + online; 143 institutions print + online; US$166 institutions print or online; 129 institutions print or online; EUR181 institutions print + online; US$277 institutions, other countries print + online; US$252 institutions, other countries print or online. **URL:** http://www.wiley.com/bw/journal.asp?ref=1098-1616.

56197 ■ The Russian Review
John Wiley & Sons Inc.
Wiley-Blackwell
9600 Garsington Rd.
Oxford OX4 2DQ, United Kingdom
Ph: 44 1865 776868
Fax: 44 1865 714591
Regional focus/area studies journal. **Subtitle:** An American Quarterly Devoted to Russia Past and Present. **Freq:** Quarterly. **Key Personnel:** Eve Levin, Editor, phone 785864-1121, fax 785864-3800, rusrev@ku.edu; Eugene Huskey, Assoc. Ed.; Irene Masing-Delic, Co-Ed. **ISSN:** 0036-0341. **Subscription Rates:** US$48 individuals print and online; EUR61 individuals print and online; 41 individuals print and online; US$46 individuals online; EUR58 individuals online; US$251 institutions print and online; US$384 institutions, other countries print and online; US$226 institutions print, online; US$349 institutions, other countries print, online. **Remarks:** Accepts advertising. **Online:** Gale. **URL:** http://www.wiley.com/bw/journal.asp?ref=0036-0341&site=1. **Circ:** (Not Reported)

56198 ■ Scandinavian Journal of Caring Sciences
John Wiley & Sons Inc.
Wiley-Blackwell
9600 Garsington Rd.
Oxford OX4 2DQ, United Kingdom
Ph: 44 1865 776868
Fax: 44 1865 714591
Peer-reviewed journal covering research focusing on a patient, family or community, promoting an interdisciplinary team approach. **Freq:** Quarterly. **Key Personnel:** Margret Lepp, Assoc. Ed.; Wendy Chaboyer, Editorial Board; Prof. Ingegerd Bergbom, Editor-in-Chief; Herdis Sveinsdottir, Editorial Board; Alvisa Palese, Editorial Board; Michael A. Carter, Editorial Board; Kirsten Lomborg, Editorial Board; Britta Hordam, Editorial Board; Arne W. Rehnsfeldt, Editorial Board. **ISSN:** 0283-9318. **Subscription Rates:** US$779 institutions print and online; 423 institutions print and online; US$708 institutions print, online; US$910 institutions, other countries print and online; US$827 institutions, other countries print, online; EUR537 institutions print and online; US$164 individuals print and online; EUR134 individuals print and online; 94 individuals print and online; 98 other countries print and online. **URL:** http://www.wiley.com/

bw/journal.asp?ref=0283-9318&site=1.

56199 ■ The Scandinavian Journal of Economics
John Wiley & Sons Inc.
Wiley-Blackwell
9600 Garsington Rd.
Oxford OX4 2DQ, United Kingdom
Ph: 44 1865 776868
Fax: 44 1865 714591
Peer-reviewed journal focusing in all areas of economics. **Freq:** Quarterly. **Key Personnel:** Ragnar Torvik, Editor; Christian Schultz, Assoc. Ed.; Juuso Valimaki, Assoc. Ed.; Nils Gottfries, Assoc. Ed.; Espen R. Moen, Assoc. Ed.; Niels Haldrup, Assoc. Ed.; John Hassler, Assoc. Ed.; Geir B. Asheim, Assoc. Ed.; Birgitte Sloth, Assoc. Ed. **ISSN:** 0347-0520. **Subscription Rates:** US$90 individuals print + online; US$481 institutions print + online; US$437 institutions print, online; 285 institutions print and online; EUR93 individuals print + online; 258 institutions print, online; EUR361 institutions print + online; EUR327 institutions print, online; US$591 institutions, other countries print + online; US$537 institutions, other countries print, online. **Remarks:** Accepts advertising. **Online:** Gale. **URL:** http://www.wiley.com/bw/journal.asp?ref=0347-0520&site=1. **Circ:** (Not Reported)

56200 ■ Scandinavian Political Studies
John Wiley & Sons Inc.
Wiley-Blackwell
9600 Garsington Rd.
Oxford OX4 2DQ, United Kingdom
Ph: 44 1865 776868
Fax: 44 1865 714591
Journal focusing on policy and electoral issues affecting the Scandinavian countries, in connection with the Nordic Political Science Association. **Freq:** Quarterly. **Key Personnel:** Christoffer Green-Pedersen, Editor, phone 45 89421297, cgp@ps.au.dk; Peter Munk Christiansen, Editor, phone 45 89421276, pmc@ps.au.dk; Karina Kosiara-Pedersen, Editor, phone 45 35323416, kp@ifs.ku.dk; Marcus Buck, Editorial Board; Baard H. Borge, Editorial Board. **ISSN:** 0080-6757. **Subscription Rates:** US$73 individuals print + online; EUR67 individuals print + online; 44 individuals print + online; US$47 students print + online; EUR42 students print + online; 28 students, other countries print + online; US$388 institutions print + online; EUR293 institutions print + online; 231 institutions print + online; US$451 institutions, other countries print + online. **Remarks:** Advertising accepted; rates available upon request. **URL:** http://www.wiley.com/bw/journal.asp?ref=0080-6757&site=1. **Circ:** (Not Reported)

56201 ■ Schizophrenia Bulletin
Oxford University Press
Great Clarendon St.
Oxford OX2 6DP, United Kingdom
Ph: 44 1865 556767
Fax: 44 1865 353485
Publisher E-mail: webenquiry.uk@oup.com
Journal reviewing recent developments and empirically-based hypotheses regarding the etiology and treatment of schizophrenia and publishing new knowledge ranging from the molecular basis to social and cultural factors. **Freq:** 6/yr. **Key Personnel:** William T. Carpenter, Editor-in-Chief; Gunvant Thaker, MD, Dep. Ed.; Susan M. Essock, Assoc. Ed.; Paul D. Shepard, MD, Assoc. Ed.; Thomas H. McGlashan, Assoc. Ed.; Janet Smith, MD, Managing Editor; Michael J. Owen, Assoc. Ed. **ISSN:** 0586-7614. **Subscription Rates:** 333 institutions corporate; print and online; 247 institutions corporate; online only; 305 institutions corporate; print only; 267 institutions print and online; 198 institutions online only; 244 institutions print only; 62 individuals print. **Remarks:** Accepts advertising. **URL:** http://schizophreniabulletin.oxfordjournals.org/. **Circ:** (Not Reported)

56202 ■ SIAM Journal on Optimization
Society for Industrial & Applied Mathematics
c/o Raphael A. Hauser, Assoc. Ed.
Oxford University Computing Laboratory
Wolfson Bldg.
Oxford OX1 3QD, United Kingdom
Publisher E-mail: service@siam.org
Journal featuring research and expository articles on the theory and practice of optimization. **Founded:** 1991. **Freq:** Quarterly. **Print Method:** Offset. **Trim Size:** 6 3/4 x 10. **Key Personnel:** Charles Audet, Assoc. Ed., charles.audet@gerad.ca; Heinz H. Bauschke, Assoc.

Ed., heinz.bauschke@ubc.ca; Lorenz T. Biegler, Assoc. Ed., lb01@andrew.cmu.edu; William J. Cook, Assoc. Ed., bico@isye.gatech.edu; Darinka Dentcheva, Assoc. Ed., ddentche@stevens-tech.edu; Masao Fukushima, Assoc. Ed., fuku@amp.i.kyoto u.ac.jp; Nicholas I.M. Gould, Editor-in-Chief, n.i.m.gould@rl.ac.uk; Raphael A. Hauser, Assoc. Ed., hauser@comlab.ox.ac.uk. **ISSN:** 1052-6234. **Subscription Rates:** US$101 individuals domestic; US$105 other countries; US$85 individuals electronic only (1997-present). **Remarks:** Accepts advertising. **URL:** http://www.siam.org/journals/siopt. php. **Ad Rates:** BW: 400. **Circ:** (Not Reported)

56203 ■ Significance
John Wiley & Sons Inc.
Wiley-Blackwell
9600 Garsington Rd.
Oxford OX4 2DQ, United Kingdom
Ph: 44 1865 776868
Fax: 44 1865 714591
Magazine for anyone interested in statistics and the analysis and interpretation of data. **Subtitle:** Statistics Making Sense. **Freq:** Quarterly. **Key Personnel:** Helen Joyce, Editorial Board; Mario Cortina Borja, Editorial Board; Daniela De Angelis, Editorial Board; Julian Champkin, Editor; Simon Briscoe, Editorial Board; Philip Woodward, Editorial Board. **ISSN:** 1740-9705. **Subscription Rates:** US$50 individuals; US$25 students; US$252 institutions print and online; US$228 institutions print, online; 121 institutions print and online; 110 institutions print, online; EUR154 institutions print and online; EUR154 institutions print, online; US$268 institutions, other countries print and online; US$243 institutions, other countries print, online. **Remarks:** Accepts advertising. **URL:** http://www.wiley.com/bw/journal.asp?ref=1740-9705&site=1. **Circ:** (Not Reported)

56204 ■ Singapore Journal of Tropical Geography
John Wiley & Sons Inc.
Wiley-Blackwell
9600 Garsington Rd.
Oxford OX4 2DQ, United Kingdom
Ph: 44 1865 776868
Fax: 44 1865 714591
Geography journal. **Freq:** 3/yr. **Key Personnel:** Victor R. Savage, Editor; James D. Sidaway, Editor; Lim Kim Leng, Editorial Asst. **ISSN:** 0129-7619. **Subscription Rates:** US$82 individuals print and online; 203 institutions print and online; US$397 institutions, other countries print and online; US$292 institutions print and online; EUR257 institutions print and online; US$397 institutions, other countries print, online; US$265 institutions print, online; 184 institutions print, online; EUR234 institutions print, online; EUR65 individuals print and online. **Remarks:** Accepts advertising. **URL:** http://www.wiley.com/bw/journal.asp?ref=0129-7619&site=1. **Ad Rates:** BW: 260. **Circ:** (Not Reported)

56205 ■ Sleep and Biological Rhythm
John Wiley & Sons Inc.
Wiley-Blackwell
9600 Garsington Rd.
Oxford OX4 2DQ, United Kingdom
Ph: 44 1865 776868
Fax: 44 1865 714591
Peer-reviewed journal providing scientific research into sleep science, sleep disorder medicine and the management of sleep. **Freq:** Quarterly. **Key Personnel:** Masako Okawa, Assoc. Ed.; Tadao Hori, Assoc. Ed.; Kiyohisa Takahashi, Editorial Board; Toshinori Kobayashi, Editorial Board; Makoto Uchiyama, Assoc. Ed.; Prof. Ken-Ichi Honma, Editor-in-Chief; Toshio Yamauchi, Editorial Board; Taneyoshi Nozawa, Editorial Board; Takuya Kojima, Editorial Board; Soichiro Miyazaki, Editorial Board. **ISSN:** 1446-9235. **Subscription Rates:** US$179 individuals print + online; EUR164 individuals print + online; 110 other countries print + online; US$450 institutions print + online; EUR356 institutions print + online; 279 institutions print + online; US$547 institutions, other countries print + online; US$409 institutions print or online; US$498 institutions, other countries print or online; EUR323 institutions print or online. **Remarks:** Accepts advertising. **URL:** http://www.wiley.com/bw/journal.asp?ref=1446-9235. **Circ:** (Not Reported)

56206 ■ Sobornost
Fellowship of St. Alban and St. Sergius
1 Canterbury Rd.
Oxford OX2 6LU, United Kingdom
Ph: 44 18 65552991
Theological journal covering Eastern Orthodox Churches and Ecumenism. **Founded:** 1934. **Freq:** Semiannual.

Key Personnel: Rev. Stephen Platt, Editor. **ISSN:** 0144-8722. **Subscription Rates:** 25 individuals all foreign p.a.; 20 individuals U.K. p.a.; 12 students for U.K. / foreign p.a.; 5 individuals inclusive of fellowship news. **Remarks:** Accepts advertising. **URL:** http://www.sobornost.org/publications.html. **Circ:** 1,600

56207 ■ Social Anthropology
John Wiley & Sons Inc.
Wiley-Blackwell
9600 Garsington Rd.
Oxford OX4 2DQ, United Kingdom
Ph: 44 1865 776868
Fax: 44 1865 714591
Journal covering sociology and social work. **Freq:** Quarterly. **Key Personnel:** Dorle Drackle, Editor; Helena Wulff, Editor. **ISSN:** 0964-0282. **Subscription Rates:** 240 institutions online only; 267 institutions print + online; 48 individuals print + online. **URL:** http://www3.interscience.wiley.com/journal/118488932/home.

56208 ■ Socio-Economic Review
Oxford University Press
Great Clarendon St.
Oxford OX2 6DP, United Kingdom
Ph: 44 1865 556767
Fax: 44 1865 353485
Publisher E-mail: webenquiry.uk@oup.com
Journal encouraging work on the relationship between society, economy, institutions and markets, moral commitments and the rational pursuit of self-interest by seeking articles that focus on economic action in its social and historical context. **Freq:** 4/yr. **Key Personnel:** Bruno Amable, Editor; Wolfgang Streeck, Editor-in-Chief, streeck@mpifg.de; Jens Beckert, Editor, beckert@mpifg.de; Lane Kenworthy, Editor; Jurgen Feick, Managing Editor, jf@mpifg.de; Marc Schneiberg, Editor. **ISSN:** 1475-1461. **Subscription Rates:** 398 institutions corporate; print and online; 332 institutions corporate; online only; 365 institutions corporate; print only; 319 institutions print and online; 266 institutions online only; 293 institutions print only; 62 individuals print. **Remarks:** Advertising accepted; rates available upon request. **URL:** http://ser.oxfordjournals.org/. **Circ:** (Not Reported)

56209 ■ The Sociological Quarterly
John Wiley & Sons Inc.
Wiley-Blackwell
9600 Garsington Rd.
Oxford OX4 2DQ, United Kingdom
Ph: 44 1865 776868
Fax: 44 1865 714591
Journal publishing research and theory in all areas of sociological inquiry, focusing on publishing sociological research and writing. **Freq:** Quarterly. **Key Personnel:** Peter Kivisto, Advisory Ed.; Brian L. Donovan, Editor; William G. Staples, Editor; Patricia Adler, Advisory Ed. **ISSN:** 0038-0253. **Subscription Rates:** US$438 institutions print and online; US$398 institutions print or online; 261 institutions print and online; 238 institutions print or online; EUR302 institutions print or online; US$512 institutions, other countries print and online; US$466 institutions, other countries print or online. **Remarks:** Accepts display advertising. **URL:** http://www.wiley.com/bw/journal.asp?ref=0038-0253&site=1. **Circ:** (Not Reported)

56210 ■ The Sociological Review
John Wiley & Sons Inc.
Wiley-Blackwell
9600 Garsington Rd.
Oxford OX4 2DQ, United Kingdom
Ph: 44 1865 776868
Fax: 44 1865 714591
Journal covering sociology and social work. **Freq:** Quarterly. **Key Personnel:** Mike Savage, Editorial Board; Rosemary Deem, Editorial Board; Jack Barbalet, Editorial Board. **ISSN:** 0038-0261. **Subscription Rates:** US$59 individuals print and online; EUR54 individuals print and online; 36 other countries print and online; US$573 institutions print and online; 294 institutions print and online; US$667 institutions, other countries print and online; US$520 institutions online; 266 institutions online; EUR338 institutions online; US$605 institutions, other countries online. **Remarks:** Accepts advertising. **Online:** Gale. **URL:** http://www.wiley.com/bw/journal.asp?ref=0038-0261&site=1. **Circ:** (Not Reported)

56211 ■ Sociology of Health & Illness
John Wiley & Sons Inc.
Wiley-Blackwell

9600 Garsington Rd.
Oxford OX4 2DQ, United Kingdom
Ph: 44 1865 776868
Fax: 44 1865 714591
Journal publishing sociological articles on all aspects of health, illness and medicine. **Freq:** 6/yr. **Key Personnel:** Hannah Bradby, Monographs Ed., h.bradby@warwick.ac.uk; Jonathan Gabe, Editor, phone 44 1784 443144, j.gabe@rhul.ac.uk; Liz Ackroyd, Editorial Admin., phone 44 20 78822511, shi@brunel.ac.uk; David Locker, Editorial Advisor; Steven P. Wainwright, Editor, steven.wainwright@kcl.ac.uk; Claire Williams, Editor, clare.2.williams@kcl.ac.uk; Clive Seale, Managing Editor, c.seale@qmul.ac.uk; Mildred Blaxter, Book Review Ed., m.blaxter@medsoc.eclipse.co.uk; Gary Albrecht, Editorial Advisor; Susan E. Bell, Editorial Advisor, mary.shaw@bristol.ac.uk; Stefan Timmermans, Editorial Advisor; Alan Petersen, Editorial Advisor. **ISSN:** 0141-9889. **Subscription Rates:** US$1,082 institutions print or online; US$1,190 institutions print + online; US$103 individuals print + online; 480 institutions print or online; 527 institutions print + online; 62 other countries print + online; EUR609 institutions print or online; 669 institutions print + online; EUR92 individuals print + online; US$1,261 institutions, other countries print or online. **Remarks:** Accepts advertising. **URL:** http://www.blackwellpublishing.com/shil_enhanced/default.asp. **Circ:** (Not Reported)

56212 ■ South African Journal of Economics
John Wiley & Sons Inc.
Wiley-Blackwell
9600 Garsington Rd.
Oxford OX4 2DQ, United Kingdom
Ph: 44 1865 776868
Fax: 44 1865 714591
International regional journal publishing economics research affecting African countries, papers from internationally-recognised authors on a wide range of subjects and accepts contributions on all the known fields of the discipline, including methodology and economic history and econometrics. **Founded:** 1925. **Freq:** Quarterly. **Key Personnel:** Johannes Fedderke, Managing Editor; J. Burns, Editor; P. Burger, Editor. **ISSN:** 0038-2280. **Subscription Rates:** US$339 institutions print and online; US$308 institutions print, online; 207 institutions print and online; 190 institutions print, online; EUR265 institutions print and online; EUR241 institutions print, online; US$411 institutions, other countries print and online; US$373 institutions, other countries print, online; US$310 institutions print and online (South Africa); US$281 institutions print, online (South Africa). **Remarks:** Advertising not accepted. **URL:** http://www.wiley.com/bw/journal.asp?ref=0038-2280&site=1. **Circ:** (Not Reported)

56213 ■ Teaching Statistics
John Wiley & Sons Inc.
Wiley-Blackwell
9600 Garsington Rd.
Oxford OX4 2DQ, United Kingdom
Ph: 44 1865 776868
Fax: 44 1865 714591
Journal for teachers of students who use statistics in their work, in connection with Teaching Statistics Trust. **Freq:** 3/yr. **Key Personnel:** Prof. Roger Johnson, Editor, roger.johnson@sdsmt.edu; Mr. N.A. Sheldon, Reviews Ed.; Prof. Vic Barnett, Editorial Board. **ISSN:** 0141-982X. **Subscription Rates:** US$56 individuals print and online; US$32 students print and online; US$109 institutions print + online; US$98 institutions print or online; EUR66 individuals print and online; EUR30 students print and online; 33 other countries print and online; US$128 institutions, other countries print and online; US$116 institutions, other countries print or online; EUR73 institutions print and online. **Remarks:** Advertising accepted; rates available upon request. **URL:** http://www.wiley.com/bw/journal.asp?ref=0141-982X&site=1. **Circ:** (Not Reported)

56214 ■ Teaching Theology and Religion
John Wiley & Sons Inc.
Wiley-Blackwell
9600 Garsington Rd.
Oxford OX4 2DQ, United Kingdom
Ph: 44 1865 776868
Fax: 44 1865 714591
Journal dealing with the study of theology. **Freq:** Quarterly. **Key Personnel:** Patricia Killen, Editor; Thomas Pearson, Managing Editor; Paul O. Myhre, book and Resource Review Ed. **ISSN:** 1368-4868. **Subscription Rates:** US$72 individuals print + online; US$48

students print + online; US$504 institutions print + online; US$457 institutions print or online; EUR65 individuals; 44 other countries; 22 students, other countries; EUR43 students Europe; 379 institutions print + online; EUR379 institutions print + online. **Remarks:** Advertising accepted; rates available upon request. **URL:** http://www.wiley.com/bw/journal.asp?ref=1368-4868. **Circ:** (Not Reported)

56215 ■ Tertiary Education and Management
Taylor & Francis Group Ltd.
2 & 4 Park Sq.
Milton Pk.
Oxford OX14 4RN, United Kingdom
Ph: 44 20 70176000
Fax: 44 20 70176699
Publisher E-mail: international@tandf.co.uk
Journal dealing with higher education management. **Freq:** 4/yr. **Key Personnel:** Barbara Sporn, Editor; Barbara M. Kehm, Editor; Jeroen Huisman, Editor; Bjorn Stensaker, Editor-in-Chief. **ISSN:** 1358-3883. **Subscription Rates:** 220 institutions print + online; US$401 institutions print + online; EUR318 institutions print + online; 209 institutions online; US$381 institutions online; EUR302 institutions online; 91 individuals; US$165 individuals; EUR130 individuals. **Remarks:** Accepts advertising. **URL:** http://www.tandf.co.uk/journals/titles/13583883.asp. **Circ:** (Not Reported)

56216 ■ Tetrahedron
Elsevier Science
c/o Prof. S.G. Davies, Ed.-in-Ch.
Chemistry Research Laboratory
Dept. of Chemistry
University of Oxford, Mansfield Rd.
Oxford OX1 3QR, United Kingdom
Publisher E-mail: nlinfo-f@elsevier.com
Journal publishing original contributions related to all the aspects of the chemical, physical and theoretical properties of non-racemic organic and inorganic materials and processes. **Subtitle:** Asymmetry. **Founded:** 1990. **Freq:** Semimonthly. **Key Personnel:** Prof. S.G. Davies, Editor-in-Chief, asymm@chem.ox.ac.uk; Prof. T. Hayashi, Editor, tetasy@kuchem.kyoto-u.ac.jp; Dr. C.H. Wong, Exec. Board of Ed.; Prof. D.L. Boger, Exec. Board of Ed.; Prof. L. Ghosez, Exec. Board of Ed.; Prof. H.H. Wasserman, Ed. Emeritus; Prof. B. Ganem, Exec. Board of Ed.; Prof. K.D. Janda, Exec. Board of Ed.; Prof. H. Waldmann, Chm. **ISSN:** 0957-4166. **Subscription Rates:** 436,700¥ institutions; US$3,678 institutions for all countries except Europe and Japan; EUR3,288 institutions for European countries; EUR271 individuals for European countries; 35,900¥ individuals; US$302 individuals for all countries except Europe and Japan. **Remarks:** Accepts advertising. **URL:** http://www.elsevier.com/wps/find/journaldescription.cws_home/937/descriptio n. **Circ:** (Not Reported)

56217 ■ Textile
Berg Publishers
1st Fl., Angel Ct.
81 St. Clements St.
Oxford OX4 1AW, United Kingdom
Ph: 44 18 65245104
Fax: 44 18 65791165
Peer-reviewed Journal bringing together research in textiles in an academic forum and providing a platform for points of departure between art and craft; gender and identity; cloth, body and architecture; labor and technology; techno-design and practice - all situated within the broader contexts of material and visual culture. **Subtitle:** The Journal of Cloth and Culture. **Founded:** 2003. **Freq:** 3/yr. **Key Personnel:** Mary Littrell, Assoc. Ed.; Doran Ross, Editor; Catherine Harper, Editor. **ISSN:** 1475-9756. **Subscription Rates:** 49 individuals print only; 144 institutions online only; 170 institutions print and online; 144 individuals online. **Remarks:** Accepts advertising. **URL:** http://www.bergpublishers.com/JournalsHomepage/Textile/tabid/518/Default.aspx. **Ad Rates:** BW: 325. **Circ:** (Not Reported)

56218 ■ Toxicological Sciences
Oxford University Press
Great Clarendon St.
Oxford OX2 6DP, United Kingdom
Ph: 44 1865 556767
Fax: 44 1865 353485
Publisher E-mail: webenquiry.uk@oup.com
Peer-reviewed Scientific journal on toxicology; contains articles assessing the risk of exposure to toxic agents to human and animal health. **Subtitle:** An Official Journal

of the Society of Toxicology. **Founded:** 1981. **Freq:** 12/yr. **Print Method:** Sheetfed offset. **Trim Size:** 8 1/2 x 11. **Cols./Page:** 2. **Key Personnel:** Lois D. Lehman-McKeeman, Editor-in-Chief; Virginia F. Hawkins, Managing Editor; Barbara Abbott, Assoc. Ed.; Michael L. Cunningham, Assoc. Ed.; Howard P. Glauert, Assoc. Ed.; Douglas Keller, Assoc. Ed. **ISSN:** 1096-6080. **Subscription Rates:** 277 individuals print; 217 members print; 1,385 institutions print and online; US$2,077 institutions print and online; US$1,679 institutions online; US$415 individuals online; 1,269 institutions print. **Remarks:** Accepts advertising. **URL:** http://toxsci.oxfordjournals.org/. **Circ:** (Not Reported)

56219 ■ Transactions of the Institute of British Geographers
John Wiley & Sons Inc.
Wiley-Blackwell
9600 Garsington Rd.
Oxford OX4 2DQ, United Kingdom
Ph: 44 1865 776868
Fax: 44 1865 714591
Peer-reviewed journal covering all aspects of geography. **Founded:** 1935. **Freq:** Quarterly. **Key Personnel:** Alison Blunt, Editor; Madeleine Hatfield, Managing Editor; Klaus Dodds, Editorial Advisory Board. **ISSN:** 0020-2754. **Subscription Rates:** US$673 institutions print + online; 401 institutions print + online; US$785 institutions, other countries print + online; US$611 institutions print, online; 401 institutions print, online; US$713 institutions, other countries print, online; EUR509 institutions print + online; EUR463 institutions print, online. **Remarks:** Advertising accepted; rates available upon request. **URL:** http://www.wiley.com/bw/journal.asp?ref=0020-2754&site=1. **Circ:** (Not Reported)

56220 ■ Transboundary and Emerging Diseases
John Wiley & Sons Inc.
Wiley-Blackwell
9600 Garsington Rd.
Oxford OX4 2DQ, United Kingdom
Ph: 44 1865 776868
Fax: 44 1865 714591
Journal dealing with veterinary medicines and related topics. **Freq:** 10/yr. **Key Personnel:** Paul Kitching, Editor-in-Chief; Marta Sabara, Assoc. Ed.; Gavin Thomson, Assoc. Ed. **ISSN:** 1865-1674. **Subscription Rates:** US$246 individuals print and online; EUR193 individuals print and online; 129 individuals print and online; 140 other countries print and online; US$2,151 institutions print and online; 1,164 institutions print and online; US$2,507 institutions, other countries print and online; 1,058 institutions print or online; US$1,854 institutions print or online; US$2,279 institutions, other countries print or online. **Remarks:** Advertising accepted; rates available upon request. **URL:** http://www.wiley.com/bw/journal.asp?ref=1865-1674&site=1. **Formerly:** Journal of Veterinary Medicine: Series A. **Circ:** (Not Reported)

56221 ■ Transfusion Medicine
John Wiley & Sons Inc.
Wiley-Blackwell
9600 Garsington Rd.
Oxford OX4 2DQ, United Kingdom
Ph: 44 1865 776868
Fax: 44 1865 714591
Peer-reviewed journal publishing articles on transfusion medicine including blood transfusion practice. **Freq:** Bimonthly. **Key Personnel:** Maria Davie, Editorial Asst., phone 44 7968 075652, transmed.edit@gmail.com; C. Prowse, Assoc. Ed.; M. Olsson, Assoc. Ed.; J. Wallis, Assoc. Ed.; Prof. Jean-Pierre Allain, Editor, phone 44 1223 568050, fax 44 1223 548155, jpa1000@cam.ac.uk; D. Roberts, Assoc. Ed. **ISSN:** 0958-7578. **Subscription Rates:** US$208 individuals print and online; EUR170 individuals print and online; 113 individuals print and online; 124 other countries print and online; US$1,014 institutions print and online; 547 institutions print and online; 498 institutions print, online; US$1,186 institutions, other countries print and online; US$1,077 institutions, other countries print; EUR696 institutions print and online. **Remarks:** Advertising accepted; rates available upon request. **URL:** http://www.wiley.com/bw/journal.asp?ref=0958-7578&site=1. **Circ:** (Not Reported)

56222 ■ Transplant International
John Wiley & Sons Inc.
Wiley-Blackwell
9600 Garsington Rd.
Oxford OX4 2DQ, United Kingdom
Ph: 44 1865 776868
Fax: 44 1865 714591
Journal serving as a forum for the exchange of scientific

information in the form of original and high quality papers in the field of transplantation and on the biology, physiology, and immunology of transplantation of tissues and organs. **Freq:** Monthly. **Key Personnel:** Ferdinand Muhlbacher, Editor-in-Chief; Thomas Wekerle, Co-Ed.-in-Ch. **ISSN:** 0934-0874. **Subscription Rates:** US$1,436 institutions print or online; 854 institutions print or online; EUR1,085 institutions print or online; US$1,675 institutions, other countries print or online. **Remarks:** Advertising accepted; rates available upon request. **URL:** http://www.wiley.com/bw/journal.asp?ref=0934-0874. **Circ:** (Not Reported)

56223 ■ Tropical Medicine and International Health
John Wiley & Sons Inc.
Wiley-Blackwell
9600 Garsington Rd.
Oxford OX4 2DQ, United Kingdom
Ph: 44 1865 776868
Fax: 44 1865 714591
Publication E-mail: tmih@aig.umcn.nl
Journal publishing work in the field of tropical medicine and international health. **Freq:** Monthly. **Key Personnel:** H. Van Asten, Editor, h.vanasten@aig.umcn.nl; S. Jaffar, Editor, shabbar.jaffar@lshtm.ac.uk; S. Cairncross, Editor, sandy.cairncross@lshtm.ac.uk; T. Junghanss, Editor, thomas.junghanss@urz.uni-heidelberg.de; R.D. Walter, Editor, walter@bni.hamburg.de. **ISSN:** 1360-2276. **Subscription Rates:** US$141 individuals print + online; US$97 members print + online; US$1,881 institutions print + online; US$1,709 institutions print or online; US$2,198 institutions, other countries print + online; 80 individuals print + online; 1,018 institutions print + online; 925 institutions print or online; EUR1,293 institutions print + online; EUR1,175 institutions print or online. **Remarks:** Advertising accepted; rates available upon request. **URL:** http://www.wiley.com/bw/journal.asp?ref=1360-2276&site=1. **Circ:** (Not Reported)

56224 ■ The Utilities Journal
OXERA—Oxford Economic Research Associates
Park Central
40/41 Park End St.
Oxford OX1 1JD, United Kingdom
Ph: 44 18 65253000
Fax: 44 18 65251172
Publisher E-mail: enquiries@oxera.com
Journal covering developments in the utilities field for professionals. **Founded:** Jan. 1998. **Freq:** Monthly. **Trim Size:** A4. **ISSN:** 1461-0256. **Subscription Rates:** 40 single issue; 45 single issue overseas; 7.50 single issue electronic version. **Remarks:** Advertising not accepted. **URL:** http://www.oxera.com/main.aspx?id=3286. **Circ:** 1,000

56225 ■ Veterinary Anaesthesia and Analgesia
John Wiley & Sons Inc.
Wiley-Blackwell
9600 Garsington Rd.
Oxford OX4 2DQ, United Kingdom
Ph: 44 1865 776868
Fax: 44 1865 714591
Peer-reviewed journal covering all branches of anaesthesia and the pain relief in animals. **Freq:** Bimonthly. **Key Personnel:** Eddie Clutton, Editorial Board; Peter J. Pascoe, Editor, pjpascoe@ucdavis.edu; Peter Pascoe, Editor, pjpascoe@ucdavis.edu. **ISSN:** 1467-2987. **Subscription Rates:** US$733 institutions print and online; 397 institutions print and online; EUR505 institutions print and online; US$856 institutions, other countries print and online; US$666 institutions print or online; 120 individuals print and online; US$221 individuals print and online; EUR181 individuals print and online; US$131 other countries print and online. **Remarks:** Accepts advertising. **URL:** http://www.wiley.com/bw/journal.asp?ref=1467-2987. **Ad Rates:** BW: 400, 4C: 900. **Circ:** (Not Reported)

56226 ■ Veterinary and Comparative Oncology
John Wiley & Sons Inc.
Wiley-Blackwell
9600 Garsington Rd.
Oxford OX4 2DQ, United Kingdom
Ph: 44 1865 776868
Fax: 44 1865 714591
Peer-reviewed journal focusing on the clinical and scientific studies for all veterinary oncologists concerned with aetiology, diagnosis and clinical course of cancer in domestic animals and its prevention. **Freq:** Quarterly. **Key Personnel:** Prof. David Argyle, Co-Ed., david.

argyle@ed.ac.uk; James Wood, Editorial Board; Paolo Buracco, Editorial Board; Mathew Breen, Editorial Board; Tim Scase, Editorial Board; Prof. David M. Vail, Co-Ed., vaild@svm.vetmed.wisc.edu; Eva Hellmen, Editorial Board; Douglas Thamm, Editorial Board; Marlene Hauck, Editorial Board. **ISSN:** 1476-5810. **Subscription Rates:** US$173 individuals print + online; EUR141 individuals print + online; 94 individuals print + online; 103 institutions, other countries print + online; US$92 members print + online; EUR78 members print + online; 50 members print + online; US$605 institutions print + online; 327 institutions print + online; 297 institutions print, online. **Remarks:** Accepts advertising. **URL:** http://www.wiley.com/bw/journal.asp?ref=1476-5810&site=1. **Circ:** (Not Reported)

56227 ■ World Bank Research Observer
Oxford University Press
Great Clarendon St.
Oxford OX2 6DP, United Kingdom
Ph: 44 1865 556767
Fax: 44 1865 353485
Publisher E-mail: webenquiry.uk@oup.com
Journal seeking to inform non-specialist readers about research being undertaken within the bank and outside the bank in areas of economics relevant for development policy. **Freq:** Semiannual. **Key Personnel:** Luis Serven, Co-Ed.; Emmanuel Jimenez, Editor; Sudhir Shetty, Editorial Board; Ravi Kanbur, Editorial Board; Barry Eichengreen, Editorial Board; Howard Pack, Editorial Board; Luis Serven, Co-Ed. **ISSN:** 0257-3032. **Subscription Rates:** 181 institutions corporate; print and online; 151 institutions corporate; online only; 167 institutions corporate; print only; 120 institutions print and online; 100 institutions online only; 110 institutions print only; 37 individuals print; 18 members print. **Remarks:** Advertising accepted; rates available upon request. **URL:** http://wbro.oxfordjournals.org/. **Circ:** (Not Reported)

56228 ■ The World Economy
John Wiley & Sons Inc.
Wiley-Blackwell
9600 Garsington Rd.
Oxford OX4 2DQ, United Kingdom
Ph: 44 1865 776868
Fax: 44 1865 714591
Peer-reviewed journal covering economics. **Freq:** Monthly. **Key Personnel:** David Greenaway, Managing Editor, phone 44 115 9515469, fax 44 115 9515552; Michael Bleaney, Book Review Ed., phone 44 115 9515464, fax 44 115 9514159, michael.bleaney@nottingham.ac.uk; Richard Baldwin, Advisory Board. **ISSN:** 0378-5920. **Subscription Rates:** US$136 individuals print and online; EUR123 individuals print and online; 82 individuals print and online; US$116 members print and online; EUR105 members print and online; 70 members print and online; US$2,695 institutions print and online; 1,698 institutions print and online; US$2,695 institutions, other countries print and online; US$2,450 institutions, other countries print, online. **Remarks:** Accepts advertising. **URL:** http://www.wiley.com/bw/journal.asp?ref=0378-5920&site=1. **Circ:** (Not Reported)

56229 ■ The Yale Review
John Wiley & Sons Inc.
Wiley-Blackwell
9600 Garsington Rd.
Oxford OX4 2DQ, United Kingdom
Ph: 44 1865 776868
Fax: 44 1865 714591
Journal covering literature and writing. **Freq:** Quarterly. **Key Personnel:** J.D. McClatchy, Editor, phone 203432-0499, fax 203432-0510, yalerev@yale.edu; Susan Bianconi, Managing Editor, susan.bianconi@yale.edu; Claude Rawson, Editorial Board. **ISSN:** 0044-0124. **Subscription Rates:** US$34 individuals print + online; EUR55 individuals print + online; 37 other countries print + online; US$166 institutions print + online; 128 institutions print + online; EUR162 institutions print + online; US$251 institutions, other countries print and online; US$151 institutions print or online; 116 institutions print or online; US$227 institutions, other countries print or online. **Remarks:** Accepts advertising. **Online:** Gale. **URL:** http://www.wiley.com/bw/journal.asp?ref=0044-0124&site=1. **Circ:** (Not Reported)

56230 ■ Zoonoses and Public Health
John Wiley & Sons Inc.
Wiley-Blackwell
9600 Garsington Rd.
Oxford OX4 2DQ, United Kingdom
Ph: 44 1865 776868

Fax: 44 1865 714591
Journal covering all aspects of veterinary microbiology and parasitology. **Freq:** 8/yr. **Key Personnel:** Prof. Klaus Osterrieder, Assoc. Ed.; Mary Torrence, Editor-in-Chief; Richard Isaacson, Assoc. Ed.; Katherine A. Feldman, Assoc. Ed.; Phillip Tarr, Assoc. Ed.; Gareth Watkins, Editorial Asst., gwatkins@wiley.com. **ISSN:** 1863-1959. **Subscription Rates:** US$246 individuals print + online; US$2,151 institutions print + online; US$1,954 institutions print or online; US$2,507 institutions, other countries print + online; EUR193 individuals print + online; 1,164 institutions print + online; 1,058 institutions print or online; EUR1,479 institutions print + online; EUR1,344 institutions print or online; US$2,279 institutions, other countries print or online. **Remarks:** Advertising accepted; rates available upon request. **URL:** http://www.wiley.com/bw/journal.asp?ref=1863-1959&site=1. **Formerly:** Journal of Veterinary Medicine Series B. **Circ:** (Not Reported)

56231 ■ Zygon
John Wiley & Sons Inc.
Wiley-Blackwell
9600 Garsington Rd.
Oxford OX4 2DQ, United Kingdom
Ph: 44 1865 776868
Fax: 44 1865 714591
Journal covering philosophy and religion. **Subtitle:** Journal of Religion & Science. **Freq:** Quarterly. **Key Personnel:** Karl E. Peters, Editor, phone 860653-3754; Philip Hefner, Editor, phone 773256-0671, fax 773256-0682, pnhefner@sbcglobal.net; Peggy Blomenberg, Exec. Ed. **ISSN:** 0591-2385. **Subscription Rates:** US$82 individuals print and online; EUR107 individuals print and online; 71 individuals print and online; US$66 members print and online; EUR84 members print and online; 56 members print and online; US$263 institutions print and online; 240 institutions print and online; US$470 institutions, other countries print and online; EUR304 institutions print and online. **Remarks:** Accepts advertising. **Online:** Gale. **URL:** http://www.wiley.com/bw/journal.asp?ref=0591-2385&site=1. **Circ:** (Not Reported)

56232 ■ BBC Radio Oxford-FM - 95.2
269 Banbury Rd.
Oxford OX2 7DW, United Kingdom
Ph: 44 8459 311444
Fax: 44 8459 311555
E-mail: oxford@bbc.co.uk
Format: Talk; News; Oldies; Sports; Eclectic; Jazz; Folk; Blues; Big Band/Nostalgia; Country. **Owner:** British Broadcasting Corporation, Broadcasting House, Portland Pl., London W1A 1AA, United Kingdom. **Operating Hours:** 5 a.m.-10 p.m. weekdays; 6 a.m.-9 p.m. Sat. 6 a.m.-10 p.m. Sun. **URL:** http://news.bbc.co.uk/local/oxford/hi/tv_and_radio/.

56233 ■ Heart-FM - 97.4
Radio House
Pony Rd.
Cowley
Oxford OX4 2XR, United Kingdom
Ph: 44 1865 871000
Format: Contemporary Hit Radio (CHR). **Formerly:** Fox-FM. **URL:** http://www.heart.co.uk/oxfordshire/.

56234 ■ Oxford-FM - 107.9
270 Woodstock Rd.
Oxford OX2 7NW, United Kingdom
Ph: 44 870 4441079
E-mail: studio@fm1079.com
Format: Urban Contemporary. **URL:** http://www.fm1079.co.uk/.

Oxted

56235 ■ Biscuit World
Crier Media Group Ltd.
1st Fl. Offices
1-3 Station Rd. E
Limpsfield
Oxted RH8 0BD, United Kingdom
Publisher E-mail: jennie@crier.co.uk
Trade magazine covering machinery, ingredients and processes for biscuit processors worldwide. **Founded:** May 1997. **Freq:** Weekly. **Trim Size:** 210 x 297 mm. **Key Personnel:** Andre Erasmus, Editor. **Subscription Rates:** 60 individuals; 96 two years; EUR89 individuals; EUR142 two years; US$122 individuals; US$195 two years. **Remarks:** Accepts advertising. **URL:** http://www.worldbakers.com/. **Ad Rates:** BW: 1,630, 4C: 2,750. **Circ:** 4,335

56236 ■ Drinks Network
Crier Media Group Ltd.
1st Fl. Office
1-3 Station Rd. E
Limpsfield
Oxted RH8 0BD, United Kingdom
Ph: 44 1883 734582
Fax: 44 1883 713640
Publisher E-mail: jennie@crier.co.uk
Trade magazine covering drink buying. **Freq:** 10/yr. **Key Personnel:** Jennie Puxty, Admin., jennie@crier.co.uk; Andre Erasmus, Editor, andre@crier.co.uk; Evie Serventi, Dep. Ed., evie@crier.co.uk. **ISSN:** 1468-6902. **Subscription Rates:** 130 individuals; EUR192 individuals; EUR247 individuals; 235 two years; EUR348 two years; US$447 two years. **Remarks:** Accepts advertising. **URL:** http://www.crier.co.uk/drinks.php. **Formerly:** Drinks Buyer - Asia Pacific. **Ad Rates:** BW: 1,900, 4C: 2,750. **Circ:** Combined ‡21,000

56237 ■ Potato Processing International
Crier Media Group Ltd.
1-3 Station Rd. E, 1st Fl.
Limpsfield
Surrey
Oxted RH8 0BD, United Kingdom
Ph: 44 1883 734582
Fax: 44 1883 713640
Publisher E-mail: jennie@crier.co.uk
Professional magazine for potato processors, covering news, product updates, features, machinery and plant visits. **Founded:** Apr. 1992. **Freq:** Bimonthly. **Print Method:** Offset. **Trim Size:** 210 x 297 mm. **Cols./Page:** 3. **Col. Width:** 50 millimeters. **Col. Depth:** 240 millimeters. **Key Personnel:** Robert Goldring, Production Mgr.; Jennie Puxty, Admin.; Andre Erasmus, Editor; Ivana Hromin, Sales Mgr. **Subscription Rates:** 85 individuals; EUR126 individuals; EUR173 individuals; 145 two years; EUR215 two years; US$294 two years. **Remarks:** Accepts advertising. **URL:** http://www.potatobusiness.com/. **Ad Rates:** BW: 1,850, 4C: 1,850. **Circ:** Controlled ‡3,616

Paddock Wood

56238 ■ Plastics & Rubber Asia
The Stables
Willow Ln.
Paddock Wood TN12 6PF, United Kingdom
Ph: 44 1892 839200
Fax: 44 1892 839210
Publisher E-mail: tim@plasticsandrubberasia.com
Business publication. **Freq:** 8/yr. **Key Personnel:** Arthur Schavemaker, Publisher. **ISSN:** 1360-1245. **Remarks:** Accepts advertising. **URL:** http://plasticsandrubberasia.com. **Ad Rates:** BW: 4,500, 4C: 6,220. **Circ:** (Not Reported)

Paisley

56239 ■ BAPOMAG
British Association of Prosthetists and Orthotists
Sir James Clark Bldg.
Paisley PA1 1TJ, United Kingdom
Ph: 44 141 5617217
Publication covering orthotics and prosthetics. **Freq:** Periodic 3/yr. **Trim Size:** A4. **Remarks:** Accepts advertising. **URL:** http://www.bapo.org/site/content/view/44/75/. **Ad Rates:** 4C: 650. **Circ:** (Not Reported)

56240 ■ Journal of the Law Society of Scotland
Law Society of Scotland
Connect Communications
Studio 2001, Mile End
Paisley PA1 1JS, United Kingdom
Ph: 44 141 5610300
Fax: 44 141 5610400
Publisher E-mail: lawscot@lawscot.org.uk
Journal covering the Law Society of Scotland. **Freq:** Monthly. **Key Personnel:** Peter Nicholson, Editor, phone 44 141 5603018, peter@connectcommunications.co.uk. **ISSN:** 0458-8711. **Subscription Rates:** 84 individuals; 108 other countries; Free trainees. **Remarks:** Advertising accepted; rates available upon request. **URL:** http://www.journalonline.co.uk/. **Circ:** ∗11,477

Penarth

56241 ■ Reviews in Clinical Gerontology
Cambridge University Press
c/o Dr. Antony Bayer, Ed.-in-Ch.

University Dept. of Geriatric Medicine
Cardiff University, 3rd Fl., Academic Center
University Hospital Llandough
Penarth CF64 2XX, United Kingdom
Publication E-mail: bayer@cf.ac.uk
Publisher E-mail: information@cambridge.org
Journal publishing latest developments in geriatric medicine and in biological, psychological and social gerontology, including current developments in rehabilitation, nursing care and psychiatry of old age. **Freq:** Quarterly. **Key Personnel:** Dr. Anthony Bayer, Editor-in-Chief. **ISSN:** 0959-2598. **Subscription Rates:** 345 institutions online and print; US$610 institutions online and print. **Remarks:** Accepts advertising. **URL:** http://journals.cambridge.org/action/displayJournal?jid=RCG. **Ad Rates:** BW: 385. **Circ:** 400

Penicuik

56242 ■ Agricultural and Forest Entomolgy
John Wiley & Sons Inc.
Wiley-Blackwell
c/o Dr. Allan D. Watt, Ed.
Center for Ecology & Hydrology
Bush Estate
Midlothian
Penicuik EH26 0QB, United Kingdom
Ph: 44 131 4454343
Fax: 44 131 4453943
Journal focusing on all aspects of agricultural and forest entomology to other researchers, policy makers and professionals. **Freq:** Quarterly. **Key Personnel:** Dr. Allan D. Watt, Editor, adw@ceh.ac.uk; Hugh Evans, Editorial Board, h.evans@forestry.gov.uk; Mark Fellowes, Editorial Board, m.fellowes@reading.ac.uk; Hefin Jones, Editor, jonesth@cardiff.ac.uk; Joseph C. Dickens, Editorial Board, jdickens@asrr.arsusda.gov; Keith R. Day, Editorial Board, kr.day@ulst.ac.uk; Richard Harrington, Editorial Board, richard.harrington@bbsrc.ac.uk; Gary P. Fitt, Editorial Board, garyf@mv.pi.csiro.au. **ISSN:** 1461-9555. **Subscription Rates:** US$212 individuals print and online; EUR173 individuals print and online (Euro zone); 117 individuals print and online (non Euro zone); 127 other countries print and online; US$1,200 institutions, other countries print or online; US$1,029 institutions print or online; 557 institutions print or online; EUR708 institutions print or online. **Remarks:** Accepts advertising. **URL:** http://www.wiley.com/bw/journal.asp?ref=1461-9555&site=1. **Circ:** (Not Reported)

56243 ■ Animal
British Society of Animal Science
PO Box 3
Penicuik EH26 0RZ, United Kingdom
Ph: 44 13 14454508
Fax: 44 13 15353120
Publisher E-mail: bsas@sac.ac.uk
Publication covering animal science. **Freq:** Bimonthly. **Key Personnel:** Michel Doreau, Editor-in-Chief. **ISSN:** 1357-7298. **Remarks:** Advertising not accepted. **URL:** http://www.bsas.org.uk/Publications/Animal/; http://www.animal-journal.eu/. **Formerly:** Animal Science (July 2, 2000). **Circ:** Combined 10,400

Penistone

56244 ■ Dearne-FM - 97.1
Unit 7, Network Ctr.
Zenith Pk.
Whaley Rd.
Barnsley S75 1HT, United Kingdom
Ph: 44 1226 321733
Fax: 44 1226 321755
E-mail: enquiries@dearnefm.co.uk
Format: Full Service. **Ad Rates:** Advertising accepted; rates available upon request. **URL:** http://www.dearnefm.co.uk/.

Penrith

56245 ■ Horizons
Institute for Outdoor Learning
The Barn
Plumpton Old Hall
Plumpton
Penrith CA11 9NP, United Kingdom
Ph: 44 1768 885800
Fax: 44 1768 885801

Publisher E-mail: institute@outdoor-learning.org
Publication covering education. **Freq:** Quarterly. **Key Personnel:** Fiona Exon, Contact, fiona@outdoor-learning.org. **ISSN:** 1462-0677. **Subscription Rates:** 21 members; 25 members Europe; 35 members rest of World; 35 individuals; 40 individuals Europe; 45 other countries. **URL:** http://www.outdoor-learning.org/our_publications/horizons/index.htm. **Ad Rates:** 4C: 790. **Circ:** (Not Reported)

56246 ■ Journal of Adventure Education and Outdoor Learning
Institute for Outdoor Learning
The Barn
Plumpton Old Hall
Plumpton
Penrith CA11 9NP, United Kingdom
Ph: 44 1768 885800
Fax: 44 1768 885801
Publication E-mail: jaeol@outdoor-learning.org
Publisher E-mail: institute@outdoor-learning.org
Peer-reviewed journal promoting dialogue, research, thinking, understanding, teaching and practice in the field of adventure education and outdoor learning. **Freq:** Semiannual. **Key Personnel:** Barbara Humberstone, Editor; Linda Allin, Editor; Nic Tucker-Welton, Editor. **ISSN:** 1472-9679. **Subscription Rates:** 102 institutions; 105 libraries in Europe; 110 institutions, other countries; 24 individuals; 25 individuals in Europe; 26 other countries. **URL:** http://www.outdoor-learning.org/our_publications/jaeol/index.htm.

56247 ■ CFM Radio-FM - 102.5
PO Box 964
Carlisle CA1 3NG, United Kingdom
Ph: 44 1228 818964
Format: Contemporary Hit Radio (CHR). **URL:** http://www.cfmradio.com/.

Penzance

56248 ■ Cornish World
Cornish World Media
Jennings House
Jennings St.
Penzance TR18 2LU, United Kingdom
Ph: 44 17 36365896
Fax: 44 17 36330538
Publisher E-mail: editor@cornish-world.fsnet.co.uk
Consumer magazine covering Cornish heritage and genealogy. **Founded:** 1994. **Freq:** Bimonthly. **Print Method:** Litho. **Key Personnel:** Philip Hosken, Editor. **Subscription Rates:** 24 individuals; 30 individuals overseas. **Remarks:** Accepts advertising. **URL:** http://www.cornishworldmagazine.co.uk/. **Ad Rates:** 4C: 500. **Circ:** Paid 5,000

56249 ■ Inside Cornwall
Creative Copy
2-4 The Fradgan
Newlyn
Penzance TR18 5BE, United Kingdom
Ph: 44 17 36334800
Fax: 44 17 36334808
Publisher E-mail: mail@insidecornwall.co.uk
Consumer magazine covering local arts, food, gardens and entertainment. **Subtitle:** Arts, Gardens, Food & Top Events. **Founded:** 1990. **Freq:** Monthly. **Print Method:** Sheetfed offset. **Key Personnel:** Mawgan Lewis, Creative Dir., mawgan@insidecornwall.co.uk; Alison Waghorn, Managing Editor, alison@insidecornwall.co.uk; Ian Waghorn, Publisher, ian@insidecornwall.co.uk; Kathy Hill, Editor, kathy@insidecornwall.co.uk. **ISSN:** 7713-6258. **Subscription Rates:** 27 individuals includes postage, packaging & priority delivery. **Remarks:** Accepts advertising. **URL:** http://www.insidecornwall.co.uk/. **Circ:** Paid 8,000

56250 ■ Songwriting and Composing Magazine
Guild of International Songwriters and Composers
Sovereign House
12 Trewartha Rd.
Praa Sands
Penzance TR20 9ST, United Kingdom
Ph: 44 17 36762826
Fax: 44 17 36763328
Publisher E-mail: songmag@aol.com
Publication covering general music industry topics, including contacts, publishing, and record company

reviews for songwriters, composers, and performing musicians. **Subtitle:** The Magazine for International Songwriters and Composers. **Founded:** 1986. **Freq:** Quarterly. **Subscription Rates:** Free to all members. **Remarks:** Advertising not accepted. **URL:** http://www.songwriters-guild.co.uk/songcompose.htm. **Circ:** 10,000

56251 ■ Ultrafit
Ultrafit Publications
Champions House
5 Princes St.
Penzance TR18 2NL, United Kingdom
Ph: 44 173 6350204
Fax: 44 173 6368587
Consumer magazine covering fitness and sports, including nutrition, fitness equipment and training techniques. **Founded:** 1984. **Freq:** Monthly 8/yr. **Print Method:** Web offset. **Trim Size:** 210 x 297 mm. **Key Personnel:** Charles Mays, Publisher. **Subscription Rates:** 18 individuals for U.K.; 24.82 two years for U.K.; 38.73 individuals 3 years; for U.K. **Remarks:** Accepts advertising. **URL:** http://www.ultra-fitmagazine.co.uk/. **Ad Rates:** 4C: 2,000. **Circ:** Combined 50,000

Peterborough

56252 ■ Bird Watching
H. Bauer Publishing
Media House
Lynchwood
Peterborough PE2 6EA, United Kingdom
Ph: 44 1733 468201
Magazine for bird watchers. **Freq:** Monthly. **Key Personnel:** Sheena Harvey, Editor; Trevor Ward, Art Ed.; Jayne Phillips, Commercial Mgr. **Subscription Rates:** EUR35 individuals direct debit; EUR51.35 individuals credit/debit card. **URL:** http://www.greatmagazines.co.uk/store/displaystore.asp?sid=329.

56253 ■ British Sugar Beet Review
British Sugar PLC
Sugar Way
Peterborough PE2 9AY, United Kingdom
Ph: 44 1733 422106
Publication E-mail: beetreview@britishsugar.com
Publisher E-mail: beetreview@britishsugar.com
Technical magazine covering sugar beet production for growers in the UK. **Freq:** Quarterly. **Print Method:** Litho. **Key Personnel:** Robin Limbs, Editor; Denise Chandler, Asst. Ed. **Remarks:** Accepts advertising. **URL:** http://www.beetreview.co.uk/Login.asp. **Ad Rates:** BW: 1,402, 4C: 1,977. **Circ:** Non-paid 14,000

56254 ■ Classic Car Weekly
Kelsey Publishing Ltd.
Bauer Consumer Media Ltd.
Media House
Lynch Wood
Peterborough PE1 1JA, United Kingdom
Publication E-mail: editorial@classiccarweekly.co.uk
Publisher E-mail: info@kelsey.co.uk
Newspaper containing news, information and advertisements about classic cars. **Subtitle:** Buying,Selling,News. **Founded:** 1990. **Freq:** Weekly. **Key Personnel:** Matt Carson, Advertising Mgr. **Subscription Rates:** 48.50 individuals 6 months; 92 individuals; 137 other countries. **Remarks:** Accepts advertising. **URL:** http://www.classic-car-weekly.co.uk. **Circ:** (Not Reported)

56255 ■ Custom Car Magazine
Kelsey Publishing Ltd.
PO Box 978
Peterborough PE1 1JA, United Kingdom
Publisher E-mail: info@kelsey.co.uk
Lifestyle magazine for hot rod, custom and drag racing enthusiasts. **Founded:** Mar. 1970. **Freq:** Monthly. **Key Personnel:** David Biggadyke, Editor, cc.ed@kelsey.co.uk; Gavin Williams, Advertising Mgr., cc.adsales@kelsey.co.uk. **Subscription Rates:** 43.92 individuals; 49.44 individuals in Europe; 54.96 other countries. **Remarks:** Accepts advertising. **URL:** http://www.customcarmag.co.uk/. **Circ:** (Not Reported)

56256 ■ The Essential Guide to UK Farm & Outdoor Power Equipment
Agricultural Engineers' Association
Samuelson House
62 Forder Way
Hampton
Peterborough PE7 8JB, United Kingdom

Circulation: ★ = ABC; △ = BPA; ♦ = CAC; • = CCAB; ❑ = VAC; ⊕ = PO Statement; ‡ = Publisher's Report; Boldface figures = sworn; Light figures = estimated.

Gale Directory of Publications & Broadcast Media/147th Ed.   5839

Ph: 44 845 6448748
Fax: 44 1733 314767
Publisher E-mail: ab@aea.uk.com
British agricultural outdoor power equipment guide in English, French, German and Spanish. **Freq:** Biennial In January and July. **Remarks:** Advertising not accepted. **URL:** http://www.aea.uk.com/export/export.htm. **Formerly:** British Farm and Outdoor Power Equipment Guide. **Circ:** (Not Reported)

56257 ■ Fall-Line Skiing
Fall.Line Media Limited
S Wing, Broadway Ct.
Peterborough PE1 1RP, United Kingdom
Ph: 44 1733 293250
Fax: 44 1733 293269
Publisher E-mail: info@fall-line.co.uk
Magazine featuring skiing. **Key Personnel:** Jonny Richards, Editor; Richard Fincher, Publisher, richard@fall-line.co.uk; Susan Williams, Office Mgr. **URL:** http://www.fall-line.co.uk/.

56258 ■ The Garden
Royal Horticultural Society
4th Fl., Churchgate, New Rd.
Peterborough PE1 1TT, United Kingdom
Ph: 44 84 52600909
Fax: 44 17 33341633
Publication E-mail: thegarden@rhs.org.uk
Publisher E-mail: info@rhs.org.uk
Journal covering the Royal Horticulture Society. **Freq:** Monthly. **Key Personnel:** Ian Hodgson, Editor. **Remarks:** Advertising accepted; rates available upon request. **URL:** http://www.rhs.org.uk/Plants/RHS-Publications/Journals/The-Garden. **Circ:** (Not Reported)

56259 ■ Peterborough Evening Telegraph
Johnston Press PLC
57 Priestgate
Peterborough PE1 1JW, United Kingdom
Ph: 44 1733 555111
Fax: 44 1733 313147
Publication E-mail: news@peterboroughtoday.co.uk
Local community newspaper. **Freq:** Mon.-Sat. **Key Personnel:** Richard Kendall, Web Ed., richard.kendall@peterboroughtoday.co.uk. **Remarks:** Accepts advertising. **URL:** http://www.peterboroughtoday.co.uk/. **Circ:** (Not Reported)

56260 ■ Railways Illustrated
Ian Allan Publishing Ltd.
PO Box 877
Peterborough PE2 2BD, United Kingdom
Publisher E-mail: info@ianallanpublishing.co.uk
Magazine offering editorial content and photographic coverage of the railway scene, covering all news aspects from the UK, with each issue containing news from the railway network and national train operators, as well as featuring main line steam, heritage operations and the principal private railway sites. **Freq:** Monthly. **Key Personnel:** Pip Dunn, Editor, pip.dunn@eastfieldmedia.com. **Remarks:** Accepts advertising. **URL:** http://www.railwaysillustrated.com. **Circ:** (Not Reported)

56261 ■ Sign Directions
British Sign & Graphics Association
5 Orton Enterprise Ctr.
Bakewell Rd.
Orton Southgate
Peterborough PE2 6XU, United Kingdom
Ph: 44 1733 230033
Publisher E-mail: info@bsga.co.uk
Publication covering advertising. **Freq:** 8/yr. **Trim Size:** 210 x 297 mm. **Key Personnel:** Val Hirst, Publisher, phone 44 1623 882398, signdirections@btconnect.com; Mike Connolly, Dep. Ed., phone 44 1306 885430, themc@btinternet.com. **Remarks:** Advertising accepted; rates available upon request. **URL:** http://www.bsga.co.uk; http://www.bsga.co.uk/sd_web/sd_index.html. **Circ:** ★7,302

56262 ■ Skydive
Skydive Mag
5 Station Rd.
Ailsworth
Peterborough PE7 5AH, United Kingdom
Publication E-mail: editor@skydivemag.com
Publisher E-mail: editor@skydivemag.com
Magazine of the British Parachute Association covering skydiving. **Subtitle:** The Mag. **Founded:** 1961. **Freq:**

Bimonthly. **Print Method:** Sheetfed offset. **Trim Size:** A4. **Key Personnel:** Liz Ashley, Editor, editor@skydivethemag.com. **Subscription Rates:** 25 individuals U.K. and U.S.; EUR30 individuals Europe; 40 other countries. **Remarks:** Accepts advertising. **URL:** http://www.skydivemag.com. **Former name:** Sport Parachutist. **Ad Rates:** GLR: 15, BW: 255, 4C: 600. **Circ:** Combined ‡6,000

56263 ■ Veterinary Times
Veterinary Business Development Ltd.
Olympus House
Werrington Center
Peterborough PE4 6NA, United Kingdom
Ph: 44 1733 325522
Fax: 44 1733 352512
Professional magazine for the veterinary field. **Freq:** 48/yr. **Key Personnel:** Paul Imrie, Editor, phone 44 1733 383554, paulimrie@vbd.uk.com; Darren Taylor, Production Mgr., phone 44 1733 383542, darrentaylor@vbd.com. **Subscription Rates:** 145 individuals 6 months (surface mail); 175 individuals; 270 elsewhere surface mail; 95 individuals 6 months. **Remarks:** Accepts advertising. **URL:** http://www.vbd.co.uk/. **Circ:** (Not Reported)

56264 ■ Connect-FM - 97.2
5 Church St., 2nd Fl.
Peterborough PE1 1XB, United Kingdom
Ph: 44 844 8001769
E-mail: studio@connectfm.com
Format: Adult Contemporary; Top 40; Full Service; Oldies. **Operating Hours:** 6 a.m.-12 a.m. weekdays; 7 a.m.-12 a.m. Weekend. **Key Personnel:** Gregg Nunney, Prog. Controller, gregg@connectfm.com. **Ad Rates:** Advertising accepted; rates available upon request. **URL:** http://www.connectfm.com/.

56265 ■ Connect-FM - 107.4
2nd Fl., 5 Church St.
Peterborough PE1 1XB, United Kingdom
Ph: 44 1733 704113
Format: Adult Contemporary. **URL:** http://www.connectfm.com/.

56266 ■ Lite-FM - 106.8
5 Church St., 2nd Fl.
Peterborough PE1 1XB, United Kingdom
Ph: 44 1733 898106
Format: Adult Contemporary; Contemporary Hit Radio (CHR); Eighties. **URL:** http://www.lite1068.com/.

Petersfield

56267 ■ Petersfield Post
Johnston Press PLC
33 High St.
Petersfield GU32 3JR, United Kingdom
Ph: 44 1730 232600
Local community newspaper. **Freq:** Weekly (Wed.). **Key Personnel:** Graeme Moir, Editor, phone 44 1730 232606, fax 44 1730 266721, graeme.moir@thepost.co.uk; Jo Barlow, Advertising Sales, phone 44 1730 232603, fax 44 1730 266721, jo.barlow@thepost.co.uk. **Remarks:** Accepts advertising. **URL:** http://www.petersfieldpost.co.uk/. **Circ:** (Not Reported)

Pevensey

56268 ■ Pet Talk
Bay View Publishing
PO Box 109
Pevensey BN24 9AA, United Kingdom
Ph: 44 1323 767804
Publisher E-mail: enquiries@pet-talk.co.uk
Magazine featuring pets and animals. **Freq:** Bimonthly. **Remarks:** Accepts advertising. **URL:** http://www.pet-talk.co.uk. **Circ:** (Not Reported)

Pewsey

56269 ■ Army Families Federation Families Journal
Army Families Federation
Trenchard Lines
Upavon
Pewsey SN9 6BE, United Kingdom
Ph: 44 1980 615525
Fax: 44 1980 615526
Publication E-mail: info@afj.org.uk

Publisher E-mail: us@aff.org.uk
Journal covering unique lifestyle of military families. **Founded:** 1990. **Freq:** Quarterly. **Key Personnel:** Catharine Moss, Editor. **Subscription Rates:** Free to Army families. **Remarks:** Advertising accepted; rates available upon request. **URL:** http://www.army.mod.uk. **Formerly:** Army Wives Journal; Army Families Journal. **Circ:** 64,000

Plymouth

56270 ■ The Hydrographic Journal
International Federation of Hydrographic Societies
PO Box 103
Plymouth PL4 7YP, United Kingdom
Ph: 44 1752 223512
Fax: 44 1752 223512
Publisher E-mail: helen@hydrographicsociety.org
Journal covering surveying. **Founded:** 1972. **Freq:** Quarterly January, April, July and October. **Trim Size:** A4. **Key Personnel:** David Goodfellow, Contact. **ISSN:** 0309-7846. **Subscription Rates:** 65 nonmembers. **Remarks:** Accepts advertising. **URL:** http://www.hydrographicsociety.org. **Ad Rates:** 4C: 1,050. **Circ:** 2,000

56271 ■ International Journal for Technology in Mathematics Education
Research Information Ltd.
Centre for Teaching Mathematics
University of Plymouth
Drake Circus
Plymouth PL4 8AA, United Kingdom
Publication E-mail: jtombs@plymouth.ac.uk
Publisher E-mail: info@researchinformation.co.uk
Journal publishing articles about the use of computer algebra systems in teaching and learning mathematics. **Freq:** Quarterly. **Key Personnel:** Stewart Townend, Asst. Ed., s.townend@plymouth.ac.uk; Dr. Ted Graham, Editor, e.graham@plymouth.ac.uk; Dr. Paul Drijvers, Asst. Ed., p.drijvers@fi.uu.nl; Prof. John Berry, Asst. Ed., j.berry@plymouth.ac.uk; Kathleen M. Heid, Asst. Ed., ik8@psu.edu; Prof. Kaye Stacey, Asst. Ed., k.stacey@edfac.unimelb.edu.au; John Monaghan, Asst. Ed., j.d.monaghan@education.leeds.ac.uk; Robert Mayes, Asst. Ed., rmayes@math.wvu.edu. **ISSN:** 1744-2710. **Subscription Rates:** US$448 individuals; 224 individuals. **Remarks:** Advertising not accepted. **URL:** http://www.researchinformation.co.uk/time.php. **Circ:** (Not Reported)

56272 ■ Journal of the Marine Biological Association of the United Kingdom (JMBA)
Cambridge University Press
c/o Dr. P.R. Dando, Ed.-in-Ch.
Plymouth Marine Laboratory
Citadel Hill
Plymouth PL1 2PB, United Kingdom
Publisher E-mail: customer_service@cup.org
Journal of marine biology. **Founded:** 1990. **Freq:** Bimonthly. **Key Personnel:** Dr. P.R. Dando, Editor-in-Chief, journal@mba.ac.uk; Prof. J.A. Raven, Assoc. Ed., j.a.raven@dundee.ac.uk; Dr. B. Bett, Editorial Board; Dr. Ann L. Pulsford, Exec. Ed., jmba@mba.eclipse.co.uk. **ISSN:** 0025-3154. **Subscription Rates:** 822 institutions online; 988 institutions print & online; US$1,400 institutions online only; US$1,710 institutions print & online. **Remarks:** Accepts display advertising. **URL:** http://journals.cambridge.org/action/displayJournal?jid=MBI. **Ad Rates:** BW: 520. **Circ:** 1,600

56273 ■ TAG Bulletin
Technical Advisors Group
Roy Fairclough Consultancy
County House
12/13 Sussex St.
Plymouth PL1 2HR, United Kingdom
Ph: 44 17 52213665
Fax: 44 17 52222678
Publisher E-mail: tag@rfconsultancy.co.uk
Magazine containing information for members of the Technical Advisors Group. **Freq:** Quarterly. **Remarks:** Accepts advertising. **URL:** http://www.tagonline.co.uk/. **Circ:** (Not Reported)

56274 ■ Thinking & Reasoning
Psychology Press
c/o Jonathan St. Evans, Ed.
Center for Thinking & Language
Dept. of Psychology

University of Plymouth
Plymouth PL4 8AA, United Kingdom
Peer-reviewed journal devoted to the understanding of human thought processes, with particular focus on studies on reasoning. **Freq:** Quarterly. **Key Personnel:** Jonathan St. Evans, Editor, j.evans@plymouth.ac.uk; Ken Gilhooly, Assoc. Ed.; Ben Newell, Assoc. Ed.; David Over, Assoc. Ed. **ISSN:** 1354-6783. **Subscription Rates:** US$293 individuals personal; US$556 institutions online only; US$618 institutions print & online. **URL:** http://www.tandf.co.uk/journals/titles/13546783.asp.

56275 ■ Tremblestone
Stowford House
43 Seymour Ave.
St. Judes
Plymouth PL4 8RB, United Kingdom
Magazine featuring contemporary poetry. **Founded:** Nov. 1999. **ISSN:** 1463-9181. **URL:** http://www.tremblestone.co.uk/.

56276 ■ Western Morning News
West Country Publications Ltd.
17 Brest Rd.
Derriford Business Pk.
Plymouth PL6 5AA, United Kingdom
Ph: 44 17 52765500
Regional morning newspaper serving the South West of England. **Freq:** Mon.-Sat. **Key Personnel:** Alan Qualtrough, Editor, aqualtrough@westernmorningnews.co.uk; Phillip Bowern, Dep. Ed., pbowern@westernmorningnews.co.uk; Steve Grant, News Ed., sgrant@westernmorningnews.co.uk; David Wells, Night News Ed., dwells@westernmorningnews.co.uk; Eleanor McGillie, Dep. News Ed., emcgillie@westernmorningnews.co.uk; Scott Harrison, Web Ed., sharrison@westernmorningnews.co.uk; Loiuse Vennels, Sen. Reporter, lvennells@westernmorningnews.co.uk; Jackie Butler, Dep. Features Ed., jbutler@westernmorningnews.co.uk; Emma Corlett, Asst. Ed., ecorlett@westernmorningnews.co.uk; David Wilcock, Asst. News Ed., dwilcock@westernmorningnews.co.uk. **Subscription Rates:** 296 individuals 6 days per week; 338 individuals 5 days per week; 312 individuals 4 days per week; 234 individuals 3 days per week; 208 individuals 2 days per week; 104 individuals 1 day per week; 3 individuals Europe (overseas); 5 individuals other overseas; 148 individuals 6 days per week (six months); 169 individuals 5 days per week (six months). **Remarks:** Accepts advertising. **URL:** http://www.thisiswesternmorningnews.co.uk/. **Circ:** (Not Reported)

56277 ■ Heart-FM - 97
Earl's Acre
Plymouth PL3 4HX, United Kingdom
Ph: 44 1752 275600
Fax: 44 1752 275609
Format: Adult Contemporary. **Formerly:** Plymouth Sound-FM. **Operating Hours:** Continuous. **Key Personnel:** Victoria Ford, Mng. Dir., phone 44 1752 275611, victoria.ford@heart.co.uk; Claire Troughton, Sales Mgr., phone 44 1752 275616, claire.troughton@heart.co.uk; Richard Spencer, Prog. Controller, phone 44 1752 275625, richard.spencer@heart.co.uk. **Ad Rates:** Advertising accepted; rates available upon request. **URL:** http://www.heartplymouth.co.uk/.

Pontypridd

56278 ■ GT-FM - 107.9
Pinewood Studios
Pinewood Ave.
Rhydyfelin
Pontypridd CF37 5EA, United Kingdom
Ph: 44 1443 406111
E-mail: mail@gtfm.co.uk
Format: Easy Listening; Top 40; Blues; Eclectic; News; Oldies. **Founded:** 1999. **Operating Hours:** Continuous. **Key Personnel:** Dave Jones, Chm.; Mary Traynor, Co. Sec. **Ad Rates:** Advertising accepted; rates available upon request. **URL:** http://www.gtfm.co.uk/.

Poole

56279 ■ Black Theology
Orca Journals
Stanley House

3 Fleets Ln.
Poole BH15 3AJ, United Kingdom
Ph: 44 12 02785712
Fax: 44 12 02666219
Publisher E-mail: journals@orcabookservices.co.uk
Journal providing a forum for the articulation and expression of issues of faith amongst black people across the world with contributors reflecting on their faith in relation to African, Caribbean, American or Asian origins and other contexts relevant to the black experience. **Subtitle:** An International Journal. **Freq:** Semiannual. **Key Personnel:** Michael N. Jagessar, Reviews Ed.; Dr. Anthony G. Reddie, Editor; Joe Aldred, Editorial Board. **Subscription Rates:** 20 individuals U.K./Europe/rest of World; 60 institutions U.K./Europe/rest of World; 25 individuals U.K./Europe/rest of World (special parish); US$30 individuals; US$90 institutions; US$39.50 individuals 3 copies per parish. **Remarks:** Advertising accepted; rates available upon request. **URL:** http://web.ukonline.co.uk/blacktheology/journal.htm. **Formerly:** Black Theology in Britain. **Circ:** (Not Reported)

56280 ■ Boys Toys
Freestyle Publications Ltd.
Alexander House
Ling Rd.
Tower Pk.
Poole BH12 4NZ, United Kingdom
Ph: 44 1202 735090
Publication E-mail: boystoys@freestyle-group.com
Publisher E-mail: enquiries@freestyle-group.com
Men's lifestyle magazine covering everything from essential gadgets to the meanest motors, via the latest in home entertainment, fashion, and adventure. **Founded:** 1999. **Freq:** Monthly. **Key Personnel:** Tom Perkins, Editor, tperkins@freestyle-group.com; Christian Dickinson, Advertising Mgr., christian.dickinson@freestyle-group.com. **Subscription Rates:** 45.60 individuals; 90 individuals Europe; 120 other countries. **URL:** http://www.boystoys.com/. **Circ:** 55,000

56281 ■ Practical Boat Owner
Time Inc.
IPC Media Ltd.
Westover House
West Quay Rd.
Poole BH15 1JG, United Kingdom
Ph: 44 1202 440820
Fax: 44 1202 440860
Publication E-mail: pbo@ipcmedia.com
Publisher E-mail: information@timeinc.com
Magazine focusing on boating. **Founded:** 1967. **Freq:** Monthly. **Key Personnel:** Sarah Norbury, Editor; Simon Owen, Publisher; David Pugh, Dep. Ed. **Subscription Rates:** US$36.57 individuals; US$73.14 two years. **Remarks:** Accepts advertising. **URL:** http://www.pbo.co.uk/pbo/home.htm. **Circ:** (Not Reported)

56282 ■ Progress in Crystal Growth and Characterization of Materials
Elsevier Science
c/o J.B. Mullin, Ed.-in-Ch.
EMC-Hoo Two, 22, Branksome Towers
Westminster Rd.
Poole BH13 6JT, United Kingdom
Publisher E-mail: nlinfo-f@elsevier.com
Peer-reviewed journal publishing article and reviews on crystal growth and characterization of materials. **Founded:** 1978. **Freq:** Quarterly. **Key Personnel:** J.B. Mullin, Editor-in-Chief; K. Byrappa, Assoc. Ed.; C.R. Schwab, Assoc. Ed. **ISSN:** 0960-8974. **Subscription Rates:** 486,500¥ institutions; US$4,098 institutions for all countries except Europe, Japan & Iran; EUR3,664 institutions for European countries & Iran; EUR131 individuals for European countries & Iran; US$175 individuals for all countries except Europe, Japan & Iran; 20,100¥ individuals. **Remarks:** Advertising accepted; rates available upon request. **URL:** http://www.elsevier.com/wps/find/journaldescription.cws_home/492/description. **Circ:** (Not Reported)

Portadown

56283 ■ Craigavon Echo
Morton Newspapers
14 Church St.
Craigavon
Portadown BT62 3LQ, United Kingdom
Community newspaper. **Freq:** Weekly (Wed.). **Print Method:** Offset. **Cols./Page:** 8. **Col. Depth:** 450

millimeters. **Key Personnel:** David Armstrong, Editor; Diane Murphy, Advertising Mgr. **Remarks:** Accepts advertising. **URL:** http://www.londonfreelance.org/rates/titles/_morton.html. **Circ:** Controlled ‡21,685

56284 ■ Portadown Times
Morton Newspapers
14 Church St.
Portadown BT62 3LQ, United Kingdom
Ph: 44 2838 336111
Community newspaper. **Freq:** Weekly (Fri.). **Print Method:** Offset. **Cols./Page:** 8. **Col. Depth:** 450 millimeters. **Key Personnel:** Alistair Bushe, Editor, fax 44 2839 350203, alistair.bushe@portadowntimes.co.uk. **Remarks:** Accepts advertising. **URL:** http://www.portadowntimes.co.uk. **Circ:** Combined 11,568

Portree

56285 ■ Cuillin-FM - 102.7
Stormyhill Rd.
Portree IV51 9DY, United Kingdom
Ph: 44 1478 611234
E-mail: admin@cuillinfm.co.uk
Format: Ethnic. **Ad Rates:** Advertising accepted; rates available upon request. **URL:** http://www.cuillinfm.co.uk/.

56286 ■ Cuillin-FM - 106.2
Stormyhill Rd.
Portree IV51 9DY, United Kingdom
Ph: 44 1478 611234
E-mail: admin@cuillinfm.co.uk
Format: Ethnic. **Ad Rates:** Advertising accepted; rates available upon request. **URL:** http://www.cuillinfm.co.uk/.

Portsmouth

56287 ■ Blue Band Magazine
HQ Band Service Royal Marines
Eastney Block
HMS Nelson
Portsmouth PO1 3HH, United Kingdom
Magazine featuring news of Royal Marines bands and Royal Naval Volunteer bands. **Freq:** 3/yr (April, August, and December). **Key Personnel:** Ann Day, Subscriptions Sec. **Remarks:** Advertising not accepted. **URL:** http://www.royalmarinesbands.co.uk/pages/Bluebandonline_index.htm. **Circ:** (Not Reported)

56288 ■ Bus & Coach Preservation
Ian Allan Publishing Ltd.
PO Box 636
Portsmouth PO2 9XR, United Kingdom
Ph: 44 23 92655224
Publisher E-mail: info@ianallanpublishing.co.uk
Magazine featuring news and views of restoration, old buses and coaches. **Freq:** Monthly. **Key Personnel:** Philip Lamb, Editor, presbusps@aol.com. **Remarks:** Accepts advertising. **URL:** http://www.ianallanmagazines.com/busandcoachpreservation. **Circ:** (Not Reported)

56289 ■ International Journal of Computational Economics and Econometrics
Inderscience Enterprises Limited
c/o Dr. Christos Floros, Ed.-in-Ch.
Richmond Bldg., RB1.07
Department of Economics, Portsmouth Business School
University of Portsmouth, Portland St.
Portsmouth PO1 3DE, United Kingdom
Peer-reviewed journal covering economics and econometrics including the application of computational techniques. **Freq:** Quarterly. **Key Personnel:** Dr. Christos Floros, Editor-in-Chief, christos.floros@port.ac.uk. **ISSN:** 1757-1170. **Subscription Rates:** EUR494 individuals print or online; EUR672 individuals print and online. **URL:** http://www.inderscience.com/browse/index.php?journalCODE=ijcee.

56290 ■ International Journal of Financial Markets and Derivatives
Inderscience Enterprises Limited
c/o Dr. Christos Floros, Ed.-in-Ch.
Richmond Bldg., (RB1.07)
Department of Economics, Portsmouth Business School
University of Portsmouth
Portsmouth PO1 3DE, United Kingdom
Peer-reviewed journal covering financial markets and

Circulation: ★ = ABC; △ = BPA; ♦ = CAC; • = CCAB; ❏ = VAC; ⊕ = PO Statement; ‡ = Publisher's Report; Boldface figures = sworn; Light figures = estimated.

Gale Directory of Publications & Broadcast Media/147th Ed.

5841

derivatives. **Freq:** Quarterly. **Key Personnel:** Dr. Christos Floros, Editor-in-Chief. **ISSN:** 1756-7130. **Subscription Rates:** EUR494 individuals print or online; EUR672 individuals print and online. **URL:** http://www.inderscience.com/browse/index.php?journalCODE=ijfmd.

56291 ■ Navy News
HMS Nelson
Queen St.
Portsmouth PO1 3HH, United Kingdom
Ph: 44 23 92725061
Publisher E-mail: edit@navynews.co.uk
Publication covering naval news. **Freq:** Monthly. **Key Personnel:** Jim Allaway, Editor. **Subscription Rates:** 18 individuals; 36 two years. **URL:** http://www.navynews.co.uk.

56292 ■ Positive Health
Positive Health Publications Ltd.
105 Madeira Rd.
Portsmouth PO2 0SY, United Kingdom
Ph: 44 23 92653266
Fax: 44 23 926653266
Publisher E-mail: admin@positivehealth.com
Magazine covering all aspects of complementary medicine for professionals and consumers. **Founded:** Jan. 1, 1994. **Freq:** Monthly. **Print Method:** Web. **Trim Size:** A4. **Key Personnel:** Mike Howell, Co-Founder, mike@positivehealth.com; Dr. Sandra Goodman, Ed. & Dir., sandra@positivehealth.com. **ISSN:** 1356-3963. **Subscription Rates:** 60 individuals; EUR88 other countries; US$118 other countries. **Remarks:** Accepts advertising. **URL:** http://www.positivehealth.net/. **Ad Rates:** 4C: 800. **Circ:** 8,000

56293 ■ Practical Diabetes International
John Wiley & Sons Inc.
c/o Ms. Sue Cradock, Ed.
Queen Alexandra Hospital
Cosham
Portsmouth PO6 3LY, United Kingdom
Ph: 44 23 92286000
Publisher E-mail: info@wiley.com
Journal covering all aspects of the worldwide clinical science and practice of diabetes medicine. **Freq:** 9/yr. **Key Personnel:** Ms. Sue Cradock, Editor, sue.cradock@porthosp.nhs.uk; Dr. Simon Croxson, Editor, simon.croxson@virgin.net; Dr. Miles Fisher, Editor, miles.fisher@northglasgow.scot.nhs.uk. **ISSN:** 1357-8170. **Subscription Rates:** 92 institutions UK (print only); EUR96 institutions, other countries print only; US$202 institutions, other countries print only. **Remarks:** Accepts advertising. **URL:** http://www3.interscience.wiley.com/journal/70003726/home. **Circ:** (Not Reported)

56294 ■ Express-FM - 93.7
Highbury Arundel Bldg.
49 Arundel St.
Portsmouth PO1 1SA, United Kingdom
Ph: 44 23 92751530
E-mail: studio@expressfm.com
Format: Eclectic; Information; Educational. **Operating Hours:** Continuous. **URL:** http://www.expressfm.com.

56295 ■ The Quay-FM - 107.4
Media Houses
Twyford Ave.
Portsmouth PO2 8YG, United Kingdom
Ph: 44 23 92351074
Format: Adult Contemporary; News; Sports. **Owner:** The Local Radio Company plc., 11 Duke St., High Wycombe HP13 6EE, United Kingdom, Fax: 44 1494 688201. **Operating Hours:** Continuous. **Ad Rates:** Advertising accepted; rates available upon request. **URL:** http://www.quayradio.com/.

Potters Bar

56296 ■ The Grieg Companion
Grieg Society of Great Britain
Pipers End, Dove Ln.
Potters Bar EN6 2SG, United Kingdom
Ph: 44 1707 643366
Fax: 44 1707 643366
Publisher E-mail: presse.london@mfa.no
Journal containing collected articles on Grieg's life and music and association events and persons. **Freq:** Annual. **Subscription Rates:** Included in membership. **Remarks:** Advertising not accepted. **URL:** http://www.griegsociety.org/default.asp?kat=1016&id=4581&sp=1. **Circ:** (Not Reported)

56297 ■ Manufacturing & Logistics IT
Interactive Business Communications Ltd.
Latimer House
189 High St.
Herts
Potters Bar EN6 5DA, United Kingdom
Ph: 44 1707 664200
Fax: 44 1707 664800
Publication E-mail: editor@ibcpub.com
Publisher E-mail: info@ibcpub.com
Magazine covering manufacturing, logistics and supply chain technology. **Key Personnel:** Ed Holden, Editor-in-Chief. **Remarks:** Accepts advertising. **URL:** http://www.ibcpub.com/magazines.html. **Circ:** (Not Reported)

Poynton

56298 ■ Journal of the Stephenson Locomotive Society
Stephenson Locomotive Society
c/o M.D. Dickin
1A Lockstock Ave.
Poynton SK12 1DR, United Kingdom
Journal containing news, articles and photographs. **Freq:** Bimonthly. **ISSN:** 1139-0090. **Subscription Rates:** Included in membership. **Remarks:** Accepts advertising. **URL:** http://www.stephensonloco.org.uk/SLSjournal.htm. **Circ:** (Not Reported)

Preston

56299 ■ Durham County Life
Archant Life
3 Tustin Ct.
Port Way
Ashton on Ribble
Preston PR2 2YQ, United Kingdom
Ph: 44 1772 722022
Fax: 44 1772 760905
Publisher E-mail: anne.basey-fisher@archant.co.uk
Magazine featuring life and leisure in Durham County. **Key Personnel:** Roger Borrell, Editor, phone 44 1772 329383, roger.borrell@archant.co.uk; Robert Hughes, Circulation Mgr., phone 44 7713 083188, bob.hughes@archant.co.uk; Andy Phelan, Publisher, andy.phelan@lancashirelife.co.uk. **URL:** http://www.archantlife.co.uk/contact-us-regions-north-durham-county-life-contacts--7314.

56300 ■ Journal of Financial Management of Property and Construction
Emerald Group Publishing Ltd.
c/o Prof. Akintola Akintoye, Editor
School of Built & Natural Environment, Harris Bldg.
Corporation St.
Preston PR1 2HE, United Kingdom
Publisher E-mail: emerald@emeraldinsight.com
Journal providing an international forum which brings together theoretical and practical based developments and new thinking in the financial management of property and construction. **Freq:** 6/yr. **Key Personnel:** Prof. Akintola Akintoye, Editor, aakintoye@uclan.ac.uk; Dr. Jim Birnie, Editor, jwbirnie@talktalk.net; Aimee Wood, Publisher, awood@emeraldinsight.com. **ISSN:** 1366-4387. **URL:** http://info.emeraldinsight.com/products/journals/journals.htm?id=jfmpc.

56301 ■ Lake District Life
Archant Life
3 Tustin Ct.
Portway
Preston PR2 2YQ, United Kingdom
Ph: 44 1772 722022
Fax: 44 1772 736496
Publication E-mail: enquiries@lakedistrict-life.co.uk
Publisher E-mail: johnny.hustler@archant.co.uk
Magazine celebrating the finer aspects of Life in the Lakes. **Freq:** Bimonthly. **Key Personnel:** Roger Borrell, Editor, roger.borrell@lancashirelife.co.uk; Amanda Griffiths, Writer, amanda.griffiths@archant.co.uk; Paul Mackenzie, Dep. Ed., paul.mackenzie@archant.co.uk. **Subscription Rates:** 25 individuals. **Remarks:** Accepts advertising. **URL:** http://www.lakedistrict-life.co.uk. **Ad Rates:** BW: 750. **Circ:** (Not Reported)

56302 ■ Lancashire Evening Post
Johnston Press PLC
Oliver's Pl.
Preston PR2 9ZA, United Kingdom

Ph: 44 1772 254841
Local community newspaper. **Freq:** Mon.-Sat. **Remarks:** Accepts advertising. **URL:** http://www.lep.co.uk/. **Circ:** (Not Reported)

56303 ■ Lancashire Life
Archant Life
3 Tustin Ct.
Port Way
Ashton on Ribble
Preston PR2 2YQ, United Kingdom
Ph: 44 1772 722022
Fax: 44 1772 736496
Publisher E-mail: anne.basey-fisher@archant.co.uk
Magazine featuring life and leisure in Lancashire. **Freq:** Monthly. **Key Personnel:** Roger Borrell, Editor, phone 44 1772 329383, roger.borrell@lancashirelife.co.uk; Richard Shelvin, Circulation Mgr., phone 44 7970 047024, richard.shevlin@archant.co.uk; Andy Phelan, Publisher, andy.phelan@lancashirelife.co.uk. **Subscription Rates:** 25 individuals. **Remarks:** Accepts advertising. **URL:** http://www.archantlife.co.uk/contact-us-regions-north-lancashire-life-contacts--7318; http://lancashire.greatbritishlife.co.uk/. **Circ:** ★23,455

56304 ■ Maternal and Child Nutrition
John Wiley & Sons Inc.
Wiley-Blackwell
Maternal & Infant Nutrition & Nurture Unit
Brook Bldg.
University of Central Lancashire
Preston PR1 2HE, United Kingdom
Ph: 44 1772 893830
Fax: 44 1772 892914
Publication E-mail: mcnjournal@uclan.ac.uk
Journal for health professionals, academics and service users with interests in maternal and infant nutrition, presenting original research findings in a variety of topics including nutritional needs of mothers and their children in health and illness, physiological, socio-cultural, psychological, economic and political aspects of the nutrition of mothers and their children, health promotion, health education, health policy and assessment in practice, inter-agency initiatives and programmes, consideration of United Nations and other organisations' activities, food safety, and related environmental and regulatory issues, discussion of foods for specific medical purposes, food and drink as health promoting, studies relating nutrition to health or disease riskin mothers and their children. evaluation of effectiveness of intervention studies aimed at improving health, role of nutrition in healthy groups and in high risk and vulnerable groups, development of research methods and validation of measures. **Freq:** Quarterly. **Key Personnel:** Victoria Hall Moran, Sen. Ed.; Kathryn Dewey, Sen. Ed.; James Bunn, Editorial Board; Rosalind Gibson, Editorial Board. **ISSN:** 1740-8695. **Subscription Rates:** US$228 individuals print + online; EUR185 individuals print + online; 124 individuals print + online; 137 other countries print + online; US$173 members print + online; EUR139 members print + online; 93 members print + online; 330 institutions print + online; US$613 institutions print + online; EUR418 institutions print + online. **Remarks:** Advertising not accepted. **URL:** http://www.wiley.com/bw/journal.asp?ref=1740-8695&site=1. **Circ:** (Not Reported)

56305 ■ Pure Weddings
Archant Life
3 Tustin Ct.
Portway
Preston PR2 2YQ, United Kingdom
Publisher E-mail: anne.basey-fisher@archant.co.uk
Magazine featuring wedding plans and preparations. **Freq:** Semiannual. **Key Personnel:** Jenny McDougall, Advertising Mgr.; Denise Evers, Advertising Mgr., denise.evers@archant.co.uk. **URL:** http://www.archantlife.co.uk/advertising-regions-south-east-and-east-pureweddings--7412.

56306 ■ Magic-AM - 999
St. Paul's Sq.
Lancashire
Preston PR1 1YE, United Kingdom
Ph: 44 1772 477700
Fax: 44 1772 477701
Format: Oldies. **URL:** http://www.magic999.co.uk/.

Quedgeley

56307 ■ Cattle Practice
British Cattle Veterinary Association
Pure Offices, Unit B4
Kestrel Ct.
Waterwells Dr.
Gloucestershire
Quedgeley GL2 7EP, United Kingdom
Ph: 44 14 52260125
Fax: 44 14 52886484
Publisher E-mail: office@cattlevet.co.uk
Publication covering veterinary medicine. **Freq:** Quarterly. **URL:** http://www.bcva.org.uk/.

Ramsgate

56308 ■ Bonjour!
Natural Leisure Ltd.
PO Box 196
Ramsgate CT11 9GG, United Kingdom
Ph: 44 1843 570381
Magazine offering articles on French lifestyle. **Key Personnel:** Susan Mayfield, Contact. **Subscription Rates:** 100 individuals. **URL:** http://www.jbwb.co.uk/arts_b.htm.

Reading

56309 ■ The Archaeologist
Institute of Field Archaeologists
SHES, University of Reading
Whiteknights
PO Box 227
Reading RG6 6AB, United Kingdom
Ph: 44 118 3786446
Fax: 44 118 3786448
Publisher E-mail: admin@archaeologists.net
Publication covering archaeology. **Freq:** Quarterly. **Key Personnel:** Alison Taylor, Editor, alison.taylor@archaeologists.net. **Subscription Rates:** 10 single issue non-members; Free to members. **Remarks:** Advertising accepted; rates available upon request. **URL:** http://www.archaeologists.net/modules/icontent/index.php?page=40. **Circ:** 2,000

56310 ■ The Bible Translator
United Bible Societies
Reading Bridge House
Reading RG1 8PJ, United Kingdom
Ph: 44 11 89500200
Fax: 44 11 89500857
Publication E-mail: bibletranslator@ubs-wsc.org
Peer-reviewed journal covering the Bible. **Freq:** Quarterly. **Remarks:** Advertising not accepted. **URL:** http://www.biblesociety.org/bibtrans.htm. **Circ:** (Not Reported)

56311 ■ Blah Blah
PO Box 2622
Reading RG1 9DJ, United Kingdom
Ph: 44 118 9753577
Fax: 44 118 9753577
Consumer magazine covering local arts, music, news, and entertainment. **Founded:** Dec. 1993. **Freq:** Monthly. **Print Method:** Litho. **Trim Size:** A4. **Cols./Page:** 4. **Col. Width:** 45 millimeters. **Col. Depth:** 257 millimeters. **Key Personnel:** Marc Wiles, Editor, marc@blahblah.co.uk. **ISSN:** 1471-1494. **Subscription Rates:** 15 individuals. **Remarks:** Accepts advertising. **URL:** http://www.blahblah.co.uk/. **Ad Rates:** BW: 500, 4C: 600. **Circ:** Non-paid ★40,000

56312 ■ E.Learning Age
Bizmedia Ltd
Royal Sta. Ct.
Sta. Rd.
Twyford
Reading RG10 9NF, United Kingdom
Ph: 44 118 9602820
Fax: 44 118 9602821
Publisher E-mail: admin@bizmedia.co.uk
Magazine for the e-learning community. **Subtitle:** The Magazine for the Learning Organisation. **Freq:** 10/yr. **Key Personnel:** Peter Williams, Editor-in-Chief, phone 44 20 89959345, peterw@bizmedia.co.uk. **Subscription Rates:** 75 individuals; 105 individuals Europe; 145 other countries. **Remarks:** Accepts advertising. **URL:** http://www.elearningage.co.uk/home.aspx. **Circ:** 12,000

56313 ■ Electronic Journal of e-Government
Academic Conferences Limited
Curtis Farm
Kidmore End
Reading RG4 9AY, United Kingdom
Ph: 44 1189 724148
Fax: 44 1189 724691
Publication E-mail: info@ejeg.com
Publisher E-mail: info@academic-conferences.org
Peer-reviewed journal publishing perspectives on topics relevant to the study, implementation and management of e-Government. **Freq:** Semiannual. **Key Personnel:** Frank Bannister, Ch. Ed.; Gil ad Ariely, Editorial Board; Matthias Finger, Editorial Board; Mary Griffiths, Editorial Board; Paul Foley, Editorial Board; Seungbong Park, Editorial Board; David Parker, Editorial Board; Tibor Vamos, Editorial Board; Panos Hahamis, Editorial Board; Briony Oates, Editorial Board. **ISSN:** 1479-439X. **URL:** http://www.ejeg.com.

56314 ■ Electronic Journal of e-Learning
Academic Conferences Limited
Curtis Farm
Kidmore End
Reading RG4 9AY, United Kingdom
Ph: 44 1189 724148
Fax: 44 1189 724691
Publisher E-mail: info@academic-conferences.org
Journal publishing topics to the study, implementation and management of e-Learning initiatives. **Freq:** Semiannual. **Key Personnel:** Shirley Williams, Editor; Roy Williams, Editorial Board; David Edgar, Editorial Board; Mark Saunders, Editorial Board. **ISSN:** 1479-4403. **URL:** http://www.ejel.org/main.html.

56315 ■ Electronic Journal of Information Systems Evaluation (EJISE)
Academic Conferences Limited
Curtis Farm
Kidmore End
Reading RG4 9AY, United Kingdom
Ph: 44 1189 724148
Fax: 44 1189 724691
Publisher E-mail: info@academic-conferences.org
Journal covering critical perspectives on topics relevant to Information Systems Evaluation, with an emphasis on the organizational and management implications. It contributes to the development of both the theory and practice of all aspects of IT/IS evaluation. **Freq:** Semiannual. **Key Personnel:** Dan Remenyi, Editorial Board; Frank Bannister, Editorial Board; Peter Bednar, Editorial Board; Prof. Shaun Pather, Editor-in-Chief; David Barnes, Editorial Board; Roger Clarke, Editorial Board. **ISSN:** 1566-6379. **URL:** http://www.ejise.com/.

56316 ■ Electronic Journal of Knowledge Management
Academic Conferences Limited
Curtis Farm
Kidmore End
Reading RG4 9AY, United Kingdom
Ph: 44 1189 724148
Fax: 44 1189 724691
Publication E-mail: info@ejkm.com
Publisher E-mail: info@academic-conferences.org
Peer-reviewed journal publishing articles and papers that contribute to the development of both theory and practice in the field of Knowledge Management. **Freq:** Semiannual. **Key Personnel:** Dave O'Donnell, Editor; Geoff Turner, Editor; Jan Aidemark, Editorial Board. **ISSN:** 1479-4411. **URL:** http://www.ejkm.com.

56317 ■ Food Science and Technology Abstracts
International Food Information Service Publishing
Ln. End House
Shinfield Rd.
Reading RG2 9BB, United Kingdom
Ph: 44 118 9883895
Fax: 44 118 9885065
Publisher E-mail: ifis@ifis.org
Publication covering food science and technology. **Founded:** 1969. **Freq:** Monthly. **ISSN:** 0015-6574. **Remarks:** Advertising not accepted. **URL:** http://www.fstadirect.com. **Circ:** (Not Reported)

56318 ■ FORWARD
The Guide Dogs for the Blind Association
Burghfield Common
Reading RG7 3YG, United Kingdom
Ph: 44 118 9835555
Fax: 44 118 9835433
Publisher E-mail: guidedogs@guidedogs.org.uk
Publication covering visual impairment and guide dogs. **Subtitle:** Magazine of the Guide Dogs for the Blind Association. **Founded:** 1941. **Freq:** Quarterly. **Print Method:** Sheetfed. **Trim Size:** 240 x 330 mm. **Subscription Rates:** Free. **Remarks:** Accepts advertising. **URL:** http://www.guidedogs.org.uk/aboutus/updates/forward/. **Ad Rates:** 4C: 2,000. **Circ:** 80,000

56319 ■ GrowthPoint
Thrive
Geoffrey Udall Center
Beech Hill
Reading RG7 2AT, United Kingdom
Ph: 44 11 89885688
Fax: 44 11 89885677
Magazine for members and others with an interest in social and therapeutic horticulture. **Subtitle:** Journal of Social and Therapeutic Horticulture. **Founded:** 1970. **Freq:** Quarterly. **ISSN:** 9051-7774. **Remarks:** Accepts advertising. **URL:** http://www.thrive.org.uk. **Circ:** Paid 1,000

56320 ■ Image and Vision Computing
Elsevier Science Inc.
c/o K.D. Baker, Founding. Ed.
University of Reading
Dept. of Computer Science
PO Box 225
Reading RG6 6AY, United Kingdom
Ph: 44 118 9318602
Publisher E-mail: usinfo-ehelp@elsevier.com
Journal featuring image processing and computational vision. **Freq:** Monthly. **Print Method:** Offset. **Cols./Page:** 6. **Col. Width:** 26 nonpareils. **Col. Depth:** 294 agate lines. **Key Personnel:** K.D. Baker, Founding Ed., keith.baker@reading.ac.uk; M. Jenkin, Advisory Board, jenkin@cs.yorku.ca; A. Pentland, Advisory Ed.; J.K. Aggarwal, Advisory Ed.; Tieniu Tan, Assoc. Ed.; A. Blake, Advisory Ed.; J. Barron, Assoc. Ed.; T. Cootes, Assoc. Ed. **ISSN:** 0262-8856. **Subscription Rates:** 217,800¥ institutions; US$1,831 institutions, other countries except Europe, Japan and Iran; EUR1,640 institutions for European countries and Iran; 14,000¥ individuals; US$118 other countries except Europe, Japan and Iran; EUR105 individuals for European countries and Iran. **URL:** http://www.elsevier.com/wps/find/journaldescription.cws_home/525443/descriptiondescription.

56321 ■ International Journal of Climatology
Royal Meteorological Society
104 Oxford Rd.
Grenville Pl.
Reading RG1 7LL, United Kingdom
Ph: 44 11 89568500
Fax: 44 11 89568571
Publisher E-mail: info@rmets.org
Journal covering worldwide climatology. **Freq:** 15/yr. **Key Personnel:** Prof. G.R. McGregor, Editor, g.mcgregor@auckland.ac.nz; Prof. Andrew C. Comrie, Reg. Ed., comrie@arizona.edu; Dr. Chris Kidd, Book Review Ed., c.kidd@bham.ac.uk. **ISSN:** 0899-8418. **Subscription Rates:** US$3,8/1 institutions print & online; US$3,366 institutions print or online; 1,976 institutions print & online. **Remarks:** Advertising accepted; rates available upon request. **URL:** http://www.rmets.org/activities/publications/index.php; http://onlinelibrary.wiley.com/journal/10.1002/(ISSN)1097-0088/issues. **Circ:** (Not Reported)

56322 ■ International Journal of Green Economics
Inderscience Publishers
c/o Miriam Kennet, Ed.
Green Economics Institute
6 Strachey Close
Reading RG8 8EP, United Kingdom
Publisher E-mail: editor@inderscience.com
Peer-reviewed journal proposing and fostering discussion on all aspects of green economics, contributing to international research and practice in green economics with the aim of encouraging economic change and the positioning of green economics at the centre of the economics disciplines. **Freq:** Quarterly. **Key Personnel:** Miriam Kennet, Editor, greeneconomicsinstitute@yahoo.

Circulation: ★ = ABC; △ = BPA; ♦ = CAC; • = CCAB; ❑ = VAC; ⊕ = PO Statement; ‡ = Publisher's Report; Boldface figures = sworn; Light figures = estimated.

com; Victor Anderson, Editorial Board Member; Dr. Priscilla Alderson, Editorial Board Member; Dr. John Barry, Advisory Board; Veronica Alam, MD, Editorial Board Member; Volker Heinemann, Dep. Ed.; Dr. Hirofumi Aizawa, Advisory Board. **ISSN:** 1744-9928. **Subscription Rates:** EUR494 individuals print only (surface mail); EUR672 individuals print and online; EUR840 individuals online only (2-3 users); EUR672 individuals print and online. **URL:** http://www.inderscience.com/browse/index.php?journalCODE=ijge.

56323 ■ Journal of General Virology
Society for General Microbiology
Marlborough House
Basingstoke Rd.
Spencers Wood
Reading RG7 1AG, United Kingdom
Ph: 44 11 89881800
Fax: 44 11 89885656
Publication E-mail: jgv@sgm.ac.uk
Professional journal covering virology. **Freq:** Monthly. **Trim Size:** 275 x 210 mm. **Key Personnel:** R. Bartenschlager, Editor, ralf_bartenschlager@med.uni-heidelberg.de; R.M. Elliot, Editor-in-Chief, fax 44 1334 462595, elliottjgv@st-andrews.ac.uk; B. Berkhout, Editor, b.berkhout@amc.uva.nl. **ISSN:** 0022-1317. **Subscription Rates:** 855 individuals print & online; US$1,940 individuals print & online; 800 other countries online; US$1,430 individuals online. **Remarks:** Accepts advertising. **URL:** http://jgv.sgmjournals.org. **Ad Rates:** BW: 495, 4C: 945. **Circ:** 2,000

56324 ■ Journal of the Royal Meteorological Society
Royal Meteorological Society
104 Oxford Rd.
Grenville Pl.
Reading RG1 7LL, United Kingdom
Ph: 44 11 89568500
Fax: 44 11 89568571
Publisher E-mail: info@rmets.org
Journal covering the Royal Meteorological Society. **Freq:** Quarterly. **Key Personnel:** John Thuburn, Editor; Mark P. Baldwin, Editor. **ISSN:** 0035-9009. **Subscription Rates:** EUR774 institutions print & online; 613 institutions print & online; US$1,199 institutions print & online. **Remarks:** Advertising accepted; rates available upon request. **URL:** http://www.rmets.org/activities/publications/index.php; http://onlinelibrary.wiley.com/journal/10.1002/(ISSN)1477-870X. **Circ:** (Not Reported)

56325 ■ Microbiology
Society for General Microbiology
Marlborough House
Basingstoke Rd.
Spencers Wood
Reading RG7 1AG, United Kingdom
Ph: 44 11 89881800
Fax: 44 11 89885656
Publication covering microbiology. **Founded:** 1947. **Freq:** Monthly. **Print Method:** Offset Line. **Trim Size:** 275 x 210 mm. **Key Personnel:** S.J. Foster, Editor; Agnes Fouet, Editor-in-Chief, agnes.fouet@pasteur.fr; D.J. Kelly, Editor; A. Holmes, Editor; S. Spiro, Editor; T. Parish, Editor; J.M. van Dijl, Editor; R.J. Lamont, Editor. **ISSN:** 1350-0872. **Subscription Rates:** 855 individuals UK (print and online); 800 individuals UK (online only); US$1,490 individuals print and online; 1,430 individuals. **Remarks:** Accepts advertising. **URL:** http://mic.sgmjournals.org. **Ad Rates:** BW: 495, 4C: 945. **Circ:** (Not Reported)

56326 ■ Microbiology Today
Society for General Microbiology
Marlborough House
Basingstoke Rd.
Spencers Wood
Reading RG7 1AG, United Kingdom
Ph: 44 11 89881800
Fax: 44 11 89885656
Magazine focusing on current research in the field of microbiology. **Freq:** Quarterly Feb., May, Aug., and Nov. **Key Personnel:** Ian Atherton, Managing Editor, i.atherton@sgm.ac.uk; Yvonne Taylor, Asst. Ed., y.taylor@sgm.ac.uk; Dr. Paul Hoskisson, Editor, paul.hoskisson@strath.ac.uk. **Remarks:** Accepts advertising. **URL:** http://www.socgenmicrobiol.org.uk/pubs/micro_today/. **Ad Rates:** BW: 490, 4C: 1,092. **Circ:** (Not Reported)

56327 ■ Molecular Plant Pathology
British Society for Plant Pathology

Marlborough House
Basingstoke Rd.
Spencers Wood
Reading RG7 1AG, United Kingdom
Publisher E-mail: secretary@bspp.org.uk
Publication covering botany. **Freq:** Bimonthly. **Key Personnel:** Gary D. Foster, Editor-in-Chief, phone 44 117 3317021, gary.foster@bristol.ac.uk; Mary Beth Mudgett, Sen. Ed., phone 650723-3252, fax 650723-6132, mudgett@stanford.edu; Ken Shirasu, Editorial Board; Howard Judelson, Sen. Ed., phone 951827-4199, fax 951827-4294, howard.judelson@ucr.edu; Barbara Howlett, Sen. Ed., phone 61 3 83445062, fax 61 3 93475460, bhowlett@unimelb.edu.au; Dawn L. Arnold, Pathogen Profile Ed., phone 44 117 3283819, fax 44 117 3282904, dawn.arnold@uwe.ac.uk. **ISSN:** 1464-6722. **Subscription Rates:** US$162 individuals print + online; EUR130 institutions print + online (Euro zone); 87 individuals print + online (non Euro zone); 97 other countries print + online; US$1,267 institutions print + online; 687 institutions print + online; EUR873 institutions print + online; US$1,480 institutions, other countries print + online; US$1,151 institutions print or online; 624 institutions print or online. **Remarks:** Accepts advertising. **URL:** http://www.bspp.org.uk/publications/molecular-plant-pathology/index.php; http://www.wiley.com/bw/journal.asp?ref=1464-6722. **Circ:** (Not Reported)

56328 ■ New Disease Reports
British Society for Plant Pathology
Marlborough House
Basingstoke Rd.
Spencers Wood
Reading RG7 1AG, United Kingdom
Publication E-mail: ndr@bspp.org.uk
Publisher E-mail: secretary@bspp.org.uk
International online journal of the British Society for Plant Pathology, accepting submissions on new plant disease situations for: fungi, bacteria, phytoplasmas, viruses and viroids. **Freq:** Semiannual. **Key Personnel:** Rick Mumford, Editor; Robert Black, Sen. Ed. **URL:** http://www.ndrs.org.uk/.

56329 ■ Quarterly Journal of the Royal Meteorological Society
Royal Meteorological Society
104 Oxford Rd.
Reading RG1 7LL, United Kingdom
Ph: 44 11 89568500
Fax: 44 11 89568571
Publisher E-mail: chiefexec@rmets.org
Journal covering atmospheric sciences, applied meteorology and physical oceanography. **Founded:** 1871. **Freq:** 8/yr. **Trim Size:** 170 x 245 mm. **Cols./Page:** 1. **Col. Width:** 135 millimeters. **Col. Depth:** 210 millimeters. **Key Personnel:** John Thuburn, Editor; Mark P. Baldwin, Editor. **ISSN:** 0035-9009. **Subscription Rates:** US$825 institutions, Canada and Mexico print only; US$825 institutions rest of world; US$908 institutions print with online access; US$908 institutions, Canada and Mexico print and online. **Remarks:** Accepts advertising. **URL:** http://www.rmets.org/activities/publications/index.php; http://onlinelibrary.wiley.com/journal/10.1002/(ISSN)1477-870X. **Ad Rates:** BW: 420. **Circ:** Paid 1,100

56330 ■ Ratio
John Wiley & Sons Inc.
Wiley-Blackwell
c/o Prof. John Cottingham, Ed.
University of Reading
Reading RG6 6AA, United Kingdom
Ph: 44 11 89318325
Fax: 44 11 89318295
Journal covering analytical philosophy. **Subtitle:** An International Journal of Analytic Philosophy. **Freq:** Quarterly. **Key Personnel:** Prof. John Cottingham, Editor, j.g.cottingham@reading.ac.uk; Brad Hooker, Assoc. Ed.; A. Kemmerling, Editorial Board; P. Bieri, Editorial Board; Emma Borg, Assoc. Ed.; Jonathan Dancy, Assoc. Ed.; John M. Cooper, Editorial Board; Alice Drewery, Assoc. Ed.; Philip Pettit, Editorial Board. **ISSN:** 0034-0006. **Subscription Rates:** US$127 individuals print + online; US$101 members APA/BPA: print + online; US$1,089 institutions, other countries print + online; US$935 institutions print + online; US$850 institutions print, online; 435 institutions print + online; EUR88 individuals print + online; EUR71 members APA/BPA: print + online; EUR552 institutions print + online; 395 institutions print or online. **Remarks:** Advertising ac-

cepted; rates available upon request. **URL:** http://www.wiley.com/bw/journal.asp?ref=0034-0006&site=1. **Circ:** (Not Reported)

56331 ■ Reading
The University of Reading
Development & Alumni Relations Office
Whiteknights
PO Box 217
Reading RG6 6AH, United Kingdom
Ph: 44 11 89875123
Fax: 44 11 89314404
University magazine. **Founded:** 1985. **Freq:** Semiannual. **Print Method:** Web offset. **Trim Size:** A4. **Key Personnel:** Marion Armson, Dep. Dir.; Ian Burn, Editor, i.j.burn@reading.ac.uk; Brenda Morris, Office Mgr., b.l.morris@reading.ac.uk. **Remarks:** Advertising not accepted. **URL:** http://www.reading.ac.uk. **Formerly:** Alumni & Friends. **Circ:** Controlled 70,000

56332 ■ Utilitas
International Society for Utilitarian Studies
c/o Brad Hooker, Ed.
Department of Philosophy
Faculty of Letters Bldg.
Reading RG6 6AA, United Kingdom
Publication covering philosophy. **Founded:** 1989. **Freq:** Triennial. **Key Personnel:** Prof. Brad Hooker, Editor. **ISSN:** 0938-8208. **Subscription Rates:** US$292 institutions print; US$270 institutions online; US$294 institutions print and online; 154 institutions print; 142 institutions online; 156 institutions print and online; US$62 individuals print; 37 individuals print. **Remarks:** Advertising accepted; rates available upon request. **URL:** http://www.ucl.ac.uk/Bentham-Project/isus; http://journals.cambridge.org/action/displayJournal?jid=UTI. **Circ:** 500

56333 ■ Weather
Royal Meteorological Society
104 Oxford Rd.
Reading RG1 7LL, United Kingdom
Ph: 44 11 89568500
Fax: 44 11 89568571
Publisher E-mail: chiefexec@rmets.org
Professional magazine covering meteorology. **Founded:** 1946. **Freq:** Monthly. **Trim Size:** A4. **Cols./Page:** 3. **Key Personnel:** Bob Prichard, Editor; Liz Bentley, Editorial Board; Edward Hanna, Editorial Board; Laura Baker, Editorial Board. **ISSN:** 0043-1656. **Subscription Rates:** US$106 individuals print only; US$109 institutions print only; US$126 institutions print with online access; 54 individuals print only, U.K.; US$118 individuals print with online access; EUR81 institutions print with online access; 65 institutions print with online access; 60 individuals print with online access, U.K. **Remarks:** Accepts advertising. **URL:** http://www.rmets.org; http://www3.interscience.wiley.com/journal/113388511/home. **Ad Rates:** 4C: 420. **Circ:** Paid 5,000

56334 ■ BBC Radio Berkshire-FM - 94.6
PO Box 104.4
Reading RG4 8FH, United Kingdom
Ph: 44 118 9464200
Fax: 44 118 9464555
E-mail: berkshire.online@bbc.co.uk
Format: News; Sports; Talk. **Owner:** British Broadcasting Corp., Broadcasting House, Portland Pl., London W1A 1AA, United Kingdom. **Key Personnel:** Marianne Bell, Managing Editor, marianne.bell@bbc.co.uk. **URL:** http://www.bbc.co.uk/berkshire/local_radio/.

56335 ■ BBC Radio-FM - 95.4
Caversham Pk., Peppard Rd.
Reading RG4 8TZ, United Kingdom
Ph: 44 118 9462400
Fax: 44 118 9464555
E-mail: radio.berkshire.news@bbc.co.uk
Format: News; Information; Sports. **Owner:** British Broadcasting Corp., Broadcasting House, Portland Pl., London W1A 1AA, United Kingdom. **Operating Hours:** Continuous. **URL:** http://www.bbc.co.uk/berkshire/local_radio/.

56336 ■ BBC Radio-FM - 104.1
Caversham Pk., Peppard Rd.
Reading RG4 8FH, United Kingdom
Ph: 44 118 9462400
Fax: 44 118 9464555
E-mail: radio.berkshire.news@bbc.co.uk
Format: News; Sports; Information. **Owner:** British Broadcasting Corp., Broadcasting House, Portland Pl., London W1A 1AA, United Kingdom. **Operating Hours:**

Continuous. **URL:** http://www.bbc.co.uk/berkshire/local_radio/.

56337 ■ Blast 1386-AM - 1386
Thames Valley University
Crescent Rd.
Reading RG1 5RQ, United Kingdom
Ph: 44 118 9675068
Fax: 44 118 9675083
E-mail: news@blast1386.com
Format: Eclectic; Alternative/New Music/Progressive; Urban Contemporary; Jazz; Blues. **Operating Hours:** Continuous. **Key Personnel:** Bob Goertz, Station Mgr. **URL:** http://193.63.27.204/ReadingCollegeRadio/.

56338 ■ Heart-FM - 102.9
The Chase
Calcot
Reading RG31 7RB, United Kingdom
Ph: 44 11 89454400
Format: Contemporary Hit Radio (CHR); Information. **Owner:** Global Radio UK Ltd., 30 Leicester Sq., London WC2H 7LA, United Kingdom, 44 20 7666000, Fax: 44 20 7666111, Formerly: 2-Ten-FM. **Operating Hours:** Continuous. **Ad Rates:** Advertising accepted; rates available upon request. **URL:** http://www.heartberkshire.co.uk.

56339 ■ Heart-FM - 97
The Chase
Calcot
Reading RG31 7RB, United Kingdom
Ph: 44 11 89454400
Format: Contemporary Hit Radio (CHR); Information. **Owner:** Global Radio UK Ltd., 30 Leicester Sq., London WC2H 7LA, United Kingdom, 44 20 7666000, Fax: 44 20 7666111. Formerly: 2-Ten-FM. **Ad Rates:** Advertising accepted; rates available upon request. **URL:** http://www.heartberkshire.co.uk.

56340 ■ Reading 107-FM - 107
Radio House
Madejski Stadium
Reading RG2 0FN, United Kingdom
Ph: 44 118 9860107
Format: Adult Contemporary; Oldies; News; Sports; Easy Listening. **Founded:** Oct. 22, 2002. **Operating Hours:** Continuous. **Ad Rates:** Advertising accepted; rates available upon request. **URL:** http://www.reading107fm.com/.

Redditch

56341 ■ Redditch Standard
Observer Standard Newspapers Ltd.
Webb House
Church Green E
Redditch B98 8BP, United Kingdom
Ph: 44 1527 588688
Fax: 44 1527 584371
Publication E-mail: editor@redditchstandard.co.uk
Publisher E-mail: hq@observerstandard.com
Local community newspaper. **Freq:** Weekly. **Key Personnel:** Chris Bullivant, Founder; Pat Bullivant, Founder; Vanessa Bradford, Contact, vanessa.bradford@bullivantmedia.com. **Remarks:** Accepts advertising. **URL:** http://www.redditchstandard.co.uk/. **Circ:** (Not Reported)

Redhill

56342 ■ Arroword Selection
Puzzler Media Ltd.
Stonecroft, 69 Station Rd.
Surrey
Redhill RH1 1EY, United Kingdom
Ph: 99944 1737 378700
Fax: 99944 1737 781800
Publisher E-mail: info@puzzler.com
Magazine featuring collection of quizzes and cash competitions. **Freq:** 13/yr. **Trim Size:** 7.1 x 10. **Subscription Rates:** 2.20 single issue. **URL:** http://www.puzzler.com/magazines/ArrowordSelection.htm.

56343 ■ Beyond Sudoku
Puzzler Media Ltd.
Stonecroft, 69 Station Rd.
Surrey
Redhill RH1 1EY, United Kingdom
Ph: 99944 1737 378700

Fax: 99944 1737 781800
Publisher E-mail: info@puzzler.com
Magazine featuring collection of popular logic puzzles. **Freq:** 6/yr. **Trim Size:** 7.5 x 10.6. **Subscription Rates:** 3.40 single issue. **URL:** http://www.puzzler.com/magazines/BeyondSudoku.htm.

56344 ■ Chat Arrowords
Puzzler Media Ltd.
Stonecroft, 69 Station Rd.
Surrey
Redhill RH1 1EY, United Kingdom
Ph: 99944 1737 378700
Fax: 99944 1737 781800
Publisher E-mail: info@puzzler.com
Magazine featuring 70 puzzles with prizes. **Freq:** 13/yr. **Trim Size:** 185 x 255 mm. **Subscription Rates:** 1.80 single issue. **URL:** http://www.puzzler.com/magazines/ChatArrowords.htm.

56345 ■ Chat Crosswords
Puzzler Media Ltd.
Stonecroft, 69 Station Rd.
Surrey
Redhill RH1 1EY, United Kingdom
Ph: 99944 1737 378700
Fax: 99944 1737 781800
Publisher E-mail: info@puzzler.com
Magazine featuring 90 crosswords ranging from arrowords, codewords, general knowledge, and showbiz quizzes. **Freq:** 13/yr. **Trim Size:** 217 x 290. **Subscription Rates:** 2 single issue. **URL:** http://www.puzzler.com/magazines/ChatCrosswords.htm.

56346 ■ Chat Puzzles Select
Puzzler Media Ltd.
Stonecroft, 69 Station Rd.
Surrey
Redhill RH1 1EY, United Kingdom
Ph: 99944 1737 378700
Fax: 99944 1737 781800
Publisher E-mail: info@puzzler.com
Magazine featuring selection of inviting puzzles ranging from wordsearches to classic crosswords. **Freq:** 13/yr. **Trim Size:** 7.3 x 10. **Subscription Rates:** 2.20 single issue. **URL:** http://www.puzzler.com/magazines/ChatPuzzlesSelect.htm.

56347 ■ Chat Wordsearch
Puzzler Media Ltd.
Stonecroft, 69 Station Rd.
Surrey
Redhill RH1 1EY, United Kingdom
Ph: 99944 1737 378700
Fax: 99944 1737 781800
Publisher E-mail: info@puzzler.com
Magazine featuring wordsearch puzzles, real-life stories, quizzes, jokes plus three great competitions in every issue. **Freq:** 13/yr. **Trim Size:** 7.3 x 10. **Subscription Rates:** 1.80 single issue. **URL:** http://www.puzzler.com/magazines/ChatWordsearch.htm.

56348 ■ Code Words
Puzzler Media Ltd.
Stonecroft, 69 Station Rd.
Surrey
Redhill RH1 1EY, United Kingdom
Ph: 99944 1737 378700
Fax: 99944 1737 781800
Publisher E-mail: info@puzzler.com
Magazine featuring collection of puzzles together with topical references, quotes or photographs. **Freq:** 13/yr. **Trim Size:** 7.1 x 10. **Subscription Rates:** 2.20 single issue. **URL:** http://www.puzzler.com/magazines/CodeWords.htm.

56349 ■ Crossword Selection
Puzzler Media Ltd.
Stonecroft, 69 Station Rd.
Surrey
Redhill RH1 1EY, United Kingdom
Ph: 99944 1737 378700
Fax: 99944 1737 781800
Publisher E-mail: info@puzzler.com
Magazine featuring comprehensive range of quality crossword puzzles. **Freq:** 10/yr. **Trim Size:** 7.1 x 10. **Subscription Rates:** 2.20 single issue. **URL:** http://www.puzzler.com/magazines/CrosswordSelection.htm.

56350 ■ Dredging and Port Construction
IHS Global Limited
Lloyd's Register--Fairplay Ltd.
Lombard House
3 Princess Way
Surrey
Redhill RH1 1UP, United Kingdom
Ph: 44 1737 379000
Fax: 44 1737 379001
Publisher E-mail: info@lrfairplay.com
Magazine focusing on port construction, development and dredging campaigns of all types. **Freq:** Monthly. **Trim Size:** 210 x 297 mm. **Key Personnel:** Paul Gunton, Managing Editor, phone 44 1737 379142, paul.gunton@ihs.com; Tony Slinn, Editor-in-Chief, phone 44 1737 379159, tony.slinn@ihs.com. **Subscription Rates:** EUR325 individuals; 225 other countries; 195 individuals; US$460 individuals. **Remarks:** Accepts advertising. **URL:** http://www.dpcmagazine.com/default.html. **Circ:** (Not Reported)

56351 ■ Fundoku
Puzzler Media Ltd.
Stonecroft, 69 Station Rd.
Surrey
Redhill RH1 1EY, United Kingdom
Ph: 99944 1737 378700
Fax: 99944 1737 781800
Publisher E-mail: info@puzzler.com
Magazine featuring selection of Sudoku puzzles for beginners. **Freq:** 5/yr. **Trim Size:** 5.8 x 8.3. **Subscription Rates:** 2.10 single issue. **URL:** http://www.puzzler.com/magazines/Fundoku.htm.

56352 ■ Furnaces International
DMG Business Media Ltd.
Westgate House
120/130 Station Rd.
Redhill RH1 1ET, United Kingdom
Ph: 44 17 37855000
Fax: 44 17 37855475
Publication E-mail: furnaces@dmgworldmedia.com
Publisher E-mail: miaeng@dmgworldmedia.com
Magazine containing features, news, product stories, industry updates and events relating to the thermal processing of metals and materials. **Subtitle:** Furnace Technology for Thermal Processing of Metals & Materials. **Freq:** Quarterly. **Print Method:** Litho. **Trim Size:** 210 x 297 mm. **Key Personnel:** Melanie Chiles, Production Mgr., phone 44 17 37855336, fax 44 17 37855034, melaniechiles@uk.dmgworldmedia.com; Phil Chandler, Vice President, phone 44 17 37855086, philchandler@dmgworldmedia.com; Anne Considine, Area Sales Mgr., phone 44 17 37855139, anneconsidine@uk.dmgworldmedia.com; Annie Baker, Production Ed., phone 44 17 37855130, anniebaker@uk.dmgworldmedia.com; Tony Meyer, Sales Mgr., phone 44 12 76470182, fax 44 12 76470182. **Remarks:** Accepts advertising. **URL:** http://www.furnacesinternational.com/. **Ad Rates:** BW: 1,245, 4C: 2,000. **Circ:** 2,000

56353 ■ Hanjie
Puzzler Media Ltd.
Stonecroft, 69 Station Rd.
Surrey
Redhill RH1 1EY, United Kingdom
Ph: 99944 1737 378700
Fax: 99944 1737 781800
Publisher E-mail: info@puzzler.com
Magazine featuring a compulsive form of painting by numbers. **Freq:** 13/yr. **Trim Size:** 7.3 x 7.5. **Subscription Rates:** 3.00 single issue. **URL:** http://www.puzzler.com/magazines/Hanjie.htm.

56354 ■ Junior Puzzles
Puzzler Media Ltd.
Stonecroft, 69 Station Rd.
Surrey
Redhill RH1 1EY, United Kingdom
Ph: 99944 1737 378700
Fax: 99944 1737 781800
Publisher E-mail: info@puzzler.com
Magazine featuring a collection of spot the difference, wordsearch, crosswords, mazes and much more for 7-12 year olds. **Freq:** 6/yr. **Trim Size:** 7.1 x 10. **Subscription Rates:** 2.70 single issue. **URL:** http://www.puzzler.com/magazines/JuniorPuzzles.htm.

56355 ■ Kakuro
Puzzler Media Ltd.

Stonecroft, 69 Station Rd.
Surrey
Redhill RH1 1EY, United Kingdom
Ph: 99944 1737 378700
Fax: 99944 1737 781800
Publisher E-mail: info@puzzler.com
Magazine featuring a sudoku with a twist. **Freq:** 9/yr.
Trim Size: 5.8 x 8.3. **Subscription Rates:** 2.70 single
issue. **URL:** http://www.puzzler.com/magazines/Kakuro.
htm.

56356 ■ Killer Sudoku
Puzzler Media Ltd.
Stonecroft, 69 Station Rd.
Surrey
Redhill RH1 1EY, United Kingdom
Ph: 99944 1737 378700
Fax: 99944 1737 781800
Publisher E-mail: info@puzzler.com
Magazine featuring sudoku with an extra challenge.
Freq: 13/yr. **Trim Size:** 5.8 x 8.3. **Subscription Rates:**
2.50 single issue. **URL:** http://www.puzzler.com/
magazines/KillerSudoku.htm.

56357 ■ Kriss Kross
Puzzler Media Ltd.
Stonecroft, 69 Station Rd.
Surrey
Redhill RH1 1EY, United Kingdom
Ph: 99944 1737 378700
Fax: 99944 1737 781800
Publisher E-mail: info@puzzler.com
Magazine featuring a selection of quick crosswords,
wordsearches, and codeword puzzles. **Freq:** 14/yr. **Trim
Size:** 7.1 x 10. **Subscription Rates:** 2.20 single issue.
URL: http://www.puzzler.com/magazines/KrissKross.
htm.

56358 ■ 100 Codewords
Puzzler Media Ltd.
Stonecroft, 69 Station Rd.
Surrey
Redhill RH1 1EY, United Kingdom
Ph: 99944 1737 378700
Fax: 99944 1737 781800
Publisher E-mail: info@puzzler.com
Magazine featuring collection of puzzles. **Freq:** 13/yr.
Trim Size: 6.6 x 9.4. **Subscription Rates:** 1.95 single
issue. **URL:** http://www.puzzler.com/magazines/
100Codewords.htm.

56359 ■ 100 Crosswords
Puzzler Media Ltd.
Stonecroft, 69 Station Rd.
Surrey
Redhill RH1 1EY, United Kingdom
Ph: 99944 1737 378700
Fax: 99944 1737 781800
Publisher E-mail: info@puzzler.com
Magazine featuring 100 newspaper style crosswords.
Freq: 13/yr. **Trim Size:** 6.6 x 9.4. **Subscription Rates:**
1.95 single issue. **URL:** http://www.puzzler.com/
magazines/100Crosswords.htm.

56360 ■ 100 Wordsearch
Puzzler Media Ltd.
Stonecroft, 69 Station Rd.
Surrey
Redhill RH1 1EY, United Kingdom
Ph: 99944 1737 378700
Fax: 99944 1737 781800
Publisher E-mail: info@puzzler.com
Magazine featuring 100 wordsearch puzzles. **Freq:** 13/
yr. **Trim Size:** 6.6 x 9.4. **Subscription Rates:** 1.90
single issue. **URL:** http://www.puzzler.com/magazines/
100Wordsearch.htm.

56361 ■ Puzzle Compendium
Puzzler Media Ltd.
Stonecroft, 69 Station Rd.
Surrey
Redhill RH1 1EY, United Kingdom
Ph: 99944 1737 378700
Fax: 99944 1737 781800
Publisher E-mail: info@puzzler.com
Magazine featuring a collection of mixed puzzles. **Freq:**
12/yr. **Trim Size:** 7.1 x 10. **Subscription Rates:** 2.65
single issue. **URL:** http://www.puzzler.com/magazines/
PuzzleCompendium.htm.

56362 ■ Puzzle Corner Special
Puzzler Media Ltd.
Stonecroft, 69 Station Rd.
Surrey
Redhill RH1 1EY, United Kingdom
Ph: 99944 1737 378700
Fax: 99944 1737 781800
Publisher E-mail: info@puzzler.com
Magazine featuring a wide variety of puzzles suitable for
a range of abilities. **Freq:** 10/yr. **Trim Size:** 7.1 x 10.
Subscription Rates: 2.70 single issue. **URL:** http://
www.puzzler.com/magazines/PuzzleCornerSpecial.htm.

56363 ■ Puzzler
Puzzler Media Ltd.
Stonecroft, 69 Station Rd.
Surrey
Redhill RH1 1EY, United Kingdom
Ph: 99944 1737 378700
Fax: 99944 1737 781800
Publisher E-mail: info@puzzler.com
Magazine featuring puzzles from the nation's top
compilers. **Freq:** 14/yr. **Trim Size:** 7.3 x 10. **Subscrip-
tion Rates:** 1.80 single issue. **URL:** http://www.puzzler.
com.

56364 ■ Puzzler Arrowords
Puzzler Media Ltd.
Stonecroft, 69 Station Rd.
Surrey
Redhill RH1 1EY, United Kingdom
Ph: 99944 1737 378700
Fax: 99944 1737 781800
Publisher E-mail: info@puzzler.com
Magazine featuring arroword puzzles. **Freq:** 13/yr. **Trim
Size:** 7.3 x 10. **Subscription Rates:** 1.80 single issue.
URL: http://www.puzzler.com/magazines/
PuzzlerArrowords.htm.

56365 ■ Puzzler Brain Trainer
Puzzler Media Ltd.
Stonecroft, 69 Station Rd.
Surrey
Redhill RH1 1EY, United Kingdom
Ph: 99944 1737 378700
Fax: 99944 1737 781800
Publisher E-mail: info@puzzler.com
Magazine featuring variety of great puzzles and specially
created short workouts. **Freq:** 13/yr. **Trim Size:** 7.3 x
10. **Subscription Rates:** 2.90 single issue. **URL:** http://
www.puzzler.com/magazines/PuzzlerBrainTrainer.htm.

56366 ■ Puzzler Codewords
Puzzler Media Ltd.
Stonecroft, 69 Station Rd.
Surrey
Redhill RH1 1EY, United Kingdom
Ph: 99944 1737 378700
Fax: 99944 1737 781800
Publisher E-mail: info@puzzler.com
Magazine featuring 75 lively code-cracking puzzles.
Freq: 13/yr. **Trim Size:** 7.3 x 10. **Subscription Rates:**
1.80 single issue. **URL:** http://www.puzzler.com/
magazines/PuzzlerCodeWords.htm.

56367 ■ Puzzler Collection
Puzzler Media Ltd.
Stonecroft, 69 Station Rd.
Surrey
Redhill RH1 1EY, United Kingdom
Ph: 99944 1737 378700
Fax: 99944 1737 781800
Publisher E-mail: info@puzzler.com
Magazine featuring over 100 quality puzzles. **Freq:** 14/
yr. **Trim Size:** 7.3 x 10. **Subscription Rates:** 2.40 single
issue. **URL:** http://www.puzzler.com/magazines/
PuzzlerCollection.htm.

56368 ■ Puzzler Crossword
Puzzler Media Ltd.
Stonecroft, 69 Station Rd.
Surrey
Redhill RH1 1EY, United Kingdom
Ph: 99944 1737 378700
Fax: 99944 1737 781800
Publisher E-mail: info@puzzler.com
Magazine featuring popular crosswords and a few
interesting variants in a stylish, uncluttered, and handy
sized format. **Freq:** 13/yr. **Trim Size:** 5.8 x 8.3. **Sub-
scription Rates:** 2.40 single issue. **URL:** http://www.

puzzler.com/magazines/PuzzlerCrossword.htm.

56369 ■ Puzzler Kriss Kross
Puzzler Media Ltd.
Stonecroft, 69 Station Rd.
Surrey
Redhill RH1 1EY, United Kingdom
Ph: 99944 1737 378700
Fax: 99944 1737 781800
Publisher E-mail: info@puzzler.com
Magazine featuring over 60 fun and lively puzzles. **Freq:**
13/yr. **Trim Size:** 7.3 x 10. **Subscription Rates:** 1.80
single issue. **URL:** http://www.puzzler.com/magazines/
PuzzlerKrissKross.htm.

56370 ■ Puzzler Pocket Crosswords
Puzzler Media Ltd.
Stonecroft, 69 Station Rd.
Surrey
Redhill RH1 1EY, United Kingdom
Ph: 99944 1737 378700
Fax: 99944 1737 781800
Publisher E-mail: info@puzzler.com
Pocket size magazine featuring crossword puzzles.
Freq: 13/yr. **Trim Size:** 4.7 x 6.5. **Subscription Rates:**
1.35 single issue. **URL:** http://www.puzzler.com/
magazines/PocketCrosswords.htm.

56371 ■ Puzzler Pocket Crosswords Collection
Puzzler Media Ltd.
Stonecroft, 69 Station Rd.
Surrey
Redhill RH1 1EY, United Kingdom
Ph: 99944 1737 378700
Fax: 99944 1737 781800
Publisher E-mail: info@puzzler.com
Magazine featuring a collection of popular pocket
crosswords. **Freq:** 11/yr. **Trim Size:** 4.7 x 6.5. **Subscrip-
tion Rates:** 1.85 single issue. **URL:** http://www.puzzler.
com/magazines/PocketCodewordsCollection.htm.

56372 ■ Puzzler Pocket Wordsearch
Puzzler Media Ltd.
Stonecroft, 69 Station Rd.
Surrey
Redhill RH1 1EY, United Kingdom
Ph: 99944 1737 378700
Fax: 99944 1737 781800
Publisher E-mail: info@puzzler.com
Pocket size magazine featuring a collection of puzzles
with fun illustrations and a mixture of themes. **Freq:** 13/
yr. **Trim Size:** 4.7 x 6.5. **Subscription Rates:** 1.35
single issue. **URL:** http://www.puzzler.com/magazines/
PocketWordsearch.htm.

56373 ■ Puzzler Pocket Wordsearch Collection
Puzzler Media Ltd.
Stonecroft, 69 Station Rd.
Surrey
Redhill RH1 1EY, United Kingdom
Ph: 99944 1737 378700
Fax: 99944 1737 781800
Publisher E-mail: info@puzzler.com
Magazine featuring collection of wordsearches in a
handy-sized format. **Freq:** 11/yr. **Trim Size:** 4.7 x 6.5.
Subscription Rates: 1.85 single issue. **URL:** http://
www.puzzler.com/magazines/
PocketWordsearchCollection.htm.

56374 ■ Puzzler Quick Crosswords
Puzzler Media Ltd.
Stonecroft, 69 Station Rd.
Surrey
Redhill RH1 1EY, United Kingdom
Ph: 99944 1737 378700
Fax: 99944 1737 781800
Publisher E-mail: info@puzzler.com
Magazine featuring fun and quick-to-solve crosswords.
Freq: 13/yr. **Trim Size:** 7.3 x 10. **Subscription Rates:**
1.80 single issue. **URL:** http://www.puzzler.com/
magazines/PuzzlerQuickCrosswords.htm.

56375 ■ Puzzler Quiz Kids
Puzzler Media Ltd.
Stonecroft, 69 Station Rd.
Surrey
Redhill RH1 1EY, United Kingdom
Ph: 99944 1737 378700
Fax: 99944 1737 781800
Publisher E-mail: info@puzzler.com
Magazine featuring collection of puzzles for 7-11 years

old. **Freq:** 6/yr. **Trim Size:** 7.1 x 10. **Subscription Rates:** 2.60 single issue. **URL:** http://www.puzzler.com/magazines/QuizKids.htm.

56376 ■ Puzzler Wordsearch
Puzzler Media Ltd.
Stonecroft, 69 Station Rd.
Surrey
Redhill RH1 1EY, United Kingdom
Ph: 99944 1737 378700
Fax: 99944 1737 781800
Publisher E-mail: info@puzzler.com
Magazine featuring over 90 puzzles. **Freq:** 13/yr. **Trim Size:** 7.3 x 10. **Subscription Rates:** 1.80 single issue. **URL:** http://www.puzzler.com.

56377 ■ Register of Ships
IHS Global Limited
Lloyd's Register--Fairplay Ltd.
Lombard House
3 Princess Way
Surrey
Redhill RH1 1UP, United Kingdom
Ph: 44 1737 379000
Fax: 44 1737 379001
Publisher E-mail: info@lrfairplay.com
Trade magazine covering maritime information. **Key Personnel:** Jim Kemp, Contact. **Remarks:** Advertising not accepted. **Circ:** (Not Reported)

56378 ■ Safety at Sea International
DMG Business Media Ltd.
Lombard House
3 Princess Way
Redhill RH1 1UP, United Kingdom
Ph: 44 1737379700
Fax: 44 1737379001
Publication E-mail: sas@dmgworldmedia.com
Publisher E-mail: miaeng@dmgworldmedia.com
Trade magazine covering commercial marine safety. **Founded:** 1967. **Freq:** Monthly. **Print Method:** Web. **Trim Size:** 210 x 297 mm. **Key Personnel:** Paul Gunton, Managing Editor, phone 44 1737379142, paul.gunton@lrfairplay.com; Daniel Goncalves, Advertising Mgr., phone 44 1737379706, daniel.goncalves@lrfairplay.com; Nick Blackmore, Editor, phone 44 1737379176, nick.blackmore@lrfairplay.com. **Subscription Rates:** 330 individuals. **Remarks:** Accepts advertising. **URL:** http://www.safetyatsea.net/. **Circ:** Paid 6,000

56379 ■ Speciality Chemicals Magazine
DMG Business Media Ltd.
Westgate House
120/130 Station Rd.
Redhill RH1 1ET, United Kingdom
Ph: 44 17 37855000
Fax: 44 17 37855475
Publisher E-mail: miaeng@dmgworldmedia.com
Professional magazine covering technical, commercial and legal issues for the fine and speciality chemical industry. **Subtitle:** Global Application of Organic Chemistry. **Founded:** 1981. **Freq:** Monthly. **Trim Size:** 216 x 303 mm. **Key Personnel:** Dr. Andrew Warmington, Editor, phone 44 17 37855080, andrewwarmington@dmgworldmedia.com. **Subscription Rates:** 115 individuals; 130 other countries. **Remarks:** Accepts advertising. **URL:** http://www.specchemonline.com/. **Circ:** Non-paid ∗22,000

56380 ■ Sudoku Puzzles
Puzzler Media Ltd.
Stonecroft, 69 Station Rd.
Surrey
Redhill RH1 1EY, United Kingdom
Ph: 99944 1737 378700
Fax: 99944 1737 781800
Publisher E-mail: info@puzzler.com
Pocket size magazine featuring a collection of sudoku puzzles. **Freq:** 13/yr. **Trim Size:** 4.7 X 6.5. **Subscription Rates:** 2.40 single issue. **URL:** http://www.puzzler.com/magazines/SudokuPuzzles.htm.

56381 ■ Super Hanjie
Puzzler Media Ltd.
Stonecroft, 69 Station Rd.
Surrey
Redhill RH1 1EY, United Kingdom
Ph: 99944 1737 378700

Fax: 99944 1737 781800
Publisher E-mail: info@puzzler.com
Magazine featuring a collection of picture forming logic puzzles in sumo-size. **Freq:** 7/yr. **Trim Size:** 8.9 x 11. **Subscription Rates:** 3.50 single issue. **URL:** http://www.puzzler.com/magazines/SuperHanjie.htm.

56382 ■ Word Search
Puzzler Media Ltd.
Stonecroft, 69 Station Rd.
Surrey
Redhill RH1 1EY, United Kingdom
Ph: 99944 1737 378700
Fax: 99944 1737 781800
Publisher E-mail: info@puzzler.com
Magazine featuring wordsearches on imaginative topics with fun-shaped puzzles, hidden messages, and word trails. **Freq:** 14/yr. **Subscription Rates:** 2.20 single issue. **URL:** http://www.puzzler.com/magazines/Wordsearch.htm.

Redruth

56383 ■ Pirate-FM - 102.8
Wilson Way
Cornwall
Redruth TR15 3XX, United Kingdom
Ph: 44 1209 313900
Format: Adult Contemporary. **Key Personnel:** Bob McCreadie, Program Dir.; Beverley Warne, Mng. Dir. **URL:** http://www.piratefm.co.uk/.

56384 ■ Pirate-FM - 102.2
Wilson Way
Cornwall
Redruth TR15 3XX, United Kingdom
Ph: 44 1209 313900
E-mail: reception@piratefm.co.uk
Format: Adult Contemporary. **Key Personnel:** Bob McCreadie, Program Dir.; Beverly Warne, Mng. Dir. **URL:** http://www.piratefm.co.uk/.

Reepham

56385 ■ ELT Journal
Oxford University Press
c/o Keith Morrow, Ed.
Homerton House
Cawston Rd.
Reepham NR10 4LT, United Kingdom
Fax: 44 16 03872955
Publisher E-mail: webenquiry.uk@oup.com
Journal providing information on the field of teaching English as a second language. **Freq:** Quarterly. **Key Personnel:** Keith Morrow, Editor, editor@eltj.org; Charles Hadfield, Text Messages Ed.; Barbara Skinner, Editorial Panel; Annamaria Pinter, Editorial Panel; Jane Spiro, Editorial Panel; Simon Greenall, Advisory Board; Philip Prowse, Reviews Ed., phone 44 1223 572390, philip.prowse@ntlworld.com; Norman Whitney, Advisory Board. **ISSN:** 0951-0893. **Subscription Rates:** 174 institutions corporate; print and online; 145 institutions corporate; online only; 160 institutions corporate; print only; 139 institutions print and online; 116 institutions online only; 128 institutions print only; 51 individuals print; 26 students print; 38 members print. **URL:** http://eltj.oxfordjournals.org.

Reigate

56386 ■ Brewers' Guardian
Advantage Publishing Ltd.
3rd Fl., Alma House
Alma Rd.
Reigate RH2 0AX, United Kingdom
Fax: 44 17 37241243
Publisher E-mail: info@advantagepublishing.co.uk
Trade magazine for the brewing and distilling industries worldwide. **Founded:** 1871. **Freq:** Monthly 10/yr. **Print Method:** Sheetfed Litho. **Trim Size:** 297 x 210 mm. **Key Personnel:** Larry Nelson, Editor and Publisher, phone 44 17 37221232, larry@advantagepublishing.co.uk; Nigel Smith, Office Mgr., nigel@advantagepublishing.co.uk. **ISSN:** 0006-9728. **Remarks:** Accepts advertising. **URL:** http://www.brewersguardian.com. **Ad Rates:** GLR: 17, BW: 700, 4C: 1,050. **Circ:** 3,200

Rhyl

56387 ■ Rhyl Journal
NWN Media Ltd.
Accent House, 23 Kinmel St.
Denbighshire
Rhyl LL18 1AH, United Kingdom
Ph: 44 1745 357500
Fax: 44 1745 343510
Publisher E-mail: internet@nwn.co.uk
Newspaper featuring news coverage and human interest stories. **Key Personnel:** Steve Rogers, Editor; Claire Bryce, Advertising Mgr. **URL:** http://www.rhyljournal.co.uk/.

Richmond

56388 ■ BG Journal
Botanical Gardens Conservation International
Descanso House, 199 Kew Rd.
Surrey
Richmond TW9 3BW, United Kingdom
Ph: 44 20 83325953
Fax: 44 20 83325956
Publisher E-mail: info@bgci.org
Journal featuring profiles of gardens and case studies of conservation work in gardens. **Freq:** Semiannual. **URL:** http://www.bgci.org/resources/bgjournal/.

56389 ■ Chamaerops Magazine
European Palm Society
c/o The Palm Ctr., Ham Central Nursery
Ham St., Ham
Surrey
Richmond TW10 7HA, United Kingdom
Ph: 44 20 82556191
Fax: 44 20 82556192
Publisher E-mail: info@palmsociety.org
Magazine containing articles on palms in a temperate climate. **Subscription Rates:** included in membership dues. **URL:** http://www.palmsociety.org/public/english/chamaerops/.

56390 ■ Dive
British Sub-Aqua Club
One Victoria Villas
Richmond TW9 2GW, United Kingdom
Publisher E-mail: info@bsac.com
Publication covering diving. **Freq:** Monthly. **Key Personnel:** Simon Rogerson, Editor; Graeme Gourlay, Exec.; Paul Critcher, Publisher. **Subscription Rates:** 35 individuals. **Remarks:** Accepts advertising. **URL:** http://www.divemagazine.co.uk/. **Circ:** 41,622

56391 ■ eltonjohnworld.com
Elton John Fan Club - United Kingdom
PO Box 315
Richmond TW9 3QX, United Kingdom
Ph: 44 77 13725242
Fax: 44 87 01307752
Publisher E-mail: news@eltonjohnworld.com
Publication covering Elton John in English, German and Italian. **Freq:** Continuous. **Key Personnel:** Cheryl Herman, Editor, habits@eltonjohnworld.com. **Remarks:** Advertising accepted; rates available upon request. **URL:** http://www.eltonjohnworld.com. **Circ:** (Not Reported)

56392 ■ Systematics and Biodiversity
Cambridge University Press
c/o Dr. Henk Beentje, Assoc. Ed.
Royal Botanic Gardens, Kew
Surrey
Richmond TW9 3AE, United Kingdom
Publisher E-mail: information@cambridge.org
International life science journal devoted to whole-organism biology, especially systematics and taxonomic biodiversity, emphasizing the importance and multi-disciplinary significance of systematics. **Key Personnel:** Dr. Gaden S. Robinson, Assoc. Ed.; Dr. P.J. Hayward, Assoc. Ed.; Dr. Henk Beentje, Assoc. Ed.; Dr. B.T. Clarke, Assoc. Ed.; Dr. Andrew Brower, Assoc. Ed. **ISSN:** 1477-2000. **Remarks:** Accepts advertising. **URL:** http://journals.cambridge.org/action/displayJournal?jid=SYS. **Circ:** ‡700

Circulation: ★ = ABC; △ = BPA; ◆ = CAC; • = CCAB; ❑ = VAC; ⊕ = PO Statement; ‡ = Publisher's Report; Boldface figures = sworn; Light figures = estimated.

Gale Directory of Publications & Broadcast Media/147th Ed.   5847

Rickmansworth

56393 ▪ Ingredients, Health & Nutrition
Turret Group Company
173 High St.
Rickmansworth WD3 1AY, United Kingdom
Ph: 44 1923 692660
Fax: 44 1923 692679
Technical, trade magazine covering health and nutritional information for the food manufacturing industry in Western Europe. **Founded:** Jan. 1998. **Freq:** Bimonthly. **Print Method:** Litho. **Trim Size:** 210 x 297 mm. **Cols./Page:** 4. **ISSN:** 1464-0074. **Subscription Rates:** Free to qualified subscribers. **Remarks:** Accepts advertising. **URL:** http://www.turretgroup.com/. **Circ:** Controlled 4,682

56394 ▪ International Aquafeed
Turret Group Company
173 High St.
Rickmansworth WD3 1AY, United Kingdom
Ph: 44 1923 692660
Fax: 44 1923 692679
Trade magazine covering the aquaculture feed industry worldwide. **Founded:** Nov. 1998. **Freq:** Quarterly. **Key Personnel:** Prof. Simon Davies, Editor, phone 44 1242 267706, simond@aquafeed.co.uk; Nicky Barnes, Production Ed., nickyb@aquafeed.co.uk. **Subscription Rates:** 43 individuals. **Remarks:** Accepts advertising. **URL:** http://www.aquafeed.co.uk/. **Circ:** (Not Reported)

Ringwood

56395 ▪ Doctor Who Battles in Time
GE Fabbri Ltd.
Unit 4, Pullman Business Pk.
Pullman Way
Ringwood BH24 1HD, United Kingdom
Ph: 44 871 2770067
Publication E-mail: drwho@dbfactory.co.uk
Publisher E-mail: mailbox@gefabbri.co.uk
Magazine featuring trading card game. **Freq:** Semimonthly. **Key Personnel:** Peter Edwards, Mng. Dir.; Liz Glaze, Director; Katie Preston, Editor-in-Chief. **Subscription Rates:** 10 individuals. **URL:** http://www.gefabbri.co.uk/publication_doctorwhobattlesintime.

56396 ▪ Felicity Wishes
GE Fabbri Ltd.
4 Pullman Business Pk.
Pullman Way
Ringwood BH24 1HD, United Kingdom
Publisher E-mail: mailbox@gefabbri.co.uk
Magazine featuring Felicity and her friends. **Freq:** Semimonthly. **Key Personnel:** Peter Edwards, Mng. Dir.; Liz Glaze, Director; Katie Preston, Editor-in-Chief. **Subscription Rates:** 2.99 single issue. **URL:** http://www.felicitywishescollection.com/; http://www.gefabbri.co.uk/publication_felicitywishes.

56397 ▪ 007 Spy Cards
GE Fabbri Ltd.
4 Pullman Business Pk.
Pullman Way
Ringwood BH24 1HD, United Kingdom
Ph: 44 871 2770116
Publication E-mail: spycards@dbfactory.co.uk
Publisher E-mail: mailbox@gefabbri.co.uk
Magazine featuring James Bond spy cards. **Freq:** Semimonthly. **Key Personnel:** Peter Edwards, Mng. Dir.; Liz Glaze, Director; Katie Preston, Editor-in-Chief. **Subscription Rates:** 2.95 single issue. **URL:** http://www.007spycards.com/; http://www.gefabbri.co.uk/publication_007spycards.

Ripley

56398 ▪ Ripley & Heanor News
Johnston Press PLC
27 Grosvenor Rd.
Ripley DE5 3JE, United Kingdom
Ph: 44 1773 514150
Publication E-mail: news@rhnews.co.uk
Local community newspaper. **Key Personnel:** Sarah Bould, Contact. **Remarks:** Accepts advertising. **URL:** http://www.ripleyandheanornews.co.uk/. **Circ:** (Not Reported)

Ripon

56399 ▪ Ripon Gazette & Boroughbridge Herald
Johnston Press PLC
5 Kirkgate
Ripon HG4 1PA, United Kingdom
Ph: 44 1765 601248
Publication E-mail: news@ripongazette.co.uk
Local community newspaper. **Key Personnel:** Jean MacQuarrie, Editor. **Remarks:** Accepts advertising. **URL:** http://www.ripongazette.co.uk/. **Circ:** (Not Reported)

56400 ▪ Yorkshire Life
Archant Life
PO Box 163
Ripon HG4 9AG, United Kingdom
Publisher E-mail: johnny.hustler@archant.co.uk
Lifestyle magazine featuring Yorkshire. **Subtitle:** Yorkshire's best selling county magazine. **Key Personnel:** Esther Leach, Editor, esther.leach@yorkshirelife.co.uk; Robert Hughes, Retail Sales Mgr., phone 44 7713 83188, bob.hughes@archant.co.uk; Andy Phelan, Publisher, andy.phelan@archant.co.uk. **Subscription Rates:** 25 individuals. **Remarks:** Accepts advertising. **URL:** http://www.yorkshirelife.co.uk. **Circ:** ★22,531

Rochdale

56401 ▪ Asian Leader
Johnston Press PLC
PO Box 303
Rochdale OL111WA, United Kingdom
Ph: 44 1706 670119
Local community newspaper. **Remarks:** Accepts advertising. **URL:** http://www.asianleader.co.uk/. **Circ:** (Not Reported)

Rochester

56402 ▪ KM-FM - 107.9
Medway House
Ginsbury Close
Sir Thomas Longley Rd.
Medway City Estate, Strood
Rochester ME2 4DU, United Kingdom
Ph: 44 1634 227800
E-mail: okemp@kmfm.co.uk
Format: Adult Contemporary. **Operating Hours:** Continuous. **Ad Rates:** Advertising accepted; rates available upon request. **URL:** http://www.kmfm.co.uk/goto.php?sess=x184372lu184259lp111ln0lc0ll0lg2ld0.

56403 ▪ KM-FM - 105.6
Medway House
Ginsbury Close
Sir Thomas Longley Rd.
Medway City Estate, Strood
Rochester ME2 4DU, United Kingdom
Ph: 44 1634 227800
Fax: 44 1622 662501
E-mail: okemp@kmfm.co.uk
Format: Contemporary Hit Radio (CHR). **Founded:** Oct. 18, 2003. **Formerly:** CTR-FM. **Ad Rates:** Advertising accepted; rates available upon request. **URL:** http://www.kmfm.co.uk/goto.php?sess=x9lg9.

Romford

56404 ▪ Link-FM - 92.2
St George's Church & Ctr.
Chippenham Rd.
Harold Hill
Romford RM3 8HX, United Kingdom
Ph: 44 1708 342200
Fax: 44 1708 345500
E-mail: studio@linkfm.net
Format: Alternative/New Music/Progressive; Jazz; New Age. **URL:** http://www.linkfm.net/.

56405 ▪ Time-FM - 107.5
Lambourne House
7 Western Rd.
Romford RM1 3LD, United Kingdom
Ph: 44 1708 741075
Format: Adult Contemporary. **Key Personnel:** Peter Stremes, Station Mng. Dir., peter@timefm.com; Sarah Ross, Head of Sales, sross@timefm.com; Mark Dover, Program Mgr., mdover@timefm.com; Sam Rigby, News Ed., 1075news@timefm.com. **Ad Rates:** Advertising accepted; rates available upon request. **URL:** http://www.time1075.com/.

Romsey

56406 ▪ Crossword
Crossword Club
Coombe Farm
Awbridge
Romsey SO51 0HN, United Kingdom
Ph: 44 17 94524346
Fax: 44 17 94514988
Publisher E-mail: bh@crosswordclub.co.uk
Publication covering crossword puzzles. **Founded:** 1978. **Freq:** Monthly. **Print Method:** Laser. **Trim Size:** A5. **ISSN:** 0267-3711. **Remarks:** Advertising accepted; rates available upon request. **URL:** http://www.thecrosswordclub.co.uk/. **Circ:** 750

56407 ▪ Photogrammetric Record
Remote Sensing and Photogrammetry Society
c/o Paul Newby, Ed.
9 Merrytree Close, West Wellow
Romsey SO51 6RB, United Kingdom
Publisher E-mail: rspsoc@rspsoc.org
Journal covering geomatics and engineering. **Founded:** 1953. **Freq:** Quarterly. **Key Personnel:** Paul Newby, Editor; K.B. Atkinson, Ed. Emeritus; J. Walstra, Book Review Ed. **ISSN:** 0031-868X. **Subscription Rates:** US$606 institutions print & online; 355 institutions print and online; EUR450 institutions; US$694 institutions, other countries print & online; US$551 institutions print only; 322 institutions print only; EUR409 institutions print only; US$360 institutions, other countries print only. **Remarks:** Accepts advertising. **URL:** http://www.rspsoc.org; http://www.rspsoc.org/publications/the-photogrammetric-record/; http://www.wiley.com/bw/editors.asp?ref=0031-868X. **Circ:** (Not Reported)

Roslin

56408 ▪ British Poultry Science
Taylor & Francis Group Journals
c/o Dr. G.A. Meiras, Editorial Asst.
Roslin Institute (Edinburgh)
Roslin EH25 9PS, United Kingdom
Publisher E-mail: customerservice@taylorandfrancis.com
Journal for poultry scientists and advisers to the poultry industry. **Freq:** Bimonthly. **Key Personnel:** Barry O. Hughes, Asst. Ed.; Murdo G. MacLeod, Editor; M. Choct, Asst. Ed.; G.K. Baggott, Asst. Ed.; S.P. Rose, Asst. Ed. **ISSN:** 0007-1668. **Subscription Rates:** US$428 institutions print and online; US$407 institutions online; US$223 individuals; 238 institutions print and online; 227 institutions online; 112 individuals; EUR343 institutions print and online; EUR327 institutions online; EUR179 individuals. **URL:** http://www.tandf.co.uk/journals/tf/00071668.html.

Ross-on-Wye

56409 ▪ Garden Design Journal
Society of Garden Designers
Katepwa House
Ashfield Park Ave.
Ross-on-Wye HR9 5AX, United Kingdom
Ph: 44 1989 566695
Fax: 44 1989 567676
Publisher E-mail: info@sgd.org.uk
Journal covering landscaping, gardening, and architecture. **Freq:** Monthly. **ISSN:** 1356-6458. **Subscription Rates:** 5 individuals UK; 27 individuals Europe; 54 other countries; Free members. **Remarks:** Advertising accepted; rates available upon request. **URL:** http://www.sgd.org.uk/mainpages/garden_design_publications.htm. **Circ:** 3,000

56410 ▪ Marine Conservation
Marine Conservation Society
Unit 3
Wolf Business Pk.
Alton Rd.
Ross-on-Wye HR9 5NB, United Kingdom
Ph: 44 19 89566017
Fax: 44 19 89567815
Publication E-mail: info@mcsuk.org
Professional journal covering marine conservation. **Freq:** Quarterly. **Print Method:** Sheetfed Offset. **Trim Size:** A4. **Cols./Page:** 3. **Key Personnel:** Richard Harrington,

Editor. **Subscription Rates:** 30 other countries; 25 individuals. **Remarks:** Accepts advertising. **URL:** http://www.mcsuk.org/magazine/magazine.php. **Circ:** Paid 5,000

56411 ■ Person-Centered and Experimental Psychotherapies
PCCS Books Ltd.
2 Cropper Row
Alton Rd.
Ross-on-Wye HR9 5LA, United Kingdom
Ph: 44 1989 763900
Fax: 44 1989 763901
Publisher E-mail: contact@pccs-books.co.uk
Official journal of the World Association for Person-Centered and Experiential Psychotherapy and Counseling. **Freq:** Quarterly. **ISSN:** 1477-9757. **Subscription Rates:** 50 individuals; 54 individuals European Union; 58 other countries; 130 institutions; 134 institutions European Union; 138 institutions, other countries. **URL:** http://www.pccs-books.co.uk/section.php?xSec=140.

Rotherham

56412 ■ The School Librarian
School Library Association
c/o Steve Hird, Ed.
7, Clifton Bank
S Yorkshire
Rotherham S60 2NA, United Kingdom
Publication E-mail: info@sla.org.uk
Publisher E-mail: info@sla.org.uk
Journal covering school library management, literacy, publishing and related information, including reviews of books, CD-ROMs and websites for school libraries. **Founded:** 1937. **Freq:** Quarterly. **Key Personnel:** Steve Hird, Editor, sleditor@sla.org.uk. **Remarks:** Accepts advertising. **URL:** http://www.sla.org.uk/school-librarian.php. **Circ:** Paid 4,000

56413 ■ Rother-FM - 96.1
Aspen Ct.
Bessemar Way
Rotherham S60 1FB, United Kingdom
Ph: 44 1709 369991
Fax: 44 1709 369993
E-mail: enquiries@rotherfm.co.uk
Format: Adult Contemporary; News; Information. **URL:** http://www.rotherfm.co.uk/.

Rothesay

56414 ■ The Buteman
Johnston Press PLC
5 Victoria St.
Rothesay PA20 0AJ, United Kingdom
Ph: 44 1700 502503
Local community newspaper. **Remarks:** Accepts advertising. **URL:** http://www.buteman.co.uk/. **Circ:** (Not Reported)

Royston

56415 ■ Royston Crow
Archant Regional Ltd.
Hoyston Crow
3 Angel Pavement
Royston SG8 9AS, United Kingdom
Ph: 44 1763 244977
Publisher E-mail: sandra.roantree@archant.co.uk
Local community newspaper. **Freq:** Weekly (Thurs.). **Key Personnel:** Darren Isted, Editor, editor@royston-crow.co.uk. **Subscription Rates:** 1.50 individuals latest issue only; 19.50 individuals 13 weeks; 39 individuals 26 weeks; 78 individuals. **Remarks:** Accepts advertising. **URL:** http://www.royston-crow.co.uk/home. **Circ:** ★16,003

Rugby

56416 ■ Chemical Engineering Research and Design (ChERD)
Institution of Chemical Engineers
Davis Bldg.
165-189 Railway Ter.
Rugby CV21 3HQ, United Kingdom
Ph: 44 1788 578214
Fax: 44 1788 560833

Publisher E-mail: onlineassistance@icheme.org
Journal covering all aspects of experimentation, development and theory in chemical engineering. **Founded:** 1923. **Freq:** Monthly. **Key Personnel:** Prof. Stephen Richardson, Exec. Ed., s.m.richardson@imperial.ac.uk; Prof. Nikolai Kulov, Editorial Board, kulov@igic.ras.ru; Prof. J.B. Joshi, Editorial Board, jbj@udct.org; Prof. John Perkins, Honorary Ed., john.perkins@manchester.ac.uk; Catherine Cliffe, Managing Editor, ccliffe@icheme.org.uk. **ISSN:** 0263-8762. **Subscription Rates:** EUR1,418 institutions European countries and Iran; 223,000¥ institutions Japan; US$1,830 institutions, other countries. **URL:** http://cms.icheme.org/mainwebsite/general-bar7ddc91997e4763f.aspx?map=95bba0b8893755ba6cdc608d3327d1ec.

56417 ■ Education for Chemical Engineers
Institution of Chemical Engineers
Davis Bldg.
165-189 Railway Ter.
Rugby CV21 3HQ, United Kingdom
Ph: 44 1788 578214
Fax: 44 1788 560833
Publisher E-mail: onlineassistance@icheme.org
Online journal providing research information on chemical engineering for education. **Key Personnel:** Dr. David Shallcross, Editor-in-Chief, dcshal@unimelb.edu.au; Prof. Stephen Richardson, Exec. Ed., s.m.richardson@lboro.ac.uk; Prof. John Perkins, Honorary Ed., john.perkins@manchester.ac.uk. **ISSN:** 1749-7728. **Subscription Rates:** 25 members UK, online only plus VAT; 25 members rest of the world, online only plus VAT; $A 60 nonmembers Australia, online only; M$150 nonmembers Malaysia, online only. **URL:** http://www.portlandpress.com; http://cms.icheme.org/mainwebsite/General-Bar7ddc91997e4763f.aspx?Map=3C5FC51347648EA242939429F89D8727.

56418 ■ Enterprise Development and Microfinance
Practical Action Publing
The Schumacher Ctr. for Technology and Development
Bourton on Dunsmore
Rugby CV23 9QZ, United Kingdom
Ph: 44 19 26634501
Fax: 44 19 26634502
Publisher E-mail: publishinginfo@practicalaction.org.uk
Journal covering small enterprise development. **Subtitle:** International journal of microfinance and business development. **Freq:** Quarterly. **Key Personnel:** Clare Tawney, Editor. **Subscription Rates:** 75 individuals; 125 institutions. **Remarks:** Accepts advertising. **URL:** http://practicalactionpublishing.org/?id=publishing_journals. **Formerly:** Small Enterprise Development Journal. **Ad Rates:** BW: 800. **Circ:** (Not Reported)

56419 ■ Food & Bioproducts Processing
Institution of Chemical Engineers
Davis Bldg.
165-189 Railway Ter.
Rugby CV21 3HQ, United Kingdom
Ph: 44 1788 578214
Fax: 44 1788 560833
Publisher E-mail: onlineassistance@icheme.org
Journal dedicated to the processing of food and bioproducts. **Freq:** Quarterly. **Key Personnel:** Prof. Stephen Richardson, Exec. Ed., s.m.richardson@imperial.ac.uk; Ken Morison, Editor-in-Chief, ken.morison@canterbury.ac.nz. **ISSN:** 0960-3085. **Subscription Rates:** EUR558 institutions European countries and Iran; 87,900¥ institutions; US$719 institutions, other countries. **URL:** http://cms.icheme.org/mainwebsite/General-Bar7ddc91997e4763f.aspx?Map=E7CFCED36C7387B07ACCF6553C1576D8.

56420 ■ The Lighting Journal
Institution of Lighting Engineers
Regent House
Regent Pl.
Rugby CV21 2PN, United Kingdom
Ph: 44 17 88576492
Fax: 44 17 88540145
Publication E-mail: lj@ile.org.uk
Publisher E-mail: info@ile.org.uk
Professional magazine covering technical information and news for the lighting industry. **Founded:** 1936. **Freq:** Bimonthly. **Print Method:** Litho. **Trim Size:** 210 x 297 mm. **Cols./Page:** 3. **Key Personnel:** Ian Marshall, Contact. **ISSN:** 0950-4559. **Subscription Rates:** 43 individuals; 55 individuals Europe; 55 other countries.

Remarks: Accepts advertising. **URL:** http://www.ile.org.uk/. **Circ:** Paid 4,500

56421 ■ Loss Prevention Bulletin
Institution of Chemical Engineers
Davis Bldg.
165-189 Railway Ter.
Rugby CV21 3HQ, United Kingdom
Ph: 44 1788 578214
Fax: 44 1788 560833
Publisher E-mail: onlineassistance@icheme.org
Trade journal covering process safety in chemical engineering. **Founded:** 1974. **Freq:** 6/yr. **Key Personnel:** Tracey Donaldson, Editor, phone 44 1788 578214, tdonaldson@icheme.org. **ISSN:** 0260-9576. **Subscription Rates:** 220 members print & online plus VAT; $A 510 individuals Australia; print & online; M$1,320 individuals Malaysia; print & online; 220 members UK & rest of world; online only plus VAT; $A 105 individuals Australia; online only; M$270 individuals Malaysia; online only; 45 members UK & rest of world; online only; $A 80 individuals Australia; online only (archive); M$210 individuals Malaysia; online only (archive); 312 nonmembers print. **Remarks:** Advertising not accepted. **URL:** http://cms.icheme.org/MainWebSite/General-Barfb7d65aa69ef5027.aspx?Map=49C04834433BEF0CA60153732CF0B3BE. **Circ:** (Not Reported)

56422 ■ Process Safety and Environmental Protection (PSEP)
Institution of Chemical Engineers
Davis Bldg.
165-189 Railway Ter.
Rugby CV21 3HQ, United Kingdom
Ph: 44 1788 578214
Fax: 44 1788 560833
Publisher E-mail: onlineassistance@icheme.org
Publication covering chemistry. **Freq:** Bimonthly. **Key Personnel:** Catherine Cliffe, Managing Editor, ccliffe@icheme.org; Prof. Stephen Richardson, Exec. Ed., s.m.richardson@imperial.ac.uk; Prof. John Perkins, Editor, john.perkins@manchester.ac.uk. **ISSN:** 0957-5820. **Subscription Rates:** 105 members UK; print with online; plus VAT; 105 other countries print and online; plus VAT; $A 245 nonmembers Australia; print and online; M$630 nonmembers Malaysia; print and online; 45 members UK & rest of world; online only + VAT; $A 105 nonmembers Australia; online only; M$270 nonmembers Malaysia; online only. **URL:** http://cms.icheme.org/mainwebsite/General-Bar7ddc91997e4763f.aspx?Map=9414B5FF7079D8C017EE917274D0EEFC.

56423 ■ Rugby Advertiser
Johnston Press PLC
2 Albert St.
Rugby CV21 2RS, United Kingdom
Ph: 44 1788 539999
Local community newspaper. **Founded:** 1846. **Freq:** Weekly (Thurs.). **Key Personnel:** Melissa Lynch, Contact, phone 44 1604 251195, melissa.lynch@jpress.co.uk. **Remarks:** Accepts advertising. **URL:** http://www.rugbytoday.co.uk/. **Circ:** (Not Reported)

56424 ■ TCE
Institution of Chemical Engineers
Davis Bldg.
165-189 Railway Ter.
Rugby CV21 3HQ, United Kingdom
Ph: 44 1788 578214
Fax: 44 1788 560833
Publication E-mail: journals@icheme.org
Publisher E-mail: onlineassistance@icheme.org
Publication covering process engineering. **Subtitle:** The Chemical Engineer. **Founded:** 1922. **Freq:** Monthly. **Print Method:** Web. **Trim Size:** A4. **Key Personnel:** Delyth Forsdyke, Managing Editor, dforsdyke@icheme.org.uk; David Brown, Publisher, dbrown@icheme.org; Claudia Flavell-While, Editor, claudia@icheme.org; Alex Revell, Magazine Graphic Designer, arevell@icheme.org; Adam Duckett, Sen. Reporter, aduckett@icheme.org; Helen Tunnicliffe, Reporter, htunnicliffe@icheme.org. **Subscription Rates:** 16 individuals one month; 16 other countries one month; 160 individuals print only; 175 other countries print only; 160 individuals online only plus VAT; 175 other countries online only plus VAT; 176 individuals print & online comb plus VAT; 192 other countries print & online comb plus VAT. **Remarks:** Ac-

Circulation: ★ = ABC; △ = BPA; ♦ = CAC; • = CCAB; ❑ = VAC; ⊕ = PO Statement; ‡ = Publisher's Report; Boldface figures = sworn; Light figures = estimated.

Gale Directory of Publications & Broadcast Media/147th Ed.

5849

cepts advertising. **URL:** http://www.tcetoday.com. **Formerly:** The Chemical Engineer. **Ad Rates:** 4C: EUR2,495. **Circ:** ★24,000

56425 ■ Waterlines
Practical Action Publishing
The Schumacher Centre for Technology & Development
Bourton on Dunsmore
Warwickshire
Rugby CV23 9QZ, United Kingdom
Ph: 44 1926 634501
Fax: 44 1926 634502
Publisher E-mail: publishinginfo@practicalaction.org.uk
Peer-reviewed journal covering low-cost water supplies and sanitation facilities in developing countries. **Founded:** 1982. **Key Personnel:** Richard Carter, Editor; Clare Tawney, Managing Editor. **ISSN:** 0262-8104. **URL:** http://www.itdgpublishing.org.uk/publishing/waterlines.

Rushden

56426 ■ Nutrition & Food Science
Emerald Group Publishing Ltd.
c/o Dr. Mabel Blades, Ed.
Denehurst
202 Newton Rd.
Rushden NN10 0SY, United Kingdom
Publisher E-mail: emerald@emeraldinsight.com
Publication for the food and beverage industries. **Freq:** Bimonthly. **Key Personnel:** Dr. Mabel Blades, Editor, mabel@qmnds.demon.co.uk; Dr. Stephen Fallows, PhD, Internet Ed., sjfallows@aol.com; Kate Snowden, Publisher, ksnowden@emeraldinsight.com; Dr. Sam Sumar, PhD, Regional Ed., sumars@wmin.ac.uk. **ISSN:** 0034-6659. **URL:** http://www.emeraldinsight.com/products/journals/journals.htm?id=nfs.

56427 ■ UK Irrigation
U.K. Irrigation Association
c/o Moorland House
Hayway
Rushden NN10 6AG, United Kingdom
Ph: 44 1427 717627
Publisher E-mail: m.kay@ukia.org
Publication covering agricultural equipment. **Freq:** Annual. **ISSN:** 0265-5136. **Remarks:** Accepts advertising. **URL:** http://www.ukia.org/publications.htm. **Formerly:** Irrigation News. **Circ:** 500

Ruyton XI Towns

56428 ■ Polymer Testing
Elsevier Science
c/o R. Brown, Ed.
Brownhill House
Ruyton XI Towns SY4 1LR, United Kingdom
Publisher E-mail: nlinfo-f@elsevier.com
Journal dealing with testing of polymers and polymeric products. **Founded:** 1980. **Freq:** 8/yr. **Key Personnel:** R. Brown, Editor, roger@eleventowns.com; M. Forrest, Editorial Board; P. Roumagnac, Editorial Board. **ISSN:** 0142-9418. **Subscription Rates:** US$1,967 institutions for all countries except Europe, Japan & Iran; EUR1,762 institutions for European countries & Iran; 233,500¥ institutions. **Remarks:** Advertising accepted; rates available upon request. **URL:** http://www.elsevier.com/wps/find/journaldescription.cws_home/405943/descriptiondescription. **Circ:** (Not Reported)

Saffron Walden

56429 ■ Photography Monthly
Archant Life
The Mill
Bearwalden Business Park
Wendens Ambo
Essex
Saffron Walden CB11 4GB, United Kingdom
Publication E-mail: photography.monthly@photographymonthly.co.uk
Publisher E-mail: johnny.hustler@archant.co.uk
Magazine targeting photography enthusiasts throughout the world. **Freq:** Monthly. **Subscription Rates:** 5 individuals 5 issues, direct debit; 42 other countries; 40 individuals europe. **URL:** http://www.photographymonthly.com.

56430 ■ Saffron Walden Reporter
Archant Regional Ltd.

54 High St.
Saffron Walden CB10 1EE, United Kingdom
Ph: 44 1799 525100
Fax: 44 1799 527310
Publication E-mail: editor@saffronwalden-reporter.co.uk
Publisher E-mail: sandra.roantree@archant.co.uk
Local community newspaper. **Freq:** Weekly (Thurs.). **Subscription Rates:** 1.50 individuals latest issue only; 19.50 individuals 13 weeks; 39 individuals 26 weeks; 78 individuals. **Remarks:** Accepts advertising. **URL:** http://www.saffronwaldenreporter.co.uk/home. **Circ:** (Not Reported)

Saint Agnes

56431 ■ Atlantic-FM - 107
10 Wheal Kitty Workshops
Saint Agnes TR5 0RD, United Kingdom
Ph: 44 18 72554466
Fax: 44 18 72554244
E-mail: studio@atlantic.fm
Format: Music of Your Life; Contemporary Hit Radio (CHR); News. **Owner:** Atlantic Broadcasting Ltd., at above address. **Operating Hours:** Continuous. **Ad Rates:** Advertising accepted; rates available upon request. **URL:** http://www.atlantic.fm.

56432 ■ Atlantic-FM - 105.1
10 Wheal Kitty Workshops
Saint Agnes TR5 0RD, United Kingdom
Ph: 44 18 72554466
Fax: 44 18 72554244
E-mail: studio@atlantic.fm
Format: Music of Your Life; Contemporary Hit Radio (CHR); News. **Owner:** Atlantic Broadcasting Ltd., at above address. **Operating Hours:** Continuous. **URL:** http://www.atlantic.fm.

Saint Albans

56433 ■ Acoustics Bulletin
Institute of Acoustics
77A St. Peter's St.
Saint Albans AL1 3BN, United Kingdom
Ph: 44 17 27848195
Fax: 44 17 27850553
Publisher E-mail: ioa@ioa.org.uk
Publication covering acoustics. **Freq:** Bimonthly. **Key Personnel:** I.F. Bennett, Editor. **Remarks:** Advertising accepted; rates available upon request. **URL:** http://www.ioa.org.uk/publications/acoustics-bulletin.asp. **Circ:** (Not Reported)

56434 ■ Asian Environmental Technology
Environmental Technology Publications Ltd.
Oak Ct., Sandridge Pk.
Porters Wood
Saint Albans AL3 6PH, United Kingdom
Ph: 44 1727 858840
Fax: 44 1727 840310
Publisher E-mail: info@envirotech-online.com
Journal covering the testing, monitoring, and analysis of water, air and soil. **Founded:** 1996. **Freq:** Quarterly. **Trim Size:** 252 x 340 mm. **Key Personnel:** Marcus Pattison, Publisher. **ISSN:** 1363-7134. **Remarks:** Accepts advertising. **URL:** http://www.envirotech-online.com/; http://www.aet-pub.com/; http://www.envirotech-online.com/assets/docs/iet/advertise/AET_Rates_and_Data.pdf. **Circ:** Controlled 23,334

56435 ■ Galpin Society Journal
The Galpin Society
37 Townsend Dr.
Saint Albans AL3 5RF, United Kingdom
Publisher E-mail: administrator@galpinsociety.org
Scholarly journal covering research in music history. **Founded:** 1946. **Freq:** Annual. **Key Personnel:** Dr. Bradley Strauchen-Scherer, Reviews Ed., bstrauchen@horniman.ac.uk; Dr. Michael Fleming, Editor, editor@galpinsociety.org. **ISSN:** 0072-0127. **Subscription Rates:** 22 individuals; 36 institutions; 28 individuals Europe; 34 elsewhere individuals. **Remarks:** Accepts advertising. **URL:** http://www.music.ed.ac.uk/euchmi/galpin/. **Circ:** Paid 850

56436 ■ Herts Advertiser
Archant Regional Ltd.
Sandridge Pk., Unit 1
Saint Albans AL3 6PH, United Kingdom
Fax: 44 1727 736527

Publisher E-mail: sandra.roantree@archant.co.uk
Local community newspaper. **Freq:** Weekly (Thurs.). **Key Personnel:** Matt Adams, Editor; Stuart McCreery, Mng. Dir. **Subscription Rates:** 3 individuals latest issue only; 39 individuals 3 months; 78 individuals 6 months; 156 individuals. **Remarks:** Accepts advertising. **URL:** http://www.hertsad.co.uk/home. **Circ:** ★51,584

56437 ■ International Environmental Technology
Environmental Technology Publications Ltd.
Oak Ct., Sandridge Pk.
Porters Wood
Saint Albans AL3 6PH, United Kingdom
Ph: 44 1727 858840
Fax: 44 1727 840310
Publisher E-mail: info@envirotech-online.com
Journal covering the testing, monitoring, and analysis of water, air and soil. **Founded:** 1990. **Freq:** Bimonthly. **Trim Size:** 252 x 340 mm. **Key Personnel:** Michael Pattison, Mng. Dir., michael@intlabmate.com; Marcus Pattison, Director, marcus@envirotechpubs.com. **ISSN:** 0963-7362. **Remarks:** Accepts advertising. **URL:** http://www.iet-pub.com/; http://www.envirotech-online.com/. **Circ:** Controlled 39,239

56438 ■ The Rose
Royal National Rose Society
The Gardens of the Rose
Chiswell Green Ln.
Saint Albans AL2 3NR, United Kingdom
Ph: 44 17 27850461
Fax: 44 17 27850360
Publisher E-mail: mail@rnrs.org.uk
Publication covering roses and rose gardening. **Founded:** 1984. **Freq:** Quarterly. **Key Personnel:** Ann Bird, President; Rod Petty, Dep. Pres. **Remarks:** Accepts advertising. **URL:** http://www.rnrs.org. **Circ:** (Not Reported)

56439 ■ TEXT
Textile Society for the Study of Art, Design and History
PO Box 1012
Saint Albans AL1 9NE, United Kingdom
Ph: 44 20 73597678
Publication E-mail: text@textilesociety.org.uk
Publisher E-mail: chair@textilesociety.org.uk
Journal of the Textile Society for the Study of Art, Design and History. **Freq:** Annual. **Subscription Rates:** 18 individuals; 23 individuals household (family); 35 institutions; 20 institutions; 10 students. **URL:** http://www.textilesociety.org.uk/text-journal/.

56440 ■ Oasis-FM - 96.6
9 Christopher Pl., Shopping Ctr.
Saint Albans AL3 5DQ, United Kingdom
Ph: 44 1727 831966
Fax: 44 1727 834456
E-mail: studios@oasisfm.co.uk
Format: Oldies; Adult Contemporary; Easy Listening. **Operating Hours:** Continuous. **Ad Rates:** Advertising accepted; rates available upon request. **URL:** http://www.oasisfm.co.uk/.

Saint Andrews

56441 ■ Forum for Modern Language Studies
Oxford University Press
c/o Dr. Ian Johnson, Editorial Consultant
University of St. Andrews
School of English
Saint Andrews KY16 9AL, United Kingdom
Ph: 44 1334 462648
Fax: 44 1334 462655
Publisher E-mail: webenquiry.uk@oup.com
Journal publishing articles on all aspects of literary and linguistic studies, from the Middle Ages to the present day, reflecting the essential pluralism of modern language and literature studies and to providing a forum for worldwide scholarly discussion. **Founded:** 1965. **Freq:** 4/yr. **Key Personnel:** Prof. Lorna Milne, Editor, lcm2@st-and.ac.uk; Dr. Nicholas Martin, Editor, n.c.martin@bham.ac.uk. **ISSN:** 0015-8518. **Subscription Rates:** 229 institutions corporate; print and online; 191 institutions corporate; online only; 210 institutions corporate; print only; 184 institutions print and online; 153 institutions online only; 168 institutions print only; 49 individuals print; 44 members print. **Remarks:** Advertising accepted; rates available upon request. **URL:** http://fmls.oxfordjournals.org. **Circ:** (Not Reported)

Saint Annes

56442 ■ Lytham St. Annes Express
Johnston Press PLC
12 St. Annes Rd. W
Saint Annes FY8 1RF, United Kingdom
Ph: 44 1253 724236
Local community newspaper. **Freq:** Weekly (Wed.). **Key Personnel:** Jeff Travis, Contact. **Remarks:** Accepts advertising. **URL:** http://www.lythamstannesexpress.co.uk/. **Circ:** (Not Reported)

Saint Helens

56443 ■ St. Helens Reporter
Johnston Press PLC
Bank House
Claughton St.
Saint Helens WA10 1RL, United Kingdom
Ph: 44 1744 22285
Local community newspaper. **Founded:** 1859. **Remarks:** Accepts advertising. **URL:** http://www.sthelensreporter.co.uk/. **Circ:** (Not Reported)

Saint Helier

56444 ■ BBC Radio-FM - 88.8
18-21 Parade Rd.
Saint Helier JE2 3PL, United Kingdom
Ph: 44 15 34870000
E-mail: jersey@bbc.co.uk
Format: News; Talk. **Owner:** British Broadcasting Corp., Broadcasting House, Portland Pl., London W1A 1AA, United Kingdom. **Operating Hours:** Continuous. **URL:** http://www.bbc.co.uk/jersey/bbc_in_jersey/index.shtml.

Saint Leonards-On-Sea

56445 ■ Hastings & St. Leonards Observer
Johnston Press PLC
Woods House
Telford Rd.
Saint Leonards-On-Sea TN38 9LZ, United Kingdom
Ph: 44 1424 845242
Local community newspaper. **Founded:** 1859. **Freq:** Weekly (Fri.). **Key Personnel:** Keith Ridley, Editor-in-Chief, phone 44 1424 856790, fax 44 1424 854284, keith.ridley@jpress.co.uk; Hayley Scott, Advertising Mgr., fax 44 1424 852850, hayley.scott@trbeckett.co.uk. **Remarks:** Accepts advertising. **URL:** http://www.hastingsobserver.co.uk/. **Circ:** (Not Reported)

56446 ■ Rye & Battle Observer
Johnston Press PLC
Woods House
Telford Rd.
Saint Leonards-On-Sea TN38 9LZ, United Kingdom
Ph: 44 1424 854242
Local community newspaper. **Founded:** 1991. **Freq:** Weekly (Fri.). **Key Personnel:** Keith Ridley, Editor-in-Chief, phone 44 1424 854790, fax 44 1424 854284, keith.ridley@jpress.co.uk; Hayley Scott, Advertising Mgr., phone 44 1424 854242, fax 44 1424 852850, hayley.scott@trbeckett.co.uk. **Remarks:** Accepts advertising. **URL:** http://www.ryeandbattleobserver.co.uk/. **Circ:** (Not Reported)

Saint Sampsons

56447 ■ BBC Radio Guernsey-FM - 93.2
Bulwer Ave.
Saint Sampsons GY2 4LA, United Kingdom
Ph: 44 1481 200600
Fax: 44 1481 200361
E-mail: guernsey@bbc.co.uk
Format: News; Talk; Sports. **Owner:** British Broadcasting Corporation, Broadcasting House, Portland Pl., London W1A 1AA, United Kingdom. **Founded:** Mar. 16, 1982. **Operating Hours:** 6 a.m.-1 a.m. weekdays; 6 a.m.-2 p.m. Sat. & Sun. **URL:** http://www.bbc.co.uk/guernsey/local_radio.

56448 ■ Island-FM - 104.7
12 Westerbrook
Saint Sampsons GY2 4QQ, United Kingdom
Ph: 44 14 81248888
E-mail: studio@islandfm.com
Format: News; Eclectic. **Operating Hours:** Continuous. **Ad Rates:** Advertising accepted; rates available upon request. **URL:** http://www.islandfm.com.

Saintfield

56449 ■ SelfBuild
SelfBuild Ireland Ltd.
119 Cahard Rd.
Saintfield BT24 7LA, United Kingdom
Ph: 44 48 97510570
Fax: 44 48 97510576
Publisher E-mail: info@selfbuild.ie
Magazine covering all of Ireland for people who either wish to build a new home or extend/renovate. **Subtitle:** Extend & Renovate. **Freq:** Quarterly. **Subscription Rates:** 16 individuals; EUR22 individuals. **URL:** http://www.selfbuild.ie/supplier/supplierhome.asp. **Circ:** ★11,574

Sale

56450 ■ Qercus
Finnybank Ltd.
30 Finnybank Rd.
Sale M33 6LR, United Kingdom
Ph: 44 161 9699820
Fax: 44 8700 519527
Publisher E-mail: info@finnybank.com
Magazine for RISC OS users. **Subtitle:** The Whole Picture for RISC OS Users. **Freq:** Monthly. **Subscription Rates:** 44.55 individuals; 53.55 individuals in Europe; 62.55 other countries; 31.20 individuals six issues; 37.20 individuals six issues, in Europe; 43.20 other countries six issues; 16.30 individuals 3 issues; 19.30 individuals in Europe; 3 issues; 22.30 other countries 3 issues. **Remarks:** Accepts advertising. **URL:** http://www.finnybank.com/qercus/index.html. **Circ:** (Not Reported)

Salford

56451 ■ Radiography
Elsevier Science
c/o P. Hogg, Editorial Board
Directorate of Radiography
University of Salford
Salford M6 6PU, United Kingdom
Publisher E-mail: nlinfo-f@elsevier.com
Peer-reviewed journal covering various aspects of diagnostic imaging and radiation therapy. **Freq:** Quarterly. **Key Personnel:** P. Hogg, Editorial Board; E. Aird, Editorial Board; S. Boynes, Editorial Board. **ISSN:** 1078-8174. **Subscription Rates:** EUR150 individuals for European countries; US$139 individuals for all countries except Europe and Japan; 16,300¥ individuals; US$413 institutions for all countries except Europe and Japan; 47,700¥ institutions; EUR443 institutions for European countries. **Remarks:** Accepts advertising. **URL:** http://www.elsevier.com/wps/find/journaldescription.cws_home/623068/description. **Circ:** (Not Reported)

Salisbury

56452 ■ Basingstoke Gazette Extra
Newsquest Media Group Ltd.
8-12 Rollestone St.
Salisbury SP1 1DY, United Kingdom
Newspaper providing up to date information on news and events. **Key Personnel:** Kassey Chandler, Contact. **Remarks:** Accepts advertising. **URL:** http://www.basingstokegazette.co.uk/. **Circ:** (Not Reported)

56453 ■ Facilities-UK
A&D Media
Jesses Farm
Snow Hill
Dinton
Wiltshire
Salisbury SP3 5HN, United Kingdom
Ph: 44 1722 716997
Magazine covering topics on facilities management. **Freq:** Monthly. **Key Personnel:** Jane Kennedy, Advertising Mgr., jane.k@markallengroup.co.uk. **Remarks:** Accepts advertising. **URL:** http://www.facilities-uk.co.uk. **Circ:** (Not Reported)

56454 ■ Hampshire
A&D Media
Jesses Farm
Snow Hill
Dinton
Wiltshire
Salisbury SP3 5HN, United Kingdom
Ph: 44 1722 716997
Magazine covering the local life in towns and villages of Hampshire county. **Subtitle:** The County Magazine. **Founded:** 1960. **Freq:** Monthly. **Key Personnel:** Mark Allen, Editor and Publisher; Fiona Richards, Publisher; Claire Waring, Managing Editor. **Subscription Rates:** 32.40 individuals UK & Eire; EUR63.90 individuals Europe; US$115.20 other countries. **Remarks:** Accepts advertising. **URL:** http://www.hampshiremagazine.com. **Circ:** (Not Reported)

56455 ■ Land Mobile
A&D Media
Jesses Farm
Snow Hill
Dinton
Wiltshire
Salisbury SP3 5HN, United Kingdom
Ph: 44 1722 716997
Magazine covering wireless services and technologies for business and public service applications. **Founded:** Dec. 1993. **Freq:** Monthly. **Key Personnel:** Mark Allen, Publisher; Richard Lambley, Editor, richard@landmobile.co.uk. **Subscription Rates:** Free to qualified subscribers for UK addresses only; US$50 other countries. **Remarks:** Accepts advertising. **URL:** http://www.landmobile.co.uk. **Circ:** Paid 8,500

56456 ■ Pro Shop Europe
A&D Media
Jesses Farm
Snow Hill
Dinton
Wiltshire
Salisbury SP3 5HN, United Kingdom
Ph: 44 1722 716997
Magazine for golf traders and retailers. **Freq:** Monthly. **Key Personnel:** Geraldine Faulker, Editor; Jane Kennedy, Publisher. **Remarks:** Accepts advertising. **URL:** http://www.proshopeurope.co.uk. **Circ:** (Not Reported)

56457 ■ Recycling & Waste World
A&D Media
Jesses Farm
Snow Hill
Dinton
Wiltshire
Salisbury SP3 5HN, United Kingdom
Ph: 44 1722 716997
Magazine for the recycling and waste management industry. **Freq:** Weekly. **Key Personnel:** Tom Freyberg, Editor; Geraldine Faulkner, Editor-in-Chief; Jane Kennedy, Publisher. **Subscription Rates:** 92 individuals UK & Eire; EUR150 individuals Europe; US$350 other countries. **Remarks:** Accepts advertising. **URL:** http://www.recyclingwasteworld.co.uk. **Circ:** (Not Reported)

56458 ■ Wiltshire Life
A&D Media
Jesses Farm
Snow Hill
Dinton
Wiltshire
Salisbury SP3 5HN, United Kingdom
Ph: 44 1722 716997
Magazine covering the local life in Wiltshire county. **Founded:** 1946. **Freq:** Monthly. **Key Personnel:** Mark Allen, Editor and Publisher; Fiona Richards, Publisher; Claire Waring, Managing Editor. **Subscription Rates:** 41.40 individuals UK & Eire; EUR75.60 individuals Europe; US$131.40 other countries. **Remarks:** Accepts advertising. **URL:** http://www.wiltshirelife.co.uk. **Circ:** (Not Reported)

56459 ■ Spire-FM - 102.0
City Hall Studios
Malthouse Ln.
Salisbury SP2 7QQ, United Kingdom
Ph: 44 1722 410102
Format: Adult Contemporary; Oldies. **URL:** http://www.spirefm.co.uk/.

Sandy

56460 ■ Bird Life
Royal Society for the Protection of Birds
The Lodge
Potton Rd.
Sandy SG19 2DL, United Kingdom

Circulation: ★ = ABC; △ = BPA; ♦ = CAC; • = CCAB; ❑ = VAC; ⊕ = PO Statement; ‡ = Publisher's Report; Boldface figures = sworn; Light figures = estimated.

Gale Directory of Publications & Broadcast Media/147th Ed.   5851

Ph: 44 1767 680551
Fax: 44 1767 692446
Publisher E-mail: peter.smith@rspb.org.uk
Publication covering bird conservation. **Freq:** Bimonthly.
Remarks: Advertising accepted; rates available upon
request. **URL:** http://www.rspb.org.uk/supporting/join/
benefits.asp. **Circ:** (Not Reported)

56461 ■ Wingbeat
Royal Society for the Protection of Birds
The Lodge
Potton Rd.
Sandy SG19 2DL, United Kingdom
Ph: 44 1767 680551
Fax: 44 1767 692446
Publication E-mail: phoenix@rspb.org.uk
Publisher E-mail: peter.smith@rspb.org.uk
Publication covering wildlife conservation. **Freq:**
Quarterly. **URL:** http://www.rspb.org.uk/supporting/join/
benefits.asp.

Scarborough

56462 ■ Ayton Today
Johnston Press PLC
17-23 Aberdeen Walk
Scarborough YO11 1BB, United Kingdom
Ph: 44 1723 363636
Local community newspaper. **URL:** http://www.
scarboroughevingnews.co.uk/sectionhome.aspx?
sectionID=1304.

56463 ■ Burniston Today
Johnston Press PLC
17-23 Aberdeen Walk
Scarborough YO11 1BB, United Kingdom
Ph: 44 1723 363636
Local community newspaper. **Remarks:** Accepts
advertising. **URL:** http://www.scarboroughevingnews.
co.uk/sectionhome.aspx?sectionid=1303. **Circ:** (Not
Reported)

56464 ■ Scarborough Evening News
Johnston Press PLC
17-23 Aberdeen Walk
Scarborough YO11 1BB, United Kingdom
Ph: 44 1723 363636
Publication E-mail: newsdesk@yrnltd.co.uk
Local community newspaper. **Founded:** July 10, 1882.
Remarks: Accepts advertising. **URL:** http://www.
scarboroughevingnews.co.uk/. **Circ:** (Not Reported)

56465 ■ Yorkshire Coast Radio-FM - 96.2
PO Box 962
Scarborough YO11 3ZP, United Kingdom
Ph: 44 1723 581700
Fax: 44 1723 588990
E-mail: info@yorkshirecoastradio.com
Format: Adult Contemporary. **Owner:** The Local Radio
Company plc., c/o UKRD Group, Ltd., Carn Brea
Studios, Barncoose Industrial Estate, Cornwall, Redruth
TR15 3RQ, United Kingdom, 44 1209 310435, Fax: 44
1209 310406. **Operating Hours:** Continuous. **Ad Rates:**
Advertising accepted; rates available upon request.
URL: http://www.yorkshirecoastradio.com/; http://www.
thelocalradiocompany.com/

Yorkshire Coast Radio-FM - See Bridlington

Yorkshire Coast Radio-FM - See Whitby

Scotland

56466 ■ Scottish Geographical Journal
Royal Scottish Geographical Society
Lord John Murray House
15-19 N Port
Perth
Scotland PH1 5LU, United Kingdom
Ph: 44 1738 455050
Publisher E-mail: enquiries@rsgs.org
Scottish journal covering geography. **Founded:** 1885.
Freq: Quarterly. **Key Personnel:** Dr. Tim Mighall, Editor-
in-Chief; Dr. Lorna Phillip, Editor-in-Chief. **ISSN:** 1470-
2541. **Subscription Rates:** 209 institutions print & on-
line; 188 institutions online; US$63 individuals print only;
US$376 institutions print & online; US$338 institutions
online; US$106 individuals print only. **Remarks:** Accepts
advertising. **URL:** http://www.rsgs.org/publications/. **Formerly:** Scottish Geographical Magazine. **Ad Rates:** BW:
400. **Circ:** (Not Reported)

Scunthorpe

56467 ■ Cromwelliana
Cromwell Association
c/o Gary Baker
190 Cemetery Rd.
Scunthorpe DN16 1NU, United Kingdom
Publisher E-mail: cromwellmuseum@cambridgeshire.
gov.uk
Publication covering world notables. **Founded:** 1970.
Freq: Annual. **Trim Size:** A5. **Subscription Rates:**
Included in membership; 7.50 nonmembers. **Remarks:**
Advertising accepted; rates available upon request.
URL: http://www.olivercromwell.org/cromwelliana.htm.
Circ: Controlled 550

Selby

56468 ■ Selby Times
Johnston Press PLC
74-76 Gowthorpe
Selby YO8 4ET, United Kingdom
Ph: 44 1757 702802
Publication E-mail: editorial@selbytimes.co.uk
Local community newspaper. **Key Personnel:** Chris
Page, Editor; Richard Parker, Dep. Ed. **Remarks:** Ac-
cepts advertising. **URL:** http://www.selbytoday.co.uk/.
Circ: (Not Reported)

Selkirk

56469 ■ Selkirk Weekend Advertiser
Johnston Press PLC
The Hermitage
High St.
Selkirk TD7 4DA, United Kingdom
Ph: 44 1750 21581
Local community newspaper. **Freq:** Weekly. **Key Per-
sonnel:** Susan Windram, Gp. Ed.; Edith Scott, Advertis-
ing Mgr. **Remarks:** Accepts advertising. **URL:** http://
www.selkirkweekendadvertiser.co.uk/. **Circ:** (Not
Reported)

Sevenoaks

56470 ■ BMW Car
Unity Media Plc
Becket House
Vestry Rd.
Kent
Sevenoaks TN14 5EJ, United Kingdom
Ph: 44 1732 748000
Fax: 44 1732 748001
Magazine featuring information on BMW cars. **Freq:**
Monthly. **Trim Size:** 220 x 285 mm. **Key Personnel:**
Bob Harper, Editor, phone 44 1732 748033, bharper@
unity-media.com; Colin Wilkinson, Publisher; Seb de La-
tour, Dep. Ed. **Subscription Rates:** 43.20 individuals.
Remarks: Accepts advertising. **URL:** http://www.unity-
media.com/bmwcar.asp; http://www.bmwcarmagazine.
com/. **Ad Rates:** BW: 1,650. **Circ:** (Not Reported)

56471 ■ Conservatory
Unity Media Plc
Becket House
Vestry Rd.
Kent
Sevenoaks TN14 5EJ, United Kingdom
Ph: 44 1732 748000
Fax: 44 1732 748001
Magazine covering the conservatory industry in United
Kingdom. **Freq:** 6/yr. **Trim Size:** 210 x 297 mm. **Key
Personnel:** Davinia Gill, Editor, dgill@unity-media.com;
Colin Wilkinson, Publisher. **Subscription Rates:** Free to
qualified subscribers. **Remarks:** Accepts advertising.
URL: http://www.unity-media.com/
conservatorymagazine.asp; http://www.ggpmag.com/
aboutconsmag.asp. **Circ:** ★7,411

56472 ■ FENSA News
Unity Media Plc
Becket House
Vestry Rd.
Kent
Sevenoaks TN14 5EJ, United Kingdom
Ph: 44 1732 748000
Fax: 44 1732 748001
Magazine covering the glass and glazing industry. **Freq:**
Quarterly. **Trim Size:** 210 x 297 mm. **Key Personnel:**

Michael Gannon, Editor, phone 44 20 73858123,
m.gannon1@btinternet.com; Colin Wilkinson, Publisher;
Sheila Skinner, Circulation Mgr., sskinner@unity-media.
com. **URL:** http://www.unity-media.com/fensanews.asp.

56473 ■ GT Purely Porsche
Unity Media Plc
Becket House
Vestry Rd.
Kent
Sevenoaks TN14 5EJ, United Kingdom
Ph: 44 1732 748000
Fax: 44 1732 748001
Publication E-mail: gtpurelyporsche@unity-media.com
Magazine featuring Porsche automobiles. **Freq:** Monthly.
Trim Size: 220 x 285 mm. **Key Personnel:** Stuart Gal-
lagher, Editor. **Subscription Rates:** 43.20 individuals.
Remarks: Accepts advertising. **URL:** http://www.unity-
media.com/gtporsche.asp; http://www.gtpurelyporsche.
com/. **Ad Rates:** BW: 1,350. **Circ:** (Not Reported)

56474 ■ Heating & Plumbing Monthly
Unity Media Plc
Becket House
Vestry Rd.
Kent
Sevenoaks TN14 5EJ, United Kingdom
Ph: 44 1732 748000
Fax: 44 1732 748001
Magazine for heating, plumbing, and ventilation install-
ers and contractors. **Freq:** 11/yr. **Key Personnel:** Tim
Wood, Editor, phone 44 1732 748041, twood@unity-
media.com; Lisa White, Production Mgr., phone 44 1732
748049, lwhite@unity-media.com. **Remarks:** Accepts
advertising. **URL:** http://www.unity-media.com/hpm.asp.
Circ: ★30,214

56475 ■ Japanese Cars Banzai
Unity Media Plc
Becket House
Vestry Rd.
Kent
Sevenoaks TN14 5EJ, United Kingdom
Ph: 44 1732 748000
Fax: 44 1732 748001
Publication E-mail: banzai@unity-media.com
Magazine featuring Japanese cars. **Freq:** Monthly. **Trim
Size:** 210 x 297 mm. **Key Personnel:** Joe Clifford, Edi-
tor, phone 44 1732 748030, jclifford@unity-media.com.
Subscription Rates: 43.20 individuals. **Remarks:** Ac-
cepts advertising. **URL:** http://www.unity-media.com/
banzai.asp; http://www.banzaimagazine.com/. **Circ:** (Not
Reported)

56476 ■ Performance BMW
Unity Media Plc
Becket House
Vestry Rd.
Kent
Sevenoaks TN14 5EJ, United Kingdom
Ph: 44 1732 748000
Fax: 44 1732 748001
Publication E-mail: pbmw@unity-media.com
Magazine featuring the finest tuned BMWs. **Freq:**
Monthly. **Trim Size:** 220 x 285 mm. **Key Personnel:**
Louise Woodhams, Editor, phone 44 1732 748028,
lwoodhams@unity-media.com. **Subscription Rates:**
43.20 individuals. **Remarks:** Accepts advertising. **URL:**
http://www.unity-media.com/performancebmw.asp;
http://www.performancebmwmag.com/. **Ad Rates:** BW:
950. **Circ:** (Not Reported)

56477 ■ Performance Car
Unity Media Plc
Becket House
Vestry Rd.
Kent
Sevenoaks TN14 5EJ, United Kingdom
Ph: 44 1732 748000
Fax: 44 1732 748001
Publication E-mail: performancecar@unity-media.com
Magazine featuring high performance cars. **Freq:**
Monthly. **Trim Size:** 220 x 285 mm. **Key Personnel:**
Dom Holtam, Editor, dholtam@unity-media.com; Colin
Wilkinson, Publisher. **Subscription Rates:** 39.50
individuals. **Remarks:** Accepts advertising. **URL:** http://
www.unity-media.com/performancecar.asp; http://www.
performancecarmagazine.co.uk/. **Circ:** (Not Reported)

56478 ■ Performance Ford
Unity Media Plc
Becket House
Vestry Rd.
Kent
Sevenoaks TN14 5EJ, United Kingdom
Ph: 44 1732 748000
Fax: 44 1732 748001
Publication E-mail: performanceford@unity-media.com
Magazine featuring the best tuned and styled Ford cars.
Freq: Monthly. **Trim Size:** 210 x 297 mm. **Key Personnel:** Luke Wood, Editor, lwood@unity-media.com; Colin Wilkinson, Publisher. **Subscription Rates:** 40.32 individuals. **Remarks:** Accepts advertising. **URL:** http://www.unity-media.com/performanceford.asp; http://www.performancefordmag.com/. **Circ:** (Not Reported)

56479 ■ Performance VW
Unity Media Plc
Becket House
Vestry Rd.
Kent
Sevenoaks TN14 5EJ, United Kingdom
Ph: 44 1732 748000
Fax: 44 1732 748001
Publication E-mail: pvw@unity-media.com
Magazine featuring the latest styling and tuning from the VW scene. **Founded:** 1996. **Freq:** Monthly. **Trim Size:** 210 x 297 mm. **Key Personnel:** Elliott Roberts, Editor, phone 44 1732 748026, eroberts@unity-media.com; Colin Wilkinson, Publisher. **Subscription Rates:** 43.20 individuals. **Remarks:** Accepts advertising. **URL:** http://www.unity-media.com/performancevw.asp; http://www.performancevwmag.com/. **Circ:** (Not Reported)

56480 ■ Public Sector & Local Government Building
Unity Media Plc
Becket House
Vestry Rd.
Kent
Sevenoaks TN14 5EJ, United Kingdom
Ph: 44 1732 748000
Fax: 44 1732 748001
Magazine covering building and construction areas of the public sector market. **Freq:** Monthly. **Trim Size:** 210 x 297 mm. **Key Personnel:** Jo White, Editor, phone 44 1732 748039, jwhite@unity-media.com; Lisa White, Production Mgr., phone 44 1732 748049, lwhite@unity-media.com. **Subscription Rates:** Free to qualified subscribers. **Remarks:** Accepts advertising. **URL:** http://www.pslgbuilding.com/; http://www.unity-media.com/pslg.asp. **Ad Rates:** 4C: 1,950. **Circ:** ★16,100

56481 ■ Retro Cars
Unity Media Plc
Becket House
Vestry Rd.
Kent
Sevenoaks TN14 5EJ, United Kingdom
Ph: 44 1732 748000
Fax: 44 1732 748001
Publication E-mail: retrocars@unity-media.com
Magazine featuring old and classic cars. **Freq:** Monthly. **Trim Size:** 210 x 297 mm. **Key Personnel:** Simon Jackson, Editor, sjackson@unity-media.com; Andy Basoo, Dep. Ed., abasoo@unity-media.com; Colin Wilkinson, Publisher. **Subscription Rates:** 40.32 individuals. **Remarks:** Accepts advertising. **URL:** http://www.unity-media.com/retrocars.asp; http://www.retrocarsmag.com/. **Circ:** (Not Reported)

56482 ■ Retro Ford
Unity Media Plc
Becket House
Vestry Rd.
Kent
Sevenoaks TN14 5EJ, United Kingdom
Ph: 44 1732 748000
Fax: 44 1732 748001
Magazine featuring old and classic Ford cars. **Freq:** Monthly. **Trim Size:** 210 x 297 mm. **Key Personnel:** Ben Morley, Editor, bmorley@unity-media.com; Colin Wilkinson, Publisher. **Subscription Rates:** 40.32 individuals. **Remarks:** Accepts advertising. **URL:** http://www.unity-media.com/retroford.asp; http://www.retrofordmagazine.co.uk/. **Circ:** (Not Reported)

56483 ■ Roofing, Cladding & Insulation
Unity Media Plc
Becket House
Vestry Rd.
Kent
Sevenoaks TN14 5EJ, United Kingdom
Ph: 44 1732 748000
Fax: 44 1732 748001
Magazine featuring articles about the roofing, cladding and insulation industry. **Founded:** 1980. **Freq:** Monthly. **Key Personnel:** Matthew Downs, Editor, phone 44 1732 748032, mdowns@unity-media.com; Colin Wilkinson, Publisher. **Remarks:** Accepts advertising. **URL:** http://www.unity-media.com/rci.asp; http://www.rcimag.co.uk/. **Circ:** (Not Reported)

56484 ■ Who's Who in Heating & Plumbing
Unity Media Plc
Becket House
Vestry Rd.
Kent
Sevenoaks TN14 5EJ, United Kingdom
Ph: 44 1732 748000
Fax: 44 1732 748001
Magazine featuring the heating and plumbing industry. **Trim Size:** 245 x 271 mm. **Key Personnel:** Tim Wood, Editor, phone 44 1732 748041, twood@unity-media.com; Jenny Wallace, Advertising Mgr., jwallace@unity-media.com; Colin Wilkinson, Publisher. **Remarks:** Accepts advertising. **URL:** http://www.unity-media.com/whoswhoinhp.asp. **Circ:** (Not Reported)

Shaftesbury

56485 ■ Vale-FM - 96.6
Longmead Studios
Shaftesbury SP7 8QQ, United Kingdom
Ph: 44 17 47855711
Format: Contemporary Hit Radio (CHR). **Owner:** The Local Radio Co. PLC, 11 Duke St., High Wycombe HP13 6EE, United Kingdom, 44 14 94688200, Fax: 44 14 94688201. **Operating Hours:** Continuous. **Ad Rates:** Advertising accepted; rates available upon request. **URL:** http://www.midwestradio.co.uk.

56486 ■ Vale-FM - 97.4
Longmead Studios
Shaftesbury SP7 8QQ, United Kingdom
Ph: 44 17 47855711
Format: Contemporary Hit Radio (CHR). **Owner:** The Local Radio Co. PLC, 11 Duke St., High Wycombe HP13 6EE, United Kingdom, 44 14 94688200, Fax: 44 14 94688201. **Operating Hours:** Continuous. **Ad Rates:** Advertising accepted; rates available upon request. **URL:** http://www.midwestradio.co.uk.

Sharpham

56487 ■ Journal of Church Monuments Society
Church Monuments Society
c/o Sue Kelland
Rose Cottage
Somerset
Sharpham BA16 9SF, United Kingdom
Publication E-mail: info@kellandconservation.co.uk
Publisher E-mail: churchmonuments@aol.com
Journal covering church monuments. **Founded:** 1985. **Freq:** Annual. **Key Personnel:** Sue Kelland, Contact. **ISSN:** 3268-7518. **Subscription Rates:** 10 members; 15 nonmembers. **Remarks:** Advertising not accepted. **URL:** http://www.churchmonumentssociety.org/The_Journal.html. **Circ:** 500

Sheffield

56488 ■ Advances in Applied Probability
University of Sheffield
Applied Probability Trust
School of Mathematics & Statistics
Sheffield S3 7RH, United Kingdom
Ph: 44 11 42223920
Fax: 44 11 42729782
Publisher E-mail: l.nash@sheffield.ac.uk
Scholarly journal covering original research and reviews on applications of probability theory. **Founded:** 1964. **Freq:** Quarterly. **Print Method:** Offset. **Trim Size:** 170 x 254 mm. **Cols./Page:** 1. **Col. Width:** 130 millimeters. **Col. Depth:** 210 millimeters. **Key Personnel:** S. As-mussen, Editor-in-Chief. **ISSN:** 0001-8678. **Subscription Rates:** 186 institutions libraries; 62 individuals; US$312 institutions libraries; US$104 individuals; $A 390 institutions libraries; $A 130 individuals. **Remarks:** Advertising not accepted. **URL:** http://www.appliedprobability.org/ap.html; http://www.appliedprobability.org/content.aspx?Group=journals&Page=apjournals. **Circ:** (Not Reported)

56489 ■ Comparative European Politics
Palgrave Macmillan
c/o Prof. Colin Hay, Ed.
Department of Politics
University of Sheffield, Elmfield
Northumberland Rd.
Sheffield S10 2TU, United Kingdom
Publisher E-mail: booksellers@palgrave.com
Peer-reviewed journal focusing on European politics. **Freq:** 4/yr. **Key Personnel:** Martin A. Schain, Editor; Prof. Colin Hay, Editor, cep@palgrave.com; Ben Rosamond, Editor. **ISSN:** 1472-4790. **Subscription Rates:** 510 institutions, other countries print; US$949 institutions print; 70 other countries print and online; US$130 individuals print and online. **URL:** http://www.palgrave-journals.com/cep/index.html.

56490 ■ Connection Science
Taylor & Francis Group Journals
Dept. of Computer Science
University of Sheffield
Regent Ct.
211 Portobello St.
Sheffield S1 4DP, United Kingdom
Publisher E-mail: customerservice@taylorandfrancis.com
Journal focusing on research in both living and artificial systems with an emphasis on cognition and AI. **Freq:** Quarterly. **Key Personnel:** Prof. Noel E. Sharkey, Editor-in-Chief, n.sharkey@dcs.shef.ac.uk; Andy Clark, Assoc. Ed.; Ronan Reilly, Assoc. Ed.; Garrison W. Cottrell, Assoc. Ed.; Niall Griffith, Assoc. Ed.; Amanda J.C. Sharkey, Editor, n.sharkey@dcs.shef.ac.uk. **ISSN:** 0954-0091. **Subscription Rates:** US$1,384 institutions print + online; US$1,384 institutions online; US$474 individuals; US$53 individuals society; 789 institutions print + online; 749 institutions print + online; 288 individuals; 32 individuals society; EUR1,101 institutions print + online; EUR1,046 institutions online. **URL:** http://www.tandf.co.uk/journals/titles/09540091.asp.

56491 ■ Digest of Information and Patent Review
British Glass
9 Churchill Way
Sheffield S35 2PY, United Kingdom
Ph: 44 11 42901850
Fax: 44 11 42901851
Publication covering glass. **Freq:** Quarterly. **Subscription Rates:** Free to members; 100 individuals per copy. **Remarks:** Advertising accepted; rates available upon request. **URL:** http://www.britglass.org.uk/index.html; http://www.britglass.org.uk/Industry/Publications.html. **Circ:** (Not Reported)

56492 ■ Fatigue & Fracture of Engineering Materials & Structures
John Wiley & Sons Inc.
Wiley-Blackwell
c/o T.J. Hickman
Dept. of Mechanical Engineering
University of Sheffield
Mappin St.
Sheffield S1 3JD, United Kingdom
Ph: 44 114 2227795
Fax: 44 114 2227890
Publication E-mail: ffems@sheffield.ac.uk
Journal focusing on the mechanics of fatigue and fracture, and the reliability and effectiveness of structural components of any scale, geometry or material. **Freq:** Monthly. **Key Personnel:** M.R. Bache, Editorial Board; Y. Murakami, Assoc. Ed., ymura@mech.kyushu-u.ac.jp; Youshi Hong, Assoc. Ed., phone 86 10 62613730, fax 86 10 62561284, hongys@imech.ac.cn; Craig R. McClung, PhD, Assoc. Ed., phone 210522-2422, craig.mcclung@swri.org; X.R. Wu, Editorial Board; John Yates, Editor; Feargal Brennan, Editor; R.M. Andrews, Editorial Board; Eann Patterson, Editor. **ISSN:** 8756-758X. **Subscription Rates:** US$322 members print + online; US$3,736 institutions print and online; US$3,451

---

institutions print or online;, 2,055 institutions print and online; EUR261 members print + online; EUR2,608 institutions print + online; EUR2,371 institutions print or online; US$4,429 institutions, other countries print and online; 174 members print + online (non Euro zone); US$4,026 institutions, other countries print or online. **Remarks:** Accepts advertising. **URL:** http://www.wiley.com/bw/journal.asp?ref=8756-758X&site=1. **Circ:** (Not Reported)

56493 ■ Geography
Geographical Association
160 Solly St.
Sheffield S1 4BF, United Kingdom
Ph: 44 114 2960088
Fax: 44 114 2967176
Publisher E-mail: info@geography.org.uk
Publication covering geography. **Subtitle:** An International Journal. **Founded:** 1901. **Freq:** 3/yr, January, May, October. **Trim Size:** 245 x 190 mm. **Key Personnel:** Anne Greaves, Contact, agreaves@geography.org.uk. **ISSN:** 0016-7487. **URL:** http://www.geography.org.uk. **Ad Rates:** BW: 310. **Circ:** Paid 4,500

56494 ■ Glass Technology
Society of Glass Technology
Unit 9, Twelve O'Clock Ct.
21 Attercliffe Rd.
Sheffield S4 7WW, United Kingdom
Ph: 44 11 42634455
Fax: 44 11 42634411
Publication E-mail: info@sgt.org
Publisher E-mail: info@sgt.org
Trade magazine covering glass making and technology from raw material to end product. **Subtitle:** European Journal of Glass Science and Technology Part A. **Founded:** 1960. **Freq:** Bimonthly. **Print Method:** Sheetfed Offset. **Trim Size:** A4. **Cols./Page:** 2. **Col. Width:** 19 picas. **Col. Depth:** 56 picas. **Key Personnel:** P.F. Hart, Editor; D. Moore, Gen. Mgr.; R.J. Hand, PhD, Sen. Ed. **ISSN:** 0017-1050. **Subscription Rates:** 215 single issue; 240 individuals. **Remarks:** Accepts advertising. **URL:** http://www.societyofglasstechnology.org.uk/cgi-bin/open.cgi?page=publications&sessionid=44008110; http://www.ingentaconnect.com/content/sgt/gt. **Ad Rates:** BW: 400, 4C: 800. **Circ:** Paid 990

56495 ■ Greener Management International
Greenleaf Publishing
Aizlewood Business Center
Aizlewood's Mill, Nursery St.
Nursery St.
Sheffield S3 8GG, United Kingdom
Ph: 44 11 42823475
Fax: 44 11 42823476
Publication E-mail: journals@greenleaf-publishing.com
Publisher E-mail: info@greenleaf-publishing.com
Journal covering environmental issues as they affect organizations worldwide. **Subtitle:** The Journal of Corporate Environmental Strategy and Practice. **Founded:** 1993. **Freq:** Quarterly. **Print Method:** Offset Litho. **Trim Size:** 171 x 248 mm. **Cols./Page:** 1. **Col. Depth:** 211 millimeters. **Key Personnel:** Walter Wehrmeyer, Gen. Ed.; John Stuart, Managing Editor. **ISSN:** 0966-9671. **Subscription Rates:** 150 institutions organizations; 75 individuals. **Remarks:** Advertising accepted; rates available upon request. **URL:** http://www.greenleaf-publishing.com/default.asp?ContentID=8. **Circ:** Combined 600

56496 ■ Hazards
PO Box 4042
Sheffield S8 2DG, United Kingdom
Ph: 44 114 2014265
Publication E-mail: editor@hazards.org
Magazine featuring information on occupational health and safety. **Freq:** Quarterly. **Key Personnel:** Rory O'Neill, Editor. **ISSN:** 0267-7296. **Subscription Rates:** 15 individuals; 20 other countries; US$40 other countries; 28 institutions United Kingdom and Europe; 32 institutions, other countries; US$64 institutions, other countries. **URL:** http://www.hazards.org/index.htm.

56497 ■ The Indexer
Society of Indexers
Woodbourn Business Center
10 Jessell St.
Sheffield S9 3HY, United Kingdom
Ph: 44 114 2449561
Fax: 44 114 2449563
Publication E-mail: info@theindexer.org

Publisher E-mail: info@indexers.org.uk
Professional journal for indexers. **Founded:** 1958. **Freq:** 4/yr. **Key Personnel:** Maureen MacGlashan, Editor, editor@theindexer.org. **ISSN:** 0019-4131. **Subscription Rates:** Included in membership; 40 nonmembers. **Remarks:** Accepts advertising. **URL:** http://www.theindexer.org/; http://www.indexers.org.uk/. **Ad Rates:** 4C: 175. **Circ:** 2,200

56498 ■ Inflammopharmacology
Springer Netherlands
c/o K.D. Rainsford, Ed.-in-Ch.
Biomedical Research Centre
Division of Biomedical Sciences, Sheffield Hallam University
Howard St.
Sheffield S1 1WB, United Kingdom
Publisher E-mail: permissions.dordrecht@springer.com
Journal on biosciences. **Subtitle:** Experimental and Therapeutic Studies. **Freq:** Bimonthly. **Print Method:** Offset. **Cols./Page:** 6. **Col. Width:** 2 1/16 inches. **Col. Depth:** 21 1/2 inches. **Key Personnel:** D.E. Furst, Editorial Consultant; S.A. Laufer, Section Ed.; N. Bellamy, Editorial Board; M.W. Whitehouse, Editorial Consultant; W.F. Kean, Asst. Ed., keanmac@cogeco.ca; L. Lichtenberger, Section Ed.; M.C. Powanda, Section Ed.; C. Bolton, Section Ed.; K. Takeuchi, Regional Ed.; G.P. Velo, Section Ed. **ISSN:** 0925-4692. **Subscription Rates:** EUR895 institutions print incl. free access or e-only; EUR1074 institutions print incl. enhanced access. **URL:** http://www.springer.com/birkhauser/biosciences/journal/10787.

56499 ■ International Journal of Enterprise Network Management
Inderscience Publishers
c/o Prof. Siau Ching Lenny Koh, Ed.-in-Ch.
University of Sheffield
Management School
9 Mappin St.
Sheffield S1 4DT, United Kingdom
Publisher E-mail: editor@inderscience.com
Peer-reviewed journal covering the interaction, collaboration, partnership and cooperation between small and medium sized enterprises and larger enterprises in a supply chain. **Founded:** 2006. **Freq:** 4/yr. **Key Personnel:** Prof. Siau Ching Lenny Koh, Editor-in-Chief, s.c.l.koh@sheffield.ac.uk; Prof. Walter W.C. Chung, Asian Ed.; Prof. Angappa Gunasekaran, American Ed. **ISSN:** 1748-1252. **Subscription Rates:** EUR494 individuals includes surface mail, print only; EUR672 individuals print and online. **URL:** http://www.inderscience.com/browse/index.php?journalCODE=ijenm

56500 ■ International Journal of Knowledge Management in Tourism and Hospitality
Inderscience Enterprises Limited
c/o Dr. Dimitrios Diamantis, Ed.-in-Ch.
Sheffield Hallam University
Center of International Tourism Research
City Campus, Howard St.
Sheffield S1 1WB, United Kingdom
Journal focusing on the study of management and hospitality. **Freq:** 4/yr. **Key Personnel:** Dr. Dimitrios Diamantis, Editor-in-Chief, d.diamantis@shu.ac.uk. **ISSN:** 1756-0322. **Subscription Rates:** EUR494 individuals print or online; EUR672 individuals print and online. **URL:** http://www.inderscience.com/browse/index.php?journalID=292.

56501 ■ International Journal of Logistics Economics & Globalisation
Inderscience Publishers
c/o Prof. Siau Ching Lenny Koh, Ed.-in-Ch.
University of Sheffield
Management School
9 Mappin St.
Sheffield S1 4DT, United Kingdom
Publisher E-mail: editor@inderscience.com
Peer-reviewed journal covering development & application of logistics information system. **Founded:** 2007. **Freq:** 4/yr. **Key Personnel:** Prof. Siau Ching Lenny Koh, Editor-in-Chief, s.c.l.koh@sheffield.ac.uk; Prof. Tzong-Ru Lee, Editor, trlee@nchu.edu.tw; Prof. Panayiotis H. Ketikidis, Assoc. Ed.; Dr. K. Ganesh, Assoc. Ed.; Prof. Lynne M. Markus, Assoc. Ed.; Prof. Amrik Sohal, Assoc. Ed. **ISSN:** 1741-5373. **Subscription Rates:** EUR494 individuals includes surface mail, print only; EUR672 individuals print and online. **URL:** http://www.inderscience.com/browse/index.php?journalCODE=ijleg.

56502 ■ International Journal of Systems Science
Taylor & Francis Group Journals
c/o Peter Fleming, Ed.-in-Ch.
Dept. of Automatic Control & Systems Engineering
University of Sheffield
Mappin St.
Sheffield S1 3JD, United Kingdom
Publisher E-mail: customerservice@taylorandfrancis.com
Journal covering the exciting and demanding field of intelligent systems engineering and its applications. **Freq:** Monthly. **Key Personnel:** Peter Fleming, Editor-in-Chief, ijss@sheffield.ac.uk; V. Kadirkamanathan, Co-Ed.; R.F. Harrison, Editorial Ed.; B. Chen, Editorial Board; A. Back, Editorial Board. **ISSN:** 0020-7721. **Subscription Rates:** US$4,914 institutions print + online; US$4,668 institutions online; 3,389 institutions print + online; 3,220 institutions online; EUR3,912 institutions print + online; EUR3,716 institutions online. **Remarks:** Advertising accepted; rates available upon request. **URL:** http://www.tandf.co.uk/journals/titles/00207721.asp. **Circ:** (Not Reported)

56503 ■ Journal of Applied Probability
University of Sheffield
Applied Probability Trust
School of Mathematics & Statistics
Sheffield S3 7RH, United Kingdom
Ph: 44 11 42223920
Fax: 44 11 42729782
Publisher E-mail: l.nash@sheffield.ac.uk
Scholarly journal covering original research on application of probability theory. **Founded:** 1964. **Freq:** Quarterly. **Print Method:** Offset. **Trim Size:** 170x 254 mm. **Cols./Page:** 1. **Col. Width:** 130 millimeters. **Col. Depth:** 210 millimeters. **Key Personnel:** N.H. Bingham, Coord. Ed.; S. Asmussen, Editor-in-Chief. **ISSN:** 0021-9002. **Subscription Rates:** 186 institutions for libraries; US$312 institutions for libraries; $A 390 institutions for libraries; 62 individuals; US$104 individuals; $A 130 individuals. **Remarks:** Advertising not accepted. **URL:** http://www.apt.group.shef.ac.uk/page6.html; http://www.appliedprobability.org/content.aspx?Group=journals&Page=apjournals. **Circ:** (Not Reported)

56504 ■ The Journal of Corporate Citizenship
Greenleaf Publishing
Aizlewood Business Center
Aizlewood's Mill, Nursery St.
Nursery St.
Sheffield S3 8GG, United Kingdom
Ph: 44 11 42823475
Fax: 44 11 42823476
Publication E-mail: journals@greenleaf-publishing.com
Publisher E-mail: info@greenleaf-publishing.com
Journal covering corporate responsibility in a global economy for researchers and practitioners. **Founded:** Jan. 2001. **Freq:** Quarterly. **Print Method:** Offset Litho. **Trim Size:** 171 x 248 mm. **Cols./Page:** 1. **Col. Depth:** 211 millimeters. **Key Personnel:** David Cooperrider, Gen. Ed.; John Stuart, Publisher; Sandra Waddock, Regional Ed.; Carol Adams, Editorial Board; Jerry Calton, Book Review Ed.; Dean Bargh, Production Ed. **ISSN:** 1470-5001. **Subscription Rates:** 150 institutions organizations; 75 individuals; 210 two years organisations. **Remarks:** Advertising accepted; rates available upon request. **URL:** http://www.greenleaf-publishing.com; http://www.greenleaf-publishing.com/default.asp?contentid=7. **Circ:** ‡750

56505 ■ Journal of Radiotherapy in Practice
Cambridge University Press
c/o Prof. Angela Duxbury, Ed.-in-Ch.
Sheffield Hallam University
Faculty of Health & Wellbeing
Collegiate Cres. Campus
Sheffield S10 2BP, United Kingdom
Publisher E-mail: information@cambridge.org
Peer-reviewed journal dealing with clinical oncology and radiotherapy. **Key Personnel:** Prof. Angela Duxbury, Editor-in-Chief; Hazel Colyer, Editorial Board; Andy Beavis, Editorial Board. **ISSN:** 1460-3969. **Subscription Rates:** 222 institutions print and online; US$444 institutions print and online; 193 institutions online only; US$385 institutions online only. **Remarks:** Accepts advertising. **URL:** http://journals.cambridge.org/action/displayJournal?jid=jrp. **Ad Rates:** BW: US$425, 4C: US$915. **Circ:** (Not Reported)

56506 ■ Managing Leisure
Routledge
Taylor & Francis Group Ltd.
c/o Peter Taylor, Ed.-in-Ch.
Support Industry Research Centre
Sheffield Hallam University
Collegiate Campus
Sheffield S10 2BP, United Kingdom
Ph: 44 11 42255320
Fax: 44 11 42254341
Publisher E-mail: webmaster.books@tandf.co.uk
Peer-reviewed journal on leisure management. **Freq:** Quarterly. **Key Personnel:** Peter Taylor, Editor-in-Chief, peter.taylor@shu.ac.uk; Jonathan Long, Book Review Ed.; Bohdah Jung, Exec. Editorial Board. **ISSN:** 1360-6719. **Subscription Rates:** US$233 individuals; US$882 institutions online only; US$928 institutions print + online; US$71 members; 557 institutions print + online; 529 institutions online only; 142 individuals print only; 48 members; EUR739 institutions print and online; EUR702 institutions online only. **Remarks:** Advertising accepted; rates available upon request. **URL:** http://www.tandf.co.uk/journals/titles/13606719.asp. **Circ:** (Not Reported)

56507 ■ The Mathematical Scientist
University of Sheffield
Applied Probability Trust
School of Mathematics & Statistics
Sheffield S3 7RH, United Kingdom
Ph: 44 11 42223920
Fax: 44 11 42729782
Publisher E-mail: l.nash@sheffield.ac.uk
Scholarly journal covering research in mathematical modeling. **Founded:** 1976. **Freq:** Semiannual. **Print Method:** Offset. **Trim Size:** 172 x 244 mm. **Cols./Page:** 1. **Col. Width:** 132 millimeters. **Col. Depth:** 240 millimeters. **Key Personnel:** J. Gani, Editor-in-Chief. **ISSN:** 0312-3685. **Subscription Rates:** $A 28 individuals; 13 individuals; US$23 individuals; $A 28 institutions; 13 institutions; US$23 institutions. **Remarks:** Advertising not accepted. **URL:** http://www.appliedprobability.org; http://apt.group.shef.ac.uk/tms.html. **Circ:** (Not Reported)

56508 ■ Mathematical Spectrum
University of Sheffield
Applied Probability Trust
School of Mathematics & Statistics
Sheffield S3 7RH, United Kingdom
Ph: 44 11 42223920
Fax: 44 11 42729782
Publication E-mail: spectrum@sheffield.ac.uk
Publisher E-mail: l.nash@sheffield.ac.uk
Magazine covering mathematics for high school and college students, teachers, and enthusiasts. **Founded:** 1968. **Freq:** 3/yr. **Print Method:** Offset. **Trim Size:** 208 x 296 mm. **Cols./Page:** 2. **Col. Width:** 85 millimeters. **Col. Depth:** 252 millimeters. **Key Personnel:** D.W. Sharpe, Editor. **ISSN:** 0025-5653. **Subscription Rates:** US$20 individuals for volume 43 only; 13.65 individuals volume 43; $A 24 individuals volume 43; 25.20 two years for volume 43 & 44; US$37 two years volume 43 & 44; $A 24 two years volume 43 & 44. **Remarks:** Accepts advertising. **URL:** http://ms.appliedprobability.org/; http://apt.group.shef.ac.uk/ms.html. **Circ:** (Not Reported)

56509 ■ Phoenix
Association of Graduate Careers Advisory Services
Millennium House
30 Jct. Rd.
Sheffield S11 8XB, United Kingdom
Ph: 44 114 2515750
Fax: 44 114 2515751
Magazine covering counseling. **Freq:** 3/yr. **Subscription Rates:** 30 individuals. **URL:** http://www.agcas.org.uk/agcas_resources/25-Phoenix.

56510 ■ Physics & Chemistry of Glasses
Society of Glass Technology
Unit 9, Twelve O'Clock Ct.
21 Attercliffe Rd.
Sheffield S4 7WW, United Kingdom
Ph: 44 11 42634455
Fax: 44 11 42634411
Publisher E-mail: info@sgt.org
Journal covering inorganic glasses of all kinds. **Founded:** 1960. **Freq:** Bimonthly. **Print Method:** Sheetfed Offset. **Trim Size:** A4. **Cols./Page:** 2. **Col. Width:** 19 picas. **Col. Depth:** 56 picas. **ISSN:** 0031-9090. **Subscription Rates:** 319 individuals; 288 individuals overseas. **Remarks:** Advertising not accepted. **URL:** http://www.societyofglasstechnology.org.uk/cgi-bin/open.cgi?page=journal&sessionid=43196110. **Circ:** Paid 725

56511 ■ Planning Theory & Practice
Routledge
Taylor & Francis Group Ltd.
c/o Kiera Chapman
Dept. of Town & Regional Planning
University of Sheffield
Sheffield S10 2TN, United Kingdom
Publisher E-mail: webmaster.books@tandf.co.uk
Peer-reviewed journal focusing on theory and practice of spatial planning in public policy. **Freq:** Quarterly. **Key Personnel:** Heather Campbell, Editor; Patsy Healey, Editorial Board; Robert Upton, Editor; Leonie Sandercock, Editorial Board; Zhang Bing, Editorial Board; Prof. Mark Scott, Review Ed.; Rachelle Alterman, Editorial Board; Angela Barbanente, Editorial Board; John Forester, Editor. **ISSN:** 1464-9357. **Subscription Rates:** US$234 individuals print only; US$672 institutions online; US$707 institutions print + online; US$53 members; 425 institutions print + online; 404 institutions online; 145 individuals print only; 31 members; EUR563 institutions print and online; EUR535 institutions online only. **Remarks:** Advertising accepted; rates available upon request. **URL:** http://www.tandf.co.uk/journals/routledge/14649357.html. **Circ:** (Not Reported)

56512 ■ Political Studies
Political Studies Association of the United Kingdom
c/o Rene Bailey, Mgr.
Department of Politics
University of Sheffield, Elmfield
Northumberland Rd.
Sheffield S10 2TU, United Kingdom
Ph: 44 114 2221673
Fax: 44 114 2221717
Publication E-mail: politicalstudies@sheffield.ac.uk
Publisher E-mail: psa@ncl.ac.uk
Publication covering political science. **Freq:** Periodic. **Key Personnel:** Rene Bailey, Manager; Matthew Festenstein, Editor, mf517@york.ac.uk; Martin Smith, Editor, m.j.smith@sheffield.ac.uk. **URL:** http://www.politicalstudies.org/.

56513 ■ Quiet
British Tinnitus Association
Ground Fl.
Unit 5
Acorn Business Pk.
Woodseats Close
Sheffield S8 0TB, United Kingdom
Ph: 44 114 2509922
Fax: 44 114 2582279
Publication E-mail: info@tinnitus.org.uk
Publisher E-mail: info@tinnitus.org.uk
Publication covering speech and hearing. **Freq:** Quarterly. **ISSN:** 0968-1264. **Subscription Rates:** Free for members. **Remarks:** Advertising accepted; rates available upon request. **URL:** http://www.tinnitus.org.uk/index.php?q=BTAMagazineQuiet. **Circ:** 10,000

56514 ■ Skamania County Pioneer
Green Leaf Publishing Inc.
Aizelewood Business Ctr.
Nursery St.
Sheffield S3 8GG, United Kingdom
Ph: 44 144282 3475
Fax: 44 144282 3476
Publication E-mail: scpioneer@gorge.net
Publisher E-mail: info@greenleaf-publishing.com
Community newspaper. **Founded:** 1892. **Freq:** Weekly. **Trim Size:** 15 x 21 3/4. **Cols./Page:** 7. **Col. Width:** 12 picas. **Col. Depth:** 427 agate lines. **Key Personnel:** Jim Price, Editor and Publisher. **Remarks:** Accepts advertising. **Ad Rates:** GLR: .295, BW: 558.60. **Circ:** 2,600

56515 ■ Surface and Coatings Technology
Elsevier Science Inc.
c/o Prof. A. Matthews, Ed.
Dept. of Engineering Materials
Sheffield University
Sir Robert Hadfield Bldg., Mappin St.
Sheffield S1 3JD, United Kingdom
Ph: 44 114 2225466
Fax: 44 114 2225943
Publisher E-mail: usinfo-ehelp@elsevier.com
Peer-reviewed journal covering the science and application of advanced surface treatments for improvement of material properties. **Founded:** 1973. **Freq:** 24/yr. **Key Personnel:** Prof. A. Matthews, Editor, a.matthews@sheffield.ac.uk; Prof. H.C. Man, Editor, mfhcman@inet.polyu.edu.hk; Dr. J. Patscheider, Editor, joerg.patscheider@empa.ch. **ISSN:** 0257-8972. **Subscription Rates:** US$9,199 institutions, other countries except Europe, Japan and Iran; EUR8,224 institutions for European countries and Iran; 1,092,500¥ institutions. **URL:** http://www.elsevier.com/wps/find/journaldescription.cws_home/504101/descriptiondescription.

56516 ■ Transactions of the Philological Society
Philological Society
c/o Andrew Linn, Ed.
Department of English Language & Linguistics
University of Sheffield
Sheffield, United Kingdom
Publication E-mail: transactions@philsoc.org.uk
Publisher E-mail: secretary@philsoc.org.uk
Publication covering the Philological Society. **Freq:** 3/yr. **Key Personnel:** Andrew Linn, Editor; Paul Rowlett, Editor. **ISSN:** 0079-1636. **Subscription Rates:** US$360 individuals print and online; US$305 members print and online; US$1,072 institutions print & online; 463 institutions print only; EUR588 institutions print only; EUR266 individuals print and online; EUR152 members print and online; US$1,089 other countries print only; 214 other countries print & online; 182 members print and online. **Remarks:** Advertising accepted; rates available upon request. **URL:** http://www.philsoc.org.uk/transactions.asp; http://www.wiley.com/bw/journal.asp?ref=0079-1636. **Circ:** (Not Reported)

56517 ■ BBC Radio Sheffield-FM - 104.1
54 Shoreham St.
Sheffield S1 4RS, United Kingdom
Ph: 44 114 2731177
E-mail: south.yorkshire@bbc.co.uk
Format: Talk; News; Oldies; Sports; Information; Eclectic; Religious; Top 40. **Owner:** British Broadcasting Corp., Broadcasting House, Portland Pl., London W1A 1AA, United Kingdom. **Operating Hours:** Continuous weekdays; 5 a.m.-1:30 a.m.Sat; 6 a.m.-1:30 a.m. Sun. **URL:** http://news.bbc.co.uk/local/sheffield/hi/tv_and_radio/.

56518 ■ Hallam-FM - 97.4
900 Herries Rd.
Sheffield S6 1RH, United Kingdom
Ph: 44 114 2091000
Fax: 44 114 2855472
Format: Contemporary Hit Radio (CHR). **Key Personnel:** Simon Monk, Program Dir.; Lynn Dixon, News Ed. **URL:** http://www.hallamfm.co.uk/.

Hallam-FM - See Barnsley

Hallam-FM - See Doncaster

Shenley

56519 ■ Dentistry
Finlayson Media Communications Ltd.
1 Hertford House
Farm Close
Shenley WD7 9AB, United Kingdom
Ph: 44 1923 851777
Fax: 44 1923 851778
Professional magazine covering dentistry. **Founded:** Jan. 1995. **Freq:** published every two weeks. **Print Method:** Web. **Trim Size:** A3. **Cols./Page:** 4. **Key Personnel:** Julian English, MCIJ, Exec. Ed., phone 44 1923 851750, julian.english@fmc.co.uk. **Subscription Rates:** 95 individuals 12 months (UK); 145 single issue 12 months (Europe); 195 elsewhere. **Remarks:** Accepts advertising. **URL:** http://www.dentistry.co.uk/; http://www.fmc.co.uk/pages/fmc_publication_detail.php?id=1. **Former name:** Dentistry Monthly. **Circ:** 21,500

Shepperton

56520 ■ Bookbinder
Society of Bookbinders
c/o Hilary Henning, Membership Sec.
102 Hetherington Rd.
Shepperton TW17 0SW, United Kingdom
Publication E-mail: publications@societyofbookbinders.com

Publisher E-mail: info@societyofbookbinders.com
Publication covering publishing. **Freq:** Annual. **Subscription Rates:** 15 nonmembers volume 2; 12 individuals volume 3-4; 14 individuals volume 7; 15 individuals volume 9-10; 16 individuals volume 11-12; 18 individuals volume 14-21; Free to members. **Remarks:** Advertising accepted; rates available upon request. **URL:** http://www.societyofbookbinders.com/bookbinder/bookbinder_frames.html. **Circ:** (Not Reported)

Shoreham-by-Sea

56521 ■ Aluminium Times
Modern Media Communications Ltd.
Gresham House
54 High St.
Shoreham-by-Sea BN43 5DB, United Kingdom
Ph: 44 1273 453033
Fax: 44 1273 453085
Publisher E-mail: info@mmcpublications.co.uk
Trade magazine for aluminum producers and fabricators in Europe and Middle East. **Founded:** Jan. 1999. **Freq:** 5/yr. **Print Method:** Litho. **Trim Size:** 210 x 297 mm. **Cols./Page:** 2. **Col. Width:** 87 millimeters. **Col. Depth:** 265 millimeters. **Key Personnel:** John Clarke, Editor, johnclarke@mmcpublications.co.uk. **ISSN:** 1465-8240. **Subscription Rates:** 85 individuals; 100 other countries; EUR143 other countries; US$176 other countries. **Remarks:** Accepts advertising. **URL:** http://www.mmcpublications.co.uk/at.html. **Ad Rates:** BW: 1,710. **Circ:** Controlled 5,200

56522 ■ Cast Metal & Diecasting Times
Modern Media Communications Ltd.
Gresham House
54 High St.
Shoreham-by-Sea BN43 5DB, United Kingdom
Ph: 44 1273 453033
Fax: 44 1273 453085
Publisher E-mail: info@mmcpublications.co.uk
Trade magazine for specifiers and buyers of foundry plant equipment and services throughout Europe and South America. **Founded:** Nov. 1998. **Freq:** 5/yr. **Print Method:** Litho. **Trim Size:** 210 x 297 mm. **Cols./Page:** 3. **Col. Width:** 87 millimeters. **Col. Depth:** 265 millimeters. **ISSN:** 1465-9123. **Subscription Rates:** 84 individuals; 99 other countries; EUR142 other countries; US$174 other countries. **Remarks:** Accepts advertising. **URL:** http://www.mmcpublications.co.uk/cmt.html. **Ad Rates:** BW: 1,350. **Circ:** Controlled 5,000

56523 ■ Fire Times
Modern Media Communications Ltd.
Gresham House
54 High St.
Shoreham-by-Sea BN43 5DB, United Kingdom
Ph: 44 1273 453033
Fax: 44 1273 453085
Publisher E-mail: info@mmcpublications.co.uk
Trade & Technical magazine for procurement managers who purchase firefighting equipment in public, private, and military sectors. **Founded:** Nov. 1998. **Freq:** Bimonthly. **Print Method:** Litho. **Trim Size:** 210 x 297 mm. **Cols./Page:** 3 and 4. **Col. Width:** 60 and 43 millimeters. **Col. Depth:** 255 and 255 millimeters. **Key Personnel:** David Holden, Editor, davidholden@mmcpublications.co.ult; Colin Robinson, Advertising Mgr., colinrobinson@mmcpublications.co.ult. **ISSN:** 1465-8798. **Subscription Rates:** 83 individuals UK; 97 other countries; EUR140 other countries; US$172 other countries. **Remarks:** Accepts advertising. **URL:** http://www.mmcpublications.co.uk/ft.html. **Ad Rates:** BW: 1,495. **Circ:** Controlled ‡5,000

56524 ■ International Journal of Knowledge-Based and Intelligent Engineering Systems
IOS Press, B.V.
KES International (Journal Dept.)
PO Box 2115
West Sussex
Shoreham-by-Sea BN43 9AF, United Kingdom
Publication E-mail: kesjournal@kesinternational.org
Publisher E-mail: info@iospress.nl
International journal providing a forum for publishing the results of recent research into the applications of intelligent systems, and also the tools and techniques necessary for them. **Freq:** Quarterly. **Key Personnel:** Dr. R.J. Howlett, Editor-in-Chief; Prof. B. Gabrys, Editor-in-Chief; Prof. L.C. Jain, Founding Ed. **ISSN:** 1327-2314. **Subscription Rates:** EUR308 individuals print and online; US$435 individuals print and online. **URL:** http://www.

iospress.nl/loadtop/load.php?isbn=13272314.

56525 ■ Learned Publishing
Association of Learned and Professional Society Publishers
1-3 Ship St.
West Sussex
Shoreham-by-Sea BN43 5DH, United Kingdom
Ph: 44 523 579826
Publication covering publishing. **Subtitle:** The Journal of the Association of Learned and Professional Society. **Founded:** 1988. **Freq:** Quarterly. **Trim Size:** 210 x 280 mm. **Key Personnel:** Pippa Smart, Reviews Ed.; Allan Singleton, Editor-in-Chief, editorc@alpsp.org. **ISSN:** 0953-1513. **URL:** http://www.learned-publishing.org. **Ad Rates:** BW: 395, 4C: 510. **Circ:** 700

Shrewsbury

56526 ■ Bag-o-Fun
Redan Publishing
Prospect House, Ste. 2
Belle Vue Rd.
Shrewsbury SY3 7NR, United Kingdom
Ph: 44 1743 364433
Fax: 44 1743 271528
Publisher E-mail: info@redan.com
Magazine featuring character fun tales and activities. **Freq:** 8/yr. **Trim Size:** 206 x 276 mm. **Subscription Rates:** 3.99 single issue. **Remarks:** Accepts advertising. **URL:** http://78.136.37.243/BagoFun.asp. **Ad Rates:** 4C: 1,800. **Circ:** 80,000

56527 ■ Cellular Polymers
RAPRA Technology
Shawbury
Shrewsbury SY4 4NR, United Kingdom
Ph: 44 1939 250383
Publisher E-mail: info@rapra.net
Publication covering cellular polymers. **Freq:** Bimonthly. **Key Personnel:** Kate Evans, Asst. Ed., phone 44 1939 252455, fax 44 1939 251118, kmevans@rapra.net. **ISSN:** 0262-4893. **Subscription Rates:** 455 individuals; 40 individuals; 45 individuals overseas. **Remarks:** Advertising not accepted. **URL:** http://www.rapra.net/journals/j_issuelist_cp.asp?j_type=cp. **Circ:** (Not Reported)

56528 ■ The Farmer (Shropshire and the Welsh Borders)
Shropshire Newspapers Ltd.
Chronicle House
Castle Foregate
Shrewsbury SY1 2DN, United Kingdom
Ph: 44 17 43248248
Fax: 44 17 43353601
Publisher E-mail: newsroom@shropshirestar.co.uk
Trade journal covering farming. **Freq:** Monthly. **Key Personnel:** Heather Jones, Editor, thefarmer@shropshirestar.co.uk. **Remarks:** Accepts advertising. **URL:** http://www.thefarmer.com/. **Circ:** Non-paid 15,000

56529 ■ Field Studies
Field Studies Council
Preston Montford
Montford Bridge
Shrewsbury SY4 1HW, United Kingdom
Ph: 44 1743 852100
Fax: 44 1743 852101
Publisher E-mail: enquiries@field-studies-council.org
Publication covering natural sciences. **Freq:** Annual. **ISSN:** 0428-304X. **Subscription Rates:** 15 individuals. **Remarks:** Advertising not accepted. **URL:** http://www.field-studies-council.org/publications/fieldstudies.aspx. **Circ:** (Not Reported)

56530 ■ Fun to Learn Barney
Redan Publishing
Prospect House, Ste. 2
Belle Vue Rd.
Shrewsbury SY3 7NR, United Kingdom
Ph: 44 1743 364433
Fax: 44 1743 271528
Publisher E-mail: info@redan.com
Magazine featuring stories, activities and puzzles based on the character of Barney, the purple dinosaur. **Freq:** Monthly. **Trim Size:** 220 x 295 mm. **Subscription Rates:** 1.99 single issue. **Remarks:** Accepts advertising. **URL:** http://78.136.37.243/Barney.asp. **Ad Rates:** 4C: 1,550. **Circ:** 50,000

56531 ■ Fun to Learn Best of Barney
Redan Publishing
Prospect House, Ste. 2
Belle Vue Rd.
Shrewsbury SY3 7NR, United Kingdom
Ph: 44 1743 364433
Fax: 44 1743 271528
Publisher E-mail: info@redan.com
Magazine featuring stories, activities and puzzles based on the character of Barney, the purple dinosaur. **Freq:** Bimonthly. **Subscription Rates:** 3.85 single issue. **Remarks:** Accepts advertising. **URL:** http://78.136.37.243/BOBarney.asp. **Ad Rates:** 4C: 1,300. **Circ:** 30,000

56532 ■ Fun to Learn Discovery
Redan Publishing
Prospect House, Ste. 2
Belle Vue Rd.
Shrewsbury SY3 7NR, United Kingdom
Ph: 44 1743 364433
Fax: 44 1743 271528
Publisher E-mail: info@redan.com
Magazine covering the National Curriculum's Early Learning Goals. **Freq:** Semiannual. **Trim Size:** 210 x 297 mm. **Subscription Rates:** 3.85 single issue. **Remarks:** Accepts advertising. **URL:** http://78.136.37.243/Discovery.asp. **Ad Rates:** 4C: 1,300. **Circ:** 40,000

56533 ■ Fun to Learn Favourites
Redan Publishing
Prospect House, Ste. 2
Belle Vue Rd.
Shrewsbury SY3 7NR, United Kingdom
Ph: 44 1743 364433
Fax: 44 1743 271528
Publisher E-mail: info@redan.com
Magazine featuring stories and activities of the children's TV characters. **Freq:** Biweekly. **Trim Size:** 220 x 300 mm. **Subscription Rates:** 1.99 single issue. **Remarks:** Accepts advertising. **URL:** http://78.136.37.243/Favourites.asp. **Ad Rates:** 4C: 2,000. **Circ:** ★45,542

56534 ■ Fun to Learn Friends
Redan Publishing
Prospect House, Ste. 2
Belle Vue Rd.
Shrewsbury SY3 7NR, United Kingdom
Ph: 44 1743 364433
Fax: 44 1743 271528
Publisher E-mail: info@redan.com
Magazine featuring children's TV characters. **Freq:** Biweekly. **Trim Size:** 220 x 300 mm. **Subscription Rates:** 1.99 single issue. **Remarks:** Accepts advertising. **URL:** http://78.136.37.243/Friends.asp. **Ad Rates:** 4C: 2,000. **Circ:** ★76,846

56535 ■ Fun to Learn Letterland
Redan Publishing
Prospect House, Ste. 2
Belle Vue Rd.
Shrewsbury SY3 7NR, United Kingdom
Ph: 44 1743 364433
Fax: 44 1743 271528
Publisher E-mail: info@redan.com
Magazine featuring stories and activities for the children. **Freq:** 4/week. **Subscription Rates:** 2.25 single issue. **URL:** http://78.136.37.243/Letterland.asp. **Circ:** 40,000

56536 ■ Fun to Learn Peppa Pig
Redan Publishing
Prospect House, Ste. 2
Belle Vue Rd.
Shrewsbury SY3 7NR, United Kingdom
Ph: 44 1743 364433
Fax: 44 1743 271528
Publisher E-mail: info@redan.com
Magazine featuring stories, activities, and puzzles based on the TV show, Peppa Pig. **Freq:** 3/week. **Trim Size:** 220 x 300 mm. **Subscription Rates:** 1.99 single issue. **Remarks:** Accepts advertising. **URL:** http://78.136.37.243/Peppa.asp. **Ad Rates:** 4C: 1,550. **Circ:** 82,498

56537 ■ Hounds
Ravensworld Ltd.
Rose Cottage
Hughley
Shrewsbury SY5 6HX, United Kingdom
Ph: 44 1746 785637
Fax: 44 1746 891719

Publication E-mail: houndsmagazine@foxhunters.net Magazine covering hunting with hounds. **Freq:** 8/yr. **Print Method:** Web offset. **Trim Size:** 210 x 297 mm. **Cols./Page:** 2. **Col. Width:** 57.2 millimeters. **Col. Depth:** 253 millimeters. **Key Personnel:** Michael Sagar, Editor; Bryan H. Jackson, Advertising Mgr., bryanjackson@ bushinternet.com. **Subscription Rates:** US$29 individuals; US$3 single issue. **Remarks:** Accepts advertising. **URL:** http://www.foxhunters.net/hounds/about.htm. **Circ:** (Not Reported)

56538 ■ My Little Pony
Redan Publishing
Prospect House, Ste. 2
Belle Vue Rd.
Shrewsbury SY3 7NR, United Kingdom
Ph: 44 1743 364433
Fax: 44 1743 271528
Publisher E-mail: info@redan.com
Magazine featuring stories, activities, and puzzles based on My Little Ponies and their friends. **Freq:** 4/week. **Trim Size:** 220 x 295 mm. **Subscription Rates:** 2.35 single issue. **Remarks:** Accepts advertising. **URL:** http://78.136.37.243/MyLittlePony.asp. **Ad Rates:** 4C: 1,550. **Circ:** 50,000

56539 ■ BBC Radio Shropshire-FM - 96
PO Box 96
Shrewsbury SY1 3WW, United Kingdom
Ph: 44 1743 248321
Fax: 44 1743 271702
E-mail: shropshire@bbc.co.uk
Format: Talk; News; Classic Rock; Sports; Information; Eclectic. **Owner:** British Broadcasting Corporation, Broadcasting House, Portland Pl., London W1A 1AA, United Kingdom. **Founded:** Apr. 23, 1985. **Operating Hours:** Continuous. **URL:** http://news.bbc.co.uk/local/shropshire/hi/tv_and_radio/.

Sidcup

56540 ■ Bexley Times
Archant Regional Ltd.
Roxby House
Station Rd.
Sidcup DA15 7EJ, United Kingdom
Ph: 44 20 82697000
Publisher E-mail: sandra.roantree@archant.co.uk
Local community newspaper. **Freq:** Weekly (Thurs.). **Key Personnel:** Melody Foreman, Editor, melody. foreman@archant.co.uk. **Subscription Rates:** 11.80 individuals 4 weeks; 23.60 individuals 2 months; 35.40 individuals 3 months; 70.80 individuals 6 months; 153.40 individuals. **Remarks:** Accepts advertising. **URL:** http://www.bexleytimes.co.uk/home. **Circ:** (Not Reported)

56541 ■ Cranes Today
Wilmington Publishing Ltd.
Wilmington House
Maidstone Rd.
Sidcup DA14 5HZ, United Kingdom
Ph: 44 20 82697720
Fax: 44 20 82697730
Publication E-mail: cranestoday@wilmington.co.uk
Trade magazine covering the crane industry worldwide. **Founded:** 1972. **Freq:** Monthly. **Print Method:** Web Offset. **Trim Size:** 210 x 287 mm. **Key Personnel:** Martin McCarthy, Gp. Sales Mgr., phone 44 20 82697720, fax 44 20 82697803, mmccarthy@ worldmarketintelligence.com; Guy Chapman, Contact, phone 44 20 82697816, fax 44 20 82697877, gchapman@progressivemediagroup.com; Will North, Dep. Ed., phone 44 20 82697779, fax 44 20 82697803, wnorth@progressivemediagroup.com; Kate Hearn, classified Sales Exec., phone 44 20 82697743, fax 44 20 82697803, khearn@progressivemediagroup.com; Richard Howes, Gp. Ed., phone 44 20 82697861, fax 44 20 82697803, rhowes@cranestodaymagazine.com. **ISSN:** 0307-0018. **Remarks:** Accepts advertising. **URL:** http://www.cranestodaymagazine.com. **Ad Rates:** BW: US$4,250, 4C: US$5,985. **Circ:** Combined △15,201

56542 ■ Dartford Times
Archant Regional Ltd.
Roxby House
Station Rd.
Sidcup DA15 7EJ, United Kingdom
Ph: 44 20 82697000

Publisher E-mail: sandra.roantree@archant.co.uk
Local community newspaper. **Freq:** Weekly (Thurs.). **Key Personnel:** Melody Foreman, Editor, melody. foreman@archant.co.uk. **Subscription Rates:** 11.80 individuals 1 month; 28.80 individuals 3 months; 70.80 individuals 6 months; 153.40 individuals. **Remarks:** Accepts advertising. **URL:** http://www.dartfordtimes.com/home. **Circ:** (Not Reported)

56543 ■ Hoist
Wilmington Publishing Ltd.
Wilmington House
Maidstone Rd.
Sidcup DA14 5HZ, United Kingdom
Ph: 44 20 82697720
Fax: 44 20 82697730
Publication E-mail: hoist@wilmington.co.uk
Trade magazine covering factory crane news, product information and analysis for users of overhead cranes worldwide. **Founded:** Feb. 1998. **Freq:** 10/yr. **Trim Size:** 210 x 297 mm. **Key Personnel:** Will North, Editor, phone 44 208 2697779, fax 44 208 2697877, wnorth@ worldmarketintelligence.com. **ISSN:** 1462-0162. **Subscription Rates:** 32; 35 individuals in UK; 35 other countries. **Remarks:** Accepts advertising. **URL:** http://www.hoistmagazine.com/. **Ad Rates:** BW: US$2,725, 4C: US$3,875. **Circ:** Controlled △8,643

56544 ■ Legal Abacus
The Institute of Legal Cashiers and Administrators
2nd Fl., Marlowe House
109 Station Rd.
Sidcup DA15 7ET, United Kingdom
Ph: 44 20 83022867
Fax: 44 20 83027481
Publisher E-mail: info@ilca.org.uk
Professional magazine covering finance and administration of legal practices and reports on the activities of the ILCA. **Founded:** July 1990. **Freq:** Bimonthly. **Print Method:** Litho. **Cols./Page:** 3. **Key Personnel:** Margaret MacDonald, Exec. Sec. **Subscription Rates:** 30 individuals; Included in membership. **Remarks:** Accepts advertising. **URL:** http://www.ilca.org.uk/PUBLICATIONS/tabid/60/Default.aspx. **Ad Rates:** BW: 685. **Circ:** Combined 3,000

56545 ■ Packaging Today
Progressive Media Markets
Maidstone Rd.
Sidcup DA14 5HZ, United Kingdom
Ph: 44 20 82697751
Fax: 44 20 82697874
Publisher E-mail: mwallace@progressivemediagroup. com
Magazine featuring latest developments in the packaging industry. **Freq:** Monthly. **Key Personnel:** Maureen Byrne, Gp. Ed., maureenbyrne@globaltrademedia.com; Daniel Trigueirinho, Circulation Mgr., dtrigueirinho@ progressivemediagroup.com; Joanne Hunter, Dep. Ed., joannehunter@globaltrademedia.com. **URL:** http://www. packagingtoday.co.uk/.

56546 ■ Tunnels & Tunnelling
British Tunnelling Society
Progressive House
2 Maidstone Rd.
Sidcup DA14 5HZ, United Kingdom
Ph: 44 20 82697780
Fax: 44 20 82697840
Publisher E-mail: bts@britishtunnelling.org.uk
Publication covering transportation. **Freq:** Monthly. **Key Personnel:** Jon Young, Editor, jyoung@tunnelsonline. info; Patrick Reynolds, Contact, preynolds@ tunnelsonline.info. **Remarks:** Accepts display advertising. **URL:** http://www.tunnelsonline.info. **Circ:** (Not Reported)

Sittingbourne

56547 ■ DIY Week
Pro Sport Media Ltd.
45 Woodside Gardens
Sittingbourne ME10 1SG, United Kingdom
Ph: 44 17 95424631
Fax: 44 18 95424631
Publisher E-mail: grahambeaudwell@blueyonder.co.uk
Trade magazine for home improvement and garden superstores in the UK and Europe. **Founded:** 2000. **Freq:** Weekly. **Key Personnel:** Fiona Hodge, Asst. Ed.; Will

Parsons, Editor. **Remarks:** Accepts advertising. **URL:** http://www.diyweek.net/index.asp. **Formerly:** DIY Superstore. **Circ:** (Not Reported)

56548 ■ Hardware & Garden Review
Pro Sport Media Ltd.
45 Woodside Gardens
Sittingbourne ME10 1SG, United Kingdom
Ph: 44 17 95424631
Fax: 44 18 95424631
Publisher E-mail: grahambeaudwell@blueyonder.co.uk
Trade magazine for independent garden and home improvement retailers, specialists and wholesalers. **Freq:** Monthly. **Trim Size:** 285 x 405 mm. **Key Personnel:** Colin Petty, Editor and Publisher, phone 44 20 86517165, colin.petty@fav-house.com; Rachael Pearson, Contact, rachael.pearson@fav-house.com. **Remarks:** Accepts advertising. **URL:** http://www.fhgmedia. com/in_print/hgr.asp. **Circ:** (Not Reported)

56549 ■ Housewares (UK)
Pro Sport Media Ltd.
45 Woodside Gardens
Sittingbourne ME10 1SG, United Kingdom
Ph: 44 17 95424631
Fax: 44 18 95424631
Publisher E-mail: grahambeaudwell@blueyonder.co.uk
Business publication. **Freq:** Bimonthly. **Key Personnel:** Jane Oliphant, Editor, phone 44 20 86517093; Clare Turner, Editor, phone 44 20 86517136; Colin Petty, Publisher, phone 44 20 86517165. **ISSN:** 0264-8563. **Online:** Gale. **URL:** http://www.fhgmedia.com/in_print/hwm.asp.

56550 ■ Moneywise
Moneywise Publishing Limited
PO Box 326
Sittingbourne ME9 8FA, United Kingdom
Ph: 44 8442 490215
Publication E-mail: moneywise@servicehelpline.co.uk
Publisher E-mail: moneywise@servicehelpline.co.uk
Magazine reporting on financial issues and information. **Founded:** 1990. **Freq:** Monthly. **Subscription Rates:** 40 individuals. **URL:** http://www.moneywise.magazine. co.uk/.

56551 ■ The PGA Professional
Pro Sport Media Ltd.
45 Woodside Gardens
Sittingbourne ME10 1SG, United Kingdom
Ph: 44 17 95424631
Fax: 44 18 95424631
Publication E-mail: grahambeardwell@blueyonder.co.uk
Publisher E-mail: grahambeaudwell@blueyonder.co.uk
Professional Golfers Association official magazine. **Freq:** 10/yr. **Print Method:** Sheetfed. **Trim Size:** 210 x 297 mm. **Cols./Page:** 3. **Col. Width:** 54 millimeters. **Col. Depth:** 248 millimeters. **Key Personnel:** Adrian Milledge, Editor, editor@pga.org.uk. **ISSN:** 1366-6428. **Remarks:** Accepts advertising. **URL:** http://www.pga. info/PGAPublications/40867686.htm. **Formerly:** PGA Profile. **Ad Rates:** BW: 1,034, 4C: 1,335. **Circ:** 7,557

Skegness

56552 ■ Skegness Standard
Johnston Press PLC
The Hildreds, Unit 22
Skegness PE25 3NU, United Kingdom
Ph: 44 1754 897120
Local community newspaper. **Key Personnel:** Rebekah Gunn, Editor, fax 44 1754 610987, rebekah.gunn@ jpress.co.uk; Tim Robinson, Managing Editor, phone 44 1476 562291, fax 44 1476 560564, tim.robinson@ jpress.co.uk; Lisa Mitchell, Gp. Advertising Mgr. **Remarks:** Accepts advertising. **URL:** http://www. skegnessstandard.co.uk/. **Circ:** (Not Reported)

Skipton

56553 ■ Dalesman Magazine
Country Publications Limited
The Water Mill
Broughton Hall
Skipton BD23 3AG, United Kingdom
Ph: 44 1756 701381
Fax: 44 1756 701326
Publication E-mail: subscriptions@dalesman.co.uk

Circulation: * = ABC; △ = BPA; ♦ = CAC; • = CCAB; ❑ = VAC; ⊕ = PO Statement; ‡ = Publisher's Report; Boldface figures = sworn; Light figures = estimated.

Publisher E-mail: editorial@thecountryman.co.uk

Magazine featuring the people, places and life in Yorkshire. **Founded:** 1939. **Key Personnel:** Paul Jackson, Editor, paul@dalesman.co.uk; Tracy Horsfall, Gp. Advertisement Mgr., phone 44 1756 693478, tracy@dalesman.co.uk; Toni Armitage, Lineage Advertising, toni@dalesman.co.uk. **Remarks:** Accepts advertising. **URL:** http://www.dalesman.co.uk/. **Circ:** (Not Reported)

56554 ■ Eye Spy
Eye Spy Publishing Ltd.
PO Box 10
Skipton BD23 5US, United Kingdom
Ph: 44 1756 770199
Publisher E-mail: sales@eyespymag.com
Magazine devoted to intelligence and espionage. **Freq:** 8/yr. **Key Personnel:** Mark I. Birdsall, Managing Editor. **Subscription Rates:** 25 individuals; US$48 individuals; C$60 individuals in Canada; 50 two years in UK; US$96 two years in US; C$120 two years in Canada. **Remarks:** Accepts advertising. **URL:** http://www.eyespymag.com/newindex/subscribe.htm. **Circ:** (Not Reported)

56555 ■ Warmer Bulletin
Residua Ltd.
The British School
Otley St.
Skipton BD23 1EP, United Kingdom
Fax: 44 17 56709801
Publication E-mail: bulletin@residua.com
Trade journal covering waste management and environmental issues worldwide. **Subtitle:** The Journal of Sustainable Waste Management & Resource Recovery. **Founded:** 1983. **Freq:** Bimonthly. **Trim Size:** A4. **Key Personnel:** Kit Strange, Editor; Liz Shotter, Contact, liz@pagefast.co.uk. **ISSN:** 1362-654X. **Remarks:** Advertising not accepted. **URL:** http://www.residua.com. **Circ:** Combined 1,000

Fresh Radio-AM - See Hawes

56556 ■ Fresh Radio-FM - 107.1
The Watermill
Broughton Hall
Skipton BD23 3AG, United Kingdom
Ph: 44 84 52242052
Fax: 44 84 52242062
E-mail: studio@freshradio.co.uk
Format: Contemporary Hit Radio (CHR). **Owner:** Fresh Radio Limited, at above address. **Operating Hours:** Continuous. **Key Personnel:** James Wilson, Hd. of News. **Ad Rates:** Advertising accepted; rates available upon request. **URL:** http://www.freshradio.co.uk.

56557 ■ Fresh Radio-FM - 102.6
The Watermill
Broughton Hall
Skipton BD23 3AG, United Kingdom
Ph: 44 84 52242052
Fax: 44 84 52242062
E-mail: info@freshradio.co.uk
Format: Contemporary Hit Radio (CHR). **Owner:** Fresh Radio Limited, at above address. **Operating Hours:** Continuous. **Key Personnel:** James Wilson, Hd. of News. **Ad Rates:** Advertising accepted; rates available upon request. **URL:** http://www.freshradio.co.uk.

Sleaford

56558 ■ Sleaford Standard
Johnston Press PLC
28 Handley St.
Sleaford NG34 7TQ, United Kingdom
Ph: 44 1529 413646
Local community newspaper. **Key Personnel:** John Lavery, Editor, phone 44 1529 413646, fax 44 1529 413239, john.lavery@jpress.co.uk; Karen Maw, Sales Mgr., phone 44 1205 311433, fax 44 1205 352913, karen.maw@jpress.co.uk; Tim Robinson, Managing Editor, phone 44 1507 353246, fax 44 1507 353201, tim.robinson@jpress.co.uk. **Remarks:** Accepts advertising. **URL:** http://www.sleafordstandard.co.uk/. **Circ:** (Not Reported)

Slough

56559 ■ Journal of the Audio Engineering Society
Audio Engineering Society - British Section
PO Box 645
Slough SL1 8BJ, United Kingdom

Ph: 44 1628 663725
Journal covering the Audio Engineering Society. **Freq:** Monthly except Jan./Feb. & July/Aug. **Key Personnel:** William T. McQuaide, Managing Editor; John Vanderkooy, Editor. **ISSN:** 1549-4950. **Subscription Rates:** US$695 individuals printed and online,; US$280 individuals print; US$525 individuals online,. **Remarks:** Accepts advertising. **URL:** http://www.aes.org/journal/masthead.cfm. **Circ:** (Not Reported)

56560 ■ Star 106.6-FM - 106.6
The Observatory Shopping Ctr.
Slough SL1 1LH, United Kingdom
Ph: 44 1753 551818
E-mail: studio@time1066.com
Format: Adult Contemporary. **Operating Hours:** Continuous. **URL:** http://time1066.com.

Smallfield

56561 ■ Auto Vending
Rephoto Publishing Ltd.
Plough Rd.
Smallfield RH6 9EZ, United Kingdom
Ph: 44 1342 844444
Fax: 44 1342 844488
Magazine featuring vending industry in United Kingdom. **Subtitle:** The Industry's Preferred Choice. **Founded:** 1991. **Freq:** Monthly. **Trim Size:** 210 x 297 mm. **Key Personnel:** Phil Reynolds, Managing Editor; Amanda Roberts, Editorial Dir., amanda-roberts@btconnect.co.uk. **Subscription Rates:** 60 individuals United Kingdom; 70 individuals Europe; 125 other countries. **Remarks:** Accepts advertising. **URL:** http://www.auto-vending.co.uk/. **Ad Rates:** 4C: 1,995. **Circ:** ‡7,180

56562 ■ Cafe Business
Rephoto Publishing Ltd.
Plough Rd.
Smallfield RH6 9EZ, United Kingdom
Ph: 44 1342 844444
Fax: 44 1342 844488
Magazine featuring beverage service industry. **Subtitle:** An essential read for the beverage service professional. **Freq:** Monthly. **Trim Size:** 210 x 297 mm. **Key Personnel:** Phil Reynolds, Managing Editor, phil.reynolds@rephotopublishing.co.uk; Amanda Roberts, Editorial Dir., amanda-roberts@btconnect.com. **Subscription Rates:** 60 individuals UK; 70 individuals to European countries; 125 other countries. **Remarks:** Accepts advertising. **URL:** http://www.cafe-business.co.uk/. **Ad Rates:** BW: 750, 4C: 995. **Circ:** 7,128

Solihull

56563 ■ Funeral Director Monthly
National Association of Funeral Directors
618 Warwick Rd.
Solihull B91 1AA, United Kingdom
Ph: 44 12 17111343
Fax: 44 12 17111351
Publisher E-mail: info@nafd.org.uk
Publication covering funeral directors. **Freq:** Monthly. **Subscription Rates:** 48 nonmembers U.K; 72 nonmembers Europe and Ireland; 90 nonmembers rest of the world. **Remarks:** Advertising accepted; rates available upon request. **URL:** http://www.nafd.org.uk/funeral-profession/funeral-director-monthly.aspx. **Circ:** 2,000

56564 ■ Interiors Focus
Association of Interior Specialists
Olton Bridge
245 Warwick Rd.
Solihull B92 7AH, United Kingdom
Ph: 44 12 17070077
Fax: 44 12 17061949
Publisher E-mail: info@ais-interiors.org.uk
Magazine of the Association of Interior Specialists. **Freq:** Semiannual. **Remarks:** Accepts advertising. **URL:** http://ais-interiors.org.uk/index.php?option=com_content&task=view&id=27&Itemid=49. **Circ:** (Not Reported)

South Croydon

56565 ■ Reverberations
Handbell Ringers of Great Britain
87 The Woodfields
Sanderstead
South Croydon CR2 OHJ, United Kingdom

Publisher E-mail: sandra@hrgb.org.uk
Publication covering music. **Freq:** Semiannual. **Key Personnel:** Lindsay Trevarthen, Editor, reverberations@hrgb.org.uk. **Remarks:** Advertising accepted; rates available upon request. **URL:** http://www.hrgb.org.uk/index.php/reverberations-mainmenu-41. **Circ:** (Not Reported)

South Shields

56566 ■ Shields Gazette
Johnston Press PLC
Chapter Row
South Shields NE33 1BL, United Kingdom
Ph: 44 191 4274800
Local community newspaper. **Freq:** Daily. **Key Personnel:** John Szymanski, Editor; Ross Gregory, Sports Ed. **Remarks:** Accepts advertising. **URL:** http://www.shieldsgazette.com/. **Circ:** (Not Reported)

Southall

56567 ■ Time-FM - 106.6
Radio House
Middlesex
Southall UB2 4AT, United Kingdom
Ph: 44 845 1941066
E-mail: studio@time1066.com
Format: Adult Contemporary. **Ad Rates:** Advertising accepted; rates available upon request. **URL:** http://time1066.com/.

Southampton

56568 ■ Biomedical Signal Processing and Control
Elsevier Science Inc.
University of Southampton
Institute of Sound & Vibration Research
Highfield
Southampton SO17 1BJ, United Kingdom
Publisher E-mail: usinfo-ehelp@elsevier.com
Peer-reviewed journal providing information on signals and images in clinical medicine and the biological sciences. **Founded:** 2006. **Freq:** 4/yr. **Print Method:** Offset. **Trim Size:** 8 1/4 x 10 7/8. **Cols./Page:** 3. **Col. Width:** 27 nonpareils. **Col. Depth:** 140 agate lines. **Key Personnel:** J.W. Clark, Editorial Advisory Board; Robert Allen, PhD, Editor-in-Chief; M. Akay, Editorial Advisory Board; S. Cerutti, Editorial Advisory Board; D. Simpson, Editorial Advisory Board; G. Chase, Editorial Advisory Board. **ISSN:** 1746-8094. **Subscription Rates:** US$1,084 institutions, other countries except Europe, Japan and Iran; EUR718 institutions for European countries and Iran; 146,000¥ institutions; US$183 other countries except Europe, Japan and Iran; 20,900¥ individuals; EUR137 individuals for European countries and Iran. **URL:** http://www.elsevier.com/wps/find/journaldescription.cws_home/706718/descriptiondescription.

56569 ■ Continental Shelf Research
Elsevier Science Inc.
c/o Michael B. Collins, Ed.
University of Southampton
Southampthon Oceanography Centre
School of Ocean & Earth Science
Southampton SO14 3ZH, United Kingdom
Ph: 44 238 0592786
Fax: 44 238 0593052
Publisher E-mail: usinfo-ehelp@elsevier.com
Journal of physical oceanography, sedimentology, geology, chemistry, biology and ecology. **Founded:** 1982. **Freq:** 20/yr. **Print Method:** Offset. **Trim Size:** 7 7/8 x 10 1/2. **Cols./Page:** 3. **Key Personnel:** Richard W. Sternberg, Editor, phone 206543-6492, fax 206543-6128, csr@ocean.washington.edu; Michael B. Collins, Editor, mbc@noc.soton.ac.uk; P. Ciavola, Editorial Advisory Board; J. Oltman-Shay, Editorial Advisory Board; M. Pinkerton, Assoc. Ed., phone 64 43860369, fax 64 43862153, m.pinkerton@niwa.co.nz; M. Dagg, Editorial Advisory Board; A. Borja, Editorial Advisory Board; L.D. Wright, Editorial Advisory Board; E. Wolanski, Editorial Advisory Board. **ISSN:** 0278-4343. **Subscription Rates:** EUR297 individuals for European countries and Iran; US$334 other countries except Europe, Japan and Iran; 39,700¥ individuals; 342,100¥ institutions; US$2,881 institutions, other countries except Europe, Japan and Iran; EUR2,576 institutions for European countries and Iran. **URL:** http://www.elsevier.com/wps/find/journaldescription.cws_home/662/descriptiondescription.

56570 ■ The English Historical Review
Oxford University Press
c/o G.W. Bernard, Articles Ed.
Department of History
University of Southampton
Highfield
Southampton SO17 1BJ, United Kingdom
Publisher E-mail: webenquiry.uk@oup.com
Journal dealing with British history as well as with almost all aspects of European and world history since the classical era. **Freq:** 6/yr. **Key Personnel:** Martin Conway, Book Review Ed.; G.W. Bernard, Articles Ed. **ISSN:** 0013-8266. **Subscription Rates:** 323 institutions corporate; print and online; 269 institutions corporate; online only; 296 institutions corporate; print only; 258 institutions print and online; 215 institutions online only; 237 institutions print only; 90 individuals print; 53 students and senior; print; 67 members print. **Remarks:** Advertising accepted; rates available upon request. **URL:** http://ehr.oxfordjournals.org. **Circ:** (Not Reported)

56571 ■ Greece and Rome
Cambridge University Press
c/o Dr. Vedia Izzet, Ed.
Archaeology, University of Southampton
Ave. Campus
Highfield
Southampton SO17 1BF, United Kingdom
Publisher E-mail: information@cambridge.org
Periodical focusing on history. **Freq:** Semiannual. **Key Personnel:** Dr. Vedia Izzet, Editor; Dr. Robert Shorrock, Editor; Dr. John Taylor, Editor. **ISSN:** 0017-3835. **Subscription Rates:** 93 institutions online and print; US$174 institutions online and print; 88 institutions online only; US$164 institutions online only. **URL:** http://journals.cambridge.org/action/displayJournal?jid=GAR.

56572 ■ Health Education
Emerald Group Publishing Ltd.
c/o Prof. Katherine Weare, Ed.
School of Education
University of Southampton
Highfield
Southampton SO17 1BJ, United Kingdom
Publisher E-mail: emerald@emeraldinsight.com
Journal on health education. **Freq:** Bimonthly. **Key Personnel:** Prof. Katherine Weare, Editor, skw@soton.ac.uk; Dr. Peter Eachus, Internet Ed.; Viv Speller, Book Review Ed.; Kate Snowden, Publisher, ksnowden@emeraldinsight.com. **ISSN:** 0965-4283. **URL:** http://www.emeraldinsight.com/products/journals/journals.htm?id=he.

56573 ■ Journal of Economic Geography
Oxford University Press
c/o Prof. Neil Wrigley, Ed.
Dept. of Geography
University of Southampton
Southampton SO17 1BJ, United Kingdom
Ph: 44 2380 593762
Fax: 44 1703 593295
Publisher E-mail: webenquiry.uk@oup.com
Journal presenting research on the relationship between economics and geography. **Freq:** 6/yr. **Key Personnel:** Prof. Neil Wrigley, Editor, n.wrigley@soton.ac.uk; Dr. Henry G. Overman, Editor, geog.joeg.editor@lse.ac.uk; Trevor Barnes, Editorial Board; Peter Dicken, Editorial Board; Meric Gertler, Assoc. Ed.; Ronald L. Martin, Assoc. Ed. **ISSN:** 1468-2702. **Subscription Rates:** 522 institutions corporate; print and online; 435 institutions corporate; online only; 479 institutions corporate; print only; 418 institutions print and online; 348 institutions online only; 383 institutions print only; 67 individuals print. **URL:** http://joeg.oxfordjournals.org.

56574 ■ Journal of Medieval History
Elsevier Science
c/o C.M. Woolgar, Ed.
Dept. of History
University of Southampton
Southampton SO17 1BJ, United Kingdom
Publisher E-mail: nlinfo-f@elsevier.com
Journal dealing with the history of Europe in the Middle Ages between the fall of Rome and the Renaissance. **Founded:** 1975. **Freq:** 4/yr. **Key Personnel:** C.M. Woolgar, Editor, c.m.woolgar@soton.ac.uk. **ISSN:** 0304-4181. **Subscription Rates:** US$255 individuals except Europe and Japan; EUR227 individuals European countries;

30,200¥ individuals Japan; US$749 institutions, other countries except Europe and Japan; EUR669 institutions European countries; 89,000¥ institutions Japan. **Remarks:** Accepts advertising. **URL:** http://www.elsevier.com/wps/find/journaldescription.cws_home/505591/description. **Circ:** (Not Reported)

56575 ■ Naturwissenschaften
Springer-Verlag
c/o Sven Thatje, Ed.-in-Ch.
School of Ocean & Earth Science
University of Southampton
European Way
Southampton SO14 3ZH, United Kingdom
Ph: 44 23 80593059
Journal publishing reviews, original articles, and short communications on scientific fields. **Founded:** 1913. **Key Personnel:** Ekkehard Fluck, Editor; Bernd Herrmann, Editor; Oskar Mahrenholtz, Editor; Gerald Mayr, Editor; Horst J. Neugebauer, Editor. **ISSN:** 0028-1042. **Subscription Rates:** EUR821 institutions print incl. free access; EUR985.20 institutions print incl. enhanced access. **Remarks:** Advertising accepted; rates available upon request. **URL:** http://www.springer.com/lifesci/journal/114. **Circ:** (Not Reported)

56576 ■ Progress in Nuclear Magnetic Resonance Spectroscopy
Mountain Association for Community Economic Development
Dept. of Chemistry
University of Southampton
Southampton, United Kingdom
Publisher E-mail: info@maced.org
Journal publishing review papers describing research related to theory and application of NMR spectroscopy. **Freq:** 8/yr. **Key Personnel:** J.W. Emsley, Exec. Ed.; J. Feeney, Exec. Ed. **ISSN:** 0079-6565. **Subscription Rates:** US$168 individuals; US$1,652 institutions. **Remarks:** Accepts advertising. **URL:** http://www.us.elsevierhealth.com/product.jsp?isbn=00796565. **Circ:** (Not Reported)

56577 ■ RYA Magazine
Royal Yachting Association
RYA House
Ensign Way
Hamble
Southampton SO31 4YA, United Kingdom
Ph: 44 23 80604100
Fax: 44 23 80604299
Magazine covering boating. **Freq:** Quarterly. **Subscription Rates:** 5.99 members; 5.09 nonmembers. **Remarks:** Advertising accepted; rates available upon request. **URL:** http://www.rya.org.uk/joinrenew/benefits/Pages/RYACommunications.aspx. **Circ:** 87,500

56578 ■ Sedimentology
John Wiley & Sons Inc.
Wiley-Blackwell
c/o Prof. Paul A. Carling, Ch. Ed.
School of Geography
University of Southampton
Highfield
Southampton SO17 1BJ, United Kingdom
Ph: 44 23 80592214
Fax: 44 23 80593295
Publication covering sedimentology. **Freq:** 7/yr. **Key Personnel:** Prof. Paul A. Carling, Ch. Ed., p.a.carling@soton.ac.uk; Prof. Peter K. Swart, Ch. Ed., phone 305421-4103, fax 305421-4632, pswart@rsmas.miami.edu; Elaine Richardson, Office Mgr., e.richardson@soton.ac.uk. **ISSN:** 0037-0746. **Subscription Rates:** US$1,943 institutions print + online; 1,053 institutions print + online; US$2,267 institutions, other countries print + online; US$1,766 institutions print; 957 institutions print; US$2,060 institutions, other countries print; EUR1,338 institutions print + online; EUR1,216 institutions print. **Remarks:** Advertising not accepted. **URL:** http://www.wiley.com/bw/journal.asp?ref=0037-0746&site=1. **Circ:** (Not Reported)

56579 ■ Wessex Scene
Southampton University
Student Union
University Rd.
Highfield
Southampton SO17 1BJ, United Kingdom
Ph: 44 23 80595000
Fax: 44 23 80593939
Publication E-mail: editor@soton.ac.uk

Publisher E-mail: comms@soton.ac.uk
Student newspaper. **Subtitle:** Edge. **Founded:** Sept. 22, 2000. **Freq:** Triweekly. **Key Personnel:** Vicky Horrigan, Mktg. Mgr. **Remarks:** Accepts advertising. **URL:** http://www.wessexscene.co.uk. **Circ:** Non-paid 4,000

56580 ■ BBC Radio Solent-FM - 96.1
Broadcasting House
Havelock Rd.
Southampton SO14 7PU, United Kingdom
Ph: 44 23 80631311
E-mail: hampshire@bbc.co.uk
Format: Talk; News; Classic Rock; Sports; Information; Alternative/New Music/Progressive; Eclectic; Religious; Jazz. **Owner:** British Broadcasting Corporation, Broadcasting House, Portland Pl., London W1A 1AA, United Kingdom. **Operating Hours:** Continuous. **Key Personnel:** Mia Costello, Editor. **URL:** http://news.bbc.co.uk/local/hampshire/hi/tv_and_radio/.

56581 ■ Dream 107.2 - 107.2
Friends Provident St. Mary's Stadium
Britannia Rd.
Southampton SO14 5FP, United Kingdom
Ph: 44 23 80330300
Fax: 44 23 80206400
E-mail: studio@radiohampshire.com
Format: News; Music of Your Life; Sports; Contemporary Hit Radio (CHR). **Owner:** Tindle Radio Ltd., Radio House, Orion Ct., Ground Fl., Great Blakenham IP6 0LW, United Kingdom, 44 1473 836100, Fax: 44 1473 836136. **Formerly:** Win-FM. **Operating Hours:** Continuous. **Ad Rates:** Advertising accepted; rates available upon request. **URL:** http://www.radiohampshire.com.

56582 ■ Surge-AM - 1287
Southampton University Students' Union
University of Southampton
Southampton SO17 1BJ, United Kingdom
Ph: 44 23 80595226
Fax: 44 23 80595252
E-mail: studio@surgeradio.co.uk
Format: Eclectic; News; Sports. **Key Personnel:** Tom Stacey, Station Mgr. **URL:** http://www.surgeradio.co.uk/.

56583 ■ Unity-FM - 101.1
107 St. Mary's Rd.
Southampton SO14 0AN, United Kingdom
Ph: 44 23 80233239
E-mail: info@unity101.org
Format: Ethnic; Talk. **Owner:** Cultural Media Enterprise Ltd., at above address. **Operating Hours:** 10 hours Daily. **Key Personnel:** Ram Kalyan, Station Mgr., kelly@unity101.org; Matthew Auckland, Hd. of Info. Tech. & Production, mauckland@unity101.org. **Ad Rates:** Advertising accepted; rates available upon request. **URL:** http://www.unity101.org.

Southend-on-Sea

56584 ■ Boards
BOARDS Magazine
196 E Esplanade
Southend-on-Sea SS1 3AB, United Kingdom
Ph: 44 1702 582245
Publication E-mail: editorial@boards.co.uk
Magazine about windsurfing, featuring tips, news, techniques, travel, competition, products, and more. **Founded:** Dec. 1982. **Freq:** 10/yr. **Subscription Rates:** 33 individuals; 45 individuals Europe; 53 individuals elsewhere; 60 two years individual; 82 two years European + 2 free issue; 96 two years out side Europe + 2 free issue. **Remarks:** Accepts advertising. **URL:** http://boards.mpora.com/. **Circ:** (Not Reported)

56585 ■ IMA Journal of Numerical Analysis
Institute of Mathematics and its Applications
IMA
16 Nelson St.
Essex
Southend-on-Sea SS1 1EF, United Kingdom
Ph: 44 17 02354020
Fax: 44 17 02354111
Publisher E-mail: post@ima.org.uk
Journal containing original contributions to all fields of numerical analysis. **Freq:** Quarterly. **Key Personnel:** Arieh Iserles, Editor; Endre Suli, Editor. **ISSN:** 0272-4979. **Subscription Rates:** US$808 institutions print

Circulation: ★ = ABC; △ = BPA; ♦ = CAC; • = CCAB; ❑ = VAC; ⊕ = PO Statement; ‡ = Publisher's Report; Boldface figures = sworn; Light figures = estimated.

Gale Directory of Publications & Broadcast Media/147th Ed. 5859

and online; US$674 institutions online only; US$742 institutions print only; 404 institutions print and online; 337 institutions online only; 371 institutions print only; EUR606 institutions print and online; EUR506 institutions online only; EUR557 institutions print only; 332 individuals print. **URL:** http://www.ima.org.uk/mathematics/journals.htm; http://imajna.oxfordjournals.org/.

56586 ■ Chelmsford Radio-FM - 107.7
Icon Bldg.
Western Esplanade
Southend-on-Sea SS1 1EE, United Kingdom
Ph: 44 845 3651077
Format: Adult Contemporary. **Former name:** Chelmer-FM. **Formerly:** Dream 107. **Operating Hours:** 5 a.m.-0 a.m. weekdays; Continuous Weekend. **Ad Rates:** Advertising accepted; rates available upon request. **URL:** http://www.chelmsfordradio.com/.

Southport

56587 ■ Linedancer
Clare House
166 Lord St.
Southport PR9 0QA, United Kingdom
Ph: 44 1704 392300
Fax: 44 1704 501678
Publication E-mail: editor@linedancermagazine.com
Magazine featuring line dancing. **Key Personnel:** Betty Drummond, Publisher, betty.drummond@linedancermagazine.com; Laurent Saletto, Editor, editor_@_linedancermagazine.com; Phil Drummond, Circulation Mgr. **Remarks:** Accepts advertising. **URL:** http://www.linedancermagazine.com/. **Circ:** (Not Reported)

56588 ■ Podiatry Review
Institute of Chiropodists and Podiatrists
The Institute of Chiropodists & Podiatrists
27 Wright St.
Southport PR9 0TL, United Kingdom
Publisher E-mail: secretary@iocp.org.uk
Medical journal covering chiropody and podiatry. **Freq:** Bimonthly. **ISSN:** 0009-4714. **Subscription Rates:** 25 individuals including postage and packaging; 5 single issue including postage and packaging. **Remarks:** Accepts advertising. **URL:** http://www.inst-chiropodist.org.uk; http://www.iocp.org.uk/. **Formerly:** Chiropody Review. **Ad Rates:** BW: EUR395, 4C: EUR525. **Circ:** Controlled 2,500

56589 ■ Dune-FM - 107.9
The Power Sta.
Victoria Way
Southport PR8 1RR, United Kingdom
Ph: 44 1704 502500
Fax: 44 1704 502240
Format: Adult Contemporary. **Operating Hours:** 12 a.m.-11 p.m. Mon.-Sat.; 12 a.m-10 p.m. Sun. **Key Personnel:** David Duffy, Mng. Dir.; Kim Cooper, Sales Mgr.; Phil Johnson, Prog. Controller. **Ad Rates:** Advertising accepted; rates available upon request. **URL:** http://www.dune1079.co.uk/.

Spalding

56590 ■ Dance Expression
A.E. Morgan Publications Ltd.
38 Amblesidr Dr.
Spalding PE11 1JU, United Kingdom
Ph: 44 1775 712856
Fax: 44 1775 712856
Publisher E-mail: info@aemorgan.co.uk
Magazine covering all forms of dance. **Freq:** Monthly. **Key Personnel:** Chris Cattrall, Designer/Ed., chris@themag.fsnet.co.uk; Terence Morgan, Publisher, sue@aemorgan.co.uk. **Subscription Rates:** EUR25.25 individuals. **URL:** http://www.danceexpression.co.uk/index.php?=8.

Stafford

56591 ■ International Journal of Learning Technology
Inderscience Publishers
c/o Dr. Lorna Uden, Exec. Ed.
Staffordshire University
Faculty of Computing, Engineering & Technology
The Octagon, Beaconside
Stafford ST18 0AD, United Kingdom

Publisher E-mail: editor@inderscience.com
Peer-reviewed journal providing information on interdisciplinary forum for the presentation and discussion of important ideas, concepts, and exemplars that can influence the role of learning technologies in learning and instruction. **Freq:** Quarterly. **Key Personnel:** Prof. Lorna Uden, Exec. Ed., l.uden@staffs.ac.uk; Jon Mason, Assoc. Ed.; Dr. Jonathan Brinkerhoff, Editorial Board Member; Dr. Fu-Kwun Hwang, Editorial Board Member; Dr. Rachid Benlamri, Editorial Board Member; Dr. Scotty D. Craig, Editorial Board Member. **ISSN:** 1477-8386. **Subscription Rates:** EUR494 individuals print only (surface mail); EUR840 individuals online only (2-3 users); EUR672 individuals print and online. **URL:** http://www.inderscience.com/browse/index.php?journalCODE=ijlt.

56592 ■ International Journal of Web Engineering and Technology
Inderscience Publishers
c/o Dr. Lorna Uden, Exec. Ed.
Faculty of Computing Engineering & Technology
Staffordshire University
The Octagon, Beaconside
Stafford ST18 0AD, United Kingdom
Publisher E-mail: editor@inderscience.com
Peer-reviewed international journal providing a forum and an authoritative source of information in the fields of web engineering and web technology, devoted to innovative research in the analysis, design, development, use, evaluation and teaching of web-based systems, applications, sites and technologies. **Freq:** Quarterly. **Key Personnel:** Dr. Lorna Uden, Exec. Ed., l.uden@staffs.ac.uk; Prof. Olga De Troyer, Editorial Board Member; Prof. Ruth Breu, Editorial Board Member; Prof. Christophe Claramunt, Editorial Board Member. **ISSN:** 1476-1289. **Subscription Rates:** EUR494 individuals print only; EUR840 individuals online only (2-3 users); EUR672 individuals print and online. **URL:** http://www.inderscience.com/browse/index.php?journalCODE=ijwet.

Stamford

56593 ■ Airports International
Key Publishing Ltd.
Units 1-4
Gwash Way Industrial Estate
Ryhall Rd.
Stamford PE9 1XQ, United Kingdom
Ph: 44.17 80755131
Fax: 44 17 80757261
Publisher E-mail: info@keypublishing.com
Publication for the aerospace and defense industries. **Freq:** Monthly. **Key Personnel:** Tom Allett, Editor. **ISSN:** 0002-2853. **Subscription Rates:** Free to qualified subscribers. **Remarks:** Accepts advertising. **URL:** http://www.airportsinternational.co.uk/. **Circ:** (Not Reported)

56594 ■ Airports of the World
Key Publishing Ltd.
Units 1-4
Gwash Way Industrial Estate
Ryhall Rd.
Stamford PE9 1XQ, United Kingdom
Ph: 44 17 80755131
Fax: 44 17 80757261
Publisher E-mail: info@keypublishing.com
Magazine covering airports and the global airport industry. **Freq:** Bimonthly. **Key Personnel:** Richard Maslen, Contact; Mark Nicholls, Editor, aow@keypublishing.com; Andrew Mason, Advertising Mgr., andrew.mason@keypublishing.com. **Subscription Rates:** 21 individuals; EUR26 individuals; US$21 U.S. and Canada; 47 two years; EUR47 two years; US$35 two years. **Remarks:** Accepts advertising. **URL:** http://www.airportsworld.com/. **Circ:** (Not Reported)

56595 ■ CAA Newsnet
Commonwealth Association of Architects
PO Box 1166
Stamford PE2 2HL, United Kingdom
Ph: 44 178 0238091
Publisher E-mail: info@comarchitect.org
Publication covering architecture. **Freq:** Semiannual. **URL:** http://www.comarchitect.org.

56596 ■ FlyPast
Key Publishing Ltd.
Units 1-4
Gwash Way Industrial Estate
Ryhall Rd.

Stamford PE9 1XQ, United Kingdom
Ph: 44 17 80755131
Fax: 44 17 80757261
Publisher E-mail: info@keypublishing.com
Consumer magazine covering aviation history. **Subtitle:** Britain's Top-Selling Aviation Monthly. **Founded:** 1982. **Freq:** Monthly. **Key Personnel:** Ken Ellis, Editor, flypast@keypublishing.com; Sue Kelly, Advertising Mgr., sue.keily@keypublishing.com. **ISSN:** 0262-6950. **Subscription Rates:** 41 individuals; EUR51 individuals; US$41 individuals; US$79 two years; 51 other countries. **Remarks:** Accepts advertising. **URL:** http://www.flypast.com/. **Circ:** Paid ★44,188

56597 ■ Today's Pilot
Key Publishing Ltd.
Units 1-4
Gwash Way Industrial Estate
Ryhall Rd.
Stamford PE9 1XQ, United Kingdom
Ph: 44 17 80755131
Fax: 44 17 80757261
Publisher E-mail: info@keypublishing.com
Magazine for people who fly. **Subtitle:** For People Who Fly. **Key Personnel:** Rhona York, Advertising Mgr., rhona.york@keypublishing.com; Dave Unwin, Editor, todayspilot@keypublishing.com. **Subscription Rates:** 32.95 individuals; EUR47 individuals; US$37 U.S. and Canada; 47 other countries; 53 two years; EUR89 two years; US$69 two years; 89 other countries two years. **Remarks:** Accepts advertising. **URL:** http://www.todayspilot.co.uk/. **Circ:** (Not Reported)

56598 ■ Rutland Radio-FM - 97.4
40 Melton Rd.
Oakham LE15 6AY, United Kingdom
Ph: 44 1572 757868
Fax: 44 1572 757744
E-mail: enquiries@rutlandradio.co.uk
Format: Oldies; Contemporary Hit Radio (CHR). **Operating Hours:** Continuous. **Ad Rates:** Advertising accepted; rates available upon request. **URL:** http://www.rutlandradio.co.uk/.

Stevenage

56599 ■ Computing and Control Engineering Journal
Institution of Engineering and Technology
Michael Faraday House
Stevenage SG1 2AY, United Kingdom
Ph: 44 1438 313311
Fax: 44 1438 765526
Publisher E-mail: postmaster@theiet.org
Journal covering computing and control engineering. **Freq:** Bimonthly. **Key Personnel:** Dickson Ross, Editor-in-Chief, dmross@iee.org.uk. **ISSN:** 0956-3385. **Remarks:** Accepts advertising. **URL:** http://ieeexplore.ieee.org/xpl/RecentIssue.jsp?punumber=2218; http://www.theiet.org/. **Ad Rates:** BW: 1,248, 4C: 1,804. **Circ:** 19,639

56600 ■ Electronics and Communication Engineering Journal
Institution of Engineering and Technology
Michael Faraday House
Stevenage SG1 2AY, United Kingdom
Ph: 44 1438 313311
Fax: 44 1438 765526
Publisher E-mail: postmaster@theiet.org
Journal covering electronics and communication engineering. **Founded:** Feb. 1989. **Freq:** Bimonthly. **ISSN:** 0954-0695. **Remarks:** Advertising accepted; rates available upon request. **URL:** http://ieeexplore.ieee.org/xpl/RecentIssue.jsp?punumber=2219. **Circ:** ‡38,000

56601 ■ Electronics Education
Institution of Engineering and Technology
The IEE
Michael Faraday House
Six Hills Way
Stevenage SG1 2AY, United Kingdom
Ph: 44 1438 767373
Publisher E-mail: postmaster@theiet.org
Publication covering electronics engineering. **Freq:** 3/yr. **Key Personnel:** Christine Faulkner, Contact, cfaulkner@iee.org.uk. **ISSN:** 0265-0096. **Subscription Rates:** 18 individuals; 12 individuals for teacher. **Remarks:** Accepts advertising. **URL:** http://www.theiet.org/education/supportteachers/ete/index.cfm. **Circ:** (Not Reported)

56602 ■ Electronics Letters
Institution of Electrical Engineers
Publishing Dept.
Michael Faraday House
Six Hills Way
Stevenage SG1 2AY, United Kingdom
Ph: 44 14 38313311
Fax: 44 14 38765526
Publication E-mail: ietdl@theiet.org
Publisher E-mail: postmaster@iee.org
Peer-reviewed journal containing the latest developments and research in the entire field of modern electronics, providing an invaluable source of new information and results on important topics of interest across the spectrum of electronic science and engineering, telecommunications, optoelectronics and optical communication. **Freq:** Semimonthly 25/yr. **Key Personnel:** Chris Toumazou, Editor-in-Chief, c.toumazou@imperial.ac.uk; Ian White, Editor-in-Chief. **ISSN:** 0013-5194. **Subscription Rates:** 1,285 individuals print or online; US$2,523 individuals print or online; 1,542 individuals print and online; US$3,027 individuals print and online. **URL:** http://www.ietdl.org/EL.

56603 ■ Engineering & Technology
Institution of Engineering and Technology
Michael Faraday House
Stevenage SG1 2AY, United Kingdom
Ph: 44 1438 313311
Fax: 44 1438 765526
Publisher E-mail: postmaster@theiet.org
Publication covering engineering. **Freq:** 21/yr. **Key Personnel:** Peter Wason, Ch. Exec. **Remarks:** Advertising accepted; rates available upon request. **URL:** http://www.theiet.org/publishing/magazines/index.cfm. **Circ:** 40,000

56604 ■ Flipside Magazine
Institution of Engineering and Technology
Michael Faraday House
Stevenage SG1 2AY, United Kingdom
Ph: 44 1438 313311
Fax: 44 1438 765526
Publication E-mail: flipside@flipside.org.uk
Publisher E-mail: postmaster@theiet.org
Magazine for teenagers covering everything from music and films to sport and adventure. **Freq:** 8/yr. **Key Personnel:** Dickon Ross, Editor, flipside@flipside.org.uk. **Subscription Rates:** EUR22 individuals; EUR27.50 members; EUR20 individuals cover price; US$55 individuals non member. **URL:** http://www.flipside.org.uk.

56605 ■ IEE Proceedings Circuits, Devices & Systems
Institution of Electrical Engineers
Publishing Dept.
Michael Faraday House
Six Hills Way
Stevenage SG1 2AY, United Kingdom
Ph: 44 14 38313311
Fax: 44 14 38765526
Publication E-mail: ieeproc_cds@iee.org
Publisher E-mail: postmaster@iee.org
Journal covering circuit theory and design, circuit analysis and simulation, computer aided design; filters (analogue and switched capacitor); circuit implementations, cells and architectures for integration including VLSI; testability, fault tolerant design, minimisation of circuits and CAD for VLSI; novel or improved electronic devices for both traditional and emerging technologies including nanoelectronics and MEMs, device and process characterisation, device parameter extraction schemes; mathematics of circuits and systems theory; test and measurement techniques involving electronic circuits, circuits for industrial applications, sensors and transducers. **Freq:** Bimonthly. **Key Personnel:** Asim Ray, Editor-in-Chief, a.k.ray@qmul.ac.uk. **ISSN:** 1751-858X. **Subscription Rates:** 813 individuals print or online; US$1,915 individuals print and online. **URL:** http://scitation.aip.org/IET-CDS.

56606 ■ IEE Proceedings Control Theory & Applications
Institution of Electrical Engineers
Publishing Dept.
Michael Faraday House
Six Hills Way
Stevenage SG1 2AY, United Kingdom
Ph: 44 14 38313311

Fax: 44 14 38765526
Publication E-mail: ieeproc_cta@iee.org
Publisher E-mail: postmaster@iee.org
Journal covering new theoretical results and the applications of new and established control methods with topics such as: system modelling, identification and simulation, the analysis and design of control systems (including computer-aided design), and practical implementation (including transducers, actuators and online computers), encompassing technological, economic, physiological (biomedical) and other systems, including manmachine interfaces. **Freq:** Bimonthly. **Key Personnel:** Sirish Shah, Editorial Board; Brett Ninness, Editor-in-Chief; Frank Allgower, Editorial Board; James Lam, Editorial Board. **ISSN:** 1751-8644. **Subscription Rates:** US$2,013 individuals print or online; US$2,416 individuals print and online. **URL:** http://www.ietdl.org/IET-CTA.

56607 ■ IEE Proceedings Electric Power Applications
Institution of Electrical Engineers
Publishing Dept.
Michael Faraday House
Six Hills Way
Stevenage SG1 2AY, United Kingdom
Ph: 44 14 38313311
Fax: 44 14 38765526
Publication E-mail: ieeproc_epa@iee.org
Publisher E-mail: postmaster@iee.org
Journal publishing papers of technical standard with a suitable balance of practice and theory, covering a wide range of applications and apparatus in the power field such as: rotating electrical machines, linear motors and actuators; the design of motors and generators of all sizes; industrial and non-industrial applications and processes; railway traction and signaling; variable speed drives; electrically powered vehicles and power electronics. **Freq:** Bimonthly. **Key Personnel:** Emil Levi, Editor-in-Chief; Antero Arkkio, Editorial Board; Nicola Bianchi, Editorial Board. **ISSN:** 1751-8660. **Subscription Rates:** US$1,755 individuals print or online; US$2,106 individuals combined. **URL:** http://www.ietdl.org/IET-EPA.

56608 ■ IEE Proceedings Generation, Transmission & Distribution
Institution of Electrical Engineers
Publishing Dept.
Michael Faraday House
Six Hills Way
Stevenage SG1 2AY, United Kingdom
Ph: 44 14 38313311
Fax: 44 14 38765526
Publication E-mail: ieeproc_gtd@iee.org
Publisher E-mail: postmaster@iee.org
Journal covering current practice and future developments in the electric power generation, transmission and distribution, including the following: operation and control of power generation, power system management and planning, power system operation and control, power system measurement and correction and computer applications and computational intelligence in power flexible AC transmission systems. **Freq:** Bimonthly. **Key Personnel:** Goran Andersson, Editor-in-Chief, andersson@eeh.ee.ethz.ch; Bikash Pal, Editor-in-Chief, b.pal@imperial.ac.uk; Akihiro Ametani, Editorial Board. **ISSN:** 1751-8687. **Subscription Rates:** US$1,722 individuals print or online; US$2,066 individuals combined. **URL:** http://www.ietdl.org/IET-GTD.

56609 ■ IEE Proceedings Microwaves, Antennas & Propagation
Institution of Electrical Engineers
Publishing Dept.
Michael Faraday House
Six Hills Way
Stevenage SG1 2AY, United Kingdom
Ph: 44 14 38313311
Fax: 44 14 38765526
Publication E-mail: ieeproc_map@iee.org
Publisher E-mail: postmaster@iee.org
Journal covering all aspects of microwave and antenna engineering and propagation. **Freq:** Bimonthly. **Key Personnel:** Stavros Iezekiel, Editor-in-Chief, iezekiel@ucy.ac.cy; Ben Allen, Editorial Board; Dominique Baillargeat, Editorial Board. **ISSN:** 1751-8725. **Subscription Rates:** US$1,980 individuals print or online; US$2,376 individuals print and online. **URL:** http://www.ietdl.org/IET-MAP.

56610 ■ IEE Proceedings Nanobiotechnology
Institution of Electrical Engineers
Publishing Dept.
Michael Faraday House
Six Hills Way
Stevenage SG1 2AY, United Kingdom
Ph: 44 14 38313311
Fax: 44 14 38765526
Publisher E-mail: postmaster@iee.org
Journal covering all aspects of research and emerging technologies including, but not limited to: biological nanostructures and novel bionanomaterials, fabrication and application of sensors, devices and machines, interactions between biological nanostructures and microsystems and single molecule spectroscopies. **Freq:** Bimonthly. **Key Personnel:** Ronald Pethig, Editor-in-Chief, ron.pethig@ed.ac.uk; Chris Backhouse, Editorial Board; Tony Cass, Editorial Board. **ISSN:** 1751-8741. **Subscription Rates:** US$441 individuals print or online; US$529 individuals print and online. **URL:** http://www.ietdl.org/IET-NBT.

56611 ■ IEE Proceedings Optoelectronics
Institution of Electrical Engineers
Publishing Dept.
Michael Faraday House
Six Hills Way
Stevenage SG1 2AY, United Kingdom
Ph: 44 14 38313311
Fax: 44 14 38765526
Publication E-mail: ieeproc_opt@iee.org
Publisher E-mail: postmaster@iee.org
Journal publishing articles on optical communication systems; optical fibres, cables and connectors; light sources, optical modulation and multiplexing; optical amplifiers; photodetectors and optical receivers; optical information theory; guided optical waves and integrated optics; optical fibre sensors; theory, development and applications of lasers; nonlinear optics and optical computing; holography; displays; optoelectronic materials. **Freq:** Bimonthly. **Key Personnel:** Richard Penty, Editor-in-Chief, rvp11@cam.ac.uk; John Abbott, Editorial Board. **ISSN:** 1751-8768. **Subscription Rates:** US$1,155 individuals print or online; US$1,386 individuals print and online. **URL:** http://www.ietdl.org/IET-OPT.

56612 ■ IEE Proceedings Radar, Sonar & Navigation
Institution of Electrical Engineers
Publishing Dept.
Michael Faraday House
Six Hills Way
Stevenage SG1 2AY, United Kingdom
Ph: 44 14 38313311
Fax: 44 14 38765526
Publication E-mail: ieeproc_rsn@iee.org
Publisher E-mail: postmaster@iee.org
Journal publishing theory and practice of systems involving the processing of signals for radar, radio location, radio navigation and surveillance purposes. **Freq:** Bimonthly. **Key Personnel:** Hugh Griffiths, Editor-in-Chief; Chris Baker, Editorial Board; Shannon Blunt, Editorial Board. **ISSN:** 1751-8784. **Subscription Rates:** 842 individuals print or online; US$1,654 individuals print or online; 1,011 individuals print and online; US$1,984 individuals print and online. **URL:** http://www.ietdl.org/IET-RSN.

56613 ■ IEE Proceedings Science, Measurement & Technology
Institution of Electrical Engineers
Publishing Dept.
Michael Faraday House
Six Hills Way
Stevenage SG1 2AY, United Kingdom
Ph: 44 14 38313311
Fax: 44 14 38765526
Publisher E-mail: postmaster@iee.org
Journal publishing papers in three main areas: materials, magnetics and measurement, and is specifically focused on all aspects of micro- and nanotechnology. **Freq:** Bimonthly. **Key Personnel:** Mike Cunningham, Editor-in-Chief, michael.cunningham@manchester.ac.uk; Giulio Antonini, Editorial board; Laurie Besley, Editorial board. **ISSN:** 1751-8822. **Subscription Rates:** US$1,145 individuals print or online; US$1,373 individuals print and online. **URL:** http://www.ietdl.org/IET-SMT.

Circulation: ★ = ABC; △ = BPA; ◆ = CAC; • = CCAB; ❑ = VAC; ⊕ = PO Statement; ‡ = Publisher's Report; Boldface figures = sworn; Light figures = estimated.

56614 ■ IEE Proceedings Software
Institution of Electrical Engineers
Publishing Dept.
Michael Faraday House
Six Hills Way
Stevenage SG1 2AY, United Kingdom
Ph: 44 14 38313311
Fax: 44 14 38765526
Publisher E-mail: postmaster@iee.org
Journal publishing papers on all aspects of the software lifecycle, including design, development, implementation and maintenance, focusing on the methods used to develop and maintain software, and their practical application. **Freq:** Bimonthly. **Key Personnel:** Susan Eisenbach, Editorial Board; Mark Harman, Editorial Board; Alessandra Russo, Editor-in-Chief; Eric Dubois, Editorial Board; Eric Yu, Editorial Board; Robert Hall, Editorial Board; Rachel Harrison, Editorial Board. **ISSN:** 1751-8806. **Subscription Rates:** US$1,712 individuals print or online; US$2,054 individuals print and online. **URL:** http://www.ietdl.org/IET-SEN.

56615 ■ IEE Proceedings Vision, Image & Signal Processing
Institution of Electrical Engineers
Publishing Dept.
Michael Faraday House
Six Hills Way
Stevenage SG1 2AY, United Kingdom
Ph: 44 14 38313311
Fax: 44 14 38765526
Publication E-mail: ieeproc_vis@iee.org
Publisher E-mail: postmaster@iee.org
Journal publishing articles on computer vision topics, including reconstruction of 3D depth information, estimation of object motion, attribute based recognition and high level scene understanding and image processing, including topics such as image enhancement and restoration, feature extraction, low level segmentation and colour and texture analysis. **Freq:** Bimonthly. **Key Personnel:** John Thompson, Editor-in-Chief, john.thompson@ed.ac.uk. **ISSN:** 1751-9675. **URL:** http://scitation.aip.org/IP-VIS.

56616 ■ IET Communications
Institution of Electrical Engineers
Publishing Dept.
Michael Faraday House
Six Hills Way
Stevenage SG1 2AY, United Kingdom
Ph: 44 14 38313311
Fax: 44 14 38765526
Publication E-mail: ieeproc_com@iee.org
Publisher E-mail: postmaster@iee.org
Journal covering theory and practice of systems, networks and applications involving line, mobile radio, satellite and optical technologies for telecommunications, and internet and multimedia communications. **Freq:** Bimonthly. **Key Personnel:** Habib F. Rashvand, Editor-in-Chief; Han-Chieh Chao, Editor-in-Chief. **ISSN:** 1751-8628. **Subscription Rates:** US$2,024 individuals print or online; US$2,429 individuals print and online. **URL:** http://scitation.aip.org/IET-COM. **Formerly:** IEE Proceedings Communications.

56617 ■ IET Computers & Digital Techniques
Institution of Electrical Engineers
Publishing Dept.
Michael Faraday House
Six Hills Way
Stevenage SG1 2AY, United Kingdom
Ph: 44 14 38313311
Fax: 44 14 38765526
Publication E-mail: ieeproc_cdt@iee.org
Publisher E-mail: postmaster@iee.org
Journal publishing technical papers describing recent research and development work in all aspects of digital system-on-chip design and test of electronic and embedded systems, including the development of design automation tools (methodologies, algorithms and architecture), aimed at researchers, engineers and educators in the fields of computer and digital systems design and test. **Freq:** Bimonthly. **Key Personnel:** Bashir Al-Hashimi, Editor-in-Chief, bmah@ecs.soton.ac.uk; Petru Eles, Editorial Board; Andrew Tyrrell, Editorial Board; Peter Kollig, Editorial Board. **ISSN:** 1751-8601. **Subscription Rates:** US$1,596 individuals print or online; US$1,915 individuals print and online. **URL:** http://www.ietdl.org/IET-CDT. **Formerly:** IEE Proceedings

Computers & Digital Techniques.

56618 ■ Systems Biology
Institution of Electrical Engineers
Publishing Dept.
Michael Faraday House
Six Hills Way
Stevenage SG1 2AY, United Kingdom
Ph: 44 14 38313311
Fax: 44 14 38765526
Publication E-mail: systemsbiology@iee.org
Publisher E-mail: postmaster@iee.org
Journal containing studies of intra- and inter-cellular dynamics, using systems- and signal-oriented approaches, papers that analyse genomic data and manuscripts on molecular and cell biological studies. **Freq:** Quarterly. **Key Personnel:** Kwang-Hyun Cho, Editor-in-Chief. **ISSN:** 1751-8849. **Subscription Rates:** 717 individuals print and online; US$1,407 individuals print and online; 860 individuals combined; US$1,688 individuals combined. **URL:** http://scitation.aip.org/IET-SYB.

56619 ■ Wiring Matters
Institution of Engineering and Technology
Michael Faraday House
Stevenage SG1 2AY, United Kingdom
Ph: 44 1438 313311
Fax: 44 1438 765526
Publisher E-mail: postmaster@theiet.org
Professional magazine covering wiring regulations for electrical contractors and others. **Founded:** 1991. **Freq:** Quarterly. **Print Method:** Litho. **Key Personnel:** Keith Shipston, Publisher, kshipston@iee.org.uk; Louise Hall, Advertising Mgr. **Remarks:** Accepts advertising. **Available Online.** **URL:** http://www.theiet.org/publishing/wiring-regulations/mag/index.cfm. **Ad Rates:** 4C: 2,040. **Circ:** Non-paid 42,500.

56620 ■ The Woman Engineer
Women's Engineering Society
The IET, Michael Faraday House
Six Hills Way
Stevenage SG1 2AY, United Kingdom
Ph: 44 1438 765506
Publisher E-mail: info@wes.org.uk
Publication covering the woman engineer. **Freq:** Quarterly. **ISSN:** 0043-7298. **Subscription Rates:** Free to members. **Remarks:** Advertising accepted; rates available upon request. **URL:** http://www.wes.org.uk/. **Circ:** 18,000

Stirling

56621 ■ Childminding
Scottish Childminding Association
7 Melville Ter.
Stirling FK8 2ND, United Kingdom
Ph: 44 17 86445377
Fax: 44 17 86449062
Publisher E-mail: information@childminding.org
Professional magazine covering child care and development. **Founded:** 1995. **Freq:** Quarterly. **Key Personnel:** Leigh McEwan, Editor, phone 44 1786 434954, leigh.mcewan@childminding.org. **Subscription Rates:** Free to qualified subscribers. **Remarks:** Accepts advertising. **URL:** http://www.childminding.org. **Circ:** Combined 18,000

56622 ■ The Forth Naturalist & Historian
Forth Naturalist & Historian
University of Stirling
Stirling FK9 4LA, United Kingdom
Ph: 44 17 86467839
Fax: 44 17 86467269
Journal covering history and environmental issues of the Forth Valley in Scotland. **Founded:** 1975. **Freq:** Annual. **Trim Size:** A5. **Cols./Page:** 1. **Key Personnel:** Dr. Neville Dix, Editor; Prof. Mike Thomas, Chm. **ISSN:** 0309-7560. **Subscription Rates:** 8 single issue. **Remarks:** Advertising not accepted. **URL:** http://www.fnh.stir.ac.uk. **Circ:** Combined 350

56623 ■ The International Review of Retail, Distribution and Consumer Research
Taylor & Francis Group Journals
University of Stirling
Institute for Retail Studies
Faculty of Management
Stirling FK9 4LA, United Kingdom

Ph: 44 1786 467384
Fax: 44 1786 46529
Publisher E-mail: customerservice@taylorandfrancis.com
Peer-reviewed journal providing information on retail, distribution and consumer research. **Founded:** 1990. **Freq:** Periodic 5/yr. **Print Method:** Offset. **Cols./Page:** 6. **Col. Width:** 25 nonpareils. **Col. Depth:** 301 agate lines. **Key Personnel:** John A. Dawson, Editor, john.dawson@ed.ac.uk; Leigh Sparks, Editor, leigh.sparks@stir.ac.uk. **ISSN:** 0959-3969. **Subscription Rates:** 635 institutions print and online; 603 institutions online; 77 individuals; US$1,058 institutions print and online; US$1,005 institutions online; US$130 individuals; EUR842 institutions print and online; EUR800 institutions online only; EUR104 individuals. **URL:** http://www.tandf.co.uk/journals/titles/09593969.asp.

56624 ■ Literature and Theology
Oxford University Press
c/o Dr. Andrew Hass, Ed.
School of Languages, Cultures, & Religions
University of Stirling
Stirling FK9 4LA, United Kingdom
Ph: 44 1786 466240
Fax: 44 1786 466088
Publisher E-mail: webenquiry.uk@oup.com
Journal providing a forum for interdisciplinary dialogue, inviting both close textual analysis and broader theoretical speculation as ways of exploring how religion is embedded within culture, encouraging contributions addressing questions of interest to both the disciplines of literature and theology, such as biblical criticism, literary criticism, philosophy, politics, history, cultural studies and contemporary critical theory or practice. **Freq:** 4/yr. **Key Personnel:** Dr. Andrew Haas, Editor, andrew.hass@stir.ac.uk; Prof. Eric Ziolkowski, Editor, 610330-5181, ziolkowe@lafayette.edu; Dr. Darren Middleton, Editor; Dr. Jeff Keuss, Editor; Dr. Cleo McNelly Kearns, Editor; Dr. Alison Jasper, Book Review Ed., a.e.jasper@stir.ac.uk. **ISSN:** 0269-1205. **Subscription Rates:** 238 institutions corporate; print and online; 198 institutions corporate; online only; 218 institutions corporate; print only; 190 institutions print and online; 158 institutions online only; 174 institutions print only; 50 individuals print; 41 members print. **Remarks:** Advertising accepted; rates available upon request. **URL:** http://litthe.oxfordjournals.org/. **Circ:** (Not Reported)

56625 ■ New Technology, Work and Employment
John Wiley & Sons Inc.
Wiley-Blackwell
c/o Chris Baldry, Ed.
University of Stirling
Stirling FK9 4LA, United Kingdom
Ph: 44 17 86467328
Fax: 44 17 86467329
Journal dealing with technological changes in the workplace. **Freq:** 3/yr. **Key Personnel:** Chris Baldry, Editor, c.j.baldry@stir.ac.uk; Prof. Rosemary Batt, Editorial Advisory Board; Prof. Richard Brown, Editorial Advisory Board; Prof. Robin Fincham, Editorial Advisory Board; Geert Van Hootegem, Editorial Advisory Board; Rowena Barrett, Editorial Advisory Board; Prof. Irene Hardill, Editorial Advisory Board; Prof. Carol Haddad, Assoc. Ed., phone 734487-1161, chaddad@emich.edu; Jos Benders, Assoc. Ed., j.benders@fm.ru.nl; Terry Wallace, Editorial Advisory Board; Niki Panteli, Editorial Advisory Board; Christian Koch, Editorial Advisory Board. **ISSN:** 0268-1072. **Subscription Rates:** US$187 individuals print and online; EUR127 individuals print and online; 85 individuals print and online; 112 other countries print and online; US$83 students print and online; EUR56 students print and online; 38 students print and online; 49 students, other countries print and online; US$698 institutions print and online; EUR419 institutions print and online. **Remarks:** Advertising accepted; rates available upon request. **URL:** http://www.wiley.com/bw/journal.asp?ref=0268-1072&site=1. **Circ:** (Not Reported)

Stockport

56626 ■ Defence Management Journal
Public Sector Information Ltd.
Petersgate House
St. Petersgate
Stockport SK1 1HE, United Kingdom
Ph: 44 1782620088

Fax: 44 1782740066
Publisher E-mail: mailbox@psigroup.co.uk
Professional magazine covering the activity of the U.K.'s Ministry of Defence. **Founded:** 1995. **Freq:** Quarterly. **Print Method:** Litho. **Trim Size:** 210 x 297 mm. **Cols./Page:** 3. **Col. Width:** 53 millimeters. **Key Personnel:** Stephen Tucker, Managing Dir.; David Cross, Commercial Dir.; Matthew D'Arcy, Editor, mdarcy@publicservice.co.uk; Philip Cunliffe, Group Ed.; David White, Advertising Sales Mgr. **ISSN:** 1464-2646. **Subscription Rates:** US$295 individuals; US$525 two years. **Remarks:** Accepts advertising. **URL:** http://www.defencemanagement.com/journal.asp. **Circ:** (Not Reported)

56627 ■ Imagine-FM - 104.9
Regent House
Heaton Ln.
Stockport SK4 1BX, United Kingdom
Ph: 44 161 6091049
Fax: 44 161 6091401
Format: Adult Contemporary; News; Sports; Top 40; Oldies. **Operating Hours:** Continuous. **Key Personnel:** Paul Willett, Contact, paul.willett@imaginefm.net; Steve Howarth, Station Dir., steve.howarth@imaginefm.net. **Ad Rates:** Advertising accepted; rates available upon request. **URL:** http://www.imaginefm.net/.

Stoke-on-Trent

56628 ■ The Artisan
Association of Painting Craft Teachers
c/o Mr. Peter Walters, Pres.
56 Eastbank Ride
Stoke-on-Trent ST11 9DS, United Kingdom
Ph: 44 1782 393849
Publisher E-mail: walters317@btinternet.com
Magazine containing information on members of the Association of Painting Craft Teachers. **Freq:** Quarterly. **Remarks:** Accepts advertising. **URL:** http://www.apct.co.uk. **Circ:** (Not Reported)

56629 ■ Design & Technology
Trentham Books Ltd.
Westview House
734 London Rd.
Oakhill
Stoke-on-Trent ST4 5NP, United Kingdom
Ph: 44 17 82745567
Fax: 44 17 82745553
Publisher E-mail: tb@trentham-books.co.uk
Professional magazine covering design and technology education. **Subtitle:** An International Journal. **Freq:** 3/yr. **Trim Size:** A4. **Key Personnel:** Dr. Eddie Norman, Editor. **ISSN:** 1360-1431. **Subscription Rates:** 64 individuals UK; 69 other countries; 56 institutions; 61 institutions; 22 single issue back issue. **URL:** http://www.trentham-books.co.uk. **Formerly:** The Journal of Design & Technology Education. **Circ:** 8,500

56630 ■ Race Equality Teaching
Trentham Books Ltd.
Westview House
734 London Rd.
Oakhill
Stoke-on-Trent ST4 5NP, United Kingdom
Ph: 44 17 82745567
Fax: 44 17 82745553
Publisher E-mail: tb@trentham-books.co.uk
Professional magazine covering education. **Founded:** Nov. 2002. **Freq:** 3/yr. **Trim Size:** A4. **Key Personnel:** Ros Garside, Assoc. Ed.; Gillian Klein, Editor. **ISSN:** 1478-8551. **Subscription Rates:** 186 individuals print and online; 56 institutions UK; 66 institutions overseas; 23 single issue; 39 individuals UK private addresses; 49 individuals overseas, private addresses. **Remarks:** Accepts advertising. **URL:** http://www.trentham-books.co.uk/acatalog/Race_Equality_Teaching.html. **Formerly:** MCT—Multicultural Teaching (Dec. 2002). **Ad Rates:** BW: 200. **Circ:** (Not Reported)

56631 ■ BBC Radio Stoke-FM - 94.6
Cheapside
Hanley
Stoke-on-Trent ST1 1JJ, United Kingdom
Ph: 44 1782 208080
E-mail: stoke@bbc.co.uk
Format: Talk; News; Jazz; Sports; Information; Eclectic;

Classical; Classic Rock; Religious; Folk. **Owner:** British Broadcasting Corporation, Broadcasting House, Portland Pl., London W1A 1AA, United Kingdom. **Operating Hours:** Continuous. **Key Personnel:** Sue Owen, Editor, sue.owen@bbc.co.uk. **URL:** http://www.bbc.co.uk/stoke/radiostoke.

56632 ■ Signal 1-FM - 102.6
Stoke Rd.
Stoke-on-Trent ST4 2SR, United Kingdom
Ph: 44 1782 441300
Fax: 44 1782 441301
Format: Adult Contemporary; Top 40; News; Sports. **Operating Hours:** Continuous. **Key Personnel:** Iain Fowler, Station Dir., iain.fowler@signalradio.com. **Ad Rates:** Advertising accepted; rates available upon request. **URL:** http://www.signal1.co.uk/.

56633 ■ Signal 2-AM - 1170
Signal Radio, Stoke Rd.
Stoke-on-Trent ST4 2SR, United Kingdom
Ph: 44 17 82441300
Fax: 44 17 82441301
Format: Full Service; Contemporary Hit Radio (CHR). **Owner:** UTV Radio GB Ltd., 18 Hatfields, London SE1 8DJ, United Kingdom, 44 20 79597900. **Operating Hours:** Continuous. **Key Personnel:** Lisa Hughes, Director, lisa.hughes@signalradio.co.uk; Lee Williams, Sales Dir., lee.williams@signalradio.co.uk; Mike Mac-Donald, Promotions Mgr., mike.mcdonald@signalradio.co.uk. **Ad Rates:** Advertising accepted; rates available upon request. **URL:** http://www.signal2.co.uk.

Stone

56634 ■ NORM News
National Organization of Restoring Men - UK
PO Box 71
Stone ST15 OSF, United Kingdom
Ph: 44 1785 814044
Publisher E-mail: info@norm-uk.org
Journal of the National Organization of Restoring Men - UK. **Freq:** Quarterly. **URL:** http://www.norm-uk.org/news.html.

Stoneleigh

56635 ■ Country Way
Arthur Rank Centre
B4113 Stoneleigh Rd.
Stoneleigh CV8 2LZ, United Kingdom
Ph: 44 24 76853060
Fax: 44 24 76414808
Publisher E-mail: admin@arthurrankcentre.org.uk
Consumer magazine covering religion and rural lifestyle. **Founded:** 1992. **Freq:** 3/yr. **Print Method:** Offset litho. **Trim Size:** 210 x 297 mm. **Cols./Page:** 3. **Col. Width:** 42 millimeters. **Key Personnel:** Rev. David Emison, Editor. **ISSN:** 0969-6172. **Subscription Rates:** 9 individuals includes p&p; 13 individuals Europe, includes p&p; 18 individuals US and Canada, including p&p. **Remarks:** Accepts advertising. **URL:** http://www.arthurrankcentre.org.uk/publications_and_resources/publications/country_way/index.html. **Ad Rates:** 4C: 420. **Circ:** Paid 4,000

56636 ■ NFU Countryside
National Farmers' Union
Agriculture House
Stoneleigh Pk.
Warwickshire
Stoneleigh CV8 2TZ, United Kingdom
Ph: 44 24 76858500
Fax: 44 24 76858501
Membership magazine for NFU countryside. **Founded:** 1992. **Freq:** Monthly. **Print Method:** Sheetfed offset. **Trim Size:** 186 x 271 mm. **Col. Width:** 43.5 millimeters. **Key Personnel:** Rebecca Shepherd, Product Mgr.; Lesley Bayley, Editor. **ISSN:** 1462-0839. **Remarks:** Accepts advertising. **URL:** http://www.countrysideonline.co.uk. **Formerly:** NFU Countryside. **Ad Rates:** 4C: 3,500. **Circ:** Controlled ★60,000

Stornoway

56637 ■ Stornoway Gazette
Johnston Press PLC
10 Francis St.
Stornoway HS1 2XE, United Kingdom

Ph: 44 1851 702687
Publication E-mail: newsdesk@stornowaygazette.co.uk
Local community newspaper. **Freq:** Weekly. **Remarks:** Accepts advertising. **URL:** http://www.stornowaygazette.co.uk/. **Circ:** (Not Reported)

56638 ■ Isles-FM - 103
PO Box 333
Stornoway HS1 2PU, United Kingdom
Ph: 44 1851 703333
Fax: 44 1851 703322
E-mail: admin@isles.fm
Format: Ethnic; News. **Ad Rates:** Advertising accepted; rates available upon request. **URL:** http://www.isles.fm/.

Stourbridge

56639 ■ Dudley News
Newsquest Media Group Ltd.
St. John's Rd.
Stourbridge DY8 1EH, United Kingdom
Newspaper featuring local news and events. **Freq:** Weekly. **Key Personnel:** Paul Walker, Editor, paul.walker@midlands.newsquest.co.uk. **Subscription Rates:** Free. **Remarks:** Accepts advertising. **URL:** http://www.dudleynews.co.uk/. **Circ:** (Not Reported)

56640 ■ Lace
Lace Guild
The Hollies
53 Audnam
Stourbridge DY8 4AE, United Kingdom
Ph: 44 13 84390739
Fax: 44 13 84444415
Publisher E-mail: hollies@laceguild.org
Magazine containing articles on lace and related subjects, patterns, suppliers new and book reviews. **Freq:** Quarterly. **ISSN:** 6308-3039. **Subscription Rates:** Included in membership. **Remarks:** Accepts advertising. **URL:** http://www.laceguild.demon.co.uk. **Circ:** (Not Reported)

Stowmarket

56641 ■ BDS Yearbook
British Driving Society
83 New Rd.
Helmingham
Stowmarket IP14 6EA, United Kingdom
Ph: 44 14 73892001
Fax: 44 14 73892005
Publisher E-mail: email@britishdrivingsociety.co.uk
Publication covering horses. **Founded:** 1957. **Freq:** Annual Published in March. **Subscription Rates:** Free for all members. **Remarks:** Accepts advertising. **URL:** http://www.britishdrivingsociety.co.uk; http://www.britishdrivingsociety.co.uk/publications/publications.htm. **Circ:** (Not Reported)

56642 ■ Countryside Building
Rural Design and Building Association
c/o Tony Hutchinson
5a The Maltings
Stowpland Rd.
Suffolk
Stowmarket IP14 5AG, United Kingdom
Ph: 44 1449 676049
Fax: 44 1449 770028
Publisher E-mail: secretary@ridba.org.uk
Technical journal of the Rural Design and Building Association. **Freq:** Quarterly. **Key Personnel:** Tony Hutchinson, Editor. **Subscription Rates:** 20 individuals; 35 two years; 45 individuals three years; 30 other countries; 65 other countries three years. **Remarks:** Accepts advertising. **URL:** http://www.ridba.org.uk/countrysidebuilding.htm. **Circ:** (Not Reported)

Strawberry Hill

56643 ■ Holy Land Studies
Edinburgh University Press
c/o Dr. Nur Masalha, Ed.
School of Theology, Philosophy & History
St. Mary's College, University of Surrey
Waldegrave Rd.
Strawberry Hill TW1 4SX, United Kingdom
Publisher E-mail: marketing@eup.ed.ac.uk
Peer-reviewed journal aimed at an academic and public readership, drawing upon expertise from virtually all

Circulation: ★ = ABC; △ = BPA; ◆ = CAC; • = CCAB; ▢ = VAC; ⊕ = PO Statement; ‡ = Publisher's Report; Boldface figures = sworn; Light figures = estimated.

Gale Directory of Publications & Broadcast Media/147th Ed.

5863

relevant disciplines (history, culture, politics, religion, archaeology, sociology). **Subtitle:** A Multidisciplinary Journal. **Freq:** Semiannual. **Key Personnel:** Dr. Nur Masalha, Editor, masalhan@smuc.ac.uk; Ilan Pappe, Editorial Board; Stephanie Cronin, Editorial Board; Yasir Suleiman, Editorial Board; Salim Tamari, International Advisory Board; Donald Wagner, International Advisory Board. **ISSN:** 1474-9475. **Subscription Rates:** 120 institutions print and online; 134 institutions, other countries print and online; US$255.50 institutions print and online (North America); 57 individuals print and online; 62 other countries print and online; US$118 individuals print and online (North America). **Remarks:** Accepts advertising. **URL:** http://www.eupjournals.com/journal/hls. **Circ:** (Not Reported)

Strood

56644 ■ KM-FM - 96.2
Medway House
Ginsbury Close
Sir Thomas Longley Rd.
Medway City Estate, Rochester
Strood ME2 4DU, United Kingdom
Ph: 44 1634 227800
E-mail: okemp@kmfm.co.uk
Format: Adult Contemporary. **URL:** http://www.kmfm.co.uk/goto.php?sess=x183806lu183694lp111ln0lc0ll0lg1ld0.

56645 ■ KM-FM - 101.6
Medway House
Ginsbury Close
Sir Thomas Longley Rd.
Medway City Estate, Rochester
Strood ME2 4DU, United Kingdom
Ph: 44 1634 227800
E-mail: okemp@kmfm.co.uk
Format: Adult Contemporary. **URL:** http://www.kmfm.co.uk/goto.php?sess=x183806lu183694lp111ln0lc0lg1ld0.

56646 ■ KM-FM - 100.4
Medway House
Ginsbury Close
Sir Thomas Longley Rd.
Medway City Estate, Rochester
Strood ME2 4DU, United Kingdom
Ph: 44 1634 227800
E-mail: okemp@kmfm.co.uk
Format: Adult Contemporary. **URL:** http://www.kmfm.co.uk/goto.php?sess=x183807lu183694lp111ln0lc0lg2ll0ld0.

Stroud

56647 ■ Musical Traditions
c/o Rod Stradling
1 Castle St,
Stroud GL5 2HP, United Kingdom
Ph: 44 1453 759475
Publisher E-mail: rod@mustrad.org.uk
Internet magazine covering traditional and folk music throughout the world. **Founded:** 1983. **Key Personnel:** Rod Stradling, Editor; Fred McCormick, Contact. **Remarks:** Accepts advertising. **URL:** http://www.mustrad.org.uk/. **Circ:** (Not Reported)

56648 ■ Star and Furrow
Bio-Dynamic Agricultural Association
c/o The Painswick Inn Project
Gloucester St.
Stroud GL5 1QG, United Kingdom
Ph: 44 14 53759501
Fax: 44 14 53759501
Publisher E-mail: office@biodynamic.org.uk
Journal containing articles, reports and research from around the world. **Freq:** Semiannual. **Trim Size:** 210 x 297 mm. **Key Personnel:** Richard Swann, Editor, rswann@biodynamic.org.uk. **ISSN:** 1472-4634. **Subscription Rates:** 11 nonmembers; 13 by mail Europe; 16 other countries airmail; Free to members. **Remarks:** Accepts advertising. **URL:** http://www.biodynamic.org.uk/about-bdaa/star-and-furrow.html. **Circ:** (Not Reported)

56649 ■ 21st Century Worker
Telecottage Association
The Other Cottage
Shortwood
Nailsworth

Stroud GL6 0SH, United Kingdom
Ph: 44 80 0616008
Publication E-mail: advertising@telework.org.uk
Journal covering new technology and methods of working for professionals working from home. **Founded:** 1993. **Freq:** Bimonthly 6/yr. **Trim Size:** 190 x 267 mm. **Key Personnel:** Shirley Borrett, Contact, shirley@telework.org.uk. **ISSN:** 1358-1465. **Subscription Rates:** EUR4 individuals. **Remarks:** Accepts advertising. **URL:** http://www.telework.org.uk/. **Former name:** Teleworker. **Circ:** Combined 4,000

Sudbury

56650 ■ Horn Player Magazine
British Horn Society
52 Friars St.
Suffolk
Sudbury CO10 2AG, United Kingdom
Magazine covering music. **Freq:** 3/yr. **Key Personnel:** Barry Tuckwell, President; Rev. John Wates, Chm. **URL:** http://www.british-horn.org/hornplayer.html.

56651 ■ Total Tattoo Magazine
PO Box 10038
Sudbury C010 7WL, United Kingdom
Ph: 44 1787 242100
Publication E-mail: editor@totaltattoo.co.uk
Magazine covering information on the tattoo industry. **Freq:** Monthly. **Subscription Rates:** 10.50 individuals for U.K residents only. **URL:** http://www.totaltattoo.co.uk/TTMWEB/.

Sunbury-on-Thames

56652 ■ BTE Journal
Institute of Telecommunications Professionals
Sunbury TE
Green St.
Sunbury-on-Thames TW16 6QJ, United Kingdom
Ph: 44 19 32788861
Fax: 44 19 32785205
Publisher E-mail: enquiries@theitp.org
Journal covering engineering. **Freq:** Quarterly. **ISSN:** 0262-401X. **Subscription Rates:** 112 nonmembers including postage & packaging; 120 nonmembers including postage & packaging, Europe; 124 nonmembers including postage & packaging, rest of the world; Free individual members of the communications network. **Remarks:** Accepts advertising. **URL:** http://www.theitp.org/The-Journal. **Circ:** 21,000

Sunderland

56653 ■ Buddhist Studies Review
Equinox Publishing Ltd.
c/o Peter Harvey, Ed.
Priestman Bldg.
School of Art, Design, Media & Culture
Green Ter.
Sunderland SR2 3PZ, United Kingdom
Peer-reviewed journal covering aspects of Buddhism. **Subtitle:** Journal of the UK Association for Buddhist Studies. **Freq:** Semiannual. **Key Personnel:** Peter Harvey, Editor, peter.harvey@sunderland.ac.uk; Alice Collett, Book Review Ed., a.collett@yorksj.ac.uk. **ISSN:** 0256-2897. **Subscription Rates:** 95 institutions, other countries print and online; US$190 institutions print and online; 40 individuals print; US$80 individuals print; 90 institutions, other countries print; US$181 institutions print. **Remarks:** Accepts advertising. **URL:** http://www.equinoxjournals.com/ojs/index.php/BSR. **Circ:** (Not Reported)

56654 ■ Neural Computing & Applications
Springer-Verlag London Ltd.
c/o John MacIntyre, Ed.-in-Ch.
School of Computing, Engineering & Technology
University of Sunderland
St. Peter's Campus
Sunderland SR6 0DD, United Kingdom
Ph: 44 191 5153778
Fax: 44 191 5152781
Journal covering research in the field of practical applications of neural computing and related techniques. **Freq:** 6/yr. **Trim Size:** 210 x 277 mm. **Cols./Page:** 2. **Col. Width:** 85 millimeters. **Key Personnel:** John MacIntyre, Editor-in-Chief, john.macintyre@sunderland.ac.uk; A.J. Jones, Editorial Board; K.S. Narendra, Editorial Board; F. Girosi, Editorial Board; M.F. Augusteijn, Edito-

rial Board; S.J. Hanson, Editorial Board; A. Browne, Editorial Board; A.U. Levin, Editorial Board; M. Fiddy, Editorial Board; T. Harris, Editorial Board. **ISSN:** 0941-0643. **Subscription Rates:** EUR1,000 institutions print & e-access; EUR1,200 institutions print & enhanced access. **Remarks:** Accepts advertising. **URL:** http://www.springer.com/uk/home/generic/search/results?SGWID=3-40109-70-1106505-0; http://www.springerlink.com/content/0941-0643. **Circ:** Paid 720

56655 ■ Star Series
Northeast Press Ltd.
Echo House
Pennywell
Sunderland SR4 9ER, United Kingdom
Community newspaper and niche publication. **Freq:** Weekly. **Key Personnel:** Betty Long, Editor. **Remarks:** Accepts advertising. **URL:** http://www.newspapersoc.org.uk/Default.aspx?page=942. **Circ:** 230,000

56656 ■ Sun-FM - 103.4
PO Box 1034
Sunderland SR5 2YL, United Kingdom
Ph: 44 191 5481034
E-mail: hello@sun-fm.com
Format: Adult Contemporary; Oldies. **Owner:** Local Radio Company, at above address. **URL:** http://www.sun-fm.com/.

Surbiton

56657 ■ Bulk Distributor
Oakhill Media Ltd.
Oakhill House
22 Williams Grove
Surbiton KT6 5RN, United Kingdom
Ph: 44 20 83989048
Fax: 44 87 07620434
Publisher E-mail: pwh@oakhillmedia.com
Trade magazine covering distribution and transportation of bulk liquids and solids worldwide. **Subtitle:** Hazardous, Non-Hazardous & Foodgrade Logistics. **Founded:** Mar. 1990. **Freq:** Bimonthly 6/yr. **Trim Size:** 210 x 297 mm. **Key Personnel:** Richard Miller, Contact, phone 44 14 24446003, richard.miller@oakhillmedia.com; Neil Madden, Managing Editor, phone 33 3 88603068, neil.madden@wanadoo.fr; Anne Williams, Advertising enquiries, phone 44 19 32225632, anne.bulkd@btinternet.com. **Subscription Rates:** 100 institutions online; US$176 individuals online; EUR146 individuals online; 150 individuals full; US$265 individuals full; EUR220 individuals full; 275 two years full; US$485 two years full; EUR400 two years full. **Remarks:** Accepts advertising. **URL:** http://www.oakhillmedia.com; http://www.bulkdistributor.co.uk/. **Ad Rates:** BW: 2,750, 4C: 3,250. **Circ:** 7,100

56658 ■ Radio Jackie-FM - 107.8
110 Tolworth Broadway
Surbiton KT6 7JD, United Kingdom
Ph: 44 20 82881300
Fax: 44 20 82881312
E-mail: info@radiojackie.com
Format: Classic Rock. **Founded:** 1969. **Operating Hours:** Continuous. **Key Personnel:** James Murray, Advertising Sales Team; Guy Gravenell, Advertising Sales Team; Kevin Cousins, Advertising Sales Team; Susan Kemp, Advertising Sales Team; Liz Cragg, Advertising Sales Team; Jan Ashley, Advertising Sales Team. **Ad Rates:** Advertising accepted; rates available upon request. **URL:** http://www.radiojackie.com/.

Surrey

56659 ■ Alexandria
Ashgate Publishing Ltd.
Union Rd.
Croft Rd.
Surrey GU9 7PT, United Kingdom
Ph: 44 1252 331551
Fax: 44 1252 736736
Professional journal covering library and information issues worldwide. **Freq:** 3/yr. **Key Personnel:** Ian McGowan, Editor. **ISSN:** 0955-7490. **Subscription Rates:** 115 individuals; 103 individuals online. **URL:** http://www.ashgate.com/default.aspx?page=637&calcTitle=1&pageSubject=1056&title_id=10283&edition_id=11280.

56660 ■ Concrete Quarterly
British Cement Association

Riverside House
4 Meadows Business Pk.
Sta. Approach
Blackwater, Camberley
Surrey GU17 9AB, United Kingdom
Ph: 44 1276 608700
Fax: 44 1276 608701
Publisher E-mail: info@bca.org.uk
Trade publication covering concrete. **Freq:** Quarterly.
URL: http://www.concretecentre.com/online_sevices/
publication_library/concrete_quarterly.aspx.

56661 ■ Crusades
Ashgate Publishing Ltd.
Union Rd.
Croft Rd.
Surrey GU9 7PT, United Kingdom
Ph: 44 1252 331551
Fax: 44 1252 736736
Scholarly journal covering the crusades from the First
Crusade (1095-1102) to the fall of Malta (1798). **Key
Personnel:** Prof. Benjamin Z. Kedar, Editor; Prof.
Jonathan Riley-Smith, Editor; Dr. Jonathan Phillips,
Editor. **ISSN:** 1476-5276. **Subscription Rates:** 65
individuals; 58.50 individuals online. **URL:** http://www.
ashgate.com/default.aspx?page=637&calcTitle=1&title_
id=10566&edition_id=11233.

**56662 ■ The European Yearbook of Business
History**
Ashgate Publishing Ltd.
Union Rd.
Croft Rd.
Surrey GU9 7PT, United Kingdom
Ph: 44 1252 331551
Fax: 44 1252 736736
Scholarly journal covering business history in Europe.
Freq: Annual. **Key Personnel:** Terry Gourvish, Editor.
ISSN: 1462-186X. **Subscription Rates:** 60 individuals;
54 individuals online. **URL:** http://www.ashgate.com/
default.aspx?page=637&calcTitle=1&title_id=4185&edit
ion_id=4403.

56663 ■ Global Cement Magazine
PRo Publications International Ltd.
Adelphi Ct., 1st Fl.
1 East St.
Surrey KT17 1BB, United Kingdom
Ph: 44 1372 743837
Fax: 44 1372 743838
Publisher E-mail: system@propubs.com
Magazine featuring the cement industry. **Freq:** Monthly.
Key Personnel: Dr. Robert McCaffrey, Editorial Dir.,
robert.mccaffrey@propubs.com; Paul Brown, Contact,
paul.brown@propubs.com. **Subscription Rates:**
EUR150 individuals; EUR270 two years with 10 percent
discount; EUR382 individuals 3 years (with 10 percent
discount). **Remarks:** Accepts advertising. **URL:** http://
www.propubs.com/global-cement/. **Ad Rates:** BW:
2,896, 4C: 4,267. **Circ:** ★5,346

56664 ■ Global Gypsum Magazine
PRo Publications International Ltd.
Adelphi Ct., 1st Fl.
1 East St.
Surrey KT17 1BB, United Kingdom
Ph: 44 1372 743837
Fax: 44 1372 743838
Publisher E-mail: system@propubs.com
Magazine featuring gypsum production and use around
the world. **Key Personnel:** Dr. Robert McCaffrey, Editorial Dir. **Subscription Rates:** EUR250 individuals; EUR450
two years with 10 percent discount; EUR637 individuals
3 years (with 10 percent discount). **Remarks:** Accepts
advertising. **URL:** http://www.propubs.com/global-
gypsum/. **Ad Rates:** BW: 2,896, 4C: 4,267. **Circ:** 3,247

56665 ■ Global Insulation Magazine
PRo Publications International Ltd.
Adelphi Ct., 1st Fl.
1 East St.
Surrey KT17 1BB, United Kingdom
Ph: 44 1372 743837
Fax: 44 1372 743838
Publisher E-mail: system@propubs.com
Magazine featuring equipment and services of thermal
insulation. **Key Personnel:** Paul Brown, Contact,
pgbrown@propubs.com. **Remarks:** Accepts advertising.
URL: http://www.propubs.com/global-insulation/. **Circ:**
(Not Reported)

56666 ■ Human Factors and Aerospace Safety
Ashgate Publishing Ltd.
Union Rd.
Croft Rd.
Surrey GU9 7PT, United Kingdom
Ph: 44 1252 331551
Fax: 44 1252 736736
Journal covering the study of the human element in the
aerospace system and its role either avoiding or
contributing to accidents and incidents, and promoting
safe operations worldwide. **Freq:** Quarterly. **Key Per-
sonnel:** Helen C. Muir, Editor; Don Harris; Don Harris,
Editor. **ISSN:** 1468-9456. **Subscription Rates:** 50
individuals; US$120 institutions.

56667 ■ Japanese Performance
CHPublications Ltd.
Nimax House
20 Ullswater Cres.
Ullswater Business Park
Surrey CR5 2HR, United Kingdom
Ph: 44 208 6556400
Fax: 44 208 7631001
Publisher E-mail: chp@chpltd.com
Consumer magazine for Japanese car owners and
enthusiasts. **Freq:** Monthly. **Print Method:** Web Offset.
Trim Size: 210 x 297 mm. **Subscription Rates:** 70
individuals; 120 two years. **Remarks:** Accepts
advertising. **URL:** http://www.chpltd.com; http://www.
japaneseperformancemagazine.co.uk. **Circ:** Paid 25,000

56668 ■ Mediterranean Studies
Ashgate Publishing Ltd.
Union Rd.
Croft Rd.
Surrey GU9 7PT, United Kingdom
Ph: 44 1252 331551
Fax: 44 1252 736736
Peer-reviewed journal concerning the ideas and ideals
of Mediterranean cultures from Late Antiquity to the
Enlightenment and their influence beyond these geo-
graphical and temporal boundaries, including topics
concerning any aspect of the history, literature, politics,
arts, geography, or any subject focused on the Mediter-
ranean region and the influence of its cultures. **Freq:**
Annual. **Key Personnel:** Prof. Richard W. Clement,
Assoc. Ed., rclement@mediterraneanstudies.org; Prof.
Geraldo U. De Sousa, Editor, sousa@ku.edu; Prof.
Angel F. Lago, Corresponding Ed. **ISSN:** 1074-164X.
URL: http://www.mediterraneanstudies.org/ms/medstud.
html.

56669 ■ 911 & Porsche World
CHPublications Ltd.
Nimax House
20 Ullswater Cres.
Ullswater Business Park
Surrey CR5 2HR, United Kingdom
Ph: 44 208 6556400
Fax: 44 208 7631001
Publisher E-mail: chp@chpltd.com
Consumer magazine for Porsche owners and enthusi-
asts worldwide. **Freq:** Monthly. **Print Method:** Web
Offset. **Trim Size:** 210 x 297 mm. **Key Personnel:** Chris
Horton, Editor. **Subscription Rates:** 80 individuals; 140
two years. **Remarks:** Accepts advertising. **URL:** http://
www.911porscheworld.com. **Circ:** Paid 36,000

56670 ■ Nineteenth-Century Music Review
Ashgate Publishing Ltd.
Union Rd.
Croft Rd.
Surrey GU9 7PT, United Kingdom
Ph: 44 1252 331551
Fax: 44 1252 736736
Peer-reviewed journal covering music of the era from
1789 to 1914. **Freq:** Semiannual. **Trim Size:** 169 x 244
mm. **Key Personnel:** Prof. Anna Celenza, Book Review
Ed.; Dr. Bennett Zon, Gen. Ed. **ISSN:** 1479-4098. **Sub-
scription Rates:** 65 individuals; US$58.50 individuals
online only. **URL:** https://www.ashgate.com/default.
aspx?page=637&calcTitle=1&title_id=11056&edition_id=
12075. **Formerly:** Music Review.

**56671 ■ Parliaments, Estates and Representa-
tion**
Ashgate Publishing Ltd.
Union Rd.
Croft Rd.

Surrey GU9 7PT, United Kingdom
Ph: 44 1252 331551
Fax: 44 1252 736736
Publication covering parliaments, estates and represen-
tation and political theory related to those topics. **Freq:**
Annual. **Key Personnel:** Henry J. Cohn, Dir of Publica-
tions; Valerie Cromwell, Advisory Board; Alexander
Cowan, Editor; Janusz Mallek, Advisory Board; John
Young, Advisory Board; John Rogister, Advisory Board;
Thomas N. Bisson, Advisory Board. **ISSN:** 0260-6755.
Subscription Rates: 70 individuals; 63 individuals
online. **URL:** http://www.ashgate.com/default.aspx?
page=637&calcTitle=1&title_id=10743&edition_id=
11422; http://www.ashgate.com/default.aspx?page=
2688.

56672 ■ A Place in the Sun
Brooklands Media Group
120-128 Station Rd.
Redhill
Surrey RH1 1ET, United Kingdom
Ph: 44 1737 786800
Fax: 44 1737 786801
Publisher E-mail: mail@brooklandsgroup.com
Magazine covering international property news, inspira-
tional homes and property related advice. **Founded:**
Mar. 2004. **Freq:** 13/yr. **Trim Size:** 213 x 278 mm. **Key
Personnel:** Matt Havercroft, Editor; Nigel Lewis, Manag-
ing Editor. **Subscription Rates:** 89.99 individuals rest
of the world; EUR51.99 individuals; 32 individuals for UK.
Remarks: Accepts advertising. **URL:** http://www.
aplaceinthesun.com/magazine. **Ad Rates:** 4C: 3,995.
Circ: ★35,818

56673 ■ Polymers Paint Colour Journal
Quartz Business Media Ltd.
Westgate House
120/130 Station Rd.
Redhill
Surrey RH1 1ET, United Kingdom
Ph: 44 1737 855000
Fax: 44 1737 855475
Business publication. **Freq:** Monthly. **Key Personnel:**
Melanie Chiles, Production Mgr., phone 44 1737
855336, melaniechiles@uk.dmgworldmedia.com; Sue
Tyler, Dep. Ed., phone 44 1737 855161, suetyler@
dmgworldmedia.com. **ISSN:** 1357-731X. **Remarks:** Ac-
cepts advertising. **Online:** Gale. **URL:** http://www.
polymerspaintcolourjournal.com. **Ad Rates:** BW: 2,367,
4C: 7,727. **Circ:** Paid 8,600

56674 ■ Renault Magazine
Brooklands Media Group
120-128 Station Rd.
Redhill
Surrey RH1 1ET, United Kingdom
Ph: 44 1737 786800
Fax: 44 1737 786801
Publisher E-mail: mail@brooklandsgroup.com
Automotive and lifestyle magazine. **Founded:** 1962.
Freq: 3/yr. **Trim Size:** 213 x 278 mm. **Key Personnel:**
Darren Styles, Publishing Ed.; Ann Wallace, Editorial
Dir. **Subscription Rates:** 3 single issue. **Remarks:** Ac-
cepts advertising. **URL:** http://www.brooklandsgroup.
com/magazines/renault-magazine/index.html. **Ad Rates:**
4C: 4,750. **Circ:** ★212,117

**56675 ■ The Shakespearean International
Yearbook**
Ashgate Publishing Ltd.
Union Rd.
Croft Rd.
Surrey GU9 7PT, United Kingdom
Ph: 44 1252 331551
Fax: 44 1252 736736
Scholarly journal covering Shakespearean studies.
Founded: Oct. 2004. **Freq:** Annual. **Trim Size:** 156 x
234 mm. **Key Personnel:** Graham Bradshaw, Editor;
Tom Bishop, Editor; Mark Turner, Editor. **ISSN:** 1465-
6098. **Subscription Rates:** 60 individuals; 54 individu-
als online. **URL:** http://www.ashgate.com/default.aspx?
page=637&calcTitle=1&title_id=7177&edition_id=7658.

56676 ■ Steel Times International
Quartz Business Media Ltd.
Westgate House
120/130 Station Rd.
Redhill
Surrey RH1 1ET, United Kingdom
Ph: 44 1737 855000

Circulation: ★ = ABC; △ = BPA; ◆ = CAC; • = CCAB; ❏ = VAC; ⊕ = PO Statement; ‡ = Publisher's Report; Boldface figures = sworn; Light figures = estimated.

Gale Directory of Publications & Broadcast Media/147th Ed.

5865

Fax: 44 1737 855475
Publication E-mail: steel@uk.dmgworldmedia.com
Magazine covering for the steel producing industries.
Founded: 1976. **Freq:** 8/yr. **Key Personnel:** Dr. Tim Smith, Editor, phone 44 1737 855154, timsmith@uk.dmgworldmedia.com; Martin Lawrence, Sen. Production Exec., phone 44 1737 855332, martinlawrence@dmgworldmedia.com; Paul Rossage, International Sales Mgr., phone 44 1737 855116, paulrossage@dmgworldmedia.com; Ken Clark, Gp. Sales Mgr., phone 44 1737 855117, kenclark@dmgworldmedia.com; Anne Considine, Area Sales Mgr., phone 44 1737 855139, anneconsidine@uk.dmgworldmedia.com; Annie Baker, Digital Production Ed., phone 44 1737 855130, anniebaker@uk.dmgworldmedia.com. **ISSN:** 0143-7798. **URL:** http://www.steeltimesint.com. **Absorbed:** Steel Times (2001). **Ad Rates:** 4C: 3,460. **Circ:** Combined ★8,000

56677 ■ Triumph World
CHPublications Ltd.
Nimax House
20 Ullswater Cres.
Ullswater Business Park
Surrey CR5 2HR, United Kingdom
Ph: 44 208 6556400
Fax: 44 208 7631001
Publisher E-mail: chp@chpltd.com
Consumer magazine covering classic triumph and standard automobiles for owners and enthusiasts.
Founded: Apr. 1995. **Freq:** Monthly. **Print Method:** Web Offset. **Trim Size:** 210 x 297 mm. **Key Personnel:** Tony Beadle, Editor. **ISSN:** 1357-4248. **Remarks:** Accepts advertising. **URL:** http://www.triumphspitfire.nl/magazines.html. **Circ:** Paid 28,000

Sutton

56678 ■ ACN: Asian Chemical News
Reed Business Information Ltd.
Quadrant House
The Quadrant
Sutton SM2 5AS, United Kingdom
Ph: 44 20 86523500
Fax: 44 20 86528932
Publisher E-mail: enquiries@mardev.com
Publication for the chemical, plastics and rubber industries. **Freq:** Weekly. **Key Personnel:** John Richardson, Editor, phone 44 656 7804356. **ISSN:** 1356-5389. **URL:** http://www.reedbusiness.co.uk/rb2_products/rb2_products_acn.htm.

56679 ■ Airline Business
Reed Business Information Ltd.
Quadrant House
The Quadrant
Sutton SM2 5AS, United Kingdom
Ph: 44 20 86523500
Fax: 44 20 86528932
Publisher E-mail: enquiries@mardev.com
Magazine providing information on trends, analysis and views on the aviation industry. **Freq:** Monthly. **Key Personnel:** Mark Pilling, Editor, phone 44 20 86524993, mark.pilling@rbi.co.uk; Shawn Buck, Sales Mgr., phone 44 20 86524998, fax 44 20 86528981, shawn.buck@rbi.co.uk. **Subscription Rates:** US$382 two years; US$225 individuals; US$506 individuals 3 years. **URL:** http://www.reedbusiness.co.uk/rb2_products/rb2_products_airline_business.htm. **Circ:** △22,907

56680 ■ Caterer & Hotelkeeper
Reed Business Information Ltd.
Quadrant House
The Quadrant
Sutton SM2 5AS, United Kingdom
Ph: 44 20 86523500
Fax: 44 20 86528932
Publisher E-mail: enquiries@mardev.com
Journal covering the hotel, restaurant, pub and contract catering industry. **Freq:** Weekly. **Trim Size:** 210 x 297 mm. **Key Personnel:** Mark Lewis, Editor, phone 44 20 86524210, mark.lewis@rbi.co.uk. **Subscription Rates:** 135 individuals; 240 two years; US$375 U.S. and Canada; US$600 U.S. and Canada 2 years. **Remarks:** Accepts advertising. **URL:** http://www.reedbusiness.co.uk/rb2_products/rb2_products_caterer_hotelkeeper.htm. **Circ:** Combined 36,000

56681 ■ Catering Update
Reed Business Information Ltd.

Quadrant House
The Quadrant
Sutton SM2 5AS, United Kingdom
Ph: 44 20 86523500
Fax: 44 20 86528932
Publisher E-mail: enquiries@mardev.com
Trade journal covering products for the catering industry.
Freq: Monthly. **Trim Size:** 210 x 297 mm. **Key Personnel:** Kathy Bowry, Editor, phone 44 20 86528307, kathy.bowry@rbi.co.uk; Duncan Kirk, Gp. Sales Dir., phone 44 20 86528838, duncan.kirk@rbi.co.uk; Wally Rogers, Display Advertising Mgr., phone 44 20 86528005, wally.rogers@rbi.co.uk; Jonathan King, Classified Sales Mgr., phone 44 20 86528412, jonathan.king@rbi.co.uk. **Remarks:** Accepts advertising. **URL:** http://www.reedbusiness.co.uk/rb2_products/rb2_products_catering_update.htm. **Ad Rates:** BW: 2,875, 4C: 3,500. **Circ:** Combined 23,423

56682 ■ Community Care
Reed Business Information Ltd.
Quadrant House
The Quadrant
Sutton SM2 5AS, United Kingdom
Ph: 44 20 86523500
Fax: 44 20 86528932
Publication E-mail: comcare.children@rbi.co.uk
Publisher E-mail: enquiries@mardev.com
Publication covering sociology and social work. **Freq:** Weekly. **Key Personnel:** Trevor Parker, Publisher, trevor.parker@rbi.co.uk. **ISSN:** 0307-5508. **Subscription Rates:** 89 individuals; US$212 individuals. **URL:** http://www.communitycare.co.uk/Home/.

56683 ■ Computer Weekly
Reed Business Information Ltd.
Quadrant House
The Quadrant
Sutton SM2 5AS, United Kingdom
Ph: 44 20 86523500
Fax: 44 20 86528932
Publisher E-mail: enquiries@mardev.com
Publication covering computers and the office automation industry. **Freq:** Weekly. **ISSN:** 0010-4787. **URL:** http://www.computerweekly.com/Home/. **Circ:** △104,559

56684 ■ European Chemical News
Reed Business Information Ltd.
Quadrant House
The Quadrant
Sutton SM2 5AS, United Kingdom
Ph: 44 20 86523500
Fax: 44 20 86528932
Publication E-mail: rbi.subscriptions@qss-uk.com
Publisher E-mail: enquiries@mardev.com
Professional magazine covering the chemical business. **Founded:** 1962. **Freq:** Weekly. **Print Method:** Sheetfed Offset. **Trim Size:** 4. **Key Personnel:** John Baker, Editor, phone 44 20 86523153, john.baker@icis.com. **ISSN:** 0014-2875. **Remarks:** Accepts advertising. **URL:** http://www.reedbusiness.co.uk/. **Circ:** Paid 9,260

56685 ■ Farmers Weekly
Reed Business Information Ltd.
Quadrant House
The Quadrant
Sutton SM2 5AS, United Kingdom
Ph: 44 20 86523500
Fax: 44 20 86528932
Publisher E-mail: enquiries@mardev.com
A magazine about farming. **Freq:** Weekly. **Trim Size:** 297 mm x 210 mm. **Key Personnel:** Jane King, Editor, phone 44 20 86528122, jane.king@rbi.co.uk; Vic Bunby, Advertising Dir., phone 44 20 86524030, vic.bunby@rbi.co.uk. **Subscription Rates:** US$335 individuals; US$600 two years; US$850 individuals 3 years. **URL:** http://www.reedbusiness.co.uk/rb2_products/rb2_products_farmers_weekly.htm; http://www.farmersmediacentre.co.uk/farmersWeekly/index.htm. **Ad Rates:** BW: 3,750. **Circ:** ★67,446

56686 ■ Farmland Market
Reed Business Information Ltd.
Quadrant House
The Quadrant
Sutton SM2 5AS, United Kingdom
Ph: 44 20 86523500
Fax: 44 20 86528932
Publisher E-mail: enquiries@mardev.com
A magazine about agriculture. **Freq:** 2/yr. **Key Person-**

nel: Ian Ashbridge, Editor, phone 44 20 86524933, ian.ashbridge@rbi.co.uk. **Subscription Rates:** 95 individuals; 171 two years. **URL:** http://www.reedbusiness.co.uk/rb2_products/rb2_products_farmland_market.htm.

56687 ■ Flight International
Reed Business Information Ltd.
Quadrant House
The Quadrant
Sutton SM2 5AS, United Kingdom
Ph: 44 20 86523500
Fax: 44 20 86528932
Publisher E-mail: enquiries@mardev.com
Publication for the aerospace and defense industries. **Freq:** Weekly. **ISSN:** 0015-3710. **Subscription Rates:** US$208 individuals; US$353 two years; US$468 3 years. **URL:** http://www.flightglobal.com/home/default.aspx.

56688 ■ Motor Transport
Reed Business Information Ltd.
Quadrant House
The Quadrant
Sutton SM2 5AS, United Kingdom
Ph: 44 20 86523500
Fax: 44 20 86528932
Publisher E-mail: enquiries@mardev.com
Business publication. **Freq:** Weekly. **Key Personnel:** Steve Hobson, Editor, phone 44 20 86523285, steve.hobson@rbi.co.uk; Dave Smith, Sales Mgr., david.john.smith@rbi.co.uk. **ISSN:** 0027-206X. **URL:** http://www.reedbusiness.co.uk/rb2_products/rb2_products_motor_transport.htm. **Circ:** 19,366

56689 ■ Mutagenesis
Oxford University Press
Institute of Cancer Research
Brookes Lawley Bldg.
Cotswold Rd.
Sutton SM2 5NG, United Kingdom
Publisher E-mail: webenquiry.uk@oup.com
International multi-disciplinary journal designed to bring together research aimed at the identification, characterization and elucidation of the mechanisms of action of physical, chemical and biological agents capable of producing genetic change in living organism and the study of the consequences of such changes. **Freq:** 6/yr. **Key Personnel:** Prof. David Phillips, Editor-in-Chief; Dr. Toshihiro Ohta, Sen. Ed.; J.L. Schwartz, Editorial Board; Prof. Charles L. Limoli, Sen. Ed.; J.M. Parry, Founding Ed. **ISSN:** 0267-8357. **Subscription Rates:** 612 institutions print and online; US$1,193 institutions print and online; EUR918 institutions print and online; 500 institutions online; US$975 institutions online; EUR750 institutions online; 561 institutions print; US$1,094 institutions print; EUR842 institutions print; 561 individuals print. **Remarks:** Advertising accepted; rates available upon request. **URL:** http://mutage.oxfordjournals.org. **Circ:** (Not Reported)

56690 ■ New Scientist
Reed Business Information Ltd.
Quadrant House
The Quadrant
Sutton SM2 5AS, United Kingdom
Ph: 44 20 86523500
Fax: 44 20 86528932
Publisher E-mail: enquiries@mardev.com
Publication covering science and technology. **Freq:** Weekly. **ISSN:** 0262-4079. **Subscription Rates:** 137 individuals. **URL:** http://www.newscientist.com/.

56691 ■ Poultry World
Reed Business Information Ltd.
Quadrant House
The Quadrant
Sutton SM2 5AS, United Kingdom
Ph: 44 20 86523500
Fax: 44 20 86528932
Publisher E-mail: enquiries@mardev.com
Trade magazine covering the poultry industry from breeding to product marketing. **Founded:** 1874. **Freq:** Monthly. **Trim Size:** 333 mm. x 244 mm. **Key Personnel:** Philip Clarke, Editor, phone 44 20 86524921, philip.clarke@rbi.co.uk. **Subscription Rates:** 36 individuals; 64 two years; 91 individuals 3 years; 18 individuals 6 months; US$115 individuals; US$205 two years; US$291.50 individuals 3 years; US$115 Canada; US$205 Canada 2 years; US$291.50 Canada 3 years. **Remarks:** Accepts advertising. **URL:** http://www.reedbusiness.co.uk/rb2_products/rb2_products_poultry_

world.htm; http://www.farmersmediacentre.co.uk/ poultryWorld/index.htm. **Ad Rates:** 4C: 2,500. **Circ:** Paid ★**3,267**

56692 ■ Railway Gazette International
Reed Business Information Ltd.
Quadrant House
The Quadrant
Sutton SM2 5AS, United Kingdom
Ph: 44 20 86523500
Fax: 44 20 86528932
Publication E-mail: info@railwaygazette.com
Publisher E-mail: enquiries@mardev.com
Trade magazine covering mainline and urban rail traffic, freight, and passenger services. **Founded:** 1905. **Freq:** Monthly. **Print Method:** Sheetfed offset litho. **Trim Size:** 8 1/4 x 11 3/8. **Key Personnel:** Chris Jackson, Editor, phone 44 2086 525201, chris.jackson@railwaygazette. com; Sheena Rennie, Publisher, phone 44 2086 525211, sheena.rennie@railwaygazette.com; Marianne Ripsher, Sales Mgr., marianne.ripsher@railwaygazette.com. **Remarks:** Accepts advertising. **URL:** http://www. railwaygazette.com/. **Ad Rates:** BW: 2,740, 4C: 4,525. **Circ:** Paid 10,000

56693 ■ Truck and Driver
Reed Business Information Ltd.
Quadrant House
The Quadrant
Sutton SM2 5AS, United Kingdom
Ph: 44 20 86523500
Fax: 44 20 86528932
Publisher E-mail: enquiries@mardev.com
Magazine for the professional truck driver. **Founded:** 1984. **Freq:** Monthly. **Trim Size:** 297 x 420 mm. **Key Personnel:** Will Shiers, Editor, phone 44 20 86523721, will.shiers@rbi.co.uk. **Subscription Rates:** 91 individuals 3 years; 64 two years; 35 individuals; US$88 individuals; US$158 two years; US$225 individuals 3 years. **Remarks:** Accepts advertising. **URL:** http://www. reedbusiness.co.uk/rb2_products/rb2_products_ truckdriver.htm. **Circ:** ★**27,973**

Sutton Coldfield

56694 ■ The Electric Railway
Electric Railway Society
17 Catherine Dr.
Sutton Coldfield B73 6AX, United Kingdom
Publication E-mail: membership@electric-rly-society. org.uk
Publisher E-mail: iwfrew@tiscali.co.uk
Journal covering railroads especially urban systems. **Subtitle:** The Journal of the Electric Railway Society. **Founded:** 1946. **Freq:** Bimonthly. **Print Method:** PhotoLitho. **Trim Size:** A5. **Subscription Rates:** 15 individuals. **Remarks:** Advertising not accepted. **URL:** http://www.electric-rly-society.org.uk/new_page_1.htm. **Formerly:** Electric Railway Society Journal. **Circ:** 400

56695 ■ Hot Dip Galvanizing
Galvanizers Association
Wrens Ct.
56 Victoria Rd.
Sutton Coldfield B72 1SY, United Kingdom
Ph: 44 121 3558838
Fax: 44 121 3558727
Publisher E-mail: ga@hdg.org.uk
Dutch, English and German publication covering the metal trade. **Freq:** Quarterly. **ISSN:** 1132-0148. **Subscription Rates:** Free to qualified subscribers. **Remarks:** Advertising not accepted. **URL:** http://hdg-online. net/?id=7&tx_hdgcategories_pi1parent=3. **Circ:** 45,000

Swaffham

56696 ■ Watton & Swaffham Times
Archant Regional Ltd.
Fitzroy House
32 Market Pl.
Swaffham PE37 7QH, United Kingdom
Ph: 44 1760 723632
Publisher E-mail: sandra.roantree@archant.co.uk
Local community newspaper. **Freq:** Weekly. **Key Personnel:** Tim Williams, Editor, tim.williams@archant.co. uk. **Subscription Rates:** 14.95 individuals 13 weeks; 29.90 individuals 26 weeks. **Remarks:** Accepts advertising. **URL:** http://www.wattonandswaffhamtimes. co.uk/home. **Circ:** (Not Reported)

Swanley

56697 ■ ITS International
Route One Publishing Ltd.
Horizon House
Azalea Dr.
Swanley BR8 8JR, United Kingdom
Ph: 44 13 22612055
Fax: 44 13 22612060
Publication E-mail: itseditor@ropl.com
Publisher E-mail: media@ropl.com
Professional magazine covering advanced technology for traffic management and urban mobility. **Founded:** Mar. 1995. **Freq:** Bimonthly. **Key Personnel:** James Foster, News Ed.; Andrew Barriball, Publisher, abarriball@ropl.com; Manuel Battista, Sales Dir., mbattista@ropl.com; Kevin O'Shea, Production Mgr., production@ropl.com; Jason Barnes, Editor, itseditor@ ropl.com. **ISSN:** 1463-6344. **Subscription Rates:** 57 individuals; US$101 individuals; EUR90 individuals; 90 two years; US$158 two years; EUR142 two years. **Remarks:** Accepts advertising. **URL:** http://www.itsinternational.com/. **Circ:** Combined △**22,283**

56698 ■ World Highways
Route One Publishing Ltd.
Horizon House
Azalea Dr.
Swanley BR8 8JR, United Kingdom
Ph: 44 13 22612055
Fax: 44 13 22612060
Publisher E-mail: media@ropl.com
Trade magazine covering road and highway industry news for road and transport authorities, construction companies, engineers, designers and contractors. **Subtitle:** Route du Monde. **Founded:** 1991. **Freq:** Monthly 10/yr. **Key Personnel:** Kevin O'Shea, Production Mgr., production@ropl.com; Yvonne Tindall, Advertising Mgr., ytindall@ropl.com; Roger Adshead, Publisher, radshead@ropl.com; Manuel Battista, Sales Mgr., mbattista@ropl.com; James Howard, Website Mgr., jhoward@ropl.com; Mike Woof, Editor, mwoof@ropl. com. **ISSN:** 0964-4598. **Subscription Rates:** 86 individuals; US$152 individuals; 135 two years; US$238 two years; EUR212 two years. **Remarks:** Accepts advertising. **URL:** http://www. worldhighways.com/. **Circ:** Combined ‡**15,133**

Swansea

56699 ■ Applied Mathematical Modelling
Elsevier Science Inc.
c/o Prof. M. Cross, Ed.
University of Wales Swansea
School of Engineering
Singleton Pk.
Swansea SA2 8PP, United Kingdom
Publisher E-mail: usinfo-ehelp@elsevier.com
Journal focused on mathematical modeling of engineering and environmental processes, manufacturing, and industrial systems. **Freq:** Monthly. **Print Method:** Offset. **Cols./Page:** 7. **Col. Width:** 26 nonpareils. **Col. Depth:** 280 agate lines. **Key Personnel:** Prof. F. Durst, Editorial Board; Prof. J.M.T. Thompson, FRS, Editorial Board; Prof. D.B. Spalding, FRS, Editorial Board; Prof. M. Cross, Editor; Prof. C.J. Malmborg, Assoc. Ed.; Prof. N.C. Markatos, Assoc. Ed. **ISSN:** 0307-904X. **Subscription Rates:** 248,000¥ institutions; US$2,089 institutions, other countries except Europe, Japan and Iran; EUR1,866 institutions for European countries and Iran. **URL:** http://www.elsevier.com/wps/find/journaldescription.cws_ home/524998/descriptiondescription.

56700 ■ Computers and Geotechnics
Elsevier Science Inc.
Dept. of Civil Engineering
University of Wales Swansea
Glamorgan
Swansea SA2 8PP, United Kingdom
Publisher E-mail: usinfo-ehelp@elsevier.com
Journal covering research in geotechnical engineering. **Founded:** 1985. **Freq:** 8/yr. **Key Personnel:** R.I. Borja, Editorial Board; P. de Buhan, Editorial Board; Y.K. Chow, Editorial Board; F. Darve, Editorial Board; P. Delage, Editorial Board; A. Gens, Editorial Board; P. Guo, Editorial Board; Gyan N. Pande, Editor, g.n.pande@swan.ac. uk; Stan Pietruszczak, Editor, pietrusz@mcmaster.ca; Scott W. Sloan, Editor, scott.sloan@newcastle.edu.au. **ISSN:** 0266-352X. **Subscription Rates:** 227,600¥

institutions; EUR1,711 institutions European countries & Iran; US$1,918 institutions all countries except Europe, Japan and Iran. **URL:** http://www.elsevier.com/wps/find/ journaldescription.cws_home/405893/ descriptiondescription.

56701 ■ Engineering Computations
Emerald Group Publishing Ltd.
c/o Prof. D.R.J. Owen, Ed.
University of Wales Swansea
Dept. of Civil Engineering
Singleton Pk.
Swansea SA2 8PP, United Kingdom
Publisher E-mail: emerald@emeraldinsight.com
Journal offering broad coverage across all branches of engineering and science of the latest development and application of new solution algorithms, innovative numerical methods and/or solution techniques directed at the utilization of computational methods in engineering analysis, design and practice, addressing the diverse disciplines involved in a numerical methods-based decision-support process, publishing advances made in computational algorithms and element methodology and encouraging innovation, particularly directed at engineering applications. **Freq:** 8/yr. **Key Personnel:** Prof. D.R.J. Owen, Editor, d.r.j.owen@swansea.ac.uk; A.K. Noor, Editorial Advisory Board; S.N. Atluri, Editorial Advisory Board; Prof. M. Ortiz, Editorial Advisory Board; Prof. John E. Akin, Editorial Advisory Board; Harry Colson, Publisher, hcolson@emeraldinsight.com; Prof. Z.P. Bazant, Editorial Advisory Board; Prof. K.J. Bathe, Advisory Ed.; Prof. J.T. Oden, Editorial Advisory Board; Prof. Peter Bettess, Editorial Advisory Board. **ISSN:** 0264-4401. **URL:** http://info.emeraldinsight.com/products/ journals/journals.htm?id=ec.

56702 ■ International Journal of Numerical Methods for Heat & Fluid Flow
Emerald Group Publishing Ltd.
c/o Prof. Roland W. Lewis, Ed.
University of Wales Swansea
Department of Mechanical Engineering
Singleton Pk.
Swansea SA2 8PP, United Kingdom
Publisher E-mail: emerald@emeraldinsight.com
Journal focusing on computer-based problem-solving techniques in heat transfer and fluid dynamics. **Freq:** 8/yr. **Key Personnel:** Prof. Roland W. Lewis, Editor, r.w. lewis@swansea.ac.uk; Prof. G. Comini, Editorial Advisory Board; M. Bellet, Editorial Advisory Board; Prof. Carlo Nonino, Editorial Advisory Board; D. Givoli, Editorial Advisory Board; Cedric Taylor, Founding Ed.; R. Codina, Editorial Advisory Board; Prof. J.I. Ramos, Advisory Ed.; Harry Colson, Publisher, hcolson@emeraldinsight. com; Prof. Michelle Napolitano, Editorial Advisory Board. **ISSN:** 0961-5539. **URL:** http://info.emeraldinsight.com/ products/journals/journals.htm?id=hff.

56703 ■ Land Degradation & Development
John Wiley & Sons Inc.
c/o Dr. Chris Barrow, Mng. Ed.
Geography Dept., Wallace Bldg.
School of the Environment & Society, University of Swansea
Singleton Pk.
Swansea SA2 8PP, United Kingdom
Ph: 44 1792 205678
Fax: 44 1792 295682
Publisher E-mail: info@wiley.com
International journal seeking to promote rational study of the recognition, monitoring, control and rehabilitation of degradation in terrestrial environments. **Freq:** Bimonthly. **Key Personnel:** Dr. Chris Barrow, Managing Editor, c.j. barrow@swansea.ac.uk; Dr. L.C. Stringer, Book Review Ed., phone 44 113 3437530, fax 44 113 3436716, l.stringer@see.leeds.ac.uk; Dr. I.P. Abrol, Editorial Board. **ISSN:** 1085-3278. **Subscription Rates:** US$1,029 other countries for print; US$1,372 institutions, other countries for print; US$1,510 institutions, other countries for print and online; 700 institutions for print; EUR886 institutions for print. **Remarks:** Accepts advertising. **URL:** http://www3.interscience.wiley.com/ journal/6175/home. **Circ:** (Not Reported)

56704 ■ New Leaves
Intervega - Movement for Compassionate Living the Vegan Way
105 Cyfyng Rd.
Ystalyfera

Swansea SA9 2BT, United Kingdom
Journal covering vegetarianism/ veganism. **Subtitle:** New Leaves. **Freq:** Quarterly. **Trim Size:** 21 x 15 cm. **Subscription Rates:** 5 individuals. **Remarks:** Advertising accepted; rates available upon request. **URL:** http://www.mclveganway.org.uk. **Circ:** (Not Reported)

56705 ■ Philosophical Investigations
John Wiley & Sons Inc.
Wiley-Blackwell
c/o Prof. H.O. Mounce, Ed.
Swansea University
Swansea SA2 8PP, United Kingdom
Ph: 44 1792 295190
Fax: 44 1792 295893
Journal on philosophy. **Freq:** Quarterly. **Key Personnel:** Peter Hacker, Assoc. Ed.; Marie McGinn, Assoc. Ed.; David Cockburn, Assoc. Ed.; Peter Lewis, Assoc. Ed.; Catherine Osborne, Assoc. Ed.; Ieuan Williams, Assoc. Ed. **ISSN:** 0190-0536. **Subscription Rates:** 332 institutions print and online; US$735 institutions print and online; EUR98 individuals print and online (Euro zone); US$146 individuals print and online; 87 other countries print and online; US$668 institutions print or online; EUR422 institutions print and online; 332 institutions print and online; 302 institutions print or online; US$73 students print and online. **Remarks:** Advertising accepted; rates available upon request. **URL:** http://www.wiley.com/bw/journal.asp?ref=0190-0536&site=1. **Circ:** (Not Reported)

56706 ■ Pulse
Welsh Secondary Schools Association
124 Walter Rd.
Swansea SA1 5RF, United Kingdom
Ph: 44 17 92455933
Fax: 44 17 92455944
Publisher E-mail: wssa@supanet.com
Journal covering WSSA activities and reports on innovative school practices. **Freq:** Quarterly. **Subscription Rates:** Included in membership. **URL:** http://www.wssa.supanet.com/English/publications.htm.

56707 ■ Studies in European Cinema
Intellect
Digital Technium Bldg.
University of Wales, Swansea
Singleton Pk.
Swansea SA2 8PP, United Kingdom
Ph: 44 1792 513375
Fax: 44 1792 513453
Publisher E-mail: info@intellectuk.org
Forum for the highest quality research being carried out on European Film, European film culture, and the changing nature of film output in Europe, and distinctive by positioning the debates within both a cultural and an historical context. **Founded:** 2004. **Freq:** 3/yr. **Trim Size:** 174 x 244 mm. **Key Personnel:** Owen Evans, Editor, owen@ecrf.org.uk; Graeme Harper, Editor, graeme.harper@bangor.ac.uk; Stephen Forcer, Reviews Ed., s.m.forcer@bham.ac.uk. **ISSN:** 1741-1548. **Subscription Rates:** 33 individuals print; 210 individuals print; 12 single issue print; US$65 individuals print; US$330 individuals print; US$24 single issue print; 177 individuals online; US$265 individuals online. **Remarks:** Accepts advertising. **URL:** http://www.intellectbooks.co.uk/journals.appx.php?issn=17411548. **Ad Rates:** BW: 100. **Circ:** (Not Reported)

56708 ■ Nation Radio-FM - 107.3
Newby House
Neath Abbey Business Pk.
Neath SA10 7DR, United Kingdom
Ph: 44 845 1062107
Fax: 44 845 0251001
E-mail: enquiries@nationwales.com; studio@nationwales.com
Format: Alternative/New Music/Progressive. **Owner:** Town & Country Broadcasting, at above address. **Ad Rates:** Advertising accepted; rates available upon request. **URL:** http://www.nationwales.com/.

56709 ■ The Wave-FM - 96.4
PO Box 964
Victoria Rd.
Gowerton
Swansea SA4 3AB, United Kingdom
Ph: 44 1792 896964
Fax: 44 1792 511964
Format: Adult Contemporary; Top 40; News; Sports. **Founded:** Nov. 1995. **Operating Hours:** Continuous.

Key Personnel: Steve Barnes, Program Dir., steve.barnes@thewave.co.uk; Carrie Mosley, Station Dir., carrie.mosley@thewave.co.uk; Richard Western, Sales Dir., richard.western@thewave.co.uk. **Ad Rates:** Advertising accepted; rates available upon request. **URL:** http://www.thewave.co.uk/.

Swindon

56710 ■ Conservation Bulletin
English Heritage
Customer Services Department
PO Box 569
Swindon SN2 2YP, United Kingdom
Ph: 44 87 03331181
Fax: 44 17 93414926
Publication E-mail: mailinglist@english-heritage.org.uk
Publisher E-mail: customers@english-heritage.org.uk
Journal reporting on conservation issues. **Subscription Rates:** Free. **URL:** http://www.english-heritage.org.uk/server/show/nav.11241.

56711 ■ Fourth World Review
PO Box 2410
Swindon SN5 4AE, United Kingdom
Ph: 44 17 93772214
Fax: 44 17 93772521
Journal covering international affairs and social and political issues. **Freq:** Bimonthly (double summer issue). **Key Personnel:** John Papworth, Editor; Sam Hains, Sub-Ed.; Jacques Boulet, Contact; Dr. Madhukar B. Nisal, Contact; Natalie D'Arbeloff, Contact; Richard Baker, Contact; Lord Beaumont, Contact; John Coleman, Contact; Helen Dew, Contact; Thomas A. Naylor, Contact. **Subscription Rates:** US$4 single issue. **Remarks:** Advertising accepted; rates available upon request. **URL:** http://www.4wr.org/. **Former name:** Resurgence. **Circ:** (Not Reported)

56712 ■ ITNOW
British Computer Society
1st Fl., Block D
North Star House
North Star House Ave.
Swindon SN2 1FA, United Kingdom
Ph: 44 1793 417417
Fax: 44 1793 417444
Publication E-mail: editor@bcs.org
Membership magazine of the British Computer Society for computer professionals. **Freq:** Bimonthly. **Print Method:** Litho. **Trim Size:** 216 x 280 mm. **Key Personnel:** Brian Runciman, Managing Editor; Helen Boddy, Asst. Ed.; Justin Richards, Asst. Ed.; Marc Arbuckle, Design Ed.; Henry Tucker, Asst. Ed. **ISSN:** 0010-4531. **Remarks:** Advertising accepted; rates available upon request. **URL:** http://www.bcs.org/server.php?show=nav.00100v003. **Formerly:** The Computer Bulletin for Information Systems Professionals. **Circ:** Combined 50,000

56713 ■ BBC Radio Wiltshire-FM - 103.5
Broadcasting House
56-58 Prospect Pl.
Swindon SN1 3RW, United Kingdom
Ph: 44 1793 513626
E-mail: bbcwiltshire@bbc.co.uk
Format: Talk; News; Eclectic; Sports; Information. **Owner:** British Broadcasting Corporation, Broadcasting House, Portland Pl., London W1A 1AA, United Kingdom. **URL:** http://news.bbc.co.uk/local/wiltshire/hi/.

56714 ■ Brunel-FM - 107.7
Shrivenham Hundred Business Pk., Unit 4
Majors Rd.
Watchfield
Swindon SN6 8TZ, United Kingdom
E-mail: studio@brunelfm.com
Format: Full Service. **URL:** http://www.brunelfm.com/.

56715 ■ Swindon 105.5-FM - 105.5
The Bentley Ctr.
Stratton Rd.
Swindon SN1 2SH, United Kingdom
Ph: 44 1793 611555
E-mail: info@swindon1055.com
Format: Public Radio. **Owner:** Community Radio Swindon, at above address. **Founded:** 2008. **Operating Hours:** Continuous. **URL:** http://www.swindon1055.com/.

Swingate

56716 ■ BBC Radio Kent - 104.2
The Great Hall
Mt. Pleasant Rd.
Tunbridge Wells TN1 1QQ, United Kingdom
Ph: 44 1892 670000
Fax: 44 1892 549118
Format: Full Service. **URL:** http://www.bbc.co.uk/kent/local_radio/.

Tamworth

56717 ■ British Journal of Special Education
National Association of Special Educational Needs
NASEN House
4/5 Amber Business Village
Amber Close
Amington
Tamworth B77 4RP, United Kingdom
Ph: 44 18 27311500
Fax: 44 18 27313005
Publisher E-mail: welcome@nasen.org.uk
British journal covering special education. **Freq:** Quarterly. **Key Personnel:** Richard Byers, Editor, rb218@cam.ac.uk. **Remarks:** Advertising accepted; rates available upon request. **URL:** http://www.nasen.org.uk; http://onlinelibrary.wiley.com/journal/10.1111/(ISSN)1467-8578/issues. **Circ:** (Not Reported)

56718 ■ Special!
National Association of Special Educational Needs
NASEN House
4/5 Amber Business Village
Amber Close
Amington
Tamworth B77 4RP, United Kingdom
Ph: 44 18 27311500
Fax: 44 18 27313005
Publisher E-mail: welcome@nasen.org.uk
Magazine covering special education issues. **Founded:** 1992. **Freq:** Triennial. **Remarks:** Accepts advertising. **URL:** http://www.nasen.org.uk/special/. **Circ:** (Not Reported)

56719 ■ Touch Radio-FM - 102.4
5-6 Aldergate
Tamworth B79 7DJ, United Kingdom
Ph: 44 1827 318000
Format: Contemporary Hit Radio (CHR). **URL:** http://www.101touchfm.co.uk/.

56720 ■ Touch Radio-FM - 101.6
5 / 6 Aldergate
Tamworth B79 7DJ, United Kingdom
Ph: 44 1827 318000
Format: Contemporary Hit Radio (CHR). **URL:** http://www.101touchfm.co.uk.

Taunton

56721 ■ Business Money
Business Money Ltd.
Bowdens Business Centre
Somerset
Hambridge
Taunton TA10 0BP, United Kingdom
Ph: 44 145 8253536
Fax: 44 145 8253538
Publisher E-mail: editor@business-money.com
Professional magazine covering finance, business banking, and related topics. **Founded:** July 1993. **Freq:** Monthly. **Key Personnel:** Robert Lefroy, Gp. Ed., editor@business-money.com; Iris Lefroy, Subscription, subscriptions@business-money.com. **Subscription Rates:** 129 individuals; 152 other countries. **Remarks:** Accepts advertising. **URL:** http://www.business-money.com. **Circ:** Controlled 14,237

56722 ■ Powys Journal
Powys Society
c/o Peter Lazare, Sec.
25 Mansfield Rd.
Taunton TA1 3NJ, United Kingdom
Ph: 44 1823278177
Publisher E-mail: enquiries@powys-society.org
Journal covering authors. **Freq:** Annual. **Key Personnel:** Richard Maxwell, Editor, richard.maxwell@yale.edu. **Subscription Rates:** Included in membership; 22 individuals; 10 students. **Remarks:** Advertising ac-

cepted; rates available upon request. **URL:** http://www.powys-society.org/. **Circ:** 400

56723 ■ Somerset County Gazette
Newsquest Media Group Ltd.
St. James St.
Taunton TA1 1JR, United Kingdom
Ph: 44 1823 365151
Fax: 44 1823 365240
Publication E-mail: newsdesk@countygazette.co.uk
Newspaper featuring local news and events. **Remarks:** Accepts advertising. **URL:** http://www.somersetcountygazette.co.uk/. **Circ:** (Not Reported)

56724 ■ BBC Radio Somerset-FM - 95.5
Broadcasting House
Park St.
Somerset
Taunton TA1 4DA, United Kingdom
Ph: 44 1823 323956
E-mail: somerset@bbc.co.uk
Format: Talk; News; Sports. **Owner:** British Broadcasting Corporation, Broadcasting House, Portland Pl., London W1A 1AA, United Kingdom. **Founded:** Sept. 1970. **Operating Hours:** Continuous. **URL:** http://news.bbc.co.uk/local/somerset/hi/tv_and_radio/.

56725 ■ Heart-FM - 102.6
Haygrove House
Somerset
Taunton TA3 7BT, United Kingdom
Ph: 44 1823 338448
Format: Adult Contemporary; Information. **Formerly:** Orchard-FM (2009). **Ad Rates:** Advertising accepted; rates available upon request. **URL:** http://www.heart.co.uk/oxfordshire/.

56726 ■ Heart-FM - 96.5
Haygrove House
Somerset
Taunton TA3 7BT, United Kingdom
Ph: 44 1823 338448
Format: Adult Contemporary; Information. **Formerly:** Orchard-FM (2009). **Ad Rates:** Advertising accepted; rates available upon request. **URL:** http://www.heart.co.uk/somerset/.

Heart-FM - See Yeovil

Tavistock

56727 ■ Dartmoor Magazine
Quay Publications (Brixham)
PO Box 16
Tavistock PL19 0XR, United Kingdom
Ph: 44 18 22614899
Publication E-mail: editor@dartmoormagazine.co.uk
Publisher E-mail: dartmoormagazine@btconnect.com
Consumer magazine covering local news, history, and information. **Founded:** 1985. **Freq:** Quarterly. **Trim Size:** A4. **Cols./Page:** 3. **Col. Width:** 57 millimeters. **Col. Depth:** 265 millimeters. **ISSN:** 0268-5027. **Subscription Rates:** 12.95 individuals; 25.75 two years. **Remarks:** Accepts advertising. **URL:** http://www.dartmoormagazine.co.uk. **Circ:** (Not Reported)

56728 ■ Zerb
Guild of Television Cameramen
1 Churchill Rd.
Whitchurch
Tavistock PL19 9BU, United Kingdom
Ph: 44 182 2614405
Fax: 44 182 2614405
Publisher E-mail: administration.07@gtc.org.uk
Broadcasting publication. **Freq:** Semiannual. **Key Personnel:** Alison Chapman, Editor, zerb.production.07@gtc.org.uk. **Subscription Rates:** 11 individuals within the U.K.; 17 individuals outside the U.K. **Remarks:** Accepts advertising. **URL:** http://www.gtc.org.uk. **Ad Rates:** BW: 745, 4C: 1,425. **Circ:** 4,000

Teddington

56729 ■ Autocar
Haymarket Motoring Publications Ltd.
Teddington Studios
Broom Rd.
Teddington TW11 9BE, United Kingdom
Ph: 44 20 82675000
Publication E-mail: autocar@haynet.com

Publisher E-mail: info@haymarket.com
Consumer magazine covering automobiles. **Founded:** 1895. **Freq:** Weekly. **Key Personnel:** Chas Hallett, Editor, phone 44 20 82675735, charles.hallett@haymarket.com. **Subscription Rates:** 88 individuals 51 issues. **Remarks:** Accepts advertising. **URL:** http://www.autocar.co.uk/; http://www.haymarketgroup.com/products/index.cfm?fuseaction=showsector&sectorid=1&productsummary=67&regionid=1&type=1. **Former name:** Autocar & Motor. **Ad Rates:** BW: 5,225, 4C: 8,225. **Circ:** Paid 66,245

56730 ■ Geophilos
Land Research Trust
7 King's Rd.
Teddington TW11 0QB, United Kingdom
Publication of the Land Research Trust. **Freq:** Semiannual. **Key Personnel:** Fred Harrison, Editor, phone 44 20 89433352, metaman@compuserve.com. **ISSN:** 1472-6300. **Subscription Rates:** 28 individuals; US$45 individuals; C$65 individuals; $A 85 individuals; 50 institutions. **URL:** http://www.interunion.org.uk/geophilos.htm.

56731 ■ International Journal of Mathematical Modelling and Numerical Optimisation
Inderscience Enterprises Limited
c/o Xin-She Yang, Ed.-in-Ch.
National Physical Laboratory
Mathematics and Scientific Computing Group
F2/A7, Middlesex
Teddington TW11 0LW, United Kingdom
Peer-reviewed journal covering mathematical modeling, computer simulation, and numerical optimization. **Freq:** Quarterly. **Key Personnel:** Xin-She Yang, Editor-in-Chief, ijmmno.editor@gmail.com. **ISSN:** 2040-3607. **Subscription Rates:** EUR494 individuals print or online; EUR672 individuals print and online. **URL:** http://www.inderscience.com/browse/index.php?journalCODE=ijmmno.

56732 ■ International Ocean Systems
Underwater World Publications Ltd.
55 High St.
Teddington TW11 8HA, United Kingdom
Ph: 44 20 89434288
Fax: 44 20 89434312
Trade magazine covering ocean data gathering and underwater surveying and instrumentation for the commercial oceanography market. **Founded:** 1979. **Freq:** Bimonthly. **Print Method:** Offset Litho. **Trim Size:** 210 x 297 mm. **Cols./Page:** 3. **Key Personnel:** Astrid Powell, Publisher, astrid@divermag.co.uk; Daniel Johnson, Editor, daniel@divermag.co.uk. **ISSN:** 1471-0188. **Subscription Rates:** 80 individuals; 100 out of country; US$195 individuals. **Remarks:** Accepts advertising. **URL:** http://www.intoceansys.co.uk. **Former name:** International Ocean Systems Design. **Formerly:** International Underwater Systems Design. **Ad Rates:** BW: US$2,145, 4C: US$2,950. **Circ:** Combined 10,021

56733 ■ Key Note Market Assessment. Tweenagers
Key Note Publications Ltd.
Harlequin House, 5th Fl.
7 High St.
Teddington TW11 8EE, United Kingdom
Ph: 44 845 5040452
Fax: 44 845 5040453
Publisher E-mail: sales@keynote.co.uk
Report covering issues of young people between two distinct life stages childhood and the teenage years. **Subscription Rates:** EUR1,054 individuals print and online. **URL:** http://www.researchandmarkets.com/reportinfo.asp?cat_id=6&report_id=3915&p=5.

56734 ■ Motor Sport
Haymarket Specialist Motoring Publications
Somerset Rd.
Teddington TW11 8RU, United Kingdom
Ph: 44 20 82675722
Fax: 44 20 82675619
Publication E-mail: info@motorsportmagazine.co.uk
Consumer magazine covering the history of motor sports. **Founded:** 1924. **Freq:** Monthly. **Print Method:** Web offset perfect bound. **Trim Size:** 265 x 210. **Key Personnel:** Martin Nott, Publisher; Nigel Roebuck, Editor-in-Chief. **Remarks:** Accepts advertising. **URL:** http://www.motorsportmagazine.co.uk/. **Ad Rates:** BW: 2,887, 4C: 3,905. **Circ:** ★35,066

56735 ■ Talkback
BackCare
16 Elmtree Rd.
Teddington TW11 8ST, United Kingdom
Ph: 44 20 89775474
Fax: 44 20 89435318
Journal covering back pain issues. **Freq:** Quarterly Jan., Apr., July, and Oct. **Print Method:** Litho. **Remarks:** Accepts advertising. **URL:** http://www.backcare.org.uk/. **Circ:** Combined 10,000

56736 ■ What Car?
Haymarket Motoring Publications Ltd.
Teddington Studios
Broom Rd.
Teddington TW11 9BE, United Kingdom
Ph: 44 20 82675000
Publication E-mail: whatcar@haynet.com
Publisher E-mail: info@haymarket.com
Consumer magazine covering automobiles for buyers. **Founded:** 1973. **Freq:** Monthly. **Trim Size:** A4. **Cols./Page:** 4. **Key Personnel:** Karen Parry, Contact, phone 44 20 82675553, karen.parry@haynet.com. **Subscription Rates:** 35.90 individuals 13 issues. **Remarks:** Accepts advertising. **URL:** http://www.whatcar.com. **Circ:** Paid 143,678

Telford

56737 ■ International Journal of Business Governance and Ethics
Inderscience Publishers
c/o Dr. Silke Machold, Assoc. Ed.
University of Wolverhampton Business School
Telford Campus, Shifnal Rd.
Telford TF2 9NT, United Kingdom
Publisher E-mail: editor@inderscience.com
Peer-reviewed journal aiming to explore business and managerial strategies, actions, responsibilities and accountabilities for survival in a highly transparent and dynamic global world. **Freq:** Quarterly. **Key Personnel:** Prof. Pervaiz K. Ahmed, Editor, pervaiz@buseco.monash.edu.my; Prof. Christopher K. Bart, Assoc. Ed.; Prof. Henri C. De Bettignies, Editorial Board Member; Prof. John Callaghan, Editorial Board Member; Prof. Christopher J. Cowton, Editorial Board Member; Prof. Steve Letza, Assoc. Ed.; Dr. Silke Machold, Assoc. Ed.; Prof. David Birch, Editorial Board Member; Dr. Douglas A. Hensler, Editorial Board Member. **ISSN:** 1477-9048. **Subscription Rates:** EUR494 individuals print only (surface mail); EUR840 individuals online only (2-3 users); EUR672 individuals print and online. **URL:** http://www.inderscience.com/browse/index.php?journalCODE=ijbge.

56738 ■ International Journal of Management Practice
Inderscience Publishers
c/o Dr. Yong Wang, Assoc. Ed.
University of Wolverhampton, Business School
Telford Campus, Shifnal Rd.
Telford TF2 9NT, United Kingdom
Publisher E-mail: editor@inderscience.com
Journal aiming to help turn management theory into management practice and endeavouring to illustrate pragmatic solutions to corporate problems and challenges. **Freq:** Quarterly. **Key Personnel:** Prof. Pervaiz K. Ahmed, Editor, pervaiz@buseco.monash.edu.my; Dr. Yong Wang, Assoc. Ed.; Prof. Glenn Hardaker, Assoc. Ed. **ISSN:** 1477-9064. **Subscription Rates:** EUR494 individuals print or online; EUR672 individuals print and online. **URL:** http://www.inderscience.com/browse/index.php?journalCODE=ijmp.

56739 ■ Severn-FM - 106.5
Waterloo Rd.
Ketley
Telford TF1 5HU, United Kingdom
Ph: 44 333 4560777
E-mail: sales@thesevern.co.uk
Format: Adult Contemporary; News; Top 40; Oldies. **Ad Rates:** Advertising accepted; rates available upon request. **URL:** http://www.the-severn.co.uk/.

56740 ■ Severn-FM - 107.1
Waterloo Rd.
Ketley
Telford TF1 5HU, United Kingdom
Ph: 44 333 4560777

E-mail: sales@thesevern.co.uk
Format: Adult Contemporary; News; Top 40; Oldies. **Ad Rates:** Advertising accepted; rates available upon request. **URL:** http://www.the-severn.co.uk/.

56741 ■ Telford-FM - 107.4
Shropshire Star Bldg.
Waterloo Rd.
Ketley
Telford TF1 5HU, United Kingdom
Ph: 44 1952 280011
Fax: 44 1952 280010
E-mail: dj@telfordfm.co.uk
Format: Full Service; Soft Rock. **Founded:** May 3, 1999. **Operating Hours:** Continuous. **Ad Rates:** Advertising accepted; rates available upon request. **URL:** http://www.telfordfm.co.uk.

Tenterden

56742 ■ The Artist
The Artists' Publishing Company Ltd.
Caxton House
63-65 High St.
Tenterden TN30 6BD, United Kingdom
Ph: 44 15 80763315
Consumer magazine covering art for amateur and professionals artists. **Founded:** 1931. **Freq:** Monthly. **Print Method:** Web. **Trim Size:** A4. **Key Personnel:** Dr. Sally Bulgin, Editor and Publisher; Jayne Notley, Advertising Mgr.; Deborah Wanstall, Dep. Ed. **ISSN:** 0004-3877. **Subscription Rates:** EUR29.50 individuals. **Remarks:** Accepts advertising. **URL:** http://www.painters-online.co.uk/. **Absorbed:** Art & Artists. **Circ:** Paid 21,500

56743 ■ Leisure Painter
The Artists' Publishing Company Ltd.
Caxton House
63-65 High St.
Tenterden TN30 6BD, United Kingdom
Ph: 44 15 80763315
Journal covering painting instruction in all media for amateur artists. **Founded:** 1967. **Freq:** Monthly. **Print Method:** Web Offset. **Trim Size:** 210 x 297 mm. **Cols./Page:** 4. **Col. Width:** 44 millimeters. **Col. Depth:** 265 millimeters. **Key Personnel:** Jane Stroud, Contributing Ed.; Ingrid Lyon, Editor. **ISSN:** 0024-0710. **Subscription Rates:** 29.50 individuals; 15.75 individuals 6 months; 55 individuals combined; 40 other countries; 75.75 two years overseas; 55 two years; 79.50 individuals 3 years; 111.50 other countries 3 years. **Remarks:** Accepts advertising. **URL:** http://www.painters-online.co.uk/magazines/issue.asp?issue=160. **Ad Rates:** BW: 700, 4C: 1,110. **Circ:** Paid 28,000

Thame

56744 ■ Thame Gazette
Johnston Press PLC
2 Swan Walk
Thame OX9 3HN, United Kingdom
Ph: 44 1844 213266
Local community newspaper. **Freq:** Weekly (Fri.). **Key Personnel:** Jean Adams, Contact, jean.adams@ccnltd.com. **Remarks:** Accepts advertising. **URL:** http://www.thametoday.co.uk/. **Circ:** (Not Reported)

Thetford

56745 ■ Ringing & Migration
British Trust for Ornithology
The Nunnery
Thetford IP24 2PU, United Kingdom
Ph: 44 18 42750050
Fax: 44 18 42750030
Publication E-mail: ringing@bto.org
Publisher E-mail: info@bto.org
Trade journal covering ornithology in the U.K. **Founded:** 1975. **Freq:** Semiannual. **Trim Size:** B5. **Cols./Page:** 2. **Key Personnel:** Jacquie Clark, Managing Editor; Franz Bairlein, Editorial Board; Dr. Chris Redfern, Editor, chris.redfern@newcastle.ac.uk; Guy Anderson, Editorial Board; Jane Reid, Editorial Board; Graham Scott, Editorial Board. **ISSN:** 0307-8698. **Subscription Rates:** 10 members; 15 nonmembers; 30 institutions. **Remarks:** Advertising not accepted. **URL:** http://www.bto.org/ringing/rmj/index.htm. **Circ:** Combined 2,200

Thornaby

56746 ■ Magic-AM - 1170
Radio House
Yale Cresent
Stockton-on-Tees
Thornaby TS17 6AA, United Kingdom
Ph: 44 1642 888222
Fax: 44 1642 868288
Format: Oldies. **Key Personnel:** Chris Rick, Station Dir. **URL:** http://www.magic1170.co.uk/.

56747 ■ TFM Radio-FM - 96.6
Yale Cres.
Teesdale
Stockton-on-Tees
Thornaby TS17 6AA, United Kingdom
Ph: 44 1642 888222
Format: Contemporary Hit Radio (CHR). **Key Personnel:** Sally Aitchison, Mng. Dir.; Chris Rick, Program Dir.; Matthew Bromham, Sales Dir., matthew.bromham@tfmradio.com. **Ad Rates:** Advertising accepted; rates available upon request. **URL:** http://www.tfmradio.com.

Thrapston

56748 ■ The Mule
British Mule Society
c/o E.M.G. Cox, Ed.
22 Roman Way
Thrapston NN14 4TE, United Kingdom
Ph: 44 18 32734253
Publisher E-mail: anndyer57@aol.com
Publication covering livestock. **Founded:** 1978. **Freq:** Quarterly. **Trim Size:** A5. **Key Personnel:** E.M.G. Cox, Editor, elizco@fish.co.uk. **Subscription Rates:** Included in membership. **Remarks:** Color advertising not accepted. **URL:** http://www.britishmulesociety.org.uk/images/pdfs/spring04Journalsmall.pdf. **Ad Rates:** BW: 20. **Circ:** (Not Reported)

Thurlby by Bourne

56749 ■ The Book Collector
The Collector Ltd.
32 Swift Way
Thurlby by Bourne PE10 0QA, United Kingdom
Ph: 44 1778 338095
Fax: 44 1778 338096
Publication E-mail: info@thebookcollector.co.uk
Publisher E-mail: info@thebookcollector.co.uk
Magazine covering the book trade. **Founded:** 1952. **Freq:** Quarterly. **Trim Size:** 101 x 164 mm. **Key Personnel:** Nicolas Barker, Editor. **Subscription Rates:** 50 individuals; 60 individuals Europe (surface mail); 65 individuals rest of the world (airmail); EUR76.50 individuals for card payments only; US$105 other countries. **Remarks:** Accepts advertising. **URL:** http://www.thebookcollector.co.uk. **Circ:** (Not Reported)

Thurso

56750 ■ Journal of the British Society of Scientific Glassblowers
British Society of Scientific Glassblowers
Glendale, Sinclair St.
Thurso KW14 7AQ, United Kingdom
Ph: 44 18 47802629
Fax: 44 18 47802971
Publisher E-mail: chris@kevic.demon.co.uk
British journal covering scientific glassblowing. **Freq:** Quarterly. **Key Personnel:** Ian Pearson, Editor, ian.pearson@dounreay.com. **Subscription Rates:** 25 individuals. **URL:** http://www.bssg.co.uk/jourrates.htm. **Ad Rates:** BW: 131.25. **Circ:** (Not Reported)

Tisbury

56751 ■ Fab Cat Care Journal
Feline Advisory Bureau
Taeselbury
High St.
Tisbury SP3 6LD, United Kingdom
Ph: 44 87 47871872
Fax: 44 17 47871873
Publisher E-mail: information@fabcats.org
Publication covering veterinary medicine. **Freq:** Quarterly. **Subscription Rates:** 26 members; 280 individuals life membership; 36 members overseas; 330 individuals overseas life membership; EUR56 members;

EUR510 individuals life membership; 32 members fab affiliate; 125 individuals fab practice membership; 145 individuals fab practice membership; EUR225 individuals fab practice membership. **Remarks:** Advertising accepted; rates available upon request. **URL:** http://www.fabcats.org/publications/index.phpFABjournal. **Formerly:** Fab Journal. **Circ:** 3,000

56752 ■ Feline Advisory Bureau Journal
Feline Advisory Bureau
Taeselbury
High St.
Tisbury SP3 6LD, United Kingdom
Ph: 44 1747 871872
Fax: 44 1747 871873
Publication E-mail: information@fabcats.org
Publisher E-mail: information@fabcats.org
Journal covering feline articles, book reviews, and letters. **Subtitle:** FAB Journal. **Freq:** Quarterly. **Key Personnel:** Claire Bessant, Editor. **Subscription Rates:** 26 individuals; 36 individuals overseas; EUR56 individuals overseas; 280 individuals; 330 individuals life memberships (overseas); EUR510 individuals life memberships (overseas). **Remarks:** Accepts advertising. **URL:** http://www.fabcats.org. **Circ:** (Not Reported)

Todmorden

56753 ■ Todmorden News
Johnston Press PLC
Fielden Sq.
Todmorden OL14 7LD, United Kingdom
Ph: 44 1706 815231
Local community newspaper. **Founded:** Nov. 5, 1853. **Remarks:** Accepts advertising. **URL:** http://www.todmordennews.co.uk/. **Circ:** (Not Reported)

Tonbridge

56754 ■ Food Processing
IML Group PLC
Blair House, High St.
Tonbridge TN9 1BQ, United Kingdom
Ph: 44 1732 359990
Fax: 44 1732 770049
Business publication. **Freq:** Monthly. **ISSN:** 0264-9462. **Online:** Gale. **URL:** http://www.imlgrouponthenet.net/.

56755 ■ Industrial Technology
New Wave Publishing
c/o Mark Simms, Ed.
PO Box 342
Tonbridge TN10 4WD, United Kingdom
Ph: 44 17 32773268
Fax: 44 17 32365676
Publisher E-mail: it.info@itmagazine.uk.com
Magazine dealing with industrial aspects of design and building machines. **Trim Size:** 240 x 310 mm. **Key Personnel:** Sarah Curl, Production Mgr., sarah.curl@itmagazine.uk.com; Mark Simms, Editor, mark.simms@itmagazine.uk.com. **Remarks:** Accepts advertising. **URL:** http://www.industrialtechnology.co.uk/d/index.php?pageld=0. **Ad Rates:** BW: 3,120. **Circ:** ★21,296

56756 ■ Outrage
Animal Aid
The Old Chapel
Bradford St.
Tonbridge TN9 1AW, United Kingdom
Ph: 44 1732 364546
Fax: 44 1732 366533
Publication E-mail: info@animalaid.org.uk
Publisher E-mail: info@animalaid.org.uk
Consumer journal covering animal welfare rights and issues. **Subtitle:** The Animal Aid Journal for Action. **Founded:** 1978. **Freq:** Quarterly. **Trim Size:** 30 cm. **Key Personnel:** Mark Gold, Editor, phone 44 1404 831763; Andrew Tyler, Editor; Becky Smith, phone 44 1732 364546. **ISSN:** 1466-206X. **Subscription Rates:** Free for members. **Remarks:** Accepts advertising. **URL:** http://www.animalaid.org.uk. **Ad Rates:** BW: 600. **Circ:** Paid 12,500

Torquay

56757 ■ Herald Express (Torquay)
Westcountry Publications Ltd.
Harmsworth House
Barton Hill Rd.
Torquay TQ2 8JN, United Kingdom
Ph: 44 1803 676000
General newspaper. **Subtitle:** Local People, Local Lives,

Local Paper. **Freq:** Daily (eve.). **Print Method:** Web offset. **Trim Size:** 300 x 400 mm. **Key Personnel:** Andy Phelan, Editor, phone 44 1803 676000, aphelan@heraldexpress.co.uk. **Subscription Rates:** 1.25 single issue 1 day/week; 15.60 individuals 1 day/week, 3 months; 31.20 individuals 1 day/week, 6 months; 62.40 individuals 1 day/week, 12 months; 31.20 individuals 2 days/week, 3 months; 62.40 individuals 2 days/week, 6 months; 124.80 individuals 2 days/week, 12 months; 46.80 3 days/week, 3 months; 93.60 3 days/week, 6 months; 187.20 3 days/week, 12 months. **Remarks:** Accepts advertising. **URL:** http://www.thisissouthdevon.co.uk/. **Circ:** Paid ★25,971

56758 ■ Torquay Pottery Collectors Society
Torquay Pottery Collectors' Society
The Kings Dr.
Torquay TQ2 5JX, United Kingdom
Publisher E-mail: torquaypottery@aol.com
Publication covering pottery collectors society. **Freq:** Quarterly. **Subscription Rates:** 18 members single; 20 members joint; 3 other countries Europe (outside U.K.); 5 individuals Australia, New Zealand, Canada, U.S. **Remarks:** Accepts advertising. **URL:** http://www.torquaypottery.com/. **Circ:** (Not Reported)

56759 ■ Heart-FM - 96.4
Harbourpoint
Victoria Parade
Torquay TQ1 2RA, United Kingdom
Ph: 44 1803 290400
Format: Adult Contemporary. **Formerly:** Gemini-FM. **Ad Rates:** Advertising accepted; rates available upon request. **URL:** http://www.heart.co.uk/torbay/.

56760 ■ Palm-FM - 105.5
Marble Ct.
Lymington Rd.
Torquay TQ1 4FB, United Kingdom
Ph: 44 1803 321055
Fax: 44 1803 321059
E-mail: studio@palm.fm
Format: Contemporary Hit Radio (CHR). **URL:** http://www.palm.fm/.

Totnes

56761 ■ Cornwall Life
Archant Life
Archant house
Babbage Rd.
Totnes TQ9 5JA, United Kingdom
Ph: 44 1803 860910
Fax: 44 1803 860922
Publication E-mail: cornwall-life@archant.co.uk
Publisher E-mail: johnny.hustler@archant.co.uk
Magazine featuring Cornwall. **Subtitle:** The Cornwall County Magazine. **Freq:** Bimonthly. **Key Personnel:** Tim Randell, Publisher, tim.randell@archant.co.uk; Jennie Cooper, Editor, jennie.wilkinson@archant.co.uk; Jonathan Nicholas, Circulation Mgr., jonathan.nicholas@archant.co.uk. **Subscription Rates:** 4 6 months; 25 individuals. **Remarks:** Accepts advertising. **URL:** http://cornwall.greatbritishlife.co.uk/. **Circ:** (Not Reported)

56762 ■ Devon Life
Archant House
Babbage Rd.
Totnes TQ9 5JA, United Kingdom
Ph: 44 18 03860910
Fax: 44 18 03860922
Publisher E-mail: devonlife@archant.co.uk
Consumer magazine covering country lifestyle. **Freq:** Monthly. **Trim Size:** 220 x 300mm. **Key Personnel:** Julian Rees, Gp. Production Mgr., julian.rees@archant.co.uk; Jane Fitzgerald, Editor, jane.fitzgerald@archant.co.uk; Rebecca Coulson, Mktg. Mgr., rebecca.coulson@archant.co.uk; Tim Randell, Publisher, tim.randell@archant.co.uk; Jonathan Nicholas, Circulation Mgr., jonathan.nicholas@archant.co.uk. **Subscription Rates:** 19.50 individuals. **Remarks:** Accepts advertising. **URL:** http://www.devonlife.co.uk/; http://devon.greatbritishlife.co.uk/. **Ad Rates:** BW: 1,036. **Circ:** Paid ★15,196

56763 ■ Somerset Life
Archant Life
Archant House
Babbage Rd.
Totnes TQ9 5JA, United Kingdom

Ph: 44 1803 860910
Fax: 44 1803 860922
Publication E-mail: somersetlifeinfo@archant.co.uk
Publisher E-mail: johnny.hustler@archant.co.uk
Magazine featuring Somerset. **Freq:** Monthly. **Print Method:** 220 x 300 mm. **Key Personnel:** Tim Randell, Publisher, tim.randell@archant.co.uk; Natalie Vizard, Editor, natalie.vizard@archant.co.uk; Jonathan Nicholas, Circulation Mgr., jonathan.nicholas@archant.co.uk. **Subscription Rates:** 25 individuals. **Remarks:** Accepts advertising. **URL:** http://www.somerset-life.co.uk. **Ad Rates:** 4C: 1,036. **Circ:** (Not Reported)

56764 ■ Wiltshire
Archant Life
Archant House
Babbage Rd.
Totnes TQ9 5JA, United Kingdom
Ph: 44 1803 860910
Fax: 44 1803 860922
Publisher E-mail: johnny.hustler@archant.co.uk
Magazine featuring the lifestyle in Wiltshire county. **Freq:** Monthly. **Key Personnel:** Tim Randell, Publisher, tim.randell@archant.co.uk. **Subscription Rates:** 25 individuals. **Remarks:** Accepts advertising. **URL:** http://www.wiltshiremagazine.co.uk/. **Circ:** (Not Reported)

Totternhoe

56765 ■ Military Illustrated
ADH Publishing Ltd.
Doolittle Mill
Doolittle Ln.
Bedfordshire
Totternhoe LU6 1QX, United Kingdom
Ph: 44 1525 222573
Fax: 44 1525 222574
Publication E-mail: enquiries@adhpublishing.com
Publisher E-mail: enquiries@adhpublishing.com
Magazine covering military history. **Founded:** 1986. **Freq:** Monthly. **Key Personnel:** Tim Newark, Editor, phone 44 20 73545215, timn@fsmail.net. **Subscription Rates:** 42 individuals inside UK; 62 individuals inside Europe; 77 individuals inside USA and rest of the world. **Remarks:** Accepts advertising. **URL:** http://www.adhpublishing.com/mi/index.htm. **Circ:** (Not Reported)

56766 ■ Model Airplane International
ADH Publishing Ltd.
Doolittle Mill
Doolittle Ln.
Bedfordshire
Totternhoe LU6 1QX, United Kingdom
Ph: 44 1525 222573
Fax: 44 1525 222574
Publication E-mail: colin@adhpublishing.com
Publisher E-mail: enquiries@adhpublishing.com
Magazine covering model aircrafts. **Freq:** Monthly. **Key Personnel:** Richard John Caruana, Editor. **Subscription Rates:** 41 individuals inside UK; 54 individuals inside Europe; 67 individuals inside USA and rest of world (airmail). **Remarks:** Accepts advertising. **URL:** http://www.modelairplaneinternational.com/. **Circ:** (Not Reported)

56767 ■ Model Military International
ADH Publishing Ltd.
Doolittle Mill
Doolittle Ln.
Bedfordshire
Totternhoe LU6 1QX, United Kingdom
Ph: 44 1525 222573
Fax: 44 1525 222574
Publisher E-mail: enquiries@adhpublishing.com
Magazine covering military modeling. **Freq:** Monthly. **Key Personnel:** Brett Green, Editor. **Subscription Rates:** 4.20 single issue UK; 5.25 single issue Europe; 6.45 single issue rest of the world; 41 individuals UK; 54 individuals Europe; 67 other countries. **URL:** http://www.modelmilitary.com/.

56768 ■ Radio Control Car RACER
ADH Publishing Ltd.
Doolittle Mill
Doolittle Ln.
Bedfordshire
Totternhoe LU6 1QX, United Kingdom
Ph: 44 1525 222573
Fax: 44 1525 222574

Publication E-mail: racermag@aol.com
Publisher E-mail: enquiries@adhpublishing.com
Magazine covering radio control car. **Freq:** Monthly. **Subscription Rates:** 38 individuals inside UK; 54 individuals inside Europe; 68 individuals rest of the world; 19 individuals inside UK; 27 individuals inside Europe; 34 individuals rest of the word. **URL:** http://www.rcracer.co.uk/.

56769 ■ Radio Control Model Flyer
ADH Publishing Ltd.
Doolittle Mill
Doolittle Ln.
Bedfordshire
Totternhoe LU6 1QX, United Kingdom
Ph: 44 1525 222573
Fax: 44 1525 222574
Publisher E-mail: enquiries@adhpublishing.com
Magazine covering radio control model flyer. **Freq:** Monthly. **Subscription Rates:** 38 individuals inside UK; 54 individuals inside Europe; 66 individuals rest of the world (air); 19 individuals inside UK; 27 individuals inside Europe; 33 individuals rest of the word. **URL:** http://www.modelflyermagazine.com/.

56770 ■ Rotorworld
ADH Publishing Ltd.
Doolittle Mill
Doolittle Ln.
Bedfordshire
Totternhoe LU6 1QX, United Kingdom
Ph: 44 1525 222573
Fax: 44 1525 222574
Publication E-mail: editor@rotorworld.co.uk
Publisher E-mail: enquiries@adhpublishing.com
Magazine covering model helicopter. **Founded:** 2003. **Freq:** Bimonthly. **Subscription Rates:** 22 individuals inside UK; 27 individuals inside Europe; 33 individuals rest of the world; 44 individuals inside UK; 54 individuals inside Europe; 66 individuals rest of the world. **Remarks:** Accepts advertising. **URL:** http://www.rotorworld.co.uk/. **Circ:** (Not Reported)

56771 ■ Tamiya Model Magazine International
ADH Publishing Ltd.
Doolittle Mill
Doolittle Ln.
Bedfordshire
Totternhoe LU6 1QX, United Kingdom
Ph: 44 1525 222573
Fax: 44 1525 222574
Publisher E-mail: enquiries@adhpublishing.com
Magazine covering Tamiya model. **Subscription Rates:** 41 individuals inside UK; 54 individuals inside Europe; 67 individuals inside USA and rest of the world; 20.50 individuals inside UK; 27 individuals inside Europe; 33.50 individuals rest of the world. **URL:** http://www.tamiyamodelmagazine.com/.

Tring

56772 ■ Quarterly Journal of Forestry
Royal Forestry Society
102 High St.
Tring HP23 4AF, United Kingdom
Ph: 44 1442 822028
Fax: 44 1442 890395
Publisher E-mail: rfshq@rfs.org.uk
Official publication of the Royal Forestry Society of England, Wales and Northern Ireland. **Founded:** 1906. **Freq:** Quarterly. **Print Method:** Litho. **Trim Size:** 148 x 210 mm. **Key Personnel:** Lesley Trotter, Editor. **ISSN:** 0022-1201. **Subscription Rates:** Free to members. **Remarks:** Accepts advertising. **URL:** http://www.rfs.org.uk/. **Circ:** Controlled 4,500

Truro

56773 ■ Best Practice & Research Clinical Rheumatology
Elsevier Science
c/o Prof. Anthony D. Woolf, Ed.-in-Ch.
Duke of Cornwall Rheumatology Unit
Royal Cornwall Hospital
Truro TR1 3LJ, United Kingdom
Publisher E-mail: nlinfo-f@elsevier.com
Journal reporting on recent advances in practice and clinical rheumatology. **Freq:** Bimonthly. **Key Personnel:** Prof. Anthony D. Woolf, Editor-in-Chief; G.S. Alarcon,

Editorial Board; R. Handa, Editorial Board; B. Bresnihan, Editorial Board; E.K. Li, Editorial Board; M. Dougados, Editorial Board. **ISSN:** 1521-6942. **Subscription Rates:** 58,900¥ institutions; EUR548 institutions for European countries & Iran; US$484 institutions for all countries except Europe, Japan & Iran; EUR291 individuals for European Countries; 31,500¥ individuals; US$204 individuals for all countries except Europe, Japan & Iran; US$178 elsewhere resident; EUR200 elsewhere resident, for European countries & Iran; 21,500¥ individuals resident; 139 trainee. **Remarks:** Advertising accepted; rates available upon request. **URL:** http://www.elsevier.com/wps/find/journaldescription.cws_home/623005/descriptiondescription. **Circ:** (Not Reported)

56774 ■ BBC Radio-FM - 95.2
Phoenix Wharf
Truro TR1 1UA, United Kingdom
Ph: 44 18 72275421
E-mail: cornwall@bbc.co.uk
Format: News; Information; Sports. **Owner:** British Broadcasting Corp., Broadcasting House, Portland Pl., London W1A 1AA, United Kingdom. **Operating Hours:** Continuous. **URL:** http://www.bbc.co.uk/cornwall/local_radio/index.shtml.

56775 ■ BBC Radio-FM - 103.9
Phoenix Wharf
Truro TR1 1UA, United Kingdom
Ph: 44 1872 275421
E-mail: radio.cornwall@bbc.co.uk
Format: News; Information; Sports. **Owner:** British Broadcasting Corp., Broadcasting House, Portland Pl., London W1A 1AA, United Kingdom. **Operating Hours:** Continuous. **URL:** http://www.bbc.co.uk/cornwall/local_radio/index.shtml.

Tunbridge Wells

56776 ■ Agra Europe Weekly
Agra Europe Ltd.
80 Calverley Rd.
Tunbridge Wells TN1 2UN, United Kingdom
Ph: 44 20 70177500
Fax: 44 20 70177599
Publisher E-mail: marketing@agra-net.com
Publication covering the agricultural industry. **Freq:** Weekly. **ISSN:** 0002-1024. **URL:** http://www.agra-net.com/portal2/home.jsp?template=productpage&pubid=ag002.

56777 ■ AgraFood East Europe
Agra Europe Ltd.
80 Calverley Rd.
Tunbridge Wells TN1 2UN, United Kingdom
Ph: 44 20 70177500
Fax: 44 20 70177599
Publisher E-mail: marketing@agra-net.com
Publication covering the agricultural industry. **Freq:** Weekly. **URL:** http://www.agra-net.com/portal2/home.jsp?template=productpage&pubid=ag027.

56778 ■ CFJ Contract Flooring Journal
Contract Flooring Journal
102 Queens Rd.
c/o Alan Bakalor
Tunbridge Wells TN4 9JU, United Kingdom
Ph: 44 18 92680816
Publisher E-mail: alancfj@btconnect.com
Official journal of the Contract Flooring Association. **Founded:** 1989. **Freq:** Monthly. **Key Personnel:** John Heath, Production Dir., phone 44 18 92752407, fax 44 18 92752404, john.heath@wellards.co.uk; Alan Bakalor, Editor, alancfj@btconnect.com; Stuart Bourne, Sales Mgr., phone 44 18 92752400, stuart.bourne@kickstartpublishing.co.uk. **Subscription Rates:** 48 individuals U.K.; 85 individuals Europe; 160 other countries. **Remarks:** Accepts advertising. **URL:** http://www.contractflooringjournal.co.uk. **Ad Rates:** BW: 990. **Circ:** Combined ★6,888

56779 ■ Contracts Flooring Journal
Contract Flooring Association
c/o Alan Bakalor, Ed. Dir.
102 Queens Rd.
Tunbridge Wells TN4 9JU, United Kingdom
Ph: 44 18 92680816
Publisher E-mail: info@cfa.org.uk
Journal covering contract flooring. **Freq:** Monthly. **Key Personnel:** Alan Bakalor, Ed. Dir., alancfj@btconnect.com. **Subscription Rates:** 48 individuals; 85 individuals

Europe; 160 other countries. **Remarks:** Accepts advertising. **URL:** http://www.contractflooringjournal.co.uk. **Circ:** ★6,888

56780 ■ Dairy Markets Weekly
Agra Europe Ltd.
80 Calverley Rd.
Tunbridge Wells TN1 2UN, United Kingdom
Ph: 44 20 70177500
Fax: 44 20 70177599
Publisher E-mail: marketing@agra-net.com
Publication covering the agricultural industry. **Freq:** Weekly. **ISSN:** 0957-8625. **Remarks:** Advertising accepted; rates available upon request. **URL:** http://www.agra-net.com/portal2/home.jsp?template=productpage&pubid=ag004. **Circ:** (Not Reported)

56781 ■ Educational Technology Abstracts
Taylor & Francis Group Journals
23 Mountfield Gardens
Tunbridge Wells TN1 1SJ, United Kingdom
Publisher E-mail: customerservice@taylorandfrancis.com
Journal covering all aspects of educational technology. **Freq:** Annual. **Print Method:** Offset. **Trim Size:** 8 1/8 x 10 7/8. **Cols./Page:** 3. **Col. Width:** 26 nonpareils. **Col. Depth:** 140 agate lines. **Key Personnel:** Paul Kelley, Editorial Advisory Board; Prof. Jon Baggaley, Editorial Advisory Board; Jessica Claridge, Editorial Advisory Board; Dr. Dennis Moss, Editorial Advisory Board; Martin Gienke, Editorial Advisory Board; Dr. Nicholas C. Farnes, Editorial Advisory Board; Dr. Vivien M. Johnston, Editor, vmj2@tutor.open.ac.uk. **ISSN:** 0266-3368. **Subscription Rates:** US$1,679 institutions print and online; US$1,595 institutions online; US$621 individuals; 1,015 institutions print + online; 965 institutions online; 373 individuals; EUR1,336 institutions print and online; EUR1,269 institutions online only; EUR494 individuals. **URL:** http://www.tandf.co.uk/journals/titles/02663368.asp.

56782 ■ Eurofood
Agra Europe Ltd.
80 Calverley Rd.
Tunbridge Wells TN1 2UN, United Kingdom
Ph: 44 20 70177500
Fax: 44 20 70177599
Publisher E-mail: marketing@agra-net.com
Publication for the food industries. **Freq:** Semimonthly. **ISSN:** 0955-5405. **Remarks:** Advertising not accepted. **URL:** http://www.agra-net.com/portal2/home.jsp?template=productpage&pubid=ag006. **Circ:** (Not Reported)

56783 ■ Transportation Professional
Barrett, Byrd Associates
BBA Linden House
Linden Close
Tunbridge Wells TN4 8HH, United Kingdom
Ph: 44 1892 524455
Fax: 44 1892 524456
Publication E-mail: info@transportation-mag.com
Publisher E-mail: two@barrett-byrd.com
Trade publication covering transportation. **Freq:** Monthly. **Key Personnel:** Ty Byrd, Editor, ty@barrett-byrd.com. **Remarks:** Accepts advertising. **URL:** http://www.barrett-byrd.com/. **Formerly:** Highways & Transportation (June 2002). **Circ:** ‡13,000

BBC Radio Kent - See Folkestone

BBC Radio Kent - See Swingate

56784 ■ BBC Radio Kent-FM - 96.7
The Great Hall
Mt. Pleasant Rd.
Tunbridge Wells TN1 1QQ, United Kingdom
Ph: 44 1892 670000
Fax: 44 1892 549118
E-mail: kent@bbc.co.uk
Format: News; Sports; Talk; Oldies. **Owner:** British Broadcasting Corporation, Broadcasting House, Portland Pl., London W1A 1AA, United Kingdom. **Operating Hours:** Continuous. **URL:** http://news.bbc.co.uk/local/kent/hi/tv_and_radio/.

Tunbridge Wells North

56785 ■ Modern Railways
Ian Allan Publishing Ltd.
c/o James Abbott, Ed.
PO Box 206

Tunbridge Wells North TN1 2XA, United Kingdom
Publisher E-mail: info@ianallanpublishing.co.uk
Magazine featuring state and developments of the British railway network. **Founded:** 1962. **Freq:** Monthly. **Key Personnel:** James Abbott, Editor; Paul Edwards, Advertising Mgr. **Remarks:** Accepts advertising. **URL:** http://www.modern-railways.com/. **Circ:** (Not Reported)

Turriff

56786 ■ NECR-FM - 97.1
The Shed
School Rd.
Kintore
Aberdeenshire
Inverurie AB51 0UX, United Kingdom
Ph: 44 1467 632909
Fax: 44 1467 632969
E-mail: enquiries@necrfm.co.uk
Format: Oldies; Contemporary Hit Radio (CHR); News; Information. **Ad Rates:** Advertising accepted; rates available upon request. **URL:** http://www.necrfm.co.uk/.

Twickenham

56787 ■ Airport World
Insight Media
Sovereign House
26-30 London Rd.
Twickenham TW1 3RW, United Kingdom
Magazine featuring airport management and airport industry. **Founded:** 1995. **Freq:** 6/yr. **Key Personnel:** Joe Bates, Editorial Dir., phone 44 20 88317507, joe@insightgrp.co.uk. **Subscription Rates:** US$75 individuals digital; US$125 two years; US$125 individuals includes postage; US$225 two years includes postage. **Remarks:** Accepts advertising. **URL:** http://airport-world.com/. **Circ:** 8,000

56788 ■ Asia-Pacific Airports
Insight Media
Sovereign House
26-30 London Rd.
Twickenham TW1 3RW, United Kingdom
Magazine featuring airport industry. **Founded:** Oct. 2007. **Freq:** Quarterly. **Trim Size:** 195 x 276 mm. **Key Personnel:** Joe Bates, Editorial Dir., phone 44 20 88317507, joe@insightgrp.co.uk. **Remarks:** Accepts advertising. **URL:** http://www.insightgrp.co.uk/asia-pacific-airports.html. **Circ:** 4,000

56789 ■ Clay Minerals
Mineralogical Society of Great Britain and Ireland
12 Baylis Mews
Amyand Park Rd.
Middlesex
Twickenham TW1 3HQ, United Kingdom
Ph: 44 20 88916600
Fax: 44 20 88916599
Publisher E-mail: info@minersoc.org
Publication covering minerology. **Freq:** Quarterly. **Key Personnel:** K.P. Murphy, Editorial Mgr.; Prof. J.M. Adams, Editor, john@treviles.com; Dr. F. Villieras, Assoc. Ed., frederic.villieras@ensg.inpl-nancy.fr; Prof. C. Breen, Assoc. Ed., c.breen@shu.ac.uk; Prof. G. Christidis, Assoc. Ed., christid@mred.tuc.gr; Dr. L.N. Warr, Assoc. Ed., warr@illite.u-strasb.fr; Dr. E. Murad, Assoc. Ed., clay.minerals@yahoo.de; Prof. M.F. Brigatti, Editorial Board. **ISSN:** 0009-8558. **Subscription Rates:** 256 individuals print and free online journal; 244 individuals agents' discounted rate; 198.99 individuals online only; 189.52 individuals agents' discounted rate; online only; 290 other countries print and free online journal; 276 other countries agents' discounted rate; 233.81 other countries online only; 222.69 other countries agents' discounted rate; online only. **Remarks:** Accepts advertising. **URL:** http://www.minersoc.org/; http://www.minersoc.org/pages/e_journals/clay.html. **Circ:** (Not Reported)

56790 ■ Conrad Studies
Rodopi
c/o Allan H. Simmons, Gen. Ed.
St. Mary's University College, Dept. of English
Strawberry Hill
Waldegrave Rd.
Twickenham TW1 4SX, United Kingdom
Fax: 44 20 82404365

Publisher E-mail: info@rodopi.nl
Journal promoting the study of Conrad. **Founded:** 1858. **Freq:** 3/week Tues, Thursday, and Sat. **Print Method:** Web. **Cols./Page:** 6. **Col. Width:** 12 picas. **Col. Depth:** 21 inches. **Key Personnel:** J.H. Stape, Gen. Ed.; Allan H. Simmons, Gen. Ed., allanhsimmons@aol.com; Owen Knowles, Advisory Ed.; Lawrence Davies, Advisory Ed. **ISSN:** 1872-1737. **URL:** http://www.rodopi.nl/senj.asp?SerieId=CONRADSTUD.

56791 ■ Fertilizer Focus
FMB Publications Ltd.
FMB House
6 Windmill Rd.
Hampton Hill
Twickenham TW12 1RH, United Kingdom
Ph: 44 20 89797866
Fax: 44 20 89794573
Publisher E-mail: fmb@fmb-group.co.uk
Trade magazine covering fertilizer worldwide. **Founded:** Feb. 1984. **Freq:** Bimonthly. **Trim Size:** 210 x 297 mm. **Key Personnel:** Mike Smith, Contact. **Subscription Rates:** US$475 individuals airmail. **Remarks:** Accepts advertising. **URL:** http://www.fmb-group.co.uk/. **Ad Rates:** BW: 1,625. **Circ:** 3,000

56792 ■ Global Airport Cities Magazine
Insight Media
Sovereign House
26-30 London Rd.
Twickenham TW1 3RW, United Kingdom
Magazine focusing on the transformation of airports into airport cities. **Founded:** Sept. 2006. **Freq:** Quarterly. **Trim Size:** 195 x 276 mm. **Key Personnel:** Jonathan Lee, Sales Dir., phone 44 20 88317563, jonathan@insightgrp.co.uk; Andrew Hazell, Advertising Mgr., phone 44 20 88317518, andrewh@insightgrp.co.uk. **Subscription Rates:** Free. **Remarks:** Accepts advertising. **URL:** http://www.insightgrp.co.uk/global-airport-cities.html. **Circ:** Controlled 5,000

56793 ■ Routes News
Insight Media
Sovereign House
26-30 London Rd.
Twickenham TW1 3RW, United Kingdom
Magazine for airline and airport executives involved in route development decision making. **Freq:** Bimonthly. **Trim Size:** 195 x 276 mm. **Key Personnel:** Rebecca Randall, Advertising Mgr., phone 44 20 88317513, rebecca.randall@routes-news.com. **Remarks:** Accepts advertising. **URL:** http://www.routesonline.com/; http://www.insightgrp.co.uk/RoutesNews.html. **Circ:** 6,000

Ugley Green

56794 ■ Health Food Business Magazine
Target Publishing Ltd.
The Old Dairy
Hudsons Farm
Fieldgate Ln.
Ugley Green CM22 6HJ, United Kingdom
Ph: 44 12 79816300
Fax: 44 12 79810081
Publisher E-mail: info@targetpublishing.com
Trade magazine for the health food retail industry. **Freq:** Monthly. **Trim Size:** 210 x 297 mm. **Cols./Page:** 3. **Key Personnel:** Rachel Symonds, Editor, editor@healthfoodbusiness.co.uk; Ruth Dodsley, Sen. Sales Exec., ruth.dodsley@targetpublishing.com; Sharon Butler, Sales Mgr., sharon.butler@targetpublishing.com. **Subscription Rates:** 54 individuals; 65 individuals Europe; 95 elsewhere international. **Remarks:** Accepts advertising. **URL:** http://www.targetpublishing.com; http://www.healthfoodbusiness.co.uk/. **Ad Rates:** 4C: 1,830. **Circ:** Controlled 3,552

Ullapool

56795 ■ Lochbroom-FM - 102.2 MHz
Radio House, Mill St.
Ullapool IV26 2UN, United Kingdom
Ph: 44 1854 613131
Fax: 44 1854 613132
E-mail: radio@lochbroomfm.co.uk
Format: Eclectic; Full Service; Religious. **Operating Hours:** Continuous. **URL:** http://www.lochbroomfm.co.uk/.

56796 ■ Lochbroom-FM - 96.8
Radio House
Mill St.
Wester Ross
Ullapool, United Kingdom
Ph: 44 1854 613131
Fax: 44 1854 613132
E-mail: radio@lochbroomfm.co.uk
Format: Eclectic. **URL:** http://www.lochbroomfm.co.uk/.

Uppingham

56797 ■ Loyalty
C & M Publications Ltd.
3A Market Pl.
Uppingham LE15 9QH, United Kingdom
Ph: 44 15 72820088
Fax: 44 15 72820099
Publisher E-mail: publisher@cm-media.net
Professional magazine covering customer relations. **Freq:** Daily. **Print Method:** Web offset. **Trim Size:** 190 x 297 mm. **Cols./Page:** 4. **Key Personnel:** Maxine Wernick, Subscriptions Mgr., maxine@cm-media.net; Annich McIntosh, Managing Editor, candmpubs@aol.com. **Subscription Rates:** 98 individuals; 146 two years. **Remarks:** Accepts advertising. **URL:** http://www.loyaltymagazine.com/. **Ad Rates:** 4C: 1,950. **Circ:** Paid ★5,000

Uxbridge

56798 ■ International Journal of Renewable Energy Technology
Inderscience Enterprises Limited
c/o Dr. Ahmed F. Zobaa, Ed.-in-Ch.
School of Engineering & Design
Middlesex
Uxbridge UB8 3PH, United Kingdom
Journal covering all aspects of renewable energy technology. **Freq:** Quarterly. **Key Personnel:** Dr. Ahmed F. Zobaa, Editor-in-Chief, ijret.editor@gmail.com. **ISSN:** 1757-3971. **Subscription Rates:** EUR494 individuals print or online; EUR672 individuals print and online. **URL:** http://www.inderscience.com/browse/index.php?journalCODE=ijret.

56799 ■ International Journal of Work Organisation & Emotion
Inderscience Publishers
Brunel University
School of Business & Management
Uxbridge UB8 3PH, United Kingdom
Publication E-mail: ijwoe@inderscience.com
Publisher E-mail: editor@inderscience.com
Journal covering processes & practices of emotion work in organizations. **Founded:** 2005. **Freq:** 4/yr. **Key Personnel:** Dr. Philip Hancock, Editor-in-Chief, philip.hancock@wbs.ac.uk; Dr. Melissa Tyler, Editor-in-Chief, m.j.tyler@lboro.ac.uk; Dr. Geraldine Lee-Treweek, Book Review Ed. **ISSN:** 1740-8938. **Subscription Rates:** EUR494 individuals print or online; EUR672 individuals print and online. **URL:** http://www.inderscience.com/browse/index.php?journalCODE=ijwoe.

56800 ■ Journal of Enterprise Information Management
Emerald Group Publishing Ltd.
c/o Prof. Zahir Irani, Ed.
Brunel Business School
Brunel University
Middlesex
Uxbridge UB8 3PH, United Kingdom
Publisher E-mail: emerald@emeraldinsight.com
Journal focusing on the latest methodologies in the field of logistics. **Freq:** 6/yr. **Key Personnel:** Prof. Zahir Irani, Editor, zahir.irani@brunel.ac.uk; Dr. Majed Al-Mashari, Editorial Advisory Board; Lucy Sootheran, Publisher, lsootheran@emeraldinsight.com; Prof. Cengiz Kahraman, Editorial Advisory Board; Prof. Norman P. Archer, Editorial Advisory Board; Dr. Philip Joyce, Editorial Advisory Board; Prof. Peter E.D. Love, Regional Ed. **ISSN:** 1741-0398. **URL:** http://info.emeraldinsight.com/products/journals/journals.htm?PHPSESSID=0onkd54o28l3c6rrkjhb05qm97&id=jeim.

56801 ■ Transforming Government
Emerald Group Publishing Ltd.
c/o Prof. Zahir Irani, Ed.
Brunel Business School
Brunel University

Middlesex
Uxbridge UB8 3PH, United Kingdom
Publisher E-mail: emerald@emeraldinsight.com
Journal covering government transpformation through its people, processes, and policy. **Subtitle:** People, Process and Policy. **Freq:** Quarterly. **Key Personnel:** Prof. Zahir Irani, Editor, zahir.irani@brunel.ac.uk; Nicola Codner, Publisher, ncodner@emeraldinsight.com. **ISSN:** 1750-6166. **URL:** http://info.emeraldinsight.com/products/journals/journals.htm?id=tg.

Verwood

56802 ■ Forest-FM - 92.3
Unit 2 Enterprise Pk.
Verwood BH31 6YS, United Kingdom
Ph: 44 12 02820006
E-mail: contact@forestfm.co.uk
Format: Eclectic; Public Radio. **Operating Hours:** Continuous. **URL:** http://www.forestfm.co.uk.

Wadebridge

56803 ■ Avicultural Magazine
The Avicultural Society
c/o Malcolm Ellis, Ed.
The Chalet Hay Farm
St. Breock
Wadebridge PL27 7LL, United Kingdom
Ph: 44 1208 812260
Publication E-mail: editor@avisoc.co.uk
Publisher E-mail: editor@avisoc.co.uk
Magazine covering aviculture (bird keeping). **Founded:** 1894. **Freq:** Annual. **Trim Size:** 207 x 134 mm. **Key Personnel:** Malcolm Ellis, Editor, mellis@avisoc.co.uk. **ISSN:** 0005-2256. **Subscription Rates:** 18 individuals; 21 other countries; overseas an additional 6 airmail. **Remarks:** Accepts advertising. **URL:** http://www.avisoc.co.uk/. **Circ:** (Not Reported)

Wadhurst

56804 ■ Access International
KHL Group
Southfields
Southview Rd.
Wadhurst TN5 6TP, United Kingdom
Ph: 44 1892 784088
Fax: 44 1892 784086
Publisher E-mail: info@khl.com
Publication covering industrial equipment in English. **Freq:** 8/yr. **Key Personnel:** Maria Hadrow, Editor, phone 44 1892 786214, maria.hadlow@khl.com; Wil Holloway, Sales Mgr., phone 44 1892 786232, wil.holloway@khl.com; Ross Dickson, Production Mgr., phone 44 1892 786245, ross.dickson@khl.com. **Subscription Rates:** 95 individuals; 170 two years; EUR120 individuals; EUR215 two years; US$170 individuals; US$300 two years. **Remarks:** Accepts advertising. **URL:** http://www.khl.com/magazines/access-international/. **Ad Rates:** 4C: 5,800. **Circ:** 8,024

56805 ■ Construction Europe
KHL Group
Southfields
Southview Rd.
Wadhurst TN5 6TP, United Kingdom
Ph: 44 1892 784088
Fax: 44 1892 784086
Publisher E-mail: info@khl.com
Magazine for European construction industry. **Freq:** Monthly. **Key Personnel:** Sandy Guthrie, Editor, phone 44 1892 786234, sandy.guthrie@khl.com; Ross Dickson, Production Mgr., phone 44 1892 786245, ross.dickson@khl.com. **Subscription Rates:** 160 individuals; 260 two years; EUR210 individuals; EUR350 two years; US$290 individuals; US$480 two years. **Remarks:** Accepts advertising. **URL:** http://www.khl.com/; http://www.khl.com/magazines/construction-europe/. **Circ:** ★14,624

56806 ■ Demolition & Recycling International
KHL Group
Southfields
Southview Rd.
Wadhurst TN5 6TP, United Kingdom
Ph: 44 1892 784088
Fax: 44 1892 784086
Publisher E-mail: info@khl.com
Magazine for the world's demolition and recycling

Circulation: ★ = ABC; △ = BPA; ♦ = CAC; • = CCAB; ❏ = VAC; ⊕ = PO Statement; ‡ = Publisher's Report; Boldface figures = sworn; Light figures = estimated.

Gale Directory of Publications & Broadcast Media/147th Ed.   5873

industry. **Freq:** Bimonthly. **Key Personnel:** Lindsay Gale, Editor, phone 44 1892 786210, fax 44 1892 784086, lindsay.gale@khl.com; Ross Dickson, Production Mgr., phone 44 1892 786245, ross.dickson@khl.com. **Subscription Rates:** 90 individuals; 145 two years; EUR115 individuals; EUR185 two years; US$160 individuals; US$260 two years. **Remarks:** Accepts advertising. **URL:** http://www.khl.com/magazines/demolition-and-recycling-international/. **Ad Rates:** 4C: 6,100. **Circ:** ‡7,481

56807 ■ International Construction China
KHL Group
Southfields
Southview Rd.
Wadhurst TN5 6TP, United Kingdom
Ph: 44 1892 784088
Fax: 44 1892 784086
Publisher E-mail: info@khl.com
Construction magazine for the massive Chinese market. **Founded:** 2006. **Freq:** Monthly. **Trim Size:** 210 x 285 mm. **Key Personnel:** David Stowe, Display Sales Mgr., phone 44 1892 786217, david.stowe@khl.com. **Subscription Rates:** 160 individuals; 260 two years; EUR210 individuals; EUR350 two years; US$290 individuals; US$480 two years. **Remarks:** Accepts advertising. **URL:** http://www.khl.com/magazines/international-construction-china/. **Ad Rates:** 4C: 2,900. **Circ:** 15,800

56808 ■ International Construction Turkiye
KHL Group
Southfields
Southview Rd.
Wadhurst TN5 6TP, United Kingdom
Ph: 44 1892 784088
Fax: 44 1892 784086
Publisher E-mail: info@khl.com
Magazine featuring Turkish construction industry. **Freq:** 6/yr. **Trim Size:** 210 x 285 mm. **Key Personnel:** Lindsay Gale, International Ed., phone 44 1892 786205, lindsay.gale@khl.com. **Subscription Rates:** 90 individuals; 145 individuals; EUR115 individuals; EUR185 two years; US$160 individuals; US$260 two years. **Remarks:** Accepts display advertising. **URL:** http://www.khl.com/magazines/international-construction-turkiye/. **Circ:** Combined 17,649

56809 ■ International Cranes and Specialized Transport
KHL Group
Southfields
Southview Rd.
Wadhurst TN5 6TP, United Kingdom
Ph: 44 1892 784088
Fax: 44 1892 784086
Publisher E-mail: info@khl.com
Magazine of Specialized Carriers & Rigging Association provides in-depth information about cranes & lifts, safety updates, lifting and specialized transport news and site reports from around the world. **Freq:** Monthly. **Key Personnel:** Alex Dahm, Editor, phone 44 1892 786206, alex.dahm@khl.com; Ross Dickson, Production Mgr., phone 44 1892 786245, ross.dickson@khl.com. **Subscription Rates:** 160 individuals; 260 two years; EUR210 individuals; EUR350 two years; US$290 individuals; US$480 two years. **Remarks:** Accepts advertising. **URL:** http://www.khl.com/magazines/international-cranes-and-specialized-transport. **Ad Rates:** 4C: 6,500. **Circ:** ‡14,381

56810 ■ International Rental News
KHL Group
Southfields
Southview Rd.
Wadhurst TN5 6TP, United Kingdom
Ph: 44 1892 784088
Fax: 44 1892 784086
Publisher E-mail: info@khl.com
Magazine focusing on equipment rental industry covering all sections of the rental market, from construction equipment, tool hire and aerial platforms, to temporary accommodation, power/temperature control rental and party/events rental. **Key Personnel:** Murray Pollok, Editor, phone 44 1505 850043, murray.pollok@khl.com. **Subscription Rates:** 115 individuals; 190 two years; EUR150 individuals; EUR240 two years; US$205 individuals; US$335 two years. **Remarks:** Accepts advertising. **URL:** http://www.khl.com/magazines/international-rental-news/. **Formerly:** European Rental News (ERN). **Circ:** Combined 14,624

Walberton

56811 ■ The Bookplate Journal
The Bookplate Society
c/o Peter Youatt, Ed.
Lansdown House
Walberton BN18 0PG, United Kingdom
Journal covering book plates (ex libris), their artists, makers and owners. **Founded:** 1983. **Freq:** Semiannual. **Key Personnel:** Bryan Welch, Editor; Peter Youatt, Editor. **ISSN:** 0264-3693. **Subscription Rates:** 30 individuals; 34 out of area; US$65 out of area; EUR45 out of area. **Remarks:** Accepts advertising. **URL:** http://www.bookplatesociety.org/publications.htm. **Circ:** Paid 250

Wales

56812 ■ International Journal of Applied Mathematics and Mechanics (IJAMM)
GBS Publishers & Distributors
c/o F.W. Williams, Ed.
Dept. of Civil Engineering
University of Cardiff
Wales CF10 3XQ, United Kingdom
Publisher E-mail: info@gbspublisher.com
Journal covering applied mathematics and mechanics, with emphasis in the integration of theory and applications. **Founded:** 1959. **Freq:** Quarterly Regular. **Print Method:** Offset. **Trim Size:** 6 1/4 x 9 1/2. **Cols./Page:** 1. **Col. Width:** 50 nonpareils. **Col. Depth:** 100 agate lines. **Key Personnel:** F.W. Williams, Editor; W.K. Liu, Editor; Raymond Lee, Assoc. Ed. **ISSN:** 0973-0184. **Subscription Rates:** US$180 individuals print; US$240 institutions print; US$260 individuals print and electronic. **URL:** http://www.gbspublisher.com/ijamm.htm.

Wallingford

56813 ■ AgBiotech News and Information
CAB International
Nosworthy Way
Wallingford OX10 8DE, United Kingdom
Ph: 44 1491 832111
Fax: 44 1491 829292
Publisher E-mail: enquiries@cabi.org
Publication covering agricultural biotechnology - including animal cloning, transgenic plants and animals. **Founded:** 1988. **Freq:** Monthly. **ISSN:** 0954-9897. **Remarks:** Accepts advertising. **URL:** http://www.cabi.org/Default.aspx?site=170&page=1016&pid=59. **Ad Rates:** BW: 90. **Circ:** 180

56814 ■ A.M.
Aston Martin Owners Club
Drayton St. Leonard
Wallingford OX10 7BG, United Kingdom
Ph: 44 18 65400400
Fax: 44 18 65400200
Trade publication covering automotive. **Freq:** Quarterly. **Remarks:** Advertising accepted; rates available upon request. **URL:** http://www.amoc.org/content/view/57/98/. **Circ:** 4,700

56815 ■ Animal Health Research Reviews
CAB International
Nosworthy Way
Wallingford OX10 8DE, United Kingdom
Ph: 44 1491 832111
Fax: 44 1491 829292
Publisher E-mail: enquiries@cabi.org
Journal providing an international forum for the publication of reviews and commentaries on all aspects of animal health, covering all facets of animal health and science, including but not limited to both infectious and non-infectious diseases in domestic and wild animals. **Freq:** Biennial. **Key Personnel:** Prof. C. Gyles, Editor-in-Chief; F. Ahrens, Editorial Board; J. Frey, Editorial Board; S.N. Cho, Editorial Board; L.B. Corbeil, Editorial Board. **ISSN:** 1466-2523. **Subscription Rates:** US$515 institutions print and online; US$300 individuals print and online; US$410 institutions online only; US$207 individuals online only. **Remarks:** Accepts advertising. **URL:** http://journals.cambridge.org/action/displayJournal?jid=AHR. **Ad Rates:** BW: 1,160. **Circ:** (Not Reported)

56816 ■ Biocontrol News and Information
CAB International
Nosworthy Way

Wallingford OX10 8DE, United Kingdom
Ph: 44 1491 832111
Fax: 44 1491 829292
Publisher E-mail: enquiries@cabi.org
Publication covering pest control. **Freq:** Quarterly. **Key Personnel:** Rebecca Murphy, Editor; D. Moore, Editorial Advisory Board; F. Bigler, Editorial Advisory Board; E. De Nardo, Editorial Advisory Board; R.L. Hill, Editorial Advisory Board; P. Neuenschwander, Editorial Advisory Board; E.S. Delfosse, Editorial Advisory Board; M. Guillon, Editorial Advisory Board. **Remarks:** Accepts advertising. **URL:** http://www.cabi.org/Default.aspx?site=170&page=1016&pid=34. **Ad Rates:** BW: 75. **Circ:** 270

56817 ■ Crop Physiology Abstracts
CAB International
Nosworthy Way
Wallingford OX10 8DE, United Kingdom
Ph: 44 1491 832111
Fax: 44 1491 829292
Publisher E-mail: enquiries@cabi.org
Scientific journal covering the physiology of all higher plants of economic importance. **Founded:** 1975. **Freq:** Bimonthly. **Cols./Page:** 2. **Key Personnel:** David Simpson, PhD, Editor, d.simpson@cabi.org. **ISSN:** 0306-7556. **Remarks:** Accepts advertising. **URL:** http://www.cabi.org/default.aspx?site=170&page=1016&pid=35. **Circ:** (Not Reported)

56818 ■ Grasslands & Forage Abstracts
CAB International
Nosworthy Way
Wallingford OX10 8DE, United Kingdom
Ph: 44 1491 832111
Fax: 44 1491 829292
Publisher E-mail: enquiries@cabi.org
Journal covering the environment. **Founded:** 1930. **Freq:** Monthly. **Key Personnel:** David Simpson, Editor. **ISSN:** 1350-9837. **Subscription Rates:** 885 institutions internet only; 1,155 institutions internet/print version; 985 nonmembers institutional (print only); EUR1,415 individuals internet only; EUR1,850 individuals internet/print version; US$1,575 individuals print only; US$1,635 institutions internet only; US$2,135 institutions internet/print version; US$1,820 nonmembers print only; US$155 individuals internet only. **Remarks:** Accepts advertising. **URL:** http://www.cabi.org/default.aspx?site=170&page=1016&pid=39. **Circ:** (Not Reported)

56819 ■ In Vitro Cellular and Developmental Biology - Plant
CABI Publishing
CAB International
Nosworthy Way
Wallingford OX10 8DE, United Kingdom
Ph: 44 1491 832111
Fax: 44 1491 829292
Publisher E-mail: enquiries@cabi.org
Journal publishing peer-reviewed original research and reviews concerned with the latest developments and state-of-the-art research in plant cell and tissue culture and biotechnology from around the globe. **Founded:** 1965. **Freq:** Bimonthly. **Key Personnel:** N.J. Taylor, Editor-in-Chief; D.T. Tomes, Editor-in-Chief. **ISSN:** 1054-5476. **Remarks:** Accepts advertising. **URL:** http://www.cabi.org. **Circ:** (Not Reported)

56820 ■ Journal of Agricultural Genomics
CABI Publishing
CAB International
Nosworthy Way
Wallingford OX10 8DE, United Kingdom
Ph: 44 1491 832111
Fax: 44 1491 829292
Publisher E-mail: enquiries@cabi.org
Journal focusing on research at interface between genomics and the social, economic and technical implication of the science. **Key Personnel:** Bill Beavis, Editor, wdb@ncqr.org; Greg May, Editor. **URL:** http://www.cabi.org; http://wheat.pw.usda.gov/jag/.

56821 ■ Ornamental Horticulture
CAB International
Nosworthy Way
Wallingford OX10 8DE, United Kingdom
Ph: 44 1491 832111
Fax: 44 1491 829292
Publisher E-mail: enquiries@cabi.org
Publication covering ornamental horticulture research. **Freq:** Bimonthly. **Key Personnel:** Alexis Rendell-Dunn, Editor. **Remarks:** Accepts advertising. **URL:** http://www.

cabi.org/Default.aspx?site=170&page=1016&pid=2182. **Circ:** (Not Reported)

56822 ■ Pig News and Information
CAB International
Nosworthy Way
Wallingford OX10 8DE, United Kingdom
Ph: 44 1491 832111
Fax: 44 1491 829292
Publisher E-mail: enquiries@cabi.org
Publication covering pest control. **Freq:** Quarterly. **Remarks:** Accepts advertising. **URL:** http://www.cabi.org/Default.aspx?site=170&page=1016&pid=2183.   **Ad Rates:** BW: 260. **Circ:** 650

56823 ■ Postharvest News and Information
CAB International
Nosworthy Way
Wallingford OX10 8DE, United Kingdom
Ph: 44 1491 832111
Fax: 44 1491 829292
Publisher E-mail: enquiries@cabi.org
Journal covering postharvest research of durable and perishable commodities. **Freq:** Bimonthly weekly updates in the Internet version. **Trim Size:** A4. **Cols./Page:** 1. **Key Personnel:** David Simpson, Editor. **ISSN:** 0957-7505. **Subscription Rates:** 760 institutions internet only; 985 institutions internet/print version; 840 nonmembers institutional (print only) EUR1,215 institutions internet only; EUR1,575 institutions internet/print version; EUR1,345 institutions print only; US$1,405 institutions internet only; US$1,820 institutions internet/print version; US$1,555 nonmembers institutional (print only). **Remarks:** Accepts advertising. **URL:** http://www.cabi.org/Default.aspx?site=170&page=1016&pid=2187. **Circ:** 150

56824 ■ Review of Agricultural Entomology
CAB International
Nosworthy Way
Wallingford OX10 8DE, United Kingdom
Ph: 44 1491 832111
Fax: 44 1491 829292
Publisher E-mail: enquiries@cabi.org
Scientific journal covering agricultural entomology. **Freq:** Monthly. **ISSN:** 0957-6762. **URL:** http://www.cabi.org/Default.aspx?site=170&page=1016&pid=2191.

56825 ■ Review of Aromatic and Medicinal Plants
CAB International
Nosworthy Way
Wallingford OX10 8DE, United Kingdom
Ph: 44 1491 832111
Fax: 44 1491 829292
Publisher E-mail: enquiries@cabi.org
Abstract journal covering cultivated and wild species of herbs and spices, essential oils, and medicinal and pesticidal plants. **Founded:** 1995. **Freq:** Bimonthly. **Trim Size:** A4. **Key Personnel:** Debbie Cousins, Editor, d.cousins@cabi.org. **ISSN:** 1356-1421. **Remarks:** Accepts advertising. **URL:** http://www.cabi.org/default.aspx?site=170&page=1016&pid=2206. **Circ:** (Not Reported)

56826 ■ Review of Medical and Veterinary Entomology
CAB International
Nosworthy Way
Wallingford OX10 8DE, United Kingdom
Ph: 44 1491 832111
Fax: 44 1491 829292
Publisher E-mail: enquiries@cabi.org
Scientific journal covering veterinary entomology. **Freq:** Monthly. **Key Personnel:** James A.H. Brooks, Editor. **Remarks:** Accepts advertising. **URL:** http://www.cabi.org/Default.aspx?site=170&page=1016&pid=2192. **Ad Rates:** BW: 100. **Circ:** 290

56827 ■ Review of Medical and Veterinary Mycology
CAB International
Nosworthy Way
Wallingford OX10 8DE, United Kingdom
Ph: 44 1491 832111
Fax: 44 1491 829292
Publisher E-mail: enquiries@cabi.org
Professional journal covering medical and veterinary mycology. **Freq:** Quarterly. **Key Personnel:** Mark Palmer, Editor, m.palmer@cabi.org. **Remarks:** Accepts advertising. **URL:** http://www.cabi.org/Default.aspx?site=

170&page=1016&pid=2193. **Ad Rates:** BW: 75. **Circ:** 200

56828 ■ Review of Plant Pathology
CAB International
Nosworthy Way
Wallingford OX10 8DE, United Kingdom
Ph: 44 1491 832111
Fax: 44 1491 829292
Publisher E-mail: enquiries@cabi.org
Professional journal covering plant pathology. **Freq:** Monthly. **Remarks:** Accepts advertising. **URL:** http://www.cabi.org/Default.aspx?site=170&page=1016&pid=2194. **Ad Rates:** BW: 250. **Circ:** 690

56829 ■ Soils and Fertilizers
CAB International
Nosworthy Way
Wallingford OX10 8DE, United Kingdom
Ph: 44 1491 832111
Fax: 44 1491 829292
Publisher E-mail: enquiries@cabi.org
Publication covering soil and fertilizers. **Freq:** Monthly. **Remarks:** Accepts advertising. **URL:** http://www.cabi.org/Default.aspx?site=170&page=1016&pid=2198. **Ad Rates:** BW: 175. **Circ:** 380

56830 ■ Soybean Abstracts
CAB International
Nosworthy Way
Wallingford OX10 8DE, United Kingdom
Ph: 44 1491 832111
Fax: 44 1491 829292
Publisher E-mail: enquiries@cabi.org
Journal covering all aspects of soybeans, including crop production, physiology, genetics, processing, uses in human and animal nutrition and economics. **Founded:** 1978. **Freq:** Weekly. **ISSN:** 0141-0172. **Subscription Rates:** 400 institutions internet only; US$695 institutions internet only; EUR640 institutions internet only; 90 individuals internet only; US$155 individuals internet only; EUR145 individuals internet only. **Remarks:** Advertising not accepted. **URL:** http://www.cabi.org/?page=1016&pid=2199&site=170. **Circ:** (Not Reported)

56831 ■ World's Poultry Science Journal
CAB International
Nosworthy Way
Wallingford OX10 8DE, United Kingdom
Ph: 44 1491 832111
Fax: 44 1491 829292
Publisher E-mail: enquiries@cabi.org
Journal for academics, researchers, students, extension workers and commercial poultry producers, providing an international forum for the exchange and dissemination of information on poultry science including research, education and industry organisation. **Freq:** Quarterly. **Key Personnel:** Dr. Lucy Tucker, Editor; S. Cherepanov, Assoc. Ed.; D.J. Farrell, Editorial Board; W. Bessei, Editorial Board; D. Kleverwal, Asst. Ed. **ISSN:** 0043-9339. **Subscription Rates:** US$238 institutions online version; US$300 institutions print and online version; 86 institutions online and print; US$137 individuals online version; US$158 individuals print and online version; 75 individuals online only; 128 institutions online version; 166 institutions print and online version. **Remarks:** Accepts advertising. **URL:** http://journals.cambridge.org/action/displayJournal?jid=WPS. **Circ:** (Not Reported)

Wallington

56832 ■ Building for Leisure
Stable Publishing
SBC House
Restmor Way
Wallington SM6 7AH, United Kingdom
Ph: 44 20 82881080
Fax: 44 20 82881099
Publication E-mail: sales@buildingforleisure.co.uk
Publisher E-mail: info@stablepublishing.co.uk
Business to business magazine covering the leisure industry. **Freq:** 9/yr. **Print Method:** Litho. **Trim Size:** 210 x 297 mm. **Key Personnel:** Toby Filby, Publisher, toby@buildingforleisure.co.uk; Vicky Kiernander, Editor, vicky@buildingforleisure.co.uk; Julian Walter, Sales Mgr., julian@buildingforleisure.co.uk. **Remarks:** Accepts advertising. **URL:** http://www.bflmagazine.co.uk/. **Circ:** Combined ‡11,706

56833 ■ Machinery Update
PPMA Ltd.
New Progress House
34 Stafford Rd.
Wallington SM6 9AA, United Kingdom
Ph: 44 20 87738111
Fax: 44 20 87730022
Publication E-mail: publishing@ppma.co.uk
Publisher E-mail: admin@ppma.co.uk
Trade magazine for the processing and packaging machinery industry. **Founded:** 1989. **Freq:** Bimonthly. **Print Method:** Sheetfed offset. **Trim Size:** 180 x 270 mm. **ISSN:** 0969-4145. **Subscription Rates:** 90 individuals online; 120 other countries online; 35 individuals; 50 individuals continental Europe; 65 other countries. **Remarks:** Accepts advertising. **URL:** http://www.machineryupdate.co.uk/; http://www.ppma.co.uk/pubs/journal.htm. **Ad Rates:** BW: 1,070, 4C: 1,520. **Circ:** ‡9,000

Wallsend

56834 ■ Galaxy-FM - 105
Kingfisher WAy
Silverlink Business Pk.
Wallsend NE28 9NX, United Kingdom
Ph: 44 191 4442500
Format: Urban Contemporary; Hip Hop; Oldies; Blues. **Operating Hours:** Continuous. **Ad Rates:** Advertising accepted; rates available upon request. **URL:** http://www.galaxynortheast.co.uk.

Walsall

56835 ■ Swim & Save
Swimming Teachers' Association
Anchor House
Birch St.
Walsall WS2 8HZ, United Kingdom
Ph: 44 1922 645097
Fax: 44 1922 720628
Publisher E-mail: sta@sta.co.uk
Publication covering swimming and rescue. **Founded:** 1932. **Freq:** Bimonthly. **Subscription Rates:** 18 individuals U.K; 24 individuals Europe; 30 other countries airmail. **Remarks:** Advertising accepted; rates available upon request. **URL:** http://www.sta.co.uk/swimming-teaching/membership/swimsave. **Circ:** (Not Reported)

Walton-on-Thames

56836 ■ Southern African Wireless Communications
Kadium Ltd.
Brassey House
New Zealand Ave.
Walton-on-Thames KT12 1QD, United Kingdom
Ph: 44 1932 886 537
Fax: 44 1932 886 539
Publisher E-mail: kadium@castlegraphics.co.za
Trade magazine covering wireless communications for Southern Africa. **Founded:** June 1996. **Freq:** Semimonthly. **Print Method:** Offset litho. **Trim Size:** A4. **Cols./Page:** 4. **Key Personnel:** Rahiel Nasir, Editor, rahieln@kadiumpublishing.com; Richard Lisney, Advertising Mgr., richardl@kadiumpublishing.com; Kathy Moynihan, Publishing Dir., phone 44 1932 886537, fax 44 1932 886539, kathym@kadiumpublishing.com. **ISSN:** 1364-4394. **Subscription Rates:** Free. **Remarks:** Accepts advertising. **URL:** http://www.kadiumpublishing.com/sawc.html. **Ad Rates:** 4C: 2,850. **Circ:** Controlled ‡7,000

56837 ■ The Woman Writer
Society of Women Writers and Journalists
c/o Wendy Hughes, Membership Sec.
27 Brayton Ave.
Walton-on-Thames KT12 2AZ, United Kingdom
Publisher E-mail: wendy@stickler.org.uk
Publication covering the press. **Freq:** 5/yr. **Key Personnel:** Sylvia Kent, Author. **Remarks:** Advertising not accepted.   **URL:**   http://www.swwj.co.uk/TheWomanWriter.htm. **Circ:** (Not Reported)

Wapping

56838 ■ The Sun (Glasgow)
News Group Newspapers Ltd.

1 Virginia St.
Wapping E98 1SN, United Kingdom
Ph: 44 20 778240000
Publication E-mail: scottish-sun@the-sun.co.uk
Publisher E-mail: corporate.info@the-sun.co.uk
General newspaper. **Remarks:** Accepts advertising.
URL: http://www.thesun.co.uk/. **Circ:** (Not Reported)

Ware

56839 ■ Bentley Magazine
FMS Publishing
New Barn
Fanhams Grange
Fanhams Hall Rd.
Ware SG12 7QA, United Kingdom
Ph: 44 1920 467492
Fax: 44 1920 460149
Lifestyle magazine for Bentley enthusiasts. **Trim Size:**
239 x 327 mm. **Key Personnel:** Julia Marozzi, Editor.
Remarks: Accepts advertising. **URL:** http://www.fms.co.
uk/enquiries.html; http://www.bentleymotors.com/. **Ad
Rates:** 4C: 7,950. **Circ:** 60,000

56840 ■ Champneys Magazine
FMS Publishing
New Barn
Fanhams Grange
Fanhams Hall Rd.
Ware SG12 7QA, United Kingdom
Ph: 44 1920 467492
Fax: 44 1920 460149
Magazine covering beauty, health, fitness, travel,
fashion, interiors, and food. **Freq:** Quarterly. **Trim Size:**
228 x 289 mm. **Key Personnel:** Nigel Fulcher, Mng.
Dir., phone 44 1920 444889, nigel@fms.co.uk; Irene
Mateides, Publishing Dir., phone 44 1920 444888,
irene@fms.co.uk. **Remarks:** Accepts advertising. **URL:**
http://www.fmspublishing.co.uk/. **Ad Rates:** 4C: 5,950.
Circ: 50,000

56841 ■ ISESnews
International Ship Electrical and Engineering Service
Association
Association Internationale des Services d'Installations
Electriques sur
Studio 204, Mill Studio
Crane Mead
Ware SG12 9PY, United Kingdom
Ph: 44 192 0444005
Fax: 44 192 0444006
Publisher E-mail: secretariat@isesassociation.com
Marine publication. **Freq:** Semiannual. **URL:** http://www.
isesassociation.com/data/publications/25_I.S.E.S.
News,2ndEdition2007.pdf.

56842 ■ Marbella Club Magazine
FMS Publishing
New Barn
Fanhams Grange
Fanhams Hall Rd.
Ware SG12 7QA, United Kingdom
Ph: 44 1920 467492
Fax: 44 1920 460149
Magazine featuring Marbella Club Hotel. **Trim Size:** 239
x 297 mm. **Key Personnel:** Nigel Fulcher, Mng. Dir.;
Irene Mateides, Publishing Dir. **Remarks:** Accepts
advertising. **URL:** http://www.marbellaclub.com/
welcome.html. **Ad Rates:** 4C: 4,950. **Circ:** 17,000

56843 ■ Paul Sheeran Magazine
FMS Publishing
New Barn
Fanhams Grange
Fanhams Hall Rd.
Ware SG12 7QA, United Kingdom
Ph: 44 1920 467492
Fax: 44 1920 460149
Publication E-mail: dundrum@paulsheeranjewellers.ie
Magazine for the Irish jewelry and watch makers. **Key
Personnel:** Nigel Fulcher, Mng. Dir.; Irene Mateides,
Publishing Dir. **URL:** http://www.paulsheeranjewellers.
ie/.

56844 ■ Ritz Magazine
FMS Publishing
New Barn
Fanhams Grange
Fanhams Hall Rd.
Ware SG12 7QA, United Kingdom

Ph: 44 1920 467492
Fax: 44 1920 460149
Magazine featuring Ritz Hotel. **Freq:** Semiannual. **Trim
Size:** 240 x 325mm. **Key Personnel:** Nigel Fulcher,
Mng. Dir.; Irene Mateides, Publishing Dir.; Alisa Stamen-
kovic, Advertising Mgr., phone 44 207 3999580, alisa@
fms.co.uk. **Remarks:** Accepts advertising. **URL:** http://
www.fms.co.uk/enquiries.html; http://www.theritzlondon.
com/. **Ad Rates:** 4C: 7,175. **Circ:** ‡35,000

56845 ■ Sunseeker Magazine
FMS Publishing
New Barn
Fanhams Grange
Fanhams Hall Rd.
Ware SG12 7QA, United Kingdom
Ph: 44 1920 467492
Fax: 44 1920 460149
Luxury lifestyle magazine featuring motoring, fashion,
watches, jewelry, gastronomy, sport, travel, and motor
yachts. **Freq:** Quarterly. **Trim Size:** 239 x 327 mm. **Key
Personnel:** Nigel Fulcher, Mng. Dir.; Irene Mateides,
Publishing Dir.; Tracey Peat, Advertising Mgr., phone 44
1920 444891, tracey@fms.co.uk. **Remarks:** Accepts
advertising. **URL:** http://www.fms.co.uk/enquiries.html;
http://www.sunseeker.com/. **Ad Rates:** 4C: 6,950. **Circ:**
170,000

56846 ■ Triumph Magazine
FMS Publishing
New Barn
Fanhams Grange
Fanhams Hall Rd.
Ware SG12 7QA, United Kingdom
Ph: 44 1920 467492
Fax: 44 1920 460149
Magazine for customers of Triumph Motorcycles.
Founded: July 2007. **Freq:** Quarterly. **Key Personnel:**
Nigel Fulcher, Mng. Dir.; Irene Mateides, Publishing Dir.;
Tue Mantoni, CEO, debra@fms.co.uk. **Remarks:** Ac-
cepts advertising. **URL:** http://www.fmspublishing.co.uk/;
http://www.triumph.co.uk/. **Ad Rates:** 4C: 5,850. **Circ:**
80,000

Warminster

56847 ■ Warminster Journal
Coates & Parker Ltd.
36 Market Pl.
Warminster BA12 9AN, United Kingdom
Ph: 44 1985 213030
Fax: 44 1985 217680
Publisher E-mail: sales@coatesandparker.co.uk
Community newspaper. **Founded:** 1881. **Freq:** Weekly.
Print Method: Litho. **Trim Size:** 315 x 415 mm. **Cols./
Page:** 5. **Col. Width:** 50 millimeters. **Col. Depth:** 355
millimeters. **ISSN:** 1470-3238. **Remarks:** Accepts
advertising. **URL:** http://www.coatesandparker.co.uk/
journal.html. **Circ:** Paid 5,500

Warrington

56848 ■ Context
AFT Publishing
7 Executive Ste.
St. James Ct.
Wilderspool Cswy.
Warrington WA4 6PS, United Kingdom
Ph: 44 1925 444414
Magazine for members of the Association of Family
Therapy and Systemic Practice in the UK. **Subtitle:** A
News Magazine of Family Therapy and Systemic
Practice. **Founded:** 1989. **Freq:** Bimonthly. **Trim Size:**
210 x 297mm. **Cols./Page:** 2. **Col. Width:** 82.5
millimeters. **Col. Depth:** 257 millimeters. **Key Person-
nel:** Brian Cade, Gen. Ed., bcade@netspace.net.au;
Ged Smith, Dep. Ed., ged59@hotmail.com. **ISSN:** 0969-
1936. **Subscription Rates:** 30 individuals; 40 institutions; 45 institutions, other countries airmail; 40 other
countries airmail. **Remarks:** Accepts advertising. **URL:**
http://www.aft.org.uk/publications/context.asp. **Ad
Rates:** BW: 750. **Circ:** Controlled 1,600

56849 ■ Jimi Hendrix Magazine
Jimpress
PO Box 218
Warrington WA5 2FG, United Kingdom
Magazine featuring articles, comment, news, and
reviews about Jimi Hendrix and his music. **Subtitle:** The

Jimi Hendrix Collectors' Magazine. **Founded:** 1991.
Freq: Quarterly. **Trim Size:** A5. **Key Personnel:** Steven
C. Pesant, Editor-in-Chief. **ISSN:** 1350-8555. **Subscription Rates:** 24 individuals; 26 individuals Europe; 28
individuals rest of the world. **URL:** http://www.jimpress.
co.uk.

56850 ■ Nishikigoi International
Nishikigoi International Ltd.
Innovation House
Parkside Business Pk., Golborne
Lowton
Warrington WA3 3PY, United Kingdom
Ph: 44 19 42777879
Fax: 44 19 42777876
Publication E-mail: nikoimag@aol.com
Publisher E-mail: nikoimag@aol.com
Consumer magazine covering koi for hobbyists.
Founded: May 1989. **Freq:** Quarterly in August, Novem-
ber, February and May. **Subscription Rates:** US$40
individuals; 20 individuals; 35 other countries; 25
individuals Europe. **Remarks:** Accepts advertising. **On-
line:** NEXUS. **URL:** http://www.koistore.com. **Ad Rates:**
4C: 1,200. **Circ:** Combined 7,000

Warwick

56851 ■ Agreement
Association of Residential Letting Agents
Arbon House
6 Tournament Ct.
Edgehill Dr.
Warwick CV34 6LG, United Kingdom
Ph: 44 84 43870555
Fax: 44 19 26417789
Publisher E-mail: info@arla.co.uk
Magazine serving as source of information and guid-
ance to anyone with an interest in the Private Rented
Sector. **Freq:** Bimonthly. **Subscription Rates:** 54
nonmembers; Free to all members. **Remarks:** Accepts
advertising. **URL:** http://www.arla.co.uk/publications/
magazine.aspx. **Circ:** (Not Reported)

56852 ■ Annals of Applied Biology
Association of Applied Biologists
Warwick Enterprise Pk.
Wellesbourne
Warwick CV35 9EF, United Kingdom
Ph: 44 178 9472020
Fax: 44 178 9470234
Publication covering biology. **Freq:** Bimonthly. **Key Per-
sonnel:** Jari Valkonen, Editor-in-Chief, phone 358 9
19158387, fax 358 9 19158727, jpvalkon@mappi.
helsinki.fi. **ISSN:** 0003-4746. **Subscription Rates:**
US$853 institutions print + online; 464 institutions print
+ online; US$997 institutions, other countries print +
online; EUR589 institutions print + online; US$775
institutions print or online; 421 institutions print or online;
EUR535 institutions print or online; US$906 institutions,
other countries print or online. **Remarks:** Advertising accepted; rates available upon request. **URL:** http://www.
aab.org.uk/contentok.php?id=301. **Circ:** 1,100

56853 ■ The Coventry Observer
Observer Standard Newspapers Ltd.
45 The Parade Leamington Spa
Warwick CV32 4BL, United Kingdom
Ph: 44 1926 451900
Fax: 44 1926 451754
Publisher E-mail: hq@observerstandard.com
Local community newspaper. **Freq:** Weekly. **Key Per-
sonnel:** Chris Bullivant, Founder; Pat Bullivant, Founder.
Remarks: Accepts advertising. **URL:** http://www.
coventryobserver.co.uk/. **Circ:** (Not Reported)

56854 ■ The Estate Agent
National Association of Estate Agents
Arbon House
6 Tournament Ct.
Edgehill Dr.
Warwick CV34 6LG, United Kingdom
Ph: 44 19 26496800
Fax: 44 19 26400953
Publisher E-mail: info@naea.co.uk
Publication covering estate agents. **Freq:** 10/yr. **Sub-
scription Rates:** 100 nonmembers; Included in
membership. **Remarks:** Advertising accepted; rates
available upon request. **URL:** http://www.naea.co.uk/
publications/default.aspx. **Circ:** (Not Reported)

56855 ■ Rugby Observer
Observer Standard Newspapers Ltd.
45 The Parade Leamington Spa
Warwick CV32 4BL, United Kingdom
Ph: 44 1926 451900
Fax: 44 1926 451754
Publisher E-mail: hq@observerstandard.com
Local community newspaper. **Founded:** 1989. **Freq:** Weekly. **Key Personnel:** Chris Bullivant, Founder; Pat Bullivant, Founder. **Remarks:** Accepts advertising. **URL:** http://www.therugbyobserver.co.uk/. **Circ:** (Not Reported)

56856 ■ Stratford Observer
Observer Standard Newspapers Ltd.
45 The Parade Leamington Spa
Warwick CV32 4BL, United Kingdom
Ph: 44 1926 451900
Fax: 44 1926 451754
Publisher E-mail: hq@observerstandard.com
Local community newspaper. **Freq:** Weekly. **Key Personnel:** Chris Bullivant, Founder; Pat Bullivant, Founder. **Remarks:** Accepts advertising. **URL:** http://www.stratfordobserver.co.uk/. **Circ:** (Not Reported)

56857 ■ Touch-FM - 96.2
Holly Farm Business Pk.
Honiley
Kenilworth
Warwick CV8 1NP, United Kingdom
Ph: 44 192 6485600
Format: News; Contemporary Hit Radio (CHR). **Operating Hours:** Continuous. **Key Personnel:** Steve Hyden, Program Dir. **Ad Rates:** Advertising accepted; rates available upon request. **URL:** http://www.962touchfm.co.uk.

Warwickshire

56858 ■ Engineering Integrity
Engineering Integrity Society
18 Oak Close
Bedworth
Warwickshire CV12 9AJ, United Kingdom
Ph: 44 2476 730126
Fax: 44 2476 730126
Publisher E-mail: lmansfield@e-i-s.org.uk
Publication covering engineering. **Founded:** 1997. **Freq:** 2/yr. **Trim Size:** 210 x 297 mm. **Key Personnel:** Catherine Pinder, Managing Editor, catherine@cpinder.com; Dr Karen Perkins, Hon. Ed., k.m.perkins@swansea.ac.uk. **ISSN:** 1365-4101. **Remarks:** Accepts advertising. **URL:** http://www.e-i-s.org.uk/. **Ad Rates:** BW: 255, 4C: 445. **Circ:** 1,630

Waterside

56859 ■ North-West Echo
Morton Newspapers
Ste. 3, Spencer House
Spencer Rd.
Waterside BT47 6AA, United Kingdom
Community newspaper. **Freq:** Weekly (Wed.). **Print Method:** Offset **Col. Depth:** 450 millimeters. **Key Personnel:** Karen Gregson, Advertising Mgr. **Remarks:** Accepts advertising. **URL:** http://www.locallife.co.uk/londonderry/newspapers3.asp. **Circ:** Non-paid ‡32,424

Watford

56860 ■ The Business Economist
Society of Business Economists
11 Bay Tree Walk
Watford WD17 4RX, United Kingdom
Ph: 44 1923237287
Publisher E-mail: admin@sbe.co.uk
Professional magazine for business economists. **Subtitle:** Journal of the Society of Business Economists (SBE). **Founded:** 1969. **Freq:** Triennial. **Key Personnel:** Marian Marshall, Production Mgr. **ISSN:** 0306-5049. **Subscription Rates:** 40 nonmembers inside Europe; 50 nonmembers airmail, outside Europe; 20 single issue; 10 back issues. **Remarks:** Accepts advertising. **URL:** http://www.sbe.co.uk/TheJournal/tabid/59/articleType/NewsListing/currentpage/2/Default.aspx. **Ad Rates:** BW: 350. **Circ:** (Not Reported)

56861 ■ Churchman
Church Society

Dean Wace House
16 Rosslyn Rd.
Watford WD18 0NY, United Kingdom
Ph: 44 19 23235111
Fax: 44 19 23800362
Publisher E-mail: enquiries@churchsociety.org
Journal covering Anglican theology worldwide. **Founded:** 1879. **Freq:** Quarterly. **Key Personnel:** Prof. Gerald Bray, Editor. **ISSN:** 0000-961X. **Subscription Rates:** 24 individuals UK & Europe; 19 students UK; 29 other countries; 6 single issue. **Remarks:** Accepts advertising. **URL:** http://www.churchsociety.org/churchman/index.asp. **Ad Rates:** BW: 150. **Circ:** (Not Reported)

56862 ■ Code of Practice
Confederation of Aerial Industries Ltd.
Communications House
41a Market St.
Watford WD18 0PN, United Kingdom
Ph: 44 1923 803030
Fax: 44 1923 803203
Publisher E-mail: office@cai.org.uk
Journal of the Confederation of Aerial Industries. **Subscription Rates:** 4.95 members; 19.95 nonmembers. **Remarks:** Accepts advertising. **URL:** http://www.cai.org.uk/about-the-cai/benefits-of-membership. **Circ:** (Not Reported)

56863 ■ Commercial Vehicle Workshop
Hamerville Magazines Ltd.
Regal House
Regal Way
Watford WD24 4YF, United Kingdom
Ph: 44 1923 237799
Fax: 44 1923 246901
Publication E-mail: cvw@hamerville.co.uk
Publisher E-mail: office@hamerville.co.uk
Magazine for service and repair professionals working in the commercial vehicle sector. **Freq:** Monthly. **Key Personnel:** Tim Franklin, Editor; Rob Gilham, Advertising Mgr.; Oliver Shannon, Gp. Mgr. **Remarks:** Accepts advertising. **URL:** http://www.hamerville.co.uk/magazines_cvw.htm. **Circ:** ★10,013

56864 ■ Feedback
Confederation of Aerial Industries Ltd.
Communications House
41a Market St.
Watford WD18 0PN, United Kingdom
Ph: 44 1923 803030
Fax: 44 1923 803203
Publisher E-mail: office@cai.org.uk
Journal containing technical and industry news and comment. **Freq:** Quarterly. **Trim Size:** A5. **Subscription Rates:** 2.95 members; 19.95 nonmembers. **URL:** http://www.cai.org.uk/asp/publications.asp.

56865 ■ Housing Association Building & Maintenance
Hamerville Magazines Ltd.
Regal House
Regal Way
Watford WD24 4YF, United Kingdom
Ph: 44 1923 237799
Fax: 44 1923 246901
Publication E-mail: habm@hamerville.co.uk
Publisher E-mail: office@hamerville.co.uk
Magazine focusing on housing and building maintenance. **Freq:** Monthly. **Key Personnel:** Iain Aubusson, Editor; Chris Eldridge, Gp. Advertising Mgr.; Dave Jones, Advertising Mgr. **Remarks:** Accepts advertising. **URL:** http://www.hamerville.co.uk/magazines_habm.htm. **Circ:** ★11,500

56866 ■ Kitchens & Bathrooms News
Hamerville Magazines Ltd.
Regal House
Regal Way
Watford WD24 4YF, United Kingdom
Ph: 44 1923 237799
Fax: 44 1923 246901
Publisher E-mail: office@hamerville.co.uk
Magazine featuring information on the design, purchase, and specification of kitchens, bathrooms, and associated products. **Freq:** Monthly. **Key Personnel:** Philippa Turrell, Editor, pturrell@hamerville.co.uk; Anthony Scott, Advertising Mgr., ascott@hamerville.co.uk. **Remarks:** Accepts advertising. **URL:** http://www.hamerville.co.uk/

magazines_kbn.htm. **Circ:** ★14,609

56867 ■ Limited Edition
Newsquest (London)
Observer House
Caxton Way
Watford Business Pk.
Watford WD18 8RJ, United Kingdom
Publication E-mail: leeditorial@london.newsquest.co.uk
Consumer magazine covering lifestyle, beauty, fashion, health, travel, gardening, and related topics. **Founded:** 1984. **Freq:** Monthly. **Print Method:** Web offset litho. **Trim Size:** 210 x 297 mm. **Cols./Page:** 4. **Col. Width:** 45.25 millimeters. **Key Personnel:** Anthony Longden, Managing Editor. **Subscription Rates:** 24.99 individuals. **Remarks:** Advertising accepted; rates available upon request. **URL:** http://www.newsshopper.co.uk/leisure/lifestyle/limitededition/. **Former name:** Finesse. **Circ:** 114,000

56868 ■ Local Authority Building and Maintenance
Hamerville Magazines Ltd.
Regal House
Regal Way
Watford WD24 4YF, United Kingdom
Ph: 44 1923 237799
Fax: 44 1923 246901
Publisher E-mail: office@hamerville.co.uk
Magazine for local authority building professionals. **Founded:** 1985. **Freq:** Monthly. **Key Personnel:** Claire Clutten, Editor; Dave Jones, Advertising Mgr. **Remarks:** Accepts advertising. **URL:** http://www.hamerville.co.uk/magazines_labm.htm. **Circ:** ★17,500

56869 ■ Professional Builder
Hamerville Magazines Ltd.
Regal House
Regal Way
Watford WD24 4YF, United Kingdom
Ph: 44 1923 237799
Fax: 44 1923 246901
Publisher E-mail: office@hamerville.co.uk
Magazine focusing on building industry. **Freq:** 11/yr. **Key Personnel:** Terry Smith, Editor; Andrew Costin, Advertising Mgr. **Remarks:** Accepts advertising. **URL:** http://www.hamerville.co.uk/magazines_pb.htm. **Circ:** ★98,489

56870 ■ Professional Builders Merchant
Hamerville Magazines Ltd.
Regal House
Regal Way
Watford WD24 4YF, United Kingdom
Ph: 44 1923 237799
Fax: 44 1923 246901
Publisher E-mail: office@hamerville.co.uk
Business magazine for merchants. **Freq:** Monthly. **Key Personnel:** Paul Davies, Editor; Craig Jowsey, Advertising Mgr. **Remarks:** Accepts advertising. **URL:** http://www.hamerville.co.uk/magazines_pbm.htm. **Circ:** ★9,500

56871 ■ Professional Electrician & Installer
Hamerville Magazines Ltd.
Regal House
Regal Way
Watford WD24 4YF, United Kingdom
Ph: 44 1923 237799
Fax: 44 1923 246901
Publisher E-mail: office@hamerville.co.uk
Magazine for professional electrician and installer. **Freq:** Monthly. **Key Personnel:** Jonathan Cole, Editor; Tim Benwell, Advertising Mgr. **Remarks:** Accepts advertising. **URL:** http://www.hamerville.co.uk/magazines_pe.htm. **Circ:** ★60,600

56872 ■ Professional Hairdresser
Hamerville Magazines Ltd.
Regal House
Regal Way
Watford WD24 4YF, United Kingdom
Ph: 44 1923 237799
Fax: 44 1923 246901
Publisher E-mail: office@hamerville.co.uk
Magazine for hairdressing business. **Freq:** 10/yr. **Key Personnel:** Nicola Shannon, Editor; Oliver Shannon, Advertising Mgr. **Remarks:** Accepts advertising. **URL:** http://www.hamerville.co.uk/mag_hb.htm. **Circ:** ★16,385

Circulation: ★ = ABC; △ = BPA; ♦ = CAC; • = CCAB; ❏ = VAC; ⊕ = PO Statement; ‡ = Publisher's Report; Boldface figures = sworn; Light figures = estimated.

56873 ■ Professional Heating & Plumbing Installer
Hamerville Magazines Ltd.
Regal House
Regal Way
Watford WD24 4YF, United Kingdom
Ph: 44 1923 237799
Fax: 44 1923 246901
Publication E-mail: phpi@hamerville.co.uk
Publisher E-mail: office@hamerville.co.uk
Magazine covering issues that matter to heating and plumbing. **Freq:** Monthly. **Key Personnel:** Stuart Hamilton, Editor; Adrian Stapleton, Advertising Mgr. **Remarks:** Accepts advertising. **URL:** http://www.hamerville.co.uk/magazines_phpi.htm. **Circ:** ★56,067

56874 ■ Professional Motor Factor
Hamerville Magazines Ltd.
Regal House
Regal Way
Watford WD24 4YF, United Kingdom
Ph: 44 1923 237799
Fax: 44 1923 246901
Publication E-mail: pmmsales@hamerville.co.uk
Publisher E-mail: office@hamerville.co.uk
Magazine covering issues affecting factor businesses. **Freq:** Monthly. **Key Personnel:** Richard Bowler, Editor; Oliver Shannon, Manager. **Remarks:** Accepts advertising. **URL:** http://www.hamerville.co.uk/mag_pmf.htm. **Circ:** ★3,621

56875 ■ Professional Motor Mechanic
Hamerville Magazines Ltd.
Regal House
Regal Way
Watford WD24 4YF, United Kingdom
Ph: 44 1923 237799
Fax: 44 1923 246901
Publication E-mail: pmmsales@hamerville.co.uk
Publisher E-mail: office@hamerville.co.uk
Magazine covering motor mechanic. **Freq:** Monthly. **Key Personnel:** Richard Bowler, Editor; Oliver Shannon, Gp. Mgr. **Remarks:** Accepts advertising. **URL:** http://www.hamerville.co.uk/mag_pmm.htm. **Circ:** ★57,478

56876 ■ Sports of Seven Seas
International Committee on Seafarer's Welfare Office
Gresham House
53 Clarendon Rd.
Watford WD17 1LA, United Kingdom
Ph: 44 192 3222653
Fax: 44 192 3222663
Publisher E-mail: icsw@icsw.org.uk
Publication covering sports activities for seamen. Provides details for ports worldwide. **Founded:** 2000. **Freq:** Annual. **Trim Size:** A4. **Subscription Rates:** 25 single issue non-members (plus p&p); 7 single issue members and seafarers (plus p&p). **Remarks:** Accepts advertising. **URL:** http://www.seafarerswelfare.org/publications-sport-of-the-seven-seas.html. **Circ:** (Not Reported)

56877 ■ Window Fabricator & Installer
Hamerville Magazines Ltd.
Regal House
Regal Way
Watford WD24 4YF, United Kingdom
Ph: 44 1923 237799
Fax: 44 1923 246901
Publisher E-mail: office@hamerville.co.uk
Magazine for window industry. **Freq:** Monthly. **Key Personnel:** Tim Franklin, Editor; Ian Turner, Advertising Mgr. **Remarks:** Accepts advertising. **URL:** http://www.hamerville.co.uk/mag_wfi.htm. **Circ:** ★10,228

Welling

56878 ■ Launderette and Cleaning World
National Association of the Launderette Industry
146 Welling Way
Welling DA16 2RS, United Kingdom
Ph: 44 20 88569798
Fax: 44 20 88569394
Publication covering launderette. **Freq:** Quarterly. **Subscription Rates:** Included in membership. **URL:** http://www.nali.co.uk/. **Ad Rates:** GLR: 2, BW: 230. **Circ:** (Not Reported)

56879 ■ Tramway Review
Light Rail Transit Association

138 Radnor Ave.
Welling DA16 2BY, United Kingdom
Ph: 44 1179 517785
Publisher E-mail: office@lrta.org
Publication covering transportation. **Freq:** Quarterly. **Key Personnel:** Nigel C. Friswell, Editor; R.J.S. Wiseman, Editor; Prof. Richard Buckley, Editor. **Subscription Rates:** 14 members. **URL:** http://www.lrta.info/TR.html.

56880 ■ Tramways & Urban Transit
Light Rail Transit Association
138 Radnor Ave.
Welling DA16 2BY, United Kingdom
Ph: 44 1179 517785
Publisher E-mail: office@lrta.org
Publication covering transportation. **Founded:** 1937. **Freq:** Monthly. **Key Personnel:** John Symons, Home News Ed.; Howard Johnston, Editor-in-Chief; Brian Lomas, Diary Ed.; Mike Russel, European Contributors; Sue Graves, Production Mgr.; Tony Streeter, Assoc. Ed.; Michael Taplin, Overseas News Ed. **ISSN:** 1460-8324. **Remarks:** Accepts advertising. **URL:** http://www.lrta.info/mag10.html. **Circ:** Paid 6,800

Wellingborough

56881 ■ Octane Magazine
Dennis Publishing Ltd.
1 Tower Ct., Irchester Rd.
Wollaston
Wellingborough NN29 7PJ, United Kingdom
Ph: 44 20 79076585
Fax: 44 1933 663367
Publisher E-mail: reception@dennis.co.uk
Magazine for classic car enthusiasts. **Subtitle:** Fuelling the Passion. **Founded:** May 2003. **Freq:** Monthly. **Trim Size:** 285 x 222 mm. **Key Personnel:** Mark Dixon, Dep. Ed., phone 44 1733 392890, mark@octane-magazine.com; Geoff Love, Publishing Dir., phone 44 1733 392890, geoff@octane-magazine.com. **Subscription Rates:** 20.75 individuals 6 issues; 41.97 individuals; 55 individuals Europe; 72 other countries. **Remarks:** Accepts advertising. **URL:** http://www.octane-magazine.com. **Circ:** ★33,039

Welwyn Garden City

56882 ■ East Herts Edition Herald
Archant Regional Ltd.
31a Howardsgate
Welwyn Garden City AL8 6AP, United Kingdom
Ph: 44 1707 327551
Publication E-mail: herald.news@archant.co.uk
Publisher E-mail: sandra.roantree@archant.co.uk
Local community newspaper. **Freq:** Weekly (Thurs.). **Key Personnel:** Terry Mitchinson, Editor; Phil White, Production Mgr. **Subscription Rates:** Free to Hoddesdon, Hertford, Ware, Broxbourne; 19.50 individuals 3 months; 39 individuals 6 months; 78 individuals. **Remarks:** Accepts advertising. **URL:** http://www.herald24.co.uk/content/herald/default/default.aspx. **Circ:** ★43,736

56883 ■ The Recorder Magazine
Society of Recorder Players
c/o Helen Shabetai, Ed.
118 Handside Ln.
Welwyn Garden City AL8 6SZ, United Kingdom
Ph: 44 1707 889893
Fax: 44 1707 332743
Publisher E-mail: chairman@srp.org.uk
Magazine covering music. **Freq:** Quarterly. **Key Personnel:** Ruth Burbridge, Publisher, ruth@recordermail.demon.co.uk; Jeremy Burbridge, Publisher; Helen Shabetai, Editor, helen.shabetai@ntlworld.com; Laura Justice, Reviews Ed.; Madeline Seviour, Branch Reviews Ed., news@srp.org.uk. **Subscription Rates:** 22 individuals. **Remarks:** Advertising accepted; rates available upon request. **URL:** http://www.srp.org.uk. **Circ:** 2,500

56884 ■ Welwyn & Hatfield Times
Archant Regional Ltd.
31a Howardsgate
Welwyn Garden City AL8 6AP, United Kingdom
Ph: 44 1707 327551
Publication E-mail: whtimes@archant.co.uk
Publisher E-mail: sandra.roantree@archant.co.uk
Local community newspaper. **Founded:** 1928. **Key Per-**

sonnel: Terry Mitchinson, Editor. **Subscription Rates:** 39 individuals 3 months; 78 individuals 6 months; 156 individuals GBR. **Remarks:** Accepts advertising. **URL:** http://www.whtimes.co.uk/home. **Circ:** ★16,611

Wem

56885 ■ Storylines
Society for Storytelling
c/o The Morgan Library
Aston St.
Shrophire
Wem SY4 5AU, United Kingdom
Ph: 44 753 4578386
Publisher E-mail: admin@sfs.org.uk
Magazine containing articles, news, and reviews. **Freq:** Quarterly. **Remarks:** Accepts advertising. **URL:** http://sfs.org.uk/about_storytelling/contacts/. **Circ:** (Not Reported)

Wembley

56886 ■ Surface Coatings International
Oil and Colour Chemists' Association
Priory House
967 Harrow Rd.
Wembley HA0 2SF, United Kingdom
Ph: 44 20 89081086
Fax: 44 20 89091219
Publisher E-mail: membership@occa.org.uk
Technical journal on surface coatings. **Subtitle:** Part B: Coatings Transactions. **Freq:** Quarterly. **Key Personnel:** Dr. S. Lawrence, Editorial Board, simon.lawrence@cibasc.com. **ISSN:** 1356-0751. **Subscription Rates:** 190 institutions; 170 out of country surface mail; US$260 individuals North America; 50 institutions single copy. **Remarks:** Accepts advertising. **URL:** http://www.occa.org.uk/publications/sci/sci_intro.lasso?-session=lgnMdl:DD8024CF0482BD0A67894BED8E57C86F. **Formerly:** Journal of the Oil & Colour Chemists' Association (JOCCA). **Circ:** (Not Reported)

56887 ■ Surface Coatings International
Oil and Colour Chemists' Association
Priory House
967 Harrow Rd.
Wembley HA0 2SF, United Kingdom
Ph: 44 20 89081086
Fax: 44 20 89091219
Publisher E-mail: membership@occa.org.uk
Publication covering paints, inks and related coatings. **Subtitle:** Part A: Coatings Journal. **Founded:** 2000. **Freq:** 8/yr. **Print Method:** Offset. **Key Personnel:** Max Harlow, Contact, maxharlow@compuserve.com. **ISSN:** 1356-0751. **Subscription Rates:** 190 institutions; 170 out of country by surface mail; US$260 institutions in North America; add airmail surcharge. **Remarks:** Advertising accepted; rates available upon request. **URL:** http://www.occa.org.uk. **Formerly:** Journal of the Oil & Colour Chemists' Association (JOCCA). **Circ:** 3,750

West Bridgford

56888 ■ Fish
Institute of Fisheries Management
22 Rushworth Ave.
West Bridgford NG2 7LF, United Kingdom
Ph: 44 115 9822317
Fax: 44 115 9826150
Publisher E-mail: info@ifm.org.uk
Publication covering fishing industries. **Founded:** 1969. **Freq:** Quarterly. **Trim Size:** A5. **Subscription Rates:** Free to all members. **Remarks:** Advertising accepted; rates available upon request. **URL:** http://www.ifm.org.uk/publications/fish/. **Circ:** 1,500

West Bromwich

56889 ■ BMHF Yearbook & Directory
British Materials Handling Federation
National Metalforming Centre
47 Birmingham Rd.
West Bromwich B70 6PY, United Kingdom
Ph: 44 12 16016350
Fax: 44 12 16016387
Publisher E-mail: enquiry@bmhf.org.uk
Editorial and buyers' guide of the British Materials Handling Federation. **Freq:** Annual. **Remarks:** Accepts

advertising. **URL:** http://www.bmhf.org.uk/page.asp?node=24&sec=Directory. **Circ:** (Not Reported)

West Drayton

56890 ■ The Log
British Air Line Pilots Association
5 Heathrow Blvd.
278 Bath Rd.
West Drayton UB7 0DQ, United Kingdom
Ph: 44 20 84764000
Fax: 44 20 84764077
Publisher E-mail: balpa@balpa.org
House journal of BALPA covering technical, medical, and industrial topics. **Founded:** 1937. **Freq:** Bimonthly. **Trim Size:** 185 x 274 mm. **Key Personnel:** Captain Ian Saunders, Chm. **Subscription Rates:** 26.50 nonmembers; 36.50 nonmembers overseas. **Remarks:** Accepts advertising. **URL:** http://www.balpa.org/About-BALPA/Publications/The-Log.aspx. **Ad Rates:** BW: 425, 4C: 635. **Circ:** 14,000

West Hoe

56891 ■ Marine Environmental Research
Elsevier Science Inc.
c/o Dr. John Widdows, Ed.
Plymouth Marine Laboratory
Prospect Pl.
West Hoe PL2 3DH, United Kingdom
Publisher E-mail: usinfo-ehelp@elsevier.com
Peer-reviewed journal covering chemical, physical, and biological interactions in the oceans and coastal waters. **Founded:** 1978. **Freq:** 10/yr. **Print Method:** Offset. Uses mats. **Cols./Page:** 5. **Col. Width:** 2 1/16 inches. **Col. Depth:** 13 1/8 inches. **Key Personnel:** G.T. Chandler, Editorial Board; A. Goksoyr, Editorial Board; L.M. Mayer, Editorial Board; M.N. Moore, Editorial Board; N.S. Fisher, Editorial Board; Dr. Robert Spies, Editor, spies@amarine.com; V.E. Forbes, Editorial Board; R. Santos, Editorial Board; Dr. John Widdows, Editor. **ISSN:** 0141-1136. **Subscription Rates:** US$2,098 institutions, other countries except Europe, Japan and Iran; EUR1,877 institutions for European countries and Iran; 248,900¥ institutions; EUR174 individuals for European countries and Iran; US$234 other countries except Europe, Japan and Iran; 26,900¥ individuals. **URL:** http://www.elsevier.com/wps/find/journaldescription.cws_home/405865/descriptiondescription.

West Lothian

56892 ■ Continence
Association for Continence Advice
c/o Fitwise Management Ltd.
Drumcross Hall
Bathgate
West Lothian EH48 4JT, United Kingdom
Ph: 44 1506 811077
Fax: 44 1506 811477
Publisher E-mail: aca@fitwise.co.uk
Journal featuring articles covering continence research, product news, information and updates on courses and conferences. **Freq:** Quarterly. **Key Personnel:** Janette Haslam, Editor. **Subscription Rates:** Free to all members. **URL:** http://www.aca.uk.com.

West Malling

56893 ■ Mortgage Matters
New Concept Group Ltd.
60 Churchill Sq.
Kings Hill
West Malling ME19 4YU, United Kingdom
Ph: 44 17 32878800
Fax: 44 17 32878801
Consumer magazine covering finance for home buyers. **Founded:** 1997. **Freq:** Bimonthly. **Print Method:** Sheetfed offset. **Trim Size:** 210 x 297 mm. **Cols./Page:** 2. **Subscription Rates:** 15 single issue. **Remarks:** Accepts advertising. **URL:** http://www.yournewhome.co.uk/Mortgage-Matters. **Circ:** (Not Reported)

56894 ■ The Soul Survivors
PO Box 377
West Malling ME6 9DQ, United Kingdom
Ph: 44 1732 844246

Publisher E-mail: info@thesoulsurvivors.co.uk
Magazine covering jazz, funk, and soul music. **Remarks:** Accepts advertising. **URL:** http://thesoulsurvivors.co.uk/index.html. **Circ:** (Not Reported)

56895 ■ Your New Home
New Concept Group Ltd.
60 Churchill Sq.
Kings Hill
West Malling ME19 4YU, United Kingdom
Ph: 44 17 32878800
Fax: 44 17 32878801
Publication E-mail: info@yournewhome.co.uk
Consumer magazine for the home moving market and new home buyers. **Subtitle:** All you Need to Know About Buying a New Home. **Founded:** 1997. **Freq:** Bimonthly. **Trim Size:** 210 x 297 mm. **Cols./Page:** 2. **Key Personnel:** Michelle Teeman, Editor; Cherry Batchelor, Subscriptions. **Subscription Rates:** 17 individuals. **Remarks:** Accepts advertising. **URL:** http://www.yournewhome.co.uk. **Circ:** (Not Reported)

West Sussex

56896 ■ Buckinghamshire Life
Archant Life
Teville Rd.
Worthing
West Sussex BN11 1UG, United Kingdom
Publisher E-mail: johnny.hustler@archant.co.uk
Magazine featuring the lifestyle in Buckingham county. **Key Personnel:** Tessa Harris, Editor, phone 44 1344 620250, tessa.harris@archant.co.uk; Guy Hanson, Publisher, phone 44 7977 054861, guy.hanson@archant.co.uk; Phil Elcome, Circulation Mgr., phone 44 1903 703737, phil.elcome@archant.co.uk. **Subscription Rates:** 25 individuals. **Remarks:** Accepts advertising. **URL:** http://www.buckinghamshirelife.co.uk/. **Circ:** (Not Reported)

56897 ■ Dyslexia
John Wiley & Sons Inc.
c/o Dr. J. B. Talcott, Ed.
PO Box 808
1-7 Oldlands Way
Bognor Regis
West Sussex P022 9SA, United Kingdom
Ph: 44 1865 778315
Publisher E-mail: info@wiley.com
Journal reporting on studies of dyslexia and related remedial programmes and methods for professionals, academis, and researchers. **Freq:** Quarterly. **Key Personnel:** Prof. T.R. Miles, Founding Ed.; Dr. M. Thomson, Exec. Ed.; Dr. J.B. Talcott, Editor; Prof. A.J. Fawcett, Exec. Ed.; Prof. R. Nicolson, Exec. Ed. **ISSN:** 1076-9242. **Subscription Rates:** 83 individuals print; US$128 other countries print; 284 institutions print only; US$451 institutions, other countries print only; EUR291 institutions, other countries print; EUR321 institutions, other countries print and online; 312 institutions print and online (UK); US$497 institutions, other countries print and online. **Remarks:** Accepts advertising. **URL:** http://www3.interscience.wiley.com/journal/6124/home. **Circ:** (Not Reported)

56898 ■ Freight Magazine
UK Transport Press Ltd.
Bank House
High St.
West Sussex RH17 5EN, United Kingdom
Ph: 44 1444 414293
Publisher E-mail: bernardsteel@uktpl.com
Publication covering transportation. **Freq:** Monthly. **Trim Size:** A4. **Key Personnel:** Naomi Queree, Contact, phone 44 1892 552211, nqueree@fta.co.uk. **ISSN:** 0964-1513. **URL:** http://www.fta.co.uk/services/publications/freight-magazine/. **Ad Rates:** BW: 1,250, 4C: 2,080. **Circ:** ★11,464

56899 ■ The Journal of Multi-Criteria Decision Analysis
John Wiley & Sons Inc.
The Atrium
Southern Gate
Chichester
West Sussex P019 8SQ, United Kingdom
Ph: 44 1243 770254
Fax: 44 1243 770432
Publisher E-mail: info@wiley.com
Journal covering all aspects of multi-criteria decision

analysis, such as case studies, evaluations and techniques. **Freq:** Bimonthly. **Trim Size:** 7 7/8 x 10 1/4. **Key Personnel:** Theodor J. Stewart, Editor-in-Chief. **ISSN:** 1057-9214. **Subscription Rates:** 191 individuals print; US$309 other countries print; US$742 institutions, other countries print; EUR479 institutions, other countries print; EUR379 institutions UK (print). **Remarks:** Accepts advertising. **URL:** http://onlinelibrary.wiley.com/journal/10.1002/(ISSN)1099-1360. **Circ:** Paid 3,500

56900 ■ Patchwork & Quilting
UK Transport Press Ltd.
Bank House
High St.
West Sussex RH17 5EN, United Kingdom
Ph: 44 1444 414293
Publisher E-mail: bernardsteel@uktpl.com
Magazine for patchworkers and quilters everywhere. **Freq:** Monthly. **Key Personnel:** Jeremy Wright, President. **URL:** http://www.quiltingandpatchwork.com/index.php?s=subscription.

56901 ■ R/C Model World
UK Transport Press Ltd.
Bank House
High St.
West Sussex RH17 5EN, United Kingdom
Ph: 44 1444 414293
Publication E-mail: rcmw@traplet.com
Publisher E-mail: bernardsteel@uktpl.com
Magazine for radio control model aircraft enthusiasts with essential information from the Modelling World for all types of R/C aircraft. **Freq:** Monthly. **Subscription Rates:** 86 U.S. and Canada; 42.95 individuals; 74.95 two years individual; 62.95 other countries; 159 U.S. and Canada two years; US$109.95 two years outside country; 56.95 individuals Europe; 107 two years Europe. **URL:** http://www.rcmodelworld.com/.

56902 ■ Redditch Advertiser/Indicator Series
Newsquest (Midlands South) Ltd.
Berrows House
Hylton Rd.
West Sussex WR2 5JX, United Kingdom
Ph: 44 1905 7482000
Community newspaper. **Founded:** July 10, 1975. **Freq:** Weekly. **Print Method:** Web offset. **Cols./Page:** 9. **Col. Width:** 28 millimeters. **Key Personnel:** Gill Cook, Advertising Mgr.; Paul Walker, Editor, paul.walker@midlands.newsquest.co.uk; Alex Wellings, Dep. Ed., alex.wellings@midlands.newsquest.co.uk. **Remarks:** Accepts advertising. **URL:** http://www.redditchadvertiser.co.uk/. **Circ:** (Not Reported)

56903 ■ Scrapbook Magic
UK Transport Press Ltd.
Bank House
High St.
West Sussex RH17 5EN, United Kingdom
Ph: 44 1444 414293
Publication E-mail: angie@scrapbookmagic.com.au
Publisher E-mail: bernardsteel@uktpl.com
Magazine for anyone with memories they want to keep and cherish, who loves to take photos, write diaries or research the history of their family. **Freq:** Monthly. **Subscription Rates:** 4 individuals. **URL:** http://www.scrapbookmagic.com.au/index.php.

West Yorkshire

56904 ■ Kybernetes
Emerald
Howard House
Wagon Ln.
Bingley
West Yorkshire BD16 1WA, United Kingdom
Ph: 44 1274 777700
Fax: 44 1274 785201
Publisher E-mail: editorial@emeraldinsight.com
Official journal of the World Organization of Systems and Cybernetics, covering computer science, cybernetics, and systems. **Subtitle:** The International Journal of Systems and Cybernetics. **Founded:** 1971. **Freq:** Monthly 10/yr. **Key Personnel:** Prof. Brian Howard Rudall, Editor-in-Chief; Lizzie Scott, Publisher, escott@emeraldinsight.com; Dr. C.J. Mann, Book Review Ed. **ISSN:** 0368-492X. **Subscription Rates:** 6,649 individuals plus tax; EUR9,759 individuals plus tax; US$10,639 U.S. and Canada; $A 13,059 individuals. **Remarks:** Advertising not accepted. **URL:** http://info.

Circulation: ★ = ABC; △ = BPA; ◆ = CAC; • = CCAB; ❏ = VAC; ⊕ = PO Statement; ‡ = Publisher's Report; Boldface figures = sworn; Light figures = estimated.

Gale Directory of Publications & Broadcast Media/147th Ed.   5879

emeraldinsight.com/products/journals/journals.htm?
PHPSESSID=gfup8qv8rdroenhrpqplum8mf4&id=k. **For-**
merly: MCB University Press Ltd. **Circ:** (Not Reported)

Weston-super-Mare

56905 ■ Golf Club Management
Golf Club Managers' Association
7a Beaconsfield Rd.
Weston-super-Mare BS23 1YE, United Kingdom
Ph: 44 19 34641166
Publisher E-mail: hq@gcma.org.uk
Publication covering golf course management. **Freq:**
Monthly. **Key Personnel:** Keith Lloyd, Ch. Exec. **Sub-**
scription Rates: Free to members; 92 individuals U.K.;
120 nonmembers Eire/Europe/surface mail; 145 non-
members outside Europe only, airmail. **Remarks:**
Advertising accepted; rates available upon request.
URL: http://www.gcma.org.uk/12/gcma.htm. **Circ:** 1,400

56906 ■ Weston & Somerset Mercury
Archant Regional Ltd.
32 Waterloo St.
Weston-super-Mare BS23 1LW, United Kingdom
Ph: 44 1934 414010
Fax: 44 1934 422600
Publication E-mail: newsdesk@thewestonmercury.co.uk
Publisher E-mail: sandra.roantree@archant.co.uk
Local community newspaper. **Key Personnel:** Judi
Kisiel, Managing Editor; Jerard Hurst, Dep. Ed.; Sally
Cook, Sales Mgr. **Subscription Rates:** 1.75 individuals
1 week; 2.75 individuals 1 week to Europe; 5 other
countries 1 week. **Remarks:** Accepts advertising. **URL:**
http://www.thewestonmercury.co.uk/. **Circ:** (Not Re-
ported)

Westoning

56907 ■ Audi Driver
AutoMetrix Publications
1 Greenfield Rd.
Westoning MK45 5JD, United Kingdom
Ph: 44 15 25750500
Fax: 44 15 25750700
Publisher E-mail: mail@autometrix.co.uk
Consumer magazine covering Audi road tests, history,
heritage, technology and developments. **Founded:** Nov.
1997. **Freq:** Monthly. **Print Method:** Web Offset. **Trim**
Size: A4. **Key Personnel:** Harris Paul, Editor. **Subscrip-**
tion Rates: 38 individuals U.K.; 44.99 individuals airmail
to Europe; 54.99 other countries airmail. **Remarks:** Accepts advertising. **URL:** http://www.autometrix.co.uk;
http://www.audidrivermag.co.uk/. **Ad Rates:** BW: 650,
4C: 750. **Circ:** Combined ‡18,000

56908 ■ Volkswagen Driver
AutoMetrix Publications
1 Greenfield Rd.
Westoning MK45 5JD, United Kingdom
Ph: 44 15 25750500
Fax: 44 15 25750700
Publisher E-mail: mail@autometrix.co.uk
Consumer magazine covering Volkswagen road tests,
history, heritage, technology and developments.
Founded: 1982. **Freq:** Monthly. **Print Method:** Sheet-
fed Offset. **Trim Size:** A4. **Key Personnel:** Harris Paul,
Publisher. **Subscription Rates:** 38 individuals U.K.;
44.99 individuals Europe; by airmail; 54.99 other
countries airmail. **Remarks:** Accepts advertising. **URL:**
http://www.autometrix.co.uk;   http://www.
volkswagendriver.co.uk/. **Formerly:** Volkswagen Audi
Car. **Ad Rates:** BW: 650, 4C: 750. **Circ:** Combined
‡18,000

Wetherby

56909 ■ Countryside Focus
Countryside Agency
PO Box 125
Wetherby LS23 7EP, United Kingdom
Ph: 44 87 01206466
Fax: 44 87 01206467
Publisher E-mail: countryside@twoten.press.net
Newspaper of the Countryside Agency. **Founded:** Apr.
1999. **Freq:** 5/yr. **Print Method:** Offset litho. **Trim Size:**
A2. **Cols./Page:** 4. **ISSN:** 1466-2531. **Subscription**
Rates: Free. **URL:** http://www.naturalengland.org.uk/.

56910 ■ Cross & Cockade International
Cragg Cottage

The Cragg
Wetherby LS23 6QB, United Kingdom
Ph: 44 19 37845320
Publication E-mail: editor@crossandcockade.com
Journal covering World War I aviation. **Founded:** 1969.
Freq: Quarterly. **Trim Size:** A4. **Key Personnel:** Gor-
don Atkin, Treas., treasurer@crossandcockade.com;
Roger Tisdale, Membership Sec., membership.
secretary@crossandcockade.com; Paul Leaman, Vice
President, paul.leaman@tesco.net; Mick Davis, Editor;
Peter Dye, President, president@crossandcockade.
com; Marcus Williams, Advertising Mgr., meetings@
crossandcockade.com. **Subscription Rates:** 25 individuals; 33 out of country surface mail; 40 out of country
airmail. **Remarks:** Accepts advertising. **URL:** http://www.
crossandcockade.com. **Formerly:** Cross & Cockade
Great Britain. **Circ:** (Not Reported)

56911 ■ Equestrian Trade News
British Equestrian Trade Association
Stockeld Pk.
West Yorkshire
Wetherby LS22 4AW, United Kingdom
Ph: 44 1937 587062
Fax: 44 1937 582728
Publisher E-mail: info@beta-uk.org
Trade magazine for equestrian industry. **Founded:**
1979. **Freq:** Monthly. **Key Personnel:** Liz Benwell, Edi-
tor, phone 44 845 6185007, editor@
equestriantradenews.com; Nicki Lewis, Contact, phone
44 1937 582111, fax 44 1937 582147, sales@
equestriantradenews.com. **Subscription Rates:** 34.95
individuals; 68 individuals Europe and Eire (airmail); 81
other countries airmail. **Remarks:** Accepts advertising.
URL: http://www.equestriantradenews.com/. **Ad Rates:**
BW: 945, 4C: 1,260. **Circ:** 5,050

Weybridge

56912 ■ British Journal of Play Therapy
British Association of Play Therapists
1 Beacon Mews
South Rd.
Weybridge KT13 9DZ, United Kingdom
Ph: 11 44 32828638
Fax: 11 44 32820100
Publisher E-mail: info@bapt.uk.com
Journal carrying papers that are of interest for members
and other occupational group using therapeutic play
skills. **Freq:** Semiannual. **Key Personnel:** Lisa Gordon
Clark, Editor. **Subscription Rates:** 25 institutions
England, Scotland, Wales, Northern Ireland; 15 individu-
als England, Scotland, Wales, Northern Ireland; 30
institutions Europe; 17 individuals Europe; 35 institu-
tions North America and International; 20 individuals
North America and International. **URL:** http://www.bapt.
info/journalofplaytherapy.htm.

56913 ■ PLAY THERAPY
British Association of Play Therapists
1 Beacon Mews
South Rd.
Weybridge KT13 9DZ, United Kingdom
Ph: 11 44 32828638
Fax: 11 44 32820100
Publisher E-mail: info@bapt.uk.com
Magazine containing up to date news and views, current
debates and other issues about play therapy practice.
Freq: Quarterly March, June, September and December.
Key Personnel: Elise Refalo, Editor, editor@bapt.uk.
com. **Subscription Rates:** Free for members. **Remarks:**
Accepts advertising. **URL:** http://www.bapt.info/
playtherapynewsletter.htm. **Circ:** (Not Reported)

Wheathampstead

56914 ■ Animal Welfare
Universities Federation for Animal Welfare
The Old School
Brewhouse Hill
Wheathampstead AL4 8AN, United Kingdom
Ph: 44 15 82831818
Fax: 44 15 82831414
Publication E-mail: ufaw@ufaw.org.uk
Publisher E-mail: ufaw@ufaw.org.uk
Scientific and educational journal covering research on
the welfare of animals in zoos, in the wild, in laboratories
and on farms. **Founded:** 1992. **Freq:** Quarterly. **Key**
Personnel: Dr. James Kirkwood, Editor-in-Chief. **ISSN:**

0962-7286. **Subscription Rates:** 58 members including
free on-line access; 158 members corporate (including
free on-line access); 79 nonmembers including free online access; 210 nonmembers institutions & libraries.
Remarks: Advertising not accepted. **URL:** http://www.
ufaw.org.uk/animal.php. **Circ:** (Not Reported)

Whitby

56915 ■ Whitby Gazette
Johnston Press PLC
17/18 Bridge St.
Whitby YO22 4BG, United Kingdom
Ph: 44 1947 602836
Local community newspaper. **Freq:** Biweekly Tues. and
Fri. **Key Personnel:** Jonathan Stokoe, News Ed., phone
44 1947 829910, jonathan.stokoe@yrnltd.co.uk; Duncan
Atkins, Sports Ed., duncan.atkins@yrnltd.co.uk; Adam
Meads, Web Admin., adammeads@jpress.co.uk. **Re-**
marks: Accepts advertising. **URL:** http://www.
whitbygazette.co.uk/. **Circ:** (Not Reported)

56916 ■ Yorkshire Coast Radio-FM - 103.1
North Yorkshire
PO Box 962
Scarborough YO11 3ZP, United Kingdom
Ph: 44 1723 581700
Fax: 44 1723 588990
E-mail: info@yorkshirecoastradio.com
Format: Adult Contemporary; News; Information. **Ad**
Rates: Advertising accepted; rates available upon
request. **URL:** http://www.yorkshirecoastradio.com/.

Whitehaven

56917 ■ CFM Radio-FM - 103.4
PO Box 964
Carlisle CA1 3NG, United Kingdom
Ph: 44 1228 818964
Format: Contemporary Hit Radio (CHR). **URL:** http://
www.cfmradio.com/.

Whitley Bay

56918 ■ Applied Thermal Engineering
Elsevier Science Inc.
c/o David A. Reay, Ed.-in-Ch.
PO Box 25
Whitley Bay NE26 1QT, United Kingdom
Publisher E-mail: usinfo-ehelp@elsevier.com
Peer-reviewed journal covering information on fundamental research to trouble-shoot existing plant and
equipment. **Founded:** 1980. **Freq:** 18/yr. **Print Method:**
Offset. **Trim Size:** 8 x 10 7/8. **Cols./Page:** 3. **Col. Width:**
30 nonpareils. **Col. Depth:** 140 agate lines. **Key Per-**
sonnel: David A. Reay, Editor-in-Chief, dareay@aol.
com; S. Devotta, Editorial Advisory Board; P.A. Pilava-
chi, Assoc. Regional Ed.; W.M. Worek, Regional Ed.,
wworek@uic.edu; T.S. Zhao, Regional Ed., metzhao@
ust.hk; A. Akbarzadeh, Assoc. Regional Ed.; R. Best
Brown, Assoc. Regional Ed.; Y. He, Assoc. Regional
Ed.; S. Murthy, Regional Ed., ssmurthy@iitm.ac.in; Y.
Takata, Assoc. Regional Ed. **ISSN:** 1359-4311. **Sub-**
scription Rates: 344,600¥ institutions; EUR2,595 institutions for European countries and Iran; US$2,904 institu-
tions, other countries except Europe, Japan and Iran.
URL: http://www.elsevier.com/wps/find/
journaldescription.cws_home/630/descriptiondescription.

56919 ■ News Post Leader
Johnston Press PLC
Guardian House
33-35 Park View
Whitley Bay NE26 2TP, United Kingdom
Ph: 44 191 2518383
Local community newspaper. **Key Personnel:** Ross
Weeks, Editor. **Remarks:** Accepts advertising. **URL:**
http://www.newspostleader.co.uk/. **Circ:** (Not Reported)

56920 ■ Rider Haggard Journal
Rider Haggard Society
c/o Mr. Roger Allen
27 Deneholm
Monkseaton
Whitley Bay NE25 9AU, United Kingdom
Ph: 44 19 12524516
Fax: 44 19 12524516
Publisher E-mail: rb27allen@aol.com
Journal focusing on one book, plus news and comments.
Freq: Quarterly. **Subscription Rates:** Included in
membership. **Remarks:** Accepts advertising. **URL:** http://

www.riderhaggardsociety.org.uk/. **Circ:** (Not Reported)

Whitstable

56921 ▪ Heart-FM - 103.1
Radio House
PO Box 100
Whitstable CT5 3QX, United Kingdom
Ph: 44 1227 772004
Fax: 44 1227 774409
Format: Full Service; Information. **Owner:** Global Radio,
30 Leicester Sq., London WC2 H7LA, United Kingdom.
Formerly: Invicta-FM. **Operating Hours:** Continuous.
Ad Rates: Advertising accepted; rates available upon
request. **URL:** http://www.heartkent.co.uk/.

Wigan

56922 ▪ Tower-FM - 107.4
Orrell Lodge
Orrell Rd.
Wigan WN5 8HJ, United Kingdom
Ph: 44 845 2081074
Fax: 44 12 04534065
Format: Top 40; Contemporary Hit Radio (CHR).
Owner: UTV PLC Group, 18 Hatfields, London SE1
8DJ, United Kingdom. **Operating Hours:** Continuous.
Key Personnel: Tony Wilkinson, Station Dir., tony.
wilkinson@utvradio.co.uk; Daniel Vincent, Sales Dir.,
daniel.vincent@towerfm.co.uk. **Ad Rates:** Advertising
accepted; rates available upon request. **URL:** http://
www.towerfm.co.uk.

56923 ▪ Wire-FM - 107.2
c/o UTV Media
Orrell Lodge
Orrell Rd.
Orrell
Wigan WN5 8HJ, United Kingdom
Ph: 44 1925 431072
Fax: 44 1942 761024
Format: Adult Contemporary. **Operating Hours:**
Continuous. **Key Personnel:** Brian Paige, Prog. Control-
ler, brian.paige@wirefm.com; Mark Wheaton, Sales
Mgr., mark.wheaton@wirefm.com; Mike Baker, Station
Dir., mike.baker@wirefm.com. **Ad Rates:** Advertising
accepted; rates available upon request. **URL:** http://
www.wirefm.com/.

56924 ▪ Wish-FM - 102.4
Orrell Lodge
Orrell Rd.
Orrell
Wigan WN5 8HJ, United Kingdom
Ph: 44 1942 761024
Fax: 44 1942 761024
Format: Top 40; News; Sports; Adult Contemporary.
Operating Hours: Continuous. **Key Personnel:** Gra-
ham Sarath, Commercial Dir., graham.sarath@wish-fm.
com; Tony Wilkinson, Station Dir., tony.wilkinson@utvgb.
co.uk. **Ad Rates:** Advertising accepted; rates available
upon request. **URL:** http://www.wishfm.net/.

Wigston

**56925 ▪ Policy and Practice in Health and
Safety**
IOSH Services Ltd.
The Grange
Highfield Dr.
Leicester
Wigston LE18 1NN, United Kingdom
Ph: 44 116 2573100
Fax: 44 116 2573101
Journal covering occupational safety. **Founded:** May
2003. **Freq:** Semiannual. **Print Method:** Offset Litho.
Trim Size: Crown quarto. **Key Personnel:** Prof. David
Walters, Editor; Prof. Kaj Frick, Editorial Board; Prof.
Peter Dorman, Editorial Board; Dr. Tom Dwyer, Editorial
Board; Matthias Beck, Editorial Board; Dr. Tim Carter,
Editorial Board; Richard Booth, Editorial Board; Joan M.
Eakin, Editorial Board; Dennis Else, Editorial Board.
ISSN: 1477-3996. **Subscription Rates:** EUR29 members; US$30 members; EUR58 nonmembers; US$60
nonmembers; EUR169 institutions; US$175 institutions;
20 members; 40 nonmembers; 115 institutions. **URL:**
http://www.iosh.co.uk/information_and_resources/buy_
our_books/our_journal_-_pphs.aspx. **Formerly:** Journal
of the Institution of Occupational Safety and Health.

56926 ▪ The Safety and Health Practitioner
Institution of Occupational Safety and Health
The Grange
Highfield Dr.
Leicestershire
Wigston LE18 1NN, United Kingdom
Ph: 44 11 62573100
Fax: 44 11 62573101
Publisher E-mail: enquiries@iosh.co.uk
Magazine containing legislative updates, European and
parliamentary news, management and technology
features, and Institution of Occupational Safety and
Health news. **Freq:** Monthly. **Key Personnel:** Martina
Weadick, Editor, phone 44 20 79218046, shpeditor@
ubm.com. **ISSN:** 0958-479X. **Subscription Rates:** 105
individuals; 126 other countries. **Remarks:** Accepts
advertising. **URL:** http://www.iosh.co.uk/news_and_
events/news/our_magazine_-_shp.aspx. **Circ:** 32,000.

Wimbledon

56927 ▪ Dockwalk
Boat International Group
41-47 Hartfield Rd., 1st Fl.
Wimbledon SW19 3RQ, United Kingdom
Ph: 44 20 85459330
Fax: 44 20 85459333
Publisher E-mail: info@boatinternational.co.uk
Magazine for yachting industry professionals. **Founded:**
1998. **Freq:** Monthly. **Trim Size:** 247.65 x 304.8 mm.
Key Personnel: Tony Harris, CEO; Tony Euden, Pub-
lishing Dir., tony.euden@boatinternationalmedia.com.
Subscription Rates: US$75 individuals; US$150 other
countries. **Remarks:** Accepts advertising. **URL:** http://
www.boatinternationalmedia.com/mags/mag06.htm. **Ad
Rates:** 4C: 1,475. **Circ:** 20,000.

Wimborne

56928 ▪ International Camellia Journal
International Camellia Society
c/o Jennifer Trehane, Ed.
353 Church Cottage
Wimborne BH21 7LX, United Kingdom
Journal covering worldwide gardening. **Freq:** Annual.
Key Personnel: Jennifer Trehane, Editor, jennifer@
trehane.co.uk. **ISSN:** 0159-656X. **Remarks:** Advertising
accepted; rates available upon request. **URL:** http://
camellia-ics.org/. **Circ:** 1,600.

56929 ▪ Soft Drinks International
PO Box 4173
Wimborne BH21 1YX, United Kingdom
Ph: 44 12 02842222
Fax: 44 12 02848494
Publication E-mail: softdrinksjournal@msn.com
Publisher E-mail: info@softdrinksdinternational.com
Trade magazine covering the manufacture, distribution
and marketing of soft drinks, fruit juices and bottled
water. **Founded:** 1888. **Freq:** Monthly. **Print Method:**
Sheetfed litho. **Trim Size:** 210 x 297 mm. **Cols./Page:**
3. **Key Personnel:** Philip Tappenden, Editor, phone 44
12 02842222, editorial@softdrinksinternational.com; Annette Sessions, News Ed., news@
softdrinksinternational.com. **Subscription Rates:** 110
individuals European Union; EUR150 individuals European Union; 125 other countries; EUR170 other countries;
US$200 other countries. **Remarks:** Accepts advertising.
URL: http://www.softdrinksjournal.com. **Circ:** Combined
3,100.

Winchester

56930 ▪ In Practice
Institute of Ecology and Environmental Management
43 Southgate St.
Winchester SO23 9EH, United Kingdom
Ph: 44 19 62868626
Fax: 44 19 62868625
Publisher E-mail: enquiries@ieem.net
Professional journal covering issues for ecologists,
environmental managers and interested others.
Founded: 1991. **Freq:** Quarterly. **Cols./Page:** 2. **Key
Personnel:** Dr. Jim Thompson, Editor. **ISSN:** 0996-
2200. **Subscription Rates:** 30 individuals; 40 individu-
als outside U.K. **Remarks:** Accepts advertising. **URL:**
http://www.ieem.org.uk/. **Ad Rates:** BW: 400. **Circ:**
Combined 2,300.

Windermere

56931 ▪ School Sailing Matters
National School Sailing Association
4 Green Moss
Oakthwaite Rd.
Windermere LA23 2BB, United Kingdom
Publication covering boating. **Freq:** Quarterly. **Key Per-
sonnel:** John Dowd, Editor, dowd@blueyonder.co.uk.
Remarks: Advertising accepted; rates available upon
request. **URL:** http://www.nssa.org.uk; http://www.nssa.
org.uk/SSMSPRING06.pdf. **Circ:** 500.

Windsor

56932 ▪ Marine News
World Ship Society
Mayes House
Vansittart Estate
Arthur Rd.
Windsor SL4 1SE, United Kingdom
Ph: 44 7768 234507
Publication covering boating industry. **Founded:** 1947.
Freq: Monthly. **ISSN:** 0025-3243. **Subscription Rates:**
Free. **Remarks:** Advertising accepted; rates available
upon request. **URL:** http://worldshipsociety.org/6346.
html. **Circ:** 4,000.

56933 ▪ Wanderlust
Wanderlust Magazine
PO Box 1832
Windsor SL4 1YT, United Kingdom
Ph: 44 1753 620426
Fax: 44 1753 620474
Publisher E-mail: info@wanderlust.co.uk
Magazine featuring photos and articles about travel.
Founded: 1993. **Freq:** Monthly 8/yr. **Trim Size:** 297 x
210 mm. **Key Personnel:** Amy Bellew, Picture Ed.;
Graham Berridge, Art Dir.; Dan Linstead, Editor; Lyn
Hughes, Publisher, Ed.-in-Ch.; Paul Bloomfield, Com-
mercial, Gear Ed. **ISSN:** 1351-4733. **Subscription
Rates:** 22.80 individuals U.K.; 30 individuals Europe
airmail; 40 other countries airmail; 30 other countries
surface mail. **Remarks:** Accepts advertising. **URL:** http://
www.wanderlust.co.uk. **Ad Rates:** 4C: 2,215. **Circ:**
37,000.

Winsford

56934 ▪ Cheshire-FM - 92.5
Verdin Exchange
Winsford CW7 2AN, United Kingdom
Ph: 44 1606 555925
Format: Full Service. **Key Personnel:** Garry Fuller, Sta-
tion Mgr. **Ad Rates:** Advertising accepted; rates avail-
able upon request. **URL:** http://www.cheshirefm.co.uk/.

Wisbech

56935 ▪ Fenland Citizen
Johnston Press PLC
11 Union St.
Wisbech PE13 1DN, United Kingdom
Ph: 44 1945 586100
Fax: 44 1945 465912
Local community newspaper. **Key Personnel:** Jon Buss,
Editor, Sue Irving, Dep. Ed., sue.irving@tenlandcitizen.
co.uk. **Remarks:** Accepts advertising. **URL:** http://www.
fenlandcitizen.co.uk/. **Circ:** (Not Reported)

Withernsea

56936 ▪ Seaside-FM - 105.3
27 Seaside Rd.
Withernsea, United Kingdom
Ph: 44 01964 611427
E-mail: info@seasideradio.co.uk
Format: Adult Contemporary. **URL:** http://www.
seasideradio.co.uk/.

Witherslack

56937 ▪ Environment International
Elsevier Science Inc.
c/o R.E. Alcock, Ed.-in-Ch.
Environmental Research Solutions
Ghyll Cottage
Mill Side
Witherslack LA11 6SG, United Kingdom

Ph: 44 153 9552345

Publisher E-mail: usinfo-ehelp@elsevier.com

Journal covering human environment. **Founded:** 1978. **Freq:** 8/yr. **Print Method:** Offset. **Cols./Page:** 6. **Col. Width:** 2 1/16 inches. **Col. Depth:** 21 inches. **Key Personnel:** P. Bhattacharya, Editorial Board; R. Lal, Editorial Board; O.I. Kalantzi, Editorial Board; P. Behnisch, Editorial Board; J.N.B. Bell, Editorial Board; P. Brimblecombe, Editorial Board; R. Duarte-Davidson, Editorial Board; R.E. Alcock, Editor-in-Chief, ruth.alcock@virgin.net; J. Hofman, Editorial Board. **ISSN:** 0160-4120. **Subscription Rates:** US$1,786 institutions, other countries except Europe, Japan and Iran; 237,100¥ institutions; EUR1,786 institutions European countries and Iran; US$296 other countries except Europe, Japan and Iran; EUR221 individuals European countries and Iran; 34,000¥ individuals. **URL:** http://www.elsevier.com/wps/find/journaldescription.cws_home/326/descriptiondescription.

Witney

56938 ■ Amon Hen
The Tolkien Society
c/o Claire Chambers, Secretary
8 Queens Ln.
Eysham
Witney OX29 4HL, United Kingdom
Journal covering works of the Tolkien society. **Subtitle:** The Bulletin of the Tolkien Society. **Founded:** 1971. **Freq:** Bimonthly. **Print Method:** Offset. **Trim Size:** A5. **Cols./Page:** 1. **Col. Width:** 120 millimeters. **Col. Depth:** 175 millimeters. **Key Personnel:** David Brawn, Publisher. **ISSN:** 0306-8781. **Subscription Rates:** 21 members U.K.; 23 members surface mail worldwide; 24 members air mail to Europe; 27 members Americas, Canada, Africa, Middle East, air mail; 27 members Australia, Japan, Hong Kong, air mail. **URL:** http://www.tolkiensociety.org/ts_info/amonhen.html. **Circ:** Paid 600

56939 ■ Bio-science Law Review
Lawtext Publishing Ltd.
55 W End, Spinners Ct., Office G18
Witney OX28 1NH, United Kingdom
Ph: 44 19 93706183
Fax: 44 19 93709410
Publisher E-mail: ltp@lawtext.com
Journal covering the legal issues in bio-science and biotechnology. **Freq:** 6/yr. **Key Personnel:** Penny Gilbert, Editorial Advisory Board; Richard Hacon, Editorial Advisory Board; Nigel Jones, Editorial Advisory Board. **ISSN:** 1365-8867. **Subscription Rates:** 375 individuals; US$610 individuals; EUR431 individuals. **URL:** http://www.lawtext.com/lawtextweb/default.jsp?PageID=2.

56940 ■ Contemporary Issues in Law
Lawtext Publishing Ltd.
55 W End, Spinners Ct., Office G18
Witney OX28 1NH, United Kingdom
Ph: 44 19 93706183
Fax: 44 19 93709410
Publication E-mail: cil@lawtext.com
Publisher E-mail: ltp@lawtext.com
Journal reporting contemporary law issues. **Freq:** 4/yr. **Trim Size:** 154 x 242 mm. **Key Personnel:** Prof. Deborah Lockton, Editor, dlockton@dmu.ac.uk. **ISSN:** 1357-0374. **Subscription Rates:** 100 individuals; US$136 individuals; EUR106 individuals. **URL:** http://www.lawtext.com/lawtextweb/default.jsp?PageID=2.

56941 ■ Environmental Law & Management
Lawtext Publishing Ltd.
55 W End, Spinners Ct., Office G18
Witney OX28 1NH, United Kingdom
Ph: 44 19 93706183
Fax: 44 19 93709410
Publisher E-mail: ltp@lawtext.com
Journal focusing on environmental law and management for lawyers, environmentalists, local government executives, and senior managers. **Freq:** Bimonthly. **Trim Size:** A4. **Key Personnel:** Sarah Hendry, Scottish Ed.; Dr. Ben Pontin, Managing Editor; Malcolm Forster, Editorial Board. **ISSN:** 1067-6058. **Subscription Rates:** 522 individuals; US$484 individuals; EUR600 individuals. **Remarks:** Accepts advertising. **URL:** http://www.lawtext.com/lawtextweb/default.jsp?PageID=2. **Formerly:** Land Management and Environmental Law Report. **Circ:** (Not Reported)

56942 ■ Environmental Liability
Lawtext Publishing Ltd.
55 W End, Spinners Ct., Office G18

Witney OX28 1NH, United Kingdom
Ph: 44 19 93706183
Fax: 44 19 93709410
Publisher E-mail: ltp@lawtext.com
Journal focusing environmental issues. **Freq:** 6/yr. **Key Personnel:** Brian Jones, Editor. **ISSN:** 0966-2030. **Subscription Rates:** 398 individuals; US$648 individuals; EUR458 individuals. **URL:** http://www.lawtext.com/lawtextweb/default.jsp?PageID=2.

56943 ■ Information Technology Law Reports
Lawtext Publishing Ltd.
55 W End, Spinners Ct., Office G18
Witney OX28 1NH, United Kingdom
Ph: 44 19 93706183
Fax: 44 19 93709410
Publisher E-mail: ltp@lawtext.com
Journal covering law reports in the field of computers, telecommunications, and data protection. **Freq:** 6/yr. **Trim Size:** 156 x 245 mm. **Key Personnel:** Richard Budworth, Editor. **ISSN:** 1365-8859. **Subscription Rates:** 396 individuals; US$644 individuals; EUR455 individuals. **URL:** http://www.lawtext.com/lawtextweb/default.jsp?PageID=2.

56944 ■ The Journal of International Maritime Law
Lawtext Publishing Ltd.
55 W End, Spinners Ct., Office G18
Witney OX28 1NH, United Kingdom
Ph: 44 19 93706183
Fax: 44 19 93709410
Publisher E-mail: ltp@lawtext.com
Journal covering the field of international maritime law. **Freq:** 6/yr. **Trim Size:** 186 x 265 mm. **Key Personnel:** Prof. D. Rhidian Thomas, Editor-in-Chief. **ISSN:** 1478-8586. **Subscription Rates:** 411 individuals; US$688 individuals; EUR472 individuals. **URL:** http://www.lawtext.com/lawtextweb/default.jsp?PageID=2.

56945 ■ The Journal of Water Law
Lawtext Publishing Ltd.
55 W End, Spinners Ct., Office G18
Witney OX28 1NH, United Kingdom
Ph: 44 19 93706183
Fax: 44 19 93709410
Publisher E-mail: ltp@lawtext.com
Journal publishing a legal analysis of environmental, business, and regulatory changes that impact the water industry. **Freq:** Bimonthly. **Trim Size:** A4. **Key Personnel:** Prof. Stuart Bell, Advisory Board; Prof. William Howarth, Editor; Sarah Hendry, Editorial Board; Martha Grekos, Editorial Board; Peter Carty, Editorial Board; Agustin Garcia Ureta, Editorial Board; Simon Payne, Editorial Board; Jenny Bough, Editorial Board; Simon Jackson, Editorial Board. **ISSN:** 1478-5277. **Subscription Rates:** 512 individuals; US$832 individuals; EUR588 individuals. **Remarks:** Accepts advertising. **URL:** http://www.lawtext.com/lawtextweb/default.jsp?PageID=2. **Circ:** (Not Reported)

56946 ■ Utilities Law Review
Lawtext Publishing Ltd.
55 W End, Spinners Ct., Office G18
Witney OX28 1NH, United Kingdom
Ph: 44 19 93706183
Fax: 44 19 93709410
Publisher E-mail: ltp@lawtext.com
Journal focusing on laws that relate to the utilities sector. **Founded:** 1989. **Freq:** Bimonthly. **Trim Size:** A4. **Key Personnel:** Leigh Hancher, Editor; Cosmo Graham, Editor; Prof. John A.K. Huntley, Asst. Ed.; Charlotte Villiers, Asst. Ed.; Jeffrey Goh, Asst. Ed.; Prof. Lorna Woods, Asst. Ed. **ISSN:** 0960-2356. **Subscription Rates:** 483 individuals; US$786 individuals; EUR556 individuals. **Remarks:** Accepts advertising. **URL:** http://www.lawtext.com/lawtextweb/default.jsp?PageID=2. **Circ:** (Not Reported)

56947 ■ Whitney Gazette
Newsquest Media Group Ltd.
47 Market Sq.
Oxfordshire
Witney, United Kingdom
Ph: 44 1993 773133
Fax: 44 1993 706797
Newspaper featuring local news and events. **Freq:** Weekly (Wed.). **Key Personnel:** Derek Holmes, Editor, dholmes@nqo.com; David Duffy, Dep. Ed., dduffy@nqo.com; Simon O'Neill, Gp. Ed., soneill@nqo.com. **Subscription Rates:** 52 individuals; 1 single issue. **Remarks:** Accepts advertising. **URL:** http://www.

witneygazette.net/. **Circ:** (Not Reported)

Woking

56948 ■ Recruitment Matters
Recruitment & Employment Confederation
Albion House
Chertsey Rd.
Woking GU21 6BT, United Kingdom
Ph: 44 20 70092100
Fax: 44 20 79354112
Publisher E-mail: info@rec.uk.com
Publication covering employment. **Founded:** Jan. 2002. **Freq:** Quarterly. **Key Personnel:** Anne Sadler, Publisher, phone 44 20 78806213, anne.sadler@redactive.co.uk; Mick James, Editor, phone 44 20 78806200, mick.james@redactive.co.uk; Steve Smith, Contact, phone 44 20 78806222, steven.smith@redactive.co.uk. **Remarks:** Accepts advertising. **URL:** http://www.rec.uk.com/press/recruitmentmatters. **Circ:** 13,500

Wokingham

56949 ■ Canal Boat
Archant Specialist Ltd.
3 The Courtyard
Denmark St.
Wokingham RG40 2AZ, United Kingdom
Ph: 44 118 9897215
Publisher E-mail: miller.hogg@atarchant.co.uk
Magazine featuring waterways and boating. **Freq:** Monthly. **Key Personnel:** Nick Wall, Editor, nick.wall@archant.co.uk; Martin Ludgate, Dep. Ed., martin.ludgate@archant.co.uk. **Subscription Rates:** 28 individuals. **URL:** http://www.canalboat.co.uk/.

Wolsingham

56950 ■ Recusant History
Catholic Record Society
12 Melbourne Pl.
Wolsingham DL13 3EH, United Kingdom
Ph: 44 13 88527747
Publisher E-mail: archive@ampleforth.org.uk
Publication covering Catholicism. **Freq:** 3/yr. **URL:** http://www.catholic-history.org.uk/.

Wolverhampton

56951 ■ At the Sign Of
Inn Sign Society
c/o Alan Rose
9 Denmead Dr.
Wednesfield
Wolverhampton WV11 2QS, United Kingdom
Ph: 44 1902 721808
Publisher E-mail: info@innsignsociety.com
Journal containing full color photographs. **Freq:** Quarterly. **ISSN:** 0957-8498. **URL:** http://www.innsignsociety.com/.

56952 ■ Cry Wolf
University of Wolverhampton SU
Wulfruna St.
Wolverhampton WV1 1LY, United Kingdom
Ph: 44 190 2322021
Fax: 44 190 2322020
Publication E-mail: crywolf@wolvesunion.org
Publisher E-mail: info@wolvesunion.org
College newspaper for students. **Founded:** 1970. **Freq:** Monthly. **Subscription Rates:** Free. **Remarks:** Accepts advertising. **URL:** http://www.wolvesunion.org/crywolf/. **Former name:** Predator (1997); Sheep's Clothing. **Circ:** Non-paid 26,000

56953 ■ Beacon - 97.2
267 Tettenhall Rd.
Wolverhampton WV6 0DE, United Kingdom
Ph: 44 1902 754123
Format: Talk; Contemporary Hit Radio (CHR). **Owner:** GCap Media PLC, 30 Leicester Sq., London WC2H 7LA, United Kingdom. **Operating Hours:** Continuous. **Ad Rates:** Advertising accepted; rates available upon request. **URL:** http://www.beaconradiowestmids.co.uk.

56954 ■ Beacon - 103.1
267 Tettenhall Rd.
Wolverhampton WV6 0DE, United Kingdom
Ph: 44 1743 204000
Format: Contemporary Hit Radio (CHR); Top 40.

Owner: GCAP Media PLC, 30 Leicester Sq., London WC2H 7LA, United Kingdom. **Operating Hours:** Continuous. **URL:** http://www.beaconshropshire.co.uk.

56955 ■ The Wolf-FM - 107.7
2nd Fl., Mander House
Wolverhampton WV1 3NB, United Kingdom
Ph: 44 1902 571077
Fax: 44 1902 571079
Format: Adult Contemporary; News; Sports; Top 40. **Operating Hours:** Continuous. **Key Personnel:** Richard Dodd, Prog. Controller, richard.dodd@thewolf.co.uk; Marie Wright, Station Dir., marie.wright@thewolf.co.uk. **Ad Rates:** Advertising accepted; rates available upon request. **URL:** http://www.thewolf.co.uk/.

Woodbridge

56956 ■ International School
John Catt Educational Ltd.
12 Deben Mill Business Ctr.
Old Maltings Approach
Woodbridge IP12 1BL, United Kingdom
Ph: 44 1394 389850
Fax: 44 1394 386893
Publisher E-mail: enquries@johncatt.com
Publication covering International schools. **Subtitle:** The Official Magazine for ECIS Members. **Freq:** 3/yr. **Key Personnel:** Caroline Ellwood, Editor, phone 44 1730 268244, fax 44 1730 267914, carolineellwood@ecis.org; Derek Bingham, Managing Editor. **ISSN:** 1461-3956. **Subscription Rates:** 15 individuals. **URL:** http://www.is-mag.co.uk/. **Ad Rates:** BW: 1,950. **Circ:** (Not Reported)

56957 ■ is
John Catt Educational Ltd.
12 Deben Mill Business Ctr.
Old Maltings Approach
Woodbridge IP12 1BL, United Kingdom
Ph: 44 1394 389850
Fax: 44 1394 386893
Publisher E-mail: enquries@johncatt.com
Magazine for the European Council of International Schools. **Freq:** 3/yr. **Trim Size:** 210 x 297 mm. **Key Personnel:** Caroline Ellwood, Editor; John Catt, Publisher. **Subscription Rates:** 15 individuals. **URL:** http://johncattbookshop.com/is_Magazine_vol_12_1_Autumn_2009-details.aspx.

56958 ■ Prep School
John Catt Educational Ltd.
12 Deben Mill Business Ctr.
Old Maltings Approach
Woodbridge IP12 1BL, United Kingdom
Ph: 44 1394 389850
Fax: 44 1394 386893
Publisher E-mail: enquries@johncatt.com
Magazine for preparatory schools. **Subtitle:** Reflecting the Best in the Prep and Junior School World. **Freq:** 3/yr. **Trim Size:** 210 x 297 mm. **Key Personnel:** Michele Kito, Editor, editor@preschoolmag.co.uk; John Catt, Publisher. **ISSN:** 0963-8601. **Subscription Rates:** 25 two years. **URL:** http://www.schoolsearch.co.uk/browse.asp?catID=1302&pID=29&cID=3.

Woodford

56959 ■ West Essex Life
Archant Life
427 High Rd.
Woodford IG8 OXE, United Kingdom
Publisher E-mail: anne.basey-fisher@archant.co.uk
Magazine covering lifestyle in West Essex. **Founded:** 2003. **Freq:** Monthly. **Key Personnel:** Julian Read, Editor; Chris Boosey, Advertising Mgr., chris.boosey@archant.co.uk. **Subscription Rates:** Free. **URL:** http://www.archantlife.co.uk/advertising-regions-south-east-and-east-westessex-life-magazine--7413; http://www.essexlifemag.co.uk/west-essex-life--2637. **Circ:** Free ★32,000

Worcester

56960 ■ Berrow's Worcester Journal
Newsquest Media Group Ltd.
Hylton Rd.
Worcester WR2 5JX, United Kingdom
Ph: 44 1905 748200
Newspaper providing up to date information on news and sports. **Founded:** 1690. **Key Personnel:** Kevin Ward, Editor, kevin.ward@midlands.newsquest.co.uk; Stephanie Preece, News Ed., stephanie.preece@midlands.newsquest.co.uk. **Remarks:** Accepts advertising. **URL:** http://www.berrowsjournal.co.uk/. **Circ:** (Not Reported)

56961 ■ EEMA Briefing
EEMA European Forum for Electronic Business
Midsummer House
Earls Common Rd.
Stock Green
Worcester B96 6SY, United Kingdom
Ph: 44 13 86793028
Fax: 44 13 86793268
Publication covering telecommunications. EEMA membership publication, e-business. **Freq:** Quarterly. **ISSN:** 1023-7135. **Remarks:** Advertising accepted; rates available upon request. **URL:** http://www.eema.org/. **Circ:** 3,000

56962 ■ Malvern Gazette
Newsquest Media Group Ltd.
Hylton Rd.
Worcester WR2 5JX, United Kingdom
Newspaper featuring local news and events. **Founded:** 1897. **Freq:** Weekly. **Key Personnel:** John Murphy, Editor, john.murphy@midlands.newsquest.co.uk. **Remarks:** Accepts advertising. **URL:** http://www.malverngazette.co.uk/. **Circ:** (Not Reported)

56963 ■ Worcester Standard
Observer Standard Newspapers Ltd.
51a Upper Tything
Worcester WR1 1JZ, United Kingdom
Ph: 44 1905 574111
Fax: 44 1905 613915
Publisher E-mail: hq@observerstandard.com
Local community newspaper. **Founded:** Sept. 2000. **Freq:** Weekly. **Key Personnel:** James Iles, Editor, editor@worcesterstandard.co.uk. **Remarks:** Accepts advertising. **URL:** http://www.worcesterstandard.co.uk/. **Circ:** (Not Reported)

56964 ■ Wyvern-FM - 102.8
1st Fl., Kirkham House
John Comyn Dr.
Worcester WR3 7NS, United Kingdom
Ph: 44 1905 545510
Format: Contemporary Hit Radio (CHR). **Ad Rates:** Advertising accepted; rates available upon request. **URL:** http://www.wyvernfm.co.uk/.

Wyvern-FM - See Hereford

Wyvern-FM - See Kidderminster

Worcester Park

56965 ■ Parents News UK
10 The Manor Dr.
Worcester Park KT4 7LG, United Kingdom
Ph: 44 20 83376337
Fax: 44 20 87152842
Magazine with articles and news about parenting and caring for children; lists events for families. **Founded:** 1993. **Freq:** Monthly 11/yr. **Key Personnel:** Fergus McCarthy, Contact, fergus@parents-news.co.uk. **ISSN:** 1362-5551. **Subscription Rates:** Free. **URL:** http://www.parents-news.co.uk/. **Circ:** 175,000

Worcestershire

56966 ■ British Journal of Learning Disabilities
British Institute of Learning Disabilities
Campion House, Green St.
Kidderminster
Worcestershire DY10 1JL, United Kingdom
Ph: 44 1562 723010
Fax: 44 1562 723029
Publisher E-mail: enquiries@bild.org.uk
Peer-reviewed British journal covering issues related to people with learning disabilities. **Freq:** Quarterly. **Key Personnel:** Prof. Duncan Mitchell, Editor. **Remarks:** Accepts advertising. **URL:** http://www.blackwellpublishing.com/journal.asp?ref=1354-4187&site=1; http://www.bild.org.uk/03journals_bjld.htm. **Circ:** (Not Reported)

56967 ■ Good Autism Practice
British Institute of Learning Disabilities
Campion House, Green St.
Kidderminster
Worcestershire DY10 1JL, United Kingdom
Ph: 44 1562 723010
Fax: 44 1562 723029
Publisher E-mail: enquiries@bild.org.uk
Journal dedicated to promoting good practice with children and adults with autism and Asperger's syndrome, for those working and living with children and adults with an autistic spectrum disorder. **Freq:** Semiannual. **Key Personnel:** Glenys Jones, Editor, g.e.jones@bham.ac.uk. **Subscription Rates:** 48 individuals; 38 students; 68 institutions; 68 individuals Europe; 88 institutions Europe; 78 individuals outside Europe; 98 institutions outside Europe. **URL:** http://www.bildservices.org.uk/acatalog/Journals_from_BILD.html; http://www.bildservices.org.uk/.

56968 ■ Journal of Applied Research in Intellectual Disability
British Institute of Learning Disabilities
Campion House, Green St.
Kidderminster
Worcestershire DY10 1JL, United Kingdom
Ph: 44 1562 723010
Fax: 44 1562 723029
Publisher E-mail: enquiries@bild.org.uk
Professional journal covering issues related to people with learning disabilities. **Freq:** Quarterly. **Key Personnel:** David Felce, Editor, felce@cf.ac.uk; Glynis Murphy, Editor, g.h.murphy@kent.ac.uk; Eric Emerson, Assoc. Ed. **Remarks:** Advertising accepted; rates available upon request. **URL:** http://www.bildservices.org.uk/acatalog/Other_BILD_journals.html; http://www.wiley.com/bw/journal.asp?ref=1360-2322; http://www.bild.org.uk/03journals_jarid.htm. **Circ:** (Not Reported)

Workington

56969 ■ CFM Radio-FM - 102.2
PO Box 964
Carlisle CA1 3NG, United Kingdom
Ph: 44 1228 818964
Format: Contemporary Hit Radio (CHR). **URL:** http://www.cfmradio.com/.

Worksop

56970 ■ Worksop Guardian
Johnston Press PLC
21-27 Ryton St.
Worksop S80 2AY, United Kingdom
Ph: 44 1909 500500
Local community newspaper. **Freq:** Weekly. **Key Personnel:** George Robinson, Editor, fax 44 1909 474894, george.robinson@worksop-guardian.co.uk; James Mitchinson, Dep. Ed., james.mitchinson@worksop-guardian.co.uk. **Remarks:** Accepts advertising. **URL:** http://www.worksopguardian.co.uk/. **Circ:** (Not Reported)

Worthing

56971 ■ Clinical Approaches in Bipolar Disorders
Cambridge Medical Publications
Wicker House
High St.
Worthing BN11 1DJ, United Kingdom
Ph: 44 1903 288255
Fax: 44 1903 288292
Publication E-mail: bipolardisorders@hbase.com
Publisher E-mail: bipolardisorders@parexel.com
Peer-reviewed international journal enhancing communication and discussion of the key issues affecting those active in the diagnosis, treatment, and overall care of patients with bipolar disorders, including psychiatrists, psychiatric nurses, and primary care physicians. **Key Personnel:** Hans-Jurgen Moller, Editor-in-Chief; Siegfried Kasper, Editorial Board; Hagop S. Akiskal, Editorial Board; Charles L. Bowden, Editorial Board; Paul Keck, Jr., Editorial Board; Ellen Frank, Editorial Board; Jules Angst, Editorial Board; Fred Goodwin, Editorial Board; Heinz Grunze, Editorial Board; Gary S. Sachs, Editorial Board. **ISSN:** 1473-6713. **URL:** http://www.bipolardisorders.net/.

56972 ■ Funeral Service Journal
FSJ Communications
The Media Centre

Circulation: ★ = ABC; △ = BPA; ♦ = CAC; ● = CCAB; ❑ = VAC; ⊕ = PO Statement; ‡ = Publisher's Report; Boldface figures = sworn; Light figures = estimated.

Gale Directory of Publications & Broadcast Media/147th Ed. 5883

Garcia Estate
Canterbury Rd.
Worthing BN13 1EH, United Kingdom
Publisher E-mail: info@fsj.co.uk
Trade journal for funeral directors and ancillary service providers in the UK. **Founded:** 1886. **Freq:** Monthly. **Print Method:** Litho. **Trim Size:** 132 x 193 mm. **Cols./Page:** 2. **Col. Width:** 62 millimeters. **Col. Depth:** 180 millimeters. **Key Personnel:** D. L. Kaye, Publisher; Brian Parsons, Editor; Denise Walker, Advertising Mgr. **ISSN:** 0016-2809. **Subscription Rates:** 20 individuals; 30 individuals Europe; 40 elsewhere. **Remarks:** Accepts advertising. **URL:** http://www.board.org.uk/. **Ad Rates:** BW: 149, 4C: 345. **Circ:** Paid 2,400

56973 ■ HERPES
Cambridge Medical Publications
Wicker House
High St.
Worthing BN11 1DJ, United Kingdom
Ph: 44 1903 288255
Fax: 44 1903 288292
Publisher E-mail: bipolardisorders@parexel.com
Peer-reviewed Journal serving physicians with latest information on key issues and inputs relating to all aspects of the patient management with herpes virus infections and their sequelae. **Freq:** 3/yr. **Key Personnel:** Per Ljungman, Editorial Board; Antonio Volpi, Editor-in-Chief; Larry Stanberry, Editor-in-Chief; Laurent Belec, Editorial Board; David Brown, Editorial Board; Paul Griffiths, Editorial Board; Adrian Mindel, Editorial Board; Robert Johnson, Editorial Board; Jan Andersson, Editorial Board; Ann Arvin, Editorial Board. **ISSN:** 0969-7667. **URL:** http://www.ihmf.org/journal/journal.asp.

56974 ■ A Kentish Partnership
Archant Life
28 Teville Rd.
Worthing BN11 1UG, United Kingdom
Ph: 44 1903 703730
Fax: 44 1903 703770
Publisher E-mail: anne.basey-fisher@archant.co.uk
Magazine featuring civil partnership in Kent. **Freq:** Annual. **Key Personnel:** Alyn Thomas, Mktg. Mgr.; Rhiannon Wragg, Sen. Advertisement Mgr., rhiannon.wragg@archant.co.uk. **Remarks:** Accepts advertising. **URL:** http://www.archantlife.co.uk/contact-us-regions-south-east-and-east-a-kentish-partnership-contacts--19976; http://www.akentishceremony.com/uk/akp-magazine. **Circ:** (Not Reported)

56975 ■ A Kentish Wedding
Archant Life
28 Teville Rd.
Worthing BN11 1UG, United Kingdom
Ph: 44 1903 703730
Fax: 44 1903 703770
Publisher E-mail: anne.basey-fisher@archant.co.uk
Magazine featuring wedding in Kent. **Freq:** Quarterly. **Key Personnel:** Alyn Thomas, Mktg. Mgr.; Rhiannon Wragg, Sen. Advertisement Mgr., phone 44 1903 703733, rhiannon.wragg@archant.co.uk. **Remarks:** Accepts advertising. **URL:** http://www.archantlife.co.uk/contact-us-regions-south-east-and-east-a-kentish-wedding-contacts--19975; http://www.akentishceremony.com/uk/akw-magazine. **Circ:** (Not Reported)

56976 ■ Shoreham Herald
Johnston Press PLC
Cannon House
Chatsworth Rd.
Worthing BN11 1NA, United Kingdom
Ph: 44 1903 282390
Publication E-mail: letters@shorehamherald.co.uk
Local community newspaper. **Founded:** 1920. **Freq:** Weekly (Thurs.). **Key Personnel:** Stephen Reed, Contact, phone 44 1903 282360, fax 44 1903 216087, stephen.reed@jpress.co.uk. **Remarks:** Accepts advertising. **URL:** http://www.shorehamherald.co.uk/. **Circ:** (Not Reported)

56977 ■ Surrey Life
Archant Life
c/o 28 Teville Rd.
Worthing BN11 1UG, United Kingdom
Ph: 44 1903 703730
Fax: 44 1903 703770
Publisher E-mail: johnny.hustler@archant.co.uk
Lifestyle magazine featuring Surrey. **Freq:** Monthly. **Key Personnel:** Caroline Harrap, Editor. **Subscription**

Rates: 25 individuals. **Remarks:** Accepts advertising. **URL:** http://surrey.greatbritishlife.co.uk/. **Circ:** (Not Reported)

56978 ■ Sussex Life
Archant Life
28 Teville Rd.
Worthing BN11 1UG, United Kingdom
Ph: 44 1903 703730
Fax: 44 1903 703770
Publisher E-mail: johnny.hustler@archant.co.uk
Lifestyle magazine featuring Sussex. **Subtitle:** Your County, Your Life. **Founded:** 1968. **Freq:** Monthly. **Key Personnel:** Simon Irwin, Gp. Ed., simon.irwin@archant.co.uk; Phil Elcome, Circulation Mgr., phone 44 1903 604222, phil.elcome@archant.co.uk. **Remarks:** Accepts advertising. **URL:** http://sussex.greatbritishlife.co.uk/. **Circ:** (Not Reported)

56979 ■ Worthing Herald
Johnston Press PLC
Cannon House
Chatsworth Rd.
Worthing BN11 1NA, United Kingdom
Ph: 44 1903 230051
Local community newspaper. **Founded:** 1920. **Freq:** Weekly (Thurs.). **Key Personnel:** Nicola Caines, Content Ed., nicola.caines@worthingherald.co.uk; Stephen Reed, Sales Mgr., phone 44 1903 282336, fax 44 1903 216087, stephen.reed@jpress.co.uk. **Remarks:** Accepts advertising. **URL:** http://www.worthingherald.co.uk/. **Circ:** (Not Reported)

56980 ■ Splash-FM - 107.7
Guildbourne Ctr.
Worthing BN11 1LZ, United Kingdom
Ph: 44 1903 233005
Fax: 44 1903 233271
E-mail: studio@splashfm.com
Format: Adult Contemporary; News. **Ad Rates:** Advertising accepted; rates available upon request. **URL:** http://www.splashfm.com/.

Wrexham

56981 ■ International Journal of Engineering Systems Modelling and Simulation
Inderscience Enterprises Limited
c/o Dr. Xiaogang Yang, Ed.-in-Ch.
Glyndwr University
School of Science & Technology
Plas Coch Campus, Mold Rd.
Wrexham LL11 2AW, United Kingdom
Journal featuring developments in the field of modeling and simulation. **Freq:** 4/yr. **Key Personnel:** Dr. Xiaogang Yang, Editor-in-Chief, x.yang@glyndwr.ac.uk; Dr. Zoubir Zouaoui, Editor-in-Chief, z.zouaoui@glyndwr.ac.uk. **ISSN:** 1755-9758. **Subscription Rates:** EUR494 individuals print or online; EUR672 individuals print and online. **URL:** http://www.inderscience.com/browse/index.php?journalCODE=ijesms.

56982 ■ Wrexham Leader
NWN Media Ltd.
45 King St.
Wrexham LL11 1HR, United Kingdom
Ph: 44 1978 355151
Fax: 44 1978 311421
Publisher E-mail: internet@nwn.co.uk
Newspaper featuring communities of Wrexham and the surrounding villages with comprehensive digest of news, views, and sports. **Founded:** 1920. **Freq:** Weekly. **URL:** http://www.leaderlive.co.uk/.

Yeovil

56983 ■ Heart-FM - 97.1
Haygrove House
Somerset
Taunton TA3 7BT, United Kingdom
Ph: 44 1823 338448
Format: Adult Contemporary; Information. **Formerly:** Orchard-FM (2009). **Ad Rates:** Advertising accepted; rates available upon request. **URL:** http://www.heart.co.uk.

56984 ■ Ivel-FM - 105.6
Middle St.
Somerset
Yeovil BA20 1DJ, United Kingdom

Ph: 44 1935 848484
Format: Adult Contemporary. **URL:** http://www.midwestradio.co.uk/.

56985 ■ Ivel-FM - 106.6
Middle St.
Somerset
Yeovil BA20 1DJ, United Kingdom
Ph: 44 1935 848484
Format: Adult Contemporary. **URL:** http://www.midwestradio.co.uk/.

York

56986 ■ Aesthetica Magazine
Aesthetica Magazine Ltd.
PO Box 371
York YO23 1WL, United Kingdom
Ph: 44 1904 527560
Publisher E-mail: info@aestheticamagazine.com
Magazine covering literature, visual arts, music, film, and theatre. **Founded:** 2002. **Freq:** Bimonthly. **Key Personnel:** Cherie Federico, Mng. Dir. & Ed.; Dale Donley, Production Dir. **Subscription Rates:** 18.98 individuals; 37.90 two years; 48 students. **URL:** http://www.aestheticamagazine.com/. **Circ:** 20,000

56987 ■ Antiquity
Antiquity Publications Ltd.
King's Manor
York YO1 7EP, United Kingdom
Publication E-mail: editor@antiquity.ac.uk
Publisher E-mail: editor@antiquity.ac.uk
Publication covering world archaeology. **Founded:** 1927. **Freq:** Quarterly. **Key Personnel:** Martin Carver, Editor, editor@antiquity.ac.uk. **ISSN:** 0003-598X. **Subscription Rates:** 309 institutions premium; 173 institutions combined; 155 institutions print only; 146 institutions online only; EUR418 institutions premium; EUR230 institutions combined; EUR205 institutions print only; EUR200 institutions online only; US$77 individuals premium; EUR111 individuals premium. **Remarks:** Accepts advertising. **URL:** http://www.antiquity.ac.uk. **Circ:** Paid 2,190

56988 ■ British Archaeology
Council for British Archaeology
St. Mary's House, 66 Bootham
York YO30 7BZ, United Kingdom
Ph: 44 19 04671417
Fax: 44 19 04671384
Journal dealing with latest developments in archaeology. **Freq:** Bimonthly February, April, June, August, October and December. **Key Personnel:** Mike Pitts, Editor, editor@britarch.ac.uk. **ISSN:** 1357-4442. **Subscription Rates:** 27 individuals UK; 34 other countries; EUR49 other countries; 4.50 single issue. **URL:** http://www.britarch.ac.uk/ba/ba.html.

56989 ■ Defence and Peace Economics
Taylor & Francis Group Journals
c/o Keith Hartley, Ed.
University of York
Heslington
York YO1 5DD, United Kingdom
Ph: 44 1904 433753
Fax: 44 1904 433759
Publisher E-mail: customerservice@taylorandfrancis.com
Journal covering all aspects of the economics of defense, disarmament, conversion, and peace. **Freq:** Bimonthly. **Key Personnel:** Keith Hartley, Editor; John T. Warner, Editorial Ed.; S. Mehay, Editorial Board. **ISSN:** 1024-2694. **Subscription Rates:** US$180 individuals print only; US$986 individuals online only; US$1,038 individuals print & online; EUR827 institutions print & online; 624 institutions print & online; EUR786 institutions online only; 593 institutions online only; EUR143 individuals; 110 individuals. **Remarks:** Advertising accepted; rates available upon request. **URL:** http://www.tandf.co.uk/journals/titles/10242694.asp. **Circ:** (Not Reported)

56990 ■ Economic Journal
Royal Economic Society
University of York
Heslington
York YO1 5DD, United Kingdom
Ph: 44 1334 462479
Publisher E-mail: royaleconsoc@st-andrews.ac.uk
Publication covering economics. **Freq:** 8/yr. **Key Personnel:** Antonio Ciccone, Editor, s.machin@ucl.ac.uk; Andrew Scott, Managing Editor, econjournal@london.edu. **ISSN:** 0013-0133. **Subscription Rates:** US$768

institutions print & online; US$667 institutions print only; US$667 institutions online only; 482 institutions print & online; 419 institutions print only; 419 institutions online only. **Remarks:** Advertising accepted; rates available upon request. **URL:** http://www.res.org.uk/economic/economichome.asp. **Circ:** (Not Reported)

56991 ■ Greenkeeper International
British and International Golf Greenkeepers' Association
Bigga House
Aldwark
Alne
York YO61 1UF, United Kingdom
Ph: 44 1347 833800
Fax: 44 1347 833801
Publisher E-mail: info@bigga.co.uk
Publication covering greenkeeping. **Freq:** Monthly. **Key Personnel:** John Pemberton, Ch. Exec., john@bigga.co.uk. **Subscription Rates:** 50 individuals; 65 individuals Europe and Ireland; 95 other countries. **Remarks:** Accepts advertising. **URL:** http://www.bigga.org.uk/about-us/magazine/. **Ad Rates:** BW: 1,180, 4C: 1,425. **Circ:** ‡6,000

56992 ■ International Journal of Public Theology
Brill Academic Publishers
Faculty of Education & Theology
St. John University
Lord Mayor's Walk
York YO31 7EX, United Kingdom
Publisher E-mail: marketing@brill.nl
Journal covering the field of public theology. **Founded:** 1970. **Freq:** 4/yr. **Print Method:** Offset. **Trim Size:** 10 x 12 7/8. **Cols./Page:** 8. **Col. Width:** 6.5 picas. **Col. Depth:** 77 picas. **Key Personnel:** Sebastian Kim, Editor. **ISSN:** 1872-5171. **Subscription Rates:** EUR60 individuals print only; US$82 individuals print only; EUR199 institutions print and electronic; US$270 institutions print and electronic; EUR166 institutions online only; US$226 institutions online only; EUR183 institutions print only; US$249 institutions print only. **URL:** http://www.brill.nl/default.aspx?partid=18&pid=26552.

56993 ■ Medical Engineering and Physics
Institute of Physics and Engineering in Medicine
Fairmount House
230 Tadcaster Rd.
York YO24 1ES, United Kingdom
Ph: 44 19 04610821
Fax: 44 19 04612279
Publication E-mail: mep@elsevier.com
Publisher E-mail: office@ipem.ac.uk
Publication covering physics and medical engineering. **Freq:** 10/yr. **Key Personnel:** Dr. Sally Clift, Editor, s.e.clift@bath.ac.uk; Rory Cooper, Assoc. Ed.; Mark J. Pearcy, Assoc. Ed. **ISSN:** 1350-4533. **Subscription Rates:** US$315 individuals for all countries except Europe, Japan and Iran; US$2,454 institutions for all countries except Europe, Japan and Iran; 291,400¥ institutions; EUR2,193 institutions for European countries and Iran; EUR284 individuals for European countries and Iran; 37,500¥ individuals. **Remarks:** Advertising accepted; rates available upon request. **URL:** http://www.ipem.ac.uk/ipem_public/default.asp?id=363; http://www.elsevier.com/wps/find/journaldescription.cws_home/30456/descriptiondescription. **Circ:** (Not Reported)

56994 ■ Mind
Oxford University Press
c/o Prof. Thomas Baldwin, Ed.
Dept. of Philosophy
University of York
Heslington
York YO10 5DD, United Kingdom
Publisher E-mail: webenquiry.uk@oup.com
Publication covering philosophy and religion. **Freq:** Quarterly. **Key Personnel:** Paul Noordhof, Reviews Ed.; David Efird, Asst. Ed.; Prof. Thomas Baldwin, Editor; Warren Goldfarb, International Advisor; Frank Jackson, International Advisor; Barry Lee, Editorial Admin.; Tom

Stoneham, Asst. Ed.; T.M. Scanlon, International Advisor. **ISSN:** 0026-4423. **Subscription Rates:** 126 institutions print and online; US$239 institutions print and online; EUR189 institutions print and online; 105 institutions online, print; US$200 institutions online, print; EUR158 institutions online, print; 34 individuals print only; US$65 individuals print only; EUR51 individuals print only; 36 individuals online only. **Remarks:** Accepts advertising. **URL:** http://mind.oupjournals.org/. **Circ:** (Not Reported)

56995 ■ Quality in Higher Education
Routledge
Taylor & Francis Group Ltd.
c/o Prof. Lee Harvey, Ed.
Higher Education Academy
Innovation Way
York Science Pk.
York YO10 5BR, United Kingdom
Publisher E-mail: webmaster.books@tandf.co.uk
Peer-reviewed journal focusing on the theory, practice and policies relating to the control, management and improvement of quality in higher education. **Freq:** 3/yr. **Key Personnel:** Prof. Lee Harvey, Editor; Prof. David Dill, Exec. Board; Prof. Diane Green, Exec. Board; Dr. James Williams, Assoc. Ed.; Prof. Jethro Newton, Exec. Board; Luisa Ribolzi, Exec. Board. **ISSN:** 1353-8322. **Subscription Rates:** US$172 individuals print only; US$558 institutions online; US$587 institutions print + online; 101 institutions print only; 336 institutions online; 354 institutions print + online; EUR468 institutions print and online; EUR444 institutions online only; EUR138 individuals. **Remarks:** Advertising accepted; rates available upon request. **URL:** http://www.tandf.co.uk/journals/cqhe. **Circ:** (Not Reported)

56996 ■ The Quilter
Quilters' Guild of the British Isles
St. Anthony's Hall
York Y01 7PW, United Kingdom
Ph: 44 1904 613242
Fax: 44 1904 632394
Publisher E-mail: info@quiltersguild.org.uk
Publication covering crafts. **Freq:** Quarterly. **Key Personnel:** Anne Williams, Editor, editorquilter@quiltersguild.org.uk. **ISSN:** 0954-4933. **Subscription Rates:** Free members. **Remarks:** Advertising accepted; rates available upon request. **URL:** http://www.quiltersguild.org.uk/index.php?page=28. **Circ:** 7,000

56997 ■ Reference Reviews
Emerald Group Publishing Ltd.
c/o Mr. Anthony Chalcraft, Ed.
York St., John University
Lord Mayor's Walk
York YO31 7EX, United Kingdom
Publisher E-mail: emerald@emeraldinsight.com
Journal for librarians offering comprehensive analyses of the latest and most significant reference material available today and offering a comprehensive and unbiased appraisal by professionals who understand the criteria used when purchasing a resource. **Freq:** 8/yr. **Key Personnel:** Mr. Anthony Chalcraft, Editor, a.chalcraft@yorksj.ac.uk; Eileen Breen, Publisher, ebreen@emeraldinsight.com; Dr. David D. Oberhelman, Regional Ed., d.oberhelman@okstate.edu; Christine Reid, Editorial Advisory Board, c.reid@strath.ac.uk; Robert J. Duckett, Editorial Advisory Board, duckettbob@yahoo.co.uk; Martin Guha, Editorial Advisory Board; Stuart James, Editorial Advisory Board. **ISSN:** 0950-4125. **URL:** http://info.emeraldinsight.com/products/journals/journals.htm?id=rr.

56998 ■ Scope
Institute of Physics and Engineering in Medicine
Fairmount House
230 Tadcaster Rd.
York YO24 1ES, United Kingdom
Ph: 44 19 04610821
Fax: 44 19 04612279
Publication E-mail: scope@ipem.ac.uk

Publisher E-mail: office@ipem.ac.uk
Publication covering physics. **Freq:** Quarterly March, June, September and December. **Key Personnel:** Mark Miguel, Editor, m.e.miquel@qmul.ac.uk. **ISSN:** 0964-9565. **Subscription Rates:** Free to members; 35 nonmembers; 10 nonmembers single copy. **Remarks:** Advertising accepted; rates available upon request. **URL:** http://www.ipem.ac.uk/ipem_public/default.asp?id=362. **Circ:** 2,400

56999 ■ Shoe World
Catherine House
Northminster Business Pk.
Northfield Ln.
York YO26 6QU, United Kingdom
Ph: 44 844 8440809
Fax: 44 1904 528791
Publication E-mail: info@shoeworld.co.uk
Publisher E-mail: helpdesk@shoe-shop.com
Online consumer magazine covering footwear in Europe. **Subtitle:** Let Your Feet do the Talking. **Remarks:** Accepts advertising. **URL:** http://www.shoeworld.com. **Circ:** Non-paid 8,000

57000 ■ Yorkshire Advertiser (Ryedale and North York Moors)
Yorkshire Advertiser Ltd.
Kirkdale Rd.
Kirbymoorside
York YO62 6YB, United Kingdom
Ph: 44 1751434609
Publication E-mail: yorkshireadvertiser@ryedalegroup.co.uk
Publisher E-mail: yorkshireadvertiser@ryedalegroup.co.uk
Shopping guide magazine. **Founded:** 1986. **Freq:** Monthly. **Key Personnel:** Sarah Beattie, Editor. **Subscription Rates:** Free; 11 by mail. **Remarks:** Accepts advertising. **URL:** http://www.yorkshireadvertiser.co.uk/. **Circ:** Non-paid 15,000

57001 ■ Minster-FM - 104.7
PO Box 123
York YO19 5ZX, United Kingdom
Ph: 44 1904 488888
Format: Adult Contemporary; Contemporary Hit Radio (CHR). **URL:** http://www.minsterfm.com/.

57002 ■ URY-AM - 1350
c/o Vanbrugh College
University of York
Heslington
York YO10 5DD, United Kingdom
Ph: 44 1904 433840
E-mail: ury@ury.york.ac.uk
Format: Eclectic; Alternative/New Music/Progressive. **Founded:** 1967. **Operating Hours:** Continuous. **Key Personnel:** Scott Bryan, Station Mgr., station.manager@ury.york.ac.uk; Jon Cook, Prog. Controller, programme.controller@ury.york.ac.uk. **Ad Rates:** Advertising accepted; rates available upon request. **URL:** http://ury.york.ac.uk/.

Zeals Warminster

57003 ■ Conference & Common Room
John Catt Educational Ltd.
c/o Tom Wheare
63 Chapel Ln.
Zeals Warminster IP12 1BL, United Kingdom
Publisher E-mail: enquries@johncatt.com
Magazine of the Headmasters' and Headmistresses' Conference associated schools. **Subtitle:** The Magazine for Leading Independent Schools. **Founded:** 1963. **Freq:** 3/yr. **Trim Size:** 210 x 297 mm. **Key Personnel:** Tom Wheare, Editor; John Catt, Publisher. **Subscription Rates:** 25 two years. **URL:** http://www.johncatt.com/en/school-magazines.

Circulation: ★ = ABC; △ = BPA; ◆ = CAC; • = CCAB; ❏ = VAC; ⊕ = PO Statement; ‡ = Publisher's Report; Boldface figures = sworn; Light figures = estimated.

Gale Directory of Publications & Broadcast Media/147th Ed.　　　　　　　　　　　　　**5885**

Artigas

57004 ■ Radio Cuareim-AM - 1270
Avda. Lecueder 167
55000 Artigas, Uruguay
Ph: 598 77 22867
Fax: 598 77 23867
E-mail: racua@adinet.com.uy
Format: Information. **Founded:** Aug. 25, 1975. **URL:**
http://www.radiocuareim.com.

Canelones

57005 ■ Ideal-FM - 90.1
18 de Julio 542
Santa Lucia
Canelones, Uruguay
Ph: 598 33 47819
E-mail: radio@fmideal.com
Format: Adult Contemporary; Ethnic. **Operating Hours:**
18 hours Daily. **Ad Rates:** Advertising accepted; rates
available upon request. **URL:** http://www.fmideal.com.

57006 ■ Inolvidable-FM - 93.1
Capitan Valdenegro y Libres
Las Piedras
90200 Canelones, Uruguay
Ph: 598 2 3643333
Fax: 598 2 3640088
E-mail: 93.1@inolvidablefm.com
Format: World Beat; Ethnic; Eclectic. **Owner:** Inolvid-
able FM, at above address. **Operating Hours:**
Continuous. **Ad Rates:** Advertising accepted; rates
available upon request. **URL:** http://www.inolvidablefm.
com.

Montevideo

57007 ■ Bibliographic Journal
Inter-American Children's Institute
Instituto Interamericano del Nino
Casilla de Correos 16212
Avenida 8 de Octubre 2904
11600 Montevideo, Uruguay
Ph: 598 2 4872150
Fax: 598 2 4873242
Publication E-mail: biblioteca@iinoea.org
Publisher E-mail: iin@oas.org
Spanish language publication covering families. **Freq:**
Semiannual. **URL:** http://www.iin.oea.org/
Referencias%20bibliograficas/Revista_bibliografica_
2005_ingles.htm.

57008 ■ Ciudad de Montevideo-AM - 1370 KHz
Arenal Grande 2093 Esq. Hocquard
11800 Montevideo, Uruguay
Ph: 598 9291370
Fax: 598 9240700
E-mail: cx42@emisoraciudaddemontevideo.com.uy
Format: Ethnic; World Beat; Folk. **Owner:** Emisora
Ciudad De Montevideo, at above address. **Founded:**
Sept. 23, 1930. **Operating Hours:** 16 hours Daily. **URL:**
http://www.emisoraciudaddemontevideo.com.uy.

57009 ■ Radio Rural-AM - 610
Av. Suarez 3409
Prado
Montevideo, Uruguay
Ph: 598 2 3360610
E-mail: comerciales@cx4radiorural.com
Format: Information. **Operating Hours:** Continuous.

URL: http://www.cx4radiorural.com.

57010 ■ Radio Sarandi - 690
Enriqueta Compte y Rique 1250
Montevideo, Uruguay
Ph: 598 2 2082612
Format: Full Service. **URL:** http://www.sarandi690.com.
uy.

57011 ■ Radio Universal-AM - 970
Avenida 18 de Julio 1220
Montevideo, Uruguay
Ph: 598 2 9032222
E-mail: info@22universal.com
Format: Full Service. **URL:** http://www.22universal.
com/.

Punta del Este

57012 ■ Aspen-FM - 103.5
Calle 28 casi Gorlero
20100 Punta del Este, Uruguay
Ph: 598 42 446792
E-mail: aspenfm@puntaweb.com
Format: Ethnic; World Beat. **Operating Hours:**
Continuous. **URL:** http://www.aspenpunta.com.

Salto

57013 ■ America-FM - 103.3 MHz
Ave. Batlle 2265
Terminal Salto Shopping local 19
50000 Salto, Uruguay
Ph: 598 73 39200
Format: Ethnic; World Beat. **Operating Hours:**
Continuous. **URL:** http://www.fmamericadigital.com.

Tashkent

57014 ■ Applied Solar Energy
Maik Nauka/Interperiodica Publishing
Physical Technical Institute
2B, G. Mavlyanov St.

100084 Tashkent, Uzbekistan
Ph: 998 71 1331271
Publication E-mail: avezov@uzsci.net
Publisher E-mail: compmg@maik.ru
Journal covering the main lines of investigations and developments on solar energy conversion and use. **Key**

Personnel: Prof. Moukhtar S. Saidov, Editor-in-Chief; Romen A. Zahidov, Dep. Ed.-in-Ch. **ISSN:** 0003-701X. **Subscription Rates:** EUR2,290 institutions print incl. free access or e-only; EUR2,748 institutions print incl. enhanced access. **URL:** http://www.maik.ru/cgi-perl/journal.pl?lang=eng&name=appsolen.

Circulation: ★ = ABC; △ = BPA; ◆ = CAC; • = CCAB; ❑ = VAC; ⊕ = PO Statement; ‡ = Publisher's Report; Boldface figures = sworn; Light figures = estimated.

Gale Directory of Publications & Broadcast Media/147th Ed.

5889

Vatican City

57015 ■ People on the Move
Pontifical Council for the Pastoral Care of Migrants and
Itinerant People
Palazzo San Calisto

I-00120 Vatican City, Vatican City
Ph: 39 066 9887131
Fax: 39 669 887111
Publisher E-mail: office@migrants.va
Publication covering the Mission religion in English, French, German, Italian and Spanish. **Freq:** 3/yr. **Subscription Rates:** US$5 individuals. **Remarks:** Advertising accepted; rates available upon request. **URL:** http://www.vatican.va/. **Circ:** (Not Reported)

Circulation: ★ = ABC; △ = BPA; ◆ = CAC; • = CCAB; ❑ = VAC; ⊕ = PO Statement; ‡ = Publisher's Report; Boldface figures = sworn; Light figures = estimated.

Gale Directory of Publications & Broadcast Media/147th Ed.

5891

Aragua

57016 ■ Master-FM - 107.3
Calle del Tanque de Hidrocentro
Maracay Edo.
Aragua, Venezuela
Ph: 58 243 2323773
Fax: 58 243 2328873
Format: Contemporary Hit Radio (CHR); Ethnic. **Ad Rates:** Advertising accepted; rates available upon request. **URL:** http://www.masterfm.net.

Barquisimeto

57017 ■ SOMOS-FM - 93.5
Av. Los Leones
Centro Empresarial Barquisimeto, Piso 6, Ofic. 6-7
Barquisimeto, Venezuela
Ph: 58 251 2543614
E-mail: contacto@corporacionsomos.com
Format: Full Service. **Owner:** Corporacion Somos Media, at above address. **Founded:** May 14, 2003. **URL:** http://www.corporacionsomos.com.

Carabobo

57018 ■ Universitaria-FM - 104.5
C.C. Prebo Av. 107
Calle 130
Carabobo 2001, Venezuela
Ph: 58 241 8244080
Fax: 58 241 8245747
Format: Jazz; Ethnic; World Beat. **Operating Hours:** Continuous. **URL:** http://www.dimetel.uc.edu.ve.

Caracas

57019 ■ Acta Botanica Venezuelica
Universidad Central de Venezuela
Jardin Botanico de Caracas
Fundacion Instituto Botanico de Venezuela dr. Tobias Lasser
Avenida Salvador Allende
Apartado 2156
Caracas, Venezuela
Publisher E-mail: arrivile@camelot.rect.ucv.ve
Scientific magazine on ecology and plant life of Venezuela and ecologically similar regions of other countries. **Key Personnel:** Dr. Silvia Perez-Cortez, Editor. **ISSN:** 0084-5906. **URL:** http://www.scielo.org.ve/scielo.php?script=sci_serial&lng=en&pid=0084-5906&.

57020 ■ Acta Cientifica Venezolana
Venezuelan Association for the Advancement of Science
Asociation Venezolana para el Avance de la Ciencia
Colinas de Bello Monte Av. Neveri
Edificio: Fundavac-Asovac Aptdo.
Caracas 47286, Venezuela
Ph: 58 212 7531002
Fax: 58 212 7511420
Publication E-mail: jdelcas@ivic.ve
English and Spanish language publication covering science. **Founded:** 1950. **Freq:** Quarterly. **Key Personnel:** Jesus R. del Castillo, Publishers partners; Juscelino

Tovar, Editor. **ISSN:** 0001-5504. **Subscription Rates:** US$100 other countries; US$180 institutions, other countries libraries. **Remarks:** Advertising not accepted. **URL:** http://acta.ivic.ve/; http://www2.scielo.org.ve/scielo.php/script_sci_serial/pid_0001-5504/lng_en/nrm_iso. **Circ:** Non-paid ‡500

57021 ■ Estrella-FM - 96.3
Av. Rio Caura, Centro Comercial Concresa
Nivel 1, FM Ctr., Prados del Este
Caracas, Venezuela
Ph: 58 212 9764545
Format: Music of Your Life. **URL:** http://www.fmcenter.com.ve.

57022 ■ Radio Sintonia-AM - 1420
Calle la Joya
Edificio Cosmos
Piso 9, Oficina 9A
Chacao
Caracas, Venezuela
Ph: 58 212 2650782
E-mail: rsintonia1420am@cantv.net
Format: Talk; World Beat. **Operating Hours:** Continuous. **URL:** http://www.radiosintonia1420.com.ve.

57023 ■ RQ-AM - 910
Av. Rio Caura
Centro Comercial Concresa
Nivel 1, FM Ctr.
Prados del Este
Caracas, Venezuela
Ph: 58 212 9764545
Format: Ethnic; Information; Sports. **Operating Hours:** 18 hours Daily. **Ad Rates:** Advertising accepted; rates available upon request. **URL:** http://www.fmcenter.com.ve/.

Isla de Margarita

57024 ■ Noticias-FM - 97.3
Av. Bolivar, Cruce con Aldonza Manrique
Centro Comercial AB
Nivel PL, Oficina 10
Isla de Margarita 6301, Venezuela
Ph: 58 295 2628022
E-mail: info@fmnoticias.com
Format: Ethnic; News; World Beat. **Operating Hours:** Continuous. **Key Personnel:** Mireya Mata, Director, mireyamata@fmnoticias.com; Luis Aguilera, Director, luisaguilera@fmnoticias.com; Juan Carlos Peralta, Contact, produccion@fmnoticias.com. **URL:** http://www.fmnoticias.com.

Los Teques

57025 ■ Metropolitana-FM - 97.1
Calle Ribas
Edificio Centro Empresarial (Torre Chocolate), Piso 7
Estado Miranda
Los Teques, Venezuela
Ph: 58 212 3227580
Fax: 58 212 3647505
Format: Ethnic; World Beat. **Ad Rates:** Advertising accepted; rates available upon request. **URL:** http://www.radiometropolitana.com.

Maracaibo

57026 ■ Gaceta Laboral
Universidad del Zulia
Apartado Postal 526
Maracaibo 4001, Venezuela
Ph: 58 261 7596716
Publisher E-mail: jcanez@luz.edu.ve
Journal covering changes that have occurred in labor relations and their impact on workers. Focusing on subjects such as transformations in workers and their organizations, new forms of labor syndicates in Venezuela, the future of labor unions in Venezuela, and informality as a new format in labor organizations. **Founded:** 1909. **Freq:** Quarterly. **Print Method:** Offset. **Trim Size:** 8 1/4 x 10 7/8. **Cols./Page:** 2. **Col. Width:** 26 nonpareils. **Col. Depth:** 140 agate lines. **Key Personnel:** Luis Eduardo Diaz, Editor; Jose Ignacio Beltran, Assoc. Ed.; Napoleon Goizueta, Assoc. Ed. **ISSN:** 1315-8597. **Subscription Rates:** US$30 individuals. **URL:** http://www.serbi.luz.edu.ve/scielo.php?script=sci_serial&pid=1315-8597&lng=es&nrm=is.

57027 ■ Sabor-FM - 106.5
Av. 8 Santa Rita con calle 73
Edificio Radiolandia N 72-75
Apto. Postal 674
Maracaibo, Venezuela
Ph: 58 261 7975070
Fax: 58 261 7971333
Format: Ethnic; World Beat. **Operating Hours:** Continuous. **Key Personnel:** Nancy Fig Tree, Vice President; Jaime Fornez, Mgr. Trade and Sales; Gisela Villalobos, Asst. of Presidency; Ricardo Garnier, Admin. Mgr.; Angi D'Moya, Admin Asst.-Accounting; Melquiades Reyes, Coord. Computer Sci. **Ad Rates:** Advertising accepted; rates available upon request. **URL:** http://www.sabor106.com.

Merida

57028 ■ Journal of Surfactants and Detergents
AOCS Press
Chemical Engineering School
Universidad de Los Andes
Merida 5101, Venezuela
Publisher E-mail: general@aocs.org
Peer-reviewed journal covering practical and theoretical aspects of chemical and petrochemical surfactants, soaps, and detergents. **Founded:** Oct. 1926. **Freq:** Monthly. **Print Method:** Offset. **Trim Size:** 11.975 x 21 1/2. **Cols./Page:** 6. **Col. Width:** 11 picas. **Col. Depth:** 301 agate lines. **Key Personnel:** Jean-Louis Salager, Editor-in-Chief, salager@ula.ve. **ISSN:** 1097-3958. **Subscription Rates:** US$150 members includes airmail. **Remarks:** Accepts advertising. **URL:** http://www.aocs.org/press/journals.cfm. **Ad Rates:** BW: Bs 1,500, 4C: Bs 1,225. **Circ:** (Not Reported)

Tachira

57029 ■ Nueva Revista Rotaria
Revista Rotaria Foundation
Apartado Postal 717
Tachira 5001, Venezuela

Circulation: ★ = ABC; △ = BPA; ♦ = CAC; • = CCAB; ❑ = VAC; ⊕ = PO Statement; ‡ = Publisher's Report; Boldface figures = sworn; Light figures = estimated.

Ph: 58 276 3441551
Fax: 58 276 3429950
Publisher E-mail: nuevarevista@cantv.net
Membership magazine of Rotary International covering current news about Rotary-related subjects. **Freq:** Bimonthly. **Key Personnel:** Fouad Souki, Editor, fswh@telcel.net.ve; Maria Souki, Editor. **URL:** http://www.

revistarotaria.com/; http://www.rotary.org/en/mediaandnews/morepublications/regionalmagazines/pages/ridefault.aspx. **Circ:** 9,900

Valencia

57030 ■ Radio Valencia-AM - 1220
Edificio El Parque, Planta Baja Local 2

Urbanizacion Lomas del Este Avenida Rosario
Valencia, Venezuela
Format: Ethnic; World Beat. **Operating Hours:** Continuous. **Key Personnel:** Gonzalo Matie, Director. **URL:** http://www.radiovenezuela.com.ve.

Ba Ria Vung tau

57031 ■ Voice of Vietnam - Ba Ria Vung tau - 1500 KHz
58 Quan Su St.
Hanoi, Vietnam
Ph: 84 4 9344231
Fax: 84 4 9344230
E-mail: toasoan@vovnews.vn
Format: Eclectic. **Owner:** Voice of Vietnam, at above address. **Key Personnel:** Vu Van Hien, Chm.; Nguyen Thuy Hoa, Dep. Ed.-in-Ch.; Vu Bich Ngoc, Editor-in-Chief. **URL:** http://vovnews.vn/.

Binh Thuan

57032 ■ Voice of Vietnam - Binh Thuan - 765 KHz
58 Quan Su St.
Hanoi, Vietnam
Ph: 84 4 9344231
Fax: 84 4 9344230
E-mail: toasoan@vovnews.vn
Format: Full Service. **Owner:** Voice of Vietnam, at above address. **Operating Hours:** 0300-1250. **Key Personnel:** Dr. Vu Van Hien, Chm.; Vu Bich Ngoc, Editor-in-Chief; Nguyen Thuy Hoa, Dep. Ed.-in-Ch. **URL:** http://www.vov.org.vn/.

57033 ■ Voice of Vietnam - Binh Thuan - 5000 KHz
58 Quan Su St.
Hanoi, Vietnam
Ph: 84 4 9344231
Fax: 84 4 9344230
E-mail: toasoan@vovnews.vn
Format: Full Service. **Owner:** Voice of Vietnam, at above address. **Key Personnel:** Dr. Vu Van Hien, Chm.; Nguyen Thuy Hoa, Dep. Ed.-in-Ch.; Vu Bich Ngoc, Editor-in-Chief. **URL:** http://vovnews.vn/.

57034 ■ Voice of Vietnam - Binh Thuan - 1100 KHz
58 Quan Su St.
Hanoi, Vietnam
Ph: 84 4 9344231
Fax: 84 4 9344230
E-mail: toasoan@vovnews.vn
Format: News; Sports. **Owner:** Voice of Vietnam, at above address. **Key Personnel:** Dr. Vu Van Hien, Chm.; Nguyen Thuy Hoa, Dep. Ed.-in-Ch.; Vu Bich Ngoc, Editor-in-Chief. **URL:** http://vovnews.vn/.

Can Tho

57035 ■ Voice of Vietnam - Can Tho - 780 KHz
58 Quan Su St.
Hanoi, Vietnam
Ph: 84 4 9344231
Fax: 84 4 9344230
E-mail: toasoan@vovnews.vn
Format: Full Service. **Owner:** Voice of Vietnam, at above address. **Key Personnel:** Dr. Vu Van Hien, Chm.; Vu Bich Ngoc, Editor-in-Chief; Nguyen Thuy Hoa, Dep. Ed.-in-Ch. **URL:** http://www.vov.org.vn/.

Cao Bang

57036 ■ Voice of Vietnam - Radio Cao Bang - 6530 KHz
58 Quan Su St.
Hanoi, Vietnam
Ph: 84 4 9344231
Fax: 84 4 9344230
E-mail: toasoan@vovnews.vn
Format: News; Sports. **Owner:** Voice of Vietnam, at above address. **Key Personnel:** Dr. Vu Van Hien, Chm.; Vu Bich Ngoc, Editor-in-Chief; Nguyen Thuy Hoa, Dep. Ed.-in-Ch. **URL:** http://www.vov.org.vn/.

Da Nang

57037 ■ Voice of Vietnam - Da Nang - 600 KHz
58 Quan Su St.
Hanoi, Vietnam
Ph: 84 4 9344231
Fax: 84 4 9344230
E-mail: toasoan@vovnews.vn
Format: Full Service. **Owner:** Voice of Vietnam, at above address. **Key Personnel:** Dr. Vu Van Hien, Chm.; Nguyen Thuy Hoa, Dep. Ed.-in-Ch.; Vu Bich Ngoc, Editor-in-Chief. **URL:** http://vovnews.vn/.

Dac Lac

57038 ■ Voice of Vietnam - Dac Lac - 4800 KHz
58 Quan Su St.
Hanoi, Vietnam
Ph: 84 4 9344231
Fax: 84 4 9344230
E-mail: toasoan@vovnews.vn
Format: News; Sports. **Owner:** Voice of Vietnam, at above address. **Key Personnel:** Dr. Vu Van Hien, Chm.; Nguyen Thuy Hoa, Dep. Ed.-in-Ch.; Vu Bich Ngoc, Editor-in-Chief. **URL:** http://vovnews.vn/.

57039 ■ Voice of Vietnam - Dac Lac - 1089 KHz
58 Quan Su St.
Hanoi, Vietnam
Ph: 84 4 9344231
Fax: 84 4 9344230
E-mail: toasoan@vovnews.vn
Format: Full Service; Educational. **Owner:** Voice of Vietnam, at above address. **Founded:** July 1, 1994. **Operating Hours:** 19 hours Daily. **Key Personnel:** Vu Van Hien, Chm.; Nguyen Thuy Hoa, Dep. Ed.-in-Ch.; Vu Bich Ngoc, Editor-in-Chief. **URL:** http://vovnews.vn/.

Dai Tieng Noi

57040 ■ Voice of Vietnam - Dai Tieng Noi (Hmong Service) - 5030 KHz
58 Quan Su St.
Hanoi, Vietnam
Ph: 84 4 9344231
Fax: 84 4 9344230
E-mail: toasoan@vovnews.vn
Format: Full Service. **Owner:** Voice of Vietnam, at above address. **Key Personnel:** Dr. Vu Van Hien, Chm.; Vu Bich Ngoc, Editor-in-Chief; Nguyen Thuy Hoa, Dep. Ed.-in-Ch. **URL:** http://www.vov.org.vn/.

Dong Hoi

57041 ■ Voice of Vietnam - Dong Hoi - 630 KHz
58 Quan Su St.
Hanoi, Vietnam
Ph: 84 4 9344231
Fax: 84 4 9344230
E-mail: toasoan@vovnews.vn
Format: News. **Owner:** Voice of Vietnam, at above address. **Founded:** July 1, 1994. **Operating Hours:** 5 a.m.-12 a.m. **Key Personnel:** Dr. Vu Van Hien, Chm.; Vu Bich Ngoc, Editor-in-Chief; Nguyen Thuy Hoa, Dep. Ed.-in-Ch. **URL:** http://www.vov.org.vn/.

Dong Thap

57042 ■ Voice of Vietnam - Dong Thap - 710 KHz
58 Quan Su St.
Hanoi, Vietnam
Ph: 84 4 9344231
Fax: 84 4 9344230
E-mail: toasoan@vovnews.vn
Format: Full Service. **Owner:** Voice of Vietnam, at above address. **Key Personnel:** Dr. Vu Van Hien, Chm.; Vu Bich Ngoc, Editor-in-Chief; Nguyen Thuy Hoa, Dep. Ed.-in-Ch. **URL:** http://www.vov.org.vn/.

Gia Lai

57043 ■ Voice of Vietnam - Gia Lai - 630 KHz
58 Quan Su St.
Hanoi, Vietnam
Ph: 84 4 9344231
Fax: 84 4 9344230
E-mail: toasoan@vovnews.vn
Format: News; Full Service. **Owner:** Voice of Vietnam, at above address. **Founded:** July 1, 1994. **Operating Hours:** 5a.m.-12a.m. Daily. **Key Personnel:** Dr. Vu Van Hien, Chm.; Vu Bich Ngoc, Editor-in-Chief; Nguyen Thuy Hoa, Dep. Ed.-in-Ch. **URL:** http://www.vov.org.vn/.

An Giang

57044 ■ Voice of Vietnam - An Giang - 1070 KHz
58 Quan Su St.
Hanoi, Vietnam
Ph: 84 4 9344231
Fax: 84 4 9344230
E-mail: toasoan@vovnews.vn
Format: News; Sports. **Owner:** Voice of Vietnam, at above address. **Key Personnel:** Dr. Vu Van Hien, Chm.; Nguyen Thuy Hoa, Dep. Ed.-in-Ch.; Vu Bich Ngoc, Editor-in-Chief. **URL:** http://www.vov.org.vn/.

Ha Giang

57045 ■ Voice of Vietnam - Ha Giang - 570 KHz
58 Quan Su St.
Hanoi, Vietnam
Ph: 84 4 9344231
Fax: 84 4 9344230
E-mail: toasoan@vovnews.vn
Format: News; Sports. **Owner:** Voice of Vietnam, at above address. **Key Personnel:** Dr. Vu Van Hien, Chm.;

Circulation: ★ = ABC; △ = BPA; ♦ = CAC; • = CCAB; ❑ = VAC; ⊕ = PO Statement; ‡ = Publisher's Report; Boldface figures = sworn; Light figures = estimated.

Gale Directory of Publications & Broadcast Media/147th Ed.

5895

Vu Bich Ngoc, Editor-in-Chief; Nguyen Thuy Hoa, Dep. Ed.-in-Ch. URL: http://vovnews.vn/.

Ha Tay

57046 ■ Voice of Vietnam - Ha Tay - 1180 KHz
58 Quan Su St.
Hanoi, Vietnam
Ph: 84 4 9344231
Fax: 84 4 9344230
E-mail: toasoan@vovnews.vn
Format: Eclectic. **Owner:** Voice of Vietnam, at above address. **Key Personnel:** Vu Van Hien, Chm.; Nguyen Thuy Hoa, Dep. Ed.-in-Ch.; Vu Bich Ngoc, Editor-in-Chief. **URL:** http://www.vov.org.vn/.

Ha Tinh

57047 ■ Ha Tinh Broadcast - Television Station - 21
28 Phan Dinh Phung
Ha Tinh, Vietnam
Ph: 84 855440
Fax: 84 857410
Operating Hours: 18 hours Daily. **Key Personnel:** Nguyen Cong Tien, Editor-in-Chief. **Wattage:** 2000. **Ad Rates:** Advertising accepted; rates available upon request. **URL:** http://www.vnnews.com/.

57048 ■ Ha Tinh Broadcast - Television Station - 6
28 Phan Dinh Phung
Ha Tinh, Vietnam
Ph: 84 855440
Fax: 84 857410
Founded: July 9, 1956. **Operating Hours:** 4 hours Daily. **Key Personnel:** Nguyen Cong Tien, Editor-in-Chief. **Wattage:** 1000. **Ad Rates:** Advertising accepted; rates available upon request. **URL:** http://www.vnnews.com/.

57049 ■ Voice of Vietnam - Ha Tinh - 900 KHz
58 Quan Su St.
Hanoi, Vietnam
Ph: 84 4 9344231
Fax: 84 4 9344230
E-mail: toasoan@vovnews.vn
Format: Full Service. **Owner:** Voice of Vietnam, at above address. **Operating Hours:** 2200-1600. **Key Personnel:** Dr. Vu Van Hien, Chm.; Vu Bich Ngoc, Editor-in-Chief; Nguyen Thuy Hoa, Dep. Ed.-in-Ch. **URL:** http://www.vov.org.vn/.

Hai Hung

57050 ■ Voice of Vietnam - Hai Hung - 1195 KHz
58 Quan Su St.
Hanoi, Vietnam
Ph: 84 4 9344231
Fax: 84 4 9344230
E-mail: toasoan@vovnews.vn
Format: News; Sports. **Owner:** Voice of Vietnam, at above address. **Key Personnel:** Dr. Vu Van Hien, Chm.; Nguyen Thuy Hoa, Dep. Ed.-in-Ch.; Vu Bich Ngoc, Editor-in-Chief. **URL:** http://vovnews.vn/.

Hanoi

57051 ■ Humanity
Red Cross of Vietnam
Croix Rouge Vietnamienne
82 Nguyen Du Str.
Hanoi, Vietnam
Ph: 84 482 63703
Fax: 84 494 24285
Publisher E-mail: vnrchq@netnam.org.vn
Vietnamese language publication covering relief. **Freq:** Semimonthly. **Key Personnel:** Le Ha, Editor-in-Chief. **Remarks:** Advertising accepted; rates available upon request. **URL:** http://www.vnrc.org.vn/. **Circ:** (Not Reported)

57052 ■ Nhan Dan
71 Hang Trong St.
Hoan Kiem District
Hoan Kiem
Hanoi, Vietnam
Ph: 84 4 8254231
Fax: 84 4 8255593

Publisher E-mail: toasoan@nhandan.org.vn
Political newspaper. **Subtitle:** The Central Organ of the Communist Party of Vietnam. **Founded:** Mar. 11, 1951. **Freq:** Daily. **Key Personnel:** Dinh Huynh, Editor-in-Chief. **URL:** http://www.nhandan.com.vn. **Circ:** Mon.-Fri. 220,000, Mon. 130,000

57053 ■ Thoi Bao Kinh Te Vietnam
Thoi Bao Kinh Te Viet Nam
96 Hoang Quoc Viet
Cau Giay
Hanoi, Vietnam
Ph: 84 475 52060
Fax: 84 475 52046
Consumer magazine covering business and lifestyle. **Subtitle:** The Insider's Guide to Business and Lifestyle. **Founded:** 1994. **Freq:** Monthly. **Trim Size:** A4. **Cols./Page:** 4. **Col. Width:** 5.5 centimeters. **Col. Depth:** 4.5 centimeters. **Key Personnel:** Prof. Dao Nguyen Cat, Editor-in-Chief. **Remarks:** Accepts advertising. **URL:** http://www.vneconomy.com.vn. **Circ:** Controlled 35,000

57054 ■ Vietnam Investment Review
Vietnam Investment Review Ltd.
47 Quan Thanh Str., Ba Dinh Dist.
Hanoi, Vietnam
Ph: 84 4 3845 0537
Fax: 84 4 3845 7937
Publisher E-mail: vir.hn@vir.com.vn
Banking, finance and accounting industries newspaper. **Freq:** Weekly. **Key Personnel:** Dr. Nguyen Anh Tuan, Editor-in-Chief. **Subscription Rates:** US$99 individuals; US$300 Asia; US$350 Japan, Australia, New Zealand; US$400 out of country. **Remarks:** Accepts advertising. **URL:** http://www.vir.com.vn/news/home. **Circ:** (Not Reported)

Voice of Vietnam - An Giang - See An Giang

Voice of Vietnam - An Nhon - See An Nhon

Voice of Vietnam - Ba Ria Vung tau - See Ba Ria Vung tau

Voice of Vietnam - Binh Thuan - See Binh Thuan

Voice of Vietnam - Binh Thuan - See Binh Thuan

Voice of Vietnam - Binh Thuan - See Binh Thuan

Voice of Vietnam - Can Tho - See Can Tho

Voice of Vietnam - Da Nang - See Da Nang

Voice of Vietnam - Dac Lac - See Dac Lac

Voice of Vietnam - Dac Lac - See Dac Lac

Voice of Vietnam - Dai Tieng Noi (Hmong Service) - See Dai Tieng Noi

Voice of Vietnam - Dong Hoi - See Dong Hoi

Voice of Vietnam - Dong Thap - See Dong Thap

Voice of Vietnam - Gia Lai - See Gia Lai

Voice of Vietnam - Ha Giang - See Ha Giang

Voice of Vietnam - Ha Tay - See Ha Tay

Voice of Vietnam - Ha Tinh - See Ha Tinh

Voice of Vietnam - Hai Hung - See Hai Hung

57055 ■ Voice of Vietnam - Hanoi - 675 KHz
58 Quan Su St.
Hanoi, Vietnam
Ph: 84 4 9344231
Fax: 84 4 9344230
E-mail: toasoan@vovnews.vn
Format: News. **Owner:** Voice of Vietnam, at above address. **Founded:** July 1, 1994. **Operating Hours:** 5 a.m.-12 a.m. Daily. **Key Personnel:** Dr. Vu Van Hien, Chm.; Vu Bich Ngoc, Editor-in-Chief; Nguyen Thuy Hoa, Dep. Ed.-in-Ch. **URL:** http://www.vov.org.vn/.

57056 ■ Voice of Vietnam - Hanoi - 1242 KHz
58 Quan Su St.
Hanoi, Vietnam
Ph: 84 4 9344231
Fax: 84 4 9344230
E-mail: toasoan@vovnews.vn
Format: Eclectic. **Owner:** Voice of Vietnam, at above address. **Operating Hours:** 2200-0030, 0900-1700. **Key Personnel:** Vu Van Hien, Chm.; Nguyen Thuy Hoa, Dep. Ed.-in-Ch.; Vu Bich Ngoc, Editor-in-Chief. **URL:** http://vovnews.vn.

Voice of Vietnam - Ho Chi Minh City --See Ho Chi Minh City

Voice of Vietnam - Khanh Hoa - See Khanh Hoa

Voice of Vietnam - Kien Giang - See Kien Giang

Voice of Vietnam - Kon Tum - See Kontum

Voice of Vietnam - Lai Cau 1 - See Lai Cau Town

Voice of Vietnam - Lam Dong - See Lam Dong

Voice of Vietnam - Lam Dong - See Lam Dong

Voice of Vietnam - Lao Cai - See Lao Cai

Voice of Vietnam - Lao Cai - See Lao Cai

Voice of Vietnam - Me Tri 1 - See Me Tri

Voice of Vietnam - Me Tri 1 - See Me Tri

Voice of Vietnam - Minh Hai - See Minh Hai

Voice of Vietnam - Nam Ha - See Nam Ha

Voice of Vietnam - Nghe An - See Nghe An

Voice of Vietnam - Nghe An - See Nghe An

Voice of Vietnam - Nhatrang - See Nhatrang

Voice of Vietnam - Quan Tre - See Quan Tre

Voice of Vietnam - Quan Tre - See Quan Tre

Voice of Vietnam - Quan Tre - See Quan Tre

Voice of Vietnam - Quang Binh - See Quang Binh

Voice of Vietnam - Quang Nam - See Quang Nam

Voice of Vietnam - Quang Ngai - See Quang Ngai

Voice of Vietnam - Quang Ninh - See Quang Ninh

Voice of Vietnam - Radio Cao Bang - See Cao Bang

Voice of Vietnam - Radio Lai Cau 2 - See Lai Cau Town

Voice of Vietnam - Radio Lao Cai - See Lao Cai

Voice of Vietnam - Radio Son La - See Son La

Voice of Vietnam - Radio Son La 1 - See Son La

Voice of Vietnam - Radio TV Gia Lai - See Playcu

Voice of Vietnam - Radio TV Kontum - See Kontum

Voice of Vietnam - Radio Yen Bai - See Yen Bai

Voice of Vietnam - Soc Trang - See Soc Trang

Voice of Vietnam - Song Be - See Song Be

Voice of Vietnam - Song Be - See Song Be

Voice of Vietnam - Tay Ninh - See Tay Ninh

Voice of Vietnam - Thai Binh - See Thai Binh

Voice of Vietnam - Thanh Hoa - See Thanh Hoa

Voice of Vietnam - Thua Thien Hue - See Thua Thien Hue

Voice of Vietnam - Tien Giang - See Tien Giang

Voice of Vietnam - Tra Vinh - See Tra Vinh

Voice of Vietnam - Tuyen Quang - See Tuyen Quang

Voice of Vietnam - Vinh Long - See Vinh Long

Voice of Vietnam - Yen Bai - See Yen Bai

Voice of Vietnam - Yen Bai - See Yen Bai

Ho Chi Minh City

57057 ■ Saigon Times Weekly
Saigon Times Group
35 Nam Ky Khol Nghia St.
District 1
Ho Chi Minh City, Vietnam
Ph: 84 882 95936
Fax: 84 882 94294
Publication E-mail: saigon.times@hcm.vnn.vn
Publisher E-mail: sgt@hcm.vnn.vn
English-language publication covering business, economic, and cultural news. **Freq:** Weekly (Thurs.). **Trim Size:** 20 X 28 cm. **Key Personnel:** Tran Thi Ngoc, Ch. Ed.; Tran Minh Hung, Dep. Ed.; Tran Minh Hung, Assoc. Ed. **Subscription Rates:** 332,800 Dg individuals. **Remarks:** Accepts advertising. **URL:** http://www.saigontimes.com.vn/quangcao.asp. **Ad Rates:** BW: 6,500,000 Dg, 4C: 7,500,000 Dg. **Circ:** 30,000

57058 ■ Voice of Vietnam - Ho Chi Minh City - 655 KHz
58 Quan Su St.
Hanoi, Vietnam
Ph: 84 4 9344231
Fax: 84 4 9344230
E-mail: toasoan@vovnews.vn
Format: News; Full Service. **Owner:** Voice of Vietnam, at above address. **Founded:** July 1, 1994. **Operating Hours:** 5 a.m.-12 a.m. Daily. **Key Personnel:** Vu Van Hien, Chm.; Vu Bich Ngoc, Editor-in-Chief; Nguyen Thuy Hoa, Dep. Ed.-in-Ch. **URL:** http://www.vov.org.vn/.

Khanh Hoa

57059 ■ Voice of Vietnam - Khanh Hoa - 576 KHz
58 Quan Su St.
Hanoi, Vietnam
Ph: 84 4 9344231
Fax: 84 4 9344230
E-mail: toasoan@vovnews.vn
Format: Full Service. **Owner:** Voice of Vietnam, at above address. **Operating Hours:** 2200-1600. **Key Personnel:** Dr. Vu Van Hien, Chm.; Nguyen Thuy Hoa, Dep. Ed.-in-Ch.; Vu Bich Ngoc, Editor-in-Chief. **URL:** http://vovnews.vn/.

Kien Giang

57060 ■ Voice of Vietnam - Kien Giang - 970 KHz
58 Quan Su St.
Hanoi, Vietnam
Ph: 84 4 9344231
Fax: 84 4 9344230
E-mail: toasoan@vovnews.vn
Format: Full Service. **Owner:** Voice of Vietnam, at above address. **Key Personnel:** Dr. Vu Van Hien, Chm.; Vu Bich Ngoc, Editor-in-Chief; Nguyen Thuy Hoa, Dep. Ed.-in-Ch. **URL:** http://www.vov.org.vn/.

Kontum

57061 ■ Voice of Vietnam - Kon Tum - 980 KHz
58 Quan Su St.
Hanoi, Vietnam
Ph: 84 4 9344231
Fax: 84 4 9344230
E-mail: toasoan@vovnews.vn
Format: News; Sports. **Owner:** Voice of Vietnam, at above address. **Key Personnel:** Vu Bich Ngoc, Editor-in-Chief; Nguyen Thuy Hoa, Dep. Ed.-in-Ch. **URL:** http://www.vov.org.vn/.

57062 ■ Voice of Vietnam - Radio TV Kontum - 4800 KHz
58 Quan Su St.
Hanoi, Vietnam
Ph: 84 4 9344231
Fax: 84 4 9344230
E-mail: toasoan@vovnews.vn
Format: News; Sports. **Owner:** Voice of Vietnam, at above address. **Key Personnel:** Dr. Vu Van Hien, Chm.; Nguyen Thuy Hoa, Dep. Ed.-in-Ch.; Vu Bich Ngoc, Editor-in-Chief. **URL:** http://vovnews.vn/.

Lai Cau Town

57063 ■ Voice of Vietnam - Lai Cau 1 - 4215 KHz
58 Quan Su St.
Hanoi, Vietnam
Ph: 84 4 9344231
Fax: 84 4 9344230
E-mail: toasoan@vovnews.vn
Format: News; Sports. **Owner:** Voice of Vietnam, at above address. **Key Personnel:** Dr. Vu Van Hien, Chm.; Nguyen Thuy Hoa, Dep. Ed.-in-Ch.; Vu Bich Ngoc, Editor-in-Chief. **URL:** http://vovnews.vn/.

57064 ■ Voice of Vietnam - Radio Lai Cau 2 - 6395 KHz
58 Quan Su St.
Hanoi, Vietnam
Ph: 84 4 9344231
Fax: 84 4 9344230
E-mail: toasoan@vovnews.vn
Format: News; Sports. **Owner:** Voice of Vietnam, at above address. **Key Personnel:** Dr. Vu Van Hien, Chm.;

Vu Bich Ngoc, Editor-in-Chief; Nguyen Thuy Hoa, Dep. Ed.-in-Ch. **URL:** http://www.vov.org.vn/.

Lam Dong

57065 ■ Voice of Vietnam - Lam Dong - 4675 KHz
58 Quan Su St.
Hanoi, Vietnam
Ph: 84 4 9344231
Fax: 84 4 9344230
E-mail: toasoan@vovnews.vn
Format: News; Sports. **Owner:** Voice of Vietnam, at above address. **Key Personnel:** Dr. Vu Van Hien, Chm.; Nguyen Thuy Hoa, Dep. Ed.-in-Ch.; Vu Bich Ngoc, Editor-in-Chief. **URL:** http://vovnews.vn/.

57066 ■ Voice of Vietnam - Lam Dong - 550 KHz
58 Quan Su St.
Hanoi, Vietnam
Ph: 84 4 9344231
Fax: 84 4 9344230
E-mail: toasoan@vovnews.vn
Format: News; Sports. **Owner:** Voice of Vietnam, at above address. **Key Personnel:** Dr. Vu Van Hien, Chm.; Vu Bich Ngoc, Editor-in-Chief; Nguyen Thuy Hoa, Dep. Ed.-in-Ch. **URL:** http://vovnews.vn/.

Lao Cai

57067 ■ Voice of Vietnam - Lao Cai - 5597 KHz
58 Quan Su St.
Hanoi, Vietnam
Ph: 84 4 9344231
Fax: 84 4 9344230
E-mail: toasoan@vovnews.vn
Format: News; Sports. **Owner:** Voice of Vietnam, at above address. **Operating Hours:** 0300-0430, 0945-1100, 1145-1400. **Key Personnel:** Dr. Vu Van Hien, Chm.; Vu Bich Ngoc, Editor-in-Chief; Nguyen Thuy Hoa, Dep. Ed.-in-Ch. **URL:** http://www.vov.org.vn/.

57068 ■ Voice of Vietnam - Lao Cai - 4677 KHz
58 Quan Su St.
Hanoi, Vietnam
Ph: 84 4 9344231
Fax: 84 4 9344230
E-mail: toasoan@vovnews.vn
Format: Eclectic. **Owner:** Voice of Vietnam, at above address. **Key Personnel:** Dr. Vu Van Hien, Chm.; Nguyen Thuy Hoa, Dep. Ed.-in-Ch.; Vu Bich Ngoc, Editor-in-Chief. **URL:** http://vovnews.vn/.

57069 ■ Voice of Vietnam - Radio Lao Cai - 6702 KHz
58 Quan Su St.
Hanoi, Vietnam
Ph: 84 4 9344231
Fax: 84 4 9344230
E-mail: toasoan@vovnews.vn
Format: News; Sports. **Owner:** Voice of Vietnam, at above address. **Key Personnel:** Dr. Vu Van Hien, Chm.; Vu Bich Ngoc, Editor-in-Chief; Nguyen Thuy Hoa, Dep. Ed.-in-Ch. **URL:** http://www.vov.org.vn/.

Me Tri

57070 ■ Voice of Vietnam - Me Tri 1 - 570 KHz
58 Quan Su St.
Hanoi, Vietnam
Ph: 84 4 9344231
Fax: 84 4 9344230
E-mail: toasoan@vovnews.vn
Format: News; Sports. **Owner:** Voice of Vietnam, at above address. **Key Personnel:** Dr. Vu Van Hien, Chm.; Nguyen Thuy Hoa, Dep. Ed.-in-Ch.; Vu Bich Ngoc, Editor-in-Chief. **URL:** http://www.vov.org.vn/.

57071 ■ Voice of Vietnam - Me Tri 1 - 549 KHz
58 Quan Su St.
Hanoi, Vietnam
Ph: 84 4 9344231
Fax: 84 4 9344230
E-mail: toasoan@vovnews.vn
Format: News; Sports. **Owner:** Voice of Vietnam, at above address. **Founded:** July 1, 1994. **Operating Hours:** 19 hours Daily. **Key Personnel:** Dr. Vu Van Hien, Chm.; Vu Bich Ngoc, Editor-in-Chief; Nguyen Thuy Hoa, Dep. Ed.-in-Ch. **URL:** http://vovnews.vn/.

Minh Hai

57072 ■ Voice of Vietnam - Minh Hai - 1120 KHz
58 Quan Su St.
Hanoi, Vietnam
Ph: 84 4 9344231
Fax: 84 4 9344230
E-mail: toasoan@vovnews.vn
Format: News; Sports. **Owner:** Voice of Vietnam, at above address. **Key Personnel:** Dr. Vu Van Hien, Chm.; Nguyen Thuy Hoa, Dep. Ed.-in-Ch.; Vu Bich Ngoc, Editor-in-Chief. **URL:** http://www.vov.org.vn/.

Nam Ha

57073 ■ Voice of Vietnam - Nam Ha - 1280 KHz
58 Quan Su St.
Hanoi, Vietnam
Ph: 84 4 9344231
Fax: 84 4 9344230
E-mail: toasoan@vovnews.vn
Format: News; Sports. **Owner:** Voice of Vietnam, at above address. **Key Personnel:** Dr. Vu Van Hien, Chm.; Nguyen Thuy Hoa, Dep. Ed.-in-Ch.; Vu Bich Ngoc, Editor-in-Chief. **URL:** http://vovnews.vn/.

Nghe An

57074 ■ Voice of Vietnam - Nghe An - 5200 KHz
58 Quan Su St.
Hanoi, Vietnam
Ph: 84 4 9344231
Fax: 84 4 9344230
E-mail: toasoan@vovnews.vn
Format: News; Sports. **Owner:** Voice of Vietnam, at above address. **Key Personnel:** Dr. Vu Van Hien, Chm.; Vu Bich Ngoc, Editor-in-Chief; Nguyen Thuy Hoa, Dep. Ed.-in-Ch. **URL:** http://www.vov.org.vn/.

57075 ■ Voice of Vietnam - Nghe An - 782 KHz
58 Quan Su St.
Hanoi, Vietnam
Ph: 84 4 9344231
Fax: 84 4 9344230
E-mail: toasoan@vovnews.vn
Format: Full Service. **Owner:** Voice of Vietnam, at above address. **Operating Hours:** 2200-2400, 0400-0600. **Key Personnel:** Dr. Vu Van Hien, Chm.; Vu Bich Ngoc, Editor-in-Chief; Nguyen Thuy Hoa, Dep. Ed.-in-Ch. **URL:** http://www.vov.org.vn/.

Nhatrang

57076 ■ Voice of Vietnam - Nhatrang - 580 KHz
58 Quan Su St.
Hanoi, Vietnam
Ph: 84 4 9344231
Fax: 84 4 9344230
E-mail: toasoan@vovnews.vn
Format: Full Service. **Owner:** Voice of Vietnam, at above address. **Key Personnel:** Dr. Vu Van Hien, Chm.; Nguyen Thuy Hoa, Dep. Ed.-in-Ch.; Vu Bich Ngoc, Editor-in-Chief. **URL:** http://vovnews.vn/.

An Nhon

57077 ■ Voice of Vietnam - An Nhon - 648 KHz
58 Quan Su St.
Hanoi, Vietnam
Ph: 84 4 9344231
Fax: 84 4 9344230
E-mail: toasoan@vovnews.vn
Format: News. **Owner:** Voice of Vietnam, at above address. **Founded:** July 1, 1994. **Operating Hours:** 5 a.m.-12 a.m. Daily. **Key Personnel:** Vu Van Hien, Chm.; Vu Bich Ngoc, Editor-in-Chief; Nguyen Thuy Hoa, Dep. Ed.-in-Ch. **Wattage:** 50,000. **URL:** http://www.vov.org.vn/.

Playcu

57078 ■ Voice of Vietnam - Radio TV Gia Lai - 4722.5 KHz
58 Quan Su St.
Hanoi, Vietnam
Ph: 84 4 9344231
Fax: 84 4 9344230
E-mail: toasoan@vovnews.vn
Format: News; Sports. **Owner:** Voice of Vietnam, at

above address. **Key Personnel:** Dr. Vu Van Hien, Chm.; Nguyen Thuy Hoa, Dep. Ed.-in-Ch.; Vu Bich Ngoc, Editor-in-Chief. **URL:** http://vovnews.vn/.

Quan Tre

57079 ■ Voice of Vietnam - Quan Tre - 747 KHz
58 Quan Su St.
Hanoi, Vietnam
Ph: 84 4 9344231
Fax: 84 4 9344230
E-mail: toasoan@vovnews.vn
Format: Ethnic; News; Full Service. **Owner:** Voice of Vietnam, at above address. **Key Personnel:** Dr. Vu Van Hien, Chm.; Vu Bich Ngoc, Editor-in-Chief; Nguyen Thuy Hoa, Dep. Ed.-in-Ch. **URL:** http://www.vov.org.vn/.

57080 ■ Voice of Vietnam - Quan Tre - 657 KHz
58 Quan Su St.
Hanoi, Vietnam
Ph: 84 4 9344231
Fax: 84 4 9344230
E-mail: toasoan@vovnews.vn
Format: Full Service. **Owner:** Voice of Vietnam, at above address. **Operating Hours:** 2200-1700. **Key Personnel:** Dr. Vu Van Hien, Chm.; Vu Bich Ngoc, Editor-in-Chief; Nguyen Thuy Hoa, Dep. Ed.-in-Ch. **URL:** http://www.vov.org.vn/.

57081 ■ Voice of Vietnam - Quan Tre - 558 KHz
58 Quan Su St.
Hanoi, Vietnam
Ph: 84 4 9344231
Fax: 84 4 9344230
E-mail: toasoan@vovnews.vn
Format: Educational. **Owner:** Voice of Vietnam, at above address. **Founded:** July 1, 1994. **Operating Hours:** 19 hours Daily. **Key Personnel:** Dr. Vu Van Hien, Chm.; Vu Bich Ngoc, Editor-in-Chief; Nguyen Thuy Hoa, Dep. Ed.-in-Ch. **URL:** http://vovnews.vn/.

Quang Binh

57082 ■ Voice of Vietnam - Quang Binh - 846 KHz
58 Quan Su St.
Hanoi, Vietnam
Ph: 84 4 9344231
Fax: 84 4 9344230
E-mail: toasoan@vovnews.vn
Format: Full Service. **Owner:** Voice of Vietnam, at above address. **Operating Hours:** 0400-1030. **Key Personnel:** Dr. Vu Van Hien, Chm.; Vu Bich Ngoc, Editor-in-Chief; Nguyen Thuy Hoa, Dep. Ed.-in-Ch. **URL:** http://www.vov.org.vn/.

Quang Nam

57083 ■ Voice of Vietnam - Quang Nam - 600 KHz
58 Quan Su St.
Hanoi, Vietnam
Ph: 84 4 9344231
Fax: 84 4 9344230
E-mail: toasoan@vovnews.vn
Format: Full Service. **Owner:** Voice of Vietnam, at above address. **Key Personnel:** Dr. Vu Van Hien, Chm.; Nguyen Thuy Hoa, Dep. Ed.-in-Ch.; Vu Bich Ngoc, Editor-in-Chief. **URL:** http://vovnews.vn/.

Quang Ngai

57084 ■ Voice of Vietnam - Quang Ngai - 774 KHz
58 Quan Su St.
Hanoi, Vietnam
Ph: 84 4 9344231
Fax: 84 4 9344230
E-mail: toasoan@vovnews.vn
Format: Full Service. **Owner:** Voice of Vietnam, at above address. **Key Personnel:** Dr. Vu Van Hien, Chm.; Vu Bich Ngoc, Editor-in-Chief; Nguyen Thuy Hoa, Dep. Ed.-in-Ch. **URL:** http://www.vov.org.vn/.

Quang Ninh

57085 ■ Voice of Vietnam - Quang Ninh - 700 KHz
58 Quan Su St.
Hanoi, Vietnam

Ph: 84 4 9344231
Fax: 84 4 9344230
E-mail: toasoan@vovnews.vn
Format: Eclectic. **Owner:** Voice of Vietnam, at above address. **Key Personnel:** Dr. Vu Van Hien, Chm.; Vu Bich Ngoc, Editor-in-Chief; Nguyen Thuy Hoa, Dep. Ed.-in-Ch. **URL:** http://www.vov.org.vn/.

Soc Trang

57086 ■ Voice of Vietnam - Soc Trang - 1200 KHz
58 Quan Su St.
Hanoi, Vietnam
Ph: 84 4 9344231
Fax: 84 4 9344230
E-mail: toasoan@vovnews.vn
Format: News; Sports. **Owner:** Voice of Vietnam, at above address. **Key Personnel:** Dr. Vu Van Hien, Chm.; Nguyen Thuy Hoa, Dep. Ed.-in-Ch.; Vu Bich Ngoc, Editor-in-Chief. **URL:** http://vovnews.vn/.

Son La

57087 ■ Voice of Vietnam - Radio Son La - 4965 KHz
58 Quan Su St.
Hanoi, Vietnam
Ph: 84 4 9344231
Fax: 84 4 9344230
E-mail: toasoan@vovnews.vn
Format: Full Service. **Owner:** Voice of Vietnam, at above address. **Key Personnel:** Dr. Vu Van Hien, Chm.; Nguyen Thuy Hoa, Dep. Ed.-in-Ch.; Vu Bich Ngoc, Editor-in-Chief. **URL:** http://vovnews.vn/.

57088 ■ Voice of Vietnam - Radio Son La 1 - 4739.5 KHz
58 Quan Su St.
Hanoi, Vietnam
Ph: 84 4 9344231
Fax: 84 4 9344230
E-mail: toasoan@vovnews.vn
Format: News; Sports. **Owner:** Voice of Vietnam, at above address. **Key Personnel:** Dr. Vu Van Hien, Chm.; Nguyen Thuy Hoa, Dep. Ed.-in-Ch.; Vu Bich Ngoc, Editor-in-Chief. **URL:** http://vovnews.vn/.

Song Be

57089 ■ Voice of Vietnam - Song Be - 970 KHz
58 Quan Su St.
Hanoi, Vietnam
Ph: 84 4 9344231
Fax: 84 4 9344230
E-mail: toasoan@vovnews.vn
Format: Full Service. **Owner:** Voice of Vietnam, at above address. **Key Personnel:** Dr. Vu Van Hien, Chm.; Vu Bich Ngoc, Editor-in-Chief; Nguyen Thuy Hoa, Dep. Ed.-in-Ch. **URL:** http://www.vov.org.vn/.

57090 ■ Voice of Vietnam - Song Be - 572 KHz
58 Quan Su St.
Hanoi, Vietnam
Ph: 84 4 9344231
Fax: 84 4 9344230
E-mail: toasoan@vovnews.vn
Format: Full Service. **Owner:** Voice of Vietnam, at above address. **Key Personnel:** Dr. Vu Van Hien, Chm.; Nguyen Thuy Hoa, Dep. Ed.-in-Ch.; Vu Bich Ngoc, Editor-in-Chief. **URL:** http://vovnews.vn/.

Tay Ninh

57091 ■ Voice of Vietnam - Tay Ninh - 580 KHz
58 Quan Su St.
Hanoi, Vietnam
Ph: 84 4 9344231
Fax: 84 4 9344230
E-mail: toasoan@vovnews.vn
Format: Full Service. **Owner:** Voice of Vietnam, at above address. **Key Personnel:** Dr. Vu Van Hien, Chm.; Nguyen Thuy Hoa, Dep. Ed.-in-Ch.; Vu Bich Ngoc, Editor-in-Chief. **URL:** http://vovnews.vn/.

Thai Binh

57092 ■ Voice of Vietnam - Thai Binh - 1250 KHz
58 Quan Su St.
Hanoi, Vietnam

Ph: 84 4 9344231
Fax: 84 4 9344230
E-mail: toasoan@vovnews.vn
Format: News; Sports. **Owner:** Voice of Vietnam, at above address. **Key Personnel:** Dr. Vu Van Hien, Chm.; Nguyen Thuy Hoa, Dep. Ed.-in-Ch.; Vu Bich Ngoc, Editor-in-Chief. **URL:** http://vovnews.vn/.

Thanh Hoa

57093 ■ Voice of Vietnam - Thanh Hoa - 850 KHz
58 Quan Su St.
Hanoi, Vietnam
Ph: 84 4 9344231
Fax: 84 4 9344230
E-mail: toasoan@vovnews.vn
Format: Full Service. **Owner:** Voice of Vietnam, at above address. **Key Personnel:** Dr. Vu Van Hien, Chm.; Vu Bich Ngoc, Editor-in-Chief; Nguyen Thuy Hoa, Dep. Ed.-in-Ch. **URL:** http://www.vov.org.vn/.

Thua Thien Hue

57094 ■ Voice of Vietnam - Thua Thien Hue - 720 KHz
58 Quan Su St.
Hanoi, Vietnam
Ph: 84 4 9344231
Fax: 84 4 9344230
E-mail: toasoan@vovnews.vn
Format: Full Service. **Owner:** Voice of Vietnam, at above address. **Operating Hours:** 2200-1310. **Key Personnel:** Dr. Vu Van Hien, Chm.; Vu Bich Ngoc, Editor-in-Chief; Nguyen Thuy Hoa, Dep. Ed.-in-Ch. **URL:** http://www.vov.org.vn/.

Tien Giang

57095 ■ Voice of Vietnam - Tien Giang - 828 KHz
58 Quan Su St.
Hanoi, Vietnam
Ph: 84 4 9344231
Fax: 84 4 9344230
E-mail: toasoan@vovnews.vn
Format: Full Service. **Owner:** Voice of Vietnam, at above address. **Operating Hours:** 2200-1155. **Key Personnel:** Dr. Vu Van Hien, Chm.; Vu Bich Ngoc, Editor-in-Chief; Nguyen Thuy Hoa, Dep. Ed.-in-Ch. **URL:** http://www.vov.org.vn/.

Tra Vinh

57096 ■ Voice of Vietnam - Tra Vinh - 1053 KHz
58 Quan Su St.
Hanoi, Vietnam
Ph: 84 4 9344231
Fax: 84 4 9344230
E-mail: toasoan@vovnews.vn
Format: News; Sports. **Owner:** Voice of Vietnam, at above address. **Key Personnel:** Dr. Vu Van Hien, Chm.; Nguyen Thuy Hoa, Dep. Ed.-in-Ch.; Vu Bich Ngoc, Editor-in-Chief. **URL:** http://vovnews.vn/.

Tuyen Quang

57097 ■ Voice of Vietnam - Tuyen Quang - 4740 KHz
58 Quan Su St.
Hanoi, Vietnam
Ph: 84 4 9344231
Fax: 84 4 9344230
E-mail: toasoan@vovnews.vn
Format: News; Sports. **Owner:** Voice of Vietnam, at above address. **Key Personnel:** Dr. Vu Van Hien, Chm.; Nguyen Thuy Hoa, Dep. Ed.-in-Ch.; Vu Bich Ngoc, Editor-in-Chief. **URL:** http://vovnews.vn/.

Vinh Long

57098 ■ Voice of Vietnam - Vinh Long - 950 KHz
58 Quan Su St.
Hanoi, Vietnam
Ph: 84 4 9344231
Fax: 84 4 9344230
E-mail: toasoan@vovnews.vn
Format: Full Service. **Owner:** Voice of Vietnam, at above address. **Key Personnel:** Dr. Vu Van Hien, Chm.; Vu Bich Ngoc, Editor-in-Chief; Nguyen Thuy Hoa, Dep. Ed.-in-Ch. **URL:** http://www.vov.org.vn/.

Yen Bai

57099 ■ Voice of Vietnam - Radio Yen Bai - 5000 KHz
58 Quan Su St.
Hanoi, Vietnam
Ph: 84 4 9344231
Fax: 84 4 9344230
E-mail: toasoan@vovnews.vn
Format: Eclectic. **Owner:** Voice of Vietnam, at above address. **Key Personnel:** Dr. Vu Van Hien, Chm.;

Nguyen Thuy Hoa, Dep. Ed.-in-Ch.; Vu Bich Ngoc, Editor-in-Chief. **URL:** http://vovnews.vn/.

57100 ■ Voice of Vietnam - Yen Bai - 6541.8 KHz
58 Quan Su St.
Hanoi, Vietnam
Ph: 84 4 9344231
Fax: 84 4 9344230
E-mail: toasoan@vovnews.vn
Format: News; Sports. **Owner:** Voice of Vietnam, at above address. **Key Personnel:** Dr. Vu Van Hien, Chm.; Vu Bich Ngoc, Editor-in-Chief; Nguyen Thuy Hoa, Dep.

Ed.-in-Ch. **URL:** http://www.vov.org.vn/.

57101 ■ Voice of Vietnam - Yen Bai - 580 KHz
58 Quan Su St.
Hanoi, Vietnam
Ph: 84 4 9344231
Fax: 84 4 9344230
E-mail: toasoan@vovnews.vn
Format: Full Service. **Owner:** Voice of Vietnam, at above address. **Key Personnel:** Dr. Vu Van Hien, Chm.; Nguyen Thuy Hoa, Dep. Ed.-in-Ch.; Vu Bich Ngoc, Editor-in-Chief. **URL:** http://vovnews.vn/.

Circulation: ★ = ABC; △ = BPA; ◆ = CAC; • = CCAB; ❑ = VAC; ⊕ = PO Statement; ‡ = Publisher's Report; Boldface figures = sworn; Light figures = estimated.

Gale Directory of Publications & Broadcast Media/147th Ed.

5899

East Caribbean

57102 ■ Praise-FM - 105.7
St. Vincent & the Grenadines
PO Box 443
East Caribbean, West Indies
Ph: 784 4561057
Fax: 784 4561696
E-mail: info@praisefmsvg.com
Format: Contemporary Christian; Religious; Gospel.
Founded: 1998. **Operating Hours:** Continuous. **URL:**
http://www.praisefmsvg.com.

Saint Johns

57103 ■ Liberty Radio-FM - 97.1
Bryant Pasture
Bird Rd. Ottos
PO Box 1100
Saint Johns, West Indies
Ph: 268 4621111
Fax: 268 4621116
E-mail: mail@radiozdk.com
Format: Ethnic; Talk; World Beat. **Owner:** Greenville
Radio Ltd., at above address. **Key Personnel:** Ivor G.T.
Bird, Mng. Dir. **Ad Rates:** Advertising accepted; rates

available upon request. **URL:** http://www.radiozdk.com.

Saint Kitts

57104 ■ KYSS-FM - 102.5
51 A Stadium View, Sandy Point
Saint Kitts, West Indies
Ph: 869 4665978
Fax: 869 4661746
E-mail: info@kyssonline.com
Format: Eclectic; News. **Operating Hours:** Continuous.
Ad Rates: Advertising accepted; rates available upon
request. **URL:** http://www.kyssonline.com.

Sana'a

57105 ■ Yemen Observer
Mohammed al-Shokani St.
PO Box 19183
Sana'a, Yemen
Ph: 967 1 505466
Fax: 967 1 260504
Publication E-mail: contact@yobserver.com
Publisher E-mail: editor@yobserver.com
English language newspaper covering local news.

Founded: 1996. **Freq:** Weekly (Sat.). **Key Personnel:** Mohammed Alasaadi, Editor-in-Chief; Faris Sanabani, Founder. **Remarks:** Accepts advertising. **URL:** http://www.yobserver.com. **Circ:** (Not Reported)

57106 ■ Yemen Times
PO Box 2579
Sana'a, Yemen
Ph: 967 1 268661
Fax: 967 1 268276
Publication E-mail: yementimes@yementimes.com
Publisher E-mail: yementimes@yementimes.com
English language general newspaper (Semi-weekly). **Founded:** 1990. **Freq:** Semiweekly. **Print Method:** Sheet offset Color. **Trim Size:** 45 x 30. **Key Personnel:** Nadia Abdulaziz Al-Saqqaf, Editor-in-Chief. **Subscription Rates:** US$80 individuals Yemen; US$450 individuals Middle East; US$650 elsewhere. **Remarks:** Accepts advertising. **URL:** http://www.yementimes.com/. **Ad Rates:** BW: US$1,200, 4C: US$1,800. **Circ:** 35,000

Circulation: ★ = ABC; △ = BPA; ◆ = CAC; • = CCAB; ❏ = VAC; ⊕ = PO Statement; ‡ = Publisher's Report; Boldface figures = sworn; Light figures = estimated.

Gale Directory of Publications & Broadcast Media/147th Ed.   **5903**

Fringilla

57107 ■ Black Lewche
Langmead & Baker Ltd.
PO Box 81
Fringilla, Zambia
Ph: 260 1 213939
Publication E-mail: blacklewche@langmead.com
Publisher E-mail: blacklechwe@langmead.com
Journal focusing on wildlife and environmental issues in Zambia. **Subtitle:** The Journal of the Wildlife and Environmental Conservation Society of Zambia. **Freq:** Quarterly. **Key Personnel:** Margaret Thompson, Managing Editor. **ISSN:** 1992-4984. **Remarks:** Accepts advertising. **URL:** http://www.langmead.com/blacklechwe/. **Ad Rates:** 4C: 3,000,000 ZKw. **Circ:** 2,000

Lusaka

57108 ■ Radio Phoenix-FM - 89.5
ZIMCO House, 12th Fl.
Cairo Rd.
Lusaka, Zambia
Ph: 260 1 226292
Fax: 260 1 222403
E-mail: rphoenix@zamnet.zm
Format: Full Service. **Operating Hours:** Continuous. **Key Personnel:** Elizabeth Pemba, Mng. Dir.; Chilombo Nakazala, General Mgr.; Alice Kaseba, Asst. Gen. Mgr.; Nathan Pemba, Mktg. Exec.; Errol Hickey, Chm./Proprietor, phone 260 1 223581, fax 260 1 232151, errolhickey@zamnet.zm. **Ad Rates:** Advertising accepted; rates available upon request. **URL:** http://www.radiophoenixzambia.com.

57109 ■ ZNBC Four-FM - 88.2
Mass Media Complex
Alick Nkhata Rd.
PO Box 50015
Lusaka, Zambia
Ph: 260 1 251983
Format: Full Service. **Owner:** Zambia National Broadcasting Corp., at above address. **URL:** http://www.znbc.co.zm.

57110 ■ ZNBC One-FM - 102.6
Mass Media Complex
Alick Nkhata Rd.
PO Box 50015
Lusaka, Zambia
Ph: 260 1 251983
Fax: 260 1 251983
Format: Full Service. **Owner:** Zambia National Broadcasting Corp., at above address. **URL:** http://www.znbc.co.zm.

57111 ■ ZNBC Two-FM - 95.8
Mass Media Complex
Alick Nkhata Rd.
PO Box 50015
Lusaka, Zambia
Ph: 260 1 251983
Fax: 260 1 251983
Format: Full Service. **Owner:** Zambia National Broadcasting Corp., at above address. **URL:** http://www.znbc.co.zm.

Circulation: ★ = ABC; △ = BPA; ◆ = CAC; • = CCAB; ❑ = VAC; ⊕ = PO Statement; ‡ = Publisher's Report; Boldface figures = sworn; Light figures = estimated.

Gale Directory of Publications & Broadcast Media/147th Ed.   **5905**

Bindura

57112 ■ Southern Africa Journal of Science and Technology
African Journals Online
Bindura University of Science Education
P. Bag 1020
Bindura, Zimbabwe
Ph: 263 71 7531
Fax: 263 71 7534
Publisher E-mail: info@ajol.info
Peer-reviewed journal covering the fields of education, science and technology. **Freq:** Semiannual. **Key Personnel:** Dr. J.F. Mupangwa, Editor-in-Chief, sajest@buse.ac.za; A. Mhlanga, Production Ed., library@buse.ac.zw; Tinashe Mugwisi, Contact, tmugwisi@buse.ac.zw. **ISSN:** 1819-3692. **URL:** http://ajol.info/index.php/sajest.

Harare

57113 ■ Central African Journal of Medicine
African Journals Online
PO Box A195
Avondale
Harare, Zimbabwe
Publisher E-mail: info@ajol.info
Peer-reviewed journal containing information about the science of medicine. **Key Personnel:** Prof. I.T. Gangaidzo, Contact, phone 263 4 791630, fax 263 4 791995, cajm@medsch.uz.ac.zw. **ISSN:** 0008-9176. **Subscription Rates:** US$150 individuals Africa (surface mail); US$250 individuals Africa (airmail); US$190 other countries surface mail; US$280 other countries airmail; US$200 institutions Africa (surface mail); US$260 institutions Africa (airmail); US$210 institutions, other countries surface mail; US$300 institutions, other countries airmail. **URL:** http://ajol.info/index.php/cajm.

57114 ■ The Hospitality Magazine
Hospitality Association of Zimbabwe
9th Fl., Travel Ctr
93 Jason Moyo Ave.
Cswy.
PO Box CY 398
Harare, Zimbabwe
Ph: 26 347 33211
Fax: 26 347 08872
Publisher E-mail: hazceaz@internet.co.zn
Magazine covering hospitality industries. **Freq:** Monthly. **Subscription Rates:** Included in membership. **Remarks:** Accepts advertising. **URL:** http://www.haz.co.zw/. **Circ:** (Not Reported)

57115 ■ Journal of Applied Science in Southern Africa
African Journals Online

PO Box MP 203
Mount Pleasant
Harare, Zimbabwe
Publisher E-mail: info@ajol.info
Peer-reviewed journal containing information on applied research that is considered important to the region. **Freq:** Semiannual. **Key Personnel:** Prof. C.F.B. Nhachi, Editor-in-Chief; Prof. M.F. Zaranyika, Dep. Ed. **ISSN:** 1019-7788. **Subscription Rates:** Z$30 individuals + postage; US$15 individuals Africa, + postage; US$20 other countries + postage. **URL:** http://ajol.info/index.php/jassa.

57116 ■ The Manica Post
Zimbabwe Newspapers Ltd.
Herald House
Cor. G. Silundika Ave. S Nujoma St.
Harare, Zimbabwe
Ph: 263 4 795771
Fax: 263 4 791311
Newspaper featuring news and events. **Founded:** 1893. **Remarks:** Accepts advertising. **URL:** http://www.manicapost.com/index.aspx. **Circ:** (Not Reported)

57117 ■ New Farmer
Zimbabwe Newspapers Ltd.
Herald House
Cor. G. Silundika Ave. S Nujoma St.
Harare, Zimbabwe
Ph: 263 4 795771
Fax: 263 4 791311
Magazine featuring agriculture. **Founded:** 2002. **Key Personnel:** Tony Zindoga, Contact. **Remarks:** Accepts advertising. **URL:** http://www.newfarmer.co.zw/. **Circ:** (Not Reported)

57118 ■ The Sunday Mail
Zimbabwe Newspapers Ltd.
Herald House
Cor. G. Silundika Ave. S Nujoma St.
Harare, Zimbabwe
Ph: 263 4 795771
Fax: 263 4 791311
Newspaper featuring news and events. **Founded:** 1935. **Remarks:** Accepts advertising. **URL:** http://www.sundaymail.co.zw/index.aspx; http://www.zimpapers.co.zw/site.aspx?sectId=13. **Circ:** (Not Reported)

57119 ■ Sunday News
Zimbabwe Newspapers Ltd.
Herald House
Cor. G. Silundika Ave. S Nujoma St.
Harare, Zimbabwe
Ph: 263 4 795771
Fax: 263 4 791311
Newspaper featuring news and events in Zimbabwe. **Founded:** 1930. **Remarks:** Accepts advertising. **URL:**

http://www.sundaynews.co.zw/index.aspx. **Circ:** (Not Reported)

57120 ■ Zambezia
African Journals Online
PO Box MP 203
Mount Pleasant
Harare, Zimbabwe
Ph: 263 4 303211
Fax: 263 4 333407
Publisher E-mail: info@ajol.info
Peer-reviewed journal covering humanities in Zimbabwe and the surrounding region. **Subtitle:** The Journal of Humanities of the University of Zimbabwe. **Freq:** Semiannual. **Key Personnel:** Dr. A.S. Mlambo, Editor-in-Chief, uzpub@admin.uz.ac.zw. **ISSN:** 0379-0622. **Subscription Rates:** 20 individuals. **URL:** http://ajol.info/index.php/zjh.

57121 ■ Zimbabwe Independent
Zimind Publishers (Private) Ltd.
1 Kwame Nkrumah Ave.
1st Blk., 3rd Fl., Ernest & Young Bldg.
Harare, Zimbabwe
Ph: 263 4 773930
Fax: 263 4 798897
Local business newspaper. **Freq:** Weekly. **Key Personnel:** Iden Wetherell, Editor; Trevor Ncube, Chm.; Silent Kamambo, Asst. Sales Mgr. **Subscription Rates:** US$30 individuals 25 issues; US$58 individuals 50 issues; US$65 institutions 25 issues; US$78 institutions 50 issues; 45 individuals 25 issues (European); 90 individuals 50 issues (European); 68 institutions 25 issues (European); 135 institutions 50 issues (European); 56 other countries 25 issues; 110 other countries 50 issues. **Remarks:** Accepts advertising. **URL:** http://www.theindependent.co.zw. **Circ:** (Not Reported)

57122 ■ Zimbabwe Journal of Educational Research
African Journals Online
Human Resources Research Ctr.
Faculty of Education, University of Zimbabwe
PO Box MP 167
Mount Pleasant
Harare, Zimbabwe
Publisher E-mail: info@ajol.info
Peer-reviewed journal containing issues in education and human resources in sub-Saharan Africa. **Freq:** 3/yr. **Key Personnel:** Dr. Rosemary Moyana, Acting Ed.-in-Ch., rosemarymoyana@education.uz.ac.zw. **ISSN:** 1013-3445. **Subscription Rates:** US$150 individuals; US$180 institutions; US$50 single issue; US$60 single issue institution. **URL:** http://ajol.info/index.php/zjer.

Circulation: ★ = ABC; △ = BPA; ◆ = CAC; • = CCAB; ❑ = VAC; ⊕ = PO Statement; ‡ = Publisher's Report; Boldface figures = sworn; Light figures = estimated.

Gale Directory of Publications & Broadcast Media/147th Ed.

5907

Index entries are arranged alphabetically by publishing company name. Publishers with multiple addresses are arranged alphabetically by country, and then by city. Citations in the index include publishing company name; street address; phone, fax, toll-free, cable, and telex numbers; publication titles published at that address; and corresponding entry numbers. Publications are arranged alphabetically under each publishing company address.

A-lehdet Oy
Risto Rytin tie 33
FIN-00081 Helsinki, Finland
Phone: 358 9 75961
Fax: 358 9 75983153
Publications: Apu (43817) • Avotakka (43820) • Demi (43824) • Eeva (43825) • Fakta (43827) • F1 Racing (43829) • Katso (43838) • Kauneus ja Terveys (43839) • Meidan Mokki (43846) • Meidan Talo (43847) • Soundi (43857) • Tuulilasi (43862) • Viherpiha (43865) • Voi Hyvin (43866)

A/S Forlaget Boersen
Montergade 19
1140 Copenhagen, Denmark
Phone: 99945 33320102
Fax: 99945 33122445
Publications: Boersen (43657)

A.A.E.N. Proprietary Ltd.
PO Box 271
Brisbane, Queensland 4030, Australia
Phone: 61 733 566155
Fax: 61 733 566130
Publications: Automotive Electrical & Air Conditioning News (41644)

A&D Media
Jesses Farm
Snow Hill
Dinton
Wiltshire
Salisbury SP3 5HN, United Kingdom
Phone: 44 1722 716997
Publications: Facilities-UK (56453) • Hampshire (56454) • Land Mobile (56455) • Pro Shop Europe (56456) • Recycling & Waste World (56457) • Wiltshire Life (56458)

Abaco Journal
Marsh Harbour
PO Box AB 20642
Abaco, Bahamas
Phone: 242367-2580
Publications: Abaco Journal (42782)

ABCM
Av. Rio Branco, 124/14 Andar-Centro
20040-001 Rio de Janeiro, Rio de Janeiro, Brazil
Phone: 55 21 22210438
Fax: 55 21 25097128
Publications: Journal of the Brazilian Society of Mechanical Sciences (43010)

Aberdeen University Students' Association
Butchart Centre
University Rd.
Aberdeen AB24 3UT, United Kingdom
Phone: 44 122 4272965
Publications: Gaudie (51676)

Abhivyakti Media for Development
31-A, Survey No. 8, Kalyani Nagar
Anandvali Shiwar, Gangapur Rd.
Nasik 422 005, Maharashtra, India
Phone: 91 253 346128
Publications: Abhivyakti and Expressions (45473)

ABK Publications
PO Box 6288
Tweed Heads, New South Wales 2486, Australia
Phone: 61 7 55907777
Fax: 61 7 55907130
Publications: Australian Birdkeeper Magazine (42655)

Aboriginal Studies Press
AIATSIS
GPO Box 553
Canberra, Australian Capital Territory 2601, Australia
Phone: 61 2 62461111
Fax: 61 2 62614285
Publications: Australian Aboriginal Studies (41700)

ABP Pvt. Ltd.
6 Prafulla Sarkar St.
Kolkata 700 001, West Bengal, India
Phone: 91 33 22345374
Fax: 91 33 22253243
Publications: The Telegraph (45306)

ABP Pvt. Limited Publication
6 Prafulla Sarkar St.
Kolkata 700 001, West Bengal, India
Phone: 91 33 22345374
Fax: 91 33 22253241
Publications: Business World (45261)

ABS-CBN Publishing Inc.
Eugenio Lopez Communications Ctr., 4th Fl.
Eugenio Lopez Dr.
Quezon City 1104, Philippines
Phone: 63 2 4152272
Fax: 63 2 4151215
Publications: The Buzz Magasin (49587) • CHALK (49588) • FOOD (49593) • Metro (49599) • Metro hiM (49600) • Metro Home & Entertaining (49601) • Metro Society (49602) • Metro Weddings (49603) • MetroActive (49604) • Pink (49615) • StarStudio (49617) • Working Mom (49619)

Academi - Yr Academi Gymreig
3rd Fl., Mount Stuart Houco
Mount Stuart Sq.
Cardiff CF10 5FQ, United Kingdom
Phone: 44 29 20472266
Fax: 44 29 20492930
Publications: A470 (52923)

Academia de las Artes y las Ciencias Cinematograficas de Espana
Sagasta, 20-3 Dcha
E-28004 Madrid, Spain
Phone: 34 915 934648
Fax: 34 915 931492
Publications: Academia (50722) • Cuadernos de la Academia (50743)

Academia Brasileira de Ciencias
R. Anfilofio de Carvalho, 29, 3, Rio de
20030-060 Rio de Janeiro, Rio de Janeiro, Brazil
Phone: 55 213 9078100
Fax: 55 213 9078101
Publications: Anais da Academia Brasileira de Ciencias (43003)

Academia Brasileira de Neurologia - ABNEURO
St. Captain Cavalcanti

327 Vila Mariana
04017-000 Sao Paulo, Sao Paulo, Brazil
Phone: 55 115 0849463
Publications: Arquivos de Neuro-Psiquiatria (43024)

Academia Scientiarum Fennica
University of Helsinki
Dept. of Mathematics & Statistics
PO Box 68
FIN-00014 Helsinki, Finland
Phone: 358 9 19151502
Fax: 358 9 19151400
Publications: Annales Academiae Scientiarum Fennicae Mathematica (43816)

Academia Sinica
128 Academia Rd., Section 2
Nankang
Taipei 115, Taiwan
Publications: Statistica Sinica (51360)

Academia Sinica Sun Yat-Sen Institute for Social Sciences and Philosophy
128 Academia Rd., Section 2
Nankang
Taipei 11529, Taiwan
Phone: 886 2 27822120
Publications: Journal of Social Sciences and Philosophy (51355)

Academic Conferences Limited
Curtis Farm
Kidmore End
Reading RG4 9AY, United Kingdom
Phone: 44 1189 724148
Fax: 44 1189 724691
Publications: Electronic Journal of e-Government (56313) • Electronic Journal of e-Learning (56314) • Electronic Journal of Information Systems Evaluation (EJISE) (56315) • Electronic Journal of Knowledge Management (56316)

Academic Electronic Press
Bajzova 7
821 08 Bratislava, Slovakia
Phone: 42 124 3637984
Fax: 42 124 3637986
Publications: Acta Virologica (50316) • Endocrine Regulations (50319)

Academic Journals
73023 Victoria Island
Lagos, Lagos, Nigeria
Publications: African Journal of Agricultural Research (49129) • African Journal of Biochemistry Research (49130) • African Journal of Business Management (49131) • African Journal of Food Science (49132) • African Journal of Microbiology Research (49133) • African Journal of Pharmacy & Pharmacology (47754) • African Journal of Plant Science (49134) • African Journal of Political Science & International Relations (49135) • African Journal of Pure & Applied Chemistry (49136) • Biotechnology & Molecular Biology Reviews (47588) • Educational Research & Reviews (49137) • International Journal of Physical Sciences (43478) • International NGO Journal (49138) • Journal of Cell & Animal Biology (49139) • Scientific Research & Essays (49143)

Academic Press
Harcourt Pl.
32 Jamestown Rd.
London NW1 7BY, United Kingdom
Phone: 44 20 74244200
Fax: 44 20 74832293
Publications: Animal Behaviour (53945) • Biologicals (54022) • Lebensmittel-Wissenschaft und-Technologie (54863) • Religion (55184)

Academic Publication Council
PO Box 5969
Safat 13060, Kuwait
Phone: 965 498 4349
Fax: 965 484 5372
Publications: Annals of the Arts and Social Sciences (47333) • Arab Journal of Administrative Sciences (47334) • Arab Journal for the Humanities (47335) • The Educational Journal (47336) • Journal of the Gulf and Arabian Peninsula Studies (47338) • Journal of the Social Sciences (47339)

Academy of Cancer Immunology
Cancer Research Institute
One Exchange Plz.
55 Broadway, Ste. 1802
New York, NY 10006
Publications: Cancer Immunity (51184)

Academy for Ethics in Medicine
Humboldtallee 36
D-37073 Gottingen, Germany
Phone: 49 551 399680
Publications: Ethik in der Medizin (44396)

Academy of Medicine, Singapore
142 Neil Rd.
Runme Shaw Bldg.
Singapore 088871, Singapore
Phone: 65 62238968
Fax: 65 62255155
Publications: Annals, Academy of Medicine, Singapore (50103)

Academy Publishing
Academy House
818 Colombo St., Level 3
PO Box 1879
Christchurch 8013, New Zealand
Phone: 64 3 9615050
Fax: 64 3 9615112
Publications: Auckland Today (48862) • Canterbury Today (48864) • Central Today (48865) • Hospitality Today (48869) • Principals Today (48877) • Retirement Today (48878) • Wellington Today (48879)

Academy of Science of South Africa
PO Box 72135
Lynnwood Ridge 0040, Republic of South Africa
Phone: 27 128 436482
Fax: 27 866 810143
Publications: Quest (50550) • South African Journal of Science (50551)

Academy of Taiwan Information Systems Research
PO Box 4-1
Taipei 23799, Taiwan
Publications: Contemporary Management Research (51336) • International Journal of Business and Information (IJBI) (51342) • International Journal of Cyber Society and Education (51343)

Acarological Society of Japan
c/o Gen-ichi Kuriki, PhD, Sec.
Dept. of Biology
Ohu University
Tomita 31-1
Koriyama 963-8611, Japan
Fax: 81 24 9337372
Publications: Journal of Acarological Society of Japan (46447)

Accent Magazines Ltd.
11 Causey St.
Tyne & Wear
Newcastle upon Tyne NE3 4DJ, United Kingdom
Phone: 44 191 2849994
Publications: Accent (55666) • Manchester Living (55571) • North East Househunter (55675) • North East Times (55676) • South Tyne & Wear HouseHunter (55679)

Accommodation Times
Anmol Bldg., Gr. Fl.
1st Ln.
7th Rd.
Santacruz E
Mumbai 400 055, Maharashtra, India
Phone: 91 226 114221
Publications: Accommodation Times (45349)

Accountancy Ireland
Chartered Accountants House
47-49 Pearse St.
Dublin IRL-4, Dublin, Ireland
Phone: 353 163 77200
Fax: 353 166 80842
Publications: Accountancy Ireland (45942)

ACE Bulletin
Advisory Centre for Education
Ic Aberdeen Studios, 22 Highbury Grove
London N5 2DQ, United Kingdom
Phone: 44 20 77043370
Fax: 44 20 73549069
Publications: ACE Bulletin (53894)

Ace International
Via. Mocomero 26
I-29010 Vernasca, Italy
Phone: 39 991 0719
Fax: 39 991 0719
Publications: Flortecnica (46278) • Flortecnica Data e Fiori (46279)

Aceville Publications Ltd.
Unit 21-23 Phoenix Ct.
Hawkins Rd.
Colchester CO2 8JY, United Kingdom
Phone: 44 12 06505900
Fax: 44 12 06505905
Publications: Craftbusiness (53032) • Crafts Beautiful (53033) • Disability Product News (53034) • Grow Your Own (53036) • Gun Mart (53037) • Hotel Business (53038) • Let's Knit! (53040) • Let's Make Cards! (53041) • Natural Health (53042) • Natural Health & Well-Being (53043) • Period Ideas (53046) • Quick & Crafty! (53047) • Shooting Sports (53050) • Slim at Home (53051) • Sound Vision Install (53052) • Speciality Food (53053)

Acharya N G Ranga Agricultural University
Rajendranagar
Hyderabad 500 030, Andhra Pradesh, India
Publications: Journal of Research—ANGRAU (45175)

ACP Custom Media
54 Park St.
Sydney, New South Wales 2000, Australia
Phone: 61 292 828019
Fax: 61 292 673625
Publications: Official PlayStation Magazine Australia (42557)

ACP Magazines Ltd.
54-58 Park St.
Sydney, New South Wales 2000, Australia
Phone: 61 2 92828000
Fax: 61 2 92674361
Publications: APC (42447) • Australian Auto Action (42451) • Australian Dirt Bike Magazine (42452) • Australian Geographic Outdoor (42453) • Australian Gourmet Traveller (42454) • Australian House & Garden (42455) • Australian Motorcycle News (42460) • Australian Mountain Bike (42461) • Australian & NZ Snowboarding (42463) • Australian PC User (42464) • Australian Personal Computer (42465) • Australian Table (42466) • The Australian Women's Weekly (42469) • Autralian & New Zealand Skiing (42470) • The Bulletin with Newsweek (42479) • COLES (42495) • Cosmopolitan (Australia) (42498) • Fernwood (42503) • 4x4 Australia (42505) • Gourmet Traveller WINE (42509) • Harper's Bazaar (Australia) (42512) • Inside Cricket (42516) • Inside Rugby (42517) • Men's Style Australia (42542) • Mother & Baby (42548) • Myer Emporium (42550) • The Picture Premium (42562) • Real Living (42569) • Slimming & Health (42579) • Take 5 (42587)

Acronym Institute for Disarmament Diplomacy
24 Colvestone Cres.
London E8 2LH, United Kingdom
Phone: 44 20 75038857

Fax: 44 20 75038857
Publications: Disarmament Diplomacy (54329)

Acta Biochimica Polonica
L. Pasteura 3
02-093 Warsaw, Poland
Phone: 48 225 892471
Fax: 48 225 892471
Publications: Acta Biochimica Polonica (49678)

ActionAid
33-39 Bowling Green Ln.
London EC1R 0BJ, United Kingdom
Phone: 44 20 31220561
Fax: 44 20 72785667
Publications: Common Cause (54239)

Active Exmoor
7-9 Fore St.
Dulverton TA22 9EX, United Kingdom
Phone: 44 1398 324599
Publications: Active Exmoor (53209)

Acumen Publishing Ltd.
4 Saddler St.
Durham DH1 3NP, United Kingdom
Phone: 44 191 3831889
Fax: 44 191 3862542
Publications: Critical Horizons (53227)

Addico Cornix Ltd.
Tregannick Sancreed Penzance
Cornwall TR20 8QW, United Kingdom
Phone: 44 1736 332736
Fax: 44 1736 334702
Publications: The European Journal of Teleworking (53065)

ADH Publishing Ltd.
Doolittle Mill
Doolittle Ln.
Bedfordshire
Totternhoe LU6 1QX, United Kingdom
Phone: 44 1525 222573
Fax: 44 1525 222574
Publications: Military Illustrated (56765) • Model Airplane International (56766) • Model Military International (56767) • Radio Control Car RACER (56768) • Radio Control Model Flyer (56769) • Rotorworld (56770) • Tamiya Model Magazine International (56771)

Adis International Ltd.
41 Centorian Dr.
PO Box 65901
Mairangi Bay 0754, New Zealand
Phone: 64 9 4770700
Fax: 64 9 4770766
Publications: American Journal of Cancer (48931) • American Journal of Cardiovascular Drugs (48932) • American Journal of Clinical Dermatology (48933) • Clinical Drug Investigation (48934) • Clinical Pharmacokinetics (48935) • High Blood Pressure & Cardiovascular Prevention (46232)

Adonis & Abbey Publishers Ltd.
PO Box 43418
London SE11 4XZ, United Kingdom
Phone: 44 845 3887248
Publications: African Journal of Business and Economic Research (53921) • African Performance Review (53923) • African Renaissance (53924) • Review of Nigeria Affairs (55199)

ADPR Consult (M) Sdn Bhd
PO Box 10762
No. 2, Jalan Sultan Sulaiman
50724 Kuala Lumpur, Malaysia
Phone: 60 3 77812903
Fax: 60 3 77812915
Publications: Asia-Pacific Military Balance (47597) • Show Daily (47635)

Adrenalin Publishing Ltd.
14C Vega Pl.
Mairangi Bay
Auckland, New Zealand
Phone: 64 9 8173818
Publications: BeautyNZ (48953) • DEMM Engineering & Manufacturing Magazine (48954) • Diesel Industry News (48952) • Electrical Automation Technology (48955) • Motor Equipment News (48956) • New Zealand Company Vehicle (48957) • New Zealand 4WD

(48958) • NZ Business (48959) • NZBusiness (48824) • NZ4WD (48825)

Adrenaline Media
One Great Cumberland Pl.
Marble Arch
London W1H 7AL, United Kingdom
Phone: 44 870 0600663
Fax: 44 870 0600664
Publications: News on the Block (55002)

Adsale Publishing Co.
6th Fl., 321 Java Rd.
N Point
Hong Kong, People's Republic of China
Phone: 852 28118897
Fax: 852 25165119
Publications: Asia Textile & Apparel Journal (43271)

Advanstar Communications
Advanstar House Park West
Sealand Rd.
Chester CH1 4RN, United Kingdom
Phone: 44 1244 378888
Fax: 44 1244 370011
Publications: Managed Healthcare Executive (52997) • Pharmaceutical Technology Europe (52998)

Advanstar Communications (UK) Ltd.
Advanstar House
Park W
Sealand Rd.
Chester CH1 4RN, United Kingdom
Phone: 44 1244 378888
Fax: 44 1244 370011
Publications: Automotive Manufacturing Solutions (53989) • LCGC Europe (52996)

Advantage Publishing Ltd.
3rd Fl., Alma House
Alma Rd.
Reigate RH2 0AX, United Kingdom
Fax: 44 17 37241243
Publications: Brewers' Guardian (56386)

Advent-Verlag
Leissigenstrasse 17
CH-3704 Krattigen, Switzerland
Phone: 41 336 541065
Fax: 41 336 544431
Publications: Leben und Gesundheit (Life and Health) (51181)

Advertising & Media Consultants Company Ltd.
18 Fl., Richmond Bldg., Klongtoey
75/65 Sukhumvit 26
Bangkok 10110, Thailand
Phone: 66 662 2042449
Fax: 66 662 2042984
Publications: LookEast (51426) • Thailand Airline Timetable (51441)

The Advocate Company Ltd.
PO Box 230
Fontabelle
Bridgetown, Barbados
Phone: 246467-2000
Fax: 246434-2020
Publications: Barbados Advocate (42827)

Aegean Neurological Society
Ege University Hospital
Dept. of Neurological Surgery
Bornova
TR-35100 Izmir, Turkey
Fax: 90 232 3731330
Publications: Journal of Neurological Sciences (51575)

Aesthetica Magazine Ltd.
PO Box 371
York YO23 1WL, United Kingdom
Phone: 44 1904 527560
Publications: Aesthetica Magazine (56986)

Africa Institute
Africa Institute of South Africa
PO Box 630
Pretoria 0001, Republic of South Africa
Publications: Africa Institute Occasional Papers (50582)

Africa Magna Verlag
J. W Goethe-University

60323 Frankfurt am Main, Germany
Publications: Journal of African Archaeology (44366)

African Centre for the Constructive Resolution or Disputes
2 Golf Course Dr.
Mount Edgecombe 4320, Republic of South Africa
Phone: 27 31 5023908
Fax: 27 31 5024160\
Publications: African Journal on Conflict Resolution (50557) • Conflict Trends Magazine (50558)

African Centre for Technology Studies
PO Box 45917
ICRAF Complex
United Nations Ave.
Gigiri
Nairobi, Kenya
Phone: 254 20 7126889
Fax: 254 20 2339093
Publications: Innovation (47184)

African Crop Science Society
PO Box 7062
Kampala, Uganda
Phone: 256 414 540464
Fax: 256 41 531641
Publications: African Crop Science Journal (51583)

African Elephant Specialist Group
PO Box 68200
Nairobi, Kenya
Phone: 254 20 89060512
Fax: 254 20 890615
Publications: Pachyderm (47195)

African Finance Association
PO Box 610
Bellville 7535, Republic of South Africa
Phone: 27 219 184469
Fax: 27 219 184262
Publications: African Finance Journal (50353)

African Journals Online
PO Box 377
Grahamstown 6140, Republic of South Africa
Phone: 27 466 229698
Fax: 27 466 229550
Publications: Africa Insight (50581) • African Health Sciences (51584) • African Journal of Applied Zoology and Environmental Biology (49165) • African Journal of Biomedical Research (50487) • African Journal of Biotechnology (47170) • African Journal of Clinical and Experimental Microbiology (49117) • African Journal of Cross-Cultural Psychology and Sport Facilitation (50583) • African Journal of Economic Policy (50488) • African Journal of Educational Studies in Mathematics and Sciences (44740) • African Journal of Finance and Management (51399) • African Journal of Food, Agriculture, Nutrition and Development (47172) • African Journal of Health Sciences (47173) • African Journal of International Affairs and Development (49083) • African Journal of Library, Archives and Information Science (49084) • African Journal of Livestock Extension (49085) • African Journal of Marine Science (50489) • African Journal of Oral Health (49110) • African Journal of Paediatric Surgery (49123) • African Journal for the Psychological Study of Social Issues (49086) • African Journal of Reproductive Health (49062) • African Journal of Traditional, Complementary and Alternative Medicines (49111) • African Journal of Tropical Hydrobiology and Fisheries (51582) • African Journal of Urology (43750) • African Research Review (43804) • African Safety Promotion (50547) • African Studies Monographs (50491) • Afrique Science (43555) • Agricultural and Food Science Journal of Ghana (50492) • Agrosearch (49118) • Animal Production Research Advances (49161) • Animal Research International (49155) • Annals of Biomedical Science (49063) • Annals of Ibadan Postgraduate Medicine (50493) • Annals of Nigerian Medicine (49181) • Archives of Ibadan Medicine (49087) • Bio-Research (49156) • Botswana Journal of Technology (42943) • Bulletin of the Chemical Society of Ethiopia (43796) • Cameroon Journal of Agricultural Science (43128) • Cameroon Journal of Experimental Biology (43125) • Central African Journal of Medicine (57113) • Clinics in Mother and Child Health (43129) • Democracy & Development (49106) • Discovery and Innovation (47177) • East African Agricultural and Forestry Journal (47179) • East African

Journal of Public Health (51400) • East African Journal of Sciences (43805) • East African Journal of Statistics (47180) • East African Medical Journal (47181) • East and Central African Journal of Pharmaceutical Sciences (47182) • Eastern Africa Journal of Rural Development (51586) • Economic and Policy Review (49109) • Egyptian Journal of Biochemistry and Molecular Biology (43756) • Egyptian Journal of Biology (43773) • Egyptian Journal of Biomedical Sciences (43757) • Egyptian Journal of Biotechnology (43758) • Egyptian Journal of Medical Laboratory Sciences (43760) • Egyptian Journal of Natural History (43774) • ES-ARBICA Journal (50567) • Ethiopian Economic Journal of Economics (43797) • Ethiopian Journal of Biological Sciences (43798) • Ethiopian Journal of Development Research (43799) • Ethiopian Journal of Health Development (43800) • Ethiopian Journal of the Social Sciences and Humanities (43801) • Ethiopian Pharmaceutical Journal (50494) • Gender and Behaviour (49112) • Ghana Journal of Agricultural Science (50495) • Ghana Journal of Development Studies (44738) • Ghana Journal of Forestry (44735) • Ghana Library Journal (44739) • Ghana Medical Journal (44726) • Global Approaches to Extension Practice (49162) • Global Journal of Agricultural Sciences (49069) • Global Journal of Educational Research (49070) • Global Journal of Engineering Research (50496) • Global Journal of Environmental Sciences (49071) • Global Journal of Geological Sciences (49072) • Global Journal of Humanities (49073) • Global Journal of Mathematical Sciences (50497) • Global Journal of Medical Sciences (49074) • Global Journal of Social Sciences (49076) • Health SA Gesondheid (50348) • Highland Medical Research Journal (49124) • Huria (51401) • IFE PsychologIA (49113) • Information Technologist (49147) • Institute of African Studies (44728) • International Journal of Agriculture and Rural Development (49163) • International Journal of Biological and Chemical Sciences (43126) • International Journal of Development and Policy Studies (49145) • International Journal of Emotional Psychology and Sport Ethics (50346) • International Journal of Humanistic Studies (50943) • International Journal of Natural and Applied Sciences (50498) • International Journal of Tropical Agriculture and Food Systems (50499) • Internet Journal of Medical Update (47752) • Journal of Agricultural Research and Development (49120) • Journal of Agriculture and Social Research (49088) • Journal of Applied Chemistry and Agricultural Research (49061) • Journal of Applied Science, Engineering and Technology (50500) • Journal of Applied Science in Southern Africa (57115) • Journal of Applied Sciences and Environmental Management (49166) • Journal of Aquatic Sciences (49125) • Journal of Biomedical Investigation (49148) • Journal of Building and Land Development (51402) • Journal of the Cameroon Academy of Sciences (43124) • Journal of Child and Adolescent Mental Health (50501) • Journal of Civil Engineering (47186) • Journal of Civil Engineering Research and Practice (47187) • Journal of College of Medicine (49080) • Journal of Community Medicine and Primary Health Care (49182) • Journal of Endocrinology, Metabolism and Diabetes of South Africa (50573) • Journal of Environmental Extension (49089) • Journal of Ethiopian Medical Practice (43802) • Journal of Experimental and Clinical Anatomy (49176) • Journal of Food Technology in Africa (47188) • Journal of Health and Visual Sciences (49177) • Journal for Language Teaching (50349) • Journal of Language, Technology & Entrepreneurship in Africa (47189) • Journal of Librarianship and Information Science in Africa (49090) • Journal of Medical Investigation and Practice (49055) • Journal of Medical Laboratory Sciences (49077) • Journal of Medicine and Biomedical Research (49064) • Journal of Mining and Geology (49091) • Journal of Modeling, Design & Management of Engineering Systems (49167) • Journal of the Musical Arts in Africa (50618) • Journal of the Nigerian Association of Mathematical Physics (49065) • Journal of the Obafemi Awolowo University Medical Student's Association (49114) • Journal of Pharmaceutical and Allied Sciences (49157) • Journal of Pharmacy and Bioresources (49127) • Journal of Philosophy and Culture (50502) • Journal for Phytomedicine and Therapeutics (49056) • Journal of Research in National Development (49164) • Journal for the Study of Religion (50619) • Journal of Technology and Education in Nigeria (49168) • Journal of Tropical Microbiology and Biotechnology (47190) • Journal Tunisien d'ORL et de chirurgie cervico-faciale (51482) • Kenya Veterinarian (47191) • Lagos Business School Management Review (49178) • Lagos Historical Review (49179) • Lagos Journal of Library and Information Science (49140) • Libyan Journal of Medicine (47458) • Lwati (50946) • Makerere Journal of Higher Education (50504) • Malawi Journal of Science and Technology (47573) • Malawi Medical Journal (47566) • Marang (42944) • Mary Slessor Journal of Medicine (49078) • Mathematics Connection (44741) • Moor Journal of Agricultural Research (49092) • Mtafiti Mwafrika (51588) • New Egyptian Journal of Microbiology (43763) • Nigeria Journal of Business Administration (50505) • Nigeria Journal of Pure and Applied Physics (49060) • Nigerian Agricultural Journal (49175) • Nigerian Dental Journal (49105) • Nigerian Food Journal (49160) • Nigerian Hospital Practice (49107) • Nigerian Journal of Animal Production (49093) • Nigerian Journal of Chemical Research (49183) • Nigerian Journal of Clinical and Counselling Psychology (49094) • Nigerian Journal of Clinical Practice (49149) • Nigerian Journal of Economic History (49095) • Nigerian Journal of Fisheries (49146) • Nigerian Journal of Genetics (49096) • Nigerian Journal of Guidance and Counselling (49121) • Nigerian Journal of Health and Biomedical Sciences (49141) • Nigerian Journal of Horticultural Science (49097) • Nigerian Journal of Natural Products and Medicine (49115) • Nigerian Journal of Ophthalmology (49098) • Nigerian Journal of Orthopaedics and Trauma (49170) • Nigerian Journal of Otorhinolaryngology (49082) • Nigerian Journal of Paediatrics (49099) • Nigerian Journal of Parasitology (50506) • Nigerian Journal of Pharmaceutical Research (49128) • Nigerian Journal of Physics (50507) • Nigerian Journal of Physiological Sciences (49079) • Nigerian Journal of Plastic Surgery (49100) • Nigerian Journal of Psychiatry (49171) • Nigerian Journal of Soil & Environmental Research (49184) • Nigerian Journal of Soil Science (50508) • Nigerian Libraries (49180) • Nigerian Medical Practitioner (49108) • Nigerian Music Review (49116) • Nigerian Quarterly Journal of Hospital Medicine (49142) • Nigerian Veterinary Journal (49186) • Obstetrics and Gynaecology Forum (50532) • Orient Journal of Medicine (49081) • OYE (49059) • Philosophical Papers (50510) • Plant Products Research Journal (49152) • Port Harcourt Medical Journal (49169) • Sahara J (50599) • Sahel Medical Journal (49174) • Samaru Journal of Information Studies (49187) • Sciences & Nature (43557) • Scientific Medical Journal (43765) • Securities Market Journal (50512) • SINET (43803) • South African Actuarial Journal (50643) • South African Family Practice (50639) • South African Gastroenterology Review (50534) • South African Journal of Agricultural Extension (50601) • South African Journal of Bioethics and Law (50412) • South African Journal of Child Health (50413) • South African Journal Clinical Nutrition (50514) • South African Journal of Obstetrics and Gynaecology (50574) • South African Journal of Philosophy (53237) • South African Journal of Psychiatry (50575) • South African Journal of Radiology (50576) • South African Journal for Research in Sport, Physical Education and Recreation (50635) • South African Journal of Surgery (50577) • South African Psychiatry Review (50535) • Southern Africa Journal of Science and Technology (57112) • Southern African Journal of Anaesthesia and Analgesia (50536) • Southern African Linguistics and Applied Language Studies (50515) • Sudan Journal of Medical Sciences (50516) • Sudanese Journal of Dermatology (50939) • Tanzania Dental Journal (50517) • Tanzania Journal of Forestry and Nature Conservation (51407) • Tanzania Journal of Science (51403) • Tanzania Medical Journal (51404) • Tanzania Veterinary Journal (51408) • Tanzanian Journal of Health Research (51405) • Tropical Freshwater Biology (49066) • Tropical Journal of Animal Science (49101) • Tropical Journal of Health Sciences (49122) • Tropical Journal of Medical Research (49151) • Tropical Journal of Obstetrics and Gynaecology (49102) • Tropical Veterinarian (49103) • Tydskrif vir letterkunde (50607) • UNISWA Journal of Agriculture (50945) • UNISWA Research Journal of Agriculture, Science and Technology (50944) • University of Dar es Salaam Library Journal (51406) • West African Journal of Applied Ecology (44730) • West African Journal of Medicine (49104) • West African Journal of Pharmacol-

ogy and Drug Research (49068) • West African Journal of Radiology (49153) • Zambezia (57120) • Zimbabwe Journal of Educational Research (57122)

African Network of Scientific and Technological Institutions
PO Box 30592
Nairobi, Kenya
Phone: 254 2 7622619
Fax: 254 2 7622538
Publications: African Journal of Science and Technology (47174)

African Soccer Magazine
Unit F, Octagon Ct.
443-449 Holloway Rd.
London N7 6LJ, United Kingdom
Phone: 44 207 5610011
Fax: 44 207 2812377
Publications: African Soccer Magazine (53926)

Afro-Asian Rural Development Organization
2, State Guest Houses Complex
Chanakyapuri
New Delhi 100 021, Delhi, India
Phone: 91 11 24100475
Fax: 91 11 24672045
Publications: Afro-Asian Journal of Rural Development (45479)

Afro Universe Media
25B Admiral St.
London SE8 4HY, United Kingdom
Phone: 44 20 86946680
Fax: 44 20 86922454
Publications: Cas London (54186)

AFT Publishing
7 Executive Ste.
St. James Ct.
Wilderspool Cswy.
Warrington WA4 6PS, United Kingdom
Phone: 44 1925 444414
Publications: Context (56848)

AFTC Publishing Pty Ltd.
PO Box 322
Gosford, New South Wales 2250, Australia
Phone: 61 243 292400
Fax: 61 243 292444
Publications: Australian Family Tree Connections (41904)

Age Concern England
207-221 Pentonville Rd.
London N1 9UZ, United Kingdom
Publications: Information Bulletin (54602)

Aged and Community Services Australia
Level 1, 36 Albert Rd.
South Melbourne, Victoria 3205, Australia
Phone: 61 3 96863460
Fax: 61 3 96863453
Publications: Agendas (42366) • Australasian Journal on Ageing (42367)

AGEFI Luxembourg
111b Rte. d'Arlon
L-8311 Capellen, Luxembourg
Phone: 352 305 7571
Publications: AGEFI Luxembourg (47488)

Agencia Espanola de Cooperacion Internacional
Avda. de los Reyes Catolicos, 4
E-28040 Madrid, Spain
Phone: 34 915 838100
Fax: 34 915 838310
Publications: Cuadernos Hispanoamericanos (50744)

Agora S.A.
Czerska 8/10
PL-00-732 Warsaw, Poland
Phone: 48 22 5556880
Fax: 48 22 5556674
Publications: Kwietnik (49729)

Agra Europe Ltd.
80 Calverley Rd.
Tunbridge Wells TN1 2UN, United Kingdom
Phone: 44 20 70177500
Fax: 44 20 70177599
Publications: Agra Europe Weekly (56776) • AgraFood East Europe (56777) • Dairy Markets Weekly (56780) • Eurofood (56782)

Agri-Horticultural Society of India
1 Alipore Rd.
Kolkata 700 027, West Bengal, India
Phone: 91 33 24791713
Fax: 91 33 24793580
Publications: Horticultural Journal (45268)

Agribusiness Association of Australia
PO Box 504
Farrell Flat, South Australia 5416, Australia
Phone: 61 44884 0232
Fax: 61 88127 8052
Publications: Agribusiness Connections (41865)

Agricultural Biotechnology Research Institute of Iran
Seed & Plant Improvement Institutes Campus
Mahdasht Rd.
PO Box 31535-1897
Karaj, Iran
Phone: 98 261 2703536
Fax: 98 261 2704539
Publications: Applied Entomology and Phytopathology (45887)

Agricultural Economics Association of South Africa
Private Bag x935
Pretoria 0001, Republic of South Africa
Publications: Agrekon (50552)

Agricultural Engineers' Association
Samuelson House
62 Forder Way
Hampton
Peterborough PE7 8JB, United Kingdom
Phone: 44 845 6448748
Fax: 44 1733 314767
Publications: The Essential Guide to UK Farm & Outdoor Power Equipment (56256)

Agricultural Research Information Centre
1314 HIG-II (GF)
Housing Board Colony
Sec. 15A
Hisar 125 001, Haryana, India
Publications: Crop Research (45346)

Agricultural University of Poznan Press
Wolynska 33
PL-60-637 Poznan, Poland
Publications: Acta Scientarum Polonorum - Technologia Alimentaria (49673)

Agrimedia Ltd.
Ashcroft House
Tancreds Rd., R D 2
PO Box 37-151
Christchurch, New Zealand
Phone: 64 3 3296555
Fax: 64 3 3296550
Publications: Australian AG Contractor and Large Scale Farmer (48863) • New Zealand AgriBusiness (48871) • New Zealand AgriVet (48872) • New Zealand Rural Contractor and Large Scale Farmer (48875)

Agronomic Scientific Society of Portugal
Rua de Junqueira 299
P-1300 Lisbon, Portugal
Phone: 351 213633719
Publications: Revista de Ciencias Agrarias (49805)

Agudath Israel World Organization
5 Yehudah Hamacabi St.
PO Box 1306
IL-91002 Jerusalem, Israel
Phone: 972 2 538 9255
Fax: 972 2 500 3384
Publications: Hamodia (Israel) (46082)

Ahl al-Bayt ('a) World Assembly
PO Box 15815-1956
Tehran, Iran
Phone: 98 21 890226
Publications: Message of Thaqalayn (45912)

Aide et Action
53 blvd. de Charonne
F-75545 Paris, France
Phone: 33 155 257000
Fax: 33 155 257029
Publications: Aide et Action (44023)

Air-Britain Historians
Victoria House
Stanbridge Pk.
Staplefield Ln.
Staplefield RH17 6AS, United Kingdom
Phone: 44 1932783888
Publications: Aeromilitaria (55614)

Airfleet Review
PO Box 77
125057 Moscow, Russia
Phone: 7 95 4575244
Publications: Airfleet (49869)

AK Wien
Prinz Eugen Str. 20-22
A-1040 Vienna, Austria
Phone: 43 150 1650
Publications: Wirschaft und Gesellschaft (42774)

Akademiai Kiado Rt.
Prielle Kornelia u. 19/D
PO Box 245
H-1117 Budapest, Hungary
Phone: 36 146 48282
Fax: 36 146 48251
Publications: Across Languages and Cultures (44804) • Acta Agronomica Hungarica (44890) • Acta Alimentaria (44805) • Acta Antiqua Academiae Scientiarum Hungaricae (44806) • Acta Archaeologica Academiae Scientiarum Hungaricae (44807) • Acta Biologica Hungarica (44808) • Acta Botanica Hungarica (44893) • Acta Ethnographica Hungarica (44894) • Acta Geodaetica et Geophysica Hungarica (44809) • Acta Geologica Hungarica (44810) • Acta Historiae Artium (44811) • Acta Juridica Hungarica (44812) • Acta Linguistica Hungarica (44813) • Acta Microbiologica et Immunologica Hungarica (44814) • Acta Oeconomica (44815) • Acta Orientalia Academiae Scientiarum Hungaricae (44816) • Acta Physiologica Hungarica (44817) • Acta Phytopathologica et Entomologica Hungarica (44818) • Acta Veterinaria Hungarica (44819) • Agrokemia es Talajtan (44821) • Antik Tanulmanyok (44822) • Archaeologiai Ertesito (44823) • Community Ecology (44827) • Epites - Epiteszettudomany (44828) • Hungarian Medical Journal (44835) • Hungarian Studies (44837) • Journal of Evolutionary Psychology (44841) • Journal of Planar Chromatography (44842) • Magyar Pszichologiai Szemle (44846) • Magyar Sebeszet (44847) • Mentalhigiene es Pszichoszomatika (44852) • Muveszettorteneti Ertesito (44853) • Nanopages (44854) • Orvosi Hetilap (44862) • Pollack Periodica (44864) • Progress in Agricultural Engineering Sciences (44866) • Review of Sociology of the Hungarian Sociological Association (44867) • Scientometrics (44869) • Society and Economy (44870) • Studia Musicologica Academiae Scientiarum Hungaricae (44875) • Studia Scientiarum Mathematicarum Hungarica (44876) • Tarsadalom es Gazdasag (Society and Economy) (44879) • Tarsadalomkutatas (44880) • Verbum (44889)

Akademikerforbundet SSR
PO Box 12800
S-112 96 Stockholm, Sweden
Phone: 46 861 74400
Publications: Socionomen (51040)

Akedemi Gizi
Jl. Hang Jebat III/F3
Kebayoran Baru
PO Box 8 KBB
Jakarta, Indonesia
Publications: Gizi Indonesia (45798)

AKG Actuaries & Consultants Ltd.
Anderton House
92 S St.
Dorking RH4 2EW, United Kingdom
Phone: 44 130 6876439
Fax: 44 130 6885325
Publications: Company Profile & Financial Strength Update (53194)

Al Habtoor Group L.L.C.
PO Box 25444
Dubai, United Arab Emirates
Phone: 971 4 3431111
Fax: 971 4 3431140
Publications: Al Shindagah (51629)

Al Hilal Publishing & Marketing Group
Hilal Al Khaleej
Al Moosa Business Ctr.
Umm Hurair Rd.
PO Box 6387
Dubai, United Arab Emirates
Phone: 971 4 3371366
Fax: 971 4 3371344
Publications: Gulf Industry Magazine (51644)

Al Hilal Publishing & Marketing Group
PO Box 224
Manama, Bahrain
Phone: 973 172 93131
Fax: 973 172 93400
Publications: Gulf Construction (42788) • Gulf Daily News (42789) • Gulf Industry (42790) • Gulf Weekly (42791) • Oil and Gas News (42793) • Travel & Tourism News Middle East (42794)

Alain Charles Publishing Ltd.
University House
11-13 Lower Grosvenor Pl.
London SW1W 0EX, United Kingdom
Phone: 44 20 78347676
Fax: 44 20 79730076
Publications: African Farming and Food Processing (53920) • African Review of Business and Technology (53925) • China Economic Review (54207) • Communications Africa (54246) • Far Eastern Agriculture (54443) • Oil Review Middle East (55027) • Technical Review Middle East (55294)

Albanian Political Science Association
PO Box 8199
Tirana, Albania
Publications: Southeast European Politics (44871)

Albatross Publications
PO Box 523
Horsham RH12 4WL, United Kingdom
Phone: 44 1293 871201
Fax: 44 1293 871301
Publications: Kennel and Cattery Management (53596) • Prestige Corporate Interiors (53597) • Prestige High Street Interiors (53598) • Prestige Hotel & Restaurant Interiors (53599) • Professional Landscaper & Groundsman (53600)

Album, Letras y Artes S.L.
Juan Alvarez Mendizabal, 58
E-28008 Madrid, Spain
Phone: 34 915 479742
Fax: 34 915 599027
Publications: Album (50727)

Alcohol Concern
64 Leman St.
London E1 8EU, United Kingdom
Phone: 44 20 72640510
Fax: 44 20 74889213
Publications: Drug and Alcohol Findings (54344)

Alcoholics Anonymous - Brazil
Av. Senador Queiros 101, 2 Andar, cj 205
PO Box 580
01060-970 Sao Paulo, Sao Paulo, Brazil
Phone: 55 11 32293611
Publications: Revista Vivencia (43048)

Alfa Lotfeeding Magazine
Unit 6, 99-101 Western Ave.
Tullamarine, Victoria 3043, Australia
Publications: Alfa Lotfeeding Magazine (42645)

Aligarh Muslim University
Dept. of Political Science
Aligarh 202 002, Uttar Pradesh, India
Publications: Aligarh Journal of English Studies (44917)

All China Women's Federation
15 Jia Guo Men Nei St.
Beijing 100730, People's Republic of China
Phone: 86 106 5103556
Fax: 86 106 5112107
Publications: Women of China (43223)

All England Netball Association
Netball House
9 Paynes Pk.
Hitchin SG5 1EH, United Kingdom
Phone: 44 1462 442344

Fax: 44 1462 442343
Publications: Netball Magazine (53581)

All India Catholic University Federation
St. Xavier's College
30 Mother Teresa Sarani
Kolkata 700 016, West Bengal, India
Publications: Rally (45302)

All India Industrial Gases Manufacturers Association
66 Masjid Moth, 2nd Fl.
Near Uday Pk.
New Delhi 110 049, Delhi, India
Phone: 91 11 26251688
Fax: 91 11 26255732
Publications: Gas News (45518)

All India Institute of Medical Sciences
Ansari Nagar
New Delhi 110 029, Delhi, India
Phone: 91 11 26588500
Fax: 91 11 26588663
Publications: The National Medical Journal of India (45629)

All India Occupational Therapists' Association
Dept. of Occupational Therapy
Manipal College of Allied Sciences
Udupi 576 104, Karnataka, India
Phone: 91 820 2574136
Fax: 91 820 2571915
Publications: Indian Journal of Occupational Therapy (45763)

All India Ophthalmological Society
c/o Dr. Rajvardhan Azad, Pres.
M-18 Saket
Road No. 50
New Delhi 110 017, Punjab, India
Phone: 91 11 26198126
Publications: Indian Journal of Ophthalmology (45385)

All India Organisation of Employers
Federation House
Tansen Marg
New Delhi 110 001, Delhi, India
Phone: 91 112 3738770
Fax: 91 112 3320714
Publications: AIOE Labour News (45481)

All India Reporter Pvt.Ltd.
Congress Nagar
Nagpur 440 012, Maharashtra, India
Phone: 91 712 2526991
Fax: 91 712 2526283
Publications: All India Reporter (45464) • Criminal Law Journal (45465) • Labour and Industrial Cases (45469) • Taxation Law Reports (45446)

All India Women's Conference
Sarojini House
6 Bhagwan Dass Rd.
New Delhi 110 001, Delhi, India
Phone: 91 112 3389680
Fax: 91 112 3384092
Publications: Roshni (45646)

Allergy Society of South Africa
PO Box 88
Observatory 7935
Cape Town 7935, Republic of South Africa
Phone: 27 21 4479019
Fax: 27 21 4480846
Publications: Current Allergy & Clinical Immunology (50372)

Alliance Francaise
1 Sarkies Rd.
Singapore 258130, Singapore
Phone: 65 67378422
Fax: 65 67333023
Publications: Lien (50216)

Alliance of Registered Homeopaths
Millbrook
Millbrook Hill
Nutley TN22 3PJ, United Kingdom
Phone: 44 1825 714506
Fax: 44 1825 714506
Publications: Homeopathy in Practice (55779)

Allied Press Ltd.
52 Stuart St.

PO Box 517
Dunedin, New Zealand
Phone: 64 3 4774760
Fax: 64 3 4747424
Publications: Courier Country (48987) • The Ensign (48902) • Greymouth Star (48904) • Hurunui News (48782) • Otago Daily Times (48892) • Southern Rural Life (48893) • The West Coast Messenger (48905) • West Coast Times (48917)

Alpha Newspaper Group
83 Wellington St.
Ballymena BT43 6AD, United Kingdom
Phone: 44 28 25641221
Fax: 44 28 25653920
Publications: Ballymena Guardian (52159)

Alphabet Media
12 Prince Edward Rd.
No. 03-01, Podium A Bestway Bldg.
Singapore City 079212, Singapore
Phone: 65 63363136
Fax: 65 6324 1228
Publications: Asian Security Review (50311) • Future-Gov (50312)

AltaMira Press
4501 Forbes Blvd., Ste. 200
Lanham, MD 20706
Phone: 301459-3366
Fax: 301429-5748
Free: 800462-6420
Publications: Archaeologies (50617)

The Alumni Relations Committee, NUS Law School
13 Law Link
Kent Ridge
Singapore 117590, Singapore
Fax: 65 677 90979
Publications: LawLink (50213)

The Alvar Aalto Academy
PO Box 461
FIN-40101 Jyvaskyla, Finland
Phone: 358 14 624809
Fax: 358 14 619009
Publications: ptah (43871)

Amateur Entomologists' Society
PO Box 8774
London SW7 5ZG, United Kingdom
Publications: AES Bug Club Magazine (53914) • The Bulletin (54156)

Amateur Yacht Research Society
BCM, AYRS
London WC1N 3XX, United Kingdom
Phone: 44 1727 862268
Fax: 44 1727 862268
Publications: Journal (54694)

Ambergris Today Newspaper
Pescador Dr.
Ambergris Caye
PO Box 23
San Pedro Town, Belize
Phone: 501 2263462
Fax: 501 2263483
Publications: Ambergris Today (42919)

Ambit
17 Priory Gardens
Highgate
London N6 5QY, United Kingdom
Publications: Ambit (53938)

AmCham Argentina
Viamonte 1133, Piso 8
1053 Buenos Aires, Argentina
Phone: 54 114 3714500
Fax: 54 114 3718400
Publications: Comments on Argentine Trade (41471)

American in Britain Ltd.
Yewlands House
Millbrook House
East Sussex
Nutley TN22 3PH, United Kingdom
Phone: 44 18 25713676
Fax: 44 18 25713687
Publications: American in Britain (55778)

American Chamber of Commerce in Korea
No. 4501, Trade Twr.
159-1 Samsung-dong, Kangnam-gu
Seoul 135-729, Republic of Korea
Phone: 82 25642040
Fax: 82 25642050
Publications: American Chamber of Commerce in Korea (47252)

American Chamber of Commerce - People's Republic of China
The Office Park, Tower AB, 6th Fl.
No. 10 Jintongxi Rd.
Beijing 100005, People's Republic of China
Phone: 86 10 85190800
Fax: 86 10 85190899
Publications: China Brief (43176)

American Chamber of Commerce of the Philippines
2/F Corinthian Plz., Paseo de Roxas
CPO 2562
Makati City 1229, Philippines
Phone: 63 2 8187911
Fax: 63 2 8113081
Publications: AmCham Business Journal (49514)

The American Chamber of Commerce in Thailand
7th Fl., GPF Witthayu A
93/1 Wireless Rd.
Lumphini
Pathumwan
Bangkok 10330, Thailand
Phone: 66 2254 1041
Fax: 66 2651 1605
Publications: Thai-American Business (51437)

American Psychological Association
750 1st St. NE
Washington, DC 20002-4242
Phone: 202336-5500
Fax: 202336-5549
Free: 800374-2721
Publications: European Psychologist (44488) • Psychology, Public Policy, and Law (42564)

American Scientific Publishers
26650 The Old Rd., Ste. 208
Valencia, CA 91381-0751
Phone: 661799-7200
Fax: 661799-7230
Publications: Journal of Biopharmaceutics and Biotechnology (46088)

American Studies Association of Turkey
c/o Gulriz Buken, Pres.
Bilkent University
Department of History
Faculty of Economic, Administrative & Social Sciences
Ankara, Turkey
Phone: 90 312 2902341
Publications: Journal of American Studies of Turkey (51494)

American Women's Association of Hong Kong
C-7 Monticello
48 Kennedy Rd.
Hong Kong, People's Republic of China
Phone: 852 25272961
Fax: 852 28657737
Publications: Aware (43282)

Amnesty International - AI Swiss Section
PO Box 3001
CH 3001 Bern, Switzerland
Phone: 41 313 072222
Fax: 41 313 072233
Publications: Amnestie (51069)

Amnesty International Dutch Section
PO Box 1968
NL-1000 BZ Amsterdam, Netherlands
Phone: 31 206 264436
Publications: Wordt Vervolgd (48271)

Anand Aaron
No. 12, 6th Main Rd.
Kasthuribai Nagar
Adyar
Chennai 600 020, Tamil Nadu, India
Phone: 91 44 24450587
Publications: Chess Mate (45029)

Anatolia
P.K. 589
TR-06444 Ankara, Turkey
Phone: 90 312 4791084
Fax: 90 312 4791084
Publications: Anatolia (51554)

Anatomical Society
U.S. Department of of Human Anatomy & Genetics
University of Oxford
South Parks Rd.
Oxford OX1 3QX, United Kingdom
Publications: Annals of Anatomy (55868)

Andolu University
Yunusemre Campus
TR-26470 Eskisehir, Turkey
Phone: 90 222 3350580
Fax: 90 222 3353616
Publications: Turkish Online Journal of Distance Education (51555)

Andromeda Spaceways
PO Box 7311
Kaleen, Australian Capital Territory 2617, Australia
Publications: Andromeda Spaceways Inflight Magazine (41981)

Angel Business Communications Ltd.
Unit 6, Bow Ct.
Fletchworth Gate
Burnsall Rd.
Coventry CV5 6SP, United Kingdom
Phone: 44 2476 718970
Fax: 44 2476 718971
Publications: EurOhs Magazine (53081)

AngelWoche/Deutsche Sportfischer Zeitung
Troplowitzstrasse 5
D-22529 Hamburg, Germany
Phone: 49 40 38906131
Fax: 49 40 38906307
Publications: AngelWoche (44409)

Anglican Communion Office
St. Andrew's House
16 Tavistock Cres.
London W11 1AP, United Kingdom
Phone: 44 20 73133900
Fax: 44 20 73133999
Publications: Anglican World (53943)

The Anglo-Celt
Sta. House
Cavan, Cavan, Ireland
Phone: 353 49 4331100
Publications: The Anglo-Celt (45930)

The Angry Corrie
3 Ferry Orchard
Cambuskenneth FK9 5ND, United Kingdom
Phone: 44 1786 450047
Publications: The Angry Corrie (52912)

ANIGP—Asociacion Nacional de Informadores Graficos de Prensa y T.V.
Espronceda, 32
5a Planta
E-28003 Madrid, Spain
Phone: 34 914 413045
Fax: 34 914 420897
Publications: ANIGP-TV (50728)

Animal Aid
The Old Chapel
Bradford St.
Tonbridge TN9 1AW, United Kingdom
Phone: 44 1732 364546
Fax: 44 1732 366533
Publications: Outrage (56756)

Animal Feed Manufacturers Association
PO Box 8144
Centurion 0046, Republic of South Africa
Phone: 27 126 639097
Fax: 27 126 639612
Publications: AFMA Matrix (50436)

Animal Health Australia
Ste. 15, 26-28 Napier Close
Deakin, Australian Capital Territory 2600, Australia
Phone: 61 262 325522
Fax: 61 262 325511
Publications: Animal Health Australia (41832)

Animals Australia
37 O'Connell St.
North Melbourne, Victoria 3051, Australia
Phone: 61 3 93296333
Fax: 61 3 93296441
Publications: Animals Today (42156)

Ankara University Rectorate
Dogol Caddesi
06100 Tandogan
Ankara, Turkey
Phone: 90 312 2126040
Fax: 90 312 2126049
Publications: Journal of Modern Turkish Studies
(JMTS) (51495)

Anon
67 Learmonth Grove
Edinburgh EH4 1BL, United Kingdom
Publications: Anon (53250)

Another Publishing Ltd.
112 Old St.
London EC1V 9BG, United Kingdom
Phone: 44 20 73660766
Fax: 44 20 73660966
Publications: Another Magazine (53953)

Anthem Publishing Limited
Piccadilly House, Ste. 6
London Rd.
Bath BA1 6PL, United Kingdom
Phone: 44 1225 489984
Fax: 44 1225 489980
Publications: Italia! (52246) • Music Tech Magazine
(52252) • Sporting Legends (52259) • Taste Italia
(52260)

Anthroposophical Society in Great Britain
Rudolf Steiner House
35 Pk. Rd.
London NW1 6XT, United Kingdom
Phone: 44 20 77234400
Fax: 44 20 77244364
Publications: New View (55000)

Antiques & Art Independent
PO Box 3369
Wilts
Chippenham SN15 9DU, United Kingdom
Phone: 44 1225 742240
Publications: Antiques & Art Independent (53020)

Antiques Information Services Ltd.
PO Box 93
Broadstairs CT10 3YR, United Kingdom
Phone: 44 1843 862069
Fax: 44 1843 862014
Publications: Antiques Info (52744)

Antiquity Publications Ltd.
King's Manor
York YO1 7EP, United Kingdom
Publications: Antiquity (56987)

Anton Melik Geographical Institute
PO Box 306
SI-1001 Ljubljana, Slovenia
Publications: Acta Geographica Slovenica (50336)

ANU Reporter
Australian National University
Canberra, Australian Capital Territory 0200, Australia
Phone: 61 261 255111
Fax: 61 261 255931
Publications: ANU Reporter (41697)

ANWB Media
PO Box 93557
NL-2509 AN The Hague, Netherlands
Publications: Autokampioen (48608) • Kampioen
(48619) • KCK (48620) • Op Pad (48623) • Pro Motor
(48626) • Reizen (48627) • Waterkampioen (48629)

AOCS Press
2710 S Boulder
Urbana, IL 61802-6996
Phone: 217359-2344
Fax: 217351-8091
Publications: Journal of Surfactants and Detergents
(57028)

AP Energy Business Publications Private Ltd.
63 Robinson Rd., No. 02-16

Singapore 68894, Singapore
Phone: 65 622 23422
Fax: 65 622 25587
Publications: Hydrocarbon Asia (50168) • Petromin
(50237)

AP Publications Ltd.
58 Ryecroft Way
Luton LU2 7TU, United Kingdom
Phone: 44 15 82722219
Publications: Database and Network Journal (55502) •
Software World (55505)

Apex Publishing
PO Box 2616
Muscat 112, Oman
Phone: 968 247 99388
Fax: 968 247 93316
Publications: Business Today (49220) • Oman Today
(49223)

APN Educational Media
Level 1, Saatchi & Saatchi Bldg.
Wellington, New Zealand
Phone: 64 4 4711600
Fax: 64 4 4711080
Publications: Campus Review (42484) • New Zealand
Education Gazette (49019)

APN New Zealand Ltd.
PO Box 1467
Christchurch, New Zealand
Publications: The Christchurch Star (48866)

APN News & Media Ltd.
100 William St., Level 4
Sydney, New South Wales 2011, Australia
Phone: 61 2 93334999
Fax: 61 2 93334900
Publications: Ballina Shire Advocate (42472) • Ba-
lonne Beacon (42473) • Big Rigs (42474) • Blackwater
Herald (42475) • Bribie Weekly (42476) • Buderim
Chronicle (42478) • Bush Telegraph (42480) • Byron
Shire News (42481) • Caboolture News (42482) •
Caloundra Weekly (42483) • Capricorn Coast Mirror
(42485) • Central & North Burnett Times (42487) •
Central Queensland News (42488) • Central Telegraph
(42489) • Chinchilla News and Murilla Advertiser
(42491) • COAST (42492) • Coastal Views (42493) •
The Coffs Coast Advocate (42494) • Cooloola Adver-
tiser (42497) • The Daily Examiner (42499) • Dalby
Herald (42500) • Fraser Coast Chronicle (42506) •
Gatton, Lockyer and Brisbane Valley Star (42507) •
Gold Coast Mail (42508) • The Gympie Times (42511) •
Hawke's Bay Today (48915) • Hervey Bay Observer
(42514) • The Ipswich Advertiser (42522) • Isis Town &
Country (42523) • Island & Mainland News (42524) •
The Kolan Recorder (42533) • Mackay & Sarina Mid-
Week (42537) • Maroochy Weekly (42540) • The Mary-
borough Herald (42541) • Miners MidWeek (42546) •
The Morning Bulletin (42547) • Nambour Weekly
(42551) • NewsMail (42552) • North West Country
(42553) • The North West Star (42554) • Northern
Downs News (42555) • The Northern Rivers Echo
(42556) • Port Curtis Post (42563) • QT (42566) • The
Range News (42568) • The Richmond River Express
Examiner (42570) • The Rivertown Times (42571) •
Rockhampton and Fitzroy News (42572) • Rural Weekly
(Central Queensland edition) (42573) • Rural Weekly
(North CQ edition) (42574) • Rural Weekly (Southern
edition) (42575) • Rural Weekly (Wide Bay edition)
(42576) • The Satellite (42577) • South Burnett Times
(42580) • The Stanthorpe Border Post (42581) •
Sunshine Coast Daily (42583) • Sunshine Coast
Sunday (42584) • Surat Basin News (42585) • Too-
woomba's Mail (42588) • Tweed/Border Mail (42589) •
Tweed Daily News (42590) • Warwick Daily News
(42591) • Warwick & Southern Downs Weekly
(42592) • Whitsunday Times (42593)

Applied Linguistics Association of New Zealand
c/o Dr. Gillian Skyrme
School of Language Studies
Massey University
Private Bag 11 222
Palmerston North, New Zealand
Publications: New Zealand Studies in Applied Linguis-
tics (48964)

Aquamedia N.V.
Vrijheidslaan 4

B-9000 Gent, Belgium
Phone: 32 921 11816
Fax: 32 921 11817
Publications: Varen (42884)

Aquaristik
Postfach 250
D-76256 Ettlingen, Germany
Phone: 49 724 3575105
Fax: 49 724 3575100
Publications: Aquaristik (44348)

Arab Horse Society
Windsor House
The Sq.
Marlborough SN8 2PE, United Kingdom
Phone: 44 16 72521411
Publications: Arab Horse Society News (55599)

**Arab League Educational, Cultural and
Scientific Organization**
BP 1120
Mohamed V Ave.
TN-1120 Tunis, Tunisia
Phone: 216 71 785751
Publications: Journal of the Arabization Bureau (51489)

Arab Organization for Agricultural Development
PO Box 474 S, No. 7
Al Amarat
Khartoum, Sudan
Phone: 24 911 472176
Fax: 24 911 471402
Publications: Agriculture and Development in the Arab
World (50938)

Aranda Editora Ltda.
Alameda Olga, 315
01155-900 Sao Paulo, Sao Paulo, Brazil
Phone: 55 113 8245300
Fax: 55 113 6629585
Publications: Eletricidade Moderna (43039) • Fundi-
cao e Servicos (43040) • Maquinas e Metals (43042) •
Plastico Industrial (43044) • RTI Redes Telecom Insta-
lacoes (43049)

**Arbeitsgemeinschaft der Wissenschaftlichen
Medizinischen Fachgesellschaften**
Ubierstr. 20
D-40223 Dusseldorf, Germany
Phone: 49 211 312828
Fax: 49 211 316819
Publications: German Medical Science (44326) •
Psycho-Social-Medicine (44332)

Arboricultural Association
Ullenwood Ct.
Hampshire
Gloucestershire
Cheltenham GL53 9QS, United Kingdom
Phone: 44 1242 522152
Fax: 44 1242 577766
Publications: Arboricultural Journal (52963)

**Archaeological and Historical Research Center
Medieval**
University of Caen-Low-Normandy
Esplanade of Peace
F-14032 Caen Cedex, France
Phone: 33 231 565725
Fax: 33 231 565495
Publications: Tabularia (43926)

Archaeological Society of India
B-17, Qutab Institutional Area
New Delhi 110 016, Delhi, India
Phone: 91 11 26523728
Fax: 91 11 26960654
Publications: Epigraphia Indica (45510)

Archant Life
Prospect House
Rouen Rd.
Norwich NR1 1RE, United Kingdom
Phone: 44 1603 772101
Publications: Birmingham Life (52964) • Brighton &
Hove Life (55726) • Buckinghamshire Life (56896) •
Cheltenham Oracle (52965) • Compass South
(55729) • Compass Wessex (55730) • Cornwall Life
(56761) • Durham County Life (56299) • French
Property News (55731) • Herefordshire Life (52153) •
Islington Gazette (EC1 Edition) (54684) • A Kentish
Partnership (56974) • A Kentish Wedding (56975) •

Lake District Life (56301) • Lancashire Life (56303) • Leicestershire Magazine (53165) • Living Edge (53503) • Living Hadley (53674) • Living North (53675) • North (55010) • North East Life (53569) • Northwest (55012) • The Oracle Gloucester Life (52973) • Oxfordshire Life (52974) • Peak District Life (53167) • Photography Monthly (56429) • Pure Weddings (56305) • Pure Weddings North (55740) • The Resident (London) (55191) • Rise (55203) • Shropshire Life (52976) • Somerset Life (56763) • Staffordshire County (52977) • Surrey Life (56977) • Sussex Life (56978) • Warwickshire Life (52979) • West Essex Life (56959) • Westside Magazine (55399) • Wiltshire (56764) • Wood & Vale Express (55744) • Worcestershire Life (52981) • Yorkshire Life (56400)

Archant Regional Ltd.
Prospect House
Rouen Rd.
Norwich NR1 1RE, United Kingdom
Phone: 44 1603 772772
Publications: Agricultural Trader (52190) • Anglia Afloat (55722) • Beccles & Bungay Journal (55724) • Bexley Times (56540) • Cambridgeshire Agenda (52800) • Cambridgeshire Property Plus (52801) • Cambs Times (55592) • Camden Gazette (54169) • Coastal Advertiser (53653) • Country Smallholding (53350) • Dartford Times (56542) • Dereham Times (53171) • Diss Mercury (53185) • East Anglian Daily Times (53655) • East Anglian Daily Times Suffolk (53656) • East Herts Edition Herald (56882) • East London Advertiser (54347) • Ely Standard (53331) • Exmouth Herald (53357) • Gravesend Reporter (53479) • Great Yarmouth Advertiser (53482) • Great Yarmouth Mercury (53483) • Green Un (Ipswich) (53657) • Hackney Gazette (54528) • Harlow Edition Herald (53511) • health24 (55732) • Herts Advertiser (56436) • Hornsey & Crouch End Journal (54568) • The Hunts Post (53635) • Ilford & Redbridge Post (53639) • Kilburn Times (54844) • Let's Talk! (55733) • Lowestoft Journal (55496) • Midweek Herald (55734) • Newham Recorder (53341) • North Devon Gazette (52191) • North Norfolk Advertiser (55736) • North Norfolk News (53118) • Norwich Advertiser (55737) • The Pink 'Un (55738) • Romford & Havering Post (53342) • Royston Crow (56415) • Saffron Walden Reporter (56430) • Stratford & Newham Express (53640) • Thetford & Brandon Times (55742) • Watton & Swaffham Times (56696) • Waveney Advertiser (53484) • Welwyn & Hatfield Times (56884) • Wembley & Kingsbury Times (55397) • Weston & Somerset Mercury (56906) • Willesden & Brent Times (55406) • Wisbech Standard (55593) • Wymondham & Attleborough Mercury (55745)

Archant Specialist Ltd.
Archant House
Oriel Rd.
Wendens Ambo
Cheltenham GL50 1BB, United Kingdom
Phone: 44 1242 216052
Publications: Canal Boat (56949) • The English Garden (52969) • The English Home (52970) • Go Flying (52315) • Grafik (52972) • Realm (52975) • Whisky (52980)

Architectural Heritage Society of Scotland
The Glasite Meeting House
33 Barony St.
Edinburgh EH3 6NX, United Kingdom
Phone: 44 131 5570019
Fax: 44 131 5570049
Publications: Architectural Heritage (53252)

Architectural Institute of Japan
26-20 Shiba 5-chome
Minato-Ku
Tokyo 108-8414, Japan
Phone: 81 334 562051
Fax: 81 334 562058
Publications: Journal of Architecture, Planning and Environmental Engineering (46885) • Journal of Asian Architecture and Building Engineering (46887) • Journal of Structural and Construction Engineering (46942) • Journal of Structural Engineering B (46943)

Architectural Society of China
No. 9, Sanlihe Rd.
Beijing 100835, People's Republic of China
Phone: 86 108 8082239

Fax: 86 108 8082222
Publications: Architectural Journal (43169) • Journal of Building Structure (43203)

Architecture Media Pvt. Ltd.
Level 3, 4 Princes St.
Port Melbourne, Victoria 3207, Australia
Phone: 61 396 464760
Fax: 61 396 464918
Publications: Houses (42264)

Arena Printing and Publications Proprietary Ltd.
PO Box 18
Melbourne, Victoria 3054, Australia
Phone: 61 3 9416 0232
Fax: 61 3 9416 0684
Publications: Arena Magazine (42046)

Argentina Oils and Fats Association
Hipolito Yrigoyen 1284
Piso 3 Depto 5
Capital Federal
Buenos Aires, Argentina
Phone: 54 11 43810555
Fax: 54 11 43810555
Publications: A & G Magazine (41468)

Argentinian Association of Dermatology
Mexico 1720
1100 Buenos Aires, Argentina
Phone: 54 143 812737
Publications: Journal of Argentine Dermatology (41476)

Ariesdue S.R.L.
Via. Airoldi 11
I-22060 Carimate, Italy
Phone: 39 31 792135
Fax: 39 31 790743
Publications: Doctor Os (46130) • Journal of Osseointegration (46131)

Aristotle University of Thessaloniki
School of Biology
GR-541 24 Thessaloniki, Greece
Publications: Journal of Biological Research (44775)

Ark Group Ltd.
266/276 Upper Richmond Rd.
Putney
London SW15 6TQ, United Kingdom
Phone: 44 20 87852700
Fax: 44 20 87859373
Publications: Ei Magazine (54357) • Managing Partner (54905)

Armada International
Hagenholzstrasse 65
CH-8050 Zurich, Switzerland
Phone: 41 1 3085050
Fax: 41 1 3085055
Publications: Armada International (51253)

Armed Forces Medical Services
c/o Armed Forces Medical College
Pune 411 040, Maharashtra, India
Phone: 91 20 32927071
Fax: 91 20 26813065
Publications: Medical Journal Armed Forces India (45697)

Arms and Armour Society
Anthony Dove
PO Box 10232
London SW19 2ZD, United Kingdom
Publications: Journal of Arms and Armour Society (54701)

Army Families Federation
Trenchard Lines
Upavon
Pewsey SN9 6BE, United Kingdom
Phone: 44 1980 615525
Fax: 44 1980 615526
Publications: Army Families Federation Families Journal (56269)

Arquitectura Viva S.L.
Calle de Aniceto Marinas, 32
E-28008 Madrid, Spain
Phone: 34 915 487317
Fax: 34 915 488191
Publications: Arquitectura Viva (50729) • AV Monografias (50731)

The Arran Banner Printing & Publishing Co.
Brodick
Isle of Arran KA27 8AJ, United Kingdom
Publications: Arran Banner (53661)

Array Publications B.V.
Lemelerberg 19-23
NL-2402 ZN Alphen aan den Rijn, Netherlands
Phone: 31 172 469030
Fax: 31 172 424381
Publications: Database Magazine (47867) • IT Service Magazine (47868) • Optimize (47870) • Process Control (47871) • Software Release Magazine (47872) • Telecommagazine (47873)

Art Review
1 Sekforde St.
London EC1R 0BE, United Kingdom
Phone: 44 20 72364880
Fax: 44 20 71072761
Publications: Art Review (53969)

Artasia Press Co., Ltd.
143/1-2 Soi Dumex
Charoen Nakorn Rd.
Klong Tonsai, Klongsarn
Bangkok 10600, Thailand
Phone: 66 2 8613360
Fax: 66 2 8613363
Publications: Asia-Pacific Tropical Homes (51412)

Arte y Parte S.L.
Three of November, 31
E-39010 Santander, Spain
Phone: 34 942 373131
Publications: Arte y Parte (50830)

Arthur Rank Centre
B4113 Stoneleigh Rd.
Stoneleigh CV8 2LZ, United Kingdom
Phone: 44 24 76853060
Fax: 44 24 76414808
Publications: Country Way (56635)

The Artists' Publishing Company Ltd.
Caxton House
63-65 High St.
Tenterden TN30 6BD, United Kingdom
Phone: 44 15 80763315
Publications: The Artist (56742) • Leisure Painter (56743)

ArtNexus
Cra 5 No. 67, 19
Bogota, Colombia
Phone: 57 1 2495514
Fax: 57 1 3129252
Publications: ArtNexus (43542)

Arts of Asia Publications Ltd.
Kowloon Centre, Stes. 803-6
29-39 Ashley Rd.
Kowloon
Hong Kong, People's Republic of China
Phone: 852 23762228
Fax: 852 23763713
Publications: Arts of Asia (43267)

Arts and Humanities Research Centre in Intellectual Property and Technology
School of Law
University of Edinburgh
Old College
Edinburgh EH8 9YL, United Kingdom
Phone: 44 131 6502014
Fax: 44 131 6506317
Publications: Script-ed (53318)

Artthrob
PO Box 30
Faerie Glen
Pretoria 0043, Republic of South Africa
Publications: Artthrob (50585)

Ascent Publishing Ltd.
2 Sugarbrook Ct.
Aston Rd.
Bromsgrove B60 3ES, United Kingdom
Phone: 44 1527 834484
Publications: Homebuilding & Renovating (52748)

ASEAN Neurological Association
The ASEAN Secretariat
70A Jalan Sisingamangaraja

12110 Jakarta, Indonesia
Phone: 62 217 262991
Fax: 62 217 398234
Publications: Neurology Asia (47629)

Ashdown Publishing
19 River Rd.
Partridge Green
Arundel BN18 9EY, United Kingdom
Phone: 44 19 3884988
Publications: Cat World (52133) • Dolls House World (52134) • Toy Soldier & Model Figure (52135)

Ashgate Publishing Ltd.
Union Rd.
Croft Rd.
Surrey GU9 7PT, United Kingdom
Phone: 44 1252 331551
Fax: 44 1252 736736
Telex: 317210 BUNEAU G
Publications: Alexandria (56659) • Crusades (56661) • The European Yearbook of Business History (56662) • Human Factors and Aerospace Safety (56666) • Mediterranean Studies (56668) • Nineteenth-Century Music Review (56670) • Parliaments, Estates and Representation (56671) • Reformation (52630) • The Shakespearean International Yearbook (56675) • Sophia (42086)

Ashley Mark Publishing Co.
1 Vance Ct.
Trans Britannia Enterprise Pk.
Blaydon-on-Tyne NE21 5NH, United Kingdom
Phone: 44 19 14149006
Fax: 44 19 14149001
Publications: Classical Guitar (52387)

Ashley Publications Ltd.
Telephone House
69-77 Paul St.
London EC2A 4LQ, United Kingdom
Phone: 44 20 70175000
Fax: 44 20 70177667
Publications: Expert Opinion on Investigational Drugs (54417)

Ashville Media Group
Longboat Quay
57-59 Sir John Rogerson's Quay
Dublin 2, Dublin, Ireland
Phone: 353 1 4322200
Fax: 353 1 6727100
Publications: Business Ireland (45948) • FireCall (45958) • Ireland at Your Leisure (45969) • It's All About Living (45989) • Maternity & Infant (45991)

Asia Asset Management
1701, Singga Commercial Ctr.
148 Connaught Rd. W
Hong Kong, People's Republic of China
Phone: 852 25477331
Fax: 852 25489544
Publications: Asia Asset Management (43269)

Asia-Pacific Cultural Centre for Unesco
6 Fukuro-Machi
Shinjuku-ku
Tokyo 162-8484, Japan
Phone: 81 332 694435
Fax: 81 332 694510
Publications: Asian-Pacific Book Development (46755)

Asia Pacific Orthopaedic Association
c/o Ms. Shannon Tan
17 Jalan Mesin, No. 04-01
Lee Hwa Industrial Bldg.
Singapore 368816, Singapore
Phone: 65 63 398687
Fax: 65 63 399536
Publications: Journal of Orthopaedic Surgery (43360)

Asia Pacific Tourism Association
School of Tourism Management
Dong-A University
1 Bumin-Dong 2-Ga
Seo-gu
Busan 602-072, Republic of Korea
Phone: 82 512008429
Fax: 82 512014335
Publications: Asia Pacific Journal of Tourism Research (47209)

Asia Systems Media Corp.
Jian Wai SOHO, Bldg. 11, No. 2805
Chao Yang District
Beijing 100 022, People's Republic of China
Phone: 86 10 51661575
Fax: 86 10 59002947
Publications: Beijing This Month (43173) • Business Beijing (43175)

Asia Theological Association
54 Scout Madrinan St.
PO Box 1454-1154
PO Box 616
Quezon City 1103, Philippines
Phone: 63 2 4100312
Publications: Journal of Asian Evangelical Theology (50199) • Journal of Asian Mission (49597)

Asian Affairs
PO Box 10086
15th Fl., Supreme Commercial Bldg.
368 King's Rd., N Point
Hong Kong, People's Republic of China
Phone: 86 852 29802240
Fax: 86 852 29802824
Publications: Asian Affairs (43273)

The Asian Age
S 7, Green Pk. Main Market
New Delhi 110 016, Delhi, India
Phone: 91 11 2653001
Fax: 91 11 26530027
Publications: The Asian Age (45486)

The Asian Age
145, Mathuradas Mills Compound
Near Sai Mandir, N.M. Joshi Marg
Lower Parel
Mumbai 400 013, Maharashtra, India
Phone: 91 22 24955825
Fax: 91 22 24965847
Publications: The Asian Age (45352)

Asian Age (Eastern) India Publishers Ltd.
7th Fl., Kankaria Estate
6, Little Russell St.
Kolkata 700 071, West Bengal, India
Phone: 91 33 22890676
Fax: 91 33 22890686
Publications: The Asian Age (45259)

Asian Age (South) Ltd.
68 Lavelle Rd.
Bangalore 560 001, Karnataka, India
Phone: 91 80 2270830
Fax: 91 80 2273561
Publications: The Asian Age (44950)

Asian Art Newspaper
PO Box 22521
London W8 4GT, United Kingdom
Phone: 44 20 72296040
Fax: 44 20 75652913
Publications: Asian Art (53974)

Asian Association for Agricultural Engineering
Agricultural Systems & Engineering
School of Environment, Resources & Development
Asian Institute of Technology
PO Box 4, Klong Luang
Pathumthani 12120, Thailand
Phone: 66 2 5245480
Fax: 66 2 5246200
Publications: International Agricultural Engineering Journal (51460)

Asian Association for Agricultural Engineering
PO Box 4
Klong Luang
Pathumthani 12120, Thailand
Phone: 66 252 45480
Fax: 66 252 46200
Publications: International Agricultural Journal (51461)

Asian-Australasian Association of Animal Production Societies
Rm. 708, Sammo Sporex
1638-32 Sillimbon-dong
Gwanak-gu
Seoul 151-730, Republic of Korea
Phone: 02 200 00550

Fax: 82 288 86559
Publications: Asian-Australasian Journal of Animal Sciences (47254)

Asian Bankers Association
13F No. 3 Sung-shou Rd.
Taipei 00110, Taiwan
Phone: 886 2 27255663
Fax: 886 2 27255665
Publications: Journal of Banking and Finance (51348)

Asian Development Bank
6 ADB Ave.
Mandaluyong
Manila 0980, Philippines
Phone: 63 263 24444
Fax: 63 263 62444
Publications: ADB Business Opportunities (49546) • Asian Development Review (49547)

Asian Diver Magazine
MediaCorp Publishing Pte Ltd.
Techpoint No. 01-06/08
10 Ang Mo Kio St. 65
Singapore 569059, Singapore
Phone: 65 64838399
Fax: 65 64842512
Publications: Asian Diver (50108)

Asian Fisheries Society
Unit A, Mayaman Townhomes
25 Mayaman St.
UP Village
Quezon City 1101, Philippines
Phone: 63 2921 1914
Fax: 63 2920 2757
Publications: Asian Fisheries Science (49581)

Asian Folklore Studies
Nanzan University
18, Yamazato-cho
Showa-ku
Nagoya 466-8673, Japan
Phone: 81 52 8323111
Fax: 81 52 8336157
Publications: Asian Ethnology (46551)

Asian Home Gourmet
18 Cross St., No. 12-01/08
China Sq. Central
Singapore 048423, Singapore
Phone: 65 621 20100
Fax: 65 622 63935
Publications: Asian Home Gourmet (50110)

Asian Human Rights Commission
19th Fl., Go-Up Commercial Bldg.
998 Canton Rd.
Kowloon
Hong Kong, People's Republic of China
Phone: 86 852 26986339
Fax: 86 852 26986367
Publications: Human Rights Solidarity (43347)

Asian Interactive Media
Accessory House
Cox Ln.
Chessington KT9 1SD, United Kingdom
Phone: 44 8707 555502
Fax: 44 8707 555503
Publications: Asian Bride (52988) • Asian Groom & Man (52989) • Asian Woman (52990)

Asian Journal of Chemistry
11-100 Rajendra Nagar
Sector 3, Sahibabad
Ghaziabad 201 005, Uttar Pradesh, India
Phone: 91 120 4102551
Publications: Asian Journal of Chemistry (45121)

Asian Media Information & Communication Centre
Jurong Point PO Box 360
Singapore 916412, Singapore
Phone: 65 679 27570
Fax: 65 679 27129
Publications: Asian Journal of Communication (50111)

Asian Network for Scientific Information
308-Lasani Town, Sargodha Rd.
Faisalabad 38850, Pakistan
Phone: 92 41 8787087

Fax: 92 41 8815544

Publications: Asian Journal of Cell Biology (49235) • Asian Journal of Plant Sciences (49237) • Biotechnology (49239) • Information Technology Journal (49247) • International Journal of Botany (49249) • International Journal of Pharmacology (49252) • International Journal of Poultry Science (49254) • Journal of Agronomy (49259) • Journal of Applied Sciences (49261) • Journal of Biological Sciences (49264) • Journal of Entomology (49267) • Journal of Medical Sciences (49270) • Pakistan Journal of Biological Sciences (49276) • Pakistan Journal of Nutrition (49277) • Plant Pathology Journal (49278)

Asian and Pacific Centre for Transfer of Technology
C-2 Qutab Institutional Area
PO Box 4575
New Delhi 110 016, Delhi, India
Phone: 91 11 26966509
Fax: 91 11 26856274
Publications: Asia Pacific Tech Monitor (45485) • VATIS Update Biotechnology (45662) • VATIS Update Food Processing (45663) • VATIS Update Non-Conventional Energy (45664) • VATIS Update Ozone Layer Protection (45665) • VATIS Update Waste Management (45666)

Asian & Pacific Coconut Community
3rd Fl., Lina Bldg.
Jl. H.R. Rasuna Said Kav.B7
Kuningan
12920 Jakarta, Indonesia
Phone: 62 21 5221712
Fax: 62 21 5221714
Publications: Cocoinfo International (45794) • Cord (45795)

Asian Regional Exchange for New Alternatives
c/o Institute of Democracy & Society
Sungkonghoe University
1-1 Hang-dong
Guro-gu
Seoul 152 176, Republic of Korea
Phone: 82 2 26104751
Fax: 82 2 26104752
Publications: Asian Exchange (47255)

Asian Studies Association of Australia
Department of Anthropology
Research School of Pacific & Asian Studies
Australian National University
Canberra, Australian Capital Territory 0200, Australia
Publications: Asian Studies Review (41699)

Asian Surgical Association
Dept. of Surgery
University of Hong Kong Medical Center
Queen Mary Hospital
Hong Kong, People's Republic of China
Phone: 852 28554235
Fax: 852 28181186
Publications: Asian Journal of Surgery (43279)

Asian Vegetable Research and Development Center
Shanhua, PO Box 42
Tainan 74199, Taiwan
Phone: 886 65 837801
Fax: 886 65 830009
Publications: Centerpoint (51326)

Asociacion Andaluza de Medicos Forenses
Palacio de Justicia
Prado de San Sebastian S/N
E-41004 Seville, Spain
Publications: Cuadernos de Medicina Forense (50833)

Asociacion Cultural por la Danza
Calle Antonio Vicent, 65
E-28019 Madrid, Spain
Phone: 34 915 695195
Fax: 34 914 698582
Publications: Por la Danza (50791)

Asociacion Demografica Salvadorena
Edificio Profamilia
25 Av. Norte No. 583
Apartado Postal 1338
San Salvador, El Salvador
Phone: 503 22448100

Fax: 503 22448179
Publications: BMC Public Health (43777)

Asociacion de Directores de Escena de Espana
Costanilla de los Angeles
13 Bajo Izq.
E-28013 Madrid, Spain
Phone: 34 915 591246
Fax: 34 915 483012
Publications: Ade-Teatro (50724)

Asociacion Historia y Fuente Oral
Sta. Llucia, 1
E-08002 Barcelona, Spain
Phone: 34 933 181195
Fax: 34 933 178327
Publications: Historia, Antropologia y Fuentes Orales (50678)

Asociacion Paleontologica Argentina
Maipu 645 1 Piso
1006 Buenos Aires, Argentina
Phone: 54 114 3267463
Fax: 54 114 3267463
Publications: Ameghiniana (41469)

Asociacion Quimica Argentina
Sanchez de Bustamante 1749
C1425DUI Buenos Aires, Argentina
Phone: 54 11 48224886
Fax: 54 11 48224886
Publications: Industria & Quimica (41473) • Journal of the Argentine Chemical Society (41475)

Asociacion de Tecnicos de Informatica
Via Laietana, 46
E-08003 Barcelona, Spain
Phone: 34 93 4125235
Fax: 34 93 4127713
Publications: Upgrade (English Edition) (50705)

Aspermont Limited
613-619 Wellington St.
Perth, Western Australia 6000, Australia
Phone: 61 8 62639100
Fax: 61 8 62639186
Publications: Australian Longwall Magazine (42004) • Australia's Mining Monthly (42005) • Cranes and Lifting Australia (42006) • RESOURCESTOCKS (42007)

Assam Tribune Private Ltd.
Tribune Bldg.
Guwahati 718 003, Assam, India
Publications: Assam Tribune (45129)

Asser International Sports Law Centre
PO Box 30461
NL-2500 GL The Hague, Netherlands
Phone: 31 70 3420300
Fax: 31 70 3420359
Publications: The International Sports Law Journal (48618)

Asset Publishing & Research Ltd.
Ste. 2404, 24th Fl., Chinachem Exchange Sq.
1 Hoi Wan St.
Quarry Bay
Hong Kong, People's Republic of China
Phone: 852 25736078
Fax: 852 25737436
Publications: The Asset (43281)

Associacao Brasileira de Engenharia Quimica
Rua Libero Badaro, 152-11 andar
01008-903 Sao Paulo, Sao Paulo, Brazil
Phone: 55 113 1078747
Fax: 55 113 1044649
Publications: Brazilian Journal of Chemical Engineering (43025)

Associacao do Comercio Automovel de Portugal
Av. Torre de Belem, 29
P-1400-342 Lisbon, Portugal
Phone: 351 21 3035300
Fax: 351 21 3021474
Publications: Revistacap (49806)

Associacao Paulista de Medicina
Av. Brigadeiro Luis Antonio 278-7 andar
278 - Bela Vista
01318-901 Sao Paulo, Sao Paulo, Brazil
Phone: 55 113 1884200

Fax: 55 113 1884255
Publications: Sao Paulo Medical Journal (43050)

Associated Cement Companies Ltd.
ACC Thane Complex
Lal Bahadur Shastri Marg
Near Teen Haath Naka
Thane 400 604, Maharashtra, India
Phone: 91 222 5823631
Fax: 91 222 5837378
Publications: Indian Concrete Journal (ICJ) (45745)

Associated Chambers of Commerce and Industry of India
Corporate Office, 1, Community Ctr. Zamrudpur
Kailash Colony
New Delhi 110 048, Delhi, India
Phone: 91 11 46550555
Fax: 91 11 46536481
Publications: Asso Cham Bulletin (45487) • Asso Cham News & Views (45488) • Overseas Business Contacts (45634)

Associated Management Consultants (P) Ltd.
Y-21 Hauz Khas
New Delhi 110 016, Delhi, India
Phone: 91 11 42654857
Publications: Indian Journal of Marketing (45559)

The Associated Newspapers of Ceylon Ltd.
35 D.R. Wijewardene Mawatha
PO Box 1217
Colombo 10, Sri Lanka
Phone: 94 112 429231
Fax: 94 112 429230
Telex: 22262 ANCL CE
Publications: Daily News (50853) • Sunday Observer (50872)

Associated Society of Locomotive Engineers and Firemen
9 Arkwright Rd.
Hampstead
London NW3 6AB, United Kingdom
Phone: 44 20 73178600
Fax: 44 20 77946406
Publications: Locomotive Journal (54882)

Association for Advancement of Entomology
c/o Dept. of Zoology
University of Kerala
Trivandrum
Kariavattom 695 581, Kerala, India
Publications: Entomon (45241)

Association of Anaesthetists of Great Britain and Ireland
21 Portland Pl.
London W1B 1PY, United Kingdom
Phone: 44 20 76311650
Fax: 44 20 76314352
Publications: Anaesthesia (53940)

Association of Anglican Women
Raffles & Bower St.
Napier, New Zealand
Phone: 64 6 8358230
Fax: 64 6 8350680
Publications: Circle (48939)

Association of Applied Biologists
Warwick Enterprise Pk.
Wellesbourne
Warwick CV35 9EF, United Kingdom
Phone: 44 178 9472020
Fax: 44 178 9470234
Publications: Annals of Applied Biology (56852)

Association of Automotive Technical Societies in Finland
Koydenpunojankatu 8
FIN-00180 Helsinki, Finland
Phone: 358 96 944724
Fax: 358 96 944027
Publications: Suomen Autolehti (43859)

Association Belge de Documentation
Chaussee de Wavre 1683
B-1160 Brussels, Belgium
Phone: 32 2 6755862
Fax: 32 2 6727446
Publications: Cahiers de la Documentation (42846)

Association of Breastfeeding Mothers
PO Box 207
Bridgwater TA6 7YT, United Kingdom
Phone: 44 8444 122948
Publications: ABM Magazine (52595)

Association of British Choral Directors
Braelees, Kirkandrews on Eden
Carlisle CA5 6DU, United Kingdom
Publications: Mastersinger (52946)

Association of British Credit Unions Limited
Holyoake House, Hanover St.
Manchester M60 0AS, United Kingdom
Phone: 44 16 18323694
Fax: 44 16 18323706
Publications: Credit Union News (55550)

Association of British Dispensing Opticians
199 Gloucester Ter.
London W2 6LD, United Kingdom
Phone: 44 20 72985100
Fax: 44 20 72985111
Publications: Dispensing Optics (53120)

Association of British Theatre Technicians
55 Farringdon Rd.
London EC1M 3JB, United Kingdom
Phone: 44 20 72429200
Fax: 44 20 72429303
Publications: Sightline (55238)

Association of Building Engineers
Lutyens House
Billing Brook Rd.
Weston Favell
Northampton NN3 8NW, United Kingdom
Phone: 44 84 51261058
Fax: 44 16 04784220
Publications: Building Engineer (55706)

Association of Certified Treasury Managers
52 Nagarjuna Hills
Hyderabad 500 082, Andhra Pradesh, India
Phone: 91 402 343536874
Fax: 91 402 3352521
Publications: Treasury Management (45184)

Association of Charitable Foundations
Central House
14 Upper Woburn Pl.
London WC1H 0AE, United Kingdom
Phone: 44 20 72554499
Publications: Trust & Foundation News (55343)

Association for Child and Adolescent Mental Health
St. Saviours House
39-41 Union St.
London SE1 1SD, United Kingdom
Phone: 44 20 74037458
Fax: 44 20 74037081
Publications: Journal of Child Psychology and Psychiatry (54722)

Association of Child Psychotherapists
120 W Heath Rd.
London NW3 7TU, United Kingdom
Phone: 44 20 84581609
Fax: 44 20 84581482
Publications: Journal of Child Psychotherapy (54723)

Association of Clinical Biochemists of India
Bibliographic Informatics Division
Dept. of Information Technology
A-Block, CGO Complex, Lodhi Rd.
New Delhi 110 003, Delhi, India
Publications: Indian Journal of Clinical Biochemistry (45195)

Association of Clinical Pathologists
189 Dyke Rd..
Hove BN3 1TL, United Kingdom
Phone: 44 12 73775700
Fax: 44 12 73773303
Publications: Journal of Clinical Pathology (53608)

Association of Commonwealth Universities
20-24 Tavistock Sq.
London WC1H 9HF, United Kingdom
Phone: 44 20 73806700
Fax: 44 20 73872655
Publications: ACU Bulletin (53896)

Association for Computing Machinery
2 Penn Plz., Ste. 701
PO Box 30777
New York, NY 10121-0701
Phone: 212626-0500
Fax: 212944-1318
Free: 800342-6626
Publications: ACM Transactions on Computational Logic (TOCL) (47877)

Association of Consulting Engineers of Germany
Budapester Strasse 31
D-10787 Berlin, Germany
Phone: 49 30 260620
Fax: 49 30 26062100
Publications: VBI-Nachrichten (44234)

Association for Continence Advice
c/o Fitwise Management Ltd.
Drumcross Hall
Bathgate
West Lothian EH48 4JT, United Kingdom
Phone: 44 1506 811077
Fax: 44 1506 811477
Publications: Continence (56892)

Association of Corporate Treasurers
51 Moorgate
London EC2R 6BH, United Kingdom
Phone: 44 20 78472540
Fax: 44 20 73748744
Publications: The Treasurer (55338)

Association of Corporate Treasurers of Southern Africa
PO Box 5853
Cresta 2118, Republic of South Africa
Phone: 27 114 821512
Fax: 27 114 821996
Publications: The Southern African Treasurer (50466)

Association des Etudes Francaises et Franco-phones d'Irlande
Dept. of French
Trinity College Dublin
Dublin 2, Dublin, Ireland
Publications: The Irish Journal of French Studies (45976)

Association of Fashion Retailers in Finland
Mannerheimintie 76 B
FIN-00250 Helsinki, Finland
Phone: 358 968 447300
Fax: 358 968 447344
Publications: Modin (43848)

Association of French-Language Leprologists
4 rue Jean Jacques Bel
F-33000 Bordeaux, France
Phone: 33 556 523214
Fax: 33 556 523214
Publications: Bulletin de l'ALLF (43921)

Association of Friends of Classical Art
Schoenbeinstrasse 20
CH-4056 Basel, Switzerland
Publications: Antike Kunst (51058)

Association of Graduate Careers Advisory Services
Millennium House
30 Jct. Rd.
Sheffield S11 8XB, United Kingdom
Phone: 44 114 2515750
Fax: 44 114 2515751
Publications: Phoenix (56509)

Association of Guilds of Weavers, Spinners and Dyers
51 Farmdale Dr.
Guisborough TS14 8JJ, United Kingdom
Phone: 44 12 87280469
Publications: The Journal for Weavers, Spinners and Dyers (53499)

The Association for Information Management
Howard House
Wagon Ln.
Bingley
London BD16 1WA, United Kingdom
Phone: 44 1274 777700
Fax: 44 1274 785201
Publications: Managing Information (54004)

Association of Interior Specialists
Olton Bridge
245 Warwick Rd.
Solihull B92 7AH, United Kingdom
Phone: 44 12 17070077
Fax: 44 12 17061949
Publications: Interiors Focus (56564)

Association of International Marathons and Distance Races
c/o Hugh Jones, AIMS Sec.
19 Kelly St.
London NW1 8PG, United Kingdom
Phone: 44 20 72093193
Publications: Distance Running (54334)

Association of Irish Musical Societies
25 Harcourt Lodge
Goldenbridge
Dublin 8, Dublin, Ireland
Publications: Show Times (45998)

Association Ivoirienne des Sciences Agronomiques
Agronomie Africaine
Abidjan BP 703, Cote d'Ivoire
Publications: Agronomie Africaine (43556)

Association of Jewish Religious Professionals from the Former Soviet Union
PO Box 5749
6 David Yellin St.
Jerusalem, Israel
Phone: 97 226 427521
Fax: 97 226 427521
Publications: B'Or Ha'Torah (46081)

Association for Language Learning
University of Leicester
University Rd.
Leicester LE1 7RH, United Kingdom
Phone: 44 116 2297600
Fax: 44 116 2231488
Publications: Deutsch (53795) • Francophonie (53801) • Language Learning Journal (53809) • Rusis-tika (53823) • Tuttitalia (53831) • Vida Hispanica (53833)

Association of Law Teachers
Nottingham Law School
Burton St.
Nottingham NG1 4BU, United Kingdom
Phone: 44 1158482550
Fax: 44 1159486569
Publications: The Law Teacher (55765)

Association of Learned and Professional Society Publishers
1-3 Ship St.
West Sussex
Shoreham-by-Sea BN43 5DH, United Kingdom
Phone: 44 523 579826
Publications: Learned Publishing (56525)

Association for Learning Technology
Gipsy Ln.
Headington
Oxford OX3 0BP, United Kingdom
Phone: 44 18 65484125
Fax: 44 18 65484165
Publications: ALT-J (55863)

Association Luxembourgeoise du Diabete
143, rue de Muhlenbach
L-2168 Luxembourg, Luxembourg
Phone: 352 485361
Fax: 352 26123748
Publications: Journal du Diabetique (47492)

Association des Maisons d'Accueil
Rue Gheude, 49
B-1070 Brussels, Belgium
Phone: 32 2 5136225
Fax: 32 2 5142300
Publications: Echos AMA (42849)

Association for Medical Education in Europe
Secretariat Office
Tay Pk. House
484 Perth Rd.
Dundee DD2 1LR, United Kingdom
Phone: 44 1382 381953
Fax: 44 1382 381987
Publications: Medical Teacher (53215)

Association of Microbiologists of India
c/o R.C. Kuhad
Division of Microbiology
University of Delhi, South Campus
Benito Juarez Rd.
New Delhi 110 012, Delhi, India
Phone: 91 112 68885270
Publications: Indian Journal of Microbiology (45562)

Association of Modern Scientific Investigation
Mosashvili 1/15
380062 Tbilisi, Georgia
Phone: 995 32 225993
Publications: Journal of Biological Physics and Chemistry (44134)

Association Nazionale Razza Bruna
Localita Ferlina 204
I-37012 Bussolengo, Italy
Phone: 39 456 760111
Fax: 39 457 156655
Publications: La Razza Bruna (46129)

Association of Otolaryngologists of India
397 Jagriti Enclave
Delhi 110 092, Delhi, India
Publications: Indian Journal of Otolaryngology and Head and Neck Surgery (45097)

Association of Painting Craft Teachers
c/o Mr. Peter Walters, Pres.
56 Eastbank Ride
Stoke-on-Trent ST11 9DS, United Kingdom
Phone: 44 1782 393849
Publications: The Artisan (56628)

Association of Pediatricians of Pakistan
37/B, GOR-2, Bahawalpur House
Lahore, Pakistan
Publications: Pakistan Pediatric Journal (49386)

Association for Perioperative Practice
Daisy Ayris House
6 Grove Park Ct.
Harrogate HG1 4DP, United Kingdom
Phone: 44 14 23508079
Fax: 44 14 23531613
Publications: Journal of Perioperative Practice (53517)

Association of Photographers
81 Leonard St.
London EC2A 4QS, United Kingdom
Phone: 44 20 77396669
Fax: 44 20 77398707
Publications: IMAGE (54583)

Association of Physicians of India
Turf Estate, No. 6 & 7, Ground Fl.
Opposite Shakti Mills Compound
Dr. E. Moses Rd.
Mumbai 400 011, Maharashtra, India
Phone: 91 222 4912218
Fax: 91 222 4920263
Publications: Journal of Association of Physicians of India (45395)

Association of Plastic Surgeons of India
Hridaykunj 21, Napier Rd.
Colony (Part-2)
Lucknow 226 003, Uttar Pradesh, India
Phone: 91 522 2257446
Fax: 91 522 2243100
Publications: Indian Journal of Plastic Surgery (45387)

Association for the Prevention of Atmospheric Pollution
10 rue Pierre Brossolette
Le Kremlin Bicetre
F-94270 Paris, France
Phone: 33 142 111500
Fax: 33 142 111501
Publications: Pollution Atmospherique (44077)

Association of Qualitative Research
Davey House
31 St. Neots Rd.
Eaton Ford
Saint Neots PE19 7BA, United Kingdom
Phone: 44 1480 407227
Fax: 44 1480 211267
Publications: In Brief (54590)

Association for Qualitative Research
Faculty of Business & Economics

Monash University
Melbourne, Victoria, Australia
Publications: Qualitative Research Journal (42083)

Association of Radical Midwives
c/o Ishbel Kargar, Membership Sec.
62 Greetby Hill
Lancashire
Ormskirk L39 2DT, United Kingdom
Phone: 44 1695 571748
Publications: Midwifery Matters (55850)

Association of Residential Letting Agents
Arbon House
6 Tournament Ct.
Edgehill Dr.
Warwick CV34 6LG, United Kingdom
Phone: 44 84 43870555
Fax: 44 19 26417789
Publications: Agreement (56851)

Association de la Revue Militaire Suisse
Av. Florimont 3
CH-1006 Lausanne, Switzerland
Phone: 41 213 114817
Publications: Revue Militaire Suisse (51199)

Association for Science Education
College Ln.
Hatfield AL10 9AA, United Kingdom
Phone: 44 1707 283000
Fax: 44 1707 266532
Publications: School Science Review (53541)

Association for the Scientific Study of Anomalous Phenomena
27 Old Gloucester St.
London WC1N 3XX, United Kingdom
Phone: 44 845 6521648
Publications: Anomaly (53952)

Association of Secretaries General of Parliaments
Committee Office
House of Commons
London SW1A 0AA, United Kingdom
Publications: Constitutional and Parliamentary Information (54260)

Association of Sign Language Interpreters
Fortuna House
S 5th St.
Milton Keynes MK9 2EU, United Kingdom
Phone: 44 87 14740522
Fax: 44 19 08325259
Publications: NEWSLI (55640)

Association of State Road Transport Undertakings
Plot No.4-A, PSP Block
Pocket-14, Sector-8
New Delhi 110 075, Delhi, India
Phone: 91 11 26499784
Fax: 91 11 43294242
Publications: Indian Journal of Transport Management (45568)

Association for the Study of Ethnicity and Nationalism
Dept. of Government
London School of Economics
Houghton St.
London WC2A 2AE, United Kingdom
Phone: 44 20 79556801
Fax: 44 20 79556218
Publications: Studies in Ethnicity and Nationalism (55273)

Association for the Study of Medical Education
12 Queen St.
Edinburgh EH2 1JE, United Kingdom
Phone: 44 13 12259111
Fax: 44 13 12259444
Publications: Journal of Medical Education (53293)

Association for the Study and Preservation of Roman Mosaics
61 Norwich St.
Cambridge CB2 1ND, United Kingdom
Publications: Mosaic (52872)

Association of Teachers and Lecturers
7 Northumberland St.
London WC2N 5RD, United Kingdom

Phone: 44 20 79306441
Fax: 44 20 79301359
Publications: Report (55189)

Association of Teachers of Lipreading to Adults
c/o Hearing Concern LINK
27-28 The Waterfront
Eastbourne
East Sussex BN23 5UZ, United Kingdom
Publications: Catchword (53242)

Association of Teachers of Singing
Weir House
108 Newton Rd.
Burton-on-Trent DE15 0TT, United Kingdom
Phone: 44 12 83542198
Fax: 44 12 83542198
Publications: Singing (52772)

Association for Tertiary Education Management
PO Box 6050
O'Connor, Australian Capital Territory 2602, Australia
Phone: 61 411 186199
Fax: 61 2 61255262
Publications: Journal of Higher Education Policy and Management (41864)

Association of University Administrators
University of Manchester
Oxford Rd.
Manchester M13 9PL, United Kingdom
Phone: 44 161 2752063
Fax: 44 161 2752036
Publications: Perspectives (52715)

Association of Women Educators
PO Box 229
Sandgate, Queensland 4017, Australia
Phone: 61 7 38693433
Fax: 61 7 38693436
Publications: Redress (42353)

Associazione Centro Aiuti Volontari Cooperazione Sviluppo Terzo Mondo
Via Sighele, 3
I-38100 Trento, Italy
Phone: 39 461 935893
Fax: 39 461 935893
Publications: ACAV Informa (46260)

Associazione Italia-Australia
Via Lombardia 14
I-00187 Rome, Italy
Phone: 39 6 916508992
Fax: 39 6 233201031
Publications: Attualita Italia-Australia (46222)

Aston Martin Owners Club
Drayton St. Leonard
Wallingford OX10 7BG, United Kingdom
Phone: 44 18 65400400
Fax: 44 18 65400200
Publications: A.M. (56814)

Astrological Association of Great Britain
Unit 168, Lee Valley Technopark
Tottenham Hale
London N17 9LN, United Kingdom
Phone: 44 20 88804848
Fax: 44 20 88804849
Publications: Astrological Journal (53978) • Correlation (54268)

Astronomical Society of Australia
c/o Prof. J.W. O'Byrne
School of Physics
The University of Sydney
Sydney, New South Wales 2006, Australia
Publications: Publications of the Astronomical Society of Australia (42565)

Astronomical Society of Japan
c/o National Astronomical Observatory of Japan
2-21-1 Osawa
Mitaka-shi
Tokyo 181-8588, Japan
Phone: 81 422 311359
Fax: 81 422 315487
Publications: Publications of Astronomical Society of Japan (47028)

Astronomy Ireland
PO Box 2888
Dublin IRL-5, Dublin, Ireland

Phone: 353 1 8470777
Fax: 353 1 8470771
Publications: Astronomy and Space Magazine (45946)

a+t ediciones
General Alava, 15-2oA
E-01005 Vitoria-Gasteiz, Spain
Phone: 34 945 134276
Fax: 34 945 134901
Publications: at (50849)

Ateneo de Manila University Press
ADMU Campus
Bellarmine Hall
Katipunan Ave., Loyola Hts.
Quezon City 1108, Philippines
Phone: 63 2 4265984
Publications: Kritika Kultura (49598) • Philippine Studies (49614)

Athene Publishing Ltd.
Axe & Bottle Ct.
70 Newcomen St.
London SE1 1YT, United Kingdom
Phone: 44 844 4774740
Fax: 44 20 79404843
Publications: Credit Today (54284)

Athens Center of Ekistics
24 Strat. Syndesmou St.
GR-106 73 Athens, Greece
Phone: 30 2103623216
Fax: 30 2103629337
Publications: EKISTICS (44742)

Atoll Media
Umgeni Business Pk.
47 Intersite Ave., 1st Fl.
Durban 4098, Republic of South Africa
Phone: 27 31 2632772
Fax: 27 31 2632771
Publications: blunt (50467) • Saltwater GIRL (50468) • Saltwater GIRL SURF (50469) • Zigzag (50472)

Atomic Energy Society of Japan
3-7 Shimbashi 2-chome
Minato-ku
Tokyo 105-0004, Japan
Phone: 81 335 081261
Fax: 81 335 816128
Publications: Journal of Nuclear Science and Technology (46930)

Attic Futura (UK) Ltd.
17-18 Berners St.
London W1P 3DD, United Kingdom
Phone: 44 20 76646490
Fax: 44 20 76642250
Publications: Westlife (55398)

Audience Media Ltd.
26 Dorset St.
London W1U 8AP, United Kingdom
Phone: 44 20 74867007
Fax: 44 20 74862002
Publications: Audience (53980)

Audio Engineering Society - British Section
PO Box 645
Slough SL1 8BJ, United Kingdom
Phone: 44 1628 663725
Publications: Journal of the Audio Engineering Society (56559)

Auslib Press
PO Box 622
Adelaide, South Australia 5051, Australia
Phone: 61 8 82784363
Fax: 61 8 82784000
Publications: Australasian Public Libraries and Information Services (41502)

Austral Internet Publishing
PO Box 156
Endeavour Hills, Victoria 3802, Australia
Publications: Australian Journal of Mathematical Analysis and Applications (42050)

Australasian Association of Clinical Biochemists
PO Box 278
Mount Lawley, Western Australia 6929, Australia
Phone: 61 893 705224

Fax: 61 893 704409
Publications: The Clinical Biochemist Reviews (42249)

Australasian College for Emergency Medicine
34 Jeffcott St.
West Melbourne, Victoria 3003, Australia
Phone: 61 393 200444
Fax: 61 393 200400
Publications: Emergency Medicine Australasia (42697)

Australasian Epidemiological Association
c/o Leigh Blizzard, Pres.
Menzies Research Institute
Private Bag 23
Hobart, Tasmania 7001, Australia
Phone: 61 39 2517244
Fax: 61 39 2446017
Publications: Australasian Epidemiologist (41957)

Australasian Farmers' & Dealers' Journal
Norley Australia Pty. Ltd.
22 Stradbroke Ave.
East Brighton, Victoria 3187, Australia
Phone: 61 395 927167
Publications: Australasian Farmers' Dealers' Journal (AFDJ) (41844)

Australasian Institute of Mining and Metallurgy
PO Box 660
Carlton, Victoria 3053, Australia
Phone: 61 396 623166
Fax: 61 396 623662
Publications: The AUSIMM Bulletin (41724)

Australasian Journal of Educational Technology
Ascilite Secretariat
PO Box 44
Figtree, New South Wales 2525, Australia
Publications: Australasian Journal of Educational Technology (41840)

Australasian Medical Publishing Company Ltd.
Locked Bag 3030
Strawberry Hills, New South Wales 2012, Australia
Phone: 61 2 95626666
Fax: 61 2 95626699
Publications: ADF Health (42393) • Australian Health Review (42395) • The Medical Journal of Australia (42396)

Australasian Raptor Association
c/o Birds Australia
Green Bldg., Ste. 2-05
60 Leicester St.
Carlton, Victoria 3053, Australia
Phone: 61 3 93470757
Fax: 61 3 93479323
Publications: Boobook (41725)

Australasian Sound Recordings Association
c/o Mr. Bruce Skilton
4 Swiss Mountain Ave.
Hepburn Springs, Victoria 3461, Australia
Publications: Australasian Sound Archive (41952)

Australasian Victorian Studies Association
c/o Dr. Monica Anderson, Treas.
English, Communication & Cultural Studies M202
University of Western Australia
Crawley, Western Australia 6009, Australia
Publications: Australasian Journal of Victorian Studies (41819)

Australian Academic Press
32 Jeays St.
Bowen Hills, Queensland 4006, Australia
Phone: 61 7 32571176
Fax: 61 7 32525908
Publications: Australasian Journal of Special Education (41623)

Australian Academic Press Pty. Ltd.
32 Jeays St.
Bowen Hills, Queensland 4006, Australia
Phone: 61 7 32571176
Fax: 61 7 32525908
Publications: Australian Journal of Guidance and Counselling (41640) • The Australian Journal of Rehabilitation Counselling (41624) • Australian and New Zealand Journal of Audiology (41738) • Australian and New Zealand Journal of Criminology (41757) • Australian and New Zealand Journal of Family Therapy (42699) • Australian Voice (42364) • Brain Impairment

(41625) • International Journal of Disability Management Research (41626) • Journal of Pacific Rim Psychology (41627) • Journal of Smoking Cessation (41628) • Twin Research and Human Genetics (41653)

Australian Academy of Forensic Sciences
207 Albion St.
Surry Hills, New South Wales 2010, Australia
Phone: 61 2 83565868
Publications: Australian Journal of Forensic Sciences (42413)

Australian Acoustical Society
PO Box 1843
Toowong DC, Queensland 4066, Australia
Phone: 61 7 31222605
Publications: Acoustics Australia (42445)

Australian Archaeological Association
3 Queens Rd.
Railway Estate
Townsville, Queensland 4810, Australia
Publications: Australian Archaeology (42634)

Australian Association for Cognitive and Behaviour Therapy
PO Box 853
West Perth, Western Australia 6872, Australia
Publications: Behaviour Change (42698)

Australian Association of Jewish Studies
Holme Bldg., Box 233
University of Sydney
Sydney, New South Wales 2006, Australia
Phone: 61 2 93514162
Fax: 61 2 93512890
Publications: Australian Journal of Jewish Studies (42458)

Australian Association of Massage Therapists
85 Queen St., Level 6
Melbourne, Victoria 3000, Australia
Phone: 61 3 96913700
Fax: 61 3 96023088
Publications: AMTA Journal (42045)

The Australian Association of Mathematics Teachers Inc.
GPO Box 1729
Bldg. D, 80 Payneham Rd.
Stepney, South Australia 5069, Australia
Phone: 61 8 83630288
Fax: 61 8 83629288
Publications: Australian Mathematics Teacher (AMT) (42387) • Australian Primary Mathematics Classroom (APMC) (42388) • Australian Senior Mathematics Journal (ASMJ) (42389)

Australian Association of Social Workers
PO Box 4956
Kingston, Australian Capital Territory 2604, Australia
Phone: 61 2 62323900
Fax: 61 2 62304399
Publications: Australian Social Work (41993)

Australian Association for the Teaching of English
English House
416 Magill Rd.
Kensington Gardens, South Australia 5000, Australia
Phone: 61 1800 248379
Fax: 61 8 83330394
Publications: English in Australia (41985)

Australian Automobile Association
103 Northbourne Ave.
PO Box 1555
Canberra, Australian Capital Territory 2601, Australia
Phone: 61 2 62477311
Fax: 61 2 62575320
Publications: Motoring Directions (41710)

Australian Book Review Inc.
PO Box 2320
Richmond South, Victoria 3121, Australia
Phone: 61 394 296700
Fax: 61 394 292288
Publications: ABR (Australian Book Review) (42311)

Australian Braford Society
122 Denham St.
PO Box 749
Rockhampton, Queensland 4700, Australia
Phone: 61 7 49275196

Fax: 1 7 49275708
Publications: Braford Annual (42314)

Australian Breastfeeding Association
PO Box 4000
Glen Iris, Victoria 3146, Australia
Phone: 61 398 850855
Fax: 61 398 850866
Publications: Breastfeeding Review (41891)

Australian Catholic University
1100 Nudgee Rd.
Banyo, Queensland 4014, Australia
Phone: 61 7 36237100
Publications: Australian Ejournal of Theology (41575)

The Australian Christian
1st Fl., 582 Heidelberg Rd.
Melbourne, Victoria 3078, Australia
Phone: 61 3 94888847
Fax: 61 3 94818543
Publications: The Australian Christian (42048)

Australian Classic Motoring Press 2000
PO Box 369
Strawberry Hills, New South Wales 2031, Australia
Phone: 61 293 194277
Fax: 61 293 192677
Publications: Australian Classic Car Monthly (42394)

Australian College of Ambulance Professionals
PO Box 1425
Brisbane, Queensland 4001, Australia
Publications: Journal of Emergency Primary Health Care (41873)

Australian Computer Society Inc.
Queen Victoria Bldg.
PO Box Q534
Sydney, New South Wales 1230, Australia
Phone: 61 2 92993666
Fax: 61 2 92993997
Publications: The Journal of Research and Practice in Information Technology (42530)

Australian Conservation Foundation
60 Leicester St., Fl. 1
Carlton, Victoria 3053, Australia
Fax: 61 3 93451166
Publications: Habitat Australia (41726)

Australian Consolidated Press NZ Ltd.
Private Bag 92512
Auckland 1036, New Zealand
Phone: 64 9 3082700
Fax: 64 9 3082878
Publications: Australian Women's Weekly (48786) • Fashion Quarterly (48792) • Home New Zealand (48795) • KiaOra (48801) • Little Treasures (48803). • North & South (48822)

Australian Council for Educational Leaders
PO Box 1891
Penrith, New South Wales 2751, Australia
Phone: 61 2 47321201
Fax: 61 2 47321711
Publications: The Australian Educational Leader (42239)

Australian Council for Educational Research
19 Prospect Hill Rd.
PO Box 55
Camberwell, Victoria 3124, Australia
Phone: 61 392 775555
Fax: 61 392 775500
Publications: Australian Journal of Career Development (41693) • Australian Journal of Education (41694)

Australian Dental Association
14-16 Chandos St.
PO Box 520
Saint Leonards, New South Wales 2065, Australia
Phone: 61 299 064412
Fax: 61 299 064917
Publications: Australian Dental Journal (42330)

Australian Diabetes Council
GPO Box 9824
Sydney, New South Wales 2001, Australia
Phone: 61 1300 342238
Fax: 61 296 603633
Publications: Issues (42525)

Australian Education Union
163 Greenhill Rd.
Parkside, South Australia 5063, Australia
Phone: 61 8 82721399
Fax: 61 8 83731254
Publications: Australian Educator (42230)

Australian Environmental Pest Managers Association
PO Box 4886
Sydney, New South Wales 2001, Australia
Phone: 61 2 92328929
Fax: 61 2 92328929
Publications: PESTALK (42560)

Australian Farm Institute Ltd.
Ste. 73, 61 Marlborough St.
Surry Hills, New South Wales 2010, Australia
Phone: 61 2 96901388
Fax: 61 2 96997270
Publications: Farm Policy Journal (42429)

Australian Flexible Learning Framework
GPO Box 1326
Brisbane, Queensland 4001, Australia
Phone: 61 7 33074700
Fax: 61 7 32594371
Publications: The Knowledge Tree (41651)

Australian Garden History Society
Gate Lodge
100 Birdwood Ave.
Melbourne, Victoria 3004, Australia
Phone: 61 396 505043
Fax: 61 396 508470
Publications: Australian Garden History (42049)

Australian Government Department of Health and Ageing
GPO Box 9848
Canberra, Australian Capital Territory 2601, Australia
Phone: 61 2 62891555
Publications: Communicable Diseases Intelligence (41704)

Australian Graduate School of Management
University of New South Wales
Sydney, New South Wales 2052, Australia
Phone: 61 2 93851000
Publications: Australian Journal of Management (42459)

Australian Graphic Design Association
PO Box 816
Unley, South Australia 5061, Australia
Phone: 11 61 84113888
Fax: 11 61 82768003
Publications: Agenda (42659)

Australian Historical Association
Australian Historical Association
Morven Brown Bldg., Level 3
University of New South Wales
Sydney, New South Wales 2052, Australia
Phone: 61 2 93858355
Fax: 61 2 93851251
Publications: History Australia (42515)

Australian Homoeopathic Association
PO Box 104
Seddon West, Victoria 3011, Australia
Phone: 61 1300 789896
Publications: Similia (42356)

Australian Indigenous HealthInfoNet
Kurongkurl Katitjin
2 Bradford St.
Mt. Lawley
Perth, Western Australia 6050, Australia
Phone: 61 8 93706336
Fax: 61 8 93706022
Publications: Australian Indigenous HealthBulletin (42246)

Australian Institute of Biology
PO Box 3014
Syndal, Victoria 3149, Australia
Phone: 61 3 98847405
Publications: Australian Biologist (42610)

Australian Institute of Energy
PO Box 534
Raymond Terrace, New South Wales 2324, Australia
Phone: 61 2 49649599

Fax: 61 2 49649599
Publications: AIE News Journal (42297)

Australian Institute of Family Studies
485 La Trobe St., Level 20
Melbourne, Victoria 3000, Australia
Phone: 61 3 92147888
Fax: 61 3 92147839
Publications: Family Matters (42059)

Australian Institute of Geoscientists
36 Brisbane St.
Perth, Western Australia 6000, Australia
Phone: 61 894 270820
Fax: 61 894 270821
Publications: AIG Journal (42242)

Australian Institute of Physics
61 Danks St. W
Port Melbourne, Victoria 3207, Australia
Phone: 61 3 96469515
Fax: 61 3 96456322
Publications: Australian Physics (42262)

Australian Institute of Quantity Surveyors
National Surveyors House
27-29 Napier Close
Deakin, Australian Capital Territory 2600, Australia
Phone: 61 2 62822222
Fax: 61 2 62852427
Publications: Australian Journal of Construction Economics and Building (41701)

Australian Library and Information Association
ALIA House, 9-11 Napier Close
Deakin, Australian Capital Territory 2600, Australia
Phone: 61 2 62158222
Fax: 61 2 62822249
Publications: The Australian Library Journal (41878) • inCite (41836)

Australian Library and Information Association
PO Box 6335
Kingston, Australian Capital Territory 2604, Australia
Phone: 61 2 62158222
Fax: 61 2 62822249
Publications: Australian Academic & Research Libraries (41990)

Australian Literacy Educators' Association
PO Box 3203
Norwood, South Australia 5067, Australia
Phone: 61 8 83322845
Fax: 61 8 83330394
Publications: Australian Journal of Language and Literacy (42214)

Australian Mathematical Publication Association Inc.
Australian National University
Canberra, Australian Capital Territory 0200, Australia
Phone: 61 261 258922
Fax: 61 261 258923
Publications: The Australian Mathematical Society Gazette (42627)

The Australian Mathematical Society Inc.
Dept. of Mathematics
Australian National University
Canberra, Australian Capital Territory 0200, Australia
Phone: 61 261 258922
Fax: 61 261 258923
Publications: The ANZIAM Journal (The Australian & New Zealand Industrial & Applied Mathematics Journal) (41698) • Journal of the Australian Mathematical Society (41709)

Australian Medical Association
42 Macquarie St.
Barton, Australian Capital Territory 2600, Australia
Phone: 61 262 705400
Fax: 61 262 705499
Publications: Australian Medicine (41576)

Australian Model Engineering
PO Box 4721
Higgins, Australian Capital Territory 2615, Australia
Phone: 61 2 62541641
Publications: Australian Model Engineering (41954)

Australian Music Centre
PO Box N690
Grosvenor Place, New South Wales 1220, Australia
Phone: 61 2 92474677

Fax: 61 2 92412873
Publications: Resonate Journal (41935)

Australian NetGuide Proprietary Ltd.
Level 18
Civic Towers
66-68 Goulburn St.
Sydney, New South Wales 2000, Australia
Phone: 61 29288 9105
Fax: 61 29267 4909
Publications: Australian NetGuide (42462)

Australian and New Zealand Institute of Insurance and Finance
Level 8, 600 Bourke St.
Melbourne, Victoria 3000, Australia
Phone: 61 3 96137200
Fax: 61 3 96424166
Publications: Australian and New Zealand Institute of Insurance and Finance Journal (42052)

Australian and New Zealand Regional Science Association Inc.
School of Economics & Information Systems
University of Wollongong
PO Box U236
Wollongong, New South Wales 2500, Australia
Phone: 61 2 409973329
Fax: 61 2 42213725
Publications: Sustaining Regions (41513)

Australian Nursing Federation
Unit 3
28 Eyre St.
Kingston, Australian Capital Territory 2604, Australia
Phone: 61 2 62326533
Fax: 61 2 62326610
Publications: Australian Journal of Advanced Nursing (AJAN) (41991) • Australian Nursing Journal (ANJ) (41992)

Australian Olive Association
PO Box 309
Pendle Hill, New South Wales 2145, Australia
Phone: 61 417 098527
Fax: 61 2 80081520
Publications: The Olive Press (42151)

Australian Options Publishing Inc.
PO Box 431
Goodwood, South Australia 5034, Australia
Publications: Australian Options (41903)

Australian Pharmaceutical Publishing Company
8 Thomas St., Level 5
Chatswood, New South Wales 2067, Australia
Phone: 61 2 81179500
Fax: 61 2 81179511
Publications: Australian Journal of Pharmacy (41737) • Natural Health & Beauty (41741) • Post Script (41743)

Australian Physiotherapy Association
Level 1
1175 Toorak Rd.
Camberwell, Victoria 3124, Australia
Phone: 61 3 90920888
Fax: 61 3 90900899
Publications: Australian Journal of Physiotherapy (41695)

Australian Pipeline Industry Association
1st Fl., 7 National Circuit
Barton, Australian Capital Territory 2600, Australia
Phone: 61 262 730577
Fax: 61 262 730588
Publications: Australian Pipeliner (41577)

Australian Political Economy Movement
University of Sydney
PO Box 76
Sydney, New South Wales 2006, Australia
Publications: Journal of Australian Political Economy (42526)

Australian Prescriber
Ste. 3, 2 Phipps Close
Deakin, Australian Capital Territory 2600, Australia
Phone: 61 2 62023100
Fax: 61 2 62826855
Publications: Australian Prescriber (41835)

Australian Property Institute
6 Campion St.
Deakin, Australian Capital Territory 2600, Australia

Phone: 61 2 62822411
Fax: 61 2 62852194
Publications: Australian and New Zealand Property Journal (41833)

Australian Science Teachers Association
Unit 7, 18 Napier Close
PO Box 334
Deakin, Australian Capital Territory 2600, Australia
Phone: 61 2 62829377
Fax: 61 2 62829477
Publications: Teaching Science (41838)

Australian Skeptics
PO Box 268
Roseville, New South Wales 2069, Australia
Phone: 61 294 172071
Fax: 61 294 177930
Publications: The Skeptic (42320)

Australian Small Animal Veterinary Association
Unit 40, 6 Herbert St.
Saint Leonards, New South Wales 2065, Australia
Phone: 61 294 315090
Fax: 61 294 379068
Publications: Australian Veterinary Practitioner (42332)

Australian Society for Classical Studies
3 Lorna Close
Bundanoon, New South Wales 2578, Australia
Publications: Antichthon (41668)

Australian Society for Microbiology
Ste. 23, 20 Commercial Rd.
Melbourne, Victoria 3004, Australia
Phone: 61 398 678699
Fax: 61 398 678722
Publications: Microbiology Australia (42076)

Australian Sports Industry Directory
PO Box 9351
Port Macquarie, New South Wales 2444, Australia
Phone: 61 265 812105
Fax: 61 265 812958
Publications: AusSport (42260)

Australian Stainless Steel Development Association
215 Adelaide St., Level 15
Brisbane, Queensland 4000, Australia
Phone: 61 7 32200722
Fax: 61 7 32200733
Publications: Australian Stainless Magazine (41641)

Australian Theological Forum Inc.
Rm. S7, Adelaide College of Divinity
34 Lipsett Ter.
Adelaide, South Australia 5032, Australia
Phone: 61 883 542299
Fax: 61 883 542399
Publications: Australian Theological Book Reviewer (41504) • Interface (41507)

Australian Veterinary Association
Unit 40, 6 Herbert St.
Sydney, New South Wales 2065, Australia
Phone: 61 294 315000
Fax: 61 294 379068
Publications: Australian Veterinary Journal (42468)

Australians Association of Convenience Stores
8 Norris St., Surrey Hills
Coburg
Melbourne, Victoria 3127, Australia
Fax: 61 382 560143
Publications: Convenience World (42057)

Austrian Automobile Touring and Motorcycle Club
Rechtsdienste
Schubertring 1-3
A-1010 Vienna, Austria
Phone: 43 171 1990
Fax: 43 171 9921511
Publications: Auto Touring (42748)

Austrian Institute of Economic Research
Arsenal, Objekt 20
A-1030 Vienna, Austria
Phone: 43 179 82601
Fax: 43 179 89386
Publications: Austrian Economic Quarterly (42747)

Austrian National Union of Students
Taubstummengasse 7-9

A-1040 Vienna, Austria
Phone: 43 131 08880
Fax: 43 131 0888036
Publications: Progress (42766)

Auto & Design
Corso Francia 54
I-10143 Turin, Italy
Fax: 39 114 88120
Publications: Auto & Design (46269)

Auto Retro
BP 40419
F-77309 Fontainebleau Cedex, France
Phone: 33 160 396969
Fax: 33 160 396900
Publications: Auto Retro (43952)

Automatizace S.R.O.
Karlovo namesti 30
CZ-120 00 Prague 2, Czech Republic
Phone: 42 224 934513
Publications: Automatizace (43611)

AutoMetrix Publications
1 Greenfield Rd.
Westoning MK45 5JD, United Kingdom
Phone: 44 15 25750500
Fax: 44 15 25750700
Publications: Audi Driver (56907) • Volkswagen Driver (56908)

Automobile Association of Singapore
336 River Valley Rd., No. 03-00
AA Ctr.
Singapore 238366, Singapore
Phone: 65 63338811
Fax: 65 67335094
Publications: Highway Magazine (50166)

Automobile Association of Upper India
C-8 Qutab Institutional Area
Behind of Qutab Hotel
New Delhi 110 016, Delhi, India
Phone: 91 11 26965397
Fax: 91 11 26866302
Publications: The Upper India Motorist (45660)

AUUG Inc.
PO Box 7071
Baulkham Hills, New South Wales 2153, Australia
Phone: 61 2 88249511
Fax: 61 2 88249522
Publications: AUUGN on the Web (41584)

A.V. Sociedad Editorial Sintesis
Claudio Coello, 101
E-28006 Madrid, Spain
Phone: 34 915 770640
Fax: 34 915 763070
Publications: Sintesis (50806)

L'Avenc S.L.
Passeig de Sant Joan, 26, 2n 1a
E-08007 Barcelona, Spain
Phone: 34 93 2457921
Fax: 34 93 2654416
Publications: L'Avenc (50653)

Aviation Industry Press Ltd.
Ludgate House, 2nd Fl.
245 Blackfriars Rd.
London SE1 9UY, United Kingdom
Phone: 44 20 75794840
Fax: 44 20 75794848
Publications: Aircraft Technology Engineering & Maintenance (53930)

Aviation Trader
PO Box 266
Lismore, New South Wales 2480, Australia
Phone: 61 2 66222133
Fax: 61 2 66222123
Publications: Aviation Trader (42011)

The Avicultural Society
The Chalet Hay Farm
St. Breock
Wadebridge PL27 7LH, United Kingdom
Publications: Avicultural Magazine (56803)

Aviva
41 Royal Cres.
London W11 4SN, United Kingdom

Phone: 44 20 76020140
Fax: 44 20 73716315
Publications: Aviva (53993)

Axel Springer Verlag
Axel-Springer-Platz 1
D-20350 Hamburg, Germany
Phone: 49 40 34700
Publications: Auto Bild (44410) • BILD der FRAU (44411) • FRAU von HEUTE (44416) • HORZU (44418) • MADCHEN (44570) • Metal Hammer (44571) • MUSIKEXPRESS (44573) • POPCORN (44578) • STARFLASH (44582) • YAM! (44588)

Axis Inc.
5-17-1 Roppongi
Minato-ku
Tokyo 106-0032, Japan
Phone: 81 3 35872781
Publications: Axis (46758)

Axon Publishing
11 Plough Yard
London EC2A 3LP, United Kingdom
Phone: 44 20 76847111
Fax: 44 20 76847122
Publications: Eukanuba (54389) • Hildon Magazine (54552) • Live It (54877) • Theatregoer Magazine (55304)

Ayub Medical College
Karakoram Hwy.
Abbottabad 22040, Pakistan
Phone: 92 992 381907
Fax: 92 992 382321
Publications: Journal of Ayub Medical College (49227)

The Ayurvedic Trust
136, 137 Trichy Rd.
PO Box 7102
Ramanathapuram
Coimbatore 641 045, Tamil Nadu, India
Phone: 91 422 2313188
Fax: 91 422 2314953
Publications: Ancient Science of Life (45077)

AZ Fachverlage AG
Neumattstrasse 1
CH-5001 Aarau, Switzerland
Phone: 41 58 2005858
Fax: 41 58 2005644
Publications: Fit for Life (51054) • MegaLink (51055)

The Azeri Times
44 J. Jabbarly Str.
Caspian Plz.
AZ-1065 Baku, Azerbaijan
Phone: 994 12 4367750
Fax: 994 12 4367751
Publications: The Azeri Times (42779)

Aztec Press Services
1 Bankside
Churt Rd.
Hindhead GU26 6NR, United Kingdom
Phone: 44 1428 605605
Fax: 44 1428 714278
Publications: Transport Engineer (53575)

B & L Verlags AG
Steinwiesenstr. 3
CH-8952 Schlieren, Switzerland
Phone: 41 44 7333999
Fax: 41 44 7333989
Publications: Aktuelle Technik (51230)

Bachudo Science Co. Ltd.
Dept. of Geology
University of Calabar
PO Box 3651
Unical Post Office
Calabar, Cross River, Nigeria
Publications: Global Journal of Pure and Applied Sciences (49075)

BackCare
16 Elmtree Rd.
Teddington TW11 8ST, United Kingdom
Phone: 44 20 89775474
Fax: 44 20 89435318
Publications: Talkback (56735)

Backhuys Publishers BV
PO Box 321

NL-2300 AH Leiden, Netherlands
Phone: 31 71 5170208
Fax: 31 71 5171856
Publications: Cainozoic Research (48660)

Badminton Association of England
National Badminton Ctr.
Milton Keynes MK8 9LA, United Kingdom
Phone: 44 19 08268400
Publications: Badminton (55630)

The Balkan Society of Geometers
Splaiul Independentei 313
RO-060042 Bucharest, Romania
Fax: 40 21 4115365
Publications: Balkan Journal of Geometry and its Applications (49832)

Baltzer Science Publishers
PO Box 221
NL-1400 AE Bussum, Netherlands
Phone: 31 356 954250
Fax: 31 256 954258
Publications: Analysis in Theory and Applications (48278) • Japanese Heart Journal (48303) • Topics in Catalysis (48307)

Banaras Hindu University
A-Block, CGO Complex, Lodhi Rd.
Varanasi 110 003, Uttar Pradesh, India
Publications: Indian Journal of Preventive and Social Medicine (45765)

Banbridge Chronicle Press Ltd.
14 Bridge St.
Co. Down
Banbridge BT32 3JS, United Kingdom
Phone: 44 28 40662322
Fax: 44 284 0624397
Publications: Banbridge Chronicle (52163)

Bangabandhu Sheikh Mujibur Rahman Agricultural University
Salna
Gazipur 1706, Bangladesh
Phone: 880 2 9205310
Fax: 880 2 9205333
Publications: Annals of Bangladesh Agriculture (42819)

Bangkok Babies & Mothers International
PO Box 1078
Suanphlu
Bangkok 10121, Thailand
Publications: BAMBI Magazine (51413)

Bangladesh Institute of Development Studies
E-17 Agargaon
Sher-e-Bangla Nagar
GPO Box 3854
Dhaka 1207, Bangladesh
Phone: 880 281 10759
Fax: 880 281 13023
Publications: Bangladesh Development Studies (42803)

Bangladesh Insurance Academy
53 Mohakhali Commercial Area
Dhaka 1212, Bangladesh
Phone: 880 2 9899292
Fax: 880 2 9882071
Publications: Insurance Journal (42812)

Bangladesh National Scientific and Technical Documentation Centre
Dr. Qudrat-I-Kuda Rd.
Dhanmondi
Dhaka 1205, Bangladesh
Publications: Bangladesh Journal of Scientific and Industrial Research (42805)

Bangladesh Pharmaceutical Society
House No. 22
Dhanmondi, Rd. No. 2
Dhaka 1205, Bangladesh
Phone: 880 2 8611370
Fax: 880 2 8613588
Publications: Bangladesh Pharmaceutical Journal (42806)

Bangladesh Sociological Society
Rm. 1054, Arts Faculty Bldg.
University of Dhaka

Dhaka 1000, Bangladesh
Publications: Bangladesh e-Journal of Sociology (42804)

The Bangladesh Today
Concord Royal Ct., 4th Fl.
Plot No. 275(G), Rd. No. 27
Dhaka 1209, Bangladesh
Phone: 880 2 9118807
Fax: 880 2 9118853
Publications: The Bangladesh Today (42807)

Bank of England
Threadneedle St.
London EC2R 8AH, United Kingdom
Phone: 44 20 76014444
Fax: 44 20 76015460
Publications: Bank of England Quarterly Bulletin (54000) • The Old Lady (55028)

Baptist Churches of New Zealand
PO Box 12149
Penrose
Auckland 1642, New Zealand
Phone: 64 9 5260333
Fax: 64 9 5260334
Publications: New Zealand Baptist (48806)

Baptist Union of Victoria
PO Box 377
Hawthorn, Victoria 3122, Australia
Phone: 61 3 98806100
Fax: 61 3 98816123
Publications: The Victoria Baptist Witness (41943)

Bar-Ilan University
Faculty of Jewish Studies
IL-59200 Ramat Gan, Israel
Phone: 972 3 5318111
Publications: Jewish Studies, an Internet Journal (46095)

The Barcelona Review
Correu Vell, 12 - 2
E-08002 Barcelona, Spain
Fax: 34 933 191596
Publications: The Barcelona Review (50654)

Barrett, Byrd Associates
BBA Linden House
Linden Close
Tunbridge Wells TN4 8HH, United Kingdom
Phone: 44 1892 524455
Fax: 44 1892 524456
Publications: Transportation Professional (56783)

Batteries International Ltd.
17 Westmeston Ave.
Rottingdean
East Sussex
Brighton BN2 8AL, United Kingdom
Phone: 44 1798 839338
Publications: Batteries International (52606)

Bauer Consumer Media Ltd.
21 Holborn Viaduct
London EC1A 2DY, United Kingdom
Publications: Yours (55435)

Bay View Publishing
PO Box 109
Pevensey BN24 9AA, United Kingdom
Phone: 44 1323 767804
Publications: Pet Talk (56268)

Bayerische Landesarztekammer
Muhlbaurstr. 16
D-81677 Munich, Germany
Phone: 49 89 41470
Fax: 49 89 4147280
Publications: Bayerisches Arzteblatt (44551)

BBC Magazines
Media Center
201 Wood Ln.
London W12 7TQ, United Kingdom
Phone: 44 20 84332000
Publications: BBC Gardeners' World Magazine (54003) • BBC Learning is Fun! (54005) • Live & Kicking (54878)

BBC Worldwide Ltd.
Media Ctr.
201 Wood Ln.

London W12 7TQ, United Kingdom
Phone: 44 20 84332000
Publications: Top Gear Magazine (55326)

BBC Worldwide Publishing Ltd.
Media Centre
201 Wood Ln.
London W12 7TQ, United Kingdom
Phone: 44 20 84332000
Fax: 44 20 87490538
Publications: All About Animals (53932) • Amy (53939) • Balamory (53998) • BBC Countryfile (52641) • BBC Good Food (54004) • BBC History (52642) • BBC The Magic Key (54006) • BBC Wildlife Magazine (52643) • Bob the Builder (54095) • CBee-bies Weekly Magazine (54188) • Charlie and Lola (54198) • Doctor Who Adventures (54338) • Easy Cook (54348) • Fifi and the Flowertots (54452) • Fimbles Magazine (54453) • Gardens Illustrated (52672) • Girl Talk (54507) • Girl Talk Extra (54508) • Good Homes (54520) • Homes & Antiques (54567) • In the Night Garden (54592) • Learn with Bob the Builder (54860) • Me Too! (54917) • Olive (55030) • Radio Times (55170) • Robin Hood Adventures (55207) • Sky at Night Magazine (52730) • Teletubbies (55298) • Top of the Pops (55328) • Toybox (55333) • Tweenies (55347) • Underground Ernie (55358) • Who Do You Think You Are? (52736) • W.I.T.C.H. (55409)

BDFM Publishers (Pty) Ltd.
4 Biermann Ave.
Rosebank
Johannesburg 2196, Republic of South Africa
Publications: Business Day (50529)

Beatles Unlimited
PO Box 602
NL-3430 AP Nieuwegein, Netherlands
Phone: 31 306 063678
Publications: Beatles Unlimited Magazine (48740)

Beaumont Publishing
PO Box 161
Congleton CW12 3WJ, United Kingdom
Phone: 44 1260 278044
Fax: 44 1260 278044
Publications: Armourer (53059)

Bees for Development
PO Box 105
Monmouth NP25 9AA, United Kingdom
Phone: 44 1600 713648
Publications: Bees for Development Journal (55644)

The Behaviormetric Society of Japan
c/o Associate Professor Kenichi Kikuchi
2-2-1 Miyama, Funabashi
Chiba 274-8510, Japan
Phone: 81 47 4721182
Fax: 81 47 4721241
Publications: Behaviormetrika (46315)

Beijing Language and Culture University Press
No. 15, Xueyuan Rd.
Haidian District
Beijing 100083, People's Republic of China
Phone: 86 10 82303668
Publications: Chinese Tales and Stories (43190) • Learning Chinese (43210) • Life in China (43211)

Beijing Review Publishing Co.
24 Baiwanzhuang Rd.
Beijing 100037, People's Republic of China
Phone: 86 106 8996288
Fax: 86 106 8328738
Publications: Beijing Review (43171)

Beilstein - Institut zur Foerderung der Chemischen Wissenschaften
Trakehner Strasse 7-9
D-60487 Frankfurt am Main, Germany
Phone: 49 69 7167320
Fax: 49 69 71673219
Publications: Beilstein Journal of Organic Chemistry (44364)

Belgian Geological Society
c/o Eric Goemaere, Sec.
Rue Jenner 13
B-1000 Brussels, Belgium
Phone: 32 278 87622
Publications: Geologica Belgica (42856)

Belgian Road Safety Institute
Chaussee de Haecht 1405
B-1130 Brussels, Belgium
Phone: 32 224 41511
Fax: 32 221 64342
Publications: Via Secura (42873)

The Beliza Times Press Ltd.
No. 3, Queen St.
PO Box 506
Belize City, Belize
Phone: 501 224 5757
Publications: The Belize Times (42915)

Bellydance Oasis Magazine
14 Anstie Way
Perth, Western Australia 6149, Australia
Phone: 43 8 223914
Publications: Bellydance Oasis (42247)

Bengal Engineering and Science University
PO Botanic Garden
Howrah 711 103, West Bengal, India
Phone: 91 33 26684561
Fax: 91 33 26682916
Publications: Journal of Technology (45138)

John Benjamins Publishing Co.
Klaprozenweg 105
PO Box 36224
NL-1033 NN Amsterdam, Netherlands
Phone: 31 206 304747
Fax: 31 206 739773
Publications: Babel (47902) • Diachronica (47957) • English Text Construction (47965) • English World-Wide (47966) • Functions of Language (FOL) (47992) • Gesture (48000) • Historiographia Linguistica (HL) (48012) • Information Design Journal (48018) • Interaction Studies (48022) • International Journal of Corpus Linguistics (48026) • Interpreting (48033) • Journal of Asian Pacific Communication (48052) • Journal of Historical Pragmatics (48083) • Journal of Language & Politics (48090) • Journal of Pidgin and Creole Languages (JPCL) (48110) • Language Problems and Language Planning (48133) • Languages in Contrast (48134) • Linguistic Variations Yearbook (48138) • Lingvisticae Investigationes (48139) • The Mental Lexicon (48153) • Narrative Inquiry (48169) • Pragmatics & Cognition (48211) • Review of Cognitive Linguistics (48223) • Sign Language and Linguistics (48232) • Spanish in Context (48235) • Studies in Language (48239) • Target (48241) • Terminology (48245) • Written Language and Literacy (48273)

Bennet, Coleman & Company Ltd.
Times House
7 Bahadurshah Zafar Marg
New Delhi 400 002, Delhi, India
Phone: 91 11 23302000
Publications: The Economic Times (45031) • The Economic Times (44958) • The Economic Times (45505) • The Economic Times (45368) • The Economic Times (45264)

Tom Bennion
Harbour City Tower, Ste. 512
29 Brandon St.
Wellington, New Zealand
Phone: 64 4 4735755
Fax: 64 4 4735751
Publications: The Maori Law Review (49016)

Bentham Science Publishers Ltd.
PO Box 294
NL-1400 AG Bussum, Netherlands
Publications: Anti-Cancer Agents in Medicinal Chemistry (48279) • Anti-Inflammatory & Anti-Allergy Agents in Medicinal Chemistry (51576) • Cardiovascular & Hematological Agents in Medicinal Chemistry (45343) • Cardiovascular & Hematological Disorders - Drug Targets (48280) • Clinical Practice and Epidemiology in Mental Health (48281) • CNS & Neurological Disorders - Drug Targets (48282) • Current Analytical Chemistry (49341) • Current Bioactive Compounds (49342) • Current Bioinformatics (48283) • Current Clinical Pharmacology (48284) • Current Computer-Aided Drug Design (48285) • Current Diabetes Reviews (51675) • Current Drug Delivery (41647) • Current Drug Discovery Technologies (48286) • Current Drug Metabolism (48287) • Current Drug Safety (48288) • Current Drug Therapy (48289) • Current Enzyme Inhibition (45344) •

Current Gene Therapy (44012) • Current Genomics (44035) • Current Hypertension Reviews (48290) • Current Nanoscience (49343) • Current Neuropharmacology (54296) • Current Nutrition & Food Science (48291) • Current Organic Synthesis (48292) • Current Pediatric Reviews (54303) • Current Pharmaceutical Analysis (49344) • Current Pharmaceutical Biotechnology (48293) • Current Pharmaceutical Design (48294) • Current Pharmacogenomics and Personalized Medicine (48295) • Current Proteomics (48296) • Current Signal Transduction Therapy (48297) • Current Topics in Medicinal Chemistry (48298) • Current Vascular Pharmacology (54304) • Current Women's Health Reviews (48299) • Drug Metabolism Letters (48300) • Endocrine, Metabolic & Immune Disorders - Drug Targets (46121) • Infectious Disorders - Drug Targets (48301) • Inflammation & Allergy - Drug Targets (48302) • Letters in Drug Design & Discovery (49360) • Letters in Organic Chemistry (49361) • Medicinal Chemistry (49363) • Mini-Reviews in Organic Chemistry (49364) • Recent Patents on Cardiovascular Drug Discovery (48304) • Recent Patents on Drug Delivery & Formulation (48305) • Recent Patents on Nanotechnology (48306) • Vascular Disease Prevention (55366)

Berg Publishers
1st Fl., Angel Ct.
81 St. Clements St.
Oxford OX4 1AW, United Kingdom
Phone: 44 18 65245104
Fax: 44 18 65791165
Publications: Anthrozoos (52789) • Cultural Politics (55920) • Cultural & Social History (55921) • The Design Journal (55924) • Fashion Theory (55953) • Home Cultures (54565) • Material Religion (56094) • Textile (56217)

Berita Publishing Sdn Bhd
16-20 Jalen 4/109E
Desa Business Pk., Taman Desa
Off Jalan Kelang Lama
58100 Kuala Lumpur, Malaysia
Phone: 60 376 208111
Fax: 60 376 208026
Publications: Malaysian Business (47614)

Berkeley Electronic Press
2809 Telegraph Ave., Ste. 202
Berkeley, CA 94705-1167
Phone: 510665-1200
Fax: 510665-1201
Publications: Theoretical Inquiries in Law (46114)

The Bermuda Press (Holdings) Ltd.
PO Box HM1025
Hamilton, Bermuda
Phone: 441295-5881
Publications: Mid-Ocean News (42921) • The Royal Gazette (42922)

Bermuda Sun Ltd.
PO Box HM 1241
Hamilton, Bermuda
Phone: 809295-3902
Fax: 809292-5597
Publications: Bermuda Sun (42920)

Bornoulli Society for Mathematical Statistics and Probability
c/o Ms. Margaret de Ruiter-Molloy, Membership Off.
428 Prinses Beatrixlaan
PO Box 950
NL-2270 AZ Voorburg, Netherlands
Phone: 31 70 3375726
Fax: 31 70 3860025
Publications: Bernoulli (48769) • Journal of Time Series Analysis (48770)

Berufsverband Osterreichischer Psychologinnen und Psychologen
Mollnaldplatz 4/4/39
A-1040 Vienna, Austria
Phone: 43 140 726710
Fax: 43 140 7267130
Publications: Psychologie in Osterreich (42767)

BH & HP Association
Chichester House
6 Pullman Ct.
Great Western Rd.
Gloucester GL1 3ND, United Kingdom
Phone: 44 1452 526911

Fax: 44 1452 508508
Publications: Journal—British Holiday & Home Parks Association (53471)

Bharat Times
PO Box 6100
West Footscray, Victoria 3012, Australia
Phone: 61 3 96896406
Fax: 61 3 96896489
Publications: Bharat Times (42694)

Bharath Prakashan (Delhi) Ltd.
Sanskriti Bhavan
D.B. Gupta Rd.
New Delhi 110 055, Delhi, India
Phone: 91 11 47642022
Fax: 91 11 47642023
Publications: Organiser (45632)

Bhatkal Media Publishing Society
SahilOnline, First Fl., Jamaat Complex
Next to KSRTC Bus Stand
Bhatkal 581 320, Karnataka, India
Phone: 91 838 5320768
Fax: 91 838 5223252
Publications: Sahil Daily (45003)

Bhutan Observer Pvt. Ltd.
Norzin Lam
PO Box 1112
Thimphu, Bhutan
Phone: 975 2 334891
Fax: 975 2 327981
Publications: Bhutan Observer (42924)

Bibliographical Society
c/o Institute of English Studies
University of London
Senate House
Malet St.
London WC1E 7HU, United Kingdom
Publications: The Library (54869)

Bicycle Federation of Australia Inc.
PO Box 499
Civic Square, Australian Capital Territory 2608, Australia
Phone: 61 262 496761
Publications: Australian Cyclist (41753)

Big Cheese Publishing
Unit 7, Clarendon Bldg.
25 Horsell Rd.
Highbury
London N5 1XL, United Kingdom
Phone: 44 20 76070303
Publications: Big Cheese (54015)

The Big Issue
PO Box 5094
Cape Town 8000, Republic of South Africa
Phone: 27 214 616690
Fax: 27 214 616662
Publications: The Big Issue (50364)

Big Issue Namibia
1-5 Wandsworth Rd.
London SW8 2LN, United Kingdom
Phone: 44 20 75263200
Publications: Big Issue Namibia (54016)

Bikersweb.co.uk
PO Box 8341
Birmingham B33 8DA, United Kingdom
Phone: 44 21 7847018
Publications: Bikersweb (52329)

Bio-Dynamic Agricultural Association
c/o The Painswick Inn Project
Gloucester St.
Stroud GL5 1QG, United Kingdom
Phone: 44 14 53759501
Fax: 44 14 53759501
Publications: Star and Furrow (56648)

Bio-Ritter GmbH
Montashauserstr. 8
D-82327 Tutzing, Germany
Publications: BIO—Gesundheit fur Korper Geist und Seele (44695)

Bio Verlag Gmbh
Magnolienweg 23
D-63741 Aschaffenburg, Germany

Phone: 49 6021 44890
Fax: 49 6021 4489499
Publications: Schrot & Korn (44139)

The Biochemical Society
Charles Darwin House
12 Roger St.
London WC1N 2JU, United Kingdom
Phone: 44 20 76852400
Fax: 44 20 76852470
Publications: The Biochemist (54019)

Biocom AG
Stralsunder Str. 58-59
D-13355 Berlin, Germany
Phone: 49 30 2649210
Fax: 49 30 26492111
Publications: European Biotechnology Science & Industry News (44173)

Bioline International
Usmanu Danfodiyo University Teaching Hospital
Sokoto, Sokoto, Nigeria
Phone: 234 602 31514
Fax: 234 602 31514
Publications: Annals of African Medicine (49172) • BIOKEMISTRI (49119) • European Journal of General Medicine (49173)

Biological Farmers of Australia
PO Box 530
Chermside, Queensland 4032, Australia
Phone: 61 7 33505716
Fax: 61 7 33505996
Publications: Australian Organic Journal (41750)

BioMed Central Ltd.
236 Gray's Inn Rd., Fl. 6
34-42 Cleveland St.
London WC1X 8HL, United Kingdom
Phone: 44 20 31922000
Fax: 44 20 31922010
Publications: AIDS Research and Therapy (53928) • Annals of Clinical Microbiology and Antimicrobials (53947) • Annals of General Psychiatry (53948) • Behavioral and Brain Functions (54009) • Bioinformation (54020) • Biological Knowledge (54021) • Biomedical Digital Libraries (54028) • BioMedical Engineering OnLine (54029) • BMC Anesthesiology (54035) • BMC Biochemistry (54036) • BMC Bioinformatics (54037) • BMC Biology (54038) • BMC Biotechnology (54039) • BMC Blood Disorders (54040) • BMC Cancer (54041) • BMC Cardiovascular Disorders (54042) • BMC Cell Biology (54043) • BMC Chemical Biology (54044) • BMC Clinical Pathology (54045) • BMC Clinical Pharmacology (54046) • BMC Complementary and Alternative Medicine (54047) • BMC Dermatology (54048) • BMC Developmental Biology (54049) • BMC Ear, Nose and Throat Disorders (54050) • BMC Ecology (54051) • BMC Emergency Medicine (54052) • BMC Endocrine Disorders (54053) • BMC Evolutionary Biology (54054) • BMC Family Practice (54055) • BMC Gastroenterology (54056) • BMC Genetics (54057) • BMC Genomics (54058) • BMC Geriatrics (54059) • BMC Health Services Research (54060) • BMC Immunology (54061) • BMC Infectious Diseases (54062) • BMC International Health and Human Rights (54063) • BMC Medical Education (54064) • BMC Medical Ethics (54065) • BMC Medical Genetics (54066) • BMC Medical Imaging (54067) • BMC Medical Informatics and Decision Making (54068) • BMC Medical Physics (54069) • BMC Medical Research Methodology (54070) • BMC Medicine (54071) • BMC Microbiology (54072) • BMC Molecular Biology (54073) • BMC Musculoskeletal Disorders (54074) • BMC Nephrology (54075) • BMC Neurology (54076) • BMC Neuroscience (54077) • BMC Nursing (54078) • BMC Ophthalmology (54079) • BMC Oral Health (54080) • BMC Palliative Care (54081) • BMC Pediatrics (54082) • BMC Pharmacology (54083) • BMC Physiology (54084) • BMC Plant Biology (54085) • BMC Pregnancy and Childbirth (54086) • BMC Psychiatry (54087) • BMC Pulmonary Medicine (54088) • BMC Structural Biology (54089) • BMC Surgery (54090) • BMC Urology (54091) • BMC Veterinary Research (54092) • BMC Women's Health (54093) • Cancer Cell International (54171) • Carbon Balance and Management (54175) • Cardiovascular Diabetology (54178) • Cardiovascular Ultrasound (54179) • Cell Communication and Signaling (54190) • Cerebrospinal Fluid Research (54196) • Chiropractic & Osteopathy (42136) • Comparative Hepatology (54250) • Cost Effectiveness and Resource Allocation (54272) • Critical Care (54288) • Current Opinion in Drug Discovery & Development (54298) • Current Opinion in Molecular Therapeutics (54301) • CytoJournal (54307) • Diagnostic Pathology (54325) • Emerging Themes in Epidemiology (54364) • Environmental Health (54376) • Epidemiologic Perspectives & Innovations (54379) • Faculty of 1000 Medicine (54437) • Frontiers in Zoology (54486) • Genetic Vaccines and Therapy (54501) • Genetics Selection Evolution (43960) • Genome Biology (Online Edition) (54502) • Geochemical Transactions (54503) • Globalization and Health (54514) • Harm Reduction Journal (54531) • Head & Face Medicine (54534) • Health Research Policy and Systems (54541) • Human Resources for Health (54580) • Immunity & Ageing (54584) • Immunome Research (54586) • International Breastfeeding Journal (54620) • International Journal of Behavioral Nutrition and Physical Activity (54634) • International Journal for Equity in Health (54648) • International Journal of Health Geographics (54649) • International Seminars in Surgical Oncology (54671) • Journal of Autoimmune Diseases (54703) • Journal of Carcinogenesis (54717) • Journal of Cardiovascular Magnetic Resonance (54718) • Journal of Cardiovascular Magnetic Resonance (54719) • Journal of Circadian Rhythms (54724) • Journal of Dermatological Treatment (54736) • Journal of Ethnobiology and Ethnomedicine (54746) • Journal of Experimental & Clinical Assisted Reproduction (54749) • Journal of Immune Based Therapies and Vaccines (54765) • Journal of Inflammation (54767) • Journal of Nanobiotechnology (54783) • Journal of Negative Results in BioMedicine (54784) • Journal of NeuroEngineering and Rehabilitation (JNER) (54785) • Journal of Neuroinflammation (54786) • Journal of Translational Medicine (54830) • Lipids in Health and Disease (54875) • Malaria Journal (54900) • Microbial Cell Factories (54929) • Molecular Cancer (54945) • Molecular Pain (54947) • Nutrition Journal (55019) • Nutrition & Metabolism (55020) • Particle and Fibre Toxicology (55059) • Philosophy, Ethics, and Humanities in Medicine (55082) • Plant Methods (55093) • Population Health Metrics (55102) • Proteome Science (55145) • Reproductive Health (55190) • Respiratory Research (55194) • Retrovirology (55198) • Saline Systems (55217) • Theoretical Biology and Medical Modelling (55306) • Thrombosis Journal (55316) • Virology Journal (55372)

Biometric Society of Japan
c/o Statistical Information Institute for Consulting & Analy
Nougakushorin Bldg., 5th Fl.
3-6 Kanda Jimbocho
Chiyoda-ku
Tokyo 101-0051, Japan
Fax: 81 3 32347472
Publications: Japanese Journal of Biometrics (46866)

BioScientifica Ltd.
Euro House
22 Apex Ct.
Woodlands
Bradley Stoke
Bristol BS32 4JT, United Kingdom
Phone: 44 14 54642220
Fax: 44 14 54642201
Publications: Endocrine Abstracts (52662) • Reproduction (52726)

Bioversity International
Via dei Tre Denari, 472a
Maccarese
I-00057 Rome, Italy
Phone: 39 06 61181
Fax: 39 06 61181
Publications: Geneflow (46230)

BIPP
1 Prebendal Ct.
Oxford Rd.
Bucks
Aylesbury HP19 8EY, United Kingdom
Phone: 44 1296 718530
Fax: 44 1296 336367
Publications: The Photographer (52148)

Birbal Sahni Institute of Palaeobotany
53 University Rd.
Lucknow 226 007, Uttar Pradesh, India
Phone: 91 522 2740008
Fax: 91 522 2740485
Publications: Palaeobotanist (45325)

Bird Observation & Conservation Australia
PO Box 185
Nunawading, Victoria 3131, Australia
Phone: 61 3 98775342
Fax: 61 3 98944048
Publications: Australian Field Ornithology (42218)

Birding World
Stonerunner
Coast Rd.
Cley-next-the-Sea
Holt NR25 7RZ, United Kingdom
Phone: 44 1263 741139
Fax: 44 1263 741173
Publications: Birding World (53583)\

BirdLife International
Wellbrook Ct.
Girton Rd.
Cambridge CB3 0NA, United Kingdom
Phone: 44 12 23277318
Fax: 44 12 23277200
Publications: Bird Conservation International (52793) •
World Birdwatch (52906)

BirdLife Malta
57/28 Triq Abate Rigord
Ta' Xbiex XBX 1120, Malta
Phone: 356 21347646
Fax: 356 21343239
Publications: Birds Eye View (47743) • Il-Merill
(47744)

Birkhauser Publishing Ltd.
Viaduktstrasse 42
CH-4051 Basel, Switzerland
Phone: 41 612 050775
Fax: 41 612 050792
Publications: Geometric and Functional Analysis
(GAFA) (46100)

Birkhauser Verlag AG
Heidelberger Platz 3
PO Box 14302
14197 Berlin, Germany
Phone: 49 30 827875431
Fax: 49 30 827875707
Publications: Journal of Applied Mathematics and
Physics (ZAMP) (51269)

Bizmedia Ltd
Royal Sta. Ct.
Sta. Rd.
Twyford
Reading RG10 9NF, United Kingdom
Phone: 44 118 9602820
Fax: 44 118 9602821
Publications: E.Learning Age (56312)

Black Inc.
37-39 Langridge St.
Collingwood, Victoria 3066, Australia
Phone: 61 3 94860288
Fax: 61 3 94860244
Publications: Quarterly Essay (41795)

Blackwell Munksgaard
1 Rosenorns Alle
DK-1970 Frederiksberg C, Denmark
Phone: 45 773 33333
Fax: 45 773 33377
Publications: Acta Crystallographica. Section E
(43689) • Genes, Brain and Behavior (43690) • International Journal of Dental Hygiene (55993) • Orthodontics
& Craniofacial Research (43694) • Pediatric Diabetes
(43695) • Traffic (43696)

Blah Blah
PO Box 2622
Reading RG1 9DJ, United Kingdom
Phone: 44 118 9753577
Fax: 44 118 9753577
Publications: Blah Blah (56311)

Blauw Media Uitgeverij B.V.
Straatweg 28

NL-3604 BB Maarssen, Netherlands
Phone: 31 346 574040
Fax: 31 346 576056
Publications: Fietsmarkt (48731) • Mannenmode
(48732) • Tred (48733) • Trend Boutique (48734) •
Trends (48735)

Blur Ediciones
Abtao 25
Interior Nave C.
E-28007 Madrid, Spain
Phone: 34 91434 8178
Publications: Visual (50815)

BMI Publications Ltd.
Suffolk House
George St.
Croydon CR9 1SR, United Kingdom
Phone: 44 20 86497233
Fax: 44 20 86497234
Publications: Selling Long Haul (53132) • Selling Short
Breaks (53133)

BMJ Publishing Group
BMA House
Tavistock Sq.
London WC1H 9JR, United Kingdom
Phone: 44 20 73834410
Fax: 44 20 73876400
Publications: Annals of the Rheumatic Disease
(53949) • Archives of Disease in Childhood. Education
and Practice Edition (53963) • British Journal of
Ophthalmology (54129) • British Medical Journal Clinical Evidence (54140) • Journal of Medical Ethics
(54779) • Journal of Medical Genetics (54780) •
Journal of Neurology, Neurosurgery, and Psychiatry
(54787) • Medical Humanities (54923) • Postgraduate
Medical Journal (55109) • Quality and Safety in Health
Care (55162)

BMJ Publishing Group Ltd.
BMA House
Tavistock Sq.
London WC1H 9JR, United Kingdom
Phone: 44 20 73874410
Fax: 44 20 73836400
Publications: Best Treatments (54014) • British
Journal of Sports Medicine (54137) • British Medical
Journal (54139) • Evidence-Based Mental Health
(EBMH) (54415) • Gut (55757) • Heart (54545) •
Journal of Epidemiology and Community Health
(54745) • Practical Neurology (55115) • Sexually
Transmitted Infections (55231) • Student BMJ
(55268) • Thorax (55315) • Tobacco Control (55325)

BMP N.V. Book & Media Publishing
Lakborslei 114
B-2100 Deurne, Belgium
Phone: 32 336 07800
Fax: 32 336 07801
Publications: Ambiance (42837)

Boarding Schools Association
Grosvenor Gardens House
35-37, Grosvenor Gardens
London SW1W 0BS, United Kingdom
Phone: 44 20 77981580
Fax: 44 20 77981581
Publications: Boarding School (54094)

BOARDS Magazine
196 E Esplanade
Southend-on-Sea SS1 3AB, United Kingdom
Phone: 44 1702 582245
Publications: Boards (56584)

Boat International Group
41-47 Hartfield Rd., 1st Fl.
Wimbledon SW19 3RQ, United Kingdom
Phone: 44 20 85459330
Fax: 44 20 85459333
Publications: Boat International Russia (49884) •
Dockwalk (56927) • Meer & Yachten (44506) • Mer &
Bateaux (43915)

Boats & Yachting Ltd.
42 Catacomb St.
Marsascala ZBR 12, Malta
Phone: 356 822 940
Fax: 356 829 464
Publications: Boats and Yachting (47738)

Boer Goat Breeders Association of Australia
c/o Agricultural Business Research Institute
University of New England
Armidale, New South Wales 2351, Australia
Phone: 61 267 735177
Fax: 61 267 721943
Publications: Boer Briefs (41559)

Bogazici University
Southern Campus No:10
Bebek
TR-34342 Istanbul, Turkey
Phone: 90 212 3595400
Fax: 90 212 3597461
Publications: Bogazici Journal (51557)

Bohol Chronicle Press
56 B. Inting St.
Tagbilaran 6300, Philippines
Phone: 63 38 4113100
Fax: 63 38 4113100
Publications: The Bohol Chronicle (49637)

BOLA SportsLine
Jl. Palmerah Barath, No. 33-37
10270 Jakarta, Indonesia
Phone: 62 21 53677835
Fax: 62 21 5301952
Publications: BOLA SportsLine (45793)

Bombay Chartered Accountants' Society
Jolly Bhavan 2
7, New Marine Lines
Churchgate
Mumbai 400 020, Maharashtra, India
Phone: 91 22 61377600
Fax: 91 22 61377666
Publications: Bombay Chartered Accountant Journal
(45357)

Bombay Hospital Institute of Medical Sciences
4th Fl., Medical Research Center Ext. Bldg.
12 Marine Lines
Mumbai 400 020, Maharashtra, India
Phone: 91 222 2067676
Fax: 92 222 2080871
Publications: Bombay Hospital Journal (45358)

Bond Law School Review Editorial Committee
Bond University
Faculty of Law
Gold Coast, Queensland 4229, Australia
Phone: 61 7 559 552008
Publications: Bond Law Review (41898)

Bond University
University Dr. (Off Cottesloe Dr.) Robina
BOND University 4229
Gold Coast, Queensland 4229, Australia
Phone: 61 755 9552008
Publications: Revenue Law Journal (41899) • Spreadsheets in Education (41900)

Bonnier Tidskrifter AB
Sveavagen 53
SE-105 44 Stockholm, Sweden
Phone: 46 87365300
Publications: Damernas Varld (51014)

The Bookplate Society
11 Nella Rd.
London W6 9PB, United Kingdom
Publications: The Bookplate Journal (56811)

Books for Keeps
1 Effingham Rd.
London SE12 8NZ, United Kingdom
Phone: 44 20 88524953
Fax: 44 20 83187580
Publications: Books for Keeps (54098)

**Booksellers Association of The United Kingdom
and Ireland**
Minster House
272 Vauxhall Bridge Rd.
London SW1V 1BA, United Kingdom
Phone: 44 20 78020802
Fax: 44 20 78020803
Publications: Bookselling Essentials (54099)

Booksellers New Zealand
Level 1, Survey House
PO Box 13248
21-29 Broderick Rd.

Johnsonville
Wellington, New Zealand
Phone: 64 447 85511
Fax: 64 447 85519
Publications: Booksellers News (49002)

The Bosnian Institute
SAVO, 8th Fl.
Hannibal House
Elephant and Castle
London SE1 6TE, United Kingdom
Publications: Bosnia Report (54100)

Botanical Gardens Conservation International
Descanso House, 199 Kew Rd.
Surrey
Richmond TW9 3BW, United Kingdom
Phone: 44 20 83325953
Fax: 44 20 83325956
Publications: BG Journal (56388)

Botanical Society of Japan
Toshin Bldg.
2-27-2 Hongo
Bunkyo-ku
Tokyo 113-0003, Japan
Phone: 81 3 38145675
Fax: 81 3 38145352
Publications: Journal of Plant Research (46938)

Botanical Society of Korea
968-3 Pongchon-dong, Kwanak-gu
402 Keumsong Bldg.
Seoul 151-821, Republic of Korea
Phone: 82 288 40384
Fax: 82 288 40385
Publications: Journal of Plant Biology (47277)

Bourgas University, Technical College
1 Prof. Yakimov Blvd.
BG-8010 Bourgas, Bulgaria
Phone: 359 56 858409
Publications: Academic Open Internet Journal (43086)

Boys' Brigade
Felden Lodge
Hemel Hempstead HP3 0BL, United Kingdom
Phone: 44 14 42231681
Fax: 44 14 42235391
Publications: Boys' Brigade Gazette (53555)

Brandes und Apsel Verlag GmbH
Scheidswaldstr. 22
D-60385 Frankfurt am Main, Germany
Publications: Selbstpsychologie (44369)

Brasilian Kant Society, Campinas Section
PO Box 6133
13083-970 Campinas, Sao Paulo, Brazil
Publications: Kant e-Prints (42970)

Braybrooke Press Ltd.
Remenham House
Remenham Hill
Henley-on-Thames RG9 3EP, United Kingdom
Phone: 44 14 91412061
Fax: 44 14 91411428
Publications: Journal of General Management (53561)

Brazilian Association for the Advancement of Science
294 - 4 andar
01222-010 Sao Paulo, Sao Paulo, Brazil
Phone: 55 11 32592766
Fax: 55 11 31061002
Publications: Ciencia e Cultura (43033) • Ciencia Hoje (43034) • Ciencia Hoje das Criancas (43035) • Jornal da Ciencia Hoje (43041)

Brazilian Association of Sanitary and Environmental Engineering
Av. Beira Mar, 216 - 13 Andar - Castelo
Rio de Janeiro, Rio de Janeiro, Brazil
Phone: 55 212 2103221
Fax: 55 212 2626838
Publications: Engenharia Sanitaria e Ambiental (43004)

The Brazilian Association of Social Psychology
R. Ramiro Barcelos 2600 Sala 13
90035-030 Porto Alegre, Rio Grande do Sul, Brazil
Phone: 55 513 3165149
Publications: Psicologia & Sociedade (42993)

Brazilian Ceramic Society
Av. Lineu Prestes

2242 - Cidade Universitaria
05508-900 Sao Paulo, Sao Paulo, Brazil
Phone: 55 113 8169343
Fax: 55 113 8169343
Publications: Ceramica (43032)

Brazilian Chamber of Commerce in Great Britain
32 Green St.
London W1K 7AT, United Kingdom
Phone: 44 20 73999281
Fax: 44 20 74990186
Publications: Brazil Business Brief (54103)

Brazilian Federation of Endocrinology and Metabolism Societies
Rua Botucatu, 572
Conjunto 83
04023-062 Sao Paulo, Sao Paulo, Brazil
Phone: 55 115 753011
Fax: 55 115 5499089
Publications: Arquivos Brasileiros de Endocrinologia & Metabologia (43022)

Brazilian Foundation for the Conservation of Nature
103, Miranda Valverde St.
Botafogo
22281-020 Rio de Janeiro, Rio de Janeiro, Brazil
Phone: 55 212 5377565
Fax: 55 212 5371343
Publications: Informativo FBCN (43006)

The Brazilian Journal of Infectious Diseases and Contexto Publishing
Rua Alfredo Magalhaes, 04/Barra
40140-140 Salvador, Bahia, Brazil
Phone: 55 71 2642971
Fax: 55 71 2643326
Publications: Brazilian Journal of Infectious Diseases (43014)

Brazilian Journal of Medical and Biological Research
Av. Bandeirantes, 3900
14049-900 Ribeirao Preto, Sao Paulo, Brazil
Phone: 55 163 6333825
Fax: 55 163 6333825
Publications: Brazilian Journal of Medical and Biological Research (42996)

Brazilian Metallurgy and Materials Association
Rua Antonio Comparato 218
04605-030 Sao Paulo, Sao Paulo, Brazil
Phone: 55 11 55344333
Fax: 55 11 55344330
Publications: ABM Metalurgia e Materials (43019)

Brazilian Society of Anesthesiology
Rua Prof. Alfredo Gomes, 36
22251-080 Botafogo, Rio de Janeiro, Brazil
Phone: 55 212 5378100
Fax: 55 212 5378188
Publications: Revista Brasileira de Anestesiologia (42955)

Brazilian Society of Applied and Computational Mathematics
Av. Getulio Vargas 333 Quitandinha
25651-070 Petropolis, Rio de Janeiro, Brazil
Phone: 55 242 336125
Fax: 55 242 315595
Publications: Computational & Applied Mathematics (42990)

Brazilian Society of Cardiology
Sede Sao Paulo
Av. Beira Rio 45 - 3 Andar
04548-050 Vila Olimpia, Sao Paulo, Brazil
Phone: 55 113 8496438
Publications: Arquivos Brasileiros de Cardiologia (43067)

Brazilian Society of Urology
Rua Bambina, 153
Botafogo, Rio de Janeiro, Brazil
Phone: 55 212 2464092
Fax: 55 212 2464194
Publications: International Braz J Urol (42954)

Brentwood Gazette
16 St. Thomas Rd.
Brentwood CM14 4DE, United Kingdom
Phone: 44 12 77219222

Fax: 44 12 77219172
Publications: Brentwood Gazette Series (52568)

Brill Academic Publishers
PO Box 9000
NL-2300 PA Leiden, Netherlands
Phone: 31 71 5353500
Fax: 31 71 5317532
Publications: Advanced Composite Materials (48641) • Advanced Robotics (48642) • African and Asian Studies (48643) • African Diaspora (48644) • Amphibia-Reptilia (48645) • Ancient Civilizations from Scythia to Siberia (48646) • Animal Biology (48647) • Applied Herpetology (48648) • Arab Law Quarterly (48649) • Arabica (48650) • Archive for the Psychology of Religion (48651) • Aries (48652) • Asian Journal of Social Science (48653) • Asian Medicine (48654) • Austrian Review of International and European Law (48655) • Behaviour (48656) • Biblical Interpretation (48657) • Brill's Annual of Afroasiatic Languages and Linguistics (48658) • The China Nonprofit Review (43179) • Comparative Sociology (48662) • Composite Interfaces (48663) • Computing Letters (48664) • Crustaceana (48665) • Dead Sea Discoveries (48666) • Designed Monomers and Polymers (48667) • Die Welt des Islams (48668) • Early Science and Medicine (48743) • East Central Europe (48669) • European Journal of East Asian Studies (48670) • European Journal of Jewish Studies (48671) • Exchange (48672) • Global Responsibility to Protect (48673) • Grotiana (48674) • Historical Materialism (54557) • Historiography East and West (48675) • Hobbes Studies (48676) • Index Islamicus (48677) • Indo-Iranian Journal (48602) • Insect Systematics & Evolution (48678) • International Community Law Review (48679) • International Journal of Myriapodology (48681) • International Journal of the Platonic Tradition (48682) • International Journal of Public Theology (56992) • International Review of Pragmatics (49670) • Iran and the Caucasus (48684) • Islamic Law and Society (48685) • Journal of Adhesion Science and Technology (48686) • Journal of Ancient Near Eastern Religions (48687) • Journal of Arabic Literature (48688) • Journal of Biomaterials Science, Polymer Edition (48690) • Journal of Cognition and Culture (48691) • Journal of Early Modern History (48692) • Journal of the Economic and Social History of the Orient (48693) • Journal of Egyptian History (48694) • Journal of Electromagnetic Waves and Applications (48695) • Journal of Empirical Theology (48696) • Journal for European Environmental & Planning Law (48698) • The Journal of Jewish Thought and Philosophy (48699) • Journal of Phenomenological Psychology (48700) • Journal of Reformed Theology (48701) • Journal of Religion in Africa (48702) • Journal of Religion in Europe (48703) • Journal for the Study of Judaism (48704) • KronoScope (48705) • Late Antique Archaeology (48706) • Medieval Encounters (48708) • Method & Theory in the Study of Religion (48709) • Middle East Journal of Culture and Communication (48710) • Middle East Law and Governance (48711) • Nematology (48713) • Nordic Journal of International Law (48714) • Novum Testamentum (48715) • Oud Hollad (48624) • Phronesis (48716) • Proceedings of the Boston Area Colloquium in Ancient Philosophy (48717) • Religion and Human Rights (48719) • Religion and Theology (48720) • Research in Phenomenology (48721) • Russian History (48722) • Seeing and Perceiving (48723) • Social Sciences and Missions (48724) • Southeastern Europe (48725) • The Soviet and Post-Soviet Review (48726) • Terrestrial Arthropod Reviews (48727) • T'oung Pao (48728) • Zutot (48730)

Brill Academic Publishers Inc.
153 Milk St., 6th Fl.
Boston, MA 02109-4809
Phone: 617263-2323
Fax: 617263-2324
Publications: Journal of Greek Linguistics (52324)

Britannia Art Publications
28 Charing Cross Rd., 4th Fl.
London WC2H 0DB, United Kingdom
Phone: 44 20 72400389
Fax: 44 20 74970726
Publications: Art Monthly (53968)

Britball.com
3-4 Madeira St.

Edinburgh EH6 64AJ, United Kingdom
Phone: 44 77 10509728
Publications: Britball (53257)

British Actors' Equity Association
Guild House
Upper St. Martins Ln.
London WC2H 9EG, United Kingdom
Phone: 44 20 73796000
Fax: 44 20 73797001
Publications: Equity (54382)

British Agents Register
5A Cheltenham Mt.
North Yorkshire
Harrogate HG1 1DW, United Kingdom
Phone: 44 1423 560608
Publications: British Commercial Agents Review (53515)

British Air Line Pilots Association
5 Heathrow Blvd.
278 Bath Rd.
West Drayton UB7 0DQ, United Kingdom
Phone: 44 20 84764000
Fax: 44 20 84764077
Publications: The Log (56890)

British Artist Blacksmiths Association
60 Buchanan St.
Balfron G63 0TW, United Kingdom
Fax: 44 1360 440830
Publications: Artist Blacksmith (52155)

British Association for Adoption and Fostering
Saffron House
6-10 Kirby St.
London EC1N 8TS, United Kingdom
Phone: 44 20 74212600
Fax: 44 20 74212601
Publications: Adoption and Fostering (53903) • Be My Parent (54008)

British Association for Cancer Research
c/o Leeds Industry of Molecular Medicine
Clinical Science Bldg.
St. James's University Hospital
Beckett St.
Leeds LS9 7TF, United Kingdom
Phone: 44 113 2065611
Fax: 44 113 2429886
Publications: British Journal of Cancer (54113)

British Association for Cardiac Rehabilitation
Town Hall Exchange
Castle St.
Farnham GU9 7ND, United Kingdom
Phone: 44 1252 720640
Fax: 44 1252 720601
Publications: The British Journal of Cardiology (53380)

British Association and College of Occupational Therapists
106-114 Borough High St.
Southwark
London SE1 1LB, United Kingdom
Phone: 44 20 73576480
Publications: British Journal of Occupational Therapy (54128)

British Association for Counselling and Psychotherapy
15 St. John's Business Pk.
Leicestershire
Lutterworth LE17 4HB, United Kingdom
Phone: 44 145 5883300
Fax: 44 145 5550243
Publications: Healthcare Counselling and Psychotherapy Journal (55512)

British Association of Dermatologists
4 Fitzroy Sq.
Willan House
London W1T 5HQ, United Kingdom
Phone: 44 20 73830266
Fax: 44 20 73885263
Publications: British Journal of Dermatology (54118)

British Association of Play Therapists
1 Beacon Mews
South Rd.
Weybridge KT13 9DZ, United Kingdom
Phone: 11 44 32828638

Fax: 11 44 32820100
Publications: British Journal of Play Therapy (56912) • PLAY THERAPY (56913)

British Association of Prosthetists and Orthotists
Sir James Clark Bldg.
Paisley PA1 1TJ, United Kingdom
Phone: 44 141 5617217
Publications: BAPOMAG (56239)

British Association of Teachers of the Deaf
175 Dashwood Ave.
High Wycombe HP12 3DB, United Kingdom
Phone: 44 14 94464190
Fax: 44 14 94464190
Publications: Association Magazine (52319) • Deafness and Education International (53572)

British Astronomical Association
Burlington House
Piccadilly
London W1J 0DU, United Kingdom
Phone: 44 20 77344145
Fax: 44 20 74394629
Publications: Journal of the British Astronomical Association (54712)

British Balloon and Airship Club
Cushy Dingle
Watery Ln.
Llanishen
Wales NP16 6QT, United Kingdom
Publications: Aerostat (55527)

British Blind and Shutter Association
36 Broadway
London SW1H OBH, United Kingdom
Phone: 44 20 7994050
Fax: 44 20 73406261
Publications: Openings (55034)

British Bryological Society
Wheelock St.
Middlewich CW10 9AB, United Kingdom
Publications: Journal of Bryology (55624)

British Canoe Union
18 Market Pl.
Nottingham
Bingham NG13 8AP, United Kingdom
Phone: 44 845 3709500
Fax: 44 845 3709501
Publications: Canoe Focus (52325)

British Cartographic Society
c/o Royal Geographic Society
1 Kensington Gore
London SW9 2AR, United Kingdom
Phone: 44 115 9328684
Fax: 44 115 9328684
Publications: The Cartographic Journal (54185)

British Cattle Veterinary Association
Pure Offices, Unit B4
Kestrel Ct.
Waterwells Dr.
Gloucestershire
Quedgeley GL2 7EP, United Kingdom
Phone: 44 14 52260125
Fax: 44 14 52886484
Publications: Cattle Practice (56307)

British Cement Association
Riverside House
4 Meadows Business Pk.
Sta. Approach
Blackwater, Camberley
Surrey GU17 9AB, United Kingdom
Phone: 44 1276 608700
Fax: 44 1276 608701
Publications: Concrete Quarterly (56660)

British Chamber of Commerce in China
The British Ctr., Rm. 1001
China Life Tower
No. 16 Chaoyangmenwai Ave.
Beijing 100020, People's Republic of China
Phone: 86 108 5251111
Fax: 86 108 5251100
Publications: British Business in China (43174)

British Chamber of Commerce for Italy
Via Dante 12

I-20121 Milan, Italy
Phone: 39 287 7798
Fax: 39 286 461885
Publications: Focus on Italy (46171)

British Chess Magazine
44 Baker St.
London W1U 7RT, United Kingdom
Phone: 44 20 73882404
Fax: 44 20 74863355
Publications: British Chess Magazine (54109)

British Computer Society
1st Fl., Block D
North Star House
North Star House Ave.
Swindon SN2 1FA, United Kingdom
Phone: 44 1793 417417
Fax: 44 1793 417444
Publications: ITNOW (56712)

British Dental Association
64 Wimpole St.
London W1G 8YS, United Kingdom
Phone: 44 20 79350875
Fax: 44 20 74875232
Publications: British Dental Journal (54110)

British Dental Trade Association
Mineral Ln.
Chesham HP5 1NL, United Kingdom
Phone: 44 1494 782873
Fax: 44 1494 786659
Publications: Dental Trader (52986)

British Double Reed Society
c/o Maxine Moody, Sec.
5 North Ave., Stoke Park
Coventry CV2 4DH, United Kingdom
Publications: Double Reed News (53573)

British Dragonfly Society
23, Bowker Way
Whittlesey
Peterborough PE7 1PY, United Kingdom
Publications: British Dragonfly Society Journal (53758)

British Driving Society
83 New Rd.
Helmingham
Stowmarket IP14 6EA, United Kingdom
Phone: 44 14 73892001
Fax: 44 14 73892005
Publications: BDS Yearbook (56641)

British Ecological Society
26 Blades Ct.
Putney
London SW15 2NU, United Kingdom
Phone: 44 20 88719797
Fax: 44 20 88719779
Publications: Journal of Animal Ecology (54697) • Journal of Applied Ecology (54698) • Journal of Functional Ecology (54755)

British Editorial Society of Bone and Joint Surgery
22 Buckingham St.
London WC2N 6ET, United Kingdom
Phone: 44 20 77820010
Fax: 44 20 77820995
Publications: Journal of Bone & Joint Surgery (British Volume) (54709)

British Equestrian Trade Association
Stockeld Pk.
West Yorkshire
Wetherby LS22 4AW, United Kingdom
Phone: 44 1937 587062
Fax: 44 1937 582728
Publications: Equestrian Trade News (56911)

British Flute Society
c/o Anna Munks, Sec.
27 Eskdale Gardens
London CR8 1ET, United Kingdom
Phone: 44 20 86683360
Publications: Flute (54469)

British Geological Survey
Kingsley Dunham Center
Keyworth
Nottingham NG12 5GG, United Kingdom
Phone: 44 11 59363143

Fax: 44 11 59363276
Publications: Earthwise (55754)

British Glass
9 Churchill Way
Sheffield S35 2PY, United Kingdom
Phone: 44 11 42901850
Fax: 44 11 42901851
Publications: Digest of Information and Patent Review (56491)

British Gliding Association
8 Merus Ct.
Meridian Business Pk.
Leicester LE19 1RJ, United Kingdom
Phone: 44 116 2892956
Fax: 44 116 2895025
Publications: Sailplane & Gliding (53824)

British Hang Gliding and Paragliding Association
8 Merus Ct.
Meridian Business Pk.
Leicester LE19 1RJ, United Kingdom
Phone: 44 116 2894316
Fax: 44 116 2814949
Publications: Skywings (53826)

British Holistic Medical Association
PO Box 371
Somerset
Bridgwater TA6 9BG, United Kingdom
Phone: 44 1278 722000
Publications: Journal of Holistic Healthcare (52596)

British Horn Society
52 Friars St.
Suffolk
Sudbury CO10 2AG, United Kingdom
Publications: Horn Player Magazine (56650)

British Horological Institute
Upton Hall
Upton
Newark NG23 5TE, United Kingdom
Phone: 44 16 36813795
Fax: 44 16 36812258
Publications: Horological Journal (55659)

The British Housewives League
17 Osborne Rd.
London N13 5PT, United Kingdom
Publications: The Lantern (54854)

British Institute of Innkeeping
Wessex House
80 Park St.
Camberley GU15 3PT, United Kingdom
Phone: 44 12 76684449
Fax: 44 12 7623045
Publications: BIIBUSINESS (52782)

British Institute of International & Comparative Law
Charles Clore House
17 Russell Sq.
London WC1B 5JP, United Kingdom
Phone: 44 2078 625151
Fax: 44 2078 625152
Publications: International and Comparative Law Quarterly (54624)

British Institute of Learning Disabilities
Campion House, Green St.
Kidderminster
Worcestershire DY10 1JL, United Kingdom
Phone: 44 1562 723010
Fax: 44 1562 723029
Publications: British Journal of Learning Disabilities (56966) • Good Autism Practice (56967) • Journal of Applied Research in Intellectual Disability (56968)

British Institute of Non-Destructive Testing
Newton Bldg.
St. George's Ave.
Northampton NN2 6JB, United Kingdom
Phone: 44 1604 893811
Fax: 44 1604 893861
Publications: Insight (55710)

British Institute of Persian Studies
1553 Dr. Ali Shariati Ave.
Qolhak
Tehran 19396, Iran

Phone: 98 21 2601937
Fax: 98 21 2604901
Publications: Iran (45891)

British Institute of Radiology
36 Portland Pl.
London W1B 1AT, United Kingdom
Phone: 44 20 73071400
Fax: 44 20 7307 1414
Publications: British Journal of Radiology (54133)

British and International Golf Greenkeepers' Association
Bigga House
Aldwark
Alne
York YO61 1UF, United Kingdom
Phone: 44 1347 833800
Fax: 44 1347 833801
Publications: Greenkeeper International (56991)

British Interplanetary Society
27-29 S Lambeth Rd.
London SW8 1SZ, United Kingdom
Phone: 44 20 77353160
Fax: 44 20 78201504
Publications: Journal of the British Interplanetary Society (54713) • Spaceflight (55259)

British and Irish Association of Law Librarians
c/o Elaine Bird, Hon. Sec.
12 S Bridge, Box 123
Edinburgh EH1 1DD, United Kingdom
Publications: Legal Information Management (53298)

British Materials Handling Federation
National Metalforming Centre
47 Birmingham Rd.
West Bromwich B70 6PY, United Kingdom
Phone: 44 12 16016350
Fax: 44 12 16016387
Publications: BMHF Yearbook & Directory (56889)

British Medical Acupuncture Society
BMAS House
3 Winnington Ct.
Northwich CW8 1AQ, United Kingdom
Phone: 44 16 06786782
Fax: 44 16 06786783
Publications: Acupuncture in Medicine (55718)

The British Medical Association
BMA House
Tavistock Sq.
London WC1H 9JP, United Kingdom
Phone: 44 20 73874499
Fax: 44 20 73836400
Publications: BMA News (54034)

British Menopause Society
4-6 Eton Pl.
Marlow SL7 2QA, United Kingdom
Phone: 44 162 8890199
Fax: 44 162 8474042
Publications: Menopause International (55600)

British Microlight Aircraft Association
The Bullring, Deddington
Banbury
Oxford OX15 0TT, United Kingdom
Phone: 44 18 69338888
Fax: 44 18 69337116
Publications: Microlight Flying (56098)

British Mule Society
2 Boscombe Rd.
Swindon SN25 3EY, United Kingdom
Phone: 44 17 93615478
Publications: The Mule (56748)

The British Museum
Great Russell St.
London WC1B 3DG, United Kingdom
Phone: 44 20 73238000
Fax: 44 20 73238616
Publications: British Museum Studies in Ancient Egypt and Sudan (BMSAES) (54141)

British Numismatic Society
c/o Warburg Institute
Woburn Sq.
London WC1H 0AB, United Kingdom
Publications: British Numismatic Journal (54143)

British Occupational Hygiene Society
5/6 Melboune Business Ct.
Millenium Way
Pride Pk.
Derby DE24 8LZ, United Kingdom
Phone: 44 13 32298101
Fax: 44 13 32298099
Publications: Annals of Occupational Hygiene (53163)

British Orthoptic Society
Tavistock House N
Tavistock Sq.
London WC1H 9HX, United Kingdom
Phone: 44 20 73877992
Fax: 44 20 73872584
Publications: British Orthoptic Journal (54144)

British Parachute Association
5 Wharf Way
Glen Parva
Leicester LE2 9TF, United Kingdom
Phone: 44 11 62785271
Fax: 44 11 62477662
Publications: Skydive Magazine (53825)

British Parking Association
Stuart House
41-43 Perrymount Rd.
Haywards Heath RH16 3BN, United Kingdom
Phone: 44 144 4447300
Fax: 44 144 4454105
Publications: Parking News (53550)

British Pest Control Association
Ground Fl.
1 Gleneagles House
Vernon Gate
South St.
Derby DE1 1UP, United Kingdom
Phone: 44 1332 294288
Publications: Professional Pest Controller (53168)

British Pharmacological Society
16 Angel Gate
City Rd.
London EC1V 2PT, United Kingdom
Phone: 44 20 74170110
Publications: British Journal of Clinical Pharmacology (54116) • British Journal of Pharmacology (54130)

British Phycological Society
Centre for Marine & Environmental Sciences
Scarborough Campus
University of Hull
Filey Rd.
Scarborough YO11 3AZ, United Kingdom
Phone: 44 1723 357362
Publications: European Journal of Phycology (54404)

The British Psychological Society
St. Andrews House
48 Princess Rd. E
Leicester LE1 7DR, United Kingdom
Phone: 44 116 2549568
Fax: 44 116 2271314
Publications: British Journal of Clinical Psychology (53786) • British Journal of Developmental Psychology (53787) • British Journal of Educational Psychology (53788) • British Journal of Health Psychology (53789) • British Journal of Mathematical and Statistical Psychology (53790) • British Journal of Psychology (53791) • British Journal of Social Psychology (53792) • Journal of Occupational and Organizational Psychology (53807) • Legal and Criminological Psychology (53810) • Psychologist Appointments (53819) • Psychology and Psychotherapy (53820)

British Safety Council
70 Chancellors Rd.
London W6 9RS, United Kingdom
Phone: 44 20 87411231
Fax: 44 20 87414555
Publications: Safety Management (55215)

British Sandwich Association
Association House
18c Moor St.
Chepstow NP16 5DB, United Kingdom
Fax: 44 1291 630402
Publications: Sandwich and Snack News (52983)

The British School at Rome at British Academy
10 Carlton House Ter.

London SW1Y 5AH, United Kingdom
Phone: 44 20 79695202
Fax: 44 20 79695401
Publications: Papers of the British School at Rome (55055)

British Science Association
The Wellcome Wolfson Bldg.
165 Queens Gate
London SW7 5HE, United Kingdom
Phone: 44 870 7707101
Fax: 44 20 75816587
Publications: People & Science (55066)

British Sign & Graphics Association
5 Orton Enterprise Ctr.
Bakewell Rd.
Orton Southgate
Peterborough PE2 6XU, United Kingdom
Phone: 44 1733 230033
Publications: Sign Directions (56261)

British Society of Animal Science
PO Box 3
Penicuik EH26 0RZ, United Kingdom
Phone: 44 13 14454508
Fax: 44 13 15353120
Publications: Animal (56243)

British Society for Antimicrobial Chemotherapy
Griffin House
53 Regent Pl.
Birmingham B1 3NJ, United Kingdom
Phone: 44 121 2361988
Fax: 44 121 2621830
Publications: Journal of Antimicrobial Chemotherapy (52345)

British Society of Clinical and Academic Hypnosis
28 Dale Park Gardens
Cookridge
Leeds LS16 7PT, United Kingdom
Phone: 44 113 8843116
Fax: 44 113 8843116
Publications: Contemporary Hypnosis (53763)

British Society for Developmental Disabilities
13 Coalway Rd.
Penn WV3 7LR, United Kingdom
Fax: 44 19 02341010
Publications: The British Journal of Developmental Disabilities (42736)

British Society for the History of Science
PO Box 3401
Norwich NR7 7JF, United Kingdom
Phone: 44 1603 516236
Fax: 44 1603 208563
Publications: British Journal for the History of Science (55727)

British Society for Immunology
Vintage House
37 Albert Embankment
London SE1 7TL, United Kingdom
Phone: 44 20 30319800
Fax: 44 20 75822882
Publications: Clinical & Experimental Immunology (54223) • Immunology (54585)

British Society of Master Glass Painters
6 Queen Sq.
London WC1N 3AR, United Kingdom
Phone: 44 16 43862807
Publications: The Journal of Stained Glass (54824)

British Society for Middle Eastern Studies
Institute for Middle Eastern & Islamic Studies
University of Durham
Durham DH1 3TU, United Kingdom
Phone: 44 19 13345179
Fax: 44 19 13345661
Publications: British Journal of Middle Eastern Studies (53759)

British Society for Music Therapy
24-27 White Lion St.
London N1 9PD, United Kingdom
Phone: 44 20 78376100
Fax: 44 20 78376142
Publications: British Journal of Music Therapy (54126)

British Society for Plant Pathology
Marlborough House
Basingstoke Rd.
Spencers Wood
Reading RG7 1AG, United Kingdom
Publications: Molecular Plant Pathology (56327) • New Disease Reports (56328)

British Society for Rheumatology
Bride House
18-20 Bride Ln.
London EC4Y 8EE, United Kingdom
Phone: 44 20 78420900
Fax: 44 20 78420901
Publications: Rheumatology (55202)

British Society of Scientific Glassblowers
c/o Chris Pitttock
15 Crompton St.
Chelmsford CM1 3BW, United Kingdom
Phone: 44 12 45355981
Publications: Journal of the British Society of Scientific Glassblowers (56750)

British Society of Soil Science
Building 53
Cranfield University
Craigie Buckler
Bedfordshire MK43 0AL, United Kingdom
Phone: 44 12 34752983
Fax: 44 12 34752970
Publications: European Journal of Soil Science (52278)

British Sociological Association
Bailey Ste.
Palatine House
Belmont Business Pk.
Belmont DH1 1TW, United Kingdom
Phone: 44 19 13830839
Fax: 44 19 13830782
Publications: Sociology (52307) • Work, Employment, and Society (52308)

British Sub-Aqua Club
Telford's Quay
S Pier Rd.
Ellesmere Port CH65 4FL, United Kingdom
Phone: 44 15 13506200
Publications: Dive (56390)

British Sugar PLC
Sugar Way
Peterborough PE2 9AY, United Kingdom
Phone: 44 1733 422106
Publications: British Sugar Beet Review (56253)

British Sulphur Publishing
31 Mount Pleasant
London WC1X 0AD, United Kingdom
Phone: 44 20 79032000
Fax: 44 20 78370976
Publications: Nitrogen & Methanol (55005)

British Tarantula Society
3 Shepham Ln.
Polegate
East Sussex
London BN20 CLZ, United Kingdom
Phone: 44 95 6438187
Publications: The Journal of the British Tarantula Society (54714) • Journal News (54788)

British Thematic Association
9 Oaklands Pk.
British Philatelic Centre
107 Charterhouse St.
Bishop's Stortford CM23 2BY, United Kingdom
Publications: Themescene (52382)

British Tinnitus Association
Ground Fl.
Unit 5
Acorn Business Pk.
Woodseats Close
Sheffield S8 0TB, United Kingdom
Phone: 44 114 2509922
Fax: 44 114 2582279
Publications: Quiet (56513)

British Trust for Ornithology
The Nunnery
Thetford IP24 2PU, United Kingdom
Phone: 44 18 42750050

Fax: 44 18 42750030
Publications: Bird Study (52330) • Ringing & Migration (56745)

British Tunnelling Society
1 Great George St.
London SW1P 3AA, United Kingdom
Publications: Tunnels & Tunnelling (56546)

British Universities Film and Video Council
77 Wells St.
London W1T 3QJ, United Kingdom
Phone: 44 20 73931500
Fax: 44 20 73931555
Publications: Viewfinder (55370)

British Veterinary Association
7 Mansfield St.
London W1G 9NQ, United Kingdom
Phone: 44 20 76366541
Fax: 44 20 79086349
Publications: The Journal of Small Animal Practice (54817)

British Wood Preserving and Damp-Proofing Association
5C Flemming Ct.
Castleford WF10 5HW, United Kingdom
Publications: Wood Protection (52953)

Brittle Star
PO Box 56108
London E17 0AY, United Kingdom
Publications: Brittle Star (54149)

Brooklands Media Group
120-128 Station Rd.
Redhill
Surrey RH1 1ET, United Kingdom
Phone: 44 1737 786800
Fax: 44 1737 786801
Publications: A Place in the Sun (56672) • Renault Magazine (56674)

The Brooklands Society Ltd.
Copse Heath
38 Coxheath Rd.
Church Crookham
Fleet GU52 6QG, United Kingdom
Phone: 44 12 52408877
Fax: 44 12 408878
Publications: The Brooklands Society Gazette (53389)

Brown, Son & Ferguson Ltd.
4-10 Darnley St.
Glasgow G41 2SD, United Kingdom
Phone: 44 141 4291234
Fax: 44 141 4201694
Publications: Brown's Nautical Almanac (53410) • The Nautical Magazine (53433)

BRT Reise Publishing GmbH
Schulstr. 34
D-80634 Munich, Germany
Phone: 49 891 679971
Fax: 49 891 679937
Publications: Business Traveller (44552)

Brunei Press Sdn Bhd
Locked Bay No. 2
MPC Berakas
Bandar Seri Begawan 3510, Brunei Darussalam
Phone: 67 324 51468
Publications: Borneo Bulletin (43072)

The Brunei Times
3rd Fl., Wisma Haji Mohd. Taha
Jalan Gadong
Bandar Seri Begawan BE 4119, Brunei Darussalam
Phone: 673 2 428333
Fax: 673 2 428555
Publications: The Brunei Times (43073)

Brunel Press Ltd.
Temple Way
Bristol B599 7HD, United Kingdom
Phone: 44 117 9343733
Fax: 44 117 9343755
Publications: Primary Times (52723)

B.R.W. Media
Fairfax Business Media
GPO BOX 55
Melbourne, Victoria 3000, Australia

Phone: 61 3 96033888
Fax: 61 2 92821799
Publications: BRW (42055)

BTTB Marketing Pty Ltd.
PO Box 825
Paradise Point, Queensland 4216, Australia
Phone: 61 7 55491092
Fax: 61 7 55491093
Publications: Procurement Professional (42228)

Buddhist Society
58 Eccleston Sq.
London SW1V 1PH, United Kingdom
Phone: 44 20 78345858
Fax: 44 20 79765238
Publications: The Middle Way (54931)

Buenos Aires Herald Ltd.
San Juan 141
1063 Buenos Aires, Argentina
Phone: 54 11 43491524
Fax: 54 11 43491524
Publications: Buenos Aires Herald (41470)

Buick Club of Australia
PO Box 168
Merrylands, New South Wales 2160, Australia
Phone: 61 2 96015005
Publications: Buick News (42103)

The Builder Group PLC
Ludgate House
245 Blackfriars Rd.
London SE1 9UY, United Kingdom
Phone: 44 20 79215000
Publications: Building (54152)

Builders' Association of India
G-1/G-20 7th Fl.
Commerce Ctr.
J. Dadajee Rd.
Tardeo
Mumbai 400034, Maharashtra, India
Phone: 91 222 3514802
Fax: 91 222 3520507
Publications; Indian Construction (45376)

Building Services Research and Information Association
Old Bracknell Ln. W
Bracknell RG12 7AH, United Kingdom
Phone: 44 1344 465600
Fax: 44 1344 465626
Publications: International Building Services Abstracts (52434)

Bulgarian Academy of Sciences
1, 15 Noemvri Str.
BG-1040 Sofia, Bulgaria
Phone: 359 2 9898446
Fax: 359 2 9862523
Publications: Balkan Linguistics (43093) • Bulgarian Chemical Communications (43094) • Bulgarian Folklore (43095) • Bulgarian Geophysical Journal (43096) • Bulgarian Musicology (43097) • Fractional Calculus and Applied Analysis (43099) • Genetics and Breeding (43100) • Geologica Balcanica (43101) • Journal of Bulgarian Historical Review (43102) • Mathematica Plus (43105) • Serdica Mathematical Journal (43107)

Bulgarian Society of Endocrinology
Bolnitsa po Endokrinologia
6 D. Gruev Str.
BG-1303 Sofia, Bulgaria
Phone: 359 298 84933
Fax: 359 298 71553
Publications: Journal of Endocrinology (43103)

Bulgarian Sociological Association
Bul. Tzrigradsko Shosse, No. 125
Block 2, Rm. 240
BG-1113 Sofia, Bulgaria
Phone: 35 929 809892
Publications: Sotsiologicheski Problemi (43108)

Bund Deutscher Landschaftsarchitekten
Bundesgeschaeftstelle
Koepenicker St. 48/49
D-10179 Berlin, Germany
Phone: 49 302 787150
Fax: 49 302 7871555
Publications: Landschaftsarchitekten (44214)

Bund der Steuerzahler
Franzosische Str 9-12
10117 Berlin, Germany
Phone: 49 30 2593960
Fax: 49 30 25939625
Publications: Der Steuezahler (44170)

Bundes-Verlag GmbH
Bodenborn 43
D-58452 Witten, Germany
Phone: 49 230 2930930
Fax: 49 230 293093689
Publications: TeensMag (44714)

Bundesamt fur Landwirtschaft
Mattenhofstrasse 5
CH-3003 Bern, Switzerland
Phone: 41 313 228516
Fax: 41 313 227080
Publications: Agrarforschung Schweiz (51221)

Bundesverband Bildender Kuenstlerinnen und Kuenstler
Weberstr. 61
Anzeigenabteilung
D-53113 Bonn, Germany
Phone: 49 228 216107
Fax: 49 228 96699690
Publications: Kultur Politik (44265)

Bureau for Economic Research
Vineyard Centre, Cor. Adam Tas & Devon Valley Rd.
Unit N, 1st Fl.
Onder-Papegaaiberg
Stellenbosch 7600, Republic of South Africa
Phone: 27 218 872810
Fax: 27 218 839225
Publications: Studies in Economics and Econometrics (50636)

Bureau of Indian Standards
Manak Bhavan
9 Bahadur Shah Zafar Marg
New Delhi 110 002, Delhi, India
Phone: 91 112 3230131
Fax: 91 112 3234062
Publications: Standards India (45653)

Bureau of Labour Publications
8 Business Ctr., Ground Fl.
Mumtaz Hasan Rd.
PO Box 5833
Karachi 74000, Pakistan
Phone: 92 21 2414975
Publications: Eastern Worker (49348) • Labour Code of Pakistan (49359)

Burke's Backyard
PO Box 929
Crows Nest, New South Wales 1585, Australia
Phone: 61 2 94144800
Fax: 61 2 94144801
Publications: Burke's Backyard Magazine (41821)

The Burlington Magazine Publication Ltd.
14-16 Duke's Rd.
London WC1H 9SZ, United Kingdom
Phone: 44 20 73881228
Fax: 44 20 73881229
Publications: The Burlington Magazine (54158)

Burton Daily Mail Ltd.
65-68 High St.
Burton-on-Trent DE14 1LE, United Kingdom
Publications: Burton Mail (52770)

Bus and Coach Association of New Zealand Inc.
PO Box 9336
Wellington, New Zealand
Phone: 64 449 97334
Fax: 64 449 97353
Publications: Circular (49004)

Business Center for Academic Societies
Gakkai Center C21
5-16-9 Honkomagome
Bunkyo-ku
Tokyo 113-8622, Japan
Phone: 81 3 58145800
Fax: 81 3 58145823
Publications: Food Science and Technology Research (46826)

Business Center for Academic Societies Japan
Gakkai Ctr. C21
5-16-9 Honkomagome
Bunkyo-Ku
Tokyo 113-8622, Japan
Phone: 81 358 145800
Fax: 81 358 145823
Publications: Anthropological Science (46743) • Geochemical Journal (46830) • Japanese Journal of Bacteriology (46865) • Japanese Journal of Medical Mycology (46871) • Soil Science and Plant Nutrition (47041)

Business Day Company Ltd.
Olympia Tower, 22nd Fl.
444 Ratchadapisak Rd.
Bangkok 10320, Thailand
Phone: 66 251 23579
Fax: 66 251 235656
Publications: Business Day (51416)

Business Money Ltd.
Somerset
Hambridge
Taunton TA10 0BP, United Kingdom
Phone: 44 145 8253536
Fax: 44 145 8253538
Publications: Business Money (56721)

Business Monitor International Ltd.
Mermaid House
2 Puddle Dock
London EC4V 3DS, United Kingdom
Phone: 44 20 72480468
Fax: 44 20 72480467
Publications: Africa Monitor. West & Central Africa (53917) • Central Europe Monitor (54194) • South East Europe Monitor (55258)

Business Perspectives
Dzerzhynsky Ln., 10
40022 Sumy, Ukraine
Phone: 380 542 775771
Fax: 380 542 775771
Publications: Investment Management & Financial Innovations (51617) • Problems & Perspectives in Management (51618)

Business Recorder
Recorder House
531 Business Recorder Rd.
Karachi 74550, Pakistan
Phone: 92 225 0311
Fax: 92 228 644
Telex: 20762 MATBR PK
Publications: Business Recorder (49340)

Business and Technical Communications Ltd.
35 Station Sq.
Petts Wood
London BR5 1LZ, United Kingdom
Phone: 44 16 89616000
Fax: 44 16 89826622
Publications: CAD User (54165) • DM Magazine (54337)

Business & Tourism Publishing
189 Kent St., Ste. 3
Sydney, New South Wales 2000, Australia
Phone: 61 2 82644444
Fax: 61 2 82644401
Publications: miceAsia.net (42543) • mice.net (42544) • miceNZ.net (42545)

BusinessWorld Online, Inc.
Raul L. Locsin Bldg. I
95 Balete Dr. Ext.
New Manila
Quezon City 1112, Philippines
Phone: 63 2 5359901
Fax: 63 2 5359926
Publications: I.T. Matters (49596)

BusinessWorld Publishing Corp.
Raul L. Locsin Bldg. I
95 Balete Dr. Ext.
New Manila
Quezon City 1112, Philippines
Phone: 63 2 5359901
Fax: 63 2 5359926
Publications: Business World (49586)

BUTT magazine
Kleine-Gartmanplantsoen 21-I
NL-1017 RP Amsterdam, Netherlands
Publications: Butt (47919)

Butterworths Tolley
Halsbury House
35 Chancery Ln.
London WC2A 1EL, United Kingdom
Phone: 44 20 74002500
Fax: 44 20 74002842
Publications: Counsel (54273)

Buzzword Media Corporation
Rm. 14, Ground Fl., Maya Bldg.
678 EDSA
Cubao
Quezon City 1109, Philippines
Publications: Planet Philippines (49616)

BVA Bielefelder Verlag GmbH & Co. KG
Niederwall 53
D-33602 Bielefeld, Germany
Phone: 49 521 595514
Fax: 49 521 595518
Publications: Sun & Wind Energy (44247)

B.Verkin Institute for Low Temperature Physics and Engineering
47 Lenin Ave.
61103 Kharkov, Ukraine
Phone: 380 57 3402223
Fax: 380 57 3403370
Publications: Fizika Nizkikh Temperatur (51592)

Bygg & Teknik
PO Box 19099
S-104 32 Stockholm, Sweden
Phone: 46 861 21750
Fax: 46 861 25481
Publications: Bygg & Teknik (51011)

Byggfakta AB
Lojtnantsgatan 9
S-827 81 Ljusdal, Sweden
Phone: 46 651 552500
Fax: 46 651 552585
Publications: Byggfakta Projektnytt (50979)

C-4
16 Glencairn Ave.
Leopardstown
Dublin IRL-18, Dublin, Ireland
Publications: C-4 (45949)

C & M Publications Ltd.
3A Market Pl.
Uppingham LE15 9QH, United Kingdom
Phone: 44 15 72820088
Fax: 44 15 72820099
Publications: Loyalty (56797)

C. Raveendra
AB-10, Safdarjung Enclave
New Delhi 110 029, Delhi, India
Phone: 91 112 6191421
Fax: 91 112 6191420
Publications: Outlook (45633)

CAB International
Nosworthy Way
Wallingford OX10 8DE, United Kingdom
Phone: 44 1491 832111
Fax: 44 1491 829292
Publications: AgBiotech News and Information (56813) • Animal Health Research Reviews (56815) • Biocontrol News and Information (56816) • Bulletin of Entomological Research (52926) • Crop Physiology Abstracts (56817) • Grasslands & Forage Abstracts (56818) • Ornamental Horticulture (56821) • Pig News and Information (56822) • Postharvest News and Information (56823) • Review of Agricultural Entomology (56824) • Review of Aromatic and Medicinal Plants (56825) • Review of Medical and Veterinary Entomology (56826) • Review of Medical and Veterinary Mycology (56827) • Review of Plant Pathology (56828) • Soils and Fertilizers (56829) • Soybean Abstracts (56830) • World's Poultry Science Journal (56831)

CABEQ
PO Box 123
Berislaviceva 6
CT-10000 Zagreb, Croatia
Publications: Chemical and Biochemical Engineering Quarterly (43563)

CABI Publishing
Nosworthy Way
Wallingford OX10 8DE, United Kingdom
Phone: 44 1491 832111
Fax: 44 1491 829292
Publications: In Vitro Cellular and Developmental Biology - Plant (56819) • Journal of Agricultural Genomics (56820)

Cairo Times
14 Al Saraya Al Kubra St., Ste. 6
Garden City
Cairo, Egypt
Phone: 20 279 43396
Fax: 20 279 43396
Publications: Cairo Times (43753)

Calcutta Statistical Association
Calcutta University
New Science Bldg.
35 B.C. Rd.
Kolkata 700 019, West Bengal, India
Publications: Calcutta Statistical Association Bulletin (45262)

Calicut Medical College Calicut Medical College P.O
PO Thiruvanathapuram
Trivandrum, Kerala, India
Publications: Calicut Medical Journal (45758) • Journal of Orthopaedics (45759)

CALL-EJ Online
School of Languages & Linguistics
Griffith University
Kessels Rd.
Brisbane, Queensland 4111, Australia
Publications: CALL-EJ Online (41646)

Callcraft
The Loft
Dean House Farm
Church Rd.
Newdigate
Dorking RH5 5DL, United Kingdom
Phone: 44 13 06631661
Publications: Call Centre Focus (53192)

Calligraphy and Lettering Arts Society
54 Boileau Rd.
London SW13 9BL, United Kingdom
Publications: The Edge (54353)

CAMA
Via Rosales, 3
I-20124 Milan, Italy
Phone: 39 265 3270
Fax: 39 229 060005
Publications: Sipario (46194)

Cambria
PO Box 22
Caerfyrddin SA32 7YH, United Kingdom
Phone: 44 845 1662147
Publications: Cambria (52781)

Cambridge International Science Publishing
7 Meadow Walk
Great Abington
Cambridge CB1 6AZ, United Kingdom
Phone: 44 1223 893295
Fax: 44 1223 894539
Publications: International Journal of Nonlinear Modelling in Science and Engineering (43477) • Journal of Advanced Materials (52841) • Journal of Advances in Chemical Physics (49926) • Journal of Applied Systems Studies (44769)

Cambridge Medical Publications
Wicker House
High St.
Worthing BN11 1DJ, United Kingdom
Phone: 44 1903 288255
Fax: 44 1903 288292
Publications: Clinical Approaches in Bipolar Disorders (56971) • HERPES (56973)

Cambridge University Press
The Edinburgh Bldg.
Shaftesbury Rd.
Cambridge CB2 2RU, United Kingdom
Phone: 44 122 3312393
Fax: 44 122 3315052
Publications: Ageing and Society (52785) • Behavioral and Brain Sciences (52791) • Breast Cancer Online (55749) • British Journal of Anaesthetic and Recovery Nursing (54111) • British Journal of Nutrition (52795) • British Journal of Political Science (52796) • Bulletin of the School of Oriental and African Studies (54157) • The Cambridge Law Journal (52798) • Cardiology in the Young (54177) • The China Quarterly (54208) • Chinese Journal of Agricultural Biotechnology (52806) • The Classical Quarterly (55910) • The Classical Review (55547) • Comparative Exercise Physiology (52808) • Comparative Studies in Society and History (52809) • Contemporary European History (52811) • Eighteenth Century Music (52816) • Environmental Practice (52818) • European Review (42896) • Geological Magazine (52823) • Glasgow Mathematical Journal (53421) • Greece and Rome (56571) • The Historical Journal (52828) • International and Comparative Law Quarterly (52831) • International Journal of Asian Studies (52832) • International Journal of Astrobiology (52833) • International Journal of Cultural Property (52834) • International Journal of Law in Context (52835) • International Journal of Middle East Studies (52836) • The International Journal of Neuropsychopharmacology (52837) • International Journal of Tropical Insect Science (52838) • International Review of Social History (52839) • The Journal of African History (52842) • Journal of African Law (52843) • Journal of American Studies (52845) • Journal of Biosocial Science (52846) • The Journal of Ecclesiastical History (52849) • The Journal of Economic History (52850) • Journal of Global History (54757) • Journal of Helminthology (52854) • Journal of the Institute of Mathematics of Jussieu (44064) • Journal of Institutional Economics (52855) • Journal of Latin American Studies (53875) • Journal of Linguistics (52858) • The Journal of Modern African Studies (52860) • Journal of Pension Economics and Finance (54794) • Journal of Psychiatric Intensive Care (53472) • Journal of Public Policy (52861) • Journal of Radiotherapy in Practice (56505) • Journal of Social Policy (52862) • Journal of Southeast Asian Studies (52863) • Modern Asian Studies (52870) • Neuron Glia Biology (52874) • New Testament Studies (52877) • New Theatre Quarterly (52878) • Nutrition Research Reviews (52879) • Organised Sound (53816) • Philosophy (55081) • Plant Genetic Resources (52884) • Popular Music (55739) • Proceedings of the Edinburgh Mathematical Society (53306) • Proceedings of the International Astronomical Union (52886) • Proceedings of the Nutrition Society (52887) • Public Health Nutrition (52888) • Quarterly Reviews of Biophysics (52889) • Religious Studies (55186) • Renewable Agriculture and Food Systems (52890) • Reviews in Clinical Gerontology (56241) • Scottish Journal of Theology (52892) • Seed Science Research (52893) • Shakespeare Survey (52894) • Social Policy and Society (52896) • Systematics and Biodiversity (56392) • Theatre Research International (52901) • Theory and Practice of Logic Programming (TPLP) (52902) • Twentieth Century Music (52903)

Cambridge University Press
32 Ave. of the Americas
New York, NY 10013-2473
Phone: 212924-3900
Fax: 212691-3239
Publications: Combinatorics, Probability and Computing (52807) • Epidemiology and Infection (54380) • European Journal of Anaesthesiology (44397) • European Journal of Applied Mathematics (55945) • Experimental Agriculture (52170) • Journal of the Marine Biological Association of the United Kingdom (JMBA) (56272) • Leiden Journal of International Law (48621)

Camel Publishing House
67 Gandhi Nagar W
Near Lalgarh Palace
Bikaner 334 001, Rajasthan, India
Phone: 91 151 2521282
Fax: 91 151 2204100
Publications: Journal of Camel Practice and Research (45017)

Campaign Against Euro-Federalism
PO Box 46295
London W5 2UG, United Kingdom

Phone: 44 845 3458902
Publications: The Democrat (54316)

Campaign for Press & Broadcasting Freedom
Second Fl.
Vi & Garner Smith House
23 Orford Rd.
Walthamstow E17 9NL, United Kingdom
Phone: 44 20 85215932
Publications: Free Press (53620)

Campden Publishing Ltd.
1 St. John's Sq.
London EC1M 4PN, United Kingdom
Phone: 44 20 72140500
Fax: 44 20 72140501
Publications: Clinical Pharmacy Europe (54228) • Families in Business (54439) • Hospital Healthcare Europe (54572) • Hospital Imaging and Radiology Europe (54573) • Nursing in Practice (55016) • Private Hospital Healthcare Europe (55122)

The Camping and Caravanning Club
Greenfields House
Westwood Way
Coventry CV4 8JH, United Kingdom
Phone: 44 845 1307632
Publications: Camping and Caravanning (53079)

Campus fur Christus Schweiz
Josefstr. 206
CH-8005 Zurich, Switzerland
Phone: 41 1 2748434
Fax: 41 1 2748483
Publications: Christliches Zeugnis (51256)

CAP&Design
Karlbergsv 77
106 78 Stockholm, Sweden
Publications: CAP&Design (51012)

Cape Business News
30 Study St.
PO Box 60567
Cape Town 7441, Republic of South Africa
Phone: 27 215 574061
Fax: 27 215 574707
Publications: Cape Business News (50369)

Cape Media
28 Main Rd.
Rondebosch
Cape Town 7700, Republic of South Africa
Phone: 27 21 6817000
Fax: 27 21 6854445
Publications: Achiever (50360) • BBQ Scorecard (50363) • Black Business Quarterly (50365) • Blue Chip (50367) • Energy Forecast (50376) • Explore South Africa (50377) • Leadership in HIV/AIDS (50387) • Opportunity (50398) • Road Ahead (50406) • Service (50410) • Shipyear (50411)

Captain Cook Society
13 Cowdry Close, Thornhill
West Yorkshire
Dewsbury WF12 OLW, United Kingdom
Publications: Cook's Log (53178)

The Caravan Club
East Grinstead House
East Grinstead RH19 1UA, United Kingdom
Phone: 44 1342 336804
Fax: 44 1342 410258
Publications: The Caravan Club Magazine (53235)

Cardiff University
Bute Bldg., King Edward VII Ave.
Cardiff CF10 3NB, United Kingdom
Phone: 44 29 20874600
Fax: 44 29 20874601
Publications: CEBE Transactions (52928)

Cardiff University School of Social Sciences
Glamorgan Bldg.
King Edward VII Ave.
Cardiff CF10 3WT, United Kingdom
Phone: 44 29 20875345
Fax: 44 29 20874678
Publications: Building Research Capacity (52925)

The Cardiological Society of India
P-60 C.I.T Rd.
Scheme VII-M
Kankurgachi

Kolkata 700 054, West Bengal, India
Phone: 91 33 23557837
Fax: 91 33 23556308
Publications: Indian Heart Journal (45271)

CARF
BM PO Box 8784
London WC1N 3XX, United Kingdom
Phone: 44 20 78371450
Publications: CARF (54180)

Caribbean Community
PO Box 10827
Georgetown, Guyana
Phone: 592 22 20001
Fax: 592 22 20171
Publications: CARICOM Perspective (44799)

Caritas Lithuania
Aukstaiciu 10
LT-44147 Kaunas, Lithuania
Phone: 370 37 205427
Fax: 370 37 205549
Publications: Caritas (47464)

Carl Ed. Schuenemann KG
Zweite Schlachtpforte 7
D-28195 Bremen, Germany
Phone: 49 421 369030
Fax: 49 421 3690339
Publications: Modell Fan (44281)

Carmelite Third Order
Via. Giovanni Lanza, 138
I-00184 Rome, Italy
Phone: 39 64620181
Fax: 39 646201847
Publications: Carmel in the World (46223)

Carnyx Group Ltd.
Mercat Bldg., 4th Fl.
26 Gallowgate
Glasgow G1 5AB, United Kingdom
Phone: 44 141 5525858
Publications: The Drum (53414) • The Firm (53418) • Urban Realm (53456)

Carpe Diem Publications Ltd.
8th Fl., Trust Tower
68 Johnston Rd.
Wanchai
Hong Kong, People's Republic of China
Phone: 86 229 760876
Fax: 86 229 760973
Publications: bc Magazine (43283)

Carreteras
c/o Marta Rodrigo, Exec. Mgr.
Goya, 23 4-Dcha
E-28001 Madrid, Spain
Phone: 34 915 779972
Fax: 34 915 766522
Publications: Carreteras (50733)

Cartref Communications
57 Lake Rd. W
Cardiff CF23 5PH, United Kingdom
Phone: 44 29 20766318
Fax: 44 29 20747929
Publications: Catholic Teachers Gazette (52927)

CASA
PO Box 2005
Canberra, Australian Capital Territory 2601, Australia
Phone: 61 262 131757
Fax: 61 262 171209
Publications: Flight Safety Australia (41706)

Casa Editrice Krea S.R.L.
Piazza Don Bosco 6
I-90143 Palermo, Italy
Phone: 39 91 543506
Fax: 39 91 6373378
Publications: Sikania (46208)

Cashew Export Promotion Council of India
Chittoor Rd.
PO Box 1709
Cochin 682 016, Kerala, India
Phone: 91 484 2376459
Fax: 91 484 2377973
Publications: Cashew Bulletin (45070) • Indian Cashew Journal (45074)

Casino World
The Maltings
50 Bath St.
Gravesend DA11 0DF, United Kingdom
Phone: 44 14 74335087
Publications: Casino World (53478)

Caspian Business News
219 Bashir Safaroglu St.
AZ1000 Baku, Azerbaijan
Phone: 99 412 4933189
Fax: 99 412 4932478
Publications: Caspian Business News (42780)

Caspian Publishing
198 King's Rd.
London SW3 5XP, United Kingdom
Phone: 44 20 73687100
Fax: 44 20 73687201
Publications: Real Business (55176)

Catalogue & e-business
151 High St.
Ilfracombe EX34 9EZ, United Kingdom
Phone: 44 1271 866221
Fax: 44 1271 866281
Publications: Catalogue & E-business (53641)

Catcha.com Private Ltd.
45-7 The Blvd. Mid Valley City
No. 08-01 HDB HUB
59200 Kuala Lumpur, Malaysia
Phone: 60 3 22970999
Fax: 60 3 22970888
Publications: Juice (47609)

Cathay Pacific Airways Ltd.
5/F, South Tower
Cathay Pacific City
8 Scenic Rd.
Hong Kong International Airport, Lantau
Hong Kong, People's Republic of China
Phone: 852 27471888
Fax: 852 25601411
Publications: The Club (43292) • Shop (43382)

The Catholic News
2 Highland Rd., 01-03
Singapore 549102, Singapore
Phone: 65 685 83055
Fax: 65 685 82055
Publications: The Catholic News (50118)

Catholic Record Society
12 Melbourne Pl.
Wolsingham DL13 3EH, United Kingdom
Phone: 44 13 88527747
Publications: Recusant History (56950)

Catholic Youth Council
43 rue de la charite
B-1210 Brussels, Belgium
Phone: 32 223 03283
Fax: 32 223 06811
Publications: Jeunes en Mouvement (42861)

British Cave Research Association
The Old Methodist Chapel
Great Hucklow
Buxton SK17 8RG, United Kingdom
Phone: 44 1298 873810
Fax: 44 1298 873801
Publications: Cave & Karst Science (52778) • Speleology (52779)

Cavendish Publishing Ltd.
The Glass House
Wharton St.
London WC1X 9PX, United Kingdom
Publications: Student Law Review (55269)

Cayman Free Press Ltd.
The Compass Ctr.
Shedden Rd.
PO Box 1365 GT
Grand Cayman, Cayman Islands
Phone: 345949-5111
Fax: 345949-7675
Publications: The Caymanian Compass (43130)

Cayman Islands Real Estate Brokers Association
PO Box 1977
Grand Cayman, Cayman Islands

Phone: 345949-7099
Fax: 345949-6819
Publications: C.I. Real Estate Magazine (43131)

CCP Ltd.
PO Box 17911
London SWIP 4YX, United Kingdom
Phone: 44 2073161472
Fax: 44 2073161453
Publications: Christianity (54209) • Youthwork (55436)

Centaur Communications Ltd.
50 Poland St.
London W1F 7AX, United Kingdom
Phone: 44 20 79704000
Publications: AB Europe (53889) • In-Store Marketing (54593) • Marketing Week (54909)

Centaur Media PLC
50 Poland St.
London W1F 7AX, United Kingdom
Phone: 44 20 79704000
Publications: Mortgage Strategy (54955) • Period Living (55068)

Centaur Publishing Ltd.
50 Poland St.
London W1F 7AX, United Kingdom
Phone: 44 20 79704000
Fax: 44 20 79704189
Publications: Creative Review (54282) • Design Week (54321) • Employee Benefits (54366) • The Engineer (54372) • Money Marketing (54950) • MWP (54967) • New Media Age (54994) • Precision Marketing (55117) • Process Engineering (55126)

Center for Academic Publications Japan
2-4-16 Yayoi
Bunkyo-Ku
Tokyo 113-0032, Japan
Phone: 81 3 38175821
Publications: Earth Planets and Space (46803) • Japanese Journal of Physiology (46874) • Microbiology and Immunology (46968)

Center for Documentation and Research of Peace and Conflicts
187 Montee de Choulans
F-69005 Lyon, France
Phone: 33 478 369303
Fax: 33 478 363683
Publications: Damocles (43968)

The Center for the Study of Venoms and Venomous Animals
Rua Jose de Barros, 1780
Caixa Postal 577
Botucatu, Sao Paulo, Brazil
Phone: 55 14 38145555
Fax: 55 14 38145446
Publications: The Journal of Venomous Animals and Toxins including Tropical Diseases (42957)

Central Bank of the Republic of China
2 Roosevelt Rd., Section 1
Taipei 10006, Taiwan
Phone: 886 223 936161
Fax: 886 223 571974
Publications: Financial Statistics Monthly (51340)

Central European University
Nador u. 9
1051 Budapest, Hungary
Phone: 36 1 3273000
Publications: Southeast European Politics Online (44872)

Central Fisheries Research Institute
Kasustu Beldesi
Yomra
TR-61250 Trabzon, Turkey
Phone: 90 462 3411056
Fax: 90 462 3411152
Publications: Turkish Journal of Fisheries and Aquatic Sciences (51578)

Central Marine Fisheries Research Institute
PO Box 1603
Ernakulam N P.O.
Cochin 682 018, Kerala, India
Phone: 91 484 2394867
Fax: 91 484 2394909
Publications: Central Marine Fisheries Research Institute Bulletin (45071) • Central Marine Fisheries Research Institute Special Publication (45072) • Indian Journal of Fisheries (45075)

Central Queensland University, Division of Teaching and Learning Services
Bldg. 5, Bruce Hwy.
Rockhampton, Queensland 4702, Australia
Phone: 61 7 49309000
Fax: 61 7 49232100
Publications: Ejournalist (42315) • Studies in Learning, Evaluation, Innovation and Development (42317)

Central Reference Library
Government of India
Ministry of Culture
Kolkata, West Bengal, India
Phone: 91 33 24791721
Fax: 91 33 24791722
Publications: Indian National Bibliography (45274)

Central Sericultural Research & Training Institute
Srirampuram
Mysore 570 008, Karnataka, India
Phone: 91 821 480314
Fax: 91 821 480845
Publications: Indian Journal of Sericulture (45457)

Central Silk Board
CSB Complex
B.T.M. Layout, Madivala
Hosur Rd.
Bangalore 560 068, Karnataka, India
Phone: 91 80 26282699
Fax: 91 80 26681511
Publications: Indian Silk (44962)

Central Social Welfare Board
Samaj Kalyan Bhawan
B-12, Qutab Institutional Area
New Delhi 110 016, Delhi, India
Phone: 91 112 6960059
Publications: Social Welfare (45651)

Central South University
Central South University
Changsha 410083, Hunan, People's Republic of China
Phone: 86 731 8877114
Fax: 86 731 8877197
Publications: Transactions of Nonferrous Metals Society of China (43246)

Central Statistical Organization—India
Sardar Patel Bhavan
Sansad Marg
New Delhi 110 001, Delhi, India
Phone: 91 233 89604
Fax: 91 233 86384
Publications: India Central Statistical Organization Monthly Abstract of Statistics' (45533) • India Central Statistical Organization Statistical Abstract (45534) • Statistical Pocket Book (45654)

Central Union of Swedish Speaking Agricultural Producers in Finland
Fredriksgatan 61 A 34
FIN-00100 Helsinki, Finland
Phone: 358 95 860460
Fax: 358 96 941358
Publications: Landsbygdens Folk (43843)

Centre for Alternative Technology
Powys
Machynlleth SY20 9AZ, United Kingdom
Phone: 44 165 4705950
Fax: 44 165 4702782
Publications: Clean Slate (55522)

The Centre for Bhutan Studies
PO Box 1111
Langjophakha
Thimphu, Bhutan
Phone: 975 2 321005
Fax: 975 2 321001
Publications: Journal of Bhutan Studies (42925)

Centre for Development of Advanced Computing
8th Fl. Air India Bldg.
Nariman Point
Mumbai 400 021, Maharashtra, India
Phone: 91 22 22024641

Fax: 91 22 22049573
Publications: Vivek (45449)

Centre for Development of Advanced Computing
Ganeshkhind
Pune 411 007, Maharashtra, India
Phone: 91 20 25704100
Fax: 91 20 25694004
Publications: C-DAC Connect (45696)

Centre for Development and Population Activities - Nigeria
Ground Fl., Bel House
22, Port Harcourt Cres.
Off Gimbiya St.
Area 11, Garki
Abuja, Lagos, Nigeria
Phone: 234 9 4618863
Fax: 234 9 4618864
Publications: Women on the Move (49058)

Centre for Health and Population Research
68 Shaheed Tajuddin Ahmed Sharani
Mohakhali
Dhaka 1212, Bangladesh
Phone: 880 288 60523
Fax: 880 288 19133
Publications: Equity Dialogue (42809)

Centre of Indian Trade Unions
B.T. Ranadive Bhawan
13-A, Rouse Ave.
New Delhi 110 002, Delhi, India
Phone: 91 11 23221288
Fax: 91 11 23221284
Publications: Working Class (45669)

Centre on Integrated Rural Development for Asia and the Pacific
Chameli House
17 Topkhana Rd.
GPO Box 2883
Dhaka 1000, Bangladesh
Phone: 880 2 9558751
Fax: 880 2 9562035
Publications: Asia-Pacific Journal of Rural Development (42802)

Centre for Irish Studies
National University of Ireland
Galway, University Rd.
Galway 6150, Galway, Ireland
Phone: 353 91 492051
Fax: 353 91 524411
Publications: Australian Journal of Irish Studies (46016)

Centre for Irish Studies in Aarhus
University of Aarhus
Bldg. 467, Jens Chr. Skous Vej 7
DK-8000 Arhus, Denmark
Phone: 45 894 26501
Fax: 45 894 26540
Publications: Nordic Irish Studies (43648)

Centre for Language Studies
Faculty of Arts & Social Sciences
National University of Singapore
9 Arts Link
Singapore 117570, Singapore
Publications: Electronic Journal of Foreign Language Teaching (50144)

Centre for Latin American Monetary Studies
Durango 54
Col. Roma
06700 Mexico City, Federal District, Mexico
Phone: 52 55 50616640
Publications: Boletin (47782) • Monetaria (47786) • Money Affairs (47787)

Centre for Latin American Research and Documentation
Keizersgracht 395-397
NL-1016 EK Amsterdam, Netherlands
Phone: 31 20 5253498
Fax: 31 20 6255127
Publications: Revista Europea de Estudios Latinoamericanos y del Caribe (48225)

Centre for Strategic and International Studies
Jakarta Post Bldg., 3rd Fl.
Jl. Palmerah Barat 142-243
10270 Jakarta, Indonesia

Phone: 62 21 53654601
Fax: 62 21 53654607
Publications: Indonesian Quarterly (45800)

Centre for Tourism Research and Development
A-965/6 Indira Nagar
Lucknow 226 016, Uttar Pradesh, India
Phone: 91 522 2310144
Fax: 91 522 2340313
Publications: Tourism Recreation Research (45329)

Centro Atlantico de Arte Moderno
Los Balcones, 11
E-35001 Las Palmas de Gran Canaria, Spain
Phone: 34 928 311800
Fax: 34 928 321629
Publications: Atlantica Internacional (50720)

Centro de Estudios y Cooperacion para America Latina
Pisuerga 2, 1o 3o
E-08028 Barcelona, Spain
Publications: Guaraguao (50675)

Centro de Estudos Educacao e Sociedade, CEDES
Caixa Postal 6022 - Unicamp
13084-971 Campinas, Sao Paulo, Brazil
Publications: Cadernos CEDES (42965) • Educacao & Sociedade (42968)

Centro de Filosofia
Faculdade de Letras da Universidade de Lisboa
Alameda da Universidade
1600-214 Lisbon, Portugal
Phone: 35 121 7920091
Fax: 35 121 7920091
Publications: Disputatio (49802)

Centro de Referencia em Informacao Ambiental
Av Romeu Tortima, 388
Barao Geraldo
13083-791 Campinas, Sao Paulo, Brazil
Phone: 55 193 2880466
Fax: 55 193 2490960
Publications: Biota Neotropica (42962)

Ceramic Review Publishing Ltd.
25 Fouberts Pl.
London W1F 7QF, United Kingdom
Phone: 44 20 74393377
Fax: 44 20 72879954
Publications: Ceramic Review (54195)

Ceramics: Art and Perception Proprietary Ltd.
120 Glenmore Rd.
Westminster, New South Wales 2021, Australia
Phone: 61 2 93615286
Fax: 61 2 93615402
Publications: Ceramics (42700)

Chabad-Lubavitch Media Center
Ilmarinkatu 10B, Ste. 66
FIN-00100 Helsinki, Finland
Phone: 358 9 444770
Publications: Chabad-Lubavitch of Finland (43823)

S.K. Chakraborti
Indian Museum
27 Jawaharlal Nehru Rd.
Kolkata 700 016, West Bengal, India
Phone: 91 332 495699
Fax: 91 332 495696
Publications: Indian Museum Bulletin (45273)

Chamber of Argentine Plastics Industries
Jeronimo Salguero 1939/41
1425 Buenos Aires, Argentina
Phone: 54 482 19603
Fax: 54 482 65480
Publications: Plasticos (41478)

Chamber of Commerce of the Grand-Duchy of Luxembourg
7, Rue Alcide de Gasperi
Kirchberg
L-2981 Luxembourg, Luxembourg
Phone: 35 242 39391
Fax: 35 243 8326
Publications: De Letzeburger Merkur (47491)

Chamber of Commerce and Industry of Western Australia
180 Hay St.
Perth, Western Australia 6004, Australia

Phone: 61 893 657627
Publications: Business Pulse (42248)

Chamber of Commerce - Malta
Exchange Bldg.
Republic St.
Valletta VLT 05, Malta
Phone: 356 21 233873
Fax: 356 21 245223
Publications: Commercial Courier (47745)

Chamber of Commerce of the Republic of Cuba
Calle 21, No. 661 esq. a A
Vedado Ciudad de La Habana
Havana, Cuba
Fax: 53 833 6810
Publications: Cuba Foreign Trade (43576)

Chandrabhaga
Tinkonia Bagicha
Cuttack 753 001, Orissa, India
Publications: Chandrabhaga (45080)

The Chap
2 Mount Pl.
Lewes BN7 1YH, United Kingdom
Publications: The Chap (53848)

Chapman Publishing
4 Broughton Pl.
Edinburgh EH1 3RX, United Kingdom
Phone: 44 13 15572207
Publications: Chapman (53261)

Charles Sturt University
PO Box 789
Albury, New South Wales 2640, Australia
Phone: 61 2 60519849
Fax: 61 2 60519849
Publications: Micronesian Journal of the Humanities and Social Sciences (41527)

Charlton Media Group
15B Stanley St.
Singapore 68734, Singapore
Phone: 65 622 37660
Publications: MSDN Magazine. Southeast Asia Edition (50223)

Chartered Institute of Architectural Technologists
397 City Rd.
London EC1V 1NH, United Kingdom
Phone: 44 20 72782206
Fax: 44 20 78373194
Publications: AT Magazine (53979)

Chartered Institute of Building
Englemere
Kings Ride
Ascot SL5 7TB, United Kingdom
Phone: 44 13 44630700
Fax: 44 13 44630777
Publications: Construction Information Quarterly (52137) • Construction Manager (52138)

Chartered Institute of Environmental Health
Chadwick Ct.
15 Hatfields
London SE1 8DJ, United Kingdom
Phone: 44 20 79286006
Fax: 44 20 78275862
Publications: Environmental Health Practitioner (54377) • Journal of Environmental Health Research (54744)

Chartered Institute of Housing
Octavia House
Westwood Way
Coventry CV4 8JP, United Kingdom
Phone: 44 24 76851700
Fax: 44 24 76695110
Publications: Housing (53084)

Chartered Institute of Journalists
2 Dock Offices
Surrey Quays Rd.
London SE16 2XU, United Kingdom
Phone: 44 20 72521187
Fax: 44 20 72322302
Publications: The Journal (54693)

Chartered Institute of Library and Information Professionals
7 Ridgmount St.

London WC1E 7AE, United Kingdom
Phone: 44 20 72550500
Fax: 44 20 72550501
Publications: Library Information Update (54871)

Chartered Institute of Management Accountants
26 Chapter St.
London SW1P 4NP, United Kingdom
Phone: 44 20 88492251
Fax: 44 20 88492450
Publications: Financial Management (54455)

Chartered Institute of Patent Attorneys
95 Chancery Ln.
London WC2A 1DT, United Kingdom
Phone: 44 20 74059450
Fax: 44 20 74300471
Publications: The CIPA Journal (54211)

Chartered Institute of Public Finance and Accountancy
3 Robert St.
London WC2N 6RL, United Kingdom
Phone: 44 20 75435600
Fax: 44 20 75435700
Publications: Journal of Finance and Management in Public Services (54751) • Public Finance (55151)

Chartered Institution of Water and Environmental Management
15 John St.
London WC1N 2EB, United Kingdom
Phone: 44 20 78313110
Fax: 44 20 74054967
Publications: Water and Environment Manager (55382)

Chartered Insurance Institute
42-48 High Rd.
S Woodford
London E18 2JP, United Kingdom
Phone: 44 20 89898464
Fax: 44 20 85303052
Publications: The Journal (54695) • Society of Fellows Journal (55252)

Chartered Quality Institute
12 Grosvenor Cres.
London SW1X 7EE, United Kingdom
Phone: 44 20 72456722
Fax: 44 20 72456788
Publications: Quality World (55163)

The Chartered Society of Physiotherapy
14 Bedford Row
London WC1R 4ED, United Kingdom
Phone: 44 20 73066666
Publications: Physiotherapy (53704)

Chaser Publishing Proprietary Ltd.
PO Box 293
Darlinghurst, New South Wales 1300, Australia
Phone: 61 292 804554
Fax: 61 292 804564
Publications: The Chaser (41827)

Chatila Publishing House
PO Box 13-5121
Chouran
Beirut, Lebanon
Fax: 961 1 352419
Publications: Arab Construction World (ACW) (47390) • Arab Water World (AWW) (47392) • Middle East Food (MEF) (47399)

Chem-Bio Informatics Society
Iida Bldg., Rm. 301
4-3-16, Yoga
Setagaya-ku
Tokyo 158-0097, Japan
Phone: 81 3 54915423
Fax: 81 3 54915462
Publications: Chem-Bio Informatics Journal (46782)

Chemical Daily Company Ltd.
16-8, Nihonbashi-Hamacho 3-Chome
Chuo-ku
Tokyo 103-8485, Japan
Phone: 81 33 6637931
Fax: 81 33 6632330
Telex: 2422362 NIPPO J
Publications: Japan Chemical Week (46854)

Chemical Society of Japan
1-5 Kanda-Surugadai

Chiyoda-Ku
Tokyo 101-8307, Japan
Phone: 81 332 926161
Fax: 81 332 926318
Publications: Bulletin of the Chemical Society of Japan (46769) • Chemistry Letters (46468) • Journal of Computer-Aided Chemistry (46893)

Chemical Software Society of Japan
Dept. of Chemistry & Biology Engineering
Fukui National College of Technology
Geshi-cho, Sabae
Fukui 916-0064, Japan
Phone: 81 778 621111
Fax: 81 778 621108
Publications: Journal of Chemical Software (46332)

Chess & Bridge Ltd.
369 Euston Rd.
London NW1 3AR, United Kingdom
Phone: 44 20 73882404
Fax: 44 20 73882407
Publications: Bridge (54105) • Chess (54202)

Chiangmai Mail Publishing Company Ltd.
209/5 Moo 6
T. Faham
A. Muang
Chiang Mai 50000, Thailand
Phone: 66 538 52557
Fax: 66 532 60788
Publications: Chiangmai Mail (51456)

Child Workers in Nepal Concerned Center
Ravi Bhawan
Kathmandu, Nepal
Phone: 977 1 4282255
Publications: Voice of Child Workers (47848)

Children's International Summer Villages International
MEA House
Ellison Pl.
Newcastle upon Tyne NE1 8XS, United Kingdom
Phone: 44 191 2324998
Fax: 44 191 2614710
Publications: Interspectives (55673)

Chilean Computer Science Society
Blanco Encalada 2120
Casilla 2777
Santiago, Chile
Publications: Revista de la SCCC (43148)

China Airlines Ltd.
131 Nanking E Rd., Sec. 3
Taipei, Taiwan
Phone: 886 22 7151212
Fax: 886 22 5146004
Publications: Dynasty (51338)

China-Britain Business Council
Portland House, 3rd Fl.
Bressenden Pl.
London SW1E 5BH, United Kingdom
Phone: 44 20 78022000
Fax: 44 20 78022029
Publications: China-Britain Business Review (54206)

China Business (Press) Hong Kong
103 No. 23 Bldg.
Guanying Yuan Xiqu
Xicheng District
Beijing 100035, People's Republic of China
Phone: 86 10 66561371
Fax: 86 10 66561412
Publications: China Business (43177)

China Chamber of International Commerce
1 Fuxingmenwai St.
Beijing 100860, People's Republic of China
Phone: 86 10 88075716
Fax: 86 10 68030747
Publications: China's Foreign Trade (43181)

China Daily
6th Fl., B3 Tower, Ziguang Bldg.
No. 11 Huixin Dongjie
Chaoyang District
Beijing 100029, People's Republic of China
Phone: 86 10 84883300

Fax: 86 10 84883600
Publications: Auto China (43170) • China Daily (Hong Kong Edition) (43178)

China Economic News Service
555 Chunghsiao E Rd., Sec. 4
Taipei 110, Taiwan
Phone: 886 2 2642 2629
Fax: 886 2 2642 7422
Publications: The Taiwan Economic News (51363)

China Pictorial Publishing House
33 Chegongzhuang W Rd.
Haidian District
Beijing 100044, People's Republic of China
Publications: China Pictorial (43180)

The China Post
8 Fu Shun St.
Taipei 104, Taiwan
Phone: 886 2 25969971
Fax: 886 2 25957962
Publications: The China Post (51334)

China Trend Building Press Ltd.
Rm. 703, 9 Chong Yip St.
Kwun Tong
Kowloon
Hong Kong, People's Republic of China
Phone: 86 228 026299
Fax: 86 228 026458
Publications: Building Journal Hong Kong (43284)

China University of Geosciences
No. 388 Lumo Rd.
Wuhan 430074, Hubei, People's Republic of China
Phone: 86 27 87481030
Fax: 86 27 87481030
Publications: Earth Science (43519) • Earth Sciences (43521) • Gems and Gemmology (43522) • Safety and Environmental Engineering (43525) • Social Sciences Edition (43526)

China Welding Association
111 Hexing Rd.
Harbin 150080, Heilongjiang, People's Republic of China
Phone: 86 451 86340850
Fax: 86 451 86333949
Publications: China Welding (43263)

Chinese Automatic Control Society
c/o Li-Chen Fu, Society Pres.
Dept. of Electrical Engineering, EE II-524
National Taiwan University
Taipei, Taiwan
Phone: 886 223 622209
Publications: Asian Journal of Control (51332)

Chinese Chemical Society
PO Box 2709
Beijing 100080, People's Republic of China
Phone: 86 10 62564020
Fax: 86 10 62568157
Publications: Chinese Journal of Applied Chemistry (43183) • Chinese Journal of Polymer Science (43186) • Journal of Molecular Structure (43208)

Chinese Coordination Centre of World Evangelism
PO Box 98435
Tsimshatsui
Hong Kong, People's Republic of China
Phone: 86 852 23910411
Fax: 86 852 27894740
Publications: Chinese Around the World (43288)

Chinese Folk Literature and Art Society
10 Nongzhanguan Nanli
Nongzhanguan
Beijing 100026, People's Republic of China
Phone: 86 106 5004622
Fax: 86 106 5004622
Publications: Folk Literature (43193)

Chinese Institute of Engineers
3rd Fl., No. 1, Ren-ai Rd., Section 2
Taipei, Taiwan
Phone: 886 22 3925128
Fax: 886 22 3973003
Publications: Journal of Chinese Institute of Engineers (51350)

Chinese Manufacturers' Association of Hong Kong
64-66 Connaught Rd.
Hong Kong, People's Republic of China
Phone: 85 225 456166
Fax: 85 225 414541
Publications: Hong Kong Entrepreneur (43324)

Chinese Medical Association
c/o Wang Mouyue
42 Dongsi Xidajie
Beijing 100710, People's Republic of China
Phone: 86 10 85158321
Fax: 86 10 85158333
Publications: Chinese Medical Journal (43187)

Chinese and Oriental Languages Information Processing Society
School of Computing, Lower Kent Ridge
National Univ. of Singapore
Singapore 119260, Singapore
Publications: International Journal of Chinese & Oriental Languages Processing (50177)

Chinese Photographers Association
61 Hongxing Huntong, Dongdan
Dongcheng District
Beijing 100005, People's Republic of China
Phone: 86 106 5252277
Publications: Chinese Photography (43188)

Chinese Radio Sports Association
No. 14-A, Tiantan Dongli Zhongqu
PO Box 6106
Beijing 100061, People's Republic of China
Phone: 86 10 67050878
Fax: 86 10 67050899
Publications: Ham's CQ (43195)

Chinese Society of Microbiology
National Taiwan University Hospital
No. 7, Chung Shan S Rd.
Taipei 100, Taiwan
Phone: 886 22 3123456
Fax: 886 22 3955072
Publications: Journal of Microbiology, Immunology and Infection (51354)

Chinese Society for Plant Pathology
435 Plant Protection Bldg.
Beijing 100094, People's Republic of China
Phone: 86 106 2891025
Fax: 86 106 2813785
Publications: Chinese Journal of Plant Pathology (43185)

Chinese University Press
Shatin Galleria, 9th Fl., Unit 1-3 & 18
18-24 Shan Mei St.
Fo Tan, Shatin
Hong Kong, People's Republic of China
Phone: 852 29465300
Fax: 852 26037355
Publications: Asian Anthropology (43274) • Asian Journal of English Language Teaching (43276) • Ching Feng (43289) • Hong Kong Journal of Sociology (43333) • Journal of Translation Studies (43362) • Translation Quarterly (43385)

Chintha Printing and Publishing Co. (P) Ltd.
Kerala State Committee
Kochi 695 001, Kerala, India
Phone: 91 484 2530739
Fax: 91 484 2530006
Publications: Deshabhimani (45249)

Chiriotti Editori SpA
Viale Rimembranza, 60
10064 Pinerolo, Italy
Phone: 39 121 393127
Fax: 39 121 794480
Publications: Ingredienti Alimentari (46217)

Chiropractors' Association of Australia (National) Ltd.
PO Box 335
2/36 Woodriff St.
Sydney, New South Wales 2751, Australia
Phone: 61 2 47318011
Fax: 61 2 47318088
Publications: Chiropractic Journal of Australia (42667)

Chitraleka
22, Andheri Ind.Est., Off Veera Desai Rd.

Andheri W
Mumbai 400 053, Maharashtra, India
Phone: 91 225 6921692
Fax: 91 222 6730858
Publications: Chitraleka (45363)

CHOICE
57 Carrington Rd.
Marrickville, New South Wales 2204, Australia
Phone: 61 295 773399
Fax: 61 295 773377
Publications: Choice (42039)

The Chosun Ilbo
62-4 Taepyeongro 1-ga
Jung-gu
Seoul 100-101, Republic of Korea
Phone: 82 272 45114
Publications: The Choogan Chosun (47260) • Chosen Ilbo (47261) • Feel (47265) • The Sonyon Chosun (47287) • The Sports Chosun (47288) • The Wolgan Chosun (47289) • The Wolgan Naksi (47290) • The Wolgan San (47291)

CHPublications Ltd.
Nimax House
20 Ullswater Cres.
Ullswater Business Park
Surrey CR5 2HR, United Kingdom
Phone: 44 208 6556400
Fax: 44 208 7631001
Publications: Japanese Performance (56667) • 911 & Porsche World (56669) • Triumph World (56677)

Christian Dance Fellowship of Australia
c/o Cathy Wright, Membership Sec.
2/3A Nield Ave.
Sydney, New South Wales 2093, Australia
Publications: Leaping (42535)

Christian Education Publications
1020 Bristol Rd.
Selly Oak
Birmingham B29 6LB, United Kingdom
Phone: 44 121 4724242
Fax: 44 121 4727575
Publications: The British Journal of Religious Education (52334) • REtoday (52363)

Christian Solidarity International
Zelglistr 64
PO Box 70
CH-8122 Binz, Switzerland
Phone: 41 449 823333
Fax: 41 449 823334
Publications: CSI Magazine (51081)

The Chronicle
PO Box 1764
Roseau, Dominica
Phone: 767448-7887
Fax: 767448-0047
Publications: The Chronicle (Dominica) (43739)

Chulalongkorn University
254 Phyathai Rd.
Patumwan
Bangkok 10330, Thailand
Phone: 66 2 2150871
Fax: 66 2 2154804
Publications: Buffalo Journal (51415)

Church Lane Publishing Ltd.
200 Eastgate
Deeping Saint James PE6 8RD, United Kingdom
Phone: 44 1778 342814
Fax: 44 1778 342814
Publications: Best of British (53162)

Church Monuments Society
55, Bowden Park Rd.
Crownhill
Plymouth PL6 5NG, United Kingdom
Publications: Journal of Church Monuments Society (56487)

Church of Scotland
121 George St.
Edinburgh EH2 4YN, United Kingdom
Phone: 44 131 2255722
Publications: Life and Work (53299)

Church Society
Dean Wace House

16 Rosslyn Rd.
Watford WD18 0NY, United Kingdom
Phone: 44 19 23235111
Fax: 44 19 23800362
Publications: Churchman (56861)

Church's Ministry Among Jewish People
Eagle Lodge, Hexgreave Hall Business Pk.
Farnsfield NG22 8LS, United Kingdom
Phone: 44 1623 883960
Fax: 44 1623 884295
Publications: Shalom (53382)

CIAUD-ICASD
Rue Ravenstein 23
B-1000 Brussels, Belgium
Phone: 32 264 57910
Fax: 32 264 02795
Publications: A Architecture/A Architectuur (42842)

CICEES
C/ La Muralla 3 entlo
E-33202 Gijon, Spain
Phone: 34 985 319385
Fax: 34 985 319385
Publications: Abaco (50716)

Cidob
Elisabets, 12
E-08001 Barcelona, Spain
Phone: 34 933 026495
Publications: Afers Internacionals (50647)

CILIP Cymru/Wales
Dept. of Information Studies
Llanbadarn Fawr
Aberystwyth SY23 3AS, United Kingdom
Phone: 44 1970 622174
Fax: 44 1970 622190
Publications: Y Ddolen (51689)

Cinema Vision India
501, Adarsh Nagar
M.H.B. Colony
New Link Rd.
Jogeshwari (W)
Mumbai 400 102, Maharashtra, India
Phone: 91 22 6320739
Fax: 91 22 6366642
Publications: Surabhi (45445)

Citizens Advice Notes Service Trust
89 Albert Embankment
London SE1 7TP, United Kingdom
Publications: CANS Digest of Social Legislation (54173)

Citrus Australia Ltd.
PO Box 5091
Mildura, Victoria 3502, Australia
Phone: 61 350 236333
Publications: Australian Citrus News (42106)

Civic Education Project
Bd. Unirii, nr. 76
Bl. J3A, sc. A, ap 2
Sector 3
Bucharest, Romania
Phone: 40 1 3206532
Publications: Romanian Journal of Society and Politics (49843)

Nigel J. Clarke Publications
Befferlands Farm Workshops
Charmouth DT6 6RD, United Kingdom
Phone: 44 1297 561577
Fax: 44 1297 561577
Publications: Tide Times (52958)

Clarkson Research Studies
St. Magnus House
3 Lower Thames St.
London EC3R 6HE, United Kingdom
Phone: 44 20 73340000
Fax: 44 20 76264189
Telex: 8812927 CLTNKG
Publications: Container Intelligence Quarterly (54262)

Classic Wings
PO Box 534
Blenheim, New Zealand
Phone: 64 357 89609
Fax: 64 357 76451
Publications: Classic Wings (42134)

The Clay Minerals Society
3635 Concorde Pky., Ste. 500
Chantilly, VA 20151-1125
Phone: 703652-9960
Fax: 703652-9951
Publications: Clays and Clay Minerals (45936)

Cleantech Investor Limited
PO Box 63865
London SE1 3SN, United Kingdom
Phone: 44 20 73947110
Fax: 44 20 72520910
Publications: Cleantech (54216)

Clothing Manufacturers' Association of India
902 Mahalaxmi Chambers
22 Bhulabhai Desai Rd.
Mumbai 400 026, Maharashtra, India
Phone: 91 22 23538245
Fax: 91 22 23515908
Publications: Apparel (45351)

Club Marine Ltd.
40 The Esplanade
Brighton, Victoria 3186, Australia
Fax: 61 386 158178
Publications: Club Marine (41638)

CMP Information Ltd.
Ludgate House
245 Blackfriars Rd.
London SE1 9UY, United Kingdom
Phone: 44 20 79215000
Publications: Cabinet Maker (54163) • Carpet & Flooring Retail (CFR) (54183) • EE Times UK (42850) • Property Week (55142) • Pulse (55156) • The Safety & Health Practitioner (55214)

CMP-WEKA Verlag GmbH & Company KG
Gruber Str. 46 A
D-85586 Poing, Germany
Phone: 49 812 1951512
Fax: 49 812 1951597
Publications: Computer Reseller News (44634) • Datacom (44635) • Information Week (44636) • Network Computing (44637)

CMPMedica
Rue du Bourdon 100
B-1180 Brussels, Belgium
Phone: 32 233 33411
Fax: 32 233 23958
Publications: Pharmacy Today (42869)

CMPMedica (NZ) Ltd
3 Shea Ter.
Takapuna
PO Box 31 348
Milford
Auckland, New Zealand
Phone: 64 9 4884278
Fax: 64 9 4896240
Publications: New Zealand Doctor (48809)

CNJA
14 St. Boetie
F-75382 Paris, France
Publications: Jeunes Agriculteurs (44062)

Coast Publishing Ltd.
St. Joseph's
St. Mawgan
Cornwall TR8 4ES, United Kingdom
Phone: 44 1637 860031
Publications: Adventure Cornwall (53064)

Coates & Parker Ltd.
36 Market Pl.
Warminster BA12 9AN, United Kingdom
Phone: 44 1985 213030
Fax: 44 1985 217680
Publications: Warminster Journal (56847)

Coconut Development Board
PO Box 1021
Kera Bhavan
Kochi 682 011, Kerala, India
Phone: 91 484 2376265
Fax: 91 484 2377902
Publications: Indian Coconut Journal (45250)

CodeBreakers Journal
Lange Strasse 31
32051 Herford, Germany

Phone: 49 5221 6913324
Publications: CodeBreakers Journal (CBJ) (44483)

CODESRIA - Council for the Development of Social Science Research in Africa
Ave. Cheikh Anta Diop x
Canal IV
BP 3304
Dakar, Senegal
Phone: 22 182 59822
Fax: 22 182 41289
Publications: Africa Development (50077) • Africa Media Review (50078) • African Journal of International Affairs (50079) • African Sociological Review (50490) • Afro-Arab Selections for Social Sciences (43751) • CODESRIA Bulletin (50080) • Journal of Higher Education in Africa (50081)

Col. legi d'Aquitectues de Catalunya
Pl. Nova, 5
E-08002 Barcelona, Spain
Phone: 34 933 015000
Fax: 34 933 186029
Publications: Quaderns d'Arquitectura (50694)

The Colegio Brasileiro de Patologia Animal
Embrapa-CNPAB/PSA
Km 47-Seropedica
23851-970 Rio de Janeiro, Rio de Janeiro, Brazil
Phone: 55 212 6822940
Fax: 55 212 6821081
Publications: Pesquisa Veterinaria Brasileira (43013)

Colegio de Postgraduados
Guerrero Num. 9.
Reconciled Cor. Hidalgo
56251 San Luis Huexotla, Mexico, Mexico
Phone: 52 159 59284427
Fax: 52 159 59284427
Publications: Agrociencia (47797)

The Collector Ltd.
20 Maple Grove
London NW9 8QY, United Kingdom
Phone: 44 20 82005004
Fax: 44 20 77923492
Publications: The Book Collector (56749)

College of Family Physicians Singapore
16 College Rd., No. 01-02
Singapore 169854, Singapore
Phone: 65 622 30606
Fax: 65 622 20204
Publications: The Singapore Family Physician (50255)

College of General Practitioners of Sri Lanka
Wijerama House
6 Wijerama Mawatha
Colombo 00700, Sri Lanka
Publications: Sri Lankan Family Physician (50868)

College of Nyiregyhaza
Institute of Mathematics & Computer Science
PO Box 166
H-4401 Nyiregyhaza, Hungary
Publications: Acta Mathematica Academiae Paedagogicae Nyiregyhaziensis (44892)

College of Optometrists
42 Craven St.
London WC2N 5NG, United Kingdom
Phone: 44 20 78396000
Fax: 44 20 78396800
Publications: Ophthalmic and Physiological Optics (55039) • Optometry in Practice (55041)

College of Physicians and Surgeons Pakistan
7th Central St.
Defence Housing Authority
Karachi 75500, Pakistan
Phone: 92 21 9207100
Fax: 92 21 9207120
Publications: Journal of College of Physicians and Surgeons Pakistan (49357)

The College of Teachers
Institute of Education
20 Bedford Way
London WC1H 0AL, United Kingdom
Phone: 44 20 79115536
Fax: 44 20 76314865
Publications: Education Today (54354)

Colloquy
Centre for Comparative Literature and Cultural Studies
Bldg. 11
Monash University
Clayton, Victoria 3800, Australia
Phone: 61 399 059009
Fax: 61 399 055593
Publications: Colloquy (41759)

Colombia Rotaria
Calle 5 No. 62C-53
Apartado Aereo 5925
Cali, Colombia
Phone: 57 2 5515380
Fax: 57 2 5531614
Publications: Colombia Rotaria (43550)

Colombian Academy of Exact, Physical, and Natural Sciences
Transversal 27 No. 39A-63
Bogota, Colombia
Phone: 57 126 80365
Fax: 57 124 43186
Publications: Revista (43545)

ComexPeru Peruvian Foreign Trading Society
Bartolome Herrera 254
Miraflores
Lima 18, Peru
Phone: 51 1 44225784
Fax: 51 1 44225942
Publications: Negocios Internacionales (49424)

Commemorative Collectors Society
Lumless House
77 Gainsborough Rd.
Winthorpe
Newark NG24 2NR, United Kingdom
Phone: 44 1636 671377
Publications: Members Journal (55660)

Commonwealth Association of Architects
PO Box 1166
Stamford PE2 2HL, United Kingdom
Phone: 44 178 0238091
Publications: CAA Newsnet (56595)

Commonwealth Association of Surveying and Land Economy
c/o Mrs. Susan Spedding
Faculty of Built Environment
University of W of England, Frenchay Campus
Coldharbour Ln.
Bristol BS16 1QY, United Kingdom
Phone: 44 17 3283036
Fax: 44 17 3283036
Publications: Survey Review (52732)

Commonwealth Broadcasting Association
17 Fleet St.
London EC4Y 1AA, United Kingdom
Phone: 44 207 5835550
Fax: 44 207 5835549
Publications: Commonwealth Broadcaster (54240)

Commonwealth Forestry Association
Crib
Dinchope
Cravon Arms SY7 9JJ, United Kingdom
Phone: 44 1588 672868
Fax: 44 870 0116645
Publications: Commonwealth Forestry News (53098)

Commonwealth Magistrates and Judges' Association
Uganda House
58-59 Trafalgar Sq.
London WC2N 5DX, United Kingdom
Phone: 44 207 9761007
Fax: 44 207 9762394
Publications: Commonwealth Judicial Journal (54241)

Commonwealth Parliamentary Association
Westminster House, Ste. 700
7 Millbank
London SW1P 3JA, United Kingdom
Phone: 44 2077991460
Fax: 44 2072226073
Publications: The Parliamentarian (55057)

Commonwealth Secretariat
Marlborough House
Pall Mall
London SW1Y 5HX, United Kingdom

Phone: 44 20 77476500
Fax: 44 20 79300827
Publications: Commonwealth Law Bulletin (54242)

Communication Workers Union - England
150 The Broadway
Wimbledon
London SW19 1RX, United Kingdom
Phone: 44 20 89717200
Fax: 44 20 89717300
Publications: CWU Voice (54306)

Communications International Group
Linen Hall
162/168 Regent St.
London W1R 5TB, United Kingdom
Phone: 44 20 7341530
Fax: 44 20 7370915
Publications: Cosmetic Products Report (54270) • Cosmetics International (54271)

Communications and Public Affairs Office
The Hong Kong Polytechnic University
Hung Hom
Kowloon
Hong Kong, People's Republic of China
Phone: 852 27665100
Fax: 852 23640246
Publications: Profile (43376)

Communist Party of Australia
74 Buckingham St.
Surry Hills, New South Wales 2010, Australia
Phone: 61 2 96998844
Fax: 61 2 96999833
Publications: The Australian Marxist Review (42414)

Community and District Nursing Association
367 Chiswick High Rd.
London W4 4AG, United Kingdom
Phone: 44 20 89714268
Publications: PNC (55096)

Community Matters
12-20 Baron St.
London N1 9LL, United Kingdom
Phone: 44 20 78377887
Fax: 44 20 72789253
Publications: Community (54247)

Community Newspaper
120 Roe St.
Northbridge, Western Australia 6003, Australia
Phone: 61 892 132013
Fax: 61 892 371056
Publications: Cockburn Gazette (42212) • Comment News (41984) • Eastern Reporter (42224) • Hills Gazette (42104) • Kalamunda Reporter (42105) • Wanneroo Times (41975)

Compagnie Mediterraneenne d'Edition
Europarc Pichaury C10
1330 Ave. Guillibert de la Lauziere
BP 439
F-13591 Aix-en-Provence Cedex 3, France
Phone: 33 442 371450
Fax: 33 442 242886
Publications: Maisons et Decors Mediterranees (43913)

The Company of Biologists Ltd.
140 Cowley Rd.
Cambridge CB4 0DL, United Kingdom
Phone: 44 12 23426164
Fax: 44 12 23423353
Publications: Journal of Cell Science (52847) • Journal of Experimental Biology (52852)

Company Law Institute of India Private Ltd.
2 Vaithyaram St.
T. Nagar
Chennai 600 017, Tamil Nadu, India
Phone: 91 44 24350752
Fax: 91 44 24322015
Publications: Income Tax Reports (45037)

Compound Livestock Feed Manufacturers' Association of India
111 Mittal Chamber, 11th Fl.
Nariman Pt.
Mumbai 400 021, Maharashtra, India
Phone: 91 222 2026103
Fax: 91 222 2880128
Publications: Feed Trends (45370)

Compress AG
Seestrasse 99
CH-8800 Thalwil, Switzerland
Phone: 41 44 7227700
Fax: 41 44 7227701
Publications: Infoweek.ch (51234)

Computer Press Agora S.R.L.
Str. T. Vladimirescu 63/1
PO Box 230
R-4300 Tg-Mures, Romania
Publications: BYTE Romania (49848)

Computer Society of India
122 TV Industrial Estate
S.K. Ahire Marg, Worli
Worli
Mumbai 400 030, Maharashtra, India
Phone: 91 22 24943422
Fax: 91 22 24950543
Publications: Computer Society of India Journal (45364) • CSI Adhyayan (45365) • CSI Communications (45366)

Comunita Ebraica di Roma
Lungotevere Cenci (Tempio)
I-00186 Rome, Italy
Phone: 39 6 6840061
Fax: 39 6 68400684
Publications: Shalom (46241)

Conchological Society of Great Britain and Ireland
88 Peperharow Rd.
Godalming GU7 2PN, United Kingdom
Phone: 44 14 83417782
Publications: Mollusc World (53475)

Concrete Repair Association
Kingsley House
Ganders Business Park, Kingsley
Hampshire
Bordon GU35 9LU, United Kingdom
Phone: 44 1420 471615
Publications: Cracking Matters (52407)

The Concrete Society
Riverside House, 4 Meadows Business Pk.
Sta. Approach, Blackwater
Camberley GU17 9AB, United Kingdom
Phone: 44 12 76607140
Fax: 44 12 76607141
Publications: Concrete (52784)

Conde Nast Publications Ltd.
Vogue House
Hanover Sq.
London W1S 1JU, United Kingdom
Phone: 44 20 74999080
Publications: The World of Interiors (55421)

Confederation of Aerial Industries Ltd.
Communications House
41a Market St.
Watford WD18 0PN, United Kingdom
Phone: 44 1923 803030
Fax: 44 1923 803203
Publications: Code of Practice (56862) • Feedback (56864)

Confederation of Asia-Pacific Chambers of Commerce and Industry
14 Fl., No. 11 Songgao Rd.
Xinyi District
Taipei 11073, Taiwan
Phone: 886 27 255663
Fax: 886 27 255665
Publications: Journal of Commerce and Industry (51351)

Confederation of Netherlands Industry and Employers
PO Box 93002
NL-2509 AA The Hague, Netherlands
Phone: 31 703 490349
Fax: 31 703 490300
Publications: Forum (48616)

Conference of Socialist Economists
25 Horsell Rd.
London N5 1XL, United Kingdom
Publications: Capital & Class (54174)

Congress of South African Trade Unions
1 Leyds St.
Braamfontein
Johannesburg 2000, Republic of South Africa
Phone: 27 11 3394911
Fax: 27 11 3395080
Publications: The Shopsteward (50533)

Connacht Tribune Ltd.
15 Market St.
Galway, Galway, Ireland
Phone: 353 915 36222
Fax: 353 915 67970
Publications: City Tribune (46017) • Connacht Sentinel (46018) • Connacht Tribune (46019)

Connaught Telegraph Ltd.
Cavendish Ln.
Castlebar, Mayo, Ireland
Phone: 353 94 9021711
Fax: 353 94 9024007
Publications: Connaught Telegraph (45928)

Connolly Publications Ltd.
244 Gray's Inn Rd.
London WC1X 8JR, United Kingdom
Publications: Irish Democrat (54682)

Consejo General de Colegios Oficiales de Psicologos
Conde de Penalver
45 Planta 5
28006 Madrid, Spain
Phone: 34 91 4449020
Fax: 34 91 3095615
Publications: Psychology in Spain (50793)

Conselho Brasileiro de Oftalmologia
Alameda Santos
1343 - 11 Andar CJ. 1110
01419-001 Sao Paulo, Sao Paulo, Brazil
Phone: 55 113 2664000
Fax: 55 113 1710953
Publications: Arquivos Brasileiros de Oftalmologia (43023)

Conservancy Association
9/F Breakthrough Ctr.
191-197 Woosung St.
Kowloon
Hong Kong, People's Republic of China
Phone: 852 27286781
Fax: 852 27285538
Publications: Green Alert (43301)

Conservation Foundation
1 Kensington Gore
London SW7 2AR, United Kingdom
Phone: 44 20 75913111
Fax: 44 20 75913110
Publications: Network 21 (54988)

Instituto de Ciencias de la Construccion Eduardo Torroja
Serrano Galvache, s/n
Aptdo. 19002
E-28033 Madrid, Spain
Phone: 34 913 020440
Fax: 34 913 020700
Publications: Informes de la Construccion (50770) • Materiales de Construccion (50782)

Consumer Council of Hong Kong
K Wah Centre, 22/F
191 Java Rd.
North Point
Hong Kong, People's Republic of China
Phone: 852 28563113
Fax: 852 28563611
Publications: Choice (43290)

Consumer Guidance Society of India
Block 'J' Mahapalika Marg
Mumbai 400 001, Maharashtra, India
Phone: 91 22 621612
Fax: 91 22 659715
Publications: Keemat (45407)

Consumers' Association of Ireland
43-44 Chelmsford Rd.
Dublin 6, Dublin, Ireland
Phone: 35 314 978600
Fax: 35 314 978601
Publications: Consumer Choice (45952)

Contemporary Review Company Ltd.
PO Box 1242
Oxford OX1 4FJ, United Kingdom
Publications: Contemporary Review (55916)

Contract Flooring Association
4C St. Mary's Pl.
The Lace Market
Nottingham NG1 1PH, United Kingdom
Phone: 44 11 59411126
Fax: 44 11 59412238
Publications: Contracts Flooring Journal (56779)

Contract Flooring Journal
102 Queens Rd.
Tunbridge Wells TN4 9JU, United Kingdom
Phone: 44 1892 680816
Publications: CFJ Contract Flooring Journal (56778)

Copernicus Gesellschaft
Max-Planck-Str. 13
D-37191 Katlenburg-Lindau, Germany
Phone: 49 5556 995550
Fax: 49 5556 9955570
Publications: Natural Hazards and Earth System Sciences (NHESS) (44501)

Copernicus GmbH
Bahnhofsallee 1e
D-37081 Gottingen, Germany
Phone: 49 551 900339
Fax: 49 551 900339
Publications: Advances in Geosciences (44389) • Advances in Radio Science (44390) • Astrophysics and Space Sciences Transactions (44392) • Biogeosciences (44538) • Biogeosciences Discussions (44394) • Climate of the Past (44412) • Hydrology and Earth System Sciences Discussions (48309) • Ocean Science (44400) • Ocean Science Discussions (44401) • Social Geography (44402)

Cornish World Media
Jennings House
Jennings St.
Penzance TR18 2LU, United Kingdom
Phone: 44 17 36365896
Fax: 44 17 36330538
Publications: Cornish World (56248)

Cornucopia K.K.
8F Mita Hillside Bldg.
4-1-9, Mita
Minato-ku
Tokyo 108-0073, Japan
Phone: 81 354 846680
Fax: 81 354 846683
Publications: Eat (46805)

Corporate Watch
Office 14, Unit 6
Wilmer Industrial Estate
Wilmer Pl.
London N16 0LW, United Kingdom
Phone: 44 20 79237082
Publications: Corporate Watch (54267)

Corps of Drums Society
103 Clare Ln.
East Malling
Maidstone ME19 6JB, United Kingdom
Publications: The Drummer's Call (55528)

Corvinus University of Budapest
Fovam ter 8
H-1093 Budapest, Hungary
Fax: 36 1 4825000
Publications: Journal Applied Ecology and Environmental Research (44840)

Cosmos Publishing Cooperative
c/o Arran Gare
Philosophy & Cultural Inquiry
Swinburne Univ.
PO Box 218
Hawthorn, Victoria 3122, Australia
Publications: Cosmos and History (41942)

Council for British Archaeology
St. Mary's House, 66 Bootham
York YO30 7BZ, United Kingdom
Phone: 44 19 04671417
Fax: 44 19 04671384
Publications: British Archaeology (56988)

Council to Homeless Persons
2 Stanley St.
Collingwood, Victoria 3066, Australia
Phone: 61 3 94198699
Fax: 61 3 94197445
Publications: Parity (41793)

Council for Leather Exports
CMDA Tower-II, 3rd Fl.
Gandhi Irwin Bridge Rd., Egmore
Chennai 600 008, Tamil Nadu, India
Phone: 91 44 28594367
Fax: 91 44 28594363
Publications: Leather News India (45052)

Council for the Protection of Rural England
128 Southwark St.
London SE1 0SW, United Kingdom
Phone: 44 20 79812800
Publications: CPRE Voice (54280)

Country Doctor
5 Manor Farm Close
Gate Ln.
Broughton
Kettering
Northampton NN14 1ND, United Kingdom
Phone: 44 15 36791515
Fax: 44 15 36791175
Publications: Country Doctor (55707)

Country Publications Limited
The Water Mill
Broughton Hall
Skipton BD23 3AG, United Kingdom
Phone: 44 1756 701381
Fax: 44 1756 701326
Publications: Dalesman Magazine (56553)

Countryside Agency
PO Box 125
Wetherby LS23 7EP, United Kingdom
Phone: 44 87 01206466
Fax: 44 87 01206467
Publications: Countryside Focus (56909)

Countrywide Editions Ltd.
24 Maddox St.
London W1S 1PP, United Kingdom
Fax: 44 20 7409083
Publications: Rare Book Review (55173)

CPA Australia
Level 20, 28 Freshwater Pl.
Southbank, Victoria 3006, Australia
Phone: 61 3 96069606
Fax: 61 3 96708901
Publications: In The Black (42064)

Crafts Council
44a Pentonville Rd.
Islington
London N1 9BY, United Kingdom
Phone: 44 20 78062500
Fax: 44 20 78376891
Publications: Crafts (54281)

Crain Communications Ltd.
3rd Fl., 21 St. Thomas St.
London SE1 9RY, United Kingdom
Phone: 44 20 74571400
Publications: Urethanes Technology (55362)

Creamer Media (Pty) Ltd.
PO Box 75316
Garden View 2047, Republic of South Africa
Phone: 27 116 223744
Fax: 27 116 229350
Publications: Engineering News (50479) • Mining Weekly (50480)

Creative Copy
2-4 The Fradgan
Newlyn
Penzance TR18 5BE, United Kingdom
Phone: 44 17 36334800
Fax: 44 17 36334808
Publications: Inside Cornwall (56249)

Creative Crafts Publishing Ltd.
Well Oast
Brenley Ln.
Faversham ME13 9LY, United Kingdom
Phone: 44 1227 750215

Fax: 44 1227 751813
Publications: New Stitches (53384)

Creative Endeavors
25 Amir Khusro Rd.
Blk. 7 & 8, CP Berar Society
Karachi 75350, Pakistan
Phone: 92 215 845467
Fax: 92 215 845467
Publications: Infectious Diseases Journal (49355)

Creative Living Media
PO Box 645
Rozelle, New South Wales 2039, Australia
Phone: 61 2 95559322
Fax: 61 2 95556188
Publications: Beads etc. . . (42323) • Creative Weddings (42324) • Down Under Quilts (42325) • For Keeps Creative Scrapbooking (42326) • i can make it myself (42327) • Parties for Kids (42328)

Crediton Country Courier
102 High St.
Crediton EX17 3LF, United Kingdom
Phone: 44 13 63774263
Fax: 44 13 63773545
Publications: Crediton Country Courier (53117)

Cremation Society of Great Britain
Brecon House, 1st Fl.
16/16A Albion Pl.
Maidstone ME14 5DZ, United Kingdom
Phone: 44 16 22688292
Fax: 44 16 22686698
Publications: Pharos International (55530)

Crier Media Group Ltd.
1-3 Station Rd. E, 1st Fl.
Limpsfield
Surrey
Oxted RH8 0BD, United Kingdom
Phone: 44 1883 734582
Fax: 44 1883 713640
Publications: Biscuit World (56235) • Drinks Network (56236) • Potato Processing International (56237)

Criminological Society of Southern Africa
PO Box 28936
Sunnyside 0132, Republic of South Africa
Publications: Acta Criminologica (50637)

Crisscross KK
3F Maison Tomoe Bldg.
3-16-1 Minami-Aoyama
Minato-ku
Tokyo 107-0062, Japan
Phone: 81 3 34236932
Fax: 81 3 34236931
Publications: Metropolis (46967)

Croatian Chemical Society
Horvatovac 102 A
CT-10000 Zagreb, Croatia
Phone: 385 146 06163
Fax: 385 146 06131
Publications: Croatica Chemica Acta (43566)

Croatian Pharmaceutical Society
Acta Pharmaceutica, HFD, Masarykova 2
HR-10000 Zagreb, Croatia
Phone: 385 1 4872849
Fax: 385 1 4872853
Publications: Acta Pharmaceutica (43562)

Cromwell Association
c/o Gary Baker
190 Cemetery Rd.
Scunthorpe DN16 1NU, United Kingdom
Publications: Cromwelliana (56467)

Crop Science Society of China
12 Zhonggguancun Nan Dajie
Beijing 100081, People's Republic of China
Phone: 86 106 8918616
Fax: 86 106 8918616
Publications: Acta Agronomica Sinica (43165)

Crop Science Society of Japan
Tokyo Secretariat
2F Shin-Kyoritsu Bldg.
Shinkawa 2-22-4, Chuo-Ku
Tokyo 104-0033, Japan
Fax: 81 3 35532047
Publications: Japanese Journal of Crop Science

(46868) • Plant Production Science (47018)

Crops Research Institute
PO Box 3785
Kumasi, Ghana
Phone: 233 51 60396
Publications: Agricultural and Food Science Journal of Ghana (44734)

Croquet Association
Old Bath Rd.
Cheltenham GL53 7DF, United Kingdom
Phone: 44 12 42242318
Publications: Croquet Gazette (52966)

Cross & Cockade International
Cragg Cottage
The Cragg
Wetherby LS23 6QB, United Kingdom
Phone: 44 19 37845320
Publications: Cross & Cockade International (56910)

Cross River University of Technology
Obubra Campus
State PMB 1123
Obubra, Cross River, Nigeria
Publications: Journal of Agriculture, Forestry and the Social Sciences (49158)

Crossword Club
Coombe Farm
Awbridge
Romsey SO51 0HN, United Kingdom
Phone: 44 17 94524346
Fax: 44 17 94514988
Publications: Crossword (56406)

CSF Medical Communications Ltd.
Ste. 119, Eagle Tower
Montpellier Dr.
Cheltenham GL50 1TA, United Kingdom
Phone: 44 1242 223890
Fax: 44 1242 243406
Publications: Drugs in Context (52968)

CSIRO Publishing
PO Box 1139
Collingwood, Victoria 3066, Australia
Phone: 61 396 627500
Fax: 61 396 627555
Publications: Animal Production Science (41780) • Australasian Plant Disease Notes (41781) • Australasian Plant Pathology (42245) • Australian Journal of Chemistry (41782) • Australian Journal of Zoology (41783) • Crop & Pasture Science (41784) • Earthmatters (41785) • Ecos (41786) • Emu - Austral Ornithology (41787) • Environmental Chemistry (41788) • Functional Plant Biology (41789) • Historical Records of Australian Science (42231) • Invertebrate Systematics (41791) • Marine & Freshwater Research (41792) • PASA (41794) • The Rangeland Journal (41560) • Reproduction, Fertility and Development (41796) • Sexual Health (42085) • Wildlife Research (41797)

CSL Publishing Ltd.
Alliance House
49 Sidney St.
Cambridge CB2 3HX, United Kingdom
Phone: 44 1223 460490
Fax: 44 1223 315960
Publications: Boat and Yacht Buyer (52794) • Jet Skier & PW Magazine (52840) • Sportsboat (52898)

Cuadernos de Jazz Editores S.L.
Hotraleze, 75
E-28004 Madrid, Spain
Phone: 34 913 080302
Fax: 34 913 080599
Publications: Cuadernos de Jazz (50745)

Cultural Center for the Philippines
CCP Complex, Roxas Blvd.
Pasay City 1300, Philippines
Phone: 63 283 21125
Fax: 63 283 23683
Publications: Ani (49568)

Culture and Cosmos
PO Box 1071
Bristol BS99 1HE, United Kingdom
Publications: Culture and Cosmos (52659)

Cumberland Newspaper Group
142-154 Macquarie St.

Parramatta, New South Wales 2150, Australia
Phone: 61 2 96895500
Publications: Blacktown Advocate (42233) • Canterbury-Bankstown Express (42012) • Central Coast Express Advocate (42695) • Fairfield Advance (42013) • The Glebe (41867) • Hills Shire Times (41731) • Hornsby & Upper North Shore Advocate (41965) • Inner-West Weekly (42234) • Lake Macquarie News (41722) • Liverpool Leader (42014) • Macarthur Chronicle (41696) • The Manly Daily (42032) • Mt. Druitt - St. Marys Standard (42124) • North Shore Times (41742) • Northern District Times (41856) • Parramatta Advertiser (42235) • Penrith Press (42240) • Rouse Hill Times (42237)

Current Drugs Ltd.
34-42 Cleveland St.
London W1T 4LB, United Kingdom
Phone: 44 20 73442800
Fax: 44 20 73442900
Publications: Current Opinion in Investigational Drugs (54300)

Current Science Association
C.V. Raman Ave.
PO Box 8001
Bangalore 560 080, Karnataka, India
Phone: 91 802 3612310
Fax: 91 802 3616094
Publications: Current Colorectal Cancer Reports (44952) • Current Heart Failure Reports (44953) • Current Hematology Reports (44954) • Current Hepatitis Reports (44955) • Current Science (44956)

C.V. Computern-Verlags GmbH
Beethovenplatz 2
D-80336 Munich, Germany
Phone: 49 895 446560
Fax: 49 895 31327
Publications: Computern im Handwerk (44555)

Cyber Media India Ltd.
B-35, Sector 32, Institutional
Gurgaon 122001, Haryana, India
Phone: 91 124 4031234
Fax: 91 124 2380694
Publications: Dataquest (45126)

Cyprus Chamber of Commerce & Industry
38, Grivas Dhigenis Ave. & 3, Deligiorgis St.
PO Box 21455
Nicosia CY-1509, Cyprus
Phone: 357 228 89800
Fax: 357 226 69048
Publications: Emporoviomichaniki (43594)

Cytologia
c/o Japan Mendel Society
Toshin Bldg.
Hongo 2-27-2
Bunkyo-ku
Tokyo 113-0033, Japan
Fax: 81 3 38145352
Publications: Cytologia (46798)

CYWEEKLY Ltd.
1 Diogenous
Engomi
PO Box 21094
Nicosia 1306, Cyprus
Phone: 357 22 744400
Fax: 357 22 668665
Publications: The Cyprus Weekly (43593)

Czech Medical Association J.E. Purknye— Publishing Div.
Sokolska 31
CZ-120 26 Prague 2, Czech Republic
Phone: 420 2 24266223
Fax: 420 2 24266212
Publications: Acta Chirurgiae Plasticae (43608) • Anaesthesiology & Intensive Critical Care Medicine (43609) • Ceska Revmatologie (43612) • Cesko-Slovenska Patologie/Soudni Lekarstvi (43613) • Ceskoslovenska Pediatrie (43614) • Czech Gynaecology (43616) • Czech Radiology (43617) • Czech and Slovak Neurology and Neurosurgery (43618) • Czech and Slovak Ophthalmology (43619) • Czech and Slovak Pharmacy (43620) • Czech and Slovak Psychiatry (43621) • Czecho-Slovak Dermatology (43622) • Epidemiology, Microbiology, Immunology (43624) • Internal Medicine (43625) • Journal of Czech Physi-

cians (43627) • Otorhinolaryngology and Phoniatrics (43632) • Revizni a Posudkove Lekarstvi (43637)

Czech Multiple Sclerosis Society
PO Box 38
CZ-120 00 Prague, Czech Republic
Phone: 42 241 728619
Fax: 42 266 712511
Publications: Roska (43638)

Czech Radiological Society
c/o Prof. Jiri Ferda, MD
University Hospital, Clinic of Diagnostic Radiology
Alej Svobody 80
306 40 Plzen, Czech Republic
Phone: 42 377 103436
Fax: 42 377 103438
Publications: Ceska Radiologie (43607)

Czech Society for Cybernetics and Informatics
Pod Vodarenskou vezi 2
CZ-182 07 Prague 8, Czech Republic
Phone: 42 266 053901
Fax: 42 285 885789
Publications: Journal Kybernetika (43628)

D C Thomson & Company Ltd.
185 Fleet St.
London EC4A 2HS, United Kingdom
Phone: 44 20 74001030
Fax: 44 20 78319440
Publications: Animals and You (53946) • Shout Magazine (55235)

Dabbagh Information Technology
PO Box 60934
Dubai, United Arab Emirates
Phone: 971 4 2240700
Fax: 971 4 2240750
Publications: PC Magazine Middle & Near East (51652)

Daehne Verlag GmbH
PO Box 100 250
D-76256 Ettlingen, Germany
Phone: 49 724 35750
Fax: 49 724 3575200
Publications: DIY (44349) • Pet in Europe (44350)

Dag Hammarskjold Foundation
Ovre Slottsgatan 2
S-753 10 Uppsala, Sweden
Phone: 46 184 101000
Fax: 46 181 22072
Publications: Development Dialogue (51051)

Daily Champion
PO Box 2276
Oshodi, Lagos, Nigeria
Phone: 234 145 25807
Fax: 234 145 24421
Publications: Daily Champion (49159)

The Daily Dipolognon
Reyes Bldg.
Gonzales St.
Dipolog City, Philippines
Phone: 63 62 2122673
Publications: The Daily Dipolognon (49487)

The Daily Star
Marine Twr., 6th Fl.
Rue de La Ste. Famille
Gemaizeh, Achrafieh
Beirut, Lebanon
Phone: 961 1 587277
Fax: 961 1 561333
Publications: The Daily Star (Lebanon) (47394)

The Daily Star
19 Karwan Bazar
Dhaka 1215, Bangladesh
Phone: 880 281 24944
Fax: 880 281 25155
Publications: The Daily Star (42808)

Daily Thanthi
86, E.V.K. Sampath Rd.
Vepary
Chennai 600 007, Tamil Nadu, India
Phone: 91 442 6618661
Fax: 91 442 6618797
Publications: Daily Thanthi (45030)

Daily Times
41-N, Industrial Area
Gulberg II
Lahore, Pakistan
Phone: 92 42 5878614
Fax: 92 42 5878620
Publications: Daily Times (49384)

Daily Zamboanga Times
Mayor Jaldon St.
Canelar
Zamboanga City, Philippines
Publications: Daily Zamboanga Times (49647)

Dainik Bhaskar
6, Dwarka Sadan, Press Complex
Bhopal 462 011, Madhya Pradesh, India
Phone: 91 755 3988884
Fax: 91 755 270466
Publications: Dainik Bhaskar (45006)

Dairy UK
93 Baker St.
London W1U 6QQ, United Kingdom
Phone: 44 20 74867244
Fax: 44 20 74874734
Publications: Milk Industry (53383)

Dalriada Celtic Heritage Trust
2 Brathwic Pl.
Brodick
Isle of Arran KA27 8BN, United Kingdom
Phone: 44 17 70302431
Fax: 44 17 70302431
Publications: Dalriada (53662)

Dance Aotearoa New Zealand
Wellington Arts Ctr.
Ground Fl., 69 Abel Smith St.
PO Box 9885
Wellington 6141, New Zealand
Phone: 64 801 9885
Publications: DANZ (49006)

Dancing Times Ltd.
45-47 Clerkenwell Green
London EC1R 0EB, United Kingdom
Phone: 44 20 72503006
Fax: 44 20 72536679
Publications: Dance Today! (54310) • Dancing Times (54311)

Danish Association for International Cooperation - Denmark
Faelledvej 12
DK-2200 Copenhagen K, Denmark
Phone: 45 773 10000
Fax: 45 773 10101
Publications: Kontakt (43678)

Danish Medical Association
Trondhjemsgade 9
DK-2100 Copenhagen, Denmark
Phone: 45 354 48500
Fax: 45 354 48503
Publications: Bibliotek for Laeger (43656) • Danish Medical Bulletin (43660) • Ugeskrift for Laeger (43685)

Danish National Association for Building
Vimmelskaftet 47/1
DK-1161 Copenhagen, Denmark
Phone: 45 331 36637
Fax: 45 339 37890
Publications: Byggeforum (43658)

Danish National Union of Upper Secondary Teachers
Vesterbrogade 16
DK-1620 Copenhagen, Denmark
Phone: 45 332 90900
Fax: 45 332 90901
Publications: Gymnasieskolen (43672)

Danish Orienteering Federation
Idraetten hus
Eroentby Statotion 20
DK-2605 Brondby, Denmark
Phone: 45 434 57730
Fax: 45 434 57790
Publications: O-Posten (43652)

Danish Shooting Union
Idraettens Hus
Brondby Stadion 20

DK-2605 Brondby, Denmark
Phone: 45 432 62626
Publications: Skyttebladet (43653)

Danish Writers Association
Strandgade 6, stuen
DK-1401 Copenhagen, Denmark
Phone: 45 329 55100
Publications: Forfatteren (43669)

Danmarks Badminton Forbund
Idraettens Hus
Brondby Stadion 20
DK-2605 Brondby, Denmark
Phone: 45 432 62152
Fax: 45 432 62150
Publications: Badminton (43651)

DANSK
Hoejbro Plads 15
DK-1200 Copenhagen K, Denmark
Phone: 45 33130444
Fax: 45 33130844
Publications: DANSK (43662)

Dansk Landbrug
Vesterbrogade 4A, 4´
Postboks 119
DK-1620 Copenhagen, Denmark
Phone: 45 333 94600
Fax: 45 333 94606
Publications: Dansk Landbrug (43663)

Dansk Samvirke
Kobmagergade 67, 2 sal.
DK-1150 Copenhagen K, Denmark
Phone: 45 33320913
Fax: 45 33325352
Publications: Danmarksposten (43661)

Dansk Transport Forlag A/S
Jernbanegade 18
DK-6330 Padborg, Denmark
Phone: 45 701 00506
Fax: 45 746 74047
Publications: Danmarks Transport-Tidende (43732) • Trans-Inform (43733)

Dar Assayad
Saeed Frayha St.
PO Box 11-1038
Beirut, Lebanon
Phone: 961 5 457261
Fax: 961 5 452700
Publications: Achabaka (47385) • Al Anwar (47386) • Al-Fares (47388) • AL IDARI (47389) • Arab Defence Journal (47391) • Assayad (47393) • Sahar (47401)

Daruma Publishing
c/o Takeguchi Momoko
Mukonoso Higashi 1-12-5
Amagasaki 661-0032, Japan
Phone: 81 664 365874
Fax: 81 664 381882
Publications: Daruma Magazine (46302)

Datateam Publishing Ltd.
15A London Rd.
Maidstone
Kent ME16 8LY, United Kingdom
Phone: 44 16 22687031
Fax: 44 16 22757646
Publications: Casino International (53676) • Footwear Today (53677) • The Independent Electrical Retailer (53678) • Printwear & Promotion (53679) • Screen Process & Digital Imaging (53680) • SGB Golf (53681)

Datateam Publishing Ltd.
15A London Rd.
Maidstone ME16 8LY, United Kingdom
Phone: 44 16 22687031
Fax: 44 16 22757646
Publications: Education Today (55529) • Stationery & Office Update (55531)

The DAWN Group of Newspapers
Haroon House
Dr. Ziauddin Ahmed Rd.
Karachi 74200, Pakistan
Phone: 92 111 444777
Fax: 92 21 5693995
Publications: Aurora (49339) • Dawn (49346) • Dawn Magazine (49347) • Herald (49353) • Images

(49354) • The Review (49375) • Spider (49376) • Star (49377) • Young World (49380)

dB Magazine
179A Hindley St.
PO Box 8260
Adelaide, South Australia 5000, Australia
Phone: 61 8 82314211
Fax: 61 8 82314393
Publications: dB Magazine (41505)

De Architect
Postbus 49
NL-2501 The Hague, Netherlands
Phone: 31 703 789911
Fax: 31 703 854321
Publications: De Architect (48611)

Walter de Gruyter GmbH & Co. KG
Genthiner Strasse 13
D-10785 Berlin, Germany
Phone: 49 302 60050
Fax: 49 302 6005251
Publications: Advances in Calculus of Variations (44148) • Advances in Geometry (44716) • Anglia (44149) • Antike und Abendland (44150) • Arbitrium (44152) • arcadia (44153) • Archiv fur Geschichte der Philosophie (44154) • Archiv fur Papyrusforschung (44155) • Aschkenas (44157) • Beitrage zur Geschichte der deutschen Sprache und Literatur (44159) • Biological Chemistry (44160) • Biomedizinische Technik (44161) • Botanica Marina (44162) • Byzantinische Zeitschrift (44164) • Clinical Chemistry and Laboratory Medicine (44165) • Der Islam (44413) • Deutsche Zeitschrift fur Wirtschafts- und Insolvenzrecht (44172) • Fabula (44178) • Folia Linguistica (44181) • Forum Mathematicum (44182) • Fruhmittelalterliche Studien (44185) • Germanistik (44186) • Holzforschung (44189) • Iberoromania (44190) • Indogermanische Forschungen (44376) • Intercultural Pragmatics (50772) • International African Bibliography (54619) • International Journal of Practical Theology (44194) • International Journal of the Sociology of Language (44195) • International Review of Applied Linguistics in Language Teaching (44196) • Internationales Archiv fur Sozialgeschichte der deutschen Literatur (44197) • Internationales Jahrbuch des Deutschen Idealismus (44198) • Jahrbuch fur Wissenschaft und Ethik (44199) • Journal of African Languages and Linguistics (44200) • Journal of Ancient Christianity (44201) • Journal of Applied Geodesy (44203) • Journal of Group Theory (56036) • Journal of Literary Semantics (JLS) (52347) • Journal of Literary Theory (44206) • Journal of Mathematical Cryptology (44207) • Journal fur die reine und angewandte Mathematik (44600) • Journal of Non-Equilibrium Thermodynamics (44208) • Journal of Perinatal Medicine (44209) • Juristische Rundschau (JR) (44327) • Kadmos (44297) • Kant-Studien (44211) • Kritikon Litterarum (44212) • Laboratoriums-Medizin (44213) • Language and Cognition (44215) • Lebende Sprachen (44218) • Liber Quarterly (48137) • Libri (44219) • Linguistic Typology (44514) • Mammalia (44220) • Microform & Imaging Review (44221) • Naharaim (44223) • Neue Zeitschrift fur Systematische Theologie und Religionsphilosophie (44224) • PIK (44226) • Praehistorische Zeitschrift (44227) • Probus (48215) • Random Operators and Stochastic Equations (51607) • Restaurator (44353) • Romanistisches Jahrbuch (44229) • Semiotica (44230) • Text & Talk (44231) • Theoretical Linguistics (44232) • Trends in Classics (44233) • Zeitschrift fur die Alttestamentliche Wissenschaft (44343) • Zeitschrift fur Antikes Christentum (44344) • Zeitschrift fur Assyriologie und Vorderasiatische Archaologie (44589) • Zeitschrift fur germanistische Linguistik (44499) • Zeitschrift fur die Neutestamentliche Wissenschaft (44273) • Zeitschrift fur Orient-Archaologie (44239) • Zeitschrift fur romanische Philologie (44240) • Zeitschrift fur Rezensionen zur germanistischen Sprachwissenschaft (44241) • Zeitschrift fur Sprachwissenschaft (44687) • Zeitschrift fur die gesamte Strafrechtswissenschaft (44694) • Zeitschrift fur Unternehmens- und Gesellschaftsrecht (ZGR) (44480)

Walter de Gruyter Inc.
545 8th Ave., Ste. 2410
New York, NY 10018-4307
Phone: 212564-9223
Fax: 212564-9224

Free: 800208-8144
Publications: Advances in Pure and Applied Mathematics (51488) • Economic Quality Control (44720) • Georgian Mathematical Journal (44133) • Groups — Complexity — Cryptology (44417) • Journal of Applied Analysis (49671)

Mouton de Gruyter
Genthiner Strasse 13
D-10785 Berlin, Germany
Phone: 49 30 260050
Fax: 49 30 26005251
Publications: Communication and Medicine (44166) • Corpus Linguistics and Linguistic Theory (44167) • Journal of Politeness Research (55483) • Linguistics (42839) • Multilingua (51076)

De Gruyter Rechtswissenschaften Verlags GmbH
Genthiner Strasse 13
D-10785 Berlin, Germany
Phone: 49 302 60050
Fax: 49 302 6005251
Publications: European Company and Financial Law Review (44174) • European Review of Contract Law (44176) • Journal of International Biotechnology Law (44205)

De La Salle University
2401 Taft Ave.
Manila 1004, Philippines
Publications: Manila Journal of Science (49553)

Deafblind International
c/o 11-13 Clifton Ter.
Finsbury Pk.
London N4 3SR, United Kingdom
Phone: 44 20 72727881
Fax: 44 20 72726012
Publications: DBI Review (54313)

DeAgostini Professionale S.p.A.
Mazzini Tree-Lined Ave., 25
I-00195 Rome, Italy
Phone: 39 632 17538
Fax: 39 632 17808
Publications: Il Fiasco (46233)

Deakin University
Faculty Of Arts
Pigdons Rd.
Geelong, Victoria 3217, Australia
Phone: 61 3 52272477
Fax: 61 3 52272001
Publications: Rural and Remote Health (41880)

Deanship of Academic Research - University of Jordan
Deanship of Academic Research
University of Jordan
Amman, Jordan
Phone: 962 653 55000
Fax: 962 653 55599
Publications: Dirasat Administrative Sciences (47152) • Dirasat Agricultural Sciences (47153) • Dirasat Engineering Sciences (47154) • Dirasat Human and Social Sciences (47155) • Dirasat Medical and Biological Sciences (47156) • Dirasat Pure Sciences (47157) • Dirasat Sharia and Law Sciences (47158)

Dedicated Systems Experts
Bergensesteenweg 421, B12
B-1600 Saint-Pieters-Leeuw, Belgium
Phone: 32 233 11284
Publications: Dedicated Systems Magazine (42911)

Defence Scientific Information & Documentation Centre
Defence Research & Development Organisation (DRDO)
Ministry of Defence, Metcalfe House
Delhi 110 054, Delhi, India
Phone: 91 122 3902482
Publications: Defence Science Journal (45090) • DESIDOC Bulletin of Information Technology (45092) • Technology Focus (45106)

Delft University Press
Nieuwe Hemweg 6B
1013 BG Amsterdam, Netherlands
Phone: 31 20 6883355
Fax: 31 20 6203419
Publications: European Journal of Transport and

Infrastructure Research (47975)

Delhi Press Patra Prakashan Ltd.
E-3 Jhandewala Estate
New Delhi 110 055, Delhi, India
Phone: 91 112 3529557
Fax: 91 112 3625020
Publications: Champak (English) (45491) • Champak (Gujarati) (45492) • Champak (Hindi) (45493) • Champak (Kannada) (45494) • Champak (Marathi) (45495) • Woman's Era (45668)

Delibros
SL. Eloy Gonzalo, 27-3
E-28010 Madrid, Spain
Fax: 34 91 5943053
Publications: Delibros (50751)

Delius Klasing Verlag GmbH
Siekerwall 21
D-33602 Bielefeld, Germany
Phone: 49 521 5590
Fax: 49 521 55988114
Publications: Tour Das Rennrad-Magazin (44584)

Democratic Action Party of Malaysia
DAP Malaysia
Ibu Pejabat Kebangsaan
Jalan Yew
55100 Kuala Lumpur, Malaysia
Phone: 60 3 92005000
Fax: 60 3 92007000
Publications: Rocket (47633)

Democratic Socialist Perspective
23 Abercrombie St., Chippendale
Sydney, New South Wales 2007, Australia
Publications: Green Left Weekly (42510)

Dempa Publications Inc.
1-11-15 Higashi Gotanda
Shinagawa-Ku
Tokyo 141-8715, Japan
Phone: 81 334 456111
Fax: 81 334 447515
Publications: Asia Electronics Industry (46753) • Journal of the Electronics Industry (46895)

Dennis Publishing Ltd.
30 Cleveland St.
London W1T 4JD, United Kingdom
Phone: 44 20 79076000
Fax: 44 20 79076020
Publications: Auto Express (53985) • Custom PC (54305) • Maxim Fashion (54916) • Octane Magazine (56881) • PokerPlayer (55098)

Dental Foundation of Ribeirao Preto
Campus Universitario - Bairro Monte Alegre
14040-010 Ribeirao Preto, Sao Paulo, Brazil
Phone: 55 16 6023952
Fax: 55 16 6023953
Publications: Brazilian Dental Journal (42995)

Dental Laboratories Association Ltd.
44-46 Wollaton Rd.
Beeston
Nottingham NG9 2NR, United Kingdom
Phone: 44 115 9254888
Fax: 44 115 9254800
Publications: Dental Laboratory (55751)

Department of Atomic Energy
Anushakti Bhavan
Chatrapathi Shivaji Maharaj Marg
Mumbai 400 001, Maharashtra, India
Phone: 91 222 2029328
Fax: 91 222 2048476
Publications: Nuclear India (45421)

Department of Classics, University of Nottingham
University Pk.
Nottingham NG7 2RD, United Kingdom
Phone: 44 115 9515151
Fax: 44 115 9513666
Publications: Digressus (55752)

Department of Criminology and Criminal Justice
Abishekapatti
Tirunelveli 627 012, Tamil Nadu, India
Publications: International Journal of Criminal Justice Sciences (IJCJS) (45753)

Department of Curriculum Studies, RAU
Rm. F211, Aldoel Bldg.
Cnr of George Storrar & Leyds St.
Groenkloof Campus
Pretoria, Republic of South Africa
Phone: 27 124 202966
Fax: 27 124 203003
Publications: Education as Change (50590)

Department of Labor and Employment
5th Fl., DOLE Bldg.
Gen. Luna St., Intramuros
Manila 1002, Philippines
Phone: 63 2 5273490
Fax: 63 2 5273448
Publications: Philippine Labor Review (49557)

Department of Peace Studies
Pemberton Bldg.
University of Bradford
Richmond Rd.
Bradford BD7 1DP, United Kingdom
Phone: 44 1274 232323
Publications: Peace, Conflict & Development (52535)

Department of Sports Medicine
Medical Faculty of Uludag University
16059 Bursa, Turkey
Phone: 90 224 4428200
Fax: 90 224 4428727
Publications: Journal of Sports Science and Medicine (JSSM) (51551)

Dept of Oriental and African Languages
PO Box 100
S-405 30 Goteborg, Sweden
Phone: 46 31 7731000
Publications: Africa & Asia (50956)

Derwent Howard
Level 7, 35 Grafton St.
Bondi Junction, New South Wales 2022, Australia
Phone: 61 2 83056900
Fax: 61 2 83056999
Publications: Australian T3 (41606) • Australian Windows XP (41607) • Creative Knitting (41608) • PlayStation 2 (41609) • Urban Hitz (41610)

Det Norske Baptistsamfunn
Micheletsvei 62c
N-1368 Stabekk, Norway
Phone: 47 67 103560
Fax: 47 67 103569
Publications: Banneret (49212)

Deutsch-Armenische Gesellschaft
Pruefeninger Str. 55
D-93049 Regensburg, Germany
Phone: 49 941 27768
Fax: 49 941 21221
Publications: Armenisch-Deutsche Korrespondenz (44642)

Deutscher Anwaltverlag GmbH
Suffering Rd., 11 Office Brussels
D-10179 Berlin, Germany
Phone: 49 307 261520
Fax: 49 307 26152
Publications: Anwaltsblatt (44151)

Deutscher Bundeswehr-Verband e.V.
Sudstrasse 123
D-53175 Bonn, Germany
Phone: 49 228 38230
Fax: 49 228 3823220
Publications: Die Bundeswehr (44254)

Deutscher Fleischer-Verband
Kennedyallee 53
D-60596 Frankfurt, Germany
Phone: 49 696 33020
Fax: 49 696 3302150
Publications: Allgemeine Fleischer Zeitung (44357)

Deutscher Landwirtschaftsverlag GmbH
Lothstrasse 29
D-80797 Munich, Germany
Phone: 49 89 127051
Fax: 49 89 12705335
Publications: Die Pirsch (44557) • DLZ Agrarmagazin (44558) • Rinderzucht/Fleckvieh (44580) • Unsere Jagd (44585)

Deutscher Psychologen Verlag GmbH
Am Kollnischen Park 2
D-10179 Berlin, Germany
Phone: 49 30 209166410
Fax: 49 30 209166413
Publications: Report Psychologie (44228)

Development Studies and Promotion Center
Jr. Leon de la Fuente No. 110
Lima 17, Peru
Phone: 51 1 6138300
Fax: 51 1 6138308
Publications: Quehacer (49425) • Resomeu Senaual (49426)

Devon County Council
County Hall
Topsham Rd.
Exeter EX2 4QR, United Kingdom
Phone: 44 845 1551020
Fax: 44 845 1551003
Publications: Devon Link (53351)

Devon Life
Archant House
Babbage Rd.
Totnes TQ9 5JA, United Kingdom
Phone: 44 18 03860910
Fax: 44 18 03860922
Publications: Devon Life (56762)

Dharitri
B - 26, Industrial Estate
PO Box 144
Bhubaneswar 751 010, Orissa, India
Phone: 91 674 2580348
Fax: 91 674 2586854
Publications: Dharitri (45009)

Di PP - NRW
Julicher Strasse 6
D-50674 Cologne, Germany
Phone: 49 221 400750
Fax: 49 221 40075180
Publications: Brains, Minds and Media (44289) • E-Learning and Education (44293) • German Risk and Insurance Review (44295) • Journal of Virtual Reality and Broadcasting (44296) • Language@internet (44298) • RT eJournal (44301) • Social Work and Society (44302)

Diabetes UK
Macleod House
10 Pky.
London NW1 7AA, United Kingdom
Phone: 44 20 74241000
Fax: 44 20 74241001
Publications: Balance (53999) • Diabetes Update (54324)

Dienas Zurnali
Mukusalas str. 41
Midlothian
LV-1004 Riga, Latvia
Phone: 371 6 7273311
Fax: 371 6 7292701
Publications: Dari Pats (47363) • Darza Pasaule (47364) • Ilustreta Junioriem (47366) • Ilustreta Pasaules Vesture (47367) • Ilustreta Zinatne (47368) • Journal of Business Ethics Education (47369) • Journal of International Business Education (47370) • Journal of Organizational Behavior Education (47371) • Legendas (47372) • Musmajas (47373) • Una (47374) • Veseliba (47375)

Dietitians Association of Australia
1/8 Phipps Close
Deakin, Australian Capital Territory 2600, Australia
Phone: 61 2 61635200
Fax: 61 2 62829888
Publications: Nutrition & Dietetics (41837)

Digital Information Research Foundation
New No. 11, Ramanujam St.
T. Nagar
Chennai 600 017, Tamil Nadu, India
Phone: 91 44 24340861
Publications: Journal of Digital Information Management (45046)

DigiTimes Publication Inc.
12F, 133, Section 4, Mingsheng E Rd.
Songshan District

Taipei 105, Taiwan
Phone: 886 2 87128866
Fax: 886 2 87123366
Publications: Digitimes (51337)

Chambre de Commerce et d'Industrie de Dijon
Pl. Jean Bouhey
BP 17440
F-21074 Dijon Cedex, France
Phone: 33 3 80659100
Fax: 33 3 80653709
Publications: Impact (43944)

Dinamalar
T.V.R. House
Dinamalar Ave.
Madurai 625 016, Tamil Nadu, India
Phone: 91 452 2380903
Fax: 91 452 2380907
Publications: Dinamalar (45336)

Dinosaur Society
PO Box 20
East Sussex
Heathfield TN21 8GY, United Kingdom
Phone: 44 14 35860881
Publications: Quarterly Journal (53551)

Diorama Publishers Ltd.
132 Syngrou Ave.
Kallithea
GR-176 71 Athens, Greece
Phone: 30 210 9214205
Fax: 30 210 9214675
Publications: Naftiliaki (44752)

Diproedisa S.L.
Javier Ferrero, 2
E-28002 Madrid, Spain
Phone: 34 915 199756
Fax: 34 914 151254
Publications: Nueva Revista (50786)

Diputacion Provincial
Hortaleza, 75
E-15917 Madrid, Spain
Phone: 34 913086066
Fax: 34 913199267
Publications: El Extramundi y los papeles de Iria Flavia (50755)

Directorate of Economics and Statistics, Rajasthan
Tilak Marg
C-Scheme
Jaipur, Rajasthan, India
Fax: 91 2229756
Publications: Statistical Abstract of Rajasthan (45199)

Dirigido por. . .
Consell de Cent, 304-2-1
E-08007 Barcelona, Spain
Phone: 34 934 876202
Fax: 34 934 880896
Publications: Dirigido (50663)

Disabled People's Association
No, 04-77 German Ctr.
25 International Business Park
Singapore 609916, Singapore
Phone: 65 68991220
Fax: 65 68991232
Publications: Integrator (50174)

Discrete Mathematics & Theoretical Computer Science
62 rue du Cardinal Mathieu
F-54000 Nancy, France
Publications: Discrete Mathematics & Theoretical Computer Science (44010)

Diskrepancija
Filozofski fakultet
Ivana Lucica 3
10000 Zagreb, Croatia
Phone: 385 1 6120000
Fax: 385 1 6156879
Publications: Diskrepancija (43567)

Distribucion Actualidad
Enrique Larreta 9 1b A
E-28036 Madrid, Spain
Publications: Distribucion Actualidad (50752)

Div. of Building Technology
Brinellvagen 34
Avdelningen for byggnadsteknik
SE-100 44 Stockholm, Sweden
Phone: 46 879 06000
Fax: 46 841 18432
Publications: Nordic Journal of Building Physics (51027)

Diverse Media Ltd.
164 Deansgate
Manchester M60 2RD, United Kingdom
Phone: 44 845 0508040
Fax: 44 161 8320870
Publications: Jobs North West (55563)

Divine Life Society
PO Shivananda Nagar
Tehri-Garhwal
Garhwal 249 192, Uttar Pradesh, India
Phone: 91 135 2430040
Fax: 91 135 2442046
Publications: Divine Life (45120)

Divya Bhaskar
280, Sarkhej-Gandhinagar Hwy.
Near YMCA Club
Ahmedabad 380 015, Gujarat, India
Phone: 91 793 9888850
Publications: Divya Bhaskar (44908)

DJ Magazine Ltd.
The Old Truman Brewery
London E1 6QL, United Kingdom
Phone: 44 20 72478855
Fax: 44 20 84170466
Publications: DJ Magazine (54336)

Djembe
Vestergade 5, 1st Fl.
DK-1456 Copenhagen K, Denmark
Phone: 45 33 918009
Publications: Djembe (43665)

DMG Business Media Ltd.
Westgate House
120/130 Station Rd.
Redhill RH1 1ET, United Kingdom
Phone: 44 17 37855000
Fax: 44 17 37855475
Publications: Furnaces International (56352) • Safety at Sea International (56378) • Speciality Chemicals Magazine (56379)

DMG World Media
Northcliffe House
2 Derry St.
London W8 5TT, United Kingdom
Phone: 44 20 79386000
Publications: Aluminium International Today (53933) • Asia Pacific Coatings Journal (53971) • Glass (54509) • Glass International (54510) • Metallurgia (54928) • World Tobacco (55425)

DMG World Media Ltd.
Equitable House Lyon Rd., Harrow
2 Derry St.
London HA1 2EW, United Kingdom
Phone: 44 20 85152000
Fax: 44 20 85152088
Publications: Communicate •(54244) • Fire International (54460)

DNG Media
96 High St.
Annan DG12 6EJ, United Kingdom
Phone: 44 1461 202078
Publications: Annandale Herald (52122) • Annandale Observer (52123) • Dumfries Courier (52124) • Moffat News (52125)

Dr. Harnisch International Publications
Blumenstrasse 15
D-90402 Nuremberg, Germany
Phone: 49 911 20180
Fax: 49 911 2018100
Publications: dedica (44608) • Element BAU (44610) • Food Marketing & Technology (44611) • Food Technologie (44612) • Getranke! Technologie & Marketing (44613) • Industrie Diamanten Rundschau (44615) • Wellness Foods Europe (44617) • WOODWORKING INTERNATIONAL (44618)

Dr. Stephen Hui Research Centre for Physical Recreation and Wellness
Kowloon Tong
Kowloon
Hong Kong, People's Republic of China
Phone: 852 34117400
Fax: 852 23387644
Publications: Asian Journal of Physical Education & Recreation (43278) • The Hong Kong Journal of Sports Medicine and Sports Science (43334)

Donna Hay Magazine
83-97 Kippax St., Level 5
Surry Hills, New South Wales 2010, Australia
Phone: 61 2 92826500
Fax: 61 2 92111541
Publications: Donna Hay Magazine (42427)

Doping Journal
Do Vostrebovania
121359 Moscow, Russia
Publications: Doping Journal (49901)

Doshisha University Center for American Studies
Graduate School of American Studies
Doshisha University
Kyoto 602-8580, Japan
Phone: 81 752 513931
Fax: 81 752 513091
Publications: Doshisha American Studies (46471)

Dove Medical Press Ltd.
Beechfield House
Winterton Way
Macclesfield SK11 0JL, United Kingdom
Phone: 44 1625 509130
Fax: 44 1625 617 933
Publications: Biologics (55514) • Clinical Interventions in Aging (55515) • Clinical Ophthalmology (55516) • International Journal of Nanomedicine (55517) • Neuropsychiatric Disease and Treatment (55518) • Therapeutics and Clinical Risk Management (55519) • Vascular Health and Risk Management (55520)

Drain Trader Ltd.
Home Farm, Unit 6-8
Quat Goose Ln.
Swindon Village
Cheltenham GL51 9RP, United Kingdom
Phone: 44 1242 576777
Fax: 44 1242 577733
Publications: The Drain Trader (52967)

Drama Australia
PO Box 15163
City East, Queensland 4002, Australia
Phone: 61 730 090664
Fax: 61 730 090668
Publications: NJ (41752)

Dream Catcher
4 Church St.
Market Rasen
Lincoln LN8 3ET, United Kingdom
Phone: 44 1673 844325
Publications: Dream Catcher (53855)

Dream Weddings Publication Philippines
94C Sct. de Guia
Diliman
Quezon City, Philippines
Publications: Dream Weddings (49590)

Driving Instructors Association
Safety House
Beddington Farm Rd.
Croydon CR0 4XZ, United Kingdom
Phone: 44 20 86655151
Fax: 44 20 86655565
Publications: Driving Instructor (53125)

Drustvo za Proucevanje Ptic in Varstvo Narave
Ptujska c. 91
SLO-2327 Racice, Slovenia
Publications: Biota (50331)

DSN Publishing
The Landsdowne Bldg.
Crowhurst Rd.
Hollingbury
Brighton BN1 8AF, United Kingdom
Phone: 44 1273 566058

Fax: 44 1273 566059
Publications: ADI News (52603)

Duke of Edinburgh's Award International Association
Award House
7-11 St. Matthew St.
London SW1P 2JT, United Kingdom
Phone: 44 20 72224242
Fax: 44 20 72224141
Publications: Award World (53994)

Duke University Press
905 W Main St., Ste. 18B
PO Box 90660
Durham, NC 27701-2054
Phone: 919688-5134
Fax: 919688-4574
Free: 888651-0122
Publications: Common Knowledge (46092) • Socialist Review (55250)

Dulwich Centre Publications Pty. Ltd.
Hutt St.
PO Box 7192
Adelaide, South Australia 5000, Australia
Phone: 61 882 233966
Fax: 61 882 324441
Publications: International Journal of Narrative Therapy and Community Work (41511)

DVS-Verlag GmbH
Aachener Strasse 172
D-40223 Dusseldorf, Germany
Phone: 49 2 1115910
Fax: 49 2 11159150
Publications: Der Praktiker (44323) • Schweissen & Schneiden (44334)

Dyflin Media Ltd.
Cunningham House, 1st Fl.
130 Francis St.
Dublin, Dublin, Ireland
Phone: 353 1 4167900
Fax: 353 1 4167901
Publications: Confetti (45951) • Irish Kitchens and Bathrooms (45979) • Prudence (45995)

Dyslexia Action
Park House
Wick Rd.
Egham TW20 0HH, United Kingdom
Phone: 44 17 84222300
Fax: 44 17 84222333
Publications: Dyslexia Review (53328)

Dyspraxia Foundation
8 West Alley
Hitchin SG5 1EG, United Kingdom
Phone: 44 1462 454986
Fax: 44 1462 455052
Publications: Dyspraxia Foundation Professional Journal (53577)

E-Beratungsjournal
Ringstrabe 48
A-3500 Krems, Austria
Phone: 43 699 19201857
Publications: e-Beratungsjournal (42728)

Eaglemoss Publications Ltd.
1st Fl., Beaumont House
Kensington Village
Avonmore Rd.
London W14 8TS, United Kingdom
Phone: 44 20 76051200
Fax: 44 20 76051201
Publications: Essential Guide to Beauty (54384) • Jackie Chan Adventures (54687)

Eaglemoss Publications Ltd
Beaumont House, 1st Fl.
Kensington Village
Avonmore Rd.
London W14 8TS, United Kingdom
Phone: 44 20 76051200
Fax: 44 20 76051201
Publications: The Classic Marvel Figurine Collection (54213) • The Country Bird Collection (54274) • Horrible Science Collection (54569) • The Lord of the Rings Collector's Models (54891) • The Magical World of Roald Dahl (54896)

Early Childhood Australia
Knox St.
PO Box 7105
Watson, Australian Capital Territory 2602, Australia
Phone: 61 2 262421800
Fax: 61 2 262421818
Publications: Australian Journal of Early Childhood (42690)

Earth Science Teachers Association
ESTA Membership Secretary
PO Box 23672
Edinburgh EH3 9XQ, United Kingdom
Publications: Teaching Earth Sciences (53323)

East African Wild Life Society
PO Box 20110
Nairobi, Kenya
Phone: 254 20 3874145
Fax: 254 20 3870335
Publications: African Journal of Ecology (47171) • SWARA (47197)

East Asian Pastoral Institute
U.P. Campus
PO Box 221
Quezon City 1101, Philippines
Phone: 63 242 65901
Fax: 63 242 66143
Publications: East Asian Pastoral Review (49591)

The East Publications Inc.
Mamiana Arc Bldg., 1F
2-1 Higashi-Azabu 3
Minato-ku
Tokyo 106-0044, Japan
Phone: 81 332243751
Fax: 81 332243754
Publications: The East (46804)

Eastern African Environmental Network
PO Box 14694-00800
Nairobi, Kenya
Phone: 254 20 3749534
Publications: NJIWA (47193)

Eastern Book Co.
34 Lalbagh
Lucknow 226 001, Uttar Pradesh, India
Phone: 91 522 4033601
Fax: 91 522 2624328
Publications: Current Central Legislation (45321) • Lucknow Law Times (45324) • Supreme Court Cases (45326) • Supreme Court Cases (Criminal) (45327) • Supreme Court Cases (Labour and Services) (45328)

Eastern Holdings Ltd.
1100 Lower Delta Rd., No. 04-01
EPL Bldg.
Singapore 169206, Singapore
Phone: 65 637 92888
Fax: 65 637 92803
Publications: Computer Era (50125) • FDM Asia (50148) • Golf (50161) • Motherhood (50219) • Motherhood Handbook (50220) • Motoring (50221) • Motoring Annual (50222) • Teens Annual (50277) • Woman's World (50288)

Eastern Media Limited
B-27, Industrial Estate, Rasulgarh
Bhubaneswar 751 010, Orissa, India
Phone: 91 674 2585351
Fax: 91 674 2588517
Publications: Sambad (45013)

Eastern Mediterranean University
Gazimagusa K.K.T.C.
Mersin, Turkey
Phone: 90 392 6301111
Fax: 90 392 3654479
Publications: Kadin/Woman 2000 (51577)

Eastern Regional Organization for Public Administration
University of the Philippines
National College of Public Administration and Governance Bld
Diliman
Quezon City 1101, Philippines
Phone: 63 2 9297789
Fax: 63 2 9297789
Publications: Asian Review of Public Administration (49585)

Eastgate Publishing Corporation
704 Prestige Tower Condominium
Ortigas Center
Pasig City 1605, Philippines
Phone: 63 2 6334004
Publications: Mabuhay (49572)

Easti Arsti Ou
Pepleri 32
EE51010 Tartu, Estonia
Phone: 37 274 27825
Fax: 37 274 27825
Publications: Journal Eesti Arst (43792)

Ebner Verlag
Karlstr. 41
D-89073 Ulm, Germany
Phone: 49 731 152002
Fax: 49 731 1520171
Publications: Klassik Uhren (44696)

ECA Publications Ltd.
Ludgate House
245 Blackfriars Rd.
London SE1 9UY, United Kingdom
Phone: 44 20 79215000
Publications: Electrical/Mechanical Contractor (54359)

L'Echo Edition
1405, route de Noves
BP 12
F-84310 Morieres Les Avignon, France
Phone: 33 490 335656
Fax: 33 490 335651
Publications: L'Echo vegetable (44009)

Eco N.V.
Lammekensraamveld 6 bus 52
B-2000 Antwerp, Belgium
Phone: 32 32933176
Fax: 32 32933180
Publications: Sparraaja (42840)

Ecole Doctorale Des Etudes Anglophones
Drewry House 213 Marsh Wall
London E14 9FJ, United Kingdom
Publications: Etudes Episteme (54388)

Ecological Society of Germany, Austria and Switzerland
c/o TU Berlin, Institute of Ecology
Rothenburgstrasse 12
D-12165 Berlin, Germany
Phone: 49 30 31471396
Fax: 49 30 31471355
Publications: Basic and Applied Ecology (44393) • Verhandlungen der Gesellschaft fur Okologie (44236)

Ecologistas en Accion
Marques of Leganes, 12
E-28004 Madrid, Spain
Phone: 34 915 312739
Fax: 34 915 312611
Publications: El Ecologista (50754)

Ecomed Verlagsgesellschaft AG & Co. KG
Unternehmensbereich ecomed Medizin
Justus-von-Liebig-Str. 1
D-86899 Landsberg, Germany
Phone: 49 622 8191125
Fax: 49 622 8191125
Publications: Journal of Soils and Sediments (44516)

Economic Society of Finland
Abo Akademi/ISES
Fanriksgatan 3B
FIN-20500 Abo, Finland
Phone: 358 2 2154587
Fax: 358 2 2154677
Publications: Journal of the Economic Society of Finland (43811)

Economics and Business Education Association
The Forum
277 London Rd.
Burgess Hill RH15 9QU, United Kingdom
Phone: 44 1444 240150
Fax: 44 1444 240161
Publications: Teaching Business & Economics (52761)

The Economics Network
8-10 Berkeley Sq.
Bristol BS8 1HH, United Kingdom

Phone: 44 11 73314347
Fax: 44 11 73314396
Publications: International Review of Economics Education (52680)

The Economist Group
25 St. James St.
London SW1A 1HG, United Kingdom
Phone: 44 20 78307000
Fax: 44 20 78392968
Publications: The Economist (54352) • European Voice (42854)

Ecosystems Ltd.
102 D Lana House Studios
116-118 Commercial St.
Spitalfield
London E1 6NF, United Kingdom
Phone: 44 20 74228100
Publications: The Ecologist (54349)

Ediciones CODA S.L.
Goya 39
E-28001 Madrid, Spain
Phone: 34 915 758324
Fax: 34 915 777047
Publications: SIC Seguridad en Informatica y Comunicaciones (50805)

Ediciones Cosmobelleza
c/o Muntaner
Entlo., 401
E-08021 Barcelona, Spain
Phone: 34 932 414690
Fax: 34 932 001544
Publications: Tocado (50702)

Ediciones y Estudios S.L.
S.L. Enrique Larreta No.5 Pi.1
E-28036 Madrid, Spain
Phone: 34 913 159845
Fax: 34 913 157419
Publications: Ipmark (50775)

Ediciones Fotograficas Argentina S.A.
Maipu 671, 5th Fl.
Buenos Aires, Argentina
Phone: 54 432 22171
Fax: 54 432 22006
Publications: Fotomundo (41472)

Ediciones de Intervencion Cultural S.L.
Sant Antoni, 86 local 9
E-08031 Mataro, Spain
Phone: 34 937 550832
Fax: 34 937 906795
Publications: El Viejo Topo (50819) • Quimera (50820)

Ediciones Mayo S.A.
Aribau, 185-187, 2 planta
E-08021 Barcelona, Spain
Phone: 34 932 090255
Fax: 34 932 020643
Publications: El Farmaceutico (50667) • El Farmaceutico Hospitales (50668) • Forum (50674) • Siete Dias Medicos (50699)

Ediciones Prensa y Video, S.L.
Plz. de las Navas, 11
E-08004 Barcelona, Spain
Phone: 34 93 292 5840
Fax: 34 93 292 5841
Publications: Peluquerias Hair Styles (50693)

Ediciones SPA S.L.
Antonio Lopez 249, 1
Edificio Vertice
E-28041 Madrid, Spain
Phone: 34 915 002077
Fax: 34 915 002075
Publications: Gerokomos (50762)

Edinburgh University Press
22 George Sq.
Edinburgh EH8 9LF, United Kingdom
Phone: 44 131 6504218
Fax: 44 131 6503286
Publications: Africa (53248) • Ben Jonson Journal (53255) • Comparative Critical Studies (54249) • Corpora (53266) • Dance Research (53267) • Deleuze Studies (53268) • Derrida Today (53269) • The Edinburgh Law Review (53271) • Episteme (53272) • Holy Land Studies (56643) • Innes Review (53286) •

International Journal of Humanities and Arts Computing (53288) • International Research in Children's Literature (53290) • Journal of Arabic and Islamic Studies (53291) • Journal of British Cinema and Television (53292) • Journal of Qur'anic Studies (53294) • Journal of Scottish Philosophy (53295) • Oxford Literary Review (53304) • Paragraph (53305) • Psychoanalysis and History (53307) • Romanticism (53308) • Scottish Archaeological Journal (53312) • Scottish Historical Review (53316) • Studies in World Christianity (53321) • Surgeons' News (53322) • Translation & Literature (53455) • World Structure (53324)

Edipresse Asia
6th Fl., Guardian House
32 Oi Kwan Rd.
Hong Kong, People's Republic of China
Phone: 11 852 25477117
Fax: 11 852 28582671
Publications: Beijing Tatler (43172) • The Best of Singapore (50114) • Coutoure (43295) • Elite Homes (43298) • Essential Guide to Home & Decor (51420) • Expat Society (51421) • Home Journal (43317) • Home Journal Buyer's Guide (43318) • Hong Kong Business (43321) • Hong Kong Tatler (43346) • Luxe Living Kitchens & Bathrooms (43364) • Macau Tatler (43365) • Macau Tatler Best Restaurants (43366) • Malaysia Society (47612) • Malaysia Tatler (43367) • Malaysia's Best Restaurants (47622) • Philippine Society (49522) • Philippine Tatler (49523) • Philippines' Best Restaurants (49524) • Phuket Tatler (51429) • Regional Best Restaurants (50242) • Shanghai Tatler (43502) • Shanghai's Best Restaurants (43505) • Singapore Tatler (50262) • Singapore Tatler Homes (50263) • Singapore Tatler Society (50264) • Singapore Tatler Weddings (50265) • Singapore's Best Restaurants (50267) • Sparkle (43383) • Taiwan Tatler (51366) • Thai Spas (51440) • Thailand Society (51442) • Thailand Tatler (51443) • Thailand's Best Restaurants (51444) • Yachtstyle (43512)

Edipresse Publications S.A.
Av. de la Gare 33
CH-1001 Lausanne, Switzerland
Phone: 41 21 3494545
Fax: 41 21 3494110
Publications: Atelier Rundschau (49879) • Avantaje (49831) • Bilan (51183) • Chwila rozrywki (49704) • Clara Deco (50658) • Coches de Ocasion (50736) • Cosas de Cocina (50661) • Cuerpomente (50662) • Diana Creative (49892) • Diana Moden (49893) • Dom & Wnetrze (49705) • Edinstvennaya (51594) • Edinstvennaya - Tvoye Zdorovye (51595) • El Jueves (50669) • El Mueble (50670) • El Mueble Casas de Campo (50671) • El Mueble Cocinas y Banos (50672) • Elle Decoration (49835) • Elle Mariaj (49836) • Femina Fashion (51189) • Geneve Home Informations (51097) • Guia del Comprador de Casas (50763) • Guia del Comprador de Coches (50764) • Guia del Comprador de Furgonetas y Autocaravanas (50765) • Guia del Comprador de Ordenadores y Software (50766) • Haroshye Raditeli (51597) • Historia National Geographic (50679) • Hot Moda & Shopping (49716) • Industria Mody (49917) • Intamplari Adevarate (49838) • International Textiles (49921) • Iren (49922) • Journal de Morges (51213) • Knit&Mode (49932) • Kollektsia Idei (49933) • Kulinarny Practicum (49934) • La Broye (51220) • Labores del Hogar (50682) • Lausanne-Cites (51193) • Le Matin (51195) • Le Matin (51194) • Le Matin Dimanche (51196) • Le Temps (51153) • Lecturas (50683) • Lecturas Cocina Facil (50684) • Lecturas Especial Cocina (50685) • Lecturas Moda (50686) • Lena Rukodelie (49937) • Linea Saludable (50687) • Lucru de Mana (49839) • Lyubimaya Datcha (51601) • Malenkaya Diana (49939) • Mama I ya (51602) • Mama, eto ya! (49940) • Mamo, to ja (49735) • Natalia (49947) • Party Celebrity lives (49745) • Patrones (50691) • Polina (51604) • Povestea Mea (49841) • Prawdziwe Zycie (49757) • Privatnyi Dom (51605) • Przedszkolak (49758) • Przekroj (49759) • Przyjaciolka (49760) • Psychologies (49842) • Russian Art (49971) • Sabrina (49986) • Sabrina Baby (49987) • Samaya (49988) • Speak Up (50701) • Susanna Rukodeliye (49993) • Susanna Vjazanie (49994) • Tele top matin (51200) • Top Auto (50812) • Tribune des Arts (51161) • Tribune de Geneve (51162) • TV Ekran (51609) • Tvoy Malysh (51610) • 24 Heures (51202) • Twoj Maluszek

(49769) • Twoje dziecko (49770) • Uczucia i tesknoty (49771) • Uroda (49772) • Uyutnaya Kvartira (51611) • Veselye Ideiki (51612) • Viajes National Geographic (50706) • Vita (49774) • Viva! Beauty (51613) • Viva! Biographia (51614) • Vjazanie Vashe Hobby (49998) • Vyshitye Kartiny (49999) • Young Lady (51615)

Editions DIASSE S.P.R.L.
Rue d'Opprebais 16
B-1360 Maleves-Sainte-Marie-Wastines, Belgium
Phone: 32 10 888898
Fax: 32 10 889934
Publications: Infor Marechalerie/European Farriers Journal/Der Huf (42903)

Editions Rodopi B.V.
Tijnmuiden 7
NL-1046 AK Amsterdam, Netherlands
Phone: 31 206 114821
Fax: 31 204 472979
Publications: At the Interface/Probing the Boundaries (53399) • Contemporary Pragmatism (47940) • Critical Approaches to Ethnic American Literature (50848) • European Joyce Studies (51258) • German Monitor (47999) • Grazer Philosophische Studien (48005) • Intercultural Theology and Study of Religions (48023) • Language and Computers (44370) • Ludus (42904) • Matatu (48142) • Nature, Culture and Literature (48170) • Polish Analytical Philosophy (48208) • SCROLL (53451) • Spatial Practices (55612) • Utrecht Studies in Language and Communication (48268) • Variants (48269)

Editions Techniques et Economiques
19 rue du Banquier
F-75013 Paris, France
Phone: 33 1 55426130
Fax: 33 1 55426139
Publications: Revue de l'Energie (44080)

Editore Argo S.R.L.
Circonvaliazione Nomentana 212/214
I-00162 Rome, Italy
Phone: 39 6 8606129
Fax: 39 6 8606324
Publications: L'Orologio (46239)

Editorial Agricola Espanola S.A.
Caballero de Gracia, 24
E-28013 Madrid, Spain
Phone: 34 91 5211633
Fax: 34 91 5224872
Publications: Agricultura (50725)

Editorial America Iberica S.A.
Miguel Yuste, 33 bis
E-28037 Madrid, Spain
Phone: 34 913 277950
Fax: 34 913 044746
Publications: Quercus (50794)

Editorial Archipielago
Cardener, 23 LOW IZDA
E-08024 Barcelona, Spain
Phone: 34 932 108503
Fax: 34 932 108503
Publications: Archipielago (50649)

Editorial Board of China's Refractories
43 Xiyuan Rd.
Luoyang 471039, People's Republic of China
Fax: 86 379 64205961
Publications: China's Refractories (43452)

Editorial Grao
Hurtado 29
E-08022 Barcelona, Spain
Phone: 34 934 080464
Fax: 34 933 524337
Publications: Aula (50652)

Editorial Pablo Iglesias
Monte Esquinza, 30-2
E-28010 Madrid, Spain
Phone: 34 913 104313
Fax: 34 913 194585
Publications: Leviatan (50778) • Zona Abierta (50817)

Editoriale Domus S.p.A.
Via. Gianni Mazzocchi 1/3
I-20089 Rozzano, Italy
Publications: Autopro (46247) • Domus (46248) • Domus Kit (46249) • Il Cucchiaio D'Argento (46250) •

Meridiani (46251) • Quattroruote (46252) • Ruoteclassiche (46253) • Tuttotrasporti (46254) • Tuttoturismo (46255) • Vendo & Compro (46256) • Volare (46257)

Editoriale di Foto Shoe S.R.L.
Via. Leonardo da Vinci 43
I-20090 Trezzano Sul Naviglio, Italy
Phone: 39 02 4459091
Fax: 39 02 48402959
Publications: Foto Shoe 15 International (46263) • Foto Shoe 30 (46264)

Editoriale Genesis S.R.L.
via Vincenzo Monti 15
I-20123 Milan, Italy
Phone: 39 2 4819 4401
Fax: 39 2 4800 2708
Publications: Prima Comunicazione (46191)

Editoriale Tuttoscuola SRL
Via. Della Scrofa 39
00186 Rome, Italy
Phone: 39 6 68307851
Fax: 39 6.68802728
Publications: Tuttoscuola (46244)

The Editors Desk Proprietary Ltd.
The Summit
163 City Rd.
Southbank, Victoria 3006, Australia
Phone: 61 3 96459887
Fax: 61 3 96459882
Publications: Plastics News International (42380)

Editrice Il Campo
Via. Amendola 11
I-40121 Bologna, Italy
Phone: 39 512 55544
Fax: 39 512 55360
Publications: Il Nuovo Club (46127) • Piscine Oggi (46128)

Editrice Il Sole
Via Monte Rosa 91
I-20149 Milan, Italy
Publications: Sole 24ore (46195)

Edizione L'Informatore Agrario S.p.A.
Via. Bencivenga/Biondani 16
I-37133 Verona, Italy
Phone: 39 458 057511
Fax: 39 455 97510
Publications: L'Informatore Agrario (46280) • Vita in Campagna (46281)

Edizioni dell' Orso
Via Urbano Rattazzi n. 47
I-15100 Alessandria, Italy
Phone: 39 131 252349
Fax: 39 131 257567
Publications: Artifara (46116)

Edizioni Minerva Medica
C. So Bramante 83-85
I-10126 Turin, Italy
Phone: 39 116 78282
Fax: 39 116 74502
Publications: Acta Vulnologica (46268)

Edizioni Monografie S.R.L.
Casella Postale 2118
I-00100 Rome, Italy
Phone: 39 651 80534
Fax: 39 651 00013
Publications: Aeronautica & Difesa (46220)

EDP Sciences
17 Ave. du Hoggar
Parc d'activites de Courtaboeuf
BP 112
F-91944 Les Ulis, France
Phone: 33 1 69187575
Fax: 33 1 69288491
Publications: Agronomy for Sustainable Development (43917) • Annales de Physique (44118) • Annals of Forest Science (43929) • Apidologie (43964) • Aquatic Living Resources (44011) • Astronomy & Astrophysics (44027) • Environmental Biosafety Research (43475) • Europhysics News (44044) • Hydroecologie appliquee (43965) • Materiaux & Techniques (43966) • Mecanique & Industries (44071) • Natures Sciences Societes (43927) • Quadrature (43967) • Radioprotection (43955)

Education International
5, Blvd. du Roi Albert II, 8th Fl.
B-1210 Brussels, Belgium
Phone: 32 2 2240611
Fax: 32 2 2240606
Publications: Worlds of Education (42875)

Educational Institute of Scotland, Edinburgh
46 Moray Pl.
Edinburgh EH3 6BH, United Kingdom
Phone: 44 13 12256244
Fax: 44 13 12203151
Publications: Scottish Educational Journal (53313)

EEMA European Forum for Electronic Business
Midsummer House
Earls Common Rd.
Stock Green
Worcester B96 6SY, United Kingdom
Phone: 44 13 86793028
Fax: 44 13 86793268
Publications: EEMA Briefing (56961)

EFY Enterprises Private Ltd.
D-87/1
Okhla Industrial Area Phase-I
New Delhi 110 020, Delhi, India
Phone: 91 11 26810601
Fax: 91 11 26817563
Publications: Electronics For You (45506) • Facts for You (45511)

E.G. Enterprises Ltd.
Apt. 41
Surrey
East Molesey KT8 9AU, United Kingdom
Phone: 44 20 89431229
Fax: 44 20 89779882
Publications: Stitch with the Embroiders' Guild (53240)

Ege University
Fen Fakultesi Dekanligi
Bornova
TR-35100 Izmir, Turkey
Phone: 90 232 3881092
Fax: 90 232 3881036
Publications: Journal of the Faculty of Science, Ege University, Series A (51574)

Egmont Magazines
184-192 Drummond St., 4th Fl.
London NW1 3HP, United Kingdom
Phone: 44 20 73806430
Publications: Daisy (54308) • Disney Fairies (54332) • Disney and Me (54333) • Fireman Sam (54461) • GO Girl (54515) • Noddy (55007) • Power Rangers (55112) • Thomas & Friends (55314)

Egypt Today
3a Rd. 199
IBA Media Bldg.
Degla, Maadi
Cairo, Egypt
Phone: 20 2 27555000
Fax: 20 2 27555050
Publications: Business Today Egypt (43752) • Egypt Today (43755)

Egyptian Computer Society
Nasr City
PO Box 9009
Cairo, Egypt
Phone: 20 2 2608182
Fax: 20 2 2603880
Publications: Egyptian Journal of Computer Science (43759)

Eireann Healthcare Publications
122 Lower Baggot St.
Dublin IRL-2, Dublin, Ireland
Phone: 353 147 53300
Fax: 353 166 24927
Publications: CancerWise (45950) • DiabetesWise (45953) • HeartWise (45963) • Irish Psychiatrist (45984) • OsteoWise (45993)

E.J. Brill
PO Box 9000
NL-2300 PA Leiden, Netherlands
Phone: 31 715 353500
Fax: 31 715 317532
Publications: Journal of Asian and African Studies (48689) • Mnemosyne (48712)

EJSE International Ltd.
Dept. of Civil & Environmental Engineering
University of Melbourne
Melbourne, Victoria 3052, Australia
Publications: Electronic Journal of Structural Engineering (42058)

Ekoloji
Murselpasa Bulvari 1265 Sokak No. 10/10
Basmane-Konak-Izmir, Pk. 63
TR-35230 Izmir, Turkey
Phone: 90 232 4459999
Fax: 90 232 4453131
Publications: Ekoloji (51573)

El Ciervo 96 S.A.
Calvet, 56
E-08021 Barcelona, Spain
Phone: 34 932 005145
Publications: El Ciervo (50666)

El Croquis
Avda. De los Reyes Catolicas, 9
E-28280 Madrid, Spain
Phone: 34 918 969410
Fax: 34 918 969411
Publications: El Croquis (50753)

El Rotario de Chile
Casilla 413
Los Angeles, Chile
Phone: 56 46 43363178
Fax: 56 46 43363350
Publications: El Rotario de Chile (43140)

El Rotario Peruano
c/o Juan Scander Juayeq
Los Sauces 312, Santa Victoria
Chiclayo, Peru
Phone: 51 74 227127
Fax: 51 74 233651
Publications: El Rotario Peruano (49418)

El Universal, Compania Periodistica Nacional S.A. de C.V.
Bucareli 8
Mexico City, Federal District, Mexico
Phone: 52 570 91313
Publications: El Universal (47784)

Electoral Institute of Southern Africa
14 Park Rd.
PO Box 740
Johannesburg 2006, Republic of South Africa
Phone: 27 113 816000
Fax: 27 114 826163
Publications: Journal of African Elections (50530)

Electric Railway Society
17 Catherine Dr.
Sutton Coldfield B73 6AX, United Kingdom
Publications: The Electric Railway (56694)

The Electrical and Electronics Association of Malaysia
No. 5-B Jalan Gelugor
Off Jalan Kenanga
55200 Kuala Lumpur, Malaysia
Phone: 60 392 214417
Fax: 60 392 218212
Publications: Suara TEEAM (47636)

Electrical World
PO Box 5023
Sydney, New South Wales 2261, Australia
Phone: 61 2 43881186
Fax: 61 2 43886614
Publications: Electrical World (42502)

Electronic Design Automation Ltd.
63-66 Hatton Garden
London EC1N 8SR, United Kingdom
Phone: 44 20 76811000
Fax: 44 20 72425124
Publications: Prototype (55147)

Electronic Journal of Theoretical Physics
PO Box 48210
Abu Dhabi, United Arab Emirates
Publications: Electronic Journal of Theoretical Physics (51619)

Electronics and Telecommunications Research Institute
138 Gajeongno, Yuseong-Gu

Daejeon 305-700, Republic of Korea
Phone: 82 42 8606127
Fax: 82 42 8606737
Publications: ETRI Journal (47226)

Electronique International Hebdo
12 rue d'Oradour sur Glane
F-75015 Paris Cedex 15, France
Publications: Electronique International Hebdo (44039)

Electrophysiological Technologists' Association
Carbis
55 Tennal Rd.
Birmingham B32 2JD, United Kingdom
Publications: Journal of Electrophysiological Technology (52346)

Elektronik Report
Dresdner Strasse 45
A-1200 Vienna, Austria
Phone: 43 1 97000100
Fax: 43 1 970005100
Publications: Elektronik Report (42750)

Elite Publishing
PO Box 800
Templestowe, Victoria 3106, Australia
Phone: 61 3 98441728
Fax: 61 3 98445300
Publications: FB Magazine (42616) • Promotional Products Magazine (42617) • Supplier Woodworking magazine (42618)

Elsevier
The Blvd., Langford Ln.
Kidlington OX5 1GB, United Kingdom
Phone: 44 1865 843000
Fax: 44 1865 843010
Publications: Acta Ecologica Sinica (53688) • Acta Mathematica Scientia (53689) • Complementary Therapies in Medicine (53349) • Computers in Human Behavior (53690) • Food and Chemical Toxicology (53692) • The History of the Family (53693) • International Journal of Law, Crime and Justice (53694) • International Journal of Project Management (53236) • Journal of Adolescence (53695) • Journal of Cranio-Maxillofacial Surgery (53696) • Journal of Environmental Management (53697) • Journal of Environmental Sciences (53698) • Journal of Historical Geography (53699) • Journal of Reproductive Immunology (53700) • Journal of Rural Studies (53701) • Journal of Rural Studies (53362) • Long Range Planning (42763) • Materials Today (53702) • Particuology (43212) • Psychology of Sport and Exercise (55487) • Radiotherapy and Oncology (43650) • Science & Justice (53706) • The Surgeon (53707) • Transportation Research Part E (53708)

Elsevier
23 rue Linois
F-75724 Paris Cedex 15, France
Phone: 33 171 724646
Fax: 33 171 724664
Publications: Acta Astronautica (44020) • Annales Francaises d'Anesthesie et de Reanimation (44025) • Combustion and Flame (44033) • Transfusion Clinique et Biologique (44086)

Elsevier Advanced Technology
The Blvd., Langford Ln.
Kidlington OX5 1GB, United Kingdom
Phone: 44 1865 843638
Fax: 44 1865 843973
Publications: Metal Powder Report (53703) • Reinforced Plastics (53705)

Elsevier Science
PO Box 211
NL-1000 AE Amsterdam, Netherlands
Phone: 31 204 853757
Fax: 31 204 853432
Publications: ACC Cardiosource Review Journal (47875) • Accident Analysis & Prevention (47876) • Acta Histochemica (55860) • Acta Psychologica (47879) • Acta Tropica (47880) • Advanced Engineering Informatics (47881) • Advanced Powder Technology (46466) • Advances in Colloid and Interface Science (47882) • Advances in Space Research (47883) • Aerospace Science and Technology (47884) • Agricultural Systems (47885) • Agriculture, Ecosystems & Environment (47886) • Annals of the ICRP (51008) • Behavioural Brain Research (44321) • Behavioural Processes (43943) • Best Practice & Research Clinical Anesthesiology (44597) • Best Practice & Research Clinical Endocrinology & Metabolism (47903) • Best Practice & Research Clinical Hematology (47904) • Best Practice & Research Clinical Obstetrics & Gynecology (54013) • Best Practice & Research Clinical Rheumatology (56773) • Biochemical Engineering Journal (55544) • Biochimica et Biophysica Acta (BBA) (47906) • Biochimica et Biophysica Acta (BBA)-General Subjects (47907) • Biochimica et Biophysica Acta (BBA)-Molecular Basis of Disease (47908) • Biochimica et Biophysica Acta (BBA)-Molecular and Cell Biology of Lipids (47909) • Biochimica et Biophysica Acta (BBA)-Proteins & Proteomics (47910) • Bioelectrochemistry (47911) • Biological Conservation (53869) • Brain Research Bulletin (47914) • Building and Environment (47917) • Bulletin des Sciences Mathematiques (47918) • Carbohydrate Polymers (47921) • Catena (44553) • Cellular Signalling (53412) • Cement and Concrete Composites (47924) • Cement and Concrete Research (51185) • Ceramics International (47925) • Chemical Engineering Journal (47926) • Chemical Physics Letters (55906) • Chemie der Erde / Geochemistry (44487) • Chemistry and Physics of Lipids (44899) • Chemosphere (47927) • Chinese Astronomy and Astrophysics (43453) • Clinica Chimica Acta (42882) • Clinical Therapeutics (47928) • Cognitive Development (47929) • Cognitive Systems Research (47931) • Colloids and Surfaces A (41670) • Communications in Nonlinear Science and Numerical Simulation (47932) • Composite Structures (47933) • Composites Part A (47934) • Computational Biology and Chemistry (55500) • Computational Materials Science (44112) • Computational Statistics & Data Analysis (47935) • Cretaceous Research (47941) • Critical Reviews in Oncology/Hematology (51174) • Current Biology (47943) • Current Opinion in Biotechnology (47944) • Current Opinion in Cell Biology (47945) • Current Opinion in Chemical Biology (47946) • Current Opinion in Genetics & Development (47947) • Current Opinion in Microbiology (47948) • Current Opinion in Plant Biology (47949) • Current Problems in Cancer (47950) • Desalination (47953) • Design Studies (55633) • Developmental & Comparative Immunology (47955) • Differential Geometry and its Applications (43604) • Dyes and Pigments (47960) • Electric Power Systems Research (47963) • Energy and Buildings (50082) • Environmental & Experimental Botany (47968) • European Management Journal (47976) • Fire Safety Journal (53276) • Flow Measurement and Instrumentation (50981) • Forest Ecology and Management (47988) • Forest Policy and Economics (44398) • Free Radical Biology and Medicine (47990) • Future Generation Computer Systems (47995) • Fuzzy Sets and Systems (44120) • Geotextiles and Geomembranes (47997) • Geothermics (47998) • Global Environmental Change (48002) • Global and Planetary Change (48003) • Habitat International (48008) • Hearing Research (48009) • Heart, Lung and Circulation (48010) • History of European Ideas (52612) • HOMO - Journal of Comparative Human Biology (41506) • Human Movement Science (48014) • Human Resource Management Review (48015) • Information Economics and Policy (48019) • Information Processing & Management (48020) • Inorganic Chemistry Communications (46205) • Insurance (51192) • International Journal of Applied Earth Observation and Geoinformation (48593) • International Journal of Industrial Organization (48028) • International Journal of Machine Tools and Manufacture (52343) • International Journal of Mechanical Sciences (48030) • International Journal of Multiphase Flow (46076) • International Journal of Pharmaceutics (48031) • International Journal of Pressure Vessels and Piping (53470) • Japan and the World Economy (48035) • Journal of Accounting and Economics (48036) • Journal of Accounting and Public Policy (48037) • Journal of African Earth Sciences (50593) • Journal of Alloys and Compounds (48040) • Journal of Analytical and Applied Pyrolysis (48043) • Journal of Applied Developmental Psychology (48045) • Journal of Applied Geophysics (48046) • Journal of Applied Mathematics and Mechanics (48047) • Journal of Arid Environments (48049) • Journal of Asian Earth Sciences (48050) • Journal of Asian Economics (48051) • Journal of Autoimmunity (48053) • Journal of Business Research (48054) • Journal of Business Venturing (48055) • Journal of Cereal Science (48056) • Journal of Chemical Health and Safety (48057) • Journal of Chemical Neuroanatomy (48738) • The Journal of Chemical Thermodynamics (48058) • Journal of Chromatography A (48059) • Journal of Computational and Applied Mathematics (42900) • Journal of Constructional Steel Research (53493) • Journal of Cultural Heritage (48066) • Journal of Development Economics (48067) • Journal of Economic Dynamics and Control (42528) • Journal of Economic Psychology (48070) • Journal of English for Academic Purposes (48072) • Journal of Ethnopharmacology (48697) • Journal of the European Ceramic Society (56031) • Journal of Fluency Disorders (48078) • Journal of Fluorine Chemistry (46897) • Journal of Forest Economics (51046) • Journal of Geochemical Exploration (46201) • Journal of Geodynamics (48081) • Journal of Geometry and Physics (46265) • Journal of Hazardous Materials (48082) • Journal of Human Evolution (48085) • Journal of Loss Prevention in the Process Industries (48092) • Journal of Marine Systems (44648) • Journal of Materials Processing Technology (48094) • Journal of Medieval History (56574) • Journal of Molecular Biology (48097) • Journal of Molecular Graphics and Modeling (55764) • Journal of Molecular Liquids (48098) • Journal of Neurolinguistics (48102) • Journal of Neuroscience Methods (52935) • Journal of Non-Newtonian Fluid Mechanics (48103) • Journal for Nurse Practitioners (48105) • Journal of Organometallic Chemistry (48106) • Journal of Pharmaceutical and Biomedical Analysis (44135) • Journal of Pharmacological and Toxicological Methods (54797) • Journal of Phonetics (48109) • Journal of Physiology - Paris (43956) • Journal of Policy Modeling (48111) • Journal of Power Sources (48112) • Journal of Pragmatics (43730) • Journal of Proteomics (48113) • Journal of Sea Research (48115) • Journal of Sound and Vibration (48117) • The Journal of Steroid Biochemistry and Molecular Biology (48118) • Journal of Stored Products Research (53329) • Journal of Structural Geology (44541) • Journal of Substance Abuse Treatment (JSAT) (48120) • Journal of Systems and Software (48123) • Journal of Terramechanics (48124) • Journal of The Franklin Institute (48125) • Journal of Thermal Biology (53230) • Journal of Transport Geography (55568) • Journal of Virological Methods (54833) • Journal of Visual Languages and Computing (48129) • Journal of Volcanology and Geothermal Research (48131) • Journal of Wind Engineering & Industrial Aerodynamics (48132) • Marine Micropaleontology (47125) • Marine Policy (52936) • Marine Structures (48141) • Materials Characterization (48143) • Materials Chemistry and Physics (51327) • Materials Science and Engineering (48145) • Materials Science and Engineering (48146) • Materials Science and Engineering (48144) • Materials Science in Semiconductor Processing (48147) • Mathematical Social Sciences (48148) • Mathematics and Computers in Simulation (42865) • Matrix Biology (48149) • Meat Science (55485) • Mechanical Systems and Signal Processing (46078) • Mechanics of Materials (48150) • Mechanism and Machine Theory (44320) • Mechatronics (48151) • Membrane Technology (56096) • Microbes and Infection (48157) • Microbial Pathogenesis (48158) • Microelectronic Engineering (42901) • Microelectronics Journal (43958) • Microelectronics Reliability (50091) • Micron (44543) • Microporous and Mesoporous Materials (49203) • Microprocessors and Microsystems (50987) • Minerals Engineering (53372) • Molecular Aspects of Medicine (48162) • Molecular and Biochemical Parasitology (48163) • Molecular and Cellular Endocrinology (54946) • Molecular and Cellular Probes (48165) • Molecular Immunology (48167) • Neural Networks (48172) • Neuropharmacology (52709) • Neuropsychiatrie de l'Enfance et de l'Adolescence (48175) • Neuropsychologia (48176) • Neuroscience Letters (48177) • Neuroscience Research (48178) • Neurotoxicology and Teratology (48179) • New Astronomy (48180) • New Astronomy Reviews (48181) • Nuclear Engineering and Design (44674) • Nuclear Instruments and Methods in Physics Research Section B (43680) • Nuclear Physics A (48185) • Nuclear Physics B (48187) • Nuclear Physics B (48186) • Nurse Education Today (48188) • Nutrition (48189) • Operations Research Letters (48190) • Optical Materials (48192) • Optics Communications (48193) • Optics & Laser Technology (48194) • Optics and Lasers in Engineering (51198) • Ore Geology Reviews (48195) •

Pacific-Basin Finance Journal (48198) • Performance Evaluation (44108) • Personality and Individual Differences (55071) • Pharmacological Research (48199) • Physica A (42888) • Physica B (48200) • Physica E (48201) • Physics and Chemistry of the Earth (48202) • Physics Reports (48203) • Planetary and Space Science (48204) • Plant Physiology and Biochemistry (48205) • Plant Science (44093) • Plastics, Additives and Compounding (56162) • Poetics (48207) • Polymer (48209) • Polymer Degradation and Stability (52628) • Polymer Testing (56428) • Powder Technology (48210) • Pratiques Psychologiques (48212) • Precambrian Research (48213) • Progress in Biophysics & Molecular Biology (56170) • Progress in Crystal Growth and Characterization of Materials (56282) • Progress in Histochemistry and Cytochemistry (51065) • Progress in Materials Science (44652) • Progress in Nuclear Energy (52362) • Progress in Particle and Nuclear Physics (44693) • Progress in Planning (55575) • Progress in Retinal and Eye Research (56171) • Progress in Solid State Chemistry (44142) • Progress in Surface Science (48216) • Psychologie Francaise (48218) • Pulmonary Pharmacology and Therapeutics (55155) • Pump Industry Analyst (56180) • Quaternary Science Reviews (42706) • Radiation Physics and Chemistry (48219) • Radiography (56451) • Review of Palaeobotany and Palynology (44601) • Safety Science (48313) • Scandinavian Journal of Management (48229) • Stochastic Processes and Their Applications (48237) • Technovation (48243) • Tectonophysics (49035) • Telecommunications Policy (50967) • Telematics and Informatics (48244) • Tetrahedron (48246) • Tetrahedron (56216) • Theoretical and Applied Fracture Mechanics (43507) • Thermochimica Acta (48248) • Thin-Walled Structures (55488) • Topology (48250) • Topology and its Applications (48251) • Tourism Management (48911) • Toxicology (48252) • Toxicon (53454) • Transportation Research Part A: Policy and Practice (48254) • Transportation Research Part C (44759) • Transportation Research Part F (48255) • Trends in Analytical Chemistry (48256) • Trends in Biochemical Sciences (48257) • Trends in Biotechnology (48258) • Trends in Cell Biology (48259) • Trends in Cognitive Sciences (48260) • Trends in Ecology & Evolution (48261) • Trends in Endocrinology and Metabolism (TEM) (55339) • Trends in Food Science & Technology (48262) • Trends in Genetics (48263) • Trends in Microbiology (48264) • Trends in Neurosciences (48265) • Trends in Parasitology (48266) • Trends in Pharmacological Sciences (48267) • Tribology International (55341)

Elsevier Science B.V.
Radarweg 29
NL-1043 Amsterdam, Netherlands
Phone: 31 204 853911
Fax: 31 204 852457
Publications: American Journal of Ophthalmology (47888) • American Journal of Preventive Medicine (47889) • Anaerobe (47891) • Analytical Biochemistry (47892) • Annals of Physics (47895) • Applied and Computational Harmonic Analysis (47897) • Archives of Biochemistry and Biophysics (47898) • Atomic Data and Nuclear Data Tables (47900) • Biochemical and Biophysical Research Communications (47905) • Blood Cells, Molecules, & Diseases (47912) • Brain and Language (47913) • Cell Biology International (47923) • Cognitive Psychology (47930) • Computer Speech & Language (47936) • Computer Vision and Image Understanding (47937) • Consciousness and Cognition (47938) • Contemporary Educational Psychology (47939) • Cryobiology (47942) • Cytokine (47952) • Developmental Biology (47954) • Developmental Review (47956) • Digital Signal Processing (47958) • Ecotoxicology and Environmental Safety (47962) • Environmental Research (47970) • Epilepsy & Behavior (47972) • Evolution and Human Behavior (47977) • Experimental Cell Research (47978) • Experimental Eye Research (47979) • Experimental and Molecular Pathology (47980) • Experimental Neurology (47981) • Experimental Parasitology (47982) • Explorations in Economic History (47983) • Finite Fields and Their Applications (47986) • Food Microbiology (47987) • Frontiers in Neuroendocrinology (47991) • Fungal Genetics and Biology (47994) • Games and Economic Behavior (47996) • Graphical Models (48004) • Gynecologic Oncology (48007) • Historia Mathematica (48011) • Hormones and Behavior (48013) • International Biodeterioration and Biodegradation (48024) • International Journal of Food Microbiology (46155) • Journal of Algebra (48038) • Journal of Algorithms in Cognition, Informatics and Logic (48039) • Journal of the American College of Surgeons (48042) • Journal of Anthropological Archaeology (48044) • Journal of Approximation Theory (48048) • Journal of Colloid and Interface Science (48060) • Journal of Combinatorial Theory, Series A (48061) • Journal of Combinatorial Theory, Series B (48062) • Journal of Computational Physics (48064) • Journal of Computer and System Sciences (48065) • Journal of Differential Equations (48068) • Journal of Environmental Management (48073) • Journal of Environmental Psychology (48074) • Journal of Experimental Child Psychology (48075) • Journal of Experimental Social Psychology (48076) • Journal of Financial Intermediation (48077) • Journal of Food Composition and Analysis (48079) • Journal of Functional Analysis (48080) • Journal of Housing Economics (48084) • Journal of Invertebrate Pathology (48088) • Journal of the Japanese and International Economics (48089) • Journal of Magnetic Resonance (48093) • Journal of Mathematical Psychology (48095) • Journal of Memory and Language (48096) • Journal of Molecular Spectroscopy (48099) • Journal of Multivariate Analysis (48100) • Journal of Network and Computer Applications (48101) • Journal of Number Theory (48104) • Journal of Parallel and Distributed Computing (48107) • Journal of Research in Personality (48114) • The Journal of Socio-Economics (48116) • Journal of Structural Biology (48119) • The Journal of Supercritical Fluids (48121) • Journal of Surgical Research (48122) • Journal of Urban Economics (48126) • Journal of Visual Communication and Image Representation (48128) • Journal of Vocational Behavior (48130) • Learning and Motivation (48135) • Metabolic Engineering (48154) • Metal Finishing (48155) • Methods (48156) • Microvascular Research (48159) • Molecular and Cellular Neurosciences (48164) • Molecular Genetics and Metabolism (48166) • Molecular Phylogenetics and Evolution (48168) • Neurobiology of Disease (48173) • NeuroImage (48174) • Nitric Oxide (48182) • North American Journal of Economics and Finance (48183) • Nuclear Data Sheets (48184) • Optical Fiber Technology (48191) • Organizational Behavior and Human Decision Processes (48196) • Plasmid (48206) • Preventive Medicine (48214) • Protein Expression and Purification (48217) • Regulatory Toxicology and Pharmacology (48220) • Research in Economics (48221) • Review of Economic Dynamics (48224) • Seminars in Cell & Developmental Biology (48230) • Social Science Research (48233) • Thrombosis Research (48249) • Toxicology and Applied Pharmacology (48253)

Elsevier Science Inc.
360 Park Ave. S
New York, NY 10010-1710
Phone: 212633-3730
Fax: 212462-1974
Free: 888437-4636
Publications: AEU - International Journal of Electronics and Communications (44319) • Applied Mathematical Modelling (56699) • Applied Surface Science (46615) • Applied Thermal Engineering (56918) • Arthropod Structure & Development (44655) • Artificial Intelligence (53754) • Atmospheric Environment (55723) • Australasian Emergency Nursing Journal (41675) • Best Practice & Research (48748) • Biomedical Signal Processing and Control (56568) • Biosystems Engineering (42974) • Cancer Radiotherapie (44032) • Chemical Engineering and Processing (44315) • Chemical Physics (44378) • Chinese Journal of Catalysis (43253) • Chinese Journal of Chemical Engineering (43184) • Computer-Aided Design (48308) • Computer Science Review (50660) • Computers and Geotechnics (56700) • Computers in Industry (48599) • Continental Shelf Research (56569) • Control Engineering Practice (50587) • Crop Protection (53238) • Dendrochronologia (51082) • Ecological Modelling (43666) • Economic Systems (44643) • Electrochemistry Communications (55935) • Engineering Analysis with Boundary Elements (52145) • Engineering Applications of Artificial Intelligence (44116) • Engineering Failure Analysis (41887) • Environment International (56937) • Environmental Modelling & Software (41705) • Environmental Science & Policy (55938) • Environmental Toxicology and Pharmacology (47971) • European Economic Review (48736) • European Journal of Agronomy (50713) • European Journal of Cell Biology (44560) • European Journal of Internal Medicine (46168) • European Journal of Mechanics - A/Solids (43725) • European Journal of Mechanics - B/Fluids (43925) • European Journal of Medical Genetics (44041) • European Journal of Medicinal Chemistry (44042) • European Journal of Operational Research (53082) • European Journal of Pharmaceutical Sciences (43826) • European Journal of Pharmaceutics and Biopharmaceutics (51095) • European Journal of Political Economy (46093) • European Journal of Protistology (42737) • L'Evolution Psychiatrique (44102) • Experimental and Toxicologic Pathology (44431) • Expositiones Mathematicae (51205) • FEBS Letters (44457) • Filtration Industry Analyst (53691) • Fisheries Research (50714) • Flora (44407) • Fluid Dynamics Research (46648) • Focus on Catalysts (52821) • Food Policy (52140) • Food Quality and Preference (52671) • Fuel (55671) • Fungal Biology Reviews (53279) • Genomics, Proteomics & Bioinformatics (43194) • Gerontology and Geriatrics (44888) • Image and Vision Computing (56320) • Immunobiology (53804) • Immunology Letters (43641) • Indagationes Mathematicae (48601) • Infant Behavior and Development (48016) • Information Processing Letters (49718) • Information and Software Technology (50997) • Integration, the VLSI Journal (50834) • Interacting with Computers (55617) • Intermetallics (43196) • International Journal of Adhesion and Adhesives (52676) • International Journal of Biochemistry & Cell Biology (54635) • International Journal of Educational Development (55760) • International Journal of Electrical Power & Energy Systems (41597) • International Journal of Hygiene and Environmental Health (44250) • International Journal for Parasitology (41685) • International Journal of Production Economics (50976) • International Journal of Refractory Metals and Hard Materials (42738) • International Journal of Rock Mechanics and Mining Sciences (54661) • ISPRS Journal of Photogrammetry and Remote Sensing (48596) • Journal of Genetics and Genomics (43206) • Journal of Hydrodynamics (43527) • Journal of Informetrics (42880) • The Journal of Logic and Algebraic Programming (48091) • Journal of Mathematical Economics (44065) • Journal of Molecular Catalysis A (52690) • Journal of Molecular Catalysis B (48311) • Journal of Natural Gas Chemistry (43254) • Journal for Nature Conservation (50719) • Journal of Purchasing & Supply Management (48751) • Journal of Science and Medicine in Sport (42531) • Journal of Veterinary Cardiology (43971) • Knowledge-Based Systems (42532) • Language & Communication (56084) • Language Sciences (50620) • Limnologica (44657) • Lithos (50633) • LWT - Food Science and Technology (51274) • Mammalian Biology (44504) • Marine Environmental Research (56891) • Materials & Design (53166) • Microbiological Research (43679) • Network Security (56113) • Neurocomputing (48745) • Nuclear Science and Techniques (43491) • Optik (44311) • Option/Bio (44073) • Paediatrics & Child Health (52937) • Palaeoworld (43454) • Pedosphere (43455) • Process Biochemistry (44122) • Protist (44300) • Quaternary Geochronology (41711) • Reactive and Functional Polymers (55576) • Regulatory Peptides (44251) • Research in International Business and Finance (43379) • Research Policy (52631) • Resources, Conservation and Recycling (48765) • Respiratory Physiology & Neurobiology (44252) • Revue du Soignant en Sante Publique (44082) • Russian Literature (48228) • Scientia Horticulturae (50569) • Sedimentary Geology (48314) • Seminars in Cancer Biology (51036) • Sensors and Actuators A (48315) • Sensors and Actuators B (46546) • Signal Processing (51037) • Solid State Ionics (44679) • Solid State Nuclear Magnetic Resonance (55654) • Space Policy (55526) • Space Research Today (51077) • Spectrochimica Acta Part B (48316) • Studies in Educational Evaluation (42841) • Studies in History and Philosophy of Science Part A (52899) • Studies in History and Philosophy of Science Part C (52900) • Surface and Coatings Technology (56515) • Systematic and Applied Microbiology (44375) • Thinking Skills and Creativity (53365) • Tsinghua Science & Technology (43222) • Ultramicroscopy (52904) • Women and Birth (41691)

Elsevier Science Inc. - Japan Regional Office
9-15 Higashi-Azabu 1-chome
Minato-ku
Tokyo 106-0044, Japan
Phone: 81 335 896370
Fax: 81 335 896371
Publications: Journal of Operations Research Society of Japan (46933)

Elsevier (Singapore) Pte. Ltd.
3 Killiney Rd., No. 08-01
Winsland House 1
Singapore 239519, Singapore
Phone: 65 6 3490222
Fax: 65 6 7331510
Publications: Acta Biomaterialia (50101) • Ad Hoc Networks (50102) • Applied Soft Computing (52272) • Catalysis Communications (44646) • Chinese Medical Association Journal (50121) • Chirurgie de la Main (50122) • Comptes Rendus (50124) • Current Applied Physics (47263) • Digital Investigation (50132) • Discrete Optimization (50134) • Drug Discovery Today (50139) • Drug Discovery Today (50137) • Drug Discovery Today (50138) • Drug Discovery Today (50135) • Drug Discovery Today (50136) • Ecological Indicators (50140) • Ecological Informatics (50141) • Economics and Human Biology (44559) • Emerging Markets Review (50145) • Gene Expression Patterns (50151) • Harmful Algae (50163) • Infection, Genetics and Evolution (43978) • Information Fusion (50171) • Infosecurity (50172) • Innovative Food Science and Emerging Technologies (44191) • International Immunopharmacology (50175) • International Journal of Osteopathic Medicine (50191) • International Journal of Surgery (50193) • ITBM - RBM (50197) • Journal of Applied Logic (50198) • Journal of Discrete Algorithms (Amsterdam) (54738) • Journal of Men's Health (50209) • Journal of Pediatric Urology (50211) • Journal of Photochemistry and Photobiology, C (46936) • Optical Switching and Networking (50232) • Organic Electronics (50233) • Organisms Diversity & Evolution (44577) • Pervasive and Mobile Computing (50236) • Photodiagnosis and Photodynamic Therapy (50238) • Photonics and Nanostructures (51499) • Physics of Life Reviews (50239) • Statistical Methodology (50272) • Urban Forestry & Urban Greening (50283)

Elton John Fan Club - United Kingdom
PO Box 315
Richmond TW9 3QX, United Kingdom
Phone: 44 77 13725242
Fax: 44 87 01307752
Publications: eltonjohnworld.com (56391)

EMAP Automotive Ltd.
40 Bernard St.
London WC1N 1LW, United Kingdom
Publications: Fleet News Europe (54465)

EMAP Construct
151 Rosebery Ave.
Hampstead Rd.
London EC1R 4GB, United Kingdom
Phone: 44 207 5056600
Publications: The Architectural Review (53962)

EMAP Healthcare Ltd.
Greater London House
Hampstead Rd.
London NW1 7EJ, United Kingdom
Phone: 44 20 77285000
Publications: HSJ (54576) • Journal of Wound Care (54838)

EMAP Ltd.
Greater London House
Hampstead Rd.
London NW1 7EJ, United Kingdom
Phone: 44 20 77285000
Publications: Closer (54234) • Drapers (London) (54343) • New Woman (55001) • Zoo Weekly (55437)

EMAP Metro Ltd.
Greater London House
Hampstead Rd.
London NW1 7EJ, United Kingdom
Phone: 44 20 7728500
Publications: Empire (54365) • FHM (54449)

Embroiderers' Guild
Apt. 41 Hampton Ct. Palace

East Molesey KT8 9AU, United Kingdom
Phone: 44 20 89431229
Fax: 44 20 89779822
Publications: The World of Embroidery (53241)

Emel Media Ltd.
1 Canfield Pl.
London NW3 5HT, United Kingdom
Phone: 44 20 73287300
Publications: Emel (54363)

Emerald
Howard House
Wagon Ln.
Bingley
West Yorkshire BD16 1WA, United Kingdom
Phone: 44 1274 777700
Fax: 44 1274 785201
Publications: Aircraft Engineering and Aerospace Technology (52639) • Kybernetes (56904)

Emerald Group Publishing Ltd.
Howard House, Wagon Ln.
Bradford BD16 1WA, United Kingdom
Phone: 44 1274 777700
Fax: 44 1274 785201
Publications: Accounting, Auditing & Accountability Journal (42444) • Accounting Research Journal (52435) • Anti-Corrosion Methods & Materials (52436) • Asia Pacific Journal of Marketing and Logistics (42244) • Aslib Proceedings (53976) • Assembly Automation (53644) • Baltic Journal of Management (52437) • British Food Journal (52438) • Business Process Management Journal (50061) • Business Strategy Series (52439) • Campus-Wide Information Systems (53617) • Career Development International (52440) • Chinese Management Studies (50120) • Circuit World (55478) • Clinical Governance (52441) • Collection Building (52442) • COMPEL (52444) • Construction Innovation (52445) • Corporate Communications (52446) • Corporate Governance (52447) • Critical Perspectives on International Business (52448) • Development and Learning in Organizations (52449) • Disaster Prevention and Management (52450) • Education, Business and Society (52451) • Education Training (52452) • Electronic Library (52453) • Employee Relations (52454) • Engineering Computations (56701) • Engineering, Construction and Architectural Management (52455) • Equality, Diversity and Inclusion (52456) • European Business Review (52457) • European Journal of Innovation Management (47696) • European Journal of Marketing (52458) • Facilities (52459) • Foresight (52461) • Gender in Management (55556) • Health Education (56572) • Human Resource Management International Digest (52462) • Humanomics (52463) • Indian Growth and Development Review (45475) • Industrial and Commercial Training (52464) • Industrial Lubrication and Tribology (52465) • Industrial Management and Data Systems (52466) • Industrial Robot (53646) • Information Management & Computer Security (52467) • Information Technology & People (52468) • Interactive Technology and Smart Education (52469) • Interlending & Document Supply (52470) • International Journal of Accounting and Information Management (52473) • International Journal of Bank Marketing (52474) • International Journal of Clothing Science and Technology (53403) • International Journal of Contemporary Hospitality Management (52475) • International Journal of Educational Management (52476) • International Journal of Emerging Markets (52477) • International Journal of Energy Sector Management (53214) • International Journal of Entrepreneurial Behaviour & Research (52478) • International Journal of Health Care Quality Assurance (52479) • International Journal of Housing Markets and Analysis (42520) • International Journal of Intelligent Computing and Cybernetics (43197) • International Journal of Islamic and Middle Eastern Finance and Management (54652) • International Journal of Law and Management (53874) • International Journal of Managerial Finance (52480) • International Journal of Managing Projects in Business (42067) • International Journal of Manpower (52481) • International Journal of Numerical Methods for Heat & Fluid Flow (56702) • International Journal of Operations and Production Management (52482) • International Journal of Pervasive Computing and Communications (52483) • International Journal of Physical Distribution and Logistics Management (52484) • International

Journal of Productivity and Performance Management (52485) • International Journal of Public Sector Management (55762) • International Journal of Quality and Reliability Management (52486) • International Journal of Retail and Distribution Management (53289) • International Journal of Social Economics (52487) • International Journal of Sustainability in Higher Education (52488) • International Journal of Web Information Systems (52489) • International Journal of Wine Business Research (IJWBR) (44502) • International Marketing Review (52490) • Internet Research (52491) • Journal of Accounting and Organisational Change (52492) • Journal of Applied Accounting Research (53806) • Journal of Business Strategy (52493) • Journal of Chinese Economic and Foreign Trade Studies (43204) • Journal of Communication Management (52494) • Journal of Corporate Real Estate (52495) • Journal of Documentation (52496) • Journal of Educational Administration (52497) • Journal of Enterprise Information Management (56800) • Journal of Enterprising Communities (52498) • Journal of European Industrial Training (52499) • Journal of European Real Estate Research (53075) • Journal of Facilities Management (52500) • Journal of Fashion Marketing and Management (52501) • Journal of Financial Management of Property and Construction (56300) • Journal of Health, Organization and Management (52502) • Journal of Information, Communication & Ethics in Society (52503) • Journal of Intellectual Capital (52504) • Journal of International Trade Law and Policy (52505) • The Journal of Investment Compliance (52506) • Journal of Knowledge Management (52507) • Journal of Management Development (53097) • Journal of Management History (52508) • Journal of Managerial Psychology (52509) • Journal of Manufacturing Technology Management (52348) • Journal of Money Laundering Control (52510) • Journal of Organizational Change Management (52511) • Journal of Place Management and Development (55564) • Journal of Product & Brand Management (52512) • Journal of Property Investment & Finance (52513) • Journal of Quality in Maintenance Engineering (52514) • The Journal of Risk Finance (52515) • Journal of Service Management (52516) • Journal of Small Business and Enterprise Development (52354) • Journal of Strategy and Management (52517) • Journal of Systems and Information Technology (41974) • Journal of Workplace Learning (52518) • Leadership in Health Services (52520) • Leadership and Organization Development Journal (55702) • The Learning Organization (52521) • Library Management (52522) • Library Review (53429) • Management of Environmental Quality (52523) • Managerial Auditing Journal (52524) • Marketing Intelligence & Planning (52525) • Measuring Business Excellence (52526) • Microelectronics International (52527) • Multicultural Education & Technology Journal (53623) • Multidiscipline Modeling in Materials and Structures (52528) • New Library World (52530) • Nutrition & Food Science (56426) • OCLC Systems & Services (52532) • On the Horizon (52533) • Online Information Review (52534) • Performance Measurements and Metrics (52536) • Personnel Review (55677) • Pigment & Resin Technology (52537) • Policing (52538) • Qualitative Market Research (52539) • Qualitative Research in Accounting and Management (52540) • Qualitative Research in Organizations and Management (55160) • Quality Assurance in Education (52541) • Rapid Prototyping Journal (52542) • Records Management Journal (55678) • Reference Reviews (56997) • Sensor Review (52543) • Social Enterprise Journal (53878) • Social Responsibility Journal (53827) • Society and Business Review (52544) • Soldering & Surface Mount Technology (52545) • Strategic Direction (52546) • Strategic HR Review (52547) • Strategic Outsourcing (52548) • Structural Survey (52549) • Team Performance Management (52550) • Tourism Review (52553) • The TQM Journal (52554) • Training & Management Development Methods (52555) • Transforming Government (56801) • VINE (52556) • Young Consumers (53366)

Emergency Management Australia
601 Mt. Macedon Rd.
Mount Macedon, Victoria 3411, Australia
Phone: 61 3 54215100
Fax: 61 3 54215272
Publications: Australian Journal of Emergency Management (42133)

EMH Swiss Medical Publishers Ltd.
Farnsburgerstrasse 8
CH-4132 Muttenz, Switzerland
Phone: 41 614 678555
Fax: 41 614 678556
Publications: Schweizerische Arztezeitung/Bulletin des Medecins Suisses (51214) • Swiss Medical Weekly (51215)

Empire of India Philatelic Society
EIPS, S.A. Vijaykar & Company
1008 Raheja Center
10th Fl., Nariman Point
Mumbai 400 021, Maharashtra, India
Publications: India's Stamp Journal (45390)

Empire Publications Ltd.
1 Newton St.
Manchester M1 1HW, United Kingdom
Phone: 44 16 18723319
Fax: 44 16 18724721
Publications: Ancient Egypt (55541)

En Franquicia
Calle Alcala, 128
E-28009 Madrid, Spain
Phone: 34 913096515
Publications: En Franquicia (50756)

Endocrine Research Center
24 Parvaneh St.
Tehran 19395, Iran
Phone: 98 212 2432500
Fax: 98 212 2416264
Publications: Iranian Journal of Endocrinology and Metabolism (45901)

Energy Institute
61 New Cavendish St.
London W1G 7AR, United Kingdom
Phone: 44 20 74677100
Fax: 44 20 72551472
Publications: Energy World (54371) • Petroleum Review (55075)

The Energy and Resources Institute
Darbari Seth Block
IHC Complex, Lodhi Rd.
New Delhi 110 003, Delhi, India
Phone: 91 11 24682100
Fax: 91 11 24682144
Publications: TerraGreen (45658)

Engineering Integrity Society
18 Oak Close
Bedworth
Warwickshire CV12 9AJ, United Kingdom
Phone: 44 2476 730126
Fax: 44 2476 730126
Publications: Engineering Integrity (56858)

English Association
University of Leicester
University Rd.
Leicester LE1 7RH, United Kingdom
Phone: 44 116 2297622
Fax: 44 116 2297623
Publications: English Four to Eleven (53797) • Use of English (53832)

English Bridge Union Ltd.
Broadfields, Bicester Rd.
Aylesbury HP19 8AZ, United Kingdom
Phone: 44 12 96317200
Fax: 44 12 96317220
Publications: English Bridge (52147)

English Folk Dance and Song Society
Cecil Sharp House
2 Regents Park Rd.
London NW1 7AY, United Kingdom
Phone: 44 20 74852206
Fax: 44 20 72840534
Publications: Folk Music Journal (54476)

English Heritage
PO Box 569
Swindon SN2 2YP, United Kingdom
Phone: 44 87 03331181
Fax: 44 17 93414926
Publications: Conservation Bulletin (56710)

English Literary Society of Japan
Kenkyusha Eigo Centre Bldg.

1-2 Kagurazaka
Shinjuku-ku
Tokyo 162-0825, Japan
Phone: 81 3 52611922
Publications: Studies in English Literature (47044)

English Place-Name Society
School of English Studies
University of Nottingham
Nottingham NG7 2RD, United Kingdom
Phone: 44 11 59515919
Fax: 44 11 58467526
Publications: EPNS Journal (55755)

Enigma Magazine
15 Mahmoud Azmy St., off 26 July St.
2nd Fl., Zamalek
Cairo, Egypt
Phone: 20 2 7382554
Fax: 20 2 7367759
Publications: Enigma Magazine (43761)

Enigma Publishing Ltd.
Unit 3, Bldg. H
Apollo Technical Park
5 Orbit Dr.
Albany, New Zealand
Phone: 64 991 29106
Fax: 64 991 29101
Publications: Health Care and Informatics Review On-line (48778)

Ensign Media Co. Ltd.
K Building, 4th Fl.
22 Sukhumvit Rd., Soi 35
Wattana
Bangkok 10110, Thailand
Phone: 66 2 2607643
Fax: 66 2 2607644
Publications: Property Report Thailand (51432)

Entomological Society of Brazil
c/o Adalecio Kovaleski
Embrapa Una e Vinho
Estacao Experimental de Vacaria
Caixa Postal 1513
95200-000 Vacaria, Rio Grande do Sul, Brazil
Phone: 55 54 32321715
Publications: Anais da Sociedade Entomologica do Brasil (43052) • Neotropical Entomology (43053)

Entomological Society of Japan
National History Laboratory
Faculty of Science
Ibaraki Univ.
Mito 310-8512, Japan
Phone: 81 292 288377
Fax: 81 292 288403
Publications: Entomological Science (46513)

Entomological Society of Shinshu
Shinshu Daigaku Nogakubu Oyo
Konchugaku Kyoshitsu
8304 Kamiina-gun
Nagano 399-4598, Japan
Phone: 81 265 771400
Fax: 81 265 771400
Publications: New Entomologist (46537)

Entomological Society of Southern Africa
PO Box 13162
Hatfield 0028, Republic of South Africa
Publications: African Entomology (50521)

The Environment Council
212 High Holborn
London WC1V 7BF, United Kingdom
Phone: 44 20 78362626
Fax: 44 20 72421180
Publications: Elements (54360)

Environmental Engineering Association of Thailand
122/4 Soi Rawadee, Rama VI Rd.
Samsen Nai, Phayathai
Bangkok 10400, Thailand
Phone: 66 2 6171530
Fax: 66 2 2799720
Publications: EEAT Journal (51419)

Environmental Protection Administration
No. 83 Section 1, Jhonghua Rd.
Taipei 10042, Taiwan

Phone: 886 22 3117722
Publications: Environmental Policy Monthly (51339)

Environmental Services Association
154 Buckingham Palace Rd.
London SW1W 9TR, United Kingdom
Phone: 44 20 78248882
Fax: 44 20 78248753
Publications: Resource Management & Recovery (55192)

Environmental Technology Publications Ltd.
Oak Ct., Sandridge Pk.
Porters Wood
Saint Albans AL3 6PH, United Kingdom
Phone: 44 1727 858840
Fax: 44 1727 840310
Publications: Asian Environmental Technology (56434) • International Environmental Technology (56437)

L'Epe-Eurl El Moudjahid
20 rue de la Liberte
Algiers, Algeria
Phone: 213 2 1737081
Fax: 213 2 1739043
Publications: El Moudjahid (41460)

EPESA
Orense, 28-2C
E-28020 Madrid, Spain
Phone: 34 917 990080
Fax: 34 913 528882
Publications: IH Industria Hostelera (50768)

Ephemera Society
PO Box 112
Northwood HA6 2WT, United Kingdom
Phone: 44 19 23829079
Fax: 44 19 23825207
Publications: The Ephemerist (55720)

Epilepsy Action
New Anstey House
Gate Way Dr.
Yeadon
Leeds LS19 7XY, United Kingdom
Phone: 44 11 32108800
Fax: 44 11 33910300
Publications: Epilepsy Today (53764)

Equinox Publishing Ltd.
1 Chelsea Manor Studios
Flood St.
London SW3 5SR, United Kingdom
Phone: 44 20 78233748
Fax: 44 20 78233748
Publications: Australian Religion Studies Review (53981) • Black Theology (52331) • Buddhist Studies Review (56653) • Fieldwork in Religion (53872) • Gender and Language (54498) • Implicit Religion (54588) • International Journal of Speech, Language and the Law (54662) • Jazz Research Journal (54688) • Journal of Adult Theological Education (54696) • Journal of Applied Linguistics (54699) • Journal of Critical Realism (54733) • Journal of Mediterranean Archaeology (43596) • Linguistics and the Human Sciences (54874) • Political Theology (55099) • Popular Music History (55101) • Reformation and Renaissance Review (53445) • Religions of South Asia (55185) • Religious Studies and Theology (55187) • Sociolinguistic Studies (55253)

Erasmus Law and Economics Review
c/o Dennis Khong, MAN
Faculty of Business & Law
Multimedia University
Jalan Ayer Keroh Lama
75450 Melaka, Malaysia
Publications: Erasmus Law and Economics Review (47680)

Eretz Hatzvi Ltd.
5 Ma'avar Yabok St.
IL-67440 Tel Aviv, Israel
Phone: 97 236 912211
Fax: 97 236 091890
Publications: ERETZ (46099)

Ergon Verlag
Keesburgstr. 11
D-97074 Wurzburg, Germany
Phone: 49 931 280084

Fax: 49 931 282872
Publications: Knowledge Organization (44721)

Ergonomics Society of South Africa
c/o Schu Schutte
CSIR Mining Technology
PO Box 91230
Auckland Park 2006, Republic of South Africa
Phone: 27 113 580202
Fax: 27 114 823267
Publications: Ergonomics SA (50347)

ErhvervsBladet
Pilestraede 34
DK-1147 Copenhagen, Denmark
Phone: 45 337 53801
Fax: 45 337 53696
Publications: ErhvervsBladet (43667)

Eric Tan
Ste. 201, Block A, Mentari Business Pk.
Jalan PJS 8/5, Bandar Sunway
46150 Petaling Jaya, Malaysia
Phone: 60 356 319395
Fax: 60 356 374062
Publications: B & I Magazine (47695)

Eryl Morgan Publications Proprietary Ltd.
785 High St.
Melbourne, Victoria 3071, Australia
Phone: 61 394 169900
Fax: 61 394 169633
Publications: Local Government Focus (42070)

ES Burioni Ricerche Bibliografiche
Corso Firenze 41/2
I-16136 Genoa, Italy
Phone: 39 108 605500
Fax: 39 108 605530
Publications: Journal of the Pancreas (46151)

Escarre International Center for the Ethnic Minorities and Nations
Rocafort, 242, bis
Catalonia
E-08029 Barcelona, Spain
Phone: 34 934 443800
Fax: 34 934 443809
Publications: Europa de les Nacions (50673)

Espacio Apicola
Punilla 1784
5006 Cordova, Argentina
Phone: 54 351 4564337
Publications: Espacio Apicola (41487)

Essential Publishing Ltd.
The Towes
Phoenix Sq.
Colchester CO4 9HU, United Kingdom
Phone: 44 12 06851117
Publications: Period House (53045)

Essentials
Box 1346
Parklands 2121, Republic of South Africa
Phone: 27 011 8890808
Fax: 27 011 8890792
Publications: Essentials (50562)

Estates Gazette Ltd.
1 Procter St.
London WC1V 6EU, United Kingdom
Phone: 44 207 9111701
Publications: Estates Gazette (54385)

Estonian Institute
Suur-Karja 14
PO Box 3469
EE-10506 Tallinn, Estonia
Phone: 372 2 6314355
Fax: 372 2 6314356
Publications: Estonian Literary Magazine (43783)

Estonian University of Life Sciences
Kreutzwaldi 1
EE51014 Tartu, Estonia
Phone: 37 273 13001
Publications: Agronomy Research (43791)

Estrategias Alimentarias S.L.
Fermin Caballero, 64
E-28034 Madrid, Spain
Phone: 34 91 3780922

Fax: 34 91 3780711
Publications: Eurocarne (50758)

Estudios de Politica Exterior S.A.
Nunez de Balboa, 49
E-28001 Madrid, Spain
Phone: 34 91 4312628
Fax: 34 91 5777252
Publications: Politica Exterior (50790)

ETH Swiss Federal Institute of Technology
RZ Bldg., Clausiusstrasse 59
CH-8092 Zurich, Switzerland
Fax: 41 446 321435
Publications: Journal of Object Technology (JOT) (51271)

Ethnic Media Group
65 Whitechapel Rd., Unit 2
London E1 1DU, United Kingdom
Phone: 44 20 76502000
Fax: 44 20 76502001
Publications: Caribbean Times (54181)

ETP Ltd.
Rosebery House
41 Springfield Rd.
Chelmsford CM2 6JJ, United Kingdom
Phone: 44 12 45491717
Fax: 44 12 45499110
Publications: Blueprint (52960)

Eurasia Press, Inc.
67 Koptevskaya Ul., Office 111,
125009 Moscow, Russia
Phone: 7 495 7818837
Fax: 7 495 7818836
Publications: Oil & Gas Eurasia (49950)

Euro-American Association of Economic Development Studies
Faculty of Economics, Rm. 119-B
University of Santiago de Compostela
15782 Santiago de Compostela, Spain
Phone: 34 981 563100
Publications: Applied Econometrics and International Development (50831)

The Euro Weekly News Group
Calle Moscatel
10 Poligono Industrial Arroyo dela Miel
E-29631 Benalmadena, Spain
Phone: 34 952 561245
Fax: 34 952 440887
Publications: The Euro Weekly News (50709)

EUROGRAPHICS Association
Ave. Frontenex 32
CH-1207 Geneva, Switzerland
Publications: Computer Graphics Forum Journal (51090)

Euroman Publications S/A
Hellerupvej 51
DK-2900 Hellerup, Denmark
Phone: 45 394 57700
Fax: 45 394 57780
Publications: Euroman (43720)

Euromed Communications Ltd.
The Old Surgery Liphook Rd.
Lynchborough Rd.
Passfield
Hampshire
Haslemere GU27 1NL, United Kingdom
Phone: 44 14 28656665
Fax: 44 14 28656643
Publications: Drug Delivery Systems and Sciences (53536)

Euromoney Publications (Jersey) Ltd.
5th & 17th Fl. Printing House
6 Duddell St., Central
Hong Kong, People's Republic of China
Phone: 85 225 233399
Publications: Asia Law and Practice (43270)

Euromoney Publications PLC
Nestor House
Playhouse Yard
London EC4V 5EX, United Kingdom
Phone: 44 20 77798888
Publications: Airfinance Journal (53931) • Asiamoney (43272) • Euromoney (54390) • Global Investor

(54511) • Institutional Investor (54608) • International Securities Finance (54670) • International Tax Review (54674) • Journal of Portfolio Management (54804) • LatinFinance (54856) • Med Ad News (54919) • Petroleum Economist (55074)

Europa Cantat - European Federation of Young Choirs
c/o Haus del Kultur
Weberstr. 59a
D-53113 Bonn, Germany
Phone: 49 228 9125663
Fax: 49 228 9125658
Publications: Europa Cantat Magazine (44256)

Europa Nostra Pan European Federation for Heritage
35 Lange Voorhout
NL-2514 EC The Hague, Netherlands
Phone: 31 70 3024050
Fax: 31 70 3617865
Publications: Europa Nostra (48614)

Europe Real Estate Publishers
PO Box 84416
NL-2508 AK The Hague, Netherlands
Phone: 31 703 023300
Fax: 31 703 023330
Publications: Amsterdam Real Estate City Book (48606)

European Academy of Allergology and Clinical Immunology
c/o C. Ostrom, Exec. Mgr.
PO Box 24140
S-10451 Stockholm, Sweden
Phone: 46 8 4596623
Fax: 46 8 6633815
Publications: Allergy (51005)

European Accounting Association
European Institute for Advanced Studies in Management
Pl. de Brouckere Plein, 31
B-1000 Brussels, Belgium
Phone: 32 222 66660
Fax: 32 251 21929
Publications: European Accounting Review (42852)

European Association of Development Research and Training Institutes
Matiere de Development
Kaiser-Friedrich-Strasse 11
53113 Bonn, Germany
Phone: 49 228 2618101
Fax: 49 228 2618103
Publications: European Journal of Development Research (44257)

European Association of Geoscientists and Engineers
PO Box 59
NL-3990 DB Houten, Netherlands
Phone: 31 88 995055
Fax: 31 30 6343524
Publications: Basin Research (48638) • First Break (48639) • Geophysical Prospecting (48640)

European Association of Hospital Pharmacists
rue Abbe Cuypers, 3
B-1040 Brussels, Belgium
Phone: 32 2 7416822
Fax: 32 2 7347910
Publications: European Journal of Hospital Pharmacy (42853)

European Association for International Education
PO Box 11189
NL-1001 GD Amsterdam, Netherlands
Phone: 31 20 445100
Fax: 31 20 3445119
Publications: EAIE Forum (47961)

European Association for Microprocessing and Microprogramming
PO Box 2043
D-53743 Saint Augustin, Germany
Phone: 49 224 19326633
Fax: 49 224 19326746
Publications: Journal of Systems Architecture (44654)

European Association of National Productivity Centres
c/o Marc de Greef, Sec. Gen.
Rue Gachard 88
B-1050 Brussels, Belgium
Phone: 32 264 34451
Fax: 32 264 34450
Publications: EPI (42851)

European Association of Remote Sensing Laboratories
c/o Gesine Bottcher, Secretary
Nienburger Strasse 1
D-30167 Hannover, Germany
Phone: 49511 762 2482
Fax: 49511 762 2483
Publications: EARSeL eProceedings (44624)

European Association for Theoretical Computer Science
c/o Ioannis Chatzigiannakis, Sec.
Research and Academy Computer Technology International
1 N Kazantzaki St.
University of Patras Campus
26500 Patras, Greece
Publications: Theoretical Computer Science (44766)

European Association of Urology
PO Box 30016
NL-6803 AA Arnhem, Netherlands
Phone: 31 263 890680
Fax: 31 263 890674
Publications: European Urology (48276)

European Bioethical Research
191 Leith Walk
Edinburgh EH6 8NX, United Kingdom
Publications: Human Reproduction & Genetic Ethics (53285)

EBU—European Broadcasting Union
L'Ancienne-Rte. 17A
CH-1218 Grand-Saconnex, Switzerland
Phone: 41 22 7172111
Fax: 41 22 7474000
Publications: Diffusion (51177) • EBU Technical Review (51178)

European Cancer Prevention Organization
Dr. Willems Instituut
Gebouw C, Universitaire Campus
B-3590 Diepenbeek, Belgium
Phone: 32 112 75734
Fax: 32 112 83677
Publications: European Journal of Cancer Prevention (42879)

European Centre for the Development of Vocational Training - Cedefop
PO Box 22427
GR-551 02 Thessaloniki, Greece
Phone: 30 231 0490111
Fax: 30 231 0490049
Publications: European Journal (44771)

European Centre for Higher Education
39, Stirbei Voda St.
R-010102 Bucharest, Romania
Phone: 40 211 3130839
Fax: 40 211 3123567
Publications: Higher Education in Europe (49837)

European Centre for Minority Issues
Schiffbrucke 12
D-24939 Flensburg, Germany
Phone: 49 4 61141490
Fax: 49 4 611414919
Publications: ECMI Journal on Ethnopolitics and Minority Issues in Europe (44354)

European Federation of National Organisations Working with the Homeless
Chaussee de Louvain 194
B-1210 Brussels, Belgium
Phone: 32 253 86669
Fax: 32 253 94174
Publications: Homeless in Europe (42858)

European Federation of Societies of Ultrasound in Medicine and Biology
36 Portland Pl.
London W1B 1LS, United Kingdom
Phone: 44 20 70997140
Fax: 44 20 74367934
Publications: European Journal of Ultrasound (54406)

European Hematology Association
Koninginnegracht 12b
NL-2514 AA The Hague, Netherlands
Phone: 31 70 3020099
Publications: Haematologica/The Hematology Journal (46209)

European Information Association
PO Box 28
Flintshire
Mold CH7 6FE, United Kingdom
Publications: European Information (55642) • Focus (55643)

European Journals, Inc.
PO Box 1123
Vienna, Austria
Publications: The European Journal of Economics, Finance and Administrative Sciences (42752) • European Journal of Scientific Research (42753) • The European Journal of Social Sciences (42754) • The European Journal of Technology and Advanced Engineering Research (42755)

European League of Institutes of the Arts
Beulingstraat 8
NL-1017 BA Amsterdam, Netherlands
Phone: 31 20 6265417
Fax: 31 20 6267751
Publications: European Journal of Arts Education (47974)

European Marketing Academy
Pl. de Brouckere Plein, 31
B-1000 Brussels, Belgium
Phone: 32 222 66660
Fax: 32 251 21929
Publications: International Journal of Research in Marketing (42859)

European Mathematical Society
EMS Secretariat
Dept. of Mathematics & Statistics
PO Box 68 (Gustaf Hallstromink. 2b)
FIN-00014 Helsinki, Finland
Phone: 358 919 151503
Fax: 358 919 151400
Publications: Bulletin, Classe des Sciences Mathematiques et Naturelles, Sciences mathematiques (43822) • Journal of Analysis and its Applications (43834) • Journal of Lie Theory (43835) • Oberwolfach Reports (43852)

European Palm Society
c/o The Palm Ctr., Ham Central Nursery
Ham St., Ham
Surrey
Richmond TW10 7HA, United Kingdom
Phone: 44 20 82556191
Fax: 44 20 82556192
Publications: Chamaerops Magazine (56389)

European Patent Office
Erhardtstrasse 27
D-80469 Munich, Germany
Phone: 49 89 23990
Publications: Official Journal of the European Patent Office (44576)

European Photography
PO Box 08 02 27
D-10002 Berlin, Germany
Publications: European Photography (44175)

European Polymer Federation
Den Dolech 2
NL-5612 AZ Eindhoven, Netherlands
Publications: E-Polymers (48589)

European Public Health Association
Otterstraat 118-124
PO Box 1568
NL-3500 BN Utrecht, Netherlands
Phone: 31 302 729709
Fax: 31 302 729729
Publications: European Journal of Public Health (48757)

European Rhinologic Society
Tuomiokirkonkatu 17 B 31
33100 Tampere, Finland
Phone: 358 3 2604266
Fax: 358 3 2541251
Publications: Rhinology (48226)

European Society of Cardiology
The European Heart House
2035 Rte. des Colles
Les Templiers
F-06903 Sophia Antipolis, France
Phone: 33 492 947600
Fax: 33 492 947601
Publications: Cardiovascular Research (44106) • European Heart Journal (44107)

European Society for the Cognitive Sciences of Music
c/o Reinhard Kopiez, Pres.
Hochschule fur Musik und Theater
Emmichplatz 1
30175 Hannover, Germany
Phone: 49 511 3100608
Fax: 49 511 3100600
Publications: Musicae Scientiae (44434)

European Society for Magnetic Resonance in Medicine and Biology
Neutorgasse 9/2A
A-1010 Vienna, Austria
Phone: 43 153 51306
Fax: 43 153 57041
Publications: MAGMA (43973)

European Society for Microcirculation
Dept. of Physiology
Freie Universitat Berlin
Arnimallee 22
D-14195 Berlin, Germany
Phone: 49 308 4451632
Fax: 49 308 4451634
Publications: Journal of Vascular Research (44210)

European Society for the Study of Cognitive Systems
University of Groningen
Grote Kruisstraat 2/1
NL-9712 TS Groningen, Netherlands
Fax: 31 503 636304
Publications: Cognitive Systems (48598)

European Society for Therapeutic Radiology and Oncology
Av. E Mounierlaan 83
B-1200 Brussels, Belgium
Phone: 32 277 59340
Fax: 32 277 95494
Publications: Journal of Radiotherapy and Oncology (42863)

European Vegetarian Union
Niederfeldstrasse 92
CH-8408 Winterthur, Switzerland
Phone: 41 71 4773377
Fax: 41 71 4773378
Publications: European Vegetarian (51240)

European Weed Research Society
c/o drs Ben Post
Postbus 28
NL-6865 ZG Doorwerth, Netherlands
Fax: 31 26 3706896
Publications: Weed Research (48317)

European Weightlifting Federation
Via Gino Giacomini, 83
San Marino 47890, San Marino
Phone: 39 378 995639
Fax: 39 378 913795
Publications: European Weightlifter (50053)

European Youth Forum
rue Joseph II straat 120
B-1000 Brussels, Belgium
Phone: 32 2 2306490
Fax: 32 2 2302123
Publications: Youth Opinion (42876)

Eurostitch Magazine
Palmpolstraat 20
NL-1327 AB Almere, Netherlands
Phone: 31 365 314505
Fax: 31 365 349003
Publications: Eurostitch Magazine (47864)

EuroSurveillance
ECDC
S-171 83 Stockholm, Sweden
Phone: 46 85 8601000
Fax: 46 85 8601001
Publications: EuroSurveillance (51015)

Evangelical Fellowship of India
805/92 Deepali Bldg.
Nehru Pl.
New Delhi 110 019, Delhi, India
Phone: 91 11 26431133
Fax: 91 11 26285350
Publications: Aim (45480)

Evangelischer Frauenbund der Schweiz
Winterthurerstrasse 60
CH-8033 Zurich, Switzerland
Phone: 41 1 443630608
Fax: 41 1 443630760
Publications: Approches (51252) • Schritte ins Offene (51277)

Evegate Publishing Ltd.
South East Business
Spicer House
Lympne Business Park
Hythe
Kent CT21 4LR, United Kingdom
Phone: 44 1303 233880
Fax: 44 1303 239517
Publications: South East Business (53682) • South East Farmer (53683)

Event Services Association
Association House
18c Moor St.
Chepstow NP16 5DB, United Kingdom
Fax: 44 12 91630402
Publications: Event Organiser (52982)

Evolution Publishing
Olivetti House, Level 3
140 William St.
East Sydney, New South Wales 2010, Australia
Phone: 61 2 93608934
Fax: 61 2 93609497
Publications: Cherrie (41849) • Fellow Traveller (41850) • Melbourne Community Voice (42073) • Queensland Pride (41870) • SX News (41852)

EWHA Womans University Press
EWHA Womans University
85-1 Daesin-dong
Seodaemun-gu
Seoul 120-750, Republic of Korea
Phone: 82 2 32773164
Fax: 82 2 3124312
Publications: Asian Journal of Women's Studies (47256)

Excel Publishing Company Ltd.
127-129 Portland St.
Manchester M1 4PZ, United Kingdom
Phone: 44 16 12362782
Fax: 44 16 12362783
Publications: Food Science and Technology (54478)

The Exile
Ul Novaya Basmanaya 10
Pod 6, Etazh 4 1/2
117418 Moscow, Russia
Phone: 7 495 6233565
Fax: 7 495 6235442
Publications: The Exile (49903)

Expert Information
Hamilton House
1 Temple Ave.
London EC4Y 0HA, United Kingdom
Publications: Index to Theses (54595)

Expert Reviews
Unitec House
2 Albert Pl.
London N3 1QB, United Kingdom
Phone: 44 20 83716090
Fax: 44 20 83432313
Publications: Expert Review of Anti-Infective Therapy (54418) • Expert Review of Anticancer Therapy (54419) • Expert Review of Cardiovascular Therapy (54420) • Expert Review of Clinical Immunology (54421) • Expert Review of Clinical Pharmacology (54422) • Expert Review of Endocrinology & Metabolism (54423) • Expert Review of Gastroenterology & Hepatology (54424) • Expert Review of Hematology (54425) • Expert Review of Medical Devices (54426) • Expert Review of Molecular Diagnostics (54427) • Expert Review of Neurotherapeutics (54428) • Expert Review of Obstetrics & Gynecology (54429) • Expert Review of Ophthalmology (54430) • Expert Review of Pharmacoeconomics & Outcomes Research (54431) • Expert Review of Proteomics (54432) • Expert Review of Respiratory Medicine (54433) • Expert Review of Vaccines (54434) • Expert Reviews of Dermatology (54435) • Therapy (55309)

The Expo Times
45 Constable Rd.
Bristol BS7 9YF, United Kingdom
Phone: 44 117 9081303
Publications: Expo Times (52668)

Exposure Youth Enterprises
Muswell Hill Center
Hillfield Pk.
London N10 3QJ, United Kingdom
Phone: 44 20 88830260
Fax: 44 20 88832906
Publications: Exposure (54436)

Express Publications (Madurai) Ltd.
Express Gardens
29 2nd Rd.
Ambattur Industrial Estate
Chennai 600 058, Tamil Nadu, India
Publications: The New Indian Express (45252) • The New Indian Express (45177) • The New Indian Express (45053) • The New Indian Express (45012) • The New Indian Express (44978)

Express Publications Pty. Ltd.
Locked Bag 111
Silverwater, New South Wales 1811, Australia
Phone: 61 297 413899
Fax: 61 297 378017
Publications: Australian Country Craft and Decorating (42359) • Australian Country Threads (42360) • Patchwork & Stitching (42361)

Eye Spy Publishing Ltd.
PO Box 10
Skipton BD23 5US, United Kingdom
Phone: 44 1756 770199
Publications: Eye Spy (56554)

Ezyhealth Holdings Pte. Ltd.
53A Science Park Dr.
The Faraday
Singapore Science Pk.
Singapore 118234, Singapore
Phone: 65 639 59393
Fax: 65 639 59394
Publications: Ezyhealth Singapore (50146)

Fachverlag Hans Carl GmbH
Andernacher St. 33a
D-90411 Nuremberg, Germany
Phone: 49 911 95250
Fax: 49 911 9528581
Publications: Brauwelt Chinese (44603) • Brauwelt Deutsch (44604) • Brauwelt en Espanol (44605) • Brauwelt International (44606) • Brauwelt in Russian (44607) • Der Weihenstephaner (44609) • Getrankemarkt (44614) • Kunst Chronik (44568) • Monatsschrift fur Brauwissenschaft (44616)

Fachverlag Wien
DOK 4 NW 21-22
A-2301 Gross Enzersdorf, Austria
Phone: 43 223 94104
Fax: 43 224 97481
Publications: Labor Direct (42726)

Factory Media
1 W Smithfield
London EC1A 9JU, United Kingdom
Phone: 44 20 73329700
Publications: Cooler (54265) • Dig BMX Magazine (53413) • Dirt Mountain Bike Magazine (54326) • Document Skateboard (54339) • Kingpin (54846) • Moto Magazine (54956) • Onboard (55031) • Sidewalk (55237) • Surf Europe (55280) • The Surfer's Path (55282) • Whitelines Snowboard Magazine (55404)

Faculdade De Odontologia De Bauru - USP
Servico de Biblioteca e Documentacao FO-USP
Al. Dr. Octavio Pinheiro Brisolla 9-75
17012-901 Bauru, Sao Paulo, Brazil
Publications: Journal of Applied Oral Science (42948)

Faculdade de Medicina Veterinaria e Zootecnia USP
Av. Prof. Dr. Orlando Marques de Paiva, 87
Cidade Universitaria Armando de Salles Oliveira
05508-270 Sao Paulo, Sao Paulo, Brazil
Phone: 55 11 30917636
Fax: 55 11 30313074
Publications: Brazilian Journal of Veterinary Research and Animal Science (43029)

Faculty of Actuaries
Maclaurin House
18 Dublin St.
Edinburgh EH1 3PP, United Kingdom
Phone: 44 20 76322100
Fax: 44 13 12401313
Publications: British Actuarial Journal (54108)

Faculty of Asia Pacific Theological Seminary
PO Box 377
Baguio City 2600, Philippines
Phone: 63 744 427068
Fax: 63 744 426378
Publications: Asian Journal of Pentecostal Studies (49450)

Faculty of Computer Science and Information Technology
University of Malaya
50603 Kuala Lumpur, Malaysia
Phone: 60 379 676300
Fax: 60 379 579249
Publications: Malaysian Journal of Library and Information Science (47617)

Faculty of Public Health
4 St. Andrew's Pl.
London NW1 4LB, United Kingdom
Phone: 44 20 79350243
Fax: 44 20 72246973
Publications: Journal of Public Health (54806)

Fagbladet Folkeskolen
Postboks 2139
Vandkunsten 12
DK-1015 Copenhagen K, Denmark
Phone: 45 336 96300
Fax: 45 336 96426
Publications: Folkeskolen (43668)

Fair Organ Preservation Society
c/o Norman Rogers, Membership Sec.
Gaythorpe, Blacketts Wood Dr.
Chorleywood WD3 5QQ, United Kingdom
Publications: The Key Frame (53024)

Fair Play for Children Association
32 Longford Rd.
Bognor Regis
Bognor Regis PO21 1AG, United Kingdom
Phone: 44 845 3307635
Publications: Play Action (52401)

Faire Savoire Plus
46 Pl. Jules Ferry
92120 Montrouge, France
Phone: 33 1 55580606
Fax: 33 1 55580600
Publications: Faire Savoir Faire (43991)

Fairfax Business Media
40 Boulcott, Level 3
PO Box 2595
Wellington 2000, New Zealand
Phone: 64 4 496 9800
Fax: 64 4 496 9841
Publications: AFR Smart Investor (48999) • Asset (42449) • Bayside Bulletin (41766) • MIS Australia (49017) • The Redland Times (41769)

Fairfax Community Newspapers
182 Forest Rd.
PO Box 210
Hurstville, New South Wales 2220, Australia
Phone: 61 295 983999
Fax: 61 295 983985
Publications: The Journal (41970)

Fairfax Media Limited
GPO 506
Sydney, New South Wales 2001, Australia
Phone: 61 2 92822833
Publications: Brisbane Times (42477) • The Sydney Morning Herald (42586)

Fairfax New Zealand Ltd.
Level 3, 40 Boulcott St.
PO Box 2595
Wellington, New Zealand
Phone: 64 4 4969800
Fax: 64 4 4969841
Publications: Boating New Zealand (48787) • Fish and Game New Zealand (48793) • New Zealand Fishing News (48810) • New Zealand Gardener (48812) • New Zealand Horse and Pony (48815) • New Zealand Lifestyle Block (48818) • New Zealand Trucking (48821) • onHoliday (48827) • Truck & Machinery Trader (48831)

Fairkehr Verlags GmbH
Niebuhrstr. 16b
D-53113 Bonn, Germany
Phone: 49 228 9858545
Publications: Fairkehr (44259)

Fall Line Media Limited
S Wing, Broadway Ct.
Peterborough PE1 1RP, United Kingdom
Phone: 44 1733 293250
Fax: 44 1733 293269
Publications: Fall-Line Skiing (56257)

Famedram Publishers Ltd.
PO Box 3
Ellon AB41 9EA, United Kingdom
Phone: 44 16 51842429
Fax: 44 16 51842180
Publications: ArtWork (53330)

Famille Chretienne
15-27 rue Moussorgski
F-75018 Paris Cedex 18, France
Phone: 33 153 263500
Publications: Famille Chretienne (44045)

Family Planning Association of India
Bajaj Bhavan
Nariman Point
Mumbai 400 021, Maharashtra, India
Phone: 91 22 22029080
Fax: 91 22 40863201
Publications: Journal of Family Welfare (45399)

Fanar Publishing WLL
Bahrain Tower, 8th Fl.
PO Box 10131
Manama, Bahrain
Phone: 973 17213900
Fax: 973 17211765
Publications: Arab World Agribusiness (42786)

Fantastic Man Magazine
Kleine-Gartmanplantsoen 21
NL-1017 RP Amsterdam, Netherlands
Phone: 31 20 3209032
Fax: 31 842 248511
Publications: Fantastic Man (47984)

Farma Maaseutukeskus
Artturinkatu 2
FIN-20200 Turku, Finland
Phone: 358 10 2731500
Fax: 358 10 2337570
Publications: Farma Sanomat (43909)

Fauna and Flora International
Jupiter House, 4th Fl.
Station Rd.
Cambridge CB1 2JD, United Kingdom
Phone: 44 122 3571000
Fax: 44 122 3461481
Publications: Oryx (52881)

Fayaz Ahmad Kaloo
6 Pratap Pk.
Residency Rd.
Srinagar 190 001, Jammu and Kashmir, India
Phone: 91 192 474339
Fax: 91 192 477782
Publications: Greater Kashmir (45737)

FDA
8 Leake St.

London SE1 7NN, United Kingdom
Phone: 44 20 73431111
Publications: Public Service Magazine (PSM) (55153)

FDI World Dental Press
5 Battery Green Rd.
Lowestoft NR32 IDE, United Kingdom
Phone: 44 15 02511522
Fax: 44 15 02583152
Publications: Community Dental Health (55493) • The European Journal of Prosthodontics and Restorative Dentistry (55494) • International Dental Journal (55495)

FeBe—Federation de l'Industrie du Beton
Bd du Souverain 68
B-1170 Brussels, Belgium
Phone: 32 273 58015
Fax: 32 273 47795
Publications: Beton (42844)

Federal National Association of the German Brick Industry
Schaumburg-Lippe-Strasse 4
D-53113 Bonn, Germany
Phone: 49 228 914930
Fax: 49 228 9149328
Publications: Zl-Ziegelindustrie International (44406)

The Federal Publishing Company
170-180 Bourke Rd.
Alexandria, New South Wales 2015, Australia
Phone: 61 2 93536666
Fax: 61 2 93536699
Publications: Australian Country Style (41534) • Australian Golf Digest (41535) • Australian Good Taste (41536) • Australian Parents (41537) • delicious. (41538) • Fast Fours Magazine (41539) • Gardening Australia (41540) • Lifestyle Pools (41541) • Live to Ride (41542) • Modern Boating (41543) • Modern Fishing (41544) • Overlander 4WD (41545) • Super Food Ideas (41546) • Truck Australia (41547) • Truckin' Life (41548) • twowheels (41549)

Federal University of Minas Gerais
Avenida Antonio Carlos
6627 Campus Pampulha
31270-301 Belo Horizonte, Mato Grosso, Brazil
Phone: 55 313 4995020
Fax: 55 313 4995060
Publications: Kriterion (42949)

Federation of Andhra Pradesh Chambers of Commerce and Industry
11-6-841
PO Box 14, Red Hills
Hyderabad 500 004, Andhra Pradesh, India
Phone: 91 40 23395515
Fax: 91 40 23395525
Publications: FAPCCI Review (45139)

Federation of Danish Painting Contractors
Postboks 1989
DK-2300 Copenhagen, Denmark
Phone: 45 32 630370
Publications: De Farver (43664)

Federation of Danish Textile and Clothing
Birk Centerpark 38
PO Box 507
DK-7400 Herning, Denmark
Phone: 45 971 17200
Fax: 45 971 17215
Publications: Textile and Clothing (43723)

Federation of Family History Societies
PO Box 8857
Lutterworth LE17 9BJ, United Kingdom
Phone: 44 1455 203133
Publications: Family History News and Digest (53485)

Federation Francophone d'Equitation et d'attelage de loisir
Rue du Tienne 12
B-5140 Ligny, Belgium
Phone: 32 718 15052
Fax: 32 718 17615
Publications: Hippo News (42902)

Federation of Hong Kong Industries
Unit 415 , Hankow Ctr.
5-15 Hankow Rd.
Tsim Sha Tsui
Kowloon
Hong Kong, People's Republic of China

Phone: 86 230 21621
Fax: 86 273 60211
Publications: Hong Kong Industrialist (43325)

Federation Internationale de Motocyclisme
11 Rte. Suisse
CH-1295 Mies, Switzerland
Phone: 41 229 509500
Fax: 41 229 509501
Publications: FIM Magazine (51212)

Federation of Jewish Communities
5A 2nd Vysheslavtzev Pereulok
127055 Moscow, Russia
Phone: 7 495 7378275
Fax: 7 495 7838471
Publications: Lechaim (49936) • World of Jewish Woman (51616) • Yevreiski Dom (47169) • A Yidishe Mame (51591)

Federation of Malaysian Manufacturers
Wisma FMM, No. 3
Persiaran Dagang
PJU 9, Bandar Sri Damansara
52200 Kuala Lumpur, Malaysia
Phone: 60 362 867200
Fax: 60 362 741266
Publications: FMM Directory of Malaysian Industries (47602)

Federation of Master Builders
14-15 Great James St.
London WC1N 3DP, United Kingdom
Phone: 44 20 72427583
Fax: 44 20 74040296
Publications: Master Builder (54912)

Federation of Obstetric & Gynaecological Societies of India
Gr Fl., Model Residency Tower
605, Baburao Jagtap Rd.
Jacob Cir.
Mahalaxmi E
Mumbai 400 001, Maharashtra, India
Phone: 91 22 23021648
Fax: 91 22 23021383
Publications: The Journal of Obstetrics and Gynaecology of India (45404)

Federation of Petroleum Suppliers
6 Royal Ct.
Tatton St.
Knutsford WA16 6EN, United Kingdom
Phone: 44 15 65631313
Fax: 44 15 65631314
Publications: Downstream (53730)

Federation of the Retail Licensed Trade
91 University St.
Belfast BT7 1HP, United Kingdom
Phone: 44 28 90327578
Fax: 44 28 90327578
Publications: Hospitality Review (52285)

Federation of Specialists Restaurant
PO Box 416
London KT1 9BJ, United Kingdom
Phone: 44 20 83994831
Publications: Mood Food (54952)

Federation of Women's Institutes of Northern Ireland
209-211 Upper Lisburn Rd.
Belfast BT10 0LL, United Kingdom
Phone: 44 28 90301506
Fax: 44 28 90431127
Publications: Ulster Countrywoman (52296)

Federauto
avenue Jules Bordet 164
B-1140 Brussels, Belgium
Phone: 32 277 86200
Fax: 32 277 86222
Publications: Federauto Magazine (42855)

Feline Advisory Bureau
Taeselbury
High St.
Tisbury SP3 6LD, United Kingdom
Phone: 44 87 47871872
Fax: 44 17 47871873
Publications: Fab Cat Care Journal (56751) • Feline Advisory Bureau Journal (56752)

Fellowship of St. Alban and St. Sergius
1 Canterbury Rd.
Oxford OX2 6LU, United Kingdom
Phone: 44 18 65552991
Publications: Sobornost (56206)

Fenman Ltd.
Unit 2 e-space N
181 Wisbech Rd.
Cambridgeshire
Littleport CB6 1RA, United Kingdom
Phone: 44 13 53865350
Fax: 44 13 53865351
Publications: Training Journal (53867)

The Ferrari Owners Club Ltd.
Snettisham
PO Box 111
King's Lynn PE31 7TF, United Kingdom
Publications: Ferrari Magazine (53712) • Ferrari News (53713)

Fertiliser Association of India
10 Shaheed Jit Singh Marg
New Delhi 110 067, Delhi, India
Phone: 91 11 26567144
Fax: 91 11 26960052
Publications: FAI Abstract Service (45512) • Fertiliser Association of India's Fertiliser Statistics (45513) • Fertiliser Marketing News (45514)

Ffestiniog Railway Society
PO Box 1832
Warrington WA4 2FR, United Kingdom
Fax: 44 8707 063351
Publications: Ffestiniog Railway Magazine (53500)

Field Studies Council
Preston Montford
Montford Bridge
Shrewsbury SY4 1HW, United Kingdom
Phone: 44 1743 852100
Fax: 44 1743 852101
Publications: Field Studies (56529)

55 North Ltd.
Waterloo Chambers
19 Waterloo St.
Glasgow G2 6AY, United Kingdom
Phone: 44 141 2222100
Fax: 44 141 2222177
Publications: First Link 4 Parents (53420) • On-Trade Scotland (53436) • Scottish Local Retailer (53449)

Fiji Institute of Applied Studies
PO Box 7580
Lautoka, Fiji
Publications: Fijian Studies (43806)

Filmbase
Curved Street Bldg.
Temple Bar
Dublin 2, Dublin, Ireland
Phone: 353 1 6796716
Fax: 353 1 6796717
Publications: Film Ireland (45956)

Filmbulletin/Kino in Augenhohe
Hard 4
Postfach 68
CH-8408 Winterthur, Switzerland
Phone: 41 52 2260555
Fax: 41 52 2260556
Publications: Filmbulletin/Kino in Augenhohe (51241)

Filtration Society
19 Clyst Valley Rd.
Clyst St Mary
Exeter EX5 1DD, United Kingdom
Phone: 44 1392 874398
Fax: 44 1392 874398
Publications: Filtration (53358)

Financial Mirror Ltd.
PO Box 16077
Nicosia CY-2085, Cyprus
Phone: 357 22 678666
Fax: 357 22 678664
Publications: Financial Mirror (43595)

Financial News Ltd.
Commodity Quay
East Smithfield
London E1W 1AZ, United Kingdom

Phone: 44 20 34261111
Fax: 44 20 77292910
Publications: eFinancial News (54356) • Financial News (54457)

Financial Times Business Ltd.
One Southwark Bridge
London SE1 9HL, United Kingdom
Phone: 44 20 77756653
Fax: 44 20 77756413
Publications: The Banker (54001) • Investors Chronicle (54680)

Financial Times (Japan) Ltd.
Yamato Seimei Bldg. 21F
1-1-7 Uchisaiwaicho
Chiyoda-ku
Tokyo 100-0011, Japan
Phone: 81 335 811422
Fax: 81 335 811423
Publications: Financial Times Japan (46823)

The Financial Times Ltd.
1 Southwark Bridge
London SE1 9HL, United Kingdom
Phone: 44 20 78733000
Publications: The Financial Times (54459)

Finansradets HUS
Amaliegade 7
DK-1256 Copenhagen, Denmark
Phone: 45 337 01000
Fax: 45 339 30260
Publications: kapital (43677)

Fine Art Trade Guild
16-18 Empress Pl.
London SW6 1TT, United Kingdom
Phone: 44 20 73816616
Fax: 44 20 73812596
Publications: Art Business Today (53966)

Fingerprint Society
Fingerprint Bureau
2nd Fl., Norwich House
Water St.
Liverpool L2 9XR, United Kingdom
Publications: Fingerprint Whorld (53873)

Finlayson Media Communications Ltd.
1 Hertford House
Farm Close
Shenley WD7 9AB, United Kingdom
Phone: 44 1923 851777
Fax: 44 1923 851778
Publications: Dentistry (56519)

Finnish Amateur Musicians' Association
Klaneettitie 6-8
FIN-00420 Helsinki, Finland
Phone: 358 10 8200220
Fax: 358 10 8200222
Publications: Sulasol (43858)

Finnish Association of Architects
Runeberginkatu 5 A
FIN-00100 Helsinki, Finland
Phone: 35 9 584448
Fax: 35 9 58444222
Publications: Arkkitehti/Finnish Architectural Review (43818)

Finnish Association on Mental Retardation/ Kehitysvammaliitto
Viljatie 4 A
FIN-00700 Helsinki, Finland
Phone: 358 934 8090
Fax: 358 938 53398
Publications: Ketju (43841)

Finnish Dental Association
Fabianinkatu 9 B
FIN-00130 Helsinki, Finland
Phone: 358 9 6220250
Fax: 358 9 6223050
Publications: Suomen Hammaslaakarilehti/Finnish Dental Journal (43860)

Finnish Diabetes Association
Diabetes Center
Kirjoniementie 15
FIN-33680 Tampere, Finland
Phone: 35 832 860111

Fax: 35 833 600462
Publications: Diabetes (43907)

Finnish Folklore Society
University of Turku
School of Cultural Production & Landscape Studies
University Consortium of Pori
Siltapuistonkatu 2
FIN-28100 Pori, Finland
Phone: 358 627 2964
Fax: 358 627 2707
Publications: Elore (43904)

Finnish Institute of Occupational Health
Topeliuksenkatu 41 A
FIN-00250 Helsinki, Finland
Phone: 358 304 741
Publications: African Newsletter on Occupational Health and Safety (43814) • Asian-Pacific Newsletter (43819) • Tyo Terveys Turvallisuus (43863)

The Finnish Literature Society
PO Box 259
FIN-00171 Helsinki, Finland
Phone: 358 201 131231
Fax: 358 9 13123220
Publications: Books from Finland (43821)

Finnish Museums Association
Annankatu 16 B 50
FIN-00120 Helsinki, Finland
Phone: 358 9 58411700
Fax: 358 9 58411750
Publications: Museo (43849)

Finnish Music Quarterly
Pieni Roobertinkatu 16
FIN-00120 Helsinki, Finland
Phone: 358 9 68034048
Fax: 358 9 68034033
Publications: Finnish Music Quarterly (43828)

Finnish Newspapers Association
PO Box 415
FIN-00121 Helsinki, Finland
Phone: 358 9 22877300
Fax: 358 9 607989
Publications: Suomen Lehdisto (43861)

Finnish Paper Engineers Association
PO Box 118
FIN-00171 Helsinki, Finland
Phone: 35 891 326688
Fax: 35 89 630365
Publications: Paper and Timber (43854)

Finnish Peatland Society
c/o Birgit Hyyrylainen
Turveteollisuusliitto
Vapaudenkatu 12
FIN-40100 Jyvaskyla, Finland
Phone: 35 814 3385420
Fax: 35 814 3385410
Publications: Suo - Mires and Peat (43872)

Finnish Sports Federation
Radiokatu 20, 7th Fl.
FIN-00240 Helsinki, Finland
Phone: 358 9 348121
Fax: 358 9 34812602
Publications: Liikunnan ja Urheilun Maailma (43845)

The Finnish Watchmaker Association
Opinkuja 2
FIN-02100 Espoo, Finland
Phone: 35 894 520560
Fax: 35 894 5205656
Publications: Kello and Kulta (43812)

Finnybank Ltd.
30 Finnybank Rd.
Sale M33 6LR, United Kingdom
Phone: 44 161 9699820
Fax: 44 8700 519527
Publications: Qercus (56450)

Fintel Publications Ltd.
6 The Mall, Beacon Ct.
Sandyford
Dublin IRL-18, Dublin, Ireland
Phone: 353 129 30565
Fax: 353 129 30560
Publications: Finance Dublin (45957)

Fire Brigades Union
Bradley House
68 Coombe Rd.
Kingston upon Thames KT2 7AE, United Kingdom
Phone: 44 20 85411765
Fax: 44 20 85465187
Publications: Firefighter (53721)

The Fire Protection Association
London Rd.
Moreton-in-Marsh GL56 0RH, United Kingdom
Phone: 44 16 08812500
Fax: 44 16 08812501
Publications: Fire Prevention (55650)

Fire Protection Association Australia
13 Ellingworth Parade
PO Box 1049
Box Hill, Victoria 3128, Australia
Phone: 61 3 98901544
Fax: 61 3 98901577
Publications: Fire Australia (41632)

Firenze University Press
Borgo Albizi 28
50122 Florence, Italy
Phone: 39 552 743051
Fax: 39 552 743058
Publications: Aestimum (46139) • Annali di Storia di
Firenze (46141) • Cromohs (46142) • Global Bioethics
(46144)

Fireworks
PO Box 40
Bexhill-on-Sea TN40 1GX, United Kingdom
Publications: Fireworks (52321)

First Charlton Communications Proprietary Ltd.
Level 8, 122 Arthur St.
56 Berry St.
North Sydney, New South Wales 2060, Australia
Phone: 61 2 99556299
Fax: 61 2 99571512
Publications: Australian Banking & Finance (42206) •
Australian Society & Events (42208) • Australian Tele-
com (42209) • Business Asia (42210)

First Empire Ltd.
59 Whitburn St.
Bridgnorth WV16 4QP, United Kingdom
Phone: 44 17 46765691
Fax: 44 87 09157965
Publications: First Empire (52594)

First Magazine Ltd.
56 Haymarket
London SW1Y 4RN, United Kingdom
Phone: 44 20 73899650
Fax: 44 20 73899644
Publications: First (54462)

FirstLaw Ltd.
Top Fl.
Merchants Ct.
Merchants Quay
Dublin IRL-8, Dublin, Ireland
Phone: 353 1 6790370
Fax: 353 1 6790057
Publications: Employment Law Review (45955)

Fisco Press Pvt. Ltd.
Flat No. 1, St. No. 38
Umar Market
Canal Park Gulberg-II
Lahore, Pakistan
Phone: 92 42 5787978
Fax: 92 42 8492837
Publications: Weekly Cutting Edge (49389)

Fish Farmer Magazine
Special Publications
Craigcrook Castle
Criagcrook Rd.
Edinburgh EH4 3PE, United Kingdom
Phone: 44 13 13124550
Fax: 44 13 13124551
Publications: Fish Farmer (53277)

National Federation of Fish Friers Ltd.
4 Greenwood Mount
Leeds LS6 4LQ, United Kingdom
Phone: 44 11 32307044

Fax: 44 11 32307010
Publications: Fish Friers Review (53766)

Flag Institute
38 Hill St.
London W1J 5NS, United Kingdom
Publications: Flagmaster (54464)

Flagship Media Group Ltd.
48-50 York St.
Belfast BT15 1AS, United Kingdom
Phone: 44 28 90319008
Fax: 44 28 90727800
Publications: Keystone (52289)

Flame Ltd.
12 Kings Pk.
Primrose Hill
Kings Langley WD4 8ST, United Kingdom
Phone: 44 19 23272920
Publications: The Grocery Trader (53710) • Ware-
house & Logistics News (53711)

Fleet Air Arm Officers' Association
4 St. James's Sq.
London SW1Y 4JU, United Kingdom
Phone: 44 20 79307722
Fax: 44 20 79307728
Publications: Fly Navy (54471)

Fly Enterprises Ltd.
59-65 Worship St.
London EC2A 2DU, United Kingdom
Publications: The Fly (54470)

Flyfishers Club
69 Brook St.
London W1K 4ER, United Kingdom
Phone: 44 20 76295958
Publications: Flyfishers' Journal (54472)

FMB Publications Ltd.
FMB House
6 Windmill Rd.
Hampton Hill
Twickenham TW12 1RH, United Kingdom
Phone: 44 20 89797866
Fax: 44 20 89794573
Publications: Fertilizer Focus (56791)

FMS Publishing
New Barn
Fanhams Grange
Fanhams Hall Rd.
Ware SG12 7QA, United Kingdom
Phone: 44 1920 467492
Fax: 44 1920 460149
Publications: Bentley Magazine (56839) • Champneys
Magazine (56840) • Marbella Club Magazine (56842) •
Paul Sheeran Magazine (56843) • Ritz Magazine
(56844) • Sunseeker Magazine (56845) • Triumph
Magazine (56846)

Focolare Movement
Via. di Frascati 306
I-00040 Rocca di Papa, Italy
Phone: 39 694 7989
Fax: 39 694 749320
Publications: New Humanity (46219)

Focus Publications (Int.) S.A.
PO Box 0819-06908
El Dorado
Panama City, Panama
Phone: 507 225 6638
Fax: 507 225 0466
Publications: Focus on Panama (49401)

Foinse
An Cheathru Rua
Gaillimhe, Galway, Ireland
Phone: 353 91 595520
Fax: 353 91 595524
Publications: Foinse (46015)

Folk Music Society of Ireland
c/o The Irish Traditional Music Archive
63 Merrion Sq.
Dublin IRL-2, Dublin, Ireland
Phone: 35 316 619699
Fax: 35 316 624585
Publications: Irish Folk Music Studies (45973)

The Folly Fellowship
Tarantostraat 41
NL-5632 RE Eindhoven, Netherlands
Phone: 31 402423648
Publications: The Follies Journal (48590)

Forbund Djurens Ratt
PO Box 2005
SE-125 02 Alvsjo, Sweden
Phone: 46 8 55591400
Fax: 46 8 55591450
Publications: Djurens Ratt (50948)

Foreign Correspondents' Club
2 Lower Albert Rd. N Block
Central
Hong Kong, People's Republic of China
Phone: 86 225 211511
Fax: 86 228 684092
Publications: The Correspondent (43294)

Forest and Bird
Level 1, 90 Ghuznee St.
PO Box 631
Wellington, New Zealand
Phone: 64 438 57374
Fax: 64 438 57373
Publications: Forest and Bird Magazine (49008)

Forest Research Institute Malaysia
52109 Kepong
52109 Selangor, Malaysia
Phone: 60 3 62797000
Fax: 60 3 62731314
Publications: Journal of Tropical Forest Science
(47712)

Formatex Research Centre
C/Zurbaran
1 2a Planta
Oficina 1
E-06002 Badajoz, Spain
Phone: 34 924 258615
Fax: 34 924 263053
Publications: Journal of Digital Contents (50645)

Formosan Medical Association
No. 1 Chang-Te St.
Taipei 10016, Taiwan
Phone: 886 2 23810367
Fax: 886 2 23896716
Publications: Journal of the Formosan Medical As-
sociation (51352)

Forth Naturalist & Historian
University of Stirling
Stirling FK9 4LA, United Kingdom
Phone: 44 17 86467839
Fax: 44 17 86467269
Publications: The Forth Naturalist & Historian (56622)

Foto8 Ltd.
1-5 Honduras St.
London EC1Y 0TH, United Kingdom
Phone: 44 20 72538801
Fax: 44 20 72532752
Publications: Ei8ht (54358)

**Foundation for Organisational Research and
Education**
Adhitam Kendra
B-18 Qutab Institutional Area
New Delhi 110 016, Delhi, India
Phone: 91 11 41242424
Fax: 91 11 26964229
Publications: Abhigyan (45476)

Foundation for Revitalization of Local Health
74/2 Jarakbhande Kaval
Attur Post, Via. Yelehanka
Bangalore 560 064, Karnataka, India
Phone: 91 808 568000
Fax: 91 808 567926
Publications: Amruth (44948)

Fourth Military Medical University
17 Changlexi St.
Xi'an 710032, Shaanxi, People's Republic of China
Phone: 86 29 83374315
Publications: Chinese Heart Journal (43528) • Chinese
Journal of Cells and Molecular Immunology (43529) •
Chinese Journal of Conservative Dentistry (43530) •
Chinese Journal of Neuroanatomy (43531) • Journal of

Fourth Military University (43533) • Journal of Practical Stomatology (43534)

Fourth World Review
PO Box 2410
Swindon SN5 4AE, United Kingdom
Phone: 44 17 93772214
Fax: 44 17 93772521
Publications: Fourth World Review (56711)

FRAME Finnish Fund for Art Exchange
Tallberginkatu 1 C 96
FIN-00150 Helsinki, Finland
Phone: 358 40 5070809
Fax: 358 9 47800818
Publications: Framework (43830)

Francophone Primatological Society
Sta. Biologique de Paimpont
F-35380 Plelan le Grand, France
Phone: 33 299 618156
Fax: 33 299 618188
Publications: Folia Primatologica (44095)

Frankfurter Allgemeine Zeitung GmbH
Hellerhofstr. 2-4
D-60327 Frankfurt, Germany
Publications: Frankfurter Allgemeine (44360)

Frauen-Union der Christian Demokratischen Union Deutschlands
Konrad-Adenauer-Haus
Friedrich-Ebert-Alle 73-75
D-53113 Bonn, Germany
Phone: 49 228 544315
Fax: 49 228 544586
Publications: Frau und Politik (44261)

Fraunhofer-Gesellschaft zur Forderung der Angewandten Forschung
Hansastrasse 27c
D-80686 Munich, Germany
Phone: 49 89 12050
Fax: 49 89 12057531
Publications: Fraunhofer (English) (44562) • Fraunhofer Magazin (44563)

Free Press Ltd.
32 Kazi Nazrul Islam Ave.
Karwan Bazar
Dhaka 1215, Bangladesh
Phone: 880 291 29938
Fax: 880 291 27722
Publications: The Independent (Bangladesh) (42811)

Freedom from Debt Coalition
11 Matimpiin St.
Barangay Pinyahan
Quezon City 1100, Philippines
Phone: 63 2 9211985
Fax: 63 2 9246399
Publications: PAID (49605)

Freemasonry Today Ltd.
Freemason's Hall
Great Queeen St.
London WC2B 5AZ, United Kingdom
Phone: 44 20 78319811
Fax: 44 20 78319811
Publications: Freemasonry Today (54480)

Freestyle Publications Ltd.
Alexander House
Ling Rd.
Tower Pk.
Poole BH12 4NZ, United Kingdom
Phone: 44 1202 735090
Publications: Boys Toys (56280)

French Chamber of Commerce in Great Britain
Lincoln House, 4th Fl.
300 High Holborn
London WC1V 7JH, United Kingdom
Phone: 44 207 0926600
Fax: 44 207 0926601
Telex: 269132 FRACOM-G
Publications: Info (54600)

French Society of Musicology
2 rue Louvois
F-75002 Paris, France
Phone: 33 1 53798845
Publications: Revue de Musicologie (44081)

Freund Publishing House Ltd.
PO Box 35010
61350 Tel Aviv, Israel
Phone: 972 3 5628540
Fax: 972 3 5628538
Publications: Corrosion Reviews (46097) • Drug Metabolism and Drug Interactions (46098) • Heterocyclic Communications (46102) • High Temperature Materials and Processes (46666) • International Journal of Adolescent Medicine and Health (46083) • International Journal on Disability and Human Development (46084) • International Journal of Nonlinear Sciences and Numerical Simulation (46104) • International Journal of Turbo and Jet Engines (46105) • Journal of Basic & Clinical Physiology & Pharmacology (46087) • Journal of the Mechanical Behavior of Materials (46108) • Main Group Metal Chemistry (46110) • Reviews in Analytical Chemistry (46079) • Reviews in Chemical Engineering (46091) • Reviews in Inorganic Chemistry (46111) • Science and Engineering of Composite Materials (46112)

The Friday Times
72 FCC Gulberg IV
Lahore, Pakistan
Phone: 92 425 763510
Fax: 92 425 751025
Publications: The Friday Times (49385)

Friedrich Berlin Publishing Group
Knesebeckstr. 59-61
D-10719 Berlin, Germany
Phone: 49 30 25449520
Fax: 49 30 25449524
Publications: ballettanz (44158)

Friend Publications Ltd.
173 Euston Rd.
London NW1 2BJ, United Kingdom
Phone: 44 207 6631010
Fax: 44 207 6631182
Publications: The Friend (54483)

Friends of the Earth - Australia
PO Box 222
Fitzroy, Victoria 3065, Australia
Phone: 61 3 94198700
Fax: 61 3 94162081
Publications: Chain Reaction (41866)

Friends of the Earth - Cyprus
PO Box 53411
Limassol 3302, Cyprus
Phone: 357 5 347042
Fax: 357 5 347043
Publications: Earthlines (43589)

Friends of the Earth Latvia
11 Novembra Krastmala 34, Rooms 103 & 104
LV-1966 Riga, Latvia
Phone: 371 72 26042
Fax: 371 72 13697
Publications: Vides Vestis (47376)

Friends of the National Maritime Museum
Greenwich
London SE10 9NF, United Kingdom
Phone: 44 20 83126632
Publications: Journal for Maritime Research (54775)

Frieze
81 Rivington St.
London EC2A 3AY, United Kingdom
Phone: 44 20 33726111
Publications: Frieze (54484)

The Frontier Publications Private Ltd.
27 Abdara Rd.
PO Box 1161
University Town
Peshawar, Pakistan
Phone: 92 300 5182252
Publications: The Frontier Post (49392)

FSJ Communications
The Media Centre
Garcia Estate
Canterbury Rd.
Worthing BN13 1EH, United Kingdom
Publications: Funeral Service Journal (56972)

FSJU
Espace Rachi, 39, Rue Broca

F-75005 Paris, France
Phone: 33 421 71010
Fax: 33 421 71031
Publications: L'Arche (44026)

Fuji Technology Press Ltd.
4F Toranomon Sangyo Bldg.
2-29 Toranomon
Minato-Ku
Tokyo 105-0001, Japan
Phone: 81 335 080051
Fax: 81 335 920648
Publications: Journal of Advanced Computational Intelligence and Intelligent Informatics (JACIII) (46880) • Journal of the Ceramic Society of Japan (46890) • Journal of Robotics and Mechatronics (46940)

Fukuoka Now Ltd.
3F Abundant Bldg.
1-5-11 Akasaka
Chuo-ku
Fukuoka 810-0042, Japan
Phone: 81 927 622505
Fax: 81 927 622509
Publications: Fukuoka Now (46341)

Fullhouse Communications Private Ltd.
246 MacPherson Rd., No. 06-01
Betime Bldg.
Singapore 348578, Singapore
Phone: 65 68427266
Fax: 65 68427133
Publications: Wedding & Travel (50285)

Fundacao Carlos Chagas
Av. Prof. Francisco Morato, 1565
05513-900 Sao Paulo, Sao Paulo, Brazil
Phone: 55 113 7233000
Fax: 55 113 7211059
Publications: Cadernos de Pesquisa (43031)

Fundacao Oswaldo Cruz
Av. Brasil, 4365
Manguinhos
21040-360 Rio de Janeiro, Rio de Janeiro, Brazil
Phone: 55 212 5984242
Publications: Historia, Ciencias, Saude-Manguinhos (43005)

Fundacao de Pesquisas Cientificas de Ribeirao Preto
Av. Presidente Vargas, 2627
2 andar - Itamarati
14020-260 Ribeirao Preto, Sao Paulo, Brazil
Phone: 55 16 6201251
Fax: 55 16 6211991
Publications: Genetics and Molecular Research (42999)

Fundacao SEADE
Av. Casper Libero, 464
01033-000 Sao Paulo, Sao Paulo, Brazil
Phone: 55 11 33135777
Fax: 55 11 21717297
Publications: Sao Paulo em Perspectiva (43051)

Fundacion Centro de Investigacion y Accion Social
Rodriguez Pena 356, 1 Π.
1334 4A Buenos Aires, Argentina
Phone: 54 11 52387730
Publications: Revista del CIAS (41479)

Fundacion de los Ferrocarriles Espanoles
Santa Isabel 44
E-28012 Madrid, Spain
Phone: 34 911 5110701
Publications: Via Libre (50814)

Fundacion Hispano Cubana
C/ Orfila, 8 1o A
E-28010 Madrid, Spain
Phone: 34 913 196313
Fax: 34 913 197008
Publications: Revista Hispano Cubana HC (50798)

Fundacion Infancia y Aprendizaje
C/Naranjo de Bulnes 69
San Sebastian de los Reyes
E-28707 Madrid, Spain
Phone: 34 91 6589100
Fax: 34 91 6589100
Publications: Cognitiva (50737) • Cultura y Educacion

(50746) • Estudios de Psicologia (50757) • Infancia y Aprendizaje/Journal for the Study of Education and Development (50769)

Fundacion Instituto de Historia Social UNED Valencia
Casa de la Misericordia, 34
E-46014 Valencia, Spain
Phone: 34 963 132621
Publications: Historia Social (50845)

Fundacion de Investigaciones Marxistas
Calle Alameda
5 2o Izda
E-28014 Madrid, Spain
Phone: 34 91 4201388
Fax: 34 91 4202004
Publications: Papeles de la FIM (Fundacion de Investigaciones Marxistas) (50787)

Fundacion Jose Ortega y Gasset
Fortuny, 53
E-28010 Madrid, Spain
Phone: 34 917 004100
Fax: 34 917 003530
Publications: Revista de Occidente (50799)

Fundacion Puntos de Encuentro
De la Rotonda El Gueguense
4 cuadras al Oeste
Managua, Nicaragua
Phone: 50 526 81227
Fax: 50 526 66305
Publications: La Boletina (49054)

Fundacion Sistema
Fuencarral, 127-1
E-28010 Madrid, Spain
Phone: 34 914 487319
Fax: 34 914 487339
Publications: Sistema (50807)

Furniture History Society
1 Mercedes Cottages
St. Johns Rd.
West Sussex
Haywards Heath RH16 4EH, United Kingdom
Phone: 44 1444 413845
Fax: 44 1444 413845
Publications: Furniture History (53548)

Fusion Flowers
Hillcroft
Fore Rd.
Kippen FK8 3DT, United Kingdom
Phone: 44 01786 870204
Fax: 44 01786 201102
Publications: Fusion Flowers (53726)

Future Medicine Ltd.
Unitec House
2 Albert Pl.
London N3 1QB, United Kingdom
Phone: 44 20 83716080
Fax: 44 20 83432313
Publications: Aging Health (53927) • Biomarkers in Medicine (54026) • Clinical Lipidology (54224) • Future Cardiology (54487) • Future Microbiology (54488) • Future Neurology (54489) • Future Oncology (54490) • Future Virology (54491) • HIV Therapy (54563) • Immunotherapy (54587) • International Journal of Clinical Rheumatology (54639) • Nanomedicine (54970) • Pediatric Health (55064) • Personalized Medicine (55072) • Pharmacogenomics (55077) • Regenerative Medicine (55180) • Women's Health (55414)

Future Publishing
Beauford Ct.
30 Monmouth St.
Bath BA1 2BW, United Kingdom
Phone: 44 12 25442244
Fax: 44 12 25822836
Publications: Good Woodworking (52242) • Quick & Easy Cross Stitch Magazine (52256) • Total Vauxhall (52261) • T3 (52263)

Future Publishing Ltd.
2 Balcombe St.
London NW1 6NW, United Kingdom
Phone: 44 20 70424000
Publications: Digital Home (52238) • The Jetix Magazine (48435) • PaperCraft Inspirations (55054) • PC-

Plus (52253) • Truckstop News (52262) • What Mountain Bike? (55401)

Fylde Tramway Society
PO Box 1264
Blackpool FY1 9EG, United Kingdom
Publications: Fylde Tramway News (52385)

Fyne Times
Linde Bldg.
7 Nuffield Way
Abingdon OX14 1RJ, United Kingdom
Phone: 44 1235 468428
Publications: Fyne Times (51792)

Fyrat University
Firat Typ Dergisi
Firat Universitesi
Tip Fakultesi Dekanligi
TR-23119 Elazig, Turkey
Phone: 90 424 2122960
Fax: 90 424 2379138
Publications: Firat Tip Dergisi (51553)

The Gaijin Gleaner
2084-22 Ooaza Masue
Nijou-Machi
Itoshima-gun
Fukuoka 819-16, Japan
Phone: 81 923 292041
Fax: 81 923 292041
Publications: The Gaijin Gleaner (46342)

Galadari Printing and Publishing L.L.C.
PO Box 11243
Dubai, United Arab Emirates
Phone: 971 433 83535
Fax: 971 433 83345
Publications: City Times (51636) • Khaleej Times (51646) • Young Times (51658)

The Galpin Society
37 Townsend Dr.
Saint Albans AL3 5RF, United Kingdom
Publications: Galpin Society Journal (56435)

Galvanizers Association
Wrens Ct.
56 Victoria Rd.
Sutton Coldfield B72 1SY, United Kingdom
Phone: 44 121 3558838
Fax: 44 121 3558727
Publications: Hot Dip Galvanizing (56695)

The Game Conservancy Trust
Game Conservancy
Fordingbridge SP6 1EF, United Kingdom
Phone: 44 1425 652381
Fax: 44 1245 655848
Publications: Game Conservancy Magazine (53395)

Game & Wildlife Conservancy Trust
Fordingbridge
Farnborough SP6 1EF, United Kingdom
Phone: 44 14 25652381
Publications: Gamewise (53378)

Gamingfloor.com Ltd.
72 New Bond St.
London W1S 1RR, United Kingdom
Phone: 44 8700 113020
Publications: Gaming Floor (54492)

Ganashtaki
74A Acharya Jagadish Chandra Bose Rd.
Kolkata 700 016, West Bengal, India
Publications: Ganashtaki (45266)

Garden History Society
70 Cowcross St.
London EC1M 6EJ, United Kingdom
Phone: 44 20 76082409
Fax: 44 20 74902974
Publications: Garden History (54493)

Gas Matters
35 New Bridge St.
London EC4V 6BW, United Kingdom
Phone: 44 20 73329900
Publications: Gas Matters (54494) • Gas Matters Today (54495)

Gatra.com
Gedung Gatra
Jl. Kalibata Timur IV, No. 15

12740 Jakarta, Indonesia
Phone: 62 21 7973535
Fax: 62 21 79196941
Publications: Gatra (45797)

Gaurav Society of Agricultural Research Information Centre
Systematic Printers, Near Video Market, Udayapuria St.
Mohalla Udayapuria
Udayapuria St.
Hisar 125 001, Haryana, India
Phone: 91 16 62230467
Publications: Research on Crops (45136)

Gazi University
Besevler
TR-06500 Ankara, Turkey
Phone: 90 312 2024444
Fax: 90 312 4444848
Publications: Gazi Medical Journal (51493)

GBS Publishers & Distributors
4866/24, Ground Fl.
Ansari Rd.
Darya Ganj
New Delhi 110 002, Delhi, India
Phone: 91 11 23264904
Fax: 91 11 27893171
Publications: Global Journal of Mathematics and Mathematical Sciences (GJMMS) (45881) • International Journal of Applied Mathematics and Mechanics (IJAMM) (56812) • International Journal of Pure & Applied Mathematical Sciences (IJPAMS) (45880) • International Journal of Theoretical and Applied Computer Sciences (IJTACS) (45587)

GE Fabbri Ltd.
The Communications Bldg., 7th Fl.
48 Leicester Sq.
London WC2H 7LT, United Kingdom
Phone: 44 20 30317600
Fax: 44 20 30317601
Publications: Doctor Who Battles in Time (56395) • Dora Dress Up and Go (54340) • Dora the Explorer (54341) • Felicity Wishes (56396) • Midsomer Murders Magazine (54933) • Sabrina's Secrets (55213) • 007 Spy Cards (56397) • Shrek's Quests (55236) • Totally Tracy Beaker (55330)

Nigel Gearing Ltd.
4 Red Barn Mews
High St.
Battle TN33 0AG, United Kingdom
Phone: 44 142 4774982
Fax: 44 142 4774321
Publications: Furniture News (52269) • Furniture Production (52270)

Gebruder Borntraeger Verlagsbuchhandlung
Johannesstr. 3A
D-70176 Stuttgart, Germany
Phone: 49 711 351456
Fax: 49 711 351456
Publications: Advances in Bryology (44659) • Bibliotheca Mycologica (44662) • Bibliotheca Phycologica (44663) • Contributions to Sedimentary Geology (44664) • Diatom Research (44665) • Eiszeitalter und Gegenwart Quaternary Science Journal (44666) • Entomologia Generalis (44244) • European Journal of Mineralogy (44043) • Fundamental and Applied Limnology (44668) • Meteorologische Zeitschrift (44669) • Neues Jahrbuch fur Geologie und Palaontologie (44672) • Neues Jahrbuch fur Mineralogie Abhandlungen (44494) • Nova Hedwigia (44673) • Phytocoenologia (44676) • Plinius (44677) • Senckenbergiana biologica (44678) • Zeitschrift der Deutschen Geologischen Gesellschaft (44685) • Zeitschrift fur Geomorphologie (44686)

The Geelong Advertiser Pty. Ltd.
PO Box 91
Geelong, Victoria 3220, Australia
Phone: 61 352 274300
Publications: Geelong Advertiser (41879)

Gem & Jewellery Information Centre
A-95 Journal House
Janta Colony
Jaipur 302 004, Rajasthan, India
Phone: 91 141 2614398
Fax: 91 141 2602973
Publications: Journal of Gem Industry (45197)

Gemmological Association and Gem Testing Laboratory of Great Britain
27 Greville St.
London EC1N 8TN, United Kingdom
Phone: 44 20 74043334
Fax: 44 20 74048843
Publications: The Journal of Gemmology (54756)

Geneesmiddelenbulletin
Postbus 2190
3500 GD Utrecht, Netherlands
Phone: 31 30 2823360
Fax: 31 20 7978500
Publications: Geneesmiddelenbulletin (48758)

General Association of Engineers in Romania
Calea Victoriei 118, 1st Fl.
R-70179 Bucharest, Romania
Phone: 40 21 3168994
Fax: 40 21 3125531
Publications: Buletin AGIR (49833) • Univers Ingineresc (49845)

General Association of Romanian Economists
Calea Grivitei N 21, Sector 1
R-010702 Bucharest, Romania
Phone: 40 21 3122248
Fax: 40 21 3129717
Publications: Economistul - The Economist (49834)

The General Dental Practitioners' Association
61 Harley St., 2nd Fl.
London W1G 8QU, United Kingdom
Phone: 44 20 76361072
Fax: 44 20 76361086
Publications: The GDP (54497)

General Osteopathic Council
176 Tower Bridge Rd.
London SE1 3LU, United Kingdom
Phone: 44 70 3576655
Fax: 44 70 3570011
Publications: The Osteopath (55044)

General Porfolio Ltd.
PO Box 4775
Kumasi, Ghana
Phone: 233 302232713
Fax: 233 302232608
Publications: The Ghanaian Chronicle (44727)

Genetics Society of Japan
c/o National Institute of Genetics
1111 Yata
Mishima
Shizuoka 411-8540, Japan
Phone: 81 559 816736
Publications: Genes & Genetic Systems (46617)

GeoConnexion Ltd.
PO Box 594
Cambridge CB1 0FY, United Kingdom
Phone: 44 1223 279151
Fax: 44 1223 279148
Publications: GEO (52822)

Geodetic Society of Japan
c/o Japanese Association of Surveyors
1-3-4 Koishikawa
Bunkyo-ku
Tokyo 112-0002, Japan
Phone: 81 3 56843358
Fax: 81 3 56843366
Publications: Journal of Geodetic Society of Japan (46901)

Geographical Association
160 Solly St.
Sheffield S1 4BF, United Kingdom
Phone: 44 114 2960088
Fax: 44 114 2967176
Publications: Geography (56493)

Geographical Society of Ireland
Geography Dept.
National University of Ireland
Belfield
Dublin IRL-4, Dublin, Ireland
Phone: 35 317 167777
Publications: Irish Geography (45974)

Geological Society of Australia
104 Bathurst St., Ste. 61
Sydney, New South Wales 2000, Australia
Phone: 61 2 92902194
Fax: 61 2 92902198
Publications: Australian Journal of Earth Sciences (42457)

Geological Society of China
26 Baiwanzhuang Rd.
Beijing 100037, People's Republic of China
Phone: 86 10 68999024
Fax: 86 10 68995305
Publications: Acta Geologica Sinica (43166)

Geological Society of Denmark
Geological Museum
Oster Voldgade 5-7
DK-1350 Copenhagen, Denmark
Phone: 45 353 22354
Publications: Geologisk Tidsskrift (43671)

Geological Society of India
No. 63, 12th Cross
Basappa Layout
Gavipuram
Bangalore 560 019, Karnataka, India
Phone: 91 80 26522943
Fax: 91 80 26613352
Publications: Journal of the Geological Society of India (44972)

Geological Society of London
Burlington House
Piccadilly
London W1J 0BG, United Kingdom
Phone: 44 20 74349944
Fax: 44 20 74398975
Publications: Journal of Micropalaeontology (52249)

Geological Society Publishing House
Unit 7, Brassmill Enterprise Center
Brassmill Ln.
Bath BA1 3JN, United Kingdom
Phone: 44 12 25445046
Fax: 44 12 25442836
Publications: Geochemistry (52241) • Journal of the Geological Society (52248) • Petroleum Geoscience (52254) • Quarterly Journal of Engineering Geology & Hydrogeology (52255)

Geological Survey of India
27 Jawaharlal Nehru Rd.
Kolkata 700 016, West Bengal, India
Phone: 91 33 22861676
Fax: 91 33 22861656
Publications: Geological Survey of India News (45267)

Geometry & Topology Publications
Mathematics Institute
University of Warwick
Coventry CV4 7AL, United Kingdom
Publications: Geometry & Topology (53083)

Georg Thieme Verlag
PO Box 301120
D-70451 Stuttgart, Germany
Phone: 49 711 89310
Fax: 49 711 8931410
Publications: Synthesis-Stuttgart (44682)

George MacDonald Society
9 Medway Dr.
Forest Row RH18 5NU, United Kingdom
Publications: North Wind (53397)

Georgian Internet Academy
17a, Chavchavadze Ave.
380028 Tbilisi, Georgia
Phone: 79 953 2913198
Publications: Computer Science and Telecommunications (44131) • Education Sciences & Psychology (44132)

Geotec
PO Box 1127
SE-221 04 Lund, Sweden
Phone: 46 75 7008820
Fax: 46 75 7008829
Publications: Borrsavangen (50984)

German Agricultural Society
Eschborner Landstrasse 122
D-60489 Frankfurt, Germany
Phone: 49 69 247880
Fax: 49 69 24788110
Publications: Agrifuture (44356) • DLG-Mitteilungen (44359)

German Appropriate Technology Exchange
Postfach 5180
D-65726 Eschborn, Germany
Phone: 49 619 6790
Fax: 49 619 679115
Publications: Gate Technology and Development (44345)

German Ceramic Society
Am Grott 7
D-51147 Cologne, Germany
Phone: 49 220 396648
Fax: 49 220 369301
Publications: Ceramic Forum International (44290)

German Direct Marketing Association
Hasengartenstr. 14
65189 Wiesbaden, Germany
Phone: 49 611 977930
Fax: 49 611 9779399
Publications: Dialog (44712)

German as a Foreign Language
Dept. of Languages & Intercultural Communication
Anglia Ruskin University
East Rd.
Cambridge CB1 1PT, United Kingdom
Publications: German as a Foreign Language (52824)

German Informatics Society
Ahrstrasse 45
D-53175 Bonn, Germany
Phone: 49 228 302145
Fax: 49 228 302167
Publications: Informatik Spektrum (44263)

German Neuroscience Society
c/o Meino Alexandra Gibson, Sec.
Max Delbruck Center for Moleculare Medizin
Robert Roessle Str. 10
D-13122 Berlin, Germany
Phone: 49 30 94063133
Fax: 49 30 94063819
Publications: Neuroforum (44225)

German Youth Hostel Association
Bismarck Rte. 8
D-32756 Detmold, Germany
Phone: 49 523 174010
Fax: 49 523 1740149
Publications: Extratour (44313)

Gesellschaft fur Deutsch-Chinesische Freundschaft Berlin e.v.
Innsbrucker Strasse 3
D-10825 Berlin, Germany
Phone: 49 308 545744
Fax: 49 308 547629
Publications: Das Neue China (44169)

Gesellschaft fur Selbstspielende Musikinstrumente
Emmastr. 56
D-45130 Essen, Germany
Phone: 49 201 784927
Fax: 49 201 7266240
Publications: Das Mechanische Musikinstrument (44346)

Gestalt Australia and New Zealand
PO Box 3728
Robina, Queensland 4230, Australia
Phone: 61 7 55809060
Publications: Gestalt Journal of Australia and New Zealand (42313)

Ghana Science Association
PO Box 7
Legon, Ghana
Phone: 233 302 937886
Publications: Ghana Journal of Science (44736) • Journal of the Ghana Science Association (44737)

Ghana Wildlife Society
PO Box 13252
Accra, Ghana
Publications: Bongo News (44725) • NKO Magazine (44729)

Ghanaian Newsrunner
Poederooienstraat 66

NL-1106 CK Amsterdam, Netherlands
Phone: 31 20 6977764
Fax: 31 20 6971978
Publications: Ghanaian Newsrunner (48001)

Gilbert and Sullivan Society
7 Mace Walk
Essex
Chelmsford CM1 2GE, United Kingdom
Publications: Gilbert & Sullivan News (52961)

Giramondo Publishing Company
PO Box 752
Artarmon, New South Wales 1570, Australia
Phone: 61 297 726350
Fax: 61 294 197934
Publications: Heat Magazine (41564)

Girgenti Editore S.R.L.
Casella Postale 10016
I-20100 Milan, Italy
Fax: 39 266 983333
Publications: La Rivista della Scuola (46185)

GIT Sicherheit + Management
Postfach 11 05 64
D-64420 Darmstadt, Germany
Phone: 49 61 5180910
Fax: 49 61 518090146
Publications: GIT Sicherheit Management (44307)

GIT Verlag GmbH
KG, Rosslerstrasse 90
D-64293 Darmstadt, Germany
Phone: 49 615 180900
Fax: 49 615 18090146
Publications: Hospital Post (44308) • Screening (44312)

G+J Espana
c/o Albasanz, 15 Edificio A
E-28037 Madrid, Spain
Phone: 34 914 369800
Fax: 34 915 767881
Publications: Cosmopolital (Spain) (50741) • Geo (50761) • Marie Claire (50780) • Mia (50784) • Muy Interesante (50785) • Ser Padres Bebe (50803) • Ser Padres Hoy (50804)

The Glade
Withnell Farm
Bury Ln.
Chorley PR6 8SD, United Kingdom
Phone: 44 1254 832849
Fax: 44 1254 832849
Publications: The Glade (53022)

The Gleaner Company Ltd.
7 N St.
PO Box 40
Kingston, Jamaica
Phone: 876922-3400
Fax: 809922-6223
Free: 888453-2637
Publications: The Children's Own (46282) • The Gleaner (46285) • The Star (46288) • The Sunday Gleaner (46289) • Track and Pools (46290) • The Weekend Star (46292)

Global Amitech
House No. 16, Rd. 127
Gulshan
Dhaka 1212, Bangladesh
Phone: 880 2 8827413
Fax: 880 2 9895247
Publications: News from Bangladesh (42814)

Global Business Press Pte. Ltd.
Level 34, Centennial Tower
3 Temasek Ave.
Singapore 039190, Singapore
Phone: 65 65497706
Fax: 65 65497011
Publications: Asian Airlines & Aerospace (50105) • Asian Defence and Diplomacy (50107)

Global Facilitation Network for Security Sector Reform
International Development Department
University of Birmingham
Birmingham B15 2TT, United Kingdom
Phone: 44 121 4145038

Fax: 44 121 4147995
Publications: Journal of Security Sector Management (52352)

Global Initiative on Psychiatry
PO Box 1282
NL-1200 BG Hilversum, Netherlands
Phone: 31 356 838727
Fax: 31 356 833646
Publications: Mental Health Reforms (48631)

Global NEST
University of the Aegean
Voulgaroktonou st. 30
GR-114 72 Athens, Greece
Phone: 30 210 6492450
Fax: 30 210 6492499
Publications: Global Nest (44743)

Global Science Press
Unit No. 1521, Level 15
Tower 1, Grand Central Plz.
138 Sha Tin Rural Committee Rd.
Shatin, N.T.
Hong Kong, People's Republic of China
Phone: 852 31051607
Fax: 852 31050207
Publications: Journal of Computational Mathematics (43353)

Global Sources
c/o Media Data Systems Pte. Ltd.
Raffles City
PO Box 0203
Singapore 911707, Singapore
Phone: 65 65472800
Fax: 65 65472888
Publications: Computer Products (50126) • Electronic & Components (50143) • Global Sources Auto Parts & Accessories (50152) • Global Sources Baby & Childrens Products (50153) • Global Sources Fashion Accessories (50154) • Global Sources Garments & Textiles (50155) • Global Sources Gifts & Premiums (50156) • Global Sources Hardware & DIY (50157) • Global Sources Home Products (50158) • Global Sources Sports & Leisure (50159) • Global Sources Telecom Products (50160)

Globe White Page Ltd.
New Hibernia House
Winchester Walk
London Bridge
London SE1 9AG, United Kingdom
Phone: 44 20 72340606
Fax: 44 20 72340808
Publications: Intellectual Asset Management (54613)

GNPHE
Rabat, Morocco
Phone: 21 237 771834
Fax: 21 237 778973
Publications: African Journal of Mathematical Physics (47814)

GoDubai.com
PO Box 112664
Dubai, United Arab Emirates
Phone: 971 4 2292675
Fax: 971 4 2292674
Publications: Arabian Woman (51632)

Goldcrest Broadcasting Ltd.
Crown House
25 High St.
Rothwell
Kettering NN14 6AD, United Kingdom
Phone: 44 15 36418558
Fax: 44 15 36418539
Publications: The Radio Magazine (53685)

Golden Egg Productions
Harris House
Tuam Rd.
Clarenbridge, Galway, Ireland
Phone: 353 91 384350
Fax: 353 91 384351
Publications: CORKnow (45932) • GALWAYnow (45933)

The Goldsmiths' Co.
Goldsmiths' Hall
Foster Ln.
London EC2V 6BN, United Kingdom

Phone: 44 20 76067010
Fax: 44 20 76061511
Publications: Goldsmiths Review (54517)

Golem
Emdener Str. 33
D-10551 Berlin, Germany
Phone: 49 176 51003202
Fax: 49 30 39731371
Publications: Golem (44187)

Golf Club Managers' Association
7a Beaconsfield Rd.
Weston-super-Mare BS23 1YE, United Kingdom
Phone: 44 19 34641166
Publications: Golf Club Management (56905)

Golf (Malaysia) Publications Sdn. Bhd.
No. 7-5 Block E2
Dataran Prima
Jalan PJU 1/42A
47301 Petaling Jaya, Malaysia
Phone: 60 378 805060
Fax: 60 378 805171
Publications: Golf Malaysia (47698)

Good Morning Chiangmai News Magazine Company Ltd.
20/1 Ratchamanka Rd.
A. Muang
Chiang Mai 50200, Thailand
Phone: 66 53 278516
Fax: 66 53 278516
Publications: Good Morning Chiangmai News Magazine (51458)

Goodwood Estate Company Ltd.
Goodwood
Chichester PO18 0PX, United Kingdom
Phone: 44 124 3755000
Fax: 44 124 3755005
Publications: Goodwood Magazine (53011)

Gospel Standard Publications
12b Roundwood Ln.
Hertfordshire
Harpenden AL5 3DD, United Kingdom
Phone: 44 1582 765448
Publications: Gospel Standard (53514)

Government College
Katchery Rd.
Lahore 5400, Pakistan
Phone: 92 42 9213340
Publications: Psychology Quarterly (49387)

Government of India Department of Periodicals
Civil Lines
Delhi 110 054, Delhi, India
Phone: 91 112 517409
Publications: Indian Labour Journal (45098)

GP London
32 Fredericks Pl.
London N12 8QE, United Kingdom
Phone: 44 20 84463604
Fax: 44 20 89228257
Publications: The Antique Trade Calendar (53958)

Graduate Journal of Social Science
c/o Mia Liinason, Managing Editor
Centre for Gender Studies
PO Box 117, Lund University
S-221 00 Lund, Sweden
Phone: 46 46 221000
Publications: Graduate Journal of Social Science (50986)

Grand Lodge of Antient Free and Accepted Masons of New Zealand
Marion Sq.
PO Box 6439
Wellington 6141, New Zealand
Phone: 64 4 3856622
Fax: 64 4 3855749
Publications: New Zealand Freemason (49020)

Grand Lodge of India
Freemasons' Hall
PO Box 681
Janpath
New Delhi 110001, Delhi, India
Phone: 91 11 23321956

Fax: 91 11 23320276
Publications: The Square and Compasses (45183)

Grand Lodge of the Philippines
New Plaridel Masonic Temple, 2nd Fl.
1440 San Marcelino St.
PO Box 990
Ermita
Manila 1000, Philippines
Phone: 63 2 522 2218
Publications: Cabletow (49548)

Grand Lodge of Scotland
Freemasons Hall
96 George St.
Edinburgh EH2 3DH, United Kingdom
Phone: 44 131 2255577
Fax: 44 131 2253953
Publications: Ashlar (53253)

Grand Lodge of Tasmania
3 Sandy Bay Rd.
Hobart, Tasmania 7005, Australia
Phone: 61 3 62235814
Fax: 61 3 62238159
Publications: Freemasonry Tasmania (41958)

Grand National Archery Society
Lilles Hall National Sports Ctr.
Newport TF10 9AT, United Kingdom
Phone: 44 1952 677888
Fax: 44 1952 606019
Publications: Archery UK (55688)

Grande Loge de France
8, rue de puteaux
F-75017 Paris, France
Publications: Points de Vues Initiatives (44076)

Greek Orthodontic Society
95-97 Mavromichali St.
GR-114 72 Athens, Greece
Phone: 30 210 3615432
Fax: 30 210 3615432
Publications: Hellenic Orthodontic Review (44744)

Green Leaf Publishing Inc.
Aizelewood Business Ctr.
Nursery St.
Sheffield S3 8GG, United Kingdom
Phone: 44 144282 3475
Fax: 44 144282 3476
Publications: Skamania County Pioneer (56514)

W. Green & Son Ltd.
21 Alva St.
Edinburgh EH2 4PS, United Kingdom
Phone: 44 13 12254879
Fax: 44 13 12252104
Publications: Greens Business Law Bulletin (53280) •
Greens Criminal Law Bulletin (53281) • Greens Property
Law Bulletin (53282) • Greens Weekly Digest (53283) •
Juridical Review (53296) • The Scots Law Times
(53311)

GreenCross Publishing
Lower Ground Fl.
5 Harrington St.
Dublin 8, Ireland
Phone: 353 147 89770
Fax: 353 147 89764
Publications: Irish Pharmacist (45983)

Greenleaf Publishing
Aizlewood Business Center
Aizlewood's Mill, Nursery St.
Nursery St.
Sheffield S3 8GG, United Kingdom
Phone: 44 11 42823475
Fax: 44 11 42823476
Publications: Greener Management International
(56495) • The Journal of Corporate Citizenship (56504)

Greenpeace Austria
Fernkorngasse 10
A-1100 Vienna, Austria
Phone: 43 154 54580
Fax: 43 154 5458098
Publications: ACT! The Magazine of Greenpeace
Austria (42742)

Greenpeace Belgium
Chaussee de Haecht, 159
B-1030 Brussels, Belgium

Phone: 32 2 2740200
Fax: 32 2 2740230
Publications: Greenpeace Magazine (42857)

Greer Publications
5B Edgewater Business Pk.
Belfast Harbour Estate
Belfast BT3 9JQ, United Kingdom
Phone: 353 28 90783200
Fax: 353 28 90783210
Publications: Garage Trader (52283) • Industrial &
Manufacturing Engineer Magazine (52286) • Northern
Woman (52290) • Specify (52293) • Ulster Business
(52295) • Ulster Grocer (52297)

Grey Literature Network Service
Javastraat 194-HS
NL-1095 CP Amsterdam, Netherlands
Phone: 31 20 3312420
Publications: The Grey Journal (48006)

Greycoat Publishing Ltd.
148 Buckingham Palace Rd.
Kensington
London SW1W 9TR, United Kingdom
Phone: 44 20 77307995
Fax: 44 20 77303884
Publications: British Journal of Intensive Care
(54124) • Cardiology International (54176) • Interna-
tional Journal of Adipose Tissue (54630) • Interna-
tional Journal of Intensive Care (54650) • International
Journal of Respiratory Care (54659) • Ophthalmology
International (55040)

Grieg Society of Great Britain
Pipers End, Dove Ln.
Potters Bar EN6 2SG, United Kingdom
Phone: 44 1707 643366
Fax: 44 1707 643366
Publications: The Grieg Companion (56296)

GRIPS media GmbH
Eichendorffstr. 64
D-38667 Bad Harzburg, Germany
Phone: 49 532 254575
Fax: 49 532 254574
Publications: Steel Grips (44144)

Groove
Kopenicker Str. 178/179
D-10997 Berlin, Germany
Phone: 49 30 44312020
Fax: 49 30 2807098
Publications: Groove (44188)

Group Diario de Coimbra
Av. Antonio Augusto de Aguiar, 88-1
1050 Lisbon, Portugal
Phone: 351 21 0040407
Fax: 351 21 0040499
Publications: Diario de Aveiro (49785) • Diario de
Coimbra (49790) • Diario de Leiria (49799) • Diario
Regional Viseu (49813)

Groupe Liaison
1 Ave. Edouard Belin
F-92856 Rueil-Malmaison, France
Phone: 33 141 299999
Fax: 33 141 299513
Publications: La Tribune de l'Assurance (44100)

Grupo Asesoramiento Comercial GM2 S.L.
Oslo, 1
Portal 1, 1
Oficina 1
28224 Pozuelo de Alarcon, Spain
Phone: 34 91 7150307
Fax: 34 91 7158421
Publications: Conectronica (50827)

Grupo Edefa S.A.
C/Puerto Principe No. 3-B 1A
E-28043 Madrid, Spain
Phone: 34 91 3821945
Fax: 34 91 7630021
Publications: Airline Ninety Two (50726) • Defensa
(50750)

Gruppo Editoriale Faenza Editrice S.p.A.
Via Granarolo 175/3
I-48018 Faenza, Italy
Phone: 39 546 673781

Fax: 39 546 660440
Publications: Giornale del Marmo—International Stone
Magazine (46137)

Gruppo Editoriale JCE S.R.L.
Via. Patecchio
I-20141 Cinisello Balsamo, Italy
Phone: 39 257 316011
Fax: 39 257 316291
Publications: Sicurezza (46135)

GSK
Pavillonweg 2
CH-3012 Bern, Switzerland
Phone: 41 31 3083838
Fax: 41 31 3016991
Publications: Kunst & Architektur in der Schweiz
(51075)

Guadalupe Missioners
Cantera 29
Col. Tlalpan
Del. Tlalpan
14000 Mexico City, Federal District, Mexico
Phone: 15 556 552691
Publications: Almas (47781)

Guardian Newspapers Ltd.
Kings Pl.
90 York Way
London N1 9GU, United Kingdom
Phone: 44 20 33532000
Publications: The Guardian (54525) • The Guardian
Weekend (54526) • Money Observer (54951) • The
Observer (55023)

Guernsey Chamber of Commerce
Ste. 1
16 Glategny Esplanande
St. Peter Port
Guernsey GY1 1WN, United Kingdom
Phone: 44 14 81727483
Fax: 44 14 81710755
Publications: Contact (53487)

The Guide Association
17-19 Buckingham Palace Rd.
London SW1W 0PT, United Kingdom
Phone: 44 20 78346242
Fax: 44 20 78288317
Publications: Guiding Magazine (54527)

The Guide Dogs for the Blind Association
Burghfield Common
Reading RG7 3YG, United Kingdom
Phone: 44 118 9835555
Fax: 44 118 9835433
Publications: FORWARD (56318)

Guideline Publications
Enigma Bldg., Unit 3
Bilton Rd.
Denbigh E
Bletchley MK1 1HW, United Kingdom
Phone: 44 1908 274433
Fax: 44 1908 270614
Publications: Military Modelcraft International (52389) •
Scale Aircraft Modelling (52390) • Toy Soldier Collector
(52391)

Guides et Scouts d'Europe - France
Le Relais de Poste
BP 17
F-77570 Chateau Landon, France
Phone: 33 164 455360
Fax: 33 164 294456
Publications: Maitrises (43930)

Guild of Air Traffic Control Officers
4 St. Mary's Rd.
Bingham NG13 8DW, United Kingdom
Phone: 44 19 49876405
Fax: 44 19 49876405
Publications: Transmit (52326)

Guild of Church Musicians
Hillbrow
Godstone Rd.
Blechingley RH1 4PJ, United Kingdom
Phone: 44 18 83743168
Publications: Laudate Magazine (52388)

Guild of Experienced Motorists
Sta. Rd.

GEM Motoring Assist
Forest Row RH18 5EN, United Kingdom
Fax: 44 13 42824847
Publications: Good Motoring Magazine (53396)

Guild of International Songwriters and Composers
Sovereign House
12 Trewartha Rd.
Praa Sands
Penzance TR20 9ST, United Kingdom
Phone: 44 17 36762826
Fax: 44 17 36763328
Publications: Songwriting and Composing Magazine (56250)

Guild of Master Craftsmen Publications Ltd.
166 High St.
E Sussex
Lewes BN7 1XU, United Kingdom
Phone: 44 1273 477374
Publications: Black and White Photography (53847) • Furniture and Cabinetmaking (53849) • Organic Life (53850) • Wood Working Plans and Projects (53851) • Woodcarving (53852)

Guild of Television Cameramen
1 Churchill Rd.
Whitchurch
Tavistock PL19 9BU, United Kingdom
Phone: 44 182 2614405
Fax: 44 182 2614405
Publications: Zerb (56728)

Guiton Group Limited
Guiton House
Five Oaks, St. Saviour
Jersey JE4 8XQ, United Kingdom
Phone: 44 1534 611800
Fax: 44 1534 611825
Publications: Guernsey Press (53665) • Jersey Evening Post (53666)

Gujarat Engineering Research Institute
Race Course
Vadodara 390 007, Gujarat, India
Publications: Navnirman (45764)

Gulf Publishing & Printing Company
PO Box 533
Doha, Qatar
Phone: 974 43 50478
Fax: 974 43 50474
Publications: The Gulf Times (49821)

GyJ Espana Ediciones
C/Albasanz, 15. Edif. A.
E-28037 Madrid, Spain
Phone: 91 4369800
Fax: 91 5767881
Publications: Ser Padres (50802)

H. Bauer Publishing
Academic House
24-28 Oval Rd.
London NW1 7DT, United Kingdom
Phone: 44 20 72418000
Fax: 44 20 72418030
Publications: Angling Times (53944) • Arrowwords (53965) • Bella (54010) • Big Value Codebreakers (54017) • Bird Watching (56252) • Codebreakers (54235) • Criss Cross (54287) • Fate & Fortune (54445) • Fiction Feast (54450) • Grazia (54521) • Hide 'n' Seek Wordsearch (54550) • Kerrang! (54842) • Mojo (54944) • Pet Product Marketing (55073) • Picture Arrowwords (55089) • Practical Fishkeeping (55113) • Puzzle Selection (55158) • Quick-X-words (55165) • Spirit & Destiny (55262) • Su-doku (55274) • Su-doku Selection (55275) • Take a Break (55286) • Take a Break's Su-doku (55287) • Take a Crossword (55288) • Take a Puzzle (55289) • that's life! (55302) • Total TVguide (55329) • TVChoice (55345) • TVQuick (55346) • Wordsearches (55416) • Wordsearches Collection (55417)

Hachette Filipacchi
Avda. Cardenal Herrera
Oria, 3
E-28034 Madrid, Spain
Phone: 34 917 287000
Fax: 34 917 289129
Publications: Car and Driver (Spain) (50732)

Hachette Filipacchi (UK) Ltd.
64 North Row
London W1K 7LL, United Kingdom
Phone: 44 20 71507000
Fax: 44 20 71507001
Publications: ELLEgirl (54361)

Haigazian University
Rue Mexique
Kantari
PO Box 11-1748
Beirut, Lebanon
Phone: 961 1 349230
Fax: 961 1 353012
Publications: Haigazian Armenological Review (47395)

David Hall Publishing
2 Stephenson Close
Drayton Fields
Northamptonshire
Daventry NN11 8RF, United Kingdom
Phone: 44 1327 311999
Fax: 44 1327 311190
Publications: Advanced Carp Fishing (53158) • Match Fishing Magazine (53160)

Halls Creek Herald
PO Box 370
Halls Creek, Western Australia 6770, Australia
Phone: 61 891 685199
Fax: 61 891 685299
Publications: Halls Creek Herald (41938)

Hamdard Foundation Pakistan
Al-Majeed, Hamdard Centre
Nazimabad No.3
Karachi 74600, Pakistan
Phone: 92 216 616001
Fax: 92 216 611755
Publications: Hamdard Islamicus (49350) • Hamdard Medicus (49351) • Hamdard Naunehal (49352)

Hamerville Magazines Ltd.
Regal House
Regal Way
Watford WD24 4YF, United Kingdom
Phone: 44 1923 237799
Fax: 44 1923 246901
Publications: Commercial Vehicle Workshop (56863) • Housing Association Building & Maintenance (56865) • Kitchens & Bathrooms News (56866) • Local Authority Building and Maintenance (56868) • Professional Builder (56869) • Professional Builders Merchant (56870) • Professional Electrician & Installer (56871) • Professional Hairdresser (56872) • Professional Heating & Plumbing Installer (56873) • Professional Motor Factor (56874) • Professional Motor Mechanic (56875) • Window Fabricator & Installer (56877)

Handbell Ringers of Great Britain
87 The Woodfields
Sanderstead
South Croydon CR2 OHJ, United Kingdom
Publications: Reverberations (56565)

Hanyang University Ceramic Processing Research Center
17 Haengdang-dong
Seongdong-gu
Seoul 133-791, Republic of Korea
Phone: 82 222 201828
Fax: 82 222 917395
Publications: Journal of Ceramic Processing Research (47271)

Happy Publishing Limited
27 York Pl.
Aberdeen AB11 4DH, United Kingdom
Phone: 44 1224 594659
Publications: Good Time Guide (51677) • Lady Biker Magazine (51679) • Star Flyer Magazine (51680)

Hardware Zone Private Ltd.
20 Ayer Rajah Cres.
NO. 09-04/05, Technopreneur Centre
Singapore 139964, Singapore
Phone: 65 6 8722725
Fax: 65 6 8722724
Publications: Hardwage Mag (50162)

Haribon Foundation
2nd Fl., Santos & Sons Bldg.
No. 973 Aurora Blvd.

Cubao
Quezon City, Philippines
Phone: 63 2 4344642
Fax: 63 2 4344696
Publications: Haring Ibon (49594)

Harmonia
Rosemount House
Dundrum Rd.
Dundrum
Dublin 16, Dublin, Ireland
Phone: 353 1 2405300
Publications: Auto Ireland (45947) • Food & Wine Magazine (45960) • Irish Tatler (45987) • U Magazine (45999)

Harrassowitz Verlag
Kreuzberger Ring 7b-d
D-65205 Wiesbaden, Germany
Phone: 49 611 5300
Fax: 49 611 530
Publications: Anatolian Archaeological Studies (44710) • Central Asiatic Journal (44711)

Hart Publishing Ltd.
16C Worcester Pl.
Oxford OX1 2JW, United Kingdom
Phone: 44 1865 517530
Fax: 44 1865 510710
Publications: European Competition Journal (54392) • European Law Reports (55948) • The Journal of Corporate Law Studies (56025) • Journal of Private International Law (51678) • Judicial Review (56080) • King's Law Journal (56081) • Law and Financial Markets Review (56085) • Law and Humanities (53088) • Legal Ethics (56089) • Legisprudence (42864) • Oxford University Commonwealth Law Journal (56138)

The Hat Magazine Ltd.
170 Brick Ln.
London E1 6RU, United Kingdom
Phone: 44 20 72471120
Fax: 44 20 73752199
Publications: The HAT Magazine (54533)

Haveeru Daily
PO Box 20103
Ameenee Magu
Male, Maldives
Phone: 96 032 5671
Fax: 96 032 3103
Publications: Haveeru Daily (47725)

Hawker Publications
Culvert House
Culvert Rd.
London SW11 5DH, United Kingdom
Phone: 44 20 77202108
Fax: 44 20 74983023
Publications: Caring Times (54182)

Hawkes Design
c/o The White Hill Centre
White Hill
Chesham HP5 1AG, United Kingdom
Phone: 44 494 793000
Fax: 44 494 776331
Publications: Chesham Town Talk (52985)

Haworth Press Inc.
10 Alice St.
Binghamton, NY 13904
Phone: 607722-5857
Fax: 607722-6362
Free: 800429-6784
Publications: Journal of Travel & Tourism Marketing (43363)

Haymarket Business Magazines
174 Hammersmith Rd.
London W6 7JP, United Kingdom
Phone: 44 20 82674210
Publications: AV Magazine (53992) • The Ends Report (54369) • Event (54413) • Human Resources (54579) • MIMS (54935) • Packaging News (55048) • Print Buyer (55118) • Promotions & Incentives (55140) • Regeneration & Renewal (55179)

Haymarket Business Publications Ltd.
174 Hammersmith Rd.
London W6 7JP, United Kingdom
Phone: 44 20 82675000

Fax: 44 20 82674268
Publications: PrintWeek (55119) • Revolution (55201)

Haymarket Magazines Ltd.
174 Hammersmith Rd.
London W6 7JP, United Kingdom
Phone: 44 20 82674210
Publications: Autocar (55615)

Haymarket Marketing Publications
174 Hammersmith Rd.
London W6 7JP, United Kingdom
Phone: 44 20 82675000
Publications: Conference & Incentive Travel (54259)

Haymarket Media GmbH & Co. KG
Frankfurter Str., 3d (ARTmax)
D-38122 Braunschweig, Germany
Phone: 49 531 380040
Fax: 49 531 3800425
Publications: Deutsche Baumschule (44275) • Friedhofs Kultur (44276) • Gb - Das Magazin fur Zierpflanzenbau (44137) • Gestalten & Verkaufen (44277) • TASPO (44279)

Haymarket Media Limited
23/F The Centrium
60 Wyndham St. Central
Hong Kong, People's Republic of China
Phone: 852 31751900
Publications: CEI Asia Pacific (43287) • Digital Media (43296) • FinanceAsia (43300) • Media (43369)

Haymarket Media Pty. Ltd.
52 Victoria St.
McMahons Point
Sydney, New South Wales 2060, Australia
Phone: 61 2 83993611
Fax: 61 2 83993622
Publications: FourFourTwo (42504) • Limelight (42536) • PC Authority (42558)

Haymarket Motoring Publications Ltd.
Teddington Studios
Broom Rd.
Teddington TW11 9BE, United Kingdom
Phone: 44 20 82675000
Publications: Autocar (56729) • What Car? (56736)

Haymarket Publishing Ltd.
174 Hammersmith Rd.
London W6 7JP, United Kingdom
Phone: 44 20 82674210
Publications: Atomic Maximum Power Computing (Australia) Magazine (42042) • Autosport Magazine (53547) • Campaign (54170) • Management Today (54902) • Marketing (54908) • PRWeek Magazine (55148) • Third Sector Magazine (55311)

Haymarket Specialist Motoring Publications
Somerset Rd.
Teddington TW11 8RU, United Kingdom
Phone: 44 20 82675722
Fax: 44 20 82675619
Publications: Motor Sport (56734)

Hayward Medical Communications
The Pines
Fordham Rd.
Newmarket CB8 7LG, United Kingdom
Phone: 44 1638 723560
Fax: 44 1638 723561
Publications: British Journal of Cancer Management (54114) • British Journal of Dermatology Nursing (54119) • British Journal of Renal Medicine (54134) • British Journal of Sexual Medicine (54136) • Dermatology in Practice (54320) • European Journal of Palliative Care (54403) • Headache in Practice (54535) • Lung Cancer in Practice (54893) • Myeloproliferative Disorders in practice (54968) • Respiratory Disease in Practice (55193) • Thrombus (55317)

Hazards
PO Box 4042
Sheffield S8 2DG, United Kingdom
Phone: 44 114 2014265
Publications: Hazards (56496)

HDRA
Garden Organic Ryton
Coventry CV8 3LG, United Kingdom
Phone: 44 247 6303517

Fax: 44 247 6639229
Publications: The Organic Way (53089)

Headway - The Brain Injury Association
Bradbury House.
190 Bagnall Rd.
Nottingham NG6 8SF, United Kingdom
Phone: 44 11 59240800
Fax: 44 11 59584446
Publications: Headway News (55758)

Health and Beauty Business Media GmbH & Co. KG
Karl-Friedrich-Strasse 14-18
D-76133 Karlsruhe, Germany
Phone: 49 721 1650
Publications: COSSMA (44492)

Health Protection Agency
Holborn Gate
330 High Holborn, 7th Fl.
London WC1V 7PP, United Kingdom
Phone: 44 20 77592783
Fax: 44 20 77592789
Publications: Communicable Disease Report Weekly (54243)

Health Systems Trust
34 Essex Ter., Westville, 3630
PO Box 808
Durban 4000, Republic of South Africa
Phone: 27 31 2669090
Fax: 27 31 2669199
Publications: South African Health Review (50470)

L'Hebdo
Pont Bessieres 3
PO Box 6682
CH-1002 Lausanne, Switzerland
Phone: 41 213 317600
Fax: 41 213 317601
Publications: L'Hebdo (51190)

Hecate Press
PO Box 6099
Brisbane, Queensland 4067, Australia
Publications: Australian Women's Book Review (41643) • Hecate (41648)

Hector Kobbekaduwa
Agrarian Research and Training Institute
114 Wijerama Mawatha
Colombo 7, Sri Lanka
Phone: 94 112 696981
Publications: Sri Lanka Journal of Agrarian Studies (50864)

Heian Bunka Center
35 Minamigoshomachi
Okazaki
Sakyo-ku
Kyoto 606-8334, Japan
Phone: 81 757 611433
Fax: 81 757 511196
Publications: Kyoto Journal (46479)

Heise Zeitschriften Verlag GmbH & Co. KG
Helstorfer Str. 7
D-30625 Hannover, Germany
Phone: 49 511 53520
Fax: 49 511 5352129
Publications: c't magazine (44430) • iX (44433) • Telepolis (44436)

Heldermann Verlag
Langer Graben 17
D-32657 Lemgo, Germany
Phone: 49 526 110226
Fax: 49 526 115264
Publications: Computational Methods and Function Theory (44718) • Contributions to Algebra and Geometry (44531) • Journal of Convex Analysis (44532) • Journal for Geometry and Graphics (44533)

Hellenic Foundation for European and Foreign Policy
Vas. Sofias 49
GR-10676 Athens, Greece
Phone: 30 210 7257110
Fax: 30 210 7257114
Publications: Journal of Southeast European and Black Sea Studies (44751)

Hellenic Radiological Society
P. Kyriakou 21
GR-115 21 Athens, Greece
Phone: 30 164 51489
Publications: Hellenic Radiology Journal (44745)

Hemming Information Services
32 Vauxhall Bridge Rd.
London SW1V 2SS, United Kingdom
Phone: 44 207 79736400
Fax: 44 207 72335056
Publications: Bridge Design & Engineering (54106)

Henry George Foundation of Great Britain Ltd.
212 Piccadilly
London W1J 9HG, United Kingdom
Phone: 44 20 79171899
Fax: 44 20 79171899
Publications: Land & Liberty (54849)

Henry Martyn Institute
6-3-128/1
Hyderabad 500 052, Andhra Pradesh, India
Phone: 91 40 24014258
Fax: 91 40 24014565
Publications: Journal of the Henry Martyn Institute (45174)

Henry Stewart Publications
Russell House
28-30 Little Russell St.
London WC1A 2HN, United Kingdom
Phone: 44 20 74043040
Fax: 44 20 74042081
Publications: Human Genomics (54577) • Journal of Financial Crime (54752) • Journal of Financial Regulation and Compliance (54753)

The Heraldry Society
PO Box 772
Guildford GU3 3ZX, United Kingdom
Phone: 44 14 83237373
Fax: 44 14 83237373
Publications: Coat of Arms (53489)

Heraldry Society of Scotland
25 Craigentinny Cres.
Edinburgh EH7 6QA, United Kingdom
Phone: 44 131 5532232
Publications: Double Tressure (53270)

The Herb Society
Sulgrave Manor
PO Box 946
Northampton NN3 0BN, United Kingdom
Phone: 44 1295768899
Publications: Herbs (55708)

Herpetological Association of Africa
c/o Mandi Alblas
Dept. of Biomedical Sciences
PO Box 19063
Tygerberg 7505, Republic of South Africa
Phone: 27 21 9389394
Fax: 27 21 9389317
Publications: African Journal of Herpetology (50638)

Herpetological Society of Japan
Dept. of Zoology
Graduate School of Science
Kyoto University
Kitashirakawa-Oiwakecho Sakyo-ku
Kyoto 606-8502, Japan
Publications: Current Herpetology (46470)

Het Houtblad
Postbus 8632
NL-3009 AP Rotterdam, Netherlands
Phone: 31 10 2894078
Fax: 31 10 2894076
Publications: Het Houtblad (48750)

H.G. Wells Society
c/o Mark Egerton, Hon. Gen. Sec.
Flat 3, 21b Church Rd.
London NW4 4EB, United Kingdom
Publications: The Wellsian (53233)

High Court of Jammu and Kashmir
Srinagar 190 001, Jammu and Kashmir, India
Publications: Jammu and Kashmir Law Reporter (45738)

High Spirit
105 High St., 1st Fl.
Brentwood CM14 4RR, United Kingdom
Phone: 44 01277 264284
Fax: 44 01277 264123
Publications: High Spirit (52574)

Higher Education Academy
Innovation Way
York Science Pk.
Heslington YO10 5BR, United Kingdom
Phone: 44 19 04717500
Publications: Discourse (53566) • Innovations in
Teaching and Learning in Information and Computer
Sciences (53567) • Journal of Hospitality, Leisure,
Sports & Tourism Education (53568)

**Higher Education Research and Development
Society of Australasia**
c/o Jennifer Ungaro, Admin. Mgr.
PO Box 27
Milperra, New South Wales 2214, Australia
Phone: 61 297 713911
Fax: 61 297 714299
Publications: Higher Education Research and Develop-
ment (HERD) (42107)

Hikari Ltd.
PO Box 15
BG-7005 Ruse, Bulgaria
Phone: 359 82 582277
Publications: Advanced Studies in Theoretical Physics
(43087) • Applied Mathematical Sciences (43088) •
International Journal of Algebra (43089) • International
Journal of Contemporary Mathematical Sciences
(43090) • International Journal of Mathematical Analysis
(43091) • International Mathematical Forum (43092)

Hindawi Publishing Corp.
410 Park Ave., 15th Fl.
287 PMB
New York, NY 10022-4407
Fax: 215893-4392
Publications: International Journal of Image and Video
Processing (IJIVP) (43914) • International Journal of
Photoenergy (43762) • Journal of Automated Methods
and Management in Chemistry (55853)

Hindustan Publishing Corp.
4805 Bharat Ram Rd.
24 Darya Ganj
New Delhi 110 002, Delhi, India
Phone: 91 113 254401
Fax: 91 116 193511
Publications: Contributions to Himalayan Geology
(45498) • Demography India (45091) • Folklore Research Journal (45517) • Recent Researches in Geology (45642)

Hinge Marketing Ltd.
Empire Land Commerical Centre, 24th Fl.
81 Lockhart Rd.
Wanchai
Hong Kong, People's Republic of China
Publications: Hinge (43302)

Hippopotamus Press
Roland John, 22 Whitewell Rd.
Frome BA11 4EL, United Kingdom
Phone: 44 13 73466653
Fax: 44 13 73466653
Publications: Outposts Poetry Quarterly (53400)

Hiragana Times
3F Ebisawa Bldg., 5-10-10 Shinjuku
Shinjuku-Ku
Tokyo 160-0065, Japan
Phone: 81 3 33418989
Fax: 81 3 33418987
Publications: Hiragana Times (46833)

Hiroshima University
1-1-1 Kagamiyama
Higashi-Hiroshima
Hiroshima 739-8524, Japan
Phone: 81 824 246810
Fax: 81 824 227076
Publications: Hiroshima Journal of Mathematics Educa-
tion (46379)

Hiroshima University
1-3-1 Kagamiyama
Higashi-Hiroshima

Hiroshima 739-8526, Japan
Phone: 81 82 4247350
Fax: 81 82 4240710
Publications: Hiroshima Mathematical Journal (46380)

Historic Motor Racing News Ltd.
34-35 Southhampton St.
London WC2E 7HF, United Kingdom
Phone: 44 20 74209348
Fax: 44 20 74209346
Publications: Historic Motor Racing News (51265)

Historical Association
59 A Kennington Park Rd.
London SE11 4JH, United Kingdom
Phone: 44 20 77353901
Fax: 44 20 75824989
Publications: Historian (54554) • Teaching History
(55293)

Historical Metallurgy Society
17A Thorncote Rd.
Bedfordshire
Northill SG18 9AQ, United Kingdom
Publications: Historical Metallurgy (55717)

History Scotland
31-32 Park Row
Leeds LS1 5JD, United Kingdom
Phone: 44 113 2002922
Publications: History Scotland (53767)

History Today Ltd.
25 Bedford Ave.
London WC1B 3AT, United Kingdom
Phone: 44 20 32197810
Fax: 44 20 32197829
Publications: History Review (54560) • History Today
(54561)

Hitachi Cable Company Ltd.
4-14-1 Sotokanda
Chiyoda-ku
Tokyo 101-8971, Japan
Publications: Hitachi Cable Review (46834)

Hitek Magazine
Hazmieh Damascus Rd.
Karam Bldg., 3rd Fl., Near Sea Sweet
Beirut, Lebanon
Phone: 961 545 0212
Fax: 961 545 5477
Publications: Hitek Magazine (47396)

Hogrefe & Huber Publishers
875 Massachusetts Ave, 7th Fl.
Cambridge, MA 02139-3015
Fax: 617354-6875
Free: 866823-4726
Publications: Allergy and Clinical Immunology International (44391) • European Journal of Psychological Assessment (48744) • Journal of Individual Differences
(44387)

Hohai University
1 Xikang Rd.
Nanjing 210098, Jiangsu, People's Republic of China
Publications: Advances in Science and Technology of
Water Resources (43456) • Journal of Economics of
Water Resources (43458) • Journal of Hohai University
(43459) • Water Resources Protection (43460) • Water
Science and Engineering (43461)

Hokkaido University
kita 10
Nishi 8
Kita-ku
Sapporo 060-0810, Japan
Fax: 81 11 7561244
Publications: Hokkaido Mathematical Journal (46650)

**Hokkaido University Faculty of Veterinary
Medicine**
Kita 18
Nishi 9
Kita-ku
Sapporo 060-0818, Japan
Fax: 81 117 065190
Publications: Japanese Journal of Veterinary Research
(46651)

Holiday Publication Ltd.
30, Tejgaon Industrial Area
Dhaka 1208, Bangladesh

Phone: 880 291 22950
Fax: 880 291 27927
Publications: Holiday (42810)

Holstein Freisian Association of Australia
PO Box 489
Hawthorn, Victoria 3122, Australia
Phone: 61 3 98357600
Fax: 61 3 98357699
Publications: The Australian Holstein Journal (41941)

Groupe de Presse Michel Hommell
48-50 Blvd. Senard
F-92210 Saint Cloud, France
Publications: Echappement (44101)

Honduras This Week
Colonia Payaqui
frente al Instituto San Miguel, casa No. 3644
Tegucigalpa, Honduras
Phone: 504 239 0285
Fax: 504 232 2300
Publications: Honduras This Week (44803)

Hong Kong Academy of Medicine
99 Wong Chuk Hang Rd.
Aberdeen
Hong Kong, People's Republic of China
Phone: 86 852 28718888
Fax: 86 852 25055577
Publications: HK Medical Journal (43303)

Hong Kong Arts Centre
2 Harbour Rd., Wanchai
Hong Kong, People's Republic of China
Phone: 852 25820200
Publications: Artslink (43268)

The Hong Kong College of Psychiatrists
Rm. 906, Hong Kong Academy of Medicine, Jockey
Club Bldg.
99 Wong Chuk Hang Rd.
Aberdeen
Hong Kong, People's Republic of China
Fax: 852 28701391
Publications: East Asian Archives of Psychiatry (43297)

Hong Kong Economic Association
GPO Box 4004
Hong Kong, People's Republic of China
Phone: 86 226 167178
Fax: 86 228 917940
Publications: Pacific Economic Review (43374)

The Hong Kong Exporters' Association
Star House, Rm. 825
3 Salisbury Rd.
Tsimshatsui
Kowloon
Hong Kong, People's Republic of China
Phone: 86 227 309851
Fax: 86 227 301869
Publications: Exporters Bulletin (43299)

The Hong Kong General Chamber of Commerce
22nd Fl., United Ctr.
95 Queensway
Hong Kong, People's Republic of China
Phone: 85 252 99229
Fax: 85 252 79843
Publications: The Bulletin (43285)

Hong Kong Institute of Landscape Architects
Hennessy Rd. Post Office
PO Box 20561
Wanchai
Hong Kong, People's Republic of China
Phone: 85 28962833
Fax: 85 28963938
Publications: Yuen Lin (43387)

The Hong Kong Institute of Surveyors
Jardine House, Ste. 801
1 Connaught Pl.
Central
Hong Kong, People's Republic of China
Phone: 86 225 263679
Fax: 86 228 684612
Publications: Hong Kong Surveyor (43345)

Hong Kong Institution of Engineering Surveyors
PO Box No. 79
Tsuen Wan

Hong Kong, People's Republic of China
Publications: Journal of Geospatial Engineering (43356)

Hong Kong Institution of Textile and Apparel
63 Tai Yip St.
Kowloon Bay
Kowloon
Hong Kong, People's Republic of China
Phone: 8522263-6313
Fax: 8522758-9935
Publications: Research Journal of Textile and Apparel (43380)

Hong Kong Jewelry Manufacturers Association
Unit G, 2nd Fl., Phase 2, Kaiser Estate
51 Man Yue St.
Hunghom
Kowloon
Hong Kong, People's Republic of China
Phone: 852 27663002
Fax: 852 23623647
Publications: Hong Kong Jewelry Express (43326)

Hong Kong Management Association
W Haking Management Development Ctr.
14/F Fairmont House
8 Cotton Tree Dr.
Hong Kong, People's Republic of China
Phone: 852 27663303
Publications: The Hong Kong Manager (43337)

Hong Kong Medical Journal
Rm. 901
99 Wong Chuk Hang Rd.
Aberdeen
Hong Kong, People's Republic of China
Phone: 85 228 718822
Fax: 85 225 159061
Publications: Hong Kong Medical Journal (43339)

Hong Kong Occupational Therapy Association
PO Box 98241
TST Post-office
Hong Kong, People's Republic of China
Phone: 852 28051278
Publications: Hong Kong Journal of Occupational Therapy (43329)

Hong Kong Physiotherapy Association Ltd.
PO Box 10139
General Post Office
Rm. 901, 9/F Rightful Ctr., No. 12 Tak Hing St.
Hong Kong, People's Republic of China
Phone: 852 23360172
Fax: 852 23380252
Publications: Hong Kong Physiotherapy Journal (43341)

The Hong Kong Psychological Society Ltd.
University of Hong Kong
Pokfulam Rd.
Hong Kong, People's Republic of China
Phone: 852 25490364
Publications: Journal of Psychology in Chinese Societies (43361)

Hong Kong Public Administration Association
PO Box 3350
Hong Kong, People's Republic of China
Publications: Public Administration & Policy (43378)

The Hong Kong Racing Journal Ltd.
23 Fl., Wing On Ctr., Rm. 2303-04
No. 111 Connaught Rd., Central
Hong Kong, People's Republic of China
Phone: 852 81980632
Publications: The Hong Kong Racing Journal (43344)

Hong Kong Social Workers Association Ltd.
Hong Kong Wanzai Xuannishi Rd. 15
Dukes Social Service Bldg. 703 Rm.
Hong Kong, People's Republic of China
Phone: 852 25281802
Fax: 852 25280068
Publications: The Hong Kong Journal of Social Work (43332)

Hong Kong Society of Accountants
Wu Chung House, 37 Fl.
213 Queen's Rd. E
Hong Kong, People's Republic of China
Phone: 862 22877228

Fax: 862 28656603
Publications: The Hong Kong Accountant (43319) • The Prospective Accountant (43377)

Hong Kong Trade Development Council
38th Fl., Office Tower, Convention Plz.
1 Harbour Rd.
Wanchai
Hong Kong, People's Republic of China
Phone: 852 1830668
Fax: 852 28240249
Publications: HKTDC Electronic Components & Parts (43304) • HKTDC Electronics (43305) • HKTDC Enterprise (43306) • HKTDC Fashion - Leather Goods & Bags (43307) • HKTDC Fasion - Fabrics & Accessories (43308) • HKTDC Fasion - Footwear (43309) • HKTDC Gifts, Premium & Stationery (43310) • HKTDC Houseware (43311) • HKTDC Jewellery (43312) • HKTDC Optical (43313) • HKTDC Packaging (43314) • HKTDC Toys & Games (43315) • HKTDC Watch & Clock (43316) • Hong Kong Apparel (43320) • Hong Kong for the Business Visitor (43322) • Hong Kong Design Services (43323) • Hong Kong Printing (43343)

Hortilien - Bond Horticultural
36 Ave. Louis Pasteur
CS 40001
F-34473 Perols Cedex, France
Phone: 33 4 67504260
Fax: 33 4 67501902
Publications: Lien Horticole (44092)

Horwitz Publications Proprietary Ltd.
Horwitz House, Level 5
55 Chandos St.
Sydney, New South Wales 2065, Australia
Phone: 61 2 99016100
Fax: 61 2 99016198
Publications: Australian Penthouse (42331) • Golf Australia (42333) • Penthouse Couples (42334) • Smart Home Ideas (42335) • TV Soap (42336)

Hospitality Association of Zimbabwe
9th Fl., Travel Ctr.
93 Jason Moyo Ave.
Cswy.
PO Box CY 398
Harare, Zimbabwe
Phone: 26 347 33211
Fax: 26 347 08872
Publications: The Hospitality Magazine (57114)

Hot English Publishing
Paseo del Rey 22, Planta 1, Oficina 1,
E-28008 Madrid, Spain
Phone: 34 915 498523
Publications: Hot English Magazine (50767)

House Builders Federation
1st Fl.
7-9 St. James's St.
London SW1A 1DW, United Kingdom
Phone: 44 20 79601600
Fax: 44 20 79601601
Publications: House Builder (54575)

House of Words Ltd.
7 Greding Walk
Hutton
Brentwood CM13 2UF, United Kingdom
Phone: 44 1277 225402
Publications: Credit Control (52571)

HQ Band Service Royal Marines
Eastney Block
HMS Nelson
Portsmouth PO1 3HH, United Kingdom
Publications: Blue Band Magazine (56287)

the HR Director
Brook Farm
Heathened
Cromhall GL12 8AT, United Kingdom
Phone: 44 1454 292060
Publications: the HR Director (53119)

Hughes Graphics & Design Proprietary Ltd.
PO Box 2455
Mansfield, Queensland 4152, Australia
Phone: 61 7 3349 0322
Fax: 61 7 3349 0181
Publications: The Jag Mag (42033)

Human Kinetics Publishers Inc.
PO Box 5076
Champaign, IL 61825-5076
Phone: 217403-7570
Fax: 217351-1549
Free: 800747-4457
Publications: International Journal of Sports Physiology and Performance (41708)

Human Resource Management & Employment Relations
West St.
Toowoomba, Queensland 4350, Australia
Phone: 61 7 46312100
Fax: 61 7 46312893
Publications: Australian Journal of Organisational Behavior & Management (42626)

Human Resources Institute of New Zealand
Level 1, 11 Chews Ln.
PO Box 11 450
Wellington, New Zealand
Phone: 64 449 92966
Fax: 64 449 92965
Publications: New Zealand Journal of Human Resources Management (49026)

Humanist Institute for Co-Operation with Developing Countries
PO Box 85565
NL-2508 CG The Hague, Netherlands
Phone: 31 703 765500
Fax: 31 703 624600
Publications: Hivos Magazine (48617)

Hungarian Natural History Museum and Hungarian Academy of Sciences
Ludovika ter 2-6
H-1083 Budapest, Hungary
Phone: 36 1 2101085
Fax: 36 1 2101075
Publications: Acta Zoologica Academiae Scientiarum Hungaricae (44820)

The Hungarian Quarterly
8 Naphegy Ter.
H-1016 Budapest, Hungary
Phone: 36 148 80024
Fax: 36 148 80023
Publications: The Hungarian Quarterly (44836)

Zakir Husain Institute of Islamic Studies
Jamia Millia Islamia
Jamia Nagar
New Delhi 110 025, Delhi, India
Phone: 91 112 6981717
Fax: 91 112 6980229
Publications: Islam and the Modern Age (45592)

Hydrocarbon Development Institute of Pakistan
Plot No. 18, St. 6, H-9/1
Islamabad, Pakistan
Phone: 92 51 9258301
Fax: 92 51 9258310
Publications: Pakistan Journal of Hydrocarbon Research (49307)

i-documentsystems
Tontine House
8 Gordon St.
Glasgow G1 3PL, United Kingdom
Phone: 44 870 3337101
Fax: 44 870 3337131
Publications: Scottish Planning and Environmental Law (53450)

Ian Allan Publishing Ltd.
Riverdene Business Pk., Molesey Rd.
Hersham
Kingston upon Thames KT12 4RG, United Kingdom
Phone: 44 1932 266600
Fax: 44 1455 266601
Publications: Aircraft Illustrated (53719) • Bus & Coach Preservation (56288) • Buses (53845) • Classic Bus (53262) • Combat Aircraft (53720) • Hornby Magazine (53722) • Modern Railways (56785) • Railways Illustrated (56260) • The Square (53724) • Vintage Roadscene (53725)

Ibrahim Najjar Law Firm
11 Madrassat El-Salam St.
PO Box 116/2270
Beirut, Lebanon

Phone: 961 1 202100
Fax: 961 1 201974
Publications: Lebanese Review of Arab and International Arbitration (47397)

IC News
c/o Island Connections
c/o Rodeo Aptos
Royal Palm, Local 236
Los Cristianos, Canary Islands
E-38650 Tenerife, Spain
Phone: 34 922750609
Fax: 34 922795810
Publications: Island Connections (50836)

IC Publications Ltd.
7 Coldbath Sq.
London EC1R 4QL, United Kingdom
Phone: 44 20 78413210
Fax: 44 20 78413211
Publications: African Business (53919) • The Middle East (54930)

ICA - Australia
23 Appel St.
Highgate Hill, Queensland 4101, Australia
Publications: Pacific Waves (41955)

Icaria Editorial
Arc de Sant Cristofol, 11-23
E-08003 Barcelona, Spain
Phone: 34 933 011723
Fax: 34 932 954916
Publications: Ecologia Politica (50665)

Ice Cream Alliance
3 Melbourne Ct.
Pride Pk.
Derby DE24 8LZ, United Kingdom
Phone: 44 13 32203333
Fax: 44 13 32203420
Publications: Ice Cream (53164)

Iceland Review
Borgartuni 23-105
IS-105 Reykjavik, Iceland
Phone: 354 512 7575
Fax: 354 561 8646
Publications: Atlantica (44897) • Iceland Review (44901)

Icelandic Library and Information Science Association
Lagmuli 7
IS-108 Reykjavik, Iceland
Phone: 35 455 37290
Fax: 35 458 89239
Publications: Bokasafnid (44898)

ICFAI University Press
Plot. 6-3-354/1, Stellar Sphinx
Rd. 1, Banjara Hills
Panjagutta
Hyderabad 500 082, Andhra Pradesh, India
Phone: 91 40 23430449
Fax: 91 40 23430447
Publications: The Icfai Journal of Accounting Research (45140) • The Icfai Journal of Alternative Dispute Resolution (45141) • The Icfai Journal of Audit Practice (45142) • The Icfai Journal of Bank Management (45143) • The Icfai Journal of Behavioral Finance (45144) • The Icfai Journal of Corporate and Securities Law (45145) • The Icfai Journal of Cyber Law (45146) • The Icfai Journal of Derivatives Markets (45147) • The Icfai Journal of Employment Law (45148) • The Icfai Journal of Entrepreneurship Development (45149) • The Icfai Journal of Environmental Economics (45150) • The Icfai Journal of Financial Economics (45151) • The Icfai Journal of Financial Risk Management (45152) • The Icfai Journal of Governance and Public Policy (45153) • The Icfai Journal of Healthcare Law (45154) • The Icfai Journal of History and Culture (45155) • The Icfai Journal of International Business Law (45156) • The Icfai Journal of Knowledge Management (45157) • The Icfai Journal of Life Sciences (45158) • The Icfai Journal of Managerial Economics (45159) • The Icfai Journal of Mergers & Acquisitions (45160) • The Icfai Journal of Monetary Economics (45161) • The Icfai Journal of Operations Management (45162) • The Icfai Journal of Organizational Behavior (45163) • The Icfai Journal of Public Finance (45164) • The Icfai Journal of Risk & Insurance (45165) • The Icfai Journal of Science

& Technology (45166) • The Icfai Journal of Services Marketing (45167) • The Icfai Journal of Soft Skills (45168) • The Icfai Journal of Urban Policy (45169) • Icfai Reader (45170) • Insurance Chronicle (45173) • Porfolio Organizer (45179) • Professional Banker (45180) • Projects & Profits (45181)

I.C.M.P.E.
Via Daniele Crespi, 7
I-20123 Milan, Italy
Phone: 39 2 58106901
Fax: 39 2 58106901
Publications: Journal of Mental Health Policy and Economics (46183)

ICR Publishers Ltd.
Crispin House
12A S Approach
Moor Pk.
Northwood HA6 2ET, United Kingdom
Phone: 44 1923 836871
Fax: 44 1923 836872
Publications: Journal of Heart Valve Disease (55721)

ICUs and Nursing Web Journal
Tzavella 121
GR-184 50 Nikea, Greece
Phone: 30 104 902095
Publications: ICUs and Nursing Web Journal (44763)

IDATE
BP 4167
F-34092 Montpellier Cedex 5, France
Phone: 33 467 144444
Fax: 33 467 144400
Publications: Communications and Strategies (43977)

IDG Communications (HK) Ltd.
Ste. 601, Kah Wah Centre
191 Java Rd.
North Point
Hong Kong, People's Republic of China
Phone: 86 852 28613238
Fax: 86 852 28610953
Publications: Computer World Hong Kong (43293) • PC World Hong Kong (43375)

IDG Communications Pty. Limited - Australia
PO Box 1753
North Sydney, New South Wales 2059, Australia
Phone: 61 2 94395133
Fax: 61 2 94395512
Publications: Australian PC World (42207)

IDG Communications (S) Private Ltd.
80 Marine Parade Rd.
No. 17-01A Pky. Parade
Singapore 449269, Singapore
Phone: 65 63458383
Fax: 65 63456735
Publications: Computerworld Singapore (50127)

IDG Communications S.A.
Claudio Coello 123, 5 Planta
E-28006 Madrid, Spain
Phone: 34 913 496600
Publications: ComputerWorld/Espana (50738) • Comunicaciones World (50739) • Dealer World & Dealer World 15 (50749) • iWorld (50776) • Macworld Espana (50779) • PC World Espana (50788)

IDG the Netherlands
Richard Holkade 8
2033 PZ Haarlem, Netherlands
Phone: 31 23 5461111
Fax: 31 23 546 1155
Publications: Computer!Totaal (48605)

Idomeneo A.S.
Holmaveien 21
PO Box 25
1306 Baerum
N-1306 Baerum, Norway
Phone: 47 671 76875
Fax: 47 671 76851
Publications: The Norway Post (49188)

IEEE Circuits and Systems Society
c/o ENDIF, University of Ferrara
Via Saragat
44100 Ferrara, Italy
Phone: 39 0532 974997

Fax: 39 0532 974870
Publications: Circuits and Systems II (46138)

IEEE Communications Society
3 Park Ave., 17th Fl.
New York, NY 10016
Phone: 212705-8900
Fax: 212705-8999
Publications: Communications Letters, IEEE (42113)

The IEEE Components, Packaging and Manufacturing Technology Society
445 Hoes Ln.
PO Box 1331
Piscataway, NJ 08855-1331
Phone: 732562-5528
Fax: 732981-1769
Publications: IEEE Transactions on Components and Packaging Technologies (43451)

IEEE Control Systems Society
445 Hoes Ln.
PO Box 1331
Piscataway, NJ 08855-1331
Phone: 908562-5528
Free: 800678-4333
Publications: Transactions on Control Systems Technology (46267)

Ifo Institute for Economic Research
Poschingerstr. 5
D-81679 Munich, Germany
Phone: 49 899 2240
Fax: 49 899 85369
Publications: CESifo Forum (44554)

Igitur, Utrecht Publishing & Archiving Services
Heidelberglaan 3
NL-3584 CS Utrecht, Netherlands
Phone: 31 302 536635
Publications: Ars Disputandi (48755) • International Journal of Integrated Care (48760) • Utrecht Law Review (48767) • Veterinary Sciences Tomorrow (48768)

Ihlas Holding Mrk.
29 Ekim Cad
Yenibosna
TR-34197 Istanbul, Turkey
Phone: 90 212 4542000
Fax: 90 212 4542136
Publications: Konfeksiyon & Teknik (51559) • Matbaa & Teknik (51561) • Medikal & Teknik (51562) • Tekstil & Teknik (51563)

IHS Global Limited
Lombard House
3 Princess Way
Surrey
Redhill RH1 1UP, United Kingdom
Phone: 44 1737 379000
Fax: 44 1737 379001
Publications: Dredging and Port Construction (56350) • Register of Ships (56377)

IHT Ha'aretz
21 Schocken St.
IL-61001 Tel Aviv, Israel
Phone: 972 3 5121205
Fax: 927 3 6810012
Publications: Ha'aretz (46101)

Ileostomy and Internal Pouch Support Group
Peverill House
1 - 5 Mill Rd.
Ballyclare BT39 9DR, United Kingdom
Phone: 44 28 93344043
Fax: 44 28 93324606
Publications: IA Journal (52157)

Illawarra Mercury
21 Auburn St.
PO Box 1215
Wollongong, New South Wales 2500, Australia
Phone: 61 24 2212333
Publications: Illawarra Mercury (42703)

ILO Staff Union
4 rte. des Morillons
CH-1211 Geneva, Switzerland
Phone: 41 22 7996111
Fax: 41 22 7988685
Publications: Union (51164)

Ilocos Publishing Corp.
Barangay 23
M.H. del Pilar St.
Laoag City 2900, Philippines
Phone: 63 77 7720976
Fax: 63 77 7711378
Publications: The Ilocos Times (49509)

IM Publications L.L.P.
6 Charlton Mill
Carlton
Chichester PO18 0HY, United Kingdom
Phone: 44 1243 811334
Fax: 44 1243 811711
Publications: European Journal of Mass Spectrometry (53009) • Journal of Near Infrared Spectroscopy (42715)

Image Centre Publishing
34 Westmoreland St. W
Grey Lynn
Auckland, New Zealand
Phone: 64 9 3605700
Fax: 64 9 3605702
Publications: New Zealand Fishing World (48811)

Imagine Publishing Ltd.
Richmond House
33 Richmond Hill
Dorset
Bournemouth BH2 6EZ, United Kingdom
Phone: 44 1202 586200
Publications: Advanced Photoshop (52410) • Corel Painter Official Magazine (52411) • Digital Camera Buyer (52412) • Digital Photographer (52413) • gamesTM (52414) • High Definition Review (52415) • iCreate (52416) • nRevolution (52417) • Paint Shop Pro Photo (52418) • Photoshop Creative (52419) • Play (52420) • PowerStation (52421) • Practical Digital Video (52422) • Retro Gamer (52423) • SciFiNow (52424) • Smartphone & PDA Essentials (52425) • 360 (52426) • Total 911 (52427) • Total PC Gaming (52428) • Web Designer (52429)

IML Group PLC
Blair House, High St.
Tonbridge TN9 1BQ, United Kingdom
Phone: 44 1732 359990
Fax: 44 1732 770049
Publications: Food Processing (56754)

Immigrant-institutet
Katrinedalsgatan 43
504 51 Boras, Sweden
Phone: 46 331 36070
Fax: 46 331 36075
Publications: Journal of Intercultural Communication (50950)

Immunology, Asthma & Allergy Research Institute
No. 62 Dr. Gharib St., Keshavarz Blvd.
PO Box 14185-863
Tehran 14194, Iran
Phone: 98 216 6935855
Fax: 98 216 6428995
Publications: Iranian Journal of Allergy, Asthma and Immunology (45897)

Imperial College Press
57 Shelton St.
Covent Garden
London WC2H 9HE, United Kingdom
Phone: 44 20 78363954
Fax: 44 20 78362002
Publications: International Journal of Computational Intelligence and Applications (42316) • Journal of Bioinformatics and Computational Biology (54705)

Importers & Exporters Association of Taipei
350 Sung Chiang Rd.
Taipei 104, Taiwan
Phone: 886 2 25813521
Fax: 886 2 25238782
Publications: Taiwan International Trade (51364)

Impress Media, Inc.
4th Roschinsky proezd, 20 bld. 5,9
115191 Moscow, Russia
Phone: 7 495 9267340
Fax: 7 495 9267215
Publications: Flooring Professional Magazine (49904)

Imprint Academic
PO Box 200
Exeter EX5 5YX, United Kingdom
Phone: 44 13 92851550
Fax: 44 13 92851178
Publications: Collingwood and British Idealism Studies (53348) • History of Political Thought (53360) • Mind and Matter (44371)

In Touch
35 Parnell Sq.
Dublin IRL-1, Dublin, Ireland
Phone: 353 1 8047700
Fax: 353 1 8722462
Publications: In Touch (45966)

Incisive Media Limited
Haymarket House
28-29 Haymarket
London SW1Y 4RX, United Kingdom
Phone: 44 870 2408859
Fax: 44 207 4849797
Publications: Accountancy Age (53892) • Asia Risk (53972) • Asian Venture Capital Journal (43280) • Benelux unquote (54012) • British Journal of Photography (54131) • Buy-Side Technology (54161) • Computeractive (54255) • Computing (54256) • COVER (54278) • Credit (54283) • Deutsche unquote (54322) • Energy Risk (54370) • Financial Director (54454) • Financial Marketing (54456) • Focus Europe (54475) • Global Pensions (54512) • Hedge Funds Review (54547) • Information World Review (54604) • Insurance Age (54610) • International Custody & Fund Administration (54626) • International Investment (54628) • Investment Week (54679) • The Journal of Computational Finance (54729) • Journal of Credit Risk (54732) • The Journal of Operational Risk (54789) • The Journal of Risk (54809) • Legal Week (54865) • Life & Pensions (54872) • Mortgage Edge (54953) • Mortgage Solutions (54954) • Nordic unquote (55009) • Operational Risk & Regulation (55038) • Personal Computer World (55069) • Post Magazine (55107) • Private Equity Europe (55121) • Professional Adviser (55127) • Professional Broking (55129) • Professional Pensions (55132) • Reinsurance (55183) • Retirement Planner (55197) • Risk (55204) • Sell-Side Technology (55227) • Structured Products (55267) • UK Unquote (55355) • Wealth (55394) • Your Mortgage (55434)

The Incorporated Council of Law Reporting for England and Wales
Megarry House
119 Chancery Ln.
London WC2A 1PP, United Kingdom
Phone: 44 20 72426471
Fax: 44 20 78315247
Publications: Industrial Cases Reports (54597)

Incorporated Society of Musicians
10 Stratford Pl.
London W1C 1AA, United Kingdom
Phone: 44 20 76294413
Fax: 44 20 74081538
Publications: Music Journal (54963)

Independent News & Media PLC
Independent House
2023 Bianconi Ave.
Citywest Business Campus
Naas Rd.
Dublin 24, Dublin, Ireland
Phone: 353 1 466 3200
Fax: 353 1 466 3222
Publications: Sunday Tribune (South Africa) (50518)

Independent University of Moscow
Bolshoy Vlasyevskiy Pereulok 11
119002 Moscow, Russia
Phone: 7 495 2414086
Fax: 7 499 7951015
Publications: Moscow Mathematical Journal (49945)

Inderscience Enterprises Limited
World Trade Center Bldg. II
29, Rte. de Pre-Bois
Case Postale 896
CH-1215 Geneva 15, Switzerland
Phone: 41 1234 240515
Fax: 41 22 7910885
Publications: Afro-Asian Journal of Finance and Accounting (48784) • The Botulinum Journal (51088) • European Journal of Cross-Cultural Competence and Management (42751) • Global Business and Economics Review (48759) • Interdisciplinary Environmental Review (51099) • International Journal of Adaptive and Innovative Systems (43963) • International Journal of Advanced Intelligence Paradigms (49830) • International Journal of Advanced Mechatronic Systems (46844) • International Journal of Advanced Operations Management (43727) • International Journal of Agricultural Resources, Governance and Ecology (42143) • International Journal of Applied Cryptography (42704) • International Journal of Applied Decision Sciences (51100) • International Journal of Applied Management Science (51101) • International Journal of Applied Nonlinear Science (51102) • International Journal of Arab Culture, Management and Sustainable Development (50826) • International Journal of Artificial Intelligence and Soft Computing (45295) • International Journal of Arts and Technology (44762) • International Journal of Auditing Technology (51103) • International Journal of Autonomous and Adaptive Communications Systems (44761) • International Journal of Aviation Management (44049) • International Journal of Banking, Accounting and Finance (52172) • International Journal of Behavioural Accounting and Finance (52244) • International Journal of Behavioural and Healthcare Research (44770) • International Journal of Bio-Inspired Computation (43515) • International Journal of Biomechatronics and Biomedical Robotics (48798) • International Journal of Biomedical Nanoscience and Nanotechnology (51104) • International Journal of Biometrics (49666) • International Journal of Border Security and Immigration Policy (51105) • International Journal of Business Competition and Growth (47785) • International Journal of Business and Emerging Markets (51106) • International Journal of Business Excellence (51107) • International Journal of Business Forecasting and Marketing Intelligence (51108) • International Journal of Business Innovation and Research (IJBIR) (51109) • International Journal of Business Performance Management (54636) • International Journal of Business Performance and Supply Chain Modelling (43728) • International Journal of Cognitive Biometrics (43771) • International Journal of Cognitive Performance Support (43772) • International Journal of Communication Networks and Distributed Systems (45246) • International Journal of Complexity in Applied Science and Engineering (51110) • International Journal of Complexity in Leadership and Management (50178) • International Journal of Computational Biology and Drug Design (51111) • International Journal of Computational Economics and Econometrics (56289) • International Journal of Computational Intelligence in Bioinformatics and Systems Biology (43447) • International Journal of Computational Intelligence Studies (46118) • International Journal of Computational Medicine and Healthcare (51112) • International Journal of Computational Vision and Robotics (45010) • International Journal of Computer Aided Engineering and Technology (44309) • International Journal of Computer Applications in Technology (52677) • International Journal of Computers in Healthcare (41508) • International Journal of Continuing Engineering Education and Life-Long Learning (53287) • International Journal of Corporate Governance (51113) • International Journal of Critical Accounting (51114) • International Journal of Critical Computer-Based Systems (46200) • International Journal of Data Analysis Techniques and Strategies (51115) • International Journal of Decision Sciences, Risk and Management (44764) • International Journal of Digital Culture and Electronic Tourism (43833) • International Journal of Digital Enterprise Technology (43537) • International Journal of Economics and Accounting (54644) • International Journal of Economics and Business Research (51116) • International Journal of Education Economics and Development (47822) • International Journal of Electronic Banking (51117) • International Journal of Electronic Democracy (54646) • International Journal of Electronic Trade (46177) • International Journal of Electronic Transport (42065) • International Journal of Engineering Management and Economics (46204) • International Journal of Engineering Systems Modelling and Simulation (56981) • International Journal of Enterprise Systems Integration and Interoperability (46122) • International Journal of Entertainment Technology and Management (44747) • International Journal of Entre-

preneurial Venturing (51020) • International Journal of Environment and Pollution (51118) • International Journal of Environment, Workplace and Employment (42066) • International Journal of Environmental Policy and Decision Making (51119) • International Journal of Exergy (51120) • International Journal of Financial Markets and Derivatives (56290) • International Journal of Food Safety, Nutrition and Public Health (51121) • International Journal of Forensic Software Engineering (46140) • International Journal of Functional Informatics and Personalised Medicine (51122) • International Journal of Global Energy Issues (42730) • International Journal of Granular Computing, Rough Sets and Intelligent Systems (51123) • International Journal of Healthcare Technology and Management (48594) • International Journal of Heavy Vehicle Systems (51124) • International Journal of Hydrology Science and Technology (45878) • International Journal of Industrial Electronics and Drives (45247) • International Journal of Information and Coding Theory (45248) • International Journal of Information and Decision Sciences (51125) • International Journal of Information Privacy, Security and Integrity (51126) • International Journal of Information Technology, Communications and Convergence (47269) • International Journal of Innovation in Education (44193) • International Journal of Innovation and Regional Development (44773) • International Journal of Intelligent Defence Support Systems (41510) • International Journal of Intelligent Engineering Informatics (43198) • International Journal of Inventory Research (51127) • International Journal of Knowledge-Based Development (41650) • International Journal of Knowledge Engineering and Data Mining (43351) • International Journal of Knowledge Engineering and Soft Data Paradigms (47110) • International Journal of Knowledge Management in Tourism and Hospitality (56500) • International Journal of Lean Enterprise Research (48603) • International Journal of Legal Information Design (51266) • International Journal of Leisure and Tourism Marketing (51128) • International Journal of Management and Network Economics (46119) • International Journal of Managerial and Financial Accounting (47683) • International Journal of Manufacturing Technology and Management (51129) • International Journal of Materials Engineering Innovation (49787) • International Journal of Materials and Product Technology (44633) • International Journal of Mathematical Modelling and Numerical Optimisation (56731) • International Journal of Mechatronics and Manufacturing Systems (51130) • International Journal of Medical Engineering and Informatics (51131) • International Journal of Metaheuristics (52931) • International Journal of Mining and Mineral Engineering (51132) • International Journal of Modelling in Operations Management (47584) • International Journal of Molecular Engineering (49788) • International Journal of Multicriteria Decision Making (44749) • International Journal of Multimedia Intelligence and Security (43199) • International Journal of Nano and Biomaterials (51133) • International Journal of Nanoparticles (43266) • International Journal of Nuclear Knowledge Management (44054) • International Journal of Ocean Systems Management (43590) • International Journal of Oil, Gas and Coal Technology (47362) • International Journal of Organisational Design and Engineering (49800) • International Journal of Petroleum Engineering (51134) • International Journal of Physiotherapy and Life Physics (44656) • International Journal of Power and Energy Conversion (45011) • International Journal of Powertrain (51135) • International Journal of Quality Engineering and Technology (51136) • International Journal of Quality and Innovation (49255) • International Journal of Reasoning-based Intelligent Systems (46378) • International Journal of Remanufacturing (51137) • International Journal of Renewable Energy Technology (56798) • International Journal of Satellite Communications Policy and Management (43520) • International Journal of Security and Networks (51138) • International Journal of Services, Economics and Management (43523) • International Journal of Services Sciences (51139) • International Journal of Services Technology and Management (46848) • International Journal of Shipping and Transport Logistics (43352) • International Journal of Signal and Imaging Systems Engineering (44758) • International Journal of Social Computing and Cyber-Physical Systems (51140) • International Journal of Social and Humanistic Computing (51021) • International Journal of Social Network Mining (41450) • International Journal of Society Systems Science (51141) • International Journal of Strategic Engineering Asset Management (49213) • International Journal of Structural Engineering (43260) • International Journal of Sudan Research, Policy and Sustainable Development (50940) • International Journal of Sustainable Design (41671) • International Journal of Sustainable Economy (50332) • International Journal of Sustainable Manufacturing (51142) • International Journal of Sustainable Society (51143) • International Journal of Sustainable Strategic Management (51144) • International Journal of System Control and Information Processing (43479) • International Journal of Systems, Control and Communications (43252) • International Journal of Technology Enhanced Learning (51022) • International Journal of Tourism Anthropology (43248) • International Journal of Transitions and Innovation Systems (43568) • International Journal of Ultra Wideband Communications and Systems (45130) • International Journal of Vehicle Design (51145) • International Journal of Vehicle Performance (51146) • Luxury Intelligence (47810) • World Review of Intermodal Transportation Research (51168)

Inderscience Publishers
PO Box 735
Olney MK46 5WB, United Kingdom
Fax: 44 12 34240515
Publications: Atoms for Peace (44028) • European Journal of Industrial Engineering (47337) • European Journal of International Management (44900) • International Journal of Abrasive Technology (42518) • International Journal of Accounting, Auditing and Performance Evaluation (42792) • International Journal of Ad Hoc and Ubiquitous Computing (55786) • International Journal of Advanced Media and Communication (55787) • International Journal of Aerodynamics (55788) • International Journal of Agent-Oriented Software Engineering (46262) • International Journal of Agile and Extreme Software Development (49798) • International Journal of Agile Systems and Management (53626) • International Journal of Alternative Propulsion (55789) • International Journal of Applied Systemic Studies (44767) • International Journal of Automotive Technology and Management (55790) • International Journal of Autonomic Computing (55791) • International Journal of Biomedical Engineering and Technology (55792) • International Journal of Business Environment (50717) • International Journal of Business Governance and Ethics (56737) • International Journal of Business Intelligence and Data Mining (41761) • International Journal of Chinese Culture & Management (50823) • International Journal of Cognitive Performance Support (IJCPS) (55793) • International Journal of Collaborative Enterprise (55794) • International Journal of Complexity (55795) • International Journal of Computational Materials Science & Surface Engineering (55796) • International Journal of Computing Science and Mathematics (43539) • International Journal of Critical Infrastructures (55797) • International Journal of Design Engineering (55759) • International Journal of Dynamical Systems and Differential Equations (43540) • International Journal of Economic Policy in Emerging Economies (46157) • International Journal of Electric and Hybrid Vehicles (44127) • International Journal of Electronic Business (51345) • International Journal of Electronic Customer Relationship Management (51320) • International Journal of Electronic Governance (44746) • International Journal of Electronic Security and Digital Forensics (54647) • International Journal of Embedded Systems (55798) • International Journal of Emergency Management (55799) • International Journal of Energy Technology and Policy (55800) • International Journal of Enterprise Network Management (56499) • International Journal of Entrepreneurial Venturing (55801) • International Journal of Entrepreneurship and Innovation Management (55802) • International Journal of Environment and Health (46234) • International Journal of Environment and Sustainable Development (55803) • International Journal of Environmental Technology and Management (55804) • International Journal of Financial Services Management (55805) • International Journal of Forensic Engineering (55638) • International Journal of Forensic Engineering and Management (55806) • International Journal of Foresight and Innovation Policy (55807) • International Journal of Global Environmental Issues (55808) • International Journal of Globalisation and Small Business (44355) • International Journal of Green Economics (56322) • International Journal of Grid & Utility Computing (49217) • International Journal of High Performance Computing and Networking (55809) • International Journal of High Performance System Architecture (43007) • International Journal of Human Resources Development and Management (55810) • International Journal of Information and Computer Security (51346) • International Journal of Information Quality (42628) • International Journal of Information Technology and Management (55811) • International Journal of Innovation and Sustainable Development (55812) • International Journal of Innovative Computing and Applications (43008) • International Journal of Intellectual Property Management (55813) • International Journal of Intelligent Information and Database Systems (49780) • International Journal of Intelligent Systems Technologies and Applications (55814) • International Journal of Internet and Enterprise Management (55815) • International Journal of Internet Manufacturing & Services (43532) • International Journal of Internet Marketing and Advertising (51308) • International Journal of Internet Protocol Technology (55816) • International Journal of Internet Technology & Secured Transactions (54651) • International Journal of Knowledge and Learning (44748) • International Journal of Knowledge Management Studies (55817) • International Journal of Learning and Change (48799) • International Journal of Learning and Intellectual Capital (50824) • International Journal of Learning Technology (56591) • International Journal of Liability and Scientific Enquiry (55818) • International Journal of Logistics Economics & Globalisation (56501) • International Journal of Low Radiation (55819) • International Journal of Machining and Machinability of Materials (49786) • International Journal of Management Concepts and Philosophy (55820) • International Journal of Management and Decision Making (55821) • International Journal of Management Practice (56738) • International Journal of Manufacturing Research (55822) • International Journal of Materials & Structural Integrity (55823) • International Journal of Metadata, Semantics and Ontologies (55824) • International Journal of Microstructure and Materials Properties (50338) • International Journal of Mobile Network Design and Innovation (52932) • International Journal of Modelling, Identification and Control (52679) • International Journal of Monetary Economics & Finance (46158) • International Journal of Nanomanufacturing (55825) • International Journal of Networking and Virtual Organisations (55826) • International Journal of Nuclear Desalination (44050) • International Journal of Nuclear Energy Science and Technology (44051) • International Journal of Nuclear Governance, Economy and Ecology (44052) • International Journal of Nuclear Hydrogen Production and Applications (44053) • International Journal of Nuclear Law (44055) • International Journal of Postharvest Technology and Innovation (50631) • International Journal of Precision Technology (47681) • International Journal of Process Management and Benchmarking (53560) • International Journal of Product Development (55827) • International Journal of Product Lifecycle Management (43924) • International Journal of Product Sound Quality (55828) • International Journal of Project Organisation and Management (55829) • International Journal of Public Policy (55830) • International Journal of Public Sector Performance Management (43912) • International Journal of Risk Assessment and Management (55831) • International Journal of Simulation and Process Modelling (49814) • International Journal of Six Sigma and Competitive Advantage (55832) • International Journal of Sport Management and Marketing (55833) • International Journal of Strategic Change Management (50825) • International Journal of Surface Science & Engineering (49789) • International Journal of Teaching & Case Studies (55834) • International Journal of Technoentrepreneurship (50194) • International Journal of Technological Learning, Innovation & Development (43009) • International Journal of Technology and Globalisation (46235) • International Journal of Technology Intelligence and Planning (55835) • International Journal of Technology Policy and Law (42521) • International Journal of Technology Policy and Management (51267) • International Journal of Technology Transfer and Commercialisation (55836) • International Journal of Tourism Policy (44765) • International

Journal of Trade and Global Markets (46159) • International Journal of Value Chain Management (51321) • International Journal of Vehicle Autonomous Systems (55837) • International Journal of Vehicle Information & Communication System (55838) • International Journal of Vehicle Systems Modelling and Testing (50835) • International Journal of Virtual Technology and Multimedia (55839) • International Journal of Water (55840) • International Journal of Web-Based Communities (48595) • International Journal of Web Engineering and Technology (56592) • International Journal of Web and Grid Services (41762) • International Journal of Wireless and Mobile Computing (55841) • International Journal of Work Organisation & Emotion (56799) • Journal of Design Research (55842) • Journal for Global Business Advancement (55843) • Journal for International Business and Entrepreneurship Development (55844) • Progress in Computational Fluid Dynamics (44331) • Progress in Industrial Ecology (43910) • World Review of Entrepreneurship, Management and Sustainable Development (55846) • World Review of Science, Technology and Sustainable Development (55847)

India Trade Promotion Organisation
Pragati Bhavan, Pragati Maidan
New Delhi 110 001, Delhi, India
Phone: 91 11 23371540
Fax: 91 11 23371492
Publications: Indian Export Bulletin (45542)

Indian Academy of Clinical Medicine
A-Block
CGO Complex
Lodhi Rd.
New Delhi 110 003, Delhi, India
Phone: 91 243 56446
Fax: 91 435 9445
Publications: Journal, Indian Academy of Clinical Medicine (45599)

Indian Academy of Forensic Medicine
SCO-3, Chowk Dukhniwaran Sahib, Sirhind Rd.
Shaheed-E-Azam Press
Patiala 147 005, Punjab, India
Phone: 91 175 2357981
Publications: Journal of Indian Academy of Forensic Medicine (45685)

Indian Academy of Geoscience
Osmania University
Hyderabad 500 007, Andhra Pradesh, India
Publications: Indian Academy of Geoscience Journal (45171)

Indian Academy of Pediatrics
Kailas Darshan
Kennedy Bridge
Mumbai 400 007, Maharashtra, India
Phone: 91 22 23889565
Fax: 91 22 23851713
Publications: Indian Pediatrics (45575)

Indian Academy of Sciences
C.V. Raman Ave.
PO Box 8005
Sadashivanagar
Bangalore 560 080, Karnataka, India
Phone: 91 802 3612546
Fax: 91 802 3616094
Publications: Bulletin of Materials Science (44951) • Journal of Astrophysics and Astronomy (44965) • Journal of Biosciences (44966) • Journal of Chemical Sciences (44967) • Journal of Earth System Science (44970) • Journal of Genetics (44971) • Pramana - Journal of Physics (44981) • Proceedings of the Indian Academy of Sciences (44982) • Profound (The Dialog Corporation) - Mathematical Sciences (44983) • Resonance (44985) • Sadhana (44986)

The Indian Anaesthetists' Forum
A 54/3 Arvind Nagar
Golf Link Rd.
Jodhpur 342 011, Rajasthan, India
Publications: The Indian Anaesthetists' Forum (45218)

Indian Association for Angiosperm Taxonomy
c/o University of Calicut
Dept. of Botany
Calicut 673 635, Kerala, India
Publications: Rheedea (45022)

Indian Association of Cardiovascular Thoracic Anaesthesiologists
624, Academic Block
GB Pant Hospital
New Delhi 110 002, Delhi, India
Phone: 91 112 3232877
Publications: Annals of Cardiac Anaesthesia (45483)

Indian Association for Child and Adolescent Mental Health
Vihar, Newada
PO Sunderpur
Varanasi 221 005, Uttar Pradesh, India
Publications: Journal of Indian Association for Child and Adolescent Mental Health (45600)

Indian Association for the Cultivation of Science
2A & 2B Raja S C Mullick Rd.
Kolkata 700 032, West Bengal, India
Phone: 91 332 4734971
Fax: 91 332 4732805
Publications: Indian Journal of Physics, Part A (45021)

Indian Association of Gastrointestinal Endosurgeons
Mettupalayam Rd.
Perumbakkam
Coimbatore 641 034, Tamil Nadu, India
Phone: 91 44 222642071
Publications: Journal of Minimal Access Surgery (JMAS) (45403)

Indian Association of Medical Microbiologists
A-3 No. 38 Rue Labourdonnaise
Pondicherry 605 001, Pondicherry, India
Phone: 91 423 2227422
Fax: 91 413 2223052
Publications: Indian Journal of Medical Microbiology (45692)

Indian Association of Pediatric Surgeons
A-108/109, Kanara Business Ctr., Off Link Rd.
Ghatkopar E
Mumbai 400 075, Maharashtra, India
Phone: 91 226 6491818
Fax: 91 226 6491817
Publications: Journal of Indian Association of Pediatric Surgeons (45601)

Indian Association of Preventive & Social Medicine
Postgraduate Institute of Medical Education & Research
Chandigarh 160 012, Chandigarh, India
Phone: 91 172 2744993
Fax: 91 172 2744993
Publications: Indian Journal of Community Medicine (45024)

Indian Association of Special Libraries and Information Centres
P-291 CIT Scheme No. 6M
Kankurgachi
Kolkata 700 054, West Bengal, India
Phone: 91 33 23629651
Publications: IASLIC Bulletin (45269)

Indian Association for the Study of Sexually Transmitted Diseases
11/34, Shri Girdhar Hospital & Research Ctr.
Girdhar Marg
Malviya Nagar
Jaipur 302 017, Rajasthan, India
Publications: Indian Journal of Sexually Transmitted Diseases (45196)

Indian Bureau of Mines
2nd Fl., Indira Bhawan, Civil Lines
Nagpur 440 002, Maharashtra, India
Phone: 91 712 2560041
Fax: 91 712 2565073
Publications: Indian Minerals Year Book (45467)

Indian Cancer Society
M. Karve Rd., Cooperage
Mumbai 400 021, Maharashtra, India
Phone: 91 22 22029941
Fax: 91 22 22872745
Publications: Indian Journal of Cancer (45378)

Indian Chemical Manufacturers Association
Bombay Regional Office
Sir Vithaldas Chambers
16 Mumbai Samachar Marg
Mumbai 400 001, Maharashtra, India
Phone: 91 222 2048043
Fax: 91 222 2048057
Publications: Chemical News (45360)

Indian College of Allergy Asthma and Immunology
A-12/1, Naraina Industrial Area, Phase I
New Delhi 110 028, Delhi, India
Publications: Indian Journal of Allergy Asthma and Immunology (45096)

Indian Council of Agricultural Research
Krishi Anusandhan Bhaven
Dr. Rajendra Prasad Rd.
New Delhi 110 114, Delhi, India
Phone: 91 112 5843657
Publications: Indian Farming (45544) • Indian Horticulture (45546) • Indian Journal of Agricultural Engineering (45547) • Indian Journal of Agricultural Sciences (45548) • Indian Journal of Animal Sciences (45549)

Indian Council for Cultural Relations
Azad Bhavan
Indraprastha Estate
New Delhi 110 002, Delhi, India
Phone: 91 11 23379309
Fax: 91 11 23378639
Publications: Africa Quarterly (45478)

Indian Council of Medical Research
V. Ramalingaswami Bhawan
Ansari Nagar
New Delhi 110 029, Delhi, India
Phone: 91 112 6588895
Fax: 91 112 6588662
Publications: ICMR Bulletin (45525) • Indian Journal of Medical Research (45561)

Indian Council of Social Science Research
J.N.U. Institutional Area
Aruna Asaf Ali Marg
New Delhi 110 067, Delhi, India
Phone: 91 11 26179849
Fax: 91 11 26179836
Publications: ICSSR Journal of Abstracts and Reviews (45529) • ICSSR Journal of Abstracts and Reviews (45528) • ICSSR Journal of Abstracts and Reviews (45526) • ICSSR Journal of Abstracts and Reviews (45527)

Indian Dairy Association
IDA House
Sector IV
R.K. Puram
New Delhi 110 022, Delhi, India
Phone: 91 116 170781
Fax: 91 116 174719
Publications: Indian Dairyman (45537) • Indian Journal of Dairy Science (45551)

Indian Drug Manufacturers Association
102-B Poonan Chambers
Dr. A.B. Rd.
Worli
Mumbai 400 018, Maharashtra, India
Phone: 91 22 24944624
Fax: 91 22 24950723
Publications: Indian Drugs (45377)

Indian Electrical and Electronics Manufacturers' Association
501 Kakad Chambers
132 Dr. Annie Besant Rd.
Worli
Mumbai 400 018, Maharashtra, India
Phone: 91 222 4930532
Fax: 91 222 4932705
Publications: IEEMA Journal (45372)

Indian Endodontic Society
C-44, Gulmohan Pk.
New Delhi 110 049, Delhi, India
Phone: 91 22 23082714
Fax: 91 22 25243223
Publications: Endontology (45508)

Indian Express Newspapers (Bombay) Ltd.
9&10, Bhadur Shah Zafar Marg
Express Bldg.
New Delhi 110002, Delhi, India
Phone: 91 11 23702618

Fax: 91 11 23702141
Publications: The Financial Express (45516) • The Indian Express (45543)

Indian Express Newspapers (Bombay) Private Ltd.
9&10 Bhadur Shah Zafar Marg
Express Bldg., ITO
New Delhi 110 002, Delhi, India
Phone: 91 11 23702618
Fax: 91 11 23702141
Publications: Screen (45649)

Indian Institute of Advanced Study
Rashtrapati Nivas
Shimla 171 005, Himachal Pradesh, India
Phone: 91 177 2831275
Fax: 91 177 2831389
Publications: Studies in Humanities and Social Sciences (45731)

Indian Institute of Chemical Engineers
Dr. H.L. Roy Bldg.
Jadavpur University Campus.
188 Raja Subodh Chandra Mullick Rd.
Calcutta 700 032, West Bengal, India
Phone: 91 332 4146670
Fax: 91 332 4146670
Publications: Indian Chemical Engineer (45095)

Indian Institute of Finance
Ashok Vihar
PO Box 8486
New Delhi 110 052, Delhi, India
Phone: 91 11 27136257
Fax: 91 11 27454128
Publications: Finance India (45515)

Indian Institute of Management
Publication Division Institute of Management
D.H. Rd.
Joka
PO Box 16757
Kolkata 700 104, West Bengal, India
Phone: 91 33 24678300
Fax: 91 33 24678307
Publications: Decision (45263)

Indian Institute of Metals
Metals House, Plot 13/4
Block AQ, Sector V, Salt Lake City
Kolkata 700091, West Bengal, India
Phone: 91 33 23675004
Fax: 91 33 23675335
Publications: IIM Metal News (45270) • Indian Institute of Metals Transactions (45272)

Indian Institute of Packaging
E-2, MIDC Area
Andheri E
Mumbai 400 093, Maharashtra, India
Phone: 91 228 219803
Publications: Packaging India (45426)

Indian Institute of Science
The Registrar
Bangalore 560 012, Karnataka, India
Phone: 91 802 3600757
Fax: 91 802 3600683
Publications: Indian Institute of Science Journal (44959)

Indian Institute of Toxicology Research
Mahatma Gandhi Marg
PO Box 80
Lucknow 226 001, Uttar Pradesh, India
Phone: 91 522 2621856
Fax: 91 522 2628227
Publications: Abstracts of Current Literature in Toxicology (45320)

Indian Institute of Welding
3A, Doctor U.N. Brahmachari St.
Kolkata 700 017, West Bengal, India
Phone: 91 33 22813208
Fax: 91 33 22401350
Publications: Indian Welding Journal (45275)

Indian Institute of World Culture
No. 6, B.P. Wadia Rd.
Basavanagudi
Bangalore 560 004, Karnataka, India

Phone: 91 80 6678581
Publications: Indian Institute of World Culture Bulletin (44960)

Indian Journal of Medical Sciences Trust
A-109, Kanara Business Center
Off Link Rd., Ghatkopar (E)
Kurla W
Mumbai 400 075, Maharashtra, India
Phone: 91 22 66491818
Fax: 91 22 66491817
Publications: Indian Journal of Medical Sciences (45383)

Indian Journal of Pediatrics
125, 2nd Fl.
Gautam Nagar
PO Box 3875
New Delhi 110 049, Delhi, India
Phone: 91 112 6568098
Fax: 91 112 6857587
Publications: Indian Journal of Pediatrics (45564)

Indian Journal of Psychiatry
B-8, Sector A
Mahanagar
Lucknow 226 006, Uttar Pradesh, India
Publications: Indian Journal of Psychological Medicine (45322)

Indian Law Institute
Bhagwandas Rd.
New Delhi 110 001, Delhi, India
Phone: 91 11 23387526
Fax: 91 11 23782140
Publications: Journal of Indian Law Institute (45603)

Indian Leather
120 Vepery High Rd.
Periamet
Chennai 600 003, Tamil Nadu, India
Phone: 91 44 25386566
Fax: 91 44 28343685
Publications: Indian Leather (45038)

Indian Medical Association
I.M.A. House
Indraprastha Marg
New Delhi 110 002, Delhi, India
Phone: 91 112 3370009
Fax: 91 112 3379178
Publications: Journal of the Indian Medical Association (JIMA) (45296)

Indian Medical Association, Karnataka State Branch
IMA House
Alur Venkata Rao Rd.
Bangalore 560 018, Karnataka, India
Publications: Karnataka Medical Journal (44977)

Indian Meteorological Society
601, Satellite Bldg.
India Meteorological Department
Lodi Rd.
New Delhi 110 003, Delhi, India
Phone: 91 11 24620701
Fax: 91 11 24699216
Publications: Vayu Mandal (45667)

Indian Military Historical Society
33 High St.
Tilbrook
Huntingdon PE18 0JP, United Kingdom
Phone: 44 14 80860437
Publications: Durbar (53634)

Indian Mountaineering Foundation
6 Benito Juarez Rd.
New Delhi 110 021, Delhi, India
Phone: 91 112 4111211
Fax: 91 112 4113412
Publications: Indian Mountaineer (45572)

Indian National Science Academy
Bahadur Shah Zafar Marg
New Delhi 110 002, Delhi, India
Phone: 91 11 23221931
Fax: 91 11 23235648
Publications: Indian Journal of History of Science (45555) • Indian Journal of Pure and Applied Mathematics (45565) • Indian National Science Academy Biographical Memoirs of Fellows (45573) • Indian National

Science Academy Year Book (45574)

Indian National Shipowners' Association
22 Maker Tower-F, 2nd Fl.
Cuffe Parade
Mumbai 400 005, Maharashtra, India
Phone: 91 22 22182103
Fax: 91 22 22182104
Publications: Indian Shipping (45389)

Indian Periodical
5 New Pali Rd.
PO Box 33
Jodhpur 342001, Rajasthan, India
Phone: 91 291 2433323
Fax: 91 291 2512580
Publications: Advances in Horticulture and Forestry (45212) • Advances in Plant Physiology (45213) • Annual Review of Plant Pathology (45215) • Bulletin of Pure and Applied Mathematics (45216) • Indian Journal of Applied Entomology (45219) • Journal of Arid Legumes (45225) • Journal of Phytopharmacotherapy and Natural Products (45227)

The Indian Pharmaceutical Association
Kalina
Santacruz (E)
Mumbai 400 098, Maharashtra, India
Phone: 91 222 6671072
Fax: 91 222 6670744
Publications: Indian Journal of Pharmaceutical Sciences (45386) • Pharma Times (45429)

Indian Pharmacological Society
Food & Drug Toxicology Research Centre
National Institute of Nutrition
Tarnaka
Hyderabad 500 007, Andhra Pradesh, India
Phone: 91 40 27008921
Publications: Indian Journal of Pharmacology (45172)

Indian Political Science Association
Dept. of Public Administration
University of Lucknow
Lucknow 226 007, Uttar Pradesh, India
Phone: 91 522 2740131
Publications: Indian Journal of Political Science (45345)

Indian Roads Congress
Jamnagar House
Shahjahan Rd.
New Delhi 110 011, Delhi, India
Phone: 91 112 6716778
Fax: 91 112 6183669
Publications: Highway Research Record (45523) • Indian Highways (45545) • Indian Roads Congress Highway Research Bulletin (45576) • Journal of Indian Roads Congress (45604)

Indian Society of Aerospace Medicine
Indian Air Force
Vimanapura
Bangalore 560 017, Karnataka, India
Phone: 91 802 5224131
Publications: Indian Journal of Aerospace Medicine (44961)

Indian Society of Critical Care Medicine
Bldg. No.3 Office No.12, 5th Fl.
Navjivan Premises Co-op Society Ltd.
Dr. D. Bhadkamkar Rd.
Mumbai 400 008, Maharashtra, India
Phone: 91 22 65268504
Fax: 91 22 23054843
Publications: Indian Journal of Critical Care Medicine (45379)

Indian Society for Development and Environment Research
PO Box 113
Roorkee 247-667, Uttar Pradesh, India
Publications: International Journal of Ecology and Development (45718) • International Journal of Mathematics and Statistics (IJMS) (45719) • International Journal of Tomography and Statistics (45236)

Indian Society of Gastroenterology
23 Bombay Mutual Ter.
534 Sandhurst Bridge
Mumbai 400 007, Maharashtra, India
Phone: 91 22 23613333

Fax: 91 22 24175626
Publications: Indian Journal of Gastroenterology (45380)

Indian Society of Nephrology
Postgraduate Institute of Medical Education & Research
Chandigarh 160 012, India
Phone: 91 172 2756733
Fax: 91 172 2744401
Publications: Indian Journal of Nephrology (45023)

Indian Society of Pedodontics and Preventive Dentistry
Dr. A. L. Nair Rd.
Nair Hospital Dental College
House Number 688, 1st Fl.
Scetor 16
Mumbai 400 008, Maharashtra, India
Phone: 91 22 23082714
Fax: 91 22 23080655
Publications: Indian Society of Pedodontics and Preventive Dentistry Journal (45086)

Indian Society of Soil Science
Indian Agricultural Research Institute
Division of Soil Science & Agricultural Chemistry
Dev Prakash Shastri Marg, Pusa
New Delhi 110 012, Delhi, India
Phone: 91 11 25841991
Fax: 91 11 25841529
Publications: Journal of the Indian Society of Soil Science (45605)

Indian Society for Technical Education
Shaheed Jeet Singh Marg
Near Katwaria Sarai
Opp. Sanskrit Vidyapeeth
New Delhi 110 016, Delhi, India
Phone: 91 11 26963431
Fax: 91 11 26852421
Publications: Indian Journal of Technical Education (45567)

Indian Statistical Institute
8th Mile, Mysore Rd.
R.V. College Post
Bangalore 560 059, Karnataka, India
Phone: 91 802 8483002
Fax: 91 802 8484265
Publications: Sankhya (45303)

Indian Sugar Mills Association
C Block, 2nd Fl.
Ansal Plz., August Kranti Marg, Andrews Ganj
New Delhi 110 049, Delhi, India
Phone: 91 11 26262294
Fax: 91 11 26263231
Publications: Indian Sugar (45578)

Indiana University Press
601 N Morton St.
Bloomington, IN 47404-3797
Phone: 812855-8817
Fax: 812855-8507
Free: 800842-6796
Publications: History & Memory (46103)

Indiavarta
Express Gardens, II Main Rd.
Ambatur Industrial Estate
Chennai 600 058, Tamil Nadu, India
Phone: 91 442 3457655
Fax: 91 44 23457619
Publications: Indiavarta (45039)

Indilinga: African Journal of Indigenous Knowledge Systems
PO Box 266
Msunduzi
Pietermaritzburg 3231, Republic of South Africa
Publications: Indilinga (50568)

Indo-American Chamber of Commerce
1-C, Vulcan Insurance Bldg.
Veer Nariman Rd., Churchgate
Mumbai 400 020, Maharashtra, India
Phone: 91 22 22821413
Fax: 91 22 22046141
Publications: Indo - US Business (45040)

Indonesian Resources and Information Programme
PO Box 1326

Collingwood, Victoria 3066, Australia
Phone: 61 394 194504
Fax: 61 394 194774
Publications: Inside Indonesia (41790)

Industrial Minerals
16 Lower Marsh
Playhouse Yard
London SE1 7RJ, United Kingdom
Phone: 44 20 78279977
Fax: 44 20 78275292
Publications: Industrial Minerals (IM) (54598)

Industrial Technology Development Institute
DOST Compound
Gen. Santos Ave.
Bicutan
Taguig City 1631, Philippines
Phone: 63 28372071
Fax: 63 28373167
Publications: Philippine Journal of Science (49641)

Infofish
1st Fl. Wisma PKNS
Jalan Raja Laut
PO Box 10899
50728 Kuala Lumpur, Malaysia
Phone: 603 26914466
Fax: 603 26916804
Publications: INFOFISH International (47605)

Infomedia 18 Ltd.
A Wing, Rugby House
J.K. Sawant Marg, Dadar
Mumbai 400 028, Maharashtra, India
Phone: 91 22 30245000
Fax: 91 22 30034499
Publications: Auto Monitor (45353) • AV Max (45354) • Better Interiors (45355) • Better Photography (45356) • Chip (45362) • Electrical & Electronics (45369) • Modern Food Processing (45414) • Modern Machine Tools (45415) • Modern Medicare (45416) • Modern Packaging & Design (45417) • Modern Pharmaceuticals (45418) • Modern Plastics & Polymers (45419) • Modern Textiles (45420) • Overdrive (45425) • Photo Imaging (45431) • Tomorrow's Technology Today (45448)

Informa Healthcare
52 Vanderbilt Ave., 7th Fl.
New York, NY 10017-3846
Publications: Acta Orthopaedica (50983) • Addiction Research and Theory (53409) • Journal of Intellectual & Developmental Disability (42008) • The World Journal of Biological Psychiatry (42775)

Informa P.L.C.
325 Chestnut St., Ste. 800
Philadelphia, PA 19106
Phone: 215625-8900
Fax: 215625-8914
Free: 800354-1420
Publications: Journal of Visual Communication in Medicine (52355)

Informa Professional Publishing
69-77 Paul St.
London EC2A 4LQ, United Kingdom
Phone: 44 20 70175532
Publications: Competition Law Insight (54253)

Informa Publishing Group
Informa House
30-32 Mortimer St.
London W1W 7RE, United Kingdom
Phone: 44 20 70175000
Publications: Banking Technology (54002) • Health Insurance (54539) • Insurance Day (54611) • The International Construction Law Review (54625) • Pathology (55062)

Information & Libraries Scotland
First Fl., Bldg. C
Brandon Gate, Leechlee Rd.
Hamilton ML3 6AU, United Kingdom
Phone: 44 169 8458888
Fax: 44 169 8283170
Publications: Information Scotland (53424)

Information on Low External Input and Sustainable Agriculture
PO Box 2067
NL-3800 CB Amersfoort, Netherlands

Phone: 31 334 673870
Fax: 31 334 632410
Publications: LEISA Magazine (47874)

Information Processing Society of Japan
Kagaku-Kaikan Bldg., 4th Fl.
1-5 Kanda-Surugadai
Chiyoda-ku
Tokyo 101-0062, Japan
Phone: 81 335 188374
Fax: 81 335 188375
Publications: Joho-Shori (46878)

Information Systems Research in Scandinavia Association
Viktoria Research Institute
Box 620
SE-405 30 Goteborg, Sweden
Phone: 46 31 7735540
Fax: 46 31 7734754
Publications: Scandinavian Journal of Information Systems (50965)

The Information & Technology Publishing Company Ltd.
PO Box 500024
Dubai, United Arab Emirates
Phone: 971 4 21008000
Fax: 971 4 21008080
Publications: Arabian Business (51630) • Arabian Computer News (51631) • Channel Middle East (51634) • Charged Middle East (51635) • Communications Middle East & Africa (51637) • Digital Studio (51638) • Network Middle East (51650) • Time Out Dubai (51654) • Windows Middle East (51657)

Informed Publishing Ltd.
2nd Fl. Asia House
31-33 Lime St.
London EC3M 7HT, United Kingdom
Phone: 44 20 73970618
Publications: IQ Magazine (54681)

Infothai CM Company Ltd.
299/50 Moo 5
Tasala, Muang
Chiang Mai, Thailand
Phone: 66 53 248859
Fax: 66 53 248859
Publications: Bangkok Magazine (51455)

Iniciativas Editoriales Sistema S.A.
Fuencarral, 127 1
E-28010 Madrid, Spain
Phone: 34 914 487319
Fax: 34 914 487339
Publications: Temas para el Debate (50809)

Inish Times
42 Upper Main St.
Buncrana, Donegal, Ireland
Publications: Inish Times Newspaper (45925)

Ink Publishing
141-143 Shoreditch High St.
London E1 6JE, United Kingdom
Phone: 44 20 7613 8777
Fax: 44 207 613 8776
Publications: Fah Thai (54438) • Ryanair Magazine (55211)

Inn Sign Society
c/o Alan Rose
9 Denmead Dr.
Wednesfield
Wolverhampton WV11 2QS, United Kingdom
Phone: 44 1902 721808
Publications: At the Sign Of (56951)

The Insight
Globe House, 1st Fl. E
3 Morley St.
Brighton BN2 9RA, United Kingdom
Phone: 44 1273 245956
Fax: 44 1273 245960
Publications: The Insight (52615)

Insight Media
Sovereign House
26-30 London Rd.
Twickenham TW1 3RW, United Kingdom
Publications: Airport World (56787) • Asia-Pacific Airports (56788) • Global Airport Cities Magazine

(56792) • Routes News (56793)

Insight Publishing Pty. Ltd.
478 Kingsford Smith Dr.
PO Box 880
Brisbane, Queensland 4007, Australia
Phone: 61 7 36301388
Fax: 61 7 36301344
Publications: Beanscene (41645) • Insight into..
Healing (41649)

Insituto de Agriquimica y Tecnologia de Alimentos
Apdo Correos, 73
E-46100 Burjasot, Spain
Phone: 34 9 63900022
Fax: 34 9 63636301
Publications: Food Science and Technology International (50711)

Insolvency Practitioners Association of Australia
GPO Box 9985
Sydney, New South Wales 2001, Australia
Phone: 61 292 905700
Fax: 61 292 902820
Publications: Australian Insolvency Journal (42456)

Institut Africain pour le Developpement Economique et Social - Rwanda
BP 866
Kigali, Rwanda
Phone: 250 84713
Fax: 250 84713
Publications: HIV Plus (50048)

Institut fur Afrikanistik
Albertus-Magnus-Platz
D-50923 Cologne, Germany
Phone: 49 221 4700
Fax: 49 221 4705158
Publications: Stichproben - Wiener Zeitschrift fur Kritische Afrikastudien (42768)

Institut Bank-Bank Malaysia
Wisma IBI, No. 5 Jalan Semantan
Damansara Hts.
50490 Kuala Lumpur, Malaysia
Phone: 60 3 20956833
Fax: 60 3 20952322
Publications: Banker's Journal Malaysia (47599)

Institut Ciencies del Mar de Barcelona
Passeig Martim de la Barceloneta 37-49
E-08003 Barcelona, Spain
Phone: 34 93 2309500
Fax: 34 93 2309555
Publications: Scientia Marina (50697)

Institut Europlace de Finance
Palais Brongniart
Place de la Bourse
F-75002 Paris, France
Phone: 33 1 49271417
Fax: 33 1 49275628
Publications: Annales d'Economie et de Statistique (44024)

Institut fuer Klinische Psychologie und Gemeindepsychologie
Freie Universitat
Habelschwerdter Allee 45
D-14195 Berlin, Germany
Phone: 49 308 3855753
Fax: 49 308 3851233
Publications: Forum Qualitative Sozialforschung (44183)

Institut fur betriebswirtschaftliches Management
Leonardo-Campus 1
D-48149 Munster, Germany
Phone: 49 251 8331810
Fax: 49 251 8331818
Publications: Journal of Business Chemistry (JoBC) (44599)

Institut National de la Recherche Agronomique
147 rue de l'universite
F-75338 Paris Cedex 07, France
Phone: 33 142 759000
Publications: Cahiers d'Economie et Sociologie Rurales (44031)

Institute of Acoustics
77A St. Peter's St.
Saint Albans AL1 3BN, United Kingdom
Phone: 44 17 27848195
Fax: 44 17 27850553
Publications: Acoustics Bulletin (56433)

Institute of Administrative Management
6 Graphite Sq.
Vauxhall Walk
London SE11 5EE, United Kingdom
Phone: 44 207 0912600
Publications: Manager, British Journal of Administrative Management (54903)

Institute of Advanced Motorists
IAM House
510 Chiswick High Rd.
London W4 5RG, United Kingdom
Phone: 44 20 89969600
Fax: 44 20 89969601
Publications: Advanced Driving (53904)

Institute of Agricultural Medicine
Instytut Medycyny Wsi
Jaczewskiego 2
PO Box 185
PL-20-950 Lublin, Poland
Phone: 48 81 7184410
Fax: 48 817 478646
Publications: Annals of Agricultural and Environmental Medicine (49672)

Institute of Applied Manpower Research
A-7, Narela Institutional Area
Delhi 110 040, Delhi, India
Phone: 91 11 27787214
Fax: 91 11 27783467
Publications: IAMR Report (45093) • IAMR Working Paper (45094) • Manpower Journal (45103)

Institute of Balkan Studies
1000 Sofia, 45 Moskovska St.
BG-1000 Sofia, Bulgaria
Phone: 35 929 806297
Fax: 35 929 806297
Publications: Etudes Balkaniques (43098)

Institute of Biochemistry and Cell Biology
319 Yue Yang Rd.
Shanghai 200031, People's Republic of China
Phone: 86 21 54920000
Fax: 86 21 54920011
Publications: Cell Research (43467)

Institute of Biology
9 Red Lion Ct.
London EC4A 3EF, United Kingdom
Phone: 44 20 79365900
Publications: Biologist (54023) • Journal of Biological Education (54706)

Institute of Biomedical Science
12 Coldbath Sq.
London EC1R 5HL, United Kingdom
Phone: 44 20 77130214
Fax: 44 20 78379658
Publications: Biomedical Scientist (54030) • British Journal of Biomedical Science (54112)

Institute of Chartered Accountants in Australia
33 Erskine St.
Sydney, New South Wales 2000, Australia
Phone: 61 2 92901344
Fax: 61 2 92621512
Publications: Charter (42490)

Institute of Chartered Accountants in England & Wales
Chartered Accountants' Hall
PO Box 433
London EC2R 6EA, United Kingdom
Phone: 44 20 79208100
Fax: 44 20 79200547
Publications: Accountancy (53891) • Accounting and Business Research (53893)

Institute of Chartered Accountants of New Zealand
Level 7, Tower Bldg.
50 Cstomhouse Quay
PO Box 11342
Wellington 6142, New Zealand

Phone: 64 4 4747840
Fax: 64 4 4736303
Publications: Chartered Accountants Journal of New Zealand (49003)

Institute of Chartered Accountants of Pakistan
Chartered Accountants Ave.
Clifton
Karachi 75600, Pakistan
Phone: 92 21 111000422
Fax: 92 21 9251626
Publications: Pakistan Accountant (49366)

Institute of Chartered Accountants of Scotland
CA House
21 Haymarket Yards
Edinburgh EH12 5BH, United Kingdom
Phone: 44 131 3470100
Fax: 44 131 3470105
Publications: CA Magazine (53259)

Institute of Chartered Accountants of Sri Lanka
30A Malalasekera Mawatha
Colombo 00700, Sri Lanka
Phone: 94 11 2352000
Fax: 94 11 2352060
Publications: Chartered Accountants (50851)

Institute of Chartered Foresters
59 George St.
Edinburgh EH2 2JG, United Kingdom
Phone: 44 13 12401425
Fax: 44 13 12401424
Publications: Forestry Journal (53278)

Institute of Chartered Secretaries and Administrators
16 Park Cres.
London W1B 1AH, United Kingdom
Phone: 44 20 75804741
Fax: 44 20 73231132
Publications: Chartered Secretary (54199)

Institute of Chemical Industry of Forest Products, CAF
Suojin Wucun, No. 16
Nanjing 210042, Jiangsu, People's Republic of China
Phone: 86 258 5482401
Fax: 86 258 5413445
Publications: Chemistry and Industry of Forest Products (43457)

Institute of Chemistry, Ceylon
341/22 Kotte Rd.
Welikada
Rajagiriya, Sri Lanka
Phone: 94 112 863154
Fax: 94 112 861231
Publications: Chemistry in Sri Lanka (50935)

Institute of Chemistry of Ireland
Cardiff Ln.
PO Box 9322
Dublin 2, Dublin, Ireland
Publications: Irish Chemical News (45972)

Institute of Chiropodists and Podiatrists
27 Wright St.
Southport PR9 0TL, United Kingdom
Phone: 44 17 04546141
Fax: 44 17 04500477
Publications: Podiatry Review (56588)

Institute of Computing Technology, Chinese Academy of Sciences
No. 6 Kexueyuan South Rd.
Zhongguancun
Haidian District
PO Box 2704
Beijing 100090, People's Republic of China
Phone: 86 10 62601166
Fax: 86 10 62567724
Publications: Journal of Computer Science and Technology (JCST) (43205)

Institute of Cost and Management Accountants of Pakistan
ICMAP Bldg., ST-18/C, Block 6
Gulshan-e-Iqbal
PO Box 17642
Karachi 75300, Pakistan
Phone: 92 21 9243900
Fax: 92 21 9243342
Publications: Management Accountant (49362)

Institute of Cost and Works Accountants of India
12 Sudder St.
Kolkata 700 016, West Bengal, India
Phone: 91 33 22441031
Fax: 91 33 22440993
Publications: The Management Accountant (45298)

Institute of Credit Management
The Water Mill
Station Rd.
South Luffenham
Oakham LE15 8NB, United Kingdom
Phone: 44 17 80722900
Fax: 44 17 80721333
Publications: Credit Management (55780)

Institute for Defence Studies and Analyses
1, Development Enclave, (near USI)
Rau Tula Ram Marg
New Delhi 110 010, Delhi, India
Phone: 91 11 26717983
Fax: 91 11 26154191
Publications: Strategic Analysis (45655) • Strategic Digest (45656)

Institute of Development Studies
c/o University of Sussex
Brighton BN1 9RE, United Kingdom
Phone: 44 1273 606261
Fax: 44 1273 621202
Publications: IDS Bulletin (52614)

Institute for Development Studies
Lot 2-5 Wisma SEDIA
Off Jalan Pintas, Penampang
Locked Bag 127
88994 Kota Kinabalu, Malaysia
Phone: 60 88 450500
Fax: 60 88 450599
Publications: Borneo Review (47589)

Institute of Eastern Culture
2-4-1 Nishi Kanda
Chiyoda-ku
Tokyo 101-0065, Japan
Phone: 81 332 627221
Fax: 81 332 627227
Publications: Acta Asiatica (46721)

Institute for Eastern Studies
28-42 Samchung-dong, Chongro-ku
Seoul 110-230, Republic of Korea
Publications: Asian Perspective (47257)

Institute of Ecology and Environmental Management
43 Southgate St.
Winchester SO23 9EH, United Kingdom
Phone: 44 19 62868626
Fax: 44 19 62868625
Publications: In Practice (56930)

Institute for Education Policy Studies
University of Northampton
Boughton Green Rd.
Northampton NN2 7AL, United Kingdom
Publications: Journal for Critical Education Policy Studies (55711)

Institute of Educational Technology
Walton Hall
The Open University
Milton Keynes MK7 6AA, United Kingdom
Phone: 44 1908 274066
Publications: Journal of Interactive Media in Education (55639)

Institute of Electronics, Information and Communication Engineers
Kikai-Shinko-Kaikan Bldg.
5-8, Shibakoen 3 chome
Minato-ku
Tokyo 105-0011, Japan
Phone: 81 334 336691
Fax: 81 334 336659
Publications: IEICE Electronics Express (46838)

Institute of Electronics, Information and Communication Engineers
Kikai-Shinko-Kaikan Bldg., Annex 3F
5-22 Shibakoen 3 chome
Minato-Ku
Tokyo 105-0011, Japan

Phone: 81 334 336692
Fax: 81 334 336616
Publications: IEICE Transactions on Communications (46839) • IEICE Transactions on Electronics (46840) • IEICE Transactions on Information and Systems (46841) • Journal of IEICE (46908)

Institute of Field Archaeologists
SHES, University of Reading
Whiteknights
PO Box 227
Reading RG6 6AB, United Kingdom
Phone: 44 118 3786446
Fax: 44 118 3786448
Publications: The Archaeologist (56309)

Institute of Financial Planning
Whitefriars Centre
Lewins Mead
Bristol BS1 2NT, United Kingdom
Phone: 44 117 9452470
Fax: 44 117 9292214
Publications: Financial Planning (52670)

Institute of Financial Services - England
IFS House,4-9 Burgate Ln.
Canterbury CTI 2XJ, United Kingdom
Phone: 44 1227 818609
Fax: 44 1227 784331
Publications: Financial World (52919)

Institute for Fiscal Studies
7 Ridgmount St., 3rd Fl.
London WC1E 7AE, United Kingdom
Phone: 44 20 72914800
Fax: 44 20 73234780
Publications: Fiscal Studies (54463)

Institute of Fisheries Management
22 Rushworth Ave.
West Bridgford NG2 7LF, United Kingdom
Phone: 44 115 9822317
Fax: 44 115 9826150
Publications: Fish (56888)

Institute of Health Promotion and Education
c/o Helen Draper, Sec.
School of Dentistry
University of Manchester
Coupland 3, Oxford Rd.
Manchester M13 9PL, United Kingdom
Publications: International Journal of Health Promotion and Education (55559)

Institute of Heraldic and Genealogical Studies
79-82 Northgate
Canterbury CT1 1BA, United Kingdom
Phone: 44 1227 768664
Fax: 44 1227 765617
Publications: Family History (52918)

Institute of Historical Research
Malet St.
London WC1E 7HU, United Kingdom
Phone: 44 20 78628740
Fax: 44 20 78628745
Publications: Reviews in History (55200)

Institute of Integrated Electrical Engineers of the Philippines Inc.
No. 41 Monte de Piedad St.
Cubao
Quezon City 1109, Philippines
Phone: 63 2 7227383
Fax: 63 2 7273545
Publications: Electrical Engineer Magazine (49592)

Institute for the Integration of Latin America and the Caribbean
Esmeralda 130, Pisos 16
C1035ABD Buenos Aires, Argentina
Phone: 54 11 43232350
Fax: 54 11 43232365
Publications: Integration and Trade (41474)

Institute of Internal Auditors - U.K. and Ireland
13 Abbeville Mews
88 Clapham Pk. Rd.
London SW4 7BX, United Kingdom
Phone: 44 20 74980101
Fax: 44 20 79782492
Publications: Internal Auditing and Business Risk (54617)

Institute of International Marketing
PO Box 70
London E13 0UU, United Kingdom
Phone: 44 20 8700422072
Fax: 44 20 8700422062
Publications: Journal of International Marketing (54771)

Institute for International Relations
Ulica Ljudevita Farkasa Vukotinovica 2
PO Box 303
CT-10000 Zagreb, Croatia
Phone: 385 148 77460
Fax: 385 148 28361
Publications: Croatian International Relations Review (43564) • Razvoj/Development (43570)

Institute of International Relations - Czech Republic
Nerudova 3
CZ-118 50 Prague 1, Czech Republic
Phone: 42 251 108111
Fax: 42 251 108222
Publications: Mezinarodni Politika International Politics (43629) • Mezinarodni Vztahy International Relations (43630) • Perspectives - The Central European Review of International Affairs (43634)

The Institute of Legal Cashiers and Administrators
2nd Fl., Marlowe House
109 Station Rd.
Sidcup DA15 7ET, United Kingdom
Phone: 44 20 83022867
Fax: 44 20 83027481
Publications: Legal Abacus (56544)

Institute of Legal Executives
Kempston Manor
Bedfordshire
Kempston MK42 7AB, United Kingdom
Phone: 44 1234 841000
Fax: 44 1234 840373
Publications: Legal Executive Journal (53669)

Institute for the Management of Information Systems
5 Kingfisher House
New Mill Rd.
Orpington BR5 3QG, United Kingdom
Phone: 44 70 00023456
Fax: 44 70 00023023
Publications: IMIS Journal (55852)

Institute of Management Services
Brooke House
24 Dam St.
Staffordshire
Lichfield WS13 6AB, United Kingdom
Phone: 44 1543 266909
Fax: 44 1543 257848
Publications: Management Services (53853)

Institute of Materia Medica
1 Xian Nong Tan St.
Beijing 100050, People's Republic of China
Phone: 86 10 63037394
Fax: 86 10 63017757
Publications: Chinese Chemical Letters (43182)

Institute of Materials, Minerals & Mining
1 Carlton House Ter.
London SW1Y 5DB, United Kingdom
Phone: 44 20 74517300
Fax: 44 20 78391702
Publications: Materials World (54914)

Institute of Mathematical Statistics
PO Box 22718
Beachwood, OH 44122-0708
Phone: 216295-2340
Fax: 216295-5661
Free: 877557-4674
Publications: Electronic Communications in Probability (44013)

Institute of Mathematics and its Applications
16 Nelson St.
Essex
Southend-on-Sea SS1 1EF, United Kingdom
Phone: 44 17 02354020
Fax: 44 17 02354111
Publications: IMA Journal of Numerical Analysis (56585)

Institute of Mathematics of the Polish Academy of Sciences
PO Box 21
ul. Sniadeckich 8
00-956 Warsaw, Poland
Phone: 48 225 228100
Fax: 48 226 293997
Publications: Bulletin of the Polish Academy of Sciences Mathematics (49698)

Institute of Measurement and Control
87 Gower St.
London WC1E 6AA, United Kingdom
Phone: 44 207 3874949
Fax: 44 207 3888431
Publications: Measurement and Control (54918)

Institute of Metal Finishing
Exeter House
48 Holloway Head
Birmingham B1 1NQ, United Kingdom
Phone: 44 121 6227387
Fax: 44 121 6666316
Publications: Transactions of the Institute of Metal Finishing (52370)

Institute of the Motor Industry
Fanshaws
Hertford
Brickendon SG13 8PQ, United Kingdom
Phone: 44 1992 511521
Fax: 44 1992 511548
Publications: Motor Industry Magazine (52592)

Institute of Nuclear Chemistry and Technology
16 Dorodna St.
03-195 Warsaw, Poland
Phone: 48 225 041220
Fax: 48 228 111532
Publications: Nukleonika (49739)

Institute of Objective Studies
PO Box 9725
162-Joga Bai Ext.
Jamia Nagar
New Delhi 110 025, Delhi, India
Phone: 91 11 26981187
Fax: 91 11 26981104
Publications: Journal of Objective Studies (45614) • Religion and Law Review (45643)

Institute of Oceanography and Fisheries
Setaliste Ivana Mestrovica 63
CT-21000 Split, Croatia
Phone: 385 214 08000
Fax: 385 213 58650
Publications: Acta Adriatica (43560) • Acta Adriatica (43559)

Institute of Oncology of Vojvodina
Institutski Put 4
YU-21204 Sremska Kamenica, Serbia
Phone: 381 21 4805500
Fax: 381 21 6613741
Publications: Archive of Oncology (50094)

Institute of Operations Management
Earlstrees Ct.
Earlstrees Rd.
Corby NN17 4AX, United Kingdom
Phone: 44 1536 740105
Fax: 44 1536 740101
Publications: Operations Management (53063)

Institute for Outdoor Learning
The Barn
Plumpton Old Hall
Plumpton
Penrith CA11 9NP, United Kingdom
Phone: 44 1768 885800
Fax: 44 1768 885801
Publications: Horizons (56245) • Journal of Adventure Education and Outdoor Learning (56246)

Institute of Parasitology
Biology Centre, ASCR, v.v.i.
Branisovska 31
370 05 Ceske Budejovice, Czech Republic
Phone: 420 38 5310351
Fax: 420 38 5310388
Publications: Folia Parasitologica (43605)

Institute of Pharmacology
Smetna 12
31-343 Krakow, Poland
Phone: 48 126 623220
Fax: 48 126 374500
Publications: Pharmacological Reports (49667)

Institute of Physics
Dubravska cesta 9
845 11 Bratislava, Slovakia
Phone: 421 2 59410501
Fax: 421 2 54776085
Publications: Acta Physica Slovaca (50315)

Institute of Physics
Dirac House
Temple Back
Bristol BS1 6BE, United Kingdom
Phone: 44 117 9297481
Fax: 44 117 9294318
Publications: Science and Technology of Advanced Materials (52729)

Institute of Physics
Vidya Mandiraya
120/10 Wijerama Mawatha
Colombo 00700, Sri Lanka
Publications: Journal of Physics (50858) • Physical Biology (50862) • Sri Lankan Journal of Physics (50870)

Institute of Physics
76 Portland Pl.
London W1B 1NT, United Kingdom
Phone: 44 20 74704800
Fax: 44 20 74704848
Publications: Inverse Problems (54677) • Journal of Physics B (54799) • Journal of Physics C (54800) • Journal of Physics G (54801) • Physics Education (55086) • Physics World (55087) • Semiconductor Science and Technology (55228) • Superconductor Science and Technology (55278)

Institute of Physics and Engineering in Medicine
Fairmount House
230 Tadcaster Rd.
York Y024 1ES, United Kingdom
Phone: 44 19 04610821
Fax: 44 19 04612279
Publications: Medical Engineering and Physics (56993) • Scope (56998)

Institute of Physics, Singapore
c/o Dept. of Physics
National University of Singapore
2 Science Dr. 3
Singapore 117542, Singapore
Phone: 65 687 43056
Fax: 65 677 76126
Publications: Singapore Journal of Physics (50257)

Institute of Plant and Microbial Biology
128 Sec. 2, Academia Rd.
Nankang
Taipei 11529, Taiwan
Phone: 886 2 27899590
Fax: 886 2 27827954
Publications: Botanical Studies (51333)

Institute of Problems of Mechanical Engineering
V.O., Bolshoj pr., 61
199178 Saint Petersburg, Russia
Phone: 78 123 214778
Fax: 78 123 214771
Publications: Reviews on Advanced Materials Science (50025)

Institute of Public Administration, Australia
37 Little Bourke St.
Melbourne, Victoria 3000, Australia
Phone: 61 3 96532000
Fax: 61 3 96399663
Publications: Australian Journal of Public Administration (42051)

Institute of Risk Management
Lloyds Ave. House
6 Lloyds Ave.
London EC3N 3AX, United Kingdom
Phone: 44 20 77099808
Fax: 44 20 77090716
Publications: InfoRM (54601)

Institute of Road Safety Officers
Pin Point, Rosslyn Cres.
Harrow HA1 2SU, United Kingdom
Phone: 44 870 0104442
Fax: 44 870 3337772
Publications: Inroads (53524)

Institute for Science of Labour
2-8-14 Sugao
Miyamae-ku
Kawasaki 216-8501, Japan
Phone: 81 44 9772121
Fax: 81 44 9777504
Publications: Journal of Science of Labour (46422)

The Institute of Scientific and Technical Communicators
Airport House
Purley Way
Croydon CR0 0XZ, United Kingdom
Phone: 44 208 2534506
Fax: 44 208 2534510
Publications: Communicator (53121)

Institute for Security Studies
PO Box 3077
Cape Town 8001, Republic of South Africa
Phone: 27 214 617211
Fax: 27 214 617213
Publications: African Security Review (50362) • Institute for Security Studies Monographs (50383) • SA Crime Quarterly (50407)

The Institute for Social Development and Policy Research
Seoul National University
Seoul 151-742, Republic of Korea
Phone: 82 28808799
Fax: 82 28736764
Publications: Development and Society (47264)

Institute of Southeast Asian Studies
30 Heng Mui Keng Ter.
Pasir Panjang 119614, Singapore
Phone: 65 677 80955
Fax: 65 677 81735
Publications: ASEAN Economic Bulletin (50098) • Contemporary Southeast Asia (50099) • SOJOURN (50100)

Institute of Southeast Asian Studies
30 Heng Mui Keng Ter.
Pasir Panjang
Singapore 119614, Singapore
Phone: 65 67780955
Fax: 65 67781735
Publications: Regional Outlook (50243) • Southeast Asian Affairs (50270)

Institute of Telecommunications Professionals
Sunbury TE
Green St.
Sunbury-on-Thames TW16 6QJ, United Kingdom
Phone: 44 19 32788861
Fax: 44 19 32785205
Publications: BTE Journal (56652)

Institute of Town Planners, India
4-A Ring Rd.
I.P. Estate
New Delhi 110 002, Delhi, India
Phone: 91 112 3702455
Fax: 91 112 3702453
Publications: Institute of Town Planners, India Journal (45579)

Institute of Transport Management
14-20 George St.
Birmingham B12 9RG, United Kingdom
Phone: 44 12 14403003
Fax: 44 12 14404644
Publications: Transport Journal (52371)

Institute of Vitreous Enamellers
39 Sweetbriar Way
Heath Hayes
Staffordshire
Cannock WS12 2US, United Kingdom
Phone: 44 15 43450596
Fax: 44 87 00941237
Publications: The Vitreous Enameller (52916)

Institute of Zoology
N Star 1 Hospital 5 Industry
W Rd., Chaong District
Beijing 100101, People's Republic of China
Phone: 86 10 64807098
Fax: 86 10 64807099
Publications: Current Zoology (43192)

Institute of Zoology
Academia Sinica
Nankang
Taipei 115, Taiwan
Phone: 886 22 7899515
Fax: 886 22 7858059
Publications: Zoological Studies (51368)

Institution of Agricultural Engineers
The Bullock Bldg.
University Way
Bedford MK43 0GH, United Kingdom
Phone: 44 1234 750876
Fax: 44 1234 751319
Publications: Landwards (53297)

Institution of Chemical Engineers
Davis Bldg.
165-189 Railway Ter.
Rugby CV21 3HQ, United Kingdom
Phone: 44 1788 578214
Fax: 44 1788 560833
Publications: Chemical Engineering Research and Design (ChERD) (56416) • Education for Chemical Engineers (56417) • Food & Bioproducts Processing (56419) • Loss Prevention Bulletin (56421) • Process Safety and Environmental Protection (PSEP) (56422) • TCE (56424)

Institution of Civil Engineers
1 Great George St.
Westminster
London SW1P 3AA, United Kingdom
Phone: 44 20 72227722
Publications: Municipal Engineer (54962)

Institution of Diesel and Gas Turbine Engineers
Bedford Hts.
Manton Ln.
Bedford MK41 7PH, United Kingdom
Phone: 44 1234 214340
Fax: 44 1234 355493
Publications: The Power Engineer (52275)

Institution of Electrical Engineers
Publishing Dept.
Michael Faraday House
Six Hills Way
Stevenage SG1 2AY, United Kingdom
Phone: 44 14 38313311
Fax: 44 14 38765526
Publications: Electronics Letters (56602) • IEE Proceedings Circuits, Devices & Systems (56605) • IEE Proceedings Control Theory & Applications (56606) • IEE Proceedings Electric Power Applications (56607) • IEE Proceedings Generation, Transmission & Distribution (56608) • IEE Proceedings Microwaves, Antennas & Propagation (56609) • IEE Proceedings Nanobiotechnology (56610) • IEE Proceedings Optoelectronics (56611) • IEE Proceedings Radar, Sonar & Navigation (56612) • IEE Proceedings Science, Measurement & Technology (56613) • IEE Proceedings Software (56614) • IEE Proceedings Vision, Image & Signal Processing (56615) • IET Communications (56616) • IET Computers & Digital Techniques (56617) • Systems Biology (56618)

Institution of Electronics and Telecommunication Engineers
2 Institutional Area
Lodi Rd.
New Delhi 110 003, Delhi, India
Phone: 91 11 43538800
Fax: 91 11 24649429
Publications: IETE Journal of Education (45530) • IETE Journal of Research (45531) • IETE Technical Review (45532)

Institution of Engineering Designers
Courtleigh
Westbury Leigh
Westbury BA13 3TA, United Kingdom
Phone: 44 1373 822801
Fax: 44 1373 858085
Publications: Engineering Designer (52917)

Institution of Engineering and Technology
Michael Faraday House
Stevenage SG1 2AY, United Kingdom
Phone: 44 1438 313311
Fax: 44 1438 765526
Publications: Computing and Control Engineering Journal (56599) • Electronics and Communication Engineering Journal (56600) • Electronics Education (56601) • Engineering & Technology (56603) • Flipside Magazine (56604) • Wiring Matters (56619)

The Institution of Engineers
8 Gokhale Rd.
Kolkata 700 020, West Bengal, India
Phone: 91 332 2238230
Publications: Institution of Engineers (India) Aerospace Engineering Division Journal (45276) • Institution of Engineers (India) Agricultural Engineering Division Journal (45277) • Institution of Engineers (India) Architectural Engineering Division Journal (45278) • Institution of Engineers (India) Chemical Engineering Division Journal (45279) • Institution of Engineers (India) Civil Engineering Division Journal (45280) • The Institution of Engineers (India) Computer Engineering Division Journal (45281) • The Institution of Engineers (India) Electrical Engineering Division Journal (45282) • Institution of Engineers (India) Electronics and Telecommunication Engineering Division Journal (45283) • Institution of Engineers (India) Environmental Engineering Division Journal (45284) • Institution of Engineers (India) Hindi Journal (45285) • The Institution of Engineers (India) Inter-disciplinary Panels Journal (45286) • Institution of Engineers (India) Marine Engineering Division Journal (45287) • The Institution of Engineers (India) Mechanical Engineering Division Journal (45288) • The Institution of Engineers (India) Metallurgical and Materials Engineering Division Journal (45289) • Institution of Engineers (India) Mining Engineering Division Journal (45290) • Institution of Engineers (India) Production Engineering Division Journal (45291) • Institution of Engineers (India) Technicians' Journal (45292) • Institution of Engineers (India) Technorama (45293) • Institution of Engineers (India) Textile Engineering Division Journal (45294)

The Institution of Engineers, Malaysia
Lots 60/62, Jalan 52/4
Peti Surat 223, Jalan Sultan
Selangor Darul Ehsan
46720 Petaling Jaya, Malaysia
Phone: 60 796 84001
Fax: 60 795 77678
Publications: IEM Journal (47699) • Jurutera (47700)

Institution of Engineers, Sri Lanka
120-15 Wijerama Mawatha
Colombo 7, Sri Lanka
Phone: 94 11 2698426
Fax: 94 11 2699202
Publications: Engineer (50854) • Sri Lanka Engineering News (50863)

Institution of Environmental Sciences
2nd Fl., 34 Grosvenor Gardens
London SW1W 0DH, United Kingdom
Phone: 44 20 77305516
Fax: 44 20 77305519
Publications: The Environmental Scientist (54378)

Institution of Fire Engineers - England
London Rd.
Gloucestershire
Moreton-in-Marsh GL56 0RH, United Kingdom
Phone: 44 1608 812580
Fax: 44 1608 812581
Publications: Fire Risk Management (55651)

Institution of Lighting Engineers
Regent House
Regent Pl.
Rugby CV21 2PN, United Kingdom
Phone: 44 17 88576492
Fax: 44 17 88540145
Publications: The Lighting Journal (56420)

Institution of Mechanical Engineers
1 Birdcage Walk
London SW1H 9JJ, United Kingdom
Phone: 44 20 72227899
Fax: 44 20 72224557
Publications: Automotive Engineer (53987) • Environmental Engineering (54375) • Journal of Strain Analysis for Engineering Design (54825) • Professional Engineering (55130)

Institution of Occupational Safety and Health
The Grange
Highfield Dr.
Leicestershire
Wigston LE18 1NN, United Kingdom
Phone: 44 11 62573100
Fax: 44 11 62573101
Publications: The Safety and Health Practitioner (56926)

The Institution of Professional Engineers New Zealand
158 The Ter.
PO Box 12 241
Wellington, New Zealand
Phone: 64 447 39444
Fax: 64 447 48933
Publications: e.nz magazine (49007)

Institution of Surveyors, Malaysia
3rd Fl., Bangunan Juruukur
64-66 Jalan 52-4
46200 Petaling Jaya, Malaysia
Phone: 60 3 79551773
Fax: 60 3 79550253
Publications: The Malaysian Surveyor (47701)

Instituto Agronomico de Campinas
Avenida Barao de Itapura, 1481
13012-970 Campinas, Sao Paulo, Brazil
Phone: 55 193 2315422
Fax: 55 193 2314943
Publications: Bragantia (42964) • Bragantia (42963)

Instituto de Economia
Vicuna Mackenna, Macul
Santiago 4860, Chile
Phone: 56 235 44303
Fax: 56 255 32377
Publications: Cuadernos de Economia (43143)

Instituto Espanol de Comercio Exterior
Paseo de la Castellana, 14-16
E-28046 Madrid, Spain
Phone: 34 913 496100
Publications: Spain Gourmetour (50808)

Instituto de Estudios Documentales sobre Ciencia y Tecnologia
Joaquin Costa, 22
E-28002 Madrid, Spain
Phone: 34 915 635482
Fax: 34 915 642644
Publications: Cybermetrics (50748)

Instituto de Estudios Turolenses
C/Amantes, 15
Planta 2
E-44001 Teruel, Spain
Phone: 34 978 617860
Fax: 34 978 617861
Publications: Turia (50830)

Instituto de Investigacion de Recursos Biologicos Alexander von Humboldt
Cr. 13 No. 28-01
Bogota, Colombia
Phone: 57 1 2877514
Publications: Biota Colombiana (43543)

Instituto Nacional de Matematica Pura e Aplicada
Estrada Dona Castorina 110
22460-320 Rio de Janeiro, Rio de Janeiro, Brazil
Phone: 55 212 5295000
Fax: 55 212 5124115
Publications: ALEA (43002) • ALEA (43001)

Instituto Nacional de Pesquisas da Amazonia
Av. Andre Araujo, 2936 Aleixo
69060-001 Manaus, Amazonas, Brazil
Phone: 55 92 36433377
Publications: Acta Amazonica (42987)

Instituto Nacional de Salud Publica
Av. Universidad, 655
Col. Santa Maria Ahuacatitlan

62100 Cuernavaca, Morelos, Mexico
Phone: 52 777 1012900
Publications: Salud Publica de Mexico (47771)

Instituto Oswaldo Cruz
Av. Brasil, 4365
21040-360 Rio de Janeiro, Rio de Janeiro, Brazil
Phone: 55 212 5984242
Publications: Memorias do Instituto Oswaldo Cruz (43012)

Instituto de Psicologia
Av. Prof. Lucio Martins Rodrigues, Trav. 4, 399 Bl. 23
Cidade Universitaria Armando de Salles Oliveira
05508-900 Sao Paulo, Sao Paulo, Brazil
Phone: 55 113 0914452
Fax: 55 113 0914462
Publications: Psicologia USP (43045)

Instituto Universitario ISEDET
Camacua 282
1406 Buenos Aires, Argentina
Phone: 54 114 6325030
Fax: 54 114 6332825
Publications: Journal of Latin American Hermeneutics (41477)

Instytut Lacznosci
ul. Szachowa 1
PL-04-894 Warsaw, Poland
Phone: 48 225 128100
Fax: 48 225 128625
Publications: Journal of Telecommunications and Information Technology (49727)

Instytut Paleobiologii PAN
ul. Twarda 51/55
00-818 Warsaw, Poland
Phone: 48 22 6978850
Fax: 48 22 6206225
Publications: Acta Palaeontologica Polonica (49681)

Insula, Libreria
Via. of the Two Castillas
33 Atica Complex, Bldg. 4
Pozuelo de Alarcon
E-28224 Madrid, Spain
Publications: Insula (50771)

Insurance Institute of India
Universal Insurance Bldg., 6th Fl.
Sir Pherozshah Mehta Rd.
Mumbai 400 001, Maharashtra, India
Phone: 91 22 22872923
Fax: 91 22 22873491
Publications: Insurance Institute of India Journal (45391)

Integrated Bar of the Philippines
IBP Bldg.
No. 15 Julia Vargas Ave.
Ortigas Center
Pasig City, Philippines
Phone: 63 2 6314697
Fax: 63 2 6313014
Publications: IBP Journal (49571)

Intellect
Russell Square House
10-12 Russell Sq.
London WC1B 5EE, United Kingdom
Phone: 44 20 73312000
Fax: 44 20 73312040
Publications: Art, Design & Communication in Higher Education (53967) • European Journal of American Culture (54396) • International Journal of Education through Art (54645) • International Journal of Media and Cultural Politics (54654) • International Journal of Performance Arts and Digital Media (54658) • International Journal of Technology Management & Sustainable Development (54664) • Journal of Media Practice (54777) • Journal of Organisational Transformation and Social Change (54790) • New Cinemas (54989) • Portuguese Journal of Social Science (55104) • The Radio Journal (53444) • Studies in European Cinema (56707) • Studies in French Cinema (53363) • Studies in Hispanic Cinemas (53829) • Studies in Theatre and Performance (53364) • Technoetic Arts (55295)

Inter-African Bureau for Animal Resources
PO Box 30786
Nairobi, Kenya
Phone: 254 2 3674000

Fax: 254 2 3674341
Publications: Bulletin of Animal Health and Production in Africa (47175)

Inter-American Children's Institute
Casilla de Correos 16212
Avenida 8 de Octubre 2904
11600 Montevideo, Uruguay
Phone: 598 2 4872150
Fax: 598 2 4873242
Publications: Bibliographic Journal (57007)

Inter-Research
Nordbunte 23
D-21385 Oldendorf, Germany
Phone: 49 413 27127
Fax: 49 413 28883
Publications: Ethics in Science and Environmental Politics (44628) • Marine Ecology Progress Series (MEPS) (44629)

Inter-Research Science Center
Nordbunte 23 (3, 5, 28, 30)
D-21385 Oldendorf, Germany
Phone: 49 413 27127
Fax: 49 413 28883
Publications: Aquatic Biology (44625) • Aquatic Microbial Ecology (44124) • Climate Research (49195) • Diseases of Aquatic Organisms (44626) • Endangered Species Research (44627)

Interactive Africa
PO Box 7735
Roggebaai 8012, Republic of South Africa
Phone: 27 21 4659966
Fax: 27 21 4659978
Publications: Design Indaba Magazine (50615)

Interactive Business Communications Ltd.
Latimer House
189 High St.
Herts
Potters Bar EN6 5DA, United Kingdom
Phone: 44 1707 664200
Fax: 44 1707 664800
Publications: Manufacturing & Logistics IT (56297)

Interline International Club
Via Nazionale, 204
I-00184 Rome, Italy
Phone: 39 6 4871721
Fax: 39 6 4871618
Publications: Travelling Interline International (46243)

The Intermedia Group
100 Harris St., Unit 39
Pyrmont, New South Wales 2009, Australia
Phone: 61 2 96602113
Fax: 61 2 96604419
Publications: Appliance Retailer (42269) • Australian Giftguide (42272) • Australian Hotelier (42273) • bars♣ (42275) • ESTETICA Australia and New Zealand (42278) • Hilton Australasia (42279) • Hotel and Accommodation Management (42280) • Interior Fitout (42282) • National Liquor News (42284) • Natural Source (42285) • The Production Book (42286) • Professional Beauty (42287) • Signature Cocktails (42288) • Smoke and Mirrors (42289) • Spa Australasia (42290) • The Wanderer (42291)

Internationaal Informatiecentrum en Archief voor de Vrouwenbeweging
Obiplein 4
NL-1094 RB Amsterdam, Netherlands
Phone: 31 20 6650820
Fax: 31 20 6655812
Publications: LOVER (48140)

International African Institute
School of Oriental and African Studies
Thornhaugh St.
Russell Sq.
London WC1H 0XG, United Kingdom
Phone: 44 20 78984420
Fax: 44 20 78984419
Publications: Africa (53915)

International Association of Air Travel Couriers - UK
The Old Cottage, Tidenham
Chepstow NP16 7JL, United Kingdom
Publications: Travel Guide International (52984)

International Association for Bridge and Structural Engineering
ETH-Honggerberg
CH-8093 Zurich, Switzerland
Phone: 41 44 6332647
Fax: 41 44 6331241
Publications: Structural Engineering International (51288)

International Association for Cross-Cultural Psychology
University of Athens
Dept. of Psychology
11 Herodou Attikou St.
GR-10674 Athens, Greece
Phone: 30 210 7241194
Fax: 30 210 7277534
Publications: Journal of Cross-Cultural Psychology (44750)

International Association of Dredging Cos.
Alexanderveld 84
NL-2585 DB The Hague, Netherlands
Phone: 31 703 523334
Fax: 31 703 512654
Publications: Terra et Aqua (48628)

International Association for the History of Religions
Department of the Study of Religion
University of Aarhus
Main Bldg.
DK-8000 Arhus, Denmark
Publications: NUMEN (43649)

International Association of Hydraulic Engineering and Research
Paseo Bajo Virgen del Puerto, 3
E-28005 Madrid, Spain
Phone: 34 91 3357908
Fax: 34 91 3357935
Publications: International Journal of River Basin Management (50773)

International Association of Jewish Lawyers and Jurists
10 Daniel Frish St.
IL-64731 Tel Aviv, Israel
Phone: 97 236 910673
Fax: 97 236 953855
Publications: Justice (46109)

International Association of Oral Pathologists
Dorevitch Pathology
18 Banksia St.
Heidelberg, Victoria 3084, Australia
Phone: 61 39244 0305
Fax: 61 39244 0366
Publications: Journal of Oral Pathology and Medicine (41948)

International Association of Paediatric Dentistry
c/o FDI World Dental Federation
L' Avant Centre
13, chemin du Levant
F-01210 Ferney-Voltaire, France
Phone: 33 4 50426994
Fax: 33 4 50405555
Publications: International Journal of Paediatric Dentistry (43948)

International Association of Ports and Harbors
7F, S Twr., New Pier Takeshiba
1-16-1 Kaigan
Minato-ku
Tokyo 105-0022, Japan
Phone: 81 354 032770
Fax: 81 354 037651
Publications: Ports and Harbors (47023)

International Association of Sound and Audiovisual Archives
c/o Kevin Bradley, P
National Library of Australia
Canberra, Australian Capital Territory 2600, Australia
Phone: 61 2 62621636
Fax: 61 2 62621653
Publications: IASA Journal (41707)

International Association for the Study of German Politics
Department of Politics & Contemporary European Studies

University of Sussex
Falmer
Brighton BN1 9SN, United Kingdom
Phone: 44 1273 877648
Publications: German Politics (52608)

International Association for the Study of Insurance Economics
53 Rte. de Malagnou
CH-1208 Geneva, Switzerland
Phone: 41 227 076600
Fax: 41 227 367536
Publications: Geneva Risk and Insurance Review (51096)

International Association for Suicide Prevention
Central Administrative Office
La Barade
F-32330 Gondrin, France
Phone: 33 562 291947
Fax: 33 562 291947
Publications: Crisis (43957)

International Association of Universities
Unesco House
1, rue Miollis
F-75732 Paris Cedex 15, France
Phone: 33 1 45684800
Fax: 33 1 47347605
Publications: Higher Education Policy (44047)

International Association for Vegetation Science
c/o Nina A.C. Smits
Wes Beekhuizenweg 3
NL-6871 VJ Renkum, Netherlands
Publications: Journal of Vegetation Science (48746)

International Association of Youth and Family Judges and Magistrates
175, Andersonstown Rd.
Belfast BT11 9EA, United Kingdom
Phone: 44 289 0615164
Fax: 44 289 0618374
Publications: The Chronicle (52281)

International Atomic Energy Agency - Austria
Wagramer Strasse 5
PO Box 100
A-1400 Vienna, Austria
Phone: 43 126 000
Fax: 43 126 007
Publications: INIS Database (42760)

International Baccalaureate Organization
Rte. des Morillons 15
CH-1218 Geneva, Switzerland
Phone: 41 22 791 7740
Fax: 41 22 791 0277
Publications: IB World (51098)

International Bar Association
1 Stephen St., 10th Fl.
London W1T 1AT, United Kingdom
Phone: 44 20 76916868
Fax: 44 20 76916544
Publications: International Business Lawyer (54621)

International Board on Books for Young People
Nonnenweg 12
CH-4003 Basel, Switzerland
Phone: 41 61 272 29 17
Fax: 41 61 272 27 57
Publications: Bookbird (51060)

International Bureau of Education
Case Postale 199
CH-1211 Geneva 20, Switzerland
Phone: 41 229177800
Fax: 41 229177801
Publications: Prospects (51156)

International Camellia Society
Westwyn, 44 Kelland Rd.
Waipipi
Waiuku, New Zealand
Publications: International Camellia Journal (56928)

The International Centre for Diarrhoeal Disease Research
PO Box 128
Dhaka 1000, Bangladesh
Phone: 880 2 8860523

Fax: 880 2 8823116
Publications: Journal of Health, Population and Nutrition (42813)

International Centre for Ethnic Studies
554/6A, Peradeniya Rd.
Kandy, Sri Lanka
Phone: 94 812 234892
Fax: 94 812 234892
Publications: Ethnic Studies Report (50906) • Identity Culture and Politics (50907) • Nethra (50908)

International Centre of Insect Physiology and Ecology
PO Box 30772
Nairobi, Kenya
Phone: 25 420 8632000
Fax: 25 420 8632001
Publications: International Journal of Tropical Insect Science (47185)

International Children's Center
Bilkent University
Merkez Kutuphane Binasi
Bilkent
TR-06800 Ankara, Turkey
Phone: 90 312 2902366
Fax: 90 312 2664678
Publications: Turkish Journal of Pediatrics (51514)

International Clematis Society
c/o Ken Woolfenden, Ed.
3 Cuthberts Close
Cheshunt EN7 5RB, United Kingdom
Publications: Clematis International (52987)

The International Commission on Irrigation and Drainage
48 Nyaya Marg
Chanakyapuri
New Delhi 110 021, Delhi, India
Phone: 91 112 6116837
Fax: 91 112 6115962
Publications: Irrigation and Drainage (45591)

International Commission on Irrigation and Drainage - England
c/o Institution of Civil Engineers
1 Great George St.
Westminster
London SW1P 3AA, United Kingdom
Phone: 44 20 86652234
Fax: 44 20 87991325
Publications: News and Views (55003)

International Committee of Military Medicine
Hopital Militaire Reine Astrid
B-1120 Brussels, Belgium
Fax: 32 226 44367
Publications: International Review of the Armed Forces Medical Services (42860)

International Committee of Plastics in Agriculture
65, rue de Prony
F-75854 Paris Cedex 17, France
Phone: 33 144 011649
Fax: 33 144 011655
Publications: Plasticulture Journal (50789)

International Committee on Seafarer's Welfare Office
Gresham House
53 Clarendon Rd.
Watford WD17 1LA, United Kingdom
Phone: 44 192 3222653
Fax: 44 192 3222663
Publications: Sports of Seven Seas (56876)

International Council on Alcohol and Addictions
PO Box 189
CH-1001 Lausanne, Switzerland
Phone: 41 21 3209865
Fax: 41 21 3209868
Publications: Alcoholism (51182)

International Council of Associations for Science Education
College Ln.
Hatfield AL10 9AA, United Kingdom
Phone: 44 1707 271034
Fax: 44 1707 270142
Publications: Science Education International (53542)

International Council of Christians and Jews
Martin Buber House
Postfach 1129
D-64629 Heppenheim, Germany
Phone: 49 625 26896810
Fax: 49 625 268331
Publications: From the Martin Buber House (44482)

International Council for the Exploration of the Sea
H.C. Andersens Blvd. 44-46
DK-1553 Copenhagen V, Denmark
Phone: 45 333 86700
Fax: 45 339 34215
Publications: ICES Cooperative Research Reports (43673) • ICES Journal of Marine Science (43674)

International Council of Nurses
3, Pl. Jean Marteau
CH-1201 Geneva, Switzerland
Phone: 41 229 080100
Fax: 41 229 080101
Publications: International Nursing Review (51148)

International Council for Science
5 rue Auguste Vacquerie
F-75116 Paris, France
Phone: 33 145 250329
Fax: 33 142 889431
Publications: Data Science Journal (44036)

International Diabetes Federation
Chaussee de la Hulpe 166
B-1000 Brussels, Belgium
Phone: 32 253 85511
Fax: 32 253 85114
Publications: Diabetes Voice (42848)

International Digital Organization for Scientific Information
P-08, Omer Homes
Satyana Rd.
Bat. 15, Campus de Beaulieu
Faisalabad 35042, Pakistan
Phone: 92 41 8501147
Fax: 92 41 8501146
Publications: Academic Journal of Cancer Research (49228) • Academic Journal of Financial Management (49229) • Advances in Biological Research (49230) • American-Eurasian Journal of Agricultural & Environmental Sciences (49232) • American-Eurasian Journal of Botany (49233) • American-Eurasian Journal of Scientific Research (49234) • Global Journal of Biotechnology & Biochemistry (49241) • Global Journal of Environmental Research (49242) • Global Journal of Molecular Sciences (49243) • Global Journal of Pharmacology (49244) • Global Veterinaria (49245) • Humanity & Social Sciences Journal (49246) • International Journal of Planetary and Space Research (49253) • Middle East Journal of Scientific Research (49274) • Universal Science and Engineering for Marine Environment (49295) • World Applied Sciences Journal (49297) • World Information Technology Journal (49298) • World Journal of Agricultural Sciences (49299) • World Journal of Chemistry (49300) • World Journal of Dairy & Food Sciences (49301) • World Journal of Medical Sciences (49302) • World Journal of Zoology (49303)

International Farm Management Association
38 W End
Whittlesford
Cambridge CB22 4LX, United Kingdom
Phone: 44 122 3832527
Publications: Journal of International Farm Management (52857)

International Federation of Beekeepers' Associations
Corso Vittorio Emanuele 101
I-00186 Rome, Italy
Phone: 39 668 52286
Fax: 39 668 52287
Publications: Apiacta (46221)

International Federation for Computational Logic
King's College Strand
London WC2R 2LS, United Kingdom
Publications: Logical Methods in Computer Science (54883)

The International Federation of Film Archives
Rue Defacqz 1
B-1000 Brussels, Belgium
Phone: 32 253 83065
Fax: 32 253 44774
Publications: Journal of Film Preservation (42862)

International Federation of Hydrographic Societies
PO Box 103
Plymouth PL4 7YP, United Kingdom
Phone: 44 1752 223512
Fax: 44 1752 223512
Publications: The Hydrographic Journal (56270)

International Federation of Medical Students Associations
c/o WMA
Boite Postale 63
F-01212 Ferney-Voltaire Cedex 63, France
Fax: 33 450 405937
Publications: Medical Student International (43949)

International Federation of Organic Agriculture Movements
Charles-de-Gaulle-St. 5
D-53113 Bonn, Germany
Phone: 49 228 9265010
Fax: 49 228 9265099
Publications: Ecology and Farming (44255)

International Federation of Red Cross and Red Crescent Societies
PO Box 372
CH-1211 Geneva 19, Switzerland
Phone: 41 227 304222
Fax: 41 227 330395
Publications: Red Cross, Red Crescent (51157)

International Federation of Societies of Cosmetic Chemists
Ste. 6, Langham House E
Mill St.
Luton LU1 2NA, United Kingdom
Phone: 44 158 2726661
Fax: 44 158 2405217
Publications: IFSCC Magazine (44140)

International Federation for Theatre Research
Department of Theatre Studies
University of Amsterdam
Nieuwe Doelenstraat 16
1012 Amsterdam, Netherlands
Fax: 31 20 5252938
Publications: Theatre Research International (48247)

International Food Information Service Publishing
Ln. End House
Shinfield Rd.
Reading RG2 9BB, United Kingdom
Phone: 44 118 9883895
Fax: 44 118 9885065
Publications: Food Science and Technology Abstracts (56317)

International Glaciological Society - Scott Polar Research Institute
Lensfield Rd.
Cambridge CB2 1ER, United Kingdom
Phone: 44 12 23355974
Fax: 44 12 23354931
Publications: Annals of Glaciology (52788) • Journal of Glaciology (52853)

International Gottfried Wilhelm Leibniz Society
Niedersaechsische Landesbibliothek
Waterloostrasse 8
D-30169 Hannover, Germany
Phone: 49 511 1267331
Fax: 49 511 1267202
Publications: Studia Leibnitiana (44435)

International Herald Tribune
6 Bis, rue des Graviers
F-92521 Neuilly Cedex, France
Phone: 33 141 439361
Publications: International Herald Tribune (44014)

International Hospital Federation
13 Chemin du Levant
Immeuble JB SAY
F-01210 Ferney-Voltaire, France
Phone: 33 450,426000

Fax: 33 450 426001
Publications: World Hospitals and Health Services (43950)

International Institute of Anticancer Research
1st km Kapandritiou-Kalamou Rd.
PO Box 22
GR-190 14 Kapandriti, Greece
Phone: 30 229 5053389
Fax: 30 229 5052945
Publications: Anticancer Research (44760)

International Institute for Applied Systems Analysis
Schlossplatz 1
A-2361 Laxenburg, Austria
Phone: 43 223 68070
Fax: 43 223 671313
Publications: Options (42731)

International Institute for Conservation of Historic and Artistic Works
6 Buckingham St.
London WC2N 6BA, United Kingdom
Phone: 44 20 78395975
Fax: 44 20 79761564
Publications: Studies in Conservation (55272)

International Institute for Environment and Development
3 Endsleigh St.
London WC1H 0DD, United Kingdom
Phone: 44 20 73882117
Fax: 44 20 73882826
Publications: Environment and Urbanization (54374)

International Institute Of Forecasters
PO Box 211
NL-1000 AE Amsterdam, Netherlands
Phone: 31-20 4853757
Fax: 31 20 4853432
Publications: International Journal of Forecasting (42665)

International Institute of Peace Studies and Global Philosophy
Castle of the Muses
Craigard
Argyll and Bute PA24 6AH, United Kingdom
Publications: The Muses Journal (52132)

International Institute of Political Science
Jostova 10
602 00 Brno, Czech Republic
Phone: 420 549 495769
Fax: 420 549 495769
Publications: Central European Political Studies Review (43603)

International Institute of Public Finance
PO Box 86 04 46
D-81631 Munich, Germany
Phone: 49 899 2241281
Fax: 49 899 077952281
Publications: International Tax and Public Finance (44565)

International Institute of Refrigeration
177, Blvd. Malesherbes
F-75017 Paris, France
Phone: 33 142 273235
Fax: 33 147 631798
Publications: International Journal of Refrigeration (44056)

International Institute for the Science of Sintering
Knez-Mhailova 35/IV
PO Box 315
YU-11001 Belgrade, Serbia
Phone: 381 11 637367
Fax: 381 11 637239
Publications: Science of Sintering (50083)

International Journal of Advanced Robotic Systems
Kirchengasse 43/3
A-1070 Vienna, Austria
Publications: International Journal of Advanced Robotic Systems (42761)

International Journal House
A-95 Journal House
Janta Colony

Jaipur 302 004, Rajasthan, India
Phone: 91 141 2614398
Fax: 91 141 2602973
Publications: Diamond World (45193) • Gem & Jewellery Yearbook (45194)

International Labour Office
4, Rte. Des Morillons
CH1211 Geneva, Switzerland
Phone: 41 122 7996111
Fax: 44 122 79888685
Publications: International Labour Review (51147)

International Labour Organization - Switzerland
4, Rte. des Morillons
CH-1211 Geneva 22, Switzerland
Phone: 41 227 996111
Fax: 41 227 988685
Publications: World of Work (51169)

International Law Book Co.
1562 Church Rd.
Kashmere Gate
New Delhi 110 006, Delhi, India
Phone: 91 11 3867810
Fax: 91 11 23864769
Publications: Current Consumer Cases (45502) • Drugs Cases (45504) • Labour and Industrial Law Reporter (45621) • Municipalities and Corporation Cases (45627) • Prevention of Food Adulteration Cases (45637)

International Library & Information Group of CILIP
Scarsdale Cottage
Woodhouse
Loughborough LE12 8UA, United Kingdom
Phone: 44 15 09890050
Fax: 44 15 09890050
Publications: Focus on International Library & Information Work (55480)

International Maize and Wheat Improvement Center
Apartado Postal 6-641
06600 Mexico City, Federal District, Mexico
Phone: 52 55 58042004
Fax: 52 555 8047558
Publications: CIMMYT Annual Report (47783)

International Map Collectors' Society
c/o Rogues Roost
Poundsgate
Newton Abbot
Devon TQ13 7PS, United Kingdom
Fax: 44 1364 631042
Publications: IMCoS Journal (53176)

International Maritime Organization, World Maritime University
PO Box 500
S-201 24 Malmo, Sweden
Phone: 46 403 56300
Fax: 46 401 28442
Publications: World Maritime University Journal of Maritime Affairs (50992)

International Meat Secretariat
6 rue de la Victoire
F-75009 Paris, France
Phone: 33 145 266897
Fax: 33 145 266898
Publications: Meat Processing Global Edition (44070)

International Media Network Nepal Pvt. Ltd.
APCA House
Baidya Khana Rd.
Anam Nagar
PO Box 11651
Kathmandu, Nepal
Phone: 977 1 4771489
Fax: 977 1 4770701
Publications: The Himalayan Times (47837)

International Medical Society of Japan
Inoue Bldg., No. 502 1-4-10
Kamiuma
Setagaya-ku
Tokyo 154-0011, Japan
Phone: 81 3 54860601
Fax: 81 3 54860599
Publications: International Medical News (46849)

International Monarchist League
PO Box 5307
Bishop's Stortford CM23 3DZ, United Kingdom
Phone: 44 127 9465551
Publications: Monarchy (52381)

International Movement of Catholic Agricultural and Rural Youth
53, Rue J. Coosemans
B-1030 Brussels, Belgium
Phone: 32 273 49211
Fax: 32 273 49225
Publications: MIJARC News (42866)

International Network for the History of Public Health
c/o Marie C. Nelson
Division of History/ISAK
Linkoping University
S-581 83 Linkoping, Sweden
Phone: 46 132 84465
Fax: 46 132 81843
Publications: Hygiea Internationalis (50974)

International Network for Scientific Information
Haseeb Shaheed Colony, P-112, No. 10
Hilal Rd.
Faisalabad, Pakistan
Phone: 92 333 6616624
Fax: 92 333 2227333
Publications: Australian Journal of Basic and Applied Sciences (49238) • Journal of Applied Sciences Research (49262) • Research Journal of Agriculture and Biological Sciences (49280) • Research Journal of Animal and Veterinary Sciences (49283) • Research Journal of Cell and Molecular Biology (49286) • Research Journal of Fisheries and Hydrobiology (49288) • Research Journal of Medicine and Medical Sciences (49290) • Research Journal of Telecommunication and Information Technology (49293)

International Network for Terminology
TermNet
Zieglergasse 28
A-1070 Vienna, Austria
Phone: 43 152 4060611
Fax: 43 152 4060699
Publications: TermNet News (42769)

International Neuropsychiatric Association
c/o Mrs. Angela Russell
Neuropsychiatric Institute
Prince of Wales Hospital
Randwick, New South Wales 2031, Australia
Phone: 61 293 823816
Fax: 61 293 823774
Publications: Neuropsychiatric Disease and Treatment (42296)

International Nut Council
Calle Boule 2, 3
E-43201 Reus, Spain
Phone: 34 977 331416
Fax: 34 977 315028
Publications: The Cracker (50828)

International Organization for the Study of The Old Testament
Faculty of Theology, Leiden Univ.
PO Box 9515
NL-2300 RA Leiden, Netherlands
Phone: 31 715 272577
Fax: 31 715 272571
Publications: Vetus Testamentum (48729)

International Organization for Succulent Plant Study
Sukkulenten-Sammlung Zurich
Mythenquai 88
CH-8002 Zurich, Switzerland
Publications: IOS Bulletin (51268)

International Orienteering Federation
Radiokatu 20
FIN-00093 Helsinki, Finland
Phone: 358 93 4813112
Fax: 358 93 4813113
Publications: Scientific Journal of Orienteering (43856)

International Pharmaceutical Federation
PO Box 84200
NL-2508 The Hague, Netherlands
Phone: 31 70 3021970

Fax: 31 70 3021999
Publications: Pharmacy Education (48625)

International Philatelic Federation
Biberlinstrasse 6
CH-8032 Zurich, Switzerland
Phone: 41 1 4223839
Fax: 41 1 4223843
Publications: FLASH (51260)

International Press of Boston Inc.
387 Somerville Ave.
PO Box 43502
Somerville, MA 02143-2950
Phone: 617623-3016
Fax: 617623-3101
Publications: Asian Journal of Mathematics (43277)

International Research and Training Center on Erosion and Sedimentation
20 West Chegongzhuang Rd.
PO Box 366
Beijing 100044, People's Republic of China
Phone: 86 106 8413372
Fax: 86 106 8411174
Publications: International Journal of Sediment Research (43200)

International Rubber Study Group
111 North Bridge Rd.
No. 23-06 Peninsula Plz.
Singapore 179098, Singapore
Phone: 65 68372411
Fax: 65 63394369
Publications: Rubber Industry Report (50248) • Rubber Statistical Bulletin (50249)

International Seed Testing Association
Zurichstrasse 50
CH-8303 Bassersdorf, Switzerland
Phone: 41 183 86000
Fax: 41 183 86001
Publications: Seed Science and Technology (51067)

International Sericultural Commission
26 rue Bellecordiere
F-69002 Lyon, France
Phone: 33 478 504198
Fax: 33 478 860957
Publications: Sericologia (43970)

International Ship Electrical and Engineering Service Association
Studio 204, Mill Studio
Crane Mead
Ware SG12 9PY, United Kingdom
Phone: 44 192 0444005
Fax: 44 192 0444006
Publications: ISESnews (56841)

International Society for Bioelectromagnetism
PO Box 692
FIN-33101 Tampere, Finland
Phone: 358 40849 0020
Fax: 358 33115 2162
Publications: International Journal of Bioelectromagnetism (43908)

International Society of Chemotherapy
c/o Kurt G. Naber, Pres.
Department of Urology
Hospital St. Elisabeth
St. Elisabeth 23
D-94315 Straubing, Germany
Phone: 49 9421 7101700
Fax: 49 9421 710270
Publications: International Journal of Antimicrobial Agents (44658)

International Society for Contemporary Music - Netherlands
c/o Muziek Centrum Nederland
Rokin 111
NL-1012 KN Amsterdam, Netherlands
Phone: 31 20 3446060
Publications: World New Music Magazine (48272)

International Society of Developmental Biologists
Netherlands Institute for Developmental Biology
Hubrecht Laboratory
Uppsalalaan 8
NL-3584 CT Utrecht, Netherlands
Phone: 31 302 121883

Fax: 31 302 516464
Publications: Mechanisms of Development (48763)

International Society for Diseases of the Esophagus
Department of Surgical Oncology and Digestive Surgery
Kagoshima University
8-35-1, Sakuragaoka
Kagoshima 890-8520, Japan
Phone: 9 9275 5361
Fax: 9 9265 7426
Publications: Diseases of the Esophagus (46403)

International Society of Electrochemistry
Rue de Sebeillon 9b
CH-1004 Lausanne, Switzerland
Fax: 41 21 6483975
Publications: Electrochimica Acta (51187)

International Society for Equity in Health
5ta. Calle 20-15 zona 11
Colonia Mirador 1
01011 Guatemala City, Guatemala
Phone: 502 2472 8530
Fax: 502 2475 2974
Publications: International Journal for Equity in Health (44785)

International Society for Gerontechnology
Den Dolech 2, Matrix 1.05
PO Box 513
NL-5600 MB Eindhoven, Netherlands
Phone: 31 402 475040
Fax: 31 402 475923
Publications: Gerontechnology (48591)

International Society for Horticultural Science
PO Box 500
B-3001 Leuven, Belgium
Phone: 32 162 29427
Fax: 32 162 29450
Publications: Acta Horticulturae (42890)

International Society for Military Law and Law of War
Av. de la Renaissance 30
B-1000 Brussels, Belgium
Phone: 32 273 76178
Fax: 32 273 76178
Publications: Military Law and Law of War Review (42867)

International Society for Optical Engineering
1000 20th St.
PO Box 10
Bellingham, WA 98225-6705
Phone: 360676-3290
Fax: 360647-1445
Free: 888504-8171
Publications: Journal of Micro/Nanolithography, MEMS, and MOEMS (51306)

International Society for Quality in Health Care
2 Parnell Sq. E
Dublin 3002, Dublin, Ireland
Phone: 353 1 8717049
Fax: 353 1 8783845
Publications: International Journal for Quality in Health Care (45967)

International Society for Rock Mechanics
Av. Brasil, 101
P-1700 Lisbon, Portugal
Phone: 351 218 443419
Fax: 351 218 443021
Publications: ISRM News Journal (49803)

International Society for Utilitarian Studies
University College London
Bentham Project
Endsleigh Gardens
London WC1H 0EG, United Kingdom
Phone: 44 20 76791407
Publications: Utilitas (56332)

International Solar Energy Society
Villa Tannheim
Wiesentalstrasse 50
D-79115 Freiburg, Germany
Phone: 49 761 459060
Fax: 49 761 4590699
Publications: Renewable Energy Focus (44372) •

Solar Energy Journal (44373)

International Sport Press Association
AIPS Headquarters
H-1054 Budapest, Hungary
Phone: 36 1 3112689
Fax: 36 1 3533807
Publications: International Sports Magazine (44838)

International Sufi Movement
Banstraat 24
NL-2517 GJ The Hague, Netherlands
Publications: Caravanserai (48609)

International Telecommunication Union
Palais des Nations
CH-1211 Geneva 20, Switzerland
Phone: 41 22 7305111
Fax: 41 22 7337256
Publications: ITU News (51151)

International Tennis Federation
Bank Ln.
Roehampton
London SW15 5X2, United Kingdom
Phone: 44 20 88786464
Fax: 44 20 88787799
Publications: ITF World (54686)

International Trade Centre UNCTAD/WTO
Palais des Nations
CH-1211 Geneva 10, Switzerland
Publications: International Trade FORUM (51150)

International Union Against Tuberculosis and Lung Disease
68 Blvd. St. Michel
F-75006 Paris, France
Phone: 33 144 320360
Fax: 33 143 299087
Publications: The International Journal of Tuberculosis and Lung Disease (44057)

International Union Association of Public Transport
rue St. Marie 6
B-1080 Brussels, Belgium
Phone: 32 267 36100
Fax: 32 266 01072
Publications: Public Transport International (42870)

International Union of Biological Sciences
Bat 442 Universite Paris-Sud 11
Orsay cedex
F-91405 Paris, France
Phone: 33 169 155027
Fax: 33 169 155747
Publications: Biology International (44029)

International Union of Crystallography
5 Abbey Sq.
Chester CH1 2HU, United Kingdom
Phone: 44 12 44342878
Fax: 44 12 44344888
Publications: Acta Crystallographica Section A (52991) • Journal of Applied Crystallography (44202) • Synchrotron Radiation (53000)

International Union for Health Promotion and Education
42 Blvd. de la Liberation
93203 Saint Denis Cedex, France
Phone: 33 148 137120
Fax: 33 148 091767
Publications: Global Health Promotion (44103)

International Union of Microbiological Societies
Institut de Biologie Moleculaire er Cellulaire de CNRS
15 Rue Descartes
F-67000 Strasbourg, France
Phone: 33 388 417022
Fax: 33 388 610680
Publications: Archives of Virology (44110) • World Journal of Microbiology and Biotechnology (44114)

International Union for Quaternary Research
Dept. of Geography, Museum Bldg.
Trinity College
Dublin 2, Dublin, Ireland
Phone: 353 1 6081213
Publications: Quaternary International (45996)

International Union of Railways
16, rue Jean Rey
F-75015 Paris, France

Phone: 33 144 492020
Fax: 33 144 492029
Publications: International Railway Statistics (44059)

International Union of Speleology
Kalisnicka 4-6
130 00 Prague 3, Czech Republic
Phone: 42 022 0922392
Fax: 42 022 0922670
Publications: International Journal of Speleology (43626)

International Veterinary Students' Association
KVL, DSR
Dyrlaegevej 9
DK-1870 Frederiksberg, Denmark
Fax: 45 352 82152
Publications: The International Veterinary Student (43691)

International Water Services Association
Alliance House
12 Caxton St.
London SW1H 0QS, United Kingdom
Phone: 44 207 6545500
Fax: 44 207 6545555
Publications: Journal of Water Supply (54835) • Water Supply (55388)

International Weightlifting Federation
Istvanmezei ut 1-3
H-1146 Budapest, Hungary
Phone: 36 135 30530
Fax: 36 135 30199
Publications: IWF Handbook (44839) • World Weightlifting (44883)

International Whaling Commission
The Red House
135 Sta. Rd.
Impington
Cambridge CB24 9NP, United Kingdom
Phone: 44 122 3233971
Fax: 44 122 3232876
Publications: Journal of Cetacean Research and Management (52848)

Internationale Coronelli-Gesellschaft fuer Globenkunde
Dominikanerbastei 21/28
A-1010 Vienna, Austria
Phone: 43 1 5320824
Publications: Globe Studies (42759)

Internationales Zentralinstitut fur das Jugend- und Bildungsfernsehen
Rundfunkplatz 1
D-80335 Munich, Germany
Phone: 49 895 9002991
Fax: 49 895 9002379
Publications: Televizion (44583)

Intersentia N.V.
Groenstraat 31
B-2640 Mortsel, Belgium
Phone: 32 368 01550
Fax: 32 365 87121
Publications: Journal of Network Industries (42906)

Intervega - Movement for Compassionate Living the Vegan Way
105 Cyfyng Rd.
Ystalyfera
Swansea SA9 2BT, United Kingdom
Publications: New Leaves (56704)

Intramuros
29 rue de Meaux
F-75019 Paris, France
Phone: 33 142 039595
Fax: 33 142 039577
Publications: Intramuros (44061)

Intras Ltd.
46 Holly Walk
Warwickshire
Leamington Spa CV32 4HY, United Kingdom
Phone: 44 1926 334137
Fax: 44 1926 314755
Publications: Eurowire (53745) • Tube & Pipe Technology (53749)

Investment Now
70 Singer Way

Kempston MK42 7PU, United Kingdom
Phone: 44 12 34843905
Fax: 44 12 34843901
Publications: Investment Now (53668)

IOP Publishing Ltd.
Dirac House
Temple Back
Bristol BS1 6BE, United Kingdom
Phone: 44 117 9297481
Fax: 44 117 9294318
Publications: Astrophysical Journal Supplement Series (52640) • Biofabrication (52645) • Bioinspiration & Biomimetics (52646) • Biomedical Materials (52647) • CERN Courier (52651) • Chinese Journal of Chemical Physics (52652) • Chinese Physics Letters (43189) • Classical and Quantum Gravity (52653) • Communications in Theoretical Physics (43191) • Compound Semiconductor (52654) • European Journal of Physics (52665) • Europhysics Letters (EPL) (52666) • FibreSystems Europe (52669) • Journal of Breath Research (52682) • Journal of Cosmology and Astroparticle Physics (52684) • Journal of Geophysics and Engineering (52686) • Journal of Instrumentation (52687) • Journal of Micromechanics and Microengineering (52689) • Journal of Neural Engineering (52692) • Journal of Optics (52693) • Journal of Physics A (52694) • Journal of Physics D (52695) • Journal of Radiological Protection (52697) • Journal of Semiconductors (52698) • Journal of Statistical Mechanics (52699) • Measurement Science & Technology (52705) • Metrologia (52706) • Modelling and Simulation in Materials Science and Engineering (52707) • Nanotechnology (52708) • New Journal of Physics (NJP) (52710) • Nonlinearity (52712) • Nuclear Fusion (42765) • Optics & Laser Europe (52713) • Physica Scripta (52716) • Physics in Medicine and Biology (52717) • Physiological Measurement (52718) • Plasma Physics and Controlled Fusion (52720) • Plasma Sources Science and Technology (52721) • Reports on Progress in Physics (52725) • Research in Astronomy and Astrophysics (52727) • Smart Materials and Structures (52731)

IOS Press, B.V.
Nieuwe Hemweg 6B
NL-1013 BG Amsterdam, Netherlands
Phone: 31 20 6883355
Fax: 31 20 6203419
Publications: AI Communications (47887) • Analytical Cellular Pathology/Cellular Oncology (47893) • Applied Ontology (46261) • Asian Journal of Water, Environment and Pollution (47899) • Asymptotic Analysis (44119) • Bio-Medical Materials and Engineering (46664) • BioFactors (46616) • Breast Disease (47915) • Bridge Structures (47916) • Cancer Biomarkers (47920) • Clinical Hemorheology and Microcirculation (46258) • Disease Markers (47959) • Education for Information (55554) • Environmental Policy and Law (47969) • Fundamenta Informaticae (47993) • In Silico Biology (44399) • Informatica (48017) • Information Polity (53423) • Information Services & Use (48021) • International Journal of Applied Electromagnetics and Mechanics (46667) • International Journal of Artificial Intelligence in Education (48025) • International Journal of Hybrid Intelligent Systems (48027) • International Journal of Hybrid Intelligent Systems (47268) • International Journal of Knowledge-Based and Intelligent Engineering Systems (56524) • International Journal of Regulation and Governance (48032) • International Journal of Risk and Safety in Medicine (48742) • Intervention Research (48034) • Isokinetics and Exercise Science (46106) • Journal of Alzheimer's Disease (48041) • Journal of Back and Musculoskeletal Rehabilitation (48597) • Journal of Computational Methods in Sciences and Engineering (48063) • Journal of E-Governance (48069) • Journal of Economic and Social Measurement (48071) • Journal of Integrated Design & Process Science (48086) • Journal of Intelligent & Fuzzy Systems (48087) • Journal of Pediatric Infectious Diseases (51581) • Journal of Pediatric Neurology (48108) • Journal of Vestibular Research (48127) • Mobile Information Systems (41763) • Model Assisted Statistics and Applications (48161) • Multiagent and Grid Systems (53431) • Pharmaceuticals Policy and Law (50718) • Restorative Neurology and Neuroscience (44536) • Shock and Vibration (48231) • Space Communications (48234) • Statistical Journal of the IAOS (48236) • Strength, Fracture and Complexity

(48238) • Technology and Disability (48630) • Technology and Health Care (48242) • Web Intelligence and Agent Systems (48270)

IOS Press Inc.
4502 Rachael Manor Dr.
Fairfax, VA 22032-3631
Phone: 703323-5600
Fax: 703323-3668
Publications: International Shipbuilding Progress (48310) • Journal of Dynamical Systems and Geometric Theories (45882) • Journal on Satisfiability, Boolean Modeling and Computation (48312)

IOSH Services Ltd.
The Grange
Highfield Dr.
Leicester
Wigston LE18 1NN, United Kingdom
Phone: 44 116 2573100
Fax: 44 116 2573101
Publications: Policy and Practice in Health and Safety (56925)

IP Publishing Ltd.
258 Belsize Rd.
London NW6 4BT, United Kingdom
Phone: 44 20 73161870
Fax: 44 20 76249994
Publications: Industry and Higher Education (54599) • International Journal of Entrepreneurship and Innovation (53856) • Outlook on Agriculture (55046) • South East Asia Research (55257) • Tourism Economics (55331)

IPC tx
Blue Fin Bldg.
110 Southwark St.
London SE1 0SU, United Kingdom
Phone: 44 20 31485000
Publications: Soaplife (55244)

IPC Country & Leisure Media Ltd.
King's Reach Tower
Stamford St.
London SE1 9LS, United Kingdom
Publications: Web User (55395)

IPC ignite! Ltd.
Blue Fin Bldg.
110 Southwark St.
London SE1 0SU, United Kingdom
Phone: 44 203 1485000
Publications: Nuts (55022)

IPC Magazine Media Ltd.
222 Branston Rd.
Burton-on-Trent DE14 3BT, United Kingdom
Phone: 44 12 83542721
Publications: Ships Monthly (52771)

IPC Media Ltd.
Blue Fin Bldg.
110 Southwark St.
London SE1 0SU, United Kingdom
Phone: 44 203 1485000
Publications: Aeroplane Monthly (53912) • Amateur Gardening (53936) • Amateur Gardening (53935) • Amateur Photographer (53937) • Angler's Mail (53942) • Cage and Aviary Birds (54166) • Chat - It's Fate (54200) • Country Life (54275) • The Field (54451) • Golf Monthly (54518) • Hi Fi News (54549) • Horse & Hound (54571) • Ideal Home (54582) • Livingetc (54879) • Motor Boat and Yachting (54957) • Motor Caravan (54958) • The Railway Magazine (55171) • Rugby World (55210) • Sporting Gun (55263) • 25 Beautiful Homes (55348) • 25 Beautiful Kitchens (55349) • Wallpaper* (55377) • What Digital Camera (55400) • Woman (55412) • Woman & Home (55413)

IPE International Publishers Ltd.
320 Great Guildford House
30 Great Guildford St.
London SE1 0HS, United Kingdom
Phone: 44 20 72610666
Publications: Investment & Pensions Europe (IPE) (54678)

Iran Exports Publication Co. Ltd.
No. 44, Golpar Alley
20th St., Khaled Slamboli Ave.
Tehran, Iran
Phone: 98 21 22200646

Fax: 98 21 22200632
Publications: Iran Exports & Imports (45892)

Iran News
PO Box 15875-8551
Tehran, Iran
Phone: 98 21 44253450
Fax: 98 21 44253478
Publications: Iran News (45893)

Iran Polymer Institute
PO Box 14965-115
Tehran, Iran
Phone: 98 21 4580000
Fax: 98 21 4580021
Publications: Iranian Polymer Journal (45910)

Iran University of Medical Sciences, Razi Institute for Drug Research
PO Box 14155-6183
Tehran, Iran
Phone: 98 21 88052977
Fax: 98 21 88052977
Publications: Iranian Journal of Pharmacology and Therapeutics (45907)

Iran Weekly Press Digest
2 Hessar Faraj Alley
Golabdareh St.
Darband Ave.
Tehran 19736, Iran
Phone: 98 212 733291
Fax: 98 212 708364
Publications: Iran Weekly Press Digest (45894)

Iranian Fisheries Research Organization
PO Box 14155-6116
Tehran, Iran
Phone: 98 21 66919133
Fax: 98 21 66420731
Publications: Iranian Journal of Fisheries Science (45903)

Iranian Public Health Association
c/o Dr. Bijan Sadrizadeh, Pres.
Ministry of Health & Medical Education
14th Fl., Simaye Iran St., Phase 5
Sharak Gharb
Tehran, Iran
Phone: 98 21 88364369
Fax: 98 21 88364111
Publications: Iranian Journal of Public Health (45908)

Irish Association for American Studies
School of English, Media & Theatre Studies
National University of Ireland
Maynooth, Kildare, Ireland
Publications: Irish Journal of American Studies (46038)

Irish Association of Teachers in Special Education
Drumconda Education Ctr.
Drumconda
Dublin 9, Dublin, Ireland
Publications: Reach (45997)

Irish Business and Employers' Confederation
Confederation House
84-86 Lower Baggot St.
Dublin IRL-2, Dublin, Ireland
Phone: 353 16 051500
Fax: 353 16 381500
Publications: IBEC Economic Trends (45965)

Irish Examiner
City Quarter
Lapps Quay
Cork, Cork, Ireland
Phone: 353 214 72722
Publications: Irish Examiner (45937)

Irish Family History Society
PO Box 36
Naas, Kildare, Ireland
Publications: Irish Family History Journal (46042)

Irish Genealogical Research Society
18 Stratford Ave.
Rainham
Gillingham ME8 OEP, United Kingdom
Publications: The Irish Genealogist (53408)

Irish Georgian Society
74 Merrion Sq.
Dublin IRL-2, Dublin, Ireland

Phone: 353 1 6767053
Fax: 353 1 6620290
Publications: Irish Architectural and Decorative Studies (45970)

Irish Marine Press
2 Lower Glenageary Rd.
Dun Laoghaire, Dublin, Ireland
Phone: 353 01 2846161
Fax: 353 01 2846192
Publications: Afloat (46007)

Irish Mathematical Society Bulletin
Belfast, United Kingdom
Publications: Bulletin of the Irish Mathematical Society (52280)

Irish Medical Journal
IMO House
10 Fitzwilliam Pl.
Dublin IRL-2, Dublin, Ireland
Phone: 353 167 67273
Fax: 353 166 12758
Publications: Irish Medical Journal (45980)

Irish Pages
The Linen Hall Library
17 Donegall Sq. N
Belfast BT1 5GB, United Kingdom
Phone: 44 28 90434800
Publications: Irish Pages (52287)

Irish Society for Archives
UCD Archives, University College Dublin
James Joyce Library
Belfield
Dublin 4, Dublin, Ireland
Phone: 35 317 167555
Fax: 35 317 161146
Publications: Irish Archives (45971)

The Irish Times
24-28 Tara St.
Dublin 2, Dublin, Ireland
Phone: 353 1 6758000
Fax: 353 1 6758035
Publications: Irish Times (45988)

Iron and Steel Institute of Japan
Niikura Bldg., 2nd Fl.
2 Kanda, Tsukasacho, 2-chome
Chiyoda-Ku
Tokyo 101-0048, Japan
Phone: 81 3 52097011
Fax: 81 3 32571110
Publications: Ferrum (46822) • ISIJ International (46851) • Tetsu-to-Hagane (47049)

ISCO Careerscope
St. George's House
Knoll Rd.
Surrey
Camberley GU15 3SY, United Kingdom
Phone: 44 1276 687525
Publications: CareerScope (52783)

Isfahan University of Medical Sciences
PO Box 81745-319
Isfahan 81745, Iran
Publications: Journal of Research in Medical Sciences (45879)

Ishiyaku Publishers Inc.
7-10 Honkomagome 1-chome
Bunkyo-ku
Tokyo 113-8612, Japan
Phone: 81 3 53957600
Fax: 81 3 53957603
Publications: Journal of Clinical and Experimental Medicine (46892)

Isis International
3 Marunong St.
Barangay Central
Quezon City 1100, Philippines
Phone: 63 2 9281956
Fax: 63 2 9241065
Publications: Women in Action (49618)

Islamic Academy of Sciences
PO Box 830036
Amman, Jordan
Phone: 962 6 5522104

Fax: 962 6 5511803
Publications: Medical Journal of Islamic Academy of Sciences (47161)

Islamic Centre for Development of Trade
Ave. des FAR
Tours des Habous
B.P. 13545 Casa Principal
Casablanca 20000, Morocco
Phone: 21 222 314974
Fax: 21 222 310110
Publications: Tijaris (47813)

Islamic Thought Foundation
No. 766, Valiy-e Asr St.
PO Box 14155-3899
Tehran 14158, Iran
Phone: 98 21 8897663
Fax: 98 21 8902725
Publications: Mahjubah (45911)

Island Publishing Services Ltd.
PO Box 133
Road Town
Pasea Estate
Tortola, British Virgin Islands
Phone: 284494-2413
Fax: 284494-6589
Publications: The British Virgin Islands Welcome Tourist Guide (43069)

The Islander
Ascension Island ASCN 1ZZ, United Kingdom
Phone: 44 00 2476327
Fax: 44 00 2476327
Publications: The Islander (52136)

Israel Exploration Society
PO Box 7041
IL-91070 Jerusalem, Israel
Phone: 972 262 57991
Fax: 972 262 47772
Publications: Israel Exploration Journal (46085)

Israel Heart Society
1 Twin Towers, 5th Fl., Rm. 509
33 Jabotinsky
IL-52511 Ramat Gan, Israel
Phone: 97 236 122577
Fax: 97 236 122588
Publications: Journal of the Israel Heart Society (46096)

Israel Medical Association
2 Twin Towers, 35 Jabotinsky St.
PO Box 3566
Ramat Gan, Israel
Phone: 97 236 100444
Fax: 97 235 753303
Publications: Israel Medical Association Journal (IMAJ) (46094)

Israel Translators' Association
PO Box 16173
IL-61161 Tel Aviv, Israel
Publications: Targima (46113)

Israel Veterinary Medical Association
PO Box 22
IL-43100 Raanana, Israel
Phone: 97 297 419929
Fax: 97 297 431778
Publications: Israel Journal of Veterinary Medicine (46090)

ISTA Mielke GmbH
Langenberg 25
D-21077 Hamburg, Germany
Phone: 49 407 610500
Publications: Oil World Monthly (44421)

Italia Turistica S.A.S.
Via. G. Fiocco, 9
I-35124 Padua, Italy
Phone: 39 498 011180
Fax: 39 498 011182
Publications: Italia Turistica (46206)

Italian Association of Precision Moulds, Dies and Tooling Manufacturers
viale Fulvio Testi 128
I-20092 Milan, Italy
Phone: 39 226 255392

Fax: 39 226 255214
Publications: Stampi (46196)

Italian Mathematical Union
Piazza di Porta San Donato, 5
I-40126 Bologna, Italy
Phone: 39 51 243190
Fax: 39 51 4214169
Publications: Bollettino di Storia delle Scienze Matematiche (46125)

Italy Down Under Pty. Ltd.
478 William St.
Melbourne, Victoria 3003, Australia
Publications: Italy Down Under (42068)

IUCN-The World Conservation Union
Rue Mauverney 28
CH 1196 Gland, Switzerland
Phone: 41 22 9990000
Fax: 41 22 9990002
Publications: Parks (51175)

Ivyspring International Publisher
PO Box 9338
Womying, New South Wales 2250, Australia
Phone: 61 243 295886
Fax: 61 243 284886
Publications: International Journal of Biological Sciences (42710) • International Journal of Medical Sciences (42711)

IWA Publishing Ltd.
Alliance House
12 Caxton St.
London SW1H 0QS, United Kingdom
Phone: 44 20 76545500
Fax: 44 20 76545555
Publications: Journal of Hydroinformatics (54764) • Journal of Water and Health (54834) • Water Asset Management International (55381) • Water Intelligence Online (55383) • Water Policy (55384) • Water Practice and Technology (55385) • Water Science & Technology (55387) • Water Science & Technology (55386) • Water 21 (55389) • Water Utility Management International (55390)

Izdatel'skii Dom Uchitel'
82-53 Bystrova St.
400067 Volgograd, Russia
Phone: 7 8442 448553
Fax: 7 8442 448553
Publications: Social Evolution & History (50044)

Iziko Museums of Cape Town
PO Box 61
Cape Town 8000, Republic of South Africa
Phone: 27 214 813800
Fax: 27 214 813993
Publications: African Natural History (50361)

Jacket
c/o Australian Literary Management
2-A Booth St.
Balmain, New South Wales 2041, Australia
Publications: Jacket (41573)

Jacques Leblanc Editions
54 Rue St. Lazare
F-75009 Paris, France
Phone: 33 1 55078107
Publications: Jukebox Magazine (44066)

Jagiellonian University
ul. Grodzka 52
PI-31-041 Krakow, Poland
Phone: 48 12 6631732
Fax: 48 12 4224916
Publications: Diametros (49665)

Jagiellonian University
ul. Reymonta 4
30-059 Krakow, Poland
Phone: 48 12 6336377
Fax: 48 12 6337086
Publications: Acta Physica Polonica B (49664)

Jahad Daneshgahi
PO Box 16765-1899
Tehran, Iran
Phone: 98 21 7453382
Fax: 98 21 7453106
Publications: Iranian Journal of Electrical and Computer Engineering (45900)

Jahr Top Special Verlag
Troplowitzstrasse 5
D-22529 Hamburg, Germany
Phone: 49 403 89060
Fax: 49 403 8906300
Publications: Flieger Magazin (44415)

Jahreszeiten Verlag GmbH
Possmoorweg 2
D-22301 Hamburg, Germany
Phone: 49 402 7170
Fax: 49 402 7172056
Publications: Merian (44420) • Petra (44422) • ZuhauseWohnen (44425)

Jamaica Agricultural Society
67 Church St.
PO Box 609
Kingston, Jamaica
Phone: 809922-6102
Fax: 809922-6103
Publications: The Farmer (46284)

Jamaica Hotel and Tourist Association
2 Ardenne Rd.
St. Ann
Kingston, Jamaica
Phone: 876920-3482
Fax: 876929-1054
Publications: Destination Jamaica (46283)

The Jamaica Observer Ltd.
40-42 1/2 Beechwood Ave.
Kingston 5, Jamaica
Phone: 809920-8136
Fax: 876968-2025
Publications: The Jamaica Observer (46287)

James Cook University
101 Angus
Smith Dr.
Townsville, Queensland 4811, Australia
Phone: 61 747 814111
Fax: 61 747 796371
Publications: The Electronic Journal of Australian and New Zealand History (42635)

James Cook University
101 Angus Smith Dr.
Townsville, Queensland 4811, Australia
Phone: 61 747 814111
Fax: 61 747 796371
Publications: James Cook University Law Review (42636)

James Cook University
Tourism Program
Townsville, Queensland 4811, Australia
Phone: 61 7 47814942
Fax: 61 7 47816116
Publications: Journal of Rural and Tropical Public Health (42637)

James and James/Earthscan
Dunstan House
14a St., Cross St.
London EC1N 8XA, United Kingdom
Phone: 44 20 78411930
Fax: 44 20 72421474
Publications: Advances in Building Energy Research (53905) • Advances in Solar Energy (53909) • Architectural Engineering and Design Management (53961) • Climate Policy (54217) • Environmental Hazards (55616) • International Journal of Agricultural Sustainability (54633) • Studies in Conservation (55271)

James Nicholas Publishers, Pty. Ltd.
PO Box 5179
South Melbourne, Victoria 3205, Australia
Phone: 61 3 96905955
Fax: 61 3 96992040
Publications: Curriculum and Teaching (42369) • Educational Practice and Theory (42370) • Information Technology, Education and Society (42372) • Journal of Postcolonial Education (42373) • Learning and Teaching (42374) • Political Crossroads (42375) • World Studies in Education (42376)

JamO—Jamstalldhetsombudsmannen
Box 3397
SE-103 68 Stockholm, Sweden
Phone: 46 84401060

Fax: 46 8210047
Publications: Jamsides (51023)

JAN Corp.
6-5-4 Shinbashi
Minato-ku
Tokyo 105-0004, Japan
Publications: Japan Automotive News (46853)

Jane's Information Group Ltd.
Sentinel House
163 Brighton Rd.
Coulsdon CR5 2YH, United Kingdom
Phone: 44 20 87003700
Fax: 44 20 87003751
Publications: Jane's Airport Review (53067) • Jane's Defence Weekly (53068) • Jane's Intelligence Review (53069) • Jane's International Defense Review (53070) • Jane's Navy International (53071) • Jane's Police Review (53072) • Jane's Simulation & Training Systems (53073) • Jane's Transport Finance (53074)

Jang Group of Newspapers
Printing House
I.I. Chundrigar Rd.
Karachi 74200, Pakistan
Phone: 92 212 637111
Fax: 92 212 636066
Publications: Daily Jang (49345) • Fashion Mag (49349) • Investor's Business & Financial Journal (49356) • The News International (49365) • US (49378) • You (49379)

The Japan Academy
7-32, Ueno Pk.
Taito-ku
Tokyo 110-0007, Japan
Phone: 81 3 38222101
Fax: 81 3 38222105
Publications: Proceedings of the Japan Academy, Series A (47026) • Proceedings of the Japan Academy, Series B (47027)

Japan Antibiotics Research Association
2-20-8 Kamiosaki
Shinagawa-ku
Tokyo 141-0021, Japan
Fax: 81 3 34910179
Publications: Journal of Antibiotics (46884)

Japan Architect Company Ltd.
2-31-2 Yushima
Bunkyo-ku
Tokyo 113-0034, Japan
Phone: 81 3 38162532
Fax: 81 3 38128229
Publications: Japan Architect (46852)

Japan Association for International Horse Racing
Roppongi Hills Gate Tower
11-1, Roppongi 6-chome, Minato-ku
Tokyo 106-8401, Japan
Phone: 81 3 57857373
Fax: 81 3 57857376
Publications: Japan Racing Journal (46860)

Japan Association of Ion Exchange
Showa Pharmaceutical Univ.
Higashi-Tamagawagakuon
Machida
Tokyo 194-8543, Japan
Publications: Journal of Ion Exchange (46910)

Japan Association for Language Teaching
Urban Edge Bldg. 5F
1-37-9 Taito
Taito-ku
Tokyo 110-0016, Japan
Phone: 81 338 371630
Fax: 81 338 371631
Publications: Language Teacher (46959)

Japan Association for Quaternary Research
3F Rakuyo bld., 519 Waseda-tsurumaki-cho,
Shinjuku-ku
Tokyo 162-0041, Japan
Publications: Quaternary Research (47029)

Japan Atherosclerosis Society
c/o Kyowa Kikaku Ltd.
2-20-15 Shinbashi
Minato-ku

Tokyo 105-0004, Japan
Phone: 81 3 35714605
Fax: 81 3 35714606
Publications: Journal of Atherosclerosis and Thrombosis (46888)

Japan Atomic Industrial Forum
Dai-ichi Chojiya Bldg. 5th Fl.
1-2-13, Shiba-daimon
Minato-ku
Tokyo 105-8605, Japan
Phone: 81 3 57770750
Fax: 81 3 57770760
Publications: Atoms in Japan (46757)

Japan Echo Inc.
Nippon Press Center Bldg.
2-2-1 Uchisaiwai-cho
Chiyoda-ku
Tokyo 100-0011, Japan
Phone: 81 335 193511
Fax: 81 335 193519
Publications: Japan Echo (46855)

Japan Evangelical Missionary Association
Ochanomizu Christian Ctr. Bldg.
2-1 Kanda-Surugadai
Chiyoda-ku
Tokyo 101-0062, Japan
Phone: 81 3 32951949
Fax: 81 3 32951949
Publications: Japan Harvest (46856)

Japan Fashion Color Association
Fukushima Bldg. 6F
1-5-3, Nihonbashi-Muromachi
Chuo-ku
Tokyo 103-0022, Japan
Phone: 81 3 32421680
Fax: 81 3 32421686
Publications: Fashion Color (46821)

Japan Forest Technology Association
7 Rokuban-cho
Chiyoda-ku
Tokyo 102-0085, Japan
Phone: 81 3 32615281
Fax: 81 3 32615393
Publications: Forestry Technology (46827)

Japan Heterocerists' Society
c/o National Museum Society
Hyakuninchou 3 chome
Shinjuku-ku
Tokyo, Japan
Publications: Japan Heterocerists Journal (46857)

Japan Incorporated Communications K.K.
Minami-Aoyama 1st Bldg., 10th Fl.
7-8-1 Minami Aoyama, Minato-Ku
Tokyo 107-0062, Japan
Phone: 81 334 992099
Fax: 81 334 993109
Publications: Computing Japan (46793) • J@pan Inc Magazine (46947)

The Japan Institute for Labour Policy and Training
4-8-23 Kami-Shakujii
Nerima-ku
Tokyo 177-8502, Japan
Phone: 81 3 59036111
Fax: 81 3 35941113
Publications: Japan Labor Review (46858)

Japan Management Association
3-1-22 Shiba Koen
Minato-ku
Tokyo 105-8522, Japan
Phone: 81 334 341246
Fax: 81 334 340269
Publications: JMA Management Review (46877)

Japan Radiation Research Society
c/o National Institute of Radiological Sciences
4-9-1 Anagawa
Inage-ku
Chiba 263-8555, Japan
Publications: Journal of Radiation Research (46381)

Japan Scientists Association
Chasu Bldg. 9F
1-9-15 Yushima

Bunkyo-Ku
Tokyo 113-0034, Japan
Fax: 81 3 38132363
Publications: Journal of Japanese Scientists (46916)

Japan Society for Analytical Chemistry
Gotanda Sanhaitsu
26-2 Nishigotanda
Shinagawa-ku
Tokyo 141-0031, Japan
Phone: 81 3 34903351
Fax: 81 3 34903572
Publications: Analytical Sciences (46734)

Japan Society of Applied Physics
Kudan-Kita Bldg., 5th Fl.
Kudan-Kita 1-12-3 Chiyoda-Ku
Tokyo 102-0073, Japan
Phone: 81 3 32381041
Fax: 81 3 32216245
Publications: Japanese Journal of Applied Physics (46864)

Japan Society of Applied Physics
Kudan-Kita Bldg., 5th Fl.
1-12-3 Kudan-Kita
Chiyoda-ku
Tokyo 102-0073, Japan
Phone: 81 3 32381041
Fax: 81 3 32216245
Publications: Ionizing Radiation (46850)

Japan Society for Bioscience, Biotechnology and Agrochemistry
Gakkai Ctr. Bldg.
2-4-16 Yayoi
Bunkyo-ku
Tokyo 113-0032, Japan
Phone: 81 3 38118789
Fax: 81 3 38151920
Publications: Bioscience, Biotechnology, and Biochemistry (46767)

Japan Society of Calorimetry and Thermal Analysis
Miyazawa Bldg. 601
1-6-7 Iwamoto-chyo
Chiyoda-ku
Tokyo 101-0032, Japan
Fax: 81 3 58217439
Publications: Calorimetry and Thermal Analysis (46774)

Japan Society of Civil Engineers
Yotsuya 1-Chome
Shinjuku-ku
Tokyo 160-0004, Japan
Phone: 81 3 33553452
Fax: 81 3 53592769
Publications: Concrete Library International (46795)

Japan Society of Histochemistry and Cytochemistry
c/o Nakanishi Printing Co., Ltd.
Shimotachiuri-Ogawa
Kamikyo-ku
Kyoto 602-8048, Japan
Phone: 81 75 4153661
Fax: 81 75 4153662
Publications: Acta Histochemica et Cytochemica (46465)

Japan Society of Home Economics
Rm. 502, Gakuendai Hts.
502-2-1-15 Otsuka
Bunkyo-ku
Tokyo 112-0012, Japan
Phone: 81 3 39472627
Fax: 81 3 39472627
Publications: Journal of Home Economics of Japan (46905)

Japan Society of Mechanical Engineers
Shinanomachi-Rengakan Bldg.
35 Shinano-Machi
Shinjuku-Ku
Tokyo 160-0016, Japan
Phone: 81 353 603505
Fax: 81 353 603509
Publications: JSME International Journal Series A (46948) • JSME International Journal Series B (46949) • JSME International Journal Series C (46950)

Japan Society of Medical Entomology and Zoology
c/o Mutsuo Kobayashi
Dept. of Medical Entomology
National Institute of Infectious Diseases
1-23-1 Shinjuku-ku
Tokyo 162-8640, Japan
Phone: 81 352 851111
Fax: 81 352 851147
Publications: Medical Entomology and Zoology (46965)

Japan Society of Nuclear and Radiochemical Sciences
c/o Prof. Seiichi Shibata, Sec.
Research Reactor Institute
Kyoto University
2 Asahiro-nishi, Kumatori-cho, Sennann-gun
Osaka 590-0494, Japan
Fax: 81 72 4512632
Publications: Journal of Nuclear and Radiochemical Sciences (46623)

Japan Society for Occupational Health
IPEC Inc.
1-24-11 sugamo
Toshima-ku
Tokyo 170-0002, Japan
Phone: 81 3 59784067
Fax: 81 3 59784068
Publications: Journal of Occupational Health (46931)

Japan Society of Plasma Science and Nuclear Fusion Research
3-1-1-4F, Uchiyama
Chikusa-ku
Nagoya 464-0073, Japan
Phone: 81 527 353185
Fax: 81 527 353485
Publications: Journal of Plasma and Fusion Research (46554)

Japan Society for Precision Engineering
Kudan-Seiwa Bldg., 1-5-9
Kudan-kita
Chiyoda-ku
Tokyo 102-0073, Japan
Phone: 81 3 52265191
Fax: 81 3 52265192
Publications: International Journal of Japan Society for Precision Engineering (46847)

Japan Society of Radiological Technology
View-Fort Gojokarasuma
167 Higashikazariya-cho, Shinmachi-higashiiru
Gojodori, Shimogyo-ku
Kyoto 600-8107, Japan
Phone: 81 753 548989
Fax: 81 753 522556
Publications: Japanese Journal of Radiological Technology (46474)

Japan Society of Refrigerating and Air Conditioning Engineers
Sanei Bldg.
8 Sanei-cho
Shinjuku-ku
Tokyo 160-0008, Japan
Phone: 81 333 595231
Fax: 81 333 595233
Publications: Refrigeration (47031)

The Japan Times Ltd.
5-4 Shibaura 4-chome
Minato-Ku
Tokyo 108-8071, Japan
Phone: 81 3 34535312
Publications: The Japan Times (46861) • Shukan ST (47039)

Japanese Association of Hydrological Science
c/o Geologican Survey of Japan
AIST
Tsukuba-shi
Ibaraki 305-8567, Japan
Phone: 81 298613693
Fax: 81 298613684
Publications: Journal of Japanese Association of Hydrological Sciences (46393)

Japanese Association for Laboratory Animal Science
Akamon Royal Hts., Rm. 1103
5-29-12 Hongo

Bunkyo-ku
Tokyo 113-0033, Japan
Phone: 81 338 148276
Fax: 81 338 143990
Publications: Experimental Animals (46819)

Japanese Association of Mathematical Sciences
Shin Sakai-Higashi Bldg.
2-1-18 Minami Hanadaguchi-cho
Sakai
Osaka 590-0075, Japan
Phone: 81 722 221850
Fax: 81 722 227987
Publications: Mathematica Japonica (46626)

Japanese Association of Regenerative Dentistry
5-1, 2-Chome
Shikata-Cho
Okayama 700-8525, Japan
Phone: 81 86 2356672
Fax: 81 86 2356674
Publications: Journal of Oral Tissue Engineering (46598)

Japanese Association of University Women
11-6-101 Samon-cho
Shinjuku-ku
Tokyo 160, Japan
Phone: 81 333 582882
Fax: 81 333 582889
Publications: JAUW (46875)

Japanese Breast Cancer Society
C/O Cancer Institute Hospital
1-37-1, Kami-Ikebukuro
Toshima-ku
Tokyo 170-8455, Japan
Publications: Japanese Journal of Breast Cancer (46867)

Japanese Circulation Society
8th Fl., Cube Oike Bldg.
599 Bano-cho Karasuma Aneyakoji
Nakagyo-ku
Kyoto 604-8172, Japan
Phone: 81 752 575830
Fax: 81 752 131675
Publications: Japanese Circulation Journal (46473)

Japanese Dermatological Association
cosmos Hongo Bldg., 6th Fl.
1-4, Hongo 4-chome
Bunkyo-ku
Tokyo 113-0033, Japan
Publications: Journal of Dermatology (46894)

Japanese Environmental Mutagen Society
c/o Oral Health Association of Japan
Konagome TS Bldg., 4th Fl.
1-43-9 Komagome
Toshima-ku
Tokyo 170-0003, Japan
Publications: Environmental Mutagen Research (46813)

Japanese Forestry Society
7 Roku-Ban-cho
Chiyoda-ku
Tokyo 102-0085, Japan
Phone: 81 332612766
Publications: Journal of Japanese Forestry Society (46915)

Japanese Geotechnical Society
2-chome Sengoku
Bunkyo-ku
Tokyo 112-0011, Japan
Phone: 81 339 468677
Fax: 81 339 468678
Publications: Soils & Foundations (47042)

Japanese Nematological Society
Laboratory of Plant Nematology, Dept. of Plant Protection
National Agriculture Research Ctr.
3-1-1 Kannondai
Tsukuba 305-0866, Japan
Phone: 81 298 388839
Fax: 81 298 388837
Publications: Japanese Journal of Nematology (47111)

Japanese Pharmacological Society
Kantohya Bldg.

Gokomachi-Ebisugawa
Nakagyo-ku
Kyoto 604-0982, Japan
Phone: 81 752 524641
Fax: 81 752 524618
Publications: Journal of Pharmacological Sciences (46478)

Japanese Rocket Society
5-16-9 Honkomagome
Bunkyo-ku
Tokyo 113-0021, Japan
Phone: 81 3 58145801
Fax: 81 3 58145820
Publications: Journal of Space Technology and Science (46941)

Japanese Society for Animal Psychology
c/o K & U Co., Ltd.
MSK Bldg., 3rd Fl.
3-32-7 Hongo
Bunkyo-ku
Tokyo 113-0033, Japan
Publications: Japanese Journal of Animal Psychology (46863)

Japanese Society of Animal Science
201 Nagatani Corporas
Ikenohata 2-9-4
Taito-ku
Tokyo 110-0008, Japan
Phone: 81 3 38288409
Fax: 81 3 38287649
Publications: Animal Science Journal (46735)

Japanese Society of Applied Entomology and Zoology
c/o Japan Plant Protection Association
1-43-11 Komagome
Toshima-ku
Tokyo 170-8484, Japan
Fax: 81 298 386077
Publications: Applied Entomology and Zoology (46746)

Japanese Society for Biological Sciences in Space
c/o Institute of Space & Astronautical Science /JAXA
Yoshino-dai
Sagamihara
Kanagawa 229-8510, Japan
Phone: 81 42 7598230
Fax: 81 42 7598449
Publications: Biological Sciences in Space (46412)

Japanese Society of Breeding
c/o Administrative Office of Japanese Society of Breeding
Nakanishi Printing Co., Ltd.
Shimotachiuri Ogawa-higashi
Kamikyo-ku
Kyoto 602-8048, Japan
Phone: 81 754 153661
Fax: 81 754 153662
Publications: Breeding Science (46467)

Japanese Society of Computational Statistics
c/o Statistical Information Institute for Consulting and Ana
Daiwa Bldg., 2F
6-3-9 Minami-Aoyama
Minato-ku
Tokyo 107-0062, Japan
Phone: 81 3 54676946
Fax: 81 3 54676946
Publications: Journal of Japanese Society of Computational Statistics (46621)

Japanese Society for Dialysis Therapy
2-38-21 Hongo
Bunkyo-ku
Tokyo 113-0033, Japan
Phone: 81 358 000786
Fax: 81 358 000787
Publications: Journal of Japanese Society of Dialysis Therapy (46917)

Japanese Society of Environmental Entomology and Zoology
Seiyu Bldg.
12-19 Nishi-Hon-Machi 1-chome
Nishi-ku
Osaka 550-0005, Japan
Publications: Japanese Journal of Environment,

Entomology and Zoology (46618)

Japanese Society of Equine Science
Equine Research Institute 321-4 Tokami-cho
Utsunomiya-Shi
Tochigi 320-0856, Japan
Publications: Journal of Equine Science (46710)

Japanese Society of Fish Pathology
c/o Laboratory Genetics & Biochemistry
Tokyo University of Fisheries
4-5-7 Konan
Minato
Tokyo 108-8477, Japan
Publications: Fish Pathology (46824)

Japanese Society of Grassland Science
c/o National Institute of Livestock & Grassland Science
Senbonmatsu
Nasushiobara
Tochigi 329-2793, Japan
Phone: 81 287 377684
Fax: 81 287 377684
Publications: Grassland Science (46518)

Japanese Society of Hematology
Kinki Invention Ctr.
14 Yoshida Kawahara-cho
Sakyo-ku
Kyoto 606-8305, Japan
Phone: 81 757 522844
Fax: 81 757 522842
Publications: International Journal of Hematology
(46472)

Japanese Society for Horticultural Science
c/o Nakanishi Printing
Shimotachiuri Ogawa Higashi
Kamikyoku
Tokyo 602-8048, Japan
Phone: 81 754153661
Fax: 81 754153662
Publications: Journal of Japanese Society for Horticultural Science (46918)

Japanese Society of Hypertension Center for Academic Societies Osaka
3-28-8 Hongo, Bunkyo-ku
Tokyo 113-0033, Japan
Phone: 81 3 68019786
Fax: 81 3 68019787
Publications: Hypertension Research (46835)

Japanese Society of Internal Medicine
28-8, 3 chome
Hongo
Bunkyo-ku
Tokyo 113-8433, Japan
Phone: 81 338181556
Publications: Internal Medicine (46843)

Japanese Society of Irrigation Drainage and Reclamation Engineering
c/o Nogyo Doboku Kaikan
34-4 Shinbashi 5-Chome
Minato-ku
Tokyo 105-0004, Japan
Phone: 81 334 363418
Fax: 81 334 358494
Publications: Rural and Environmental Engineering (47034)

Japanese Society of Nuclear Medicine
2-28-45 Honkomagome
Bunkyo-ku
Tokyo 113-0021, Japan
Phone: 81 339 470976
Fax: 81 339 472535
Publications: Annals of Nuclear Medicine (46739)

Japanese Society for Oral and Maxillofacial Radiology
c/o Hitotsubashi Printing Co. Ltd.
4-11, Fukagawa 2-chome
Koutou-ku
Tokyo 135-0033, Japan
Publications: Oral Radiology (46382)

Japanese Society of Pediatric Dentistry Oral Health Association
1-43-9 Komagome TS Bldg.
Toshima-ku
Tokyo 170-0003, Japan
Publications: Pediatric Dental Journal (47017)

Japanese Society for Pediatric Endocrinology
Academic Sq.
2-348-302 Ryogae-cho
Kyoto 612-8082, Japan
Phone: 81 75 4688772
Fax: 81 75 4688773
Publications: Clinical Pediatric Endocrinology (46469)

Japanese Society of Pharmacometrics
2-11-12 Ichibancho
Sendai 980-0811, Japan
Phone: 81 22 2673810
Fax: 81 22 2220515
Publications: Pharmacometrics (46668)

Japanese Society of Radiation Safety Management
Radiation Sciences Division, Radioisotope Research Center
Nagoya University
Furo-cho Chikusa-ku
Nagoya 464-8602, Japan
Phone: 81 527 892569
Fax: 81 527 895048
Publications: Radiation Safety Management (46558)

Japanese Society of Smooth Muscle Research
Office Tanaka
4-40-206 Hasekura-machi
Aoba
Sendai 980-0824, Japan
Phone: 81 22 7177587
Fax: 81 22 7177508
Publications: Journal of Smooth Muscle Research (46555)

Jasubhai Media Private Ltd.
Taj Bldg., 4th Fl.
210 Dr. D.N. Rd.
Fort
Mumbai 400 001, Maharashtra, India
Phone: 91 22 40373636
Fax: 91 22 40373635
Publications: Chemical Engineering World (45359) • Digit (45367) • Offshore World (OW) (45422) • Pharma Bio World (45428) • SKOAR (45439)

Jawaharlal Handoo
Central Institute of Indian Languages
Manasagangothri, Hunsur Rd.
Manasagangotri
Mysore 570 006, Karnataka, India
Phone: 91 821 2345000
Fax: 91 821 2515032
Publications: Journal of Indian Folkloristics (45458)

Jaypee Brothers Medical Publishers Private Ltd.
4838/24 Ansari Rd.
Daryaganj
PO Box 7193
New Delhi 110 002, Delhi, India
Phone: 91 11 23272143
Fax: 91 11 23276490
Publications: Recent Advances in Pediatrics (45641)

Jazz Newspapers Ltd.
1st Fl., 132 Southwark St.
Castle Arcade
London SE1 0SW, United Kingdom
Phone: 44 20 79289089
Fax: 44 20 74016870
Publications: Jazz UK (54689)

Jazz Publishing
The Old School
Main Rd.
Higher Kinerton
Chester CH4 9AJ, United Kingdom
Phone: 44 1244 663400
Publications: Skin Deep (52999)

Jazzbladet KS
Havnegade 41
DK-1058 Copenhagen, Denmark
Phone: 45 333 38760
Fax: 45 333 38730
Publications: Jazz Special (43676)

Jazzwise Publications Ltd.
2(b) Gleneagle Mews
London SW16 6AE, United Kingdom
Phone: 44 20 87697725

Fax: 44 20 86777128
Publications: Jazzwise Magazine (54690)

Jemma Publications
Grattan House
Temple Rd.
Blackrock, Dublin, Ireland
Phone: 353 1 7642700
Fax: 353 1 7642750
Publications: Hotel & Catering Review (45920) • Irish Hardware (45921) • Irish Printer (45922) • Licensing World (45923)

Jerusalem Media and Communication Center
PO Box 25047
Khalil El Sakakeeni St.
IL-97300 East Jerusalem, israel
Phone: 972 2 5838266
Fax: 972 2 5836837
Publications: Palestine Report (46075)

Jesuit Publications
PO Box 553
Richmond, Victoria 3121, Australia
Phone: 61 3 94219666
Fax: 61 3 94219600
Publications: Australian Catholics (42301)

Jewellers and Watchmakers of New Zealand
10a Athelstan St.
Barrington
Christchurch 8024, New Zealand
Phone: 64 3 3376576
Fax: 64 3 3376576
Publications: Jewellery Time (48870)

Jewish Literary Trust Ltd.
Haskell House
152 West End Ln.
London NW6 1SD, United Kingdom
Publications: Jewish Quarterly (54691)

JF Media Ltd.
GolfPunk Towers
Sussex Innovation Ctr., Unit 10-13
Science Pk. Sq.
Brighton BN1 9SB, United Kingdom
Publications: Golf Punk (52609)

Jikei University School of Medicine
3-25-8 Nishi-Shinbashi
Minato-ku
Tokyo 105-8461, Japan
Publications: Jikeikai Medical Journal (46876)

Jilin University
2699 Qianjin St.
Changchun 130012, Jilin, People's Republic of China
Phone: 86 431 85166885
Fax: 86 431 85166570
Publications: Jilin University Journal Social Sciences Edition (43239) • Journal of Jilin University Earth Science Edition (43240) • Journal of Jilin University Engineering and Technology Edition (43241) • Journal of Jilin University Information Science Edition (43242) • Journal of Jilin University Medicine Edition (43243) • Journal of Jilin University Science Edition (43244)

Jimpress
PO Box 218
Warrington WA5 2FG, United Kingdom
Publications: Jimi Hendrix Magazine (56849)

JJDS Publications
D'Alton St.
Fairview
Claremorris 3, Mayo, Ireland
Phone: 353 94 9372819
Fax: 353 94 9373571
Publications: Fleet Transport (45931)

Joenkoeping International Business School, Media Management and Transformation Centre
Jonkoping International Business School
Jonkoping University
PO Box 1026
SE-551 11 Jonkoping, Sweden
Publications: Journal of Media Business Studies (50970)

Johannes Gutenberg Universitaet Mainz
Forum Universitatis 6
D 55099 Mainz, Germany
Phone: 49 6131 3922798

Fax: 49 6131 3923730
Publications: Swahili - Forum (44545)

John Brown Citrus Publishing
136-142 Bramley Rd.
London W10 6SR, United Kingdom
Phone: 44 20 75653000
Fax: 44 20 75653060
Publications: Waitrose Food Illustrated (55376)

John Brown Publishing
136-142 Bramley Rd.
London W10 6SR, United Kingdom
Phone: 44 17 15653000
Fax: 44 20 75653060
Publications: Bizarre (54032)

John Catt Educational Ltd.
12 Deben Mill Business Ctr.
Old Maltings Approach
Woodbridge IP12 1BL, United Kingdom
Phone: 44 1394 389850
Fax: 44 1394 386893
Publications: Conference & Common Room (57003) • International School (56956) • is (56957) • Prep School (56958)

John Libbey Eurotext
127, Ave. de la Republique
92120 Montrouge, France
Phone: 33 1 46730660
Fax: 33 1 40840999
Publications: Annales de Biologie Clinique (43980) • Annales de Gerontologie (43981) • Bulletin du Cancer (43982) • Bulletin Infirmier du Cancer (43983) • Cahiers d'etudes et de recherches francophones/ Agricultures (43984) • Cahiers d'etudes et de recherches francophones/Sante (43985) • Environnement, Risques & Sante (43986) • Epilepsies (43987) • Epileptic Disorders (43988) • European Cytokine Network (43989) • European Journal of Dermatology (43990) • Hepato-Gastro (43992) • L'Information Psychiatrique (43993) • Journal de Pharmacie Clinique (43994) • La Lettre de l'Internat (43995) • Magnesium Research (43996) • Medecine therapeutique cardiologie (43998) • Medecine therapeutique (43997) • Medecine therapeutique/Endocrinologie (43999) • Medecine Therapeutique/medecine de la reproduction (44000) • Medecine therapeutique/Pediatrie (44001) • MT Cardio (44002) • Oleagineux, Corps Gras, Lipides (44003) • Psychologie & NeuroPsychiatrie du vieillissement (44004) • Revue de neuropsychologie (44005) • Sang Thrombose Vaisseaux (44006) • Science et changements planetaires/Secheresse (44007) • Sciences Sociales et Sante (44125) • Virologie (44008)

John Wiley & Sons Ltd.
1-7 Oldlands Way
Bognor Regis PO21 9FF, United Kingdom
Phone: 44 1865 778315
Publications: Briefings in Real Estate Finance (52393) • ChemMedChem (44704) • Cochlear Implants International (52394) • European Diabetes Nursing (52395) • The International Journal of Applied Psychoanalytic Studies (52396) • International Journal of Medical Robotics and Computer-Assisted Surgery (52397) • Journal of Consumer Behaviour (52398) • Journal of Public Affairs (52399) • Musculoskeletal Care (52400) • Practice Development in Health Care (52402) • Psychotherapy and Politics International (52403) • Spirituality and Health International (53736)

Johnson Matthey PLC
40-42 Hatton Garden
London EC1N 8EE, United Kingdom
Phone: 44 20 72698400
Fax: 44 20 72698433
Publications: Platinum Metals Review (55095)

Johnson Society of London
16 Laurier Rd.
London NW5 1SG, United Kingdom
Publications: The New Rambler (54996)

Johnston Press PLC
c/o Richard Cooper
53 Manor Pl.
Edinburgh EH3 7EG, United Kingdom
Phone: 44 13 12253361
Publications: Antrim Times (52158) • Arbroath Herald (52127) • Asian Leader (56401) • Ayton Today (56462) • Banbury Guardian (52166) • Batley News

(52267) • Bellshill Speaker (52305) • Belper News (52309) • Berwick Advertiser (52317) • Berwickshire News (52318) • Beverley Guardian (53199) • Bexhill Observer (52320) • Biggleswade Chronicle (52323) • Birstall News (52268) • Bognor Regis Observer (52392) • Bo'ness Journal (53858) • Boston Standard (52408) • Brechin Advertiser (52563) • Bridlington Free Press (52597) • Brighouse Echo (52600) • Buckingham & Winslow Advertiser (52755) • Bucks Herald (52146) • Burniston Today (56463) • Bury Free Press (52773) • Business Citizen (53258) • The Buteman (56414) • Buxton Advertiser (52777) • Carluke Gazette (52950) • Carnoustie Guide & Gazette (52128) • Chichester Observer (53007) • Chorley Guardian (53021) • Clitheroe Advertiser & Times (53026) • Crawley Observer (53101) • Cumbernauld News (53149) • Daventry Express (53159) • Deeside Piper & Herald (52168) • Derbyshire Times (53002) • Derry Journal (53172) • Dewsbury Reporter (53179) • Dinnington Guardian (53183) • Diss Express (53184) • Doncaster Free Press (53186) • Donside Piper & Herald (52169) • Driffield Times (53201) • East Antrim Advertiser (53741) • East Lothian News (53152) • Eastbourne Herald (53243) • Eastwood Advertiser (53245) • Fenland Citizen (56935) • Fife Free Press (53387) • Fleetwood Weekly News (53390) • Gainsborough Standard (53401) • Galloway Gazette (55698) • Garstang Courier (53404) • Harborough Mail (53507) • Harrogate Advertiser (53516) • Hartlepool Mail (53533) • Hastings & St. Leonards Observer (56445) • Haverhill Echo (53544) • Hawick News (53546) • Hebden Bridge Times (53552) • Hemel Gazette (53557) • Horncastle News (53591) • Hucknall Dispatch (53615) • Ilkeston Advertiser (53642) • Inverurie Herald (53649) • Kenilworth Weekly News (53746) • Kettering Evening Telegraph (53684) • Kilsyth Chronicle (53150) • Kincardineshire Observer (55645) • Kirkintilloch Herald (53727) • Kirriemuir Herald (53398) • Knaresborough Post (53728) • Lakeland Echo (55648) • Lanark Gazette (53731) • Lancashire Evening Post (56302) • Leamington Spa Courier (53748) • Leighton Buzzard Observer (53839) • Leyland Guardian (53023) • Linlithgow Gazette (53859) • Littlehampton Gazette (53865) • Londonderry Sentinel (55473) • Lytham St. Annes Express (56442) • Malton & Pickering Mercury (55532) • Mansfield Chad (55590) • Market Rasen Mail (55595) • Matlock Mercury (55604) • Melton Times (55606) • Mid Sussex Times (53549) • Midhurst & Petworth Observer (55625) • Midlothian Advertiser (53153) • Milngavie Herald (55629) • Mirfield Reporter (53181) • Montrose Review (55646) • Morley Observer & Advertiser (55652) • Newmarket Journal (55686) • News Post Leader (56919) • Newtonabbey Times (53469) • Northampton Chronicle & Echo (55713) • Northumberland Gazette (52101) • Pateley Bridge & Nidderdale Herald (53519) • Peterborough Evening Telegraph (56259) • Peterlee Mail (53534) • Petersfield Post (56267) • Pontefract & Castleford Express (52952) • Queensferry Gazette (53860) • Ripley & Heanor News (56398) • Ripon Gazette & Boroughbridge Herald (56399) • Rugby Advertiser (56423) • Rye & Battle Observer (56446) • St. Helens Reporter (56443) • Scarborough Evening News (56464) • Selby Times (56468) • Selkirk Weekend Advertiser (56469) • Shields Gazette (56566) • Shoreham Herald (56976) • Skegness Standard (56552) • Sleaford Standard (56558) • South Yorkshire Times (55610) • Spenborough Guardian (53025) • Stornoway Gazette (56637) • Thame Gazette (56744) • Todmorden News (56753) • Warwick Courier (53750) • West Sussex County Times (53602) • Whitby Gazette (56915) • Worksop Guardian (56970) • Worthing Herald (56979) • Yorkshire Evening Post (53776)

Johnston Press PLC
108 Holyrood Rd.
Edinburgh EH8 8AS, United Kingdom
Phone: 44 131 2253361
Fax: 44 131 2254580
Publications: Luton News and Dunstable Gazette (53300) • Rutland & Stamford Mercury Series (53309) • Tyrone Times (53224) • Ulster Star (53863)

Joint Stock Company Diena
Mukusalas Str. 15
LV-1004 Riga, Latvia
Phone: 371 706 3150

Fax: 371 706 3167
Publications: Diena (Latvian Edition) (47365)

Joint University Council
College of Business, Law & Social Science
Victoria House, Rm. 517
Nottingham Trent University
Nottingham NG1 4BU, United Kingdom
Phone: 44 11 58488117
Fax: 44 11 58486808
Publications: Public Policy and Administration (55771)

Jordan Press Foundation
Queen Rania Al Abdullah St.
PO Box 6710
Amman, Jordan
Phone: 962 656 00800
Fax: 962 656 96183
Publications: Jordan Times (47160)

JOTMI Research Group
Universidad Alberto Hurtado
Facultad de Economia y Negocios
erasmo Escala 1835
Santiago, Chile
Phone: 56 2 8897356
Publications: Journal of Technology Management & Innovation (43145)

Journal of Buddhist Ethics
c/o Prof. Damien Keown
Dept. of Historical & Cultural Studies
Univ. of London, Goldsmiths' College
London SE14 6NW, United Kingdom
Phone: 44 20 79197171
Publications: Journal of Buddhist Ethics (54715)

Journal of Chinese Chemical Society
PO Box 1-18
Nankang
Taipei 115, Taiwan
Phone: 886 2 33668206
Fax: 886 2 23648940
Publications: Journal of Chinese Chemical Society (51349)

Journal of Dharma
Dharmaram Vidya Kshetram
Bangalore 560 029, Karnataka, India
Publications: Journal of Dharma (44969)

Journal of Geographical Sciences
11 A Datun Rd.
Beijing 100101, People's Republic of China
Publications: Journal of Geographical Sciences (43207)

Journal of Maps
School of Geography, Geology & the Environment
Kingston University
Penrhyn Rd.
Kingston upon Thames KT1 2EE, United Kingdom
Phone: 44 20 70992817
Fax: 44 870 0633061
Publications: Journal of Maps (53723)

Journal Ophthalmological Society
Molla Gurani Cad. 22/2
Findikzade
34093 Istanbul, Turkey
Phone: 90 212 6219925
Fax: 90 212 6219927
Publications: Journal of Turkish Ophthalmology (51558)

Journal of Social Development in Africa
PO Box 377
PO Box 66022, Kopje
Grahamstown, Republic of South Africa
Phone: 27 46 6228058
Fax: 27 46 6229550
Publications: Journal of Social Development in Africa (50503)

Jowett Car Club
15 2nd Ave.
Chemsford
Essex CM1 4ET, United Kingdom
Phone: 44 1274 604455
Fax: 44 1274 604455
Publications: The Jowetteer (53339)

JRAAS Ltd.
Edgbaston House
3 Duchess Pl.
Edgbaston

Birmingham B16 8NH, United Kingdom
Phone: 44 121 4544114
Fax: 44 121 4541190
Publications: Journal of the Renin-Angiotensin-Aldosterone System (52351)

Justice
59 Carter Ln.
London EC4V 5AQ, United Kingdom
Phone: 44 20 73295100
Fax: 44 20 73295055
Publications: Justice Journal (54841)

Justice and Peace Scotland
65 Bath St.
Glasgow G2 2BX, United Kingdom
Phone: 44 14 13330238
Fax: 44 14 13330238
Publications: Justice and Peace (53428)

Justis Publishing Ltd
Grand Union House
20 Kentish Town Rd.
London NW1 9NR, United Kingdom
Phone: 44 20 72848080
Fax: 44 20 72671133
Publications: Criminal Appeal Reports (54285)

JUTA Law
1st fl. Suncare Bldg.
21 Dreyer St.
Claremont 7708, Republic of South Africa
Phone: 27 21 6592300
Fax: 27 21 6592360
Publications: Acta Juridica (50459) • African Human Rights Law Journal (50460) • Jutas Business Law (50461) • SA Mercantile Law Journal (50462) • South African Journal of Criminal Justice (50463) • South African Journal on Human Rights (50464) • Stellenbosch Law Review (50465)

Jyvaskylan Yliopisto, Agora Center
University of Jyvaskyla
PO Box 35
FIN-40014 Jyvaskyla, Finland
Phone: 35 814 2601211
Fax: 35 814 2601021
Publications: Human Technology (43869)

K. Kumar
34 Heavy Industrial Area
Jodhpur 342 003, Rajasthan, India
Phone: 91 291 2745452
Fax: 91 291 2745470
Publications: Current Tax Reporter (45217)

Kadium Ltd.
Brassey House
New Zealand Ave.
Walton-on-Thames KT12 1QD, United Kingdom
Phone: 44 1932 886 537
Fax: 44 1932 886 539
Publications: Southern African Wireless Communications (56836)

Kagoshima University Research Center for the Pacific Islands
1-21-24 Korimoto
Kagoshima 890-8580, Japan
Phone: 81 992 857394
Fax: 81 992 856197
Publications: South Pacific Studies (46405)

Kamla-Raj Enterprises
PO Box 1120
Delhi 110 006, Delhi, India
Phone: 91 11 23284126
Fax: 91 12 44361193
Publications: International Journal of Human Genetics (45099) • Studies of Tribes and Tribals (45104)

Kamla-Raj Enterprises
2273 Gali Bari Paharwali
Chawri Bazar
PO Box 1120
Delhi 110 006, Delhi, India
Phone: 91 112 3284126
Fax: 91 124 4361193
Publications: The Anthropologist (45087) • Journal of Human Ecology (45100) • Journal of Social Sciences (Delhi) (45101)

Kandy Society of Medicine
KSM Office
Postgraduate Medical Ctr.
General (Teaching) Hospital
Kandy, Sri Lanka
Phone: 94 820 1702
Fax: 94 820 1702
Publications: Sri Lanka Journal of Medicine (50909)

Kansai Society of Naval Architects
c/o Graduate School of Engineering, Osaka University
2-1 Yamada-oka
Suita
Osaka 565-0871, Japan
Publications: Journal of Kansai Society of Naval Architects (46622)

Kansai Time Out
402 Shinko Bldg.
8 Kaigan-dori
Chuo-ku
Kobe 650-0024, Japan
Phone: 81 783 937033
Fax: 81 783 937039
Publications: Kansai Time Out (46431)

Kanto Poetry Center
Kanto Gakuin University
Kamariya Minami 3-22-1
Kanazawa-ku
Yokohama 236-8502, Japan
Publications: Poetry Kanto (47141)

Kaohsiung Medical University
100 Shih-Chuan 1st Rd.
Kaohsiung 80708, Taiwan
Phone: 886 7 3121101
Fax: 886 7 3212062
Publications: Kaohsiung Journal of Medical Sciences (51310)

S. Karger Publishers Inc.
26 W Avon Rd.
PO Box 529
Unionville, CT 06085-1162
Phone: 860675-7834
Fax: 203675-7302
Free: 800828-5479
Publications: Annals of Nutrition and Metabolism (42744) • Cytogenetic and Genome Research (44719) • European Addiction Research (44414) • Nephron Physiology (54987) • Neuroembryology and Aging (43370) • Neuroendocrinology (53302) • Tumor-Biology (51048) • Viszeralmedizin (44374)

Karnataka News Pulications Pvt. Ltd.
11/2, Queens Rd.
Bangalore 560 052, Karnataka, India
Publications: Sanjevani (44987)

Kashmir Observer
Haza Complex
Residency Rd.
Kashmir
Srinagar 190 001, Jammu and Kashmir, India
Publications: Kashmir Observer (45739)

Kashmir Times Publications
Residency Rd.
Jammu 180 001, Jammu and Kashmir, India
Phone: 91 19 15247937
Fax: 91 19 12542028
Publications: Kashmir Times (45205)

Kassel University Press GmbH
Diagonale 10
D-34127 Kassel, Germany
Phone: 49 561 8042159
Fax: 49 561 8043429
Publications: Journal of Agriculture and Rural Development in the Tropics and Subtropics (44498)

Kasturi & Sons Ltd.
859-860 Anna Salai
Chennai 600 002, Tamil Nadu, India
Phone: 91 442 8413344
Fax: 91 442 8415325
Publications: Frontline (45032) • The Hindu (45524) • Hindu Business Line (45033) • Hindu Index (45034) • Hindu International Edition (45035) • The Hindu Weekly (45036) • The Sportstar (45057)

Kathmandu University, Kathmandu Medical College
Sinamangal
PO Box 21266
Kathmandu, Nepal
Publications: Kathmandu University Medical Journal (47841)

Katholieke Universiteit Leuven
Oude Markt 13
B-3000 Leuven, Belgium
Phone: 32 163 24010
Fax: 32 163 24014
Publications: Campuskrant (42893) • Image & Narrative (42897)

Kaunas University of Medicine
Mickeviciaus 9
44307 Kaunas, Lithuania
Phone: 370 37 327201
Fax: 370 37 220733
Publications: Medicina (47465)

Keio University
35 Shinanomachi
Shinjuku
Tokyo 160-8582, Japan
Phone: 81 3 33531211
Fax: 81 3 53617091
Publications: The Keio Journal of Medicine (46953)

Keio University
2-19-30 Mita
Minato-ku
Tokyo 108-8346, Japan
Fax: 81 3 34547029
Publications: Keio Economic Studies (46952)

Kelsey Publishing Ltd.
Cudham Tithe Barn
Berry's Hill
Cudham TN16 3AG, United Kingdom
Phone: 44 1959 541444
Fax: 44 1959 541400
Publications: Classic Car Weekly (56254) • Classic Military Vehicle (53138) • Classic Plant & Machinery (53139) • Classic Van and Pick-up (53140) • Classic and Vintage Commercials (53141) • Custom Car Magazine (56255) • Farm and Horticultural Equipment (53142) • Ford & Fordson Tractors (53385) • Jaguar World Monthly (53143) • Modern MINI (53144) • Old Tractor (53145) • Practical Poultry (53146) • Stationary Engine (53147) • Tractor & Machinery (53148)

Keppler Verlag GmbH
Postfach 1353
D-63131 Heusenstamm, Germany
Phone: 49 6104 6060
Fax: 49 6104 606121
Publications: Allgemeine Papier-Rundschau (44485)

Kerala Agricultural University
KAU
PO Box 680656
Thrissur 680 656, Kerala, India
Phone: 91 487 2370432
Fax: 91 487 2370019
Publications: Journal of Tropical Agriculture (45750)

Keren Hayesod
48 king George St.
PO Box 7583
91074 Jerusalem, Israel
Phone: 972 2 6701811
Fax: 972 2 6701925
Publications: Menorah (46089)

Kerry's Eye
22 Ashe St.
Tralee, Kerry, Ireland
Phone: 353 667 149200
Publications: Kerry's Eye (46060)

Keskisuomalainen Oyi
Aholaidantie 3
PO Box 159
FIN-40101 Jyvaskyla, Finland
Phone: 35 814 622000
Publications: Keskisuomalainen (43870)

Key Note Publications Ltd.
Harlequin House, 5th Fl.
7 Hight St.

Teddington TW11 8EE, United Kingdom
Phone: 44 845 5040452
Fax: 44 845 5040453
Publications: Key Note Market Assessment. Tweenagers (56733)

Key Publishing Ltd.
Units 1-4
Gwash Way Industrial Estate
Ryhall Rd.
Stamford PE9 1XQ, United Kingdom
Phone: 44 17 80755131
Fax: 44 17 80757261
Publications: Airports International (56593) • Airports of the World (56594) • FlyPast (56596) • Today's Pilot (56597)

K.G. Saur Verlag KG
Mies-van-der-Rohe-Strasse 1
D-80807 Munich, Germany
Phone: 49 89 769020
Fax: 49 89 76902150
Publications: The African Book Publishing Record (44098)

KHL Group
Southfields
Southview Rd.
Wadhurst TN5 6TP, United Kingdom
Phone: 44 1892 784088
Fax: 44 1892 784086
Publications: Access International (56804) • Construction Europe (56805) • Demolition & Recycling International (56806) • International Construction China (56807) • International Construction Turkiye (56808) • International Cranes and Specialized Transport (56809) • International Rental News (56810)

Kilvert Society
c/o Alan Brimson, Honorable Sec.
30, Bromley Heath Ave.
Downend
Bristol BS16 6JP, United Kingdom
Publications: Journal of the Kilvert Society (52688)

Kindred Spirit
Unit 101, The Perfume Factory
140 Wales Farm Rd.
London W3 6UG, United Kingdom
Phone: 44 208 7528172
Fax: 44 208 7528185
Publications: Kindred Spirit (54845)

King Fahd University of Petroleum and Minerals
PO Box 5033
Dhahran 31261, Saudi Arabia
Phone: 966 3 8605418
Fax: 966 3 8605458
Publications: Arabian Journal for Science and Engineering (50054)

King Saud University
PO Box 2454
Riyadh 11451, Saudi Arabia
Fax: 966 1 4677580
Publications: Journal of King Saud University (50062)

King Saud University Libraries
PO Box 2454
Riyadh 11451, Saudi Arabia
Phone: 966 1 4670112
Fax: 966 1 4677580
Publications: Journal of King Saud University: Agricultural Sciences (50063) • Journal of King Saud University: Architecture and Planning (50064) • Journal of King Saud University: Arts (50065) • Journal of King Saud University: Computer & Information Sciences (50066) • Journal of King Saud University: Educational Sciences & Islamic Studies (50067) • Journal of King Saud University: Science (50068)

Kingdom Magazine
Dalgety Bay Business Ctr.
Ridge Way
Dalgety Bay
Fife KY11 9JN, United Kingdom
Phone: 44 01383 823333
Fax: 44 01383 824444
Publications: Kingdom Magazine (53388)

Kiosk Europe
17 Sturton St.
Cambridge CB1 2SN, United Kingdom

Phone: 44 1223 350515
Fax: 44 1223 351725
Publications: Kiosk Europe (52865)

KK Aiki News
14-17-103 Matsugae-cho
Kanagawa
Sagamihara 228-0813, Japan
Phone: 81 427 482423
Publications: Aikido Journal (46643)

Klocke Publishing Company
Hoefeweg 40
D-33619 Bielefeld, Germany
Phone: 49 5 2191111
Fax: 49 5 2191112
Publications: HIDEAWAYS (44246) • YACHTING & STYLE (44248)

KlubKat
15 Saddlers Pl.
Martlesham Heath IP5 3SS, United Kingdom
Publications: KlubKat Music Magazine (55602)

Kluwer Academic/Plenum Publishing Corp.
101 Philip Dr.
Norwell, MA 02061
Phone: 781871-6600
Fax: 781871-6528
Publications: European Foreign Affairs Review (53799)

Kluwer Datalex
PO Box 85889
The Hague, Netherlands
Phone: 31 78 6546454
Fax: 31 78 6546474
Publications: Asian International Arbitration Journal (48607) • Common Market Law Review (48610) • EC Tax Review (48613) • European Business Law Review (48615)

Kluwer Law International
PO Box 316
NL-2400 AH Alphen aan den Rijn, Netherlands
Phone: 31 172 641500
Fax: 31 172 641555
Publications: Air & Space Law (47865) • Arbitration International (47866) • Journal of International Arbitration (47869)

KMK Scientific Press Ltd.
c/o Dr. K.G. Mikhailov
Zoological Museum MGU
Bolshaya Nikitskaya Str. 6
125009 Moscow, Russia
Publications: Acarina (49867) • Russian Entomological Journal (49974) • Russian Journal of Theriology (49983)

Knee High Media Japan
1-23-3 Higashi Shibuya
Shibuya-ku
Tokyo 150-0011, Japan
Phone: 81 3 54699318
Fax: 81 3 54695656
Publications: Paper Sky (47016)

Know-Center
Inffeldgasse 21a/II
A-8010 Graz, Austria
Phone: 43 316 8739251
Fax: 43 316 8739254
Publications: J.UCS (Journal of Universal Computer Science) (42724)

Kobe Journal of Mathematics
Tsurukabuto 1-2-1
Nada
Kobe 657-8501, Japan
Publications: Kobe Journal of Mathematics (46432)

Kobe University
7-5-1 Kusunoki-cho
Chuo-ku
Kobe 650-0017, Japan
Publications: Kobe Journal of Medical Sciences (46433)

Kobe University Graduate School of Economics
2-1 Rokkodai-cho
Nada-ku
Kobe 657-8501, Japan

Phone: 81 78 8811212
Publications: Kobe University Economic Review (46434)

Kodak Limited & Eastman Kodak Co.
Hemel One
Boundary Way
Hemel Hempstead HP2 7YU, United Kingdom
Phone: 44 1442 261122
Fax: 44 1442 240609
Publications: In Camera (53558)

Kodansha Ltd.
2-12-21 Otowa
Bunkyo-ku
Tokyo 112-8001, Japan
Phone: 81 3 3946 6201
Fax: 81 3 3944 9915
Publications: Afternoon (46729) • Afternoon Season Zokan (46730) • Be Love (46759) • Be Love Parfait (46760) • Bessatsu Friend (46761) • Dessert (46801) • Evening (46818) • Gekkan Shonen Magazine (46829) • Juliet (46951) • Kiss (46954) • Magazine Special (46962) • Magazine Z (46963) • Morning (46972) • Nakayoshi (46974) • One More Kiss (47014) • Shukan Shonen Magazine (47038) • Young Magazine (47057) • Young Magazine Uppers (47058)

Koganemushi-Kenkyukai (The Japanese Society of Scarabaeoideans)
c/o Shinya Kawai
4-16-3, Shimouma
Setagaya-ku
Tokyo 154-0002, Japan
Publications: Kogane (46955)

KONGPOSH Publications Pvt. Ltd.
ICS House, 2nd Fl., C-19
Commercial Complex
New Delhi 110 016, Delhi, India
Phone: 91 11 26855839
Fax: 91 11 26855876
Publications: The Pharma Review (45635)

Koninklijke Vereniging van Marineofficieren
Wassaenaarseweg 2 B
NL-2596 The Hague, Netherlands
Phone: 31 70 3839504
Fax: 31 70 3835911
Publications: Marineblad (48622)

Konradin Publishing Group
Ernst-Mey-Strasse 8
70771 Leinfelden-Echterdingen, Germany
Phone: 49 711 75940
Fax: 49 711 7594390
Publications: bild der wissenschaft (44517) • DAMALS (44518) • DER AUGENOPTIKER (44519) • Der Deutsche Tabakbau (44520) • die Kontaktlinse (44521) • ErgoMed (44524) • Lackiererblatt (44525) • Malerblatt (44526) • Metamorphose (44527) • naturkosmos (44403) • Sicherheitsbeauftragter (44529) • Sicherheitsingenieur (44530)

Konradin Verlag Robert Kohlhammer GmbH
Ernst-Mey-Str.8
D-70771 Leinfelden-Echterdingen, Germany
Phone: 49 711 75940
Fax: 49 711 7594390
Publications: Elektro Automation (44522) • EPP Europe (44523) • Quality Engineering (44528)

Korea Foundation
10-11F, Diplomatic Center Bldg.
1376-1 Seocho 2-dong, Seocho-gu
Seoul 137-863, Republic of Korea
Phone: 82 234635600
Fax: 82 234636076
Publications: Koreana (47283)

Korea Institute for Defense Analyses
PO Box 250
Cheong Ryang
Seoul, Republic of Korea
Fax: 82 2 9611172
Publications: The Korean Journal of Defense Analysis (47281)

The Korea Post
2nd Fl., Daeok Bldg.
241-4 Oksu-dong
Songdong-gu
Seoul 133-839, Republic of Korea

Phone: 82 2 22981740
Fax: 82 2 22989506
Publications: The Korea Post (47279)

The Korea Times Company Ltd.
43, Chungmuro 3-ga
Chung-ku
Seoul 100-013, Republic of Korea
Phone: 82 2 7242359
Fax: 82 2 7364061
Publications: Korea Times (47280)

Korean Chemical Society
34-1, 5-ga, Anam-dong
Seongbuk-gu
Seoul 136-075, Republic of Korea
Phone: 82 2 9532095
Fax: 82 2 9532093
Publications: Bulletin of the Korean Chemical Society (47259)

The Korean Mathematical Society
The Korea Science & Technology Center 202
635-4 Yeoksam-dong
Gangnam-gu
Seoul 135-703, Republic of Korea
Phone: 82 2 5650361
Fax: 82 2 5650364
Publications: Bulletin of the Korean Mathematical Society (47247) • Communications of the Korean Mathematical Society (47262)

Korean National Commission for UNESCO
50-14 Myong-dong 2-ga
Jung-gu
Seoul 100-810, Republic of Korea
Phone: 82 2 7551105
Fax: 82 2 7556667
Publications: Korea Journal (47278)

Korean Radiological Society
69 Yangjaecheon-gil
Seocho-gu
Seoul 137-891, Republic of Korea
Phone: 82 257 88003
Fax: 82 252 97113
Publications: The Journal of Korean Radiological Society (47274) • Korean Journal of Radiology (47282)

Korean Society for Biochemistry and Molecular Biology
Rm. 801, The Korea Science & Technology Center
635-4 Yeoksam-dong, Kangnam-gu
Seoul 135-703, Republic of Korea
Phone: 82 2 5087434
Fax: 82 2 5087578
Publications: Biochemistry and Molecular Biology Reports (47258)

Korean Society of Pharmacognosy
Medicinal Studies Bldg., 1st Fl.
Soegyo-dong 448-13
Mapo-gu
Seoul 121-841, Republic of Korea
Phone: 82 25260370
Fax: 82 23260371
Publications: Natural Product Sciences (47284)

Korean Society of Plastic and Reconstructive Surgery
Seocho World officetel 1814
Seocho-dong 1355-3 Seocho-ku
Seoul 137-070, Republic of Korea
Phone: 82 2 34724252
Fax: 82 2 34724254
Publications: Journal of the Korean Society of Plastic and Reconstructive Surgery (47275)

Korean Society of Soil Science and Fertilizer
249 Seodun-dong
Kweonseon-gu
GyeongGi-Do
Suwon 441-709, Republic of Korea
Phone: 82 312 957335
Fax: 82 312 900207
Publications: Journal of Korean Society of Soil Science and Fertilizer (47327)

Koster Publishing S.p.A.
Via. della Liberazione, 1
I-20068 Peschiera Borromeo, Italy
Phone: 39 255 305067

Fax: 39 255 305068
Publications: Agri Parts (46212) • Bellauto (46213) • Euro Electric News (46214) • Il Giornale dei Veicoli Commerciali (46215) • Il Gommone e la Nautica per Tutti (46216)

KP Media
14-A Bazhana Ave., 7th Fl.
02140 Kiev, Ukraine
Phone: 380 44 4964563
Fax: 380 44 4964567
Publications: Afisha (51593) • Interior Magazine (51598) • Korrespondent (51599) • Kyiv Post (51600) • Novynar (51603)

Krishnamurti Foundation
Vasanta Vihar
124 Greenways Rd.
RA Puram
Chennai 600 028, Tamil Nadu, India
Phone: 91 24937803
Publications: Krishnamurti Foundation Bulletin (45051)

Kristdemokratiska Ungdomsforbundet
Munkbron 1
PO Box 2373
SE-10318 Stockholm, Sweden
Phone: 46 87232530
Fax: 46 87232510
Publications: Ny Framtid (51029)

Kruzak D.o o.
Zastavnice 29
CT-10251 Hrvatski Leskovac, Croatia
Phone: 385 1 6590416
Fax: 385 9 8235527
Publications: Croatian Journal of Philosophy (43558)

Kuensel Corporation
PO Box 204
Thimphu, Bhutan
Phone: 975 23 21544
Fax: 975 23 22975
Publications: Kuensel (42926)

Kuldeforlaget
Marielundsveien 5
N-1358 Jar, Norway
Phone: 47 671 20659
Fax: 47 671 2061790
Publications: Kulde Skandinavia (49192)

Kumamoto University
39-1 Kurokami 2-chome
Kumamoto 860-8555, Japan
Phone: 81 963 442111
Publications: Kumamoto Journal of Mathematics (46453)

Kungliga Vetenskapsakademien
PO Box 50005
SE-104 05 Stockholm, Sweden
Phone: 46 8 6739500
Fax: 46 8 155670
Publications: Ambio (51006)

Kunst Bulletin
Zeughausstr. 55
CH-8004 Zurich, Switzerland
Phone: 44 298 3030
Fax: 44 298 3038
Publications: Kunst Bulletin (51273)

The Kuppuswami Sastri Research Institute
84 Thiru Vi Ka Rd.
Mylapore
Chennai 600 004, Tamil Nadu, India
Phone: 91 442 4985320
Fax: 91 442 4985320
Publications: Journal of Oriental Research (45050)

Kurtis Editrice
via Luigi Zoja, 30
20153 Milan, Italy
Phone: 39 2 48202740
Fax: 39 2 48201219
Publications: Aggiornamento Medico (46160) • Aging Clinical and Experimental Research (46161) • Annali dell'Istituto Superiore di Sanita (46163) • Eating and Weight Disorders (46166) • L'Endocrinologo (46167) • Il Cardiologo (46173) • Il Ginecologo (46174) • Ipertensione (46178) • Journal of Endocrinological Investiga-

tion (46182) • Obesity and Metabolism (46188) • Urodinamica (46198)

Kustannus oy Kampanja
Office House, 7 krs.
Bulevardi 2-4 A
FIN-00120 Helsinki, Finland
Phone: 358 961507482
Fax: 358 96923063
Publications: Kampanja (43837)

Kustannus Oy Kauppalehti
Etelaesplanadi 20
PO Box 830
FIN-00101 Helsinki, Finland
Phone: 358 950 781
Fax: 358 950 78641
Publications: Kauppalehti Optio (43840)

Kuwait Medical Association
PO Box 1202
Safat 13013, Kuwait
Phone: 965 53 17972
Fax: 965 53 12630
Publications: The Kuwait Medical Journal (47340)

Kuwait University Health Science Centre
Karger
Faculty of Medicine 4th Fl.
PO Box 24923
Safat 13110, Kuwait
Fax: 965 25 330472
Publications: Medical Principles and Practice (47341)

KVINFO, Danish Center for Information on Women and Gender
Christians Brygge 3
DK-1219 Copenhagen, Denmark
Phone: 45 33135088
Fax: 45 33141156
Publications: Forum, Tidsskrift for Kon Og Kultur (43670)

KVS Foundation
Haapaniemenkatu 7-9 B, 11
FIN-00530 Helsinki, Finland
Phone: 358 207 511500
Fax: 358 207 511502
Publications: Aikuiskasvatus (43815) • Lifelong Learning in Europe (43844)

Kwani Trust
PO Box 2895
Nairobi, Kenya
Phone: 25 420 4441801
Fax: 25 420 4441802
Publications: Kwani? (47192)

KWF Kankerbestrijding - Dutch Cancer Society
Delflandlaan 17
NL-1062 EA Amsterdam, Netherlands
Phone: 31 020 5700500
Fax: 31 020 6750302
Publications: Overleven (48197)

Kyodo News
Shiodome Media Tower 15th Fl.
1-7-1 Higashi-Shimbashi
Minato-ku
Tokyo 105-7201, Japan
Fax: 81 3 62528306
Publications: Kyodo News (46956)

The Kyoto Shimbun Newspaper Company Ltd.
Karasuma Ebisugawa-agaru
Nakagyo-ku
Kyoto 604-8577, Japan
Phone: 81 752 415277
Fax: 81 752 221956
Publications: The Kyoto Shimbun News (46481)

Kyoto University
Yoshida-Honmachi
Sakyo-Ku
Kyoto 606-8501, Japan
Phone: 81 757 537531
Publications: Kyoto Review of Southeast Asia (46480) • Publications of Seto Marine Biological Laboratory (46486)

Kyushu University
Kyushu University 12
6-10-1 Hakozaki
Higashi-ku, Fukuoka-shi

Fukuoka 812-8581, Japan
Phone: 81 926 423066
Fax: 81 926 423069
Publications: International Journal of Biotronics (46343)

La Fabrica Gestion + Cultura
Alameda 9
Veronica 13
E-28014 Madrid, Spain
Phone: 34 913 601320
Publications: Matador (50781)

La Pagina Ediciones S.L.
Ramon y Cajal, 56
E-38006 Santa Cruz de Tenerife, Spain
Phone: 34 922 248559
Fax: 34 922 248559
Publications: La Pagina (50829)

La Trobe University
PO Box 821
Wodonga, Victoria 3689, Australia
Phone: 61 260 249700
Fax: 61 260 249797
Publications: The Weaver (42702)

La Vie de l'Auto
BP 40419
F-77309 Fontainebleau Cedex, France
Phone: 33 160 396969
Fax: 33 160 396900
Publications: La Vie de l'Auto (43953)

Lace Guild
The Hollies
53 Audnam
Stourbridge DY8 4AE, United Kingdom
Phone: 44 13 84390739
Fax: 44 13 84444415
Publications: Lace (56640)

Lancaster & Morecambe Newspapers
12 Victoria St.
Morecambe LA4 4AG, United Kingdom
Phone: 44 15 24833111
Fax: 44 15 24420939
Publications: Dirt Bike Rider (55647) • Trials & Motocross News (55649)

Lancer Publishers & Distributors
K-32A (F.F) Green Park Main
New Delhi 110 016, Delhi, India
Phone: 91 11 6867339
Fax: 91 11 6862077
Publications: Indian Defence Review (45538)

Land Research Trust
7 King's Rd.
Teddington TW11 0QB, United Kingdom
Publications: Geophilos (56730)

Land Research Unit Ltd.
Studio Crown Reach
149a Grosvenor Rd.
London SW1V 3JY, United Kingdom
Phone: 44 20 78349471
Fax: 44 20 78349470
Publications: Planning in London (55091)

Land -und forstwirtschaftliche Berufsgenossen-schaft Franken und Oberbayern
Neumarkter Strasse 35
D-81673 Munich, Germany
Phone: 49 89 45480382
Fax: 49 89 436639813
Publications: LSV aktuell (44569)

Landes Bioscience
1002 W Ave.
Austin, TX 78701
Phone: 512637-6050
Fax: 512637-6079
Publications: Cell Adhesion & Migration (44111) • Plant Signaling & Behavior (44269)

Landscape Institute
Charles Darwin House
12 Roger St.
London WC1N 2JU, United Kingdom
Phone: 44 20 72994500
Fax: 44 20 72994501
Publications: Landscape Design (54850)

Landscape Research Group
PO Box 1482
Oxford OX4 9DN, United Kingdom
Publications: Landscape Research (56083)

Langmead & Baker Ltd.
PO Box 81
Fringilla, Zambia
Phone: 260 1 213939
Publications: Black Lewche (57107)

Larchdrift Projects Ltd.
Unit 12, Moor Pl. Farm
Plough Ln.
Bramshill
Hook RG27 0RF, United Kingdom
Phone: 44 11 89326665
Publications: Project Manager Today (53587)

Latin American Association of Communications Researchers
Avenida Prof. Lucio M. Rodrigues, 443-Bloco B, Rm. 27
Cidade Universitaria
Butanta
05508-900 Sao Paulo, Sao Paulo, Brazil
Phone: 55 11 30914082
Fax: 55 11 30914224
Publications: Revista Latinoamericana de Ciencias de la Comunicacion (43047)

Latin American and Caribbean Women's Health Network
Casilla Postal 50610
Santiago 1
Santiago, Chile
Phone: 56 2 2237077
Fax: 56 2 2231066
Publications: Cuadernos Mujer Salud (43144) • Revista Mujer Salud (43147) • Women's Health Collection (43149)

Law Council of Australia
GPO Box 1989
Canberra, Australian Capital Territory 2601, Australia
Phone: 61 2 62463788
Fax: 61 2 62480639
Publications: Australian Law Management Journal (41702)

Law Institute of Victoria
470 Bourke St.
Melbourne, Victoria 3000, Australia
Phone: 61 396 079311
Fax: 61 396 025270
Publications: LIJ (42069)

The Law Society of Hong Kong
3rd Fl., Wing On House
71 Des Voeux Rd., Central
Hong Kong, People's Republic of China
Phone: 852 28460500
Fax: 852 28450387
Publications: Hong Kong Lawyer (43336)

Law Society of Ireland
Blackhall Pl.
Dublin 7, Dublin, Ireland
Phone: 35 316 724800
Fax: 35 316 724801
Publications: Gazette (45962)

The Law Society of New South Wales
170 Phillip St.
Sydney, New South Wales 2000, Australia
Phone: 61 2 99260333
Fax: 61 2 92315809
Publications: Caveat (42486) • Law Society Journal (42534)

Law Society of Scotland
26 Drumsheugh Gardens
Edinburgh EH3 7YR, United Kingdom
Phone: 44 131 2267411
Fax: 44 131 2252934
Publications: Journal of the Law Society of Scotland (56240)

The Law Society of Singapore
39 S Bridge Rd.
Singapore 058673, Singapore
Phone: 65 65382500
Fax: 65 65335700
Publications: Law Gazette (50212)

The Law Society of South Africa
304 Brooks St.
PO Box 36626
Pretoria 0102, Republic of South Africa
Phone: 27 123 668800
Fax: 27 123 620969
Publications: De Rebus (50589)

LAWASIA: The Law Association for Asia and the Pacific
Law Society House, Ground Fl.
179 Ann St.
Brisbane, Queensland 4000, Australia
Phone: 61 732 225888
Fax: 61 732 225850
Publications: LAWASIA Journal (41652)

Lawbook Co.
Level 5, 100 Harris St.
Pyrmont, New South Wales NSW 2009, Australia
Phone: 61 2 85877980
Fax: 61 2 85877981
Publications: Australasian Dispute Resolution Journal (42270) • Australian Business Law Review (42271) • Australian Law Journal (42274) • Criminal Law Journal (42276) • Environmental and Planning Law Journal (42277) • Insolvency Law Journal (42281) • Journal of Banking and Finance Law and Practice (42283)

Lawrence & Wishart Ltd.
99a Wallis Rd.
London E9 5LN, United Kingdom
Phone: 44 20 85332506
Fax: 44 20 85337369
Publications: Mediactive (54922)

Lawtext Publishing Ltd.
55 W End, Spinners Ct., Office G18
Witney OX28 1NH, United Kingdom
Phone: 44 19 93706183
Fax: 44 19 93709410
Publications: Bio-science Law Review (56939) • Contemporary Issues in Law (56940) • Environmental Law & Management (56941) • Environmental Liability (56942) • Information Technology Law Reports (56943) • The Journal of International Maritime Law (56944) • The Journal of Water Law (56945) • Utilities Law Review (56946)

Le Carrousel
27 rue Danielle Casanova
F-75001 Paris, France
Phone: 33 1 42615142
Fax: 33 1 49279190
Publications: Phytoma La Defense des Vegetaux (44075)

Le Cavalier Romand—Pro Cheval
Rue du Port 24
CH-1009 Pully, Switzerland
Phone: 41 217 298683
Fax: 41 217 298761
Publications: Le Cavalier Romand (51222)

Le Rotarien
34 rue Pierre-Dupont
FR-69001 Lyon, France
Phone: 33 4 72003214
Fax: 33 4 72000507
Publications: Le Rotarien (43969)

Lea-Francis Owners Club
French's
Long Wittenham
Abingdon OX14 4QQ, United Kingdom
Publications: LeaFlet (51967)

Leader Community Newspapers
636 St. Kilda Rd.
Melbourne, Victoria 3004, Australia
Phone: 61 3 99149000
Fax: 61 3 98758077
Publications: Bayside Leader (41745) • Berwick Leader (41598) • Brimbank Leader (42650) • Caulfield Glen Eira Leader (41892) • Cranbourne Leader (41599) • Dandenong Leader (41746) • Diamond Valley Leader (41635) • Frankston Standard Leader (42117) • Free Press Leader (41618) • Heidelberg Leader (42063) • Hobsons Bay Leader (42144) • Hume Leader (42651) • Knox Leader (41619) • Lilydale & Yarra Valley Leader (42010) • Macedon Ranges Leader (42402) • Manningham Leader (42071) • Maribyrnong

Leader (42145) • Maroondah Leader (42072) • Melbourne Leader (42074) • Melton Leader (42403) • Moonee Valley Leader (42077) • Moorabbin Glen Eira Leader (41747) • Moorabbin Kingston Leader (41748) • Moorabool Leader (42078) • Mordialloc Chelsea Leader (41749) • Moreland Leader (42079) • Mornington Peninsula Leader (42118) • Northcote Leader (42213) • Oakleigh Monash Leader (42080) • Pakenham Cardinia Leader (41600) • Port Phillip Leader (41893) • Preston Leader (42082) • Progress Leader (41894) • Stonnington Leader (41895) • Sunbury Leader (42404) • Waverley Leader (42089) • Whitehorse Leader (42090) • Whittlesea Leader (41636) • Wyndham Leader (42692)

Leader Publication Ltd.
1st Fl., Colombo Commercial Bldg.
121, Sir James Peiris Mawatha
Colombo 2, Sri Lanka
Phone: 94 753 65892
Fax: 94 753 65891
Publications: The Sunday Leader (50871)

Leaf Coppin Publishing Ltd.
PO Box 46387
London SW17 8WF, United Kingdom
Phone: 44 20 86821001
Publications: Lubrication Science (54892)

League Publications Ltd.
Wellington House
Briggate
Brighouse HD6 1DN, United Kingdom
Phone: 44 14 84401895
Fax: 44 14 84401995
Publications: Rugby League World (52601) • Rugby Leaguer & League Express (52602)

Leatherhead Food International Ltd.
Randalls Rd.
Leatherhead KT22 7RY, United Kingdom
Phone: 44 1372 376761
Fax: 44 1372 386228
Publications: Food Allergy and Intolerance Journal (53751)

Lebensmittel Zeitung DIREKT
Mainzer Landstr. 251
D-60326 Frankfurt am Main, Germany
Fax: 49 69 7595 01
Publications: Deutscher Fachuerlag GmbH (44365)

Leeds Guide Ltd.
80 North St.
West Yorkshire
Leeds LS2 7PN, United Kingdom
Phone: 44 113 2441000
Fax: 44 113 2441002
Publications: The Leeds Guide (53771)

Leeds United AFC Ltd.
Elland Rd.
Leeds LS11 0ES, United Kingdom
Publications: Leeds, Leeds, Leeds (53772)

Legal Service Bulletin Co-operative Ltd.
Law Faculty
Monash University
Clayton, Victoria 3000, Australia
Phone: 61 3 95440974
Fax: 61 3 99055305
Publications: Alternative Law Journal (41755)

Legalese Ltd.
Kensington Sq. House
12-14 Ansdell St.
London W8 5BN, United Kingdom
Phone: 44 20 73969292
Fax: 44 20 73969303
Publications: Employment Law Journal (54368) • Family Law Journal (54442) • The In-House Lawyer (54591) • Legal Business (54864) • Lex (54866) • The Practical Lawyer (55114) • Property Law Journal (55141) • Trusts and Estates Law & Tax Journal (55344) • Wills & Trusts Law Reports (55407)

Leicester City Council
New Walk Center
Welford Pl.
Leicester LE1 6ZG, United Kingdom
Phone: 44 116 2527000
Publications: Leicester Link (53811)

Leicester University Students Union
University Rd.
Leicester LE1 7RH, United Kingdom
Phone: 44 11 62231148
Publications: Ripple (53822)

The Leisure Media Company Ltd.
Portmill House
Portmill Ln.
Hitchin SG5 1DJ, United Kingdom
Phone: 44 14 62431385
Fax: 44 14 62433909
Publications: Attractions Management (53576) • Health Club Management (53578) • Leisure Management (53579) • Leisure Opportunities (53580) • Sports Management (53582)

Leopold Stokowski Society
12 Market St.
Deal CT14 6HS, United Kingdom
Publications: Tocatta (53161)

Les Editions du Verbe
LP 28
F-28270 Brezolles, France
Phone: 33 237 436660
Fax: 33 237 436271
Publications: Chorus (43923)

Lexicon Group Ltd.
371 Beach Rd.
03-18 Keypoint
Singapore 199597, Singapore
Phone: 65 629 20300
Fax: 65 629 34294
Publications: Newman (50227) • Singapore Visitor (50266) • Smart Investor (50268) • Space (50271) • Today's Parents (50279) • Wine & Dine (50287)

Lexington Press Ltd.
PO Box 51
Lexington, MA 02420-0001
Phone: 781862-8900
Fax: 781861-0375
Publications: Parliamentary Brief (55058)

LexisNexis UK
Halsbury House
35 Chancery Ln.
London WC2A 1EL, United Kingdom
Phone: 44 20 74002500
Fax: 44 20 74002842
Publications: Competency & Emotional Intelligence (54251) • Employment Law Bulletin (54367) • Equal Opportunities Review (54381) • European Industrial Relations Review (54395) • Health and Safety Bulletin (54542) • Health & Safety at Work (54543) • IRS Employment Review (53127) • New Law Journal (54992) • Occupational Pensions (55025) • Taxation (53136) • The Times Law Reports (55324)

Lexxion Verlagsgesellschaft mbH
Guntzelstr. 63
10717 Berlin, Germany
Phone: 49 30 8145060
Fax: 49 30 81450622
Publications: European State Aid Law Quarterly (44177)

Liberal International
1 Whitehall Pl.
London SW1A 2HD, United Kingdom
Phone: 44 20 78395905
Fax: 44 20 79252685
Publications: Liberal Matters (54867)

Liberal Party of Norway
Moellergaten 16
N-0179 Oslo, Norway
Phone: 47 22 404350
Fax: 47 22 404351
Publications: Liberalt Forum (49201)

Liberator Publications
Flat 1, 24 Alexandra Grove
London N4 2LF, United Kingdom
Publications: Liberator (54868)

Libertas Academica Ltd.
PO Box 302-874
North Harbour
Albany 0751, New Zealand
Phone: 64 9 4763930

Fax: 64 9 3531397
Publications: Cancer Informatics (48776) • Evolutionary Bioinformatics Online (48777)

Liberte
37 rue Larbi Ben M'hidi
Algiers, Algeria
Phone: 213 2 1736480
Fax: 213 2 1730487
Publications: Liberte (41461)

Librairie du Liban Publishers
Sayegh Bldg. Zouk Mosbeh
Keserwan, Lebanon
Phone: 96 192 17735
Fax: 96 199 77435
Publications: International Journal of Arabic-English Studies (47159)

Librarians' Christian Fellowship
c/o Graham Hedges
34 Thurlestone Ave.
Seven Kings
Ilford IG3 9DU, United Kingdom
Phone: 44 20 85991310
Publications: Christian Librarian (53638)

Library Association of Ireland
53 Upper Mount St.
Dublin IRL-2, Dublin, Ireland
Publications: An Leabharlann (45944)

Library and Information Association of New Zealand
PO Box 12-212
Wellington 6144, New Zealand
Phone: 64 447 35834
Fax: 64 449 91480
Publications: Library Life (49015)

Library and Information Research Group
c/o CILIP
7 Ridgmount St.
London WC1E 7AE, United Kingdom
Phone: 44 20 72550500
Fax: 44 20 72550501
Publications: Library and Information Research (54870)

Library of Tibetan Works & Archives
Gangchen Kyishong
Dharamsala 176 215, Himachal Pradesh, India
Phone: 91 1892 22467
Fax: 91 1892 23723
Publications: Tibet Journal (45112)

Mary Ann Liebert Incorporated Publishers
140 Huguenot St., 3rd Fl.
New Rochelle, NY 10801-5215
Phone: 914740-2100
Fax: 914740-2101
Free: 800654-3237
Publications: Cloning and Stem Cells (53263) • The Journal of Alternative & Complementary Medicine (53563)

Light Rail Transit Association
138 Radnor Ave.
Welling DA16 2BY, United Kingdom
Phone: 44 1179 517785
Publications: Tramway Review (56879) • Tramways & Urban Transit (56880)

LighterLife UK Ltd.
Cavendish House
Parkway
Harlow Business Park
Essex CM 19 5QF, United Kingdom
Publications: LighterLife (53340)

Limbless Association
Jubilee House; 3 The Dr.
Warley Hill
Brentwood CM13 3FR, United Kingdom
Phone: 44 1277 725182
Fax: 44 1277 725379
Publications: Step Forward (52589)

Limerick Leader Ltd.
54 O'Connell St.
Limerick, Limerick, Ireland
Phone: 353 61 214500
Publications: Limerick Leader (46029)

Limerick Post Newspaper
The Red Church
Henry St.
Limerick, Limerick, Ireland
Phone: 353 614 13322
Fax: 353 614 17684
Publications: Limerick Post (46030)

Linedancer
Clare House
166 Lord St.
Southport PR9 0QA, United Kingdom
Phone: 44 1704 392300
Fax: 44 1704 501678
Publications: Linedancer (56587)

Lingnan University
8 Castle Peak Rd., Tuen Mun, New Territories
Hong Kong, People's Republic of China
Phone: 852 26168888
Fax: 852 24638363
Publications: Journal of Modern Literature in Chinese
(43359) • Review of Modern Literature in Chinese
(43381)

Linguistic Association of Finland
c/o Department of General Linguistics
PO Box 9
University of Helsinki
FIN-00014 Helsinki, Finland
Publications: SKY Journal of Linguistics (43906)

Linguistic Society of the Philippines
De La Salle University
2401 Taft Ave.
Manila 1004, Philippines
Publications: Philippine Journal of Linguistics (49555)

Linkoping University Electronic Press
Linkoping University/ISV
S-581 83 Linkoping, Sweden
Phone: 46 132 81000
Fax: 46 131 49403
Publications: The International Journal of Ageing and
Later Life (IJAL) (50975)

Lippincott Williams & Wilkins
351 W Camden St.
Baltimore, MD 21201
Phone: 410528-4000
Free: 800638-3030
Publications: Anti-Cancer Drugs (47896)

Lippincott, Williams and Wilkins Ltd.
250 Waterloo Rd.
London SE1 8RD, United Kingdom
Phone: 44 20 79810500
Fax: 44 20 79810501
Publications: Current Opinion in Clinical Nutrition &
Metabolic Care (54297) • Current Opinion in Infectious
Diseases (54299) • Current Opinion in Neurology
(54302)

Lira Editorial S.A.
Isábel Colbrand, 10
Oficina 87
E-28050 Madrid, Spain
Phone: 34 913 588774
Fax: 34 913 588944
Publications: Ritmo (50800)

Lithuanian Physical Society
A. Gostauto 12
LT-2600 Vilnius, Lithuania
Phone: 37 526 20668
Fax: 37 521 25361
Publications: Lithuanian Journal of Physics (47482)

Lithuanian Society of Cardiology
Eiveniu 2
LT-50009 Kaunas, Lithuania
Phone: 370 37 326449
Fax: 370 37 331395
Publications: Seminars in Cardiology (47466)

Living Media India Ltd.
Trade Ctr.
2nd Fl.Kamla City,
S.B. Marg Lower Parel (W)
Mumbai 400 013, Maharashtra, India
Phone: 91 22 24983355
Publications: Business Today (45490) • Computers
Today (45497) • Cosmopolitan (India) (45501) • India

Today (45373) • India Today Plus (45374)

Living Media India Pvt. Ltd.
Videocon Tower, 13th Fl.
E-1, Jhandewalan Ext.
New Delhi 110 055, Delhi, India
Phone: 91 112 3684848
Fax: 91 112 3684841
Publications: Good Housekeeping (45521)

Livsmedelsverket
PO Box 622
SE-751 26 Uppsala, Sweden
Phone: 46 181 75500
Fax: 46 181 05848
Publications: Var Foda (51053)

Lobster
214 Westbourne Ave.
Hull HU5 3JB, United Kingdom
Phone: 44 1482 447558
Publications: Lobster (53627)

Lockwood Press
1 Nine Elms Ln.
London SW8 5NN, United Kingdom
Phone: 44 20 75010300
Fax: 44 20 77202047
Publications: Fresh Produce Journal (54482)

Lockwood Publications
Vanit Bldg. II, Rm. 1403A
1126/2 New Petchburi Rd.
Bangkok 10400, Thailand
Phone: 66 225 56625
Fax: 66 265 52211
Publications: Tobacco Asia (51445)

Lodgemark Press
15 Moorfield Rd.
Orpington BR6 OXD, United Kingdom
Phone: 44 1689 897123
Fax: 44 1689 890998
Publications: Karting (55854)

Logistics and Transport New Zealand
c/o John Partridge, Devel. Executive
PO Box 1281
Shortland St.
Auckland, New Zealand
Phone: 64 936 84970
Fax: 64 936 84971
Publications: Transportant (48829)

London Business School Alumni Association
Regent's Pk.
London NW1 4SA, United Kingdom
Phone: 44 20 70007000
Fax: 44 20 70007001
Publications: Alumni News (53934)

London City Mission
175 Tower Bridge Rd.
London SE1 2AH, United Kingdom
Phone: 44 20 74077585
Fax: 44 20 74036711
Publications: Span (55260)

London Councils
59 1/2 Southwark St.
London SE1 0AL, United Kingdom
Phone: 44 20 79349999
Publications: London Bulletin (54886)

London Mathematical Society
De Morgan House
57-58 Russell Sq.
London WC1 B4HS, United Kingdom
Phone: 44 20 76373686
Fax: 44 20 73233655
Publications: LMS Journal of Computation and Math-
ematics (54880) • Proceedings (55124)

London Natural History Society
19 Mecklenburgh Sq.
London WC1N 2AD, United Kingdom
Publications: The London Bird Report (54885) • The
London Naturalist (53884)

The London Picture Book Ltd.
3rd Fl.
45 Albemarle St., Mayfair
London W1X 4FE, United Kingdom
Phone: 44 208 8744905
Publications: The London Picture Book (54889)

**London School of Economics and Political Sci-
ence**
Houghton St.
London WC2A 2AE, United Kingdom
Phone: 44 20 74057686
Publications: Millennium (54934) • Risk and Regula-
tion (55205)

Longford Leader Ltd.
Leader House
Dublin Rd.
Longford, Longford, Ireland
Phone: 353 434 5241
Publications: Longford Leader (46034)

Lord's Day Observance Society
Day One Christian Ministries
Ryelands Rd.
Leominster HR6 8NZ, United Kingdom
Phone: 44 15 68613740
Fax: 44 15 68611473
Publications: Day One Diary (53840)

Loughborough Students' Union
Union Bldg.
Ashby Rd.
Loughborough LE11 3TT, United Kingdom
Phone: 44 1509 635000
Fax: 44 1509 635003
Publications: Label (55484)

Lovatts Publications Pty Ltd.
PO Box 999
Gosford, New South Wales 2250, Australia
Phone: 61 2 43254199
Publications: Christine's BIG Crossword (41905) •
Christine's Cryptic Crossword Collection (41906) •
Cluewords (41907) • Codecracker Starhunts (41908) •
Colossus Crosswords (41909) • FindaWord (41910) •
Handy ADDoku Plus Kakuro (41911) • Handy Arrowords
(41912) • Handy Codecrackers (41913) • Handy
Crosswords (41914) • Handy Cryptic Crosswords
(41915) • Handy Fill-Ins (41916) • Handy Wordhunt
(41917) • Holiday Crossword Collection (41918) •
Large Print Crosswords (41919) • MEGA! (41920) •
Puzzle Fun for Kids (41921) • Super Sudoku (41922) •
Variety Puzzles (41923)

Loyola College of Social Sciences
Sreekariyam PO
Thiruvananthapuram 695 017, Kerala, India
Phone: 91 471 2591018
Fax: 91 471 2591760
Publications: Loyola Journal of Social Sciences
(45748)

LR Presse S.A.R.L.
12 St. of Sablen
F-56400 Auray Cedex, France
Phone: 33 297 240165
Fax: 33 297 242830
Publications: Vole Libre (43916)

LRB Ltd.
28 Little Russell St.
London WC1A 2HN, United Kingdom
Phone: 44 20 72091141
Fax: 44 20 72091151
Publications: London Review of Books (54890)

LTSN Centre for Bioscience
Rm. 9.15 Worsley Bldg.
University of Leeds
Leeds LS2 9JT, United Kingdom
Phone: 44 11 33433001
Fax: 44 11 33435894
Publications: Bioscience Education E-journal (53757)

Lulea University of Technology
Lulea University of Technology
S-971 87 Lulea, Sweden
Phone: 46 920 491000
Fax: 46 920 491399
Publications: Journal of Nonlinear Mathematical Phys-
ics (50982)

Luxury Publishing Limited
5 Jubilee Pl.
Chelsea
London SW3 3TD, United Kingdom
Phone: 44 20 75912900
Fax: 44 20 75912929
Publications: Aspinalls (53977) • Candid (54172)

Cartier International Polo @MAG (54184) • Derby Festival @MAG (54319) • Harrods Estates @MAG (54532) • PrivatAir (55120) • PrivatSea (55123) • Quintessentially (55166) • TenGoal (55299) • Ultra (55356) • WMS (55410)

LZ Fachverlag AG
Maihofstrasse 76
CH-6002 Lucerne, Switzerland
Phone: 41 429 5252
Fax: 41 429 5367
Publications: Schweizerische Kirchenzeitung (51210)

M D Periodicals Private Ltd.
11 Darya Ganj
New Delhi 110 002, Delhi, India
Phone: 91 11 3268645
Fax: 91 11 3275542
Publications: International Journal of Sociology of the Family (45585)

M. Mustafa Aldur
Hacettepe University
Faculty of Medicine
Department of Anatomy
06100 Ankara, Turkey
Phone: 90 312 3052466
Fax: 90 312 4785200
Publications: Neuroanatomy (51498)

MA Healthcare Ltd.
St. Jude's Church
Dulwich Rd.
Herne Hill
London SE24 0PB, United Kingdom
Phone: 44 20 77385454
Fax: 44 20 77332325
Publications: African Journal of Midwifery and Women's Health (53922) • British Journal of Cardiac Nursing (54115) • British Journal of Community Nursing (54117) • British Journal of Health Care Management (54121) • British Journal of Healthcare Assistants (54122) • British Journal of Hospital Medicine (54123) • British Journal of Midwifery (54125) • British Journal of Neuroscience Nursing (54127) • British Journal of School Nursing (54135) • Dental Nursing (54317) • Gastrointestinal Nursing (54496) • International Journal of Palliative Nursing (54657) • International Journal of Therapy and Rehabilitation (IJTR) (54665) • Journal of Paramedic Practice (54792) • Journal of Renal Nursing (54808) • Nurse Prescribing (55014) • Nursing and Residential Care (55017)

Mac Communications
Taney Hall
Eglinton Terr.
Dundrum 14, Dublin, Ireland
Phone: 353 1 2960000
Fax: 353 1 2960383
Publications: FINS (46008) • Irish Medical News (46009) • Living It (46010) • Visitor (46011)

Macmillan Publishers Ltd.
Houndmills
Basingstoke RG21 6XS, United Kingdom
Phone: 44 1256 329242
Fax: 44 1256 479476
Publications: Nature (52226)

Macquarie University
School of Law
Sydney, New South Wales 2109, Australia
Phone: 61 298 507111
Publications: Macquarie Law Journal (42538) • Perfect Beat (42559) • Scan (42578)

Made in Germany Publication GmbH
Siemensstrasse 18
D-63303 Dreieich, Germany
Phone: 49 610 3936597
Fax: 49 610 334175
Publications: Made in Germany—International Edition (44318)

Madhyamam
PO Box 2014, Pulleppady
Kochi 682 018, Kerala, India
Publications: Madhyamam (45251)

Madicinska Naklada
Cankarova ulica 13
10000 Zagreb, Croatia
Phone: 385 1 3779444
Fax: 385 1 3907041
Publications: Croatian Medical Journal (43565)

Madras Institute of Development Studies
79 Second Main Rd.
Gandhi Nagar
Adyar
Chennai 600 020, Tamil Nadu, India
Phone: 91 442 4412589
Fax: 91 442 4910872
Publications: Review of Development and Change (45055)

The Magazine Publishing Co.
34 Station St.
PO Box 406
Nundah, Queensland 4012, Australia
Phone: 61 7 38660000
Fax: 61 7 38660066
Publications: Australian Baking Business (42219) • The Circuit (42220) • Council Leader (42221) • Developers Digest (42222) • Queensland Racing Magazine (42223)

Magenta Uitgeverij
Bijsterhuizen 31-47
NL-6604 LV Wijchen, Netherlands
Phone: 31 243 454150
Fax: 31 243 976071
Publications: CBM (48773)

The Magic Circle
12 Stephenson Way
Euston
London NW1 2HD, United Kingdom
Publications: The Magic Circular Magazine (54895)

Magicalia Ltd.
15-18 White Lion St.
Islington
London N1 9PG, United Kingdom
Phone: 44 20 78438800
Fax: 44 20 78438999
Publications: Practical Parenting and Pregnancy (55116)

Magisterbladet
Nimbusparken 16
DK-2000 Frederiksberg, Denmark
Phone: 45 381 56600
Fax: 45 381 56666
Publications: Magisterbladet (43692)

Magistrates' Association of England and Wales
28 Fitzroy Sq.
London W1T 6DD, United Kingdom
Phone: 44 207 3872353
Fax: 44 207 3834020
Publications: The Magistrate (54897)

Magna Publishing Company Ltd.
Magna House
100/E Old Prabhadevi Rd.
Prabhadevi
Mumbai 400 025, Maharashtra, India
Phone: 91 224 362270
Fax: 91 224 306523
Publications: Health (45371) • Society (45441) • Starduct (45442)

Magnetics Society of Japan
5th Fl., Mitsui-Sumitomo, Kaijo Ogawamachi Bldg.
2-8 Kanda Ogawamachi
Chiyoda-ku
Tokyo 101-0052, Japan
Phone: 81 3 52810106
Fax: 81 3 52810107
Publications: Journal of Magnetics Society of Japan (46920)

Magnolia Press
PO Box 41383
St. Lukes
Auckland 1346, New Zealand
Publications: Zootaxa (48833)

Magpie Publications
70 Winifred Ln.
Aughton
Ormskirk L39 5DL, United Kingdom
Phone: 44 16 95423470
Fax: 44 16 54200185
Publications: Card Times (55849)

Magyar Tajekozodasi Futo Szovestseg
Dozsa Gyorgy ut 1-3
H-1143 Budapest, Hungary
Phone: 36 1 2215878
Fax: 36 1 2514602
Publications: Tajfutas (44878)

Magyar Tudomanyos Akademia, Szazadveg Politikai Iskola
Benczur 33
H-1068 Budapest, Hungary
Publications: Central European Political Science Review (44826)

Maik Nauka/Interperiodica Publishing
Profsoyuznaia St. 90
117997 Moscow, Russia
Phone: 7 953 361600
Fax: 7 953 360666
Publications: Applied Biochemistry and Microbiology (49875) • Applied Solar Energy (57014) • Astronomy Letters (49877) • Astronomy Reports (49878) • Automatic Control and Computer Sciences (49880) • Automatic Documentation and Mathematical Linguistics (49881) • Automation and Remote Control (49882) • Biochemistry (Moscow) (49883) • Bulletin of the Crimean Astrophysical Observatory (49885) • Cell and Tissue Biology (50020) • Coke and Chemistry (49887) • Colloid Journal (49888) • Computational Mathematics and Mathematical Physics (49889) • Cosmic Research (49890) • Crystallography Reports (49891) • Doklady Biochemistry and Biophysics (49894) • Doklady Biological Sciences (49895) • Doklady Chemistry (49896) • Doklady Earth Sciences (49897) • Doklady Mathematics (49898) • Doklady Physical Chemistry (49899) • Doklady Physics (49900) • Entomological Review (50021) • Geochemistry International (49906) • Geology of Ore Deposits (49907) • Geomagnetism and Aeronomy (49908) • Geotectonics (49909) • Glass Physics and Chemistry (50022) • Herald of the Russian Academy of Sciences (49912) • High Energy Chemistry (49913) • High Temperature (49914) • Human Physiology (49915) • Inorganic Materials (49919) • Izvestiya, Atmospheric and Oceanic Physics (49924) • Izvestiya, Physics of the Solid Earth (49925) • Journal of Analytical Chemistry (49927) • Journal of Computer and Systems Sciences International (49928) • Journal of Evolutionary Biochemistry and Physiology (50023) • Journal of Ichthyology (49929) • Kinetics and Catalysis (49931) • Laser Physics (49935) • Lithology and Mineral Resources (49938) • Oceanology (49949) • Pattern Recognition and Image Analysis (49952) • Petroleum Chemistry (49954) • Petrology (49955) • Physics of Atomic Nuclei (49956) • Physics of Metals and Metallography (49855) • Physics of Particles and Nuclei Letters (49957) • Physics of the Solid State (50024) • Plasma Physics Reports (49959) • Polymer Science (49960) • Polymer Science, Series C (49961) • Protection of Metals (49968) • Russian Journal of Bioorganic Chemistry (49975) • Russian Journal of Biotechnology (49976) • Russian Journal of General Chemistry (50026) • Russian Journal of Inorganic Chemistry (49977) • Russian Journal of Marine Biology (50040) • Russian Journal of Organic Chemistry (50027) • Russian Journal of Physical Chemistry (49980) • Russian Metallurgy (49985) • Stratigraphy and Geological Correlation (49991) • Studies on Russian Economic Development (49992) • Thermal Engineering (49996) • Thermophysics and Aeromechanics (50015)

The Mainichi Newspapers Co
1-1-1 Hitotsubashi
Chiyoda-ku
Tokyo 100-8051, Japan
Phone: 81 332120885
Fax: 81 332112509
Publications: Mainichi Daily News (46964)

Malacological Society of Japan
c/o National Science Museum
3-23-1 Hiyakunin-cho
Shinjuku-ku
Tokyo 169-0073, Japan
Publications: Venus: Japanese Journal of Malacology (47055)

The Malacological Society of London
Canterbury Christ Church University
Kent CT1 1QU, United Kingdom

Phone: 44 20 75942949
Publications: Bulletin of the Malacological Society of London (55545)

Malaria Research Centre
22 Sham Nath Marg
Delhi 110 054, Delhi, India
Phone: 91 112 3981690
Fax: 91 112 3946150
Publications: Journal of Vector Borne Diseases (45102)

Malayan Nature Society
JKR 641, Jalan Kelantan
Bukit Persekutuan
50480 Kuala Lumpur, Malaysia
Phone: 60 3 22879422
Fax: 60 3 22878773
Publications: Malayan Nature Journal (47611) • Malaysian Naturalist (47621)

Malaysian Agricultural Research and Development Institute
PO Box 12301
50774 Kuala Lumpur, Malaysia
Phone: 60 389 437111
Fax: 60 389 483664
Publications: Journal of Tropical Agriculture & Food Science (47608)

Malaysian Branch of the Royal Asiatic Society
2nd Fl., 4B Jalan Kemuja
Bangsar
59000 Kuala Lumpur, Malaysia
Phone: 60 3 22835345
Fax: 60 3 22822458
Publications: Journal of the Malaysian Branch of the Royal Asiatic Society (47606)

Malaysian Chamber of Mines
W Block, Wisma Selangor Dredging, 8th Fl.
Jalan Ampang
50450 Kuala Lumpur, Malaysia
Phone: 60 3 21616171
Fax: 60 3 21616179
Publications: Malaysian Chamber of Mines Year Book (47615)

Malaysian Cocoa Board
Locked Bag 211
88999 Kota Kinabalu, Malaysia
Phone: 60 88 234477
Fax: 60 88 239575
Publications: Banci Estet Koko (47587) • Malaysian Cocoa Monitor (47591)

Malaysian Medical Association
4th Fl., Bangunan MMA, No. 124
Jalan Pahang
53000 Kuala Lumpur, Malaysia
Phone: 60 3 40411375
Fax: 60 3 40418187
Publications: The Medical Journal of Malaysia (47627)

Malaysian Paper Board
Tanah Putih
PO Box 1653
93916 Kuching, Malaysia
Phone: 60 823 31811
Fax: 60 823 36877
Publications: Pepper Market Bulletin (47667)

Malaysian Rubber Board
148 Jalan Ampang
50450 Kuala Lumpur, Malaysia
Phone: 60 3 92062000
Fax: 60 3 21613139
Publications: Journal of Rubber Research (47607)

Maltese Diabetes Association
British Legion Premises
111 Melita St.
Valletta CMR 01, Malta
Phone: 356 21 221518
Publications: Id-Dijabete u Sahhtek (47746)

Management Development Institute
Mehrauli Rd.
Sukhrali
Gurgaon 122 007, Haryana, India
Phone: 91 124 4560000
Fax: 91 124 4560456
Publications: Vision (45128)

Manas Chaudhuri
Rilbong
Shillong 793 004, Meghalaya, India
Phone: 91 364 2223488
Fax: 91 364 2229488
Publications: The Shillong Times (45729)

Manchester University Press
Oxford Rd.
Manchester M13 9NR, United Kingdom
Phone: 44 161 2752310
Fax: 44 161 2743346
Publications: Critical Studies in Television (55551) • Gothic Studies (52243) • International Journal of Electrical Engineering Education (55558) • International Journal of Mechanical Engineering Education (55560) • The Journal of Transport History (55569) • Literature & History (55570) • Nineteenth Century Theatre and Film (55574) • The Seventeenth Century (53231)

Maney Publishing
1 Carlton House Ter.
London SW1Y 5AF, United Kingdom
Phone: 44 20 74517300
Fax: 44 20 74517307
Publications: Annals of Tropical Paediatrics (53950) • Applied Earth Science (53959) • Arms & Armour (53964) • Austrian Studies (53982) • Breathe (54104) • Bronte Studies (54150) • Bubble Science, Engineering and Technology (54151) • Byzantine and Modern Greek Studies (54162) • Central Europe (54193) • Comparative American Studies (54248) • Competition & Change (54252) • Corrosion Engineering, Science and Technology (54269) • Dutch Crossing (54345) • Early Medieval China (54346) • Family & Community History (54440) • The Hardy Review (54530) • Hematology (54548) • Hispanic Research Journal (54553) • The Historic Environment (54555) • Industrial Archaeology Review (54596) • Interdisciplinary Science Reviews (54615) • International Heat Treatment and Surface Engineering (54627) • International Journal of Cast Metals Research (54638) • International Wood Products Journal (54675) • Ironmaking & Steelmaking (54683) • The Italianist (54685) • Journal of the British Archaeological Association (54711) • Journal of the Energy Institute (54743) • Journal of Manual & Manipulative Therapy (54774) • Labour History Review (54848) • Language & History (54851) • Materials Science and Technology (54913) • Medieval Sermon Studies (54924) • Midland History (54932) • Mineral Processing and Extractive Metallurgy (54936) • Ming Studies (54938) • Mining Technology (54942) • Names (54969) • Northern History (55011) • Nutritional Neuroscience (55021) • Packaging, Transport, Storage & Security of Radioactive Material (55049) • Palestine Exploration Quarterly (55051) • Physical Therapy Reviews (55085) • Plastics, Rubber and Composites (55094) • Post-Medieval Archaeology (55108) • Powder Metallurgy (55110) • Progress in Palliative Care (55136) • Public Archaeology (55150) • Publications of the English Goethe Society (55154) • Seventeenth-Century French Studies (55229) • Slavonica (55242) • Slovo (55243) • Surface Engineering (55281) • T'ang Studies (55292) • Tel Aviv (55296) • Terrae Incognitae (55300) • Textile History (55301) • Usus Antiquior (55364) • Vernacular Architecture (55367) • War & Society (55379)

Mani Tese
Piazza Gambara 7/9
I-20146 Milan, Italy
Phone: 39 240 75165
Fax: 39 240 46890
Publications: Mani Tese (46187)

Manila Bulletin
Muralla Cor. Recoletos Sts.
PO Box 769.
Intramuros 1002, Philippines
Publications: Manila Bulletin (49501) • Tempo (49502)

Manoramaonline
Malayala Manorama
PO Box 26
Kottayam 686 001, Kerala, India
Phone: 91 481 2563646
Fax: 91 481 2565398
Publications: Malayala Manorama (45315)

Manufacturers' Agents' Association of Great Britain and Ireland
Unit 16, Thrales End
Harpenden AL5 3NS, United Kingdom
Phone: 44 15 82767618
Fax: 44 15 82766092
Publications: Agents News (53513)

Manushi Trust
C 1/3, Sangam Estate
1 Under Hill Rd.
Civil Lines
New Delhi 110 054, Delhi, India
Phone: 91 11 23916437
Publications: Manushi (45622)

Marg Publications
Army & Navy Bldg., 3rd Fl.
148 Mahatma Gandhi Rd.
Mumbai 400 001, Maharashtra, India
Phone: 91 22 22842520
Fax: 91 22 22047102
Publications: Marg (45409)

Marga Institute, Sri Lanka Centre for Development Studies
941/1 Jayanthi Mawatha, Kotte Rd.
Ethul Kotte, Sri Lanka
Phone: 94 112 888790
Fax: 94 112 888794
Publications: Marga Journal (50894)

Margery Allingham Society
c/o Barry Pike, Chm.
42 Scarborough Rd.
Leytonstone
London E11 4AL, United Kingdom
Phone: 44 20 85565243
Publications: The Bottle Street Gazette (54101)

Maria Sheila Cremaschi
Calle Ayala, N 7
2 Derecha
E-28001 Madrid, Spain
Phone: 34 915 779506
Fax: 34 917 811402
Publications: Intramuros (50774)

Marine Connection
PO Box 2404
London W2 3WG, United Kingdom
Publications: Seventh Wave (55601)

Marine Conservation Society
Unit 3
Wolf Business Pk.
Alton Rd.
Ross-on-Wye HR9 5NB, United Kingdom
Phone: 44 19 89566017
Fax: 44 19 89567815
Publications: Marine Conservation (56410)

Marine Media Ltd.
Ballymoon Industrial Estate
Kilcar, Donegal, Ireland
Phone: 353 749 738836
Fax: 353 749 738841
Publications: Marine Times Newspaper (46025)

Marine Society
202 Lambeth Rd.
London SE1 7JW, United Kingdom
Phone: 44 20 76547000
Fax: 44 20 79288914
Publications: Seafarer (55224)

Maritime Books
Lodge Hill
Liskeard PL14 4EL, United Kingdom
Phone: 44 15 79343663
Fax: 44 15 79346747
Publications: Warship World (53864)

Maritime Union of Australia
Level 2, 365 Sussex St.
Sydney, New South Wales 2000, Australia
Phone: 61 2 92679134
Fax: 61 2 92613481
Publications: Maritime Workers Journal (42539)

Market House
Market Pl.
Alston CA9 3HS, United Kingdom

Phone: 44 14 34382680
Publications: In the Sticks (52103)

Marketing Federation of Southern Africa
JSE Bldg., 17 Diagonal St.
Newtown
Johannesburg 2000, Republic of South Africa
Phone: 27 11 8323500
Fax: 27 11 7263639
Publications: Journal of Marketing (50531)

Marketletter (Publications) Ltd.
Appleton House
139 King St.
London W6 9JG, United Kingdom
Phone: 44 20 87356625
Fax: 44 20 87356688
Publications: Nutraceuticals International (55018)

MarketSource International Pty Ltd.
PO Box 60
Mona Vale, New South Wales 2103, Australia
Phone: 61 2 99863522
Fax: 61 2 99863599
Publications: Your Trading Edge (42112)

Marmara University
Goztepe Kampusu
Kadikoy
TR-81040 Istanbul, Turkey
Phone: 90 216 3384196
Fax: 90 216 3474543
Publications: Marmara Journal of European Studies (51560)

Martinus Nijhoff
Plantijnstraat 2
NL-2321 JC Leiden, Netherlands
Phone: 31 715 353500
Fax: 31 715 317532
Publications: International Criminal Law Review (48680) • International Organizations Law Review (48683) • The Law and Practice of International Courts and Tribunals (48707)

Maruzen Company Ltd.
9-2 Nihombashi 3-chome
Chuo-Ku
PO Box 5050
Tokyo 103-8244, Japan
Phone: 81 3 32733234
Fax: 81 3 32731144
Publications: Journal of Japanese Trade and Industry (46919) • Journal of Veterinary Medical Science (46944) • Structural Engineering Earthquake Engineering (47043)

Masarykova Universita
Zerotinovo nam. 617/9
CZ-601 77 Brno, Czech Republic
Phone: 42 549 491011
Fax: 42 549 491070
Publications: Archivum Mathematicum (43602)

Mashriq Group of Newspapers
Bilal Town, GT Rd.
PO Box 1107
Peshawar, Pakistan
Phone: 92 91 2651151
Fax: 92 91 2651197
Publications: Statesman (49395)

Maskinbladet
Birk Centerpark 36
DK-7400 Herning, Denmark
Phone: 45 962 65266
Fax: 45 962 65296
Publications: Maskinbladet (43722)

Massage World
PO Box 54879
London SW1P 9FW, United Kingdom
Phone: 44 20 73879111
Publications: Massage World (54911)

Massey University
Private Bag 11-222
Palmerston North, New Zealand
Phone: 64 6 2569099
Fax: 64 6 3505673
Publications: Australasian Journal of Disaster and Trauma Studies (48962) • NZ Journal of Teachers' Work (48965)

Master Builders Association - Malaysia
2-1 Jalan 2/109E, 1st Fl.
Desa Business Pk., Taman Desa
Off Jalan Kelang Lama
58100 Kuala Lumpur, Malaysia
Phone: 60 3 79848636
Fax: 60 3 79826811
Publications: Master Builders Journal (47625)

Master Photographers Association
Jubilee House
1 Chancery Ln.
Darlington DL1 5QP, United Kingdom
Phone: 44 13 25356555
Fax: 44 13 25357813
Publications: Master Photographers (53155)

Materials and Energy Research Center
PO Box 14155-4777
Tehran 15169, Iran
Phone: 98 21 88771626
Fax: 98 21 88773352
Publications: International Journal of Engineering (45890)

The Mathematical Association
259 London Rd.
Leicester LE2 3BE, United Kingdom
Phone: 44 116 2210013
Fax: 44 116 2122835
Publications: Equals (53798) • Mathematical Gazette (53813) • Mathematical Pie (53814) • Mathematics in School (53815) • Primary Mathematics (53817) • Symmetry Plus (53830)

Mathematical Society of Japan
c/o Faculty of Science
Kobe Univ.
Kobe 657-8501, Japan
Publications: Funkcialaj Ekvacioj, Serio Internacia (46430)

Mathematical Society of Japan
34-8, Taito 1-chome
Taito-ku
Tokyo 110-0016, Japan
Phone: 81 3 38353483
Fax: 81 3 38353485
Publications: Japanese Journal of Mathematics (46870)

The Mathematical Society of the Republic of China
Dept. of Applied Mathematics
101, Sec. 2, Guangfu Rd.,
Hsinchu 300, Taiwan
Phone: 886 3 5713784
Fax: 886.3 5723888
Publications: The Taiwanese Journal of Mathematics (51307)

Mathrubhumi
Dr. A R Menon Rd.
K.P.Kesavamenon Rd.
Palakkad 678 001, Kerala, India
Phone: 91 491 2504446
Fax: 91 491 2521600
Publications: Mathrubhumi (45680)

Matt Publishing
7 Unity St.
Bristol BS1 5HH, United Kingdom
Phone: 44 117 9300255
Fax: 44 117 9300245
Publications: DNJ (52661)

Mauritius News
583 Wandsworth Rd.
London SW8 3JD, United Kingdom
Phone: 44 20 74983066
Publications: Mauritius News (54915)

Max-Planck-Gesellschaft (Max Planck Society)
Hofgartenstr. 8
D-80539 Munich, Germany
Phone: 49 892 1080
Fax: 49 892 1081111
Publications: Demographic Research (44647)

Max-Planck-Institut for Solar System Research
Max-Planck-Str. 2
D-37191 Katlenburg-Lindau, Germany
Phone: 49 555 69790

Fax: 49 555 6979240
Publications: Living Reviews in Solar Physics (44500)

Max Publishing Ltd.
United House
North Rd.
London N7 9DP, United Kingdom
Phone: 44 20 77006740
Fax: 44 20 76076411
Publications: Progressive Gifts and Home Worldwide (55137) • Progressive Greetings Worldwide (55138) • Progressive Housewares (55139)

The Mayo News
The Fairgreen
Westport, Mayo, Ireland
Phone: 353 98 25311
Fax: 353 98 26108
Publications: The Mayo News (46069)

McKenzie Publishing Ltd.
Longhouse, 460 Bath Rd.
Longford
Middlesex UB7 0EB, United Kingdom
Phone: 44 17 53775511
Fax: 44 17 53775512
Publications: The Squash Player (55620)

McQuillan Young Communications
1 Sekforde St.
Clerkenwell
London EC1R 0BE, United Kingdom
Phone: 44 20 72536450
Fax: 44 20 72536455
Publications: SPE Review (55261)

Meanjin Company Ltd.
187 Grattan St.
Carlton, Victoria 3053, Australia
Phone: 61 39 420317
Fax: 61 39 420399
Publications: Meanjin (41727)

Meath Chronicle Group of Publications
Market Sq.
Navan, Meath, Ireland
Phone: 353 46 9079600
Publications: Meath Chronicle (46046)

Medcom Ltd.
Rm. 504-5, Cheung Tat Ctr.
18 Cheung Lee St.
Hong Kong, People's Republic of China
Phone: 86 852 25783833
Fax: 86 852 25783929
Publications: Hong Kong Journal of Dermatology & Venereology (43328) • Hong Kong Journal of Paediatrics (43331) • Hong Kong Medical Diary (43338) • The Hong Kong Nursing Journal (43340) • The Hong Kong Practitioner (43342) • Journal of the Hong Kong College of Cardiology (43357) • Journal of the Hong Kong Geriatrics Society (43358)

Media Africa
PO Box 752
Pinegowrie 2123, Republic of South Africa
Phone: 27 117 827003
Fax: 27 117 827063
Publications: Gadget (50571)

Media Corporation Publishing Private Ltd.
Caldecott Broadcast Centre
Andrew Rd.
Singapore 299939, Singapore
Phone: 65 63333888
Fax: 65 62515628
Publications: 8 Days (50142)

Media Enterprises Ltd.
31 Shirley Park Ave.
PO Box 9240
Nassau, Bahamas
Phone: 242325-8210
Fax: 242325-8065
Publications: Bahamas Journal of Science (42783)

Media G8way Publishing Corp.
Unit P5 VGP Ctr.
6772 Ayala Ave.
Makati City 1226, Philippines
Phone: 632 812 8401
Fax: 632 894 2487
Publications: Computer World Philippines (49515) •

Enterprise (49516) • PC World Philippines (49518)

Media, Marketing & Publications Unit
Rm. G07, Mitchell Bldg.
Adelaide, South Australia 5005, Australia
Phone: 61 883 035174
Fax: 61 883 034838
Publications: The Adelaidean (41500)

Media Services (Private) Ltd.
59 Ward Pl.
Colombo 00700, Sri Lanka
Phone: 94 11 2672017
Fax: 94 11 2672019
Publications: Lanka Monthly Digest (50860)

Media Wales Ltd.
Six Park St.
Cardiff CF10 1XR, United Kingdom
Phone: 44 29 20223333
Publications: South Wales Echo (52939) • Western
Mail (52941)

MediaCorp Publishing
Caldecott Broadcast Centre
Andrew Rd.
Singapore 299939, Singapore
Phone: 65 633 33888
Fax: 65 625 15628
Publications: Style (50274)

MediaNavigering A.S.
PO Box 253
N-1379 Nesbru, Norway
Phone: 47 66 774060
Fax: 47 66 774061
Publications: SEIL Magasinet (49194)

Mediaspazio S.R.L.
Via. M. Melloni 17
I-20129 Milan, Italy
Publications: Foto-Notiziario (46172)

Media24
Nasper Ctr.
Heerengracht 40
PO Box 2271
Cape Town 8000, Republic of South Africa
Phone: 27 21 4062489
Fax: 27 21 4063753
Publications: Beeld (50527) • Bloemnews (50366) •
Caledon Kontreinuus (50368) • Carletonville Herald
(50370) • City Vision (50371) • Die Breederivier
Gazette (50373) • Die Burger (50541) • DistrictMail
(50374) • Eikestadnuus (50375) • Fairlady (50378) •
Gazette (50379) • HelderMail (50380) • Hermanus
Times (50381) • Huisgenoot (50626) • Idees (50382) •
Kouga Express (50526) • Kroonnuus (50385) • Land-
bouweekblad (50386) • Leef met hart & siel (50388) •
Maluti (50389) • Max Power (50390) • Meyerton Ster
(50392) • Move! (50393) • Mshana (50627) • Noord-
Vrystaatse Gazette (50394) • Noordkaap (50395) •
Northwest Gazette (50396) • Ons Stad (50397) • Over-
berg Venster (50399) • Paarl Post (50400) • Port
Elizabeth Express (50401) • Potchefstroom Herald
(50402) • Psychologies South Africa (50403) •
QwaQwa News (50404) • Rapport (50405) • SARIE
My inspirasie (50408) • Sasolburg Ster (50409) •
Swartlander (50414) • TOPbike (50415) • TopCar
(50416) • topMotor (50417) • True Love (50418) • Tuis
(50419) • tvplus (50420) • TygerBurger (50421) • Vaal
Vision (50422) • Vaal Weekly (50423) • Vanderbijlpark
Ster (50424) • Vereeniging Ster (50425) • Volksblad
(50426) • Vrystaat (50427) • Weskus News (50428) •
Weslander (50429)

Medical Association of Nippon Medical School
1-1-5 Sendagi
Bunkyo-ku
Tokyo 113-8602, Japan
Fax: 81 338 223759
Publications: Journal of Nippon Medical School
(46929)

Medical Association of Thailand
4th Royal Golden Jubilee Bldg., 2 Soi Soonvijai
New Pechburi Rd., Huaykwang
Bangkok 10310, Thailand
Phone: 66 231 44333
Fax: 66 231 46305
Publications: Journal of the Medical Association of
Thailand (51423)

Medical Assurance Society
PO Box 13402
Johnsonville
Wellington, New Zealand
Phone: 64 447 88863
Publications: Hi Society (49009)

Medical Tribune Inc.
2-1 Nibancho
Chiyoda-ku
Tokyo 102-0084, Japan
Phone: 81 3 32397217
Fax: 81 3 32399375
Publications: Annals of Thoracic and Cardiovascular
Surgery (46741)

Medicom Publishing Ltd.
Churston House
Portsmouth Rd.
Esher KT10 9AD, United Kingdom
Phone: 44 137 2471671
Fax: 44 137 2471672
Publications: Pharmacy in Practice (53338)

MediNews (Diabetes) Ltd.
Edgbaston House
3 Duchess Pl.
Edgbaston
Birmingham B16 8NH, United Kingdom
Phone: 44 12 14544114
Fax: 44 121 4541190
Publications: The British Journal of Diabetes and
Vascular Disease (52333) • Diabetes and Vascular
Disease Research (52339)

**Mediterranean Council for Burns and Fire
Disasters**
Via C. Lazzaro
90127 Palermo, Italy
Phone: 39 916 663631
Fax: 39 915 96404
Publications: Annals of Burns and Fire Disasters
(46207)

Meditsina Publishers
Bolshaya Pirogovskaya, 5, Bldg. 2
119435 Moscow, Russia
Phone: 7 95 2453355
Fax: 7 95 2453355
Publications: Anesthesiology & Intensive Care
(49870) • Annals of Ophthalmology (49871) • Annals
of the Russian Academy of Medical Sciences (49872) •
Annals of Surgery (49873) • Annals of Traumatology &
Orthopedics (49874) • Clinical Laboratory Diagnosis
(49886) • Epidemiology & Infectious Diseases
(49902) • Forensic Medical Examination (49905) •
Haematology & Trasfusiology (49910) • Health Care of
the Russian Federation (49911) • Hygiene & Sanitation
(49916) • Journal of Neurosurgical Problems (49930) •
Medical Care (49941) • Medico-Social Expert Evalua-
tion and Rehabilitation (49942) • Molecular Genetics,
Microbiology & Virology (49943) • Molecular Medicine
(49944) • Obstetrics & Gynaecology (49948) • Patho-
logical Physiology & Experimental Therapy (49951) •
Pediatric Surgery (49953) • Physitherapy, Balneology
and Rehabilitation (49958) • Problems of Biological,
Medical and Pharmaceutical Chemistry (49962) •
Problems of Endocrinology (49963) • Problems of
Health Resort Treatment, Physiotherapy & Exercise
Therapy (49964) • Problems of Social Hygiene, Health
Care & History of Medicine (49965) • Problems of
Tuberculosis (49966) • Problems of Virology (49967) •
Russian Journal of Oncology (49978) • Russian Journal
of Pediatrics (49979) • Russian Journal of Skin and
Sexually Transmitted Diseases (49981) • Russian
Journal of Stomatology (49982) • Russian Medical
Journal (49984) • Sociology of Medicine (49990) •
Therapeutic Archives (49995) • Thoracic & Cardiovas-
cular Surgery (49997)

Medknow Publications Pvt Ltd.
B-9, Kanara Business Center
Off Link Rd., Ghatkopar E
Mumbai 400075, Maharashtra, India
Phone: 91 22 56491818
Fax: 91 22 56491817
Publications: Annals of Indian Academy of Neurology
(45757) • Annals of Pediatric Cardiology (45350) • An-
nals of Thoracic Medicine (50059) • Asian Journal of
Pharmaceutics (45338) • Asian Journal of Transfusion

Science (45258) • Hepatitis B Annual (45081) • Indian
Journal of Human Genetics (45381) • Indian Journal of
Medical and Paediatric Oncology (45382) • Indian
Journal of Occupational and Environmental Medicine
(45746) • Indian Journal of Palliative Care (45563) •
International Journal for Ayurveda Research (45392) •
International Journal of Diabetes in Developing Coun-
tries (45393) • International Journal of Green Pharmacy
(45339) • International Journal of Shoulder Surgery
(50384) • International Journal of Trichology (45043) •
International Journal of Yoga (44964) • Journal of
Cancer Research and Therapeutics (45396) • Journal
of Conservative Dentistry (45045) • Journal of Craniovertebral Junction and Spine (45397) • Journal of
Cutaneous and Aesthetic Surgery (44968) • Journal of
Cytology (45594) • Journal of Dental Implants (45398) •
Journal of Forensic Dental Sciences (45028) • Journal
of Gynecological Endoscopy and Surgery (45401) •
Journal of Human Reproductive Sciences (44973) •
Journal of Indian Academy of Oral Medicine and Radiol-
ogy (44996) • Journal of Indian Prosthodontic Society
(44974) • Journal of Indian Society of Periodontology
(45048) • Journal of Laboratory Physicians (45612) •
Journal of Medical Physics (45402) • Journal of Neurosciences in Rural Practice (45770) • Journal of Oral
and Maxillofacial Pathology (45049) • Journal of
Pediatric Neurosciences (45615) • Journal of Young
Pharmacists (44976) • Lung India (45198) • Medical
Law Cases for Doctors (45410) • Mens Sana Monographs (45411) • Middle East African Journal of Ophthalmology (45413) • Noise and Health (55008) •
Oman Journal of Ophthalmology (45423) • Pharmacognosy @MAG (44980) • Pharmacognosy Research
(45430) • PVRI Review (45433) • Saudi Journal of
Anaesthesia (45436) • Systematic Reviews in Pharmacy (44988) • Urology Annals (50072) • Young
Scientists Journal (45451)

MedMedia Group
25 Adelaide St.
Dun Laoghaire
Dublin, Dublin, Ireland
Phone: 35 312 803967
Fax: 35 312 807076
Publications: Irish Journal of Psychological Medicine
(45978)

Medpharm Publications
The Centurion Wine & Art Ctr.
123 Amcor Rd., Ground Level
Gauteng 0157, Republic of South Africa
Phone: 64 126 647460
Fax: 64 126 646276
Publications: Professional Nursing Today (50482) •
SA Pharmaceutical Journal (50483)

Medwell Journals
ANSInet Bldg.
308-Lasani Town
Sargodha Rd.
Faisalabad, Pakistan
Phone: 92 41 5004000
Fax: 92 41 8815599
Publications: Agricultural Journal (49231) • Asian
Journal of Information Technology (49236) • Botany
Research Journal (49240) • International Business
Management (49248) • International Journal of Electri-
cal and Power Engineering (49250) • International
Journal of Molecular Medicine and Advance Sciences
(49251) • International Journal of Soft Computing
(49256) • International Journal of Systems Signal
Control and Engineering Application (49257) • Interna-
tional Journal of Tropical Medicine (49258) • Journal of
Animal and Veterinary Advances (49260) • Journal of
Aquaculture Feed Science and Nutrition (49263) •
Journal of Economics Theory (49265) • Journal of
Engineering and Applied Sciences (49266) • Journal of
Fisheries International (49268) • Journal of Food
Technology (49269) • Journal of Mobile Communication
(49271) • Journal of Modern Mathematics and Statistics
(49272) • Journal of Molecular Genetics (49273) • Online Journal of Earth Sciences (49275) • Plant Sciences
Research (49279) • Research Journal of Agronomy
(49281) • Research Journal of Animal Sciences
(49282) • Research Journal of Applied Sciences
(49284) • Research Journal of Biological Sciences
(49285) • Research Journal of Dairy Sciences
(49287) • Research Journal of Medical Sciences
(49289) • Research Journal of Pharmacology (49291) •

Research Journal of Poultry Sciences (49292) • Surgery Journal (49294) • Veterinary Research (49296)

MEED Communications
Dubai Media City
PO Box 25960
Al Thuraya Tower 1
Dubai, United Arab Emirates
Phone: 971 4 3900045
Fax: 971 4 3904560
Publications: MEED - The Middle East Business Weekly (51648)

Meeleven
Postbus 10887
NL-1001 EW Amsterdam, Netherlands
Phone: 31 20 5317600
Fax: 31 20 4203528
Publications: Meeleven (48152)

Melcrum Publishing
The Glassmills
322B King St.
London W6 0AX, United Kingdom
Phone: 44 20 86004670
Fax: 44 20 87419975
Publications: Internal Comms Hub (54618)

Mensa International
15 The Ivories
6-8 Northampton St.
London N1 2HY, United Kingdom
Publications: International Journal (54629)

Mental Health Association New South Wales
80 William St., Level 5
East Sydney, New South Wales 2011, Australia
Fax: 61 293 396066
Publications: Mental Health Matters (41851)

Mental Health Association Queensland
473 Annerley Rd.
Annerley, Queensland 4103, Australia
Phone: 61 1300 729686
Fax: 61 7 31124399
Publications: Balance (41556)

Mercantile Communications Pvt. Ltd.
PO Box 876
Durbar Marg
Kathmandu, Nepal
Phone: 977 4 445920
Fax: 977 1 4439360
Publications: Kathmandu Post (47840) • Nepali Times (47843) • New Business Age (47844) • Spotlight (47846) • The Telegraph Weekly (47847)

Mercantile Gazette Marketing Ltd.
8 Sheffield Cres.
PO Box 20034
Christchurch 05003, New Zealand
Phone: 64 3 3583219
Fax: 64 3 3584490
Publications: The New Zealand Shipping Gazette (48876)

Mercator Media Ltd.
The Old Mill
Lower Quay
Fareham PO16 0RA, United Kingdom
Phone: 44 1329 825335
Fax: 44 1329 825330
Publications: Maritime Journal (53373) • Motor Ship (53374)

Merricks Media Ltd.
3-4 Riverside Ct.
Lower Bristol Rd.
Bath BA2 3DZ, United Kingdom
Phone: 44 12 25786800
Fax: 44 12 25786801
Publications: French Magazine (52240)

Merumpress AG
Verlag und Agentur fur italienische Lebensfreuden
Thiersteinerallee 17
Postfach
CH-4018 Basel, Switzerland
Publications: Merum (51064)

Messenger Newspapers
1 Baynes Pl.
PO Box 197
Port Adelaide, South Australia 5015, Australia

Phone: 61 8 83475722
Publications: Adelaide Matters (41499) • East Torrens Messenger (42215) • Eastern Courier Messenger (42216) • Guardian Messenger (41986) • Hills & Valley Messenger (42119) • Leader Messenger (42343) • News Review Messenger (42344) • Portside Messenger (41987) • Southern Times Messenger (42120) • Standard Messenger (42345) • Weekly Times Messenger (42257)

Metal Bulletin
Nestor House
Playhouse Yard
London EC4V 5EX, United Kingdom
Phone: 44 20 78279977
Fax: 44 20 78276470
Publications: Metal Bulletin Monthly (54927)

Metal Bulletin PLC
Nestor House
Playhouse Yard
London EC4V 5EX, United Kingdom
Phone: 44 20 78279977
Fax: 44 20 78276470
Publications: World Mining Equipment (55422)

Meteorological Society of Japan
c/o Japan Meteorological Agency
1-3-4 Ote-Machi
Chiyoda-ku
Tokyo 100-0004, Japan
Phone: 81 3 32128341
Fax: 81 3 32164401
Publications: Journal of Meteorological Society of Japan (46927)

The Metropolis Group
140 Wales Farm Rd.
London W3 6UG, United Kingdom
Phone: 44 20 87528181
Fax: 44 20 87528185
Publications: Book and Magazine Collector (54097) • Family History Monthly (54441) • Frontier Brands (54485) • Laboratory News (53128) • The Landscaper (52776) • Record Collector (55177)

Mezhdunarodnyi Institut Sotsioniki
a/s 23
2206 Kiev, Ukraine
Phone: 38 44 5580935
Publications: Fizika Soznaniya i Zhyzni, Kosmologiya i Astrofizika (Physics of Consciousness and Life, Cosmology and Astrophysics) (51596)

MG Car Club
Kimber House
Cemetery Rd.
Abingdon OX14 1AS, United Kingdom
Phone: 44 12 35555552
Publications: Safety Fast! (52046)

MGP Ltd.
Salter House
263-265 High St.
Berkhamsted HP4 1AB, United Kingdom
Phone: 44 1442 876100
Fax: 44 1442 877100
Publications: Guidelines (52310) • Guidelines in Practice (52311) • Medendum (52313)

Microbiological Society of Korea
The Korea Science & Technology Ctr., Rm. 810
635-4 Yeogsam-dong
Gangnam-gu
Seoul 135-703, Republic of Korea
Phone: 82 2 34533321
Fax: 82 2 34533322
Publications: The Journal of Microbiology (47276)

Microbiology Research Foundation
Center of Academic Publications Japan Bldg.
4-16, Yayoi 2 chome
Bunkyo-ku
Tokyo 113-0032, Japan
Publications: Journal of General and Applied Microbiology (46900)

Mid Day Publications Ltd.
64 Sitaram Mills Compound
N.M. Joshi Marg, Lower Parel
Lower Parel (E)
Mumbai 400 011, Maharashtra, India

Phone: 91 22 23017171
Publications: Mid-Day (45412) • Sunday Mid-Day (45444)

Middle East Technical University
Dept. of Economics
Balgat
TR-06531 Ankara, Turkey
Phone: 90 312 2102001
Fax: 90 312 2101107
Publications: METU Studies in Development (51497)

Military History Society of Ireland
Newman House
86 St. Stephen's Green
Dublin 2, Dublin, Ireland
Publications: Irish Sword (45986)

Miller Publishing Group L.L.C.
1918 Main St., 3rd Fl.
Santa Monica, CA 90405
Phone: 310893-5300
Publications: WHERE Budapest (44882) • WHERE Hong Kong (43386) • WHERE London (55403) • WHERE Rome (46245)

Millivres Prowler Group
Spectrum House, Unit M
32-34 Gordon House Rd.
London NW5 1LP, United Kingdom
Phone: 44 20 74247400
Fax: 44 20 74247401
Publications: axm (53996) • Diva (54335)

MIND - Mental Health Charity
Granta House
15-19 Broadway
London E15 4BQ, United Kingdom
Phone: 44 20 85192122
Fax: 44 20 85221725
Publications: OpenMIND (55035)

Mineralogical Society of Great Britain and Ireland
12 Baylis Mews
Amyand Park Rd.
Middlesex
Twickenham TW1 3HQ, United Kingdom
Phone: 44 20 88916600
Fax: 44 20 88916599
Publications: Clay Minerals (56789) • Mineralogical Magazine (54937)

Mining Journal Ltd.
Albert House
1 Singer St.
London EC2A 4BQ, United Kingdom
Phone: 44 20 72166060
Fax: 44 20 72166050
Publications: Mining Environmental Management (54939) • Mining Journal (54940) • Mining Magazine (54941) • World Gold Analyst (55420) • World Tunnelling (55427)

Ministry of Commerce
Sugandha Bhavan
Palarivattom P.O.
Cochin 682 025, Kerala, India
Phone: 91 484 2330010
Fax: 91 484 2331429
Publications: Spices India (45076)

Ministry of Defence
Ordnance Rd.
Aldershot GU11 2DU, United Kingdom
Fax: 44 1252 347358
Publications: Soldier Magazine (52098)

Ministry of External Affairs—India
Rm. 152, A Wing
Shastri Bhavan
New Delhi 110 001, Delhi, India
Phone: 91 112 3389471
Fax: 91 112 3384319
Publications: India Perspectives (45535)

Ministry of Information & Broadcasting
Smt. Stuti Narain Kacker
Rm. No. 552, A-Wing, Shastri Bhawan
New Delhi 110 001, Delhi, India
Phone: 91 112 3384453
Publications: Employment News (45507) • Mass Media in India (45624) • Yojana (45670)

Ministry of Public Health
PO Box 3050
Doha, Qatar
Phone: 97 443 92132
Fax: 97 443 14564
Publications: Qatar Medical Journal (49823)

Ministry of Rural Development
National Institute of Rural Development
Rajendranagar
Hyderabad 500 030, Andhra Pradesh, India
Phone: 91 402 4008526
Fax: 91 402 4015277
Publications: Journal of Rural Development (45176)

Ministry of Social Development
PO Box 1556
Wellington 6140, New Zealand
Phone: 64 4 9163300
Fax: 64 4 9180099
Publications: Social Policy Journal of New Zealand (49034)

Miskolci Egyetem
University of Miskolc
H-3515 Miskolc-Egyetemvaros, Hungary
Phone: 36 465 65111
Publications: Journal of Computational and Applied Mechanics (44891)

The Mission to Seafarers
St. Michael Paternoster Royal
College Hill
London EC4R 2RL, United Kingdom
Phone: 44 20 72485202
Fax: 44 20 72484761
Publications: Flying Angel News (54473) • The Sea (55223)

Missionary Society of Saint Columban
St. Columban's
Dalgan Pk.
Navan, Meath, Ireland
Phone: 35 346 9021525
Publications: Columban Mission (46044) • The Far East (46045)

MIT Press
55 Hayward St.
Cambridge, MA 02142-1315
Phone: 617253-2889
Fax: 617577-2889
Publications: Biological Theory (42721) • Computational Linguistics (42496)

Mita Society for Library and Information Science
c/o School of Library & Information Science
Keio University
2-15-45 Mita
Minato-ku
Tokyo 108-8345, Japan
Publications: Library and Information Science (46960)

Mitsubishi Electric Corp.
Tokyo Bldg.
2-7-3, Marunouchi
Chiyoda-ku
Tokyo 100-8310, Japan
Phone: 81 3 32182111
Publications: Mitsubishi Electric Advance (46969)

Mitsubishi Heavy Industries Ltd.
3-1 Minatomirai 3-chome
Nishi-ku
Yokohama 220-8401, Japan
Phone: 81 3 67163111
Fax: 81 3 67165800
Publications: Mitsubishi Heavy Industries Technical Review (47140)

Mkini Dotcom Sdn. Bhd.
48 Jalan Kemuja
Bangsar Utama
59000 Kuala Lumpur, Malaysia
Phone: 60 322 835567
Fax: 60 322 892579
Publications: Malaysiakini (47613)

Mladina
Dunajska cesta 51
SI-1000 Ljubljana, Slovenia
Phone: 386 123 06500
Fax: 386 123 06510
Publications: Mladina Magazine (50340)

Mmegi/The Reporter
PO Box BR 50
Gaborone, Botswana
Phone: 267 397 4784
Fax: 267 390 5508
Publications: Mmegi/The Reporter (42945)

Model Activity Press Ltd.
5 Chiltern Business Ctr.
63-65 Woodside Rd.
Amersham HP6 6AA, United Kingdom
Phone: 44 1494 433453
Fax: 44 1494 433468
Publications: Aviation Modeller International (52105) • Flying Scale Models (52106) • Military Machines International (52108)

Modern Churchpeople's Union
MCU Office
9 Westward View
Liverpool L17 7EE, United Kingdom
Phone: 44 15 17269730
Publications: Modern Believing (53876)

Modern English Publishing
211 E Ontario St., Ste. 1800
Chicago, IL 60611
Publications: ESL Magazine (53008)

Modern Humanities Research Association
1 Carlton House Ter.
London SW1Y 5AF, United Kingdom
Publications: Annual Bibliography of English Language & Literature (53951) • Modern Language Review (54943) • Portuguese Studies (55105) • Slavonic and East European Review (55241)

Modern Media Communications Ltd.
Gresham House
54 High St.
Shoreham-by-Sea BN43 5DB, United Kingdom
Phone: 44 1273 453033
Fax: 44 1273 453085
Publications: Aluminium Times (56521) • Cast Metal & Diecasting Times (56522) • Fire Times (56523)

Mohr Siebeck
Postfach 2040
72010 Tubingen, Germany
Publications: Journal of Institutional & Theoretical Economics (44692)

Molecular Diversity Preservation International
Kandererstrasse 25
CH-4057 Basel, Switzerland
Phone: 41 793 223379
Fax: 41 613 028918
Publications: International Journal of Molecular Sciences (51062) • Marine Drugs (51063)

Moller Buch und Zeitschriften Verlag KG
Oraniendamm 48
D-13469 Berlin, Germany
Phone: 49 30 419090
Fax: 49 30 41909599
Publications: Flieger Revue (44180)

Monash University
Clayton campus
Wellington Rd.
Clayton, Victoria 3800, Australia
Phone: 61 3 99026000
Fax: 61 3 99054007
Publications: Monash University Law Review (41764)

Monash University ePress
Bldg. 4
Monash University
Wellington Rd.
Clayton, Victoria 3800, Australia
Fax: 61 3 99058450
Publications: Applied GIS (41756) • The Bible and Critical Theory (41758)

Monch Publishing Group
Heilsbachstrasse 26
W-53123 Bonn, Germany
Phone: 49 228 64830
Fax: 49 228 6483109
Publications: Al Defaiya (47387) • MILITARY TECHNOLOGY (44266) • Nato's Nations and Partners for Peace (44267) • Naval Forces (44268) • Rivista Italiana Difesa (46133) • Safety & Security International (44270) • Savunma Ve Havacilik (51500) • TECNOLOGIA MILITAR (44271) • WEHRTECHNIK (44272)

Monday Morning
Dimitri Trad Bldg.
Issa Maalouf St., Sioufi
PO Box 165612
Beirut, Lebanon
Phone: 961 1 200961
Fax: 961 1 335079
Publications: Monday Morning (47400)

Moneyfacts Group PLC
66-70 Thorpe Rd.
Norwich NR1 1BJ, United Kingdom
Publications: Moneyfacts (55735)

Moneywise Publishing Limited
Standon House, 1st Fl.
21 Mansell St.
London E1 8AA, United Kingdom
Publications: Moneywise (56550)

Monitor CE Media Services
Laubova 6
CZ-130 00 Prague 3, Czech Republic
Phone: 42 222 365216
Fax: 42 222 365271
Publications: Prague Daily Monitor (43635)

Monitor Publications Ltd.
PO Box 12141
Kampala, Uganda
Phone: 256 412 32367
Fax: 256 412 32369
Publications: The Monitor (51587)

Montessori Tidningen
Drottninggatan 31
SE-411 14 Goteborg, Sweden
Publications: Montessori Tidningen (50960)

Montres Passion/Uhren Welt
Pont Bessieres 3
CH-1002 Lausanne, Switzerland
Phone: 41 21 331 7000
Fax: 41 21 331 7121
Publications: Montres Passion/Uhren Welt (51197)

MONTSAME News Agency
PO Box 1514
Ulaanbaatar, Mongolia
Fax: 976 11 327857
Publications: Khumuun Bichig (47811) • The Mongol Messenger (47812)

A.E. Morgan Publications Ltd.
8a High St.
Surrey
Epsom KT19 8AD, United Kingdom
Phone: 44 1372 741411
Fax: 44 1372 744493
Publications: Dance Expression (56590)

Morrison Media Services
Level 1, 25 Lemana Ln.
Burleigh, Queensland 4220, Australia
Phone: 61 7 55761388
Fax: 61 7 55761527
Publications: Freerider MX Magazine (41672)

Morton Newspapers
108 Holyrood Rd.
Edinburgh EH8 8AS, United Kingdom
Phone: 44 131 2253361
Fax: 44 131 2254580
Publications: Ballymena Times (52160) • Ballymoney Times (52162) • Banbridge Leader (52164) • Carrick Times (52951) • Coleraine Times (53264) • Craigavon Echo (56283) • Dromore Leader (53207) • Larne Times (53742) • Lisburn Echo (53862) • Lurgan Mail (55499) • Mid-Ulster Mail (53060) • North-West Echo (56859) • Portadown Times (56284) • Roe Valley Sentinel (53854)

Mortons Media Group
Media Ctr.
Morton Way
Horncastle LN9 6JR, United Kingdom
Phone: 44 1507 523456
Fax: 44 1507 529490
Publications: Heritage Railway Magazine (53590) •

Old Glory (53592) • Scootering (53593)

Mortons Motorcycle Media Ltd.
Media Ctr.
Morton Way
Horncastle LN9 6JR, United Kingdom
Phone: 44 15 07523456
Publications: Classic and Motorcycle Mechanics (53588) • Classic Racer International (53589)

Mosby Inc.
11830 Westline Industrial Dr.
Saint Louis, MO 63146-3313
Phone: 314872-8370
Fax: 314432-1380
Free: 800325-4177
Publications: Archives of Gerontology and Geriatrics (44887) • Autonomic Neuroscience (53991) • Biomaterials (42845) • Cancer Letters (55902) • Cardiovascular Research (44384) • Cell Calcium (55546) • Clinical Biomechanics (53618) • Clinical Neurology and Neurosurgery (42838) • Computer Methods and Programs in Biomedicine (51050) • Contact Lens & Anterior Eye (52838) • Dental Materials (55553) • Diabetes Research and Clinical Practice (55925) • EJVES Extra (55934) • European Journal of Cancer (53274) • European Journal of Cardio-Thoracic Surgery (51188) • European Journal of Cardiovascular Nursing (48600) • European Journal of Cardiovascular Prevention & Rehabilitation (54397) • European Journal of Obstetrics & Gynecology (53765) • European Journal of Oncology Nursing (53354) • Growth Hormone & IGF Research (43646) • Hepatology Research (46404) • International Journal of Cardiology (42519) • International Journal of Nursing Studies (54656) • International Journal of Oral & Maxillofacial Surgery (53490) • Journal of Behavior Therapy and Experimental Psychiatry (48737) • Journal of Biomechanics (48592) • Journal of Bodywork and Movement Therapies (54708) • Journal of Cranio-Maxillofacial Surgery (44503) • Journal of Dentistry (53361) • Journal of Hand Surgery (British & European Volume) (54758) • Journal of Psychiatric Research (44567) • Journal of Psychosomatic Research (55565) • Legal Medicine (46345) • Medical Engineering and Physics (52251) • Nutrition, Metabolism, & Cardiovascular Diseases (46202) • Oral Oncology (56129) • Pathophysiology (43877) • Seminars in Fetal & Neonatal Medicine (53774) • Theriogenology (46197) • Tissue & Cell (46259)

Moscow News
4, Zubovsky Blvd.
119021 Moscow, Russia
Phone: 7 495 6456565
Publications: Moscow News (49946)

The Mothers' Union
Mary Sumner House
24 Tufton St.
London SW1P 3RB, United Kingdom
Phone: 44 20 72225533
Fax: 44 20 72279737
Publications: Home & Family (54566)

Motivate Publishing
Al Wahaibi Bldg.
Al Garhoud Bridge Rd., Deira
PO Box 2331
Dubai, United Arab Emirates
Phone: 971 428 24060
Fax: 971 428 20428
Publications: Ad-Vocate (51628) • Business Traveller Middle East (51633) • Dubai Voyager (51639) • Emaar Properties Magazine (51640) • Emirates Bride (51641) • Emirates Woman (51642) • Gulf Business (51643) • Jumeirah (51645) • Living in the Gulf (51647) • Middle East MICE & Events (51649) • Open Skies (51651) • Souk (51653) • tv&radio (51655) • What's On (51656)

Motor Neurone Disease Association
PO Box 246
Northampton NN1 2PR, United Kingdom
Phone: 44 160 4250505
Fax: 44 160 4624726
Publications: Thumbprint (55715)

Motor Press Lisbon
Rua Policarpo Anjos, No. 4
P-1495-742 Cruz Quebrada-Dafundo, Portugal
Phone: 351 214 154500

Fax: 351 214 154501
Publications: Auto Hoje (Car Today) (49791) • Automagazine (49792) • Bike Magazine (49793) • Guia do Automovel (49794) • Motociclismo (49795) • Pais & Filhos (49796)

Motor-Presse Bohemia
At Sta. 36 of Krk
140 00 Prague 4, Czech Republic
Phone: 420 2 41093410
Fax: 420 2 41721905
Publications: Auto Motor a Sport (Czech) (43610) • Motorcykl (Czech) (43631)

Motor-Presse Verlag GmbH & Company KG
Leuschnerstr. 1
D-70174 Stuttgart, Germany
Phone: 49 711 18201
Fax: 49 711 18217779
Publications: Aerokurier (44660) • Flug Revue (44260)

Motoring Life
48 N Great Georges St.
Dublin IRL-1, Dublin, Ireland
Phone: 353 187 80444
Fax: 353 187 87740
Publications: Motoring Life (45992)

Mountain Association for Community Economic Development
433 Chestnut St.
Berea, KY 40403-1510
Phone: 859986-2373
Fax: 859986-1299
Publications: Progress in Nuclear Magnetic Resonance Spectroscopy (56576) • Reviews in Gynaecological Practice (52728)

Mountaineering Council of Ireland
Sport HQ
13 Joyce Way
Parkwest Business Pk.
Dublin IRL-12, Dublin, Ireland
Phone: 35 316 251115
Fax: 35 316 251116
Publications: Irish Mountain Log (45981)

Mourne Observer Ltd.
Castlewellan Rd.
County Down
Newcastle BT33 0JX, United Kingdom
Phone: 44 284 3722666
Fax: 44 284 3724566
Publications: Mourne Observer (55665)

MSM Media Ltd.
Thames House
18 Park St.
London SE1 9ER, United Kingdom
Phone: 44 20 73781605
Publications: SHARES (55232)

MTG Learning Media (P) Ltd.
406, Taj Apt., Ring Rd.
Near Safdarjung Hospital
New Delhi 110 029, Delhi, India
Phone: 91 11 46686000
Fax: 91 26 191601
Publications: Biology Today (45489) • Chemistry Today (45496) • Mathematics Today (45625) • Physics For You (45636)

M2 Communications Ltd.
1 Soulsbury View
The Normans
Bathampton
Bath BA2 6TF, United Kingdom
Phone: 44 20 70470200
Fax: 44 20 70570200
Publications: Airline Industry Information (52236) • Corporate IT Update (52237) • Internet Business News (52245) • Worldwide Computer Products News (52264)

Partha N. Mukherji
Tata Institute of Social Sciences
Sion-Trombay Rd.
PO Box 8313
Mumbai 400 088, Maharashtra, India
Phone: 91 22 25563289
Fax: 91 22 25562912
Publications: Indian Journal of Social Work (45388)

Reto Muller
Oberer Burghaldenweg 22
CH-4410 Liestal, Switzerland
Publications: Organic Chemistry Highlights (51207)

Multi-Science Publishing Company Ltd.
5 Wates Way
Brentwood CM15 9TB, United Kingdom
Phone: 44 12 77224632
Fax: 44 12 77223453
Publications: Acoustics Abstracts (52564) • Adsorption Science & Technology (52565) • Advances in Structural Engineering (52566) • Biomass Bulletin (52567) • Building Acoustics (52569) • Energy and Environment (52572) • Energy Exploration & Exploitation (52573) • International Journal of Aeroacoustics (52575) • International Journal of Aerospace Innovations (44963) • International Journal of Architectural Computing (52576) • International Journal of Emerging and Multidisciplinary Fluid Science (45394) • International Journal of Innovation Science (52577) • International Journal of Space Structures (52578) • International Journal of Spray and Combustion Dynamics (45042) • The Journal of Computational Multiphase Flows (52579) • Journal of Low Frequency Noise, Vibration & Active Control (52580) • Low Frequency Noise, Vibration and Active Control (52581) • Noise Notes (52582) • Noise & Vibration Bulletin (52583) • Noise & Vibration in Industry (52584) • Noise & Vibration Worldwide (52585) • Rare Earth Bulletin (52587) • Renewable Energy Bulletin (52588) • Wind Engineering (52590) • Wind Engineering Abstracts (52591)

Multiple Sclerosis Society of Great Britain and Northern Ireland
MS National Centre
372 Edgware Rd.
London NW2 6ND, United Kingdom
Phone: 44 20 84380700
Fax: 44 20 84380701
Publications: MS Matters (54959)

Mundipress S.L.
San Ambrosio, 6 bajo
E-28011 Madrid, Spain
Phone: 34 91 3655700
Fax: 34 91 3662682
Publications: Revista del Calzado (50796)

Mundo Recambio y Taller
Paris 150 4b 3a
E-08036 Barcelona, Spain
Phone: 34 934 395564
Fax: 34 934 306853
Publications: Mundo Recambio y Taller (Spares and Workshop World) (50689)

Munster Express
37 The Quay
Waterford, Waterford, Ireland
Phone: 353 51 872141
Publications: Munster Express (46062)

Murdoch University
90 South St.
Murdoch, Western Australia 6150, Australia
Phone: 61 893 602393
Fax: 61 893 606571
Publications: Intersections (42137)

D.J. Murphy (Publishers) Ltd.
Headley House
Headley Rd.
Grayshott GU26 6TU, United Kingdom
Phone: 44 14 28601020
Fax: 44 14 28601030
Publications: Horse & Rider (53480) • Pony Magazine (53481)

Muscat Press and Publishing House
PO Box 770
Ruwi
Muscat 112, Oman
Phone: 968 24811953
Fax: 968 24813153
Publications: Times of Oman (49225)

Museu de Ciencies Naturals de la Ciutadella, Museu de Zoologia
Parc de la Ciutadella, s/n
E-08003 Barcelona, Spain
Phone: 34 93 2562200

Fax: 34 933 104999
Publications: Arxus de Miscel-lania Zoologica (50651)

Museum national d'Histoire naturelle
57 rue Cuvier
F-75005 Paris Cedex 05, France
Phone: 33 014 0794856
Fax: 33 014 0793858
Publications: Adansonia (44022)

Music Farm Ltd.
1-3 Love Ln.
London SE18 6QT, United Kingdom
Phone: 44 20 88547217
Fax: 44 30 99666370
Publications: Country Music People (54276)

Music (Scotland) Ltd.
11 Lynedoch Pl.
Glasgow G3 6AB, United Kingdom
Phone: 44 14 13531118
Fax: 44 14 13531448
Publications: M8 Magazine (53430)

Musica e Dischi
Via. de Amicis 47
I-20123 Milan, Italy
Phone: 39 02 89402837
Fax: 39 02 8323843
Publications: M&D/Musica e Dischi (46186)

Musical Opinion Ltd.
1 Exford Rd.
London SE12 9HD, United Kingdom
Phone: 44 14 24855544
Fax: 44 14 24863686
Publications: Musical Opinion (54965)

Musical Stages Ltd.
PO Box 8365
London W14 0GL, United Kingdom
Phone: 44 20 76032227
Fax: 44 20 76032227
Publications: Musical Stages (54966)

Musical Times Publications Ltd.
7 Brunswick Mews
Hove BN3 1HD, United Kingdom
Phone: 44 1442 879097
Fax: 44 1442 872279
Publications: Musical Times (53611)

Musical Traditions
c/o Rod Stradling
1 Castle St.
Stroud GL5 2HP, United Kingdom
Phone: 44 1453 759475
Publications: Musical Traditions (56647)

Muslim Association for the Advancement of Science
Darul Fikr
The Main Rd., Iqra Colony
New Sir Sayyed Nagar
Aligarh 202 002, Uttar Pradesh, India
Phone: 91 571 3290443
Publications: MAAS Journal of Islamic Science (44918)

MyHobbyStore Ltd.
Hadlow House
9 High St.
Orpington BR6 6BG, United Kingdom
Phone: 44 844 4122262
Publications: Gardens Monthly (55851) • Popular Patchwork (55855)

MysoreSamachar
Samachar Bldg. No. 49, 1st Fl.
Devaraj Urs Rd.
Mysore 570 001, Karnataka, India
Phone: 91 821 2423574
Publications: Samachar (45459)

Mythic Society
Nrupatunga Rd.
Bangalore 560 001, Karnataka, India
Phone: 91 80 2215034
Publications: Quarterly Journal of the Mythic Society (44984)

MYU
1-23-3-303 Sendagi
Bunkyo-ku
Tokyo 113-0022, Japan

Phone: 81 3 38227374
Fax: 81 3 38278547
Publications: Sensors and Materials (47036)

Nagasaki University
Sakamoto 1-12-4
Nagasaki-shi
Nagasaki 852-8523, Japan
Phone: 81 95 8497000
Fax: 81 95 8497166
Publications: Acta Medica Nagasakiensia (46545)

Nagoya University
Furo-cho, Chikusa-ku
Nagoya 464-8601, Japan
Phone: 81 52 7895111
Publications: Nagoya Mathematical Journal (46556)

Naidunia News & Networks Pvt. Ltd.
60/1, Babu Labhchand Chhajlani Marg
Indore 452 009, Madhya Pradesh, India
Phone: 91 731 2763111-14
Fax: 91 731 2763118-120
Publications: Naidunia (45188)

The Namibia Economist
7 Schuster St.
PO Box 49
Windhoek 9000, Namibia
Phone: 264 612 21925
Fax: 264 612 20615
Publications: The Namibia Economist (47823)

The Namibian
42 John Meinert St.
PO Box 20783
Windhoek, Namibia
Phone: 264 612 79660
Fax: 264 612 79602
Publications: The Namibian Newspaper (47824)

The Nanyang Chronicle
School of Communication & Information
Nanyang Technological University
31 Nanyang Link
Singapore 639798, Singapore
Phone: 65 679 06446
Fax: 65 6794 0096
Publications: Digital Nanyang Chronicle (50133)

Nanyang Technological University
50 Nanyang Ave.
Singapore 639798, Singapore
Phone: 65 67911744
Fax: 65 67911604
Publications: NTU (50228)

Nanzan Institute for Religion and Culture
Nanzan University
18 Yamazato-cho
Showa-ku
Nagoya 466-8673, Japan
Phone: 81 52 8323111
Fax: 81 52 8336157
Publications: Japanese Journal of Religious Studies (46553)

Nanzan University
18 Yamazato-cho
Showa-ku
Nagoya-shi
Nagoya 466-8673, Japan
Phone: 81 52 8323111
Fax: 81 52 8336985
Publications: Nanzan Review of American Studies (46557)

The Nassau Guardian
PO Box N-3011
Nassau, Bahamas
Phone: 242302-2300
Publications: The Nassau Guardian (42784)

Natal Sharks Board
PO Box 2
Umhlanga 4320, Republic of South Africa
Phone: 27 315 660400
Fax: 27 315 660499
Publications: African Journal of Marine Science (50640)

Nation Media Group
Nation Center, Kimathi St.
PO Box 49010

Nairobi, Kenya
Publications: Daily Nation (Kenya) (47176) • The East African (47178)

Nation Multimedia Group
1854 Bangna-Trat Rd.
Bangna
Bangkok 10260, Thailand
Phone: 66 233 83333
Fax: 66 233 83334
Publications: The Nation (51428)

National Aquatic Resources Research Development Agency
Crow Island
Colombo 01500, Sri Lanka
Phone: 94 112 521000
Fax: 94 112 521932
Publications: Journal of the National Aquatic Resources Research & Development Agency of Sri Lanka (50856)

National Assembly of Women
92 Wansbeck Ave.
Cullercoats
Tyne and Wear
North Tyneside NE30 3DJ, United Kingdom
Phone: 44 191 2520961
Publications: SISTERS (Sisterhood and International Solidarity to End Racism and Sexism) (55705)

National Association of Adult Education
2nd Fl., 83-87 Main St.
Ranelagh
Dublin IRL-6, Dublin, Ireland
Phone: 353 1 4068220
Fax: 353 1 4068227
Publications: Adult Learner (45943)

National Association for Clean Air
PO Box 8370
Halfway House 1685, Republic of South Africa
Phone: 27 71 6839770
Fax: 27 11 8057010
Publications: Clean Air Journal (50520)

National Association for Educational Guidance for Adults
c/o Meeting Makers Ltd.
Crawfurd Bldg.
Jordanhill Campus
76 Southbrae Dr.
Glasgow G13 1PP, United Kingdom
Phone: 44 141 4341500
Fax: 44 141 4341519
Publications: News and Views (53434)

National Association of Estate Agents
Arbon House
6 Tournament Ct.
Edgehill Dr.
Warwick CV34 6LG, United Kingdom
Phone: 44 19 26496800
Fax: 44 19 26400953
Publications: The Estate Agent (56854)

National Association of Flower Arrangement Societies
Osborne House
12 Devonshire Sq.
London EC2M 4TE, United Kingdom
Phone: 44 20 72475567
Fax: 44 20 72477232
Publications: The Flower Arranger (54468)

National Association of Funeral Directors
618 Warwick Rd.
Solihull B91 1AA, United Kingdom
Phone: 44 12 17111343
Fax: 44 12 17111351
Publications: Funeral Director Monthly (56563)

National Association of the Launderette Industry
146 Welling Way
Welling DA16 2RS, United Kingdom
Phone: 44 20 88569798
Fax: 44 20 88569394
Publications: Launderette and Cleaning World (56878)

National Association of Local Councils
109 Great Russell St.
London WC1B 3LD, United Kingdom
Phone: 44 20 76371865

Fax: 44 20 74367451
Publications: LCR (54858)

National Association for Pastoral Care in Education
PO Box 6005
Nuneaton CVII 9GY, United Kingdom
Phone: 44 24 76765639
Fax: 44 24 76765639
Publications: Pastoral Care in Education (55777)

National Association of Special Educational Needs
NASEN House
4/5 Amber Business Village
Amber Close
Amington
Tamworth B77 4RP, United Kingdom
Phone: 44 18 27311500
Fax: 44 18 27313005
Publications: British Journal of Special Education (56717) • Special! (56718) • Support for Learning (55714)

National Association of Swedish Handicraft Societies
Kungsgatan 51
SE-903 26 Umea, Sweden
Phone: 46 90 718302
Fax: 46 90 718305
Publications: Hemslojden (51045)

National Association for Teaching English and other Community Languages to Adults
South Birmingham College
Hall Green Campus
Cole Bank Rd.
Rm. HA205
Birmingham B28 8ES, United Kingdom
Phone: 44 12 16888121
Fax: 44 12 16945062
Publications: Language Issues (52357)

National Association of Woodturners New Zealand Inc.
c/o Mark von Dadelszen, Pres.
25 Muritai Cres.
Hasting
Havelock North 4130, New Zealand
Phone: 6 8778136
Fax: 6 8778174
Publications: Creative Wood (49005)

National Autistic Society
393 City Rd.
London EC1V 1NG, United Kingdom
Phone: 44 20 78332299
Fax: 44 20 78339666
Publications: Communication (54245)

National Caravan Council
Catherine House
Victoria Rd.
Aldershot GU11 1SS, United Kingdom
Phone: 44 12 52318251
Fax: 44 12 52322596
Publications: The Business (52007)

National Christian Council of Japan
Karasuma-Shimotachiuri
Kamikyo-ku
Kyoto 602-8011, Japan
Phone: 81 75 4321945
Publications: Japanese Religions (46475)

National Cooperative Union of India
3 Siri Institutional Area
August Kranti Marg
New Delhi 110 016, Delhi, India
Phone: 91 11 26861472
Fax: 91 11 26863248
Publications: Cooperator (45500) • Indian Cooperative Review (45536)

National Council of Applied Economic Research
Parisila Bhawan
11 Indraprastha Estate
New Delhi 110 002, Delhi, India
Phone: 91 11 23379861
Fax: 91 11 23370164
Publications: Artha Suchi (45484) • Margin (45623)

National Council for the Conservation of Plants and Gardens
12 Home Farm
Loseley Pk.
Guildford GU3 1HS, United Kingdom
Phone: 44 1483 447540
Fax: 44 1483 458933
Publications: Plant Heritage (53494)

National Council of Educational Research and Training
Sri Aurbindo Marg
New Delhi 110 016, Delhi, India
Phone: 91 112 6560620
Fax: 91 112 6868419
Publications: Indian Educational Review (45541) • Journal of Indian Education (45602) • School Science (45647)

National Council for Scientific Research - Lebanon
PO Box 11-8281
Riad El-Solh 1107
59, Zahia Selman St.
Beirut, Lebanon
Phone: 961 1850 125
Fax: 961 1822 639
Publications: Lebanese Science Journal (47398)

National Council for Voluntary Organisations
Regent's Wharf
8 All Saints St.
London N1 9RL, United Kingdom
Phone: 44 20 77136161
Fax: 44 20 77136300
Publications: Voluntary Sector (55375)

National Deaf Children's Society
15 Dufferin St.
London EC1Y 8UR, United Kingdom
Phone: 44 20 74908656
Fax: 44 20 72515020
Publications: Talk (55290)

National Drama Publications
Diorama Arts
34 Osnaburch St.
London NW1 3ND, United Kingdom
Publications: Drama Magazine (54342)

National Eczema Society
Hill House
Highgate Hill
London N19 5NA, United Kingdom
Phone: 44 20 72813553
Publications: Exchange (54416)

National Environmental Engineering Research Institute
Nehru Marg
Nagpur 440 020, Maharashtra, India
Phone: 91 712 2249885
Fax: 91 712 2249900
Publications: Indian Literature in Environmental Engineering (45466) • Journal of Environmental Science and Engineering (45468)

National Farmers' Union
Agriculture House
Stoneleigh Pk.
Warwickshire
Stoneleigh CV8 2TZ, United Kingdom
Phone: 44 24 76858500
Fax: 44 24 76858501
Publications: NFU Countryside (56636)

National Federation of Demolition Contractors
Resurgam House
Paradise
Herts
Hemel Hempstead HP2 4TF, United Kingdom
Phone: 44 1442 217144
Fax: 44 1442 218268
Publications: Demolition and Dismantling (53556)

National Federation of Retail Newsagents
Yeoman House
Sekforde St.
London EC1R 0HF, United Kingdom
Phone: 44 20 72534225
Fax: 44 20 72500927
Publications: Retail Newsagent (55195)

National Indigenous Times
66 Fitchett St.
Garran, Australian Capital Territory 2605, Australia
Publications: National Indigenous Times (41877)

National Information Centre for Textile and Allied Subjects
c/o ATIRA
PO Box Ambawadi Vistar
Ahmedabad 380 015, Gujarat, India
Phone: 91 79 26307921
Fax: 91 79 26304677
Publications: Texincon (44910)

National Inquiry Services Centre (Pty.) Ltd.
1 Dundas St.
PO Box 377
Grahamstown 6140, Republic of South Africa
Phone: 27 466 229698
Fax: 27 466 229550
Publications: African Journal of AIDS Research (50486) • African Journal of Aquatic Science (50564) • Ostrich (50509)

National Institute of Adult Continuing Education
Renaissance House
20 Princess Rd. W
Leicester LE1 6TP, United Kingdom
Phone: 44 116 2044200
Fax: 44 116 2044201
Publications: Adults Learning (53782) • Studies in the Education of Adults (53828)

National Institute of Bank Management
NIBM Post Office
Kondhwe Khurd
Pune 411 048, Maharashtra, India
Phone: 91 20 26833080
Fax: 91 20 26834478
Publications: Prajnan (Pune) (45699)

National Institute of Development Administration
118 Moo3, Sereethai Rd.
Khwaeng Klong-Chan
Khet Bangkapi
Bangkok 10240, Thailand
Phone: 66 2 7273000
Fax: 66 2 3758798
Publications: Thai Journal of Development Administration (51439)

National Institute of Educational Planning and Administration
17-B Sri Aurobindo Marg
New Delhi 110 016, Delhi, India
Phone: 91 112 6863562
Fax: 91 112 6853041
Publications: Journal of Educational Planning and Administration (45596)

National Institute of Health and Family Welfare
Baba Gang Nath Marg
Munirka
New Delhi 110 067, Delhi, India
Phone: 91 11 26165959
Fax: 91 11 26101623
Publications: Health and Population (45522)

National Institute of Industrial Health
6-21-1, Nagao
Tama-ku
Kawasaki 214-8585, Japan
Phone: 81 44 8656111
Fax: 81 44 8656116
Publications: Industrial Health (46421)

National Institute of Infectious Diseases
Toyama 1-23-1
Shinjuku-ku
Tokyo 162-8640, Japan
Phone: 81 3 52851111
Fax: 81 3 52851150
Publications: Japanese Journal of Infectious Diseases (46869)

National Institute of Medical Herbalists
Elm House
54 Mary Arches St.
Exeter EX4 3BA, United Kingdom
Phone: 44 13 92426022

Fax: 44 13 92498963
Publications: European Journal of Herbal Medicine (53353)

National Institute of Nutrition
Indian Council of Medical Research
Jamai-Osmania
Hyderabad 500 007, Andhra Pradesh, India
Phone: 91 40 27008921
Fax: 91 40 27019074
Publications: Nutrition (45178)

National Institute of Personnel Management
3 Fl., Tower Block 1582
Rajdanga Main Rd.
Kolkata 700 107, West Bengal, India
Phone: 91 33 24417253
Fax: 91 33 24417256
Publications: Personnel Today (45301)

National Institute of Polar Research
10-3 Midoricho
Tachikawa
Tokyo 190-8518, Japan
Phone: 81 42 5120608
Fax: 81 42 5283146
Publications: Antarctic Record (46742) • Polar Bioscience (47020)

National Institute of Science Communication
Dr. K.S. Krishnan Marg Pusa Campus
New Delhi 110 012, Delhi, India
Phone: 91 11 25841647
Fax: 91 11 25847062
Publications: Medicinal and Aromatic Plants Abstracts (45626)

National Institute of Science Communication and Information Resources
Dr. K S Krishnan Marg
Pusa Campus
New Delhi 110 012, Delhi, India
Phone: 91 11 25841647
Fax: 91 11 25847062
Publications: Journal of Scientific and Industrial Research (45617)

National Institute of Science and Information Resources
Anusandhan Bhawan
2 Rafi Marg
New Delhi 110001, Delhi, India
Phone: 91 11 23710340
Fax: 91 11 23320932
Publications: Indian Journal of Fibre & Textile Research (45553) • Indian Journal of Marine Sciences (45558) • Indian Journal of Radio & Space Physics (45566)

National Library of Australia
Parkes Pl.
Parkes, Australian Capital Territory 2600, Australia
Phone: 61 2 62621111
Fax: 61 2 62571703
Publications: National Library of Australia Gateways (42229)

The National Library of Wales
Aberystwyth
Ceredigion SY23 3BU, United Kingdom
Phone: 44 19 70632800
Fax: 44 19 70615709
Publications: Cylchgrawn Llyfrgell Genedlaethol Cymru (52954)

National Magazine Company Ltd.
72 Broadwick St.
London W1F 9EP, United Kingdom
Phone: 44 20 74395000
Publications: You & Your Wedding (55433)

National Museum, Bloemfontein
PO Box 266
Bloemfontein 9300, Republic of South Africa
Phone: 27 514 479609
Fax: 27 514 476273
Publications: Navorsinge van die Nasionale Musium, Bloemfontein (50355)

National Olympic Committee for Germany
Otto-Fleck-Schneise 12
D-60528 Frankfurt am Main, Germany
Phone: 49 69 67000

Fax: 49 69 674906
Publications: Olympisches Feuer (44367)

National Organization of Battered Women's Shelters in Sweden
Hornsgatan 66
S-118 21 Stockholm, Sweden
Phone: 46 8 4429930
Fax: 46 8 6127325
Publications: Kvinnotryck (51024)

National Organization of Restoring Men - UK
PO Box 71
Stone ST15 OSF, United Kingdom
Phone: 44 1785 814044
Publications: NORM News (56634)

National Pest Technicians Association
NPTA House, Hall Ln., Kinoulton
Nottingham NG12 3EF, United Kingdom
Phone: 44 115 194981133
Fax: 44 115 1949823905
Publications: Today's Technician (55773)

National Productivity Council
Utpadakta Bhawan, 5-6 Institutional Area
Lodhi Rd.
New Delhi 110 003, Delhi, India
Phone: 91 112 4690331
Fax: 91 112 4615002
Publications: Energy Management (45509) • Productivity (45638) • Productivity News (45639)

National Research Council of the Philippines
General Santos Ave.
Bicutan
Taguig City, Philippines
Phone: 63 2 8378142
Fax: 63 2 8390275
Publications: NRCD Research Journal of the Philippines (49639)

National Research Development Corporation
20-22 Zamroodpur Community Ctr.
Kailash Colony Ext.
New Delhi 110 048, Delhi, India
Phone: 91 11 29240410
Fax: 91 11 29230506
Publications: Invention Intelligence (45590)

National Safety Council of Australia
Bldg. 4, Brandon Office Pk.
540 Srpingvale Rd.
Glen Waverley, Victoria 3150, Australia
Phone: 61 385 621555
Fax: 61 385 621590
Publications: National Safety (41896)

National School Sailing Association
4 Green Moss
Oakthwaite Rd.
Windermere LA23 2BB, United Kingdom
Publications: School Sailing Matters (56931)

National Science Foundation of Sri Lanka
47/5 Maitland Pl.
Colombo 00700, Sri Lanka
Phone: 94 112 696771
Fax: 94 112 694754
Publications: Journal of the National Science Foundation (50857) • Sri Lanka Journal of Social Sciences (50867)

National Sheep Association
The Sheep Centre
Malvern WR13 6PH, United Kingdom
Phone: 44 16 84892661
Fax: 44 16 84892663
Publications: The Sheep Farmer (55540)

National Society for Education in Art and Design
3 Masons Wharf
Potley Ln.
Wiltshire
Corsham SN13 9FY, United Kingdom
Phone: 44 12 25810134
Fax: 44 12 25812730
Publications: International Journal of Art & Design Education (53066)

National Space Society of Australia
GPO Box 7048
Sydney, New South Wales 2001, Australia

Phone: 61 291 504553
Publications: Ad Astra (42446)

National Spiritual Assembly of the Baha'is of the UK
27 Rutland Gate
London SW7 1PD, United Kingdom
Phone: 44 20 75842566
Fax: 44 20 75849402
Publications: UK Baha'i Journal (55353)

National Statistics Office
Ramon Magsaysay Blvd.
Box 779
Sta. Mesa
Manila 1008, Philippines
Phone: 63 2 7160807
Fax: 63 2 7156503
Publications: Journal of Philippine Statistics (49550)

National Taiwan University
No. 1, Sec. 4, Roosevelt Rd.
Taipei 107, Taiwan
Phone: 886 23 3664187
Fax: 886 22 3622005
Publications: Acta Zoologica Taiwanica (51330)

National Taiwan University
No. 1, Section 4, Roosevelt Rd.
Taipei 10617, Taiwan
Phone: 886 2 33663366
Fax: 886 2 23627651
Publications: Journal of Geographical Science (51353)

National Taiwan University
6th Fl., Shih-liang Hall
1, Sec. 4, Roosevelt Rd.
Taipei 106 ROC, Taiwan
Phone: 886 2 33664187
Fax: 886 2 23622005
Publications: Acta Oceanographica Taiwanica (51328)

National Tertiary Education Union
PO Box 1323
South Melbourne, Victoria 3205, Australia
Phone: 61 392 541910
Fax: 61 392 541915
Publications: Advocate (42365) • Australian Universities Review (42368) • Frontline (42371)

National Tuberculosis Institute—India
No. 8 Bellary Rd.
Bangalore 560 003, Karnataka, India
Phone: 91 80 3441192
Fax: 91 80 3440952
Publications: NTI Bulletin (44979)

National Union of Journalists - England
Headland House
308-312 Gray's Inn Rd.
London WC1X 8DP, United Kingdom
Phone: 44 20 72787916
Fax: 44 20 78378143
Publications: Journalist (54840)

National Union of Knitwear, Footwear & Apparel Trades
55 New Walk
Leicester LE1 7EB, United Kingdom
Phone: 44 116 2556703
Publications: KFAT News (53808)

National Union of Rail, Maritime and Transport Workers
Unity House
39 Chalton St.
London NW1 1JD, United Kingdom
Phone: 44 20 73874771
Fax: 44 20 73874123
Publications: RMT News (55206)

National University Of Ireland
49 Merrion Sq.
Dublin 2, Dublin, Ireland
Phone: 353 1 4392424
Fax: 353 1 4392466
Publications: Eigse (45954)

National University of Singapore
21 Lower Kent Ridge Rd.
Singapore 119077, Singapore
Phone: 65 6516 6666
Fax: 65 6775 9330
Publications: Biomolecular Frontiers (50116) • China

(50119) • The Dental Mirror (50131) • Journal of Chinese Overseas (50201) • NUS Economic Journal (50229) • Singapore Journal of Legal Studies (50256) • Singapore Law Review (50258) • Singapore National Academy of Science Journal (50261)

National Veterinary Research Institute
Al. Partyzantow 57
24-100 Pulawy, Poland
Phone: 48 81 8893000
Fax: 48 81 8862595
Publications: The Bulletin of the Veterinary Institute in Pulawy (49674)

National Youth Agency
Eastgate House
19-23 Humberstone Rd.
Leicester LE5 3GJ, United Kingdom
Phone: 44 116 2427350
Fax: 44 116 2427444
Publications: The Edge (53796) • Young People Now (53834) • Youth Policy Update (53835)

Nationwide Group Staff Union
Middleton Farmhouse
37 Main Rd.
Oxfordshire
Middleton Cheney OX17 2QT, United Kingdom
Phone: 44 12 95710767
Fax: 44 12 95712580
Publications: Rapport (55623)

Nationwide News Proprietary Ltd.
PO Box 4245
Sydney, New South Wales 2001, Australia
Phone: 61 2 92883000
Fax: 61 2 92882250
Publications: Australian (42450)

Natsiyanal'naya Akademiya Navuk Belarusi (National Academy of Sciences of Belarus)
66 Independence Ave.
BY-220072 Minsk, Belarus
Phone: 375 17 2841801
Fax: 375 17 2842816
Publications: Computational Methods in Applied Mathematics (42832)

Natural Leisure Ltd.
PO Box 196
Ramsgate CT11 9GG, United Kingdom
Phone: 44 1843 570381
Publications: Bonjour! (56308)

Natural Remedies Private Ltd.
Plot No.5B Veerasandra Indl. Area
19 K.M. Stone, Hosur Rd.
Bangalore 560 100, Karnataka, India
Phone: 91 804 1859999
Fax: 91 804 0209817
Publications: Journal of Natural Remedies (44975)

Nature Kenya
PO Box 44486
Nairobi, Kenya
Phone: 259 420 3749957
Publications: Journal of East African Natural History (50632) • Scopus (47196)

Nature Publishing Group
Brunel Rd.
Houndmills
Basingstoke RG21 6XS, United Kingdom
Phone: 44 12 56329242
Fax: 44 12 56842754
Publications: Clinical Pharmacology and Therapeutics (52198) • European Journal of Clinical Nutrition (52200) • EYE (52203) • International Journal of Obesity (52211) • Molecular Therapy (52224) • Prostate Cancer and Prostatic Diseases (55144)

Nature Publishing Group
The Macmillan Bldg.
4 Crinan St.
London N1 9XW, United Kingdom
Phone: 44 20 78334000
Fax: 44 20 78434640
Publications: Acta Pharmacologica Sinica (53895) • Asian Journal of Andrology (53975) • BDJ British Dental Journal (54007) • Cell Death & Differentiation (54191) • EMBO Reports (54362) • Evidence-Based Dentistry (EBD) (54414) • Gene Therapy (54499) • Journal of Exposure Science and Environmental Epidemiology (JE-

SEE) (54750) • Journal of Human Genetics (46906) • Journal of Human Hypertension (54763) • Molecular Psychiatry (54948) • Molecular Systems Biology (54949) • Nature Cell Biology (54971) • Nature Materials (54972) • Nature Methods (54973) • Nature Physics (54974) • Nature Reviews Cancer (54975) • Nature Reviews Cardiology (54976) • Nature Reviews Clinical Oncology (54977) • Nature Reviews Drug Discovery (54978) • Nature Reviews Gastroenterology & Hepatology (54979) • Nature Reviews Genetics (54980) • Nature Reviews Immunology (54981) • Nature Reviews Microbiology (54982) • Nature Reviews Molecular Cell Biology (54983) • Nature Reviews Neuroscience (54984) • Nature Reviews Urology (54985) • Oncogene (55032) • The Pharmacogenomics Journal (55078) • Vital (55374)

Nature Publishing Group
75 Varick St., 9th Fl.
New York, NY 10013-1917
Phone: 212726-9200
Fax: 212696-9006
Free: 888331-6288
Publications: Journal of Cerebral Blood Flow and Metabolism (44204) • Leukemia (44068)

Nature Society (Singapore, Singapore)
510 Geylang Rd.
No. 02-05, The Sunflower
Singapore 389466, Singapore
Phone: 65 6741 2036
Fax: 65 6741 0871
Publications: Nature Watch (50225)

Nautical Institute
202 Lambeth Rd.
London SE1 7LQ, United Kingdom
Phone: 44 207 9281351
Fax: 44 207 4012817
Publications: Seaways (55225)

Naval Historical Collectors and Research Association
9 Lyngate Gardens
Lyngate Rd.
N Walsham
Norfolk NR28 0NE, United Kingdom
Publications: The Review (55703)

Navhind Papers & Publication Ltd.
Navhind Bhavan
Panaji 403 001, Goa Daman and Diu, India
Publications: The Navhind Times (45681)

Navy News
HMS Nelson
Queen St.
Portsmouth PO1 3HH, United Kingdom
Phone: 44 23 92725061
Publications: Navy News (56291)

Neagari Press
Plz. Fray Luis Colomer, 3-Entlo. B
E-46021 Valencia, Spain
Phone: 34 902 131331
Fax: 34 963 610673
Publications: Bonsai Autoctono (50843)

NEC Creative Ltd.
29-11 Shiba 5-Chome
Minato-Ku
Tokyo 108-0014, Japan
Phone: 81 3 54764079
Publications: NEC Journal of Advanced Technology (46976) • NEC Technical Journal (46977)

Neckar-Verlag GmbH
Klosterring 1
D-78050 Villingen-Schwenningen, Germany
Phone: 49 772 189870
Fax: 49 772 1898750
Publications: Modell (44699)

Nederlandse Maatschappij tot bevordering der Tandheelkunde
Postbus 2000
NL-3430 CA Nieuwegein, Netherlands
Phone: 31 306076276
Fax: 31 306048994
Publications: Nederlands Tandartsenblad (48741)

Nederlandse Vegetariersbond
Nieuwezijds Voorburgwal 153

NL-1012 RK Amsterdam, Netherlands
Phone: 31 20 3300044
Fax: 31 20 4203737
Publications: Leven (48136)

Nelson Mandela Metropolitan University
PO Box 77000
Port Elizabeth 6031, Republic of South Africa
Phone: 27 41 5042593
Fax: 27 41 5042574
Publications: Obiter (50578)

Nenagh Guardian
13 Summerhill
Nenagh, Tipperary, Ireland
Phone: 353 673 1214
Fax: 353 673 3401
Publications: Nenagh Guardian (46047)

The Nencki Institute Of Experimental Biology
3 Pasteur St.
PL-02-093 Warsaw, Poland
Phone: 48 226 598571
Fax: 48 228 225342
Publications: Acta Neurobiologiae Experimentalis (49680) • Acta Protozoologica (49682)

Nepal Agricultural Research Council
PO Box 5459
Kathmandu, Nepal
Phone: 977 14 256837
Fax: 977 14 262500
Publications: Nepal Agriculture Research Journal (47842)

Nepal Dental Association
PO Box 21506
Nagpokhari
Kathmandu, Nepal
Phone: 977 1 2120450
Publications: Journal of the Nepal Dental Association (47838)

Nepal Forum for Environmental Journalists
Thapathali
PO Box 5143
Kathmandu, Nepal
Phone: 97 714 261991
Publications: Aankhijhyal (47836)

Nepal Medical Association
Siddhi Sadan
Exhibition Rd.
PO Box 189
Kathmandu, Nepal
Phone: 977 14 225860
Fax: 977 14 225300
Publications: Journal of the Nepal Medical Association (47839)

Netherlands Institute of Human Rights
Janskerkhof 3
NL-3512 BK Utrecht, Netherlands
Publications: Netherlands Quarterly of Human Rights (48764)

Netherlands Institute for Southern Africa
Postbus 10707
NL-1001 ES Amsterdam, Netherlands
Phone: 31 205 206210
Fax: 31 205 206249
Publications: Zuidelyk Afrika (48274)

Netherlands Royal Society for Agricultural Sciences
PO Box 79
NL-6700 AB Wageningen, Netherlands
Phone: 31 317 455191
Fax: 31 317 483976
Publications: NJAS (48772)

Netherlands Society for Jewish Genealogy
PO Box 94703
NL-1090 GS Amsterdam, Netherlands
Publications: Misjpoge (48160)

The Network University
Nijnburg 2a
NL-1081 GG Amsterdam, Netherlands
Phone: 31 205 040008
Fax: 31 204 420977
Publications: Tailoring Biotechnologies (48240)

Neurological Society of India
c/o Dr. B.S. Sharma
Dept. of Neurosurgery
Neurosciences Centre, All India Institute of Medical Science
New Delhi 110 029, Delhi, India
Phone: 91 11 26593291
Publications: Neurology India (45630)

New Cicada Press
40-11 Kubo
Date-gun
Hobara-machi
Fukushima 960-0602, Japan
Publications: New Cicada (46355)

New Concept Group Ltd.
60 Churchill Sq.
Kings Hill
West Malling ME19 4YU, United Kingdom
Phone: 44 17 32878800
Fax: 44 17 32878801
Publications: Mortgage Matters (56893) • Your New Home (56895)

New Consumer Ltd.
1-5 Wandsworth Rd.
London SW8 2LN, United Kingdom
Phone: 44 20 75263314
Publications: New Consumer (54990)

New Economics Foundation
3 Jonathan St.
London SE11 5NH, United Kingdom
Phone: 44 20 78206300
Fax: 44 20 78206301
Publications: Radical Economics (55169)

New Hall Publications Ltd.
New Hall Ln.
Wirral
Hoylake CH47 4BQ, United Kingdom
Phone: 44 870 7453004
Fax: 44 844 5458103
Publications: Candis (53614)

New Internationalist
Tower House
Lathkill St.
Market Harborough LE16 9EF, United Kingdom
Phone: 44 1858 438896
Fax: 44 1858 461739
Publications: New Internationalist (56117)

New Japan Sewing Machine News Ltd.
2nd Fl., Kosumo Bldg.
8-5 Sugamo 1-chome
Toshima-ku
Tokyo 170-0002, Japan
Phone: 81 3 39422574
Fax: 81 3 39421827
Publications: Apparel Production News (46744)

New Left Review
6 Meard St.
London W1F 0EG, United Kingdom
Phone: 44 20 77348830
Fax: 44 20 74393869
Publications: New Left Review (54993)

New Life Publishing Co.
PO Box 777
Nottingham NG11 6ZZ, United Kingdom
Phone: 44 115 8240777
Publications: Direction (55753)

New Sabah Times
PO Box 15141
Kota Kinabalu
88861 Sabah, Malaysia
Phone: 60 882 30055
Fax: 60 882 41155
Publications: New Sabah Times (47709)

New Start
Centre for Local Economic Strategies
Express Networks
One George Leigh St.
Manchester M4 5DL, United Kingdom
Phone: 44 114 2816130
Publications: New Start (55573)

New Statesman Ltd.
Boundary House, 1st Fl.

91-93 Charterhouse St.
London EC1M 6HR, United Kingdom
Phone: 44 20 77303444
Fax: 44 20 72590181
Publications: New Statesman (54999)

The New Straits Times Press (Malaysia) Bhd.
Balai Berita
31 Jalan Riong
59100 Kuala Lumpur, Malaysia
Phone: 60 322 823131
Fax: 60 322 821428
Publications: Business Times (47601) • New Straits Times (47630) • New Sunday Times (47631) • Tech & U (47637)

New Testament Society of South Africa
School of Religion & Theology
University of KwaZulu-Natal
PO Box X01
Scottsville 3209, Republic of South Africa
Publications: Neotestamentica (50629)

New Wave Publishing
Hesketh House, 1st Fl.
3 School Rd.
Sale M33 7XY, United Kingdom
Phone: 44 16 13745615
Fax: 44 16 13746436
Publications: Industrial Technology (56755)

The New Writer
PO Box 60
Cranbrook TN17 2ZR, United Kingdom
Phone: 44 15 80212626
Fax: 44 15 80212041
Publications: The New Writer (53096)

New Zealand Archaeological Association Inc.
PO Box 6337
Dunedin North 9059, New Zealand
Publications: Archaeology in New Zealand (48861) • Journal of Pacific Archaeology (48897)

New Zealand Association of Economists
97 Cuba St.
PO Box 568
Wellington, New Zealand
Phone: 64 4 8017139
Fax: 64 4 8017106
Publications: New Zealand Economic Papers (49018)

New Zealand Association for Gifted Children
PO Box 46
Waitomo Caves, New Zealand
Phone: 64 3 9601252
Publications: Apex (48908) • Tall Poppies (48993)

New Zealand Association of Radio Transmitters
19 Main St., Ste. 9
Upper Hutt 5018, New Zealand
Phone: 64 4 9392189
Fax: 64 4 9392190
Publications: Break In (48992)

New Zealand Association of Rationalists and Humanists
Rationalist House
64 Symonds St.
Auckland 1010, New Zealand
Phone: 64 9 3735131
Fax: 64 9 3798233
Publications: The Open Society (48828)

New Zealand Automobile Association
99 Albert St.
PO Box 5
Auckland, New Zealand
Phone: 64 996 68800
Fax: 64 996 68891
Publications: AA Directions (48783)

New Zealand Avocado Growers Association
Level 5, Harrington House
Harrington St.
PO Box 13267
Tauranga 3141, New Zealand
Phone: 64 7 5716147
Fax: 64 7 5716145
Publications: Avoscene (48980)

New Zealand Book Council
Level 7, Alan Burns Insurance House
69 Boulcott St.

Wellington 6011, New Zealand
Phone: 64 449 91569
Fax: 64 449 91424
Publications: Booknotes (49001)

New Zealand Camellia Society
c/o Mrs. V. Cave, Ed.
Seafield R.D. 4
Wanganui, New Zealand
Publications: New Zealand Camellia Bulletin (48995)

New Zealand College of Midwives
376 Manchester St.
Christchurch 8014, New Zealand
Phone: 64 3 3772732
Fax: 64 3 3775662
Publications: New Zealand College of Midwives (48873)

New Zealand Council for Educational Research
10th Fl., W Block, Education House
178-182 Willis St.
Wellington 6011, New Zealand
Phone: 64 438 47939
Fax: 64 438 47933
Publications: New Zealand Journal of Educational Studies (49024)

New Zealand Democratic Party
PO Box 18-907
New Brighton
Christchurch 8641, New Zealand
Phone: 64 3 3829544
Fax: 64 3 3829544
Publications: The Guardian (48867)

New Zealand Dental Association
PO Box 28084
Remuera
Auckland 1541, New Zealand
Phone: 64 9 579 8001
Fax: 64 9 580 0010
Publications: New Zealand Dental Journal (48808)

New Zealand Geographical Society Inc.
c/o School of Geography, Geology & Environmental Science
The University of Auckland
PO Box 92019
Auckland, New Zealand
Phone: 64 937 37599
Publications: New Zealand Geographer (48813) • New Zealand Journal of Geography (48816)

New Zealand Magazines Ltd.
Piccadilly House
74 New North Rd.
Eden Ter.
Auckland, New Zealand
Phone: 64 9 3090296
Publications: New Zealand Listener (48819)

New Zealand Mathematical Society
c/o Dr. Alex James, Sec.
Dept. of Mathematics & Statistics
University of Canterbury
Private Bag 4800
Christchurch 8140, New Zealand
Publications: New Zealand Journal of Mathematics (48874)

New Zealand Nurses Organization
PO Box 2128
Wellington 6140, New Zealand
Phone: 64 4 4999533
Fax: 64 4 3829993
Publications: Kai Tiaki (49013)

New Zealand Railway & Locomotive Society Inc.
PO Box 5134
Wellington 6145, New Zealand
Phone: 64 4 5684938
Fax: 64 4 5865554
Publications: The New Zealand Railway Observer (49030)

New Zealand Red Cross
L3 Red Cross House
69 Molesworth St.
Thorndon
Wellington 6038, New Zealand
Phone: 64 447 23750
Publications: Red Cross News (49032)

New Zealand Snowboarder
27 Seddon Cres.
Gisborne, New Zealand
Phone: 64 6 8687974
Fax: 64 6 8687971
Publications: New Zealand Snowboarder (48898)

New Zealand Society of Authors
PO Box 7701
Wellesley St.
Auckland 1141, New Zealand
Phone: 64 937 94801
Fax: 64 937 94801
Publications: New Zealand Author (48805)

New Zealand Society for Music Therapy
The Terrace
PO Box 10352
Wellington 6143, New Zealand
Publications: Journal (49010)

New Zealand Statistical Association
PO Box 1731
Wellington, New Zealand
Publications: Australian and New Zealand Journal of Statistics (49000)

New Zealand Veterinary Association
PO Box 11-212
Wellington, New Zealand
Phone: 64 4 4710484
Fax: 64 4 4710494
Publications: New Zealand Veterinary Journal (49031)

New Zealand Water and Wastes Association
PO Box 1316
Wellington 6140, New Zealand
Phone: 64 4 4728925
Fax: 64 4 4728926
Publications: Water and Wastes in New Zealand (49036)

Newcomen Society for the Study of the History of Engineering and Technology
The Science Museum
London SW7 2DD, United Kingdom
Phone: 44 20 73714445
Fax: 44 20 73714445
Publications: Transactions (55334)

News Corporation
3D Stefanias Ave.
Palea Penteli, Greece
Phone: 30 210 6136999
Fax: 30 210 6136899
Publications: New Europe (42868)

News Group Newspapers Ltd.
1 Virginia St.
Wapping
London E98 1SN, United Kingdom
Phone: 44 20 77824000
Publications: The Sun (Glasgow) (56838)

News Today Printers & Publishers Private Ltd.
15 Vellala St.
Kodambakkam
Chennai 600 024, Tamil Nadu, India
Publications: News Today (45054)

NewsAfrica
Ste. 16 Canon Wharf Business Ctr,
35 Evelyn St.
London SE8 5RT, United Kingdom
Phone: 44 20 73944030
Fax: 44 20 73948600
Publications: NewsAfrica (55004)

Newsquest (London)
Mega House
Crest View Dr.
Petts Wood
Orpington BR5 1BT, United Kingdom
Phone: 44 16 89836211
Fax: 44 16 89877823
Publications: Limited Edition (56867)

Newsquest Magazines
30 Cannon St.
London EC4M 6YJ, United Kingdom
Phone: 44 20 76183456
Publications: Classic Record Collector (54214)

Newsquest Media Group Ltd.
58 Church St.

Weybridge KT13 8DP, United Kingdom
Phone: 44 1932 821212
Fax: 44 1932 836164
Publications: Andover Advertiser (52110) • The Argus Lite (52605) • Armley & Wortley Advertiser (53643) • Banbury Cake (52165) • The Barrow Browser (53670) • Barry & District News (52192) • Basildon and Wickford Recorder (52193) • Basingstoke Gazette (52195) • Basingstoke Gazette Extra (56452) • Berrow's Worcester Journal (56960) • The Bolton News (52405) • Bridport & Lyme Regis News (52599) • Darlington & Stockton Times (53154) • Dudley News (56639) • Evesham Journal (53343) • Ilkley Gazette (53645) • Leigh Journal (53838) • Malvern Gazette (56962) • Somerset County Gazette (56723) • South Wales Argus (55690) • Telegraph & Argus (52551) • Whitney Gazette (56947) • Yeovil Express (52957)

Newsquest (Midlands South) Ltd.
Berrows House
Hylton Rd.
West Sussex WR2 5JX, United Kingdom
Phone: 44 1905 7482000
Publications: Redditch Advertiser/Indicator Series (56902)

Newton Mann Ltd.
Fourteen Business Centre
14 Town St.
Duffield DE56 4EH, United Kingdom
Phone: 44 1332 843107
Fax: 44 845 0098871
Publications: Forge (53208)

NeXXus Communications K.K.
BIG Office Plz. 1002-1007
2-62-8 Higashi-Ikebukuro
Toshima-ku
Tokyo 170-0013, Japan
Phone: 81 339 845200
Fax: 81 339 866850
Publications: Tokyo Journal (47051)

Nhan Dan
71 Hang Trong St.
Hoan Kiem District
Hoan Kiem
Hanoi, Vietnam
Phone: 84 4 8254231
Fax: 84 4 8255593
Publications: Nhan Dan (57052)

Nicholson Media Group Proprietary Ltd.
1st Fl., 457 Malvern Rd.
Melbourne, Victoria 3141, Australia
Phone: 61 398 268448
Fax: 61 398 278808
Publications: Australian Tennis Magazine (42053)

Nielsen Business Media
770 Broadway
New York, NY 10003-9595
Publications: Europa Star (51093) • Europa Star International (51094)

NIGEB - National Research Center for Genetic Engineering and Biotechnology
Pajoohesh Blvd. Tehran -Karaj Hwy., 15th km.
Tehran, Iran
Phone: 90 214 4580301
Fax: 98 214 4580396
Publications: Iranian Journal of Biotechnology (IJB) (45898)

The Nigerian Journal of Surgical Research
c/o Pediatric Surgery Unit
Ahmadu Bello University Teaching Hospital
Zaria, Kaduna, Nigeria
Phone: 234 69 333 311
Fax: 234 69 334 150
Publications: Nigerian Journal of Surgical Research (49185)

Nigerian Medical Association
PO Box 8829
Wuse
Abuja, Lagos, Nigeria
Phone: 23 414 801569
Publications: Nigerian Medical Journal (49150)

Nigerian Society of Engineers
National Engineering Center
off National Mosque-Labour House Rd.

Central Business Area
Abuja, Lagos, Nigeria
Phone: 234 9 6735096
Publications: The Nigerian Engineer (49057)

Hero Joy Nightingale
3 Sandbank Cottages
St. Stephen's Hill
Canterbury CT2 7AU, United Kingdom
Phone: 44 12 27456625
Fax: 44 12 27459963
Publications: From the Window (52920)

Nihon Daekisen Gakkai
2-1-1 Otsuka
Bunkyo-ku
Tokyo 1604, Japan
Fax: 81 3 59761478
Publications: Journal of Japan Salivary Gland Society (46913)

Nihon Jikoketsu Yuketsu Kenkyukai
Kawasaki Ika Daigaku Masuika
577 Matsushima
Kurashiki-shi
Okayama 701-0114, Japan
Publications: Journal of Japanese Society of Autologous Blood Transfusion (46597)

Nihon Keizai Shimbun Inc.
1-3-7 Otemachi
Chiyoda-Ku
Tokyo 100-8066, Japan
Phone: 81 3 62567158
Fax: 81 3 52233661
Publications: Nikkei Net Interactive (47000) • The Nikkei Weekly (47010)

Nihon Konkurito Kogaku Kyokai (Japan Concrete Institute)
Sogo Hanzomon Bldg., 12F
1-7 Kojimachi
Chiyoda-ku
Tokyo 102-0083, Japan
Phone: 81 332 631571
Fax: 81 332 632115
Publications: Journal of Advanced Concrete Technology (46881)

Nihon Parapurejia Igakkai
Keio Gijuku Daigaku Igakubu Seikei
Gekagaku Kyoshitsu
35 Shinano-Machi
Shinjuku-ku
Tokyo 160-0016, Japan
Publications: Journal of Japan Medical Society of Paraplegia (46912)

Nihon Ryokunaisho
Miyazaki Ika Daigaku Gankagaku Kyoshitsu
5200 Kihara
Miyazaki-gun
Kiyotake-cho
Miyazaki 889-1601, Japan
Publications: Journal of Japan Glaucoma Society (46519)

Nihon Ryumachi Kansetsu Geka Gakkai
Shiga Ika Daigaku Seikei Gekagaku Kyoshitsu
Seta Tsukiwacho
Otsu-shi
Shiga, Japan
Publications: Japanese Journal of Rheumatism and Joint Surgery (46682)

Nihon Seitai Jiki Gakkai
Daigaku Igakubu
Iyo Denshi Kenkyu Shisetsu
3-1 Hongo 7-chome
Bunkyo-ku
Tokyo 113-0033, Japan
Publications: Journal of Japan Biomagnetism and Bioelectromagnetics Society (46911)

Nihon Sekitsui Geka Gakkai
Seikei Geka Kyoshitsu
35 Shinano-Machi
Shinjuku-ku
Tokyo 160-0016, Japan
Publications: Journal of Japan Spine Research Society (46914)

Nihon University School of Dentistry
1-8-13 Kanda-Surugadai
Chiyoda-ku
Tokyo 101-8310, Japan
Phone: 81 3 32198001
Fax: 81 3 32198310
Publications: Journal of Oral Science (46934)

Niigata University
Dept. of Mathematics
Faculty of Science
Niigata 950-2181, Japan
Phone: 81 252 627000
Fax: 81 252 626539
Publications: Nihonkai Mathematical Journal (46573)

Nikkei Business Publications Asia Ltd.
Stanhope House, 17th Fl., Unit 1701A
734 King's Rd.
Quarry Bay
Hong Kong, People's Republic of China
Phone: 852 25758301
Fax: 852 25748175
Publications: Nikkei Electronics Asia (43371)

Nikkei Business Publications Inc.
1-17-3 Shirokane
Minato-ku
Tokyo 108-8646, Japan
Phone: 81 3 68118502
Fax: 81 3 54219058
Publications: National Geographic Japanese Edition (46975) • Nikkei Architecture (46978) • Nikkei Board Guide (46979) • Nikkei BP Government Technology (46980) • Nikkei Business (46981) • Nikkei Business Associe (46982) • Nikkei Communications (46983) • Nikkei Computer (46984) • Nikkei Construction (46985) • Nikkei Design (46986) • Nikkei Drug Information (46987) • Nikkei Ecology (46988) • Nikkei Electronics (46989) • Nikkei Electronics China (46990) • Nikkei Entertainment! (46991) • Nikkei Health (46992) • Nikkei Healthcare (46993) • Nikkei Home Builder (46994) • Nikkei Information Strategy (46995) • Nikkei Linux (46996) • Nikkei Medical (46997) • Nikkei Microdevices (46998) • Nikkei Monozukuri (46999) • Nikkei Network (47001) • Nikkei PC Beginners (47002) • Nikkei PC21 (47003) • Nikkei Personal Computing (47004) • Nikkei Restaurants (47005) • Nikkei Software (47006) • Nikkei Solution Business (47007) • Nikkei Systems (47008) • Nikkei Venture (47009) • Nikkei WinPC (47011) • Priv. (47025) • Real Simple Japan (47030)

Nippon Kaiji Kyokai
4-7 Kioi-cho
Chiyoda-ku
Tokyo 102-8567, Japan
Phone: 81 332 301201
Fax: 81 352 262012
Publications: ClassNK Magazine (46786)

Nippon Steel Corp.
Marunouchi Pk. Bldg.
2-6-1, Marunouchi
Chiyoda Ward
Tokyo 100-8071, Japan
Phone: 81 332 424111
Fax: 81 332 755607
Publications: Nippon Steel News (47012)

NISC Proprietary Ltd.
1 Dundas St.
PO Box 377
Grahamstown 6140, Republic of South Africa
Phone: 27 466 229698
Fax: 27 466 229550
Publications: African Journal of Range and Forage Science (50565)

Nishikigoi International Ltd.
Innovation House
Parkside Business Pk., Golborne
Lowton
Warrington WA3 3PY, United Kingdom
Phone: 44 19 42777879
Fax: 44 19 42777876
Publications: Nishikigoi International (56850)

Nordic Association for Architectural Research
Faculty for Architecture & Fine Arts
The Norwegian University of Science & Technology
NTNU

N-7491 Trondheim, Norway
Phone: 47 735 95007
Publications: Nordic Journal for Architectural Research (49218)

Nordic Association for Hydrology
c/o Hans Stjarnskog, Treas.
Swedish Meteorological & Hydrological Inst.
SE-601 76 Norrkoping, Sweden
Phone: 46 114958313
Fax: 46 114958573
Publications: Hydrology Research (50995)

Nordic Information Center for Media and Communication Research (Nordicom)
Goteborgs University
PO Box 713
S-405 30 Goteborg, Sweden
Phone: 46 31 7860000
Fax: 46 31 7864655
Publications: Nordicom Review (50961)

Norges Frisormester Forbund
Postboks 7071
N-0306 Oslo, Norway
Phone: 47 230 87960
Fax: 47 230 87970
Publications: Frisor (49199)

Norges Handels & Sjofartstidende
Christian Krohgs gate 16
PO Box 1182
Sentrum
N-0107 Oslo, Norway
Phone: 47 22001000
Publications: Dagens Naeringsliv (49196)

The Norse Federation
Radhusgaten 23 B
NO-0158 Oslo, Norway
Phone: 47 233 57170
Fax: 47 233 57175
Publications: The Norseman (49205)

Norsk Aero Klubb
Radhusgaten 5B
Postboks 383
Sentrum
N-0102 Oslo, Norway
Phone: 47 230 10450
Fax: 47 230 10451
Publications: Flynytt (49198)

Norsk Atferdsanalytisk Forening
Kapellveien 6
N-0487 Oslo, Norway
Phone: 47 33 806570
Fax: 47 21 012449
Publications: European Journal of Behavior Analysis (49197)

Norsk Radiografforbund
Radhusgata 4
N-0105 Oslo, Norway
Phone: 47 23100470
Fax: 47 23100480
Publications: Hold Pusten (49200)

Norske Meierifolks Landsforening
Postboks 9370
Gronland
N-0135 Oslo, Norway
Phone: 47 230 02710
Publications: Meieriposten (49202)

North West University
PO Box X2046
Mmabatho 2735, Republic of South Africa
Phone: 27 183 892111
Fax: 27 183 925775
Publications: Potchefstroom Electronic Law Journal (50556)

Northeast Press Ltd.
Echo House
Pennywell
Sunderland SR4 9ER, United Kingdom
Publications: Morpeth Herald (55653) • Star Series (56655)

Northern Daily Leader
92 Brisbane St.
PO Box 525

Tamworth, New South Wales 2340, Australia
Publications: Northern Daily Leader (42612)

Northern Earth
10 Jubilee St.
Mytholmroyd
West Yorkshire
Hebden Bridge HX7 5NP, United Kingdom
Publications: Northern Earth (53553)

Northland Age Ltd.
PO Box 45
Kaitaia, New Zealand
Phone: 64 940 80330
Fax: 64 940 82955
Publications: Northland Age (48928)

Northumbria Law Press
Northumbria University
Sutherland Bldg.
Northumberland Rd.
Newcastle upon Tyne NE1 8ST, United Kingdom
Phone: 44 19 12437587
Fax: 44 19 12437506
Publications: International Journal of Clinical Legal Education (55672) • Journal of Obligations & Remedies (55674)

Now Publishers
PO Box 1024
Hanover, MA 02339-1001
Phone: 781871-0245
Publications: International Review of Environmental and Resource Economics (43738)

NSW Department of Health
73 Miller St.
Sydney, New South Wales 2060, Australia
Phone: 61 293 919000
Fax: 61 293 919101
Publications: NSW Public Health Bulletin (42211)

Nucleo de Estudos de Genero
Universidade Estadual de Campinas
Caixa Postal 6110
13083-970 Campinas, Sao Paulo, Brazil
Phone: 55 19 35217873
Fax: 55 19 37881704
Publications: Cadernos Pagu (42966)

NWN Media Ltd.
Mold Business Pk.
Wrexham Rd.
Flintshire
Mold CH7 1XY, United Kingdom
Phone: 44 1352 707707
Fax: 44 1352 707748
Publications: Border Counties Advertizer (55856) • Chester Standard (52992) • Denbighshire Free Press (55641) • Ellesmere Port Standard (52993) • North Wales Chronicle (52173) • North Wales Pioneer (53058) • Rhyl Journal (56387) • Wrexham Leader (56982)

NZ Catholic
PO Box 147-000
Ponsonby
Auckland 1034, New Zealand
Phone: 64 936 03067
Fax: 64 936 03065
Publications: NZ Catholic (48823)

O Informador Fiscal
c/o Mr. Rua Dias Ferreira, No. 370, 1 pt.
Apartado 8012
P-4100-246 Porto, Portugal
Phone: 351 22 3394030
Fax: 351 22 3394029
Publications: O Informador Fiscal (49809)

OAG Worldwide
Church St.
Dunstable LU5 4HB, United Kingdom
Phone: 44 15 82600111
Fax: 44 15 82695230
Publications: OAG Rail Guide (53225)

Oakhill Media Ltd.
Oakhill House
22 Williams Grove
Surbiton KT6 5RN, United Kingdom
Phone: 44 20 83989048

Fax: 44 87 07620434
Publications: Bulk Distributor (56657)

Observer Standard Newspapers Ltd.
Webb House
Church Green E
Redditch B98 8BP, United Kingdom
Phone: 44 1527 588688
Fax: 44 1527 584371
Publications: Bromsgrove Standard (52746) • The Coventry Observer (56853) • Droitwich Standard (52747) • The Leamington Observer (53747) • Redditch Standard (56341) • Rugby Observer (56855) • Stratford Observer (56856) • Worcester Standard (56963)

The College of Occupational Therapists Ltd.
106-114 Borough High St.
London SE1 1LB, United Kingdom
Phone: 44 20 73576480
Publications: Occupational Therapy News (55026)

Ocean Media Events Ltd.
1 Canada Sq.
London E14 5AA, United Kingdom
Phone: 44 20 77728300
Fax: 44 20 77728599
Publications: Access All Areas (53890) • Geriatric Medicine (54505) • Inside Housing (54606)

Oceanographic Society of Japan
c/o JOS/Mainichi Admin. Center for Academic Societies
9th Fl., Palace-side Bldg.
1-1-1 Hitotsubashi
Chiyoda-ku
Tokyo 100-0003, Japan
Fax: 81 332 111413
Publications: Journal of Oceanography (46932)

Odsgard A/S
Stationsparken 25
DK-2600 Glostrup, Denmark
Phone: 45 434 32900
Fax: 45 434 31328
Publications: Byggeri (43698) • BygTek (43699) • BygTek Mester & Svend (43700) • Elektronik & Data (43702) • Puff - Fagtidsskrift for Tralast og Byggemarkeder (43713) • Telekommunikation (43718)

Office International des Epizooties
12 rue de Prony
F-75017 Paris, France
Phone: 33 144 151888
Fax: 33 142 670987
Publications: Scientific and Technical Review (44083)

Offshore Investment
Lombard House
10-20 Lombard St.
Belfast BT1 1BW, United Kingdom
Phone: 44 28 90328777
Fax: 44 28 90328555
Publications: Offshore Investment (52291)

Ohmsha Ltd.
3-1 Kanda-Nishiki-cho
Chiyoda-ku
Tokyo 101-8460, Japan
Phone: 81 3 32332425
Fax: 81 3 32332426
Publications: Journal of Visualization (46945)

OIE
12, rue de Prony
F-75017 Paris, France
Phone: 33 1 44151888
Fax: 33 1 42670987
Publications: Disease Information (44038)

Oil and Colour Chemists' Association
Priory House
967 Harrow Rd.
Wembley HA0 2SF, United Kingdom
Phone: 44 20 89081086
Fax: 44 20 89091219
Publications: Surface Coatings International (56887) • Surface Coatings International (56886)

Okayama University
3-1-1 Tsushima-Naka
Okayama 700-8530, Japan
Publications: Mathematical Journal of Okayama University (46599)

Okayama University
2-5-1 Shikata-cho
Shikata-cho
Okayama 700-8558, Japan
Phone: 81 862 357057
Fax: 81 862 357059
Publications: Acta Medica Okayama (46596)

Okaz Organization for Press and Publication
PO Box 5034
Jeddah 21422, Saudi Arabia
Phone: 966 2 6722775
Fax: 966 2 6712355
Publications: Saudi Gazette (50057)

O.L. Society Ltd.
9 David St.
Melbourne, Victoria 3001, Australia
Phone: 61 3 99194163
Fax: 61 3 96877614
Publications: Overland (42081)

Old City Publishing
628 N 2nd St.
Philadelphia, PA 19123-3002
Phone: 215925-4390
Fax: 215925-4371
Publications: Journal of Cellular Automata (52683)

Oldie Publications Ltd.
65 Newman St.
London W1T 3EG, United Kingdom
Phone: 44 20 74368801
Fax: 44 20 74368804
Publications: The Oldie (55029)

Olympia-Verlag GmbH
Badstr. 4-6
D-90402 Nuremberg, Germany
Phone: 49 911 2160
Publications: Berge (44602)

Om Sai Ram Centre for Financial Management Research
15 Prakash Co-operative Housing Society
Relief Rd.
Santacruz W
Mumbai 400 054, Maharashtra, India
Publications: Journal of Financial Management and Analysis (45400)

Oman Chamber of Commerce and Industry
PO Box 1400
Ruwi 112, Oman
Phone: 968 24707674
Fax: 968 24708497
Publications: Al Ghorfa (49226)

The Oman Establishment for Press, News, Publication and Advertising
PO Box 974
Muscat 113, Oman
Publications: Oman Daily Observer (49222)

Oman Tribune
PO Box 463
Muscat 113, Oman
Phone: 968 24491919
Fax: 968 24498444
Publications: Oman Tribune (49224)

Omnicon
Seis de diciembre, s/n, local 25
E-28023 Madrid, Spain
Phone: 34 91 7402081
Fax: 34 91 3579295
Publications: Foto Video (50759) • FV—Foto-Video Actualidad (50760)

Onderstepoort Veterinary Institute
1134 Park St.
Hatfield
PO Box 8783
Pretoria 0001, Republic of South Africa
Phone: 27 12 4279700
Fax: 27 12 3423948
Publications: Onderstepoort Journal of Veterinary Research (50598)

One Caribbean Media
Express House
35 Independence Sq.
Port of Spain, Trinidad and Tobago
Phone: 868623-1711

Fax: 868627-4886
Publications: Trinidad & Tobago Express (51468)

1st Industrial Magazine Online
E-3, Industrial Estate
Kota 321 006, Rajasthan, India
Phone: 91 744 360835
Fax: 91 744 450276
Publications: 1st Industrial Magazine (45311)

Open Government
c/o Steve Wood
School of Business Information
Liverpool John Moores University
Liverpool L3 5UZ, United Kingdom
Phone: 44 15 12313589
Fax: 44 15 17070423
Publications: Open Government (53877)

Open Spaces Society
25A Bell St.
Henley-on-Thames RG9 2BA, United Kingdom
Phone: 44 1491 573535
Fax: 44 1491 573051
Publications: Open Space (53562)

Opera Actual S.L.
Bruc, 6 Ppal 2a
E-08010 Barcelona, Spain
Phone: 34 933 191300
Fax: 34 933 107338
Publications: Opera Actual (50690)

Opera Magazine Ltd.
36 Black Lion Ln.
London W6 9BE, United Kingdom
Phone: 44 20 85638893
Fax: 44 20 85638635
Publications: Opera (55036)

Operational Research Society of India
39, Mahanirvan Rd.
Kolkata 700029, West Bengal, India
Publications: Opsearch (45300)

Operational Research Society of the United Kingdom
Seymour House
12 Edward St.
Birmingham B1 2RX, United Kingdom
Phone: 44 12 12339300
Fax: 44 12 12330321
Publications: European Journal of Information Systems (52341) • OR Insight (53628)

Opportunities Today Publication Pvt. Ltd.
Radio Bhuvan
3/35 Kamal Mansion
Arthur Bunder Rd.
Near Radio Club, Colaba
Mumbai 400 005, Maharashtra, India
Phone: 91 222 2853081
Fax: 91 222 2875269
Publications: Opportunities Today (45424)

Optical Society of India
92 Acharya Prafulla Chandra Rd.
Kolkata 700 009, West Bengal, India
Phone: 91 33 23522411
Fax: 91 33 23522411
Publications: Journal of Optics (45297)

Optical Society of Japan
Imon Kudan-Kita Bldg., 5th Fl.
1-12-3 Kudan-kita
Chiyoda-ku
Tokyo 102-0073, Japan
Phone: 81 3 32381043
Fax: 81 3 32216245
Publications: Optical Review (47015)

Options Publications Private Ltd.
PO Box 784
Marine Parade
Singapore 914410, Singapore
Phone: 65 634 84007
Publications: BigO (50115)

Oral History Society
c/o Dept. of History
Essex University
Colchester CO4 3SQ, United Kingdom
Phone: 44 20 74127405
Publications: Oral History Journal (53044)

Orca Journals
Stanley House
3 Fleets Ln.
Poole BH15 3AJ, United Kingdom
Phone: 44 12 02785712
Fax: 44 12 02666219
Publications: Black Theology (56279)

Orca Publications
Berry Rd. Studios
Newquay TR7 1AT, United Kingdom
Phone: 44 16 37878074
Fax: 44 16 37850226
Publications: Carve (55693)

Orchid Society of Great Britain
103 North Rd.
Three Bridges
Crawley RH10 1SQ, United Kingdom
Phone: 44 1293 528615
Publications: Journal (53107)

Ord & Bild
Box 31120
SE-400 32 Goteborg, Sweden
Phone: 46 317439905
Fax: 46 317439906
Publications: Ord & Bild (50962)

Orfeo Ediciones
Bloque 3 Oficina 2
Avda Espana 133
E-28231 Madrid, Spain
Phone: 34 913510253
Fax: 34 913510587
Publications: Melomano (50783)

Organization of Islamic Capitals and Cities
PO Box 13621
Jeddah 21414, Saudi Arabia
Phone: 66 626 9821414
Fax: 66 626 981053
Publications: Islamic Capitals and Cities Magazine (50056)

Oriens Institute for Religious Research
2-28-5 Matsubara
Setagaya-ku
Tokyo 156-0043, Japan
Phone: 81 3 3322 7601
Fax: 81 3 3325 5322
Publications: Japan Mission Journal (46859)

Orientations Magazine Ltd.
815, 8th Fl., Zung Fu Industrial Bldg.
1067 King's Rd.
Quarry Bay
Hong Kong, People's Republic of China
Phone: 852 25111368
Fax: 852 25074620
Publications: Orientations (43373)

Orienteering Federation of Australia
PO Box 284
Mitchell, Australian Capital Territory 2911, Australia
Phone: 61 2 61621200
Publications: The Australian Orienteer (42686)

Origin Publishing Ltd.
Tower House
Fairfax St.
Bristol BS1 3BN, United Kingdom
Phone: 44 117 9279009
Fax: 44 117 9349008
Publications: Beautiful Cards (52644) • Blonde Hair (52648) • Card Making & Papercraft (52650) • Cross Stitch Card Shop (52656) • Cross Stitch Crazy (52657) • Cross Stitch Gold (52658) • Hair Ideas (52673) • Knit Today (52700) • Koi (52701) • Quick Cards Made Easy (52724) • 220 Triathlon (52733) • The World of Cross Stitching (52737) • Your Hair (Bristol) (52738)

Ornithological Society of Japan
c/o National Science Museum
3-23-1, Hyakunin-cho
Shinjuku-ku
Tokyo 169-0073, Japan
Phone: 81 3 33647108
Fax: 81 3 33647104
Publications: Japanese Journal of Ornithology (46873)

Osaka University
1-1 Machikaneyama-cho
Toyonaka-shi
Osaka 560-0043, Japan
Fax: 81 668 505288
Publications: Osaka Journal of Mathematics (46627)

Osprey Publishing
Midland House
West Way
Botley
Oxford OX2 0PH, United Kingdom
Phone: 44 1865 727022
Fax: 44 1865 242009
Publications: HyperScale (55982)

Osterreichischer Naturschutzbund
Museumsplatz 2
A-5020 Salzburg, Austria
Phone: 43 662 642909
Fax: 43 662 6437344
Publications: Natur und Land (42741)

Osterreichisches Getranke Institut
Michaelerstrasse 25
A-1180 Vienna, Austria
Phone: 43 1 47969240
Fax: 43 1 479692433
Publications: Mitteilungen Osterreiches Getranke Institut (42764)

Osterreichisches Normungsinstitut
Heinestr. 38
A-1020 Vienna, Austria
Phone: 43 121 3000
Fax: 43 121 300818
Publications: Connex (42749)

Otago Polytechnic
PO Box 16
Cromwell 9310, New Zealand
Phone: 64 344 59900
Fax: 64 344 59909
Publications: Junctures (48888)

Otavamedia Ltd.
Maistraatinportti 1
FIN-00015 Kuvalehdet, Finland
Phone: 358 9 156665
Fax: 358 9 1566511
Publications: Alibi (43878) • Anna (43879) • Era (43880) • Hymy (43881) • Kaksplus (43882) • Kanava (43883) • Kaytannon Maamies (KM) (43884) • Kippari (43885) • Kodutohter (43886) • Kotiliesi (43887) • Koululainen (43888) • Lemmikki (43889) • Leppis (43890) • Metsastys ja Kalastus (43891) • MODA (43892) • Parnasso (43893) • Seura (43894) • Suomen Kuvalehti (43895) • Suosikki (43896) • Tekniikan Maailma (43897) • Tom & Jerry (43898) • TV-maailma (43899) • Vauhdin Maailma (43900) • Vene (43901) • Villivarsa (43902)

Outdoors New Zealand
PO Box 6027
Marion Sq.
Wellington 6141, New Zealand
Phone: 64 4 3857287
Fax: 64 4 3857366
Publications: New Zealand Journal of Outdoor Education (49028)

Overseas Radio & Television Inc.
No. 10, Ln. 62, Dajhih St.
Jhongshan District
PO Box 104-127
Taipei 00104, Taiwan
Phone: 886 2 25338082
Fax: 886 2 25331009
Publications: Let's Talk in English (51356) • Studio Classroom (51361)

OXERA—Oxford Economic Research Associates
Park Central
40/41 Park End St.
Oxford OX1 1JD, United Kingdom
Phone: 44 18 65253000
Fax: 44 18 65251172
Publications: The Utilities Journal (56224)

Oxfam GB
Oxfam House
John Smith Dr.

Oxford OX4 2JY, United Kingdom
Phone: 44 1865 472602
Publications: Gender & Development (55962)

Oxford University Press
YMCA Library Bldg.
1st Fl.
Jai Singh Rd.
PO Box 43
New Delhi 110 001, Delhi, India
Phone: 91 11 43600300
Fax: 91 11 23360897
Publications: Journal of Intellectual Property Law & Practice (45607) • Nicotine and Tobacco Research (53217)

Oxford University Press
Great Clarendon St.
Oxford OX2 6DP, United Kingdom
Phone: 44 1865 556767
Fax: 44 1865 353485
Publications: African Affairs (53249) • Age and Ageing (52638) • Alcohol and Alcoholism (55704) • American Law and Economics Review (55865) • Annals of Botany (53784) • Annals of Oncology (51237) • Applied Mathematics Research eXpress (55870) • Behavioral Ecology (55879) • Bioinformatics (55881) • Biometrika (55882) • Biostatistics (55883) • Brain (55887) • Brief Treatment and Crisis Intervention (55888) • Briefings in Bioinformatics (55889) • Briefings in Functional Genomics & Proteomics (55890) • The British Journal of Aesthetics (55891) • British Journal of Anaesthesia (55892) • The British Journal of Criminology (55893) • The British Journal for the Philosophy of Science (52649) • The British Journal of Social Work (52279) • British Medical Bulletin (55895) • British Yearbook of International Law (52797) • Cambridge Journal of Economics (55900) • The Cambridge Quarterly (52799) • Carcinogenesis (55904) • CESifo Economic Studies (55905) • Chinese Journal of International Law (55908) • Community Development Journal (53080) • The Computer Journal (54254) • Continuing Education in Anaesthesia, Critical Care & Pain (55917) • Contributions to Political Economy (52812) • Critical Survey (55919) • Current Legal Problems (55922) • DNA Research (46317) • Early Music (52815) • ELT Journal (56385) • The English Historical Review (56570) • Enterprise & Society (55937) • Epidemiologic Reviews (55939) • ESHRE Monographs (55940) • Essays in Criticism (55941) • European Heart Journal (55944) • European Journal of Echocardiography (55946) • European Journal of International Law (46143) • European Journal of Orthodontics (54402) • European Journal of Public Health (55947) • European Review of Agricultural Economics (44258) • European Sociological Review (44145) • European Sociological Review (55949) • Evidence-based Complementary and Alternative Medicine (55950) • Family Practice (55952) • Forestry (55960) • Forum for Modern Language Studies (56441) • French History (55961) • German History (55965) • Glycobiology (55967) • Health Education Research (55971) • Health Promotion International (55972) • History Workshop Journal (54562) • Holocaust and Genocide Studies (55976) • Human Molecular Genetics (55979) • Human Reproduction (53018) • Human Reproduction Update (52829) • Human Rights Law Review (55981) • ICES Journal of Marine Science (55983) • IMA Journal of Applied Mathematics (52342) • IMA Journal of Management Mathematics (55984) • IMA Journal of Mathematical Control and Information (55985) • IMA Journal of Numerical Analysis (55986) • IMRN (55987) • Industrial and Corporate Change (46175) • Industrial Law Journal (52830) • International Immunology (55991) • International Journal of Constitutional Law (55992) • International Journal of Epidemiology (52678) • International Journal of Law and Information Technology (55996) • International Journal of Law, Policy and the Family (55997) • International Journal of Lexicography (55998) • International Journal of Public Opinion Research (56001) • International Journal for Quality in Health Care (56002) • International Journal of Refugee Law (53039) • International Mathematics Research Papers (56005) • International Relations of the Asia-Pacific (56006) • Japanese Journal of Clinical Oncology (56009) • Journal of African Economies (56012) • Journal of Antimicrobial Chemotherapy (56014) • The Journal of Biochemistry (56017) • Journal of Competi-

tion Law and Economics (56022) • Journal of Conflict and Security Law (56024) • Journal of Design History (56026) • Journal of Digital Information (55481) • Journal of Economic Geography (56573) • Journal of Electron Microscopy (56028) • Journal of Environmental Law (56029) • Journal of Experimental Botany (56032) • Journal of Financial Econometrics (56034) • Journal of Heredity (56037) • Journal of the History of Collections (56039) • Journal of the ICRU (56040) • Journal of International Criminal Justice (56044) • Journal of Islamic Studies (56046) • Journal of Law, Economics, and Organization (56047) • Journal of Logic and Computation (54773) • The Journal of Medicine and Philosophy (56051) • Journal of Molluscan Studies (56052) • Journal of the National Cancer Institute (56053) • Journal of Petrology (53768) • Journal of Plankton Research (56059) • Journal of Public Administration Research and Theory (56062) • Journal of Public Health (56064) • Journal of Refugee Studies (56065) • Journal of the Royal Musical Association (53770) • Journal of Semantics (56071) • Journal of Semitic Studies (55566) • The Journal of Theological Studies (56075) • Journal of Tropical Pediatrics (56076) • Law, Probability and Risk (56087) • Literary and Linguistic Computing (54876) • Literature and Theology (56624) • Logic Journal of the IGPL (56091) • Mathematical Medicine and Biology (55766) • Medical Law Review (56095) • Mind (56994) • Molecular Biology and Evolution (56105) • Molecular Human Reproduction (53019) • Music & Letters (54964) • Mutagenesis (56689) • Nephrology Dialysis Transplantation (42887) • Notes and Queries (56120) • Nucleic Acids Research (56121) • Oral History Review (56128) • Oxford Art Journal (56130) • Oxford Economic Papers (56133) • Oxford Journal of Legal Studies (56135) • Oxford Review of Economic Policy (56136) • Parliamentary Affairs (56141) • Past & Present (56142) • Philosophia Mathematica (56153) • Plant and Cell Physiology (56160) • Political Analysis (56164) • Proceedings of the London Mathematical Society (56168) • Protein Engineering, Design and Selection (56172) • Public Opinion Quarterly (56178) • Publius (56179) • QJM (56181) • The Quarterly Journal of Mathematics (56182) • The Quarterly Journal of Mechanics and Applied Mathematics (56183) • Radiation Protection Dosimetry (56185) • The Review of English Studies (56191) • Schizophrenia Bulletin (56201) • Social Politics (51039) • Social Science Japan Journal (47040) • Socio-Economic Review (56208) • Statute Law Review (53197) • Teaching Mathematics and Its Applications (52404) • Toxicological Sciences (56218) • Twentieth Century British History (52634) • World Bank Research Observer (56227)

Oxford University Press
4-5-10-8F Shiba, Minato-ku
Tokyo 108-8386, Japan
Phone: 81 3 54445858
Fax: 81 3 34542929
Publications: Adaptation (46728) • American Literary History (46733) • Cambridge Journal of Regions, Economy & Society (46775) • Capital Markets Law Journal (46779) • Health Policy and Planning (54540) • IEICE Transactions on Fundamentals of Electronics, Communications and Computer Sciences (46318) • Journal of Medicine & Philosophy (46926) • Tree Physiology (47053)

P R Gupta
A-25 Priyadarshini Vihar
Delhi 110 092, Delhi, India
Phone: 91 112 2543326
Fax: 91 112 2543039
Publications: Dairy India Yearbook (45089)

Pablo Publishing Pte Ltd.
Block 61, Kallang Pl., No. 07-01
Singapore 339156, Singapore
Phone: 65 63967877
Fax: 65 63967177
Publications: DENTAL ASIA (50130) • Food & Beverage Asia (50150) • PANELS & FURNITURE ASIA (50234) • Water & Wastewater Asia (50284)

Pabst Science Publishers
Eichengrund 28
D-49525 Lengerich, Germany
Publications: Transplantationsmedizin (44534)

Pacific Magazines
8 Central Ave.
Eveleigh, New South Wales 2015, Australia
Phone: 61 2 93942000
Publications: Diabetic Living (41859) • Heart Healthy Living (41860) • That's Life (41861) • Total Girl (41862) • TV Hits (41863)

Pacific Prospect Group Ltd.
20 Fl., Admiralty Ctr., Tower 2
18 Harcourt Rd.
Hong Kong, People's Republic of China
Phone: 852 34114700
Fax: 852 34114701
Publications: Asian Credit Investor (43275) • Innovative Investor (43348)

Pacific Seabird Group
c/o Ron LeValley, Treas.
PO Box 324
Little River, CA 95456-0324
Publications: Marine Ornithology (50621)

Page7 Media
Arena House
Arena Rd.
Sandyford 18, Dublin, Ireland
Phone: 353 1 2405528
Publications: Bike Buyers Guide (46054) • Farm & Plant Buyers Guide (46055) • Modified Motors (46056) • The Stock Market (46057) • Used Car Price Guide (46058)

Paint Research Association
14 Castle Mews
High St.
Middlesex
Hampton TW12 2NP, United Kingdom
Phone: 44 20 84870800
Fax: 44 20 84870801
Publications: Coatings Comet (53505) • World Surface Coatings Abstracts (53506)

Pakistan Agricultural Research Council
PO Box 1031
Islamabad, Pakistan
Phone: 92 519 203071
Fax: 92 519 202968
Publications: Pakistan Journal of Agricultural Research (49306) • Progressive Farming (49311)

Pakistan Association of Pathologists
Sindlab Private Ltd.
Z-74, D.M.C. Society, Tariq Rd.
Karachi 74800, Pakistan
Phone: 92 91 9212041
Publications: Pakistan Journal of Pathology (49370)

Pakistan Botanical Society
Dr. Abdul Ghaffar , Ch.Ed.
Dept. of Botany
University of Karachi
Karachi 75270, Pakistan
Phone: 92 221 4387867
Publications: Pakistan Journal of Botany (49368)

Pakistan Christian Post
912-B UNI Shopping Centre
A. H. Rd. Saddar
Karachi, Pakistan
Publications: Pakistan Christian Post (49367)

Pakistan Council of Scientific and Industrial Research
Constitution Ave.
Sector G-5/2
Islamabad, Pakistan
Phone: 92 51 9225395
Fax: 92 51 9219266
Publications: Pakistan Journal of Scientific and Industrial Research (49309)

Pakistan Forest Institute
BPO Forest Institute
NWFP
Peshawar, Pakistan
Phone: 92 521 40580
Publications: Pakistan Journal of Forestry (49394)

Pakistan Medical Association
P.M.A. House
Aga Khan III Rd.
Karachi 74400, Pakistan

Phone: 92 21 5418192
Fax: 92 21 5418192
Publications: Journal of the Pakistan Medical Association (49358)

Pakistan Medical Research Council
Shahrah-e-Jumhuriat, Sector G-5/2
PO Box 2598
Islamabad 44000, Pakistan
Phone: 92 920 7386
Fax: 92 921 6774
Publications: Pakistan Journal of Medical Research (49308)

Pakistan Petroleum Ltd.
PIDC House
Dr. Ziauddin Ahmed Rd.
PO Box 3942
Karachi 75530, Pakistan
Phone: 92 21 5651480
Fax: 92 21 5680005
Publications: Progress (49373)

Pakistan Psychiatric Society
c/o Saeed Farooq, Ed.
Journal of Pakistan Psychiatric Society
29-30 Habib Medical Complex
Dabgari Gardens
Peshawar, Pakistan
Publications: Journal of Pakistan Psychiatric Society (49393)

Pakistan Textile Journal
B4 2nd Fl., 64/21, Miran Mohd Shah Rd.
Karachi, Pakistan
Phone: 92 21 4533616
Fax: 92 21 5206188
Publications: Pakistan Textile Journal (49372)

PakTribune
House 6, Khyaban-e-Iqbal, Margalla Rd.
F-7/3
Islamabad, Pakistan
Phone: 92 51 111888666
Fax: 92 51 2871236
Publications: PakTribune (49310)

Palestine Times
PO Box 10355
London NW2 3WH, United Kingdom
Publications: Palestine Times (55052)

Palgrave Macmillan
Houndsmills
Basingstoke RG21 6XS, United Kingdom
Phone: 44 1256 329242
Fax: 44 1256 479476
Publications: Acta Politica (47878) • Asian Business & Management (52194) • BioSocieties (52196) • British Politics (52197) • Comparative European Politics (56489) • Corporate Reputation Review (48749) • Crime Prevention & Community Safety (55668) • Economic & Labour Market Review (52199) • European Management Review (52201) • European Political Science (52202) • Family Spending (52204) • Feminist Review (54447) • French Politics (45961) • Geneva Papers on Risk and Insurance Issues and Practice (52205) • Health Statistics Quarterly (52206) • Information Visualization (52207) • International Abstracts in Operations Research (52208) • International Journal of Disclosure and Governance (52209) • International Journal of Educational Advancement (52210) • Journal of Asset Management (54702) • Journal of Banking Regulation (52212) • Journal of Brand Management (54710) • Journal of Building Appraisal (52213) • Journal of Commercial Biotechnology (52214) • Journal of Database Marketing & Customer Strategy Management (54734) • Journal of Derivatives & Hedge Funds (54735) • Journal of Digital Asset Management (52215) • Journal of Direct, Data and Digital Marketing Practice (54737) • Journal of Financial Services Marketing (52216) • Journal of Generic Medicines (52217) • Journal of Information Technology (56042) • Journal of International Relations and Development (50339) • Journal of Medical Marketing (52218) • Journal of the Operational Research Society (52350) • Journal of Public Health Policy (52219) • Journal of Retail and Leisure Property (52220) • Journal of Revenue and Pricing Management (52221) • Journal of Simulation (52353) • Journal of Targeting, Measurement and Analysis for Marketing (54826) • Knowledge Manage-

ment Research & Practice (52356) • Latino Studies (52222) • Maritime Economics and Logistics (52223) • Monthly Digest of Statistics (52225) • Pensions (52227) • Place Branding (52228) • Regional Trends (52229) • Social Theory & Health (55249) • Social Trends (52230) • Subjectivity (52231) • Tourism and Hospitality Research (52232) • United Kingdom Economic Accounts (52233) • Urban Design International (52234)

Pallasite Press
PO Box 296
Silverdale
Auckland, New Zealand
Phone: 64 942 69311
Fax: 64 942 69312
Publications: Meteorite (48804)

Pamela Youde Nethersole Eastern Hospital
3 Lok Man Rd.
Chai Wan
Hong Kong, People's Republic of China
Publications: The Hong Kong Journal of Orthopaedic Surgery (43330)

Paneuropa-Union Deutschland e.V.
Dachauer Str. 17
D-80335 Munich, Germany
Phone: 49 895 54683
Fax: 49 895 94768
Publications: Paneuropa Deutschland (44141)

The Pantaneto Forum
1st Fl., 3 Gordon St.
Luton LU1 2QP, United Kingdom
Publications: The Pantaneto Forum (55504)

The Paper
725 Bainbridge St.
Barry, IL 62312
Phone: 217335-2112
Fax: 217335-2112
Publications: The Paper (50837)

Paper Industry Technical Association
5 Frecheville Ct.
Bury BL9 0UF, United Kingdom
Phone: 44 16 17645858
Fax: 44 16 17645353
Publications: Paper Technology (55053)

Paperi ja Puu
Snellmaninkatu 13
PO Box 155
FIN-00171 Helsinki, Finland
Phone: 358 91326688
Publications: Paperi Ja Puu (43855)

Paragraph Publishing Limited
St. Faiths House
Mountergate
Norwich NR1 1PY, United Kingdom
Phone: 44 1603 633808
Fax: 44 1603 632808
Publications: Beers of the World (55725) • Cigar Buyer Magazine (55728) • Scotland Magazine (55741) • Whisky Magazine (55743)

Parents Centres New Zealand
Unit 4, Bridgepoint
13 Marina View
Mana, New Zealand
Phone: 64 423 32022
Fax: 64 423 32063
Publications: Kiwi Parent (48936)

Parents News UK
10 The Manor Dr.
Worcester Park KT4 7LG, United Kingdom
Phone: 44 20 83376337
Fax: 44 20 87152842
Publications: Parents News UK (56965)

Paris Woman Journal
34 rue de Picpus
F-75012 Paris, France
Publications: Paris Woman Journal (44074)

Parkinson's Disease Society of the UK
215 Vauxhall Bridge Rd.
London SW1V 1EJ, United Kingdom
Phone: 44 20 79318080
Fax: 44 20 72339908
Publications: The Parkinson Magazine (55056)

ParksideMedia
PO Box 46020
Herne Bay
Auckland 1147, New Zealand
Phone: 64 9 3601480
Fax: 64 9 3601470
Publications: D-Photo (48790) • New Zealand Classic Car (48807) • New Zealand Performance Car (48820) • NZV8 (48826)

Parrot Society of Australia
PO Box 75
Salisbury, Queensland 4107, Australia
Fax: 61 7 54331921
Publications: Parrot Society of Australia News (42342)

Parsiana Publications Private Ltd.
K.K. (Navsari) Chambers, Ground Fl.
39B Amrit Keshav Nayak Rd., Fort
Mumbai 400 001, Maharashtra, India
Phone: 91 22 078104
Fax: 91 22 075572
Publications: Parsiana (45427)

The Parthenon Publishing Group Ltd.
Richmond House, White Cross
South Rd.
Lancaster LA1 4XF, United Kingdom
Phone: 44 1524 585700
Fax: 44 1524 389659
Publications: Gynecological Endocrinology (53733)

Partido Comunista de Espana
Mt. Olympus, 35
E-28043 Madrid, Spain
Phone: 34 91 3004969
Fax: 34 91 3004744
Publications: Utopias/Nuestra Bandera (50813)

PASOS
Tesnov 3
CZ-110 00 Prague, Czech Republic
Phone: 420 222 313644
Fax: 420 222 313644
Publications: Pasos (43633)

Passerella Network S.A.
72-74 Aspasias St.
Cholargos
GR-155 61 Athens, Greece
Phone: 30 210 6548344
Fax: 30 210 6537149
Publications: NY-LONDON Shows (44753) • Paris Catwalks (44754) • Passerella di Donna (44755)

Pasteur Institute of Iran
Pasteur Ave.
Tehran 1316943551, Iran
Phone: 98 216 6492596
Fax: 98 216 6492596
Publications: Iranian Biomedical Journal (45895)

The Paton Publishing House
E.O. Paton Welding Institute
11 Bozhenko St.
03680 Kiev, Ukraine
Phone: 380 44 2876302
Fax: 380 44 5280486
Publications: Technical Diagnostics and Nondestructive Testing (51608)

Patrimonio Nacional Palacio Real de Madrid
Palacio Real
E-28071 Madrid, Spain
Phone: 34 91 4548700
Publications: Reales Sitios (50795)

Pattaya Mail Publishing Company Ltd.
370/7-8 Pattaya Second Rd.
Pattaya City 20260, Thailand
Phone: 66 384 11240
Fax: 66 384 27596
Publications: Pattaya Mail (51463)

Pavilion Publishing
Richmond House
Richmond Rd.
Brighton BN2 3RL, United Kingdom
Phone: 44 1273 623222
Fax: 44 0844 8805062
Publications: Advances in Mental Health and Intellectual Disabilities (52604) • The British Journal of Forensic Practice (52607) • Healthmatters (52611) •

Housing, Care and Support (52613) • The International Journal of Leadership in Public Services (52616) • International Journal of Migration, Health and Social Care (52617) • The Journal of Adult Protection (52618) • Journal of Children's Services (52619) • Journal of Integrated Care (52621) • The Journal of Mental Health Training, Education and Practice (52622) • Journal of Public Mental Health (52623) • Learning Disability Review (52624) • Learning Disability Today (52625) • Mental Health Review Journal (52626) • Mental Health Today (52627) • Quality in Ageing (52629) • Safer Communities (52632) • Working with Older People (52635)

Pax Christi - Italy
Via Quintole Per Le Rose 131
I-50029 Tavarnuzze, Italy
Phone: 39 055 2020375
Fax: 39 055 2020608
Publications: Mosaico di Pace (46124)

Payer & Payer GesmbH
Winzerstrasse 23
A-1130 Vienna, Austria
Phone: 43 171 80246
Fax: 43 171 8024622
Publications: Extra Golf (42757)

PBWnews
6 The Rickyard
Clifton Reynes
Olney MK46 5LQ, United Kingdom
Phone: 44 12 34714644
Fax: 44 12 34714633
Publications: PBWnews (55845)

PCCS Books Ltd.
2 Cropper Row
Alton Rd.
Ross-on-Wye HR9 5LA, United Kingdom
Phone: 44 1989 763900
Fax: 44 1989 763901
Publications: Person-Centered and Experimental Psychotherapies (56411)

Pedal Power ACT Inc.
GPO Box 581
Canberra, Australian Capital Territory 2601, Australia
Phone: 61 2 62487995
Fax: 61 2 62487774
Publications: Canberra Cyclist (41703)

Peebles Media Group
Bergius House
Clifton St.
Glasgow G3 7LA, United Kingdom
Phone: 44 141 5676000
Fax: 44 141 3311395
Publications: Envirotec (53416) • OS (53437) • Packaging Scotland (53438) • Project Plant (53441) • Project Scotland (53442) • scottish grocer (53447)

PEETERS - Leuven
Bondgenotenlaan 153
B-3000 Leuven, Belgium
Phone: 32 162 35170
Fax: 32 162 28500
Publications: Bijdragen (42892) • Bulletin Antieke Beschaving (BABESCH) (48659) • Ethical Perspectives (42894) • Iranica Antiqua (42899) • Journal Asiatique (44063)

PEETERS - USA
141 Endean Dr.
Walpole, MA 02032-1061
Fax: 508734-5670
Publications: Ancient Society (42891) • ASTIN Bulletin (53254) • INTAMS review (42898) • Journal of Coptic Studies (44352) • Journal of the European Society of Women in Theological Research (44146) • Karthago (44067) • Khil'a (42912)

Pelican Magazines Ltd.
2 Cheltenham Mount
Harrogate HG1 1DL, United Kingdom
Phone: 44 1423 569676
Fax: 44 1423 569677
Publications: Orthopaedic Product News (53518)

Pender Beekeeping Supplies Proprietary Ltd.
PMB 19
Maitland, New South Wales 2320, Australia
Phone: 61 2 49327999

Fax: 61 2 49325994
Publications: Australasian Beekeeper (42028)

Pendragon Press Ltd.
April Arcade
124 Ocean View Rd.
PO Box 5
Oneroa, New Zealand
Phone: 64 937 25055
Fax: 64 937 25055
Publications: Gulf News (Waiheke) (48961)

Penerbit Universiti Kebangsaan Malaysia
University Kebangsaan Malaysia
43600 Bangi, Malaysia
Phone: 60 3 89215321
Fax: 60 3 89254575
Publications: Jurnal Ekonomi Malaysia (47574)

Pension Publications Ltd.
Hope House, E Wing, 4th Fl.
45 Great Peter St.
London SW1P 3LT, United Kingdom
Phone: 44 20 72220288
Fax: 44 20 77992163
Publications: Benefits & Compensation International (54011)

People's Daily Online
Jintaixi Rd. No. 2
Chaoyang District
Beijing 100733, People's Republic of China
Phone: 86 10 65363470
Publications: People's Daily (43213)

People's Independent Media Inc.
Leyland Bldg.
Railroad St.
Port Area
Manila 1018, Philippines
Phone: 63 2 5271841
Fax: 63 2 5271836
Publications: Malaya (49552)

People's Progressive Party
41 Robb St.
Georgetown, Guyana
Phone: 592 272095
Fax: 592 272096
Publications: Thunder (44801)

Perdix Publishing Ltd.
Bridge Farm
Chediston
Halesworth IP19 0AE, United Kingdom
Phone: 44 1986 873688
Publications: Deer (53504)

Performance Textiles Association
Priory Ct.
Pilgrim St.
London EC4V 6DR, United Kingdom
Phone: 44 207 6189196
Fax: 44 207 3297301
Publications: Performance Textiles (55067)

Periodical Publishers Association
Queens House
28 Kingsway
London WC2B 6JR, United Kingdom
Phone: 44 207 4044166
Fax: 44 207 4044167
Publications: Magazine News (54894)

Periodici San Paolo
Via. Alessandro Severo 58
I-00145 Rome, Italy
Phone: 39 065 978600
Fax: 39 065 978660
Publications: Club 3 (46224) • Famiglia Cristiana (46229) • Jesus (46236)

Periodiek en Partners
Postbus 41
NL-7940 AA Meppel, Netherlands
Phone: 31 572855333
Fax: 31 572855300
Publications: Kijk op Oost Nederland (48739)

Permanent Way Institution
4 Coombe Rd.
Folkestone CT19 4EG, United Kingdom

Phone: 44 130 3274534
Publications: Journal and Report of Proceedings (53392)

Permanyer Publications
Mallorca, 310
08037 Barcelona, Spain
Phone: 34 932 075920
Fax: 34 934 576642
Publications: AIDS Reviews (50648) • Cancer & Chemotherapy Reviews (50655) • Cirugia Cardiovascular (50656) • Hepatology Reviews (50677) • Revista Espanola de Ortodoncia (50695) • Trends in Transplantation (50703)

Persatuan Ekonomi Malaysia
c/o University of Malaya
Faculty of Economics & Administration
50603 Kuala Lumpur, Malaysia
Publications: Malaysian Journal of Economic Studies (47616)

Perspective Publishing
3 London Wall Bldgs., 6th Fl.
London EC2M 5PD, United Kingdom
Phone: 44 20 75622400
Fax: 44 20 73742701
Publications: Cable & Satellite International (54164) • Charity Times (54197) • Continuity, Insurance & Risk (54264) • European Pensions (54408) • Financial Sector Technology (54458) • Pensions Age (55065) • Retail Systems (55196)

Peruvian - German Chamber of Commerce and Industry
Av. Camino Real 348, of. 1502
San Isidro 27, Peru
Phone: 51 1 4418616
Fax: 51 1 4426014
Publications: Made in Germany (49441)

Pesticide Science Society of Japan
1-43-11 Komagome
Toshima-ku
Tokyo 170-8484, Japan
Phone: 81 3 39436021
Fax: 81 3 39436086
Publications: Journal of Pesticide Science (46477)

Pet Care Trust
Bedford Business Ctr.
170 Mile Rd.
Bedford MK42 9TW, United Kingdom
Phone: 44 1234 273933
Fax: 44 1234 273550
Publications: Petcare (52274)

Peter Knipp Holdings Private Ltd.
7 Jalan Kilang, 5th Fl.
Singapore 159407, Singapore
Phone: 65 62737707
Fax: 65 62701763
Publications: CW Magazine (50129)

Pharmaceutical Press
1 Lambeth High St.
London SE1 7JN, United Kingdom
Phone: 44 20 77359141
Fax: 44 20 75722509
Publications: British National Formulary (54142) • Clinical Pharmacist (54227)

Pharmaceutical Society of Australia
44 Thesiger Ct.
Deakin, Australian Capital Territory 2600, Australia
Phone: 61 262 834777
Fax: 61 262 852869
Publications: Australian Pharmacist (41834)

Pharmaceutical Society of Japan
12-15 Shibuya 2-chome
Shibuya-Ku
Tokyo 150-0002, Japan
Fax: 81 334 981835
Publications: Biological & Pharmaceutical Bulletin (46764) • Chemical & Pharmaceutical Bulletin (46783) • Journal of Health Science (46903)

Pharmaceutical Society of Korea
1489-3 Suhcho 3-Dong, Suhcho-Ku
Suhcho-ku
Seoul 137-071, Republic of Korea
Phone: 82 2 5843257

Fax: 82 2 5211781
Publications: Archives of Pharmacal Research (47253)

Pharmacotherapy Group
Faculty of Pharmacy
University of Benin
Benin City, Nigeria
Phone: 234 802 3360318
Fax: 234 52 602257
Publications: Tropical Journal of Pharmaceutical Research (49067)

Pharos Media & Publishing (P) Ltd.
D-84 Abul Fazl Enclave-I
Jamia Nagar
New Delhi 110 025, Delhi, India
Phone: 91 11 26947483
Fax: 91 11 26945825
Publications: Journal of Islamic History (45610) • Muslim & Arab Perspectives (45628)

Philatelic Group
GPO Box 1777
Melbourne, Victoria 3001, Australia
Publications: Stamp Bulletin (42087) • Stamp Explorer (42088)

Philip Allan Updates
338 Euston Rd.
London NW1 3BH, United Kingdom
Phone: 44 20 78736000
Fax: 44 20 78736299
Publications: Economic Review (UK) (54351) • Sociology Review (55254) • 20th Century History Review (55350)

Philippine Academy of Ophthalmology
Unit 815, Medical Plz. Makati
Amorsolo St.
Cor. De la Rosa St.
Makati City 1000, Philippines
Phone: 63 2 8135318
Fax: 63 2 8135331
Publications: Philippine Journal of Ophthalmology (49521)

Philippine Association of Entomologists
c/o Department of Entomology
University of the Phillipines at Los Banos College
Laguna 4031, Philippines
Phone: 63 49 536 1315
Publications: The Philippine Entomologist (49508)

Philippine Association of Nutrition
General Santos Ave.
Bicutan
Taguig City 1631, Philippines
Phone: 63 283 91842
Fax: 63 283 91842
Publications: Philippine Journal of Nutrition (49640)

Philippine College of Physicians
Unit 2201-2203, 22nd Fl.
San Miguel Ave. Cor. Shaw Blvd.
Ortigas Center
Pasig City 1600, Philippines
Phone: 63 2 9102250
Fax: 63 2 9102251
Publications: Philippino Journal of Internal Medicine (49573)

The Philippine Daily Inquirer Inc.
Chino Roces Ave.
Cor. Yague & Mascardo Sts.
PO Box 2353
Makati City 1263, Philippines
Phone: 63 2 8978808
Fax: 63 2 8974793
Publications: Philippine Daily Inquirer (49519)

Philippine Headline News Online
1991 M.H. del Pilar
Malate
Manila, Philippines
Phone: 63 2 5232040
Fax: 63 2 5217366
Publications: Philippine Headline News Online (49554)

Philippine Institute of Certified Public Accountants
PICPA Bldg.
700 Shaw Blvd.
Mandaluyong City, Philippines

Phone: 63 2 723 0691
Fax: 63 2 723 6305
Publications: Accountant's Journal (49531)

Philippine Institute for Development Studies
Rm. 304, NEDA Makati Bldg.
106 Amorsolo St.
Legaspi Village
Makati City 1229, Philippines
Phone: 63 289 35705
Fax: 63 289 39589
Publications: Philippine Journal of Development (49520)

Philippine Nurses Association
1663 F.T. Benitez St.
Malate
Manila 1004, Philippines
Phone: 63 2 5210937
Fax: 63 2 5251596
Publications: Philippine Journal of Nursing (49556)

Philippine Sociological Society
Philippine Social Science Council
PSSCenter, Commonwealth Ave.
Diliman
Quezon City 1101, Philippines
Phone: 63 2 9292671
Fax: 63 2 9229621
Publications: Philippine Sociological Review (49613)

Phillipine Rotary
87 Visayas Ave.
Quezon City 1100, Philippines
Phone: 63 2 9267453
Fax: 63 2 9291912
Publications: Philippine Rotary (49611)

Philological Society
c/o Dr. Martin Orwin, Hon. Sec.
School of Oriental & African Studies
Department of Africa
Thornhaugh St.
London WC1H 0XG, United Kingdom
Phone: 44 20 78984376
Fax: 44 20 78984399
Publications: Transactions of the Philological Society (56516)

Phnom Penh Post
888 Bldg. F, 8th Fl.
Phnom Penh, Cambodia
Phone: 855 23 214311
Fax: 855 23 214318
Publications: Phnom Penh Post (43113)

An Phoblacht/Republican News
58 Parnell Sq.
Dublin IRL-1, Dublin, Ireland
Phone: 353 187 33611
Fax: 353 187 33074
Publications: An Phoblacht (45945)

The Phuket Gazette Company Ltd.
79/94 Moo 4
Thepkrasattri Rd.
T. Koh Keaw, A. Muang
Phuket 83000, Thailand
Phone: 66 762 73555
Fax: 66 766 15240
Publications: Phuket Gazette (51464)

Physical Society of Japan
5F Eishin-kaihatsu Bldg.
5-34-3 Shimbashi
Minato-ku
Tokyo 105-0004, Japan
Phone: 81 3 34342671
Fax: 81 3 34320997
Publications: Journal of Physical Society of Japan (46937)

The Physical Society of the Republic of China
PO Box 23-30
Taipei 106, Taiwan
Phone: 886 2 23634923
Fax: 886 2 23626538
Publications: Chinese Journal of Physics (51335)

Physiological Society - England
Peer House
Verulam St.
London WC1X 8LZ, United Kingdom

Phone: 44 20 72695710
Fax: 44 20 72695720
Publications: The Journal of Physiology (54802)

Phytochemical Society of Europe
Espinardo-Murcia
de Alimentos
E-30100 Murcia, Spain
Publications: Phytochemistry (50822)

Picture-Box Media Ltd.
Dulwich Lodge
62 Pemberton Rd.
East Molesey KT8 9LH, United Kingdom
Phone: 44 20 89410249
Fax: 44 20 89411088
Publications: Ag Magazine (53239)

Pier Professional
The Old Market, Ste. N4
Upper Market St.
Hove BN3 1AS, United Kingdom
Phone: 44 1273 783720
Fax: 44 1273 783723
Publications: Advances in Dual Diagnosis (53603) • Drugs and Alcohol Today (53604) • Ethnicity and Inequalities in Health and Social Care (53605) • Journal of Aggression, Conflict and Peace Research (53606) • Journal of Assistive Technologies (53607) • Journal of Learning Disabilities and Offending Behaviour (53609) • A Life in the Day (53610) • Safer Communities (53612) • Social Care and Neurodisability (53613)

Pilotmagazinet
PO Box 301
S-77126 Ludvika, Sweden
Phone: 46 240 84890
Fax: 46 240 18015
Publications: pilotmagazinet (50980)

Pinede Publishing
16-18 Hawkesyard Hall
Armitage Pk.
Rugeley WS15 1PU, United Kingdom
Phone: 44 1889 577222
Fax: 44 1889 579177
Publications: Plumbing, Heating & Air Movement News (53391)

Pink Ink
MBE Surawong NO. 227
173/3 Surawong Rd.
Bangkok 10500, Thailand
Phone: 66 2 6613150
Publications: Pink Ink (51430)

Pinpoint Scotland Ltd.
9 Gayfield Sq.
Edinburgh EH1 3NT, United Kingdom
Phone: 44 131 5574184
Fax: 44 131 4788405
Publications: Cardiology News (53260) • Eye News (53275) • Scotland's New Homebuyer (53310)

Pion Ltd.
207 Brondesbury Pk.
London NW2 5JN, United Kingdom
Phone: 44 20 84590066
Fax: 44 20 84516454
Publications: Environment & Planning A (54373) • European Research in Regional Science (54410) • High Temperatures-High Pressures (54551)

Pioneer Total Abstinence Association
27 Upper Sherrard St.
Dublin IRL-1, Dublin, Ireland
Phone: 35 318 749464
Fax: 35 318 748485
Publications: Pioneer (45994)

Pipeline Industries Guild
14/15 Belgrave Sq.
London SW1X 8PS, United Kingdom
Phone: 44 20 72357938
Fax: 44 20 72350074
Publications: Pipeline World (55090)

Pira International
Cleeve Rd.
Leatherhead KT22 7RU, United Kingdom
Phone: 44 1372 802000
Fax: 44 1372 802079

Telex: 929810
Publications: Packaging Month (53752)

Piracicaba Dental School - UNICAMP
Av. Limeira 901, Piracicaba
Caixa Postal 52
13414-903 Sao Paulo, Sao Paulo, Brazil
Phone: 55 19 21065200
Fax: 55 19 34210144
Publications: Brazilian Journal of Oral Sciences (43027)

Pireme Publishing Ltd.
c/o Andrew Hubback
Strelley Hall
Nottingham NG8 6PE, United Kingdom
Phone: 44 115 9061200
Fax: 44 115 9061251
Publications: Miniature Wargames (55767)

Piton Publishing House Ltd.
79/81 High St.
Godalming GU7 1AW, United Kingdom
Phone: 44 1483425454
Publications: Monocle Magazine (53476)

Pius Branzeu Center
2 Eftimie Murgu St.
RO-300041 Timisoara, Romania
Phone: 40 256 216510
Fax: 40 256 216510
Publications: Timisoara Medical Journal (TMJ) (49849)

PJB Publications Ltd.
Telephone House
69-77 Paul St.
London EC2A 4LQ, United Kingdom
Phone: 44 20 70175000
Fax: 44 20 70176792
Publications: BioVenture View (54031) • Clinica World Medical Device and Diagnostic News (54218) • Good Clinical Practice Journal (GCPj) (54519) • Instrumenta (54609) • Journal of Clinical Research (54726) • Journal of Drug Assessment (54739) • Journal of Outcomes Research (54791) • Regulatory Affairs Journal (55181) • Regulatory Affairs Journal (Devices) (55182) • Scrip Magazine (55221)

Placencia Chapter of the Belize Tourism Industry Association
10 N Park St.
Belize City, Belize
Phone: 501 5234045
Fax: 501 5233294
Publications: Placencia Breeze (42916)

Plan International Deutschland e.V.
Bramfelder Str. 70
D-22305 Hamburg, Germany
Phone: 49 406 11400
Fax: 49 406 1140140
Publications: Plan Post (44423)

Planera Bygga Bo
Boverket
Box 534
SE-371 23 Karlskrona, Sweden
Publications: Planera Bygga Bo (50971)

Planetary Gemologists Association
131 Soi Asoke
Sukhumvit Rd.
Bangkok 10110, Thailand
Phone: 66 266 16479
Fax: 66 226 02833
Publications: Journal of the Planetary Gemologists Association (51424)

Plankton Society of Japan
c/o Mar. Biodiversity Lab.
3-1-1 Minatomachi
Hokkaido
Hakodate 041-8611, Japan
Phone: 81 138 405543
Fax: 81 138 405542
Publications: Plankton and Benthos Research (46372)

Plastics Historical Society
c/o Susan Lambert
Brick Hill
Burghclere
Berkshire RG20 9HJ, United Kingdom
Publications: Plastiquarian (52316)

Plastics and Rubber Institute of Singapore
Tanglin PO Box 354
Singapore 912412, Singapore
Publications: Plastics & Rubber Singapore Journal
(50241)

The Poetry Society
22 Betterton St.
London WC2H 9BX, United Kingdom
Phone: 44 20 74209880
Fax: 44 20 72404818
Publications: Poetry Review (55097)

Pogranicze Foundation
ul. Pilsudskiego St. 37
PL-16-500 Sejny, Poland
Phone: 48 87 5162765
Fax: 48 87 5162765
Publications: Krasnogruda (49675)

Police Federation of England and Wales
Federation House
Highbury Dr.
Leatherhead KT22 7UY, United Kingdom
Phone: 44 1372 352000
Publications: Police (53753)

Policy Press
University of Bristol
Beacon House, 4th Fl.
Queen's Road
Bristol BS8 1QU UK, United Kingdom
Phone: 44 0117 331 4054
Fax: 44 0117 331 4093
Publications: Policy and Politics (52722) • Voluntary
Sector Review (52735)

The Policy Press
University of Bristol, Fourth Fl.
Beacon House, Queen's Rd.
Bristol BS8 1QU, United Kingdom
Phone: 44 117 3314054
Fax: 44 117 3314093
Publications: Evidence & Policy (52667) • The Journal
of Poverty and Social Justice (52696)

Polish Academy of Sciences
PO Box 21
ul. Sniadeckich 8
00-956 Warsaw, Poland
Fax: 48 226 293997
Publications: Acta Arithmetica (49677)

Polish Football Association
ul. Miodowa 1
PL-00-080 Warsaw, Poland
Phone: 48 22 5512300
Fax: 48 22 5512240
Publications: Trener (49768)

Political Party Democrats 66
PO Box 660
NL-2501 CR The Hague, Netherlands
Phone: 31 703 566066
Fax: 31 703 641917
Publications: Democraat (48612)

Political Studies Association of the UK
Department of Politics
University of Newcastle
Newcastle upon Tyne NE1 7RU, United Kingdom
Phone: 44 19 12228021
Fax: 44 19 12223499
Publications: The British Journal of Politics and
International Relations (55750)

**Political Studies Association of the United
Kingdom**
Dept. of Politics
University of Newcastle
Newcastle upon Tyne NE1 7RU, United Kingdom
Phone: 44 191 2228021
Fax: 44 191 2223499
Publications: Political Studies (56512)

Polska Akademia Nauk
ul. Parkowa 5
PL-62-035 Kornik, Poland
Phone: 48 61 8170 033
Fax: 48 61 8170 166
Publications: Dendrobiology (49663)

**Pontifical Council for the Pastoral Care of
Migrants and Itinerant People**
Palazzo San Calisto
I-00120 Vatican City, Vatican City
Phone: 39 066 9887131
Fax: 39 669 887111
Publications: People on the Move (57015)

Pontificia Universidad Catolica de Chile
Alameda 340
Oficina 13
Santiago, Chile
Fax: 56 222 23116
Publications: Psykhe (43146)

Pontificia Universidad Catolica De Valparaiso
Av. Brasil 2950
PO Box 4059
Valparaiso, Chile
Publications: Electronic Journal of Biotechnology
(43162)

Pontificia Universidade Catolica de Sao Paulo
Rua Monte Alegre, 984
05014-001 Sao Paulo, Sao Paulo, Brazil
Publications: Documentacao de Estudos em Linguistica Teorica e Aplicada (DELTA) (43037)

The Pool Newspaper
Third Fl., Ste. No. 1, Short St.
Freetown, Sierra Leone
Phone: 232 222 20102
Fax: 232 222 20102
Publications: The Pool Newspaper (50096)

PopMatters Media, Inc.
1555 Sherman Ave. No. 324
Evanston, IL 60201
Publications: Chapter&Verse (53760)

Popular Flying Association
Turweston Aerodrome
Northants
Brackley NN13 5YD, United Kingdom
Phone: 44 12 80846786
Fax: 44 12 80846780
Publications: Popular Flying (52433)

Population Association of New Zealand
PO Box 225
Wellington, New Zealand
Phone: 64 4 4638225
Fax: 64 4 4638088
Publications: New Zealand Population Review (49029)

Portland Press Ltd.
Commerce Way
Colchester C02 8HP, United Kingdom
Phone: 44 1206 796351
Fax: 44 1206 799331
Publications: Annals of The Royal College of Surgeons
of England (53028) • Biochemical Society Symposia
(53029) • Biochemical Society Transactions (53030) •
Bulletin of Medical Ethics (53031) • Essays in Biochem-
istry (53035)

**Portsmouth & South East Hampshire Chamber
of Commerce & Industry**
Harts Farm Way
Havant PO9 1HR, United Kingdom
Phone: 44 23 92449449
Fax: 44 23 92449444
Publications: Business News (South East Hampshire)
(53543)

Positif Press
130 Southfield Rd.
Oxford OX4 1PA, United Kingdom
Phone: 44 1865 243220
Fax: 44 1865 243272
Publications: Journal of the BIOS (56018)

Positive Action Publications Ltd.
PO Box 4
Driffield YO25 9DJ, United Kingdom
Phone: 44 13 77241724
Fax: 44 13 77253640
Publications: International Dairy Topics (53202) •
International Food Hygiene (53203) • International
Hatchery Practice (53204) • International Pig Topics
(53205) • International Poultry Production (53206)

Positive Health Publications Ltd.
105 Madeira Rd.

Portsmouth PO2 0SY, United Kingdom
Phone: 44 23 92653266
Fax: 44 23 926653266
Publications: Positive Health (56292)

The Post Publishing Public Company Ltd.
Bangkok Post Bldg.
136 Na Ranong Rd.
Klong Toey
Bangkok 10110, Thailand
Phone: 66 224 03700
Fax: 66 224 03790
Publications: Bangkok Post Student Weekly (51414)

Postgraduate Institute of Management
University of Sri Jayewardenepura
28 Lesley Ranagala Mawatha
Colombo 8, Sri Lanka
Phone: 94 11 2689639
Fax: 94 11 2689643
Publications: Sri Lankan Journal of Management
(50869)

Posthornet
Mollergaten 10
N-0179 Oslo, Norway
Phone: 47 23061561
Fax: 47 23062271
Publications: Posthornet (49206)

Poundbury Publishing Ltd.
Middle Farm
Middle Farm Way
Poundbury
Dorset DT1 3RS, United Kingdom
Phone: 44 1305 266360
Fax: 44 1305 262760
Publications: Minor Monthly (53195) • Point to Point
and Hunter Chase Magazine (53196)

Pour nos Jardins
40 Rte. d'Aulnoy
F-59300 Valenciennes, France
Phone: 33 3 27463750
Fax: 33 3 27290812
Publications: Pour nos Jardins (44121)

The Powys Review
Beeches House
Harborough Rd.
Desborough NN14 2QX, United Kingdom
Publications: The Powys Review (53175)

Powys Society
c/o Peter Lazare, Sec.
25 Mansfield Rd.
Taunton TA1 3NJ, United Kingdom
Phone: 44 1823278177
Publications: Powys Journal (56722)

PPGAS-Museu Nacional
Quinta da Boa Vista S/N - Sao Cristovao
20940-040 Rio de Janeiro, Rio de Janeiro, Brazil
Phone: 55 212 5689642
Fax: 55 212 2546695
Publications: Mana - Estudos de Antropologia Social
(43011)

PPMA Ltd.
New Progress House
34 Stafford Rd.
Wallington SM6 9AA, United Kingdom
Phone: 44 20 87738111
Fax: 44 20 87730022
Publications: Machinery Update (56833)

Practical Action Publing
The Schumacher Ctr. for Technology and Development
Bourton on Dunsmore
Rugby CV23 9QZ, United Kingdom
Phone: 44 19 26634501
Fax: 44 19 26634502
Telex: 888 941 A/B LCCIG
Publications: Enterprise Development and Microfi-
nance (56418)

Practical Action Publishing
The Schumacher Centre for Technology & Develop-
ment
Bourton on Dunsmore
Warwickshire
Rugby CV23 9QZ, United Kingdom
Phone: 44 1926 634501

Fax: 44 1926 634502
Publications: Waterlines (56425)

Pragativadi
178/B, Mancheswar Industrial Estate
Bhubaneswar 751 010, West Bengal, India
Phone: 91 674 2588297
Fax: 91 674 2582709
Publications: Pragativadi (45014)

The Prague Post S.R.O.
Stepanska 20
CZ-110 00 Prague 1, Czech Republic
Phone: 420 2 96334400
Fax: 420 2 96334450
Publications: The Prague Post (43636)

Pre-Raphaelite Society
c/o Barry Johnson
37 Larchmere Dr.
Hall Green
Birmingham B28 8JB, United Kingdom
Publications: Review (52364)

Premier Magazines
Haymarket House
1 Oxendon St.
London SW1Y 4EE, United Kingdom
Phone: 44 20 79252544
Publications: The London Magazine (54887)

Prensa del Espectaculo S.L.
Paris, 151-155
esc. izda
Despacho, 7
E-08036 Barcelona, Spain
Phone: 34 3 4393511
Fax: 34 3 4107921
Publications: Show Press (50698)

Presbyterian Church in Ireland
Church House
Belfast BT1 6DW, United Kingdom
Phone: 44 28 90322284
Publications: The Presbyterian Herald (52292)

Price Communications, Inc.
PO Box 23498
91234 Jerusalem, Israel
Phone: 972 2 5862031
Fax: 972 2 5863019
Publications: Jerusalem Magazine (46086)

Primary Care Respiratory Society UK
Smithy House
Waterbeck
Lockerbie 1G11 3EY, United Kingdom
Phone: 44 121 3514455
Fax: 44 121 3361914
Publications: Primary Care Respiratory Journal (53888)

Prime Marketing Publications Ltd.
Cavendish House
Cavendish Ct.
44-47 Hill Ave.
Amersham HP6 5FA, United Kingdom
Phone: 44 870 9088767
Fax: 44 870 1340931
Publications: International Consultants' Guide (52107)

Primer Acto
Ricardo de la Vega, 18
E-28028 Madrid, Spain
Phone: 34 917 258085
Fax: 34 917 263711
Publications: Primer Acto (50792)

Primus Publishing Ltd.
Hammerstrasse 81
Postfach 1331
CH-8032 Zurich, Switzerland
Phone: 41 44 3875757
Fax: 41 44 3875707
Publications: Travel Inside (51292) • Travel Inside Francais (51293) • Travel Manager (51294)

Princeton University
164/6 Prince Anwar Shah Rd.
Kolkata 700 045, West Bengal, India
Phone: 91 33 242288645
Publications: Energy for Sustainable Development (45265)

The Printers (Mysore) Ltd.
75 Mahatma Gandhi Rd.
PO Box 5331
Bangalore 560 001, Karnataka, India
Phone: 91 80 25880000
Fax: 91 80 25880523
Publications: Deccan Herald (44957)

Pro Familia: Deutsche Gesellschaft fur Familien-planung,
Stresemannallee 3
D-60596 Frankfurt am Main, Germany
Phone: 49 69 639002
Fax: 49 69 639852
Publications: Pro Familia Magazin (44368)

Pro Helvetia Arts Council of Switzerland
Hirschengraben 22
CH-8024 Zurich, Switzerland
Phone: 41 1 4472677171
Fax: 41 1 442677106
Publications: Passages (51276)

PRo Publications International Ltd.
Adelphi Ct., 1st Fl.
1 East St.
Surrey KT17 1BB, United Kingdom
Phone: 44 1372 743837
Fax: 44 1372 743838
Publications: Global Cement Magazine (56663) • Global Gypsum Magazine (56664) • Global Insulation Magazine (56665)

Pro Sport Media Ltd.
45 Woodside Gardens
Sittingbourne ME10 1SG, United Kingdom
Phone: 44 17 95424631
Fax: 44 18 95424631
Publications: DIY Week (56547) • Hardware & Garden Review (56548) • Housewares (UK) (56549) • The PGA Professional (56551)

Probability Surveys
c/o Geoffrey Grimmett, Mng. Ed.
Centre for Mathematical Sciences
University of Cambridge
Wilberforce Rd.
Cambridge CB3 0WB, United Kingdom
Phone: 44 1223 337957
Fax: 44 1223 337956
Publications: International Journal of Design (51344) • Probability Surveys (52885)

Process Products Ltd.
Passfield Business Center
Lynchborough Rd.
Passfield
Liphook GU30 7SB, United Kingdom
Phone: 44 1428 751188
Fax: 44 1428 751199
Publications: Process Industry Informer (53861)

Producers Alliance for Cinema and Television
3rd Fl. Fitzrovia House
153-157 Cleveland St.
London W1T 6QW, United Kingdom
Phone: 44 20 73808230
Publications: Pact (55050)

Association des Professeurs d'Histoire et de Geographie
BP 6541
75065 Paris Cedex 2, France
Phone: 33 142 336237
Fax: 33 142 331208
Publications: Historiens et Geographes (44048)

Professional Engineering Publishing
1 Birdcage Walk
London SW1H 9JJ, United Kingdom
Phone: 44 20 79731300
Fax: 44 20 79736844
Publications: Journal of Engineering Manufacture (52247)

Professional Lighting & Sound Association
Redoubt House
1 Edward Rd.
Eastbourne BN23 8AS, United Kingdom
Phone: 44 1323 524120
Fax: 44 1323 524121
Publications: Lighting & Sound International (53244)

Professional Marketing International
Warnford Ct.
29 Throgmorton St.
London EC2N 2AT, United Kingdom
Phone: 44 20 77869786
Fax: 44 20 77869799
Publications: Professional Marketing (55131)

Professional Medical Publications
Rm. No. 522, 5th Fl., Panorama Centre
Bldg. No. 2, Saddar
PO Box 8766
Karachi, Pakistan
Phone: 92 21 5689285
Fax: 92 21 5689860
Publications: Pakistan Journal of Medical Sciences (49369) • Pulse International (49374)

Program for Research and Documentation for a Sustainable Society
University of Oslo
PO Box 1116
Blindern
N-0317 Oslo, Norway
Phone: 47 228 58900
Fax: 47 228 58790
Publications: Monitor 21 (49204)

Programa de Pos-Graduacao em Letras Neolati-nas
Av. Brigadeiro Trompovsky s/n
Ilha do Fundao
Rio de Janeiro, Rio de Janeiro, Brazil
Phone: 55 2598 9798
Publications: Alea (43000)

Progresa
Julian Camarillo, 29 B
1 planta
E-28037 Madrid, Spain
Phone: 34 91 5386104
Fax: 34 91 5229508
Publications: Claves de Razon Practica (50735)

Progressive Media Markets
Maidstone Rd.
Sidcup DA14 5HZ, United Kingdom
Phone: 44 20 82697751
Fax: 44 20 82697874
Publications: Packaging Today (56545)

ProLitteris
Postfach
CH-8033 Zurich, Switzerland
Phone: 41 433 006615
Fax: 41 433 006668
Publications: Gazzetta (51261)

The Property Executive
216 St. Vincent St.
Glasgow G2 5SG, United Kingdom
Phone: 44 1506 204913
Publications: The Property Executive (53443)

Property Print Services
Banner House
Briar Close
Evesham WR11 4XA, United Kingdom
Phone: 44 1386 765832
Publications: Oldham & District Property News (53344)

ProPress Publishing Group Ltd.
Am Buschhof 8
D-53227 Bonn, Germany
Publications: Behorden Spiegel (44253)

Prospect Publishing Ltd.
2 Bloomsbury Pl.
London WC1A 2QA, United Kingdom
Phone: 44 20 72551281
Fax: 44 20 72551279
Publications: Prospect (55143)

Protestant Truth Society Inc.
184 Fleet St.
London EC4A 2HJ, United Kingdom
Phone: 44 20 74054960
Publications: Protestant Truth (55146)

Prous Science S.A.
Provenza 388
08025 Barcelona, Spain
Phone: 34 93 4592220

Fax: 34 93 4581535
Publications: Drug News & Perspectives (50664)

PS Narayanan
10 (Old No. 14) First St.
Kasturi Ranga Rd.
Chennai 600 018, Tamil Nadu, India
Phone: 91 44 28128070
Fax: 91 44 28111902
Publications: Sruti (45058)

PSB Design & Print Consultants Ltd.
PO Box 5
Driffield YO25 8JD, United Kingdom
Phone: 44 13 77255213
Publications: craft&design (53200)

PSBN Verlags GmbH
Eisenhuttenstr. 4
40882 Ratingen, Germany
Phone: 49 21022046830
Fax: 49 2102895825
Publications: Deutsche Briefmarken Revue (44641)

PSP Publishing Ltd.
50 High Craighall Rd.
Glasgow G4 9UD, United Kingdom
Phone: 44 141 3532222
Fax: 44 141 3323839
Publications: Bunkered (53411) • English Club Golfer
(53415) • Nationwide Bowler (53432) • No.1 (53435) •
Scottish Club Golfer (53446) • Scottish Hosteller
(53448) • Welsh Club Golfer (53459)

Psychologia Society
Dept. of Cognitive Psychology in Education
Graduate School of Education
Kyoto University
Kyoto 606-8501, Japan
Fax: 81 757 533049
Publications: Psychologia (46485)

Psychological Association of the Philippines
Philippine Social Science Council
PSSC Bldg.
Commonwealth Ave.
Diliman
Quezon City 1101, Philippines
Publications: Philippine Journal of Psychology (49606)

Psychological Society of Northern Greece
School of Psychology
Aristotle University of Thessaloniki
GR-541 24 Thessaloniki, Greece
Publications: Hellenic Journal of Psychology (44772)

Psychology Graduate Course
2600 Sala 110
90035-003 Porto Alegre, Rio Grande do Sul, Brazil
Publications: Psicologia (42992)

Psychology Press
270 Madison Ave.
New York, NY 10016-0601
Phone: 212216-7800
Fax: 212563-2269
Free: 800634-7064
Publications: European Journal of Developmental
Psychology (48756) • Neuropsychological Rehabilita-
tion (52875) • Thinking & Reasoning (56274)

PT Bina Media Tenggara
Jl. Palmera Selatan 15
10270 Jakarta, Indonesia
Phone: 62 21 5300476
Fax: 62 21 5350050
Publications: The Jakarta Post (45801)

PT Bumi Dian Kusuma
Jl. Bypass Ngurah Rai 120C
Lt. 2
80361 Kuta, Indonesia
Phone: 62 361 752764
Fax: 62 361 762096
Publications: Bali & Beyond Magazine (45824)

P.T. Data Consult Inc.
Maya Indah Bldg.
Jalan Kramat Raya, No. 5-L
10450 Jakarta, Indonesia
Phone: 62 21 3904711
Fax: 62 21 3901877
Publications: Indonesian Commercial Newsletter
(45799)

PT Kubu Dua Media
Jl. Petitenget 12A
Kerobokan
Bali
Seminyak, Indonesia
Phone: 62 7463751
Fax: 62 8475458
Publications: The Beat (45854)

PT. Tempo Inti Media
Kebayoran Center Blok A11 - A15
Jl. Kebayoran Baru - Mayestik
12440 Jakarta, Indonesia
Phone: 62 21 7255625
Fax: 62 21 7256995
Publications: Tempo Interactive (45802)

The Ptolemaic Terrascope
PO Box 2152
Melksham SN12 7UQ, United Kingdom
Phone: 44 12 25706134
Publications: The Ptolemaic Terrascope Magazine
(55605)

Publiafinsa
Lagasca, 88 4o
E-28001 Madrid, Spain
Phone: 34 915 767007
Fax: 34 915 756117
Publications: Cronica Filatelica (50742)

Public Health Association of Australia
PO Box 319
Curtin, Australian Capital Territory 2605, Australia
Phone: 61 262 852373
Fax: 61 262 825438
Publications: Australian and New Zealand Journal of
Public Health (41826)

Public Monuments and Sculpture Association
70 Cowcross St.
London EC1M 6EJ, United Kingdom
Publications: The Sculpture Journal (55222)

Public Sector Information Ltd.
Petersgate House
St. Petersgate
Stockport SK1 1HE, United Kingdom
Phone: 44 1782620088
Fax: 44 1782740066
Publications: Defence Management Journal (56626)

Public Sector Publishing Ltd.
226 High Rd.
Loughton IG10 1ET, United Kingdom
Phone: 44 20 85320055
Fax: 44 20 85320066
Publications: Education Business (55489) • Govern-
ment Business (55490) • Government Technology
(55491) • Health Business (55492)

Public Services International
BP 9
F-01211 Ferney-Voltaire Cedex, France
Phone: 33 450 406464
Fax: 33 450 407320
Publications: Focus on the Public Services (43947)

Publicadora Atlantico
Rua N Senhora da Piedade
Sabugo
P-2715 Almargem do Bispo, Portugal
Phone: 351 21 9626200
Fax: 351 21 9626201
Publications: Saude e Lar (49784)

Publicis Blueprint
23 Howland St.
London W1A 1AQ, United Kingdom
Phone: 44 207 4627777
Publications: ASDA Magazine (53755) • AYGO Maga-
zine (53997) • Vanguard (55365) • Via Inmarsat
Magazine (55368)

Publicity Press Proprietary Ltd.
1121 High St.
Melbourne, Victoria 3143, Australia
Phone: 61 398044700
Fax: 61 398044711
Publications: Australian Triathlete (42054)

Publishing House Leo S. Olschki
Viuzzo del Pozzetto, 8
I-50126 Florence, Italy

Phone: 39 556 530684
Fax: 39 556 530214
Publications: Nuncius (46145)

**Publishing House of the Siberian Branch of the
Russian Academy of Sciences**
Morskoy pr. 2
630090 Novosibirsk, Russia
Phone: 7 383 3301758
Publications: Earth's Cryosphere (50010) • Geography
and Natural Resources (49856) • Journal Chemistry for
Sustainable Development (50011) • Journal of Mining
Sciences (50012) • Siberian Journal of Ecology
(50013) • Siberian Journal of Numerical Mathematics
(50014)

Pudhari
Pudhari Bhavan, 2318 C, Bhausingji Rd.
Kolhapur 416 002, Maharashtra, India
Phone: 91 231 2543111
Fax: 91 231 2543124
Publications: Pudhari (45256)

Pulp and Paper Technical Association
Janequeo 884 dep. 404
Concepcion, Chile
Phone: 56 41 2888131
Publications: Celulosa y Papel (43136)

Pulse Weekly
Mezzaine No.8, 47-W Dossul Arcade
Jinnah Ave., Blue Area
Islamabad, Pakistan
Phone: 92 51 812257
Publications: Pulse Weekly (49312)

Punjabi University
Punjabi University
Patiala 147 002, Punjab, India
Phone: 91 175 3046366
Publications: Panjab Past and Present (45686)

Pusat Penelitian Fisika LIPI
Kompleks PUSPIPTEK Serpong
15310 Tangerang, Indonesia
Phone: 62 217 560570
Fax: 62 217 560554
Publications: Physics Journal of the Indonesian Physi-
cal Society (45870)

Pushpa Publishing House
Vijaya Niwas
198 Mumfordganj
Allahabad 211002, Uttar Pradesh, India
Publications: Advances and Applications in Discrete
Mathematics (44919) • Advances and Applications in
Statistics (44920) • Advances in Computer Science and
Engineering (44921) • Advances in Differential Equa-
tions and Control Processes (44922) • Advances in
Fuzzy Sets and Systems (44923) • Current Develop-
ment in Theory and Applications of Wavelets (44924) •
Far East Journal of Applied Mathematics (44925) • Far
East Journal of Dynamical Systems (44926) • Far East
Journal of Electronics and Communications (44927) •
Far East Journal of Experimental and Theoretical
Artificial Intelligence (44928) • Far East Journal of
Mathematical Education (44929) • Far East Journal of
Mathematical Sciences (44930) • International Journal
of Functional Analysis, Operator Theory and Applica-
tions (44932) • International Journal of Information Sci-
ence and Computer Mathematics (43258) • Interna-
tional Journal of Materials Engineering and Technology
(47694) • International Journal of Numerical Methods
and Applications (44933) • JP Journal of Algebra,
Number Theory and Applications (44935) • JP Journal
of Biostatistics (44936) • JP Journal of Fixed Point
Theory and Applications (44937) • JP Journal of
Geometry and Topology (46375) • JP Journal of Heat
and Mass Transfer (44938) • JP Journal of Solids and
Structures (44939)

Pushpa Raj Pradhan
Pipalbot
Dillibazar
Kathmandu, Nepal
Phone: 977 1 4438797
Publications: People's Review (47845)

Puzzler Media Ltd.
Stonecroft, 69 Station Rd.
Surrey
Redhill RH1 1EY, United Kingdom

Phone: 99944 1737 378700
Fax: 99944 1737 781800
Publications: Arroword Selection (56342) • Beyond Sudoku (56343) • Chat Arrowords (56344) • Chat Crosswords (56345) • Chat Puzzles Select (56346) • Chat Wordsearch (56347) • Code Words (56348) • Crossword Selection (56349) • Fundoku (56351) • Hanjie (56353) • Junior Puzzles (56354) • Kakuro (56355) • Killer Sudoku (56356) • Kriss Kross (56357) • 100 Codewords (56358) • 100 Crosswords (56359) • 100 Wordsearch (56360) • Puzzle Compendium (56361) • Puzzle Corner Special (56362) • Puzzler (56363) • Puzzler Arrowords (56364) • Puzzler Brain Trainer (56365) • Puzzler Codewords (56366) • Puzzler Collection (56367) • Puzzler Crossword (56368) • Puzzler Kriss Kross (56369) • Puzzler Pocket Crosswords (56370) • Puzzler Pocket Crosswords Collection (56371) • Puzzler Pocket Wordsearch (56372) • Puzzler Pocket Wordsearch Collection (56373) • Puzzler Quick Crosswords (56374) • Puzzler Quiz Kids (56375) • Puzzler Wordsearch (56376) • Sudoku Puzzles (56380) • Super Hanjie (56381) • Word Search (56382)

Pyongyang Times
Sochon-dong
Pyongyang, Democratic People's Republic of Korea
Phone: 850 2 18111
Fax: 850 2 3814598
Publications: The Pyongyang Times (47207)

Pyramyd NTCV S.A.
15 rue Turbigo
F-75002 Paris, France
Phone: 33 140 260099
Fax: 33 140 260703
Publications: Bloc Notes Publishing (44030) • Etapes (44040)

Q News International
Dexion House
2-4 Empire Way
Wembley HA9 0XA, United Kingdom
Phone: 44 181 9030819
Publications: Q News (55159)

Qatar Info
PO Box 6124
Doha, Qatar
Phone: 974 4371773
Fax: 974 4371776
Publications: Qatar Info Magazine (49822)

Quadrant Magazine Company Inc.
PO Box 82
Sydney, New South Wales 2041, Australia
Phone: 61 2 98181155
Fax: 61 2 85804664
Publications: Quadrant (42567)

Qualified Private Medical Practitioners Association
Vallamattan Estate
Ravipuram
M.G. Rd.
Kochi 682015, Kerala, India
Phone: 91 484 2383287
Publications: QPMPA Journal of Medical Sciences (45253)

Quantum Business Media
Quantum House
19 Scarbrook Rd.
Croydon CR9 1LX, United Kingdom
Publications: Media Week (53130)

Quantum Business Media Ltd.
Quantum House
19 Scarbrook Rd.
Croydon CR9 1LX, United Kingdom
Phone: 44 20 85654200
Fax: 44 20 85654202
Publications: Building Products (53122)

Quartz Business Media Ltd.
Westgate House
120/130 Station Rd.
Redhill
Surrey RH1 1ET, United Kingdom
Phone: 44 1737 855000
Fax: 44 1737 855475
Publications: Polymers Paint Colour Journal (56673) •

Steel Times International (56676)

Quay Publications (Brixham)
PO Box 16
Tavistock PL19 0XR, United Kingdom
Phone: 44 18 22614899
Publications: Dartmoor Magazine (56727)

Quest Community Newspapers
PO Box 104
Alderley, Queensland 4051, Australia
Phone: 61 7 33520700
Fax: 61 7 33520636
Publications: Albert & Logan News (41530) • Caboolture Shire Herald (41681) • City North News (42386) • City South News (42129) • Ipswich News (42155) • Logan West Leader (42384) • Northside Chronicle (41531) • Pine Rivers Press (42392) • Redcliffe & Bayside Herald (42298) • South-East Advertiser (42130) • Westside News (42108) • Wynnum Herald (42718)

Quilters' Guild of the British Isles
St. Anthony's Hall
York Y01 7PW, United Kingdom
Phone: 44 1904 613242
Fax: 44 1904 632394
Publications: The Quilter (56996)

Quintessenz Verlags-GmbH
Komturstr.18
D-12099 Berlin, Germany
Phone: 49 307 61805
Fax: 49 307 6180692
Publications: International Poster Journal of Dentistry and Oral Medicine (44540)

QX Forlag AB
PO Box 17 218
SE-104 62 Stockholm, Sweden
Phone: 46 8 7203001
Publications: QX (51031)

Radcliffe Publishing Ltd.
18 Marcham Rd.
Abingdon OX14 1AA, United Kingdom
Phone: 44 1235 528820
Fax: 44 1235 528830
Publications: Diversity in Health and Social Care (52340)

Radio, Electrical and Television Retailers' Association
RETRA House, St. John's Ter.
1 Ampthill St.
Bedford MK42 9EY, United Kingdom
Phone: 44 1234 269110
Fax: 44 1234 269609
Publications: Alert Magazine (52271)

Radio Society of Great Britain
3 Abbey Ct.
Fraser Rd.
Priory Business Park
Bedford MK44 3WH, United Kingdom
Phone: 44 1234 832700
Fax: 44 1234 831496
Publications: Radio Communication (52276)

Railfuture
12 Home Close
Bracebridge Heath LN4 2LP, United Kingdom
Publications: Railwatch (52432)

Railway Preservation Society of Ireland
PO Box 461
County Antrim
Newtownabbey BT36 9BT, United Kingdom
Phone: 44 28 93373968
Publications: Five Foot Three (55701)

Rainbow Warriors International
PO Box 1154
Oranjestad, Aruba
Publications: Eco Aruba (41491)

Ramakrishna Math
1 Udbodhan Ln.
Kolkata 700 003, West Bengal, India
Phone: 91 33 25542248
Publications: Udbodhan (45307)

Ramakrishna Mission Institute of Culture
Gol Pk.
Kolkata 700 029, West Bengal, India
Phone: 91 33 24641303

Fax: 91 33 24661235
Publications: Bulletin of the Ramakrishna Mission Institute of Culture (45260)

The Ramblers' Association
2nd Fl., Camelford House
87-90 Albert Embankment
London SE1 7TW, United Kingdom
Phone: 44 20 73398500
Fax: 44 20 73398501
Publications: The Rambler (55172)

A Ramp Magazine
Dept. of Media Arts
Wintec
Private Bag 3036
Hamilton, New Zealand
Fax: 64 7 8580227
Publications: Ramp (48910)

Ranchi Express
55 Baralal St.
Ranchi 834 001, Bihar, India
Phone: 91 651 2206320
Fax: 91 651 2206213
Publications: Ranchi Express (45712)

R&M Afzal
PO Box 14155-4364
Tehran, Iran
Phone: 98 21 6497572
Publications: Iranian Journal of Chemistry and Chemical Engineering (45899)

RAPRA Technology
Shawbury
Shrewsbury SY4 4NR, United Kingdom
Phone: 44 1939 250383
Publications: Cellular Polymers (56527)

Rare Metals
No. 30
Xueyuanlu
Beijing 100083, People's Republic of China
Phone: 86 106 2333436
Fax: 86 106 2332875
Publications: Rare Metals (43214)

RAS Publishing Ltd.
The Old Town Hall
Lewisham Rd.
Slaithwaite
Huddersfield HD7 5AL, United Kingdom
Phone: 44 14 84846069
Fax: 44 14 84846232
Publications: Bridal Buyer (53616) • CWB (53619) • Lingerie Buyer (53622) • MWB (53624) • WWB (53625)

Rashtra Deepika Ltd.
PO Box 7
Kottayam 686 001, Kerala, India
Phone: 91 481 2566706
Fax: 91 481 2567947
Publications: Deepika (45314)

Rationalist Press Association Ltd.
One Gower St.
London WC1E 6HD, United Kingdom
Phone: 44 20 74361151
Fax: 44 20 70793588
Publications: New Humanist (54991)

Ravensworld Ltd.
Hunters Moon
Exford
Minehead TA24 7PP, United Kingdom
Phone: 44 16 43831695
Fax: 44 16 43831576
Publications: Hounds (56537)

RBA Edipresse
PO Box 14776
28080 Madrid, Spain
Phone: 34 91 902392396
Publications: Arquitectura y Diseno (50650) • Casa al Dia (50734) • Clara (50657) • Comer Bien (50659) • Cosas de Casa (50740) • Habitania (50676) • Mente Sana (50688) • PC Actual (50692) • Saber Vivir (50696) • Tu Bebe (50704)

RCN Publishing Co.
The Heights
59-65 Lowlands Rd.
Harrow HA1 3AW, United Kingdom

Phone: 44 20 84231066
Publications: Emergency Nurse (53522) • Evidence-Based Nursing (53523) • Mental Health Practice (53525) • Nurse Researcher (53527) • Nursing Management (53528) • Nursing Older People (53529) • Nursing Standard (53530) • Pediatric Nursing (53531) • Primary Health Care (53532)

Reach
PO Box 54
Helston TR13 8WD, United Kingdom
Phone: 44 845 1306225
Fax: 44 845 1300262
Publications: Within Reach (53554)

Readershouse/Hearst
Aletta Jacobslaan 7
NL-1006 BP Amsterdam, Netherlands
Phone: 31 20 3551010
Publications: Carros Magazine (47922)

Real Federacion Espanola de Atletismo
Avenida de Valladolid, 81, esc. Dcha. 1
E-28008 Madrid, Spain
Phone: 34 915 482423
Fax: 34 915 480638
Publications: Atletismo Espanol (50730)

Reality Bites bvba
Ad!dict Creative Lab
Barthelemylaan 20
B-1000 Brussels, Belgium
Phone: 32 228 95101
Publications: Ad!dict (42843)

Recoletos Grupo de Comunicacion
P de la Castellana, No. 66
E-28046 Madrid, Spain
Phone: 34 913 373220
Publications: Actualidad Economica (50723)

Recruitment & Employment Confederation
Albion House
Chertsey Rd.
Woking GU21 6BT, United Kingdom
Phone: 44 20 70092100
Fax: 44 20 79354112
Publications: Recruitment Matters (56948)

Red Cross of Vietnam
82 Nguyen Du Str.
Hanoi, Vietnam
Phone: 84 482 63703
Fax: 84 494 24285
Publications: Humanity (57051)

Red House Marketing
PO Box 20461
Manama, Bahrain
Phone: 973 178 13777
Fax: 973 178 13700
Publications: Bahrain This Month (BTM) (42787)

Red House Publishing Group
PO Box 20461
Manama, Bahrain
Phone: 973 17 813777
Fax: 973 17 813700
Publications: Woman This Month (42795)

Red Pepper
1B Waterlow Rd.
London N19 5NJ, United Kingdom
Phone: 44 20 72817024
Publications: red pepper (55178)

Redactive Media Group
17-18 Britton St.
London EC1M 5TP, United Kingdom
Phone: 44 20 78806200
Fax: 44 20 78807691
Publications: CPO Agenda (54279) • FM World (54474) • Getting There (54506) • Leadership Focus (54859) • Make the Grade (54899) • Stroke News (55266) • Supply Management (55279) • UCU (55352) • UK Excellence (55354)

Redan Publishing
Prospect House, Ste. 2
Belle Vue Rd.
Shrewsbury SY3 7NR, United Kingdom
Phone: 44 1743 364433
Fax: 44 1743 271528
Publications: Bag-o-Fun (56526) • Fun to Learn Bar-

ney (56530) • Fun to Learn Best of Barney (56531) • Fun to Learn Discovery (56532) • Fun to Learn Favourites (56533) • Fun to Learn Friends (56534) • Fun to Learn Letterland (56535) • Fun to Learn Peppa Pig (56536) • My Little Pony (56538)

Redgauntlet Publications Ltd.
PO Box 464
Berkhamsted HP4 2UR, United Kingdom
Publications: Steam Days (52314)

REDRESS
87 Vauxhall Walk
London SE11 5HJ, United Kingdom
Phone: 44 20 77931777
Fax: 44 20 77931719
Publications: The Reparation Report (55188)

Reed Business Information Ltd.
Quadrant House
The Quadrant
Sutton SM2 5AS, United Kingdom
Phone: 44 20 86523500
Fax: 44 20 86528932
Publications: ACN: Asian Chemical News (56678) • Airline Business (56679) • Caterer & Hotelkeeper (56680) • Catering Update (56681) • Community Care (56682) • Computer Weekly (56683) • European Chemical News (56684) • Farmers Weekly (56685) • Farmland Market (56686) • Flight International (56687) • Motor Transport (56688) • New Scientist (56690) • New Scientist (54998) • Poultry World (56691) • Railway Gazette International (56692) • Truck and Driver (56693)

Reed Business Information Norway A.S.
Vaerftsgata 7
Postboks 1024
N-1510 Moss, Norway
Phone: 47 699 12400
Publications: Byggaktuelt (49193)

Reed Business Information Proprietary Ltd.
Tower 2, 475 Victoria Ave.
Locked Bag 2999
Chatswood, New South Wales 2067, Australia
Phone: 61 2 94222999
Fax: 61 2 94222922
Publications: Australian Doctor (41736) • B&T Weekly (42263) • Construction Contractor (41739) • Manufacturers Monthly (41740) • Professional Marketing (42265)

Reed Business Information S.p.a.
Viale G. Richard 1/A
I-20143 Milan, Italy
Phone: 39 281 8301
Fax: 39 281 830406
Publications: CDA (46164)

The Reference Publishing Co.
PO Box 26269
Epsom
Auckland, New Zealand
Phone: 64 93582749
Fax: 64 93582741
Publications: Commercial Horticulture Magazine (48789)

Regional Centre for Energy, Heat and Mass Transfer for Asia and the Pacific
IIT Madras, Campus
Chennai 600 036, Tamil Nadu, India
Phone: 91 442 2574932
Fax: 91 442 2570094
Publications: Journal of Energy, Heat and Mass Transfer (45047)

Regional Energy Resources Information Center
Asian Institute of Technology
Khlong Luang
PO Box 4
Pathumthani 12120, Thailand
Phone: 66 252 45866
Fax: 66 252 45439
Publications: RERIC International Energy Journal (51462)

Registered Nursing Home Association
John Hewitt House, Tunnel Ln.
Off Lifford Ln.
Kings Norton
Birmingham B30 3JN, United Kingdom

Phone: 44 121 4511088
Fax: 44 121 4863175
Publications: Nursing Home News (52359)

Reiner H. Nitschke Verlags-GmbH
Eifelring 28
D-53879 Euskirchen, Germany
Phone: 49 2251650460
Fax: 49 22516504699
Publications: Tourenfahrer/Motorrad Reisen (44351)

Reise & Preise
Hauptstr. 14
D-21614 Buxtehude, Germany
Phone: 49 416 171690
Fax: 49 416 1716915
Publications: Reise & Preise (44288)

Remedica Medical Education and Publishing
1 New Oxford St.
London WC1A 1NU, United Kingdom
Phone: 44 20 77592999
Fax: 44 20 77592951
Publications: Advances in Osteoporotic Fracture Management (53906) • Depression (54318) • International Journal of Advances in Rheumatology (54631)

Remedica Publishing Ltd
Commonwealth House
1 New Oxford St.
London WC1A 1NUN, United Kingdom
Phone: 44 20 77592999
Fax: 44 20 77592951
Publications: Acute Coronary Syndromes (53897) • Advances in Sepsis (53908) • Heart Failure Monitor (54546)

Remote Sensing and Photogrammetry Society
U.S. Department of Geography
University of Nottingham
University Pk.
Nottingham NG7 2RD, United Kingdom
Phone: 44 11 59515435
Fax: 44 11 59515249
Publications: International Journal of Remote Sensing (55763) • Photogrammetric Record (56407)

Renaissance
51-K Model Town
Lahore, Pakistan
Phone: 92 42 5865145
Fax: 92 42 5864856
Publications: Renaissance (49388)

Renaissance Publishing Ltd.
PO Box 28849
London SW13 0WA, United Kingdom
Phone: 44 20 88761891
Publications: Jewish Renaissance (54692)

Renaissance Universal
3a Cazenove Rd.
London N16 6PA, United Kingdom
Phone: 44 20 88064250
Publications: New Renaissance (54997)

Repeat Fanzine & Records
PO Box 438
Cambridge CB4 1FX, United Kingdom
Publications: Repeat (52891)

Rephoto Publishing Ltd.
Plough Rd.
Smallfield RH6 9EZ, United Kingdom
Phone: 44 1342 844444
Fax: 44 1342 844488
Publications: Auto Vending (56561) • Cafe Business (56562)

Reprohuset
Dueoddevej 14
DK-7400 Herning, Denmark
Phone: 45 97 22 48 85
Fax: 45 97 22 01 80
Publications: Frisorfaget (43721)

Republic of Singapore Yacht Club
52 W Coast Ferry Rd.
Singapore 126887, Singapore
Phone: 65 676 89288
Fax: 65 676 89280
Publications: RSYC (50247)

Research India Publications
D1/71, Top Fl., Rohini Sec-16
New Delhi 110 089, Delhi, India
Phone: 91 11 65394240
Fax: 91 11 27297815
Publications: Advances in Aerospace and Applications (45886) • Advances in Algebra (47218) • Advances in Applied Mathematical Analysis (46614) • Advances in Computational Sciences and Technology (53783) • Advances in Dynamical Systems and Applications (45477) • Advances in Fuzzy Mathematics (46276) • Advances in Theoretical and Applied Mathematics (47242) • Communications in Differential and Difference Equations (43538) • Global Journal of Pure and Applied Mathematics (47266) • International Journal of Applied Engineering Research (47715) • International Journal of Applied Environmental Sciences (47267) • International Journal of Biotechnology & Biochemistry (IJBB) (43745) • International Journal of Computational and Applied Mathematics (43259) • International Journal of Computational Intelligence Research (49216) • International Journal of Computational Physical Sciences (41828) • International Journal of Dynamics of Fluids (IJDF) (55618) • International Journal of Educational Administration (44947) • International Journal of Engineering Studies (45582) • International Journal of Lakes and Rivers (43746) • International Journal of Materials Science (43770) • International Journal of Mathematics Manuscripts (51626) • International Journal of Nanotechnology and Applications (43747) • International Journal of Oceans and Oceanography (IJOO) (43748) • International Journal of Petroleum Science and Technology (51620) • International Journal of Pure and Applied Physics (43749) • International Journal of Statistics and Systems (45586) • International Journal of Theoretical and Applied Mechanics (47227) • Journal of Bio-Inspired Computation Research (45593) • Journal of Computational Intelligence in Bioinformatics (47272) • Mathematical Modelling and Applied Computing (43368) • Mathematical Modelling of Natural Phenomena (44126) • Mathematics Applied in Science and Technology (46482)

Research Information Ltd.
Grenville Ct.
Britwell Rd.
Burnham SL1 8DF, United Kingdom
Phone: 44 1628 600499
Fax: 44 1628 600488
Publications: Appropriate Technology (52763) • Electronic Materials & Packaging (52764) • International Journal of Micrographics & Optical Technology (52765) • International Journal for Technology in Mathematics Education (56271) • International Pest Control (52766) • The Journal of Grey System (43524) • Journal of Systems Science and Information (43209) • Outlooks on Pest Management (52767) • World Food Regulation Review (52768)

Research Institute for Austrian and International Literature and Cultural Studies
PF 74
Vienna, Austria
Phone: 43 1 7481633
Fax: 43 1 7481615
Publications: TRANS (42770)

Research Institute of Nuclear Medicine
Tehran University of Medical Sciences
PO Box 14155-6559
Tehran, Iran
Phone: 98 216 491070
Fax: 98 216 419537
Publications: DARU (45888) • Iranian Journal of Nuclear Medicine (45904)

Research Institute of the Wood Industry
Chinese Academy of Forestry
Wan Shou Shan
Beijing 100091, People's Republic of China
Phone: 86 10 62889410
Fax: 86 10 62881937
Publications: Wood Industry (43224)

Reserve Bank of India—Department of Economic Analysis & Policy/Division of Reports Reviews & Publications
Fort
Mumbai 400 001, Maharashtra, India
Publications: Reserve Bank of India Bulletin—Weekly Statistical Supplement (45434) • Reserve Bank of India Occasional Papers (45435)

Reserve Bank of New Zealand
2 The Ter.
PO Box 2498
Wellington 6011, New Zealand
Phone: 64 4 4722029
Fax: 64 4 4738554
Publications: The Reserve Bank of New Zealand (49033)

Residua Ltd.
The British School
Otley St.
Skipton BD23 1EP, United Kingdom
Fax: 44 17 56709801
Publications: Warmer Bulletin (56555)

Restaurang Guiden
Stenklevsgatan 5
S-414 65 Goteborg, Sweden
Phone: 46 317 412545
Fax: 46 317 044810
Publications: Restaurang Guiden (50963)

Resurgence Ltd.
Ford House
Hartland
Bideford EX39 6EE, United Kingdom
Phone: 44 12 37441293
Publications: Resurgence (52322)

Retail Pharmacy
Level 1, 410 Church St.
North Parramatta, New South Wales 2151, Australia
Phone: 61 2 98901199
Fax: 61 2 98901877
Publications: Retail Pharmacy (42158)

Retreat Association
Kerridge House
42 Woodside Close
Buckinghamshire
Amersham HP6 5EF, United Kingdom
Phone: 44 1494 433004
Fax: 44 871 7151917
Publications: Retreats (52109)

Retroviseur
BP 40419
F-77309 Fontainebleau Cedex 15, France
Phone: 33 1 60396969
Fax: 33 1 60396900
Publications: Retroviseur (43954)

Revista Litoral
Urb. La Roca, 107 C
E-29630 Torremoinos, Spain
Phone: 34 952 388257
Fax: 34 952 380758
Publications: Litoral (50841)

Revista Rotaria Foundation
Apartado Postal 717
Tachira 5001, Venezuela
Phone: 58 276 3441551
Fax: 58 276 3429950
Publications: Nueva Revista Rotaria (57029)

Rex Publications Ltd.
64 Charlotte St.
Eltham
London W1T 4QD, United Kingdom
Phone: 44 20 74364006
Fax: 44 20 74363458
Publications: Majesty Magazine (54898)

Rhinegold Publishing
241 Shaftesbury Ave.
London WC2H 8TF, United Kingdom
Phone: 44 20 73331720
Fax: 44 20 73331765
Publications: Classical Music (54215) • International Piano (54666) • Opera Now (55037)

Rhodes University
PO Box 94
Grahamstown 6140, Republic of South Africa
Phone: 27 46 6037100
Fax: 27 46 6037101
Publications: Rhodes Journalism Review (50511)

Rhodos International Science and Art Publishers
Horsholmvej 17
DK-3050 Humlebaek, Denmark
Phone: 45 32543020
Fax: 45 32543022
Publications: Scandinavian Journal of Design History (43724)

Richard Jefferies Society
Pear Tree Cottage
Longcot SN7 7SS, United Kingdom
Phone: 44 179 3783040
Publications: The Richard Jefferies Society Journal (55475)

Richmond House Publishing Company Ltd.
70-76 Bell St.
Marylebone
London NW1 6SP, United Kingdom
Phone: 44 20 72249666
Fax: 44 20 72249688
Publications: The British Theatre Directory (54148)

Rider Haggard Society
c/o Mr. Roger Allen
27 Deneholm
Monkseaton
Whitley Bay NE25 9AU, United Kingdom
Phone: 44 19 12524516
Fax: 44 19 12524516
Publications: Rider Haggard Journal (56920)

Rigaku Corp.
4-14-4 Sendagaya
Shibuya-Ku
Tokyo 151-0051, Japan
Phone: 81 334 790618
Fax: 81 334 796112
Publications: The Rigaku Journal (47032)

Rila Publications Ltd.
73 Newman St.
London W1A 4PG, United Kingdom
Phone: 44 20 76311299
Fax: 44 20 75807166
Publications: Acute Medicine (53898) • Clinical Focus (53794) • The Otorhinolaryngologist (55045)

Ringier Publishing House Switzerland
Dufourstrasse 23
CH-8008 Zurich, Switzerland
Phone: 41 44 2596111
Publications: Betty Bossi (51254) • Edelweiss (51186) • FdH (51259) • Gesundheit Sprechstunde (51262) • GlucksPost (51263) • Heute (51264) • il caffe (51209) • L'illustre (51191) • Schweizer Illustrierte (51278) • Schweizer Illustrierte Style (51279) • SonntagsBlick (51284) • SonntagsBlick Magazin (51285) • SPORTmagazin (51287) • TV8 (51201) • TVtaglich (51295)

RISI
326 Ave. Louise, Bte 22
B-1050 Brussels, Belgium
Phone: 32 253 60748
Fax: 32 253 75626
Publications: Pulp & Paper International (PPI) (42871)

River Publishing Limited
Victory House
14 Leicester Pl.
London WC2H 7BZ, United Kingdom
Phone: 44 20 73060304
Publications: DARE (54312)

Riverina Media Group
48 Trl. St.
Wagga Wagga, New South Wales 2650, Australia
Publications: Daily Advertiser (42668)

Riviera Maritime Media Limited
Mitre House
66 Abbey Rd.
Enfield EN1 2QN, United Kingdom
Phone: 44 208 3641551
Publications: LNG World Shipping (53332) • LPG World Shipping (53333) • Marine Electronics & Communications (53334) • Marine Propulsion & Auxiliary Machinery (53335) • Offshore Support Journal (53336) • Tanker Shipping & Trade (53337)

Riyadh Armed Forces Hospital
PO Box 7897
Riyadh 11159, Saudi Arabia
Phone: 966 14 791000
Fax: 966 14 761810
Publications: Saudi Medical Journal (50071)

The Rock s.r.o.
Lazaretska 12
811 08 Bratislava, Slovakia
Phone: 421 2 59233300
Publications: The Slovak Spectator (50322) • SPEX (50323)

Rodeo
Superstudio 13
Via Forcella 13
I-20144 Milan, Italy
Phone: 39 2 89405560
Fax: 39 2 80420126
Publications: Rodeo (46193)

Rodopi
248 E 44th St., 2nd Fl.
New York, NY 10017-4358
Fax: 800853-3881
Free: 800225-3998
Publications: Amsterdam Monographs in American Studies (47890) • Architecture, Technology, Culture (ATC) (44550) • Australian Playwrights (41669) • Central-European Value Studies (50317) • Clio Medica (54233) • Conrad Studies (56790) • Cross/Cultures (44385) • Currents of Encounter (47951)

Rolling River Publications Ltd.
The Locus Ctr.
The Square
Perthshire
Aberfeldy PH15 2DD, United Kingdom
Phone: 44 1887 829868
Fax: 44 1887 829856
Publications: FlyFishing and FlyTying (51686)

Romanian Association for Nuclear Energy
Str. Polona, Nr. 65, Sector 1
Bucharest, Romania
Phone: 40 21 2038200
Fax: 40 21 2119400
Publications: Nuclear Energy (49840)

Romanian Union of Public Transport
6-8 Gh. Magheru Blvd., 6th Fl., Rm. 15-16, District 1
010332 Bucharest, Romania
Phone: 40 314 025702
Fax: 40 314 025701
Publications: TRANSURB (49844)

ROOM, the National Council for Housing and Planning
41 Botolph Ln.
London EC3R 8DL, United Kingdom
Phone: 44 20 79299494
Fax: 44 20 79299490
Publications: AXIS (53995)

Roskilde University
Bldg. 11.2, RUC
PO Box 260
4000 Roskilde, Denmark
Phone: 45 467 42120
Fax: 45 467 43041
Publications: The Journal of Transdisciplinary Environmental Studies (TES) (43734)

Ross Publishing Ltd.
Baan Klang Muang, The Paris Patchavipha
55/96 Moo 2, Lad Yao
Chatuchak
Bangkok 10900, Thailand
Phone: 66 2 1581146
Fax: 66 2 1581152
Publications: Travel Trade Report (51446)

Rotarian
Redactie De Rotarian
Stichting Rotary Administratie Nederland
Amstel 266
NL-1017 AM Amsterdam, Netherlands
Phone: 31 206 232405
Fax: 31 206 227642
Publications: Rotarian (48227)

The Rotarian Monthly
3rd Fl., 18-1 Ln. 14
Chi Lin Rd.
Taipei 104, Taiwan
Phone: 886 2 25418580
Fax: 886 2 5418608
Publications: The Rotarian Monthly (51357)

Rotarismo en Mexico
Paseo de la Reforma
No. 195-Piso 13
Col. Cuauhetemoc
06500 Mexico City, Federal District, Mexico
Phone: 52 554 94543
Fax: 52 551 03837
Publications: Rotarismo en Mexico (47789)

Rotary
c/o Pernice Editori s.r.l.
Via. Verdi 1
IT-24121 Bergamo, Italy
Phone: 39 35 241227
Fax: 39 35 4220153
Publications: Rotary (46123)

Rotary Africa
PO Box 563
Westville
KwaZulu-Natal 3630, Republic of South Africa
Phone: 27 312 671848
Fax: 27 312 671849
Publications: Rotary Africa (50544)

Rotary Contact
Av. De L'Exposition Universelle 68
B-1083 Brussels, Belgium
Phone: 32 2 4203500
Fax: 32 2 4201110
Publications: Rotary Contact (42872)

Rotary Dergisi
1571 Sokak No. 16
TR-35110 Cinarli-Izmir, Turkey
Phone: 90 232 4619642
Fax: 90 232 4619646
Publications: Rotary Dergisi (51552)

Rotary Down Under
PO Box 779
Parramatta, New South Wales 2124, Australia
Phone: 61 296 334888
Fax: 61 298 915984
Publications: Rotary Down Under (42236)

Rotary International in Great Britain and Ireland
Kinwarton Rd.
Alcester B49 6PB, United Kingdom
Phone: 44 1789 765411
Fax: 44 1789 764916
Publications: Rotary Magazine (GB & I) (52095)

The Rotary Korea
Royal Bldg. 930
5 Dangjudong
Chongno-Ku
Seoul 110-0721, Republic of Korea
Phone: 82 2 7302511
Fax: 82 2 7302515
Publications: The Rotary Korea (47205)

Rotary Magazine
19 El Shahid Mohamed El Shibany St.
Heliopolis
Cairo 11341, Egypt
Phone: 20 22918822
Fax: 20 23924270
Publications: Rotary Magazine (43764)

Rotary News/Rotary Samachar
3rd Fl., Dugar Towers
34 Marshalls Rd.
Egmore
Chennai 600 008, Tamil Nadu, India
Phone: 91 444 2145666
Fax: 91 442 8528818
Publications: Rotary News/Rotary Samachar (45056)

The Rotary-No-Tomo
4th Fl., Kokuryu Shibakoen Bldg.
Shibakoen 2-6-15
Minato-ku
Tokyo 105-0011, Japan
Publications: The Rotary-No-Tomo (47033)

Rotary Norden
c/o Markus Orn Antonsson
Vesturgata 36A
ICE-101 Reykjavik, Iceland
Phone: 354 545 1400
Publications: Rotary Norden (44902)

Rotary Suisse-Liechtenstein
Aathalstr. 34
8613 Uster, Switzerland
Phone: 41 44 9941666
Fax: 41 44 9941665
Publications: Rotary Suisse-Liechtenstein (51236)

Route One Publishing Ltd.
Horizon House
Azalea Dr.
Swanley BR8 8JR, United Kingdom
Phone: 44 13 22612055
Fax: 44 13 22612060
Publications: ITS International (56697) • World Highways (56698)

Routledge
2 Park Sq.
Milton Pk.
Abingdon OX14 4RN, United Kingdom
Phone: 44 20 70176000
Fax: 44 20 70176699
Publications: Accounting, Business & Financial History (51693) • Accounting Education (55476) • Action Learning (51696) • Adelphi Series (51698) • African Studies (51699) • Aging and Mental Health (51700) • AIDS Care (51701) • Anthropological Forum (51704) • Applied Economics (51705) • Asia Pacific Journal of Education (51706) • Asian Philosophy (51707) • Asian Population Studies (51708) • Australasian Journal of Philosophy (51710) • Australian Feminist Studies (51711) • Australian Geographer (51712) • Australian Historical Studies (51713) • Australian Journal of International Affairs (51714) • Australian Journal of Political Science (51715) • British Journal of Guidance and Counselling (51718) • British Journal for the History of Philosophy (51719) • The British Journal of Sociology (51721) • Building Research & Information (54153) • Bulletin of Spanish Studies (51722) • Business History (51723) • Cambridge Journal of Education (51724) • Cambridge Review of International Affairs (51725) • Central Asian Survey (51726) • Changing English (51727) • Child Care in Practice (51728) • Children's Geographies (51729) • Citizenship Studies (51730) • Cognitive Behaviour Therapy (50973) • Commonwealth & Comparative Politics (51733) • Communication and Critical/Cultural Studies (51734) • Communication Reports (51735) • Communication Research Reports (51736) • Communication Teacher (51737) • Community, Work & Family (51738) • Comparative Education (51739) • Contemporary Music Review (53265) • Criminal Justice Studies (51743) • Critical Discourse Studies (51744) • Critical Public Health (55611) • Critical Review of International Social and Political Philosophy (51745) • Critical Studies in Education (51746) • Cultural Studies (51747) • Cultural Trends (51748) • Culture, Health and Sexuality (54294) • Culture and Organization (52660) • Culture and Religion (51749) • Current Issues in Language Planning (51750) • Current Issues in Tourism (51751) • Curriculum Journal (51752) • Defence and Security Analysis (53732) • Defence Studies (51753) • Democratization (51754) • Development in Practice (51755) • Development Southern Africa (51756) • Diplomacy & Statecraft (51758) • Disability and Society (54328) • Distance Education (51759) • Early Child Development and Care (51761) • Early Popular Visual Culture (51762) • Early Years (51763) • East European Jewish Affairs (51764) • Economic System Research (51765) • Economy and Society (51766) • Education Economics (51767) • Education, Knowledge & Economy (51768) • Education and the Law (51769) • Educational Action Research (51770) • Ethics and Education (51772) • Ethics and Social Welfare (51773) • Ethnic and Racial Studies (51774) • Ethnography & Education (51775) • Ethnomusicology Forum (51776) • Ethnopolitics (51777) • Europe-Asia Studies (51778) • European Journal of Teacher Education (EJTE) (51782) • The European Legacy (51783) • European Security (51784) • European Societies (51785) • European Sport Management Quarterly (ESMQ) (51786) • Evaluation & Research in Education (51787) • Feminist

Economics (51788) • Folklore (51790) • Gender and Education (51793) • Gender, Place and Culture (51688) • Geopolitics (51794) • Global Change, Peace & Security (51795) • Global Crime (51796) • Global Society (51798) • Globalisation, Societies and Education (51799) • Globalizations (51800) • Health, Risk and Society (51801) • High Ability Studies (51802) • Historical Journal of Film, Radio and Television (51803) • History and Anthropology (51804) • History of Photography (51805) • Housing Studies (51806) • Housing, Theory & Society (51807) • Human Resource Development International (51809) • Immigrants & Minorities (51811) • India Review (51812) • Indonesia and the Malay World (51813) • Industry & Innovation (51814) • Infant Observation (51815) • Information, Communication and Society (51817) • Information and Communications Technology Law (51818) • Innovations in Education & Teaching International (51819) • Intellectual History Review (54614) • Intelligence & National Security (51820) • Inter-Asia Cultural Studies (51821) • Intercultural Education (51822) • International Economic Journal (51823) • International Feminist Journal of Politics (51824) • International Gambling Studies (51825) • International Journal for Academic Development (51826) • International Journal of Art Therapy (51827) • International Journal of Bilingual Education & Bilingualism (51828) • International Journal of Children's Spirituality (51829) • International Journal of Construction Education and Research (51830) • International Journal of Cultural Policy (51831) • International Journal of Disability, Development and Education (IJDDE) (51832) • International Journal of the Economics of Business (51833) • International Journal of Heritage Studies (51836) • International Journal of the History of Sport (51837) • International Journal of Human Resource Management (52930) • The International Journal of Human Rights (51838) • International Journal of the Legal Profession (51840) • The International Journal of Multilingualism (51841) • International Journal of Philosophical Studies (51843) • International Journal of Research and Method in Education (51845) • International Journal of Water Resources Development (51847) • International Planning Studies (51848) • International Public Management Journal (51849) • International Research in Geography & Environment Education (51850) • International Review of Applied Economics (51851) • International Review of Law Computers & Technology (51852) • The International Spectator (51855) • International Studies in Sociology of Education (51856) • Interventions (51857) • Iranian Studies (51858) • Irish Political Studies (51859) • Irish Studies Review (51860) • Islam and Christian-Muslim Relations (51861) • Israel Affairs (51863) • Japan Forum (51865) • Japanese Studies (51866) • Jazz Perspectives (51867) • Journal of African Cultural Studies (51868) • The Journal of Agricultural Education and Extension (48771) • Journal of Applied Statistics (51869) • The Journal of Architecture (54700) • Journal of the Asia Pacific Economy (51870) • Journal of Balkan and Near Eastern Studies (51871) • Journal of Baltic Studies (53426) • Journal of Beliefs & Values (51872) • Journal of Change Management (51873) • Journal of Children and Media (46107) • Journal of Children and Poverty (51874) • Journal of Chinese Economic and Business Studies (53492) • Journal of Civil Society (51875) • Journal of Commonwealth Law and Legal Education (51876) • The Journal of Communist Studies and Transition Politics (51877) • Journal of Contemporary African Studies (51878) • Journal of Contemporary China (51879) • Journal of Contemporary European Studies (51880) • Journal of Contemporary Religion (51881) • Journal for Cultural Research (51883) • Journal of Development Studies (51885) • Journal of Economic Methodology (51888) • Journal of Ecotourism (51889) • Journal of Education for Teaching (51890) • Journal of Education and Work (51891) • Journal of Educational Administration and History (51892) • Journal of Elections, Public Opinion & Parties (51893) • Journal of Environmental Planning and Management (51894) • Journal of Environmental Policy & Planning (51895) • Journal of Ethnic and Migration Studies (JEMS) (52620) • Journal of European Public Policy (51896) • Journal of Further and Higher Education (51898) • Journal of Gender Studies (51899) • Journal of Genocide Research (51900) • Journal of Geography in Higher Education (51901) • Journal of Global Ethics (51902) • Journal of Heritage Tourism (51903) • Journal of Human Development and Capabilities (51904) • Journal of Human Rights (51905) • Journal of Iberian & Latin American Studies (51906) • The Journal of Imperial & Commonwealth History (51907) • Journal of Intercultural Studies (51909) • The Journal of International Trade and Economic Development (41676) • Journal of Intervention and Statebuilding (51911) • Journal of Israeli History (51912) • Journal of Latin American Cultural Studies (51913) • Journal of Legal History (51914) • Journal of Legal Medicine (51915) • The Journal of Legislative Studies (51916) • Journal of Marketing Communications (51917) • Journal of Modern Italian Studies (51919) • Journal of Modern Jewish Studies (51920) • Journal of Moral Education (51921) • Journal of Multicultural Discourses (51922) • Journal of Multilingual & Multicultural Development (51923) • Journal of Muslim Minority Affairs (51924) • Journal of New Music Research (53735) • Journal of North African Studies (51925) • The Journal of Pacific History (51928) • Journal of Peace Education (51929) • Journal of Peasant Studies (51930) • Journal of Poetry Therapy (51932) • Journal of Political Ideologies (51933) • The Journal of Positive Psychology (51934) • Journal of Postcolonial Writing (51935) • Journal of Property Research (51936) • Journal of Quantitative Linguistics (51938) • Journal of Reproductive and Infant Psychology (51940) • Journal of Risk Research (54810) • Journal of Sexual Aggression (51941) • Journal of Social Welfare and Family Law (51942) • Journal of Social Work Practice (51943) • Journal of Southern African Studies (51944) • Journal of Spanish Cultural Studies (51945) • Journal of Sport & Tourism (51946) • Journal of Strategic Marketing (51947) • Journal of Strategic Studies (51948) • Journal of Sustainable Tourism (51950) • Journal of Tourism & Cultural Change (51952) • Journal of Urban Design (51953) • Journal of Urban Technology (51954) • Journal of Victorian Culture (51955) • Journal of Vocational Education & Training (51956) • Journal of Wine Research (51957) • Journal of Youth Studies (51958) • Journalism Studies (51959) • Justice Quarterly (51960) • Labor History (51961) • Language Awareness (51962) • Language Culture & Curriculum (51963) • Language and Education (51964) • Language and Intercultural Communication (51965) • Latin American and Caribbean Ethnic Studies (51966) • Life Writing (51969) • London Review of Education (51971) • Managing Leisure (56506) • Media History (51972) • Medicine, Conflict & Survival (51974) • Mediterranean Historical Review (51975) • Mediterranean Politics (51976) • Mental Health, Religion and Culture (51977) • Middle Eastern Literatures (51979) • Middle Eastern Studies (51980) • Military Balance (51981) • Mobilities (51984) • Modern & Contemporary France (51985) • Modern Italy (51986) • Mortality (51987) • National Identities (51988) • Nationalism & Ethnic Politics (51989) • Nationalities Papers (51990) • New Genetics & Society (51992) • New Political Economy (51993) • New Political Science (51994) • New Review of Academic Librarianship (51995) • New Review of Children's Literature and Librarianship (51996) • New Review of Film & Television Studies (51997) • New Review of Information Networking (51998) • New Writing (51999) • Nonproliferation Review (52000) • Open Learning (52002) • Oxford Development Studies (56132) • The Pacific Review (52003) • Peace Review (52004) • Pedagogy, Culture and Society (52005) • Performance Research (52007) • Perspectives (52008) • Perspectives on European Politics and Society (52009) • Philosophical Explorations (52010) • Philosophical Psychology (52011) • Physical Education & Sport Pedagogy (52012) • Planning Perspectives (55769) • Planning Practice and Research (52014) • Planning Theory & Practice (56511) • Police Practice and Research (52015) • Policing and Society (52016) • Policy Studies (52017) • Political Communication (52018) • Politikon (52019) • Population Studies (55103) • Post-Communist Economies (52020) • Postcolonial Studies (52021) • Professional Development in Education (52022) • Prometheus (52023) • Prose Studies (52024) • Psychoanalytic Psychotherapy (52026) • Psychodynamic Practice (52027) • Psychology Crime and Law (52028) • Psychology and Health (52029) • Psychology, Health and Medicine (52030) • Public Management Review (52031) • Quality in Higher Education (56995) • Race, Ethnicity and Education (52033) • Reflective Practice (52035) • Regional Studies (52036) • Research in Post-Compulsory Education (52037) • Rethinking History (52038) • Review (52039) • Review of African Political Economy (52040) • The Review of Communication (52041) • Review of International Political Economy (52042) • Review of Political Economy (52043) • Review of Social Economy (52044) • Revolutionary Russia (52045) • Scandinavian Journal of Disability Research (49207) • Scandinavian Journal of Educational Research (49208) • Scandinavian Journal of History (44903) • Scandinavian Journal of Hospitality and Tourism (52049) • Scando-Slavica (43683) • School Leadership & Management (52053) • Science as Culture (52054) • The Service Industries Journal (52055) • Sex Education (55230) • Sexual Addiction & Compulsivity (52056) • Shakespeare (52057) • Sikh Formations (52058) • Social History (52059) • Socialism and Democracy (52061) • Spatial Economic Analysis (53452) • Sport in History (52063) • Sports Biomechanics (52064) • Strategic Survey (52065) • Studies in Conflict and Terrorism (52066) • Studying Teacher Education (52067) • Survival (55283) • Teacher Development (52069) • Teachers and Teaching (52070) • Teaching in Higher Education (52071) • Technical Education & Training Abstracts (52072) • Technology Analysis & Strategic Management (52073) • Technology, Pedagogy and Education (52074) • Terrorism and Political Violence (52075) • Textual Practice (52076) • Theology and Science (52077) • Third Text (55312) • Third World Quarterly (52078) • Total Quality Management & Business Excellence (52079) • Totalitarian Movements and Political Religions (52080) • Tourism Geographies (52081) • Tourism and Hospitality Planning & Development (52082) • Twenty-first Century Society (52084) • Visual Culture in Britain (52086) • Vulnerable Children and Youth Studies (52087) • Wasafiri (52088) • West European Politics (52090) • Women (52091) • Women & Performance (52092) • Women's Writing (52093) • World Archaeology (52094)

Rover P4 Drivers Guild
32 Arundel Rd.
Luton LU4 8DY, United Kingdom
Publications: Overdrive (55503)

Royal Academy of Arts
Burlington House
Piccadilly
London W1J 0BD, United Kingdom
Phone: 44 20 73008000
Publications: RA Magazine (55167)

Royal Academy of Dancing
36 Battersea Sq.
London SW11 3RA, United Kingdom
Phone: 44 20 73268000
Publications: Dance Gazette (54309)

Royal Academy of Dutch Language and Literature
Koningstraat 18
B-9000 Gent, Belgium
Phone: 32 926 59340
Fax: 32 926 59349
Publications: Jaarboek (42883) • Verslagen en Mededelingen (42885)

Royal Academy of Medicine in Ireland
Frederick House, 4th Fl.
19 S Frederick St.
Dublin 2, Dublin, Ireland
Phone: 353 1 6334820
Fax: 353 1 6334918
Publications: Irish Journal of Medical Science (45977)

Royal Aeronautical Society
4 Hamilton Pl.
London W1J 7BQ, United Kingdom
Phone: 44 20 76704300
Fax: 44 20 76704309
Publications: Aeronautical Journal (53911) • Aerospace International (53913)

Royal Aeronautical Society - Australian Div.
PO Box 573
Mascot, New South Wales 2020, Australia
Publications: Australian Aeronautics (42041)

Royal African Society
36 Gordon Sq.
London WC1H 0PD, United Kingdom

Phone: 44 20 30738335
Fax: 44 20 30738340
Publications: African Affairs (53918)

Royal Anthropological Institute of Great Britain and Ireland
50 Fitzroy St.
London W1T 5BT, United Kingdom
Phone: 44 20 73870455
Fax: 44 20 73888817
Publications: Journal of the Royal Anthropological Institute (54812)

Royal Asiatic Society of Sri Lanka
Mahaweli Centre & Royal Asiatic Society Bldg., 1st Fl.
96 Ananda Coomaraswamy Mawatha
Colombo 7, Sri Lanka
Phone: 94 11 2699249
Publications: Journal of the Royal Asiatic Society of Sri Lanka (50859)

Royal Australian Chemical Institute
1/21 Vale St.
North Melbourne, Victoria 3051, Australia
Phone: 61 393 282033
Fax: 61 393 282670
Publications: Chemistry in Australia (42056)

Royal Australian Navy News
R8-LG-042 Russell Offices
Dept. of Defence
Canberra, Australian Capital Territory 2600, Australia
Publications: Royal Australian Navy News (41712)

Royal College of Anesthesiologists of Thailand
Dept. of Anesthesiology
Faculty of Medicine
Chulalongkorn University
Rama 4 Rd., Pathumwan
Bangkok, Thailand
Publications: Thai Journal of Anesthesiology (51438)

Royal College of General Practitioners
1 Bow Churchyard
London EC4M 9DQ, United Kingdom
Phone: 44 20 31887400
Fax: 44 020 31887401
Publications: British Journal of General Practice (54120)

Royal College of Pathologists
2 Carlton House Ter.
London SW1Y 5AF, United Kingdom
Phone: 44 20 74516700
Fax: 44 20 74516701
Publications: College Bulletin (54238)

Royal College of Physicians
11 St., Andrew's Pl.
Regents Pk.
London NW1 4LE, United Kingdom
Phone: 44 20 79351174
Fax: 44 20 74875218
Publications: Clinical Medicine (54225)

The Royal College of Psychiatrists
17 Belgrave Sq.
London SW1X 8PG, United Kingdom
Phone: 44 20 72352351
Fax: 44 20 72451231
Publications: Advances in Psychiatric Treatment (53907) • British Journal of Psychiatry (54132) • The Psychiatrist (55149)

Royal College of Radiologists
38 Portland Pl.
London W1B 1JQ, United Kingdom
Phone: 44 20 76364432
Fax: 44 20 73233100
Publications: Clinical Oncology (54226) • Clinical Radiology (54229)

Royal College of Speech and Language Therapists
2 White Hart Yard
London SE1 1NX, United Kingdom
Phone: 44 20 73781200
Publications: Bulletin (54155)

Royal Dutch Geographical Society
PO Box 805
NL-3500 AV Utrecht, Netherlands
Phone: 31 30 2534056

Fax: 31 30 2535523
Publications: Journal of Economic and Social Geography (48762)

Royal Economic Society
University of York
Heslington
York YO1 5DD, United Kingdom
Phone: 44 1334 462479
Publications: Economic Journal (56990)

Royal Forestry Society
102 High St.
Tring HP23 4AF, United Kingdom
Phone: 44 1442 822028
Fax: 44 1442 890395
Publications: Quarterly Journal of Forestry (56772)

Royal Geographical Society - The Institute of British Geographers
1 Kensington Gore
London SW7 2AR, United Kingdom
Phone: 44 20 75913000
Fax: 44 20 75913001
Publications: Glacial Geology and Geomorphology (52284)

Royal Horticultural Society
80 Vincent Sq.
London SW1P 2PE, United Kingdom
Phone: 44 84 52605000
Publications: The Garden (56258)

The Royal Institute of International Affairs
Chatham House
10 St. James's Sq.
London SW1Y 4LE, United Kingdom
Phone: 44 20 79575700
Fax: 44 20 79575710
Publications: The World Today (55426)

RINA—The Royal Institute of Naval Architects
10 Upper Belgrave St.
London SW1X 8BQ, United Kingdom
Phone: 44 20 72354622
Fax: 44 20 72595912
Publications: The Naval Architect (54986) • Ship & Boat International (55233) • Ship Repair & Conversion Technology (55234) • Significant Ships (55239) • Warship Technology (55380)

Royal Institution of Chartered Surveyors - England
RICS Contact Ctr.
Surveyor Ct.
Westwood Way
Coventry CV4 8JE, United Kingdom
Phone: 44 870 3331600
Fax: 44 207 3343811
Publications: Abstracts and Reviews (53076)

Royal Irish Academy
19 Dawson St.
Dublin 2, Dublin, Ireland
Phone: 353 1 6762570
Fax: 353 1 6762346
Publications: Irish Studies in International Affairs (45985)

Royal Jordanian
PO Box 302
Amman, Jordan
Phone: 962 6 5202000
Fax: 962 6 5672527
Telex: 21501 ALIA JO
Publications: Royal Wings (Jordan) (47162)

Royal Mail
148 Old St.
London EC1V 9HQ, United Kingdom
Publications: British Philatelic Bulletin (54145) • British Postmark Bulletin (54146)

Royal Mencap Society
123 Golden Ln.
London EC1Y 0RT, United Kingdom
Phone: 44 20 74540454
Fax: 44 20 76083254
Publications: Viewpoint (55371)

Royal Meteorological Society
104 Oxford Rd.
Grenville Pl.
Reading RG1 7LL, United Kingdom

Phone: 44 11 89568500
Fax: 44 11 89568571
Publications: International Journal of Climatology (56321) • Journal of the Royal Meteorological Society (56324)

Royal Meteorological Society
104 Oxford Rd.
Reading RG1 7LL, United Kingdom
Phone: 44 11 89568500
Fax: 44 11 89568571
Publications: Quarterly Journal of the Royal Meteorological Society (56329) • Weather (56333)

Royal National Institute for Deaf People
19-23 Featherstone St.
London EC1Y 8SL, United Kingdom
Phone: 44 207 2968000
Fax: 44 207 2968001
Publications: One in Seven (55033)

Royal National Rose Society
Chiswell Green Ln.
Saint Albans AL2 3NR, United Kingdom
Phone: 44 17 27850461
Fax: 44 17 27850360
Publications: The Rose (56438)

Royal Over-Seas League
Over-Seas House
Pk. Pl.
St. James's St.
London SW1A 1LR, United Kingdom
Phone: 44 207 4080214
Fax: 44 207 4996738
Publications: Overseas (55047)

The Royal Philatelic Society London
41 Devonshire Pl.
London W1G 6JY, United Kingdom
Phone: 44 20 74861044
Fax: 44 20 74860803
Publications: The London Philatelist (54888)

The Royal Photographic Society of Great Britain
Fenton House
122 Wells Rd.
Bath BA2 3AH, United Kingdom
Phone: 44 1225 325733
Publications: RPS Journal (52257)

Royal School of Church Music
19 The Close
Salisbury
Wiltshire
Dorking SP1 2EB, United Kingdom
Phone: 44 1722 424848
Fax: 44 1722 424849
Publications: Church Music Quarterly (53193)

Royal Scottish Forestry Society
c/o Richard Kay, Dir.
4 Doonhill Way
Newton Stewart DG8 6JF, United Kingdom
Phone: 44 1671 401591
Publications: Scottish Forestry (55699)

Royal Scottish Geographical Society
Lord John Murray House
15-19 N Port
Perth
Scotland PH1 5LU, United Kingdom
Phone: 44 1738 455050
Publications: Scottish Geographical Journal (56466)

Royal Society
6-9 Carlton House Ter.
London SW1Y 5AG, United Kingdom
Phone: 44 20 74512500
Fax: 44 20 79302170
Publications: Biology Letters (54024) • Journal of the Royal Society Interface (54813) • Notes & Records of the Royal Society (55013) • Philosophical Transactions of the Royal Society A (55079) • Philosophical Transactions of the Royal Society B (55080) • Profound (The Dialog Corporation) of the Royal Society A (55133) • Profound (The Dialog Corporation) of the Royal Society B (55134) • The Royal Society Yearbook (55209)

Royal Society for Asian Affairs
2 Belgrave Sq.
London SW1X 8PJ, United Kingdom

Phone: 44 20 72355122
Publications: Asian Affairs (53973)

Royal Society of Chemistry
Thomas Graham House
The Science Pk., Milton Rd.
Milton Rd.
Cambridge CB4 0WF, United Kingdom
Phone: 44 12 23420066
Fax: 44 12 23423623
Publications: Analyst (52786) • Analytical Abstract (52787) • Catalysts & Catalysed Reactions (52802) • Chemical Communications (52803) • Chemical Society Reviews (52804) • Chemistry Education Research and Practice (52805) • CrystEngComm (52813) • Dalton Transactions (52814) • Energy & Environmental Science (52817) • Faraday Discussions (52819) • Green Chemistry (52825) • Highlights in Chemical Biology (52826) • Highlights in Chemical Science (52827) • Journal of Environmental Monitoring (52851) • Journal of Materials Chemistry (52859) • Lab on a Chip (52866) • Metallomics (52868) • Methods in Organic Synthesis (52869) • Molecular Biosystems (52871) • Natural Product Reports (52873) • New Journal of Chemistry (52876) • Organic & Biomolecular Chemistry (52880) • Photochemical & Photobiological Science (52882) • Physical Chemistry, Chemical Physics (52883) • Softmatter (52897)

Royal Society of Medicine
1 Wimpole St.
London W1G 0AE, United Kingdom
Phone: 44 20 72902900
Fax: 44 20 72902989
Publications: International Journal of STD and AIDS (54663) • Journal of Medical Biography (54778) • Journal of Telemedicine and Telecare (54827)

Royal Society of Medicine Press Ltd.
1 Wimpole St.
London W1G 0AE, United Kingdom
Phone: 44 20 72902921
Fax: 44 20 72902929
Publications: Clinical Ethics (54220) • Clinical Risk (54231) • Handbook of Practice Management (54529) • Health Services Management Research (54544) • International Journal of Care Pathways (54637) • Journal of Health Services Research & Policy (54760) • Journal of Medical Screening (54781) • Journal of the Royal Society of Medicine (54814) • Laboratory Animals (54847) • Menopause International (54926) • Phlebology (55084) • Tropical Doctor (55342)

Royal Society of New Zealand
4 Halswell St.
PO Box 598
Wellington 6011, New Zealand
Phone: 64 4 4727421
Fax: 64 4 4731841
Publications: Journal of the Royal Society of New Zealand (49011) • Kotuitui (49014) • New Zealand Journal of Agricultural Research (49021) • New Zealand Journal of Botany (49022) • New Zealand Journal of Crop and Horticultural Science (49023) • New Zealand Journal of Geology and Geophysics (49025) • New Zealand Journal of Marine and Freshwater Research (49027) • New Zealand Journal of Zoology (48909)

Royal Society for the Prevention of Accidents
RoSPA House, Edgbaston Pk.
353 Bristol Rd.
Birmingham B5 7ST, United Kingdom
Phone: 44 12 12482000
Publications: Occupational Safety & Health (52360) • Safety Education (52365) • Safety Express (52366) • Staying Alive (52368)

Royal Society for the Prevention of Cruelty to Animals
Wilberforce Way
Southwater
Horsham RH13 9RS, United Kingdom
Fax: 44 87 07530284
Publications: Animal Action (53594) • Animal Life (53595) • Science Review (53601)

Royal Society for the Protection of Birds
The Lodge
Potton Rd.
Sandy SG19 2DL, United Kingdom
Phone: 44 1767 680551

Fax: 44 1767 692446
Publications: Bird Life (56460) • Wingbeat (56461)

Royal Society for Public Health
28 Portland Pl.
London W1B 1DE, United Kingdom
Phone: 44 20 75802731
Fax: 44 20 75806157
Publications: Health and Hygiene (54538) • Public Health (55152)

Royal Society of Tropical Medicine and Hygiene
50 Bedford Sq.
London WC1B 3DP, United Kingdom
Phone: 44 20 75802127
Fax: 44 20 74361389
Publications: Transactions of the Royal Society of Tropical Medicine and Hygiene (55335)

Royal Town Planning Institute
41 Botolph Ln.
London EC3R 8DL, United Kingdom
Phone: 44 20 79299494
Fax: 44 20 79299490
Publications: Planning (UK) (55092)

Royal Yachting Association
RYA House
Ensign Way
Hamble
Southampton SO31 4YA, United Kingdom
Phone: 44 23 80604100
Fax: 44 23 80604299
Publications: RYA Magazine (56577)

RPA Publishing Ltd.
PO Box 1479
Maidenhead SL6 8DP, United Kingdom
Phone: 44 1628783080
Publications: Machine Knitting Monthly (55523)

RPS-yhtiot
Hietakummuntie 18
FIN-00700 Helsinki, Finland
Phone: 358 934 78070
Fax: 358 934 780710
Publications: Julkaisija (43836)

Rudiger Koppe Verlag
Wendelinstrasse 73-75
D-50933 Cologne, Germany
Phone: 49 221 4911236
Fax: 49 221 4994336
Publications: Frankfurter Afrikanistische Blatter (44294) • Law in Africa (44299) • Sprache und Geschichte in Afrika (44303) • Yearbook of African Law (44304)

Rural Design and Building Association
c/o Tony Hutchinson
5a The Maltings
Stowupland Rd.
Suffolk
Stowmarket IP14 5AG, United Kingdom
Phone: 44 1449 676049
Fax: 44 1449 770028
Publications: Countryside Building (56642)

Rural and Isolated Libraries Special Interest Group
PO Box 6335
Kingston, Victoria 2604, Australia
Phone: 61 2 62158222
Fax: 61 2 62822249
Publications: Aphelion (41994)

Rural Press Ltd.
159 Bells Line of Rd.
North Richmond, New South Wales 2754, Australia
Phone: 61 2 45704444
Fax: 61 2 45704663
Publications: AgTrader (48907) • Australasian Flowers (42646) • Australian Cotton Outlook (42625) • Australian Dairyfarmer (42647) • Australian Farm Journal (42160) • Australian Horticulture (42648) • Australian Landcare (42649) • Camden Haven Courier (42003) • Cobar Age (41772) • Collie Mail (41779) • Country Music Capital News (42611) • Dairyman (48791) • Eyre Peninsula Tribune (41765) • Farm Equipment Trader (42161) • Farm Weekly (42666) • Farming Small Areas (42162) • Farming Small Blocks (42115) • Good Fruits & Vegetables (41767) • Goulburn Post (41927) • Great Lakes Advocate (41869) • Grenfell Record (41934) •

Horticulture News (48796) • Irrigation and Water Resources (42652) • The Land (42163) • The Lifestyle Farmer (48802) • New Zealand Grapegrower (48814) • North Queensland Register (42638) • NSW Agriculture Today (42164) • Pig Industry News (42660) • Queensland Country Life (42165) • Queensland Farmer (42024) • Queensland Farmer & Grazier (42629) • Queensland Smart Farmer (41768) • Stock Journal (42661) • Stock & Land (42653) • Turfcraft (41723)

Rural Press Regional Publishing Proprietary Ltd.
159 Bells Line of Rd.
Sydney, New South Wales 2754, Australia
Phone: 61 2 45704444
Fax: 61 2 45704663
Publications: Blue Mountains Gazette (41603) • Hawkesbury Courier (42513) • Hawkesbury Gazette (42299)

Russell Publishing Limited
Ct. Lodge
Hogtbough Hill
Brasted TN16 1NU, United Kingdom
Phone: 44 19 59563311
Fax: 44 19 59563123
Publications: European Pharmaceutical Review (52561) • International Airport Review (52562)

S Z Husainy
101/22 Shivaji Nagar
Bhopal 462001, Madhya Pradesh, India
Publications: The Annals of Medical Entomology (45005)

SA ePublications
1021 Bank Ave.
PO Box 9785
Centurion 0046, Republic of South Africa
Phone: 27 126 439500
Fax: 27 126 633543
Publications: African Journal of Research in Mathematics, Science and Technology Education (50437) • English in Africa (50438) • IMFO (50439) • IMIESA (50440) • Journal for Christian Scholarship (50441) • Journal of Engineering, Design and Technology (50442) • Journal of Literary Studies (50443) • Old Testament Essays (50444) • Perspectives in Education (50445) • SA Irrigation (50446) • SA Journal of Human Resource Management (50447) • SA Journal of Industrial Psychology (50448) • Scriptura (50449) • South African Computer Journal (50450) • South African Journal of Business Management (50451) • South African Journal of Cultural History (50452) • South African Journal of Diabetes and Vascular Disease (50453) • South African Journal of Information Management (50454) • Southern African Journal of Critical Care (50455) • Tax Breaks Newsletter (50456) • Transactions of the Centre for Business Law (50457)

Sabah Publishing House SDN BHD
PO Box 10139
88801 Kota Kinabalu, Malaysia
Phone: 60 88238711
Fax: 60 88238611
Publications: Daily Express (47590) • Overseas Chinese Daily (47592)

SACCAR - Southern African Centre for Cooperation in Agricultural Research and Natural Resources Research and Training
PO Box 00108
Gaborone, Botswana
Phone: 267 32 8847
Fax: 267 32 8806
Publications: ZJAR (42946)

Sadhu Vaswani Mission
10 Sadhu Vaswani Path
Pune 411 001, Maharashtra, India
Phone: 91 20 40064447
Fax: 91 20 26127474
Publications: Mira (45698)

SAEH Verlag AG
Schaffhausersh 13
CH-8212 Neuhausen, Switzerland
Phone: 41 526 755060
Fax: 41 526 755061
Publications: Ars Medici (51216) • Gynakologie (51217) • Padiatrie (51218)

Saga Publishing Ltd.
The Saga Bldg.
Enbrook Pk.
Folkestone CT20 3SE, United Kingdom
Phone: 44 1303 771111
Publications: Saga (53393)

Sage Periodicals India Private Ltd.
PO Box 4215
New Delhi 110 048, Delhi, India
Phone: 91 11 6419884
Fax: 91 11 6472426
Publications: Indian Social Science Review (45577)

Sage Publications Inc.
2455 Teller Rd.
Thousand Oaks, CA 91320-2218
Phone: 805499-9774
Fax: 805583-2665
Free: 800818-7243
Publications: Animation (53379) • China Information (48661) • European Union Politics (44512) • Management & Organizational History (52704)

Sage Publications India Private Ltd.
B-1/I-1 Mohan Cooperative Industrial Area
Mathura Rd.
New Delhi 110 044, Delhi, India
Phone: 91 11 40539222
Fax: 91 11 40539234
Publications: Contributions to Indian Sociology (45499) • Gender, Technology & Development (45519) • Indian Economic and Social History Review (45540) • Indian Journal of Gender Studies (45554) • The Journal of Entrepreneurship (45597) • Journal of Human Values (45598) • Psychology and Developing Societies (45640) • Science, Technology & Society (45648) • South Asian Survey (45652) • Studies in History (New Delhi) (45657)

Sage Publications Ltd.
1 Oliver's Yard
55 City Rd.
London EC1Y 1SP, United Kingdom
Phone: 44 20 73248500
Fax: 44 20 73248600
Publications: Anthropological Theory (53954) • Autism (53984) • Body & Society (54096) • British Journalism Review (54138) • Building Services Engineering Research and Technology (54154) • Child Language and Teaching Therapy (54203) • Childhood (54204) • Chronic Respiratory Disease (54210) • Clinical Child Psychology and Psychiatry (54219) • Clinical Trials (54232) • Concurrent Engineering (54257) • Cooperation and Conflict (54266) • Criminology & Criminal Justice (54286) • Critical Social Policy (54289) • Critical Sociology (54290) • Critique of Anthropology (54291) • Cultural Dynamics (54292) • Cultural Geographies (54293) • Culture & Psychology (54295) • Current Sociology (50747) • Dementia (54315) • Discourse & Society (54330) • Discourse Studies (54331) • Economic and Industrial Democracy (54350) • Educational Management Administration and Leadership (54355) • Ethnicities (54386) • Ethnography (54387) • European History Quarterly (54394) • European Journal of Archaeology (53273) • European Journal of Communication (54398) • European Journal of Cultural Studies (54399) • European Journal of Industrial Relations (54400) • European Journal of International Relations (54401) • European Journal of Social Theory (53871) • The European Journal of Women's Studies (54407) • European Physical Education Review (52994) • European Urban and Regional Studies (54411) • Evaluation (54412) • Feminism & Psychology (54446) • Feminist Theory (54448) • French Cultural Studies (54481) • Global Social Policy (54513) • Group Analysis (54522) • Group Processes & Intergroup Relations (54523) • Health (54536) • Health Education Journal (54537) • History of the Human Sciences (54559) • The Holocene (54564) • Human Relations (54578) • Improving Schools (54589) • Information Development (54603) • Innate Immunity (54605) • International Communication Gazette (54623) • International Journal of Cross Cultural Management (54641) • International Journal of Cultural Studies (54642) • International Journal of Damage Mechanics (54643) • International Journal of Music Education (54655) • International Journal of Robotics Research (54660) • The International Political Science Review/Revue internationale de science politique (54667) • International Review of Administrative Sciences (54668) • International Review for the Sociology of Sport (54669) • International Social Work (54672) • International Sociology (54673) • Journal of Bioactive and Compatible Polymers (54704) • Journal of Biomaterials Applications (54707) • Journal of Building Physics (54716) • Journal of Cellular Plastics (54720) • Journal of Classical Sociology (54725) • The Journal of Commonwealth Literature (54727) • Journal of Composite Materials (54728) • Journal of Consumer Culture (54730) • Journal of Contemporary History (54731) • Journal of Early Childhood Literacy (54740) • Journal of Elastomers and Plastics (54742) • Journal of European Social Policy (54747) • Journal of European Studies (54748) • Journal of Fire Sciences (54754) • Journal of Health Psychology (54759) • Journal of Industrial Textiles (54766) • Journal of Information Science (54768) • Journal of Intellectual Disabilities (54769) • Journal of Intelligent Material Systems and Structures (54770) • Journal of Librarianship & Information Science (55482) • Journal of Material Culture (54776) • Journal of Peace Research (54793) • Journal of Plastic Film and Sheeting (54803) • Journal of Psychopharmacology (54805) • Journal of Reinforced Plastics and Composites (54807) • Journal of Sandwich Structures and Materials (54815) • Journal of Social Archaeology (54818) • Journal of Social and Personal Relationships (54819) • Journal of Social Work (54820) • Journal of Sociology (54823) • Journal of Theoretical Politics (54828) • Journal of Thermoplastic Composite Materials (54829) • Journal of Wide Bandgap Materials (54836) • Journalism (54839) • Language and Literature (54852) • Language Teaching Research (54853) • Law, Culture & the Humanities (54857) • Lighting Research and Technology (54873) • Management Learning (54901) • Marketing Theory (53812) • Media, Culture & Society (54920) • Multiple Sclerosis (54961) • New Media & Society (54995) • Nursing Ethics (55015) • Organization (55042) • Organization Studies (55043) • Party Politics (55060) • Philosophy & Social Criticism (55083) • Politics, Philosophy & Economics (55100) • Progress in Development Studies (55135) • Punishment & Society (55157) • Qualitative Research (52938) • Qualitative Research in Psychology (55161) • Race & Class (55168) • Rationality and Society (55174) • SAGE Race Relations Abstracts (55216) • Scandinavian Journal of Public Health (51047) • School Psychology International (55219) • Security Dialogue (55226) • Sexualities (53049) • Social Compass (55245) • Social & Legal Studies (55246) • Social Science Information (55247) • Social Studies of Science (55248) • Statistical Modelling (55264) • Theoretical Criminology (55307) • Theory, Culture & Society (55772) • Theory & Psychology (55308) • Thesis Eleven (55310) • Time & Society (55319) • Tourist Studies (55332) • Transactions of the Institute of Measurement and Control (52294) • Transcultural Psychiatry (55336) • Urban Studies (55360) • Visual Communication (55373)

Sahabat Alam Malaysia
21, Lindang Delima 15
11700 Penang, Malaysia
Phone: 604 6596960
Fax: 604 6596931
Publications: Suara SAM (47691)

Sahitya Akademi
Rabindra Bhavan
35 Ferozeshah Rd.
New Delhi 110 001, Delhi, India
Phone: 91 112 3386626
Fax: 91 112 3382428
Publications: Indian Literary Index (45570)

Saigon Times Group
35 Nam Ky Khoi Nghia St.
District 1
Ho Chi Minh City, Vietnam
Phone: 84 882 95936
Fax: 84 882 94294
Publications: Saigon Times Weekly (57057)

St. Jerome Publishing
2 Maple Rd. W
Brooklands
Manchester M23 9HH, United Kingdom
Phone: 44 161 9739856

Fax: 44 161 9053498
Publications: Interpreter and Translator Trainer (55561) • Sign Language Translator & Interpreter (55577) • The Translator (55580)

St. Patrick's College
Dublin IRL-9, Dublin, Ireland
Phone: 353 1 8373789
Fax: 353 1 8378997
Publications: Irish Journal of Education (45975)

Saint Patrick's Missionary Society
St. Patrick's
Kiltegan, Wicklow, Ireland
Phone: 35 359 6473600
Fax: 35 359 6473622
Publications: Africa (46028)

The St. Petersburg Times
4 St. Isaac's Sq.
190000 Saint Petersburg, Russia
Phone: 7 812 3256080
Fax: 7 812 3256080
Publications: The St. Petersburg Times (50028)

Saint Scholastica's College Institute of Women's Studies
931 Estrada St., Malate
Manila 1004, Philippines
Phone: 63 252 23551
Fax: 63 252 30693
Publications: Lila (49551)

Sakal Paper Limited
595, Budhwar Peth
Pune 411 002, Maharashtra, India
Phone: 91 20 24405500
Publications: Sakal (45700)

Sakia.org
Farm 2538 Murray Rd.
PO Box 508
Hanwood, New South Wales 2680, Australia
Phone: 61 269 630881
Fax: 61 269 630781
Publications: Journal of Applied Irrigation Science (41940)

Salisbury Sarum Ltd.
PO Box 1523
London N2 9HZ, United Kingdom
Phone: 44 20 84420654
Fax: 44 20 84421640
Publications: POWDEReporter (55111)

The Salvation Army
2nd Fl., 33/35 Kings Exchange
Tileyard Rd.
London N7 9AH, United Kingdom
Phone: 44 20 76196100
Fax: 44 20 76196111
Publications: Kids Alive! (54843) • The War Cry (55378)

Salvation Army - Caribbean Territory
3 Waterloo Rd.
PO Box 378
Kingston 10, Jamaica
Phone: 876929-6190
Fax: 876929-7960
Publications: The War Cry (46291)

Samedan Ltd.
16, Hampden Gurney St.
London W1H 5AL, United Kingdom
Phone: 44 20 77243456
Fax: 44 20 77242632
Publications: European BioPharmaceutical Review (54391) • European Pharmaceutical Contractor (54409) • International Clinical Trials (54622) • Pharmaceutical Manufacturing and Packing Sourcer (55076)

G. John Samuel
Institute of Asian Studies
Sholinganallur
Madras 600 119, Tamil Nadu, India
Phone: 91 442 4502212
Publications: Institute of Asian Studies Journal (45335)

The San Pedro Sun
PO Box 35
San Pedro Town
Ambergris Caye, Belize
Phone: 501 226 2070

Fax: 501 226 2905
Publications: The San Pedro Sun (42914)

Sandesh
Sandesh Bhavan, Lad Society Rd., Vastrapur
Ahmedabad 380 054, Gujarat, India
Phone: 91 794 0004000
Fax: 91 794 0004242
Publications: Sandesh (44909)

Sandron Publishing Ltd.
Bouverie House
43a Effra Rd.
Wimbledon
London SW19 8PS, United Kingdom
Phone: 44 20 85439799
Fax: 44 20 85406519
Publications: Esprit Magazine (54383)

SANE Australia
PO Box 226
Melbourne, Victoria 3205, Australia
Phone: 61 396 825933
Fax: 61 396 825944
Publications: SANE News (42084)

Sanei-shobo Publishing Company Ltd.
Honshio 19
Shinjyuku-ku
Tokyo 160-8547, Japan
Phone: 81 3 53695111
Fax: 81 3 53695117
Publications: Moto-Champ (46973)

Sanoma Budapest Kiadoi Rt.
Montevideo utca 9
H-1037 Budapest, Hungary
Phone: 36 1 4371100
Fax: 36 1 4372303
Publications: Atrium (44824) • Baratok Kozt Magazin (44825) • Fakanal (44829) • Fakanal Recepttar (44830) • Figyelo (44831) • Figyelo TOP 200 (44832) • Figyelo Trend (44833) • Fules (44834) • Kismama (44843) • Kismama Mintaszam (44844) • Kismama 9 Honap (44845) • Market!ng&Media (44848) • Maxima Special (44849) • Meglepetes (44850) • Meglepetes Raadas (44851) • National Geographic Kids (44855) • National Geographic Special (44856) • Nok Lapja (44857) • Nok Lapja Egeszseg (44858) • Nok Lapja Eskuvo (44859) • Nok Lapja Evszakok (44860) • Nok Lapja Konyha (44861) • Otthon (44863) • Praktika (44865) • RTV Musormagazin (44868) • Story Special (44873) • Szines RTV (44877) • UZLET & SIKER (44881)

Sanoma Corp.
Ludviginkatu 6-8
PO Box 1229
FIN-00101 Helsinki, Finland
Phone: 358 105 1999
Fax: 358 105 195068
Publications: Helsingin Sanomat (43832)

Santa Barbara Publishing Corp.
105 Labrador Bldg.
Epifanio Delos Santos Ave.
Mandaluyong City, Philippines
Phone: 63 253 27974
Fax: 63 253 10838
Publications: Design and Architecture (49534)

SARP Publishers
PO Box 828
Pretoria 0001, Republic of South Africa
Phone: 27 12 3285282
Publications: Servamus (50600)

Satish Serial Publishing House
115, Express Tower
Commercial Complex
Azadpur
New Delhi 110033, Delhi, India
Phone: 91 11 27672852
Fax: 91 11 27672046
Publications: The Indian Journal of Crop Science (45550) • Indian Media Studies Journal (45571)

Saudi Center for Organ Transplantation
PO Box 27049
Riyadh 11417, Saudi Arabia
Phone: 966 1 4451100

Fax: 966 1 4453934
Publications: Saudi Journal of Kidney Diseases and Transplantation (50070)

Saudi Gastroenterology Association
c/o King Saud University
PO Box 2454
Riyadh 11451, Saudi Arabia
Phone: 966 1 4670112
Fax: 966 1 4677580
Publications: The Saudi Journal of Gastroenterology (50069)

Saudi Heart Foundation
PO Box 6615
Jeddah 21452, Saudi Arabia
Publications: Saudi Heart Journal (50058)

Saudi Research & Publishing Co.
PO Box 478
Riyadh 11411, Saudi Arabia
Phone: 966 1 4419933
Fax: 966 1 4400453
Publications: Arab News (50060) • Asharq Al-Awsat (53970)

SB Communications Group
3.05 Enterprise House
1-2 Hatfields
London SE1 9PG, United Kingdom
Phone: 44 20 76271510
Fax: 44 20 76271570
Publications: Diabetes & Primary Care (54323)

Scalabrini Migration Center
4 13th St.
New Manila
Quezon City 1112, Philippines
Phone: 63 272 43512
Fax: 63 272 14296
Publications: Asian Migrant (49582) • Asian Migration News (49583) • Asian and Pacific Migration Journal (49584)

Scandinavia Now
PO Box 26174
S-100 41 Stockholm, Sweden
Phone: 46 867 83230
Fax: 46 861 12358
Publications: Scandinavia Now (51032)

Scandinavian Society for Economic and Social History
School of Business, Economics & Law
Goteborg University
PO Box 600
S-405 30 Goteborg, Sweden
Phone: 46 317 860000
Fax: 46 317 864970
Publications: Scandinavian Economic History Review (50964)

Scandinavian Society for Laboratory Animal Science
c/o Barbro Salomonsson
Erstaviksvagen 6
S-135 47 Stockholm, Sweden
Phone: 46 8546 44281
Publications: Scandinavian Journal of Laboratory Animal Science (43681)

Scandinavian Yoga and Meditation School
Haa Course Center
S-340 13 Hamneda, Sweden
Phone: 46 372 55063
Fax: 46 372 55036
Publications: Bindu (50968)

ScanPub ApS
Vejlbovej 31
DK-8600 Silkeborg, Denmark
Phone: 45 868 00299
Fax: 45 868 05839
Publications: ScanRef (43735)

SCAS
The Blue Cross
Shilton Rd.
Burford OX18 4PF, United Kingdom
Phone: 44 19 93825597
Fax: 44 19 93825598
Publications: Journal of Society for Companion Animal Studies (52760)

SCFAB
AlbaNova University Ctr.
Dept. of Astronomy
Roslagstullsbacken 21
S-106 91 Stockholm, Sweden
Phone: 46 855 378500
Fax: 46 855 378510
Publications: Popular Astronomi (51030)

Schaper Philatelie-Verlag GmbH
Postfach 1642
D-31046 Alfeld, Germany
Phone: 49 5181 80090
Fax: 49 5181 800933
Publications: Deutsche Briefmarken Zeitung/Sammler Express (DBZ/SE) (44138)

Schattauer Publishers
Hoelderlinstr. 3
D-70174 Stuttgart, Germany
Phone: 49 711 229870
Fax: 49 711 2298750
Publications: Methods of Information in Medicine (44670) • Nervenheilkunde (44671) • Nuklearmedizin (44675) • Thrombosis and Haemostasis (44683) • V.C. O.T. (44684)

Scherzo Editorial S.A.
C/Cartagena, 10-1 C
E-28028 Madrid, Spain
Phone: 34 913 567622
Fax: 34 917 261864
Publications: Scherzo (50801)

School Library Association
Unit 2 Lotmead Business Village
Wanborough
Swindon SN4 0UY, United Kingdom
Phone: 44 1793 791787
Fax: 44 1793 791786
Publications: The School Librarian (56412)

School of Pharmacy
Evin Ave.
Tehran 19395, Iran
Phone: 98 21 88774283
Fax: 98 21 88795008
Publications: Iranian Journal of Pharmaceutical Research (45906)

The School Times International
PO Box 137
DK-3480 Fredensborg, Denmark
Phone: 45 491 33394
Fax: 45 497 17755
Publications: The School Times International (43687)

Schott Musik International
Weihergarten 5
D-55116 Mainz, Germany
Phone: 49 613 12460
Fax: 49 613 1246211
Publications: Das Orchester (44539)

Schweizer Alpen-Club
3000 Berne 23
Bern, Switzerland
Phone: 41 313 701818
Fax: 41 313 701800
Publications: Die Alpen (51071)

Schweizer Monatshefte
Vogelsangstr. 52
CH-8006 Zurich, Switzerland
Phone: 41 443 612606
Fax: 41 443 637005
Publications: Schweizer Monatshefte fur Politik, Wirtschaft und Kultur (51281)

Schweizerische Wasserwirtschaftsverband
Rutistr. 3A
CH-5401 Baden, Switzerland
Phone: 41 562225069
Fax: 41 562211083
Publications: Wasser Energie Luft/Eau Energie Air (51057)

Science in China Press
16, Dong-huang-cheng-gen N St.
Beijing 100717, People's Republic of China
Phone: 86 10 64016350
Publications: Science in China Series A (43215) • Science in China Series B (43216) • Science in China

Series C (43217) • Science in China Series D (43218) • Science in China Series E (43219) • Science in China Series F (43220) • Science in China Series G (43221)

Science Fiction Foundation
Middlesex University
White Hart Ln.
London N17 8HR, United Kingdom
Phone: 44 15 17943142
Fax: 44 15 17942681
Publications: Foundation (54479)

Science a GoGo
PO Box 254
Scarborough, Western Australia 6019, Australia
Publications: Science a GoGo (42354)

Science History Publications Ltd.
16 Rutherford Rd.
Cambridge CB2 8HH, United Kingdom
Phone: 44 1638 605464
Fax: 44 1638 605465
Publications: History of Science (52955)

Science Society of Thailand
c/o Public Information Dept.
NSTDA
111 Phaholyothin Rd.
Klong 1, Klong Luang
Pathumthani 10400, Thailand
Phone: 66 256 47000
Publications: Science Asia (51434)

Sciences Today
rue de Rixensart 18/17
B-1332 Genval, Belgium
Phone: 32 26532158
Fax: 32 26532158
Publications: Health and Food (42886)

Scientific Publishers
5-A, New Pali Rd.
PO Box 91
Jodhpur 342 001, Rajasthan, India
Phone: 91 291 2433323
Fax: 91 291 2624154
Publications: Journal of Economic and Taxonomic Botany (45226)

Scientific Publishers - India
5-A New Pali Rd.
PO Box 91
Jodhpur 342 001, Rajasthan, India
Phone: 91 291 2433323
Fax: 91 291 2624154
Publications: Annals of Arid Zone (45214) • Indian Journal of Biochemistry and Biophysics (45220) • Indian Journal of Chemical Technology (45221) • Indian Journal of Engineering and Materials Sciences (45222) • Indian Journal of Experimental Biology (45223) • Indian Journal of Pure & Applied Physics (45224) • Phytomorphology (45228) • Reserve Bank of India Bulletin (45229)

Scientific Research Council
Hope Gardens
PO Box 350
Kingston 06, Jamaica
Phone: 876927-1771
Fax: 876927-1990
Publications: Jamaica Journal of Science and Technology (46286)

The Scientific and Technical Research Council of Turkey
Tunus Caddesi No. 80
Kavaklidere
TR-06100 Ankara, Turkey
Phone: 90 312 4272302
Fax: 90 312 4274024
Publications: Turkish Journal of Agriculture and Forestry (51503) • Turkish Journal of Biology (51504) • Turkish Journal of Botany (51505) • Turkish Journal of Chemistry (51507) • Turkish Journal of Earth Sciences (51508) • Turkish Journal of Electrical Engineering and Computer Sciences (51509) • Turkish Journal of Engineering and Environmental Sciences (51510) • Turkish Journal of Mathematics (51512) • Turkish Journal of Medical Sciences (51513) • Turkish Journal of Physics (51515) • Turkish Journal of Veterinary and Animal Sciences (51516) • Turkish Journal of Zoology (51517)

The Scientific World Journal
Saflaksintie 70
02400 Kirkkonummi, Finland
Publications: The Scientific World Journal (43874) • TSW Development & Embryology (43875) • TSW Holistic Health & Medicine (43876)

SCIVAC
Via. Trecchi 20
I-26100 Cremona, Italy
Phone: 39 372 460440
Fax: 39 372 457091
Publications: Ippologia (46136)

Scope
6 Market Rd.
London N7 9PW, United Kingdom
Phone: 44 20 76197100
Publications: Disability Now (54327)

The Scotsman Publications Ltd.
Barclay House
108 Holyrood Rd.
Edinburgh EH8 8AS, United Kingdom
Phone: 44 13 16208620
Publications: Spectrum Magazine Scotland on Sunday (53320)

T.G. Scott & Son Ltd.
Brettenham House
10 Savoy St.
London WC2E 7HR, United Kingdom
Phone: 44 20 72402032
Fax: 44 20 73797118
Publications: RCM Midwives' Journal (55175)

Scott Taylor Ltd.
Beacon House
2 Beacon Hill
London N7 9LY, United Kingdom
Phone: 44 20 76095100
Publications: British Style (54147) • Savile Row (55218)

Scottish Beekeepers' Association
c/o Ian Craig, Pres.
30 Burnside Ave.
Brookfield PA5 8UT, United Kingdom
Publications: The Scottish Beekeeper (52749)

Scottish Braille Press
Craigmillar Pk.
Edinburgh EH16 5NB, United Kingdom
Phone: 44 13 16624445
Fax: 44 13 16621968
Publications: The Braille Sporting Record (53256) • Home Help (53284)

Scottish Childminding Association
7 Melville Ter.
Stirling FK8 2ND, United Kingdom
Phone: 44 17 86445377
Fax: 44 17 86449062
Publications: Childminding (56621)

Scottish Field
Craigcrook Castle
Craigcrook Rd.
Edinburgh EH4 3PE, United Kingdom
Phone: 44 131 3124550
Fax: 44 131 3124551
Publications: Scottish Field (53314)

Scottish Genealogy Society
15 Victoria Ter.
Edinburgh EH1 2JL, United Kingdom
Phone: 44 13 12203677
Fax: 44 13 12203677
Publications: Scottish Genealogist (53315)

Scottish Natural Heritage
Great Glen House
Leachkin Rd.
Inverness IV3 8NW, United Kingdom
Phone: 44 1463 725000
Fax: 44 1463 725067
Publications: Scotland's Natural Heritage (53647)

Scottish Pre-School Play Association
21-23 Granville St.
Glasgow G3 7EE, United Kingdom
Phone: 44 14 12214148
Fax: 44 14 12216043
Publications: First Five (53419)

Scottish Railway Preservation Society
Bo'ness Sta.
Union St.
Bo'ness EH51 9AQ, United Kingdom
Phone: 44 1506 825855
Publications: Blastpipe (52406)

Scottish Women's Rural Institutes
42 Heriot Row
Edinburgh EH3 6ES, United Kingdom
Phone: 44 131 2251724
Fax: 44 131 2258129
Publications: Scottish Home and Country (53317)

The Scout Association
Gilwell Pk.
Chingford
London E4 7QW, United Kingdom
Phone: 44 20 84337100
Fax: 44 20 84337103
Publications: Scouting Magazine (55220)

Screen World Publication
H/9 171, Snehankoor Soc.
New M.H.L.B.T. Rd.
Borivali
Mumbai 4000 092, Maharashtra, India
Phone: 91 22 28692244
Publications: Screen World (45437)

Scripture Union in New Zealand
PO Box 760
Wellington, New Zealand
Phone: 64 438 50485
Fax: 64 438 50483
Publications: The Adventure (48998)

Scripture Union Publishing
207-209 Queensway
Bletchley
Milton Keynes MK2 2EB, United Kingdom
Phone: 44 1908 856000
Publications: Closer to God (55631) • Daily Bread (55632) • Encounter with God (55634)

S.D. Rohmetra
Excelsior House
Janipura
Jammu 180 007, Jammu and Kashmir, India
Phone: 91 191 2537901
Fax: 91 191 2537831
Publications: Daily Excelsior (45204)

Se-Education Public Company Ltd.
1858/87-90 Nation Tower Bldg.
19th Fl., Bangna-Trad Rd., Km. 4.5
Bangkok 10260, Thailand
Phone: 66 2 7398000
Publications: Hobby Electronics (51422) • Microcomputer (51427) • Update Magazine (51447)

Seager Publishing
9 Riverside Ct.
Lower Bristol Rd.
Bath BA2 3DZ, United Kingdom
Phone: 44 12 25481440
Fax: 44 12 25481262
Publications: Flyer (52230)

Seagull Foundation for the Arts
26 Circus Ave.
Kolkata 700 019, West Bengal, India
Phone: 91 33 22873636
Publications: Seagull Theatre Quarterly (45304)

Seahorse
5 Brittania Pl.
Station St.
Lymington SO41 3BA, United Kingdom
Phone: 44 1590 671899
Fax: 44 1590 671116
Publications: Seahorse (55513)

SEAMEO Regional Centre for Education in Science and Mathematics
11700 Gelugor
11700 Penang, Malaysia
Phone: 60 465 22700
Fax: 60 465 22737
Publications: The Classroom Teacher (47688) • Journal of Science and Mathematics Education in Southeast Asia (47689)

SEAMEO Regional Centre for Educational Innovation and Technology
UP PO Box 207
University of the Philippines
Diliman
Quezon City 1101, Philippines
Phone: 63 292 47681
Fax: 63 292 10224
Publications: INNOTECH Journal (49595)

SEAMEO Regional Language Centre
30 Orange Grove Rd.
Singapore 258352, Singapore
Phone: 65 68857855
Fax: 65 67342753
Publications: SEAMEO Regional Language Centre Guidelines (50250)

SEAMEO Secretariat
Mom Luang Pin Malakul Bldg.
4th Fl., 920 Sukhumvit Rd.
Bangkok 10110, Thailand
Phone: 66 23910144
Fax: 66 23812587
Publications: Journal of Southeast Asian Education (51425)

Seatrade Communications Ltd.
Seatrade House
42 N Station Rd.
Colchester CO1 1RB, United Kingdom
Phone: 44 12 06545121
Fax: 44 12 06545190
Publications: Seatrade Magazine (53048)

Secours Catholique Secteur International
106, rue du Bac
F-75007 Paris Cedex 07, France
Phone: 33 145 497300
Publications: Messages du Secours Catholique (44072)

Seibundo Shinkosha Publishing Company Ltd.
1-13-7 Yayoi-cho
Nakano-ku
Tokyo 164-0013, Japan
Fax: 81 333 737313
Publications: Idea (46837)

Sejong University
98 Gunja-Dong, Gwangjin-Gu
Seoul 143-747, Republic of Korea
Phone: 82 2 34083973
Fax: 82 2 34083813
Publications: Journal of Economic Integration (47273)

SEJT
21 St. Martissot
F-92110 Clichy, France
Phone: 33 141 279737
Fax: 33 141 279730
Publications: Autocar Infos (43931) • Forum Chantiers (43932) • Guide des Relais Routiers (43933) • Les Routiers (43934) • Stations-Service Acutalites (43936) • Transport Service (43937)

SELECT
The Walled Garden
Bush Estate
Midlothian EH26 0SB, United Kingdom
Phone: 44 131 4455577
Fax: 44 131 4455548
Publications: Cabletalk (55627)

SelfBuild Ireland Ltd.
119 Cahard Rd.
Saintfield BT24 7LA, United Kingdom
Phone: 44 48 97510570
Fax: 44 48 97510576
Publications: SelfBuild (56449)

Seminarul de Cercetare a Religiilor si Ideologiilor
Et. 1, sala 130
St. M. Kogalniceanu nr. 1
3400 Cluj-Napoca, Romania
Phone: 40 744 698826
Publications: Journal for the Study of Religions and Ideologies (49847)

Senate Hall Academic Publishing
PO Box 8261
Shankill
Dublin, Dublin, Ireland
Publications: International Review of Entrepreneurship

(45968) • Journal of Strategic Management Education (45990)

Sense
101 Pentonville Rd.
London N1 9LG, United Kingdom
Phone: 44 845 1270060
Fax: 44 845 1270061
Publications: Talking Sense (55291)

Seoul National University Institute of Economic Research
Seoul National University
Seoul 151-746, Republic of Korea
Fax: 82 288 84454
Publications: Seoul Journal of Economics (47286)

Serials Publications
4830-24 Ansari Rd.
Darya Ganj
New Delhi 110 002, Delhi, India
Phone: 91 11 23245225
Fax: 91 11 23272135
Publications: Global Review of Business and Economic Research (45520) • Indian Development Review (45539) • Indian Journal of Economics & Business (45552) • Indian Journal of Human Rights and Justice (45556) • Indian Journal of Human Rights and the Law (45557) • Indian Journal of Mathematics and Mathematical Sciences (45560) • International Journal of Applied Business and Economic Research (45580) • International Journal for Computational Vision and Biomechanics (45581) • International Journal of Computing and Applications (45747) • International Journal of Economic Research (44768) • International Journal of Environment and Development (45583) • International Journal of Jurisprudence and Philosophy of Law (45728) • International Journal of Mathematical Sciences (47243) • International Journal of Scientific Computing (45584) • International Review of Fuzzy Mathematics (45588) • International Review of Pure and Applied Chemistry (45589) • International Review of Pure and Applied Physics (43201) • Journal of Agricultural and Food Economics (44774) • Journal of Approximation Theory and Applications (46619) • Journal of Contemporary Mathematics (51580) • Journal of International Economic Review (45609) • Journal of Islamic Law Review (45611) • Journal of Mathematical Analysis and Approximation Theory (45613) • Journal of Social Anthropology (45618) • Journal of Social and Economic Policy (45619) • Review of Applied Economics (45645)

Sestre milosrdnice University Hospital and Institute for Clinical Medical Research
Vinogradska cesta 29
Zagreb, Croatia
Fax: 385 1 3787111
Publications: Acta Clinica Croatica (45561)

Seth G.S. Medical College and K.E.M. Hospital
Acharya Donde Marg
Parel
Mumbai 400 012, Maharashtra, India
Phone: 91 22 24136051
Fax: 91 22 24143435
Publications: Journal of Postgraduate Medicine (45405)

Sevak Publications
602, 6th Fl., B-Wing, Godrej Coliseum
Off Eastern Express Hwy.
K.J. Somaiya Hospital Rd.
Sio E
Mumbai 400 022, Maharashtra, India
Phone: 91 22 24044477
Fax: 91 22 24044450
Publications: Chemical Weekly (45361)

The Seychelles Nation Newspaper
Long Pier Rd.
PO Box 800
Victoria, Seychelles
Phone: 248 225 775
Fax: 248 321 006
Publications: Seychelles Nation (50095)

Shakespeare Society of Japan
B1-23 Kenkyusha-Eigo Ctr. Bldg.
1-2, Kagurazaka
Shinjuku-ku
Tokyo 162-0825, Japan

Phone: 81 3 32608109
Publications: Shakespeare Studies (47037)

Shakespeare Society of Southern Africa
Rhodes University
PO Box 94
Grahamstown 6140, Republic of South Africa
Phone: 27 466 226093
Publications: Shakespeare in Southern Africa (50513)

The Shalem Center
13 Yehoshua Bin-Nun St.
93102 Jerusalem, Israel
Phone: 972 2 560 5555
Publications: Azure (46080)

Shanghai Brilliant Books
Changle Rd., Ln. 672, No. 33, Section E
Shanghai 200040, People's Republic of China
Phone: 86 21 54030490
Fax: 86 21 54045466
Publications: Charity Matters (43468) • Shanghai Pictorial (43499)

Shanghai Fine Arts Publishing House
593 Yan'an Rd. W
Shanghai 200050, People's Republic of China
Phone: 86 21 61229008
Fax: 86 21 61229015
Publications: Calligraphy (43464) • Calligraphy and Painting (43465) • Shanghai Residence (43500)

Shanghai Jiao Tong University
1954 Huashan Rd.
Shanghai 200030, People's Republic of China
Phone: 86 21 62932444
Fax: 86 21 62821369
Publications: Academic Journal of Shanghai Jiao Tong University Social Science Section (43462) • Die & Mould Technology (43472) • Drive System Technique (43473) • English of Science and Technology Learning (43474) • Journal of Noise and Vibration Control (43481) • Journal of Shanghai Jiaotong University (43482) • Journal of Shanghai Jiaotong University Agricultural Science (43483) • Journal of Vibration and Shock (43484) • Laboratory Research and Exploration (43485) • Machine Design & Research (43486) • Micro- and Nanometer Science & Technology (43488) • Microcomputer Applications (43489) • Ocean Engineering (43492) • Systems Engineering (43506)

Shanghai Literature & Arts Publishing House
74 Shaoxing Rd.
Shanghai 200020, People's Republic of China
Phone: 86 21 64336243
Fax: 86 21 64740676
Publications: Fiction World (43476) • Oriental Sword (43493)

Shanghai Music Publishing House
74 Shaoxing Rd.
Shanghai 200020, People's Republic of China
Phone: 86 21 64376483
Fax: 86 21 64674944
Publications: Music Lover (43490)

Shanghai New Printing Technology Co., Ltd.
Ln. 1209, No. 60
Xinzha Rd.
Shanghai 200041, People's Republic of China
Phone: 86 21 62539220
Fax: 86 21 62553562
Publications: Printing Field (43495)

Shanghai People's Fine Arts Publishing House
D Bldg., No. 33
Changle Rd., Ln. 672
Shanghai 200040, People's Republic of China
Phone: 86 21 54044520
Fax: 86 21 54032331
Publications: Comic King (43471) • World Traveller (43511)

Shanghai Scientific & Technical Publishers
71 Qinzhou Rd.
Shanghai 200235, People's Republic of China
Phone: 86 21 64089888
Fax: 86 21 64845082
Publications: Car & Fan (43466) • Popular Medicine (43494) • Radio & TV (43496) • Science Journal (43497) • Scientific Pictorial (43498) • Shanghai Style (43501)

Shanghai Stories Culture Media Co., Ltd.
74 Shaoxing Rd.
Shanghai 200020, People's Republic of China
Phone: 86 21 64376635
Fax: 86 21 64376635
Publications: Travelling Scope (43508) • With (43510)

Shanghai Using the Right Word Culture Media Co., Ltd.
Jia, 384/11 Jianguo Rd. W
Shanghai 200031, People's Republic of China
Phone: 86 21 64330669
Fax: 86 21 64330669
Publications: Journal of Editorial Study (43480) • Using the Right Word (43509)

Shanghai Weekly Culture Media Co., Ltd.
5th Fl., 593 W Yan'an Rd.
Shanghai 200050, People's Republic of China
Phone: 86 21 61229133
Fax: 86 21 61229129
Publications: Beauty Home (43463) • Man & Nature (43487) • Shanghai Weekly (43504)

Shanvik Publications Private Ltd.
D-32/276
M.I.G. Bandra E
Mumbai 400 051, Maharashtra, India
Phone: 91 222 6550022
Fax: 91 222 6550088
Publications: Process & Plant Engineering (45432)

Sharif University of Technology
PO Box 11365-8639
Tehran, Iran
Phone: 98 21 66022727
Fax: 98 21 66005310
Publications: Scientia Iranica (45913)

Sheen Publishing Ltd.
50 Queens Rd.
Buckhurst Hill IG9 5DD, United Kingdom
Phone: 44 20 85041661
Fax: 44 20 85054336
Publications: Machinery World (52750) • Plant World (52751) • Refurbishment Projects (52752) • Secure Times (52753)

Shelter
88 Old St.
London EC1V 9HU, United Kingdom
Fax: 44 20 75052030
Publications: Roof (55208)

Shetland Council of Social Service
14 Market St.
Lerwick ZE1 0JP, United Kingdom
Phone: 44 1595743900
Fax: 44 1595696787
Publications: The New Shetlander (53841)

Shetland Seafood News Ltd.
Shetland Seafood Centre
Stewart Bldg.
Lerwick ZE1 0LL, United Kingdom
Publications: Shetland Fishing News (53842)

Shiraz University
Zand Ave.
Shiraz, Iran
Phone: 98 711 6286531
Fax: 98 711 2337852
Publications: Iranian Journal of Science and Technology (45884)

Shiraz University of Medical Sciences
PO Box 71348-1878
Shiraz 71934, Iran
Phone: 98 71 12122454
Fax: 98 71 12351865
Publications: Iranian Journal of Medical Sciences (45883)

Shoe World
Catherine House
Northminster Business Pk.
Northfield Ln.
York YO26 6QU, United Kingdom
Phone: 44 844 8440809
Fax: 44 1904 528791
Publications: Shoe World (56999)

Shogakukan Inc.
2-3-1, Hitotsubashi

Chiyoda-ku
Tokyo 101-8001, Japan
Publications: Big Comic Original (46762) • Big Comic Spirits (46763) • CanCam (46776) • Josei Seven (46879) • SARAI (47035) • Weekly Shonen Sunday (47056)

SHP Media Sdn. Bhd.
C-17-1, 17th Fl., Tower C, Megan Ave. II
12, Jalan Yap Kwan Seng
PO Box 10836
50726 Kuala Lumpur, Malaysia
Phone: 60 3 21660852
Fax: 60 3 21610541
Publications: Asian Defence Journal (47598)

Shree Ramana Maharishi Academy for the Blind
CA-1B, 3rd Cross, 3rd Phase
J.P. Nagar
Bangalore 560 078, Karnataka, India
Phone: 91 80 26631076
Fax: 91 80 26580325
Publications: Asia Pacific Disability Rehabilitation Journal (44949)

Shropshire Newspapers Ltd.
Chronicle House
Castle Foregate
Shrewsbury SY1 2DN, United Kingdom
Phone: 44 17 43248248
Fax: 44 17 43353601
Publications: The Farmer (Shropshire and the Welsh Borders) (56528)

The Siasat Daily
Jawaharlal Nehru Rd.
Hyderabad 500 001, Andhra Pradesh, India
Phone: 91 402 4744180
Fax: 91 402 4603188
Publications: The Siasat Daily (45182)

The Simon Community
129 Malden Rd.
89-93 Fonthill Rd.
London NW5 4HS, United Kingdom
Phone: 44 20 74856639
Publications: Simon Star (55240)

Singapore Academy of Law
1 Supreme Court Ln., Level 6
Singapore City 178879, Singapore
Phone: 65 63324388
Fax: 65 63344940
Publications: Annual Review of Singapore Cases (50310) • Inter Se Print (50313) • Singapore Academy of Law Journal (50314)

Singapore Association of the Visually Handicapped
47 Toa Payoh Rise
Singapore 298104, Singapore
Phone: 65 625 14331
Fax: 65 625 37191
Publications: White Cane (50286)

Singapore Human Resources Institute
2 Serangoon Rd.
Level 6, Tekka Mall
Singapore 218227, Singapore
Phone: 65 64380012
Fax: 65 62994864
Publications: Research and Practice in Human Resource Management (50244)

Singapore Institute of Architects
79B Neil Rd.
Singapore 088904, Singapore
Phone: 65 62262668
Fax: 65 62262663
Publications: Singapore Architect (50253)

Singapore Institute of Management
461 Clementi Rd.
Singapore 599491, Singapore
Phone: 65 62489777
Publications: Singapore Management Review (50259)

Singapore Institute of Planners
93 Toa Payoh Central, No. 05-01
Toa Payoh Community Bldg.
Singapore 319194, Singapore
Phone: 65 62515503

Fax: 65 62524533
Publications: Planews (50240)

Singapore International Chamber of Commerce
John Hancock Twr.
6 Raffles Quay, No. 10-01
Singapore 048580, Singapore
Phone: 65 65000988
Fax: 65 62242785
Publications: Investor's Guide to Singapore (50196)

Singapore Medical Association
Alumni Medical Ctr.
2 College Rd., Level 2
Singapore 169850, Singapore
Phone: 65 622 31264
Fax: 65 622 47827
Publications: Singapore Medical Journal (50260)

Singapore Press Holdings Ltd.
News Ctr.
1000 Toa Payoh N
Singapore 318994, Singapore
Phone: 65 63196319
Fax: 65 63198150
Publications: Berita Harian (50112) • Berita Minggu (50113) • The Business Times (50117) • Citta Bella (50123) • Female Business (50149) • Her World (50164) • Her World Brides (50165) • Home & Decor (50167) • Icon Moments (50169) • Lianhe Wanbao (50214) • Lianhe Zaobao (50215) • My Paper (50224) • The New Paper on Sunday (50226) • NuYou (50230) • NuYou Time (50231) • Shin Min Daily News (50251) • Simply Her (50252) • The Straits Times (50273) • Tamil Murasu (50276) • Thumbs Up (50278) • Torque (50280) • Young Parents (50289) • Young Parents Baby (50290) • Young Parents Preschool Guide (50291) • zbCOMMA (50292)

SISSA/ISAS
Via Bonomea, 265
34136 Trieste, Italy
Phone: 39 40 3787111
Fax: 39 40 3787249
Publications: PoS (Proceedings of Science) (46266)

SKAL Kustannus Oy
Nuijamiestentie 7
PO Box 38
FIN-00401 Helsinki, Finland
Phone: 358 947 8999
Fax: 358 958 78520
Publications: Kuljetusyrittaja (43842)

Skandinavisk Bladforlag A/S
Kongevej 3B
DK-1610 Copenhagen V, Denmark
Phone: 45 332 38099
Fax: 45 332 37042
Publications: Take Off (43684)

Ski Forum A/S
Postboks 6
Post Terminal
N-1306 Baerum, Norway
Publications: SkiSport (49189)

Skills Publishing Proprietary Ltd.
PO Box 514
Hazelbrook, New South Wales 2779, Australia
Phone: 61 2 47592844
Fax: 61 2 47593721
Publications: The Australian Woodworker (41944) • House & Home (41945)

Skydive Mag
5 Station Rd.
Ailsworth
Peterborough PE7 5AH, United Kingdom
Publications: Skydive (56262)

Slimming World
PO Box 55
Alfreton DE55 4UE, United Kingdom
Phone: 44 844 8920400
Fax: 44 844 8920401
Publications: Slimming World Magazine (52099)

Slojdforum
Pl. 6610 Mariedal 1
S-713 94 Nora, Sweden
Phone: 46 587 60015

Fax: 46 587 60032
Publications: Slojdforum (50994)

Slovak Academy of Sciences
Dubravska cesta 9
845 07 Bratislava, Slovakia
Phone: 42 125 9411204
Fax: 42 125 4771004
Publications: Computing and Informatics (50318) •
Measurement Science Review (50321)

Slovak Academy of Sciences
Racianska 75
831 02 Bratislava, Slovakia
Phone: 421 2 44259404
Fax: 421 2 44259404
Publications: Journal of Hydrology and Hydromechanics (50320)

Slovenian Chemical Society
Hajdrihova 19
p.p. 660
SI-1000 Ljubljana, Slovenia
Phone: 386 1 4760252
Fax: 386 1 4760300
Publications: Acta Chimica Slovenica (ACSi) (50334)

The Slovenian Museum of Natural History
Presernova 20
p.p. 290
SI-1001 Ljubljana, Slovenia
Phone: 386 1 2410940
Fax: 386 1 2410953
Publications: Acta Entomologica Slovenica (50335) •
Illiesia (50337) • Scopolia (50341)

Smart Card News Ltd.
Anchor Springs, Ste. 3
Duke St.
Littlehampton BN17 6BP, United Kingdom
Phone: 44 1903 734677
Fax: 44 1903 734318
Publications: Smart Card News (53866)

SMZ
Bellariastr. 82
CH-8038 Zurich, Switzerland
Phone: 41 442 812321
Fax: 41 442 812353
Publications: Schweizer Musikzeitung (51282)

Social, Emotional and Behavioural Difficulties Association
The Triangle, Rm. 211
Exchange Sq.
Manchester M4 3TR, United Kingdom
Phone: 44 161 2402418
Fax: 44 161 8385601
Publications: Emotional and Behavioral Difficulties (55555)

The Socialist Party of Great Britain
52 Clapham High St.
London SW4 7UN, United Kingdom
Phone: 44 20 76223811
Publications: Socialist Standard (55251)

Sociedade Botanica do Brasil
Caixa Postal 4005
Sao Paulo, Sao Paulo, Brazil
Phone: 55 51 33086955
Fax: 55 51 33086955
Publications: Acta Botanica Brasilica (43020)

Sociedade Brasileira de Ciencia do Solo
Cx. Postal 231
36570 000 Vicosa, Minas Gerais, Brazil
Phone: 55 31 38992471
Publications: Agora (43054) • Arquivo Brasileiro de Medicina Veterinaria e Zootecnia (43055) • Ciencia & Saude Coletiva (43056) • Ensaio (43057) • Entomologia y Vectores (43058) • Journal of Epilepsy and Clinical Neurophysiology (43059) • Materials Research (43060) • Novos Estudos Cebrap (43061) • Papeis Avulsos de Zoologia (Sao Paulo) (43043) • Pro-Fono Revista de Atualizacao Cientifica (43062) • Radiologia Brasileira (43063) • RAE eletronica (43064) • Rem (43065)

Sociedade Brasileira de Ciencia e Tecnologia de Alimentos
Caixa Postal 271
Avenida Brazil, 2880

13001-970 Campinas, Sao Paulo, Brazil
Phone: 55 19 32415793
Fax: 55 19 32410527
Publications: Ciencia e Tecnologia de Alimentos (42967)

Sociedade Brasileira de Computacao
Av. Bento Goncalves 9500, B. Agronomia
Caixa Postal 15064
91501-970 Porto Alegre, Rio Grande do Sul, Brazil
Phone: 55 51 3166835
Fax: 55 51 3166835
Publications: Journal of the Brazilian Computer Society (42991)

Sociedade Brasileira para o Desenvolvimento da Pesquisa em Cirurgia
Al. Rio Claro, 179, 14
01332-010 Sao Paulo, Sao Paulo, Brazil
Phone: 55 113 2878814
Fax: 55 113 2878814
Publications: Acta Cirurgica Brasileira (43021)

Sociedade Brasileira de Fisica
Rua do Matao, travessa R, 187 - Edificio Sede
Cidade Universitaria
05508-090 Sao Paulo, Sao Paulo, Brazil
Phone: 55 11 30340429
Fax: 55 11 38146293
Publications: Brazilian Journal of Physics (43028)

Sociedade Brasileira de Fisiologia Vegetal
Departamento de Botanica
Universidade Federal de Pelotas
96010-900 Pelotas, Rio Grande do Sul, Brazil
Phone: 55 53 32757336
Fax: 55 53 32757169
Publications: Brazilian Journal of Plant Physiology (42989)

Sociedade Brasileira de Fitopatologia
SGAS 902 Bloco B, Lote 74 - Salas 102/103
Edificio Athenas
70390-020 Brasilia, Federal District, Brazil
Phone: 55 613 2252421
Fax: 55 613 2252421
Publications: Fitopatologia Brasileira (42958)

Sociedade Brasileira de Genetica
Rua Cap. Adelmio Norberto da Silva, 736
Alto da Boa Vista
14025-670 Ribeirao Preto, Sao Paulo, Brazil
Phone: 55 16 36218540
Fax: 55 16 33696164
Publications: Genetics and Molecular Biology (42998)

Sociedade Brasileira de Microbiologia
Av. Prof. Lineu Prestes, 1374 - Sala 214
Cidade Universitaria
05508-900 Sao Paulo, Sao Paulo, Brazil
Phone: 55 113 8139647
Fax: 55 113 8139647
Publications: Brazilian Journal of Microbiology (43026)

Sociedade Brasileira de Microondas e Opto-eletronica - SBMO
Praca Maua, No. 1
09580-900 Sao Caetano do Sul, Sao Paulo, Brazil
Phone: 55 114 2388988
Fax: 55 114 2388988
Publications: Journal of Microwaves, Optoelectronics and Electromagnetic Applications (43018)

Sociedade Brasileira de Pesquisa Odontologica
Av. Lineu Prestes, 2227
Cid. Universitaria
Sao Paulo, Sao Paulo, Brazil
Phone: 55 113 0917855
Fax: 55 113 0917855
Publications: Brazilian Oral Research (43030)

Sociedade Brasileira de Quimica
Instituto de Quimica - UNICAMP
Caixa Postal 6154
13083-970 Campinas, Sao Paulo, Brazil
Phone: 55 19 37883151
Fax: 55 19 37883151
Publications: Journal of the Brazilian Chemical Society (42969)

Sociedade Brasileira de Quimica
Av. Prof. Lineu Prestes, 748 - Bloco 3 - Superior
Sala 371

05508-000 Sao Paulo, Sao Paulo, Brazil
Phone: 55 113 0322299
Fax: 55 113 8143602
Publications: Quimica Nova (43046)

Sociedade de Investigaoes Florestais
Departamento de Engenharia Florestal
Av. P.H. Rolfs s/n - Campus UFV
36570-000 Vicosa, Minas Gerais, Brazil
Phone: 55 313 8992476
Fax: 55 313 8912166
Publications: Revista Arvore (43066)

Societe Francais de Chimie
250, rue St. Jacques
F-75005 Paris, France
Phone: 33 140 467160
Fax: 33 140 467161
Publications: L'Actualite Chimique (44021)

Societe Royale Belge de Geographie
CP 246 ULB Campus de la Plaine
bvd. du Triomphe
B-1050 Ixelles, Belgium
Phone: 32 2 6505079
Fax: 32 2 6505092
Publications: Revue Belge de Geographie (42889)

Society for Actinomycetes, Japan
c/o Kitasato Institute for Life Sciences
Kitasato University
5-9-1 Shirokane
Minato-ku
Tokyo 108-8641, Japan
Phone: 81 3 57916133
Fax: 81 3 57916133
Publications: Actinomycetologica (46727)

Society for the Advancement of Breeding Researches in Asia and Oceania
c/o Ms. Marlyn Rala
International Rice Research Institute
Los Banos
Laguna 4031, Philippines
Phone: 63 2 5805600
Fax: 63 2 5805699
Publications: SABRAO Journal of Breeding and Genetics (49559)

Society for Advancement of Electrochemical Science and Technology
CECRI Campus
Karaikudi 630 006, Maharashtra, India
Phone: 91 456 5224198
Fax: 91 456 5227713
Publications: Current Titles in Electrochemistry (45239)

Society of Antiquaries of London
Burlington House
Piccadilly
London W1J 0BE, United Kingdom
Phone: 44 20 74797080
Fax: 44 20 72876967
Publications: Antiquaries Journal (53956)

Society of Antiquaries of Newcastle-upon-Tyne
Great North Museum
Hancock, Barras Bridge
Newcastle upon Tyne NE2 4PT, United Kingdom
Phone: 44 19 12312700
Publications: Archaeologia Aeliana (55667)

Society for Applied Microbiology
Bedford Hts.
Brickhill Dr.
Bedford MK41 7PH, United Kingdom
Phone: 44 123 4326661
Fax: 44 123 4326678
Publications: Journal of Applied Microbiology (52273)

Society of Archer-Antiquaries
29 Batley Ct. Oldland
S Glousteshire B
London BS30 8YZ, United Kingdom
Phone: 44 117 9323276
Publications: Journal of the Society of Archer-Antiquaries (54821)

Society of Archivists
Prioryfield House
20 Canon St.
Taunton TA1 1SW, United Kingdom
Phone: 44 1823 327030

Fax: 44 1823 271719
Publications: Journal of the Society of Archivists (54822)

Society of Australian Genealogists
120 Kent St.
Sydney, New South Wales 2000, Australia
Phone: 61 292 473953
Fax: 61 292 414872
Publications: Descent (42501)

Society of Authors - England
84 Drayton Gardens
London SW10 9SB, United Kingdom
Phone: 44 20 73736642
Fax: 44 20 73735768
Publications: Author (53983)

Society for Biomaterials and Artificial Organs
Sree Chitra Tirunal Institute for Medical Sciences & Technol
Poojapura
Thiruvananthapuram 695 012, Kerala, India
Phone: 91 471 2520214
Fax: 91 471 2341814
Publications: Trends in Biomaterials & Artificial Organs (45749)

Society for Biotechnology, Japan
c/o Faculty of Engineering
Osaka University
2-1 Yamada-Oka
Suita-shi
Osaka 565-0871, Japan
Phone: 81 6 68762731
Fax: 81 6 68792034
Publications: Journal of Bioscience and Bioengineering (46620)

Society of Bookbinders
c/o Hilary Henning, Membership Sec.
102 Hetherington Rd.
Shepperton TW17 0SW, United Kingdom
Publications: Bookbinder (56520)

Society of Business Economists
11 Bay Tree Walk
Watford WD17 4RX, United Kingdom
Phone: 44 1923237287
Publications: The Business Economist (56860)

Society of Chemical Engineers Japan
Kyoritsu Bldg.
4-6-19 Kohinata
Bunkyo-ku
Tokyo 112-0006, Japan
Phone: 81 3 39433527
Fax: 81 3 39433530
Publications: Journal of Chemical Engineering of Japan (46891)

Society of Chemical Industry
14-15 Belgrave Sq.
London SW1X 8PS, United Kingdom
Phone: 44 20 75981500
Fax: 44 20 75981545
Publications: Chemistry & Industry (54201) • Journal of Chemical Technology and Biotechnology (54721) • Journal of the Science of Food and Agriculture (54816)

Society for Computers and Law
10 Hurle Cres.
Clifton
Bristol BS8 2TA, United Kingdom
Phone: 44 11 79237393
Fax: 44 11 79239305
Publications: Computers and Law (52655)

Society of Cosmetic Scientists
G.T. House
24/26 Rothesay Rd.
Luton LU1 1QX, United Kingdom
Phone: 44 15 82726661
Fax: 44 15 82405217
Publications: International Journal of Cosmetic Science (55719)

Society of Dairy Technology
PO Box 12
Appleby-in-Westmorland CA16 6YJ, United Kingdom
Phone: 44 1768 354034
Publications: International Journal of Dairy Technology (52126)

Society for Endocrinology
22 Apex Ct.
Woodlands, Bradley Stoke
Bradley Stoke
Bristol BS32 4JT, United Kingdom
Phone: 44 1454 642200
Fax: 44 1454 642222
Publications: Endocrine-Related Cancer (52663) • European Journal of Endocrinology (52664) • Journal of Endocrinology (52685) • Journal of Molecular Endocrinology (52691)

Society for Environmental Communications
41, Tughlakabad Institutional Area
New Delhi 110062, Delhi, India
Phone: 91 11 29955124
Fax: 91 11 29955879
Publications: Down To Earth (45503)

Society of Environmental Engineers
The Manor House, High St.
Buntingford SG9 9AB, United Kingdom
Phone: 44 17 63271209
Fax: 44 17 63273255
Publications: Environmental Engineering (52759)

Society for Experimental Biology
Charles Darwin House
12 Roger St.
London WC1N 2JU, United Kingdom
Phone: 44 207 6852600
Fax: 44 207 6852601
Publications: Journal of Experimental Botany (53734)

Society of Fisheries Technologists (India)
Matsyapuri PO
Cochin 682 029, Kerala, India
Phone: 91 484 2666845
Fax: 91 484 2668212
Publications: Fishery Technology (45073)

Society of Food Hygiene Technology
Middleton House Farm
Tamworth Rd.
Middleton B78 2BD, United Kingdom
Phone: 44 1827 872500
Fax: 44 1827 875800
Publications: SOFHT Focus (55622)

Society of Garden Designers
Katepwa House
Ashfield Park Ave.
Ross-on-Wye HR9 5AX, United Kingdom
Phone: 44 1989 566695
Fax: 44 1989 567676
Publications: Garden Design Journal (56409)

Society of Genealogists
14 Charterhouse Bldgs.
Goswell Rd.
London EC1M 7BA, United Kingdom
Phone: 44 20 7251 8799
Fax: 44 20 7250 1800
Publications: Genealogists' Magazine (54500)

Society for General Microbiology
Marlborough House
Basingstoke Rd
Spencers Wood
Reading RG7 1AG, United Kingdom
Phone: 44 11 89881800
Fax: 44 11 89885656
Publications: International Journal of Systematic and Evolutionary Microbiology (44386) • Journal of General Virology (56323) • Journal of Medical Microbiology (52349) • Microbiology (56325) • Microbiology Today (56326)

Society of Glass Technology
Unit 9, Twelve O'Clock Ct.
21 Attercliffe Rd.
Sheffield S4 7WW, United Kingdom
Phone: 44 11 42634455
Fax: 44 11 42634411
Publications: Glass Technology (56494) • Physics & Chemistry of Glasses (56510)

Society of Homeopaths
11 Brookfield, Duncan Close
Moultan Pk.
Northampton NN3 6WL, United Kingdom
Phone: 44 84 54506611

Fax: 44 84 54506622
Publications: The Homeopath Journal (55709)

Society of Indexers
Woodbourn Business Center
10 Jessell St.
Sheffield S9 3HY, United Kingdom
Phone: 44 114 2449561
Fax: 44 114 2449563
Publications: The Indexer (56497)

Society for Industrial & Applied Mathematics
3600 Market St., 6th Fl.
Philadelphia, PA 19104-2688
Phone: 215382-9800
Fax: 215386-7999
Free: 800447-7426
Publications: SIAM Journal on Optimization (56202) • SIAM Journal on Scientific Computing (44341)

Society for International Development - Italy
Via. Panisperna 207
I-00184 Rome, Italy
Phone: 39 648 72172
Fax: 39 648 72170
Publications: Development (46226)

Society for Italian Studies
c/o Spencer Pearce, Treas.
School of Languages Linguistics and Cultures
University of Manchester
Oxford Rd.
Manchester M13 9PL, United Kingdom
Phone: 44 161 2753125
Publications: Italian Studies (55562)

Society for Japanese Arts
Overste den Oudenlaan 7
Aerdenhout
NL-2111 WB Amsterdam, Netherlands
Phone: 31 23 5240129
Fax: 31 23 5248913
Publications: Andon (47894)

Society of Lamellicornians
c/o Mr. Masaaki Ishida
23-5 Miyamae 3-chome
Suginami-ku
Tokyo 168-0081, Japan
Publications: Lamellicornia (46957)

Society of Leather Technologists and Chemists
49 N Park St.
Dewsbury WF13 4LZ, United Kingdom
Phone: 44 19 24460864
Fax: 44 19 24460864
Publications: Journal of the Society of Leather Technologists and Chemists (53180)

Society of Medical Laboratory Technologists of South Africa
PO Box 6014
Roggebaai
Cape Town 8012, Republic of South Africa
Phone: 27 21 4194857
Fax: 27 21 4212566
Publications: Medical Technology (50391)

Society for Name Studies in Britain and Ireland
c/o Medical Library, School of Medical Science
University of Bristol
University Walk
Bristol BS8 1TD, United Kingdom
Publications: NOMINA (52711)

Society for Nautical Research
The Lodge
The Drive
Hellingly
East Sussex
Hailsham BN27 4EP, United Kingdom
Publications: Mariner's Mirror (53501)

Society of Nuclear Medicine, India
c/o Radiation Medicine Ctr., B.A.R.C.
T.M.C. Annexe
Parel
Mumbai 400 012, Maharashtra, India
Phone: 91 022 24149428
Fax: 91 022 24157098
Publications: Indian Journal of Nuclear Medicine (45384)

Society of Occupational Medicine
6 St. Andrew's Pl.
Regent's Pk.
London NW1 4LB, United Kingdom
Phone: 44 20 74862641
Fax: 44 20 74860028
Publications: Occupational Medicine Journal (55024)

Society of Petroleum Engineers
3rd Fl., Portland House
4 Great Portland St.
London W1W 8QJ, United Kingdom
Phone: 44 20 72993300
Fax: 44 20 72993309
Publications: Journal of Petroleum Technology (54795)

Society of Pharmaceutical Medicine
9 Red Lion Ct.
London EC4A 3EF, United Kingdom
Phone: 44 20 79365903
Fax: 44 20 79365901
Publications: Journal of Pharmaceutical Medicine (54796)

Society for Plant Biochemistry and Biotechnology
Division of Biochemistry
Indian Agricultural Research Institute
New Delhi 110 012, Delhi, India
Publications: Journal of Plant Biochemistry and Biotechnology (45616)

Society of Polymer Science Japan
Shintomicho Bldg.
3-10-9 Irifune
Chuo-ku
Tokyo 104-0042, Japan
Phone: 81 3 55403776
Fax: 81 3 55403737
Publications: Polymer Journal (47021)

Society for Popular Astronomy
79 Chadwick Ave.
Rednal
Birmingham B45 8ED, United Kingdom
Publications: Popular Astronomy (52361)

Society for Promoting Christian Knowledge
36 Causton St.
London SW1P 4ST, United Kingdom
Phone: 44 20 75923900
Fax: 44 20 75923939
Publications: Theology (55305)

Society for the Promotion of African, Asian, and Latin American Literature
PO Box 10 01 16
D-60001 Frankfurt, Germany
Phone: 49 69 2102143
Fax: 49 69 2102227
Publications: Literaturnachrichten (44362)

Society for the Promotion of Hellenic Studies
Senate House
Malet St.
London WC1E 7HU, United Kingdom
Phone: 44 20 78628730
Fax: 44 20 78628731
Publications: Archaeological Reports (53960) • Journal of Hellenic Studies (54761)

Society for the Promotion of Roman Studies
Senate House
Malet St.
London WC1E 7HU, United Kingdom
Phone: 44 20 78628727
Fax: 44 20 78628728
Publications: Britannia (54107) • Journal of Roman Studies (54811)

Society of Radiographers of South Africa
PO Box 6014
Roggebaai 8012, Republic of South Africa
Phone: 27 21 4194857
Fax: 27 21 4212566
Publications: The South African Radiographer (50616)

Society of Recorder Players
c/o Dick Pyper, Chm.
35 Meads Rd.
Guildford GU1 2NA, United Kingdom
Phone: 44 1483 505104
Publications: The Recorder Magazine (56883)

Society for Reproduction and Development
c/o Hiroko Tsukamura, PhD
Nagoya University
Graduate School of Bioagricultural Science
Furo-cho, Chikusa-ku
Nagoya 464-8601, Japan
Phone: 81 527 894162
Fax: 81 527 894072
Publications: Journal of Reproduction and Development (46939)

Society for Research in Music
PO Box 3211
Matieland 7602, Republic of South Africa
Phone: 27 82 8815825
Fax: 27 86 5253704
Publications: South African Music Studies (50554)

Society of Resource Geology
Nogizaka Bldg.
9-6-41 Akasaka
Minato-ku
Tokyo 107-0052, Japan
Phone: 81 3 34755287
Fax: 81 3 34750824
Publications: Resource Geology (47109)

Society of St. Paul, Inc.
PO Box 1722
Makati City 1257, Philippines
Publications: Home Life (49517)

Society for the Scientific Investigation of Para-Science
Arheilger Weg 11
D-64380 Rossdorf, Germany
Phone: 49 6154 695021
Fax: 49 6154 695022
Publications: Skeptiker (44645)

Society of South African Geographers
Dept. of Environmental & Geographical Science
University of Cape Town
Rondebosch 7701, Republic of South Africa
Phone: 27 216 502873
Publications: The South African Geographical Journal (50623)

Society of Statistic and Operations Research
Faculty of Mathematical Sciences
Facultad de Matematicas
Despacho 502
Plaza de Ciencias, 3
28040 Madrid, Spain
Phone: 34 91 5449102
Fax: 34 91 5449102
Publications: TEST (50811)

Society for Storytelling
c/o The Morgan Library
Aston St.
Shrophire
Wem SY4 5AU, United Kingdom
Phone: 44 753 4578386
Publications: Storylines (56885)

Society for the Study of German Art
Geschaftsstelle Berlin
Jebensstrasse 2
D-10623 Berlin, Germany
Phone: 49 3 3139932
Fax: 49 3 75632108
Publications: Zeitschrift des Deutschen Vereins fur Kunstwissenschaft (44238)

Society for the Study of Human Biology
University of Sheffield
Regent Ct.
30 Regent Rd.
Sheffield S1 4DA, United Kingdom
Phone: 44 1629 56409
Publications: Annals of Human Biology (55477)

Society for the Study of Inborn Errors of Metabolism
c/o Dr. Nenad Blau
University Children's Hospital
Division of Clinical Chemistry and Biochemistry
Steinwiesstrasse 75
8032 Zurich, Switzerland
Phone: 41 44 2667544

Fax: 41 44 2667169
Publications: Journal of Inherited Metabolic Disease (51270)

Society for the Study of the Origin and Evolution of Life
c/o Dr. Akihiko Shimada
University of Tsukuba
Graduate School of Life & Environmental Sciences
1-1-1, Tennodai
Tsukuba 305-8572, Japan
Phone: 81 298 534367
Publications: Viva Origino (46629)

Society of Surgeons of Pakistan
c/o Prof. Ahmed Memon
Surgical Unit III
Chandka Medical College
Larkana, Pakistan
Publications: Pakistan Journal of Surgery (49391)

Society for Theatre Research
c/o The National Theatre Archive
The Cut
London SE1 8LL, United Kingdom
Publications: Theatre Notebook (52633)

Society for Underwater Technology
80 Coleman St.
London EC2R 5BJ, United Kingdom
Phone: 44 20 7382 2601
Fax: 44 20 7382 2684
Publications: Underwater Technology (55359)

Society of Women Writers and Journalists
c/o Wendy Hughes, Membership Sec.
27 Brayton Ave.
Walton-on-Thames KT12 2AZ, United Kingdom
Publications: The Woman Writer (56837)

Sofcom
Level 19, The Como Centre
644 Chapel St.
Melbourne, Victoria 3141, Australia
Phone: 61 3 98268300
Publications: 4wdonline (42060)

SOFETEC
66 rue Escudier
F-92100 Boulogne, France
Phone: 33 148 255030
Fax: 33 148 259054
Publications: Werkzeug Technik (43922)

Soft Drinks International
PO Box 4173
Wimborne BH21 1YX, United Kingdom
Phone: 44 12 02842222
Fax: 44 12 02848494
Publications: Soft Drinks International (56929)

Sogn og Fjordane Univiversity College
PO Box 133
Sogndal, Norway
Phone: 47 576 76000
Fax: 47 576 76100
Publications: Nordic Journal of Music Therapy (49211)

Soiel International S.R.L.
Via. Martiri Oscuri 3
I-20125 Milan, Italy
Phone: 39 2 26148855
Fax: 39 2 26149333
Publications: Office Automation (46189) • Officelayout (46190)

Soil Association
South Plz.
Marlborough St.
Bristol BS1 3NX, United Kingdom
Phone: 44 117 3145000
Fax: 44 117 3145001
Publications: Living Earth (52702)

Soil Science Society of South Africa
PO Box 65217
Erasmusrand 0165, Republic of South Africa
Publications: South African Journal of Plant and Soil (50478)

Solvent Extractors' Association of India
142 Jolly Maker Chambers No. 2, 14th Fl.
225 Nariman Point
Mumbai 400 021, Maharashtra, India

Phone: 91 222 2021475
Fax: 91 222 2021692
Publications: SEA Monthly News Circular (45438)

Songlines
PO Box 54209
London W14 0WU, United Kingdom
Phone: 44 20 73712777
Fax: 44 20 73712220
Publications: Songlines (55255)

Sonntag Aktuell
Postfach 10 44 62
70039 Stuttgart, Germany
Phone: 49 711 72050
Fax: 49 711 72057138
Publications: Sonntag Aktuell (44680)

Soochow University
Wai Shuang Hsi Campus
70, Lin-shi Rd., Shilin
Taipei 111, Taiwan
Phone: 86 228 819471
Fax: 86 223 890224
Publications: Soochow Journal of History (51358) •
Soochow Journal of Political Science (51359)

Sophia University
7-1 Kioi-cho
Chiyoda-Ku
Tokyo 102-8554, Japan
Phone: 81 3 32383179
Fax: 81 3 32383539
Publications: Journal of American and Canadian Studies (46882) • Monumenta Nipponica (46971)

Sotelo Blanco Edicions S.L.
San Marcos, 77
E-15820 Santiago de Compostela, Spain
Phone: 34 981 582571
Fax: 34 981 587290
Publications: A Trabe de Ouro (50832)

Sothis Editrice S.R.L.
Via. Pietro Maestri 3
I-00191 Rome, Italy
Phone: 39 6 3296563
Fax: 39 6 3295624
Publications: La Clessidra (46237)

The Soul Survivors
PO Box 377
West Malling ME6 9DQ, United Kingdom
Phone: 44 1732 844246
Publications: The Soul Survivors (56894)

The Sound Projector
BM Bemused
London WC1N 3XX, United Kingdom
Publications: Sound Projector (55256) •

South African Association for Food Science and Technology
PO Box 35233
Menlo Pk.
Gauteng 0102, Republic of South Africa
Phone: 27 12 3492788
Fax: 27 86 6984784
Publications: Food Review (50481)

South African Chemical Institute
The Secretary
PO Box 407
Wits 2050, Republic of South Africa
Phone: 27 11 7176741
Fax: 27 11 7176779
Publications: South African Journal of Chemistry (50644)

South African Communist Party
PO Box 1027
Johannesburg 2000, Republic of South Africa
Phone: 27 11 3393621
Fax: 27 11 3396880
Publications: Umsebenzi (50538)

South African Historical Society
c/o Prof. Julie Parle, Pres.
University of KwaZulu-Natal
Howard College
King George V Ave.
KwaZulu-Natal 4041, Republic of South Africa
Phone: 27 31 2602624

Fax: 27 31 2602621
Publications: South African Historical Journal (50545)

South African Institute of Architects
Private Bag 10063
Randburg 2125, Republic of South Africa
Phone: 27 117 821315
Fax: 27 117 828717
Publications: SA Architect (50610)

South African Institution of Civil Engineering
Private Bag X200
Halfway House 1685, Republic of South Africa
Phone: 27 11 8055947
Fax: 27 11 8055971
Publications: Civil Engineering (50519)

South African Jewish Board of Deputies
PO Box 87557
Houghton 2041, Republic of South Africa
Phone: 27 114 861434
Fax: 27 116 464940
Publications: Jewish Affairs (50524)

South African Medical Association
PO Box 74789
Lynnwood Ridge
Pretoria 0040, Republic of South Africa
Phone: 27 124812010
Fax: 27 124812061
Publications: Southern African Journal of HIV Medicine (50605)

South African National Museum of Military History
PO Box 52090
Saxonwold 2132, Republic of South Africa
Phone: 27 116 465513
Fax: 27 116 465256.
Publications: The Military History Journal (50628)

South African Orthopaedic Association
PO Box 12918
Brandhof 9324, Republic of South Africa
Phone: 27 51 4303280
Fax: 27 51 4303284
Publications: Journal of Bone and Joint Surgery (50358)

South African Society of Animal Science
PO Box 13884
Hatfield
Pretoria 0028, Republic of South Africa
Phone: 27 124 205017
Fax: 27 124 203290
Publications: South African Journal of Animal Science (50602)

South African Sports Medicine Association
PO Box 2491
Bedfordview 2008, Republic of South Africa
Phone: 27 117 173372
Fax: 27 117 173379
Publications: SA Journal of Sports Medicine (50352)

South African Translators Institute
PO Box 1710
Rivonia 2128, Republic of South Africa
Phone: 27 11 8032681
Fax: 27 86 5114971
Publications: Muratho (50611)

South African Water Research Commission
Marumati Bldg.
Frederika Street & 18th Ave.
Rietfontein
Pretoria 0003, Republic of South Africa
Phone: 27 123 300340
Fax: 27 123 312565
Publications: Water Wheel (50608)

South Australian Apple Users Club
PO Box 411
Glenside, South Australia 5065, Australia
Publications: AppleSauce (41897)

South Edinburgh Community Newspaper Ltd.
64 Gilmerton Dykes St.
Edinburgh EH17 8PL, United Kingdom
Phone: 44 131 6217065
Fax: 44 131 6217064
Publications: South Edinburgh Echo (53319)

South Pacific Post Proprietary Ltd.
PO Box 85
Lawes Rd.
Port Moresby, Papua New Guinea
Phone: 675 3091000
Fax: 675 3212721
Publications: Post-Courier (49403)

SOUTH Poetry
PO Box 3744
Cookham
Maidenhead SL6 9UY, United Kingdom
Publications: SOUTH Poetry (55525)

South Seas Society
PO Box 709
Singapore 901409, Singapore
Fax: 65 64665510
Publications: South Seas Society Journal (50269)

Southampton University
University Rd.
Highfield
Southampton SO17 1BJ, United Kingdom
Phone: 44 23 80595000
Fax: 44 23 80593939
Publications: Wessex Scene (56579)

Southeast Asian Geotechnical Society
c/o Asian Institute of Technology
Klong Luang
Pathumthani 12120, Thailand
Phone: 66 2 5245864
Fax: 66 2 5162126
Publications: Geotechnical Engineering (51459)

Southeast Asian Ministers of Education Organization
Mom Luang Pin Malakul Centenary Bldg., 4th Fl.
920 Sukhumvit Rd.
Bangkok 10110, Thailand
Phone: 66 2391 0144
Fax: 66 2381 2587
Publications: SEAMEO Journal of Southeast Asian Education (51435)

Southern Africa Places
PO Box 3422
Paarl 7620, Republic of South Africa
Phone: 27 218 723210
Fax: 27 218 723212
Publications: Encounter Southern Africa (50561)

Southern African Institute of Forestry
Postnet, Ste. 329
Private Bag X4
Menlo Park
Pretoria 0102, Republic of South Africa
Phone: 27 123 481745
Fax: 27 123 481745
Publications: Southern Forest (50606)

Southern African Institute of Government Auditors
PO Box 36303
Menlo Pk.
Pretoria 0102, Republic of South Africa
Phone: 27 123 621221
Fax: 27 123 621418
Publications: Southern African Journal of Accountability and Auditing Research (50604)

Southern African Institute for Industrial Engineering
PO Box 141
Bruma 2026, Republic of South Africa
Phone: 27 11 5596143
Fax: 27 11 269759
Publications: South African Journal of Industrial Engineering (50359)

Southern African Institute for Management Scientists
Faculty of Economic & Management Sciences
University of Pretoria
Pretoria 0002, Republic of South Africa
Phone: 27 124 203816
Fax: 27 123 625058
Publications: Management Dynamics (50596)

Southern African Society of Legal Historians
Dept. of Jurisprudence
Pretoria 0003, Republic of South Africa

Phone: 27 012 4298412
Publications: Fundamina (50592)

Southern African Wildlife Management Association
PO Box 217
Bloubergstrand 7436, Republic of South Africa
Phone: 27 21 5541297
Fax: 27 86 6729882
Publications: South African Journal of Wildlife Research (50357)

Sozialdienst Katholischer Frauen
Agnes-Neuhaus-Str. 5
D-44135 Dortmund, Germany
Phone: 49 231 5570260
Fax: 49 231 55702660
Publications: Korrespondenzblatt (44317)

Sozialverband VdK Deutschland
In den Ministergarten 4
D-10117 Berlin, Germany
Phone: 49 30 726290400
Fax: 49 30 726290499
Publications: VdK Zeitung (44235)

Spanish Association of Dance Sport and Competition Dancing
C. St. Quinti, 37-45
ESC. A Entr. 2
E-08041 Barcelona, Spain
Phone: 34 93 4565167
Fax: 34 93 4557078
Publications: AEBDC News (50646)

Spanish Paleontology Society
Museo Nacional de Ciencias Naturales
Jose Gutierrez Abascal, 2
E-28006 Madrid, Spain
Publications: Revista Espanola de Paleontologia (50797)

Spanish Society for Microbiology
Vitruvio, 8
E-28006 Madrid, Spain
Phone: 34 915 613381
Fax: 34 915 613299
Publications: International Microbiology (50681)

Specialised Publications Ltd.
57 Bath St.
Gravesend
London DA11 0DF, United Kingdom
Phone: 44 1474 532202
Fax: 44 1474 532203
Publications: Confectionery Production (54258)

Spectrum Press
264/192 Allenganj
Allahabad 211 002, Uttar Pradesh, India
Publications: Journal of the Interdisciplinary Crossroads (44934)

Speech & Language Therapy in Practice
33 Kinnear Sq.
Laurencekirk AB30 1UL, United Kingdom
Phone: 44 1561 377415
Publications: Speech & Language Therapy in Practice (53743)

SPEEDUP Society: Swiss forum for GRID and High Performance Computing
c/o Prof. Peter Arbenz
Chair of Computational Science
CAB G 69.3
Universitaetsstrasse 6
CH-8092 Zurich, Switzerland
Phone: 41 44 6327432
Publications: SPEEDUP Journal (51286)

Speleological Society of Japan
c/o Kitakyushu Museum of Natural History & Human History
2-4-1 Higashida, Yahatahigashi-ku
Kitakyushyu
Fukuoka 805-0071, Japan
Publications: Caving Journal (46340) • Journal of the Speleological Society of Japan (46344)

SPG Media Group Plc.
Brunel House
55-57 N Wharf Rd.
London W2 1LA, United Kingdom
Phone: 44 20 79159660
Fax: 44 20 77242089
Publications: Hospital Management International (54574) • World Cruise Industry Review (55418) • World Expro (55419) • World Superyacht Review (55424)

SPIEGLHOF media GmbH
Grammelkam 3
D-84036 Kumhausen, Germany
Phone: 49 8743 303570
Fax: 49 8743 967654
Publications: AgrarMEGA (44515)

SPN Publishing Company
4a Novodanilovskaya nab
117105 Moscow, Russia
Publications: Aeroflot Premium (49868) • Inflight Review (49918) • Russian Digital (49973)

Sports Coach UK
114 Cardigan Rd.
Headingley
Leeds LS6 3BJ, United Kingdom
Phone: 44 11 32744802
Fax: 44 11 32755019
Publications: Coaching Edge (53761)

Sports Turf Research Institute
St. Ives Estate
Bingley BD16 1AU, United Kingdom
Phone: 44 12 74565131
Fax: 44 12 74561891
Publications: International Turfgrass Bulletin (52327) • Journal of Turfgrass Science (Incorporating the Journal of the Sports Turf Research Institute) (52328)

Springer Netherlands
Van Godewijckstraat 30
3311 GX Dordrecht, Netherlands
Phone: 31 786 576210
Fax: 31 786 576744
Publications: Acta Applicandae Mathematicae (48318) • Acta Biotheoretica (48319) • Advances in Computational Mathematics (48320) • Aerobiologia (48321) • African Archaeological Review (48322) • Agroforestry Systems (48323) • American Journal of Community Psychology (48324) • Annals of Mathematics and Artificial Intelligence (48325) • Annals of Operations Research (48326) • Applied Mathematics and Mechanics (48327) • Archives of Sexual Behavior (48328) • Arkiv for Matematik (50952) • Autonomous Agents and Multi-Agent Systems (48329) • BioControl (48330) • Biodegradation (48331) • Biogeochemistry (48332) • Biologia Plantarum (48333) • Biology and Philosophy (48334) • Boundary-Layer Meteorology (48335) • Brain and Mind (48336) • Breast Cancer Research and Treatment (48337) • Bulletin of the Brazilian Mathematical Society, New Series (48338) • Bulletin of Earthquake Engineering (48339) • Bulletin of Mathematical Biology (48340) • Bundesgesundheitsblatt - Gesundheitsforschung - Gesundheitsschutz (44163) • Cancer and Metastasis Reviews (48341) • Cardiac Electrophysiology Review (48342) • Cardiovascular Drugs and Therapy (48343) • Catalysis Letters (48344) • Catalysis Surveys from Asia (48345) • Celestial Mechanics & Dynamical Astronomy (48346) • Cell Biology and Toxicology (48347) • Cellular & Molecular Biology Letters (49777) • Central European Journal of Biology (48348) • Central European Journal of Medicine (48349) • Chemosensory Perception (48350) • Chinese Annals of Mathematics, Series B (43469) • Chinese Science Bulletin (48351) • Climatic Change (48352) • Clinical and Experimental Medicine (48353) • Clinical & Experimental Metastasis (48354) • Clinical Neuroradiology (48355) • Clinical Research in Cardiology (44486) • CME (48356) • Coloproctology (48357) • Complex Analysis and Operator Theory (46074) • Computer Supported Cooperative Work (CSCW) (48358) • Constitutional Political Economy (55549) • Contemporary Family Therapy (48359) • Contemporary Islam (48360) • Crime, Law and Social Change (48361) • Criminal Law Forum (48362) • Critical Criminology (48363) • De Economist (48364) • Der Anaesthesist (48365) • Der Chirurg (48366) • Der Gastroenterologe (48367) • Der Nephrologe (48368) • Der Nervenarzt (48369) • Der Radiologe (48370) • Der Schmerz (48371) • Designs, Codes and Cryptography (48372) • Dialectical Anthropology (48373) • Digestive Diseases and Sciences (48374) • Discrete Event Dynamic Systems (48375) • Distributed and Parallel Databases (48376) • Documenta Ophthalmologica (48377) • Economic Change and Restructuring (48378) • Economic Theory (48379) • Education Assessment, Evaluation and Accountability (48380) • Educational Research for Policy and Practice (50097) • European Journal of Clinical Microbiology & Infectious Diseases (48381) • European Journal on Criminal Policy and Research (48382) • European Journal of Pediatrics (42895) • European Journal of Plastic Surgery (48383) • European Radiology Supplements (48384) • European Review of Aging and Physical Activity (46115) • European Surgery (42756) • Evolution: Education and Outreach (48385) • Feminist Legal Studies (48386) • Financial Markets and Portfolio Management (48387) • Flexible Services and Manufacturing Journal (48388) • Food Biophysics (48389) • Forschung im Ingenieurwesen (48390) • Forum der Psychoanalyse (48391) • Foundations of Science (48392) • Frontiers of Biology in China (48393) • Frontiers of Chemistry in China (48394) • Frontiers of Economics in China (48395) • Frontiers of Education in China (48396) • Frontiers of Electrical and Electronic Engineering in China (48397) • Frontiers of Forestry in China (48398) • Frontiers of History in China (48399) • Frontiers of Law in China (48400) • Frontiers of Mathematics in China (48401) • Frontiers of Mechanical Engineering in China (48402) • Frontiers of Philosophy in China (48403) • Frontiers of Physics in China (48404) • Genes & Nutrition (46231) • Genetica (48405) • GeoInformatica (48406) • Geometriae Dedicata (48407) • Grammars (48408) • Grundwasser (48409) • Gynakologische Endokrinologie (48410) • Gynecological Surgery (48411) • Health Care Analysis (48412) • HealthCare Ethics Committee Forum (48413) • Helminthologia (48414) • Herzschrittmachertherapie & Elektrophysiologie (44361) • Higher Education (48415) • HNO (48416) • Holz als Roh- und Werkstoff (48417) • Human Ecology (48418) • Hydrobiologia (48419) • Hyperfine Interactions (48420) • Inflammopharmacology (56498) • Informatik-Spektrum (48421) • Information Technology and Management (48422) • Integrated Assessment (48423) • Intensivmedizin und Notfallmedizin (48424) • International Economics and Economic Policy (44715) • International Journal for the Advancement of Counseling (48425) • International Journal of Computer Assisted Radiology and Surgery (48426) • International Journal for Educational and Vocational Guidance (48427) • International Journal of Historical Archaeology (48428) • International Journal of Information Security (44419) • International Journal for Philosophy of Religion (48429) • International Journal of Politics, Culture, and Society (48430) • International Journal of Public Health (51074) • International Journal for the Semiotics of Law (48431) • International Review of Education (48432) • Invertebrate Neuroscience (48433) • Ionics (48434) • Journal of Academic Ethics (48436) • Journal of Applied Electrochemistry (48437) • Journal of Archaeological Research (48438) • Journal of the Association for Research in Otolaryngology (48439) • Journal of Atmospheric Chemistry (48440) • Journal of Autism and Developmental Disorders (48441) • Journal of Bamboo and Rattan (48442) • Journal of Behavioral Education (48443) • Journal of Bioethical Inquiry (48444) • Journal of Biomedical Science (48445) • Journal of Business Ethics (48446) • Journal of Cardiovascular Translational Research (48447) • Journal of Clinical Monitoring and Computing (48448) • Journal of Cluster Science (48449) • Journal of Computational Electronics (48450) • Journal of Computational Neuroscience (48451) • Journal in Computer Virology (48452) • Journal of Consumer Policy (48453) • Journal of Dynamical and Control Systems (48454) • Journal of Dynamics and Differential Equations (48455) • Journal of East Asian Linguistics (48456) • The Journal of Economic Inequality (48457) • Journal of Experimental Criminology (48458) • Journal of Financial Services Research (48459) • Journal of Fusion Energy (48460) • Journal of Gambling Studies (48461) • Journal of Genetic Counseling (48462) • Journal of Geographical Systems (48463) • Journal of Geometry (48464) • Journal of Global Optimization (48465) • Journal of Grid Computing (48466) • Journal of Housing and the Built Environment (48467) • Journal of Immigrant and Minority Health (48468) • Journal of Inorganic and Organometallic Polymers and Materials (48469) • Journal of Low Temperature Physics (48470) • Journal of Manage-

ment and Governance (48471) • Journal of Maritime Archaeology (48472) • Journal of Materials Science (48473) • Journal of Mathematical Chemistry (48474) • Journal of Mathematical Modelling and Algorithms (48475) • Journal of Medical Humanities (48476) • Journal of Neuro-Oncology (48477) • Journal of Neuroimmune Pharmacology (48478) • Journal of Nonverbal Behavior (48479) • Journal of Optimization Theory and Applications (48480) • Journal of Orofacial Orthopedics/Fortschritte der Kieferorthopadie (48481) • Journal of Pest Science (48482) • Journal of Pharmaceutical Innovation (48483) • Journal of Polymer Research (48484) • Journal of Polymers and the Environment (48485) • The Journal of Primary Prevention (48486) • Journal of Productivity Analysis (48487) • Journal of Psycholinguistic Research (48488) • Journal of Psychopathology & Behavioral Assessment (48489) • Journal of Risk and Uncertainty (48490) • Journal of Scheduling (48491) • Journal of Science Teacher Education (48492) • Journal of Statistical Physics (48493) • Journal of Structural and Functional Genomics (48494) • Journal of Superconductivity and Novel Magnetism (48495) • Journal of Systems Science and Complexity (48496) • Journal of Systems Science and Systems Engineering (48497) • Journal of Thrombosis and Thrombolysis (48498) • Journal of World Prehistory (48499) • Knee Surgery, Sports Traumatology, Arthroscopy (48500) • Knowledge and Information Systems (48501) • La radiologia medica (48502) • La Lettre de medecine physique et de readaptation (48503) • Landslides (48504) • Language Policy (48505) • Language Resources and Evaluation (48506) • Law and Philosophy (48507) • Liverpool Law Review (48508) • L1-Educational Studies in Language and Literature (48509) • Manuelle Medizin (48510) • Marketing Letters (48511) • Maternal and Child Health Journal (48512) • Mathematical Physics, Analysis and Geometry (48513) • Meccanica (48514) • Metabolic Brain Disease (48515) • Mycopathologia (48516) • Natural Computing (48517) • Netnomics (48518) • Neurochemical Research (48519) • Numerical Algorithms (48520) • Optical and Quantum Electronics (55768) • Optimization and Engineering (48521) • Order (48522) • Origins of Life and Evolution of the Biosphere (48523) • Periodica Mathematica Hungarica (48524) • Pharmaceutical Research (48525) • Philosophical Studies (48526) • Photonic Network Communications (48527) • Photosynthesis Research (48528) • Photosynthetica (48529) • Phytoparasitica (48530) • Pituitary (48531) • Plant Cell, Tissue and Organ Culture (48532) • Plant Ecology (48533) • Plant Foods for Human Nutrition (48534) • Plant Molecular Biology (48535) • Plant and Soil (48536) • Plasma Chemistry and Plasma Processing (48537) • Polfcy Sciences (48538) • Population Research and Policy Review (48539) • Potential Analysis (48540) • Precision Agriculture (48541) • Public Choice (48542) • Quality of Life Research (48543) • Quality & Quantity (48544) • Queueing Systems (48545) • The Ramanujan Journal (48546) • Reading and Writing (48547) • Real-Time Systems (48548) • Reliable Computing (48549) • Res Publica (55689) • Research in Higher Education (48550) • Review of Accounting Studies (48551) • The Review of Austrian Economics (48552) • Review of Derivatives Research (48553) • Review of Industrial Organization (48554) • Review of Quantitative Finance and Accounting (48555) • Reviews in Endocrine & Metabolic Disorders (48556) • Reviews in Fish Biology and Fisheries (48557) • Russian Linguistics (48558) • Science & Education (48559) • Sensing and Imaging (48560) • Social Indicators Research (48561) • Social Justice Research (48562) • Software Quality Journal (48563) • Solar Physics (48564) • Somatic Cell and Molecular Genetics (48565) • Space Science Reviews (48566) • Spanish Economic Review (50700) • Sport Sciences for Health (48567) • Statistical Inference for Stochastic Processes (44084) • Statistical Methods and Applications (46242) • Statistical Papers (42734) • Statistics and Computing (48568) • Strahlentherapie und Onkologie (44342) • Structural and Multidisciplinary Optimization (44874) • Studia Logica (48569) • Studies in Philosophy and Education (48570) • Supportive Care in Cancer (48571) • Surgical and Radiologic Anatomy (48572) • Surveys in Geophysics (48573) • Sustainability Science (48574) • Synthese (48575) • Systematic Parasitology (55284) • Systemic Practice and Action Research

(48576) • Systems and Synthetic Biology (47142) • Theoretical Medicine and Bioethics (48577) • Theory in Biosciences (44491) • Theory and Decision (48578) • Theory and Society (48579) • Transition Metal Chemistry (48580) • Transport in Porous Media (48581) • Transportation (48582) • Tropical Animal Health and Production (48583) • Urban Ecosystems (48584) • User Modeling and User-Adapted Interaction (48585) • Vietnam Journal of Mathematics (48586) • Wireless Networks (48587) • World Wide Web (48588)

Springer Publishing Co.
11 W 42nd St., 15th Fl.
New York, NY 10036
Phone: 212431-4370
Fax: 212941-7842
Free: 877687-7476
Publications: Wood Science and Technology (44587)

Springer-VDI-Verlag
VDI-Platz 1
D-14197 Dusseldorf, Germany
Phone: 49 211 61030
Fax: 49 211 6103300
Publications: European Physical Journal E. Soft Matter (44324) • Gefahrstoffe-Reinhaltung der Luft (44325)

Springer-Verlag
Tiergartenstrasse 17
D-69121 Heidelberg, Germany
Phone: 49 6221 4878808
Publications: Acta Ethologica (49801) • Annals of Software Engineering (44439) • Climate Dynamics (44446) • Cluster Computing (44448) • Computational Geosciences (44449) • Diabetologia (44452) • Environmental Modeling & Assessment (44454) • European Archives of Otorhinolaryngology (44455) • The European Physical Journal A-Hadrons and Nuclei (46146) • European Spine Journal (44456) • Experimental Brain Research (46228) • Geo-Marine Letters (44713) • Graefe's Archive for Clinical and Experimental Ophthalmology (53422) • Granular Matter (44097) • Health Care Management Science (44458) • Heat and Mass Transfer (44497) • Helgoland Marine Research (44481) • Hernia (44459) • Histochemistry and Cell Biology (44460) • Information Systems and E-Business Management (ISeB) (44598) • Innovations in Systems and Software Engineering (44461) • International Archives of Occupational and Environmental Health (44339) • International Journal on Digital Libraries (44310) • International Journal of Legal Medicine (44462) • International Journal on Software Tools for Technology Transfer (STTT) (44316) • Inventiones Mathematicae (44019) • Journal fur Betriebswirtschaft (44463) • Journal of Cancer Research and Clinical Oncology (44490) • Journal of Comparative Physiology B (44548) • Journal of Geodesy (44464) • Journal of Mathematical Biology (44465) • Journal of Population Economics (44264) • Journal of Solid State Electrochemistry (44404) • Marine Biology (44505) • Mathematische Annalen (44466) • Mathematische Zeitschrift (44069) • Microsystem Technologies (44222) • Mineralium Deposita (44467) • Molecular Genetics and Genomics (50959) • Multimedia Systems (44468) • Mycorrhiza (43945) • Naturwissenschaften (56575) • Naunyn-Schmiedeberg's Archives of Pharmacology (48171) • Neurogenetics (44388) • Neuroradiology (44469) • Numerische Mathematik (46210) • Oecologia (44470) • Pediatric Surgery International (44471) • Pflugers Archiv (44472) • Physics and Chemistry of Minerals (44147) • Plant Cell Reports (44473) • Polar Biology (44507) • Polymer Bulletin (44544) • Probability Theory and Related Fields (44078) • Psychological Research Psychologische Forschung (48718) • Radiation and Environmental Biophysics (44579) • Review of Economic Design (44474) • Review of World Economics (44508) • Teaching Business Ethics (44476) • Telecommunication Systems (44477) • Theoretical and Applied Genetics (44478) • Tribology Letters (44479)

Springer-Verlag
Sachsenplatz 4-6
Postfach 89
A-1201 Vienna, Austria
Phone: 43 133 024150
Fax: 43 133 02426261
Publications: Architektur Aktuell (42746) • Few-Body Systems (47985) • Journal of Neural Transmission

(42762) • Protoplasma (44495) • Rock Mechanics and Rock Engineering (46274)

Springer-Verlag GmbH & Company KG
Tiergartenstr. 17
D-69121 Heidelberg, Germany
Phone: 49 622 14870
Fax: 49 622 13454229
Publications: Analytical and Bioanalytical Chemistry (44437) • Animal Cognition (44438) • Applied Physics A (44440) • Asia Europe Journal (50104) • Basic Research in Cardiology (44441) • Biological Cybernetics (44443) • Bioprocess and Biosystems Engineering (44377) • Cell and Tissue Research (44444) • Chinese-German Journal of Clinical Oncology (44445) • Clinical Oral Investigations (44447) • Cognitive Processing (46225) • Computational Management Science (44450) • Coral Reefs (44451) • Environmental Earth Sciences (44453) • Journal of Molecular Modeling (44340) • Parasitology Research (44330) • Rheumatology International (44475)

Springer-Verlag London Ltd.
236 Gray's Inn Rd., 6th Fl.
London WC1X 8HB, United Kingdom
Phone: 44 20 31922000
Publications: Anatomical Science International (53941) • Clinical Rheumatology (54230) • Cognition, Technology & Work (54236) • Comparative Clinical Pathology (53521) • Formal Aspects of Computing (55670) • Journal of High Energy Physics (54762) • Journal of Urban Health (54831) • Lasers in Medical Science (54855) • Neural Computing & Applications (56654) • Pattern Analysis & Applications (55486) • Personal and Ubiquitous Computing (55070) • Progress in Osteoporosis (41947)

Springer-Verlag New York Inc.
233 Spring St.
New York, NY 10013-1578
Phone: 212460-1500
Fax: 212460-1575
Free: 800777-4643
Publications: 4OR (46126) • Journal of Neurology (44566) • Theoretical and Applied Climatology (44424)

Springer-Verlag Tokyo
No. 2, Funato Bldg.
1-11-11 Kudan-kita
Chiyoda-ku
Tokyo 102-0073, Japan
Phone: 81 368 317000
Fax: 81 368 317001
Publications: Accreditation and Quality Assurance (44314) • Acta Diabetologica (46722) • Acta Endoscopica (46723) • Acta Mathematica Sinica (46724) • Acta Mathematicae Applicatae Sinica (43167) • Acta Mechanica (46725) • Acta Mechanica Sinica (46726) • Acta Neuropathologica (44594) • Aequationes Mathematicae (44886) • AI & Society (55687) • Algebra Universalis (46731) • Amino Acids (42743) • Annales Henri Poincare (44018) • Annali di Matematica Pura ed Applicata (46736) • Annals of Combinatorics (46737) • Annals of Finance (46738) • Annals of Hematology (44429) • Annals of Regional Science (46740) • Applicable Algebra in Engineering, Communication and Computing (46745) • Applied Magnetic Resonance (46747) • Applied Microbiology and Biotechnology (44595) • Applied Physics B (50009) • Aquatic Sciences (51180) • Archiv der Mathematik (44651) • Archive of Applied Mechanics (44280) • Archive for History of Exact Sciences (46748) • Archive for Mathematical Logic (44596) • Archive for Rational Mechanics and Analysis (55872) • Archives of Dermatological Research (46749) • Archives of Gynecology and Obstetrics (51059) • Archives of Microbiology (46750) • Archives of Orthopaedic and Trauma Surgery (46751) • Archives of Toxicology (46752) • Artificial Life and Robotics (46590) • Astronomy and Astrophysics Review (46756) • Behavioral Ecology and Sociobiology (44442) • Biology and Fertility of Soils (46765) • Biomechanics and Modeling in Mechanobiology (46766) • Brain Tumor Pathology (46768) • Bulletin of the Brazilian Mathematical Society (51010) • Bulletin of Engineering Geology and the Environment (46770) • Bulletin of Volcanology (46771) • Calcolo (46772) • Calculus of Variations and Partial Differential Equation (46773) • Cancer Chemotherapy and Pharmacology (46777) • Cancer Immunology, Immunotherapy (46778) • Cellular

and Molecular Life Sciences (46780) • Central European Journal of Operations Research (46781) • Chemoecology (42847) • Child's Nervous System (46784) • Chromatographia (46785) • Chromosoma (51061) • Clean Technologies and Environmental Policy (46787) • Clinical Autonomic Research (46788) • Clinical and Experimental Nephrology (46789) • Colloid and Polymer Science (44136) • Computational Complexity (46790) • Computational Mechanics (46791) • Computational Statistics (46792) • Computing and Visualization in Science (46794) • Continuum Mechanics and Thermodynamics (46796) • Contributions to Mineralogy and Petrology (46797) • Current Genetics (50958) • Decisions in Economics and Finance (46800) • Development Genes and Evolution (46802) • Ecological Research (46665) • Economics of Governance (46806) • Ecosystems (46807) • Electrical Engineering (46808) • Emergency Radiology (46809) • Engineering with Computers (46810) • Environmental Chemistry Letters (46811) • Environmental Economics and Policy Studies (46812) • Esophagus (46814) • European Archives of Psychiatry and Clinical Neuroscience (46815) • European Biophysics Journal (55942) • European Food Research and Technology (46816) • European Journal of Ageing (47973) • European Journal of Applied Physiology (46817) • Extremophiles (46820) • Gastric Cancer (46828) • Graphs and Combinatorics (46831) • Heart and Vessels (46832) • Ichthyological Research (46836) • Immunogenetics (48747) • Inflammation Research (46842) • International Journal of Asian Management (46845) • International Journal of Clinical Oncology (46846) • International Journal of Colorectal Disease (44192) • Japanese Journal of Ophthalmology (46872) • Journal of Anesthesia (46883) • Journal of Artificial Organs (46886) • Journal of Bone and Mineral Metabolism (46889) • Journal of Ethology (46896) • Journal of Forest Research (46898) • Journal of Gastroenterology (46899) • Journal of General Plant Pathology (46476) • Journal of Headache and Pain (46902) • Journal of Hepato-Biliary-Pancreatic Sciences (46904) • Journal of Infection and Chemotherapy (46909) • Journal of Marine Science and Technology (46921) • Journal of Material Cycles and Waste Management (46922) • Journal of Medical Ultrasonics (46925) • Journal of Molecular Medicine (46928) • Journal of Orthopaedic Science (46935) • Journal of Wood Science (46946) • Landscape and Ecological Engineering (46958) • Limnology (46961) • Medical Microbiology and Immunology (44542) • Medical Molecular Morphology (46966) • Modern Rheumatology (46970) • Mycoscience (46320) • Odontology (47013) • Population Ecology (47022) • Primates (47024) • Surgery Today (47045) • Techniques in Coloproctology (47047) • Urological Research (55363)

Spuren
Rudolfstrasse 13
CH-8400 Winterthur, Switzerland
Phone: 41 522 123361
Fax: 41 522 123371
Publications: Spuren (51243)

Squires Kitchen Magazine Publishing Ltd.
Squires House
3 Waverley Ln.
Farnham GU9 8BB, United Kingdom
Phone: 44 845 2255671
Fax: 44 845 2255673
Publications: Cakes & Sugarcraft (53381)

Sri Aurobindo Ashram Trust
123 S.V. Patel Salai
Pondicherry 605 001, Pondicherry, India
Phone: 91 413 2233656
Fax: 91 413 2223328
Publications: The Advent (45690) • The Bulletin of Sri Aurobindo International Centre of Education (45691) • Mother India (45693)

Sri Lanka College of Paediatricians
Wijerama House, No. 6
Wijerama Mawatha
Colombo 00700, Sri Lanka
Phone: 94 11 2683178
Fax: 94 11 2683178
Publications: Sri Lanka Journal of Child Health (50865)

Sri Lanka Institute of Development Administration
28-10 Mallasekara Mawatha

Colombo 00700, Sri Lanka
Phone: 94 11 2582181
Fax: 94 11 2553215
Publications: Journal of Development Administration (50855)

Sri Ramakrishna Math
31 Ramakrishna Math Rd.
Mylapore
Chennai 600 004, Tamil Nadu, India
Phone: 91 44 24621110
Fax: 91 44 24934589
Publications: The Vedanta Kesari (45060)

Stable Publishing
SBC House
Restmor Way
Wallington SM6 7AH, United Kingdom
Phone: 44 20 82881080
Fax: 44 20 82881099
Publications: Building for Leisure (56832)

The Stables
Willow Ln.
Paddock Wood TN12 6PF, United Kingdom
Phone: 44 1892 839200
Fax: 44 1892 839210
Publications: Plastics & Rubber Asia (56238)

Stadt Leoben
Erzherzog-Johann-Str 2
A-8700 Leoben, Austria
Phone: 43 384 240620
Fax: 43 384 24062320
Publications: Stadt Leoben (42732)

Standard Publications Ltd.
Standard House
Birkirkara Hill
Saint Julians STJ 1149, Malta
Phone: 356 21345888
Publications: The Malta Business Weekly (47739) • The Malta Independent (47740) • The Malta Independent on Sunday (47741)

Standfirst
66 John Finnie St.
Kilmarnock KA1 1BS, United Kingdom
Phone: 44 15 63530830
Fax: 44 15 63549503
Publications: The Scottish Review (53709)

Stanford, a.s.
Provaznicka 13
CZ-110 00 Prague, Czech Republic
Phone: 42 2 34071370
Fax: 42 2 34071377
Publications: Czech Business Weekly (43615)

Stansted News Ltd.
134 S St.
Bishop's Stortford CM23 3BQ, United Kingdom
Phone: 44 127 9714501
Fax: 44 127 9714519
Publications: European Business Air News (52378) • Global Business Jet (52379) • Journal of Neonatal Nursing (52380)

Star of Mysore
15-C, Industrial 'A' Layout
Academy Newspapers Pvt. Ltd.
Mysore 570 015, India
Phone: 91 821 2496520
Publications: Star of Mysore (45456)

Star Publications (M) Bhd
Menara Star, 15 Jalan 16/11
Selangor Darul Ehsan
46350 Petaling Jaya, Malaysia
Phone: 60 3 79671388
Fax: 60 3 79554039
Publications: Galaxie (47697) • The Star (47702)

The Statesman Ltd.
Statesman House
4 Chowringhee Sq.
Kolkata 700 001, West Bengal, India
Phone: 91 33 22127070
Fax: 91 33 22126181
Publications: The Statesman (45305)

Statuscourt Ltd.
Greenwich
PO Box 805

London SE10 8TD, United Kingdom
Phone: 44 20 86914820
Publications: Antique Dealer & Collectors Guide (53957)

Steel Institute VDEh
Sohnstr. 65
D-40237 Dusseldorf, Germany
Publications: Literaturschau Stahl Eisen (44328) • MPT International (44329)

Stellenbosch University
Private Bag X2
Saldanha 7395, Republic of South Africa
Phone: 27 22 7023107
Fax: 27 22 7023060
Publications: Scientia Militaria (50624)

Stepe Group Chantiers de France
202 quai de Clichy
F-92110 Clichy, France
Phone: 33 147561723
Fax: 33 147561432
Publications: Route Actualite/Roads News (43935)

Stephenson Locomotive Society
c/o M.D. Dickin
1A Lockstock Ave.
Poynton SK12 1DR, United Kingdom
Publications: Journal of the Stephenson Locomotive Society (56298)

Stereoscopic Society
6 Sheppards Ct., Horsenden Ln., N
Greenford
Middlesex UB6 7QJ, United Kingdom
Publications: Journal of 3-D Imaging (55619)

Stichting Ons Erfdeel vzw
Murissonstraat 260
B-8930 Rekkem, Belgium
Phone: 32 56 411201
Fax: 32 56 414707
Publications: Ons Erfdeel (42909) • Septentrion (42910)

Stiftelsen Contra
PO Box 8052
SE-104 20 Stockholm, Sweden
Phone: 46 8 7200145
Fax: 46 8 7200195
Publications: Contra (51013)

Stomatological Society of Greece
17 Kallirroes St.
GR-117 43 Athens, Greece
Phone: 30 210 9214325
Fax: 30 210 9214204
Publications: Stomatologia (44756)

Strategic Planning Society
Mayfair House
14-18 Heddon St.
London W1B 4DA, United Kingdom
Phone: 44 845 0563663
Fax: 44 845 0563663
Publications: Strategy (55265)

Studio Magazines
101-111 William St., Level 3
Sydney, New South Wales 2011, Australia
Phone: 61 2 93601422
Fax: 61 2 93609742
Publications: My Perfect Wedding Planner (42549) • Studio Bambini (42582)

Studio Systems
6/C-5, Sangeeta Apts.
Ground Fl., Juhu Rd.
Santacruz (W)
Mumbai 400 049, Maharashtra, India
Phone: 91 22 26609147
Publications: Studio Systems (45443)

Stumpf & Kossendey
Postfach 1361
D-26183 Edewecht, Germany
Phone: 49 440 591810
Fax: 49 440 5918133
Publications: Rettungsdienst (44336)

Raymond Stuyck Consultants BVBA
Koralenhoeve 4
B-2160 Wommelgem, Belgium

Phone: 32 335 53838
Fax: 32 335 55339
Publications: Exclusief (42913)

Succulent Society of South Africa
PO Box 12580
Hatfield 0028, Republic of South Africa
Phone: 27 12 9933588
Fax: 27 12 9933588
Publications: Aloe (50522)

Sumangal Press Private Ltd.
G-8
Cross Rd. A
MIDC
Andheri (E)
Mumbai 400 093, Maharashtra, India
Phone: 91 22 28234745
Publications: Kalnirnay (45406)

Summit Media
6F & 7F Robinsons Cybergate Ctr., Tower 3
Robinsons Pioneer Complex
Pioneer St.
Mandaluyong City 1550, Philippines
Phone: 63 2 4518888
Fax: 63 2 6317788
Publications: Candy Magazine (49532) • Cosmopolitan Philippines (49533) • Disney Princess Magazine (49535) • For Him Magazine Philippines (49536) • Good Housekeeping Philippines (49537) • High School Musical (49538) • Preview (49539) • Seventeen Philippines (49540) • Smart Parenting (49541) • Star Teacher (49542) • Yes! (49543) • Yummy (49544)

Sun Enterprises (BVI) Ltd.
PO Box 21
Tortola
Road Town, British Virgin Islands
Phone: 284494-2476
Fax: 284494-5854
Publications: The Island Sun (43068)

The Sun Newspapers
1 Virginia St.
London E98 1SN, United Kingdom
Phone: 44 20 77824000
Publications: The Sun Journal (55277)

Sunday Herald
200 Renfield St.
Glasgow G2 3QB, United Kingdom
Phone: 44 14 13027300
Publications: Sunday Herald (53453)

Sunday Times
341 St. Paul St.
Valletta VLT 1211, Malta
Phone: 356 25594100
Fax: 356 25594116
Publications: Sunday Times (Malta) (47747)

Sun.Star Network Exchange
Sun. Star Bldg.
3rd Fl., Sun. Star Bldg.
P. del Rosario cor. P. Cui Sts.
Cebu City 6000, Philippines
Phone: 63 322 546100
Fax: 63 322 546530
Publications: Sun.Star Network (49464)

Suntory and Toyota International Centres for Economics and Related Disciplines
London School of Economics & Political Science
Houghton St.
London WC2A 2AE, United Kingdom
Phone: 44 20 79556699
Fax: 44 20 79556951
Publications: CASEpapers (54187)

Suomen Palloliitto
Finnair Stadium
Urheilukatu 5
FIN-00250 Helsinki, Finland
Phone: 358 9 742151
Fax: 358 9 74215200
Publications: Futari (43831)

Svensk Mjolk
Kungsgatan 43
PO Box 1146
SE-631 80 Eskilstuna, Sweden
Phone: 46 771 191900

Fax: 46 162 1216
Publications: Husdjur (50953)

Sveriges Filatelist-Forbund
Box 91
SE-568 22 Skillingaryd, Sweden
Phone: 46 370 70566
Publications: SFF Filatelisten/Svensk Filatelistisk Tidskrift (50998)

Sveriges Schackforbund
Kabelvagen 19
S-602 20 Norrkoping, Sweden
Phone: 46 111 07420
Fax: 46 111 82341
Publications: Tidskrift for Schack (50996)

SVP Generalsekretariat
Bruckfeldstr. 18
Postfach 8252
CH-3001 Bern 26, Switzerland
Phone: 41 313 005858
Fax: 41 313 005859
Publications: SVPja (51078)

Swamy Botanical Club
c/o Dr. K.V. Krishnamurthy
Dept. of Plant Sciences
Bharathidasan University
Tiruchirapalli 620 024, Tamil Nadu, India
Phone: 91 431 2407048
Fax: 91 431 2407032
Publications: Swamy Botanical Club Journal (45751)

Swazi MTN Ltd.
PO Box 5050
Mbabane, Swaziland
Phone: 268 4060000
Fax: 268 4046215
Publications: Y'ello (50947)

Swedish Anti-Nuclear Movement
Tegelviksgatan 40
SE-116 41 Stockholm, Sweden
Phone: 46 884 1490
Fax: 46 884 5181
Publications: MEDSOLS (51025)

Swedish Archaeological Society
c/o Tore Artelius
Kvarnbygatan 12
S-431 34 Molndal, Sweden
Publications: Current Swedish Archaeology (50993)

Swedish Archival Association
c/o Stockholms stadsarkiv
PO Box 22063
S-104 22 Stockholm, Sweden
Publications: Arkiv Samhalle och Forskning (51009)

Swedish Association of Registered Physical Therapists
Vasagatan 48
PO Box 3196
S-103 63 Stockholm, Sweden
Phone: 46 8 56706100
Fax: 46 8 56706199
Publications: Nordisk Fysioterapi (51028) • Sjukgymnasten (51038)

Swedish Association of Translators
PO Box 1091
S-269 21 Bastad, Sweden
Phone: 46 431 75500
Fax: 46 431 76990
Publications: Fackoversattaren (50949)

Swedish Dance Sport Federation
Idrottshuset Farsta
Marbackagatan 19
S-123 43 Farsta, Sweden
Phone: 46 8 6996000
Fax: 46 8 6996531
Publications: Svensk Danssport (50954)

Swedish-English Literary Translators' Association
c/o Peter Linton
3 Roseacre Close
London W13 8DG, United Kingdom
Phone: 44 20 89971218
Publications: Swedish Book Review (55608)

Swedish Orienteering Federation
PO Box 22

S-171 18 Solna, Sweden
Phone: 46 8 58772000
Fax: 46 8 58772088
Publications: Skogssport (51000)

Swedish Pulp and Paper Research Institute
STFI-Packforsk AB
Drottning Kristinas vag 61
SE-114 86 Stockholm, Sweden
Phone: 46 867 67000
Fax: 46 841 15518
Publications: STFI Kontakt (51041)

Swedish Society for Anthropology and Geography
Socialantropologiska institutionen Stockholms universitet
Villavagen 16
S-106 91 Stockholm, Sweden
Phone: 46 736466095
Publications: Geografiska Annaler, Series A, Physical Geography (51017) • Geografiska Annaler, Series B, Social Geography (51018)

Swedish Society for Musicology
PO Box 7448
SE-103 91 Stockholm, Sweden
Publications: Swedish Journal of Musicology (50966)

Swedish Writers' Union
PO Box 3157
Drottninggatan 88 B
S-103 63 Stockholm, Sweden
Phone: 46 854 513200
Fax: 46 854 513210
Publications: Fortattaren (51016)

Sweet & Maxwell Asia
10 Fl. Cityplaza 3,
Taikoo Shing
Hong Kong, People's Republic of China
Phone: 852 37623227
Fax: 852 25206646
Publications: Hong Kong Law Reports & Digest (43335)

Sweet & Maxwell Ltd.
PO Box 2000
North Way
Andover SP10 5BE, United Kingdom
Phone: 44 1264 332424
Fax: 44 207 3938074
Publications: British Tax Review (52111) • Civil Justice Quarterly (52112) • Construction Law Journal (52113) • Conveyancer and Property Lawyer (52114) • Criminal Law Review (52115) • EIPR: European Intellectual Property Review (52116) • Intellectual Property Quarterly (52117) • Journal of Business Law (52118) • Journal of Planning and Environment Law (52119) • Law Quarterly Review (52120) • Public Law (52121)

Sweets Global Network e.V.
Grillparzerstr. 38
D-81675 Munich, Germany
Phone: 49 89 4706093
Fax: 49 89 4703783
Publications: SG Susswarenhandel (44581)

Swimming Teachers' Association
Anchor House
Birch St.
Walsall WS2 8HZ, United Kingdom
Phone: 44 1922 645097
Fax: 44 1922 720628
Publications: Swim & Save (56835)

Swiss Alliance Mission
Wolfensbergstrasse 47
CH-8400 Winterthur, Switzerland
Phone: 41 52 2690469
Fax: 41 52 2135681
Publications: SAM-Focus (51242)

Swiss Businesspress SA
Koschenrutistrasse 109
8052 Zurich, Switzerland
Phone: 41 1 306 47 00
Fax: 41 1 306 47 11
Publications: Swiss News (51289)

Swiss Chemical Society
Schwarztorstrasse 9
CH-3007 Bern, Switzerland

Phone: 41 313 104090
Fax: 41 313 104029
Publications: Chimia (51070) • Helvetica Chimica Acta (51073)

Swiss Dietetic Association
Postgasse 17
Postfatch 686
CH-3000 Bern, Switzerland
Phone: 41 31 3138870
Fax: 41 31 3138899
Publications: Ernahrungs Info (51072)

Swiss Teachers Federation
Ringstrasse 54
Postfach 189
CH-8057 Zurich, Switzerland
Phone: 41 131 55454
Fax: 41 131 18315
Publications: Schweizer Lehrerinnen- und Lehrer-Zeitung (51280)

Swisspack International
Postfach
CH-8048 Zurich, Switzerland
Phone: 41 44 4316445
Fax: 41 44 4316497
Publications: Swisspack International (51290)

Symposium of General Topology
Uzumasa Higashiga-oka
13-2 Neyagawa-shi
Osaka 572-0841, Japan
Publications: Questions and Answers in General Topology (46628)

Symposium Journals Ltd.
PO Box 204
Oxford OX11 9ZQ, United Kingdom
Phone: 44 1235 818062
Fax: 44 1235 817275
Publications: Citizenship, Social and Economics Education (55909)

Synthetic and Art Silk Mills' Research Association
Sasmira Marg
Worli
Mumbai 400 030, Maharashtra, India
Phone: 91 22 24935351
Fax: 91 22 24930225
Publications: Man-Made Textiles in India (45408)

Systematic and Applied Acarology Society
c/o Dr. Ting-Kui Qin, Treas.
Plant Biosecurity
Biosecurity Australia
Canberra, Australian Capital Territory 2601, Australia
Phone: 61 2 62723719
Fax: 61 2 6272330
Publications: SAA (55212) • Systematic and Applied Acarology (41713)

Tablet Publishing Company Ltd.
1 King St. Cloisters
Clifton Walk
London W6 0QZ, United Kingdom
Phone: 44 20 87488484
Fax: 44 20 87481550
Publications: The Pastoral Review (55061) • The Tablet (55285)

Taipei Times
14th Fl., No. 399
Ruiguang Rd.
Taipei 11492, Taiwan
Phone: 886 226 561000
Fax: 886 226 561099
Publications: Taipei Times (51362)

Taiwan Agricultural Research Institute
189 Jhongjheng Rd., Wufeng
Taipei 41301, Taiwan
Phone: 886 4 23302301-5
Publications: Journal of Agricultural Research of China (51347)

Taiwan News
9th Fl., 290 Jhongsiao E Rd., Sec. 4
Taipei 10600, Taiwan
Phone: 886 22 3491500
Publications: Taiwan News (51365)

Taiwan Pediatric Association
10F/1 No. 69 Sec. 1 Hang Chow S Rd.
Taipei 100, Taiwan
Phone: 886 22 3516446
Fax: 886 22 3516448
Publications: Acta Paediatrica Taiwanica (51329)

Talent Media
Studio 37, Riverside Bldg.
Trinity Buoy Wharf
64 Ochard Pl.
London E14 0JW, United Kingdom
Phone: 44 20 70010754
Publications: Black History Month (54033) • Leaving School (54862) • Mela UK (54925) • Positive Nation (55106) • Student Times (55270)

Tambek International
PO Box 2395
Addis Ababa, Ethiopia
Phone: 251 161 5228
Fax: 251 161 5227
Publications: The Addis Tribune (43795)

Tamil Nadu Science Forum
Balaji Sampath, C2 Ratna Apts.
AH 250, Shanti Colony, Annanagar
Chennai 600 040, Tamil Nadu, India
Phone: 91 446 213638
Publications: Jantar Mantar (45044)

Tamkang University
151 Ying-chuan Rd.
Tamsui 25137, Taiwan
Phone: 886 22 6215656
Fax: 886 22 6223204
Publications: Journal of Educational Media and Library Sciences (51394)

Tamkang University
151 Ying-Chuan Rd.
Republic of China
Tamsui 25137, Taiwan
Phone: 886 2 26215656
Fax: 886 2 26223204
Publications: International Journal of Information and Management Sciences (51393)

Tamkang University
151 Ying-chuan Rd.
Taipei County
Tamsui 25137, Taiwan
Phone: 886 2 26215656
Fax: 886 2 26209916
Publications: Tamkang Journal of Mathematics (51397)

Tamkang University
151 Ying-chuan Rd.
Tamsui 25137, Taiwan
Phone: 886 2 26215656
Fax: 886 2 26223204
Publications: Tamkang Journal of Tamkang Review (51398)

Tamkang University
Taipei County Rd. 151, Taipei Hsien
Tamsui 25137, Taiwan
Phone: 886 22 6215656
Publications: Tamkang Journal of International Affairs (51396)

Tamkang University
Tamsui Campus
151 Ying-chuan Rd.
Tamsui 25137, Taiwan
Phone: 886 22 6215656
Fax: 886 22 6223204
Publications: Tamkang Journal of Futures Studies (51395)

Taqasim Magazine
PO Box 72
Devon EX39 1FA, United Kingdom
Publications: Taqasim (53177)

Tara Publishing Company Ltd.
Poolbeg House
1-2 Poolbeg St.
Dublin 2, Dublin, Ireland
Phone: 353 124 13000
Fax: 353 124 13020
Publications: Food Ireland (45959) • Irish Pharma-chem Industry Buyers' Guide (45982)

Target Publishing Ltd.
The Old Dairy
Hudsons Farm
Fieldgate Ln.
Ugley Green CM22 6HJ, United Kingdom
Phone: 44 12 79816300
Fax: 44 12 79810081
Publications: Health Food Business Magazine (56794)

Taru Publications
G-159, Pushkar Enclave
Pashchim Vihar
New Delhi 110 063, Delhi, India
Phone: 91 114 2331159
Fax: 91 114 2321126
Publications: Algebraic Hyperstructures and Applications (45482) • Journal of Discrete Mathematical Sciences and Cryptography (45595) • Journal of Information & Optimization Sciences (45606) • Journal of Interdisciplinary Mathematics (45608) • Journal of Statistics and Management Systems (45620)

Tarun Bharat Daily Pvt. Ltd.
3524, Narvekar Galli
Belgaum 590 002, Maharashtra, India
Phone: 91 831 2404333
Fax: 91 831 2428603
Publications: Tarun Bharat (44997)

Taste of Scotland Scheme Ltd.
c/o Expresss Media
Bush House
Bush State
Midlothian EH26 0BB, United Kingdom
Phone: 44 13 68865444
Fax: 44 13 68865777
Publications: Taste of Scotland (55628)

Tata Energy Research Institute
Darbari Seth Block
IHC Complex, Lodhi Rd.
Lodhi Rd.
New Delhi 110 003, Delhi, India
Phone: 91 112 4682100
Fax: 91 112 4682144
Publications: Resources, Energy and Development (45644) • SESI Journal (45650) • TIDEE—Teri Information Digest on Energy and Environment (45659)

Taxation Institute of Australia
Level 2, 95 Pitt St.
Sydney, New South Wales 2000, Australia
Phone: 61 2 8223 0000
Fax: 61 2 8223 0077
Publications: Australian Tax Forum (42467)

Taxi Trade Promotions Ltd.
429-431 Caledonian Rd.
London N7 9BG, United Kingdom
Phone: 44 20 77005681
Fax: 44 20 77005684
Publications: CallSign (54168)

Taylor & Francis Group Journals
325 Chestnut St., Ste. 800
Philadelphia, PA 19106-2608
Phone: 215625-8900
Fax: 215625-2940
Free: 800354-1420
Publications: Acta Agriculturae Scandinavica—Section C, Food Economics (43688) • Alcheringa (51004) • Applied Artificial Intelligence (42745) • Applied Economics Letters (53077) • Applied Financial Economics (53078) • Aquatic Insects (44661) • Archives of Animal Nutrition (44156) • Asia Pacific Review (46754) • Astronomical and Astrophysical Transactions (49876) • Biocatalysis and Biotransformation (54018) • Biofouling (52754) • Biomarkers (54025) • British Poultry Science (56408) • BSHM Bulletin (55896) • Chemistry and Ecology (46117) • Computational & Mathematical Methods in Medicine (53762) • Connection Science (56490) • Crystallography Reviews (55552) • Defence and Peace Economics (56989) • Disability and Rehabilitation (53654) • Dynamical Systems (53352) • Economics of Innovation and New Technology (46271) • Educational Technology Abstracts (56781) • Engineering Optimization (53870) • European Journal of Psychotherapy and Counselling (54405) • European Journal of Special Needs Education (53355) • European Planning Studies (52929) • Food and Agricultural Immunology (52995) • Geomechanics and Geoengineering

(55756) • Geophysical & Astrophysical Fluid Dynamics (53359) • Grana (51019) • High Pressure Research (44046) • Historical Biology (45964) • Integral Transforms and Special Functions (49920) • International Journal of Computer Mathematics (54640) • International Journal of Food Properties (49221) • International Journal of Systems Science (56502) • The International Review of Retail, Distribution and Consumer Research (56623) • International Reviews in Physical Chemistry (53229) • Journal of Asian Natural Products Research (43202) • Journal of Carbohydrate Chemistry (44640) • Journal of Location Based Services (54772) • Journal of Microencapsulation (54782) • Norsk Geologisk Tidsskrift (49219) • Phase Transitions (43959) • Polycyclic Aromatic Compounds (44115) • Scandinavian Actuarial Journal (51033) • Scandinavian Journal of Forest Research (50972) • Urban Water Journal (55361)

Taylor & Francis Group Ltd.
270 Madison Ave.
New York, NY 10016-0601
Phone: 212216-7800
Fax: 212563-2269
Free: 800634-7064
Publications: Environmental Politics (51771)

Taylor & Francis Group Ltd.
2 & 4 Park Sq.
Milton Pk.
Oxford OX14 4RN, United Kingdom
Phone: 44 20 70176000
Fax: 44 20 70176699
Publications: Comparative Strategy (55914) • Emotional and Behavioral Difficulties (55936) • Tertiary Education and Management (56215)

Taylor and Francis Group Ltd
2 Park Sq., Milton Park
Abingdon OX14 4RN, United Kingdom
Phone: 44 20 70176000
Fax: 44 20 70176699
Publications: Journal of Systematic Palaeontology (51951)

Taylor & Francis Ltd.
2 & 4 Park Sq.
Milton Pk.
Abingdon OX14 4RN, United Kingdom
Phone: 44 20 70176000
Fax: 44 20 70176336
Publications: Acta Dermato-Venereologica (51694) • Acta Odontologica Scandinavica (50969) • Acta Oncologica (50999) • Acta Oto-Laryngologica (51001) • Acta Radiologica (51695) • Acute Cardiac Care (51697) • Addiction Abstracts (53901) • Advances in Physiotherapy (51003) • American Journal on Addictions (51702) • Amyloid (51703) • Amyotrophic Lateral Sclerosis (51007) • Augmentative & Alternative Communication (51709) • Australian & New Zealand Journal of Psychiatry (51716) • Avian Pathology (55661) • Behaviour and Information Technology (51717) • Blood Pressure (50957) • Body, Movement and Dance in Psychotherapy (53538) • British Journal of Neurosurgery (51720) • Clinical Linguistics & Phonetics (51731) • CoDesign (51732) • Cognitive Neuropsychiatry (54237) • Computer Methods in Biomechanics and Biomedical Engineering (51740) • Connective Tissue Research (51741) • Contemporary Physics (54263) • Counselling and Psychotherapy Research (51742) • Developmental Neurorehabilitation (51757) • Drug and Alcohol Review (42428) • Drugs (51760) • Ergonomics (55479) • European Journal of Contraception and Reproductive Health Care (51779) • European Journal of Engineering Education (51780) • European Journal of Sport Science (51781) • Fetal and Pediatric Pathology (51789) • Free Radical Research (51791) • Global Public Health (51797) • Growth Factors (42062) • Human Fertility (51808) • Hypertension in Pregnancy (51810) • Informatics for Health and Social Care (51816) • International Journal of Environmental Health Research (51834) • International Journal of Food Sciences & Nutrition (51835) • International Journal of Injury Control and Safety Promotion (48029) • International Journal of Language & Communication Disorders (51839) • International Journal of Neuroscience (51842) • International Journal of Prisoner Health (51844) • International Journal of Speech-Language Pathology (51846) • International Review of

Psychiatry (51853) • International Reviews of Immunology (51854) • Isotopes in Environmental and Health Studies (51862) • IUBMB Life (51864) • Journal of Cosmetic and Laser Therapy (51882) • Journal of Dermatological Treatment (51884) • Journal of Drug Targeting (51886) • Journal of Early Childhood Teacher Education (51887) • Journal of Enzyme Inhibition and Medicinal Chemistry (52933) • Journal of Experimental Nanoscience (51897) • Journal of Intellectual and Developmental Disability (51908) • Journal of Interprofessional Care (51910) • Journal of Medical Engineering and Technology (52934) • Journal of Mental Health (51918) • Journal of Nutritional & Environmental Medicine (51926) • Journal of Organ Dysfunctions (51927) • Journal of Plant Interactions (51931) • Journal of Psychosomatic Obstetrics and Gynecology (51937) • Journal of Rehabilitation Medicine (51939) • Journal of Substance Use (51949) • Leukemia and Lymphoma (51968) • Liquid Crystals (51970) • Logopedics Phoniatrics Vocology (54884) • Medical Mycology (51973) • Microbial Ecology in Health and Disease (51026) • Microcirculation (51978) • Minimally Invasive Therapy and Allied Technologies (51982) • Mitochondrial DNA (51983) • Nanotoxicology (53301) • Network (51991) • Nordic Journal of Psychiatry (43851) • Ocean Development and International Law (52001) • Pediatric Hematology & Oncology (52006) • Physiotherapy Theory and Practice (52013) • Platelets (55770) • Prosthetics & Orthotics International (52025) • Quarterly Journal of Experimental Psychology (52032) • Reading & Writing Quarterly (52034) • SAR and QSAR in Environmental Research (44099) • Scandinavian Cardiovascular Journal (51034) • Scandinavian Journal of Clinical and Laboratory Investigation (52047) • Scandinavian Journal of Food and Nutrition (50990) • Scandinavian Journal of Gastroenterology (52048) • Scandinavian Journal of Occupational Therapy (51035) • Scandinavian Journal of Primary Health Care (52050) • Scandinavian Journal of Rheumatology (52051) • Scandinavian Journal of Urology and Nephrology (52052) • Social Influence (52060) • Strabismus (48753) • Synthesis and Reactivity in Inorganic, Metal-Organic, and Nano-Metal Chemistry (52068) • Toxic Substance Mechanisms (52083) • Upsala Journal of Medical Sciences (51052) • Virtual and Physical Prototyping (52085) • Waves in Random and Complex Media (52089)

Tbilisi State Medical University
33 Vazha-Pshavela Ave.
0177 Tbilisi, Georgia
Phone: 7 995 32391879
Fax: 7 995 32392284
Publications: Annals of Biomedical Research and Education (44130)

Tear Australia
4 Solwood Ln.
PO Box 164
Blackburn, Victoria 3130, Australia
Phone: 61 3 98777000
Fax: 61 3 98777944
Publications: Target (41601)

TechMedia A/S
Neverland 35
DK-2600 Glostrup, Denmark
Phone: 45 43242628
Fax: 45 43242626
Publications: Aktuel Elektronik (43697) • Dansk Kemi (43701) • Elektronik Nyt (43703) • Elteknik (43704) • HVAC Magasinet (43705) • IN-PAK (43706) • Installations Nyt (43707) • Installations Nyt Special (43708) • Levnedsmiddel Bladet (43709) • Maskin Aktuelt (43710) • PackPlast (43711) • Plus Process (43712) • Rens & Vask samt Tekstiludlejning (43714) • Scandinavian Food & Drink (43715) • Teknisk Nyt (43716) • Teknisk Nyt Special Edition (43717) • Trae- & Mobelindustri (43719)

Technews (Pty) Ltd.
PO Box 626
Kloof 3640, Republic of South Africa
Phone: 27 31 7640593
Fax: 27 31 7640386
Publications: Dataweek (50542)

Technical Advisors Group
Roy Fairclough Consultancy
County House

12/13 Sussex St.
Plymouth PL1 2HR, United Kingdom
Phone: 44 17 52213665
Fax: 44 17 52222678
Publications: TAG Bulletin (56273)

Technical Association of the Pulp and Paper Industry of Korea
Ste. 701, Chungmu Bldg.
44-13, Yoido-dong
Yongdungpo-gu
Seoul 150-890, Republic of Korea
Phone: 82 2 7868620
Fax: 82 2 7868621
Publications: Journal (47270)

Technical Association of Refractories - Japan
New Ginza Bldg. 4th Fl.
7-3-13 Ginza
Chuo-ku
Tokyo 104-0061, Japan
Phone: 81 335 720705
Fax: 81 335 720175
Publications: Taikabutsu (47046)

Technical University of Kosice
Letna
042 00 Kosice, Slovakia
Publications: Acta Montanistica Slovaca (50325)

Tecpar
Prof. R. Algacyr Munhoz Mader, 3775 - CIC
81350-010 Curitiba, Paraiba, Brazil
Phone: 55 41 33163052
Fax: 55 41 33462872
Publications: Brazilian Archives of Biology and Technology (BABT) (42976)

Tehran Hepatitis Center
PO Box 14155-3651
Tehran, Iran
Phone: 98 218 967923
Fax: 98 218 958048
Publications: Hepatitis Monthly (45889)

Tehran Times
No. 18 Bimeh Ln.
Nejatollahi St.
PO Box 14155-4843
Tehran, Iran
Phone: 98 21 88800295
Fax: 98 21 88808214
Publications: Tehran Times (45914)

Tehran University of Medical Sciences
PO Box 14155-6559
Tehran, Iran
Phone: 98 216 491070
Fax: 98 216 419537
Publications: Iranian Journal of Environmental Health Science & Engineering (45902)

Tehran University of Medical Sciences Faculty of Medicine
PO Box 14155-6447
Tehran 1417613151, Iran
Phone: 08 21 88953001
Fax: 98 21 66404377
Publications: Acta Medica Iranica (45885) • Iranian Journal of Pediatrics (45905) • Iranian Journal of Radiology (45909)

Teknoscienze S.R.L.
Via. Brianza 22
I-20127 Milan, Italy
Phone: 39 2 26809375
Fax: 39 2 2847226
Publications: Agro Food (46162) • Chimica Oggi (Chemistry Today) (46165)

Telcom Journal Company Ltd.
327/17-19 Soi Sri-Amporn (Phaholyothin 32)
Senanikom Rd., Ladyao
Chatuchak
Bangkok 10900, Thailand
Phone: 66 2 5614993
Fax: 66 2 5615033
Publications: Telcom Journal (51436)

TELE-Satellite Medien GmbH
PO Box 1234

D-85766 Unterfoehring, Germany
Publications: TELE-satellite International Magazine (44697)

Telecom Tribune
Shobunsha Blgd. No. 2
1-17-5 Uchikanda
Chiyoda-City
Tokyo 101-0047, Japan
Phone: 81 3 32946191
Fax: 81 3 32949066
Publications: Telecom Tribune (47048)

Telecommunications Heritage Group
Dalton House
60 Windsor Ave.
London SW19 2RR, United Kingdom
Phone: 44 20 80991699
Publications: Telecommunications Heritage Group Journal (55297)

Telecottage Association
The Other Cottage
Shortwood
Nailsworth
Stroud GL6 0SH, United Kingdom
Phone: 44 80 0616008
Publications: 21st Century Worker (56649)

Templar Poetry
PO Box 7082
Bakewell DE45 9AF, United Kingdom
Phone: 44 1629 582500
Publications: Iota Magazine (55603)

Termedia Publishing House
ul. Kleeberga 2
61-615 Poznan, Poland
Phone: 48 61 8227781
Fax: 48 61 8227781
Publications: Folia Neuropathologica (49710)

Terra Incognita
Apartado de Correos 14401
E-28080 Madrid, Spain
Publications: Terra Incognita (50810)

Terra Verlag GmbH
Neuhauser Strasse 21
D-78464 Konstanz, Germany
Phone: 49 75 3181220
Fax: 49 75 31812299
Publications: Hochzeit (44513)

Teshreen Foundation for Press and Publication
PO Box 5452
Damascus, Syrian Arab Republic
Phone: 963 11 2131100
Fax: 963 11 2231374
Publications: Syria Times (51300)

Textile Association
Dinesh Hall
Ashram Rd.
Ahmedabad 380 009, Gujarat, India
Phone: 91 79 26582123
Fax: 91 79 26586311
Publications: Textile Association (India) Journal (44911)

The Textile Institute
1st Fl., St. James's Bldg., Oxford St.
Manchester M1 6FQ, United Kingdom
Phone: 44 161 2371188
Fax: 44 161 2361991
Publications: Journal of the Textile Institute (55567) • Textile Progress (55579)

Textile Machinery Society of Japan
8-4 Utsubo Honmachi 1 chome
Nishi-ku
Osaka 550-0004, Japan
Phone: 81 6 64434691
Fax: 81 6 64434694
Publications: Journal of Textile Engineering (46625)

Textile Society for the Study of Art, Design and History
PO Box 1012
Saint Albans AL1 9NE, United Kingdom
Phone: 44 20 73597678
Publications: TEXT (56439)

Theatre Institute
Celetna 17

CZ-110 00 Prague, Czech Republic
Phone: 42 224 809111
Fax: 42 224 809226
Publications: Divadelni Noviny (43623)

Theatre Record
131 Sherringham Ave.
London N17 9RU, United Kingdom
Phone: 44 20 88083656
Fax: 44 20 83500211
Publications: Theatre Record (55303)

The Theosophical Publishing House
The Theosophical Society
Adyar
Chennai 600 020, Tamil Nadu, India
Phone: 91 44 24912474
Publications: Theosophist (45059)

Theosophical Society in England
50 Gloucester Pl.
London W1U 8EA, United Kingdom
Phone: 44 20 75639817
Fax: 44 20 79359543
Publications: Insight (54607)

Theosophy Company (India) Private Ltd.
40 New Marine Lines
Mumbai 400 020, Maharashtra, India
Publications: The Theosophical Movement (45447)

Thermal and Nuclear Power Engineering Society
Terayama Pacific Bldg.
1-23-11 Toranomon, Minato-ku
Tokyo 105-0001, Japan
Phone: 81 335 920380
Fax: 81 335 920335
Publications: The Thermal and Nuclear Power (47050)

Georg Thieme Verlag Stuttgart
Rudigerstr. 14
Postfach 30 11 20
D-70469 Stuttgart, Germany
Phone: 49 711 89310
Fax: 49 711 8931298
Publications: European Journal of Pediatric Surgery (44667) • Synfacts (44681)

Think Publishing
The Pal Mall Deposit
124-128 Barlby Rd.
London W10 6BL, United Kingdom
Phone: 44 20 89623020
Fax: 44 20 89628689
Publications: Historic Scotland Magazine (54556) • Summit (55276) • WRVS Action (55428)

Think Publishing
The Pall Mall Deposit
124-128 Barlby Rd.
London W10 6BL, United Kingdom
Phone: 44 20 89623020
Fax: 44 20 89628689
Publications: Countryside Voice (54277) • Waterlife (55391) • WDCS (55392) • Wildabout (55405)

Third Way Publications Ltd.
PO Box 1243
London SW7 3PB, United Kingdom
Publications: Third Way Voice of the Radical Centre (55313)

Third World Network
131, Jalan Macalister
10400 Penang, Malaysia
Phone: 60 422 66159
Fax: 60 422 64505
Publications: Third World Economics (47692) • Third World Resurgence (47693)

This England Ltd.
PO Box 52
Cheltenham GL50 1YQ, United Kingdom
Phone: 44 1242 537900
Fax: 44 1242 537901
Publications: Evergreen (52971) • This England (52978)

Thoi Bao Kinh Te Viet Nam
96 Hoang Quoc Viet
Cau Giay
Hanoi, Vietnam
Phone: 84 475 52060

Fax: 84 475 52046
Publications: Thoi Bao Kinh Te Vietnam (57053)

Thomas
St. Anne's House
France St.
Blackburn BB2 1LX, United Kingdom
Phone: 44 12 25459240
Fax: 44 12 25456884
Publications: Edges Magazine (52383)

Thomas Hardy Society
PO Box 1438
High West St.
Dorchester DT1 1YH, United Kingdom
Phone: 44 1305 251501
Fax: 44 1305 251501
Publications: Thomas Hardy Journal (53190)

Thomas Telford Ltd.
One Great George St.
London SW1P 3AA, United Kingdom
Phone: 44 20 79876999
Publications: Geosynthetics International (54504)

D.C. Thomson & Company Ltd.
Courier Bldg.
2 Albert Sq.
Dundee DD1 9QJ, United Kingdom
Phone: 44 20 74001030
Fax: 44 20 78319440
Publications: My Weekly (53216)

D.C. Thomson & Company Ltd.
2 Albert Sq.
Dundee DD1 9QJ, United Kingdom
Phone: 44 1382 223131
Fax: 44 1382 322214
Publications: Animals and You (53213) • The Scots Magazine (53218)

3 Dimensional Media Ltd.
Seymour House
South St.
Bromley BR1 1RH, United Kingdom
Phone: 44 20 84606060
Fax: 44 20 84606050
Publications: FQ (52745)

3S Shorten Publications
PO Box 92026
Johannesburg 2117, Republic of South Africa
Phone: 27 11 5313300
Fax: 27 11 4401516
Publications: Building Women (50528) • Transport World Africa (50537)

Thrive
Geoffrey Udall Center
Beech Hill
Reading RG7 2AT, United Kingdom
Phone: 44 11 89885688
Fax: 44 11 89885677
Publications: GrowthPoint (56319)

Through the Loop Consulting Ltd.
PO Box 2528
Maidenhead SL6 9WS, United Kingdom
Phone: 44 1628 898542
Fax: 44 1628 474836
Publications: Pool (55524)

Tibetan Review
c/o Tibetan SOS Hostel
Sector 14 Ext., Rohini
Delhi 110 085, Delhi, India
Phone: 91 11 27860828
Fax: 91 11 27569702
Publications: Tibetan Review (45107)

Tibetan Women's Association
Bhagsunath Rd.
PO McLeod Ganj
Dharamsala 176219, Himachal Pradesh, India
Phone: 91 1892 221527
Fax: 91 1892 221528
Publications: DOLMA (45110)

Tibetan Youth Congress
PO McLeod Ganj
Dharamsala 176 219, Himachal Pradesh, India
Phone: 91 1892 21554
Fax: 91 1892 21849
Publications: Rangzen (45111)

The Tico Times S.A.
PO Box 4632
San Jose 1000, Costa Rica
Phone: 506 258 1558
Fax: 506 233 6378
Publications: The Tico Times (43552)

Tiempos Modernos
Sant Isidre, 83
08221 Terrassa, Spain
Publications: Tiempos Modernos (50838)

Tiles and Architectural Ceramics Society
27 Spurn Ln.
Holden Smithy, Diggle
Oldham OL3 5QP, United Kingdom
Publications: Glazed Expressions (55783) • Journal of
the Tiles and Architectural Ceramic Society (55784)

Tilgher-Genova
Via Assarotti 31/15
16122 Genoa, Italy
Phone: 39 10 8391140
Fax: 39 10 870653
Publications: Epistemologia (46148) • Giornale di
Metafisica (46149) • Nuova Corrente (46152) • Rivista
di Biologia (46153) • Textus (46154)

Time Inc.
1271 Ave. of the Americas
New York, NY 10020
Phone: 212522-1212
Publications: Caravan (53123) • Cycling Weekly
(53124) • Decanter (54314) • Horse (54570) • International
Boat Industry (53126) • MBR - Mountain Bike
Rider (53129) • Practical Boat Owner (56281) • Prediction
(53131) • Stamp Magazine (53134) • Superbike
(53135) • Uncut (55357) • VolksWorld (53137) • World
Soccer (55423) • Yachting Monthly (55429) • Yachting
World (55430)

TIME Magazine
30/F Oxford House, Taikoo Pl.
979 King's Rd.
Quarry Bay
Hong Kong, People's Republic of China
Phone: 852 31283333
Fax: 852 31285043
Publications: Time Asia (43384)

Time Out Group Ltd.
Universal House
251 Tottenham Ct. Rd.
London W1T 7AB, United Kingdom
Phone: 44 20 78133000
Fax: 44 20 78136001
Publications: Time Out Kids Out (55318) • Timeout.
com (55320)

The Times of Central Asia
175A, Abdrahmanova St., Office 304-305
720000 Bishkek, Kirgizstan
Phone: 996 312 661737
Fax: 996 312 665086
Publications: The Times of Central Asia (47202)

Times Internet Ltd.
I World Tower
DLF City Phas V (Opp DLF Golf Course)
Gurgaon 122 002, Haryana, India
Publications: The Times of India (45127)

Times Newspapers Ltd.
3 thomas More Sq.
London E98 1XY, United Kingdom
Phone: 44 20 78601133
Publications: The Times (55321)

Tjeck Magazine
Vesterbro 42
1. Sal th.
DK-9000 Alborg, Denmark
Phone: 45 331 84200
Publications: Tjeck Magazine (43644)

TOCH
Wing House, 3rd Fl.
Britannia St.
Aylesbury HP20 1QS, United Kingdom
Phone: 44 1296 331099
Fax: 44 1296 331135
Publications: Point 3 (52149)

Today Publications Ltd.
10/F Peng Xin Apt.
811 Tian Yao Qiao Rd.
Shanghai 200030, People's Republic of China
Phone: 86 216 4825237
Fax: 86 216 4825237
Publications: Shanghai Today (43503)

Today's Outlook
PO Box 90792
Jdeidet el Metn
Beirut, Lebanon
Phone: 961 1 696927
Fax: 961 1 696928
Publications: Today's Outlook (47402)

Toffee Publications Ltd.
PO Box 28
Harleston IP20 OWT, United Kingdom
Fax: 44 1986 788655
Publications: CARPology (53510)

Tohoku University
2-1 Seiryo-machi
Aoba-ku
Sendai-shi
Miyagi 980-8575, Japan
Publications: Research and Practice in Forensic
Medicine (46517)

Tohoku University
Aramaki aza Aoba
6-3 Aoba-ku
Miyagi
Sendai 980-8578, Japan
Fax: 81 22 7956400
Publications: Tohoku Mathematical Journal (46670)

Tohoku University
Kawauchi
Aoba-ku
Miyagi
Sendai 980-8576, Japan
Phone: 81 22 7956048
Fax: 81 22 7953703
Publications: Tohoku Psychologica Folia (46671)

Tohoku University Medical Press
2-1 Seiryo-machi
Aoba-ku
Miyagi
Sendai 980-8575, Japan
Fax: 81 22 7178185
Publications: Tohoku Journal of Experimental Medicine
(46669)

Tokai University
20-1 Ori-Do 3-chome
ShimizuOrido
Shizuoka 424-8610, Japan
Phone: 81 543340472
Fax: 81 243357109
Publications: Journal of Faculty of Marine Science and
Technology of Tokai University (46688)

Token Publishing Ltd.
Orchard House
Duchy Rd.
Heathpark
Honiton EX14 1YD, United Kingdom
Publications: Coin News (53586)

Tokushima University
3-18-15, Kuramoto-cho
Tokushima 770-8503, Japan
Phone: 81 88 6337104
Fax: 81 88 6337115
Publications: Journal of Medical Investigation (46715)

Tokyo Dental College Society
Tokyo Dental College
1-2-2 Masago, Mihama-ku
Chiba 261-8502, Japan
Publications: The Bulletin of Tokyo Dental College
(46316)

Tokyo Keizai University
1-7-34, Minami-cho
Kokubunji-shi
Tokyo 185-8502, Japan
Phone: 81 423287728

Fax: 81 423287769
Publications: Journal of Humanities and Natural Sciences
(46907)

Tokyo Medical and Dental University
1-5-45 Yushima
Bunkyo-ku
Tokyo 113-8510, Japan
Publications: Journal of Medical and Dental Sciences
(46924)

Tokyo Weekender
5th Fl., Chou Iikura Bldg.
8-5-8 Azabudai, Minato-ku
Tokyo 106-0041, Japan
Phone: 81 368 465615
Fax: 81 368 465616
Publications: Tokyo Weekender (47052)

The Tolkien Society
c/o Claire Chambers, Secretary
8 Queens Ln.
Eysham
Witney OX29 4HL, United Kingdom
Publications: Amon Hen (56938)

Tool and Trades History Society
Woodbine Cottage
Budleigh Hill
East Budleigh EX9 7DT, United Kingdom
Publications: Tools and Trades (53234)

Topwave Ltd.
40 Morpeth Rd.
London E9 7LD, United Kingdom
Phone: 44 20 89864141
Fax: 44 20 89864145
Publications: Boxing Monthly (54102)

Torch Publishing Company Pty. Ltd.
PO Box 113
Bankstown, New South Wales 1885, Australia
Phone: 61 2 97950000
Fax: 61 2 97950096
Publications: Auburn Review Pictorial (41801) • Bankstown
Canterbury Torch (41802) • Cooks River Valley
Times (41803)

Torquay Pottery Collectors' Society
The Kings Dr.
Torquay TQ2 5JX, United Kingdom
Publications: Torquay Pottery Collectors Society
(56758)

Total Tattoo Magazine
PO Box 10038
Sudbury C010 7WL, United Kingdom
Phone: 44 1787 242100
Publications: Total Tattoo Magazine (56651)

Toucan Publications Ltd.
322-C King George's Ave.
Singapore 0820, Singapore
Phone: 65 2997121
Fax: 65 2997545
Publications: Asian Furniture (50109)

Townswomen's Guilds
Tomlinson House, 1st Fl.
329 Tyburn Rd.
Erdington
Birmingham B24 8HJ, United Kingdom
Phone: 44 121 3260400
Fax: 44 121 3261976
Publications: Townswoman (52369)

Toyama University
3190 Gofuku
Toyama 930-8555, Japan
Phone: 81 764 456011
Publications: Mathematics Journal of Toyama University
(47096)

TPL Media
308 Gt South Rd.
Greenlane
Auckland 1051, New Zealand
Phone: 64 9 5293000
Fax: 64 9 5293001
Publications: Catering Plus (48788) • Food & Beverage
Today (48794) • Traveltrade (48830) • Wine
Technology in New Zealand (48832)

Trade Science Inc.
126, Prasheel Pk.
SanjayRaj Farm House
Nr. Saurashtra University
Rajkot 360 005, Gujarat, India
Fax: 91 281 3042233
Publications: Analytical Chemistry (45717) • Biochemistry (45706) • Biotechnology (45707) • Chemical Technology (45708) • Chemistry (50710) • Environmental Science (45756) • Inorganic Chemistry (50846) • Materials Science (45709) • Nano Science and Nano Technology (45299) • Natural Products (49804) • Physical Chemistry (50840)

Trade Union of Education in Finland
Rautatielaisenkatu 6
FIN-00520 Helsinki, Finland
Phone: 358 20 7489600
Fax: 358 9145821
Publications: Opettaja (43853)

Trade Winds Inc.
No. 7, Ln. 75, Yung Kang St.
Taipei 106, Taiwan
Phone: 886 2 23913251
Fax: 886 2 23964022
Publications: Industry Weekly (51341)

Trader Media Group
41-47 Hartfield Rd., 3rd & 4th Fl.
Wimbledon
London SW19 3RQ, United Kingdom
Phone: 44 208 5447000
Fax: 44 208 8791879
Publications: Ad Trader (53899) • Auto Freeway (55542) • Auto Trader (53986) • Bike Trader (55543) • Boat Trader (53005) • Classic American (54212) • Farmers Trader (54444) • Fast and Modified (52306) • Motorhome and Caravan Trader (55572) • Top Marques (55327) • Truck and Plant Trader (55581)

Trades Exhibitions Ltd.
Professional Beauty
3rd Fl., Broadway House
2-6 Fulham Broadway
London SW6 1AA, United Kingdom
Phone: 44 20 76103001
Fax: 44 20 76103566
Publications: Professional Beauty/LNE English Edition (55128)

Traditional Irish Music, Singing and Dancing Society
32 Belgrave Sq.
Monkstown, Dublin, Ireland
Phone: 353 12 800295
Fax: 353 12 803759
Publications: Treoir (46040)

Trained Nurses Association of India
Florence Nightingale Ln.
L-17 Green Pk.
New Delhi 110 016, Delhi, India
Phone: 91 112 6566665
Fax: 91 112 6858304
Publications: The Nursing Journal of India (45631)

Trakia University
Students Campus
BG-6000 Stara Zagora, Bulgaria
Phone: 359 42 673012
Publications: Bulgarian Journal of Veterinary Medicine (BJVM) (43110)

Trans Tech Publications Inc.
Laubisrutistr. 24
CH-8712 Zurich, Switzerland
Fax: 41 44 9221033
Publications: Advances in Science and Technology (51251) • Defect and Diffusion Forum (51257) • Journal of Biomimetics, Biomaterials, and Tissue Engineering (42527) • Key Engineering Materials (51272) • Materials Science Forum (51275) • Solid State Phenomena (51283)

Transformation
PO Box 37432
Overport 4067, Republic of South Africa
Publications: Transformation (50560)

Transitions Online
Baranova 33
CZ-130 00 Prague 3, Czech Republic

Phone: 42 222 780805
Fax: 42 222 780804
Publications: Transitions Online (TOL) (43639)

Transnet Internet Services GmbH
Lilienstr. 3-5
D-81669 Munich, Germany
Phone: 49 894 8903350
Fax: 49 894 8903355
Publications: Munich Found (44572)

Transport Planning Society
1 Great George St.
London SW1P 3AA, United Kingdom
Phone: 44 20 76652238
Fax: 44 20 77991325
Publications: Local Transport Today (54881)

Transport Ticket Society
6 Breckbank, Forest Town
Notts
Mansfield NG19 0PZ, United Kingdom
Publications: Transport Ticket Society Journal (55591)

Transportbedriftenes Landsforening
PO Box 5477, Majorstuen
N-0305 Oslo, Norway
Phone: 47 23088600
Fax: 47 23088601
Publications: Transportforum (49209)

Traplet Publications Ltd.
Traplet House
Pendragon Close
Malvern WR14 1GA, United Kingdom
Phone: 44 16 84588500
Fax: 44 16 84578558
Publications: Craft Stamper (55533) • Marine Modelling International (55534) • QFI Quiet Flight International (55535) • Quiet & Electric Flight International (55536) • R/C Jet International (55537) • Radio Control Model World (55538) • Radio Race Car International (55539)

Travel Productions N.V.
Hanswijkstraat 23
B-2800 Mechelen, Belgium
Phone: 32 154 50350
Fax: 32 154 50360
Publications: Travel Magazine (42905)

Tremblestone
Stowford House
43 Seymour Ave.
St. Judes
Plymouth PL4 8RB, United Kingdom
Publications: Tremblestone (56275)

Trentham Books Ltd.
Westview House
734 London Rd.
Oakhill
Stoke-on-Trent ST4 5NP, United Kingdom
Phone: 44 17 82745567
Fax: 44 17 82745553
Publications: Design & Technology (56629) • Race Equality Teaching (56630)

Trespass
32 Addison Grove
London W4 1ER, United Kingdom
Phone: 44 20 84005882
Fax: 44 20 89941713
Publications: Trespass (55340)

TRI Global Company Ltd.
72 PAV Bldg., 4A Fl.
Ladprao Rd., Soi 42
Huay Khwang
Bangkok 10310, Thailand
Phone: 66 2 5122128
Fax: 66 2 5122129
Publications: The Rubber International (51433)

The Tribune Publishing Co. Inc.
The Penthouse Stes.
GLC Bldg.
T.M. Kalaw cor. A. Mabini Sts.
Ermita
Manila, Philippines
Phone: 63 2 5215511
Publications: Daily Tribune (49549)

The Tribune Trust
The Tribune House

Sector 29-C
Chandigarh 160 030, Chandigarh, India
Phone: 91 172 2655066
Fax: 91 172 2651293
Publications: The Tribune (45025)

Trinidad Publishing & Trinidad Broadcasting Company Ltd.
22-24 St. Vincent St.
PO Box 122
Port of Spain, Trinidad and Tobago
Phone: 809623-8871
Fax: 809625-1782
Publications: The Trinidad Guardian (51467)

Trinity College London
89 Albert Embankment
London SE1 7TP, United Kingdom
Phone: 44 20 78206100
Fax: 44 20 78206161
Publications: Flourish (54467)

Trinity Publications
92-93 Edward House, Edward St.
Birmingham B1 2RA, United Kingdom
Phone: 44 12 12338712
Fax: 44 12 12338715
Publications: Boat Mart (52332) • Build It (52335) • Classic Car Mart (52337) • Micro Mart (52358)

Trisila Company Ltd.
3 Chom Doi Rd.
T. Suthep
A.Muang
Chiang Mai 50200, Thailand
Phone: 66 532 25201
Fax: 66 533 57491
Publications: Citylife (51457)

Triveni Enterprises
1/206 Vikas Nagar
Lucknow 226 022, Uttar Pradesh, India
Phone: 91 522 2769181
Fax: 91 522 2769018
Publications: Journal of Environmental Biology (45323)

Trofima kai Pota
110 Sigrou Ave.
GR-117 41 Athens, Greece
Phone: 30 210 9240748
Fax: 30 210 9242650
Publications: Trofima kai Pota (44757)

TSL Education Ltd.
26 Red Lion Sq.
London WC1R 4HQ, United Kingdom
Phone: 44 20 31943000
Publications: Times Educational Supplement (55322) • Times Higher Education Supplement (55323)

Tsuda College
2-1-1 Tsuda-Machi
Kodaira-shi
Tokyo 187-8577, Japan
Phone: 81 423425113
Publications: Tsuda Review (47054)

Tsukuba Sago Fund
Institute of Applied Biochemistry
791-27 Inaoka
Tsukuba-shi
Ibaraki 305-0071, Japan
Phone: 81 298380152
Fax: 81 298380152
Publications: Sago Communication (46394)

TTG Asia Media Private Ltd.
1 Science Park Rd.
No. 04-07 The Capricorn
Singapore Science Park II
Singapore 117528, Singapore
Phone: 65 63957575
Fax: 65 65362972
Publications: Travel Trade Gazette Asia (50281) • TTGmice (50282)

TTG—De Telegraaf Tijdschriften Groep B.V.
Basiweg 30
PO Box 36
NL-1000 AC Amsterdam, Netherlands
Phone: 31 20 5852913
Publications: Autovisie (47901) • Elegance (47964) • Residence (48222)

TTG Italia S.p.A.
Via Nota 6
I-10122 Turin, Italy
Phone: 39 11 4366300
Fax: 39 11 4366500
Publications: TTG Italia (46275)

TTS Institute
PO Box 5
FIN-05201 Rajamaki, Finland
Phone: 358 9 29041200
Fax: 358 9 29041285
Publications: Teho (43905)

Tuberculosis Association of India
3 Red Cross Rd.
New Delhi 110 001, Delhi, India
Phone: 91 11 23715217
Fax: 91 11 23711303
Publications: Indian Journal of Tuberculosis (45569)

Tudor Rose
6 Friar Ln.
Leicester LE1 5RA, United Kingdom
Phone: 44 116 2229900
Publications: Finance on Windows (53800) • Global Municipal Investor (53802) • Golf Course Architecture (53803) • Prime (53818) • Retailspeak (53821)

Tun Abdul Razak Research Centre
Brickendebberry
Hertford SG13 8NL, United Kingdom
Phone: 44 19 92584966
Fax: 44 19 92554837
Publications: Rubber Developments (53565)

Turkish Academy of Sciences
Piyade Sokak No. 27
Kavaklidere
TR-06550 Ankara, Turkey
Phone: 90 312 4422903
Fax: 90 312 4426491
Publications: TUBA-AR (51501)

Turkish Association for Cancer Research and Control
Hacettepe University Institute of Oncology
Sihhiye
TR-06100 Ankara, Turkey
Phone: 90 312 3092904
Fax: 90 312 3092905
Publications: Turkish Journal of Cancer (51506)

Turkish Association of Orthopaedics and Traumatology
Istanbul School of Medicine
Dept. of Orthopaedics & Traumatology
Topkapi
TR-34390 Istanbul, Turkey
Publications: Acta Orthopaedica et Traumatologica Turcica (51556)

Turkish Biochemical Society
Hirfanli Sokak Banu Apt. 9/3
Gaziosmanpasa
TR-06700 Ankara, Turkey
Phone: 90 312 4470997
Fax: 90 312 4470963
Publications: Biyokimya Dergisi (51490)

Turkish Cooperative Association
Mithatpaba Caddesi 38-A
Kizilay
TR-06420 Ankara, Turkey
Phone: 90 312 4359899
Fax: 90 312 4304292
Publications: Cooperation in Turkiye (51491) • Karinca (51496) • Ucuncu Sektor Kooperatifcilik (51518)

Turkish Psychological Association
Mesrutiyet Cad. 22/12
Kizilay
TR-06640 Ankara, Turkey
Phone: 90 312 4256765
Publications: Turk Psikoloji Dergisi (Turkish Journal of Psychology) (51502)

Turkish Society of Gastroenterology
Gaziler Sokak 22/1
Abidinpapa
TR-06620 Ankara, Turkey
Phone: 90 312 3622145

Fax: 90 312 3625948
Publications: Turkish Journal of Gastroenterology (51511)

Turkish Society of Radiology
Hosdere Caddesi, Guzelkent Sokak
Cankaya Evleri, F Blok, No. 2
Cankaya
06540 Ankara, Turkey
Phone: 90 312 4423653
Fax: 90 312 4423654
Publications: Diagnostic and Interventional Radiology (51492)

Turpion - Moscow Ltd.
MIAN
8 Gubkina St., Rm. 915
119991 Moscow, Russia
Phone: 7 495 1354509
Fax: 7 495 9300604
Publications: Izvestiya (49923) • Quantum Electronics (49969) • Regular & Chaotic Dynamics (49970) • Russian Chemical Reviews (49972) • Sbornik (49989)

Turret Group Company
173 High St.
Rickmansworth WD3 1AY, United Kingdom
Phone: 44 1923 692660
Fax: 44 1923 692679
Publications: Ingredients, Health & Nutrition (56393) • International Aquafeed (56394)

TV Trend Verlag GmbH
Hertener Mark 7
D-45699 Herten, Germany
Phone: 49 2366 808248
Fax: 49 2366 808248
Publications: VW Scene International (44484)

TWI Ltd.
Granta Pk.
Great Abington
Cambridge CB21 6AL, United Kingdom
Phone: 44 12 23899000
Fax: 44 12 23892588
Publications: Connect (52810)

Tzeng Brothers Information Group
PO Box 43-345
7G-09 World Trade Ctr.
Taipei 105, Taiwan
Publications: Asian Air Transport (51331)

U-Kan Inc.
Yoyogi 2-32-1
Shibuya-ku
Tokyo 151-0053, Japan
Phone: 81 333 793881
Fax: 81 333 793882
Publications: The Plaza (47019)

The Uganda Society
PO Box 4980
Kampala, Uganda
Publications: The Uganda Journal (51589)

Uitgeverij Bis B.V.
Oude Braak 16
NL-1012 PS Amsterdam, Netherlands
Phone: 31 20 423717
Fax: 31 20 4280653
Publications: Frame (47989)

Uitgeverij de Groeve
Postbus 728
B-8400 Oostende, Belgium
Publications: Old Timer Dreamcar Magazine (42907) • Zwerfauto Magazine (42908)

U.K. Irrigation Association
c/o Moorland House
Hayway
Rushden NN10 6AG, United Kingdom
Phone: 44 1427 717627
Publications: UK Irrigation (56427)

UK Transport Press Ltd.
Bank House
High St.
West Sussex RH17 5EN, United Kingdom
Phone: 44 1444 414293
Publications: Freight Magazine (56898) • Patchwork & Quilting (56900) • R/C Model World (56901) • Scrapbook Magic (56903)

Ukrainian Gerontological and Geriatric Society
Vyshgorodskaya St. 67
254114 Kiev, Ukraine
Phone: 380 44 4304068
Fax: 380 44 4329956
Publications: Problems of Aging & Longevity (51606)

Ulster Folk and Transport Museum
153 Bangor Rd.
Cultra
Holywood BT18 0EU, United Kingdom
Phone: 44 28 90428428
Fax: 44 28 90428728
Publications: Ulster Folklife (53584)

Ulster Historical Foundation
Unit 7, Cotton Ct.
30-42 Waring St.
Belfast BT1 2ED, United Kingdom
Phone: 44 28 90332288
Fax: 44 28 90661977
Publications: Directory of Irish Family History Research (52282)

Ultima Media Ltd.
Lamb House
Church St.
London W4 2PD, United Kingdom
Phone: 44 20 89870900
Fax: 44 20 89870948
Publications: Automotive Logistics (53988) • Automotive Production China (53990) • Interior Motives (54616)

Ultra Scientist of Physical Sciences
PO Box 93, GPO
Bhopal 462 001, Madhya Pradesh, India
Phone: 91 755 2533437
Publications: Ultra Scientist of Physical Sciences (45007)

Ultrafit Publications
Champions House
5 Princes St.
Penzance TR18 2NL, United Kingdom
Phone: 44 173 6350204
Fax: 44 173 6368587
Publications: Ultrafit (56251)

UMG Verlag GmbH
Frielenger Str. 31
D-28215 Bremen, Germany
Phone: 49 421 3649714
Fax: 49 421 4984252
Publications: Umwelt-Medizin-Gesellschaft (44282)

UMIST Students Association
Oxford Rd.
Manchester M13 9PL, United Kingdom
Phone: 44 161 3066000
Publications: Grip (55557)

UN Special
Palais des Nations
Bureau C507
CH-1211 Geneva, Switzerland
Phone: 41 22 9172501
Fax: 41 22 9170505
Publications: UN Special (51163)

UN System - Standing Committee on Nutrition
c/o World Health Organisation
20 Ave. Appia
CH-1211 Geneva 27, Switzerland
Phone: 41 227 910456
Fax: 41 227 988891
Publications: Nutrition Information in Crisis Situations (51154) • SCN News (51160)

Underwater World Publications Ltd.
55 High St.
Teddington TW11 8HA, United Kingdom
Phone: 44 20 89434288
Fax: 44 20 89434312
Publications: International Ocean Systems (56732)

UNESCO
1 rue Miollis
F-75732 Paris Cedex 15, France
Phone: 33 1 45681000
Fax: 33 1 45671690
Publications: Copyright Bulletin (44034) • Diogenes (44037) • Diversities (44395)

UNESCO Courier
7 Pl. de Fontenoy
F-75352 Paris 07, France
Publications: UNESCO Courier (44087)

UNESCO International Centre for Engineering Education
Faculty of Engineering
Monash University
Melbourne, Victoria 3800, Australia
Phone: 61 399 055575
Fax: 61 399 051547
Publications: Global Journal of Engineering Education (42061)

UNESP - Universidade Estadual Paulista
Alameda Santos 647
01419-901 Sao Paulo, Sao Paulo, Brazil
Publications: Ecletica Quimica (43038)

UNHCR Library
Case Postale 2500
CH-1211 Geneva, Switzerland
Phone: 41 22 7398111
Publications: Refugee Survey Quarterly (51159)

Uni Foundation and Unesp - Sao Paulo State University
Caixa Postal 592
18618-000 Botucatu, Sao Paulo, Brazil
Phone: 55 143 8153133
Fax: 55 143 8153133
Publications: Interface (42956)

Unidad de Bioetica de la Organizacion Pan-americana de la Salud/Organizacion Mundial de la Salud
Avenida Providencia No. 1017, Piso 7
Casilla 61-T
Santiago, Chile
Phone: 56 2 2360330
Fax: 56 2 7692377
Publications: Acta Bioethica (43142)

Union of Bulgarian Film Makers
67 Dondukoz Blvd.
BG-1504 Sofia, Bulgaria
Phone: 359 2 9461069
Fax: 359 2 9461069
Publications: Kino (43104)

Union Editorial S.A. de C.V.
Independencia No. 300
Col. Centro C.P.
44100 Guadalajara, Jalisco, Mexico
Phone: 52 333 6146340
Publications: El Informador (47774)

Union of the Electric Industry - Eurelectric
Blvd. de l'Imperatrice 66
PO Box 2
B-1000 Brussels, Belgium
Phone: 32 251 51000
Fax: 32 251 51010
Publications: Watt's NEW? (42874)

Union of German Catholic Women
Kaesenstrasse 18
D-50677 Cologne, Germany
Phone: 49 2 21860920
Fax: 49 2 218609279
Publications: Christliche Frau (44291)

Union of Science and Education
1, rue Jean-Pierre Sauvage
Kirchberg
L-2514 Luxembourg, Luxembourg
Phone: 352 26096969
Fax: 352 26096969
Publications: Sew-Journal (47493)

Union of Scientists in Bulgaria
39, Madrid Blvd. Fl. 2
BG-1505 Sofia, Bulgaria
Phone: 35 929 430128
Fax: 35 929 441590
Publications: Nauka (43106)

UNISON
1 Mabledon Pl.
London WC1H 9AJ, United Kingdom
Phone: 44 845 3550845
Publications: U Magazine (55351)

United Advertising Publications Ltd.
C.I. Twr.
St. George's Sq.
New Malden KT3 4JA, United Kingdom
Phone: 44 208 3290100
Fax: 44 208 3290101
Publications: Dalton's Weekly (55658)

United Bible Societies
Reading Bridge House
Reading RG1 8PJ, United Kingdom
Phone: 44 11 89500200
Fax: 44 11 89500857
Publications: The Bible Translator (56310)

United Business Media
245 Blackfriars Rd.
London SE1 9UY, United Kingdom
Phone: 44 20 79215000
Publications: BioMechanics (54027) • Call Center Magazine (54167) • CCTV Today (54189) • IBM Database Magazine (54581) • Insurance & Technology (54612) • MSDN Magazine (54960)

United Grand Lodge of England
Freemason's Hall
60 Great Queen St.
London WC2B 5AZ, United Kingdom
Phone: 44 20 78319811
Fax: 44 20 78316021
Publications: Masonic Quarterly (54910)

United Kingdom Lubricants Association
Berkhamstead House
121 High St.
Berkhamsted HP4 2DJ, United Kingdom
Phone: 44 1442 230589
Fax: 44 1442 259232
Publications: Lube (52312)

United Kingdom Maritime Pilots' Association
Transport House
128 Theobald's Rd.
London WC1X 8TN, United Kingdom
Phone: 44 20 76112568
Fax: 44 20 76112757
Publications: The Maritime Pilot (54906)

United Kingdom Wayfarer Association
c/o Sarah Burgess
49 Seaview Ave.
West Mersea
Colchester CO5 8BY, United Kingdom
Phone: 44 12 06384043
Publications: Wayfarer News (53054)

United Nations Association of Sri Lanka
39/1 Cyril Jansz Mawatha
Panadura, Sri Lanka
Phone: 94 38 2243080
Fax: 94 38 2232123
Publications: Losetha (50922)

United Nations Centre for Human Settlements
PO Box 30030
Nairobi, Kenya
Phone: 254 20 7621234
Fax: 254 20 7624266
Publications: Habitat Debate (47183)

United Nations Centre for Regional Development
1-47-1 Nagono
Nakamura-ku
Nagoya 450-0001, Japan
Phone: 81 52 5619377
Fax: 81 52 5619375
Publications: Regional Development Dialogue (46559)

United Nations Economic and Social Commission for Asia and the Pacific
United Nations Bldg.
Rajadamnern Nok Ave.
Bangkok 10200, Thailand
Phone: 66 228 81234
Fax: 66 228 81000
Publications: Asia Pacific Development Journal (51410) • Asia-Pacific Population Journal (51411) • Confluence (51417) • e-TISNET Monthly News/e-TISNET Monthly Information Services (51418) • Population Headliners (51431) • Water Resources Journal (51448)

United Nations Environment Programme
United Nations Ave.
Gigiri
PO Box 30552
Nairobi, Kenya
Phone: 254 20 7621234
Fax: 254 20 7624489
Publications: Our Planet (47194)

United Nations High Commission for Refugees - Regional Office Mexico
Apartado Postal 105-39
11581 Mexico City, Federal District, Mexico
Phone: 52 52802072
Fax: 52 52802133
Publications: Refugees (47788)

United Reformed Church History Society
Westminster College
Madingley Rd.
Cambridge CB3 0AA, United Kingdom
Phone: 44 1223 741300
Publications: Journal of the United Reformed Church History Society (52864)

United Service Institution of India
Rao Tula Ram Marg (Opp. Signal Enclave)
PO Box 8
Vasant Vihar PO
New Delhi 110 057, Delhi, India
Phone: 91 11 26146755
Fax: 91 11 26149773
Publications: USI Journal (45661)

Unity Media Plc
Becket House
Vestry Rd.
Kent
Sevenoaks TN14 5EJ, United Kingdom
Phone: 44 1732 748000
Fax: 44 1732 748001
Publications: BMW Car (56470) • Conservatory (56471) • FENSA News (56472) • GT Purely Porsche (56473) • Heating & Plumbing Monthly (56474) • Japanese Cars Banzai (56475) • Performance BMW (56476) • Performance Car (56477) • Performance Ford (56478) • Performance VW (56479) • Public Sector & Local Government Building (56480) • Retro Cars (56481) • Retro Ford (56482) • Roofing, Cladding & Insulation (56483) • Who's Who in Heating & Plumbing (56484)

Universal Magazines
6-8 Byfield St., Unit 5
North Ryde, New South Wales 2113, Australia
Phone: 61 2 98050399
Fax: 61 2 98050714
Publications: Australian Beading (42166) • Australian Country Collections (42167) • Australian Road Rider (42168) • Australian Trailrider (42169) • Backyard Design Ideas (42170) • Barb's Factory Shopping Guide (42171) • Bargain Shopper Guide to Melbourne (42172) • Bathroom Yearbook (42173) • BuildHOME Vic (42174) • Choosing a School for Your Child - New South Wales (42175) • Choosing a School for Your Child - Victoria (42176) • Complete Wedding Guide Melbourne (42177) • Complete Wedding Sydney (42178) • Contemporary Home Design (42179) • Dirt Action (42180) • Dogs Life (42181) • 4WD Buyers Guide (42182) • Homespun (42183) • Kit Homes (42184) • Kitchen Yearbook (42185) • Kitchens and Bathrooms Quarterly (42186) • Life Etc. (42187) • New Car Buyer (42188) • Outdoor Design & Living (42189) • Outdoor Design Source (42190) • Outdoor Space (42191) • Performance Buildups (42192) • Poolside (42193) • Poolside Showcase (42194) • Quilters Companion (42195) • Scrapbook Creations (42196) • Smart Kitchens & Bathrooms (42197) • Stone (42198) • Sydney Eats (42199) • Used Car Buyers Guide (42200) • WellBeing (42201)

Universidad Autonoma de Baja California
Avenida Alvaro Obregon Y Julian Carrillo
21100 Mexicali, Baja California, Mexico
Publications: Estudios Fronterizos (47780)

Universidad Catolica del Norte Departamento de Matematicas
Casilla 1280
Antofagasta, Chile
Phone: 56 553 55571

Fax: 56 553 55599
Publications: Proyecciones Journal of Mathematics (43132)

Universidad Central de Venezuela
Avenida Salvador Allende
Apartado 2156
Caracas, Venezuela
Publications: Acta Botanica Venezuelica (57019)

Universidad de Concepcion
Victor Lamas 1290
Casilla 160-C
Concepcion, Chile
Phone: 56 412 204000
Fax: 56 412 227455
Publications: Acta Literaria (43135)

Universidad de Murcia, Servicio de Publicaciones
Teniente Flomesta, N 5
E-30003 Murcia, Spain
Phone: 34 968 363000
Publications: Anales de Psicologia (50821)

Universidad Nacional de Colombia
Carrera 45, No. 26-85
Edificio Uriel Gutierrez
Bogota, Colombia
Phone: 57 131 65000
Publications: Acta Biologica Colombiana (43541) • Caldasia (43544)

Universidad Nacional Mayor de San Marcos
Av. Grau 755
Lima 01, Peru
Phone: 51 1 6197000
Publications: Anales de la Facultad de Medicina (49423)

Universidad de Tarapaca
Casilla 6-D
Arica, Chile
Phone: 56 58 205501
Fax: 56 58 205503
Publications: IDESIA (43133)

Universidad del Zulia
Apartado Postal 526
Maracaibo 4001, Venezuela
Phone: 58 261 7596716
Publications: Gaceta Laboral (57026)

Universidade Federal de Minas Gerais
Av. Antonio Carlos
6627 Campus Pampulha
31270-901 Belo Horizonte, Mato Grosso, Brazil
Phone: 55 31 34095000
Publications: Nova Economia (42950)

Universidade Federal do Parana
Rua XV de Novembro 1299
80060-000 Curitiba, Paraiba, Brazil
Phone: 55 413 3605002
Fax: 55 413 2642243
Publications: Electronic Musicological Review (42977)

Universidade Federal de Pernambuco
Av Prof. Moraes Rego, 1235
Recife, Pernambuco, Brazil
Publications: The Brazilian Electronic Journal of Economics (BEJE) (42994)

Universidade Federal de Santa Maria
Avenida Roraima No. 1000
Cidade Universitaria
Bairro Camobi
97105-900 Santa Maria, Rio Grande do Sul, Brazil
Publications: Ciencia Rural (43016)

Universidade Federal de Sao Carlos
Caixa Postal 676
13565-905 Sao Carlos, Sao Paulo, Brazil
Publications: Gestao & Producao (43017)

Universidade de Sao Paulo
Avenida dos Bandeirantes, 3900
14040-900 Ribeirao Preto, Sao Paulo, Brazil
Phone: 55 163 6024746
Fax: 55 163 6023884
Publications: Economia Aplicada (42997)

Universita Cattolica Del Sacro Cuore
Largo F. Vito 1
I-00168 Rome, Italy

Phone: 39 6 30151
Publications: Medicina e Morale (46238)

Universita di Pisa
Via Serafini, 3
56126 Pisa, Italy
Phone: 39 502 212412
Fax: 39 502 212400
Publications: Bollettino Telematico di Filosofia Politica (46218)

Universita degli Studi di Modena e Reggio Emilia
Via Universita 4
I-41100 Modena, Italy
Phone: 39 52 2522604
Publications: Invertebrate Survival Journal (ISJ) (46199)

Universitat Bielefeld
Postfach 100131
D-33501 Bielefeld, Germany
Phone: 49 521 10600
Fax: 49 521 1065844
Publications: Documenta Mathematica (44245)

Universitat Oberta de Catalunya
Av. Tibidabo 39-43
E-08035 Barcelona, Spain
Phone: 34 93 2532323
Fax: 34 93 4175129
Publications: IDP (50680)

Universitat St. Gallen
Dufourstrasse 50
CH-9000 Saint Gallen, Switzerland
Phone: 41 71 2242111
Fax: 41 71 2242816
Publications: Thexis (51224)

Universite de Fribourg
Av. Europe 20
CH-1700 Fribourg, Switzerland
Phone: 41 26 3007111
Fax: 41 26 3009700
Publications: Universitas Friburgensis (51087)

Universite Marc Bloch
22 Rue Descartes
F-67084 Strasbourg, France
Phone: 33 388 417300
Fax: 33 388 417354
Publications: ALSIC (Apprentissage des Langues et Systemes d'Information et de Communication) (44109)

Universiti Putra Malaysia
43400 Serdang, Malaysia
Phone: 60 3 89466000
Fax: 60 3 89487273
Publications: Asia-Pacific Journal of Molecular Biology & Biotechnology (47714)

Universiti Putra Malaysia Press
Serdang, Malaysia
Phone: 60 3 89468555
Fax: 60 3 89416172
Publications: Pertanika Journal of Social Science and Humanities (47716) • Pertanika Journal of Tropical Agricultural Science (47717)

Universities Federation for Animal Welfare
The Old School
Brewhouse Hill
Wheathampstead AL4 8AN, United Kingdom
Phone: 44 15 82831818
Fax: 44 15 82831414
Publications: Animal Welfare (56914)

University of Allahabad
PO Box 2005
Allahabad 211002, Uttar Pradesh, India
Phone: 91 0532460846
Fax: 91 0532609857
Publications: Indian Journal of Economics (44931)

University of Auckland
Faculty of Law
PO Box 92019
Auckland 1142, New Zealand
Phone: 64 937 37599
Fax: 64 937 37473
Publications: Auckland University Law Review (48785) • The New Zealand Journal of History (48817)

University of Bath
Claverton Down
Bath BA2 7AY, United Kingdom
Phone: 44 1225 386302
Fax: 44 1225 386767
Publications: Journal of Transport Economics and Policy (52250)

University of Buckingham Press
University of Buckingham
Buckingham MK18 1EG, United Kingdom
Phone: 44 1280 814080
Publications: The Denning Law Journal (52756) • The Journal of Gambling Business and Economics (52757) • The Journal of Prediction Markets (52758)

University of Campinas
Caixa Postal 6110
13081-970 Campinas, Sao Paulo, Brazil
Phone: 55 193 5217093
Fax: 55 193 2894309
Publications: Opiniao Publica (42971)

University of Canterbury
Private Bag 4800
Christchurch 8140, New Zealand
Phone: 64 3 3367001
Publications: History Now (48868)

University of Cape Town
PO Box X3
Rondebosch 7701, Republic of South Africa
Phone: 27 21 6509111
Publications: Monday Paper (50622)

University of Central England Union of Students
Franchise St.
Perry Barr
Birmingham B42 2SZ, United Kingdom
Phone: 44 121 3316801
Fax: 44 121 3316802
Publications: Spaghetti Junction (52367)

University Centre of Journalism Teaching
11, rue du Marechal Juin
F-67043 Strasbourg Cedex, France
Phone: 33 68 858300
Fax: 33 68 858574
Publications: News d'Ill (44113)

University College of Boras
Swedish Library Research
SE-501 90 Boras, Sweden
Phone: 46 33 4354000
Publications: Svensk Biblioteksforskning/Swedish Library Research (50951)

University College London
Gower St.
London WC1E 6BT, United Kingdom
Phone: 44 20 76792000
Publications: PIA (Papers from the Institute of Archaeology) (55088)

University of Colombo
c/o The Registrar
94, Cumaratunga Munidasa Mawatha
PO Box 1490
Colombo 00300, Sri Lanka
Phone: 94 158 1835
Fax: 94 158 3810
Publications: Ceylon Journal of Medical Sciences (50850)

University of Colombo
94 Cumaratunga Munidasa Mawatha
Colombo 3, Sri Lanka
Phone: 94 1 581835
Fax: 94 1 583810
Publications: Sri Lanka Journal of International Law (50866)

University of Cyprus
PO Box 20537
Nicosia 1678, Cyprus
Phone: 357 22 894000
Publications: POLIS (43597)

University of Durham
Old Elvet
Durham DH1 3HP, United Kingdom
Phone: 44 191 3342000
Publications: Durham Anthropology Journal (53228)

University of Dusseldorf
Universitatsstr. 1
D-40225 Dusseldorf, Germany
Phone: 49 211 8100
Publications: Constructions (44322)

University of Exeter
Devonshire House
Stocker Rd.
Exeter EX4 4PZ, United Kingdom
Phone: 44 1392 723528
Fax: 44 1392 263546
Publications: Exepose (53356)

University of Glasgow
University Ave.
Glasgow G12 8QQ, United Kingdom
Phone: 44 141 3302000
Publications: eSharp (53417) • Journal of eLiteracy
(JeLit) (53427)

University of Haifa
Mount Carmel
IL-31905 Haifa, Israel
Phone: 972 4 8240111
Publications: Khulyot (46077)

University of Hertfordshire
Innovation Ctr.
College Ln.
Hatfield AL10 9AB, United Kingdom
Phone: 44 170 7281060
Fax: 44 170 7281061
Publications: Information Management & Technology
(53539)

The University of Hong Kong
Main Bldg., Rm. 126
The University of Hong Kong
Pokfulam Rd.
Hong Kong, People's Republic of China
Phone: 852 28578606
Fax: 852 25464943
Publications: The Journal of Dagaare Studies (JDS)
(43355)

The University of Hong Kong
Pokfulam Rd.
Hong Kong, People's Republic of China
Phone: 852 28592006
Fax: 852 25473409
Publications: Hong Kong Journal of Applied Linguistics
(43327)

University of Illinois Press
1325 S Oak St.
Champaign, IL 61820-6903
Phone: 217333-0950
Fax: 217244-8082
Publications: Journal of Symbolic Logic (49012)

University of Indonesia
Jalan Raya Salemba 4
10430 Jakarta, Indonesia
Phone: 62 217 78880139
Publications: Economics and Finance in Indonesia
(45796)

University of Jos
c/o The Deans Office
University of Jos
PMB 2084
Jos, Plateau, Nigeria
Phone: 23 473 55952
Publications: Journal of Medicine in the Tropics (49126)

University of Karachi
University Rd.
Karachi 75720, Pakistan
Publications: Pakistan Journal of Pharmaceutical Sci-
ences (49371)

University of Kent Student's Union
Kent Union
Mandela Bldg.
University of Kent
Canterbury CT2 7NW, United Kingdom
Phone: 44 1227 824200
Fax: 44 1227 824204
Publications: inQuire (52921)

University of Leeds
University of Leeds
The School of Computing

Leeds LS2 9JT, United Kingdom
Phone: 44 11 33435430
Fax: 44 11 33435468
Publications: Tangentium (53775)

University of Leicester
Ken Edwards Bldg.
Leicester LE1 7RH, United Kingdom
Phone: 44 11 62525520
Publications: International Journal of Community Cur-
rency Research (53805)

University of Ljubljana
Jamnikarjeva 101
SI-1000 Ljubljana, Slovenia
Phone: 38 613 203000
Fax: 38 612 565782
Publications: Acta Agriculturae Slovenica (50333)

University of Luton Press
75 Castle St.
Luton LU1 3AJ, United Kingdom
Phone: 44 1582 743297
Fax: 44 1582 743298
Publications: Convergence (55501)

University of Malaya
Faculty of Arts & Social Sciences
50603 Kuala Lumpur, Malaysia
Phone: 60 3 79675504
Fax: 60 3 79675457
Publications: Malaysian Journal of Science Series A:
Life Sciences (47618) • Malaysian Journal of Science
Series B: Physical & Earth Sciences (47619) • Malay-
sian Journal of Tropical Geography (47620)

University of Malaya Medical Centre
Lembah Pantai
59100 Kuala Lumpur, Malaysia
Phone: 60 3 79494422
Fax: 60 3 79562253
Publications: Biomedical Imaging and Intervention
Journal (47600)

University of Malaya Press
Pantai Valley
50603 Kuala Lumpur, Malaysia
Phone: 60 3 79574361
Fax: 60 3 79574473
Publications: Man and Society (47623)

University of Manchester
Steve Biko Bldg.
Oxford Rd.
Manchester M13 9PR, United Kingdom
Phone: 44 16 12752930
Fax: 44 16 12752936
Publications: Student Direct (55578)

University of Melbourne
John Medley Bldg.
Parkville Campus
Carlton, Victoria 3010, Australia
Phone: 61 3 83446565
Fax: 61 3 83447906
Publications: Melbourne Journal of Politics (41728)

The University of Melbourne
Law School
Melbourne, Victoria 3010, Australia
Phone: 61 3 83444000
Fax: 61 3 83445104
Publications: Melbourne University Law Review
(42075)

University of Naples
c/o Presidenza
Facolta di Studi Arabo-Islamici e del Mediterraneo
L'Orientale
via Nuova Marina n. 59
80133 Naples, Italy
Phone: 39 0816909303
Fax: 39 0816909396
Publications: Web Journal on Cultural Patrimony
(46203)

University of New England
Armidale
Armidale, New South Wales 2351, Australia
Phone: 61 2 67733333
Fax: 61 2 67733100
Publications: Australian Folklore (41558)

The University of Newcastle
Callaghan Campus
University Dr.
Callaghan, New South Wales 2308, Australia
Phone: 61 2 49215000
Fax: 61 2 49214200
Publications: Australian Journal of Educational &
Developmental Psychology (41690)

University of Nigeria
University of Nigeria
Nsukka, Anambra, Nigeria
Publications: Agro-Science (49154)

**University of Nis, Faculty of Medicine and Clinic
of Stomatology in Nis**
52 Brace Taskovic St.
18000 Nis, Serbia
Publications: Acta Stomatologica Naissi (50090)

University of the Orange Free State
PO Box 339
Bloemfontein 9300, Republic of South Africa
Phone: 27 514 019111
Publications: Acta Theologica (50354)

University of Oslo
Boks 89
Blindern
N-0314 Oslo, Norway
Phone: 47 22 853336
Fax: 47 22 853274
Publications: Universitas (49210)

University of Otago Press
Level 1, 398 Cumberland St.
PO Box 56
Dunedin, New Zealand
Phone: 64 3 4791100
Fax: 64 3 4798385
Publications: JNZL: Journal of New Zealand Literature
(48889) • Landfall (48891)

University of Peradeniya
PO Box 35
Peradeniya 20400, Sri Lanka
Phone: 94 812 388301
Fax: 94 812 388102
Publications: Ceylon Journal of Science, Biological
Sciences (50927) • Ceylon Journal of Science, Physi-
cal Sciences (50928)

University of the Philippines
Diliman
Quezon City 1101, Philippines
Phone: 63 2 9283861
Fax: 63 2 9261432
Publications: Philippine Journal of Public Administra-
tion (49607) • Philippine Law Journal (49608)

University of the Philippines
E Jacinto St.
Diliman
Quezon City 1101, Philippines
Phone: 63 2 9206853
Publications: Philippine Planning Journal (49609)

University of the Philippines
Guerrero St.
Quezon City 1101, Philippines
Phone: 63 2 9279686
Fax: 63 2 9205463
Publications: Philippine Review of Economics (49610)

University of the Philippines
Palma Hall
Diliman
Quezon City 1101, Philippines
Phone: 63 2 9818500
Fax: 63 2 9263486
Publications: Philippine Social Sciences Review
(49612)

University of the Philippines
2nd Fl., Palma Hall Annex
Diliman
Quezon City 1101, Philippines
Fax: 63 2 9818500
Publications: Diliman Review (49589)

University of the Philippines at Los Banos
College
Laguna 4031, Philippines
Phone: 63 495 362379

Fax: 63 495 362379
Publications: The Philippine Agricultural Scientist (49507)

University Press Inc.
c/o the American Mathematical Society
201 Charles St.
Providence, RI 02904-2294
Phone: 401455-4000
Fax: 401331-3842
Free: 800321-4AMS
Publications: Journal of Algebraic Geometry (52844)

University of Pretoria
Sciences Bldg.
University of Pretoria, Lynnwood Rd.
Hillcrest 0002, Republic of South Africa
Phone: 27 124 203111
Fax: 27 124 204555
Publications: South African Journal of Economic and Management Sciences (50523)

The University of Queensland
The University of Queensland
Brisbane, Queensland 4072, Australia
Phone: 61 733 651111
Publications: Access (41639) • Australian Studies in Journalism (41642)

University of Queensland Press
Staff House Rd.
PO Box 6042
Saint Lucia, Queensland 4067, Australia
Phone: 61 733 657244
Fax: 61 733 657579
Publications: The Australian Journal of Politics and History (42338) • Australian Literary Studies (42339) • Journal of Australian Studies (42340) • University of Queensland Law Journal (42341)

The University of Reading
Whiteknights
PO Box 217
Reading RG6 6AH, United Kingdom
Phone: 44 11 89875123
Fax: 44 11 89314404
Publications: Reading (56331)

University of San Carlos
P. del Rosario St.
Cebu City 6000, Philippines
Phone: 63 32 2531000
Fax: 63 32 2554341
Publications: Philippine Quarterly of Culture and Society (49462) • Philippine Scientist (49463)

University of Santo Tomas
Ecclesiastical Publications Office
Espana St.
Manila 1015, Philippines
Phone: 63 2 4061611
Publications: Philippiniana Sacra (49558)

University of Santo Tomas Publishing House
Beato Angelico Bldg.
UST Compound
Espana, Sampaloc
Manila 1008, Philippines
Phone: 63 2 7313101
Fax: 63 2 7313522
Publications: Unitas (49560)

University of Sao Paulo
Av. Dr. Eneas de Carvalho Aguiar, 255
Cerqueira Cesar
05403-000 Sao Paulo, Sao Paulo, Brazil
Phone: 55 113 0696000
Publications: Clinics (43036)

University of Sheffield
School of Mathematics & Statistics
Sheffield S3 7RH, United Kingdom
Phone: 44 11 42223920
Fax: 44 11 42729782
Publications: Advances in Applied Probability (56488) • Journal of Applied Probability (56503) • The Mathematical Scientist (56507) • Mathematical Spectrum (56508)

University of Silesia
12 Bankowa st.
40-007 Katowice, Poland
Publications: Acta Chromatographica (49661)

University of South Africa
PO Box 392
Pretoria 0003, Republic of South Africa
Phone: 27 124 296813
Publications: Africanus (50584) • Communicatio (50586)

University of South Africa
PO Box 392
Muckleneuk
Pretoria 0003, Republic of South Africa
Phone: 27 116 709000
Publications: Freeskier (50591) • Musicus (50597)

University of South Africa
PO Box 392
Pretoria 0003, Republic of South Africa
Phone: 27 11 6520000
Fax: 27 11 6520299
Publications: South African Journal of Labour Relations (50603)

University of South Africa
Sunnyside Campus, Bldg. 12C
PO Box 392
Pretoria 0003, Republic of South Africa
Phone: 27 11 6709000
Publications: De Arte (50588)

University of South Africa
Unisa Press
PO Box 392
Muckleneuk
Pretoria 0003, Republic of South Africa
Phone: 27 11 6709000
Publications: Language Matters (50595)

University of South Australia
PO Box 2471
Adelaide, South Australia 5001, Australia
Phone: 61 883 026611
Fax: 61 883 022466
Publications: Accounting Forum (41498) • International Journal for Educational Integrity (41509)

University of South Bohemia
Jirovcova 24
370 04 Ceske Budejovice, Czech Republic
Phone: 420 387 315181
Fax: 420 387 438389
Publications: Journal of Applied Biomedicine (43606)

University of Southern Denmark
Campusvej 55
DK-5230 Odense, Denmark
Phone: 45 655 01000
Fax: 45 655 01090
Publications: The Journal of Music and Meaning (43729)

University of Stellenbosch
c/o Director - CTPS
Drama Dept.
PO Box X1
Matieland 7602, Republic of South Africa
Phone: 27 218 083216
Fax: 27 218 083086
Publications: SATJ (50553)

University of Stellenbosch
PO Box X1
Stellenbosch 7602, Republic of South Africa
Phone: 27 218 089111
Publications: Per Liguam (50634)

University of Sydney
A20 - John Woolley Bldg.
Sydney, New South Wales 2006, Australia
Phone: 61 293 512222
Publications: Philament (42561)

University of Technology Sydney
PO Box 123
Broadway, New South Wales 2007, Australia
Phone: 61 2 95142000
Publications: African Journal of Information & Communication Technology (41660)

University of Tehran
Kargar Shomali Ave.
PO Box 14155-6445
Tehran 14114, Iran
Phone: 98 21 88634001

Fax: 98 21 88632472
Publications: Iranian Economic Review (45896)

University of Tokushima
2-1 Minamijosanjima-cho
Tokushima 770-8506, Japan
Phone: 81 88 6567103
Publications: Journal of Mathematics (46714) • Social Science Research of University of Tokushima (46716)

University of Tokyo
3-8-1 Komaba
Meguro
Tokyo 153-8914, Japan
Phone: 81 3 54657001
Fax: 81 3 54657011
Publications: Journal of Mathematical Sciences (46923)

University of Tokyo
3-8-1 Komaba
Meguro-ku
Tokyo 153-8902, Japan
Phone: 81 354 546163
Fax: 81 354 546163
Publications: The Japanese Journal of American Studies (46862)

University of Toronto Press-Journal Div.
5201 Dufferin St.
Toronto, ON, Canada M3H 5T8
Phone: 416667-7810
Fax: 416667-7881
Free: 800221-9985
Publications: The Tocqueville Review/La Revue Tocqueville (44085)

University of Tsukuba
Tsukuba-shi
Tennoudai 1-1-1
Ibaraki 305-8571, Japan
Phone: 81 29 8534235
Fax: 81 29 8536201
Publications: Tsukuba Journal of Mathematics (46395)

University of Valencia
Avda. Blasco Ibanez, 13
E-46010 Valencia, Spain
Phone: 34 963 864100
Publications: Anglogermanica online (50842) • Celestinesca (50844)

University of Veterinary and Pharmaceutical Sciences
Palackeho 1-3
612 42 Brno, Czech Republic
Phone: 420 541561111
Publications: Acta Veteriniaria Brno (43601)

University of Warwick
University of Warwick
Coventry CV4 7AL, United Kingdom
Phone: 44 24 76523523
Fax: 44 24 76461606
Publications: Journal of Information, Law & Technology (JILT) (53086)

The University of the West Indies
St. Augustine Campus
Saint Augustine, Trinidad and Tobago
Phone: 868662-2002
Fax: 868663-9684
Publications: The International Journal of Education and Development using Information and Communication Technology (IJEDICT) (42828)

The University of Western Australia
35 Stirling Hwy.
Crawley, Western Australia 6009, Australia
Phone: 61 864 882066
Fax: 61 864 881030
Publications: Outskirts (41820)

University of Wollongong
Northfields Ave.
Wollongong, New South Wales 2522, Australia
Phone: 61 242 213555
Publications: Journal of University Teaching and Learning Practice (JUTLP) (42705)

University of Wolverhampton SU
Wulfruna St.
Wolverhampton WV1 1LY, United Kingdom
Phone: 44 190 2322021

Fax: 44 190 2322020
Publications: Cry Wolf (56952)

Urdd Gobaith Cymru
Swyddfar Urdd
Uned 13 Llys Castan, Parc Menai
Bangor LL57 4FH, United Kingdom
Phone: 44 1248 672100
Fax: 44 1248 672101
Publications: IAW! (52171)

Urological Society of India
c/o Dr. Kim Mammmen
Christian Medical Colorado & Hospital
Sathya Gardens, Saligramam
Ludhiana 141008, Punjab, India
Phone: 91 161 5026999
Fax: 91 161 5010909
Publications: Indian Journal of Urology (45331)

Utillaje Inc.
Apartado Postal 19-467
03910 Mexico City, Federal District, Mexico
Phone: 52 55 55932787
Fax: 52 55 55636542
Publications: Utillaje (47790)

UTK Media
Frauenfelderstr. 49
CH-8370 Sirnach, Switzerland
Phone: 41 719 666080
Fax: 41 719 666081
Publications: Professional Computing (51231)

Utusan Melayu (M) Bhd
46 M, Jalan Lima Off
Jalan Chan Sow Lin
55200 Kuala Lumpur, Malaysia
Phone: 60 3 92217055
Fax: 60 3 92227876
Publications: Al-Islam (47596) • Harmoni (47603) • i-Sihat (47604) • Kosmo! (47610) • Mangga (47624) • Mastika (47626) • Mingguan Malaysia (47628) • Pemikir (47632) • Saji (47634) • URTV (47638) • Utusan Malaysia (47639) • Utusan Melayu Mingguan (47640) • Wanita (47641)

Valencia Maritima
Dr. J.J. Domine, 5 1-1a
E-46011 Valencia, Spain
Phone: 34 963 164515
Fax: 34 963 678555
Publications: Valencia Maritima (50847)

Valkea Media
ul. Elblaska 15/17
PL-01-747 Warsaw, Poland
Phone: 48 22 6398567
Fax: 48 22 6398569
Publications: Warsaw Insider (49775)

Valmonde & Cie
6 rue d'Uzes
F-75081 Paris, France
Phone: 33 14233 2184
Publications: Revue des Deux Mondes (44079)

Variant
1/2 189b Maryhill Rd.
Glasgow G20 7XJ, United Kingdom
Phone: 44 141 3339522
Publications: Variant (53457)

Vathek Publishing
Bridge House
Dalby
Isle of Man IM5 3BP, United Kingdom
Phone: 44 16 24844056
Fax: 44 16 24845043
Publications: Common Law World Review (53663) • Environmental Law Review (55669) • International Journal of Evidence and Proof (55761) • International Journal of Police Science and Management (53370) • The Police Journal (53664)

VCO Verkehrsclub Osterreich
Braeuhausgasse 7-9
A-1050 Vienna, Austria
Phone: 43 1 8932697
Fax: 43 1 8932431
Publications: VCO Magazin (42773)

V.D. Padmanaban
Indian Veterinary Association

New No. 11 , Old No. 7, Chamiers Rd.
Nandanam
Madras 600 035, Tamil Nadu, India
Phone: 91 444 351006
Fax: 91 444 338894
Publications: Indian Veterinary Journal (45334)

VDI Verlag
VDI-Platz 1
D-40468 Dusseldorf, Germany
Phone: 49 211 61880
Fax: 49 211 6188112
Publications: VDI Nachrichten (44335)

Vecherny Minskt
44 Skorina Ave.
220805 Minsk, Belarus
Phone: 375 172 335044
Publications: Vecherny Minskt (42833)

Veetech Ltd.
7A Barclays Venture Center
University of Warwick Science Pk.
Sir William Lyons Rd.
Coventry CV4 7EZ, United Kingdom
Phone: 44 24 1189477231
Fax: 44 24 1189477223
Publications: The International Journal of Ventilation (53085)

Vegan Society - England
Donald Watson House
21 Hylton St.
Birmingham B18 6HJ, United Kingdom
Phone: 44 121 5231730
Fax: 44 121 5231749
Publications: The Vegan (52372)

Vegan Society of Finland
Hameentie 48
FIN-00500 Helsinki, Finland
Phone: 358 50 3449524
Fax: 358 97 732328
Publications: Vegaia (43864)

Vegetarian Society of the United Kingdom
Parkdale
Dunham Rd.
Altrincham WA14 4QG, United Kingdom
Phone: 44 161 9252000
Fax: 44 161 9269182
Publications: The Vegetarian (52104)

Venezuelan Association for the Advancement of Science
Colinas de Bello Monte Av. Neveri
Edificio: Fundavac-Asovac Aptdo.
Caracas 47286, Venezuela
Phone: 58 212 7531002
Fax: 58 212 7511420
Publications: Acta Cientifica Venezolana (57020)

Verlag Coating Thomas & Co.
Schmiedgasse 5
Postfach 1762
CH-9001 Saint Gallen, Switzerland
Phone: 41 712 282011
Fax: 41 712 282014
Publications: Coating (51223)

Verlag Lebensmittelindustrie
Spielhof 14A
CH-8750 Glarus, Switzerland
Phone: 41 556 453750
Fax: 41 556 402171
Publications: Lebensmittel Industrie (51176)

Verlag Natur & Heilen
Nikolaistr. 5
D-80802 Munich, Germany
Phone: 49 89 38015910
Fax: 49 89 38015916
Publications: Natur & Heilen (44575)

Verlag Pro Senectute Schweiz
Lavaterstr. 60
CH-8027 Zurich, Switzerland
Phone: 49 44 2838989
Fax: 49 44 2838980
Publications: Zeitlupe (51297)

Verlag Schweizer Jager
Postfach 261
CH-8840 Einsiedeln, Switzerland

Phone: 41 55 4184343
Fax: 41 55 4184344
Publications: Schweizer Jager (51086)

Verlagsgemeinschaft Viscom/St. Galler Tagblatt AG
Furstenlandstr. 122
CH-9001 Saint Gallen, Switzerland
Phone: 41 71 2727248
Fax: 41 71 2727487
Publications: Viscom (51225)

Verlagsgenossenschaft Caprovis
Industriestr. 9
Postfach 2
CH-3362 Niederonz, Switzerland
Phone: 41 62 9566874
Fax: 41 62 9566879
Publications: Forum Kleinwiederkaeuer (51219)

Verlagsgruppe Handelsblatt GmbH
Kasernenstr. 67
D-40213 Dusseldorf, Germany
Phone: 49 211 8870
Fax: 49 211 8872980
Publications: Schmalenbach Business Review (44333)

Verlagsgruppe Rhein Main
Erich-Dombrowski-Strasse 2
D-55127 Mainz, Germany
Phone: 49 613 1484950
Fax: 49 613 1484933
Publications: Tobacco Journal International (44546)

Versita
Solipska 14A/1 St.
PL-02-482 Warsaw, Poland
Phone: 48 22 7015015
Fax: 48 22 4335126
Publications: Acta Geophysica (49679) • Acta Zoologica Lituanica (49683) • Advances in Cell Biology (49684) • Advances in Cognitive Psychology (49685) • Advances in Materials Science (49686) • Advances in Medical Sciences (49687) • Advances in Rehabilitation (49688) • Annals of Warsaw University of Life Sciences, Land Reclamation (49689) • Anthropological Review (49690) • Archives of Industrial Hygiene and Toxicology (49691) • Archives of Polish Fisheries (49692) • Artificial Satellites (49693) • Balkan Journal of Medical Genetics (49694) • Baltic Journal of Law & Politics (49695) • Biologija (49696) • Biomedical Human Kinetics (49697) • Central European Journal of Chemistry (49699) • Central European Journal of Geosciences (49700) • Central European Journal of Mathematics (49701) • Central European Journal of Physics (49702) • Chemical Papers (49703) • Ecological Questions (49706) • Economics and Organization of Enterprise (49707) • Ekologija (49708) • European Countryside (49709) • Folia Oeconomica Stetinensia (49711) • Formalized Mathematics (49712) • Geodesy and Cartography (49713) • Geologija (49714) • Hacquetia (49715) • Human Movement (49717) • International Journal of Applied Mathematics and Computer Science (49719) • International Journal of Strategic Property Management (49720) • Issues of Business and Law (49721) • Journal of Human Kinetics (49722) • Journal of Konbin (49723) • Journal of Medical Biochemistry (49724) • Journal of Plant Protection Research (49725) • Journal of Teacher Education for Sustainability (49726) • Journal of Water and Land Development (49728) • Latvian Journal of Physics and Technical Sciences (49730) • Limes (49731) • Linguistica Pragensia (49732) • Lodz Papers in Pragmatics (49733) • Macedonian Journal of Medical Sciences (49734) • Mathematica Slovaca (49736) • Medicina Sportiva (49737) • Mineralogia (49738) • Oceanological and Hydrobiological Studies (49740) • Old and New Concepts of Physics (49741) • Opto-Electronics Review (49742) • Organizacija (49743) • Paladyn (49744) • Philologia (49746) • Physical Education and Sport (49747) • Polish Journal of Chemical Technology (49748) • Polish Journal of Medical Physics and Engineering (49749) • Polish Journal of Natural Sciences (49750) • Polish Journal of Surgery (49751) • Polish Maritime Research (49752) • Polish Psychological Bulletin (49754) • Poznan Studies in Contemporary Linguistics (49756) • Psychology of Language and Communication (49761) • Radiology and Oncology (49762) • Ring (49763) • South East European Journal of Economics and Business (49765) • Town Planning and Architecture

(49767) • Vestnik Zoologii (49773) • Zoologica Polo-niae (49776)

Veterinary Business Development Ltd.
Olympus House
Werrington Center
Peterborough PE4 6NA, United Kingdom
Phone: 44 1733 325522
Fax: 44 1733 352512
Publications: Veterinary Times (56263)

Via Medica
ul. Swietokrzyska 73
PL-80-180 Gdansk, Poland
Phone: 48 58 3209494
Fax: 48 58 3209460
Publications: Acta Angiologica (49652) • Advances in Palliative Medicine (49653) • Annales Academiae Medicae Silesiensis (49781) • Arterial Hypertension (49655) • Cardiovascular Forum (49669) • Endocrinology, Obesity and Metabolic Disorders (49656) • Experimental and Clinical Diabetology (49782) • Folia Morphologica (49657) • Interdisciplinary Problems of Stroke (49779) • Nuclear Medicine Review (49658) • Nursing Topics (49659) • Polish Gerontology (49668) • Polish Journal of Endocrinology (49783) • Polish Pneumology and Allergology (49753) • Polish Sexology (49755) • Polish Surgery (49662) • Psychiatry in General Practice (49654) • Psychooncology (49660) • Suicidology (49766)

Victim Support
Hallam House
56-60 Hallam St.
London W1W 6JL, United Kingdom
Phone: 44 20 72680200
Fax: 44 20 72680210
Publications: Victim Support (55369)

Victoria University
PO Box 14428
Melbourne, Victoria 8001, Australia
Phone: 61 3 99194333
Fax: 61 3 99194901
Publications: Asian Review of Accounting (42047)

Victorian Military Society
PO Box 5837
Newbury RG14 7FJ, United Kingdom
Publications: Soldiers of the Queen (55662)

Vida Rotaria
Calle Cordoba 954
Oficinas 24
S2000AWL Rosario, Argentina
Phone: 54 341 5300057
Fax: 54 341 5300058
Publications: Vida Rotaria (41488)

Vidyajyoti College of Theology
4-A, Raj Niwas Marg
Delhi 110054, Delhi, India
Phone: 91 11 23943556
Publications: Ave (45088) • Tattvaviveka (45105) • Vachan Sudha (45108) • Vidyajyoti Journal of Theological Reflection (45109)

Vienna University of Economics and Business Administration
Augasse 2-6
A-1090 Vienna, Austria
Phone: 43 1 313364310
Fax: 43 1 31336752
Publications: Transfer Werbeforschung & Praxis (42771)

Vietnam Investment Review Ltd.
47 Quan Thanh Str., Ba Dinh Dist.
Hanoi, Vietnam
Phone: 84 4 3845 0537
Fax: 84 4 3845 7937
Publications: Vietnam Investment Review (57054)

Vintage Austin Register Ltd.
The Briars
Wingfield Rd.
Oakerthorpe
Alfreton DE55 7LH, United Kingdom
Phone: 44 173 3831646
Publications: Vintage Austin Magazine (52100)

Violet Needham Society
Blunsden, Faringdon Rd.

Abingdon OX14 1BQ, United Kingdom
Publications: Souvenir (52062)

Vision International Publishing Co.
10F-3/5, No. 2 Fuxing North Rd.
Taipei, Taiwan
Phone: 886 2 7115403
Fax: 886 2 7212790
Publications: Travel in Taiwan (51367)

Visitcrest Ltd.
PO Box 380
Harrow HA2 6LL, United Kingdom
Phone: 44 20 88638586
Fax: 44 20 88639370
Publications: The Muslim News (53526)

Visor Distribuciones
Tomas Breton, 66
E-28045 Madrid, Spain
Phone: 34 914681102
Fax: 34 914681098
Publications: La Balsa de la Medusa (50777)

S. Viswanathan
S-15, Industrial Estate, Guindy
Chennai 600 032, Tamil Nadu, India
Phone: 91 442 342248
Fax: 91 442 349382
Publications: Industrial Economist (45041)

Vit Kabourek
Sokolska 3923
CZ-760 01 Zlin, Czech Republic
Phone: 420 577 437870
Fax: 420 577 437870
Publications: Folia Heyrovskyana (43642)

Vitesse Media
Octavia House
50 Banner St.
London EC1Y 8ST, United Kingdom
Phone: 44 20 72507010
Fax: 44 20 72507011
Publications: The AIM Guide (53929) • Business XL (54160) • Growth Company Investor (54524)

Vivekananda Kendra Prakashan Trust
5 Singarachari St.
Triplicane
Chennai 600 005, Tamil Nadu, India
Phone: 91 442 8440042
Fax: 91 442 8442960
Publications: Vivekananda Kendra Patrika (45061) • Yuva Bharati (45062)

Vladivostok Novosti Ltd.
13 Narodny Prospect
690014 Vladivostok, Russia
Phone: 7 423 2415590
Fax: 7 423 2415615
Publications: Vladivostok News (50041)

VNU Business Media S.A.
Rte. des Acacias 25
PO Box 1355
CH-1211 Geneva 26, Switzerland
Phone: 41 22 3077837
Fax: 41 22 3003748
Publications: Europa Star (51092)

VNU Business Publications Italia
Via. Gorki 69
I-20092 Cinisello Balsamo, Italy
Phone: 39 556 60341
Fax: 39 556 6034238
Publications: RMO—Rivista di Meccanica Oggi (46134)

Vogel Verlag und Druck GmbH & Company KG
Max-Planck-Str. 7/9
D-97082 Wurzburg, Germany
Phone: 49 931 4180
Fax: 49 931 4182100
Publications: CHIP (44717) • MM Industrial Magazine Western Europe (44722) • MM Maschinenmarkt (44723) • Process (44724)

Vogt-Schild/Habegger Media
Zuchwilerstr. 21
PO Box 716
CH-4501 Solothurn, Switzerland
Phone: 41 326 247111
Fax: 41 326 247444
Publications: Schweizer Waffen-Magazin (51232)

Vorarlberger Gebietskrankenkasse
Gebietskrankenkasse
Jahngasse 4
A-6850 Dornbirn, Austria
Phone: 43 50 84551111
Fax: 43 50 84551040
Publications: Forum Gesundheit Vorarlberg (42723)

VRL Publishing
The Colonnades
34 Porchester Rd.
London W2 6ES, United Kingdom
Phone: 44 20 75635600
Fax: 44 20 75635601
Publications: Leasing Life (54861)

Vulture Study Group
Private Bag X11
Parkview 2122, Republic of South Africa
Phone: 27 11 6468617
Fax: 27 11 4861506
Publications: Vulture News (50563)

W & V Werben & Verkaufen
Hultschiner Strasse 8
81677 Munich, Germany
Phone: 49 89 21837999
Publications: W & V Werben & Verkaufen (44586)

Wadhera Publications
General Assurance Bldg., 1st Fl.
232 D.N. Rd.
Mumbai 400 001, Maharashtra, India
Publications: Indian Cement Review (45375) • Soaps, Detergents & Toiletries Review (45440)

Wairarapa Times-Age Company Ltd.
Cor. Chapel & Perry St.
PO Box 445
Masterton, New Zealand
Phone: 64 637 89999
Fax: 64 637 82371
Publications: Wairarapa Times-Age (48937)

Wanderlust Magazine
PO Box 1832
Windsor SL4 1YT, United Kingdom
Phone: 44 1753 620426
Fax: 44 1753 620474
Publications: Wanderlust (56933)

Wanganui Newspapers
59 Taupo Quay
PO Box 433
Wanganui, New Zealand
Phone: 64 646 3490710
Fax: 64 646 3490721
Publications: Wanganui Chronicle (48996)

WARC Ltd.
85 Newman St.
London W1T 3EX, United Kingdom
Phone: 44 20 74678100
Publications: Admap (53902) • International Journal of Advertising (54632) • International Journal of Market Research (54653)

Warners Group Publications plc
The Maltings
West St.
Bourne PE10 9PH, United Kingdom
Phone: 44 1778 391000
Publications: Caravan, Motorhome & Camping Mart (52409)

Warragul Gazette
97-103 Queen St.
PO Box 305
Warragul, Victoria 3820, Australia
Phone: 61 356 235666
Fax: 61 356 232367
Publications: Warragul & Drovin Gazette (42685)

Warsaw School of Social Psychology
ul. Chodakowska 19/31
03-815 Warsaw, Poland
Publications: Scalable Computing (49764)

Waterford News & Star
25 Michael St.
Waterford, Waterford, Ireland
Phone: 353 518 74951
Fax: 353 518 55281
Publications: Waterford News & Star (46063)

Waterford Today
36 Mayor's Walk
Waterford City, Waterford, Ireland
Phone: 353 51 854135
Fax: 353 51 854140
Publications: Waterford Today (46065)

WAVE Network & European Info Centre Against Violence
Bacherplatz 10-4
A-1050 Vienna, Austria
Phone: 43 154 82720
Fax: 43 154 82720
Publications: Fempower (42758)

The Week
30 Cleveland St.
London WIT 4JT, United Kingdom
Phone: 44 20 79076180
Fax: 44 20 79850052
Publications: The Week (55396)

The Weir Group PLC
Clydesdale Bank Exchange
20 Waterloo St.
Glasgow G2 6DB, United Kingdom
Phone: 44 141 6377111
Fax: 44 141 2219789
Publications: Weir Bulletin (53458)

WEKA Fachzeitschriften Verlag GmbH
Gruber Strasse 46A
D-85586 Kissing, Germany
Phone: 49 812 1950
Publications: Elektronik (44509)

Welsh Music Guild
71 Broad St.
Vale of Glamorgan
Barry CF62 7AG, United Kingdom
Publications: Welsh Music (53885)

Welsh Secondary Schools Association
124 Walter Rd.
Swansea SA1 5RF, United Kingdom
Phone: 44 17 92455933
Fax: 44 17 92455944
Publications: Pulse (56706)

Werk, Bauen und Wohnen
Talstrasse, 39
CH-8001 Zurich, Switzerland
Phone: 41 102 181430
Fax: 41 102 181434
Publications: Werk, Bauen und Wohnen (51296)

Werner Publishing Company Ltd.
PO Box 5134
1211 Geneva 11, Switzerland
Phone: 41 22 3103422
Fax: 41 22 3114592
Publications: The Journal of World Investment and Trade (51152)

West Country Publications Ltd.
17 Brest Rd.
Derriford Business Pk.
Plymouth PL6 5AA, United Kingdom
Phone: 44 17 52765500
Publications: Western Morning News (56276)

Westburn Publishers Ltd.
23 Millig St.
Helensburgh
Argyll G84 9LD, United Kingdom
Phone: 44 1436 678699
Fax: 44 1436 670328
Publications: Journal of Customer Behaviour (52129) • Journal of Marketing Management (52130) • The Marketing Review (52131)

Westcountry Publications Ltd.
Harmsworth House
Barton Hill Rd.
Torquay TQ2 8JN, United Kingdom
Phone: 44 1803 676000
Publications: Herald Express (Torquay) (56757)

Western Academic & Specialist Press Limited
PO Box 191
Liverpool L23 3WZ, United Kingdom
Phone: 44 15 19321312
Publications: Before Farming, the Archaeology and Anthropology of Hunter-Gatherers (53868)

Western Cape Department of Agriculture
PO Box X1
Elsenburg 7607, Republic of South Africa
Phone: 27 218 085111
Fax: 27 218 085120
Publications: Agriprobe (50477)

Western Indian Ocean Marine Science Association
Mizingani St., House No. 13644/10
PO Box 3298
Zanzibar, United Republic of Tanzania
Phone: 255 24 2233472
Fax: 255 24 2233852
Publications: Western Indian Ocean Journal of Marine Science (51409)

Westwick-Farrow Publishing
Locked Bag 1289
Wahroonga, New South Wales 2076, Australia
Phone: 61 2 94872700
Fax: 61 2 94891265
Publications: Electrical Solutions (42672) • Industrial Workwear Solutions (42673) • InMotion (42674) • Radio Comms Asia-Pacific (42675) • Safety Solutions (42676) • Sustainability Matters (42677) • Voice&Data (42678) • What's New in Electronics (42679) • What's New in Food Technology and Manufacturing (42680) • What's New in LAB Technology (42681) • What's New in Process Technology (42682)

Wharncliffe Publishing Ltd.
47 Church St.
Barnsley S70 2AS, United Kingdom
Phone: 44 1226 734639
Fax: 44 1226 734478
Publications: The Main Event Magazine (52182)

Wharncliffe Publishing Ltd.
47 Church St.
South Yorkshire
Barnsley S70 2AS, United Kingdom
Phone: 44 1226 734639
Fax: 44 1226 734478
Publications: Assistive Technologies (52177) • Caring UK (52178) • Destination UK (52179) • Future Fitness (52180) • Horse Health Magazine (52181) • Out on a Limb (52183) • Wedding Professional (52184) • Work-Out Ireland (52185) • WorkOut UK (52186)

Whitehouse Publishing
1 The Lynch
Mere BA12 6DQ, United Kingdom
Phone: 44 1747 860168
Fax: 44 1747 860168
Publications: Advances in Clinical Neuroscience & Rehabilitation (55609)

Wichtig Editore Srl
Via Friuli 72
20135 Milan, Italy
Phone: 39 255 195443
Fax: 39 255 195971
Publications: European Journal of Ophthalmology (46169) • International Journal of Artificial Organs (46120) • International Journal of Biological Markers (46176) • Journal of Applied Biomaterials & Biomechanics (46181) • The Journal of Vascular Access (46184)

Wieler Revue b.v.
Postbus 5070
NL-9700 GB Groningen, Netherlands
Phone: 31 505 445830
Publications: Wieler Revue (48604)

Wijeya Newspapers Ltd.
No. 8, Hunupitiya Cross Rd.
Colombo 02, Sri Lanka
Publications: Daily Mirror (50852) • Lanka Woman (50861) • The Sunday Times (50873)

Wilbury & Claymore
PO Box 2177
Pinegowrie 2123, Republic of South Africa
Phone: 27 117 874696
Fax: 27 117 871819
Publications: LMS—Laboratory Marketing Spectrum (50572)

Wild Places Publishing
PO Box 100
Abergavenny NP7 9WY, United Kingdom
Publications: Descent (51687)

Wildfire Communications Ltd.
Unit 2.4 Paintworks
Arnos Vale
Totterdown
Bristol BS4 3EN, United Kingdom
Phone: 44 117 9029977
Fax: 44 117 9029978
Publications: Imagine Magazine (52675) • Irish Dancing & Culture (52681) • University Caterer (52734)

Wildlife and Environment Society of South Africa
1 Karkloof Rd.
PO Box 394
Howick 3290, Republic of South Africa
Phone: 27 33 3303931
Fax: 27 33 3304576
Publications: African Wildlife (50525)

Wildlife Preservation Society of Queensland
95 William St.
Brisbane, Queensland 4000, Australia
Phone: 61 7 32210194
Fax: 61 7 32210701
Publications: Wildlife Australia (41654)

Wiley InterScience
111 River St.
Hoboken, NJ 07030-5774
Phone: 201748-6000
Fax: 201748-6088
Publications: HPB (55978)

John Wiley & Sons (Asia) Private Ltd.
2 Clementi Loop, No. 02-01
Singapore 129809, Singapore
Phone: 65 646 32400
Fax: 65 646 34605
Publications: Clinical Oral Implants Research (43291) • Congenital Anomalies (46683) • Fisheries Science (46825)

John Wiley & Sons Inc.
350 Main St., Commerce Pl.
Malden, MA 02148-5089
Phone: 781388-8200
Fax: 781388-8210
Publications: Acta Paediatrica (51002) • Addiction (53900) • Africa Confidential (53916) • Agricultural and Forest Entomology (55626) • Allergology International (46732) • Biological Reviews (52792) • The Clinical Respiratory Journal (43659) • Entomologia Experimentalis et Applicata (47967) • Geostandards & Geoanalytical Research (55636) • Insect Conservation and Diversity (52139) • Journal of Flood Risk Management (53574) • Journal of Nursing and Healthcare of Chronic Illness (56054) • Literacy (45938) • Oikos (50988) • Oxford Journal of Archaeology (56134) • Oxford Today (56137) • Polar Research (49214) • Proceedings of the Aristotelian Society (55125) • Reproduction in Domestic Animals (50977) • Statistica Neerlandica (48752) • Tijdschrift voor economische en sociale geografie (48766) • Weed Biology and Management (46333)

John Wiley & Sons Inc.
111 River St.
Hoboken, NJ 07030-5774
Phone: 201748-6000
Fax: 201748-6088
Free: 800825-7550
Publications: Advanced Synthesis & Catalysis (44631) • Aquatic Conservation (53251) • Archiv der Pharmazie (44358) • Asia-Pacific Journal of Chemical Engineering (42243) • Astronomische Nachrichten (44638) • Atmospheric Science Letters (53347) • Berichte zur Wissenschaftsgeschichte (44535) • BioEssays (44701) • Biometrical Journal (51255) • Business Strategy and the Environment (43286) • Chemkon - Chemie konkret, Forum fuer Unterricht und Didaktik (44623) • Chinese Journal of Chemistry (43470) • Comparative and Functional Genomics (55548) • Contrast Media & Molecular Imaging (46270) • Crystal Research and Technology (44168) • Deutsche Entomologische Zeitschrift (44171) • Diabetes/Metabolism Research and Reviews (46227) • Drug Testing and Analysis (44292) • Dyslexia (56897) • Ecohydrology (42250) • Environmental Toxicology (41557) • European Transactions on Telecommunications (46170) • Feddes Repertorium (44179) • Forschungsberichte aus

Technik und Naturwissenschaften (44432) • Fortschritte der Physik/Progress of Physics (44561) • Fossil Record (44184) • GAMM - Mitteilungen (44338) • Genes, Chromosomes & Cancer (50985) • Geomechanics and Tunnelling (42740) • german research (44262) • Hydrological Processes (52674) • International Journal for Numerical Methods in Fluids (52344) • International Journal of Satellite Communications and Networking (53491) • Journal of Basic Microbiology (44489) • Journal of Community & Applied Social Psychology (48761) • Journal of Investigative Psychology and Offender Profiling (53621) • The Journal of Multi-Criteria Decision Analysis (56899) • Land Degradation & Development (56703) • Laser Technik Journal (44217) • Mathematische Nachrichten (44644) • Microscopy and Analysis (53014) • MLQ - Mathematical Logic Quarterly (44405) • NMR in Biomedicine (55006) • Particle and Particle Systems Characterization (44632) • Personality and Mental Health (53439) • physica status solidi (a) (44379) • physica status solidi (b) (44380) • physica status solidi (c) (44381) • Practical Diabetes International (56293) • Review of Behavioral Finance (53773) • Spectroscopy Asia (53017) • Starch/Staerke (44708) • Structural Control and Health Monitoring (46211) • ZAAC - Zeitschrift fur anorganische und allgemeine Chemie (44237) • ZAMM - Zeitschrift fur Angewandte Mathematik und Mechanik (44650)

John Wiley & Sons Inc.
9600 Garsington Rd.
Oxford OX4 2DQ, United Kingdom
Phone: 44 1865 776868
Fax: 44 1865 714591
Publications: Abacus (55857) • Accounting and Finance (55858) • Acta Anaesthesiologica Scandinavica (49215) • Acta Archaeologica (43654) • Acta Biochimica et Biophysica Sinica (55859) • Acta Crystallographica Section A (51246) • Acta Crystallographica Section B (51247) • Acta Crystallographica Section C (51248) • Acta Crystallographica Section D (51249) • Acta Crystallographica Section F (51250) • Acta Neurologica Scandanavica (50955) • Acta Neuropsychiatrica (42329) • Acta Ophthalmologica (44896) • Acta Psychiatrica Scandinavica (43643) • Acta Zoologica (51049) • Addiction Biology (44547) • Africa Research Bulletin (53345) • Africa Research Bulletin (53346) • African Journal of Ecology (51585) • Agricultural Economics (55861) • Agricultural and Forest Entomology (56242) • Allergy (55862) • American Business Law Journal (55864) • Anaesthesia (55866) • Anatomia, Histologia, Embryologia (44549) • Andrologia (44383) • Animal Science Journal (55867) • Annals of Public and Cooperative Economics (55869) • Anthropology Today (53955) • ANZ Journal of Surgery (42300) • APMIS (43655) • Aquaculture Nutrition (49190) • Arabian Archaeology and Epigraphy (42448) • Archaeometry (55871) • Area (55873) • Art History (55874) • Asia-Pacific Journal of Clinical Oncology (55875) • Astronomy and Geophysics (53756) • Austral Ecology (41501) • Australian Economic History Review (41503) • Australian Economic Review (55876) • Australian Endodontic Journal (55877) • The Australian Journal of Agricultural and Resource Economics (55878) • Australian & New Zealand Journal of Statistics (48963) • Australian Occupational Therapy Journal (42302) • Autonomic and Autacoid Pharmacology (52924) • Basic & Clinical Pharmacology & Toxicology (43726) • Bioethics (55880) • BJIR: British Journal of Industrial Relations (55884) • BJOG (55885) • BloodMed (55886) • Boreas (43645) • British Journal of Management (55894) • Bulletin of Economic Research (55897) • Business Ethics (55898) • Business and Society Review (55899) • Business Strategy Review (54159) • Canadian Journal of Agricultural Economics (55901) • Cancer Science (55903) • Cell Proliferation (54192) • Cephalalgia (52570) • Child (55907) • Child and Family Social Work (52336) • Children & Society (54205) • Clinical & Experimental Allergy (53793) • Clinical and Experimental Allergy Reviews (54221) • Clinical & Experimental Dermatology (54222) • Clinical and Experimental Optometry (55911) • Clinical Physiology and Functional Imaging (50991) • The Clinical Teacher (55912) • Coloration Technology (52443) • Communication Theory (55913) • Contact Dermatitis (54261) • Critical Quarterly (55918) • Decision Sciences Journal of Innovative Education (55923) • Diabetic Medicine (55926) • Dialectica (55927) • Ecological Management & Restoration (42713) • The Economic History Review (55928) • Economic Inquiry (55929) • The Economic Journal (55930) • The Economic Record (55931) • Economica (55932) • Educational Measurement (55933) • Family Court Review (55951) • Fatigue & Fracture of Engineering Materials & Structures (56492) • FEBS Journal (52820) • FEMS Immunology and Medical Microbiology (55954) • FEMS Microbiology Reviews (55955) • FEMS Yeast Research (55956) • Financial Accountability and Management (55957) • Fiscal Studies (55958) • Foreign Policy Analysis (55959) • Geographical Journal (55963) • Geographical Research (42251) • Geriatrics & Gerontology International (55964) • Global Networks (Oxford) (55966) • Government and Opposition (52610) • Grassland Science (55968) • Ground Water (55969) • Ground Water Monitoring & Remediation (55970) • Historical Research (54558) • History (55973) • History Compass (55974) • History and Theory (55975) • The Howard Journal of Criminal Justice (55977) • Human Resource Management Journal (55980) • Industrial Relations Journal (55988) • infocus Magazine (55989) • Insect Science (55990) • International Journal of Economic Theory (55994) • International Journal of Evidence-based Healthcare (55995) • International Journal of Nursing Terminologies and Classifications (55999) • International Journal of Older People Nursing (56000) • International Journal of Rheumatic Diseases (56003) • International Journal of Urban and Regional Research (56004) • International Social Science Journal (44060) • International Studies Quarterly (56007) • The Japanese Economic Review (56008) • JCMS: Journal of Common Market Studies (56010) • Journal of Advanced Transportation (56011) • Journal of the American Ceramic Society (56013) • Journal of Applied Corporate Finance (56015) • Journal of Architectural Education (56016) • Journal of Business Finance and Accounting (56019) • Journal of Child and Adolescent Psychiatric Nursing (56020) • Journal of Communication (56021) • Journal of Computer-Mediated Communication (56023) • The Journal of Ecology (54741) • Journal of Educational Measurement (56027) • Journal of Eukaryotic Microbiology (56030) • Journal of the European Academy of Dermatology and Venereology (44016) • Journal of Finance (56033) • Journal of Food Processing and Preservation (56035) • Journal of Gastroenterology and Hepatology (42303) • Journal of Historical Sociology (56038) • Journal of Human Nutrition and Dietetics (53540) • Journal of Industrial Economics (56041) • Journal of Integrative Plant Biology (56043) • Journal of Intellectual Disability Research (JIDR) (52856) • Journal of International Financial Management & Accounting (56045) • Journal of Law and Society (56048) • Journal of Legal Studies Education (56049) • Journal of Management Studies (56050) • Journal of Neuroendocrinology (48890) • Journal of Nursing Management (56055) • Journal of Oral Rehabilitation (43647) • Journal of Paediatrics and Child Health (56056) • Journal of Periodontal Research (46624) • Journal of Personality (56057) • Journal of Philosophy of Education (54798) • Journal of Phytopathology (56058) • Journal of Policy and Practice in Intellectual Disabilities (56060) • The Journal of Political Philosophy (56061) • Journal of Psychiatric and Mental Health Nursing (53769) • Journal of Public Economic Theory (56063) • Journal of Regional Science (56066) • Journal of Religious History (42529) • Journal of Research in Reading (53087) • The Journal of Research in Special Educational Needs (55712) • Journal of the Royal Statistical Society (56069) • Journal of the Royal Statistical Society (56067) • Journal of the Royal Statistical Society (56068) • Journal of School Health (56070) • Journal of Sexual Medicine (56072) • Journal of Sleep Research (56073) • Journal of Sociolinguistics (48800) • Journal of Supply Chain Management (56074) • Journal of Urban Affairs (56077) • Journal of Veterinary Emergency and Critical Care (56078) • Journal of Viral Hepatitis (54832) • The Journal of World Intellectual Property (56079) • Journal of Zoological Systematics and Evolutionary Research (44630) • KYKLOS (56082) • Law & Policy (56086) • Learning in Health and Social Care (56088) • Literature Compass (56090) • Mammal Review (52703) • Management and Organization Review (56092) • The Manchester School (56093) • Marine Ecology (46156) • Maternal and Child Nutrition (56304) • Medical and Veterinary Entomology (52959) • Metaphilosophy (56097) • Metroeconomica (42725) • Midwest Studies in Philosophy (56099) • The Milbank Quarterly (56100) • Mind & Language (56101) • The Modern Language Journal (56102) • The Modern Law Review (56103) • Modern Theology (56104) • Molecular Ecology (56106) • Molecular Ecology Resources (56107) • Molecular Oral Microbiology (56108) • Monthly Notices of the Royal Astronomical Society (56109) • Museum International (56110) • Music Analysis (56111) • Mycoses (44574) • Natural Resources Forum (56112) • Nephrology (42304) • Neuromodulation (56114) • Neuropathology (56115) • Neuropathology and Applied Neurobiology (56116) • New Blackfriars (53303) • New Perspectives Quarterly (56118) • New Technology, Work and Employment (56625) • New Zealand Geographer (56119) • Nursing and Health Sciences (56122) • Nursing Philosophy (56123) • Nutrition Bulletin (56124) • Obesity Reviews (56125) • Oil and Energy Trends (56126) • OPEC Energy Review (56127) • Oral Diseases (43693) • Orbis Litterarum (43731) • Oxford Bulletin of Economics & Statistics (56131) • Pacific Philosophical Quarterly (56139) • Paediatric and Perinatal Epidemiology (52714) • Palaeontology (56140) • Parasite Immunology (52586) • Pathology International (56143) • Peace & Change (56144) • Pediatric Allergy and Immunology (56145) • Pediatric Anesthesia (56146) • Pediatric Dermatology (56147) • Pediatrics International (56148) • Periodontology 2000 (56149) • Personnel Psychology (56150) • Perspectives in Psychiatric Care (56151) • Perspectives on Psychological Science (56152) • The Philosophical Forum (56154) • Philosophical Investigations (56705) • The Philosophical Quarterly (56155) • Photodermatology, Photoimmunology and Photomedicine (56156) • Phycological Research (46436) • Physiologia Plantarum (50989) • Physiological Entomology (56157) • Pigment Cell and Melanoma Research (56158) • Plant Biotechnology Journal (52719) • Plant Breeding (56159) • Plant Species Biology (56161) • Poe Studies/Dark Romanticism (56163) • The Political Quarterly (56165) • Political Studies (56166) • Political Studies Review (56167) • Politics (53440) • The Professional Geographer (56169) • Psychogeriatrics (56173) • Psychological Science in the Public Interest (56174) • Psychology of Women Quarterly (56175) • Public Administration (56176) • Public Health Nursing (56177) • R & D Management (56184) • Ratio (56330) • Ratio Juris (56186) • Restoration Ecology (56188) • Review of Development Economics (56189) • The Review of Economic Studies (56190) • The Review of Income and Wealth (56192) • Review of International Economics (56193) • Review of Policy Research (56194) • Review of Urban & Regional Development Studies (56195) • Risk Management & Insurance Review (56196) • The Russian Review (56197) • Scandinavian Journal of Caring Sciences (56198) • The Scandinavian Journal of Economics (56199) • Scandinavian Journal of Immunology (49191) • Scandinavian Journal of Medicine and Science in Sports (43682) • Scandinavian Journal of Psychology (50978) • Scandinavian Journal of Statistics (43868) • Scandinavian Political Studies (56200) • Sedimentology (56578) • Significance (56203) • Singapore Journal of Tropical Geography (56204) • Sleep and Biological Rhythm (56205) • Social Anthropology (56207) • The Sociological Quarterly (56209) • The Sociological Review (56210) • Sociology of Health & Illness (56211) • South African Journal of Economics (56212) • Strain (44776) • Teaching Statistics (56213) • Teaching Theology and Religion (56214) • Tellus (51042) • Tellus (51043) • Tissue Antigens (42232) • Transactions of the Institute of British Geographers (56219) • Transboundary and Emerging Diseases (56220) • Transfusion Medicine (56221) • Transplant International (56222) • Transplant International (42772) • Tropical Medicine and International Health (56223) • Veterinary Anaesthesia and Analgesia (56225) • Veterinary and Comparative Oncology (56226) • Veterinary Dermatology (53508) • The World Economy (56228) • The Yale Review (56229) • Zoonoses and Public Health (56230) • Zygon (56231)

John Wiley & Sons Ltd.
The Atrium
Southern Gate
Chichester PO19 8SQ, United Kingdom
Phone: 44 1243 779777

Fax: 44 1243 775878

Publications: Applied Cognitive Psychology (53785) • Applied Organometallic Chemistry (53004) • British Journal of Surgery (53006) • European Journal of Social Psychology (53010) • International Journal of Adaptive Control & Signal Processing (53425) • International Journal of Robust & Nonlinear Control (53012) • Journal of Analytical Atomic Spectrometry (53013) • Journal of Pathology (52288) • Magnetic Resonance in Chemistry (52867) • Optimal Control Applications & Methods (53015) • Quality & Reliability Engineering International (53016)

Wiley-VCH Verlag GmbH
PO Box 101161
D-69451 Weinheim, Germany
Phone: 49 620 16060
Fax: 49 620 1606328
Publications: Chemie Ingenieur Technik (44702) • Chemistry (44703) • ChemSusChem (44705) • CLEAN (44274) • Journal of Biophotonics (44706) • Laser & Photonics Reviews (44216) • Lipid Technology (44707) • Molecular Informatics (44278)

William Herschel Society
Herschel House
19 New King St.
Bath BA1 2BL, United Kingdom
Phone: 44 12 25446865
Publications: Speculum (52258)

William Morris Society
Kelmscott House
26 Upper Mall
Hammersmith
London W6 9TA, United Kingdom
Phone: 44 20 87413735
Fax: 44 20 87485207
Publications: Journal of William Morris Studies (54837)

William Reed Publishing Ltd.
Broadfield Pk.
Crawley RH11 9RT, United Kingdom
Phone: 44 1293 613400
Publications: British Baker (53099) • Convenience Store (53100) • Drinks International (53102) • Food Manufacture (53103) • Forecourt Trader (53104) • Grocer (53105) • H - The Hotel Magazine (53106) • Meat Trades Journal (53108) • Morning Advertiser (53109) • Off Licence News (53110) • PubChef (53111) • Restaurant Equipment (53112) • Shopping Centre (53113) • Shopping Centre Ireland (53114) • Wine & Spirit (53115)

Wilmington Media
6-14 Underwood St.
London N1 7JQ, United Kingdom
Phone: 44 20 75498626
Fax: 44 20 75498622
Publications: European Cosmetics Markets (54393)

Wilmington Publishing Ltd.
Wilmington House
Maidstone Rd.
Sidcup DA14 5HZ, United Kingdom
Phone: 44 20 82697720
Fax: 44 20 82697740
Publications: Cranes Today (56541) • Hoist (56543)

Wilmington Quest Magazines Ltd.
Global Trade Media
Progressive House
Maidstone Rd.
Foots Cray
London DA14 5HZ, United Kingdom
Phone: 44 20 82697741
Publications: What Van? (55402)

Wilson Press HK Ltd.
Ste. 3D, Tung Shan Villa
2, Tung Shan Ter., Happy Valley
Hong Kong, People's Republic of China
Phone: 86 289 33676
Fax: 86 228 922846
Publications: Orient Aviation (43372)

Wimborne Publishing Ltd.
113 Lynwood Dr.
Ferndown BH21 1UU, United Kingdom
Phone: 44 12 02873872
Fax: 44 12 02874562
Publications: Everyday Practical Electronics (53386)

WIN verlags
Johann-Sebastian-Bach-Str. 5
D-85591 Vaterstetten, Germany
Phone: 49 810 63500
Fax: 49 810 6350190
Publications: E-Commerce Magazin (44698)

WIND- J. Wojewoda Publishing Company
Kuropatwia 2
PL-44-100 Wroclaw, Poland
Publications: Geochronometria (49778)

Winetitles/Wine Publishers Proprietary Ltd.
PO Box 1006
Prospect East, South Australia 5082, Australia
Phone: 61 8 83699500
Fax: 61 8 83699501
Publications: The Australian & New Zealand Wine Industry Journal (42267) • Australian Viticulture (42268)

Winkler Medien Verlag GmbH
Nymphenburger Strasse 1
D-80335 Munich, Germany
Phone: 49 89 2900110
Fax: 49 89 29001199
Publications: DECO (44556)

The Wire Magazine
23 Jack's Pl.
6 Corbet Pl.
London E1 6NN, United Kingdom
Phone: 44 20 74225010
Fax: 44 20 74225011
Publications: The Wire (55408)

The WJG Press
Biomed Scientific Co. Ltd.
Rm. 903, Bldg. D, Ocean
International Ctr., No. 62
Dongsihuan Zhonglu, Chaoyang
Beijing 100025, People's Republic of China
Phone: 86 105 9080039
Fax: 86 108 5381893
Publications: World Journal of Gastroenterology (43225)

Wochenschrift fuer Anthroposophie
In den Zielbaumen 7
Postfach
CH-4143 Dornach 1, Switzerland
Phone: 41 617 064464
Fax: 41 617 064465
Publications: Das Goetheanum (51085)

The Wolf
3, Holly Mansions
Fortune Green Rd.
W Hampstead
London NW6 1UB, United Kingdom
Publications: The Wolf (55411)

Women's Engineering Society
The IET, Michael Faraday House
Six Hills Way
Stevenage SG1 2AY, United Kingdom
Phone: 44 1438 765506
Publications: The Woman Engineer (56620)

Women's Infoteka
Varsavska 16
CT-10000 Zagreb, Croatia
Phone: 38 514 830557
Fax: 38 514 830552
Publications: Kruh i Ruze (43569)

Women's International League for Peace and Freedom - Australia
Rundle Mall
PO Box 345
Adelaide, South Australia 5000, Australia
Phone: 61 8 82964357
Publications: Peace and Freedom (41512)

W1 Magazine
26, York St.
London W1U 6PZ, United Kingdom
Phone: 44 207 7887547
Publications: W1 Magazine (55415)

Woodhead Publishing Ltd.
Abington Hall, Granta Park
Great Abington
Cambridge CB21 6AH, United Kingdom
Phone: 44 12 23891358

Fax: 44 12 23893694
Publications: Applied Bionics and Biomechanics (52790) • Ships and Offshore Structures (52895)

Woodpublishers Oy Ltd.
PL 211, Puistokatu 9 A
FIN-15101 Lahti, Finland
Phone: 358 373 31501
Fax: 358 373 31511
Publications: Woodworking Puuntyosto WIN (43903)

Wordhouse Publishing Group
68 1st Ave.
Mortlake
London SW14 8SR, United Kingdom
Phone: 44 20 89396470
Fax: 44 20 88789983
Publications: Florist & Wholesale Buyer (54466)

Workers' Educational Association
96-100 Clifton St.
London EC2A 4TP, United Kingdom
Phone: 44 20 74263450
Fax: 44 20 74299821
Publications: Fonstret (54477)

Working People's Alliance
Walter Rodney House
80 Croal St.
Stabroek
Georgetown, Guyana
Phone: 592 2 53679
Fax: 592 2 53679
Publications: Dayclean (44800)

Workplace Law Group
110 hills Rd.
Cambridge CB2 1LQ, United Kingdom
Phone: 44 871 7778881
Fax: 44 871 7778882
Publications: Workplace Law (52905)

World Advertising Research Center
85 Newman St.
London W1T 3EX, United Kingdom
Phone: 44 20 74678100
Fax: 44 20 74678101
Publications: Advertising Forecast (53910) • Market Leader (54907) • Quarterly Survey of Advertising Expenditure (55164)

World Airnews
PO Box 35082
Northway
Durban 4065, Republic of South Africa
Phone: 27 31 5641319
Fax: 27 31 5637115
Publications: World Airnews (50471)

World Alliance of Reformed Churches
150 rte. de Ferney
PO Box 2100
CH-1211 Geneva, Switzerland
Phone: 41 227 916240
Fax: 41 227 916505
Publications: Reformed World (51158)

World Apostolate of Fatima
International Secretariat
Rua S Vicente Paulo, 32
Apartado 1
P-2495-438 Fatima, Portugal
Phone: 351 249532865
Fax: 351 249539864
Publications: Soul (49797)

World Association for Christian Communication
71 Lambeth Walk
London SE11 6DX, United Kingdom
Phone: 44 20 77352877
Publications: Media Development (54921)

World Christian Life Community
Borgo Santo Spirito, 4
I-00195 Rome, Italy
Phone: 39 668 977792
Fax: 39 668 977220
Publications: Progressio (46240)

World Congress of Faiths
London Inter Faith Center
125 Salusbury Rd.
London NW6 6RG, United Kingdom
Phone: 44 20 89593129

Fax: 44 20 76043052
Publications: Interreligious Insight (54676)

World Council of Churches
150 Rte. de Ferney
PO Box 2100
CH-1211 Geneva 2, Switzerland
Phone: 41 227 916111
Fax: 41 227 910361
Publications: The Ecumenical Review (51091) •
International Review of Mission (51149)

World Development Movement
66 Offley Rd.
London SW9 0LS, United Kingdom
Phone: 44 207 8204900
Fax: 44 207 8204949
Publications: WDM in Action (55393)

World Expeditionary Association
45-49 Brompton Rd.
Knightsbridge
London SW3 1DE, United Kingdom
Phone: 44 84 56436568
Fax: 44 20 78380837
Publications: Traveller (55337)

World Federation of Occupational Therapists
PO Box 30
Forrestfield, Western Australia 6058, Australia
Fax: 61 894 539746
Publications: WFOT Bulletin (41868)

World Gold Council
55 Old Broad St.
London EC2M 1RX, United Kingdom
Phone: 44 20 78264700
Fax: 44 20 78264799
Publications: Gold Bulletin (54516)

World Health Organization
20 Appia Ave.
CH-1211 Geneva 27, Switzerland
Phone: 41 22 7912111
Fax: 41 22 7913111
Publications: Bulletin of the World Health Organization
(51089) • Pan American Journal of Public Health
(51155) • Weekly Epidemiological Record (51165) •
WHO Drug Information (51166)

World Health Organization - Regional Office for the Eastern Mediterranean
Abdul Razzak Al Sanhouri St.
PO Box 7608, Nasr City
Cairo 11371, Egypt
Phone: 20 2 22765000
Fax: 20 2 26702492
Publications: Eastern Mediterranean Health Journal
(43754)

World Medical Association
13 Ch. du Levant
CIB - Batiment A
F-01210 Ferney-Voltaire, France
Phone: 33 450 407575
Fax: 33 450 405937
Publications: World Medical Journal (43951)

World Meteorological Organization
7 Bis, Ave. de la Paix
Case postale No. 2300
12112 Geneva, Switzerland
Phone: 41 22 7308111
Fax: 41 22 7308181
Telex: 41 41 99 OMM CH
Publications: WMO Bulletin (51167)

World Organization of Family Doctors
College of Medicine Bldg.
16 College Rd., No. 01-02
Singapore 169854, Singapore
Phone: 65 6224 2886
Fax: 65 6324 2029
Publications: The Family Doctor (50147)

World Scientific Publishing Company Inc.
27 Warren St., Ste. 401-402
Hackensack, NJ 07601
Phone: 201487-9655
Fax: 201487-9656
Free: 800227-7562
Publications: Advances in Adaptive Data Analysis
(51304) • Journal of Construction Research (43354)

World Scientific Publishing Company Private Ltd.
5 Toh Tuck Link
Singapore 596224, Singapore
Phone: 99965 646 65775
Fax: 99965 646 77667
Publications: Algebra Colloquium (43168) • Asian
Case Research Journal (50106) • Biophysical Reviews
and Letters (44639) • Coastal Engineering Journal
(46552) • COSMOS (50128) • Division of Labour &
Transaction Costs (41760) • Gene Therapy and Regula-
tion (44015) • Hand Surgery (46649) • Infinite Dimen-
sional Analysis, Quantum Probability and Related Topics
(50170) • Innovation (50173) • International Game
Theory Review (43675) • International Journal of
Algebra and Computation (50176) • International
Journal of Computational Methods (IJCM) (50179) •
International Journal of Cooperative Information Systems
(48754) • International Journal of Geometric Methods
in Modern Physics (IJGMMP) (50180) • International
Journal of Humanoid Robotics (IJHR) (50181) • International Journal of Image and Graphics (50182) • International Journal of Information Acquisition (50183) •
International Journal of Innovation Management
(50184) • International Journal of Modern Physics A
(50185) • International Journal of Modern Physics B
(44493) • International Journal of Modern Physics C
(50186) • International Journal of Modern Physics D
(50187) • International Journal of Modern Physics E
(50188) • International Journal of Nanoscience
(50189) • International Journal of Neural Systems
(50190) • International Journal of Pattern Recognition
and Artificial Intelligence (44564) • International Journal
of PIXE (50192) • International Journal of Shape Modeling (46150) • International Journal of Uncertainty, Fuzziness and Knowledge-Based Systems (44058) • International Journal on Wireless & Optical Communications
(50195) • Journal of Biological Systems (50200) •
Journal of Computational Acoustics (50202) • Journal
of Developmental Entrepreneurship (50203) • Journal
of Enterprising Culture (50204) • Journal of Environmental Assessment Policy and Management (50205) •
Journal of Graph Algorithms and Applications (50206) •
Journal of Integrative Neuroscience (50207) • Journal
of Knot Theory and Its Ramifications (50208) • Journal
of Musculoskeletal Research (50210) • Mathematical
Models and Methods in Applied Sciences (46273) •
Modern Physics Letters A (50217) • Modern Physics
Letters B (50218) • Parallel Processing Letters
(50235) • Review of Pacific Basin Financial Markets
and Policies (50245) • Reviews in Mathematical Phys-
ics (50246) • Singapore Economic Review (50254) •
Surface Review and Letters (50275)

World Scientific Publishing (HK) Company Ltd.
Kowloon Central Post Office
PO Box 72482
Hong Kong, People's Republic of China
Phone: 852 27718791
Fax: 852 27718155
Publications: International Journal of Computer Pro-
cessing of Languages (43349) • International Journal of
Image and Graphics (43350)

World Ship Society
Mayes House
Vansittart Estate
Arthur Rd.
Windsor SL4 1SE, United Kingdom
Phone: 44 7768 234507
Publications: Marine News (56932)

World Student Christian Federation
5 rte. des Morillons
PO Box 2100
CH-1211 Geneva, Switzerland
Phone: 41 22 7916358
Fax: 41 22 7916152
Publications: WSCF Journal (51170)

World Taekwondo Federation
4th Fl., Joyang Bldg. 113
Samseong-dong
Gangnam-gu
Seoul 135-090, Republic of Korea
Phone: 82 256 62505
Fax: 82 255 34728
Publications: WTF Taekwondo (47292)

World Textile Publications Ltd.
Perkin House
1 Longlands St.
Bradford BD1 2TP, United Kingdom
Phone: 44 1274 378800
Fax: 44 1274 378811
Publications: Fashion Business International (52460) •
International Carpet Bulletin (ICB) (52471) • Interna-
tional Dyer (52472) • Knitting International (52519) •
Nonwovens Report International (52531) • Textile
Month (TM) (52552) • Wool Record (52557)

World Vision Australia
1 Vision Dr.
Burwood East, Victoria 3151, Australia
Phone: 61 392 872233
Fax: 61 392 872427
Publications: Global Future (41677)

World Vision - New Zealand
Private Bag 92078
Auckland, New Zealand
Phone: 64 9 5807700
Fax: 64 9 5807799
Publications: Impact (48797)

World War Two Railway Study Group
c/o Mike Christensen, Membership Sec.
25 Woodcote Rd.
Warwickshire
Leamington Spa CV32 6PZ, United Kingdom
Phone: 44 1926 429378
Publications: Bulletin (53744)

World Watch
Gobernador 3
E-28014 Madrid, Spain
Phone: 34 914 293774
Fax: 34 936 926675
Publications: World Watch (50816)

World Wide Fund for Nature - Germany
Rebstocker StraBe 55
D-60326 Frankfurt, Germany
Phone: 49 697 91440
Fax: 49 696 17221
Publications: WWF Journal (44363)

WorldFish Center
11960 Bayan Lepas
Jalan Batu Maung, Batu Maung
PO Box 500
10670 Penang, Malaysia
Phone: 60 4 626 1606
Fax: 60 4 626 5530
Publications: NAGA (47690)

World's Poultry Science Association - The Netherlands
PO Box 31
NL-7360 AA Beekbergen, Netherlands
Phone: 31 55 5063250
Fax: 31 55 5064858
Publications: World Poultry Science Journal (48277)

Wound Care Society
PO Box 170
Huntingdon PE29 1PL, United Kingdom
Phone: 44 1480 434401
Publications: Wound Care (53636)

Writers and Scholars International Ltd.
Lancaster House
6-8 Anwell St.
London EC1R 3GA, United Kingdom
Phone: 44 20 73242522
Publications: Index on Censorship (54594)

Writing Equipment Society
c/o Mr. Martin Roberts
53 Horsecroft Rd.
Suffolk
Bury Saint Edmunds IP33 2DT, United Kingdom
Phone: 44 1284 750978
Publications: Journal of the Writing Equipment Society
(52774)

wwwords Ltd.
Didcot
PO Box 204
Oxford OX11 9ZQ, United Kingdom
Phone: 44 1235 818062

Fax: 44 1235 817275
Publications: Contemporary Issues in Early Childhood (55915) • European Educational Research Journal (55943) • Research in Comparative and International Education (56187)

Wydawnictwo Naukowe Akademii Rolniczej W Szczecinie
ul. Doktora Judyman 22
PL-71-466 Szczecin, Poland
Phone: 48 914 541639
Publications: Acta Ichthyologica et Piscatoria (49676)

Wyvex Media Limited
Lochavullin Estate
Argyll PA34 4HB, United Kingdom
Phone: 44 1631 568000
Fax: 44 1631 568001
Publications: Argyllshire Advertiser (53887)

Xene Inc.
Oji Fudosan Sapporo Bldg.
1st Fl., Minami 1 Nishi 11
Chuo-ku
Hokkaido
Sapporo 060-0061, Japan
Phone: 81 11 2720757
Fax: 81 11 2720758
Publications: Xene (46652)

Xi'an University of Architecture and Technology
No. 13, Yanta Rd.
Xi'an 710055, Shaanxi, People's Republic of China
Publications: Journal of Xauat (Natural Sciences) (43535) • Journal of Xauat (Social Sciences) (43536)

XLRI
Circuit House Area E
Jamshedpur 831 001, Bihar, India
Phone: 91 657 3983333
Fax: 91 657 2227814
Publications: Management and Labour Studies (45207)

Yaffa Publishing Group
17-21 Bellevue St.
Surry Hills, New South Wales 2010, Australia
Phone: 61 292 812333
Fax: 61 292 812750
Publications: AdNews (42407) • Australasian Paint & Panel (42408) • Australasian Sporting Shooter (42409) • Australian Creative (42410) • Australian Defence Magazine (42411) • Australian Flying (42412) • Australian National Security Magazine (42415) • Australian Photography (42416) • Australian Power Boat (42417) • Australian Sailing (42418) • Australian Yachting (42419) • Aviation Business Magazine (42420) • Bacon Busters (42421) • Capture (42422) • Climate Control News (CCN) (42423) • Cruising Helmsman (42424) • Dance Australia (42425) • Digital Photography and Design (42426) • Flightpath (42430) • Food & Drink Business (42431) • FoodService News (42432) • Greetings & Gifts (42433) • Hospital & Agedcare (42434) • Marine Business (42435) • Nature & Health (42436) • Packaging News (42437) • Ragtrader (42438) • Sporting Shooter (42439) • Stationery News (42440) • Toy & Hobby Retailer (42441)

Yamashina Institute for Ornithology
115 Konoyama
Abiko-shi
Chiba 270-1145, Japan
Phone: 81 4 71821101
Fax: 81 4 71821106
Publications: Journal of Yamashina Institute for Ornithology (46319)

Yandell Publishing Ltd.
PO Box 5116
Milton Keynes MK15 8ZQ, United Kingdom
Phone: 44 190 8613323
Fax: 44 190 8210656
Publications: Food Marketing & Manufacturing (55635) • Group Leisure (55637)

Yemen Observer
Mohammed al-Shokani St.
PO Box 19183
Sana'a, Yemen
Phone: 967 1 505466
Fax: 967 1 260504
Publications: Yemen Observer (57105)

Yemen Times
PO Box 2579
Sana'a, Yemen
Phone: 967 1 268661
Fax: 967 1 268276
Publications: Yemen Times (57106)

YHA—New South Wales
422 Kent St.
Sydney, New South Wales 2000, Australia
Phone: 02 92 611111
Fax: 02 92 611969
Publications: Backpacker Essentials (42471)

The Yoga Institute
Shri Yogendra Marg
Prabhat Colony
Santa Cruz E
Mumbai 400 055, Maharashtra, India
Phone: 91 22 26110506
Publications: Yoga and Total Health (45450)

YOGA Magazine Limited
26 York St.
London W1U 6PZ, United Kingdom
Phone: 44 20 77295454
Fax: 44 20 77390181
Publications: YOGA Magazine (55432)

Yoga Today Ltd.
PO Box 16969
London E1W 1FY, United Kingdom
Phone: 44 207 4805456
Publications: Yoga and Health (55431)

Yokohama Association for International Communications and Exchanges
Yokohama International Organizations Center 5th Fl.
Pacifico Yokohama
1-1-1 Minato Mirai
Nishi-ku
Yokohama 220-0012, Japan
Phone: 81 452 221171
Fax: 81 452 212210
Publications: The Yoke (47143)

The Yomiuri Shimbun
1-7-1 Otemachi
Chiyoda-Ku
Tokyo 100-8055, Japan
Publications: Daily Yomiuri (46799)

Yonsei University College of Medicine
134 Shinchon-dong
Seodaemun-gu
Seoul 120-752, Republic of Korea
Phone: 82 2 22282034
Fax: 82 2 3934945
Publications: Yonsei Medical Journal (47293)

Yorkshire Advertiser Ltd.
Kirkdale Rd.
Kirbymoorside
York YO62 6YB, United Kingdom
Phone: 44 1751434609
Publications: Yorkshire Advertiser (Ryedale and North York Moors) (57000)

Yorkshire Naturalists' Union
The University of Bradford
Bradford BD7 1DP, United Kingdom
Phone: 44 12 74234212
Publications: The Naturalist (52529)

Yorkshire Post Newspapers Ltd.
Wellington St.
PO Box 168
Leeds LS1 1RF, United Kingdom
Phone: 44 11 32432701
Publications: Yorkshire Post (53777) • Yorkshire Sport (53778)

Young Men's Christian Association and Young Women's Christian Association
Valby Langgade 19
DK-2500 Valby, Denmark
Phone: 45 36 141533
Publications: Horysont (Good News) (43736)

Young Women's Christian Association - Finland
P. Rautatiekatu 23 B
FIN-00100 Helsinki, Finland
Phone: 35 894 342290

Fax: 35 894 3422920
Publications: NNKY-NAKY (43850)

Young Women's Christian Association - Italy
Via San Secondo 70
I-10128 Turin, Italy
Phone: 39 11 5683369
Fax: 39 11 5131427
Publications: Impegno (46272)

Youth Hostels Association of India
5 Nyaya Marg
Chanakyapuri
New Delhi 110 021, Delhi, India
Phone: 91 112 6110250
Fax: 91 112 6113469
Publications: Youth Hosteller (45671)

Yr Academi Gymreig—The Welsh Academy
3rd Fl., Mount Stuart House
Mount Stuart Sq.
Cardiff CF10 5FQ, United Kingdom
Phone: 44 29 20472266
Fax: 44 29 20492930
Publications: Taliesin (52940)

Yukawa Institute for Theoretical Physics
Kitashirakawa Oiwake-Cho
Kyoto 606-8502, Japan
Phone: 81 75 7537000
Fax: 81 75 7537020
Publications: Progress of Theoretical Physics (46483) • Progress of Theoretical Physics - Supplement (46484)

Zahra Publishing
1st Fl.
Barker House
Church Rd.
Greystone, Wicklow, Ireland
Phone: 353 1 2557566
Publications: Easy Food (46023) • Easyhealth (46024)

Zecchini Editore
Via. Tonale 60
I-21100 Varese, Italy
Phone: 39 332 331041
Fax: 39 332 331013
Publications: Musica (46277)

Zee Publications Inc.
PDI Bldg.
Archbishop Reyes Ave.
Cebu City 6000, Philippines
Phone: 63 32 2342636
Publications: Zee Lifestyle (49465)

Zentralsekretariat Zurich
Josefstrasse 59
Postfach
CH-8031 Zurich, Switzerland
Phone: 41 44 2797171
Fax: 41 44 2797172
Publications: Syna die Gewerkschaft (51291)

Zeus International S.R.L.
Viale Lunigiana, 14
I-20125 Milan, Italy
Phone: 39 2 67100605
Fax: 39 2 67100621
Publications: Italian Food Machines (46179) • Italian Magazine Food Processing (46180) • Rassegna Alimentare (46192)

Ziff-Davis UK Ltd.
International House
1 St. Katherine's Way
London E1 9UN, United Kingdom
Publications: PC Magazine (55063)

Zimbabwe Newspapers Ltd.
Herald House
Cor. G. Silundika Ave. S Nujoma St.
Harare, Zimbabwe
Phone: 263 4 795771
Fax: 263 4 791311
Publications: The Manica Post (57116) • New Farmer (57117) • The Sunday Mail (57118) • Sunday News (57119)

Zimind Publishers (Private) Ltd.
PO Box BE 1165
Belvedere
Harare, Zimbabwe

Phone: 263 773 934
Fax: 263 773 941
Publications: Zimbabwe Independent (57121)

Ziua
Strada Ion Campineanu Numarul 4
Sect. 1
Bucharest, Romania
Phone: 40 315 9111
Fax: 40 310 3119
Publications: Ziua (49846)

ZOA Refugee Care - Netherlands
Sleutelbloemstraat 8
PO Box 4130
NL-7320 AC Apeldoorn, Netherlands
Phone: 31 553 663339
Fax: 31 553 668799
Publications: Direct Mailings (48275)

Zoological Society of London
Outer Cir.
Regent's Pk.

London NW1 4RY, United Kingdom
Phone: 44 20 77223333
Publications: Journal of Zoology (50594)

Zoological Society of Southern Africa
Post Bag X01
Pietermaritzburg 3209, Republic of South Africa
Phone: 27 332 605127
Fax: 27 332 605105
Publications: African Zoology (50566)

This is a consolidated alphabetical listing of subject terms appearing in the following six subject indexes: Agricultural Publications (by Subject); Ethnic Publications; Fraternal Publications; Magazines of General Circulation; Radio Station Formats index; and Trade, Technical, and Professional Publications. Citations are followed by page numbers referring to indexes where the subject terms appear. In addition to actual subject headings being used, the Index to Subject Terms provides "see" and "see also" references to guide users to appropriate headings.

A

[Abortion] 6093
[Abstracts]--see Indexes, Abstracts, Reports, Proceedings, and Bibliographies
[Accident Prevention]--see Safety
[Accountants and Accounting] 6131
[Acoustics]--see Physics
[Acquired Immune Deficiency Syndrome].......6131
[Adult Entertainment]--see Sex/Erotica
[Adventure]--see Science Fiction, Mystery, Adventure, and Romance
[Advertising and Marketing]...........................6131
[Aeronautics]--see Aviation
[African-American Publications]--see Black Publications
[Agents and Salesmen]--see Selling and Salesmanship
[Agricultural College Publications]--see Scientific Agricultural Publications
[Agricultural Implements]--see Farm Implements and Supplies
[Air Conditioning and Refrigeration]...............6132
[Air Force]--see Military and Navy
[Air Pollution]--see Ecology and Conservation
[Aircraft]--see Aviation
[Airlines]--see In-Flight Publications; also Travel and Tourism; also Aviation
[Alcoholic Beverages]--see Beverages, Brewing, and Bottling
[Alcoholism]--see Substance Abuse and Treatment
[Alternative and Underground] 6093
[Amateur Sports]--see General Sports
[American Indian]--see Native American Interests
[American Legion]--see Veterans
[Anatomy]--see Physiology and Anatomy
[Animal Rights]--see Society for the Prevention of Cruelty to Animals and Anti-Vivisection
[Animals]--see Pets; also Dogs; also Cats; also Ornithology and Oology; also Zoology
[Anthropology and Ethnology]........................6132
[Anti-Vivisection]--see Society for the Prevention of Cruelty to Animals and Anti-Vivisection
[Antiques]...6093
[Apartments]--see Building Management and Maintenance
[Apiculture]--see Beekeeping
[Apparel]--see Clothing; also Fashion
[Appliances]...6133
[Appraisals]--see Banking, Finance, and Investments
[Arabic]...6071
[Archaeology]...6133
[Archery]...6112
[Architecture]..6134
[Arenas]--see Building Management and Maintenance
[Armenian]..6071
[Army]--see Military and Navy
[Art]..6093
[Art and Art History] 6134
[Arts]--see Art; also Art and Art History; also Architecture; also Humanities; also Literature and Literary Reviews; also Music and Musical Instruments; also Drama and Theatre; also Performing Arts

[Asbestos]--see Stone and Rock Products
[Astrology]...6093
[Astronautics]...6135
[Astronomy and Meteorology] 6135
[Atheism]..6093
[Athletic Clubs]--see Physical Fitness; also Clubs and Societies
[Athletics]--see Physical Education and Athletics; also Sports
[Atomic Science and Engineering]--see Astronautics; also Nuclear Engineering
[Authors]--see Book Trade and Author News; also Journalism and Publishing; also Literature and Literary Reviews
[Auto Racing]..6112
[Automatic Machines]--see Vending Machines
[Automation]...6136
[Automotive (Consumer)]..............................6093
[Automotive (Trade)] 6136
[Aviation]..6094, 6137
[Awnings]--see Textiles

B

[Babies] 6094
[Bacteriology]--see Biology; also Medicine and Surgery
[Badminton]--see Racquet Sports
[Baking]..6137
[Banking, Finance, and Investments]...............6137
[Barbers]--see Hairstyling
[Baseball]..6112
[Basketball]..6112
[Batteries]--see Automotive (Trade)
[Beauty Culture]--see Hairstyling; also Cosmetics and Toiletries
[Bedding]--see Furniture and Furnishings
[Beekeeping]...6067
[Beer]--see Beverages, Brewing, and Bottling
[Benevolent and Protective Order of Elks]--see Elks, Benevolent and Protective Order of
[Beverages, Brewing, and Bottling] 6139
[Bibliography]--see Indexes, Abstracts, Reports, Proceedings, and Bibliographies
[Bicycling]...6112
[Billboard Advertising]--see Advertising and Marketing
[Biochemistry]--see Chemistry, Chemicals, and Chemical Engineering; also Biology
[Biography (Current)]--see General Editorial
[Biology]...6140
[Birds]--see Ornithology and Oology; also Pets
[Blind and Visually Challenged].....................6095
[Blueprints]--see Engineering (Various branches)
[Boards of Trade]--see Chambers of Commerce and Boards of Trade
[Boating and Yachting] 6112
[Body Building]--see Physical Fitness
[Bonds]--see Banking, Finance, and Investments
[Book Reviews]--see Literature; also Literature and Literary Reviews
[Book Trade and Author News].......................6143
[Bookkeeping]--see Accountants and Accounting
[Boots]--see Shoes, Leather, and Luggage
[Botany]...6144

[Bottling]--see Beverages, Brewing, and Bottling
[Bowling] 6112
[Boxing and Wrestling] 6112
[Boy Scouts]--see Youths' Interests
[Boy's Magazine]--see Children's Interests; also Youths' Interests
[Breed Publications]--see Livestock
[Brewing]--see Beverages, Brewing, and Bottling
[Bricks]--see Building Materials, Concrete, Brick, and Tile
[Brides]..6095
[Broadcasting]--see Radio, Television, Cable, and Video
[Building]--see Construction, Contracting, Building, and Excavating; also Building Materials, Concrete, Brick, and Tile; also Wood and Woodworking; also Architecture; also Engineering (Various branches); also Roofing
[Building Materials, Concrete, Brick, and Tile] 6145
[Bulgarian]...6071
[Buses]--see Transportation, Traffic, and Shipping; also Public Transportation
[Business]..6095, 6145
[Business Executives]--see Management and Administration
[Butchers]--see Food and Grocery Trade
[Butter]--see Milk and Dairy Products

C

[Cable]--see Radio, Television, Cable, and Video
[Cafeterias]--see Hotels, Motels, Restaurants, and Clubs
[Camping]--see Outdoors
[Candy]--see Confectionaries and Frozen Dairy Products
[Canning]--see Food and Grocery Trade
[Canvas Goods]--see Textiles
[Car Wash]--see Automotive (Trade)
[Cards]--see Games and Puzzles
[Career Development and Employment]..........6095
[Carpentry] 6149
[Carpets]--see Furniture and Furnishings
[Catalan]...6071
[Catering]--see Hotels, Motels, Restaurants, and Clubs
[Cats]..6096
[Cattle]--see Livestock
[Cellular Communications]--see Telecommunications
[Cement]--see Building Materials, Concrete, Brick, and Tile
[Cemeteries and Monuments] 6149
[Ceramics]...6149
[Cereal]--see Food and Grocery Trade
[Chain Stores]--see Retail
[Chambers of Commerce and Boards of Trade] 6149
[Checkers]--see Games and Puzzles
[Cheese]--see Milk and Dairy Products
[Chemistry, Chemicals, and Chemical Engineering]...6149
[Chess]--see Games and Puzzles
[Child Care]--see Babies; also Parenting

[Children]--see Children's Interests; also Parenting; also Babies; also Youths' Interests; also Pediatrics
[Children's Interests] 6096
[China]--see Glass and China
[Chinese] 6071
[Chiropody]--see Podiatry
[Chiropractic]..6152
[Cigar and Cigarette Trade]--see Tobacco
[Circulation Management]--see Advertising and Marketing
[City, Hotel, Railroad, and Travel Guides] 6096
[City Life]--see Lifestyle; also Home and Garden
[City Magazines]--see Local, State, and Regional Publications
[Civic]--see Chambers of Commerce and Boards of Trade; also State, Municipal, and County Administration
[Civil Defense]--see Military and Navy
[Civil Engineering]--see Engineering (Various branches)
[Civil Rights]..6152
[Civil Service]--see Congressional and Federal Government Affairs
[Clay]--see Building Materials, Concrete, Brick, and Tile
[Cleaning]--see Laundry and Dry Cleaning; also Building Management and Maintenance
[Clocks]--see Jewelry, Watches, and Clocks
[Clothing]...6152
[Clubs]--see Hotels, Motels, Restaurants, and Clubs
[Clubs and Societies] 6096
[Coaching]--see General Sports
[Coal and Coke]--see Mining and Minerals
[Coast Guard]--see Military and Navy
[Coffee]--see Food and Grocery Trade
[Coin-Operated Machines]--see Vending Machines
[Coin and Stamping Collecting]--see Collecting
[Cold Storage]--see Air Conditioning and Refrigeration
[Collecting]...6097
[College Store Supplies]--see Stationery, Office Equipment, and College Store Supplies
[Comics and Comic Technique] 6097
[Commentary]--see General Editorial
[Commerce and Industry] 6153
[Communications] 6153
[Community Interest]--see Chambers of Commerce and Boards of Trade; also Local, State, and Regional Publications
[Compact Discs]--see Radio, Television, Cable, and Video; also Music and Musical Instruments; also Library and Information Science
[Composition Materials]--see Plastic and Composition Materials
[Computers] 6097, 6154
[Concrete]--see Building Materials, Concrete, Brick, and Tile
[Confectionaries and Frozen Dairy Products] .6158
[Congressional and Federal Government Affairs]..6158
[Conservation]--see Ecology and Conservation
[Construction, Contracting, Building, and Excavating]...6158
[Consumer Electronics] 6098
[Consumer Magazines]--see Magazines of General Circulation
[Consumerism]....................................6098, 6159
[Containers]--see Packaging
[Contests]--see Crafts, Models, Hobbies, and Contests
[Contracting]--see Construction, Contracting, Building, and Excavating
[Control Engineering]--see Automation; also Computers
[Conventions, Meetings, and Trade Fairs].......6159
[Cooking]--see Food and Cooking; also Home and Garden
[Cooling]--see Air Conditioning and Refrigeration
[Cooperative Associations]--see Farm Bureau, Grange, and Cooperative Associations
[Copyrights]--see Patents, Trademarks, and Copyrights
[Cordage and Twine]--see Packaging
[Cosmetics and Toiletries] 6159
[Cotton]--see Textiles
[Cottonseed Products]--see Oils and Fats (Animal & Vegetable)

[Counseling]--see Psychology and Psychiatry
[County Government]--see State, Municipal, and County Administration
[Court News]--see Law
[Crafts, Models, Hobbies, and Contests].........6098
[Credit]--see Banking, Finance, and Investments; also Savings and Loan
[Croatian]...6072
[Crockery]--see Ceramics
[Cryogenics]--see Air Conditioning and Refrigeration
[Current Biography]--see General Editorial
[Current Events]--see General Editorial
[Curtains]--see Home Furnishings, Curtains, Draperies
[Cutlery]--see Hardware; also Home Furnishings, Curtains, Draperies
[Cybernetics]--see Computers
[Cycles, Cycle Research]--see Economics
[Czech] 6072

D
[Dairy Products]--see Milk and Dairy Products; also Confectionaries and Frozen Dairy Products
[Dairying]...6067
[Dance]--see Performing Arts; also Entertainment
[Danish]..6072
[Data Processing]--see Computers
[Deaf]--see Hearing and Speech; also Handicapped
[Debating]--see Public Speaking and Lecturing
[Decorating]--see Interior Design/Decorating; also Paint and Wallcoverings
[Dehydration]--see Food and Grocery Trade
[Delicatessen]--see Food and Grocery Trade
[Dentistry]...6160
[Department Stores]--see General Merchandise; also Retail
[Detective]--see Science Fiction, Mystery, Adventure, and Romance
[Diesel Power]--see Power and Power Plants
[Diet]--see Health
[Diners]--see Hotels, Motels, Restaurants, and Clubs
[Diplomatic]--see Congressional and Federal Government Affairs; also International Affairs
[Direct Mail Advertising]--see Advertising and Marketing
[Discount Buying]--see Retail; also Purchasing
[Display]--see Advertising and Marketing
[Distance Running]--see Running
[Distilling]--see Beverages, Brewing, and Bottling
[Distribution]--see Transportation, Traffic, and Shipping; also Materials Handling; also Ships and Shipping
[Dogs]...6099
[Drainage]--see Water Supply and Sewage Disposal; also Plumbing and Heating
[Drama and Theatre]............................6099, 6160
[Draperies]--see Home Furnishings, Curtains, Draperies
[Dressmaking, Needlework, and Quilting].......6099
[Drug Abuse]--see Substance Abuse and Treatment
[Drugs and Pharmaceuticals].........................6160
[Dry Cleaning]--see Laundry and Dry Cleaning
[Dutch]...6072
[Dyeing]--see Laundry and Dry Cleaning

E
[Ecclesiastical]--see Religious Publications
[Ecology and Conservation] 6162
[Economics] 6164
[Education]..6099, 6167
[Electrical Engineering] 6170
[Electrical Products]--see Electrical Engineering; also Appliances; also Consumer Electronics
[Electricity]--see Physics
[Electronics Engineering] 6170
[Electrotyping]--see Printing and Typography
[Elevators]--see Construction, Contracting, Building, and Excavating
[Employment and Human Resources].............6171
[Enamel, Vitreous]--see Glass and China
[Enamels]--see Paint and Wallcoverings
[Engineering (Various Branches)]...................6172
[Engraving]--see Printing and Typography
[Entertainment]...6090
[Entomology]..6175

[Environmental and Natural Resources Conservation]..6100
[Equipment]--see Machinery and Equipment
[Erotica]--see Sex/Erotica
[Estonian]..6072
[Ethnic and Minority Studies] 6176
[Ethnic Publications] 6101
[Ethnology]--see Anthropology and Ethnology
[Evaporation]--see Food and Grocery Trade
[Excavating]--see Construction, Contracting, Building, and Excavating
[Export Consumer Magazines]........................6101
[Exports]--see International Business and Economics
[Express]--see Transportation, Traffic, and Shipping; also Postal and Shipping Supplies

F
[Facsimile]--see Telecommunications
[Fairs]--see Conventions, Meetings, and Trade Fairs
[Family]--see Marriage and Family
[Farm Bureau, Grange, and Cooperative Associations]..6067
[Farm Implements and Supplies]....................6067
[Farm Newspapers]......................................6067
[Fashion] 6101
[Federal Government]--see Congressional and Federal Government Affairs
[Feed and Grain]...6067
[Fences]--see Building Materials, Concrete, Brick, and Tile
[Fencing]--see General Sports
[Fertilizer] 6067
[Fiber Optics]--see Ophthalmology, Optometry, and Optics; also Telecommunications
[Fiction]--see Literature; also Literature and Literary Reviews; also Science Fiction, Mystery, Adventure, and Romance
[Filipino] 6072
[Film]--see Motion Pictures; also Photography
[Finance]--see Banking, Finance, and Investments
[Finnish] 6072
[Fire Fighting]..6176
[Firearms]...6102, 6176
[Fish and Commercial Fisheries] 6176
[Fishing (Sportsmen)]--see Hunting, Fishing, and Game Management
[Flooring and Floor Covering] 6177
[Florists and Floriculture] 6177
[Flour]--see Food and Grocery Trade
[Flying]--see Aviation
[Folklore]--see History and Genealogy; also Literature and Literary Reviews
[Food and Cooking]......................................6102
[Food and Grocery Trade]..............................6177
[Food Production]..6177
[Football]...6112
[Forestry]...6178
[Foundry]--see Metal, Metallurgy, and Metal Trade
[4-H Clubs]--see Farm Bureau, Grange, and Cooperative Associations
[Fraternal Order of Eagles]--see Eagles
[Free Thought]--see Agnostic and Free Thought; also Atheism
[French] 6072
[Frozen Dairy Products]--see Confectionaries and Frozen Dairy Products
[Frozen Food]--see Food and Grocery Trade
[Fruit, Fruit Products, and Produce Trade]......6179
[Fuel]--see Petroleum, Oil, and Gas; also Mining and Minerals
[Funeral Directors]......................................6179
[Fur]--see Fur Trade and Fur Farming
[Furnaces]--see Plumbing and Heating
[Furniture and Furnishings].............................6179

G
[Game Management]--see Hunting, Fishing, and Game Management
[Games and Puzzles]....................................6103
[Garages]--see Automotive (Trade)
[Gardening]--see Home and Garden; also Landscape Architecture
[Gas]--see Petroleum, Oil, and Gas
[Gay and Lesbian Interests].............................6103
[Genealogy]--see History and Genealogy
[General Agriculture]....................................6067

[General Editorial] 6103
[General Merchandise]........................6179
[General Sports] 6113
[Genetics] 6179
[Geography] 6180
[Geology] 6181
[Geophysics]--see Geology; also Seismology; also Astronomy and Meteorology; also Oceanography and Marine Studies
[German] 6073
[Gerontology] 6182
[Gifts, Toys, and Novelties].................6182
[Ginning]--see Oils and Fats (Animal & Vegetable)
[Girls' Magazine]--see Children's Interests; also Youths' Interests
[Glass and China] 6182
[Goats]--see Dairying; also Livestock
[Golf] 6113
[Golf Course Management] 6183
[Government]--see Congressional and Federal Government Affairs; also International Affairs
[Grain]--see Feed and Grain; also Food and Grocery Trade
[Grange]--see Farm Bureau, Grange, and Cooperative Associations
[Graphic Arts and Design] 6183
[Greek]...6074
[Greeting Cards]--see Gifts, Toys, and Novelties
[Grocery]--see Food and Grocery Trade
[Guides]--see City, Hotel, Railroad, and Travel Guides
[Guns]--see Firearms; also Hunting, Fishing, and Game Management
[Gymnastics]--see General Sports; also Physical Education and Athletics

H
[Hairstyling] 6183
[Handicapped] 6104, 6183
[Hard of Hearing]--see Hearing and Speech; also Handicapped
[Hardware] 6183
[Hats]--see Clothing
[Hauling]--see Transportation, Traffic, and Shipping; also Trucks and Trucking
[Hay]--see Feed and Grain
[Hazardous Materials]--see Waste Management and Recycling; also Ecology and Conservation
[Health]..6104
[Health and Fitness] 6183
[Health and Healthcare] 6184
[Healthcare Institutions]--see Hospitals and Healthcare Institutions
[Hearing and Speech] 6188
[Heat]--see Physics
[Heating]--see Plumbing and Heating
[Hebrew]...6074
[Highways]--see Roads and Streets
[Hiking]--see Outdoors
[Hindi]...6074
[History and Genealogy].............6104, 6189
[Hobbies]--see Crafts, Models, Hobbies, and Contests
[Hobby and Craft Supplies]--see Gifts, Toys, and Novelties
[Hogs]--see Livestock
[Home Appliances]--see Appliances; also Radio, Television, Cable, and Video; also Electrical Engineering; also Electronics Engineering; also Consumer Electronics
[Home Craft]--see Crafts, Models, Hobbies, and Contests
[Home Economics] 6190
[Home Furnishings, Curtains, Draperies]........6190
[Home and Garden] 6104
[Home Interests]--see Home and Garden
[Homosexual Interests]--see Gay and Lesbian Interests
[Horses and Horse Racing].................6113
[Horticulture] 6069
[Hosiery]--see Clothing
[Hospices]--see Hospitals and Healthcare Institutions
[Hospitals and Healthcare Institutions]...........6191
[Hotel Guides]--see City, Hotel, Railroad, and Travel Guides
[Hotels, Motels, Restaurants, and Clubs]........6191

[Housewares]....................................6192
[Housing]--see Building Management and Maintenance
[Human Resources]--see Employment and Human Resources
[Humanitarianism]--see Philanthropy and Humanitarianism
[Humanities] 6192
[Humor]--see Comics and Comic Technique
[Hungarian].......................................6074
[Hunting, Fishing, and Game Management] 6113
[Hygiene]--see Health; also Health and Healthcare
[Hypnosis]--see Medicine and Surgery

I
[Ice]--see Air Conditioning and Refrigeration
[Ice Cream]--see Confectionaries and Frozen Dairy Products; also Milk and Dairy Products
[Ice Hockey]--see Hockey
[Ice Skating]--see Skating
[Imports]--see International Business and Economics
[In-Flight Publications] 6105
[Income Tax]--see Taxation and Tariff
[Independent Order of Odd Fellows]--see Odd Fellows, Independent Order of
[Indexes, Abstracts, Reports, Proceedings, and Bibliographies]..................................6192
[Indians]--see Native American Interests
[Indonesian].....................................6074
[Industrial Design]--see Engineering (Various branches)
[Industrial Purchasing]--see Purchasing
[Industrial Relations]--see Labor; also Employment and Human Resources; also Management and Administration
[Industry]--see Commerce and Industry
[Infants]--see Babies; also Parenting
[Infantswear]--see Clothing
[Ink]--see Printing and Typography
[Insects]--see Entomology
[Institutions]--see Building Management and Maintenance; also Hospitals and Healthcare Institutions
[Instruments]--see Weights and Measures; also Science (General)
[Insurance] 6193
[Intercultural Interests] 6105, 6193
[Interior Design/Decorating]...............6194
[International Affairs] 6195
[International Business and Economics] 6196
[International Fellowship of Rotarians]--see Rotarians, International Fellowship of
[Inventions]--see Patents, Trademarks, and Copyrights
[Investments]--see Banking, Finance, and Investments
[Iron and Steel]--see Metal, Metallurgy, and Metal Trade
[Irrigation]--see Engineering (Various branches)
[Italian] 6074

J
[Jails]--see Police, Penology, and Penal Institutions
[Janitorial]--see Building Management and Maintenance
[Japanese].......................................6074
[Jaycees]--see Clubs and Societies
[Jet Planes]--see Aviation
[Jewelry, Watches, and Clocks] 6197
[Journalism and Publishing]...............6197
[Junk]--see Waste Management and Recycling
[Juvenile]--see Children's Interests; also Youths' Interests

K
[Kiwanis]--see Clubs and Societies
[Knitting]--see Dressmaking, Needlework, and Quilting
[Korean]..6074

L
[Labor]..6197
[Laboratory Research (Scientific and Medical)] 6198
[Lamps]--see Lighting
[Landscape Architecture]...................6201

[Language]--see Philology, Language, and Linguistics
[Latin] 6074
[Latino Publications]--see Hispanic Publications
[Latvian] 6075
[Laundry and Dry Cleaning]...............6201
[Law]...6201
[Law Enforcement]--see Police, Penology, and Penal Institutions
[Leather]--see Shoes, Leather, and Luggage
[Lecturing]--see Public Speaking and Lecturing
[Leisure]--see Crafts, Models, Hobbies, and Contests; also Entertainment; also General Sports
[Lesbian]--see Gay and Lesbian Interests
[Library and Information Science]...............6203
[Lifestyle]...6105
[Light]--see Physics
[Lighting]..6204
[Limousines]--see Transportation, Traffic, and Shipping
[Linen Supply]--see Laundry and Dry Cleaning
[Linguistics]--see Philology, Language, and Linguistics
[Lions Clubs]--see Clubs and Societies
[Liquors]--see Beverages, Brewing, and Bottling
[Literary]--see General Editorial; also Literature; also Literature and Literary Reviews; also Book Trade and Author News; also Science Fiction, Mystery, Adventure, and Romance; also Journalism and Publishing
[Literature].......................................6204
[Literature and Literary Reviews]...............6107
[Lithography]--see Printing and Typography
[Lithuanian] 6075
[Livestock]..6069
[Loans]--see Savings and Loan; also Banking, Finance, and Investments
[Local, State, and Regional Publications] 6107, 6205
[Locks]--see Hardware
[Locksmiths]--see Safety
[Logging]--see Forestry; also Lumber
[Logistics]--see Military and Navy; also Transportation, Traffic, and Shipping
[Loyal Order of Moose]--see Moose International
[Lubrication]--see Petroleum, Oil, and Gas
[Luggage]--see Shoes, Leather, and Luggage

M
[Machinery and Equipment]...............6205
[Magicians]--see Crafts, Models, Hobbies, and Contests
[Magnetism]--see Physics
[Maintenance]--see Building Management and Maintenance
[Malay]..6075
[Malt]--see Beverages, Brewing, and Bottling
[Management and Administration].................6206
[Manicurist]--see Hairstyling
[Manufacturing]--see Commerce and Industry
[Marine]--see Boats and Marine
[Marine Studies]--see Oceanography and Marine Studies
[Marines]--see Military and Navy
[Marketing]--see Advertising and Marketing
[Marking Devices]--see Rubber Stamps, Seals, and Stencils
[Marriage and Family]........................6208
[Martial Arts] 6114
[Masons]--see Construction, Contracting, Building, and Excavating, 6085
[Materials Handling]...........................6208
[Mathematics]....................................6209
[Meat]--see Food and Grocery Trade
[Mechanical Engineering]--see Engineering (Various branches)
[Mechanics]--see Commerce and Industry; also Automotive (Trade)
[Media]--see Communications; also Radio, Television, Cable, and Video; also Journalism and Publishing
[Medicine and Surgery].......................6212
[Men's Interests]...............................6108
[Mental Disorders]--see Medicine and Surgery; also Psychology and Psychiatry
[Merchandise]--see General Merchandise

[Merchandising]--see Advertising and Marketing
[Metal, Metallurgy, and Metal Trade]...............6219
[Meteorology] 6220
[Military and Navy] 6220
[Milk and Dairy Products] 6220
[Milling]--see Food and Grocery Trade
[Mineral Water]--see Beverages, Brewing, and Bottling
[Minerals]--see Mining and Minerals
[Mining and Minerals] 6221
[Missiles]--see Nuclear Engineering
[Mobile Homes]--see Trailers and Accessories
[Models]--see Fashion; also Crafts, Models, Hobbies, and Contests
[Mohair]--see Livestock; also Textiles
[Money]--see Banking, Finance, and Investments; also Savings and Loan
[Monuments]--see Cemeteries and Monuments
[Mortgages]--see Savings and Loan; also Banking, Finance, and Investments
[Motels]--see Hotels, Motels, Restaurants, and Clubs
[Motion Pictures] 6108, 6221
[Motor Boating]--see Boating and Yachting; also Boats and Marine
[Motorbikes and Motorcycles] 6108
[Motorcycles] 6221
[Motoring]--see Automotive (Trade); also Travel and Tourism
[Movies]--see Motion Pictures
[Municipal]--see State, Municipal, and County Administration
[Museums] 6221
[Music and Musical Instruments]...........6108, 6221
[Mycology]--see Botany
[Mystery]--see Science Fiction, Mystery, Adventure, and Romance

N
[National Affairs]--see Congressional and Federal Government Affairs
[Natural Gas]--see Petroleum, Oil, and Gas
[Natural History and Nature Study].................6222
[Natural Resources].......................................6223
[Natural Sciences]--see Physics; also Biology; also Chemistry, Chemicals, and Chemical Engineering
[Nature Study]--see Natural History and Nature Study
[Naval Stores]--see Boats and Marine; also Ships and Shipping
[Navy]--see Military and Navy
[Needlework]--see Dressmaking, Needlework, and Quilting
[Nervous and Mental Disorders]--see Medicine and Surgery; also Psychology and Psychiatry
[New Age]...6109
[Newspapers]--see Daily Newspapers; also Free Newspapers; also Paid Community Newspapers; also Shopping Guides; also Journalism and Publishing; also Printing and Typography
[Night Clubs]--see Hotels, Motels, Restaurants, and Clubs
[Norwegian] 6075
[Novelties]--see Gifts, Toys, and Novelties
[Nuclear Engineering]....................................6223
[Nuclear Medicine]--see Radiology, Ultrasound, and Nuclear Medicine
[Numismatic]--see Collecting
[Nursery Trade]--see Seed and Nursery Trade; also Landscape Architecture
[Nursing] 6223
[Nursing Homes]--see Hospitals and Healthcare Institutions
[Nut Culture and Trade]--see Food and Grocery Trade
[Nutrition]--see Health

O
[Occult]--see Parapsychology
[Oceanography and Marine Studies]................6224
[Office Equipment and Systems]--see Stationery, Office Equipment, and College Store Supplies; also Furniture and Furnishings; also Computers
[Oil]--see Petroleum, Oil, and Gas
[Oils and Fats (Animal & Vegetable)] 6225
[Oology]--see Ornithology and Oology
[Ophthalmology, Optometry, and Optics]........6225

[Optics]--see Ophthalmology, Optometry, and Optics
[Optimist Club]--see Clubs and Societies
[Optometry]--see Ophthalmology, Optometry, and Optics
[Ornithology and Oology] 6225
[Osteopathy]...6225
[Outdoor Advertising]--see Advertising and Marketing
[Outdoors] 6114
[Overseas Transport]--see Ships and Shipping

P
[Packaging] 6225
[Packing]--see Food and Grocery Trade
[Paint and Wallcoverings]...............................6226
[Painting]--see Art; also Paint and Wallcoverings
[Pan-American]--see International Affairs
[Paper]...6226
[Paper Boxes]--see Paper; also Packaging
[Parapsychology]..6109
[Parasitology]--see Biology
[Parenting]..6109
[Parking]--see Automotive (Trade)
[Parks]...6226
[Patents, Trademarks, and Copyrights]...........6226
[Peace]..6226
[Pediatrics] 6226
[Penal Institutions and Penology]--see Police, Penology, and Penal Institutions
[Penology]--see Police, Penology, and Penal Institutions
[Performing Arts].............................6109, 6227
[Perfume]--see Cosmetics and Toiletries
[Personnel]--see Employment and Human Resources; also Labor
[Pest Control]--see Building Management and Maintenance
[Petroleum, Oil, and Gas] 6227
[Pets]...6109, 6228
[Pharmaceuticals]--see Drugs and Pharmaceuticals
[Philanthropy and Humanitarianism]...............6228
[Philately]--see Collecting
[Philippine Publications]--see Filipino
[Philology, Language, and Linguistics]...........6228
[Philosophy]..6230
[Photo Engraving]--see Printing and Typography
[Photography]..................................6109, 6231
[Physical Education and Athletics] 6231
[Physical Fitness] 6114
[Physical Therapy]--see Medicine and Surgery
[Physics]..6231
[Physiology and Anatomy].............................6233
[Pianos]--see Music and Musical Instruments
[Pigeons]--see Poultry and Pigeons
[Pistols]--see Firearms
[Plant Food]--see Fertilizer
[Plastic and Composition Materials] 6234
[Plumbing and Heating] 6235
[Podiatry]...6235
[Police, Penology, and Penal Institutions].......6235
[Polish]..6075
[Political Science]..6235
[Politics]...6236
[Pollution]--see Ecology and Conservation; also Water Supply and Sewage Disposal
[Pools]--see Sporting Goods/Retail Sports
[Ports]--see Ships and Shipping
[Portuguese]...6075
[Postal and Shipping Supplies] 6237
[Pottery]--see Ceramics
[Poultry and Pigeons]...................................6070
[Poultry Products and Supplies].....................6237
[Power Boats]--see Boating and Yachting; also Boats and Marine
[Power Farming]--see Rural Electrification
[Power and Power Plants] 6237
[Printing Inks]--see Printing and Typography
[Printing and Typography] 6237
[Proceedings]--see Indexes, Abstracts, Reports, Proceedings, and Bibliographies
[Produce]--see Fruit, Fruit Products, and Produce Trade
[Psychology and Psychiatry] 6110, 6237
[Public Housing]--see Sociology; also Social Programs

[Public Policy]--see State, Municipal, and County Administration
[Public Relations] 6239
[Public Safety and Emergency Response] 6240
[Public Speaking and Lecturing]....................6240
[Public Transportation].................................6240
[Public Utilities]--see Power and Power Plants; also Water Supply and Sewage Disposal
[Public Works]--see State, Municipal, and County Administration; also Roads and Streets
[Publishers]--see Book Trade and Author News; also Journalism and Publishing
[Purchasing]..6240
[Puzzles]--see Games and Puzzles

Q
[Quarrying]--see Stone and Rock Products
[Quilting]--see Dressmaking, Needlework, and Quilting

R
[Rabbits]--see Livestock; also Fur Farming
[Racial Interests]--see Civil Rights; also Ethnic and Minority Studies
[Racing]--see Horses and Horse Racing; also Auto Racing; also Bicycling; also Boating and Yachting; also Running; also Skating; also Skiing
[Racquet Sports]...6114
[Racquetball]--see Racquet Sports
[Radio, Television, Cable, and Video].....6110, 6240
[Radiology, Ultrasound, and Nuclear Medicine]..6240
[Railroad]...6241
[Railroad Guides]--see City, Hotel, Railroad, and Travel Guides
[Real Estate]...6241
[Recreation]--see Sports; also Entertainment
[Recreational Vehicles]--see Trailers and Accessories
[Red Cross]--see Philanthropy and Humanitarianism
[Refrigeration]--see Air Conditioning and Refrigeration
[Regional Publications]--see Local, State, and Regional Publications
[Rental Equipment].......................................6242
[Reports]--see Indexes, Abstracts, Reports, Proceedings, and Bibliographies
[Restaurants]--see Hotels, Motels, Restaurants, and Clubs
[Retail]...6242
[Retail Selling]--see Selling and Salesmanship
[Retail Sports]--see Sporting Goods/Retail Sports
[Retirement]--see Senior Citizens' Interests
[Rifles]--see Firearms; also Hunting, Fishing, and Game Management
[Roads and Streets]......................................6242
[Robotics]--see Automation
[Rock Products]--see Stone and Rock Products
[Rockets]--see Nuclear Engineering; also Astronautics
[Rodeos]--see Horses and Horse Racing
[Romance]--see Science Fiction, Mystery, Adventure, and Romance
[Romanian]..6075
[Roofing] 6242
[Rotarians, International Fellowship of] 6085
[Rotary Clubs]--see Clubs and Societies
[Rubber Trade]...6242
[Rugby]--see General Sports
[Rugs]--see Furniture and Furnishings
[Running]..6114
[Russian]..6075
[Russian and Eurasian Interests]--see Soviet Interests

S
[Safes]--see Banking, Finance, and Investments
[Safety]..6242
[Sailing]--see Boating and Yachting
[Sales Management]--see Management and Administration
[Salesmanship]--see Selling and Salesmanship
[Sand and Gravel]--see Stone and Rock Products
[Sanitary Supplies]--see Building Management and Maintenance

[Sanitation]--see Health and Healthcare
[Savings and Loan].................................6243
[Scales]--see Weights and Measures
[Scandinavian Publications]--see Norwegian; also Dutch; also Swedish
[School and School Administration]--see Education
[Science]...6110
[Science (General)]................................6243
[Scientific Agricultural Publications]..............6070
[SCUBA Diving]--see Water Sports
[Sculpture]--see Art
[Seals]--see Rubber Stamps, Seals, and Stencils
[Secret Societies]--see Fraternal Publications
[Security]--see Safety
[Seed and Nursery Trade]........................6249
[Seismology].......................................6249
[Selling and Salesmanship].......................6249
[Senior Citizens' Interests].......................6111
[Service Industries]...............................6249
[Service Stations]--see Automotive (Trade); also Petroleum, Oil, and Gas
[Sewage Disposal]--see Water Supply and Sewage Disposal
[Sewing]--see Home Economics; also Dressmaking, Needlework, and Quilting
[Sewing Machines]--see Machinery and Equipment
[Sex/Erotica].......................................6111
[Sheep]--see Livestock
[Sheet Metal Working]--see Metal, Metallurgy, and Metal Trade
[Shipbuilding]--see Ships and Shipping
[Ships and Shipping]..............................6250
[Shoes, Leather, and Luggage]..................6250
[Signs]--see Advertising and Marketing
[Silk]--see Textiles
[Skating]...6114
[Skiing]..6114
[Skin Diving]--see Water Sports
[Slot Machines]--see Vending Machines
[Slovak]..6075
[Slovene]..6076
[Soap]--see Cosmetics and Toiletries
[Soccer]..6114
[Social and Political Issues]......................6111
[Social Programs].................................6250
[Social Sciences]--see Sociology; also Psychology and Psychiatry; also Anthropology and Ethnology; also Economics; also Politics; also History and Genealogy, 6251
[Social Studies]--see Geography; also History and Genealogy; also Sociology
[Socialism]--see Labor
[Societies]--see Clubs and Societies
[Society]..6111
[Society for the Prevention of Cruelty to Animals and Anti-Vivisection]....................6252
[Sociology]...6252
[Soft Drinks]--see Beverages, Brewing, and Bottling
[Sound]--see Physics
[Space]--see Physics; also Astronautics; also Nuclear Engineering
[Spanish]...6076
[Spas, Health]--see Physical Fitness
[Spas, Home]--see Sporting Goods/Retail Sports
[SPCA]--see Society for the Prevention of Cruelty to Animals and Anti-Vivisection
[Speech Correction]--see Hearing and Speech
[Speleology]--see Geology
[Spices]--see Food and Grocery Trade
[Sporting Goods/Retail Sports]...................6254
[Squash]--see Racquet Sports
[Stage]--see Drama and Theatre; also Performing Arts
[Stamps]--see Collecting; also Rubber Stamps, Seals, and Stencils
[State, Municipal, and County Administration]...6254
[State Publications]--see Local, State, and Regional Publications
[Statistics]...6254

[Stencils]--see Rubber Stamps, Seals, and Stencils
[Stone and Rock Products]......................6255
[Storage and Warehousing]......................6255
[Store Display]--see Advertising and Marketing
[Stoves]--see Appliances
[Streets]--see Roads and Streets
[Substance Abuse and Treatment]...............6255
[Sugar and Sugar Beets]........................6255
[Surfing]--see Water Sports
[Surgery]--see Medicine and Surgery
[Surplus]--see Commerce and Industry
[Surveying]--see Engineering (Various branches)
[Swedish]..6076
[Swimming]--see Water Sports
[Swimming Pools]--see Sporting Goods/Retail Sports
[Syrian Publications]--see Arabic

T
[Tailoring]--see Dressmaking, Needlework, and Quilting
[Tamil]...6077
[Tariff]--see Taxation and Tariff
[Taxation and Tariff]..............................6255
[Taxicabs]--see Transportation, Traffic, and Shipping
[Tea and Coffee]--see Food and Grocery Trade
[Teachers]--see Education
[Teen Magazines]--see Youths' Interests
[Telecommunications].............................6255
[Telephone and Telegraph]--see Telecommunications
[Television]--see Radio, Television, Cable, and Video
[Tennis]--see Racquet Sports
[Textiles]...6256
[Theatre]--see Drama and Theatre; also Performing Arts
[Theology]...6257
[Therapy]--see Psychology and Psychiatry
[Tile]--see Building Materials, Concrete, Brick, and Tile
[Tires]--see Automotive (Trade)
[Tobacco]..6257
[Toiletries]--see Cosmetics and Toiletries
[Tools]--see Metal, Metallurgy, and Metal Trade
[Tourism]--see Travel and Tourism; also City, Hotel, Railroad, and Travel Guides
[Town Planning]--see State, Municipal, and County Administration
[Toxicology].......................................6257
[Toys]--see Gifts, Toys, and Novelties
[Tractors]--see Machinery and Equipment; also Farm Implements and Supplies
[Trademarks]--see Patents, Trademarks, and Copyrights
[Traffic]--see Transportation, Traffic, and Shipping
[Trailers and Accessories].......................6258
[Transportation, Traffic, and Shipping]...........6258
[Trapping]--see Hunting, Fishing, and Game Management; also Fur Trade and Fur Farming
[Travel Guides]--see City, Hotel, Railroad, and Travel Guides
[Travel and Tourism]........................6115, 6258
[Triathlons and Biathlons].......................6114
[Trucks and Trucking]............................6259
[Turf and Turf Maintenance]....................6250
[Turkeys]--see Poultry and Pigeons
[Turkish]...6077
[Typography]--see Printing and Typography

U
[Ukrainian]...6077
[Ultrasound]--see Radiology, Ultrasound, and Nuclear Medicine
[Underground Publications]--see Alternative and Underground
[Undertakers]--see Funeral Directors
[Underwear]--see Clothing
[Unions]--see Labor
[U.S. Air Force]--see Military and Navy
[U.S. Army]--see Military and Navy

[U.S. Coast Guard]--see Military and Navy
[U.S. Marine Corps]--see Military and Navy
[U.S. Navy]--see Military and Navy
[Upholstery]--see Furniture and Furnishings
[Urban Affairs]--see State, Municipal, and County Administration
[Urdu]...6077

V
[Variety Stores]--see Retail
[Varnish]--see Paint and Wallcoverings
[Vegetables]--see Fruit, Fruit Products, and Produce Trade; also Horticulture; also Home and Garden
[Vending Machines]...............................6259
[Veneers]--see Wood and Woodworking
[Ventilating]--see Air Conditioning and Refrigeration; also Plumbing and Heating
[Veterans]...6259
[Veterinary Medicine].............................6260
[Video]--see Radio, Television, Cable, and Video
[Video Games]--see Entertainment; also Radio, Television, Cable, and Video
[Vietnamese]......................................6077
[Vocational Education]............................6260

W
[Walking]--see Physical Fitness
[Wallcoverings]--see Paint and Wallcoverings
[Waste Management and Recycling]............6261
[Watches and Watchmaking]--see Jewelry, Watches, and Clocks
[Water Sports].....................................6114
[Water Supply and Sewage Disposal]...........6261
[Water and Water Pollution]--see Water Supply and Sewage Disposal; also Ecology and Conservation
[Waterways]--see Boats and Marine
[Weather]--see Astronomy and Meteorology
[Weekly, Semiweekly, and Triweekly Newspapers]--see Paid Community Newspapers
[Weight Lifting]--see Physical Fitness
[Weights and Measures]..........................6261
[Welding]..6261
[Welsh]..6077
[Wigs]--see Hairstyling
[Wildlife and Exotic Animals]....................6262
[Window Display]--see Advertising and Marketing
[Wine]--see Beverages, Brewing, and Bottling
[Wire and Wire Products]--see Metal, Metallurgy, and Metal Trade
[Women's Apparel]--see Clothing; also Fashion; also Women's Interests
[Women's Clubs]--see Clubs and Societies; also Women's Interests
[Women's Political Affairs]--see Politics; also Women's Interests
[Wood and Woodworking].........................6262
[Wool and Mohair]--see Livestock
[Woolens]--see Textiles
[Wrestling]--see Boxing and Wrestling
[Writers]--see Book Trade and Author News; also Journalism and Publishing; also Literature; also Literature and Literary Reviews

X
[X-Ray]--see Radiology, Ultrasound, and Nuclear Medicine

Y
[Yachting]--see Boating and Yachting
[Yiddish]...6077
[YMCA and YWCA]--see Religious Publications
[YMHA and YWHA]--see Religious Publications
[Youths' Interests]................................6115
[Yugoslavian Publications]--see Croatian; also Serbian; also Macedonian; also Slovene

Z
[Zoology]...6262
[Zoos]--see Zoology

Index entries are arranged geographically, first by country and then by city. Within cities in this index, citations appear alphabetically by publication title. Citations include publication title, entry number (given in parentheses immediately following the title), and circulation figures.

ARGENTINA
Cordova
Espacio Apicola [41487]

AUSTRALIA
Armidale
Boer Briefs [41559]

Brisbane
Beanscene [41645]

Chermside
Australian Organic Journal
 [41750] .. .. (Paid) ‡6,000

Cleveland
Good Fruits & Vegetables [41767]
Queensland Smart Farmer [41768]

Collingwood
Animal Production Science
 [41780] .... (Paid) 600
Crop & Pasture Science [41784]

Deakin
Animal Health Australia [41832]

East Brighton
Australasian Farmers' Dealers' Journal (AFDJ) [41844]

Hawthorn
The Australian Holstein Journal
 [41941] .... (Paid) 3,000

Maitland
Australasian Beekeeper
 [42028] .. .. (Paid) 1,600

Melbourne
Australian Garden History [42049]

Mildura
Australian Citrus News
 [42106] ..../...... (Combined) 3,000

Nathan
International Journal of Agricultural
 Resources, Governance and
 Ecology [42143]

North Richmond
Australian Farm Journal
 [42160] .... ★4,456
Farming Small Areas
 [42162] .... (Paid) ★54,709

Prospect East
The Australian & New Zealand Wine
 Industry Journal [42267] 3,000
Australian Viticulture
 [42268] .. .. (Paid) 4,000

Rockhampton
Braford Annual [42314]

Surry Hills
Farm Policy Journal [42429]

Sydney
PESTALK [42560]

Tullamarine
Alfa Lotfeeding Magazine
 [42645] .... (Controlled) 8,000
Australian Dairyfarmer
 [42647] .. .. ‡14,112
Australian Horticulture
 [42648] .. .. ★2,360
Australian Landcare
 [42649] .. .. ‡33,000
Irrigation and Water Resources
 [42652] .. .. ‡14,500

Unley
Pig Industry News [42660] ...... ‡300

BAHRAIN
Manama
Arab World Agribusiness
 [42786] 18,715

BANGLADESH
Dhaka
Asia-Pacific Journal of Rural
 Development [42802]

Gazipur
Annals of Bangladesh Agriculture
 [42819] .. .. (Paid) 300

BOTSWANA
Gaborone
ZJAR [42946] 2,000

BRAZIL
Campinas
Bragantia [42963]
Bragantia [42964]

Santa Maria
Ciencia Rural [43016]

CAMEROON
Yaounde
Cameroon Journal of Agricultural
 Science [43128]

CHILE
Arica
IDESIA [43133]

PEOPLE'S REPUBLIC OF CHINA
Beijing
Acta Agronomica Sinica
 [43165] 12,000

Science in China Series C [43217]

Shanghai
Journal of Shanghai Jiaotong University Agricultural Science [43483]

COTE D'IVOIRE
Abidjan
Agronomie Africaine [43556]
Sciences & Nature [43557]

DENMARK
Copenhagen
Dansk Landbrug
 [43663] .... (Combined) 116,000

Frederiksberg
Acta Agriculturae
 Scandinavica—Section C, Food
 Economics [43688]

Herning
Maskinbladet [43722] 54,734

ESTONIA
Tartu
Agronomy Research [43791]

ETHIOPIA
Haramaya
East African Journal of Sciences
 [43805]

FINLAND
Helsinki
Landsbygdens Folk
 [43843] 10,220

Jyvaskyla
Suo - Mires and Peat [43872]

Kuvalehdet
Kaytannon Maamies (KM)
 [43884] .. .. (Combined) ‡23,791

Rajamaki
Teho [43905] .. .. (Paid) 4,662

Turku
Farma Sanomat
 [43909] .... (Combined) 9,000

FRANCE
Avignon
Agronomy for Sustainable
 Development [43917] 1,000

Montrouge
Cahiers d'etudes et de recherches
 francophones/Agricultures [43984]

Oleagineux, Corps Gras, Lipides
 [44003]

Paris
Jeunes Agriculteurs
 [44062] .. ..,.... (Paid) 30,000
Meat Processing Global Edition
 [44070]
Phytoma La Defense des Vegetaux
 [44075] 25,000

Perols
Lien Horticole [44092]

GERMANY
Aachen
Gb - Das Magazin fur
 Zierpflanzenbau [44137] 2,846

Bonn
Ecology and Farming
 [44255] 2,000
European Review of Agricultural
 Economics [44258]

Braunschweig
Deutsche Baumschule [44275]
Friedhofs Kultur [44276]
Gestalten & Verkaufen [44277]
TASPO [44279]

Frankfurt
Agrifuture [44356] 20,000
Allgemeine Fleischer Zeitung [44357]
DLG-Mitteilungen [44359] 12,000

Hamburg
Oil World Monthly [44421]

Kumhausen
AgrarMEGA [44515]

Munich
DLZ Agrarmagazin
 [44558] .... (Paid) 71,000
LSV aktuell [44569]
Rinderzucht/Fleckvieh [44580]

GHANA
Accra
West African Journal of Applied
 Ecology [44730]

Kumasi
Agricultural and Food Science Journal of Ghana [44734]

GREECE
Thessaloniki
Journal of Agricultural and Food
 Economics [44774]

HUNGARY
Budapest
Acta Phytopathologica et Entomologica Hungarica [44818]

Circulation: ★ = ABC; △ = BPA; ◆ = CAC; • = CCAB; ❑ = VAC; ⊕ = PO Statement; ‡ = Publisher's Report; Boldface figures = sworn; Light figures = estimated.

Agrokemia es Talajtan [44821]

Martonvasar
Acta Agronomica Hungarica [44890]

INDIA

Delhi
Dairy India Yearbook
[45089] .. .. (Paid) 2,500

Hyderabad
Journal of Research—ANGRAU
[45175]

Jodhpur
Advances in Horticulture and Forestry
[45212]
Annals of Arid Zone
[45214] .... (Paid) 800
Journal of Arid Legumes [45225]

Kochi
Indian Coconut Journal
[45250] .. .. (Paid) 2,000

Kolkata
Horticultural Journal [45268]
Institution of Engineers (India) Agri-
cultural Engineering Division
Journal [45277] .... (Paid) 4,000

Mohindergarh
Crop Research [45346] 2,000

Mumbai
Feed Trends [45370] 1,000
SEA Monthly News Circular
[45438] 1,500

New Delhi
Afro-Asian Journal of Rural
Development
[45479] .... (Combined) 400
FAI Abstract Service
[45512] .... (Paid) 2,200
Fertiliser Association of India's Fertil-
iser Statistics [45513] 2,000
Fertiliser Marketing News
[45514] .. .. (Paid) 3,000
Indian Cooperative Review
[45536] .. .. (Paid) 1,000
Indian Dairyman
[45537] .. .. (Paid) 2,000
Indian Farming
[45544] .. .. (Paid) 51,200
Indian Horticulture
[45546] .. .. (Paid) 12,000
Indian Journal of Agricultural
Engineering [45547] 4,000
Indian Journal of Agricultural
Sciences [45548] 2,000
The Indian Journal of Crop Science
[45550]
Indian Journal of Dairy Science
[45551]
Irrigation and Drainage
[45591] .. .. (Paid) 2,900

Thrissur
Journal of Tropical Agriculture
[45750] .... (Paid) 500

INDONESIA

Jakarta
Cocoinfo International [45794]
Cord [45795]

IRELAND

Sandyford
Farm & Plant Buyers Guide [46055]

ITALY

Bussolengo
La Razza Bruna [46129] 10,000

Fiorentino
Aestimum [46139]

Milan
Agro Food
[46162] .... (Combined) 7,000

Peschiera Borromeo
Agri Parts [46212] 10,000

Rome
Apiacta [46221] 250

Trento
ACAV Informa [46260]

Vernasca
Flortecnica
[46278] .... (Controlled) 6,800

Verona
L'Informatore Agrario
[46280] .. .. (Combined) 35,211
Vita in Campagna
[46281] .. .. (Combined) 74,211

JAMAICA

Kingston
The Farmer [46284]

JAPAN

Kyoto
Breeding Science
[46467] .. .. (Paid) 2,000
Journal of Pesticide Science
[46477] .. .. (Paid) 2,000

Miyazaki
Grassland Science
[46518] .. .. (Paid) 1,400

Tokyo
Animal Science Journal
[46735] .. .. (Paid) 3,000
Japanese Journal of Crop Science
[46868] .. .. (Paid) 2,000
Journal of Japanese Society for Horticultural Science
[46918] .. .. (Paid) 3,000
Rural and Environmental Engineering
[47034]
Soil Science and Plant Nutrition
[47041]

JORDAN

Amman
Dirasat Agricultural Sciences
[47153] .... (Controlled) 1,000

KENYA

Nairobi
African Journal of Food, Agriculture,
Nutrition and Development [47172]
East African Agricultural and Forestry
Journal [47179]

REPUBLIC OF KOREA

Seoul
Asian-Australasian Journal of Animal
Sciences [47254] 1,000

Suwon
Journal of Korean Society of Soil Science and Fertilizer [47327] 850

MALAYSIA

Kuala Lumpur
Journal of Tropical Agriculture & Food
Science [47608] .. .. (Paid) 500

Serdang
Pertanika Journal of Tropical Agricultural Science [47717]

MEXICO

Mexico City
CIMMYT Annual Report
[47783] 5,000

San Luis Huexotla
Agrociencia [47797]

NEPAL

Kathmandu
Nepal Agriculture Research Journal
[47842]

NETHERLANDS

Amersfoort
LEISA Magazine [47874] 17,000

Amsterdam
Agricultural Systems [47885]
Agriculture, Ecosystems &
Environment [47886]
Tailoring Biotechnologies [48240]

Beekbergen
World Poultry Science Journal
[48277] 7,000

Doorwerth
Weed Research [48317]

Dordrecht
Agroforestry Systems [48323]
BioControl [48330]
Phytoparasitica [48530]
Plant and Soil [48536]
Precision Agriculture [48541]

Wageningen
The Journal of Agricultural Education
and Extension [48771]
NJAS [48772]

NEW ZEALAND

Auckland
New Zealand Lifestyle Block
[48818] *8,412

Christchurch
Australian AG Contractor and Large
Scale Farmer [48863]
New Zealand AgriBusiness [48871]
New Zealand AgriVet [48872]
New Zealand Rural Contractor and
Large Scale Farmer [48875]

Wellington
New Zealand Journal of Agricultural
Research [49021]
New Zealand Journal of Crop and
Horticultural Science [49023]

NIGERIA

Asaba
Journal of Applied Chemistry and Agricultural Research [49061]

Ibadan
African Journal of Livestock
Extension [49085]
Journal of Agriculture and Social
Research [49088]
Moor Journal of Agricultural Research
[49092]
Nigerian Journal of Horticultural
Science [49097]

Ilorin
Agrosearch [49118]
Journal of Agricultural Research and
Development [49120]

Lagos
African Journal of Agricultural
Research [49129]
Scientific Research & Essays [49143]

Nsukka
Agro-Science [49154]

Obubra
Journal of Agriculture, Forestry and
the Social Sciences [49158]

Owerri
Global Approaches to Extension
Practice [49162]
International Journal of Agriculture
and Rural Development [49163]

Port Harcourt
Journal of Technology and Education
in Nigeria [49168]

Umuahia
Nigerian Agricultural Journal [49175]

PAKISTAN

Faisalabad
Agricultural Journal [49231]
American-Eurasian Journal of Agricul-
tural & Environmental Sciences
[49232]
International Journal of Poultry
Science [49254]
Research Journal of Agriculture and
Biological Sciences [49280]
Research Journal of Agronomy
[49281]
Research Journal of Dairy Sciences
[49287]
Research Journal of Poultry Sciences
[49292]
World Journal of Agricultural
Sciences [49299]

Islamabad
Pakistan Journal of Agricultural
Research [49306] .. ... (Paid) 1,000
Progressive Farming
[49311] .. .. (Paid) 1,000

PHILIPPINES

Laguna
The Philippine Agricultural Scientist
[49507] .. .. (Paid) 25,000

Manila
SABRAO Journal of Breeding and
Genetics [49559]

POLAND

Lublin
Annals of Agricultural and Environmental Medicine [49672]

Warsaw
European Countryside [49709]
Kwietnik [49729] 42,200

PORTUGAL

Lisbon
Revista de Ciencias Agrarias [49805]

SAUDI ARABIA

Riyadh
Journal of King Saud University: Agricultural Sciences
[50063] .. .. (Paid) 2,000

SLOVENIA

Ljubljana
Acta Agriculturae Slovenica [50333]

REPUBLIC OF SOUTH AFRICA

Cape Town
Landbouweekblad [50386] ... 42,628

Circulation: ★ = ABC; △ = BPA; ◆ = CAC; • = CCAB; ❑ = VAC; ⊕ = PO Statement; ‡ = Publisher's Report; Boldface figures = sworn; Light figures = estimated.

Agricultural Publications

Centurion
AFMA Matrix [50436] 2,000
SA Irrigation [50446]

Elsenburg
Agriprobe [50477]

Erasmusrand
South African Journal of Plant and
    Soil [50478]

Grahamstown
Agricultural and Food Science Jour-
    nal of Ghana [50492]
Ghana Journal of Agricultural Science
    [50495]
International Journal of Tropical Agri-
    culture and Food Systems [50499]
Journal of Social Development in
    Africa [50503] ... (Combined) 150

Matieland
Agrekon [50552]

Pietermaritzburg
African Journal of Range and Forage
    Science [50565] .... (Paid) 196
Scientia Horticulturae [50569]

Pretoria
South African Journal of Agricultural
    Extension [50601]
South African Journal of Animal
    Science [50602]

SPAIN
Burjasot
Food Science and Technology
    International [50711]

Madrid
Agricultura
    [50725] .... (Combined) ‡6,426
Eurocarne [50758] 6000

SRI LANKA
Colombo
Sri Lanka Journal of Agrarian Studies
    [50864] .... (Paid) 300

SUDAN
Khartoum
Agriculture and Development in the
    Arab World [50938]

SWAZILAND
Kwaluseni
UNISWA Research Journal of Agricul-
    ture, Science and Technology
    [50944]

Luyengo
UNISWA Journal of Agriculture
    [50945]

SWEDEN
Eskilstuna
Husdjur
    [50953] .... (Controlled) 17,900

SWITZERLAND
Niederonz
Forum Kleinwiederkaeuer
    [51219] .... (Controlled) 14,569

Posieux
Agrarforschung Schweiz
    [51221] .... (Paid) 12,500

TAIWAN
Tainan
Centerpoint [51326]

Taipei
Journal of Agricultural Research of
    China [51347]

THAILAND
Pathumthani
International Agricultural Engineering
    Journal [51460] 300
International Agricultural Journal
    [51461]

TURKEY
Ankara
Turkish Journal of Agriculture and
    Forestry [51503]
Turkish Journal of Veterinary and Ani-
    mal Sciences [51516]

UGANDA
Kampala
African Crop Science Journal [51583]
Eastern Africa Journal of Rural
    Development [51586]

UNITED KINGDOM
Abingdon
Journal of Peasant Studies [51930]

Appleby-in-Westmorland
International Journal of Dairy
    Technology [52126] 2,000

Bangor
Experimental Agriculture
    [52170] 550

Barnstaple
Agricultural Trader [52190]

Bedfordshire
European Journal of Soil Science
    [52278]

Bristol
Gardens Illustrated
    [52672] .... ★31,312

Brookfield
The Scottish Beekeeper [52749]

Burnham
International Pest Control [52766]

Cambridge
Journal of International Farm
    Management [52857]

Chester
Food and Agricultural Immunology
    [52995]

Coventry
The Organic Way [53089] 30,400

Crawley
Meat Trades Journal
    [53108] .... ★5,574

Cudham
Farm and Horticultural Equipment
    [53142]
Old Tractor [53145]
Practical Poultry [53146]

Duffield
Forge [53208] 3,400

East Malling
Crop Protection [53238]

Edinburgh
Landwards [53297] 2,000

Exeter
Country Smallholding [53350]

Felixstowe
Ford & Fordson Tractors [53385]

Kent
South East Farmer
    [53683] .... (Combined). 12,500

London
African Farming and Food
    Processing [53920] 10,755
Far Eastern Agriculture
    [54443] .... ★7,050
Farmers Trader [54444] 36,500
Journal of the Science of Food and
    Agriculture [54816]
Lebensmittel-Wissenschaft und-Technologie
    [54863]
Nitrogen & Methanol
    [55005] .... (Combined) ‡3,600
Outlook on Agriculture [55046]
World Tobacco [55425] 4,256

Loughborough
Meat Science [55485]

Malvern
The Sheep Farmer [55540]

Monmouth
Bees for Development Journal
    [55644] .... (Paid) 4,000

Nottingham
Today's Technician [55773]

Oxford
The Australian Journal of Agricultural
    and Resource Economics [55878]

Penicuik
Agricultural and Forest Entomolgy
    [56242]

Peterborough
British Sugar Beet Review
    [56253] .... (Non-paid) 14,000
The Essential Guide to UK Farm &
    Outdoor Power Equipment [56256]

The Garden [56258]

Reading
GrowthPoint [56319] ... (Paid) 1,000

Roslin
British Poultry Science [56408]

Rushden
UK Irrigation [56427] 500

Shrewsbury
The Farmer (Shropshire and the
    Welsh Borders)
    [56528] ...... (Non-paid) 15,000

Stoneleigh
NFU Countryside
    [56636] ...... (Controlled) ★60,000

Stroud
Star and Furrow [56648]

Sutton
Farmers Weekly [56685] .... ★67,446
Farmland Market [56686]
Poultry World
    [56691] .... (Paid) ★3,267

Swansea
New Leaves [56704]

Thrapston
The Mule [56748]

Tunbridge Wells
Agra Europe Weekly [56776]
AgraFood East Europe [56777]
Dairy Markets Weekly [56780]

Twickenham
Fertilizer Focus [56791] 3,000

Wallingford
AgBiotech News and Information
    [56813] 180
Biocontrol News and Information
    [56816] 270
Crop Physiology Abstracts [56817]
Ornamental Horticulture [56821]
Pig News and Information
    [56822] 650
Postharvest News and Information
    [56823] 150
Review of Agricultural Entomology
    [56824]
Review of Aromatic and Medicinal
    Plants [56825]
Soils and Fertilizers [56829] 380
Soybean Abstracts [56830]

Wimborne
International Camellia Journal
    [56928] 1,600

ZIMBABWE
Harare
New Farmer [57117]

Circulation: ★ = ABC; △ = BPA; ◆ = CAC; • = CCAB; ❑ = VAC; ⊕ = PO Statement; ‡ = Publisher's Report; Boldface figures = sworn; Light figures = estimated.

Index entries are arranged by subject (please refer to the Index to Subject Terms). Within the subject groupings, entries appear geographically by country and alphabetically within city. Citations in this index include publication title, entry number (given in parentheses), and circulation figures.

BEEKEEPING

ARGENTINA
Cordova
Espacio Apicola [41487]

AUSTRALIA
Maitland
Australasian Beekeeper
[42028] .... (Paid) 1,600

ITALY
Rome
Apiacta [46221] 250

UNITED KINGDOM
Brookfield
The Scottish Beekeeper [52749]

Monmouth
Bees for Development Journal
[55644] .... (Paid) 4,000

DAIRYING

AUSTRALIA
Hawthorn
The Australian Holstein Journal
[41941] .... (Paid) 3,000

Tullamarine
Australian Dairyfarmer
[42647] .... ‡14,112

INDIA
Delhi
Dairy India Yearbook
[45089] .... (Paid) 2,500

New Delhi
Indian Dairyman
[45537] .... (Paid) 2,000
Indian Journal of Dairy Science
[45551]

PAKISTAN
Faisalabad
Research Journal of Dairy Sciences
[49287]

SLOVENIA
Ljubljana
Acta Agriculturae Slovenica [50333]

UNITED KINGDOM
Appleby-in-Westmorland
International Journal of Dairy
Technology [52126] 2,000

FARM BUREAU, GRANGE, AND COOPERATIVE ASSOCIATIONS

AUSTRALIA
Brisbane
Beanscene [41645]

Surry Hills
Farm Policy Journal [42429]

INDIA
New Delhi
Indian Cooperative Review
[45536] .... (Paid) 1,000

FARM IMPLEMENTS AND SUPPLIES

AUSTRALIA
East Brighton
Australasian Farmers' Dealers' Journal (AFDJ) [41844]

FINLAND
Helsinki
Landsbygdens Folk
[43843] 10,220

INDIA
New Delhi
Irrigation and Drainage
[45591] .... (Paid) 2,900

IRELAND
Sandyford
Farm & Plant Buyers Guide [46055]

ITALY
Peschiera Borromeo
Agri Parts [46212] 10,000

UNITED KINGDOM
Cudham
Farm and Horticultural Equipment
[53142]
Old Tractor [53145]

East Malling
Crop Protection [53238]

Felixstowe
Ford & Fordson Tractors [53385]

London
Farmers Trader [54444] 36,500

Peterborough
The Essential Guide to UK Farm &
Outdoor Power Equipment [56256]

Rushden
UK Irrigation [56427] 500

FARM NEWSPAPERS

FINLAND
Helsinki
Landsbygdens Folk
[43843] 10,220

NETHERLANDS
Amersfoort
LEISA Magazine [47874] 17,000

UNITED KINGDOM
Barnstaple
Agricultural Trader [52190]

Exeter
Country Smallholding [53350]

FEED AND GRAIN

INDIA
Mumbai
Feed Trends [45370] 1,000
SEA Monthly News Circular
[45438] 1,500

REPUBLIC OF SOUTH AFRICA
Centurion
AFMA Matrix [50436] 2,000

FERTILIZER

FINLAND
Jyvaskyla
Suo - Mires and Peat [43872]

INDIA
New Delhi
Fertiliser Association of India's Fertiliser Statistics [45513] 2,000
Fertiliser Marketing News
[45514] ... . (Paid) 3,000

REPUBLIC OF KOREA
Suwon
Journal of Korean Society of Soil Science and Fertilizer [47327] 850

UNITED KINGDOM
London
Nitrogen & Methanol
[55005] .. .. (Combined) ‡3,600

Twickenham
Fertilizer Focus [56791] 3,000

Wallingford
Soils and Fertilizers [56829] 380

GENERAL AGRICULTURE
See also Farm Newspapers

AUSTRALIA
Brisbane
Beanscene [41645]

Cleveland
Good Fruits & Vegetables [41767]
Queensland Smart Farmer [41768]

Collingwood
Crop & Pasture Science [41784]

Mildura
Australian Citrus News
[42106] .... (Combined) 3,000

Nathan
International Journal of Agricultural
Resources, Governance and
Ecology [42143]

North Richmond
Australian Farm Journal
[42160] .... ★4,456
Farming Small Areas
[42162] .... (Paid) ★54,709

Prospect East
The Australian & New Zealand Wine
Industry Journal [42267] 3,000
Australian Viticulture
[42268] .. .. (Paid) 4,000

Sydney
PESTALK [42560]

Tullamarine
Alfa Lotfeeding Magazine
[42645] .... (Controlled) 8,000
Australian Horticulture
[42648] .... ★2,360
Australian Landcare
[42649] .... ‡33,000
Irrigation and Water Resources
[42652] .... ‡14,500

Unley
Pig Industry News [42660] ...... ‡300

BAHRAIN
Manama
Arab World Agribusiness
[42786] 18,715

Circulation: ★ = ABC; △ = BPA; ◆ = CAC; • = CCAB; ❑ = VAC; ⊕ = PO Statement; ‡ = Publisher's Report; Boldface figures = sworn; Light figures = estimated.

BANGLADESH
Dhaka
Asia-Pacific Journal of Rural Development [42802]

Gazipur
Annals of Bangladesh Agriculture [42819] .... (Paid) 300

BRAZIL
Campinas
Bragantia [42963]
Bragantia [42964]

Santa Maria
Ciencia Rural [43016]

CAMEROON
Yaounde
Cameroon Journal of Agricultural Science [43128]

PEOPLE'S REPUBLIC OF CHINA
Beijing
Acta Agronomica Sinica [43165] 12,000
Science in China Series C [43217]

COTE D'IVOIRE
Abidjan
Sciences & Nature [43557]

DENMARK
Copenhagen
Dansk Landbrug [43663] .... (Combined) 116,000

Frederiksberg
Acta Agriculturae Scandinavica—Section C, Food Economics [43688]

Herning
Maskinbladet [43722] 54,734

ETHIOPIA
Haramaya
East African Journal of Sciences [43805]

FINLAND
Helsinki
Landsbygdens Folk [43843] 10,220

Kuvalehdet
Kaytannon Maamies (KM) [43884] .. .. (Combined) ‡23,791

Rajamaki
Teho [43905] .. .. (Paid) 4,662

Turku
Farma Sanomat [43909] .... (Combined) 9,000

FRANCE
Avignon
Agronomy for Sustainable Development [43917] 1,000

Montrouge
Cahiers d'etudes et de recherches francophones/Agricultures [43984]

Paris
Jeunes Agriculteurs [44062] .. .. (Paid) 30,000
Phytoma La Defense des Vegetaux [44075] 25,000

GERMANY
Bonn
Ecology and Farming [44255] 2,000

European Review of Agricultural Economics [44258]

Frankfurt
Agrifuture [44356] 20,000
DLG-Mitteilungen [44359] 12,000

Kumhausen
AgrarMEGA [44515]

Munich
DLZ Agrarmagazin [44558] .. .. (Paid) 71,000
LSV aktuell [44569]

GHANA
Accra
West African Journal of Applied Ecology [44730]

Kumasi
Agricultural and Food Science Journal of Ghana [44734]

GREECE
Thessaloniki
Journal of Agricultural and Food Economics [44774]

HUNGARY
Martonvasar
Acta Agronomica Hungarica [44890]

INDIA
Hyderabad
Journal of Research—ANGRAU [45175]

Jodhpur
Annals of Arid Zone [45214] .... (Paid) 800
Journal of Arid Legumes [45225]

Kochi
Indian Coconut Journal [45250] .. .. (Paid) 2,000

Kolkata
Institution of Engineers (India) Agricultural Engineering Division Journal [45277] .... (Paid) 4,000

Mohindergarh
Crop Research [45346] 2,000

Mumbai
Feed Trends [45370] 1,000

New Delhi
Afro-Asian Journal of Rural Development [45479] .... (Combined) 400
FAI Abstract Service [45512] .. .. (Paid) 2,200
Fertiliser Association of India's Fertiliser Statistics [45513] 2,000
Indian Dairyman [45537] .. .. (Paid) 2,000
Indian Farming [45544] .. .. (Paid) 51,200
Indian Journal of Agricultural Engineering [45547] 4,000
Irrigation and Drainage [45591] .. .. (Paid) 2,900

Thrissur
Journal of Tropical Agriculture [45750] .... (Paid) 500

INDONESIA
Jakarta
Cocoinfo International [45794]
Cord [45795]

IRELAND
Sandyford
Farm & Plant Buyers Guide [46055]

ITALY
Fiorentino
Aestimum [46139]

Trento
ACAV Informa [46260]

Verona
L'Informatore Agrario [46280] .. .. (Combined) 35,211

JAMAICA
Kingston
The Farmer [46284]

JAPAN
Kyoto
Breeding Science [46467] .. .. (Paid) 2,000
Journal of Pesticide Science [46477] .. .. (Paid) 2,000

Miyazaki
Grassland Science [46518] .. .. (Paid) 1,400

Tokyo
Animal Science Journal [46735] .. .. (Paid) 3,000
Japanese Journal of Crop Science [46868] .. .. (Paid) 2,000
Rural and Environmental Engineering [47034]
Soil Science and Plant Nutrition [47041]

JORDAN
Amman
Dirasat Agricultural Sciences [47153] .. .. (Controlled) 1,000

KENYA
Nairobi
East African Agricultural and Forestry Journal [47179]

REPUBLIC OF KOREA
Seoul
Asian-Australasian Journal of Animal Sciences [47254] 1,000

MALAYSIA
Kuala Lumpur
Journal of Tropical Agriculture & Food Science [47608] .. .. (Paid) 500

Serdang
Pertanika Journal of Tropical Agricultural Science [47717]

MEXICO
Mexico City
CIMMYT Annual Report [47783] 5,000

San Luis Huexotla
Agrociencia [47797]

NEPAL
Kathmandu
Nepal Agriculture Research Journal [47842]

NETHERLANDS
Amersfoort
LEISA Magazine [47874] 17,000

Amsterdam
Tailoring Biotechnologies [48240]

Doorwerth
Weed Research [48317]

Dordrecht
BioControl [48330]
Precision Agriculture [48541]

Wageningen
The Journal of Agricultural Education and Extension [48771]
NJAS [48772]

NEW ZEALAND
Christchurch
Australian AG Contractor and Large Scale Farmer [48863]
New Zealand AgriBusiness [48871]
New Zealand AgriVet [48872]
New Zealand Rural Contractor and Large Scale Farmer [48875]

Wellington
New Zealand Journal of Agricultural Research [49021]

NIGERIA
Asaba
Journal of Applied Chemistry and Agricultural Research [49061]

Ibadan
Journal of Agriculture and Social Research [49088]
Moor Journal of Agricultural Research [49092]

Ilorin
Agrosearch [49118]
Journal of Agricultural Research and Development [49120]

Lagos
African Journal of Agricultural Research [49129]
Scientific Research & Essays [49143]

Nsukka
Agro-Science [49154]

Obubra
Journal of Agriculture, Forestry and the Social Sciences [49158]

Owerri
Global Approaches to Extension Practice [49162]
International Journal of Agriculture and Rural Development [49163]

Port Harcourt
Journal of Technology and Education in Nigeria [49168]

Umuahia
Nigerian Agricultural Journal [49175]

PAKISTAN
Faisalabad
Agricultural Journal [49231]
American-Eurasian Journal of Agricultural & Environmental Sciences [49232]
Research Journal of Agriculture and Biological Sciences [49280]
Research Journal of Agronomy [49281]
World Journal of Agricultural Sciences [49299]

Islamabad
Pakistan Journal of Agricultural Research [49306] .. ... (Paid) 1,000
Progressive Farming [49311] .. .. (Paid) 1,000

PHILIPPINES
Laguna
The Philippine Agricultural Scientist [49507] .. .. (Paid) 25,000

Manila
SABRAO Journal of Breeding and Genetics [49559]

Circulation: ★ = ABC; △ = BPA; ◆ = CAC; • = CCAB; ❑ = VAC; ⊕ = PO Statement; ‡ = Publisher's Report; Boldface figures = sworn; Light figures = estimated.

POLAND
Lublin
Annals of Agricultural and Environmental Medicine [49672]

Warsaw
European Countryside [49709]

PORTUGAL
Lisbon
Revista de Ciencias Agrarias [49805]

REPUBLIC OF SOUTH AFRICA
Cape Town
Landbouweekblad [50386] 42,628

Centurion
SA Irrigation [50446]

Elsenburg
Agriprobe [50477]

Erasmusrand
South African Journal of Plant and Soil [50478]

Grahamstown
Agricultural and Food Science Journal of Ghana [50492]
Ghana Journal of Agricultural Science [50495]
International Journal of Tropical Agriculture and Food Systems [50499]
Journal of Social Development in Africa [50503] ... .. (Combined) 150

Matieland
Agrekon [50552]

Pietermaritzburg
African Journal of Range and Forage Science [50565] ... . (Paid) 196

Pretoria
South African Journal of Agricultural Extension [50601]

SRI LANKA
Colombo
Sri Lanka Journal of Agrarian Studies [50864] .... (Paid) 300

SUDAN
Khartoum
Agriculture and Development in the Arab World [50938]

SWAZILAND
Kwaluseni
UNISWA Research Journal of Agriculture, Science and Technology [50944]

Luyengo
UNISWA Journal of Agriculture [50945]

SWEDEN
Eskilstuna
Husdjur
[50953] ... . (Controlled) 17,900

SWITZERLAND
Niederonz
Forum Kleinwiederkaeuer
[51219] ... . (Controlled) 14,569

TAIWAN
Tainan
Centerpoint [51326]

Taipei
Journal of Agricultural Research of China [51347]

THAILAND
Pathumthani
International Agricultural Engineering Journal [51460] 300

TURKEY
Ankara
Turkish Journal of Agriculture and Forestry [51503]
Turkish Journal of Veterinary and Animal Sciences [51516]

UGANDA
Kampala
African Crop Science Journal [51583]
Eastern Africa Journal of Rural Development [51586]

UNITED KINGDOM
Abingdon
Journal of Peasant Studies [51930]

Barnstaple
Agricultural Trader [52190]

Burnham
International Pest Control [52766]

Cambridge
Journal of International Farm Management [52857]

Coventry
The Organic Way [53089] 30,400

Duffield
Forge [53208] 3,400

Exeter
Country Smallholding [53350]

Kent
South East Farmer
[53683] ... . (Combined) 12,500

London
African Farming and Food Processing [53920] 10,755
Far Eastern Agriculture
[54443] *7,050
Journal of the Science of Food and Agriculture [54816]
Outlook on Agriculture [55046]
World Tobacco [55425] 4,256

Nottingham
Today's Technician [55773]

Peterborough
British Sugar Beet Review
[56253] .... (Non-paid) 14,000

Rushden
UK Irrigation [56427] 500

Shrewsbury
The Farmer (Shropshire and the Welsh Borders)
[56528] .... (Non-paid) 15,000

Stoneleigh
NFU Countryside
[56636] ... . (Controlled) *60,000

Stroud
Star and Furrow [56648]

Sutton
Farmers Weekly [56685] *67,446
Farmland Market [56686]

Swansea
New Leaves [56704]

Tunbridge Wells
Agra Europe Weekly [56776]
AgraFood East Europe [56777]
Dairy Markets Weekly [56780]

Wallingford
AgBiotech News and Information
[56813] 180

Biocontrol News and Information
[56816] 270
Ornamental Horticulture [56821]
Pig News and Information
[56822] 650
Review of Agricultural Entomology
[56824]
Soils and Fertilizers [56829] 380
Soybean Abstracts [56830]

ZIMBABWE
Harare
New Farmer [57117]

HORTICULTURE

AUSTRALIA
Melbourne
Australian Garden History [42049]

Tullamarine
Australian Horticulture
[42648] *2,360

FRANCE
Perols
Lien Horticole [44092]

GERMANY
Aachen
Gb - Das Magazin fur
Zierpflanzenbau [44137] 2,846

Braunschweig
Deutsche Baumschule [44275]
Friedhofs Kultur [44276]
Gestalten & Verkaufen [44277]
TASPO [44279]

INDIA
Jodhpur
Advances in Horticulture and Forestry [45212]

Kolkata
Horticultural Journal [45268]

New Delhi
Indian Horticulture
[45546] .. .. (Paid) 12,000
The Indian Journal of Crop Science [45550]

ITALY
Vernasca
Flortecnica
[46278] .... (Controlled) 6,800

Verona
Vita in Campagna
[46281] .. .. (Combined) 74,211

JAPAN
Tokyo
Journal of Japanese Society for Horticultural Science
[46918] .. .. (Paid) 3,000

NETHERLANDS
Dordrecht
Phytoparasitica [48530]

NEW ZEALAND
Auckland
New Zealand Lifestyle Block
[48818] *8,412

Wellington
New Zealand Journal of Crop and Horticultural Science [49023]

NIGERIA
Ibadan
Nigerian Journal of Horticultural Science [49097]

POLAND
Warsaw
Kwietnik [49729] 42,200

SLOVENIA
Ljubljana
Acta Agriculturae Slovenica [50333]

REPUBLIC OF SOUTH AFRICA
Pietermaritzburg
Scientia Horticulturae [50569]

UNITED KINGDOM
Bristol
Gardens Illustrated
[52672] *31,312

Cudham
Farm and Horticultural Equipment [53142]

Penicuik
Agricultural and Forest Entomolgy [56242]

Peterborough
The Garden [56258]

Reading
GrowthPoint [56319] ... (Paid) 1,000

Wimborne
International Camellia Journal
[56928] 1,600

LIVESTOCK
See also Dairying

AUSTRALIA
Armidale
Boer Briefs [41559]

Deakin
Animal Health Australia [41832]

Hawthorn
The Australian Holstein Journal
[41941] .... (Paid) 3,000

Rockhampton
Braford Annual [42314]

Tullamarine
Alfa Lotfeeding Magazine
[42645] .... (Controlled) 8,000
Australian Dairyfarmer
[42647] .. .. ‡14,112

Unley
Pig Industry News [42660] ...... ‡300

COTE D'IVOIRE
Abidjan
Sciences & Nature [43557]

ESTONIA
Tartu
Agronomy Research [43791]

FRANCE
Montrouge
Cahiers d'etudes et de recherches francophones/Agricultures [43984]

Paris
Meat Processing Global Edition [44070]

GERMANY
Frankfurt
Allgemeine Fleischer Zeitung [44357]

Hamburg
Oil World Monthly [44421]

Agricultural Publications

Munich
Rinderzucht/Fleckvieh [44580]

INDIA
Jodhpur
Annals of Arid Zone
[45214] .... (Paid) 800
Kochi
Indian Coconut Journal
[45250] .... (Paid) 2,000
Mohindergarh
Crop Research [45346] 2,000
Mumbai
SEA Monthly News Circular
[45438] 1,500
New Delhi
FAI Abstract Service
[45512] .... (Paid) 2,200
Indian Dairyman
[45537] .... (Paid) 2,000
Indian Farming
[45544] .... (Paid) 51,200

ITALY
Bussolengo
La Razza Bruna [46129] 10,000

NETHERLANDS
Dordrecht
Agroforestry Systems [48323]

NIGERIA
Ibadan
African Journal of Livestock
Extension [49085]

SLOVENIA
Ljubljana
Acta Agriculturae Slovenica [50333]

**REPUBLIC OF SOUTH AF-
RICA**
Pretoria
South African Journal of Animal
Science [50602]

SPAIN
Madrid
Eurocarne [50758] 6000

SWITZERLAND
Niederonz
Forum Kleinwiederkaeuer
[51219] .... (Controlled) 14,569

UNITED KINGDOM
Crawley
Meat Trades Journal
[53108] .... ★5,574
London
Farmers Trader [54444] 36,500
Malvern
The Sheep Farmer [55540]
Thrapston
The Mule [56748]
Wallingford
Pig News and Information
[56822] 650

POULTRY AND PIGEONS

NETHERLANDS
Beekbergen
World Poultry Science Journal
[48277] 7,000

PAKISTAN
Faisalabad
International Journal of Poultry
Science [49254]
Research Journal of Poultry Sciences
[49292]

SLOVENIA
Ljubljana
Acta Agriculturae Slovenica [50333]

UNITED KINGDOM
Cudham
Practical Poultry [53146]
Loughborough
Meat Science [55485]
Roslin
British Poultry Science [56408]
Sutton
Poultry World
[56691] .. .. (Paid) ★3,267

SCIENTIFIC AGRICULTURAL PUBLICATIONS

AUSTRALIA
Chermside
Australian Organic Journal
[41750] .. .. (Paid) ‡6,000
Collingwood
Animal Production Science
[41780] .. .. (Paid) 600
Deakin
Animal Health Australia [41832]
Nathan
International Journal of Agricultural
Resources, Governance and
Ecology [42143]

BOTSWANA
Gaborone
ZJAR [42946] 2,000

CHILE
Arica
IDESIA [43133]

**PEOPLE'S REPUBLIC OF
CHINA**
Shanghai
Journal of Shanghai Jiaotong Univer-
sity Agricultural Science [43483]

COTE D'IVOIRE
Abidjan
Agronomie Africaine [43556]
Sciences & Nature [43557]

ESTONIA
Tartu
Agronomy Research [43791]

FRANCE
Montrouge
Oleagineux, Corps Gras, Lipides
[44003]

HUNGARY
Budapest
Acta Phytopathologica et Entomo-
logica Hungarica [44818]

Agrokemia es Talajtan [44821]

INDIA
Jodhpur
Journal of Arid Legumes [45225]
New Delhi
Indian Journal of Agricultural
Sciences [45548] 2,000

INDONESIA
Jakarta
Cocoinfo International [45794]
Cord [45795]

ITALY
Milan
Agro Food
[46162] .... (Combined) 7,000

JORDAN
Amman
Dirasat Agricultural Sciences
[47153] .... (Controlled) 1,000

KENYA
Nairobi
African Journal of Food, Agriculture,
Nutrition and Development [47172]

REPUBLIC OF KOREA
Suwon
Journal of Korean Society of Soil Sci-
ence and Fertilizer [47327] 850

NETHERLANDS
Amsterdam
Agricultural Systems [47885]
Agriculture, Ecosystems &
Environment [47886]
Dordrecht
Agroforestry Systems [48323]
Plant and Soil [48536]
Wageningen
NJAS [48772]

NIGERIA
Ibadan
Moor Journal of Agricultural Research
[49092]
Ilorin
Agrosearch [49118]
Journal of Agricultural Research and
Development [49120]
Owerri
Global Approaches to Extension
Practice [49162]
International Journal of Agriculture
and Rural Development [49163]
Umuahia
Nigerian Agricultural Journal [49175]

PAKISTAN
Faisalabad
Agricultural Journal [49231]
International Journal of Poultry
Science [49254]
World Journal of Agricultural
Sciences [49299]

PORTUGAL
Lisbon
Revista de Ciencias Agrarias [49805]

SAUDI ARABIA
Riyadh
Journal of King Saud University: Agri-

cultural Sciences
[50063] .. .. (Paid) 2,000

SLOVENIA
Ljubljana
Acta Agriculturae Slovenica [50333]

**REPUBLIC OF SOUTH AF-
RICA**
Erasmusrand
South African Journal of Plant and
Soil [50478]

SPAIN
Burjasot
Food Science and Technology
International [50711]
Madrid
Agricultura
[50725] .. .. (Combined) ‡6,426

SWITZERLAND
Posieux
Agrarforschung Schweiz
[51221] .. .. (Paid) 12,500

THAILAND
Pathumthani
International Agricultural Journal
[51461]

UNITED KINGDOM
Abingdon
Journal of Peasant Studies [51930]
Appleby-in-Westmorland
International Journal of Dairy
Technology [52126] 2,000
Bangor
Experimental Agriculture
[52170] 550
Bedfordshire
European Journal of Soil Science
[52278]
Cambridge
Journal of International Farm
Management [52857]
Chester
Food and Agricultural Immunology
[52995]
Edinburgh
Landwards [53297] 2,000
London
Lebensmittel-Wissenschaft und-Technologie
[54863]
Outlook on Agriculture [55046]
Oxford
The Australian Journal of Agricultural
and Resource Economics [55878]
Penicuik
Agricultural and Forest Entomolgy
[56242]
Roslin
British Poultry Science [56408]
Wallingford
Crop Physiology Abstracts [56817]
Postharvest News and Information
[56823] 150
Review of Aromatic and Medicinal
Plants [56825]
Soybean Abstracts [56830]

Circulation: ★ = ABC; △ = BPA; ◆ = CAC; • = CCAB; ❑ = VAC; ⊕ = PO Statement; ‡ = Publisher's Report; Boldface figures = sworn; Light figures = estimated.

This index lists newspapers and other periodicals that are published entirely or partly in a language other than English. Index entries are arranged by languages (please refer to the Index to Subject Terms). Within these groupings, entries are arranged geographically by country and alphabetically within cities. Citations include the publication title, entry number (given in parentheses), and circulation figures.

ARABIC

EGYPT
Cairo
Afro-Arab Selections for Social Sciences [43751]
Egyptian Journal of Computer Science [43759] 320
Rotary Magazine [43764] 4,000

FRANCE
Paris
Copyright Bulletin [44034] 188

HUNGARY
Budapest
IWF Handbook [44839]

JORDAN
Amman
International Journal of Arabic-English Studies [47159]

LEBANON
Beirut
Al Anwar [47386] .... (Combined) 47,899
Al Defaiya [47387] .... (Combined) 24,000

MOROCCO
Casablanca
Tijaris [47813]

NETHERLANDS
Leiden
Arabica [48650]

OMAN
Ruwi
Al Ghorfa [49226] .... (Non-paid) 10,500

SENEGAL
Dakar
CODESRIA Bulletin [50080] 5000

SUDAN
Khartoum
Agriculture and Development in the Arab World [50938]

SWITZERLAND
Geneva
Prospects [51156]

UNITED ARAB EMIRATES
Dubai
Open Skies [51651] .... △73,178

UNITED KINGDOM
Edinburgh
Journal of Qur'anic Studies [53294]

ARMENIAN

GERMANY
Regensburg
Armenisch-Deutsche Korrespondenz [44642] 680

BULGARIAN

BULGARIA
Sofia
Journal of Endocrinology [43103] .... (Paid) ⊕1,500
Kino [43104] 2,000
Nauka [43106] 2,000

CATALAN

SPAIN
Barcelona
L'Avenc [50653] 8,000
The Barcelona Review [50654]
Europa de les Nacions [50673]

CHINESE

PEOPLE'S REPUBLIC OF CHINA
Beijing
Acta Agronomica Sinica [43165] 12,000
Architectural Journal [43169] 65,000
Beijing Tatler [43172] .... ‡46,500
The China Nonprofit Review [43179]
Chinese Journal of Applied Chemistry [43183]
Chinese Journal of Plant Pathology [43185] 1,500
Chinese Photography [43188] .... (Paid) ⊕7,000
Chinese Tales and Stories [43190]
Folk Literature [43193] 100,000
Ham's CQ [43195]
Journal of Chinese Economic and Foreign Trade Studies [43204]
Learning Chinese [43210]
Wood Industry [43224] 5,000
Changchun
Jilin University Journal Social Sciences Edition [43239]
Journal of Jilin University Earth Science Edition [43240]
Journal of Jilin University Engineering and Technology Edition [43241]
Journal of Jilin University Information Science Edition [43242]
Journal of Jilin University Medicine Edition [43243]
Journal of Jilin University Science Edition [43244]
Hong Kong
The Bulletin [43285] 8,500
Ching Feng [43289]
Choice [43290] 30,000
Exporters Bulletin [43299] .... (Non-paid) 5,000
Hong Kong Entrepreneur [43324] 4,200
Hong Kong Jewelry Express [43326] 7,000
The Hong Kong Manager [43337] 140,000
Journal of Psychology in Chinese Societies [43361] .... (Paid) 500
Journal of Translation Studies [43362]
Luxe Living Kitchens & Bathrooms [43364] .... ‡25,000
Macau Tatler Best Restaurants [43366] .... ‡31,100
Yuen Lin [43387] 1,000
Nanjing
Advances in Science and Technology of Water Resources [43456]
Journal of Economics of Water Resources [43458]
Journal of Hohai University [43459]
Water Resources Protection [43460]
Water Science and Engineering [43461]
Shanghai
Academic Journal of Shanghai Jiao Tong University Social Science Section [43462]
Calligraphy [43464]
Car & Fan [43466]
Die & Mould Technology [43472]
Drive System Technique [43473]
Journal of Noise and Vibration Control [43481]
Journal of Shanghai Jiaotong University [43482]
Journal of Shanghai Jiaotong University Agricultural Science [43483]
Journal of Vibration and Shock [43484]
Laboratory Research and Exploration [43485]
Machine Design & Research [43486]
Micro- and Nanometer Science & Technology [43488]
Microcomputer Applications [43489]
Ocean Engineering [43492]
Popular Medicine [43494]
Radio & TV [43496]
Science Journal [43497]
Scientific Pictorial [43498]
Shanghai Pictorial [43499]
Shanghai Residence [43500] 30,000
Shanghai Style [43501]
Shanghai Tatler [43502] ..... ‡60,000
Shanghai's Best Restaurants [43505] .... ‡38,000
Systems Engineering [43506]
Using the Right Word [43509]
Yachtstyle [43512] .. .. ‡90,000
Xi'an
Chinese Heart Journal [43528]
Chinese Journal of Cells and Molecular Immunology [43529]
Chinese Journal of Conservative Dentistry [43530]
Chinese Journal of Neuroanatomy [43531]
Journal of Fourth Military University [43533]
Journal of Practical Stomatology [43534]
Journal of Xauat (Natural Sciences) [43535]
Journal of Xauat (Social Sciences) [43536]

GERMANY
Nuremberg
Brauwelt Chinese [44603] .. .. (Combined) ‡4,221

REPUBLIC OF KOREA
Suwon
Journal of Korean Society of Soil Science and Fertilizer [47327] 850

SINGAPORE
Singapore
Citta Bella [50123] 30,000
Lianhe Zaobao [50215] .. .. (Mon.-Fri.) 176,600
NuYou Time [50231] 20,000
Thumbs Up [50278] .... (Mon.-Fri.) 39,200
zbCOMMA [50292] 60,000

SWITZERLAND
Geneva
Prospects [51156]

TAIWAN
Taipei
Acta Paediatrica Taiwanica [51329] 3,000

Circulation: ★ = ABC; △ = BPA; ◆ = CAC; • = CCAB; ❑ = VAC; ⊕ = PO Statement; ‡ = Publisher's Report; Boldface figures = sworn; Light figures = estimated.

UNITED KINGDOM
Wadhurst
International Construction China
[56807] 15,800

CROATIAN

CROATIA
Zagreb
Diskrepancija [43567]

CZECH

CZECH REPUBLIC
Plzen
Ceska Radiologie [43607]

Prague
Journal Kybernetika [43628]
Mezinarodni Politika International
    Politics [43629] 3,500
Mezinarodni Vztahy International
    Relations [43630] 7,500

POLAND
Warsaw
Linguistica Pragensia [49732]

SWITZERLAND
Binz
CSI Magazine [51081]

DANISH

DENMARK
Brondby
Badminton [43651] 600
O-Posten [43652]
Skyttebladet [43653]

Copenhagen
Forum, Tidsskrift for Kon Og Kultur
    [43670]
Gymnasieskolen [43672] 15,000
Kontakt [43678] .... (Paid) 5,000

Herning
Textile and Clothing [43723]

Valby
Horysont (Good News) [43736]

ICELAND
Reykjavik
Rotary Norden [44902] ....:.... 69,000

SWEDEN
Stockholm
Popular Astronomi [51030] 1,300

DUTCH

BELGIUM
Brussels
Cahiers de la Documentation [42846]
Federauto Magazine [42855]
Greenpeace Magazine
    [42857] 60,000
Military Law and Law of War Review
    [42867]
Rotary Contact [42872] 769,000

Gent
Jaarboek [42883] 300
Verslagen en Mededelingen
    [42885] 300

Rekkem
Ons Erfdeel
    [42909] .... (Paid) 10,000

ICELAND
Reykjavik
Rotary Norden [44902] 69,000

NETHERLANDS
Amsterdam
LOVER [48140] 2,000
Misjpoge [48160] 650
Wordt Vervolgd
    [48271] .... (Non-paid) 32,500

Apeldoorn
Direct Mailings
    [48275] .... (Non-paid) 55,000

The Hague
Democraat
    [48612] .... (Non-paid) 12,500
Forum [48616] ... . (Non-paid) 30,000
Hivos Magazine [48617]

REPUBLIC OF SOUTH AF-RICA
Bloemfontein
Acta Theologica [50354]

Mmabatho
Potchefstroom Electronic Law Journal
    [50556]

UNITED KINGDOM
Sutton Coldfield
Hot Dip Galvanizing
    [56695] 45,000

ESTONIAN

ESTONIA
Tartu
Journal Eesti Arst [43792] 3,800

FILIPINO

PHILIPPINES
Quezon City
PAID [49605] 1,000

FINNISH

FINLAND
Helsinki
Museo [43849] 2,000
NNKY-NAKY [43850] 3,500
Sulasol [43858] 1,000
Suomen Autolehti [43859] .... ‡8,473
Vegaia [43864] 400

ICELAND
Reykjavik
Rotary Norden [44902] 69,000

FRENCH

AUSTRIA
Vienna
Annals of Nutrition and Metabolism
    [42744] 1,250
Fempower [42758]
INIS Database [42760]

BELGIUM
Brussels
Cahiers de la Documentation [42846]
Echos AMA [42849]
Federauto Magazine [42855]
Greenpeace Magazine
    [42857] 60,000

Jeunes en Mouvement
    [42861] .... ‡25,000
MIJARC News [42866] 3,000
Military Law and Law of War Review
    [42867]
Public Transport International
    [42870] 6,000
Rotary Contact [42872] 769,000
Watt's NEW? [42874]
Youth Opinion [42876] 13,000

BULGARIA
Sofia
Etudes Balkaniques [43098]

COTE D'IVOIRE
Abidjan
Agronomie Africaine [43556]

EGYPT
Cairo
Rotary Magazine [43764] 4,000

FRANCE
Bordeaux
Bulletin de l'ALLF [43921]

Chateau Landon
Maitrises [43930]

Ferney-Voltaire
Focus on the Public Services
    [43947] .... (Free) 17,000

Les Ulis
Quadrature [43967]

Lyon
Sericologia [43970]

Montrouge
Annales de Biologie Clinique [43980]
Annales de Gerontologie [43981]
Bulletin du Cancer [43982]
Bulletin Infirmier du Cancer [43983]
Cahiers d'etudes et de recherches
    francophones/Agricultures [43984]
Cahiers d'etudes et de recherches
    francophones/Sante [43985]
Environnement, Risques & Sante
    [43986]
Epilepsies [43987]
Hepato-Gastro [43992]
L'Information Psychiatrique [43993]
Journal de Pharmacie Clinique
    [43994]
La Lettre de l'Internat [43995]
Medecine therapeutique [43997]
Medecine therapeutique cardiologie
    [43998]
Medecine therapeutique/Endocrinologie
    [43999]
Medecine Therapeutique/medecine
    de la reproduction [44000]
Medecine therapeutique/Pediatrie
    [44001]
MT Cardio [44002]
Oleagineux, Corps Gras, Lipides
    [44003]
Psychologie & NeuroPsychiatrie du
    vieillissement [44004]
Revue de neuropsychologie [44005]
Sang Thrombose Vaisseaux [44006]
Science et changements
    planetaires/Secheresse [44007]
Virologie [44008]

Paris
L'Actualite Chimique
    [44021] .... (Paid) 5,000
Annales Francaises d'Anesthesie et
    de Reanimation
    [44025] .... (Paid) 5,500
Copyright Bulletin [44034] 188
International Journal of Refrigeration
    [44056]

Pollution Atmospherique
    [44077] 1,500
Revue de Musicologie [44081]
Scientific and Technical Review
    [44083] 1,800
The Tocqueville Review/La Revue
    Tocqueville
    [44085] .... (Combined) 500

Saint Denis
Global Health Promotion [44103]

Strasbourg
News d'Ill [44113]

Villejuif
Sciences Sociales et Sante [44125]

GERMANY
Berlin
arcadia [44153] .... ‡500
Archiv fur Papyrusforschung
    [44155] .... ‡300
Byzantinische Zeitschrift
    [44164] .... ‡650
Kritikon Litterarum [44212] 150
Praehistorische Zeitschrift
    [44227] 500
Zeitschrift fur romanische Philologie
    [44240] 520

Bonn
Europa Cantat Magazine [44256]

Fellbach
Restaurator [44353] .... ‡3,500

Frankfurt
Agrifuture [44356] 20,000

Hamburg
Der Islam [44413] 500

Hannover
Studia Leibnitiana [44435]

Munich
Official Journal of the European
    Patent Office
    [44576] .. .. (Paid) ‡2,200
                    (Non-paid) ‡2,100

GREECE
Thessaloniki
European Journal [44771]

HUNGARY
Budapest
Acta Antiqua Academiae Scientiarum
    Hungaricae [44806]
Acta Historiae Artium [44811]
Acta Orientalia Academiae Scien-
    tiarum Hungaricae [44816]
Hungarian Studies [44837]
International Sports Magazine
    [44838] 9,000
IWF Handbook [44839]
Studia Musicologica Academiae Sci-
    entiarum Hungaricae [44875]
Studia Scientiarum Mathematicarum
    Hungarica [44876]

Egyetem
Verbum [44889]

Szeged
Acta Ethnographica Hungarica
    [44894]

IRELAND
Dublin
The Irish Journal of French Studies
    [45976]

ITALY
Bologna
Bollettino di Storia delle Scienze
    Matematiche [46125]

Circulation: ★ = ABC; △ = BPA; ♦ = CAC; • = CCAB; ❑ = VAC; ⊕ = PO Statement; ‡ = Publisher's Report; Boldface figures = sworn; Light figures = estimated.

Milan
Italian Magazine Food Processing
[46180] 5,500

Rome
Apiacta [46221] 250
Progressio [46240]

KENYA
Nairobi
African Journal of Science and
Technology [47174]
International Journal of Tropical In-
sect Science [47185]
Pachyderm [47195]

LEBANON
Beirut
Lebanese Science Journal [47398]

LUXEMBOURG
Luxembourg
Journal du Diabetique
[47492] 800
Sew-Journal [47493]

MEXICO
Mexico City
Refugees [47788] 215,000

MOROCCO
Casablanca
Tijaris [47813]

NETHERLANDS
Amersfoort
LEISA Magazine [47874] 17,000
Amsterdam
Environmental Policy and Law
[47969]
Doorwerth
Weed Research [48317]
Dordrecht
International Journal for the Semiot-
ics of Law [48431]
International Review of Education
[48432] .. .. (Paid) ‡1,200
Leiden
Vetus Testamentum [48729]

ROMANIA
Bucharest
Higher Education in Europe [49837]

SPAIN
Madrid
Plasticulture Journal [50789]
Revista Espanola de Paleontologia
[50797] 600

SWEDEN
Stockholm
Geografiska Annaler, Series A, Physi-
cal Geography [51017]
Geografiska Annaler, Series B, Social
Geography [51018]

SWITZERLAND
Basel
Antike Kunst [51058] 1,100
Bern
Amnestie [51069] 22,000
Ernahrungs Info [51072]
Helvetica Chimica Acta [51073]
Binz
CSI Magazine [51081]

Geneva
IB World [51098] 10,000
International Trade FORUM [51150]
ITU News [51151]
Prospects [51156]
Refugee Survey Quarterly [51159]
Union [51164]
World of Work [51169]
Lausanne
Le Matin [51194] .... ‡58,849
Tele top matin [51200] ...... ‡193,316
Mies
FIM Magazine [51212] 2,600
Saint Gallen
Viscom [51225] 14,595
Uster
Rotary Suisse-Liechtenstein
[51236] .. .. ‡12,000
Zurich
Approches [51252]
FLASH [51260] 2,200
Passages [51276]

UNITED KINGDOM
Belfast
The Chronicle [52281]
Hailsham
Mariner's Mirror [53501]
Leicester
Francophonie [53801] 5,500
London
Constitutional and Parliamentary
Information [54260]
Etudes Episteme [54388]
Social Science Information [55247]
Newbury
Avian Pathology [55661]
Peterborough
The Essential Guide to UK Farm &
Outdoor Power Equipment [56256]
Ramsgate
Bonjour! [56308]
Wadhurst
Access International
[56804] 8,024

VATICAN CITY
Vatican City
People on the Move [57015]

GERMAN

AUSTRALIA
Hanwood
Journal of Applied Irrigation Science
[41940]

AUSTRIA
Vienna
Annals of Nutrition and Metabolism
[42744] 1,250
Auto Touring
[42748] ..... (Combined) 2,107,000
Mitteilungen Osterreiches Getranke
Institut [42764]
Progress [42766]
Stichproben - Wiener Zeitschrift fur
Kritische Afrikastudien [42768]

BELGIUM
Brussels
MIJARC News [42866] 3,000
Military Law and Law of War Review
[42867]

Public Transport International
[42870] 6,000
Rotary Contact [42872] 769,000
Watt's NEW? [42874]
Youth Opinion [42876] 13,000

BULGARIA
Sofia
Etudes Balkaniques [43098]

FRANCE
Ferney-Voltaire
Focus on the Public Services
[43947] .. .. (Free) 17,000
Paris
Revue de Musicologie [44081]

GERMANY
Augsburg
Paneuropa Deutschland [44141]
Berlin
Anglia [44149] .... ‡540
Arbitrium [44152] .... ‡460
arcadia [44153] .... ‡500
Archiv fur Papyrusforschung
[44155] .... ‡300
Aschkenas [44157] .... ‡320
Beitrage zur Geschichte der deut-
schen Sprache und Literatur
[44159] .... ‡540
Byzantinische Zeitschrift
[44164] .... ‡650
Das Neue China [44169] 2,000
European Photography [44175]
Germanistik [44186] 1,300
Iberoromania [44190]
Internationales Archiv fur Sozialge-
schichte der deutschen Literatur
[44197]
Landschaftsarchitekten
[44214] 2,500
Lebende Sprachen [44218]
PIK [44226] .. .. ‡3,200
Praehistorische Zeitschrift
[44227] 500
VBI-Nachrichten [44234]
Verhandlungen der Gesellschaft fur
Okologie [44236]
Zeitschrift fur romanische Philologie
[44240] 520
Zeitschrift fur Rezensionen zur ger-
manistischen Sprachwissenschaft
[44241] 200
Bielefeld
HIDEAWAYS [44246] 60,000
Bonn
Europa Cantat Magazine [44256]
Frau und Politik [44261]
Informatik Spektrum
[44263] 24,000
Kultur Politik [44265]
WEHRTECHNIK [44272] 12,000
Bremen
Umwelt-Medizin-Gesellschaft
[44282] 4,000
Cologne
Ceramic Forum International [44290]
Christliche Frau [44291]
Dortmund
Korrespondenzblatt [44317] 750
Dusseldorf
Der Praktiker [44323] 17,000
Schweissen & Schneiden
[44334] 14,000
Essen
Das Mechanische Musikinstrument
[44346]
Fellbach
Restaurator [44353] .... ‡3,500

Frankfurt
Allgemeine Fleischer Zeitung [44357]
DLG-Mitteilungen [44359] 12,000
Literaturnachrichten [44362] ... 3,500
WWF Journal [44363]
Frankfurt am Main
Pro Familia Magazin
[44368] 7,000
Freiburg
Viszeralmedizin
[44374] .... (Combined) 4,000
Gottingen
Ethik in der Medizin [44396]
Gutersloh
ZI-Ziegelindustrie International
[44406]
Hamburg
Der Islam [44413] 500
Plan Post
[44423] .... (Non-paid) 176,000
Hannover
Studia Leibnitiana [44435]
Kiel
Meer & Yachten [44506] 15,025
Leinfelden-Echterdingen
Metamorphose [44527] 11,916
Lubeck
Berichte zur Wissenschaftsgeschichte
[44535]
Munich
Fraunhofer Magazin [44563]
Official Journal of the European
Patent Office
[44576] .. .. (Paid) ‡2,200
(Non-paid) ‡2,100
SG Susswarenhandel
[44581] 6,500
Nuremberg
dedica [44608] 19,993
Element + BAU [44610] 6,800
Food Technologie [44612] 11,668
Getranke! Technologie & Marketing
[44613] 8,905
Industrie Diamanten Rundschau
[44615] 6,800
Oldenburg
Chemkon - Chemie konkret, Forum
fuer Unterricht und Didaktik
[44623]
Regensburg
Armenisch-Deutsche Korrespondenz
[44642] 680
Rossdorf
Skeptiker [44645] 3,000

GREECE
Thessaloniki
European Journal [44771]

HUNGARY
Budapest
Acta Antiqua Academiae Scientiarum
Hungaricae [44806]
Acta Archaeologica Academiae Sci-
entiarum Hungaricae [44807]
Acta Orientalia Academiae Scien-
tiarum Hungaricae [44816]
Hungarian Studies [44837]

ITALY
Milan
Italian Magazine Food Processing
[46180] 5,500
Rome
Apiacta [46221] 250

Ethnic Publications

LUXEMBOURG
Luxembourg
Journal du Diabetique
[47492] 800
Sew-Journal [47493]

MEXICO
Mexico City
Refugees [47788] 215,000

NETHERLANDS
Amsterdam
German Monitor [47999]

Doorwerth
Weed Research [48317]

Dordrecht
International Review of Education
[48432] .... (Paid) ‡1,200

Leiden
Vetus Testamentum [48729]

REPUBLIC OF SOUTH AFRICA
Mmabatho
Potchefstroom Electronic Law Journal
[50556]

SWEDEN
Stockholm
Geografiska Annaler, Series A, Physical Geography [51017]
Geografiska Annaler, Series B, Social Geography [51018]

SWITZERLAND
Basel
Antike Kunst [51058] 1,100

Bern
Amnestie [51069] 22,000
Chimia [51070]
Ernahrungs Info [51072]
Helvetica Chimica Acta [51073]

Binz
CSI Magazine [51081]

Saint Gallen
Viscom [51225] 14,595

Uster
Rotary Suisse-Liechtenstein
[51236] .... ‡12,000

Winterthur
SAM-Focus [51242] 7,000

Zurich
FLASH [51260] 2,200
Passages [51276]
Schritte ins Offene [51277]
Schweizer Lehrerinnen- und
Lehrer-Zeitung [51280]
Travel Inside [51292] ... (Paid) 7,976
Travel Inside Francais
[51293] .... (Paid) 2,913

TURKEY
Ankara
Cooperation in Turkiye
[51491] 500

UNITED KINGDOM
Leicester
Deutsch [53795] 2,500

Newbury
Avian Pathology [55661]

Peterborough
The Essential Guide to UK Farm &
Outdoor Power Equipment [56256]

Sutton Coldfield
Hot Dip Galvanizing
[56695] 45,000

Wadhurst
Access International
[56804] 8,024

VATICAN CITY
Vatican City
People on the Move [57015]

GREEK

CYPRUS
Limassol
Earthlines [43589]

Nicosia
Emporoviomichaniki [43594] ... 4,000
POLIS [43597]

GERMANY
Berlin
Trends in Classics [44233] 250

GREECE
Athens
Stomatologia [44756] 2,000

UNITED KINGDOM
Biggleswade
Journal of Greek Linguistics [52324]

HEBREW
See also Yiddish

ISRAEL
Haifa
Khulyot [46077]

Jerusalem
Azure [46080]
Hamodia (Israel) [46082]

Tel Aviv
Targima [46113] 450

HINDI

INDIA
Chennai
Rotary News/Rotary Samachar
[45056] .... (Paid) ⊕75,000

HUNGARIAN

HUNGARY
Budapest
Agrokemia es Talajtan [44821]
Antik Tanulmanyok [44822]
Archaeologiai Ertesito [44823]
Epites - Epiteszettudomany [44828]
Magyar Pszichologiai Szemle [44846]
Magyar Sebeszet [44847]
Mentalhigiene es Pszichoszomatika
[44852]
Muveszettorteneti Ertesito [44853]
Orvosi Hetilap [44862]
Tajfutas [44878]
Tarsadalom es Gazdasag (Society
and Economy) [44879]
Tarsadalomkutatas [44880]

SWITZERLAND
Binz
CSI Magazine [51081]

INDONESIAN

NETHERLANDS
Amersfoort
LEISA Magazine [47874] 17,000

ITALIAN

BELGIUM
Brussels
Military Law and Law of War Review
[42867]

BULGARIA
Sofia
Etudes Balkaniques [43098]

GERMANY
Berlin
Archiv fur Papyrusforschung
[44155] .... ‡300
Byzantinische Zeitschrift
[44164] .... ‡650
Zeitschrift fur romanische Philologie
[44240] 520

HUNGARY
Budapest
Acta Antiqua Academiae Scientiarum
Hungaricae [44806]

Egyetem
Verbum [44889]

ITALY
Bisceglie
Mosaico di Pace [46124]

Bologna
Bollettino di Storia delle Scienze
Matematiche [46125]

Chiavari
Rivista Italiana Difesa
[46133] 30,000

Fiorentino
Aestimum [46139]

Genoa
Epistemologia [46148]
Giornale di Metafisica [46149]
Nuova Corrente [46152]
Rivista di Biologia [46153]

Milan
Aggiornamento Medico
[46160] 40,683
Annali dell'Istituto Superiore di Sanita
[46163]
L'Endocrinologo [46167]
Focus on Italy [46171]
Il Cardiologo [46173]
Il Ginecologo [46174]
Ipertensione [46178]
Mani Tese [46187] 36,000

Rocca di Papa
New Humanity [46219] 5,000

Rome
Carmel in the World [46223]

Trento
ACAV Informa [46260]

MEXICO
Mexico City
Refugees [47788] 215,000

SWITZERLAND
Basel
Antike Kunst [51058] 1,100

Bern
Ernahrungs Info [51072]

Binz
CSI Magazine [51081]

Saint Gallen
Viscom [51225] 14,595

Uster
Rotary Suisse-Liechtenstein
[51236] .... ‡12,000

VATICAN CITY
Vatican City
People on the Move [57015]

JAPANESE

FRANCE
Ferney-Voltaire
Focus on the Public Services
[43947] .... (Free) 17,000

JAPAN
Tokyo
Afternoon [46729]
Afternoon Season Zokan [46730]
Be Love [46759]
Be Love Parfait [46760]
Bessatsu Friend [46761]
Dessert [46801]
Evening [46818]
Fashion Color [46821]
Forestry Technology [46827]
Gekkan Shonen Magazine [46829]
JAUW [46875]
JMA Management Review
[46877] 20,000
Joho-Shori [46878] 27,000
Journal of Japanese Scientists
[46916]
Juliet [46951]
Kiss [46954]
Magazine Special [46962]
Magazine Z [46963]
Morning [46972]
Nakayoshi [46974]
Nikkei Business [46981] ... *308,561
Nikkei Business Associe
[46982] *71,610
Nikkei Design
[46986] .... (Paid) *13,370
Nikkei Ecology [46988] *16,632
Nikkei Monozukuri
[46999] *34,857
Nikkei Restaurants
[47005] *19,137
Nikkei Venture [47009] *59,790
One More Kiss [47014]
Refrigeration [47031] 10,000
Shukan Shonen Magazine [47038]
Taikabutsu [47046]
Tetsu-to-Hagane
[47049] .... (Combined) 3,000
Young Magazine [47057]
Young Magazine Uppers [47058]

MEXICO
Mexico City
Refugees [47788] 215,000

KOREAN

REPUBLIC OF KOREA
Seoul
Journal of the Korean Society of
Plastic and Reconstructive Surgery
[47275]

Suwon
Journal of Korean Society of Soil Science and Fertilizer [47327] 850

LATIN

ITALY
Bologna
Bollettino di Storia delle Scienze
Matematiche [46125]

Circulation: ★ = ABC; △ = BPA; ♦ = CAC; • = CCAB; ❑ = VAC; ⊕ = PO Statement; ‡ = Publisher's Report; Boldface figures = sworn; Light figures = estimated.

UNITED KINGDOM
Basingstoke
Latino Studies [52222]

LATVIAN

LATVIA
Riga
Vides Vestis [47376] ... (Paid) 3,000
(Non-paid) 2,000

LITHUANIAN

LITHUANIA
Kaunas
Caritas [47464] 6,000

POLAND
Warsaw
Biologija [49696]

MALAY

MALAYSIA
Penang
The Classroom Teacher
[47688] 100

NORWEGIAN

ICELAND
Reykjavik
Rotary Norden [44902] 69,000

NORWAY
Oslo
Liberalt Forum [49201]
The Norseman [49205]

SWEDEN
Stockholm
Popular Astronomi [51030] 1,300

POLISH

POLAND
Warsaw
Acta Arithmetica [49677]
Chwila rozrywki [49704]
Dom & Wnetrze [49705] ..... ‡20,283
Hot Moda & Shopping
[49716] .... ‡7,073
Mamo, to ja [49735] .... ‡98,937
Party Celebrity lives
[49745] .. .. ‡472,261
Prawdziwe Zycle [49757]
Przedszkolak [49758]
Przekroj [49759] .... ‡68,815
Przyjaciolka [49760] .... ‡460,291
Trener [49768] 2,000
Twoj Maluszek [49769] ..... ‡146,473
Twoje dziecko [49770] .. .. ‡70,524
Uczucia i tesknoty
[49771] .... ‡63,514
Uroda [49772] .. .. ‡76,342
Vita [49774] .. .. ‡72,677

PORTUGUESE

ARGENTINA
Buenos Aires
Ameghiniana [41469]

BRAZIL
Belo Horizonte
Kriterion [42949]

Botafogo
Revista Brasileira de Anestesiologia
[42955]

Botucatu
Interface [42956]

Campinas
Bragantia [42963]
Bragantia [42964]
Cadernos Pagu [42966]
Ciencia e Tecnologia de Alimentos
[42967]
Educacao & Sociedade [42968]
Opiniao Publica [42971]

Petropolis
Computational & Applied
Mathematics [42990]

Porto Alegre
Psicologia [42992]

Rio de Janeiro
Anais da Academia Brasileira de
Ciencias [43003]
Historia, Ciencias,
Saude-Manguinhos [43005]
Informativo FBCN [43006]
Mana - Estudos de Antropologia
Social [43011]
Memorias do Instituto Oswaldo Cruz
[43012]
Pesquisa Veterinaria Brasileira
[43013]

Sao Carlos
Gestao & Producao [43017]

Sao Paulo
ABM Metalurgia e Materials [43019]
Arquivos Brasileiros de Endocrinolo-
gia & Metabologia [43022]
Arquivos Brasileiros de Oftalmologia
[43023]
Arquivos de Neuro-Psiquiatria
[43024]
Cadernos de Pesquisa [43031]
Ceramica [43032] 700
Ciencia e Cultura [43033] 1,500
Ciencia Hoje
[43034] .. .. (Paid) 13,000
Ciencia Hoje das Criancas
[43035] .... (Paid) 194,000
Clinics [43036]
Documentacao de Estudos em Lin-
guistica Teorica e Aplicada (DELTA)
[43037]
Ecletica Quimica [43038]
Jornal da Ciencia Hoje [43041]
Papeis Avulsos de Zoologia (Sao
Paulo) [43043]
Quimica Nova [43046]
Revista Vivencia [43048] 10,000

Vacaria
Anais da Sociedade Entomologica do
Brasil [43052]
Neotropical Entomology [43053]

Vicosa
Agora [43054]
Arquivo Brasileiro de Medicina Veteri-
naria e Zootecnia [43055]
Ciencia & Saude Coletiva [43056]
Ensaio [43057]
Entomologia y Vectores [43058]
Journal of Epilepsy and Clinical
Neurophysiology [43059]
Materials Research [43060]
Novos Estudos Cebrap [43061]
Pro-Fono Revista de Atualizacao
Cientifica [43062]
Radiologia Brasileira [43063]
RAE eletronica [43064]
Rem [43065]
Revista Arvore [43066]

Vila Olimpia
Arquivos Brasileiros de Cardiologia
[43067]

CHILE
Arica
IDESIA [43133]

COLOMBIA
Bogota
Acta Biologica Colombiana [43541]
Caldasia [43544]

GERMANY
Berlin
Iberoromania [44190]
Zeitschrift fur romanische Philologie
[44240] 520

GREECE
Thessaloniki
European Journal [44771]

NETHERLANDS
Amersfoort
LEISA Magazine [47874] 17,000

PERU
Lima
Anales de la Facultad de Medicina
[49423]

PORTUGAL
Lisbon
Revistacap [49806]

SPAIN
Madrid
Gerokomos [50762]

Seville
Cuadernos de Medicina Forense
[50833]

ROMANIAN

ROMANIA
Bucharest
Avantaje [49831] .... ‡23,612
Buletin AGIR [49833]
Economistul - The Economist
[49834] 30,000
Elle Decoration [49835] .... ‡9,469
Elle Mariaj [49836] .. .. ‡4,387
Intamplari Adevarate
[49838] .. .. ‡30,880
Lucru de Mana [49839] ...... ‡12,516
Nuclear Energy [49840]
Povestea Mea [49841] .... ‡31,077
Psychologies [49842] .... ‡10,845
TRANSURB [49844]
Univers Ingineresc [49845]

RUSSIAN

AUSTRIA
Vienna
INIS Database [42760]

BULGARIA
Sofia
Etudes Balkaniques [43098]

FRANCE
Nancy
Discrete Mathematics & Theoretical
Computer Science [44010]

Paris
Copyright Bulletin [44034] 188

GERMANY
Berlin
Kritikon Litterarum [44212] 150

MEXICO
Mexico City
Refugees [47788] 215,000

NETHERLANDS
Amsterdam
Journal of Applied Mathematics and
Mechanics [48047]

ROMANIA
Bucharest
Higher Education in Europe [49837]

RUSSIA
Irkutsk
Geography and Natural Resources
[49856]

Moscow
Atelier Rundschau
[49879] .... ‡18,320
Diana Creative [49892] ..... ‡20,715
Diana Moden [49893] .... ‡50,230
Industria Mody [49917] .... ‡1,900
International Textiles [49921] .. ‡235
Iren [49922] .... ‡27,340
Knit&Mode [49932] .... ‡15,900
Kollektsia Idei [49933] .... ‡24,800
Kulinarny Practicum
[49934] .... ‡120,000
Lechaim [49936] .... ‡54,000
Lena Rukodelie [49937] .... ‡20,600
Malenkaya Diana [49939] ... ‡72,350
Mama, eto ya! [49940] ...... ‡86,740
Natalia [49947] .... ‡14,300
Russian Art [49971] .... ‡7,000
Sabrina [49986] .... ‡74,880
Sabrina Baby [49987] .... ‡6,110
Samaya [49988] .... ‡117,350
Susanna Rukodeliye
[49993] .... ‡20,980
Vjazanie Vashe Hobby
[49998] .... ‡64,900
Vyshitye Kartiny [49999] ..... ‡18,100

Novosibirsk
Earth's Cryosphere [50010]
Journal Chemistry for Sustainable
Development [50011]
Journal of Mining Sciences [50012]
Siberian Journal of Ecology [50013]
Siberian Journal of Numerical
Mathematics [50014]

SWITZERLAND
Geneva
Prospects [51156]

UKRAINE
Donetsk
A Yidishe Mame [51591]

Kiev
Problems of Aging & Longevity
[51606]

Lugansk
World of Jewish Woman [51616]

SLOVAK

CZECH REPUBLIC
Plzen
Ceska Radiologie [43607]

Ethnic Publications

SLOVENE

SLOVENIA
Ljubljana
Acta Agriculturae Slovenica [50333]

SPANISH

ARGENTINA
Buenos Aires
A & G Magazine [41468] 1,500
Integration and Trade [41474]
Journal of Argentine Dermatology
  [41476]
Plasticos [41478] 5,000
Revista del CIAS [41479]

AUSTRIA
Vienna
INIS Database [42760]

BELGIUM
Brussels
MIJARC News [42866] 3,000
Military Law and Law of War Review
  [42867]
Youth Opinion [42876] 13,000

BRAZIL
Botucatu
Interface [42956]

Campinas
Bragantia [42963]
Bragantia [42964]
Cadernos Pagu [42966]
Ciencia e Tecnologia de Alimentos
  [42967]
Educacao & Sociedade [42968]
Opiniao Publica [42971]

Petropolis
Computational & Applied
  Mathematics [42990]

Ribeirao Preto
Economia Aplicada [42997]

Rio de Janeiro
Anais da Academia Brasileira de
  Ciencias [43003]
Historia, Ciencias,
  Saude-Manguinhos [43005]
Pesquisa Veterinaria Brasileira
  [43013]

Sao Paulo
Arquivos Brasileiros de Endocrinolo-
  gia & Metabologia [43022]
Arquivos Brasileiros de Oftalmologia
  [43023]
Arquivos de Neuro-Psiquiatria
  [43024]
Documentacao de Estudos em Lin-
  guistica Teorica e Aplicada (DELTA)
  [43037]
Ecletica Quimica [43038]
Papeis Avulsos de Zoologia (Sao
  Paulo) [43043]
Quimica Nova [43046]

Vacaria
Anais da Sociedade Entomologica do
  Brasil [43052]
Neotropical Entomology [43053]

Vicosa
Arquivo Brasileiro de Medicina Veteri-
  naria e Zootecnia [43055]
Ciencia & Saude Coletiva [43056]
Ensaio [43057]
Entomologia y Vectores [43058]
Journal of Epilepsy and Clinical
  Neurophysiology [43059]

Materials Research [43060]
Novos Estudos Cebrap [43061]
Pro-Fono Revista de Atualizacao
  Cientifica [43062]
Radiologia Brasileira [43063]
RAE eletronica [43064]
Rem [43065]
Revista Arvore [43066]

Vila Olimpia
Arquivos Brasileiros de Cardiologia
  [43067]

CHILE
Arica
IDESIA [43133]

Concepcion
Acta Literaria [43135]
Celulosa y Papel [43136]

Los Angeles
El Rotario de Chile [43140] 5,800

Santiago
Cuadernos Mujer Salud [43144]
Revista Mujer Salud [43147]
Revista de la SCCC [43148]

COLOMBIA
Bogota
ArtNexus [43542]
Caldasia [43544]

CUBA
Havana
Cuba Foreign Trade
  [43576] 3,000

FRANCE
Ferney-Voltaire
Focus on the Public Services
  [43947] .. .. (Free) 17,000

Paris
Copyright Bulletin [44034] 188
Scientific and Technical Review
  [44083] 1,800

Saint Denis
Global Health Promotion [44103]

GERMANY
Berlin
Iberoromania [44190]
Zeitschrift fur romanische Philologie
  [44240] 520

Bonn
TECNOLOGIA MILITAR
  [44271] 10,000

Nuremberg
Brauwelt en Espanol [44605]

GREECE
Thessaloniki
European Journal [44771]

HUNGARY
Budapest
International Sports Magazine
  [44838] 9,000
IWF Handbook [44839]
World Weightlifting [44883]

ITALY
Milan
Italian Magazine Food Processing
  [46180] 5,500

Rome
Apiacta [46221] 250
Progressio [46240]

MEXICO
Mexico City
Almas [47781]
Boletin [47782]
Monetaria [47786]
Refugees [47788] 215,000
Utillaje [47790] .... (Paid) 500
            (Controlled) 30,250

San Luis Huexotla
Agrociencia [47797]

NETHERLANDS
Amersfoort
LEISA Magazine [47874] 17,000

Amsterdam
Spanish in Context [48235]

NICARAGUA
Managua
La Boletina [49054] 26,000

PERU
Lima
Anales de la Facultad de Medicina
  [49423]
Negocios Internacionales
  [49424] 6,000
Quehacer [49425] 4,000
Resomeu Senaual [49426] 500

San Isidro
Made in Germany [49441] 5,000

SPAIN
Barcelona
AEBDC News [50646]
Arquitectura y Diseno
  [50650] .... ‡47,513
The Barcelona Review [50654]
Cirugia Cardiovascular [50656]
Clara [50657] .... ‡161,874
Clara Deco [50658]
Comer Bien [50659] .... ‡49,079
Cosas de Cocina [50661] .... ‡60,144
Cuerpomente [50662] .... ‡66,291
El Jueves [50669] .... ‡74,441
El Mueble [50670] .... ‡217,434
El Mueble Casas de Campo
  [50671] .... ‡43,155
El Mueble Cocinas y Banos
  [50672] .... ‡20,535
Habitania [50676] .... ‡44,184
Historia National Geographic
  [50679] .. .. ‡142,798
IDP [50680]
Labores del Hogar
  [50682] .... ‡53,427
Lecturas [50683] .... ‡198,930
Lecturas Cocina Facil
  [50684] .... ‡81,446
Lecturas Especial Cocina
  [50685] .... ‡78,346
Lecturas Moda [50686]
Linea Saludable [50687] ..... ‡68,000
Mente Sana [50688] .... ‡118,513
Patrones [50691] .... ‡33,397
PC Actual [50692] .... ‡61,365
Revista Espanola de Ortodoncia
  [50695]
Saber Vivir [50696] .... ‡142,798
Speak Up [50701]
Tu Bebe [50704] .... ‡95,092
Viajes National Geographic
  [50706] .... ‡63,013

Madrid
Casa al Dia [50734] .... ‡87,531
Coches de Ocasion
  [50736] .... ‡17,108
Cosas de Casa [50740] .... ‡183,118
Gerokomos [50762]

Guia del Comprador de Casas
  [50763] .... ‡2,568
Guia del Comprador de Coches
  [50764] .... ‡13,348
Guia del Comprador de Furgonetas y
  Autocaravanas [50765] ..... ‡2,524
Guia del Comprador de Ordenadores
  y Software [50766] .... ‡4,054
Plasticulture Journal [50789]
Revista Espanola de Paleontologia
  [50797] 600
Top Auto [50812] .... ‡24,234

Valencia
Anglogermanica online [50842]
Celestinesca
  [50844] .... (Controlled) 412

SWITZERLAND
Geneva
IB World [51098] 10,000
International Trade FORUM [51150]
ITU News [51151]
Prospects [51156]
Union [51164]
World of Work [51169]

Zurich
FLASH [51260] 2,200

UNITED KINGDOM
Abingdon
Bulletin of Spanish Studies [51722]

Belfast
The Chronicle [52281]

London
DBI Review [54313] 3,000
Media Development [54921]

Peterborough
The Essential Guide to UK Farm &
  Outdoor Power Equipment [56256]

URUGUAY
Montevideo
Bibliographic Journal [57007]

VATICAN CITY
Vatican City
People on the Move [57015]

VENEZUELA
Caracas
Acta Botanjca Venezuelica [57019]
Acta Cientifica Venezolana
  [57020] .. .. (Non-paid) ‡500

SWEDISH

FINLAND
Abo
Journal of the Economic Society of
  Finland [43811] 950

Helsinki
Landsbygdens Folk
  [43843] 10,220
NNKY-NAKY [43850] 3,500

FRANCE
Ferney-Voltaire
Focus on the Public Services
  [43947] .... (Free) 17,000

ICELAND
Reykjavik
Rotary Norden [44902] 69,000

SWEDEN
Bastad
Fackoversattaren [50949]

Circulation: ★ = ABC; △ = BPA; ◆ = CAC; • = CCAB; ❏ = VAC; ⊕ = PO Statement; ‡ = Publisher's Report; Boldface figures = sworn; Light figures = estimated.

Farsta
Svensk Danssport [50954]

Goteborg
Swedish Journal of Musicology
[50966]

Stockholm
Arkiv Samhalle och Forskning
[51009]
Kvinnotryck [51024]
MEDSOLS [51025] .. ... (Paid) 2,000
Popular Astronomi [51030] 1,300
Sjukgymnasten [51038]
Socionomen [51040] 9,000

UNITED KINGDOM
London
Fonstret [54477]

TAMIL

SINGAPORE
Singapore
Tamil Murasu [50276] 14,400

SRI LANKA
Ethul Kotte
Marga Journal [50894]

Panadura
Losetha [50922] 2,000

TURKISH

TURKEY
Ankara
Biyokimya Dergisi [51490]
Karinca [51496] 3,500
Savunma Ve Havacilik
[51500] 15,000
Ucuncu Sektor Kooperatifcilik
[51518] 1,500

Istanbul
Acta Orthopaedica et Traumatologica
Turcica [51556] ...... (Paid) ‡1,000

UNITED KINGDOM
Wadhurst
International Construction Turkiye
[56808] .. .. (Combined) 17,649

UKRAINIAN

UKRAINE
Kharkov
Fizika Nizkikh Temperatur [51592]

Kiev
Edinstvennaya [51594] ..... ‡265,000
Edinstvennaya - Tvoye Zdorovye
[51595] .. .. ‡265,000
Haroshye Raditeli
[51597] .. .. ‡45,000
Lyubimaya Datcha
[51601] .. .. ‡20,000
Mama I ya [51602] .... ‡60,000
Polina [51604] .. .. ‡155,000
Privatnyi Dom [51605] .... ‡35,000
TV Ekran [51609] .. .. ‡100,000
Tvoy Malysh [51610] .... ‡90,000
Uyutnaya Kvartira [51611]
Veselye Ideiki [51612] .. .. ‡40,000
Viva! Beauty [51613] .. .. ‡50,000
Viva! Biographia [51614] .. ... ‡50,000
Young Lady [51615] .... ‡65,000

URDU

PAKISTAN
Karachi
Daily Jang [49345]

VIETNAMESE

VIETNAM
Hanoi
Humanity [57051]

WELSH

UNITED KINGDOM
Cardiff
A470 [52923] 6,000

YIDDISH
See also Hebrew

ISRAEL
Haifa
Khulyot [46077]

Ethnic Publications

Index entries are arranged geographically, first by states/provinces and then by cities. Within cities in this index, citations appear alphabetically by publication title. Citations include publication title, entry number (given in parentheses immediately following the title), and circulation figures.

COLOMBIA

Bogota

ArtNexus **[43542]**

SPAIN

Madrid

Cuadernos Hispanoamericanos
   [50744]
Insula **[50771]**
Ser Padres **[50802]**

UNITED KINGDOM

Abingdon

Bulletin of Spanish Studies **[51722]**
Journal of Spanish Cultural Studies
   [51945]

Index entries are arranged geographically, first by country and then by city. Within cities in this index, citations appear alphabetically by publication title. Citations include publication title, entry number (given in parentheses immediately following the title), and circulation figures.

AUSTRALIA
Sydney
Australian Journal of Jewish Studies
  [42458]

FINLAND
Helsinki
Chabad-Lubavitch of Finland **[43823]**

FRANCE
Paris
L'Arche **[44026]** .. .. (Paid) 20,000

GERMANY
Berlin
Aschkenas **[44157]** .... ‡320
Golem **[44187]**

Erlangen
Zeitschrift fur die Alttestamentliche
  Wissenschaft **[44343]** 1,200

ISRAEL
Haifa
Khulyot **[46077]**

Jerusalem
Azure **[46080]**
B'Or Ha'Torah **[46081]** 5,000
Hamodia (Israel) **[46082]**
Jerusalem Magazine **[46086]**
Menorah
  [46089] .... (Combined) 13,600

Ramat Gan
Jewish Studies, an Internet Journal
  [46095]

ITALY
Rome
Shalom
  [46241] .. .. (Combined) 10,000

KAZAKHSTAN
Almaty
Yevreiski Dom **[47169]**

NETHERLANDS
Leiden
European Journal of Jewish Studies
  [48671]
The Journal of Jewish Thought and
  Philosophy **[48699]**
Zutot **[48730]**

RUSSIA
Moscow
Lechaim **[49936]** .... ‡54,000

REPUBLIC OF SOUTH
AFRICA
Houghton
Jewish Affairs
  [50524] .. .. (Combined) ⊕1,000

UKRAINE
Donetsk
A Yidishe Mame **[51591]**

Lugansk
World of Jewish Woman **[51616]**

UNITED KINGDOM
Abingdon
East European Jewish Affairs **[51764]**
Journal of Modern Jewish Studies
  [51920]

Farnsfield
Shalom **[53382]**

London
Jewish Quarterly **[54691]**
Jewish Renaissance **[54692]**

Circulation: ★ = ABC; △ = BPA; ◆ = CAC; • = CCAB; ❑ = VAC; ⊕ = PO Statement; ‡ = Publisher's Report; Boldface figures = sworn; Light figures = estimated.

Index entries are arranged geographically, first by country and then by city. Within cities in this index, citations appear alphabetically by publication title. Citations include publication title, name of college or university, entry number (given in parentheses immediately following the title), and circulation figures.

AUSTRALIA

Adelaide
The Adelaidean—Media, Marketing & Publications Unit [41500] .... (Combined) 13,000

Canberra
ANU Reporter—ANU Reporter [41697]

Wodonga
The Weaver—La +Trobe University [42702]

BELGIUM

Leuven
Campuskrant—Katholieke Universiteit Leuven [42893]

PEOPLE'S REPUBLIC OF CHINA

Changchun
Jilin University Journal Social Sciences Edition—Jilin University [43239]
Journal of Jilin University Earth Science Edition—Jilin University [43240]
Journal of Jilin University Engineering and Technology Edition—Jilin University [43241]
Journal of Jilin University Information Science Edition—Jilin University [43242]
Journal of Jilin University Medicine Edition—Jilin University [43243]
Journal of Jilin University Science Edition—Jilin University [43244]

Hong Kong
Profile—Communications and Public Affairs Office [43376] 13,000

Nanjing
Advances in Science and Technology of Water Resources—Hohai University [43456]
Journal of Economics of Water Resources—Hohai University [43458]
Journal of Hohai University—Hohai University [43459]

Water Resources Protection—Hohai University [43460]
Water Science and Engineering—Hohai University [43461]

Shanghai
Academic Journal of Shanghai Jiao Tong University Social Science Section—Shanghai Jiao Tong University [43462]
Die & Mould Technology—Shanghai Jiao Tong University [43472]
Drive System Technique—Shanghai Jiao Tong University [43473]
English of Science and Technology Learning—Shanghai Jiao Tong University [43474]
Journal of Noise and Vibration Control—Shanghai Jiao Tong University [43481]
Journal of Shanghai Jiaotong University—Shanghai Jiao Tong University [43482]
Journal of Shanghai Jiaotong University Agricultural Science—Shanghai Jiao Tong University [43483]
Journal of Vibration and Shock—Shanghai Jiao Tong University [43484]
Laboratory Research and Exploration—Shanghai Jiao Tong University [43485]
Machine Design & Research—Shanghai Jiao Tong University [43486]
Micro- and Nanometer Science & Technology—Shanghai Jiao Tong University [43488]
Microcomputer Applications—Shanghai Jiao Tong University [43489]
Ocean Engineering—Shanghai Jiao Tong University [43492]
Systems Engineering—Shanghai Jiao Tong University [43506]

Xi'an
Journal of Xaut (Natural Sciences)—Xi'an University of Architecture and Technology [43535]
Journal of Xaut (Social Sciences)—Xi'an University of Architecture and Technology [43536]

CROATIA

Zagreb
Diskrepancija—Diskrepancija [43567]

CYPRUS

Nicosia
POLIS—University of Cyprus [43597]

IRELAND

Dublin
Eigse—National University Of Ireland [45954]

NORWAY

Oslo
Universitas—University of Oslo [49210] .... (Controlled) 15,000

POLAND

Warsaw
Annals of Warsaw University of Life Sciences, Land Reclamation—Versita [49689]

SINGAPORE

Singapore
NTU—Nanyang Technological University [50228]

REPUBLIC OF SOUTH AFRICA

Rondebosch
Monday Paper—University of Cape Town [50622]

SWITZERLAND

Fribourg
Universitas Friburgensis—Universite de Fribourg [51087] 9,500

UNITED KINGDOM

Aberdeen
Gaudie—Aberdeen University Students' Association [51676] .... (Non-paid) 4,000

Abingdon
Defence Studies—Routledge [51753]
East European Jewish Affairs—Routledge [51764]

Birmingham
Spaghetti Junction—University of Central England Union of Students [52367] .... (Controlled) 4,000

Canterbury
inQuire—University of Kent Student's Union [52921] ... (Non-paid) 2,000

Exeter
Expose—University of Exeter [53356] .... (Controlled) 2,500

Glasgow
eSharp—University of +Glasgow [53417]

Leicester
Ripple—Leicester University Students Union [53822]

Loughborough
Label—Loughborough Students' Union [55484]

Manchester
Grip—UMIST Students Association [55557] .... (Combined) 6,000
Student Direct—University of Manchester [55578] .... (Non-paid) 60,000

Nottingham
Digressus—Department of +Classics, +University of Nottingham [55752]

Oxford
Oxford Today—John #Wiley & Sons Inc. [56137]

Reading
Reading—The University of Reading [56331] .... (Controlled) 70,000

Southampton
Wessex Scene—Southampton University [56579] .... (Non-paid) 4,000

Wolverhampton
Cry Wolf—University of Wolverhampton SU [56952] .... (Non-paid) 26,000

Index entries are grouped beneath subheadings for fraternal organizations (please refer to the Index to Subject Terms). Within this broad subject arrangement, entries appear geographically by country and alphabetically within cities. Citations in this index include the publication title, entry number (given in parentheses), and circulation figures.

MASONS

AUSTRALIA
Hobart
Freemasonry Tasmania [41958]

FRANCE
Paris
Points de Vues Initiatiques [44076]

INDIA
Hyderabad
The Square and Compasses [45183]

NEW ZEALAND
Wellington
New Zealand Freemason
   [49020] .... ‡12,000

PHILIPPINES
Manila
Cabletow [49548]

UNITED KINGDOM
Edinburgh
Ashlar [53253]

Kingston upon Thames
The Square [53724]

London
Freemasonry Today
   [54480] .... (Paid) ‡240,000
Masonic Quarterly [54910]

ROTARIANS, INTERNATIONAL FELLOWSHIP OF

ARGENTINA
Rosario
Vida Rotaria [41488] 13,900

AUSTRALIA
Parramatta
Rotary Down Under
   [42236] .. .. (Paid) 50,000

BELGIUM
Brussels
Rotary Contact [42872] 769,000

CHILE
Los Angeles
El Rotario de Chile [43140] 5,800

COLOMBIA
Cali
Colombia Rotaria
   [43550] .... (Paid) 491,312

EGYPT
Cairo
Rotary Magazine [43764] 4,000

FRANCE
Lyon
Le Rotarien
   [43969] .. .. (Paid) 40,000

ICELAND
Reykjavik
Rotary Norden [44902] 69,000

INDIA
Chennai
Rotary News/Rotary Samachar
   [45056] .... (Paid) ⊕75,000

ITALY
Bergamo
Rotary [46123] 491,312

JAPAN
Tokyo
The Rotary-No-Tomo
   [47033] 120,000

REPUBLIC OF KOREA
Seoul
The Rotary Korea [47285] 48,000

MEXICO
Mexico City
Rotarismo en Mexico
   [47789] 13,500

NETHERLANDS
Amsterdam
Rotarian [48227] .... ★20,000

PERU
Chiclayo
El Rotario Peruano [49418] 3,500

PHILIPPINES
Quezon City
Philippine Rotary [49611] 15,000

REPUBLIC OF SOUTH AFRICA
KwaZulu-Natal
Rotary Africa
   [50544] .... (Paid) ⊕7,000

SWITZERLAND
Uster
Rotary Suisse-Liechtenstein
   [51236] .. .. ‡12,000

TAIWAN
Taipei
The Rotarian Monthly
   [51357] 11,300

TURKEY
Cinarli-Izmir
Rotary Dergisi [51552] 8,100

UNITED KINGDOM
Alcester
Rotary Magazine (GB & I) [52095]

VENEZUELA
Tachira
Nueva Revista Rotaria
   [57029] 9,900

Circulation: ★ = ABC; △ = BPA; ◆ = CAC; • = CCAB; ❑ = VAC; ⊕ = PO Statement; ‡ = Publisher's Report; Boldface figures = sworn; Light figures = estimated.

Index entries are arranged geographically, first by country and then by city. Within cities in this index, citations appear alphabetically by publication title. Citations include publication title, entry number (given in parentheses immediately following the title), and circulation figures.

ARGENTINA
Buenos Aires
Journal of Latin American Hermeneutics **[41477]**

AUSTRALIA
Banyo
Australian Ejournal of Theology **[41575]**

Blackburn
Target **[41601]** 17,000

Hawthorn
The Victoria Baptist Witness **[41943]** .... (Paid) 14,000

Melbourne
The Australian Christian **[42048]** .. .. (Paid) 2,205

Richmond
Australian Catholics **[42301]** 196,555

Sydney
Journal of Religious History **[42529]**

BELGIUM
Brussels
MIJARC News **[42866]** 3,000

PEOPLE'S REPUBLIC OF CHINA
Hong Kong
Chinese Around the World **[43288]** 7,000
Ching Feng **[43289]**

FRANCE
Paris
Famille Chretienne **[44045]**
Messages du Secours Catholique **[44072]**

GERMANY
Berlin
International Journal of Practical Theology **[44194]**
Journal of Ancient Christianity **[44201]** 400
Neue Zeitschrift fur Systematische Theologie und Religionsphilosophie **[44224]** 250

Bonn
Zeitschrift fur die Neutestamentliche Wissenschaft **[44273]** 1,050

Cologne
Christliche Frau **[44291]**

Dortmund
Korrespondenzblatt **[44317]** 750

Erlangen
Zeitschrift fur die Alttestamentliche Wissenschaft **[44343]** 1,200
Zeitschrift fur Antikes Christentum [44344]** 400

Hamburg
Der Islam **[44413]** 500

Heppenheim
From the Martin Buber House **[44482]**

Witten
TeensMag **[44714]** .. .. (Combined) 20,000

INDIA
Aligarh
MAAS Journal of Islamic Science **[44918]** .. .. (Paid) 1,000

Bangalore
Journal of Dharma **[44969]** .. .. (Paid) 1,800

Chennai
Krishnamurti Foundation Bulletin **[45051]** .. .. (Paid) 1,300
Theosophist **[45059]** .. . (Paid) 3,000
The Vedanta Kesari **[45060]** .. .. (Paid) 95,000

Delhi
Ave **[45088]**
Tattvaviveka **[45105]**
Vachan Sudha **[45108]**
Vidyajyoti Journal of Theological Reflection **[45109]**

Garhwal
Divine Life **[45120]**

Hyderabad
Journal of the Henry Martyn Institute **[45174]** .... (Paid) 370

Kolkata
Rally **[45302]** .. .. (Paid) 1,500
Udbodhan **[45307]** .. .. (Paid) 55,000
(Non-paid) 1,000

Mumbai
The Theosophical Movement **[45447]** .... (Paid) 380
(Non-paid) 380

New Delhi
Aim **[45480]** .. .. (Combined) 3,300
Journal of Objective Studies **[45614]**
Religion and Law Review **[45643]**

Pondicherry
The Advent **[45690]** ..... (Paid) 1,000

IRAN
Tehran
Message of Thaqalayn **[45912]**

IRELAND
Kiltegan
Africa **[46028]** 130,000

Navan
Columban Mission **[46044]** 500,000
The Far East **[46045]** 135,000

ITALY
Rocca di Papa
New Humanity **[46219]** 5,000

Rome
Carmel in the World **[46223]**
Club 3 **[46224]**
Famiglia Cristiana **[46229]** 966,671
Jesus **[46236]** 68,173
Progressio **[46240]**

JAPAN
Nagoya
Japanese Journal of Religious Studies **[46553]** .... (Combined) 510

LITHUANIA
Kaunas
Caritas **[47464]** 6,000

MALAYSIA
Kuala Lumpur
Al-Islam **[47596]**

MEXICO
Mexico City
Almas **[47781]**

NETHERLANDS
Amsterdam
Currents of Encounter **[47951]**
Intercultural Theology and Study of Religions **[48023]**
Meeleven **[48152]** .. .. (Non-paid) 9,500

Dordrecht
International Journal for Philosophy of Religion **[48429]**

The Hague
Caravanserai **[48609]**

Leiden
Archive for the Psychology of Religion **[48651]**
Islamic Law and Society **[48685]**
Journal of Ancient Near Eastern Religions **[48687]**
Journal of Reformed Theology **[48701]**
Journal of Religion in Africa **[48702]**
Journal of Religion in Europe **[48703]**
Journal for the Study of Judaism **[48704]**
Novum Testamentum **[48715]**
Religion and Human Rights **[48719]**
Religion and Theology **[48720]**
Social Sciences and Missions **[48724]**
Vetus Testamentum **[48729]**

Utrecht
Ars Disputandi **[48755]**

NEW ZEALAND
Auckland
New Zealand Baptist **[48806]** 9,800
NZ Catholic **[48823]** .. .. (Paid) 20,000

Napier
Circle **[48939]**

NORWAY
Stabekk
Banneret **[49212]**

PAKISTAN
Karachi
Hamdard Islamicus **[49350]** .. .., (Paid) 2,000
Pakistan Christian Post **[49367]**

Lahore
Renaissance **[49388]**

PHILIPPINES
Baguio City
Asian Journal of Pentecostal Studies **[49450]**

Makati City
Home Life **[49517]** .. .. (Paid) 60,000

Manila
Philippiniana Sacra **[49558]** .... (Paid) 500

Quezon City
East Asian Pastoral Review **[49591]** .... (Paid) 2,000
Journal of Asian Mission **[49597]**

Circulation: ★ = ABC; △ = BPA; ◆ = CAC; • = CCAB; ❑ = VAC; ⊕ = PO Statement; ‡ = Publisher's Report; Boldface figures = sworn; Light figures = estimated.

PORTUGAL
Fatima
Soul [49797]

ROMANIA
Cluj-Napoca
Journal for the Study of Religions
and Ideologies [49847]

SINGAPORE
Singapore
The Catholic News
[50118] 20,000
Journal of Asian Evangelical
Theology [50199]

REPUBLIC OF SOUTH AFRICA
Bloemfontein
Acta Theologica [50354]

Centurion
Journal for Christian Scholarship
[50441]
Old Testament Essays [50444]
Scriptura [50449]

Rondebosch
Journal for the Study of Religion
[50619]

Scottsville
Neotestamentica [50629]

SPAIN
Barcelona
El Ciervo [50666]

SWEDEN
Stockholm
Ny Framtid [51029]

SWITZERLAND
Binz
CSI Magazine [51081]

Geneva
The Ecumenical Review
[51091] .. .. (Paid) ‡2,000
International Review of Mission
[51149]
Reformed World
[51158] .... (Combined) 3,500
WSCF Journal [51170]

Lucerne
Schweizerische Kirchenzeitung
[51210] .. .. (Paid) 3,000

Winterthur
SAM-Focus [51242] 7,000

Zurich
Approches [51252]
Christliches Zeugnis [51256]
Schritte ins Offene [51277]

UNITED KINGDOM
Abingdon
Asian Philosophy [51707]
Islam and Christian-Muslim Relations
[51861]
Journal of Contemporary Religion
[51881]

Belfast
The Presbyterian Herald
[52292] .. .. (Paid) 16,000

Birmingham
Black Theology [52331]
The British Journal of Religious
Education [52334] .... (Paid) 2,000
REtoday [52363] .... (Paid) 7,000

Cambridge
The Journal of Ecclesiastical History
[52849] 1,250
Journal of the United Reformed
Church History Society [52864]
New Testament Studies
[52877] 2,400
Scottish Journal of Theology
[52892] 1,200

Dorking
Church Music Quarterly
[53193] .... (Paid) ‡11,500

Edinburgh
Journal of Qur'anic Studies [53294]
Life and Work
[53299] .. .. (Paid) 45,405
Studies in World Christianity [53321]

Glasgow
Reformation and Renaissance
Review [53445]

Harpenden
Gospel Standard
[53514] .. .. (Paid) 2,000

Harrow
The Muslim News [53526] 26,000

Ilford
Christian Librarian
[53638] .. .. (Paid) 500

Leominster
Day One Diary
[53840] .. .. (Combined) 160,000

Liverpool
Fieldwork in Religion [53872]
Modern Believing [53876] 750

London
Anglican World [53943]
Australian Religion Studies Review
[53981]
Christianity [54209]
Emel [54363]
The Friend [54483] .. ... (Paid) 4,500
Home & Family
[54566] .... (Paid) ★54,000
Implicit Religion [54588]
Interreligious Insight [54676] 800
Journal of Adult Theological
Education [54696]
Journal of Buddhist Ethics [54715]
Kids Alive!
[54843] .... (Non-paid) 35,000
Medieval Sermon Studies [54924]
The Middle Way [54931]
The Pastoral Review
[55061] .. .. (Paid) 3,800
Philosophy [55081] 2,000
Protestant Truth
[55146] .... (Combined) 3,030

Q News
[55159] .. .. (Combined) 15,000
Religion [55184]
Religions of South Asia [55185]
Religious Studies [55186] 1,200
Religious Studies and Theology
[55187]
Span [55260] .. ... (Non-paid) 35,000
The Tablet [55285] .. ... (Paid) 22,738
Theology [55305] 3,400
Usus Antiquior [55364]
The War Cry
[55378] .. .. (Paid) 17,000
Youthwork [55436] .... ‡2,500

Milton Keynes
Closer to God [55631]
Daily Bread [55632]
Encounter with God [55634]

Nottingham
Direction [55753] .... (Paid) 10,000

Oxford
The Journal of Theological Studies
[56075]
Material Religion [56094]
Modern Theology [56104]
Pacific Philosophical Quarterly
[56139]
The Philosophical Quarterly [56155]
Teaching Theology and Religion
[56214]
Zygon [56231]

Reading
The Bible Translator [56310]

Stoneleigh
Country Way
[56635] .. .. (Paid) 4,000

Sunderland
Buddhist Studies Review [56653]

Wolsingham
Recusant History [56950]

York
Mind [56994]

VATICAN CITY
Vatican City
People on the Move [57015]

Circulation: ★ = ABC; △ = BPA; ◆ = CAC; • = CCAB; ❑ = VAC; ⊕ = PO Statement; ‡ = Publisher's Report; Boldface figures = sworn; Light figures = estimated.

Index entries are arranged geographically, first by country and then by city. Within cities in this index, citations appear alphabetically by publication title. Citations include publication title, entry number (given in parentheses immediately following the title), and circulation figures.

AUSTRALIA
Brisbane
Australian Women's Book Review [41643]
Hecate [41648] 1,800

Callaghan
Women and Birth [41691]

Crawley
Outskirts [41820]

Eveleigh
Total Girl [41862] .... ★51,566

Sandgate
Redress [42353]

Sydney
The Australian Women's Weekly [42469] .... ★493,301
Fernwood [42503] 74,250
Harper's Bazaar (Australia) [42512] .... (Paid) ★56,119
Take 5 [42587] ... . ★222,498

AUSTRIA
Vienna
Fempower [42758]

BAHRAIN
Manama
Woman This Month [42795]

CHILE
Santiago
Cuadernos Mujer Salud [43144]
Revista Mujer Salud [43147]
Women's Health Collection [43149]

PEOPLE'S REPUBLIC OF CHINA
Beijing
Women of China [43223] 150,000

Hong Kong
Aware [43282]
Sparkle [43383] .... ‡21,500

Shanghai
Shanghai Style [43501]
With [43510]

CROATIA
Zagreb
Kruh i Ruze [43569]

DENMARK
Copenhagen
Forum, Tidsskrift for Kon Og Kultur [43670]

FINLAND
Helsinki
Eeva [43825] .... (Paid) 96,326
Kauneus ja Terveys [43839] .... (Paid) 73,290

Kuvalehdet
Anna [43879] ...... (Combined) ‡148,587
Kaksplus [43882] .. .... (Combined) ‡46,740
Kotiliesi [43887] ...... (Combined) ‡195,425

FRANCE
Paris
Paris Woman Journal [44074]

GERMANY
Augsburg
IFSCC Magazine [44140]

Bamberg
Journal of the European Society of Women in Theological Research [44146]

Bonn
Frau und Politik [44261]

Cologne
Christliche Frau [44291]

Hamburg
BILD der FRAU [44411] .... ‡1,274,182
FRAU von HEUTE [44416] .... ‡349,348
Petra [44422] .... (Paid) ‡295,102

Munich
MADCHEN [44570] .... ‡158,029
STAHLASH [44582] .... ‡69,073

HUNGARY
Budapest
Maxima Special [44849] .... (Paid) 44,183
Meglepetes [44850] ... (Paid) 94,838
Meglepetes Raadas [44851] .... (Paid) 65,900
Nok Lapja [44857] ... (Paid) 253,749
Nok Lapja Eskuvo [44859] .... ‡28,000
Nok Lapja Evszakok [44860] .... (Paid) 22,300
Praktika [44865] .... (Paid) 40,067
Story Special [44873] .... (Paid) 110,116

INDIA
Dharamsala
DOLMA [45110]

New Delhi
Cosmopolitan (India) [45501] .... (Paid) ★78,000
Good Housekeeping [45521]
Indian Journal of Human Rights and the Law [45557]
Woman's Era [45668] .... (Paid) 79,428

IRAN
Tehran
Mahjubah [45911] .. ... (Paid) 30,000

IRELAND
Clarenbridge
CORKnow [45932]
GALWAYnow [45933]

Dublin
Confetti [45951] .... ★17,000
Irish Tatler [45987] .... ★26,427
Prudence [45995] .... ★11,035
U Magazine [45999] .... ★34,103

Dundrum
Living It [46010] 10,000

JAPAN
Tokyo
Be Love [46759]
Be Love Parfait [46760]
Bessatsu Friend [46761]
CanCam [46776]
Dessert [46801]
JAUW [46875]
Juliet [46951]
Kiss [46954]
Nakayoshi [46974]
One More Kiss [47014]
Priv. [47025] .... ★173,474
Real Simple Japan [47030] .... (Paid) ★105,285

REPUBLIC OF KOREA
Seoul
Asian Journal of Women's Studies [47256] .... (Paid) 700
Feel [47265]

LEBANON
Beirut
Sahar [47401] 110,000

MALAYSIA
Kuala Lumpur
Harmoni [47603]
Wanita [47641] .... ★38,844

NETHERLANDS
Amsterdam
Elegance [47964] .. .. (Combined) ‡55,885
LOVER [48140] 2,000

NEW ZEALAND
Auckland
Australian Women's Weekly [48786] .... ★80,727

NICARAGUA
Managua
La Boletina [49054] 26,000

NIGERIA
Ibadan
Tropical Journal of Obstetrics and Gynaecology [49102]

PAKISTAN
Karachi
Fashion Mag [49349]
You [49379]

PHILIPPINES
Mandaluyong City
Cosmopolitan Philippines [49533] 72,000
Good Housekeeping Philippines [49537] 50,000
Preview [49539] 45,000

Manila
Lila [49551] .... (Paid) 500

Quezon City
Metro [49599]
Pink [49615]
Women in Action [49618] .. .. (Paid) 2,000
Working Mom [49619]

POLAND
Warsaw
Hot Moda & Shopping [49716] .... ‡7,073
Prawdziwe Zycie [49757]
Przyjaciolka [49760] .... ‡460,291
Uroda [49772] .. .. ‡76,342

PORTUGAL
Cruz Quebrada-Dafundo
Pais & Filhos [49796] .. .. (Paid) 30,712

Circulation: ★ = ABC; △ = BPA; ♦ = CAC; • = CCAB; ❑ = VAC; ⊕ = PO Statement; ‡ = Publisher's Report; Boldface figures = sworn; Light figures = estimated.

ROMANIA
Bucharest
Avantaje **[49831]** .. .. ‡23,612
Elle Mariaj **[49836]** .. .. ‡4,387
Lucru de Mana **[49839]** ..... ‡12,516
Povestea Mea **[49841]** .... ‡31,077
Psychologies **[49842]** .... ‡10,845

RUSSIA
Moscow
Atelier Rundschau
   [49879] .... ‡18,320
Diana Creative **[49892]** .. .. ‡20,715
Diana Moden **[49893]** .... ‡50,230
Industria Mody **[49917]** .... ‡1,900
International Textiles **[49921]** ... ‡235
Iren **[49922]** .. .. ‡27,340
Knit&Mode **[49932]** .... ‡15,900
Lena Rukodelie **[49937]** .. ... ‡20,600
Natalia **[49947]** .... ‡14,300
Sabrina **[49986]** .... ‡74,880
Sabrina Baby **[49987]** .. .. ‡6,110
Samaya **[49988]** .... ‡117,350
Susanna Rukodeliye
   [49993] .... ‡20,980
Susanna Vjazanie
   [49994] .... ‡75,000
Vjazanie Vashe Hobby
   [49998] .... ‡64,900
Vyshitye Kartiny **[49999]** ..... ‡18,100

SINGAPORE
Singapore
The Best of Singapore
   [50114] .. .. ‡20,000
Citta Bella **[50123]** 30,000
Female Business **[50149]** 25,000
Icon Moments
   [50169] .. .. (Combined) 20,000
NuYou **[50230]** 25,000
Simply Her **[50252]** 50,000

REPUBLIC OF SOUTH AFRICA
Cape Town
Fairlady **[50378]** .. .. ★71,898
Idees **[50382]** 85,642
Leef met hart & siel
   [50388] .... ★40,886
Move! **[50393]** 41,336
Psychologies South Africa
   [50403] 42,000
SARIE My inspirasie
   [50408] .... ★125,612

True Love **[50418]** .. .. ★99,889
Durban
Saltwater GIRL **[50468]** ...... ★32,360
Saltwater GIRL SURF **[50469]**
Johannesburg
Building Women **[50528]**
Obstetrics and Gynaecology Forum
   [50532]
Parklands
Essentials **[50562]** ... (Paid) ★76,295

SPAIN
Barcelona
Clara **[50657]** .. .. ‡161,874
Labores del Hogar
   [50682] .... ‡53,427
Lecturas **[50683]** .... ‡198,930
Lecturas Moda **[50686]**
Patrones **[50691]** .... ‡33,397
Madrid
Cosmopolital (Spain)
   [50741] .. .. (Combined) 140,000
Marie Claire
   [50780] ...... (Combined) ‡108,000
Mia
   [50784] ...... (Combined) ‡140,000
Ser Padres Bebe
   [50803] .. .. (Combined) ‡59,308

SRI LANKA
Colombo
Lanka Woman **[50861]**

SWEDEN
Stockholm
Damernas Varld **[51014]** ..... ‡87,700

SWITZERLAND
Lausanne
Edelweiss **[51186]** 24,185
Femina Fashion **[51189]** ..... ‡25,000
Zurich
GlucksPost **[51263]** 146,325

TURKEY
Mersin
Kadin/Woman 2000 **[51577]**

UKRAINE
Donetsk
A Yidishe Mame **[51591]**

Kiev
Edinstvennaya **[51594]** ..... ‡265,000
Edinstvennaya - Tvoye Zdorovye
   [51595] .. .. ‡265,000
Polina **[51604]** .. .. ‡155,000
Viva! Beauty **[51613]** .... ‡50,000
Young Lady **[51615]** .... ‡65,000
Lugansk
World of Jewish Woman **[51616]**

UNITED ARAB EMIRATES
Dubai
Emirates Bride **[51641]** 15,000

UNITED KINGDOM
Aberdeen
Lady Biker Magazine **[51679]**
Abingdon
Australian Feminist Studies **[51711]**
International Feminist Journal of
   Politics **[51824]**
Journal of Gender Studies **[51899]**
Women **[52091]**
Women & Performance **[52092]**
Women's Writing **[52093]**
Alfreton
Slimming World Magazine
   [52099] .. .. (Controlled) 248,862
Aylesbury
Point 3 **[52149]** 2,500
Belfast
Northern Woman **[52290]**
Ulster Countrywoman
   [52296] 5,000
Bristol
Irish Dancing & Culture **[52681]**
Chessington
Asian Woman **[52990]** .... ★90,339
Colchester
Slim at Home **[53051]**
Edinburgh
Home Help **[53284]**
Glasgow
OS **[53437]** .. .. ★25,520
Guisborough
The Journal for Weavers, Spinners
   and Dyers **[53499]**
Leeds
ASDA Magazine
   [53755] 3,000,000

London
African Journal of Midwifery and
   Women's Health **[53922]**
Amy **[53939]**
Aviva **[53993]** ..... (Non-paid) 20,000
Bella **[54010]** .... ★246,446
Chat - It's Fate **[54200]**
Cooler **[54265]**
Crafts **[54281]** 20,000
Daisy **[54308]** .... ★43,162
DARE **[54312]**
Essential Guide to Beauty **[54384]**
The European Journal of Women's
   Studies **[54407]**
Fate & Fortune **[54445]**
Feminism & Psychology **[54446]**
Feminist Theory **[54448]**
Girl Talk Extra **[54508]**
Grazia **[54521]**
The HAT Magazine **[54533]**
Home & Family
   [54566] .... (Paid) ★54,000
The Lantern **[54854]**
Majesty Magazine **[54898]**
Menopause International **[54926]**
New Woman **[55001]**
Practical Parenting and Pregnancy
   [55116]
Spirit & Destiny **[55262]** .. ... ★61,537
Take a Break **[55286]** .... ★855,372
that's life! **[55302]** .. .. ★386,875
Totally Tracy Beaker **[55330]**
W.I.T.C.H. **[55409]**
Woman **[55412]**
Woman & Home **[55413]**
Women's Health **[55414]**
You & Your Wedding **[55433]**
Marlow
Menopause International **[55600]**
North Tyneside
SISTERS (Sisterhood and Interna-
   tional Solidarity to End Racism and
   Sexism) **[55705]**
Norwich
health24 **[55732]**
Orpington
Popular Patchwork **[55855]**
Ringwood
Felicity Wishes **[56396]**
Shrewsbury
My Little Pony **[56538]** 50,000
Stevenage
The Woman Engineer
   [56620] 18,000

Circulation: ★ = ABC; △ = BPA; ◆ = CAC; • = CCAB; ❑ = VAC; ⊕ = PO Statement; ‡ = Publisher's Report; Boldface figures = sworn; Light figures = estimated.

Index entries are arranged geographically, first by country and then by city. Within cities in this index, citations appear alphabetically by publication title. Citations include publication title, entry number (given in parentheses immediately following the title), and circulation figures.

INDIA
Bangalore
The Economic Times
   [44958] .. .. (Paid) 24,489
Chennai
The Economic Times
   [45031] .. .. (Paid) 26,592

Kolkata
The Economic Times
   [45264] .. .. (Paid) 43,228
Mumbai
The Economic Times
   [45368] .. .. (Paid) 108,302

New Delhi
The Economic Times
   [45505] .. .. (Paid) 19,804
   (Combined) 400,000

Circulation: ★ = ABC; △ = BPA; ◆ = CAC; • = CCAB; ❑ = VAC; ⊕ = PO Statement; ‡ = Publisher's Report; Boldface figures = sworn; Light figures = estimated.

Gale Directory of Publications & Broadcast Media/147th Ed.

6091

Index entries are arranged by subject (please refer to the Index to Subject Terms). Within the subject groupings, entries appear geographically by country and alphabetically within cities. Citations in this index include publication title, entry number (given in parentheses), and circulation figures.

ABORTION

UNITED KINGDOM
London
Cas London [54186]

ALTERNATIVE AND UNDERGROUND

AUSTRALIA
Roseville
The Skeptic [42320] 3,000

PEOPLE'S REPUBLIC OF CHINA
Hong Kong
bc Magazine [43283] 30,000

GERMANY
Rossdorf
Skeptiker [44645] 3,000

INDIA
Bangalore
Amruth [44948] .... (Paid) ⊕5,000

NORWAY
Oslo
Monitor 21 [49204]

SWITZERLAND
Winterthur
Spuren
 [51243] .... (Controlled) 10,000

UNITED KINGDOM
Birmingham
The Vegan [52372] 6,000

Exeter
European Journal of Herbal Medicine
 [53353]

London
Bizarre [54032]

Northampton
The Homeopath Journal
 [55709] 3,000

ANTIQUES

AUSTRIA
Vienna
Globe Studies [42759]

HUNGARY
Budapest
Antik Tanulmanyok [44822]

JAPAN
Amagasaki
Daruma Magazine [46302]

UNITED KINGDOM
Broadstairs
Antiques Info [52744]

Chippenham
Antiques & Art Independent
 [53020] 21,000

Horncastle
Old Glory [53592]

London
Antique Dealer & Collectors Guide
 [53957] .... (Combined) 12,000
The Antique Trade Calendar
 [53958] .... (Paid) ‡12,000
Homes & Antiques
 [54567] .... ★55,100
Journal of Arms and Armour Society
 [54701]
Journal of the Society of
 Archer-Antiquaries [54821] 400

Newark
Members Journal [55660] 4,311

Newtownabbey
Five Foot Three [55701]

ART

AUSTRALIA
Sydney
Scan [42578]

PEOPLE'S REPUBLIC OF CHINA
Shanghai
Calligraphy [43464]
Calligraphy and Painting [43465]

FINLAND
Helsinki
Framework [43830]

GERMANY
Berlin
European Photography [44175]
Zeitschrift des Deutschen Vereins fur
 Kunstwissenschaft [44238]

Leinfelden-Echterdingen
DAMALS [44518] 32,799

GREECE
Nauplion
International Journal of Arts and
 Technology [44762]

ITALY
Milan
Rodeo [46193]

JAPAN
Amagasaki
Daruma Magazine [46302]

NEW ZEALAND
Hamilton
Ramp [48910]

RUSSIA
Moscow
Russian Art [49971] .... ‡7,000

REPUBLIC OF SOUTH AFRICA
Durban
blunt [50467] .... ★13,207

SWEDEN
Stockholm
CAP&Design
 [51012] .... (Paid) 15,000

SWITZERLAND
Geneva
Tribune des Arts [51161] .. .. ‡72,000

UNITED KINGDOM
Chester
Skin Deep [52999] 38,764

Colchester
Let's Make Cards! [53041]

London
Art, Design & Communication in
 Higher Education [53967]
Asian Art [53974] 8,000
Frieze [54484]
International Journal of Education
 through Art [54645]
Overseas [55047] 25,000
Quintessentially [55166] 25,000
RA Magazine [55167]
Technoetic Arts [55295]

Sudbury
Total Tattoo Magazine [56651]

Tenterden
The Artist [56742] .. ... (Paid) 21,500
Leisure Painter
 [56743] .. .. (Paid) 28,000

ASTROLOGY

INDIA
Mumbai
Kalnirnay [45406] 8,000,000

UNITED KINGDOM
Bristol
Culture and Cosmos
 [52659] .... (Paid) 300

Croydon
Prediction [53131]

London
Astrological Journal [53978] ... 1,600
Chat - It's Fate [54200]
Correlation [54268]
Fate & Fortune [54445]
Spirit & Destiny [55262] .. ... ★61,537

ATHEISM

NEW ZEALAND
Auckland
The Open Society [48828]

AUTOMOTIVE (CONSUMER)
See also (Auto Racing)

AUSTRALIA
Alexandria
Fast Fours Magazine
 [41539] .... ★30,120
Overlander 4WD [41545] .... ★24,333

Mansfield
The Jag Mag
 [42033] .. .. (Paid) 12,000

Melbourne
4wdonline [42060]
Melbourne Community Voice
 [42073] .. .. (Combined) 20,000

North Ryde
Australian Road Rider
 [42168] 27,000
Australian Trailrider [42169]
4WD Buyers Guide [42182]
New Car Buyer [42188]
Performance Buildups
 [42192] 22,000
Used Car Buyers Guide [42200]

Pyrmont
The Wanderer [42291]

Strawberry Hills
Australian Classic Car Monthly
 [42394]

Surry Hills
Australasian Paint & Panel
 [42408] .... ‡6,548

Sydney
Australian Auto Action
 [42451] .... ★12,006

Circulation: ★ = ABC; △ = BPA; ◆ = CAC; • = CCAB; ❑ = VAC; ⊕ = PO Statement; ‡ = Publisher's Report; Boldface figures = sworn; Light figures = estimated.

Australian Motorcycle News
[42460] .... ★20,132
4x4 Australia [42505] .... ★18,227

BELGIUM
Oostende
Old Timer Dreamcar Magazine
[42907] .... (Paid) ‡23,375
Zwerfauto Magazine
[42908] .... (Paid) ‡18,825

PEOPLE'S REPUBLIC OF CHINA
Shanghai
Car & Fan [43466]

CZECH REPUBLIC
Prague
Auto Motor a Sport (Czech)
[43610] 23,500

FINLAND
Helsinki
F1 Racing [43829] ... .. (Paid) 18,031
Tuulilasi [43862] .... (Paid) 80,071
Kuvalehdet
Tekniikan Maailma
[43897] ...... (Combined) ‡129,343

FRANCE
Fontainebleau
Auto Retro [43952]
La Vie de l'Auto [43953]
Retroviseur [43954]

GERMANY
Hamburg
Auto Bild [44410] .. ... (Paid) 700,244
Herten
VW Scene International [44484]

INDIA
Mumbai
Overdrive [45425]

IRELAND
Dublin
Motoring Life [45992]
Sandyford
Used Car Price Guide [46058]

ITALY
Rozzano
Quattroruote [46252] .... ‡464,393
Ruoteclassiche [46253] 50,600
Vendo & Compro
[46256] .. .. (Combined) 125,000

NETHERLANDS
Amsterdam
Autovisie [47901] ...... (Paid) 60,000
Carros Magazine
[47922] .... (Combined) 30,000
The Hague
Autokampioen
[48608] .... (Controlled) 55,000

NEW ZEALAND
Auckland
AA Directions [48783]
New Zealand Classic Car
[48807] 10,743
New Zealand Performance Car
[48820] .... ★17,432
New Zealand Trucking
[48821] .... ★10,009

NZV8 [48826]
North Shore City
New Zealand 4WD [48958] 3,403
Wellington
Circular [49004]

PORTUGAL
Cruz Quebrada-Dafundo
Auto Hoje (Car Today)
[49791] .. .. (Paid) 19,923
Automagazine
[49792] .. .. (Controlled) 19,912
Guia do Automovel
[49794] .... (Paid) 42,496

SINGAPORE
Singapore
Global Sources Auto Parts &
Accessories [50152]
Torque [50280] 25,000

REPUBLIC OF SOUTH AF-RICA
Cape Town
Max Power [50390]
TOPbike [50415]
TopCar [50416] 31,990
topMotor [50417]

SPAIN
Madrid
Car and Driver (Spain) [50732]
Coches de Ocasion
[50736] .. .. ‡17,108
Guia del Comprador de Coches
[50764] .. .. ‡13,348
Guia del Comprador de Furgonetas y
Autocaravanas [50765] ..... ‡2,524
Top Auto [50812] .. ..,..... ‡24,234
Seville
International Journal of Vehicle Sys-
tems Modelling and Testing [50835]

UNITED KINGDOM
Aberdeen
Lady Biker Magazine [51679]
Bath
Total Vauxhall [52261]
Berkhamsted
Steam Days [52314]
Birmingham
Classic Car Mart [52337]
Bourne
Caravan, Motorhome & Camping
Mart [52409]
Bournemouth
Total 911 [52427]
Croydon
VolksWorld [53137]
Cudham
Classic Military Vehicle [53138]
Classic Van and Pick-up [53140]
Classic and Vintage Commercials
[53141]
Jaguar World Monthly [53143]
Modern MINI [53144]
Old Tractor [53145]
Stationary Engine [53147]
Dorset
Minor Monthly [53195]
Edinburgh
Classic Bus [53262]
Horncastle
Old Glory [53592]

Scootering [53593]
King's Lynn
Ferrari Magazine
[53712] .. .. (Paid) 2,848
Ferrari News
[53713] .... (Controlled) 3,000
London
Auto Express [53985]
Auto Trader [53986] .... ★189,077
Classic American
[54212] ...... (Combined) 18,500
Motor Caravan [54958]
Top Gear Magazine
[55326] .... ★175,218
Top Marques [55327] .... ★24,118
What Van?
[55402] .. .. (Combined) ‡20,000
Manchester
Auto Freeway [55542] 143,000
Bike Trader [55543] .... ★17,876
Portsmouth
Bus & Coach Preservation [56288]
Sevenoaks
BMW Car [56470]
GT Purely Porsche [56473]
Japanese Cars Banzai [56475]
Performance BMW [56476]
Performance Car [56477]
Performance Ford [56478]
Performance VW [56479]
Retro Cars [56481]
Retro Ford [56482]
Surrey
Japanese Performance
[56667] .. .. (Paid) 25,000
911 & Porsche World
[56669] .. .. (Paid) 36,000
Renault Magazine
[56674] .. .. ★212,117
Triumph World
[56677] .. .. (Paid) 28,000
Teddington
Autocar [56729] .. .. (Paid) 66,245
What Car?
[56736] .... (Paid) 143,678
Tunbridge Wells North
Modern Railways [56785]
Ware
Bentley Magazine [56839] 60,000
Wellingborough
Octane Magazine
[56881] .. .. ★33,039
Westoning
Audi Driver
[56907] .. .. (Combined) ‡18,000
Volkswagen Driver
[56908] .. .. (Combined) ‡18,000

AVIATION

AUSTRALIA
Mount Ommaney
Classic Wings [42134] 13,000
Surry Hills
Australian Flying [42412] ...... ★7,377
Aviation Business Magazine
[42420] .... ★3,098
Flightpath [42430] .... ‡15,500

REPUBLIC OF SOUTH AF-RICA
Johannesburg
Transport World Africa [50537]

UNITED KINGDOM
Bath
Flyer [52239]

Berkshire
Go Flying [52315]
Brackley
Popular Flying [52433]
Chepstow
Travel Guide International [52984]
Fleet
The Brooklands Society Gazette
[53389] .... (Controlled) 1,300
Kingston upon Thames
Aircraft Illustrated [53719]
Combat Aircraft [53720]
London
Aeroplane Monthly [53912]
Airfinance Journal [53931]
PrivatAir [55120] 7,000
Maidstone
Aerostat [55527]
Oxford
HyperScale [55982]
Microlight Flying
[56098] .. .. (Paid) 4,200
Stamford
Airports of the World [56594]
FlyPast [56596] .... (Paid) ★44,188
Today's Pilot [56597]
Sutton
Airline Business [56679] .... △22,907

BABIES
See also Parenting

AUSTRALIA
Glen Iris
Breastfeeding Review [41891]

CAMEROON
Yaounde
Clinics in Mother and Child Health
[43129]

FINLAND
Kuvalehdet
Kaksplus
[43882] .. .. (Combined) ‡46,740

HUNGARY
Budapest
Kismama [44843] ...... (Paid) 19,535
Kismama Mintaszam
[44844] .. .. (Free) 130,000
Kismama 9 Honap
[44845] .. .. (Paid) 30,970

IRELAND
Dublin
Maternity & Infant [45991] 15,000

NEW ZEALAND
Auckland
Little Treasures [48803] .... ★30,713

POLAND
Warsaw
Mamo, to ja [49735] .... ‡98,937
Twoj Maluszek [49769] ..... ‡146,473
Twoje dziecko [49770] .. .. ‡70,524

RUSSIA
Moscow
Mama, eto ya! [49940] .... ‡86,740
Sabrina Baby [49987] .. .. ‡6,110

SINGAPORE
Singapore
Young Parents Baby
[50290] 25,000

Circulation: ★ = ABC; △ = BPA; ◆ = CAC; ● = CCAB; ❏ = VAC; ⊕ = PO Statement; ‡ = Publisher's Report; Boldface figures = sworn; Light figures = estimated.

SPAIN
Barcelona
Tu Bebe [50704] .... ‡95,092

Madrid
Ser Padres Bebe
[50803] .. .. (Combined) ‡59,308

UKRAINE
Kiev
Haroshye Raditeli
[51597] .... ‡45,000
Mama I ya [51602] .... ‡60,000
Tvoy Malysh [51610] .... ‡90,000

UNITED KINGDOM
Glasgow
First Link 4 Parents
[53420] .. .. (Free) 18,000

London
Practical Parenting and Pregnancy
[55116]

BLIND AND VISUALLY CHALLENGED

SINGAPORE
Singapore
White Cane [50286]

UNITED KINGDOM
Reading
FORWARD [56318] 80,000

BRIDES

AUSTRALIA
North Ryde
Complete Wedding Guide Melbourne
[42177] 15,000
Complete Wedding Sydney [42178]

Rozelle
Creative Weddings [42324]

Sydney
My Perfect Wedding Planner
[42549] 30,000

GERMANY
Konstanz
Hochzeit
[44513] .. .. (Combined) 84,400

HUNGARY
Budapest
Nok Lapja Eskuvo
[44859] .... ‡20,000

IRELAND
Dublin
Confetti [45951] .... ★17,000

PHILIPPINES
Quezon City
Metro Weddings [49603]

SINGAPORE
Singapore
Her World Brides [50165] 13,193
Singapore Tatler Weddings
[50265] .... ‡14,000
Wedding & Travel [50285]

UNITED ARAB EMIRATES
Dubai
Emirates Bride [51641] 15,000

UNITED KINGDOM
Barnsley
Wedding Professional [52184]

Chessington
Asian Bride [52988] .. .. ★89,414

London
You & Your Wedding [55433]

Norwich
Pure Weddings North [55740]

BUSINESS

AUSTRALIA
North Sydney
Australian Telecom [42209]

Perth
Business Pulse [42248]

Surry Hills
Australasian Paint & Panel
[42408] .... ‡6,548
Australian Creative
[42410] .... ‡3,007
Australian Defence Magazine
[42411] .... ★3,985
Aviation Business Magazine
[42420] .... ★3,098
Food & Drink Business
[42431] .... ★5,294
FoodService News
[42432] 12,871
Greetings & Gifts [42433] ..... ‡5,300
Hospital & Agedcare
[42434] 7,523
Marine Business [42435] 4,149
Packaging News [42437] 4,659
Stationery News
[42440] .... (Paid) ‡5,000
Toy & Hobby Retailer
[42441] 2,662

Sydney
Asset [42449]

PEOPLE'S REPUBLIC OF CHINA
Hong Kong
Hong Kong Business
[43321] .. .. (Paid) 15,000

EGYPT
Cairo
Cairo Times [43753] .... (Paid) 5,000

FINLAND
Helsinki
Kauppalehti Optio
[43840] .... ★86,577

HUNGARY
Budapest
Figyelo TOP 200
[44832] .. .. (Paid) 10,000
UZLET & SIKER [44881] .... ‡20,346

INDIA
Hyderabad
The Icfai Journal of Accounting
Research [45140]
The Icfai Journal of Corporate and
Securities Law [45145]
The Icfai Journal of Knowledge
Management [45157]
The Icfai Journal of Mergers &
Acquisitions [45160]
The Icfai Journal of Operations
Management [45162]
The Icfai Journal of Organizational
Behavior [45163]

Icfai Reader [45170]
Insurance,Chronicle [45173]
Porfolio Organizer [45179]
Projects & Profits [45181]

Mumbai
Offshore World (OW) [45422]
Pharma Bio World [45428]

IRELAND
Dublin
Business Ireland [45948] 2,500

JAPAN
Tokyo
Eat [46805]
Nikkei Business [46981] ... ★308,561
Nikkei Business Associe
[46982] .... ★71,610
Nikkei Solution Business
[47007] .... ★9,034
Nikkei Venture [47009] .... ★59,790

NAMIBIA
Windhoek
The Namibia Economist
[47823] .. .. (Paid) 7,000

NEW ZEALAND
North Shore City
NZ Business [48959] 7,579

Wellington
AFR Smart Investor [48999]

PAKISTAN
Faisalabad
International Business Management
[49248]

Karachi
Investor's Business & Financial
Journal [49356]

SINGAPORE
Singapore
Female Business [50149] 25,000

REPUBLIC OF SOUTH AFRICA
Johannesburg
Transport World Africa [50537]

Roggebaai
Design Indaba Magazine
[50615] 5,000

SWITZERLAND
Geneva
International Journal of Information
and Decision Sciences [51125]

Lausanne
Bilan [51183] 19,325

TAIWAN
Taipei
International Journal of Business and
Information (IJBI) [51342]

THAILAND
Bangkok
Thailand Tatler [51443] .... ‡54,850

UNITED KINGDOM
Colchester
Craftbusiness [53032]

Crawley
Drinks International
[53102] .. .. (Controlled) ★10,000

Morning Advertiser
[53109] .... ★31,288
Off Licence News
[53110] .... ★18,440
Shopping Centre
[53113] .... (Paid) ★12,241
Shopping Centre Ireland
[53114] .... ★12,789
Wine & Spirit [53115] .. .. ★11,044

Edinburgh
Business Citizen
[53258] .... (Non-paid) ‡98,000

Kent
South East Business
[53682] .... (Non-paid) 13,000

Leicester
Global Municipal Investor [53802]

London
The AIM Guide [53929]
Business XL [54160]
China-Britain Business Review
[54206] .... (Combined) 7,000
The Economist [54352]
Growth Company Investor [54524]
In Brief [54590]
Intellectual Asset Management
[54613]
Market Leader [54907]
PrivatAir [55120] 7,000
PRWeek Magazine
[55148] .... ★14,818
Summit
[55276] .... (Combined) 29,949
Third Sector Magazine
[55311] .... ★12,345
UK Excellence [55354] .... ‡4,000
Vanguard [55365] 80,000

Maidenhead
Pool [55524]

Newcastle upon Tyne
Accent [55666] 18,000
North East Times [55676]

Oxford
Pump Industry Analyst [56180]

Potters Bar
Manufacturing & Logistics IT [56297]

Salisbury
Land Mobile [56455] ... (Paid) 8,500

Watford
Professional Builders Merchant
[56870] .... ★9,500
Professional Hairdresser
[56872] .... ★16,385
Professional Motor Factor
[56874] .... ★3,621

West Malling
Mortgage Matters [56893]
Your New Home [56895]

VIETNAM
Hanoi
Thoi Bao Kinh Te Vietnam
[57053] .... (Controlled) 35,000

ZIMBABWE
Harare
Zimbabwe Independent [57121]

CAREER DEVELOPMENT AND EMPLOYMENT

GERMANY
Augsburg
IFSCC Magazine [44140]

SINGAPORE
Singapore
Female Business [50149] 25,000

Circulation: ★ = ABC; △ = BPA; ♦ = CAC; • = CCAB; ❑ = VAC; ⊕ = PO Statement; ‡ = Publisher's Report; Boldface figures = sworn; Light figures = estimated.

SWITZERLAND
Fribourg
Universitas Friburgensis
[51087] 9,500

UNITED KINGDOM
Camberley
CareerScope [52783]

Glasgow
OS [53437] .... ★25,520

Hitchin
Sports Management [53582]

Leicester
Psychologist Appointments [53819]

London
Leaving School [54862]

Manchester
Jobs North West
[55563] .. .. (Paid) 27,000

Woking
Recruitment Matters
[56948] 13,500

CATS
See also Pets

UNITED KINGDOM
Arundel
Cat World [52133]

CHILDREN'S INTERESTS
See also Youths' Interests

AUSTRALIA
Gosford
Puzzle Fun for Kids [41921]

Rozelle
Parties for Kids [42328]

Sydney
Studio Bambini [42582] 45,000

PEOPLE'S REPUBLIC OF CHINA
Shanghai
Comic King [43471]

DENMARK
Alborg
Tjeck Magazine
[43644] .. .. (Controlled) 160,000

FINLAND
Kuvalehdet
Koululainen
[43888] .. .. (Combined) ‡44,634
Leppis
[43890] .. .. (Combined) ‡19,992
Tom & Jerry
[43898] .. .. (Combined) ‡8,559

HUNGARY
Budapest
National Geographic Kids
[44855] .... (Paid) ‡41,873

INDIA
New Delhi
Champak (English)
[45491] .. .. (Paid) 34,185
Champak (Gujarati)
[45492] .. .. (Paid) 10,000
Champak (Hindi)
[45493] .. .. (Paid) 71,705

Champak (Kannada)
[45494] .. .. (Paid) 10,000
Champak (Marathi)
[45495] .. .. (Paid) 17,000

JAMAICA
Kingston
The Children's Own [46282]

JAPAN
Tokyo
Weekly Shonen Sunday [47056]

REPUBLIC OF KOREA
Seoul
The Sonyon Chosun [47287]

NETHERLANDS
Dordrecht
The Jetix Magazine [48435]

NEW ZEALAND
Hamilton
Apex [48908]

Waitomo Caves
Tall Poppies [48993]

PAKISTAN
Karachi
US [49378]
Young World [49380]

PHILIPPINES
Mandaluyong City
Disney Princess Magazine
[49535] 22,000

POLAND
Warsaw
Przedszkolak [49758]

RUSSIA
Moscow
Sabrina Baby [49987] .: .... ‡6,110

SINGAPORE
Singapore
Global Sources Baby & Childrens
Products [50153]

REPUBLIC OF SOUTH AFRICA
Cape Town
South African Journal of Child Health
[50413]

UKRAINE
Kiev
Veselye Ideiki [51612] .. .. ‡40,000

UNITED KINGDOM
Bognor Regis
Play Action [52401]

Bristol
Imagine Magazine [52675] 7,500

Dundee
Animals and You
[53213] .. .. (Paid) 60,000

Leicester
Mathematical Pie [53814]
Symmetry Plus [53830]

London
All About Animals [53932]
Balamory [53998]

BBC Learning is Fun!
[54005] .. .. (Controlled) 60,000
Bob the Builder [54095]
CBeebies Weekly Magazine [54188]
Charlie and Lola [54198]
Codebreakers [54235] .... ★109,000
Criss Cross [54287] .... ★63,000
Daisy [54308] .... ★43,162
Disney Fairies [54332]
Disney and Me [54333] ...... ★49,002
Doctor Who Adventures [54338]
Dora Dress Up and Go [54340]
Dora the Explorer [54341]
Fifi and the Flowertots [54452] -
Fireman Sam [54461]
Girl Talk Extra [54508]
GO Girl [54515] .... ★43,163
In the Night Garden [54592]
Jackie Chan Adventures [54687]
Kids Alive!
[54843] .... (Non-paid) 35,000
Learn with Bob the Builder [54860]
Me Too! [54917]
Noddy [55007] .... ★39,229
Power Rangers [55112] ...... ★56,047
Robin Hood Adventures [55207]
Shrek's Quests [55236]
Su-doku [55274]
Take a Break's Su-doku
[55287] .... ★100,000
Teletubbies [55298]
Thomas & Friends
[55314] .... ★50,002
Totally Tracy Beaker [55330]
Toybox [55333]
Tweenies [55347]
Underground Ernie [55358]
W.I.T.C.H. [55409]

Redhill
Junior Puzzles [56354]
Puzzler Quiz Kids [56375]

Ringwood
Doctor Who Battles in Time [56395]
Felicity Wishes [56396]
007 Spy Cards [56397]

Shrewsbury
Bag-o-Fun [56526] 80,000
Fun to Learn Barney
[56530] 50,000
Fun to Learn Best of Barney
[56531] 30,000
Fun to Learn Discovery
[56532] 40,000
Fun to Learn Favourites
[56533] .... ★45,542
Fun to Learn Friends
[56534] .... ★76,846
Fun to Learn Letterland
[56535] 40,000
Fun to Learn Peppa Pig
[56536] 82,498
My Little Pony [56538] 50,000

CITY, HOTEL, RAILROAD, AND TRAVEL GUIDES
See also Travel and Tourism

AUSTRALIA
Sydney
COAST [42492] .... ‡30,000

PEOPLE'S REPUBLIC OF CHINA
Shanghai
Shanghai's Best Restaurants
[43505] .... ‡38,000
Travelling Scope [43508]
World Traveller [43511]

IRELAND
Dublin
Ireland at Your Leisure
[45969] .... ★41,000

Dundrum
Visitor [46011] .. .. ★200,000

MALAYSIA
Kuala Lumpur
Malaysia's Best Restaurants
[47622] .... ‡20,800

PHILIPPINES
Makati City
Philippines' Best Restaurants [49524]

SINGAPORE
Singapore
Regional Best Restaurants
[50242] .... ‡16,000
Singapore's Best Restaurants
[50267] .... ‡33,000

SPAIN
Barcelona
Viajes National Geographic
[50706] .: .... ‡63,013

THAILAND
Bangkok
Thai Spas [51440]
Thailand's Best Restaurants
[51444] .... ‡115,000

UNITED ARAB EMIRATES
Dubai
Dubai Voyager [51639] ...... △29,350
Middle East MICE & Events
[51649] 33,000

UNITED KINGDOM
Aberdeen
Good Time Guide [51677]

Crawley
H - The Hotel Magazine
[53106] .... ★8,602

Horncastle
Heritage Railway Magazine [53590]

Milton Keynes
Group Leisure [55637]

Skipton
Dalesman Magazine [56553]

Ware
Marbella Club Magazine
[56842] 17,000
Ritz Magazine [56844] .. .. ‡35,000

CLUBS AND SOCIETIES

AUSTRALIA
Canberra
The ANZIAM Journal (The Australian & New Zealand Industrial & Applied Mathematics Journal)
[41698] .... (Paid) 450
Canberra Cyclist [41703] 2,000
Journal of the Australian Mathematical Society [41709] ..... (Paid) 550

Glenside
AppleSauce [41897]

PEOPLE'S REPUBLIC OF CHINA
Hong Kong
The Club [43292]

Circulation: ★ = ABC; △ = BPA; ♦ = CAC; • = CCAB; ❑ = VAC; ⊕ = PO Statement; ‡ = Publisher's Report; Boldface figures = sworn; Light figures = estimated.

DENMARK
Valby
Horysont (Good News) [43736]

FINLAND
Abo
Journal of the Economic Society of
  Finland [43811] 950

Helsinki
NNKY-NAKY [43850] 3,500

FRANCE
Chateau Landon
Maitrises [43930]

GERMANY
Bonn
Fairkehr [44259] .... ‡65,000

ITALY
Turin
Impegno [46272] 500

REPUBLIC OF KOREA
Seoul
Bulletin of the Korean Chemical
  Society [47259] 2,300

NETHERLANDS
The Hague
Kampioen
  [48619] ..... (Controlled) 3,531,785

NEW ZEALAND
Wanganui
New Zealand Camellia Bulletin
  [48995]

Wellington
Forest and Bird Magazine
  [49008] .... (Paid) 20,000

SWEDEN
Norrkoping
Tidskrift for Schack
  [50996] .... (Non-paid) 2,000

Stockholm
Ny Framtid [51029]

SWITZERLAND
Bern
Die Alpen
  [51071] .... (Controlled) 83,000

UNITED KINGDOM
Bingham
Canoe Focus
  [52325] .. .. (Paid) 24,000

Birmingham
Townswoman [52369] 34,000

Bury Saint Edmunds
Journal of the Writing Equipment
  Society [52774] 600

East Grinstead
The Caravan Club Magazine
  [53235] ...... (Controlled) ★322,820
                              383,396

Gwynedd
Ffestiniog Railway Magazine
  [53500] .... (Paid) 5,000

Hemel Hempstead
Boys' Brigade Gazette
  [53555] .. .. (Paid) 22,000

King's Lynn
Ferrari News
  [53713] .... (Controlled) 3,000

London
Flyfishers' Journal
  [54472] .... (Paid) 650
Journal of the Society of Archivists
  [54822]
The Parkinson Magazine
  [55056] .... (Combined) 26,000
Scouting Magazine
  [55220] 22,000

Peterborough
The Garden [56258]

Reading
GrowthPoint [56319] .. . (Paid) 1,000

Sheffield
Transactions of the Philological
  Society [56516]

Ware
Marbella Club Magazine
  [56842] 17,000

Wem
Storylines [56885]

COLLECTING
See also Antiques; Art

AUSTRALIA
Melbourne
Stamp Bulletin
  [42087] ...... (Non-paid) ⊕300,000
Stamp Explorer
  [42088] ...... (Non-paid) ⊕300,000

FRANCE
Paris
Jukebox Magazine
  [44066] .... (Paid) 20,000

GERMANY
Alfeld
Deutsche Briefmarken Zeitung/Sam-
  mler Express (DBZ/SE)
  [44138] .. .. (Combined) 41,000

Ratingen
Deutsche Briefmarken Revue
  [44641] .. .. (Combined) 30,000

INDIA
Mumbai
India's Stamp Journal [45390]

ITALY
Rome
L'Orologio [46239]

SPAIN
Madrid
Cronica Filatelica [50742]

SWEDEN
Skillingaryd
SFF Filatelisten/Svensk Filatelistisk
  Tidskrift [50998] .... (Paid) 9,700

SWITZERLAND
Lausanne
Montres Passion/Uhren Welt
  [51197] .... (Controlled) 180,000

Zurich
FLASH [51260] 2,200

UNITED KINGDOM
Amersham
Military Machines International
  [52108]

Arundel
Toy Soldier & Model Figure
  [52135] .... (Paid) 10,000

Bishop's Stortford
Themescene [52382]

Bletchley
Toy Soldier Collector [52391]

Bristol
Koi [52701] 15,000

Bury Saint Edmunds
Journal of the Writing Equipment
  Society [52774] 600

Croydon
Stamp Magazine [53134]

Devon
IMCoS Journal [53176]

Honiton
Coin News [53586]

London
The Antique Trade Calendar
  [53958] .... (Paid) ‡12,000
Book and Magazine Collector
  [54097]
British Numismatic Journal [54143]
British Philatelic Bulletin
  [54145] .. .. (Paid) 22,000
British Postmark Bulletin
  [54146] .. .. (Paid) 1,500
The Classic Marvel Figurine
  Collection [54213]
The Country Bird Collection [54274]
Dora the Explorer [54341]
Horrible Science Collection [54569]
Jackie Chan Adventures [54687]
Journal of Arms and Armour Society
  [54701]
The London Philatelist [54888]
The Lord of the Rings Collector's
  Models [54891]
Midsomer Murders Magazine [54933]
Record Collector [55177]

Mansfield
Transport Ticket Society Journal
  [55591] 480

Norfolk
The Review [55703]

Northwood
The Ephemerist [55720]

Ormskirk
Card Times [55849] .. ... (Paid) 2,800

Ringwood
Doctor Who Battles in Time [56395]
007 Spy Cards [56397]

COMICS AND COMIC TECHNIQUE

PEOPLE'S REPUBLIC OF CHINA
Shanghai
Comic King [43471]

FINLAND
Kuvalehdet
Tom & Jerry
  [43898] .. .. (Combined) ‡8,559

JAPAN
Tokyo
Afternoon [46729]
Afternoon Season Zokan [46730]
Be Love [46759]
Be Love Parfait [46760]
Bessatsu Friend [46761]
Big Comic Original [46762]
Big Comic Spirits [46763]
Dessert [46801]
Evening [46818]
Gekkan Shonen Magazine [46829]
Juliet [46951]
Kiss [46954]
Magazine Special [46962]
Magazine Z [46963]
Morning [46972]
Nakayoshi [46974]
One More Kiss [47014]
Shukan Shonen Magazine [47038]
Weekly Shonen Sunday [47056]
Young Magazine Uppers [47058]

COMPUTERS

ALBANIA
Tirana
International Journal of Social Net-
  work Mining [41450]

AUSTRALIA
North Ryde
Barb's Factory Shopping Guide
  [42171]

Sydney
APC [42447] .... ★28,952

GERMANY
Berlin
PIK [44226] .... ‡3,200

INDIA
Hyderabad
The Icfai Journal of Cyber Law
  [45146]

Mumbai
Chip [45362] 110,000
Digit [45367]
SKOAR [45439]

New Delhi
Journal of Bio-Inspired Computation
  Research [45593]

ITALY
Trieste
Transactions on Control Systems
  Technology [46267]

JAPAN
Himeji
International Journal of Reasoning-
  based Intelligent Systems [46378]

Tokyo
Nikkei BP Government Technology
  [46980] 11,100
Nikkei Computer [46984] .... ★48,862
Nikkei Information Strategy
  [46995] .... ★20,809
Nikkei Linux [46996] .. .. ★15,185
Nikkei Network [47001] ...... ★48,034
Nikkei PC Beginners
  [47002] 80,000
Nikkei PC21 [47003] .. .. ★161,939
Nikkei Personal Computing
  [47004] .... ★177,199
Nikkei Software [47006] ... .. ★20,928
Nikkei Systems [47008] ...... ★37,890
Nikkei WinPC [47011] .. .. ★43,791

NETHERLANDS
Haarlem
Computer!Totaal [48605] 134,000

PAKISTAN
Faisalabad
Asian Journal of Information
  Technology [49236]

Circulation: ★ = ABC; △ = BPA; ◆ = CAC; • = CCAB; ❏ = VAC; ⊕ = PO Statement; ‡ = Publisher's Report; Boldface figures = sworn; Light figures = estimated.

Magazines

International Journal of Soft
Computing [49256]
World Information Technology Journal
[49298]

RUSSIA
Moscow
Russian Digital [49973] 130,000

SPAIN
Barcelona
PC Actual [50692] .... ‡61,365

Madrid
Guia del Comprador de Ordenadores
y Software [50766] .... ‡4,054

UNITED KINGDOM
Birmingham
Micro Mart
[52358] .... (Combined) 27,090

Bournemouth
Corel Painter Official Magazine
[52411]
iCreate [52416]
nRevolution [52417]
Paint Shop Pro Photo [52418]
Photoshop Creative [52419]
Play [52420]
PowerStation [52421]
360 [52426]
Total PC Gaming [52428]

Bradford
Information Technology & People
[52468]

Cardiff
International Journal of
Metaheuristics [52931]

Leicester
Finance on Windows [53800]
Prime [53818] ... (Combined) 13,000
Retailspeak
[53821] .... (Combined) 10,000

London
Computeractive [54255] ... ★159,210

Loughton
Government Technology [55491]

CONSUMER ELECTRONICS

AUSTRALIA
North Ryde
Barb's Factory Shopping Guide
[42171]

Saint Leonards
Smart Home Ideas [42335]

Sydney
APC [42447] .... ★28,952

FINLAND
Kuvalehdet
Tekniikan Maailma
[43897] ...... (Combined) ‡129,343

GERMANY
Hamburg
HORZU [44418] .... ‡1,538,346

Munich
MUSIKEXPRESS
[44573] .... ‡52,398

INDIA
Mumbai
AV Max [45354]

Chip [45362] 110,000
SKOAR [45439]
Tomorrow's Technology Today
[45448]

JAPAN
Tokyo
Nikkei Board Guide
[46979] 60,000
Nikkei Electronics China
[46990] .... △33,220
Nikkei Microdevices
[46998] .... ★14,200

RUSSIA
Moscow
Russian Digital [49973] 130,000

REPUBLIC OF SOUTH AFRICA
Pinegowrie
Gadget [50571]

THAILAND
Bangkok
Hobby Electronics [51422]

UNITED KINGDOM
Bath
Music Tech Magazine [52252]

Bournemouth
Corel Painter Official Magazine
[52411]
nRevolution [52417]
PowerStation [52421]
Retro Gamer [52423]

Colchester
Sound Vision Install [53052]

Ferndown
Everyday Practical Electronics
[53386] .... (Paid) 19,000

London
Hi Fi News [54549]

CONSUMERISM

AUSTRALIA
North Ryde
Barb's Factory Shopping Guide
[42171]

Surry Hills
Australian Creative
[42410] .... ‡3,007
Greetings & Gifts [42433] ..... ‡5,300

INDIA
Mumbai
Parsiana [45427] .... (Paid) 3,352

PHILIPPINES
Quezon City
Pink [49615]

REPUBLIC OF SOUTH AFRICA
Johannesburg
Transport World Africa [50537]

UNITED KINGDOM
London
New Consumer [54990]

CRAFTS, MODELS, HOBBIES, AND CONTESTS
See also Collecting; Photography

AUSTRALIA
Bondi Junction
Creative Knitting [41608]

Higgins
Australian Model Engineering [41954]

North Ryde
Australian Beading
[42166] 30,000
Homespun [42183]
Scrapbook Creations [42196]

Rozelle
Beads etc... [42323]
Creative Weddings [42324]
Down Under Quilts [42325]
For Keeps Creative Scrapbooking
[42326]
i can make it myself [42327]

Silverwater
Australian Country Craft and
Decorating [42359]
Australian Country Threads [42360]
Patchwork & Stitching [42361]

Surry Hills
Toy & Hobby Retailer
[42441] 2,662

GERMANY
Bremen
Modell Fan [44281] 12,152

Villingen-Schwenningen
Modell
[44699] .... (Combined) 33,500

RUSSIA
Moscow
Kollektsia Idei [49933] .... ‡24,800

SWEDEN
Umea
Hemslojden
[51045] .... (Paid) 14,800

UKRAINE
Kiev
Veselye Ideiki [51612] .... ‡40,000

UNITED KINGDOM
Amersham
Aviation Modeller International
[52105]
Flying Scale Models [52106]
Military Machines International
[52108]

Arundel
Dolls House World [52134]
Toy Soldier & Model Figure
[52135] .... (Paid) 10,000

Bath
Good Woodworking
[52242] .... (Paid) 14,800

Bletchley
Military Modelcraft International
[52389]
Scale Aircraft Modelling [52390]
Toy Soldier Collector [52391]

Bristol
Beautiful Cards [52644] 20,000
Card Making & Papercraft [52650]

Cross Stitch Gold [52658]
Knit Today [52700]
Koi [52701] 15,000
Quick Cards Made Easy
[52724] .... ★16,927

Chester
Skin Deep [52999] 38,764

Colchester
Craftbusiness [53032]
Crafts Beautiful [53033]
Let's Make Cards! [53041]
Quick & Crafty! [53047]

Driffield
craft&design [53200]

East Molesey
Stitch with the Embroiders' Guild
[53240] .... (Combined) 12,000
The World of Embroidery
[53241] .... (Combined) 12,500

Farnham
Cakes & Sugarcraft
[53381] .... (Paid) 18,000

Faversham
New Stitches [53384]

Guisborough
The Journal for Weavers, Spinners
and Dyers [53499]

Holt
Birding World
[53583] .... (Paid) 6,000

Kingston upon Thames
Hornby Magazine [53722]

London
Charlie and Lola [54198]
The Classic Marvel Figurine
Collection [54213]
The Country Bird Collection [54274]
Crafts [54281] 20,000
Flagmaster [54464]
Horrible Science Collection [54569]
Jackie Chan Adventures [54687]
The Lord of the Rings Collector's
Models [54891]
PaperCraft Inspirations [55054]
Practical Fishkeeping [55113]
Progressive Greetings Worldwide
[55138] 6,500
The Railway Magazine
[55171] .... ★35,100

Maidenhead
Machine Knitting Monthly [55523]

Malvern
Craft Stamper [55533]
Marine Modelling International
[55534]
QFI Quiet Flight International [55535]
Quiet & Electric Flight International
[55536]
R/C Jet International [55537]
Radio Control Model World [55538]
Radio Race Car International [55539]

Nottingham
Miniature Wargames
[55767] .... (Paid) 9,000

Stourbridge
Lace [56640]

Sudbury
Total Tattoo Magazine [56651]

Tenterden
Leisure Painter
[56743] .... (Paid) 28,000

Totternhoe
Military Illustrated [56765]
Model Airplane International [56766]
Model Military International [56767]

Circulation: ★ = ABC; △ = BPA; ◆ = CAC; • = CCAB; ❑ = VAC; ⊕ = PO Statement; ‡ = Publisher's Report; Boldface figures = sworn; Light figures = estimated.

Radio Control Car RACER [56768]
Radio Control Model Flyer [56769]
Rotorworld [56770]
Tamiya Model Magazine International
   [56771]

Warrington
Nishikigoi International
   [56850] .... (Combined) 7,000

West Sussex
Patchwork & Quilting [56900]
R/C Model World [56901]
Scrapbook Magic [56903]

York
The Quilter [56996] 7,000

DOGS
See also Pets

INDIA
Chennai
Sruti [45058]

ITALY
Milan
Sipario
   [46194] .. .. (Combined) 16,000

UKRAINE
Kiev
Afisha
   [51593] .. .. (Combined) 25,000

UNITED KINGDOM
Bristol
Who Do You Think You Are?
   [52736] .. .. ★20,266
London
Musical Opinion
   [54965] .. .. (Paid) ‡5,000
                     (Non-paid) ‡1,000
Musical Stages [54966]
Theatre Record [55303]
Theatregoer Magazine [55304]

DRESSMAKING,
NEEDLEWORK, AND
QUILTING
See also Fashion

AUSTRALIA
North Ryde
Homespun [42183]
Quilters Companion [42195]
Rozelle
Down Under Quilts [42325]

FINLAND
Kuvalehdet
MODA
   [43892] .. .. (Combined) ‡38,256

ROMANIA
Bucharest
Lucru de Mana [49839] ...... ‡12,516

AUSTRALIA
North Ryde
Dogs Life [42181]

UNITED KINGDOM
London
Eukanuba [54389]

DRAMA AND THEATRE
See also Entertainment

RUSSIA
Moscow
Diana Creative [49892] ..... ‡20,715
Diana Moden [49893] .... ‡50,230
Iren [49922] .. .. ‡27,340
Knit&Mode [49932] .. .. ‡15,900
Lena Rukodelie [49937] ..... ‡20,600
Malenkaya Diana [49939] ..... ‡72,350
Natalia [49947] .. .. ‡14,300
Sabrina [49986] .... ‡74,880
Sabrina Baby [49987] .. .. ‡6,110
Susanna Rukodeliye
   [49993] .. .. ‡20,980
Susanna Vjazanie
   [49994] .. .. ‡75,000
Vjazanie Vashe Hobby
   [49998] .. .. ‡64,900
Vyshitye Kartiny [49999] ..... ‡18,100

SPAIN
Barcelona
Labores del Hogar
   [50682] .. .. ‡53,427
Patrones [50691] .. .. ‡33,397

UNITED KINGDOM
Bath
Quick & Easy Cross Stitch Magazine
   [52256] .. .. (Controlled) 27,304
Bristol
Cross Stitch Card Shop
   [52656] 56,534
Cross Stitch Crazy
   [52657] .. .. ★19,225
The World of Cross Stitching
   [52737] .. .. ★40,116
Colchester
Let's Knit! [53040]
East Molesey
Stitch with the Embroiders' Guild
   [53240] .. .. (Combined) 12,000
The World of Embroidery
   [53241] .. .. (Combined) 12,500
Faversham
New Stitches [53384]
Maidenhead
Machine Knitting Monthly [55523]
Orpington
Popular Patchwork [55855]

EDUCATION
See also Parenting

AUSTRALIA
Brisbane
The Knowledge Tree [41651]
North Ryde
Choosing a School for Your Child -
   New South Wales [42175]
Choosing a School for Your Child -
   Victoria [42176]
South Melbourne
Australian Universities Review
   [42368]
Frontline [42371]

PEOPLE'S REPUBLIC OF
CHINA
Hong Kong
Translation Quarterly [43385]

FINLAND
Kuvalehdet
Leppis
   [43890] ....: (Combined) ‡19,992

GERMANY
Berlin
International Journal of Innovation in
   Education [44193]

INDIA
Hyderabad
The Icfai Journal of Science &
   Technology [45166]

ITALY
Milan
La Rivista della Scuola [46185]
Rome
Tuttoscuola
   [46244] .... (Paid) ‡45,000
Rozzano
Domus Kit
   [46249] .... (Combined) 15,000

JAMAICA
Kingston
The Children's Own [46282]

NEW ZEALAND
Christchurch
Principals Today
   [48877] .. .. (Combined) ★8,221

PHILIPPINES
Mandaluyong City
Star Teacher [49542] 8,000
Quezon City
INNOTECH Journal [49595]

POLAND
Warsaw
Journal of Teacher Education for
   Sustainability [49726]

PORTUGAL
Almargem do Bispo
Saude e Lar [49784]

SINGAPORE
Singapore
Digital Nanyang Chronicle
   [50133] 20,000

SPAIN
Barcelona
Speak Up [50701]
Madrid
Hot English Magazine [50767]

SWITZERLAND
Fribourg
Universitas Friburgensis
   [51087] 9,500

UNITED KINGDOM
Abingdon
London Review of Education [51971]
Bangor
IAW! [52171] ...... (Combined) 2,700
Bristol
Primary Times
   [52723] .. .. (Free) 72,000
Chichester
ESL Magazine [53008]
Glasgow
First Link 4 Parents
   [53420] .. .. (Free) 18,000

Huddersfield
Multicultural Education & Technology
   Journal [53623]
London
BBC Learning is Fun!
   [54005] .. .. (Controlled) 60,000
BBC The Magic Key [54006]
Bob the Builder [54095]
Books for Keeps
   [54098] .. .. (Paid) 9,000
CBeebies Weekly Magazine [54188]
Fifi and the Flowertots [54452]
Fimbles Magazine [54453]
In the Night Garden [54592]
Learn with Bob the Builder [54860]
Leaving School [54862]
Me Too! [54917]
Teletubbies [55298]
Tweenies [55347]
UCU [55352]
Underground Ernie [55358]
Oxford
The Clinical Teacher [55912]
Decision Sciences Journal of Innova-
   tive Education [55923]
Reading
E.Learning Age [56312] 12,000
Shrewsbury
Fun to Learn Discovery
   [56532] 40,000
Swansea
Pulse [56706]
Woodbridge
is [56957]
Prep School [56958]
Zeals Warminster
Conference & Common Room
   [57003]

ENTERTAINMENT
See also Drama and The-
atre; Motion Pictures; Radio,
Television, Cable, and Video

AUSTRALIA
East Sydney
SX News
   [41852] .. .. (Combined) 25,000
Eveleigh
TV Hits [41863]
Fortitude Valley
Queensland Pride [41870]
Saint Leonards
TV Soap [42336]

BAHRAIN
Manama
Bahrain This Month (BTM)
   [42787] .. .. (Combined) 10,000

FINLAND
Helsinki
Katso [43838] .. .. (Paid) 72,741
Kuvalehdet
Hymy
   [43881] .. .. (Combined) ‡95,845
TV-maailma
   [43899] ...... (Combined) ‡400,000

GERMANY
Hamburg
BILD der FRAU
   [44411] .. .. ‡1,274,182
FRAU von HEUTE
   [44416] .. .. ‡349,348

Circulation: ★ = ABC; △ = BPA; ◆ = CAC; ● = CCAB; ❑ = VAC; ⊕ = PO Statement; ‡ = Publisher's Report; Boldface figures = sworn; Light figures = estimated.

Magazines

Munich
POPCORN [44578] .... ‡188,349
STARFLASH [44582] .... ‡69,073

GREECE
Athens
International Journal of Entertainment
Technology and Management
[44747]

HUNGARY
Budapest
Baratok Kozt Magazin
[44825] 60,000
Fules [44834] .... (Paid) ‡68,605
RTV Musormagazin
[44868] .... (Paid) ‡74,540
Szines RTV
[44877] .... (Paid) 211,125

INDIA
Mumbai
Stardust [45442] ...... (Paid) 308,170

INDONESIA
Seminyak
The Beat [45854]

IRELAND
Dublin
Film Ireland [45956]

ITALY
Milan
Rodeo [46193]
Sipario
[46194] .... (Combined) 16,000

JAMAICA
Kingston
The Star [46288]
The Weekend Star [46292]

JAPAN
Tokyo
Afternoon Season Zokan [46730]
Big Comic Original [46762]
Big Comic Spirits [46763]
Morning [46972]
Nikkei Entertainment!
[46991] .... ★90,234
Shukan Shonen Magazine [47038]
Tokyo Weekender [47052] 15,000
Weekly Shonen Sunday [47056]

LEBANON
Beirut
Achabaka
[47385] .... (Combined) 113,583
Sahar [47401] 110,000

MALAYSIA
Kuala Lumpur
Mangga [47624] .. .. ★121,465
URTV [47638] .... ★53,860
Petaling Jaya
Galaxie [47697] .... ★15,733

NEW ZEALAND
Auckland
Home New Zealand
[48795] 14,805

PHILIPPINES
Mandaluyong City
High School Musical
[49538] 20,000

Preview [49539] 45,000
Yes! [49543] 150,000

Quezon City
The Buzz Magasin [49587]
StarStudio [49617] 150,000

POLAND
Warsaw
Party Celebrity lives
[49745] .... ‡472,261

SINGAPORE
Singapore
Singapore Visitor [50266]

**REPUBLIC OF SOUTH AF-
RICA**
Cape Town
Fairlady [50378] .. .. ★71,898
Move! [50393] 41,336
tvplus [50420] 150,254
Sandton
Mshana [50627]

SPAIN
Barcelona
Lecturas [50683] .... ‡198,930

SWEDEN
Jonkoping
Journal of Media Business Studies
[50970]

UKRAINE
Kiev
Afisha
[51593] .... (Combined) 25,000
TV Ekran [51609] .. .. ‡100,000
Viva! Biographia [51614] .. .. ‡50,000

UNITED ARAB EMIRATES
Dubai
Charged Middle East
[51635] 9,000
Souk [51653] 30,000
tv&radio [51655] .. .. △43,750

UNITED KINGDOM
Aberdeen
Good Time Guide [51677]
Star Flyer Magazine [51680]
Barnsley
The Main Event Magazine
[52182] 10,000
Bexhill-on-Sea
Fireworks [52321] .... (Paid) 600
Bournemouth
High Definition Review [52415]
SciFiNow [52424]
Brighton
The Insight
[52615] .... (Non-paid) 20,000
Bristol
Irish Dancing & Culture [52681]
Primary Times
[52723] .... (Free) 72,000
Who Do You Think You Are?
[52736] .... ★20,266
Edinburgh
Journal of British Cinema and
Television [53292]
Exeter
Studies in French Cinema [53363]
Studies in Theatre and Performance
[53364]

Glasgow
M8 Magazine [53430]
No.1 [53435]
Godalming
Monocle Magazine
[53476] .... (Non-paid) 12,000
Hoylake
Candis [53614] .. .. (Paid) ★254,420
Leeds
The Leeds Guide
[53771] .. .. (Paid) 15,000
Leicester
Studies in Hispanic Cinemas [53829]
London
Amy [53939]
AV Magazine [53992] .... ★11,731
Cas London [54186]
Closer [54234]
Dance Today! [54310]
Dancing Times [54311]
DJ Magazine [54336]
Empire
[54365] .. .. (Combined) 173,000
Event [54413] .... ★15,055
Grazia [54521]
Hi Fi News [54549]
Islington Gazette (EC1 Edition)
[54684]
Live & Kicking [54878]
Midsomer Murders Magazine [54933]
Musical Stages [54966]
New Cinemas [54989]
Radio Times
[55170] .... (Paid) 1,093,850
Soaplife [55244]
Theatregoer Magazine [55304]
Top of the Pops [55328]
Total TVguide [55329] ...... ★107,681
Toybox [55333]
TVChoice [55345] .. .. ★1,335,894
TVQuick [55346] .... ★144,270
Uncut [55357]
Westlife [55398]
W1 Magazine [55415]
Manchester
Nineteenth Century Theatre and Film
[55574]
Newcastle upon Tyne
Accent [55666] 18,000
Norwich
Compass South [55729] ...... ‡40,000
Compass Wessex
[55730] .... ‡40,000
Let's Talk! [55733] .. .. ★27,205
Wood & Vale Express [55744]
Penzance
Inside Cornwall
[56249] .. .. (Paid) 8,000
Reading
Blah Blah
[56311] .. .. (Non-paid) ★40,000
Redhill
Arroword Selection [56342]
Beyond Sudoku [56343]
Chat Arrowords [56344]
Chat Crosswords [56345]
Chat Puzzles Select [56346]
Chat Wordsearch [56347]
Code Words [56348]
Crossword Selection [56349]
Fundoku [56351]
Hanjie [56353]
Junior Puzzles [56354]
Kakuro [56355]
Killer Sudoku [56356]
Kriss Kross [56357]
100 Codewords [56358]
100 Crosswords [56359]

100 Wordsearch [56360]
Puzzle Compendium [56361]
Puzzle Corner Special [56362]
Puzzler [56363]
Puzzler Arrowords [56364]
Puzzler Brain Trainer [56365]
Puzzler Codewords [56366]
Puzzler Collection [56367]
Puzzler Crossword [56368]
Puzzler Kriss Kross [56369]
Puzzler Pocket Crosswords [56370]
Puzzler Pocket Crosswords
Collection [56371]
Puzzler Pocket Wordsearch [56372]
Puzzler Pocket Wordsearch
Collection [56373]
Puzzler Quick Crosswords [56374]
Puzzler Quiz Kids [56375]
Puzzler Wordsearch [56376]
Sudoku Puzzles [56380]
Super Hanjie [56381]
Word Search [56382]
Southport
Linedancer [56587]
Swansea
Studies in European Cinema [56707]

**ENVIRONMENTAL AND
NATURAL RESOURCES
CONSERVATION**

ARUBA
Oranjestad
Eco Aruba [41491]

AUSTRALIA
Adelaide
Sustaining Regions [41513]
Collingwood
Ecos [41786] .... (Paid) 7,500
Environmental Chemistry [41788]

AUSTRIA
Salzburg
Natur und Land [42741] 12,000

FINLAND
Turku
Progress in Industrial Ecology
[43910]

FRANCE
Avignon
Agronomy for Sustainable
Development [43917] 1,000
Les Ulis
Hydroecologie appliquee [43965]
Montrouge
Environnement, Risques & Sante
[43986]

GERMANY
Bielefeld
Sun & Wind Energy [44247]
Braunschweig
CLEAN [44274]
Grasbrunn
natur+kosmos [44403] 84,278
Oldenburg
EARSeL eProceedings [44624]

GHANA
Accra
Bongo News [44725]

HUNGARY
Budapest
Progress in Agricultural Engineering
Sciences [44866]

Circulation: ★ = ABC; △ = BPA; ◆ = CAC; • = CCAB; ❑ = VAC; ⊕ = PO Statement; ‡ = Publisher's Report; Boldface figures = sworn; Light figures = estimated.

INDIA

Hyderabad
The Icfai Journal of Environmental
   Economics [45150]

New Delhi
Down To Earth [45503]

ITALY

Rome
International Journal of Environment
   and Health [46234]

JAPAN

Tokyo
National Geographic Japanese
   Edition [46975] .... ★84,124

KENYA

Nairobi
Our Planet [47194]

NETHERLANDS

Leiden
Applied Herpetology [48648]

NEW ZEALAND

Wellington
New Zealand Journal of Outdoor
   Education [49028]

NIGERIA

Calabar
Global Journal of Environmental
   Sciences [49071]

Ibadan
Journal of Environmental Extension
   [49089]

Port Harcourt
Journal of Applied Sciences and Environmental Management [49166]

POLAND

Warsaw
Annals of Warsaw University of Life
   Sciences, Land Reclamation
   [49689]
Ekologija [49708]

SINGAPORE

Singapore
Nature Watch [50225]

SPAIN

Madrid
International Journal of River Basin
   Management [50773]
World Watch
   [50816] .. .. (Paid) 15,000

SWITZERLAND

Geneva
Interdisciplinary Environmental
   Review [51099]
International Journal of Environment
   and Pollution [51118]
International Journal of Environmen-
   tal Policy and Decision Making
   [51119]

**UNITED REPUBLIC OF TAN-
ZANIA**

Dar es Salaam
Journal of Building and Land
   Development [51402]

UNITED KINGDOM

Abingdon
Environmental Politics [51771]

Bideford
Resurgence
   [52322] .. .. (Combined) 15,000

Cambridge
Environmental Practice [52818]

Glasgow
Envirotec [53416] .. .. ★8,958

Kidlington
Journal of Environmental
   Management [53697]

London
BMC Ecology [54051]
Climate Policy [54217]
Corporate Watch [54267]
Countryside Voice [54277] .. . 35,000
The Ecologist
   [54349] .. .. (Combined) 25,000
The Ends Report [54369]
The Journal of Ecology [54741]
Journal of Environmental Health
   Research [54744]
Network 21 [54988] 7,000
Studies in Conservation [55272]
WDCS [55392] 26,000

Olney
International Journal of Environment
   and Sustainable Development
   [55803]
International Journal of Environmental Technology and Management
   [55804]
International Journal of Global Environmental Issues [55808]
International Journal of Innovation
   and Sustainable Development
   [55812]
International Journal of Water
   [55840]

Reading
International Journal of Green
   Economics [56322]

Richmond
BG Journal [56388]

Salisbury
Recycling & Waste World [56457]

Swansea
International Journal of Numerical
   Methods for Heat & Fluid Flow
   [56702]

Witney
Environmental Liability [56942]

ZAMBIA

Fringilla
Black Lewche [57107] 2,000

ETHNIC PUBLICATIONS

DENMARK

Copenhagen
Danmarksposten
   [43661] .. .. (Paid) 6,500

NETHERLANDS

Amsterdam
Ghanaian Newsrunner [48001]

UNITED KINGDOM

London
Caribbean Times [54181]
Mauritius News
   [54915] .... (Combined) 5,000
Q News
   [55159] .. .. (Combined) 15,000
Studies in Ethnicity and Nationalism
   [55273]

EXPORT CONSUMER MAGAZINES

**PEOPLE'S REPUBLIC OF
CHINA**

Hong Kong
HKTDC Fasion - Fabrics &
   Accessories [43308]

SINGAPORE

Singapore
Global Sources Gifts & Premiums
   [50156]

FASHION

**See also Dressmaking,
Needlework, and Quilting**

AUSTRALIA

Melbourne
Melbourne Community Voice
   [42073] .. .. (Combined) 20,000

North Ryde
Barb's Factory Shopping Guide
   [42171]

Surry Hills
Ragtrader [42438] .. .. ‡6,000

Sydney
Harper's Bazaar (Australia)
   [42512] .. .. (Paid) ★56,119
Men's Style Australia [42542]
Myer Emporium [42550] .. . ★248,900
Studio Bambini [42582] 45,000

**PEOPLE'S REPUBLIC OF
CHINA**

Hong Kong
Coutoure [43295] 42,000
Hong Kong Apparel [43320]
Hong Kong Tatler [43346]

Shanghai
Beauty Home [43463]
Shanghai Style [43501]
With [43510]

DENMARK

Copenhagen
DANSK [43662]

FINLAND

Helsinki
Modin [43848] :. .... (Paid) 8,000

Kuvalehdet
Hymy
   [43881] .. .. (Combined) ‡95,845

GERMANY

Hamburg
Petra [44422] .... (Paid) ‡295,102

Leinfelden-Echterdingen
DER AUGENOPTIKER
   [44519] 9,836

Munich
MADCHEN [44570] .... ‡158,029
MUSIKEXPRESS
   [44573] .. .. ‡52,398

GREECE

Athens
NY-LONDON Shows [44753]
Paris Catwalks [44754]
Passerella di Donna [44755]

HUNGARY

Budapest
Maxima Special
   [44849] .. .. (Paid) 44,183

Meglepetes [44850] ... (Paid) 94,838
Nok Lapja [44857] ... (Paid) 253,749
Nok Lapja Evszakok
   [44860] .. .. (Paid) 22,300

IRELAND

Clarenbridge
CORKnow [45932]
GALWAYnow [45933]

Dublin
Irish Tatler [45987] .... ★26,427
Prudence [45995] .. .. ★11,035
U Magazine [45999] .... ★34,103

ITALY

Milan
Rodeo [46193]

JAPAN

Tokyo
CanCam [46776]
Fashion Color [46821]
Josei Seven [46879]
Priv. [47025] .. .. ★173,474

REPUBLIC OF KOREA

Seoul
Feel [47265]

LEBANON

Beirut
Al-Fares [47388] .. .. ★78,307
Sahar [47401] 110,000

NETHERLANDS

Amsterdam
Elegance
   [47964] .. .. (Combined) ‡55,885

Maarssen
Mannenmode
   [48732] .. .. (Paid) 2,400

NEW ZEALAND

Auckland
Fashion Quarterly
   [48792] .. .. (Controlled) 23,713

PAKISTAN

Karachi
Fashion Mag [49349]

PHILIPPINES

Cebu City
Zee Lifestyle [49465] 25,000

Makati City
Philippine Tatler [49523] ..... ‡45,000

Mandaluyong City
Cosmopolitan Philippines
   [49533] 72,000
Preview [49539] 45,000
Seventeen Philippines
   [49540] 30,000

Quezon City
Metro [49599]
Pink [49615]

POLAND

Warsaw
Hot Moda & Shopping
   [49716] .... ‡7,073
Przyjaciolka [49760] .... ‡460,291

ROMANIA

Bucharest
Avantaje [49831] .. .. ‡23,612

Circulation: ★ = ABC; △ = BPA; ◆ = CAC; • = CCAB; ❏ = VAC; ⊕ = PO Statement; ‡ = Publisher's Report; Boldface figures = sworn; Light figures = estimated.

Magazines

Elle Mariaj [49836] .... ‡4,387

RUSSIA
Moscow
Atelier Rundschau
  [49879] .... ‡18,320
Industria Mody [49917] .... ‡1,900
International Textiles [49921] ... ‡235
Knit&Mode [49932] .... ‡15,900
Malenkaya Diana [49939] ... ‡72,350
Natalia [49947] .... ‡14,300
Sabrina [49986] .... ‡74,880
Susanna Vjazanie
  [49994] .... ‡75,000

SINGAPORE
Singapore
The Best of Singapore
  [50114] .... ‡20,000
Global Sources Fashion Accessories
  [50154]
Her World [50164] 62,530
Icon Moments
  [50169] .... (Combined) 20,000
Newman [50227]
NuYou [50230] 25,000
Simply Her [50252] 50,000
Singapore Tatler [50262] .... ‡13,000
Singapore Tatler Weddings
  [50265] .... ‡14,000
Style [50274]
Teens Annual [50277]

REPUBLIC OF SOUTH AFRICA
Cape Town
SARIE My inspirasie
  [50408] .... ★125,612

SPAIN
Barcelona
Clara [50657] .... ‡161,874
Lecturas Moda [50686]
Patrones [50691] .... ‡33,397

SWEDEN
Nora
Slojdforum [50994]
Stockholm
Damernas Varld [51014] ..... ‡87,700

SWITZERLAND
Lausanne
Femina Fashion [51189] ..... ‡25,000
Zurich
Schweizer Illustrierte Style
  [51279] 109,983

UKRAINE
Kiev
Edinstvennaya - Tvoye Zdorovye
  [51595] .... ‡265,000
Tvoy Malysh [51610] .... ‡90,000
Viva! Beauty [51613] .... ‡50,000

UNITED KINGDOM
Barnsley
Out on a Limb [52183]
Belfast
Northern Woman [52290]
Chessington
Asian Woman [52990] .... ★90,339
Glasgow
No.1 [53435]
London
Another Magazine [53953]

Bella [54010] .... ★246,446
Cartier International Polo MAG
  [54184] 10,000
DARE [54312]
Drapers (London) [54343]
FHM [54449] .... (Paid) 710,000
Grazia [54521]
The HAT Magazine [54533]
Maxim Fashion [54916] ...... ★43,542
Mela UK [54925]
Quintessentially [55166] 25,000
Savile Row
  [55218] .... (Non-paid) 25,000
Take a Break [55286] .... ★855,372
Top of the Pops [55328]
Wallpaper [55377] .... ★113,000
You & Your Wedding [55433]

Ware
Champneys Magazine
  [56840] 50,000
Sunseeker Magazine
  [56845] 170,000

York
Shoe World
  [56999] .... (Non-paid) 8,000

FIREARMS
See also (Hunting, Fishing, and Game Management)

AUSTRALIA
Surry Hills
Australasian Sporting Shooter
  [42409] .... ★13,542

DENMARK
Brondby
Skyttebladet [43653]

SWITZERLAND
Solothurn
Schweizer Waffen-Magazin
  [51232] .... (Paid) 20,000
                 (Non-paid) 10,000

UNITED KINGDOM
Colchester
Gun Mart [53037]
Shooting Sports [53050]

FOOD AND COOKING
See also Home and Garden

AUSTRALIA
Alexandria
Australian Good Taste
  [41536] .... ★121,612
delicious. [41538] .... ★134,000
Super Food Ideas
  [41546] .... ★261,997
North Ryde
Sydney Eats [42199]
Pyrmont
Signature Cocktails [42288]
Surry Hills
Donna Hay Magazine
  [42427] .... ★89,192
Food & Drink Business
  [42431] .... ★5,294
FoodService News
  [42432] 12,871
Sydney
Australian Gourmet Traveller
  [42454] .... ★75,107
Australian Table [42466] ...... ★67,095
COLES [42495]

Gourmet Traveller WINE
  [42509] .... ★21,948

BELGIUM
Antwerp
Ambiance
  [42837] .... (Controlled) 63,638

FINLAND
Helsinki
Apu [43817] ... (Combined) 254,762
Kuvalehdet
Kotiliesi
  [43887] ...... (Combined) ‡195,425

GERMANY
Munich
SG Susswarenhandel
  [44581] 6,500
Nuremberg
Food Marketing & Technology
  [44611] 18,500
Food Technologie [44612] 11,668
Wellness Foods Europe
  [44617] 6,011

HUNGARY
Budapest
Fakanal [44829] ...... (Paid) ‡25,162
Fakanal Recepttar [44830] ... 26,425
Meglepetes Raadas
  [44851] .... (Paid) 65,900
Nok Lapja Konyha
  [44861] .... (Paid) 37,893

INDIA
Hyderabad
Nutrition [45178] .... (Paid) 4,000
Mumbai
India Today Plus
  [45374] .... (Paid) 89,000

IRELAND
Blackrock
Hotel & Catering Review [45920]
Dublin
Food & Wine Magazine
  [45960] .... ★7,429
Greystone
Easy Food [46023] .... ★27,599

ITALY
Rozzano
Il Cucchiaio D'Argento [46250]

JAPAN
Tokyo
Josei Seven [46879]
SARAI [47035]
Shukan Shonen Magazine [47038]

LATVIA
Riga
Musmajas [47373]
Una [47374] .... (Paid) 18,000

MALAYSIA
Kota Kinabalu
Banci Estet Koko [47587]
Malaysian Cocoa Monitor [47591]
Kuala Lumpur
i-Sihat [47604]
Saji [47634] .... ★57,567

NETHERLANDS
Amsterdam
Leven [48136] .... (Paid) ‡8,500

NEW ZEALAND
Auckland
Catering Plus [48788] .... ‡2,528

PHILIPPINES
Mandaluyong City
Good Housekeeping Philippines
  [49537] 50,000
Yummy [49544] 30,000
Quezon City
FOOD [49593]

RUSSIA
Moscow
Kulinarny Practicum
  [49934] .... ‡120,000

SINGAPORE
Singapore
Asian Home Gourmet [50110]
CW Magazine [50129] 12,000
Wine & Dine [50287] 40,000

REPUBLIC OF SOUTH AFRICA
Cape Town
Tuis [50419] 84,715

SPAIN
Barcelona
Clara [50657] .... ‡161,874
Comer Bien [50659] .... ‡49,079
Cosas de Cocina [50661] ... ‡60,144
Lecturas Cocina Facil
  [50684] .... ‡81,446
Lecturas Especial Cocina
  [50685] .... ‡78,346

SWITZERLAND
Zurich
Betty Bossi [51254] 850,000

UNITED KINGDOM
Basingstoke
European Journal of Clinical Nutrition
  [52200]
Bath
Taste Italia [52260] 45,000
Bristol
Living Earth [52702] 24,000
University Caterer [52734] 2,500
Colchester
Speciality Food [53053] .. .. ★8,695
Crawley
PubChef [53111]
Farnham
Cakes & Sugarcraft
  [53381] .. .. (Paid) 18,000
Hoylake
Candis [53614] ...... (Paid) ★254,420
Leatherhead
Food Allergy and Intolerance Journal
  [53751]
Lewes
Organic Life [53850]
London
BBC Good Food
  [54004] .... (Paid) ★342,375
Decanter [54314] 46,000
Easy Cook [54348]
Mela UK [54925]
Mood Food [54952]
Nutritional Neuroscience [55021]

Circulation: ★ = ABC; △ = BPA; ♦ = CAC; • = CCAB; ❏ = VAC; ⊕ = PO Statement; ‡ = Publisher's Report; Boldface figures = sworn; Light figures = estimated.

Olive [55030]
Waitrose Food Illustrated [55376]
W1 Magazine [55415]

Midlothian
Taste of Scotland [55628]

Northampton
Herbs [55708] .. .. (Combined) 3,000

Norwich
Beers of the World [55725]

Penzance
Inside Cornwall
   [56249] .... (Paid) 8,000

Ware
Champneys Magazine
   [56840] 50,000

GAMES AND PUZZLES

AUSTRALIA
Gosford
Christine's BIG Crossword [41905]
Christine's Cryptic Crossword
   Collection [41906]
Cluewords [41907]
Codecracker Starhunts [41908]
Colossus Crosswords [41909]
FindaWord [41910]
Handy ADDoku Plus Kakuro [41911]
Handy Arrowords [41912]
Handy Codecrackers [41913]
Handy Crosswords [41914]
Handy Cryptic Crosswords [41915]
Handy Fill-Ins [41916]
Handy Wordhunt [41917]
Holiday Crossword Collection [41918]
Large Print Crosswords [41919]
MEGA! [41920]
Puzzle Fun for Kids [41921]
Super Sudoku [41922]
Variety Puzzles [41923]

Sydney
Official PlayStation Magazine
   Australia [42557]

HUNGARY
Budapest
Fules [44834] .... (Paid) ‡68,605

INDIA
Chennai
Chess Mate [45029] ...,........ 3,000

Mumbai
SKOAR [45439]

ITALY
Rozzano
Domus Kit
   [46249] .... (Combined) 15,000

SWEDEN
Norrkoping
Tidskrift for Schack
   [50996] ....:........ (Non-paid) 2,000

UNITED KINGDOM
Aylesbury
English Bridge
   [52147] .... (Non-paid) 30,000

Bournemouth
gamesTM [52414]
nRevolution [52417]
Play [52420]
PowerStation [52421]
Retro Gamer [52423]
360 [52426]
Total PC Gaming [52428]

Leicester
Symmetry Plus [53830]

London
Animals and You [53946]
Arrowwords [53965]
Balamory [53998]
Big Value Codebreakers
   [54017] .... ★41,000
Bridge [54105]
British Chess Magazine [54109]
CBeebies Weekly Magazine [54188]
Chess [54202]
Codebreakers [54235] ...... ★109,000
Criss Cross [54287] .... ★63,000
Disney Fairies [54332]
Disney and Me [54333] ...... ★49,002
Gaming Floor [54492]
Hide 'n' Seek Wordsearch
   [54550] .... ★62,000
Picture Arrowwords
   [55089] .... ★74,000
Puzzle Selection [55158] .... ★93,434
Quick-X-words [55165] .... ★64,000
Su-doku [55274]
Su-doku Selection
   [55275] .... ★67,000
Take a Break [55286] .... ★855,372
Take a Break's Su-doku
   [55287] .... ★100,000
Take a Crossword
   [55288] .... ★133,604
Take a Puzzle [55289] ...... ★107,264
Thomas & Friends
   [55314] .... ★50,002
Totally Tracy Beaker [55330]
Tweenies [55347]
Wordsearches [55416] ...... ★108,000
Wordsearches Collection
   [55417] .... ★63,000

Nottingham
Miniature Wargames
   [55767] .... (Paid) 9,000

Redhill
Arroword Selection [56342]
Beyond Sudoku [56343]
Chat Arrowords [56344]
Chat Crosswords [56345]
Chat Puzzles Select [56346]
Chat Wordsearch [56347]
Code Words [56348]
Crossword Selection [56349]
Fundoku [56351]
Hanjie [56353]
Junior Puzzles [56354]
Kakuro [56355]
Killer Sudoku [56356]
Kriss Kross [56357]
100 Codewords [56358]
100 Crosswords [56359]
100 Wordsearch [56360]
Puzzle Compendium [56361]
Puzzle Corner Special [56362]
Puzzler [56363]
Puzzler Arrowords [56364]
Puzzler Brain Trainer [56365]
Puzzler Codewords [56366]
Puzzler Collection [56367]
Puzzler Crossword [56368]
Puzzler Kriss Kross [56369]
Puzzler Pocket Crosswords [56370]
Puzzler Pocket Crosswords
   Collection [56371]
Puzzler Pocket Wordsearch [56372]
Puzzler Pocket Wordsearch
   Collection [56373]
Puzzler Quick Crosswords [56374]
Puzzler Quiz Kids [56375]
Puzzler Wordsearch [56376]
Sudoku Puzzles [56380]
Super Hanjie [56381]
Word Search [56382]

Ringwood
Doctor Who Battles in Time [56395]

Romsey
Crossword [56406] 750

Shrewsbury
Fun to Learn Barney
   [56530] 50,000
Fun to Learn Best of Barney
   [56531] 30,000

GAY AND LESBIAN INTERESTS

AUSTRALIA
East Sydney
Cherrie
   [41849] .... (Combined) 19,000
Fellow Traveller
   [41850] .... (Combined) 30,000
SX News
   [41852] .... (Combined) 25,000

Fortitude Valley
Queensland Pride [41870]

Melbourne
Melbourne Community Voice
   [42073] .... (Combined) 20,000

NETHERLANDS
Amsterdam
Butt [47919]

SWEDEN
Stockholm
QX [51031] .. .... (Controlled) 32,000

THAILAND
Bangkok
Pink Ink [51430]

UNITED KINGDOM
Abingdon
Fyne Times [51792]

London
axm [53996]
Diva [54335] ..... (Combined) 55,643

Worthing
A Kentish Partnership [56974]

GENERAL EDITORIAL

AUSTRALIA
Marrickville
Choice [42039]

Sydney
The Bulletin with Newsweek
   [42479] .... ★57,039
Quadrant [42567]

PEOPLE'S REPUBLIC OF CHINA
Beijing
Beijing Review [43171] .... ‡70,000
Beijing This Month
   [43173] .... (Free) 70,000

Hong Kong
Malaysia Tatler
   [43367] .. .. (Paid) 16,400

Shanghai
Journal of Editorial Study [43480]
Shanghai Today [43503]

FRANCE
Neuilly
International Herald Tribune [44014]

INDIA
Chennai
The Sportstar
   [45057] .. .. (Paid) 98,230

Mumbai
India Today
   [45373] .... (Paid) 932,079
Opportunities Today
   [45424] 15,000
Parsiana [45427] .. .. (Paid) 3,352
Society [45441] .... (Paid) 85,093
Sunday Mid-Day
   [45444] .... (Paid) 117,449

New Delhi
Organiser [45632] .... (Paid) 8,632

INDONESIA
Jakarta
Gatra [45797]
Tempo Interactive [45802]

IRELAND
Dublin
C-4 [45949]

JAPAN
Fukuoka
Fukuoka Now [46341]
The Gaijin Gleaner
   [46342] .. .. (Paid) 1,600

Sapporo
Xene [46652] 30,000

Tokyo
Mainichi Daily News [46964]
Metropolis [46967] .... ★30,000
Tokyo Journal [47051]

REPUBLIC OF KOREA
Seoul
The Choogan Chosun [47260]
The Korea Post [47279]
The Wolgan Chosun
   [47289] .... (Paid) ‡100,000

LEBANON
Beirut
Assayad [47393] 76,192
Today's Outlook [47402]

MALAYSIA
Kuala Lumpur
Mastika [47626] .. .. ★236,541
Pemikir [47632]

Penang
Third World Resurgence [47693]

NEPAL
Kathmandu
New Business Age [47844]
Spotlight [47846]

NEW ZEALAND
Dunedin
Landfall [48891] .... (Paid) 1,250

OMAN
Muscat
Oman Today
   [49223] .. .. (Paid) 40,000

PAKISTAN
Karachi
Herald [49353]

Peshawar
Statesman [49395] ...... (Paid) 5,000

Magazines

PHILIPPINES
Quezon City
Planet Philippines [49616]

QATAR
Doha
Qatar Info Magazine [49822]

RUSSIA
Moscow
Moscow News [49946] 75,000

SPAIN
Madrid
Muy Interesante
   [50785] ...... (Combined) ‡230,000

SWITZERLAND
Lausanne
L'Hebdo
   [51190] .. .. (Controlled) 72,000

THAILAND
Chiang Mai
Good Morning Chiangmai News
   Magazine [51458]

UNITED ARAB EMIRATES
Dubai
Al Shindagah [51629]
Time Out Dubai [51654] .... △30,072

UNITED KINGDOM
London
The Guardian [54525]
The Week [55396]

Oxford
Critical Quarterly [55918]

HANDICAPPED

UNITED KINGDOM
Colchester
Disability Product News [53034]

London
Talk [55290] .... (Paid) 13,500

HEALTH

AUSTRALIA
Eveleigh
Diabetic Living [41859] .... ★53,591
Heart Healthy Living [41860]

Pyrmont
Natural Source [42285] ..·...... 11,600

Strawberry Hills
The Medical Journal of Australia
   [42396] 27,459

Surry Hills
Hospital & Agedcare
   [42434] 7,523
Nature & Health [42436] ..... ‡30,000

Sydney
Fernwood [42503] 74,250
Slimming & Health
   [42579] .... ★33,761

BANGLADESH
Dhaka
Equity Dialogue [42809]

PEOPLE'S REPUBLIC OF CHINA
Shanghai
Popular Medicine [43494]

FINLAND
Helsinki
Kauneus ja Terveys
   [43839] .. .. (Paid) 73,290
Voi Hyvin [43866] ...... (Paid) 64,246

Kuvalehdet
Kodutohter
   [43886] .... (Combined) 16,000

GERMANY
Aschaffenburg
Schrot & Korn
   [44139] .... (Non-paid) 411,689

Munich
Natur & Heilen
   [44575] .... (Paid) 55,596

Nuremberg
Wellness Foods Europe
   [44617] 6,011

HUNGARY
Budapest
Nok Lapja Egeszseg
   [44858] .... (Paid) 27,439

INDIA
Mumbai
Health [45371] .. .. (Paid) 102,214

IRELAND
Dublin
It's All About Living [45989]

ITALY
Pavia
Haematologica/The Hematology
   Journal [46209]

JAPAN
Tokyo
Josei Seven [46879]
Nikkei Health [46992] .... ★88,192
Nikkei Healthcare
   [46993] .... ★19,079
Nikkei Medical [46997] ... ... ★111,060

MALAYSIA
Kuala Lumpur
i-Sihat [47604]

NETHERLANDS
Utrecht
European Journal of Public Health
   [48757]

POLAND
Warsaw
Vita [49774] .. .. ‡72,677

PORTUGAL
Almargem do Bispo
Saude e Lar [49784]

SINGAPORE
Singapore
Ezyhealth Singapore
   [50146] ... . (Free) 100,000
Simply Her [50252] 50,000
Teens Annual [50277]

SPAIN
Barcelona
Cuerpomente [50662] .. .. ‡66,291
Saber Vivir [50696] .. .. ‡142,798

SWEDEN
Hamneda
Bindu [50968] ... (Combined) 69,000

Linkoping
Hygiea Internationalis [50974]

SWITZERLAND
Geneva
Bulletin of the World Health
   Organization [51089] 6,000

Krattigen
Leben und Gesundheit (Life and
   Health) [51181] .. .. (Paid) 15,200

Zurich
FdH [51259] 460,000
Gesundheit Sprechstunde
   [51262] 86,952

UKRAINE
Kiev
Edinstvennaya - Tvoye Zdorovye
   [51595] .... ‡265,000
Tvoy Malysh [51610] .... ‡90,000

UNITED KINGDOM
Alfreton
Slimming World Magazine
   [52099] ...... (Controlled) 248,862

Barnsley
Horse Health Magazine
   [52181] 10,000
WorkOut Ireland [52185]
WorkOut UK [52186] 8,000

Bristol
Living Earth [52702] 24,000

Essex
LighterLife [53340]

Exeter
Complementary Therapies in
   Medicine [53349]

Leeds
Epilepsy Today
   [53764] .. .. (Combined) 22,500

London
Globalization and Health [54514]
Health Education Journal [54537]
International Journal for Equity in
   Health [54648]
Kindred Spirit
   [54845] .... (Paid) 160,000
Massage World [54911]
The Parkinson Magazine
   [55056] .. .. (Combined) 26,000
Positive Nation [55106]
Stroke News [55266] .. .:...... ‡70,000

Loughton
Health Business [55492]

Norwich
health24 [55732]

Oxford
The Journal of Medicine and
   Philosophy [56051]
Sociology of Health & Illness [56211]

Portsmouth
Positive Health [56292] 8,000

Ware
Champneys Magazine
   [56840] 50,000

HISTORY AND GENEALOGY

CYPRUS
Nicosia
POLIS [43597]

LATVIA
Riga
Ilustreta Pasaules Vesture [47367]

UNITED KINGDOM
Cheltenham
Realm [52975] .... ★48,874

Fife
Kingdom Magazine [53388]

HOME AND GARDEN

AUSTRALIA
Alexandria
Gardening Australia
   [41540] .... ★88,606

Crows Nest
Burke's Backyard Magazine [41821]

Hazelbrook
House & Home [41945]

North Ryde
Australian Country Collections
   [42167] 35,000
Backyard Design Ideas
   [42170] 30,000
Bathroom Yearbook [42173]
BuildHOME Vic [42174]
Contemporary Home Design [42179]
Kitchen Yearbook [42185]
Kitchens and Bathrooms Quarterly
   [42186]
Smart Kitchens & Bathrooms
   [42197] 25,000
Stone [42198] 12,000

Saint Leonards
Smart Home Ideas [42335]

Sydney
Australian House & Garden
   [42455] .... ★105,623
Real Living [42569] .... ★62,283

PEOPLE'S REPUBLIC OF CHINA
Hong Kong
Home Journal Buyer's Guide
   [43318] .... ‡36,570

Shanghai
Shanghai Residence
   [43500] 30,000

FINLAND
Helsinki
Apu [43817] .. . (Combined) 254,762
Avotakka [43820] .... (Paid) 81,271
Meidan Mokki
   [43846] .. .. (Paid) 43,917
Meidan Talo
   [43847] .. .. (Paid) 61,222
Viherpiha [43865] ...... (Paid) 99,577

Kuvalehdet
Kotiliesi
   [43887] ...... (Combined) ‡195,425

FRANCE
Aix-en-Provence
Maisons et Decors Mediterranees
   [43913] .... (Paid) 100,582

Valenciennes
Pour nos Jardins [44121]

GERMANY
Hamburg
ZuhauseWohnen
   [44425] .. .. (Combined) 132,845

Munich
DECO [44556] .... (Paid) 68,000

HUNGARY
Budapest
Praktika [44865] .... (Paid) 40,067

Circulation: ★ = ABC; △ = BPA; ◆ = CAC; • = CCAB; ❑ = VAC; ⊕ = PO Statement; ‡ = Publisher's Report; Boldface figures = sworn; Light figures = estimated.

INDIA
Mumbai
Better Interiors [45355]

IRELAND
Blackrock
Irish Hardware [45921] .... ★1,664
Dublin
Irish Kitchens and Bathrooms
[45979] 25,000

ITALY
Verona
Vita in Campagna
[46281] .. .. (Combined) 74,211

JAPAN
Tokyo
Nikkei Home Builder
[46994] .... ★22,754

LATVIA
Riga
Dari Pats [47363] ...... (Paid) 15,000
Darza Pasaule [47364]
Musmajas [47373]
Una [47374] .. .. (Paid) 18,000

MALAYSIA
Kuala Lumpur
Harmoni [47603]

NETHERLANDS
Amsterdam
Elegance
[47964] .. .. (Combined) ‡55,885
Residence
[48222] .... (Paid) ‡33,556

NEW ZEALAND
Auckland
Home New Zealand
[48795] 14,805
New Zealand Gardener
[48812] .... ★35,880

PHILIPPINES
Mandaluyong City
Good Housekeeping Philippines
[49537] 50,000

POLAND
Warsaw
Kwietnik [49729] 42,200

SINGAPORE
Singapore
Global Sources Hardware & DIY
[50157]
Simply Her [50252] 50,000
Singapore Tatler Homes
[50263] .... ‡14,000

**REPUBLIC OF SOUTH AF-
RICA**
Cape Town
Tuis [50419] 84,715
Hatfield
Aloe [50522]

SPAIN
Madrid
Casa al Dia [50734] .... ‡87,531
Valencia
Bonsai Autoctono
[50843] .... (Combined) 9,700

THAILAND
Bangkok
Essential Guide to Home & Decor
[51420] .... ‡63,350

UKRAINE
Kiev
Interior Magazine
[51598] .... (Combined) 17,500
Lyubimaya Datcha
[51601] .... ‡20,000
Privatnyi Dom [51605] .... ‡35,000

UNITED KINGDOM
Bristol
Gardens Illustrated
[52672] .... ★31,312
Bromsgrove
Homebuilding & Renovating
[52748] .... ★41,602
Cheltenham
The English Garden
[52969] .... ★67,462
The English Home
[52970] .... ★61,355
Colchester
Grow Your Own [53036]
Period House [53045] 45,000
Period Ideas [53046]
Crawley
Journal [53107]
Edinburgh
Home Help [53284]
Scotland's New Homebuyer
[53310] .... (Non-paid) 18,000
Hoylake
Candis [53614] ...... (Paid) ★254,420
Kippen
Fusion Flowers [53726]
London
Amateur Gardening
[53935] .... ★42,691
BBC Gardeners' World Magazine
[54003] .... (Paid) 260,133
Garden History [54493] 3,000
Good Homes [54520] .... ★127,202
Homes & Antiques
[54567] .... ★55,100
Ideal Home [54582]
Livingetc [54879] .... ★92,685
Period Living [55068]
Progressive Gifts and Home
Worldwide [55137] 6,700
25 Beautiful Homes
[55348] .... ★102,868
The World of Interiors
[55421] .... (Paid) 65,000
Northampton
Herbs [55708] .. ... (Combined) 3,000
Orpington
Gardens Monthly [55851]
Saint Albans
The Rose [56438]
Saintfield
SelfBuild [56449] .. .. ★11,574
Watford
Kitchens & Bathrooms News
[56866] .... ★14,609
West Malling
Mortgage Matters [56893]
Your New Home [56895]
Wimborne
International Camellia Journal
[56928] 1,600

**IN-FLIGHT
PUBLICATIONS**

ICELAND
Reykjavik
Atlantica [44897]

JORDAN
Amman
Royal Wings (Jordan) [47162]

PHILIPPINES
Pasig City
Mabuhay [49572]

RUSSIA
Moscow
Aeroflot Premium [49868] ....., 25,000
Inflight Review [49918] 70,000

UNITED KINGDOM
Aberdeen
Star Flyer Magazine [51680]
London
Fah Thai [54438]
Ryanair Magazine [55211]

**INTERCULTURAL
INTERESTS**

AUSTRALIA
Collingwood
Inside Indonesia [41790]
Melbourne
Italy Down Under [42068]
Sydney
Australian Journal of Jewish Studies
[42458]

**PEOPLE'S REPUBLIC OF
CHINA**
Beijing
China Daily (Hong Kong Edition)
[43178]

FRANCE
Paris
L'Arche [44026] .. .. (Paid) 20,000

GERMANY
Berlin
Aschkenas [44157] .... ‡320
Golem [44187]

HUNGARY
Budapest
The Hungarian Quarterly [44836]

ICELAND
Reykjavik
Iceland Review [44901]

ISRAEL
Jerusalem
Hamodia (Israel) [46082]
Menorah
[46089] .. .. (Combined) 13,600

ITALY
Alessandria
Artifara [46116]

NETHERLANDS
Leiden
African and Asian Studies [48643]

POLAND
Sejny
Krasnogruda [49675]

UNITED KINGDOM
Abingdon
Communication and Critical/Cultural
Studies [51734]
London
International Journal of Media and
Cultural Politics [54654]
Jewish Quarterly [54691]
Nutley
American in Britain
[55778] ... .: (Controlled) ‡20,000

LIFESTYLE

AUSTRALIA
Adelaide
Adelaide Matters [41499] 97,418
Alexandria
Australian Country Style
[41534] .... ★57,780
Australian Good Taste
[41536] .... ★121,612
Artarmon
Heat Magazine [41564]
Bondi Junction
Australian T3 [41606]
Cleveland
Queensland Smart Farmer [41768]
East Sydney
SX News
[41852] .... (Combined) 25,000
Eveleigh
That's Life [41861] .... ★274,106
Melbourne
Italy Down Under [42068]
North Ryde
Life Etc. [42187] .... ★41,026
North Sydney
Australian Society & Events
[42208] 10,000
Pyrmont
Hilton Australasia [42279]
Surry Hills
Nature & Health [42436] ..... ‡30,000
Sydney
COLES [42495]
Cosmopolitan (Australia)
[42498] .... ★151,213
Fernwood [42503] 74,250
Harper's Bazaar (Australia)
[42512] .... (Paid) ★56,119
Myer Emporium [42550] ... ★248,900
Real Living [42569] .... ★62,283

BELGIUM
Antwerp
Ambiance
[42837] .. .. (Controlled) 63,638
Wommelgem
Exclusief
[42913] .. .. (Combined) 40,000

**PEOPLE'S REPUBLIC OF
CHINA**
Beijing
Beijing Tatler [43172] .. .. ‡46,500
Hong Kong
Elite Homes [43298] .. .. ‡16,350

Circulation: ★ = ABC; △ = BPA; ♦ = CAC; • = CCAB; ❑ = VAC; ⊕ = PO Statement; ‡ = Publisher's Report; Boldface figures = sworn; Light figures = estimated.

Hong Kong Tatler **[43346]**
Macau Tatler **[43365]** .... ‡30,140
Shanghai
Beauty Home **[43463]**
Shanghai Tatler **[43502]** .. .. ‡60,000
Shanghai Weekly **[43504]**
With **[43510]**

DENMARK
Copenhagen
DANSK **[43662]**
Hellerup
Euroman **[43720]**

EGYPT
Cairo
Enigma Magazine **[43761]** 45,000

FINLAND
Helsinki
Apu **[43817]** .. . (Combined) 254,762
Kauppalehti Optio
   [43840] .... ★86,577
Meidan Mokki
   [43846] .. .. (Paid) 43,917
Kuvalehdet
Seura
   [43894] ...... (Combined) ‡211,863

GERMANY
Grasbrunn
natur+kosmos **[44403]** 84,278
Hamburg
Petra **[44422]** .... (Paid) ‡295,102
ZuhauseWohnen
   [44425] .. .. (Combined) 132,845
Munich
Munich Found **[44572]** 10,000
MUSIKEXPRESS
   [44573] .... ‡52,398

HUNGARY
Budapest
Maxima Special
   [44849] .... (Paid) 44,183
Meglepetes **[44850]** ... (Paid) 94,838
Nok Lapja **[44857]** ... (Paid) 253,749
Nok Lapja Evszakok
   [44860] .... (Paid) 22,300
Otthon **[44863]** .... (Paid) 41,066

IRELAND
Clarenbridge
CORKnow **[45932]**
GALWAYnow **[45933]**
Dublin
Prudence **[45995]** .. .. ★11,035

JAPAN
Kobe
Kansai Time Out **[46431]**
Tokyo
Josei Seven **[46879]**
Nikkei Entertainment!
   [46991] .... ★90,234
Paper Sky **[47016]**
Priv. **[47025]** .... ★173,474
Real Simple Japan
   [47030] .... (Paid) ★105,285
SARAI **[47035]**

LATVIA
Riga
Veseliba **[47375]** .... (Paid) 17,000

LEBANON
Beirut
Al-Fares **[47388]** .... ★78,307

Sahar **[47401]** 110,000

MALAYSIA
Kuala Lumpur
i-Sihat **[47604]**
Juice **[47609]** .... (Free) 30,000
Malaysia Society **[47612]**

NETHERLANDS
Amsterdam
Elegance
   [47964] .. .. (Combined) ‡55,885

NEW ZEALAND
Auckland
onHoliday **[48827]**

PAKISTAN
Karachi
Dawn Magazine **[49347]**
Images **[49354]**
The Review **[49375]**

PHILIPPINES
Cebu City
Zee Lifestyle **[49465]** 25,000
Makati City
Philippine Society
   [49522] .... ‡45,000
Philippine Tatler **[49523]** ..... ‡45,000
Mandaluyong City
For Him Magazine Philippines
   [49536] 150,000
Quezon City
CHALK **[49588]**
Dream Weddings **[49590]**
Metro **[49599]**
Metro Society **[49602]**
MetroActive **[49604]**

POLAND
Warsaw
Chwila rozrywki **[49704]**
Uczucia i tesknoty
   [49771] .... ‡63,514
Uroda **[49772]** .... ‡76,342
Warsaw Insider **[49775]** 20,000

ROMANIA
Bucharest
Avantaje **[49831]** .... ‡23,612
Psychologies **[49842]** .... ‡10,845

RUSSIA
Moscow
Samaya **[49988]** .... ‡117,350

SINGAPORE
Singapore
Icon Moments
   [50169] .... (Combined) 20,000
Newman **[50227]**
NuYou **[50230]** 25,000
Simply Her **[50252]** 50,000
Singapore Tatler **[50262]** ... . ‡13,000
Singapore Tatler Society
   [50264] .... ‡12,200
Singapore Tatler Weddings
   [50265] .... ‡14,000
Woman's World **[50288]**

REPUBLIC OF SOUTH AF-RICA
Cape Town
Idees **[50382]** 85,642
Max Power **[50390]**
Move! **[50393]** 41,336

True Love **[50418]** .. .. ★99,889
Sandton
Huisgenoot **[50626]** 355,487

SRI LANKA
Colombo
Lanka Woman **[50861]**

SWITZERLAND
Lausanne
L'illustre **[51191]** 90,635
Zurich
Schweizer Illustrierte
   [51278] 204,856
Schweizer Illustrierte Style
   [51279] 109,983
SonntagsBlick Magazin
   [51285] 247,449

TAIWAN
Taipei
Taiwan Tatler **[51366]** .... ‡20,000

THAILAND
Bangkok
Expat Society **[51421]**
Phuket Tatler **[51429]** .... ‡62,850
Thailand Society **[51442]** ... ‡36,200
Thailand Tatler **[51443]** .... ‡54,850

UKRAINE
Kiev
Edinstvennaya - Tvoye Zdorovye
   [51595] .... ‡265,000
Viva! Beauty **[51613]** .... ‡50,000

UNITED ARAB EMIRATES
Dubai
Charged Middle East
   [51635] 9,000
Emaar Properties Magazine
   [51640] 18,000
Living in the Gulf
   [51647] ...... (Controlled) ‡25,000
What's On **[51656]** .... △31,055

UNITED KINGDOM
Abingdon
Fyne Times **[51792]**
Bacton
Herefordshire Life **[52153]**
Bath
French Magazine **[52240]**
Brighton
The Insight
   [52615] .... (Non-paid) 20,000
Learning Disability Today **[52625]**
Caerfyrddin
Cambria **[52781]**
Cambridge
Cambridgeshire Agenda
   [52800] .... (Combined) 30,000
Cheltenham
Birmingham Life **[52964]**
Cheltenham Oracle **[52965]**
Evergreen **[52971]** ... .. (Paid) 48,000
The Oracle Gloucester Life **[52973]**
Realm **[52975]** .... ★48,874
Shropshire Life **[52976]**
Staffordshire County **[52977]**
This England **[52978]** 170,342
Warwickshire Life **[52979]**
Worcestershire Life **[52981]**
Chessington
Asian Woman **[52990]** .... ★90,339
Chester
Skin Deep **[52999]** 38,764

Derby
Leicestershire Magazine
   [53165] 10,000
Dundee
My Weekly **[53216]** .. .. ‡198,980
East Molesey
Ag Magazine **[53239]**
Edinburgh
Scottish Field
   [53314] .... (Paid) ★14,165
Spectrum Magazine Scotland on
   Sunday **[53320]**
Folkestone
Saga **[53393]**
Glasgow
No.1 **[53435]**
Godalming
Monocle Magazine
   [53476] .... (Non-paid) 12,000
Hexham
North East Life **[53569]**
Hoylake
Candis **[53614]** ...... (Paid) ★254,420
Ipswich
East Anglian Daily Times Suffolk
   [53656]
Kensington Village
Living Hadley **[53674]**
Living North **[53675]**
Leeds
ASDA Magazine
   [53755] 3,000,000
London
Amy **[53939]**
Aspinalls **[53977]**
Bella **[54010]** .... ★246,446
Big Cheese
   [54015] .. .. (Paid) 16,000
Candid **[54172]** 8,000
Country Life **[54275]** .. .. ★36,836
Emel **[54363]**
European Journal of American
   Culture **[54396]**
Harrods Estates MAG
   [54532] 25,000
Livingetc **[54879]** .. .. ★92,685
The London Magazine **[54887]**
North **[55010]**
Northwest **[55012]** .. .. ★34,034
PrivatAir **[55120]** 7,000
PrivatSea **[55123]** 8,000
Quintessentially **[55166]** 25,000
The Rambler
   [55172] .... (Controlled) 93,202
The Resident (London) **[55191]**
Rise **[55203]** .... ★40,000
Shout Magazine **[55235]**
Spirit & Destiny **[55262]** .. .... ★61,537
TenGoal **[55299]** 7,000
that's life! **[55302]** .. .. ★386,875
Westside Magazine
   [55399] .... ★47,000
W1 Magazine **[55415]**
YOGA Magazine **[55432]**
Yours **[55435]** .... ★344,438
Manchester
Grip **[55557]** .... (Combined) 6,000
Norwich
Brighton & Hove Life
   [55726] .... (Controlled) 22,000
Compass South **[55729]** ..... ‡40,000
Compass Wessex
   [55730] .... ‡40,000
Let's Talk! **[55733]** .. .. ★27,205
Peterborough
Custom Car Magazine **[56255]**
Poole
Boys Toys **[56280]** 55,000

Circulation: ★ = ABC; △ = BPA; ◆ = CAC; • = CCAB; ❑ = VAC; ⊕ = PO Statement; ‡ = Publisher's Report; Boldface figures = sworn; Light figures = estimated.

Preston
Durham County Life [56299]
Lancashire Life [56303] ...... ★23,455

Ramsgate
Bonjour! [56308]

Ripon
Yorkshire Life [56400] .... ★22,531

Salisbury
Hampshire [56454]
Wiltshire Life [56458]

Stoneleigh
Country Way
   [56635] .... (Paid) 4,000

Sudbury
Total Tattoo Magazine [56651]

Surrey
Renault Magazine
   [56674] .. .. ★212,117

Totnes
Devon Life
   [56762] .... (Paid) ★15,196
Somerset Life [56763]
Wiltshire [56764]

Ware
Bentley Magazine [56839] 60,000
Sunseeker Magazine
   [56845] 170,000

Watford
Limited Edition [56867] 114,000

West Sussex
Buckinghamshire Life [56896]

Worthing
Surrey Life [56977]
Sussex Life [56978]

VIETNAM
Hanoi
Thoi Bao Kinh Te Vietnam
   [57053] .... (Controlled) 35,000

LITERATURE AND LITERARY REVIEWS
See also Science Fiction, Mystery, Adventure, and Romance

AUSTRALIA
Balmain
Jacket [41573]

Richmond South
ABR (Australian Book Review)
   [42311] 2,000

BELGIUM
Mechelen
Ludus [42904]

CHILE
Concepcion
Acta Literaria [43135]

PEOPLE'S REPUBLIC OF CHINA
Beijing
Life in China [43211]

Shanghai
Fiction World [43476]
Journal of Editorial Study [43480]
Oriental Sword [43493]

FINLAND
Kuvalehdet
Parnasso
   [43893] .... (Combined) ‡3,648

HUNGARY
Budapest
The Hungarian Quarterly [44836]
Story Special
   [44873] .. .. (Paid) 110,116

INDIA
Cuttack
Chandrabhaga
   [45080] ... . (Paid) ‡300

JAPAN
Kyoto
Kyoto Review of Southeast Asia
   [46480]

KENYA
Nairobi
Kwani? [47192]

LATVIA
Riga
Legendas [47372]

NEW ZEALAND
Auckland
New Zealand Listener
   [48819] ... . (Combined) 80,939

RUSSIA
Moscow
Lechaim [49936] .... ‡54,000

SPAIN
Madrid
Insula [50771]
Intramuros
   [50774] .. .. (Combined) 15,000

Mataro
Quimera [50820]

Santa Cruz de Tenerife
La Pagina [50829]

Teruel
Turia [50839]

SWITZERLAND
Zurich
European Joyce Studies [51258]

UNITED KINGDOM
Cranbrook
The New Writer [53096]

Edinburgh
Anon [53250]

Lerwick
The New Shetlander
   [53841] .... (Combined) 1,900

Lincoln
Dream Catcher [53855]

London
Ambit [53938] .... (Paid) 3,000
Another Magazine [53953]
Brittle Star [54149]
Frieze [54484]
The Hardy Review [54530]
London Review of Books
   [54890] .... (Paid) ★42,721
The Magical World of Roald Dahl
   [54896]
The Wolf [55411]

Maidenhead
SOUTH Poetry [55525]

Matlock
Iota Magazine [55603]

Oxford
Literature Compass [56090]

Plymouth
Tremblestone [56275]

Witney
Amon Hen [56938] .. .. (Paid) 600

LOCAL, STATE, AND REGIONAL PUBLICATIONS

AUSTRALIA
Adelaide
dB Magazine [41505]

Cleveland
Queensland Smart Farmer [41768]

Melbourne
Local Government Focus
   [42070] .. .. (Combined) 11,800

BAHAMAS
Abaco
Abaco Journal [42782]

BAHRAIN
Manama
Bahrain This Month (BTM)
   [42787] .. .. (Combined) 10,000

FINLAND
Kuvalehdet
Seura
   [43894] ...... (Combined) ‡211,863

GERMANY
Hamburg
Merian [44420] .. .. (Paid) ◆88,953

Munich
Munich Found [44572] 10,000

INDIA
New Delhi
Islam and the Modern Age
   [45592] .. .. (Paid) 1,000

ITALY
Padua
Italia Turistica
   [46206] .. .. (Combined) 150,000

Palermo
Sikania [46208] .... (Paid) 10,000

Rozzano
Meridiani [46251] .... ‡31,066

JAMAICA
Kingston
The Star [46288]
The Weekend Star [46292]

JAPAN
Tokyo
Tokyo Weekender [47052] 15,000

LATVIA
Riga
Darza Pasaule [47364]

NEW ZEALAND
Auckland
New Zealand Listener
   [48819] .. .. (Combined) 80,939
North & South [48822] 299,000

PAKISTAN
Karachi
Dawn Magazine [49347]

Images [49354]
The Review [49375]

POLAND
Warsaw
Warsaw Insider [49775] 20,000

SINGAPORE
Singapore
Regional Best Restaurants
   [50242] .. .. ‡16,000

THAILAND
Chiang Mai
Citylife [51457]

UKRAINE
Kiev
Korrespondent
   [51599] .. .. (Combined) 50,000

UNITED KINGDOM
Bath
Italia! [52246]

Brighton
The Insight
   [52615] .... (Non-paid) 20,000

Cambridge
Cambridgeshire Agenda
   [52800] .. .. (Combined) 30,000

Cheltenham
Realm [52975] .. .. ★48,874

Chesham
Chesham Town Talk
   [52985] .... (Non-paid) 4,500

Derby
Peak District Life [53167]

Dundee
My Weekly [53216] .. .. ‡198,980

Glasgow
Scottish Hosteller [53448]

Godalming
Monocle Magazine
   [53476] .... (Non-paid) 12,000

Hexham
North East Life [53569]

Ipswich
East Anglian Daily Times Suffolk
   [53656]

Kensington Village
Living Hadley [53674]
Living North [53675]

Kilmarnock
The Scottish Review [53709]

London
Countryside Voice [54277] .. . 35,000
The Field [54451] .. .. ★30,428
The London Picture Book
   [54889] .. .. (Combined) 125,000
The Resident (London) [55191]

Midlothian
Taste of Scotland [55628]

Norwich
Brighton & Hove Life
   [55726] .. .. (Controlled) 22,000
Compass South [55729] ..... ‡40,000
Compass Wessex
   [55730] .. .. ‡40,000
Let's Talk! [55733] .. .. ★27,205

Penzance
Inside Cornwall
   [56249] .. .. (Paid) 8,000

Ripon
Yorkshire Life [56400] .. .. ★22,531

Circulation: ★ = ABC; △ = BPA; ◆ = CAC; • = CCAB; ❑ = VAC; ⊕ = PO Statement; ‡ = Publisher's Report; Boldface figures = sworn; Light figures = estimated.

Magazines

Salisbury
Hampshire [56454]
Wiltshire Life [56458]

Skipton
Dalesman Magazine [56553]

Tavistock
Dartmoor Magazine [56727]

Totnes
Cornwall Life [56761]
Somerset Life [56763]
Wiltshire [56764]

Watford
Limited Edition [56867] 114,000

West Sussex
Buckinghamshire Life [56896]

Worthing
Surrey Life [56977]
Sussex Life [56978]

MEN'S INTERESTS

AUSTRALIA
Saint Leonards
Australian Penthouse [42331]

Surry Hills
Bacon Busters [42421] .... ‡57,000

Sydney
Men's Style Australia [42542]
The Picture Premium [42562]

DENMARK
Hellerup
Euroman [43720]

IRELAND
Dublin
Auto Ireland [45947]

Dundrum
Living It [46010] 10,000

LEBANON
Beirut
Al-Fares [47388] .... ★78,307

NETHERLANDS
Amsterdam
Fantastic Man [47984]

PHILIPPINES
Mandaluyong City
For Him Magazine Philippines
   [49536] 150,000

Quezon City
Metro hiM [49600]
MetroActive [49604]

PORTUGAL
Cruz Quebrada-Dafundo
Guia do Automovel
   [49794] .. .. (Paid) 42,496

SINGAPORE
Singapore
Journal of Men's Health [50209]

SWITZERLAND
Lausanne
Montres Passion/Uhren Welt
   [51197] .... (Controlled) 180,000

UNITED KINGDOM
Cheltenham
Whisky [52980]

Chessington
Asian Groom & Man [52989]

Lewes
The Chap [53848]

London
FHM [54449] .... (Paid) 710,000
Nuts [55022]
PokerPlayer [55098]
Savile Row
   [55218] .... (Non-paid) 25,000
Zoo Weekly [55437]

Poole
Boys Toys [56280] 55,000

Stone
NORM News [56634]

MOTION PICTURES
See also Photography; Radio, Television, Cable, and Video

FINLAND
Helsinki
Katso [43838] .... (Paid) 72,741

INDIA
Mumbai
Stardust [45442] .. ... (Paid) 308,170

IRELAND
Dublin
Film Ireland [45956]

PHILIPPINES
Mandaluyong City
High School Musical
   [49538] 20,000

SINGAPORE
Singapore
8 Days [50142]

UKRAINE
Kiev
Afisha
   [51593] .... (Combined) 25,000

UNITED KINGDOM
Bournemouth
Practical Digital Video [52422]

London
Empire
   [54365] .. .. (Combined) 173,000
Midsomer Murders Magazine [54933]

MOTORBIKES AND MOTORCYLES

AUSTRALIA
Alexandria
Live to Ride [41542] .... ‡24,039
twowheels [41549] .... ★31,453

Burleigh
Freerider MX Magazine [41672]

North Ryde
Australian Road Rider
   [42168] 27,000
Australian Trailrider [42169]
Dirt Action [42180]

Sydney
Australian Dirt Bike Magazine
   [42452] .... ★26,074

CZECH REPUBLIC
Prague
Motorcykl (Czech) [43631] .. . 17,000

GERMANY
Euskirchen
Tourenfahrer/Motorrad Reisen
   [44351] .... (Paid) ‡65,170

JAPAN
Tokyo
Moto-Champ [46973]

NETHERLANDS
The Hague
Pro Motor
   [48626] .. .. (Controlled) 38,217

PORTUGAL
Cruz Quebrada-Dafundo
Motociclismo
   [49795] .. .. (Controlled) 15,889

REPUBLIC OF SOUTH AFRICA
Cape Town
TOPbike [50415]

SWITZERLAND
Mies
FIM Magazine [51212] 2,600

UNITED KINGDOM
Aberdeen
Lady Biker Magazine [51679]

Birmingham
Bikersweb [52329]

Croydon
Superbike [53135]

Haywards Heath
Autosport Magazine [53547]

Horncastle
Classic and Motorcycle Mechanics
   [53588] 30,000
Classic Racer International [53589]

London
Moto Magazine [54956]

Manchester
Bike Trader [55543] .. .. ★17,876

Morecambe
Dirt Bike Rider
   [55647] .... (Paid) ‡25,000
Trials & Motocross News
   [55649] .... (Paid) ‡24,000

MUSIC AND MUSICAL INSTRUMENTS

AUSTRALIA
Bondi Junction
Urban Hitz [41610]

Tamworth
Country Music Capital News [42611]

PEOPLE'S REPUBLIC OF CHINA
Shanghai
Music Lover [43490]

DENMARK
Copenhagen
Jazz Special
   [43676] .. .. (Combined) 10,000

FINLAND
Helsinki
Soundi [43857] .... (Paid) 25,000

Kuvalehdet
Suosikki [43896] .... ‡45,939

FRANCE
Brezolles
Chorus [43923] .... (Paid) 20,000

Paris
Jukebox Magazine
   [44066] .. .. (Paid) 20,000

GERMANY
Berlin
Groove [44188]

Munich
Metal Hammer [44571] .... ‡42,996
MUSIKEXPRESS
   [44573] .... ‡52,398
POPCORN [44578] .... ‡188,349

INDIA
Chennai
Sruti [45058]

Mumbai
AV Max [45354]

ITALY
Varese
Musica [46277]

LEBANON
Beirut
Achabaka
   [47385] .... (Combined) 113,583

NETHERLANDS
Nieuwegein
Beatles Unlimited Magazine
   [48740] 3,575

SINGAPORE
Singapore
BigO [50115]
8 Days [50142]

REPUBLIC OF SOUTH AFRICA
Durban
blunt [50467] .... ★13,207

SPAIN
Barcelona
Opera Actual [50690]

Madrid
Cuadernos de Jazz [50745]
Melomano [50783]
Ritmo [50800]
Scherzo
   [50801] .... (Combined) 17,500

SWITZERLAND
Zurich
Schweizer Musikzeitung
   [51282] .. .. (Controlled) 21,948

UNITED KINGDOM
Bath
Music Tech Magazine [52252]

Blaydon-on-Tyne
Classical Guitar
   [52387] .... (Combined) 8,000

Cambridge
Repeat [52891] 500

Dorking
Church Music Quarterly
   [53193] .... (Paid) ‡11,500

Circulation: ★ = ABC; △ = BPA; ◆ = CAC; • = CCAB; ▢ = VAC; ⊕ = PO Statement; ‡ = Publisher's Report; Boldface figures = sworn; Light figures = estimated.

High Wycombe
Double Reed News [53573]

London
Big Cheese
[54015] .. .. (Paid) 16,000
Classic Record Collector
[54214] .... (Paid) ‡6,000
Country Music People
[54276] ... . (Paid) 20,000
DJ Magazine [54336]
Flute [54469] .... (Paid) 1,700
The Fly [54470]
International Piano
[54666] .... (Controlled) ‡8,000
Jazz UK
[54689] ... . (Combined) 30,000
Jazzwise Magazine [54690]
Kerrang! [54842]
Mojo [54944]
Musical Opinion
[54965] .. .. (Paid) ‡5,000
(Non-paid) ‡1,000
Opera [55036]
Record Collector [55177]
Songlines [55255]
Sound Projector [55256]
The Wire [55408]

Martlesham Heath
KlubKat Music Magazine [55602]

Melksham
The Ptolemaic Terrascope Magazine
[55605] 4,000

Portsmouth
Blue Band Magazine [56287]

Stroud
Musical Traditions [56647]

Warrington
Jimi Hendrix Magazine [56849]

West Malling
The Soul Survivors [56894]

NEW AGE
See also Alternative and Underground

FINLAND
Helsinki
Voi Hyvin [43866] ...... (Paid) 64,246

NORWAY
Oslo
Monitor 21 [49204]

SWEDEN
Hamneda
Bindu [50968] ... (Combined) 09,000

SWITZERLAND
Winterthur
Spuren
[51243] .... (Controlled) 10,000

UNITED KINGDOM
London
Kindred Spirit
[54845] .... (Paid) 160,000
New Renaissance
[54997] .... (Controlled) 1,500

PARAPSYCHOLOGY
See also Alternative and Underground

MALAYSIA
Kuala Lumpur
Mastika [47626] .... ★236,541

UNITED KINGDOM
London
Anomaly [53952] 500
Chat - It's Fate [54200]

PARENTING
See also Babies; Children's
Interests; Youths' Interests

AUSTRALIA
Alexandria
Australian Parents [41537]

Glen Iris
Breastfeeding Review [41891]

North Ryde
Choosing a School for Your Child -
New South Wales [42175]
Choosing a School for Your Child -
Victoria [42176]

Sydney
Mother & Baby [42548] ... .. ★134,000

BELGIUM
Brussels
Echos AMA [42849]

CAMEROON
Yaounde
Clinics in Mother and Child Health
[43129]

FINLAND
Kuvalehdet
Kaksplus
[43882] ...... (Combined) ‡46,740
Seura
[43894] ...... (Combined) ‡211,863

GERMANY
Frankfurt am Main
Pro Familia Magazin
[44368] 7,000

HUNGARY
Budapest
Kismama [44843] ...... (Paid) 19,535
Kismama Mintaszam
[44844] .. .. (Free) 130,000
Kismama 9 Honap
[44845] .. .. (Paid) 30,970

IRELAND
Dublin
Maternity & Infant [45991] 15,000

ITALY
Rome
Famiglia Cristiana
[46229] 966,671

MALAYSIA
Kuala Lumpur
Harmoni [47603]

NEW ZEALAND
Auckland
Little Treasures [48803] ...... ★30,713
Mana
Kiwi Parent
[48936] ...... (Controlled) ‡15,000

NIGERIA
Abuja
Women on the Move [49058]

PHILIPPINES
Mandaluyong City
Smart Parenting [49541] 20,000
Quezon City
Working Mom [49619]

POLAND
Warsaw
Mamo, to ja [49735] .... ‡98,937
Przedszkolak [49758]
Twoj Maluszek [49769] ..... ‡146,473
Twoje dziecko [49770] .. .. ‡70,524

PORTUGAL
Almargem do Bispo
Saude e Lar [49784]
Cruz Quebrada-Dafundo
Pais & Filhos
[49796] .. .. (Paid) 30,712

RUSSIA
Moscow
Mama, eto ya! [49940] .... ‡86,740

SINGAPORE
Singapore
Motherhood [50219]
Motherhood Handbook [50220]
Today's Parents [50279]
Young Parents [50289] 15,000
Young Parents Baby
[50290] 25,000
Young Parents Preschool Guide
[50291] 30,000

SPAIN
Barcelona
Tu Bebe [50704] .... ‡95,092
Madrid
Ser Padres [50802]
Ser Padres Bebe
[50803] .. .. (Combined) ‡59,308
Ser Padres Hoy
[50804] .. .. (Combined) ‡35,000

UKRAINE
Kiev
Haroshye Raditeli
[51597] .. .. ‡45,000
Mama I ya [51602] .... ‡60,000
Tvoy Malysh [51610] .... ‡90,000

UNITED KINGDOM
Bromley
FQ [52745]
Glasgow
First Link 4 Parents
[53420] .. .. (Free) 18,000
Hoylake
Candis [53614] ...... (Paid) ★254,420
London
Be My Parent
[54008] .. .. (Combined) 22,000
Practical Parenting and Pregnancy
[55116]
Time Out Kids Out [55318]
Stirling
Childminding
[56621] .. .. (Combined) 18,000
Worcester Park
Parents News UK
[56965] 175,000

PERFORMING ARTS

AUSTRALIA
Surry Hills
Dance Australia [42425]........ ★4,348

CZECH REPUBLIC
Prague
Divadelni Noviny [43623]

INDIA
Kolkata
Seagull Theatre Quarterly [45304]

NEW ZEALAND
Wellington
DANZ [49006] .... (Paid) 500

SPAIN
Barcelona
Opera Actual [50690]

UNITED KINGDOM
London
Dance Today! [54310]
Dancing Times [54311]
Opera [55036]
Southport
Linedancer [56587]

PETS
See also Cats; Dogs

AUSTRALIA
North Melbourne
Animals Today [42156] 3,000
North Ryde
Dogs Life [42181]
Tweed Heads
Australian Birdkeeper Magazine
[42655] 9,500

FINLAND
Kuvalehdet
Lemmikki [43889] .. .. ‡18,152

GERMANY
Ettlingen
Aquaristik
[44348] .... (Controlled) 26,364
Pet in Europe [44350]

UNITED KINGDOM
Arundel
Cat World [52133]
Dundee
Animals and You
[53213] .. .. (Paid) 60,000
London
All About Animals [53932]
Cage and Aviary Birds
[54166] .... ★15,185
Eukanuba [54389]
The Journal of the British Tarantula
Society [54714]
Pet Product Marketing [55073]
Pevensey
Pet Talk [56268]
Warrington
Nishikigoi International
[56850] .... (Combined) 7,000
Wheathampstead
Animal Welfare [56914]

PHOTOGRAPHY

ARGENTINA
Buenos Aires
Fotomundo [41472] .... (Paid) 8,000

Circulation: ★ = ABC; △ = BPA; ◆ = CAC; • = CCAB; ❑ = VAC; ⊕ = PO Statement; ‡ = Publisher's Report; Boldface figures = sworn; Light figures = estimated.

Magazines

AUSTRALIA

Surry Hills
Australian Photography
[42416] .... ★9,099
Capture [42422] .... ★2,826
Digital Photography and Design
[42426] .... ★4,593

PEOPLE'S REPUBLIC OF CHINA

Beijing
China Pictorial
[43180] .... (Paid) 500,000

Shanghai
Shanghai Pictorial [43499]

GERMANY

Berlin
European Photography [44175]

HUNGARY

Budapest
National Geographic Special
[44856] .... ‡16,000

INDIA

Mumbai
Better Photography [45356]

NEW ZEALAND

Auckland
D-Photo [48790] 12,000

UNITED KINGDOM

Bournemouth
Digital Camera Buyer [52412]
Digital Photographer [52413]

London
Amateur Photographer
[53937] .... ★22,242
British Journal of Photography
[54131] .... (Paid) ★8,015
Ei8ht [54358]
What Digital Camera [55400]

Saffron Walden
Photography Monthly [56429]

POETRY

See also Literature and Literary Reviews

AUSTRALIA

Balmain
Jacket [41573]

FINLAND

Kuvalehdet
Parnasso
[43893] .... (Combined) ‡3,648

INDIA

Cuttack
Chandrabhaga
[45080] .... (Paid) ‡300

SPAIN

Torremoinos
Litoral [50841]

UNITED KINGDOM

Belfast
Irish Pages [52287]

Cranbrook
The New Writer [53096]

Edinburgh
Anon [53250]
Chapman
[53261] .... (Combined) 2,550

Frome
Outposts Poetry Quarterly
[53400] .. .. (Paid) 2,000

Lerwick
The New Shetlander
[53841] .... (Combined) 1,900

Lincoln
Dream Catcher [53855]

London
Ambit [53938] .... (Paid) 3,000
Brittle Star [54149]
Poetry Review
[55097] .... (Paid) 4,000
Trespass [55340]
The Wolf [55411]

Maidenhead
SOUTH Poetry [55525]

Matlock
Iota Magazine [55603]

Plymouth
Tremblestone [56275]

PSYCHOLOGY AND PSYCHIATRY

MALAYSIA

Kuala Lumpur
i-Sihat [47604]

NETHERLANDS

Amsterdam
Narrative Inquiry [48169]

POLAND

Warsaw
Advances in Cognitive Psychology
[49685]
Polish Psychological Bulletin [49754]

UNITED KINGDOM

Brentwood
High Spirit [52574] .... ★40,000

RADIO, TELEVISION, CABLE, AND VIDEO

AUSTRALIA

Saint Leonards
TV Soap [42336]

PEOPLE'S REPUBLIC OF CHINA

Shanghai
Radio & TV [43496]

FINLAND

Helsinki
Katso [43838] .... (Paid) 72,741

Kuvalehdet
TV-maailma
[43899] ...... (Combined) ‡400,000

GERMANY

Hamburg
HORZU [44418] .... ‡1,538,346

HUNGARY

Budapest
RTV Musormagazin
[44868] .... (Paid) ‡74,540

Szines RTV
[44877] .... (Paid) 211,125

INDIA

Mumbai
AV Max [45354]
Tomorrow's Technology Today
[45448]

REPUBLIC OF SOUTH AFRICA

Cape Town
tvplus [50420] 150,254

SWITZERLAND

Lausanne
Tele top matin [51200] ...... ‡193,316
TV8 [51201] 84,087

Zurich
TVtaglich [51295] 1,221,000

UKRAINE

Kiev
TV Ekran [51609] .. .. ‡100,000

UNITED ARAB EMIRATES

Dubai
tv&radio [51655] .... △43,750

UNITED KINGDOM

Bedford
Radio Communication
[52276] 27,000

Bournemouth
High Definition Review [52415]
Practical Digital Video [52422]

Glasgow
The Radio Journal [53444]

London
Dora the Explorer [54341]
Midsomer Murders Magazine [54933]
Radio Times
[55170] .... (Paid) 1,093,850
Total TVguide [55329] ...... ★107,681
TVChoice [55345] .. .. ★1,335,894
TVQuick [55346] .... ★144,270

Manchester
Critical Studies in Television [55551]

SCIENCE

AUSTRALIA

Surry Hills
Climate Control News (CCN)
[42423] .... ★6,394

PEOPLE'S REPUBLIC OF CHINA

Shanghai
Scientific Pictorial [43498]

GHANA

Legon
Ghana Journal of Science [44736]
Journal of the Ghana Science
Association [44737]

INDIA

Chennai
Jantar Mantar [45044]

Hyderabad
The Icfai Journal of Science &
Technology [45166]

Mumbai
Offshore World (OW) [45422]

Pharma Bio World [45428]

JORDAN

Amman
Medical Journal of Islamic Academy
of Sciences [47161]

LATVIA

Riga
Ilustreta Junioriem [47366]
Ilustreta Pasaules Vesture [47367]
Ilustreta Zinatne [47368]

MALAWI

Zomba
Malawi Journal of Science and
Technology [47573]

NETHERLANDS

Dordrecht
Grundwasser [48409]

PAKISTAN

Faisalabad
Global Journal of Molecular Sciences
[49243]
Journal of Biological Sciences
[49264]
Research Journal of Applied
Sciences [49284]

REPUBLIC OF SOUTH AFRICA

Pretoria
Water Wheel [50608]

UNITED KINGDOM

Abingdon
Science as Culture [52054]

SCIENCE FICTION, MYSTERY, ADVENTURE, AND ROMANCE

AUSTRALIA

Kaleen
Andromeda Spaceways Inflight
Magazine [41981]

PEOPLE'S REPUBLIC OF CHINA

Shanghai
Fiction World [43476]
Oriental Sword [43493]

HUNGARY

Budapest
Story Special
[44873] .. .. (Paid) 110,116

JAPAN

Tokyo
Be Love [46759]
Bessatsu Friend [46761]
Dessert [46801]
Evening [46818]
Juliet [46951]
Kiss [46954]
Morning [46972]
Nakayoshi [46974]
One More Kiss [47014]
Shukan Shonen Magazine [47038]
Young Magazine [47057]
Young Magazine Uppers [47058]

MALAYSIA

Kuala Lumpur
Mastika [47626] .... ★236,541

Circulation: ★ = ABC; △ = BPA; ◆ = CAC; • = CCAB; ❑ = VAC; ⊕ = PO Statement; ‡ = Publisher's Report; Boldface figures = sworn; Light figures = estimated.

SPAIN
Barcelona
The Barcelona Review [50654]

UNITED KINGDOM
London
Doctor Who Adventures [54338]
Fiction Feast [54450]
Foundation [54479] 1,200
The Magical World of Roald Dahl
[54896]
Trespass [55340]
W.I.T.C.H. [55409]

Witney
Amon Hen [56938] .. .. (Paid) 600

SENIOR CITIZENS' INTERESTS

AUSTRALIA
South Melbourne
Agendas [42366]
Australasian Journal on Ageing
[42367]

IRELAND
Dundrum
Living It [46010] 10,000

ITALY
Rome
Club 3 [46224]

NEW ZEALAND
Christchurch
Retirement Today
[48878] .. .. (Combined) 40,000

SWITZERLAND
Zurich
Zeitlupe [51297]

UNITED KINGDOM
Bristol
Age and Ageing [52638]

Cambridge
Ageing and Society [52785]

London
Occupational Pensions [55025]
The Oldie [55029] .... ★26,151
Yours [55435] .. .. ★344,438

SEX/EROTICA

AUSTRALIA
Saint Leonards
Australian Penthouse [42331]
Penthouse Couples [42334]

UNITED KINGDOM
London
Trespass [55340]

SOCIAL AND POLITICAL ISSUES

AUSTRALIA
Burwood East
Global Future [41677]

Collingwood
Parity [41793]

East Sydney
Cherrie
[41849] .. .. (Combined) 19,000

Highgate Hill
Pacific Waves [41955]

Melbourne
Local Government Focus
[42070] .. .. (Combined) 11,800

Surry Hills
Australian Defence Magazine
[42411] .. .. ★3,985
Australian National Security
Magazine [42415] .... ‡3,000

Sydney
Green Left Weekly [42510]

BELGIUM
Brussels
Homeless in Europe [42858]

FINLAND
Kuvalehdet
Kanava
[43883] .. .. (Combined) ‡6,056
Suomen Kuvalehti
[43895] ...... (Combined) ‡101,000

FRANCE
Gondrin
Crisis [43957]

HONDURAS
Tegucigalpa
Honduras This Week
[44803] 6,000

INDIA
Hyderabad
The Icfai Journal of Governance and
Public Policy [45153]

IRAN
Tehran
Iran Weekly Press Digest [45894]

JAPAN
Kobe
Kansai Time Out [46431]

JORDAN
Amman
Jordan Times [47160]

REPUBLIC OF KOREA
Seoul
The Choogan Chosun [47260]
The Wolgan Chosun
[47289] .... (Paid) ‡100,000

LEBANON
Beirut
Assayad [47393] 76,192

NEW ZEALAND
Auckland
Impact [48797]
New Zealand Listener
[48819] .. .. (Combined) 80,939

Wellington
New Zealand Population Review
[49029]

PAKISTAN
Lahore
The Friday Times [49385]

POLAND
Warsaw
Przekroj [49759] .. .. ‡68,815

SINGAPORE
Singapore City
Inter Se Print [50313]

SLOVENIA
Ljubljana
Mladina Magazine
[50340] .. .. (Paid) 80,000

SPAIN
Barcelona
El Ciervo [50666]

Madrid
Leviatan [50778]
Nueva Revista [50786]

Mataro
El Viejo Topo [50819]
Quimera [50820]

SWEDEN
Goteborg
Ord & Bild [50962] ...... (Paid) 3,000

Stockholm
Contra [51013] .. .. (Paid) 1,500
Ny Framtid [51029]

SWITZERLAND
Winterthur
European Vegetarian [51240]

UNITED KINGDOM
Blackburn
Edges Magazine [52383]

Canterbury
From the Window [52920]

Hull
Lobster [53627]

Kilmarnock
The Scottish Review [53709]

Liverpool
Open Government [53877]

London
CARF [54180]
Corporate Watch [54267]
The Ecologist
[54349] .. .. (Combined) 25,000
Irish Democrat
[54682] .. .. (Combined) 2,100
New Renaissance
[54997] .. .. (Controlled) 1,500
Parliamentary Brief
[55058] .. .. (Controlled) 2,500
Political Theology [55099]
Prospect
[55143] .. .. (Controlled) ★26,767
red pepper [55178]
Third Way Voice of the Radical
Centre
[55313] .. .. (Combined) 1,000

Manchester
New Start [55573]

Oxford
New Internationalist
[56117] 75,000

Tonbridge
Outrage [56756] .... (Paid) 12,500

Witney
Contemporary Issues in Law [56940]

VIETNAM
Hanoi
Nhan Dan
[57052] .. .. (Mon.-Fri.) 220,000
(Mon.) 130,000

SOCIETY

PEOPLE'S REPUBLIC OF CHINA
Hong Kong
Macau Tatler [43365] .. .. ‡30,140

Shanghai
Shanghai Weekly [43504]

DENMARK
Arhus
Nordic Irish Studies [43648]

INDIA
Hyderabad
The Icfai Journal of Urban Policy
[45169]

JAPAN
Tokyo
Hiragana Times [46833]
Japan Echo [46855]

MALAYSIA
Kuala Lumpur
Malaysia Society [47612]

NETHERLANDS
Amsterdam
Narrative Inquiry [48169]

PHILIPPINES
Makati City
Philippine Society
[49522] .. .. ‡45,000

SENEGAL
Dakar
Africa Development [50077]

SINGAPORE
Singapore
Singapore Tatler [50262] .. ... ‡13,000
Singapore Tatler Society
[50264] .. .. ‡12,200

Singapore City
Inter Se Print [50313]

SPAIN
Barcelona
El Jueves [50669] .... ‡74,441

TAIWAN
Taipei
Taiwan Tatler [51366] .. .. ‡20,000

THAILAND
Bangkok
Expat Society [51421]
Phuket Tatler [51429] .. .. ‡62,850
Thailand Society [51442] .... ‡36,200
Thailand Tatler [51443] .... ‡54,850

UNITED ARAB EMIRATES
Dubai
Emaar Properties Magazine
[51640] 18,000

UNITED KINGDOM
Abingdon
Pedagogy, Culture and Society
[52005]

Bacton
Herefordshire Life [52153]

Circulation: ★ = ABC; △ = BPA; ◆ = CAC; • = CCAB; ❑ = VAC; ⊕ = PO Statement; ‡ = Publisher's Report; Boldface figures = sworn; Light figures = estimated.

Cheltenham
Birmingham Life [52964]
Cheltenham Oracle [52965]
The Oracle Gloucester Life [52973]
Shropshire Life [52976]
Staffordshire County [52977]
Warwickshire Life [52979]
Worcestershire Life [52981]

Derby
Leicestershire Magazine
[53165] 10,000

Hale
Living Edge [53503]

London
North [55010]
Northwest [55012] .... ★34,200
red pepper [55178]
Rise [55203] .... ★40,000
Westside Magazine
[55399] .... ★47,000
Yours [55435] .... ★344,438

Oxford
Peace & Change [56144]

Plymouth
TAG Bulletin [56273]

Preston
Durham County Life [56299]
Lancashire Life [56303] ...... ★23,455

(ARCHERY)

UNITED KINGDOM
Chorley
The Glade [53022]

London
Journal of the Society of
Archer-Antiquaries [54821] 400

Newport
Archery UK [55688] 12,500

(AUTO RACING)
See also Automotive (Consumer)

FINLAND
Helsinki
F1 Racing [43829] .... .. (Paid) 18,031

Kuvalehdet
Vauhdin Maailma
[43900] .. .. (Combined) ‡33,558

FRANCE
Fontainebleau
Auto Retro [43952]

Saint Cloud
Echappement
[44101] .. .. (Paid) 58,653

IRELAND
Dublin
Auto Ireland [45947]

Sandyford
Bike Buyers Guide [46054]
Modified Motors [46056]

NETHERLANDS
The Hague
Autokampioen
[48608] .. .. (Controlled) 55,000

PORTUGAL
Cruz Quebrada-Dafundo
Automagazine
[49792] .. .. (Controlled) 19,912

SPAIN
Madrid
Car and Driver (Spain) [50732]

SWITZERLAND
Zurich
Historic Motor Racing News
[51265] .... (Combined) 1,000

UNITED KINGDOM
Bellshill
Fast and Modified [52306] 14,000

Fleet
The Brooklands Society Gazette
[53389] .... (Controlled) 1,300

Haywards Heath
Autosport Magazine [53547]

Orpington
Karting [55854] .... (Paid) 12,800

Peterborough
Custom Car Magazine [56255]

Teddington
Motor Sport [56734] .... ★35,066

(BASEBALL)

AUSTRALIA
Sydney
Inside Cricket [42516]

(BASKETBALL)

UNITED KINGDOM
Edinburgh
Britball [53257] 13,045

(BICYCLING)

AUSTRALIA
Canberra
Canberra Cyclist [41703] 2,000

Civic Square
Australian Cyclist [41753]

Sydney
Australian Mountain Bike
[42461] 20,000

GERMANY
Munich
Tour Das Rennrad-Magazin
[44584] .. .. (Controlled) 85,000

NETHERLANDS
Groningen
Wieler Revue
[48604] .. .. (Combined) 22,740

The Hague
Op Pad
[48623] .... (Controlled) 35,796

PORTUGAL
Cruz Quebrada-Dafundo
Bike Magazine
[49793] .. .. (Paid) 5,650

REPUBLIC OF SOUTH AFRICA
Cape Town
TOPbike [50415]

UNITED KINGDOM
Bristol
220 Triathlon [52733] 23,500

Croydon
Cycling Weekly [53124]
MBR - Mountain Bike Rider [53129]

Glasgow
Dig BMX Magazine [53413]

London
Dirt Mountain Bike Magazine [54326]
What Mountain Bike? [55401]

(BOATING AND YACHTING)
See also (Water Sports)

AUSTRALIA
Alexandria
Modern Boating [41543] ..... ★11,131

Brighton
Club Marine [41638] .. .. △78,976

Surry Hills
Australian Power Boat
[42417] .... ‡3,000
Australian Sailing [42418] ..... ★4,416
Australian Yachting
[42419] .... ‡2,000
Cruising Helmsman
[42424] .... ★7,771
Marine Business [42435] 4,149

PEOPLE'S REPUBLIC OF CHINA
Shanghai
Yachtstyle [43512] .... ‡90,000

FINLAND
Kuvalehdet
Kippari
[43885] .. .. (Combined) ‡16,745
Vene
[43901] .. .. (Combined) ‡31,702

FRANCE
Antibes
Mer & Bateaux [43915] 13,500

GERMANY
Bielefeld
YACHTING & STYLE
[44248] 60,000

Kiel
Meer & Yachten [44506] 15,025

IRELAND
Dun Laoghaire
Afloat [46007]

ITALY
Peschiera Borromeo
Il Gommone e la Nautica per Tutti
[46216] .... (Combined) 31,000

MALTA
Qormi
Boats and Yachting
[47738] .... (Combined) 5,000

NETHERLANDS
The Hague
Waterkampioen
[48629] .. .. (Controlled) 37,940

NEW ZEALAND
Auckland
Boating New Zealand
[48787] .... ★15,256

NORWAY
Nesbru
SEIL Magasinet
[49194] .... (Combined) 16,000

RUSSIA
Moscow
Boat International Russia
[49884] 15,000

SINGAPORE
Singapore
RSYC [50247] 2,200

UNITED KINGDOM
Bingham
Canoe Focus
[52325] .... (Paid) 24,000

Birmingham
Boat Mart [52332]

Cambridge
Boat and Yacht Buyer
[52794] 20,000

Chichester
Boat Trader [53005]

Colchester
Wayfarer News [53054]

Croydon
International Boat Industry [53126]

London
Journal [54694] 800
Motor Boat and Yachting [54957]
PrivatSea [55123] 8,000
Yachting Monthly [55429]
Yachting World [55430]

Lymington
Seahorse [55513]

Norwich
Anglia Afloat [55722]

Poole
Practical Boat Owner [56281]

Southampton
RYA Magazine [56577] 87,500

Ware
Sunseeker Magazine
[56845] 170,000

Wimbledon
Dockwalk [56927] 20,000

Windsor
Marine News [56932] 4,000

Wokingham
Canal Boat [56949]

(BOWLING)

UNITED KINGDOM
Glasgow
Nationwide Bowler [53432]

(BOXING AND WRESTLING)

UNITED KINGDOM
London
Boxing Monthly
[54102] .. .. (Paid) 25,000

(FOOTBALL)

AUSTRALIA
Sydney
FourFourTwo [42504] 100,000

Circulation: ★ = ABC; △ = BPA; ◆ = CAC; • = CCAB; ❑ = VAC; ⊕ = PO Statement; ‡ = Publisher's Report; Boldface figures = sworn; Light figures = estimated.

Inside Rugby [42517]

UNITED KINGDOM
Bath
Sporting Legends [52259]

London
Rugby World [55210]

(GENERAL SPORTS)

AUSTRALIA
Melbourne
Australian Triathlete
[42054] 15,000

Surry Hills
Australasian Sporting Shooter
[42409] .... ★13,542
Sporting Shooter [42439] .. . ‡13,542

Sydney
Inside Cricket [42516]
Inside Rugby [42517]

PEOPLE'S REPUBLIC OF CHINA
Beijing
Beijing Tatler [43172] .. .. ‡46,500

Hong Kong
The Hong Kong Racing Journal
[43344]

Shanghai
Shanghai Tatler [43502] .. .... ‡60,000

INDIA
Chennai
Chess Mate [45029] 3,000

INDONESIA
Jakarta
BOLA SportsLine [45793]

IRELAND
Dublin
Irish Mountain Log [45981] 9,500

Dundrum
FINS [46008] .... (Combined) 10,000

JAPAN
Tokyo
Gekkan Shonen Magazine [46829]
Shukan Shonen Magazine [47038]

REPUBLIC OF KOREA
Seoul
The Sports Chosun [47288]

NETHERLANDS
The Hague
The International Sports Law Journal
[48618]

PHILIPPINES
Quezon City
MetroActive [49604]

POLAND
Warsaw
Medicina Sportiva [49737]
Physical Education and Sport
[49747]

SINGAPORE
Singapore
Global Sources Sports & Leisure
[50159]

REPUBLIC OF SOUTH AFRICA
Arcadia
International Journal of Emotional
Psychology and Sport Ethics
[50346]

Pretoria
Freeskier [50591]

Stellenbosch
South African Journal for Research in
Sport, Physical Education and
Recreation [50635]

SWITZERLAND
Aarau
Fit for Life
[51054] .. .. (Combined) ‡25,000

Zurich
SPORTmagazin [51287] 25,000

UNITED KINGDOM
Abergavenny
Descent [51687]

Abingdon
Sports Biomechanics [52064]

Bath
Sporting Legends [52259]

Brighouse
Rugby League World
[52601] ...... (Controlled) ‡25,000
Rugby Leaguer & League Express
[52602] .. .. (Paid) 37,000

Brighton
Golf Punk [52609]

Bristol
220 Triathlon [52733] 23,500

Chichester
Goodwood Magazine
[53011] .. .. (Controlled) 20,000

Edinburgh
The Braille Sporting Record [53256]

Ipswich
Green Un (Ipswich)
[53657] .. .. (Controlled) 18,000

Leeds
Yorkshire Sport [53778]

Leicester
Golf Course Architecture [53803]

London
Derby Festival MAG [54319]
The Field [54451] .. .. ★30,428
Golf Monthly [54518] .... ★61,408
TenGoal [55299] 7,000

Olney
International Journal of Sport Management and Marketing [55833]

Peterborough
Skydive
[56262] .. .. (Combined) ‡6,000

Salisbury
Pro Shop Europe [56456]

Ware
Sunseeker Magazine
[56845] 170,000

(GOLF)

AUSTRALIA
Alexandria
Australian Golf Digest
[41535] .. .. ★36,000

Saint Leonards
Golf Australia [42333]

AUSTRIA
Vienna
Extra Golf
[42757] .. .. (Controlled) 55,000

MALAYSIA
Petaling Jaya
Golf Malaysia
[47698] .. .. (Paid) 25,000

SINGAPORE
Singapore
Golf [50161]

UNITED KINGDOM
Brighton
Golf Punk [52609]

Glasgow
Bunkered [53411]

Kent
SGB Golf [53681] .... ★4,500

London
Golf Monthly [54518] .... ★61,408

Salisbury
Pro Shop Europe [56456]

Sittingbourne
The PGA Professional
[56551] 7,557

(HORSES AND HORSE RACING)

AUSTRALIA
Nundah
Queensland Racing Magazine
[42223] ./........................... 4,850

BELGIUM
Ligny
Hippo News [42902] .. . (Paid) 7,000

Maleves-Sainte-Marie-Wastines
Infor Marechalerie/European Farriers
Journal/Der Huf
[42903] .. .. (Paid) 6,500

FINLAND
Kuvalehdet
Villivarsa
[43902] .. .. (Combined) ‡13,538

JAMAICA
Kingston
Track and Pools [46200]

JAPAN
Tokyo
Japan Racing Journal [46860]

NEW ZEALAND
Auckland
New Zealand Horse and Pony
[48815] .. .. ★12,792

SWITZERLAND
Pully
Le Cavalier Romand
[51222] .. .. (Controlled) 8,000

UNITED KINGDOM
Barnsley
Horse Health Magazine
[52181] 10,000

Dorset
Point to Point and Hunter Chase
Magazine
[53196] .. .. (Controlled) 23,000

Grayshott
Horse & Rider [53480] .. .. ‡42,184
Pony Magazine
[53481] .. .. (Combined) ‡34,132

London
Horse [54570]
Horse & Hound [54571]

Stowmarket
BDS Yearbook [56641]

Wetherby
Equestrian Trade News
[56911] 5,050

(HUNTING, FISHING, AND GAME MANAGEMENT)
See also Firearms

AUSTRALIA
Alexandria
Modern Fishing [41544] .. ... ★15,556

Surry Hills
Australasian Sporting Shooter
[42409] .... ★13,542
Bacon Busters [42421] .... ‡57,000
Sporting Shooter [42439] .. . ‡13,542

FINLAND
Kuvalehdet
Metsastys ja Kalastus
[43891] .. .. (Combined) ‡36,637

GERMANY
Ettlingen
Aquaristik
[44348] .. .. (Controlled) 26,364

Hamburg
AngelWoche
[44409] .. .. (Paid) 80,000

Munich
Die Pirsch
[44557] .. .. (Combined) 48,244
Unsere Jagd
[44585] .. .. (Combined) ‡42,781

REPUBLIC OF KOREA
Seoul
The Wolgan Naksi [47290]

NEW ZEALAND
Auckland
Fish and Game New Zealand
[48793] .... ★17,435
New Zealand Fishing News
[48810] .... ★26,780

SWITZERLAND
Einsiedeln
Schweizer Jager [51086]

UNITED KINGDOM
Aberfeldy
FlyFishing and FlyTying [51686]

Daventry
Advanced Carp Fishing
[53158] 16,000
Match Fishing Magazine
[53160] .. .. (Paid) 17,500

Harleston
CARPology [53510]

Circulation: ★ = ABC; △ = BPA; ◆ = CAC; • = CCAB; ❏ = VAC; ⊕ = PO Statement; ‡ = Publisher's Report; Boldface figures = sworn; Light figures = estimated.

London
Angler's Mail [53942] .. .. ★34,413
Angling Times [53944]
Flyfishers' Journal
[54472] .... (Paid) 650
Practical Fishkeeping [55113]
Sporting Gun [55263]

Shrewsbury
Hounds [56537]

(MARTIAL ARTS)

JAPAN
Sagamihara
Aikido Journal
[46643] .. .. (Paid) 12,000

REPUBLIC OF KOREA
Seoul
WTF Taekwondo [47292] 1,900

(OUTDOORS)

AUSTRALIA
Crows Nest
Burke's Backyard Magazine [41821]

Sydney
Australian Geographic Outdoor
[42453] 20,000
FourFourTwo [42504] 100,000

Warrandyte
The Australian Orienteer
[42686] 2,000

DENMARK
Brondby
O-Posten [43652]

FINLAND
Kuvalehdet
Era [43880] .... (Combined) ‡52,088

GERMANY
Nuremberg
Berge [44602] .... (Paid) 32,000

HUNGARY
Budapest
Tajfutas [44878]

INDIA
New Delhi
Indian Mountaineer
[45572] .. .. (Paid) 2,000

REPUBLIC OF KOREA
Seoul
The Wolgan San [47291]

NETHERLANDS
The Hague
KCK [48620] ... (Controlled) 158,581
Op Pad
[48623] .. .. (Controlled) 35,796

SWITZERLAND
Bern
Die Alpen
[51071] .. .. (Controlled) 83,000

UNITED KINGDOM
Abergavenny
Descent [51687]

Amersham
Retreats [52109] 14,500

Buxton
Speleology
[52779] .... (Combined) 1,200

Cambuskenneth
The Angry Corrie [52912]

Cornwall
Adventure Cornwall [53064]

Coventry
Camping and Caravanning
[53079] .... ★237,168

Dulverton
Active Exmoor [53209]

Glasgow
Dig BMX Magazine [53413]

Holt
Birding World
[53583] .. .. (Paid) 6,000

London
Cooler [54265]
Dirt Mountain Bike Magazine [54326]
Document Skateboard [54339]
Kingpin [54846]
Moto Magazine [54956]
Onboard [55031]
Sidewalk [55237]
Surf Europe [55280]
The Surfer's Path [55282]
Whitelines Snowboard Magazine
[55404]

Penrith
Journal of Adventure Education and
Outdoor Learning [56246]

Southend-on-Sea
Boards [56584]

(PHYSICAL FITNESS)

AUSTRALIA
Surry Hills
Nature & Health [42436] ..... ‡30,000

FINLAND
Helsinki
Kauneus ja Terveys
[43839] .. .. (Paid) 73,290

HUNGARY
Budapest
IWF Handbook [44839]
World Weightlifting [44883]

POLAND
Warsaw
Medicina Sportiva [49737]
Physical Education and Sport
[49747]

SAN MARINO
San Marino
European Weightlifter [50053]

SWEDEN
Hamneda
Bindu [50968] ... (Combined) 69,000

UNITED KINGDOM
Barnsley
Future Fitness [52180]
WorkOut Ireland [52185]
WorkOut UK [52186] 8,000

Essex
LighterLife [53340]

Hitchin
Health Club Management [53578]

London
YOGA Magazine [55432]

Penzance
Ultrafit
[56251] .. .. (Combined) 50,000

Ware
Champneys Magazine
[56840] 50,000

(RUNNING)

SPAIN
Madrid
Atletismo Espanol
[50730] .. .. (Paid) 15,000

SWEDEN
Solna
Skogssport [51000]

UNITED KINGDOM
Bristol
220 Triathlon [52733] 23,500

London
Distance Running
[54334] 400,000

(SKATING)

UNITED KINGDOM
London
Document Skateboard [54339]
Kingpin [54846]
Sidewalk [55237]

(SKIING)

AUSTRALIA
Sydney
Autralian & New Zealand Skiing
[42470] 15,000

NEW ZEALAND
Gisborne
New Zealand Snowboarder [48898]

NORWAY
Baerum
SkiSport [49189] 10,000

REPUBLIC OF SOUTH AFRICA
Pretoria
Freeskier [50591]

UNITED KINGDOM
Cambridge
Jet Skier & PW Magazine [52840]

Peterborough
Fall-Line Skiing [56257]

(SOCCER)

FINLAND
Helsinki
Futari [43831] .... (Paid) 75,478

POLAND
Warsaw
Trener [49768] 2,000

UNITED KINGDOM
Leeds
Leeds, Leeds, Leeds
[53772] .. .. (Paid) 60,000

London
African Soccer Magazine [53926]
World Soccer [55423]

(TRIATHLONS AND BIATHLONS)

AUSTRALIA
Melbourne
Australian Triathlete
[42054] 15,000

(RACQUET SPORTS)

AUSTRALIA
Melbourne
Australian Tennis Magazine [42053]

DENMARK
Brondby
Badminton [43651] 600

UNITED KINGDOM
London
ITF World [54686] 7,000

Middlesex
The Squash Player [55620]

Milton Keynes
Badminton [55630] 8,000

(WATER SPORTS)
See also (Boating and Yachting)

AUSTRALIA
Surry Hills
Australian Power Boat
[42417] .... ‡3,000
Australian Sailing [42418] ..... ★4,416
Australian Yachting
[42419] .... ‡2,000
Cruising Helmsman
[42424] .... ★7,771

Sydney
Australian & NZ Snowboarding
[42463] 20,000

BELGIUM
Gent
Varen [42884] ... (Combined) 17,500

PEOPLE'S REPUBLIC OF CHINA
Shanghai
Yachtstyle [43512] .... ‡90,000

FRANCE
Antibes
Mer & Bateaux [43915] 13,500

GERMANY
Kiel
Meer & Yachten [44506] 15,025

IRELAND
Dun Laoghaire
Afloat [46007]

Dundrum
FINS [46008] .... (Combined) 10,000

NETHERLANDS
The Hague
Op Pad
[48623] .. .. (Controlled) 35,796

Circulation: ★ = ABC; △ = BPA; ◆ = CAC; • = CCAB; ❏ = VAC; ⊕ = PO Statement; ‡ = Publisher's Report; Boldface figures = sworn; Light figures = estimated.

SINGAPORE
Singapore
Asian Diver [50108]

REPUBLIC OF SOUTH AFRICA
Durban
Saltwater GIRL SURF [50469]
Zigzag [50472] .. .. ★15,252

UNITED KINGDOM
Bingham
Canoe Focus
  [52325] .. .. (Paid) 24,000
Bristol
220 Triathlon [52733] 23,500
Cambridge
Jet Skier & PW Magazine [52840]
London
Motor Boat and Yachting [54957]
Surf Europe [55280]
The Surfer's Path [55282]
Lymington
Seahorse [55513]
Newquay
Carve [55693]
Walsall
Swim & Save [56835]
Wimbledon
Dockwalk [56927] 20,000

TRAVEL AND TOURISM

AUSTRALIA
East Sydney
Fellow Traveller
  [41850] .. .. (Combined) 30,000
Sydney
Australian Gourmet Traveller
  [42454] .. .. ★75,107
Backpacker Essentials
  [42471] .... (Paid) 104,000
COAST [42492] .... ‡30,000

PEOPLE'S REPUBLIC OF CHINA
Shanghai
Travelling Scope [43508]
World Traveller [43511]

FINLAND
Helsinki
Apu [43817] .. . (Combined) 254,762

GERMANY
Bielefeld
HIDEAWAYS [44246] 60,000
Bonn
Fairkehr [44259] .. .. ‡65,000
Hamburg
Merian [44420] .. .. (Paid) ◆88,953
Munich
Business Traveller
  [44552] .... (Paid) 260,000

IRELAND
Dublin
Ireland at Your Leisure
  [45969] .. .. ★41,000
Dundrum
Visitor [46011] .. .. ★200,000

ITALY
Palermo
Sikania [46208] .... (Paid) 10,000

NEW ZEALAND
Auckland
KiaOra [48801] 45,000

PANAMA
Panama City
Focus on Panama
  [49401] .... (Non-paid) 60,000

PHILIPPINES
Cebu City
Zee Lifestyle [49465] 25,000
Pasig City
Mabuhay [49572]

POLAND
Warsaw
Warsaw Insider [49775] 20,000

RUSSIA
Moscow
Aeroflot Premium [49868] 25,000
Inflight Review [49918] 70,000

SINGAPORE
Singapore
Simply Her [50252] 50,000
Singapore Visitor [50266]

SPAIN
Barcelona
Viajes National Geographic
  [50706] .. .. ‡63,013

SWITZERLAND
Zurich
Swiss News [51289] 12,000

THAILAND
Bangkok
Thai Spas [51440]

UNITED ARAB EMIRATES
Dubai
Business Traveller Middle East
  [51633] .. .. △26,437
Dubai Voyager [51639] ...... △29,350
Open Skies [51651] .... △73,178

UNITED KINGDOM
Barnsley
Destination UK [52179] 11,902
Bath
Italia! [52246]
Bristol
DDC Countryfile [52641] ...... ★33,839
Cheltenham
Realm [52975] .... ★48,874
Glasgow
Scottish Hosteller [53448]
London
Fah Thai [54438]
The London Picture Book
  [54889] .. .. (Combined) 125,000
Olive [55030]
PrivatAir [55120] 7,000
Quintessentially [55166] 25,000
The Surfer's Path [55282]
Milton Keynes
Group Leisure [55637]
Norwich
Scotland Magazine [55741]
Ware
Champneys Magazine
  [56840] 50,000

Sunseeker Magazine
  [56845] 170,000

YOUTHS' INTERESTS
See also Children's Interests; Education; Comics and Comic Technique; Parenting

AUSTRALIA
Eveleigh
TV Hits [41863]
Sydney
Studio Bambini [42582] 45,000

BELGIUM
Brussels
Jeunes en Mouvement
  [42861] .. .. ‡25,000
Youth Opinion [42876] 13,000

PEOPLE'S REPUBLIC OF CHINA
Shanghai
Comic King [43471]

DENMARK
Alborg
Tjeck Magazine
  [43644] .. .. (Controlled) 160,000

FINLAND
Helsinki
Demi [43824] .... (Paid) 49,951
Kuvalehdet
Koululainen
  [43888] .. .. (Combined) ‡44,634
Suosikki [43896] .... ‡45,939

GERMANY
Munich
POPCORN [44578] .... ‡188,349
STARFLASH [44582] .. .. ‡69,073
YAM! [44588] .... ‡106,915
Witten
TeensMag
  [44714] .. .. (Combined) 20,000

INDIA
Chennai
Yuva Bharati [45062] ... (Paid) 6,400
Dharamsala
Rangzen [45111]
New Delhi
Youth Hosteller [45671] 45,000

JAPAN
Tokyo
Afternoon [46729]
Afternoon Season Zokan [46730]
Bessatsu Friend [46761]
Dessert [46801]
Gekkan Shonen Magazine [46829]
Juliet [46951]
Kiss [46954]
Magazine Special [46962]
Magazine Z [46963]
Nakayoshi [46974]
Weekly Shonen Sunday [47056]
Young Magazine [47057]
Young Magazine Uppers [47058]

REPUBLIC OF KOREA
Seoul
The Sonyon Chosun [47287]

LATVIA
Riga
Ilustreta Junioriem [47366]

MALAYSIA
Kuala Lumpur
Mangga [47624] .. .. ★121,465

NEW ZEALAND
Wellington
The Adventure [48998]

PAKISTAN
Karachi
US [49378]
Young World [49380]

PHILIPPINES
Mandaluyong City
Candy Magazine [49532] 40,000
High School Musical
  [49538] 20,000
Seventeen Philippines
  [49540] 30,000
Quezon City
CHALK [49588]
Pink [49615]

RUSSIA
Moscow
Kollektsia Idei [49933] .... ‡24,800
Malenkaya Diana [49939] ... ‡72,350

REPUBLIC OF SOUTH AFRICA
Durban
blunt [50467] .... ★13,207
Saltwater GIRL [50468] ...... ★32,360
Sandton
Mshana [50627]

SWEDEN
Stockholm
Ny Framtid [51029]

SWITZERLAND
Fribourg
Universitas Friburgensis
  [51087] 9,500

THAILAND
Bangkok
Bangkok Post Student Weekly
  [51414] 110,000

UKRAINE
Kiev
Young Lady [51615] .. .. ‡65,000

UNITED ARAB EMIRATES
Dubai
Young Times [51658]

UNITED KINGDOM
Bangor
IAW! [52171] ...... (Combined) 2,700
Barnsley
Future Fitness [52180]
Bristol
Imagine Magazine [52675] 7,500
Dundee
Animals and You
  [53213] .. .. (Paid) 60,000
Glasgow
First Link 4 Parents
  [53420] .. .. (Free) 18,000

Circulation: ★ = ABC; △ = BPA; ◆ = CAC; • = CCAB; ❑ = VAC; ⊕ = PO Statement; ‡ = Publisher's Report; Boldface figures = sworn; Light figures = estimated.

Magazines

Harleston
CARPology [53510]

Hemel Hempstead
Boys' Brigade Gazette
  [53555] .. .. (Paid) 22,000

Leicester
The Edge [53796]
Mathematical Pie [53814]
Symmetry Plus [53830]
Young People Now
  [53834] .. .. (Paid) 4,000

London
Award World [53994] 22,000
Big Cheese
  [54015] .. .. (Paid) 16,000
Bob the Builder [54095]
Codebreakers [54235] ...... ★109,000
Criss Cross [54287] .. .. ★63,000
Daisy [54308] .. .. ★43,162

Disney Fairies [54332]
Disney and Me [54333] ...... ★49,002
Doctor Who Adventures [54338]
Dora Dress Up and Go [54340]
Dora the Explorer [54341]
ELLEgirl [54361]
Exposure
  [54436] .... (Non-paid) 4,500
Fireman Sam [54461]
Girl Talk [54507] .... ★1,161,019
Girl Talk Extra [54508]
GO Girl [54515] .. .. ★43,163
Learn with Bob the Builder [54860]
Live & Kicking [54878]
Noddy [55007] .. .. ★39,229
Power Rangers [55112] ...... ★56,047
Robin Hood Adventures [55207]
Sabrina's Secrets [55213]
Shrek's Quests [55236]
Su-doku [55274]

Take a Break's Su-doku
  [55287] .. .. ★100,000
Thomas & Friends
  [55314] .. .. ★50,002
Totally Tracy Beaker [55330]
W.I.T.C.H. [55409]
Youthwork [55436] .... ‡2,500

Manchester
Emotional and Behavioral Difficulties
  [55555]

Redhill
Junior Puzzles [56354]
Puzzler Quiz Kids [56375]

Ringwood
Doctor Who Battles in Time [56395]
Felicity Wishes [56396]
007 Spy Cards [56397]

Shrewsbury
Bag-o-Fun [56526] 80,000

Fun to Learn Barney
  [56530] 50,000
Fun to Learn Best of Barney
  [56531] 30,000
Fun to Learn Discovery
  [56532] 40,000
Fun to Learn Favourites
  [56533] .. .. ★45,542
Fun to Learn Friends
  [56534] .. .. ★76,846
Fun to Learn Letterland
  [56535] 40,000
Fun to Learn Peppa Pig
  [56536] 82,498
My Little Pony [56538] 50,000

Stevenage
Flipside Magazine [56604]

Teddington
Key Note Market Assessment,
  Tweenagers [56733]

Circulation: ★ = ABC; △ = BPA; ◆ = CAC; • = CCAB; ❑ = VAC; ⊕ = PO Statement; ‡ = Publisher's Report; Boldface figures = sworn; Light figures = estimated.

Index entries are arranged geographically, first by country and then by city. Within cities in this index, citations appear alphabetically by publication title. Citations in the index include publication title, entry number (given in parentheses immediately following the titles), street address, postal code (in parentheses), phone number, and circulation figures.

ALGERIA
Algiers
El Moudjahid **[41460]**
20 rue de la Liberte
  Phone: 213 2 1737081
Liberte **[41461]**
37 rue Larbi Ben M'hidi
  Phone: 213 2 1736480

ARGENTINA
Buenos Aires
Buenos Aires Herald **[41470]**
San Juan 141 (1063)
  Phone: 54 11 43491524

AUSTRALIA
Sydney
The Coffs Coast Advocate
  [42494] .. .. (Paid) ‡3,245
                        (Free) ‡30,666
100 William St., Level 4 (2011)
  Phone: 61 2 93334999
The Daily Examiner
  [42499] .... (Mon.-Sat.) ★5,670
                        (Sat.) ★6,298
100 William St., Level 4 (2011)
  Phone: 61 2 93334999
The Sydney Morning Herald **[42586]**
GPO 506 (2001)
  Phone: 61 2 92822833

Tamworth
Northern Daily Leader
  [42612] .. .. (Paid) 9,214
92 Brisbane St.
PO Box 525 (2340)

Wagga Wagga
Daily Advertiser **[42668]**
48 Trl. St. (2650)

West Footscray
Bharat Times **[42694]**
PO Box 6100 (3012)
  Phone: 61 3 96896406

AZERBAIJAN
Baku
The Azeri Times **[42779]** 8000
44 J. Jabbarly Str.
  Caspian Plz. (AZ-1065)
  Phone: 994 12 4367750

BAHAMAS
Nassau
The Nassau Guardian **[42784]**
PO Box N-3011
  Phone: (242)302-2300

BAHRAIN
Manama
Gulf Daily News **[42789]**
PO Box 5300
  Phone: 973 620222

BANGLADESH
Dhaka
The Bangladesh Today **[42807]**
Concord Royal Ct., 4th Fl.
  Plot No. 275(G), Rd. No. 27 (1209)
  Phone: 880 2 9118807
The Daily Star **[42808]** 30,000
19 Karwan Bazar (1215)
  Phone: 880 281 24944
The Independent (Bangladesh)
  [42811]
32 Kazi Nazrul Islam Ave.
  Karwan Bazar (1215)
  Phone: 880 291 29938
News from Bangladesh **[42814]**
House No. 16, Rd. 127
  Gulshan (1212)
  Phone: 880 2 8827413

BARBADOS
Bridgetown
Barbados Advocate **[42827]**
PO Box 230
  Fontabelle
  Phone: 246467-2000

BELARUS
Minsk
Vecherny Minskt
  [42833] .. .. (Combined) 100,000
44 Skorina Ave. (220805)
  Phone: 375 172 335044

BERMUDA
Hamilton
The Royal Gazette
  [42922] 16,000
PO Box HM1025
  Phone: (441)295-5881

CAYMAN ISLANDS
Grand Cayman
The Caymanian Compass
  [43130] .. .. (Controlled) 10,500
The Compass Ctr.
  Shedden Rd.
  PO Box 1365 GT
  Phone: (345)949-5111

CZECH REPUBLIC
Prague
The Prague Post
  [43636] .. .. (Combined) 50,134

Stepanska 20 (CZ-110 00)
  Phone: 420 2 96334400

DOMINICA
Roseau
The Chronicle (Dominica)
  [43739] 3,000
PO Box 1764
  Phone: (767)448-7887

FINLAND
Helsinki
Helsingin Sanomat
  [43832] .. .. (Mon.-Sat.) ‡430,785
                        (Sun.) ‡482,767
Ludviginkatu 6-8
  PO Box 1229 (FIN-00101)
  Phone: 358 105 1999

Jyvaskyla
Keskisuomalainen **[43870]** ... 77,865
Aholaidantie 3
  PO Box 159 (FIN-40101)
  Phone: 35 814 622000

GERMANY
Stuttgart
Sonntag Aktuell
  [44680] .... (Paid) 506,884
Postfach 10 44 62 (70039)
  Phone: 49 7205 3501

INDIA
Ahmedabad
Divya Bhaskar **[44908]**
280, Sarkhej-Gandhinagar Hwy.
  Near YMCA Club (380 015)
  Phone: 91 793 9888850
Sandesh **[44909]**
Sandesh Bhavan, Lad Society Rd.,
  Vastrapur (380 054)
  Phone: 91 794 0004000

Bangalore
Sanjevani **[44987]**
11/2, Queens Rd. (560 052)

Belgaum
Tarun Bharat **[44997]**
3524, Narvekar Galli (590 002)
  Phone: 91 831 2404333

Bhatkal
Sahil Daily **[45003]**
SahilOnline, First Fl., Jamaat Com-
  plex
  Next to KSRTC Bus Stand
  (581 320)
  Phone: 91 838 5320768

Bhopal
Dainik Bhaskar **[45006]**
6, Dwarka Sadan, Press Complex
  (462 011)
  Phone: 91 755 3988884

Bhubaneswar
Dharitri **[45009]**
B - 26, Industrial Estate
  PO Box 144 (751 010)
  Phone: 91 674 2580348
Sambad **[45013]**
B-27, Industrial Estate, Rasulgarh
  (751 010)
  Phone: 91 674 2585351
Pragativadi **[45014]** .... ★200,921
178/B, Mancheswar Industrial Estate
  (751 010)
  Phone: 91 674 2588297

Chennai
Daily Thanthi **[45030]** .. .. ★113,404
86, E.V.K. Sampath Rd.
  Vepary (600 007)
  Phone: 91 442 6618661
Indiavarta **[45039]**
Express Gardens, II Main Rd.
  Ambatur Industrial Estate
  (600 058)
  Phone: 91 442 3457655

Gurgaon
The Times of India **[45127]**
I World Tower
  DLF City Phas V (Opp DLF Golf
  Course) (122 002)

Hyderabad
The Siasat Daily **[45182]**
Jawaharlal Nehru Rd. (500 001)
  Phone: 91 402 4744180

Indore
Naidunia **[45188]**
60/1, Babu Labhchand Chhajlani
  Marg (452 009)
  Phone: 91 731 2763111-14

Kochi
Deshabhimani **[45249]**
Kerala State Committee (695 001)
  Phone: 91 484 2530739
Madhyamam **[45251]**
PO Box 2014, Pulleppady (682 018)

Kolhapur
Pudhari **[45256]**
Pudhari Bhavan, 2318 C, Bhausingji
  Rd. (416 002)
  Phone: 91 231 2543111

Kolkata
Ganashtaki **[45266]**
74A Acharya Jagadish Chandra Bose
  Rd. (700 016)

Circulation: ★ = ABC; △ = BPA; ◆ = CAC; • = CCAB; ❑ = VAC; ⊕ = PO Statement; ‡ = Publisher's Report; Boldface figures = sworn; Light figures = estimated.

Kottayam
Deepika [45314]
PO Box 7 (686 001)
Phone: 91 481 2566706
Malayala Manorama
[45315] .... ‡1,700,192
Malayala Manorama
PO Box 26 (686 001)
Phone: 91 481 2563646

Madurai
Dinamalar [45336]
T.V.R. House
Dinamalar Ave. (625 016)
Phone: 91 452 2380903

Mysore
Star of Mysore [45456]
15-C, Industrial 'A' Layout
Academy Newspapers Pvt. Ltd.
(570 015)
Phone: 91 821 2496520
Samachar [45459]
Samachar Bldg. No. 49, 1st Fl.
Devaraj Urs Rd. (570 001)
Phone: 91 821 2423574

Palakkad
Mathrubhumi [45680]
Dr. A R Menon Rd.
K.P.Kesavamenon Rd. (678 001)
Phone: 91 491 2504446

Pune
Sakal [45700]
595, Budhwar Peth (411 002)
Phone: 91 20 24405500

Ranchi
Ranchi Express
[45712] .... (Controlled) 45,000
55 Baralal St. (834 001)
Phone: 91 651 2206320

INDONESIA
Jakarta
The Jakarta Post [45801] 30,552
Jl. Palmerah Selatan 15 (10270)
Phone: 62 215 300476

IRAN
Tehran
Iran News [45893]
PO Box 15875-8551
Phone: 98 21 44253450
Tehran Times [45914]
No. 18 Bimeh Ln.
Nejatollahi St.
PO Box 14155-4843
Phone: 98 21 88800295

IRELAND
Cork
Irish Examiner [45937]
City Quarter
Lapps Quay
Phone: 353 214 72722

Dublin
Irish Times [45988] 116,061
24-28 Tara St. (2)
Phone: 353 1 6758000

ISRAEL
Tel Aviv
Ha'aretz
[46101] .... (Combined) 75,000
(Free) 95,000
21 Schocken St. (IL-61001)
Phone: 972 3 5121205

JAMAICA
Kingston
The Gleaner [46285]

7 N St.
PO Box 40
Phone: (876)922-3400
The Jamaica Observer [46287]
40-42 1/2 Beechwood Ave. (5)
Phone: (809)920-8136

JAPAN
Tokyo
Daily Yomiuri [46799] 75,540
1-7-1 Otemachi
Chiyoda-Ku (100-8055)
Kyodo News [46956]
Shiodome Media Tower 15th Fl.
1-7-1 Higashi-Shimbashi
Minato-ku (105-7201)

JORDAN
Amman
Jordan Times [47160]
Queen Rania Al Abdullah St.
PO Box 6710
Phone: 962 656 00800

KENYA
Nairobi
Daily Nation (Kenya)
[47176] .... (Paid) 205,000
Nation Center, Kimathi St.
PO Box 49010

KIRGIZSTAN
Bishkek
The Times of Central Asia [47202]
175A, Abdrahmanova St., Office 304-
305 (720000)
Phone: 996 312 661737

REPUBLIC OF KOREA
Seoul
Chosen Ilbo
[47261] ... (Combined) ‡4,245,000
62-4 Taepyeongro 1-ga
Jung-gu (100-101)
Phone: 82 272 45114
Korea Times [47280] 150,000
43, Chungmuro 3-ga
Chung-ku (100-013)
Phone: 82 2 7242359

LATVIA
Riga
Diena (Latvian Edition)
[47365] .... (Controlled) 65,000
Mukusalas Str. 15 (LV-1004)
Phone: 371 706 3150

LEBANON
Beirut
Al Anwar
[47386] .... (Combined) 47,899
Saeed Frayha St.
PO Box 11-1038
Phone: 961 5 457261
The Daily Star (Lebanon)
[47394] .... (Combined) 10,550
Marine Twr., 6th Fl.
Rue de La Ste. Famille
Gemaizeh, Achrafieh
Phone: 961 1 587277

MALAYSIA
Kota Kinabalu
Daily Express [47590]
PO Box 10139 (88801)
Phone: 60 88238711

Overseas Chinese Daily [47592]
PO Box 10139 (88801)
Phone: 60 88238711
Kuala Lumpur
Kosmo! [47610]
46 M, Jalan Lima Off
Jalan Chan Sow Lin (55200)
Phone: 60 3 92217055

MALDIVES
Male
Haveeru Daily [47725]
PO Box 20103
Ameenee Magu
Phone: 96 032 5671

MALTA
Saint Julians
The Malta Independent [47740]
Standard House
Birkirkara Hill (STJ 1149)
Phone: 356 21345888

Valletta
Sunday Times (Malta)
[47747] .. .. (Combined) 40,000
341 St. Paul St. (VLT 1211)
Phone: 356 25594100

MEXICO
Guadalajara
El Informador [47774]
Independencia No. 300
Col. Centro C.P. (44100)
Phone: 52 333 6146340

Mexico City
El Universal
[47784] .. .. (Mon.-Fri.) 350,000
Bucareli 8
Phone: 52 570 91313

NAMIBIA
Windhoek
The Namibian Newspaper [47824]
42 John Meinert St.
PO Box 20783
Phone: 264 612 79660

NEPAL
Kathmandu
The Himalayan Times [47837]
APCA House
Baidya Khana Rd.
Anam Nagar
PO Box 11651
Phone: 977 1 4771489
Kathmandu Post [47840]
PO Box 876
Durbar Marg
Phone: 977 4 445920

NEW ZEALAND
Dunedin
Otago Daily Times
[48892] .. .. (Combined) 45,000
52 Stuart St.
PO Box 517
Phone: 64 3 4774760

Greymouth
Greymouth Star [48904]
5-9 Werita St.
PO Box 3
Phone: 64 3 7687121

Hastings
Hawke's Bay Today
[48915] .... (Paid) ‡36,665

113 Karamu Rd.
PO Box 180
Phone: 64 6 8730800

Hokitika
West Coast Times [48917]
18 Weld St.
PO Box 122
Phone: 64 3 7558422

Masterton
Wairarapa Times-Age
[48937] 7,302
Cor. Chapel & Perry St.
PO Box 445
Phone: 64 637 89999

Wanganui
Wanganui Chronicle
[48996] .. .. (Combined) ‡15,255
59 Taupo Quay
PO Box 433
Phone: 64 646 3490710

NIGERIA
Oshodi
Daily Champion [49159]
PO Box 2276
Phone: 234 145 25807

NORWAY
Baerum
The Norway Post [49188]
Holmaveien 21
PO Box 25
1306 Baerum (N-1306)
Phone: 47 671 76875

OMAN
Muscat
Oman Daily Observer [49222]
PO Box 974 (113)
Oman Tribune [49224]
PO Box 463 (113)
Phone: 968 24491919
Times of Oman [49225] 20,000
PO Box 770
Ruwi (112)
Phone: 968 24811953

PAKISTAN
Islamabad
PakTribune [49310]
House 6, Khyaban-e-Iqbal, Margalla
Rd.
F-7/3
Phone: 92 51 111888666

Karachi
Daily Jang [49345]
Printing House
I.I. Chundrigar Rd. (74200)
Phone: 92 212 637111
Dawn [49346] 138,000
Haroon House
Dr. Ziauddin Ahmed Rd. (74200)
Phone: 92 111 444777
The News International
[49365] 140,000
Printing House
I.I. Chundrigar Rd. (74200)
Phone: 92 212 637111
Star [49377]
Haroon House
Dr. Ziauddin Ahmed Rd. (74200)
Phone: 92 111 444777

Lahore
Daily Times [49384]
41-N, Industrial Area
Gulberg II
Phone: 92 42 5878614

Peshawar
The Frontier Post [49392]

Circulation: ★ = ABC; △ = BPA; ◆ = CAC; • = CCAB; ❑ = VAC; ⊕ = PO Statement; ‡ = Publisher's Report; Boldface figures = sworn; Light figures = estimated.

27 Abdara Rd.
PO Box 1161
University Town
Phone: 92 300 5182252

PAPUA NEW GUINEA
Port Moresby
Post-Courier
[49403] .. .. (Combined) 28,835
PO Box 85
Lawes Rd.
Phone: 675 3091000

PHILIPPINES
Dipolog City
The Daily Dipolognon [49487]
Reyes Bldg.
Gonzales St.
Phone: 63 62 2122673

Intramuros
Manila Bulletin [49501]
Muralla Cor. Recoletos Sts.
PO Box 769. (1002)
Tempo [49502]
Muralla Cor. Recoletos Sts.
PO Box 769. (1002)

Makati City
Philippine Daily Inquirer [49519]
Chino Roces Ave.
Cor. Yague & Mascardo Sts.
PO Box 2353 (1263)
Phone: 63 2 8978808

Manila
Daily Tribune [49549]
The Penthouse Stes.
GLC Bldg.
T.M. Kalaw cor. A. Mabini Sts.
Ermita
Phone: 63 2 5215511
Malaya [49552]
Leyland Bldg.
Railroad St.
Port Area (1018)
Phone: 63 2 5271841
Philippine Headline News Online
[49554]
1991 M.H. del Pilar
Malate
Phone: 63 2 5232040

Zamboanga City
Daily Zamboanga Times [49647]
Mayor Jaldon St.
Canelar

PORTUGAL
Aveiro
Diario de Aveiro
[49785] .... (Controlled) 5,050
Av. De. Lourenco Peixinho 15-1-G
(P-3800)
Phone: 351 234 234000031

Coimbra
Diario de Coimbra
[49790] .... (Controlled) 10,200
Rua Adriano Lucas
Apartado 542 (P-3020)
Phone: 351 239499999

Leira
Diario de Leiria
[49799] .... (Controlled) 2,010
Edificio Mariuga
Rua Sao Franciso 7-4-Esq. (P-
2400)
Phone: 351 244000031

Viseu
Diario Regional Viseu
[49813] .... (Controlled) 1,025
Rua Alexandre Herculaus 198-1-Esq.
(P-3510)
Phone: 351 232000030

QATAR
Doha
The Gulf Times [49821] 15,000
PO Box 533
Phone: 974 43 50478

ROMANIA
Bucharest
Ziua [49846] .... (Paid) 80,000
Strada Ion Campineanu Numarul 4
Sect. 1
Phone: 40 315 9111

RUSSIA
Saint Petersburg
The St. Petersburg Times
[50028] 20,000
4 St. Isaac's Sq. (190000)
Phone: 7 812 3256080

Vladivostok
Vladivostok News [50041]
13 Narodny Prospect (690014)
Phone: 7 423 2415590

SAUDI ARABIA
Jeddah
Saudi Gazette
[50057] .. .. (Paid) 60,000
PO Box 5034 (21422)
Phone: 966 2 6722775

Riyadh
Arab News [50060] 52
PO Box 478 (11411)
Phone: 966 1 4419933

SEYCHELLES
Victoria
Seychelles Nation [50095]
Long Pier Rd.
PO Box 800
Phone: 248 225 775

SINGAPORE
Singapore
Berita Harian
[50112] .. .. (Mon.-Fri.) 62,000
News Ctr.
1000 Toa Payoh N (318994)
Phone: 65 63196319
Lianhe Wanbao
[50214] .. .. (Mon.-Fri.) 107,200
News Ctr.
1000 Toa Payoh N (318994)
Phone: 65 63196319
Lianhe Zaobao
[50215] .. .. (Mon.-Fri.) 176,600
News Ctr.
1000 Toa Payoh N (318994)
Phone: 65 63196319
Tamil Murasu [50276] 14,400
News Ctr.
1000 Toa Payoh N (318994)
Phone: 65 63196319

REPUBLIC OF SOUTH AFRICA
Cape Town
Volksblad [50426] 28,062
Nasper Ctr.
Heerengracht 40
PO Box 2271 (8000)
Phone: 27 21 4062489

Johannesburg
Beeld [50527] 101,972
Kingsweg 69
Auckland Pk. (2006)

Kaapstad
Die Burger [50541] 104,808
Posbus 692 (8000)

SRI LANKA
Colombo
Daily Mirror [50852] 30,000
8 Hunupitiya Cross Rd.
PO Box 1136 (2)
Phone: 94 11 2436998
Daily News [50853] .... ‡88,000
35 D.R. Wijewardene Mawatha
PO Box 1217 (10)
Phone: 94 112 429231

SWITZERLAND
Geneva
Le Temps [51153] .... ‡45,506
3, Pl. Cornavin
Case postale 2570 (CH-1211)
Phone: 41 22 7995858
Tribune de Geneve
[51162] .. .. ‡56,333
11, rue des Rois
Case postale 5115 (CH-1211)
Phone: 41 22 3224000

Lausanne
Le Matin [51194] .... ‡58,849
Av. de la Gare 33 (CH-1001)
Phone: 41 21 3494545
Le Matin [51195] .... ‡230,873
Av. de la Gare 33 (CH-1001)
Phone: 41 21 3494545
24 Heures [51202] .... ‡85,813
Av. de la Gare 33 (CH-1001)
Phone: 41 21 3494545

SYRIAN ARAB REPUBLIC
Damascus
Syria Times [51300]
PO Box 5452
Phone: 963 11 2131100

TAIWAN
Taipei
The China Post
[51334] .... (Paid) 180,000
250,000
8 Fu Shun St. (104)
Phone: 886 2 25969971
Digitimes [51337] .... ‡65,000
12F, 133, Section 4, Mingsheng E
Rd.
Songshan District (105)
Phone: 886 2 87128866
Taipei Times [51362] 285,130
14th Fl., No. 399
Ruiguang Rd. (11492)
Phone: 886 226 561000
Taiwan News [51365]
9th Fl., 290 Jhongsiao E Rd., Sec. 4
(10600)
Phone: 886 22 3491500

TRINIDAD AND TOBAGO
Port of Spain
The Trinidad Guardian
[51467] .. .. (Combined) 45,000
22-24 St. Vincent St.
PO Box 122
Phone: (809)623-8871
Trinidad & Tobago Express [51468]
Express House
35 Independence Sq.
Phone: (868)623-1711

UGANDA
Kampala
The Monitor
[51587] .. .. (Combined) 25,000

PO Box 12141
Phone: 256 412 32367

UNITED KINGDOM
Bradford
Telegraph & Argus [52551]
Hall Ings (BD1 1JR)
Phone: 44 1274 729511

Brighton
The Argus Lite [52605]
Crowhurst Rd.
Hollingbury (BN1 8AR)
Phone: 44 1273 544544

Bristol
Expo Times [52668]
45 Constable Rd. (BS7 9YF)
Phone: 44 117 9081303

Burton-on-Trent
Burton Mail
[52770] .... (Paid) ‡15,665
65-68 High St. (DE14 1LE)

Glasgow
Sunday Herald [53453] 56,374
200 Renfield St. (G2 3QB)
Phone: 44 14 13027300

Hartlepool
Hartlepool Mail [53533]
New Clarence House
Wesley Sq. (TS24 8BX)
Phone: 44 1429 239333
Peterlee Mail [53534]
New Clarence House
Wesley Sq. (TS24 8BX)
Phone: 44 1429 239333

Leeds
Yorkshire Post [53777] 225,000
Wellington St.
PO Box 168 (LS1 1RF)
Phone: 44 11 32432701

London
Asharq Al-Awsat
[53970] .. .. (Mon.-Fri.) ★236,988
Arab Press House
184 High Holborn (WC1V 7AP)
Phone: 44 207 831818

Newport
South Wales Argus [55690]
Cardiff Rd.
Maesglas (NP20 3QN)
Phone: 44 1633 810000

Northampton
Northampton Chronicle & Echo
[55713]
Upper Mounts (NN1 3HR)
Phone: 44 1604 467000

Plymouth
Western Morning News [56276]
17 Brest Rd.
Derriford Business Pk. (PL6 5AA)
Phone: 44 17 52765500

South Shields
Shields Gazette [56566]
Chapter Row (NE33 1BL)
Phone: 44 191 4274800

Torquay
Herald Express (Torquay)
[56757] .... (Paid) ★25,971
Harmsworth House
Barton Hill Rd. (TQ2 8JN)
Phone: 44 1803 676000

Wapping
The Sun (Glasgow) [56838]
1 Virginia St. (E98 1SN)
Phone: 44 20 778240000

Newspapers

Circulation: ★ = ABC; △ = BPA; ◆ = CAC; • = CCAB; ❑ = VAC; ⊕ = PO Statement; ‡ = Publisher's Report; Boldface figures = sworn; Light figures = estimated.

VIETNAM
Hanoi
Nhan Dan
  [57052] .... (Mon.-Fri.) 220,000
                        (Mon.) 130,000

71 Hang Trong St.
  Hoan Kiem District
  Hoan Kiem
  Phone: 84 4 8254231

YEMEN
Sana'a
Yemen Times **[57106]** 35,000
PO Box 2579
  Phone: 967 1 268661

Index entries are arranged geographically, first by country and then by city. Within cities in this index, citations appear alphabetically by publication title. Citations include publication title, entry number (given in parentheses immediately following the title), and circulation figures.

AUSTRALIA

Alderley
Albert & Logan News
  [41530] .... (Wed.) ‡73,440
                (Fri.) ‡76,880
Northside Chronicle
  [41531] .... ‡62,294

Berwick
Berwick Leader
  [41598] .... (Wed.) ‡64,566
Cranbourne Leader
  [41599] .... (Wed.) ‡28,363
Pakenham Cardinia Leader **[41600]**

Boronia
Free Press Leader
  [41618] .... (Wed.) ‡14,887
Knox Leader
  [41619] .... (Tues.) ‡62,133

Briar Hill
Diamond Valley Leader
  [41635] .... (Wed.) ‡44,693
Whittlesea Leader
  [41636] .... (Tues.) ‡49,163

Caboolture
Caboolture Shire Herald
  [41681] .... ‡43,268

Campbelltown
Macarthur Chronicle
  [41696] 76,166

Cardiff
Lake Macquarie News
  [41722] 52,461

Castle Hill
Hills Shire Times **[41731]** 64,872

Chatswood
North Shore Times
  [41742] .. .. (Wed.) 56,944
               (Fri.) 73,395

Cheltenham
Bayside Leader
  [41745] .. .. (Tues.) ‡40,314
Dandenong Leader
  [41746] .... (Mon.) ‡43,672
Moorabbin Glen Eira Leader
  [41747] .... (Wed.) ‡50,576
Moorabbin Kingston Leader
  [41748] .... (Wed.) ‡50,576
Mordialloc Chelsea Leader
  [41749] .. .. (Mon.) ‡37,575

Cleve
Eyre Peninsula Tribune **[41765]**

Cobar
Cobar Age **[41772]**

Collie
Collie Mail **[41779]**

Darlinghurst
The Chaser **[41827]**

Epping
Northern District Times
  [41856] 58,337

Five Dock
The Glebe **[41867]** 51,698

Forster
Great Lakes Advocate **[41869]**

Geelong
Geelong Advertiser **[41879]**

Glen Iris
Caulfield Glen Eira Leader
  [41892] .... (Tues.) ‡84,704
Port Phillip Leader
  [41893] .... (Tues.) ‡84,704
Progress Leader
  [41894] .... (Tues.) ‡70,100
Stonnington Leader
  [41895] .... (Tues.) ‡53,310

Goulburn
Goulburn Post **[41927]**

Grenfell
Grenfell Record **[41934]**

Halls Creek
Halls Creek Herald **[41938]**

Hornsby
Hornsby & Upper North Shore
  Advocate **[41965]** 51,450

Hurstville
The Journal **[41970]**

Joondalup
Wanneroo Times **[41975]**

Kelmscott
Comment News **[41984]**

Kidman Park
Guardian Messenger
  [41986] 71,025
Portside Messenger
  [41987] 32,977

Laurieton
Camden Haven Courier
  [42003] .. .. (Wed.) ‡7,450

Lilydale
Lilydale & Yarra Valley Leader
  [42010] .... (Mon.) ‡40,479

Liverpool
Canterbury-Bankstown Express
  [42012] 74,119
Fairfield Advance **[42013]** 56,116
Liverpool Leader **[42014]** 58,271

Mackay
Queensland Farmer
  [42024] .... ‡10,000

Manly
The Manly Daily **[42032]** 92,590

Melbourne
Heidelberg Leader
  [42063] .... (Tues.) ‡29,343
Manningham Leader
  [42071] .... (Wed.) ‡44,421
Maroondah Leader
  [42072] .... (Tues.) ‡44,398
Melbourne Leader
  [42074] .... (Wed.) ‡55,689
Moonee Valley Leader
  [42077] .... (Mon.) ‡51,339
Moorabool Leader
  [42078] .... (Tues.) ‡35,575
Moreland Leader
  [42079] .... (Mon.) ‡66,973
Oakleigh Monash Leader
  [42080] .... (Tues.) ‡70,580
Preston Leader
  [42082] .... (Tues.) ‡38,044
Waverley Leader
  [42089] .... (Tues.) ‡70,580
Whitehorse Leader
  [42090] .... (Wed.) ‡66,374

Midland
Hills Gazette **[42104]**
Kalamunda Reporter **[42105]**

Milton
Westside News **[42108]** 60,423

Moonee Ponds
Farming Small Blocks **[42115]**

Mornington
Frankston Standard Leader
  [42117] .... (Mon.) ‡71,585
Mornington Peninsula Leader
  [42118] .. .. (Tues.) ‡50,495

Morphett Vale
Hills & Valley Messenger
  [42119] 19,585
Southern Times Messenger
  [42120] 60,540

Mount Druitt
Mt. Druitt - St. Marys Standard
  [42124] 44,210

Mount Gravatt
City South News **[42129]** 30,398
South-East Advertiser
  [42130] 51,802

Newport
Hobsons Bay Leader
  [42144] .... (Tues.) ‡35,503
Maribyrnong Leader
  [42145] .... (Tues.) ‡30,216

North Ipswich
Ipswich News **[42155]** .... ‡41,178

North Richmond
Farm Equipment Trader
  [42161] .... (Paid) ★53,918
The Land **[42163]** .... ★50,492
Queensland Country Life
  [42165] .... (Paid) ★35,661

Northbridge
Cockburn Gazette **[42212]**

Northcote
Northcote Leader
  [42213] .... (Tues.) ‡24,072

Norwood
East Torrens Messenger
  [42215] 33,157
Eastern Courier Messenger
  [42216] 62,673

Osborne Park
Eastern Reporter **[42224]**

Parramatta
Blacktown Advocate
  [42233] 51,400
Inner-West Weekly
  [42234] 52,892
Parramatta Advertiser
  [42235] 82,656
Rouse Hill Times **[42237]** ... ‡18,410

Penrith
Penrith Press
  [42240] .... (Tues.) 54,845
              (Fri.) 54,838

Port Adelaide
Weekly Times Messenger
  [42257] 66,079

Redcliffe
Redcliffe & Bayside Herald
  [42298] 34,835

Richmond
Hawkesbury Gazette
  [42299] .. .. (Paid) 8,830

Salisbury
Leader Messenger **[42343]** ... 43,550
News Review Messenger
  [42344] 93,621
Standard Messenger
  [42345] 35,261

Springwood
Logan West Leader
  [42384] .... ‡30,887

Stafford
City North News **[42386]** ... ‡29,154

Strathpine
Pine Rivers Press **[42392]** 35,760

Sunbury
Macedon Ranges Leader
  [42402] .... (Tues.) ‡28,456

Circulation: ★ = ABC; △ = BPA; ♦ = CAC; • = CCAB; ❑ = VAC; ⊕ = PO Statement; ‡ = Publisher's Report; Boldface figures = sworn; Light figures = estimated.

Melton Leader
[42403] .... (Tues.) ‡37,575
Sunbury Leader
[42404] .... (Tues.) ‡28,456

Sydney
Balonne Beacon [42473] ...... ★1,510
Brisbane Times [42477]
Bush Telegraph [42480] .. .... ‡4,195
Central & North Burnett Times
[42487] .... ★3,122
Central Queensland News
[42488] .... ★4,927
Central Telegraph [42489] .... ★3,595
Chinchilla News and Murilla
Advertiser [42491] ..,...... ★3,899
Dalby Herald [42500] .... ★2,452
Fraser Coast Chronicle
[42506] .... (Mon.-Fri.) ★9,400
(Sat.) ★10,851
The Gympie Times
[42511] .... (Tues.-Fri.) ★5,569
(Sat.) ★8,569
Isis Town & Country
[42523] .... ‡1,647
The Morning Bulletin
[42547] .... (Mon.-Fri.) ★17,702
(Sat.) ★22,951
NewsMail
[42552] .... (Mon.-Fri.) ★11,335
(Sat.) ★165,826
The North West Star
[42554] .... ★2,936
Port Curtis Post [42563] ..... ‡14,505
QT [42566] .... (Mon.-Fri.) ★10,792
(Sat.) ★13,999
Rural Weekly (Central Queensland
edition) [42573] .... ‡24,937
Rural Weekly (North CQ edition)
[42574] .... ‡15,608
Rural Weekly (Southern edition)
[42575] .... ‡45,592
Rural Weekly (Wide Bay edition)
[42576] .... ‡25,045
South Burnett Times
[42580] .... ★6,743
The Stanthorpe Border Post
[42581] .... ★2,406
Sunshine Coast Daily
[42583] .... (Mon.-Fri.) ★20,259
(Sat.) ★30,794
Sunshine Coast Sunday
[42584] .... ‡12,976
Surat Basin News
[42585] .... ‡12,500
Tweed Daily News
[42590] .... (Mon.-Sat.) ★4,317
Warwick Daily News
[42591] .... (Mon.-Sat.) ★3,249
(Sat.) ★3,344

Toowoomba
Australian Cotton Outlook
[42625] .... ‡21,150
Queensland Farmer & Grazier
[42629] .... ‡19,300

Townsville
North Queensland Register [42638]

Tullamarine
Brimbank Leader
[42650] .... (Tues.) ‡61,598
Hume Leader
[42651] .... (Tues.) ‡42,878
Stock & Land
[42653] .... (Paid) ★10,004

Unley
Stock Journal [42661] .... ★15,252

Victoria Park
Farm Weekly [42666] .... ★13,819

Warragul
Warragul & Drovin Gazette
[42685] .. .. (Paid) 10,700

Werribee
Wyndham Leader
[42692] .... (Tues.) ‡42,730

Wollongong
Illawarra Mercury [42703]

Wynnum Central
Wynnum Herald [42718] 34,647

BAHRAIN
Manama
Gulf Weekly [42791] 31,000

BELGIUM
Brussels
European Voice [42854] .... △18,241
Jeunes en Mouvement
[42861] .... ‡25,000
New Europe [42868]

BELIZE
Ambergris Caye
The San Pedro Sun [42914]
Belize City
The Belize Times [42915]
San Pedro Town
Ambergris Today [42919]

BERMUDA
Hamilton
Bermuda Sun [42920]
Mid-Ocean News [42921]

BHUTAN
Thimphu
Bhutan Observer [42924]
Kuensel [42926] .. .. (Paid) 6,023

BOTSWANA
Gaborone
Mmegi/The Reporter
[42945] .... (Paid) ★16,000

BRAZIL
Sao Paulo
Jornal da Ciencia Hoje [43041]

BRITISH VIRGIN ISLANDS
Road Town
The Island Sun
[43068] .... (Paid) 3,300

BRUNEI DARUSSALAM
Bandar Seri Begawan
The Brunei Times [43073]

CAMBODIA
Phnom Penh
Phnom Penh Post [43113]

COSTA RICA
San Jose
The Tico Times
[43552] ...... (Combined) ⊕15,000

CYPRUS
Nicosia
The Cyprus Weekly
[43593] 17,000

Emporoviomichaniki [43594] ... 4,000
Financial Mirror [43595] .: 4,000

CZECH REPUBLIC
Prague
Czech Business Weekly [43615]
Prague Daily Monitor [43635]

ETHIOPIA
Addis Ababa
The Addis Tribune [43795]

FINLAND
Pori
Elore [43904]

GERMANY
Dusseldorf
VDI Nachrichten [44335]

GHANA
Accra
The Ghanaian Chronicle [44727]

GUYANA
Georgetown
Dayclean [44800] 5,000

HONDURAS
Tegucigalpa
Honduras This Week
[44803] 6,000

INDIA
Bangalore
The Asian Age
[44950] .. .. (Paid) 28,870
Deccan Herald
[44957] .... (Paid) ★147,538
The New Indian Express [44978]
Bhubaneswar
The New Indian Express [45012]
Chandigarh
The Tribune
[45025] .... (Paid) 203,900
Chennai
The Hindu Weekly [45036]
The New Indian Express
[45053] .... (Paid) 324,165
News Today
[45054] .... (Paid) 39,050
Guwahati
Assam Tribune
[45129] .... (Paid) 94,196
Hyderabad
The New Indian Express [45177]
Jammu
Daily Excelsior
[45204] .... (Paid) 135,700
Kashmir Times
[45205] .... (Paid) 160,000
Kochi
The New Indian Express
[45252] .... (Paid) 67,134
Kolkata
The Asian Age [45259]
The Statesman
[45305] .... (Paid) 180,000
(Sun.) 230,000
The Telegraph
[45306] .... (Paid) 247,497

Mumbai
The Asian Age [45352] 40,436
Chitraleka [45363]
Mid-Day [45412] .. ... (Paid) 122,630
New Delhi
The Asian Age [45486] 6,722
The Hindu [45524] 1,180,000
The Indian Express
[45543] .. .. (Paid) 76,857
Panaji
The Navhind Times
[45681] .. .. (Paid) 33,287
Shillong
The Shillong Times
[45729] .. .. (Paid) 28,245
Srinagar
Greater Kashmir
[45737] .. .. (Paid) 70,820
Kashmir Observer [45739]

IRELAND
Buncrana
Inish Times Newspaper
[45925] .. .. (Paid) ‡6,000
Castlebar
Connaught Telegraph
[45928] 75,000
Cavan
The Anglo-Celt [45930] .. .. ‡16,600
Dublin
An Phoblacht [45945] 18,000
Gaillimhe
Foinse [46015]
Galway
City Tribune [46017] 29,970
Connacht Sentinel [46018] 8,480
Connacht Tribune
[46019] .. .. ★26,457
Limerick
Limerick Leader [46029]
Limerick Post [46030] .. .. ★50,000
Longford
Longford Leader
[46034] .. .. (Paid) 13,550
Navan
Meath Chronicle
[46046] .. .. (Paid) 16,010
Nenagh
Nenagh Guardian
[46047] .. .. (Paid) ★8,347
Tralee
Kerry's Eye [46060]
Waterford
Munster Express [46062] .. . 100,000
Waterford News & Star [46063]
Waterford City
Waterford Today [46065] 27,000
Westport
The Mayo News [46069]

ISRAEL
East Jerusalem
Palestine Report [46075]
Jerusalem
Hamodia (Israel) [46082]

JAMAICA
Kingston
The Star [46288]
The Sunday Gleaner [46289]
The Weekend Star [46292]

Circulation: ★ = ABC; △ = BPA; ◆ = CAC; • = CCAB; ❑ = VAC; ⊕ = PO Statement; ‡ = Publisher's Report; Boldface figures = sworn; Light figures = estimated.

KENYA
Nairobi
The East African [47178]

DEMOCRATIC PEOPLE'S REPUBLIC OF KOREA
Pyongyang
The Pyongyang Times [47207]

LEBANON
Beirut
Monday Morning [47400] 11,000

MALAYSIA
Kuala Lumpur
Malaysiakini [47613]
Mingguan Malaysia
  [47628] .... (Sun.) ★483,240
Utusan Melayu Mingguan [47640]

MALTA
Saint Julians
The Malta Business Weekly [47739]
The Malta Independent on Sunday
  [47741]

MONGOLIA
Ulaanbaatar
Khumuun Bichig [47811]
The Mongol Messenger [47812]

NEPAL
Kathmandu
Nepali Times [47843]
People's Review [47845]
The Telegraph Weekly [47847]

NEW ZEALAND
Amberley
Hurunui News [48782]

Auckland
Dairyman [48791] .... ‡25,500
Horticulture News [48796] .... ‡4,000
The Lifestyle Farmer [48802]
New Zealand Baptist
  [48806] 9,800
New Zealand Grapegrower
  [48814] .... ‡3,000

Christchurch
Auckland Today
  [48862] .... (Paid) ★20,162
Canterbury Today
  [48864] .... (Combined) 21,899
Central Today
  [48865] .... (Combined) 18,862
Hospitality Today
  [48869] .... (Combined) 13,406
Wellington Today [48879]

Gore
The Ensign [48902] .... ‡11,500

Greymouth
The West Coast Messenger [48905]

Hamilton
AgTrader [48907] .... ‡82,000

Kaitaia
Northland Age [48928] .... ★6,525

Oneroa
Gulf News (Waiheke)
  [48961] .... ‡3,129

PAKISTAN
Islamabad
Pulse Weekly [49312]

Karachi
Pakistan Christian Post [49367]

Lahore
The Friday Times [49385]
Weekly Cutting Edge [49389]

PHILIPPINES
Cebu City
Sun.Star Network [49464]

Laoag City
The Ilocos Times [49509] 5,000

Tagbilaran
The Bohol Chronicle [49637]

RUSSIA
Moscow
The Exile [49903]

SIERRA LEONE
Freetown
The Pool Newspaper
  [50096] 3,000

SINGAPORE
Singapore
Berita Minggu [50113] 62,000
Integrator [50174] 800
The New Paper on Sunday
  [50226] .... (Sun.) 109,300
Shin Min Daily News
  [50251] .... (Mon.-Fri.) 139,600
Thumbs Up
  [50278] .... (Mon.-Fri.) 39,200
zbCOMMA [50292] 60,000

SLOVAKIA
Bratislava
The Slovak Spectator
  [50322] 8,500

REPUBLIC OF SOUTH AFRICA
Cape Town
Caledon Kontreinuus [50368]
Carletonville Herald [50370] ... 5,664
Die Breederivier Gazette
  [50373] 10,280
DistrictMail [50374] 30,000
Eikestadnuus [50375] 9,000
Hermanus Times [50381] 7,921
Meyerton Ster [50392] 7,581
Noord-Vrystaatse Gazette
  [50394] 7,451
Northwest Gazette [50396] 29,786
Overberg Venster [50399] 7,145
Paarl Post [50400] 16,000
Potchefstroom Herald
  [50402] 7,805
Rapport [50405]
Sasolburg Ster [50409] 11,565
Swartlander [50414] 4,300
Vaal Vision [50422] 64,946
Vaal Weekly [50423] 8,702
Vanderbijlpark Ster
  [50424] 25,020
Vereeniging Ster [50425] 22,592
Weslander [50429] 11,300

Greyville
Sunday Tribune (South Africa)
  [50518] .... (Paid) 113,195

Johannesburg
The Shopsteward [50533]

SPAIN
Tenerife
Island Connections

  [50836] .... (Paid) 6,000
           (Non-paid) 19,000
The Paper [50837] .. .. ‡2,000

SRI LANKA
Colombo
The Sunday Leader [50871]
Sunday Observer
  [50872] .... ‡175,000
The Sunday Times
  [50873] .... (Paid) 80,000

Panadura
Losetha [50922] 2,000

SWITZERLAND
Geneva
Geneve Home Informations [51097]

Lausanne
Lausanne-Cites [51193] .... ‡157,734
Le Matin Dimanche
  [51196] .. .. ‡193,601

Morges
Journal de Morges [51213] ... ‡7,052

Payerne
La Broye [51220] .... ‡7,686

Zurich
SonntagsBlick [51284] .. .. 247,449 \

THAILAND
Pattaya City
Pattaya Mail [51463]

Phuket
Phuket Gazette
  [51464] .... (Paid) ‡15,000

UKRAINE
Kiev
Kyiv Post
  [51600] .... (Combined) 25,000

UNITED ARAB EMIRATES
Dubai
Khaleej Times [51646] 72,000

UNITED KINGDOM
Alnwick
Northumberland Gazette [52101]

Andover
Andover Advertiser [52110]

Annan
Annandale Herald [52122]
Annandale Observer [52123]
Moffat News [52125] 1,000

Arbroath
Arbroath Herald [52127]
Carnoustie Guide & Gazette [52128]

Aylesbury
Bucks Herald [52146]

Ballymena
Antrim Times [52158]
Ballymena Guardian
  [52159] .... ‡17,261
Ballymena Times
  [52160] .. .. (Combined) ‡7,981

Ballymoney
Ballymoney Times
  [52162] .... (Combined) 6,744

Banbridge
Banbridge Chronicle
  [52163] 5,984

Banbridge Leader [52164]

Banbury
Banbury Cake [52165]
Banbury Guardian [52166]

Banchory
Deeside Piper & Herald [52168]
Donside Piper & Herald [52169]

Bangor
North Wales Chronicle [52173]

Barnstaple
North Devon Gazette [52191]

Barry
Barry & District News [52192]

Basildon
Basildon and Wickford Recorder
  [52193]

Basingstoke
Basingstoke Gazette [52195]

Batley
Batley News [52267]
Birstall News [52268]

Bellshill
Bellshill Speaker [52305]

Belper
Belper News [52309]

Berwick upon Tweed
Berwick Advertiser [52317]
Berwickshire News [52318]

Bexhill-on-Sea
Bexhill Observer [52320]

Biggleswade
Biggleswade Chronicle [52323]

Birmingham
Safety Express [52366]

Bognor Regis
Bognor Regis Observer [52392]

Bolton
The Bolton News [52405]

Boston
Boston Standard [52408]

Brechin
Brechin Advertiser [52563]

Brentwood
Brentwood Gazette Series
  [52568] .. .. (Paid) 22,819

Bridlington
Bridlington Free Press [52597]

Bridport
Bridport & Lyme Regis News [52599]

Brighouse
Brighouse Echo [52600]

Buckingham
Buckingham & Winslow Advertiser
  [52755]

Bury Saint Edmunds
Bury Free Press [52773]

Buxton
Buxton Advertiser [52777]

Cardiff
South Wales Echo [52939]
Western Mail [52941]

Carluke
Carluke Gazette [52950]

Carrickfergus
Carrick Times [52951]

Castleford
Pontefract & Castleford Express
  [52952]

Chard
Yeovil Express [52957]

Chester
Ellesmere Port Standard [52993]

Chesterfield
Derbyshire Times [53002]

Chichester
Chichester Observer [53007]

Chorley
Chorley Guardian [53021]
Leyland Guardian [53023]

Cleckheaton
Spenborough Guardian [53025]

Clitheroe
Clitheroe Advertiser & Times [53026]

Cookstown
Mid-Ulster Mail
[53060] .... (Combined) 12,038

Crawley
Crawley Observer [53101]

Crediton
Crediton Country Courier
[53117] .... (Paid) 10,000

Cromer
North Norfolk News
[53118] *8,797

Croydon
Driving Instructor [53125] 18,000

Cumbernauld
Cumbernauld News [53149]
Kilsyth Chronicle [53150]

Dalkeith
East Lothian News [53152]
Midlothian Advertiser [53153]

Darlington
Darlington & Stockton Times [53154]

Daventry
Daventry Express [53159]

Dereham
Dereham Times [53171]

Derry
Derry Journal [53172]

Dewsbury
Dewsbury Reporter [53179]
Mirfield Reporter [53181]

Dinnington
Dinnington Guardian [53183]

Diss
Diss Express [53184]
Diss Mercury [53185]

Doncaster
Doncaster Free Press [53186]

Driffield
Driffield Times [53201]

Dromore
Dromore Leader [53207]

Dungannon
Tyrone Times
[53224] .... (Combined) 3,626

Eastbourne
Eastbourne Herald [53243]

Eastwood
Eastwood Advertiser [53245]

Edinburgh
The Braille Sporting Record [53256]
Business Citizen
[53258] .... (Non-paid) ‡98,000
Coleraine Times
[53264] .... (Combined) 6,744
Home Help [53284]
Luton News and Dunstable Gazette
[53300] .... (Controlled) 14,716

Rutland & Stamford Mercury Series
[53309] .. .. (Paid) 21,784

Ellon
ArtWork [53330] 100,000

Essex
Newham Recorder [53341]
Romford & Havering Post [53342]

Evesham
Evesham Journal [53343]

Exeter
Exmouth Herald [53357]

Fife
Fife Free Press [53387]

Fleetwood
Fleetwood Weekly News [53390]

Forfar
Kirriemuir Herald [53398]

Gainsborough
Gainsborough Standard [53401]

Garstang
Garstang Courier [53404]

Glasgow
English Club Golfer
[53415] 50,000
Scottish Club Golfer
[53446] 25,000
Welsh Club Golfer [53459] .. .*15,000

Glengormley
Newtonabbey Times [53469]

Gravesend
Gravesend Reporter [53479]

Great Yarmouth
Great Yarmouth Advertiser [53482]
Great Yarmouth Mercury
[53483] .. .. (Paid) 20,400
Waveney Advertiser [53484]

Harborough
Harborough Mail [53507]

Harrogate
Harrogate Advertiser [53516]
Pateley Bridge & Nidderdale Herald
[53519]

Haverhill
Haverhill Echo [53544]

Hawick
Hawick News [53546]

Haywards Heath
Mid Sussex Times [53549]

Hebden Bridge
Hebden Bridge Times [53552]

Hemel Hempstead
Hemel Gazette [53557]

Horncastle
Horncastle News [53591]

Horsham
West Sussex County Times [53602]

Hucknall
Hucknall Dispatch [53615]

Ilford
Ilford & Redbridge Post [53639]
Stratford & Newham Express [53640]

Ilkeston
Ilkeston Advertiser [53642]

Ilkley
Armley & Wortley Advertiser [53643]
Ilkley Gazette [53645]

Inverurie
Inverurie Herald [53649]

Ipswich
Coastal Advertiser [53653]

East Anglian Daily Times
[53655] 37,338

Isle of Arran
Arran Banner
[53661] .. .. (Paid) 3,600

Jersey
Guernsey Press [53665] ..... ‡16,000
Jersey Evening Post [53666]

Kendal
The Barrow Browser [53670]

Kettering
Kettering Evening Telegraph [53684]

Kirkintilloch
Kirkintilloch Herald [53727]

Knaresborough
Knaresborough Post [53728]

Lanark
Lanark Gazette [53731]

Larne
East Antrim Advertiser
[53741] ...... (Combined) ‡19,222
Larne Times [53742]

Leamington Spa
Kenilworth Weekly News [53746]
Leamington Spa Courier [53748]
Warwick Courier [53750]

Leeds
Yorkshire Evening Post [53776]
Yorkshire Sport [53778]

Leigh
Leigh Journal [53838]

Leighton Buzzard
Leighton Buzzard Observer
[53839] .... (Controlled) 7,945

Limavady
Roe Valley Sentinel
[53854] .... (Combined) 5,321

Linlithgow
Bo'ness Journal [53858]
Linlithgow Gazette [53859]
Queensferry Gazette [53860]

Lisburn
Ulster Star
[53863] .. .. (Combined) 12,684

Littlehampton
Littlehampton Gazette [53865]

Lochgilphead
Argyllshire Advertiser [53887]

London
Accountancy Age [53892]
Ad Trader [53899] 128,000
Asian Art [53974] 8,000
Be My Parent
[54008] .... (Combined) 22,000
Camden Gazette [54169]
East London Advertiser [54347]
Flying Angel News [54473] ... 18,800
The Guardian Weekend [54526]
Hackney Gazette [54528]
Hornsey & Crouch End Journal
[54568]
Investment Week [54679]
ITF World [54686] 7,000
Kilburn Times [54844]
Mauritius News
[54915] .... (Combined) 5,000
Palestine Times [55052]
The War Cry
[55378] .. .. (Paid) 17,000
Wembley & Kingsbury Times [55397]
Willesden & Brent Times [55406]

Londonderry
Londonderry Sentinel
[55473] .... (Combined) 5,321

Lowestoft
Lowestoft Journal [55496]

Lurgan
Lurgan Mail
[55499] .... (Combined) 9,390

Malton
Malton & Pickering Mercury [55532]

Mansfield
Mansfield Chad [55590]

Market Rasen
Market Rasen Mail [55595]

Matlock
Matlock Mercury [55604]

Melton Mowbray
Melton Times [55606]

Mexborough
South Yorkshire Times [55610]

Midhurst
Midhurst & Petworth Observer
[55625]

Milngavie
Milngavie Herald [55629]

Mold
Denbighshire Free Press [55641]

Montrose
Kincardineshire Observer [55645]
Montrose Review [55646]

Morecambe
Lakeland Echo [55648]

Morley
Morley Observer & Advertiser
[55652]

Morpeth
Morpeth Herald
[55653] .. .. (Paid) *3,122

Newcastle
Mourne Observer
[55665] .... (Paid) 11,988

Newmarket
Newmarket Journal
[55686] .. .. (Paid) 12,600

Newton Stewart
Galloway Gazette [55698]

Norwich
Beccles & Bungay Journal
[55724] 7,445
Midweek Herald [55734]
North Norfolk Advertiser [55736]
Norwich Advertiser [55737]
The Pink 'Un [55738]
Thetford & Brandon Times [55742]

Oswestry
Border Counties Advertizer [55856]

Peterborough
Classic Car Weekly [56254]
Peterborough Evening Telegraph
[56259]

Petersfield
Petersfield Post [56267]

Portadown
Portadown Times
[56284] .. .. (Combined) 11,568

Preston
Lancashire Evening Post [56302]

Rhyl
Rhyl Journal [56387]

Ripley
Ripley & Heanor News [56398]

Ripon
Ripon Gazette & Boroughbridge
Herald [56399]

Circulation: ★ = ABC; △ = BPA; ◆ = CAC; • = CCAB; ❑ = VAC; ⊕ = PO Statement; ‡ = Publisher's Report; Boldface figures = sworn; Light figures = estimated.

Rochdale
Asian Leader [56401]

Rothesay
The Buteman [56414]

Rugby
Rugby Advertiser [56423]

Saint Annes
Lytham St. Annes Express [56442]

Saint Helens
St. Helens Reporter [56443]

Saint Leonards-On-Sea
Hastings & St. Leonards Observer
 [56445]
Rye & Battle Observer [56446]

Salisbury
Basingstoke Gazette Extra [56452]

Scarborough
Ayton Today [56462]
Burniston Today [56463]
Scarborough Evening News [56464]

Selby
Selby Times [56468]

Selkirk
Selkirk Weekend Advertiser [56469]

Sheffield
Skamania County Pioneer
 [56514] 2,600

Sidcup
Bexley Times [56540]
Dartford Times [56542]

Skegness
Skegness Standard [56552]

Sleaford
Sleaford Standard [56558]

Stornoway
Stornoway Gazette [56637]

Stourbridge
Dudley News [56639]

Swaffham
Watton & Swaffham Times [56696]

Taunton
Somerset County Gazette [56723]

Thame
Thame Gazette [56744]

Todmorden
Todmorden News [56753]

Warminster
Warminster Journal
 [56847] .. .. (Paid) 5,500

Welwyn Garden City
Welwyn & Hatfield Times
 [56884] .. .. ★16,611

West Sussex
Redditch Advertiser/Indicator Series
 [56902]

Weston-super-Mare
Weston & Somerset Mercury [56906]

Whitby
Whitby Gazette [56915]

Whitley Bay
News Post Leader [56919]

Wisbech
Fenland Citizen [56935]

Witney
Whitney Gazette [56947]

Worcester
Berrow's Worcester Journal [56960]
Malvern Gazette [56962]

Worksop
Worksop Guardian [56970]

Worthing
Shoreham Herald [56976]
Worthing Herald [56979]

Wrexham
Wrexham Leader [56982]

YEMEN

Sana'a
Yemen Observer [57105]

ZIMBABWE

Harare
The Manica Post [57116]
The Sunday Mail [57118]
Sunday News [57119]

Newspapers

Circulation: ★ = ABC; △ = BPA; ♦ = CAC; • = CCAB; ❑ = VAC; ⊕ = PO Statement; ‡ = Publisher's Report; Boldface figures = sworn; Light figures = estimated.

Index entries are arranged geographically, first by country and then by city. Within cities in this index, citations appear alphabetically by publication title. Citations include publication title, entry number (given in parentheses immediately following the title), and circulation figures.

AUSTRALIA

Blue Mountains
Blue Mountains Gazette [41603]

Condell Park
Auburn Review Pictorial
[41801] 24,5469
Bankstown Canterbury Torch
[41802] 91,335
Cooks River Valley Times
[41803] 23,987

North Richmond
NSW Agriculture Today
[42164] .... ‡35,000

Sydney
Ballina Shire Advocate
[42472] .... ‡16,787
Big Rigs [42474] .... ‡24,660
Blackwater Herald [42475] ... ‡1,339
Bribie Weekly [42476] .... ‡11,168
Buderim Chronicle
[42478] .... ‡18,000
Byron Shire News
[42481] .... ‡17,120
Caboolture News [42482] ... ‡33,648
Caloundra Weekly
[42483] .... ‡22,116
Capricorn Coast Mirror
[42485] .... ‡10,843
Coastal Views [42493] .... ‡18,531
Cooloola Advertiser
[42497] .... ‡10,213
Gatton, Lockyer and Brisbane Valley
Star [42507] .... ‡19,970
Gold Coast Mail [42508] ..... ‡28,309
Hawkesbury Courier
[42513] .... (Non-paid) 20,470
Hervey Bay Observer
[42514] .... ‡21,122
The Ipswich Advertiser
[42522] .... ‡33,753
Island & Mainland News
[42524] .... ‡11,311
The Kolan Recorder
[42533] .... ‡2,400
Mackay & Sarina MidWeek
[42537] .... ‡28,097
Maroochy Weekly [42540] .... ‡9,865
The Maryborough Herald
[42541] .... ‡11,880
Miners MidWeek [42546] ...... ‡5,078
Nambour Weekly [42551] ... ‡10,952
North West Country
[42553] .... ‡4,250
Northern Downs News
[42555] .... ‡6,000
The Northern Rivers Echo
[42556] .... ‡22,980
The Range News [42568] .. ‡16,521

The Richmond River Express
Examiner [42570] .. .. ‡12,468
The Rivertown Times
[42571] .... ‡2,606
Rockhampton and Fitzroy News
[42572] .... ‡24,635
The Satellite [42577] .... ‡47,209
Toowoomba's Mail
[42588] .... ‡32,791
Tweed/Border Mail
[42589] .... ‡38,754
Warwick & Southern Downs Weekly
[42592] .... ‡10,821
Whitsunday Times
[42593] .... (Thurs.) ‡7,431

West Gosford
Central Coast Express Advocate
[42695] .. .. (Wed.) 63,103
(Fri.) 62,983

BANGLADESH

Dhaka
Holiday [42810]

PEOPLE'S REPUBLIC OF CHINA

Beijing
People's Daily [43213] 3,000,000

FRANCE

Caen
Tabularia [43926]

JAPAN

Kyoto
The Kyoto Shimbun News [46481]

Tokyo
Financial Times Japan
[46823] .. .. (Paid) 7,000
The Japan Times [46861]

MALAYSIA

Kuala Lumpur
New Sunday Times
[47631] 100,000
Utusan Malaysia
[47639] .... (Paid) 228,802

Petaling Jaya
The Star
[47702] .. .. (Mon.-Sat.) ★926,000

Sabah
New Sabah Times [47709]

NEW ZEALAND

Christchurch
The Christchurch Star
[48866] .. .. (Non-paid) 117,707

Dunedin
Southern Rural Life
[48893] .... ‡20,000

Timaru
Courier Country [48987] 15,200

SINGAPORE

Singapore
My Paper [50224] .. . (Free) 300,000
The Straits Times
[50273] .... (Paid) 400,000

REPUBLIC OF SOUTH AFRICA

Cape Town
Bloemnews [50366]
City Vision [50371] 80,787
Gazette [50379] 13,000
HelderMail [50380] 30,000
Kroonnuus [50385] 8,332
Maluti [50389] 7,861
Noordkaap [50395] 21,593
Ons Stad [50397] 36,681
Port Elizabeth Express
[50401] 89,800
QwaQwa News [50404] 4,069
TygerBurger
[50421] .. .. (Combined) 126,461
Vrystaat [50427] 4,673
Weskus News [50428] 15,000

Jeffreys Bay
Kouga Express [50526] 20,250

SPAIN

Benalmadena
The Euro Weekly News
[50709] .. .. (Combined) 65,000

SWITZERLAND

Locarno
il caffe [51209] ...\...... (Free) 59,733

Zurich
Heute [51264] 225,226

THAILAND

Chiang Mai
Chiangmai Mail [51456]

UNITED ARAB EMIRATES

Dubai
City Times [51636]

UNITED KINGDOM

Aberdeen
Gaudie [51676] .... (Non-paid) 4,000

Annan
Dumfries Courier [52124]

Ascension Island
The Islander
[52136] .... (Non-paid) 8,000

Bromsgrove
Bromsgrove Standard [52746]
Droitwich Standard [52747]

Chester
Chester Standard [52992]

Colwyn Bay
North Wales Pioneer
[53058] .... (Free) 25,233

Driffield
Beverley Guardian [53199]

Edinburgh
South Edinburgh Echo [53319]

Ely
Ely Standard [53331] .... ★20,474

Harlow
Harlow Edition Herald
[53511] 48,147

Huntingdon
The Hunts Post [53635] .. ... ★45,579

Leamington Spa
The Leamington Observer [53747]

Lisburn
Lisburn Echo
[53862] .. .. (Controlled) ‡18,993

London
Simon Star
[55240] .... (Non-paid) 5,000
Student Times
[55270] .... (Free) 200,000
The Sun Journal
[55277] .. .. (Free) 32,000
(Paid) 50

March
Cambs Times [55592] ....: 60,957
Wisbech Standard
[55593] .... ★17,538

Norwich
Wymondham & Attleborough Mercury
[55745]

Portadown
Craigavon Echo
[56283] .. .. (Controlled) ‡21,685

Redditch
Redditch Standard [56341]

Circulation: ★ = ABC; △ = BPA; ♦ = CAC; • = CCAB; ❑ = VAC; ⊕ = PO Statement; ‡ = Publisher's Report; Boldface figures = sworn; Light figures = estimated.

Royston
Royston Crow [56415] .. .. ★16,003

Saffron Walden
Saffron Walden Reporter [56430]

Saint Albans
Herts Advertiser [56436] ..... ★51,584

Sunderland
Star Series [56655] 230,000

Warwick
The Coventry Observer [56853]
Rugby Observer [56855]
Stratford Observer [56856]

Waterside
North-West Echo
    [56859] .... (Non-paid) ‡32,424

Welwyn Garden City
East Herts Edition Herald
    [56882] .... ★43,736

Worcester
Worcester Standard [56963]

Circulation: ★ = ABC; △ = BPA; ◆ = CAC; • = CCAB; ❑ = VAC; ⊕ = PO Statement; ‡ = Publisher's Report; Boldface figures = sworn; Light figures = estimated.

Index entries are arranged geographically, first by country and then by city. Within cities in this index, citations appear alphabetically by publication title. Citations include publication title, entry number (given in parentheses immediately following the title), and circulation figures.

AUSTRALIA
North Ryde
Bargain Shopper Guide to Melbourne
[42172] 35,000

PEOPLE'S REPUBLIC OF CHINA
Hong Kong
Home Journal Buyer's Guide
[43318] .... ‡36,570
Luxe Living Kitchens & Bathrooms
[43364] .... ‡25,000
Shop [43382]

POLAND
Warsaw
Hot Moda & Shopping
[49716] .... ‡7,073

ROMANIA
Bucharest
Elle Mariaj [49836] .. .. ‡4,387

SINGAPORE
Singapore
The Best of Singapore
[50114] .. .. ‡20,000

SPAIN
Barcelona
El Mueble [50670] .... ‡217,434

Madrid
Coches de Ocasion
[50736] .... ‡17,108
Cosas de Casa [50740] .... ‡183,118
Guia del Comprador de Casas
[50763] .... ‡2,568
Guia del Comprador de Coches
[50764] .... ‡13,348
Guia del Comprador de Furgonetas y
Autocaravanas [50765] .. ... ‡2,524
Guia del Comprador de Ordenadores
y Software [50766] .. .. ‡4,054

UNITED ARAB EMIRATES
Dubai
Souk [51653] 30,000

UNITED KINGDOM
Crawley
Shopping Centre
[53113] .... (Paid) ★12,241
Shopping Centre Ireland
[53114] .. .. ★12,789

London
Good Homes [54520] .... ★127,202

York
Yorkshire Advertiser (Ryedale and
North York Moors)
[57000] .... (Non-paid) 15,000

Index entries are arranged by subject (please refer to the Index to Subject Terms). Within the subject groupings, entries appear geographically by country and alphabetically within cities. Citations in this index include publication title, entry numbers (given in parentheses), and circulation figures.

ACCOUNTANTS AND ACCOUNTING
See also Banking, Finance, and Investments

AUSTRALIA
Melbourne
Asian Review of Accounting [42047]

Sydney
Accounting, Auditing & Accountability Journal [42444]
Charter [42490] .... ♦48,570

BAHRAIN
Manama
International Journal of Accounting, Auditing and Performance Evaluation [42792]

BELGIUM
Brussels
European Accounting Review [42852]

PEOPLE'S REPUBLIC OF CHINA
Hong Kong
The Hong Kong Accountant [43319] 35,000
The Prospective Accountant [43377]

GERMANY
Dusseldorf
Schmalenbach Business Review [44333]

INDIA
Hyderabad
The Icfai Journal of Accounting Research [45140]
The Icfai Journal of Audit Practice [45142]

Kolkata
The Management Accountant [45298] .. .. (Paid) 25,000

Mumbai
Bombay Chartered Accountant Journal [45357] ...... (Paid) 12,100

IRELAND
Dublin
Accountancy Ireland [45942] .. .... (Controlled) ★26,475

MALAYSIA
Miri
International Journal of Managerial and Financial Accounting [47683]

NETHERLANDS
Amsterdam
Journal of Accounting and Economics [48036]
Journal of Accounting and Public Policy [48037]

Dordrecht
Review of Accounting Studies [48551]
Review of Quantitative Finance and Accounting [48555]

The Hague
EC Tax Review [48613]

NEW ZEALAND
Auckland
Afro-Asian Journal of Finance and Accounting [48784]

Wellington
Chartered Accountants Journal of New Zealand [49003] 12,941

PAKISTAN
Faisalabad
Academic Journal of Financial Management [49229]

Karachi
Management Accountant [49362] .. .. (Paid) 10,000

PHILIPPINES
Mandaluyong City
Accountant's Journal [49531]

REPUBLIC OF SOUTH AFRICA
Bellville
African Finance Journal [50353]

Centurion
South African Journal of Business Management [50451]

Hillcrest
South African Journal of Economic and Management Sciences [50523]

Pretoria
Southern African Journal of Accountability and Auditing Research [50604]

SRI LANKA
Colombo
Chartered Accountants [50851] .. .. (Paid) 1,000

SWITZERLAND
Geneva
International Journal of Critical Accounting [51114]

UNITED REPUBLIC OF TANZANIA
Dar es Salaam
African Journal of Finance and Management [51399]

UNITED KINGDOM
Abingdon
Accounting, Business & Financial History [51693]

Bangor
International Journal of Banking, Accounting and Finance [52172]

Bath
International Journal of Behavioural Accounting and Finance [52244]

Bradford
Accounting Research Journal [52435]
International Journal of Accounting and Information Management [52473]
Journal of Accounting and Organisational Change [52492]
Managerial Auditing Journal [52524]
Qualitative Research in Accounting and Management [52540]

Brentwood
Credit Control [52571] .. .. (Paid) 15,000

Edinburgh
CA Magazine [53259] .... ★22,362

Leicester
Journal of Applied Accounting Research [53806]

London
Financial Management [54455] .. .. (Paid) 65,289
Internal Auditing and Business Risk [54617] 8,000
International Journal of Economics and Accounting [54644]
Journal of Finance and Management in Public Services [54751]

Loughborough
Accounting Education [55476]

Oxford
Abacus [55857]
Journal of International Financial Management & Accounting [56045]

ACQUIRED IMMUNE DEFICIENCY SYNDROME
See also Medicine and Surgery; Health and Healthcare

RWANDA
Kigali
HIV Plus [50048]

SPAIN
Barcelona
AIDS Reviews [50648]

UNITED KINGDOM
Abingdon
AIDS Care [51701]

London
International Journal of STD and AIDS [54663]
Positive Nation [55106]

ADVERTISING AND MARKETING
See also Public Relations; Selling and Salesmanship

AUSTRALIA
Perth
Asia Pacific Journal of Marketing and Logistics [42244]

Port Melbourne
B&T Weekly [42263] .... (Combined) ‡9,269
Professional Marketing [42265]

Pyrmont
The Production Book [42286]

Surry Hills
AdNews [42407]

Templestowe
Promotional Products Magazine [42617] .... (Combined) 6,000

AUSTRIA
Vienna
Transfer Werbeforschung & Praxis [42771] .... (Combined) 8,500

BELGIUM
Brussels
International Journal of Research in Marketing [42859]

PEOPLE'S REPUBLIC OF CHINA
Hong Kong
Digital Media [43296] .... (Combined) 12,000

Media
[43369] .... (Combined) 12,000

FINLAND
Helsinki
Kampanja [43837] .... (Paid) 7,000

GERMANY
Heidelberg
Journal fur Betriebswirtschaft [44463]
Kiel
International Journal of Wine Business Research (IJWBR) [44502]
Leinfelden-Echterdingen
DER AUGENOPTIKER
[44519] 9,836
Munich
W & V Werben & Verkaufen
[44586] .... (Controlled) 33,885
Nuremberg
dedica [44608] 19,993
Food Marketing & Technology
[44611] 18,500
Getranke! Technologie & Marketing
[44613] 8,905
Getrankemarkt [44614] 16,833
Wiesbaden
Dialog [44712]

HUNGARY
Budapest
Market!ng&Media
[44848] .... (Combined) ‡1,520

INDIA
Hyderabad
The Icfai Journal of Behavioral Finance [45144]
The Icfai Journal of Services Marketing [45167]
New Delhi
Indian Journal of Marketing
[45559] .... (Paid) 2,500

ITALY
Milan
Prima Comunicazione
[46191] .... (Paid) ‡15,000

JAPAN
Tokyo
Idea [46837] .... (Paid) 32,000

NETHERLANDS
Amsterdam
Japan and the World Economy
[48035]
Dordrecht
Journal of Consumer Policy [48453]
Marketing Letters [48511]

NEW ZEALAND
Christchurch
Principals Today
[48877] .... (Combined) ★8,221

PAKISTAN
Karachi
Aurora [49339]

REPUBLIC OF SOUTH AFRICA
Centurion
South African Journal of Business Management [50451]

Johannesburg
Journal of Marketing [50531]
Pretoria
Management Dynamics [50596]

SPAIN
Madrid
Ipmark [50775]

SWITZERLAND
Geneva
International Journal of Business Forecasting and Marketing Intelligence [51108]
Saint Gallen
Thexis [51224]

TAIWAN
Jhongli City
International Journal of Internet Marketing and Advertising [51308]
Taichung
International Journal of Electronic Customer Relationship Management [51320]

UNITED ARAB EMIRATES
Dubai
Ad-Vocate [51628] 5,000

UNITED KINGDOM
Abingdon
Journal of Marketing Communications [51917]
Journal of Strategic Marketing [51947]
Amersham
International Consultants' Guide
[52107] .... (Controlled) 30,000
Argyll
Journal of Marketing Management [52130]
The Marketing Review [52131]
Birmingham
Journal of Manufacturing Technology Management [52348]
Bognor Regis
Journal of Public Affairs [52399]
Bradford
Corporate Communications [52446]
European Journal of Marketing [52458]
Journal of Fashion Marketing and Management [52501]
Journal of Product & Brand Management [52512]
Marketing Intelligence & Planning [52525]
Qualitative Market Research [52539]
Croydon
Media Week [53130]
Cudham
Classic and Vintage Commercials [53141]
Glasgow
The Drum [53414]
Leicester
Global Municipal Investor [53802]
Marketing Theory [53812]
Retailspeak
[53821] .... (Combined) 10,000
London
Admap [53902] ... (Controlled) 2,500
Advertising Forecast [53910]

Campaign [54170]
Conference & Incentive Travel
[54259] ...... (Controlled) ★16,154
Financial Marketing [54456] ... 2,103
In-Store Marketing
[54593] .... (Combined) 13,084
★10,168
International Journal of Advertising [54632]
Journal of Direct, Data and Digital Marketing Practice [54737]
Journal of International Marketing [54771]
Journal of Targeting, Measurement and Analysis for Marketing
[54826] 450
Market Leader [54907]
Marketing [54908] .... ★35,615
Marketing Week [54909] 40,000
Med Ad News [54919] 16,000
Packaging News [55048] .... ★13,919
Precision Marketing
[55117] .... ★7,500
Print Buyer [55118] .... ★14,500
Professional Marketing [55131]
Promotions & Incentives
[55140] .... ★18,000
Quarterly Survey of Advertising Expenditure [55164]
Revolution
[55201] .. .. (Combined) 13,753
Peterborough
Sign Directions [56261] .... ★7,302
Smallfield
Auto Vending [56561] .. .. ‡7,180

AIR CONDITIONING AND REFRIGERATION
See also Plumbing and Heating

AUSTRALIA
Brisbane
Automotive Electrical & Air Conditioning News [41644] 3,200

DENMARK
Glostrup
HVAC Magasinet [43705] .... ‡350
Skive
ScanRef [43735] .. .. ‡4,650

ITALY
Milan
CDA [46164] .. ... (Controlled) ★3,800

NETHERLANDS
Dordrecht
Aerobiologia [48321]

NORWAY
Jar
Kulde Skandinavia
[49192] .... (Controlled) 3,550

SERBIA
Belgrade
Energy and Buildings [50082]

UNITED KINGDOM
Flitwick
Plumbing, Heating & Air Movement News
[53391] .. .. (Combined) ★27,962
Wadhurst
Construction Europe
[56805] .... ★14,624

ANTHROPOLOGY AND ETHNOLOGY

AUSTRALIA
Adelaide
HOMO - Journal of Comparative Human Biology [41506]
Armidale
Australian Folklore [41558]
Canberra
Australian Aboriginal Studies [41700]

BRAZIL
Rio de Janeiro
Mana - Estudos de Antropologia Social [43011]

PEOPLE'S REPUBLIC OF CHINA
Chengdu
International Journal of Tourism Anthropology [43248]
Hong Kong
Asian Anthropology [43274]

FRANCE
Paris
Historiens et Geographes [44048]
Plelan le Grand
Folia Primatologica [44095]
Villejuif
Sciences Sociales et Sante [44125]

HUNGARY
Szeged
Acta Ethnographica Hungarica [44894]

INDIA
Delhi
The Anthropologist
[45087] .... (Paid) 250
Journal of Human Ecology
[45100] .... (Paid) 500
New Delhi
ICSSR Journal of Abstracts and Reviews [45527] ...... (Paid) 450
Journal of Social Anthropology [45618]

JAPAN
Nagoya
Asian Ethnology
[46551] .... (Paid) 450
Tokyo
Anthropological Science
[46743] .. .. (Paid) 1,300

MALAYSIA
Kuala Lumpur
Man and Society
[47623] .. .. (Paid) 1,000

NETHERLANDS
Amsterdam
Entomologia Experimentalis et Applicata [47967]
Interaction Studies [48022]
Journal of Anthropological Archaeology [48044]
Journal of Arid Environments [48049]
Journal of Cultural Heritage [48066]
Journal of Human Evolution [48085]
Trends in Cognitive Sciences [48260]

Circulation: ★ = ABC; △ = BPA; ◆ = CAC; • = CCAB; ❑ = VAC; ⊕ = PO Statement; ‡ = Publisher's Report; Boldface figures = sworn; Light figures = estimated.

Dordrecht
African Archaeological Review [48322]
Dialectical Anthropology [48373]

Leiden
Asian Medicine [48654]
Comparative Sociology [48662]
European Journal of East Asian Studies [48670]
Journal of Ethnopharmacology [48697]

NEW ZEALAND
Christchurch
Archaeology in New Zealand [48861]

PHILIPPINES
Quezon City
Philippine Sociological Review [49613] .... (Paid) 500

POLAND
Warsaw
Anthropological Review [49690]

REPUBLIC OF SOUTH AFRICA
Bloemfontein
Navorsinge van die Nasionale Musium, Bloemfontein [50355]

Grahamstown
African Journal of AIDS Research [50486]

Lynnwood Ridge
South African Journal of Science [50551]

SPAIN
Barcelona
Archipielago [50649]
Historia, Antropologia y Fuentes Orales [50678]

SWEDEN
Stockholm
Geografiska Annaler, Series A, Physical Geography [51017]
Geografiska Annaler, Series B, Social Geography [51018]

UNITED KINGDOM
Abingdon
Anthropological Forum [51704]
Culture and Religion [51749]
Folklore [51790]
History and Anthropology [51804]
Indonesia and the Malay World [51813]
Journal of North African Studies [51925]
Journal of Southern African Studies [51944]
Mortality [51987]
World Archaeology [52094]

Cambridge
Anthrozoos [52789] .. .. (Paid) 850
(Non-paid) 50
International Journal of Asian Studies [52832]

Coventry
Journal of Research in Reading [53087]

Durham
Durham Anthropology Journal [53228]

Edgbaston
Africa [53248] .... (Paid) ‡1,000

Edinburgh
European Journal of Archaeology [53273]

Liverpool
Before Farming, the Archaeology and Anthropology of Hunter-Gatherers [53868]
Fieldwork in Religion [53872]

London
Anthropological Theory [53954]
Anthropology Today [53955]
British Museum Studies in Ancient Egypt and Sudan (BMSAES) [54141]
Bulletin of the School of Oriental and African Studies [54157] .: 900
Byzantine and Modern Greek Studies [54162]
Critique of Anthropology [54291]
Cultural Dynamics [54292]
Culture & Psychology [54295]
European History Quarterly [54394]
Journal of Ethnobiology and Ethnomedicine [54746]
Journal of Material Culture [54776]
Journal of the Royal Anthropological Institute [54812]
Journal of Social Archaeology [54818]
Names [54969] ..../..... (Paid) 850
Slovo [55243]

Oxford
Oxford Development Studies [56132]

York
Antiquity [56987] .... (Paid) 2,190

APPLIANCES

AUSTRALIA
Pyrmont
Appliance Retailer [42269] ... . ★7,112

ARCHAEOLOGY

AUSTRALIA
Canberra
Australian Aboriginal Studies [41700]

Sydney
Arabian Archaeology and Epigraphy [42448]

Townsville
Australian Archaeology [42634]

Wollongong
Quaternary Science Reviews [42706]

BELGIUM
Wilsele
Khil'a [42912]

COLOMBIA
Bogota
Caldasia [43544]

CYPRUS
Nicosia
Journal of Mediterranean Archaeology [43596]

DENMARK
Copenhagen
Acta Archaeologica [43654]
Scando-Slavica [43683]

FRANCE
Paris
Karthago [44067]

GERMANY
Berlin
Praehistorische Zeitschrift [44227] 500
Zeitschrift fur Orient-Archaologie [44239]

Feldkirchen
Journal of Coptic Studies [44352]

Frankfurt am Main
Journal of African Archaeology [44366]

Munich
Zeitschrift fur Assyriologie und Vorderasiatische Archaologie [44589] 500

Tubingen
Progress in Particle and Nuclear Physics [44693]

Wiesbaden
Anatolian Archaeological Studies [44710]
Central Asiatic Journal [44711]

HUNGARY
Budapest
Acta Archaeologica Academiae Scientiarum Hungaricae [44807]
Archaeologiai Ertesito [44823]

INDIA
New Delhi
Epigraphia Indica [45510] .... (Paid) 740

ISRAEL
Jerusalem
Israel Exploration Journal [46085] .. .. (Paid) 2,000

JAPAN
Nagoya
Asian Ethnology [46551] .... (Paid) 450

NETHERLANDS
Amsterdam
Journal of Anthropological Archaeology [48044]

Dordrecht
African Archaeological Review [48322]
International Journal of Historical Archaeology [48428]
Journal of Archaeological Research [48438]
Journal of Maritime Archaeology [48472]
Journal of World Prehistory [48499]

Leiden
Ancient Civilizations from Scythia to Siberia [48646]
Bulletin Antieke Beschaving (BABESCH) [48659]
Cainozoic Research [48660]
Late Antique Archaeology [48706]

NEW ZEALAND
Christchurch
Archaeology in New Zealand [48861]

Dunedin North
Journal of Pacific Archaeology [48897]

POLAND
Wroclaw
Geochronometria [49778]

REPUBLIC OF SOUTH AFRICA
Rondebosch
Archaeologies [50617]

SPAIN
Madrid
Revista Espanola de Paleontologia [50797] 600

SWEDEN
Molndal
Current Swedish Archaeology [50993]

TURKEY
Ankara
TUBA-AR [51501]

UNITED KINGDOM
Abingdon
Indonesia and the Malay World [51813]
World Archaeology [52094]

Bath
Journal of Micropalaeontology [52249]

Edinburgh
European Journal of Archaeology [53273]
Scottish Archaeological Journal [53312]

Hebden Bridge
Northern Earth [53553] .... (Combined) 450

Liverpool
Before Farming, the Archaeology and Anthropology of Hunter-Gatherers [53868]

London
Antiquaries Journal [53956] .... (Paid) 2,450
Archaeological Reports [53960] 3,100
Bulletin of the School of Oriental and African Studies [54157] 900
Industrial Archaeology Review [54596]
Journal of the British Archaeological Association [54711]
Journal of Hellenic Studies [54761] 3,100
Journal of Material Culture [54776]
Journal of Roman Studies [54811] 3,200
Journal of Social Archaeology [54818]
Linguistics and the Human Sciences [54874]
Palestine Exploration Quarterly [55051]
Papers of the British School at Rome [55055]
PIA (Papers from the Institute of Archaeology) [55088]
Post-Medieval Archaeology [55108]
Public Archaeology [55150]
Tel Aviv [55296]

Oxford
Archaeometry [55871]
Oxford Journal of Archaeology [56134]

Reading
The Archaeologist [56309] 2,000

York
Antiquity [56987] .... (Paid) 2,190
British Archaeology [56988]

Circulation: ★ = ABC; △ = BPA; ◆ = CAC; • = CCAB; ❏ = VAC; ⊕ = PO Statement; ‡ = Publisher's Report; Boldface figures = sworn; Light figures = estimated.

ARCHITECTURE
See also Construction, Contracting, Building, and Excavating

AUSTRALIA
Alexandria
Lifestyle Pools [41541]

North Ryde
BuildHOME Vic [42174]
Contemporary Home Design [42179]
Kitchens and Bathrooms Quarterly
  [42186]
Outdoor Design & Living [42189]
Outdoor Design Source [42190]
Poolside [42193]
Poolside Showcase
  [42194] 30,000
Stone [42198] 12,000

Port Melbourne
Houses [42264]

Pyrmont
Interior Fitout [42282] .... ★5,466

AUSTRIA
Vienna
Architektur Aktuell [42746] 10,428

BELGIUM
Brussels
A+ Architecture/A+ Architectuur
  [42842] .... (Combined) 14,010

BRAZIL
Rio de Janeiro
International Journal of High Performance System Architecture
  [43007]

PEOPLE'S REPUBLIC OF CHINA
Beijing
Architectural Journal
  [43169] 65,000
Journal of Building Structure [43203]

Hong Kong
Hinge [43302]

FINLAND
Helsinki
Arkkitehti/Finnish Architectural
  Review [43818] 4,796

Jyvaskyla
ptah [43871]

FRANCE
Paris
Intramuros
  [44061] .... (Combined) 25,000

GERMANY
Berlin
Landschaftsarchitekten
  [44214] 2,500

Leinfelden-Echterdingen
Metamorphose [44527] 11,916

Munich
Architecture, Technology, Culture
  (ATC) [44550]

GREECE
Athens
EKISTICS [44742]

HUNGARY
Budapest
Atrium [44824] 15,000

Epites – Epiteszettudomany [44828]

INDIA
Kolkata
Institution of Engineers (India) Architectural Engineering Division
  Journal [45278] .... (Paid) 5,000

Mumbai
Better Interiors [45355]

IRELAND
Dublin
Irish Architectural and Decorative
  Studies [45970]

ITALY
Rozzano
Domus
  [46248] .... (Combined) 51,000

JAPAN
Tokyo
Japan Architect
  [46852] .... (Paid) 18,000
Journal of Architecture, Planning and
  Environmental Engineering [46885]
Journal of Asian Architecture and
  Building Engineering [46887]
Journal of Structural and Construction Engineering [46942]
Nikkei Architecture
  [46978] .... ★44,461

NETHERLANDS
Amsterdam
Building and Environment [47917]
Frame
  [47989] .... (Combined) 17,000

The Hague
De Architect
  [48611] .... (Combined) 8,192
Europa Nostra [48614]

NORWAY
Moss
Byggaktuelt
  [49193] .... (Combined) 12,445

Trondheim
International Journal of Grid & Utility
  Computing [49217]
Nordic Journal for Architectural
  Research [49218]

PHILIPPINES
Mandaluyong City
Design and Architecture
  [49534] .... (Paid) 2,500

POLAND
Warsaw
Dom & Wnetrze [49705] ..... ‡20,283
Town Planning and Architecture
  [49767]

SAUDI ARABIA
Riyadh
Journal of King Saud University: Architecture and Planning
  [50064] .... (Paid) 3,000

SINGAPORE
Singapore
Singapore Architect [50253]
Space [50271]

REPUBLIC OF SOUTH AFRICA
Randburg
SA Architect [50610]

SPAIN
Barcelona
Arquitectura y Diseno
  [50650] .... ‡47,513
Quaderns d'Arquitectura [50694]

Madrid
Album [50727]
Arquitectura Viva [50729] 11,000
AV Monografias [50731] 9,000
El Croquis [50753] .... (Paid) 35,000
Informes de la Construccion [50770]

Vitoria-Gasteiz
a+t [50849]

SWEDEN
Karlskrona
Planera Bygga Bo
  [50971] .... (Controlled) 3,500

SWITZERLAND
Bern
Kunst & Architektur in der Schweiz
  [51075] 7,200

Zurich
Werk, Bauen und Wohnen
  [51296] .... (Combined) 8,500

UNITED REPUBLIC OF TANZANIA
Dar es Salaam
Journal of Building and Land
  Development [51402]

UNITED KINGDOM
Abingdon
Journal of Urban Design [51953]
Journal of Urban Technology [51954]

Basingstoke
Urban Design International [52234]

Bradford
Facilities [52459]

Brentwood
Building Acoustics [52569]
International Journal of Architectural
  Computing [52576]

Chelmsford
Blueprint
  [52960] .... (Combined) 7,400

Edinburgh
Architectural Heritage [53252]

Glasgow
Urban Realm [53456] 7,000

London
Architectural Engineering and Design
  Management [53961]
The Architectural Review
  [53962] .... (Paid) ★22,700
AT Magazine
  [53979] .... (Non-paid) 8,500
                     11,000
Building Research & Information
  [54153]
Candid [54172] 8,000
Design Week [54321]
Home Cultures [54565]
The Journal of Architecture [54700]
Journal of the British Archaeological
  Association [54711]
Period Living [55068]
Vernacular Architecture [55367]

Loughborough
Ergonomics [55479]

Milton Keynes
Design Studies [55633]

Nottingham
Planning Perspectives [55769]

Oldham
Glazed Expressions [55783]
Journal of the Tiles and Architectural
  Ceramic Society [55784]

Olney
International Journal of Embedded
  Systems [55798]

Oxford
Journal of Architectural Education
  [56016]

Saintfield
SelfBuild [56449] .... ★11,574

Sharpham
Journal of Church Monuments
  Society [56487] 500

Stamford
CAA Newsnet [56595]

Stowmarket
Countryside Building [56642]

Wadhurst
Construction Europe
  [56805] .... ★14,624

ART AND ART HISTORY

AUSTRALIA
Sydney
Philament [42561]

Westminster
Ceramics [42700] 12,200

PEOPLE'S REPUBLIC OF CHINA
Hong Kong
Arts of Asia [43267]
Artslink [43268] 16,000
The Journal of Dagaare Studies
  (JDS) [43355]
Orientations [43373]

Shanghai
Calligraphy [43464]
Calligraphy and Painting [43465]

DENMARK
Copenhagen
Djembe [43665] 1,500

Humlebaek
Scandinavian Journal of Design
  History [43724]

FINLAND
Jyvaskyla
ptah [43871]

GERMANY
Berlin
Archiv fur Papyrusforschung
  [44155] .... ‡300
Byzantinische Zeitschrift
  [44164] .... ‡650
Romanistisches Jahrbuch
  [44229] 300

Bonn
Kultur Politik [44265]

Feldkirchen
Journal of Coptic Studies [44352]

Munich
Kunst Chronik [44568] 2,869
Zeitschrift fur Assyriologie und
  Vorderasiatische Archaologie
  [44589] 500

HUNGARY
Budapest
Acta Historiae Artium [44811]

Circulation: ★ = ABC; △ = BPA; ◆ = CAC; ● = CCAB; ❑ = VAC; ⊕ = PO Statement; ‡ = Publisher's Report; Boldface figures = sworn; Light figures = estimated.

Muveszettorteneti Ertesito [44853]

INDIA
Mumbai
Marg [45409] .... (Paid) 1,500

IRELAND
Dublin
Irish Architectural and Decorative
  Studies [45970]
Irish Studies in International Affairs
  [45985]

JAPAN
Amagasaki
Daruma Magazine [46302]

NETHERLANDS
Amsterdam
European Journal of Arts Education
  [47974]
Poetics [48207]

The Hague
De Architect
  [48611] .... (Combined) 8,192
Europa Nostra [48614]
Oud Hollad [48624]

Leiden
Historiography East and West
  [48675]

NIGERIA
Ago Iwoye
OYE [49059]

RUSSIA
Moscow
Russian Art [49971] .... ‡7,000

SAUDI ARABIA
Riyadh
Journal of King Saud University: Arts
  [50065] .... (Paid) 3,000

REPUBLIC OF SOUTH AF-
RICA
Grahamstown
African Studies Monographs [50491]

Pretoria
Artthrob [50585]
De Arte [50588]

SPAIN
Barcelona
Historia National Geographic
  [50679] .... †142,798
Quaderns d'Arquitectura [50694]

Las Palmas de Gran Canaria
Atlantica Internacional [50720]

Madrid
Album [50727]
Nueva Revista [50786]
Reales Sitios [50795]
Visual [50815]

Santander
Arte y Parte
  [50830] .. .. (Paid) 40,000

Terrassa
Tiempos Modernos [50838]

SRI LANKA
Colombo
Journal of the Royal Asiatic Society
  of Sri Lanka [50859]

SWITZERLAND
Basel
Antike Kunst [51058] 1,100

Bern
Kunst & Architektur in der Schweiz
  [51075] 7,200

Zurich
Kunst Bulletin
  [51273] .. .. (Combined) 30,544

TUNISIA
Tunis
Journal of the Arabization Bureau
  [51489]

UNITED KINGDOM
Abingdon
Indonesia and the Malay World
  [51813]
International Journal of Art Therapy
  [51827]
Israel Affairs [51863]
Japan Forum [51865]
Japanese Studies [51866]
Life Writing [51969]
Visual Culture in Britain [52086]

Birmingham
Review [52364]

Cambridge
New Theatre Quarterly
  [52878] 1,00
Theatre Research International
  [52901] .... (Controlled) 1,100

Chippenham
Antiques & Art Independent
  [53020] 21,000

Corsham
International Journal of Art & Design
  Education [53066] 2,800

Coventry
Law and Humanities [53088]

Edinburgh
International Journal of Humanities
  and Arts Computing [53288]
Romanticism [53308]

Farnham
Animation [53379]

Glasgow
Variant [53457]

Haywards Heath
Furniture History
  [53548] .... (Combined) 1,750

London
Art Business Today
  [53966] .. .. (Paid) 5,500
Art Monthly
  [53968] .... (Combined) 5,000
Art Review [53969] ... . (Paid) 25,000
Britannia [54107] 1,500
The Burlington Magazine [54158]
Charlie and Lola [54198]
Home Cultures [54565]
Interdisciplinary Science Reviews
  [54615]
Journal of the British Archaeological
  Association [54711]
Journal of Hellenic Studies
  [54761] 3,100
Journal of Roman Studies
  [54811] 3,200
The Journal of Stained Glass [54824]
Papers of the British School at Rome
  [55055]
The Sculpture Journal [55222]
Studies in Conservation [55271]
Third Text [55312] .... (Paid) 3,000

Oxford
Archaeometry [55871]
Art History [55874]
The British Journal of Aesthetics
  [55891]

Contemporary Review [55916]
The Design Journal [55924]
Journal of Design History [56026]
Material Religion [56094]
Oxford Art Journal [56130]

Saint Albans
TEXT [56439]

Tenterden
The Artist [56742] .. ... (Paid) 21,500

ASTRONAUTICS
**See also Nuclear Engineer-
ing**

AUSTRALIA
Sydney
Ad Astra [42446]

FRANCE
Paris
Acta Astronautica [44020]

IRELAND
Dublin
Astronomy and Space Magazine
  [45946] 9,000

NETHERLANDS
Amsterdam
Space Communications [48234]

PAKISTAN
Faisalabad
International Journal of Planetary and
  Space Research [49253]

UNITED KINGDOM
Oxford
Monthly Notices of the Royal Astro-
  nomical Society [56109]

ASTRONOMY AND
METEOROLOGY

AUSTRALIA
Collingwood
PASA [41794]

Sydney
Publications of the Astronomical Society of Australia [42565]

PEOPLE'S REPUBLIC OF
CHINA
Beijing
Science in China Series G [43221]

Nanjing
Chinese Astronomy and Astrophysics
  [43453]

FRANCE
Paris
Astronomy & Astrophysics [44027]
Mathematische Zeitschrift [44069]

GERMANY
Gottingen
Advances in Geosciences [44389]
Astrophysics and Space Sciences
  Transactions [44392]

Hamburg
Theoretical and Applied Climatology
  [44424]

Katlenburg-Lindau
Living Reviews in Solar Physics
  [44500]

Kiel
Polar Biology [44507]

Potsdam
Astronomische Nachrichten [44638]

Stuttgart
Meteorologische Zeitschrift [44669]

INDIA
Bangalore
Journal of Astrophysics and
  Astronomy [44965] .. ... (Paid) 800
Journal of Earth System Science
  [44970]

IRELAND
Dublin
Astronomy and Space Magazine
  [45946] 9,000

JAPAN
Kanagawa
Biological Sciences in Space
  [46412] .... (Paid) 500

Tokyo
Astronomy and Astrophysics Review
  [46756]
Publications of Astronomical Society
  of Japan [47028]

NETHERLANDS
Amsterdam
Advances in Space Research
  [47883]
Few-Body Systems [47985]
Journal of Arid Environments [48049]
New Astronomy [48180]
New Astronomy Reviews [48181]

Dordrecht
Celestial Mechanics & Dynamical
  Astronomy [48346]
Solar Physics [48564]
Space Science Reviews [48566]

PAKISTAN
Faisalabad
International Journal of Planetary and
  Space Research [49253]

RUSSIA
Moscow
Astronomical and Astrophysical
  Transactions [49876]
Astronomy Letters [49877]
Astronomy Reports [49878]

Novosibirsk
Applied Physics B [50009]

SWEDEN
Stockholm
Popular Astronomi [51030] 1,300

UNITED KINGDOM
Bath
Speculum [52258]

Birmingham
Popular Astronomy
  [52361] .... (Combined) 3,000

Bristol
Astrophysical Journal Supplement
  Series [52640] .... (Paid) ‡1,800
Culture and Cosmos
  [52659] .... (Paid) 300
Journal of Cosmology and Astropar-
  ticle Physics [52684]
Research in Astronomy and
  Astrophysics [52727]

Circulation: ★ = ABC; △ = BPA; ◆ = CAC; • = CCAB; ❑ = VAC; ⊕ = PO Statement; ‡ = Publisher's Report; Boldface figures = sworn; Light figures = estimated.

Sky at Night Magazine [52730]

Cambridge
International Journal of Astrobiology
[52833] 450
Proceedings of the International Astronomical Union [52886]

Exeter
Geophysical & Astrophysical Fluid Dynamics [53359]

London
Journal of the British Astronomical Association [54712]
Journal of the British Interplanetary Society [54713]
Spaceflight [55259]

Oxford
Archive for Rational Mechanics and Analysis [55872]
Monthly Notices of the Royal Astronomical Society [56109]

Reading
International Journal of Climatology [56321]
Journal of the Royal Meteorological Society [56324]

AUTOMATION
See also Computers

AUSTRALIA
Sydney
Australian Personal Computer
[42465] .... ★28,952
The Journal of Research and Practice in Information Technology
[42530] .. .. (Combined) ‡15,500
PC Authority [42558]

Toowoomba
International Journal of Information Quality [42628]

Wahroonga
What's New in Process Technology
[42682] .... ★6,605

BRAZIL
Rio de Janeiro
International Journal of Innovative Computing and Applications
[43008]

PEOPLE'S REPUBLIC OF CHINA
Hong Kong
Journal of Travel & Tourism Marketing [43363]

Shanghai
Drive System Technique [43473]

CZECH REPUBLIC
Prague
Automatizace
[43611] .... (Combined) ‡8,500

DENMARK
Glostrup
Elteknik [43704] .... ‡3,950
Teknisk Nyt [43716] .... ‡10,131
Teknisk Nyt Special Edition
[43717] .... ‡10,000

FRANCE
Sophia Antipolis
Performance Evaluation [44108]

Villiers-Saint-Frederic
International Journal of Electric and Hybrid Vehicles [44127]

GERMANY
Dreieich
Made in Germany—International Edition
[44318] ...... (Combined) ‡110,000

Heidelberg
Multimedia Systems [44468]

Poing
Computer Reseller News
[44634] .. .. (Controlled) 33,136
Datacom
[44635] .. .. (Combined) 11,014
Information Week
[44636] .. .. (Combined) 75,253
Network Computing
[44637] .... (Combined) 52,181

INDIA
Bhubaneswar
International Journal of Computational Vision and Robotics [45010]

Pune
C-DAC Connect [45696]

ITALY
Milan
Office Automation [46189] 17,000

JAPAN
Tokyo
J@pan Inc Magazine
[46947] 24,000

NETHERLANDS
Alphen aan den Rijn
IT Service Magazine
[47868] .... (Combined) ‡4,700
Process Control
[47871] .... (Combined) 4,000
Telecommagazine [47873] 7,369

Dordrecht
Annals of Mathematics and Artificial Intelligence [48325]
Autonomous Agents and Multi-Agent Systems [48329]
Photonic Network Communications [48527]
Real-Time Systems [48548]
World Wide Web [48588]

NEW ZEALAND
North Shore City
Electrical + Automation Technology
[48955] .... ★10,315

Wellington
MIS Australia [49017]

PHILIPPINES
Makati City
Computer World Philippines [49515]

RUSSIA
Moscow
Automatic Control and Computer Sciences [49880]
Automatic Documentation and Mathematical Linguistics [49881]
Automation and Remote Control [49882]

SINGAPORE
Singapore
International Journal of Humanoid Robotics (IJHR) [50181]

SPAIN
Madrid
PC World Espana
[50788] .. .. (Combined) ‡62,450

SWITZERLAND
Aarau
MegaLink [51055] 12,500

Sirnach
Professional Computing [51231]

Thalwil
Infoweek.ch
[51234] .... (Combined) 18,000

UNITED KINGDOM
Bath
Internet Business News [52245]
Worldwide Computer Products News [52264]

Bristol
DNJ [52661]

Burnham
International Journal of Micrographics & Optical Technology [52765]

Cambridge
Kiosk Europe [52865]

Coulsdon
Jane's Simulation & Training Systems [53073]

Littlehampton
Smart Card News [53866]

London
Buy-Side Technology [54161]
Computing [54256]
Personal and Ubiquitous Computing [55070]

Luton
Software World
[55505] .... (Paid) 400

Olney
International Journal of Embedded Systems [55798]

Orpington
Journal of Automated Methods and Management in Chemistry [55853]

Sutton
Computer Weekly
[56683] .... △104,559

AUTOMOTIVE (TRADE)
See also Transportation, Traffic, and Shipping; Trailers and Accessories; Trucks and Trucking

AUSTRALIA
Brisbane
Automotive Electrical & Air Conditioning News [41644] 3,200

Canberra
Motoring Directions [41710] .. . 1,800

Melbourne
International Journal of Electronic Transport [42065]

Merrylands
Buick News [42103] 500

AUSTRIA
Vienna
Auto Touring
[42748] ..... (Combined) 2,107,000

BELGIUM
Brussels
Federauto Magazine [42855]

PEOPLE'S REPUBLIC OF CHINA
Beijing
Auto China [43170] 4,000,000

Shanghai
Car & Fan [43466]

FINLAND
Helsinki
Suomen Autolehti [43859] .... ‡8,473

FRANCE
Villiers-Saint-Frederic
International Journal of Electric and Hybrid Vehicles [44127]

GERMANY
Bad Harzburg
Steel Grips [44144] 5,000

Dreieich
Made in Germany—International Edition
[44318] ...... (Combined) ‡110,000

Leinfelden-Echterdingen
Lackiererblatt [44525] 5,904

INDIA
Mumbai
Auto Monitor [45353]

New Delhi
The Upper India Motorist
[45660] .... (Combined) 20,000

IRELAND
Dublin
Auto Ireland [45947]

Sandyford
Used Car Price Guide [46058]

ITALY
Peschiera Borromeo
Bellauto
[46213] .... (Combined) 12,400
Il Giornale dei Veicoli Commerciali
[46215] .. .. (Paid) 20,000

Rozzano
Autopro [46247] 27,000
Quattroruote [46252] .... ‡464,393
Tuttotrasporti [46254] 22,127

Turin
Auto & Design
[46269] .. .. (Paid) 12,000

JAPAN
Tokyo
Japan Automotive News
[46853] .. .. (Paid) 5,180

NEW ZEALAND
North Shore
Diesel Industry News [48952]

North Shore City
Motor Equipment News
[48956] .. .. ★11,330
New Zealand Company Vehicle
[48957] .... (Controlled) ★7,048

PORTUGAL
Lisbon
Revistacap [49806]

SINGAPORE
Singapore
Global Sources Auto Parts & Accessories [50152]
Highway Magazine [50166]
Motoring [50221]
Motoring Annual [50222]

Circulation: ★ = ABC; △ = BPA; ◆ = CAC; • = CCAB; ❏ = VAC; ⊕ = PO Statement; ‡ = Publisher's Report; Boldface figures = sworn; Light figures = estimated.

SPAIN
Barcelona
Mundo Recambio y Taller (Spares and Workshop World)
[50689] .... (Paid) 2,500
(Non-paid) 7,500

Madrid
Guia del Comprador de Coches
[50764] .... ‡13,348
Guia del Comprador de Furgonetas y Autocaravanas [50765] ...... ‡2,524

UNITED KINGDOM
Abingdon
LeaFlet [51967] 350
Safety Fast! [52046] 13,000

Aldershot
The Business [52097]

Alfreton
Vintage Austin Magazine [52100]

Belfast
Garage Trader [52283]

Bellshill
Fast and Modified [52306] 14,000

Bournemouth
Total 911 [52427]

Brickendon
Motor Industry Magazine
[52592] 24,000

Brighton
ADI News [52603] 16,000

Essex
The Jowetteer [53339]

Forest Row
Good Motoring Magazine
[53396] 53,000

Hertford
Rubber Developments
[53565] 10,000

Kingston upon Thames
Vintage Roadscene [53725]

Leven
Buses [53845]

London
Advanced Driving [53904] ... 110,000
Auto Trader [53986] .... ★189,077
Automotive Engineer [53987]
Automotive Logistics
[53988] .... △9,000
Automotive Manufacturing Solutions
[53989]
Automotive Production China
[53990] .... △5,000
AYGO Magazine [53997] 250,000
Fleet News Europe [54465]
Interior Motives [54616]
Journal of Sandwich Structures and Materials [54815]
Top Marques [55327] .... ★24,118
Vanguard [55365] 80,000
What Van?
[55402] ...... (Combined) ‡20,000

Luton
Overdrive [55503]

Manchester
Motorhome and Caravan Trader
[55572] 10,028
Truck and Plant Trader
[55581] .... ★14,383

Middlesex
Autocar [55615] .... ★47,646

Olney
International Journal of Automotive Technology and Management
[55790]

International Journal of Vehicle Autonomous Systems [55837]

Shrewsbury
Cellular Polymers [56527]

Wallingford
A.M. [56814] 4,700

Watford
Commercial Vehicle Workshop
[56863] .... ★10,013
Professional Motor Factor
[56874] .... ★3,621
Professional Motor Mechanic
[56875] .... ★57,478

AVIATION

AUSTRALIA
Canberra
Flight Safety Australia
[41706] 85,000

Lismore
Aviation Trader [42011] 16,500

Mascot
Australian Aeronautics [42041]

PEOPLE'S REPUBLIC OF CHINA
Hong Kong
Orient Aviation
[43372] .... (Paid) 10,516

FRANCE
Paris
International Journal of Aviation Management [44049]

GERMANY
Berlin
Flieger Revue
[44180] .... (Paid) 25,485

Bonn
Flug Revue
[44260] .... (Combined) 50,000
Nato's Nations and Partners for Peace [44267] 22,000

Hamburg
Flieger Magazin
[44415] .... (Paid) 25,305

Stuttgart
Aerokurier [44660]

INDIA
Bangalore
International Journal of Aerospace Innovations [44963]

Kolkata
Institution of Engineers (India) Aerospace Engineering Division Journal
[45276] .... (Paid) 4,000

New Delhi
Contributions to Himalayan Geology
[45498]

IRAN
Tehran
Advances in Aerospace and Applications [45886]

ISRAEL
Haifa
Mechanical Systems and Signal Processing [46078]

Tel Aviv
International Journal of Turbo and Jet Engines [46105]

ITALY
Rome
Aeronautica & Difesa [46220]

Rozzano
Volare [46257] 17,618

JAPAN
Tokyo
Journal of Space Technology and Science [46941]

LEBANON
Beirut
Al Defaiya
[47387] .... (Combined) 24,000
Arab Defence Journal
[47391] .... ★25,000

NETHERLANDS
Amsterdam
Aerospace Science and Technology
[47884]
Journal of Applied Mathematics and Mechanics [48047]

NORWAY
Oslo
Flynytt [49198] ... (Combined) 5,200

SINGAPORE
Singapore
Asian Airlines & Aerospace
[50105] 5,434

REPUBLIC OF SOUTH AFRICA
Durban
World Airnews
[50471] .... (Paid) 9,250
(Non-paid) 4,200

SPAIN
Madrid
Airline Ninety Two
[50726] .... ‡15,000

SWEDEN
Ludvika
pilotmagazinet
[50980] .... (Paid) 30,000

SWITZERLAND
Bern
Space Research Today [51077]

UNITED KINGDOM
Amersham
Aviation Modollor International
[52105]
Flying Scale Models [52106]

Bingham
Transmit
[52326] .... (Controlled) 2,350

Bishop's Stortford
European Business Air News
[52378] .... (Controlled) △6,244
Global Business Jet
[52379] .... (Controlled) 6,244

Bletchley
Scale Aircraft Modelling [52390]

Brasted
International Airport Review
[52562] .... (Controlled) 11,200

Bristol
Aircraft Engineering and Aerospace Technology [52639]

Coulsdon
Jane's Airport Review [53067]

Leicester
Sailplane & Gliding [53824]
Skydive Magazine [53825] ... 14,200
Skywings [53826]

London
Aeronautical Journal [53911]
Aeroplane Monthly [53912]
Aerospace International
[53913] .... △17,299
Aircraft Technology Engineering & Maintenance
[53930] .... (Controlled) △11,500
The Maritime Pilot
[54906] .... (Controlled) 1,250
Spaceflight [55259]

Maidens
Space Policy [55526]

Stamford
Airports International [56593]

Surrey
Human Factors and Aerospace Safety [56666]

Sutton
Flight International [56687]

Twickenham
Airport World [56787] 8,000
Asia-Pacific Airports [56788] ... 4,000
Global Airport Cities Magazine
[56792] .... (Controlled) 5,000
Routes News [56793] 6,000

West Drayton
The Log [56890] 14,000

Wetherby
Cross & Cockade International
[56910]

BAKING
See also Confectionaries and Frozen Dairy Products

AUSTRALIA
Nundah
Australian Baking Business
[42219] 8,348

UNITED KINGDOM
Crawley
British Baker
[53099] .... (Combined) ★6,074

London
Confectionery Production
[54258] .... (Controlled) 3,500

Oxted
Biscuit World [56235] 4,335

BANKING, FINANCE, AND INVESTMENTS
See also Accountants and Accounting; Commerce and Industry; Savings and Loan

ARGENTINA
Buenos Aires
Comments on Argentine Trade
[41471]
Integration and Trade [41474]

AUSTRALIA
Adelaide
Accounting Forum [41498]

Leederville
RESOURCESTOCKS
[42007] 15,000

Circulation: ★ = ABC; △ = BPA; ◆ = CAC; • = CCAB; ❑ = VAC; ⊕ = PO Statement; ‡ = Publisher's Report; Boldface figures = sworn; Light figures = estimated.

Melbourne
Asian Review of Accounting [42047]
In The Black [42064] 95,000

Mona Vale
Your Trading Edge [42112]

North Sydney
Australian Banking & Finance
  [42206] 3,850

Sydney
Australian Insolvency Journal [42456]

AUSTRIA
Vienna
Austrian Economic Quarterly
  [42747] 200

BELGIUM
Brussels
European Accounting Review [42852]

PEOPLE'S REPUBLIC OF CHINA
Hong Kong
Asia Asset Management [43269]
Asiamoney [43272]
Asian Credit Investor [43275]
The Asset [43281]
FinanceAsia [43300] 21,600
The Hong Kong Accountant
  [43319] 35,000
Innovative Investor [43348]
Research in International Business
  and Finance [43379]

DENMARK
Copenhagen
kapital [43677] .... (Paid) 2,840

FINLAND
Abo
Journal of the Economic Society of
  Finland [43811] 950

GERMANY
Berlin
Der Steuezahler [44170]

Frankfurt
Agrifuture [44356] 20,000
DLG-Mitteilungen [44359] 12,000

Munich
International Tax and Public Finance
  [44565]

GREECE
Piraeus
International Journal of Economic
  Research [44768]

GUYANA
Georgetown
CARICOM Perspective
  [44799] 3,000

HUNGARY
Budapest
Acta Oeconomica [44815]

INDIA
Bangalore
The Economic Times
  [44958] .. .. (Paid) 24,489

Chennai
The Economic Times
  [45031] .. .. (Paid) 26,592
Hindu Business Line
  [45033] .. .. (Paid) 24,823

Hyderabad
The Icfai Journal of Audit Practice
  [45142]
The Icfai Journal of Bank
  Management [45143]
The Icfai Journal of Behavioral
  Finance [45144]
The Icfai Journal of Financial
  Economics [45151]
The Icfai Journal of Financial Risk
  Management [45152]
The Icfai Journal of International
  Business Law [45156]
The Icfai Journal of Monetary
  Economics [45161]
The Icfai Journal of Risk & Insurance
  [45165]
Icfai Reader [45170]
Porfolio Organizer [45179]
Professional Banker [45180]
Treasury Management [45184]

Jodhpur
Current Tax Reporter
  [45217] 10,000
Reserve Bank of India Bulletin
  [45229] .. .. (Paid) 5,300

Kolkata
The Economic Times
  [45264] .. .. (Paid) 43,228

Mumbai
The Economic Times
  [45368] .... (Paid) 108,302
Journal of Financial Management and
  Analysis [45400] ...... (Paid) 3,000
Reserve Bank of India
  Bulletin—Weekly Statistical
  Supplement
  [45434] .. .. (Paid) 1,400
Reserve Bank of India Occasional
  Papers [45435] .... (Paid) 1,000
Taxation Law Reports
  [45446] .. .. (Paid) 1,500

New Delhi
The Economic Times
  [45505] .. .. (Paid) 19,804
                    (Combined) 400,000
The Financial Express
  [45516] .. .. (Paid) 11,991

Pune
Prajnan (Pune) [45699]

IRELAND
Dublin
Finance Dublin
  [45957] .. .. (Combined) ★5,000
IBEC Economic Trends [45965]

Sandyford
The Stock Market [46057]

ITALY
Messina
International Journal of Monetary
  Economics & Finance [46158]

Milan
Mani Tese [46187] 36,000

Rome
Development [46226] 3,000

JAPAN
Tokyo
Annals of Finance [46738]
Central European Journal of Opera-
  tions Research [46781]

KENYA
Nairobi
Habitat Debate [47183] 10,000
Journal of Language, Technology &
  Entrepreneurship in Africa [47189]

REPUBLIC OF KOREA
Seoul
American Chamber of Commerce in
  Korea [47252]

LUXEMBOURG
Capellen
AGEFI Luxembourg
  [47488] .. .. (Combined) 24,000

MALAYSIA
Kuala Lumpur
Banker's Journal Malaysia [47599]

Miri
International Journal of Managerial
  and Financial Accounting [47683]

MEXICO
Mexico City
Boletin [47782]
Monetaria [47786]
Money Affairs [47787]

NEPAL
Kathmandu
Aankhijhyal [47836]

NETHERLANDS
Amsterdam
Habitat International [48008]
Journal of Financial Intermediation
  [48077]
Journal of Housing Economics
  [48084]
North American Journal of Economics
  and Finance [48183] ... (Paid) 300
                    (Non-paid) 50
Pacific-Basin Finance Journal
  [48198]

Dordrecht
Economic Change and Restructuring
  [48378]
Financial Markets and Portfolio
  Management [48387]
Journal of Financial Services
  Research [48459]
Review of Derivatives Research
  [48553]
Review of Quantitative Finance and
  Accounting [48555]

The Hague
EC Tax Review [48613]
Hivos Magazine [48617]

NEW ZEALAND
Auckland
Afro-Asian Journal of Finance and
  Accounting [48784]

Wellington
AFR Smart Investor [48999]
Hi Society [49009]
The Reserve Bank of New Zealand
  [49033]

NORWAY
Stavange
International Journal of Strategic Engineering Asset Management
  [49213]

PAKISTAN
Faisalabad
Academic Journal of Financial
  Management [49229]

Karachi
Investor's Business & Financial
  Journal [49356]

PERU
Lima
Quehacer [49425] 4,000
Resomeu Senaual [49426] 500

PHILIPPINES
Manila
ADB Business Opportunities [49546]
Asian Development Review [49547]

Quezon City
Business World
  [49586] .. .. (Paid) 54,000
PAID [49605] .. ../........ 1,000

PORTUGAL
Porto
O Informador Fiscal [49809]

SINGAPORE
Singapore
The Business Times
  [50117] .... (Mon.-Fri.) 35,700
Emerging Markets Review [50145]
Investor's Guide to Singapore
  [50196] .. .. (Paid) 4,000
Review of Pacific Basin Financial
  Markets and Policies [50245]
Smart Investor [50268]

REPUBLIC OF SOUTH AFRICA
Bellville
African Finance Journal [50353]

Cape Town
BBQ Scorecard [50363] 10,000
Blue Chip [50367] 10,000
Opportunity [50398] 10,000

Centurion
IMFO [50439]

Cresta
The Southern African Treasurer
  [50466]

Grahamstown
Securities Market Journal [50512]

Hillcrest
South African Journal of Economic
  and Management Sciences [50523]

SRI LANKA
Ethul Kotte
Marga Journal [50894]

SWEDEN
Stockholm
International Journal of Entrepreneur-
  ial Venturing [51020]

Uppsala
Development Dialogue [51051]

SWITZERLAND
Geneva
International Journal of Electronic
  Banking [51117]

TAIWAN
Taipei
Journal of Banking and Finance
  [51348]

UNITED REPUBLIC OF TANZANIA
Dar es Salaam
African Journal of Finance and
  Management [51399]

Circulation: ★ = ABC; △ = BPA; ◆ = CAC; • = CCAB; ❑ = VAC; ⊕ = PO Statement; ‡ = Publisher's Report; Boldface figures = sworn; Light figures = estimated.

THAILAND

Bangkok

Asia Pacific Development Journal [51410]

Asia-Pacific Population Journal [51411] 2,000

e-TISNET Monthly News/e-TISNET Monthly Information Services [51418]

Water Resources Journal [51448]

UKRAINE

Sumy

Investment Management & Financial Innovations [51617]

UNITED KINGDOM

Abingdon

Accounting, Business & Financial History [51693]

Bangor

International Journal of Banking, Accounting and Finance [52172]

Basingstoke

Family Spending [52204]

International Journal of Disclosure and Governance [52209]

Journal of Banking Regulation [52212]

Journal of Financial Services Marketing [52216] 400

Pensions [52227]

Bath

International Journal of Behavioural Accounting and Finance [52244]

Belfast

Offshore Investment [52291]

Bradford

International Journal of Bank Marketing [52474]

International Journal of Managerial Finance [52480]

International Marketing Review [52490]

The Journal of Investment Compliance [52506]

The Journal of Risk Finance [52515]

Brentwood

Credit Control [52571] .... (Paid) 15,000

Brighton

IDS Bulletin [52614] 1,800

Bristol

Financial Planning [52670] 1,450

Buckingham

The Journal of Prediction Markets [52758]

Canterbury

Financial World [52919] ...... ★22,080

Coulsdon

Jane's Transport Finance [53074]

Coventry

Applied Economics Letters [53077]

Applied Financial Economics [53078]

Edinburgh

CA Magazine [53259] .... ★22,362

Kempston

Investment Now [53668] .... (Combined) 70,000

Leeds

Review of Behavioral Finance [53773]

Leicester

International Journal of Community Currency Research [53805]

London

Accountancy [53891] .... ★150,952

Accounting and Business Research [53893]

Asia Risk [53972]

Bank of England Quarterly Bulletin [54000]

The Banker [54001] .... ★28,771

Banking Technology [54002] .... (Combined) 8,108

Benelux unquote [54012]

Community [54247] 3,000

Credit [54283]

Deutsche unquote [54322]

DM Magazine [54337] 14,560

eFinancial News [54356]

Energy Risk [54370]

Environment and Urbanization [54374] 3,100

Euromoney [54390]

European Pensions [54408]

Financial Management [54455] .. .. (Paid) 65,289

Financial Marketing [54456] ... 2,103

Financial News [54457] .. .... (Controlled) △21,089

Financial Sector Technology [54458] .... ★12,776

The Financial Times [54459]

First [54462] ... (Combined) 157,000

Fiscal Studies [54463] 1,500

Global Investor [54511] 8,100

Global Pensions [54512]

Hedge Funds Review [54547]

Institutional Investor [54608]

International Custody & Fund Administration [54626]

International Investment [54628]

International Journal of Islamic and Middle Eastern Finance and Management [54652]

International Securities Finance [54670]

Investment & Pensions Europe (IPE) [54678]

Investors Chronicle [54680]

Journal of Asset Management [54702] .... (Combined) 650

The Journal of Computational Finance [54729]

Journal of Credit Risk [54732]

Journal of Derivatives & Hedge Funds [54735] .... (Combined) 1,400

Journal of Financial Crime [54752]

Journal of Financial Regulation and Compliance [54753]

The Journal of Operational Risk [54789]

Journal of Portfolio Management [54804]

The Journal of Risk [54809]

LatinFinance [54056] .... △29,176

Leasing Life [54861] .... (Combined) 1,000

Life & Pensions [54872]

Money Marketing [54950]

Money Observer [54951]

Mortgage Edge [54953]

Mortgage Solutions [54954]

Mortgage Strategy [54955]

Nordic unquote [55009]

The Old Lady [55028] .... (Paid) 2,000

Pensions Age [55065] .... ★14,000

Post Magazine [55107]

Private Equity Europe [55121]

Professional Adviser [55127]

Professional Pensions [55132] .... ★12,672

Retirement Planner [55197] 12,000

Risk [55204]

SHARES [55232]

The Treasurer [55338]

Trust & Foundation News [55343]

UK Unquote [55355] 3,500

Ultra [55356] 54,450

Wealth [55394] 4,000

WMS [55410] 54,450

World Gold Analyst [55420]

Your Mortgage [55434] 15,000

Loughton

Education Business [55489]

Manchester

Credit Union News [55550]

Norwich

Moneyfacts [55735]

Oakham

Credit Management [55780] ... 8,791

Olney

International Journal of Financial Services Management [55805]

Oxford

Abacus [55857]

Accounting and Finance [55858]

Annals of Public and Cooperative Economics [55869]

Financial Accountability and Management [55957]

Journal of Applied Corporate Finance [56015]

Journal of Business Finance and Accounting [56019]

Journal of Finance [56033]

Journal of Financial Econometrics [56034]

Journal of International Financial Management & Accounting [56045]

Law and Financial Markets Review [56085]

The Review of Income and Wealth [56192] .... ‡1,400

Portsmouth

International Journal of Financial Markets and Derivatives [56290]

Rugby

Enterprise Development and Microfinance [56418]

Sheffield

Managing Leisure [56506]

Sidcup

Legal Abacus [56544] .... (Combined) 3,000

Sittingbourne

Moneywise [56550]

Taunton

Business Money [56721] .... (Controlled) 14,237

York

Economic Journal [56990]

VIETNAM

Hanoi

Vietnam Investment Review [57054]

BEVERAGES, BREWING, AND BOTTLING

AUSTRALIA

Prospect East

The Australian & New Zealand Wine Industry Journal [42267] 3,000

Australian Viticulture [42268] .... (Paid) 4,000

Pyrmont

National Liquor News [42284] .... ‡12,267

Signature Cocktails [42288]

Sydney

Gourmet Traveller WINE [42509] .... ★21,948

AUSTRIA

Vienna

Mitteilungen Osterreiches Getranke Institut [42764]

DENMARK

Glostrup

Scandinavian Food & Drink [43715] .... ‡7,538

GERMANY

Nuremberg

Brauwelt Chinese [44603] .... (Combined) ‡4,221

Brauwelt Deutsch [44604] .. .. (Paid) ‡5,543

Brauwelt en Espanol [44605]

Brauwelt International [44606]

Brauwelt in Russian [44607]

Der Weihenstephaner [44609]

Getranke! Technologie & Marketing [44613] 8,905

Getrankemarkt [44614] 16,833

Monatsschrift fur Brauwissenschaft [44616]

Wellness Foods Europe [44617] 6,011

GREECE

Athens

Trofima kai Pota [44757] 3,809

NEW ZEALAND

Auckland

Food & Beverage Today [48794] 6,587

Wine Technology in New Zealand [48832] .... ‡2052

SINGAPORE

Singapore

Food & Beverage Asia [50150]

SWITZERLAND

Basel

Merum [51064]

Glarus

Lebensmittel Industrie [51176] .... (Combined) 4,300

UNITED KINGDOM

Abingdon

Journal of Wine Research [51957]

Bath

Taste Italia [52260] 45,000

Crawley

Drinks International [53102] .. .. (Controlled) ★10,000

Food Manufacture [53103] .... (Controlled) 15,491

Off Licence News [53110] .. .. ★18,440

Wine & Spirit [53115] .. .. ★11,044

Norwich

Beers of the World [55725]

Whisky Magazine [55743]

Oxford

Membrane Technology [56096]

Oxted

Drinks Network [56236] .. .. (Combined) ‡21,000

Reigate

Brewers' Guardian [56386] 3,200

Rushden
Nutrition & Food Science [56426]

Smallfield
Cafe Business [56562] 7,128

Tunbridge Wells
Eurofood [56782]

Wimborne
Soft Drinks International
[56929] .... (Combined) 3,100

BIOLOGY

AUSTRALIA

Collingwood
Australasian Plant Disease Notes [41781]
Invertebrate Systematics [41791]
Reproduction, Fertility and Development [41796]

Melbourne
Microbiology Australia [42076]

Perth
The Clinical Biochemist Reviews [42249]

Sydney
Journal of Biomimetics, Biomaterials, and Tissue Engineering [42527]

Syndal
Australian Biologist [42610]

Womying
International Journal of Biological Sciences [42710]

AUSTRIA

Altenberg
Biological Theory [42721] .... (Non-paid) 225

Vienna
Journal of Neural Transmission [42762]
The World Journal of Biological Psychiatry [42775]

BANGLADESH

Gazipur
Annals of Bangladesh Agriculture [42819] .... (Paid) 300

BELGIUM

Brussels
Biomaterials [42845]

Gent
Clinica Chimica Acta [42882]

BRAZIL

Curitiba
Brazilian Archives of Biology and Technology (BABT) [42976]

Petropolis
Computational & Applied Mathematics [42990]

Ribeirao Preto
Brazilian Journal of Medical and Biological Research [42996]
Genetics and Molecular Biology [42998]

Rio de Janeiro
Memorias do Instituto Oswaldo Cruz [43012]

Sao Paulo
Brazilian Journal of Microbiology [43026]
Papeis Avulsos de Zoologia (Sao Paulo) [43043]

Vacaria
Anais da Sociedade Entomologica do Brasil [43052]
Neotropical Entomology [43053]

CAMEROON

Dschang
Cameroon Journal of Experimental Biology [43125]
International Journal of Biological and Chemical Sciences [43126]

CHILE

Valparaiso
Electronic Journal of Biotechnology [43162]

PEOPLE'S REPUBLIC OF CHINA

Beijing
Science in China Series C [43217]

Hong Kong
Neuroembryology and Aging [43370]

Jinan
International Journal of Computational Intelligence in Bioinformatics and Systems Biology [43447]

Shanghai
Cell Research [43467]
Environmental Biosafety Research [43475]

COLOMBIA

Bogota
Acta Biologica Colombiana [43541]
Biota Colombiana [43543]

COTE D'IVOIRE

Abidjan
Afrique Science [43555]

DENMARK

Copenhagen
APMIS [43655]

Frederiksberg
Traffic [43696]

EGYPT

Alexandria
International Journal of Biotechnology & Biochemistry (IJBB) [43745]

Cairo
Egyptian Journal of Biochemistry and Molecular Biology [43756]
Egyptian Journal of Biotechnology [43758]
New Egyptian Journal of Microbiology [43763]

Ismailia
Egyptian Journal of Biology [43773]

ETHIOPIA

Addis Ababa
Ethiopian Journal of Biological Sciences [43798]

FINLAND

Kirkkonummi
TSW Development & Embryology [43875]

FRANCE

Les Ulis
Apidologie [43964] 1,000

Montrouge
Annales de Biologie Clinique [43980]

European Cytokine Network [43989]
European Journal of Dermatology [43990]
Journal de Pharmacie Clinique [43994]
La Lettre de l'Internat [43995]
Magnesium Research [43996]
Medecine therapeutique [43997]
Medecine therapeutique/Pediatrie [44001]
Oleagineux, Corps Gras, Lipides [44003]
Virologie [44008]

Nantes
Aquatic Living Resources [44011] 1,000

Nice
Gene Therapy and Regulation [44015]

Paris
Adansonia [44022]
Biology International [44029] 3,000
Option/Bio [44073]
Transfusion Clinique et Biologique [44086]

Perpignan
Plant Science [44093]

Strasbourg
Archives of Virology [44110]
World Journal of Microbiology and Biotechnology [44114]

Vandoeuvre-les-Nancy
Process Biochemistry [44122]

Villefranche-sur-Mer
Aquatic Microbial Ecology [44124]

Villeurbanne
Mathematical Modelling of Natural Phenomena [44126]

GEORGIA

Tbilisi
Journal of Biological Physics and Chemistry [44134]

GERMANY

Berlin
Biological Chemistry [44160]
Biomedizinische Technik [44161]
Clinical Chemistry and Laboratory Medicine [44165]

Bonn
Plant Signaling & Behavior [44269]

Cologne
Protist [44300]

Dusseldorf
Behavioural Brain Research [44321]
Parasitology Research [44330]

Erlangen
Journal of Molecular Modeling [44340]
Strahlentherapie und Onkologie [44342]

Freising
Systematic and Applied Microbiology [44375]

Giessen
International Journal of Systematic and Evolutionary Microbiology [44386] .... (Combined) 925
Neurogenetics [44388]

Gottingen
Biogeosciences Discussions [44394]
In Silico Biology [44399]

Heidelberg
Biological Cybernetics [44443]

Cell and Tissue Research [44444]
Histochemistry and Cell Biology [44460]
Journal of Mathematical Biology [44465]
Neuroradiology [44469]

Helgoland
Helgoland Marine Research [44481]

Jena
Journal of Basic Microbiology [44489]
Theory in Biosciences [44491]

Karlsruhe
Protoplasma [44495]

Kiel
Mammalian Biology [44504]
Marine Biology [44505]

Mainz
Biogeosciences [44538]

Munich
Economics and Human Biology [44559]
European Journal of Cell Biology [44560]
Mycoses [44574]
Organisms Diversity & Evolution [44577]

Munster
Review of Palaeobotany and Palynology [44601]

Oldendorf
Aquatic Biology [44625]
Diseases of Aquatic Organisms [44626]
Endangered Species Research [44627]

Osnabruck
Journal of Zoological Systematics and Evolutionary Research [44630]

Potsdam
Biophysical Reviews and Letters [44639]

Stuttgart
Bibliotheca Mycologica [44662]
Synthesis-Stuttgart [44682]

Weinheim
BioEssays [44701]
ChemMedChem [44704]
Lipid Technology [44707]

GREECE

Thessaloniki
Journal of Biological Research [44775]

HUNGARY

Budapest
Acta Biologica Hungarica [44808]
Acta Microbiologica et Immunologica Hungarica [44814]
Acta Phytopathologica et Entomologica Hungarica [44818]

ICELAND

Reykjavik
Chemistry and Physics of Lipids [44899]

INDIA

Allahabad
JP Journal of Biostatistics [44936]

Bangalore
Journal of Biosciences [44966] .. .. (Paid) 2,100

Delhi
The Anthropologist [45087] .... (Paid) 250

Circulation: ★ = ABC; △ = BPA; ◆ = CAC; • = CCAB; ❑ = VAC; ⊕ = PO Statement; ‡ = Publisher's Report; Boldface figures = sworn; Light figures = estimated.

Hyderabad
The Icfai Journal of Life Sciences [45158]

Jaipur
Indian Journal of Clinical Biochemistry [45195]

Jodhpur
Annual Review of Plant Pathology [45215]
Indian Journal of Experimental Biology [45223] 1,200

Lucknow
Journal of Environmental Biology [45323] 50,000

New Delhi
Biology Today [45489]
Indian Journal of Microbiology [45562]
International Journal for Computational Vision and Biomechanics [45581]
Journal of Cytology [45594]
Journal of Educational Planning and Administration [45596] .... (Paid) 700

Rajkot
Biochemistry [45706]
Biotechnology [45707]

Roorkee
Analytical Chemistry [45717]

Thiruvananthapuram
Trends in Biomaterials & Artificial Organs [45749]

IRAN
Tehran
Iranian Biomedical Journal [45895]
Iranian Journal of Biotechnology (IJB) [45898]

IRELAND
Dublin
Historical Biology [45964]

ITALY
Florence
Global Bioethics [46144]

Genoa
Rivista di Biologia [46153]

Grugliasco
International Journal of Food Microbiology [46155] 450

Milan
Journal of Applied Biomaterials & Biomechanics [46181]

Modena
Invertebrate Survival Journal (ISJ) [46199]

Rome
Experimental Brain Research [46228]
Medicina e Morale [46238]

JAPAN
Chiba
DNA Research [46317]

Fukuoka
International Journal of Biotronics [46343] .... (Free) 1,000

Hakodate
Plankton and Benthos Research [46372] .... (Paid) 700

Kanagawa
Biological Sciences in Space [46412] .... (Paid) 500

Kochi
Phycological Research [46436]

Kyoto
Acta Histochemica et Cytochemica [46465] .... (Paid) 1,800
Chemistry Letters [46468] .... ‡43,200
Mathematics Applied in Science and Technology [46482]
Publications of Seto Marine Biological Laboratory [46486] 460

Osaka
BioFactors [46616]
Viva Origino [46629]

Sendai
Bio-Medical Materials and Engineering [46664]

Tokyo
Actinomycetologica [46727]
Applied Entomology and Zoology [46746] .... (Paid) 1,900
Applied Magnetic Resonance [46747]
Biology and Fertility of Soils [46765]
Bioscience, Biotechnology, and Biochemistry [46767] .... (Paid) 3,600
Bulletin of the Chemical Society of Japan [46769] .... ‡37,200
Cellular and Molecular Life Sciences [46780]
Cytologia [46798] .... (Paid) 1,000
Development Genes and Evolution [46802]
Japanese Journal of Animal Psychology [46863] .... (Controlled) 500
Japanese Journal of Bacteriology [46865] ..!............... (Paid) 3,700
Japanese Journal of Biometrics [46866]
Japanese Journal of Medical Mycology [46871] .. .. (Paid) 1,000
Japanese Journal of Ornithology [46873] .... (Paid) 900
Journal of General and Applied Microbiology [46900] ... (Paid) 680
Journal of Japan Salivary Gland Society [46913]
Journal of Molecular Medicine [46928]
Medical Molecular Morphology [46966]

Yamagata
Marine Micropaleontology [47125]

Yokohama
Systems and Synthetic Biology [47142]

KENYA
Nairobi
African Journal of Biotechnology [47170]
Journal of Tropical Microbiology and Biotechnology [47190]

REPUBLIC OF KOREA
Seoul
Asian-Australasian Journal of Animal Sciences [47254] .. ./............. 1,000
Biochemistry and Molecular Biology Reports [47258]
Journal of Computational Intelligence in Bioinformatics [47272]
The Journal of Microbiology [47276]
Journal of Plant Biology [47277] .... (Paid) 750

MALAYSIA
Kota Kinabalu
Biotechnology & Molecular Biology Reviews [47588]

Kuala Lumpur
Malaysian Journal of Science Series A: Life Sciences [47618] 1,000
Neurology Asia [47629]

Serdang
Asia-Pacific Journal of Molecular Biology & Biotechnology [47714]

NETHERLANDS
Amsterdam
Advances in Colloid and Interface Science [47882]
Anaerobe [47891]
Analytical Biochemistry [47892]
Archives of Biochemistry and Biophysics [47898]
Biochemical and Biophysical Research Communications [47905]
Biochimica et Biophysica Acta (BBA) [47906]
Biochimica et Biophysica Acta (BBA)- General Subjects [47907]
Biochimica et Biophysica Acta (BBA)- Molecular and Cell Biology of Lipids [47909]
Biochimica et Biophysica Acta (BBA)- Proteins & Proteomics [47910]
Bioelectrochemistry [47911]
Blood Cells, Molecules, & Diseases [47912]
Brain Research Bulletin [47914]
Cell Biology International [47923]
Cryobiology [47942]
Current Biology [47943]
Current Opinion in Biotechnology [47944]
Current Opinion in Cell Biology [47945]
Current Opinion in Chemical Biology [47946]
Current Opinion in Microbiology [47948]
Cytokine [47952]
Developmental Biology [47954]
Experimental Cell Research [47978] 1,986
Experimental Neurology [47981]
Experimental Parasitology [47982]
Food Microbiology [47987]
Free Radical Biology and Medicine [47990]
Frontiers in Neuroendocrinology [47991]
Fungal Genetics and Biology [47994]
Hormones and Behavior [48013]
Interaction Studies [48022]
International Biodeterioration and Biodegradation [48024]
Journal of Autoimmunity [48053]
Journal of Cereal Science [48056]
Journal of Colloid and Interface Science [48060]
Journal of Invertebrate Pathology [48088]
Journal of Magnetic Resonance [48093]
Journal of Molecular Biology [48097]
Journal of Neurolinguistics [48102]
Journal of Proteomics [48113]
Matrix Biology [48149]
Metabolic Engineering [48154]
Methods [48156]
Microvascular Research [48159]
Molecular and Cellular Neurosciences [48164]
Molecular Genetics and Metabolism [48166]
Molecular Immunology [48167]
Molecular Phylogenetics and Evolution [48168]
Neural Networks [48172]
NeuroImage [48174]
Neuropsychologia [48176]

Neuroscience Letters [48177]
Neuroscience Research [48178]
Neurotoxicology and Teratology [48179]
Nitric Oxide [48182]
Plasmid [48206]
Protein Expression and Purification [48217]
Seminars in Cell & Developmental Biology [48230]
Tailoring Biotechnologies [48240]
Thermochimica Acta [48248]
Trends in Biochemical Sciences [48257]
Trends in Biotechnology [48258]
Trends in Cell Biology [48259]
Trends in Ecology & Evolution [48261]
Trends in Genetics [48263]
Trends in Microbiology [48264]
Trends in Neurosciences [48265]
Trends in Parasitology [48266]

Bussum
Current Bioinformatics [48283]
Current Pharmacogenomics and Personalized Medicine [48295]

Dordrecht
Acta Biotheoretica [48319]
Aerobiologia [48321]
Biogeochemistry [48332]
Biology and Philosophy [48334]
Bulletin of Mathematical Biology [48340]
Cell Biology and Toxicology [48347]
Central European Journal of Biology [48348]
Clinical & Experimental Metastasis [48354]
Frontiers of Biology in China [48393]
Genetica [48405]
Hydrobiologia [48419]
Journal of Bamboo and Rattan [48442]
Journal of Biomedical Science [48445]
Journal of Computational Neuroscience [48451]
Journal of Neuro-Oncology [48477]
Mycopathologia [48516]
Origins of Life and Evolution of the Biosphere [48523]
Photosynthetica [48529]
Plant Cell, Tissue and Organ Culture [48532]
Plant Ecology [48533]
Plant Foods for Human Nutrition [48534]
Plant Molecular Biology [48535]
Reviews in Fish Biology and Fisheries [48557]
Somatic Cell and Molecular Genetics [48565]

Eindhoven
Journal of Biomechanics [48592]

Leiden
Animal Biology [48647]
Applied Herpetology [48648]
Behaviour [48656]
Insect Systematics & Evolution [48678]
Journal of Biomaterials Science, Polymer Edition [48690]

Utrecht
Mechanisms of Development [48763]

NEW ZEALAND
Albany
Evolutionary Bioinformatics Online [48777]

Auckland
Zootaxa [48833]

Circulation: ★ = ABC; △ = BPA; ◆ = CAC; • = CCAB; ❑ = VAC; ⊕ = PO Statement; ‡ = Publisher's Report; Boldface figures = sworn; Light figures = estimated.

Dunedin
Journal of Neuroendocrinology
[48890]

Wellington
New Zealand Journal of Marine and
Freshwater Research [49027]

NIGERIA
Aba
Journal of Medical Investigation and
Practice [49055]

Asaba
Journal of Applied Chemistry and Agricultural Research [49061]

Benin City
Tropical Freshwater Biology [49066]

Calabar
Global Journal of Pure and Applied
Sciences [49075]
Journal of Medical Laboratory
Science [49077]

Ilorin
African Journal of Clinical and Experimental Microbiology [49117]

Lagos
African Journal of Biochemistry
Research [49130]
African Journal of Microbiology
Research [49133]
Journal of Cell & Animal Biology
[49139]

Nnewi
Journal of Biomedical Investigation
[49148]

Nsukka
Plant Products Research Journal
[49152]
Bio-Research [49156]

Port Harcourt
African Journal of Applied Zoology
and Environmental Biology [49165]

NORWAY
Trondheim
Norsk Geologisk Tidsskrift [49219]

PAKISTAN
Faisalabad
Advances in Biological Research
[49230]
Asian Journal of Cell Biology [49235]
Biotechnology [49239]
Global Journal of Biotechnology &
Biochemistry [49241]
International Journal of Botany
[49249]
International Journal of
Pharmacology [49252]
Pakistan Journal of Biological
Sciences [49276]
Research Journal of Agriculture and
Biological Sciences [49280]
Research Journal of Biological
Sciences [49285]
Research Journal of Cell and Mo-
lecular Biology [49286]
World Applied Sciences Journal
[49297]

Karachi
Current Bioactive Compounds
[49342]
Pakistan Journal of Pharmaceutical
Sciences [49371]

POLAND
Gdansk
Folia Morphologica [49657]

Kornik
Dendrobiology [49663]

Krakow
Polish Gerontology [49668]

Warsaw
Acta Protozoologica [49682]
Advances in Cell Biology [49684]
Biologija [49696]
Journal of Plant Protection Research
[49725]
Macedonian Journal of Medical
Sciences [49734]
Polish Journal of Natural Sciences
[49750]
Polish Sexology [49755]

Wroclaw
Cellular & Molecular Biology Letters
[49777]

PORTUGAL
Aveiro
International Journal of Molecular
Engineering [49788]

Lisbon
Acta Ethologica [49801]
Natural Products [49804]

ROMANIA
Bucharest
Balkan Journal of Geometry and its
Applications [49832]

RUSSIA
Moscow
Acarina [49867]
Applied Biochemistry and
Microbiology [49875]
Biochemistry (Moscow) [49883]
Doklady Biochemistry and Biophysics
[49894]
Doklady Biological Sciences [49895]
Human Physiology [49915]
Journal of Ichthyology [49929]
Problems of Biological, Medical and
Pharmaceutical Chemistry [49962]
Russian Journal of Bioorganic
Chemistry [49975]
Russian Journal of Biotechnology
[49976]
Russian Journal of Theriology
[49983]

Saint Petersburg
Cell and Tissue Biology [50020]
Journal of Evolutionary Biochemistry
and Physiology [50023]

Vladivostok
Russian Journal of Marine Biology
[50040]

SINGAPORE
Singapore
Biomolecular Frontiers [50116]
Harmful Algae [50163]
International Journal of Humanoid
Robotics (IJHR) [50181]
ITBM - RBM [50197]
Journal of Biological Systems
[50200]
Singapore National Academy of Sci-
ence Journal
[50261] ... (Paid) 1,500

SLOVAKIA
Bratislava
Acta Virologica [50316]

SLOVENIA
Hajdina
Biota [50331]

REPUBLIC OF SOUTH AF-
RICA
Bloemfontein
Navorsinge van die Nasionale Mu-
sium, Bloemfontein [50355]

Grahamstown
African Journal of Biomedical
Research [50487]
Journal of Applied Science, Engineer-
ing and Technology [50500]

Lynnwood Ridge
South African Journal of Science
[50551]

Pietermaritzburg
African Journal of Aquatic Science
[50564]
African Zoology [50566]

Tygerberg
African Journal of Herpetology
[50638]

SPAIN
Barcelona
International Microbiology [50681]

SRI LANKA
Colombo
Journal of the National Aquatic Re-
sources Research & Development
Agency of Sri Lanka [50856]
Physical Biology [50862]

Peradeniya
Ceylon Journal of Science, Biological
Sciences [50927] ... (Paid) 500

SWEDEN
Goteborg
Current Genetics [50958]
Molecular Genetics and Genomics
[50959]

Stockholm
Grana [51019]
Seminars in Cancer Biology [51036]

Umea
TumorBiology [51048] ... 1,000

Uppsala
Computer Methods and Programs in
Biomedicine [51050]

SWITZERLAND
Basel
Chromosoma [51061]
Progress in Histochemistry and
Cytochemistry [51065]

Geneva
International Journal of Biomedical
Nanoscience and Nanotechnology
[51104]

TURKEY
Ankara
Biyokimya Dergisi [51490]
Turkish Journal of Biology [51504]

UNITED KINGDOM
Abingdon
Connective Tissue Research [51741]
IUBMB Life [51864]
Journal of Experimental Nanoscience
[51897]
Medical Mycology [51973]

Basingstoke
BioSocieties [52196]

Bedford
Journal of Applied Microbiology
[52273]

Bradford
The Naturalist
[52529] ... (Combined) 5,800

Bristol
Biofabrication [52645]
Bioinspiration & Biomimetics [52646]
Biomedical Materials [52647]
Journal of Cellular Automata [52683]
Journal of Neural Engineering
[52692]
Nanotechnology [52708]
Reproduction [52726]

Buckingham
Biofouling [52754]

Burnham
Outlooks on Pest Management
[52767]

Cambridge
Applied Bionics and Biomechanics
[52790]
Biological Reviews [52792]
Chinese Journal of Agricultural
Biotechnology [52806]
FEBS Journal [52820]
Highlights in Chemical Biology
[52826]
Human Reproduction Update [52829]
International Journal of Tropical In-
sect Science [52838]
Journal of Biosocial Science
[52846] ... 500
Journal of Cell Science [52847]
Journal of Experimental Biology
[52852]
Metallomics [52868]
Molecular Biosystems [52871]
Neuron Glia Biology [52874]
Neuropsychological Rehabilitation
[52875]
Photochemical & Photobiological
Science [52882]
Softmatter [52897]

Cardiff
Autonomic and Autacoid
Pharmacology [52924]
Journal of Neuroscience Methods
[52935]

Childerley
Molecular Human Reproduction
[53019]

Colchester
Biochemical Society Symposia
[53029]
Biochemical Society Transactions
[53030]
Essays in Biochemistry [53035]

Durham
Journal of Thermal Biology [53230]

Edinburgh
Cloning and Stem Cells [53263]
Fungal Biology Reviews [53279]

Glasgow
Cellular Signalling [53412]

Kidlington
Food and Chemical Toxicology
[53692]

Leeds
Bioscience Education E-journal
[53757]

Leicester
Immunobiology [53804]

Liverpool
Biological Conservation [53869]

London
Anatomical Science International
[53941]
Behavioral and Brain Functions
[54009]

Circulation: ★ = ABC; △ = BPA; ◆ = CAC; • = CCAB; ❑ = VAC; ⊕ = PO Statement; ‡ = Publisher's Report; Boldface figures = sworn; Light figures = estimated.

The Biochemist
  [54019] .... (Controlled) 9,000
Bioinformation [54020]
Biological Knowledge [54021]
Biologicals [54022]
Biologist [54023] 26,000
Biology Letters [54024]
BioVenture View
  [54031] .... (Paid) 327
BMC Bioinformatics [54037]
BMC Biology [54038]
BMC Biotechnology [54039]
BMC Cancer [54041]
BMC Cell Biology [54043]
BMC Chemical Biology [54044]
BMC Clinical Pathology [54045]
BMC Complementary and Alternative
  Medicine [54047]
BMC Developmental Biology [54049]
BMC Evolutionary Biology [54054]
BMC Immunology [54061]
BMC Microbiology [54072]
BMC Molecular Biology [54073]
BMC Plant Biology [54085]
BMC Structural Biology [54089]
British Journal of Biomedical Science
  [54112]
Cancer Cell International [54171]
Cell Communication and Signaling
  [54190]
Cell Death & Differentiation [54191]
Cell Proliferation [54192]
Diagnostic Pathology [54325]
EMBO Reports [54362]
Gene Therapy [54499]
Genome Biology (Online Edition)
  [54502]
Innate Immunity [54605]
International Journal of Biochemistry
  & Cell Biology [54635]
Journal of Bioinformatics and Compu-
  tational Biology [54705]
Journal of Biological Education
  [54706] .. .. (Paid) ‡1,800
Journal of Circadian Rhythms
  [54724]
Journal of Exposure Science and En-
  vironmental Epidemiology (JESEE)
  [54750]
Journal of Nanobiotechnology
  [54783]
Journal of NeuroEngineering and Re-
  habilitation (JNER) [54785]
Journal of Virological Methods
  [54833]
Microbial Cell Factories [54929]
Molecular and Cellular Endocrinology
  [54946]
Molecular Systems Biology [54949]
Nature Cell Biology [54971]
Nature Reviews Microbiology [54982]
Nature Reviews Molecular Cell
  Biology [54983]
NMR in Biomedicine [55006]
Nutrition & Metabolism [55020]
Philosophical Transactions of the
  Royal Society B [55080]
Philosophy, Ethics, and Humanities in
  Medicine [55082]
Plant Methods [55093]
Profound (The Dialog Corporation) of
  the Royal Society B [55134]
Proteome Science [55145]
Reproductive Health [55190]
Saline Systems [55217]
Theoretical Biology and Medical
  Modelling [55306]
Trends in Endocrinology and Metabo-
  lism (TEM) [55339]

Loughborough
Annals of Human Biology [55477]

Luton
Computational Biology and Chemistry
  [55500]

Manchester
Biochemical Engineering Journal
  [55544]
Cell Calcium [55546]
International Journal of Health Pro-
  motion and Education [55559]

Nottingham
Mathematical Medicine and Biology
  [55766]

Olney
International Journal of Biomedical
  Engineering and Technology
  [55792]
International Journal of Cognitive
  Performance Support (IJCPS)
  [55793]

Oxford
Acta Biochimica et Biophysica Sinica
  [55859]
Acta Histochemica [55860]
Archaeometry [55871]
Bioethics [55880]
Bioinformatics [55881]
Briefings in Bioinformatics [55889]
Briefings in Functional Genomics &
  Proteomics [55890]
Cancer Science [55903]
European Biophysics Journal [55942]
FEMS Immunology and Medical
  Microbiology [55954]
FEMS Microbiology Reviews [55955]
FEMS Yeast Research [55956]
Insect Science [55990]
The Journal of Biochemistry [56017]
Journal of Eukaryotic Microbiology
  [56030]
Journal of Heredity [56037]
Journal of Molluscan Studies [56052]
Journal of Phytopathology [56058]
Molecular Biology and Evolution
  [56105]
Molecular Ecology Resources
  [56107]
Neuromodulation [56114]
Neuropathology [56115]
Neuropathology and Applied
  Neurobiology [56116]
Nucleic Acids Research [56121]
Palaeontology [56140]
Pigment Cell and Melanoma
  Research [56158]
Plant and Cell Physiology [56160]
Plant Species Biology [56161]
Progress in Biophysics & Molecular
  Biology [56170]
Protein Engineering, Design and
  Selection [56172]
Transplant International [56222]

Penicuik
Agricultural and Forest Entomology
  [56242]

Plymouth
Journal of the Marine Biological As-
  sociation of the United Kingdom
  (JMBA) [56272] 1,600

Reading
Journal of General Virology
  [56323] 2,000
Microbiology [56325]
Microbiology Today [56326]

Richmond
Systematics and Biodiversity
  [56392] .... ‡700

Southampton
Biomedical Signal Processing and
  Control [56568]
Continental Shelf Research [56569]

Stevenage
IEE Proceedings Nanobiotechnology
  [56610]
Systems Biology [56618]

Sutton
Mutagenesis [56689]

Wallingford
AgBiotech News and Information
  [56813] 180

Warwick
Annals of Applied Biology
  [56852] 1,100

Witney
Bio-science Law Review [56939]

BOATS AND MARINE
See also Ships and Ship-
ping

AUSTRALIA
Sydney
Maritime Workers Journal
  [42539] .... (Non-paid) ⊕10,000

JAPAN
Tokyo
ClassNK Magazine [46786]
Ports and Harbors [47023] 5,000

NETHERLANDS
Amsterdam
Marine Structures [48141]

Delft
International Shipbuilding Progress
  [48310]

The Hague
Terra et Aqua [48628]

PAKISTAN
Faisalabad
Universal Science and Engineering
  for Marine Environment [49295]

POLAND
Warsaw
Polish Maritime Research [49752]

REPUBLIC OF SOUTH AF-
RICA
Cape Town
Shipyear [50411] 10,000

UNITED KINGDOM
Cambridge
Boat and Yacht Buyer
  [52794] 20,000

Cardiff
Marine Policy [52936]

Charmouth
Tide Times [52958] ... . (Paid) 27,500

Chichester
Boat Trader [53005]

Dewsbury
Cook's Log [53178]

Enfield
LNG World Shipping
  [53332] .... ‡3,637
LPG World Shipping
  [53333] .... (Combined) 2,586
Marine Electronics &
  Communications [53334] ... ★6,944
Marine Propulsion & Auxiliary
  Machinery [53335] .... ★12,525

Offshore Support Journal
  [53336] .... ‡4,800
Tanker Shipping & Trade
  [53337] .... ★4,798

Fareham
Maritime Journal
  [53373] .... (Controlled) 6,000

Glasgow
Brown's Nautical Almanac
  [53410] 13,000
The Nautical Magazine
  [53433] .... (Combined) 52,000

Hailsham
Mariner's Mirror [53501]

London
Flying Angel News [54473] ... 18,800
Journal [54694] 800
Journal for Maritime Research
  [54775]
The Maritime Pilot
  [54906] .... (Controlled) 1,250
The Naval Architect
  [54986] .... (Combined) ★11,650
The Sea
  [55223] .... (Combined) 25,000
Seafarer [55224] 8,500
Seaways [55225] 7,500
Ship & Boat International
  [55233] .... (Combined) ★5,998
Ship Repair & Conversion
  Technology
  [55234] .... (Combined) 6,096
Significant Ships
  [55239] .... (Combined) 4,000
Warship Technology
  [55380] .... (Combined) 11,650
World Cruise Industry Review
  [55418] .... (Non-paid) 6,993
World Superyacht Review
  [55424] 10,000

Redhill
Register of Ships [56377]
Safety at Sea International
  [56378] .... (Paid) 6,000

Ware
ISESnews [56841]

Watford
Sports of Seven Seas [56876]

West Hoe
Marine Environmental Research
  [56891]

Windermere
School Sailing Matters
  [56931] .... ★500

Windsor
Marine News [56932] 4,000

Wokingham
Canal Boat [56949]

BOOK TRADE AND
AUTHOR NEWS

BULGARIA
Sofia
Bulgarian Folklore [43095]

DENMARK
Copenhagen
Forfatteren [43669]

FINLAND
Helsinki
Books from Finland
  [43821] ..:......,.. (Combined) 2,800

FRANCE
Riberac
The African Book Publishing Record
  [44098] .... (Paid) 300

NEW ZEALAND
Auckland
New Zealand Author
[48805] 1,300

Wellington
Booknotes [49001]
Booksellers News [49002]

SPAIN
Madrid
Delibros [50751]

SWITZERLAND
Basel
Bookbird [51060] 1,500

TURKEY
Istanbul
Matbaa & Teknik [51561] 9,690

UNITED KINGDOM
Dorchester
Thomas Hardy Journal [53190]

Durham City
The Wellsian [53233]

Forest Row
North Wind [53397]

London
Author [53983] 9,200
Book and Magazine Collector
[54097]
Books for Keeps
[54098] .... (Paid) 9,000
Bookselling Essentials
[54099] .... (Controlled) 3,300
Bronte Studies
[54150] .... (Paid) 750
The Edge [54353] 2,000
Foundation [54479] 1,200
Journal of William Morris Studies
[54837]
The Library [54869]
The New Rambler [54996]
Rare Book Review [55173]

Meopham
Swedish Book Review
[55608] 800

Taunton
Powys Journal [56722] 400

Thurlby by Bourne
The Book Collector [56749]

Walberton
The Bookplate Journal
[56811] .... (Paid) 250

BOTANY

AUSTRALIA
Collingwood
Australasian Plant Disease Notes
[41781]
Functional Plant Biology [41789]

Perth
Australasian Plant Pathology [42245]

BELGIUM
Leuven
Acta Horticulturae [42890]

BRAZIL
Brasilia
Fitopatologia Brasileira [42958]

Pelotas
Brazilian Journal of Plant Physiology
[42989]

Sao Paulo
Acta Botanica Brasilica [43020]

PEOPLE'S REPUBLIC OF CHINA
Beijing
Chinese Journal of Plant Pathology
[43185] 1,500

COLOMBIA
Bogota
Caldasia [43544]

COTE D'IVOIRE
Abidjan
Agronomie Africaine [43556]

FRANCE
Dijon
Mycorrhiza [43945]

Perpignan
Plant Science [44093]

GERMANY
Berlin
Botanica Marina [44162]
Feddes Repertorium [44179]

Halle
Flora [44407]

Heidelberg
Plant Cell Reports [44473]
Theoretical and Applied Genetics
[44478]

Kiel
Marine Biology [44505]
Polar Biology [44507]

Munster
Review of Palaeobotany and
Palynology [44601]

Stuttgart
Advances in Bryology [44659]
Bibliotheca Phycologica [44663]
Nova Hedwigia [44673]
Phytocoenologia [44676]
Senckenbergiana biologica [44678]

Weinheim
Lipid Technology [44707]

HUNGARY
Martonvasar
Acta Agronomica Hungarica [44890]

Pecs
Acta Botanica Hungarica [44893]

INDIA
Bangalore
Journal of Natural Remedies [44975]

Calicut
Rheedea [45022] .... (Paid) 500

Hyderabad
The Icfai Journal of Life Sciences
[45158]

Jodhpur
Journal of Economic and Taxonomic
Botany [45226]
Phytomorphology
[45228] .... (Paid) 1,200

Lucknow
Palaeobotanist
[45325] .... (Paid) 400

Mumbai
Taxation Law Reports
[45446] .. .. (Paid) 1,500

New Delhi
The Indian Journal of Crop Science
[45550]
Journal of Plant Biochemistry and
Biotechnology
[45616] .... (Paid) 750

Tiruchirapalli
Swamy Botanical Club Journal
[45751] .... (Paid) 250

ITALY
Rome
Geneflow [46230]

JAPAN
Chiba
Mycoscience [46320]

Fukui
Weed Biology and Management
[46333]

Ibaraki
Sago Communication
[46394] .... (Free) 650

Kochi
Phycological Research [46436]

Kyoto
Journal of General Plant Pathology
[46476]

Tokyo
Journal of Plant Research
[46938] .... (Paid) 2,600
Plant Production Science [47018]
Tree Physiology
[47053] .... (Paid) 600
(Non-paid) 150

REPUBLIC OF KOREA
Seoul
Journal of Plant Biology
[47277] .... (Paid) 750

NETHERLANDS
Amsterdam
Current Opinion in Plant Biology
[47949]
Environmental & Experimental
Botany [47968] 800
Journal of Arid Environments [48049]
Plant Physiology and Biochemistry
[48205]

Dordrecht
Biologia Plantarum [48333]
Photosynthesis Research [48528]
Photosynthetica [48529]
Plant Foods for Human Nutrition
[48534]
Plant Molecular Biology [48535]

Renkum
Journal of Vegetation Science
[48746]

NEW ZEALAND
Wellington
New Zealand Journal of Botany
[49022]

NIGERIA
Lagos
African Journal of Plant Science
[49134]

Nsukka
Plant Products Research Journal
[49152]

PAKISTAN
Faisalabad
American-Eurasian Journal of Botany
[49233]

Asian Journal of Plant Sciences
[49237]
Botany Research Journal [49240]
International Journal of Botany
[49249]
Plant Pathology Journal [49278]
Plant Sciences Research [49279]
Research Journal of Agronomy
[49281]

Karachi
Pakistan Journal of Botany
[49368] .... (Controlled) 1,000

POLAND
Warsaw
Journal of Plant Protection Research
[49725]

RUSSIA
Moscow
Crystallography Reports [49891]

SINGAPORE
Singapore
Singapore National Academy of Science Journal
[50261] .. .. (Paid) 1,500
Urban Forestry & Urban Greening
[50283]

SPAIN
Barcelona
Arxus de Miscel-lania Zoologica
[50651]

Murcia
Phytochemistry [50822]

SWEDEN
Lund
Physiologia Plantarum [50989]

Stockholm
Grana [51019]

SWITZERLAND
Basel
Progress in Histochemistry and
Cytochemistry [51065]

Zurich
IOS Bulletin [51268] 300

TAIWAN
Taipei
Botanical Studies [51333]

TURKEY
Ankara
Turkish Journal of Botany [51505]

UGANDA
Kampala
African Crop Science Journal [51583]

UNITED KINGDOM
Abingdon
Journal of Plant Interactions [51931]

Bristol
Plant Biotechnology Journal [52719]

Cambridge
Chinese Journal of Agricultural
Biotechnology [52806]
Plant Genetic Resources [52884]
Seed Science Research [52893]

Lancaster
Journal of Experimental Botany
[53734]

Circulation: ★ = ABC; △ = BPA; ◆ = CAC; • = CCAB; ❑ = VAC; ⊕ = PO Statement; ‡ = Publisher's Report; Boldface figures = sworn; Light figures = estimated.

Leicester
Annals of Botany [53784]

London
BMC Ecology [54051]
BMC Plant Biology [54085]
European Journal of Phycology
  [54404]
Plant Methods [55093]
Transactions of the Royal Society of
  Tropical Medicine and Hygiene
  [55335]

Middlewich
Journal of Bryology [55624]

Orpington
Gardens Monthly [55851]

Oxford
Acta Histochemica [55860]
Briefings in Functional Genomics &
  Proteomics [55890]
Journal of Experimental Botany
  [56032]
Journal of Integrative Plant Biology
  [56043]
Journal of Phytopathology [56058]
Palaeontology [56140]
Plant Breeding [56159]
Plant Species Biology [56161]

Reading
Molecular Plant Pathology [56327]
New Disease Reports [56328]

Richmond
Chamaerops Magazine [56389]

Shrewsbury
Field Studies [56529]

Wallingford
In Vitro Cellular and Developmental
  Biology - Plant [56819]
Review of Aromatic and Medicinal
  Plants [56825]
Review of Plant Pathology
  [56828] 690

VENEZUELA
Caracas
Acta Botanica Venezuelica [57019]

BUILDING MANAGEMENT AND MAINTENANCE
See also Real Estate

AUSTRALIA
Leederville
Cranes and Lifting Australia [42006]

Nundah
Developers Digest [42222] 1750

DENMARK
Glostrup
HVAC Magasinet [43705] .... ‡350

GERMANY
Leinfelden-Echterdingen
Metamorphose [44527] 11,916

Nuremberg
Element + BAU [44610] 6,800

IRELAND
Blackrock
Irish Hardware [45921] .... ⋆1,664

JAPAN
Tokyo
Nikkei Construction
  [46985] .... ⋆26,357

NETHERLANDS
Amsterdam
Building and Environment [47917]

Dordrecht
Journal of Housing and the Built
  Environment [48467]

UNITED REPUBLIC OF TANZANIA
Dar es Salaam
Journal of Building and Land
  Development [51402]

UNITED KINGDOM
Abingdon
Housing, Theory & Society [51807]

Basingstoke
Journal of Building Appraisal [52213]

Birmingham
Build It [52335]

Brighton
Housing, Care and Support [52613]

Buckhurst Hill
Refurbishment Projects
  [52752] .. .. ⋆10,138

Cheltenham
The Drain Trader
  [52967] .... (Combined) 4,500

Hemel Hempstead
Demolition and Dismantling
  [53556] 4,000

London
Building Research & Information
  [54153]
FM World [54474]
News on the Block
  [55002] 10,000
Vernacular Architecture [55367]

Preston
Journal of Financial Management of
  Property and Construction [56300]

Wadhurst
Construction Europe
  [56805] .... ⋆14,624

Watford
Housing Association Building &
  Maintenance [56865] .... ⋆11,500
Local Authority Building and
  Maintenance [56868] .. .. ⋆17,500

BUILDING MATERIALS, CONCRETE, BRICK, AND TILE

AUSTRALIA
North Ryde
Poolside Showcase
  [42194] 30,000
Stone [42198] 12,000

BELGIUM
Brussels
Beton [42844]

GERMANY
Gutersloh
ZI-Ziegelindustrie International
  [44406]

Nuremberg
Element + BAU [44610] 6,800

INDIA
Mumbai
Indian Cement Review
  [45375] .. .. (Paid) 4,000

IRELAND
Blackrock
Irish Hardware [45921] .... ⋆1,664

MALAYSIA
Perlis
International Journal of Materials En-
  gineering and Technology [47694]

NETHERLANDS
Amsterdam
Cement and Concrete Composites
  [47924]
Marine Structures [48141]

Dordrecht
Journal of Housing and the Built
  Environment [48467]

SWEDEN
Stockholm
Nordic Journal of Building Physics
  [51027]

SWITZERLAND
Lausanne
Cement and Concrete Research
  [51185]

UNITED KINGDOM
Ascot
Construction Information Quarterly
  [52137] 4,000
Construction Manager
  [52138] 33,000

Bordon
Cracking Matters [52407]

Buckhurst Hill
Refurbishment Projects
  [52752] .. .. ⋆10,138

Cambridge
Journal of Advanced Materials
  [52841]

Coventry
The International Journal of
  Ventilation [53085]

Guildford
Journal of Constructional Steel
  Research [53493]

London
Building Research & Information
  [54153]
Geosynthetics International [54504]
House Builder [54575]
Vernacular Architecture [55367]

Sevenoaks
FENSA News [56472]

Surrey
Concrete Quarterly [56660]
Global Cement Magazine
  [56663] .... ⋆5,346
Global Gypsum Magazine
  [56664] 3,247
Global Insulation Magazine [56665]

Wadhurst
Construction Europe
  [56805] .... ⋆14,624

Watford
Professional Builder
  [56869] .... ⋆98,489
Professional Builders Merchant
  [56870] .... ⋆9,500

BUSINESS
See also Accountants and
Accounting; Advertising and
Marketing; Banking; Finance, and Investments;
Chambers of Commerce and
Boards of Trade; Commerce
and Industry; Economics;
International Business and
Economics; Management
and Administration; Purchasing; Selling and Salesmanship; Taxation and Tariff

AUSTRALIA
Brisbane
International Journal of Knowledge-
  Based Development [41650]

Chatswood
Manufacturers Monthly
  [41740] .... ◆15,269

Clayton
International Journal of Business Intelligence and Data Mining [41761]

Leederville
Australian Longwall Magazine
  [42004] 3,500
Australia's Mining Monthly
  [42005] .... ⋆8,268
Cranes and Lifting Australia [42006]
RESOURCESTOCKS
  [42007] 15,000

Melbourne
BRW [42055]
International Journal of Managing
  Projects in Business [42067]

North Richmond
Australian Farm Journal
  [42160] .... ⋆4,456

Perth
Asia Pacific Journal of Marketing and
  Logistics [42244]

Pyrmont
Professional Beauty [42287] ... 9,000

Sydney
Asset [42449]
Australian [42450] 131,753
International Journal of Housing Markets and Analysis [42520]
miceAsia.net [42543] .. .. ‡17,548
mice.net [42544] .... ‡14,794
miceNZ.net [42545] .... ‡7,857

Templestowe
FB Magazine [42616] 8,960
Supplier Woodworking magazine
  [42618] 17,000

Toowoomba
Australian Journal of Organisational
  Behavior & Management [42626]

Wahroonga
Voice&Data [42678] 7,745

AUSTRIA
Linz
Statistical Papers [42734]

Vienna
Connex [42749] 2,100

AZERBAIJAN
Baku
Caspian Business News
  [42780] .. .. (Paid) 4,000

BAHRAIN
Manama
Arab World Agribusiness
  [42786] 18,715

Circulation: ⋆ = ABC; △ = BPA; ◆ = CAC; • = CCAB; ❏ = VAC; ⊕ = PO Statement; ‡ = Publisher's Report; Boldface figures = sworn; Light figures = estimated.

Gulf Industry
[42790] .. .. (Paid) 13,614

BANGLADESH
Dhaka
Bangladesh Development Studies
[42803] .. .. (Paid) 1,500

BELGIUM
Antwerp
Sparraaja
[42840] .... (Controlled) 4,000
Brussels
EE Times UK [42850]
Mortsel
Journal of Network Industries [42906]

BRAZIL
Rio de Janeiro
International Journal of Technological
Learning, Innovation &
Development [43009]

BRUNEI DARUSSALAM
Bandar Seri Begawan
Borneo Bulletin
[43072] .... (Mon.-Fri.) 20,000
(Sun.) 25,000

CHILE
Santiago
Journal of Technology Management
& Innovation [43145]

PEOPLE'S REPUBLIC OF CHINA
Beijing
British Business in China
[43174] 2,000
Business Beijing [43175] 50,000
China Business [43177]
Journal of Chinese Economic and
Foreign Trade Studies [43204]
Hong Kong
Asian Affairs [43273]
Asian Credit Investor [43275]
Asian Venture Capital Journal
[43280]
The Asset [43281]
Business Strategy and the
Environment [43286]
Hong Kong for the Business Visitor
[43322] 40,000
Hong Kong Entrepreneur
[43324] 4,200
Hong Kong Industrialist
[43325] .... (Paid) 7,000
Innovative Investor [43348]
Journal of Construction Research
[43354]
Time Asia [43384] .... ★272,363
Shanghai
Shanghai Tatler [43502] .. ...: ‡60,000
Wuhan
International Journal of Services,
Economics and Management
[43523]
Xi'an
International Journal of Digital Enter-
prise Technology [43537]

CUBA
Havana
Cuba Foreign Trade
[43576] 3,000

CYPRUS
Nicosia
Emporoviomichaniki [43594] ... 4,000

DENMARK
Copenhagen
Boersen [43657]
ErhvervsBladet
[43667] ...... (Controlled) ‡105,542
Odense
International Journal of Advanced
Operations Management [43727]
International Journal of Business Per-
formance and Supply Chain
Modelling [43728]

EGYPT
Cairo
Business Today Egypt [43752]
Egypt Today [43755] 14,500

FINLAND
Helsinki
Fakta [43827] .. .. (Paid) 30,000

FRANCE
Le Havre
International Journal of Adaptive and
Innovative Systems [43963]
Paris
Electronique International Hebdo
[44039]
Revue de l'Energie [44080]

GERMANY
Darmstadt
GIT Sicherheit Management
[44307] .... ‡28,281
Dreieich
Made in Germany—International
Edition
[44318] ...... (Combined) ‡110,000
Dusseldorf
Schmalenbach Business Review
[44333]
Ettlingen
DIY [44349] .. .. (Combined) 9,231
Flensburg
International Journal of Globalisation
and Small Business [44355]
Frankfurt
Frankfurter Allgemeine [44360]
Heidelberg
Teaching Business Ethics [44476]
Heusenstamm
Allgemeine Papier-Rundschau
[44485]
Kiel
International Journal of Wine Busi-
ness Research (IJWBR) [44502]
Munich
Computern im Handwerk
[44555] .. .. (Combined) ‡72,351
Munster
Information Systems and E-Business
Management (ISeB) [44598]
Journal of Business Chemistry
(JoBC) [44599]
Nuremberg
dedica [44608] 19,993
Industrie Diamanten Rundschau
[44615] 6,800
Poing
Computer Reseller News
[44634] .. ...:... (Controlled) 33,136
Information Week
[44636] .. .. (Combined) 75,253
Network Computing
[44637] .. .. (Combined) 52,181

Vaterstetten
E-Commerce Magazin
[44698] .... ‡14,675
Wurzburg
MM Industrial Magazine Western
Europe
[44722] .... (Controlled) 20,000
MM Maschinenmarkt
[44723] .... (Combined) 44,200

GREECE
Athens
International Journal of Multicriteria
Decision Making [44749]
Thessaloniki
International Journal of Innovation
and Regional Development [44773]

HUNGARY
Budapest
Figyelo TOP 200
[44832] .. .. (Paid) 10,000
Figyelo Trend [44833] .. .. ‡15,000
Market!ng&Media
[44848] .... (Combined) ‡1,520
UZLET & SIKER [44881] .... ‡20,346

INDIA
Allahabad
Indian Journal of Economics
[44931] 500
Chennai
Hindu Business Line
[45033] .. .. (Paid) 24,823
Delhi
IAMR Report [45093]
IAMR Working Paper [45094]
Gurgaon
Vision [45128] .. .. (Paid) 500
Hyderabad
The Icfai Journal of Entrepreneurship
Development [45149]
Professional Banker [45180]
Kolkata
Business World [45261] 37,204
Opsearch [45300] .. .. (Paid) 2,000
Kota
1st Industrial Magazine [45311]
Mumbai
Auto Monitor [45353]
Electrical & Electronics [45369]
Modern Food Processing [45414]
Modern Machine Tools [45415]
Modern Medicare [45416]
Modern Packaging & Design [45417]
Modern Pharmaceuticals [45418]
Modern Plastics & Polymers [45419]
Modern Textiles [45420]
Photo Imaging [45431]
New Delhi
Artha Suchi [45484] .... (Paid) 120
Asia Pacific Tech Monitor
[45485] .. .. (Paid) 2,000
Business Today
[45490] .. .. (Paid) 127,378
Employment News
[45507] .. .. (Paid) 426,000
Facts for You
[45511] .. .. (Paid) 5,000
Finance India
[45515] .. .. (Paid) 1,200
Global Review of Business and Eco-
nomic Research [45520]
ICSSR Journal of Abstracts and
Reviews [45528] .... (Paid) 550
Indian Economic and Social History
Review [45540] .. .. (Paid) 900

Indian Export Bulletin
[45542] .. .. (Paid) 5,000
Indian Journal of Economics &
Business [45552]
The Journal of Entrepreneurship
[45597] .. .. (Paid) 500
Journal of Interdisciplinary
Mathematics
[45608] .. .. (Paid) 240
Journal of Statistics and Management
Systems [45620] .. .. (Paid) 240
Margin [45623] .... (Paid) 600
VATIS Update Biotechnology
[45662] 700
VATIS Update Food Processing
[45663] 500
VATIS Update Non-Conventional
Energy [45664] 700
VATIS Update Ozone Layer
Protection [45665] 2,300
VATIS Update Waste Management
[45666] 500

INDONESIA
Jakarta
Economics and Finance in Indonesia
[45796] 4,000
Indonesian Commercial Newsletter
[45799]

IRAN
Tehran
Iran Exports & Imports
[45892] .. .. (Paid) 5,000

IRELAND
Dublin
Business Ireland [45948] 2,500
IBEC Economic Trends [45965]
International Review of
Entrepreneurship [45968]
Sandyford
The Stock Market [46057]

ITALY
Messina
International Journal of Economic
Policy in Emerging Economies
[46157]
International Journal of Trade and
Global Markets [46159]
Milan
Focus on Italy [46171]
Industrial and Corporate Change
[46175]
Office Automation [46189] 17,000
Sole 24ore [46195]

JAPAN
Tokyo
Asia Pacific Review [46754]
Japan Chemical Week [46854]
Journal of the Electronics Industry
[46895]
J@pan Inc Magazine
[46947] 24,000
Nikkei Business [46981] ... ★308,561
Nikkei Business Associe
[46982] .. .. ★71,610
Nikkei Monozukuri
[46999] .. .. ★34,857
Nikkei Net Interactive [47000]
Nikkei Solution Business
[47007] .. .. ★9,034
Nikkei Venture [47009] .... ★59,790
The Nikkei Weekly
[47010] .. .. (Paid) 36,500

JORDAN
Amman
Dirasat Administrative Sciences
[47152] .... (Controlled) 1,000

KENYA
Nairobi
Journal of Language, Technology & Entrepreneurship in Africa **[47189]**

REPUBLIC OF KOREA
Seoul
Seoul Journal of Economics **[47286]** .... (Paid) 300

KUWAIT
Safat
Arab Journal of Administrative Sciences **[47334]** ..... (Paid) 2,000

LATVIA
Riga
Journal of Business Ethics Education **[47369]**
Journal of International Business Education **[47370]**
Journal of Organizational Behavior Education **[47371]**

LEBANON
Beirut
AL IDARI **[47389]** .. .. ★36,988

MALAYSIA
Bangi
Jurnal Ekonomi Malaysia **[47574]** .... (Paid) 500

Kampar
International Journal of Modelling in Operations Management **[47584]**

Kota Kinabalu
Borneo Review **[47589]**

Kuala Lumpur
FMM Directory of Malaysian Industries **[47602]**
New Straits Times **[47630]** 136,273
Tech & U **[47637]** 163,287

Penang
Suara SAM **[47691]** .. .. (Paid) 2,500
Third World Economics **[47692]**

MEXICO
Mexico City
International Journal of Business Competition and Growth **[47785]**

MONACO
Monte Carlo
Luxury Intelligence **[47810]**

NAMIBIA
Windhoek
The Namibia Economist **[47823]** .. .. (Paid) 7,000

NETHERLANDS
Alphen aan den Rijn
Software Release Magazine **[47872]** .... ‡4,100

Amsterdam
Japan and the World Economy **[48035]**
Journal of Business Research **[48054]**
Journal of Business Venturing **[48055]**
Pacific-Basin Finance Journal **[48198]**
Technovation **[48243]**

Dordrecht
Journal of Business Ethics **[48446]**
Journal of Management and Governance **[48471]**
Journal of Productivity Analysis **[48487]**
Netnomics **[48518]**

Groningen
International Journal of Lean Enterprise Research **[48603]**

The Hague
European Business Law Review **[48615]**

Meppel
Kijk op Oost Nederland **[48739]** .... (Combined) 8,229

Rotterdam
Corporate Reputation Review **[48749]**

Utrecht
Global Business and Economics Review **[48759]**

NEW ZEALAND
Auckland
NZBusiness **[48824]** .... ★7,428

Christchurch
New Zealand AgriBusiness **[48871]**

North Shore City
DEMM Engineering & Manufacturing Magazine **[48954]** 9,017
New Zealand Company Vehicle **[48957]** .... (Controlled) ★7,048

Wellington
AFR Smart Investor **[48999]**

NIGERIA
Ikoyi
Economic and Policy Review **[49109]**

Lagos
African Journal of Business Management **[49131]**

NORWAY
Oslo
Dagens Naeringsliv **[49196]** 79,628

OMAN
Muscat
Business Today **[49220]**

PAKISTAN
Faisalabad
International Business Management **[49248]**
International Journal of Quality and Innovation **[49255]**

Karachi
Business Recorder **[49340]**
Eastern Worker **[49348]** .. .. (Paid) 1,000
Investor's Business & Financial Journal **[49356]**
Labour Code of Pakistan **[49359]**
Pakistan Accountant **[49366]** .... (Paid) 1,400

PHILIPPINES
Makati City
AmCham Business Journal **[49514]**

Quezon City
Business World **[49586]** .. .. (Paid) 54,000

POLAND
Warsaw
Economics and Organization of Enterprise **[49707]**

Issues of Business and Law **[49721]**
Organizacija **[49743]**
South East European Journal of Economics and Business **[49765]**

PORTUGAL
Viseu
International Journal of Simulation and Process Modelling **[49814]**

SAUDI ARABIA
Riyadh
Business Process Management Journal **[50061]**

SINGAPORE
Singapore
Asian Case Research Journal **[50106]**
The Business Times **[50117]** .. .. (Mon.-Fri.) 35,700
Infosecurity **[50172]**
International Journal of Technoentrepreneurship **[50194]**
Investor's Guide to Singapore **[50196]** .... (Paid) 4,000
Journal of Developmental Entrepreneurship **[50203]**
Journal of Enterprising Culture **[50204]**
NUS Economic Journal **[50229]** .... (Paid) 10,000
Singapore Economic Review **[50254]** .... (Paid) 800
Singapore Management Review **[50259]**

Singapore City
FutureGov **[50312]** 8,950

REPUBLIC OF SOUTH AFRICA
Cape Town
Achiever **[50360]** 10,000
BBQ Scorecard **[50363]** 10,000
Black Business Quarterly **[50365]** 10,000
Blue Chip **[50367]** 10,000
Cape Business News **[50369]** .. .. (Paid) 6,713
Explore South Africa **[50377]** .... ★10,000
Opportunity **[50398]** 10,000
Service **[50410]** 10,000

Centurion
South African Journal of Business Management **[50451]**
Tax Breaks Newsletter **[50456]**

Claremont
Jutas Business Law **[50461]**
SA Mercantile Law Journal **[50462]**

Grahamstown
Nigeria Journal of Business Administration **[50505]**

Hillcrest
South African Journal of Economic and Management Sciences **[50523]**

Johannesburg
Business Day **[50529]**

Pretoria
Management Dynamics **[50596]**

SPAIN
Barcelona
Drug News & Perspectives **[50664]**

Granada
International Journal of Business Environment **[50717]**

Madrid
Actualidad Economica **[50723]** .... (Combined) 23,000
En Franquicia **[50756]** .. .. (Paid) 30,000

Oviedo
International Journal of Chinese Culture & Management **[50823]**
International Journal of Learning and Intellectual Capital **[50824]**
International Journal of Strategic Change Management **[50825]**

Oviedo-Asturias
International Journal of Arab Culture, Management and Sustainable Development **[50826]**

SRI LANKA
Colombo
Lanka Monthly Digest **[50860]**

SWEDEN
Jonkoping
Journal of Media Business Studies **[50970]**

Stockholm
International Journal of Entrepreneurial Venturing **[51020]**
Scandinavia Now **[51032]**

SWITZERLAND
Geneva
International Journal of Applied Management Science **[51101]**
International Journal of Business and Emerging Markets **[51106]**
International Journal of Business Excellence **[51107]**
International Journal of Business Forecasting and Marketing Intelligence **[51108]**
International Journal of Business Innovation and Research (IJBIR) **[51109]**
International Journal of Complexity in Applied Science and Engineering **[51110]**
International Journal of Corporate Governance **[51113]**
International Journal of Critical Accounting **[51114]**
International Journal of Economics and Business Research **[51116]**
International Journal of Information and Decision Sciences **[51125]**
International Journal of Powertrain **[51135]**
International Journal of Remanufacturing **[51137]**
International Journal of Sustainable Manufacturing **[51142]**
UN Special **[51163]**

Thalwil
Infoweek.ch **[51234]** .... (Combined) 18,000

TAIWAN
Taichung
International Journal of Value Chain Management **[51321]**

Tainan
Centerpoint **[51326]**

Taipei
Financial Statistics Monthly **[51340]** .. .. (Paid) 2,250
Industry Weekly **[51341]** .. .. (Paid) 12,000
International Journal of Business and Information (IJBI) **[51342]**

Circulation: ★ = ABC; △ = BPA; ♦ = CAC; • = CCAB; ❑ = VAC; ⊕ = PO Statement; ‡ = Publisher's Report; Boldface figures = sworn; Light figures = estimated.

International Journal of Electronic Business **[51345]**
Journal of Banking and Finance **[51348]**

THAILAND
Bangkok
Business Day **[51416]**
The Rubber International **[51433]**
Thai-American Business
  [51437] .. .. (Paid) 3,000
Thai Journal of Development Administration
  [51439] .. .. (Paid) 1,500
Tobacco Asia **[51445]** 5,000

TURKEY
Ankara
METU Studies in Development
  [51497] .. .. (Paid) 1,500

UKRAINE
Sumy
Problems & Perspectives in Management **[51618]**

UNITED ARAB EMIRATES
Dubai
Arabian Business **[51630]** ... ‡22,995
Arabian Computer News **[51631]**
Gulf Business
  [51643] .. .. (Paid) 28,608
MEED - The Middle East Business
  Weekly **[51648]** 70,000

UNITED KINGDOM
Abingdon
Accounting, Business & Financial History **[51693]**
Business History **[51723]**
Economic System Research **[51765]**
International Journal of the Economics of Business **[51833]**
Journal of Change Management **[51873]**
New Genetics & Society **[51992]**
The Service Industries Journal **[52055]**
Technology Analysis & Strategic Management **[52073]**
Total Quality Management & Business Excellence **[52079]**

Amersham
International Consultants' Guide
  [52107] .... (Controlled) 30,000

Basingstoke
Asian Business & Management **[52194]**
Journal of Commercial Biotechnology
  [52214] 400
Journal of Digital Asset Management **[52215]**
Pensions **[52227]**

Belfast
Ulster Business **[52295]**

Birmingham
European Journal of Information Systems **[52341]**
Journal of Manufacturing Technology Management **[52348]**
Journal of the Operational Research Society **[52350]**
Journal of Small Business and Enterprise Development **[52354]**

Bradford
Business Strategy Series **[52439]**
Career Development International **[52440]**
Corporate Communications **[52446]**

Critical Perspectives on International Business **[52448]**
Education, Business and Society **[52451]**
European Business Review **[52457]**
Foresight **[52461]**
Industrial Management and Data Systems **[52466]**
Journal of Business Strategy **[52493]**
Journal of Facilities Management **[52500]**
Journal of Fashion Marketing and Management **[52501]**
Journal of Intellectual Capital **[52504]**
Journal of Organizational Change Management **[52511]**
Managerial Auditing Journal **[52524]**
Measuring Business Excellence **[52526]**
Rapid Prototyping Journal **[52542]**
Society and Business Review **[52544]**
Strategic Direction **[52546]**
Strategic Outsourcing **[52548]**

Buckingham
The Journal of Gambling Business and Economics **[52757]**
The Journal of Prediction Markets **[52758]**

Burgess Hill
Teaching Business & Economics
  [52761] 3,200

Burnham
International Journal of Micrographics & Optical Technology **[52765]**

Chester
Managed Healthcare Executive
  [52997] .. .. △41,800

Corby
Operations Management
  [53063] .. .. (Paid) 1,462

Cornwall
The European Journal of Teleworking **[53065]**

Cranfield
Journal of Management Development **[53097]**

Crawley
Grocer **[53105]**
Morning Advertiser
  [53109] .. .. ★31,288

Croydon
Taxation **[53136]** .. .. (Paid) ★7,464

Dorking
Call Centre Focus **[53192]** .. . 47,000

Edinburgh
CA Magazine **[53259]** .... ★22,362

Glasgow
On-Trade Scotland **[53436]** 9,020

Guernsey
Contact **[53487]** 1,300

Harrogate
British Commercial Agents Review **[53515]**

Havant
Business News (South East Hampshire)
  [53543] .. .. (Controlled) 1,100

Henley-on-Thames
International Journal of Process Management and Benchmarking **[53560]**
Journal of General Management **[53561]**

Hitchin
Leisure Management **[53579]**

Leisure Opportunities **[53580]**

Hook
Project Manager Today
  [53587] .. .. (Controlled) ★14,871

Horsham
Prestige Corporate Interiors
  [53597] .... (Controlled) 3,000

Hull
OR Insight **[53628]**

Ilfracombe
Catalogue & E-business
  [53641] 8,500

Kent
South East Business
  [53682] .... (Non-paid) 13,000

Kidlington
Materials Today **[53702]**

Leicester
Finance on Windows **[53800]**
Global Municipal Investor **[53802]**
Prime **[53818]** ... (Combined) 13,000
Retailspeak
  [53821] .. .. (Combined) 10,000

Lincoln
International Journal of Entrepreneurship and Innovation **[53856]**

Liverpool
International Journal of Law and Management **[53874]**
Social Enterprise Journal **[53878]**

London
AB Europe
  [53889] .... (Controlled) 8,300
African Business
  [53919] .... (Paid) ★21,332
African Journal of Business and Economic Research **[53921]**
The AIM Guide **[53929]**
Asia Risk **[53972]**
AYGO Magazine **[53997]** 250,000
Brazil Business Brief **[54103]** 500
Business Strategy Review **[54159]**
Business XL **[54160]**
Buy-Side Technology **[54161]**
Charity Times **[54197]**
Chartered Secretary
  [54199] .... (Combined) 20,057
Competency & Emotional Intelligence **[54251]**
Competition & Change **[54252]**
Continuity, Insurance & Risk **[54264]**
COVER **[54278]**
Credit **[54283]**
Credit Today **[54284]** .... ★13,670
DM Magazine **[54337]** 14,560
Economic Review (UK) **[54351]**
The Engineer
  [54372] .... (Non-paid) ‡35,466
European BioPharmaceutical Review **[54391]**
European Pensions **[54408]**
European Pharmaceutical Contractor **[54409]**
Families in Business
  [54439] 6,000
Financial Director **[54454]** ... ★20,609
Financial Management
  [54455] .. .. (Paid) 65,289
Financial Sector Technology
  [54458] .. .. ★12,776
First **[54462]** ... (Combined) 157,000
Glass **[54509]**
Glass International **[54510]** 6,000
Growth Company Investor **[54524]**
Hedge Funds Review **[54547]**
Industry and Higher Education **[54599]**
Info **[54600]** ...... (Combined) 12,100
Internal Comms Hub **[54618]**

International Journal of Business Performance Management **[54636]**
International Journal of Islamic and Middle Eastern Finance and Management **[54652]**
International Journal of Market Research **[54653]**
International Tax Review **[54674]**
The Journal of Computational Finance **[54729]**
Journal of International Marketing **[54771]**
The Journal of Risk **[54809]**
Legal Week **[54865]** .... ★32,070
Market Leader **[54907]**
Metal Bulletin Monthly
  [54927] .. .. (Paid) ★5,554
The Middle East
  [54930] .. .. (Combined) ‡20,347
Mortgage Edge **[54953]**
Operational Risk & Regulation **[55038]**
Organization Studies
  [55043] 1,000
Pensions Age **[55065]** .... ★14,000
Planning (UK) **[55092]** 21,413
Post Magazine **[55107]**
Private Equity Europe **[55121]**
Professional Adviser **[55127]**
Quality World
  [55163] .. .. (Combined) 34,000
Real Business
  [55176] .. .. (Combined) 43,000
Retail Systems **[55196]** .. .. ★13,000
Revolution
  [55201] .. .. (Combined) 13,753
Risk **[55204]**
SHARES **[55232]**
Structured Products **[55267]**
The Times **[55321]**
UK Excellence **[55354]** .... ‡4,000
UK Unquote **[55355]** 3,500
Vanguard **[55365]** 80,000
Wealth **[55394]** 4,000

Loughton
Education Business **[55489]**

Manchester
Education for Information **[55554]**
Journal of Place Management and Development **[55564]**

Newtownabbey
Leadership and Organization Development Journal **[55702]**

Olney
International Journal of Collaborative Enterprise **[55794]**
International Journal of Critical Infrastructures **[55797]**
International Journal of Entrepreneurship and Innovation Management **[55802]**
International Journal of Intellectual Property Management **[55813]**
International Journal of Six Sigma and Competitive Advantage **[55832]**
International Journal of Technology Intelligence and Planning **[55835]**
International Journal of Technology Transfer and Commercialisation **[55836]**
World Review of Entrepreneurship, Management and Sustainable Development **[55846]**

Oxford
Abacus **[55857]**
American Business Law Journal **[55864]**
British Journal of Management **[55894]**
Enterprise & Society **[55937]**

Circulation: ★ = ABC; △ = BPA; ◆ = CAC; • = CCAB; ❑ = VAC; ⊕ = PO Statement; ‡ = Publisher's Report; Boldface figures = sworn; Light figures = estimated.

Journal of Management Studies **[56050]**
Journal of Supply Chain Management **[56074]**
The Journal of World Intellectual Property **[56079]**
R & D Management **[56184]**

Paddock Wood
Plastics & Rubber Asia **[56238]**

Portsmouth
International Journal of Financial Markets and Derivatives **[56290]**

Potters Bar
Manufacturing & Logistics IT **[56297]**

Sheffield
Greener Management International **[56495]** .... (Combined) 600
International Journal of Enterprise Network Management **[56499]**
The Journal of Corporate Citizenship **[56504]** .... ‡750

Sidcup
Packaging Today **[56545]**

Sittingbourne
Housewares (UK) **[56549]**

Smallfield
Auto Vending **[56561]** .... ‡7,180

Stroud
21st Century Worker **[56649]** .... (Combined) 4,000

Surrey
The European Yearbook of Business History **[56662]**
Polymers Paint Colour Journal **[56673]** .. .. (Paid) 8,600

Sutton
Motor Transport **[56688]** 19,366

Taunton
Business Money **[56721]** .. .. (Controlled) 14,237

Telford
International Journal of Business Governance and Ethics **[56737]**

Tonbridge
Food Processing **[56754]**

Twickenham
Airport World **[56787]** 8,000
Asia-Pacific Airports **[56788]** ... 4,000
Global Airport Cities Magazine **[56792]** .... (Controlled) 5,000
Routes News **[56793]** 6,000

Uppingham
Loyalty **[56797]** .... (Paid) ★5,000

Wadhurst
Construction Europe **[56805]** .... ★14,024

Watford
The Business Economist **[56860]**

ZIMBABWE
Harare
Zimbabwe Independent **[57121]**

CARPENTRY

DENMARK
Glostrup
BygTek Mester & Svend **[43700]** .. .. (Controlled) 26,305

CEMETERIES AND MONUMENTS

GERMANY
Braunschweig
Friedhofs Kultur **[44276]**

Leinfelden-Echterdingen
Metamorphose **[44527]** 11,916

CERAMICS
See also Glass and China

AUSTRALIA
Westminster
Ceramics **[42700]** 12,200

GERMANY
Cologne
Ceramic Forum International **[44290]**

IRELAND
Cork
Clays and Clay Minerals **[45936]**

JAPAN
Tokyo
Journal of the Ceramic Society of Japan **[46890]** .. .. (Paid) 6,000

REPUBLIC OF KOREA
Seoul
Journal of Ceramic Processing Research **[47271]**

NETHERLANDS
Amsterdam
Ceramics International **[47925]**
Materials Characterization **[48143]**
Materials Science and Engineering **[48146]**
Mechanics of Materials **[48150]**

RUSSIA
Saint Petersburg
Glass Physics and Chemistry **[50022]**

UNITED KINGDOM
Bristol
Smart Materials and Structures **[52731]**

London
Ceramic Review **[54195]** .. .. (Paid) 8,800

Oxford
Journal of the American Ceramic Society **[56013]**
Journal of the European Ceramic Society **[56031]**

Torquay
Torquay Pottery Collectors Society **[56758]**

CHAMBERS OF COMMERCE AND BOARDS OF TRADE

ARGENTINA
Buenos Aires
Comments on Argentine Trade **[41471]**
Integration and Trade **[41474]**

PEOPLE'S REPUBLIC OF CHINA
Beijing
British Business in China **[43174]** 2,000
China Brief **[43176]** 2,100

Hong Kong
The Bulletin **[43285]** 8,500

Exporters Bulletin **[43299]** .... (Non-paid) 5,000

CUBA
Havana
Cuba Foreign Trade **[43576]** 3,000

CYPRUS
Nicosia
Emporoviomichaniki **[43594]** ... 4,000

FRANCE
Dijon
Impact **[43944]**

ITALY
Milan
Focus on Italy **[46171]**

REPUBLIC OF KOREA
Seoul
American Chamber of Commerce in Korea **[47252]**

LUXEMBOURG
Luxembourg
De Letzeburger Merkur **[47491]** .... (Non-paid) ‡24,300

MALTA
Valletta
Commercial Courier **[47745]** ... 1,300

MOROCCO
Casablanca
Tijaris **[47813]**

OMAN
Ruwi
Al Ghorfa **[49226]** .... (Non-paid) 10,500

PERU
Lima
Negocios Internacionales **[49424]** 6,000
San Isidro
Made in Germany **[49441]** 5,000

SWITZERLAND
Geneva
International Trade FORUM **[51150]**

TAIWAN
Taipei
Journal of Commerce and Industry **[51351]**

UNITED KINGDOM
Guernsey
Contact **[53487]** 1,300
Havant
Business News (South East Hampshire) **[53543]** ...,....... (Controlled) 1,100
London
Brazil Business Brief **[54103]** 500
Info **[54600]** ...... (Combined) 12,100
The Treasurer **[55338]**

CHEMISTRY, CHEMICALS, AND CHEMICAL ENGINEERING

ARGENTINA
Buenos Aires
Industria & Quimica **[41473]**

Journal of the Argentine Chemical Society **[41475]**

AUSTRALIA
Bundoora
Colloids and Surfaces A **[41670]**

Collingwood
Australian Journal of Chemistry **[41782]**
Environmental Chemistry **[41788]**

Melbourne
Chemistry in Australia **[42056]**

Perth
Asia-Pacific Journal of Chemical Engineering **[42243]**
The Clinical Biochemist Reviews **[42249]**

Sydney
Journal of Biomimetics, Biomaterials, and Tissue Engineering **[42527]**

Woolgoolga
Journal of Near Infrared Spectroscopy **[42715]**

AUSTRIA
Vienna
Amino Acids **[42743]**

BELGIUM
Brussels
Chemoecology **[42847]**

Gent
Clinica Chimica Acta **[42882]**

BRAZIL
Campinas
Journal of the Brazilian Chemical Society **[42969]**

Petropolis
Computational & Applied Mathematics **[42990]**

Sao Paulo
Brazilian Journal of Chemical Engineering **[43025]**
Ecletica Quimica **[43038]**
Quimica Nova **[43046]**

BULGARIA
Sofia
Bulgarian Chemical Communications **[43094]**

CAMEROON
Dschang
Cameroon Journal of Experimental Biology **[43125]**
International Journal of Biological and Chemical Sciences **[43126]**

PEOPLE'S REPUBLIC OF CHINA
Beijing
Chinese Chemical Letters **[43182]**
Chinese Journal of Applied Chemistry **[43183]**
Chinese Journal of Chemical Engineering **[43184]**
Chinese Journal of Polymer Science **[43186]**
Intermetallics **[43196]**
Journal of Molecular Structure **[43208]**
Science in China Series B **[43216]**

Shanghai
Chinese Journal of Chemistry **[43470]**

Circulation: ★ = ABC; △ = BPA; ◆ = CAC; • = CCAB; ❑ = VAC; ⊕ = PO Statement; ‡ = Publisher's Report; Boldface figures = sworn; Light figures = estimated.

Theoretical and Applied Fracture Mechanics **[43507]**

COTE D'IVOIRE
Abidjan
Afrique Science **[43555]**

CROATIA
Zagreb
Chemical and Biochemical Engineering Quarterly **[43563]**
Croatica Chemica Acta **[43566]**

DENMARK
Frederiksberg
Acta Crystallographica. Section E **[43689]**
Glostrup
Dansk Kemi **[43701]** .... ‡6,540

EGYPT
Cairo
Egyptian Journal of Biochemistry and Molecular Biology **[43756]**
International Journal of Photoenergy **[43762]**

ETHIOPIA
Addis Ababa
Bulletin of the Chemical Society of Ethiopia **[43796]**

FRANCE
Grenoble
Phase Transitions **[43959]**
Paris
L'Actualite Chimique **[44021]** .... (Paid) 5,000
European Journal of Medicinal Chemistry **[44042]**
Talence
Polycyclic Aromatic Compounds **[44115]**
Villeurbanne
Mathematical Modelling of Natural Phenomena **[44126]**

GERMANY
Aachen
Colloid and Polymer Science **[44136]**
Augsburg
Progress in Solid State Chemistry **[44142]**
Bayreuth
Physics and Chemistry of Minerals **[44147]**
Berlin
Biological Chemistry **[44160]**
Laser & Photonics Reviews **[44216]**
ZAAC - Zeitschrift fur anorganische und allgemeine Chemie **[44237]**
Braunschweig
Molecular Informatics **[44278]**
Cologne
Drug Testing and Analysis **[44292]**
Dortmund
Accreditation and Quality Assurance **[44314]**
Chemical Engineering and Processing **[44315]**
Duisburg
Mechanism and Machine Theory **[44320]**
Erlangen
Journal of Molecular Modeling **[44340]**

Frankfurt
Archiv der Pharmazie **[44358]**
Frankfurt am Main
Beilstein Journal of Organic Chemistry **[44364]**
Garching
Bioprocess and Biosystems Engineering **[44377]**
Chemical Physics **[44378]**
Gottingen
Biogeosciences Discussions **[44394]**
Greifswald
Journal of Solid State Electrochemistry **[44404]**
Heidelberg
Analytical and Bioanalytical Chemistry **[44437]**
FEBS Letters **[44457]**
Jena
Chemie der Erde / Geochemistry **[44487]**
Lubeck
Berichte zur Wissenschaftsgeschichte **[44535]**
Mainz
Biogeosciences **[44538]**
Polymer Bulletin **[44544]**
Munster
Applied Microbiology and Biotechnology **[44595]**
Journal of Business Chemistry (JoBC) **[44599]**
Oldenburg
Chemkon - Chemie konkret, Forum fuer Unterricht und Didaktik **[44623]**
Ostfildern
Advanced Synthesis & Catalysis **[44631]** 1,000
Potsdam
Journal of Carbohydrate Chemistry **[44640]**
Stuttgart
Solid State Ionics **[44679]**
Synfacts **[44681]**
Synthesis-Stuttgart **[44682]**
Weinheim
Chemie Ingenieur Technik **[44702]**
Chemistry **[44703]**
ChemMedChem **[44704]**
ChemSusChem **[44705]**
Journal of Biophotonics **[44706]**
Lipid Technology **[44707]**
Starch/Staerke **[44708]**
Wurzburg
Process **[44724]** .... (Combined) ‡28,041

HUNGARY
Budapest
Acta Veterinaria Hungarica **[44819]**
Journal of Planar Chromatography **[44842]**

ICELAND
Reykjavik
Chemistry and Physics of Lipids **[44899]**

INDIA
Bangalore
Journal of Chemical Sciences **[44967]**
Delhi
Indian Chemical Engineer **[45095]** .... (Paid) 5,000

Ghaziabad
Asian Journal of Chemistry **[45121]** .... (Paid) 700
Jaipur
Indian Journal of Clinical Biochemistry **[45195]**
Jodhpur
Indian Journal of Biochemistry and Biophysics **[45220]** 1,000
Indian Journal of Chemical Technology **[45221]** 1,200
Karaikudi
Current Titles in Electrochemistry **[45239]** .... (Combined) 900
Kolkata
Institution of Engineers (India) Chemical Engineering Division Journal **[45279]** .... (Paid) 5,000
Meerut
Cardiovascular & Hematological Agents in Medicinal Chemistry **[45343]**
Current Enzyme Inhibition **[45344]**
Mumbai
Chemical Engineering World **[45359]** 44,000
Chemical News **[45360]** 3,000
Chemical Weekly **[45361]** 87,000
Indian Journal of Nuclear Medicine **[45384]**
Modern Plastics & Polymers **[45419]**
New Delhi
Chemistry Today **[45496]**
Gas News **[45518]**
International Review of Pure and Applied Chemistry **[45589]**
Rajkot
Biochemistry **[45706]**
Biotechnology **[45707]**
Chemical Technology **[45708]**
Materials Science **[45709]**
Roorkee
Analytical Chemistry **[45717]**
Tirupati
Environmental Science **[45756]**

IRAN
Tehran
Iranian Journal of Chemistry and Chemical Engineering **[45899]** .... (Controlled) 2,000
Iranian Polymer Journal **[45910]** .. .. (Paid) 3,000

IRELAND
Dublin
Irish Chemical News **[45972]**

ISRAEL
Haifa
International Journal of Multiphase Flow **[46076]**
Reviews in Analytical Chemistry **[46079]**
Ramat Aviv
Reviews in Chemical Engineering **[46091]**
Tel Aviv
Heterocyclic Communications **[46102]**
Main Group Metal Chemistry **[46110]**
Reviews in Inorganic Chemistry **[46111]**

ITALY
Ancona
Chemistry and Ecology **[46117]**

Milan
Chimica Oggi (Chemistry Today) **[46165]** .... (Combined) 8,000
Padua
Inorganic Chemistry Communications **[46205]**

JAPAN
Fukui
Journal of Chemical Software **[46332]**
Kyoto
Advanced Powder Technology **[46466]**
Chemistry Letters **[46468]** .... ‡43,200
Mathematics Applied in Science and Technology **[46482]**
Nagasaki
Sensors and Actuators B **[46546]**
Osaka
Journal of Nuclear and Radiochemical Sciences **[46623]**
Tokyo
Analytical Sciences **[46734]** .. .. (Paid) 3,600
Applied Magnetic Resonance **[46747]**
Biological & Pharmaceutical Bulletin **[46764]**
Bulletin of the Chemical Society of Japan **[46769]** .... ‡37,200
Chem-Bio Informatics Journal **[46782]**
Chemical & Pharmaceutical Bulletin **[46783]**
Chromatographia **[46785]**
Environmental Chemistry Letters **[46811]**
Journal of Chemical Engineering of Japan **[46891]**
Journal of Computer-Aided Chemistry **[46893]**
Journal of Fluorine Chemistry **[46897]**
Journal of Ion Exchange **[46910]**
Journal of Photochemistry and Photobiology, C **[46936]**
Polymer Journal **[47021]** .. .. (Paid) 2,000

KENYA
Nairobi
African Journal of Biotechnology **[47170]**

REPUBLIC OF KOREA
Seoul
Biochemistry and Molecular Biology Reports **[47258]**
Bulletin of the Korean Chemical Society **[47259]** 2,300

MALAYSIA
Kota Kinabalu
Biotechnology & Molecular Biology Reviews **[47588]**
Petaling Jaya
Jurutera **[47700]** .. .. (Paid) 15,000

NETHERLANDS
Amsterdam
Advances in Colloid and Interface Science **[47882]**
Analytical Biochemistry **[47892]**
Archives of Biochemistry and Biophysics **[47898]**
Biochemical and Biophysical Research Communications **[47905]**

Circulation: ★ = ABC; △ = BPA; ♦ = CAC; • = CCAB; ❑ = VAC; ⊕ = PO Statement; ‡ = Publisher's Report; Boldface figures = sworn; Light figures = estimated.

Biochimica et Biophysica Acta (BBA) [47906]
Biochimica et Biophysica Acta (BBA)- General Subjects [47907]
Biochimica et Biophysica Acta (BBA)- Molecular Basis of Disease [47908]
Biochimica et Biophysica Acta (BBA)- Molecular and Cell Biology of Lipids [47909]
Bioelectrochemistry [47911]
Carbohydrate Polymers [47921]
Chemical Engineering Journal [47926]
Chemosphere [47927]
Composite Structures [47933]
Composites Part A [47934]
Current Opinion in Chemical Biology [47946]
Desalination [47953]
Dyes and Pigments [47960]
Geotextiles and Geomembranes [47997]
Journal of Alloys and Compounds [48040]
Journal of Analytical and Applied Pyrolysis [48043]
Journal of Chemical Health and Safety [48057]
Journal of Chromatography A [48059]
Journal of Colloid and Interface Science [48060]
Journal of Food Composition and Analysis [48079]
Journal of Loss Prevention in the Process Industries [48092]
Journal of Molecular Liquids [48098]
Journal of Molecular Spectroscopy [48099]
Journal of Organometallic Chemistry [48106]
Journal of Proteomics [48113]
The Journal of Supercritical Fluids [48121] .... (Paid) 229 (Controlled) 34
Materials Characterization [48143]
Materials Science and Engineering [48144]
Materials Science and Engineering [48145]
Materials Science and Engineering [48146]
Materials Science in Semiconductor Processing [48147]
Molecular Genetics and Metabolism [48166]
Nitric Oxide [48182]
Polymer [48209]
Powder Technology [48210]
Radiation Physics and Chemistry [48219]
Tetrahedron [48246]
Thermochimica Acta [40248]
Trends in Analytical Chemistry [48256]
Trends in Biochemical Sciences [48257]

Bussum
Cardiovascular & Hematological Disorders - Drug Targets [48280]
CNS & Neurological Disorders - Drug Targets [48282]
Current Organic Synthesis [48292]
Current Topics in Medicinal Chemistry [48298]
Infectious Disorders - Drug Targets [48301]
Inflammation & Allergy - Drug Targets [48302]

Dordrecht
Biogeochemistry [48332]
Biologia Plantarum [48333]
Chemosensory Perception [48350]

Frontiers of Chemistry in China [48394]
Journal of Applied Electrochemistry [48437]
Journal of Inorganic and Organometallic Polymers and Materials [48469]
Journal of Mathematical Chemistry [48474]
Journal of Polymer Research [48484]
Journal of Polymers and the Environment [48485]
Photosynthesis Research [48528]
Transition Metal Chemistry [48580]

Leiden
Composite Interfaces [48663]
Designed Monomers and Polymers [48667]
Journal of Adhesion Science and Technology [48686]

NIGERIA
Asaba
Journal of Applied Chemistry and Agricultural Research [49061]

Benin City
Journal of the Nigerian Association of Mathematical Physics [49065]

Ilorin
BIOKEMISTRI [49119]

Lagos
African Journal of Biochemistry Research [49130]
African Journal of Pure & Applied Chemistry [49136]

Zaria
Nigerian Journal of Chemical Research [49183]

NORWAY
Oslo
Microporous and Mesoporous Materials [49203]

PAKISTAN
Faisalabad
Global Journal of Biotechnology & Biochemistry [49241]
Journal of Applied Sciences [49261]
World Journal of Chemistry [49300]

Karachi
Current Analytical Chemistry [49341]
Letters in Organic Chemistry [49361]
Medicinal Chemistry [49363]
Mini-Reviews in Organic Chemistry [49364]
Pakistan Journal of Pharmaceutical Sciences [49371]

POLAND
Katowice
Acta Chromatographica [49661]

Warsaw
Central European Journal of Chemistry [49699]
Chemical Papers [49703]
Journal of Medical Biochemistry [49724]
Nukleonika [49739]
Polish Journal of Chemical Technology [49748]

PORTUGAL
Lisbon
Natural Products [49804]

ROMANIA
Bucharest
Balkan Journal of Geometry and its Applications [49832]

RUSSIA
Moscow
Applied Biochemistry and Microbiology [49875]
Biochemistry (Moscow) [49883]
Coke and Chemistry [49887]
Colloid Journal [49888]
Doklady Chemistry [49896]
Doklady Physical Chemistry [49899]
Doping Journal [49901]
High Energy Chemistry [49913]
Inorganic Materials [49919]
Journal of Advances in Chemical Physics [49926]
Journal of Analytical Chemistry [49927]
Kinetics and Catalysis [49931]
Polymer Science [49960] ... . (Paid) 1,000
Polymer Science, Series C [49961]
Problems of Biological, Medical and Pharmaceutical Chemistry [49962]
Russian Chemical Reviews [49972]
Russian Journal of Inorganic Chemistry [49977]
Russian Journal of Physical Chemistry [49980]

Novosibirsk
Journal Chemistry for Sustainable Development [50011]

Saint Petersburg
Journal of Evolutionary Biochemistry and Physiology [50023]
Reviews on Advanced Materials Science [50025]
Russian Journal of General Chemistry [50026]
Russian Journal of Organic Chemistry [50027]

SINGAPORE
Singapore
Biomolecular Frontiers [50116]
International Journal of Nanoscience [50189]
Organic Electronics [50233]

SLOVENIA
Ljubljana
Acta Chimica Slovenica (ACSi) [50334]

REPUBLIC OF SOUTH AFRICA
Wits
South African Journal of Chemistry [50644]

SPAIN
Bilbao
Chemistry [50710]

Madrid
Plasticulture Journal [50789]

Toledo
Physical Chemistry [50840]

Valencia
Inorganic Chemistry [50846]

SRI LANKA
Rajagiriya
Chemistry in Sri Lanka [50935]

SWITZERLAND
Basel
International Journal of Molecular Sciences [51062]
Progress in Histochemistry and Cytochemistry [51065]

Bern
Chimia [51070]
Helvetica Chimica Acta [51073]

Lausanne
Electrochimica Acta [51187] 1,400

Liestal
Organic Chemistry Highlights [51207]

Saint Gallen
Coating [51223] .... (Combined) 4,500

Zurich
Materials Science Forum [51275]

TAIWAN
Tainan
Materials Chemistry and Physics [51327]

Taipei
Journal of Chinese Chemical Society [51349] ... .:.... (Paid) 2,000

TURKEY
Ankara
Photonics and Nanostructures [51499]
Turkish Journal of Chemistry [51507]

UNITED KINGDOM
Abingdon
Free Radical Research [51791]
Liquid Crystals [51970]
Synthesis and Reactivity in Inorganic, Metal-Organic, and Nano-Metal Chemistry [52068]
Toxic Substance Mechanisms [52083]

Berkshire
Plastiquarian [52316]

Birmingham
Journal of Antimicrobial Chemotherapy [52345]

Bradford
Anti-Corrosion Methods & Materials [52436]
Pigment & Resin Technology [52537]
Soldering & Surface Mount Technology [52545]

Brentwood
Adsorption Science & Technology [52565]
Biomass Bulletin [52567]

Brighton
Polymer Degradation and Stability [52628]

Bristol
Biomedical Materials [52647]
Chinese Journal of Chemical Physics [52652]
Journal of Cellular Automata [52683]
Journal of Instrumentation [52687]
Nanotechnology [52708]

Burnham
Outlooks on Pest Management [52767]

Cambridge
Chemical Communications [52803] ... . (Paid) 3,000
Chemical Society Reviews [52804]
Chemistry Education Research and Practice [52805]
Dalton Transactions [52814]
Energy & Environmental Science [52817]
Faraday Discussions [52819]
Green Chemistry [52825]

Journal of Materials Chemistry
[52859]
Magnetic Resonance in Chemistry
[52867]
Methods in Organic Synthesis
[52869]
Molecular Biosystems [52871]
New Journal of Chemistry [52876]
Organic & Biomolecular Chemistry
[52880]
Photochemical & Photobiological
Science [52882]
Physical Chemistry, Chemical
Physics [52883]
Softmatter [52897]

Chester
Acta Crystallographica Section A
[52991]
Synchrotron Radiation [53000]

Chichester
Applied Organometallic Chemistry
[53004]
European Journal of Mass
Spectrometry [53009]
Journal of Analytical Atomic
Spectrometry [53013]
Spectroscopy Asia
[53017] ....‡10,000

Colchester
Biochemical Society Symposia
[53029]
Essays in Biochemistry [53035]

Dewsbury
Journal of the Society of Leather
Technologists and Chemists
[53180] ....(Paid) 900

Durham
International Reviews in Physical
Chemistry [53229]

Exeter
Filtration [53358]

Liphook
Process Industry Informer
[53861] ....‡4,000

London
Asia Pacific Coatings Journal
[53971] 5,960
The Biochemist
[54019] ....(Controlled) 9,000
BMC Biochemistry [54036]
BMC Clinical Pathology [54045]
Chemistry & Industry
[54201] ....(Combined) 9,824
Geochemical Transactions [54503]
Geosynthetics International [54504]
High Temperatures-High Pressures
[54551]
Journal of Carcinogenesis [54717]
Journal of Chemical Technology and
Biotechnology [54721]
Journal of the Science of Food and
Agriculture [54816]
Materials Science and Technology
[54913]
Materials World [54914] 34,000
Mineral Processing and Extractive
Metallurgy [54936]
Mineralogical Magazine [54937]
Nature Methods [54973]
NMR in Biomedicine [55006]
Nutrition & Metabolism [55020]
Plastics, Rubber and Composites
[55094]
Platinum Metals Review
[55095] ....(Controlled) 9,200
POWDEReporter [55111]
Process Engineering
[55126] ....(Controlled) 30,466
Surface Engineering [55281]

Loughborough
Thin-Walled Structures [55488]

Luton
Computational Biology and Chemistry
[55500]

Manchester
Biochemical Engineering Journal
[55544]
Reactive and Functional Polymers
[55576]

Nottingham
Journal of Molecular Graphics and
Modeling [55764]

Orpington
Journal of Automated Methods and
Management in Chemistry [55853]

Oxford
Acta Biochimica et Biophysica Sinica
[55859]
Chemical Physics Letters [55906]
Electrochemistry Communications
[55935]
Membrane Technology [56096]
Nucleic Acids Research [56121]
Plant and Cell Physiology [56160]
Plastics, Additives and Compounding
[56162]
Tetrahedron [56216]

Poole
Progress in Crystal Growth and Characterization of Materials [56282]

Redhill
Speciality Chemicals Magazine
[56379] ....(Non-paid) ★22,000

Rugby
Chemical Engineering Research and
Design (ChERD) [56416]
Education for Chemical Engineers
[56417]
Food & Bioproducts Processing
[56419]
Loss Prevention Bulletin [56421]
Process Safety and Environmental
Protection (PSEP) [56422]
TCE [56424] ....★24,000

Ruyton XI Towns
Polymer Testing [56428]

Sheffield
Physics & Chemistry of Glasses
[56510] ....(Paid) 725

Sutton
ACN: Asian Chemical News [56678]
European Chemical News
[56684] ....(Paid) 9,260
Mutagenesis [56689]

Wallingford
Biocontrol News and Information
[56816] 270
Ornamental Horticulture [56821]
Pig News and Information
[56822] 650
Review of Plant Pathology
[56828] 690
Soils and Fertilizers [56829] 380

VENEZUELA
Merida
Journal of Surfactants and
Detergents [57028]

CHIROPRACTIC

AUSTRALIA
Murdoch
Chiropractic & Osteopathy [42136]

AUSTRIA
Vienna
Journal of Neural Transmission
[42762]

CIVIL RIGHTS
**See also Ethnic and Minor-
ity Studies**

AUSTRALIA
Garran
National Indigenous Times [41877]

PEOPLE'S REPUBLIC OF
CHINA
Beijing
Women of China [43223] 150,000

INDIA
Dharamsala
DOLMA [45110]

NEPAL
Kathmandu
Voice of Child Workers
[47848] 5,000

NETHERLANDS
Amsterdam
LOVER [48140] 2,000
Wordt Vervolgd
[48271] ....(Non-paid) 32,500
Hilversum
Mental Health Reforms
[48631] 1,000
Utrecht
Netherlands Quarterly of Human
Rights [48764]

NICARAGUA
Managua
La Boletina [49054] 26,000

SWITZERLAND
Bern
Amnestie [51069] 22,000

UNITED KINGDOM
Abingdon
The International Journal of Human
Rights [51838]
Belfast
The Chronicle [52281]
Bradford
Equality, Diversity and Inclusion
[52456]
Glasgow
Justice and Peace [53428] 800
London
Disability and Society [54328]
Ethnicities [54386]
Race & Class [55168]
The Reparation Report [55188]
SAGE Race Relations Abstracts
[55216]
North Tyneside
SISTERS (Sisterhood and Interna-
tional Solidarity to End Racism and
Sexism) [55705]

CLOTHING
**See also General Merchan-
dise; Fashion**

AUSTRALIA
Sydney
Myer Emporium [42550] ...★248,900
Wahroonga
Industrial Workwear Solutions
[42673] 28,000

PEOPLE'S REPUBLIC OF
CHINA
Hong Kong
HKTDC Enterprise
[43306] ....(Paid) 150,000
HKTDC Fasion - Fabrics &
Accessories [43308]
HKTDC Fasion - Footwear [43309]
Research Journal of Textile and
Apparel [43380] ....(Paid) 1,000

DENMARK
Herning
Textile and Clothing [43723]

FINLAND
Helsinki
Modin [43848] ....(Paid) 8,000

GREECE
Athens
NY-LONDON Shows [44753]
Paris Catwalks [44754]
Passerella di Donna [44755]

JAPAN
Tokyo
Apparel Production News
[46744] ....(Paid) 9,000
Fashion Color [46821]
SARAI [47035]

NETHERLANDS
Almere
Eurostitch Magazine
[47864] ....(Paid) 15,000
Maarssen
Mannenmode
[48732] ....(Paid) 2,400
Tred [48733] .....(Combined) 3,100
Trend Boutique
[48734] ....(Combined) 2,200

SINGAPORE
Singapore
Global Sources Garments & Textiles
[50155]

SWEDEN
Nora
Slojdforum [50994]

TURKEY
Istanbul
Konfeksiyon & Teknik
[51559] 10,560

UNITED KINGDOM
Barnsley
Out on a Limb [52183]
Galashiels
International Journal of Clothing Sci-
ence and Technology [53403]
Huddersfield
Bridal Buyer [53616]
CWB [53619] .....(Combined) 3,000
Lingerie Buyer
[53622] ....(Combined) 3,000
MWB [53624] .....(Combined) 5,711
WWB [53625] .....(Combined) 7,259
Kent
Printwear & Promotion
[53679] ....★5,536
Leicester
KFAT News [53808]
London
The HAT Magazine [54533]

Circulation: ★ = ABC; △ = BPA; ◆ = CAC; ● = CCAB; ❑ = VAC; ⊕ = PO Statement; ‡ = Publisher's Report; Boldface figures = sworn; Light figures = estimated.

Oxford
Fashion Theory
[55953] .... (Combined) ‡716

COMMERCE AND INDUSTRY

See also Banking, Finance, and Investments; Chambers of Commerce and Boards of Trade; International Business and Economics

AUSTRALIA
Chatswood
Manufacturers Monthly
[41740] .... ♦15,269
Mona Vale
Your Trading Edge [42112]
Sydney
International Journal of Abrasive Technology [42518]

AUSTRIA
Vienna
Connex [42749] 2,100

PEOPLE'S REPUBLIC OF CHINA
Beijing
British Business in China
[43174] 2,000
Hong Kong
The Bulletin [43285] 8,500
Exporters Bulletin
[43299] .... (Non-paid) 5,000
Hong Kong Entrepreneur
[43324] 4,200

GERMANY
Leinfelden-Echterdingen
EPP Europe
[44523] .. .. (Combined) ‡20,040
Quality Engineering
[44528] .... (Controlled) 25,000
Wurzburg
MM Industrial Magazine Western Europe
[44722] .. .. (Controlled) 20,000
MM Maschinenmarkt
[44723] .. .. (Combined) 44,200

HUNGARY
Budapest
Figyelo [44831] .. .. (Paid) 11,522
Figyelo TOP 200
[44832] .. .. (Paid) 10,000
Figyelo Trend [44833] .. .. ‡15,000

INDIA
Chennai
Industrial Economist
[45041] .. .. (Paid) 25,000
Hyderabad
FAPCCI Review [45139]
Kota
1st Industrial Magazine [45311]
New Delhi
Asso Cham Bulletin
[45487] .. .. (Paid) 9,000
Asso Cham News & Views
[45488] .. .. (Paid) 1,500
Journal of Scientific and Industrial Research [45617] .. .... (Paid) 1100
Productivity [45638] .. ... (Paid) 3,000
Productivity News
[45639] .. .. (Paid) 2,500

ITALY
L'Aquila
International Journal of Management and Network Economics [46119]

MALAYSIA
Kuala Lumpur
FMM Directory of Malaysian Industries [47602]

MEXICO
Mexico City
Utillaje [47790] .. .. (Paid) 500
(Controlled) 30,250

MONACO
Monte Carlo
Luxury Intelligence [47810]

NETHERLANDS
Amsterdam
International Journal of Industrial Organization [48028]
Pacific-Basin Finance Journal [48198]
Dordrecht
Journal of Bamboo and Rattan [48442]
Review of Industrial Organization [48554]

SINGAPORE
Singapore
Journal of Developmental Entrepreneurship [50203]

REPUBLIC OF SOUTH AFRICA
Bellville
African Finance Journal [50353]
Cape Town
Achiever [50360] 10,000
Energy Forecast [50376] 10,000
Leadership in HIV/AIDS
[50387] 10,000
Opportunity [50398] 10,000

SPAIN
Oviedo-Asturias
International Journal of Arab Culture, Management and Sustainable Development [50826]
Valencia
Valencia Maritima [50847]

SWITZERLAND
Geneva
International Journal of Business and Emerging Markets [51106]
Schlieren
Aktuelle Technik
[51230] .. .. (Combined) 14,500

TAIWAN
Taipei
Contemporary Management Research [51336]

UNITED KINGDOM
Abingdon
Industry & Innovation [51814]
Basingstoke
International Journal of Disclosure and Governance [52209]
Bradford
Journal of Enterprising Communities [52498]

Rapid Prototyping Journal [52542]
Cambridge
Kiosk Europe [52865]
Galashiels
International Journal of Clothing Science and Technology [53403]
Glasgow
On-Trade Scotland [53436] .. ..·. 9,020
Gloucester
International Journal of Pressure Vessels and Piping [53470]
Guildford
Journal of Chinese Economic and Business Studies [53492]
Hook
Project Manager Today
[53587] .. .. (Controlled) ★14,871
Ilkley
Assembly Automation [53644]
Kent
Printwear & Promotion
[53679] .. .. ★5,536
Kidlington
Filtration Industry Analyst [53691]
Leicester
International Journal of Community Currency Research [53805]
Prime [53818] ... (Combined) 13,000
Retailspeak
[53821] .. .. (Combined) 10,000
London
Brazil Business Brief [54103] 500
Credit Today [54284] .... ★13,670
DM Magazine [54337] 14,560
European Journal of Industrial Relations [54400]
Financial Director [54454] ... ★20,609
International Custody & Fund Administration [54626]
Ironmaking & Steelmaking [54683]
Journal of Logic and Computation [54773]
Performance Textiles [55067]
Manchester
Education for Information [55554]
Oxford
The Journal of World Intellectual Property [56079]
Potters Bar
Manufacturing & Logistics IT [56297]
Sheffield
International Journal of Logistics Economics & Globalisation [56501]
Shoreham-by-Sea
Learned Publishing [56525] 700

COMMUNICATIONS

See also Journalism and Publishing; Public Relations; Radio, Television, Cable, and Video; Telecommunications

ALBANIA
Tirana
International Journal of Social Network Mining [41450]

AUSTRALIA
Broadway
African Journal of Information & Communication Technology [41660]

Monash
Communications Letters, IEEE [42113]
Rockhampton
Ejournalist [42315]
Wahroonga
Radio Comms Asia-Pacific
[42675] .... ★4,426

BARBADOS
Bridgetown
The International Journal of Education and Development using Information and Communication Technology (IJEDICT) [42828]

BELGIUM
Brussels
Ad!dict [42843]

BRAZIL
Sao Paulo
Revista Latinoamericana de Ciencias de la Comunicacion [43047]

PEOPLE'S REPUBLIC OF CHINA
Beijing
International Journal of Multimedia Intelligence and Security [43199]
Dalian
International Journal of Systems, Control and Communications [43252]
Hong Kong
The Correspondent [43294] .. . 1,800
Shanghai
Science Journal [43497]
Wuhan
International Journal of Satellite Communications Policy and Management [43520]

FRANCE
Strasbourg
News d'Ill [44113]

GERMANY
Berlin
International Journal of the Sociology of Language [44195]
Semiotica [44230]
Text & Talk [44231]
Theoretical Linguistics [44232]
Cologne
Kadmos [44297] 330
Dresden
AEU - International Journal of Electronics and Communications [44319]
Hannover
iX [44433]
Kassel
Zeitschrift fur germanistische Linguistik [44499] 700
Konstanz
Linguistic Typology [44514]

GREECE
Kozani
International Journal of Autonomous and Adaptive Communications Systems [44761]

INDIA
Allahabad
Far East Journal of Electronics and Communications [44927]

Circulation: ★ = ABC; △ = BPA; ♦ = CAC; • = CCAB; ❑ = VAC; ⊕ = PO Statement; ‡ = Publisher's Report; Boldface figures = sworn; Light figures = estimated.

Hyderabad
The Icfai Journal of Soft Skills [45168]

Kharagpur
International Journal of Communication Networks and Distributed Systems [45246]

New Delhi
Indian Media Studies Journal [45571]
Mass Media in India [45624]

ISRAEL
Tel Aviv
Heterocyclic Communications [46102]

JAPAN
Tokyo
IEICE Transactions on Communications [46839] 2,600
IEICE Transactions on Electronics [46840]
IEICE Transactions on Information and Systems [46841]
Nikkei Communications [46983] .... ★26,486
Nikkei Network [47001] ...... ★48,034
The Plaza [47019]

KENYA
Nairobi
Journal of Language, Technology & Entrepreneurship in Africa [47189]

REPUBLIC OF KOREA
Daejeon
ETRI Journal [47226] 3,700

Seoul
International Journal of Information Technology, Communications and Convergence [47269]

NETHERLANDS
Amsterdam
Babel [47902]
Brain and Language [47913]
English Text Construction [47965]
Information Design Journal [48018]
Information Economics and Policy [48019]
Information Processing & Management [48020]
Interpreting [48033]
Journal of Asian Pacific Communication [48052]
Journal of E-Governance [48069]
Journal of Visual Communication and Image Representation [48128]
Optical Fiber Technology [48191]
Space Communications [48234]
Target [48241]
Terminology [48245]
Utrecht Studies in Language and Communication [48268]

Dordrecht
Discrete Event Dynamic Systems [48375]

Leiden
Middle East Journal of Culture and Communication [48710]

Tilburg
International Journal of Cooperative Information Systems [48754]

NORWAY
Trondheim
International Journal of Grid & Utility Computing [49217]

PAKISTAN
Faisalabad
Journal of Mobile Communication [49271]
Research Journal of Telecommunication and Information Technology [49293]

POLAND
Lodz
International Review of Pragmatics [49670]

Warsaw
Lodz Papers in Pragmatics [49733]
Psychology of Language and Communication [49761]

SENEGAL
Dakar
Africa Media Review [50078]

SINGAPORE
Singapore
Asian Journal of Communication [50111] 750
International Journal on Wireless & Optical Communications [50195]

REPUBLIC OF SOUTH AFRICA
Kloof
Dataweek [50542] .... (Free) 4,000

Pretoria
Communicatio [50586]

SPAIN
Madrid
Album [50727]
La Balsa de la Medusa [50777]
SIC Seguridad en Informatica y Comunicaciones [50805] .. .. (Paid) 5,000
Visual [50815]

SWEDEN
Goteborg
Nordicom Review [50961]

SWITZERLAND
Aarau
MegaLink [51055] 12,500

Geneva
International Journal of Security and Networks [51138]

THAILAND
Bangkok
Microcomputer [51427]

UNITED ARAB EMIRATES
Dubai
Communications Middle East & Africa [51637] 10,000
Digital Studio [51638] .... △6,023

UNITED KINGDOM
Abingdon
Augmentative & Alternative Communication [51709]
Communication and Critical/Cultural Studies [51734]
Communication Reports [51735]
Communication Research Reports [51736]
Information, Communication and Society [51817]

International Journal of Language & Communication Disorders [51839]
Journal of Marketing Communications [51917]
Media History [51972]
New Review of Information Networking [51998]
The Review of Communication [52041]

Bath
T3 [52263]

Bradford
Corporate Communications [52446]
International Journal of Pervasive Computing and Communications [52483]
Journal of Communication Management [52494]
Journal of Information, Communication & Ethics in Society [52503]

Bristol
FibreSystems Europe [52669]

Crowthorne
Communicator [53121] 2,000

Dorking
Call Centre Focus [53192] 47,000

Enfield
Marine Electronics & Communications [53334] ... ★6,944

Exeter
Thinking Skills and Creativity [53365]

Guildford
International Journal of Satellite Communications and Networking [53491]

Huddersfield
Free Press [53620] .. ... (Paid) 5,250

London
British Journalism Review [54138]
Cable & Satellite International [54164] .... △10,000
Call Center Magazine [54167]
Commonwealth Broadcaster [54240] 3,000
Communicate [54244] 10,000
CWU Voice [54306]
European Journal of Communication [54398]
International Communication Gazette [54623]
Journal of Social and Personal Relationships [54819]
Journalism [54839]
Journalist [54840]
Magazine News [54894] .... (Non-paid) ‡10,000
Media, Culture & Society [54920]
Media Development [54921]
New Media Age [54994] .... (Controlled) 12,255 (Controlled) ‡6,503
New Media & Society [54995]
Pact [55050]
Personal and Ubiquitous Computing [55070]
Via Inmarsat Magazine [55368] 24,000
Viewfinder [55370] 5,500
Visual Communication [55373]

Loughton
Government Technology [55491]

Luton
Convergence [55501]
The Pantaneto Forum [55504]

Manchester
Interpreter and Translator Trainer [55561]
Sign Language Translator & Interpreter [55577]

The Translator [55580]

Olney
International Journal of Advanced Media and Communication [55787]
International Journal of Liability and Scientific Enquiry [55818]
International Journal of Vehicle Information & Communication System [55838]

Oxford
Journal of Communication [56021] .... (Paid) ‡5,000
Language & Communication [56084]
Public Opinion Quarterly [56178]

Tavistock
Zerb [56728] 4,000

Walton-on-Thames
The Woman Writer [56837]

Witney
Information Technology Law Reports [56943]

Worcester
EEMA Briefing [56961] 3,000

COMPUTERS

ALBANIA
Tirana
International Journal of Social Network Mining [41450]

AUSTRALIA
Adelaide
International Journal of Computers in Healthcare [41508]
International Journal of Intelligent Defence Support Systems [41510]

Baulkham Hills
AUUGN on the Web [41584]

Bondi Junction
Australian Windows XP [41607]
PlayStation 2 [41609]

Brisbane
CALL-EJ Online [41646]

Clayton
International Journal of Web and Grid Services [41762]
Mobile Information Systems [41763]

Dickson
Australasian Journal of Educational Technology [41840] .. ... (Paid) 700

Glenside
AppleSauce [41897]

Joondalup
Journal of Systems and Information Technology [41974]

McMahons Point
Atomic Maximum Power Computing (Australia) Magazine [42042] 28,555

North Sydney
Australian PC World [42207] .... (Paid) ★50,078

Rockhampton
International Journal of Computational Intelligence and Applications [42316]

Sydney
Australian NetGuide [42462] .... ★19,134
Australian PC User [42464] .... ★40,084
Australian Personal Computer [42465] .... ★28,952

Circulation: ★ = ABC; △ = BPA; ◆ = CAC; • = CCAB; ❑ = VAC; ⊕ = PO Statement; ‡ = Publisher's Report; Boldface figures = sworn; Light figures = estimated.

Computational Linguistics [42496]
The Journal of Research and Practice in Information Technology
   [42530] .. .. (Combined) ‡15,500
PC Authority [42558]

Toowoomba
International Journal of Information Quality [42628]

Wahroonga
What's New in Process Technology
   [42682] .... ★6,605

Wollongong
International Journal of Applied Cryptography [42704]

AUSTRIA
Graz
J.UCS (Journal of Universal Computer Science) [42724]

Krems
e-Beratungsjournal [42728]

Vienna
Applied Artificial Intelligence
   [42745] .... (Combined) ‡453

BARBADOS
Bridgetown
The International Journal of Education and Development using Information and Communication Technology (IJEDICT) [42828]

BELGIUM
Brussels
Mathematics and Computers in Simulation [42865]

Saint-Pieters-Leeuw
Dedicated Systems Magazine [42911]

BRAZIL
Porto Alegre
Journal of the Brazilian Computer Society [42991]

Rio de Janeiro
International Journal of High Performance System Architecture [43007]
International Journal of Innovative Computing and Applications [43008]

Sao Paulo
RTI Redes Telecom Instalacoes
   [43049] .... (Non-paid) 12,000

CHILE
Santiago
Revista de la SCCC [43148]

PEOPLE'S REPUBLIC OF CHINA
Beijing
International Journal of Intelligent Computing and Cybernetics [43197]
International Journal of Intelligent Engineering Informatics [43198]
International Journal of Multimedia Intelligence and Security [43199]
Journal of Computer Science and Technology (JCST) [43205]
Science in China Series F [43220]

Dalian
International Journal of Systems, Control and Communications [43252]

Hainan
International Journal of Information Science and Computer Mathematics [43258]

Hong Kong
Computer World Hong Kong [43293]
International Journal of Computer Processing of Languages [43349]
International Journal of Knowledge Engineering and Data Mining [43351]
Journal of Computational Mathematics [43353]
Mathematical Modelling and Applied Computing [43368]
PC World Hong Kong [43375]

Jinan
International Journal of Computational Intelligence in Bioinformatics and Systems Biology [43447]

Shanghai
International Journal of System Control and Information Processing [43479]
Microcomputer Applications [43489]

Taiyuan
International Journal of Bio-Inspired Computation [43515]

Xi'an
International Journal of Internet Manufacturing & Services [43532]

CZECH REPUBLIC
Prague
Automatizace
   [43611] .. .. (Combined) ‡8,500
Journal Kybernetika [43628]

EGYPT
Cairo
Egyptian Journal of Computer Science [43759] 320

El Sherouk City
International Journal of Cognitive Biometrics [43771]
International Journal of Cognitive Performance Support [43772]

FINLAND
Helsinki
International Journal of Digital Culture and Electronic Tourism [43833]

Kirkkonummi
The Scientific World Journal [43874]

Kuvalehdet
Tekniikan Maailma
   [43897] ...... (Combined) ‡129,343

FRANCE
Montpellier
Communications and Strategies [43977]

Nancy
Discrete Mathematics & Theoretical Computer Science [44010]

Rillieux-la-Pape
SAR and QSAR in Environmental Research [44099]

Sophia Antipolis
Performance Evaluation [44108]

Strasbourg
ALSIC (Apprentissage des Langues et Systemes d'Information et de Communication) [44109]
Computational Materials Science [44112]

GEORGIA
Tbilisi
Computer Science and Telecommunications [44131]

GERMANY
Berlin
Journal of Applied Crystallography [44202]
Microsystem Technologies [44222]
PIK [44226] .... ‡3,200

Bonn
Behorden Spiegel
   [44253] 104,000
Informatik Spektrum
   [44263] 24,000

Cologne
Journal of Virtual Reality and Broadcasting [44296]
RT eJournal [44301]

Darmstadt
International Journal of Computer Aided Engineering and Technology [44309]

Dortmund
International Journal on Software Tools for Technology Transfer (STTT) [44316]

Dusseldorf
Progress in Computational Fluid Dynamics [44331]
VDI Nachrichten [44335]

Erlangen
SIAM Journal on Scientific Computing [44341]

Freiburg
Language and Computers [44370]

Hannover
c't magazine
   [44430] .... (Paid) 379,350
                    (Paid) 233,521
iX [44433]
Telepolis [44436]

Heidelberg
Annals of Software Engineering [44439]
Cluster Computing [44448]
Innovations in Systems and Software Engineering [44461]
Multimedia Systems [44468]

Herford
CodeBreakers Journal (CBJ) [44483]

Munich
Computern im Handwerk
   [44555] .. .. (Combined) ‡72,351
Fraunhofer (English) [44562]

Poing
Computer Reseller News
   [44634] .. .. (Controlled) 33,136
Datacom
   [44635] .. .. (Combined) 11,014
Information Week
   [44636] .. .. (Combined) 75,253
Network Computing
   [44637] .. .. (Combined) 52,181

Saint Augustin
Journal of Systems Architecture [44654]

Vaterstetten
E-Commerce Magazin
   [44698] .... ‡14,675

Wurzburg
CHIP
   [44717] .. .. (Controlled) 345,780
Knowledge Organization [44721]

GREECE
Athens
International Journal of Electronic Governance [44746]

Kozani
International Journal of Autonomous and Adaptive Communications Systems [44761]

Nauplion
International Journal of Arts and Technology [44762]

Patras
Theoretical Computer Science [44766]

Piraeus
International Journal of Applied Systemic Studies [44767]
Journal of Applied Systems Studies [44769]

HUNGARY
Egyetem
Verbum [44889]

INDIA
Allahabad
Advances in Computer Science and Engineering [44921]
Advances in Differential Equations and Control Processes [44922]
Advances in Fuzzy Sets and Systems [44923]
Current Development in Theory and Applications of Wavelets [44924]
Far East Journal of Electronics and Communications [44927]
Far East Journal of Experimental and Theoretical Artificial Intelligence [44928]

Bhubaneswar
International Journal of Computational Vision and Robotics [45010]

Chennai
Journal of Digital Information Management [45046]

Gurgaon
Dataquest [45126] 40,000

Hyderabad
The Icfai Journal of Cyber Law [45146]

Kharagpur
International Journal of Communication Networks and Distributed Systems [45246]
International Journal of Information and Coding Theory [45248]

Kolkata
The Institution of Engineers (India) Computer Engineering Division Journal [45281] .... (Paid) 5,000
International Journal of Artificial Intelligence and Soft Computing [45295]

Kota
1st Industrial Magazine [45311]

Mumbai
Computer Society of India Journal
   [45364] .. .. (Paid) 3,000
CSI Adhyayan [45365]
CSI Communications [45366]
IEEMA Journal [45372] 10,000
Vivek [45449] .... (Paid) 400

New Delhi
Computers Today
   [45497] .. .. (Paid) 49,134
International Journal for Computational Vision and Biomechanics [45581]

Circulation: ★ = ABC; △ = BPA; ◆ = CAC; • = CCAB; ❑ = VAC; ⊕ = PO Statement; ‡ = Publisher's Report; Boldface figures = sworn; Light figures = estimated.

International Journal of Scientific Computing [45584]
International Journal of Theoretical and Applied Computer Sciences (IJTACS) [45587]
Journal of Bio-Inspired Computation Research [45593]
Journal of Discrete Mathematical Sciences and Cryptography [45595] .... (Paid) 240
Journal of Information & Optimization Sciences [45606] ....: (Paid) 480

Pune
C-DAC Connect [45696]

Thanjavur
International Journal of Computing and Applications [45747]

IRAN
Tehran
Iranian Journal of Electrical and Computer Engineering [45900]

ITALY
Ancona
International Journal of Computational Intelligence Studies [46118]

Bari
International Journal of Enterprise Systems Integration and Interoperability [46122]

Fisciano
International Journal of Forensic Software Engineering [46140]

Genoa
International Journal of Shape Modeling [46150]

Milan
International Journal of Electronic Trade [46177]
Office Automation [46189] 17,000

Naples
International Journal of Critical Computer-Based Systems [46200]

Trento
Applied Ontology [46261]
International Journal of Agent-Oriented Software Engineering [46262]

JAPAN
Chiba
IEICE Transactions on Fundamentals of Electronics, Communications and Computer Sciences [46318]

Fukui
Journal of Chemical Software [46332]

Himeji
International Journal of Reasoning-based Intelligent Systems [46378]

Oita
Artificial Life and Robotics [46590]

Osaka
Journal of Japanese Society of Computational Statistics [46621] .... (Paid) 400

Tokyo
Applicable Algebra in Engineering, Communication and Computing [46745]
Computing Japan [46793]
Computing and Visualization in Science [46794]
Engineering with Computers [46810]
IEICE Transactions on Communications [46839] 2,600

IEICE Transactions on Electronics [46840]
IEICE Transactions on Information and Systems [46841]
Joho-Shori [46878] 27,000
Journal of Advanced Computational Intelligence and Intelligent Informatics (JACIII) [46880]
Journal of Robotics and Mechatronics [46940]
J@pan Inc Magazine [46947] 24,000
NEC Journal of Advanced Technology [46976]
NEC Technical Journal [46977]
Nikkei BP Government Technology [46980] 11,100
Nikkei Communications [46983] .... ⋆26,486
Nikkei Computer [46984] .... ⋆48,862
Nikkei Information Strategy [46995] .... ⋆20,809
Nikkei Linux [46996] .... ⋆15,185
Nikkei PC Beginners [47002] 80,000
Nikkei PC21 [47003] .... ⋆161,939
Nikkei Personal Computing [47004] .... ⋆177,199
Nikkei Software [47006] .... ⋆20,928
Nikkei Systems [47008] ...... ⋆37,890
Nikkei WinPC [47011] .... ⋆43,791

Tsukuba
International Journal of Knowledge Engineering and Soft Data Paradigms [47110]

REPUBLIC OF KOREA
Seoul
International Journal of Information Technology, Communications and Convergence [47269]
Journal of Computational Intelligence in Bioinformatics [47272]

NETHERLANDS
Alphen aan den Rijn
Database Magazine [47867] .. .. (Paid) ‡4,000
IT Service Magazine [47868] .... (Combined) ‡4,700
Optimize [47870] .... ‡3,500
Process Control [47871] .... (Combined) 4,000
Software Release Magazine [47872] .... ‡4,100
Telecommagazine [47873] 7,369

Amsterdam
ACM Transactions on Computational Logic (TOCL) [47877]
Computational Statistics & Data Analysis [47935]
Computer Speech & Language [47936]
Computer Vision and Image Understanding [47937]
Fundamenta Informaticae [47993]
Future Generation Computer Systems [47995]
Graphical Models [48004]
Information Processing & Management [48020]
Information Services & Use [48021]
Interaction Studies [48022]
International Journal of Artificial Intelligence in Education [48025]
International Journal of Hybrid Intelligent Systems [48027]
Journal of Computer and System Sciences [48065]
Journal of Intelligent & Fuzzy Systems [48087] 3,850
Journal of Network and Computer Applications [48101]

Journal of Parallel and Distributed Computing [48107]
Journal of Systems and Software [48123]
Journal of Visual Languages and Computing [48129]
Materials Science in Semiconductor Processing [48147]
Mechatronics [48151]
Neural Networks [48172]
Web Intelligence and Agent Systems [48270]

Bussum
Current Computer-Aided Drug Design [48285]

Delft
Computer-Aided Design [48308]
Journal on Satisfiability, Boolean Modeling and Computation [48312]

Dordrecht
Annals of Mathematics and Artificial Intelligence [48325]
Autonomous Agents and Multi-Agent Systems [48329]
Computer Supported Cooperative Work (CSCW) [48358]
Designs, Codes and Cryptography [48372]
Discrete Event Dynamic Systems [48375]
Distributed and Parallel Databases [48376]
GeoInformatica [48406]
Informatik-Spektrum [48421]
The Jetix Magazine [48435]
Journal of Computational Electronics [48450]
Journal of Computational Neuroscience [48451]
Journal in Computer Virology [48452]
Journal of Grid Computing [48466]
Journal of Mathematical Modelling and Algorithms [48475]
Journal of Scheduling [48491]
Natural Computing [48517]
Netnomics [48518]
Photonic Network Communications [48527]
Queueing Systems [48545]
Real-Time Systems [48548]
Reliable Computing [48549]
Software Quality Journal [48563]
Statistics and Computing [48568]
World Wide Web [48588]

Enschede
International Journal of Healthcare Technology and Management [48594]
International Journal of Web-Based Communities [48595]

Groningen
Cognitive Systems [48598]
Computers in Industry [48599]

Leiden
Computing Letters [48664]
Seeing and Perceiving [48723]

Wijchen
CBM [48773] ...... (Combined) 6,300

NEW ZEALAND
Auckland
International Journal of Biomechatronics and Biomedical Robotics [48798]

Wellington
MIS Australia [49017]

NIGERIA
Minna
Information Technologist [49147]

NORWAY
Trondheim
International Journal of Computational Intelligence Research [49216]
International Journal of Grid & Utility Computing [49217]

PAKISTAN
Faisalabad
Asian Journal of Information Technology [49236]
Information Technology Journal [49247]
International Journal of Soft Computing [49256]
World Information Technology Journal [49298]

Karachi
Spider [49376]

PHILIPPINES
Makati City
Computer World Philippines [49515]
Enterprise [49516] 60,000
PC World Philippines [49518] 65,000

Quezon City
I.T. Matters [49596]

POLAND
Krakow
International Journal of Biometrics [49666]

Warsaw
International Journal of Applied Mathematics and Computer Science [49719]
Scalable Computing [49764]

Wroclaw
International Journal of Intelligent Information and Database Systems [49780]

PORTUGAL
Funchal
International Journal of Agile and Extreme Software Development [49798]

Lisboa
International Journal of Organisational Design and Engineering [49800]

ROMANIA
Arad
International Journal of Advanced Intelligence Paradigms [49830]

Tg-Mures
BYTE Romania [49848]

RUSSIA
Moscow
Automatic Control and Computer Sciences [49880]
Automation and Remote Control [49882]
Integral Transforms and Special Functions [49920]
Journal of Computer and Systems Sciences International [49928]
Pattern Recognition and Image Analysis [49952]

SAUDI ARABIA
Riyadh
Journal of King Saud University:

Circulation: ⋆ = ABC; △ = BPA; ◆ = CAC; • = CCAB; ❑ = VAC; ⊕ = PO Statement; ‡ = Publisher's Report; Boldface figures = sworn; Light figures = estimated.

Computer & Information Sciences
[50066] .. .. (Paid) 3,000

SINGAPORE
Singapore
Computer Era [50125]
Computer Products [50126]
Computerworld Singapore [50127]
Hardware Mag [50162]
International Journal of Computational Methods (IJCM) [50179]
Journal of Computational Acoustics
[50202]
Journal of Graph Algorithms and
Applications [50206]
MSDN Magazine. Southeast Asia
Edition [50223]
Parallel Processing Letters [50235]
Pervasive and Mobile Computing
[50236]

SLOVAKIA
Bratislava
Computing and Informatics
[50318] .... (Paid) 300

REPUBLIC OF SOUTH AFRICA
Centurion
South African Computer Journal
[50450]
South African Journal of Information
Management [50454]

Pinegowrie
Gadget [50571]

SPAIN
Barcelona
Computer Science Review [50660]
IDP [50680]
PC Actual [50692] .... ‡61,365
Upgrade (English Edition) [50705]

Madrid
ComputerWorld/Espana
[50738] .. .. (Combined) ‡10,000
Comunicaciones World
[50739] .. .. (Combined) ‡10,000
Cybermetrics [50748]
Dealer World & Dealer World 15
[50749] .. .. (Controlled) ‡13,826
Guia del Comprador de Ordenadores
y Software [50766] .. .. ‡4,054
iWorld [50776] .. .. (Paid) 7,000
Macworld Espana
[50779] .. .. (Combined) ‡9,000
PC World Espana
[50788] .. .. (Combined) ‡62,450
SIC Seguridad en Informatica y
Comunicaciones
[50805] .. .. (Paid) 5,000

Vitoria-Gasteiz
a+t [50849]

SWAZILAND
Mbabane
Y'ello [50947]

SWEDEN
Goteborg
Scandinavian Journal of Information
Systems [50965]

Lund
Microprocessors and Microsystems
[50987]

Stockholm
International Journal of Social and
Humanistic Computing [51021]
International Journal of Technology
Enhanced Learning [51022]

SWITZERLAND
Aarau
MegaLink [51055] 12,500

Geneva
Computer Graphics Forum Journal
[51090] .... (Paid) ‡844
International Journal of Auditing
Technology [51103]
International Journal of Electronic
Banking [51117]
International Journal of Granular
Computing, Rough Sets and Intelligent Systems [51123]
International Journal of Medical Engineering and Informatics [51131]
International Journal of Quality Engineering and Technology [51136]
International Journal of Security and
Networks [51138]
International Journal of Social Computing and Cyber-Physical Systems
[51140]
World Review of Intermodal Transportation Research [51168]

Lausanne
Insurance [51192]

Sirnach
Professional Computing [51231]

Thalwil
Infoweek.ch
[51234] .. .. (Combined) 18,000

Zurich
Journal of Object Technology (JOT)
[51271]
SPEEDUP Journal [51286] ... ‡2,500

TAIWAN
Chungli
Advances in Adaptive Data Analysis
[51304]

Jhongli City
International Journal of Internet Marketing and Advertising [51308]

Taichung
International Journal of Electronic
Customer Relationship
Management [51320]

Taipei
Asian Journal of Control [51332]
Digitimes [51337] .... ‡65,000
International Journal of Cyber Society
and Education [51343]
International Journal of Information
and Computer Security [51346]

Tamsui
International Journal of Information
and Management Sciences
[51393] .... (Paid) 400

THAILAND
Bangkok
Microcomputer [51427]

TURKEY
Ankara
Turkish Journal of Electrical Engineering and Computer Sciences
[51509]

UNITED ARAB EMIRATES
Dubai
Channel Middle East
[51634] .... △7,485
Network Middle East
[51650] 8,000
PC Magazine Middle & Near East
[51652] 4,870

Windows Middle East [51657]

UNITED KINGDOM
Abingdon
Behaviour and Information
Technology [51717]
Information, Communication and
Society [51817]
Information and Communications
Technology Law [51818]
International Review of Law Computers & Technology [51852]
New Review of Information
Networking [51998]
Open Learning [52002]

Bath
Digital Home [52238]
Internet Business News [52245]
PCPlus [52253] .... (Paid) ★72,698
Worldwide Computer Products News
[52264]

Bedford
Applied Soft Computing [52272]

Bournemouth
Advanced Photoshop [52410]
gamesTM [52414]
Web Designer [52429]

Bradford
Information Technology & People
[52468]
International Journal of Pervasive
Computing and Communications
[52483]
International Journal of Web Information Systems [52489]
Internet Research [52491]
Journal of Documentation [52496]
OCLC Systems & Services [52532]

Brentwood
International Journal of Architectural
Computing [52576]

Bristol
Computers and Law
[52655] 2,700
DNJ [52661]
International Journal of Computer
Applications in Technology [52677]
Journal of Instrumentation [52687]

Burnham
International Journal of Micrographics
& Optical Technology [52765]

Cambridge
Combinatorics, Probability and
Computing [52807] 300
GEO [52822]
Kiosk Europe [52865]
Theory and Practice of Logic Programming (TPLP) [52902] 300

Cardiff
International Journal of
Metaheuristics [52931]
International Journal of Mobile Network Design and Innovation
[52932]

Coulsdon
Jane's Simulation & Training Systems
[53073]

Edinburgh
International Journal of Humanities
and Arts Computing [53288]

Farnham
Animation [53379]

Glasgow
International Journal of Adaptive Control & Signal Processing [53425]

Hatfield
Information Management &
Technology
[53539] .... (Controlled) 700

Heslington
Innovations in Teaching and Learning
in Information and Computer
Sciences [53567]

Leeds
Artificial Intelligence [53754]

Leicester
Advances in Computational Sciences
and Technology [53783]
Finance on Windows [53800]

Littlehampton
Smart Card News [53866]

London
CAD User [54165] 13,000
Cognition, Technology & Work
[54236]
The Computer Journal [54254]
Computing [54256]
Custom PC [54305]
Ei Magazine [54357]
IBM Database Magazine [54581]
International Journal of Computer
Mathematics [54640]
International Journal of Electronic
Democracy [54646]
International Journal of Electronic
Security and Digital Forensics
[54647]
International Journal of Internet Technology & Secured Transactions
[54651]
Journal of Database Marketing &
Customer Strategy Management
[54734]
Literary and Linguistic Computing
[54876]
Logical Methods in Computer
Science [54883]
Managing Information
[54904] 8,000
MSDN Magazine
[54960] .. .. (Paid) 75,378
PC Magazine
[55063] .... (Paid) 218,000
Personal Computer World
[55069] .... ★54,069
Personal and Ubiquitous Computing
[55070]
Sell-Side Technology [55227]
Web User [55395]

Loughborough
Pattern Analysis & Applications
[55486] .... (Paid) 950

Loughton
Government Technology [55491]

Luton
Computational Biology and Chemistry
[55500]
Database and Network Journal
[55502] .... (Paid) 400
Software World
[55505] .... (Paid) 400

Middlesex
Interacting with Computers [55617]

Milton Keynes
Design Studies [55633]

Newcastle upon Tyne
Formal Aspects of Computing
[55670]

Newport
AI & Society [55687]

Nottingham
International Journal of Design
Engineering [55759]

Olney
International Journal of Ad Hoc and
Ubiquitous Computing [55786]

Circulation: ★ = ABC; △ = BPA; ◆ = CAC; • = CCAB; ❑ = VAC; ⊕ = PO Statement; ‡ = Publisher's Report; Boldface figures = sworn; Light figures = estimated.

Gale Directory of Publications & Broadcast Media/147th Ed.

6157

International Journal of Autonomic
Computing **[55791]**
International Journal of Computa-
tional Materials Science & Surface
Engineering **[55796]**
International Journal of Embedded
Systems **[55798]**
International Journal of High Perfor-
mance Computing and Networking
[55809]
International Journal of Internet and
Enterprise Management **[55815]**
International Journal of Internet Pro-
tocol Technology **[55816]**
International Journal of Manufacturing
Research **[55822]**
International Journal of Networking
and Virtual Organisations **[55826]**
International Journal of Teaching &
Case Studies **[55834]**
International Journal of Wireless and
Mobile Computing **[55841]**

Oxford
Journal of Computer-Mediated
Communication **[56023]**
Journal of Information Technology
[56042]
Network Security **[56113]**
SIAM Journal on Optimization
[56202]

Plymouth
International Journal for Technology
in Mathematics Education **[56271]**

Reading
Electronic Journal of e-Learning
[56314]
Electronic Journal of Information Systems Evaluation (EJISE) **[56315]**

Shoreham-by-Sea
International Journal of Knowledge-
Based and Intelligent Engineering
Systems **[56524]**

Stafford
International Journal of Web Engineering and Technology **[56592]**

Stevenage
Electronics and Communication Engi-
neering Journal
[56600] .... ‡38,000
Electronics Education **[56601]**
IEE Proceedings Control Theory &
Applications **[56606]**
IEE Proceedings Software **[56614]**
IEE Proceedings Vision, Image &
Signal Processing **[56615]**
IET Computers & Digital Techniques
[56617]

Stoke-on-Trent
Design & Technology
[56629] 8,500

Sunderland
Neural Computing & Applications
[56654] .... (Paid) 720

Sutton
Computer Weekly
[56683] .. .. △104,559

Swansea
Computers and Geotechnics **[56700]**

Swindon
ITNOW
[56712] .. .. (Combined) 50,000

Teddington
International Journal of Mathematical
Modelling and Numerical
Optimisation **[56731]**

West Yorkshire
Kybernetes **[56904]**

Witney
Information Technology Law Reports
[56943]

CONFECTIONARIES AND FROZEN DAIRY PRODUCTS
See also Baking

AUSTRALIA
Nundah
Australian Baking Business
[42219] 8,348

NORWAY
Oslo
Meieriposten **[49202]** ... (Paid) 2,050

PAKISTAN
Faisalabad
Research Journal of Dairy Sciences
[49287]
World Journal of Dairy & Food
Sciences **[49301]**

UNITED KINGDOM
Derby
Ice Cream **[53164]** 1,000

London
Confectionery Production
[54258] .... (Controlled) 3,500

Oxted
Biscuit World **[56235]** 4,335

CONGRESSIONAL AND FEDERAL GOVERNMENT AFFAIRS

AUSTRALIA
Melbourne
Australian Journal of Public
Administration **[42051]**

FRANCE
Ferney-Voltaire
Focus on the Public Services
[43947] .. .. (Free) 17,000

GREECE
Athens
International Journal of Electronic
Governance **[44746]**

GUYANA
Georgetown
Dayclean **[44800]** ....: 5,000

INDIA
New Delhi
Yojana **[45670]** .... (Paid) 150,000

JAPAN
Tokyo
Economics of Governance **[46806]**

NETHERLANDS
Leiden
Middle East Law and Governance
[48711]

NEW ZEALAND
Christchurch
The Guardian **[48867]** 2,500

SWEDEN
Stockholm
Socionomen **[51040]** 9,000

UNITED KINGDOM
Abingdon
Adelphi Series **[51698]**
Journal of Strategic Studies **[51948]**

Brighton
Government and Opposition **[52610]**

Cambridge
Journal of Public Policy
[52861] 800

Hull
Lobster **[53627]**

London
Commonwealth Judicial Journal
[54241]
Constitutional and Parliamentary
Information **[54260]**
London Bulletin
[54886] .... (Combined) 6,000
Public Finance **[55151]**

Loughton
Government Business **[55490]**

Olney
International Journal of Public Policy
[55830]

Oxford
International Journal of Urban and
Regional Research **[56004]**
Parliamentary Affairs **[56141]**
Public Administration **[56176]**
Publius **[56179]** .... (Paid) ‡1,200
(Non-paid) ‡100

Surrey
Parliaments, Estates and
Representation **[56671]**

Uxbridge
Transforming Government **[56801]**

CONSTRUCTION, CONTRACTING, BUILDING, AND EXCAVATING
See also Architecture; Building Materials, Concrete, Brick, and Tile; Engineering (Various branches); Roads and Streets; Wood and Woodworking

AUSTRALIA
Barton
Australian Pipeliner
[41577] .. .. ♦3,020

Canberra
Australian Journal of Construction
Economics and Building **[41701]**

Chatswood
Construction Contractor
[41739] ... . (Combined) 120,000

Hazelbrook
House & Home **[41945]**

Leederville
Cranes and Lifting Australia **[42006]**

North Ryde
BuildHOME Vic **[42174]**
Kit Homes **[42184]**
Outdoor Design & Living **[42189]**

Wahroonga
Safety Solutions **[42676]** 7,323

AUSTRIA
Salzburg
Geomechanics and Tunnelling
[42740]

BAHRAIN
Manama
Gulf Construction
[42788] .. .. (Paid) 49,028

BELGIUM
Brussels
Beton **[42844]**

BRAZIL
Rio de Janeiro
International Journal of High Performance System Architecture
[43007]

PEOPLE'S REPUBLIC OF CHINA
Beijing
Architectural Journal
[43169] 65,000
Journal of Building Structure **[43203]**

Hangzhou
International Journal of Structural
Engineering **[43260]**

Hong Kong
Building Journal Hong Kong **[43284]**
Hong Kong Surveyor **[43345]**
Journal of Construction Research
[43354]

DENMARK
Copenhagen
Byggeforum **[43658]** 3,500
De Farver **[43664]** 12,800

Glostrup
Byggeri
[43698] .... (Controlled) 7,743
BygTek
[43699] .... (Controlled) 21,146
Teknisk Nyt **[43716]** .... ‡10,131
Teknisk Nyt Special Edition
[43717] .... ‡10,000

FRANCE
Clichy
Forum Chantiers
[43932] .. .. (Paid) 15,000
Route Actualite/Roads News
[43935] .... (Combined) 8,000

GERMANY
Berlin
Landschaftsarchitekten
[44214] 2,500

Gutersloh
ZI-Ziegelindustrie International
[44406]

Mainz
Journal of Structural Geology **[44541]**

Nuremberg
Element + BAU **[44610]** 6,800

HUNGARY
Budapest
Atrium **[44824]** 15,000

INDIA
Mumbai
Indian Construction
[45376] .. .. (Paid) 7,000

Circulation: ★ = ABC; △ = BPA; ♦ = CAC; • = CCAB; ❑ = VAC; ⊕ = PO Statement; ‡ = Publisher's Report; Boldface figures = sworn; Light figures = estimated.

Thane
Indian Concrete Journal (ICJ)
[45745] .... (Paid) 3,000

Vadodara
Navnirman [45764] .... (Paid) 250

IRELAND
Blackrock
Irish Hardware [45921] .... ★1,664

JAPAN
Tokyo
Journal of Advanced Concrete
Technology [46881]
Nikkei Architecture
[46978] .... ★44,461
Nikkei Construction
[46985] .... ★26,357
Nikkei Home Builder
[46994] .... ★22,754

LEBANON
Beirut
Arab Construction World (ACW)
[47390] .... (Combined) ‡7,153

MALAYSIA
Kuala Lumpur
Master Builders Journal
[47625] 3,000

Petaling Jaya
B & I Magazine [47695] 10,000

NETHERLANDS
Amsterdam
Bridge Structures [47916]
Composite Structures [47933]

Dordrecht
Journal of Housing and the Built
Environment [48467]

Rotterdam
Het Houtblad
[48750] .... (Controlled) ‡16,500

NORWAY
Moss
Byggaktuelt
[49193] .... (Combined) 12,445

POLAND
Warsaw
Town Planning and Architecture
[49767]

SERBIA
Belgrade
Energy and Buildings [50082]

REPUBLIC OF SOUTH AF-RICA
Johannesburg
Building Women [50528]

Randburg
SA Architect [50610]

SPAIN
Madrid
Carreteras
[50733] .... (Controlled) 16,000
Informes de la Construccion [50770]
Materiales de Construccion [50782]

SWEDEN
Karlskrona
Planera Bygga Bo
[50971] .... (Controlled) 3,500

Ljusdal
Byggfakta Projektnytt
[50979] .... (Controlled) 23,000

Stockholm
Bygg & Teknik
[51011] .... (Controlled) 6,800
Nordic Journal of Building Physics
[51027]

UNITED REPUBLIC OF TAN-ZANIA
Dar es Salaam
Journal of Building and Land
Development [51402]

UNITED ARAB EMIRATES
Dubai
Gulf Industry Magazine
[51644] 28,808

UNITED KINGDOM
Abingdon
International Journal of Construction
Education and Research [51830]

Ascot
Construction Information Quarterly
[52137] 4,000
Construction Manager
[52138] 33,000

Belfast
Keystone
[52289] .... (Controlled) 15,000
Specify [52293]

Bracknell
International Building Services
Abstracts [52434]

Bradford
Construction Innovation [52445]
Engineering, Construction and Archi-
tectural Management [52455]
Structural Survey [52549]

Brentwood
International Journal of Space
Structures [52578]

Buckhurst Hill
Plant World [52751] .... ★11,606
Refurbishment Projects
[52752] .... ★10,138

Camberley
Concrete [52784] .... (Paid) 5,500

Cannock
The Vitreous Enameller [52916]

Coventry
Housing [53084]
The International Journal of
Ventilation [53085]

Croydon
Building Products
[53122] .... (Controlled) 23,000

Cudham
Classic Plant & Machinery [53139]

Glasgow
Project Plant [53441] .... ★5,330
Project Scotland [53442] ...... ★7,223
Urban Realm [53456] 7,000

Guildford
Journal of Constructional Steel
Research [53493]

Hemel Hempstead
Demolition and Dismantling
[53556] 4,000

London
AXIS [53995] 6,000
Bridge Design & Engineering
[54106] .... (Combined) 5,000

Building
[54152] .. .. (Combined) ★23,961
Geosynthetics International [54504]
House Builder [54575]
The Journal of Architecture [54700]
Journal of Sandwich Structures and
Materials [54815]
Journal of Wide Bandgap Materials
[54836]
Master Builder [54912]
Openings [55034] 4,000
World Tunnelling [55427] ...... ★7,000

Manchester
Progress in Planning [55575]

Northampton
Building Engineer
[55706] .... (Combined) 6,500

Olney
International Journal of Materials &
Structural Integrity [55823]

Preston
Journal of Financial Management of
Property and Construction [56300]

Redhill
Dredging and Port Construction
[56350]

Saintfield
SelfBuild [56449] .... ★11,574

Sevenoaks
Conservatory [56471] .... ★7,411
FENSA News [56472]
Public Sector & Local Government
Building [56480] .... ★16,100
Roofing, Cladding & Insulation
[56483]

Stamford
CAA Newsnet [56595]

Surrey
Concrete Quarterly [56660]

Wadhurst
Construction Europe
[56805] ...,...................... ★14,624
International Construction China
[56807] 15,800
International Construction Turkiye
[56808] .... (Combined) 17,649

Watford
Professional Builder
[56869] .... ★98,489
Window Fabricator & Installer
[56877] .... ★10,228

CONSUMERISM

PEOPLE'S REPUBLIC OF CHINA
Hong Kong
Choice [43290] 30,000

INDIA
Mumbai
Keemat [45407] .... (Paid) 2,000

IRELAND
Dublin
Consumer Choice [45952]

TAIWAN
Taichung
International Journal of Electronic
Customer Relationship
Management [51320]

UNITED KINGDOM
Argyll
Journal of Customer Behaviour
[52129]

Basingstoke
Journal of Medical Marketing
[52218] 550
Journal of Revenue and Pricing
Management [52221] 450

Bognor Regis
Journal of Consumer Behaviour
[52398]

Exeter
Young Consumers [53366]

London
Journal of Brand Management
[54710] 650
Journal of Consumer Culture [54730]
Journal of Database Marketing &
Customer Strategy Management
[54734]

Stirling
The International Review of Retail,
Distribution and Consumer
Research [56623]

CONVENTIONS, MEETINGS, AND TRADE FAIRS

SINGAPORE
Singapore
TTGmice [50282]

UNITED ARAB EMIRATES
Dubai
Middle East MICE & Events
[51649] 33,000

UNITED KINGDOM
Chepstow
Event Organiser [52982] 7,000

London
Access All Areas
[53890] .... (Controlled) 5,000

COSMETICS AND TOILETRIES
See also Hairstyling

AUSTRALIA
Chatswood
Post Script [41743] .. .. ★11,545

Pyrmont
Professional Beauty [42287] ... 9,000

FRANCE
Montrouge
Oleagineux, Corps Gras, Lipides
[44003]

GERMANY
Augsburg
IFSCC Magazine [44140]

Karlsruhe
COSSMA [44492]

INDIA
Mumbai
Soaps, Detergents & Toiletries
Review [45440] .... (Paid) 4,000

JAPAN
Tokyo
Priv. [47025] .... ★173,474

SWITZERLAND
Geneva
WHO Drug Information [51166]

Circulation: ★ = ABC; △ = BPA; ◆ = CAC; ⚬ = CCAB; ❑ = VAC; ⊕ = PO Statement; ‡ = Publisher's Report; Boldface figures = sworn; Light figures = estimated.

UNITED KINGDOM
London
British Style
[54147] .... (Non-paid) 5,000
Cosmetic Products Report
[54270] .. .. (Paid) 2,000
Esprit Magazine [54383] 5,200
Essential Guide to Beauty [54384]
European Cosmetics Markets
[54393] .... (Paid) 400
Nutraceuticals International [55018]
Professional Beauty/LNE English
Edition
[55128] .. .. (Combined) 11,867
Northwich
International Journal of Cosmetic
Science [55719]

DENTISTRY

AUSTRALIA
Saint Leonards
Australian Dental Journal
[42330] .. .. (Paid) 10,000

BRAZIL
Bauru
Journal of Applied Oral Science
[42948]
Ribeirao Preto
Brazilian Dental Journal [42995]
Sao Paulo
Brazilian Journal of Oral Sciences
[43027]
Brazilian Oral Research [43030]

PEOPLE'S REPUBLIC OF CHINA
Hong Kong
Clinical Oral Implants Research
[43291]
Xi'an
Chinese Journal of Conservative
Dentistry [43530]

DENMARK
Arhus
Journal of Oral Rehabilitation [43647]
Frederiksberg
Orthodontics & Craniofacial Research
[43694]

FINLAND
Helsinki
Suomen Hammaslaakarilehti/Finnish
Dental Journal
[43860] .... (Combined) 6,800

FRANCE
Ferney-Voltaire
International Journal of Paediatric
Dentistry [43948]

GERMANY
Heidelberg
Clinical Oral Investigations [44447]
Mainz
International Poster Journal of Den-
tistry and Oral Medicine [44540]

GREECE
Athens
Hellenic Orthodontic Review [44744]
Stomatologia [44756] 2,000

INDIA
Bangalore
Journal of Indian Prosthodontic
Society [44974]

Belgaum
Journal of Indian Academy of Oral
Medicine and Radiology [44996]
Chennai
Journal of Conservative Dentistry
[45045]
Journal of Indian Society of
Periodontology [45048]
Davangere
Indian Society of Pedodontics and
Preventive Dentistry Journal
[45086] .... (Combined) 1,500
Mumbai
Journal of Dental Implants [45398]
New Delhi
Endontology [45508]

ITALY
Carimate
Doctor Os [46130] 15,000
Journal of Osseointegration
[46131] .. .. (Controlled) ‡9,000

JAPAN
Chiba
The Bulletin of Tokyo Dental College
[46316]
Hiroshima
Oral Radiology [46382]
Okayama
Journal of Oral Tissue Engineering
[46598]
Osaka
Journal of Periodontal Research
[46624]
Tokyo
Journal of Medical and Dental
Sciences [46924] 1,000
Journal of Oral Science
[46934] .... (Controlled) 1,200
Odontology [47013]
Pediatric Dental Journal [47017]

NEPAL
Kathmandu
Journal of the Nepal Dental
Association [47838]

NETHERLANDS
Nieuwegein
Nederlands Tandartsenblad [48741]

NEW ZEALAND
Auckland
New Zealand Dental Journal [48808]

NIGERIA
Idi-Araba
Nigerian Dental Journal [49105]
Lagos
Nigerian Quarterly Journal of Hospital
Medicine [49142]
Nnewi
Nigerian Journal of Clinical Practice
[49149]
Port Harcourt
Port Harcourt Medical Journal
[49169]

RUSSIA
Moscow
Russian Journal of Stomatology
[49982]

SERBIA
Nis
Acta Stomatologica Naissi [50090]

SINGAPORE
Singapore
DENTAL ASIA [50130]
The Dental Mirror [50131]

REPUBLIC OF SOUTH AFRICA
Grahamstown
Tanzania Dental Journal [50517]

SPAIN
Barcelona
Revista Espanola de Ortodoncia
[50695]

SRI LANKA
Colombo
Ceylon Journal of Medical Sciences
[50850] .... (Controlled) 125

SWEDEN
Huddinge
Acta Odontologica Scandinavica
[50969]

UNITED KINGDOM
Chesham
Dental Trader [52986] 2,000
Exeter
Journal of Dentistry [53361]
London
BDJ British Dental Journal
[54007] 20,562
BMC Oral Health [54080]
British Dental Journal
[54110] 37,000
Dental Nursing [54317]
Evidence-Based Dentistry (EBD)
[54414]
The GDP [54497] 13,000
The Magic Circular Magazine [54895]
Vital [55374]
Lowestoft
Community Dental Health [55493]
The European Journal of Prosthodon-
tics and Restorative Dentistry
[55494]
International Dental Journal
[55495] .. .. (Paid) 2,000
Manchester
Dental Materials [55553]
Nottingham
Dental Laboratory
[55751] .... (Combined) 3,500
Oxford
Australian Endodontic Journal
[55877]
International Journal of Dental
Hygiene [55993]
Periodontology 2000 [56149]
Shenley
Dentistry [56519] 21,500

DRAMA AND THEATRE
See also Performing Arts

AUSTRALIA
Bundoora
Australian Playwrights [41669]
City East
NJ [41752]

BELGIUM
Brussels
Journal of Film Preservation [42862]

Mechelen
Ludus [42904]

BOTSWANA
Gaborone
Marang [42944]

IRELAND
Dublin
Show Times [45998]

JAPAN
Tokyo
Adaptation [46728]

NETHERLANDS
Amsterdam
Theatre Research International
[48247] 1,000

REPUBLIC OF SOUTH AFRICA
Matieland
SATJ [50553]

SPAIN
Madrid
Ade-Teatro [50724]
Por la Danza [50791]
Primer Acto [50792]

UNITED KINGDOM
Abingdon
Cultural Trends [51748]
Performance Research [52007]
Brighton
Theatre Notebook [52633]
Bristol
Who Do You Think You Are?
[52736] .. .. ★20,266
Edinburgh
Dance Research [53267]
London
African Performance Review [53923]
The British Theatre Directory
[54148] .. .. (Paid) 2,000
Drama Magazine [54342] 1200
Equity
[54382] .. .. (Controlled) 39,000
Opera Now [55037]
Sightline [55238]
Manchester
Nineteenth Century Theatre and Film
[55574]
York
Aesthetica Magazine
[56986] 20,000

DRUGS AND PHARMACEUTICALS

AUSTRALIA
Brisbane
Current Drug Delivery [41647]
Chatswood
Australian Journal of Pharmacy
[41737] .... ‡15,035
Natural Health & Beauty
[41741] .... ★11,545
Post Script [41743] .... ★11,545
Deakin
Australian Pharmacist
[41834] 9,500
Australian Prescriber [41835]

North Parramatta
Retail Pharmacy
[42158] .... (Controlled) 7,413

Surry Hills
Drug and Alcohol Review [42428]

Womying
International Journal of Medical
Sciences [42711]

BANGLADESH
Dhaka
Bangladesh Pharmaceutical Journal
[42806]

BELGIUM
Brussels
European Journal of Hospital
Pharmacy [42853]
Pharmacy Today [42869]

BRAZIL
Botucatu
The Journal of Venomous Animals
and Toxins including Tropical
Diseases [42957]

CROATIA
Zagreb
Acta Pharmaceutica [43562]

CZECH REPUBLIC
Prague
Czech and Slovak Pharmacy [43620]

DENMARK
Arhus
Growth Hormone & IGF Research
[43646]

Odense
Basic & Clinical Pharmacology &
Toxicology [43726]

FINLAND
Helsinki
European Journal of Pharmaceutical
Sciences [43826]

FRANCE
Montrouge
Journal de Pharmacie Clinique
[43994]

Nice
Gene Therapy and Regulation
[44015]

Rillieux-la-Pape
SAR and QSAR in Environmental
Research [44099]

GEORGIA
Tbilisi
Journal of Pharmaceutical and Bio-
medical Analysis [44135]

GERMANY
Braunschweig
Molecular Informatics [44278]

Cologne
Drug Testing and Analysis [44292]

Darmstadt
Screening [44312] .. .. ‡12,000

Frankfurt
Archiv der Pharmazie [44358]

Giessen
Cardiovascular Research [44384]

Heidelberg
Diabetologia [44452]
Pediatric Surgery International
[44471]

Jena
Journal of Cancer Research and
Clinical Oncology [44490]

Munster
Journal of Business Chemistry
(JoBC) [44599]

Weinheim
ChemMedChem [44704]

INDIA
Bangalore
Journal of Natural Remedies [44975]
Journal of Young Pharmacists
[44976]
Pharmacognosy @MAG [44980]
Systematic Reviews in Pharmacy
[44988]

Hyderabad
The Icfai Journal of Healthcare Law
[45154]
Indian Journal of Pharmacology
[45172] 2,000

Jodhpur
Journal of Phytopharmacotherapy
and Natural Products [45227]

Mandsaur
Asian Journal of Pharmaceutics
[45338]
International Journal of Green
Pharmacy [45339]

Meerut
Current Enzyme Inhibition [45344]

Mumbai
Indian Drugs [45377] ... (Paid) 6,000
Indian Journal of Pharmaceutical
Sciences [45386]
Journal of Association of Physicians
of India [45395] 200,000
Modern Pharmaceuticals [45418]
Pharma Times
[45429] .. .. (Paid) 6,500
Pharmacognosy Research [45430]
Saudi Journal of Anaesthesia [45436]

New Delhi
Drugs Cases [45504]
The Pharma Review [45635]

IRAN
Tehran
DARU [45888]
Iranian Biomedical Journal [45895]
Iranian Journal of Pharmaceutical
Research [45906]
Iranian Journal of Pharmacology and
Therapeutics [45907]

IRELAND
Dublin
Irish Pharmachem Industry Buyers'
Guide
[45982] .... (Combined) 2,124
Irish Pharmacist [45983] 2,089

ISRAEL
Jerusalem
Journal of Basic & Clinical Physiology
& Pharmacology [46087]
Journal of Biopharmaceutics and
Biotechnology [46088]

Tel Aviv
Drug Metabolism and Drug
Interactions [46098]

ITALY
Milan
Chimica Oggi (Chemistry Today)
[46165] .... (Combined) 8,000

JAPAN
Kyoto
Chemistry Letters
[46468] .... ‡43,200
Journal of Pharmacological Sciences
[46478] .. .. (Paid) 2,400

Sendai
Pharmacometrics
[46668] .. .. (Paid) 1,200

Tokyo
Biological & Pharmaceutical Bulletin
[46764]
Chemical & Pharmaceutical Bulletin
[46783]
Journal of Antibiotics
[46884] .. .. (Paid) 2,000
Journal of Infection and
Chemotherapy
[46909] .. .. (Paid) 1,500
Nikkei Drug Information
[46987] .. .. ★69,930

JORDAN
Amman
Dirasat Medical and Biological
Sciences
[47156] .... (Controlled) 1,000

KENYA
Nairobi
East and Central African Journal of
Pharmaceutical Sciences [47182]

REPUBLIC OF KOREA
Seoul
Archives of Pharmacal Research
[47253] .. .. (Paid) 1,500
Natural Product Sciences [47284]

MAURITIUS
Reduit
African Journal of Pharmacy &
Pharmacology [47754]

NETHERLANDS
Amsterdam
Best Practice & Research Clinical
Hematology [47904]
Clinical Therapeutics [47928]
Developmental & Comparative
Immunology [47955]
Free Radical Biology and Medicine
[47990]
International Journal of
Pharmaceutics [48031]
Journal of Autoimmunity [48053]
The Journal of Steroid Biochemistry
and Molecular Biology [48118]
Molecular Aspects of Medicine
[48162]
Naunyn-Schmiedeberg's Archives of
Pharmacology [48171]
Pharmacological Research [48199]
Regulatory Toxicology and
Pharmacology [48220]
Toxicology and Applied
Pharmacology [48253]
Trends in Pharmacological Sciences
[48267]

Bussum
Current Clinical Pharmacology
[48284]
Current Computer-Aided Drug Design
[48285]

Current Drug Discovery Technologies
[48286]
Current Drug Metabolism [48287]
Current Drug Safety [48288]
Current Drug Therapy [48289]
Current Pharmaceutical
Biotechnology [48293]
Current Pharmaceutical Design
[48294]
Current Pharmacogenomics and Per-
sonalized Medicine [48295]
Current Signal Transduction Therapy
[48297]
Drug Metabolism Letters [48300]
Recent Patents on Drug Delivery &
Formulation [48305]

Dordrecht
Cardiovascular Drugs and Therapy
[48343]
Journal of Pharmaceutical Innovation
[48483]
Pharmaceutical Research [48525]

Leiden
Journal of Ethnopharmacology
[48697]

Maastricht
Journal of Chemical Neuroanatomy
[48738]

Nigtevecht
International Journal of Risk and
Safety in Medicine [48742]

Utrecht
Geneesmiddelenbulletin
[48758] .... (Non-paid) 47,000

NEW ZEALAND
Auckland
New Zealand Doctor [48809]

Mairangi Bay
Clinical Drug Investigation [48934]
Clinical Pharmacokinetics [48935]

NIGERIA
Abuja
Journal for Phytomedicine and
Therapeutics [49056]

Benin City
Tropical Journal of Pharmaceutical
Research [49067]
West African Journal of Pharmacol-
ogy and Drug Research [49068]

Ile-Ife
Nigerian Journal of Natural Products
and Medicine [49115]

Jos
Journal of Pharmacy and
Bioresources [49127]
Nigerian Journal of Pharmaceutical
Research [49128]

Lagos
Nigerian Quarterly Journal of Hospital
Medicine [49142]

Nsukka
Journal of Pharmaceutical and Allied
Sciences [49157]

PAKISTAN
Faisalabad
Global Journal of Pharmacology
[49244]
International Journal of
Pharmacology [49252]
Research Journal of Pharmacology
[49291]

Karachi
Current Pharmaceutical Analysis
[49344]

Circulation: ★ = ABC; △ = BPA; ◆ = CAC; • = CCAB; ❑ = VAC; ⊕ = PO Statement; ‡ = Publisher's Report; Boldface figures = sworn; Light figures = estimated.

Letters in Drug Design & Discovery [49360]
Pakistan Journal of Pharmaceutical Sciences [49371]

POLAND
Krakow
Pharmacological Reports [49667]

Warsaw
Folia Neuropathologica [49710] 450

RUSSIA
Moscow
Problems of Biological, Medical and Pharmaceutical Chemistry [49962]

SINGAPORE
Singapore
Drug Discovery Today [50135]
Drug Discovery Today [50136]
Drug Discovery Today [50139]

REPUBLIC OF SOUTH AFRICA
Gauteng
SA Pharmaceutical Journal [50483]

Grahamstown
Ethiopian Pharmaceutical Journal [50494]

SPAIN
Barcelona
AIDS Reviews [50648]
El Farmaceutico [50667] .... (Non-paid) 20,000
El Farmaceutico Hospitales [50668] .... (Controlled) 2,800

Granada
Pharmaceuticals Policy and Law [50718]

SWITZERLAND
Geneva
European Journal of Pharmaceutics and Biopharmaceutics [51095]
International Journal of Computational Biology and Drug Design [51111]
International Journal of Functional Informatics and Personalised Medicine [51122]
WHO Drug Information [51166]

TAIWAN
Kaohsiung
Kaohsiung Journal of Medical Sciences [51310] ..... (Paid) 1,500

TURKEY
Mersin
Anti-Inflammatory & Anti-Allergy Agents in Medicinal Chemistry [51576]

UNITED KINGDOM
Abingdon
Drugs [51760]
Journal of Drug Targeting [51886]

Basingstoke
Clinical Pharmacology and Therapeutics [52198] .... (Combined) ‡3,800
Journal of Generic Medicines [52217]
Journal of Medical Marketing [52218] 550

Brasted
European Pharmaceutical Review [52561] .... (Controlled) 14,000

Brentwood
Parasite Immunology [52586]

Bristol
Neuropharmacology [52709]
Paediatric and Perinatal Epidemiology [52714]

Cambridge
The International Journal of Neuropsychopharmacology [52837] 1,200

Cardiff
Autonomic and Autacoid Pharmacology [52924]

Cheltenham
Drugs in Context [52968]

Chester
Pharmaceutical Technology Europe [52998] .. .. (Controlled) △18,000

Esher
Pharmacy in Practice [53338] .... (Controlled) 6,000

Haslemere
Drug Delivery Systems and Sciences [53536]

Hove
Drugs and Alcohol Today [53604]

Huddersfield
Clinical Biomechanics [53618]

London
Addiction Abstracts [53901]
Autonomic Neuroscience [53991]
Best Practice & Research Clinical Obstetrics & Gynecology [54013]
BMC Chemical Biology [54044]
BMC Clinical Pharmacology [54046]
BMC Pharmacology [54083]
British Journal of Clinical Pharmacology [54116]
British Journal of Pharmacology [54130]
British National Formulary [54142]
Clinical Pharmacist [54227] 7,500
Clinical Pharmacy Europe [54228]
Cosmetic Products Report [54270] .. .. (Paid) 2,000
Current Neuropharmacology [54296]
Current Opinion in Drug Discovery & Development [54298]
Current Opinion in Investigational Drugs [54300]
Current Vascular Pharmacology [54304]
Diagnostic Pathology [54325]
European BioPharmaceutical Review [54391]
European Pharmaceutical Contractor [54409]
Expert Opinion on Investigational Drugs [54417]
Expert Review of Clinical Pharmacology [54422]
Expert Review of Neurotherapeutics [54428]
Expert Review of Pharmacoeconomics & Outcomes Research [54431]
Gene Therapy [54499]
Good Clinical Practice Journal (GCPj) [54519] .... ⊕1,300
Harm Reduction Journal [54531]
Human Genomics [54577]
Innate Immunity [54605]
Journal of Inflammation [54767]
Journal of Microencapsulation [54782]
Journal of Pharmaceutical Medicine [54796]
Journal of Pharmacological and Toxicological Methods [54797]

Journal of Psychopharmacology [54805]
Nature Reviews Drug Discovery [54978]
Nutraceuticals International [55018]
Pharmaceutical Manufacturing and Packing Sourcer [55076]
Pharmacogenomics [55077]
The Pharmacogenomics Journal [55078]
POWDEReporter [55111]
Progress in Palliative Care [55136]
Prostate Cancer and Prostatic Diseases [55144]
Pulmonary Pharmacology and Therapeutics [55155]
Regulatory Affairs Journal [55181] .... (Paid) 810
Regulatory Affairs Journal (Devices) [55182]
Scrip Magazine [55221] .... (Combined) 10,061
Thorax [55315]

Macclesfield
International Journal of Nanomedicine [55517]

Nottingham
Journal of Molecular Graphics and Modeling [55764]

Oxford
Cancer Letters [55902]
Diabetic Medicine [55926]
Membrane Technology [56096]
Pathology International [56143]
Pediatric Allergy and Immunology [56145]
Pediatric Anesthesia [56146]
Pediatric Dermatology [56147]
Pediatrics International [56148]
Progress in Retinal and Eye Research [56171]

Truro
Best Practice & Research Clinical Rheumatology [56773]

ECOLOGY AND CONSERVATION
See also Forestry; Natural History and Nature Study; Waste Management and Recycling; Water Supply and Sewage Disposal; (Hunting, Fishing, and Game Management)

ARUBA
Oranjestad
Eco Aruba [41491]

AUSTRALIA
Adelaide
Austral Ecology [41501]

Aranda
Environmental Toxicology [41557]

Bundoora
International Journal of Sustainable Design [41671]

Carlton
Habitat Australia [41726] 17,000

Collingwood
Reproduction, Fertility and Development [41796]
Wildlife Research [41797]

Fitzroy
Chain Reaction [41866] 2,500

Nathan
International Journal of Agricultural Resources, Governance and Ecology [42143]

Perth
Ecohydrology [42250]

Tullamarine
Australian Landcare [42649] .. .. ‡33,000

Woodburn
Ecological Management & Restoration [42713]

AUSTRIA
Salzburg
Natur und Land [42741] 12,000

Vienna
ACT! The Magazine of Greenpeace Austria [42742]
VCO Magazin [42773] .. .. (Paid) 20,000

BELGIUM
Brussels
Chemoecology [42847]
Greenpeace Magazine [42857] 60,000

BRAZIL
Campinas
Biota Neotropica [42962]

Manaus
Acta Amazonica [42987]

Rio de Janeiro
Informativo FBCN [43006]

Sao Paulo
Papeis Avulsos de Zoologia (Sao Paulo) [43043]

Vacaria
Anais da Sociedade Entomologica do Brasil [43052]
Neotropical Entomology [43053]

PEOPLE'S REPUBLIC OF CHINA
Hong Kong
Business Strategy and the Environment [43286]
Green Alert [43301] 1,000

Nanjing
Pedosphere [43455]
Advances in Science and Technology of Water Resources [43456]
Journal of Hohai University [43459]
Water Resources Protection [43460]

Shanghai
Man & Nature [43487]

COLOMBIA
Bogota
Caldasia [43544]

CYPRUS
Limassol
Earthlines [43589]

DENMARK
Copenhagen
Ecological Modelling [43666]
ICES Cooperative Research Reports [43673] 500

Roskilde
The Journal of Transdisciplinary Environmental Studies (TES) [43734]

Wageningen
International Review of Environmental and Resource Economics [43738]

Circulation: ★ = ABC; △ = BPA; ◆ = CAC; • = CCAB; ❑ = VAC; ⊕ = PO Statement; ‡ = Publisher's Report; Boldface figures = sworn; Light figures = estimated.

FINLAND
Turku
Progress in Industrial Ecology [43910]

FRANCE
Champenoux
Annals of Forest Science [43929]

Dijon
Behavioural Processes [43943]
Mycorrhiza [43945]

Les Ulis
Hydroecologie appliquee [43965]

Paris
Adansonia [44022]
International Journal of Nuclear Governance, Economy and Ecology [44052]
Pollution Atmospherique [44077] 1,500

Rillieux-la-Pape
SAR and QSAR in Environmental Research [44099]

Villefranche-sur-Mer
Aquatic Microbial Ecology [44124]

GERMANY
Berlin
Botanica Marina [44162]
Verhandlungen der Gesellschaft fur Okologie [44236]

Dusseldorf
Gefahrstoffe-Reinhaltung der Luft [44325] 2,000

Frankfurt
WWF Journal [44363]

Gottingen
Basic and Applied Ecology [44393]

Grasbrunn
natur+kosmos [44403] 84,278

Heidelberg
Environmental Earth Sciences [44453]
Environmental Modeling & Assessment [44454]
Oecologia [44470]

Helgoland
Helgoland Marine Research [44481]

Jena
Journal of Basic Microbiology [44489]
Theory in Biosciences [44491]

Kiel
Polar Biology [44607]

Munich
Catena [44553]

Oldendorf
Endangered Species Research [44627]
Marine Ecology Progress Series (MEPS) [44629]

Stechlin
Limnologica [44657]

Stuttgart
Aquatic Insects [44661]
Phytocoenologia [44676]

GHANA
Accra
West African Journal of Applied Ecology [44730]

GREECE
Athens
Global Nest [44743]

HUNGARY
Budapest
Community Ecology [44827]
Journal Applied Ecology and Environmental Research [44840]

INDIA
Delhi
Journal of Human Ecology [45100] .... (Paid) 500

Lucknow
Abstracts of Current Literature in Toxicology [45320]
Journal of Environmental Biology [45323] 50,000

Nagpur
Indian Literature in Environmental Engineering [45466]
Journal of Environmental Science and Engineering [45468] 1,200

New Delhi
Down To Earth [45503]
International Journal of Environment and Development [45583]
VATIS Update Ozone Layer Protection [45665] 2,300

Roorkee
International Journal of Ecology and Development [45718]

IRAN
Tehran
Iranian Journal of Environmental Health Science & Engineering [45902]

ISRAEL
Tel Aviv
ERETZ [46099] 50,000

ITALY
Ancona
Chemistry and Ecology [46117]

Fiorentino
Aestimum [46139]

JAPAN
Fukuoka
International Journal of Biotronics [46343] .... (Free) 1,000

Sendai
Ecological Research [46665]

Tokyo
Clean Technologies and Environmental Policy [46787]
Ecosystems [46807]
Environmental Economics and Policy Studies [46812]
Landscape and Ecological Engineering [46958]
Nikkei Ecology [46988] .... ★16,632
Population Ecology [47022] .... (Paid) 25,000
Tree Physiology [47053] .... (Paid) 600
(Non-paid) 150

KENYA
Nairobi
African Journal of Ecology [47171]
NJIWA [47193]
SWARA [47197]

LATVIA
Riga
Vides Vestis [47376] ... (Paid) 3,000
(Non-paid) 2,000

MALAYSIA
Kuala Lumpur
Malaysian Naturalist [47621]

Penang
Suara SAM [47691] .. ... (Paid) 2,500

NETHERLANDS
Amsterdam
Agriculture, Ecosystems & Environment [47886]
Asian Journal of Water, Environment and Pollution [47899]
Chemosphere [47927]
Ecotoxicology and Environmental Safety [47962]
Environmental Policy and Law [47969]
Environmental Research [47970]
Forest Ecology and Management [47988]
Global Environmental Change [48002]
Global and Planetary Change [48003]
Journal of Arid Environments [48049]
Journal of Environmental Management [48073]
Journal of Environmental Psychology [48074]
Nature, Culture and Literature [48170]
Trends in Ecology & Evolution [48261]

Dordrecht
Aerobiologia [48321]
Biodegradation [48331]
Biogeochemistry [48332]
Climatic Change [48352]
Hydrobiologia [48419]
Journal of Bamboo and Rattan [48442]
Plant Ecology [48533]
Urban Ecosystems [48584]

Leiden
Crustaceana [48665]

NEW ZEALAND
Wellington
Forest and Bird Magazine [49008] .. .. (Paid) 20,000

NIGERIA
Benin City
Tropical Freshwater Biology [49066]

Ibadan
Journal of Environmental Extension [49089]

Zaria
Nigerian Journal of Soil & Environmental Research [49184]

NORWAY
Oslo
Climate Research [49195]

PAKISTAN
Faisalabad
International Journal of Botany [49249]
Plant Sciences Research [49279]

PHILIPPINES
Quezon City
Haring Ibon [49594]

POLAND
Lublin
Annals of Agricultural and Environmental Medicine [49672]

Warsaw
Acta Protozoologica [49682]
Acta Zoologica Lituanica [49683]
Annals of Warsaw University of Life Sciences, Land Reclamation [49689]
Ecological Questions [49706]
Ekologija [49708]
European Countryside [49709]
Hacquetia [49715]
Journal of Water and Land Development [49728]

RUSSIA
Novosibirsk
Siberian Journal of Ecology [50013]

SINGAPORE
Singapore
Ecological Indicators [50140]
Ecological Informatics [50141]
Journal of Environmental Assessment Policy and Management [50205]

SLOVENIA
Hajdina
Biota [50331]

Ljubljana
Acta Agriculturae Slovenica [50333]

REPUBLIC OF SOUTH AFRICA
Grahamstown
Nigerian Journal of Soil Science [50508]

Halfway House
Clean Air Journal [50520] 550

Howick
African Wildlife [50525] 10,000

Parkview
Vulture News [50563]

Pietermaritzburg
African Journal of Aquatic Science [50564]
African Zoology [50566]

Tygerberg
African Journal of Herpetology [50638]

SPAIN
Barcelona
Arxus de Miscel-lania Zoologica [50651]
Ecologia Politica [50665]

Madrid
El Ecologista [50754]
World Watch [50816] .. ....,.......... (Paid) 15,000

SWEDEN
Lund
Oikos [50988]

Norrkoping
Hydrology Research [50995]

Stockholm
Ambio [51006]
Grana [51019]
MEDSOLS [51025] .. ... (Paid) 2,000

SWITZERLAND
Geneva
International Journal of Environment and Pollution [51118]

Gland
Parks [51175] 1,700

Circulation: ★ = ABC; △ = BPA; ◆ = CAC; • = CCAB; ❑ = VAC; ⊕ = PO Statement; ‡ = Publisher's Report; Boldface figures = sworn; Light figures = estimated.

Trade, Technical, and Professional Publications

Kastanienbaum
Aquatic Sciences [51180]

TAIWAN
Taipei
Botanical Studies [51333]
Environmental Policy Monthly
[51339]

**UNITED REPUBLIC OF TAN-
ZANIA**
Morogoro
Tanzania Journal of Forestry and Na-
ture Conservation [51407]

THAILAND
Bangkok
EEAT Journal [51419] 1,500

TURKEY
Ankara
Turkish Journal of Engineering and
Environmental Sciences [51510]
Izmir
Ekoloji [51573]

UGANDA
Kampala
African Journal of Ecology [51585]

UNITED KINGDOM
Abingdon
International Journal of Heritage
Studies [51836]
International Journal of Water Re-
sources Development [51847]
Journal of Ecotourism [51889]
Journal of Environmental Planning
and Management [51894]
Journal of Environmental Policy &
Planning [51895]
Bath
Journal of the Geological Society
[52248] .... (Paid) 500
Bradford
Management of Environmental
Quality [52523]
Brentwood
Energy and Environment [52572]
Energy Exploration & Exploitation
[52573]
Bristol
Mammal Review [52703]
Buntingford
Environmental Engineering
[52759] 7,500
Cambridge
Geological Magazine [52823] 850
International Journal of Tropical In-
sect Science [52838]
Journal of Biosocial Science
[52846] 500
Journal of Cetacean Research and
Management [52848]
Journal of Helminthology [52854]
Oryx [52881] 2,800
Renewable Agriculture and Food
Systems [52890]
Seed Science Research [52893]
World Birdwatch [52906] 6,000
Chatham
Medical and Veterinary Entomology
[52959]
Edinburgh
Aquatic Conservation [53251]
Exeter
Filtration [53358]

Journal of Rural Studies [53362]
Farnborough
Gamewise [53378]
Fordingbridge
Game Conservancy Magazine
[53395] .... (Controlled) ⊕25,000
Glasgow
Envirotec [53416] .... ★8,958
Scottish Planning and Environmental
Law [53450] .... (Paid) 500
Guildford
Plant Heritage [53494]
Halesworth
Deer [53504] .... (Paid) 6,000
Henley-on-Thames
Open Space [53562]
Inverness
Scotland's Natural Heritage [53647]
Kidlington
Acta Ecologica Sinica [53688]
Journal of Environmental Sciences
[53698]
Liverpool
Biological Conservation [53869]
London
Carbon Balance and Management
[54175]
Cleantech [54216]
CPRE Voice [54280]
Elements
[54360] .... (Combined) 2,200
Environmental Health Practitioner
[54377] 11,800
The Environmental Scientist [54378]
The Historic Environment [54555]
Journal of Animal Ecology [54697]
Journal of Applied Ecology [54698]
Journal of Ethnobiology and
Ethnomedicine [54746]
Journal of Functional Ecology
[54755]
Journal of Water Supply [54835]
Mining Environmental Management
[54939] .... (Combined) 3,000
Network 21 [54988] 7,000
Water Asset Management
International [55381]
Water and Environment Manager
[55382] 12,000
Water Intelligence Online [55383]
Water Policy [55384]
Water Supply [55388]
Water 21 [55389]
Manchester
Progress in Planning [55575]
Nottingham
Earthwise
[55754] .... (Non-paid) 5,000
Oxford
Behavioral Ecology
[55879] .... (Paid) 1,300
                    (Non-paid) 35
Grassland Science [55968]
Molecular Ecology [56106]
Palaeontology [56140]
Restoration Ecology [56188]
Plymouth
Journal of the Marine Biological As-
sociation of the United Kingdom
(JMBA) [56272] 1,600
Ross-on-Wye
Marine Conservation
[56410] .... (Paid) 5,000
Saint Albans
Asian Environmental Technology
[56434] .... (Controlled) 23,334

International Environmental
Technology
[56437] .... (Controlled) 39,239
Salisbury
Recycling & Waste World [56457]
Sandy
Bird Life [56460]
Wingbeat [56461]
Sheffield
Greener Management International
[56495] .... (Combined) 600
Skipton
Warmer Bulletin
[56555] .... (Combined) 1,000
Swansea
Land Degradation & Development
[56703]
Swindon
Conservation Bulletin [56710]
Uxbridge
International Journal of Renewable
Energy Technology [56798]
Wallingford
Grasslands & Forage Abstracts
[56818]
Review of Aromatic and Medicinal
Plants [56825]
Winchester
In Practice
[56930] .... (Combined) 2,300
Witney
Environmental Law & Management
[56941]

VENEZUELA
Caracas
Acta Botanica Venezuelica [57019]

ECONOMICS

**See also Banking, Finance,
and Investments**

ARGENTINA
Buenos Aires
Integration and Trade [41474]

AUSTRALIA
Adelaide
Australian Economic History Review
[41503]
Clayton
Division of Labour & Transaction
Costs [41760]
Deakin
Australian and New Zealand Property
Journal [41833] .... ◆11,270
North Sydney
Business Asia
[42210] .... (Combined) 24,600
                       (Paid) 1,000
Sydney
Journal of Economic Dynamics and
Control [42528]
Victoria
International Journal of Forecasting
[42665]

AUSTRIA
Graz
Metroeconomica [42725]
Linz
Statistical Papers [42734]

Vienna
Austrian Economic Quarterly
[42747] 200
The European Journal of Economics,
Finance and Administrative
Sciences [42752]
Wirschaft und Gesellschaft
[42774] .... (Combined) 900

BAHRAIN
Manama
Arab World Agribusiness
[42786] 18,715
Gulf Industry
[42790] ... . (Paid) 13,614

BANGLADESH
Dhaka
Asia-Pacific Journal of Rural
Development [42802]
Bangladesh Development Studies
[42803] .... (Paid) 1,500

BRAZIL
Belo Horizonte
Nova Economia [42950]
Petropolis
Computational & Applied
Mathematics [42990]
Recife
The Brazilian Electronic Journal of
Economics (BEJE) [42994]
Ribeirao Preto
Economia Aplicada [42997]

CHILE
Santiago
Cuadernos de Economia [43143]

**PEOPLE'S REPUBLIC OF
CHINA**
Beijing
Journal of Chinese Economic and
Foreign Trade Studies [43204]
Hong Kong
Hong Kong Industrialist
[43325] .... (Paid) 7,000
Mathematical Modelling and Applied
Computing [43368]
Pacific Economic Review [43374]
Wuhan
The Journal of Grey System [43524]

DENMARK
Frederiksberg
Acta Agriculturae
Scandinavica—Section C, Food
Economics [43688]
Wageningen
International Review of Environmen-
tal and Resource Economics
[43738]

ESTONIA
Tartu
Agronomy Research [43791]

ETHIOPIA
Addis Ababa
Ethiopian Economic Journal of
Economics [43797]
Ethiopian Journal of Development
Research [43799]
Bahir Dar
African Research Review [43804]

FINLAND
Abo
Journal of the Economic Society of
Finland [43811] 950

Circulation: ★ = ABC; △ = BPA; ◆ = CAC; • = CCAB; ❑ = VAC; ⊕ = PO Statement; ‡ = Publisher's Report; Boldface figures = sworn; Light figures = estimated.

Helsinki
Fakta **[43827]** .... (Paid) 30,000

FRANCE
Dijon
Impact **[43944]**

Paris
Aide et Action **[44023]**
Annales d'Economie et de Statistique **[44024]**
Cahiers d'Economie et Sociologie Rurales **[44031]**
Journal of Mathematical Economics **[44065]**

GERMANY
Bonn
European Review of Agricultural Economics **[44258]**
Journal of Population Economics **[44264]**

Frankfurt
Agrifuture **[44356]** 20,000
DLG-Mitteilungen **[44359]** 12,000

Gottingen
Forest Policy and Economics **[44398]**

Heidelberg
Computational Management Science **[44450]**
Journal fur Betriebswirtschaft **[44463]**
Review of Economic Design **[44474]**

Kiel
Review of World Economics **[44508]**

Munich
CESifo Forum **[44554]**
International Tax and Public Finance **[44565]**
Zeitschrift fur Assyriologie und Vorderasiatische Archaologie **[44589]** 500

Regensburg
Economic Systems **[44643]**

Tubingen
Journal of Institutional & Theoretical Economics **[44692]**

Wuppertal
International Economics and Economic Policy **[44715]**

Wurzburg
Economic Quality Control **[44720]**

GREECE
Piraeus
International Journal of Economic Research **[44768]**

GUYANA
Georgetown
CARICOM Perspective **[44799]** 3,000

HUNGARY
Budapest
Acta Oeconomica **[44815]**
Figyelo **[44831]** .... (Paid) 11,522
Figyelo Trend **[44833]** .... ‡15,000
Society and Economy **[44870]**
Tarsadalom es Gazdasag (Society and Economy) **[44879]**

INDIA
Allahabad
Indian Journal of Economics **[44931]** 500

Chennai
Hindu Business Line **[45033]** .. .. (Paid) 24,823

Delhi
IAMR Report **[45093]**

Hyderabad
The Icfai Journal of Financial Economics **[45151]**
The Icfai Journal of International Business Law **[45156]**
The Icfai Journal of Managerial Economics **[45159]**
The Icfai Journal of Public Finance **[45164]**

Kolkata
Business World **[45261]** 37,204

Mumbai
Taxation Law Reports **[45446]** .. .. (Paid) 1,500

New Delhi
Indian Growth and Development Review **[45475]**
Afro-Asian Journal of Rural Development **[45479]** .... (Combined) 400
Artha Suchi **[45484]** .... (Paid) 120
Asia Pacific Tech Monitor **[45485]** .... (Paid) 2,000
Cooperator **[45500]** 2,700
Employment News **[45507]** .... (Paid) 426,000
Facts for You **[45511]** .. .. (Paid) 5,000
Finance India **[45515]** .. .. (Paid) 1,200
Global Review of Business and Economic Research **[45520]**
Indian Development Review **[45539]**
Indian Economic and Social History Review **[45540]** .... (Paid) 900
Indian Export Bulletin **[45542]** .. .. (Paid) 5,000
Indian Journal of Economics & Business **[45552]**
International Journal of Applied Business and Economic Research **[45580]**
The Journal of Entrepreneurship **[45597]** .... (Paid) 500
Journal of Interdisciplinary Mathematics **[45608]** .... (Paid) 240
Journal of International Economic Review **[45609]**
Journal of Social and Economic Policy **[45619]**
Journal of Statistics and Management Systems **[45620]** .. .. (Paid) 240
Margin **[45623]** .... (Paid) 600
Review of Applied Economics **[45645]**

INDONESIA
Jakarta
Economics and Finance in Indonesia **[45796]** 4,000

IRAN
Tehran
Iran Exports & Imports **[45892]** .. .. (Paid) 5,000

IRELAND
Dublin
IBEC Economic Trends **[45965]**

Sandyford
The Stock Market **[46057]**

ISRAEL
Ramat Gan
European Journal of Political Economy **[46093]**

Tel Aviv
Theoretical Inquiries in Law **[46114]**

ITALY
Messina
International Journal of Economic Policy in Emerging Economies **[46157]**
International Journal of Monetary Economics & Finance **[46158]**
International Journal of Trade and Global Markets **[46159]**

Milan
Journal of Mental Health Policy and Economics **[46183]**
Mani Tese **[46187]** 36,000

Napoli
International Journal of Engineering Management and Economics **[46204]**

Rome
Development **[46226]** 3,000
International Journal of Technology and Globalisation **[46235]**

Turin
Economics of Innovation and New Technology **[46271]**

JAPAN
Kobe
Kobe University Economic Review **[46434]** .. ..,............ 650

Nagoya
Regional Development Dialogue **[46559]** .. .. (Paid) 1,000

Tokyo
Annals of Regional Science **[46740]**
Cambridge Journal of Regions, Economy & Society **[46775]**
Journal of Japanese Trade and Industry **[46919]** ..... (Paid) 35,000
Journal of Operations Research Society of Japan **[46933]** .. .. (Paid) 3,000
Keio Economic Studies **[46952]** .. .. (Paid) 800
The Nikkei Weekly **[47010]** .. .. (Paid) 36,500

KENYA
Nairobi
Bulletin of Animal Health and Production in Africa **[47175]**
Habitat Debate **[47183]** 10,000

REPUBLIC OF KOREA
Seoul
Journal of Economic Integration **[47273]** .... (Paid) 250
Seoul Journal of Economics **[47286]** .... (Paid) 300

LUXEMBOURG
Capellen
AGEFI Luxembourg **[47488]** .. .. (Combined) 24,000

MALAYSIA
Bangi
Jurnal Ekonomi Malaysia **[47574]** .... (Paid) 500

Kota Kinabalu
Borneo Review **[47589]**

Kuala Lumpur
Malaysian Journal of Economic Studies **[47616]**

Melaka
Erasmus Law and Economics Review **[47680]**

MEXICO
Mexico City
Boletin **[47782]**
CIMMYT Annual Report **[47783]** 5,000
Monetaria **[47786]**
Money Affairs **[47787]**

NAMIBIA
Windhoek
International Journal of Education Economics and Development **[47822]**

NEPAL
Kathmandu
Aankhijhyal **[47836]**

NETHERLANDS
Amsterdam
Explorations in Economic History **[47983]**
Games and Economic Behavior **[47996]**
Information Economics and Policy **[48019]**
Japan and the World Economy **[48035]**
Journal of Asian Economics **[48051]**
Journal of Development Economics **[48067]**
Journal of E-Governance **[48069]**
Journal of Economic Psychology **[48070]**
Journal of Economic and Social Measurement **[48071]**
Journal of Housing Economics **[48084]**
Journal of Integrated Design & Process Science **[48086]**
Journal of the Japanese and International Economics **[48089]**
The Journal of Socio-Economics **[48116]**
Journal of Urban Economics **[48126]**
North American Journal of Economics and Finance **[48183]** ... (Paid) 300   (Non-paid) 50
Pacific-Basin Finance Journal **[48198]**
Poetics **[48207]**
Research in Economics **[48221]**
Review of Economic Dynamics **[48224]**
Technovation **[48243]**

Dordrecht
De Economist **[48364]**
Economic Change and Restructuring **[48378]**
Economic Theory **[48379]**
Frontiers of Economics in China **[48395]**
The Journal of Economic Inequality **[48457]**
Journal of Productivity Analysis **[48487]**
Journal of Risk and Uncertainty **[48490]**
Netnomics **[48518]**
Public Choice **[48542]**
The Review of Austrian Economics **[48552]**
Review of Derivatives Research **[48553]**
Review of Industrial Organization **[48554]**
Theory and Decision **[48578]**

The Hague
Hivos Magazine **[48617]**

Leiden
Journal of the Economic and Social History of the Orient **[48693]**

Circulation: ★ = ABC; △ = BPA; ◆ = CAC; • = CCAB; ❑ = VAC; ⊕ = PO Statement; ‡ = Publisher's Report; Boldface figures = sworn; Light figures = estimated.

Maastricht
European Economic Review [48736]

Utrecht
Global Business and Economics
Review [48759]

NEW ZEALAND
Wellington
New Zealand Economic Papers
[49018]

NIGERIA
Ibadan
Nigerian Journal of Economic History
[49095]

Ikoyi
Economic and Policy Review [49109]

Victoria Island
Lagos Business School Management
Review [49178]

OMAN
Muscat
Business Today [49220]

PAKISTAN
Faisalabad
Journal of Economics Theory [49265]

Karachi
Eastern Worker
   [49348] .... (Paid) 1,000
Labour Code of Pakistan [49359]
Pakistan Accountant
   [49366] .... (Paid) 1,400

PERU
Lima
Quehacer [49425] 4,000
Resomeu Senaual [49426] 500

PHILIPPINES
Manila
ADB Business Opportunities [49546]
Asian Development Review [49547]

Quezon City
PAID [49605] 1,000

POLAND
Warsaw
Economics and Organization of
Enterprise [49707]
Folia Oeconomica Stetinensia
[49711]
Issues of Business and Law [49721]
South East European Journal of Eco-
nomics and Business [49765]

ROMANIA
Bucharest
Economistul - The Economist
[49834] 30,000

RUSSIA
Moscow
Studies on Russian Economic
Development [49992]

SINGAPORE
Pasir Panjang
ASEAN Economic Bulletin [50098]

Singapore
International Journal of
Technoentrepreneurship [50194]
Journal of Developmental
Entrepreneurship [50203]

Journal of Enterprising Culture
[50204]
NUS Economic Journal
   [50229] .. .. (Paid) 10,000
Regional Outlook [50243]
Review of Pacific Basin Financial
Markets and Policies [50245]
Singapore Economic Review
   [50254] .... (Paid) 800
Singapore Management Review
[50259]

SLOVENIA
Koper
International Journal of Sustainable
Economy [50332]

Ljubljana
Acta Agriculturae Slovenica [50333]

REPUBLIC OF SOUTH AF-
RICA
Bellville
African Finance Journal [50353]

Centurion
South African Journal of Business
Management [50451]

Grahamstown
African Journal of Economic Policy
[50488]
Journal of Social Development in
Africa [50503] .... (Combined) 150
Securities Market Journal [50512]

Hillcrest
South African Journal of Economic
and Management Sciences [50523]

Matieland
Agrekon [50552]

Pretoria
Africa Insight [50581]
Africa Institute Occasional Papers
[50582]

Stellenbosch
Studies in Economics and
Econometrics [50636]

SPAIN
Barcelona
El Jueves [50669] .... ‡74,441
Spanish Economic Review [50700]

Madrid
Temas para el Debate [50809]

Oviedo
International Journal of Chinese Culture & Management [50823]

SRI LANKA
Ethul Kotte
Marga Journal [50894]

SWEDEN
Goteborg
Scandinavian Economic History
Review [50964] 500

Linkoping
International Journal of Production
Economics [50976]

Uppsala
Development Dialogue [51051]

SWITZERLAND
Geneva
International Journal of Economics
and Business Research [51116]
International Journal of Sustainable
Strategic Management [51144]

International Trade FORUM [51150]

Lausanne
Bilan [51183] 19,325
Insurance [51192]

TAIWAN
Taipei
The Taiwan Economic News [51363]

THAILAND
Bangkok
Asia Pacific Development Journal
[51410]
Asia-Pacific Population Journal
[51411] 2,000
e-TISNET Monthly News/e-TISNET
Monthly Information Services
[51418]
Thai-American Business
   [51437] .... (Paid) 3,000
Water Resources Journal [51448]

TURKEY
Ankara
METU Studies in Development
   [51497] .... (Paid) 1,500

Istanbul
Bogazici Journal
   [51557] .... (Paid) 850

UGANDA
Kampala
Mtafiti Mwafrika [51588]

UKRAINE
Kiev
Novynar
   [51603] .. .. (Combined) 150,000

UNITED KINGDOM
Abingdon
Applied Economics [51705]
Central Asian Survey [51726]
Development in Practice [51755]
Economic System Research [51765]
Education Economics [51767]
Education, Knowledge & Economy
[51768]
Feminist Economics [51788]
India Review [51812]
Industry & Innovation [51814]
International Journal of the Econom-
ics of Business [51833]
International Review of Applied
Economics [51851]
Israel Affairs [51863]
Journal of the Asia Pacific Economy
[51870]
Journal of Contemporary China
[51879]
Journal of Development Studies
[51885]
Journal of Economic Methodology
[51888]
Journal of Human Development and
Capabilities [51904]
Journal of North African Studies
[51925]
Journal of Urban Technology [51954]
New Political Economy [51993]
Post-Communist Economies [52020]
Postcolonial Studies [52021]
Review of International Political
Economy [52042]
Review of Political Economy [52043]

Basingstoke
Economic & Labour Market Review
[52199]
Maritime Economics and Logistics
[52223] 600

Monthly Digest of Statistics [52225]
Social Trends [52230]
United Kingdom Economic Accounts
[52233]

Bath
Journal of Transport Economics and
Policy [52250] 1,000

Bradford
Humanomics [52463]
International Journal of Social
Economics [52487]
Journal of Enterprising Communities
[52498]

Brighton
IDS Bulletin [52614] 1,800

Bristol
International Review of Economics
Education [52680]

Buckingham
The Journal of Gambling Business
and Economics [52757]

Burgess Hill
Teaching Business & Economics
   [52761] 3,200

Cambridge
Contributions to Political Economy
[52812]
The Journal of Economic History
   [52850] 3,300
Journal of Institutional Economics
[52855]
Renewable Agriculture and Food
Systems [52890]

Coventry
Applied Economics Letters [53077]
Applied Financial Economics [53078]
Community Development Journal
[53080]

Edinburgh
Scottish Home and Country
   [53317] 11,000

Glasgow
Information Polity [53423]
Spatial Economic Analysis [53452]

Guildford
Journal of Chinese Economic and
Business Studies [53492]

Kempston
Investment Now
   [53668] .... (Combined) 70,000

Leicester
International Journal of Community
Currency Research [53805]

London
African Affairs [53918]
African Journal of Business and Eco-
nomic Research [53921]
Capital & Class [54174] 1,100
CASEpapers [54187]
Community [54247] 3,000
Competition & Change [54252]
Cost Effectiveness and Resource
Allocation [54272]
Economic and Industrial Democracy
[54350]
Environment and Urbanization
   [54374] 3,100
Health Policy and Planning
   [54540] 720
Historical Materialism [54557]
International Journal of Economics
and Accounting [54644]
Journal of Financial Crime [54752]
Journal of Pension Economics and
Finance [54794] 400
Land & Liberty
   [54849] .... (Controlled) 1,000

Circulation: ★ = ABC; △ = BPA; ◆ = CAC; • = CCAB; ❑ = VAC; ⊕ = PO Statement; ‡ = Publisher's Report; Boldface figures = sworn; Light figures = estimated.

Politics, Philosophy & Economics [55100]
Radical Economics [55169]
Regeneration & Renewal
[55179] *10,238
Review of Nigeria Affairs [55199]
Risk and Regulation [55205]
Slovo [55243]
Supply Management
[55279] .... ‡35,000
Tourism Economics [55331]

Manchester
Constitutional Political Economy
[55549]
The Journal of Transport History
[55569]

Nottingham
Planning Perspectives [55769]

Olney
International Journal of Entrepreneurship and Innovation Management
[55802]

Oxford
Agricultural Economics [55861]
American Law and Economics
Review [55865]
Annals of Public and Cooperative
Economics [55869]
Australian Economic Review [55876]
The Australian Journal of Agricultural
and Resource Economics [55878]
Bulletin of Economic Research
[55897]
Business Ethics [55898]
Cambridge Journal of Economics
[55900]
Canadian Journal of Agricultural
Economics [55901]
CESifo Economic Studies [55905]
The Economic History Review
[55928]
Economic Inquiry [55929]
The Economic Journal [55930]
The Economic Record [55931]
Economica [55932]
Fiscal Studies [55958]
International Journal of Economic
Theory [55994]
The Japanese Economic Review
[56008]
Journal of African Economies [56012]
Journal of Competition Law and
Economics [56022]
Journal of Industrial Economics
[56041]
Journal of Public Economic Theory
[56063]
Journal of Supply Chain Management
[56074]
The Journal of World Intellectual
Property [56079]
The Manchester School [56093]
OPEC Energy Review [56127]
Oxford Bulletin of Economics &
Statistics [56131]
Oxford Development Studies [56132]
Oxford Economic Papers [56133]
Oxford Review of Economic Policy
[56136]
Review of Development Economics
[56189]
The Review of Economic Studies
[56190]
Review of International Economics
[56193]
The Scandinavian Journal of
Economics [56199]
Socio-Economic Review [56208]
World Bank Research Observer
[56227]
The World Economy [56228]

Portsmouth
International Journal of Computational Economics and Econometrics
[56289]

Reading
International Journal of Green
Economics [56322]

Rugby
Enterprise Development and
Microfinance [56418]

Sheffield
International Journal of Enterprise
Network Management [56499]
International Journal of Logistics Eco-
nomics & Globalisation [56501]
Managing Leisure [56506]

Southampton
Journal of Economic Geography
[56573]

Teddington
Geophilos [56730]

Wallingford
Journal of Agricultural Genomics
[56820]

Watford
The Business Economist [56860]

York
Defence and Peace Economics
[56989]
Economic Journal [56990]

EDUCATION
See also Vocational Educa-
tion

AUSTRALIA
Adelaide
International Journal for Educational
Integrity [41509]

Bowen Hills
Australasian Journal of Special
Education [41623]

Callaghan
Australian Journal of Educational &
Developmental Psychology [41690]

Camberwell
Australian Journal of Career
Development [41693] 700
Australian Journal of Education
[41694]

Canberra
Asian Studies Review [41699]

Dickson
Australasian Journal of Educational
Technology [41840] .. .. (Paid) 700

Fairfield
Journal of Higher Education Policy
and Management [41864]

Gold Coast
Spreadsheets in Education [41900]

Kensington Gardens
English in Australia [41985]

Lidcombe
Journal of Intellectual & Developmental Disability [42008]

Melbourne
Global Journal of Engineering
Education [42061]

Milperra
Higher Education Research and Development (HERD) [42107]

Norwood
Australian Journal of Language and
Literacy [42214]

Parkside
Australian Educator
[42230] 120,000

Rockhampton
Studies in Learning, Evaluation, Innovation and Development [42317]

South Melbourne
Advocate
[42365] .... (Non-paid) 28,000
Curriculum and Teaching [42369]
Educational Practice and Theory
[42370]
Information Technology, Education
and Society [42372]
Journal of Postcolonial Education
[42373]
Learning and Teaching [42374]
World Studies in Education [42376]

Stepney
Australian Mathematics Teacher
(AMT) [42387] .. .. (Paid) 3,000
Australian Primary Mathematics
Classroom (APMC)
[42388] .. .. (Paid) 1,500
Australian Senior Mathematics Jour-
nal (ASMJ)
[42389] .. .. (Paid) 1,500

Sydney
Campus Review
[42484] .. .. (Combined) 45,000
Knowledge-Based Systems [42532]

Wodonga
The Weaver [42702]

Wollongong
Journal of University Teaching and
Learning Practice (JUTLP) [42705]

AUSTRIA
Vienna
Progress [42766]

BARBADOS
Bridgetown
The International Journal of Education and Development using Information and Communication Technology (IJEDICT) [42828]

BELGIUM
Antwerp
Studies in Educational Evaluation
[42841]

Brussels
Worlds of Education
[42875] 12,000

Leuven
European Review [42896] 2,200

BRAZIL
Botucatu
Interface [42956]

Campinas
Cadernos CEDES [42965]

Rio de Janeiro
International Journal of Technological
Learning, Innovation &
Development [43009]

Sao Paulo
Cadernos de Pesquisa [43031]

Vicosa
Ensaio [43057]

PEOPLE'S REPUBLIC OF
CHINA
Hong Kong
Asian Journal of English Language
Teaching [43276]

Profile [43376] .....,............ 13,000

Xiangtan
Communications in Differential and
Difference Equations [43538]

DENMARK
Copenhagen
Folkeskolen [43668] 84,483
Gymnasieskolen [43672] 15,000

Fredensborg
The School Times International
[43687]

Frederiksberg
Magisterbladet [43692]

ETHIOPIA
Bahir Dar
African Research Review [43804]

Haramaya
East African Journal of Sciences
[43805]

FINLAND
Helsinki
Aikuiskasvatus
[43815] .. .. (Paid) 2,000
(Non-paid) 200
Lifelong Learning in Europe
[43844] .... (Paid) 400
(Non-paid) 1,000
Opettaja [43853] 86,000

FRANCE
Ferney-Voltaire
Medical Student International [43949]

Paris
Higher Education Policy [44047]

Saint Denis
Global Health Promotion [44103]

GEORGIA
Tbilisi
Education Sciences & Psychology
[44132]

GERMANY
Berlin
Antike und Abendland
[44150] .... ‡450
International Journal of Innovation in
Education [44193]

Cologne
E-Learning and Education [44293]

Feldkirchen
Journal of Coptic Studies [44352]

Heidelberg
Teaching Business Ethics [44476]

GHANA
Winneba
Mathematics Connection [44741]

GREECE
Athens
International Journal of Knowledge
and Learning [44748]

Piraeus
International Journal of Applied Systemic Studies [44767]

Thessaloniki
European Journal [44771]

HUNGARY
Budapest
Acta Antiqua Academiae Scientiarum
Hungaricae [44806]

Circulation: ★ = ABC; △ = BPA; ◆ = CAC; • = CCAB; ❑ = VAC; ⊕ = PO Statement; ‡ = Publisher's Report; Boldface figures = sworn; Light figures = estimated.

INDIA

Allahabad
Far East Journal of Mathematical Education [44929]

Balasore
International Journal of Educational Administration [44947]

Bangalore
Indian Institute of World Culture Bulletin [44960]
Resonance [44985] ..... (Paid) 8,000

Chandigarh
Indian Journal of Community Medicine [45024]

Koikata
Bulletin of the Ramakrishna Mission Institute of Culture [45260] .... (Paid) 4,200

Nasik
Abhivyakti and Expressions [45473] 1,000

New Delhi
IETE Journal of Education [45530] .... (Paid) 25,000
Indian Development Review [45539]
Indian Educational Review [45541] .... (Paid) 1,000
International Journal of Engineering Studies [45582]
Journal of Indian Education [45602] .... (Paid) 1,200
Mathematics Today [45625] .... (Paid) 50,000
School Science [45647] .... (Paid) 1,000

Pondicherry
The Bulletin of Sri Aurobindo International Centre of Education [45691] .... (Paid) 800

IRELAND

Cork
Literacy [45938]

Dublin
Adult Learner [45943] 500
In Touch [45966] .... (Combined) 27,100
International Review of Entrepreneurship [45968]
Irish Journal of Education [45975] .... (Paid) 500
Journal of Strategic Management Education [45990]
Reach [45997]

Maynooth
Irish Journal of American Studies [46038] 100

JAPAN

Tokyo
Language Teacher [46959]
Shukan ST [47039] .... (Paid) 150,000

KUWAIT

Safat
The Educational Journal [47336]

LATVIA

Riga
Journal of Business Ethics Education [47369]
Journal of International Business Education [47370]
Journal of Organizational Behavior Education [47371]

LUXEMBOURG

Luxembourg
Sew-Journal [47493]

NAMIBIA

Windhoek
International Journal of Education Economics and Development [47822]

NEPAL

Kathmandu
Kathmandu University Medical Journal [47841]

NETHERLANDS

Amsterdam
Contemporary Educational Psychology [47939]
EAIE Forum [47961] 2,000
Journal of English for Academic Purposes [48072]
The Journal of Logic and Algebraic Programming [48091]

Dordrecht
Designs, Codes and Cryptography [48372]
Education Assessment, Evaluation and Accountability [48380]
Frontiers of Education in China [48396]
Higher Education [48415]
International Journal for the Advancement of Counseling [48425]
International Review of Education [48432] .. .. (Paid) ‡1,200
Journal of Academic Ethics [48436]
Journal of Behavioral Education [48443]
Journal of Dynamical and Control Systems [48454]
Journal of Medical Humanities [48476]
Journal of Science Teacher Education [48492]
Knowledge and Information Systems [48501]
Reading and Writing [48547]
Research in Higher Education [48550]
Science & Education [48559]
Studies in Philosophy and Education [48570]

The Hague
Pharmacy Education [48625]

Leiden
Method & Theory in the Study of Religion [48709]

NEW ZEALAND

Auckland
International Journal of Learning and Change [48799]

Christchurch
Principals Today [48877] .... (Combined) ★8,221

Palmerston North
NZ Journal of Teachers' Work [48965]

Wellington
New Zealand Education Gazette [49019] 17,200
New Zealand Journal of Educational Studies [49024]

NIGERIA

Calabar
Global Journal of Educational Research [49070]

Ikeja
Nigerian Hospital Practice [49107]

Lagos
Educational Research & Reviews [49137]

Port Harcourt
Journal of Technology and Education in Nigeria [49168]

NORWAY

Oslo
Scandinavian Journal of Educational Research [49208]

POLAND

Warsaw
Journal of Teacher Education for Sustainability [49726]

ROMANIA

Bucharest
Higher Education in Europe [49837]

SENEGAL

Dakar
Journal of Higher Education in Africa [50081]

SINGAPORE

Nanyang
Educational Research for Policy and Practice [50097]

Singapore
Electronic Journal of Foreign Language Teaching [50144]

REPUBLIC OF SOUTH AFRICA

Auckland Park
Journal for Language Teaching [50349] 350

Centurion
African Journal of Research in Mathematics, Science and Technology Education [50437]
Journal for Christian Scholarship [50441]
Perspectives in Education [50445]

Grahamstown
Makerere Journal of Higher Education [50504]

Mount Edgecombe
African Journal on Conflict Resolution [50557]

Pietermaritzburg
Indilinga [50568]

Pretoria
Africa Insight [50581]
Education as Change [50590]
Musicus [50597]

SPAIN

Barcelona
Aula [50652] .... (Paid) 4,300
Speak Up [50701]

Madrid
Cultura y Educacion [50746] .... (Combined) 600
Infancia y Aprendizaje/Journal for the Study of Education and Development [50769]

Seville
Integration, the VLSI Journal [50834]

SWEDEN

Goteborg
Montessori Tidningen

[50960] .. .. (Paid) 10,000
(Non-paid) 11,300

SWITZERLAND

Geneva
IB World [51098] 10,000
Prospects [51156]

Zurich
Schweizer Lehrerinnen- und Lehrer-Zeitung [51280]

TAIWAN

Taipei
International Journal of Cyber Society and Education [51343]
Let's Talk in English [51356] 290,000
Studio Classroom [51361] 210,000

Tamsui
Journal of Educational Media and Library Sciences [51394] .. .. (Paid) 1,200

UNITED REPUBLIC OF TANZANIA

Dar es Salaam
Huria [51401]

THAILAND

Bangkok
Journal of Southeast Asian Education [51425]
SEAMEO Journal of Southeast Asian Education [51435]

TURKEY

Ankara
Cooperation in Turkiye [51491] 500
Karinca [51496] 3,500
Ucuncu Sektor Kooperatifcilik [51518] 1,500

Eskisehir
Turkish Online Journal of Distance Education [51555]

UNITED KINGDOM

Abingdon
Action Learning [51696]
Asia Pacific Journal of Education [51706]
British Journal of Guidance and Counselling [51718]
Cambridge Journal of Education [51724]
Changing English [51727]
Child Care in Practice [51728]
Communication Teacher [51737]
Comparative Education [51739]
Critical Studies in Education [51746]
Curriculum Journal [51752]
Democratization [51754]
Distance Education [51759]
Early Child Development and Care [51761]
Early Years [51763]
Education Economics [51767]
Education, Knowledge & Economy [51768]
Education and the Law [51769]
Educational Action Research [51770]
Ethics and Education [51772]
Ethnography & Education [51775]
European Journal of Engineering Education [51780]
European Journal of Teacher Education (EJTE) [51782]

Circulation: ★ = ABC; △ = BPA; ◆ = CAC; • = CCAB; ❑ = VAC; ⊕ = PO Statement; ‡ = Publisher's Report; Boldface figures = sworn; Light figures = estimated.

Evaluation & Research in Education [51787]
Gender and Education [51793]
Globalisation, Societies and Education [51799]
High Ability Studies [51802] 400
Human Resource Development International [51809]
Innovations in Education & Teaching International [51819]
International Journal for Academic Development [51826]
International Journal of Bilingual Education & Bilingualism [51828]
International Journal of Children's Spirituality [51829]
International Journal of Construction Education and Research [51830]
International Journal of Research and Method in Education [51845]
International Research in Geography & Environment Education [51850]
International Studies in Sociology of Education [51856]
Journal of Beliefs & Values [51872]
Journal of Early Childhood Teacher Education [51887]
Journal of Education for Teaching [51890]
Journal of Education and Work [51891]
Journal of Educational Administration and History [51892]
Journal of Further and Higher Education [51898]
Journal of Geography in Higher Education [51901]
Journal of Interprofessional Care [51910]
Journal of Moral Education [51921]
Journal of Multilingual & Multicultural Development [51923]
Journal of Vocational Education & Training [51956]
Language Awareness [51962]
Language Culture & Curriculum [51963]
Language and Education [51964]
New Review of Information Networking [51998]
Open Learning [52002]
Pedagogy, Culture and Society [52005]
Professional Development in Education [52022]
Race, Ethnicity and Education [52033]
Reading & Writing Quarterly [52034] .... (Combined) 900
Research in Post-Compulsory Education [52037]
School Leadership & Management [52053]
Studying Teacher Education [52067]
Teacher Development [52069]
Teachers and Teaching [52070]
Teaching in Higher Education [52071]
Technical Education & Training Abstracts [52072]
Technology, Pedagogy and Education [52074]

Basingstoke
International Journal of Educational Advancement [52210]
Latino Studies [52222]

Birmingham
Journal of Visual Communication in Medicine [52355]
REtoday [52363] .... (Paid) 7,000

Bradford
Education, Business and Society [52451]
Education Training [52452]

Interactive Technology and Smart Education [52469]
International Journal of Educational Management [52476]
International Journal of Sustainability in Higher Education [52488]
Journal of Educational Administration [52497]
Journal of Knowledge Management [52507]
The Learning Organization [52521]
On the Horizon [52533]
Quality Assurance in Education [52541]

Brighton
The Journal of Mental Health Training, Education and Practice [52622]

Bristol
Primary Times [52723] .... (Free) 72,000

Burgess Hill
Teaching Business & Economics [52761] 3,200

Cambridge
Journal of Biosocial Science [52846] 500
Journal of Intellectual Disability Research (JIDR) [52856] 1,400

Cardiff
Building Research Capacity [52925]
Catholic Teachers Gazette [52927]
CEBE Transactions [52928]
European Planning Studies [52929]

Corsham
International Journal of Art & Design Education [53066] 2,800

Coventry
European Journal of Operational Research [53082]
Journal of Research in Reading [53087]

Croydon
Driving Instructor [53125] 18,000

Dundee
Medical Teacher [53215]

Edinburgh
International Journal of Continuing Engineering Education and Life-Long Learning [53287]
International Research in Children's Literature [53290]
Journal of Medical Education [53293]
Scottish Educational Journal [53313] .... (Paid) 63,000
Teaching Earth Sciences [53323]

Exeter
European Journal of Special Needs Education [53355]

Glasgow
First Five [53419] 2,200
Journal of Baltic Studies [53426]
Journal of eLiteracy (JeLit) [53427]
News and Views [53434]

Hatfield
School Science Review [53541]
Science Education International [53542] 700

Heslington
Discourse [53566]
Innovations in Teaching and Learning in Information and Computer Sciences [53567]

High Wycombe
Deafness and Education International [53572] .... (Paid) 2,000

Hove
Journal of Learning Disabilities and Offending Behaviour [53609]

Huddersfield
Campus-Wide Information Systems [53617]
Multicultural Education & Technology Journal [53623]

Leeds
Tangentium [53775]

Leicester
Adults Learning [53782] .... (Paid) 3,000
British Journal of Educational Psychology [53788]
English Four to Eleven [53797]
Equals [53798]
Mathematical Gazette [53813]
Primary Mathematics [53817]
Studies in the Education of Adults [53828] .... (Paid) 750
Use of English [53832]
Young People Now [53834] .... (Paid) 4,000

London
ACE Bulletin [53894]
ACU Bulletin [53896] .... (Controlled) 5,000
Advanced Driving [53904] ... 110,000
Alumni News [53934]
Art, Design & Communication in Higher Education [53967]
BBC Learning is Fun! [54005] .... (Controlled) 60,000
Biological Knowledge [54021]
BMC Medical Education [54064]
Boarding School [54094]
Books for Keeps [54098] .... (Paid) 9,000
Breathe [54104]
Children & Society [54205]
Education Today [54354] .... (Paid) 2,000
Educational Management Administration and Leadership [54355]
Flourish [54467] .... (Non-paid) 20,000
Improving Schools [54589] .. .. (Paid) 1,000
Index to Theses [54595]
Industry and Higher Education [54599]
International Journal [54629]
International Journal of Education through Art [54645]
International Journal of Music Education [54655] .... (Paid) ‡1,000
Journal of Biological Education [54706] .... (Paid) ‡1,800
Journal of Early Childhood Literacy [54740]
Journal of Intellectual Disabilities [54769]
Journal of Media Practice [54777]
Journal of Philosophy of Education [54798]
Language Teaching Research [54853] .... (Paid) 500
Leadership Focus [54859] .... ‡28,000
Make the Grade [54899]
Menopause International [54926]
New View [55000] ... (Paid) 350,000
Report [55189] 160,000
School Psychology International [55219]
Sex Education [55230]
Teaching History [55293]
Times Educational Supplement [55322] .. .. ★118,609

Times Higher Education Supplement [55323] .... ★31,140
UCU [55352]
Viewfinder [55370] 5,500

Loughborough
Accounting Education [55476]

Loughton
Education Business [55489]

Maidstone
Education Today [55529] .. .. (Controlled) ‡21,500

Manchester
International Journal of Electrical Engineering Education [55558]
International Journal of Mechanical Engineering Education [55560]
Interpreter and Translator Trainer [55561]

Milton Keynes
Journal of Interactive Media in Education [55639]

Newcastle upon Tyne
Interspectives [55673]

Northampton
Journal for Critical Education Policy Studies [55711]
The Journal of Research in Special Educational Needs [55712]
Support for Learning [55714] 11,500

Nottingham
EPNS Journal [55755] 650
International Journal of Educational Development [55760]
Public Policy and Administration [55771] 600

Nuneaton
Pastoral Care in Education [55777] 2,000

Olney
International Journal of Information Technology and Management [55811]
International Journal of Knowledge Management Studies [55817]
International Journal of Teaching & Case Studies [55834]

Oxford
ALT-J [55863]
Educational Measurement [55933]
Emotional and Behavioral Difficulties [55936]
European Educational Research Journal [55943]
Fiscal Studies [55958]
Health Education Research [55971]
Journal of Educational Measurement [56027]
Research in Comparative and International Education [56187]
Review of Urban & Regional Development Studies [56195]
Teaching Statistics [56213]
Teaching Theology and Religion [56214]
Tertiary Education and Management [56215]

Penrith
Horizons [56245]

Reading
Electronic Journal of e-Learning [56314]
Image and Vision Computing [56320]

Reepham
ELT Journal [56385]

Rotherham
The School Librarian [56412] .. .. (Paid) 4,000

Circulation: ★ = ABC; △ = BPA; ◆ = CAC; • = CCAB; ❑ = VAC; ⊕ = PO Statement; ‡ = Publisher's Report; Boldface figures = sworn; Light figures = estimated.

Trade, Technical, and Professional Publications

Rugby
Education for Chemical Engineers [56417]

Southampton
Health Education [56572]

Stafford
International Journal of Learning Technology [56591]

Stirling
Childminding
[56621] .... (Combined) 18,000

Stoke-on-Trent
Design & Technology
[56629] 8,500
Race Equality Teaching [56630]

Tamworth
British Journal of Special Education [56717]
Special! [56718]

Tunbridge Wells
Educational Technology Abstracts [56781]

West Sussex
Dyslexia [56897]

Woodbridge
International School [56956]
is [56957]
Prep School [56958]

York
Quality in Higher Education [56995]

Zeals Warminster
Conference & Common Room [57003]

ZIMBABWE
Bindura
Southern Africa Journal of Science and Technology [57112]

Harare
Zimbabwe Journal of Educational Research [57122]

ELECTRICAL ENGINEERING
See also Electronics Engineering; Lighting; Power and Power Plants; Radio, Television, Cable, and Video; Telecommunications

AUSTRALIA
Brisbane
Automotive Electrical & Air Conditioning News [41644] 3,200

Nundah
The Circuit [42220] 9392

Raymond Terrace
AIE News Journal
[42297] .... (Paid) 1,000

Sydney
Electrical World
[42502] .... (Paid) ‡6,749

BELGIUM
Brussels
Watt's NEW? [42874]

BRAZIL
Sao Paulo
Eletricidade Moderna
[43039] .... (Non-paid) 12,000

DENMARK
Glostrup
Installations Nyt [43707] .... ‡3,907

Installations Nyt Special [43708]

FINLAND
Tampere
International Journal of Bioelectromagnetism [43908]

FRANCE
Villiers-Saint-Frederic
International Journal of Electric and Hybrid Vehicles [44127]

GERMANY
Heidelberg
Cluster Computing [44448]

Leinfelden-Echterdingen
Elektro Automation
[44522] .. .. (Combined) ‡21,617

INDIA
Allahabad
Far East Journal of Electronics and Communications [44927]

Bhubaneswar
International Journal of Power and Energy Conversion [45011]

Kolkata
Energy for Sustainable Development [45265]
The Institution of Engineers (India) Electrical Engineering Division Journal [45282] ...... (Paid) 17,000

Mumbai
Electrical & Electronics [45369]
IEEMA Journal [45372] 10,000

IRAN
Tehran
Iranian Journal of Electrical and Computer Engineering [45900]

ITALY
Peschiera Borromeo
Euro Electric News
[46214] .. .. (Paid) 15,000

JAPAN
Tokyo
Asia Electronics Industry
[46753] 51,000
Electrical Engineering [46808]
Hitachi Cable Review [46834]
Mitsubishi Electric Advance
[46969] .... (Paid) 2,000
Nikkei Board Guide
[46979] 60,000
Nikkei Electronics China
[46990] .... △33,220
Nikkei Microdevices
[46998] .... ★14,200

NETHERLANDS
Amsterdam
Electric Power Systems Research [47963]
Graphical Models [48004]
Journal of Power Sources [48112]

Dordrecht
Frontiers of Electrical and Electronic Engineering in China [48397]

Leiden
Journal of Electromagnetic Waves and Applications [48695]

NEW ZEALAND
North Shore City
Electrical + Automation Technology
[48955] .. .. ★10,315

PAKISTAN
Faisalabad
International Journal of Electrical and Power Engineering [49250]

POLAND
Warsaw
Opto-Electronics Review [49742]
Paladyn [49744]

RUSSIA
Moscow
Quantum Electronics [49969]

SWITZERLAND
Geneva
International Journal of Mechatronics and Manufacturing Systems [51130]

TURKEY
Ankara
Turkish Journal of Electrical Engineering and Computer Sciences [51509]

UNITED KINGDOM
Bedford
The Power Engineer [52275] 700

Bradford
COMPEL [52444]

Brighton
Batteries International
[52606] .... (Combined) 5,800

Bristol
Compound Semiconductor
[52654] .... △9,025
Journal of Semiconductors [52698]

Kent
The Independent Electrical Retailer
[53678] .. .. (Controlled) ★6,895

London
Electrical/Mechanical Contractor
[54359] .. .. (Paid) ★9,000
Lighting Research and Technology [54873]
Personal and Ubiquitous Computing [55070]

Manchester
International Journal of Electrical Engineering Education [55558]

Midlothian
Cabletalk [55627] 5,000

Nottingham
International Journal of Design Engineering [55759]

Rugby
The Lighting Journal
[56420] .. .. (Paid) 4,500

Slough
Journal of the Audio Engineering Society [56559]

Stevenage
Electronics and Communication Engineering Journal
[56600] .... ‡38,000
Electronics Education [56601]
IEE Proceedings Electric Power Applications [56607]
IEE Proceedings Generation, Transmission & Distribution [56608]
IEE Proceedings Radar, Sonar & Navigation [56612]
Wiring Matters
[56619] .... (Non-paid) 42,500

Watford
Professional Electrician & Installer
[56871] .... ★60,600

Wrexham
International Journal of Engineering Systems Modelling and Simulation [56981]

ELECTRONICS ENGINEERING
See also Electrical Engineering; Computers

AUSTRALIA
Melbourne
International Journal of Electronic Transport [42065]

Nundah
The Circuit [42220] 9392

Wahroonga
Electrical Solutions
[42672] .... ★7,582
What's New in Electronics
[42679] .... ★7072

AUSTRIA
Vienna
Elektronik Report [42750]

BELGIUM
Leuven
Microelectronic Engineering [42901]

BRAZIL
Sao Carlos
Journal of Microwaves, Optoelectronics and Electromagnetic Applications [43018]

PEOPLE'S REPUBLIC OF CHINA
Beijing
International Journal of Intelligent Computing and Cybernetics [43197]
Science in China Series E [43219]

Hong Kong
HKTDC Electronic Components & Parts [43304]
HKTDC Electronics
[43305] .. .. (Paid) 50,000

Shanghai
Microcomputer Applications [43489]

Xi'an
International Journal of Digital Enterprise Technology [43537]

DENMARK
Glostrup
Aktuel Elektronik [43697] .. ... ‡6,080
Elektronik & Data
[43702] .... (Controlled) 6,388
Elektronik Nyt [43703] .... ‡3,391
Elteknik [43704] .. .. ‡3,950

FINLAND
Helsinki
International Journal of Digital Culture and Electronic Tourism [43833]

FRANCE
Grenoble
Microelectronics Journal [43958]

Nantes
Electronic Communications in Probability [44013]

Circulation: ★ = ABC; △ = BPA; ◆ = CAC; • = CCAB; ❑ = VAC; ⊕ = PO Statement; ‡ = Publisher's Report; Boldface figures = sworn; Light figures = estimated.

GERMANY
Berlin
Microsystem Technologies [44222]

Dresden
AEU - International Journal of Electronics and Communications [44319]

Kissing
Elektronik
[44509] .. .. (Controlled) 30,000

Leinfelden-Echterdingen
EPP Europe
[44523] .. .. (Combined) ‡20,040

Mainz
Micron [44543]

INDIA
Allahabad
Far East Journal of Electronics and Communications [44927]

Bhubaneswar
International Journal of Computational Vision and Robotics [45010]

Kharagpur
International Journal of Communication Networks and Distributed Systems [45246]
International Journal of Industrial Electronics and Drives [45247]

Kolkata
Energy for Sustainable Development [45265]
Institution of Engineers (India) Electronics and Telecommunication Engineering Division Journal
[45283] .. .. (Paid) 10,000

Mumbai
Electrical & Electronics [45369]
IEEMA Journal [45372] 10,000

New Delhi
Electronics For You
[45506] .. .. (Paid) 47,151

ITALY
Peschiera Borromeo
Euro Electric News
[46214] .. .. (Paid) 15,000

JAPAN
Chiba
IEICE Transactions on Fundamentals of Electronics, Communications and Computer Sciences [46318]

Tokyo
Electrical Engineering [46808]
IEICE Electronics Express [46838]
Journal of IEICE
[46908] .. .. (Paid) 40,000
Nikkei Board Guide
[46979] 60,000
Nikkei Electronics
[46989] .. .. ★36,575
Nikkei Electronics China
[46990] .. .. △33,220
Nikkei Microdevices
[46998] .. .. ★14,200

MALAYSIA
Kuala Lumpur
Suara TEEAM [47636]

NETHERLANDS
Amsterdam
Digital Signal Processing [47958]
Materials Science in Semiconductor Processing [48147]

Mechatronics [48151]
Dordrecht
Frontiers of Electrical and Electronic Engineering in China [48397]
Journal of Computational Electronics [48450]

Leiden
Advanced Robotics [48642]

NEW ZEALAND
Auckland
International Journal of Biomechatronics and Biomedical Robotics [48798]

PAKISTAN
Faisalabad
International Journal of Electrical and Power Engineering [49250]
International Journal of Soft Computing [49256]
International Journal of Systems Signal Control and Engineering Application [49257]

POLAND
Warsaw
Opto-Electronics Review [49742]
Paladyn [49744]

SERBIA
Nis
Microelectronics Reliability [50091]

SINGAPORE
Singapore
Optical Switching and Networking [50232]

REPUBLIC OF SOUTH AFRICA
Kloof
Dataweek [50542] .... (Free) 4,000

SWEDEN
Lund
Microprocessors and Microsystems [50987]

SWITZERLAND
Aarau
MegaLink [51055] 12,500

Geneva
International Journal of Mechatronics and Manufacturing Systems [51130]

Schlieren
Aktuelle Technik
[51230] .. .. (Combined) 14,500

TAIWAN
Tainan
Materials Chemistry and Physics [51327]

UNITED KINGDOM
Basingstoke
Journal of Digital Asset Management [52215]

Bedford
The Power Engineer [52275] 700

Bradford
COMPEL [52444]
Information Technology & People [52468]

Microelectronics International [52527]
London
Electrical/Mechanical Contractor
[54359] .. .. (Paid) ★9,000
International Journal of Electronic Security and Digital Forensics [54647]
Journal of Wide Bandgap Materials [54836]
Personal and Ubiquitous Computing [55070]

Loughborough
Circuit World [55478]

Manchester
International Journal of Electrical Engineering Education [55558]

Olney
International Journal of Nanomanufacturing [55825]

Oxford
infocus Magazine [55989]

Slough
Journal of the Audio Engineering Society [56559]

Stevenage
Electronics and Communication Engineering Journal
[56600] .... ‡38,000
Electronics Education [56601]
Electronics Letters [56602]
IEE Proceedings Circuits, Devices & Systems [56605]
IEE Proceedings Control Theory & Applications [56606]
IEE Proceedings Science, Measurement & Technology [56613]
IET Computers & Digital Techniques [56617]

Wrexham
International Journal of Engineering Systems Modelling and Simulation [56981]

EMPLOYMENT AND HUMAN RESOURCES
See also Labor

AUSTRALIA
Bowen Hills
The Australian Journal of Rehabilitation Counselling [41624]
International Journal of Disability Management Research [41626]

Melbourne
International Journal of Environment, Workplace and Employment [42066]

AUSTRIA
Vienna
Long Range Planning [42763]

BELGIUM
Brussels
EPI [42851]

PEOPLE'S REPUBLIC OF CHINA
Hong Kong
The Hong Kong Manager
[43337] 140,000

FRANCE
Ferney-Voltaire
Focus on the Public Services
[43947] .. .. (Free) 17,000

GERMANY
Leinfelden-Echterdingen
ErgoMed [44524] 2,800

Mainz
Das Orchester
[44539] .. .. (Paid) 20,000

INDIA
Hyderabad
The Icfai Journal of Employment Law [45148]

Kolkata
Personnel Today
[45301] .. .. (Paid) 6,000

IRELAND
Dublin
Employment Law Review [45955]

JAPAN
Tokyo
JMA Management Review
[46877] 20,000

NETHERLANDS
Amsterdam
Human Resource Management Review [48015]

NEW ZEALAND
Wellington
New Zealand Journal of Human Resources Management [49026]

POLAND
Warsaw
Organizacija [49743]

SINGAPORE
Singapore
Chinese Management Studies [50120]
Research and Practice in Human Resource Management [50244]

REPUBLIC OF SOUTH AFRICA
Cape Town
Achiever [50360] 10,000

Centurion
SA Journal of Human Resource Management [50447]

Lynnwood Ridge
Quest [50550]

Pretoria
South African Journal of Labour Relations [50603]

SWEDEN
Stockholm
Socionomen [51040] 9,000

SWITZERLAND
Geneva
International Labour Review [51147]
Union [51164]

UNITED KINGDOM
Abingdon
Human Resource Development International [51809]
Journal of Education and Work [51891]
Labor History [51961]

Circulation: ★ = ABC; △ = BPA; ◆ = CAC; • = CCAB; ❑ = VAC; ⊕ = PO Statement; ‡ = Publisher's Report; Boldface figures = sworn; Light figures = estimated.

Bradford
Employee Relations [52454]
Human Resource Management International Digest [52462]
Industrial and Commercial Training [52464]
International Journal of Manpower [52481]
Journal of Managerial Psychology [52509]
Strategic HR Review [52547]
The TQM Journal [52554]

Cambridge
Workplace Law [52905]

Cardiff
International Journal of Human Resource Management [52930]

Cromhall
the HR Director
[53119] .... (Controlled) ★10,000

Croydon
IRS Employment Review [53127]

Leicester
Psychologist Appointments [53819]

London
Benefits & Compensation International
[54011] .. .. (Paid) 1,007
Competency & Emotional Intelligence [54251]
Employee Benefits [54366] ... 10,030
Equal Opportunities Review [54381]
European Industrial Relations Review [54395]
Human Resources [54579] ... 20,532
Human Resources for Health [54580]
Journal of Organisational Transformation and Social Change [54790]
Leadership Focus
[54859] .... ‡28,000
Manager, British Journal of Administrative Management
[54903] 12,500
Strategy [55265] 15,000

Manchester
Jobs North West
[55563] .. .. (Paid) 27,000

Middleton Cheney
Rapport
[55623] .... (Non-paid) 11,000

Newcastle upon Tyne
Personnel Review [55677]

Olney
International Journal of Human Resources Development and Management [55810]

Oxford
BJIR: British Journal of Industrial Relations [55884]
Human Resource Management Journal [55980]
Industrial Relations Journal [55988]

Sheffield
Hazards [56496]
Managing Leisure [56506]

Stirling
New Technology, Work and Employment [56625]

Uxbridge
International Journal of Work Organisation & Emotion [56799]

VENEZUELA
Maracaibo
Gaceta Laboral [57026]

ZIMBABWE
Harare
Zimbabwe Journal of Educational Research [57122]

ENGINEERING (VARIOUS BRANCHES)
See also Chemistry, Chemicals, and Chemical Engineering; Electrical Engineering; Electronics Engineering; Nuclear Engineering

AUSTRALIA
Bundoora
Colloids and Surfaces A [41670]

Gladstone
Engineering Failure Analysis [41887]

Melbourne
Electronic Journal of Structural Engineering [42058]
Global Journal of Engineering Education [42061]

Sydney
International Journal of Abrasive Technology [42518]
Journal of Biomimetics, Biomaterials, and Tissue Engineering [42527]

AUSTRIA
Salzburg
Geomechanics and Tunnelling [42740]

Vienna
The European Journal of Technology and Advanced Engineering Research [42755]
TermNet News [42769]

BAHRAIN
Manama
Gulf Construction
[42788] .. .. (Paid) 49,028
Gulf Industry
[42790] .. .. (Paid) 13,614

BELGIUM
Leuven
Microelectronic Engineering [42901]

Saint-Pieters-Leeuw
Dedicated Systems Magazine [42911]

BOTSWANA
Gaborone
Botswana Journal of Technology [42943]

BRAZIL
Campos dos Goytacazes
Biosystems Engineering [42974]

Petropolis
Computational & Applied Mathematics [42990]

Rio de Janeiro
Journal of the Brazilian Society of Mechanical Sciences [43010]

Sao Carlos
Gestao & Producao [43017]

Vicosa
Materials Research [43060]
Rem [43065]

PEOPLE'S REPUBLIC OF CHINA
Beijing
International Journal of Intelligent Engineering Informatics [43198]
Particuology [43212]
Rare Metals [43214] 1,000
Science in China Series E [43219]
Tsinghua Science & Technology [43222]

Changchun
Journal of Jilin University Engineering and Technology Edition [43241]

Changsha
Transactions of Nonferrous Metals Society of China [43246] 800

Hangzhou
International Journal of Structural Engineering [43260]

Hong Kong
Hong Kong Surveyor [43345]
International Journal of Knowledge Engineering and Data Mining [43351]
Journal of Geospatial Engineering [43356]
Mathematical Modelling and Applied Computing [43368]
Nikkei Electronics Asia
[43371] .. .. △28,300

Kowloon
IEEE Transactions on Components and Packaging Technologies [43451]

Nanjing
Water Science and Engineering [43461]

Shanghai
Die & Mould Technology [43472]
Journal of Noise and Vibration Control [43481]
Journal of Shanghai Jiaotong University [43482]
Journal of Vibration and Shock [43484]
Machine Design & Research [43486]
Ocean Engineering [43492]
Systems Engineering [43506]

Wuhan
Safety and Environmental Engineering [43525]

Wuxi
Journal of Hydrodynamics [43527]

Xiangtan
International Journal of Computing Science and Mathematics [43539]
International Journal of Dynamical Systems and Differential Equations [43540]

COTE D'IVOIRE
Abidjan
Afrique Science [43555]

CROATIA
Zagreb
Chemical and Biochemical Engineering Quarterly [43563]
International Journal of Transitions and Innovation Systems [43568]

DENMARK
Glostrup
Maskin Aktuelt [43710] .... ‡8,200
Teknisk Nyt [43716] .. .. ‡10,131
Teknisk Nyt Special Edition
[43717] .... ‡10,000

Lyngby
European Journal of Mechanics - A/Solids [43725]

FRANCE
Cachan
European Journal of Mechanics - B/Fluids [43925]

Grenoble
Microelectronics Journal [43958]

Paris
Mecanique & Industries [44071]

Tarbes
Engineering Applications of Artificial Intelligence [44116]

Toulouse
Fuzzy Sets and Systems [44120]

GERMANY
Berlin
Journal of Applied Geodesy [44203]
Journal of Non-Equilibrium Thermodynamics [44208] 200
Microsystem Technologies [44222]
VBI-Nachrichten [44234]

Bielefeld
Sun & Wind Energy [44247]

Bremen
Archive of Applied Mechanics [44280]

Darmstadt
International Journal of Computer Aided Engineering and Technology [44309]

Dortmund
Chemical Engineering and Processing [44315]

Duisburg
Mechanism and Machine Theory [44320]

Eschborn
Gate Technology and Development [44345]

Gottingen
Advances in Radio Science [44390]

Heidelberg
Computational Management Science [44450]
Innovations in Systems and Software Engineering [44461]

Herford
CodeBreakers Journal (CBJ) [44483]

Leinfelden-Echterdingen
Elektro Automation
[44522] .. .. (Combined) ‡21,617

Pfinztal
International Journal of Materials and Product Technology [44633]

Saarbrucken
Progress in Materials Science [44652]

Stuttgart
Nuclear Engineering and Design [44674]

GREECE
Chalkis
International Journal of Signal and Imaging Systems Engineering [44758]

Piraeus
International Journal of Applied Systemic Studies [44767]

Circulation: ★ = ABC; △ = BPA; ◆ = CAC; • = CCAB; ❏ = VAC; ⊕ = PO Statement; ‡ = Publisher's Report; Boldface figures = sworn; Light figures = estimated.

Journal of Applied Systems Studies [44769]

Xanthi
Strain [44776] .... (Non-paid) 650

HUNGARY
Budapest
Epites - Epiteszettudomany [44828]
Nanopages [44854]
Pollack Periodica [44864]
Progress in Agricultural Engineering Sciences [44866]
Structural and Multidisciplinary Optimization [44874]

INDIA
Allahabad
Advances in Computer Science and Engineering [44921]
Far East Journal of Experimental and Theoretical Artificial Intelligence [44928]
JP Journal of Solids and Structures [44939]

Bangalore
International Journal of Aerospace Innovations [44963]
Sadhana [44986] .... (Paid) 850

Bhubaneswar
International Journal of Computational Vision and Robotics [45010]

Chennai
International Journal of Spray and Combustion Dynamics [45042]

Guwahati
International Journal of Ultra Wideband Communications and Systems [45130]

Hyderabad
The Icfai Journal of Science & Technology [45166]

Jodhpur
Indian Journal of Engineering and Materials Sciences [45222]

Kharagpur
International Journal of Industrial Electronics and Drives [45247]

Kolkata
Institution of Engineers (India) Aerospace Engineering Division Journal [45276] .... (Paid) 4,000
Institution of Engineers (India) Agricultural Engineering Division Journal [45277] ...... (Paid) 4,000
Institution of Engineers (India) Architectural Engineering Division Journal [45278] .... (Paid) 5,000
Institution of Engineers (India) Civil Engineering Division Journal [45280] .. .. (Paid) 30,000
The Institution of Engineers (India) Computer Engineering Division Journal [45281] .... (Paid) 5,000
Institution of Engineers (India) Environmental Engineering Division Journal [45284] ...... (Paid) ‡8,000
Institution of Engineers (India) Hindi Journal [45285] ...... (Paid) ‡5,000
The Institution of Engineers (India) Inter-disciplinary Panels Journal [45286] ...... (Paid) 12,000
Institution of Engineers (India) Marine Engineering Division Journal [45287] .. .. (Paid) ‡4,000
The Institution of Engineers (India) Mechanical Engineering Division Journal [45288] ...... (Paid) 20,000
The Institution of Engineers (India-

) Metallurgical and Materials Engineering Division Journal [45289] .... (Paid) 4,000
Institution of Engineers (India) Mining Engineering Division Journal [45290] .... (Paid) 4,000
Institution of Engineers (India) Production Engineering Division Journal [45291] .... (Paid) 5,000
Institution of Engineers (India) Technicians' Journal [45292] .... (Paid) ‡260,000
Institution of Engineers (India) Technorama [45293] .. .. (Paid) 90,000
Institution of Engineers (India) Textile Engineering Division Journal [45294] .... (Paid) 4,000
Nano Science and Nano Technology [45299]

Mumbai
Process & Plant Engineering [45432] .. .. (Paid) 16,000

Nagpur
Indian Literature in Environmental Engineering [45466]

New Delhi
Highway Research Record [45523] .. .. (Paid) 8,500
Indian Highways [45545] .. .. (Paid) 6,500
Indian Journal of Agricultural Engineering [45547] 4,000
International Journal of Engineering Studies [45582]
Journal of Discrete Mathematical Sciences and Cryptography [45595] .... (Paid) 240
Journal of Information & Optimization Sciences [45606] .... (Paid) 480

Rajkot
Materials Science [45709]

IRAN
Shiraz
Iranian Journal of Science and Technology [45884] .. .. (Paid) 1,000

Tehran
International Journal of Engineering [45890]
Iranian Journal of Environmental Health Science & Engineering [45902]
Scientia Iranica [45913] .. .. (Paid) 5,000

ISRAEL
Haifa
Mechanical Systems and Signal Processing [46078]

Tel Aviv
Corrosion Reviews [46097]
International Journal of Turbo and Jet Engines [46105]
Journal of the Mechanical Behavior of Materials [46108]
Science and Engineering of Composite Materials [46112]

ITALY
Bari
International Journal of Enterprise Systems Integration and Interoperability [46122]

Bologna
4OR [46126]

Fisciano
International Journal of Forensic Software Engineering [46140]

Milan
European Journal of Internal Medicine [46168] 1,439

Naples
International Journal of Critical Computer-Based Systems [46200]

Napoli
International Journal of Engineering Management and Economics [46204]

Pavia
Structural Control and Health Monitoring [46211]

Trento
International Journal of Agent-Oriented Software Engineering [46262]

Turin
Rock Mechanics and Rock Engineering [46274]

JAPAN
Kyoto
Advanced Powder Technology [46466]

Nagoya
Coastal Engineering Journal [46552]

Sendai
High Temperature Materials and Processes [46666]

Tokyo
Acta Mechanica [46725]
Acta Mechanica Sinica [46726]
Biomechanics and Modeling in Mechanobiology [46766]
Clean Technologies and Environmental Policy [46787]
Computational Mechanics [46791]
Concrete Library International [46795]
Engineering with Computers [46810]
International Journal of Advanced Mechatronic Systems [46844]
International Journal of Japan Society for Precision Engineering [46847]
Journal of Medical Ultrasonics [46925]
Journal of Structural Engineering B [46943]
JSME International Journal Series A [46948] .. .. (Paid) 1,300
JSME International Journal Series B [46949]
JSME International Journal Series C [46950]
Refrigeration [47031] 10,000
Rural and Environmental Engineering [47034]
Soils & Foundations [47042] .... (Paid) 600
Structural Engineering Earthquake Engineering [47043]

Tsukuba
International Journal of Knowledge Engineering and Soft Data Paradigms [47110]

Yokohama
Systems and Synthetic Biology [47142]

JORDAN
Amman
Dirasat Engineering Sciences [47154] .. .. (Controlled) 1,000

KENYA
Nairobi
African Journal of Science and Technology [47174]

Journal of Civil Engineering [47186]
Journal of Civil Engineering Research and Practice [47187]

REPUBLIC OF KOREA
Daejeon
International Journal of Theoretical and Applied Mechanics [47227]

KUWAIT
Safat
European Journal of Industrial Engineering [47337]

MALAYSIA
Kota Kinabalu
Biotechnology & Molecular Biology Reviews [47588]

Melaka
International Journal of Precision Technology [47681]

Perlis
International Journal of Materials Engineering and Technology [47694]

Petaling Jaya
IEM Journal [47699] 15,000
Jurutera [47700] .. .. (Paid) 15,000

Serdang
International Journal of Applied Engineering Research [47715]

NETHERLANDS
Amsterdam
Advanced Engineering Informatics [47881]
Advances in Colloid and Interface Science [47882]
Applied and Computational Harmonic Analysis [47897]
Bridge Structures [47916]
Current Opinion in Biotechnology [47944]
Geotextiles and Geomembranes [47997]
International Journal of Mechanical Sciences [48030]
Journal of Applied Mathematics and Mechanics [48047]
Journal of Colloid and Interface Science [48060]
Journal of Computational Methods in Sciences and Engineering [48063]
Journal of Intelligent & Fuzzy Systems [48087] 3,850
Journal of The Franklin Institute [48125]
Journal of Visual Languages and Computing [48129]
Journal of Wind Engineering & Industrial Aerodynamics [48132]
Materials Science and Engineering [48145]
Matrix Biology [48149]
Mechanics of Materials [48150]
Mechatronics [48151]
Optical Fiber Technology [48191]
Optical Materials [48192]
Optics & Laser Technology [48194]
Shock and Vibration [48231] 4,900
Technology and Health Care [48242]
Thermochimica Acta [48248]
Trends in Biotechnology [48258]

Dordrecht
Bulletin of Earthquake Engineering [48339]
Designs, Codes and Cryptography [48372]
Discrete Event Dynamic Systems [48375]

Flexible Services and Manufacturing Journal [48388]
Forschung im Ingenieurwesen [48390]
Frontiers of Mechanical Engineering in China [48402]
Journal of Computational Electronics [48450]
Journal of Dynamical and Control Systems [48454]
Journal of Global Optimization [48465]
Journal of Scheduling [48491]
Journal of Systems Science and Systems Engineering [48497]
Landslides [48504]
Meccanica [48514]
Optimization and Engineering [48521]
Plasma Chemistry and Plasma Processing [48537]
Queueing Systems [48545]
Software Quality Journal [48563]
Transport in Porous Media [48581]
User Modeling and User-Adapted Interaction [48585]

Leiden
Advanced Composite Materials [48641]
Advanced Robotics [48642]
Composite Interfaces [48663]

NEW ZEALAND
North Shore City
DEMM Engineering & Manufacturing Magazine [48954] 9,017

Wellington
e.nz magazine [49007]

NIGERIA
Abuja
The Nigerian Engineer [49057] .. .. (Paid) 2,000

Benin City
Journal of the Nigerian Association of Mathematical Physics [49065]

Lagos
Scientific Research & Essays [49143]

Port Harcourt
Journal of Modeling, Design & Management of Engineering Systems [49167]
Journal of Technology and Education in Nigeria [49168]

NORWAY
Stavange
International Journal of Strategic Engineering Asset Management [49213]

PAKISTAN
Faisalabad
Australian Journal of Basic and Applied Sciences [49238]
Information Technology Journal [49247]
International Journal of Systems Signal Control and Engineering Application [49257]
Journal of Engineering and Applied Sciences [49266]

PHILIPPINES
Quezon City
Electrical Engineer Magazine [49592] .. .. (Paid) 17,000
Philippine Planning Journal [49609] .... (Paid) 600

POLAND
Warsaw
Advances in Materials Science [49686]
Chemical Papers [49703]
Geodesy and Cartography [49713]
International Journal of Applied Mathematics and Computer Science [49719]
Latvian Journal of Physics and Technical Sciences [49730]
Paladyn [49744]
Polish Journal of Medical Physics and Engineering [49749]

Wroclaw
International Journal of Intelligent Information and Database Systems [49780]

PORTUGAL
Aveiro
International Journal of Materials Engineering Innovation [49787]
International Journal of Molecular Engineering [49788]
International Journal of Surface Science & Engineering [49789]

Lisboa
International Journal of Organisational Design and Engineering [49800]

Lisbon
ISRM News Journal [49803] ... 6,000

ROMANIA
Bucharest
Balkan Journal of Geometry and its Applications [49832]
Buletin AGIR [49833]
Univers Ingineresc [49845]

RUSSIA
Moscow
Integral Transforms and Special Functions [49920]

SAUDI ARABIA
Dhahran
Arabian Journal for Science and Engineering [50054] .... (Paid) 800

Riyadh
Journal of King Saud University [50062] .. .. (Paid) 2,000

SERBIA
Nis
Microelectronics Reliability [50091]

SINGAPORE
Singapore
Journal of Graph Algorithms and Applications [50206]
Surface Review and Letters [50275]

SLOVAKIA
Kosice
Acta Montanistica Slovaca [50325]

REPUBLIC OF SOUTH AFRICA
Auckland Park
Ergonomics SA [50347]

Bruma
South African Journal of Industrial Engineering [50359]

Centurion
African Journal of Research in Mathematics, Science and Technology Education [50437]
Journal of Engineering, Design and Technology [50442]
SA Irrigation [50446]

Garden View
Engineering News [50479] .... (Combined) ★15,003

Grahamstown
Global Journal of Engineering Research [50496]
Journal of Applied Science, Engineering and Technology [50500]

Halfway House
Civil Engineering [50519]

Pretoria
Control Engineering Practice [50587]

SRI LANKA
Colombo
Engineer [50854] .. .. (Paid) 3,750
Sri Lanka Engineering News [50863]

SWEDEN
Lulea
Flow Measurement and Instrumentation [50981]

Lund
Microprocessors and Microsystems [50987]

SWITZERLAND
Geneva
International Journal of Complexity in Applied Science and Engineering [51110]
International Journal of Manufacturing Technology and Management [51129]
International Journal of Mining and Mineral Engineering [51132]
International Journal of Petroleum Engineering [51134]
International Journal of Quality Engineering and Technology [51136]

Lausanne
Optics and Lasers in Engineering [51198]

Zurich
Journal of Applied Mathematics and Physics (ZAMP) [51269]
Journal of Object Technology (JOT) [51271]
Key Engineering Materials [51272]
Structural Engineering International [51288] 5,500

TAIWAN
Chungli
Advances in Adaptive Data Analysis [51304]

Hsinchu
Journal of Micro/Nanolithography, MEMS, and MOEMS [51306]

Taipei
Journal of Chinese Institute of Engineers [51350] .... (Paid) 1,800

THAILAND
Pathumthani
Geotechnical Engineering [51459] 1,120
International Agricultural Engineering Journal [51460] 300

TURKEY
Ankara
Turkish Journal of Engineering and Environmental Sciences [51510]

UNITED KINGDOM
Abingdon
Computer Methods in Biomechanics and Biomedical Engineering [51740]
European Journal of Engineering Education [51780]
Virtual and Physical Prototyping [52085]

Ashurst
Engineering Analysis with Boundary Elements [52145]

Barnsley
Assistive Technologies [52177]

Bath
Journal of Engineering Manufacture [52247]

Belfast
Industrial & Manufacturing Engineer Magazine [52286]

Birmingham
International Journal for Numerical Methods in Fluids [52344]
Journal of Simulation [52353]
Progress in Nuclear Energy [52362]

Bradford
International Journal of Web Information Systems [52489]
Journal of Quality in Maintenance Engineering [52514]
Multidiscipline Modeling in Materials and Structures [52528]
Sensor Review [52543]
Soldering & Surface Mount Technology [52545]

Brentwood
Advances in Structural Engineering [52566]
Building Acoustics [52569]
International Journal of Aeroacoustics [52575]
International Journal of Space Structures [52578]
Wind Engineering [52590]

Bristol
International Journal of Modelling, Identification and Control [52679]
Journal of Cellular Automata [52683]
Journal of Geophysics and Engineering [52686]
Journal of Instrumentation [52687]
Journal of Neural Engineering [52692]
Measurement Science & Technology [52705] .... (Combined) 2,100
Science and Technology of Advanced Materials [52729]
Survey Review [52732]

Buckhurst Hill
Machinery World [52750] .. .... ★9,000

Buntingford
Environmental Engineering [52759] 7,500

Cambridge
CrystEngComm [52813]
Journal of Advanced Materials [52841]

Canterbury
Engineering Designer [52917] 6,600

Chichester
International Journal of Robust & Nonlinear Control [53012]
Optimal Control Applications & Methods [53015]
Quality & Reliability Engineering International [53016]

Circulation: ★ = ABC; △ = BPA; ◆ = CAC; • = CCAB; ❏ = VAC; ⊕ = PO Statement; ‡ = Publisher's Report; Boldface figures = sworn; Light figures = estimated.

Derby
Materials & Design [53166]

Edinburgh
Fire Safety Journal [53276]
International Journal of Continuing Engineering Education and Life-Long Learning [53287]

Glasgow
Weir Bulletin
[53458] .... (Controlled) 20,000

Gloucester
International Journal of Pressure Vessels and Piping [53470]

Guildford
Journal of Constructional Steel Research [53493]

Ilkley
Industrial Robot [53646]

Liphook
Process Industry Informer
[53861] .... ‡4,000

Liverpool
Engineering Optimization [53870]

London
Architectural Engineering and Design Management [53961]
Automotive Engineer [53987]
BioMedical Engineering OnLine [54029]
Bridge Design & Engineering
[54106] .... (Combined) 5,000
Bubble Science, Engineering and Technology [54151]
Building Services Engineering Research and Technology [54154]
CAD User [54165] 13,000
Concurrent Engineering
[54257] 185
Corrosion Engineering, Science and Technology [54269] 900
Environmental Engineering
[54375] 7,000
International Heat Treatment and Surface Engineering [54627]
International Journal of Cast Metals Research [54638]
International Journal of Damage Mechanics
[54643] .... (Controlled) 160
International Journal of Electronic Security and Digital Forensics [54647]
Journal of Building Physics
[54716] .... ‡200
Journal of Composite Materials
[54728] 800
Journal of the Energy Institute [54743]
Journal of Intelligent Material Systems and Structures
[54770] 300
Journal of NeuroEngineering and Rehabilitation (JNER) [54785]
Journal of Sandwich Structures and Materials [54815]
Journal of Strain Analysis for Engineering Design [54825]
Materials Science and Technology [54913]
Municipal Engineer [54962]
Nature Materials [54972]
Personal and Ubiquitous Computing [55070]
Planning in London
[55091] .... (Combined) 1,000
Professional Engineering
[55130] .... (Combined) 90,000
Prototype [55147]
SPE Review
[55261] .... (Controlled) 8,500

Surface Engineering [55281]
Tribology International [55341]

Loughborough
Pattern Analysis & Applications
[55486] .... (Paid) 950
Thin-Walled Structures [55488]

Machynlleth
Clean Slate [55522] 8,500

Manchester
Biochemical Engineering Journal [55544]
International Journal of Mechanical Engineering Education [55560]
Progress in Planning [55575]

Middlesex
International Journal of Dynamics of Fluids (IJDF) [55618]

Milton Keynes
Design Studies [55633]
International Journal of Forensic Engineering [55638]

Northill
Historical Metallurgy [55717]

Nottingham
Geomechanics and Geoengineering [55756]
International Journal of Design Engineering [55759]
Journal of Molecular Graphics and Modeling [55764]
Optical and Quantum Electronics [55768]

Olney
International Journal of Biomedical Engineering and Technology [55792]
International Journal of Computational Materials Science & Surface Engineering [55796]
International Journal of Forensic Engineering and Management [55806]
International Journal of Materials & Structural Integrity [55823]
International Journal of Nanomanufacturing [55825]
International Journal of Product Development [55827]
International Journal of Product Sound Quality [55828]
International Journal of Teaching & Case Studies [55834]

Orpington
Journal of Automated Methods and Management in Chemistry [55853]

Oxford
Journal of Advanced Transportation
[56011] .... (Combined) 355
SIAM Journal on Optimization [56202]

Plymouth
The Hydrographic Journal
[56270] 2,000

Romsey
Photogrammetric Record [56407]

Sheffield
Fatigue & Fracture of Engineering Materials & Structures [56492]
International Journal of Systems Science [56502]

Stevenage
Computing and Control Engineering Journal [56599] 19,639
Engineering & Technology
[56603] 40,000
IEE Proceedings Microwaves, Antennas & Propagation [56609]

The Woman Engineer
[56620] 18,000

Sunbury-on-Thames
BTE Journal [56652] 21,000

Swansea
Applied Mathematical Modelling [56699]
Engineering Computations [56701]
International Journal of Numerical Methods for Heat & Fluid Flow [56702]

Tonbridge
Industrial Technology
[56755] .... ★21,296

Uxbridge
International Journal of Renewable Energy Technology [56798]

Wadhurst
International Cranes and Specialized Transport [56809] .... ‡14,381

Warwickshire
Engineering Integrity
[56858] 1,630

Whitley Bay
Applied Thermal Engineering [56918]

Wrexham
International Journal of Engineering Systems Modelling and Simulation [56981]

ENTOMOLOGY
See also Natural History and Nature Study

AUSTRALIA
Canberra
Systematic and Applied Acarology [41713]

CZECH REPUBLIC
Ceske Budejovice
Folia Parasitologica [43605]
Zlin
Folia Heyrovskyana [43642]

GERMANY
Berlin
Deutsche Entomologische Zeitschrift [44171]
Biebergemund
Entomologia Generalis [44244]
Stuttgart
Aquatic Insects [44661]

HUNGARY
Budapest
Acta Phytopathologica et Entomologica Hungarica [44818]

INDIA
Jodhpur
Indian Journal of Applied Entomology [45219]
Kariavattom
Entomon [45241] .... (Paid) 400

IRAN
Tehran
Applied Entomology and Phytopathology [45887]

JAPAN
Koriyama
Journal of Acarological Society of Japan [46447] .... (Paid) 350

Mito
Entomological Science [46513]
Nagano
New Entomologist [46537]
Osaka
Japanese Journal of Environment, Entomology and Zoology [46618]
Tokyo
Applied Entomology and Zoology
[46746] .... (Paid) 1,900
Kogane [46955]
Lamellicornia [46957]
Medical Entomology and Zoology [46965]

KENYA
Nairobi
International Journal of Tropical Insect Science [47185]

NETHERLANDS
Amsterdam
Entomologia Experimentalis et Applicata [47967]
Leiden
Insect Systematics & Evolution [48678]
International Journal of Myriapodology [48681]
Terrestrial Arthropod Reviews [48727]

PAKISTAN
Faisalabad
Journal of Entomology [49267]

PHILIPPINES
Laguna
The Philippine Entomologist
[49508] .. .. (Paid) 1,000

RUSSIA
Moscow
Acarina [49867]
Russian Entomological Journal [49974]
Saint Petersburg
Entomological Review [50021]

SLOVENIA
Ljubljana
Acta Entomologica Slovenica [50335]

REPUBLIC OF SOUTH AFRICA
Hatfield
African Entomology [50521]

UGANDA
Kampala
African Crop Science Journal [51583]

UNITED KINGDOM
Ascot
Insect Conservation and Diversity [52139]
Cambridge
International Journal of Tropical Insect Science [52838]
Cardiff
Bulletin of Entomological Research [52926]
Chatham
Medical and Veterinary Entomology [52959]
Leeds
British Dragonfly Society Journal [53758]

Trade, Technical, and Professional Publications

London
AES Bug Club Magazine **[53914]**
The Bulletin **[54156]**
SAA **[55212]**
Midlothian
Agricultural and Forest Entomology
[55626]
Oxford
Insect Science **[55990]**
Physiological Entomology **[56157]**
Penicuik
Agricultural and Forest Entomolgy
[56242]
Wallingford
Review of Agricultural Entomology
[56824]
Review of Medical and Veterinary
Entomology **[56826]** 290

ETHNIC AND MINORITY STUDIES

AUSTRALIA
Garran
National Indigenous Times **[41877]**

BELGIUM
Leuven
Iranica Antiqua **[42899]**

GERMANY
Flensburg
ECMI Journal on Ethnopolitics and
Minority Issues in Europe **[44354]**
Gottingen
Diversities **[44395]**

INDIA
Chennai
Journal of Oriental Research
[45050] .... (Paid) 500
Delhi
Studies of Tribes and Tribals **[45104]**
New Delhi
Muslim & Arab Perspectives
[45628] .... (Paid) 3,000

IRAN
Tehran
Iran **[45891]**

REPUBLIC OF KOREA
Seoul
Koreana
[47283] .... (Non-paid) 5,500

KUWAIT
Safat
Annals of the Arts and Social
Sciences **[47333]**

LEBANON
Beirut
Haigazian Armenological Review
[47395]

NETHERLANDS
Amsterdam
Wordt Vervolgd
[48271] .... (Non-paid) 32,500
Apeldoorn
Direct Mailings
[48275] .... (Non-paid) 55,000
Dordrecht
Journal of Immigrant and Minority
Health **[48468]**

Leiden
China Information **[48661]**
Journal of Asian and African Studies
[48689]
Medieval Encounters **[48708]**
Utrecht
Netherlands Quarterly of Human
Rights **[48764]**

SPAIN
Las Palmas de Gran Canaria
Atlantica Internacional **[50720]**
Valladolid
Critical Approaches to Ethnic Ameri-
can Literature **[50848]**

SRI LANKA
Kandy
Ethnic Studies Report **[50906]**

SWITZERLAND
Geneva
Refugee Survey Quarterly **[51159]**

UNITED KINGDOM
Abingdon
Asian Population Studies **[51708]**
Ethnic and Racial Studies **[51774]**
Ethnography & Education **[51775]**
Ethnopolitics **[51777]**
Immigrants & Minorities **[51811]**
Iranian Studies **[51858]**
Irish Studies Review **[51860]**
Journal of Intercultural Studies
[51909]
Journal of Muslim Minority Affairs
[51924]
Latin American and Caribbean Ethnic
Studies **[51966]**
Nationalism & Ethnic Politics **[51989]**
Race, Ethnicity and Education
[52033]
Sikh Formations **[52058]**
Bath
Gothic Studies **[52243]**
Brighton
Journal of Ethnic and Migration Stud-
ies (JEMS) **[52620]**
Cambridge
Modern Asian Studies
[52870] 1,100
London
Africa **[53915]**
Austrian Studies **[53982]**
Bosnia Report **[54100]**
Disability and Society **[54328]**
Ethnicities **[54386]**
Ethnography **[54387]**
Race & Class **[55168]**
SAGE Race Relations Abstracts
[55216]
Studies in Ethnicity and Nationalism
[55273]
Manchester
Journal of Semitic Studies **[55566]**
Middlesbrough
Critical Public Health **[55611]**
Oxford
French History **[55961]**
Journal of Islamic Studies **[56046]**
Journal of Refugee Studies **[56065]**
Poole
Black Theology **[56279]**
Surrey
Mediterranean Studies **[56668]**
Wallingford
Postharvest News and Information
[56823] 150

FIRE FIGHTING

AUSTRALIA
Box Hill
Fire Australia **[41632]**

FRANCE
Paris
Combustion and Flame **[44033]**

IRELAND
Dublin
FireCall **[45958]** 1,500

ITALY
Cinisello Balsamo
Sicurezza **[46135]**
Palermo
Annals of Burns and Fire Disasters
[46207]

UNITED KINGDOM
Buckhurst Hill
Secure Times **[52753]** .... ‡9,306
Edinburgh
Fire Safety Journal **[53276]**
Kingston upon Thames
Firefighter **[53721]**
London
Fire International **[54460]**
Journal of Fire Sciences
[54754] 350
Moreton-in-Marsh
Fire Prevention **[55650]** 15,000
Fire Risk Management
[55651] 15,000
Shoreham-by-Sea
Fire Times
[56523] .... (Controlled) ‡5,000

FIREARMS

DENMARK
Brondby
Skyttebladet **[43653]**

FISH AND COMMERCIAL FISHERIES

INDIA
Cochin
Central Marine Fisheries Research
Institute Bulletin **[45071]**
Central Marine Fisheries Research
Institute Special Publication
[45072]
Fishery Technology
[45073] .... (Paid) 750
Indian Journal of Fisheries
[45075] 500

IRAN
Tehran
Iranian Journal of Fisheries Science
[45903]

IRELAND
Kilcar
Marine Times Newspaper
[46025] 6,250

JAPAN
Tokyo
Fisheries Science **[46825]**

MALAYSIA
Kuala Lumpur
INFOFISH International
[47605] 7,000
Penang
NAGA **[47690]**

NETHERLANDS
Dordrecht
Reviews in Fish Biology and
Fisheries **[48557]**

NEW ZEALAND
Auckland
New Zealand Fishing World
[48811] .... ★9,391

NIGERIA
Jos
Journal of Aquatic Sciences **[49125]**
Makurdi
Nigerian Journal of Fisheries **[49146]**

NORWAY
Bergen
Aquaculture Nutrition **[49190]**

PAKISTAN
Faisalabad
Journal of Aquaculture Feed Science
and Nutrition **[49263]**
Journal of Fisheries International
[49268]
Research Journal of Fisheries and
Hydrobiology **[49288]**

PHILIPPINES
Quezon City
Asian Fisheries Science **[49581]**

POLAND
Szczecin
Acta Ichthyologica et Piscatoria
[49676]
Warsaw
Archives of Polish Fisheries **[49692]**

SPAIN
Esporles
Fisheries Research **[50714]**

TURKEY
Trabzon
Turkish Journal of Fisheries and
Aquatic Sciences **[51578]**

UGANDA
Jinja
African Journal of Tropical Hydrobiol-
ogy and Fisheries **[51582]**

UNITED KINGDOM
Edinburgh
Fish Farmer
[53277] .... (Combined) 6,500
Leeds
Fish Friers Review **[53766]**
Lerwick
Shetland Fishing News
[53842] .... (Combined) 1,440
Rickmansworth
International Aquafeed **[56394]**
West Bridgford
Fish **[56888]** 1,500

Circulation: ★ = ABC; △ = BPA; ◆ = CAC; • = CCAB; ❑ = VAC; ⊕ = PO Statement; ‡ = Publisher's Report; Boldface figures = sworn; Light figures = estimated.

FLOORING AND FLOOR COVERING

RUSSIA

Moscow
Flooring Professional Magazine
[49904] 8,000

SINGAPORE

Singapore
PANELS & FURNITURE ASIA
[50234]

UNITED KINGDOM

Bradford
International Carpet Bulletin (ICB)
[52471] .... (Combined) 1,500

London
Carpet & Flooring Retail (CFR)
[54183] .... (Combined) 4,045

Tunbridge Wells
CFJ Contract Flooring Journal
[56778] .... (Combined) ★6,888
Contracts Flooring Journal
[56779] .... ★6,888

Wadhurst
Construction Europe
[56805] .... ★14,624

FLORISTS AND FLORICULTURE

See also Landscape Architecture; Seed and Nursery Trade

AUSTRALIA

Tullamarine
Australasian Flowers
[42646] .. .. (Paid) ‡1,009

ITALY

Vernasca
Flortecnica Data e Fiori
[46279] .... (Controlled) 6,800

NEW ZEALAND

Wanganui
New Zealand Camellia Bulletin
[48995]

POLAND

Warsaw
Hacquetia [49715]

SWITZERLAND

Bassersdorf
Seed Science and Technology
[51067]

UNITED KINGDOM

Cheshunt
Clematis International [52987]

Kippen
Fusion Flowers [53726]

London
Florist & Wholesale Buyer
[54466] .. .. (Combined) ★9,966
The Flower Arranger
[54468] 80,000

FOOD AND GROCERY TRADE

See also Baking; Confectionaries and Frozen Dairy Products; Fruit, Fruit Products, and Produce Trade; Milk and Dairy Products

AUSTRALIA

Wahroonga
What's New in Food Technology and
  Manufacturing [42680] .. .... ★6,892

DENMARK

Glostrup
Levnedsmiddel Bladet
  [43709] .... ‡3,400
Plus Process [43712] .... ‡5,400
Scandinavian Food & Drink
  [43715] .... ‡7,538

GERMANY

Frankfurt am Main
Deutscher Fachuerlag GmbH
  [44365] 89,208

Nuremberg
Food Marketing & Technology
  [44611] 18,500
Food Technologie [44612] 11,668

GREECE

Athens
Trofima kai Pota [44757] 3,809

HUNGARY

Budapest
Fakanal [44829] ...... (Paid) ‡25,162
Fakanal Recepttar [44830] ... 26,425

INDIA

Cochin
Cashew Bulletin [45070] 700
Indian Cashew Journal
  [45074] .... (Paid) 2,000
Spices India [45076] ... (Paid) 3,000

Mumbai
Modern Food Processing [45414]

IRELAND

Blackrock
Hotel & Catering Review [45920]

Dublin
Food Ireland
  [45959] .... (Combined) 2,000
Food & Wine Magazine
  [45960] .... ★7,429

Greystone
Easy Food [46023] .. .. ★27,599
Easyhealth [46024]

ITALY

Milan
Italian Food Machines
  [46179] 4,000
Italian Magazine Food Processing
  [46180] 5,500
Rassegna Alimentare
  [46192] 6,000

Rome
Genes & Nutrition [46231]

JAPAN

Tokyo
Food Science and Technology
  Research [46826]

LEBANON

Beirut
Middle East Food (MEF)
  [47399] .... (Combined) ‡7,182

MALAYSIA

Kuching
Pepper Market Bulletin
  [47667] .... (Combined) 390

NETHERLANDS

Amsterdam
Trends in Food Science &
  Technology [48262]

Dordrecht
Food Biophysics [48389]

NEW ZEALAND

Auckland
Catering Plus [48788] .... ‡2,528

Christchurch
Retirement Today
  [48878] .... (Combined) 40,000

NIGERIA

Lagos
African Journal of Food Science
  [49132]

REPUBLIC OF SOUTH AFRICA

Gauteng
Food Review [50481] 5,000

SPAIN

Madrid
Eurocarne [50758] 6000

Reus
The Cracker [50828] 2,500

SWEDEN

Uppsala
Var Foda
  [51053] .... (Combined) 5,000

SWITZERLAND

Basel
Merum [51064]

Geneva
International Journal of Food Safety,
  Nutrition and Public Health [51121]

Glarus
Lebensmittel Industrie
  [51176] .. .. (Combined) 4,300

UNITED KINGDOM

Ashford
Food Policy [52140]

Belfast
Hospitality Review [52285]
Ulster Grocer [52297]

Chepstow
Sandwich and Snack News
  [52983] 7,000

Crawley
British Baker
  [53099] .. .. (Combined) ★6,074
Food Manufacture
  [53103] .... (Controlled) 15,491
PubChef [53111]

Driffield
International Food Hygiene
  [53203] .... (Controlled) 10,000

Faversham
Milk Industry [53383] 2,000

Glasgow
scottish grocer [53447] .... ★8,217

Kings Langley
The Grocery Trader
  [53710] .... (Combined) 21,318

Leeds
Fish Friers Review [53766]

Middleton
SOFHT Focus [55622] 3,000

Milton Keynes
Food Marketing & Manufacturing
  [55635] .... (Controlled) 10,219

Oxted
Biscuit World [56235] 4,335

Reading
Food Science and Technology
  Abstracts [56317]

Rushden
Nutrition & Food Science [56426]

Tunbridge Wells
Eurofood [56782]

Ugley Green
Health Food Business Magazine
  [56794] .... (Controlled) 3,552

FOOD PRODUCTION

AUSTRALIA

Cleveland
Good Fruits & Vegetables [41767]

Wahroonga
What's New in Food Technology and
  Manufacturing [42680] .. .. ★6,892

COTE D'IVOIRE

Abidjan
Sciences & Nature [43557]

DENMARK

Frederiksberg
Acta Agriculturae
  Scandinavica—Section C, Food
  Economics [43688]

Glostrup
Levnedsmiddel Bladet
  [43709] .... ‡3,400
Plus Process [43712] .... ‡5,400
Scandinavian Food & Drink
  [43715] .... ‡7,538

GERMANY

Berlin
Innovative Food Science and Emerg
  ing Technologies [44191]

Bonn
Ecology and Farming
  [44255] 2,000

Frankfurt
Allgemeine Fleischer Zeitung [44357]

Munich
SG Susswarenhandel
  [44581] 6,500

Nuremberg
Food Marketing & Technology
  [44611] 18,500
Food Technologie [44612] 11,668

GREECE

Athens
Trofima kai Pota [44757] 3,809

HUNGARY
Budapest
Acta Alimentaria **[44805]**
Nok Lapja Konyha
[44861] .. .. (Paid) 37,893

INDIA
Cochin
Indian Cashew Journal
[45074] .. .. (Paid) 2,000
Hisar
Research on Crops **[45136]**
Mumbai
Modern Food Processing **[45414]**
New Delhi
Prevention of Food Adulteration
Cases **[45637]**
VATIS Update Food Processing
[45663] 500

IRELAND
Dublin
Food Ireland
[45959] .... (Combined) 2,000

ITALY
Grugliasco
International Journal of Food
Microbiology **[46155]** 450
Milan
Agro Food
[46162] .... (Combined) 7,000
Italian Food Machines
[46179] 4,000
Italian Magazine Food Processing
[46180] 5,500
Rassegna Alimentare
[46192] 6,000
Pinerolo
Ingredienti Alimentari **[46217]**
Rome
Genes & Nutrition **[46231]**

JAPAN
Tokyo
European Food Research and
Technology **[46816]**

KENYA
Nairobi
East African Agricultural and Forestry
Journal **[47179]**
Journal of Food Technology in Africa
[47188]

MALAYSIA
Kuala Lumpur
Journal of Tropical Agriculture & Food
Science **[47608]** .. .. (Paid) 500
Kuching
Pepper Market Bulletin
[47667] .... (Combined) 390

NETHERLANDS
Amsterdam
Food Microbiology **[47987]**
Tailoring Biotechnologies **[48240]**
Bussum
Current Nutrition & Food Science
[48291]

NIGERIA
Calabar
Global Journal of Agricultural
Sciences **[49069]**

Oshodi
Nigerian Food Journal **[49160]**
Owerri
Animal Production Research
Advances **[49161]**
Port Harcourt
Journal of Technology and Education
in Nigeria **[49168]**

PAKISTAN
Faisalabad
Journal of Agronomy **[49259]**
Journal of Aquaculture Feed Science
and Nutrition **[49263]**
Journal of Food Technology **[49269]**

POLAND
Poznan
Acta Scientarum Polonorum - Tech-
nologia Alimentaria **[49673]**

SINGAPORE
Singapore
Food & Beverage Asia **[50150]**

SLOVENIA
Ljubljana
Acta Agriculturae Slovenica **[50333]**

REPUBLIC OF SOUTH AF-
RICA
Gauteng
Food Review **[50481]** 5,000
Grahamstown
International Journal of Tropical Agri-
culture and Food Systems **[50499]**
Stellenbosch
International Journal of Postharvest
Technology and Innovation **[50631]**

SPAIN
Burjasot
Food Science and Technology
International **[50711]**
Reus
The Cracker **[50828]** 2,500

SWEDEN
Uppsala
Var Foda
[51053] .... (Combined) 5,000

SWITZERLAND
Geneva
International Journal of Food Safety,
Nutrition and Public Health **[51121]**
Glarus
Lebensmittel Industrie
[51176] .... (Combined) 4,300

UNITED KINGDOM
Abingdon
International Journal of Food Sci-
ences & Nutrition **[51835]**
Journal of Nutritional & Environmen-
tal Medicine **[51926]**
Belfast
Hospitality Review **[52285]**
Bradford
British Food Journal **[52438]**
Bristol
Food Quality and Preference **[52671]**
Burnham
World Food Regulation Review
[52768]

Chepstow
Sandwich and Snack News
[52983] 7,000
Coventry
The Organic Way **[53089]** 30,400
Crawley
Food Manufacture
[53103] .. .. (Controlled) 15,491
Meat Trades Journal
[53108] *5,574
PubChef **[53111]**
Driffield
International Food Hygiene
[53203] .. :...... (Controlled) 10,000
International Pig Topics **[53205]**
Egham
Journal of Stored Products Research
[53329]
London
African Farming and Food
Processing **[53920]** 10,755
Food Science and Technology
[54478]
International Journal of Agricultural
Sustainability **[54633]**
Journal of the Science of Food and
Agriculture **[54816]**
Lebensmittel-Wissenschaft und-Technologie
[54863]
Middleton
SOFHT Focus **[55622]** 3,000
Oxford
Canadian Journal of Agricultural
Economics **[55901]**
Journal of Food Processing and
Preservation **[56035]**
Oxted
Biscuit World **[56235]** 4,335
Potato Processing International
[56237] .... (Controlled) ‡3,616
Reading
Food Science and Technology
Abstracts **[56317]**
Rickmansworth
Ingredients, Health & Nutrition
[56393] .... (Controlled) 4,682
Rugby
Food & Bioproducts Processing
[56419]
Wallingford
World's Poultry Science Journal
[56831]

FORESTRY

BANGLADESH
Gazipur
Annals of Bangladesh Agriculture
[42819] .... (Paid) 300

BRAZIL
Manaus
Acta Amazonica **[42987]**
Santa Maria
Ciencia Rural **[43016]**
Vicosa
Revista Arvore **[43066]**

PEOPLE'S REPUBLIC OF
CHINA
Beijing
Wood Industry **[43224]** 5,000
Nanjing
Chemistry and Industry of Forest
Products **[43457]**

ETHIOPIA
Haramaya
East African Journal of Sciences
[43805]

FINLAND
Helsinki
Paperi Ja Puu **[43855]** 4,000
Rajamaki
Teho **[43905]** .. .. (Paid) 4,662

FRANCE
Champenoux
Annals of Forest Science **[43929]**

GERMANY
Gottingen
Forest Policy and Economics **[44398]**

GHANA
Kumasi
Ghana Journal of Forestry **[44735]**

INDIA
Jodhpur
Advances in Horticulture and Forestry
[45212]

JAPAN
Tokyo
Forestry Technology **[46827]**
Journal of Forest Research **[46898]**
Journal of Japanese Forestry Society
[46915] .. .. (Paid) 4,000
Journal of Wood Science **[46946]**
Tree Physiology
[47053] .... (Paid) 600
(Non-paid) 150

KENYA
Nairobi
East African Agricultural and Forestry
Journal **[47179]**

MALAYSIA
Selangor
Journal of Tropical Forest Science
[47712] .... (Paid) 250

NETHERLANDS
Amsterdam
Forest Ecology and Management
[47988]
Dordrecht
Agroforestry Systems **[48323]**
Frontiers of Forestry in China **[48398]**

NIGERIA
Obubra
Journal of Agriculture, Forestry and
the Social Sciences **[49158]**

PAKISTAN
Faisalabad
Plant Sciences Research **[49279]**
Peshawar
Pakistan Journal of Forestry
[49394] .... (Paid) 400

POLAND
Lublin
Annals of Agricultural and Environ-
mental Medicine **[49672]**

REPUBLIC OF SOUTH AF-
RICA
Pretoria
Southern Forest **[50606]**

Circulation: ★ = ABC; △ = BPA; ◆ = CAC; • = CCAB; ❑ = VAC; ⊕ = PO Statement; ‡ = Publisher's Report; Boldface figures = sworn; Light figures = estimated.

SWEDEN

Knivsta
Scandinavian Journal of Forest
   Research **[50972]**

Umea
Journal of Forest Economics **[51046]**

UNITED REPUBLIC OF TAN-ZANIA

Morogoro
Tanzania Journal of Forestry and Nature Conservation **[51407]**

TURKEY

Ankara
Turkish Journal of Agriculture and
   Forestry **[51503]**

UGANDA

Kampala
African Crop Science Journal **[51583]**

UNITED KINGDOM

Burnham
International Pest Control **[52766]**

Cardiff
Bulletin of Entomological Research
   [52926]

Castleford
Wood Protection **[52953]**

Cheltenham
Arboricultural Journal
   [52963] 2,300

Craven Arms
Commonwealth Forestry News
   [53098]

Edinburgh
Forestry Journal **[53278]** 1,100

Liverpool
Biological Conservation **[53869]**

Newton Stewart
Scottish Forestry **[55699]** 1,500

Oxford
Forestry **[55960]**

Penicuik
Agricultural and Forest Entomolgy
   [56242]

Tring
Quarterly Journal of Forestry
   [56772] ...:...... (Controlled) 4,500

FRUIT, FRUIT PRODUCTS, AND PRODUCE TRADE
See also Food and Grocery
Trade

AUSTRALIA

Cleveland
Good Fruits & Vegetables **[41767]**

Mildura
Australian Citrus News
   [42106] .... (Combined) 3,000

Normanhurst
The Olive Press **[42151]**

FRANCE

Morieres Les Avignon
L'Echo vegetable
   [44009] .. .. (Paid) 10,000

NEW ZEALAND

Tauranga
Avoscene **[48980]**

UNITED KINGDOM

Colchester
Grow Your Own **[53036]**

London
Fresh Produce Journal
   [54482] .... (Controlled) 3,500

Peterborough
British Sugar Beet Review
   [56253] .... (Non-paid) 14,000

FUNERAL DIRECTORS

UNITED KINGDOM

Abingdon
Mortality **[51987]**

Maidstone
Pharos International **[55530]**

Solihull
Funeral Director Monthly
   [56563] 2,000

Worthing
Funeral Service Journal
   [56972] .. .. (Paid) 2,400

FURNITURE AND FURNISHINGS

AUSTRALIA

Templestowe
FB Magazine **[42616]** 8,960

FINLAND

Lahti
Woodworking Puuntyosto WIN
   [43903] 5,000

POLAND

Warsaw
Dom & Wnetrze **[49705]** ..... ‡20,283

SINGAPORE

Singapore
Asian Furniture **[50109]**
FDM Asia **[50148]**
Global Sources Home Products
   [50158]
PANELS & FURNITURE ASIA
   [50234]

SPAIN

Barcelona
El Mueble **[50670]** .... ‡217,434
El Mueble Casas de Campo
   [50671] .... ‡43,155
El Mueble Cocinas y Banos
   [50672] .... ‡20,535
Habitania **[50676]** .... ‡44,184

Madrid
Cosas de Casa **[50740]** .... ‡183,118

UKRAINE

Kiev
Lyubimaya Datcha
   [51601] .... ‡20,000

UNITED KINGDOM

Battle
Furniture News
   [52269] .... (Non-paid) 7,000
Furniture Production
   [52270] .... (Non-paid) 5,311

Coventry
Housing **[53084]**

East Budleigh
Tools and Trades **[53234]**

Haywards Heath
Furniture History
   [53548] .... (Combined) 1,750

Lewes
Furniture and Cabinetmaking **[53849]**

London
Cabinet Maker
   [54163] .... (Combined) 4,634
Ideal Home **[54582]**
Live It **[54877]**
Period Living **[55068]**

GENERAL MERCHANDISE
See also Retail; Clothing;
Cosmetics and Toiletries;
Drugs and Pharmaceuticals

PEOPLE'S REPUBLIC OF CHINA

Hong Kong
HKTDC Enterprise
   [43306] .... (Paid) 150,000
HKTDC Gifts, Premium & Stationery
   [43310]
Research Journal of Textile and
   Apparel **[43380]** .... (Paid) 1,000

GREECE

Athens
NY-LONDON Shows **[44753]**
Paris Catwalks **[44754]**
Passerella di Donna **[44755]**

NETHERLANDS

Maarssen
Trend Boutique
   [48734] .... (Combined) 2,200

SINGAPORE

Singapore
Electronic & Components **[50143]**

SPAIN

Madrid
Distribucion Actualidad **[50752]**

UNITED KINGDOM

Bedford
Alert Magazine **[52271]**

Glasgow
Scottish Local Retailer
   [53449] 8,363

Ilfracombe
Catalogue & E-business
   [53641] 8,500

London
Retail Newsagent **[55195]**

Norwich
Cigar Buyer Magazine **[55728]**

GENETICS
See also Science (General)

AUSTRALIA

Brisbane
Twin Research and Human Genetics
   [41653]

Collingwood
Reproduction, Fertility and
   Development **[41796]**

Parkville
Tissue Antigens **[42232]**

BRAZIL

Ribeirao Preto
Genetics and Molecular Biology
   [42998]
Genetics and Molecular Research
   [42999]

BULGARIA

Sofia
Genetics and Breeding **[43100]**

PEOPLE'S REPUBLIC OF CHINA

Beijing
Journal of Genetics and Genomics
   [43206]

Shanghai
Cell Research **[43467]**

COTE D'IVOIRE

Abidjan
Agronomie Africaine **[43556]**

CZECH REPUBLIC

Ceske Budejovice
Folia Parasitologica **[43605]**

DENMARK

Frederiksberg
Genes, Brain and Behavior **[43690]**

EGYPT

Alexandria
International Journal of Biotechnology
   & Biochemistry (IJBB) **[43745]**

ESTONIA

Tartu
Agronomy Research **[43791]**

FRANCE

Jouy-en-Josas
Genetics Selection Evolution
   [43960] 1,000

Les Ulis
Apidologie **[43964]** 1,000

Montpellier
Infection, Genetics and Evolution
   [43978]

Nantes
Current Gene Therapy **[44012]**

Nice
Gene Therapy and Regulation
   [44015]

Paris
Current Genomics **[44035]**
European Journal of Medical
   Genetics **[44041]**

Perpignan
Plant Science **[44093]**

GERMANY

Berlin
Journal of International Biotechnology
   Law **[44205]**

Dusseldorf
Behavioural Brain Research **[44321]**

Giessen
Neurogenetics **[44388]**

Heidelberg
Plant Cell Reports **[44473]**
Theoretical and Applied Genetics
   [44478]

Circulation: ★ = ABC; △ = BPA; ◆ = CAC; • = CCAB; ❏ = VAC; ⊕ = PO Statement; ‡ = Publisher's Report; Boldface figures = sworn; Light figures = estimated.

Jena
Journal of Basic Microbiology [44489]

Karlsruhe
Protoplasma [44495]

Kiel
Marine Biology [44505]

HUNGARY
Budapest
Acta Biologica Hungarica [44808]

Martonvasar
Acta Agronomica Hungarica [44890]

INDIA
Bangalore
Journal of Genetics
[44971] ... . (Paid) 1,000
Delhi
International Journal of Human
Genetics [45099]
Jaipur
Indian Journal of Clinical
Biochemistry [45195]
Mumbai
Indian Journal of Human Genetics
[45381]
New Delhi
The Indian Journal of Crop Science
[45550]
Rajkot
Biotechnology [45707]

IRAN
Tehran
Iranian Biomedical Journal [45895]
Iranian Journal of Biotechnology (IJB)
[45898]

ISRAEL
Jerusalem
International Journal on Disability and
Human Development [46084]

ITALY
Ischia Porto
Marine Ecology [46156]

JAPAN
Chiba
DNA Research [46317]
Osaka
Genes & Genetic Systems
[46617] ... . (Paid) 2,000
Tokyo
Environmental Mutagen Research
[46813]
Journal of Human Genetics
[46906] ... . (Paid) 1,200

KENYA
Nairobi
African Journal of Biotechnology
[47170]

MEXICO
Mexico City
CIMMYT Annual Report
[47783] 5,000

NETHERLANDS
Amsterdam
Biochimica et Biophysica Acta (BBA)
[47906]
Biochimica et Biophysica Acta (BBA)-
Molecular Basis of Disease [47908]

Biochimica et Biophysica Acta (BBA)-
Molecular and Cell Biology of
Lipids [47909]
Bioelectrochemistry [47911]
Current Opinion in Genetics &
Development [47947]
Developmental & Comparative
Immunology [47955]
Journal of Autoimmunity [48053]
Journal of Cereal Science [48056]
Journal of Molecular Biology [48097]
Microbes and Infection [48157]
Microbial Pathogenesis [48158]
Plant Physiology and Biochemistry
[48205]
Plasmid [48206]
Protein Expression and Purification
[48217]
Trends in Genetics [48263]
Bussum
Current Bioinformatics [48283]
Dordrecht
Biodegradation [48331]
Biologia Plantarum [48333]
Cell Biology and Toxicology [48347]
Genetica [48405]
Journal of Bamboo and Rattan
[48442]
Journal of Bioethical Inquiry [48444]
Journal of Genetic Counseling
[48462]
Journal of Structural and Functional
Genomics [48494]
Plant Molecular Biology [48535]
Leiden
Animal Biology [48647]
Crustaceana [48665]

NEW ZEALAND
Albany
Evolutionary Bioinformatics Online
[48777]

NIGERIA
Ibadan
Nigerian Journal of Genetics [49096]
Ilorin
BIOKEMISTRI [49119]

PAKISTAN
Faisalabad
Global Journal of Molecular Sciences
[49243]
Journal of Molecular Genetics
[49273]

POLAND
Warsaw
Acta Biochimica Polonica [49678]
Acta Protozoologica [49682]
Balkan Journal of Medical Genetics
[49694]

RUSSIA
Moscow
Molecular Genetics, Microbiology &
Virology [49943]

SINGAPORE
Singapore
Gene Expression Patterns [50151]

SLOVAKIA
Bratislava
Acta Virologica [50316]

SLOVENIA
Ljubljana
Acta Agriculturae Slovenica [50333]

**REPUBLIC OF SOUTH AF-
RICA**
Pietermaritzburg
African Zoology [50566]
Tygerberg
African Journal of Herpetology
[50638]

SWEDEN
Goteborg
Current Genetics [50958]
Molecular Genetics and Genomics
[50959]
Lund
Genes, Chromosomes & Cancer
[50985]

SWITZERLAND
Geneva
International Journal of Biomedical
Nanoscience and Nanotechnology
[51104]

UGANDA
Kampala
African Crop Science Journal [51583]

UNITED KINGDOM
Basingstoke
Molecular Therapy [52224]
Cambridge
Journal of Biosocial Science
[52846] 500
Journal of Cell Science [52847]
Colchester
Biochemical Society Transactions
[53030]
Edinburgh
Cloning and Stem Cells [53263]
London
Asian Journal of Andrology [53975]
BMC Blood Disorders [54040]
BMC Cardiovascular Disorders
[54042]
BMC Dermatology [54048]
BMC Genetics [54057]
BMC Genomics [54058]
BMC Medical Genetics [54066]
Gene Therapy [54499]
Genetic Vaccines and Therapy
[54501]
Immunome Research [54586]
Journal of Medical Genetics
[54780] .... ‡1,495
Nature Reviews Genetics [54980]
Oncogene [55032]
Manchester
Biochemical Engineering Journal
[55544]
Comparative and Functional
Genomics [55548]
Oxford
Briefings in Bioinformatics [55889]
Human Molecular Genetics [55979]
Molecular Ecology [56106]
Pediatric Dermatology [56147]
Plant Breeding [56159]
Plant and Cell Physiology [56160]
Sutton
Mutagenesis [56689]
Wallingford
Journal of Agricultural Genomics
[56820]

GEOGRAPHY

AUSTRALIA
Hanwood
Journal of Applied Irrigation Science
[41940]

Perth
Geographical Research [42251]
Wollongong
Quaternary Science Reviews [42706]

BAHAMAS
Nassau
Bahamas Journal of Science
[42783] .... (Paid) 500

BELGIUM
Ixelles
Revue Belge de Geographie [42889]

**PEOPLE'S REPUBLIC OF
CHINA**
Beijing
Journal of Geographical Sciences
[43207] .... (Paid) ‡700
Science in China Series D [43218]

CZECH REPUBLIC
Prague
International Journal of Speleology
[43626]

GERMANY
Hamburg
Climate of the Past [44412]
Munich
Catena [44553]
Rostock
Demographic Research [44647]

HUNGARY
Budapest
Hungarian Studies [44837]
National Geographic Special
[44856] .... ‡16,000

INDIA
Allahabad
JP Journal of Fixed Point Theory and
Applications [44937]
New Delhi
ICSSR Journal of Abstracts and
Reviews [45529] .... (Paid) 550
TerraGreen [45658]

IRELAND
Dublin
Irish Geography [45974]

ITALY
Ischia Porto
Marine Ecology [46156]
Naples
Journal of Geochemical Exploration
[46201]

JAPAN
Fukuoka
Journal of the Speleological Society
of Japan [46344] .. .. (Paid) 250
Tokyo
Antarctic Record [46742] 1,000
Journal of Geodetic Society of Japan
[46901] .... (Paid) 775
National Geographic Japanese
Edition [46975] *84,124
Polar Bioscience [47020] 1,000

MALAYSIA
Kuala Lumpur
Journal of the Malaysian Branch of

Circulation: ★ = ABC; △ = BPA; ♦ = CAC; • = CCAB; ❑ = VAC; ⊕ = PO Statement; ‡ = Publisher's Report; Boldface figures = sworn; Light figures = estimated.

the Royal Asiatic Society
[47606] .. .. (Paid) 1,000
Malaysian Journal of Tropical
Geography [47620] ..... (Paid) 400

NETHERLANDS
Amsterdam
Global and Planetary Change
[48003]
Journal of Arid Environments [48049]

Dordrecht
Aerobiologia [48321]
Boundary-Layer Meteorology [48335]
GeoInformatica [48406]
Journal of Geographical Systems
[48463]

Houten
Geophysical Prospecting
[48640] .... ‡8,841

Utrecht
Journal of Economic and Social
Geography [48762]
Tijdschrift voor economische en so-
ciale geografie [48766]

NEW ZEALAND
Auckland
New Zealand Geographer [48813]
New Zealand Journal of Geography
[48816]

POLAND
Warsaw
Geodesy and Cartography [49713]
Geologija [49714]

RUSSIA
Irkutsk
Geography and Natural Resources
[49856]

SLOVENIA
Ljubljana
Acta Geographica Slovenica [50336]

REPUBLIC OF SOUTH AF-
RICA
Rondebosch
The South African Geographical
Journal [50623] .. .. (Paid) 400

SWEDEN
Stockholm
Geografiska Annaler, Series A, Physi-
cal Geography [51017]
Geografiska Annaler, Series B, Social
Geography [51018]
Tellus [51042]
Tellus [51043]

TAIWAN
Taipei
Journal of Geographical Science
[51353] .... (Paid) 500

UNITED KINGDOM
Aberystwyth
Gender, Place and Culture [51688]

Abingdon
Australian Geographer [51712]
Children's Geographies [51729]
Journal of Geography in Higher
Education [51901]
Tourism Geographies [52081]

Bristol
Survey Review [52732]

Cambridge
GEO [52822]

Kidlington
Journal of Rural Studies [53701]

Kingston upon Thames
Journal of Maps [53723]

London
The Cartographic Journal
[54185] 1,200
Cultural Geographies [54293]
Environment & Planning A [54373]
European Research in Regional
Science [54410]
European Urban and Regional
Studies [54411]
Family & Community History [54440]
The Holocene [54564]
Names [54969] .... (Paid) 850
Terrae Incognitae [55300]

Manchester
Journal of Transport Geography
[55568]

Middlesbrough
Spatial Practices [55612]

Nottingham
Planning Perspectives [55769]

Oxford
Area [55873]
Geographical Journal [55963]
New Zealand Geographer [56119]
The Professional Geographer
[56169]
Singapore Journal of Tropical
Geography [56204]
Transactions of the Institute of British
Geographers [56219]

Scotland
Scottish Geographical Journal
[56466]

Sheffield
Geography [56493] ..... (Paid) 4,500
Managing Leisure [56506]

Southampton
Journal of Economic Geography
[56573]

Swansea
Land Degradation & Development
[56703]

GEOLOGY

AUSTRALIA
Perth
AIG Journal [42242]

Sydney
Australian Journal of Earth Sciences
[42457]

Wollongong
Quaternary Science Reviews [42706]

BELGIUM
Brussels
Geologica Belgica [42856]

BULGARIA
Sofia
Bulgarian Geophysical Journal
[43096]
Geologica Balcanica [43101]

PEOPLE'S REPUBLIC OF
CHINA
Beijing
Acta Geologica Sinica [43166]

International Journal of Sediment
Research [43200]
Science in China Series D [43218]

Changchun
Journal of Jilin University Earth Science Edition [43240]

Nanjing
Palaeoworld [43454]

Wuhan
Earth Science [43519]
Earth Sciences [43521]

COTE D'IVOIRE
Abidjan
Afrique Science [43555]

CZECH REPUBLIC
Prague
International Journal of Speleology
[43626]

DENMARK
Copenhagen
Geologisk Tidsskrift [43671]

GERMANY
Berlin
Journal of Applied Geodesy [44203]

Gottingen
Advances in Geosciences [44389]

Hamburg
Climate of the Past [44412]

Heidelberg
Climate Dynamics [44446]
Computational Geosciences [44449]
Journal of Geodesy [44464]
Mineralium Deposita [44467]

Jena
Chemie der Erde / Geochemistry
[44487]

Katlenburg-Lindau
Natural Hazards and Earth System
Sciences (NHESS) [44501]

Landsberg
Journal of Soils and Sediments
[44516]

Mainz
Journal of Structural Geology [44541]

Munster
Review of Palaeobotany and
Palynology [44601]

Oldenburg
EARSeL eProceedings [44624]

Stuttgart
Contributions to Sedimentary
Geology [44664]
Neues Jahrbuch fur Geologie und
Palaontologie [44672]
Zeitschrift der Deutschen Geologis-
chen Gesellschaft [44685]
Zeitschrift fur Geomorphologie
[44686]

Wilhelmshaven
Geo-Marine Letters [44713]

HUNGARY
Budapest
Acta Geodaetica et Geophysica
Hungarica [44809]
Acta Geologica Hungarica [44810]

INDIA
Bangalore
Journal of the Geological Society of
India [44972] .... (Paid) 2,000

Hyderabad
Indian Academy of Geoscience
Journal [45171] .. .. (Paid) ★300

Kolkata
Geological Survey of India News
[45267] 2,500

New Delhi
Recent Researches in Geology
[45642]

IRAN
Tehran
Iranian Economic Review [45896]

IRELAND
Cork
Clays and Clay Minerals [45936]

Dublin
Quaternary International [45996]

ITALY
Naples
Journal of Geochemical Exploration
[46201]

Turin
Rock Mechanics and Rock
Engineering [46274]

JAPAN
Fukuoka
Caving Journal [46340]

Ibaraki
Journal of Japanese Association of
Hydrological Sciences [46393]

Tokyo
Bulletin of Engineering Geology and
the Environment [46770]
Bulletin of Volcanology [46771]
Contributions to Mineralogy and
Petrology [46797]
Earth Planets and Space
[46803] .... (Paid) 800
Environmental Chemistry Letters
[46811]
Geochemical Journal
[46830] .. .. (Paid) 1,300
Quaternary Research
[47029] .. .. (Paid) 1,900

Tsuchiura City
Resource Geology
[47109] .. .. (Paid) 1,400

Yamagata
Marine Micropaleontology [47125]

REPUBLIC OF KOREA
Seoul
International Journal of Applied Envi-
ronmental Sciences [47267]

MALAYSIA
Kuala Lumpur
Malaysian Journal of Science Series
B: Physical & Earth Sciences
[47619]

Petaling Jaya
The Malaysian Surveyor
[47701] .. .. (Paid) 3,000

NETHERLANDS
Amsterdam
Cretaceous Research [47941]
Geotextiles and Geomembranes
[47997]
Geothermics [47998]
Journal of Applied Geophysics
[48046]

Journal of Arid Environments [48049]
Journal of Asian Earth Sciences [48050]
Journal of Geodynamics [48081]
Journal of Volcanology and Geothermal Research [48131]
Ore Geology Reviews [48195]
Physics and Chemistry of the Earth [48202]
Planetary and Space Science [48204]
Precambrian Research [48213]

Delft
Sedimentary Geology [48314]

Dordrecht
Bulletin of Earthquake Engineering [48339]
Climatic Change [48352]
Journal of Atmospheric Chemistry [48440]
Surveys in Geophysics [48573]

Houten
Basin Research [48638]
First Break [48639] 25,000

NEW ZEALAND
Auckland
Meteorite [48804]

Wellington
New Zealand Journal of Geology and Geophysics [49025]
Tectonophysics [49035]

NIGERIA
Calabar
Global Journal of Geological Sciences [49072]

Ibadan
Journal of Mining and Geology [49091]

Zaria
Nigerian Journal of Soil & Environmental Research [49184]

PAKISTAN
Faisalabad
Online Journal of Earth Sciences [49275]

PHILIPPINES
Makati City
Philippine Journal of Development [49520] .... (Paid) 500

Manila
Philippine Labor Review [49557] .. .. (Paid) 2,000

Quezon City
Philippine Review of Economics [49610]

POLAND
Warsaw
Acta Geophysica [49679]
Artificial Satellites [49693]
Central European Journal of Geosciences [49700]
Geodesy and Cartography [49713]
Geologija [49714]

RUSSIA
Moscow
Doklady Earth Sciences [49897]
Geochemistry International [49906]
Geology of Ore Deposits [49907]
Geomagnetism and Aeronomy [49908]
Geotectonics [49909]

Izvestiya, Atmospheric and Oceanic Physics [49924]
Izvestiya, Physics of the Solid Earth [49925]
Lithology and Mineral Resources [49938]
Petrology [49955]
Stratigraphy and Geological Correlation [49991]

Novosibirsk
Earth's Cryosphere [50010]

SLOVAKIA
Kosice
Acta Montanistica Slovaca [50325]

REPUBLIC OF SOUTH AFRICA
Grahamstown
Nigerian Journal of Soil Science [50508]

Lynnwood Ridge
South African Journal of Science [50551]

Pretoria
Journal of African Earth Sciences [50593]

SPAIN
Madrid
Revista Espanola de Paleontologia [50797] 600

TAIWAN
Taipei
Acta Oceanographica Taiwanica [51328] .... (Paid) 800

THAILAND
Pathumthani
Geotechnical Engineering [51459] 1,120

TURKEY
Ankara
Turkish Journal of Earth Sciences [51508]

UNITED ARAB EMIRATES
Abu Dhabi
International Journal of Petroleum Science and Technology [51620]

UNITED KINGDOM
Bath
Geochemistry [52241]
Journal of the Geological Society [52248] .... (Paid) 500
Petroleum Geoscience [52254] 5,000
Quarterly Journal of Engineering Geology & Hydrogeology [52255] 4,000

Belfast
Glacial Geology and Geomorphology [52284]

Bristol
Hydrological Processes [52674]

Buxton
Cave & Karst Science [52778] .. .. (Paid) 1,000
Speleology [52779] .... (Combined) 1,200

Cambridge
Geological Magazine [52823] 850

Chester
Acta Crystallographica Section A [52991]

Synchrotron Radiation [53000]

Exeter
Geophysical & Astrophysical Fluid Dynamics [53359]

Leeds
Journal of Petrology [53768]

London
Applied Earth Science [53959] 500
Geochemical Transactions [54503]
Mineralogical Magazine [54937]

Milton Keynes
Geostandards & Geoanalytical Research [55636]

Norwich
Atmospheric Environment [55723]

Nottingham
Earthwise [55754] .... (Non-paid) 5,000
Geomechanics and Geoengineering [55756]

Oxford
Palaeontology [56140]

Southampton
Sedimentology [56578]

Swansea
Computers and Geotechnics [56700]

GERONTOLOGY

PEOPLE'S REPUBLIC OF CHINA
Hong Kong
Journal of the Hong Kong Geriatrics Society [43358] 1,800

FRANCE
Montrouge
Annales de Gerontologie [43981]

HUNGARY
Debrecen
Archives of Gerontology and Geriatrics [44887]
Gerontology and Geriatrics [44888]

ITALY
Milan
Aging Clinical and Experimental Research [46161]

NETHERLANDS
Amsterdam
Biochimica et Biophysica Acta (BBA)-Molecular Basis of Disease [47908]
Developmental & Comparative Immunology [47955]
European Journal of Ageing [47973]

Eindhoven
Gerontechnology [48591]

SWEDEN
Linkoping
The International Journal of Ageing and Later Life (IJAL) [50975]

UKRAINE
Kiev
Problems of Aging & Longevity [51606]

UNITED KINGDOM
Cambridge
Journal of Biosocial Science [52846] 500

London
Aging Health [53927]
Immunity & Ageing [54584]
Information Bulletin [54602]

Oxford
Geriatrics & Gerontology International [55964]

Penarth
Reviews in Clinical Gerontology [56241] 400

GIFTS, TOYS, AND NOVELTIES

AUSTRALIA
Pyrmont
Australian Giftguide [42272] ... 9,824

PEOPLE'S REPUBLIC OF CHINA
Hong Kong
HKTDC Gifts, Premium & Stationery [43310]
HKTDC Toys & Games [43315]

NETHERLANDS
Maarssen
Trends [48735] 4,500

SINGAPORE
Singapore
Global Sources Gifts & Premiums [50156]

UNITED KINGDOM
London
Progressive Gifts and Home Worldwide [55137] 6,700

Oxford
Journal of the History of Collections [56039]

Totternhoe
Military Illustrated [56765]
Model Airplane International [56766]
Model Military International [56767]
Radio Control Car RACER [56768]
Radio Control Model Flyer [56769]
Rotorworld [56770]
Tamiya Model Magazine International [56771]

GLASS AND CHINA
See also Ceramics

RUSSIA
Saint Petersburg
Glass Physics and Chemistry [50022]

UNITED KINGDOM
London
The Journal of Stained Glass [54824]

Oxford
Journal of the European Ceramic Society [56031]

Sheffield
Digest of Information and Patent Review [56491]
Glass Technology [56494] .... (Paid) 990
Physics & Chemistry of Glasses [56510] .... (Paid) 725

Thurso
Journal of the British Society of Scientific Glassblowers [56750]

Torquay
Torquay Pottery Collectors Society
[56758]

GOLF COURSE MANAGEMENT
See also Turf and Turf Maintenance

UNITED KINGDOM
Bingley
International Turfgrass Bulletin
[52327] .... (Controlled) 5,000

Weston-super-Mare
Golf Club Management
[56905] 1,400

GRAPHIC ARTS AND DESIGN

AUSTRALIA
Unley
Agenda [42659]

BELGIUM
Brussels
Ad!dict [42843]

Leuven
Image & Narrative [42897]

PEOPLE'S REPUBLIC OF CHINA
Hong Kong
International Journal of Image and
Graphics [43350]

Shanghai
Calligraphy [43464]
Calligraphy and Painting [43465]

FINLAND
Helsinki
Julkaisija
[43836] .... (Combined) ‡2,500

Jyvaskyla
ptah [43871]

FRANCE
Paris
Bloc Notes Publishing
[44030] .... (Combined) 8,000
Etapes
[44040] .... (Combined) 13,000
Intramuros
[44061] .... (Combined) 25,000

GREECE
Nauplion
International Journal of Arts and
Technology [44762]

IRELAND
Blackrock
Irish Printer [45922]

SINGAPORE
Singapore
International Journal of Image and
Graphics [50182]

SPAIN
Badajoz
Journal of Digital Contents [50645]

Madrid
Album [50727]

Visual [50815]

SWEDEN
Stockholm
CAP&Design
[51012] .. .. (Paid) 15,000

SWITZERLAND
Saint Gallen
Viscom [51225] 14,595

TAIWAN
Taipei
International Journal of Design
[51344]

UNITED KINGDOM
Abingdon
CoDesign [51732]
Journal of Urban Design [51953]

Bournemouth
Advanced Photoshop [52410]
Paint Shop Pro Photo [52418]
Photoshop Creative [52419]

Cheltenham
Grafik [52972] .... (Paid) 7,300

Edinburgh
International Journal of Humanities
and Arts Computing [53288]

Glasgow
eSharp [53417]

Milton Keynes
Design Studies [55633]

Oxford
The Design Journal [55924]

Sale
Qercus [56450]

Stoke-on-Trent
Design & Technology
[56629] 8,500

HAIRSTYLING
See also Cosmetics and Toiletries

AUSTRALIA
Pyrmont
ESTETICA Australia and New
Zealand [42278] ..... (Paid) ‡5,000

DENMARK
Herning
Frisorfaget [43721]

NORWAY
Oslo
Frisor [49199] .... (Paid) 2,500
(Non-paid) 10,000

SPAIN
Barcelona
Peluquerias Hair Styles [50693]
Tocado [50702] .... (Paid) 20,000

UNITED KINGDOM
Bristol
Blonde Hair [52648] 11,264
Hair Ideas [52673] .... ★62,289
Your Hair (Bristol)
[52738] .... ★30,727

London
Professional Beauty/LNE English
Edition
[55128] .... (Combined) 11,867

Watford
Professional Hairdresser
[56872] .... ★16,385

HANDICAPPED

AUSTRALIA
Lidcombe
Journal of Intellectual & Developmental Disability [42008]

AUSTRIA
Modling
The British Journal of Developmental Disabilities [42736]

FINLAND
Helsinki
Ketju [43841] .... (Paid) 3,000

GERMANY
Berlin
VdK Zeitung
[44235] .... (Paid) 1,121,210

INDIA
Bangalore
Asia Pacific Disability Rehabilitation
Journal [44949] .... (Paid) 2,000

SINGAPORE
Singapore
Integrator [50174] 800

UNITED KINGDOM
Abingdon
International Journal of Disability, Development and Education (IJDDE)
[51832]
Reading & Writing Quarterly
[52034] .... (Combined) 900

Beverley
Association Magazine
[52319] .... ‡1,800

Brentwood
Step Forward [52589] 2,000

Burford
Journal of Society for Companion
Animal Studies [52760] 500

Cambridge
Journal of Intellectual Disability Research (JIDR) [52856] 1,400

East Sussex
Catchword [53242]

Egham
Dyslexia Review [53328] 1,200

Exeter
Devon Link
[53351] .... (Non-paid) 7,000

High Wycombe
Deafness and Education International
[53572] .. .. (Paid) 2,000

Ipswich
Disability and Rehabilitation [53654]

London
Communication [54245] 12,000
DBI Review [54313] 3,000
Disability Now [54327] .... ★19,022
Occupational Therapy News
[55026] .... (Controlled) 22,000
The Parkinson Magazine
[55056] .... (Combined) 26,000
Talking Sense [55291] 5,000
Viewpoint [55371] .. ... (Paid) ‡6,300

Reading
FORWARD [56318] 80,000

Tamworth
British Journal of Special Education
[56717]

Worcestershire
British Journal of Learning Disabilities
[56966]
Journal of Applied Research in Intellectual Disability [56968]

HARDWARE

SINGAPORE
Singapore
Global Sources Hardware & DIY
[50157]

UNITED KINGDOM
Sittingbourne
DIY Week [56547]
Hardware & Garden Review [56548]

HEALTH AND FITNESS

AUSTRALIA
North Ryde
WellBeing [42201]

Perth
Australian Indigenous HealthBulletin
[42246]

Sydney
Slimming & Health
[42579] .... ★33,761

DENMARK
Copenhagen
Scandinavian Journal of Medicine
and Science in Sports [43682]

EGYPT
Cairo
Eastern Mediterranean Health
Journal [43754] 3,500

FINLAND
Helsinki
Vegaia [43864] 400

HUNGARY
Budapest
Nok Lapja Egeszseg
[44858] .. .. (Paid) 27,439

INDIA
Jodhpur
The Indian Anaesthetists' Forum
[45218]

Mumbai
Yoga and Total Health
[45450] .. .. (Paid) 2,000

IRELAND
Dublin
It's All About Living [45989]

Greystone
Easyhealth [46024]

JAPAN
Tokyo
European Journal of Applied
Physiology [46817]

MEXICO
Cuernavaca
Salud Publica de Mexico [47771]

Circulation: ★ = ABC; △ = BPA; ◆ = CAC; • = CCAB; ▫ = VAC; ⊕ = PO Statement; ‡ = Publisher's Report; Boldface figures = sworn; Light figures = estimated.

Mexico City
CIMMYT Annual Report
   [47783] 5,000

NEPAL
Kathmandu
Journal of the Nepal Medical
   Association
   [47839] .... (Paid) 1,250

NETHERLANDS
Amsterdam
Human Movement Science [48014]
Journal of Alzheimer's Disease
   [48041]

Dordrecht
Sport Sciences for Health [48567]

NEW ZEALAND
Christchurch
Retirement Today
   [48878] .... (Combined) 40,000

POLAND
Warsaw
Biomedical Human Kinetics [49697]
Physical Education and Sport
   [49747]
Przyjaciolka [49760] .... ‡460,291
Vita [49774] .. .. ‡72,677

**REPUBLIC OF SOUTH AF-
RICA**
Grahamstown
South African Journal Clinical
   Nutrition [50514]

SPAIN
Barcelona
Clara [50657] .... ‡161,874
Cuerpomente [50662] .. .. ‡66,291
Linea Saludable [50687] ..... ‡68,000
Mente Sana [50688] .... ‡118,513
Saber Vivir [50696] .... ‡142,798

SWEDEN
Lund
Scandinavian Journal of Food and
   Nutrition [50990]

SWITZERLAND
Bern
Ernahrungs Info [51072]

UKRAINE
Kiev
Edinstvennaya - Tvoye Zdorovye
   [51595] .. .. ‡265,000

UNITED KINGDOM
Abingdon
Global Public Health [51797]
The Journal of Positive Psychology
   [51934]

Altrincham
The Vegetarian [52104] 15,000

Barnsley
Future Fitness [52180]

Birmingham
Diversity in Health and Social Care
   [52340]
The Vegan [52372] 6,000

Brentwood
High Spirit [52574] *40,000

Cambridge
Nutrition Research Reviews [52879]

Public Health Nutrition [52888]
Colchester
Natural Health & Well-Being [53043]
Slim at Home [53051]

Essex
LighterLife [53340]

Lewes
Organic Life [53850]

London
Advances in Osteoporotic Fracture
   Management [53906]
British Journal of Intensive Care
   [54124]
Depression [54318]
Heart Failure Monitor [54546]
International Journal of Behavioral
   Nutrition and Physical Activity
   [54634]
Massage World [54911]
Yoga and Health
   [55431] .. .. (Paid) 15,000
YOGA Magazine [55432]

Manchester
International Journal of Health Promotion and Education [55559]

North Berwick
Alcohol and Alcoholism [55704]

Norwich
health24 [55732]

Oxford
Biostatistics [55883]
Journal of School Health [56070]

Preston
Maternal and Child Nutrition [56304]

Swansea
New Leaves [56704]

Ugley Green
Health Food Business Magazine
   [56794] .... (Controlled) 3,552

HEALTH AND
HEALTHCARE
**See also Hospitals and
Healthcare Institutions;
Medicine and Surgery; Nurs-
ing**

AUSTRALIA
Adelaide
International Journal of Computers in
   Healthcare [41508]
International Journal of Narrative
   Therapy and Community Work
   [41511]

Annerley
Balance [41556]

Barton
Australian Medicine
   [41576] ...... (Combined) ♦26,351

Bowen Hills
International Journal of Disability
   Management Research [41626]
Journal of Smoking Cessation
   [41628]

Callaghan
Women and Birth [41691]

Camberwell
Australian Journal of Physiotherapy
   [41695] .... (Combined) *11,000

Canberra
Communicable Diseases Intelligence
   [41704]
Environmental Modelling & Software
   [41705]

Chatswood
Natural Health & Beauty
   [41741] *11,545
Post Script [41743] *11,545

Curtin
Australian and New Zealand Journal
   of Public Health [41826]

Deakin
Australian Prescriber [41835]
Nutrition & Dietetics [41837]

East Sydney
Mental Health Matters [41851]

Frankston
Journal of Emergency Primary Health
   Care [41873]

Geelong
Rural and Remote Health [41880]

Glen Waverley
National Safety [41896]

Melbourne
AMTA Journal [42045] 7,000
SANE News [42084]
Sexual Health [42085]

North Sydney
NSW Public Health Bulletin [42211]

Perth
Australian Indigenous HealthBulletin
   [42246]

Richmond
Australian Occupational Therapy
   Journal [42302]

Saint Leonards
Australian Dental Journal
   [42330] .. .. (Paid) 10,000

Seddon West
Similia [42356]

Strawberry Hills
Australian Health Review [42395]

Sydney
Issues [42525]

Townsville
Journal of Rural and Tropical Public
   Health [42637]

Wagga Wagga
Chiropractic Journal of Australia
   [42667] 1,900

Westleigh
Australian and New Zealand Journal
   of Family Therapy [42699]

Womying
International Journal of Medical
   Sciences [42711]

AUSTRIA
Dornbirn
Forum Gesundheit Vorarlberg
   [42723] .... (Non-paid) 40,000

Vienna
Transplant International [42772]

BANGLADESH
Dhaka
Journal of Health, Population and
   Nutrition [42813]

BELGIUM
Brussels
Diabetes Voice [42848] 11,000

Diepenbeek
European Journal of Cancer
   Prevention [42879]

Genval
Health and Food
   [42886] .... (Non-paid) ⊕15,000

BRAZIL
Botafogo
International Braz J Urol
   [42954] 6,000
Revista Brasileira de Anestesiologia
   [42955]

Botucatu
Interface [42956]

Rio de Janeiro
Memorias do Instituto Oswaldo Cruz
   [43012]
Pesquisa Veterinaria Brasileira
   [43013]

Sao Paulo
Acta Cirurgica Brasileira [43021]
Arquivos Brasileiros de Oftalmologia
   [43023]
Arquivos de Neuro-Psiquiatria
   [43024]
Clinics [43036]
Sao Paulo Medical Journal [43050]

Vicosa
Ciencia & Saude Coletiva [43056]
Entomologia y Vectores [43058]
Journal of Epilepsy and Clinical
   Neurophysiology [43059]
Pro-Fono Revista de Atualizacao
   Cientifica [43062]
Radiologia Brasileira [43063]

Vila Olimpia
Arquivos Brasileiros de Cardiologia
   [43067]

CAMEROON
Yaounde
Clinics in Mother and Child Health
   [43129]

CHILE
Santiago
Women's Health Collection [43149]

**PEOPLE'S REPUBLIC OF
CHINA**
Beijing
World Journal of Gastroenterology
   [43225]

Hong Kong
Clinical Oral Implants Research
   [43291]
Hong Kong Physiotherapy Journal
   [43341]

Shanghai
Popular Medicine [43494]

CROATIA
Zagreb
Acta Clinica Croatica [43561]

CZECH REPUBLIC
Prague
Anaesthesiology & Intensive Critical
   Care Medicine
   [43609] .... (Paid) 1,800
Roska [43638]

DENMARK
Copenhagen
The Clinical Respiratory Journal
   [43659]

Frederiksberg
Pediatric Diabetes [43695]

EGYPT
Cairo
African Journal of Urology [43750]

Circulation: ★ = ABC; △ = BPA; ♦ = CAC; • = CCAB; ❑ = VAC; ⊕ = PO Statement; ‡ = Publisher's Report; Boldface figures = sworn; Light figures = estimated.

ETHIOPIA
Addis Ababa
Ethiopian Journal of Health
  Development [43800]

FINLAND
Helsinki
African Newsletter on Occupational
  Health and Safety [43814]
Asian-Pacific Newsletter [43819]
Ketju [43841] .... (Paid) 3,000

Kirkkonummi
TSW Holistic Health & Medicine
  [43876]

Tampere
Diabetes [43907]

FRANCE
Ferney-Voltaire
International Journal of Paediatric
  Dentistry [43948]
Medical Student International [43949]
World Hospitals and Health Services
  [43950] 2,500
World Medical Journal [43951]

Montrouge
Bulletin du Cancer [43982]
Bulletin Infirmier du Cancer [43983]
Cahiers d'etudes et de recherches
  francophones/Sante [43985]
Environnement, Risques & Sante
  [43986]
Epilepsies [43987]
Epileptic Disorders [43988]
Medecine therapeutique/Pediatrie
  [44001]
Sang Thrombose Vaisseaux [44006]

Paris
Annales Francaises d'Anesthesie et
  de Reanimation
  [44025] .. .. (Paid) 5,500
Leukemia [44068]
Revue du Soignant en Sante
  Publique [44082]

Saint Denis
Global Health Promotion [44103]

Villejuif
Sciences Sociales et Sante [44125]

GEORGIA
Tbilisi
Annals of Biomedical Research and
  Education [44130]

GERMANY
Berlin
Bundesgesundheitsblatt - Gesundheitsforschung - Gesundheitsschutz
  [44163]
Communication and Medicine
  [44166]
Journal of Vascular Research
  [44210]

Bochum
International Journal of Hygiene and
  Environmental Health [44250]

Darmstadt
Hospital Post [44308] .... ‡43,000

Edewecht
Rettungsdienst
  [44336] .. .. (Paid) 22,500

Erlangen
International Archives of Occupational
  and Environmental Health [44339]

Giessen
Andrologia [44383]

Gottingen
Allergy and Clinical Immunology
  International [44391]

Hamburg
Plan Post
  [44423] .. .. (Non-paid) 176,000

Heidelberg
Health Care Management Science
  [44458]
Pediatric Surgery International
  [44471]

Jena
Journal of Cancer Research and
  Clinical Oncology [44490]

Leinfelden-Echterdingen
Sicherheitsingenieur
  [44530] 5,020

Munich
Bayerisches Arzteblatt [44551]

Stuttgart
Thrombosis and Haemostasis
  [44683] .. .. (Paid) 3,180

Tutzing
BIO—Gesundheit fur Korper Geist
  und Seele [44695]

GREECE
Athens
Hellenic Orthodontic Review [44744]

Kapandriti
Anticancer Research [44760]

Rion
International Journal of Behavioural
  and Healthcare Research [44770]

GUATEMALA
Guatemala City
International Journal for Equity in
  Health [44785]

HUNGARY
Budapest
Acta Physiologica Hungarica [44817]
Magyar Pszichologiai Szemle [44846]
Mentalhigiene es Pszichoszomatika
  [44852]
Nok Lapja Egeszseg
  [44858] .. .. (Paid) 27,439

INDIA
Bangalore
Current Heart Failure Reports
  [44953]
Current Hematology Reports [44954]
Current Hepatitis Reports [44955]
International Journal of Yoga [44964]
Journal of Cutaneous and Aesthetic
  Surgery [44968]
Journal of Human Reproductive
  Sciences [44973]

Chandigarh
Indian Journal of Nephrology [45023]
Indian Journal of Community
  Medicine [45024]

Chennai
International Journal of Trichology
  [45043]
Journal of Oral and Maxillofacial
  Pathology [45049]

Cuttack
Hepatitis B Annual [45081]

Delhi
Indian Journal of Allergy Asthma and
  Immunology [45096]

Hyderabad
The Icfai Journal of Healthcare Law
  [45154]

Jaipur
Indian Journal of Clinical
  Biochemistry [45195]
Indian Journal of Sexually Transmit-
  ted Diseases [45196]
Lung India [45198]

Jodhpur
The Indian Anaesthetists' Forum
  [45218]

Kolkata
Asian Journal of Transfusion Science
  [45258]

Mumbai
Indian Journal of Nuclear Medicine
  [45384]
International Journal of Diabetes in
  Developing Countries [45393]
Journal of Association of Physicians
  of India [45395] 200,000
Journal of Craniovertebral Junction
  and Spine [45397]
Journal of Gynecological Endoscopy
  and Surgery [45401]
Mens Sana Monographs [45411]
Modern Medicare [45416]
PVRI Review [45433]

Nasik
Abhivyakti and Expressions
  [45473] 1,000

New Delhi
Annals of Cardiac Anaesthesia
  [45483]
Indian Development Review [45539]
Journal of Indian Association for
  Child and Adolescent Mental
  Health [45600]
Journal of Indian Association of Pedi-
  atric Surgeons [45601]
Journal of Pediatric Neurosciences
  [45615]

Thane
Indian Journal of Occupational and
  Environmental Medicine [45746]

Thiruvananthapuram
Trends in Biomaterials & Artificial
  Organs [45749]

Trivandrum
Calicut Medical Journal [45758]

Wardha
Journal of Neurosciences in Rural
  Practice [45770]

INDONESIA
Jakarta
Gizi Indonesia [45798]

IRAN
Tehran
DARU [45888]
Hepatitis Monthly [45889]
Iranian Journal of Endocrinology and
  Metabolism [45901]
Iranian Journal of Public Health
  [45908] .. .. (Paid) 2,000

IRELAND
Dublin
CancerWise [45950] 3,159
DiabetesWise [45953] 4,227
HeartWise [45963] 3,185
International Journal for Quality in
  Health Care [45967]
Irish Medical Journal
  [45980] .. .. (Paid) 8,800
It's All About Living [45989]
OsteoWise [45993] 2,921

Greystone
Easyhealth [46024]

ISRAEL
Jerusalem
International Journal of Adolescent
  Medicine and Health [46083]
International Journal on Disability and
  Human Development [46084]

Ramat Gan
Israel Medical Association Journal
  (IMAJ) [46094]
Journal of the Israel Heart Society
  [46096]

ITALY
Genoa
Journal of the Pancreas [46151]

Milan
Annali dell'Istituto Superiore di Sanita
  [46163]
Eating and Weight Disorders [46166]
L'Endocrinologo [46167]
Ipertensione [46178]
Journal of Endocrinological
  Investigation [46182]
Journal of Mental Health Policy and
  Economics [46183]
Obesity and Metabolism [46188]
Urodinamica [46198]

Naples
Nutrition, Metabolism, & Cardiovascular Diseases [46202]

Rome
Diabetes/Metabolism Research and
  Reviews [46227]
High Blood Pressure & Cardiovascu-
  lar Prevention [46232]
International Journal of Environment
  and Health [46234]

JAPAN
Kagoshima
Diseases of the Esophagus [46403]

Kawasaki
Industrial Health [46421] 1,100
Journal of Science of Labour
  [46422] .. .. (Paid) 2,500

Shimane
Congenital Anomalies [46683]

Tokyo
Allergology International [46732]
Journal of Health Science
  [46903] .... (Controlled) 1,700
Journal of Occupational Health
  [46931] .. .. (Paid) 8,000
Nikkei Health [46992] .... ★88,192
Nikkei Healthcare
  [46993] .. .. ★19,079
Nikkei Medical [46997] .. ... ★111,060

KENYA
Nairobi
African Journal of Food, Agriculture,
  Nutrition and Development [47172]
African Journal of Health Sciences
  [47173]

LATVIA
Riga
Veseliba [47375] .... (Paid) 17,000

LIBYAN ARAB JAMAHIRIYA
Zliten
Libyan Journal of Medicine [47458]

LITHUANIA
Kaunas
Medicina [47465]

Circulation: ★ = ABC; △ = BPA; ♦ = CAC; • = CCAB; ❑ = VAC; ⊕ = PO Statement; ‡ = Publisher's Report; Boldface figures = sworn; Light figures = estimated.

NETHERLANDS
Amsterdam
Accident Analysis & Prevention [47876]
Acta Tropica [47880]
American Journal of Preventive Medicine [47889] ... (Paid) ‡2,500 (Non-paid) ‡18
Best Practice & Research Clinical Endocrinology & Metabolism [47903]
Best Practice & Research Clinical Hematology [47904]
Biochimica et Biophysica Acta (BBA)- Proteins & Proteomics [47910]
Developmental & Comparative Immunology [47955]
International Journal of Injury Control and Safety Promotion [48029]
Journal of Autoimmunity [48053]
Microbes and Infection [48157]
Microbial Pathogenesis [48158]
Naunyn-Schmiedeberg's Archives of Pharmacology [48171]
Nurse Education Today [48188]
Nutrition [48189]
Overleven [48197]
Preventive Medicine [48214]
Toxicology [48252]

Bussum
Clinical Practice and Epidemiology in Mental Health [48281]
Current Hypertension Reviews [48290]

Dordrecht
Health Care Analysis [48412]
HealthCare Ethics Committee Forum [48413]
Journal of Cardiovascular Translational Research [48447]
Journal of Genetic Counseling [48462]
Journal of Immigrant and Minority Health [48468]
La Lettre de medecine physique et de readaptation [48503]
Quality of Life Research [48543]
Reviews in Endocrine & Metabolic Disorders [48556]

Enschede
International Journal of Healthcare Technology and Management [48594]
Journal of Back and Musculoskeletal Rehabilitation [48597]

Utrecht
International Journal of Integrated Care [48760]

NEW ZEALAND
Albany
Cancer Informatics [48776]
Health Care and Informatics Review Online [48778]

Auckland
New Zealand Doctor [48809]

Wellington
Journal [49010] 200

NIGERIA
Abuja
Women on the Move [49058]

Benin City
African Journal of Reproductive Health [49062]
Journal of Medicine and Biomedical Research [49064]

Enugu
Journal of College of Medicine [49080]

Ibadan
Tropical Journal of Obstetrics and Gynaecology [49102]

Ikeja
Nigerian Medical Practitioner [49108]

Ile-Ife
African Journal of Oral Health [49110]
African Journal of Traditional, Complementary and Alternative Medicines [49111]
Journal of the Obafemi Awolowo University Medical Student's Association [49114]

Ilorin
African Journal of Clinical and Experimental Microbiology [49117]
Tropical Journal of Health Sciences [49122]

Jos
Journal of Medicine in the Tropics [49126]

Lagos
Nigerian Journal of Health and Biomedical Sciences [49141]

Nnewi
Nigerian Medical Journal [49150]
Tropical Journal of Medical Research [49151]

Uturu
Journal of Health and Visual Sciences [49177]

Zaria
Journal of Community Medicine and Primary Health Care [49182]
Nigerian Journal of Surgical Research [49185]

NORWAY
Oslo
Scandinavian Journal of Disability Research [49207]

PAKISTAN
Faisalabad
Academic Journal of Cancer Research [49228]
International Journal of Tropical Medicine [49258]
Pakistan Journal of Nutrition [49277]

Karachi
Hamdard Naunehal [49352]

PERU
Lima
Anales de la Facultad de Medicina [49423]

PHILIPPINES
Taguig City
Philippine Journal of Nutrition [49640]

POLAND
Bydgoszcz
Advances in Palliative Medicine [49653]

Gdansk
Endocrinology, Obesity and Metabolic Disorders [49656]
Psychooncology [49660]

Krakow
Polish Gerontology [49668]

Warsaw
Acta Neurobiologiae Experimentalis [49680]

Advances in Rehabilitation [49688]
Archives of Industrial Hygiene and Toxicology [49691]
Macedonian Journal of Medical Sciences [49734]
Polish Pneumology and Allergology [49753]

Wroclaw
Interdisciplinary Problems of Stroke [49779]

Zabrze
Experimental and Clinical Diabetology [49782]
Polish Journal of Endocrinology [49783]

RUSSIA
Moscow
Anesthesiology & Intensive Care [49870]
Annals of the Russian Academy of Medical Sciences [49872]
Epidemiology & Infectious Diseases [49902]
Health Care of the Russian Federation [49911]
Hygiene & Sanitation [49916]
Medical Care [49941]
Pediatric Surgery [49953]
Problems of Health Resort Treatment, Physiotherapy & Exercise Therapy [49964]
Problems of Social Hygiene, Health Care & History of Medicine [49965]
Problems of Tuberculosis [49966]
Russian Journal of Pediatrics [49979]
Russian Medical Journal [49984]
Sociology of Medicine [49990]

SAUDI ARABIA
Riyadh
Annals of Thoracic Medicine [50059]
Urology Annals [50072]

SERBIA
Sremska Kamenica
Archive of Oncology [50094]

SINGAPORE
Singapore
DENTAL ASIA [50130]
The Family Doctor [50147] 130,000
Journal of Men's Health [50209]

REPUBLIC OF SOUTH AFRICA
Auckland Park
Health SA Gesondheid [50348]

Cape Town
Current Allergy & Clinical Immunology [50372]
International Journal of Shoulder Surgery [50384]
Leadership in HIV/AIDS [50387] 10,000
South African Journal of Child Health [50413]

Centurion
South African Journal of Diabetes and Vascular Disease [50453]
Southern African Journal of Critical Care [50455]

Durban
South African Health Review [50470]

Gauteng
Professional Nursing Today [50482]
SA Pharmaceutical Journal [50483]

Grahamstown
African Journal of AIDS Research [50486]
African Journal of Biomedical Research [50487]
Journal of Child and Adolescent Mental Health [50501]
South African Journal Clinical Nutrition [50514]

Johannesburg
Obstetrics and Gynaecology Forum [50532]

Pinelands
Journal of Endocrinology, Metabolism and Diabetes of South Africa [50573]

Pretoria
Sahara J [50599]

SPAIN
Barcelona
Cancer & Chemotherapy Reviews [50655]
Cuerpomente [50662] .. .. ‡66,291
Hepatology Reviews [50677]
Siete Dias Medicos [50699] .... (Controlled) 25,000

Madrid
Gerokomos [50762]

Seville
Cuadernos de Medicina Forense [50833]

SWEDEN
Goteborg
Acta Neurologica Scandanavica [50955]
Blood Pressure [50957]

Lund
Acta Orthopaedica [50983]

Solna
Acta Oncologica [50999]

Stockholm
Allergy [51005]
EuroSurveillance [51015]
Kvinnotryck [51024]
Microbial Ecology in Health and Disease [51026]
Nordisk Fysioterapi [51028]
Scandinavian Journal of Occupational Therapy [51035]
Sjukgymnasten [51038]

Umea
Scandinavian Journal of Public Health [51047]

Uppsala
Computer Methods and Programs in Biomedicine [51050]

SWITZERLAND
Bern
Ernahrungs Info [51072]
International Journal of Public Health [51074]

Geneva
International Journal of Computational Medicine and Healthcare [51112]
International Journal of Food Safety, Nutrition and Public Health [51121]
Nutrition Information in Crisis Situations [51154] 2,300
Pan American Journal of Public Health [51155]
Red Cross, Red Crescent [51157]
SCN News [51160] 8,000

Circulation: ★ = ABC; △ = BPA; ◆ = CAC; • = CCAB; ❏ = VAC; ⊕ = PO Statement; ‡ = Publisher's Report; Boldface figures = sworn; Light figures = estimated.

Weekly Epidemiological Record
[51165] .... (Combined) 6,500

Lausanne
Alcoholism [51182]

Muttenz
Schweizerische Arztezeitung/Bulletin
des Medecins Suisses
[51214] .. .. (Paid) 29,599

Neuhausen
Ars Medici [51216]

Viganello-Lugano
Annals of Oncology [51237]

Zurich
Biometrical Journal [51255]
Journal of Inherited Metabolic
Disease [51270]

UNITED REPUBLIC OF TAN-
ZANIA
Dar es Salaam
East African Journal of Public Health
[51400]
Tanzania Medical Journal [51404]
Tanzanian Journal of Health
Research [51405]

TURKEY
Ankara
Diagnostic and Interventional
Radiology [51492]

Bursa
Journal of Sports Science and Medicine (JSSM) [51551]

Istanbul
Medikal & Teknik [51562] 10,069

UGANDA
Kampala
African Health Sciences [51584]

UNITED KINGDOM
Abingdon
Acute Cardiac Care [51697]
Aging and Mental Health [51700]
AIDS Care [51701]
Child Care in Practice [51728]
Developmental Neurorehabilitation
[51757]
European Journal of Contraception
and Reproductive Health Care
[51779]
Health, Risk and Society [51801]
Hypertension in Pregnancy [51810]
Informatics for Health and Social
Care [51816]
International Journal of Environmen-
tal Health Research [51834]
International Journal of Prisoner
Health [51844]
Journal of Dermatological Treatment
[51884]
Journal of Intellectual and Develop-
mental Disability [51908]
Journal of Psychosomatic Obstetrics
and Gynecology [51937]
Journal of Social Work Practice
[51943]
Leukemia and Lymphoma [51968]
Medicine, Conflict & Survival [51974]
Minimally Invasive Therapy and Allied
Technologies [51982]
Physiotherapy Theory and Practice
[52013]
Prosthetics & Orthotics International
[52025]
Scandinavian Journal of Primary
Health Care [52050]

Scandinavian Journal of
Rheumatology [52051]
Scandinavian Journal of Urology and
Nephrology [52052]

Altrincham
The Vegetarian [52104] 15,000

Barnsley
Assistive Technologies [52177]
Caring UK [52178]

Basingstoke
Health Statistics Quarterly [52206]
International Journal of Obesity
[52211]
Journal of Public Health Policy
[52219]

Berkhamsted
Guidelines [52310]
Guidelines in Practice [52311]
Medendium [52313]

Birmingham
Journal of the Renin-Angiotensin-
Aldosterone System [52351]
Occupational Safety & Health
[52360]

Bishop's Stortford
Journal of Neonatal Nursing
[52380] .... (Combined) 5,000

Bognor Regis
Musculoskeletal Care [52400]
Practice Development in Health Care
[52402]

Bradford
Clinical Governance [52441]
Disaster Prevention and Management
[52450]
International Journal of Health Care
Quality Assurance [52479]
Journal of Health, Organization and
Management [52502]
Leadership in Health Services
[52520]

Brentwood
Cephalalgia [52570]
Parasite Immunology [52586]

Bridgwater
ABM Magazine [52595]
Journal of Holistic Healthcare [52596]

Brighton
Advances in Mental Health and Intel-
lectual Disabilities [52604]
The British Journal of Forensic
Practice [52607]
Healthmatters [52611]
International Journal of Migration,
Health and Social Care [52617]
Journal of Integrated Care [52621]
The Journal of Mental Health Train-
ing, Education and Practice
[52622]
Journal of Public Mental Health
[52623]
Learning Disability Review [52624]
Mental Health Review Journal
[52626]
Mental Health Today [52627]
Working with Older People [52635]

Bristol
Journal of Breath Research [52682]
Neuropharmacology [52709]
Paediatric and Perinatal
Epidemiology [52714]

Burford
Journal of Society for Companion
Animal Studies [52760] 500

Cambridge
British Journal of Nutrition
[52795] .... (Combined) 1,500

Journal of Biosocial Science
[52846] 500
Proceedings of the Nutrition Society
[52887]
Workplace Law [52905]

Chester
Managed Healthcare Executive
[52997] .. .. △41,800

Colchester
Bulletin of Medical Ethics [53031]
Natural Health [53042]

Dundee
Nicotine and Tobacco Research
[53217]

Edinburgh
Cardiology News [53260]
Surgeons' News [53322]

Exeter
European Journal of Herbal Medicine
[53353]

Glasgow
Addiction Research and Theory
[53409]

Harrogate
Orthopaedic Product News
[53518] .. .. (Combined) ‡8,044

Hatfield
Body, Movement and Dance in
Psychotherapy [53538]
Journal of Human Nutrition and
Dietetics [53540]

Hitchin
Dyspraxia Foundation Professional
Journal [53577]

Hove
Ethnicity and Inequalities in Health
and Social Care [53605]
Journal of Clinical Pathology [53608]
Social Care and Neurodisability
[53613]

Hoylake
Candis [53614] ...... (Paid) ★254,420

Huntingdon
Wound Care [53636]

Kidlington
Journal of Cranio-Maxillofacial
Surgery [53696]
Physiotherapy
[53704] .. .. (Controlled) 35,000

Lancaster
Gynecological Endocrinology [53733]
Spirituality and Health International
[53736]

Laurencekirk
Speech & Language Therapy in
Practice [53743] .. .... (Paid) 1,600

Leeds
Contemporary Hypnosis [53763]

Leicester
Clinical & Experimental Allergy
[53793]
Clinical Focus
[53794] .. .. (Controlled) 15,000

London
Acute Coronary Syndromes [53897]
Advances in Osteoporotic Fracture
Management [53906]
Advances in Psychiatric Treatment
[53907]
Advances in Sepsis [53908]
African Journal of Midwifery and
Women's Health [53922]
Aging Health [53927]
Annals of the Rheumatic Disease
[53949] .. .. (Paid) 9,500

Annals of Tropical Paediatrics
[53950]
Archives of Disease in Childhood.
Education and Practice Edition
[53963]
Asian Journal of Andrology [53975]
Best Practice & Research Clinical
Obstetrics & Gynecology [54013]
Best Treatments [54014]
BMA News
[54034] .... (Controlled) 116,000
BMC Complementary and Alternative
Medicine [54047]
BMC Family Practice [54055]
BMC Geriatrics [54059]
BMC Health Services Research
[54060]
BMC International Health and Human
Rights [54063]
BMC Medical Research Methodology
[54070]
BMC Palliative Care [54081]
BMC Pregnancy and Childbirth
[54086]
BMC Pulmonary Medicine [54088]
British Journal of Cancer
Management [54114]
British Journal of Community Nursing
[54117]
British Journal of Dermatology
Nursing [54119]
British Journal of Health Care
Management [54121]
British Journal of Healthcare
Assistants [54122]
British Journal of Music Therapy
[54126] 800
British Journal of Occupational
Therapy [54128] 18,000
British Journal of Ophthalmology
[54129] .... ‡2,370
British Journal of Psychiatry [54132]
British Journal of Renal Medicine
[54134]
British Journal of School Nursing
[54135]
British Journal of Sexual Medicine
[54136]
British Medical Journal Clinical
Evidence [54140]
Cardiology in the Young [54177]
Caring Times
[54182] .. .. (Controlled) ★16,967
Cerebrospinal Fluid Research
[54196]
Children & Society [54205]
Chronic Respiratory Disease [54210]
Clinical and Experimental Allergy
Reviews [54221]
Clinical & Experimental Dermatology
[54222] .... (Combined) 762
Clinical Lipidology [54224]
Clinical Risk [54231]
Clio Medica [54233]
Communicable Disease Report
Weekly [54243]
Communication [54245] 12,000
Contact Dermatitis [54261]
Cost Effectiveness and Resource
Allocation [54272]
COVER [54278]
Culture, Health and Sexuality [54294]
Current Opinion in Clinical Nutrition &
Metabolic Care [54297]
Dementia [54315]
Dermatology in Practice [54320]
Diabetes & Primary Care [54323]
Diabetes Update [54324]
Emerging Themes in Epidemiology
[54364]
Epidemiology and Infection
[54380] 1,000
European Journal of Orthodontics
[54402]

European Journal of Palliative Care [54403]
Expert Review of Anti-Infective Therapy [54418]
Expert Review of Anticancer Therapy [54419]
Expert Review of Cardiovascular Therapy [54420]
Expert Review of Clinical Immunology [54421]
Expert Review of Clinical Pharmacology [54422]
Expert Review of Endocrinology & Metabolism [54423]
Expert Review of Gastroenterology & Hepatology [54424]
Expert Review of Hematology [54425]
Expert Review of Obstetrics & Gynecology [54429]
Expert Review of Ophthalmology [54430]
Expert Review of Proteomics [54432]
Expert Review of Respiratory Medicine [54433]
Expert Reviews of Dermatology [54435]
Future Neurology [54489]
Geriatric Medicine [54505] .. .. (Controlled) ‡23,000
Headache in Practice [54535]
Health [54536]
Health and Hygiene [54538] .. .. (Paid) 2,500
Health Policy and Planning [54540] 720
Health Research Policy and Systems [54541]
Health & Safety at Work [54543] .... ★23,051
Health Services Management Research [54544]
Heart Failure Monitor [54546]
HIV Therapy [54563]
Hospital Healthcare Europe [54572]
Hospital Management International [54574] .... (Non-paid) ★10,039
Human Resources for Health [54580]
Immunotherapy [54587]
Information Bulletin [54602]
International Breastfeeding Journal [54620]
International Journal of Advances in Rheumatology [54631]
International Journal of Care Pathways [54637]
International Journal of Clinical Rheumatology [54639]
International Journal of Health Geographics [54649]
International Journal of Intensive Care [54650]
International Journal of Palliative Nursing [54657]
International Journal of Respiratory Care [54659]
International Journal of STD and AIDS [54663]
International Journal of Therapy and Rehabilitation (IJTR) [54665]
Journal of Bodywork and Movement Therapies [54708]
Journal of Cardiovascular Magnetic Resonance [54718]
Journal of Cardiovascular Magnetic Resonance [54719]
Journal of Clinical Research [54726]
Journal of Epidemiology and Community Health [54745]
Journal of Exposure Science and Environmental Epidemiology (JESEE) [54750]
Journal of Health Psychology [54759]

Journal of Health Services Research & Policy [54760]
Journal of Human Hypertension [54763]
Journal of Intellectual Disabilities [54769]
Journal of Manual & Manipulative Therapy [54774]
Journal of Outcomes Research [54791]
Journal of Paramedic Practice [54792]
Journal of Renal Nursing [54808]
Journal of Risk Research [54810]
Journal of the Royal Society of Medicine [54814] .. .. (Combined) 18,000
Journal of Urban Health [54831]
Journal of Wound Care [54838] .. ..:............... (Paid) 6,000
Lipids in Health and Disease [54875]
Lung Cancer in Practice [54893]
Malaria Journal [54900]
Myeloproliferative Disorders in practice [54968]
Nephron Physiology [54987]
Noise and Health [55008]
Nurse Prescribing [55014]
Nursing Ethics [55015] .. .. (Paid) 1,000
Nursing and Residential Care [55017]
Nutrition Journal [55019]
Nutritional Neuroscience [55021]
Occupational Therapy News [55026] .... (Controlled) 22,000
Pediatric Health [55064]
Population Health Metrics [55102]
Positive Nation [55106]
Postgraduate Medical Journal [55109] .... ‡1,475
Private Hospital Healthcare Europe [55122]
Progress in Palliative Care [55136]
Prostate Cancer and Prostatic Diseases [55144]
Pulmonary Pharmacology and Therapeutics [55155]
Pulse [55156] ... (Combined) 40,269
Quality and Safety in Health Care [55162] .... ‡6,000
RCM Midwives' Journal [55175] .. .. (Paid) 36,350
Respiratory Disease in Practice [55193]
Respiratory Research [55194]
The Safety & Health Practitioner [55214] .... (Paid) ★36,549
Sexually Transmitted Infections [55231] 1,780
Social Theory & Health [55249]
Stroke News [55266] .. .. ‡70,000
Thrombus [55317]
Tobacco Control [55325]
Women's Health [55414]

Loughton
Education Business [55489]
Health Business [55492]

Macclesfield
Vascular Health and Risk Management [55520]

Manchester
Biochemical Engineering Journal [55544]

Marlow
Menopause International [55600]

Mere
Advances in Clinical Neuroscience & Rehabilitation [55609]

Middlesbrough
Critical Public Health [55611]

Middlesex
Environmental Hazards [55616]

Northampton
Country Doctor [55707]

Northwich
Acupuncture in Medicine [55718] .... (Combined) 6,225

Nottingham
Gut [55757]
Headway News [55758]
Planning Perspectives [55769]

Nutley
Homeopathy in Practice [55779]

Olney
International Journal of Biomedical Engineering and Technology [55792]
International Journal of Low Radiation [55819]

Oxford
Allergy [55862]
Asia-Pacific Journal of Clinical Oncology [55875]
Australian Endodontic Journal [55877]
Brief Treatment and Crisis Intervention [55888]
Cancer Science [55903]
Carcinogenesis [55904]
Diabetes Research and Clinical Practice [55925]
Diabetic Medicine [55926]
Emotional and Behavioral Difficulties [55936]
Epidemiologic Reviews [55939]
European Heart Journal [55944]
European Journal of Public Health [55947]
Family Court Review [55951]
Health Education Research [55971]
Health Promotion International [55972]
HPB [55978]
International Journal of Older People Nursing [56000]
International Journal for Quality in Health Care [56002]
International Journal of Rheumatic Diseases [56003]
Journal of Child and Adolescent Psychiatric Nursing [56020]
Journal of Nursing and Healthcare of Chronic Illness [56054]
Journal of Public Health [56064]
Learning in Health and Social Care [56088]
The Milbank Quarterly [56100]
Nursing and Health Sciences [56122]
Nutrition Bulletin [56124]
Obesity Reviews [56125]
Pathology International [56143]
Pediatric Allergy and Immunology [56145]
Pediatric Dermatology [56147]
Pediatrics International [56148]
Progress in Retinal and Eye Research [56171]
Public Health Nursing [56177]
Scandinavian Journal of Caring Sciences [56198]
Sleep and Biological Rhythm [56205]
Tropical Medicine and International Health [56223]

Portsmouth
Positive Health [56292] 8,000
Practical Diabetes International [56293]

Reading
GrowthPoint [56319] ... (Paid) 1,000

Sheffield
Hazards [56496]

Phoenix [56509]
Quiet [56513] 10,000

Southampton
Health Education [56572]

Swansea
New Leaves [56704]

Teddington
Talkback [56735] .... (Combined) 10,000

Truro
Best Practice & Research Clinical Rheumatology [56773]

West Lothian
Continence [56892]

Weybridge
British Journal of Play Therapy [56912]
PLAY THERAPY [56913]

Witherslack
Environment International [56937]

Worcestershire
Good Autism Practice [56967]

ZIMBABWE
Harare
Central African Journal of Medicine [57113]

HEARING AND SPEECH

AUSTRALIA
Chatswood
Australian and New Zealand Journal of Audiology [41738]

South Bank
Australian Voice [42364]

Sydney
Acoustics Australia [42445] .. .. (Paid) ‡600

NETHERLANDS
Amsterdam
Hearing Research [48009]

UNITED KINGDOM
Abingdon
International Journal of Language & Communication Disorders [51839]
International Journal of Speech-Language Pathology [51846]

Beverley
Association Magazine [52319] .... ‡1,800

Bognor Regis
Cochlear Implants International [52394]

Brentwood
Noise Notes [52582]

East Sussex
Catchword [53242]

High Wycombe
Deafness and Education International [53572] .. .. (Paid) 2,000

London
Bulletin [54155] 11,500
Child Language and Teaching Therapy [54203]
International Journal of Speech, Language and the Law [54662]
Logopedics Phoniatrics Vocology [54884]
One in Seven [55033] 25,000
Talk [55290] .... (Paid) 13,500

Circulation: ★ = ABC; △ = BPA; ◆ = CAC; ● = CCAB; ❑ = VAC; ⊕ = PO Statement; ‡ = Publisher's Report; Boldface figures = sworn; Light figures = estimated.

Talking Sense **[55291]** 5,000

Manchester
Sign Language Translator &
  Interpreter **[55577]**

Milton Keynes
NEWSLI **[55640]**

Saint Albans
Acoustics Bulletin **[56433]**

Sheffield
Quiet **[56513]** 10,000

HISTORY AND GENEALOGY

AUSTRALIA
Brisbane
Access **[41639]**

Bundanoon
Antichthon **[41668]**

Crawley
Australasian Journal of Victorian
  Studies **[41819]** 150

Gosford
Australian Family Tree Connections
  [41904]

Melbourne
Overland
  [42081] .... (Combined) 2,000

Murdoch
Intersections **[42137]**

Parkville
Historical Records of Australian
  Science **[42231]**

Saint Lucia
The Australian Journal of Politics and
  History **[42338]**

Sydney
Descent **[42501]**
History Australia **[42515]**

Townsville
The Electronic Journal of Australian
  and New Zealand History **[42635]**

AUSTRIA
Vienna
Stichproben - Wiener Zeitschrift fur
  Kritische Afrikastudien **[42768]**

BELGIUM
Leuven
Ancient Society **[42891]**
Iranica Antiqua **[42899]**

BRAZIL
Rio de Janeiro
Historia, Ciencias,
  Saude-Manguinhos **[43005]**

BULGARIA
Sofia
Journal of Bulgarian Historical
  Review **[43102]**

DENMARK
Arhus
Nordic Irish Studies **[43648]**
NUMEN **[43649]**

Copenhagen
Scando-Slavica **[43683]**

FRANCE
Paris
Cahiers d'Economie et Sociologie
  Rurales **[44031]**

Historiens et Geographes **[44048]**
Karthago **[44067]**

GERMANY
Berlin
Antike und Abendland
  [44150] .... ‡450
Byzantinische Zeitschrift
  [44164] .... ‡650
Fruhmittelalterliche Studien **[44185]**

Cologne
Kadmos **[44297]** 330

Erlangen
Zeitschrift fur Antikes Christentum
  [44344] 400

Heidelberg
European Archives of
  Otorhinolaryngology **[44455]**

Leinfelden-Echterdingen
DAMALS **[44518]** 32,799

Munich
Architecture, Technology, Culture
  (ATC) **[44550]**
Zeitschrift fur Assyriologie und
  Vorderasiatische Archaologie
  [44589] 500

Wiesbaden
Central Asiatic Journal **[44711]**

GREECE
Piraeus
International Journal of Economic
  Research **[44768]**

HUNGARY
Budapest
Acta Antiqua Academiae Scientiarum
  Hungaricae **[44806]**
Acta Orientalia Academiae Scien-
  tiarum Hungaricae **[44816]**
Hungarian Studies **[44837]**

INDIA
Allahabad
Journal of the Interdisciplinary
  Crossroads **[44934]**

Delhi
Tibetan Review
  [45107] .... (Paid) 4,500

Dharamsala
Tibet Journal **[45112]** ... (Paid) 1,000

Hyderabad
The Icfai Journal of History and
  Culture **[45155]**

New Delhi
Journal of Islamic History
  [45610] .... (Paid) 2,000
South Asian Survey
  [45652] .... (Paid) 500
Studies in History (New Delhi)
  [45657] .... (Paid) 500

Patiala
Panjab Past and Present
  [45686] .... (Paid) 500

IRELAND
Dublin
Historical Biology **[45964]**
Irish Architectural and Decorative
  Studies **[45970]**
Irish Archives **[45971]**
Irish Sword **[45986]** 900

Naas
Irish Family History Journal **[46042]**

ISRAEL
Jerusalem
Israel Exploration Journal
  [46085] .... (Paid) 2,000

Tel Aviv
History & Memory **[46103]** 650

ITALY
Florence
Annali di Storia di Firenze **[46141]**
Cromohs **[46142]**

JAPAN
Kyoto
Doshisha American Studies
  [46471] .... (Paid) 750

Nagoya
Nanzan Review of American Studies
  [46557]

Tokyo
American Literary History **[46733]**

KUWAIT
Safat
Journal of the Gulf and Arabian Pen-
  insula Studies **[47338]**

MALAYSIA
Kuala Lumpur
Journal of the Malaysian Branch of
  the Royal Asiatic Society
  [47606] .... (Paid) 1,000

NETHERLANDS
Amsterdam
Amsterdam Monographs in American
  Studies **[47890]**
Explorations in Economic History
  [47983]
Historia Mathematica **[48011]**
Historiographia Linguistica (HL)
  [48012]
Journal of Cultural Heritage **[48066]**
Misjpoge **[48160]** 650

Dordrecht
Frontiers of History in China **[48399]**

Groningen
Indo-Iranian Journal **[48602]**

The Hague
Europa Nostra **[48614]**

Leiden
Ancient Civilizations from Scythia to
  Siberia **[48646]**
Arabica **[48650]**
Die Welt des Islams **[48668]**
International Journal of the Platonic
  Tradition **[48682]**
Iran and the Caucasus **[48684]**
Journal of Early Modern History
  [48692]
Journal of the Economic and Social
  History of the Orient **[48693]**
Journal of Egyptian History **[48694]**
The Journal of Jewish Thought and
  Philosophy **[48699]**
Journal of Reformed Theology
  [48701]
Mnemosyne **[48712]**
Phronesis **[48716]**
Religion and Human Rights **[48719]**
Russian History **[48722]**
The Soviet and Post-Soviet Review
  [48726]

NEW ZEALAND
Auckland
The New Zealand Journal of History
  [48817] 800

Christchurch
History Now **[48868]**

NIGERIA
Yaba
Lagos Historical Review **[49179]**

POLAND
Warsaw
Limes **[49731]**

SINGAPORE
Singapore
Journal of Chinese Overseas **[50201]**
South Seas Society Journal
  [50269] .... (Paid) 600

SLOVENIA
Ljubljana
Scopolia **[50341]**

REPUBLIC OF SOUTH AF-RICA
Centurion
South African Journal of Cultural
  History **[50452]**

KwaZulu-Natal
South African Historical Journal
  [50545]

Pretoria
Africanus **[50584]**
Fundamina **[50592]**

Saxonwold
The Military History Journal **[50628]**

Scottsville
Neotestamentica **[50629]**

SPAIN
Barcelona
Historia, Antropologia y Fuentes
  Orales **[50678]**

Terrassa
Tiempos Modernos **[50838]**

Valencia
Historia Social **[50845]**

SWEDEN
Goteborg
Scandinavian Economic History
  Review **[50964]** 500

Stockholm
Arkiv Samhalle och Forskning
  [51009]

TAIWAN
Taipei
Soochow Journal of History **[51358]**

TURKEY
Ankara
Journal of American Studies of
  Turkey **[51494]** .... (Paid) 325

UGANDA
Kampala
Mtafiti Mwafrika **[51588]**

UNITED KINGDOM
Abingdon
Australian Historical Studies **[51713]**
British Journal for the History of
  Philosophy **[51719]**
Central Asian Survey **[51726]**
Diplomacy & Statecraft **[51758]**
Early Popular Visual Culture **[51762]**
The European Legacy **[51783]**
Historical Journal of Film, Radio and
  Television **[51803]**
Immigrants & Minorities **[51811]**
Intelligence & National Security
  [51820]

Circulation: ★ = ABC; △ = BPA; ◆ = CAC; • = CCAB; ❑ = VAC; ⊕ = PO Statement; ‡ = Publisher's Report; Boldface figures = sworn; Light figures = estimated.

International Journal of the History of Sport [51837]
Interventions [51857]
Iranian Studies [51858]
Israel Affairs [51863]
Journal of Iberian & Latin American Studies [51906]
The Journal of Imperial & Commonwealth History [51907]
Journal of Israeli History [51912]
Journal of Modern Jewish Studies [51920]
Journal of North African Studies [51925]
The Journal of Pacific History [51928]
Journal of Postcolonial Writing [51935]
Journal of Systematic Palaeontology [51951] .... ‡500
Journal of Victorian Culture [51955] 5,700
Mediterranean Historical Review [51975]
Middle Eastern Studies [51980]
Modern & Contemporary France [51985]
Modern Italy [51986]
National Identities [51988]
Perspectives on European Politics and Society [52009]
Rethinking History [52038]
Revolutionary Russia [52045]
Social History [52059]
Souvenir [52062]
Sport in History [52063]
Women's Writing [52093]

Belfast
Directory of Irish Family History Research [52282]

Birmingham
Review [52364]

Bradford
Journal of Management History [52508]

Bridgnorth
First Empire [52594]

Brighton
History of European Ideas [52612]
Reformation [52630]
Twentieth Century British History [52634]

Bristol
BBC History [52642] 50,000
Journal of the Kilvert Society [52688]
Management & Organizational History [52704]

Caerfyrddin
Cambria [52781]

Cambridge
Comparative Studies in Society and History [52809] 2,000
Contemporary European History [52811] 650
Eighteenth Century Music [52816]
The Historical Journal [52828] 1,300
International Journal of Cultural Property [52834]
International Journal of Middle East Studies [52836] 3,700
International Review of Social History [52839] 1,200
The Journal of African History [52842] 1,600
Journal of the United Reformed Church History Society [52864]
Mosaic [52872]

Canterbury
Family History [52918]

Ceredigion
History of Science [52955] .... (Paid) 600

Colchester
Oral History Journal [53044] 795

Deeping Saint James
Best of British [53162]

Durham
The Seventeenth Century [53231]

Edgbaston
Africa [53248] .... (Paid) ‡1,000

Edinburgh
Architectural Heritage [53252]
Double Tressure [53270]
Innes Review [53286]
Journal of Scottish Philosophy [53295]
Oxford Literary Review [53304]
Psychoanalysis and History [53307]
Scottish Genealogist [53315]
Scottish Historical Review [53316]

Exeter
Collingwood and British Idealism Studies [53348]
History of Political Thought [53360]

Gillingham
The Irish Genealogist [53408]

Grimsby
Family History News and Digest [53485] 5,000

Guildford
Coat of Arms [53489]

Heathfield
Quarterly Journal [53551]

Holywood
Ulster Folklife [53584]

Huntingdon
Durbar [53634]

Kidlington
The History of the Family [53693]
Journal of Historical Geography [53699]

Leeds
History Scotland [53767]

London
Black History Month [54033] .... (Free) 100,000
British Museum Studies in Ancient Egypt and Sudan (BMSAES) [54141]
Bulletin of the School of Oriental and African Studies [54157] 900
Byzantine and Modern Greek Studies [54162]
Central Europe [54193]
The China Quarterly [54208] 2,700
Clio Medica [54233]
Early Medieval China [54346]
European History Quarterly [54394]
Family & Community History [54440]
Family History Monthly [54441]
Genealogists' Magazine [54500] .... (Paid) 15,500
Historian [54554]
The Historic Environment [54555]
Historical Research [54558]
History Review [54560] 5,000
History Today [54561] ... . (Paid) 30,000
History Workshop Journal [54562]
Intellectual History Review [54614]
Interdisciplinary Science Reviews [54615]
The Italianist [54685]

Journal of Contemporary History [54731]
Journal of Global History [54757]
Journal of the Society of Archer-Antiquaries [54821] 400
Labour History Review [54848] 1,000
Language & History [54851]
Medieval Sermon Studies [54924]
Midland History [54932]
Ming Studies [54938]
Northern History [55011]
Notes & Records of the Royal Society [55013]
Palestine Exploration Quarterly [55051]
Papers of the British School at Rome [55055]
Popular Music History [55101]
Reviews in History [55200]
Seventeenth-Century French Studies [55229]
Slavonica [55242] 200
Slovo [55243]
T'ang Studies [55292]
Teaching History [55293]
Tel Aviv [55296]
Telecommunications Heritage Group Journal [55297] 450
Terrae Incognitae [55300]
Transactions [55334] 2,500
20th Century History Review [55350]
War & Society [55379]

Maidens
Space Policy [55526]

Manchester
Ancient Egypt [55541]
The Classical Review [55547]
Literature & History [55570]

Middlesbrough
Spatial Practices [55612]

Middlesex
Aeromilitaria [55614]

Newbury
Soldiers of the Queen [55662] .... (Controlled) 1,250

Newcastle upon Tyne
Archaeologia Aeliana [55667]

Newtownabbey
Five Foot Three [55701]

Norwich
British Journal for the History of Science [55727] .... ‡1,500

Nottingham
Miniature Wargames [55767] ... .:............ (Paid) 9,000
Planning Perspectives [55769]

Oxford
BSHM Bulletin [55896]
Cultural & Social History [55921]
Enterprise & Society [55937]
French History [55961]
German History [55965]
History [55973]
History Compass [55974]
History and Theory [55975]
Holocaust and Genocide Studies [55976]
Journal of Historical Sociology [56038]
Oral History Review [56128] ... 1,065
Oxford Development Studies [56132]
Past & Present [56142]

Penzance
Cornish World [56248] .... (Paid) 5,000

Saint Albans
Galpin Society Journal [56435] .... (Paid) 850

Scunthorpe
Cromwelliana [56467] .... (Controlled) 550

Sharpham
Journal of Church Monuments Society [56487] 500

Southampton
The English Historical Review [56570]
Greece and Rome [56571]
Journal of Medieval History [56574]

Stirling
The Forth Naturalist & Historian [56622] .... (Combined) 350

Surrey
Crusades [56661]
The European Yearbook of Business History [56662]
Mediterranean Studies [56668]

Wetherby
Cross & Cockade International [56910]

Whitley Bay
Rider Haggard Journal [56920]

HOME ECONOMICS

FINLAND
Rajamaki
Teho [43905] .... (Paid) 4,662

JAPAN
Tokyo
Journal of Home Economics of Japan [46905] .... (Paid) 5,350

UNITED KINGDOM
Abingdon
Housing Studies [51806]
Housing, Theory & Society [51807]

HOME FURNISHINGS, CURTAINS, DRAPERIES
See also Furniture and Furnishings; Glass and China; Lighting

AUSTRALIA
North Ryde
BuildHOME Vic [42174]
Contemporary Home Design [42179]
Kitchens and Bathrooms Quarterly [42186]
Stone [42198] .. ..:.... 12,000

Templestowe
Supplier Woodworking magazine [42618] 17,000

PEOPLE'S REPUBLIC OF CHINA
Shanghai
Shanghai Residence [43500] 30,000

INDIA
Mumbai
Better Interiors [45355]

IRELAND
Blackrock
Irish Hardware [45921] .... ★1,664

Dublin
Irish Kitchens and Bathrooms [45979] 25,000

Circulation: ★ = ABC; △ = BPA; ◆ = CAC; • = CCAB; ❑ = VAC; ⊕ = PO Statement; ‡ = Publisher's Report; Boldface figures = sworn; Light figures = estimated.

JAPAN
Tokyo
Nikkei Home Builder
[46994] .... ★22,754

LATVIA
Riga
Dari Pats [47363] ...... (Paid) 15,000

NEW ZEALAND
Auckland
Home New Zealand
[48795] 14,805

PHILIPPINES
Quezon City
Metro Home & Entertaining [49601]

POLAND
Warsaw
Dom & Wnetrze [49705] ..... ‡20,283

SINGAPORE
Singapore
Global Sources Hardware & DIY
[50157]
Global Sources Home Products
[50158]
Singapore Tatler Homes
[50263] .... ‡14,000

SPAIN
Barcelona
El Mueble [50670] .... ‡217,434
El Mueble Casas de Campo
[50671] .... ‡43,155
El Mueble Cocinas y Banos
[50672] .... ‡20,535
Habitania [50676] .... ‡44,184
Madrid
Casa al Dia [50734] .... ‡87,531
Cosas de Casa [50740] .... ‡183,118

THAILAND
Bangkok
Essential Guide to Home & Decor
[51420] .... ‡63,350

UKRAINE
Kiev
Lyubimaya Datcha
[51601] .... ‡20,000
Privatnyi Dom [51605] .... ‡35,000

UNITED KINGDOM
Coventry
Housing [53084]
East Budleigh
Tools and Trades [53234]
London
Good Homes [54520] .... ★127,202
Homes & Antiques
[54567] .... ★55,100
Ideal Home [54582]
Live It [54877]
Period Living [55068]
25 Beautiful Kitchens
[55349] .... ★118,373

HOSPITALS AND HEALTHCARE INSTITUTIONS
See also Health and Health-care; Medicine and Surgery; Nursing

AUSTRALIA
Kingston
Australian Journal of Advanced Nurs-ing (AJAN) [41991]

Australian Nursing Journal (ANJ)
[41992] .... ‡65,000
Perth
Australian Indigenous HealthBulletin
[42246]
Strawberry Hills
Australian Health Review [42395]

CROATIA
Zagreb
Acta Clinica Croatica [43561]

FRANCE
Ferney-Voltaire
World Hospitals and Health Services
[43950] 2,500

GERMANY
Darmstadt
Hospital Post [44308] .... ‡43,000
Munster
Best Practice & Research Clinical
Anesthesiology [44597]

INDIA
Mumbai
Bombay Hospital Journal
[45358] .. .. (Paid) 5,000

IRAN
Tehran
Iranian Journal of Endocrinology and
Metabolism [45901]

IRELAND
Dundrum
Irish Medical News
[46009] .... ★6,750

JAPAN
Tokyo
Nikkei Healthcare
[46993] .... ★19,079
Nikkei Medical [46997] .. .... ★111,060

NETHERLANDS
Amsterdam
Accident Analysis & Prevention
[47876]
Best Practice & Research Clinical
Endocrinology & Metabolism
[47903]
Best Practice & Research Clinical
Hematology [47904]
Dordrecht
Health Care Analysic [48412]
HNO [48416]
Supportive Care in Cancer [48571]
Utrecht
International Journal of Integrated
Care [48760]

NEW ZEALAND
Wellington
Kai Tiaki [49013] .... ‡44,000

NORWAY
Trondheim
Acta Anaesthesiologica Scandinavica
[49215]

RUSSIA
Moscow
Medico-Social Expert Evaluation and
Rehabilitation [49942]

Problems of Health Resort Treat-
ment, Physiotherapy & Exercise
Therapy [49964]
Russian Medical Journal [49984]

SWEDEN
Stockholm
Nordisk Fysioterapi [51028]
Sjukgymnasten [51038]

SWITZERLAND
Geneva
International Nursing Review [51148]

UNITED REPUBLIC OF TAN-ZANIA
Dar es Salaam
East African Journal of Public Health
[51400]

UNITED KINGDOM
Abingdon
Child Care in Practice [51728]
Vulnerable Children and Youth
Studies [52087]
Barnsley
Assistive Technologies [52177]
Caring UK [52178]
Berkhamsted
Medendium [52313]
Birmingham
Diversity in Health and Social Care
[52340]
Chester
Managed Healthcare Executive
[52997] .... △41,800
London
Advances in Osteoporotic Fracture
Management [53906]
Advances in Psychiatric Treatment
[53907]
Advances in Sepsis [53908]
Best Practice & Research Clinical
Obstetrics & Gynecology [54013]
Clinical Risk [54231]
Critical Care [54288]
Hospital Healthcare Europe [54572]
Hospital Management International
[54574] .... (Non-paid) ★10,039
HSJ [54576] 105,000
Human Resources for Health [54580]
International Clinical Trials [54622]
International Journal of Therapy and
Rehabilitation (IJTR) [54665]
Journal of Cardiovascular Magnetic
Resonance [54718]
Journal of Health Services Research
& Policy [54760]
Pharmaceutical Manufacturing and
Packing Sourcer [55076]
Private Hospital Healthcare Europe
[55122]
Loughton
Health Business [55492]
Truro
Best Practice & Research Clinical
Rheumatology [56773]

HOTELS, MOTELS, RESTAURANTS, AND CLUBS

AUSTRALIA
North Ryde
Sydney Eats [42199]
Pyrmont
Australian Hotelier [42273] 6,508

bars♣
[42275] .... (Combined) ★6,043
Hilton Australasia [42279]
Hotel and Accommodation
Management [42280] 5,578
Spa Australasia [42290]

PEOPLE'S REPUBLIC OF CHINA
Hong Kong
Macau Tatler Best Restaurants
[43366] .... ‡31,100
Shanghai
Shanghai's Best Restaurants
[43505] .... ‡38,000

FRANCE
Clichy
Guide des Relais Routiers
[43933] .. .. (Paid) 50,000

IRELAND
Blackrock
Hotel & Catering Review [45920]
Licensing World [45923]

JAMAICA
Kingston
Destination Jamaica [46283]

JAPAN
Tokyo
Nikkei Restaurants
[47005] .... ★19,137

MALAYSIA
Kuala Lumpur
Malaysia's Best Restaurants
[47622] .... ‡20,800

PHILIPPINES
Makati City
Philippines' Best Restaurants [49524]

SINGAPORE
Singapore
Regional Best Restaurants
[50242] .... ‡16,000
Singapore's Best Restaurants
[50267] .... ‡33,000

SPAIN
Madrid
IH Industria Hostelera
[50768] .... (Combined) 7,000

SWEDEN
Goteborg
Restaurang Guiden
[50963] .. .. (Controlled) ⊕22,000

THAILAND
Bangkok
Thailand's Best Restaurants
[51444] .... ‡115,000

UNITED ARAB EMIRATES
Dubai
Jumeirah [51645] 17,500
Souk [51653] 30,000

UNITED KINGDOM
Abingdon
Tourism and Hospitality Planning &
Development [52082]
Bradford
International Journal of Contemporary
Hospitality Management [52475]

Circulation: ★ = ABC; △ = BPA; ♦ = CAC; • = CCAB; ❑ = VAC; ⊕ = PO Statement; ‡ = Publisher's Report; Boldface figures = sworn; Light figures = estimated.

Gale Directory of Publications & Broadcast Media/147th Ed.   6191

Camberley
BIIBUSINESS [52782]

Colchester
Hotel Business [53038]

Crawley
H - The Hotel Magazine
  [53106] *8,602
Restaurant Equipment
  [53112] 15,776

Gravesend
Casino World [53478]

Heslington
Journal of Hospitality, Leisure, Sports
  & Tourism Education [53568]

Hitchin
Leisure Management [53579]
Leisure Opportunities [53580]

Horsham
Prestige Hotel & Restaurant Interiors
  [53599] .... (Controlled) 3,000

Kent
Casino International
  [53676] *4,487

Leeds
Fish Friers Review [53766]

London
Mood Food [54952]
Olive [55030]
W1 Magazine [55415]

Sutton
Caterer & Hotelkeeper
  [56680] .... (Combined) 36,000
Catering Update
  [56681] .... (Combined) 23,423

Wallington
Building for Leisure
  [56832] .... (Combined) ‡11,706

Ware
Ritz Magazine [56844] .... ‡35,000

Wolverhampton
At the Sign Of [56951]

ZIMBABWE
Harare
The Hospitality Magazine [57114]

HOUSEWARES

**PEOPLE'S REPUBLIC OF
CHINA**
Hong Kong
HKTDC Houseware [43311]

NETHERLANDS
Maarssen
Trends [48735] 4,500

UNITED KINGDOM
Crawley
Restaurant Equipment
  [53112] 15,776
London
Progressive Housewares
  [55139] .... (Controlled) ‡3,500

HUMANITIES

AUSTRALIA
Albury
Micronesian Journal of the Humani-
  ties and Social Sciences [41527]

Hawthorn
Cosmos and History [41942]

BELGIUM
Leuven
Ethical Perspectives [42894]

BRAZIL
Botucatu
Interface [42956]

Vicosa
Novos Estudos Cebrap [43061]

**PEOPLE'S REPUBLIC OF
CHINA**
Changchun
Jilin University Journal Social Sci-
  ences Edition [43239]

CROATIA
Zagreb
Diskrepancija [43567]

FINLAND
Jyvaskyla
Human Technology [43869]

FRANCE
Paris
Journal Asiatique [44063]

GERMANY
Bonn
german research [44262]

Heidelberg
Zeitschrift fur Unternehmens- und
  Gesellschaftsrecht (ZGR) [44480]

GHANA
Accra
Institute of African Studies [44728]

HUNGARY
Budapest
Review of Sociology of the Hungarian
  Sociological Association [44867]
Society and Economy [44870]

INDIA
Chennai
Vivekananda Kendra Patrika
  [45061] .... (Paid) 2,000
Kolkata
Bulletin of the Ramakrishna Mission
  Institute of Culture
  [45260] .... (Paid) 4,200
Mysore
Journal of Indian Folkloristics
  [45458] .... (Paid) 1,100
New Delhi
Indian Journal of Human Rights and
  Justice [45556]
Pondicherry
Mother India [45693] ... (Paid) 1,050
Pune
Mira [45698]

ISRAEL
Ramat Gan
Common Knowledge [46092] 400

ITALY
Naples
Web Journal on Cultural Patrimony
  [46203]

JAPAN
Kyoto
Kyoto Journal
  [46479] .... (Paid) 3,000

Tokyo
Acta Asiatica
  [46721] .... (Paid) 1,000
Journal of American and Canadian
  Studies [46882] .... (Paid) 2,000
Journal of Humanities and Natural
  Sciences [46907] 2,200
Monumenta Nipponica
  [46971] .... (Paid) 1,150

JORDAN
Amman
Dirasat Human and Social Sciences
  [47155] ....: (Controlled) 1,000

KUWAIT
Safat
Arab Journal for the Humanities
  [47335] .., ... (Paid) 2,000

MALAYSIA
Serdang
Pertanika Journal of Social Science
  and Humanities
  [47716] .... (Paid) 200

NETHERLANDS
Amsterdam
Habitat International [48008]

Dordrecht
Biology and Philosophy [48334]
Dialectical Anthropology [48373]

Leiden
Aries [48652]
East Central Europe [48669]
Grotiana [48674]
Hobbes Studies [48676]

NEW ZEALAND
Cromwell
Junctures [48888]

NIGERIA
Ago Iwoye
OYE [49059]

Calabar
Global Journal of Humanities [49073]

PHILIPPINES
Cebu City
Philippine Quarterly of Culture and
  Society [49462] .... (Paid) 280
Manila
Unitas [49560] .... (Paid) 500
Quezon City
Philippine Studies
  [49614] .... (Paid) 650

SINGAPORE
Singapore
Lien [50216]

**REPUBLIC OF SOUTH AF-
RICA**
Johannesburg
Journal of African Elections [50530]

Lynnwood Ridge
Quest [50550]

SWAZILAND
Kwaluseni
International Journal of Humanistic
  Studies [50943]

Matsapha
Lwati [50946]

SWITZERLAND
Dornach
Das Goetheanum
  [51085] .. .. (Paid) 10,246

UNITED KINGDOM
Abingdon
International Gambling Studies
  [51825]
The International Journal of Human
  Rights [51838]
Japan Forum [51865]
Journal of Contemporary African
  Studies [51878]
Journal of Contemporary China
  [51879]
Life Writing [51969]
Terrorism and Political Violence
  [52075]

Buckingham
The Denning Law Journal [52756]

Cambridge
International Journal of Asian Studies
  [52832]

Coventry
Law and Humanities [53088]

Edinburgh
International Journal of Humanities
  and Arts Computing [53288]
Paragraph [53305]

Glasgow
eSharp [53417]

London
Folk Music Journal
  [54476] .... (Paid) 4,000
The Hardy Review [54530]
Interdisciplinary Science Reviews
  [54615]
Journal of European Studies [54748]
Law, Culture & the Humanities
  [54857]
Medical Humanities
  [54923] .... ‡1,770
Philosophy, Ethics, and Humanities in
  Medicine [55082]
Post-Medieval Archaeology [55108]

Oxford
Oral History Review [56128] ... 1,065

Reading
Electronic Journal of Knowledge
  Management [56316]

Southampton
Journal of Medieval History [56574]

Strawberry Hill
Holy Land Studies [56643]

ZIMBABWE
Harare
Zambezia [57120]

INDEXES, ABSTRACTS, REPORTS, PROCEEDINGS, AND BIBLIOGRAPHIES

AUSTRALIA
Parkville
Historical Records of Australian
  Science [42231]

BRAZIL
Bauru
Journal of Applied Oral Science
  [42948]

Sao Paulo
Psicologia USP [43045]

Circulation: ★ = ABC; △ = BPA; ◆ = CAC; • = CCAB; ❑ = VAC; ⊕ = PO Statement; ‡ = Publisher's Report; Boldface figures = sworn; Light figures = estimated.

FRANCE

Sophia Antipolis
Performance Evaluation [44108]

GERMANY

Berlin
Folia Linguistica [44181]

Erlangen
International Archives of Occupational
and Environmental Health [44339]

Heidelberg
Pediatric Surgery International
[44471]

INDIA

Chennai
Hindu Index [45034]

Kolkata
Indian National Bibliography
[45274] .... (Paid) 500
Journal of the Indian Medical Association (JIMA) [45296]

ITALY

Florence
Annali di Storia di Firenze [46141]

Pisa
Bollettino Telematico di Filosofia
Politica [46218]

NETHERLANDS

Amsterdam
Nuclear Physics A [48185]
Nuclear Physics B [48187]
Physics Reports [48203]

Leiden
Journal of Arabic Literature [48688]

UNITED KINGDOM

Abingdon
Psychoanalytic Psychotherapy
[52026]

Basingstoke
International Abstracts in Operations
Research [52208]

Birmingham
Journal of Simulation [52353]

Brentwood
Parasite Immunology [52586]

Cambridge
Biological Reviews [52792]

London
Annual Bibliography of English Lan-
guage & Literature [53951]
Index to Theses [54595]

Oxford
Pediatric Dermatology [56147]

Sheffield
The Indexer [56497] 2,200

INSURANCE

ARGENTINA

Buenos Aires
Journal of Argentine Dermatology
[41476]

AUSTRALIA

Forrestfield
WFOT Bulletin [41868]

Heidelberg
Journal of Oral Pathology and
Medicine [41948]

Melbourne
Australian and New Zealand Institute
of Insurance and Finance Journal
[42052] 11,379

AUSTRIA

Dornbirn
Forum Gesundheit Vorarlberg
[42723] .... (Non-paid) 40,000

BANGLADESH

Dhaka
Insurance Journal
[42812] .... (Paid) 300

BELGIUM

Brussels
European Journal of Hospital
Pharmacy [42853]

PEOPLE'S REPUBLIC OF CHINA

Hong Kong
Journal of Orthopaedic Surgery
[43360]

FRANCE

Paris
The International Journal of Tuberculosis and Lung Disease
[44057] 2,500

Rueil-Malmaison
La Tribune de l'Assurance
[44100] .... (Combined) 15,000

GERMANY

Cologne
German Risk and Insurance Review
[44295]

Munich
LSV aktuell [44569]

Stuttgart
European Journal of Pediatric
Surgery [44667]

INDIA

Hyderabad
The Icfai Journal of Risk & Insurance
[45165]
Insurance Chronicle [45173]

Mumbai
Insurance Institute of India Journal
[45391] ... . (Paid) 15,000

NETHERLANDS

Amsterdam
Rhinology [48226] 1,500

Dordrecht
Health Care Analysis [48412]

Hilversum
Mental Health Reforms
[48631] 1,000

SINGAPORE

Singapore
Singapore Medical Journal
[50260] 4,700

SWEDEN

Stockholm
Scandinavian Actuarial Journal
[51033]

SWITZERLAND

Geneva
Geneva Risk and Insurance Review
[51096] 800

Lausanne
Insurance [51192]

UNITED KINGDOM

Basingstoke
Geneva Papers on Risk and Insurance Issues and Practice
[52205] 950

Birmingham
Journal of Electrophysiological
Technology [52346]

Derby
Annals of Occupational Hygiene
[53163]

Dorking
Company Profile & Financial Strength
Update [53194]

Edinburgh
ASTIN Bulletin [53254]

London
British Actuarial Journal
[54108] 13,400
British Journal of Cancer [54113]
British Journal of Dermatology
[54118]
British Medical Journal
[54139] 28,241
Continuity, Insurance & Risk [54264]
Financial Sector Technology
[54458] *12,776
Health Insurance
[54539] .... (Combined) 10,440
InfoRM [54601] 3,500
Insurance Age
[54610] .. .. (Controlled) *15,880
Insurance Day
[54611] .. .. (Controlled) 7,000
Insurance & Technology
[54612] .. .. (Paid) 18,100
IQ Magazine [54681]
The Journal
[54695] .... (Non-paid) 61,212
Professional Broking [55129]
Public Health [55152]
Reinsurance
[55183] .... (Combined) 8,996
Society of Fellows Journal [55252]
Student BMJ [55268]

Oxford
Risk Management & Insurance
Review [56196]

INTERCULTURAL INTERESTS

AUSTRALIA

Canberra
Asian Studies Review [41699]

Collingwood
Inside Indonesia [41790]

Murdoch
Intersections [42137]

Sydney
Philament [42561]

AUSTRIA

Vienna
European Journal of Cross-Cultural
Competence and Management
[42751]

BELGIUM

Brussels
European Voice [42854] .... △18,241

Rekkem
Septentrion [42910] ... (Paid) 10,000

BHUTAN

Thimphu
Journal of Bhutan Studies [42925]

BRAZIL

Campinas
Cadernos Pagu [42966]

BULGARIA

Sofia
Etudes Balkaniques [43098]

PEOPLE'S REPUBLIC OF CHINA

Hong Kong
The Journal of Dagaare Studies
(JDS) [43355]

Shanghai
Using the Right Word [43509]

CROATIA

Zagreb
Croatian International Relations
Review [43564] 1,000
Razvoj/Development [43570] 500

DENMARK

Copenhagen
Djembe [43665] 1,500
Scando-Slavica [43683]

EGYPT

Cairo
Afro-Arab Selections for Social
Sciences [43751]

FINLAND

Helsinki
Books from Finland
[43821] .... (Combined) 2,800

FRANCE

Paris
Revue des Deux Mondes
[44079] .. .. (Combined) 27,000

GERMANY

Berlin
Das Neue China [44169] 2,000
Kritikon Litterarum [44212] 150
Lebende Sprachen [44218]

Hamburg
Der Islam [44413] 500

Regensburg
Armenisch-Deutsche Korrespondenz
[44642] 680

HUNGARY

Budapest
Hungarian Studies [44837]

ICELAND

Reykjavik
Scandinavian Journal of History
[44903]

INDIA

Allahabad
Journal of the Interdisciplinary
Crossroads [44934]

Dharamsala
Tibet Journal [45112] ... (Paid) 1,000

Hyderabad
The Icfai Journal of History and
Culture [45155]

Circulation: ★ = ABC; △ = BPA; ◆ = CAC; • = CCAB; ❑ = VAC; ⊕ = PO Statement; ‡ = Publisher's Report; Boldface figures = sworn; Light figures = estimated.

Trade, Technical, and Professional Publications

The Icfai Journal of Urban Policy
[45169]

Madras
Institute of Asian Studies Journal
[45335] .... (Paid) 500

Mumbai
Opportunities Today
[45424] 15,000
Surabhi [45445]

New Delhi
Africa Quarterly
[45478] .... (Paid) 1,900
Youth Hosteller [45671] 45,000

IRELAND
Galway
Australian Journal of Irish Studies
[46016]

Maynooth
Irish Journal of American Studies
[46038] 100

ITALY
Genoa
Textus [46154]

JAPAN
Kyoto
Kyoto Journal
[46479] .... (Paid) 3,000

Tokyo
Acta Asiatica
[46721] .... (Paid) 1,000
The East [46804]
The Japanese Journal of American
Studies [46862]
Monumenta Nipponica
[46971] .... (Paid) 1,150
The Plaza [47019]

REPUBLIC OF KOREA
Seoul
Koreana
[47283] .... (Non-paid) 5,500

NETHERLANDS
Amsterdam
Amsterdam Monographs in American
Studies [47890]
Andon [47894]
EAIE Forum [47961] 2,000
Matatu [48142]
Nature, Culture and Literature
[48170]
Revista Europea de Estudios Lati-
noamericanos y del Caribe [48225]

Dordrecht
Contemporary Islam [48360]

Groningen
Indo-Iranian Journal [48602]

Leiden
African Diaspora [48644]
Brill's Annual of Afroasiatic Lan-
guages and Linguistics [48658]
Die Welt des Islams [48668]
Index Islamicus [48677]
Medieval Encounters [48708]
Middle East Journal of Culture and
Communication [48710]
T'oung Pao [48728]
Zutot [48730]

NORWAY
Oslo
The Norseman [49205]

POLAND
Warsaw
Limes [49731]

ROMANIA
Bucharest
Romanian Journal of Society and
Politics [49843]

SINGAPORE
Singapore
China [50119]

SLOVAKIA
Bratislava
SPEX [50323]

**REPUBLIC OF SOUTH AF-
RICA**
Grahamstown
Journal of Social Development in
Africa [50503] .. .. (Combined) 150

Houghton
Jewish Affairs
[50524] .. .. (Combined) ⊕1,000

Overport
Transformation [50560]

Pretoria
African Journal of Cross-Cultural Psychology and Sport Facilitation
[50583]
Africanus [50584]

SPAIN
Barcelona
L'Avenc [50653] 8,000
Guaraguao [50675]

Madrid
Cuadernos Hispanoamericanos
[50744]
Intercultural Pragmatics [50772]
Leviatan [50778]

Oviedo
International Journal of Chinese Culture & Management [50823]

Santiago de Compostela
A Trabe de Ouro [50832]

SWEDEN
Boras
Journal of Intercultural
Communication [50950]

SWITZERLAND
Bern
Multilingua [51076]

Zurich
Passages [51276]

UKRAINE
Kiev
Novynar
[51603] .. .. (Combined) 150,000

UNITED KINGDOM
Abingdon
African Studies [51699]
Central Asian Survey [51726]
Citizenship Studies [51730]
Culture and Religion [51749]
Inter-Asia Cultural Studies [51821]
Intercultural Education [51822]
International Journal of Cultural
Policy [51831]
Israel Affairs [51863]
Journal of African Cultural Studies
[51868]
Journal of the Asia Pacific Economy
[51870]

Journal of Balkan and Near Eastern
Studies [51871]
Journal of Contemporary African
Studies [51878]
Journal of Contemporary European
Studies [51880]
Journal for Cultural Research [51883]
Journal of Latin American Cultural
Studies [51913]
Journal of Multicultural Discourses
[51922]
Journal of Southern African Studies
[51944]
Media History [51972]
Mediterranean Historical Review
[51975]
Modern Italy [51986]
Politikon [52019]

Bristol
Culture and Organization [52660]

Caerfyrddin
Cambria [52781]

Edinburgh
Journal of Scottish Philosophy
[53295]
New Blackfriars [53303]

Glasgow
Journal of Baltic Studies [53426]
Variant [53457]

Leeds
British Journal of Middle Eastern
Studies [53759]

London
Africa [53915]
Asian Affairs [53973] ... (Paid) 1,500
Austrian Studies [53982]
Black History Month
[54033] .. .. (Free) 100,000
Byzantine and Modern Greek Studies
[54162]
Comparative American Studies
[54248]
Cultural Geographies [54293]
Early Medieval China [54346]
Hispanic Research Journal [54553]
International African Bibliography
[54619]
The Italianist [54685]
Mela UK [54925]
Ming Studies [54938]
Palestine Exploration Quarterly
[55051]
Portuguese Studies [55105]
Publications of the English Goethe
Society [55154]
Seventeenth-Century French Studies
[55229]
Slavonica [55242] 200
Slovo [55243]
South East Asia Research [55257]
T'ang Studies [55292]
Tel Aviv [55296]
UK Baha'i Journal [55353]

Manchester
Italian Studies [55562] ... (Paid) 500
The Translator [55580]

Middlesbrough
Spatial Practices [55612]

Newcastle upon Tyne
Interspectives [55673]

Oxford
South African Journal of Economics
[56212]

**INTERIOR
DESIGN/DECORATING**
See also Paint and Wallcov-
erings

AUSTRALIA
North Ryde
Bathroom Yearbook [42173]
Kit Homes [42184]
Kitchen Yearbook [42185]
Kitchens and Bathrooms Quarterly
[42186]
Poolside [42193]
Poolside Showcase
[42194] 30,000
Smart Kitchens & Bathrooms
[42197] 25,000
Stone [42198] 12,000

Pyrmont
Interior Fitout [42282] .... ★5,466

**PEOPLE'S REPUBLIC OF
CHINA**
Hong Kong
Home Journal [43317]
Home Journal Buyer's Guide
[43318] .... ‡36,570
Hong Kong Design Services [43323]
Luxe Living Kitchens & Bathrooms
[43364] .... ‡25,000

Shanghai
Shanghai Residence
[43500] 30,000

FRANCE
Paris
Intramuros
[44061] .. .. (Combined) 25,000

GERMANY
Leinfelden-Echterdingen
Malerblatt [44526] 23,096

Munich
DECO [44556] .... (Paid) 68,000

HUNGARY
Budapest
Otthon [44863] .... (Paid) 41,066

INDIA
Mumbai
Better Interiors [45355]

IRELAND
Dublin
Irish Kitchens and Bathrooms
[45979] 25,000

ITALY
Milan
Officelayout [46190] 20,000

JAPAN
Tokyo
Axis [46758]
Nikkei Design
[46986] .... (Paid) ★13,370

LATVIA
Riga
Musmajas [47373]
Una [47374] .. .. (Paid) 18,000

NETHERLANDS
Amsterdam
Frame
[47989] .. .. (Combined) 17,000

Circulation: ★ = ABC; △ = BPA; ◆ = CAC; ● = CCAB; ❑ = VAC; ⊕ = PO Statement; ‡ = Publisher's Report; Boldface figures = sworn; Light figures = estimated.

The Hague
De Architect
[48611] .... (Combined) 8,192

PHILIPPINES
Quezon City
Metro Home & Entertaining [49601]

POLAND
Warsaw
Dom & Wnetrze [49705] ..... ‡20,283

ROMANIA
Bucharest
Elle Decoration [49835] .... ‡9,469

SINGAPORE
Singapore
Home & Decor [50167] 27,000
Singapore Tatler Homes
[50263] .... ‡14,000
Space [50271]

SPAIN
Barcelona
Arquitectura y Diseno
[50650] .... ‡47,513
Clara Deco [50658]
El Mueble Casas de Campo
[50671] .... ‡43,155
El Mueble Cocinas y Banos
[50672] .... ‡20,535
Habitania [50676] .... ‡44,184

Madrid
Casa al Dia [50734] .... ‡87,531

THAILAND
Bangkok
Essential Guide to Home & Decor
[51420] .... ‡63,350

UKRAINE
Kiev
Interior Magazine
[51598] .... (Combined) 17,500
Lyubimaya Datcha
[51601] .... ‡20,000
Uyutnaya Kvartira [51611]

UNITED KINGDOM
Battle
Furniture News
[52269] .... (Non-paid) 7,000

Colchester
Period Ideas [53046]

Hale
Living Edge [53503]

Horsham
Prestige Corporate Interiors
[53597] .... (Controlled) 3,000
Prestige High Street Interiors
[53598] .... (Controlled) 3,000
Prestige Hotel & Restaurant Interiors
[53599] .... (Controlled) 3,000

London
Candid [54172] 8,000
Good Homes [54520] .... ★127,202
Homes & Antiques
[54567] .... ★55,100
Ideal Home [54582]
Period Living [55068]
Wallpaper* [55377] .... ★113,000
The World of Interiors
[55421] .... (Paid) 65,000

Solihull
Interiors Focus [56564]

Wadhurst
Construction Europe
[56805] .... ★14,624

Ware
Champneys Magazine
[56840] 50,000

INTERNATIONAL AFFAIRS

BANGLADESH
Dhaka
Equity Dialogue [42809]

BRAZIL
Sao Paulo
Sao Paulo em Perspectiva [43051]

CROATIA
Zagreb
Croatian International Relations
Review [43564] 1,000
Razvoj/Development [43570] 500

CZECH REPUBLIC
Prague
Mezinarodni Vztahy International
Relations [43630] 7,500
Perspectives - The Central European
Review of International Affairs
[43634]

FIJI
Lautoka
Fijian Studies [43806]

FRANCE
Paris
UNESCO Courier
[44087] .... (Non-paid) 40,000

GERMANY
Augsburg
Paneuropa Deutschland [44141]

Berlin
European Biotechnology Science &
Industry News [44173] 15,000

Frankfurt am Main
Olympisches Feuer [44367]

Kassel
Journal of Agriculture and Rural De-
velopment in the Tropics and
Subtropics [44498]

Konstanz
European Union Politics [44512]

HUNGARY
Budapest
Acta Juridica Hungarica [44812]
Acta Oeconomica [44815]
Central European Political Science
Review [44826]

INDONESIA
Jakarta
Indonesian Quarterly
[45800] .... (Paid) 3,000

IRELAND
Dublin
Irish Studies in International Affairs
[45985]

ITALY
Florence
European Journal of International
Law [46143]

Rome
Attualita Italia-Australia
[46222] ....:... (Non-paid) 6,000

International Journal of Technology
and Globalisation [46235]

JAPAN
Tokyo
The Japanese Journal of American
Studies [46862]

KUWAIT
Safat
Journal of the Gulf and Arabian Pen-
insula Studies [47338]

MALAYSIA
Petaling Jaya
European Journal of Innovation
Management [47696]

MEXICO
Mexicali
Estudios Fronterizos [47780]

Mexico City
CIMMYT Annual Report .
[47783] 5,000

NETHERLANDS
Alphen aan den Rijn
Air & Space Law [47865]

Amsterdam
Revista Europea de Estudios Latinoamericanos y del Caribe [48225]

Dordrecht
International Journal for the Advancement of Counseling [48425]

Leiden
African Diaspora [48644]
China Information [48661]
Global Responsibility to Protect
[48673]
The Law and Practice of International
Courts and Tribunals [48707]

NIGERIA
Calabar
Global Journal of Agricultural
Sciences [49069]

Ibadan
African Journal of International Affairs
and Development [49083]

Lagos
African Journal of Political Science &
International Relations [49135]

SENEGAL
Dakar
African Journal of International Affairs
[50079]

SINGAPORE
Singapore
Asia Europe Journal [50104]

Singapore City
Asian Security Review
[50311] 10,000
Singapore Academy of Law Journal
[50314]

**REPUBLIC OF SOUTH AF-
RICA**
Grahamstown
African Journal of Economic Policy
[50488]

Mount Edgecombe
Conflict Trends Magazine [50558]

Pretoria
Africa Insight [50581]

SRI LANKA
Panadura
Losetha [50922] 2,000

SWITZERLAND
Geneva
International Journal of Border Secu-
rity and Immigration Policy [51105]

TAIWAN
Tamsui
Tamkang Journal of International
Affairs [51396]

UNITED KINGDOM
Abingdon
Asian Population Studies [51708]
Australian Journal of International
Affairs [51714]
Cambridge Review of International
Affairs [51725]
Development Southern Africa [51756]
Diplomacy & Statecraft [51758]
Europe-Asia Studies [51778]
European Security [51784]
Global Crime [51796]
Global Public Health [51797]
Global Society [51798]
Globalisation, Societies and
Education [51799]
Globalizations [51800]
International Feminist Journal of
Politics [51824]
The International Spectator [51855]
Journal of Contemporary China
[51879]
Journal of Global Ethics [51902]
Journal of Intervention and
Statebuilding [51911]
Military Balance [51981]
Nationalities Papers [51990]
Nonproliferation Review [52000]
Perspectives on European Politics
and Society [52009]
Post-Communist Economies [52020]
Strategic Survey [52065]
Third World Quarterly [52078]

Birmingham
Journal of Security Sector
Management [52352]

Bradford
Critical Perspectives on International
Business [52448]
Foresight [52461]

Brighton
International Journal of Migration,
Health and Social Care [52617]

Bristol
Policy and Politics [52722]

Edinburgh
Derrida Today [53269]

Exeter
Africa Research Bulletin [53345]
Africa Research Bulletin [53346]

Leicester
European Foreign Affairs Review
[53799]

London
Africa Confidential [53916]
Asian Affairs [53973] ... (Paid) 1,500
Big Issue Namibia
[54016] .... ★136,018
BMC International Health and Human
Rights [54063]
Bosnia Report [54100]
Cooperation and Conflict [54266]
European Journal of International
Relations [54401]

Circulation: ★ = ABC; △ = BPA; ◆ = CAC; • = CCAB; ❑ = VAC; ⊕ = PO Statement; ‡ = Publisher's Report; Boldface figures = sworn; Light figures = estimated.

Journal of Peace Research [54793]
Journal of Theoretical Politics [54828]
Millennium [54934] .... (Paid) ‡1,000
NewsAfrica [55004]
Party Politics [55060]
Politics, Philosophy & Economics [55100]
Progress in Development Studies [55135]
red pepper [55178]
Security Dialogue [55226]
Slovo [55243]
Survival [55283]
WDM in Action [55393]

Newcastle upon Tyne
Interspectives [55673]

Olney
International Journal of Environment and Sustainable Development [55803]

Oxford
Chinese Journal of International Law [55908]
Comparative Strategy [55914]
Contemporary Review [55916]
Cultural Politics [55920]
Foreign Policy Analysis [55959]
Global Networks (Oxford) [55966]
International Journal of Constitutional Law [55992]
International Relations of the Asia-Pacific [56006]
Journal of African Economies [56012]
Journal of International Criminal Justice [56044]
Journal of Refugee Studies [56065]
Political Studies Review [56167]

Skipton
Eye Spy [56554]

Swindon
Fourth World Review [56711]

Witney
The Journal of International Maritime Law [56944]

Woodbridge
International School [56956]

INTERNATIONAL BUSINESS AND ECONOMICS

ARGENTINA
Buenos Aires
Comments on Argentine Trade [41471]
Integration and Trade [41474]

AUSTRALIA
Burwood
The Journal of International Trade and Economic Development [41676]

Clayton
International Journal of Business Intelligence and Data Mining [41761]

Sydney
International Journal of Housing Markets and Analysis [42520]

PEOPLE'S REPUBLIC OF CHINA
Beijing
China's Foreign Trade [43181] .. .. (Paid) 70,000

DENMARK
Odense
International Journal of Business Per-

formance and Supply Chain Modelling [43728]

EGYPT
Cairo
Business Today Egypt [43752]
Egypt Today [43755] 14,500

FRANCE
Le Havre
International Journal of Adaptive and Innovative Systems [43963]

Paris
Aide et Action [44023]

GERMANY
Bonn
TECNOLOGIA MILITAR [44271] 10,000

Dreieich
Made in Germany—International Edition [44318] ...... (Combined) ‡110,000

HUNGARY
Budapest
Central European Political Science Review [44826]

ICELAND
Reykjavik
European Journal of International Management [44900]

INDIA
Bangalore
Indian Silk [44962]

Chennai
Indo - US Business [45040] .. .. (Paid) 1,800

Hyderabad
The Icfai Journal of Bank Management [45143]

New Delhi
Indian Growth and Development Review [45475]
International Journal of Applied Business and Economic Research [45580]
Overseas Business Contacts [45634] .. .. (Paid) 4,000

IRAN
Tehran
Iran Exports & Imports [45892] .. .. (Paid) 5,000

ITALY
Messina
International Journal of Economic Policy in Emerging Economies [46157]
International Journal of Monetary Economics & Finance [46158]
International Journal of Trade and Global Markets [46159]

Milan
Industrial and Corporate Change [46175]
Mani Tese [46187] 36,000

Rome
Attualita Italia-Australia [46222] .... (Non-paid) 6,000

JAPAN
Tokyo
Economics of Governance [46806]

International Journal of Asian Management [46845]
Nikkei Business [46981] ... ★308,561

REPUBLIC OF KOREA
Seoul
American Chamber of Commerce in Korea [47252]

LATVIA
Riga
Journal of International Business Education [47370]

MALAYSIA
Kuala Lumpur
Business Times [47601]
Malaysian Business [47614]

MEXICO
Mexico City
International Journal of Business Competition and Growth [47785]

MONACO
Monte Carlo
Luxury Intelligence [47810]

MOROCCO
Casablanca
Tijaris [47813]

NETHERLANDS
Amsterdam
Journal of Accounting and Economics [48036]
Journal of Development Economics [48067]

Dordrecht
Journal of Management and Governance [48471]

Leiden
International Organizations Law Review [48683]

Utrecht
Global Business and Economics Review [48759]

PAKISTAN
Faisalabad
International Business Management [49248]

POLAND
Warsaw
Folia Oeconomica Stetinensia [49711]

SINGAPORE
Singapore
Asian Case Research Journal [50106]

SLOVENIA
Koper
International Journal of Sustainable Economy [50332]

Ljubljana
Journal of International Relations and Development [50339]

REPUBLIC OF SOUTH AFRICA
Grahamstown
Securities Market Journal [50512]

SPAIN
Oviedo
International Journal of Chinese Culture & Management [50823]

Oviedo-Asturias
International Journal of Arab Culture, Management and Sustainable Development [50826]

Santiago de Compostela
Applied Econometrics and International Development [50831]

Valencia
Valencia Maritima [50847]

SWITZERLAND
Geneva
International Journal of Applied Decision Sciences [51100]
International Journal of Applied Management Science [51101]
International Journal of Business and Emerging Markets [51106]
International Journal of Business Excellence [51107]
International Journal of Business Forecasting and Marketing Intelligence [51108]
International Journal of Corporate Governance [51113]
International Journal of Economics and Business Research [51116]
International Journal of Information and Decision Sciences [51125]
International Journal of Inventory Research [51127]
International Journal of Sustainable Manufacturing [51142]
International Journal of Sustainable Strategic Management [51144]
International Trade FORUM [51150]

TAIWAN
Taipei
Contemporary Management Research [51336]
Taiwan International Trade [51364]

UNITED KINGDOM
Abingdon
Accounting, Business & Financial History [51693]
Globalizations [51800]
International Economic Journal [51823]
Japanese Studies [51866]
The Pacific Review [52003]
Review of International Political Economy [52042]
Strategic Survey [52065]

Basingstoke
Maritime Economics and Logistics [52223] 600

Belfast
Offshore Investment [52291]

Bradford
European Business Review [52457]
International Journal of Emerging Markets [52477]
International Journal of Entrepreneurial Behaviour & Research [52478]
International Journal of Operations and Production Management [52482]
International Journal of Physical Distribution and Logistics Management [52484]
International Journal of Quality and Reliability Management [52486]

Journal of Enterprising Communities [52498]
Journal of European Industrial Training [52499]

Chester
Pharmaceutical Technology Europe [52998] .. .... (Controlled) △18,000

Guildford
Journal of Chinese Economic and Business Studies [53492]

Kent
Casino International [53676] .... ★4,487

London
Africa Monitor. West & Central Africa [53917]
African Farming and Food Processing [53920] 10,755
African Review of Business and Technology [53925] .... ★13,440
Benelux unquote [54012]
Central Europe Monitor [54194]
China Economic Review [54207] 9,537
Communications Africa [54246] .... ★9,034
Competition & Change [54252]
Competition Law Insight [54253]
Cosmetics International [54271] .. .. (Paid) 2,000
Deutsche unquote [54322]
Environment and Urbanization [54374] 3,100
Far Eastern Agriculture [54443] .... ★7,050
First [54462] ... (Combined) 157,000
Focus Europe [54475]
Global Investor [54511] 8,100
International Journal of Business Performance Management [54636]
International Journal of Islamic and Middle Eastern Finance and Management [54652]
International Journal of Technology Management & Sustainable Development [54664]
International Securities Finance [54670]
Management Today [54902] .. .. ★100,184
NewsAfrica [55004]
Nordic unquote [55009]
Oil Review Middle East [55027] .... ★9,034
Operational Risk & Regulation [55038]
Private Equity Europe [55121]
Professional Adviser [55127]
South East Europe Monitor [55258]
Technical Review Middle East [55294] .... ★12,017
UK Unquote [55355] 3,500
Your Mortgage [55434] 15,000

Nottingham
International Journal of Public Sector Management [55762]

Olney
International Journal of Financial Services Management [55805]
Journal for Global Business Advancement [55843]
Journal for International Business and Entrepreneurship Development [55844]

Oxford
JCMS: Journal of Common Market Studies [56010]
Review of International Economics [56193]

Sheffield
The Journal of Corporate Citizenship [56504] .... ‡750

Surrey
The European Yearbook of Business History [56662]

Wadhurst
Construction Europe [56805] .. .. ★14,624

VIETNAM
Ho Chi Minh City
Saigon Times Weekly [57057] 30,000

JEWELRY, WATCHES, AND CLOCKS

PEOPLE'S REPUBLIC OF CHINA
Hong Kong
HKTDC Jewellery [43312]
HKTDC Watch & Clock [43316]
Hong Kong Jewelry Express [43326] 7,000
Sparkle [43383] .... ‡21,500

Wuhan
Gems and Gemmology [43522]

FINLAND
Espoo
Kello and Kulta [43812]

GERMANY
Nuremberg
Industrie Diamanten Rundschau [44615] 6,800

Ulm
Klassik Uhren [44696] 7,339

INDIA
Jaipur
Diamond World [45193] 8,000
Gem & Jewellery Yearbook [45194] .... (Paid) 4,500
Journal of Gem Industry [45197] 8,750

ITALY
Rome
La Clessidra [46237] .. .. (Combined) 25,000

NEW ZEALAND
Christchurch
Jewellery Time [48870]

SINGAPORE
Singapore
Global Sources Fashion Accessories [50154]
Icon Moments [50169] .... (Combined) 20,000
NuYou Time [50231] 20,000

SWITZERLAND
Geneva
Europa Star [51092] .. .. (Combined) △10,000
Europa Star [51093]
Europa Star International [51094] 10,000
Tribune des Arts [51161] .. ... ‡72,000

UNITED ARAB EMIRATES
Dubai
Jumeirah [51645] 17,500

UNITED KINGDOM
London
Goldsmiths Review [54517] 4,500
The Journal of Gemmology [54756] 4,000

Newark
Horological Journal [55659] .... (Controlled) 3,800

Ware
Paul Sheeran Magazine [56843]
Sunseeker Magazine [56845] 170,000

JOURNALISM AND PUBLISHING
See also Book Trade and Author News; Communications

AUSTRALIA
Brisbane
Australian Studies in Journalism [41642]

Rockhampton
Ejournalist [42315]

PEOPLE'S REPUBLIC OF CHINA
Hong Kong
The Correspondent [43294] .. . 1,800

FINLAND
Helsinki
Julkaisija [43836] .... (Combined) ‡2,500
Suomen Lehdisto [43861] .... (Combined) 2,404

FRANCE
Riberac
The African Book Publishing Record [44098] .... (Paid) 300

ITALY
Milan
Prima Comunicazione [46191] .... (Paid) ‡15,000

Trieste
PoS (Proceedings of Science) [46266]

JAPAN
Tokyo
Asian-Pacific Book Development [46755] .. .. (Paid) 2,500

REPUBLIC OF SOUTH AFRICA
Grahamstown
Rhodes Journalism Review [50511]

SPAIN
Madrid
Delibros [50751]

SWEDEN
Goteborg
Nordicom Review [50961]

UNITED KINGDOM
Abingdon
Journalism Studies [51959]
New Writing [51999]

Huddersfield
Free Press [53620] .. .... (Paid) 5,250

London
British Journalism Review [54138]
The Edge [54353] 2,000
The Journal [54693] .... (Controlled) 2,000
Journalism [54839]
Journalist [54840]
Magazine News [54894] .... (Non-paid) ‡10,000
Media, Culture & Society [54920]

Luton
Convergence [55501]

Nottingham
International Journal of Remote Sensing [55763]

Shepperton
Bookbinder [56520]

Shoreham-by-Sea
Learned Publishing [56525] 700

Taunton
Powys Journal [56722] 400

Walton-on-Thames
The Woman Writer [56837]

LABOR
See also Employment and Human Resources

BELGIUM
Brussels
EPI [42851]

FINLAND
Helsinki
Tyo Terveys Turvallisuus [43863] .. .. (Controlled) 62,933

FRANCE
Ferney-Voltaire
Focus on the Public Services [43947] .... (Free) 17,000

GERMANY
Leinfelden-Echterdingen
ErgoMed [44524] 2,800

INDIA
Delhi
IAMR Working Paper [45094]
Indian Labour Journal [45098] .... (Paid) 1,250
Manpower Journal [45103] .... (Paid) 500

Hyderabad
The Icfai Journal of Employment Law [45148]

Kolkata
Personnel Today [45301] .... (Paid) 6,000

Nagpur
Labour and Industrial Cases [45469] .... (Paid) 4,000

New Delhi
AIOE Labour News [45481] .... (Paid) 1,000
Labour and Industrial Law Reporter [45621]
Working Class [45669] .... (Paid) 6,500

JAPAN
Tokyo
Japan Labor Review [46858]

Circulation: ★ = ABC; △ = BPA; ◆ = CAC; • = CCAB; ❑ = VAC; ⊕ = PO Statement; ‡ = Publisher's Report; Boldface figures = sworn; Light figures = estimated.

NETHERLANDS
The Hague
Forum [48616] ... . (Non-paid) 30,000

PHILIPPINES
Manila
Philippine Labor Review
[49557] ... . (Paid) 2,000

POLAND
Warsaw
Archives of Industrial Hygiene and
Toxicology [49691]

REPUBLIC OF SOUTH AFRICA
Pretoria
South African Journal of Labour
Relations [50603]

SWEDEN
Stockholm
Jamsides
[51023] ... . (Combined) 30,000
Socionomen [51040] 9,000

SWITZERLAND
Geneva
Union [51164]
World of Work [51169]

Zurich
Syna die Gewerkschaft [51291]

UNITED KINGDOM
Abingdon
International Economic Journal
[51823]
Reflective Practice [52035]

Bradford
Journal of Workplace Learning
[52518]
The Learning Organization [52521]
Team Performance Management
[52550]

Cambridge
Workplace Law [52905]

Coventry
EurOhs Magazine
[53081] ... . (Controlled) 10,000

Cromhall
the HR Director
[53119] .... (Controlled) ★10,000

Littleport
Training Journal
[53867] ... . (Paid) 3,500

London
Fonstret [54477]
Occupational Pensions [55025]

Sheffield
Hazards [56496]

Uxbridge
International Journal of Work Organisation & Emotion [56799]

VENEZUELA
Maracaibo
Gaceta Laboral [57026]

LABORATORY RESEARCH (SCIENTIFIC AND MEDICAL)

AUSTRALIA
Melbourne
Growth Factors [42062]

Wahroonga
What's New in LAB Technology
[42681] .... ★6,233

Womying
International Journal of Biological
Sciences [42710]

Woolgoolga
Journal of Near Infrared
Spectroscopy [42715]

AUSTRIA
Gross Enzersdorf
Labor Direct
[42726] .... (Non-paid) 7,000

Laxenburg
Options [42731] 5,000

Vienna
Journal of Neural Transmission
[42762]

BELGIUM
Ghent
Nephrology Dialysis Transplantation
[42887]

BOTSWANA
Gaborone
Botswana Journal of Technology
[42943]

BRAZIL
Bauru
Journal of Applied Oral Science
[42948]

Botafogo
International Braz J Urol
[42954] 6,000

Botucatu
The Journal of Venomous Animals
and Toxins including Tropical
Diseases [42957]

Curitiba
Brazilian Archives of Biology and
Technology (BABT) [42976]

Ribeirao Preto
Brazilian Journal of Medical and Biological Research [42996]

Rio de Janeiro
Memorias do Instituto Oswaldo Cruz
[43012]

Vacaria
Neotropical Entomology [43053]

CAMEROON
Buea
Journal of the Cameroon Academy of
Sciences [43124]

CHILE
Santiago
Acta Bioethica [43142]

PEOPLE'S REPUBLIC OF CHINA
Beijing
World Journal of Gastroenterology
[43225]

Hefei
International Journal of Nanoparticles
[43266]

Hong Kong
Asian Anthropology [43274]

Shanghai
Cell Research [43467]

Laboratory Research and Exploration
[43485]

Taiyuan
International Journal of Bio-Inspired
Computation [43515]

Wuhan
Safety and Environmental
Engineering [43525]

Xi'an
Chinese Heart Journal [43528]
Journal of Fourth Military University
[43533]

COLOMBIA
Bogota
Acta Biologica Colombiana [43541]

CROATIA
Zagreb
Croatian Medical Journal [43565]

CZECH REPUBLIC
Brno
Acta Veteriniaria Brno [43601]

Ceske Budejovice
Folia Parasitologica [43605]

DENMARK
Arhus
Growth Hormone & IGF Research
[43646]

Copenhagen
The Clinical Respiratory Journal
[43659]
Danish Medical Bulletin [43660]
Nuclear Instruments and Methods in
Physics Research Section B
[43680]
Scandinavian Journal of Laboratory
Animal Science [43681]

Frederiksberg
Oral Diseases [43693]

EGYPT
Alexandria
International Journal of Biotechnology
& Biochemistry (IJBB) [43745]

Cairo
Egyptian Journal of Biomedical
Sciences [43757]
Egyptian Journal of Biotechnology
[43758]
Egyptian Journal of Medical Laboratory Sciences [43760]
New Egyptian Journal of Microbiology
[43763]

Ismailia
Egyptian Journal of Natural History
[43774]

FRANCE
Nice
Journal of the European Academy of
Dermatology and Venereology
[44016]

Paris
L'Actualite Chimique
[44021] ... . (Paid) 5,000
Leukemia [44068]

Rennes
Granular Matter [44097]

GEORGIA
Tbilisi
Annals of Biomedical Research and
Education [44130]

GERMANY
Augsburg
Progress in Solid State Chemistry
[44142]

Berlin
Clinical Chemistry and Laboratory
Medicine [44165]
International Journal of Colorectal
Disease [44192]
LaboratoriumsMedizin [44213]
Mammalia [44220]

Biebergemund
Entomologia Generalis [44244]

Bonn
European Journal of Development
Research [44257]

Erlangen
Strahlentherapie und Onkologie
[44342]

Giessen
Cardiovascular Research [44384]

Heidelberg
Basic Research in Cardiology
[44441]
European Spine Journal [44456]
Hernia [44459]
Pediatric Surgery International
[44471]
Rheumatology International [44475]

Jena
Journal of Cancer Research and
Clinical Oncology [44490]

Munich
Fraunhofer (English) [44562]
Fraunhofer Magazin [44563]

Munster
Journal of Business Chemistry
(JoBC) [44599]

Saarbrucken
Progress in Materials Science
[44652]

Stuttgart
Advances in Bryology [44659]
Bibliotheca Mycologica [44662]
Diatom Research [44665]
Eiszeitalter und Gegenwart Quaternary Science Journal [44666]
Fundamental and Applied Limnology
[44668]
Nuclear Engineering and Design
[44674]

Tubingen
Progress in Particle and Nuclear
Physics [44693]

Weinheim
ChemMedChem [44704]

Wurzburg
Cytogenetic and Genome Research
[44719]

GHANA
Accra
Ghana Medical Journal [44726]

HUNGARY
Budapest
Acta Biologica Hungarica [44808]
Acta Microbiologica et Immunologica
Hungarica [44814]
Review of Sociology of the Hungarian
Sociological Association [44867]

INDIA
Bangalore
Pharmacognosy @MAG [44980]

Circulation: ★ = ABC; △ = BPA; ◆ = CAC; • = CCAB; ❑ = VAC; ⊕ = PO Statement; ‡ = Publisher's Report; Boldface figures = sworn; Light figures = estimated.

Systematic Reviews in Pharmacy
[44988]

Chennai
International Journal of Spray and
Combustion Dynamics [45042]

Delhi
Indian Journal of Allergy Asthma and
Immunology [45096]

Jodhpur
Advances in Plant Physiology
[45213]
Journal of Phytopharmacotherapy
and Natural Products [45227]

Kolkata
Journal of the Indian Medical Association (JIMA) [45296]
Nano Science and Nano Technology
[45299]

Meerut
Current Enzyme Inhibition [45344]

Mumbai
Indian Journal of Critical Care
Medicine [45379]
International Journal for Ayurveda
Research [45392]
International Journal of Emerging and
Multidisciplinary Fluid Science
[45394]
Journal of Association of Physicians
of India [45395] 200,000
Journal of Minimal Access Surgery
(JMAS) [45403]
Pharmacognosy Research [45430]
Young Scientists Journal [45451]

New Delhi
Journal of Laboratory Physicians
[45612]

Pondicherry
Indian Journal of Medical
Microbiology [45692]

Rajkot
Materials Science [45709]

IRAN
Isfahan
Journal of Research in Medical
Sciences [45879]

IRELAND
Dundrum
Irish Medical News
[46009] .... ★6,750

ITALY
Bologna
4OR [46126]

Milan
The Journal of Vascular Access
[46184]

JAPAN
Kyoto
Chemistry Letters
[46468] .... ‡43,200

Tokyo
Acta Mathematica Sinica [46724]
Archives of Microbiology [46750]
Biological & Pharmaceutical Bulletin
[46764]
Cancer Chemotherapy and
Pharmacology [46777]
Cancer Immunology, Immunotherapy
[46778]
Cellular and Molecular Life Sciences
[46780]
Clinical Autonomic Research [46788]

Esophagus [46814]
European Food Research and
Technology [46816]
European Journal of Applied
Physiology [46817]
Inflammation Research [46842]
Journal of Headache and Pain
[46902]
Journal of Molecular Medicine
[46928]
Modern Rheumatology [46970]
Proceedings of the Japan Academy,
Series A [47026]

KENYA
Nairobi
East African Medical Journal [47181]
East and Central African Journal of
Pharmaceutical Sciences [47182]
Journal of Civil Engineering Research
and Practice [47187]
Journal of Tropical Microbiology and
Biotechnology [47190]

REPUBLIC OF KOREA
Seoul
Biochemistry and Molecular Biology
Reports [47258]

MALAWI
Blantyre
Malawi Medical Journal [47566]

MALAYSIA
Kuala Lumpur
Biomedical Imaging and Intervention
Journal [47600]

MAURITIUS
Curepipe
Internet Journal of Medical Update
[47752]

NETHERLANDS
Alphen aan den Rijn
Process Control
[47871] .... (Combined) 4,000

Amsterdam
Acta Tropica [47880]
Advances in Colloid and Interface
Science [47882]
Analytical Cellular Pathology/Cellular
Oncology [47893]
Best Practice & Research Clinical
Endocrinology & Metabolism
[47903]
Biochimica et Biophysica Acta (BBA)
[47906]
Biochimica et Biophysica Acta (BBA)-
General Subjects [47907]
Biochimica et Biophysica Acta (BBA)-
Molecular Basis of Disease [47908]
Biochimica et Biophysica Acta (BBA)-
Molecular and Cell Biology of
Lipids [47909]
Breast Disease [47915]
Cancer Biomarkers [47920]
Current Biology [47943]
Current Problems in Cancer [47950]
Developmental & Comparative
Immunology [47955]
Disease Markers [47959]
Experimental and Molecular
Pathology [47980]
Geotextiles and Geomembranes
[47997]
Geothermics [47998]
Journal of Applied Geophysics
[48046]

Journal of Applied Mathematics and
Mechanics [48047]
Journal of Autoimmunity [48053]
Journal of Chromatography A [48059]
Journal of Molecular Biology [48097]
Journal of Proteomics [48113]
Journal of Surgical Research [48122]
Molecular Aspects of Medicine
[48162]
Molecular and Cellular
Neurosciences [48164]
Molecular and Cellular Probes
[48165]
Molecular Phylogenetics and
Evolution [48168]
NeuroImage [48174]
Nuclear Physics B [48186]
Pharmacological Research [48199]
Protein Expression and Purification
[48217]

Bussum
Current Computer-Aided Drug Design
[48285]

Dordrecht
Biologia Plantarum [48333]
Breast Cancer Research and
Treatment [48337]
Cancer and Metastasis Reviews
[48341]
Evolution: Education and Outreach
[48385]
Flexible Services and Manufacturing
Journal [48388]
Journal of Neuro-Oncology [48477]
Journal of Pharmaceutical Innovation
[48483]
Journal of Structural and Functional
Genomics [48494]
Journal of Thrombosis and
Thrombolysis [48498]

Heerlen
Technology and Disability [48630]

Rijswijk
Immunogenetics [48747]

Rotterdam
Best Practice & Research [48748]

Utrecht
European Journal of Developmental
Psychology [48756]

NEW ZEALAND
Auckland
International Journal of Biomechatronics and Biomedical Robotics
[48798]

Dunedin
Journal of Neuroendocrinology
[48890]

NIGERIA
Aba
Journal of Medical Investigation and
Practice [49055]

Abuja
Journal for Phytomedicine and
Therapeutics [49056]

Akure
Nigeria Journal of Pure and Applied
Physics [49060]

Benin City
Annals of Biomedical Science
[49063]
Journal of Medicine and Biomedical
Research [49064]

Calabar
Journal of Medical Laboratory
Science [49077]

Enugu
Orient Journal of Medicine [49081]

Ibadan
West African Journal of Medicine
[49104]

Idi-Araba
Nigerian Dental Journal [49105]

Ikeja
Nigerian Medical Practitioner [49108]

Ile-Ife
African Journal of Oral Health
[49110]
African Journal of Traditional,
Complementary and Alternative
Medicines [49111]

Ilorin
African Journal of Clinical and Experi-
mental Microbiology [49117]
BIOKEMISTRI [49119]

Jos
Highland Medical Research Journal
[49124]
Journal of Aquatic Sciences [49125]
Journal of Medicine in the Tropics
[49126]
Journal of Pharmacy and
Bioresources [49127]

Lagos
African Journal of Microbiology
Research [49133]

Makurdi
Nigerian Journal of Fisheries [49146]

Nnewi
Journal of Biomedical Investigation
[49148]
Tropical Journal of Medical Research
[49151]

Nsukka
Bio-Research [49156]

Port Harcourt
Port Harcourt Medical Journal
[49169]

Sokoto
European Journal of General
Medicine [49173]
Sahel Medical Journal [49174]

Uturu
Journal of Health and Visual
Sciences [49177]

Zaria
Nigerian Journal of Chemical
Research [49183]
Nigerian Journal of Surgical
Research [49185]

NORWAY
Tromso
Polar Research [49214]

Trondheim
Norsk Geologisk Tidsskrift [49219]

PAKISTAN
Faisalabad
Academic Journal of Cancer
Research [49228]
Advances in Biological Research
[49230]
American-Eurasian Journal of Scien-
tific Research [49234]
Global Journal of Environmental
Research [49242]
Global Journal of Pharmacology
[49244]
Journal of Molecular Genetics
[49273]
Middle East Journal of Scientific
Research [49274]

Circulation: ★ = ABC; △ = BPA; ◆ = CAC; • = CCAB; ❑ = VAC; ⊕ = PO Statement; ‡ = Publisher's Report; Boldface figures = sworn; Light figures = estimated.

Research Journal of Medical Sciences [49289]
Research Journal of Medicine and Medical Sciences [49290]
Veterinary Research [49296]
World Journal of Medical Sciences [49302]

PHILIPPINES
Taguig City
NRCD Research Journal of the Philippines [49639]

POLAND
Warsaw
Acta Neurobiologiae Experimentalis [49680]
Acta Zoologica Lituanica [49683]
Advances in Medical Sciences [49687]
Archives of Polish Fisheries [49692]
Artificial Satellites [49693]
Balkan Journal of Medical Genetics [49694]
Ecological Questions [49706]
Folia Neuropathologica [49710] 450
Journal of Medical Biochemistry [49724]

PORTUGAL
Funchal
International Journal of Agile and Extreme Software Development [49798]

ROMANIA
Timisoara
Timisoara Medical Journal (TMJ) [49849]

RUSSIA
Saint Petersburg
Cell and Tissue Biology [50020]
Glass Physics and Chemistry [50022]

SAUDI ARABIA
Riyadh
Annals of Thoracic Medicine [50059]

SENEGAL
Dakar
CODESRIA Bulletin [50080] 5000

SINGAPORE
Singapore
International Journal of Geometric Methods in Modern Physics (IJGMMP) [50180]
International Journal of Information Acquisition [50183]

SLOVAKIA
Bratislava
Acta Virologica [50316]

SLOVENIA
Ljubljana
Acta Chimica Slovenica (ACSi) [50334]
Illiesia [50337]

REPUBLIC OF SOUTH AFRICA
Auckland Park
Health SA Gesondheid [50348]

Cape Town
Current Allergy & Clinical Immunology [50372]

South African Journal of Bioethics and Law [50412]
Centurion
Southern African Journal of Critical Care [50455]
Grahamstown
Annals of Ibadan Postgraduate Medicine [50493]
Journal of Applied Science, Engineering and Technology [50500]
Sudan Journal of Medical Sciences [50516]
Lynnwood Ridge
Quest [50550]
Pinegowrie
LMS—Laboratory Marketing Spectrum [50572] .... ★5,833
Pretoria
African Journal of Cross-Cultural Psychology and Sport Facilitation [50583]
Tygerberg
South African Family Practice [50639]
Wits
South African Actuarial Journal [50643]

SPAIN
Barcelona
AIDS Reviews [50648]
Toledo
Physical Chemistry [50840]

SWEDEN
Lund
Genes, Chromosomes & Cancer [50985]
Solna
Acta Oncologica [50999]
Stockholm
Acta Oto-Laryngologica [51001]
Advances in Physiotherapy [51003]
Amyotrophic Lateral Sclerosis [51007]
Microbial Ecology in Health and Disease [51026]
Scandinavian Cardiovascular Journal [51034]

SWITZERLAND
Basel
Chromosoma [51061]
Bern
International Journal of Public Health [51074]
Geneva
The Botulinum Journal [51088]
International Journal of Computational Biology and Drug Design [51111]
International Journal of Computational Medicine and Healthcare [51112]
International Journal of Medical Engineering and Informatics [51131]
International Journal of Nano and Biomaterials [51133]
Genolier
Critical Reviews in Oncology/Hematology [51174]
Lausanne
Cancer Immunity [51184]

UNITED REPUBLIC OF TANZANIA
Dar es Salaam
Tanzania Medical Journal [51404]

Tanzanian Journal of Health Research [51405]

TURKEY
Ankara
Turkish Journal of Cancer [51506]

UGANDA
Jinja
African Journal of Tropical Hydrobiology and Fisheries [51582]
Kampala
African Health Sciences [51584]

UNITED KINGDOM
Abingdon
Acta Dermato-Venereologica [51694]
Action Learning [51696]
Amyloid [51703]
Human Fertility [51808]
International Reviews of Immunology [51854]
Isotopes in Environmental and Health Studies [51862]
Journal of Genocide Research [51900]
Journal of Interprofessional Care [51910]
Journal of Rehabilitation Medicine [51939]
Leukemia and Lymphoma [51968]
Medical Mycology [51973]
Microcirculation [51978]
Mitochondrial DNA [51983]
Psychoanalytic Psychotherapy [52026]
Scandinavian Journal of Clinical and Laboratory Investigation [52047]
Scandinavian Journal of Gastroenterology [52048]
Waves in Random and Complex Media [52089]
Birmingham
Journal of the Operational Research Society [52350]
Bradford
British Food Journal [52438]
Pigment & Resin Technology [52537]
Sensor Review [52543]
Brentwood
The Journal of Computational Multiphase Flows [52579]
Parasite Immunology [52586]
Bristol
Biofabrication [52645]
Europhysics Letters (EPL) [52666]
International Journal of Epidemiology [52678]
Journal of Breath Research [52682]
New Journal of Physics (NJP) [52710]
Paediatric and Perinatal Epidemiology [52714]
Research in Astronomy and Astrophysics [52727]
Cambridge
Green Chemistry [52825]
International Journal of Astrobiology [52833] 450
Journal of Environmental Monitoring [52851]
Lab on a Chip [52866]
Natural Product Reports [52873]
Photochemical & Photobiological Science [52882]
Cardiff
Building Research Capacity [52925]
Journal of Enzyme Inhibition and Medicinal Chemistry [52933]

Journal of Neuroscience Methods [52935]
Colchester
Biochemical Society Transactions [53030]
Croydon
Laboratory News [53128] .... (Controlled) ★11,095
Dundee
Nicotine and Tobacco Research [53217]
Edinburgh
Nanotoxicology [53301]
Farnham
The British Journal of Cardiology [53380]
Glasgow
Cellular Signalling [53412]
Harrow
Comparative Clinical Pathology [53521]
Huddersfield
Clinical Biomechanics [53618]
Kidlington
Journal of Environmental Sciences [53698]
Leeds
Bioscience Education E-journal [53757]
London
Acute Coronary Syndromes [53897]
Advances in Osteoporotic Fracture Management [53906]
Advances in Sepsis [53908]
Aslib Proceedings [53976]
Autonomic Neuroscience [53991]
Best Practice & Research Clinical Obstetrics & Gynecology [54013]
Biological Knowledge [54021]
Biomarkers in Medicine [54026]
Biomedical Scientist [54030] .. .. (Paid) 14,500
British Journal of Psychiatry [54132]
Cardiovascular Ultrasound [54179]
Expert Opinion on Investigational Drugs [54417]
Expert Review of Endocrinology & Metabolism [54423]
Expert Review of Gastroenterology & Hepatology [54424]
Expert Review of Hematology [54425]
Expert Reviews of Dermatology [54435]
Future Microbiology [54488]
Future Virology [54491]
Good Clinical Practice Journal (GCPj) [54519] .... ⊕1,300
Health Services Management Research [54544]
Hematology [54548]
HIV Therapy [54563]
Immunome Research [54586]
Instrumenta [54609] .... (Paid) 7,000
Journal of Drug Assessment [54739] .... (Paid) 100
Journal of Medical Genetics [54780] .... ‡1,495
Journal of Nanobiotechnology [54783]
Journal of NeuroEngineering and Rehabilitation (JNER) [54785]
Journal of Neurology, Neurosurgery, and Psychiatry [54787]
Journal of Translational Medicine [54830]
Journal of Viral Hepatitis [54832]

Circulation: ★ = ABC; △ = BPA; ◆ = CAC; • = CCAB; ❏ = VAC; ⊕ = PO Statement; ‡ = Publisher's Report; Boldface figures = sworn; Light figures = estimated.

6200

Gale Directory of Publications & Broadcast Media/147th Ed.

Journal of Virological Methods [54833]
Laboratory Animals [54847]
Molecular Psychiatry [54948]
Nanomedicine [54970]
NMR in Biomedicine [55006]
Oncogene [55032]
Personal and Ubiquitous Computing [55070]
Philosophy, Ethics, and Humanities in Medicine [55082]
Prostate Cancer and Prostatic Diseases [55144]
Pulmonary Pharmacology and Therapeutics [55155]
Qualitative Research in Organizations and Management [55160]
Regenerative Medicine [55180]
Thorax [55315]
Urological Research [55363]

Manchester
Biochemical Engineering Journal [55544]
Cell Calcium [55546]

Middlesex
International Journal of Dynamics of Fluids (IJDF) [55618]

Northampton
Insight [55710] 2,500

Nottingham
Breast Cancer Online [55749]
Gut [55757]
Journal of Molecular Graphics and Modeling [55764]
Platelets [55770]

Oxford
Acta Histochemica [55860]
Cancer Letters [55902]
Carcinogenesis [55904]
Glycobiology [55967]
Human Molecular Genetics [55979]
infocus Magazine [55989]
Japanese Journal of Clinical Oncology [56009]
Journal of the ICRU [56040]
Journal of the National Cancer Institute [56053]
Journal of Nursing and Healthcare of Chronic Illness [56054]
Journal of Sleep Research [56073]
Molecular Oral Microbiology [56108]
Nutrition Bulletin [56124]
Pathology International [56143]
Pediatric Allergy and Immunology [56145]
Pediatric Anesthesia [56146]
Pediatric Dermatology [56147]
Pediatrics International [56148]
Photodermatology, Photoimmunology and Photomedicine [56156]
Public Health Nursing [56177]

Shoreham-by-Sea
International Journal of Knowledge-Based and Intelligent Engineering Systems [56524]

Stevenage
IEE Proceedings Nanobiotechnology [56610]

ZIMBABWE
Harare
Journal of Applied Science in Southern Africa [57115]

LANDSCAPE ARCHITECTURE
See also Botany; Florists and Floriculture; Seed and Nursery Trade

AUSTRALIA
Alexandria
Lifestyle Pools [41541]

Carisbrook
Turfcraft [41723]

North Ryde
Outdoor Design & Living [42189]
Outdoor Design Source [42190]
Outdoor Space [42191] 30,000

PEOPLE'S REPUBLIC OF CHINA
Hong Kong
Yuen Lin [43387] 1,000

ITALY
Vernasca
Flortecnica
 [46278] .... (Controlled) 6,800

JAPAN
Tokyo
Nikkei Architecture
 [46978] .... ★44,461

NETHERLANDS
Eindhoven
The Follies Journal [48590]

POLAND
Warsaw
European Countryside [49709]

SWITZERLAND
Bassersdorf
Seed Science and Technology [51067]

UNITED KINGDOM
Bushey
The Landscaper [52776] 7,000

Glasgow
Urban Realm [53456] 7,000

Horsham
Professional Landscaper & Groundsman
 [53600] .... (Combined) 3,100

London
Landscape Design [54850]

Oxford
Landscape Research [56083]

Ross-on-Wye
Garden Design Journal
 [56409] 3,000

Wadhurst
Construction Europe
 [56805] .... ★14,624

York
Greenkeeper International
 [56991] .... ‡6,000

LAUNDRY AND DRY CLEANING

DENMARK
Glostrup
Rens & Vask samt Tekstiludlejning
 [43714] .... ‡3,340

LAW

AUSTRALIA
Brisbane
LAWASIA Journal [41652] 2,000

Canberra
Australian Law Management Journal
 [41702] 700

Clayton
Alternative Law Journal
 [41755] 1,300
Australian and New Zealand Journal of Criminology [41757]
Monash University Law Review [41764]

Gold Coast
Bond Law Review [41898]
Revenue Law Journal [41899]

Melbourne
LIJ [42069] ..... (Combined) ‡11,131
Melbourne University Law Review [42075]

Pyrmont
Australasian Dispute Resolution Journal [42270]
Australian Business Law Review [42271]
Australian Law Journal [42274]
Criminal Law Journal [42276]
Environmental and Planning Law Journal [42277]
Insolvency Law Journal [42281]
Journal of Banking and Finance Law and Practice [42283]

Saint Lucia
University of Queensland Law Journal [42341]

Surry Hills
Australian Journal of Forensic Sciences [42413] .... (Paid) 498

Sydney
Australian Tax Forum [42467]
Caveat [42486]
International Journal of Technology Policy and Law [42521]
Law Society Journal
 [42534] .... (Paid) 23,943
Macquarie Law Journal [42538]

Townsville
James Cook University Law Review [42636]

BELGIUM
Brussels
Legisprudence [42864]
Military Law and Law of War Review [42867]

PEOPLE'S REPUBLIC OF CHINA
Hong Kong
Asia Law and Practice [43270]
Hong Kong Law Reports & Digest [43335]
Hong Kong Lawyer [43336]
Human Rights Solidarity [43347]

FRANCE
Paris
International Journal of Nuclear Law [44055]

GERMANY
Berlin
Anwaltsblatt
 [44151] .... (Combined) 113,000

Deutsche Zeitschrift fur Wirtschafts- und Insolvenzrecht [44172]
European Company and Financial Law Review [44174]
European Review of Contract Law [44176]
European State Aid Law Quarterly [44177]

Cologne
Law in Africa [44299]
Yearbook of African Law [44304]

Dusseldorf
Juristische Rundschau (JR) [44327]

Heidelberg
Zeitschrift fur Unternehmens- und Gesellschaftsrecht (ZGR) [44480]

Munich
Zeitschrift fur Assyriologie und Vorderasiatische Archaologie
 [44589] 500

Tubingen
Zeitschrift fur die gesamte Strafrechtswissenschaft [44694]

GREECE
Athens
Journal of Southeast European and Black Sea Studies [44751]

HUNGARY
Budapest
Acta Juridica Hungarica [44812]

INDIA
Chennai
Income Tax Reports
 [45037] .... (Paid) 16,500

Hyderabad
The Icfai Journal of Alternative Dispute Resolution [45141]
The Icfai Journal of Corporate and Securities Law [45145]

Lucknow
Current Central Legislation
 [45321] 2,500
Lucknow Law Times
 [45324] 3,000
Supreme Court Cases
 [45326] .... (Paid) 10,000
Supreme Court Cases (Criminal)
 [45327] .... (Paid) 3,000
Supreme Court Cases (Labour and Services) [45328] ..... (Paid) 2,200

Mumbai
Medical Law Cases for Doctors [45410]

Nagpur
All India Reporter
 [45464] .... (Paid) 43,000
Criminal Law Journal
 [45465] 16,800

New Delhi
Current Consumer Cases [45502]
Drugs Cases [45504]
Indian Journal of Human Rights and Justice [45556]
Indian Journal of Human Rights and the Law [45557]
Journal of Indian Law Institute [45603]
Journal of Intellectual Property Law & Practice [45607]
Journal of Islamic Law Review [45611]
Labour and Industrial Law Reporter [45621]
Municipalities and Corporation Cases [45627]

Prevention of Food Adulteration
  Cases [45637]
Religion and Law Review [45643]

Shillong
International Journal of Jurisprudence
  and Philosophy of Law [45728]

Srinagar
Jammu and Kashmir Law Reporter
  [45738] .... (Paid) 475

Tirunelveli
International Journal of Criminal Justice Sciences (IJCJS) [45753]

IRELAND
Dublin
Gazette [45962] 12,000

ISRAEL
Tel Aviv
Justice [46109] 8,100
Theoretical Inquiries in Law [46114]

ITALY
Florence
European Journal of International
  Law [46143]

Rome
Il Fiasco [46233]

JAMAICA
Kingston
The War Cry [46291] 300,000

JAPAN
Tokyo
Capital Markets Law Journal [46779]

JORDAN
Amman
Dirasat Sharia' and Law Sciences
  [47158] .... (Controlled) 1,000

LEBANON
Beirut
Lebanese Review of Arab and Inter-
  national Arbitration [47397]

MALAYSIA
Melaka
Erasmus Law and Economics Review
  [47680]

NETHERLANDS
Alphen aan den Rijn
Air & Space Law [47865]
Arbitration International [47866]
Journal of International Arbitration
  [47869]

Amsterdam
Environmental Policy and Law
  [47969]
Journal of Chemical Health and
  Safety [48057]
Regulatory Toxicology and
  Pharmacology [48220]

Dordrecht
Crime, Law and Social Change
  [48361]
Criminal Law Forum [48362]
Critical Criminology [48363]
Feminist Legal Studies [48386]
Frontiers of Law in China [48400]
Health Care Analysis [48412]
International Journal for the Semiot-
  ics of Law [48431]
Journal of Experimental Criminology
  [48458]

Law and Philosophy [48507]
Liverpool Law Review [48508]

The Hague
Asian International Arbitration Journal
  [48607]
Common Market Law Review
  [48610]
European Business Law Review
  [48615]
Leiden Journal of International Law
  [48621] 500

Leiden
Arab Law Quarterly [48649]
Austrian Review of International and
  European Law [48655]
International Community Law Review
  [48679]
International Criminal Law Review
  [48680]
International Organizations Law
  Review [48683]
Islamic Law and Society [48685]
Journal for European Environmental
  & Planning Law [48698]
The Law and Practice of International
  Courts and Tribunals [48707]
Middle East Law and Governance
  [48711]
Nordic Journal of International Law
  [48714]

Utrecht
Utrecht Law Review [48767]

NEW ZEALAND
Auckland
Auckland University Law Review
  [48785]

Wellington
The Maori Law Review [49016]

PHILIPPINES
Pasig City
IBP Journal
  [49571] .. .. (Paid) 20,000

Quezon City
Philippine Law Journal
  [49608] .... (Paid) 821

POLAND
Warsaw
Baltic Journal of Law & Politics
  [49695]
Issues of Business and Law [49721]

SINGAPORE
Singapore
Digital Investigation [50132]
Law Gazette [50212] ... (Paid) 5,000
LawLink [50213]
Singapore Journal of Legal Studies
  [50256] .. .. (Paid) 1,850
Singapore Law Review
  [50258] .. .. (Paid) 1,350

Singapore City
Annual Review of Singapore Cases
  [50310]
Singapore Academy of Law Journal
  [50314]

REPUBLIC OF SOUTH AF-RICA
Cape Town
South African Journal of Bioethics
  and Law [50412]

Centurion
Transactions of the Centre for Business Law [50457]

Claremont
Acta Juridica [50459]

African Human Rights Law Journal
  [50460]
Jutas Business Law [50461]
SA Mercantile Law Journal [50462]
South African Journal of Criminal
  Justice [50463]
South African Journal on Human
  Rights [50464]
Stellenbosch Law Review [50465]

Mmabatho
Potchefstroom Electronic Law Journal
  [50556]

Port Elizabeth
Obiter [50578]

Pretoria
De Rebus
  [50589] .. .. (Combined) *20,004
Fundamina [50592]

Sunnyside
Acta Criminologica [50637]

SPAIN
Barcelona
IDP [50680]

Granada
Pharmaceuticals Policy and Law
  [50718]

Seville
Cuadernos de Medicina Forense
  [50833]

SRI LANKA
Colombo
Sri Lanka Journal of International
  Law [50866]

SWITZERLAND
Geneva
The Journal of World Investment and
  Trade [51152]

Zurich
International Journal of Legal Information Design [51266]

UNITED KINGDOM
Aberdeen
Journal of Private International Law
  [51678]

Abingdon
Criminal Justice Studies [51743]
Education and the Law [51769]
Geopolitics [51794]
Information and Communications
  Technology Law [51818]
The International Journal of Human
  Rights [51838]
International Journal of the Legal
  Profession [51840]
International Review of Law Comput-
  ers & Technology [51852]
Journal of Children and Poverty
  [51874]
Journal of Commonwealth Law and
  Legal Education [51876]
Journal of Contemporary China
  [51879]
Journal of Legal History [51914]
Journal of Legal Medicine [51915]
The Journal of Legislative Studies
  [51916]
Journal of Social Welfare and Family
  Law [51942]
Ocean Development and Interna-
  tional Law [52001]
Psychology Crime and Law [52028]

Andover
British Tax Review [52111]
Civil Justice Quarterly [52112]

Construction Law Journal [52113]
Conveyancer and Property Lawyer
  [52114]
Criminal Law Review [52115]
EIPR: European Intellectual Property
  Review [52116]
Intellectual Property Quarterly
  [52117]
Journal of Business Law [52118]
Journal of Planning and Environment
  Law [52119]
Law Quarterly Review [52120]
Public Law [52121]

Belfast
The Chronicle [52281]

Bradford
Journal of International Trade Law
  and Policy [52505]
Journal of Money Laundering Control
  [52510]

Brighton
The British Journal of Forensic
  Practice [52607]

Bristol
Computers and Law
  [52655] 2,700
Evidence & Policy [52667]
The Journal of Poverty and Social
  Justice [52696]

Cambridge
British Yearbook of International Law
  [52797]
The Cambridge Law Journal
  [52798] 1,600
Industrial Law Journal [52830]
International and Comparative Law
  Quarterly [52831]
International Journal of Law in
  Context [52835]
Journal of African Law
  [52843] 500
Journal of Biosocial Science
  [52846] 500
Workplace Law [52905]

Colchester
International Journal of Refugee Law
  [53039]

Coventry
Journal of Information, Law & Tech-
  nology (JILT) [53086]
Law and Humanities [53088]

Douglas
Statute Law Review [53197]

Edinburgh
The Edinburgh Law Review [53271]
Greens Business Law Bulletin
  [53280]
Greens Criminal Law Bulletin [53281]
Greens Property Law Bulletin [53282]
Greens Weekly Digest [53283]
Juridical Review [53296]
Legal Information Management
  [53298] 1,200
The Scots Law Times [53311]
Script-ed [53318]

Exmouth
International Journal of Police Science and Management [53370]

Glasgow
The Firm [53418]
Scottish Planning and Environmental
  Law [53450] .... (Paid) 500

Harpenden
Agents News [53513]

Hove
Drugs and Alcohol Today [53604]

Isle of Man
Common Law World Review
  [53663] .... (Paid) 400

Kidlington
International Journal of Law, Crime and Justice [53694]
Science & Justice [53706]

Liverpool
Fingerprint Whorld [53873]
International Journal of Law and Management [53874]

London
CANS Digest of Social Legislation [54173] 1,831
Commonwealth Judicial Journal [54241]
Commonwealth Law Bulletin [54242] 1,500
Competition Law Insight [54253]
Constitutional and Parliamentary Information [54260]
Counsel [54273] 23,000
Criminal Appeal Reports [54285]
Criminology & Criminal Justice [54286]
Employment Law Bulletin [54367]
Employment Law Journal [54368]
European Competition Journal [54392]
Family Law Journal [54442]
Focus Europe [54475]
Health and Safety Bulletin [54542]
The In-House Lawyer [54591] .... (Combined) ‡5,500
Index on Censorship [54594] .... (Combined) 10,000
Industrial Cases Reports [54597]
International Business Lawyer [54621] 12,500
International and Comparative Law Quarterly [54624]
The International Construction Law Review [54625]
Journal of Financial Regulation and Compliance [54753]
Justice Journal [54841]
Law, Culture & the Humanities [54857]
Legal Business [54864] .... (Paid) 9,000
Lex [54866]
The Magistrate [54897]
Managing Partner [54905]
New Law Journal [54992]
The Practical Lawyer [55114] .... (Paid) 6,000
Property Law Journal [55141]
Social & Legal Studies [55246] .... (Paid) 800
Student Law Review [55269] .... (Non-paid) 37,000
The Times Law Reports [55324]
Trust & Foundation News [55343]
Trusts and Estates Law & Tax Journal [55344]
Victim Support [55369]
Wills & Trusts Law Reports [55407]

Newcastle upon Tyne
Environmental Law Review [55669]
International Journal of Clinical Legal Education [55672]
Journal of Obligations & Remedies [55674]

Nottingham
International Journal of Evidence and Proof [55761]
The Law Teacher [55765]

Olney
International Journal of Liability and Scientific Enquiry [55818]

Oxford
American Business Law Journal [55864]
American Law and Economics Review [55865]

The British Journal of Criminology [55893]
Business and Society Review [55899]
Chinese Journal of International Law [55908]
Current Legal Problems [55922]
European Law Reports [55948]
Family Court Review [55951]
The Howard Journal of Criminal Justice [55977]
Human Rights Law Review [55981]
International Journal of Constitutional Law [55992]
International Journal of Law and Information Technology [55996]
International Journal of Law, Policy and the Family [55997]
Journal of Competition Law and Economics [56022]
Journal of Conflict and Security Law [56024]
The Journal of Corporate Law Studies [56025]
Journal of Environmental Law [56029]
Journal of International Criminal Justice [56044]
Journal of Law, Economics, and Organization [56047]
Journal of Law and Society [56048]
Journal of Legal Studies Education [56049]
Judicial Review [56080]
King's Law Journal [56081]
Law and Financial Markets Review [56085]
Law & Policy [56086]
Law, Probability and Risk [56087]
Legal Ethics [56089]
Medical Law Review [56095]
The Modern Law Review [56103]
Oxford Journal of Legal Studies [56135]
Oxford University Commonwealth Law Journal [56138]
Ratio Juris [56186]

Paisley
Journal of the Law Society of Scotland [56240] .... ★11,477

Sheffield
Managing Leisure [56506]

Sidcup
Legal Abacus [56544] .... (Combined) 3,000

Surrey
Parliaments, Estates and Representation [56671]

Witney
Bio-science Law Review [56939]
Contemporary Issues in Law [56940]
Environmental Law & Management [56941]
Environmental Liability [56942]
Information Technology Law Reports [56943]
The Journal of International Maritime Law [56944]
The Journal of Water Law [56945]
Utilities Law Review [56946]

LIBRARY AND INFORMATION SCIENCE
See also Book Trade and Author News

AUSTRALIA
Adelaide
Australasian Public Libraries and Information Services [41502]

Canberra
IASA Journal [41707]

Deakin
inCite [41836] .... (Paid) 8,000

Geelong
The Australian Library Journal [41878]

Kingston
Australian Academic & Research Libraries [41990] .. .. (Paid) 700
Aphelion [41994]

Parkes
National Library of Australia Gateways [42229]

BELGIUM
Brussels
Cahiers de la Documentation [42846]

Diepenbeek
Journal of Informetrics [42880]

PEOPLE'S REPUBLIC OF CHINA
Beijing
Folk Literature [43193] 100,000
Science in China Series F [43220]

Changchun
Journal of Jilin University Information Science Edition [43242]

Hainan
International Journal of Information Science and Computer Mathematics [43258]

FRANCE
Toulouse
Fuzzy Sets and Systems [44120]

GERMANY
Berlin
Libri [44219] 2,900
Microform & Imaging Review [44221] 2000

Darmstadt
International Journal on Digital Libraries [44310]

Fellbach
Restaurator [44353] .... ‡3,500

Hamburg
International Journal of Information Security [44419]

Hannover
iX [44433]

Wurzburg
Knowledge Organization [44721]

GHANA
Tamale
Ghana Library Journal [44739]

ICELAND
Reykjavik
Bokasafnid [44898]

INDIA
Kolkata
IASLIC Bulletin [45269] .... (Paid) 1,600

IRELAND
Dublin
An Leabharlann [45944]
Irish Archives [45971]

ITALY
Ancona
International Journal of Computational Intelligence Studies [46118]

JAPAN
Tokyo
Library and Information Science [46960] .. .. (Paid) 1,500

MALAYSIA
Kuala Lumpur
Malaysian Journal of Library and Information Science [47617]

NETHERLANDS
Amsterdam
Information Design Journal [48018]
Liber Quarterly [48137]

Enschede
ISPRS Journal of Photogrammetry and Remote Sensing [48596]

NEW ZEALAND
Wellington
Library Life [49015] 1,600

NIGERIA
Ibadan
African Journal of Library, Archives and Information Science [49084]
Journal of Librarianship and Information Science in Africa [49090]

Lagos
Lagos Journal of Library and Information Science [49140]

Minna
Information Technologist [49147]

Yaba
Nigerian Libraries [49180]

Zaria
Samaru Journal of Information Studies [49187]

POLAND
Warsaw
Information Processing Letters [49718]

REPUBLIC OF SOUTH AFRICA
Centurion
South African Journal of Information Management [50454]

SWEDEN
Boras
Svensk Biblioteksforskning/Swedish Library Research [50951]

Ronneby
Information and Software Technology [50997]

Stockholm
Arkiv Samhalle och Forskning [51009]

SWITZERLAND
Sirnach
Professional Computing [51231]

TAIWAN
Tamsui
Journal of Educational Media and Library Sciences [51394] .. .. (Paid) 1,200

Trade, Technical, and Professional Publications

UNITED REPUBLIC OF TANZANIA
Dar es Salaam
University of Dar es Salaam Library Journal [51406]

UNITED KINGDOM
Aberystwyth
Y Ddolen
  [51689] .... (Non-paid) ‡1,500
Abingdon
New Review of Academic Librarianship [51995]
New Review of Children's Literature and Librarianship [51996]
New Review of Information Networking [51998]
Bradford
Collection Building [52442]
Electronic Library [52453]
Interlending & Document Supply [52470]
Journal of Documentation [52496]
Library Management [52522]
New Library World [52530]
Online Information Review [52534]
Performance Measurements and Metrics [52536]
VINE [52556]
Burnham
International Journal of Micrographics & Optical Technology [52765]
Ceredigion
Cylchgrawn Llyfrgell Genedlaethol Cymru [52954] ... (Combined) 350
Edinburgh
Legal Information Management
  [53298] 1,200
Glasgow
Information Scotland
  [53424] 2,500
Library Review [53429]
Hatfield
Information Management & Technology
  [53539] .... (Controlled) 700
Huddersfield
Campus-Wide Information Systems [53617]
Ilford
Christian Librarian
  [53638] .... (Paid) 500
London
Aslib Proceedings [53976]
Biomedical Digital Libraries [54028]
Information Development [54603]
Information World Review
  [54604] .... ‡15,000
Journal of Information Science [54768]
Journal of the Society of Archivists [54822]
Library and Information Research [54870]
Library + Information Update [54871]
Managing Information
  [54904] 8,000
Loughborough
Focus on International Library & Information Work
  [55480] .... (Paid) 1,500
Journal of Librarianship & Information Science [55482]
Mold
European Information [55642]
Focus [55643]
Newcastle upon Tyne
Records Management Journal [55678]

Olney
International Journal of Metadata, Semantics and Ontologies [55824]
Orpington
IMIS Journal [55852] 11,000
Rotherham
The School Librarian
  [56412] .... (Paid) 4,000
Sheffield
The Indexer [56497] 2,200
Surrey
Alexandria [56659]
York
Reference Reviews [56997]

LIGHTING

See also Electrical Engineering

INDIA
Kolkata
Energy for Sustainable Development [45265]

UNITED KINGDOM
London
Lighting Research and Technology [54873]
Rugby
The Lighting Journal
  [56420] .... (Paid) 4,500

LITERATURE

AUSTRALIA
Carlton
Meanjin [41727] 2,000
Clayton
Colloquy [41759]
Melbourne
Overland
  [42081] .... (Combined) 2,000
Richmond South
ABR (Australian Book Review)
  [42311] 2,000
Saint Lucia
Australian Literary Studies
  [42339] 750
Sydney
Philament [42561]

AUSTRIA
Vienna
TRANS [42770]

BELGIUM
Gent
Jaarboek [42883] 300
Verslagen en Mededelingen
  [42885] 300
Mechelen
Ludus [42904]

BOTSWANA
Gaborone
Marang [42944]

BRAZIL
Rio de Janeiro
Alea [43000]

BULGARIA
Sofia
Bulgarian Folklore [43095]

PEOPLE'S REPUBLIC OF CHINA
Beijing
Folk Literature [43193] 100,000
Hong Kong
Journal of Modern Literature in Chinese [43359]
Review of Modern Literature in Chinese [43381]
Shanghai
Fiction World [43476]

DENMARK
Copenhagen
Scando-Slavica [43683]
Odense
Orbis Litterarum [43731]

ESTONIA
Tallinn
Estonian Literary Magazine
  [43783] 2,000

FINLAND
Helsinki
Books from Finland
  [43821] .... (Combined) 2,800

GERMANY
Berlin
Antike und Abendland
  [44150] .... ‡450
Arbitrium [44152] .... ‡460
arcadia [44153] .... ‡500
Beitrage zur Geschichte der deutschen Sprache und Literatur
  [44159] .... ‡540
Byzantinische Zeitschrift
  [44164] .... ‡650
Fabula [44178] 450
Germanistik [44186] 1,300
Iberoromania [44190]
Internationales Archiv fur Sozialgeschichte der deutschen Literatur [44197]
Internationales Jahrbuch des Deutschen Idealismus [44198] .... ‡350
Journal of Literary Theory [44206]
Kritikon Litterarum [44212] 150
Naharaim [44223]
Romanistisches Jahrbuch
  [44229] 300
Zeitschrift fur romanische Philologie
  [44240] 520
Feldkirchen
Journal of Coptic Studies [44352]
Frankfurt
Literaturnachrichten [44362] ... 3,500
Giessen
Cross/Cultures [44385]
Wiesbaden
Central Asiatic Journal [44711]

HUNGARY
Budapest
Acta Antiqua Academiae Scientiarum Hungaricae [44806]
Acta Orientalia Academiae Scientiarum Hungaricae [44816]
Hungarian Studies [44837]
Story Special
  [44873] .... (Paid) 110,116

INDIA
Aligarh
Aligarh Journal of English Studies
  [44917] .... (Paid) 350

Hyderabad
The Square and Compasses [45183]
Madras
Institute of Asian Studies Journal
  [45335] .... (Paid) 500
New Delhi
Indian Literary Index [45570]

IRELAND
Dublin
Eigse [45954]
Irish Archives [45971]

ITALY
Genoa
Textus [46154]

JAPAN
Fukushima
New Cicada [46355]
Tokyo
American Literary History [46733]
Shakespeare Studies
  [47037] .... (Paid) 1,200
Studies in English Literature
  [47044] ...... (Controlled) 3,800
Tsuda Review [47054] 1,000
Yokohama
Poetry Kanto
  [47141] .... (Controlled) 700

NETHERLANDS
Amsterdam
The Grey Journal [48006]
Matatu [48142]
Nature, Culture and Literature [48170]
Russian Literature [48228]
Variants [48269]
Dordrecht
The Journal of Primary Prevention [48486]
L1-Educational Studies in Language and Literature [48509]
Leiden
Arabica [48650]
Journal of Arabic Literature [48688]

NEW ZEALAND
Auckland
New Zealand Author
  [48805] 1,300
Dunedin
JNZL: Journal of New Zealand Literature [48889]
Hamilton
Ramp [48910]

PHILIPPINES
Pasay City
Ani [49568] .... (Paid) 2,000
Quezon City
Diliman Review [49589]

POLAND
Warsaw
Philologia [49746]

ROMANIA
Bucharest
Intamplari Adevarate
  [49838] .... ‡30,880

SAUDI ARABIA
Riyadh
Journal of King Saud University: Arts
  [50065] .... (Paid) 3,000

Circulation: ★ = ABC; △ = BPA; ◆ = CAC; • = CCAB; ❑ = VAC; ⊕ = PO Statement; ‡ = Publisher's Report; Boldface figures = sworn; Light figures = estimated.

REPUBLIC OF SOUTH AF-RICA
Centurion
English in Africa [50438]
Journal of Literary Studies [50443]

Grahamstown
African Studies Monographs [50491]
Shakespeare in Southern Africa [50513]

Pretoria
Tydskrif vir letterkunde [50607]

SPAIN
Madrid
Intramuros
  [50774] .... (Combined) 15,000
Revista de Occidente [50799]
Terra Incognita [50810]

Mataro
Quimera [50820]

Santa Cruz de Tenerife
La Pagina [50829]

Teruel
Turia [50839]

Valencia
Anglogermanica online [50842]
Celestinesca
  [50844] .... (Controlled) 412

Valladolid
Critical Approaches to Ethnic American Literature [50848]

SWEDEN
Goteborg
Africa & Asia [50956]

Stockholm
Fortattaren [51016]

SWITZERLAND
Basel
Bookbird [51060] 1,500

Zurich
European Joyce Studies [51258]
Gazzetta [51261]

TAIWAN
Tamsui
Tamkang Journal of Tamkang Review [51398]

TURKEY
Ankara
Journal of American Studies of Turkey [51494] .... (Paid) 325
Journal of Modern Turkish Studies (JMTS) [51495]

UNITED KINGDOM
Abingdon
Changing English [51727]
Indonesia and the Malay World [51813]
Iranian Studies [51858]
Israel Affairs [51863]
Japan Forum [51865]
Japanese Studies [51866]
Journal of Iberian & Latin American Studies [51906]
The Journal of Imperial & Commonwealth History [51907]
Journal of Modern Jewish Studies [51920]
Journal of Poetry Therapy [51932]
Journal of Postcolonial Writing [51935]

Life Writing [51969]
Middle Eastern Literatures [51979]
Mortality [51987]
Prose Studies [52024]
Review [52039]
Shakespeare [52057]
Textual Practice [52076]
Wasafiri [52088]
Women's Writing [52093]

Birmingham
Journal of Literary Semantics (JLS) [52347]

Cambridge
The Cambridge Quarterly [52799]
Shakespeare Survey [52894]

Cardiff
A470 [52923] 6,000
Taliesin [52940] .... (Paid) 1,000

Coventry
Journal of Research in Reading [53087]

Desborough
The Powys Review
  [53175] .... (Controlled) 620

Durham City
The Wellsian [53233]

Edinburgh
Ben Jonson Journal [53255]
Chapman
  [53261] .... (Combined) 2,550
Corpora [53266]
Deleuze Studies [53268]
International Research in Children's Literature [53290]
Journal of Arabic and Islamic Studies [53291]
Oxford Literary Review [53304]
Paragraph [53305]
Romanticism [53308]

Forest Row
North Wind [53397]

Frome
Outposts Poetry Quarterly
  [53400] .... (Paid) 2,000

Glasgow
SCROLL [53451]
Translation & Literature
  [53455] .... (Combined) 450

Isle of Arran
Dalriada [53662]

Leeds
Chapter&Verse [53760]

Leicester
English Four to Eleven [53797]
Use of English [53832]

London
Annual Bibliography of English Language & Literature [53951]
The Bottle Street Gazette [54101]
Bronte Studies
  [54150] .... (Paid) 750
Bulletin of the School of Oriental and African Studies [54157] 900
Byzantine and Modern Greek Studies [54162]
Comparative Critical Studies [54249]
The Edge [54353] 2,000
Etudes Episteme [54388]
French Cultural Studies [54481]
Intellectual History Review [54614]
The Journal of Commonwealth Literature [54727]
Journal of William Morris Studies [54837]
Literary and Linguistic Computing [54876]

Medieval Sermon Studies [54924]
Modern Language Review [54943]
The New Rambler [54996]
Poetry Review
  [55097] .... (Paid) 4,000
Publications of the English Goethe Society [55154]
Seventeenth-Century French Studies [55229]
Slavonica [55242] 200
Slovo [55243]

Longcot
The Richard Jefferies Society Journal [55475]

Manchester
Italian Studies [55562] ... (Paid) 500
Journal of Semitic Studies [55566]
Literature & History [55570]

Meopham
Swedish Book Review
  [55608] 800

Middlesbrough
Spatial Practices [55612]

Oxford
Contemporary Review [55916]
Critical Survey [55919]
Essays in Criticism [55941]
Notes and Queries [56120]
Poe Studies/Dark Romanticism
  [56163] .... (Combined) 500
The Review of English Studies [56191]
The Yale Review [56229]

Stirling
Literature and Theology [56624]

Surrey
The Shakespearean International Yearbook [56675]

Taunton
Powys Journal [56722] 400

Twickenham
Conrad Studies [56790]

York
Aesthetica Magazine
  [56986] 20,000

LOCAL, STATE, AND REGIONAL PUBLICATIONS
See also History and Genealogy; Chambers of Commerce and Boards of Trade

AUSTRALIA
Saint Lucia
Journal of Australian Studies
  [42340] 1,000

Sydney
Perfect Beat [42559]

FRANCE
Dijon
Impact [43944]

GREECE
Thessaloniki
International Journal of Innovation and Regional Development [44773]

REPUBLIC OF KOREA
Seoul
Korea Journal [47278] 2,200

MOROCCO
Casablanca
Tijaris [47813]

NETHERLANDS
Leiden
East Central Europe [48669]
Middle East Journal of Culture and Communication [48710]
Southeastern Europe [48725]

SUDAN
Wad Medani
International Journal of Sudan Research, Policy and Sustainable Development [50940]

SWEDEN
Stockholm
Scandinavia Now [51032]

UKRAINE
Kiev
Korrespondent
  [51599] .... (Combined) 50,000

UNITED KINGDOM
Abingdon
Central Asian Survey [51726]
Regional Studies [52036]

Basingstoke
Regional Trends [52229]

Bradford
Education, Business and Society [52451]

Cambridge
Journal of American Studies [52845]
The Journal of Modern African Studies
  [52860] .... (Combined) 1,600
Journal of Southeast Asian Studies
  [52863] 1,100

Edinburgh
African Affairs [53249]

Liverpool
Journal of Latin American Studies
  [53875] 1,900

Lochgilphead
Argyllshire Advertiser [53887]

London
African Renaissance [53924]
Dutch Crossing [54345]
Review of Nigeria Affairs [55199]
Slavonic and East European Review [55241]

Oxford
The Russian Review [56197]

MACHINERY AND EQUIPMENT
See also Commerce and Industry; Metal, Metallurgy, and Metal Trade; Vending Machines

AUSTRALIA
Leederville
Australian Longwall Magazine
  [42004] 3,500
Cranes and Lifting Australia [42006]

Sydney
International Journal of Abrasive Technology [42518]

Wahroonga
InMotion [42674] *6,157

BRAZIL
Sao Paulo
Maquinas e Metals
  [43042] .... (Non-paid) 15,000

DENMARK
Glostrup
Installations Nyt [43707] .... ‡3,907
Teknisk Nyt [43716] .... ‡10,131
Teknisk Nyt Special Edition
    [43717] .... ‡10,000

FRANCE
Paris
Mecanique & Industries [44071]

GERMANY
Berlin
Laser Technik Journal [44217]

Bonn
WEHRTECHNIK [44272] 12,000

Duisburg
Mechanism and Machine Theory
    [44320]

INDIA
Mumbai
Modern Machine Tools [45415]
Modern Packaging & Design [45417]
Modern Textiles [45420]

IRELAND
Sandyford
Farm & Plant Buyers Guide [46055]

ITALY
Cinisello Balsamo
RMO—Rivista di Meccanica Oggi
    [46134] .. .. (Combined) ‡14,000

Milan
Stampi [46196]

Peschiera Borromeo
Agri Parts [46212] 10,000

JAPAN
Tokyo
Ferrum
    [46822] .... (Combined) 10,000
International Journal of Advanced
    Mechatronic Systems [46844]
ISIJ International
    [46851] .... (Combined) 1,600
Tetsu-to-Hagane
    [47049] .... (Combined) 3,000

MALAYSIA
Melaka
International Journal of Precision
    Technology [47681]

MEXICO
Mexico City
Utillaje [47790] .... (Paid) 500
                  (Controlled) 30,250

NETHERLANDS
Amsterdam
Aerospace Science and Technology
    [47884]
Journal of Terramechanics [48124]

Dordrecht
Flexible Services and Manufacturing
    Journal [48388]
Information Technology and
    Management [48422]

NEW ZEALAND
Auckland
Truck & Machinery Trader
    [48831] .... ★12,390

Christchurch
Australian AG Contractor and Large
    Scale Farmer [48863]
New Zealand Rural Contractor and
    Large Scale Farmer [48875]

North Shore
Diesel Industry News [48952]

North Shore City
Motor Equipment News
    [48956] .. .. ★11,330

PORTUGAL
Aveiro
International Journal of Machining
    and Machinability of Materials
    [49786]

REPUBLIC OF SOUTH AF-
RICA
Cape Town
Medical Technology [50391]

Roggebaai
The South African Radiographer
    [50616] 1,800

SWITZERLAND
Geneva
International Journal of Mechatronics
    and Manufacturing Systems
    [51130]
International Journal of Vehicle
    Design [51145]
International Journal of Vehicle
    Performance [51146]

UNITED KINGDOM
Abingdon
Industry & Innovation [51814]

Belfast
Transactions of the Institute of Mea-
    surement and Control [52294]

Birmingham
International Journal of Machine
    Tools and Manufacture [52343]

Buckhurst Hill
Machinery World [52750] .. ... ★9,000
Plant World [52751] .... ★11,606

Cambridge
Connect [52810]

Chichester
Microscopy and Analysis
    [53014] .... ‡46,000

Cudham
Classic Plant & Machinery [53139]
Farm and Horticultural Equipment
    [53142]
Tractor & Machinery [53148]

Felixstowe
Ford & Fordson Tractors [53385]

Glasgow
Project Plant [53441] .... ★5,330

Horncastle
Old Glory [53592]

Hove
Journal of Assistive Technologies
    [53607]

Ilkley
Assembly Automation [53644]

Leamington Spa
Tube & Pipe Technology
    [53749] .... (Combined) 12,500

London
Farmers Trader [54444] 36,500

Tribology International [55341]

Olney
International Journal of Manufacturing
    Research [55822]

Sidcup
Cranes Today
    [56541] .. .... (Combined) △15,201
Hoist [56543] ... (Controlled) △8,643
Packaging Today [56545]

Surrey
Global Gypsum Magazine
    [56664] .... ◊3,247
Global Insulation Magazine [56665]

Tonbridge
Industrial Technology
    [56755] .... ★21,296

Wadhurst
Access International
    [56804] 8,024
International Construction China
    [56807] 15,800
International Construction Turkiye
    [56808] .... (Combined) 17,649
International Rental News
    [56810] .... (Combined) 14,624

Wallington
Machinery Update [56833] ... .‡9,000

MANAGEMENT AND ADMINISTRATION

AUSTRALIA
Adelaide
International Journal of Intelligent De-
    fence Support Systems [41510]

Bowen Hills
The Australian Journal of Rehabilita-
    tion Counselling [41624]
International Journal of Disability
    Management Research [41626]

Brisbane
International Journal of Knowledge-
    Based Development [41650]

Canberra
Australian Law Management Journal
    [41702] 700

Leederville
Australian Longwall Magazine
    [42004] 3,500

Penrith
The Australian Educational Leader
    [42239]

Pyrmont
Hotel and Accommodation
    Management [42280] 5,578

Sydney
Australian Journal of Management
    [42459]

Toowoomba
Australian Journal of Organisational
    Behavior & Management [42626]

AUSTRIA
Vienna
European Journal of Cross-Cultural
    Competence and Management
    [42751]
Long Range Planning [42763]

BRAZIL
Vicosa
RAE eletronica [43064]

CHILE
Santiago
Journal of Technology Management
    & Innovation [43145]

PEOPLE'S REPUBLIC OF CHINA
Hong Kong
The Hong Kong Manager
    [43337] 140,000
Nikkei Electronics Asia
    [43371] .... △28,300

Wuhan
International Journal of Satellite Com-
    munications Policy and
    Management [43520]
International Journal of Services,
    Economics and Management
    [43523]
The Journal of Grey System [43524]

Xi'an
International Journal of Internet
    Manufacturing & Services [43532]

DENMARK
Odense
International Journal of Advanced
    Operations Management [43727]

FRANCE
Aix-en-Provence
International Journal of Public Sector
    Performance Management [43912]

Champenoux
Annals of Forest Science [43929]

Le Havre
International Journal of Adaptive and
    Innovative Systems [43963]

GERMANY
Darmstadt
GIT Sicherheit Management
    [44307] .... ‡28,281

Heidelberg
Computational Management Science
    [44450]

Kiel
International Journal of Wine Busi-
    ness Research (IJWBR) [44502]

Munster
Information Systems and E-Business
    Management (ISeB) [44598]

Nuremberg
dedica [44608] 19,993

Wurzburg
Economic Quality Control [44720]

GREECE
Athens
International Journal of Multicriteria
    Decision Making [44749]

Patras
International Journal of Decision Sci-
    ences, Risk and Management
    [44764]

ICELAND
Reykjavik
European Journal of International
    Management [44900]

INDIA
Balasore
International Journal of Educational
    Administration [44947]

Hyderabad
The Icfai Journal of Bank
    Management [45143]
The Icfai Journal of Derivatives
    Markets [45147]

Circulation: ★ = ABC; △ = BPA; ◆ = CAC; • = CCAB; ❑ = VAC; ⊕ = PO Statement; ‡ = Publisher's Report; Boldface figures = sworn; Light figures = estimated.

The Icfai Journal of Entrepreneur-
ship Development [45149]
The Icfai Journal of Financial Risk
Management [45152]
The Icfai Journal of Managerial
Economics [45159]
The Icfai Journal of Operations
Management [45162]
The Icfai Journal of Organizational
Behavior [45163]
Projects & Profits [45181]

Jamshedpur
Management and Labour Studies
[45207] .. .. (Paid) 1,500

Kolkata
Decision [45263] 300
Opsearch [45300] .. .. (Paid) 2,000

New Delhi
International Journal of Statistics and
Systems [45586]
Journal of Statistics and Management
Systems [45620] .. .. (Paid) 240

IRAN
Isfahan
International Journal of Hydrology
Science and Technology [45878]

Tehran
Iranian Journal of Environmental
Health Science & Engineering
[45902]

IRELAND
Dublin
Journal of Strategic Management
Education [45990]

ITALY
Bologna
Il Nuovo Club
[46127] .. .. (Controlled) 10,000
Piscine Oggi
[46128] .. .. (Controlled) 15,000

Napoli
International Journal of Engineering
Management and Economics
[46204]

JAPAN
Tokyo
International Journal of Services
Technology and Management
[46848]
JMA Management Review
[46877] 20,000
Nikkei Monozukuri
[46999] .... ⋆34,857

JORDAN
Amman
Dirasat Administrative Sciences
[47152] .... (Controlled) 1,000

KUWAIT
Safat
Arab Journal of Administrative
Sciences [47334] ..... (Paid) 2,000
European Journal of Industrial
Engineering [47337]

LATVIA
Riga
Journal of Organizational Behavior
Education [47371]

LEBANON
Beirut
AL IDARI [47389] .. .. ⋆36,988

MALAYSIA
Kampar
International Journal of Modelling in
Operations Management [47584]

NETHERLANDS
Amsterdam
European Management Journal
[47976]
Information Processing &
Management [48020]
Intervention Research [48034]
Japan and the World Economy
[48035]
Operations Research Letters [48190]
Scandinavian Journal of Management
[48229]
Technovation [48243]

Dordrecht
Information Technology and
Management [48422]
Journal of Academic Ethics [48436]
Journal of Global Optimization
[48465]
Journal of Productivity Analysis
[48487]
Journal of Scheduling [48491]

Groningen
International Journal of Lean Enterprise Research [48603]

Leiden
Journal for European Environmental
& Planning Law [48698]
Middle East Law and Governance
[48711]

Rotterdam
Corporate Reputation Review
[48749]

NEW ZEALAND
Auckland
New Zealand Doctor [48809]

North Shore City
New Zealand Company Vehicle
[48957] .. .. (Controlled) ⋆7,048

NIGERIA
Lagos
African Journal of Business
Management [49131]
Educational Research & Reviews
[49137]

Victoria Island
Lagos Business School Management
Review [49178]

NORWAY
Stavange
International Journal of Strategic Engineering Asset Management
[49213]

PAKISTAN
Faisalabad
Academic Journal of Financial
Management [49229]
International Journal of Quality and
Innovation [49255]

POLAND
Warsaw
Economics and Organization of
Enterprise [49707]
International Journal of Strategic
Property Management [49720]
Organizacija [49743]

Wroclaw
International Journal of Intelligent Information and Database Systems
[49780]

RUSSIA
Irkutsk
Geography and Natural Resources
[49856]

SAUDI ARABIA
Jeddah
Islamic Capitals and Cities Magazine
[50056]

SINGAPORE
Singapore
Asian Case Research Journal
[50106]
Chinese Management Studies
[50120]
International Journal of Complexity in
Leadership and Management
[50178]
International Journal of Innovation
Management [50184]

Singapore City
Asian Security Review
[50311] 10,000
FutureGov [50312] 8,950

REPUBLIC OF SOUTH AF-
RICA
Cape Town
Black Business Quarterly
[50365] 10,000
Leadership in HIV/AIDS
[50387] 10,000
Service [50410] 10,000

Centurion
IMFO [50439]
IMIESA [50440]
SA Journal of Human Resource
Management [50447]
SA Journal of Industrial Psychology
[50448]
South African Journal of Business
Management [50451]
South African Journal of Information
Management [50454]

Grahamstown
Nigeria Journal of Business
Administration [50505]

Hillcrest
South African Journal of Economic
and Management Sciences [50523]

Pretoria
Management Dynamics [50596]

SPAIN
Oviedo
International Journal of Chinese Cul-
ture & Management [50823]
International Journal of Strategic
Change Management [50825]

SRI LANKA
Colombo
Sri Lankan Journal of Management
[50869]

SWEDEN
Goteborg
Telecommunications Policy [50967]

Stockholm
International Journal of Entrepreneurial Venturing [51020]

SWITZERLAND
Geneva
International Journal of Applied Deci-
sion Sciences [51100]

International Journal of Applied Man-
agement Science [51101]
International Journal of Corporate
Governance [51113]
International Journal of Inventory
Research [51127]
International Journal of Sustainable
Strategic Management [51144]

Lausanne
Insurance [51192]

Zurich
International Journal of Technology
Policy and Management [51267]

TAIWAN
Taichung
International Journal of Electronic
Customer Relationship
Management [51320]

Taipei
Contemporary Management
Research [51336]

UNITED REPUBLIC OF TAN-
ZANIA
Dar es Salaam
African Journal of Finance and
Management [51399]

THAILAND
Bangkok
Thai Journal of Development
Administration
[51439] .. .. (Paid) 1,500

TURKEY
Istanbul
Bogazici Journal
[51557] .... (Paid) 850

UNITED KINGDOM
Abingdon
European Sport Management Quar-
terly (ESMQ) [51786]
International Public Management
Journal [51849]
International Review of Law Comput-
ers & Technology [51852]
Journal of Change Management
[51873]
Journal of Educational Administration
and History [51892]
New Genetics & Society [51992]
Planning Practice and Research
[52014]
Public Management Review [52031]
School Leadership & Management
[52053]
Technology Analysis & Strategic
Management [52073]

Argyll
Journal of Marketing Management
[52130]

Basingstoke
European Management Review
[52201]

Birmingham
Knowledge Management Research &
Practice [52356]

Bradford
Baltic Journal of Management
[52437]
Corporate Governance [52447]
Development and Learning in
Organizations [52449]
Information Management & Computer
Security [52467]

International Journal of Accounting and Information Management [52473]

International Journal of Educational Management [52476]

International Journal of Productivity and Performance Management [52485]

Journal of Communication Management [52494]

Journal of Educational Administration [52497]

Journal of Health, Organization and Management [52502]

Journal of Management History [52508]

Journal of Strategy and Management [52517]

Strategic Direction [52546]

Strategic HR Review [52547]

The TQM Journal [52554]

Training & Management Development Methods [52555]

Brighton
The International Journal of Leadership in Public Services [52616]
Research Policy [52631]

Bristol
Management & Organizational History [52704]
Perspectives [52715] .... (Combined) ‡4,000

Cambridge
Workplace Law [52905]

Corby
Operations Management [53063] .. .. (Paid) 1,462

Dundee
International Journal of Energy Sector Management [53214]

East Horsley
International Journal of Project Management [53236]

Hook
Project Manager Today [53587] .. .. (Controlled) ★14,871

Hull
International Journal of Agile Systems and Management [53626]

Kempston
Legal Executive Journal [53669] 23,000

Lichfield
Management Services [53853] 4,500

London
British Journal of Cancer Management [54114]
British Journal of Health Care Management [54121]
Charity Times [54197]
Chartered Secretary [54199] .... (Combined) 20,057
Competency & Emotional Intelligence [54251]
Continuity, Insurance & Risk [54264]
CPO Agenda [54279]
European Journal of Industrial Relations [54400]
Financial Director [54454] ... ★20,609
FM World [54474]
Handbook of Practice Management [54529]
International Journal of Business Performance Management [54636]
International Journal of Cross Cultural Management [54641]
Journal of Organisational Transformation and Social Change [54790]

Leadership Focus [54859] .... ‡28,000
London Bulletin [54886] .... (Combined) 6,000
Management Learning [54901]
Manager, British Journal of Administrative Management [54903] 12,500
Managing Partner [54905]
Operational Risk & Regulation [55038]
Organization [55042]
Qualitative Research in Organizations and Management [55160]
Strategy [55265] 15,000
Supply Management [55279] .... ‡35,000
UK Excellence [55354] .... ‡4,000

Loughton
Education Business [55489]

Manchester
Gender in Management [55556]
Progress in Planning [55575]

Olney
International Journal of Complexity [55795]
International Journal of Entrepreneurial Venturing [55801]
International Journal of Foresight and Innovation Policy [55807]
International Journal of Liability and Scientific Enquiry [55818]
International Journal of Management Concepts and Philosophy [55820]
International Journal of Management and Decision Making [55821]
International Journal of Project Organisation and Management [55829]
International Journal of Risk Assessment and Management [55831]
International Journal of Teaching & Case Studies [55834]
International Journal of Technology Intelligence and Planning [55835]
International Journal of Technology Transfer and Commercialisation [55836]

Orpington
Journal of Automated Methods and Management in Chemistry [55853]

Oxford
Human Resource Management Journal [55980]
IMA Journal of Management Mathematics [55984]
Journal of International Financial Management & Accounting [56045]
Journal of Public Administration Research and Theory [56062]
Management and Organization Review [56092]
Review of Policy Research [56194]
Review of Urban & Regional Development Studies [56195]

Reading
Electronic Journal of Information Systems Evaluation (EJISE) [56315]

Salisbury
Facilities-UK [56453]

Sheffield
International Journal of Enterprise Network Management [56499]
International Journal of Knowledge Management in Tourism and Hospitality [56500]
International Journal of Logistics Economics & Globalisation [56501]
Managing Leisure [56506]
Planning Theory & Practice [56511]

Telford
International Journal of Business Governance and Ethics [56737]
International Journal of Management Practice [56738]

Uxbridge
International Journal of Work Organisation & Emotion [56799]
Journal of Enterprise Information Management [56800]

West Sussex
The Journal of Multi-Criteria Decision Analysis [56899] .. .. (Paid) 3,500

MARRIAGE AND FAMILY

AUSTRALIA
Glen Iris
Breastfeeding Review [41891]

Melbourne
Family Matters [42059]

BELGIUM
Brussels
Echos AMA [42849]

GERMANY
Frankfurt am Main
Pro Familia Magazin [44368] 7,000

Hamburg
Plan Post [44423] .... (Non-paid) 176,000

HUNGARY
Budapest
Nok Lapja Eskuvo [44859] .. .. ‡28,000
Praktika [44865] .... (Paid) 40,067

INDIA
Nasik
Abhivyakti and Expressions [45473] 1,000

New Delhi
Health and Population [45522] .. .. (Paid) 1,000
Roshni [45646] .... (Paid) 500

JAPAN
Tokyo
Real Simple Japan [47030] .... (Paid) ★105,285

NEW ZEALAND
Christchurch
New Zealand College of Midwives [48873] 2,500

NIGERIA
Abuja
Women on the Move [49058]

SINGAPORE
Singapore
The Family Doctor [50147] 130,000

REPUBLIC OF SOUTH AFRICA
Tygerberg
South African Family Practice [50639]

SWEDEN
Stockholm
Kvinnotryck [51024]

UNITED ARAB EMIRATES
Dubai
Emirates Bride [51641] 15,000

UNITED KINGDOM
Abingdon
Journal of Youth Studies [51958]

Basingstoke
Family Spending [52204]

Belfast
The Chronicle [52281]

Bridgwater
ABM Magazine [52595]

London
Be My Parent [54008] .. .. (Combined) 22,000
Practical Parenting and Pregnancy [55116]
You & Your Wedding [55433]

Ormskirk
Midwifery Matters [55850] 1,750

Pewsey
Army Families Federation Families Journal [56269] 64,000

Worthing
A Kentish Wedding [56975]

URUGUAY
Montevideo
Bibliographic Journal [57007]

MATERIALS HANDLING

AUSTRALIA
Sydney
International Journal of Abrasive Technology [42518]
Journal of Biomimetics, Biomaterials, and Tissue Engineering [42527]

Wahroonga
InMotion [42674] .. .. ★6,157

BRAZIL
Vicosa
Materials Research [43060]

PEOPLE'S REPUBLIC OF CHINA
Shanghai
Theoretical and Applied Fracture Mechanics [43507]

EGYPT
El Mansoura
International Journal of Materials Science [43770]

FRANCE
Les Ulis
Materiaux & Techniques [43966]

GERMANY
Pfinztal
International Journal of Materials and Product Technology [44633]

INDIA
Jodhpur
Indian Journal of Engineering and Materials Sciences [45222]

ISRAEL
Tel Aviv
Journal of the Mechanical Behavior of Materials [46108]

Circulation: ★ = ABC; △ = BPA; ◆ = CAC; • = CCAB; ❏ = VAC; ⊕ = PO Statement; ‡ = Publisher's Report; Boldface figures = sworn; Light figures = estimated.

Science and Engineering of Composite Materials [46112]

JAPAN
Sendai
High Temperature Materials and Processes [46666]

MALAYSIA
Melaka
International Journal of Precision Technology [47681]

NETHERLANDS
Amsterdam
Journal of Hazardous Materials [48082]

PORTUGAL
Aveiro
International Journal of Machining and Machinability of Materials [49786]
International Journal of Materials Engineering Innovation [49787]

SERBIA
Belgrade
Science of Sintering [50083]

SWITZERLAND
Zurich
Key Engineering Materials [51272]
Solid State Phenomena [51283]
Swisspack International [51290] .... (Paid) 3,800

UNITED KINGDOM
Bradford
Industrial Lubrication and Tribology [52465]
Multidiscipline Modeling in Materials and Structures [52528]

Cambridge
Journal of Advanced Materials [52841]

London
Corrosion Engineering, Science and Technology [54269] 900
POWDEReporter [55111]

Olney
International Journal of Computational Materials Science & Surface Engineering [55796]
International Journal of Materials & Structural Integrity [55823]
International Journal of Nanomanufacturing [55825]

Sidcup
Cranes Today
[56541] .. .. (Combined) △15,201
Hoist [56543] ... (Controlled) △8,643

Wadhurst
Construction Europe
[56805] .... ★14,624
International Cranes and Specialized Transport [56809] .. .. ‡14,381

West Bromwich
BMHF Yearbook & Directory [56889]

MATHEMATICS
See also Statistics

AUSTRALIA
Canberra
The ANZIAM Journal (The Australian & New Zealand Industrial & Applied Mathematics Journal)
[41698] ....,... (Paid) 450
Journal of the Australian Mathematical Society [41709] ..... (Paid) 550

Melbourne
Australian Journal of Mathematical Analysis and Applications [42050]

Stepney
Australian Mathematics Teacher (AMT) [42387] .... (Paid) 3,000
Australian Primary Mathematics Classroom (APMC)
[42388] .... (Paid) 1,500
Australian Senior Mathematics Journal (ASMJ)
[42389] .... (Paid) 1,500

Sydney
Journal of Economic Dynamics and Control [42528]

Toowoomba
The Australian Mathematical Society Gazette [42627] 1,000

BELARUS
Minsk
Computational Methods in Applied Mathematics [42832]

BELGIUM
Brussels
Mathematics and Computers in Simulation [42865]

Leuven
Journal of Computational and Applied Mathematics [42900]

BRAZIL
Petropolis
Computational & Applied Mathematics [42990]

Rio de Janeiro
ALEA [43001]
ALEA [43002]

BULGARIA
Ruse
Advanced Studies in Theoretical Physics [43087]
Applied Mathematical Sciences [43088]
International Journal of Algebra [43089]
International Journal of Contemporary Mathematical Sciences [43090]
International Journal of Mathematical Analysis [43091]
International Mathematical Forum [43092]

Sofia
Fractional Calculus and Applied Analysis [43099]
Mathematica Plus [43105]
Serdica Mathematical Journal [43107]

CHILE
Antofagasta
Proyecciones Journal of Mathematics [43132]

PEOPLE'S REPUBLIC OF CHINA
Beijing
Acta Mathematicae Applicatae Sinica [43167]
Algebra Colloquium [43168]

Science in China Series A [43215]

Hainan
International Journal of Information Science and Computer Mathematics [43258]
International Journal of Computational and Applied Mathematics [43259]

Hong Kong
Asian Journal of Mathematics
[43277] .... (Combined) 1,100
Journal of Computational Mathematics [43353]
Mathematical Modelling and Applied Computing [43368]

Shanghai
Chinese Annals of Mathematics, Series B [43469]
International Journal of Nonlinear Modelling in Science and Engineering [43477]

Xiangtan
Communications in Differential and Difference Equations [43538]
International Journal of Computing Science and Mathematics [43539]
International Journal of Dynamical Systems and Differential Equations [43540]

COTE D'IVOIRE
Abidjan
Afrique Science [43555]

CZECH REPUBLIC
Brno
Archivum Mathematicum [43602]

Brunn
Differential Geometry and its Applications [43604]

DENMARK
Lyngby
European Journal of Mechanics - A/Solids [43725]

FINLAND
Helsinki
Annales Academiae Scientiarum Fennicae Mathematica [43816]
Bulletin, Classe des Sciences Mathematiques et Naturelles, Sciences mathematiques [43822]
Journal of Analysis and its Applications [43834]
Journal of Lie Theory [43835]
Oberwolfach Reports [43852]

FRANCE
Les Ulis
Quadrature [43967]

Nancy
Discrete Mathematics & Theoretical Computer Science [44010]

Orsay
Inventiones Mathematicae [44019]

Paris
Journal of the Institute of Mathematics of Jussieu [44064]
Journal of Mathematical Economics [44065]
Mathematische Zeitschrift [44069]
Probability Theory and Related Fields [44078]

Rillieux-la-Pape
SAR and QSAR in Environmental Research [44099]

Toulouse
Asymptotic Analysis [44119]
Fuzzy Sets and Systems [44120]

Villeurbanne
Mathematical Modelling of Natural Phenomena [44126]

GEORGIA
Tbilisi
Georgian Mathematical Journal [44133]

GERMANY
Berlin
Advances in Calculus of Variations
[44148] .... ‡200
Forum Mathematicum [44182] ... 300
Journal of Mathematical Cryptology
[44207] 170

Bielefeld
Documenta Mathematica [44245]

Dusseldorf
Progress in Computational Fluid Dynamics [44331]

Erlangen
GAMM - Mitteilungen [44338]
SIAM Journal on Scientific Computing [44341]

Gottingen
In Silico Biology [44399]

Greifswald
MLQ - Mathematical Logic Quarterly [44405]

Hamburg
Groups — Complexity — Cryptology [44417]

Heidelberg
Journal of Mathematical Biology [44465]
Mathematische Annalen [44466]

Lemgo
Contributions to Algebra and Geometry [44531]
Journal of Convex Analysis [44532]
Journal for Geometry and Graphics [44533]

Munster
Archive for Mathematical Logic [44596]
Journal fur die reine und angewandte Mathematik [44600] 750

Regensburg
Mathematische Nachrichten [44644]

Saale
ZAMM - Zeitschrift fur Angewandte Mathematik und Mechanik [44650]

Saarbrucken
Archiv der Mathematik [44651]

Wurzburg
Advances in Geometry [44716]
Computational Methods and Function Theory [44718]

GHANA
Winneba
African Journal of Educational Studies in Mathematics and Sciences [44740]
Mathematics Connection [44741]

HUNGARY
Budapest
Studia Scientiarum Mathematicarum Hungarica [44876]

Debrecen
Aequationes Mathematicae [44886]

Circulation: ★ = ABC; △ = BPA; ◆ = CAC; • = CCAB; ❑ = VAC; ⊕ = PO Statement; ‡ = Publisher's Report; Boldface figures = sworn; Light figures = estimated.

Nyiregyhaza
Acta Mathematica Academiae Paedagogicae Nyiregyhaziensis [44892]

INDIA
Allahabad
Advances and Applications in Discrete Mathematics [44919]
Advances and Applications in Statistics [44920]
Advances in Differential Equations and Control Processes [44922]
Advances in Fuzzy Sets and Systems [44923]
Current Development in Theory and Applications of Wavelets [44924]
Far East Journal of Applied Mathematics [44925]
Far East Journal of Mathematical Education [44929]
Far East Journal of Mathematical Sciences [44930]
International Journal of Functional Analysis, Operator Theory and Applications [44932]
International Journal of Numerical Methods and Applications [44933]
JP Journal of Algebra, Number Theory and Applications [44935]
JP Journal of Fixed Point Theory and Applications [44937]

Bangalore
Proceedings of the Indian Academy of Sciences [44982]
Profound (The Dialog Corporation) - Mathematical Sciences [44983]

Jodhpur
Bulletin of Pure and Applied Mathematics [45216]

Kolkata
Sankhya [45303]

New Delhi
Advances in Dynamical Systems and Applications [45477]
Algebraic Hyperstructures and Applications [45482]
Indian Journal of Mathematics and Mathematical Sciences [45560]
Indian Journal of Pure and Applied Mathematics [45565]
International Review of Fuzzy Mathematics [45588]
Journal of Discrete Mathematical Sciences and Cryptography [45595] .... (Paid) 240
Journal of Information & Optimization Sciences [45606] .... (Paid) 480
Journal of Interdisciplinary Mathematics [45608] .... (Paid) 240
Journal of International Economic Review [45609]
Journal of Mathematical Analysis and Approximation Theory [45613]
Mathematics Today [45625] .... (Paid) 50,000

Roorkee
International Journal of Mathematics and Statistics (IJMS) [45719]

IRAN
Kashan
International Journal of Pure & Applied Mathematical Sciences (IJPAMS) [45880]

Kerman
Global Journal of Mathematics and Mathematical Sciences (GJMMS) [45881]
Journal of Dynamical Systems and Geometric Theories [45882]

Tehran
Scientia Iranica [45913] .... (Paid) 5,000

ISRAEL
Beer-Sheva
Complex Analysis and Operator Theory [46074]

Tel Aviv
Geometric and Functional Analysis (GAFA) [46100]
International Journal of Nonlinear Sciences and Numerical Simulation [46104]

ITALY
Bologna
Bollettino di Storia delle Scienze Matematiche [46125]

Pavia
Numerische Mathematik [46210]

Trieste
Journal of Geometry and Physics [46265]

Turin
Mathematical Models and Methods in Applied Sciences [46273]

Udine
Advances in Fuzzy Mathematics [46276]

JAPAN
Hikone
JP Journal of Geometry and Topology [46375]

Hiroshima
Hiroshima Journal of Mathematics Education [46379]
Hiroshima Mathematical Journal [46380] 400

Ibaraki
Tsukuba Journal of Mathematics [46395]

Kobe
Funkcialaj Ekvacioj, Serio Internacia [46430]
Kobe Journal of Mathematics [46432]

Kumamoto
Kumamoto Journal of Mathematics [46453]

Kyoto
Mathematics Applied in Science and Technology [46482]

Nagoya
Nagoya Mathematical Journal [46556] .... (Controlled) 1,150

Niigata
Nihonkai Mathematical Journal [46573]

Okayama
Mathematical Journal of Okayama University [46599]

Osaka
Advances in Applied Mathematical Analysis [46614]
Journal of Approximation Theory and Applications [46619]
Mathematica Japonica [46626] .... (Paid) 950
Osaka Journal of Mathematics [46627]
Questions and Answers in General Topology [46628] .... (Paid) 200

Sapporo
Hokkaido Mathematical Journal [46650] .... (Paid) 720

Sendai
Tohoku Mathematical Journal [46670] ... . (Paid) 1,000

Tokushima
Journal of Mathematics [46714]

Tokyo
Acta Mathematica Sinica [46724]
Algebra Universalis [46731]
Annali di Matematica Pura ed Applicata [46736]
Annals of Combinatorics [46737]
Applicable Algebra in Engineering, Communication and Computing [46745]
Archive for History of Exact Sciences [46748]
Calcolo [46772]
Calculus of Variations and Partial Differential Equation [46773]
Computational Complexity [46790]
Computational Mechanics [46791]
Computing and Visualization in Science [46794]
Continuum Mechanics and Thermodynamics [46796]
Decisions in Economics and Finance [46800]
Graphs and Combinatorics [46831]
Japanese Journal of Mathematics [46870]
Journal of Mathematical Sciences [46923] .... (Paid) 850
Proceedings of the Japan Academy, Series A [47026]

Toyama
Mathematics Journal of Toyama University [47096]

Yokohama
Systems and Synthetic Biology [47142]

KENYA
Nairobi
East African Journal of Statistics [47180]

REPUBLIC OF KOREA
Chinju
Advances in Algebra [47218]

Kyungnam
Advances in Theoretical and Applied Mathematics [47242]

Masan
International Journal of Mathematical Sciences [47243]

Pohang
Bulletin of the Korean Mathematical Society [47247]

Seoul
Communications of the Korean Mathematical Society [47262]
Global Journal of Pure and Applied Mathematics [47266]

MALAYSIA
Penang
Journal of Science and Mathematics Education in Southeast Asia [47689] 100

MOROCCO
Rabat
African Journal of Mathematical Physics [47814]

NETHERLANDS
Amsterdam
Applied and Computational Harmonic Analysis [47897]

Bulletin des Sciences Mathematiques [47918]
Communications in Nonlinear Science and Numerical Simulation [47932]
Finite Fields and Their Applications [47986]
Fundamenta Informaticae [47993]
Future Generation Computer Systems [47995]
Historia Mathematica [48011]
Informatica [48017]
Journal of Algebra [48038]
Journal of Algorithms in Cognition, Informatics and Logic [48039]
Journal of Applied Mathematics and Mechanics [48047]
Journal of Approximation Theory [48048]
Journal of Colloid and Interface Science [48060]
Journal of Combinatorial Theory, Series A [48061]
Journal of Combinatorial Theory, Series B [48062]
Journal of Computational Physics [48064]
Journal of Computer and System Sciences [48065]
Journal of Differential Equations [48068]
Journal of Functional Analysis [48080]
Journal of Integrated Design & Process Science [48086]
Journal of Mathematical Psychology [48095]
Journal of Multivariate Analysis [48100]
Journal of Number Theory [48104]
Journal of The Franklin Institute [48125]
Mathematical Social Sciences [48148]
Model Assisted Statistics and Applications [48161]
Neural Networks [48172]
Stochastic Processes and Their Applications [48237]
Topology [48250]
Topology and its Applications [48251]

Bussum
Analysis in Theory and Applications [48278]

Dordrecht
Acta Applicandae Mathematicae [48318]
Acta Biotheoretica [48319]
Advances in Computational Mathematics [48320]
Annals of Mathematics and Artificial Intelligence [48325]
Applied Mathematics and Mechanics [48327]
Bulletin of the Brazilian Mathematical Society, New Series [48338]
Bulletin of Mathematical Biology [48340]
Designs, Codes and Cryptography [48372]
Discrete Event Dynamic Systems [48375]
Frontiers of Mathematics in China [48401]
Geometriae Dedicata [48407]
Journal of Computational Electronics [48450]
Journal of Dynamics and Differential Equations [48455]
Journal of Geometry [48464]
Journal of Global Optimization [48465]

Circulation: ★ = ABC; △ = BPA; ◆ = CAC; • = CCAB; ❏ = VAC; ⊕ = PO Statement; ‡ = Publisher's Report; Boldface figures = sworn; Light figures = estimated.

Journal of Mathematical Chemistry **[48474]**
Journal of Mathematical Modelling and Algorithms **[48475]**
Journal of Optimization Theory and Applications **[48480]**
Journal of Scheduling **[48491]**
Mathematical Physics, Analysis and Geometry **[48513]**
Numerical Algorithms **[48520]**
Order **[48522]**
Periodica Mathematica Hungarica **[48524]**
Potential Analysis **[48540]**
The Ramanujan Journal **[48546]**
Reliable Computing **[48549]**
Vietnam Journal of Mathematics **[48586]**

Groningen
Indagationes Mathematicae **[48601]**

Rotterdam
Statistica Neerlandica **[48752]**

Voorburg
Bernoulli **[48769]** .... (Paid) 2,000
Journal of Time Series Analysis **[48770]**

NEW ZEALAND
Christchurch
New Zealand Journal of Mathematics **[48874]**

Wellington
Australian and New Zealand Journal of Statistics **[49000]**
Journal of Symbolic Logic **[49012]**

NIGERIA
Benin City
Journal of the Nigerian Association of Mathematical Physics **[49065]**

Calabar
Global Journal of Pure and Applied Sciences **[49075]**

PAKISTAN
Faisalabad
Journal of Applied Sciences **[49261]**
Journal of Modern Mathematics and Statistics **[49272]**

POLAND
Lodz
Journal of Applied Analysis **[49671]**

Warsaw
Acta Arithmetica **[49677]**
Bulletin of the Polish Academy of Sciences Mathematics **[49698]**
Central European Journal of Mathematics **[49701]**
Formalized Mathematics **[49712]**
International Journal of Applied Mathematics and Computer Science **[49719]**
Mathematica Slovaca **[49736]**

ROMANIA
Bucharest
Balkan Journal of Geometry and its Applications **[49832]**

RUSSIA
Moscow
Computational Mathematics and Mathematical Physics **[49889]**
Doklady Mathematics **[49898]**
Integral Transforms and Special Functions **[49920]**
Izvestiya **[49923]**

Moscow Mathematical Journal **[49945]**
Regular & Chaotic Dynamics **[49970]**
Sbornik **[49989]**

Novosibirsk
Siberian Journal of Numerical Mathematics **[50014]**

SINGAPORE
Singapore
COSMOS **[50128]**
Discrete Optimization **[50134]**
Infinite Dimensional Analysis, Quantum Probability and Related Topics **[50170]**
Information Fusion **[50171]**
International Journal of Algebra and Computation **[50176]**
International Journal of Computational Methods (IJCM) **[50179]**
International Journal of Geometric Methods in Modern Physics (IJGMMP) **[50180]**
Journal of Applied Logic **[50198]**
Journal of Knot Theory and Its Ramifications **[50208]**
Reviews in Mathematical Physics **[50246]** .... (Paid) 150

REPUBLIC OF SOUTH AFRICA
Centurion
African Journal of Research in Mathematics, Science and Technology Education **[50437]**

Grahamstown
Global Journal of Mathematical Sciences **[50497]**

Wits
South African Actuarial Journal **[50643]**

SPAIN
Madrid
TEST **[50811]**

SWEDEN
Djursholm
Arkiv for Matematik **[50952]**

Lulea
Journal of Nonlinear Mathematical Physics **[50982]**

Stockholm
Bulletin of the Brazilian Mathematical Society **[51010]**
Scandinavian Actuarial Journal **[51033]**

SWITZERLAND
Geneva
International Journal of Applied Nonlinear Science **[51102]**
International Journal of Data Analysis Techniques and Strategies **[51115]**

Lausanne
Insurance **[51192]**

Lausanne-Dorigny
Expositiones Mathematicae **[51205]**

Zurich
Journal of Applied Mathematics and Physics (ZAMP) **[51269]**

TAIWAN
Hsinchu
The Taiwanese Journal of Mathematics **[51307]**

Tamsui
Tamkang Journal of Mathematics **[51397]**

TUNISIA
Tunis
Advances in Pure and Applied Mathematics **[51488]**

TURKEY
Ankara
Turkish Journal of Mathematics **[51512]**

Van
Journal of Contemporary Mathematics **[51580]**

UNITED ARAB EMIRATES
Al Ain
International Journal of Mathematics Manuscripts **[51626]**

UNITED KINGDOM
Abingdon
International Journal of Neuroscience **[51842]**

Belfast
Bulletin of the Irish Mathematical Society **[52280]**

Birmingham
IMA Journal of Applied Mathematics **[52342]**

Bognor Regis
Teaching Mathematics and Its Applications **[52404]**

Brentwood
The Journal of Computational Multiphase Flows **[52579]**

Bristol
Journal of Cellular Automata **[52683]**
Journal of Physics A **[52694]**
Nonlinearity **[52712]**

Cambridge
Journal of Algebraic Geometry **[52844]**
Probability Surveys **[52885]**

Coventry
Abstracts and Reviews **[53076]**
Geometry & Topology **[53083]**

Edinburgh
ASTIN Bulletin **[53254]**
Proceedings of the Edinburgh Mathematical Society **[53306]** 700

Exeter
Dynamical Systems **[53352]**

Glasgow
Glasgow Mathematical Journal **[53421]** 600
Multiagent and Grid Systems **[53431]**

Kidlington
Acta Mathematica Scientia **[53689]**

Leeds
Computational & Mathematical Methods in Medicine **[53762]**

Leicester
Equals **[53798]**
Mathematical Gazette **[53813]**
Mathematical Pie **[53814]**
Mathematics in School **[53815]**
Primary Mathematics **[53817]**
Symmetry Plus **[53830]**

London
Bioinformation **[54020]**
International Journal of Computer Mathematics **[54640]**

Inverse Problems **[54677]**
Journal of Discrete Algorithms (Amsterdam) **[54738]**
Journal of Logic and Computation **[54773]**
LMS Journal of Computation and Mathematics **[54880]**
Measurement and Control **[54918]** 4,500
Philosophical Transactions of the Royal Society A **[55079]**
Proceedings **[55124]**
Profound (The Dialog Corporation) of the Royal Society A **[55133]**

Nottingham
Mathematical Medicine and Biology **[55766]**

Oxford
Applied Mathematics Research eXpress **[55870]**
BSHM Bulletin **[55896]**
European Journal of Applied Mathematics **[55945]** 350
IMA Journal of Management Mathematics **[55984]**
IMRN **[55987]**
International Mathematics Research Papers **[56005]**
Journal of Group Theory **[56036]** 250
Logic Journal of the IGPL **[56091]**
Philosophia Mathematica **[56153]**
Proceedings of the London Mathematical Society **[56168]**
The Quarterly Journal of Mechanics and Applied Mathematics **[56183]**
SIAM Journal on Optimization **[56202]**

Plymouth
International Journal for Technology in Mathematics Education **[56271]**

Sheffield
Advances in Applied Probability **[56488]**
Journal of Applied Probability **[56503]**
The Mathematical Scientist **[56507]**
Mathematical Spectrum **[56508]**

Southend-on-Sea
IMA Journal of Numerical Analysis **[56585]**

Swansea
Applied Mathematical Modelling **[56699]**

Teddington
International Journal of Mathematical Modelling and Numerical Optimisation **[56731]**

Wales
International Journal of Applied Mathematics and Mechanics (IJAMM) **[56812]**

Circulation: ★ = ABC; △ = BPA; ◆ = CAC; • = CCAB; ❏ = VAC; ⊕ = PO Statement; ‡ = Publisher's Report; Boldface figures = sworn; Light figures = estimated.

MEDICINE AND SURGERY

See also Chiropractic; Drugs and Pharmaceuticals; Health and Healthcare; Hospitals and Healthcare Institutions; Laboratory Research (Scientific and Medical); Osteopathy; Physiology and Anatomy; Podiatry; Psychology and Psychiatry; Substance Abuse and Treatment; Toxicology

ARGENTINA
Buenos Aires
Journal of Argentine Dermatology [41476]

AUSTRALIA
Adelaide
International Journal of Computers in Healthcare [41508]

Barton
Australian Medicine
[41576] ...... (Combined) ◆26,351

Bowen Hills
Brain Impairment [41625]

Callaghan
Women and Birth [41691]

Camberwell
Australian Journal of Physiotherapy
[41695] .... (Combined) ★11,000

Canberra
Communicable Diseases Intelligence [41704]

Chatswood
Australian Doctor
[41736] .... (Combined) 22,005

Deakin
Australian Prescriber [41835]

Forrestfield
WFOT Bulletin [41868]

Heidelberg
Progress in Osteoporosis [41947]
Journal of Oral Pathology and Medicine [41948]

Kingston
Australian Journal of Advanced Nursing (AJAN) [41991]
Australian Nursing Journal (ANJ)
[41992] .... ‡65,000

Parkville
Tissue Antigens [42232]

Richmond
ANZ Journal of Surgery [42300]
Journal of Gastroenterology and Hepatology [42303]
Nephrology [42304]

Strawberry Hills
ADF Health [42393]

Sydney
International Journal of Cardiology [42519]
Journal of Science and Medicine in Sport [42531]

West Melbourne
Emergency Medicine Australasia [42697]

Womying
International Journal of Medical Sciences [42711]

AUSTRIA
Vienna
Annals of Nutrition and Metabolism
[42744] 1,250
European Surgery [42756]
Transplant International [42772]

BELGIUM
Antwerp
Clinical Neurology and Neurosurgery [42838]

Brussels
Diabetes Voice [42848] 11,000
International Review of the Armed Forces Medical Services [42860]
Journal of Radiotherapy and Oncology [42863]

Diepenbeek
European Journal of Cancer Prevention [42879]

Gent
Clinica Chimica Acta [42882]

Genval
Health and Food
[42886] .... (Non-paid) ⊕15,000

BRAZIL
Botafogo
International Braz J Urol
[42954] 6,000
Revista Brasileira de Anestesiologia [42955]

Botucatu
The Journal of Venomous Animals and Toxins including Tropical Diseases [42957]

Rio de Janeiro
Memorias do Instituto Oswaldo Cruz [43012]
Pesquisa Veterinaria Brasileira [43013]

Salvador
Brazilian Journal of Infectious Diseases [43014]

Sao Paulo
Acta Cirurgica Brasileira [43021]
Arquivos Brasileiros de Endocrinologia & Metabologia [43022]
Arquivos Brasileiros de Oftalmologia [43023]
Arquivos de Neuro-Psiquiatria [43024]
Clinics [43036]
Sao Paulo Medical Journal [43050]

Vicosa
Arquivo Brasileiro de Medicina Veterinaria e Zootecnia [43055]
Entomologia y Vectores [43058]
Journal of Epilepsy and Clinical Neurophysiology [43059]
Radiologia Brasileira [43063]

Vila Olimpia
Arquivos Brasileiros de Cardiologia [43067]

BULGARIA
Sofia
Journal of Endocrinology
[43103] .... (Paid) ⊕1,500

PEOPLE'S REPUBLIC OF CHINA
Beijing
Chinese Medical Journal [43187]
Journal of Asian Natural Products Research [43202]

Science in China Series C [43217]
World Journal of Gastroenterology [43225]

Changchun
Journal of Jilin University Medicine Edition [43243]

Hong Kong
Asian Journal of Surgery
[43279] .... (Combined) ‡1,350
Clinical Oral Implants Research [43291]
HK Medical Journal [43303] ... 6,000
Hong Kong Journal of Dermatology & Venereology [43328]
Hong Kong Journal of Occupational Therapy [43329]
The Hong Kong Journal of Orthopaedic Surgery [43330]
The Hong Kong Journal of Sports Medicine and Sports Science [43334]
Hong Kong Medical Diary
[43338] 8,000
Hong Kong Medical Journal
[43339] .... (Paid) 7,100
                               7,800
The Hong Kong Nursing Journal [43340]
Hong Kong Physiotherapy Journal [43341]
The Hong Kong Practitioner
[43342] 4,000
Journal of the Hong Kong College of Cardiology [43357] 1,000
Journal of Orthopaedic Surgery [43360]
Neuroembryology and Aging [43370]

Shanghai
Popular Medicine [43494]

Xi'an
Chinese Heart Journal [43528]
Chinese Journal of Cells and Molecular Immunology [43529]
Chinese Journal of Conservative Dentistry [43530]
Chinese Journal of Neuroanatomy [43531]
Journal of Fourth Military University [43533]
Journal of Practical Stomatology [43534]

CROATIA
Zagreb
Croatian Medical Journal [43565]

CZECH REPUBLIC
Ceske Budejovice
Journal of Applied Biomedicine [43606]

Prague
Acta Chirurgiae Plasticae [43608]
Anaesthesiology & Intensive Critical Care Medicine
[43609] .. .. (Paid) 1,800
Ceska Revmatologie [43612]
Cesko-Slovenska Patologie/Soudni Lekarstvi [43613]
Ceskoslovenska Pediatrie
[43614] 2,500
Czech Gynaecology [43616]
Czech Radiology [43617]
Czech and Slovak Neurology and Neurosurgery [43618]
Czech and Slovak Ophthalmology [43619]
Czech and Slovak Pharmacy [43620]
Czecho-Slovak Dermatology [43622]
Epidemiology, Microbiology, Immunology [43624]

Internal Medicine [43625]
Journal of Czech Physicians [43627]
Otorhinolaryngology and Phoniatrics [43632]
Revizni a Posudkove Lekarstvi [43637]

DENMARK
Copenhagen
APMIS [43655]
Bibliotek for Laeger [43656]
The Clinical Respiratory Journal [43659]
Scandinavian Journal of Medicine and Science in Sports [43682]
Ugeskrift for Laeger [43685]

Frederiksberg
Oral Diseases [43693]

EGYPT
Cairo
African Journal of Urology [43750]
Egyptian Journal of Biomedical Sciences [43757]
Egyptian Journal of Medical Laboratory Sciences [43760]
Scientific Medical Journal [43765]

EL SALVADOR
San Salvador
BMC Public Health [43777]

ESTONIA
Tartu
Journal Eesti Arst [43792] 3,800

ETHIOPIA
Addis Ababa
Ethiopian Journal of Health Development [43800]
Journal of Ethiopian Medical Practice [43802]

FINLAND
Helsinki
Ketju [43841] .... (Paid) 3,000

Kirkkonummi
TSW Holistic Health & Medicine [43876]

Kuopio
Pathophysiology [43877]

FRANCE
Bordeaux
Bulletin de l'ALLF [43921]

Ferney-Voltaire
Medical Student International [43949]
World Medical Journal [43951]

Gif-sur-Yvette
Journal of Physiology - Paris [43956]

Marseille
MAGMA [43973]

Montrouge
Annales de Gerontologie [43981]
Bulletin du Cancer [43982]
Cahiers d'etudes et de recherches francophones/Sante [43985]
Epilepsies [43987]
Epileptic Disorders [43988]
European Journal of Dermatology [43990]
Hepato-Gastro [43992]
La Lettre de l'Internat [43995]
Magnesium Research [43996]
Medecine therapeutique [43997]
Medecine therapeutique cardiologie [43998]

Circulation: ★ = ABC; △ = BPA; ◆ = CAC; • = CCAB; ❑ = VAC; ⊕ = PO Statement; ‡ = Publisher's Report; Boldface figures = sworn; Light figures = estimated.

Medecine therapeutique/Endocrinologie [43999]
Medecine Therapeutique/medecine de la reproduction [44000]
Medecine therapeutique/Pediatrie [44001]
MT Cardio [44002]
Revue de neuropsychologie [44005]
Sang Thrombose Vaisseaux [44006]
Virologie [44008]

Nice
Journal of the European Academy of Dermatology and Venereology [44016]

Paris
Annales Francaises d'Anesthesie et de Reanimation
[44025] .... (Paid) 5,500
Cancer Radiotherapie [44032]
The International Journal of Tuberculosis and Lung Disease
[44057] 2,500
Leukemia [44068]
Transfusion Clinique et Biologique [44086]

Sophia Antipolis
Cardiovascular Research [44106]
European Heart Journal [44107]

Strasbourg
Cell Adhesion & Migration [44111]

Villeurbanne
Mathematical Modelling of Natural Phenomena [44126]

GEORGIA
Tbilisi
Annals of Biomedical Research and Education [44130]

GERMANY
Berlin
Biomedizinische Technik [44161]
International Journal of Colorectal Disease [44192]
Journal of Cerebral Blood Flow and Metabolism [44204] 1,151
Journal of Perinatal Medicine [44209]
Journal of Vascular Research [44210]
LaboratoriumsMedizin [44213]
Laser & Photonics Reviews [44216]
Laser Technik Journal [44217]

Bonn
European Journal of Development Research [44257]

Bremen
Umwelt-Medizin-Gesellschaft [44282] 4,000

Dusseldorf
Behavioural Brain Research [44321]
German Medical Science [44326]
Parasitology Research [44330]

Edewecht
Rettungsdienst
[44336] ... . (Paid) 22,500

Freiburg
Viszeralmedizin
[44374] .... (Combined) 4,000

Giessen
Cardiovascular Research [44384]
International Journal of Systematic and Evolutionary Microbiology [44386] .... (Combined) 925

Gottingen
Allergy and Clinical Immunology International [44391]

Ethik in der Medizin [44396]

Hamburg
European Addiction Research
[44414] .... (Combined) 900

Hannover
Annals of Hematology [44429]

Heidelberg
Basic Research in Cardiology [44441]
Chinese-German Journal of Clinical Oncology [44445]
Diabetologia [44452]
European Archives of Otorhinolaryngology [44455]
European Spine Journal [44456]
Health Care Management Science [44458]
Hernia [44459]
International Journal of Legal Medicine [44462]
Pediatric Surgery International [44471]
Rheumatology International [44475]
Zeitschrift fur Unternehmens- und Gesellschaftsrecht (ZGR) [44480]

Homburg
Clinical Research in Cardiology [44486]

Jena
Journal of Cancer Research and Clinical Oncology [44490]

Kiel
Journal of Cranio-Maxillofacial Surgery [44503]

Leinfelden-Echterdingen
ErgoMed [44524] 2,800

Lengerich
Transplantationsmedizin [44534]

Magdeburg
Restorative Neurology and Neuroscience [44536]

Mainz
Medical Microbiology and Immunology [44542]

Marburg
Journal of Comparative Physiology B [44548]

Munich
Bayerisches Arzteblatt [44551]
Journal of Neurology [44566]

Munster
Acta Neuropathologica [44594]
Best Practice & Research Clinical Anesthesiology [44597]

Siegen
International Journal of Physiotherapy and Life Physics [44656]

Straubing
International Journal of Antimicrobial Agents [44658]

Stuttgart
European Journal of Pediatric Surgery [44667]
Methods of Information in Medicine [44670] .... (Paid) 800
Nervenheilkunde
[44671] .. .. (Paid) 32,500
Nuklearmedizin
[44675] .. .. (Paid) 3,100
Thrombosis and Haemostasis
[44683] .. .. (Paid) 3,180

Tubingen
Progress in Particle and Nuclear Physics [44693]

Weinheim
ChemMedChem [44704]

Journal of Biophotonics [44706]

GHANA
Accra
Ghana Medical Journal [44726]

GREECE
Athens
Hellenic Radiology Journal [44745]

Kapandriti
Anticancer Research [44760]

HUNGARY
Budapest
Acta Microbiologica et Immunologica Hungarica [44814]
Acta Physiologica Hungarica [44817]
Acta Veterinaria Hungarica [44819]
Hungarian Medical Journal [44835]
Magyar Sebeszet [44847]
Orvosi Hetilap [44862]

INDIA
Bangalore
Amruth [44948] .... (Paid) ⊕5,000
Asia Pacific Disability Rehabilitation Journal [44949] .... (Paid) 2,000
Current Colorectal Cancer Reports [44952]
Indian Journal of Aerospace Medicine [44961]
Journal of Cutaneous and Aesthetic Surgery [44968]
Journal of Human Reproductive Sciences [44973]
Journal of Young Pharmacists [44976]
Karnataka Medical Journal
[44977] .. .. (Paid) 5,000
NTI Bulletin [44979] 1,000
Pharmacognosy @MAG [44980]
Systematic Reviews in Pharmacy [44988]

Belgaum
Journal of Indian Academy of Oral Medicine and Radiology [44996]

Bhopal
The Annals of Medical Entomology
[45005] .. .. (Paid) 3,500

Chandigarh
Indian Journal of Nephrology [45023]
Indian Journal of Community Medicine [45024]

Chennai
Journal of Forensic Dental Sciences [45028]
International Journal of Trichology [45043]
Journal of Conservative Dentistry [45045]
Journal of Indian Society of Periodontology [45048]
Journal of Oral and Maxillofacial Pathology [45049]

Coimbatore
Ancient Science of Life
[45077] .. .. (Paid) 2,000

Cuttack
Hepatitis B Annual [45081]

Delhi
Indian Journal of Allergy Asthma and Immunology [45096]
Indian Journal of Otolaryngology and Head and Neck Surgery
[45097] 3,500
Journal of Vector Borne Diseases
[45102] 300

Jaipur
Indian Journal of Clinical Biochemistry [45195]

Indian Journal of Sexually Transmitted Diseases [45196]
Lung India [45198]

Jodhpur
The Indian Anaesthetists' Forum [45218]

Kochi
QPMPA Journal of Medical Sciences [45253]

Kolkata
Asian Journal of Transfusion Science [45258]
Indian Heart Journal
[45271] .. .. (Paid) 1,500
Journal of the Indian Medical Association (JIMA) [45296]

Lucknow
Indian Journal of Psychological Medicine [45322]

Mandsaur
Asian Journal of Pharmaceutics [45338]
International Journal of Green Pharmacy [45339]

Meerut
Cardiovascular & Hematological Agents in Medicinal Chemistry [45343]

Mumbai
Annals of Pediatric Cardiology [45350]
Indian Journal of Cancer
[45378] 1,600
Indian Journal of Critical Care Medicine [45379]
Indian Journal of Gastroenterology
[45380] 1,200
Indian Journal of Medical and Paediatric Oncology [45382]
Indian Journal of Medical Sciences
[45383] 3,000
Indian Journal of Nuclear Medicine [45384]
Indian Journal of Plastic Surgery
[45387] 35,000
International Journal for Ayurveda Research [45392]
International Journal of Diabetes in Developing Countries [45393]
Journal of Association of Physicians of India [45395] 200,000
Journal of Cancer Research and Therapeutics [45396]
Journal of Craniovertebral Junction and Spine [45397]
Journal of Dental Implants [45398]
Journal of Gynecological Endoscopy and Surgery [45401]
Journal of Medical Physics [45402]
Journal of Minimal Access Surgery (JMAS) [45403]
The Journal of Obstetrics and Gynaecology of India
[45404] .. .. (Paid) 18,200
Journal of Postgraduate Medicine
[45405] 2,000
Medical Law Cases for Doctors [45410]
Mens Sana Monographs [45411]
Middle East African Journal of Ophthalmology [45413]
Modern Medicare [45416]
Oman Journal of Ophthalmology [45423]
Pharmacognosy Research [45430]
PVRI Review [45433]
Saudi Journal of Anaesthesia [45436]

New Delhi
Annals of Cardiac Anaesthesia [45483]

Circulation: ★ = ABC; △ = BPA; ◆ = CAC; • = CCAB; ❏ = VAC; ⊕ = PO Statement; ‡ = Publisher's Report; Boldface figures = sworn; Light figures = estimated.

Health and Population
  [45522] .. .. (Paid) 1,000
ICMR Bulletin
  [45525] .. .. (Paid) 7,500
Indian Journal of Medical Research
  [45561] .. .. (Paid) 700
Indian Journal of Palliative Care
  [45563]
Indian Journal of Tuberculosis
  [45569] .. .. (Paid) 1,500
Journal, Indian Academy of Clinical
  Medicine [45599]
Journal of Indian Association of Pedi-
  atric Surgeons [45601]
Journal of Laboratory Physicians
  [45612]
Journal of Pediatric Neurosciences
  [45615]
Medicinal and Aromatic Plants
  Abstracts [45626] .. .. (Paid) 550
The National Medical Journal of India
  [45629] .. .. (Combined) ‡2,500
The Pharma Review [45635]

Patiala
Journal of Indian Academy of Forensic Medicine [45685]

Pondicherry
Indian Journal of Medical
  Microbiology [45692]

Pune
Medical Journal Armed Forces India
  [45697] .. .. (Paid) 5,000

Thane
Indian Journal of Occupational and
  Environmental Medicine [45746]

Thiruvananthapuram
Trends in Biomaterials & Artificial
  Organs [45749]

Trivandrum
Annals of Indian Academy of
  Neurology [45757]
Calicut Medical Journal [45758]
Journal of Orthopaedics [45759]

Udupi
Indian Journal of Occupational
  Therapy [45763] 750

Varanasi
Indian Journal of Preventive and Social Medicine [45765]

Wardha
Journal of Neurosciences in Rural
  Practice [45770]

IRAN
Shiraz
Iranian Journal of Medical Sciences
  [45883] .. .. (Paid) 3,000

Tehran
Acta Medica Iranica
  [45885] .. .., (Paid) 2,000
DARU [45888]
Hepatitis Monthly [45889]
Iranian Biomedical Journal [45895]
Iranian Journal of Allergy, Asthma
  and Immunology [45897]
Iranian Journal of Endocrinology and
  Metabolism [45901]
Iranian Journal of Nuclear Medicine
  [45904]

IRELAND
Dublin
DiabetesWise [45953] 4,227
HeartWise [45963] 3,185
International Journal for Quality in
  Health Care [45967]
Irish Journal of Medical Science
  [45977]

Irish Journal of Psychological
  Medicine [45978]
Irish Medical Journal
  [45980] .. .. (Paid) 8,800
It's All About Living [45989]
OsteoWise [45993] 2,921

Dundrum
Irish Medical News
  [46009] .. .. ★6,750

ISRAEL
Jerusalem
International Journal of Adolescent
  Medicine and Health [46083]
International Journal on Disability and
  Human Development [46084]
Journal of Basic & Clinical Physiology
  & Pharmacology [46087]
Journal of Biopharmaceutics and
  Biotechnology [46088]

Ramat Gan
Israel Medical Association Journal
  (IMAJ) [46094]

Tel Aviv
Drug Metabolism and Drug
  Interactions [46098]

ITALY
Arcavacata di Rende
International Journal of Artificial
  Organs [46120] 3,000

Bari
Endocrine, Metabolic & Immune Disorders - Drug Targets [46121]

Milan
Aggiornamento Medico
  [46160] 40,683
Eating and Weight Disorders [46166]
L'Endocrinologo [46167]
European Journal of Internal
  Medicine [46168] 1,439
Il Cardiologo [46173]
Il Ginecologo [46174]
International Journal of Biological
  Markers [46176] 1,500
Journal of Endocrinological
  Investigation [46182]
Journal of Mental Health Policy and
  Economics [46183]
The Journal of Vascular Access
  [46184]
Urodinamica [46198]

Naples
Nutrition, Metabolism, & Cardiovascular Diseases [46202]

Rome
Experimental Brain Research [46228]
High Blood Pressure & Cardiovascu-
  lar Prevention [46232]
Medicina e Morale [46238]

Siena
Tissue & Cell [46259]

Turin
Acta Vulnologica [46268]

JAPAN
Fukuoka
Legal Medicine [46345]

Hiroshima
Journal of Radiation Research
  [46381] .. .. (Paid) 1,500

Kagoshima
Diseases of the Esophagus [46403]
Hepatology Research [46404]

Kobe
Kobe Journal of Medical Sciences
  [46433] .... (Paid) 650

Kyoto
Clinical Pediatric Endocrinology
  [46469]
International Journal of Hematology
  [46472] .. .. (Paid) 5,000
Japanese Circulation Journal
  [46473] .. .. (Paid) 19,000
Japanese Journal of Radiological
  Technology [46474]

Miyagi
Research and Practice in Forensic
  Medicine [46517] .. ... (Paid) 1,000

Miyazaki
Journal of Japan Glaucoma Society
  [46519]

Nagasaki
Acta Medica Nagasakiensia
  [46545] 350

Nagoya
Journal of Smooth Muscle Research
  [46555] 950

Okayama
Acta Medica Okayama
  [46596] .... (Controlled) 580
Journal of Japanese Society of Autologous Blood Transfusion [46597]

Sapporo
Hand Surgery [46649]

Sendai
Bio-Medical Materials and
  Engineering [46664]
Tohoku Journal of Experimental
  Medicine [46669] .... (Paid) 800

Shiga
Japanese Journal of Rheumatism
  and Joint Surgery [46682]

Tokushima
Journal of Medical Investigation
  [46715]

Tokyo
Acta Diabetologica [46722]
Acta Endoscopica [46723]
Annals of Nuclear Medicine [46739]
Annals of Thoracic and Cardiovascu-
  lar Surgery [46741]
Archives of Dermatological Research
  [46749]
Archives of Orthopaedic and Trauma
  Surgery [46751]
Brain Tumor Pathology [46768]
Cancer Chemotherapy and
  Pharmacology [46777]
Cancer Immunology, Immunotherapy
  [46778]
Clinical Autonomic Research [46788]
Clinical and Experimental Nephrology
  [46789]
Emergency Radiology [46809]
Esophagus [46814]
Experimental Animals
  [46819] .. .. (Paid) · 2,300
Gastric Cancer [46828]
Heart and Vessels
  [46832] .. .. (Paid) 1,000
Hypertension Research [46835]
Inflammation Research [46842]
Internal Medicine
  [46843] .. .. (Paid) 6,500
International Journal of Clinical
  Oncology [46846]
International Medical News [46849]
Japanese Journal of Breast Cancer
  [46867]
Japanese Journal of Infectious
  Diseases [46869] 1,100
Japanese Journal of Medical
  Mycology [46871] .. ... (Paid) 1,000

Jikeikai Medical Journal
  [46876] 1,000
Journal of Anesthesia [46883]
Journal of Artificial Organs [46886]
Journal of Atherosclerosis and
  Thrombosis [46888]
Journal of Bone and Mineral
  Metabolism
  [46889] .. .. (Paid) 2,500
Journal of Clinical and Experimental
  Medicine [46892] ..... (Paid) 8,800
Journal of Dermatology [46894]
Journal of Gastroenterology
  [46899] .. .. (Paid) 4,500
Journal of Headache and Pain
  [46902]
Journal of Hepato-Biliary-Pancreatic
  Sciences [46904]
Journal of Japan Medical Society of
  Paraplegia [46912]
Journal of Japan Spine Research
  Society [46914]
Journal of Japanese Society of Dialy-
  sis Therapy [46917]
Journal of Medical and Dental
  Sciences [46924] 1,000
Journal of Medical Ultrasonics
  [46925]
Journal of Medicine & Philosophy
  [46926]
Journal of Nippon Medical School
  [46929] .... (Controlled) 2,850
Journal of Orthopaedic Science
  [46935] .. .. (Paid) 2,800
The Keio Journal of Medicine
  [46953] .. .. (Paid) 500
Microbiology and Immunology
  [46968] .. .. (Paid) 1,000
Nikkei Drug Information
  [46987] .· .... ★69,930
Surgery Today
  [47045] .· .... (Paid) 1,500
Techniques in Coloproctology [47047]

JORDAN
Amman
Dirasat Medical and Biological
  Sciences
  [47156] .... (Controlled) 1,000

KENYA
Nairobi
East African Medical Journal [47181]

REPUBLIC OF KOREA
Seoul
The Journal of Korean Radiological
  Society [47274]
Journal of the Korean Society of
  Plastic and Reconstructive Surgery
  [47275]
Korean Journal of Radiology [47282]
Yonsei Medical Journal
  [47293] .. .. (Paid) 1,400

KUWAIT
Safat
The Kuwait Medical Journal
  [47340] .. .. (Paid) 7,000
Medical Principles and Practice
  [47341]

LIBYAN ARAB JAMAHIRIYA
Zliten
Libyan Journal of Medicine [47458]

LITHUANIA
Kaunas
Medicina [47465]
Seminars in Cardiology [47466]

Circulation: ★ = ABC; △ = BPA; ◆ = CAC; • = CCAB; ❑ = VAC; ⊕ = PO Statement; ‡ = Publisher's Report; Boldface figures = sworn; Light figures = estimated.

LUXEMBOURG
Luxembourg
Journal du Diabetique
  [47492] 800

MALAWI
Blantyre
Malawi Medical Journal [47566]

MALAYSIA
Kuala Lumpur
Biomedical Imaging and Intervention
  Journal [47600]
The Medical Journal of Malaysia
  [47627] 8,000
Neurology Asia [47629]

MALTA
Valletta
Id-Dijabete u Sahhtek [47746] ... 900

MAURITIUS
Curepipe
Internet Journal of Medical Update
  [47752]

NEPAL
Kathmandu
Journal of the Nepal Medical
  Association
  [47839] .. .. (Paid) 1,250
Kathmandu University Medical
  Journal [47841]

NETHERLANDS
Amsterdam
ACC Cardiosource Review Journal
  [47875]
Accident Analysis & Prevention
  [47876]
Acta Tropica [47880]
American Journal of Preventive
  Medicine [47889] .. . (Paid) ‡2,500
            (Non-paid) ‡18
Analytical Cellular Pathology/Cellular
  Oncology [47893]
Anti-Cancer Drugs [47896]
Best Practice & Research Clinical
  Endocrinology & Metabolism
  [47903]
Best Practice & Research Clinical
  Hematology [47904]
Biochimica et Biophysica Acta (BBA)-
  Molecular Basis of Disease [47908]
Blood Cells, Molecules, & Diseases
  [47912]
Breast Disease [47915]
Cancer Biomarkers [47920]
Clinical Therapeutics [47928]
Cryobiology [47942]
Current Problems in Cancer [47950]
Developmental & Comparative
  Immunology [47955]
Disease Markers [47959]
Epilepsy & Behavior [47972]
Gynecologic Oncology [48007]
Heart, Lung and Circulation [48010]
Journal of Alzheimer's Disease
  [48041]
Journal of the American College of
  Surgeons
  [48042] .... (Paid) ‡13,176
            (Controlled) ‡6,832
Journal of Autoimmunity [48053]
Journal of Fluency Disorders [48078]
Journal of Invertebrate Pathology
  [48088]
Journal of Surgical Research [48122]
Journal of Vestibular Research
  [48127]

Molecular Aspects of Medicine
  [48162]
Molecular and Cellular Probes
  [48165]
Molecular Genetics and Metabolism
  [48166]
Neurobiology of Disease [48173]
Neuropsychiatrie de l'Enfance et de
  l'Adolescence [48175]
Nutrition [48189]
Overleven [48197]
Pharmacological Research [48199]
Rhinology [48226] 1,500
Technology and Health Care [48242]
Thrombosis Research
  [48249] .... ‡1,580
Arnhem
European Urology [48276]
Bussum
Anti-Cancer Agents in Medicinal
  Chemistry [48279]
Cardiovascular & Hematological Dis-
  orders - Drug Targets [48280]
Clinical Practice and Epidemiology in
  Mental Health [48281]
CNS & Neurological Disorders - Drug
  Targets [48282]
Current Bioinformatics [48283]
Current Hypertension Reviews
  [48290]
Current Topics in Medicinal
  Chemistry [48298]
Current Women's Health Reviews
  [48299]
Infectious Disorders - Drug Targets
  [48301]
Inflammation & Allergy - Drug Targets
  [48302]
Japanese Heart Journal [48303]
Dordrecht
Acta Biotheoretica [48319]
Breast Cancer Research and
  Treatment [48337]
Cancer and Metastasis Reviews
  [48341]
Cardiac Electrophysiology Review
  [48342]
Cardiovascular Drugs and Therapy
  [48343]
Central European Journal of
  Medicine [48349]
Clinical and Experimental Medicine
  [48353]
Clinical & Experimental Metastasis
  [48354]
Clinical Neuroradiology [48355]
CME [48356]
Coloproctology [48357]
Der Anaesthesist [48365]
Der Chirurg [48366]
Der Gastroenterologe [48367]
Der Nephrologe [48368]
Der Nervenarzt [48369]
Der Schmerz [48371]
Digestive Diseases and Sciences
  [48374] 1,700
Documenta Ophthalmologica [48377]
European Journal of Clinical Microbi-
  ology & Infectious Diseases
  [48381]
European Journal of Plastic Surgery
  [48383]
Gynakologische Endokrinologie
  [48410]
Gynecological Surgery [48411]
Health Care Analysis [48412]
Helminthologia [48414]
Intensivmedizin und Notfallmedizin
  [48424]
International Journal of Computer
  Assisted Radiology and Surgery
  [48426]

Journal of Autism and Developmental
  Disorders [48441]
Journal of Biomedical Science
  [48445]
Journal of Cardiovascular Transla-
  tional Research [48447]
Journal of Clinical Monitoring and
  Computing
  [48448] .. .. (Paid) 1,300
Journal of Genetic Counseling
  [48462]
Journal of Medical Humanities
  [48476]
Journal of Neuro-Oncology [48477]
Journal of Thrombosis and
  Thrombolysis [48498]
Knee Surgery, Sports Traumatology,
  Arthroscopy [48500]
Manuelle Medizin [48510]
Maternal and Child Health Journal
  [48512]
Metabolic Brain Disease [48515]
Neurochemical Research [48519]
Pituitary [48531]
Quality of Life Research [48543]
Reviews in Endocrine & Metabolic
  Disorders [48556]
Supportive Care in Cancer [48571]
Surgical and Radiologic Anatomy
  [48572]
Theoretical Medicine and Bioethics
  [48577]
Eindhoven
Journal of Biomechanics [48592]
Enschede
Journal of Back and Musculoskeletal
  Rehabilitation [48597]
Heerlen
Technology and Disability [48630]
Leiden
Asian Medicine [48654]
Journal of Ethnopharmacology
  [48697]
Maastricht
Journal of Behavior Therapy and Ex-
  perimental Psychiatry [48737]
Journal of Chemical Neuroanatomy
  [48738]
Nigtevecht
International Journal of Risk and
  Safety in Medicine [48742]
Nijmegen
Early Science and Medicine [48743]
Rijswijk
Immunogenetics [48747]

NEW ZEALAND
Auckland
International Journal of Biomecha-
  tronics and Biomedical Robotics
  [48798]
New Zealand Doctor [48809]
Christchurch
New Zealand College of Midwives
  [48873] 2,500
Mairangi Bay
American Journal of Cancer [48931]
American Journal of Cardiovascular
  Drugs [48932]
American Journal of Clinical
  Dermatology [48933]
Wellington
Kai Tiaki [49013] .... ‡44,000

NIGERIA
Aba
Journal of Medical Investigation and
  Practice [49055]

Abuja
Journal for Phytomedicine and
  Therapeutics [49056]
Women on the Move [49058]
Benin City
Annals of Biomedical Science
  [49063]
Journal of Medicine and Biomedical
  Research [49064]
Calabar
Global Journal of Medical Sciences
  [49074]
Journal of Medical Laboratory
  Science [49077]
Mary Slessor Journal of Medicine
  [49078]
Enugu
Journal of College of Medicine
  [49080]
Orient Journal of Medicine [49081]
Nigerian Journal of
  Otorhinolaryngology [49082]
Ibadan
Archives of Ibadan Medicine [49087]
Nigerian Journal of Paediatrics
  [49099]
Nigerian Journal of Plastic Surgery
  [49100]
West African Journal of Medicine
  [49104]
Ikeja
Nigerian Hospital Practice [49107]
Nigerian Medical Practitioner [49108]
Ile-Ife
African Journal of Traditional,
  Complementary and Alternative
  Medicines [49111]
Journal of the Obafemi Awolowo Uni-
  versity Medical Student's
  Association [49114]
Nigerian Journal of Natural Products
  and Medicine [49115]
Ilorin
African Journal of Clinical and Experi-
  mental Microbiology [49117]
Jos
African Journal of Paediatric Surgery
  [49123]
Highland Medical Research Journal
  [49124]
Journal of Medicine in the Tropics
  [49126]
Journal of Pharmacy and
  Bioresources [49127]
Nigerian Journal of Pharmaceutical
  Research [49128]
Lagos
Nigerian Journal of Health and Bio-
  medical Sciences [49141]
Nigerian Quarterly Journal of Hospital
  Medicine [49142]
Scientific Research & Essays [49143]
Nnewi
Nigerian Journal of Clinical Practice
  [49149]
Tropical Journal of Medical Research
  [49151]
Port Harcourt
Port Harcourt Medical Journal
  [49169]
Sagamu
Nigerian Journal of Orthopaedics and
  Trauma [49170]
Sokoto
Annals of African Medicine [49172]
European Journal of General
  Medicine [49173]

Circulation: ★ = ABC; △ = BPA; ◆ = CAC; ● = CCAB; ❑ = VAC; ⊕ = PO Statement; ‡ = Publisher's Report; Boldface figures = sworn; Light figures = estimated.

Gale Directory of Publications & Broadcast Media/147th Ed.

6215

Trade, Technical, and Professional Publications

Sahel Medical Journal **[49174]**

Zaria
Annals of Nigerian Medicine **[49181]**
Journal of Community Medicine and
Primary Health Care **[49182]**
Nigerian Journal of Surgical
Research **[49185]**

NORWAY
Bergen
Scandinavian Journal of Immunology
[49191]

Sogndal
Nordic Journal of Music Therapy
[49211]

Trondheim
Acta Anaesthesiologica Scandinavica
[49215]

PAKISTAN
Abbottabad
Journal of Ayub Medical College
[49227]

Faisalabad
Global Journal of Pharmacology
[49244]
International Journal of Molecular
Medicine and Advance Sciences
[49251]
International Journal of Tropical
Medicine **[49258]**
Journal of Animal and Veterinary
Advances **[49260]**
Journal of Medical Sciences **[49270]**
Research Journal of Medicine and
Medical Sciences **[49290]**
Research Journal of Pharmacology
[49291]
Surgery Journal **[49294]**

Islamabad
Pakistan Journal of Medical
Research **[49308]** .... (Paid) 1,000

Karachi
Hamdard Medicus
[49351] .... (Paid) 2,000
Infectious Diseases Journal **[49355]**
Journal of College of Physicians and
Surgeons Pakistan
[49357] .. .. (Paid) 5,000
Journal of the Pakistan Medical
Association
[49358] .... (Paid) 6,000
Pakistan Journal of Medical Sciences
[49369] .... (Paid) 2,000
Pulse International
[49374] .... (Paid) 8,000

Lahore
Pakistan Pediatric Journal **[49386]**

Larkana
Pakistan Journal of Surgery **[49391]**

PERU
Lima
Anales de la Facultad de Medicina
[49423]

PHILIPPINES
Manila
Philippine Journal of Nursing
[49556] .... (Paid) 13,000

Pasig City
Philippine Journal of Internal
Medicine **[49573]**

POLAND
Bydgoszcz
Acta Angiologica **[49652]**

Advances in Palliative Medicine
[49653]
Psychiatry in General Practice
[49654]

Gdansk
Arterial Hypertension **[49655]**
Endocrinology, Obesity and Metabolic
Disorders **[49656]**
Folia Morphologica **[49657]**
Nuclear Medicine Review **[49658]**
Psychooncology **[49660]**

Katowice
Polish Surgery **[49662]**

Krakow
Polish Gerontology **[49668]**

Lodz
Cardiovascular Forum **[49669]**

Warsaw
Acta Neurobiologiae Experimentalis
[49680]
Advances in Medical Sciences
[49687]
Advances in Rehabilitation **[49688]**
Biomedical Human Kinetics **[49697]**
Folia Neuropathologica
[49710] 450
Macedonian Journal of Medical
Sciences **[49734]**
Polish Journal of Medical Physics
and Engineering **[49749]**
Polish Journal of Surgery **[49751]**
Polish Pneumology and Allergology
[49753]
Polish Sexology **[49755]**
Radiology and Oncology **[49762]**
Suicidology **[49766]**

Wroclaw
Interdisciplinary Problems of Stroke
[49779]

Zabrze
Annales Academiae Medicae
Silesiensis **[49781]**
Experimental and Clinical
Diabetology **[49782]**
Polish Journal of Endocrinology
[49783]

QATAR
Doha
Qatar Medical Journal **[49823]**

ROMANIA
Timisoara
Timisoara Medical Journal (TMJ)
[49849]

RUSSIA
Moscow
Anesthesiology & Intensive Care
[49870]
Annals of the Russian Academy of
Medical Sciences **[49872]**
Annals of Surgery **[49873]**
Annals of Traumatology &
Orthopedics **[49874]**
Clinical Laboratory Diagnosis **[49886]**
Epidemiology & Infectious Diseases
[49902]
Forensic Medical Examination
[49905]
Haematology & Trasfusiology **[49910]**
Journal of Neurosurgical Problems
[49930]
Medical Care **[49941]**
Medico-Social Expert Evaluation and
Rehabilitation **[49942]**
Molecular Genetics, Microbiology &
Virology **[49943]**

Molecular Medicine **[49944]**
Obstetrics & Gynaecology **[49948]**
Pathological Physiology & Experi-
mental Therapy **[49951]**
Pediatric Surgery **[49953]**
Physitherapy, Balneology and
Rehabilitation **[49958]**
Problems of Biological, Medical and
Pharmaceutical Chemistry **[49962]**
Problems of Endocrinology **[49963]**
Problems of Social Hygiene, Health
Care & History of Medicine **[49965]**
Problems of Tuberculosis **[49966]**
Problems of Virology **[49967]**
Russian Journal of Oncology **[49978]**
Russian Journal of Pediatrics **[49979]**
Russian Journal of Skin and Sexually
Transmitted Diseases **[49981]**
Russian Journal of Stomatology
[49982]
Russian Medical Journal **[49984]**
Therapeutic Archives **[49995]**
Thoracic & Cardiovascular Surgery
[49997]

SAUDI ARABIA
Jeddah
Saudi Heart Journal
[50058] .... (Free) 5,000

Riyadh
Annals of Thoracic Medicine **[50059]**
The Saudi Journal of
Gastroenterology **[50069]**
Saudi Journal of Kidney Diseases
and Transplantation
[50070] .... (Paid) 3,500
Saudi Medical Journal **[50071]**
Urology Annals **[50072]**

SERBIA
Sremska Kamenica
Archive of Oncology **[50094]**

SINGAPORE
Singapore
Annals, Academy of Medicine,
Singapore **[50103]**
Chinese Medical Association Journal
[50121]
Chirúrgie de la Main **[50122]**
The Family Doctor
[50147] 130,000
International Journal of Neural
Systems **[50190]**
International Journal of Osteopathic
Medicine **[50191]**
International Journal of Surgery
[50193]
ITBM - RBM **[50197]**
Journal of Biological Systems
[50200]
Journal of Integrative Neuroscience
[50207]
Journal of Musculoskeletal Research
[50210]
Photodiagnosis and Photodynamic
Therapy **[50238]**
The Singapore Family Physician
[50255] .... ‡1,000
Singapore Medical Journal
[50260] 4,700

SLOVAKIA
Bratislava
Endocrine Regulations **[50319]**

REPUBLIC OF SOUTH AF-
RICA
Bedfordview
SA Journal of Sports Medicine
[50352]

Brandhof
Journal of Bone and Joint Surgery
[50358] .. .. (Paid) ‡4,500

Cape Town
Current Allergy & Clinical
Immunology **[50372]**
International Journal of Shoulder
Surgery **[50384]**
Leadership in HIV/AIDS
[50387] 10,000
Medical Technology **[50391]**

Centurion
South African Journal of Diabetes
and Vascular Disease **[50453]**
Southern African Journal of Critical
Care **[50455]**

Gauteng
Professional Nursing Today **[50482]**
SA Pharmaceutical Journal **[50483]**

Grahamstown
African Journal of Biomedical
Research **[50487]**
Annals of Ibadan Postgraduate
Medicine **[50493]**
Nigerian Journal of Parasitology
[50506]
Sudan Journal of Medical Sciences
[50516]

Johannesburg
South African Gastroenterology
Review **[50534]**
South African Psychiatry Review
[50535]
Southern African Journal of Anaes-
thesia and Analgesia **[50536]**

Lenasia
African Safety Promotion **[50547]**

Pinelands
South African Journal of Obstetrics
and Gynaecology **[50574]**
South African Journal of Surgery
[50577]

Pretoria
Sahara J **[50599]**
Southern African Journal of HIV
Medicine **[50605]**

Roggebaai
The South African Radiographer
[50616] 1,800

Tygerberg
South African Family Practice
[50639]

SPAIN
Barcelona
AIDS Reviews **[50648]**
Cancer & Chemotherapy Reviews
[50655]
Cirugia Cardiovascular **[50656]**
El Farmaceutico
[50667] .... (Non-paid) 20,000
El Farmaceutico Hospitales
[50668] .... (Controlled) 2,800
Forum **[50674]**
Siete Dias Medicos
[50699] .... (Controlled) 25,000
Trends in Transplantation **[50703]**

Madrid
Gerokomos **[50762]**

Seville
Cuadernos de Medicina Forense
[50833]

SRI LANKA
Colombo
Ceylon Journal of Medical Sciences
[50850] .... (Controlled) 125

Circulation: ★ = ABC; △ = BPA; ◆ = CAC; • = CCAB; ❑ = VAC; ⊕ = PO Statement; ‡ = Publisher's Report; Boldface figures = sworn; Light figures = estimated.

Sri Lankan Family Physician [50868]
Kandy
Sri Lanka Journal of Medicine [50909]

SUDAN
Khartoum
Sudanese Journal of Dermatology [50939]

SWEDEN
Lund
Acta Orthopaedica [50983]
Stockholm
Acta Oto-Laryngologica [51001]
Allergy [51005]
Nordisk Fysioterapi [51028]
Scandinavian Cardiovascular Journal [51034]
Sjukgymnasten [51038]
Umea
TumorBiology [51048] 1,000
Uppsala
Upsala Journal of Medical Sciences [51052]

SWITZERLAND
Basel
Archives of Gynecology and Obstetrics [51059]
Geneva
International Journal of Computational Biology and Drug Design [51111]
International Journal of Functional Informatics and Personalised Medicine [51122]
International Journal of Medical Engineering and Informatics [51131]
International Journal of Nano and Biomaterials [51133]
International Nursing Review [51148]
Weekly Epidemiological Record [51165] .... (Combined) 6,500
Genolier
Critical Reviews in Oncology/Hematology [51174]
Lausanne
Cancer Immunity [51184]
European Journal of Cardio-Thoracic Surgery [51188]
Muttenz
Schweizerische Arztezeitung/Bulletin des Medecins Suisses [51214] .. .. (Paid) 29,599
Swiss Medical Weekly [51215] .... (Controlled) 4,500
Neuhausen
Ars Medici [51216]
Gynakologie [51217]
Padiatrie [51218]
Viganello-Lugano
Annals of Oncology [51237]
Zurich
Biometrical Journal [51255]
Journal of Inherited Metabolic Disease [51270]

TAIWAN
Kaohsiung
Kaohsiung Journal of Medical Sciences [51310] ..... (Paid) 1,500
Taipei
Journal of the Formosan Medical Association [51352]
Journal of Microbiology, Immunology

and Infection [51354] .. .. (Paid) 4,000

UNITED REPUBLIC OF TANZANIA
Dar es Salaam
Tanzania Medical Journal [51404]

THAILAND
Bangkok
Journal of the Medical Association of Thailand [51423] 3,500
Thai Journal of Anesthesiology [51438]

TUNISIA
Sousse
Journal Tunisien d'ORL et de chirurgie cervico-faciale [51482]

TURKEY
Ankara
Gazi Medical Journal [51493] .... (Controlled) 1,000
Turkish Journal of Cancer [51506]
Turkish Journal of Gastroenterology [51511]
Turkish Journal of Medical Sciences [51513]
Bursa
Journal of Sports Science and Medicine (JSSM) [51551]
Elazig
Firat Tip Dergisi [51553]
Istanbul
Acta Orthopaedica et Traumatologica Turcica [51556] ...... (Paid) ‡1,000
Medikal & Teknik [51562] 10,069
Izmir
Journal of Neurological Sciences [51575]
Mersin
Anti-Inflammatory & Anti-Allergy Agents in Medicinal Chemistry [51576]
Van
Journal of Pediatric Infectious Diseases [51581]

UGANDA
Kampala
African Health Sciences [51584]

UNITED KINGDOM
Aberdeen
Current Diabetes Reviews [51675]
Abingdon
Acute Cardiac Care [51697]
Amyloid [51703]
British Journal of Neurosurgery [51720]
Computer Methods in Biomechanics and Biomedical Engineering [51740]
Fetal and Pediatric Pathology [51789]
Human Fertility [51808]
Informatics for Health and Social Care [51816]
Journal of Cosmetic and Laser Therapy [51882]
Journal of Nutritional & Environmental Medicine [51926]
Journal of Organ Dysfunctions [51927]
Journal of Psychosomatic Obstetrics and Gynecology [51937]

Journal of Rehabilitation Medicine [51939]
Journal of Reproductive and Infant Psychology [51940]
Mortality [51987]
Pediatric Hematology & Oncology [52006] .... (Combined) 1,312
Prosthetics & Orthotics International [52025]
Psychology and Health [52029]
Psychology, Health and Medicine [52030]
Scandinavian Journal of Primary Health Care [52050]
Scandinavian Journal of Rheumatology [52051]
Ballyclare
IA Journal [52157] 12,000
Basingstoke
BioSocieties [52196]
International Journal of Obesity [52211]
Molecular Therapy [52224]
Bath
Medical Engineering and Physics [52251]
Belfast
Journal of Pathology [52288]
Berkhamsted
Guidelines [52310]
Birmingham
The British Journal of Diabetes and Vascular Disease [52333]
Diabetes and Vascular Disease Research [52339]
Journal of Antimicrobial Chemotherapy [52345]
Journal of Electrophysiological Technology [52346]
Journal of Medical Microbiology [52349] .... (Paid) 700
Journal of the Renin-Angiotensin-Aldosterone System [52351]
Journal of Visual Communication in Medicine [52355]
Bognor Regis
International Journal of Medical Robotics and Computer-Assisted Surgery [52397]
Bradford
Clinical Governance [52441]
Brentwood
Parasite Immunology [52586]
Brighton
The British Journal of Forensic Practice [52607]
Healthmatters [52611]
Mental Health Today [52627]
Bristol
Endocrine Abstracts [52662]
Endocrine-Related Cancer [52663] 1,000
European Journal of Endocrinology [52664] 1,600
International Journal of Epidemiology [52678]
Journal of Endocrinology [52685] 1,200
Journal of Molecular Endocrinology [52691] 400
Neuropharmacology [52709]
Paediatric and Perinatal Epidemiology [52714]
Physics in Medicine and Biology [52717]
Physiological Measurement [52718]
Reviews in Gynaecological Practice [52728]

Cambridge
Journal of Helminthology [52854]
Neuropsychological Rehabilitation [52875]
Quarterly Reviews of Biophysics [52889]
Cardiff
Journal of Enzyme Inhibition and Medicinal Chemistry [52933]
Chester
Managed Healthcare Executive [52997] .. .. △41,800
Chichester
British Journal of Surgery [53006]
Microscopy and Analysis [53014] .. .. ‡46,000
Colchester
Annals of The Royal College of Surgeons of England [53028]
Derby
Annals of Occupational Hygiene [53163]
Dundee
Medical Teacher [53215]
Edinburgh
Cardiology News [53260]
Cloning and Stem Cells [53263]
European Journal of Cancer [53274]
Eye News [53275] 4,200
Human Reproduction & Genetic Ethics [53285]
Journal of Medical Education [53293]
Neuroendocrinology [53302] ... 1,650
Surgeons' News [53322]
Farnham
The British Journal of Cardiology [53380]
Glasgow
Graefe's Archive for Clinical and Experimental Ophthalmology [53422]
Toxicon [53454]
Guildford
International Journal of Oral & Maxillofacial Surgery [53490]
Harrogate
Orthopaedic Product News [53518] .. .. (Combined) ‡8,044
Harrow
Comparative Clinical Pathology [53521]
Helston
Within Reach [53554]
Hereford
The Journal of Alternative & Complementary Medicine [53563]
Hove
Advances in Dual Diagnosis [53603]
Journal of Assistive Technologies [53607]
Journal of Clinical Pathology [53608]
Social Care and Neurodisability [53613]
Huddersfield
Clinical Biomechanics [53618]
Kidlington
Journal of Cranio-Maxillofacial Surgery [53696]
Journal of Reproductive Immunology [53700]
Physiotherapy [53704] .. .. (Controlled) 35,000
The Surgeon [53707]
Lancaster
Gynecological Endocrinology [53733]
Leeds
Computational & Mathematical Methods in Medicine [53762]

European Journal of Obstetrics & Gynecology [53765]

Seminars in Fetal & Neonatal Medicine [53774]

Leicester

British Journal of Clinical Psychology [53786] .... (Combined) 3,900

British Journal of Developmental Psychology [53787] .... (Combined) 1,700

British Journal of Health Psychology [53789] .... (Combined) 2,000

British Journal of Mathematical and Statistical Psychology [53790] ....: (Combined) 700

British Journal of Psychology [53791] .... (Combined) 2,800

British Journal of Social Psychology [53792] .... (Combined) 1,500

Clinical Focus [53794] .... (Controlled) 15,000

Journal of Occupational and Organizational Psychology [53807] .... (Combined) 3,100

Legal and Criminological Psychology [53810] .... (Combined) 1,200

Psychology and Psychotherapy [53820] .... (Combined) 1,900

Liverpool

Fingerprint Whorld [53873]

Lockerbie

Primary Care Respiratory Journal [53888]

London

Acute Coronary Syndromes [53897]

Acute Medicine [53898]

Advances in Osteoporotic Fracture Management [53906]

Advances in Psychiatric Treatment [53907]

Advances in Sepsis [53908]

AIDS Research and Therapy [53928]

Anaesthesia [53940]

Anatomical Science International [53941]

Annals of Clinical Microbiology and Antimicrobials [53947]

Annals of the Rheumatic Disease [53949] .... (Paid) 9,500

Annals of Tropical Paediatrics [53950]

Autism [53984]

Autonomic Neuroscience [53991]

Balance [53999] ...... (Paid) 200,000

Best Practice & Research Clinical Obstetrics & Gynecology [54013]

Best Treatments [54014]

Biological Knowledge [54021]

Biomarkers in Medicine [54026]

BioMechanics [54027] .... (Paid) 32,000

Biomedical Digital Libraries [54028]

BioMedical Engineering OnLine [54029]

BioVenture View [54031] .... (Paid) 327

BMA News [54034] .... (Controlled) 116,000

BMC Anesthesiology [54035]

BMC Blood Disorders [54040]

BMC Cancer [54041]

BMC Cardiovascular Disorders [54042]

BMC Dermatology [54048]

BMC Ear, Nose and Throat Disorders [54050]

BMC Emergency Medicine [54052]

BMC Endocrine Disorders [54053]

BMC Gastroenterology [54056]

BMC Immunology [54061]

BMC Infectious Diseases [54062]

BMC Medical Education [54064]

BMC Medical Ethics [54065]

BMC Medical Genetics [54066]

BMC Medical Imaging [54067]

BMC Medical Informatics and Decision Making [54068]

BMC Medical Physics [54069]

BMC Medical Research Methodology [54070]

BMC Medicine [54071]

BMC Musculoskeletal Disorders [54074]

BMC Nephrology [54075]

BMC Neurology [54076]

BMC Neuroscience [54077]

BMC Pregnancy and Childbirth [54086]

BMC Pulmonary Medicine [54088]

BMC Surgery [54090]

BMC Urology [54091]

BMC Women's Health [54093]

Breathe [54104]

British Journal of Cancer [54113]

British Journal of Clinical Pharmacology [54116]

British Journal of Dermatology [54118]

British Journal of General Practice [54120] 23,000

British Journal of Hospital Medicine [54123]

British Journal of Midwifery [54125] .... ★4,051

British Journal of Occupational Therapy [54128] 18,000

British Journal of Pharmacology [54130]

British Journal of Renal Medicine [54134]

British Journal of Sexual Medicine [54136]

British Journal of Sports Medicine [54137] .... ‡1,650

British Medical Journal [54139] 28,241

British Medical Journal Clinical Evidence [54140]

Cardiology International [54176]

Cardiovascular Diabetology [54178]

Cardiovascular Ultrasound [54179]

Caring Times [54182] ... . (Controlled) ★16,967

Cerebrospinal Fluid Research [54196]

Clinica World Medical Device and Diagnostic News [54218] .... (Combined) 2,373

Clinical Ethics [54220]

Clinical & Experimental Dermatology [54222] .... (Combined) 762

Clinical & Experimental Immunology [54223]

Clinical Lipidology [54224]

Clinical Medicine [54225] .. .. (Paid) 14,000

Clinical Rheumatology [54230] .. .. (Paid) 1,500

Clinical Risk [54231]

Clinical Trials [54232]

Clio Medica [54233]

College Bulletin [54238] 7,500

Comparative Hepatology [54250]

Critical Care [54288]

Current Opinion in Clinical Nutrition & Metabolic Care [54297]

Current Opinion in Infectious Diseases [54299] ... (Paid) ‡2,612

Current Opinion in Molecular Therapeutics [54301]

Current Opinion in Neurology [54302]

CytoJournal [54307]

Depression [54318]

Diabetes & Primary Care [54323]

Diagnostic Pathology [54325]

Emerging Themes in Epidemiology [54364]

Environmental Health [54376]

Epidemiologic Perspectives & Innovations [54379]

Epidemiology and Infection [54380] 1,000

European Journal of Cardiovascular Prevention & Rehabilitation [54397]

Evidence-Based Mental Health (EBMH) [54415]

Exchange [54416] ... (Paid) ‡11,500

Expert Opinion on Investigational Drugs [54417]

Expert Review of Anti-Infective Therapy [54418]

Expert Review of Cardiovascular Therapy [54420]

Expert Review of Clinical Immunology [54421]

Expert Review of Clinical Pharmacology [54422]

Expert Review of Endocrinology & Metabolism [54423]

Expert Review of Gastroenterology & Hepatology [54424]

Expert Review of Hematology [54425]

Expert Review of Medical Devices [54426]

Expert Review of Molecular Diagnostics [54427]

Expert Review of Obstetrics & Gynecology [54429]

Expert Review of Ophthalmology [54430]

Expert Review of Respiratory Medicine [54433]

Expert Review of Vaccines [54434]

Expert Reviews of Dermatology [54435]

Faculty of 1000 Medicine [54437]

Future Cardiology [54487]

Future Microbiology [54488]

Future Neurology [54489]

Future Oncology [54490]

Future Virology [54491]

Gene Therapy [54499]

Genetic Vaccines and Therapy [54501]

Geriatric Medicine [54505] .. .. (Controlled) ‡23,000

Good Clinical Practice Journal (GCPj) [54519] .... ⊕1,300

Handbook of Practice Management [54529]

Head & Face Medicine [54534]

Heart [54545]

Heart Failure Monitor [54546]

Hematology [54548]

HIV Therapy [54563]

Hospital Management International [54574] .... (Non-paid) ★10,039

Immunology [54585] 4,500

Immunome Research [54586]

Immunotherapy [54587]

Innate Immunity [54605]

Instrumenta [54609] .... (Paid) 7,000

International Journal of Adipose Tissue [54630]

International Journal of Advances in Rheumatology [54631]

International Journal of Clinical Rheumatology [54639]

International Journal of Intensive Care [54650]

International Journal of Respiratory Care [54659]

International Journal of STD and AIDS [54663]

International Journal of Therapy and Rehabilitation (IJTR) [54665]

International Seminars in Surgical Oncology [54671]

Journal of Autoimmune Diseases [54703]

Journal of Bone & Joint Surgery (British Volume) [54709] .... (Controlled) 40,000

Journal of Carcinogenesis [54717]

Journal of Cardiovascular Magnetic Resonance [54719]

Journal of Clinical Research [54726]

Journal of Drug Assessment [54739] .... (Paid) 100

Journal of Epidemiology and Community Health [54745]

Journal of Ethnobiology and Ethnomedicine [54746]

Journal of Experimental & Clinical Assisted Reproduction [54749]

Journal of Hand Surgery (British & European Volume) [54758]

Journal of Human Hypertension [54763]

Journal of Immune Based Therapies and Vaccines [54765]

Journal of Inflammation [54767]

Journal of Intellectual Disabilities [54769]

Journal of Manual & Manipulative Therapy [54774]

Journal of Medical Biography [54778]

Journal of Medical Ethics [54779] .... ‡1,850

Journal of Medical Genetics [54780] .... ‡1,495

Journal of Medical Screening [54781]

Journal of Nanobiotechnology [54783]

Journal of Negative Results in BioMedicine [54784]

Journal of NeuroEngineering and Rehabilitation (JNER) [54785]

Journal of Neuroinflammation [54786]

Journal of Neurology, Neurosurgery, and Psychiatry [54787]

Journal of Outcomes Research [54791]

Journal of Paramedic Practice [54792]

Journal of Pharmaceutical Medicine [54796]

The Journal of Physiology [54802]

Journal of Public Health [54806]

Journal of the Royal Society of Medicine [54814] .... (Combined) 18,000

Journal of Telemedicine and Telecare [54827]

Journal of Translational Medicine [54830]

Journal of Urban Health [54831]

Journal of Viral Hepatitis [54832]

Journal of Virological Methods [54833]

Journal of Wound Care [54838] .. .. (Paid) 6,000

Lasers in Medical Science [54855]

Lipids in Health and Disease [54875]

Lung Cancer in Practice [54893]

Medical Humanities [54923] .... ‡1,770

Menopause International [54926]

MIMS [54935] .. .. (Combined) ★39,388

Molecular Cancer [54945]

MS Matters [54959]

Multiple Sclerosis [54961] .... (Paid) 700

Myeloproliferative Disorders in practice [54968]

Nanomedicine [54970]

Nature Reviews Cancer [54975]

Nature Reviews Cardiology [54976]

Nature Reviews Clinical Oncology [54977]

Circulation: ★ = ABC; △ = BPA; ♦ = CAC; • = CCAB; ❏ = VAC; ⊕ = PO Statement; ‡ = Publisher's Report; Boldface figures = sworn; Light figures = estimated.

Nature Reviews Gastroenterology & Hepatology [54979]
Nature Reviews Immunology [54981]
Nature Reviews Neuroscience [54984]
Nature Reviews Urology [54985]
NMR in Biomedicine [55006]
Notes & Records of the Royal Society [55013]
Nursing Ethics
  [55015] .... (Paid) 1,000
Occupational Medicine Journal [55024]
Occupational Therapy News
  [55026] .... (Controlled) 22,000
OpenMIND [55035] ... (Paid) ‡5,500
The Osteopath [55044]
The Otorhinolaryngologist [55045]
Pathology [55062]
Personalized Medicine [55072]
Phlebology [55084]
Physical Therapy Reviews [55085]
Postgraduate Medical Journal
  [55109] .... ‡1,475
Practical Neurology [55115]
Progress in Palliative Care [55136]
Prostate Cancer and Prostatic Diseases [55144]
Pulmonary Pharmacology and Therapeutics [55155]
Pulse [55156] ... (Combined) 40,269
Regenerative Medicine [55180]
Respiratory Disease in Practice [55193]
Retrovirology [55198]
Rheumatology [55202] 3,500
Sexually Transmitted Infections
  [55231] 1,780
Stroke News [55266] .. .. ‡70,000
Student BMJ [55268]
Systematic Parasitology [55284]
Therapy [55309]
Thorax [55315]
Thrombosis Journal [55316]
Thrombus [55317]
Transactions of the Royal Society of Tropical Medicine and Hygiene [55335]
Tropical Doctor [55342]
Urological Research [55363]
Vascular Disease Prevention [55366]
Virology Journal [55372]

Macclesfield
Biologics [55514]
Clinical Interventions in Aging [55515]
International Journal of Nanomedicine [55517]
Neuropsychiatric Disease and Treatment [55518]
Therapeutics and Clinical Risk Management [55519]

Manchester
Biochemical Engineering Journal [55544]

Marlow
Menopause International [55600]

Mere
Advances in Clinical Neuroscience & Rehabilitation [55609]

Northampton
Country Doctor [55707]
The Homeopath Journal
  [55709] 3,000
Thumbprint [55715] 9,000

Northwich
Acupuncture in Medicine
  [55718] .... (Combined) 6,225

Northwood
Journal of Heart Valve Disease [55721]

Nottingham
Breast Cancer Online [55749]
Gut [55757]

Olney
International Journal of Biomedical Engineering and Technology [55792]

Ormskirk
Midwifery Matters [55850] 1,750

Oxford
Anaesthesia [55866]
Annals of Anatomy [55868]
BJOG [55885]
BloodMed [55886]
Brain [55887]
British Journal of Anaesthesia [55892]
British Medical Bulletin [55895]
Cancer Letters [55902]
Carcinogenesis [55904]
The Clinical Teacher [55912]
Continuing Education in Anaesthesia, Critical Care & Pain [55917]
Diabetic Medicine [55926]
EJVES Extra [55934]
Epidemiologic Reviews [55939]
European Heart Journal [55944]
European Journal of Echocardiography [55946]
Evidence-based Complementary and Alternative Medicine [55950]
Family Practice [55952]
FEMS Immunology and Medical Microbiology [55954]
International Immunology [55991]
International Journal of Evidence-based Healthcare [55995]
International Journal of Rheumatic Diseases [56003]
Japanese Journal of Clinical Oncology [56009]
Journal of Antimicrobial Chemotherapy [56014]
Journal of the National Cancer Institute [56053]
Journal of Policy and Practice in Intellectual Disabilities [56060]
Journal of Sexual Medicine [56072]
Journal of Tropical Pediatrics [56076]
Medical Law Review [56095]
Molecular Oral Microbiology [56108]
Neuromodulation [56114]
Neuropathology and Applied Neurobiology [56116]
Oral Oncology [56129]
Pathology International [56143]
Pediatric Allergy and Immunology [56145]
Pediatric Anesthesia [56146]
Pediatric Dermatology [56147]
Pediatrics International [56148]
Photodermatology, Photoimmunology and Photomedicine [56156]
Progress in Retinal and Eye Research [56171]
QJM [56181]
The Quarterly Journal of Mathematics [56182]
Radiation Protection Dosimetry [56185]
Transboundary and Emerging Diseases [56220]
Transfusion Medicine [56221]
Transplant International [56222]
Tropical Medicine and International Health [56223]
Zoonoses and Public Health [56230]

Paisley
BAPOMAG [56239]

Portsmouth
Positive Health [56292] 8,000

Practical Diabetes International [56293]

Sheffield
Journal of Radiotherapy in Practice [56505]

Southampton
Biomedical Signal Processing and Control [56568]
Progress in Nuclear Magnetic Resonance Spectroscopy [56576]

Southport
Podiatry Review
  [56588] .... (Controlled) 2,500

Truro
Best Practice & Research Clinical Rheumatology [56773]

Wallingford
Review of Medical and Veterinary Entomology [56826] 290
Review of Medical and Veterinary Mycology [56827] 200

West Sussex
Dyslexia [56897]

Worthing
HERPES [56973]

York
Medical Engineering and Physics [56993]

ZIMBABWE
Harare
Central African Journal of Medicine [57113]

METAL, METALLURGY, AND METAL TRADE
See also Machinery and Equipment; Engineering (Various branches); Plumbing and Heating; Air Conditioning and Refrigeration; Mining and Minerals; Welding

AUSTRALIA
Brisbane
Australian Stainless Magazine
  [41641] .... ‡8,000

AUSTRIA
Reutte
International Journal of Refractory Metals and Hard Materials [42738]

BRAZIL
Sao Paulo
ABM Metalurgia e Materials [43019]
Fundicao e Servicos
  [43040] .... (Non-paid) 8,000

PEOPLE'S REPUBLIC OF CHINA
Beijing
Rare Metals [43214] 1,000

Changsha
Transactions of Nonferrous Metals Society of China [43246] 800

Harbin
China Welding [43263]

Luoyang
China's Refractories [43452]

DENMARK
Glostrup
Maskin Aktuelt [43710] .... ‡8,200

FRANCE
Boulogne
Werkzeug Technik
  [43922] .... (Combined) 8,000

GERMANY
Bad Harzburg
Steel Grips [44144] 5,000

Dusseldorf
Der Praktiker [44323] 17,000
Literaturschau Stahl + Eisen [44328]
MPT International [44329] 10,232
Schweissen & Schneiden [44334] 14,000

Saarbrucken
Progress in Materials Science [44652]

INDIA
Kolkata
IIM Metal News [45270]
Indian Institute of Metals Transactions
  [45272] .... (Paid) 4,000
Indian Welding Journal
  [45275] .... (Paid) 5,000
The Institution of Engineers (India-) Metallurgical and Materials Engineering Division Journal
  [45289] .... (Paid) 4,000

ISRAEL
Tel Aviv
Main Group Metal Chemistry [46110]

ITALY
Cinisello Balsamo
RMO—Rivista di Meccanica Oggi
  [46134] .. .. (Combined) ‡14,000

JAPAN
Tokyo
Ferrum
  [46822] .... (Combined) 10,000
ISIJ International
  [46851] .... (Combined) 1,600
Nippon Steel News [47012]
Taikabutsu [47046]
Tetsu-to-Hagane
  [47049] .... (Combined) 3,000

NETHERLANDS
Amsterdam
Journal of Materials Processing Technology [48094]
Materials Characterization [48143]
Materials Science and Engineering [48144]
Materials Science in Semiconductor Processing [48147]
Mechanics of Materials [48150]
Metal Finishing [48155]
Powder Technology [48210]

Dordrecht
Transition Metal Chemistry [48580]

NIGERIA
Ibadan
Journal of Mining and Geology [49091]

RUSSIA
Ekaterinburg
Physics of Metals and Metallography [49855]

Moscow
Protection of Metals [49968]

Circulation: ★ = ABC; △ = BPA; ♦ = CAC; • = CCAB; ❑ = VAC; ⊕ = PO Statement; ‡ = Publisher's Report; Boldface figures = sworn; Light figures = estimated.

Russian Metallurgy [49985]

Saint Petersburg
Reviews on Advanced Materials
  Science [50025]

SERBIA
Belgrade
Science of Sintering [50083]

UNITED KINGDOM
Balfron
Artist Blacksmith [52155] 600

Birmingham
International Journal of Machine
  Tools and Manufacture [52343]
Transactions of the Institute of Metal
  Finishing [52370] 1,400

Falmouth
Minerals Engineering [53372]

Kidlington
Metal Powder Report [53703]

Leamington Spa
Tube & Pipe Technology
  [53749] .... (Combined) 12,500

London
Aluminium International Today
  [53933] 5,500
Gold Bulletin [54516]
International Journal of Cast Metals
  Research [54638]
Metallurgia [54928]
Mineral Processing and Extractive
  Metallurgy [54936]
MWP [54967] 16,861
Platinum Metals Review
  [55095] .... (Controlled) 9,200
Powder Metallurgy [55110]
World Gold Analyst [55420]

Northill
Historical Metallurgy [55717]

Redhill
Furnaces International
  [56352] 2,000

Shoreham-by-Sea
Aluminium Times
  [56521] .... (Controlled) 5,200
Cast Metal & Diecasting Times
  [56522] .... (Controlled) 5,000

Surrey
Steel Times International
  [56676] .... (Combined) *8,000

Sutton Coldfield
Hot Dip Galvanizing
  [56695] 45,000

METEOROLOGY

GERMANY
Katlenburg-Lindau
Natural Hazards and Earth System
  Sciences (NHESS) [44501]

Stuttgart
Meteorologische Zeitschrift [44669]

INDIA
New Delhi
Standards India
  [45653] .... (Paid) 4,000
Vayu Mandal
  [45667] .... (Paid) 1,000

JAPAN
Tokyo
Journal of Meteorological Society of
  Japan [46927] .... (Paid) 2,000

NETHERLANDS
Dordrecht
Aerobiologia [48321]
Boundary-Layer Meteorology [48335]

SWEDEN
Stockholm
Tellus [51042]
Tellus [51043]

SWITZERLAND
Geneva
WMO Bulletin [51167]

UNITED KINGDOM
Cambridge
Annals of Glaciology
  [52788] .... (Paid) 500
Journal of Glaciology
  [52853] .... (Paid) 1,000

Exeter
Atmospheric Science Letters [53347]

London
Climate Policy [54217]

Reading
International Journal of Climatology
  [56321]
Journal of the Royal Meteorological
  Society [56324]
Quarterly Journal of the Royal Meteo-
  rological Society
  [56329] .... (Paid) 1,100
Weather [56333] .... (Paid) 5,000

MILITARY AND NAVY
See also Veterans

AUSTRALIA
Adelaide
International Journal of Intelligent De-
  fence Support Systems [41510]

Canberra
Royal Australian Navy News
  [41712] .... (Non-paid) 22,000

Strawberry Hills
ADF Health [42393]

BELGIUM
Brussels
International Review of the Armed
  Forces Medical Services [42860]
Military Law and Law of War Review
  [42867]

GERMANY
Bonn
Die Bundeswehr [44254]
MILITARY TECHNOLOGY
  [44266] 25,000
Nato's Nations and Partners for
  Peace [44267] 22,000
Naval Forces [44268] 16,000
TECNOLOGIA MILITAR
  [44271] 10,000
WEHRTECHNIK [44272] 12,000

INDIA
Delhi
Defence Science Journal
  [45090] 600
Technology Focus
  [45106] .... (Controlled) 3,000

New Delhi
Indian Defence Review
  [45538] .... (Paid) 4,000

Strategic Analysis
  [45655] .... (Paid) 2,200
Strategic Digest
  [45656] .... (Paid) 2,200
USI Journal [45661] .... (Paid) 9,500

Pune
Medical Journal Armed Forces India
  [45697] .... (Paid) 5,000

IRELAND
Dublin
Irish Sword [45986] 900

ITALY
Chiavari
Rivista Italiana Difesa
  [46133] 30,000

Rome
Aeronautica & Difesa [46220]

REPUBLIC OF KOREA
Seoul
The Korean Journal of Defense
  Analysis [47281]

LEBANON
Beirut
Al Defaiya
  [47387] .... (Combined) 24,000
Arab Defence Journal
  [47391] *25,000

MALAYSIA
Kuala Lumpur
Asia-Pacific Military Balance [47597]
Asian Defence Journal
  [47598] 20,000

NETHERLANDS
The Hague
Marineblad
  [48622] .... (Controlled) 6,000

NORWAY
Oslo
Flynytt [49198] ... (Combined) 5,200

RUSSIA
Moscow
Airfleet [49869]

SINGAPORE
Singapore
Asian Defence and Diplomacy
  [50107] 10,088

**REPUBLIC OF SOUTH AF-
RICA**
Saldanha
Scientia Militaria [50624]

Saxonwold
The Military History Journal [50628]

SPAIN
Madrid
Defensa
  [50750] .... (Combined) 21,000

SRI LANKA
Panadura
Losetha [50922] 2,000

SWITZERLAND
Lausanne
Revue Militaire Suisse [51199]

Zurich
Armada International
  [51253] .... (Controlled) 25,088

TURKEY
Ankara
Savunma Ve Havacilik
  [51500] 15,000

UNITED KINGDOM
Abingdon
Defence Studies [51753]
Journal of Strategic Studies [51948]
Military Balance [51981]

Aldershot
Soldier Magazine
  [52098] .... (Combined) 88,000

Bletchley
Military Modelcraft International
  [52389]

Congleton
Armourer [53059]

Coulsdon
Jane's Defence Weekly [53068]
Jane's Intelligence Review [53069]
Jane's International Defense Review
  [53070]
Jane's Navy International
  [53071] .... (Combined) ‡3,606

Lancaster
Defence and Security Analysis
  [53732]

Liskeard
Warship World
  [53864] .... (Combined) ‡4,000

London
Arms & Armour [53964]
Disarmament Diplomacy [54329]
Fly Navy [54471]
Survival [55283]
Warship Technology
  [55380] .. .. (Combined) 11,650

Newbury
Soldiers of the Queen
  [55662] .... (Controlled) 1,250

Pewsey
Army Families Federation Families
  Journal [56269] 64,000

Portsmouth
Navy News [56291]

Stockport
Defence Management Journal
  [56626]

Totternhoe
Military Illustrated [56765]
Model Military International [56767]

Wetherby
Cross & Cockade International
  [56910]

York
Defence and Peace Economics
  [56989]

MILK AND DAIRY
PRODUCTS
See also Confectionaries
and Frozen Dairy Products

BANGLADESH
Dhaka
Journal of Health, Population and
  Nutrition [42813]

IRELAND
Dublin
Food Ireland
  [45959] .... (Combined) 2,000

Circulation: ★ = ABC; △ = BPA; ◆ = CAC; • = CCAB; ❑ = VAC; ⊕ = PO Statement; ‡ = Publisher's Report; Boldface figures = sworn; Light figures = estimated.

PAKISTAN
Faisalabad
Research Journal of Dairy Sciences [49287]
World Journal of Dairy & Food Sciences [49301]

SLOVENIA
Ljubljana
Acta Agriculturae Slovenica [50333]

UNITED KINGDOM
Appleby-in-Westmorland
International Journal of Dairy Technology [52126] 2,000
Driffield
International Dairy Topics [53202] .... (Controlled) ‡20,000
Faversham
Milk Industry [53383] 2,000

MINING AND MINERALS
See also Stone and Rock Products; Petroleum, Oil, and Gas; Metal, Metallurgy, and Metal Trade

AUSTRALIA
Carlton
The AUSIMM Bulletin [41724] .... (Combined) 8,667
Collingwood
Earthmatters [41785]
Leederville
Australian Longwall Magazine [42004] 3,500
Australia's Mining Monthly [42005] .... ★8,268
Wahroonga
Safety Solutions [42676] 7,323

FRANCE
Paris
European Journal of Mineralogy [44043]

GERMANY
Bayreuth
Physics and Chemistry of Minerals [44147]
Karlsruhe
Neues Jahrbuch fur Mineralogie Abhandlungen [44494]
Stuttgart
Plinius [44677]

INDIA
Kolkata
Institution of Engineers (India) Mining Engineering Division Journal [45290] .... (Paid) 4,000
Nagpur
Indian Minerals Year Book [45467]

KUWAIT
Surra
International Journal of Oil, Gas and Coal Technology [47362]

MALAYSIA
Kuala Lumpur
Malaysian Chamber of Mines Year Book [47615] 500

NETHERLANDS
Amsterdam
Journal of Applied Geophysics [48046]
Materials Science and Engineering [48146]

NIGERIA
Ibadan
Journal of Mining and Geology [49091]

POLAND
Warsaw
Mineralogia [49738]

RUSSIA
Novosibirsk
Journal of Mining Sciences [50012]

REPUBLIC OF SOUTH AFRICA
Garden View
Mining Weekly [50480] .... (Combined) ★14,850

SWITZERLAND
Geneva
International Journal of Mining and Mineral Engineering [51132]

THAILAND
Bangkok
Journal of the Planetary Gemologists Association [51424]

UNITED KINGDOM
Crawley
Forecourt Trader [53104] .... ★10,922
Falmouth
Minerals Engineering [53372]
London
Applied Earth Science [53959] 500
Industrial Minerals (IM) [54598]
International Heat Treatment and Surface Engineering [54627]
International Journal of Rock Mechanics and Mining Sciences [54661]
The Journal of Gemmology [54756] 4,000
Mineral Processing and Extractive Metallurgy [54936]
Mineralogical Magazine [54937]
Mining Environmental Management [54939] .... (Combined) 3,000
Mining Journal [54940] .... (Combined) 3,600
Mining Magazine [54941] .... △19,900
Mining Technology [54942]
Petroleum Economist [55074]
Platinum Metals Review [55095] .... (Controlled) 9,200
World Gold Analyst [55420]
World Mining Equipment [55422] ...... (Combined) ★23,971
World Tunnelling [55427] ...... ★7,000
Manchester
Crystallography Reviews [55552]
Oxford
Membrane Technology [56096]
Twickenham
Clay Minerals [56789]

MOTION PICTURES
See also Photography

AUSTRALIA
Pyrmont
The Production Book [42286]
Smoke and Mirrors [42289] .... ★4,483

BULGARIA
Sofia
Kino [43104] 2,000

INDIA
Mumbai
Screen World [45437] 2,500
New Delhi
Screen [45649] .... (Paid) 28,700

SPAIN
Barcelona
Dirigido [50663]
Show Press [50698] .... (Non-paid) 15,000
Madrid
Academia [50722]
Cuadernos de la Academia [50743]
Foto Video [50759]

SWITZERLAND
Winterthur
Filmbulletin/Kino in Augenhohe [51241] .... (Combined) 15,000

UNITED KINGDOM
Abingdon
Early Popular Visual Culture [51762]
Eastbourne
Lighting & Sound International [53244] .... (Combined) ★10,000
Hemel Hempstead
In Camera [53558] .... (Controlled) 65,000
Manchester
Nineteenth Century Theatre and Film [55574]
York
Aesthetica Magazine [56986] 20,000

MOTORCYCLES

AUSTRALIA
Sydney
Australian Motorcycle News [42460] .... ★20,132

IRELAND
Sandyford
Bike Buyers Guide [46054]
Modified Motors [46056]

SWITZERLAND
Mies
FIM Magazine [51212] 2,600

UNITED KINGDOM
Horncastle
Scootering [53593]
London
Moto Magazine [54956]
Manchester
Bike Trader [55543] .... ★17,876

Ware
Triumph Magazine [56846] ... 80,000

MUSEUMS

FINLAND
Helsinki
Museo [43849] 2,000

INDIA
Kolkata
Indian Museum Bulletin [45273] .... (Paid) 500

UNITED KINGDOM
Abingdon
International Journal of Heritage Studies [51836]
London
British Museum Studies in Ancient Egypt and Sudan (BMSAES) [54141]
Oxford
Museum International [56110]

MUSIC AND MUSICAL INSTRUMENTS
See also Performing Arts

AUSTRALIA
Grosvenor Place
Resonate Journal [41935] 1,700
Sydney
Limelight [42536] .... ★11,299
Perfect Beat [42559]
Tamworth
Country Music Capital News [42611]

BRAZIL
Curitiba
Electronic Musicological Review [42977]

BULGARIA
Sofia
Bulgarian Musicology [43097]

DENMARK
Copenhagen
Djembe [43665] 1,500
Odense
The Journal of Music and Meaning [43729]

FINLAND
Helsinki
Finnish Music Quarterly [43828]
Sulasol [43858] 1,000

FRANCE
Paris
Revue de Musicologie [44081]

GERMANY
Bonn
Europa Cantat Magazine [44256]
Essen
Das Mechanische Musikinstrument [44346]
Hannover
Musicae Scientiae [44434]
Mainz
Das Orchester [44539] .. .. (Paid) 20,000

Circulation: ★ = ABC; △ = BPA; ◆ = CAC; • = CCAB; ▢ = VAC; ⊕ = PO Statement; ‡ = Publisher's Report; Boldface figures = sworn; Light figures = estimated.

HUNGARY
Budapest
Studia Musicologica Academiae Scientiarum Hungaricae [44875]

Egyetem
Verbum [44889]

IRELAND
Dublin
Irish Folk Music Studies [45973]
Show Times [45998]

Monkstown
Treoir [46040] 15,000

ITALY
Milan
M&D/Musica e Dischi [46186]

Varese
Musica [46277]

NETHERLANDS
Amsterdam
World New Music Magazine [48272]

Nieuwegein
Beatles Unlimited Magazine
[48740] 3,575

NIGERIA
Ile-Ife
Nigerian Music Review [49116]

NORWAY
Sogndal
Nordic Journal of Music Therapy
[49211]

REPUBLIC OF SOUTH AFRICA
Matieland
South African Music Studies
[50554] .... (Paid) 125
(Non-paid) 14

Pretoria
Musicus [50597]

Rondebosch
Journal of the Musical Arts in Africa
[50618]

SPAIN
Madrid
Cuadernos de Jazz [50745]
Melomano [50783]
Ritmo [50800]

SWEDEN
Goteborg
Swedish Journal of Musicology
[50966]

SWITZERLAND
Zurich
Schweizer Musikzeitung
[51282] .... (Controlled) 21,948

UNITED KINGDOM
Abingdon
Early Popular Visual Culture [51762]
Ethnomusicology Forum [51776]
Jazz Perspectives [51867]

Blechingley
Laudate Magazine [52388] 600

Burton-on-Trent
Singing [52772]

Cambridge
Early Music [52815]
Eighteenth Century Music [52816]
Twentieth Century Music [52903]

Carlisle
Mastersinger [52946]

Chelmsford
Gilbert & Sullivan News [52961]

Chorleywood
The Key Frame [53024] 1,000

Deal
Tocatta [53161]

Devon
Taqasim [53177]

Dorking
Church Music Quarterly
[53193] .... (Paid) ‡11,500

Edinburgh
Contemporary Music Review [53265]

Hove
Musical Times [53611]

Isle of Arran
Dalriada [53662]

Lancaster
Journal of New Music Research
[53735]

Leeds
Chapter&Verse [53760]
Journal of the Royal Musical
Association [53770]

Leicester
Organised Sound [53816] 400

Llanelli
Welsh Music [53885]

London
Audience [53980]
British Journal of Music Therapy
[54126] 800
Classical Music [54215]
Equity
[54382] .... (Controlled) 39,000
Flourish
[54467] .... (Non-paid) 20,000
Flute [54469] .... (Paid) 1,700
Folk Music Journal
[54476] .. .. (Paid) 4,000
International Journal of Music
Education
[54655] .. .. (Paid) ‡1,000
International Piano
[54666] .. .. (Controlled) ‡8,000
Jazz Research Journal [54688]
Jazz UK
[54689] .. .. (Combined) 30,000
Jazzwise Magazine [54690]
Music Journal
[54963] .... (Combined) 5,100
Music & Letters [54964]
Opera [55036]
Popular Music History [55101]
Songlines [55255]

Maidstone
The Drummer's Call [55528]

Norwich
Popular Music [55739] 800

Oxford
Journal of the BIOS [56018]
Music Analysis [56111]

Penzance
Songwriting and Composing
Magazine [56250] 10,000

Potters Bar
The Grieg Companion [56296]

Richmond
eltonjohnworld.com [56391]

Saint Albans
Acoustics Bulletin [56433]
Galpin Society Journal
[56435] .... (Paid) 850

South Croydon
Reverberations [56565]

Sudbury
Horn Player Magazine [56650]

Surrey
Nineteenth-Century Music Review
[56670]

Welwyn Garden City
The Recorder Magazine
[56883] 2,500

York
Aesthetica Magazine
[56986] 20,000

NATURAL HISTORY AND NATURE STUDY
See also Ecology and Conservation; Entomology; Ornithology and Oology

AUSTRALIA
Canberra
Quaternary Geochronology [41711]

Carlton
Habitat Australia [41726] 17,000

Nathan
International Journal of Agricultural
Resources, Governance and
Ecology [42143]

Perth
Ecohydrology [42250]

AUSTRIA
Vienna
ACT! The Magazine of Greenpeace
Austria [42742]

PEOPLE'S REPUBLIC OF CHINA
Nanjing
Journal of Hohai University [43459]

Shanghai
Journal of Shanghai Jiaotong
University [43482]
Man & Nature [43487]

Xi'an
Journal of Xauat (Natural Sciences)
[43535]

EGYPT
Ismailia
Egyptian Journal of Natural History
[43774]

FRANCE
Castanet-Tolosan
Natures Sciences Societes
[43927] 1,000

Paris
Karthago [44067]

GERMANY
Berlin
Fossil Record [44184]

Biebergemund
Entomologia Generalis [44244]

GHANA
Accra
West African Journal of Applied
Ecology [44730]

Kumasi
Ghana Journal of Forestry [44735]

ITALY
Ischia Porto
Marine Ecology [46156]

JAPAN
Tokyo
Limnology [46961] .. .. (Paid) 1,200

KENYA
Nairobi
International Journal of Tropical Insect Science [47185]
Scopus [47196]

NETHERLANDS
Amsterdam
Global Environmental Change
[48002]
Global and Planetary Change
[48003]
Journal of Arid Environments [48049]

Dordrecht
Journal of Bamboo and Rattan
[48442]

Leiden
Dead Sea Discoveries [48666]
Journal for European Environmental
& Planning Law [48698]

NIGERIA
Benin City
Tropical Freshwater Biology [49066]

NORWAY
Tromso
Polar Research [49214]

POLAND
Warsaw
Hacquetia [49715]
Polish Journal of Natural Sciences
[49750]

REPUBLIC OF SOUTH AFRICA
Bloemfontein
Navorsinge van die Nasionale Musium, Bloemfontein [50355]

Cape Town
African Natural History [50361]

Hatfield
African Entomology [50521]

Parkview
Vulture News [50563]

Rondebosch
Marine Ornithology [50621]

Stellenbosch
Journal of East African Natural
History [50632]

SPAIN
La Laguna
Journal for Nature Conservation
[50719]

Madrid
Quercus [50794]

Terrassa
Tiempos Modernos [50838]

SRI LANKA
Colombo
Journal of the National Science
Foundation [50857]

Circulation: ★ = ABC; △ = BPA; ◆ = CAC; ● = CCAB; ❑ = VAC; ⊕ = PO Statement; ‡ = Publisher's Report; Boldface figures = sworn; Light figures = estimated.

SWEDEN
Lund
Oikos [50988]

Stockholm
Alcheringa [51004]
Grana [51019]

SWITZERLAND
Geneva
Interdisciplinary Environmental
Review [51099]
International Journal of Environment
and Pollution [51118]
International Journal of Environmen-
tal Policy and Decision Making
[51119]

UNITED REPUBLIC OF TAN-ZANIA
Morogoro
Tanzania Journal of Forestry and Na-
ture Conservation [51407]

THAILAND
Bangkok
Science Asia [51434]

UGANDA
Kampala
The Uganda Journal [51589]

UNITED KINGDOM
Abingdon
International Journal of Heritage
Studies [51836]

Birmingham
Bird Study [52330] 2,500

Bradford
The Naturalist
[52529] .... (Combined) 5,800

Cambridge
Journal of Cetacean Research and
Management [52848]
World Birdwatch [52906] 6,000

Edinburgh
Aquatic Conservation [53251]

Holt
Birding World
[53583] .. .. (Paid) 6,000

Inverness
Scotland's Natural Heritage [53647]

Leeds
British Dragonfly Society Journal
[53758]

Llandovery
The London Naturalist [53884]

London
Environmental Health Practitioner
[54377] 11,800
Historic Scotland Magazine
[54556] 35,000
Journal of Applied Ecology [54698]
Journal of Functional Ecology
[54755]
The London Bird Report [54885]
Midland History [54932]
Northern History [55011]

Olney
International Journal of Emergency
Management [55799]

Shrewsbury
Field Studies [56529]

Stirling
The Forth Naturalist & Historian
[56622] .... (Combined) 350

Wadebridge
Avicultural Magazine [56803]

NATURAL RESOURCES

AUSTRALIA
Farrell Flat
Agribusiness Connections [41865]

Tullamarine
Australian Landcare
[42649] .. .. ‡33,000

AUSTRIA
Laxenburg
International Journal of Global En-
ergy Issues [42730]

PEOPLE'S REPUBLIC OF CHINA
Shanghai
Man & Nature [43487]

GERMANY
Dusseldorf
Gefahrstoffe-Reinhaltung der Luft
[44325] 2,000

JAPAN
Tokyo
National Geographic Japanese
Edition [46975] .... ★84,124
Nikkei Ecology [46988] .... ★16,632

NETHERLANDS
Amsterdam
Forest Ecology and Management
[47988]
Geothermics [47998]
International Journal of Regulation
and Governance [48032]

Dordrecht
Journal of Bamboo and Rattan
[48442]

Leiden
Journal for European Environmental
& Planning Law [48698]

RUSSIA
Irkutsk
Geography and Natural Resources
[49856]

SWEDEN
Norrkoping
Hydrology Research [50995]

UNITED REPUBLIC OF TAN-ZANIA
Morogoro
Tanzania Journal of Forestry and Na-
ture Conservation [51407]

TURKEY
Izmir
Ekoloji [51573]

UNITED KINGDOM
Abingdon
Journal of Environmental Planning
and Management [51894]
Journal of Environmental Policy &
Planning [51895]

Brentwood
Biomass Bulletin [52567]
Energy and Environment [52572]

Energy Exploration & Exploitation
[52573]
London
Advances in Building Energy
Research [53905]
Advances in Solar Energy [53909]
Gas Matters [54494]
Gas Matters Today [54495]
Journal of the Energy Institute
[54743]
Water Asset Management
International [55381]
Water Intelligence Online [55383]

Oxford
Natural Resources Forum [56112]

NUCLEAR ENGINEERING
See also Power and Power
Plants; Physics

AUSTRALIA
Port Melbourne
Australian Physics [42262]

AUSTRIA
Vienna
INIS Database [42760]

PEOPLE'S REPUBLIC OF CHINA
Beijing
Communications in Theoretical
Physics [43191]
Shanghai
Nuclear Science and Techniques
[43491]

DENMARK
Copenhagen
Nuclear Instruments and Methods in
Physics Research Section B
[43680]

FRANCE
Paris
Atoms for Peace [44028]
International Journal of Nuclear En-
ergy Science and Technology
[44051]
International Journal of Nuclear Gov-
ernance, Economy and Ecology
[44052]
International Journal of Nuclear Hy-
drogen Production and Applications
[44053]
International Journal of Nuclear
Knowledge Management [44054]
International Journal of Nuclear Law
[44055]

GERMANY
Freiburg
Renewable Energy Focus
[44372] 86,140
Solar Energy Journal [44373]

Stuttgart
Nuclear Engineering and Design
[44674]

Tubingen
Progress in Particle and Nuclear
Physics [44693]

INDIA
Mumbai
Nuclear India [45421] 5,000

ITALY
Frascati
The European Physical Journal
A-Hadrons and Nuclei [46146]

JAPAN
Nagoya
Journal of Plasma and Fusion
Research [46554]

Tokyo
Atoms in Japan [46757]
Ionizing Radiation [46850]
Journal of Nuclear Science and
Technology [46930] 1,500
The Thermal and Nuclear Power
[47050] 18,000

NETHERLANDS
Amsterdam
Nuclear Data Sheets [48184]
Nuclear Physics A [48185]
Nuclear Physics B [48186]
Nuclear Physics B [48187]

Dordrecht
Hyperfine Interactions [48420]

POLAND
Krakow
Acta Physica Polonica B [49664]

Warsaw
Nukleonika [49739]

ROMANIA
Bucharest
Nuclear Energy [49840]

RUSSIA
Moscow
Physics of Atomic Nuclei [49956]
Thermal Engineering [49996]

SINGAPORE
Singapore
International Journal of Modern Phys-
ics E [50188]
International Journal of PIXE [50192]
Modern Physics Letters A
[50217] .... (Paid) 550
Modern Physics Letters B
[50218] .... (Paid) 350

SWEDEN
Stockholm
MEDSOLS [51025] .. .... (Paid) 2,000

UNITED KINGDOM
Birmingham
Progress in Nuclear Energy [52362]

Cambridge
Journal of Advanced Materials
[52841]

Munster
Solid State Nuclear Magnetic
Resonance [55654]

NURSING
See also Hospitals and
Healthcare Institutions;
Medicine and Surgery

AUSTRALIA
Burwood
Australasian Emergency Nursing
Journal [41675]

Kingston
Australian Journal of Advanced Nursing (AJAN) [41991]
Australian Nursing Journal (ANJ)
[41992] .... ‡65,000

Circulation: ★ = ABC; △ = BPA; ◆ = CAC; • = CCAB; ❑ = VAC; ⊕ = PO Statement; ‡ = Publisher's Report; Boldface figures = sworn; Light figures = estimated.

Gale Directory of Publications & Broadcast Media/147th Ed.

6223

Trade, Technical, and Professional Publications

PEOPLE'S REPUBLIC OF CHINA
Hong Kong
The Hong Kong Nursing Journal [43340]

FRANCE
Montrouge
Bulletin Infirmier du Cancer [43983]

GREECE
Nikea
ICUs and Nursing Web Journal [44763]

INDIA
New Delhi
The Nursing Journal of India
[45631] .... (Paid) 6,000

ITALY
Milan
The Journal of Vascular Access [46184]

JAPAN
Tokyo
Nikkei Healthcare
[46993] .... ★19,079
Nikkei Medical [46997] .. ... ★111,060

JORDAN
Amman
Dirasat Medical and Biological Sciences
[47156] .... (Controlled) 1,000

NETHERLANDS
Amsterdam
Best Practice & Research Clinical Endocrinology & Metabolism [47903]
Journal for Nurse Practitioners [48105]
Nurse Education Today [48188]

Groningen
European Journal of Cardiovascular Nursing [48600]

NEW ZEALAND
Wellington
Kai Tiaki [49013] .... ‡44,000

PHILIPPINES
Manila
Philippine Journal of Nursing
[49556] .. .. (Paid) 13,000

POLAND
Gdansk
Nursing Topics [49659]

REPUBLIC OF SOUTH AFRICA
Gauteng
Professional Nursing Today [50482]

SPAIN
Madrid
Gerokomos [50762]

SWEDEN
Stockholm
Nordisk Fysioterapi [51028]
Sjukgymnasten [51038]

SWITZERLAND
Geneva
International Nursing Review [51148]

UNITED KINGDOM
Berkhamsted
Guidelines in Practice [52311]

Birmingham
Nursing Home News [52359]

Bishop's Stortford
Journal of Neonatal Nursing
[52380] .... (Combined) 5,000

Bognor Regis
European Diabetes Nursing [52395]

Exeter
European Journal of Oncology Nursing [53354]

Harrogate
Journal of Perioperative Practice
[53517] 8,000

Harrow
Emergency Nurse
[53522] .. .. (Paid) ‡5,621
Evidence-Based Nursing
[53523] .. .. ‡8,244
Mental Health Practice
[53525] .. .. (Paid) 10,925
Nurse Researcher [53527]
Nursing Management
[53528] .... ★4,564
Nursing Older People
[53529] .. .. (Paid) ★7,430
Nursing Standard [53530] ... ★67,272
Pediatric Nursing [53531] ... . ★13,048
Primary Health Care
[53532] .... ★7,271

Leeds
Journal of Psychiatric and Mental Health Nursing [53769]

London
BMC Nursing [54078]
British Journal of Anaesthetic and Recovery Nursing [54111]
British Journal of Cardiac Nursing [54115]
British Journal of Community Nursing [54117]
British Journal of Dermatology Nursing [54119]
British Journal of Neuroscience Nursing [54127]
British Journal of School Nursing [54135]
Dental Nursing [54317]
Gastrointestinal Nursing [54496]
International Journal of Nursing Studies [54656]
International Journal of Palliative Nursing [54657]
Journal of Renal Nursing [54808]
Journal of Wound Care
[54838] .. .. (Paid) 6,000
Nurse Prescribing [55014]
Nursing Ethics
[55015] .. .. (Paid) 1,000
Nursing in Practice [55016]
Nursing and Residential Care [55017]
Physical Therapy Reviews [55085]
PNC [55096]
Progress in Palliative Care [55136]

Oxford
International Journal of Evidence-based Healthcare [55995]
International Journal of Nursing Terminologies and Classifications [55999]
International Journal of Older People Nursing [56000]

Journal of Nursing and Healthcare of Chronic Illness [56054]
Journal of Nursing Management [56055]
Nursing and Health Sciences [56122]
Nursing Philosophy [56123]
Public Health Nursing [56177]

Penarth
Reviews in Clinical Gerontology
[56241] 400

OCEANOGRAPHY AND MARINE STUDIES

AUSTRALIA
Collingwood
Marine & Freshwater Research [41792]

Sydney
Maritime Workers Journal
[42539] .... (Non-paid) ⊕10,000

PEOPLE'S REPUBLIC OF CHINA
Beijing
Science in China Series D [43218]

Shanghai
Ocean Engineering [43492]

CROATIA
Split
Acta Adriatica [43559]
Acta Adriatica [43560]

CYPRUS
Limassol
International Journal of Ocean Systems Management [43590]

DENMARK
Copenhagen
ICES Journal of Marine Science [43674]

EGYPT
Alexandria
International Journal of Lakes and Rivers [43746]
International Journal of Oceans and Oceanography (IJOO) [43748]

FRANCE
Les Ulis
Hydroecologie appliquee [43965]

Nantes
Aquatic Living Resources
[44011] 1,000

Villefranche-sur-Mer
Aquatic Microbial Ecology [44124]

GERMANY
Gottingen
Ocean Science [44400]
Ocean Science Discussions [44401]

Heidelberg
Coral Reefs [44451]

Helgoland
Helgoland Marine Research [44481]

Kiel
Marine Biology [44505]
Polar Biology [44507]

Oldendorf
Aquatic Biology [44625]
Diseases of Aquatic Organisms [44626]

Marine Ecology Progress Series (MEPS) [44629]

Rostock
Journal of Marine Systems [44648]

Stuttgart
Fundamental and Applied Limnology [44668]

Wilhelmshaven
Geo-Marine Letters [44713]

INDIA
New Delhi
Indian Journal of Marine Sciences [45558]

ITALY
Ischia Porto
Marine Ecology [46156]

JAPAN
Shizuoka
Journal of Faculty of Marine Science and Technology of Tokai University [46688]

Tokyo
ClassNK Magazine [46786]
Fisheries Science [46825]
Journal of Marine Science and Technology [46921]
Journal of Oceanography [46932]

Yamagata
Marine Micropaleontology [47125]

NETHERLANDS
Amsterdam
Journal of Sea Research [48115]
Marine Structures [48141]

Dordrecht
Reviews in Fish Biology and Fisheries [48557]

The Hague
Terra et Aqua [48628]

PAKISTAN
Faisalabad
Universal Science and Engineering for Marine Environment [49295]

POLAND
Warsaw
Oceanological and Hydrobiological Studies [49740]
Polish Maritime Research [49752]

RUSSIA
Moscow
Izvestiya, Atmospheric and Oceanic Physics [49924]
Oceanology [49949]

REPUBLIC OF SOUTH AFRICA
Grahamstown
African Journal of Marine Science [50489]

Pietermaritzburg
African Journal of Aquatic Science [50564]

Rondebosch
Marine Ornithology [50621]

Umhlanga
African Journal of Marine Science [50640]

SPAIN
Barcelona
Scientia Marina
[50697] .... (Combined) 290

SWEDEN
Malmo
World Maritime University Journal of Maritime Affairs [50992]

Stockholm
Tellus [51042]

SWITZERLAND
Basel
Marine Drugs [51063]

TAIWAN
Taipei
Acta Oceanographica Taiwanica [51328] .... (Paid) 800

UNITED REPUBLIC OF TANZANIA
Zanzibar
Western Indian Ocean Journal of Marine Science [51409]

UNITED KINGDOM
Cardiff
Marine Policy [52936]

Dewsbury
Cook's Log [53178]

Edinburgh
Aquatic Conservation [53251]

Godalming
Mollusc World [53475]

Hailsham
Mariner's Mirror [53501]

London
Geochemical Transactions [54503]
Seaways [55225] 7,500
Underwater Technology [55359] 1,800

Marlow
Seventh Wave [55601]

Oxford
ICES Journal of Marine Science [55983]
Journal of Plankton Research [56059]

Plymouth
Journal of the Marine Biological Association of the United Kingdom (JMBA) [56272] 1,600

Reading
Quarterly Journal of the Royal Meteorological Society [56029] .. .. (Paid) 1,100

Southampton
Continental Shelf Research [56569]

Teddington
International Ocean Systems [56732] .. .. (Combined) 10,021

Ware
ISESnews [56841]

OILS AND FATS (ANIMAL & VEGETABLE)

ARGENTINA
Buenos Aires
A & G Magazine [41468] 1,500

GERMANY
Hamburg
Oil World Monthly [44421]

ICELAND
Reykjavik
Chemistry and Physics of Lipids [44899]

OPHTHALMOLOGY, OPTOMETRY, AND OPTICS

BRAZIL
Sao Paulo
Arquivos Brasileiros de Oftalmologia [43023]

PEOPLE'S REPUBLIC OF CHINA
Hong Kong
HKTDC Optical [43313]

CZECH REPUBLIC
Prague
Czech and Slovak Ophthalmology [43619]

GERMANY
Darmstadt
Optik [44311]

Leinfelden-Echterdingen
DER AUGENOPTIKER [44519] 9,836
die Kontaktlinse [44521] 2,569

ICELAND
Reykjavik
Acta Ophthalmologica [44896]

INDIA
Mumbai
Indian Journal of Ophthalmology [45385]
Middle East African Journal of Ophthalmology [45413]
Oman Journal of Ophthalmology [45423]

ITALY
Milan
European Journal of Ophthalmology [46169]

JAPAN
Tokyo
Japanese Journal of Ophthalmology [46872]
Optical Review [47015]

NETHERLANDS
Amsterdam
American Journal of Ophthalmology [47888]
Experimental Eye Research [47979]
Graphical Models [48004]
Optical Materials [48192]
Optics Communications [48193]
Optics & Laser Technology [48194]

Dordrecht
Documenta Ophthalmologica [48377]

Rotterdam
Strabismus [48753]

NIGERIA
Ibadan
Nigerian Journal of Ophthalmology [49098]

Uturu
Journal of Health and Visual Sciences [49177]

PHILIPPINES
Makati City
Philippine Journal of Ophthalmology [49521] .... (Paid) 1,000

RUSSIA
Moscow
Annals of Ophthalmology [49871]

SWITZERLAND
Lausanne
Optics and Lasers in Engineering [51198]

TURKEY
Istanbul
Journal of Turkish Ophthalmology [51558]

UNITED KINGDOM
Basingstoke
EYE [52203] 3,500

Birmingham
Contact Lens & Anterior Eye [52338]

Bristol
FibreSystems Europe [52669]
Optics & Laser Europe [52713]

Chichester
Microscopy and Analysis [53014] .... ‡46,000

Crowborough
Dispensing Optics [53120] 7,502

Edinburgh
Eye News [53275] 4,200

Glasgow
Graefe's Archive for Clinical and Experimental Ophthalmology [53422]

London
BMC Ophthalmology [54079]
British Journal of Ophthalmology [54129] .... ‡2,370
British Orthoptic Journal [54144] 1,500
Expert Review of Ophthalmology [54430]
Ophthalmic and Physiological Optics [55039]
Ophthalmology International [55040]
Optometry in Practice [55041]

Macclesfield
Clinical Ophthalmology [55516]

Nottingham
Optical and Quantum Electronics [55768]

Oxford
Clinical and Experimental Optometry [55911]
infocus Magazine [55989]
Progress in Retinal and Eye Research [56171]

Stevonage
IEE Proceedings Optoelectronics [56611]

ORNITHOLOGY AND OOLOGY
See also Natural History and Nature Study

AUSTRALIA
Collingwood
Emu - Austral Ornithology [41787]

Nunawading
Australian Field Ornithology [42218] .... (Paid) 621
(Non-paid) 59

JAPAN
Chiba
Journal of Yamashina Institute for Ornithology [46319] .. .. (Paid) 700

Tokyo
Japanese Journal of Ornithology [46873] .... (Paid) 900

MALTA
Ta' Xbiex
Birds Eye View [47743]
Il-Merill [47744]

POLAND
Warsaw
Ring [49763]

REPUBLIC OF SOUTH AFRICA
Grahamstown
Ostrich [50509]

Rondebosch
Marine Ornithology [50621]

UNITED KINGDOM
Birmingham
Bird Study [52330] 2,500

Cambridge
Bird Conservation International [52793]

Holt
Birding World [53583] .. .. (Paid) 6,000

Sandy
Bird Life [56460]
Wingbeat [56461]

Thetford
Ringing & Migration [56745] .... (Combined) 2,200

Wadebridge
Avicultural Magazine [56803]

OSTEOPATHY

AUSTRALIA
Murdoch
Chiropractic & Osteopathy [42136]

UNITED KINGDOM
Childerley
Human Reproduction [53018]

London
Advances in Osteoporotic Fracture Management [53906]

PACKAGING
See also Paper

CHILE
Concepcion
Celulosa y Papel [43136]

PEOPLE'S REPUBLIC OF CHINA
Hong Kong
HKTDC Packaging [43314]

DENMARK
Glostrup
IN-PAK [43706] .. .. ‡4,476
Pack+Plast [43711]

INDIA
Mumbai
Modern Packaging & Design [45417]
Packaging India [45426] .. .. (Paid) 2,500

Circulation: ★ = ABC; △ = BPA; ◆ = CAC; • = CCAB; ❑ = VAC; ⊕ = PO Statement; ‡ = Publisher's Report; Boldface figures = sworn; Light figures = estimated.

REPUBLIC OF KOREA
Seoul
Journal [47270]

SWITZERLAND
Zurich
Swisspack International
[51290] .. .. (Paid) 3,800

UNITED KINGDOM
Burnham
Electronic Materials & Packaging
[52764]

Glasgow
Packaging Scotland
[53438] *4,219

Leatherhead
Packaging Month
[53752] .. .. (Paid) 500

London
Packaging, Transport, Storage & Security of Radioactive Material
[55049]

Sidcup
Packaging Today [56545]

Wallington
Machinery Update [56833] .. . ‡9,000

PAINT AND WALLCOVERINGS
See also Interior Design/
Decorating

GERMANY
Leinfelden-Echterdingen
Lackiererblatt [44525] 5,904
Malerblatt [44526] 23,096

JAPAN
Tokyo
Nikkei Design
[46986] .... (Paid) *13,370

ROMANIA
Bucharest
Elle Decoration [49835] .... ‡9,469

UKRAINE
Kiev
Interior Magazine
[51598] .. .. (Combined) 17,500

UNITED KINGDOM
Hale
Living Edge [53503]

Hampton
Coatings Comet [53505]
World Surface Coatings Abstracts
[53506] 250

Stoke-on-Trent
The Artisan [56628]

Wadhurst
Construction Europe
[56805] *14,624

Wembley
Surface Coatings International
[56886]
Surface Coatings International
[56887] 3,750

PAPER
See also Packaging

BELGIUM
Brussels
Pulp & Paper International (PPI)
[42871] .. .. △14,180

CHILE
Concepcion
Celulosa y Papel [43136]

FINLAND
Helsinki
Paper and Timber [43854] 4000

GERMANY
Berlin
Archiv fur Papyrusforschung
[44155] .... ‡300

REPUBLIC OF KOREA
Seoul
Journal [47270]

PORTUGAL
Aveiro
International Journal of Surface Sci-
ence & Engineering [49789]

SWEDEN
Stockholm
STFI Kontakt [51041]

UNITED KINGDOM
Leatherhead
Packaging Month
[53752] .... (Paid) 500

London
Paper Technology
[55053] .... (Combined) 2,000

Oxford
Membrane Technology [56096]

PARKS

ITALY
Bologna
Piscine Oggi
[46128] .. .. (Controlled) 15,000

UNITED KINGDOM
Gloucester
Journal—British Holiday & Home
Parks Association
[53471] .... (Controlled) 2,600

PATENTS, TRADEMARKS, AND COPYRIGHTS

FRANCE
Paris
Copyright Bulletin [44034] 188

GERMANY
Munich
Official Journal of the European
Patent Office
[44576] .. .. (Paid) ‡2,200
(Non-paid) ‡2,100

INDIA
New Delhi
Invention Intelligence
[45590] .. .. (Paid) 3,000

UNITED KINGDOM
London
The CIPA Journal [54211] 3,600

Sheffield
Digest of Information and Patent
Review [56491]

PEACE

ARGENTINA
Rosario
Vida Rotaria [41488] 13,900

AUSTRALIA
Adelaide
Peace and Freedom [41512] 500

Parramatta
Rotary Down Under
[42236] .. .. (Paid) 50,000

BELGIUM
Brussels
Rotary Contact [42872] 769,000

CHILE
Los Angeles
El Rotario de Chile [43140] 5,800

COLOMBIA
Cali
Colombia Rotaria
[43550] .... (Paid) 491,312

EGYPT
Cairo
Rotary Magazine [43764] 4,000

ESTONIA
Tallinn
Estonian Literary Magazine
[43783] 2,000

FRANCE
Lyon
Damocles [43968]
Le Rotarien
[43969] .. .. (Paid) 40,000

GERMANY
Augsburg
Paneuropa Deutschland [44141]

ICELAND
Reykjavik
Rotary Norden [44902] 69,000

INDIA
Chennai
Rotary News/Rotary Samachar
[45056] .... (Paid) ⊕75,000

ITALY
Bergamo
Rotary [46123] 491,312

Bisceglie
Mosaico di Pace [46124]

JAPAN
Tokyo
The Rotary-No-Tomo
[47033] 120,000

REPUBLIC OF KOREA
Seoul
The Rotary Korea [47285] 48,000

MEXICO
Mexico City
Rotarismo en Mexico
[47789] 13,500

NETHERLANDS
Amsterdam
Rotarian [48227] *20,000

NIGERIA
Ikeja
Democracy & Development [49106]

PERU
Chiclayo
El Rotario Peruano [49418] 3,500

PHILIPPINES
Quezon City
Philippine Rotary [49611] 15,000

REPUBLIC OF SOUTH AF-RICA
KwaZulu-Natal
Rotary Africa
[50544] .... (Paid) ⊕7,000

SWITZERLAND
Uster
Rotary Suisse-Liechtenstein
[51236] .... ‡12,000

TAIWAN
Taipei
The Rotarian Monthly
[51357] 11,300

TURKEY
Cinarli-Izmir
Rotary Dergisi [51552] 8,100

UNITED KINGDOM
Abingdon
Global Change, Peace & Security
[51795]
Journal of Peace Education [51929]
Medicine, Conflict & Survival [51974]
Peace Review [52004]

Alcester
Rotary Magazine (GB & I) [52095]

Argyll and Bute
The Muses Journal [52132]

Bradford
Peace, Conflict & Development
[52535]

Hove
Journal of Aggression, Conflict and
Peace Research [53606]

London
Cooperation and Conflict [54266]
Journal of Peace Research [54793]
Security Dialogue [55226]

Oxford
Peace & Change [56144]

York
Defence and Peace Economics
[56989]

VENEZUELA
Tachira
Nueva Revista Rotaria
[57029] 9,900

PEDIATRICS

AUSTRALIA
Watson
Australian Journal of Early Childhood
[42690]

BELGIUM
Leuven
European Journal of Pediatrics
[42895]

Circulation: ★ = ABC; △ = BPA; ◆ = CAC; • = CCAB; ❑ = VAC; ⊕ = PO Statement; ‡ = Publisher's Report; Boldface figures = sworn; Light figures = estimated.

BRAZIL
Botafogo
International Braz J Urol
[42954] 6,000

PEOPLE'S REPUBLIC OF CHINA
Hong Kong
Hong Kong Journal of Paediatrics
[43331]

CZECH REPUBLIC
Prague
Ceskoslovenska Pediatrie
[43614] 2,500

DENMARK
Frederiksberg
Pediatric Diabetes [43695]

FRANCE
Montrouge
Medecine therapeutique/Pediatrie
[44001]

GERMANY
Berlin
Journal of Perinatal Medicine [44209]
Heidelberg
Pediatric Surgery International
[44471]

INDIA
Chandigarh
Indian Journal of Nephrology [45023]
Mumbai
Annals of Pediatric Cardiology
[45350]
Indian Journal of Medical and Paediatric Oncology [45382]
New Delhi
Indian Journal of Pediatrics
[45564] 20,000
Indian Pediatrics
[45575] .. .. (Paid) 17,500
Journal of Indian Association of Pediatric Surgeons [45601]
Journal of Pediatric Neurosciences
[45615]
Recent Advances in Pediatrics
[45641]

IRAN
Tehran
Iranian Journal of Pediatrics [45905]

JAPAN
Kyoto
Clinical Pediatric Endocrinology
[46469]
Tokyo
Child's Nervous System [46784]

NETHERLANDS
Amsterdam
Journal of Pediatric Neurology
[48108]

NIGERIA
Ibadan
Nigerian Journal of Paediatrics
[49099]
Jos
African Journal of Paediatric Surgery
[49123]

SINGAPORE
Singapore
Journal of Pediatric Urology [50211]

SRI LANKA
Colombo
Sri Lanka Journal of Child Health
[50865]

SWEDEN
Stockholm
Acta Paediatrica [51002]

SWITZERLAND
Neuhausen
Padiatrie [51218]

TAIWAN
Taipei
Acta Paediatrica Taiwanica
[51329] 3,000

TURKEY
Ankara
Turkish Journal of Pediatrics
[51514] .. .. (Paid) 1,500
Van
Journal of Pediatric Infectious
Diseases [51581]

UNITED KINGDOM
Abingdon
Developmental Neurorehabilitation
[51757]
Early Child Development and Care
[51761]
Pediatric Hematology & Oncology
[52006] .... (Combined) 1,312
Bridgwater
ABM Magazine [52595]
Bristol
Paediatric and Perinatal
Epidemiology [52714]
Cardiff
Paediatrics & Child Health [52937]
Leeds
Seminars in Fetal & Neonatal
Medicine [53774]
London
Annals of Tropical Paediatrics
[53950]
BMC Pediatrics [54082]
Current Pediatric Reviews [54303]
Journal of Child Psychology and
Psychiatry [54722]
Journal of Child Psychotherapy
[54723]
Pediatric Health [55064]
Progress in Palliative Care [55136]
Thorax [55315]
Oxford
Child [55907]
Journal of Paediatrics and Child
Health [56056]
Pediatric Allergy and Immunology
[56145]
Pediatric Anesthesia [56146]
Pediatric Dermatology [56147]
Pediatrics International [56148]

PERFORMING ARTS
See also Drama and Theatre; Music and Musical Instruments

AUSTRALIA
Bundoora
Australian Playwrights [41669]

Perth
Bellydance Oasis [42247]
Sydney
Leaping [42535]
Limelight [42536] .... ★11,299

BELGIUM
Mechelen
Ludus [42904]

BOTSWANA
Gaborone
Marang [42944]

GERMANY
Berlin
ballettanz [44158] 12,000
Mainz
Das Orchester
[44539] .. .. (Paid) 20,000

JAPAN
Tokyo
Adaptation [46728]

NETHERLANDS
Amsterdam
European Journal of Arts Education
[47974]
Theatre Research International
[48247] 1,000

NEW ZEALAND
Wellington
DANZ [49006] .... (Paid) 500

REPUBLIC OF SOUTH AFRICA
Matieland
SATJ [50553]
Rondebosch
Journal of the Musical Arts in Africa
[50618]

SPAIN
Barcelona
AEBDC News [50646]
Madrid
Por la Danza [50791]
Primer Acto [50792]

SRI LANKA
Colombo
Journal of the Royal Asiatic Society
of Sri Lanka [50869]

SWEDEN
Farsta
Svensk Danssport [50954]

SWITZERLAND
Basel
Antike Kunst [51058] 1,100

UNITED KINGDOM
Abingdon
Cultural Trends [51748]
Ethnomusicology Forum [51776]
Indonesia and the Malay World
[51813]
Performance Research [52007]
Women & Performance [52092]
Brighton
Theatre Notebook [52633]

Bristol
Irish Dancing & Culture [52681]
Who Do You Think You Are?
[52736] .... ★20,266
Cambridge
New Theatre Quarterly
[52878] 1,00
Theatre Research International
[52901] .... (Controlled) 1,100
Deal
Tocatta [53161]
Devon
Taqasim [53177]
Glasgow
Variant [53457]
London
African Performance Review [53923]
Britannia [54107] 1,500
The British Theatre Directory
[54148] .. .. (Paid) 2,000
Creative Review
[54282] .... (Paid) ★19,032
Dance Gazette [54309] 12,000
Equity
[54382] .. .. (Controlled) 39,000
International Journal of Music
Education
[54655] .... (Paid) ‡1,000
International Journal of Performance
Arts and Digital Media [54658]
The Magic Circular Magazine [54895]
The Observer [55023]
Opera Now [55037]
Oxford
Art History [55874]
The British Journal of Aesthetics
[55891]
Spalding
Dance Expression [56590]

PETROLEUM, OIL, AND GAS

AUSTRIA
Laxenburg
International Journal of Global Energy Issues [42730]

BAHRAIN
Manama
Oil and Gas News
[42793] .. .. (Paid) 8,539

PEOPLE'S REPUBLIC OF CHINA
Dalian
Journal of Natural Gas Chemistry
[43254]

FRANCE
Clichy
Stations-Service Acutalites
[43936] .. .. (Paid) 9,500

GERMANY
Stuttgart
Plinius [44677]

KUWAIT
Surra
International Journal of Oil, Gas and
Coal Technology [47362]

NETHERLANDS
Amsterdam
Journal of Applied Geophysics
[48046]

Circulation: ★ = ABC; △ = BPA; ◆ = CAC; • = CCAB; ❑ = VAC; ⊕ = PO Statement; ‡ = Publisher's Report; Boldface figures = sworn; Light figures = estimated.

PAKISTAN
Islamabad
Pakistan Journal of Hydrocarbon
Research [49307] .... (Paid) 500
Karachi
Progress [49373] .... (Paid) 4,750

POLAND
Warsaw
Mineralogia [49738]

RUSSIA
Moscow
Oil & Gas Eurasia
[49950] .. .. (Combined) △12,723
Petroleum Chemistry [49954]

SINGAPORE
Singapore
Hydrocarbon Asia [50168]
Petromin [50237]

REPUBLIC OF SOUTH AF-
RICA
Cape Town
Energy Forecast [50376] 10,000
Road Ahead [50406] 10,000
Stellenbosch
Lithos [50633]

SWITZERLAND
Geneva
International Journal of Petroleum
Engineering [51134]

UNITED ARAB EMIRATES
Abu Dhabi
International Journal of Petroleum
Science and Technology [51620]

UNITED KINGDOM
Berkhamsted
Lube [52312] 1,800
Brentwood
Biomass Bulletin [52567]
Energy Exploration & Exploitation
[52573]
Crawley
Forecourt Trader [53104] .... ★10,922
Dundee
International Journal of Energy Sec-
tor Management [53214]
Knutsford
Downstream [53730] 750
Leeds
Journal of Petrology [53768]
London
Energy Risk [54370]
Journal of the Energy Institute
[54743]
Journal of Petroleum Technology
[54795]
Oil Review Middle East
[55027] .... ★9,034
Petroleum Economist [55074]
Petroleum Review [55075] ... 10,000
Pipeline World [55090] 2,500
SPE Review
[55261] .... (Controlled) 8,500
World Expro [55419] .... ‡12,500
Newcastle upon Tyne
Fuel [55671]
Oxford
Oil and Energy Trends [56126]

OPEC Energy Review [56127]

PETS
See also Veterinary Medi-
cine

AUSTRALIA
Tweed Heads
Australian Birdkeeper Magazine
[42655] 9,500

BELGIUM
**Maleves-Sainte-Marie-
Wastines**
Infor Marechalerie/European Farriers
Journal/Der Huf
[42903] .. ..:.. (Paid) 6,500

PAKISTAN
Faisalabad
Global Veterinaria [49245]
Research Journal of Animal and Vet-
erinary Sciences [49283]

SWEDEN
Linkoping
Reproduction in Domestic Animals
[50977]

UNITED KINGDOM
Bedford
Petcare [52274] 1,600
Burford
Journal of Society for Companion
Animal Studies [52760] 500
Horsham
Animal Action [53594]
Animal Life [53595] ... . (Paid) 45,000
Kennel and Cattery Management
[53596] .... (Combined) 3,100
London
Animals and You [53946]
The Journal of the British Tarantula
Society [54714]
Olney
PBWnews
[55845] .... (Combined) 5,100
Oxford
Journal of Veterinary Emergency and
Critical Care [56078]
Pevensey
Pet Talk [56268]
Tisbury
Feline Advisory Bureau Journal
[56752]
Wallingford
Animal Health Research Reviews
[56815]

PHILANTHROPY AND
HUMANITARIANISM

AUSTRALIA
Hawthorn
Cosmos and History [41942]

PEOPLE'S REPUBLIC OF
CHINA
Beijing
The China Nonprofit Review [43179]
Shanghai
Charity Matters [43468]

DENMARK
Copenhagen
Kontakt [43678] .. .. (Paid) 5,000

ETHIOPIA
Addis Ababa
Ethiopian Journal of the Social Sci-
ences and Humanities [43801]

INDIA
Chennai
Rotary News/Rotary Samachar
[45056] .... (Paid) ⊕75,000

MEXICO
Mexico City
Refugees [47788] 215,000

NETHERLANDS
Leiden
Global Responsibility to Protect
[48673]

NEW ZEALAND
Wellington
Red Cross News [49032]

SWEDEN
Alvsjo
Djurens Ratt
[50948] .. .. (Combined) 50,000

SWITZERLAND
Geneva
Nutrition Information in Crisis
Situations [51154] 2,300
Red Cross, Red Crescent [51157]
SCN News [51160] 8,000

THAILAND
Bangkok
BAMBI Magazine [51413]

UNITED KINGDOM
Abingdon
Critical Review of International Social
and Political Philosophy [51745]
Cultural Trends [51748]
Development in Practice [51755]
Journal of Children and Poverty
[51874]
Birmingham
Child and Family Social Work
[52336]
Diversity in Health and Social Care
[52340]
Brighton
Housing, Care and Support [52613]
The Journal of Adult Protection
[52618]
Journal of Children's Services
[52619]
Learning Disability Review [52624]
Learning Disability Today [52625]
Working with Older People [52635]
Bristol
The Journal of Poverty and Social
Justice [52696]
Voluntary Sector Review [52735]
London
Charity Times [54197]
Common Cause
[54239] .... (Non-paid) 140,000
Voluntary Sector [55375] 5,000

VIETNAM
Hanoi
Humanity [57051]

PHILOLOGY,
LANGUAGE, AND
LINGUISTICS

AUSTRALIA
Brisbane
CALL-EJ Online [41646]
Sydney
Computational Linguistics [42496]

AUSTRIA
Vienna
Stichproben - Wiener Zeitschrift fur
Kritische Afrikastudien [42768]

BELGIUM
Antwerp
Linguistics [42839]
Gent
Jaarboek [42883] 300
Verslagen en Mededelingen
[42885] 300

BOTSWANA
Gaborone
Marang [42944]

BRAZIL
Sao Paulo
Documentacao de Estudos em Linguistica Teorica e Aplicada (DELTA)
[43037]

BULGARIA
Sofia
Balkan Linguistics [43093]

PEOPLE'S REPUBLIC OF
CHINA
Beijing
Chinese Tales and Stories [43190]
Learning Chinese [43210]
Life in China [43211]
Hong Kong
Asian Journal of English Language
Teaching [43276]
Hong Kong Journal of Applied
Linguistics [43327]
International Journal of Computer
Processing of Languages [43349]
Journal of Translation Studies
[43362]
Translation Quarterly [43385]
Shanghai
Using the Right Word [43509]

DENMARK
Fredensborg
The School Times International
[43687]
Odense
Journal of Pragmatics [43730]

FINLAND
Savonlinna
SKY Journal of Linguistics [43906]

FRANCE
Paris
Journal Asiatique [44063]
Strasbourg
ALSIC (Apprentissage des Langues
et Systemes d'Information et de
Communication) [44109]

Circulation: ★ = ABC; △ = BPA; ◆ = CAC; • = CCAB; ❑ = VAC; ⊕ = PO Statement; ‡ = Publisher's Report; Boldface figures = sworn; Light figures = estimated.

GERMANY
Berlin
Anglia [44149] .... ‡540
Beitrage zur Geschichte der deutschen Sprache und Literatur [44159] .... ‡540
Corpus Linguistics and Linguistic Theory [44167]
Folia Linguistica [44181]
Germanistik [44186] 1,300
Iberoromania [44190]
International Journal of the Sociology of Language [44195]
International Review of Applied Linguistics in Language Teaching [44196]
Internationales Jahrbuch des Deutschen Idealismus [44198] ... .. ‡350
Journal of African Languages and Linguistics [44200]
Language and Cognition [44215] 700
Lebende Sprachen [44218]
Romanistisches Jahrbuch [44229] 300
Semiotica [44230]
Text & Talk [44231]
Theoretical Linguistics [44232]
Trends in Classics [44233] 250
Zeitschrift fur Rezensionen zur germanistischen Sprachwissenschaft [44241] 200

Cologne
Frankfurter Afrikanistische Blatter [44294]
Language@internet [44298]
Sprache und Geschichte in Afrika [44303]

Dusseldorf
Constructions [44322]

Freiburg
Language and Computers [44370]

Friedland
Indogermanische Forschungen [44376] 350

Kassel
Zeitschrift fur germanistische Linguistik [44499] 700

Konstanz
Linguistic Typology [44514]

Mainz
Swahili - Forum [44545]

Munich
Zeitschrift fur Assyriologie und Vorderasiatische Archaologie [44580] .. ..,.................... 500

Stuttgart
Zeitschrift fur Sprachwissenschaft [44687] .... ‡1,400

Wiesbaden
Central Asiatic Journal [44711]

HUNGARY
Budapest
Across Languages and Cultures [44804]
Acta Antiqua Academiae Scientiarum Hungaricae [44806]
Acta Linguistica Hungarica [44813]
Acta Orientalia Academiae Scientiarum Hungaricae [44816]
Hungarian Studies [44837]

INDIA
New Delhi
Outlook [45633] .. .... (Paid) 178,276

IRELAND
Dublin
Eigse [45954]

ISRAEL
Tel Aviv
Targima [46113] 450

ITALY
Alessandria
Artifara [46116]

Genoa
Textus [46154]

JAPAN
Tokyo
Language Teacher [46959]
Shukan ST [47039] .... (Paid) 150,000

JORDAN
Amman
International Journal of Arabic-English Studies [47159]

KENYA
Nairobi
Journal of Language, Technology & Entrepreneurship in Africa [47189]

NETHERLANDS
Amsterdam
Andon [47894]
Babel [47902]
Cognitive Development [47929]
Cognitive Systems Research [47931]
Computer Speech & Language [47936]
Diachronica [47957]
English Text Construction [47965]
English World-Wide [47966]
Functions of Language (FOL) [47992]
Gesture [48000]
Historiographia Linguistica (HL) [48012]
International Journal of Corpus Linguistics [48026]
Interpreting [48033]
Journal of English for Academic Purposes [48072]
Journal of Historical Pragmatics [48083]
Journal of Language & Politics [48090]
Journal of Neurolinguistics [48102]
Journal of Phonetics [48109]
Journal of Pidgin and Creole Languages (JPCL) [48110]
Language Problems and Language Planning [48133]
Languages in Contrast [48134]
Linguistic Variations Yearbook [48138]
Lingvisticae Investigationes [48139]
The Mental Lexicon [48153]
Pragmatics & Cognition [48211]
Probus [48215]
Review of Cognitive Linguistics [48223]
Sign Language and Linguistics [48232]
Spanish in Context [48235]
Studies in Language [48239]
Target [48241]
Trends in Cognitive Sciences [48260]
Utrecht Studies in Language and Communication [48268]
Written Language and Literacy [48273]

Dordrecht
Grammars [48408]
Journal of East Asian Linguistics [48456]

Language Policy [48505]
Language Resources and Evaluation [48506]
L1-Educational Studies in Language and Literature [48509]
Reading and Writing [48547]
Russian Linguistics [48558]

Groningen
Indo-Iranian Journal [48602]

Leiden
Arabica [48650]
Brill's Annual of Afroasiatic Languages and Linguistics [48658]

NEW ZEALAND
Auckland
Journal of Sociolinguistics [48800]

Palmerston North
New Zealand Studies in Applied Linguistics [48964]

PHILIPPINES
Manila
Philippine Journal of Linguistics [49555] .... (Paid) 500

Quezon City
Kritika Kultura [49598]

POLAND
Lodz
International Review of Pragmatics [49670]

Warsaw
Linguistica Pragensia [49732]
Lodz Papers in Pragmatics [49733]
Philologia [49746]
Poznan Studies in Contemporary Linguistics [49756]
Psychology of Language and Communication [49761]

RUSSIA
Moscow
Automatic Documentation and Mathematical Linguistics [49881]

SINGAPORE
Singapore
Electronic Journal of Foreign Language Teaching [50144]
International Journal of Chinese & Oriental Languages Processing [50177] .... (Paid) 400
SEAMEO Regional Language Centre Guidelines [50250] ... (Paid) 1,000

REPUBLIC OF SOUTH AFRICA
Auckland Park
Journal for Language Teaching [50349] 350

Grahamstown
Southern African Linguistics and Applied Language Studies [50515]

Pretoria
Language Matters [50595]

Rivonia
Muratho [50611]

Rondebosch
Language Sciences [50620]

Stellenbosch
Per Liguam [50634]

SPAIN
Barcelona
Speak Up [50701]

Madrid
Intercultural Pragmatics [50772]

Valencia
Anglogermanica online [50842]

SWEDEN
Goteborg
Africa & Asia [50956]

SWITZERLAND
Bern
Multilingua [51076]

TURKEY
Ankara
Journal of Modern Turkish Studies (JMTS) [51495]

UNITED KINGDOM
Abingdon
British Journal of Guidance and Counselling [51718]
Bulletin of Spanish Studies [51722]
Changing English [51727]
Clinical Linguistics & Phonetics [51731]
Current Issues in Language Planning [51750]
Current Issues in Tourism [51751]
Indonesia and the Malay World [51813]
International Journal of Bilingual Education & Bilingualism [51828]
International Journal of Language & Communication Disorders [51839]
The International Journal of Multilingualism [51841]
International Research in Geography & Environment Education [51850]
Japan Forum [51865]
Journal of Iberian & Latin American Studies [51906]
Journal of Multicultural Discourses [51922]
Journal of Multilingual & Multicultural Development [51923]
Journal of Quantitative Linguistics [51938]
Journal of Sustainable Tourism [51950]
Language Awareness [51962]
Language Culture & Curriculum [51963]
Language and Education [51964]
Language and Intercultural Communication [51965]
Perspectives [52008] .... (Combined) 4,500

Biggleswade
Journal of Greek Linguistics [52324]

Birmingham
Journal of Literary Semantics (JLS) [52347]
Language Issues [52357] 450

Bristol
NOMINA [52711]

Cambridge
German as a Foreign Language [52824]
Journal of Linguistics [52858] ....: 2,100

Coventry
Journal of Research in Reading [53087]

Edinburgh
Corpora [53266]
Journal of Arabic and Islamic Studies [53291]

Circulation: ★ = ABC; △ = BPA; ◆ = CAC; • = CCAB; ❏ = VAC; ⊕ = PO Statement; ‡ = Publisher's Report; Boldface figures = sworn; Light figures = estimated.

World Structure **[53324]**
Glasgow
SCROLL **[53451]**
Laurencekirk
Speech & Language Therapy in
   Practice **[53743]** .. ..., (Paid) 1,600
Leicester
Deutsch **[53795]** 2,500
English For to Eleven **[53797]**
Francophonie **[53801]** 5,500
Language Learning Journal
   [53809] 3,500
Rusistika **[53823]**
Tuttitalia **[53831]** 900
Use of English **[53832]**
Vida Hispanica **[53833]** 2,000
London
Annual Bibliography of English Lan-
   guage & Literature **[53951]**
Bulletin **[54155]** 11,500
Discourse & Society **[54330]**
Discourse Studies **[54331]**
Dutch Crossing **[54345]**
Gender and Language **[54498]**
International Journal of Speech, Lan-
   guage and the Law **[54662]**
Journal of Applied Linguistics **[54699]**
Language & History **[54851]**
Language and Literature **[54852]**
Language Teaching Research
   [54853] .... (Paid) 500
Linguistics and the Human Sciences
   [54874]
Literary and Linguistic Computing
   [54876]
Names **[54969]** .... (Paid) 850
Sociolinguistic Studies **[55253]**
Loughborough
Journal of Politeness Research
   [55483]
Manchester
Interpreter and Translator Trainer
   [55561]
Journal of Semitic Studies **[55566]**
Sign Language Translator &
   Interpreter **[55577]**
The Translator **[55580]**
Oxford
The Classical Quarterly **[55910]**
Communication Theory **[55913]**
International Journal of Lexicography
   [55998]
Journal of Semantics **[56071]**
Language & Communication **[56084]**
Mind & Language **[56101]**
The Modern Language Journal
   [56102] .. .. (Paid) 4,000
               (Controlled) ‡74
Saint Andrews
Forum for Modern Language Studies
   [56441]
Sheffield
Transactions of the Philological
   Society **[56516]**

PHILOSOPHY

AUSTRALIA
Hawthorn
Cosmos and History **[41942]**
Melbourne
Sophia **[42086]**
Sydney
Journal of Religious History **[42529]**
Scan **[42578]**

BELGIUM
Leuven
Bijdragen **[42892]**

BRAZIL
Belo Horizonte
Kriterion **[42949]**

CROATIA
Hrvatski Leskovac
Croatian Journal of Philosophy
   [43558]

FINLAND
Helsinki
Chabad-Lubavitch of Finland **[43823]**

FRANCE
Paris
Diogenes **[44037]**

GERMANY
Berlin
Archiv fur Geschichte der Philosophie
   [44154] 650
Jahrbuch fur Wissenschaft und Ethik
   [44199]
Kant-Studien **[44211]** 1000
Hannover
Studia Leibnitiana **[44435]**

INDIA
Chennai
Theosophist **[45059]** ... (Paid) 3,000
The Vedanta Kesari
   [45060] .. .. (Paid) 95,000
Vivekananda Kendra Patrika
   [45061] .. .. (Paid) 2,000
Mumbai
The Theosophical Movement
   [45447] .... (Paid) 380
                     (Non-paid) 380
New Delhi
Journal of Human Values
   [45598] .... (Paid) 600
Pondicherry
The Advent **[45690]** ..... (Paid) 1,000
Mother India **[45693]** ... (Paid) 1,050
Shillong
International Journal of Jurisprudence
   and Philosophy of Law **[45728]**

ISRAEL
Jerusalem
B'Or Ha'Torah **[46081]** 5,000

ITALY
Genoa
Epistemologia **[46148]**
Giornale di Metafisica **[46149]**
Nuova Corrente **[46152]**
Pisa
Bollettino Telematico di Filosofia
   Politica **[46218]**

JAPAN
Tokyo
Journal of Medicine & Philosophy
   [46926]

NETHERLANDS
Amsterdam
Contemporary Pragmatism **[47940]**
Grazer Philosophische Studien
   [48005]
Polish Analytical Philosophy **[48208]**
Pragmatics & Cognition **[48211]**
Dordrecht
Acta Biotheoretica **[48319]**

Biology and Philosophy **[48334]**
Frontiers of Philosophy in China
   [48403]
International Journal for Philosophy
   of Religion **[48429]**
Philosophical Studies **[48526]**
Studia Logica **[48569]**
Studies in Philosophy and Education
   [48570]
Synthese **[48575]**
Theoretical Medicine and Bioethics
   [48577]
Theory and Decision **[48578]**
Leiden
Grotiana **[48674]**
Hobbes Studies **[48676]**
International Journal of the Platonic
   Tradition **[48682]**
The Journal of Jewish Thought and
   Philosophy **[48699]**
Journal of Phenomenological
   Psychology **[48700]** ... .. (Paid) 350
Phronesis **[48716]**
Proceedings of the Boston Area Col-
   loquium in Ancient Philosophy
   [48717]
Research in Phenomenology
   [48721] .... (Paid) 200

POLAND
Krakow
Diametros **[49665]**

PORTUGAL
Lisbon
Disputatio **[49802]**

SLOVAKIA
Bratislava
Central-European Value Studies
   [50317]

**REPUBLIC OF SOUTH AF-
RICA**
Grahamstown
African Studies Monographs **[50491]**
Journal of Philosophy and Culture
   [50502]
Philosophical Papers **[50510]**
Pietermaritzburg
ESARBICA Journal **[50567]**
Indilinga **[50568]**

SPAIN
Madrid
La Balsa de la Medusa **[50777]**

SWITZERLAND
Geneva
The Ecumenical Review
   [51091] .. .. (Paid) ‡2,000
International Review of Mission
   [51149]

TAIWAN
Taipei
Journal of Social Sciences and
   Philosophy
   [51355] ... . (Paid) 1,000

UNITED KINGDOM
Abingdon
Asian Philosophy **[51707]**
Australasian Journal of Philosophy
   [51710] .... (Combined) 1,200
British Journal for the History of
   Philosophy **[51719]**
Critical Review of International Social
   and Political Philosophy **[51745]**

Ethics and Social Welfare **[51773]**
International Journal of Philosophical
   Studies **[51843]**
Journal of Moral Education **[51921]**
Mental Health, Religion and Culture
   [51977]
Mortality **[51987]**
Philosophical Explorations **[52010]**
Philosophical Psychology **[52011]**
Cambridge
The Journal of Ecclesiastical History
   [52849] 1,250
New Testament Studies
   [52877] 2,400
Studies in History and Philosophy of
   Science Part A **[52899]**
Studies in History and Philosophy of
   Science Part C **[52900]**
Colchester
Bulletin of Medical Ethics **[53031]**
Coventry
Journal of Research in Reading
   [53087]
East London
South African Journal of Philosophy
   [53237]
Edinburgh
New Blackfriars **[53303]**
Exeter
Collingwood and British Idealism
   Studies **[53348]**
Freeland
At the Interface/Probing the
   Boundaries **[53399]**
Liverpool
European Journal of Social Theory
   [53871]
London
Bulletin of the School of Oriental and
   African Studies **[54157]** 900
Clinical Ethics **[54220]**
Insight **[54607]**
Journal of Critical Realism **[54733]**
New Humanist
   [54991] .... (Combined) 5,000
Philosophy **[55081]** 2,000
Philosophy, Ethics, and Humanities in
   Medicine **[55082]**
Philosophy & Social Criticism **[55083]**
Politics, Philosophy & Economics
   [55100]
Proceedings of the Aristotelian
   Society **[55125]**
Religion **[55184]**
Religious Studies **[55186]** 1,200
Slovo **[55243]**
Thesis Eleven **[55310]**
Newport
Res Publica **[55689]**
Oxford
Dialectica **[55927]**
The Journal of Theological Studies
   [56075]
Metaphilosophy **[56097]**
Midwest Studies in Philosophy
   [56099]
Modern Theology **[56104]**
Pacific Philosophical Quarterly
   [56139]
Philosophia Mathematica **[56153]**
The Philosophical Forum **[56154]**
The Philosophical Quarterly **[56155]**
Zygon **[56231]**
Reading
Ratio **[56330]**
Utilitas **[56332]** 500
Swansea
Philosophical Investigations **[56705]**

Circulation: ★ = ABC; △ = BPA; ◆ = CAC; • = CCAB; ❑ = VAC; ⊕ = PO Statement; ‡ = Publisher's Report; Boldface figures = sworn; Light figures = estimated.

York
Mind [56994]

PHOTOGRAPHY
See also Motion Pictures

ARGENTINA
Buenos Aires
Fotomundo [41472] ..... (Paid) 8,000

PEOPLE'S REPUBLIC OF CHINA
Beijing
Chinese Photography
  [43188] .... (Paid) ⊕7,000
Shanghai
Shanghai Pictorial [43499]

FRANCE
Antibes
International Journal of Image and
  Video Processing (IJIVP) [43914]

INDIA
Mumbai
Better Photography [45356]
Photo Imaging [45431]

ITALY
Milan
Foto-Notiziario [46172] 12,500
Rodeo [46193]

NETHERLANDS
Enschede
International Journal of Applied Earth
  Observation and Geoinformation
  [48593]

NEW ZEALAND
Auckland
D-Photo [48790] 12,000

SPAIN
Barcelona
Dirigido [50663]
Historia National Geographic
  [50679] .. .. ‡142,798
Madrid
Academia [50722]
Album [50727]
ANIGP-TV [50728]
Foto Video [50759]
FV—Foto-Video Actualidad
  [50760] .... (Paid) 15,000
Visual [50815]

UNITED KINGDOM
Abingdon
History of Photography [51805]
Aylesbury
The Photographer [52148]
Bath
RPS Journal [52257] 10,500
Darlington
Master Photographers [53155]
Eastbourne
Lighting & Sound International
  [53244] .. .. (Combined) ★10,000
Hemel Hempstead
In Camera
  [53558] .. .. (Controlled) 65,000
Lewes
Black and White Photography
  [53847]

London
IMAGE [54583] 2,800
Luton
The Pantaneto Forum [55504]
Middlesex
Journal of 3-D Imaging
  [55619] .. ..:............ 750
Nottingham
International Journal of Remote
  Sensing [55763]

PHYSICAL EDUCATION AND ATHLETICS

AUSTRALIA
Port Macquarie
AusSport [42260] 20,000

PEOPLE'S REPUBLIC OF CHINA
Hong Kong
Asian Journal of Physical Education
  & Recreation [43278]
The Hong Kong Journal of Sports
  Medicine and Sports Science
  [43334]

ISRAEL
Wingate
European Review of Aging and
  Physical Activity [46115]

ITALY
Bologna
Il Nuovo Club
  [46127] .. .. (Controlled) 10,000

POLAND
Warsaw
Human Movement [49717]
Journal of Human Kinetics [49722]
Medicina Sportiva [49737]
Physical Education and Sport
  [49747]

REPUBLIC OF SOUTH AFRICA
Bedfordview
SA Journal of Sports Medicine
  [50352]
Stellenbosch
South African Journal for Research in
  Sport, Physical Education and
  Recreation [50635]

SWITZERLAND
Aarau
Fit for Life
  [51054] .. .., (Combined) ‡25,000

UNITED KINGDOM
Abingdon
International Journal of the History of
  Sport [51837]
Physical Education & Sport
  Pedagogy [52012]
Chester
European Physical Education Review
  [52994]
London
British Journal of Sports Medicine
  [54137] ....:.. ‡1,650
International Review for the Sociol-
  ogy of Sport [54669]
Profound (The Dialog Corporation) of
  the Royal Society A [55133]

PHYSICS
See also Nuclear Engineering; Science (General)

AUSTRALIA
Bundoora
Colloids and Surfaces A [41670]
Darwin
International Journal of Computa-
  tional Physical Sciences [41828]
Port Melbourne
Australian Physics [42262]

AUSTRIA
Vienna
INIS Database [42760]
Nuclear Fusion [42765]

BELGIUM
Heverlee
Physica A [42888]
Leuven
Microelectronic Engineering [42901]

BRAZIL
Petropolis
Computational & Applied
  Mathematics [42990]
Sao Carlos
Journal of Microwaves, Optoelectron-
  ics and Electromagnetic
  Applications [43018]
Sao Paulo
Brazilian Journal of Physics [43028]
Ecletica Quimica [43038]

BULGARIA
Ruse
Advanced Studies in Theoretical
  Physics [43087]
Sofia
Bulgarian Geophysical Journal
  [43096]

PEOPLE'S REPUBLIC OF CHINA
Beijing
Chinese Physics Letters [43189]
Communications in Theoretical
  Physics [43191]
International Review of Pure and Ap-
  plied Physics [43201]
Science in China Series G [43221]
Nanjing
Chinese Astronomy and Astrophysics
  [43453]
Shanghai
International Journal of Physical
  Sciences [43478]

COTE D'IVOIRE
Abidjan
Afrique Science [43555]

DENMARK
Copenhagen
Nuclear Instruments and Methods in
  Physics Research Section B
  [43680]
Lyngby
European Journal of Mechanics -
  A/Solids [43725]

EGYPT
Alexandria
International Journal of Pure and Ap-
  plied Physics [43749]

Cairo
International Journal of Photoenergy
  [43762]

FINLAND
Helsinki
Journal of Analysis and its
  Applications [43834]

FRANCE
Fontenay-aux-Roses
Radioprotection [43955]
Grenoble
Microelectronics Journal [43958]
Phase Transitions [43959]
Orsay
Annales Henri Poincare [44018]
Paris
Astronomy & Astrophysics [44027]
Europhysics News [44044] ... 25,000
Mathematische Zeitschrift [44069]
Toulouse
Annales de Physique [44118]
Villeurbanne
Mathematical Modelling of Natural
  Phenomena [44126]

GERMANY
Bayreuth
Physics and Chemistry of Minerals
  [44147]
Berlin
Crystal Research and Technology
  [44168]
Forum Mathematicum [44182] ... 300
Journal of Applied Crystallography
  [44202]
Journal of Non-Equilibrium
  Thermodynamics [44208] 200
Laser & Photonics Reviews [44216]
Duisburg
Mechanism and Machine Theory
  [44320]
Dusseldorf
European Physical Journal E. Soft
  Matter [44324]
Erlangen
Strahlentherapie und Onkologie
  [44342]
Freiburg
Renewable Energy Focus
  [44372] 86,140
Solar Energy Journal [44373]
Garching
Chemical Physics [44378]
physica status solidi (a) [44379]
physica status solidi (b) [44380]
physica status solidi (c) [44381]
Greifswald
Journal of Solid State
  Electrochemistry [44404]
Heidelberg
Applied Physics A [44440]
Karlsruhe
International Journal of Modern Phys-
  ics B [44493] .... (Paid) 300
Kassel
Heat and Mass Transfer [44497]
Katlenburg-Lindau
Living Reviews in Solar Physics
  [44500]
Mainz
Micron [44543]
Munich
Fortschritte der Physik/Progress of
  Physics [44561]

Radiation and Environmental
Biophysics **[44579]**

Potsdam
Biophysical Reviews and Letters
[44639]

Stuttgart
Nuclear Engineering and Design
[44674]
Solid State Ionics **[44679]**

Tubingen
Progress in Particle and Nuclear
Physics **[44693]**

Weinheim
Journal of Biophotonics **[44706]**

HUNGARY
Budapest
Acta Geodaetica et Geophysica
Hungarica **[44809]**
Studia Scientiarum Mathematicarum
Hungarica **[44876]**

ICELAND
Reykjavik
Chemistry and Physics of Lipids
[44899]

INDIA
Allahabad
JP Journal of Heat and Mass
Transfer **[44938]**
JP Journal of Solids and Structures
[44939]

Bangalore
Pramana - Journal of Physics
[44981]

Calcutta
Indian Journal of Physics, Part A
[45021] .... (Combined) ‡800

Jodhpur
Indian Journal of Pure & Applied
Physics **[45224]** 1,200

Mumbai
Journal of Medical Physics **[45402]**

New Delhi
Indian Journal of Radio & Space
Physics **[45566]**
Physics For You **[45636]**

INDONESIA
Tangerang
Physics Journal of the Indonesian
Physical Society **[45870]**

ISRAEL
Haifa
International Journal of Multiphase
Flow **[46076]**

ITALY
Frascati
The European Physical Journal
A-Hadrons and Nuclei **[46146]**

Trieste
Journal of Geometry and Physics
[46265]

JAPAN
Kyoto
Mathematics Applied in Science and
Technology **[46482]**
Progress of Theoretical Physics
[46483]
Progress of Theoretical Physics -
Supplement **[46484]**

Osaka
Applied Surface Science **[46615]**

Sendai
International Journal of Applied Electromagnetics and Mechanics
[46667]

Tokyo
Applied Magnetic Resonance **[46747]**
Astronomy and Astrophysics Review
[46756]
Calculus of Variations and Partial Dif-
ferential Equation **[46773]**
Calorimetry and Thermal Analysis
[46774]
Continuum Mechanics and
Thermodynamics **[46796]**
Electrical Engineering **[46808]**
Environmental Chemistry Letters
[46811]
Ionizing Radiation **[46850]**
Japanese Journal of Applied Physics
[46864] 3,900
Journal of Japan Biomagnetism and
Bioelectromagnetics Society
[46911]
Journal of Magnetics Society of
Japan **[46920]**
Journal of Nuclear Science and
Technology **[46930]** 1,500
Journal of Physical Society of Japan
[46937] .. .. (Paid) 4,000
Journal of Visualization **[46945]**
Optical Review **[47015]**
Refrigeration **[47031]** 10,000
The Rigaku Journal **[47032]**
Sensors and Materials **[47036]**

REPUBLIC OF KOREA
Seoul
Current Applied Physics **[47263]**

LITHUANIA
Vilnius
Lithuanian Journal of Physics **[47482]**

MALAYSIA
Kuala Lumpur
Malaysian Journal of Science Series
B: Physical & Earth Sciences
[47619]

MOROCCO
Rabat
African Journal of Mathematical
Physics **[47814]**

NETHERLANDS
Amsterdam
Advances in Colloid and Interface
Science **[47882]**
Advances in Space Research
[47883]
Annals of Physics **[47895]**
Archives of Biochemistry and
Biophysics **[47898]**
Atomic Data and Nuclear Data Tables
[47900]
Biochemical and Biophysical Re-
search Communications **[47905]**
Biochimica et Biophysica Acta (BBA)-
General Subjects **[47907]**
Biochimica et Biophysica Acta (BBA)-
Proteins & Proteomics **[47910]**
Bioelectrochemistry **[47911]**
Dyes and Pigments **[47960]**
Few-Body Systems **[47985]**
Journal of Alloys and Compounds
[48040]
Journal of Analytical and Applied
Pyrolysis **[48043]**

Journal of Applied Geophysics
[48046]
Journal of Applied Mathematics and
Mechanics **[48047]**
The Journal of Chemical
Thermodynamics **[48058]**
Journal of Colloid and Interface
Science **[48060]**
Journal of Computational Physics
[48064]
Journal of Integrated Design & Pro-
cess Science **[48086]**
Journal of Molecular Liquids **[48098]**
Journal of Molecular Spectroscopy
[48099]
Journal of Non-Newtonian Fluid
Mechanics **[48103]**
Journal of Proteomics **[48113]**
Journal of Sound and Vibration
[48117]
Materials Characterization **[48143]**
Materials Science and Engineering
[48144]
Materials Science and Engineering
[48145]
Materials Science and Engineering
[48146]
Materials Science in Semiconductor
Processing **[48147]**
Mechanics of Materials **[48150]**
Neural Networks **[48172]**
New Astronomy **[48180]**
New Astronomy Reviews **[48181]**
Nuclear Physics A **[48185]**
Nuclear Physics B **[48186]**
Nuclear Physics B **[48187]**
Physica B **[48200]**
Physica E **[48201]**
Physics Reports **[48203]**
Powder Technology **[48210]**
Radiation Physics and Chemistry
[48219]
Technology and Health Care **[48242]**
Thermochimica Acta **[48248]**

Bussum
Recent Patents on Nanotechnology
[48306]

Delft
Sensors and Actuators A **[48315]**
Spectrochimica Acta Part B **[48316]**

Dordrecht
Biologia Plantarum **[48333]**
Celestial Mechanics & Dynamical
Astronomy **[48346]**
Food Biophysics **[48389]**
Frontiers of Physics in China **[48404]**
Hyperfine Interactions **[48420]**
Journal of Fusion Energy **[48460]**
Journal of Low Temperature Physics
[48470]
Journal of Statistical Physics **[48493]**
Mathematical Physics, Analysis and
Geometry **[48513]**
Solar Physics **[48564]**

Leiden
Journal of Electromagnetic Waves
and Applications **[48695]**

NEW ZEALAND
Wellington
Tectonophysics **[49035]**

NIGERIA
Akure
Nigeria Journal of Pure and Applied
Physics **[49060]**

Benin City
Journal of the Nigerian Association of
Mathematical Physics **[49065]**

Calabar
Global Journal of Pure and Applied
Sciences **[49075]**

NORWAY
Oslo
Microporous and Mesoporous
Materials **[49203]**

PAKISTAN
Faisalabad
Journal of Applied Sciences **[49261]**

POLAND
Krakow
Acta Physica Polonica B **[49664]**

Warsaw
Acta Geophysica **[49679]**
Central European Journal of Physics
[49702]
Latvian Journal of Physics and Tech-
nical Sciences **[49730]**
Nukleonika **[49739]**
Old and New Concepts of Physics
[49741]
Polish Journal of Medical Physics
and Engineering **[49749]**

PORTUGAL
Aveiro
International Journal of Molecular
Engineering **[49788]**

ROMANIA
Bucharest
Balkan Journal of Geometry and its
Applications **[49832]**

RUSSIA
Moscow
Bulletin of the Crimean Astrophysical
Observatory **[49885]**
Doklady Biochemistry and Biophysics
[49894]
Doklady Physics **[49900]**
Geomagnetism and Aeronomy
[49908]
High Temperature **[49914]**
Integral Transforms and Special
Functions **[49920]**
Izvestiya, Physics of the Solid Earth
[49925]
Journal of Advances in Chemical
Physics **[49926]**
Laser Physics **[49935]**
Physics of Atomic Nuclei **[49956]**
Physics of Particles and Nuclei
Letters **[49957]**
Plasma Physics Reports **[49959]**

Novosibirsk
Applied Physics B **[50009]**
Thermophysics and Aeromechanics
[50015]

Saint Petersburg
Physics of the Solid State **[50024]**

SERBIA
Nis
Microelectronics Reliability **[50091]**

SINGAPORE
Singapore
International Journal of Geometric
Methods in Modern Physics
(IJGMMP) **[50180]**
International Journal of Modern Phys-
ics A **[50185]** .... (Paid) 500
International Journal of Modern Phys-
ics C **[50186]**
International Journal of Modern Phys-
ics D **[50187]**
Organic Electronics **[50233]**

Circulation: ★ = ABC; △ = BPA; ◆ = CAC; • = CCAB; ❏ = VAC; ⊕ = PO Statement; ‡ = Publisher's Report; Boldface figures = sworn; Light figures = estimated.

Physics of Life Reviews [50239]
Reviews in Mathematical Physics
   [50246] .... (Paid) 150
Singapore Journal of Physics [50257]

SLOVAKIA
Bratislava
Acta Physica Slovaca [50315]

REPUBLIC OF SOUTH AFRICA
Grahamstown
Nigerian Journal of Physics [50507]

SPAIN
Toledo
Physical Chemistry [50840]

SRI LANKA
Colombo
Journal of Physics [50858]
Physical Biology [50862]
Sri Lankan Journal of Physics
   [50870]

SWEDEN
Lulea
Flow Measurement and
   Instrumentation [50981]
Journal of Nonlinear Mathematical
   Physics [50982]
Stockholm
MEDSOLS [51025] ..... (Paid) 2,000
Nordic Journal of Building Physics
   [51027]

SWITZERLAND
Basel
International Journal of Molecular
   Sciences [51062]
Geneva
International Journal of Exergy
   [51120]
Zurich
Journal of Applied Mathematics and
   Physics (ZAMP) [51269]

TAIWAN
Tainan
Materials Chemistry and Physics
   [51327]
Taipei
Chinese Journal of Physics [51335]

TURKEY
Ankara
Photonics and Nanostructures
   [51499]
Turkish Journal of Physics [51515]

UKRAINE
Kharkov
Fizika Nizkikh Temperatur [51592]
Kiev
Fizika Soznaniya i Zhyzni, Kos-
   mologiya i Astrofizika (Physics of
   Consciousness and Life, Cosmol-
   ogy and Astrophysics) [51596]
Random Operators and Stochastic
   Equations [51607] .... ‡140

UNITED ARAB EMIRATES
Abu Dhabi
Electronic Journal of Theoretical
   Physics [51619]

UNITED KINGDOM
Abingdon
International Journal of Neuroscience
   [51842]

Journal of Experimental Nanoscience
   [51897]
Pedagogy, Culture and Society
   [52005]

Birmingham
International Journal for Numerical
   Methods in Fluids [52344]
Progress in Nuclear Energy [52362]

Brentwood
Noise & Vibration Worldwide
   [52585] .... (Paid) 750

Bristol
CERN Courier [52651]
Chinese Journal of Chemical Physics
   [52652]
Classical and Quantum Gravity
   [52653]
European Journal of Physics [52665]
Europhysics Letters (EPL) [52666]
Journal of Cellular Automata [52683]
Journal of Geophysics and
   Engineering [52686]
Journal of Instrumentation [52687]
Journal of Micromechanics and
   Microengineering [52689]
Journal of Optics [52693]
Journal of Physics A [52694]
Journal of Physics D [52695]
Journal of Radiological Protection
   [52697]
Journal of Statistical Mechanics
   [52699]
Modelling and Simulation in Materials
   Science and Engineering [52707]
Nanotechnology [52708]
New Journal of Physics (NJP)
   [52710]
Nonlinearity [52712]
Physica Scripta [52716]
Physics in Medicine and Biology
   [52717]
Physiological Measurement [52718]
Plasma Physics and Controlled
   Fusion [52720]
Plasma Sources Science and
   Technology [52721]
Reports on Progress in Physics
   [52725]
Research in Astronomy and
   Astrophysics [52727]
Smart Materials and Structures
   [52731]

Cambridge
CrystEngComm [52813]
Faraday Discussions [52819]
Physical Chemistry, Chemical
   Physics [52883]

Chester
Acta Crystallographica Section A
   [52991]
Synchrotron Radiation [53000]

Durham
International Reviews in Physical
   Chemistry [53229]

London
Contemporary Physics [54263]
Energy World
   [54371] .... (Paid) 4,500
High Temperatures-High Pressures
   [54551]
Inverse Problems [54677]
Journal of High Energy Physics
   [54762]
Journal of Nanobiotechnology
   [54783]
Journal of Physics B [54799]
Journal of Physics C [54800]
Journal of Physics G [54801]
Materials Science and Technology
   [54913]

Nature Physics [54974]
Physics Education [55086]
Physics World [55087] .. .. ★34,495
Semiconductor Science and
   Technology [55228]
Superconductor Science and
   Technology [55278]

Middlesex
International Journal of Dynamics of
   Fluids (IJDF) [55618]

Nottingham
Journal of Molecular Graphics and
   Modeling [55764]

Oxford
Acta Biochimica et Biophysica Sinica
   [55859]
Archive for Rational Mechanics and
   Analysis [55872]
Chemical Physics Letters [55906]
infocus Magazine [55989]
Photodermatology, Photoimmunology
   and Photomedicine [56156]

Sheffield
Physics & Chemistry of Glasses
   [56510] .... (Paid) 725

York
Medical Engineering and Physics
   [56993]
Scope [56998] 2,400

PHYSIOLOGY AND ANATOMY
See also Biology; Zoology

AUSTRALIA
Canberra
International Journal of Sports Physi-
   ology and Performance [41708]
Collingwood
Reproduction, Fertility and
   Development [41796]
South Bank
Australian Voice [42364]

BELGIUM
Ghent
Nephrology Dialysis Transplantation
   [42887]

BRAZIL
Pelotas
Brazilian Journal of Plant Physiology
   [42989]
Sao Paulo
Papeis Avulsos de Zoologia (Sao
   Paulo) [43043]

CZECH REPUBLIC
Ceske Budejovice
Folia Parasitologica [43605]
Prague
Czech Gynaecology [43616]
Czech and Slovak Neurology and
   Neurosurgery [43618]
Czecho-Slovak Dermatology [43622]
Otorhinolaryngology and Phoniatrics
   [43632]

ESTONIA
Tartu
Agronomy Research [43791]

FRANCE
Dijon
Behavioural Processes [43943]

Mycorrhiza [43945]
Gif-sur-Yvette
Journal of Physiology - Paris [43956]
Montrouge
Hepato-Gastro [43992]
Medecine therapeutique cardiologie
   [43998]
Medecine therapeutique/Endocrinologie
   [43999]
Medecine Therapeutique/medecine
   de la reproduction [44000]
MT Cardio [44002]
Sang Thrombose Vaisseaux [44006]
Paris
Adansonia [44022]

GERMANY
Bochum
Respiratory Physiology &
   Neurobiology [44252]
Dusseldorf
Behavioural Brain Research [44321]
Frankfurt
Herzschrittmachertherapie &
   Elektrophysiologie [44361]
Heidelberg
European Spine Journal [44456]
Pflugers Archiv [44472]
Jena
Journal of Cancer Research and
   Clinical Oncology [44490]
Kiel
Marine Biology [44505]
Magdeburg
Restorative Neurology and
   Neuroscience [44536]
Marburg
Journal of Comparative Physiology B
   [44548]
Munich
Anatomia, Histologia, Embryologia
   [44549]

HUNGARY
Budapest
Acta Physiologica Hungarica [44817]

INDIA
Jodhpur
Advances in Plant Physiology
   [45213]
Mumbai
Indian Journal of Gastroenterology
   [45380] ....: 1,200
Journal of Family Welfare
   [45399] .. .. (Paid) 1,500
The Journal of Obstetrics and Gynae-
   cology of India
   [45404] .. .. (Paid) 18,200
New Delhi
Neurology India
   [45630] .. .. (Paid) 1,600

IRAN
Tehran
Iranian Biomedical Journal [45895]

ISRAEL
Jerusalem
Journal of Basic & Clinical Physiology
   & Pharmacology [46087]
Tel Aviv
Isokinetics and Exercise Science
   [46106]

Trade, Technical, and Professional Publications

ITALY

Arcavacata di Rende
International Journal of Artificial
Organs [46120] 3,000

Ischia Porto
Marine Ecology [46156]

Milan
L'Endocrinologo [46167]
Il Cardiologo [46173]
Il Ginecologo [46174]
Ipertensione [46178]
Journal of Endocrinological
Investigation [46182]
Obesity and Metabolism [46188]
Urodinamica [46198]

Modena
Invertebrate Survival Journal (ISJ)
[46199]

Rome
Experimental Brain Research [46228]

Siena
Clinical Hemorheology and
Microcirculation [46258]

JAPAN

Kochi
Phycological Research [46436]

Tokyo
Japanese Journal of Physiology
[46874] .... (Paid) 1,600
Journal of Molecular Medicine
[46928]
Modern Rheumatology [46970]

NETHERLANDS

Amsterdam
Acta Tropica [47880]
Biochimica et Biophysica Acta (BBA)
[47906]
Biochimica et Biophysica Acta (BBA)-
Molecular Basis of Disease [47908]
Biochimica et Biophysica Acta (BBA)-
Molecular and Cell Biology of
Lipids [47909]
Biochimica et Biophysica Acta (BBA)-
Proteins & Proteomics [47910]
Brain Research Bulletin [47914]
Human Movement Science [48014]
Journal of Arid Environments [48049]
Journal of Autoimmunity [48053]
Journal of Vestibular Research
[48127]
Methods [48156]
Microbes and Infection [48157]
Microbial Pathogenesis [48158]
Molecular Aspects of Medicine
[48162]
Plant Physiology and Biochemistry
[48205]
Trends in Cognitive Sciences [48260]
Trends in Neurosciences [48265]

Dordrecht
Documenta Ophthalmologica [48377]
Journal of Bamboo and Rattan
[48442]
Journal of Computational
Neuroscience [48451]
Sport Sciences for Health [48567]

Leiden
Crustaceana [48665]

Maastricht
Journal of Chemical Neuroanatomy
[48738]

NIGERIA

Calabar
Nigerian Journal of Physiological
Sciences [49079]

Uturu
Journal of Experimental and Clinical
Anatomy [49176]

PAKISTAN

Faisalabad
Asian Journal of Cell Biology [49235]
Research Journal of Cell and Mo-
lecular Biology [49286]

Karachi
Pakistan Journal of Pathology
[49370]

POLAND

Bydgoszcz
Acta Angiologica [49652]

Gdansk
Endocrinology, Obesity and Metabolic
Disorders [49656]

Lodz
Cardiovascular Forum [49669]

Warsaw
Acta Biochimica Polonica [49678]
Acta Protozoologica [49682]
Biomedical Human Kinetics [49697]
Human Movement [49717]
Journal of Human Kinetics [49722]
Polish Sexology [49755]

Zabrze
Polish Journal of Endocrinology
[49783]

PORTUGAL

Lisbon
Acta Ethologica [49801]

RUSSIA

Moscow
Human Physiology [49915]
Journal of Neurosurgical Problems
[49930]
Obstetrics & Gynaecology [49948]
Pathological Physiology & Experi-
mental Therapy [49951]
Problems of Endocrinology [49963]
Russian Journal of Skin and Sexually
Transmitted Diseases [49981]
Therapeutic Archives [49995]
Thoracic & Cardiovascular Surgery
[49997]

Saint Petersburg
Journal of Evolutionary Biochemistry
and Physiology [50023]

REPUBLIC OF SOUTH AFRICA

Pietermaritzburg
African Zoology [50566]

SPAIN

Barcelona
Cirugia Cardiovascular [50656]
Hepatology Reviews [50677]
Trends in Transplantation [50703]

SWEDEN

Malmo
Clinical Physiology and Functional
Imaging [50991]

Stockholm
Advances in Physiotherapy [51003]

TURKEY

Ankara
Neuroanatomy [51498]

UNITED KINGDOM

Abingdon
Connective Tissue Research [51741]

International Journal of Neuroscience
[51842]
Journal of Organ Dysfunctions
[51927]
Mitochondrial DNA [51983]
Scandinavian Journal of Clinical and
Laboratory Investigation [52047]

Bristol
Journal of Neural Engineering
[52692]

Cambridge
Comparative Exercise Physiology
[52808]
Neuron Glia Biology [52874]

Cardiff
Journal of Medical Engineering and
Technology [52934]
Journal of Neuroscience Methods
[52935]

Childerley
Molecular Human Reproduction
[53019]

Durham
Journal of Thermal Biology [53230]

London
Advances in Osteoporotic Fracture
Management [53906]
Advances in Sepsis [53908]
BMC Physiology [54084]
British Journal of Cardiac Nursing
[54115]
British Journal of Dermatology
Nursing [54119]
Cardiology International [54176]
Cell Communication and Signaling
[54190]
CytoJournal [54307]
Dermatology in Practice [54320]
Gastrointestinal Nursing [54496]
International Journal of Adipose
Tissue [54630]
Journal of Bodywork and Movement
Therapies [54708]
Journal of Neuroinflammation [54786]
The Journal of Physiology [54802]
Lung Cancer in Practice [54893]
Microbial Cell Factories [54929]
Molecular and Cellular Endocrinology
[54946]
Molecular Pain [54947]
Prostate Cancer and Prostatic
Diseases [55144]
Pulmonary Pharmacology and
Therapeutics [55155]
Respiratory Disease in Practice
[55193]
Thrombus [55317]

Oxford
Acta Histochemica [55860]
Annals of Anatomy [55868]
Insect Science [55990]
Pigment Cell and Melanoma
Research [56158]
Plant Species Biology [56161]
Transplant International [56222]

Wallingford
Animal Health Research Reviews
[56815]

PLASTIC AND COMPOSITION MATERIALS
See also Chemistry, Chemicals, and Chemical Engineering

ARGENTINA

Buenos Aires
Plasticos [41478] 5,000

AUSTRALIA

Southbank
Plastics News International
[42380] .... (Paid) ♦4,500
(Non-paid) ♦4,500

BRAZIL

Sao Paulo
Plastico Industrial
[43044] .... (Non-paid) 12,000

INDIA

Ahmedabad
Texincon [44910] .. .. (Paid) 1,000

Mumbai
Modern Plastics & Polymers [45419]

NETHERLANDS

Amsterdam
Materials Science and Engineering
[48146]

Leiden
Advanced Composite Materials
[48641]

RUSSIA

Saint Petersburg
Reviews on Advanced Materials
Science [50025]

SINGAPORE

Singapore
Plastics & Rubber Singapore Journal
[50241]

SPAIN

Madrid
Plasticulture Journal [50789]

TAIWAN

Tainan
Materials Chemistry and Physics
[51327]

UNITED KINGDOM

Abingdon
Toxic Substance Mechanisms
[52083]

Berkshire
Plastiquarian [52316]

Kidlington
Reinforced Plastics
[53705] .. .. (Controlled) △15,000

London
Asia Pacific Coatings Journal
[53971] 5,960
Journal of Bioactive and Compatible
Polymers [54704] 180
Journal of Biomaterials Applications
[54707] 160
Journal of Building Physics
[54716] .... ‡200
Journal of Cellular Plastics
[54720] .... ‡340
Journal of Composite Materials
[54728] 800
Journal of Elastomers and Plastics
[54742] .... ‡275
Journal of Intelligent Material Sys-
tems and Structures
[54770] 300
Journal of Plastic Film and Sheeting
[54803] 300
Journal of Reinforced Plastics and
Composites [54807] 320

Circulation: ★ = ABC; △ = BPA; ♦ = CAC; • = CCAB; ❑ = VAC; ⊕ = PO Statement; ‡ = Publisher's Report; Boldface figures = sworn; Light figures = estimated.

Journal of Thermoplastic Composite
Materials **[54829]** 200
Materials World **[54914]** 34,000
Process Engineering
[55126] .... (Controlled) 30,466
Urethanes Technology
[55362] .... (Controlled) 5,381

Loughborough
Thin-Walled Structures **[55488]**

Sutton
ACN: Asian Chemical News **[56678]**

PLUMBING AND HEATING
See also Air Conditioning and Refrigeration

DENMARK
Glostrup
HVAC Magasinet **[43705]** .... ‡350

ITALY
Milan
CDA **[46164]** .... (Controlled) ★**3,800**

NORWAY
Jar
Kulde Skandinavia
[49192] .... (Controlled) 3,550

UNITED KINGDOM
Flitwick
Plumbing, Heating & Air Movement News
[53391] .... (Combined) ★**27,962**

Sevenoaks
Heating & Plumbing Monthly
[56474] .... ★**30,214**
Who's Who in Heating & Plumbing **[56484]**

Wadhurst
Construction Europe
[56805] .... ★**14,624**

Watford
Professional Heating & Plumbing Installer **[56873]** .... ★**56,067**

PODIATRY

UNITED KINGDOM
Southport
Podiatry Review
[56588] .... (Controlled) 2,500

POLICE, PENOLOGY, AND PENAL INSTITUTIONS
See also Safety

FINLAND
Kuvalehdet
Alibi **[43878]** ..... (Combined) 37,103

INDIA
Lucknow
Supreme Court Cases (Criminal)
[45327] .... (Paid) 3,000

Nagpur
Criminal Law Journal
[45465] 16,800

NETHERLANDS
Dordrecht
European Journal on Criminal Policy and Research **[48382]**

Journal of Experimental Criminology **[48458]**

REPUBLIC OF SOUTH AFRICA
Cape Town
SA Crime Quarterly **[50407]**

Pretoria
Servamus **[50600]** ..... (Paid) 30,000

UNITED KINGDOM
Abingdon
International Journal of Prisoner Health **[51844]**
Justice Quarterly **[51960]**
Police Practice and Research **[52015]**
Policing and Society **[52016]**

Belfast
The Chronicle **[52281]**

Bradford
Journal of Money Laundering Control **[52510]**
Policing **[52538]**

Coulsdon
Jane's Police Review **[53072]**

Isle of Man
The Police Journal **[53664]**

Leatherhead
Police
[53753] .... (Controlled) 42,000

London
Criminology & Criminal Justice **[54286]**
Punishment & Society **[55157]**
Theoretical Criminology **[55307]**

POLITICAL SCIENCE

AUSTRALIA
Carlton
Melbourne Journal of Politics **[41728]**

Melbourne
Arena Magazine **[42046]** 1,800

Sydney
Journal of Australian Political Economy **[42526]**

AUSTRIA
Vienna
Wirschaft und Gesellschaft.
[42774] .... (Combined) 900

BRAZIL
Sao Paulo
Sao Paulo em Perspectiva **[43051]**

CYPRUS
Nicosia
POLIS **[43597]**

CZECH REPUBLIC
Brno
Central European Political Studies Review **[43603]**

FRANCE
Villejuif
Sciences Sociales et Sante **[44125]**

HUNGARY
Budapest
Southeast European Politics **[44871]**
Southeast European Politics Online **[44872]**

Tarsadalom es Gazdasag (Society and Economy) **[44879]**

INDIA
Meerut
Indian Journal of Political Science
[45345] 500

New Delhi
Africa Quarterly
[45478] .... (Paid) 1,900
ICSSR Journal of Abstracts and Reviews **[45526]** .... (Paid) 550
Social Welfare
[45651] .... (Paid) 3,000

INDONESIA
Jakarta
Indonesian Quarterly
[45800] .... (Paid) 3,000

IRELAND
Dublin
French Politics **[45961]**

JAPAN
Tokyo
Cambridge Journal of Regions, Economy & Society **[46775]**

REPUBLIC OF KOREA
Seoul
Asian Perspective
[47257] .... (Paid) 2,300

MALAYSIA
Kuala Lumpur
Rocket **[47633]**
Show Daily **[47635]**

NETHERLANDS
Amsterdam
The Journal of Socio-Economics **[48116]**

Dordrecht
Dialectical Anthropology **[48373]**
Policy Sciences **[48538]**
Public Choice **[48542]**

The Hague
Democraat
[48612] .... (Non-paid) 12,500

NEW ZEALAND
Wellington
Social Policy Journal of New Zealand **[49034]**

NIGERIA
Lagos
African Journal of Political Science & International Relations **[49135]**

NORWAY
Oslo
Liberalt Forum **[49201]**

PHILIPPINES
Quezon City
Philippine Journal of Public Administration
[49607] .... (Paid) 1,000

SINGAPORE
Pasir Panjang
Contemporary Southeast Asia
[50099] .... (Paid) 800

Singapore
Regional Outlook **[50243]**

Southeast Asian Affairs **[50270]**

SLOVAKIA
Bratislava
Central-European Value Studies **[50317]**

REPUBLIC OF SOUTH AFRICA
Johannesburg
Journal of African Elections **[50530]**

SPAIN
Madrid
Papeles de la FIM (Fundacion de Investigaciones Marxistas) **[50787]**

SRI LANKA
Colombo
Sri Lanka Journal of International Law **[50866]**

Kandy
Identity Culture and Politics **[50907]**
Nethra **[50908]**

SWEDEN
Stockholm
Social Politics **[51039]**

SWITZERLAND
Zurich
Schweizer Monatshefte fur Politik, Wirtschaft und Kultur
[51281] .... (Combined) 3,000

TAIWAN
Taipei
Soochow Journal of Political Science **[51359]**

THAILAND
Bangkok
The Nation **[51428]**

TURKEY
Istanbul
Marmara Journal of European Studies **[51560]** .. .. (Paid) 1,000

UNITED KINGDOM
Abingdon
Australian Journal of Political Science **[51715]**
Democratization **[51754]**
Geopolitics **[51794]**
India Review **[51812]**
Journal of Civil Society **[51875]**
Journal of Elections, Public Opinion & Parties **[51893]**
Journal of Intervention and Statebuilding **[51911]**
Journal of Political Ideologies **[51933]**
Nationalities Papers **[51990]**
New Political Economy **[51993]**
New Political Science **[51994]**
Political Communication **[52018]**
Postcolonial Studies **[52021]**
Socialism and Democracy **[52061]**
West European Politics **[52090]**

Basingstoke
European Political Science **[52202]**

Brighton
German Politics **[52608]**

Cambridge
British Journal of Political Science
[52796] 1,350

Circulation: ★ = ABC; △ = BPA; ◆ = CAC; • = CCAB; ❑ = VAC; ⊕ = PO Statement; ‡ = Publisher's Report; Boldface figures = sworn; Light figures = estimated.

Contemporary European History
[52811] 650

Glasgow
The Firm [53418]
Politics [53440]

London
Commonwealth Judicial Journal
[54241]
Constitutional and Parliamentary
Information [54260]
The International Political Science
Review/Revue internationale de
science politique [54667]
Millennium [54934] .... (Paid) ‡1,000
New Left Review
[54993] .... (Combined) ‡7,500
New Statesman [54999] 25,000
Party Politics [55060]
Socialist Review [55250]
Survival [55283]
The World Today [55426] 7,500

Northampton
Journal for Critical Education Policy
Studies [55711]

Nottingham
The British Journal of Politics and
International Relations [55750]

Oxford
International Studies Quarterly
[56007]
The Journal of Political Philosophy
[56061]
Journal of Public Administration Re-
search and Theory [56062]
New Perspectives Quarterly [56118]
Political Analysis [56164]
The Political Quarterly [56165]
Political Studies [56166]
Political Studies Review [56167]
Scandinavian Political Studies
[56200]

Reading
Electronic Journal of e-Government
[56313]

Sheffield
Political Studies [56512]

POLITICS
**See also Congressional and
Federal Government Affairs**

AUSTRALIA
Clayton
Australian and New Zealand Journal
of Criminology [41757]

Cleveland
Bayside Bulletin [41766]
The Redland Times [41769]

Collingwood
Quarterly Essay [41795]

Goodwood
Australian Options [41903]

Nundah
Council Leader [42221] 3125

South Melbourne
Political Crossroads [42375]

Surry Hills
The Australian Marxist Review
[42414]

AUSTRIA
Vienna
Stichproben - Wiener Zeitschrift fur
Kritische Afrikastudien [42768]

PEOPLE'S REPUBLIC OF
CHINA
Hong Kong
Asian Affairs [43273]

Human Rights Solidarity [43347]

CZECH REPUBLIC
Brno
Central European Political Studies
Review [43603]

Prague
Mezinarodni Politika International
Politics [43629] 3,500
Transitions Online (TOL)
[43639] 200,000

FRANCE
Paris
The Tocqueville Review/La Revue
Tocqueville
[44085] .... (Combined) 500

GERMANY
Bonn
Frau und Politik [44261]
TECNOLOGIA MILITAR
[44271] 10,000

Konstanz
European Union Politics [44512]

Leinfelden-Echterdingen
DAMALS [44518] 32,799

Oldendorf
Ethics in Science and Environmental
Politics [44628]

GUYANA
Georgetown
Dayclean [44800] 5,000
Thunder [44801]

INDIA
Chennai
Frontline [45032] .... (Paid) 62,348

Delhi
Tibetan Review
[45107] .... (Paid) 4,500

New Delhi
Indian Journal of Human Rights and
Justice [45556]
Indian Journal of Human Rights and
the Law [45557]

Pondicherry
Mother India [45693] ... (Paid) 1,050

JAPAN
Tokyo
Japan Echo [46855]
Nikkei BP Government Technology
[46980] 11,100

NETHERLANDS
Amsterdam
Acta Politica [47878]
Journal of Language & Politics
[48090]
Zuidelyk Afrika
[48274] .... (Paid) 2,500

The Hague
Democraat
[48612] .... (Non-paid) 12,500

NEW ZEALAND
Auckland
New Zealand Doctor [48809]

Christchurch
The Guardian [48867] 2,500

NORWAY
Oslo
Liberalt Forum [49201]

POLAND
Warsaw
Baltic Journal of Law & Politics
[49695]
Przekroj [49759] .... ‡68,815

SLOVENIA
Ljubljana
Mladina Magazine
[50340] .... (Paid) 80,000

REPUBLIC OF SOUTH AF-
RICA
Claremont
African Human Rights Law Journal
[50460]

Grahamstown
African Studies Monographs [50491]

Johannesburg
Umsebenzi [50538]

Pretoria
Africa Insight [50581]
Africa Institute Occasional Papers
[50582]

SPAIN
Barcelona
Afers Internacionals [50647]
El Jueves [50669] .... ‡74,441
Europa de les Nacions [50673]

Madrid
Claves de Razon Practica [50735]
Leviatan [50778]
Nueva Revista [50786]
Papeles de la FIM (Fundacion de
Investigaciones Marxistas) [50787]
Politica Exterior [50790]
Revista Hispano Cubana HC [50798]
Sintesis [50806]
Temas para el Debate [50809]
Utopias/Nuestra Bandera [50813]
Zona Abierta [50817]

Mataro
El Viejo Topo [50819]

Santiago de Compostela
A Trabe de Ouro [50832]

SRI LANKA
Panadura
Losetha [50922] 2,000

SWEDEN
Stockholm
Contra [51013] .. .. (Paid) 1,500

SWITZERLAND
Bern
SVPja [51078]

TURKEY
Ankara
Karinca [51496] 3,500

UGANDA
Kampala
Mtafiti Mwafrika [51588]

UKRAINE
Kiev
Novynar
[51603] .. .. (Combined) 150,000

UNITED KINGDOM
Abingdon
Central Asian Survey [51726]

Citizenship Studies [51730]
Commonwealth & Comparative
Politics [51733]
Critical Review of International Social
and Political Philosophy [51745]
Democratization [51754]
Development Southern Africa [51756]
Ethnopolitics [51777]
India Review [51812]
Intelligence & National Security
[51820]
The International Spectator [51855]
Interventions [51857]
Irish Political Studies [51859]
Japanese Studies [51866]
The Journal of Communist Studies
and Transition Politics [51877]
Journal of Contemporary China
[51879]
Journal of Contemporary European
Studies [51880]
Journal of Elections, Public Opinion &
Parties [51893]
Journal of Political Ideologies [51933]
Media History [51972]
Mediterranean Politics [51976]
Middle Eastern Studies [51980]
Nationalism & Ethnic Politics [51989]
New Political Science [51994]
The Pacific Review [52003]
Perspectives on European Politics
and Society [52009]
Politikon [52019]
Review of African Political Economy
[52040]
Review of International Political
Economy [52042]
Review of Political Economy [52043]
Terrorism and Political Violence
[52075]
Textual Practice [52076]
Totalitarian Movements and Political
Religions [52080]

Basingstoke
British Politics [52197]
Subjectivity [52231] 400

Bishop's Stortford
Monarchy [52381] 4,000

Bognor Regis
Psychotherapy and Politics
International [52403]

Brighton
German Politics [52608]

Bristol
Policy and Politics [52722]

Caerfyrddin
Cambria [52781]

Coventry
Community Development Journal
[53080]

Edinburgh
Derrida Today [53269]

Exeter
History of Political Thought [53360]

Glasgow
Information Polity [53423]
Politics [53440]

Hull
Lobster [53627]

Leeds
Tangentium [53775]

Leicester
European Foreign Affairs Review
[53799]

Liverpool
European Journal of Social Theory
[53871]

Circulation: ★ = ABC; △ = BPA; ◆ = CAC; ● = CCAB; ❑ = VAC; ⊕ = PO Statement; ‡ = Publisher's Report; Boldface figures = sworn; Light figures = estimated.

6236

Gale Directory of Publications & Broadcast Media/147th Ed.

Open Government **[53877]**

London
African Affairs **[53918]**
African Renaissance **[53924]**
Bosnia Report **[54100]**
Commonwealth Judicial Journal
   [54241]
Competition & Change **[54252]**
Constitutional and Parliamentary
   Information **[54260]**
Cooperation and Conflict **[54266]**
The Democrat
   [54316] .... (Paid) 1,000
Discourse & Society **[54330]**
Economic and Industrial Democracy
   [54350]
The Ends Report **[54369]**
European Journal of Industrial
   Relations **[54400]**
European Journal of International
   Relations **[54401]**
The European Journal of Women's
   Studies **[54407]**
European Urban and Regional
   Studies **[54411]**
Feminist Theory **[54448]**
Human Relations **[54578]**
Index on Censorship
   [54594] .... (Combined) 10,000
International Journal of Electronic
   Democracy **[54646]**
International Journal of Media and
   Cultural Politics **[54654]**
International Review of Administrative
   Sciences **[54668]**
Journal of Theoretical Politics
   [54828]
Labour History Review
   [54848] 1,000
Land & Liberty
   [54849] .... (Controlled) 1,000
Liberal Matters **[54867]** 2,000
Liberator **[54868]**
Mediactive **[54922]**
New Left Review
   [54993] .... (Combined) ‡7,500
The Parliamentarian
   [55057] .... (Combined) 15,500
Parliamentary Brief
   [55058] .... (Controlled) 2,500
Party Politics **[55060]**
Political Theology **[55099]**
Politics, Philosophy & Economics
   [55100]
Race & Class **[55168]**
red pepper **[55178]**
Review of Nigeria Affairs **[55199]**
Security Dialogue **[55226]**
Slavonica **[55242]** 200
Slovo **[55243]**
Socialist Review **[55250]**
Socialist Standard **[55251]**

Loughton
Government Business **[55490]**

Manchester
Constitutional Political Economy
   [55549]

Oxford
Contemporary Review **[55916]**
Cultural Politics **[55920]**
The Journal of Political Philosophy
   [56061]
Oxford Development Studies **[56132]**
Publius **[56179]** .... (Paid) ‡1,200
                (Non-paid) ‡100

Sheffield
Comparative European Politics
   [56489]

Surrey
Parliaments, Estates and
   Representation **[56671]**

Swindon
Fourth World Review **[56711]**

Uxbridge
Transforming Government **[56801]**

POSTAL AND SHIPPING SUPPLIES

ITALY
L'Aquila
International Journal of Management
   and Network Economics **[46119]**

NORWAY
Oslo
Posthornet
   [49206] .... (Non-paid) 31,000

POULTRY PRODUCTS AND SUPPLIES

JAPAN
Tokyo
Animal Science Journal
   [46735] .... (Paid) 3,000

NIGERIA
Owerri
Animal Production Research
   Advances **[49161]**

PAKISTAN
Faisalabad
Research Journal of Poultry Sciences
   [49292]

THAILAND
Bangkok
Buffalo Journal **[51415]**

UNITED KINGDOM
Driffield
International Hatchery Practice
   [53204]
International Poultry Production
   [53206]

Loughborough
Meat Science **[55485]**

POWER AND POWER PLANTS
See also Electrical Engineering; Nuclear Engineering

AUSTRALIA
Bentley
International Journal of Electrical
   Power & Energy Systems **[41597]**

Raymond Terrace
AIE News Journal
   [42297] .... (Paid) 1,000

Sydney
Electrical World
   [42502] .... (Paid) ‡6,749

AUSTRIA
Vienna
INIS Database **[42760]**

GERMANY
Stuttgart
Nuclear Engineering and Design
   [44674]

INDIA
Bhubaneswar
International Journal of Power and
   Energy Conversion **[45011]**

Kharagpur
International Journal of Industrial
   Electronics and Drives **[45247]**

Kolkata
Energy for Sustainable Development
   [45265]

New Delhi
Energy Management
   [45509] .... (Paid) 1,500
Resources, Energy and Development
   [45644] .... (Paid) 1,800
SESI Journal
   [45650] .... (Paid) 2,000
TIDEE—Teri Information Digest on
   Energy and Environment
   [45659] .... (Paid) 2,200

NETHERLANDS
Amsterdam
Electric Power Systems Research
   [47963]

PAKISTAN
Faisalabad
International Journal of Electrical and
   Power Engineering **[49250]**

REPUBLIC OF SOUTH AFRICA
Cape Town
Energy Forecast **[50376]** 10,000

SWEDEN
Stockholm
MEDSOLS **[51025]** ..... (Paid) 2,000

THAILAND
Pathumthani
RERIC International Energy Journal
   [51462] .... ‡4,247

UNITED KINGDOM
Birmingham
Progress in Nuclear Energy **[52362]**

Brentwood
Energy and Environment **[52572]**
Energy Exploration & Exploitation
   [52573]
Renewable Energy Bulletin **[52588]**
Wind Engineering **[52590]**
Wind Engineering Abstracts **[52591]**

Brighton
Batteries International
   [52606] .... (Combined) 5,800

Dundee
International Journal of Energy Sector
   Management **[53214]**

London
Energy World
   [54371] .... (Paid) 4,500
Gas Matters **[54494]**
Gas Matters Today **[54495]**

Oxford
The Utilities Journal **[56224]** ... 1,000

Stevenage
IEE Proceedings Generation, Transmission & Distribution **[56608]**

PRINTING AND TYPOGRAPHY

PEOPLE'S REPUBLIC OF CHINA
Hong Kong
Hong Kong Printing **[43343]**

Shanghai
Printing Field **[43495]**

FINLAND
Helsinki
Julkaisija
   [43836] .. .. (Combined) ‡2,500

IRELAND
Blackrock
Irish Printer **[45922]**

TURKEY
Istanbul
Matbaa & Teknik **[51561]** 9,690

UNITED KINGDOM
Kent
Screen Process & Digital Imaging
   [53680] .... ★7,500

London
PrintWeek
   [55119] .... (Controlled) ★16,536

Nottingham
International Journal of Remote
   Sensing **[55763]**

PSYCHOLOGY AND PSYCHIATRY

AUSTRALIA
Bowen Hills
The Australian Journal of Rehabilitation Counselling **[41624]**
Brain Impairment **[41625]**
Journal of Pacific Rim Psychology
   [41627]
Journal of Smoking Cessation
   [41628]

Brisbane
Australian Journal of Guidance and
   Counselling **[41640]**

Callaghan
Australian Journal of Educational &
   Developmental Psychology **[41690]**

Clayton
Australian and New Zealand Journal
   of Criminology **[41757]**

Lidcombe
Journal of Intellectual & Developmental Disability **[42008]**

Randwick
Neuropsychiatric Disease and
   Treatment **[42296]**

Robina
Gestalt Journal of Australia and New
   Zealand **[42313]**

Saint Leonards
Acta Neuropsychiatrica **[42329]**

Sydney
Psychology, Public Policy, and Law
   [42564] 2,100

West Perth
Behaviour Change **[42698]**

Westleigh
Australian and New Zealand Journal
   of Family Therapy **[42699]**

AUSTRIA
Vienna
Journal of Neural Transmission
   [42762]
Psychologie in Osterreich
   [42767] .. .. (Combined) ⊕2,146

Circulation: ★ = ABC; △ = BPA; ◆ = CAC; • = CCAB; ❑ = VAC; ⊕ = PO Statement; ‡ = Publisher's Report; Boldface figures = sworn; Light figures = estimated.

The World Journal of Biological
Psychiatry **[42775]**

BRAZIL
Porto Alegre
Psicologia **[42992]**
Psicologia & Sociedade
[42993] 1,000

Sao Paulo
Psicologia USP **[43045]**

Vicosa
Agora **[43054]**

CHILE
Santiago
Psykhe **[43146]**

PEOPLE'S REPUBLIC OF CHINA
Hong Kong
East Asian Archives of Psychiatry
[43297]
Journal of Psychology in Chinese
Societies **[43361]** .... (Paid) 500

CZECH REPUBLIC
Prague
Czech and Slovak Psychiatry **[43621]**

DENMARK
Alborg
Acta Psychiatrica Scandinavica
[43643]

FINLAND
Helsinki
Nordic Journal of Psychiatry **[43851]**

FRANCE
Montrouge
Epilepsies **[43987]**
Epileptic Disorders **[43988]**
L'Information Psychiatrique **[43993]**
Psychologie & NeuroPsychiatrie du
vieillissement **[44004]**
Revue de neuropsychologie **[44005]**

Saint Denis
L'Evolution Psychiatrique **[44102]**

GEORGIA
Tbilisi
Education Sciences & Psychology
[44132]

GERMANY
Berlin
Language and Cognition
[44215] 700
Report Psychologie
[44228] 13,000

Dusseldorf
Psycho-Social-Medicine **[44332]**

Frankfurt am Main
Selbstpsychologie **[44369]**

Giessen
Neurogenetics **[44388]**

Heidelberg
Neuroradiology **[44469]**

Jena
European Psychologist **[44488]**

Munich
Journal of Psychiatric Research
[44567]

Stuttgart
Nervenheilkunde
[44671] .. .. (Paid) 32,500

GREECE
Athens
Journal of Cross-Cultural Psychology
[44750]

Thessaloniki
Hellenic Journal of Psychology
[44772]

HUNGARY
Budapest
Journal of Evolutionary Psychology
[44841]
Magyar Pszichologiai Szemle **[44846]**
Mentalhigiene es Pszichoszomatika
[44852]

INDIA
Mumbai
Mens Sana Monographs **[45411]**

New Delhi
Psychology and Developing Societies
[45640] .... (Paid) 500

IRELAND
Dublin
Irish Journal of Psychological
Medicine **[45978]**
Irish Psychiatrist **[45984]** 3,322

ISRAEL
Tel Aviv
Journal of Children and Media
[46107]

ITALY
Milan
Journal of Mental Health Policy and
Economics **[46183]**

JAPAN
Chiba
Behaviormetrika **[46315]**

Kyoto
Mathematics Applied in Science and
Technology **[46482]**
Psychologia **[46485]** .. .. (Paid) 900

Sendai
Tohoku Psychologica Folia
[46671] 525

Tokyo
European Archives of Psychiatry and
Clinical Neuroscience **[46815]**

MALAYSIA
Kuala Lumpur
Neurology Asia **[47629]**

NETHERLANDS
Amsterdam
Acta Psychologica **[47879]**
Brain and Language **[47913]**
Cognitive Development **[47929]**
Cognitive Psychology **[47930]**
Cognitive Systems Research **[47931]**
Consciousness and Cognition
[47938]
Contemporary Educational
Psychology **[47939]**
Developmental Review **[47956]**
Hormones and Behavior **[48013]**
Interaction Studies **[48022]**
Journal of Applied Developmental
Psychology **[48045]**
Journal of Economic Psychology
[48070]

Journal of Environmental Psychology
[48074]
Journal of Experimental Child
Psychology **[48075]**
Journal of Experimental Social
Psychology **[48076]**
Journal of Mathematical Psychology
[48095]
Journal of Memory and Language
[48096]
Journal of Neurolinguistics **[48102]**
Journal of Research in Personality
[48114]
The Journal of Socio-Economics
[48116]
Journal of Vocational Behavior
[48130]
Learning and Motivation **[48135]**
Narrative Inquiry **[48169]**
Neural Networks **[48172]**
Neuropsychiatrie de l'Enfance et de
l'Adolescence **[48175]**
Neuropsychologia **[48176]**
Neuroscience Letters **[48177]**
Neuroscience Research **[48178]**
Neurotoxicology and Teratology
[48179]
Organizational Behavior and Human
Decision Processes **[48196]**
Poetics **[48207]**
Pratiques Psychologiques **[48212]**
Psychologie Francaise **[48218]**
Transportation Research Part F
[48255]
Trends in Neurosciences **[48265]**

Dordrecht
American Journal of Community
Psychology **[48324]**
Archives of Sexual Behavior **[48328]**
Brain and Mind **[48336]**
Contemporary Family Therapy
[48359]
Forum der Psychoanalyse **[48391]**
Journal of Behavioral Education
[48443]
Journal of Gambling Studies **[48461]**
Journal of Genetic Counseling
[48462]
Journal of Nonverbal Behavior
[48479]
Journal of Psycholinguistic Research
[48488]
Journal of Psychopathology & Behav-
ioral Assessment **[48489]**
Journal of Risk and Uncertainty
[48490]
Marketing Letters **[48511]**
Theory and Decision **[48578]**

Eindhoven
Journal of Biomechanics **[48592]**

Leiden
Archive for the Psychology of
Religion **[48651]**
Biblical Interpretation **[48657]**
Journal of Cognition and Culture
[48691]
Journal of Phenomenological
Psychology **[48700]** ... .. (Paid) 350
Phronesis **[48716]**
Psychological Research Psycholo-
gische Forschung **[48718]**

Maastricht
Journal of Behavior Therapy and Experimental Psychiatry **[48737]**

Nijmegen
European Journal of Psychological
Assessment **[48744]** 800

Utrecht
European Journal of Developmental
Psychology **[48756]**
Journal of Community & Applied So-

cial Psychology
[48761] .. .. (Paid) 2,800

NEW ZEALAND
Palmerston North
Australasian Journal of Disaster and
Trauma Studies **[48962]**

Wellington
Journal **[49010]** 200

NIGERIA
Ibadan
African Journal for the Psychological
Study of Social Issues **[49086]**
Nigerian Journal of Clinical and
Counselling Psychology **[49094]**

Ile-Ife
Gender and Behaviour **[49112]**
IFE PsychologIA **[49113]**

Ilorin
Nigerian Journal of Guidance and
Counselling **[49121]**

Shomolu
Nigerian Journal of Psychiatry
[49171]

NORWAY
Oslo
European Journal of Behavior
Analysis **[49197]**

PAKISTAN
Lahore
Psychology Quarterly
[49387] .... (Paid) 300

Peshawar
Journal of Pakistan Psychiatric
Society **[49393]**

PHILIPPINES
Quezon City
Philippine Journal of Psychology
[49606] .... (Paid) 175

POLAND
Bydgoszcz
Psychiatry in General Practice
[49654]

Gdansk
Psychooncology **[49660]**

Krakow
Polish Gerontology **[49668]**

Warsaw
Advances in Cognitive Psychology
[49685]
Paladyn **[49744]**
Polish Psychological Bulletin **[49754]**
Psychology of Language and
Communication **[49761]**
Suicidology **[49766]**

PORTUGAL
Lisbon
Acta Ethologica **[49801]**

ROMANIA
Bucharest
Psychologies **[49842]** .... ‡10,845

SINGAPORE
Singapore
International Journal of Humanoid
Robotics (IJHR) **[50181]**

REPUBLIC OF SOUTH AFRICA
Arcadia
International Journal of Emotional
Psychology and Sport Ethics
[50346]

Circulation: ★ = ABC; △ = BPA; ◆ = CAC; • = CCAB; ❑ = VAC; ⊕ = PO Statement; ‡ = Publisher's Report; Boldface figures = sworn; Light figures = estimated.

Cape Town
Psychologies South Africa
[50403] 42,000

Centurion
SA Journal of Industrial Psychology
[50448]

Grahamstown
Journal of Child and Adolescent Mental Health [50501]

Johannesburg
South African Psychiatry Review
[50535]

Pinelands
South African Journal of Psychiatry
[50575]

Pretoria
African Journal of Cross-Cultural Psychology and Sport Facilitation
[50583]
Sahara J [50599]

SPAIN

Madrid
Cognitiva [50737]
Cultura y Educacion
[50746] .... (Combined) 600
Estudios de Psicologia [50757]
Infancia y Aprendizaje/Journal for the Study of Education and Development [50769]
Psychology in Spain [50793]

Murcia
Anales de Psicologia [50821]

SWEDEN

Djursholm
Arkiv for Matematik [50952]

Linkoping
Cognitive Behaviour Therapy [50973]
Scandinavian Journal of Psychology
[50978]

TURKEY

Ankara
Turk Psikoloji Dergisi (Turkish Journal of Psychology) [51502]

Izmir
Journal of Neurological Sciences
[51575]

UNITED KINGDOM

Abingdon
Aging and Mental Health [51700]
Australian & New Zealand Journal of Psychiatry [51716] ... (Paid) 3,000
Behaviour and Information Technology [51717]
British Journal of Guidance and Counselling [51718]
Child Care in Practice [51728]
Counselling and Psychotherapy Research [51742]
Infant Observation [51815]
International Journal of Art Therapy
[51827]
International Review of Psychiatry
[51853]
Journal of Mental Health [51918]
Journal of Reproductive and Infant Psychology [51940]
Journal of Sexual Aggression [51941]
Mental Health, Religion and Culture
[51977]
Mortality [51987]
Philosophical Psychology [52011]
Psychoanalytic Psychotherapy
[52026]

Psychodynamic Practice [52027]
Psychology Crime and Law [52028]
Psychology and Health [52029]
Psychology, Health and Medicine
[52030]
Quarterly Journal of Experimental Psychology [52032]
Reflective Practice [52035]
Sexual Addiction & Compulsivity
[52056]
Vulnerable Children and Youth Studies [52087]

Belmont
Sociology [52307]
Work, Employment, and Society
[52308]

Bognor Regis
The International Journal of Applied Psychoanalytic Studies [52396]
Psychotherapy and Politics International [52403]

Brighton
Mental Health Today [52627]

Bristol
Neuropharmacology [52709]

Cambridge
Behavioral and Brain Sciences
[52791] ... . (Paid) 2,100
The International Journal of Neuropsychopharmacology
[52837] 1,200
Journal of Biosocial Science
[52846] 500
Neuropsychological Rehabilitation
[52875]

Chichester
European Journal of Social Psychology [53010]

Coventry
Journal of Research in Reading
[53087]

Edinburgh
Psychoanalysis and History [53307]
World Structure [53324]

Glasgow
Addiction Research and Theory
[53409]
Personality and Mental Health
[53439]

Gloucester
Journal of Psychiatric Intensive Care
[53472]

Harrow
Mental Health Practice
[53525] .. .. (Paid) 10,925

Hove
Advances in Dual Diagnosis [53603]
Journal of Aggression, Conflict and Peace Research [53606]
Journal of Learning Disabilities and Offending Behaviour [53609]
A Life in the Day [53610]

Huddersfield
Journal of Investigative Psychology and Offender Profiling [53621]

Kidlington
Computers in Human Behavior
[53690]
Journal of Adolescence [53695]

Lancaster
Journal of New Music Research
[53735]

Leeds
Contemporary Hypnosis [53763]
Journal of Psychiatric and Mental Health Nursing [53769]

Leicester
Applied Cognitive Psychology
[53785]
British Journal of Clinical Psychology
[53786] .... (Combined) 3,900
British Journal of Developmental Psychology
[53787] .... (Combined) 1,700
British Journal of Educational Psychology [53788]
British Journal of Health Psychology
[53789] .... (Combined) 2,000
British Journal of Mathematical and Statistical Psychology
[53790] .... (Combined) 700
British Journal of Psychology
[53791] ....: (Combined) 2,800
British Journal of Social Psychology
[53792] .... (Combined) 1,500
Journal of Occupational and Organizational Psychology
[53807] .... (Combined) 3,100
Legal and Criminological Psychology
[53810] .... (Combined) 1,200
Psychologist Appointments [53819]
Psychology and Psychotherapy
[53820] .... (Combined) 1,900

London
Addiction Abstracts [53901]
Advances in Psychiatric Treatment
[53907]
Annals of General Psychiatry [53948]
Autism [53984]
BMC Psychiatry [54087]
British Journal of Psychiatry [54132]
Clinical Child Psychology and Psychiatry [54219]
Cognitive Neuropsychiatry [54237]
Communication [54245] 12,000
Culture & Psychology [54295]
European Journal of Psychotherapy and Counselling [54405]
Evidence-Based Mental Health (EBMH) [54415]
Feminism & Psychology [54446]
Group Analysis [54522]
Group Processes & Intergroup Relations [54523]
Journal of Child Psychology and Psychiatry [54722]
Journal of Child Psychotherapy
[54723]
Journal of Health Psychology [54759]
Journal of Neurology, Neurosurgery, and Psychiatry [54787]
Journal of Psychopharmacology
[54805]
Journal of Social and Personal Relationships [54819]
Molecular Psychiatry [54948]
Multiple Sclerosis
[54961] .... (Paid) 700
Names [54969] .... (Paid) 850
OpenMIND [55035] ... (Paid) ‡5,500
Personality and Individual Differences
[55071]
The Psychiatrist [55149]
Qualitative Research in Psychology
[55161]
School Psychology International
[55219]
Statistical Modelling [55264]
Theory & Psychology [55308]
Transcultural Psychiatry [55336]

Loughborough
Psychology of Sport and Exercise
[55487]

Lutterworth
Healthcare Counselling and Psychotherapy Journal [55512]

Manchester
Journal of Psychosomatic Research
[55565]

Oxford
Brief Treatment and Crisis Intervention [55888]
Child [55907]
Emotional and Behavioral Difficulties
[55936]
Gender & Development [55962]
Journal of Personality [56057]
Neuropathology [56115]
Neuropathology and Applied Neurobiology [56116]
Personnel Psychology [56150]
Perspectives in Psychiatric Care
[56151]
Perspectives on Psychological Science [56152]
Psychogeriatrics [56173]
Psychological Science in the Public Interest [56174]
Psychology of Women Quarterly
[56175]
Schizophrenia Bulletin [56201]

Penarth
Reviews in Clinical Gerontology
[56241] 400

Plymouth
Thinking & Reasoning [56274]

Ross-on-Wye
Person-Centered and Experimental Psychotherapies [56411]

Sheffield
Managing Leisure [56506]

Warrington
Context
[56848] .... (Controlled) 1,600

West Sussex
Dyslexia [56897]

Worthing
Clinical Approaches in Bipolar Disorders [56971]

PUBLIC RELATIONS
See also Advertising and Marketing; Communications

BELGIUM
Brussels
International Journal of Research in Marketing [42859]

BRAZIL
Campinas
Opiniao Publica [42971]

INDIA
Hyderabad
The Icfai Journal of Governance and Public Policy [45153]

NETHERLANDS
Dordrecht
Journal of Consumer Policy [48453]

NIGERIA
Lagos
African Journal of Political Science & International Relations [49135]

SINGAPORE
Singapore City
FutureGov [50312] 8,950

SWITZERLAND
Zurich
International Journal of Technology Policy and Management [51267]

Trade, Technical, and Professional Publications

TAIWAN
Taichung
International Journal of Electronic
   Customer Relationship
   Management [51320]

UNITED KINGDOM
Abingdon
International Public Management
   Journal [51849]

Bognor Regis
Journal of Public Affairs [52399]

Bradford
European Journal of Marketing
   [52458]
Marketing Intelligence & Planning
   [52525]

Glasgow
The Drum [53414]

London
Campaign [54170]
Marketing [54908] *35,615
Med Ad News [54919] 16,000
Precision Marketing
   [55117] *7,500

Luton
The Pantaneto Forum [55504]

PUBLIC SAFETY AND EMERGENCY RESPONSE

IRELAND
Dublin
FireCall [45958] 1,500

NETHERLANDS
Amsterdam
Accident Analysis & Prevention
   [47876]

Delft
Safety Science [48313]

NIGERIA
Ikeja
Democracy & Development [49106]

POLAND
Warsaw
Journal of Konbin [49723]

UNITED KINGDOM
Bradford
Disaster Prevention and Management
   [52450]

Brighton
Safer Communities [52632]

High Wycombe
Journal of Flood Risk Management
   [53574]

Hove
Safer Communities [53612]

Kingston upon Thames
Firefighter [53721]

London
Journal of Paramedic Practice
   [54792]
Journal of Public Health [54806]

Walsall
Swim & Save [56835]

PUBLIC SPEAKING AND LECTURING

FRANCE
Paris
International Railway Statistics
   [44059]

ROMANIA
Bucharest
TRANSURB [49844]

UNITED KINGDOM
Blackpool
Fylde Tramway News [52385] ... 650

Folkestone
Journal and Report of Proceedings
   [53392] 7,000

Luton
The Pantaneto Forum [55504]

Welling
Tramway Review [56879]
Tramways & Urban Transit
   [56880] .. .. (Paid) 6,800

PUBLIC TRANSPORTATION

NETHERLANDS
Dordrecht
Transportation [48582]

REPUBLIC OF SOUTH AFRICA
Cape Town
Road Ahead [50406] 10,000
Shipyear [50411] 10,000

UNITED KINGDOM
Berkhamsted
Steam Days [52314]

London
Getting There [54506]

Manchester
The Journal of Transport History
   [55569]
Progress in Planning [55575]

Swanley
ITS International
   [56697] .. .. (Combined) △22,283
World Highways
   [56698] .. .. (Combined) ‡15,133

Tunbridge Wells North
Modern Railways [56785]

PURCHASING

AUSTRALIA
Paradise Point
Procurement Professional
   [42228] 4,500

Wahroonga
Electrical Solutions
   [42672] *7,582
What's New in Electronics
   [42679] *7072

NETHERLANDS
Rotterdam
Journal of Purchasing & Supply
   Management [48751]

UNITED KINGDOM
London
CPO Agenda [54279]
Supply Management
   [55279] .... ‡35,000

RADIO, TELEVISION, CABLE, AND VIDEO
See also Electrical Engineering; Electronics Engineering; Music and Musical Instruments

AUSTRALIA
Hepburn Springs
Australasian Sound Archive [41952]

Pyrmont
The Production Book [42286]
Smoke and Mirrors
   [42289] *4,483

Sydney
Limelight [42536] *11,299

Wahroonga
Radio Comms Asia-Pacific
   [42675] *4,426

PEOPLE'S REPUBLIC OF CHINA
Shanghai
Radio & TV [43496]

FINLAND
Helsinki
Suomen Lehdisto
   [43861] .... (Combined) 2,404

FRANCE
Antibes
International Journal of Image and
   Video Processing (IJIVP) [43914]

GERMANY
Gottingen
Advances in Radio Science [44390]

Heidelberg
Multimedia Systems [44468]

Munich
Televizion [44583]

Unterfoehring
TELE-satellite International Magazine
   [44697] .... ‡148,430

HUNGARY
Budapest
RTV Musormagazin
   [44868] .... (Paid) ‡74,540

INDIA
Kolkata
Energy for Sustainable Development
   [45265]

Mumbai
Screen World [45437] 2,500
Studio Systems
   [45443] .. .. (Paid) 12,500

New Delhi
Indian Media Studies Journal [45571]

ISRAEL
Tel Aviv
Journal of Children and Media
   [46107]

ITALY
Ferrara
Circuits and Systems II [46138]

Milan
Prima Comunicazione
   [46191] .... (Paid) ‡15,000

NEW ZEALAND
Upper Hutt
Break In [48992]

SINGAPORE
Singapore
Asian Journal of Communication
   [50111] 750

SPAIN
Madrid
ANIGP-TV [50728]

Pozuelo de Alarcon
Conectronica
   [50827] .... (Controlled) 4,000

SWEDEN
Goteborg
Nordicom Review [50961]

SWITZERLAND
Grand-Saconnex
Diffusion
   [51177] .. .. (Non-paid) ⊕5,000
EBU Technical Review [51178]

Lausanne
TV8 [51201] 84,087

Zurich
TVtaglich [51295] 1,221,000

UNITED ARAB EMIRATES
Dubai
Digital Studio [51638] .... △6,023
tv&radio [51655] .... △43,750

UNITED KINGDOM
Abingdon
New Review of Film & Television
   Studies [51997]

Bournemouth
Practical Digital Video [52422]
SciFiNow [52424]

Huddersfield
Free Press [53620] ..... (Paid) 5,250

Kettering
The Radio Magazine
   [53685] .... (Combined) 4,000

Leamington Spa
Eurowire
   [53745] .. .. (Controlled) ‡25,338

London
British Journalism Review [54138]
Cable & Satellite International
   [54164] .. .. △10,000
Commonwealth Broadcaster
   [54240] 3,000
Media, Culture & Society [54920]
Pact [55050]
Viewfinder [55370] 5,500

Luton
Convergence [55501]

Midlothian
Cabletalk [55627] 5,000

Stevenage
IEE Proceedings Radar, Sonar &
   Navigation [56612]

Tavistock
Zerb [56728] 4,000

RADIOLOGY, ULTRASOUND, AND NUCLEAR MEDICINE

BELGIUM
Brussels
Journal of Radiotherapy and
   Oncology [42863]

Circulation: ★ = ABC; △ = BPA; ◆ = CAC; • = CCAB; ❏ = VAC; ⊕ = PO Statement; ‡ = Publisher's Report; Boldface figures = sworn; Light figures = estimated.

BRAZIL
Vicosa
Radiologia Brasileira [43063]

CZECH REPUBLIC
Plzen
Ceska Radiologie [43607]

Prague
Czech Radiology [43617]

DENMARK
Arhus
Radiotherapy and Oncology [43650]

FRANCE
Fontenay-aux-Roses
Radioprotection [43955]

Paris
Cancer Radiotherapie [44032]

GERMANY
Erlangen
Strahlentherapie und Onkologie [44342]

Heidelberg
Neuroradiology [44469]

GREECE
Chalkis
International Journal of Signal and Imaging Systems Engineering [44758]

INDIA
Belgaum
Journal of Indian Academy of Oral Medicine and Radiology [44996]

Mumbai
Indian Journal of Nuclear Medicine [45384]

IRAN
Tehran
Iranian Journal of Radiology [45909]

ITALY
Turin
Contrast Media & Molecular Imaging [46270]

JAPAN
Hiroshima
Journal of Radiation Research [46381] .... (Paid) 1,500
Oral Radiology [46382]

Tokyo
Annals of Nuclear Medicine [46739]
Emergency Radiology [46809]

MALAYSIA
Kuala Lumpur
Biomedical Imaging and Intervention Journal [47600]

NETHERLANDS
Amsterdam
Journal of Structural Biology [48119]

Dordrecht
Der Radiologe [48370]
European Radiology Supplements [48384]
International Journal of Computer Assisted Radiology and Surgery [48426]

La radiologia medica [48502]
Surgical and Radiologic Anatomy [48572]

NIGERIA
Nsukka
West African Journal of Radiology [49153]

NORWAY
Oslo
Hold Pusten [49200] .... (Combined) ‡1,970

POLAND
Warsaw
Radiology and Oncology [49762]

REPUBLIC OF SOUTH AFRICA
Pinelands
South African Journal of Radiology [50576]

SWEDEN
Malmo
Clinical Physiology and Functional Imaging [50991]

Stockholm
Annals of the ICRP [51008] .. .. (Paid) ‡1,800

TURKEY
Ankara
Diagnostic and Interventional Radiology [51492]

UNITED KINGDOM
Abingdon
Acta Radiologica [51695]

Cambridge
Magnetic Resonance in Chemistry [52867]

London
British Journal of Cancer [54113]
British Journal of Radiology [54133] 3,000
Cardiovascular Ultrasound [54179]
Clinical Oncology [54226]
Clinical Radiology [54229]
European Journal of Ultrasound [54406]
Hospital Imaging and Radiology Europe [54573] 8,750

Oxford
Photodermatology, Photoimmunology and Photomedicine [56156]
Radiation Protection Dosimetry [56185]

Salford
Radiography [56451]

Sheffield
Journal of Radiotherapy in Practice [56505]

RAILROAD
See also Public Transportation

FRANCE
Auray
Voie Libre [43916] .... (Combined) 5,150

Paris
International Railway Statistics [44059]

NEW ZEALAND
Wellington
The New Zealand Railway Observer [49030] .... (Combined) 1,450

SPAIN
Madrid
Via Libre [50814] .. .. (Controlled) 15,000

UNITED KINGDOM
Berkhamsted
Steam Days [52314]

Blackpool
Fylde Tramway News [52385] ... 650

Bo'ness
Blastpipe [52406]

Bracebridge Heath
Railwatch [52432] 4,500

Folkestone
Journal and Report of Proceedings [53392] 7,000

Gwynedd
Ffestiniog Railway Magazine [53500] .. .. (Paid) 5,000

Leamington Spa
Bulletin [53744]

London
Locomotive Journal [54882]
The Railway Magazine [55171] .. .. ★35,100

Manchester
The Journal of Transport History [55569]

Peterborough
Railways Illustrated [56260]

Poynton
Journal of the Stephenson Locomotive Society [56298]

Stevenage
IEE Proceedings Electric Power Applications [56607]

Sutton
Railway Gazette International [56692] .. .. (Paid) 10,000

Sutton Coldfield
The Electric Railway [56694] 400

Tunbridge Wells North
Modern Railways [56785]

REAL ESTATE

CAYMAN ISLANDS
Grand Cayman
C.I. Real Estate Magazine [43131] 13,000

PEOPLE'S REPUBLIC OF CHINA
Hong Kong
Elite Homes [43298] .. .. ‡16,350

NETHERLANDS
The Hague
Amsterdam Real Estate City Book [48606]

POLAND
Warsaw
International Journal of Strategic Property Management [49720]

SPAIN
Madrid
Guia del Comprador de Casas [50763] .... ‡2,568

UNITED REPUBLIC OF TANZANIA
Dar es Salaam
Journal of Building and Land Development [51402]

THAILAND
Bangkok
Property Report Thailand [51432] 25,000

UNITED KINGDOM
Abingdon
Journal of Property Research [51936]

Alston
In the Sticks [52103] .. .. (Combined) 10,000

Basingstoke
Journal of Retail and Leisure Property [52220]

Bognor Regis
Briefings in Real Estate Finance [52393]

Bradford
Journal of Corporate Real Estate [52495]
Journal of Property Investment & Finance [52513]

Cambridge
Cambridgeshire Property Plus [52801]

County Antrim
Journal of European Real Estate Research [53075]

Edinburgh
Scotland's New Homebuyer [53310] .... (Non-paid) 18,000

Evesham
Oldham & District Property News [53344] .. .. (Combined) 15,000

Glasgow
The Property Executive [53443] .... (Combined) 9,600

London
Estates Gazette [54385]
Inside Housing [54606] .. .. (Combined) ★26,343
Mortgage Strategy [54955]
News on the Block [55002] 10,000
Property Week [55142] .. .. ★27,520

Manchester
Manchester Living [55571] .. .. (Paid) 12,000
Progress in Planning [55575]

New Malden
Dalton's Weekly [55658] .... (Paid) ★32,124

Newcastle upon Tyne
North East Househunter [55675] 14,500
South Tyne & Wear HouseHunter [55679] 17,000

Norwich
French Property News [55731] .. .. (Controlled) 50,000

Surrey
A Place in the Sun [56672] .... ★35,818

Wadhurst
Construction Europe [56805] .... ★14,624

Warwick
Agreement [56851]

Circulation: ★ = ABC; △ = BPA; ◆ = CAC; • = CCAB; ▢ = VAC; ⊕ = PO Statement; ‡ = Publisher's Report; Boldface figures = sworn; Light figures = estimated.

The Estate Agent [56854]

RENTAL EQUIPMENT
See also Machinery and Equipment

FRANCE
Clichy
Forum Chantiers
[43932] .. .. (Paid) 15,000

UNITED KINGDOM
Wadhurst
International Rental News
[56810] .. .. (Combined) 14,624

RETAIL
See also General Merchandise

AUSTRALIA
Melbourne
Convenience World [42057]

Pyrmont
Appliance Retailer [42269] .. · ★7,112

BELGIUM
Antwerp
Sparraaja
[42840] .. .. (Controlled) 4,000

PEOPLE'S REPUBLIC OF CHINA
Hong Kong
HKTDC Enterprise
[43306] .. .. (Paid) 150,000

DENMARK
Glostrup
Puff - Fagtidsskrift for Tralast og Byggemarkeder
[43713] .. .. (Controlled) ‡1,843

FRANCE
Montrouge
Faire Savoir Faire
[43991] .. .. (Combined) 27,802

GERMANY
Ettlingen
DIY [44349] .. .. (Combined) 9,231

NETHERLANDS
Maarssen
Trends [48735] 4,500

Wijchen
CBM [48773] .. .. (Combined) 6,300

SPAIN
Madrid
Dealer World & Dealer World 15
[50749] .. .. (Controlled) ‡13,826
Distribucion Actualidad [50752]
En Franquicia
[50756] .. .. (Paid) 30,000

UNITED KINGDOM
Bedford
Alert Magazine [52271]

Crawley
Convenience Store
[53100] .. .. ★40,587

Edinburgh
International Journal of Retail and Distribution Management [53289]

Glasgow
scottish grocer [53447] .... ★8,217
Scottish Local Retailer
[53449] 8,363

Horsham
Prestige High Street Interiors
[53598] .. .. (Controlled) 3,000

Ilfracombe
Catalogue & E-business
[53641] 8,500

Kent
Footwear Today [53677]
The Independent Electrical Retailer
[53678] .. .. (Controlled) ★6,895

London
Frontier Brands [54485] 4,000
In-Store Marketing
[54593] .. .. (Combined) 13,084
.... ★10,168
Progressive Greetings Worldwide
[55138] 6,500
Retail Newsagent [55195]
Retail Systems [55196] .. .. ★13,000

Sittingbourne
DIY Week [56547]
Hardware & Garden Review [56548]

Stirling
The International Review of Retail, Distribution and Consumer Research [56623]

ROADS AND STREETS
See also Construction, Contracting, Building, and Excavating

FRANCE
Clichy
Route Actualite/Roads News
[43935] .. .. (Combined) 8,000

INDIA
New Delhi
Indian Roads Congress Highway Research Bulletin
[45576] .. .. (Paid) 8,500
Journal of Indian Roads Congress
[45604] .. .. (Paid) 8,500

LEBANON
Beirut
Arab Construction World (ACW)
[47390] .. ..: (Combined) ‡7,153

POLAND
Warsaw
Town Planning and Architecture
[49767]

SPAIN
Madrid
Carreteras
[50733] .. .. (Controlled) 16,000

UNITED KINGDOM
Lewes
Wood Working Plans and Projects
[53851]

Manchester
The Journal of Transport History
[55569]
Progress in Planning [55575]

Wadhurst
Construction Europe
[56805] .. .. ★14,624

ROOFING
See also Building Materials, Concrete, Brick, and Tile; Metal, Metallurgy, and Metal Trade; Construction, Contracting, Building, and Excavating

UNITED KINGDOM
Sevenoaks
Roofing, Cladding & Insulation
[56483]

Wadhurst
Construction Europe
[56805] .. .. ★14,624

RUBBER TRADE
See also Automotive (Trade)

MALAYSIA
Kuala Lumpur
Journal of Rubber Research
[47607] .. .. (Paid) 1,000

SINGAPORE
Singapore
Plastics & Rubber Singapore Journal
[50241]
Rubber Industry Report [50248]
Rubber Statistical Bulletin [50249]

UNITED KINGDOM
Hertford
Rubber Developments
[53565] 10,000

Shrewsbury
Cellular Polymers [56527]

SAFETY

AUSTRALIA
Canberra
Flight Safety Australia
[41706] 85,000

Mount Macedon
Australian Journal of Emergency Management
[42133] .. .. (Non-paid) 5,200

Wahroonga
Industrial Workwear Solutions
[42673] 28,000
Safety Solutions [42676] 7,323

BELGIUM
Brussels
Via Secura [42873]

PEOPLE'S REPUBLIC OF CHINA
Wuhan
Safety and Environmental Engineering [43525]

FINLAND
Helsinki
African Newsletter on Occupational Health and Safety [43814]
Asian-Pacific Newsletter [43819]
Tyo Terveys Turvallisuus
[43863] .. .. (Controlled) 62,933

GERMANY
Bonn
Safety & Security International
[44270]

Braunschweig
CLEAN [44274]

Darmstadt
GIT Sicherheit Management
[44307] .. .. ‡28,281

Leinfelden-Echterdingen
Sicherheitsbeauftragter
[44529] 14,092
Sicherheitsingenieur
[44530] 5,020

Munich
LSV aktuell [44569]

IRAN
Tehran
Iranian Journal of Public Health
[45908] .. ..: (Paid) 2,000

IRELAND
Dublin
International Journal for Quality in Health Care [45967]

ITALY
Cinisello Balsamo
Sicurezza [46135]

JAPAN
Nagoya
Radiation Safety Management
[46558]

NETHERLANDS
Amsterdam
Journal of Chemical Health and Safety [48057]

Bussum
Current Drug Safety [48288]

PHILIPPINES
Quezon City
Philippine Journal of Public Administration
[49607] .. .. (Paid) 1,000

POLAND
Warsaw
Journal of Konbin [49723]

SINGAPORE
Singapore City
Asian Security Review
[50311] 10,000

REPUBLIC OF SOUTH AFRICA
Cape Town
African Security Review [50362]
Institute for Security Studies Monographs [50383]

Lenasia
African Safety Promotion [50547]

SPAIN
Madrid
SIC Seguridad en Informatica y Comunicaciones
[50805] .. .. (Paid) 5,000

SWITZERLAND
Geneva
International Journal of Information Privacy, Security and Integrity
[51126]
International Journal of Vehicle Design [51145]

Circulation: ★ = ABC; △ = BPA; ◆ = CAC; • = CCAB; ❏ = VAC; ⊕ = PO Statement; ‡ = Publisher's Report; Boldface figures = sworn; Light figures = estimated.

UNITED KINGDOM

Basingstoke
Molecular Therapy [52224]

Birmingham
Occupational Safety & Health [52360]
Safety Education [52365]
Safety Express [52366]
Staying Alive
　[52368] .. .. (Paid) 2,000

Brighton
Safer Communities [52632]

Buckhurst Hill
Secure Times [52753] .... ‡9,306

Coventry
EurOhs Magazine
　[53081] .. .. (Controlled) 10,000

Driffield
International Food Hygiene
　[53203] .. .. (Controlled) 10,000

Edinburgh
Fire Safety Journal [53276]

Forest Row
Good Motoring Magazine
　[53396] 53,000

Harrow
Inroads [53524] 2,000

Hove
Safer Communities [53612]

London
CCTV Today
　[54189] .... (Paid) ‡8,000
Fire International [54460]
Health & Safety at Work
　[54543] .... ★23,051
Quality and Safety in Health Care
　[55162] .... ‡6,000
The Safety & Health Practitioner
　[55214] .... (Paid) ★36,549
Safety Management [55215]

Moreton-in-Marsh
Fire Prevention [55650] 15,000

Newcastle upon Tyne
Crime Prevention & Community
　Safety [55668]

Olney
International Journal of Risk Assess-
　ment and Management [55831]

Redhill
Safety at Sea International
　[56378] .. .. (Paid) 6,000

Sheffield
Hazards [56496]

Surrey
Human Factors and Aerospace
　Safety [56666]

Walsall
Swim & Save [56835]

Wigston
Policy and Practice in Health and
　Safety [56925]
The Safety and Health Practitioner
　[56926] 32,000

SAVINGS AND LOAN

UNITED KINGDOM

London
European Pensions [54408]
Pensions Age [55065] .... ★14,000

Norwich
Moneyfacts [55735]

Sittingbourne
Moneywise [56550]

SCIENCE (GENERAL)
See also Anthropology and
Ethnology; Archaeology;
Astronautics; Biology;
Botany; Chemistry, Chemi-
cals, and Chemical Engi-
neering; Engineering (Vari-
ous branches); Entomology;
Forestry; Genetics; Geol-
ogy; Laboratory Research
(Scientific and Medical), etc.

ARGENTINA

Buenos Aires
Ameghiniana [41469]

AUSTRALIA

Armidale
The Rangeland Journal [41560]

Cairns
International Journal for Parasitology
　[41685]

Canberra
Communicable Diseases Intelligence
　[41704]

Clayton
Applied GIS [41756]

Collingwood
Australasian Plant Disease Notes
　[41781]
Emu - Austral Ornithology [41787]
Invertebrate Systematics [41791]
Marine & Freshwater Research
　[41792]
PASA [41794]
Reproduction, Fertility and
　Development [41796]
Wildlife Research [41797]

Darwin
International Journal of Computa-
　tional Physical Sciences [41828]

Deakin
Nutrition & Dietetics [41837]
Teaching Science [41838] .... ‡4,000

Hanwood
Journal of Applied Irrigation Science
　[41940]

Hobart
Australasian Epidemiologist [41957]

Melbourne
Growth Factors [42062]
Qualitative Research Journal [42083]

Parkville
Historical Records of Australian
　Science [42231]
Tissue Antigens [42232]

Perth
AIG Journal [42242]
Australasian Plant Pathology [42245]

Port Melbourne
Australian Physics [42262]

Saint Leonards
Australian Dental Journal
　[42330] .. .. (Paid) 10,000

Scarborough
Science a GoGo [42354]

Sydney
Acoustics Australia
　[42445] .... (Paid) ‡600
Journal of Science and Medicine in
　Sport [42531]

Wahroonga
What's New in LAB Technology
　[42681] .... ★6,233

Woolgoolga
Journal of Near Infrared
　Spectroscopy [42715]

AUSTRIA

Laxenburg
Options [42731] 5,000

Mondsee
European Journal of Protistology
　[42737]

Vienna
European Journal of Scientific
　Research [42753]
International Journal of Advanced
　Robotic Systems [42761]
TermNet News [42769]

BAHAMAS

Nassau
Bahamas Journal of Science
　[42783] .... (Paid) 500

BANGLADESH

Dhaka
Bangladesh Journal of Scientific and
　Industrial Research [42805]

BELGIUM

Leuven
Journal of Computational and Applied
　Mathematics [42900]

BRAZIL

Bauru
Journal of Applied Oral Science
　[42948]

Botafogo
Revista Brasileira de Anestesiologia
　[42955]

Botucatu
Interface [42956]

Brasilia
Fitopatologia Brasileira [42958]

Campinas
Ciencia e Tecnologia de Alimentos
　[42967]
Kant e-Prints [42970]

Campos dos Goytacazes
Biosystems Engineering [42974]

Porto Alegre
Psicologia [42992]
Psicologia & Sociedade
　[42993] 1,000

Rio de Janeiro
Anais da Academia Brasileira de
　Ciencias [43003]
Mana - Estudos de Antropologia
　Social [43011]
Memorias do Instituto Oswaldo Cruz
　[43012]

Sao Paulo
Acta Cirurgica Brasileira [43021]
Arquivos Brasileiros de Endocrinolo-
　gia & Metabologia [43022]
Arquivos Brasileiros de Oftalmologia
　[43023]
Arquivos de Neuro-Psiquiatria
　[43024]
Ceramica [43032] 700
Ciencia e Cultura [43033] 1,500
Ciencia Hoje
　[43034] .. .. (Paid) 13,000

Ciencia Hoje das Criancas
　[43035] .... (Paid) 194,000
Clinics [43036]
Ecletica Quimica [43038]
Jornal da Ciencia Hoje [43041]
Quimica Nova [43046]

Vacaria
Anais da Sociedade Entomologica do
　Brasil [43052]
Neotropical Entomology [43053]

Vicosa
Agora [43054]
Arquivo Brasileiro de Medicina Veteri-
　naria e Zootecnia [43055]
Entomologia y Vectores [43058]
Journal of Epilepsy and Clinical
　Neurophysiology [43059]
Pro-Fono Revista de Atualizacao
　Cientifica [43062]

Vila Olimpia
Arquivos Brasileiros de Cardiologia
　[43067]

BULGARIA

Bourgas
Academic Open Internet Journal
　[43086]

Ruse
Advanced Studies in Theoretical
　Physics [43087]

Sofia
Bulgarian Geophysical Journal
　[43096]
Genetics and Breeding [43100]
Nauka [43106] 2,000

CAMEROON

Buea
Journal of the Cameroon Academy of
　Sciences [43124]

Dschang
Cameroon Journal of Experimental
　Biology [43125]

Yaounde
Cameroon Journal of Agricultural
　Science [43128]

CHILE

Arica
IDESIA [43133]

Santiago
Psykhe [43146]
Revista de la SCCC [43148]

PEOPLE'S REPUBLIC OF CHINA

Beijing
Communications in Theoretical
　Physics [43191]
Genomics, Proteomics &
　Bioinformatics [43194]
International Journal of Intelligent
　Computing and Cybernetics
　[43197]
Journal of Geographical Sciences
　[43207] .... (Paid) ‡700
Journal of Systems Science and
　Information [43209]
Particuology [43212]
Tsinghua Science & Technology
　[43222]
World Journal of Gastroenterology
　[43225]

Changchun
Journal of Jilin University Earth Sci-
　ence Edition [43240]
Journal of Jilin University Information
　Science Edition [43242]

Circulation: ★ = ABC; △ = BPA; ◆ = CAC; • = CCAB; ❏ = VAC; ⊕ = PO Statement; ‡ = Publisher's Report; Boldface figures = sworn; Light figures = estimated.

Journal of Jilin University Medicine Edition [43243]
Journal of Jilin University Science Edition [43244]

Dalian
Chinese Journal of Catalysis [43253]

Hefei
International Journal of Nanoparticles [43266]

Hong Kong
The Journal of Dagaare Studies (JDS) [43355]

Nanjing
Chemistry and Industry of Forest Products [43457]
Journal of Hohai University [43459]
Water Science and Engineering [43461]

Shanghai
English of Science and Technology Learning [43474]
International Journal of Nonlinear Modelling in Science and Engineering [43477]
International Journal of Physical Sciences [43478]
Micro- and Nanometer Science & Technology [43488]
Nuclear Science and Techniques [43491]
Science Journal [43497]
Scientific Pictorial [43498]

Xiangtan
International Journal of Computing Science and Mathematics [43539]
International Journal of Dynamical Systems and Differential Equations [43540]

COLOMBIA
Bogota
Acta Biologica Colombiana [43541]
Caldasia [43544]
Revista [43545]

COTE D'IVOIRE
Abidjan
Agronomie Africaine [43556]

CROATIA
Split
Acta Adriatica [43559]
Acta Adriatica [43560]

Zagreb
Croatica Chemica Acta [43566]

CZECH REPUBLIC
Prague
Epidemiology, Microbiology, Immunology [43624]
International Journal of Speleology [43626]
Journal Kybernetika [43628]

Videnska
Immunology Letters [43641]

DENMARK
Arhus
Boreas [43645]

Copenhagen
ICES Journal of Marine Science [43674]
International Game Theory Review [43675]
Microbiological Research [43679]
Nuclear Instruments and Methods in Physics Research Section B [43680]

Wageningen
International Review of Environmental and Resource Economics [43738]

EGYPT
Alexandria
International Journal of Biotechnology & Biochemistry (IJBB) [43745]
International Journal of Lakes and Rivers [43746]
International Journal of Nanotechnology and Applications [43747]
International Journal of Pure and Applied Physics [43749]

Cairo
African Journal of Urology [43750]
Egyptian Journal of Biochemistry and Molecular Biology [43756]
Egyptian Journal of Biomedical Sciences [43757]
Egyptian Journal of Biotechnology [43758]
Egyptian Journal of Computer Science [43759] 320
Egyptian Journal of Medical Laboratory Sciences [43760]

El Mansoura
International Journal of Materials Science [43770]

Ismailia
Egyptian Journal of Biology [43773]

ETHIOPIA
Addis Ababa
Bulletin of the Chemical Society of Ethiopia [43796]
Ethiopian Journal of Biological Sciences [43798]
SINET [43803]

Haramaya
East African Journal of Sciences [43805]

FINLAND
Helsinki
Annales Academiae Scientiarum Fennicae Mathematica [43816]
Journal of Analysis and its Applications [43834]

Kirkkonummi
The Scientific World Journal [43874]
TSW Development & Embryology [43875]

FRANCE
Bron
International Journal of Product Lifecycle Management [43924]

Castanet-Tolosan
Natures Sciences Societes [43927] 1,000

Montrouge
Science et changements planetaires/Secheresse [44007]

Nice
Gene Therapy and Regulation [44015]

Paris
L'Actualite Chimique [44021] .. .. (Paid) 5,000
Combustion and Flame [44033]
Data Science Journal [44036]
European Journal of Mineralogy [44043]
High Pressure Research [44046]
International Journal of Nuclear Hydrogen Production and Applications [44053]

International Journal of Nuclear Knowledge Management [44054]
International Journal of Refrigeration [44056]
International Journal of Uncertainty, Fuzziness and Knowledge-Based Systems [44058]
Leukemia [44068]
Revue du Soignant en Sante Publique [44082]

Rennes
Granular Matter [44097]

Strasbourg
Computational Materials Science [44112]

Vandoeuvre-les-Nancy
Process Biochemistry [44122]

Villeurbanne
Mathematical Modelling of Natural Phenomena [44126]

GEORGIA
Tbilisi
Annals of Biomedical Research and Education [44130]
Education Sciences & Psychology [44132]

GERMANY
Augsburg
Progress in Solid State Chemistry [44142]

Berlin
Archives of Animal Nutrition [44156]
Biomedizinische Technik [44161]
Clinical Chemistry and Laboratory Medicine [44165]
Crystal Research and Technology [44168]
Fossil Record [44184]
Jahrbuch fur Wissenschaft und Ethik [44199]
Journal of Applied Crystallography [44202]
Journal of Applied Geodesy [44203]
Journal of Non-Equilibrium Thermodynamics [44208] 200
Neuroforum [44225]
Praehistorische Zeitschrift [44227] 500

Bielefeld
Documenta Mathematica [44245]

Bochum
Regulatory Peptides [44251]

Bonn
European Journal of Development Research [44257]
german research [44262]
Informatik Spektrum [44263] 24,000
Plant Signaling & Behavior [44269]

Cologne
Brains, Minds and Media [44289]

Dusseldorf
European Physical Journal E. Soft Matter [44324]

Eschborn
Gate Technology and Development [44345]

Freiburg
Mind and Matter [44371]
Renewable Energy Focus [44372] 86,140
Solar Energy Journal [44373]

Giessen
International Journal of Systematic and Evolutionary Microbiology [44386] .... (Combined) 925

Journal of Individual Differences [44387] 400

Gottingen
European Journal of Anaesthesiology [44397] 8,600

Hannover
Forschungsberichte aus Technik und Naturwissenschaften [44432]

Heidelberg
Analytical and Bioanalytical Chemistry [44437]
Animal Cognition [44438]
Behavioral Ecology and Sociobiology [44442]
Climate Dynamics [44446]
Computational Geosciences [44449]
Environmental Modeling & Assessment [44454]
Health Care Management Science [44458]
Journal of Geodesy [44464]
Tribology Letters [44479]
Zeitschrift fur Unternehmens- und Gesellschaftsrecht (ZGR) [44480]

Jena
Journal of Basic Microbiology [44489]

Karlsruhe
Neues Jahrbuch fur Mineralogie Abhandlungen [44494]

Leinfelden-Echterdingen
bild der wissenschaft [44517] 105,059

Mainz
Medical Microbiology and Immunology [44542]

Munich
Fortschritte der Physik/Progress of Physics [44561]
Fraunhofer (English) [44562]
International Journal of Pattern Recognition and Artificial Intelligence [44564]
Journal of Neurology [44566]
Radiation and Environmental Biophysics [44579]

Oldendorf
Ethics in Science and Environmental Politics [44628]
Marine Ecology Progress Series (MEPS) [44629]

Paderborn
Particle and Particle Systems Characterization [44632]

Rostock
Catalysis Communications [44646]

Saarbrucken
Progress in Materials Science [44652]

Seewiesen
Arthropod Structure & Development [44655]

Stuttgart
Advances in Bryology [44659]
Bibliotheca Mycologica [44662]
Bibliotheca Phycologica [44663]
Contributions to Sedimentary Geology [44664]
Diatom Research [44665]
Eiszeitalter und Gegenwart Quaternary Science Journal [44666]
Neues Jahrbuch fur Geologie und Palaontologie [44672]
Nova Hedwigia [44673]
Nuclear Engineering and Design [44674]
Synthesis-Stuttgart [44682]

Circulation: ★ = ABC; △ = BPA; ◆ = CAC; • = CCAB; ❏ = VAC; ⊕ = PO Statement; ‡ = Publisher's Report; Boldface figures = sworn; Light figures = estimated.

Zeitschrift der Deutschen Geologis-
chen Gesellschaft [44685]
Zeitschrift fur Geomorphologie
[44686]
Weinheim
Starch/Staerke [44708]
Wurzburg
Cytogenetic and Genome Research
[44719]

GHANA
Winneba
African Journal of Educational Studies in Mathematics and Sciences
[44740]

GREECE
Kapandriti
Anticancer Research [44760]
Patras
Theoretical Computer Science
[44766]
Piraeus
International Journal of Applied Sys-
temic Studies [44767]
Journal of Applied Systems Studies
[44769]

HUNGARY
Budapest
Acta Alimentaria [44805]
Acta Biologica Hungarica [44808]
Acta Geodaetica et Geophysica
Hungarica [44809]
Acta Geologica Hungarica [44810]
Acta Microbiologica et Immunologica
Hungarica [44814]
Acta Physiologica Hungarica [44817]
Acta Phytopathologica et Entomo-
logica Hungarica [44818]
Acta Veterinaria Hungarica [44819]
Acta Zoologica Academiae Scien-
tiarum Hungaricae [44820]
Agrokemia es Talajtan [44821]
Epites - Epiteszettudomany [44828]
Journal of Planar Chromatography
[44842]
Magyar Pszichologiai Szemle [44846]
Nanopages [44854]
Pollack Periodica [44864]
Scientometrics [44869]
Studia Scientiarum Mathematicarum
Hungarica [44876]
Martonvasar
Acta Agronomica Hungarica [44890]
Miskolc-Egyetemvaros
Journal of Computational and Applied
Mechanics [44891]
Nyiregyhaza
Acta Mathematica Academiae Paeda-
gogicae Nyiregyhaziensis [44892]
Pecs
Acta Botanica Hungarica [44893]
Szeged
Acta Ethnographica Hungarica
[44894]

INDIA
Allahabad
Far East Journal of Dynamical
Systems [44926]
JP Journal of Heat and Mass
Transfer [44938]
JP Journal of Solids and Structures
[44939]
Bangalore
Bulletin of Materials Science
[44951] 2,228

Current Science [44956] 5,500
Indian Institute of Science Journal
[44959] .... (Paid) 500
Journal of Cutaneous and Aesthetic
Surgery [44968]
Resonance [44985] ..... (Paid) 8,000
Bhopal
Ultra Scientist of Physical Sciences
[45007]
Chandigarh
Indian Journal of Nephrology [45023]
Chennai
Journal of Forensic Dental Sciences
[45028]
International Journal of Spray and
Combustion Dynamics [45042]
Journal of Energy, Heat and Mass
Transfer [45047] .... (Paid) 200
Coimbatore
Ancient Science of Life
[45077] .... (Paid) 2,000
Cuttack
Hepatitis B Annual [45081]
Delhi
DESIDOC Bulletin of Information
Technology [45092] ... .. (Paid) 700
Indian Journal of Allergy Asthma and
Immunology [45096]
Howrah
Journal of Technology
[45138] .... (Paid) 250
Jaipur
Indian Journal of Clinical
Biochemistry [45195]
Indian Journal of Sexually Transmit-
ted Diseases [45196]
Jodhpur
Annual Review of Plant Pathology
[45215]
Indian Journal of Applied Entomology
[45219]
Kochi
QPMPA Journal of Medical Sciences
[45253]
Kolkata
Asian Journal of Transfusion Science
[45258]
Journal of Optics
[45297] .... (Paid) 600
Nano Science and Nano Technology
[45299]
Ludhiana
Indian Journal of Urology [45331]
Mumbai
Indian Journal of Nuclear Medicine
[45384]
International Journal of Diabetes in
Developing Countries [45393]
International Journal of Emerging and
Multidisciplinary Fluid Science
[45394]
Mens Sana Monographs [45411]
Young Scientists Journal [45451]
New Delhi
Advances in Dynamical Systems and
Applications [45477]
Algebraic Hyperstructures and
Applications [45482]
Annals of Cardiac Anaesthesia
[45483]
Gas News [45518]
The Indian Journal of Crop Science
[45550]
Indian Journal of History of Science
[45555] 380
Indian Journal of Mathematics and
Mathematical Sciences [45560]

Indian Journal of Palliative Care
[45563]
Indian National Science Academy
Biographical Memoirs of Fellows
[45573]
Indian National Science Academy
Year Book [45574] ... (Paid) 1,000
International Journal for Computa-
tional Vision and Biomechanics
[45581]
International Journal of Scientific
Computing [45584]
International Journal of Theoretical
and Applied Computer Sciences
(IJTACS) [45587]
International Review of Pure and Ap-
plied Chemistry [45589]
Journal of Cytology [45594]
Journal of Indian Association of Pedi-
atric Surgeons [45601]
Journal of the Indian Society of Soil
Science [45605] .... (Paid) 2,500
Journal of International Economic
Review [45609]
Journal of Mathematical Analysis and
Approximation Theory [45613]
Journal of Pediatric Neurosciences
[45615]
Journal of Scientific and Industrial
Research [45617] .. ... (Paid) 1100
Journal of Social Anthropology
[45618]
School Science
[45647] .... (Paid) 1,000
Science, Technology & Society
[45648] .... (Paid) 500
VATIS Update Biotechnology
[45662] 700
VATIS Update Non-Conventional
Energy [45664] 700
VATIS Update Ozone Layer
Protection [45665] 2,300
VATIS Update Waste Management
[45666] 500
Patiala
Journal of Indian Academy of Foren-
sic Medicine [45685]
Rajkot
Biochemistry [45706]
Biotechnology [45707]
Roorkee
Analytical Chemistry [45717]
Tirupati
Environmental Science [45756]
Trivandrum
Annals of Indian Academy of
Neurology [45757]

IRAN
Kashan
International Journal of Pure & Ap-
plied Mathematical Sciences
(IJPAMS) [45880]
Kerman
Global Journal of Mathematics and
Mathematical Sciences (GJMMS)
[45881]
Journal of Dynamical Systems and
Geometric Theories [45882]
Shiraz
Iranian Journal of Science and
Technology
[45884] .... (Paid) 1,000
Tehran
Advances in Aerospace and
Applications [45886]
DARU [45888]
Hepatitis Monthly [45889]
Scientia Iranica
[45913] .... (Paid) 5,000

IRELAND
Dublin
Historical Biology [45964]
Irish Studies in International Affairs
[45985]

ISRAEL
Tel Aviv
Corrosion Reviews [46097]
International Journal of Nonlinear Sci-
ences and Numerical Simulation
[46104]

ITALY
Florence
Global Bioethics [46144]
Nuncius [46145]
Genoa
Epistemologia [46148]
Milan
Journal of Applied Biomaterials &
Biomechanics [46181]
Rome
Cognitive Processing [46225]
Udine
Advances in Fuzzy Mathematics
[46276]

JAMAICA
Kingston
Jamaica Journal of Science and
Technology [46286]

JAPAN
Chiba
DNA Research [46317]
Kagoshima
South Pacific Studies
[46405] .... (Controlled) 700
Kyoto
Chemistry Letters
[46468] .... ‡43,200
Mathematics Applied in Science and
Technology [46482]
Osaka
Advances in Applied Mathematical
Analysis [46614]
Applied Surface Science [46615]
Journal of Approximation Theory and
Applications [46619]
Journal of Bioscience and
Bioengineering [46620]
Sakyo-ku
Fluid Dynamics Research [46648]
Sendai
High Temperature Materials and
Processes [46666]
Tochigi
Journal of Equine Science [46710]
Tokyo
Biology and Fertility of Soils [46765]
Cancer Chemotherapy and
Pharmacology [46777]
Computing and Visualization in
Science [46794]
Development Genes and Evolution
[46802]
Extremophiles [46820]
Joho-Shori [46878] 27,000
Journal of Bone and Mineral
Metabolism
[46889] .... (Paid) 2,500
Journal of Japanese Scientists
[46916]
Journal of Nuclear Science and
Technology [46930] 1,500

Medical Molecular Morphology
[46966]
Microbiology and Immunology
[46968] .. .. (Paid) 1,000
Proceedings of the Japan Academy,
Series B [47027]

Yokohama

Mitsubishi Heavy Industries Technical
Review [47140] 3,000

JORDAN
Amman

Dirasat Engineering Sciences
[47154] .... (Controlled) 1,000
Dirasat Pure Sciences
[47157] .... (Controlled) 1,000

KENYA
Nairobi

African Journal of Biotechnology
[47170]
African Journal of Health Sciences
[47173]
African Journal of Science and
Technology [47174]
Discovery and Innovation [47177]
East and Central African Journal of
Pharmaceutical Sciences [47182]
Innovation [47184]

REPUBLIC OF KOREA
Chinju

Advances in Algebra [47218]

Kyungnam

Advances in Theoretical and Applied
Mathematics [47242]

Masan

International Journal of Mathematical
Sciences [47243]

Seoul

Biochemistry and Molecular Biology
Reports [47258]
International Journal of Applied Envi-
ronmental Sciences [47267]
International Journal of Hybrid Intelli-
gent Systems [47268]
Journal of Computational Intelligence
in Bioinformatics [47272]

LEBANON
Beirut

Lebanese Science Journal [47398]

MALAWI
Zomba

Malawi Journal of Science and
Technology [47573]

MALAYSIA
Kuala Lumpur

Malayan Nature Journal
[47611] .. .. (Paid) 2,500

Penang

The Classroom Teacher
[47688] 100
Journal of Science and Mathematics
Education in Southeast Asia
[47689] 100

Serdang

Asia-Pacific Journal of Molecular Biology & Biotechnology [47714]

MAURITIUS
Reduit

African Journal of Pharmacy &
Pharmacology [47754]

MEXICO
Mexico City

CIMMYT Annual Report
[47783] 5,000

NETHERLANDS
Amsterdam

Advances in Space Research
[47883]
AI Communications [47887]
American Journal of Preventive
Medicine [47889] ... (Paid) ‡2,500
(Non-paid) ‡18
Cell Biology International [47923]
Communications in Nonlinear Sci-
ence and Numerical Simulation
[47932]
Cytokine [47952]
European Journal of Transport and
Infrastructure Research [47975]
Evolution and Human Behavior
[47977]
Finite Fields and Their Applications
[47986]
Frontiers in Neuroendocrinology
[47991]
Future Generation Computer
Systems [47995]
Geothermics [47998]
Infant Behavior and Development
[48016]
Journal of Applied Mathematics and
Mechanics [48047]
Journal of Asian Earth Sciences
[48050]
Journal of Autoimmunity [48053]
Journal of Chromatography A [48059]
Journal of Computational Methods in
Sciences and Engineering [48063]
Journal of Cultural Heritage [48066]
Journal of Geodynamics [48081]
Journal of Magnetic Resonance
[48093]
Journal of Multivariate Analysis
[48100]
Journal of Neurolinguistics [48102]
Journal of Non-Newtonian Fluid
Mechanics [48103]
Journal of Proteomics [48113]
Metabolic Engineering [48154]
Neurobiology of Disease [48173]
Nuclear Data Sheets [48184]
Nuclear Physics A [48185]
Nuclear Physics B [48186]
Nuclear Physics B [48187]
Physics and Chemistry of the Earth
[48202]
Planetary and Space Science
[48204]
Pragmatics & Cognition [48211]
Progress in Surface Science [48216]
Seminars in Cell & Developmental
Biology [48230]
Strength, Fracture and Complexity
[48238]

Beekbergen

World Poultry Science Journal
[48277] 7,000

Bussum

Current Proteomics [48296]
Current Signal Transduction Therapy
[48297]
Japanese Heart Journal [48303]
Recent Patents on Cardiovascular
Drug Discovery [48304]
Recent Patents on Nanotechnology
[48306]
Topics in Catalysis [48307]

Delft

Hydrology and Earth System Sci-
ences Discussions [48309]
International Shipbuilding Progress
[48310]
Journal of Molecular Catalysis B
[48311]
Journal on Satisfiability, Boolean
Modeling and Computation [48312]

Doorwerth

Weed Research [48317]

Dordrecht

Annals of Operations Research
[48326]
Brain and Mind [48336]
Catalysis Letters [48344]
Catalysis Surveys from Asia [48345]
Chemosensory Perception [48350]
Chinese Science Bulletin [48351]
Discrete Event Dynamic Systems
[48375]
European Journal of Clinical Microbi-
ology & Infectious Diseases
[48381]
Evolution: Education and Outreach
[48385]
Foundations of Science [48392]
GeoInformatica [48406]
Gynecological Surgery [48411]
Hyperfine Interactions [48420]
Informatik-Spektrum [48421]
Integrated Assessment [48423]
Invertebrate Neuroscience [48433]
Ionics [48434]
Journal of Applied Electrochemistry
[48437]
Journal of the Association for Re-
search in Otolaryngology [48439]
Journal of Atmospheric Chemistry
[48440]
Journal of Cluster Science [48449]
Journal of Global Optimization
[48465]
Journal of Materials Science [48473]
Journal of Neuroimmune
Pharmacology [48478]
Journal of Orofacial Orthopedics/
Fortschritte der Kieferorthopadie
[48481]
Journal of Pest Science [48482]
Journal of Scheduling [48491]
Journal of Science Teacher
Education [48492]
Journal of Superconductivity and
Novel Magnetism [48495]
Journal of Systems Science and
Complexity [48496]
Journal of Systems Science and Sys-
tems Engineering [48497]
Landslides [48504]
Mycopathologia [48516]
Natural Computing [48517]
Optimization and Engineering
[48521]
Origins of Life and Evolution of the
Biosphere [48523]
Photosynthesis Research [48528]
Pituitary [48531]
Plant Cell, Tissue and Organ Culture
[48532]
Plant Foods for Human Nutrition
[48534]
Plant and Soil [48536]
Science & Education [48559]
Studia Logica [48569]
Surveys in Geophysics [48573]
Synthese [48575]

Eindhoven

E-Polymers [48589]

Enschede

International Journal of Applied Earth
Observation and Geoinformation
[48593]

Houten

Basin Research [48638]
First Break [48639] 25,000
Geophysical Prospecting
[48640] .... ‡8,841

Leiden

Animal Biology [48647]
Behaviour [48656]

Insect Systematics & Evolution
[48678]
International Journal of
Myriapodology [48681]
Journal of Biomaterials Science,
Polymer Edition [48690]
KronoScope [48705]
Seeing and Perceiving [48723]
Terrestrial Arthropod Reviews [48727]

Nijmegen

Early Science and Medicine [48743]
European Journal of Psychological
Assessment [48744] 800
Neurocomputing [48745]

Wageningen

NJAS [48772]

NEW ZEALAND
Auckland

Meteorite [48804]

Wellington

Journal of the Royal Society of New
Zealand [49011]
New Zealand Journal of Agricultural
Research [49021]
New Zealand Journal of Crop and
Horticultural Science [49023]
New Zealand Journal of Geology and
Geophysics [49025]
New Zealand Journal of Marine and
Freshwater Research [49027]

NIGERIA
Aba

Journal of Medical Investigation and
Practice [49055]

Abuja

Journal for Phytomedicine and
Therapeutics [49056]

Asaba

Journal of Applied Chemistry and Agricultural Research [49061]

Benin City

African Journal of Reproductive
Health [49062]
Journal of the Nigerian Association of
Mathematical Physics [49065]

Calabar

Global Journal of Pure and Applied
Sciences [49075]
Journal of Medical Laboratory
Science [49077]

Enugu

Nigerian Journal of
Otorhinolaryngology [49082]

Ibadan

African Journal for the Psychological
Study of Social Issues [49086]
Nigerian Journal of Horticultural
Science [49097]
Tropical Journal of Animal Science
[49101]
West African Journal of Medicine
[49104]

Ile-Ife

African Journal of Traditional,
Complementary and Alternative
Medicines [49111]

Ilorin

African Journal of Clinical and Experimental Microbiology [49117]
Tropical Journal of Health Sciences
[49122]

Jos

Highland Medical Research Journal
[49124]
Journal of Aquatic Sciences [49125]

Circulation: ★ = ABC; △ = BPA; ◆ = CAC; • = CCAB; ❏ = VAC; ⊕ = PO Statement; ‡ = Publisher's Report; Boldface figures = sworn; Light figures = estimated.

Journal of Pharmacy and Bioresources [49127]

Lagos
African Journal of Food Science [49132]
African Journal of Microbiology Research [49133]
African Journal of Plant Science [49134]
African Journal of Pure & Applied Chemistry [49136]
Journal of Cell & Animal Biology [49139]
Scientific Research & Essays [49143]

Nnewi
Journal of Biomedical Investigation [49148]

Nsukka
Agro-Science [49154]
Bio-Research [49156]

Port Harcourt
Journal of Applied Sciences and Environmental Management [49166]
Journal of Technology and Education in Nigeria [49168]

Sagamu
Nigerian Journal of Orthopaedics and Trauma [49170]

Uturu
Journal of Health and Visual Sciences [49177]

Zaria
Annals of Nigerian Medicine [49181]
Nigerian Journal of Surgical Research [49185]

OMAN
Muscat
International Journal of Food Properties [49221]

PAKISTAN
Faisalabad
Academic Journal of Cancer Research [49228]
Advances in Biological Research [49230]
American-Eurasian Journal of Agricultural & Environmental Sciences [49232]
American-Eurasian Journal of Botany [49233]
American-Eurasian Journal of Scientific Research [49234]
Australian Journal of Basic and Applied Sciences [49238]
Biotechnology [49239]
Botany Research Journal [49240]
Global Journal of Environmental Research [49242]
Global Journal of Molecular Sciences [49243]
International Journal of Molecular Medicine and Advance Sciences [49251]
Journal of Applied Sciences Research [49262]
Journal of Engineering and Applied Sciences [49266]
Journal of Food Technology [49269]
Journal of Molecular Genetics [49273]
Middle East Journal of Scientific Research [49274]
Online Journal of Earth Sciences [49275]
Plant Sciences Research [49279]
Research Journal of Agriculture and Biological Sciences [49280]

Research Journal of Agronomy [49281]
Research Journal of Animal Sciences [49282]
Research Journal of Applied Sciences [49284]
Research Journal of Biological Sciences [49285]
Research Journal of Cell and Molecular Biology [49286]
Research Journal of Dairy Sciences [49287]
Research Journal of Fisheries and Hydrobiology [49288]
Research Journal of Medical Sciences [49289]
Research Journal of Medicine and Medical Sciences [49290]
World Applied Sciences Journal [49297]
World Journal of Chemistry [49300]
World Journal of Medical Sciences [49302]
World Journal of Zoology [49303]

Islamabad
Pakistan Journal of Scientific and Industrial Research
[49309] .... (Paid) 800

Karachi
Current Nanoscience [49343]

Peshawar
Journal of Pakistan Psychiatric Society [49393]

PERU
Lima
Anales de la Facultad de Medicina [49423]

PHILIPPINES
Cebu City
Philippine Scientist
[49463] .... (Paid) 200

Manila
Manila Journal of Science
[49553] .... (Paid) 300
Unitas [49560] .... (Paid) 500

Taguig City
NRCD Research Journal of the Philippines [49639]
Philippine Journal of Science
[49641] .... (Paid) 1,300

POLAND
Kornik
Dendrobiology [49663]

Krakow
Acta Physica Polonica B [49664]

Warsaw
Acta Geophysica [49679]
Acta Neurobiologiae Experimentalis [49680]
Advances in Cell Biology [49684]
Advances in Materials Science [49686]
Advances in Medical Sciences [49687]
Annals of Warsaw University of Life Sciences, Land Reclamation [49689]
Anthropological Review [49690]
Artificial Satellites [49693]
Biologija [49696]
Central European Journal of Geosciences [49700]
Journal of Human Kinetics [49722]
Journal of Medical Biochemistry [49724]

Latvian Journal of Physics and Technical Sciences [49730]
Macedonian Journal of Medical Sciences [49734]
Nukleonika [49739]
Old and New Concepts of Physics [49741]
Polish Journal of Chemical Technology [49748]

Zabrze
Annales Academiae Medicae Silesiensis [49781]

PORTUGAL
Aveiro
International Journal of Surface Science & Engineering [49789]

Lisbon
Revista de Ciencias Agrarias [49805]

RUSSIA
Moscow
Astronomical and Astrophysical Transactions [49876]
Bulletin of the Crimean Astrophysical Observatory [49885]
Cosmic Research [49890]
Crystallography Reports [49891]
Herald of the Russian Academy of Sciences [49912]
Izvestiya [49923]
Molecular Genetics, Microbiology & Virology [49943]
Moscow Mathematical Journal [49945]
Pattern Recognition and Image Analysis [49952]
Problems of Virology [49967]
Russian Journal of Bioorganic Chemistry [49975]
Russian Journal of Oncology [49978]

Novosibirsk
Journal of Mining Sciences [50012]

Saint Petersburg
Reviews on Advanced Materials Science [50025]

SAUDI ARABIA
Riyadh
Annals of Thoracic Medicine [50059]
Journal of King Saud University: Science [50068] .... (Paid) 3,000

SERBIA
Sremska Kamenica
Archive of Oncology [50094]

SINGAPORE
Singapore
Acta Biomaterialia [50101]
Comptes Rendus [50124]
COSMOS [50128]
Drug Discovery Today [50137]
Drug Discovery Today [50138]
Innovation [50173] 10,000
International Immunopharmacology [50175]
International Journal of Geometric Methods in Modern Physics (IJGMMP) [50180]
International Journal of Modern Physics D [50187]
International Journal of Nanoscience [50189]
International Journal of Neural Systems [50190]

SLOVAKIA
Bratislava
Acta Physica Slovaca [50315]

Journal of Hydrology and Hydromechanics [50320]
Measurement Science Review [50321]

Kosice
Acta Montanistica Slovaca [50325]

SLOVENIA
Ljubljana
Acta Geographica Slovenica [50336]
International Journal of Microstructure and Materials Properties [50338]

REPUBLIC OF SOUTH AFRICA
Bloemfontein
Navorsinge van die Nasionale Musium, Bloemfontein [50355]

Cape Town
International Journal of Shoulder Surgery [50384]

Centurion
African Journal of Research in Mathematics, Science and Technology Education [50437]
Southern African Journal of Critical Care [50455]

Grahamstown
African Journal of Biomedical Research [50487]
African Journal of Marine Science [50489]
Ethiopian Pharmaceutical Journal [50494]
Ghana Journal of Agricultural Science [50495]
International Journal of Natural and Applied Sciences [50498]
Journal of Applied Science, Engineering and Technology [50500]
Nigerian Journal of Parasitology [50506]
Sudan Journal of Medical Sciences [50516]

Johannesburg
South African Gastroenterology Review [50534]
Southern African Journal of Anaesthesia and Analgesia [50536]

Lynnwood Ridge
Quest [50550]
South African Journal of Science [50551]

Pietermaritzburg
African Journal of Range and Forage Science [50565] .. .. (Paid) 196
Indilinga [50568]

Pinelands
South African Journal of Obstetrics and Gynaecology [50574]

Pretoria
African Journal of Cross-Cultural Psychology and Sport Facilitation [50583]
Journal of African Earth Sciences [50593]
Sahara J [50599]

Rondebosch
Language Sciences [50620]

SPAIN
Bilbao
Chemistry [50710]

Burjasot
Food Science and Technology International [50711]

Cordoba
European Journal of Agronomy [50713]

Madrid
Cognitiva [50737]
Gerokomos [50762]
Revista Espanola de Paleontologia
[50797] 600

Murcia
Anales de Psicologia [50821]

Toledo
Physical Chemistry [50840]

Valencia
Inorganic Chemistry [50846]

SRI LANKA
Colombo
Journal of the National Aquatic Re-
sources Research & Development
Agency of Sri Lanka [50856]

Peradeniya
Ceylon Journal of Science, Physical
Sciences [50928]

SUDAN
Khartoum
Sudanese Journal of Dermatology
[50939]

SWAZILAND
Kwaluseni
UNISWA Research Journal of Agriculture, Science and Technology
[50944]

SWEDEN
Stockholm
Alcheringa [51004]
EuroSurveillance [51015]
Seminars in Cancer Biology [51036]
Signal Processing [51037]

SWITZERLAND
Bassersdorf
Seed Science and Technology
[51067]

Birmensdorf
Dendrochronologia [51082]

Geneva
The Botulinum Journal [51088]
Computer Graphics Forum Journal
[51090] .. .. (Paid) ‡844
International Journal of Applied Non-
linear Science [51102]
International Journal of Biomedical
Nanoscience and Nanotechnology
[51104]
International Journal of Complexity in
Applied Science and Engineering
[51110]
International Journal of Exergy
[51120]
International Journal of Nano and
Biomaterials [51133]

Zurich
Acta Crystallographica Section A
[51246]
Acta Crystallographica Section B
[51247]
Acta Crystallographica Section C
[51248]
Acta Crystallographica Section D
[51249]
Acta Crystallographica Section F
[51250]
Advances in Science and Technology
[51251]
Defect and Diffusion Forum [51257]
LWT - Food Science and Technology
[51274]

Solid State Phenomena [51283]

**UNITED REPUBLIC OF TAN-
ZANIA**
Dar es Salaam
Tanzania Journal of Science [51403]

THAILAND
Bangkok
Update Magazine [51447]

TUNISIA
Tunis
Journal of the Arabization Bureau
[51489]

TURKEY
Ankara
Biyokimya Dergisi [51490]

Izmir
Journal of the Faculty of Science,
Ege University, Series A [51574]

Van
Journal of Contemporary
Mathematics [51580]

UGANDA
Kampala
African Health Sciences [51584]

UKRAINE
Kharkov
Fizika Nizkikh Temperatur [51592]

Kiev
Random Operators and Stochastic
Equations [51607] .. .. ‡140
Technical Diagnostics and Nonde-
structive Testing [51608]

UNITED ARAB EMIRATES
Abu Dhabi
International Journal of Petroleum
Science and Technology [51620]

UNITED KINGDOM
Abingdon
Educational Action Research [51770]
European Journal of Sport Science
[51781]
Isotopes in Environmental and Health
Studies [51862]
Journal of Experimental Nanoscience
[51897]
Liquid Crystals [51970]
Network [51991]
Theology and Science [52077]

Bath
Journal of Micropalaeontology
[52249]
Petroleum Geoscience
[52254] 5,000

Bedfordshire
European Journal of Soil Science
[52278]

Birmingham
Progress in Nuclear Energy [52362]

Bradford
Coloration Technology [52443]
Industrial Lubrication and Tribology
[52465]
International Journal of Productivity
and Performance Management
[52485]

Brentwood
Acoustics Abstracts [52564]

Biomass Bulletin [52567]
Building Acoustics [52569]
International Journal of Aeroacoustics
[52575]
International Journal of Innovation
Science [52577]
The Journal of Computational Mul-
tiphase Flows [52579]
Journal of Low Frequency Noise, Vi-
bration & Active Control [52580]
Low Frequency Noise, Vibration and
Active Control [52581]
Noise & Vibration Bulletin [52583]
Noise & Vibration in Industry [52584]
Rare Earth Bulletin [52587]
Renewable Energy Bulletin [52588]
Wind Engineering [52590]
Wind Engineering Abstracts [52591]

Bristol
Bioinspiration & Biomimetics [52646]
Biomedical Materials [52647]
The British Journal for the Philosophy
of Science [52649]
Classical and Quantum Gravity
[52653]
Computers and Law
[52655] 2,700
Endocrine Abstracts [52662]
European Journal of Physics [52665]
Europhysics Letters (EPL) [52666]
International Journal of Adhesion and
Adhesives [52676]
International Journal of Modelling,
Identification and Control [52679]
Journal of Instrumentation [52687]
Journal of Molecular Catalysis A
[52690]
Journal of Physics A [52694]
Journal of Physics D [52695]
Journal of Radiological Protection
[52697]
Measurement Science & Technology
[52705] .. .. (Combined) 2,100
Nonlinearity [52712]
Plant Biotechnology Journal [52719]
Plasma Physics and Controlled
Fusion [52720]

Buckingham
Biofouling [52754]

Cambridge
Analyst [52786]
Analytical Abstract [52787]
Biological Reviews [52792]
Catalysts & Catalysed Reactions
[52802]
Chemical Communications
[52803] .. .. (Paid) 3,000
Chemical Society Reviews [52804]
Energy & Environmental Science
[52817]
Faraday Discussions [52819]
FEBS Journal [52820]
Focus on Catalysts [52821]
Highlights in Chemical Science
[52827]
Journal of Advanced Materials
[52841]
Journal of Biosocial Science
[52846] 500
Journal of Environmental Monitoring
[52851]
Journal of Materials Chemistry
[52859]
Lab on a Chip [52866]
Metallomics [52868]
Methods in Organic Synthesis
[52869]
Natural Product Reports [52873]
New Journal of Chemistry [52876]
Nutrition Research Reviews [52879]
Organic & Biomolecular Chemistry
[52880]

Photochemical & Photobiological
Science [52882]
Physical Chemistry, Chemical
Physics [52883]
Quarterly Reviews of Biophysics
[52889]
Studies in History and Philosophy of
Science Part A [52899]
Studies in History and Philosophy of
Science Part C [52900]
Ultramicroscopy [52904]

Chester
Food and Agricultural Immunology
[52995]
LCGC Europe
[52996] .. .. (Controlled) △26,000

Chichester
European Journal of Mass
Spectrometry [53009]
Journal of Analytical Atomic
Spectrometry [53013]
Optimal Control Applications &
Methods [53015]

Croydon
Laboratory News
[53128] .... (Controlled) ★11,095

Edinburgh
Cloning and Stem Cells [53263]
Nanotoxicology [53301]
Teaching Earth Sciences [53323]

Exeter
Geophysical & Astrophysical Fluid
Dynamics [53359]

Glasgow
Addiction Research and Theory
[53409]
Graefe's Archive for Clinical and Experimental Ophthalmology [53422]
International Journal of Adaptive Control & Signal Processing [53425]

Hatfield
Science Education International
[53542] 700

Horsham
Science Review [53601]

Kidlington
Journal of Environmental Sciences
[53698]

Leeds
Astronomy and Geophysics [53756]

Liverpool
Fingerprint Whorld [53873]

London
Acta Pharmacologica Sinica [53895]
Anatomical Science International
[53941]
Applied Earth Science
[53959] 500
Biocatalysis and Biotransformation
[54018]
Bioinformation [54020]
Biologist [54023] 26,000
Biomarkers [54025]
Biomedical Scientist
[54030] .. .. (Paid) 14,500
BioVenture View
[54031] .. .. (Paid) 327
Britannia [54107] 1,500
British Journal of Biomedical Science
[54112]
British Journal of Ophthalmology
[54129] .... ‡2,370
British Journal of Psychiatry [54132]
British Medical Journal Clinical
Evidence [54140]
Bubble Science, Engineering and
Technology [54151]

Circulation: ★ = ABC; △ = BPA; ♦ = CAC; • = CCAB; ❑ = VAC; ⊕ = PO Statement; ‡ = Publisher's Report; Boldface figures = sworn; Light figures = estimated.

Bulletin of the School of Oriental and
  African Studies [54157] 900
Clinical Risk [54231]
Corrosion Engineering, Science and
  Technology [54269] 900
Current Neuropharmacology [54296]
Current Opinion in Neurology [54302]
The Environmental Scientist [54378]
Etudes Episteme [54388]
European Research in Regional
  Science [54410]
Food Science and Technology
  [54478]
Gene Therapy [54499]
Gold Bulletin [54516]
High Temperatures-High Pressures
  [54551]
Interdisciplinary Science Reviews
  [54615]
International Journal of Robotics
  Research [54660]
Inverse Problems [54677]
Journal of Bioactive and Compatible
  Polymers [54704] 180
Journal of Biomaterials Applications
  [54707] 160
Journal of Cellular Plastics
  [54720] .. .. ‡340
Journal of Elastomers and Plastics
  [54742] .. .. ‡275
Journal of Fire Sciences
  [54754] 350
Journal of Global History [54757]
Journal of Hydroinformatics [54764]
Journal of Industrial Textiles
  [54766] .. .. ‡260
Journal of Physics B [54799]
Journal of Physics C [54800]
Journal of Physics G [54801]
Journal of Plastic Film and Sheeting
  [54803] 300
Journal of Reinforced Plastics and
  Composites [54807] 320
Journal of the Royal Society Interface
  [54813]
Journal of the Science of Food and
  Agriculture [54816]
Journal of Thermoplastic Composite
  Materials [54829] 200
Journal of Translational Medicine
  [54830]
Journal of Water Supply [54835]
Laboratory Animals [54847]
Lebensmittel-Wissenschaft und-Technologie
  [54863]
Lubrication Science [54892]
Molecular Cancer [54945]
Nature Materials [54972]
Nature Methods [54973]
Nature Reviews Microbiology [54982]
New Scientist [54998]
Notes & Records of the Royal
  Society [55013]
Pathology [55062]
People & Science [55066] 3,000
Personal and Ubiquitous Computing
  [55070]
Philosophical Transactions of the
  Royal Society A [55079]
Philosophical Transactions of the
  Royal Society B [55080]
Phlebology [55084]
Physics Education [55086]
Physics World [55087] *34,495
Powder Metallurgy [55110]
Profound (The Dialog Corporation) of
  the Royal Society A [55133]
Profound (The Dialog Corporation) of
  the Royal Society B [55134]
The Psychiatrist [55149]
Semiconductor Science and
  Technology [55228]
Superconductor Science and
  Technology [55278]

Systematic Parasitology [55284]
Technoetic Arts [55295]
Tropical Doctor [55342]

Macclesfield
Biologics [55514]
Clinical Interventions in Aging
  [55515]

Machynlleth
Clean Slate [55522] 8,500

Manchester
Crystallography Reviews [55552]
Reactive and Functional Polymers
  [55576]

Marlow
Menopause International [55600]

Mere
Advances in Clinical Neuroscience &
  Rehabilitation [55609]

Middlewich
Journal of Bryology [55624]

Newcastle upon Tyne
Formal Aspects of Computing
  [55670]

Northwich
International Journal of Cosmetic
  Science [55719]

Norwich
British Journal for the History of
  Science [55727] .. .. ‡1,500

Nottingham
International Journal of Remote
  Sensing [55763]

Olney
International Journal of Aerodynamics
  [55788]
International Journal of Alternative
  Propulsion [55789]
International Journal of Cognitive
  Performance Support (IJCPS)
  [55793]
International Journal of Critical
  Infrastructures [55797]
International Journal of Energy Tech-
  nology and Policy [55800]
International Journal of Intelligent
  Systems Technologies and
  Applications [55814]
International Journal of Virtual Tech-
  nology and Multimedia [55839]
World Review of Science, Technology
  and Sustainable Development
  [55847]

Oxford
Animal Science Journal [55867]
Briefings in Functional Genomics &
  Proteomics [55890]
Contemporary Issues in Early
  Childhood [55915]
Environmental Science & Policy
  [55938]
ESHRE Monographs [55940]
European Biophysics Journal [55942]
Glycobiology [55967]
infocus Magazine [55989]
Journal of Electron Microscopy
  [56028]
Journal of the ICRU [56040]
Nursing and Health Sciences [56122]

Penicuik
Animal
  [56243] .. .. (Combined) 10,400

Plymouth
The Hydrographic Journal
  [56270] 2,000

Reading
Molecular Plant Pathology [56327]

Ross-on-Wye
Marine Conservation
  [56410] .. .. (Paid) 5,000

Sheffield
Connection Science [56490]
Inflammopharmacology [56498]
International Journal of Systems
  Science [56502]
Surface and Coatings Technology
  [56515]

Southampton
Naturwissenschaften [56575]

Stevenage
Systems Biology [56618]

Sunderland
Neural Computing & Applications
  [56654] .. .. (Paid) 720

Sutton
New Scientist [56690]

Swansea
Engineering Computations [56701]

Thurso
Journal of the British Society of Scientific Glassblowers [56750]

Twickenham
Clay Minerals [56789]

Wales
International Journal of Applied Mathematics and Mechanics (IJAMM)
  [56812]

Wallingford
Postharvest News and Information
  [56823] 150

West Yorkshire
Kybernetes [56904]

Witney
Bio-science Law Review [56939]

York
Medical Engineering and Physics
  [56993]
Scope [56998] 2,400

UZBEKISTAN
Tashkent
Applied Solar Energy [57014]

VENEZUELA
Caracas
Acta Cientifica Venezolana
  [57020] .. .. (Non-paid) ‡500

ZIMBABWE
Bindura
Southern Africa Journal of Science
  and Technology [57112]

Harare
Central African Journal of Medicine
  [57113]
Journal of Applied Science in Southern Africa [57115]

SEED AND NURSERY TRADE
See also Florists and Floriculture; Landscape Archi-
tecture; Turf and Turf Maintenance

ITALY
Vernasca
Flortecnica Data e Fiori
  [46279] .... (Controlled) 6,800

NEW ZEALAND
Auckland
Commercial Horticulture Magazine
  [48789] .. .. (Paid) 2,000

SWITZERLAND
Bassersdorf
Seed Science and Technology
  [51067]

UNITED KINGDOM
Cambridge
Seed Science Research [52893]

SEISMOLOGY

HUNGARY
Budapest
Acta Geodaetica et Geophysica
  Hungarica [44809]

SELLING AND SALESMANSHIP
See also Advertising and
Marketing; General Mer-
chandise

BELGIUM
Brussels
International Journal of Research in
  Marketing [42859]

GERMANY
Munich
W & V Werben & Verkaufen
  [44586] .. .. (Controlled) 33,885

INDIA
Hyderabad
The Icfai Journal of Services
  Marketing [45167]

UNITED KINGDOM
Harrogate
British Commercial Agents Review
  [53515]

SERVICE INDUSTRIES

PEOPLE'S REPUBLIC OF CHINA
Wuhan
International Journal of Services,
  Economics and Management
  [43523]

Xi'an
International Journal of Internet
  Manufacturing & Services [43532]

GREECE
Thessaloniki
International Journal of Innovation
  and Regional Development [44773]

INDIA
Hyderabad
The Icfai Journal of Knowledge
  Management [45157]
The Icfai Journal of Services
  Marketing [45167]

IRELAND
Blackrock
Hotel & Catering Review [45920]
Licensing World [45923]

JAPAN
Tokyo
International Journal of Services
  Technology and Management
  [46848]

Nikkei Restaurants
[47005] .... ★19,137

PORTUGAL
Viseu
International Journal of Simulation
and Process Modelling [49814]

SWITZERLAND
Geneva
International Journal of Services
Sciences [51139]

UNITED KINGDOM
Bradford
Journal of Service Management
[52516]
Bristol
University Caterer [52734] 2,500
Buckhurst Hill
Secure Times [52753] .... ‡9,306
Cambridge
Kiosk Europe [52865]
Derby
Professional Pest Controller
[53168] 3,000
Glasgow
Envirotec [53416] .. .. ★8,958
Kent
The Independent Electrical Retailer
[53678] .. .. (Controlled) ★6,895
London
British Journal of Healthcare
Assistants [54122]
COVER [54278]
Olney
International Journal of Six Sigma
and Competitive Advantage
[55832]
Salisbury
Land Mobile [56455] .. . (Paid) 8,500
Smallfield
Cafe Business [56562] 7,128
Welling
Launderette and Cleaning World
[56878]

SHIPS AND SHIPPING
See also Boats and Marine

PEOPLE'S REPUBLIC OF CHINA
Hong Kong
International Journal of Shipping and
Transport Logistics [43352]

GREECE
Athens
Naftiliaki [44752] .... (Paid) 4,000

INDIA
Mumbai
Indian Shipping
[45389] .. .. (Paid) 1,000

JAPAN
Osaka
Journal of Kansai Society of Naval
Architects [46622]
Tokyo
Ports and Harbors [47023] 5,000

NETHERLANDS
Delft
International Shipbuilding Progress
[48310]

NEW ZEALAND
Christchurch
The New Zealand Shipping Gazette
[48876]

REPUBLIC OF SOUTH AFRICA
Cape Town
Shipyear [50411] 10,000

UNITED KINGDOM
Birmingham
Transport Journal
[52371] .. .. (Controlled) 17,500
Burton-on-Trent
Ships Monthly [52771]
Cambridge
Ships and Offshore Structures
[52895]
Cardiff
Marine Policy [52936]
Charmouth
Tide Times [52958] ... . (Paid) 27,500
Colchester
Seatrade Magazine
[53048] .... ★6,426
Enfield
LNG World Shipping
[53332] .... ‡3,637
LPG World Shipping
[53333] .... (Combined) 2,586
Marine Electronics &
Communications [53334] ... ★6,944
Marine Propulsion & Auxiliary
Machinery [53335] .... ★12,525
Offshore Support Journal
[53336] .... ‡4,800
Tanker Shipping & Trade
[53337] .... ★4,798
Glasgow
Brown's Nautical Almanac
[53410] 13,000
London
Container Intelligence Quarterly
[54262]
Journal for Maritime Research
[54775]
The Naval Architect
[54986] .... (Combined) ★11,650
Ship & Boat International
[55233] .. .. (Combined) ★5,998
Ship Repair & Conversion
Technology
[55234] .... (Combined) 6,096
Significant Ships
[55239] .... (Combined) 4,000
Warship Technology
[55380] .... (Combined) 11,650
World Superyacht Review
[55424] 10,000
Redhill
Register of Ships [56377]
Safety at Sea International
[56378] .. .. (Paid) 6,000

SHOES, LEATHER, AND LUGGAGE

PEOPLE'S REPUBLIC OF CHINA
Hong Kong
HKTDC Fashion - Leather Goods &
Bags [43307]

INDIA
Chennai
Indian Leather
[45038] .. .. (Paid) 1,500

Leather News India
[45052] .. .. (Paid) 3,000

ITALY
Trezzano Sul Naviglio
Foto Shoe 15 International
[46263] .. .. (Combined) 8,000
Foto Shoe 30
[46264] .. .. (Combined) 8,000

NETHERLANDS
Maarssen
Tred [48733] .. .... (Combined) 3,100
Trend Boutique
[48734] .... (Combined) 2,200

SPAIN
Madrid
Revista del Calzado
[50796] 4,500

UNITED KINGDOM
Dewsbury
Journal of the Society of Leather
Technologists and Chemists
[53180] .... (Paid) 900
Kent
Footwear Today [53677]
Leicester
KFAT News [53808]

SOCIAL PROGRAMS
See also Philanthropy and Humanitarianism

AUSTRALIA
Hawthorn
Cosmos and History [41942]
Kingston
Australian Social Work
[41993] 6,500

BHUTAN
Thimphu
Journal of Bhutan Studies [42925]

PEOPLE'S REPUBLIC OF CHINA
Hong Kong
The Hong Kong Journal of Social
Work [43332]
Shanghai
Charity Matters [43468]

DENMARK
Copenhagen
Kontakt [43678] .. .. (Paid) 5,000

GERMANY
Cologne
Social Work and Society [44302]

GHANA
Navrongo
Ghana Journal of Development
Studies [44738]

HUNGARY
Budapest
Acta Juridica Hungarica [44812]

INDIA
Chennai
Rotary News/Rotary Samachar
[45056] .... (Paid) ⊕75,000

New Delhi
Journal of Social and Economic
Policy [45619]

REPUBLIC OF KOREA
Seoul
Asian Exchange [47255] 800

NETHERLANDS
Dordrecht
The Journal of Economic Inequality
[48457]
Theory and Society [48579]

NIGERIA
Makurdi
International Journal of Development
and Policy Studies [49145]

SINGAPORE
Pasir Panjang
SOJOURN [50100] .... (Paid) 700

REPUBLIC OF SOUTH AFRICA
Cape Town
The Big Issue [50364]
Claremont
South African Journal on Human
Rights [50464]
Grahamstown
Journal of Social Development in
Africa [50503] .... (Combined) 150

TURKEY
Ankara
Cooperation in Turkiye
[51491] 500
Ucuncu Sektor Kooperatifcilik
[51518] 1,500

UNITED ARAB EMIRATES
Dubai
Middle East MICE & Events
[51649] 33,000

UNITED KINGDOM
Abingdon
The British Journal of Sociology
[51721]
Child Care in Practice [51728]
Children's Geographies [51729]
Community, Work & Family [51738]
Cultural Studies [51747]
Ethics and Social Welfare [51773]
Review of Social Economy [52044]
Studies in Conflict and Terrorism
[52066]
Belfast
The British Journal of Social Work
[52279]
Birmingham
Child and Family Social Work
[52336]
Diversity in Health and Social Care
[52340]
Brighton
The International Journal of Leadership in Public Services [52616]
International Journal of Migration,
Health and Social Care [52617]
The Journal of Adult Protection
[52618]
Journal of Children's Services
[52619]
Journal of Integrated Care [52621]

Circulation: ★ = ABC; △ = BPA; ◆ = CAC; • = CCAB; ❑ = VAC; ⊕ = PO Statement; ‡ = Publisher's Report; Boldface figures = sworn; Light figures = estimated.

Learning Disability Review [52624]
Learning Disability Today [52625]
Quality in Ageing [52629]
Working with Older People [52635]

Bristol
Culture and Organization [52660]

Cambridge
Journal of Social Policy
[52862] 2,000

Kidlington
Journal of Rural Studies [53701]

Leicester
Youth Policy Update
[53835] 1,250

London
African Affairs [53918]
Critical Social Policy [54289]
Global Social Policy [54513]
Guiding Magazine
[54527] .... (Controlled) 28,000
International Social Work [54672]
Journal of European Social Policy
[54747]
Journal of Social Work [54820]
Population Studies
[55103] .... (Paid) ‡1,300
The Royal Society Yearbook [55209]
Sociology Review [55254]
U Magazine
[55351] ...... (Non-paid) 1,400,000
Urban Studies [55360]
WRVS Action [55428] 90,000

Oxford
International Journal of Public Opin-
ion Research [56001]
Journal of Urban Affairs [56077]
Social Anthropology [56207]
The Sociological Review [56210]

Sutton
Community Care [56682]

SOCIAL SCIENCES

ARGENTINA
Buenos Aires
Revista del CIAS [41479]

AUSTRALIA
Albury
Micronesian Journal of the Humani-
ties and Social Sciences [41527]

Clayton
Australian and New Zealand Journal
of Criminology [41757]

Goodwood
Australian Options [41903]

South Melbourne
Political Crossroads [42375]

Westleigh
Australian and New Zealand Journal
of Family Therapy [42699]

AUSTRIA
Vienna
European Journal of Cross-Cultural
Competence and Management
[42751]
The European Journal of Social
Sciences [42754]
TRANS [42770]

BANGLADESH
Dhaka
Bangladesh Development Studies
[42803] .... (Paid) 1,500

BELGIUM
Leuven
Iranica Antiqua [42899]

Rekkem
Ons Erfdeel
[42909] .. .. (Paid) 10,000
Septentrion [42910] ... (Paid) 10,000

BRAZIL
Campinas
Opiniao Publica [42971]

Petropolis
Computational & Applied
Mathematics [42990]

Sao Paulo
Sao Paulo em Perspectiva [43051]

PEOPLE'S REPUBLIC OF CHINA
Changchun
Jilin University Journal Social Sci-
ences Edition [43239]

Hong Kong
Hong Kong Journal of Sociology
[43333]

Shanghai
Academic Journal of Shanghai Jiao
Tong University Social Science
Section [43462]

Wuhan
Social Sciences Edition [43526]

Xi'an
Journal of Xauat (Social Sciences)
[43536]

Xiangtan
International Journal of Computing
Science and Mathematics [43539]

CROATIA
Zagreb
Diskrepancija [43567]
International Journal of Transitions
and Innovation Systems [43568]

CYPRUS
Nicosia
POLIS [43597]

DENMARK
Copenhagen
Kontakt [43678] .. .. (Paid) 5,000

EGYPT
Cairo
Afro-Arab Selections for Social
Sciences [43751]

ETHIOPIA
Addis Ababa
Ethiopian Journal of the Social Sci-
ences and Humanities [43801]

FRANCE
Aix-en-Provence
International Journal of Public Sector
Performance Management [43912]

Paris
Acta Astronautica [44020]
International Social Science Journal
[44060]
Journal Asiatique [44063]
The Tocqueville Review/La Revue
Tocqueville
[44085] .... (Combined) 500

GERMANY
Berlin
arcadia [44153] .... ‡500

Forum Qualitative Sozialforschung
[44183]
Dusseldorf
Psycho-Social-Medicine [44332]

Gottingen
Social Geography [44402]

Leinfelden-Echterdingen
bild der wissenschaft
[44517] 105,059
DAMALS [44518] 32,799

GHANA
Accra
Institute of African Studies [44728]

GREECE
Patras
International Journal of Decision Sciences, Risk and Management
[44764]

HUNGARY
Budapest
Antik Tanulmanyok [44822]
Mentalhigiene es Pszichoszomatika
[44852]
Muveszettorteneti Ertesito [44853]
Society and Economy [44870]
Tarsadalomkutatas [44880]

INDIA
Bangalore
Quarterly Journal of the Mythic
Society [44984] .... (Paid) 340

Chennai
Hindu International Edition
[45035] .. .. (Paid) 5,000
Review of Development and Change
[45055] .... (Paid) 300

Delhi
The Anthropologist
[45087] .... (Paid) 250
Journal of Human Ecology
[45100] .... (Paid) 500
Journal of Social Sciences (Delhi)
[45101] .... (Paid) 300
Studies of Tribes and Tribals [45104]

Hyderabad
Journal of Rural Development
[45176] .... (Paid) 1,000

Mumbai
Indian Journal of Social Work
[45388] 1,200

New Delhi
Abhigyan [45476] .. .. (Paid) 500
Folklore Research Journal [45517]
Gender, Technology & Development
[45519] 400
India Perspectives [45535]
Indian Journal of Gender Studies
[45554]
Indian Social Science Review
[45577]
Manushi [45622] .... (Paid) 10,000

Shimla
Studies in Humanities and Social
Sciences [45731] ..... (Paid) 1,000

Thiruvananthapuram
Loyola Journal of Social Sciences
[45748] .... (Paid) 300

ISRAEL
Tel Aviv
Theoretical Inquiries in Law [46114]

JAPAN
Tokushima
Social Science Research of Univer-
sity of Tokushima [46716]

Tokyo
Social Science Japan Journal
[47040]

Yokohama
The Yoke [47143]

KENYA
Nairobi
Discovery and Innovation [47177]

KUWAIT
Safat
Journal of the Social Sciences
[47339] .. .. (Paid) 3,000

LEBANON
Beirut
Haigazian Armenological Review
[47395]

MALAYSIA
Serdang
Pertanika Journal of Social Science
and Humanities
[47716] .... (Paid) 200

NETHERLANDS
Amsterdam
Contemporary Pragmatism [47940]
Journal of Applied Developmental
Psychology [48045]
Journal of Cultural Heritage [48066]
Language Problems and Language
Planning [48133]
Mathematical Social Sciences
[48148]
Telematics and Informatics [48244]

Dordrecht
Dialectical Anthropology [48373]
Quality & Quantity [48544]
Social Indicators Research [48561]
Sustainability Science [48574]
Systemic Practice and Action
Research [48576]
Theory and Society [48579]

Leiden
Asian Journal of Social Science
[48653]
East Central Europe [48669]
Historiography East and West
[48675]
Journal of the Economic and Social
History of the Orient [48693]
Late Antique Archaeology [48706]
Social Sciences and Missions
[48724]
Southeastern Europe [48725]
The Soviet and Post-Soviet Review
[48726]

Utrecht
Tijdschrift voor economische en sociale geografie [48766]

NEW ZEALAND
Cromwell
Junctures [48888]

NIGERIA
Calabar
Global Journal of Social Sciences
[49076]

Ibadan
African Journal for the Psychological
Study of Social Issues [49086]
Journal of Agriculture and Social
Research [49088]

Ile-Ife
Gender and Behaviour [49112]

Trade, Technical, and Professional Publications

Obubra
Journal of Agriculture, Forestry and
the Social Sciences [49158]

Owerri
Journal of Research in National
Development [49164]

PAKISTAN
Faisalabad
Humanity & Social Sciences Journal
[49246]

PHILIPPINES
Quezon City
Philippine Social Sciences Review
[49612] .... (Controlled) 1,000

ROMANIA
Bucharest
Romanian Journal of Society and
Politics [49843]

RUSSIA
Moscow
Sociology of Medicine [49990]
Volgograd
Social Evolution & History [50044]

SINGAPORE
Singapore
Asia Europe Journal [50104]

SLOVAKIA
Bratislava
Central-European Value Studies
[50317]

REPUBLIC OF SOUTH AFRICA
Centurion
South African Journal of Cultural
History [50452]
Claremont
African Human Rights Law Journal
[50460]
Overport
Transformation [50560]
Pretoria
Africa Institute Occasional Papers
[50582]

SPAIN
Barcelona
Afers Internacionals [50647]
Archipielago [50649]
L'Avenc [50653] 8,000
Gijon
Abaco [50716]
Madrid
La Balsa de la Medusa [50777]
Matador [50781]
Revista de Occidente [50799]
Sistema [50807]
Zona Abierta [50817]
Oviedo
International Journal of Chinese Culture & Management [50823]

SRI LANKA
Colombo
Sri Lanka Journal of Social Sciences
[50867]

SWAZILAND
Matsapha
Lwati [50946]

SWEDEN
Lund
Graduate Journal of Social Science
[50986]

SWITZERLAND
Dornach
Das Goetheanum
[51085] .. .. (Paid) 10,246
Geneva
International Journal of Society Systems Science [51141]
International Journal of Sustainable
Society [51143]

TAIWAN
Taipei
Journal of Social Sciences and
Philosophy
[51355] .. .. (Paid) 1,000

THAILAND
Bangkok
Population Headliners
[51431] 5,500

TURKEY
Ankara
Journal of American Studies of
Turkey [51494] .... (Paid) 325
Istanbul
Bogazici Journal
[51557] .... (Paid) 850

UNITED KINGDOM
Abingdon
Anthropological Forum [51704]
Critical Discourse Studies [51744]
Development Southern Africa [51756]
Economy and Society [51766]
Geopolitics [51794]
Health, Risk and Society [51801]
History and Anthropology [51804]
Information, Communication and
Society [51817]
Irish Studies Review [51860]
Japan Forum [51865]
Japanese Studies [51866]
Journal of Contemporary China
[51879]
Journal for Cultural Research [51883]
Journal of European Public Policy
[51896]
Journal of Genocide Research
[51900]
Journal of Human Development and
Capabilities [51904]
Journal of Modern Italian Studies
[51919]
Journal of Modern Jewish Studies
[51920]
Journal of Southern African Studies
[51944]
Journal of Youth Studies [51958]
New Political Economy [51993]
Philosophical Explorations [52010]
Social Influence [52060]
Totalitarian Movements and Political
Religions [52080]
Twenty-first Century Society [52084]
Basingstoke
BioSocieties [52196]
Information Visualization
[52207] .. ..:............ 350
Social Trends [52230]
Belmont
Sociology [52307]
Work, Employment, and Society
[52308]

Bradford
Education, Business and Society
[52451]
Equality, Diversity and Inclusion
[52456]
Brighton
International Journal of Migration,
Health and Social Care [52617]
Journal of Children's Services
[52619]
Journal of Integrated Care [52621]
Learning Disability Today [52625]
Quality in Ageing [52629]
Bristol
International Journal of Modelling,
Identification and Control [52679]
Journal of Cellular Automata [52683]
The Journal of Poverty and Social
Justice [52696]
Voluntary Sector Review [52735]
Buckingham
The Journal of Prediction Markets
[52758]
Burnham
Appropriate Technology
[52763] .... (Controlled) 3,000
Cambridge
Social Policy and Society
[52896] 1,000
Cardiff
Qualitative Research [52938]
Edinburgh
Episteme [53272]
Journal of Arabic and Islamic Studies
[53291]
Paragraph [53305]
Glasgow
eSharp [53417]
Hove
Drugs and Alcohol Today [53604]
Ethnicity and Inequalities in Health
and Social Care [53605]
Journal of Learning Disabilities and
Offending Behaviour [53609]
A Life in the Day [53610]
Social Care and Neurodisability
[53613]
Leicester
Social Responsibility Journal [53827]
Liverpool
European Journal of Social Theory
[53871]
London
Adoption and Fostering
[53903] 4,800
African Renaissance [53924]
Body & Society [54096]
Comparative Critical Studies [54249]
European Journal of Cultural Studies
[54399]
The European Journal of Women's
Studies [54407]
Evaluation [54412] 1,500
Feminist Review [54447] 1,300
Gender and Language [54498]
Human Relations [54578]
Interdisciplinary Science Reviews
[54615]
International African Bibliography
[54619]
International Journal of Cultural
Studies [54642]
Jazz Research Journal [54688]
Journal of Consumer Culture [54730]
Journal of Risk Research [54810]
Journal of Social and Personal
Relationships [54819]

Linguistics and the Human Sciences
[54874]
Media, Culture & Society [54920]
New Humanist
[54991] .... (Combined) 5,000
New Media & Society [54995]
Philosophy & Social Criticism [55083]
Portuguese Journal of Social Science
[55104]
Public Archaeology [55150]
Review of Nigeria Affairs [55199]
Slavonica [55242] 200
Social & Legal Studies
[55246] .... (Paid) 800
Sociolinguistic Studies [55253]
Thesis Eleven [55310]
Tourist Studies [55332]
War & Society [55379]
Nottingham
Planning Perspectives [55769]
Theory, Culture & Society [55772]
Olney
Journal of Design Research [55842]
Oxford
Citizenship, Social and Economics
Education [55909]
Fashion Theory
[55953] .... (Combined) ‡716
Gender & Development [55962]
Journal of Regional Science [56066]
KYKLOS [56082]
Perspectives on Psychological
Science [56152]
Public Opinion Quarterly [56178]
Stirling
New Technology, Work and
Employment [56625]
Strawberry Hill
Holy Land Studies [56643]
Swindon
Fourth World Review [56711]

SOCIETY FOR THE PREVENTION OF CRUELTY TO ANIMALS AND ANTI-VIVISECTION

AUSTRALIA
North Melbourne
Animals Today [42156] 3,000

SWEDEN
Alvsjo
Djurens Ratt
[50948] .... (Combined) 50,000

UNITED KINGDOM
Horsham
Animal Action [53594]
Animal Life [53595] ... (Paid) 45,000

SOCIOLOGY
See also Philanthropy and
Humanitarianism

AUSTRALIA
Armidale
Australian Folklore [41558]
Crawley
Australasian Journal of Victorian
Studies [41819] 150
Murdoch
Intersections [42137]

AUSTRIA
Vienna
Wirschaft und Gesellschaft
[42774] .... (Combined) 900

Circulation: ★ = ABC; △ = BPA; ◆ = CAC; • = CCAB; ❑ = VAC; ⊕ = PO Statement; ‡ = Publisher's Report; Boldface figures = sworn; Light figures = estimated.

BANGLADESH

Dhaka
Bangladesh e-Journal of Sociology [42804]

BRAZIL

Campinas
Cadernos Pagu [42966]

Rio de Janeiro
Mana - Estudos de Antropologia Social [43011]

BULGARIA

Sofia
Sotsiologicheski Problemi [43108]

PEOPLE'S REPUBLIC OF CHINA

Hong Kong
Hong Kong Journal of Sociology [43333]
The Journal of Dagaare Studies (JDS) [43355]

ETHIOPIA

Addis Ababa
Ethiopian Journal of the Social Sciences and Humanities [43801]

FRANCE

Castanet-Tolosan
Natures Sciences Societes [43927] 1,000

Paris
Cahiers d'Economie et Sociologie Rurales [44031]

GERMANY

Bamberg
European Sociological Review [44145]

HUNGARY

Budapest
Review of Sociology of the Hungarian Sociological Association [44867]
Tarsadalom es Gazdasag (Society and Economy) [44879]

INDIA

New Delhi
Contributions to Indian Sociology [45499] 900
ICSSR Journal of Abstracts and Reviews [45527] .... (Paid) 450
International Journal of Sociology of the Family [45585] .. (Paid) 1,200
Journal of Social Anthropology [45618]
Journal of Social and Economic Policy [45619]

ISRAEL

Tel Aviv
Journal of Children and Media [46107]

JAPAN

Kyoto
Mathematics Applied in Science and Technology [46482]

REPUBLIC OF KOREA

Seoul
Development and Society [47264]

MALAYSIA

Kuala Lumpur
Man and Society [47623] .... (Paid) 1,000

NETHERLANDS

Amsterdam
Evolution and Human Behavior [47977]
Journal of Arid Environments [48049]
The Journal of Socio-Economics [48116]
Poetics [48207]
Social Science Research [48233]
Telematics and Informatics [48244]

Dordrecht
Human Ecology [48418]
International Journal of Politics, Culture, and Society [48430]
The Journal of Economic Inequality [48457]
Population Research and Policy Review [48539]
Social Justice Research [48562]

Leiden
Journal of the Economic and Social History of the Orient [48693]
Journal of Religion in Europe [48703]

NIGERIA

Makurdi
International Journal of Development and Policy Studies [49145]

PAKISTAN

Faisalabad
Humanity & Social Sciences Journal [49246]

PHILIPPINES

Quezon City
Asian Migrant [49582]
Asian Migration News [49583]
Asian and Pacific Migration Journal [49584]
Philippine Sociological Review [49613] .... (Paid) 500

POLAND

Warsaw
European Countryside [49709]
Limes [49731]

SINGAPORE

Pasir Panjang
SOJOURN [50100] .... (Paid) 700

REPUBLIC OF SOUTH AFRICA

Centurion
African Journal of Research in Mathematics, Science and Technology Education [50437]
South African Journal of Cultural History [50452]

Grahamstown
African Sociological Review [50490]

Overport
Transformation [50560]

Pretoria
Sahara J [50599]

SPAIN

Madrid
Current Sociology [50747]
El Extramundi y los papeles de Iria Flavia [50755]
La Balsa de la Medusa [50777]
Matador [50781]
Revista Hispano Cubana HC [50798]
Revista de Occidente [50799]

Temas para el Debate [50809]
Utopias/Nuestra Bandera [50813]

Mataro
El Viejo Topo [50819]
Quimera [50820]

SRI LANKA

Kandy
Nethra [50908]

SWEDEN

Djursholm
Arkiv for Matematik [50952]

Linkoping
The International Journal of Ageing and Later Life (IJAL) [50975]

SWITZERLAND

Geneva
International Journal of Society Systems Science [51141]
International Journal of Sustainable Society [51143]

TAIWAN

Tamsui
Tamkang Journal of Futures Studies [51395]

TURKEY

Ankara
Journal of Modern Turkish Studies (JMTS) [51495]

UNITED ARAB EMIRATES

Dubai
Arabian Woman [51632]
Emirates Woman [51642] .... (Paid) △20,324

UNITED KINGDOM

Aberystwyth
Gender, Place and Culture [51688]

Abingdon
African Studies [51699]
The British Journal of Sociology [51721]
Citizenship Studies [51730]
Critical Review of International Social and Political Philosophy [51745]
Cultural Studies [51747]
Development in Practice [51755]
European Societies [51785]
International Planning Studies [51848]
International Studies in Sociology of Education [51856]
Iranian Studies [51858]
Journal of Beliefs & Values [51872]
Journal of Civil Society [51875]
Journal of Contemporary China [51879]
Journal of Human Rights [51905]
Journal of North African Studies [51925]
Journal of Southern African Studies [51944]
Mortality [51987]
Review of Social Economy [52044]
Social Influence [52060]
Studies in Conflict and Terrorism [52066]
Terrorism and Political Violence [52075]

Basingstoke
Subjectivity [52231] 400

Belfast
The British Journal of Social Work [52279]

Belmont
Sociology [52307]
Work, Employment, and Society [52308]

Bradford
Humanomics [52463]

Cambridge
International Review of Social History [52839] 1,200
Journal of Biosocial Science [52846] 500
Journal of Social Policy [52862] 2,000

Chester
European Physical Education Review [52994]

Colchester
Bulletin of Medical Ethics [53031]
Sexualities [53049]

Coventry
Journal of Research in Reading [53087]

Durham
Critical Horizons [53227]

Edinburgh
Derrida Today [53269]
World Structure [53324]

Hove
Journal of Aggression, Conflict and Peace Research [53606]

Kidlington
Journal of Rural Studies [53701]

Lancaster
Journal of New Music Research [53735]

London
Advances in Psychiatric Treatment [53907]
Body & Society [54096]
Childhood [54204]
Critical Sociology [54290] .... (Paid) 850
Dementia [54315]
Discourse & Society [54330]
Discourse Studies [54331]
Feminist Review [54447] 1,300
Health [54536]
History of the Human Sciences [54559]
Human Relations [54578]
International Review for the Sociology of Sport [54669]
International Sociology [54673]
Journal of Classical Sociology [54725]
Journal of Sociology [54823]
New Media & Society [54995]
Organization [55042]
Population Studies [55103] .. .. (Paid) ‡1,300
Punishment & Society [55157]
Rationality and Society [55174]
Slovo [55243]
Social Compass [55245]
Social Science Information [55247]
Social Studies of Science [55248] ....:............ 1,100
Sociology Review [55254]
Theoretical Criminology [55307]
Time & Society [55319]
Tourist Studies [55332]
Urban Studies [55360]
Visual Communication [55373]

Nottingham
Planning Perspectives [55769]
Theory, Culture & Society [55772]

Oxford
Cambridge Journal of Economics [55900]

Circulation: ★ = ABC; △ = BPA; ◆ = CAC; • = CCAB; ❑ = VAC; ⊕ = PO Statement; ‡ = Publisher's Report; Boldface figures = sworn; Light figures = estimated.

European Sociological Review
[55949]
International Journal of Public Opinion Research [56001]
Journal of Urban Affairs [56077]
Oxford Development Studies [56132]
Social Anthropology [56207]
The Sociological Quarterly [56209]
The Sociological Review [56210]

Sheffield
Managing Leisure [56506]

Sutton
Community Care [56682]

SPORTING GOODS/RETAIL SPORTS

AUSTRALIA
Port Macquarie
AusSport [42260] 20,000

Warrandyte
The Australian Orienteer
[42686] 2,000

DENMARK
Brondby
Badminton [43651] 600
O-Posten [43652]

FINLAND
Helsinki
Liikunnan ja Urheilun Maailma
[43845]
Scientific Journal of Orienteering
[43856]

GERMANY
Frankfurt am Main
Olympisches Feuer [44367]

HUNGARY
Budapest
International Sports Magazine
[44838] 9,000
IWF Handbook [44839]
Tajfutas [44878]

NETHERLANDS
Maarssen
Fietsmarkt
[48731] .... (Combined) 3,600

POLAND
Warsaw
Trener [49768] 2,000

SINGAPORE
Singapore
Global Sources Sports & Leisure
[50159]

UNITED KINGDOM
Cheltenham
Croquet Gazette [52966]

Hitchin
Netball Magazine [53581] 65,000

Leeds
Coaching Edge [53761] 4,000

Leicester
Golf Course Architecture [53803]

London
Distance Running
[54334] 400,000
ITF World [54686] 7,000

Loughborough
Psychology of Sport and Exercise
[55487]

Marlborough
Arab Horse Society News
[55599] 3,000

Milton Keynes
Badminton [55630] 8,000

Newport
Archery UK [55688] 12,500

Richmond
Dive [56390] 41,622

Salisbury
Pro Shop Europe [56456]

Walsall
Swim & Save [56835]

STATE, MUNICIPAL, AND COUNTY ADMINISTRATION
See also Chambers of Commerce and Boards of Trade

AUSTRALIA
Mount Macedon
Australian Journal of Emergency
Management
[42133] .... (Non-paid) 5,200

AUSTRIA
Leoben
Stadt Leoben
[42732] .. .. (Combined) ‡13,500

BARBADOS
Bridgetown
The International Journal of Education and Development using Information and Communication Technology (IJEDICT) [42828]

PEOPLE'S REPUBLIC OF CHINA
Hong Kong
Public Administration & Policy
[43378] 1,000

INDIA
New Delhi
India Central Statistical Organization
Monthly Abstract of Statistics
[45533] .... (Paid) 650
Institute of Town Planners, India
Journal [45579]

NETHERLANDS
Amsterdam
Habitat International [48008]
Journal of Accounting and Public
Policy [48037]
Journal for Nurse Practitioners
[48105]
Journal of Policy Modeling [48111]

PHILIPPINES
Quezon City
Asian Review of Public Administration
[49585]

SINGAPORE
Singapore
Planews [50240] .... (Paid) 1,000

SRI LANKA
Colombo
Journal of Development
Administration
[50855] .. .. (Paid) 1,000

UNITED KINGDOM
Abingdon
Journal of European Public Policy
[51896]
Policy Studies [52017]

Leicester
Leicester Link
[53811] .... (Controlled) 112,000

London
Constitutional and Parliamentary
Information [54260]
LCR [54858] .... ‡12,000
Public Service Magazine (PSM)
[55153] .... (Combined) 10,364
Roof [55208] .... (Paid) 9,000

Preston
Durham County Life [56299]
Lancashire Life [56303] *23,455

Sheffield
Planning Theory & Practice [56511]

STATIONERY, OFFICE EQUIPMENT, AND COLLEGE STORE SUPPLIES

UNITED KINGDOM
Maidstone
Stationery & Office Update
[55531] .. .. (Combined) *5,586

STATISTICS
See also Mathematics

AUSTRALIA
Sydney
Journal of Economic Dynamics and
Control [42528]

AUSTRIA
Linz
Statistical Papers [42734]

BRAZIL
Rio de Janeiro
ALEA [43001]
ALEA [43002]

PEOPLE'S REPUBLIC OF CHINA
Beijing
Science in China Series A [43215]

Xiangtan
International Journal of Computing
Science and Mathematics [43539]

FINLAND
Joensuu
Scandinavian Journal of Statistics
[43868]

FRANCE
Paris
Journal of the Institute of Mathematics of Jussieu [44064]
Statistical Inference for Stochastic
Processes [44084]

Rillieux-la-Pape
SAR and QSAR in Environmental
Research [44099]

HUNGARY
Budapest
Studia Scientiarum Mathematicarum
Hungarica [44876]

INDIA
Allahabad
Advances and Applications in
Statistics [44920]
JP Journal of Biostatistics [44936]

Delhi
Demography India [45091] 950

Hyderabad
The Icfai Journal of Financial
Economics [45151]

Jaipur
Statistical Abstract of Rajasthan
[45199]

Kanpur
International Journal of Tomography
and Statistics [45236]

Kolkata
Calcutta Statistical Association
Bulletin [45262] 350
Sankhya [45303]

New Delhi
India Central Statistical Organization
Monthly Abstract of Statistics
[45533] .... (Paid) 650
India Central Statistical Organization
Statistical Abstract [45534]
International Journal of Statistics and
Systems [45586]
International Review of Fuzzy
Mathematics [45588]
Journal of Statistics and Management
Systems [45620] .. .. (Paid) 240
Statistical Pocket Book [45654]

Roorkee
International Journal of Mathematics
and Statistics (IJMS) [45719]

ITALY
Rome
Statistical Methods and Applications
[46242]

JAPAN
Kyoto
Mathematics Applied in Science and
Technology [46482]

Osaka
Advances in Applied Mathematical
Analysis [46614]

Tokyo
Computational Statistics [46792]

Tsukuba
International Journal of Knowledge
Engineering and Soft Data
Paradigms [47110]

KENYA
Nairobi
East African Journal of Statistics
[47180]

REPUBLIC OF KOREA
Masan
International Journal of Mathematical
Sciences [47243]

NETHERLANDS
Amsterdam
Computational Statistics & Data
Analysis [47935]
Model Assisted Statistics and
Applications [48161]
Statistical Journal of the IAOS
[48236]
Stochastic Processes and Their
Applications [48237]

Circulation: ★ = ABC; △ = BPA; ◆ = CAC; • = CCAB; ❑ = VAC; ⊕ = PO Statement; ‡ = Publisher's Report; Boldface figures = sworn; Light figures = estimated.

Dordrecht
Marketing Letters [48511]
Statistics and Computing [48568]
Theory and Decision [48578]

Enschede
International Journal of Applied Earth Observation and Geoinformation [48593]

Rotterdam
Statistica Neerlandica [48752]

Voorburg
Bernoulli [48769] .... (Paid) 2,000
Journal of Time Series Analysis [48770]

NEW ZEALAND

Palmerston North
Australian & New Zealand Journal of Statistics [48963]

Wellington
Australian and New Zealand Journal of Statistics [49000]

PAKISTAN

Faisalabad
Journal of Modern Mathematics and Statistics [49272]

PHILIPPINES

Manila
Journal of Philippine Statistics [49550] .... (Paid) 250

Quezon City
Asian Migrant [49582]
Asian Migration News [49583]
Asian and Pacific Migration Journal [49584]

SINGAPORE

Singapore
Statistical Methodology [50272]

REPUBLIC OF SOUTH AFRICA

Wits
South African Actuarial Journal [50643]

SPAIN

Madrid
TEST [50811]

SWITZERLAND

Geneva
International Journal of Data Analysis Techniques and Strategies [51115]

Lausanne
Insurance [51192]

Zurich
Biometrical Journal [51255]

TAIWAN

Taipei
Statistica Sinica [51360]

UNITED ARAB EMIRATES

Al Ain
International Journal of Mathematics Manuscripts [51626]

UNITED KINGDOM

Abingdon
Journal of Applied Statistics [51869]

Basingstoke
Health Statistics Quarterly [52206]

Monthly Digest of Statistics [52225]
Regional Trends [52229]
Social Trends [52230]

Cambridge
Probability Surveys [52885]

Coventry
Abstracts and Reviews [53076]

London
Measurement and Control [54918] 4,500
Quarterly Survey of Advertising Expenditure [55164]
Statistical Modelling [55264]

Oxford
Biometrika [55882]
Biostatistics [55883]
IMA Journal of Mathematical Control and Information [55985]
IMA Journal of Numerical Analysis [55986]
Journal of Financial Econometrics [56034]
Journal of the Royal Statistical Society [56067]
Journal of the Royal Statistical Society [56068]
Journal of the Royal Statistical Society [56069]
Significance [56203]
Teaching Statistics [56213]

Portsmouth
International Journal of Computational Economics and Econometrics [56289]

Sheffield
Advances in Applied Probability [56488]
Journal of Applied Probability [56503]

STONE AND ROCK PRODUCTS
See also Building Materials, Concrete, Brick, and Tile; Cemeteries and Monuments; Mining and Minerals

GERMANY

Mannheim
Addiction Biology [44547]

Nuremberg
Industrie Diamanten Rundschau [44615] 6,800

ITALY

Faenza
Giornale del Marmo—International Stone Magazine [46137] .... (Combined) 7,000

NETHERLANDS

Amsterdam
Mechanics of Materials [48150]

POLAND

Warsaw
Mineralogia [49738]

UNITED KINGDOM

London
International Journal of Rock Mechanics and Mining Sciences [54661]

Manchester
Crystallography Reviews [55552]

Wadhurst
Construction Europe [56805] .... ★14,624

STORAGE AND WAREHOUSING

UNITED KINGDOM

Kings Langley
Warehouse & Logistics News [53711] 27,822

London
Packaging, Transport, Storage & Security of Radioactive Material [55049]

Surbiton
Bulk Distributor [56657] 7,100

SUBSTANCE ABUSE AND TREATMENT

AUSTRALIA

Surry Hills
Drug and Alcohol Review [42428]

BRAZIL

Sao Paulo
Revista Vivencia [43048] 10,000

IRELAND

Dublin
Pioneer [45994]

ITALY

Milan
Journal of Mental Health Policy and Economics [46183]

NETHERLANDS

Amsterdam
Journal of Substance Abuse Treatment (JSAT) [48120]
Meeleven [48152] .... (Non-paid) 9,500

SWITZERLAND

Lausanne
Alcoholism [51182]

UNITED KINGDOM

Abingdon
American Journal on Addictions [51702]
Drugs [51760]
Journal of Substance Use [51949]

London
Addiction [53900] .... (Paid) 1,200
Drug and Alcohol Findings [54344]

Sheffield
Phoenix [56509]

SUGAR AND SUGAR BEETS

INDIA

New Delhi
Indian Sugar [45578] ... (Paid) 1,100

TAXATION AND TARIFF

AUSTRALIA

Melbourne
Asian Review of Accounting [42047]

INDIA

Chennai
Income Tax Reports [45037] .. .. (Paid) 16,500

Hyderabad
The Icfai Journal of International Business Law [45156]
The Icfai Journal of Monetary Economics [45161]
The Icfai Journal of Public Finance [45164]

ITALY

Rome
Il Fiasco [46233]

NETHERLANDS

The Hague
EC Tax Review [48613]

REPUBLIC OF SOUTH AFRICA

Centurion
Tax Breaks Newsletter [50456]

UNITED KINGDOM

London
Fiscal Studies [54463] 1,500
International Investment [54628]

TELECOMMUNICATIONS

AUSTRALIA

Dickson
Australasian Journal of Educational Technology [41840] ... (Paid) 700

Monash
Communications Letters, IEEE [42113]

Wahroonga
Radio Comms Asia-Pacific [42675] .... ★4,426
Voice&Data [42678] 7,745

BRAZIL

Sao Paulo
RTI Redes Telecom Instalacoes [43049] .... (Non-paid) 12,000

DENMARK

Glostrup
Telekommunikation [43718] .... (Controlled) 6,077

FRANCE

Montpellier
Communications and Strategies [43977]

GEORGIA

Tbilisi
Computer Science and Telecommunications [44131]

GERMANY

Bonn
Behorden Spiegel [44253] 104,000

Heidelberg
Telecommunication Systems [44477]

Munich
Computern im Handwerk [44555] .. .. (Combined) ‡72,351

Poing
Datacom [44635] .. .. (Combined) 11,014

Unterfoehring
TELE-satellite International Magazine [44697] .... ‡148,430

Circulation: ★ = ABC; △ = BPA; ◆ = CAC; • = CCAB; ❏ = VAC; ⊕ = PO Statement; ‡ = Publisher's Report; Boldface figures = sworn; Light figures = estimated.

GREECE
Kozani
International Journal of Autonomous and Adaptive Communications Systems [44761]

INDIA
Delhi
DESIDOC Bulletin of Information Technology [45092] .. .. (Paid) 700

Guwahati
International Journal of Ultra Wideband Communications and Systems [45130]

Kharagpur
International Journal of Information and Coding Theory [45248]

Kolkata
Energy for Sustainable Development [45265]

New Delhi
IETE Journal of Research [45531] .. .. (Paid) 2,000
IETE Technical Review [45532] .. .. (Paid) 8,000
Journal of Information & Optimization Sciences [45606] .... (Paid) 480

ITALY
Milan
European Transactions on Telecommunications [46170]
Office Automation [46189] 17,000

JAPAN
Tokyo
Nikkei Network [47001] .. .. ★48,034
Telecom Tribune [47048]

REPUBLIC OF KOREA
Daejeon
ETRI Journal [47226] 3,700

LEBANON
Beirut
Hitek Magazine [47396] 10,000

NETHERLANDS
Alphen aan den Rijn
Telecommagazine [47873] 7,369

Amsterdam
Information Economics and Policy [48019]
Information Services & Use [48021]
Journal of E-Governance [48069]

Dordrecht
Wireless Networks [48587]

PAKISTAN
Faisalabad
Journal of Mobile Communication [49271]
Research Journal of Telecommunication and Information Technology [49293]

PHILIPPINES
Quezon City
I.T. Matters [49596]

POLAND
Warsaw
Journal of Telecommunications and Information Technology [49727]

SINGAPORE
Singapore
Ad Hoc Networks [50102]

Asian Journal of Communication [50111] 750
Global Sources Telecom Products [50160]

REPUBLIC OF SOUTH AFRICA
Kloof
Dataweek [50542] .... (Free) 4,000

SPAIN
Madrid
Comunicaciones World [50739] .. .. (Combined) ‡10,000

Pozuelo de Alarcon
Conectronica [50827] .... (Controlled) 4,000

SWEDEN
Goteborg
Telecommunications Policy [50967]

SWITZERLAND
Geneva
ITU News [51151]

THAILAND
Bangkok
Telcom Journal [51436] 120,000

UNITED ARAB EMIRATES
Dubai
Channel Middle East [51634] .. .. △7,485
Windows Middle East [51657]

UNITED KINGDOM
Abingdon
Prometheus [52023]

Bath
Corporate IT Update [52237]

Bournemouth
Smartphone & PDA Essentials [52425]

Bradford
Internet Research [52491]

Guildford
International Journal of Satellite Communications and Networking [53491]

Leamington Spa
Eurowire [53745] .. .. (Controlled) ‡25,338

London
Cable & Satellite International [54164] .... △10,000
Call Center Magazine [54167]
Commonwealth Broadcaster [54240] 3,000
Communicate [54244] 10,000
Communications Africa [54246] .... ★9,034
Health Research Policy and Systems [54541]
International Journal of Internet Technology & Secured Transactions [54651]
Journal of Location Based Services [54772]
Personal and Ubiquitous Computing [55070]
Telecommunications Heritage Group Journal [55297] 450
Via Inmarsat Magazine [55368] 24,000

Loughborough
Journal of Digital Information [55481]

Olney
International Journal of Vehicle Information & Communication System [55838]
International Journal of Wireless and Mobile Computing [55841]

Oxford
Journal of Communication [56021] .. .. (Paid) ‡5,000
Network Security [56113]
The Utilities Journal [56224] ... 1,000

Salisbury
Land Mobile [56455] ... (Paid) 8,500

Stevenage
Electronics Letters [56602]
IET Communications [56616]

Stroud
21st Century Worker [56649] .... (Combined) 4,000

Tavistock
Zerb [56728] 4,000

Walton-on-Thames
Southern African Wireless Communications [56836] .... (Controlled) ‡7,000

Watford
Code of Practice [56862]
Feedback [56864]

Witney
Information Technology Law Reports [56943]

Worcester
EEMA Briefing [56961] 3,000

TEXTILES

PEOPLE'S REPUBLIC OF CHINA
Hong Kong
Asia Textile & Apparel Journal [43271] .. .. (Controlled) 15,893
Research Journal of Textile and Apparel [43380] .... (Paid) 1,000

DENMARK
Herning
Textile and Clothing [43723]

FINLAND
Helsinki
Modin [43848] .. .. (Paid) 8,000

FRANCE
Lyon
Sericologia [43970]

INDIA
Ahmedabad
Texincon [44910] .. .. (Paid) 1,000
Textile Association (India) Journal [44911] .... (Paid) 10,000

Bangalore
Indian Silk [44962]

Kolkata
Institution of Engineers (India) Textile Engineering Division Journal [45294] .... (Paid) 4,000

Mumbai
Apparel [45351] .. .. (Paid) 10,000
Man-Made Textiles in India [45408] .... (Paid) 1,500
Modern Textiles [45420]

Mysore
Indian Journal of Sericulture [45457] .... (Paid) 700

New Delhi
Indian Journal of Fibre & Textile Research [45553] :........... (Combined) ‡300

ITALY
Trezzano Sul Naviglio
Foto Shoe 15 International [46263] .... (Combined) 8,000
Foto Shoe 30 [46264] .... (Combined) 8,000

JAPAN
Osaka
Journal of Textile Engineering [46625]

NETHERLANDS
Almere
Eurostitch Magazine [47864] .. .. (Paid) 15,000

Amsterdam
Geotextiles and Geomembranes [47997]

PAKISTAN
Karachi
Pakistan Textile Journal [49372] .... (Paid) 2,500

SINGAPORE
Singapore
Global Sources Garments & Textiles [50155]

TURKEY
Istanbul
Konfeksiyon & Teknik [51559] 10,560
Tekstil & Teknik [51563] 12,381

UNITED KINGDOM
Bradford
Fashion Business International [52460] .... (Combined) 7,500
International Carpet Bulletin (ICB) [52471] .... (Combined) 1,500
International Dyer [52472]
Journal of Fashion Marketing and Management [52501]
Knitting International [52519] 22,500
Nonwovens Report International [52531]
Textile Month (TM) [52552]
Wool Record [52557]

Guisborough
The Journal for Weavers, Spinners and Dyers [53499]

Leicester
KFAT News [53808]

London
British Style [54147] .... (Non-paid) 5,000
Journal of Industrial Textiles [54766] .... ‡260
Performance Textiles [55067]
Textile History [55301]

Manchester
Journal of the Textile Institute [55567] .... (Combined) 700
Textile Progress [55579]

Oxford
Fashion Theory [55953] .... (Combined) ‡716
Textile [56217]

Circulation: ★ = ABC; △ = BPA; ◆ = CAC; • = CCAB; ❑ = VAC; ⊕ = PO Statement; ‡ = Publisher's Report; Boldface figures = sworn; Light figures = estimated.

THEOLOGY

AUSTRALIA
Adelaide
Australian Theological Book
    Reviewer [41504]
Interface [41507] 550
Banyo
Australian Ejournal of Theology
    [41575]
Brisbane
Insight into...Healing [41649]
Clayton
The Bible and Critical Theory [41758]
Melbourne
Sophia [42086]

BELGIUM
Leuven
Bijdragen [42892]
INTAMS review [42898]

GERMANY
Bamberg
Journal of the European Society of
    Women in Theological Research
    [44146]
Berlin
International Journal of Practical
    Theology [44194]
Neue Zeitschrift fur Systematische
    Theologie und Religionsphilosophie
    [44224] 250
Bonn
Zeitschrift fur die Neutestamentliche
    Wissenschaft [44273] 1,050
Erlangen
Zeitschrift fur die Alttestamentliche
    Wissenschaft [44343] 1,200
Zeitschrift fur Antikes Christentum
    [44344] 400

INDIA
Kolkata
Udbodhan [45307] .. .. (Paid) 55,000
                    (Non-paid) 1,000
Pondicherry
The Advent [45690] ..... (Paid) 1,000

IRAN
Tehran
Mahjubah [45911] .. ... (Paid) 30,000
Message of Thaqalayn [45912]

JAPAN
Kyoto
Japanese Religions
    [46475] .... (Paid) 500
Tokyo
Japan Harvest
    [46856] .. .. (Paid) 1,200
Japan Mission Journal
    [46859] .. .. (Paid) 1,000

NETHERLANDS
Amsterdam
Intercultural Theology and Study of
    Religions [48023]
Leiden
Archive for the Psychology of
    Religion [48651]
Biblical Interpretation [48657]
Exchange [48672]
Journal of Empirical Theology
    [48696]

Journal of Reformed Theology
    [48701]
Journal of Religion in Africa [48702]
Method & Theory in the Study of
    Religion [48709]
Religion and Theology [48720]

PAKISTAN
Karachi
Hamdard Islamicus
    [49350] .. .. (Paid) 2,000
Lahore
Renaissance [49388]

PHILIPPINES
Baguio City
Asian Journal of Pentecostal Studies
    [49450]
Makati City
Home Life [49517] .. .. (Paid) 60,000
Manila
Philippiniana Sacra
    [49558] .. .. (Paid) 500
Quezon City
East Asian Pastoral Review
    [49591] .. .. (Paid) 2,000

SAUDI ARABIA
Riyadh
Journal of King Saud University: Edu-
    cational Sciences & Islamic Studies
    [50067] .. .. (Paid) 2,000

REPUBLIC OF SOUTH AF-
RICA
Bloemfontein
Acta Theologica [50354]
Centurion
Old Testament Essays [50444]
Scriptura [50449]
Rondebosch
Journal for the Study of Religion
    [50619]

SWITZERLAND
Lucerne
Schweizerische Kirchenzeitung
    [51210] .. .. (Paid) 3,000

UNITED KINGDOM
Abingdon
International Journal of Children's
    Spirituality [51829]
Islam and Christian-Muslim Relations
    [51861]
Journal of Beliefs & Values [51872]
Journal of Contemporary Religion
    [51881]
Theology and Science [52077]
Birmingham
Black Theology [52331]
Cambridge
Journal of the United Reformed
    Church History Society [52864]
Scottish Journal of Theology
    [52892] 1,200
Edinburgh
New Blackfriars [53303]
Studies in World Christianity [53321]
Glasgow
Reformation and Renaissance
    Review [53445]
London
Journal of Adult Theological
    Education [54696]

Journal of Buddhist Ethics [54715]
Political Theology [55099]
Religious Studies and Theology
    [55187]
Social Compass [55245]
Oxford
Sobornost [56206] 1,600
Teaching Theology and Religion
    [56214]
Stirling
Literature and Theology [56624]
Watford
Churchman [56861]
York
International Journal of Public
    Theology [56992]

TOBACCO

AUSTRALIA
Bowen Hills
Journal of Smoking Cessation
    [41628]

GERMANY
Leinfelden-Echterdingen
Der Deutsche Tabakbau
    [44520] 3,000
Mainz
Tobacco Journal International
    [44546] 6,000

UNITED KINGDOM
London
Tobacco Control [55325]
Norwich
Cigar Buyer Magazine [55728]

TOXICOLOGY
See also Drugs and Pharmaceuticals; Ecology and Conservation

AUSTRALIA
Aranda
Environmental Toxicology [41557]

BRAZIL
Botucatu
The Journal of Venomous Animals
    and Toxins including Tropical
    Diseases [42957]

DENMARK
Odense
Basic & Clinical Pharmacology &
    Toxicology [43726]

FRANCE
Les Ulis
Apidologie [43964] 1,000
Montrouge
Environnement, Risques & Sante
    [43986]

GERMANY
Hannover
Experimental and Toxicologic
    Pathology [44431]

HUNGARY
Budapest
Acta Biologica Hungarica [44808]

INDIA
Lucknow
Abstracts of Current Literature in
    Toxicology [45320]

JAPAN
Tokyo
Archives of Toxicology [46752]

NETHERLANDS
Amsterdam
Chemosphere [47927]
Ecotoxicology and Environmental
    Safety [47962]
Environmental Toxicology and
    Pharmacology [47971]
Free Radical Biology and Medicine
    [47990]
Neurotoxicology and Teratology
    [48179]
Regulatory Toxicology and
    Pharmacology [48220]
Toxicology [48252]
Toxicology and Applied
    Pharmacology [48253]
Trends in Pharmacological Sciences
    [48267]
Dordrecht
Cell Biology and Toxicology [48347]

NIGERIA
Benin City
West African Journal of Pharmacol-
    ogy and Drug Research [49068]
Lagos
African Journal of Biochemistry
    Research [49130]
Port Harcourt
Journal of Applied Sciences and En-
    vironmental Management [49166]

POLAND
Warsaw
Archives of Industrial Hygiene and
    Toxicology [49691]

REPUBLIC OF SOUTH AF-
RICA
Pietermaritzburg
African Journal of Aquatic Science
    [50564]

UNITED KINGDOM
Bristol
Biomedical Materials [52647]
Glasgow
Toxicon [53454]
London
Environmental Health [54376]
Innate Immunity [54605]
Journal of Exposure Science and En-
    vironmental Epidemiology (JESEE)
    [54750]
Journal of Pharmacological and Toxi-
    cological Methods [54797]
Journal of Virological Methods
    [54833]
Particle and Fibre Toxicology [55059]
Pulmonary Pharmacology and
    Therapeutics [55155]
Oxford
Toxicological Sciences [56218]

TRAILERS AND ACCESSORIES
See also Transportation, Traffic, and Shipping

SWITZERLAND
Geneva
International Journal of Heavy Vehicle Systems [51124]

UNITED KINGDOM
Manchester
Truck and Plant Trader
[55581] .... ★14,383

TRANSPORTATION, TRAFFIC, AND SHIPPING
See also Trucks and Trucking

AUSTRALIA
Melbourne
International Journal of Electronic Transport [42065]

AUSTRIA
Vienna
VCO Magazin
[42773] .. .. (Paid) 20,000

BELGIUM
Brussels
Public Transport International
[42870] 6,000

PEOPLE'S REPUBLIC OF CHINA
Hong Kong
International Journal of Shipping and Transport Logistics [43352]

DENMARK
Padborg
Danmarks Transport-Tidende
[43732] .. .. (Paid) ◆4,000
Trans-Inform
[43733] .. .. (Paid) ◆4,000

FINLAND
Helsinki
Kuljetusyrittaja
[43842] .... (Controlled) 8,423

FRANCE
Auray
Voie Libre
[43916] .... (Combined) 5,150
Clichy
Autocar Infos
[43931] .. .. (Paid) 23,000
Les Routiers
[43934] .. .. (Paid) 45,000
Transport Service
[43937] .. .. (Paid) 30,000

GREECE
Crete
Transportation Research Part C [44759]

INDIA
New Delhi
Indian Journal of Transport Management [45568] 2,000

Indian Roads Congress Highway Research Bulletin
[45576] .. .. (Paid) 8,500
Journal of Indian Roads Congress
[45604] .. .. (Paid) 8,500

IRELAND
Claremorris
Fleet Transport
[45931] .... (Combined) 6,200

ITALY
Rozzano
Tuttotrasporti [46254] 22,127

JAPAN
Osaka
Journal of Kansai Society of Naval Architects [46622]
Tokyo
Japan Automotive News
[46853] .. .. (Paid) 5,180

NETHERLANDS
Amsterdam
Transportation Research Part A: Policy and Practice
[48254] .... ‡1,500
Transportation Research Part F
[48255]
Dordrecht
Transportation [48582]

NEW ZEALAND
Auckland
Transportant [48829]

NORWAY
Oslo
Transportforum
[49209] .... (Combined) 5,000

ROMANIA
Bucharest
TRANSURB [49844]

REPUBLIC OF SOUTH AFRICA
Cape Town
Road Ahead [50406] 10,000

SPAIN
Madrid
Carreteras
[50733] .. .. (Controlled) 16,000
Valencia
Valencia Maritima [50847]

SWITZERLAND
Geneva
International Journal of Vehicle Performance [51146]

TAIWAN
Taipei
Asian Air Transport
[51331] .. .. (Paid) 11,750

THAILAND
Bangkok
Thailand Airline Timetable
[51441] .. .. (Paid) 40,000

UNITED KINGDOM
Abingdon
Mobilities [51984]

Bath
Airline Industry Information [52236]
Birmingham
Transport Journal
[52371] .. .. (Controlled) 17,500
Brighton
ADI News [52603] 16,000
Coulsdon
Jane's Airport Review [53067]
Jane's Transport Finance [53074]
Fareham
Motor Ship [53374]
Haywards Heath
Parking News [53550] 1,600
Hindhead
Transport Engineer
[53575] .. .. (Combined) 15,622
Kidlington
Transportation Research Part E [53708]
London
CallSign
[54168] .... (Controlled) 2,000
Getting There [54506]
Local Transport Today [54881]
Packaging, Transport, Storage & Security of Radioactive Material [55049]
RMT News [55206]
Manchester
Journal of Transport Geography [55568]
Oxford
Journal of Advanced Transportation
[56011] .... (Combined) 355
Sidcup
Tunnels & Tunnelling [56546]
Surbiton
Bulk Distributor [56657] 7,100
Sutton
Railway Gazette International
[56692] .. .. (Paid) 10,000
Swanley
ITS International
[56697] .. .. (Combined) △22,283
World Highways
[56698] .. .. (Combined) ‡15,133
Tunbridge Wells
Transportation Professional
[56783] .. .. ‡13,000
Wadhurst
International Cranes and Specialized Transport [56809] .. .. ‡14,381
West Sussex
Freight Magazine [56898] ... ★11,464

TRAVEL AND TOURISM

AUSTRALIA
Collingwood
Inside Indonesia [41790]
Sydney
COAST [42492] .... ‡30,000

BAHRAIN
Manama
Travel & Tourism News Middle East
[42794] .. .. (Paid) 6,428

BELGIUM
Antwerp
Ambiance
[42837] .. .. (Controlled) 63,638

Mechelen
Travel Magazine
[42905] .... (Combined) 7,000

BELIZE
Belize City
Placencia Breeze [42916] 2,500

BRITISH VIRGIN ISLANDS
Tortola
The British Virgin Islands Welcome Tourist Guide
[43069] .... (Non-paid) 165,000

PEOPLE'S REPUBLIC OF CHINA
Chengdu
International Journal of Tourism Anthropology [43248]
Hong Kong
Hong Kong for the Business Visitor
[43322] 40,000
Journal of Travel & Tourism Marketing [43363]
WHERE Hong Kong [43386]
Shanghai
Travelling Scope [43508]
World Traveller [43511]

CZECH REPUBLIC
Prague
Pasos [43633]

DENMARK
Copenhagen
Take Off [43684] .. .. (Paid) 5,800
.... (Combined) ‡18,000

FINLAND
Helsinki
International Journal of Digital Culture and Electronic Tourism [43833]
Meidan Mokki
[43846] .. .. (Paid) 43,917

GERMANY
Buxtehude
Reise & Preise
[44288] .. .. (Combined) 125,000
Detmold
Extratour [44313] 900,000

GREECE
Patras
International Journal of Tourism Policy [44765]

HUNGARY
Budapest
WHERE Budapest [44882]

ICELAND
Reykjavik
Atlantica [44897]
Iceland Review [44901]

INDIA
Lucknow
Tourism Recreation Research
[45329] .. .. (Paid) 2,000
Mumbai
Accommodation Times
[45349] .. .. (Paid) 19,254
India Today Plus
[45374] .. .. (Paid) 89,000

Circulation: ★ = ABC; △ = BPA; ◆ = CAC; • = CCAB; ❑ = VAC; ⊕ = PO Statement; ‡ = Publisher's Report; Boldface figures = sworn; Light figures = estimated.

New Delhi
Youth Hosteller [45671] 45,000

INDONESIA
Kuta
Bali & Beyond Magazine
[45824] 20,000

IRELAND
Dublin
Ireland at Your Leisure
[45969] .... ★41,000

Dundrum
Visitor [46011] .... ★200,000

ITALY
Padua
Italia Turistica
[46206] .... (Combined) 150,000

Peschiera Borromeo
Il Gommone e la Nautica per Tutti
[46216] .... (Combined) 31,000

Rome
Travelling Interline International
[46243] .... (Combined) 20,000
WHERE Rome [46245]

Rozzano
Meridiani [46251] .... ‡31,066
Tuttoturismo
[46255] .... (Combined) ‡41,623

Turin
TTG Italia [46275] 9,000

JAPAN
Tokyo
Paper Sky [47016]

REPUBLIC OF KOREA
Busan
Asia Pacific Journal of Tourism
Research [47209] 400

NETHERLANDS
The Hague
Kampioen
[48619] ..... (Controlled) 3,531,785
Reizen [48627] 55,350

NEW ZEALAND
Auckland
Home New Zealand
[48795] 14,805
KiaOra [48801] 45,000
onHoliday [48827]
Traveltrade [48830] .... ‡1,393

Hamilton
Tourism Management [48911]

SINGAPORE
Singapore
Travel Trade Gazette Asia
[50281] .... ‡16,800
Wedding & Travel [50285]
Wine & Dine [50287] 40,000

REPUBLIC OF SOUTH AF-RICA
Cape Town
Explore South Africa
[50377] .... ★10,000

Paarl
Encounter Southern Africa [50561]

SPAIN
Barcelona
Viajes National Geographic
[50706] .... ‡63,013

Madrid
Geo [50761] ..... (Combined) 31,000
IH Industria Hostelera
[50768] .... (Combined) 7,000
Spain Gourmetour
[50808] .... (Non-paid) 25,000

SUDAN
Wad Medani
International Journal of Sudan Re-
search, Policy and Sustainable
Development [50940]

SWITZERLAND
Geneva
International Journal of Leisure and
Tourism Marketing [51128]

Zurich
Travel Inside [51292] ... (Paid) 7,976
Travel Inside Francais
[51293] .... (Paid) 2,913
Travel Manager
[51294] ....:. (Combined) 2,900

TAIWAN
Taipei
Dynasty [51338] .... (Paid) 60,000
Travel in Taiwan [51367]

THAILAND
Bangkok
Asia-Pacific Tropical Homes [51412]
LookEast [51426]
Travel Trade Report
[51446] .. .. (Paid) 15,000

Chiang Mai
Bangkok Magazine [51455]
Citylife [51457]

TURKEY
Eskisehir
Anatolia [51554] .. .. (Paid) 1,500

UNITED ARAB EMIRATES
Dubai
Business Traveller Middle East
[51633] .... △26,437
Dubai Voyager [51639] ...... △29,350
Open Skies [51651] .... △73,178

UNITED KINGDOM
Abingdon
Current Issues in Tourism [51751]
International Journal of Heritage
Studies [51836]
Journal of Ecotourism [51889]
Journal of Heritage Tourism [51903]
Journal of Sport & Tourism [51946]
Journal of Sustainable Tourism
[51950]
Journal of Tourism & Cultural Change
[51952]
Scandinavian Journal of Hospitality
and Tourism [52049]
Tourism Geographies [52081]
Tourism and Hospitality Planning &
Development [52082]

Barnsley
Destination UK [52179] 11,902

Basingstoke
Place Branding [52228] 400
Tourism and Hospitality Research
[52232]

Bradford
Tourism Review [52553]

Bristol
BBC Countryfile [52641] ..... ★33,839

Cambridge
Sportsboat [52898] .... (Paid) 10,000

Cheltenham
Evergreen [52971] ... .. (Paid) 48,000
Oxfordshire Life [52974]
This England [52978] 170,342

Croydon
Caravan [53123]
Selling Long Haul
[53132] .... (Non-paid) 16,500
Selling Short Breaks
[53133] .... (Non-paid) 16,500

Dulverton
Active Exmoor [53209]

Dundee
The Scots Magazine [53218]

Dunstable
OAG Rail Guide
[53225] .... (Paid) 5,000

Heslington
Journal of Hospitality, Leisure, Sports
& Tourism Education [53568]

Hitchin
Attractions Management [53576]

London
AB Europe
[53889] .... (Controlled) 8,300
Cartier International Polo @MAG
[54184] 10,000
Conference & Incentive Travel
[54259] .. .. (Controlled) ★16,154
Motor Caravan [54958]
Timeout.com [55320]
Tourism Economics [55331]
Tourist Studies [55332]
Traveller [55337] 35,000
Wallpaper* [55377] .... ★113,000
WHERE London [55403]
World Cruise Industry Review
[55418] .... (Non-paid) 6,993

Manchester
Journal of Transport Geography
[55568]

Preston
Lake District Life [56301]
Lancashire Life [56303] ...... ★23,455

Sheffield
International Journal of Knowledge
Management in Tourism and
Hospitality [56500]

Wallington
Building for Leisure
[56832] .... (Combined) ‡11,706

Windsor
Wanderlust [56933] 37,000

TRUCKS AND TRUCKING
**See also Transportation,
Traffic, and Shipping**

AUSTRALIA
Alexandria
Truck Australia [41547] .. .. ★12,881
Truckin' Life [41548] .. .. ★21,539

DENMARK
Padborg
Trans-Inform
[43733] .... (Paid) ◆4,000

FINLAND
Helsinki
Kuljetusyrittaja
[43842] .... (Controlled) 8,423

FRANCE
Clichy
Les Routiers
[43934] .. .. (Paid) 45,000

IRELAND
Claremorris
Fleet Transport
[45931] .... (Combined) 6,200

NEW ZEALAND
Auckland
New Zealand Trucking
[48821] .... ★10,009

North Shore
Diesel Industry News [48952]

SWITZERLAND
Geneva
International Journal of Heavy Ve-
hicle Systems [51124]
International Journal of Vehicle
Design [51145]

UNITED KINGDOM
Bath
Truckstop News
[52262] .. .. (Combined) ‡41,033

Cudham
Tractor & Machinery [53148]

Felixstowe
Ford & Fordson Tractors [53385]

Manchester
Truck and Plant Trader
[55581] .... ★14,383

Sutton
Truck and Driver [56693] .... ★27,973

West Sussex
Freight Magazine [56898] ... ★11,464

TURF AND TURF MAINTENANCE

AUSTRALIA
Carisbrook
Turfcraft [41723]

SWITZERLAND
Bassersdorf
Seed Science and Technology
[51067]

UNITED KINGDOM
Bingley
International Turfgrass Bulletin
[52327] .. .. (Controlled) 5,000
Journal of Turfgrass Science (Incor-
porating the Journal of the Sports
Turf Research Institute) [52328]

Weston-super-Mare
Golf Club Management
[56905] 1,400

VENDING MACHINES

UNITED KINGDOM
Smallfield
Auto Vending [56561] .... ‡7,180

VETERANS

NIGERIA
Ibadan
Tropical Veterinarian [49103]

VETERINARY MEDICINE

AUSTRALIA
Deakin
Animal Health Australia [41832]

Saint Leonards
Australian Veterinary Practitioner [42332]

Sydney
Australian Veterinary Journal
[42468] .... ‡25,000

BELGIUM
Maleves-Sainte-Marie-Wastines
Infor Marechalerie/European Farriers Journal/Der Huf
[42903] .... (Paid) 6,500

BRAZIL
Rio de Janeiro
Pesquisa Veterinaria Brasileira [43013]

Santa Maria
Ciencia Rural [43016]

Sao Paulo
Brazilian Journal of Veterinary Research and Animal Science [43029]

Vicosa
Arquivo Brasileiro de Medicina Veterinaria e Zootecnia [43055]
Entomologia y Vectores [43058]

BULGARIA
Stara Zagora
Bulgarian Journal of Veterinary Medicine (BJVM) [43110]

CZECH REPUBLIC
Brno
Acta Veteriniaria Brno [43601]

DENMARK
Frederiksberg
The International Veterinary Student [43691]

FRANCE
Maisons-Alfort
Journal of Veterinary Cardiology [43971]

Paris
Disease Information [44038]
Scientific and Technical Review
[44083] 1,800

GERMANY
Dusseldorf
Parasitology Research [44330]

Munich
Anatomia, Histologia, Embryologia [44549]

Stuttgart
V.C.O.T. [44684] .... (Paid) 1,800

HUNGARY
Budapest
Acta Microbiologica et Immunologica Hungarica [44814]
Acta Veterinaria Hungarica [44819]

INDIA
Bikaner
Journal of Camel Practice and Research [45017] .... (Paid) 750

Madras
Indian Veterinary Journal
[45334] .... (Paid) 8,000

New Delhi
Indian Journal of Animal Sciences
[45549] 2,000

ISRAEL
Raanana
Israel Journal of Veterinary Medicine [46090]

ITALY
Cremona
Ippologia [46136]

Milan
Theriogenology [46197]

JAPAN
Sapporo
Japanese Journal of Veterinary Research [46651] 650

Tochigi
Journal of Equine Science [46710]

Tokyo
Journal of Reproduction and Development [46939]
Journal of Veterinary Medical Science
[46944] .. .. (Paid) 5,000

KENYA
Nairobi
Bulletin of Animal Health and Production in Africa [47175]
Kenya Veterinarian [47191]

NETHERLANDS
Dordrecht
Tropical Animal Health and Production [48583]

Utrecht
Veterinary Sciences Tomorrow [48768]

NEW ZEALAND
Christchurch
New Zealand AgriVet [48872]

Wellington
New Zealand Veterinary Journal
[49031] .. .. (Paid) 2,000

NIGERIA
Ibadan
Tropical Journal of Animal Science [49101]

Zaria
Nigerian Veterinary Journal [49186]

PAKISTAN
Faisalabad
Global Veterinaria [49245]
Journal of Animal and Veterinary Advances [49260]
Research Journal of Animal and Veterinary Sciences [49283]
Veterinary Research [49296]

Islamabad
Pakistan Journal of Agricultural Research [49306] .. ... (Paid) 1,000

PHILIPPINES
Manila
SABRAO Journal of Breeding and Genetics [49559]

POLAND
Pulawy
The Bulletin of the Veterinary Institute in Pulawy [49674]

REPUBLIC OF SOUTH AFRICA
Grahamstown
Nigerian Journal of Parasitology [50506]

Pretoria
Onderstepoort Journal of Veterinary Research
[50598] .... (Combined) 300
South African Journal of Animal Science [50602]

SRI LANKA
Colombo
Ceylon Journal of Medical Sciences
[50850] .... (Controlled) 125

SWEDEN
Linkoping
Reproduction in Domestic Animals [50977]

UNITED REPUBLIC OF TANZANIA
Morogoro
Tanzania Veterinary Journal [51408]

THAILAND
Bangkok
Buffalo Journal [51415]
Confluence [51417] 600

TURKEY
Ankara
Turkish Journal of Veterinary and Animal Sciences [51516]

UNITED KINGDOM
Bedford
Petcare [52274] 1,600

Cambridge
Journal of Helminthology [52854]
Nutrition Research Reviews [52879]

Chatham
Medical and Veterinary Entomology [52959]

Harlescott
Veterinary Dermatology [53508]

London
BMC Veterinary Research [54092]
Comparative Hepatology [54250]
The Journal of Small Animal Practice
[54817] .. .. (Paid) 6,500
Laboratory Animals [54847]

Newbury
Avian Pathology [55661]

Oxford
Animal Science Journal [55867]
Journal of Veterinary Emergency and Critical Care [56078]
Transboundary and Emerging Diseases [56220]
Veterinary Anaesthesia and Analgesia [56225]
Veterinary and Comparative Oncology [56226]
Zoonoses and Public Health [56230]

Penicuik
Animal
[56243] .. .. (Combined) 10,400

Peterborough
Veterinary Times [56263]

Quedgeley
Cattle Practice [56307]

Tisbury
Fab Cat Care Journal
[56751] 3,000

Wallingford
Review of Medical and Veterinary Entomology [56826] 290
Review of Medical and Veterinary Mycology [56827] 200

VOCATIONAL EDUCATION

AUSTRALIA
Camberwell
Australian Journal of Career Development [41693] 700

AUSTRIA
Vienna
Progress [42766]

BELGIUM
Brussels
Worlds of Education
[42875] 12,000

DENMARK
Frederiksberg
The International Veterinary Student [43691]

FRANCE
Ferney-Voltaire
Medical Student International [43949]

Paris
Higher Education Policy [44047]

GREECE
Thessaloniki
European Journal [44771]

INDIA
New Delhi
Indian Journal of Technical Education
[45567] .. .. (Paid) 12,000

IRELAND
Dublin
Adult Learner [45943] 500

NETHERLANDS
Dordrecht
Higher Education [48415]
International Journal for the Advancement of Counseling [48425]
International Journal for Educational and Vocational Guidance [48427]

NIGERIA
Port Harcourt
Journal of Technology and Education in Nigeria [49168]

ROMANIA
Bucharest
Higher Education in Europe [49837]

REPUBLIC OF SOUTH AFRICA
Pretoria
Musicus [50597]

SWITZERLAND
Geneva
IB World [51098] 10,000

Circulation: ★ = ABC; △ = BPA; ◆ = CAC; • = CCAB; ❑ = VAC; ⊕ = PO Statement; ‡ = Publisher's Report; Boldface figures = sworn; Light figures = estimated.

Prospects [51156]

THAILAND
Bangkok
SEAMEO Journal of Southeast Asian
Education [51435]

UNITED KINGDOM
Abingdon
European Journal of Engineering
Education [51780]
Journal of Education and Work
[51891]
Journal of Vocational Education &
Training [51956]
Technical Education & Training
Abstracts [52072]

Bradford
Education Training [52452]

Corsham
International Journal of Art & Design
Education [53066] 2,800

Dundee
Medical Teacher [53215]

Edinburgh
Journal of Medical Education [53293]
Teaching Earth Sciences [53323]

High Wycombe
Deafness and Education International
[53572] .... (Paid) 2,000

London
Boarding School [54094]
Education Today
[54354] .... (Paid) 2,000
International Journal [54629]

Loughborough
Accounting Education [55476]

Newcastle upon Tyne
Interspectives [55673]

Nottingham
The Law Teacher [55765]

WASTE MANAGEMENT AND RECYCLING
See also Water Supply and Sewage Disposal; Ecology and Conservation

AUSTRALIA
Wahroonga
Sustainability Matters
[42677] .... ★5,757

BRAZIL
Rio de Janeiro
Engenharia Sanitaria e Ambiental
[43004]

FRANCE
Paris
Pollution Atmospherique
[44077] 1,500

GREECE
Athens
Global Nest [44743]

INDIA
New Delhi
VATIS Update Waste Management
[45666] 500

Tirupati
Environmental Science [45756]

JAPAN
Tokyo
Journal of Material Cycles and Waste
Management [46922]

NETHERLANDS
Amsterdam
Asian Journal of Water, Environment
and Pollution [47899]
Chemosphere [47927]

Dordrecht
Biodegradation [48331]

Utrecht
Resources, Conservation and
Recycling [48765]

NEW ZEALAND
Wellington
Water and Wastes in New Zealand
[49036] .... ‡1,450

NIGERIA
Calabar
Global Journal of Environmental
Sciences [49071]

POLAND
Warsaw
Annals of Warsaw University of Life
Sciences, Land Reclamation
[49689]
Journal of Water and Land
Development [49728]

SINGAPORE
Singapore
Water & Wastewater Asia [50284]

THAILAND
Bangkok
EEAT Journal [51419] 1,500

TURKEY
Izmir
Ekoloji [51573]

UNITED KINGDOM
Bradford
Management of Environmental
Quality [52523]

Cambridge
Renewable Agriculture and Food
Systems [52890]

London
The Environmental Scientist [54378]
Hildon Magazine [54552]
Journal of Water Supply [54835]
Resource Management & Recovery
[55192]
Water and Environment Manager
[55382] 12,000
Water Policy [55384]
Water Supply [55388]
Water 21 [55389]

Salisbury
Recycling & Waste World [56457]

Skipton
Warmer Bulletin
[56555] .... (Combined) 1,000

Wadhurst
Demolition & Recycling International
[56806] .... ‡7,481

WATER SUPPLY AND SEWAGE DISPOSAL
See also Ecology and Conservation; Waste Management and Recycling

AUSTRALIA
Tullamarine
Irrigation and Water Resources
[42652] .... ‡14,500

BRAZIL
Rio de Janeiro
Engenharia Sanitaria e Ambiental
[43004]

PEOPLE'S REPUBLIC OF CHINA
Nanjing
Advances in Science and Technology
of Water Resources [43456]
Journal of Economics of Water
Resources [43458]
Water Resources Protection [43460]
Water Science and Engineering
[43461]

FRANCE
Paris
International Journal of Nuclear
Desalination [44050]

GHANA
Accra
West African Journal of Applied
Ecology [44730]

JAPAN
Tokyo
Limnology [46961] .. .... (Paid) 1,200

LEBANON
Beirut
Arab Water World (AWW)
[47392] 8,909

POLAND
Warsaw
Journal of Water and Land
Development [49728]

SINGAPORE
Singapore
Water & Wastewater Asia [50284]

REPUBLIC OF SOUTH AFRICA
Centurion
SA Irrigation [50446]

SPAIN
Madrid
International Journal of River Basin
Management [50773]

SWEDEN
Lund
Borrsavangen [50984]

Norrkoping
Hydrology Research [50995]

SWITZERLAND
Baden
Wasser Energie Luft/Eau Energie Air
[51057]

THAILAND
Bangkok
EEAT Journal [51419] 1,500

TURKEY
Izmir
Ekoloji [51573]

UNITED KINGDOM
Exeter
Filtration [53358]

London
The Environmental Scientist [54378]
Hildon Magazine [54552]
Journal of Water and Health [54834]
Journal of Water Supply [54835]
News and Views [55003]
Urban Water Journal [55361]
Water Asset Management
International [55381]
Water and Environment Manager
[55382] 12,000
Water Intelligence Online [55383]
Water Policy [55384]
Water Practice and Technology
[55385]
Water Science & Technology [55386]
Water Science & Technology [55387]
Water Supply [55388]
Water 21 [55389]
Water Utility Management
International [55390]

Olney
International Journal of Water
[55840]

Oxford
Ground Water [55969]
Ground Water Monitoring &
Remediation [55970]
The Utilities Journal [56224] ... 1,000

Ross-on-Wye
Marine Conservation
[56410] .... (Paid) 5,000

Rugby
Waterlines [56425]

Witney
The Journal of Water Law [56945]

WEIGHTS AND MEASURES

UNITED KINGDOM
Bristol
Metrologia [52706]

Essex
LighterLife [53340]

WELDING
See also Metal, Metallurgy, and Metal Trade

PEOPLE'S REPUBLIC OF CHINA
Harbin
China Welding [43263]

GERMANY
Dusseldorf
Der Praktiker [44323] 17,000
Schweissen & Schneiden
[44334] 14,000

UNITED KINGDOM
Wadhurst
Construction Europe
[56805] .... ★14,624

Circulation: ★ = ABC; △ = BPA; ◆ = CAC; • = CCAB; ❑ = VAC; ⊕ = PO Statement; ‡ = Publisher's Report; Boldface figures = sworn; Light figures = estimated.

WILDLIFE AND EXOTIC ANIMALS

AUSTRALIA
Brisbane
Wildlife Australia [41654]

Collingwood
Wildlife Research [41797]

EGYPT
Ismailia
Egyptian Journal of Natural History [43774]

GERMANY
Frankfurt
WWF Journal [44363]

HUNGARY
Budapest
National Geographic Kids
[44855] .... (Paid) ‡41,873
National Geographic Special
[44856] .... ‡16,000

KENYA
Nairobi
African Journal of Ecology [47171]
Pachyderm [47195]
SWARA [47197]

NIGERIA
Lagos
Journal of Cell & Animal Biology [49139]

Nsukka
Animal Research International [49155]

REPUBLIC OF SOUTH AFRICA
Bloubergstrand
South African Journal of Wildlife Research [50357]

Howick
African Wildlife [50525] 10,000

UNITED KINGDOM
Abingdon
International Journal of Heritage Studies [51836]

Basingstoke
Nature [52226] .... ‡65,955

Bristol
BBC Wildlife Magazine
[52643] .... ★44,564

Cambridge
Journal of Cetacean Research and Management [52848]
World Birdwatch [52906] 6,000

Farnborough
Gamewise [53378]

Liverpool
Biological Conservation [53869]

London
Journal of Animal Ecology [54697]
Waterlife [55391] 87,000
WDCS [55392] 26,000
Wildabout [55405] 30,000

Oxford
Animal Science Journal [55867]

Peterborough
Bird Watching [56252]

Tonbridge
Outrage [56756] .... (Paid) 12,500

Wallingford
Animal Health Research Reviews [56815]

ZAMBIA
Fringilla
Black Lewche [57107] 2,000

WOOD AND WOODWORKING
See also Forestry

AUSTRALIA
Hazelbrook
The Australian Woodworker [41944]

DENMARK
Glostrup
Puff - Fagtidsskrift for Tralast og Byggemarkeder
[43713] .... (Controlled) ‡1,843
Trae- & Mobelindustri
[43719] .... ‡6,315

FINLAND
Lahti
Woodworking Puuntyosto WIN
[43903] 5,000

GERMANY
Berlin
Holzforschung [44189] 400

Munich
Wood Science and Technology [44587]

Nuremberg
WOODWORKING INTERNATIONAL
[44618] 12,000

NETHERLANDS
Dordrecht
Holz als Roh- und Werkstoff [48417]

Rotterdam
Het Houtblad
[48750] ...... (Controlled) ‡16,500

NEW ZEALAND
Wellington
Creative Wood [49005] 1,000

UNITED KINGDOM
Bath
Good Woodworking
[52242] ... . (Paid) 14,800

Battle
Furniture Production
[52270] .... (Non-paid) 5,311

Lewes
Furniture and Cabinetmaking [53849]
Woodcarving [53852]

London
International Wood Products Journal [54675]

Wadhurst
Construction Europe
[56805] .... ★14,624

ZOOLOGY

AUSTRALIA
Brisbane
Wildlife Australia [41654]

Carlton
Boobook [41725]

Collingwood
Australian Journal of Zoology [41783]

Richmond
Nephrology [42304]

Salisbury
Parrot Society of Australia News [42342]

PEOPLE'S REPUBLIC OF CHINA
Beijing
Current Zoology [43192]

COLOMBIA
Bogota
Caldasia [43544]

CZECH REPUBLIC
Ceske Budejovice
Folia Parasitologica [43605]

FRANCE
Dijon
Behavioural Processes [43943]

GERMANY
Berlin
Mammalia [44220]

Kiel
Marine Biology [44505]
Polar Biology [44507]

Osnabruck
Journal of Zoological Systematics and Evolutionary Research [44630]

Stuttgart
Senckenbergiana biologica [44678]

GHANA
Accra
NKO Magazine [44729]

HUNGARY
Budapest
Acta Zoologica Academiae Scientiarum Hungaricae [44820]

INDIA
Hyderabad
The Icfai Journal of Life Sciences [45158]

ITALY
Ischia Porto
Marine Ecology [46156]

JAPAN
Kyoto
Current Herpetology [46470]

Tokyo
Fish Pathology
[46824] .... (Paid) 1,000
Ichthyological Research
[46836] .... (Paid) 700
Japan Heterocerists Journal [46857]
Japanese Journal of Animal Psychology
[46863] .... (Controlled) 500
Journal of Ethology [46896]
Primates [47024] .... (Paid) 800
Venus: Japanese Journal of Malacology [47055] .. .. (Paid) 900

Tsukuba
Japanese Journal of Nematology [47111]

Yamagata
Marine Micropaleontology [47125]

NETHERLANDS
Amsterdam
Journal of Arid Environments [48049]
Microbes and Infection [48157]
Microbial Pathogenesis [48158]
Molecular and Biochemical Parasitology [48163]

Dordrecht
Evolution: Education and Outreach [48385]
Hydrobiologia [48419]

Leiden
Amphibia-Reptilia [48645]
Animal Biology [48647]
Crustaceana [48665]
Nematology [48713]

NEW ZEALAND
Dunedin
Journal of Neuroendocrinology [48890]

Hamilton
New Zealand Journal of Zoology [48909]

NIGERIA
Ibadan
Nigerian Journal of Animal Production [49093]
Tropical Journal of Animal Science [49101]

Nsukka
Animal Research International [49155]

Port Harcourt
African Journal of Applied Zoology and Environmental Biology [49165]

PAKISTAN
Faisalabad
Research Journal of Animal Sciences [49282]
World Journal of Zoology [49303]

PHILIPPINES
Quezon City
Asian Fisheries Science [49581]

POLAND
Warsaw
Acta Palaeontologica Polonica [49681]
Acta Zoologica Lituanica [49683]
Ring [49763]
Vestnik Zoologii [49773]
Zoologica Poloniae [49776]

PORTUGAL
Lisbon
Acta Ethologica [49801]

RUSSIA
Moscow
Journal of Ichthyology [49929]

SLOVENIA
Ljubljana
Acta Agriculturae Slovenica [50333]

REPUBLIC OF SOUTH AFRICA
Bloemfontein
Navorsinge van die Nasionale Museum, Bloemfontein [50355]

Circulation: ★ = ABC; △ = BPA; ◆ = CAC; • = CCAB; ❏ = VAC; ⊕ = PO Statement; ‡ = Publisher's Report; Boldface figures = sworn; Light figures = estimated.

Pietermaritzburg
African Zoology [50566]

Pretoria
Journal of Zoology [50594]

SWEDEN
Uppsala
Acta Zoologica [51049]

TAIWAN
Taipei
Acta Zoologica Taiwanica
    [51330] .... (Controlled) 500
Zoological Studies [51368]

UNITED REPUBLIC OF TAN-ZANIA
Morogoro
Tanzania Veterinary Journal [51408]

TURKEY
Ankara
Turkish Journal of Zoology [51517]

UNITED KINGDOM
Basingstoke
Nature [52226] .. .. ‡65,955

Bristol
Mammal Review [52703]

Cardiff
Journal of Neuroscience Methods
    [52935]

London
Animal Behaviour [53945]
Cage and Aviary Birds
    [54166] .. .. ★15,185
Frontiers in Zoology [54486]
Journal News [54788]

Manchester
Bulletin of the Malacological Society
    of London [55545]

Oxford
Acta Histochemica [55860]

Behavioral Ecology
    [55879] .. .. (Paid) 1,300
                              (Non-paid) 35
Palaeontology [56140]

Penicuik
Animal
    [56243] .. .. (Combined) 10,400

Reading
Microbiology Today [56326]

Circulation: ★ = ABC; △ = BPA; ◆ = CAC; • = CCAB; ❑ = VAC; ⊕ = PO Statement; ‡ = Publisher's Report; Boldface figures = sworn; Light figures = estimated.

The Master Index is a comprehensive listing of all entries, both print and broadcast, included in this Directory. Citations in this index are interfiled alphabetically throughout regardless of media type. Publications are cited according to title and important keywords within titles; broadcast citations are by station call letters or cable company names. Indexed here also are: notices of recent cessations; former call letters or titles; foreign language and other alternate publication titles; other types of citations. Indexing is word-by-word rather than letter-by-letter, so that "New York" files before "News". Listings in the Master Index include geographic locations and entry numbers. An asterisk (*) after a number indicates that the title is mentioned within the text of the cited entry.

A

A+ Architecture/A+ Architectuur (Brussels, BEL) **[42842]**

A to B (Castle Cary, GBR) Unable to locate

AA Directions (Auckland, NZL) **[48783]**

A & G Magazine (Buenos Aires, ARG) **[41468]**

A & U (Tokyo, JPN) Unable to locate

AAD Outlook (Sydney, NW, AUS) Unable to locate

Aamar-FM - 106.2 (Kolkata, WB, IND) **[45308]**

Aandrijftechniek (Doetinchem, NLD) Unable to locate

Aankhijhyal (Kathmandu, NPL) **[47836]**

Aaraaichi (Tirunelveli, TN, IND) Unable to locate

Aavesh (New Delhi, DH, IND) Unable to locate

AB Europe (London, GBR) **[53889]**

Abaco (Gijon, SPA) **[50716]**

Abaco Journal (Abaco, BHS) **[42782]**

Abacus (Oxford, GBR) **[55857]**

ABAS Journal (London, GBR) Unable to locate

Abbey-FM (Barrow, GBR) Ceased

ABC Brisbane-AM - 612 (Brisbane, QL, AUS) **[41655]**

ABC Canberra - 666 KHz (Canberra, AC, AUS) **[41714]**

ABC Coast-FM - 91.7 (Gold Coast City, QL, AUS) **[41901]**

ABC Illawara-FM - 97.3 (Wollongong, NW, AUS) **[42707]**

ABC NewsRadio-AM - 630 (Sydney, NW, AUS) **[42594]**

ABC NewsRadio-FM - 103.9 (Sydney, NW, AUS) **[42595]**

ABC North Queensland - 630 KHz (Townsville, QL, AUS) **[42639]**

ABC Northern Territory-AM - 783 (Alice Springs, NT, AUS) **[41550]**

ABC Radio National-AM - 576 (Sydney, NW, AUS) **[42596]**

ABCE Noticias (Rio de Janeiro, RJ, BRZ) Unable to locate

Abhigyan (New Delhi, DH, IND) **[45476]**

Abhivyakti and Expressions (Nasik, MH, IND) **[45473]**

Able Update (Wellington, NZL) Unable to locate

ABM Magazine (Bridgwater, GBR) **[52595]**

ABM Metalurgia e Materials (Sao Paulo, SP, BRZ) **[43019]**

Aboriginal and Torres Strait Islander health bulletin **[42246]***

ABR (Australian Book Review) (Richmond South, VI, AUS) **[42311]**

ABS-FM - 93.3 (Auburn, NW, AUS) **[41566]**

Abstract of Statistics for Tamil Nadu (Chennai, TN, IND) Unable to locate

Abstracts (Kirgat Tivon, ISR) Unable to locate

Abstracts of Congress (London, GBR) Unable to locate

Abstracts of Current Literature in Toxicology (Lucknow, UP, IND) **[45320]**

Abstracts and Reviews (Coventry, GBR) **[53076]**

ABTT Update **[55238]***

ACA Review (Leominster, GBR) Unable to locate

Academia (Madrid, SPA) **[50722]**

Academic Journal of Agriculture **[43165]***

Academic Journal of Cancer Research (Faisalabad, PAK) **[49228]**

Academic Journal of Financial Management (Faisalabad, PAK) **[49229]**

Academic Journal of Shanghai Jiao Tong University Social Science Section (Shanghai, CHN) **[43462]**

Academic Open Internet Journal (Bourgas, BUL) **[43086]**

Academy (Ilford, GBR) Unable to locate

Academy Law Review (Trivandrum, KE, IND) Unable to locate

Acao Anti AIDS (Rio de Janeiro, RJ, BRZ) Unable to locate

Acarina (Moscow, RUS) **[49867]**

ACAV Informa (Trento, ITA) **[46260]**

ACC Cardiosource Review Journal (Amsterdam, NLD) **[47875]**

Accelerator Machine Physics (Bristol, GBR) Unable to locate

Accent (Newcastle upon Tyne, GBR) **[55666]**

Access (Brisbane, QL, AUS) **[41639]**

Access All Areas (London, GBR) **[53890]**

Access International (Wadhurst, GBR) **[56804]**

Accident Analysis & Prevention (Amsterdam, NLD) **[47876]**

Accidents Claims Journal (New Delhi, DH, IND) Unable to locate

Accommodation Times (Mumbai, MH, IND) **[45349]**

Accountancy (London, GBR) **[53891]**

Accountancy Age (London, GBR) **[53892]**

Accountancy Ireland (Dublin, DU, IRL) **[45942]**

Accountant's Journal (Mandaluyong City, PHL) **[49531]**

The Accountants Magazine **[53259]***

Accounting, Auditing & Accountability Journal (Sydney, NW, AUS) **[42444]**

Accounting, Business & Financial History (Abingdon, GBR) **[51693]**

Accounting and Business Research (London, GBR) **[53893]**

Accounting Education (Loughborough, GBR) **[55476]**

Accounting and Finance (Oxford, GBR) **[55858]**

Accounting Forum (Adelaide, SA, AUS) **[41498]**

Accounting Organisations & Society (Oxford, GBR) Unable to locate

Accounting Personnel (Hong Kong, CHN) Unable to locate

Accounting Research Journal (Bradford, GBR) **[52435]**

Accounting Technician (London, GBR) Unable to locate

Accreditation and Quality Assurance (Dortmund, GER) **[44314]**

ACE Bulletin (London, GBR) **[53894]**

Aceem Radio-FM - 103.4 (Antananarivo, MDG) **[47563]**

Achabaka (Beirut, LBN) **[47385]**

Achiever (Cape Town, SAF) **[50360]**

Achilles Heel (Plymouth, DN, GBR) Unable to locate

Acik Radyo - Istanbul - 94.9 MHz (Istanbul, TUR) **[51564]**

ACM Transactions on Computational Logic (TOCL) (Amsterdam, NLD) **[47877]**

ACN: Asian Chemical News (Sutton, GBR) **[56678]**

Acoustics Abstracts (Brentwood, GBR) **[52564]**

Acoustics Australia (Sydney, NW, AUS) **[42445]**

Acoustics Bulletin (Saint Albans, GBR) **[56433]**

Acquisition Update (New Delhi, DH, IND) Unable to locate

Acquisitions Monthly (Tunbridge Wells, GBR) Unable to locate

Across Languages and Cultures (Budapest, HUN) **[44804]**

ACT (Ahmedabad, GJ, IND) Unable to locate

ACT! The Magazine of Greenpeace Austria (Vienna, AUT) **[42742]**

Acta Acoustics (Beijing, CHN) Unable to locate

Acta Adriatica (Split, CTA) **[43559]**

Acta Adriatica (Split, CTA) **[43560]**

ACTA Aeronautica et Astronautica Sinica (Beijing, CHN) Unable to locate

Acta Agriculturae Scandinavica—Section C, Food Economics (Frederiksberg, DEN) **[43688]**

Acta Agriculturae Slovenica (Ljubljana, SVA) **[50333]**

Acta Agronomica Hungarica (Martonvasar, HUN) **[44890]**

Acta Agronomica Sinica (Beijing, CHN) **[43165]**

Acta Alimentaria (Budapest, HUN) **[44805]**

Acta Amazonica (Manaus, AZ, BRZ) **[42987]**

Acta Anaesthesiologica Scandinavica (Trondheim, NOR) **[49215]**

Acta Anatomica Nipponica (Tokyo, JPN) Unable to locate

Acta Angiologica (Bydgoszcz, POL) **[49652]**

Acta Anthropogenetica (New Delhi, DH, IND) Unable to locate

Acta Antiqua Academiae Scientiarum Hungaricae (Budapest, HUN) **[44806]**

Acta Applicandae Mathematicae (Dordrecht, NLD) **[48318]**

Acta Arachnologica (Osaka, JPN) Unable to locate

Acta Archaeologica (Copenhagen, DEN) **[43654]**

Acta Archaeologica Academiae Scientiarum Hungaricae (Budapest, HUN) **[44807]**

Acta Arithmetica (Warsaw, POL) **[49677]**

Acta Asiatica (Tokyo, JPN) **[46721]**

Acta Astronautica (Paris, FRA) **[44020]**

Acta Automatica Sinica, Information and Control, Robot and Automation (Beijing, CHN) Unable to locate

Acta Biochimica et Biophysica Sinica (Oxford, GBR) **[55859]**

Acta Biochimica Polonica (Warsaw, POL) **[49678]**

Acta Bioethica (Santiago, CHL) **[43142]**

Acta Biologica Colombiana (Bogota, COL) **[43541]**

Acta Biologica Hungarica (Budapest, HUN) **[44808]**

Acta Biomaterialia (Singapore, SGP) **[50101]**

Acta Biotheoretica (Dordrecht, NLD) **[48319]**

Acta Botanica Brasilica (Sao Paulo, SP, BRZ) **[43020]**

Numbers cited in bold after listings are entry numbers rather than page numbers.

Acta Botanica Hungarica (Pecs, HUN) [**44893**]

Acta Botanica Indica (Meerut, UP, IND) *Unable to locate*

Acta Botanica Venezuelica (Caracas, VEN) [**57019**]

Acta Chimica Slovenica (ACSi) (Ljubljana, SVA) [**50334**]

Acta Chirurgiae Plasticae (Prague, CZE) [**43608**]

Acta Chromatographica (Katowice, POL) [**44961**]

Acta Ciencia Indica Physics (Meerut, UP, IND) *Unable to locate*

Acta Cientifica Venezolana (Caracas, VEN) [**57020**]

Acta Cirurgica Brasileira (Sao Paulo, SP, BRZ) [**43021**]

Acta Clinica Croatica (Zagreb, CTA) [**43561**]

Acta Criminologiae et Medicinae Legalis Japonica (Tokyo, JPN) *Unable to locate*

Acta Criminologica (Sunnyside, SAF) [**50637**]

Acta Crystallographica Section A (Zurich, SWI) [**51246**]

Acta Crystallographica Section A (Chester, GBR) [**52991**]

Acta Crystallographica Section B (Zurich, SWI) [**51247**]

Acta Crystallographica Section C (Zurich, SWI) [**51248**]

Acta Crystallographica Section D (Zurich, SWI) [**51249**]

Acta Crystallographica. Section E (Frederiksberg, DEN) [**43689**]

Acta Crystallographica Section F (Zurich, SWI) [**51250**]

Acta Dermato-Venereologica (Abingdon, GBR) [**51694**]

Acta Diabetologica (Tokyo, JPN) [**46722**]

Acta Dipterologica (Fukuoka, JPN) *Unable to locate*

Acta Ecologica (Kota, RJ, IND) *Unable to locate*

Acta Ecologica Sinica (Kidlington, GBR) [**53688**]

Acta Endoscopica (Tokyo, JPN) [**46723**]

Acta Entomologica Bulgarica (Sofia, BUL) *Unable to locate*

Acta Entomologica Slovenica (Ljubljana, SVA) [**50335**]

Acta Ethnographica Hungarica (Szeged, HUN) [**44894**]

Acta Ethologica (Lisbon, PRT) [**49801**]

Acta Genica Sinica [**43206**]*

Acta Geodaetica et Geophysica Hungarica (Budapest, HUN) [**44809**]

Acta Geographica Sinica (Beijing, CHN) *Unable to locate*

Acta Geographica Slovenica (Ljubljana, SVA) [**50336**]

Acta Geologica Hungarica (Budapest, HUN) [**44810**]

Acta Geologica Sinica (Beijing, CHN) [**43166**]

Acta Geophysica (Warsaw, POL) [**49679**]

Acta Histochemica (Oxford, GBR) [**55860**]

Acta Histochemica et Cytochemica (Kyoto, JPN) [**46465**]

Acta Historiae Artium (Budapest, HUN) [**44811**]

Acta Horticulturae (Leuven, BEL) [**42890**]

Acta Horticulturae Sinica (Beijing, CHN) *Unable to locate*

Acta Ichthyologica et Piscatoria (Szczecin, POL) [**49676**]

Acta Juridica (Claremont, SAF) [**50459**]

Acta Juridica Hungarica (Budapest, HUN) [**44812**]

Acta Linguistica Hungarica (Budapest, HUN) [**44813**]

Acta Literaria (Concepcion, CHL) [**43135**]

Acta Manilana (Manila, PHL) *Unable to locate*

Acta Mathematica Academiae Paedagogicae Nyiregyhaziensis (Nyiregyhaza, HUN) [**44892**]

Acta Mathematica Scientia (Kidlington, GBR) [**53689**]

Acta Mathematica Sinica (Tokyo, JPN) [**46724**]

Acta Mathematicae Applicatae Sinica (Beijing, CHN) [**43167**]

Acta Mechanica (Tokyo, JPN) [**46725**]

Acta Mechanica Sinica (Tokyo, JPN) [**46726**]

Acta Medica et Biologica (Niigata, JPN) *Unable to locate*

Acta Medica Iranica (Tehran, IRN) [**45885**]

Acta Medica Kinki University (Osaka, JPN) *Unable to locate*

Acta Medica Nagasakiensia (Nagasaki, JPN) [**46545**]

Acta Medica Okayama (Okayama, JPN) [**46596**]

Acta Medica Philippina (Manila, PHL) *Unable to locate*

Acta Microbiologica et Immunologica Hungarica (Budapest, HUN) [**44814**]

Acta Montanistica Slovaca (Kosice, SLK) [**50325**]

Acta Musicologica (Kassel, GER) *Unable to locate*

Acta Neurobiologiae Experimentalis (Warsaw, POL) [**49680**]

Acta Neurochirurgica (Copenhagen, DEN) *Unable to locate*

Acta Neurologica Scandanavica (Goteborg, SWE) [**50955**]

Acta Neurologica Taiwanica (Taipei, TWN) *Unable to locate*

Acta Neuropathologica (Munster, GER) [**44594**]

Acta Neuropsychiatrica (Saint Leonards, NW, AUS) [**42329**]

Acta Obstetrica Gynecologica Scandinavica (Trondheim, NOR) *Unable to locate*

Acta Oceanographica Taiwanica (Taipei, TWN) [**51328**]

Acta Odontologica Scandinavica (Huddinge, SWE) [**50969**]

Acta Oeconomica (Budapest, HUN) [**44815**]

Acta Oncologica (Solna, SWE) [**50999**]

Acta Ophthalmologica (Reykjavik, ICE) [**44896**]

Acta Ophthalmologica Scandinavica [**44896**]*

Acta Orientalia Academiae Scientiarum Hungaricae (Budapest, HUN) [**44816**]

Acta Orthopaedica (Lund, SWE) [**50983**]

Acta Orthopaedica et Traumatologica Turcica (Istanbul, TUR) [**51556**]

Acta Oto-Laryngologica (Stockholm, SWE) [**51001**]

Acta Paediatrica (Stockholm, SWE) [**51002**]

Acta Paediatrica Japonica [**56148**]*

Acta Paediatrica Sinica [**51329**]*

Acta Paediatrica Taiwanica (Taipei, TWN) [**51329**]

Acta Palaeontologica Polonica (Warsaw, POL) [**49681**]

Acta Pharmaceutica (Zagreb, CTA) [**43562**]

Acta Pharmacologica Sinica (London, GBR) [**53895**]

Acta Physica Polonica B (Krakow, POL) [**49664**]

Acta Physica Slovaca (Bratislava, SLK) [**50315**]

Acta Physiologica Hungarica (Budapest, HUN) [**44817**]

Acta Physiologica et Pharmacologica Latinoamericana (Santiago, CHL) *Unable to locate*

Acta Phytopathologica et Entomologica Hungarica (Budapest, HUN) [**44818**]

Acta Phytotaxonomica et Geobotanica (Kyoto, JPN) *Unable to locate*

Acta Politica (Amsterdam, NLD) [**47878**]

Acta Protozoologica (Warsaw, POL) [**49682**]

Acta Psychiatrica Scandinavica (Alborg, DEN) [**43643**]

Acta Psychologica (Amsterdam, NLD) [**47879**]

Acta Radiologica (Abingdon, GBR) [**51695**]

Acta Reproductiva Turcica (Ankara, TUR) *Unable to locate*

Acta Scientarum Polonorum - Technologia Alimentaria (Poznan, POL) [**49673**]

Acta Stomatologica Naissi (Nis, SER) [**50090**]

Acta Theologica (Bloemfontein, SAF) [**50354**]

Acta Tropica (Amsterdam, NLD) [**47880**]

Acta Veterinaria Hungarica (Budapest, HUN) [**44819**]

Acta Veteriniaria Brno (Brno, CZE) [**43601**]

Acta Virologica (Bratislava, SLK) [**50316**]

Acta Vulnologica (Turin, ITA) [**46268**]

Acta Zoologica (Uppsala, SWE) [**51049**]

Acta Zoologica Academiae Scientiarum Hungaricae (Budapest, HUN) [**44820**]

Acta Zoologica Lituanica (Warsaw, POL) [**49683**]

Acta Zoologica Sinica [**43192**]*

Acta Zoologica Taiwanica (Taipei, TWN) [**51330**]

Actas del Cabildo de Santiago (Santiago, CHL) *Unable to locate*

Actes de Congres (Villeneuved'Ascq, FRA) *Unable to locate*

Actinomycetologica (Tokyo, JPN) [**46727**]

Action (Bridgetown, BRB) *Unable to locate*

Action Cancer News Update (Belfast, GBR) *Unable to locate*

Action Learning (Abingdon, GBR) [**51696**]

Action Packed (Adelaide, SA, AUS) *Unable to locate*

Active Exmoor (Dulverton, GBR) [**53209**]

Activity Report (Paris, FRA) *Unable to locate*

Actual (Lisbon, PRT) *Unable to locate*

Actualidad Economica (Madrid, SPA) [**50723**]

L'Actualite Chimique (Paris, FRA) [**44021**]

ACU Bulletin (London, GBR) [**53896**]

ACUM News (Tel Aviv, ISR) *Unable to locate*

Acupuncture in Medicine (Northwich, GBR) [**55718**]

Acute Cardiac Care (Abingdon, GBR) [**51697**]

Acute Coronary Syndromes (London, GBR) [**53897**]

Acute Medicine (London, GBR) [**53898**]

Ad Astra (Sydney, NW, AUS) [**42446**]

Ad Hoc Networks (Singapore, SGP) [**50102**]

Ad Trader (London, GBR) [**53899**]

Ad-Vocate (Dubai, UAE) [**51628**]

ADAC Motorwelt (Munich, GER) *Unable to locate*

Adam and Eve (Chennai, TN, IND) *Unable to locate*

Adansonia (Paris, FRA) [**44022**]

Adaptation (Tokyo, JPN) [**46728**]

ADB Business Opportunities (Manila, PHL) [**49546**]

ADB Roost (Haymarket, NW, AUS) *Unable to locate*

Ad!dict (Brussels, BEL) [**42843**]

Addiction (London, GBR) [**53900**]

Addiction Abstracts (London, GBR) [**53901**]

Addiction Biology (Mannheim, GER) [**44547**]

Addiction Research and Theory (Glasgow, GBR) [**53409**]

The Addis Tribune (Addis Ababa, ETH) [**43795**]

Ade-Teatro (Madrid, SPA) [**50724**]

Adelaide Matters (Adelaide, SA, AUS) [**41499**]

The Adelaidean (Adelaide, SA, AUS) [**41500**]

Adelphi Papers [**51698**]*

The Adelphi Papers (Oxford, GBR) *Unable to locate*

Adelphi Series (Abingdon, GBR) [**51698**]

ADF Health (Strawberry Hills, NW, AUS) [**42393**]

Adhesive Technology (London, GBR) *Unable to locate*

ADHUNA (Dhaka, BGD) *Unable to locate*

ADI News (Brighton, GBR) [**52603**]

Admap (London, GBR) [**53902**]

Administration (Bangalore, KA, IND) *Unable to locate*

Administrative Tribunals Cases (Lucknow, UP, IND) *Ceased*

The Administrator (Mussoorie, UP, IND) *Unable to locate*

AdNews (Surry Hills, NW, AUS) [**42407**]

Adobo Interactive (Makati, PHL) *Unable to locate*

Adoption and Fostering (London, GBR) [**53903**]

ADSGM Strategic Journal for Business Research (Makati City, PHL) *Unable to locate*

Adsorption Science & Technology (Brentwood, GBR) [**52565**]

Adult Learner (Dublin, DU, IRL) [**45943**]

Adults Learning (Leicester, GBR) [**53782**]

Advance in Frontiers of Plant Sciences (New Delhi, DH, IND) *Unable to locate*

Advanced Carp Fishing (Daventry, GBR) [**53158**]

Advanced Composite Materials (Leiden, NLD) [**48641**]

Advanced Driving (London, GBR) [**53904**]

Numbers cited in bold after listings are entry numbers rather than page numbers.

Advanced Engineering Informatics (Amsterdam, NLD) **[47881]**

Advanced Manufacturing Technology (Dun Laoghaire, DU, IRL) *Unable to locate*

Advanced Photoshop (Bournemouth, GBR) **[52410]**

Advanced Powder Technology (Kyoto, JPN) **[46466]**

Advanced Robotics (Leiden, NLD) **[48642]**

Advanced Studies in Theoretical Physics (Ruse, BUL) **[43087]**

Advanced Synthesis & Catalysis (Ostfildern, GER) **[44631]**

Advances in Adaptive Data Analysis (Chungli, TWN) **[51304]**

Advances in Aerospace and Applications (Tehran, IRN) **[45886]**

Advances in Algebra (Chinju, KOR) **[47218]**

Advances and Applications in Discrete Mathematics (Allahabad, UP, IND) **[44919]**

Advances and Applications in Statistics (Allahabad, UP, IND) **[44920]**

Advances in Applied Ceramics (London, GBR) *Unable to locate*

Advances in Applied Mathematical Analysis (Osaka, JPN) **[46614]**

Advances in Applied Probability (Sheffield, GBR) **[56488]**

Advances in Biological Research (Faisalabad, PAK) **[49230]**

Advances in Bryology (Stuttgart, GER) **[44659]**

Advances in Building Energy Research (London, GBR) **[53905]**

Advances in Calculus of Variations (Berlin, GER) **[44148]**

Advances in Cell Biology (Warsaw, POL) **[49684]**

Advances in Clinical Neuroscience & Rehabilitation (Mere, GBR) **[55609]**

Advances in Cognitive Psychology (Warsaw, POL) **[49685]**

Advances in Colloid and Interface Science (Amsterdam, NLD) **[47882]**

Advances in Computational Mathematics (Dordrecht, NLD) **[48320]**

Advances in Computational Sciences and Technology (Leicester, GBR) **[53783]**

Advances in Computer Science and Engineering (Allahabad, UP, IND) **[44921]**

Advances in Differential Equations and Control Processes (Allahabad, UP, IND) **[44922]**

Advances in Dual Diagnosis (Hove, GBR) **[53603]**

Advances in Dynamical Systems and Applications (New Delhi, DH, IND) **[45477]**

Advances in Education (Baroda, GJ, IND) *Unable to locate*

Advances in Fish Biology and Fisheries (New Delhi, DH, IND) *Unable to locate*

Advances in Fuzzy Mathematics (Udine, ITA) **[46276]**

Advances in Fuzzy Sets and Systems (Allahabad, UP, IND) **[44923]**

Advances in Geometry (Wurzburg, GER) **[44716]**

Advances in Geosciences (Gottingen, GER) **[44389]**

Advances in Horticulture and Forestry (Jodhpur, RJ, IND) **[45212]**

Advances in Horticulture & Forestry (Jodhpur, RJ, IND) *Unable to locate*

Advances in Library and Information Science (Jodhpur, RJ, IND) *Ceased*

Advances in Materials Science (Warsaw, POL) **[49686]**

Advances in Medical Sciences (Warsaw, POL) **[49687]**

Advances in Mental Health and Intellectual Disabilities (Brighton, GBR) **[52604]**

Advances in Mental Health and Learning Disabilities **[52604]***

Advances in Modelling and Analysis (Barcelona, SPA) *Unable to locate*

Advances in Neurotrauma Research (Tokyo, JPN) *Unable to locate*

Advances in Osteoporotic Fracture Management (London, GBR) **[53906]**

Advances in Palliative Medicine (Bydgoszcz, POL) **[49653]**

Advances in Physiotherapy (Stockholm, SWE) **[51003]**

Advances in Plant Physiology (Jodhpur, RJ, IND) **[45213]**

Advances in Plant Sciences (New Delhi, DH, IND) *Unable to locate*

Advances in Pollen Spore Research (New Delhi, DH, IND) *Unable to locate*

Advances in Psychiatric Treatment (London, GBR) **[53907]**

Advances in Pure and Applied Mathematics (Tunis, TUN) **[51488]**

Advances in Radio Science (Gottingen, GER) **[44390]**

Advances in Rehabilitation (Warsaw, POL) **[49688]**

Advances in Science and Technology (Zurich, SWI) **[51251]**

Advances in Science and Technology of Water Resources (Nanjing, JS, CHN) **[43456]**

Advances in Sepsis (London, GBR) **[53908]**

Advances in Solar Energy (London, GBR) **[53909]**

Advances in Space Research (Amsterdam, NLD) **[47883]**

Advances in Speech Language Pathology **[51846]***

Advances in Structural Engineering (Brentwood, GBR) **[52566]**

Advances in Theoretical and Applied Mathematics (Kyungnam, KOR) **[47242]**

The Advent (Pondicherry, PN, IND) **[45690]**

The Adventure (Wellington, NZL) **[48998]**

Adventure Cornwall (Cornwall, GBR) **[53064]**

Advertising Forecast (London, GBR) **[53910]**

Advertlink (Calcutta, WB, IND) *Unable to locate*

Advocate (South Melbourne, VI, AUS) **[42365]**

Advocate (Moscow, RUS) *Unable to locate*

Advocate (London, GBR) *Unable to locate*

AEBDC News (Barcelona, SPA) **[50646]**

AEGEE News Bulletin (Brussels, BEL) *Unable to locate*

Aequationes Mathematicae (Debrecen, HUN) **[44886]**

Aero Lloyd Journal (Oberursel, GER) *Unable to locate*

Aerobiologia (Dordrecht, NLD) **[48321]**

Aeroflot (Moscow, RUS) *Unable to locate*

Aeroflot Premium (Moscow, RUS) **[49868]**

Aerokurier (Stuttgart, GER) **[44660]**

Aeromilitaria (Middlesex, GBR) **[55614]**

Aeronautica & Difesa (Rome, ITA) **[46220]**

Aeronautica Meridiana (Sinoville, SAF) *Ceased*

Aeronautical Journal (London, GBR) **[53911]**

Aeronautical Society of India Journal (New Delhi, DH, IND) *Unable to locate*

Aeroplane Monthly (London, GBR) **[53912]**

Aerospace International (London, GBR) **[53913]**

Aerospace Journal (Moscow, RUS) *Unable to locate*

Aerospace Knowledge (Beijing, CHN) *Unable to locate*

Aerospace Science and Technology (Amsterdam, NLD) **[47884]**

Aerostat (Maidstone, GBR) **[55527]**

Aerztin (Cologne, GER) *Unable to locate*

AES Bug Club Magazine (London, GBR) **[53914]**

Aesthetica Magazine (York, GBR) **[56986]**

Aestimum (Fiorentino, ITA) **[46139]**

The Aether Sanctum,) *Unable to locate*

AEU - International Journal of Electronics and Communications (Dresden, GER) **[44319]**

Afers Internacionals (Barcelona, SPA) **[50647]**

Affinity (London, GBR) *Unable to locate*

Afghanerposten (Holme Olstrup, DEN) *Unable to locate*

Afisha (Kiev, URE) **[51593]**

Afloat (Dun Laoghaire, DU, IRL) **[46007]**

AFMA Matrix (Centurion, SAF) **[50436]**

AFN Korea Radio & Television, KOR) *Unable to locate*

AFN Korea Radio & Television (Ch'unch'on, KOR) *Unable to locate*

AFN Korea Radio & Television (Ch'unch'on, KOR) *Unable to locate*

AFN Korea Radio & Television - 88.5 MHz (Daegu, KOR) **[47224]**

AFN Korea Radio & Television - 1197 KHz (Dongducheon, KOR) **[47232]**

AFN Korea Radio & Television - 88.3 MHz (Dongducheon, KOR) **[47231]**

AFN Korea Radio & Television - 1512 KHz (Jinhae, KOR) **[47241]**

AFN Korea Radio & Television - 1440 KHz (Pyongtaek, KOR) **[47250]**

AFN Korea Radio & Television - 88.3 MHz (Pyongtaek, KOR) **[47251]**

AFN Korea Radio & Television - 102.7 MHz (Seoul, KOR) **[47295]**

AFN Korea Radio & Television - 1530 KHz (Seoul, KOR) **[47294]**

AFN Korea Radio & Television - 88.5 MHz (Songtan, KOR) **[47326]**

AFN Korea Radio & Television - 1359 KHz (Songtan, KOR) **[47325]**

AFN Korea Radio & Television - 88.5 MHz (Uijongbu, KOR) **[47330]**

AFN Korea Radio & Television - 1161 KHz (Uijongbu, KOR) **[47329]**

AFN Korea Radio & Television - 1440 KHz (Wonju-si, KOR) **[47331]**

AFN-Tokyo - 810 KHz (Tokyo, JPN) **[47059]**

Aeroflot Premium (Moscow, RUS) **[49868]**

A4 (Rotterdam, NLD) *Ceased*

A470 (Cardiff, GBR) **[52923]**

AFR Smart Investor (Wellington, NZL) **[48999]**

Africa (Kiltegan, WI, IRL) **[46028]**

Africa (Edgbaston, GBR) **[53248]**

Africa (London, GBR) **[53915]**

Africa America Latina (Madrid, SPA) *Unable to locate*

Africa & Asia (Goteborg, SWE) **[50956]**

Africa Confidential (London, GBR) **[53916]**

Africa Development (Dakar, SEN) **[50077]**

Africa Health (Cambridge, GBR) *Unable to locate*

Africa INFO (Brussels, BEL) *Unable to locate*

Africa Info (Nairobi, KEN) *Unable to locate*

Africa Insight (Pretoria, SAF) **[50581]**

Africa Institute Occasional Papers (Pretoria, SAF) **[50582]**

Africa Letter (Calcutta, WB, IND) *Unable to locate*

Africa Link (Nairobi, KEN) *Unable to locate*

Africa Media Review (Dakar, SEN) **[50078]**

Africa Monitor. West & Central Africa (London, GBR) **[53917]**

Africa N 1-FM - 90.3 (Paris, FRA) **[44089]**

Africa N 1-FM - 102 (Paris, FRA) **[44090]**

Africa N 1-FM - 89.6 (Paris, FRA) **[44088]**

Africa Quarterly (New Delhi, DH, IND) **[45478]**

Africa Research Bulletin (Exeter, GBR) **[53345]**

Africa Research Bulletin (Exeter, GBR) **[53346]**

Africa Affairs (Edinburgh, GBR) **[53249]**

African Affairs (London, GBR) **[53918]**

African Archaeological Review (Dordrecht, NLD) **[48322]**

African and Asian Studies (Leiden, NLD) **[48643]**

The African Book Publishing Record (Riberac, FRA) **[44098]**

African Business (London, GBR) **[53919]**

African Crop Science Journal (Kampala, UGA) **[51583]**

African Diaspora (Leiden, NLD) **[48644]**

African Entomology (Hatfield, SAF) **[50521]**

African Farming and Food Processing (London, GBR) **[53920]**

African Finance Journal (Bellville, SAF) **[50353]**

African Health Sciences (Kampala, UGA) **[51584]**

African Human Rights Law Journal (Claremont, SAF) **[50460]**

African Journal of Agricultural Research (Lagos, LG, NGA) **[49129]**

African Journal of AIDS Research (Grahamstown, SAF) **[50486]**

African Journal of Applied Zoology and Environmental Biology (Port Harcourt, RV, NGA) **[49165]**

African Journal of Aquatic Science (Pietermaritzburg, SAF) **[50564]**

African Journal of Biochemistry Research (Lagos, LG, NGA) **[49130]**

African Journal of Biomedical Research (Grahamstown, SAF) **[50487]**

Numbers cited in bold after listings are entry numbers rather than page numbers.

African Journal of Biotechnology (Nairobi, KEN) [47170]

African Journal of Business and Economic Research (London, GBR) [53921]

African Journal of Business Management (Lagos, LG, NGA) [49131]

African Journal of Clinical and Experimental Microbiology (Ilorin, KW, NGA) [49117]

African Journal on Conflict Resolution (Mount Edgecombe, SAF) [50557]

African Journal of Cross-Cultural Psychology and Sport Facilitation (Pretoria, SAF) [50583]

African Journal of Ecology (Nairobi, KEN) [47171]

African Journal of Ecology (Kampala, UGA) [51585]

African Journal of Economic Policy (Grahamstown, SAF) [50488]

African Journal of Educational Studies in Mathematics and Sciences (Winneba, GHA) [44740]

African Journal of Farm Child and Youth Development (Centurion, SAF) Ceased

African Journal of Fertility, Sexuality and Reproductive Health (Nairobi, KEN) Unable to locate

African Journal of Finance and Management (Dar es Salaam, TZA) [51399]

African Journal of Food, Agriculture, Nutrition and Development (Nairobi, KEN) [47172]

African Journal of Food Science (Lagos, LG, NGA) [49132]

African Journal of Health Sciences (Nairobi, KEN) [47173]

African Journal of Herpetology (Tygerberg, SAF) [50638]

African Journal of Information & Communication Technology (Broadway, NW, AUS) [41660]

African Journal of International Affairs (Dakar, SEN) [50079]

African Journal of International Affairs and Development (Ibadan, OY, NGA) [49083]

African Journal of International and Comparative Law (London, GBR) Unable to locate

African Journal of Library, Archives and Information Science (Ibadan, OY, NGA) [49084]

African Journal of Livestock Extension (Ibadan, OY, NGA) [49085]

African Journal of Marine Science (Grahamstown, SAF) [50489]

African Journal of Marine Science (Umhlanga, SAF) [50640]

African Journal of Mathematical Physics (Rabat, MOR) [47814]

African Journal of Microbiology Research (Lagos, LG, NGA) [49133]

African Journal of Midwifery and Women's Health (London, GBR) [53922]

African Journal of Neurological Sciences (Nairobi, KEN) Unable to locate

African Journal of Oral Health (Ile-Ife, NGA) [49110]

African Journal of Paediatric Surgery (Jos, PL, NGA) [49123]

African Journal of Pharmacy & Pharmacology (Reduit, MUS) [47754]

African Journal of Plant Science (Lagos, LG, NGA) [49134]

African Journal of Political Science (Harare, ZWE) Unable to locate

African Journal of Political Science & International Relations (Lagos, LG, NGA) [49135]

African Journal for the Psychological Study of Social Issues (Ibadan, OY, NGA) [49086]

African Journal of Pure & Applied Chemistry (Lagos, LG, NGA) [49136]

African Journal of Range and Forage Science (Pietermaritzburg, SAF) [50565]

African Journal of Reproductive Health (Benin City, NGA) [49062]

African Journal of Research in Mathematics, Science and Technology Education (Centurion, SAF) [50437]

African Journal of Science and Technology (Nairobi, KEN) [47174]

African Journal of Traditional, Complementary and Alternative Medicines (Ile-Ife, NGA) [49111]

African Journal of Tropical Hydrobiology and Fisheries (Jinja, UGA) [51582]

African Journal of Urology (Cairo, EGY) [43750]

African Mining Monitor (Bath, GBR) Ceased

African Natural History (Cape Town, SAF) [50361]

African Newsletter on Occupational Health and Safety (Helsinki, FIN) [43814]

African Performance Review (London, GBR) [53923]

African Recorder (New Delhi, DH, IND) Unable to locate

African Renaissance (London, GBR) [53924]

African Research Review (Bahir Dar, ETH) [43804]

African Review of Business and Technology (London, GBR) [53925]

African Safety Promotion (Lenasia, SAF) [50547]

African Security Review (Cape Town, SAF) [50362]

African Soccer Magazine (London, GBR) [53926]

African Sociological Review (Grahamstown, SAF) [50490]

African Studies (Taipei, TWN) Unable to locate

African Studies (Abingdon, GBR) [51699]

African Studies Monographs (Grahamstown, SAF) [50491]

African Target (Addis Ababa, ETH) Unable to locate

African Wildlife (Howick, SAF) [50525]

African Zoology (Pietermaritzburg, SAF) [50566]

Africanus (Pretoria, SAF) [50584]

AFRING News (Rondebosch, SAF) Unable to locate

Afrique Automobile (Paris, FRA) Unable to locate

Afrique Science (Abidjan, COT) [43555]

Afro-Arab Selections for Social Sciences (Cairo, EGY) [43751]

Afro-Asian Journal of Finance and Accounting (Auckland, NZL) [48784]

Afro-Asian Journal of Rural Development (New Delhi, DH, IND) [45479]

Afro-Asian Nematology Network (Faizabad, UP, IND) Unable to locate

Afro-Asian and World Affairs (New Delhi, DH, IND) Unable to locate

Afsaar Magazine (Dubai, UAE) Unable to locate

Afternoon (Tokyo, JPN) [46729]

The Afternoon Despatch & Courier (Mumbai, MH, IND) Unable to locate

Afternoon Season Zokan (Tokyo, JPN) [46730]

Afternoon on Sunday (Mumbai, MH, IND) Unable to locate

Aftersales Management (Peterborough, GBR) Ceased

Afya (Nairobi, KEN) Unable to locate

Ag Magazine (East Molesey, GBR) [53239]

Agazen (Addis Ababa, ETH) Unable to locate

AgBiotech News and Information (Wallingford, GBR) [56813]

Age and Ageing (Bristol, GBR) [52638]

AGEFI Luxembourg (Capellen, LUX) [47488]

Ageing and Society (Cambridge, GBR) [52785]

Agenda (Unley, SA, AUS) [42659]

Agenda (Oslo, NOR) Unable to locate

Agenda (Dalbridge, SAF) Unable to locate

Agendas (South Melbourne, VI, AUS) [42366]

Agents News (Harpenden, GBR) [53513]

Aggiornamento Medico (Milan, ITA) [46160]

Aghamtao (Quezon City, PHL) Unable to locate

Aging Clinical and Experimental Research (Milan, ITA) [46161]

Aging Health (London, GBR) [53927]

Aging and Mental Health (Abingdon, GBR) [51700]

Agora (Vicosa, MI, BRZ) [43054]

Agora-FM - 91 (Montpellier, FRA) [43979]

Agra Europe Weekly (Tunbridge Wells, GBR) [56776]

Agra University Bulletin (Agra, UP, IND) Unable to locate

Agra University Journal of Research (Science) (Agra, UP, IND) Unable to locate

AgraFood East Europe (Tunbridge Wells, GBR) [56777]

Agrarforschung Schweiz (Posieux, SWI) [51221]

AgrarMEGA (Kumhausen, GER) [44515]

Agreement (Warwick, GBR) [56851]

Agrekon (Matieland, SAF) [50552]

Agri Parts (Peschiera Borromeo, ITA) [46212]

Agribusiness Connections (Farrell Flat, SA, AUS) [41865]

Agricultura (Madrid, SPA) [50725]

Agricultura Radio-FM - 92.1 (Santiago, CHL) [43150]

Agricultural Banker (New Delhi, DH, IND) Unable to locate

Agricultural and Biological Research (Lucknow, UP, IND) Unable to locate

Agricultural Chemistry (Moscow, RUS) Ceased

Agricultural Economics (Oxford, GBR) [55861]

Agricultural Economist (Madras, TN, IND) Unable to locate

Agricultural Engineer [53297]*

Agricultural Engineering (Peradeniya, SRI) Unable to locate

Agricultural Engineering Today (Jodhpur, RJ, IND) Unable to locate

Agricultural Extension Review (New Delhi, DH, IND) Unable to locate

Agricultural Films and Television Programmes (Beijing, CHN) Unable to locate

Agricultural and Food Science Journal of Ghana (Kumasi, GHA) [44734]

Agricultural and Food Science Journal of Ghana (Grahamstown, SAF) [50492]

Agricultural and Forest Entomolgy (Penicuik, GBR) [56242]

Agricultural and Forest Entomology (Midlothian, GBR) [55626]

Agricultural Journal (Faisalabad, PAK) [49231]

Agricultural Journal of Kyushu University (Fukuoka, JPN) Unable to locate

Agricultural Manpower (Didcot, GBR) Unable to locate

Agricultural Marketing (Faridabad, HY, IND) Unable to locate

Agricultural Prices in India (New Delhi, DH, IND) Unable to locate

Agricultural Reviews (Karnal, HY, IND) Unable to locate

Agricultural Science Digest (Karnal, HY, IND) Unable to locate

Agricultural Situation in India (Jodhpur, RJ, IND) Unable to locate

Agricultural Student's News (Leuven, BEL) Unable to locate

Agricultural Systems (Amsterdam, NLD) [47885]

Agricultural Trader (Barnstaple, GBR) [52190]

Agricultural Wages in India (New Delhi, DH, IND) Unable to locate

Agriculture and Agro-Industries Journal (Mumbai, MH, IND) Unable to locate

Agriculture; Australian Journal of Experimental [41780]*

Agriculture Checklist (Calcutta, WB, IND) Unable to locate

Agriculture and Development in the Arab World (Khartoum, SDN) [50938]

Agriculture, Ecosystems & Environment (Amsterdam, NLD) [47886]

Agriculture & Equipment International [52763]*

Agriculture at Los Banos (Laguna, PHL) Unable to locate

AGRIFACK (Stockholm, SWE) Unable to locate

Agrifuture (Frankfurt, GER) [44356]

Agriprobe (Elsenburg, SAF) [50477]

Agro-Bonus (Leopoldsdorf, AUT) Ceased

Agro Food (Milan, ITA) [46162]

Agro-Science (Nsukka, AN, NGA) [49154]

Agrociencia (San Luis Huexotla, ME, MEX) [47797]

Agroforestry Magazine (Turrialba, CRI) Unable to locate

Agroforestry Systems (Dordrecht, NLD) [48323]

Agrokemia es Talajtan (Budapest, HUN) [44821]

Agronomie Africaine (Abidjan, COT) [43556]

Agronomy Research (Tartu, EST) [43791]

Agronomy for Sustainable Development (Avignon, FRA) [43917]

Agrosearch (Ilorin, KW, NGA) [49118]

AgTrader (Hamilton, NZL) [48907]

Ahead (Vienna, AUT) Unable to locate

Numbers cited in bold after listings are entry numbers rather than page numbers.

Ahlen-FM (Amman, JOR) *Unable to locate*

Ahmadiyya Bulletin (London, GBR) *Unable to locate*

AI Communications (Amsterdam, NLD) **[47887]**

AI & Society (Newport, GBR) **[55687]**

AIA News (Genoa, ITA) *Unable to locate*

Aide et Action (Paris, FRA) **[44023]**

AIDS Abstracts (Abingdon, GBR) *Ceased*

AIDS Care (Abingdon, GBR) **[51701]**

AIDS Research and Therapy (London, GBR) **[53928]**

AIDS Reviews (Barcelona, SPA) **[50648]**

AIE News Journal (Raymond Terrace, NW, AUS) **[42297]**

AIESEC SG Yearbook (Saint Gallen, SWI) *Unable to locate*

AIG Journal (Perth, WA, AUS) **[42242]**

Aikakauskirja (Helsinki, FIN) *Unable to locate*

Aikido Journal (Sagamihara, JPN) **[46643]**

Aikuiskasvatus (Helsinki, FIN) **[43815]**

Aim (New Delhi, DH, IND) **[45480]**

The AIM Guide (London, GBR) **[53929]**

AIM Magazine (Hilversum, NLD) *Unable to locate*

AIOE Labour News (New Delhi, DH, IND) **[45481]**

AIPM Flash (Moscow, RUS) *Unable to locate*

Air Ambulance (Slough, GBR) *Unable to locate*

Air-Britain Digest (Staplefield, GBR) *Unable to locate*

Air Cargo Agents Association of India News (On Board) (Mumbai, MH, IND) *Unable to locate*

Air Conditioning and Refrigeration in India (Mumbai, MH, IND) *Unable to locate*

Air et Cosmos (Paris, FRA) *Unable to locate*

Air Enthusiast (Stamford, GBR) *Ceased*

AIR-FM - 106.4 (New Delhi, DH, IND) **[45672]**

Air New Zealand's Inflight Magazine (Auckland, NZL) *Unable to locate*

Air & Space Law (Alphen aan den Rijn, NLD) **[47865]**

Aircraft Engineering and Aerospace Technology (Bristol, GBR) **[52639]**

Aircraft Illustrated (Kingston upon Thames, GBR) **[53719]**

Aircraft Technology Engineering & Maintenance (London, GBR) **[53930]**

Airfinance Journal (London, GBR) **[53931]**

Airfleet (Moscow, RUS) **[49869]**

Airline Business (Stockholm, SWE) *Unable to locate*

Airline Business (Sutton, GBR) **[56679]**

Airline Industry Information (Bath, GBR) **[52236]**

Airline Ninety Two (Madrid, SPA) **[50726]**

Airlines (Bishop's Stortford, GBR) *Unable to locate*

Airone (Milan, ITA) *Unable to locate*

Airport World (Twickenham, GBR) **[56787]**

Airports International (Stamford, GBR) **[56593]**

Airports of the World (Stamford, GBR) **[56594]**

Airship (Folkestone, GBR) *Unable to locate*

AiRUnion Magazine (Moscow, RUS) *Unable to locate*

AIRUT (Helsinki, FIN) *Unable to locate*

Airways Journal (London, GBR) *Ceased*

Aiyu Broadcasting Station (Changhua, TWN) *Unable to locate*

Ajia no Kenko (Aichi, JPN) *Unable to locate*

Ajia no Kodomo (Children in Asia) (Aichi, JPN) *Unable to locate*

Ajoblanco (Barcelona, SPA) *Unable to locate*

Akademiker (Stockholm, SWE) *Unable to locate*

AKAHATA (Tokyo, JPN) *Unable to locate*

Akash Radio-AM (Southall, GBR) *Unable to locate*

AKAVA UUTISET (Helsinki, FIN) *Unable to locate*

Akita Journal of Medicine (Akita, JPN) *Unable to locate*

AKK-Motorsport (Helsinki, FIN) *Unable to locate*

Akoestiek (Schiphol Centrum, NLD) *Unable to locate*

Aksyon Radyo-AM (Cebu City, PHL) *Unable to locate*

Aktuel Elektronik (Glostrup, DEN) **[43697]**

Aktuel Sikkerhed (Glostrup, DEN) *Unable to locate*

Aktuelle Technik (Schlieren, SWI) **[51230]**

AL-AKHBAR (Salimiyah, KWT) *Unable to locate*

Al-An Kabout (Jerusalem, ISR) *Unable to locate*

Al Anwar (Beirut, LBN) **[47386]**

Al-Arabieh (Damascus, SYR) *Unable to locate*

Al Defaiya (Beirut, LBN) **[47387]**

Al-Fares (Beirut, LBN) **[47388]**

Al Ghorfa (Ruwi, OMN) **[49226]**

AL IDARI (Beirut, LBN) **[47389]**

Al-Islam (Kuala Lumpur, MYS) **[47596]**

Al Koran Al Karim (Al Mazraa Beirut, LBN) *Unable to locate*

Al Madina-FM - 101.5 (Damascus, SYR) **[51302]**

Al Madina-FM - 100.5 (Damascus, SYR) **[51301]**

Al-Madinah Al-Arabiyah (Kaifar, KWT) *Unable to locate*

Al-Majarra (Kuwait, KWT) *Unable to locate*

Al Mouhamoun (Damascus, SYR) *Unable to locate*

Al-Nahdah (Kuala Lumpur, MYS) *Unable to locate*

Al Noor - Baalbek (Beirut, LBN) *Unable to locate*

Al Noor - Beirut (Beirut, LBN) *Unable to locate*

Al Noor - Beit Meri (Beirut, LBN) *Unable to locate*

Al Noor - Beit Meri (Beirut, LBN) *Unable to locate*

Al Noor - Saida (Beirut, LBN) *Unable to locate*

Al Quran Al Kareem Radio (Al Mazraa Beirut, LBN) *Unable to locate*

Al Shindagah (Dubai, UAE) **[51629]**

Al-Subah (Bonn, GER) *Unable to locate*

Al Volante (Milan, ITA) *Unable to locate*

Al-Warak (Baghdad, IRQ) *Unable to locate*

Albanian Observer (Tirana, ALB) *Unable to locate*

Albany Community Radio-FM - 100.9 (Albany, WA, AUS) **[41525]**

Albert & Logan News (Alderley, QL, AUS) **[41530]**

Alborada-FM - 107.7 (Chillan, CHL) **[43134]**

Album (Madrid, SPA) **[50727]**

Alcheringa (Stockholm, SWE) **[51004]**

Alcohol and Alcoholism (North Berwick, GBR) **[55704]**

Alcoholism (Lausanne, SWI) **[51182]**

ALEA (Rio de Janeiro, RJ, BRZ) **[43002]**

Alea (Rio de Janeiro, RJ, BRZ) **[43000]**

ALEA (Rio de Janeiro, RJ, BRZ) **[43001]**

Alem FM - Istanbul - 89.3 MHz (Istanbul, TUR) **[51565]**

Alert Magazine (Bedford, GBR) **[52271]**

Alerta Verde (Quito, ECU) *Unable to locate*

Alexander Journal (London, GBR) *Unable to locate*

Alexandria (Surrey, GBR) **[56659]**

Alfa Echo (Paris, FRA) *Unable to locate*

Alfa Lotfeeding Magazine (Tullamarine, VI, AUS) **[42645]**

Alfaomega-FM - 106.5 (Curico, CHL) **[43137]**

Algebra Colloquium (Beijing, CHN) **[43168]**

Algebra Universalis (Tokyo, JPN) **[46731]**

Algebraic Hyperstructures and Applications (New Delhi, DH, IND) **[45482]**

Alger Chaine 1-AM (Algiers, ALG) *Unable to locate*

Algoa FM - 94.8 (Walmer, SAF) **[50642]**

Alibi (Kuvalehdet, FIN) **[43878]**

Alicerce (Lisbon, PRT) *Unable to locate*

Aligarh Journal of English Studies (Aligarh, UP, IND) **[44917]**

Aligarh Journal of Oriental Studies (Aligarh, UP, IND) *Unable to locate*

Aligarh Journal of Statistics (Aligarh, UP, IND) *Unable to locate*

Aliran Monthly (Pulau Pinang, MYS) *Unable to locate*

Alicca Radio-FM - 94.3 (Szekszard, HUN) **[44895]**

All About Animals (London, GBR) **[53932]**

All-Age Digest (Hohoe V.R., GHA) *Unable to locate*

All-FM - 96.9 (Levenshulme, GBR) **[53846]**

All-India Anglo-Indian Association Review (New Delhi, DH, IND) *Unable to locate*

All India Appointment Gazette (Calcutta, WB, IND) *Unable to locate*

All India Congress Committee Congress Bulletin (New Delhi, DH, IND) *Unable to locate*

All India Institute of Local Self Government Quarterly Journal (Mumbai, MH, IND) *Unable to locate*

All India Institute of Speech and Hearing Journal (Mysore, KA, IND) *Unable to locate*

All India Magic Circle Bulletin (Calcutta, WB, IND) *Unable to locate*

All India Radio Adilabad - 1485 KHz (Adilabad, AP, IND) **[44905]**

All India Radio Agartala - 1269 KHz (Agartala, TR, IND) **[44906]**

All India Radio Agra - 1530 KHz (Agra, UP, IND) **[44907]**

All India Radio Ahmedabad - 846 KHz (Ahmedabad, GJ, IND) **[44912]**

All India Radio Ahmednagar - 100.1 KHz (Ahmednagar, MH, IND) **[44913]**

All India Radio Ahwa (Dangs) - 1485 KHz (Ahwa, GJ, IND) **[44914]**

All India Radio Aizawl - 540 KHz (Aizawl, MZ, IND) **[44915]**

All India Radio Akola - 102.4 KHz (Akola, MH, IND) **[44916]**

All India Radio Allahabad - 100.3 MHz (Allahabad, UP, IND) **[44940]**

All India Radio Almora - 999 KHz (Almora, DH, IND) **[44941]**

All India Radio Alwar - 103.1 MHz (Alwar, RJ, IND) **[44942]**

All India Radio Ambikapur - 1260 KHz (Ambikapur, MP, IND) **[44943]**

All India Radio Anantpur - 101.7 MHz (Anantpur, AP, IND) **[44944]**

All India Radio Aurangabad - 1521 KHz (Aurangabad, MH, IND) **[44945]**

All India Radio Balaghat - 101.3 KHz (Balaghat, KA, IND) **[44946]**

All India Radio Bangalore - 612 KHz (Bangalore, KA, IND) **[44989]**

All India Radio Banswara - 101.3 MHz (Banswara, RJ, IND) **[44990]**

All India Radio Bareilly - 100.4 MHz (Bareilly, UP, IND) **[44991]**

All India Radio Baripada - 1485 KHz (Baripada, OR, IND) **[44992]**

All India Radio Barmer - 1458 KHz (Barmer, RJ, IND) **[44993]**

All India Radio Beed - 102.9 KHz (Beed, MH, IND) **[44995]**

All India Radio Belonia - 103.7 MHz (Belonia, TR, IND) **[44998]**

All India Radio Berhampur - 100.6 MHz (Berhampur, OR, IND) **[44999]**

All India Radio Betul - 103.1 KHz (Betul, MP, IND) **[45000]**

All India Radio Bhadrawati - 675 KHz (Bhadrawati, KA, IND) **[45001]**

All India Radio Bhagalpur - 1458 KHz (Bhagalpur, BH, IND) **[45002]**

All India Radio Bhatinda - 101.1 MHz (Bathinda, PJ, IND) **[44994]**

All India Radio Bhawanipatna - 1206 KHz (Bhawanipatna, OR, IND) **[45004]**

All India Radio Bhopal - 1593 KHz (Bhopal, MP, IND) **[45008]**

All India Radio Bhuj - 1314 KHz (Bhuj, GJ, IND) **[45015]**

All India Radio Bijapur - 101.8 MHz (Bijapur, KA, IND) **[45016]**

All India Radio Bikaner - 1395 KHz (Bikaner, RJ, IND) **[45018]**

All India Radio Bilaspur - 103.2 KHz (Bilaspur, MP, IND) **[45019]**

All India Radio Bolangir - 101.9 MHz (Bolangir, OR, IND) **[45020]**

All India Radio Calcutta 'A' - 657 KHz (Kolkata, WB, IND) **[45309]**

All India Radio Calcutta 'B' - 1008 KHz (Kolkata, WB, IND) **[45310]**

All India Radio Calcutta 'D' (Calcutta, WB, IND) *Unable to locate*

All India Radio Cannanore - 101.5 MHz (Kannur, KE, IND) **[45235]**

Numbers cited in bold after listings are entry numbers rather than page numbers.

All India Radio Chaibasa (Chaibasa, BH, IND) *Unable to locate*

All India Radio Chandigarh (Chandigarh, CH, IND) *Unable to locate*

All India Radio Chandigarh - 103.1 MHz (Chandigarh, CH, IND) **[45026]**

All India Radio Chandrapur - 103.0 KHz (Chandrapur, MH, IND) **[45027]**

All India Radio Chennai 'A' - 720 KHz (Chennai, TN, IND) **[45063]**

All India Radio Chennai 'B' - 1017 KHz (Chennai, TN, IND) **[45064]**

All India Radio Chhatarpur - 675 KHz (Chhatarpur, MP, IND) **[45065]**

All India Radio Chindwara - 102.2 KHz (Chindwara, MP, IND) **[45066]**

All India Radio Chitradurga - 102.6 MHz (Chitradurga, KA, IND) **[45067]**

All India Radio Chittorgarh - 102.9 MHz (Chittorgarh, RJ, IND) **[45068]**

All India Radio Churu - 100.7 MHz (Churu, RJ, IND) **[45069]**

All India Radio Cochin - 102.3 MHz (Kochi, KE, IND) **[45254]**

All India Radio Coimbatore - 999 KHz (Coimbatore, TN, IND) **[45078]**

All India Radio Cuddapah - 900 KHz (Cuddapah, AP, IND) **[45079]**

All India Radio Cuttack - 972 KHz (Cuttack, OR, IND) **[45082]**

All India Radio Daltonganj - 103.0 MHz (Daltonganj, DH, IND) **[45083]**

All India Radio Daman - 102.3 KHz (Daman, GD, IND) **[45084]**

All India Radio Darbhanga - 1296 KHz (Darbhanga, BH, IND) **[45085]**

All India Radio Delhi 'A' - 819 KHz (New Delhi, DH, IND) **[45673]**

All India Radio Delhi 'B' - 666 KHz (New Delhi, DH, IND) **[45674]**

All India Radio Dharamsala - 103.4 MHz (Dharamsala, HP, IND) **[45113]**

All India Radio Dharwad - 765 KHz (Dharwad, KA, IND) **[45114]**

All India Radio Dhule - 100.5 MHz (Dhule, MH, IND) **[45115]**

All India Radio Dibrugarh - 567 KHz (Dibrugarh, AS, IND) **[45116]**

All India Radio Diphu - 1584 kHz (Diphu, AS, IND) **[45117]**

All India Radio Faizabad - 101.9 MHz (Faizabad, UP, IND) **[45118]**

All India Radio Gangtok - 1404 KHz (Gangtok, SK, IND) **[45119]**

All India Radio Godhra - 102.2 KHz (Godhra, GJ, IND) **[45122]**

All India Radio Gorakhpur - 909 KHz (Gorakhpur, UP, IND) **[45123]**

All India Radio Gulbarga - 1107 KHz (Gulbarga, KA, IND) **[45124]**

All India Radio Guna - 102.3 KHz (Guna, MP, IND) **[45125]**

All India Radio Guwahati - 729 KHz (Guwahati, AS, IND) **[45131]**

All India Radio Gwalior - 1386 KHz (Gwalior, MP, IND) **[45132]**

All India Radio Haflong - 100.2 MHz (Haflong, AS, IND) **[45133]**

All India Radio Hamirpur - 101.8 MHz (Hamirpur, HP, IND) **[45134]**

All India Radio Hassan - 102.2 MHz (Hassan, KA, IND) **[45135]**

All India Radio Hazaribagh - 102.1 MHz (New Delhi, DH, IND) **[45675]**

All India Radio Hospet - 100.5 MHz (Hospet, KA, IND) **[45137]**

All India Radio Hyderabad 'A' - 738 KHz (Hyderabad, AP, IND) **[45185]**

All India Radio Hyderabad 'B' - 1377 KHz (Hyderabad, AP, IND) **[45186]**

All India Radio Imphal - 882 KHz (Imphal, MN, IND) **[45187]**

All India Radio Indore - 648 KHz (Indore, MP, IND) **[45189]**

All India Radio Itanagar - 675 KHz (Itanagar, AR, IND) **[45190]**

All India Radio Jabalpur - 801 KHz (Jabalpur, MP, IND) **[45191]**

All India Radio Jagdalpur - 756 KHz (Jagdalpur, MP, IND) **[45192]**

All India Radio Jaipur - 1476 KHz (Jaipur, RJ, IND) **[45200]**

All India Radio Jaisalmer - 101.8 MHz (Jaisalmer, RJ, IND) **[45201]**

All India Radio Jalandhar 'A' - 873 KHz (Jalandhar, PJ, IND) **[45202]**

All India Radio Jalgaon - 963 KHz (Jalgaon, MH, IND) **[45203]**

All India Radio Jammu - 990 KHz (Jammu, JK, IND) **[45206]**

All India Radio Jamshedpur - 1584 KHz (Jamshedpur, DH, IND) **[45208]**

All India Radio Jeypore - 1467 KHz (Jeypore, OR, IND) **[45209]**

All India Radio Jhalawar - 103.2 MHz (Jhalawar, RJ, IND) **[45210]**

All India Radio Jhansi - 103.0 MHz (Jhansi, UP, IND) **[45211]**

All India Radio Jodhpur - 102.1 MHz (Jodhpur, RJ, IND) **[45230]**

All India Radio Joranda - 1485 KHz (Joranda, OR, IND) **[45231]**

All India Radio Jorhat - 103.4 MHz (Jorhat, AS, IND) **[45232]**

All India Radio Jowai - 101.1 MHz (Jowai, MG, IND) **[45233]**

All India Radio Kailashahar - 103.2 MHz (Kailashahar, TR, IND) **[45234]**

All India Radio Kanpur - 1449 KHz (Kanpur, UP, IND) **[45237]**

All India Radio Karaikal - 100.3 MHz (Karaikal, PN, IND) **[45238]**

All India Radio Kargil 'B' - 1584 KHz (Kargil, JK, IND) **[45240]**

All India Radio Karwar - 102.3 MHz (Karwar, KA, IND) **[45242]**

All India Radio Kathua - 102.2 MHz (Kathua, JK, IND) **[45243]**

All India Radio Keonjhar - 1584 KHz (Keonjhar, OR, IND) **[45244]**

All India Radio Khandwa - 101.2 KHz (Khandwa, MP, IND) **[45245]**

All India Radio Kohima - 639 KHz (Kohima, NG, IND) **[45255]**

All India Radio Kolhapur - 102.7 KHz (Kolhapur, MH, IND) **[45257]**

All India Radio Kota - 1413 KHz (Kota, RJ, IND) **[45312]**

All India Radio Kothagudem - 100.1 MHz (Kothagudem, AP, IND) **[45313]**

All India Radio Kurnool - 102.4 MHz (Kurnool, AP, IND) **[45316]**

All India Radio Kurseong - 1440 KHz (Kurseong, WB, IND) **[45317]**

All India Radio Kurukshetra - 101.4 MHz (Kurukshetra, HY, IND) **[45318]**

All India Radio Leh - 1053 KHz (Leh, JK, IND) **[45319]**

All India Radio Lucknow - 747 KHz (Lucknow, UP, IND) **[45330]**

All India Radio Lunglei - 101.9 MHz (Lunglei, MZ, IND) **[45332]**

All India Radio Madurai - 1269 KHz (Madurai, TN, IND) **[45337]**

All India Radio Mangalore - 100.3 MHz (Mangalore, KA, IND) **[45340]**

All India Radio Markapur - 101.5 MHz (Markapur, AP, IND) **[45341]**

All India Radio Mathura - 1584 KHz (Mathura, UP, IND) **[45342]**

All India Radio Mercara - 103.1 MHz (Madikeri, KA, IND) **[45333]**

All India Radio Mokokchung - 100.9 MHz (Mokokchung, NG, IND) **[45347]**

All India Radio Mount Abu - 103.5 MHz (Mount Abu, RJ, IND) **[45348]**

All India Radio Mumbai 'A' - 1044 KHz (Mumbai, MH, IND) **[45452]**

All India Radio Mumbai 'B' - 558 KHz (Mumbai, MH, IND) **[45453]**

All India Radio Murshidabad - 102.2 MHz (Murshidabad, WB, IND) **[45455]**

All India Radio Mysore - 100.6 MHz (Mysore, KA, IND) **[45460]**

All India Radio Nagaur - 103.7 MHz (Nagaur, RJ, IND) **[45462]**

All India Radio Nagercoil - 101.0 MHz (Nagercoil, TN, IND) **[45463]**

All India Radio Nagpur - 100.6 MHz (Nagpur, MH, IND) **[45470]**

All India Radio Najibabad - 954 KHz (Najibabad, UP, IND) **[45471]**

All India Radio Nanded - 101.1 MHz (Nanded, MH, IND) **[45472]**

All India Radio Nasik - 101.4 KHz (Nasik, MH, IND) **[45474]**

All India Radio Nizamabad - 103.2 MHz (Nizamabad, AP, IND) **[45676]**

All India Radio Nowgong - 102.7 MHz (Nagaon, AS, IND) **[45461]**

All India Radio Obra - 102.7 MHz (Obra, RJ, IND) **[45677]**

All India Radio Ootacamund - 1602 KHz (Ootacamund, TN, IND) **[45678]**

All India Radio Osmanabad - 101.3 KHz (Osmanabad, MH, IND) **[45679]**

All India Radio Panaji - 1287 KHz (Panaji, GD, IND) **[45682]**

All India Radio Parbhani - 1305 KHz (Parbhani, MH, IND) **[45683]**

All India Radio Pasighat - 1062 KHz (Pasighat, AR, IND) **[45684]**

All India Radio Patiala - 100.2 MHz (Patiala, PJ, IND) **[45687]**

All India Radio Patna 'A' - 621 KHz (Patna, BH, IND) **[45688]**

All India Radio Pauri - 1602 KHz (Pauri, DH, IND) **[45689]**

All India Radio Poonch - 100.7 MHz (Poonch, JK, IND) **[45694]**

All India Radio Port Blair (A&N Islands) - 684 KHz (Port Blair, AN, IND) **[45695]**

All India Radio Pune - 101.0 MHz (Pune, MH, IND) **[45701]**

All India Radio Puri - 103.4 MHz (Puri, OR, IND) **[45702]**

All India Radio Purnia - 102.3 MHz (Purnia, BH, IND) **[45703]**

All India Radio Raigarh - 100.7 KHz (Raigarh, MP, IND) **[45704]**

All India Radio Raipur - 981 KHz (Raipur, MP, IND) **[45705]**

All India Radio Rajkot - 810 KHz (Rajkot, GJ, IND) **[45710]**

All India Radio Rampur - 891 KHz (Rampur, UP, IND) **[45711]**

All India Radio Ranchi - 549 KHz (Ranchi, BH, IND) **[45713]**

All India Radio Ratnagiri - 1143 KHz (Ratnagiri, MH, IND) **[45714]**

All India Radio Rewa - 1179 KHz (Rewa, MP, IND) **[45715]**

All India Radio Rohtak - 1143 KHz (Rohtak, HY, IND) **[45716]**

All India Radio Rourkela - 102.6 MHz (Rourkela, OR, IND) **[45720]**

All India Radio Sagar - 102.6 KHz (Sagar, MP, IND) **[45721]**

All India Radio Sambalpur - 945 KHz (Sambalpur, OR, IND) **[45722]**

All India Radio Sangli - 1251 KHz (Sangli, MH, IND) **[45723]**

All India Radio Sasaram - 103.4 MHz (Sasaram, BH, IND) **[45724]**

All India Radio Satara - 103.1 KHz (Satara, MH, IND) **[45725]**

All India Radio Sawaimadhopur - 101.5 MHz (Sawaimadhopur, RJ, IND) **[45726]**

All India Radio Shahdol - 102.0 KHz (Shahdol, MP, IND) **[45727]**

All India Radio Shillong - 864 KHz (Shillong, MG, IND) **[45730]**

All India Radio Shimla - 774 KHz (Shimla, HP, IND) **[45732]**

All India Radio Shivpuri - 100.2 KHz (Shivpuri, MP, IND) **[45733]**

All India Radio Silchar - 828 KHz (Silchar, AS, IND) **[45734]**

All India Radio Siliguri - 711 KHz (Siliguri, WB, IND) **[45735]**

All India Radio Solapur - 1602 kHz (Solapur, MH, IND) **[45736]**

All India Radio Srinagar - 1116 KHz (Srinagar, JK, IND) **[45740]**

All India Radio Surat - 101.1 MHz (Surat, GJ, IND) **[45741]**

All India Radio Suratgarh - 918 KHz (Suratgarh, RJ, IND) **[45742]**

All India Radio Tawang - 1521 KHz (Tawang, AR, IND) **[45743]**

All India Radio Tezu - 1332 KHz (Tezu, AR, IND) **[45744]**

All India Radio Tiruchirapalli - 936 KHz (Tiruchirapalli, TN, IND) **[45752]**

All India Radio Tirunelveli - 1197 KHz (Tirunelveli, TN, IND) **[45754]**

All India Radio Tirupati - 103.2 MHz (Tirupati, AP, IND) **[45755]**

All India Radio Tura - 1233 KHz (Tura, MG, IND) **[45760]**

All India Radio Tuticorin - 1053 KHz (Tuticorin, TN, IND) **[45761]**

All India Radio Udaipur - 1125 KHz (Udaipur, RJ, IND) **[45762]**

All India Radio Vadodara (Vadodara, GJ, IND) *Unable to locate*

All India Radio Varanasi - 1242 KHz (Varanasi, UP, IND) **[45766]**

All India Radio Vijayawada - 837 KHz (Vijayawada, AP, IND) **[45767]**

All India Radio Vishakhapatnam - 927 KHz (Visakhapatnam, AP, IND) **[45768]**

All India Radio Warangal - 103.5 MHz (Warangal, AP, IND) **[45769]**

All India Radio Yavatmal - 102.7 KHz (Yavatmal, MH, IND) **[45771]**

All India Reporter (Nagpur, MH, IND) **[45464]**

All India Services Law Journal (New Delhi, DH, IND) *Unable to locate*

All Pakistan Legal Decisions (Lahore, PAK) *Unable to locate*

All Sport & Leisure Monthly (Hayes, GBR) *Unable to locate*

Allahabad Law Journal (Allahabad, UP, IND) *Unable to locate*

Allegra (Hamburg, GER) *Unable to locate*

Allelopathy Journal (Hisar, HY, IND) *Unable to locate*

Allergie et Immunologie (Lisbon, PRT) *Unable to locate*

Allergology International (Tokyo, JPN) **[46732]**

Allergy (Stockholm, SWE) **[51005]**

Allergy (Oxford, GBR) **[55862]**

Allergy and Clinical Immunology International (Gottingen, GER) **[44391]**

Numbers cited in bold after listings are entry numbers rather than page numbers.

Allers (Oslo, NOR) *Unable to locate*

Allgemeine Fleischer Zeitung (Frankfurt, GER) **[44357]**

Allgemeine Papier-Rundschau (Heusenstamm, GER) **[44485]**

Allgemeines Statistisches Archive (Tokyo, JPN) *Unable to locate*

L'Alliance Agricole (Brussels, BEL) *Unable to locate*

The Alliance Life (Bouake, COT) *Unable to locate*

Alliances (Paris, FRA) *Ceased*

Allied Trades Association Commercial News (New Delhi, DH, IND) *Unable to locate*

AllTrends Tuttotendenze (Sesto S. Giovanni, ITA) *Unable to locate*

Almas (Mexico City, DF, MEX) **[47781]**

Almaty Herald (Almaty, KAZ) *Unable to locate*

Aloe (Hatfield, SAF) **[50522]**

Alpha Communications Monthly (Mumbai, MH, IND) *Unable to locate*

Alpha Digest (Mumbai, MH, IND) *Unable to locate*

Alpha-FM - 103.2 (Darlington, GBR) **[53156]**

Alpin (Nuremberg, GER) *Unable to locate*

Alpinisme et Randonnee (Saint Cloud, FRA) *Unable to locate*

ALSIC (Apprentissage des Langues et Systemes d'Information et de Communication) (Strasbourg, FRA) **[44109]**

ALT-J (Oxford, GBR) **[55863]**

The Alternative (Chisholm, AC, AUS) *Unable to locate*

Alternative (New Delhi, DH, IND) *Unable to locate*

Alternative Law Journal (Clayton, VI, AUS) **[41755]**

Aluminium International Today (London, GBR) **[53933]**

Aluminium Times (Shoreham-by-Sea, GBR) **[56521]**

Aluminium Today **[53933]***

Alumni & Friends; **[56331]***

Alumni & Friends **[56331]***

Alumni News (London, GBR) **[53934]**

Alumni Publications (New Delhi, DH, IND) *Unable to locate*

Alxa People's Broadcasting Station (Alxa Zuoqi, NM, CHN) *Unable to locate*

Alxa People's Broadcasting Station (Alxa Zuoqi, NM, CHN) *Unable to locate*

Alxa People's Broadcasting Station (Alxa Zuoqi, NM, CHN) *Unable to locate*

Alzheimer Magazine (Bunnik, NLD) *Unable to locate*

A.M. (Wallingford, GBR) **[56814]**

AM Kobe (Kobe, JPN) *Unable to locate*

Amadeus-FM - 103.7 (Buenos Aires, ARG) **[41480]**

Amateur Cine Enthusiast (Looe, GBR) *Unable to locate*

Amateur Gardening (London, GBR) **[53936]**

Amateur Gardening (London, GBR) **[53935]**

Amateur Photographer (London, GBR) **[53937]**

Amber & Fossils (Kaliningrad, RUS) *Unable to locate*

Ambergris Today (San Pedro Town, BLZ) **[42919]**

Ambiance (Antwerp, BEL) **[42837]**

Ambio (Stockholm, SWE) **[51006]**

Ambit (London, GBR) **[53938]**

Ambix (Sutton, GBR) *Unable to locate*

AMC LOVE RADIO-FM - 90.7 (Tirana, ALB) **[41451]**

AmCham Business Journal (Makati City, PHL) **[49514]**

Ameghiniana (Buenos Aires, ARG) **[41469]**

America-FM - 103.3 MHz (Salto, URY) **[57013]**

America Stereo-FM (Quito, ECU) *Unable to locate*

America Stereo-FM (Quito, ECU) *Unable to locate*

American in Britain (Nutley, GBR) **[55778]**

American Business Law Journal (Oxford, GBR) **[55864]**

American Chamber of Commerce in Korea (Seoul, KOR) **[47252]**

American-Eurasian Journal of Agricultural & Environmental Sciences (Faisalabad, PAK) **[49232]**

American-Eurasian Journal of Botany (Faisalabad, PAK) **[49233]**

American-Eurasian Journal of Scientific Research (Faisalabad, PAK) **[49234]**

American Journal on Addictions (Abingdon, GBR) **[51702]**

American Journal of Cancer (Mairangi Bay, NZL) **[48931]**

American Journal of Cardiovascular Drugs (Mairangi Bay, NZL) **[48932]**

American Journal of Clinical Dermatology (Mairangi Bay, NZL) **[48933]**

American Journal of Community Psychology (Dordrecht, NLD) **[48324]**

American Journal of Drug Delivery (Mairangi Bay, NZL) *Ceased*

American Journal of Ophthalmology (Amsterdam, NLD) **[47888]**

American Journal of Preventive Medicine (Amsterdam, NLD) **[47889]**

American Journal of Reproductive Immunology (Frederiksberg, DEN) *Unable to locate*

American Law and Economics Review (Oxford, GBR) **[55865]**

American Literary History (Tokyo, JPN) **[46733]**

American Market (New Delhi, DH, IND) *Unable to locate*

American Studies in Scandinavia (Odense, DEN) *Unable to locate*

Amerikastudien/American Studies (Halle, GER) *Unable to locate*

Amida Magazine (Canberra, AC, AUS) *Unable to locate*

Amigos De La Tierra (Madrid, SPA) *Unable to locate*

Amino Acids (Vienna, AUT) **[42743]**

Amis de la Terre (Dave, BEL) *Unable to locate*

Amity (New Delhi, DH, IND) *Unable to locate*

Ammattiautoilija **[43842]***

Amnestie (Bern, SWI) **[51069]**

Amon Hen (Witney, GBR) **[56938]**

Amor-FM - 91.9 (Papagayo, DOM) **[43740]**

Amphibia-Reptilia (Leiden, NLD) **[48645]**

AMPO (Tokyo, JPN) *Unable to locate*

Amrita Bazar Patrika (Calcutta, WB, IND) *Unable to locate*

Amruth (Bangalore, KA, IND) **[44948]**

AMSPAR (London, GBR) *Unable to locate*

Amsterdam-FM (Amsterdam, NLD) *Unable to locate*

Amsterdam-FM - 104.4 (Hilversum, NLD) **[48632]**

Amsterdam Journal (Avenhorn, NLD) *Unable to locate*

Amsterdam Monographs in American Studies (Amsterdam, NLD) **[47890]**

Amsterdam Real Estate City Book (The Hague, NLD) **[48606]**

Amsterdam The Magazine (Amstelveen, NLD) *Unable to locate*

AMTA Journal (Melbourne, VI, AUS) **[42045]**

Amusement Business **[53889]***

Amy (London, GBR) **[53939]**

Amyloid (Abingdon, GBR) **[51703]**

Amyotrophic Lateral Sclerosis (Stockholm, SWE) **[51007]**

Amyotrophic Lateral Sclerosis and Other Motor Neuron Disorders **[51007]***

AMZ - Auto Motor Zubehor (Hannover, GER) *Unable to locate*

An Leabharlann (Dublin, DU, IRL) **[45944]**

An Phoblacht (Dublin, DU, IRL) **[45945]**

Anaerobe (Amsterdam, NLD) **[47891]**

Anaesthesia (London, GBR) **[53940]**

Anaesthesia (Oxford, GBR) **[55866]**

Anaesthesia Essays and Researches (Amman, JOR) *Unable to locate*

Anaesthesiology & Intensive Critical Care Medicine (Prague, CZE) **[43609]**

Anais da Academia Brasileira de Ciencias (Rio de Janeiro, RJ, BRZ) **[43003]**

Anais da Sociedade Entomologica do Brasil (Vacaria, RN, BRZ) **[43052]**

Analecta (Rome, ITA) *Unable to locate*

Anales de la Academia de Geografia e Historia de Guatemala (Guatemala City, GTM) *Unable to locate*

Anales de la Facultad de Medicina (Lima, PER) **[49423]**

Anales de Medicina Interna (Madrid, SPA) *Ceased*

Anales de Psicologia (Murcia, SPA) **[50821]**

Analisis Filosofico (Buenos Aires, ARG) *Unable to locate*

Analusis (Paris, FRA) *Unable to locate*

Analysis in Theory and Applications (Bussum, NLD) **[48278]**

Analyst (Cambridge, GBR) **[52786]**

Analyst (London, GBR) *Unable to locate*

Analytical Abstract (Cambridge, GBR) **[52787]**

Analytical and Bioanalytical Chemistry (Heidelberg, GER) **[44437]**

Analytical Biochemistry (Amsterdam, NLD) **[17892]**

Analytical Bulletin (Minsk, BLH) *Unable to locate*

Analytical Cellular Pathology/Cellular Oncology (Amsterdam, NLD) **[47893]**

Analytical Chemistry (Roorkee, UP, IND) **[45717]**

Analytical Instrument Industry Report **[54609]***

Analytical Laboratory (Changsha, HA, CHN) *Unable to locate*

Analytical Sciences (Tokyo, JPN) **[46734]**

Ananda Acharya Universal Series (Hoshiarpur, PJ, IND) *Unable to locate*

Ananda Varta (Calcutta, WB, IND) *Unable to locate*

Anatolia (Eskisehir, TUR) **[51554]**

Anatolian Archaeological Studies (Wiesbaden, GER) **[44710]**

Anatomia, Histologia, Embryologia (Wilrijk, BEL) *Unable to locate*

Anatomia, Histologia, Embryologia (Munich, GER) **[44549]**

Anatomical Science **[53941]***

Anatomical Science International (London, GBR) **[53941]**

Anatomical Society of India Journal (Jhansi, UP, IND) *Unable to locate*

Anatomy and Embryology (Tokyo, JPN) *Unable to locate*

Ancient Ceylon (Colombo, SRI) *Unable to locate*

Ancient Civilizations from Scythia to Siberia (Leiden, NLD) **[48646]**

Ancient Egypt (Manchester, GBR) **[55541]**

Ancient Nepal (Kathmandu, NPL) *Unable to locate*

Ancient Science of Life (Coimbatore, TN, IND) **[45077]**

Ancient Society (Leuven, BEL) **[42891]**

Andaia-FM - 104.3 (San Antonio de Jesus, BH, BRZ) **[43015]**

Andhra Agricultural Journal (Guntur, AP, IND) *Unable to locate*

Andhra Historical Research Society Journal (Hyderabad, AP, IND) *Unable to locate*

Andhra Pradesh, India Department of Archaeology and Museums—Archaeological Series (Hyderabad, AP, IND) *Unable to locate*

Andhra Pradesh, India—Department of Archaeology and Museums Archaeological Series: A.P. Journal (Hyderabad, AP, IND) *Unable to locate*

Andhra Pradesh, India Department of Archaeology and Museums—Epigraphy Series (Hyderabad, AP, IND) *Unable to locate*

ANDID Notizie (Bologna, ITA) *Unable to locate*

Andon (Amsterdam, NLD) **[47894]**

Andover Advertiser (Andover, GBR) **[52110]**

Andrologia (Giessen, GER) **[44383]**

Andromeda Spaceways Inflight Magazine (Kaleen, AC, AUS) **[41981]**

Anesthesiology & Intensive Care (Moscow, RUS) **[49870]**

Angeiologie (Paris, FRA) *Unable to locate*

AngelWoche (Hamburg, GER) **[44409]**

Angewandte Botanik (Gottingen, GER) *Unable to locate*

Angiosperm Taxonomy (New Delhi, DH, IND) *Unable to locate*

Angler's Mail (London, GBR) **[53942]**

Anglia (Berlin, GER) **[44140]**

Anglia Afloat (Norwich, GBR) **[55722]**

Anglican World (London, GBR) **[53943]**

Angling Times (London, GBR) **[53944]**

Anglo-American Law Review **[53663]***

Anglo-American Law Review (Chichester, GBR) *Unable to locate*

The Anglo-Celt (Cavan, CV, IRL) **[45930]**

Anglogermanica online (Valencia, SPA) **[50842]**

The Angry Corrie (Cambuskenneth, GBR) **[52912]**

Anhui People's Broadcasting Station (Hefei, AN, CHN) *Unable to locate*

Anhui People's Broadcasting Station (Hefei, AN, CHN) *Unable to locate*

Numbers cited in bold after listings are entry numbers rather than page numbers.

Anhui People's Broadcasting Station (Hefei, AN, CHN) *Unable to locate*

Ani (Pasay City, PHL) **[49568]**

ANIGP-TV (Madrid, SPA) **[50728]**

Animal (Penicuik, GBR) **[56243]**

Animal Action (Horsham, GBR) **[53594]**

Animal Behaviour (London, GBR) **[53945]**

Animal Biology (Leiden, NLD) **[48647]**

Animal Cognition (Heidelberg, GER) **[44438]**

Animal Health Australia (Deakin, AC, AUS) **[41832]**

Animal Health Research Reviews (Wallingford, GBR) **[56815]**

Animal Life (Horsham, GBR) **[53595]**

Animal Production Research Advances (Owerri, IM, NGA) **[49161]**

Animal Production Science (Collingwood, VI, AUS) **[41780]**

Animal Research International (Nsukka, AN, NGA) **[49155]**

Animal Science **[56243]***

Animal Science Journal (Tokyo, JPN) **[46735]**

Animal Science Journal (Oxford, GBR) **[55867]**

Animal Welfare (Wheathampstead, GBR) **[56914]**

Animalia (Helsinki, FIN) *Unable to locate*

Animals Today (North Melbourne, VI, AUS) **[42156]**

Animals and You (Dundee, GBR) **[53213]**

Animals and You (London, GBR) **[53946]**

Animation (Farnham, GBR) **[53379]**

Animations (London, GBR) *Ceased*

The Animist (Strathfieldsaye, VI, AUS) *Ceased*

Ankara Polis Radyosu (Ankara, TUR) *Unable to locate*

Anna (Kuvalehdet, FIN) **[43879]**

Anna (Estonia) (Kuvalehdet, FIN) *Unable to locate*

Annales Academiae Medicae Silesiensis (Zabrze, POL) **[49781]**

Annales Academiae Scientiarum Fennicae Mathematica (Helsinki, FIN) **[43816]**

Annales de Biologie Clinique (Montrouge, FRA) **[43980]**

Annales d'Economie et de Statistique (Paris, FRA) **[44024]**

Annales Francaises d'Anesthesie et de Reanimation (Paris, FRA) **[44025]**

Annales de Gerontologie (Montrouge, FRA) **[43981]**

Annales Henri Poincare (Orsay, FRA) **[44018]**

Annales de l'IFORD (Yaounde, CMR) *Unable to locate*

Annales de Physique (Toulouse, FRA) **[44118]**

Annali dell'Istituto Superiore di Sanita (Milan, ITA) **[46163]**

Annali di Matematica Pura ed Applicata (Tokyo, JPN) **[46736]**

Annali di Storia di Firenze (Florence, ITA) **[46141]**

Annals of Abbasi Shaheed Hospital and Karachi Medical & Dental College (Karachi, PAK) *Unable to locate*

Annals, Academy of Medicine, Singapore (Singapore, SGP) **[50103]**

Annals of African Medicine (Sokoto, SK, NGA) **[49172]**

Annals of Agri Bio Research (Hisar, HY, IND) *Unable to locate*

Annals of Agricultural and Environmental Medicine (Lublin, POL) **[49672]**

Annals of Agricultural Research (New Delhi, DH, IND) *Unable to locate*

Annals of Anatomy (Oxford, GBR) **[55868]**

Annals of Applied Biology (Warwick, GBR) **[56852]**

Annals of Arid Zone (Jodhpur, RJ, IND) **[45214]**

Annals of the Arts and Social Sciences (Safat, KWT) **[47333]**

Annals of Bangladesh Agriculture (Gazipur, BGD) **[42819]**

Annals of Biology (Hisar, HY, IND) *Unable to locate*

Annals of Biomedical Research and Education (Tbilisi, GRG) **[44130]**

Annals of Biomedical Science (Benin City, NGA) **[49063]**

Annals of Botany (Leicester, GBR) **[53784]**

Annals of Burns and Fire Disasters (Palermo, ITA) **[46207]**

Annals of Cardiac Anaesthesia (New Delhi, DH, IND) **[45483]**

Annals of Clinical Microbiology and Antimicrobials (London, GBR) **[53947]**

Annals of Combinatorics (Tokyo, JPN) **[46737]**

Annals of Diagnostic Paediatric Pathology (Warsaw, POL) *Unable to locate*

Annals of Entomology (Dehradun, UP, IND) *Unable to locate*

Annals of Finance (Tokyo, JPN) **[46738]**

Annals of Forest Science (Champenoux, FRA) **[43929]**

Annals of Forestry (Dehradun, UP, IND) *Unable to locate*

Annals of General Psychiatry (London, GBR) **[53948]**

Annals of Glaciology (Cambridge, GBR) **[52788]**

Annals of Hematology (Hannover, GER) **[44429]**

Annals of Human Biology (Loughborough, GBR) **[55477]**

Annals of Ibadan Postgraduate Medicine (Grahamstown, SAF) **[50493]**

Annals of the ICRP (Stockholm, SWE) **[51008]**

Annals of Indian Academy of Neurology (Trivandrum, KE, IND) **[45757]**

Annals of King Edward Medical College (Lahore, PAK) *Unable to locate*

Annals of Library Science and Documentation (New Delhi, DH, IND) *Unable to locate*

Annals of Mathematics and Artificial Intelligence (Dordrecht, NLD) **[48325]**

The Annals of Medical Entomology (Bhopal, MP, IND) **[45005]**

Annals of Nigerian Medicine (Zaria, KD, NGA) **[49181]**

Annals of Nuclear Medicine (Tokyo, JPN) **[46739]**

Annals of Nutrition and Metabolism (Vienna, AUT) **[42744]**

Annals of Occupational Hygiene (Derby, GBR) **[53163]**

Annals of Oncology (Viganello-Lugano, SWI) **[51237]**

Annals of Operations Research (Dordrecht, NLD) **[48326]**

Annals of Ophthalmology (Moscow, RUS) **[49871]**

Annals of Oriental Research (Chennai, TN, IND) *Unable to locate*

Annals of Pediatric Cardiology (Mumbai, MH, IND) **[45350]**

Annals of Physics (Amsterdam, NLD) **[47895]**

Annals of Plant Protection Sciences (New Delhi, DH, IND) *Unable to locate*

Annals of Public and Cooperative Economics (Oxford, GBR) **[55869]**

Annals of Regional Science (Tokyo, JPN) **[46740]**

Annals of the Rheumatic Disease (London, GBR) **[53949]**

Annals of the Russian Academy of Medical Sciences (Moscow, RUS) **[49872]**

Annals of Software Engineering (Heidelberg, GER) **[44439]**

Annals of Surgery (Moscow, RUS) **[49873]**

Annals of The Royal College of Surgeons of England (Colchester, GBR) **[53028]**

Annals of Thoracic and Cardiovascular Surgery (Tokyo, JPN) **[46741]**

Annals of Thoracic Medicine (Riyadh, SAU) **[50059]**

Annals of Traumatology & Orthopedics (Moscow, RUS) **[49874]**

Annals of Tropical Paediatrics (London, GBR) **[53950]**

Annals of Tropical Research (Leyte, PHL) *Unable to locate*

Annals of Warsaw University of Life Sciences, Land Reclamation (Warsaw, POL) **[49689]**

Annals of Zoology (Agra, UP, IND) *Unable to locate*

Annandale Herald (Annan, GBR) **[52122]**

Annandale Observer (Annan, GBR) **[52123]**

Anne Frank Krant (Amsterdam, NLD) *Unable to locate*

Anne Frank Zeitung (Amsterdam, NLD) *Unable to locate*

Anniversary Magazine (San Salvador, ELS) *Unable to locate*

Annotated Bibliography of Literature on Cooperative Movements in South-East Asia (New Delhi, DH, IND) *Unable to locate*

Annotated Index to Indian Social Science Journals (New Delhi, DH, IND) *Unable to locate*

Annual Bibliography of English Language & Literature (London, GBR) **[53951]**

Annual Handbook (Bedford Gardens, SAF) *Unable to locate*

Annual Home Industries Prize List (Harare, ZWE) *Unable to locate*

Annual Review of Cognitive Linguistics **[48223]***

Annual Review of Plant Pathology (Jodhpur, RJ, IND) **[45215]**

Annual Review of Singapore Cases (Singapore City, SGP) **[50310]**

Anomaly (London, GBR) **[53952]**

Anon (Edinburgh, GBR) **[53250]**

Another Magazine (London, GBR) **[53953]**

ANPHI Papers (Manila, PHL) *Unable to locate*

Anqing People's Broadcasting Station (Anqing, AN, CHN) *Unable to locate*

Anritsu Technical Review (Kanagawa, JPN) *Unable to locate*

Anshan People's Broadcasting Station (Anshan, LI, CHN) *Unable to locate*

Anshan People's Broadcasting Station (Anshan, LI, CHN) *Unable to locate*

Anshan People's Broadcasting Station (Anshan, LI, CHN) *Unable to locate*

Anshun People's Broadcasting Station (Anshun, GZ, CHN) *Unable to locate*

Anshun People's Broadcasting Station (Anshun, GH, CHN) *Unable to locate*

Anshun People's Broadcasting Station (Anshun, GH, CHN) *Unable to locate*

ANSTO Program of Research (Menai, NW, AUS) *Unable to locate*

Antarctic Record (Tokyo, JPN) **[46742]**

Antena Uno-FM - 107.9 (Santa Fe, ARG) **[41489]**

Antenna5 - Berovo - 97.9 (Berovo, MEC) **[47501]**

Antenna5 - Bitola - 93.9 (Bitola, MEC) **[47502]**

Antenna5 - Bitola - 92.9 (Bitola, MEC) **[47503]**

Antenna5 - Bogdanci - 89.2 (Bogdanci, MEC) **[47505]**

Antenna5 - Bogdanci - 106.3 (Bogdanci, MEC) **[47506]**

Antenna5 - Delcevo - 97.90 (Delcevo, MEC) **[47507]**

Antenna5 - Demir Kapija - 104.2 (Demir Kapija, MEC) **[47510]**

Antenna5 - Demir Kapija - 88.8 (Demir Kapija, MEC) **[47509]**

Antenna5 - Demir Kapija - 91.9 (Demir Kapija, MEC) **[47508]**

Antenna5 - Dojran - 106.3 (Dojran, MEC) **[47511]**

Antenna5 - Dusegubica - 103.3 (Dusegubica, MEC) **[47512]**

Antenna5 - FM Radovis - 91.9 (Radovis, MEC) **[47545]**

Antenna5 - FM Resen - 92.9 (Resen, MEC) **[47546]**

Antenna5 - FM Skopje - 95.5 (Skopje, MEC) **[47547]**

Antenna5 - Galicnik - 92.9 (Galicnik, MEC) **[47513]**

Antenna5 - Gevgelija - 106.3 (Gevgelija, MEC) **[47515]**

Antenna5 - Gevgelija - 89.2 (Gevgelija, MEC) **[47514]**

Antenna5 - Gostivar - 106.9 (Gostivar, MEC) **[47516]**

Antenna5 - Gostivar - 105.5 (Gostivar, MEC) **[47517]**

Antenna5 - Kavadarci - 104.2 (Kavadarci, MEC) **[47519]**

Antenna5 - Kavadarci - 91.9 (Kavadarci, MEC) **[47518]**

Antenna5 - Kicevo - 95.5 (Kicevo, MEC) **[47520]**

Antenna5 - Kocani - 97.9 (Kocani, MEC) **[47521]**

Antenna5 - Kocani - 104.8 (Kocani, MEC) **[47522]**

Antenna5 - Kratovo - 105.5 (Kratovo, MEC) **[47524]**

Antenna5 - Kratovo - 106.9 (Kratovo, MEC) **[47523]**

Antenna5 - Kriva Palanka - 105.5 (Kriva Palanka, MEC) **[47526]**

Antenna5 - Kriva Palanka - 95.5 (Kriva Palanka, MEC) **[47525]**

Antenna5 - Krusevo - 92.9 (Krusevo, MEC) **[47527]**

Antenna5 - Kumanovo - 106.3 (Kumanovo, MEC) **[47529]**

Antenna5 - Kumanovo - 104.8 (Kumanovo, MEC) **[47530]**

Numbers cited in bold after listings are entry numbers rather than page numbers.

Antenna5 - Kumanovo - 106.9 (Kumanovo, MEC) **[47528]**

Antenna5 - M. Radobil - 97.9 (M. Radobil, MEC) **[47531]**

Antenna5 - Makedonska Kamenica - 104.8 (Makedonska Kamenica, MEC) **[47533]**

Antenna5 - Makedonska Kamenica - 97.90 (Makedonska Kamenica, MEC) **[47532]**

Antenna5 - Mavrovo - 95.5 (Mavrovo, MEC) **[47534]**

Antenna5 - Mavrovo - 105.5 (Mavrovo, MEC) **[47535]**

Antenna5 - Negotino - 104.2 (Negotino, MEC) **[47538]**

Antenna5 - Negotino - 91.9 (Negotino, MEC) **[47536]**

Antenna5 - Negotino - 88.8 (Negotino, MEC) **[47537]**

Antenna5 - Ohrid - 103.3 (Ohrid, MEC) **[47540]**

Antenna5 - Ohrid - 92.0 (Ohrid, MEC) **[47539]**

Antenna5 - Pesocan - 101.9 (Pesocan, MEC) **[47541]**

Antenna5 - Popova Sapka - 106.9 (Popova Sapka, MEC) **[47542]**

Antenna5 - Prilep - 92.9 (Prilep, MEC) **[47543]**

Antenna5 - Prilep - 106.3 (Prilep, MEC) **[47544]**

Antenna5 - Stip - 91.9 (Stip, MEC) **[47548]**

Antenna5 - Stip - 104.8 (Stip, MEC) **[47549]**

Antenna5 - Stracin - 105.5 (Stracin, MEC) **[47551]**

Antenna5 - Struga - 103.3 (Struga, MEC) **[47553]**

Antenna5 - Struga - 92.0 (Struga, MEC) **[47552]**

Antenna5 - Strumica - 100.5 (Strumica, MEC) **[47555]**

Antenna5 - Strumica - 91.9 (Strumica, MEC) **[47554]**

Antenna5 - Sveti Nikole - 91.9 (Sveti Nikole, MEC) **[47556]**

Antenna5 - Tetovo - 106.9 (Tetovo, MEC) **[47557]**

Antenna5 - Tetovo - 105.5 (Tetovo, MEC) **[47558]**

Antenna5 - Valandovo - 106.3 (Valandovo, MEC) **[47559]**

Antenna5 - Veles - 91.9 (Veles, MEC) **[47560]**

Antenna5 - Vinica - 104.8 (Vinica, MEC) **[47562]**

Antenna5 - Vinica - 97.9 (Vinica, MEC) **[47561]**

Antenne AC-FM (Wurselen, GER) *Unable to locate*

Antenne Kaernten-FM - 104.9 (Klagenfurt, AUT) **[42727]**

Antenne Koblenz-FM - 98.0 (Koblenz, GER) **[44511]**

Antenne Niederrhein-FM - 87.65 (Kleve, GER) **[44510]**

Antenne Ruhr-FM (Oberhausen, GER) *Unable to locate*

Antenne Ruhr-FM (Oberhausen, GER) *Unable to locate*

Antenne Thuringen-FM - 107.2 (Weimar, GER) **[44700]**

Anthropological Forum (Abingdon, GBR) **[51704]**

Anthropological Review (Warsaw, POL) **[49690]**

Anthropological Science (Tokyo, JPN) **[46743]**

Anthropological Theory (London, GBR) **[53954]**

The Anthropologist (Delhi, DH, IND) **[45087]**

Anthropology Research Association Research Bulletin (Lucknow, UP, IND) *Unable to locate*

Anthropology Today (London, GBR) **[53955]**

Anthropos (Rome, ITA) *Unable to locate*

Anthrozoos (Cambridge, GBR) **[52789]**

Anti-Cancer Agents in Medicinal Chemistry (Bussum, NLD) **[48279]**

Anti-Cancer Drugs (Amsterdam, NLD) **[47896]**

Anti-Corrosion Methods & Materials (Bradford, GBR) **[52436]**

Anti-Inflammatory & Anti-Allergy Agents in Medicinal Chemistry (Mersin, TUR) **[51576]**

Anticancer Research (Kapandriti, GRC) **[44760]**

Antichthon (Bundanoon, NW, AUS) **[41668]**

Antik Tanulmanyok (Budapest, HUN) **[44822]**

Antike und Abendland (Berlin, GER) **[44150]**

Antike Kunst (Basel, SWI) **[51058]**

Antiquarian Book Monthly **[55173]***

Antiquarian Book Review **[55173]***

Antiquarian Horology and the Proceedings of the Antiquarian Horological (Wadhurst, GBR) *Unable to locate*

Antiquaries Journal (London, GBR) **[53956]**

Antique Collecting (Woodbridge, GBR) *Unable to locate*

Antique Dealer & Collectors Guide (London, GBR) **[53957]**

The Antique Trade Calendar (London, GBR) **[53958]**

Antiques & Art Independent (Chippenham, GBR) **[53020]**

Antiques Info (Broadstairs, GBR) **[52744]**

Antiquity (York, GBR) **[56987]**

The Antiseptic (Madurai, TN, IND) *Unable to locate*

Antrim Times (Ballymena, GBR) **[52158]**

ANU Reporter (Canberra, AC, AUS) **[41697]**

Anuario de Estudios Indigenas (San Cristobal de Las Casas, CP, MEX) *Unable to locate*

Anuario da Sociedade Broteriana (Coimbra, PRT) *Unable to locate*

Anuvad (New Delhi, DH, IND) *Unable to locate*

Anvesak (Ahmedabad, GJ, IND) *Unable to locate*

Anwaltsblatt (Berlin, GER) **[44151]**

Anyang People's Broadcasting Station (Anyang, HN, CHN) *Unable to locate*

ANZ Journal of Surgery (Richmond, VI, AUS) **[42300]**

Anzen to Kenko (Tokyo, JPN) *Unable to locate*

The ANZIAM Journal (The Australian & New Zealand Industrial & Applied Mathematics Journal) (Canberra, AC, AUS) **[41698]**

AP & A Magazine Auto Parts & Accessories (Virginia Water, GBR) *Unable to locate*

APC (Sydney, NW, AUS) **[42447]**

Apeldoorn-FM - 88.2 (Hilversum, NLD) **[48633]**

Apex (Hamilton, NZL) **[48908]**

Aphelion (Kingston, VI, AUS) **[41994]**

Aphrodite (Rumbeke, BEL) *Unable to locate*

Apiacta (Rome, ITA) **[46221]**

Apicultural Abstracts (Cardiff, GBR) *Ceased*

Apidologie (Les Ulis, FRA) **[43964]**

APJML **[42244]***

APLAR Journal of Rheumatology **[56003]***

APMIS (Copenhagen, DEN) **[43655]**

APO Productivity Journal (Tokyo, JPN) *Unable to locate*

Apoteket - Tidningen (Stockholm, SWE) *Unable to locate*

Apparel (Mumbai, MH, IND) **[45351]**

Apparel Production News (Tokyo, JPN) **[46744]**

Appita Journal (Carlton, VI, AUS) *Unable to locate*

AppleSauce (Glenside, SA, AUS) **[41897]**

Appliance Retailer (Pyrmont, NW, AUS) **[42269]**

Applicable Algebra in Engineering, Communication and Computing (Tokyo, JPN) **[46745]**

Applied Artificial Intelligence (Vienna, AUT) **[42745]**

Applied Biochemistry and Microbiology (Moscow, RUS) **[49875]**

Applied Bioinformatics (Mairangi Bay, NZL) *Ceased*

Applied Bionics and Biomechanics (Cambridge, GBR) **[52790]**

Applied Botany Abstracts (Lucknow, UP, IND) *Unable to locate*

Applied Cognitive Psychology (Leicester, GBR) **[53785]**

Applied and Computational Harmonic Analysis (Amsterdam, NLD) **[47897]**

Applied Earth Science (London, GBR) **[53959]**

Applied Econometrics and International Development (Santiago de Compostela, SPA) **[50831]**

Applied Economic Papers (Secunderabad, AP, IND) *Unable to locate*

Applied Economics (Abingdon, GBR) **[51705]**

Applied Economics Letters (Coventry, GBR) **[53077]**

Applied Entomology and Phytopathology (Tehran, IRN) **[45887]**

Applied Entomology and Zoology (Tokyo, JPN) **[46746]**

Applied Financial Economics (Coventry, GBR) **[53078]**

Applied GIS (Clayton, VI, AUS) **[41756]**

Applied Health Economics and Health Policy (Mairangi Bay, NZL) *Ceased*

Applied Herpetology (Leiden, NLD) **[48648]**

Applied Magnetic Resonance (Tokyo, JPN) **[46747]**

Applied Mathematical Modelling (Swansea, GBR) **[56699]**

Applied Mathematical Sciences (Ruse, BUL) **[43088]**

Applied Mathematics and Mechanics (Dordrecht, NLD) **[48327]**

Applied Mathematics Research eXpress (Oxford, GBR) **[55870]**

Applied Microbiology and Biotechnology (Munster, GER) **[44595]**

Applied Ontology (Trento, ITA) **[46261]**

Applied Organometallic Chemistry (Chichester, GBR) **[53004]**

Applied Physics A (Heidelberg, GER) **[44440]**

Applied Physics B (Novosibirsk, RUS) **[50009]**

Applied Soft Computing (Bedford, GBR) **[52272]**

Applied Solar Energy (Tashkent, UZN) **[57014]**

Applied Surface Science (Osaka, JPN) **[46615]**

Applied Thermal Engineering (Whitley Bay, GBR) **[56918]**

Appointments Memorandum **[53819]***

Approches (Zurich, SWI) **[51252]**

Appropriate Technology (Burnham, GBR) **[52763]**

Approximation Theory and its Applications **[48278]***

APRC Journal of Experimental Psychology (Agra, UP, IND) *Unable to locate*

APROMUJER (San Jose, CRI) *Unable to locate*

Apu (Helsinki, FIN) **[43817]**

Apuraportti (Helsinki, FIN) *Unable to locate*

Aquaculture Europe incorporated in World Aquaculture (Oostende, BEL) *Unable to locate*

Aquaculture Nutrition (Bergen, NOR) **[49190]**

Aquaristik (Ettlingen, GER) **[44348]**

Aquatic Biology (Oldendorf, GER) **[44625]**

Aquatic Conservation (Edinburgh, GBR) **[53251]**

Aquatic Insects (Stuttgart, GER) **[44661]**

Aquatic Living Resources (Nantes, FRA) **[44011]**

Aquatic Microbial Ecology (Villefranche-sur-Mer, FRA) **[44124]**

Aquatic Resources, Culture and Development (Wallingford, GBR) *Ceased*

Aquatic Sciences (Kastanienbaum, SWI) **[51180]**

Aquazone (Loughborough, GBR) *Unable to locate*

Aquinas Journal (Colombo, SRI) *Unable to locate*

ARA City Radio-FM - 105.2 (Luxembourg, LUX) **[47495]**

ARA City Radio-FM - 103.3 (Luxembourg, LUX) **[47494]**

The Arab (Tokyo, JPN) *Unable to locate*

Arab Agricultural Research Journal (Khartoum, SDN) *Unable to locate*

Arab Construction World (ACW) (Beirut, LBN) **[47390]**

Arab Defence Journal (Beirut, LBN) **[47391]**

Arab Food Industries (Baghdad, IRQ) *Unable to locate*

Arab Gulf Journal of Scientific Research (Manama, BHR) *Ceased*

Arab Historical Review for Ottoman Studies (Zaghouan, TUN) *Unable to locate*

Arab Horse Society News (Marlborough, GBR) **[55599]**

Arab Journal of Administrative Sciences (Safat, KWT) **[47334]**

Arab Journal of Culture (Tunis, TUN) *Ceased*

Arab Journal of Education (Tunis, TUN) *Ceased*

Arab Journal for the Humanities (Safat, KWT) **[47335]**

Arab Journal of Information (Tunis, TUN) *Unable to locate*

Arab Journal of Irrigation Water Management (Khartoum, SDN) *Unable to locate*

Arab Journal of Library and Information Science (Riyadh, SAU) *Unable to locate*

Arab Journal of Plant Protection (Beirut, LBN) *Unable to locate*

Numbers cited in bold after listings are entry numbers rather than page numbers.

Arab Journal of Science (Tunis, TUN) *Ceased*

Arab Land Transport's Magazine (Amman, JOR) *Unable to locate*

Arab Law Quarterly (Leiden, NLD) **[48649]**

Arab News (Riyadh, SAU) **[50060]**

Arab Water World (AWW) (Beirut, LBN) **[47392]**

The Arab Woman (Damascus, SYR) *Unable to locate*

Arab Women (Baghdad, IRQ) *Unable to locate*

The Arab World (Jounieh, LBN) *Unable to locate*

Arab World Agribusiness (Manama, BHR) **[42786]**

Arabian Archaeology and Epigraphy (Sydney, NW, AUS) **[42448]**

Arabian Business (Dubai, UAE) **[51630]**

Arabian Computer News (Dubai, UAE) **[51631]**

Arabian Journal for Science and Engineering (Dhahran, SAU) **[50054]**

Arabian Woman (Dubai, UAE) **[51632]**

Arabic Voice of Beirut (Beirut, LBN) *Unable to locate*

Arabica (Leiden, NLD) **[48650]**

The ARACHIM Torah Journal (Bnei Brak, ISR) *Unable to locate*

Araksha (New Delhi, DH, IND) *Unable to locate*

Arandu (Quito, ECU) *Unable to locate*

Arbeitgeber (Cologne, GER) *Unable to locate*

Arbetsterapeuten (Nacka, SWE) *Unable to locate*

Arbitration (London, GBR) *Ceased*

Arbitration International (Alphen aan den Rijn, NLD) **[47866]**

Arbitrium (Berlin, GER) **[44152]**

Arboricultural Journal (Cheltenham, GBR) **[52963]**

Arbroath Herald (Arbroath, GBR) **[52127]**

L'Arca (Milan, ITA) *Unable to locate*

arcadia (Berlin, GER) **[44153]**

Arcana (Malmo, SWE) *Unable to locate*

L'Arcaplus (Milan, ITA) *Unable to locate*

Archaeologia Aeliana (Newcastle upon Tyne, GBR) **[55667]**

Archaeologiai Ertesito (Budapest, HUN) **[44823]**

The Archaeological Journal (London, GBR) *Unable to locate*

Archaeological Reports (London, GBR) **[53960]**

Archaeologies (Rondebosch, SAF) **[50617]**

The Archaeologist (Reading, GBR) **[56309]**

Archaeology (Sofia, BUL) *Unable to locate*

Archaeology in New Zealand (Christchurch, NZL) **[48861]**

Archaeometry (Oxford, GBR) **[55871]**

L'Arche (Paris, FRA) **[44026]**

Archeologia Zambiana (Livingstone, ZMB) *Unable to locate*

Archery UK (Newport, GBR) **[55688]**

Archipelago (Manila, PHL) *Unable to locate*

Archipielago (Barcelona, SPA) **[50649]**

Architect and Surveyor **[55706]***

Architects India (Mumbai, MH, IND) *Unable to locate*

Architects' Journal (London, GBR) *Unable to locate*

Architectural Engineering and Design Management (London, GBR) **[53961]**

Architectural Heritage (Edinburgh, GBR) **[53252]**

Architectural Ironmongery Journal (London, GBR) *Unable to locate*

Architectural Journal (Beijing, CHN) **[43169]**

The Architectural Review (London, GBR) **[53962]**

Architectural Technology **[53979]***

Architecture (Moscow, RUS) *Unable to locate*

Architecture and Building Industry (Meerut, UP, IND) *Unable to locate*

Architecture, Construction, Design - ACD (Moscow, RUS) *Unable to locate*

Architecture and Construction of Moscow (Moscow, RUS) *Unable to locate*

Architecture and Construction of Russia (Moscow, RUS) *Unable to locate*

Architecture plus Design (New Delhi, DH, IND) *Unable to locate*

Architecture, Technology, Culture (ATC) (Munich, GER) **[44550]**

Architecture - Theory and History (Sofia, BUL) *Unable to locate*

Architecturny Vestnik (Moscow, RUS) *Unable to locate*

Architekt (Prague, CZE) *Unable to locate*

Architektur Aktuell (Vienna, AUT) **[42746]**

Archiv fur Geschichte der Philosophie (Berlin, GER) **[44154]**

Archiv der Mathematik (Saarbrucken, GER) **[44651]**

Archiv fur Papyrusforschung (Berlin, GER) **[44155]**

Archiv der Pharmazie (Frankfurt, GER) **[44358]**

Archive of Applied Mechanics (Bremen, GER) **[44280]**

Archive for History of Exact Sciences (Tokyo, JPN) **[46748]**

Archive for Mathematical Logic (Munster, GER) **[44596]**

Archive of Oncology (Sremska Kamenica, SER) **[50094]**

Archive for the Psychology of Religion (Leiden, NLD) **[48651]**

Archive for Rational Mechanics and Analysis (Oxford, GBR) **[55872]**

Archives (London, GBR) *Unable to locate*

Archives of Animal Nutrition (Berlin, GER) **[44156]**

Archives of Biochemistry and Biophysics (Amsterdam, NLD) **[47898]**

Archives of Dermatological Research (Tokyo, JPN) **[46749]**

Archives of Disease in Childhood. Education and Practice Edition (London, GBR) **[53963]**

Archives of Gerontology and Geriatrics (Debrecen, HUN) **[44887]**

Archives of Gynecology and Obstetrics (Basel, SWI) **[51059]**

Archives of Histology and Cytology (Niigata, JPN) *Unable to locate*

Archives of Ibadan Medicine (Ibadan, OY, NGA) **[49087]**

Archives of Industrial Hygiene and Toxicology (Warsaw, POL) **[49691]**

Archives Internationales d'Histoire des Sciences (Paris, FRA) *Unable to locate*

Archives of Microbiology (Tokyo, JPN) **[46750]**

Archives of Orthopaedic and Trauma Surgery (Tokyo, JPN) **[46751]**

Archives of Pharmacal Research (Seoul, KOR) **[47253]**

Archives for Philosophy of Law and Social Philosophy (Bologna, ITA) *Unable to locate*

Archives of Polish Fisheries (Warsaw, POL) **[49692]**

Archives of Sexual Behavior (Dordrecht, NLD) **[48328]**

Archives of Toxicology (Tokyo, JPN) **[46752]**

Archives of the Turkish Society of Cardiology (Istanbul, TUR) *Unable to locate*

Archives of Virology (Strasbourg, FRA) **[44110]**

Archivos de la Filmoteca (Valencia, SPA) *Unable to locate*

Archivum Mathematicum (Brno, CZE) **[43602]**

ARCONIS - Wissen zum Planen und Bauen und zum Baumarkt (Stuttgart, GER) *Unable to locate*

Area (Oxford, GBR) **[55873]**

Area and Production of Principal Crops in India Summary Tables (New Delhi, DH, IND) *Unable to locate*

ARENA (Manchester, GBR) *Unable to locate*

Arena Magazine (Melbourne, VI, AUS) **[42046]**

Arena Magazine (Dublin, DU, IRL) *Unable to locate*

Argos (Aylesford, GBR) *Unable to locate*

The Argus Lite (Brighton, GBR) **[52605]**

Argyll FM - 106.5 (Campbeltown, GBR) **[52915]**

Argyll FM - 107.7 (Campbeltown, GBR) **[52913]**

Argyll FM - 107.1 (Campbeltown, GBR) **[52914]**

Argyllshire Advertiser (Lochgilphead, GBR) **[53887]**

Arhitektuuriajakiri MAJA (Tallinn, EST) *Unable to locate*

ARIANA Radio-FM - 93.5 (Kabul, AFG) **[41426]**

Ariel (Sindh, PAK) *Unable to locate*

Aries (Leiden, NLD) **[48652]**

ARIPO Quarterly Journal (Harare, ZWE) *Unable to locate*

Arise (Kampala, UGA) *Unable to locate*

Ark File (Edinburgh, GBR) *Unable to locate*

Arkhangelsk (Arkhangelsk, RUS) *Unable to locate*

Arkhangelsk (Arkhangelsk, RUS) *Unable to locate*

Arkhangelsk (Arkhangelsk, RUS) *Unable to locate*

Arkitekten (Stockholm, SWE) *Unable to locate*

Arkiv for Matematik (Djursholm, SWE) **[50952]**

Arkiv Samhalle och Forskning (Stockholm, SWE) **[51009]**

Arkkitehti/Finnish Architectural Review (Helsinki, FIN) **[43818]**

ARL-FM - 90.0 (Langon, FRA) **[43962]**

ARL-FM - 98.1 (Langon, FRA) **[43961]**

Armada International (Zurich, SWI) **[51253]**

Arman-FM - 98.1 (Kabul, AFG) **[41427]**

Armenisch-Deutsche Korrespondenz (Regensburg, GER) **[44642]**

Armley & Wortley Advertiser (Ilkley, GBR) **[53643]**

Armonia (Gerakas, GRC) *Unable to locate*

Armourer (Congleton, GBR) **[53059]**

Arms & Armour (London, GBR) **[53964]**

Army Families Federation Families Journal (Pewsey, GBR) **[56269]**

Army Families Journal **[56269]***

Army Magazine (Canberra, AC, AUS) *Unable to locate*

Army Wives Journal **[56269]***

ARN Al Arabiya Info-FM - 99.0 (Dubai, UAE) **[51659]**

ARN Al Khaleejia Info-FM - 100.9 (Dubai, UAE) **[51660]**

ARN Awaaz-FM **[51670]***

ARN City Info-FM - 101.6 (Dubai, UAE) **[51661]**

ARN Eye-FM - 103.8 (Dubai, UAE) **[51662]**

ARN-FM - 96.7 (Dubai, SAU) **[50055]**

ARN-FM - 100.9 (Dubai, UAE) **[51664]**

ARN-FM - 92 (Dubai, UAE) **[51663]**

ARN-FM (Dubai, UAE) *Unable to locate*

ARN Noor Dubai-FM - 93.9 (Dubai, UAE) **[51665]**

Arnhem-FM - 87.8 (Hilversum, NLD) **[48634]**

Arogya (Manipal, KA, IND) *Unable to locate*

Aromatherapy World (Hinckley, GBR) *Unable to locate*

Arpan Weekly (Kathmandu, NPL) *Unable to locate*

Arquitectura y Diseno (Barcelona, SPA) **[50650]**

Arquitectura Viva (Madrid, SPA) **[50729]**

Arquivo Brasileiro de Medicina Veterinaria e Zootecnia (Vicosa, MI, BRZ) **[43055]**

Arquivos Brasileiros de Cardiologia (Vila Olimpia, SP, BRZ) **[43067]**

Arquivos Brasileiros de Endocrinologia & Metabologia (Sao Paulo, SP, BRZ) **[43022]**

Arquivos Brasileiros de Oftalmologia (Sao Paulo, SP, BRZ) **[43023]**

Arquivos de Neuro-Psiquiatria (Sao Paulo, SP, BRZ) **[43024]**

Arran Banner (Isle of Arran, GBR) **[53661]**

Arran Voice (Brodick, GBR) *Ceased*

Arrow-FM - 92.7 (Masterton, NZL) **[48938]**

Arrow-FM - 107.8 (Hastings, GBR) **[53537]**

Arroword Selection (Redhill, GBR) **[56342]**

Arrowwords (London, GBR) **[53965]**

Ars Disputandi (Utrecht, NLD) **[48755]**

Ars Medici (Neuhausen, SWI) **[51216]**

ARS Medicina (Sofia, BUL) *Unable to locate*

Art & Artists **[56742]***

ART AsiaPacific (Saint Leonards, NW, AUS) *Unable to locate*

The Art Book (London, GBR) *Unable to locate*

Art Business Today (London, GBR) **[53966]**

Art, Design & Communication in Higher Education (London, GBR) **[53967]**

Art History (London, GBR) *Unable to locate*

Art History (Oxford, GBR) **[55874]**

Numbers cited in bold after listings are entry numbers rather than page numbers.

Art Libraries Journal (Bromsgrove, GBR) *Unable to locate*

Art and Life (Varanasi, UP, IND) *Unable to locate*

Art Monthly (London, GBR) **[53968]**

Art and Poetry Today (New Delhi, DH, IND) *Unable to locate*

Art Review (London, GBR) **[53969]**

Arte y Joya (Barcelona, SPA) *Unable to locate*

Arte y Parte (Santander, SPA) **[50830]**

Arterial Hypertension (Gdansk, POL) **[49655]**

Artha Suchi (New Delhi, DH, IND) **[45484]**

Artha Vijnana (Pune, MH, IND) *Unable to locate*

Artha Vijnana Reprint Series (Pune, MH, IND) *Unable to locate*

Arthaniti (Calcutta, WB, IND) *Unable to locate*

Arthropod Structure & Development (Seewiesen, GER) **[44655]**

Articulate (London, GBR) *Unable to locate*

Artifact (Abingdon, GBR) *Ceased*

Artifara (Alessandria, ITA) **[46116]**

Artificial Intelligence (Leeds, GBR) **[53754]**

Artificial Life and Robotics (Oita, JPN) **[46590]**

Artificial Satellites (Warsaw, POL) **[49693]**

The Artisan (Stoke-on-Trent, GBR) **[56628]**

The Artist (Tenterden, GBR) **[56742]**

Artist Blacksmith (Balfron, GBR) **[52155]**

ArtNexus (Bogota, COL) **[43542]**

The Arts (Singapore, SGP) *Unable to locate*

Arts en Apotheker (Amsterdam, NLD) *Unable to locate*

Arts of Asia (Hong Kong, CHN) **[43267]**

Artslink (Hong Kong, CHN) **[43268]**

ArtSound-FM - 92.7 (Manuka, AC, AUS) **[42034]**

Artthrob (Pretoria, SAF) **[50585]**

ArtWork (Ellon, GBR) **[53330]**

Aruba Holiday! (Curacao, NAT) *Unable to locate*

Arut Perum Jothi (Chennai, TN, IND) *Unable to locate*

Arxus de Miscel-lania Zoologica (Barcelona, SPA) **[50651]**

Arzt & Praxis (Neuhausen, SWI) *Ceased*

ASA News (London, GBR) *Unable to locate*

Asahi Camera (Tokyo, JPN) *Unable to locate*

Asahi Evening News (Tokyo, JPN) *Unable to locate*

Asahi Shimbun/Asahi Evening News (Tokyo, JPN) *Unable to locate*

Aschkenas (Berlin, GER) **[44157]**

ASDA Magazine (Leeds, GBR) **[53755]**

ASEAN Economic Bulletin (Pasir Panjang, SGP) **[50098]**

ASEKO Journal (Obinsk, RUS) *Unable to locate*

ASGARD (Glasgow, GBR) *Unable to locate*

Asharq Al-Awsat (London, GBR) **[53970]**

Ashlar (Edinburgh, GBR) **[53253]**

ASI Journal (Chippenham, GBR) *Ceased*

Asia - Africa World Trade Register (New Delhi, DH, IND) *Unable to locate*

Asia Asset Management (Hong Kong, CHN) **[43269]**

Asia Electronics Industry (Tokyo, JPN) **[46753]**

Asia Europe Journal (Singapore, SGP) **[50104]**

Asia-Inc (Singapore, SGP) *Unable to locate*

Asia Journal of Theology (Manila, PHL) *Unable to locate*

Asia Law and Practice (Hong Kong, CHN) **[43270]**

Asia Life Sciences (Laguna, PHL) *Unable to locate*

Asia-Pacific Airports (Twickenham, GBR) **[56788]**

Asia-Pacific Aviation and Engineering Journal (Singapore, SGP) *Unable to locate*

Asia Pacific Coatings Journal (London, GBR) **[53971]**

Asia Pacific Development Journal (Bangkok, THA) **[51410]**

Asia Pacific Disability Rehabilitation Journal (Bangalore, KA, IND) **[44949]**

Asia Pacific; Drinks Buyer - **[56236]***

Asia-Pacific Information Technology Times (Singapore, SGP) *Unable to locate*

Asia-Pacific Journal of Chemical Engineering (Perth, WA, AUS) **[42243]**

Asia-Pacific Journal of Clinical Oncology (Oxford, GBR) **[55875]**

Asia-Pacific Journal of Education (Singapore, SGP) *Unable to locate*

Asia Pacific Journal of Education (Abingdon, GBR) **[51706]**

Asia Pacific Journal of Human Resources (Mulgrave, VI, AUS) *Unable to locate*

Asia Pacific Journal of Marketing and Logistics (Perth, WA, AUS) **[42244]**

Asia-Pacific Journal of Molecular Biology & Biotechnology (Serdang, MYS) **[47714]**

Asia-Pacific Journal of Rural Development (Dhaka, BGD) **[42802]**

Asia Pacific Journal of Tourism Research (Busan, KOR) **[47209]**

Asia-Pacific Military Balance (Kuala Lumpur, MYS) **[47597]**

Asia-Pacific Population Journal (Bangkok, THA) **[51411]**

Asia-Pacific Purchasing & Materials Management (Vienna, AUT) *Ceased*

Asia Pacific Rail (Epsom, GBR) *Unable to locate*

Asia Pacific Review (Tokyo, JPN) **[46754]**

Asia-Pacific Rural Finance (Bangkok, THA) *Unable to locate*

Asia Pacific Satellite (Sutton, GBR) *Unable to locate*

Asia Pacific Tech Monitor (New Delhi, DH, IND) **[45485]**

Asia-Pacific Tropical Homes (Bangkok, THA) **[51412]**

Asia Risk (London, GBR) **[53972]**

Asia Textile & Apparel Journal (Hong Kong, CHN) **[43271]**

The Asia Water (Singapore, SGP) *Unable to locate*

AsiaInfo Journal (Bendigo, VI, AUS) *Unable to locate*

Asiamoney (Hong Kong, CHN) **[43272]**

Asian Affairs (Hong Kong, CHN) **[43273]**

Asian Affairs (London, GBR) **[53973]**

The Asian Age (Bangalore, KA, IND) **[44950]**

The Asian Age (Kolkata, WB, IND) **[45259]**

The Asian Age (Mumbai, MH, IND) **[45352]**

The Asian Age (New Delhi, DH, IND) **[45486]**

Asian Air Transport (Taipei, TWN) **[51331]**

Asian Airlines & Aerospace (Singapore, SGP) **[50105]**

Asian Anthropology (Hong Kong, CHN) **[43274]**

Asian Archives of Anaesthesiology and Resuscitation (New Delhi, DH, IND) *Unable to locate*

Asian Art (London, GBR) **[53974]**

Asian-Australasian Journal of Animal Sciences (Seoul, KOR) **[47254]**

Asian Banking Digest (Makati City, PHL) *Unable to locate*

Asian Bride (Chessington, GBR) **[52988]**

Asian Business (Hong Kong) (Hong Kong, CHN) *Unable to locate*

Asian Business & Management (Basingstoke, GBR) **[52194]**

Asian Case Research Journal (Singapore, SGP) **[50106]**

Asian Church Today (Hyderabad, AP, IND) *Unable to locate*

Asian Communications (Sutton, GBR) *Unable to locate*

Asian Community and Science Policy (Dehradun, UP, IND) *Unable to locate*

Asian Credit Investor (Hong Kong, CHN) **[43275]**

Asian Cultural Studies (Tokyo, JPN) *Unable to locate*

Asian Culture (Singapore, SGP) *Unable to locate*

Asian Defence and Diplomacy (Singapore, SGP) **[50107]**

Asian Defence Journal (Kuala Lumpur, MYS) **[47598]**

Asian Development Review (Manila, PHL) **[49547]**

Asian Diver (Singapore, SGP) **[50108]**

Asian Economic Review (Hyderabad, AP, IND) *Unable to locate*

Asian Economic and Social Review (Mumbai, MH, IND) *Unable to locate*

Asian Enterprise (New Delhi, DH, IND) *Unable to locate*

Asian Environment (Makati, PHL) *Unable to locate*

Asian Environmental Technology (Saint Albans, GBR) **[56434]**

Asian Ethnology (Nagoya, JPN) **[46551]**

Asian Exchange (Seoul, KOR) **[47255]**

Asian Express (Almaty, KAZ) *Unable to locate*

Asian Financial Law Briefing (Hong Kong, CHN) *Unable to locate*

Asian Fisheries Science (Quezon City, PHL) **[49581]**

Asian Folklore Studies **[46551]***

Asian Furniture (Singapore, SGP) **[50109]**

Asian Groom & Man (Chessington, GBR) **[52989]**

Asian Home Gourmet (Singapore, SGP) **[50110]**

Asian International Arbitration Journal (The Hague, NLD) **[48607]**

Asian IP (Hong Kong, CHN) *Unable to locate*

Asian Journal of Aesthetic Dentistry (Singapore, SGP) *Unable to locate*

Asian Journal of Andrology (London, GBR) **[53975]**

Asian Journal of Cell Biology (Faisalabad, PAK) **[49235]**

Asian Journal of Chemistry (Ghaziabad, UP, IND) **[45121]**

Asian Journal of Communication (Singapore, SGP) **[50111]**

Asian Journal of Control (Taipei, TWN) **[51332]**

Asian Journal of English Language Teaching (Hong Kong, CHN) **[43276]**

Asian Journal of Information Technology (Faisalabad, PAK) **[49236]**

Asian Journal of Mathematics (Hong Kong, CHN) **[43277]**

Asian Journal of Microbiology, Biotechnology and Environmental Sciences (Aligarh, UP, IND) *Unable to locate*

Asian Journal of Oral and Maxillofacial Surgery (Yokohama, JPN) *Unable to locate*

Asian Journal of Pentecostal Studies (Baguio City, PHL) **[49450]**

Asian Journal of Pharmaceutics (Mandsaur, MP, IND) **[45338]**

Asian Journal of Physical Education & Recreation (Hong Kong, CHN) **[43278]**

Asian Journal of Physics (Ghaziabad, UP, IND) *Unable to locate*

Asian Journal of Plant Science (Secunderabad, AP, IND) *Unable to locate*

Asian Journal of Plant Sciences (Faisalabad, PAK) **[49237]**

Asian Journal of Psychology and Education (Agra, UP, IND) *Unable to locate*

Asian Journal of Social Science (Leiden, NLD) **[48653]**

Asian Journal of Surgery (Hong Kong, CHN) **[43279]**

Asian Journal of Transfusion Science (Kolkata, GJ, IND) **[45258]**

Asian Journal of Water, Environment and Pollution (Amsterdam, NLD) **[47899]**

Asian Journal of Women's Studies (Seoul, KOR) **[47256]**

Asian Leader (Rochdale, GBR) **[56401]**

Asian Literary Market Review (Kottayam, KE, IND) *Unable to locate*

The Asian Manager (Makati, PHL) *Unable to locate*

Asian Medicine (Leiden, NLD) **[48654]**

Asian Migrant (Quezon City, PHL) **[49582]**

Asian Migration News (Quezon City, PHL) **[49583]**

Asian Oil and Gas (Tokyo, JPN) *Unable to locate*

Asian-Pacific Book Development (Tokyo, JPN) **[46755]**

Asian Pacific Culture Quarterly (Taipei, TWN) *Unable to locate*

Asian Pacific Journal of Allergy and Immunology (Bangkok, THA) *Unable to locate*

Asian Pacific Journal of Social Work and Development (Singapore, SGP) *Unable to locate*

Asian and Pacific Labour (Singapore, SGP) *Unable to locate*

Asian and Pacific Migration Journal (Quezon City, PHL) **[49584]**

Asian-Pacific Newsletter (Helsinki, FIN) **[43819]**

Asian Perspective (Seoul, KOR) **[47257]**

Master Index

Numbers cited in bold after listings are entry numbers rather than page numbers.

Asian Philosophy (Abingdon, GBR) [51707]

Asian Population Studies (Abingdon, GBR) [51708]

Asian Printer (Singapore, SGP) Unable to locate

Asian Recorder (Mumbai, MH, IND) Unable to locate

Asian Research Trends (Tokyo, JPN) Unable to locate

Asian Review of Accounting (Melbourne, VI, AUS) [42047]

Asian Review of Business and Technology (London, GBR) Ceased

Asian Review of Public Administration (Quezon City, PHL) [49585]

Asian Science Bulletin (Faisalabad, PAK) Unable to locate

Asian Security Review (Singapore City, SGP) [50311]

Asian Sound Radio-AM - 963 (Manchester, GBR) [55582]

Asian Sound Radio-AM - 1377 (Manchester, GBR) [55583]

Asian Sources Computer Products [50126]*

Asian Sources Electronic Components [50143]*

Asian Sources Gifts & Home Products (Phoenix, AZ, USA) Ceased

Asian Sources Multimedia Products [50126]*

Asian Sources Security Products (Singapore, SGP) Unable to locate

Asian Student News (Hong Kong, CHN) Unable to locate

Asian Studies Review (Canberra, AC, AUS) [41699]

The Asian Studies WWW Monitor (Canberra, AC, AUS) Unable to locate

Asian Timber (Singapore, SGP) Unable to locate

Asian Times (London, GBR) Unable to locate

Asian Venture Capital Journal (Hong Kong, CHN) [43280]

Asian Woman (Chessington, GBR) [52990]

AsiaWeek (Makati City, PHL) Ceased

Aside (Chennai, TN, IND) Unable to locate

Asklepios (Sofia, BUL) Unable to locate

Aslib Proceedings (London, GBR) [53976]

Aspen-FM - 103.5 (Punta del Este, URY) [57012]

Asphalt (Bonn, GER) Unable to locate

Aspinalls (London, GBR) [53977]

Assam Academy Review (Guwahati, AS, IND) Unable to locate

Assam Economic Journal (Dibrugarh, AS, IND) Unable to locate

Assam Information (Mumbai, MH, IND) Unable to locate

Assam Tribune (Guwahati, AS, IND) [45129]

Assayad (Beirut, LBN) [47393]

Assembly Automation (Ilkley, GBR) [53644]

Asset (Sydney, NW, AUS) [42449]

Asset (New Delhi, DH, IND) Ceased

The Asset (Hong Kong, CHN) [43281]

Assistive Technologies (Barnsley, GBR) [52177]

Asso Cham Bulletin (New Delhi, DH, IND) [45487]

Asso Cham News & Views (New Delhi, DH, IND) [45488]

Association of Engineers, India Journal (Calcutta, WB, IND) Unable to locate

Association of Engineers, Kerala PWD News Letter (Trivandrum, KE, IND) Unable to locate

Association Executive (Essex, GBR) Unable to locate

Association of Exploration Geophysicists Journal (New Delhi, DH, IND) Unable to locate

Association Magazine (Beverley, GBR) [52319]

Association of Medical Women in India Journal (Mumbai, MH, IND) Unable to locate

Association of Scientific Workers of India Bulletin (New Delhi, DH, IND) Unable to locate

Asthetische Chirurgrie (Berlin, GER) Ceased

ASTIN Bulletin (Edinburgh, GBR) [53254]

Astra & Orama (Gerakas, GRC) Unable to locate

Astragalo (Madrid, SPA) Unable to locate

Astrolab (Limoges, FRA) Unable to locate

Astrological Journal (London, GBR) [53978]

The Astrological Magazine (Bangalore, KA, IND) Ceased

Astrology and Athrishta (Chennai, TN, IND) Unable to locate

Astronautyka (Warsaw, POL) Unable to locate

Astronomical and Astrophysical Transactions (Moscow, RUS) [49876]

Astronomical Ephemeris of Geocentric Places of Planets (Ujjain, MP, IND) Unable to locate

Astronomical Society of India Bulletin (Bangalore, KA, IND) Unable to locate

Astronomische Nachrichten (Potsdam, GER) [44638]

Astronomisk Tidskrift [51030]*

Astronomy & Astrophysics (Paris, FRA) [44027]

Astronomy and Astrophysics Review (Tokyo, JPN) [46756]

Astronomy and Geophysics (Leeds, GBR) [53756]

Astronomy Letters (Moscow, RUS) [49877]

Astronomy Reports (Moscow, RUS) [49878]

Astronomy and Space Magazine (Dublin, DU, IRL) [45946]

Astrophysical Journal Supplement Series (Bristol, GBR) [52640]

Astrophysics and Space Sciences Transactions (Gottingen, GER) [44392]

Asymptotic Analysis (Toulouse, FRA) [44119]

a+t (Vitoria-Gasteiz, SPA) [50849]

At the Interface/Probing the Boundaries (Freeland, GBR) [53399]

AT Magazine (London, GBR) [53979]

At the Sign Of (Wolverhampton, GBR) [56951]

Atelier Rundschau (Moscow, RUS) [49879]

Athletic Turf Maintenance and Technology (Chester, GBR) Unable to locate

Athofu (Reykjavik, ICE) Unable to locate

A3V-FM - 89.1 (Nuku'alofa, TGA) [51465]

ATIC Magazine (Lisbon, PRT) Unable to locate

Atlantic-FM - 107 (Saint Agnes, GBR) [56431]

Atlantic-FM - 105.1 (Saint Agnes, GBR) [56432]

Atlantic Perspective (The Hague, NLD) Unable to locate

Atlantic Seabird (Portlethen, GBR) Ceased

Atlantica (Reykjavik, ICE) [44897]

Atlantica Internacional (Las Palmas de Gran Canaria, SPA) [50720]

Atlantico Sul-FM - 105.7 (Fortaleza, CE, BRZ) [42979]

Atlantis-FM - 101.7 (Macher, SPA) [50721]

L'Atlas des Regions des Echos (Paris, FRA) Unable to locate

ATLETIK'en (Brondby, DEN) Unable to locate

Atletismo Espanol (Madrid, SPA) [50730]

Atmospheric Environment (Norwich, GBR) [55723]

Atmospheric Science Letters (Exeter, GBR) [53347]

ATO Bulletin of Information (Libreville, GAB) Unable to locate

Atom Indonesia (Jakarta, IDN) Unable to locate

Atomic Data and Nuclear Data Tables (Amsterdam, NLD) [47900]

Atomic Maximum Power Computing (Australia) Magazine (McMahons Point, NW, AUS) [42042]

Atoms in Japan (Tokyo, JPN) [46757]

Atoms for Peace (Paris, FRA) [44028]

ATPAS (Walsall, GBR) Unable to locate

Atra Mirada (San Jose, CRI) Unable to locate

Atrium (Budapest, HUN) [44824]

Atrium, SAAT News [53979]*

Attractions Management (Hitchin, GBR) [53576]

Attualita Italia-Australia (Rome, ITA) [46222]

ATVC Revista tu Cable (Buenos Aires, ARG) Unable to locate

Auburn Review Pictorial (Condell Park, NW, AUS) [41801]

Auckland Today (Christchurch, NZL) [48862]

Auckland University Law Review (Auckland, NZL) [48785]

Audi Driver (Westoning, GBR) [56907]

Audience (London, GBR) [53980]

Augmentative & Alternative Communication (Abingdon, GBR) [51709]

Aula (Barcelona, SPA) [50652]

Aunt Webby (Singapore, SGP) Unable to locate

Aurealis (Mount Waverley, VI, AUS) Unable to locate

Aurora (Karachi, PAK) [49339]

The AUSIMM Bulletin (Carlton, VI, AUS) [41724]

AusSport (Port Macquarie, NW, AUS) [42260]

Austral Ecology (Adelaide, SA, AUS) [41501]

Australasian Beekeeper (Maitland, NW, AUS) [42028]

Australasian Biotechnology (Brighton, VI, AUS) Unable to locate

Australasian Chiropractic & Osteopathy [42136]*

Australasian Dispute Resolution Journal (Pyrmont, NW, AUS) [42270]

Australasian Emergency Nursing Journal (Burwood, NW, AUS) [41675]

Australasian Epidemiologist (Hobart, TA, AUS) [41957]

Australasian Farmers' Dealers' Journal (AFDJ) (East Brighton, VI, AUS) [41844]

Australasian Flowers (Tullamarine, VI, AUS) [42646]

Australasian Journal on Ageing (South Melbourne, VI, AUS) [42367]

Australasian Journal of Disaster and Trauma Studies (Palmerston North, NZL) [48962]

Australasian Journal of Educational Technology (Dickson, AC, AUS) [41840]

Australasian Journal of Philosophy (Abingdon, GBR) [51710]

Australasian Journal of Special Education (Bowen Hills, QL, AUS) [41623]

Australasian Journal of Victorian Studies (Crawley, WA, AUS) [41819]

Australasian Marketing Journal (Sydney, NW, AUS) Unable to locate

Australasian Paint & Panel (Surry Hills, NW, AUS) [42408]

Australasian Plant Disease Notes (Collingwood, VI, AUS) [41781]

Australasian Plant Pathology (Perth, WA, AUS) [42245]

Australasian Public Libraries and Information Services (Adelaide, SA, AUS) [41502]

Australasian Sound Archive (Hepburn Springs, VI, AUS) [41952]

Australasian Sporting Shooter (Surry Hills, NW, AUS) [42409]

Australasian Victorian Studies Journal [41819]*

Australia Drama Education Magazine (City East, QL, AUS) Ceased

Australia Magazine (Surry Hills, NW, AUS) Unable to locate

Australia and New Zealand Health Policy (London, GBR) Ceased

Australia and New Zealand Journal of Developmental Disabilities [42008]*

Australia & Pacific Islands Letter (Calcutta, WB, IND) Unable to locate

Australia Tibet Council News (Darlinghurst, NW, AUS) Unable to locate

Australian (Sydney, NW, AUS) [42450]

Australian Aboriginal Studies (Canberra, AC, AUS) [41700]

Australian Academic & Research Libraries (Kingston, AC, AUS) [41990]

Australian Accountant (Southbank, VI, AUS) Unable to locate

Australian Aeronautics (Mascot, NW, AUS) [42041]

Australian AG Contractor and Large Scale Farmer (Christchurch, NZL) [48863]

Australian Archaeology (Townsville, QL, AUS) [42634]

Australian Auto Action (Sydney, NW, AUS) [42451]

Australian Baking Business (Nundah, QL, AUS) [42219]

Australian Banking & Finance (North Sydney, NW, AUS) [42206]

Australian Bar Review (North Ryde, NW, AUS) Unable to locate

Australian Beading (North Ryde, NW, AUS) [42166]

Numbers cited in bold after listings are entry numbers rather than page numbers.

Australian Biologist (Syndal, VI, AUS) [42610]

The Australian Bird Watcher [42218]*

Australian Birdkeeper Magazine (Tweed Heads, NW, AUS) [42655]

Australian Building News (Surry Hills, NW, AUS) Unable to locate

Australian Business Law Review (Pyrmont, NW, AUS) [42271]

Australian Catholics (Richmond, VI, AUS) [42301]

The Australian Christian (Melbourne, VI, AUS) [42048]

Australian Citrus News (Mildura, VI, AUS) [42106]

Australian Classic Car Monthly (Strawberry Hills, NW, AUS) [42394]

Australian Cotton Outlook (Too-woomba, QL, AUS) [42625]

Australian Country Collections (North Ryde, NW, AUS) [42167]

Australian Country Craft and Decorating (Silverwater, NW, AUS) [42359]

Australian Country Style (Alexandria, NW, AUS) [41534]

Australian Country Threads (Silver-water, NW, AUS) [42360]

Australian CPA [42064]*

Australian Creative (Surry Hills, NW, AUS) [42410]

Australian Cultural History (Geelong, VI, AUS) Unable to locate

Australian Cyclist (Civic Square, AC, AUS) [41753]

Australian Dairyfarmer (Tullamarine, VI, AUS) [42647]

Australian Defence Magazine (Surry Hills, NW, AUS) [42411]

Australian Dental Journal (Saint Leonards, NW, AUS) [42330]

Australian Dirt Bike Magazine (Sydney, NW, AUS) [42452]

Australian Doctor (Chatswood, NW, AUS) [41736]

Australian Doctor Weekly [41736]*

Australian Economic History Review (Adelaide, SA, AUS) [41503]

Australian Economic Review (Oxford, GBR) [55876]

Australian Educational Computing (Belconnen, AC, AUS) Unable to locate

The Australian Educational Leader (Penrith, NW, AUS) [42239]

Australian Educator (Parkside, SA, AUS) [42230]

Australian Ejournal of Theology (Banyo, QL, AUS) [41575]

Australian Endodontic Journal (Oxford, GBR) [55877]

Australian Family Tree Connections (Gosford, NW, AUS) [41904]

Australian Farm Journal (North Richmond, NW, AUS) [42160]

Australian Feminist Studies (Abingdon, GBR) [51711]

Australian Field Ornithology (Nunawading, VI, AUS) [42218]

Australian Financial Review (Sydney, NW, AUS) Unable to locate

Australian Flying (Surry Hills, NW, AUS) [42412]

Australian Folklore (Armidale, NW, AUS) [41558]

Australian Garden History (Melbourne, VI, AUS) [42049]

Australian Geographer (Abingdon, GBR) [51712]

Australian Geographic (Terrey Hills, NW, AUS) Unable to locate

Australian Geographic Outdoor (Sydney, NW, AUS) [42453]

Australian Geographical Studies [42251]*

Australian Giftguide (Pyrmont, NW, AUS) [42272]

Australian Gliding (Adelaide, SA, AUS) Unable to locate

Australian Golf Digest (Alexandria, NW, AUS) [41535]

Australian Good Taste (Alexandria, NW, AUS) [41536]

Australian Gourmet Traveller (Sydney, NW, AUS) [42454]

Australian Health Review (Strawberry Hills, NW, AUS) [42395]

Australian Historical Studies (Abingdon, GBR) [51713]

The Australian Holstein Journal (Hawthorn, VI, AUS) [41941]

Australian Horticulture (Tullamarine, VI, AUS) [42648]

Australian Hotelier (Pyrmont, NW, AUS) [42273]

Australian House & Garden (Sydney, NW, AUS) [42455]

Australian Indigenous HealthBulletin (Perth, WA, AUS) [42246]

Australian Industry Group (North Sydney, NW, AUS) Unable to locate

Australian Innovation Magazine (Canberra, AC, AUS) Ceased

Australian Insolvency Journal (Sydney, NW, AUS) [42456]

Australian Insurance Institute Journal [42052]*

Australian Journal of Advanced Nursing (AJAN) (Kingston, AC, AUS) [41991]

Australian Journal of Agricultural Research [41784]*

The Australian Journal of Agricultural and Resource Economics (Oxford, GBR) [55878]

The Australian Journal of Anthropology (Sydney, NW, AUS) Unable to locate

Australian Journal of Basic and Applied Sciences (Faisalabad, PAK) [49238]

Australian Journal of Career Development (Camberwell, VI, AUS) [41693]

Australian Journal of Chemistry (Collingwood, VI, AUS) [41782]

The Australian Journal of Comedy (Oakleigh, VI, AUS) Unable to locate

Australian Journal of Construction Economics and Building (Canberra, AC, AUS) [41701]

Australian Journal of Early Childhood (Watson, AC, AUS) [42690]

Australian Journal of Earth Sciences (Sydney, NW, AUS) [42457]

Australian Journal of Ecology [41501]*

Australian Journal of Education (Camberwell, VI, AUS) [41694]

Australian Journal of Educational & Developmental Psychology (Callaghan, NW, AUS) [41690]

Australian Journal of Educational Technology [41840]*

Australian Journal of Emergency Management (Mount Macedon, VI, AUS) [42133]

Australian Journal of Environmental Management (North Ryde, NW, AUS) Unable to locate

Australian Journal of Experimental Agriculture [41780]*

Australian Journal of Family Law (North Ryde, NW, AUS) Unable to locate

Australian Journal of Forensic Sciences (Surry Hills, NW, AUS) [42413]

Australian Journal of Guidance and Counselling (Brisbane, QL, AUS) [41640]

Australian Journal of Holistic Nursing (East Lismore, NW, AUS) Unable to locate

Australian Journal of International Affairs (Abingdon, GBR) [51714]

Australian Journal of Irish Studies (Galway, GL, IRL) [46016]

Australian Journal of Jewish Studies (Sydney, NW, AUS) [42458]

Australian Journal of Labour Law (North Ryde, NW, AUS) Unable to locate

Australian Journal of Language and Literacy (Norwood, SA, AUS) [42214]

Australian Journal of Law and Society (Sydney, NW, AUS) Unable to locate

Australian Journal of Legal Philosophy (Canberra, AC, AUS) Unable to locate

Australian Journal of Management (Sydney, NW, AUS) [42459]

Australian Journal of Management & Organisational Behaviour [42626]*

Australian Journal of Mathematical Analysis and Applications (Melbourne, VI, AUS) [42050]

Australian Journal of Medical Science (Toowong, QL, AUS) Unable to locate

Australian Journal of Music Therapy (Turramurra, NW, AUS) Unable to locate

Australian Journal of Nutrition and Dietetics [41837]*

Australian Journal of Organisational Behavior & Management (Toowoomba, QL, AUS) [42626]

Australian Journal of Pharmacy (Chatswood, NW, AUS) [41737]

Australian Journal of Physics (Collingwood, VI, AUS) Ceased

Australian Journal of Physiotherapy (Camberwell, VI, AUS) [41695]

Australian Journal of Plant Physiology [41789]*

Australian Journal of Political Science (Abingdon, GBR) [51715]

The Australian Journal of Politics and History (Saint Lucia, QL, AUS) [42338]

Australian Journal of Public Administration (Melbourne, VI, AUS) [42051]

Australian Journal of Reading [42214]*

The Australian Journal of Rehabilitation Counselling (Bowen Hills, QL, AUS) [41624]

Australian Journal of Social Issues (Redfern, NW, AUS) Unable to locate

The Australian Journal of Statistics and The New Zealand Statistician [49000]*

Australian Journal of Zoology (Collingwood, VI, AUS) [41783]

Australian Landcare (Tullamarine, VI, AUS) [42649]

Australian Law Journal (Pyrmont, NW, AUS) [42274]

Australian Law Management Journal (Canberra, AC, AUS) [41702]

Australian Legal Practice [41702]*

Australian Legal Practice Management Journal [41702]*

The Australian Library Journal (Geelong, VI, AUS) [41878]

Australian Literary Studies (Saint Lucia, QL, AUS) [42339]

Australian Longwall Magazine (Leederville, WA, AUS) [42004]

Australian Mammalogy (North Ryde, NW, AUS) Unable to locate

The Australian Marxist Review (Surry Hills, NW, AUS) [42414]

The Australian Mathematical Society Gazette (Toowoomba, QL, AUS) [42627]

Australian Mathematics Teacher (AMT) (Stepney, SA, AUS) [42387]

The Australian Meat News (Hawthorn, VI, AUS) Unable to locate

Australian Medicine (Barton, AC, AUS) [41576]

Australian Model Engineering (Higgins, AC, AUS) [41954]

Australian Motorcycle News (Sydney, NW, AUS) [42460]

Australian Mountain Bike (Sydney, NW, AUS) [42461]

Australian National Security Magazine (Surry Hills, NW, AUS) [42415]

Australian NetGuide (Sydney, NW, AUS) [42462]

Australian & New Zealand Industry Defence Equipment Capability Catalogue (Melbourne, VI, AUS) Unable to locate

Australian and New Zealand Institute of Insurance and Finance Journal (Melbourne, VI, AUS) [42052]

Australian and New Zealand Journal of Audiology (Chatswood, NW, AUS) [41738]

Australian and New Zealand Journal of Criminology (Clayton, VI, AUS) [41757]

Australian and New Zealand Journal of Family Therapy (Westleigh, NW, AUS) [42699]

Australian & New Zealand Journal of Psychiatry (Abingdon, GBR) [51716]

Australian and New Zealand Journal of Public Health (Curtin, AC, AUS) [41826]

Australian & New Zealand Journal of Statistics (Palmerston North, NZL) [48963]

Australian and New Zealand Journal of Statistics (Wellington, NZL) [49000]

Australian and New Zealand Property Journal (Deakin, AC, AUS) [41833]

The Australian & New Zealand Wine Industry Journal (Prospect East, SA, AUS) [42267]

Australian Nursing Journal (ANJ) (Kingston, AC, AUS) [41992]

Australian & NZ Snowboarding (Sydney, NW, AUS) [42463]

Australian Occupational Therapy Journal (Richmond, VI, AUS) [42302]

Australian Options (Goodwood, SA, AUS) [41903]

Australian Organic Journal (Chermside, QL, AUS) [41750]

The Australian Orienteer (Warrandyte, VI, AUS) [42686]

Australian Outlook [51714]*

Australian Parents (Alexandria, NW, AUS) [41537]

Australian PC User (Sydney, NW, AUS) [42244]

Australian PC World (North Sydney, NW, AUS) [42207]

Numbers cited in bold after listings are entry numbers rather than page numbers.

Australian Penthouse (Saint Leonards, NW, AUS) **[42331]**

Australian Personal Computer (Sydney, NW, AUS) **[42465]**

Australian Pharmacist (Deakin, AC, AUS) **[41834]**

Australian Photography (Surry Hills, NW, AUS) **[42416]**

Australian Physics (Port Melbourne, VI, AUS) **[42262]**

Australian Pipeliner (Barton, AC, AUS) **[41577]**

Australian Playwrights (Bundoora, VI, AUS) **[41669]**

Australian Power Boat (Surry Hills, NW, AUS) **[42417]**

Australian Preschool Quarterly **[42690]***

Australian Prescriber (Deakin, AC, AUS) **[41835]**

Australian Primary Mathematics Classroom (APMC) (Stepney, SA, AUS) **[42388]**

Australian Professional Hairdresser (Nundah, QL, AUS) *Unable to locate*

Australian Property Journal **[41833]***

Australian Religion Studies Review (London, GBR) **[53981]**

Australian Road Rider (North Ryde, NW, AUS) **[42168]**

Australian Sailing (Surry Hills, NW, AUS) **[42418]**

Australian Senior Mathematics Journal (ASMJ) (Stepney, SA, AUS) **[42389]**

Australian Social Work (Kingston, AC, AUS) **[41993]**

Australian Society & Events (North Sydney, NW, AUS) **[42208]**

Australian Stainless Magazine (Brisbane, QL, AUS) **[41641]**

Australian Studies in Journalism (Brisbane, QL, AUS) **[41642]**

Australian Table (Sydney, NW, AUS) **[42466]**

Australian Tax Forum (Sydney, NW, AUS) **[42467]**

Australian Tax Review (North Ryde, NW, AUS) *Unable to locate*

Australian Telecom (North Sydney, NW, AUS) **[42209]**

Australian Tennis Magazine (Melbourne, VI, AUS) **[42053]**

Australian Theological Book Reviewer (Adelaide, SA, AUS) **[41504]**

Australian Trailrider (North Ryde, NW, AUS) **[42169]**

Australian Triathlete (Melbourne, VI, AUS) **[42054]**

Australian T3 (Bondi Junction, NW, AUS) **[41606]**

Australian Universities Review (South Melbourne, VI, AUS) **[42368]**

Australian Veterinary Journal (Sydney, NW, AUS) **[42468]**

Australian Veterinary Practitioner (Saint Leonards, NW, AUS) **[42332]**

Australian Viticulture (Prospect East, SA, AUS) **[42268]**

Australian Voice (South Bank, QL, AUS) **[42364]**

Australian Windows XP (Bondi Junction, NW, AUS) **[41607]**

Australian Women's Book Review (Brisbane, QL, AUS) **[41643]**

The Australian Women's Weekly (Sydney, NW, AUS) **[42469]**

Australian Women's Weekly (Auckland, NZL) **[48786]**

The Australian Woodworker (Hazelbrook, NW, AUS) **[41944]**

Australian Yachting (Surry Hills, NW, AUS) **[42419]**

Australian Yearbook of International Law (Canberra, AC, AUS) *Unable to locate*

Australia's Mining Monthly (Leederville, WA, AUS) **[42005]**

Austrian Economic Quarterly (Vienna, AUT) **[42747]**

Austrian Review of International and European Law (Leiden, NLD) **[48655]**

Austrian Studies (London, GBR) **[53982]**

Author (London, GBR) **[53983]**

Autism (London, GBR) **[53984]**

Auto Age (Kalyani, WB, IND) *Unable to locate*

Auto Bild (Hamburg, GER) **[44410]**

Auto China (Beijing, CHN) **[43170]**

Auto & Design (Turin, ITA) **[46269]**

Auto Express (London, GBR) **[53985]**

Auto Freeway (Manchester, GBR) **[55542]**

Auto Hoje (Car Today) (Cruz Quebrada-Dafundo, PRT) **[49791]**

Auto International (Kuala Lumpur, MYS) *Unable to locate*

Auto Ireland (Dublin, DU, IRL) **[45947]**

Auto Magazin (Hungary) (Budapest, HUN) *Unable to locate*

Auto Monitor (Mumbai, MH, IND) **[45353]**

Auto-Moto Monthly (Warsaw, POL) *Unable to locate*

Auto Motor Klassiek (Ulft, NLD) *Unable to locate*

Auto Motor a Sport (Czech) (Prague, CZE) **[43610]**

Auto & Motortechnick (Schagen, NLD) *Unable to locate*

Auto & Reise (Bad Windsheim, GER) *Unable to locate*

Auto Retro (Fontainebleau, FRA) **[43952]**

Auto Touring (Vienna, AUT) **[42748]**

Auto Trader (London, GBR) **[53986]**

Auto Vending (Smallfield, GBR) **[56561]**

Autocar (Middlesex, GBR) **[55615]**

Autocar (Teddington, GBR) **[56729]**

Autocar Infos (Clichy, FRA) **[43931]**

Autocar & Motor **[56729]***

Autoclub (Buenos Aires, ARG) *Unable to locate*

Autoguide (New Delhi, DH, IND) *Unable to locate*

Autohaus (Ottobrunn, GER) *Unable to locate*

Autokampioen (The Hague, NLD) **[48608]**

Autokoerier (Budel, NLD) *Unable to locate*

Automagazine (Cruz Quebrada-Dafundo, PRT) **[49792]**

Automatic Control and Computer Sciences (Moscow, RUS) **[49880]**

Automatic Documentation and Mathematical Linguistics (Moscow, RUS) **[49881]**

Automation and Remote Control (Moscow, RUS) **[49882]**

Automatizace (Prague, CZE) **[43611]**

Automobile India (New Delhi, DH, IND) *Unable to locate*

Automobile Press Digest (Mumbai, MH, IND) *Unable to locate*

Automobile, Tractor, Scooter Report (Allahabad, UP, IND) *Unable to locate*

Automotive Digest (Peterborough, GBR) *Ceased*

Automotive Electrical & Air Conditioning News (Brisbane, QL, AUS) **[41644]**

Automotive Engineer (London, GBR) **[53987]**

Automotive Logistics (London, GBR) **[53988]**

Automotive Management (London, GBR) *Unable to locate*

Automotive Manufacturing Solutions (London, GBR) **[53989]**

Automotive Production China (London, GBR) **[53990]**

Automotive Technology International (London, GBR) *Unable to locate*

Autonews CC (North Riding, SAF) *Unable to locate*

Autonomic and Autacoid Pharmacology (Cardiff, GBR) **[52924]**

Autonomic Neuroscience (London, GBR) **[53991]**

Autonomous Agents and Multi-Agent Systems (Dordrecht, NLD) **[48329]**

Autopiac (Budapest, HUN) *Unable to locate*

Autopro (Rozzano, ITA) **[46247]**

Autospark (Mumbai, MH, IND) *Unable to locate*

Autosport Magazine (Haywards Heath, GBR) **[53547]**

AutoTecnica (Locate Triulzi, ITA) *Unable to locate*

Autotuning Zubehor Katalog (Schwabach, GER) *Unable to locate*

Autovisie (Amsterdam, NLD) **[47901]**

Autralian & New Zealand Skiing (Sydney, NW, AUS) **[42470]**

AUUGN on the Web (Baulkham Hills, NW, AUS) **[41584]**

AV Magazine (London, GBR) **[53992]**

AV Max (Mumbai, MH, IND) **[45354]**

AV Monografias (Madrid, SPA) **[50731]**

AV State of the Art (Shanghai, CHN) *Unable to locate*

Avant Magazine (Chelmsford, GBR) *Unable to locate*

Avantaje (Bucharest, ROM) **[49831]**

AvD Motor und Reisen (Frankfurt, GER) *Unable to locate*

Ave (Delhi, DH, IND) **[45088]**

L'Avenc (Barcelona, SPA) **[50653]**

Avian Pathology (Newbury, GBR) **[55661]**

Aviation Business Magazine (Surry Hills, NW, AUS) **[42420]**

Aviation Industry Development (London, GBR) *Unable to locate*

Aviation Medicine (New Delhi, DH, IND) *Unable to locate*

Aviation Modeller International (Amersham, GBR) **[52105]**

Aviation & Pilote (Lognes, FRA) *Unable to locate*

Aviation & Space Journal (Mumbai, MH, IND) *Unable to locate*

Aviation Trader (Lismore, NW, AUS) **[42011]**

Aviation and Transport Developments for China (London, GBR) *Unable to locate*

Avicultural Magazine (Wadebridge, GBR) **[56803]**

Aviva (London, GBR) **[53993]**

Avoscene (Tauranga, NZL) **[48980]**

Avotakka (Helsinki, FIN) **[43820]**

Avtoradio (Arkhangelsk, RUS) *Unable to locate*

Avtoradio (Izhevsk, RUS) *Unable to locate*

Avtoradio (Moscow, RUS) *Unable to locate*

Avtoradio (Moscow, RUS) *Unable to locate*

Avtoradio - 90.3 MHz (Moscow, RUS) **[50000]**

Avtoradio (Perm, RUS) *Unable to locate*

Avtoradio (Perm, RUS) *Unable to locate*

Avtoradio (Perm, RUS) *Unable to locate*

Avtoradio (Perm, RUS) *Unable to locate*

Avtoradio (Perm, RUS) *Unable to locate*

Avtoradio (Yekaterinburg, RUS) *Unable to locate*

Avtoradio-AM - 810 KHz (Krasnoyarsk, RUS) **[49863]**

Avtoradio - Bishkek (Bishkek, KGA) *Unable to locate*

Avtoradio-FM (Krasnoyarsk, RUS) *Unable to locate*

Avtoradio - Izhevsk (Izhevsk, RUS) *Unable to locate*

Awa-FM - 91.2 (Whanganui, NZL) **[49049]**

AWA Magazine (Banjul, GMB) *Unable to locate*

Award World (London, GBR) **[53994]**

Aware (Hong Kong, CHN) **[43282]**

Awaz-FM - 107.2 (Glasgow, GBR) **[53460]**

Axis (Tokyo, JPN) **[46758]**

AXIS (London, GBR) **[53995]**

axm (London, GBR) **[53996]**

AYGO Magazine (London, GBR) **[53997]**

Ayton Today (Scarborough, GBR) **[56462]**

Ayu (Jamnagar, GJ, IND) *Unable to locate*

Ayurveda Doot (Jaipur, RJ, IND) *Unable to locate*

Ayurveda Saukhyam Series (New Delhi, DH, IND) *Unable to locate*

The Azeri Times (Baku, AJN) **[42779]**

Azimut (Smederevska Palanka, SER) *Unable to locate*

Azimuth (Chateau Landon, FRA) *Unable to locate*

Azure (Jerusalem, ISR) **[46080]**

B

b-FM - 95 (Auckland, NZL) **[48834]**

B & I Magazine (Petaling Jaya, MYS) **[47695]**

B-ROCK-FM - 99.3 (Bathurst, NW, AUS) **[41580]**

BA 89-FM (Buenos Aires, ARG) *Unable to locate*

Ba Ria - Vung Tau Broadcast - Television Station (Vung Tau City, VNM) *Unable to locate*

Ba Ria - Vung Tau Broadcast - Television Station (Vung Tau City, VNM) *Unable to locate*

Babayevskoye Radio (Babayevo, RUS) *Unable to locate*

Babel (Amsterdam, NLD) **[47902]**

Bac Lieu Broadcast - Television Station (Bac Lieu Town, VNM) *Unable to locate*

Back Office Magazine (London, GBR) *Unable to locate*

Backer und Konditor (Zurich, SWI) *Unable to locate*

Backpacker Essentials (Sydney, NW, AUS) **[42471]**

Backyard Design Ideas (North Ryde, NW, AUS) **[42170]**

Bacon Busters (Surry Hills, NW, AUS) **[42421]**

Badmagasinet (Herlev, DEN) *Unable to locate*

Badminton (Brondby, DEN) **[43651]**

Numbers cited in bold after listings are entry numbers rather than page numbers.

Badminton (Rome, ITA) *Unable to locate*

Badminton (Milton Keynes, GBR) **[55630]**

Bag-o-Fun (Shrewsbury, GBR) **[56526]**

Baha'i Journal UK **[55353]***

Bahamas Journal of Science (Nassau, BHS) **[42783]**

Bahrain Radio - General Programme (Manama, BHR) *Unable to locate*

Bahrain Radio - General Programme (Manama, BHR) *Unable to locate*

Bahrain Radio - General Programme (Manama, BHR) *Unable to locate*

Bahrain Radio - Holy Koran Programme (Manama, BHR) *Unable to locate*

Bahrain Radio - Second Programme (Manama, BHR) *Unable to locate*

Bahrain Radio - Second Programme (Manama, BHR) *Unable to locate*

Bahrain Radio - Second Programme (Manama, BHR) *Unable to locate*

Bahrain Radio - The Sports Service (Manama, BHR) *Unable to locate*

Bahrain Television (Manama, BHR) *Unable to locate*

Bahrain Television (Manama, BHR) *Unable to locate*

Bahrain Television (Manama, BHR) *Unable to locate*

Bahrain Television (Manama, BHR) *Unable to locate*

Bahrain This Month (BTM) (Manama, BHR) **[42787]**

Bahrain Today Magazine (Isa Town, BHR) *Unable to locate*

Baicheng People's Broadcasting Station (Baicheng, JI, CHN) *Unable to locate*

The BAIF Journal (Pune, MH, IND) *Unable to locate*

Bailrigg-FM - 87.7 (Bailrigg, GBR) **[52154]**

Baishan People's Broadcasting Station (Baishan, JI, CHN) *Unable to locate*

Baishan People's Broadcasting Station (Baishan, JI, CHN) *Unable to locate*

BAJT Computer Magazine (Prague, CZE) *Unable to locate*

Balamory (London, GBR) **[53998]**

Balance (Annerley, QL, AUS) **[41556]**

Balance (London, GBR) **[53999]**

Baleares Magazine (Bendinat/Calvia, SPA) *Unable to locate*

Bali & Beyond Magazine (Kuta, IDN) **[45824]**

Balkan Journal of Geometry and its Applications (Bucharest, ROM) **[49832]**

Balkan Journal of Medical Genetics (Warsaw, POL) **[49694]**

Balkan Linguistics (Sofia, BUL) **[43093]**

ballettanz (Berlin, GER) **[44158]**

Ballina Shire Advocate (Sydney, NW, AUS) **[42472]**

Ballroom Dancing Times **[54310]***

Ballymena Guardian (Ballymena, GBR) **[52159]**

Ballymena Times (Ballymena, GBR) **[52160]**

Ballymoney Times (Ballymoney, GBR) **[52162]**

Balonne Beacon (Sydney, NW, AUS) **[42473]**

Baltic Journal of Law & Politics (Warsaw, POL) **[49695]**

Baltic Journal of Management (Bradford, GBR) **[52437]**

Bama (Givatayim, ISR) *Unable to locate*

BAMBI Magazine (Bangkok, THA) **[51413]**

Bamboo Journal (Tokyo, JPN) *Unable to locate*

Bamtock Society (Bristol, GBR) *Ceased*

Banach Journal of Mathematics (New Delhi, DH, IND) *Unable to locate*

Banaras Metallurgist (Varanasi, UP, IND) *Unable to locate*

Banasthali Patrika (Jaipur, RJ, IND) *Unable to locate*

Banbridge Chronicle (Banbridge, GBR) **[52163]**

Banbridge Leader (Banbridge, GBR) **[52164]**

Banbury Cake (Banbury, GBR) **[52165]**

Banbury Guardian (Banbury, GBR) **[52166]**

Banca Nazionale Del Lavoro Quarterly Review (Rome, ITA) *Unable to locate*

Banci Estet Koko (Kota Kinabalu, MYS) **[47587]**

Bandolier (Oxford, GBR) *Ceased*

B&T Weekly (Port Melbourne, VI, AUS) **[42263]**

Bangalore Theological Forum (Bangalore, KA, IND) *Unable to locate*

Bangkok Broadcasting & TV Company Ltd - Channel 7 (Bangkok, THA) *Unable to locate*

Bangkok Entertainment Company Limited - Channel 3 (Bangkok, THA) *Unable to locate*

Bangkok Magazine (Chiang Mai, THA) **[51455]**

Bangkok Post Student Weekly (Bangkok, THA) **[51414]**

Bangla Academy Journal (Dhaka, BGD) *Unable to locate*

Bangladesh Betar - Chittagong - 873 KHz (Chittagong, BGD) **[42799]**

Bangladesh Betar - Chittagong (Dhaka, BGD) *Unable to locate*

Bangladesh Betar - Comilla - 1413 KHz (Comilla, BGD) **[42801]**

Bangladesh Betar - Dhaka (Dhaka, BGD) *Unable to locate*

Bangladesh Betar - Dhaka A - 693 KHz (Dhaka, BGD) **[42815]**

Bangladesh Betar - Dhaka B - 630 KHz (Dhaka, BGD) **[42816]**

Bangladesh Betar - Dhaka C - 1170 KHz (Dhaka, BGD) **[42817]**

Bangladesh Betar - Khulna (Dhaka, BGD) *Unable to locate*

Bangladesh Betar - Khulna - 558 KHz (Khulna, BGD) **[42820]**

Bangladesh Betar - Rajshahi (Dhaka, BGD) *Unable to locate*

Bangladesh Betar - Rajshahi (Dhaka, BGD) *Unable to locate*

Bangladesh Betar - Rajshahi - 1080 KHz (Rajshahi, BGD) **[42821]**

Bangladesh Betar - Rangamati - 1161 KHz (Rangamati, BGD) **[42822]**

Bangladesh Betar - Rangpur (Dhaka, BGD) *Unable to locate*

Bangladesh Betar - Rangpur - 1053 KHz (Rangpur, BGD) **[42823]**

Bangladesh Betar - Shavar (Dhaka, BGD) *Unable to locate*

Bangladesh Betar - Shavar (Dhaka, BGD) *Unable to locate*

Bangladesh Betar - Sylhet (Dhaka, BGD) *Unable to locate*

Bangladesh Betar - Sylhet - 963 KHz (Sylhet, BGD) **[42824]**

Bangladesh Betar - Thakurgaon - 999 KHz (Thakurgaon, BGD) **[42826]**

Bangladesh Development Studies (Dhaka, BGD) **[42803]**

Bangladesh e-Journal of Sociology (Dhaka, BGD) **[42804]**

Bangladesh Journal of Agricultural Sciences (Mymensingh, BGD) *Unable to locate*

Bangladesh Journal of Animal Science (Mymensingh, BGD) *Unable to locate*

Bangladesh Journal of Biological Sciences (Dhaka, BGD) *Unable to locate*

Bangladesh Journal of Botany (Dhaka, BGD) *Unable to locate*

Bangladesh Journal of Extension Education (Mymensingh, BGD) *Unable to locate*

Bangladesh Journal of Jute & Fibre Research (Dhaka, BGD) *Unable to locate*

Bangladesh Journal of Nuclear Agriculture (Mymensingh, BGD) *Unable to locate*

Bangladesh Journal of Psychology (Dhaka, BGD) *Unable to locate*

Bangladesh Journal of Scientific and Industrial Research (Dhaka, BGD) **[42805]**

Bangladesh Journal of Scientific Research (Dhaka, BGD) *Unable to locate*

Bangladesh Journal of Soil Science (Dhaka, BGD) *Unable to locate*

Bangladesh Journal of Zoology (Dhaka, BGD) *Unable to locate*

Bangladesh Medical College (Dhaka, BGD) *Unable to locate*

Bangladesh Medical Journal (Dhaka, BGD) *Unable to locate*

Bangladesh News (New Delhi, DH, IND) *Unable to locate*

Bangladesh Pharmaceutical Journal (Dhaka, BGD) **[42806]**

Bangladesh Television - Chittagong (Dhaka, BGD) *Unable to locate*

Bangladesh Television - Cox's Bazar (Dhaka, BGD) *Unable to locate*

Bangladesh Television - Dhaka (Dhaka, BGD) *Unable to locate*

Bangladesh Television - Khulna (Dhaka, BGD) *Unable to locate*

Bangladesh Television - Mymensingh (Dhaka, BGD) *Unable to locate*

Bangladesh Television - Naokhali (Dhaka, BGD) *Unable to locate*

Bangladesh Television - Natore (Dhaka, BGD) *Unable to locate*

Bangladesh Television - Rangamati (Dhaka, BGD) *Unable to locate*

Bangladesh Television - Rangpur (Dhaka, BGD) *Unable to locate*

Bangladesh Television - Satkhira (Dhaka, BGD) *Unable to locate*

Bangladesh Television - Sylhet (Dhaka, BGD) *Unable to locate*

The Bangladesh Today (Dhaka, BGD) **[42807]**

Bangladesh Veterinary Journal (Dhaka, BGD) *Unable to locate*

Banijya Barta (Calcutta, WB, IND) *Unable to locate*

Bank of England Quarterly Bulletin (London, GBR) **[54000]**

Bank of India Bulletin (Mumbai, MH, IND) *Unable to locate*

Bank Karamchari (Kanpur, UP, IND) *Unable to locate*

Bank of Korea Quarterly Economic Review (Seoul, KOR) *Unable to locate*

Bank Quest (Mumbai, MH, IND) *Unable to locate*

The Banker (London, GBR) **[54001]**

Banker's Journal Malaysia (Kuala Lumpur, MYS) **[47599]**

Banking Technology (London, GBR) **[54002]**

Bankinsurance News (Karachi, PAK) *Unable to locate*

Banks and Exchanges Weekly (Moscow, RUS) *Unable to locate*

Bankside Bulletin (London, GBR) *Unable to locate*

Bankstown Canterbury Torch (Condell Park, NW, AUS) **[41802]**

Banneret (Stabekk, NOR) **[49212]**

Banter (Singapore, SGP) *Unable to locate*

Bantu Studies **[51699]***

Baoding People's Broadcasting Station (Baoding, HB, CHN) *Unable to locate*

Baoding People's Broadcasting Station (Baoding, HB, CHN) *Unable to locate*

Baoding People's Broadcasting Station (Baoding, HB, CHN) *Unable to locate*

Baoji People's Broadcasting Station (Baoji, SH, CHN) *Unable to locate*

Baoji People's Broadcasting Station (Baoji, SH, CHN) *Unable to locate*

Baoji People's Broadcasting Station (Baoji, SH, CHN) *Unable to locate*

Baoji People's Broadcasting Station (Baoji, SH, CHN) *Unable to locate*

Baotou People's Broadcasting Station (Baotou, NM, CHN) *Unable to locate*

Baotou Stereo People's Broadcasting Station (Baotou, NM, CHN) *Unable to locate*

BAPOMAG (Paisley, GBR) **[56239]**

Baptist (Copenhagen, DEN) *Unable to locate*

Baptist Historical Magazine (Swansea, GBR) *Unable to locate*

Baratok Kozt Magazin (Budapest, HUN) **[44825]**

Barbados Advocate (Bridgetown, BRB) **[42827]**

Barb's Factory Shopping Guide (North Ryde, NW, AUS) **[42171]**

The Barcelona Review (Barcelona, SPA) **[50654]**

Barclays Economic Review (Poole, GBR) *Ceased*

Bardymskiye zori (Barda, RUS) *Unable to locate*

Barg e Sabz (Paris, FRA) *Unable to locate*

Bargain Shopper Guide to Melbourne (North Ryde, NW, AUS) **[42172]**

Barn och Familj (Skillingfors, SWE) *Ceased*

Baroda Reporter (Baroda, GJ, IND) *Unable to locate*

The Barrow Browser (Kendal, GBR) **[53670]**

Barry & District News (Barry, GBR) **[52192]**

bars♣ (Pyrmont, NW, AUS) **[42275]**

Bartimee (Yaounde, CMR) *Unable to locate*

Basava Journal (Bangalore, KA, IND) *Unable to locate*

Basic and Applied Ecology (Gottingen, GER) **[44393]**

Basic & Clinical Pharmacology & Toxicology (Odense, DEN) **[43726]**

Numbers cited in bold after listings are entry numbers rather than page numbers.

Master Index

Basic Course in Songwriting (Limerick, LI, IRL) *Unable to locate*

Basic Port Statistics of India (New Delhi, DH, IND) *Unable to locate*

Basic Research in Cardiology (Heidelberg, GER) **[44441]**

Basic Road Statistics (London, GBR) *Unable to locate*

Basildon and Wickford Recorder (Basildon, GBR) **[52193]**

Basin Research (Houten, NLD) **[48638]**

Basingstoke Gazette (Basingstoke, GBR) **[52195]**

Basingstoke Gazette Extra (Salisbury, GBR) **[56452]**

Basis (Brussels, BEL) *Unable to locate*

Basis (Brussels, BEL) *Unable to locate*

Basis (Oslo, NOR) *Unable to locate*

Baskent Radyo TV - Bakanlıklar (Ankara, TUR) *Unable to locate*

Basket Ball (Paris, FRA) *Unable to locate*

Batborsen (Bekkestua, NOR) *Unable to locate*

Batborsen (Vaxjo, SWE) *Unable to locate*

Bath-FM - 107.9 (Bath, GBR) **[52265]**

Bathroom Yearbook (North Ryde, NW, AUS) **[42173]**

Batley News (Batley, GBR) **[52267]**

BATOD Journal **[53572]***

Batteries International (Brighton, GBR) **[52606]**

BATU Monitor (Manila, PHL) *Unable to locate*

BATU Research and Documentation (Manila, PHL) *Unable to locate*

Bau & Baustoff (Duisburg, GER) *Unable to locate*

Bay & Basin-FM - 92.7 (Sanctuary Point, NW, AUS) **[42349]**

Bay-FM - 99.9 (Byron Bay, NW, AUS) **[41679]**

Bay-FM - 100.3 (Cleveland, QL, AUS) **[41770]**

BAY-FM - 93.9 (Geelong, VI, AUS) **[41881]**

Bay-FM - 89.7 (Saint Julian's, MAL) **[47742]**

The Bay-FM - 102.3 (Lancaster, GBR) **[53739]**

The Bay-FM - 96.9 (Lancaster, GBR) **[53737]**

The Bay-FM - 103.2 (Lancaster, GBR) **[53738]**

Bay News (Tauranga, NZL) *Unable to locate*

Bayannur People's Broadcasting Station (Bayannur, NM, CHN) *Unable to locate*

Bayannur People's Broadcasting Station (Linhe, NM, CHN) *Unable to locate*

Bayerisches Arzteblatt (Munich, GER) **[44551]**

Bayern 4 Klassik-FM - 103.2 (Munich, GER) **[44590]**

BayFM - 107.9 (Linton Grange, SAF) **[50549]**

Bayrock-FM - 97.7 (Whakatane, NZL) **[49047]**

Bayside Bulletin (Cleveland, QL, AUS) **[41766]**

Bayside Leader (Cheltenham, VI, AUS) **[41745]**

BBC Countryfile (Bristol, GBR) **[52641]**

BBC Gardeners' World Magazine (London, GBR) **[54003]**

BBC GMR-FM **[55584]***

BBC Good Food (London, GBR) **[54004]**

BBC History (Bristol, GBR) **[52642]**

BBC Learning is Fun! (London, GBR) **[54005]**

BBC London-FM - 94.9 (London, GBR) **[55438]**

BBC Merseyside-FM - 95.8 (Liverpool, GBR) **[53879]**

BBC Northampton-FM - 104.2 (Northampton, GBR) **[55716]**

BBC Radio-AM - 1548 (Bristol, GBR) **[52739]**

BBC Radio-AM - 1026 (Cambridge, GBR) **[52907]**

BBC Radio-AM - 1116 (Derby, GBR) **[53169]**

BBC Radio-AM - 792 (Londonderry, GBR) **[55474]**

BBC Radio Berkshire-FM - 94.6 (Reading, GBR) **[56334]**

BBC Radio Cambridgeshire-FM - 96 (Cambridge, GBR) **[52908]**

BBC Radio Cleveland-FM **[55613]***

BBC Radio Cumbria-FM - 95.6 (Carlisle, GBR) **[52947]**

BBC Radio Derby-FM - 104.5 (Derby, GBR) **[53170]**

BBC Radio Essex-FM - 103.5 (Chelmsford, GBR) **[52962]**

BBC Radio 5-AM (London, GBR) *Unable to locate*

BBC Radio 5 Live-AM (London, GBR) *Unable to locate*

BBC Radio-FM - 94.9 (Bristol, GBR) **[52740]**

BBC Radio-FM - 95.7 (Cambridge, GBR) **[52909]**

BBC Radio-FM - 94.8 (Coventry, GBR) **[53090]**

BBC Radio-FM - 103.7 (Coventry, GBR) **[53091]**

BBC Radio-FM - 104.1 (Reading, GBR) **[56336]**

BBC Radio-FM - 95.4 (Reading, GBR) **[56335]**

BBC Radio-FM (Reading, GBR) *Unable to locate*

BBC Radio-FM - 88.8 (Saint Helier, GBR) **[56444]**

BBC Radio-FM - 103.9 (Truro, GBR) **[56775]**

BBC Radio-FM - 95.2 (Truro, GBR) **[56774]**

BBC Radio 4-FM - 92 (London, GBR) **[55439]**

BBC Radio Guernsey-FM - 93.2 (Saint Sampsons, GBR) **[56447]**

BBC Radio Humberside-FM - 95.9 (Hull, GBR) **[53629]**

BBC Radio Kent - 97.6 (Folkestone, GBR) **[53394]**

BBC Radio Kent - 104.2 (Swingate, GBR) **[56716]**

BBC Radio Kent-FM - 96.7 (Tunbridge Wells, GBR) **[56784]**

BBC Radio Lancashire-FM - 103.9 (Blackburn, GBR) **[52384]**

BBC Radio Leeds-FM - 92.4 (Leeds, GBR) **[53779]**

BBC Radio Leicester-FM - 104.9 (Leicester, GBR) **[53836]**

BBC Radio Manchester-FM - 95.1 (Manchester, GBR) **[55584]**

BBC Radio Newcastle-FM - 95.4 (Newcastle upon Tyne, GBR) **[55680]**

BBC Radio Norfolk-FM - 95.1 (Norwich, GBR) **[55746]**

BBC Radio Nottingham-FM - 95.5 (Nottingham, GBR) **[55774]**

BBC Radio 1-FM - 97 (London, GBR) **[55440]**

BBC Radio Oxford-FM - 95.2 (Oxford, GBR) **[56232]**

BBC Radio Scotland-FM - 92 (Glasgow, GBR) **[53461]**

BBC Radio Sheffield-FM - 104.1 (Sheffield, GBR) **[56517]**

BBC Radio Shropshire-FM - 96 (Shrewsbury, GBR) **[56539]**

BBC Radio Solent-FM - 96.1 (Southampton, GBR) **[56580]**

BBC Radio Somerset-FM - 95.5 (Taunton, GBR) **[56724]**

BBC Radio Stoke-FM - 94.6 (Stoke-on-Trent, GBR) **[56631]**

BBC Radio Surrey-FM - 104 (Guildford, GBR) **[53495]**

BBC Radio 3-FM - 90.2 (London, GBR) **[55441]**

BBC Radio 2-FM - 88 (London, GBR) **[55442]**

BBC Radio Wiltshire-FM - 103.5 (Swindon, GBR) **[56713]**

BBC Radio WM-FM - 95.6 (Birmingham, GBR) **[52373]**

BBC Southern Counties-FM **[53495]***

BBC Tees-FM - 95 (Middlesbrough, GBR) **[55613]**

BBC Thai Service (Bangkok, THA) *Unable to locate*

BBC Thai Service (Bangkok, THA) *Unable to locate*

BBC Thai Service (Bangkok, THA) *Unable to locate*

BBC Thai Service (Bangkok, THA) *Unable to locate*

BBC Thai Service (Bangkok, THA) *Unable to locate*

BBC Thai Service (Bangkok, THA) *Unable to locate*

BBC Thai Service (Bangkok, THA) *Unable to locate*

BBC Thai Service (Bangkok, THA) *Unable to locate*

BBC Thai Service (Bangkok, THA) *Unable to locate*

BBC Thai Service (Bangkok, THA) *Ceased*

BBC Thai Service (Bangkok, THA) *Unable to locate*

BBC Thai Service (Bangkok, THA) *Unable to locate*

BBC Thai Service (Bangkok, THA) *Unable to locate*

BBC Thai Service (Bangkok, THA) *Unable to locate*

BBC Thai Service (Bangkok, THA) *Unable to locate*

BBC The Magic Key (London, GBR) **[54006]**

BBC Three Counties Radio-AM - 1161 (Luton, GBR) **[55506]**

BBC Three Counties Radio-FM - 95.5 (Luton, GBR) **[55509]**

BBC Three Counties Radio-FM - 103.8 (Luton, GBR) **[55507]**

BBC Three Counties Radio-FM - 104.5 (Luton, GBR) **[55508]**

BBC 3CR-FM - 95.5 (Luton, GBR) **[55510]**

BBC Wildlife Magazine (Bristol, GBR) **[52643]**

BBQ Scorecard (Cape Town, SAF) **[50363]**

BC-FM - 93.2 (Bristol, GBR) **[52741]**

bc Magazine (Hong Kong, CHN) **[43283]**

BCB-FM - 106.6 (Bradford, GBR) **[52558]**

BCB-FM (Bradford, GBR) *Unable to locate*

BCCI (Thimphu, BTN) *Unable to locate*

BCDTA (Crewe, GBR) *Unable to locate*

BDJ British Dental Journal (London, GBR) **[54007]**

BDS Yearbook (Stowmarket, GBR) **[56641]**

be (London, GBR) *Unable to locate*

Be Love (Tokyo, JPN) **[46759]**

Be Love Parfait (Tokyo, JPN) **[46760]**

Be My Parent (London, GBR) **[54008]**

The Beach-FM - 103.4 (Lowestoft, GBR) **[55498]**

The Beach-FM - 97.4 (Lowestoft, GBR) **[55497]**

An Beachaire (Enfield, ME, IRL) *Unable to locate*

Beacon - 103.1 (Wolverhampton, GBR) **[56954]**

Beacon - 97.2 (Wolverhampton, GBR) **[56953]**

Beads etc... (Rozelle, NW, AUS) **[42323]**

Beanscene (Brisbane, QL, AUS) **[41645]**

The Beat (Seminyak, IDN) **[45854]**

Beat-FM - 103 (Waterford City, WA, IRL) **[46067]**

Beat-FM - 102 (Waterford City, WA, IRL) **[46066]**

Beatles-Nytt (Stockholm, SWE) *Unable to locate*

Beatles Unlimited Magazine (Nieuwegein, NLD) **[48740]**

Beaumont Magazine (London, GBR) *Unable to locate*

Beautiful Cards (Bristol, GBR) **[52644]**

Beauty Counter (Tonbridge, GBR) *Unable to locate*

Beauty and Hair (Beijing, CHN) *Unable to locate*

Beauty Home (Shanghai, CHN) **[43463]**

BeautyNZ (North Shore City, NZL) **[48953]**

Beccles & Bungay Journal (Norwich, GBR) **[55724]**

BEC40 (Hualien, TWN) *Unable to locate*

BEC44 (Penghu, TWN) *Unable to locate*

BEC42 (Taipei, TWN) *Ceased*

BEC30 (Taipei, TWN) *Unable to locate*

BEC38 (Penghu, TWN) *Unable to locate*

BEC35 (Hualien, TWN) *Unable to locate*

BEC34 (Taipei, TWN) *Unable to locate*

BEC39 (Taipei, TWN) *Unable to locate*

BEC31 (Taipei, TWN) *Unable to locate*

BEC37 (Kaohsiung, TWN) *Unable to locate*

BEC36 (Kaohsiung, TWN) *Unable to locate*

BEC33 (Hualien, TWN) *Unable to locate*

BEC32 (Tainan, TWN) *Unable to locate*

BEC28 (Tainan, TWN) *Unable to locate*

BEC25 (Taipei, TWN) *Unable to locate*

BEC24 (Taipei, TWN) *Unable to locate*

BEC29 (Kaohsiung, TWN) *Unable to locate*

BEC27 (Taichung, TWN) *Unable to locate*

Numbers cited in bold after listings are entry numbers rather than page numbers.

BEC26 (Taipei, TWN) *Unable to locate*

BEC22 (Taipei, TWN) *Unable to locate*

BEC22 (Taipei, TWN) *Unable to locate*

Bedding magazine **[42616]***

BED80 (Taitung, TWN) *Unable to locate*

BED85, TWN) *Unable to locate*

BED89, TWN) *Unable to locate*

BED81 (Hualien, TWN) *Unable to locate*

BED87, TWN) *Unable to locate*

BED82 (Chia-I, TWN) *Unable to locate*

BED48 (Kaohsiung, TWN) *Unable to locate*

BED47, TWN) *Unable to locate*

BED92, TWN) *Unable to locate*

Bedrijfsvoering/EuroPress (Bilthoven, NLD) *Unable to locate*

BED78, TWN) *Unable to locate*

BED77, TWN) *Unable to locate*

BED65 (Ilan, TWN) *Unable to locate*

BED63, TWN) *Unable to locate*

BED34 (Taipei, TWN) *Unable to locate*

BED28, TWN) *Unable to locate*

BED24, TWN) *Unable to locate*

The Bee-FM - 107 (Darwen, GBR) **[53157]**

BEE43 (Taipei, TWN) *Unable to locate*

Beehive-FM - 105 (Phnom Penh, CMB) **[43114]**

Beeld (Johannesburg, SAF) **[50527]**

Beers of the World (Norwich, GBR) **[55725]**

Bees for Development Journal (Monmouth, GBR) **[55644]**

BEE38 (Taitung, TWN) *Unable to locate*

BEE35, TWN) *Ceased*

BEE34 (Changhua, TWN) *Unable to locate*

BEE37 (Hualien, TWN) *Unable to locate*

BEE36 (Kaohsiung, TWN) *Unable to locate*

BEE33 (Taipei, TWN) *Unable to locate*

BEE32 (Taipei, TWN) *Unable to locate*

BEF 21 (Taipei, TWN) *Unable to locate*

BEF 23 (Taipei, TWN) *Unable to locate*

BEF 22 (Taipei, TWN) *Unable to locate*

Before Farming, the Archaeology and Anthropology of Hunter-Gatherers (Liverpool, GBR) **[53868]**

BEG51 (Ilan, TWN) *Unable to locate*

BEG78, TWN) *Unable to locate*

BEG77, TWN) *Unable to locate*

BEG28 (Kaohsiung, TWN) *Unable to locate*

BEG25 - 93.1 MHz (Taipei, TWN) **[51369]**

BEG29 (Kaohsiung, TWN) *Unable to locate*

BEG26 - 1134 KHz (Taipei, TWN) **[51370]**

Behavioral and Brain Functions (London, GBR) **[54009]**

Behavioral and Brain Sciences (Cambridge, GBR) **[52791]**

Behavioral Ecology (Oxford, GBR) **[55879]**

Behavioral Ecology and Sociobiology (Heidelberg, GER) **[44442]**

Behaviormetrika (Chiba, JPN) **[46315]**

Behaviorometric (Gaya, BH, IND) *Unable to locate*

Behaviour (Leiden, NLD) **[48656]**

Behaviour Change (West Perth, WA, AUS) **[42698]**

Behaviour and Information Technology (Abingdon, GBR) **[51717]**

Behavioural Brain Research (Dusseldorf, GER) **[44321]**

Behavioural Processes (Dijon, FRA) **[43943]**

BEH56 (Kaohsiung, TWN) *Unable to locate*

BEH5 (Taipei, TWN) *Unable to locate*

BEH44 (Kaohsiung, TWN) *Unable to locate*

Behorden Spiegel (Bonn, GER) **[44253]**

BEH7 (Taipei, TWN) *Unable to locate*

BEH38 (Taichung, TWN) *Unable to locate*

BEH34 (Taichung, TWN) *Unable to locate*

BEH3 (Taipei, TWN) *Unable to locate*

BEH2 (Taipei, TWN) *Unable to locate*

Beihai People's Broadcasting Station (Beihai, GZ, CHN) *Unable to locate*

Beihai People's Broadcasting Station (Beihai, GZ, CHN) *Unable to locate*

Beijing Communications Radio (Beijing, CHN) *Unable to locate*

Beijing Culture Radio (Beijing, CHN) *Unable to locate*

Beijing Economic Radio (Beijing, CHN) *Unable to locate*

Beijing Margins to Maintstream (Belfast, GBR) *Unable to locate*

Beijing Music Radio (Beijing, CHN) *Unable to locate*

Beijing People's Broadcasting Station (Beijing, CHN) *Unable to locate*

Beijing People's Broadcasting Station (Beijing, CHN) *Unable to locate*

Beijing People's Broadcasting Station (Beijing, CHN) *Unable to locate*

Beijing People's Broadcasting Station (Beijing, CHN) *Unable to locate*

Beijing People's Broadcasting Station (Beijing, CHN) *Unable to locate*

Beijing People's Broadcasting Station - 103.9 MHz (Beijing, CHN) **[43226]**

Beijing Review (Beijing, CHN) **[43171]**

Beijing Tatler (Beijing, CHN) **[43172]**

Beijing This Month (Beijing, CHN) **[43173]**

Beilstein Journal of Organic Chemistry (Frankfurt am Main, GER) **[44364]**

Beipiao People's Broadcasting Station (Beipiao, LI, CHN) *Unable to locate*

Beitrage zur Geschichte der deutschen Sprache und Literatur (Berlin, GER) **[44159]**

Beitrage zur Sexualforschung (Hamburg, GER) *Unable to locate*

The Belize Times (Belize City, BLZ) **[42915]**

Bella (London, GBR) **[54010]**

Bellauto (Peschiera Borromeo, ITA) **[46213]**

Bell'Europa (Milan, ITA) *Unable to locate*

Bellshill Speaker (Bellshill, GBR) **[52305]**

Bellydance Oasis (Perth, WA, AUS) **[42247]**

Belper News (Belper, GBR) **[52309]**

Belser Kunst Quartal (Ostfildern, GER) *Unable to locate*

BEL3 (Kaohsiung, TWN) *Unable to locate*

BEL2 (Kaohsiung, TWN) *Unable to locate*

BEM30 - 99.9 MHz (Kaohsiung, TWN) **[51311]**

BEM31 (Taipei, TWN) *Unable to locate*

BEM3 (Taipei, TWN) *Unable to locate*

BEM28 (Taoyuan, TWN) *Unable to locate*

BEM25 (Hualien, TWN) *Unable to locate*

BEM24 (Yunlin, TWN) *Unable to locate*

BEM29 (Taichung, TWN) *Unable to locate*

BEM27 (Tainan, TWN) *Unable to locate*

BEM26 (Taichung, TWN) *Unable to locate*

BEM23 (Taipei, TWN) *Unable to locate*

BEM22 (Taipei, TWN) *Unable to locate*

Ben Advertising (Bangkok, THA) *Unable to locate*

Ben Jonson Journal (Edinburgh, GBR) **[53255]**

Benefits & Compensation International (London, GBR) **[54011]**

Benelux unquote (London, GBR) **[54012]**

Bengal Medical Journal (Calcutta, WB, IND) *Unable to locate*

Bengal Natural History Society Journal (Darjeeling, WB, IND) *Unable to locate*

Bengal—Past and Present (Calcutta, WB, IND) *Unable to locate*

Bengali International (Calcutta, WB, IND) *Unable to locate*

Bengbu People's Broadcasting Station (Bengbu, AN, CHN) *Unable to locate*

Bengbu People's Broadcasting Station (Bengbu, AN, CHN) *Unable to locate*

Bengbu People's Broadcasting Station (Bengbu, AN, CHN) *Unable to locate*

Bengbu People's Broadcasting Station (Bengbu, AN, CHN) *Unable to locate*

Bensiiniuutiset (Helsinki, FIN) *Unable to locate*

Bensin & Butik (Helsingborg, SWE) *Unable to locate*

Bentley Magazine (Ware, GBR) **[56839]**

Benxi People's Broadcasting Station (Benxi, LI, CHN) *Unable to locate*

Benxi People's Broadcasting Station (Benxi, LI, CHN) *Unable to locate*

Benxi People's Broadcasting Station (Benxi, LI, CHN) *Unable to locate*

BE144 (Taichung, TWN) *Unable to locate*

BEP44 (Hualien, TWN) *Unable to locate*

BEP41 (Taipei, TWN) *Unable to locate*

BEP43 (Taichung, TWN) *Unable to locate*

BEP42 (Kaohsiung, TWN) *Unable to locate*

BEP30 (Ilan, TWN) *Unable to locate*

BEP35 (Hualien, TWN) *Unable to locate*

BEP39 (Taitung, TWN) *Unable to locate*

BEP31 (Tainan, TWN) *Unable to locate*

BEP32 (Kaohsiung, TWN) *Unable to locate*

BEP32 (Tainan, TWN) *Unable to locate*

BEP25 (Kaohsiung, TWN) *Unable to locate*

BEP24 (Taichung, TWN) *Unable to locate*

BEP24 (Taichung, TWN) *Unable to locate*

BEP29 (Taipei, TWN) *Unable to locate*

BEP29 (Taitung, TWN) *Unable to locate*

BEP26 (Chupei, TWN) *Unable to locate*

BEP22 (Taipei, TWN) *Unable to locate*

Beratende Ingenieure (Berlin, GER) *Unable to locate*

Berge (Nuremberg, GER) **[44602]**

Bergerac-FM - 95 (Bergerac, FRA) **[43920]**

Berichte der Bunsen-Gesellschaft **[52883]***

Berichte zur Wissenschaftsgeschichte (Lubeck, GER) **[44535]**

Berichten Broeders Maastricht (Maastricht, NLD) *Unable to locate*

Berita Harian (Singapore, SGP) **[50112]**

Berita IPTEK (Jakarta, IDN) *Unable to locate*

Berita Minggu (Singapore, SGP) **[50113]**

Berliner Rundfunk-FM - 91.4 (Berlin, GER) **[44242]**

Bermuda Sun (Hamilton, BMU) **[42920]**

Bernoulli (Voorburg, NLD) **[48769]**

Berrow's Worcester Journal (Worcester, GBR) **[56960]**

Bertrand Vacances (Paris, FRA) *Unable to locate*

Berwick Advertiser (Berwick upon Tweed, GBR) **[52317]**

Berwick Leader (Berwick, VI, AUS) **[41598]**

Berwickshire News (Berwick upon Tweed, GBR) **[52318]**

Bessatsu Friend (Tokyo, JPN) **[46761]**

Besser Wohnen (Better Living) (Vienna, AUT) *Unable to locate*

Best of British (Deeping Saint James, GBR) **[53162]**

Best 104 (Johor Bahru, MYS) *Unable to locate*

Best 104 (Johor Bahru, MYS) *Unable to locate*

Best Practice & Research (Rotterdam, NLD) **[48748]**

Best Practice & Research Clinical Anesthesiology (Munster, GER) **[44597]**

Best Practice & Research Clinical Endocrinology & Metaboliom (Amsterdam, NLD) **[47903]**

Best Practice & Research Clinical Hematology (Amsterdam, NLD) **[47904]**

Best Practice & Research Clinical Obstetrics & Gynecology (London, GBR) **[54013]**

Best Practice & Research Clinical Rheumatology (Truro, GBR) **[56773]**

The Best of Singapore (Singapore, SGP) **[50114]**

Best Solutions (Northampton, GBR) *Unable to locate*

Best Treatments (London, GBR) **[54014]**

Beton (Brussels, BEL) **[42844]**

Betong (Stockholm, SWE) *Unable to locate*

Numbers cited in bold after listings are entry numbers rather than page numbers.

Better Business (Baroda, GJ, IND) *Unable to locate*

Better Interiors (Mumbai, MH, IND) **[45355]**

Better Photography (Mumbai, MH, IND) **[45356]**

Betty Bossi (Zurich, SWI) **[51254]**

Between the Flags **[53196]***

Beur-FM - 106.7 (Paris, FRA) **[44091]**

BEV88 (Taoyuan, TWN) *Unable to locate*

BEV85 (Tainan, TWN) *Unable to locate*

BEV84 (Nantou, TWN) *Unable to locate*

Beverage and Food World (Mumbai, MH, IND) *Unable to locate*

Beverley Guardian (Driffield, GBR) **[53199]**

BEV50 (Taipei, TWN) *Unable to locate*

BEV58 (Taichung, TWN) *Unable to locate*

BEV54 (Changhua, TWN) *Unable to locate*

BEV59 (Taichung, TWN) *Unable to locate*

BEV51 (Taipei, TWN) *Unable to locate*

BEV57 (Tainan, TWN) *Unable to locate*

BEV56 (Tainan, TWN) *Unable to locate*

BEV52 (Taichung, TWN) *Unable to locate*

BEV45 (Taipei, TWN) *Unable to locate*

BEV46 (Taipei, TWN) *Unable to locate*

BEV98 (Kaohsiung, TWN) *Unable to locate*

BEV94 (Taichung, TWN) *Unable to locate*

BEV96 (Tainan, TWN) *Unable to locate*

BEV92 (Taipei, TWN) *Unable to locate*

BEVP38 (Ilan, TWN) *Unable to locate*

BEVP34 (Hualien, TWN) *Unable to locate*

BEV70 (Taipei, TWN) *Unable to locate*

BEV78 (Keelung, TWN) *Unable to locate*

BEV74 (Pingtung, TWN) *Unable to locate*

BEV79 (Keelung, TWN) *Unable to locate*

BEV71 (Taipei, TWN) *Unable to locate*

BEV76 (Miaoli, TWN) *Unable to locate*

BEV72 (Chia-I, TWN) *Unable to locate*

BEV60, TWN) *Unable to locate*

BEV68 (Kaohsiung, TWN) *Unable to locate*

BEV64 (Hualien, TWN) *Unable to locate*

BEV67 (Kaohsiung, TWN) *Unable to locate*

BEV62 (Hsinchu, TWN) *Unable to locate*

BEV35 (Taipei, TWN) *Unable to locate*

BEV37 - 1269 KHz (Taitung, TWN) **[51391]**

BEV36 (Yunlin, TWN) *Unable to locate*

BEV24 (Taipei, TWN) *Unable to locate*

BEV23 (Taipei, TWN) *Unable to locate*

Bexhill Observer (Bexhill-on-Sea, GBR) **[52320]**

Bexley Times (Sidcup, GBR) **[56540]**

Beyond the Horizon (London, GBR) *Unable to locate*

Beyond Sudoku (Redhill, GBR) **[56343]**

BFBS Brunei-FM - 101.7 (Gerrards Cross, GBR) **[53407]**

BFBS Gurkha Radio-FM (Gerrards Cross, GBR) *Unable to locate*

BFBS Gurkha Radio-FM (Gerrards Cross, GBR) *Unable to locate*

B5 Aktuell-FM - 87.8 (Munich, GER) **[44592]**

B5 Aktuell-FM - 90 (Munich, GER) **[44591]**

Bfp fuhrpark management (Hannover, GER) *Unable to locate*

BG Journal (Richmond, GBR) **[56388]**

Bhagalpur University Journal (Bhagalpur, BH, IND) *Unable to locate*

Bhagirath (New Delhi, DH, IND) *Unable to locate*

Bharat Sevak (Chandigarh, CH, IND) *Unable to locate*

Bharat Times (West Footscray, VI, AUS) **[42694]**

Bharata Manisha Quarterly (Varanasi, UP, IND) *Unable to locate*

Bharata Varsha (Cuttack, OR, IND) *Unable to locate*

Bharati Research Institute Journal (Indore, MP, IND) *Unable to locate*

Bharatiya Samajik Chintan (New Delhi, DH, IND) *Unable to locate*

Bharatya Vidya (Mumbai, MH, IND) *Unable to locate*

Bhartiya Krishi Anusandhan Patrika (Karnal, HY, IND) *Unable to locate*

Bhau Vishnu Ashetar Vedic Research Series (Pune, MH, IND) *Unable to locate*

Bhavan's Journal (Mumbai, MH, IND) *Unable to locate*

Bhopal University Research Journal (Bhopal, MP, IND) *Unable to locate*

Bhushan's World Trade Enquiries (Jagadhri, HY, IND) *Unable to locate*

Bhutan Broadcasting Service - 6035 KHz (Thimphu, BTN) **[42928]**

Bhutan Broadcasting Service - Channel 5 (Thimphu, BTN) **[42927]**

Bhutan Broadcasting Service - Dobchula - 88.1 MHz (Dobchula, BTN) **[42923]**

Bhutan Observer (Thimphu, BTN) **[42924]**

The Bible and Critical Theory (Clayton, VI, AUS) **[41758]**

The Bible Translator (Reading, GBR) **[56310]**

Biblebhashyam (Kottayam, KE, IND) *Unable to locate*

Biblical Interpretation (Leiden, NLD) **[48657]**

Bibliegrafski vjesnik (Cetinje, MON) *Unable to locate*

Bibliographic Journal (Montevideo, URY) **[57007]**

Bibliographic Reprints (New Delhi, DH, IND) *Unable to locate*

Bibliography of Doctoral Dissertations: Natural and Applied Sciences (New Delhi, DH, IND) *Unable to locate*

Bibliography of Indian Writing in English Series (New Delhi, DH, IND) *Unable to locate*

Bibliography on Irrigation, Drainage,

River Training and Flood Control (New Delhi, DH, IND) *Unable to locate*

Bibliography of Research Studies, Papers, and Other Documents (Ethul Kotte, SRI) *Unable to locate*

Bibliotek for Laeger (Copenhagen, DEN) **[43656]**

Bibliotheca Mycologica (Stuttgart, GER) **[44662]**

Bibliotheca Phycologica (Stuttgart, GER) **[44663]**

Bibliotheek Blad (The Hague, NLD) *Unable to locate*

Big Cheese (London, GBR) **[54015]**

Big Comic Original (Tokyo, JPN) **[46762]**

Big Comic Spirits (Tokyo, JPN) **[46763]**

Big Daddy Magazine (Nottingham, GBR) *Unable to locate*

Big-FM - 87.8 (Stuttgart, GER) **[44688]**

Big-FM - 92.6 (Stuttgart, GER) **[44689]**

BIG-FM - 101.2 (Pokhara, NPL) **[47859]**

The Big Issue (Cape Town, SAF) **[50364]**

Big Issue Namibia (London, GBR) **[54016]**

The Big Picture (Auckland, NZL) *Unable to locate*

Big Rigs (Sydney, NW, AUS) **[42474]**

Big Value Codebreakers (London, GBR) **[54017]**

Biggleswade Chronicle (Biggleswade, GBR) **[52323]**

BigO (Singapore, SGP) **[50115]**

Bihar Industries (Patna, BH, IND) *Unable to locate*

Bihar Law Journal Reports (Allahabad, UP, IND) *Unable to locate*

Bihar Research Society Journal (Patna, BH, IND) *Unable to locate*

BIIBUSINESS (Camberley, GBR) **[52782]**

Bijdragen (Leuven, BEL) **[42892]**

Bijoux Magazine (Brussels, BEL) *Unable to locate*

Bike Buyers Guide (Sandyford, DU, IRL) **[46054]**

Bike Europe (Maarssen, NLD) *Unable to locate*

Bike Fitness (Euskirchen, GER) *Ceased*

Bike Magazine (Cruz Quebrada-Dafundo, PRT) **[49793]**

Bike Trader (Manchester, GBR) **[55543]**

Biker (Leeds, GBR) *Unable to locate*

Bikersweb (Birmingham, GBR) **[52329]**

Bil Magasinet (Copenhagen, DEN) *Unable to locate*

Bil & Motor (Frederiksberg, DEN) *Unable to locate*

Bilan (Lausanne, SWI) **[51183]**

bild der wissenschaft (Leinfelden-Echterdingen, GER) **[44517]**

BILD der FRAU (Hamburg, GER) **[44411]**

Bimbisani & Belli (Milan, ITA) *Unable to locate*

BIMCO Bulletin (Bagsvaerd, DEN) *Unable to locate*

Bindu (Hamneda, SWE) **[50968]**

Binh Dinh Broadcast - Television Station (Qui Nhon City, VNM) *Unable to locate*

Binh Dinh Broadcast - Television Station (Qui Nhon City, VNM) *Unable to locate*

Binh Duong Broadcast - Television Station (Thu Dau Mot Town, VNM) *Unable to locate*

Binzhou People's Broadcasting Station (Binzhou, SD, CHN) *Unable to locate*

Binzhou People's Broadcasting Station (Binzhou, SD, CHN) *Unable to locate*

Bio-Bio-FM - 96.9 (Santiago, CHL) **[43151]**

BIO—Gesundheit fur Korper Geist und Seele (Tutzing, GER) **[44695]**

Bio Med (Mumbai, MH, IND) *Unable to locate*

Bio-Medical Materials and Engineering (Sendai, JPN) **[46664]**

Bio-Research (Nsukka, AN, NGA) **[49156]**

Bio-science Law Review (Witney, GBR) **[56939]**

Bio-Science Research Bulletin (New Delhi, DH, IND) *Unable to locate*

Biocatalysis and Biotransformation (London, GBR) **[54018]**

Biochemical and Biophysical Research Communications (Amsterdam, NLD) **[47905]**

Biochemical Engineering Journal (Manchester, GBR) **[55544]**

Biochemical and Molecular Medicine **[48166]***

Biochemical Reviews (Bangalore, KA, IND) *Unable to locate*

Biochemical Society Symposia (Colchester, GBR) **[53029]**

Biochemical Society Transactions (Colchester, GBR) **[53030]**

The Biochemist (London, GBR) **[54019]**

Biochemistry (Rajkot, GJ, IND) **[45706]**

Biochemistry and Molecular Biology Reports (Seoul, KOR) **[47258]**

Biochemistry (Moscow) (Moscow, RUS) **[49883]**

Biochimica et Biophysica Acta (BBA) (Amsterdam, NLD) **[47906]**

Biochimica et Biophysica Acta (BBA)-General Subjects (Amsterdam, NLD) **[47907]**

Biochimica et Biophysica Acta (BBA)-Molecular Basis of Disease (Amsterdam, NLD) **[47908]**

Biochimica et Biophysica Acta (BBA)-Molecular and Cell Biology of Lipids (Amsterdam, NLD) **[47909]**

Biochimica et Biophysica Acta (BBA)-Proteins & Proteomics (Amsterdam, NLD) **[47910]**

Biocommerce Abstracts (London, GBR) *Ceased*

BioControl (Dordrecht, NLD) **[48330]**

BioControl (Delemont, SWI) *Unable to locate*

Biocontrol News and Information (Wallingford, GBR) **[56816]**

Biodegradation (Dordrecht, NLD) **[48331]**

Bioelectrochemistry (Amsterdam, NLD) **[47911]**

BioEssays (Weinheim, GER) **[44701]**

Bioethics (Oxford, GBR) **[55880]**

Biofabrication (Bristol, GBR) **[52645]**

BioFactors (Osaka, JPN) **[46616]**

Biofilms (Cambridge, GBR) *Ceased*

Biofouling (Buckingham, GBR) **[52754]**

Biogenic Amines (Leiden, NLD) *Unable to locate*

Biogeochemistry (Dordrecht, NLD) **[48332]**

Biogeographica (Paris, FRA) *Unable to locate*

Numbers cited in bold after listings are entry numbers rather than page numbers.

Biogeosciences (Mainz, GER) **[44538]**

Biogeosciences Discussions (Gottingen, GER) **[44394]**

Bioinformatics (Oxford, GBR) **[55881]**

Bioinformation (London, GBR) **[54020]**

Bioingenieren (Oslo, NOR) *Unable to locate*

Bioinspiration & Biomimetics (Bristol, GBR) **[52646]**

BIOKEMISTRI (Ilorin, KW, NGA) **[49119]**

Biologia (Lahore, PAK) *Unable to locate*

Biologia Plantarum (Dordrecht, NLD) **[48333]**

Biologica (Madrid, SPA) *Unable to locate*

Biological Chemistry (Berlin, GER) **[44160]**

Biological Conservation (Liverpool, GBR) **[53869]**

Biological Cybernetics (Heidelberg, GER) **[44443]**

Biological Knowledge (London, GBR) **[54021]**

Biological & Pharmaceutical Bulletin (Tokyo, JPN) **[46764]**

Biological Reviews (Cambridge, GBR) **[52792]**

Biological Sciences in Space (Kanagawa, JPN) **[46412]**

Biological Theory (Altenberg, AUT) **[42721]**

Biologicals (London, GBR) **[54022]**

Biologics (Macclesfield, GBR) **[55514]**

Biologija (Warsaw, POL) **[49696]**

Biologisches Zentralblatt **[44491]***

Biologist (London, GBR) **[54023]**

Biology Education (New Delhi, DH, IND) *Unable to locate*

Biology and Fertility of Soils (Tokyo, JPN) **[46765]**

Biology of Inland Waters (Nara, JPN) *Unable to locate*

Biology International (Paris, FRA) **[44029]**

Biology Letters (London, GBR) **[54024]**

Biology and Philosophy (Dordrecht, NLD) **[48334]**

Biology Today (New Delhi, DH, IND) **[45489]**

BioMagnetic Research and Technology (London, GBR) *Ceased*

Biomarkers (London, GBR) **[54025]**

Biomarkers in Medicine (London, GBR) **[54026]**

Biomass Bulletin (Brentwood, GBR) **[52567]**

Biomaterials (Brussels, BEL) **[42845]**

BioMechanics (London, GBR) **[54027]**

Biomechanics and Modeling in Mechanobiology (Tokyo, JPN) **[46766]**

Biomedica (Lahore, PAK) *Unable to locate*

Biomedical Digital Libraries (London, GBR) **[54028]**

BioMedical Engineering OnLine (London, GBR) **[54029]**

Biomedical Human Kinetics (Warsaw, POL) **[49697]**

Biomedical Imaging and Intervention Journal (Kuala Lumpur, MYS) **[47600]**

Biomedical Materials (Bristol, GBR) **[52647]**

Biomedical Research (Tokyo, JPN) *Unable to locate*

Biomedical Research on Trace Elements (Tokyo, JPN) *Unable to locate*

Biomedical Scientist (London, GBR) **[54030]**

Biomedical Signal Processing and Control (Southampton, GBR) **[56568]**

Biomedizinische Technik (Berlin, GER) **[44161]**

Biometrical Journal (Zurich, SWI) **[51255]**

Biometrika (Oxford, GBR) **[55882]**

Biomolecular Frontiers (Singapore, SGP) **[50116]**

Bionature (New Delhi, DH, IND) *Unable to locate*

BioPeople (London, GBR) *Unable to locate*

Biophysical Reviews and Letters (Potsdam, GER) **[44639]**

Biophysics (Tokyo, JPN) *Unable to locate*

Bioprocess and Biosystems Engineering (Garching, GER) **[44377]**

Bioscience, Biotechnology, and Biochemistry (Tokyo, JPN) **[46767]**

Bioscience Education E-journal (Leeds, GBR) **[53757]**

Bioscience Research Bulletin (New Delhi, DH, IND) *Unable to locate*

Bioseparation (Dordrecht, NLD) *Ceased*

BioSocieties (Basingstoke, GBR) **[52196]**

Biostatistics (Oxford, GBR) **[55883]**

BioSynopsis (Chisinau, MDI) *Unable to locate*

Biosystems Engineering (Campos dos Goytacazes, RJ, BRZ) **[42974]**

Biota (Hajdina, SVA) **[50331]**

Biota Colombiana (Bogota, COL) **[43543]**

Biota Neotropica (Campinas, SP, BRZ) **[42962]**

Biotechnology (Rajkot, GJ, IND) **[45707]**

Biotechnology (Faisalabad, PAK) **[49239]**

Biotechnology and Development Monitor **[48240]***

Biotechnology & Molecular Biology Reviews (Kota Kinabalu, MYS) **[47588]**

Biotronics **[46343]***

Biotropia (Bogor, IDN) *Unable to locate*

Bioved (Allahabad, UP, IND) *Unable to locate*

BioVenture View (London, GBR) **[54031]**

Bird Conservation International (Cambridge, GBR) **[52793]**

Bird Life (Sandy, GBR) **[56460]**

Bird Study (Birmingham, GBR) **[52330]**

Bird Watching (Peterborough, GBR) **[56252]**

Birding World (Holt, GBR) **[53583]**

Birds (Sandy, GBR) *Unable to locate*

Birds Eye View (Ta' Xbiex, MAL) **[47743]**

Birlik (Ankara, TUR) *Unable to locate*

Birmingham Life (Cheltenham, GBR) **[52964]**

Birsa Agricultural University Journal of Research (Ranchi, BH, IND) *Unable to locate*

Birstall News (Batley, GBR) **[52268]**

Biscuit World (Oxted, GBR) **[56235]**

Bitidningen (Hallsberg, SWE) *Unable to locate*

Biyokimya Dergisi (Ankara, TUR) **[51490]**

Bizarre (London, GBR) **[54032]**

Biznes i Investitsii v SNG (Moscow, RUS) *Unable to locate*

BJA **[55892]***

BJIR: British Journal of Industrial Relations (Oxford, GBR) **[55884]**

BJOG (Oxford, GBR) **[55885]**

BKR Radio-FM - 94.5 (Birkirkara, MAL) **[47727]**

Black Business Quarterly (Cape Town, SAF) **[50365]**

Black History Month (London, GBR) **[54033]**

Black Lewche (Fringilla, ZMB) **[57107]**

Black Theology (Birmingham, GBR) **[52331]**

Black Theology (Poole, GBR) **[56279]**

Black Theology in Britain **[56279]***

Black and White Photography (Lewes, GBR) **[53847]**

Blacktown Advocate (Parramatta, NW, AUS) **[42233]**

Blackwater Herald (Sydney, NW, AUS) **[42475]**

BladNA (Amsterdam, NLD) *Unable to locate*

Blah Blah (Reading, GBR) **[56311]**

Blast 1386-AM - 1386 (Reading, GBR) **[56337]**

Blastpipe (Bo'ness, GBR) **[52406]**

Blitz (Mumbai, MH, IND) *Unable to locate*

Blitz Illu (Wiesbaden, GER) *Unable to locate*

Bloc Notes Publishing (Paris, FRA) **[44030]**

Bloemnews (Cape Town, SAF) **[50366]**

Blomster (Holbaek, DEN) *Unable to locate*

Blonde Hair (Bristol, GBR) **[52648]**

Blood Cells, Molecules, & Diseases (Amsterdam, NLD) **[47912]**

Blood Pressure (Goteborg, SWE) **[50957]**

Blood Therapies in Medicine (London, GBR) *Unable to locate*

Blood Therapy Journal International (New Delhi, DH, IND) *Unable to locate*

BloodMed (Oxford, GBR) **[55886]**

Blue Band Magazine (Portsmouth, GBR) **[56287]**

Blue Chip (Cape Town, SAF) **[50367]**

Blue Mountains Gazette (Blue Mountains, NW, AUS) **[41603]**

Blue Moves (Edinburgh, GBR) *Unable to locate*

Blue Triangle (Lagos, LG, NGA) *Unable to locate*

Blueprint (Chelmsford, GBR) **[52960]**

Bluestocking (Rondebosch, SAF) *Unable to locate*

blunt (Durban, SAF) **[50467]**

BM Radio-FM - 99.3 (Zenica, HBO) **[42942]**

BMA News (London, GBR) **[54034]**

BMA News Review **[54034]***

BMC Anesthesiology (London, GBR) **[54035]**

BMC Biochemistry (London, GBR) **[54036]**

BMC Bioinformatics (London, GBR) **[54037]**

BMC Biology (London, GBR) **[54038]**

BMC Biotechnology (London, GBR) **[54039]**

BMC Blood Disorders (London, GBR) **[54040]**

BMC Cancer (London, GBR) **[54041]**

BMC Cardiovascular Disorders (London, GBR) **[54042]**

BMC Cell Biology (London, GBR) **[54043]**

BMC Chemical Biology (London, GBR) **[54044]**

BMC Clinical Pathology (London, GBR) **[54045]**

BMC Clinical Pharmacology (London, GBR) **[54046]**

BMC Complementary and Alternative Medicine (London, GBR) **[54047]**

BMC Dermatology (London, GBR) **[54048]**

BMC Developmental Biology (London, GBR) **[54049]**

BMC Ear, Nose and Throat Disorders (London, GBR) **[54050]**

BMC Ecology (London, GBR) **[54051]**

BMC Emergency Medicine (London, GBR) **[54052]**

BMC Endocrine Disorders (London, GBR) **[54053]**

BMC Evolutionary Biology (London, GBR) **[54054]**

BMC Family Practice (London, GBR) **[54055]**

BMC Gastroenterology (London, GBR) **[54056]**

BMC Genetics (London, GBR) **[54057]**

BMC Genomics (London, GBR) **[54058]**

BMC Geriatrics (London, GBR) **[54059]**

BMC Health Services Research (London, GBR) **[54060]**

BMC Immunology (London, GBR) **[54061]**

BMC Infectious Diseases (London, GBR) **[54062]**

BMC International Health and Human Rights (London, GBR) **[54063]**

BMC Medical Education (London, GBR) **[54064]**

BMC Medical Ethics (London, GBR) **[54065]**

BMC Medical Genetics (London, GBR) **[54066]**

BMC Medical Imaging (London, GBR) **[54067]**

BMC Medical Informatics and Decision Making (London, GBR) **[54068]**

BMC Medical Physics (London, GBR) **[54069]**

BMC Medical Research Methodology (London, GBR) **[54070]**

BMC Medicine (London, GBR) **[54071]**

BMC Microbiology (London, GBR) **[54072]**

BMC Molecular Biology (London, GBR) **[54073]**

BMC Musculoskeletal Disorders (London, GBR) **[54074]**

BMC Nephrology (London, GBR) **[54075]**

BMC Neurology (London, GBR) **[54076]**

BMC Neuroscience (London, GBR) **[54077]**

BMC Nuclear Medicine **[54069]***

BMC Nursing (London, GBR) **[54078]**

BMC Ophthalmology (London, GBR) **[54079]**

BMC Oral Health (London, GBR) **[54080]**

BMC Palliative Care (London, GBR) **[54081]**

BMC Pediatrics (London, GBR) **[54082]**

BMC Pharmacology (London, GBR) **[54083]**

Numbers cited in bold after listings are entry numbers rather than page numbers.

BMC Physiology (London, GBR) **[54084]**

BMC Plant Biology (London, GBR) **[54085]**

BMC Pregnancy and Childbirth (London, GBR) **[54086]**

BMC Psychiatry (London, GBR) **[54087]**

BMC Public Health (San Salvador, ELS) **[43777]**

BMC Pulmonary Medicine (London, GBR) **[54088]**

BMC Structural Biology (London, GBR) **[54089]**

BMC Surgery (London, GBR) **[54090]**

BMC Urology (London, GBR) **[54091]**

BMC Veterinary Research (London, GBR) **[54092]**

BMC Women's Health (London, GBR) **[54093]**

BMHF Yearbook & Directory (West Bromwich, GBR) **[56889]**

BMJ Specialist Journals (London, GBR) *Unable to locate*

BMW Car (Sevenoaks, GBR) **[56470]**

Boadland-FM **[55747]***

Boarding School (London, GBR) **[54094]**

Boards (Southend-on-Sea, GBR) **[56584]**

Boat International Russia (Moscow, RUS) **[49884]**

Boat Mart (Birmingham, GBR) **[52332]**

Boat Mart International **[52332]***

Boat Trader (Chichester, GBR) **[53005]**

Boat and Yacht Buyer (Cambridge, GBR) **[52794]**

Boating New Zealand (Auckland, NZL) **[48787]**

Boats and Yachting (Qormi, MAL) **[47738]**

Bob the Builder (London, GBR) **[54095]**

Body & Beauty Care (Mumbai, MH, IND) *Unable to locate*

Body Language (Hove, GBR) *Unable to locate*

Body, Movement and Dance in Psychotherapy (Hatfield, GBR) **[53538]**

Body & Society (London, GBR) **[54096]**

Bodybuilding Journal (Hong Kong, CHN) *Unable to locate*

Boer Briefs (Armidale, NW, AUS) **[41559]**

Boersen (Copenhagen, DEN) **[43657]**

Bogazici Journal (Istanbul, TUR) **[51557]**

Bognor Regis Observer (Bognor Regis, GBR) **[52392]**

The Bohol Chronicle (Tagbilaran, PHL) **[49637]**

Bok og Samfunn (Oslo, NOR) *Unable to locate*

Bokasafnid (Reykjavik, ICE) **[44898]**

Bokatidindi (Reykjavik, ICE) *Unable to locate*

Bokatidindi (Reykjavik, ICE) *Unable to locate*

BOLA SportsLine (Jakarta, IDN) **[45793]**

Bolero (Zurich, SWI) *Unable to locate*

Boletim da Sociedade Broteriana (Coimbra, PRT) *Unable to locate*

Boletin (Mexico City, DF, MEX) **[47782]**

Boletin Bibliografico (Bogota, COL) *Unable to locate*

Boletin de Estudios Latinoamericanos y del Caribe **[48225]***

Boletin La Chiva (Panama, PAN) *Unable to locate*

Boletin de Oneutacion (Madrid, SPA) *Unable to locate*

Boletin Proaft (Mexico City, DF, MEX) *Unable to locate*

Boletin de la Sociedad Geografica de Lima (Lima, PER) *Unable to locate*

Bolivian Times (La Paz, BOL) *Unable to locate*

Bolletino di Collegamento e d'Informazione (Rome, ITA) *Unable to locate*

Bollettino (Rome, ITA) *Unable to locate*

Bollettino AIB (Rome, ITA) *Unable to locate*

Bollettino di Storia delle Scienze Matematiche (Bologna, ITA) **[46125]**

Bollettino Telematico di Filosofia Politica (Pisa, ITA) **[46218]**

The Bolton Evening News **[52405]***

The Bolton News (Bolton, GBR) **[52405]**

Bombay (Mumbai, MH, IND) *Unable to locate*

Bombay Chartered Accountant Journal (Mumbai, MH, IND) **[45357]**

Bombay Hospital Journal (Mumbai, MH, IND) **[45358]**

Bombay Labour Journal (Mumbai, MH, IND) *Unable to locate*

Bombay Law Reporter (Mumbai, MH, IND) *Unable to locate*

Bombay Market (Mumbai, MH, IND) *Unable to locate*

Bomsel (Patna, BH, IND) *Unable to locate*

Bonaire Holiday! (Curacao, NAT) *Unable to locate*

Bond Law Review (Gold Coast, QL, AUS) **[41898]**

Bondi-FM - 88.0 (Bondi Beach, NW, AUS) **[41605]**

Bo'ness Journal (Linlithgow, GBR) **[53858]**

Bongo News (Accra, GHA) **[44725]**

Bonjour! (Ramsgate, GBR) **[56308]**

Bonsai Autoctono (Valencia, SPA) **[50843]**

Boobook (Carlton, VI, AUS) **[41725]**

Boogie Woogie en Blues Collector (Amsterdam-Zuidoost, NLD) *Unable to locate*

The Book Collector (Thurlby by Bourne, GBR) **[56749]**

Book and Magazine Collector (London, GBR) **[54097]**

Book Monthly; Antiquarian **[55173]***

Book Review (New Delhi, DH, IND) *Unable to locate*

Book Review Index: Africa (New Delhi, DH, IND) *Unable to locate*

The Book Trade Yearbook (London, GBR) *Unable to locate*

Bookbinder (Shepperton, GBR) **[56520]**

Bookbird (Basel, SWI) **[51060]**

Bookbird: A Journal of International Children's Literature (Toronto, ON, CAN) *Unable to locate*

Bookeeping & Development **[55644]***

Booknotes (Wellington, NZL) **[49001]**

The Bookplate Journal (Walberton, GBR) **[56811]**

Books from Finland (Helsinki, FIN) **[43821]**

Books for Keeps (London, GBR) **[54098]**

Books Quarterly (London, GBR) *Unable to locate*

Bookseller (Lahore, PAK) *Unable to locate*

Booksellers News (Wellington, NZL) **[49002]**

Bookselling **[54099]***

Bookselling Essentials (London, GBR) **[54099]**

Bookselling News **[54099]***

B'Or Ha'Torah (Jerusalem, ISR) **[46081]**

Border Counties Advertizer (Oswestry, GBR) **[55856]**

Boreas (Arhus, DEN) **[43645]**

Borgyogyaszati es Venerologiai Szemle (Debrecen, HUN) *Unable to locate*

Born & Unge (Copenhagen, DEN) *Unable to locate*

Borneo Bulletin (Bandar Seri Begawan, BRN) **[43072]**

Borneo Review (Kota Kinabalu, MYS) **[47589]**

Borns Hverdag (Copenhagen, DEN) *Unable to locate*

Borrsavangen (Lund, SWE) **[50984]**

Bose Institute Transactions (Calcutta, WB, IND) *Unable to locate*

Bosnia Report (London, GBR) **[54100]**

Bostausslituationen i Norden (Oslo, NOR) *Unable to locate*

Boston Standard (Boston, GBR) **[52408]**

The Botanica (Delhi, DH, IND) *Unable to locate*

Botanica Marina (Berlin, GER) **[44162]**

Botanical Studies (Taipei, TWN) **[51333]**

Botanical Survey of India Bulletin (New Delhi, DH, IND) *Unable to locate*

Botanicheski Zhurnal (Saint Petersburg, RUS) *Unable to locate*

Botanique (Nagpur, MH, IND) *Unable to locate*

Botany Research Journal (Faisalabad, PAK) **[49240]**

Botou People's Broadcasting Station (Botou, HB, CHN) *Unable to locate*

Botswana Journal of Technology (Gaborone, BWA) **[42943]**

Botswana Notes and Records (Gaborone, BWA) *Unable to locate*

The Bottle Street Gazette (London, GBR) **[54101]**

The Botulinum Journal (Geneva, SWI) **[51088]**

Boundary-Layer Meteorology (Dordrecht, NLD) **[48335]**

Boundary and Security Bulletin (Durham, GBR) *Ceased*

BouwNed Belang (Gouda, NLD) *Unable to locate*

Boxing Monthly (London, GBR) **[54102]**

Boys' Brigade Gazette (Hemel Hempstead, GBR) **[53555]**

Boys Toys (Poole, GBR) **[56280]**

Braford Annual (Rockhampton, QL, AUS) **[42314]**

Bragantia (Campinas, SP, BRZ) **[42964]**

Bragantia (Campinas, SP, BRZ) **[42963]**

Braille Science Journal (Edinburgh, GBR) *Ceased*

The Braille Sporting Record (Edinburgh, GBR) **[53256]**

Brain (Oxford, GBR) **[55887]**

Brain Impairment (Bowen Hills, QL, AUS) **[41625]**

Brain and Language (Amsterdam, NLD) **[47913]**

Brain and Mind (Dordrecht, NLD) **[48336]**

Brain News (Calcutta, WB, IND) *Unable to locate*

Brain Research Bulletin (Amsterdam, NLD) **[47914]**

Brain Tumor Pathology (Tokyo, JPN) **[46768]**

Brains, Minds and Media (Cologne, GER) **[44289]**

BRAK - Mitteilungen (Bonn, GER) *Unable to locate*

Bram Stoker Society Journal (Dublin, DU, IRL) *Unable to locate*

Branch-FM - 101.8 (Dewsbury, GBR) **[53182]**

Brandpunt (Brussels, BEL) *Unable to locate*

Brasil Rotario (Rio de Janeiro, RJ, BRZ) *Unable to locate*

Brass Band World (High Peak, GBR) *Unable to locate*

Brauwelt Chinese (Nuremberg, GER) **[44603]**

Brauwelt Deutsch (Nuremberg, GER) **[44604]**

Brauwelt en Espanol (Nuremberg, GER) **[44605]**

Brauwelt International (Nuremberg, GER) **[44606]**

Brauwelt in Russian (Nuremberg, GER) **[44607]**

Brazil Business Brief (London, GBR) **[54103]**

Brazilian Archives of Biology and Technology (BABT) (Curitiba, PR, BRZ) **[42976]**

Brazilian Dental Journal (Ribeirao Preto, SP, BRZ) **[42995]**

The Brazilian Electronic Journal of Economics (BEJE) (Recife, PB, BRZ) **[42994]**

Brazilian Journal of Chemical Engineering (Sao Paulo, SP, BRZ) **[43025]**

Brazilian Journal of Infectious Diseases (Salvador, BH, BRZ) **[43014]**

Brazilian Journal of Medical and Biological Research (Ribeirao Preto, SP, BRZ) **[42996]**

Brazilian Journal of Microbiology (Sao Paulo, SP, BRZ) **[43026]**

Brazilian Journal of Oral Sciences (Sao Paulo, SP, BRZ) **[43027]**

Brazilian Journal of Physics (Sao Paulo, SP, BRZ) **[43028]**

Brazilian Journal of Plant Physiology (Pelotas, RN, BRZ) **[42989]**

Brazilian Journal of Veterinary Research and Animal Science (Sao Paulo, SP, BRZ) **[43029]**

Brazilian Oral Research (Sao Paulo, SP, BRZ) **[43030]**

Break In (Upper Hutt, NZL) **[48992]**

Breakthrough (Taipei, TWN) *Unable to locate*

Breast Cancer Online (Nottingham, GBR) **[55749]**

Breast Cancer Research and Treatment (Dordrecht, NLD) **[48337]**

Breast Disease (Amsterdam, NLD) **[47915]**

Breastfeeding Review (Glen Iris, VI, AUS) **[41891]**

Breathe (London, GBR) **[54104]**

Brechin Advertiser (Brechin, GBR) **[52563]**

Breeding Science (Kyoto, JPN) **[46467]**

Breeze-FM (Browns Plains, QL, AUS) *Unable to locate*

The Breeze-FM - 94 (Auckland, NZL) **[48835]**

The Breeze-FM - 94.5 (Christchurch, NZL) **[48880]**

The Breeze-FM - 99.3 (Hamilton, NZL) **[48912]**

Numbers cited in bold after listings are entry numbers rather than page numbers.

Bremen Eins-FM - 89.3 (Bremen, GER) **[44286]**

Bremen Eins-FM - 92.75 (Bremen, GER) **[44284]**

Bremen Eins-FM - 93.8 (Bremen, GER) **[44285]**

Bremen Eins-FM - 87.85 (Bremen, GER) **[44283]**

Brentwood Gazette Series (Brentwood, GBR) **[52568]**

Brewer's Contract (Edinburgh, GBR) *Unable to locate*

Brewers' Guardian (Reigate, GBR) **[56386]**

Bribie Weekly (Sydney, NW, AUS) **[42476]**

Bridal Buyer (Huddersfield, GBR) **[53616]**

Bridge (London, GBR) **[54105]**

Bridge Design & Engineering (London, GBR) **[54106]**

Bridge-FM - 106.3 (Bridgend, GBR) **[52593]**

Bridge Structures (Amsterdam, NLD) **[47916]**

Bridlington Free Press (Bridlington, GBR) **[52597]**

Bridport & Lyme Regis News (Bridport, GBR) **[52599]**

Brief Treatment and Crisis Intervention (Oxford, GBR) **[55888]**

Briefings in Bioinformatics (Oxford, GBR) **[55889]**

Briefings in Functional Genomics & Proteomics (Oxford, GBR) **[55890]**

Briefings in Real Estate Finance (Bognor Regis, GBR) **[52393]**

Brighouse Echo (Brighouse, GBR) **[52600]**

Bright 106.4-FM - 106.4 (Burgess Hill, GBR) **[52762]**

Brighton & Hove Life (Norwich, GBR) **[55726]**

Brihanmumbai Mahanagarpalika Patrika (Mumbai, MH, IND) *Unable to locate*

Brill's Annual of Afroasiatic Languages and Linguistics (Leiden, NLD) **[48658]**

Brimbank Leader (Tullamarine, VI, AUS) **[42650]**

Brisbane Feel Good-FM - 97.3 (Brisbane, QL, AUS) **[41656]**

Brisbane Times (Sydney, NW, AUS) **[42477]**

Britain Overseas (London, GBR) *Unable to locate*

Britannia (London, GBR) **[54107]**

Britball (Edinburgh, GBR) **[53257]**

British Actuarial Journal (London, GBR) **[54108]**

British Airways News (Harmondsworth, GBR) *Unable to locate*

British Archaeology (York, GBR) **[56988]**

The British Audio Journal (New Malden, GBR) *Unable to locate*

British Baker (Crawley, GBR) **[53099]**

The British Bandsman (Beaconsfield, GBR) *Unable to locate*

British Blacksmith **[52155]***

British Broadcasting Corporation (BBC) WS (Moscow, RUS) *Unable to locate*

British Broadcasting Corporation (BBC) WS (Moscow, RUS) *Unable to locate*

British Business in China (Beijing, CHN) **[43174]**

British Chess Magazine (London, GBR) **[54109]**

The British China Painter (Grantham, GBR) *Unable to locate*

British Commercial Agents Review (Harrogate, GBR) **[53515]**

British Corrosion Journal (London, GBR) *Unable to locate*

British Dental Journal (London, GBR) **[54110]**

British Dragonfly Society Journal (Leeds, GBR) **[53758]**

British Economy Survey (London, GBR) *Unable to locate*

British Elections & Parties Review **[51893]***

British European Flying Colours (Croydon, GBR) *Unable to locate*

British Farm and Outdoor Power Equipment Guide **[56256]***

British Food Journal (Bradford, GBR) **[52438]**

British Heart Journal **[54545]***

British Homeopathic Journal (Basingstoke, GBR) *Ceased*

The British Journal of Aesthetics (Oxford, GBR) **[55891]**

British Journal of Anaesthesia (Oxford, GBR) **[55892]**

British Journal of Anaesthetic and Recovery Nursing (London, GBR) **[54111]**

British Journal of Applied Physics **[52695]***

British Journal of Biomedical Science (London, GBR) **[54112]**

British Journal of Cancer (London, GBR) **[54113]**

British Journal of Cancer Management (London, GBR) **[54114]**

British Journal of Cardiac Nursing (London, GBR) **[54115]**

The British Journal of Cardiology (Farnham, GBR) **[53380]**

British Journal of Clinical Pharmacology (London, GBR) **[54116]**

British Journal of Clinical Psychology (Leicester, GBR) **[53786]**

British Journal of Clinical Research **[54726]***

British Journal of Community Nursing (London, GBR) **[54117]**

The British Journal of Criminology (Oxford, GBR) **[55893]**

British Journal of Dermatology (London, GBR) **[54118]**

British Journal of Dermatology Nursing (London, GBR) **[54119]**

The British Journal of Developmental Disabilities (Modling, AUT) **[42736]**

British Journal of Developmental Psychology (Leicester, GBR) **[53787]**

The British Journal of Diabetes and Vascular Disease (Birmingham, GBR) **[52333]**

British Journal of Educational Psychology (Leicester, GBR) **[53788]**

British Journal of Ethnomusicology **[51776]***

The British Journal of Forensic Practice (Brighton, GBR) **[52607]**

British Journal of General Practice (London, GBR) **[54120]**

British Journal of Guidance and Counselling (Abingdon, GBR) **[51718]**

British Journal of Haematology (London, GBR) *Unable to locate*

British Journal of Health Care Management (London, GBR) **[54121]**

British Journal of Health Psychology (Leicester, GBR) **[53789]**

British Journal of Healthcare Assistants (London, GBR) **[54122]**

British Journal for the History of Philosophy (Abingdon, GBR) **[51719]**

British Journal for the History of Science (Norwich, GBR) **[55727]**

British Journal of Hospital Medicine (London, GBR) **[54123]**

British Journal of Intensive Care (London, GBR) **[54124]**

British Journal of Learning Disabilities (Worcestershire, GBR) **[56966]**

British Journal of Management (Oxford, GBR) **[55894]**

British Journal of Mathematical and Statistical Psychology (Leicester, GBR) **[53790]**

British Journal of Medical Psychology **[53820]***

British Journal of Middle Eastern Studies (Leeds, GBR) **[53759]**

British Journal of Midwifery (London, GBR) **[54125]**

British Journal of Music Therapy (London, GBR) **[54126]**

British Journal of Neuroscience Nursing (London, GBR) **[54127]**

British Journal of Neurosurgery (Abingdon, GBR) **[51720]**

The British Journal of NonDestructive Testing **[55710]***

British Journal of Nutrition (Cambridge, GBR) **[52795]**

British Journal of Obstetrics and Gynaecology **[55885]***

British Journal of Occupational Therapy (London, GBR) **[54128]**

British Journal of Ophthalmology (London, GBR) **[54129]**

British Journal of Perioperitive Nurses **[53517]***

British Journal of Pharmacology (London, GBR) **[54130]**

The British Journal for the Philosophy of Science (Bristol, GBR) **[52649]**

British Journal of Photography (London, GBR) **[54131]**

British Journal of Phytotherapy (Battle, GBR) *Unable to locate*

British Journal of Play Therapy (Weybridge, GBR) **[56912]**

British Journal of Political Science (Cambridge, GBR) **[52796]**

The British Journal of Politics and International Relations (Nottingham, GBR) **[55750]**

British Journal of Psychiatry (London, GBR) **[54132]**

British Journal of Psychology (Leicester, GBR) **[53791]**

British Journal of Radiology (London, GBR) **[54133]**

The British Journal of Religious Education (Birmingham, GBR) **[52334]**

British Journal of Renal Medicine (London, GBR) **[54134]**

British Journal of Rheumatology **[55202]***

British Journal of School Nursing (London, GBR) **[54135]**

British Journal of Sexual Medicine (London, GBR) **[54136]**

British Journal of Social Psychology (Leicester, GBR) **[53792]**

The British Journal of Social Work (Belfast, GBR) **[52279]**

The British Journal of Sociology (Abingdon, GBR) **[51721]**

British Journal of Special Education (Tamworth, GBR) **[56717]**

British Journal of Sports Medicine (London, GBR) **[54137]**

British Journal of Surgery (Chichester, GBR) **[53006]**

British Journal of Theatre Nurses **[53517]***

British Journal of Therapy and Rehabilitation (BJTR) **[54665]***

British Journalism Review (London, GBR) **[54138]**

British Manager, Journal of Administrative Management **[54903]***

British Medical Bulletin (Oxford, GBR) **[55895]**

British Medical Journal (London, GBR) **[54139]**

British Medical Journal Clinical Evidence (London, GBR) **[54140]**

British Museum Studies in Ancient Egypt and Sudan (BMSAES) (London, GBR) **[54141]**

British Music (Upminster, GBR) *Unable to locate*

British National Formulary (London, GBR) **[54142]**

British Numismatic Journal (London, GBR) **[54143]**

British Orthoptic Journal (London, GBR) **[54144]**

British Philatelic Bulletin (London, GBR) **[54145]**

British Plastics & Rubber (Tattenhall, GBR) *Unable to locate*

British Politics (Basingstoke, GBR) **[52197]**

British Postmark Bulletin (London, GBR) **[54146]**

British Poultry Science (Roslin, GBR) **[56408]**

British Register of Wanted Publications Updated Daily - 8 Parts (Oxford, GBR) *Unable to locate*

British Style **[54147]***

British Style (London, GBR) **[54147]**

British Sugar Beet Review (Peterborough, GBR) **[56253]**

British Tax Review (Andover, GBR) **[52111]**

The British Theatre Directory (London, GBR) **[54148]**

The British Virgin Islands Welcome Tourist Guide (Tortola, BVI) **[43069]**

British Yearbook of International Law (Cambridge, GBR) **[52797]**

Brittle Star (London, GBR) **[54149]**

Briviba (Riga, LAT) *Unable to locate*

BRMB-FM - 96.4 (Birmingham, GBR) **[52374]**

Broadcast (London, GBR) *Unable to locate*

Broadcaster (Colombo, SRI) *Unable to locate*

Broadcasting Corporation of China - Chentoshan, TWN) *Unable to locate*

Broadcasting Corporation of China - Chentoshan (Chia-I, TWN) *Ceased*

Broadcasting Corporation of China - Hualien, TWN) *Unable to locate*

Broadcasting Corporation of China - Huoyenshan, TWN) *Unable to locate*

Broadcasting Corporation of China - Huoyenshan (Huoyenshan, TWN) *Unable to locate*

Broadcasting Corporation of China - Ilan, TWN) *Ceased*

Broadcasting Corporation of China - Ilan, TWN) *Ceased*

Broadcasting Corporation of China - Kaohsiung, TWN) *Unable to locate*

Broadcasting Corporation of China - Taichung, TWN) *Unable to locate*

Broadcasting Corporation of China - Taichung, TWN) *Unable to locate*

Broadcasting Corporation of China - Taipei, TWN) *Unable to locate*

Broadcasting Corporation of China - Taitung, TWN) *Unable to locate*

Broadcasting Corporation of China - Taitung, TWN) *Unable to locate*

The Broadsheet (Madrid, SPA) *Unable to locate*

Numbers cited in bold after listings are entry numbers rather than page numbers.

Broken Gardenia (Birmingham, GBR) *Ceased*

The Broker (London, GBR) *Unable to locate*

Bromsgrove Standard (Bromsgrove, GBR) [52746]

Bronte Society Transactions [54150]*

Bronte Studies (London, GBR) [54150]

The Brooklands Society Gazette (Fleet, GBR) [53389]

Brooks Bulletin (Hong Kong, CHN) *Unable to locate*

BrotherSister (Richmond, VI, AUS) *Unable to locate*

Brownie (London, GBR) *Ceased*

Brown's Nautical Almanac (Glasgow, GBR) [53410]

BRPT Bulletin (Agartala, TR, IND) *Unable to locate*

The Brundland Report (Port Louis, MUS) *Unable to locate*

The Brunei Times (Bandar Seri Begawan, BRN) [43073]

Brunel-FM - 107.7 (Swindon, GBR) [56714]

BRW (Melbourne, VI, AUS) [42055]

BSHM Bulletin (Oxford, GBR) [55896]

BSP Magazine (Bhilai, MP, IND) *Unable to locate*

BTE Journal (Sunbury-on-Thames, GBR) [56652]

BTV-3 (Beijing, CHN) *Unable to locate*

BTV-2 (Beijing, CHN) *Unable to locate*

Bubble Science, Engineering and Technology (London, GBR) [54151]

Buch Journal (Frankfurt, GER) *Unable to locate*

Buckingham & Winslow Advertiser (Buckingham, GBR) [52755]

Buckinghamshire Life (West Sussex, GBR) [56896]

Bucks Herald (Aylesbury, GBR) [52146]

Buddhist Studies (New Delhi, DH, IND) *Unable to locate*

Buddhist Studies Review (Sunderland, GBR) [56653]

Buddhist Tradition Series (New Delhi, DH, IND) *Unable to locate*

Buderim Chronicle (Sydney, NW, AUS) [42478]

Buenos Aires Herald (Buenos Aires, ARG) [41470]

Buffalo Journal (Bangkok, THA) [51415]

Bug (Seoul, KOR) *Unable to locate*

Buick News (Merrylands, NW, AUS) [42103]

Build It (Birmingham, GBR) [52335]

Builders of Indian Anthropology (Varanasi, UP, IND) *Unable to locate*

BuildHOME Vic (North Ryde, NW, AUS) [42174]

Building (London, GBR) [54152]

Building Acoustics (Brentwood, GBR) [52569]

Building Design (London, GBR) *Unable to locate*

Building Engineer (Northampton, GBR) [55706]

Building and Environment (Amsterdam, NLD) [47917]

Building and Estate Management Society Proceedings (Singapore, SGP) *Unable to locate*

Building Journal Hong Kong (Hong Kong, CHN) [43284]

Building for Leisure (Wallington, GBR) [56832]

Building Products (Croydon, GBR) [53122]

Building Research Capacity (Cardiff, GBR) [52925]

Building Research & Information (London, GBR) [54153]

Building Sciences; Journal of Thermal Envelope and [54716]*

Building Services Engineering Research and Technology (London, GBR) [54154]

Building Women (Johannesburg, SAF) [50528]

The Building Worker (Wellington, NZL) *Unable to locate*

Bula-FM - 102.0 (Suva, FIJ) [43807]

Bulatlat (Quezon City, PHL) *Unable to locate*

Buletin AGIR (Bucharest, ROM) [49833]

Bulgarian Army (Sofia, BUL) *Unable to locate*

Bulgarian Chemical Communications (Sofia, BUL) [43094]

Bulgarian Chemistry and Industry (Sofia, BUL) *Unable to locate*

Bulgarian Folklore (Sofia, BUL) [43095]

Bulgarian Geophysical Journal (Sofia, BUL) [43096]

Bulgarian Journal of Veterinary Medicine (BJVM) (Stara Zagora, BUL) [43110]

Bulgarian Musicology (Sofia, BUL) [43097]

Bulgarian Review of Opthalmology (Sofia, BUL) *Unable to locate*

Bulk Distributor (Surbiton, GBR) [56657]

Bullet (New Delhi, DH, IND) *Unable to locate*

Bulletin (Dhaka, BGD) *Unable to locate*

Bulletin (Tehran, IRN) *Unable to locate*

Bulletin (Skopje, MEC) *Unable to locate*

The Bulletin (Hong Kong, CHN) [43285]

Bulletin (Ljubljana, SVA) *Unable to locate*

The Bulletin (Geneva, SWI) *Unable to locate*

Bulletin (Leamington Spa, GBR) [53744]

Bulletin (London, GBR) [54155]

The Bulletin (London, GBR) [54156]

Bulletin (Princes Risborough, GBR) *Unable to locate*

Bulletin Academia de Ciencias Fisicas, Matematicas y Naturales (Caracas, VEN) *Unable to locate*

Bulletin of Agriculture Prices (New Delhi, DH, IND) *Unable to locate*

Bulletin of Animal Health and Production in Africa (Nairobi, KEN) [47175]

Bulletin Antieke Beschaving (BABESCH) (Leiden, NLD) [48659]

Bulletin of the Brazilian Mathematical Society (Stockholm, SWE) [51010]

Bulletin of the Brazilian Mathematical Society, New Series (Dordrecht, NLD) [48338]

Bulletin of the Calcutta Mathematical Society (Calcutta, WB, IND) *Unable to locate*

Bulletin du Cancer (Montrouge, FRA) [43982]

Bulletin de Centre Scientifique de Monaco (Monte Carlo, MCO) *Ceased*

Bulletin of the Chemical Society of Ethiopia (Addis Ababa, ETH) [43796]

Bulletin of the Chemical Society of Japan (Tokyo, JPN) [46769]

Bulletin Circulaire de L'OIE [44083]*

Bulletin, Classe des Sciences Mathematiques et Naturelles, Sciences mathematiques (Helsinki, FIN) [43822]

Bulletin on Consumption of Non-Ferrous Metals—Copper, Lead & Zinc (New Delhi, DH, IND) *Unable to locate*

Bulletin of the Crimean Astrophysical Observatory (Moscow, RUS) [49885]

Bulletin of Earth Sciences (Pune, MH, IND) *Unable to locate*

Bulletin of Earthquake Engineering (Dordrecht, NLD) [48339]

Bulletin of Economic Research (Oxford, GBR) [55897]

Bulletin of Engineering Geology and the Environment (Tokyo, JPN) [46770]

Bulletin of Entomological Research (Cardiff, GBR) [52926]

Bulletin of the Geological Society of Malaysia (GSM) (Kuala Lumpur, MYS) *Unable to locate*

Bulletin Infirmier du Cancer (Montrouge, FRA) [43983]

Bulletin of the Institute of Zoology, Academia Sinica [51368]*

Bulletin of the Irish Mathematical Society (Belfast, GBR) [52280]

Bulletin of the Korean Chemical Society (Seoul, KOR) [47259]

Bulletin of the Korean Mathematical Society (Pohang, KOR) [47247]

Bulletin de l'ALLF (Bordeaux, FRA) [43921]

Bulletin of Legal Developments (London, GBR) *Ceased*

Bulletin de Liaison (Coulonges-les-Sablons, FRA) *Unable to locate*

Bulletin of the Malacological Society of London (Manchester, GBR) [55545]

Bulletin of Materials Science (Bangalore, KA, IND) [44951]

Bulletin of Mathematical Biology (Dordrecht, NLD) [48340]

Bulletin of Medical Ethics (Colchester, GBR) [53031]

Bulletin of the Military Historical Society (London, GBR) *Unable to locate*

The Bulletin with Newsweek (Sydney, NW, AUS) [42479]

Bulletin of the Polish Academy of Sciences Mathematics (Warsaw, POL) [49698]

Bulletin of Pure and Applied Mathematics (Jodhpur, RJ, IND) [45216]

Bulletin of Pure & Applied Sciences Section A: Zoology (Shahdara, DH, IND) *Unable to locate*

Bulletin of Pure & Applied Sciences Section B: Botany (Shahdara, DH, IND) *Unable to locate*

Bulletin of Pure & Applied Sciences Section C: Chemistry (Shahdara, DH, IND) *Unable to locate*

Bulletin of Pure & Applied Sciences Section E: Mathematics (Shahdara, DH, IND) *Unable to locate*

Bulletin of the Ramakrishna Mission Institute of Culture (Kolkata, WB, IND) [45260]

Bulletin of the School of Oriental and African Studies (London, GBR) [54157]

Bulletin des Sciences Mathematiques (Amsterdam, NLD) [47918]

Bulletin of the Scientific Instrument Society (Faringdon, GBR) *Unable to locate*

Bulletin of Spanish Studies (Abingdon, GBR) [51722]

The Bulletin of Sri Aurobindo International Centre of Education (Pondicherry, PN, IND) [45691]

Bulletin of State Savings Bank (Sofia, BUL) *Unable to locate*

Bulletin Strijela (Zagreb, CTA) *Unable to locate*

The Bulletin of Tokyo Dental College (Chiba, JPN) [46316]

The Bulletin of the Veterinary Institute in Pulawy (Pulawy, POL) [49674]

Bulletin of Volcanology (Tokyo, JPN) [46771]

Bulletin of the World Health Organization (Geneva, SWI) [51089]

Bulletin Zen - Journal de l'AZI (Paris, FRA) *Unable to locate*

Bund Magazine (Berlin, GER) *Unable to locate*

Bundesgesundheitsblatt - Gesundheitsforschung - Gesundheitsschutz (Berlin, GER) [44163]

Bunkered (Glasgow, GBR) [53411]

Bunsen-Magazin (Frankfurt, GER) *Unable to locate*

Burke's Backyard Magazine (Crows Nest, NW, AUS) [41821]

The Burlington Magazine (London, GBR) [54158]

Burniston Today (Scarborough, GBR) [56463]

BURNS (Tokyo, JPN) *Unable to locate*

B.U.R.O. (Vienna, AUT) *Unable to locate*

Burton Mail (Burton-on-Trent, GBR) [52770]

Bury Free Press (Bury Saint Edmunds, GBR) [52773]

Bus und Bahn (Dusseldorf, GER) *Unable to locate*

Bus & Coach Preservation (Portsmouth, GBR) [56288]

Buses (Leven, GBR) [53845]

Bush Telegraph (Sydney, NW, AUS) [42480]

The Business (Aberdeen, GBR) *Unable to locate*

The Business (Aldershot, GBR) [52097]

The Business (Dundee, GBR) *Unable to locate*

The Business (London, GBR) *Unable to locate*

The Business (Northampton, GBR) *Unable to locate*

Business Analyst (New Delhi, DH, IND) *Unable to locate*

Business Asia (North Sydney, NW, AUS) [42210]

Business Beijing (Beijing, CHN) [43175]

Business Citizen (Edinburgh, GBR) [53258]

Business Colombia (Bogota, COL) *Unable to locate*

The Business Communicator [54618]*

Business Computer (Mumbai, MH, IND) *Unable to locate*

Business Contact (Moscow, RUS) *Unable to locate*

Business Contact magazine (Durham, GBR) *Unable to locate*

Business Day (Johannesburg, SAF) [50529]

Numbers cited in bold after listings are entry numbers rather than page numbers.

Business Day (Bangkok, THA) **[51416]**

Business Day (Thailand) (Bangkok, THA) *Unable to locate*

Business East Midlands (Mansfield, GBR) *Unable to locate*

The Business Economist (Watford, GBR) **[56860]**

Business El Salvador (San Salvador, ELS) *Unable to locate*

Business Ethics (Oxford, GBR) **[55898]**

Business Forums (Hanoi, VNM) *Unable to locate*

Business Herald (Trivandrum, KE, IND) *Unable to locate*

Business History (Abingdon, GBR) **[51723]**

Business History Studies (Calcutta, WB, IND) *Unable to locate*

Business India (Mumbai, MH, IND) *Unable to locate*

Business and Industry: Taiwan (Taipei, TWN) *Unable to locate*

Business Info (Mitcham, GBR) *Unable to locate*

Business Ireland (Dublin, DU, IRL) **[45948]**

Business Jets International (Staplefield, GBR) *Unable to locate*

Business Journal (Makati City, PHL) *Unable to locate*

Business Korea (Seoul, KOR) *Unable to locate*

Business Lanka (Colombo, SRI) *Unable to locate*

Business Luxembourg (Luxembourg, LUX) *Unable to locate*

Business Matters (London, GBR) *Unable to locate*

Business Mexico (Mexico City, DF, MEX) *Ceased*

Business Money (Taunton, GBR) **[56721]**

Business News (Aberdeen, Grampian & Highlands) (Aberdeen, GBR) *Unable to locate*

Business News Review (Cambodia) (Makati City, PHL) *Unable to locate*

Business News (South East Hampshire) (Havant, GBR) **[53543]**

Business Outlook (London, GBR) *Unable to locate*

Business Process Management Journal (Riyadh, SAU) **[50061]**

Business Pulse (Perth, WA, AUS) **[42248]**

Business Recorder (Karachi, PAK) **[49340]**

Business Report (West Midlands) (Birmingham, GBR) *Unable to locate*

Business in Russia (Moscow, RUS) *Unable to locate*

Business and Society Review (Oxford, GBR) **[55899]**

Business South East **[53682]***

Business Stone (Rho, ITA) *Unable to locate*

Business Strategy and the Environment (Hong Kong, CHN) **[43286]**

Business Strategy Review (London, GBR) **[54159]**

Business Strategy Series (Bradford, GBR) **[52439]**

Business in Thailand Magazine (Bangkok, THA) *Unable to locate*

Business Times (Kuala Lumpur, MYS) **[47601]**

The Business Times (Singapore, SGP) **[50117]**

Business Times (Bangkok, THA) *Unable to locate*

Business Today (New Delhi, DH, IND) **[45490]**

Business Today (Muscat, OMN) **[49220]**

Business Today Egypt (Cairo, EGY) **[43752]**

Business Travel Magazine (Antwerp, BEL) *Unable to locate*

Business Travel News (Makati City, PHL) *Unable to locate*

Business Traveller (Munich, GER) **[44552]**

Business Traveller Middle East (Dubai, UAE) **[51633]**

Business 2 Business Magazine - Bendigo Region (Strathfieldsaye, VI, AUS) *Unable to locate*

Business Voice (Chesterfield, GBR) *Unable to locate*

Business West Times (Derby, GBR) *Unable to locate*

Business Woman (Vanadzor, AMA) *Unable to locate*

Business World (Kolkata, WB, IND) **[45261]**

Business World (Quezon City, PHL) **[49586]**

Business XL (London, GBR) **[54160]**

Businessman (Hyderabad, AP, IND) *Unable to locate*

BusinessWorld (Mumbai, MH, IND) *Unable to locate*

BusinessWorld (Philippines) (Makati City, PHL) *Unable to locate*

The Buteman (Rothesay, GBR) **[56414]**

Butt (Amsterdam, NLD) **[47919]**

Butterflies (Tokyo, JPN) *Unable to locate*

Buxton Advertiser (Buxton, GBR) **[52777]**

Buy and Sell (Calcutta, WB, IND) *Unable to locate*

Buy Sell Magazine (Wrexham, GBR) *Unable to locate*

Buy-Side Technology (London, GBR) **[54161]**

Buzz-FM (Birkenhead, GBR) *Unable to locate*

The Buzz Magasin (Quezon City, PHL) **[49587]**

BWP Update (Oxford, GBR) *Ceased*

By the Way (Tokyo, JPN) *Unable to locate*

Bygg & Jarnhandeln (Stockholm, SWE) *Unable to locate*

Bygg & Teknik (Stockholm, SWE) **[51011]**

Byggaktuelt (Moss, NOR) **[49193]**

Byggeforum (Copenhagen, DEN) **[43658]**

Byggekunst (Oslo, NOR) *Unable to locate*

Byggeri (Glostrup, DEN) **[43698]**

Byggfakta Projektnytt (Ljusdal, SWE) **[50979]**

Byggnadskonst **[51011]***

BygTek (Glostrup, DEN) **[43699]**

BygTek Mester & Svend (Glostrup, DEN) **[43700]**

Byron Shire News (Sydney, NW, AUS) **[42481]**

BYTE Romania (Tg-Mures, ROM) **[49848]**

Byzantine and Modern Greek Studies (London, GBR) **[54162]**

Byzantinische Zeitschrift (Berlin, GER) **[44164]**

BZ Bauzentralblatt (Isernhagen, GER) *Unable to locate*

C

C-DAC Connect (Pune, MH, IND) **[45696]**

C-4 (Dublin, DU, IRL) **[45949]**

CA Charter **[42490]***

CA Magazine (Edinburgh, GBR) **[53259]**

CAA Newsnet (Stamford, GBR) **[56595]**

Cab Trade News (London, GBR) *Unable to locate*

Cabala (Caracas, VEN) *Ceased*

Cabanuelas: Auto Suficiencia Rural (Barinas, VEN) *Unable to locate*

Cabinet Maker (London, GBR) **[54163]**

Cable & Satellite International (London, GBR) **[54164]**

Cabletalk (Midlothian, GBR) **[55627]**

Cabletow (Manila, PHL) **[49548]**

Cabo Mil-FM - 96.3 (Cabo San Lucas, BS, MEX) **[47755]**

Caboolture News (Sydney, NW, AUS) **[42482]**

Caboolture Shire Herald (Caboolture, QL, AUS) **[41681]**

CAD User (London, GBR) **[54165]**

Cadernos CEDES (Campinas, SP, BRZ) **[42965]**

Cadernos Luso-Brasileiros de Alergia e Imunologia (Lisbon, PRT) *Unable to locate*

Cadernos Pagu (Campinas, SP, BRZ) **[42966]**

Cadernos de Pesquisa (Sao Paulo, SP, BRZ) **[43031]**

CAECILIA (Brussels, BEL) *Unable to locate*

Cafe Business (Smallfield, GBR) **[56562]**

Caffe (Rome, ITA) *Unable to locate*

Cage and Aviary Birds (London, GBR) **[54166]**

Cagimaira Development Ass. (Ba, FIJ) *Unable to locate*

Cahiers d'Economie et Sociologie Rurales (Paris, FRA) **[44031]**

Cahiers d'etudes et de recherches francophones/Agricultures (Montrouge, FRA) **[43984]**

Cahiers d'etudes et de recherches francophones/Sante (Montrouge, FRA) **[43985]**

Cahiers de la Documentation (Brussels, BEL) **[42846]**

Cainozoic Research (Leiden, NLD) **[48660]**

Cairo Times (Cairo, EGY) **[43753]**

Cakes & Sugarcraft (Farnham, GBR) **[53381]**

Calcolo (Tokyo, JPN) **[46772]**

Calculus of Variations and Partial Differential Equation (Tokyo, JPN) **[46773]**

Calcutta Gazette (Calcutta, WB, IND) *Unable to locate*

Calcutta Historical Journal (Calcutta, WB, IND) *Unable to locate*

Calcutta Journal of Political Studies (Calcutta, WB, IND) *Unable to locate*

Calcutta Medical Journal (Calcutta, WB, IND) *Unable to locate*

Calcutta Municipal Gazette (Calcutta, WB, IND) *Unable to locate*

Calcutta Statistical Association Bulletin (Kolkata, WB, IND) **[45262]**

Calcutta Weekly Notes (Calcutta, WB, IND) *Unable to locate*

Calcuttan (Calcutta, WB, IND) *Unable to locate*

Caldasia (Bogota, COL) **[43544]**

Caledon Kontreinuus (Cape Town, SAF) **[50368]**

Calendario Demografico (Guatemala City, GTM) *Unable to locate*

Calicut Medical Journal (Trivandrum, KE, IND) **[45758]**

Calidad (Madrid, SPA) *Unable to locate*

Call (New Delhi, DH, IND) *Unable to locate*

Call (Colombo, SRI) *Unable to locate*

Call Center Magazine (London, GBR) **[54167]**

Call Centre Focus (Dorking, GBR) **[53192]**

CALL EJ **[41646]***

CALL-EJ Online (Brisbane, QL, AUS) **[41646]**

Calligraphy (Shanghai, CHN) **[43464]**

Calligraphy and Painting (Shanghai, CHN) **[43465]**

CallSign (London, GBR) **[54168]**

Calorimetry and Thermal Analysis (Tokyo, JPN) **[46774]**

Caloundra Weekly (Sydney, NW, AUS) **[42483]**

Calypso-FM - 106.7 (Fortaleza, CE, BRZ) **[42980]**

Calypso Ten 18-FM - 101.8 (Luqa, MAL) **[47734]**

Cambodian Television (Phnom Penh, CMB) *Unable to locate*

Cambria (Caerfyrddin, GBR) **[52781]**

Cambrian Law Review (Aberystwyth, GBR) *Unable to locate*

Cambridge Journal of Economics (London, GBR) *Ceased*

Cambridge Journal of Economics (Oxford, GBR) **[55900]**

Cambridge Journal of Education (Abingdon, GBR) **[51724]**

Cambridge Journal of Regions, Economy & Society (Tokyo, JPN) **[46775]**

The Cambridge Law Journal (Cambridge, GBR) **[52798]**

The Cambridge Quarterly (Cambridge, GBR) **[52799]**

Cambridge Review of International Affairs (Abingdon, GBR) **[51725]**

Cambridgeshire Agenda (Cambridge, GBR) **[52800]**

Cambridgeshire Property Plus (Cambridge, GBR) **[52801]**

Cambs Times (March, GBR) **[55592]**

Camden Gazette (London, GBR) **[54169]**

Camden Haven Courier (Laurieton, NW, AUS) **[42003]**

Cameroon Journal of Agricultural Science (Yaounde, CMR) **[43128]**

Cameroon Journal of Experimental Biology (Dschang, CMR) **[43125]**

Campaign (London, GBR) **[54170]**

The Campaigner (London, GBR) *Unable to locate*

Camping and Caravanning (Coventry, GBR) **[53070]**

Camping Revue (Klosterneuburg, AUT) *Unable to locate*

Campus-FM - 103.7 (Msida, MAL) **[47735]**

Campus Radio-FM - 97.1 (Laoag City, PHL) **[49510]**

Campus Review (Sydney, NW, AUS) **[42484]**

Campus-Wide Information Systems (Huddersfield, GBR) **[53617]**

Campuskrant (Leuven, BEL) **[42893]**

Canada-FM (Edeia, GO, BRZ) *Unable to locate*

Canadian Journal of Agricultural Economics (Oxford, GBR) **[55901]**

Canal Boat (Wokingham, GBR) **[56949]**

Canal-Melodia - 91.1 MHz (Saint Petersburg, RUS) **[50029]**

Numbers cited in bold after listings are entry numbers rather than page numbers.

Canal & Riverboat (Epsom, GBR) *Unable to locate*

The Canara Times (Mangalore, KA, IND) *Unable to locate*

Canberra Cyclist (Canberra, AC, AUS) **[41703]**

CanCam (Tokyo, JPN) **[46776]**

Cancer Biomarkers (Amsterdam, NLD) **[47920]**

Cancer Cell International (London, 'GBR) **[54171]**

Cancer Chemotherapy and Pharmacology (Tokyo, JPN) **[46777]**

Cancer & Chemotherapy Reviews (Barcelona, SPA) **[50655]**

Cancer Immunity (Lausanne, SWI) **[51184]**

Cancer Immunology, Immunotherapy (Tokyo, JPN) **[46778]**

Cancer Informatics (Albany, NZL) **[48776]**

Cancer Letters (Oxford, GBR) **[55902]**

Cancer and Metastasis Reviews (Dordrecht, NLD) **[48341]**

Cancer Radiotherapie (Paris, FRA) **[44032]**

Cancer Research on Prevention and Treatment (Tianjin, CHN) *Unable to locate*

Cancer Science (Oxford, GBR) **[55903]**

Cancer Treatment (Saint Louis, MO, USA) *Unable to locate*

CancerWise (Dublin, DU, IRL) **[45950]**

Cancun (Cancun, QR, MEX) *Unable to locate*

Candid (London, GBR) **[54172]**

Candis (Hoylake, GBR) **[53614]**

Candy Magazine (Mandaluyong City, PHL) **[49532]**

Cangzhou People's Broadcasting Station (Cangzhou, HB, CHN) *Unable to locate*

Cangzhou People's Broadcasting Station (Cangzhou, HB, CHN) *Unable to locate*

Cani (Sesto Fiorentino, ITA) *Unable to locate*

Canoe Focus (Bingham, GBR) **[52325]**

Canoeist (Appleford-on-Thames, GBR) *Unable to locate*

CANS Digest of Social Legislation (London, GBR) **[54173]**

Canterbury-Bankstown Express (Liverpool, NW, AUS) **[42012]**

Canterbury Today (Christchurch, NZL) **[48864]**

Canto Grande-FM - 97.7 (San Juan de Lurigancho, PER) **[49442]**

Cao Bang Broadcast - Television Station (Cao Bang, VNM) *Unable to locate*

Cao Bang Broadcast - Television Station (Cao Bang, VNM) *Unable to locate*

CAPA Journal (Nairobi, KEN) *Unable to locate*

CAP&Design (Stockholm, SWE) **[51012]**

Cape Business News (Cape Town, SAF) **[50369]**

Cape Talk-AM - 567 (Cape Town, SAF) **[50430]**

Capital (Calcutta, WB, IND) *Unable to locate*

Capital & Class (London, GBR) **[54174]**

Capital Community Radio-FM - 90.5 (Booragoon, WA, AUS) **[41613]**

Capital Equipement Medical (Boulogne Billancourt, FRA) *Unable to locate*

Capital-FM - 95.8 (London, GBR) **[55443]**

Capital Gold-AM (London, GBR) *Unable to locate*

Capital Markets Law Journal (Tokyo, JPN) **[46779]**

Capital Radio (Colombo, SRI) *Unable to locate*

Capital Radio - Ankara - 99.5 MHz (Ankara, TUR) **[51519]**

Capital Radio-FM - 88.7 (Valletta, MAL) **[47748]**

Capital Radio Malawi-FM - 102.5 (Blantyre, MWI) **[47567]**

Capital Radio 95.8 FM - 95.8 FM (Singapore, SGP) **[50293]**

Capitalist (New Delhi, DH, IND) *Unable to locate*

Capitol Gold-AM (London, GBR) *Unable to locate*

Capricorn Coast Mirror (Sydney, NW, AUS) **[42485]**

Capture (Surry Hills, NW, AUS) **[42422]**

Car Buyers Guide. Irish New Car Guide (Dublin, DU, IRL) *Unable to locate*

Car and Driver Hong Kong (Hong Kong, CHN) *Unable to locate*

Car and Driver (Spain) (Madrid, SPA) **[50732]**

Car & Fan (Shanghai, CHN) **[43466]**

Caravan (Croydon, GBR) **[53123]**

Caravan Business **[52097]***

The Caravan Club Magazine (East Grinstead, GBR) **[53235]**

Caravan, Motorcaravan & Camping Mart **[52409]***

Caravan, Motorhome & Camping Mart (Bourne, GBR) **[52409]**

Caravanserai (The Hague, NLD) **[48609]**

Carbohydrate Polymers (Amsterdam, NLD) **[47921]**

Carbon Balance and Management (London, GBR) **[54175]**

Carcinogenesis (Oxford, GBR) **[55904]**

Card Making & Papercraft (Bristol, GBR) **[52650]**

Card Technology Today (New York, NY, USA) *Ceased*

Card Times (Ormskirk, GBR) **[55849]**

Cardamom Statistics (Kochi, KE, IND) *Unable to locate*

Cardiac Electrophysiology Review (Dordrecht, NLD) **[48342]**

The Cardinal (Godalming, GBR) *Unable to locate*

Cardinal-AM - 730 (Lambare, PAR) **[49412]**

Cardinal-FM - 92.3 (Lambare, PAR) **[49413]**

Cardiologia Hungarica (Budapest, HUN) *Unable to locate*

Cardiologia Practica (Barcelona, SPA) *Unable to locate*

Cardiologie (Utrecht, NLD) *Unable to locate*

Cardiology International (London, GBR) **[54176]**

Cardiology News (Edinburgh, GBR) **[53260]**

Cardiology in the Young (London, GBR) **[54177]**

Cardiovascular Diabetology (London, GBR) **[54178]**

Cardiovascular Drugs and Therapy (Dordrecht, NLD) **[48343]**

Cardiovascular Forum (Lodz, POL) **[49669]**

Cardiovascular & Hematological Agents in Medicinal Chemistry (Meerut, UP, IND) **[45343]**

Cardiovascular & Hematological Disorders - Drug Targets (Bussum, NLD) **[48280]**

Cardiovascular Medicine; Nature Clinical Practice **[54976]***

Cardiovascular Research (Sophia Antipolis, FRA) **[44106]**

Cardiovascular Research (Giessen, GER) **[44384]**

Cardiovascular Surgery (Yvoir, BEL) *Unable to locate*

Cardiovascular Ultrasound (London, GBR) **[54179]**

Career & Competition Times (New Delhi, DH, IND) *Unable to locate*

Career Development International (Bradford, GBR) **[52440]**

Career Teacher (Birmingham, GBR) *Unable to locate*

Careers Digest (Delhi, DH, IND) *Unable to locate*

Careers Education and Guidance (Usk, GBR) *Unable to locate*

CareerScope (Camberley, GBR) **[52783]**

CARF (London, GBR) **[54180]**

Cargo Tomorrow (Romford, GBR) *Unable to locate*

Caribbean Beacon (Saint Michael, BRB) *Unable to locate*

Caribbean Health (Incorporating Medicine Digest) (Cambridge, GBR) *Ceased*

Caribbean Insight (London, GBR) *Unable to locate*

Caribbean Issues (Saint Augustine, TTO) *Ceased*

Caribbean Times (London, GBR) **[54181]**

Caribe-FM - 104.9 (Iquique, CHL) **[43138]**

Caricia-FM - 104.5 (Melipilla, CHL) **[43141]**

CARICOM Perspective (Georgetown, GUY) **[44799]**

The Caring Business (Hebden Bridge, GBR) *Unable to locate*

Caring Times (London, GBR) **[54182]**

Caring UK (Barnsley, GBR) **[52178]**

Caritas (Kaunas, LIT) **[47464]**

Caritas Newspaper (Lucerne, SWI) *Unable to locate*

Carletonville Herald (Cape Town, SAF) **[50370]**

Carlisle-FM - 96.4 (Carlisle, GBR) **[52948]**

Carluke Gazette (Carluke, GBR) **[52950]**

Carmel in the World (Rome, ITA) **[46223]**

Carnica 2000 (Madrid, SPA) *Unable to locate*

Carnoustie Guide & Gazette (Arbroath, GBR) **[52128]**

Caroados-FM - 103.3 (Nova Prata, RN, BRZ) **[42988]**

Carolina-FM - 99.3 (Santiago, CHL) **[43152]**

Carpet and Floorcoverings Review **[54183]***

Carpet & Flooring Retail (CFR) (London, GBR) **[54183]**

CARPology (Harleston, GBR) **[53510]**

Carreteras (Madrid, SPA) **[50733]**

Carriage Driving (Salisbury, GBR) *Unable to locate*

Carrick Times (Carrickfergus, GBR) **[52951]**

Carros Magazine (Amsterdam, NLD) **[47922]**

Cartier International Polo @MAG (London, GBR) **[54184]**

The Cartographic Journal (London, GBR) **[54185]**

Cartoons International (Lucknow, UP, IND) *Unable to locate*

Carve (Newquay, GBR) **[55693]**

Cas London (London, GBR) **[54186]**

Casa al Dia (Madrid, SPA) **[50734]**

CASCADE (London, GBR) *Unable to locate*

Case Law of the European Court of Human Rights, Judgments, Commentaries (Kiev, URE) *Unable to. locate*

Case Studies on Disaster Mitigation (Ahmedabad, GJ, IND) *Unable to locate*

CASEpapers (London, GBR) **[54187]**

Cash & Carry Management Inc. Delivered Wholesaler (East Grinstead, GBR) *Unable to locate*

The Cashew (Cochin, KE, IND) *Unable to locate*

Cashew Bulletin (Cochin, KE, IND) **[45070]**

Casino International (Kent, GBR) **[53676]**

Casino World (Gravesend, GBR) **[53478]**

Caspian Business News (Baku, AJN) **[42780]**

The CASSL Magazine (London, GBR) *Unable to locate*

Cast Metal & Diecasting Times (Shoreham-by-Sea, GBR) **[56522]**

Castings S.A. (Bryanston, SAF) *Unable to locate*

CASTME Journal (London, GBR) *Ceased*

Cat World (Arundel, GBR) **[52133]**

Catalogue & E-business (Ilfracombe, GBR) **[53641]**

Catalysis Communications (Rostock, GER) **[44646]**

Catalysis Letters (Dordrecht, NLD) **[48344]**

Catalysis Surveys from Asia (Dordrecht, NLD) **[48345]**

Catalysis Surveys from Japan **[48345]***

Catalysts & Catalysed Reactions (Cambridge, GBR) **[52802]**

Catchword (East Sussex, GBR) **[53242]**

Catena (Munich, GER) **[44553]**

Caterer & Hotelkeeper (Sutton, GBR) **[56680]**

Catering Avisen (Copenhagen, DEN) *Unable to locate*

Catering and Licensing Review **[52285]***

The Catering Manager (Whitby, GBR) *Unable to locate*

Catering Plus (Auckland, NZL) **[48788]**

Catering UK (Bewdley, GBR) *Unable to locate*

Catering Update (Sutton, GBR) **[56681]**

The Catholic News (Singapore, SGP) **[50118]**

Catholic Teachers Gazette (Cardiff, GBR) **[52927]**

Cattech (Dordrecht, NLD) *Ceased*

Cattle Practice (Quedgeley, GBR) **[56307]**

Caulfield Glen Eira Leader (Glen Iris, VI, AUS) **[41892]**

Caustic (Kochi, KE, IND) *Unable to locate*

Cave & Karst Science (Buxton, GBR) **[52778]**

Caveat (Sydney, NW, AUS) **[42486]**

Numbers cited in bold after listings are entry numbers rather than page numbers.

Caves & Caving [52779]*

Caving Journal (Fukuoka, JPN) [46340]

The Caymanian Compass (Grand Cayman, CYM) [43130]

CBeebies Weekly Magazine (London, GBR) [54188]

CBFM [50549]*

CBM (Wijchen, NLD) [48773]

CCAMLR Science (Hobart, TA, AUS) Unable to locate

CCHHR-AM - 1350 (Hemel Hempstead, GBR) [53559]

CCTV 8 - Channel 8 (Beijing, CHN) [43227]

CCTV 5 - Channel 5 (Beijing, CHN) [43228]

CCTV 4 - International - Channel 4 (Beijing, CHN) [43229]

CCTV 1 - Channel 1 (Beijing, CHN) [43230]

CCTV 7 - Channel 7 (Beijing, CHN) [43231]

CCTV 6 - Channel 6 (Beijing, CHN) [43232]

CCTV 3 - Channel 3 (Beijing, CHN) [43233]

CCTV Today (London, GBR) [54189]

CCTV 2 - Channel 2 (Beijing, CHN) [43234]

CD Compact (Barcelona, SPA) Unable to locate

CDA (Milan, ITA) [46164]

CDDE [43538]*

CDR Weekly [54243]*

CEA Info (Paris, FRA) Ceased

CEAP Perspective (Quezon City, PHL) Ceased

CEBE Transactions (Cardiff, GBR) [52928]

Cebecoskoop (Rotterdam, NLD) Unable to locate

Cecidologia Internationale (Allahabad, UP, IND) Unable to locate

CEI Asia Pacific (Hong Kong, CHN) [43287]

Celestial Mechanics & Dynamical Astronomy (Dordrecht, NLD) [48346]

Celestinesca (Valencia, SPA) [50844]

Cell Adhesion & Migration (Strasbourg, FRA) [44111]

Cell Biology International (Amsterdam, NLD) [47923]

Cell Biology and Toxicology (Dordrecht, NLD) [48347]

Cell Calcium (Manchester, GBR) [55546]

Cell & Chromosome (London, GBR) Ceased

Cell and Chromosome Research Journal (Calcutta, WB, IND) Unable to locate

Cell Communication and Signaling (London, GBR) [54190]

Cell Death & Differentiation (London, GBR) [54191]

Cell Proliferation (London, GBR) [54192]

Cell Research (Shanghai, CHN) [43467]

Cell Research; Pigment [56158]*

Cell Structure and Function (Kyoto, JPN) Unable to locate

Cell and Tissue Biology (Saint Petersburg, RUS) [50020]

Cell and Tissue Research (Heidelberg, GER) [44444]

Cellular & Molecular Biology Letters (Wroclaw, POL) [49777]

Cellular and Molecular Life Sciences (Tokyo, JPN) [46780]

Cellular Polymers (Shrewsbury, GBR) [56527]

Cellular Signalling (Glasgow, GBR) [53412]

Celtic Music Radio-AM - 1530 (Glasgow, GBR) [53462]

Celulosa y Papel (Concepcion, CHL) [43136]

Cement and Concrete Composites (Amsterdam, NLD) [47924]

Cement and Concrete Research (Lausanne, SWI) [51185]

Centerpoint (Tainan, TWN) [51326]

Central African Journal of Medicine (Harare, ZWE) [57113]

Central Asia (Peshawar, PAK) Unable to locate

Central Asian Survey (Abingdon, GBR) [51726]

Central Asiatic Journal (Wiesbaden, GER) [44711]

Central Broadcasting System [51387]*

Central Broadcasting System [51384]*

Central Broadcasting System [51371]*

Central Broadcasting System - 7445 KHz (Taipei, TWN) [51371]

Central Broadcasting System (Taipei, TWN) Unable to locate

Central Broadcasting System (Taipei, TWN) Unable to locate

Central Broadcasting System (Taipei, TWN) Unable to locate

Central Broadcasting System (Taipei, TWN) Unable to locate

Central Broadcasting System (Taipei, TWN) Unable to locate

Central Broadcasting System (Taipei, TWN) Unable to locate

Central Broadcasting System (Taipei, TWN) Unable to locate

Central Broadcasting System (Taipei, TWN) Unable to locate

Central Broadcasting System (Taipei, TWN) Unable to locate

Central Broadcasting System (Taipei, TWN) Unable to locate

Central Broadcasting System (Taipei, TWN) Unable to locate

Central Building Research Institute Building Research Note (Roorkee, UP, IND) Unable to locate

Central Building Research Institute Publications Index (Roorkee, UP, IND) Unable to locate

Central Coast Express Advocate (West Gosford, NW, AUS) [42695]

Central Europe (London, GBR) [54193]

Central Europe Monitor (London, GBR) [54194]

Central European (London, GBR) Unable to locate

Central European History (Boston, MA, USA) Unable to locate

Central European Journal of Biology (Dordrecht, NLD) [48348]

Central European Journal of Chemistry (Warsaw, POL) [49699]

Central European Journal of Geosciences (Warsaw, POL) [49700]

Central European Journal of Mathematics (Warsaw, POL) [49701]

Central European Journal of Medicine (Dordrecht, NLD) [48349]

Central European Journal of Operations Research (Tokyo, JPN) [46781]

Central European Journal of Physics (Warsaw, POL) [49702]

Central European Political Science Review (Budapest, HUN) [44826]

Central European Political Studies Review (Brno, CZE) [43603]

Central-European Value Studies (Bratislava, SLK) [50317]

Central-FM - 103.1 (Falkirk, GBR) [53371]

Central Glass and Ceramic Research Institute Bulletin (Calcutta, WB, IND) Unable to locate

The Central Hawke's Bay Mail (Waipukarau, NZL) Unable to locate

Central Marine Fisheries Research Institute Bulletin (Cochin, KE, IND) [45071]

Central Marine Fisheries Research Institute Special Publication (Cochin, KE, IND) [45072]

Central Mine Planning & Design Institute Current Awareness Service (Ranchi, BH, IND) Unable to locate

Central Mine Planning and Design Institute Manuals (Ranchi, BH, IND) Unable to locate

Central & North Burnett Times (Sydney, NW, AUS) [42487]

Central Queensland News (Sydney, NW, AUS) [42488]

Central Telegraph (Sydney, NW, AUS) [42489]

Central Today (Christchurch, NZL) [48865]

Centralian Advocate (Alice Springs, NT, AUS) Unable to locate

Centre Calling (New Delhi, DH, IND) Unable to locate

Centre Court (Hilversum, NLD) Unable to locate

Centre Line (Fareham, GBR) Unable to locate

Centrepoint (London, GBR) Unable to locate

Century-FM [55587]*

Century Radio - 105.4 (Manchester, GBR) [55585]

Cephalalgia (Brentwood, GBR) [52570]

Ceramic Forum International (Cologne, GER) [44290]

Ceramic Review (London, GBR) [54195]

Ceramica (Sao Paulo, SP, BRZ) [43032]

Ceramica Keramos (Madrid, SPA) Unable to locate

Ceramics (Westminster, NW, AUS) [42700]

Ceramics International (Amsterdam, NLD) [47925]

Cerddoriaeth Cymru [53885]*

Cerebrospinal Fluid Research (London, GBR) [54196]

Ceres (Rome, ITA) Ceased

CERN Courier (Bristol, GBR) [52651]

Certified Accountant (London, GBR) Unable to locate

Cervenake-FM - 99,1 MHz (Pogradec, ALB) [41442]

CESifo Economic Studies (Oxford, GBR) [55905]

CESifo Forum (Munich, GER) [44554]

Ceska Radiologie (Plzen, CZE) [43607]

Ceska Revmatologie (Prague, CZE) [43612]

Cesko-Slovenska Patologie/Soudni Lekarstvi (Prague, CZE) [43613]

Ceskoslovenska Pediatrie (Prague, CZE) [43614]

Ceskoslovenska Radiologie [43607]*

The Ceylon Churchman (Colombo, SRI) Unable to locate

Ceylon Historical Journal (Dehiwala, SRI) Unable to locate

Ceylon Journal of Medical Sciences (Colombo, SRI) [50850]

Ceylon Journal of Science, Biological Sciences (Peradeniya, SRI) [50927]

Ceylon Journal of Science, Physical Sciences (Peradeniya, SRI) [50928]

The Ceylon Medical Journal (Colombo, SRI) Unable to locate

CFJ Contract Flooring Journal (Tunbridge Wells, GBR) [56778]

CFM-FM - 89.1 (Kingaroy, QL, AUS) [41988]

CFM-FM - 100.7 (Toowoomba, QL, AUS) [42630]

CFM Radio-FM - 96.4 (Carlisle, GBR) [52949]

CFM Radio-FM - 102.5 (Penrith, GBR) [56247]

CFM Radio-FM - 103.4 (Whitehaven, GBR) [56917]

CFM Radio-FM - 102.2 (Workington, GBR) [56969]

CFO Asia (Hong Kong, CHN) Ceased

Chabad-Lubavitch of Finland (Helsinki, FIN) [43823]

Chacarera (Lima, PER) Unable to locate

Chain Reaction (Fitzroy, VI, AUS) [41866]

CHALK (Quezon City, PHL) [49588]

The Challenge (Karachi, PAK) Unable to locate

Chamaerops Magazine (Richmond, GBR) [56389]

Champak (English) (New Delhi, DH, IND) [45491]

Champak (Gujarati) (New Delhi, DH, IND) [45492]

Champak (Hindi) (New Delhi, DH, IND) [45493]

Champak (Kannada) (New Delhi, DH, IND) [45494]

Champak (Marathi) (New Delhi, DH, IND) [45495]

Champion-FM - 103 (Bangor, GBR) [52174]

Champneys Magazine (Ware, GBR) [56840]

Chandamama (Palani, TN, IND) Unable to locate

Chandigarh Post (Chandigarh, CH, IND) Unable to locate

Chandrabhaga (Cuttack, OR, IND) [45080]

Chandrabhaga: A Magazine of World Writing [45080]*

Chandrika Daily (Calicut, KE, IND) Unable to locate

Changchun People's Broadcasting Station (Changchun, JI, CHN) Unable to locate

Changchun People's Broadcasting Station (Changchun, JI, CHN) Unable to locate

Changchun People's Broadcasting Station (Changchun, JI, CHN) Unable to locate

Changchun People's Broadcasting Station (Changchun, JI, CHN) Unable to locate

Changde People's Broadcasting Station (Changde, HA, CHN) Unable to locate

Changemakers (Darjeeling, WB, IND) Unable to locate

Changhua FM Broadcasting Station - 98.7 MHz (Taichung, TWN) [51322]

Changing English (Abingdon, GBR) [51727]

Changing Families (London, GBR) Unable to locate

Changji People's Broadcasting Station (Changji, XU, CHN) Unable to locate

Numbers cited in bold after listings are entry numbers rather than page numbers.

Gale Directory of Publications & Broadcast Media/147th Ed.

6289

Master Index

Changjiang People's Broadcasting Station (Wuhan, HB, CHN) *Unable to locate*

Changshu People's Broadcasting Station (Changshu, JS, CHN) *Unable to locate*

Changshu People's Broadcasting Station (Changshu, JS, CHN) *Unable to locate*

Changzhi People's Broadcasting Station (Changzhi, SX, CHN) *Unable to locate*

Changzhou People's Broadcasting Station (Changzhou, JS, CHN) *Unable to locate*

Changzhou People's Broadcasting Station (Changzhou, JS, CHN) *Unable to locate*

Changzhou People's Broadcasting Station (Changzhou, JS, CHN) *Unable to locate*

Changzhou People's Broadcasting Station (Changzhou, JS, CHN) *Unable to locate*

Changzhou People's Broadcasting Station (Changzhou, JS, CHN) *Unable to locate*

Channel Africa-AM - 7230 (Auckland Park, SAF) [50350]

Channel 4 Ajman - 104.8 MHz (Ajman, UAE) [51623]

Channel Middle East (Dubai, UAE) [51634]

Channel 103-FM - 103.7 (Jersey, GBR) [53667]

Chant Choral (Lyon, FRA) *Unable to locate*

Chaohu People's Broadcasting Station (Chaohu, AN, CHN) *Unable to locate*

Chaoyang People's Broadcasting Station (Chaoyang, LI, CHN) *Unable to locate*

Chaoyang People's Broadcasting Station (Chaoyang, LI, CHN) *Unable to locate*

Chaoyang People's Broadcasting Station (Chaoyang, LI, CHN) *Unable to locate*

The Chap (Lewes, GBR) [53848]

Chapman (Edinburgh, GBR) [53261]

Chapter&Verse (Leeds, GBR) [53760]

Charge Utile Magazine (Paris, FRA) *Unable to locate*

Charged Middle East (Dubai, UAE) [51635]

Chariot (Cuttack, OR, IND) *Unable to locate*

Charity Matters (Shanghai, CHN) [43468]

Charity Times (London, GBR) [54197]

Charivari-FM - 95.5 (Munich, GER) [44593]

Charivari-FM - 98.6 (Nuremberg, GER) [44619]

Charlie and Lola (London, GBR) [54198]

Charter (Sydney, NW, AUS) [42490]

Chartered Accountants (Colombo, SRI) [50851]

Chartered Accountants Journal of New Zealand (Wellington, NZL) [49003]

Chartered Banker [52919]*

Chartered Secretary (New Delhi, DH, IND) *Unable to locate*

Chartered Secretary (London, GBR) [54199]

Chartered Surveyor Weekly [55142]*

The Chaser (Darlinghurst, NW, AUS) [41827]

Chat Arrowords (Redhill, GBR) [56344]

Chat Crosswords (Redhill, GBR) [56345]

Chat - It's Fate (London, GBR) [54200]

Chat Puzzles Select (Redhill, GBR) [56346]

Chat Wordsearch (Redhill, GBR) [56347]

Chatterers World (Telford, GBR) *Unable to locate*

Cheering Words (Stamford, GBR) *Unable to locate*

Chelmer-FM [56586]*

Chelmsford Radio-FM - 107.7 (Southend-on-Sea, GBR) [56586]

Cheltenham Oracle (Cheltenham, GBR) [52965]

Chem-Bio Informatics Journal (Tokyo, JPN) [46782]

Chemexcil Export Bulletin (Mumbai, MH, IND) *Unable to locate*

Chemical Age of India (Mumbai, MH, IND) *Unable to locate*

Chemical and Biochemical Engineering Quarterly (Zagreb, CTA) [43563]

Chemical Biology [52826]*

Chemical Communications (Cambridge, GBR) [52803]

Chemical Digest (New Delhi, DH, IND) *Unable to locate*

Chemical Education (Seoul, KOR) *Unable to locate*

The Chemical Engineer [56424]*

Chemical Engineering Journal (Amsterdam, NLD) [47926]

Chemical Engineering and Processing (Dortmund, GER) [44315]

Chemical Engineering Research and Design (ChERD) (Rugby, GBR) [56416]

Chemical Engineering World (Mumbai, MH, IND) [45359]

Chemical and Environmental Research (Aligarh, UP, IND) *Unable to locate*

Chemical Era (Calcutta, WB, IND) *Unable to locate*

Chemical Health and Safety [48057]*

The Chemical Industry in Finland (Helsinki, FIN) *Unable to locate*

Chemical Industry News [45360]*

Chemical News (Mumbai, MH, IND) [45360]

Chemical Papers (Warsaw, POL) [49703]

Chemical Perspective (Wits, SAF) *Unable to locate*

Chemical & Pharmaceutical Bulletin (Tokyo, JPN) [46783]

Chemical Physics (Garching, GER) [44378]

Chemical Physics Letters (Oxford, GBR) [55906]

Chemical Processing Developments Asia (London, GBR) *Unable to locate*

Chemical Products Finder (Mumbai, MH, IND) *Unable to locate*

Chemical Science [52827]*

Chemical Society Reviews (Cambridge, GBR) [52804]

Chemical Take-Off (New Delhi, DH, IND) *Unable to locate*

Chemical Technology (Rajkot, GJ, IND) [45708]

Chemical Weekly (Mumbai, MH, IND) [45361]

Chemicals and Allied Products Export News (New Delhi, DH, IND) *Unable to locate*

Chemicals, Drugs, Pharmaceuticals,

Petroleum, Petrochemicals, Fertilizers (Allahabad, UP, IND) *Unable to locate*

Chemicals - International (New Delhi, DH, IND) *Unable to locate*

Chemicke Listy (Prague, CZE) *Unable to locate*

Chemie der Erde / Geochemistry (Jena, GER) [44487]

Chemie Ingenieur Technik (Weinheim, GER) [44702]

Chemie Plus/Sigwerb Ag (Solothurn, SWI) *Unable to locate*

Chemische Rundschau (Solothurn, SWI) *Unable to locate*

Chemist & Drugstore News (Mumbai, MH, IND) *Unable to locate*

Chemistry (Weinheim, GER) [44703]

Chemistry (Bilbao, SPA) [50710]

Chemistry in Australia (Melbourne, VI, AUS) [42056]

Chemistry in Britain (Chichester, GBR) *Unable to locate*

Chemistry and Ecology (Ancona, ITA) [46117]

Chemistry Education (Bangalore, KA, IND) *Unable to locate*

Chemistry Education Research and Practice (Cambridge, GBR) [52805]

Chemistry & Industry (London, GBR) [54201]

Chemistry and Industry of Forest Products (Nanjing, JS, CHN) [43457]

Chemistry Letters (Kyoto, JPN) [46468]

Chemistry and Physics of Lipids (Reykjavik, ICE) [44899]

Chemistry in Sri Lanka (Rajagiriya, SRI) [50935]

Chemistry Today (New Delhi, DH, IND) [45496]

Chemkon - Chemie konkret, Forum fuer Unterricht und Didaktik (Oldenburg, GER) [44623]

ChemMedChem (Weinheim, GER) [44704]

Chemoecology (Brussels, BEL) [42847]

Chemosensory Perception (Dordrecht, NLD) [48350]

Chemosphere (Amsterdam, NLD) [47927]

ChemSusChem (Weinheim, GER) [44705]

Cheng Sheng Broadcasting Co. (Chia-I, TWN) *Unable to locate*

Cheng Sheng Broadcasting Co. - 819 KHz (Taliao, TWN) [51392]

Chengde People's Broadcasting Station 1 (Chengde, HB, CHN) *Unable to locate*

Chengde People's Broadcasting Station 1 (Chengde, HB, CHN) *Unable to locate*

Chengde People's Broadcasting Station 1 (Chengde, HB, CHN) *Unable to locate*

Chengdu People's Broadcasting Station (Chengdu, SI, CHN) *Unable to locate*

Chengdu People's Broadcasting Station (Chengdu, SI, CHN) *Unable to locate*

Chengdu People's Broadcasting Station (Chengdu, SI, CHN) *Unable to locate*

Chengdu People's Broadcasting Station (Chengdu, SI, CHN) *Unable to locate*

Chengdu People's Broadcasting Station 1 (Chengdu, SI, CHN) *Unable to locate*

Chenghai People's Broadcasting Station (Shantou, GD, CHN) *Unable to locate*

Chenzhou People's Radio (Chenzhou, HA, CHN) *Unable to locate*

Chenzhou People's Radio (Chenzhou, HA, CHN) *Unable to locate*

Chernomorskaya zdravnitsa (Sochi, RUS) *Unable to locate*

Cherrie (East Sydney, NW, AUS) [41849]

Chesham Town Talk (Chesham, GBR) [52985]

Cheshire-FM - 92.5 (Winsford, GBR) [56934]

Chess (London, GBR) [54202]

Chess Asia (Makati, PHL) *Unable to locate*

Chess in China (Beijing, CHN) *Unable to locate*

Chess Mate (Chennai, TN, IND) [45029]

Chester Standard (Chester, GBR) [52992]

The Chesterton Review (Poole, GBR) *Unable to locate*

Chiale Broadcasting Station (Chia-I, TWN) *Unable to locate*

Chiang Mai News Online [51457]*

Chiangmai Mail (Chiang Mai, THA) [51456]

Chibi People's Broadcasting Station (Chibi, HU, CHN) *Unable to locate*

Chichester Observer (Chichester, GBR) [53007]

Chiefeng People's Broadcasting Station (Chifeng, NM, CHN) *Unable to locate*

Chien Kuo Broadcasting Station (Tainan, TWN) *Unable to locate*

Chien Kuo Broadcasting Station (Tainan, TWN) *Unable to locate*

Chifeng People's Broadcasting Station (Chifeng, NM, CHN) *Unable to locate*

Chifeng People's Broadcasting Station (Chifeng, NM, CHN) *Unable to locate*

Chifeng People's Broadcasting Station (Chifeng, NM, CHN) *Unable to locate*

Chifeng People's Broadcasting Station (Chifeng, NM, CHN) *Unable to locate*

Chifeng People's Broadcasting Station (Chifeng, NM, CHN) *Unable to locate*

Child (Oxford, GBR) [55907]

Child Care in Practice (Abingdon, GBR) [51728]

Child and Family Social Work (Birmingham, GBR) [52336]

Child Language and Teaching Therapy (London, GBR) [54203]

Childcare Now (London, GBR) *Unable to locate*

Childhood (London, GBR) [54204]

Childminding (Stirling, GBR) [56621]

Children and Books (Copenhagen, DEN) *Unable to locate*

Children First (Monaco, MCO) *Unable to locate*

Children & Society (London, GBR) [54205]

Children Worldwide (Geneva, SWI) *Unable to locate*

Children's Digest (Mumbai, MH, IND) *Unable to locate*

Children's Geographies (Abingdon, GBR) [51729]

The Children's Own (Kingston, JAM) [46282]

Children's Social and Economics Education [55909]*

Numbers cited in bold after listings are entry numbers rather than page numbers.

Child's Nervous System (Tokyo, JPN) [46784]

Chile News (Stedham, GBR) Ceased

Chiltern-FM [52277]*

Chiltern-FM - 97.6 (Dunstable, GBR) [53226]

Chimia (Bern, SWI) [51070]

Chimica Acta Turcica (Istanbul, TUR) Unable to locate

Chimica Oggi (Chemistry Today) (Milan, ITA) [46165]

Chin Ma chih sheng Broadcasting Station (Kinmen, TWN) Unable to locate

China (Singapore, SGP) [50119]

China Aero Information (Beijing, CHN) Unable to locate

China and Africa (Beijing, CHN) Unable to locate

China Auto (Beijing, CHN) Unable to locate

China Bicycle (Beijing, CHN) Unable to locate

China Books (Beijing, CHN) Unable to locate

China Brief (Beijing, CHN) [43176]

China-Britain Business Review (London, GBR) [54206]

China Business (Beijing, CHN) [43177]

China Chemical Reporter (Beijing, CHN) Unable to locate

China Computer Reseller World (Beijing, CHN) Unable to locate

China Daily (Hong Kong Edition) (Beijing, CHN) [43178]

China Economic Review (London, GBR) [54207]*

China Environment News (Beijing, CHN) Unable to locate

China in Focus (Cheltenham, GC, GBR) Ceased

China Heavy Machinery Industry Association News Report (Beijing, CHN) Unable to locate

China Huayi Broadcasting Company (Private) (Fuzhou, FJ, CHN) Unable to locate

China Huayi Broadcasting Station (Fuzhou, FJ, CHN) Unable to locate

China Huayi Broadcasting Station (Fuzhou, FJ, CHN) Unable to locate

China Huayi Broadcasting Station (Fuzhou, FJ, CHN) Unable to locate

China Huayi Broadcasting Station (Fuzhou, FJ, CHN) Unable to locate

China Huayi People's Broadcasting Station (Fuzhou, FJ, CHN) Unable to locate

China Information (Leiden, NLD) [48661]

China Land Sciences (Beijing, CHN) Unable to locate

China Law Review (Abingdon, GBR) Ceased

China Leprosy and Skin Diseases Journal (Beijing, CHN) Unable to locate

China Mail (Singapore, SGP) Unable to locate

China National Radio Minorities (Beijing, CHN) Unable to locate

China National Radio Minorities (Beijing, CHN) Unable to locate

China National Radio Minorities (Beijing, CHN) Unable to locate

China National Radio Minorities (Beijing, CHN) Unable to locate

China National Radio 1 (Beijing, CHN) Unable to locate

China National Radio 1 (Beijing, CHN) Unable to locate

China National Radio 1 (Beijing, CHN) Unable to locate

China National Radio 1 (Beijing, CHN) Unable to locate

China National Radio 1 (Beijing, CHN) Unable to locate

China National Radio 1 (Beijing, CHN) Unable to locate

China National Radio 1 (Beijing, CHN) Unable to locate

China National Radio 1 (Beijing, CHN) Unable to locate

China National Radio 1 (Beijing, CHN) Unable to locate

China National Radio 1 (Beijing, CHN) Unable to locate

China National Radio 1 - 540 KHz (Beijing, CHN) [43237]

China National Radio 1 - 567 KHz (Beijing, CHN) [43235]

China National Radio 1 - 639 KHz (Beijing, CHN) [43236]

China National Radio 1 Minorities (Beijing, CHN) Unable to locate

China National Radio Taiwan 1 (Beijing, CHN) Unable to locate

China National Radio Taiwan 1 (Beijing, CHN) Unable to locate

China National Radio Taiwan 1 (Beijing, CHN) Unable to locate

China National Radio Taiwan 2 (Beijing, CHN) Unable to locate

China National Radio Taiwan 2 (Beijing, CHN) Unable to locate

China National Radio Taiwan 2 (Beijing, CHN) Unable to locate

China National Radio Taiwan 2 (Beijing, CHN) Unable to locate

China National Radio 2 (Beijing, CHN) Unable to locate

China National Radio 2 (Beijing, CHN) Unable to locate

China National Radio 2 (Beijing, CHN) Unable to locate

China National Radio 2 (Beijing, CHN) Unable to locate

China National Radio 2 (Beijing, CHN) Unable to locate

China National Radio 2 (Beijing, CHN) Unable to locate

China National Radio 2 (Beijing, CHN) Unable to locate

China National Radio 2 (Beijing, CHN) Unable to locate

China National Radio 2 (Beijing, CHN) Unable to locate

China National Radio 2 - 630 KHz (Beijing, CHN) [43238]

The China News (Taipei, TWN) Unable to locate

The China Nonprofit Review (Beijing, CHN) [43179]

China Paint (Beijing, CHN) Unable to locate

China Particuology [43212]*

China Philately (Beijing, CHN) Unable to locate

China Pictorial (Beijing, CHN) [43180]

The China Post (Taipei, TWN) [51334]

The China Quarterly (London, GBR) [54208]

China Radio International (Beijing, CHN) Unable to locate

China Radio International (Beijing, CHN) Unable to locate

China Radio International (Beijing, CHN) Unable to locate

China Radio International (Beijing, CHN) Unable to locate

China Radio International (Beijing, CHN) Unable to locate

China Radio International (Beijing, CHN) Unable to locate

China Radio International (Beijing, CHN) Unable to locate

China Radio International (Beijing, CHN) Unable to locate

China Red Cross Fraternity (Beijing, CHN) Unable to locate

China Reports (Beijing, CHN) Unable to locate

China Review on Administration of Industry and Commerce (Beijing, CHN) Unable to locate

China Salt Industry (Beijing, CHN) Unable to locate

China Screen (Beijing, CHN) Unable to locate

China Shooting and Archery (Beijing, CHN) Unable to locate

China Southeast Broadcasting Company (Fuzhou, FJ, CHN) Unable to locate

China Southeast Broadcasting Company (Fuzhou, FJ, CHN) Unable to locate

China Sports (Beijing, CHN) Unable to locate

China University of Geosciences; Journal of the [43519]*

China Welding (Harbin, HL, CHN) [43263]

China & the World (Beijing, CHN) Unable to locate

China's Foreign Trade (Beijing, CHN) [43181]

China's Refractories (Luoyang, CHN) [43452]

Chinchilla News and Murilla Advertiser (Sydney, NW, AUS) [42491]

Chinese Annals of Mathematics (Bussum, NLD) Unable to locate

Chinese Annals of Mathematics (Singapore, SGP) Ceased

Chinese Annals of Mathematics, Series B (Shanghai, CHN) [43469]

Chinese Around the World (Hong Kong, CHN) [43288]

Chinese Astronomy and Astrophysics (Nanjing, CHN) [43453]

Chinese Chemical Letters (Beijing, CHN) [43182]

Chinese-German Journal of Clinical Oncology (Heidelberg, GER) [44445]

Chinese Heart Journal (Xi'an, SH, CHN) [43528]

Chinese Journal of Acoustics (Beijing, CHN) Unable to locate

Chinese Journal of Administration (Taipei, TWN) Unable to locate

Chinese Journal of Aeronautics (Beijing, CHN) Unable to locate

Chinese Journal of Agricultural Biotechnology (Cambridge, GBR) [52806]

Chinese Journal of Applied Chemistry (Beijing, CHN) [43183]

Chinese Journal for Cancer Research (Tianjin, CHN) Unable to locate

Chinese Journal of Catalysis (Dalian, LI, CHN) [43253]

Chinese Journal of Cells and Molecular Immunology (Xi'an, SH, CHN) [43529]

Chinese Journal of Chemical Engineering (Beijing, CHN) [43184]

Chinese Journal of Chemical Physics (Bristol, GBR) [52652]

Chinese Journal of Chemistry (Shanghai, CHN) [43470]

Chinese Journal of Chromotography (Beijing, CHN) Unable to locate

Chinese Journal of Clinical Oncology (Tianjin, CHN) Unable to locate

Chinese Journal of Conservative Dentistry (Xi'an, SH, CHN) [43530]

Chinese Journal of Inorganic Chemistry (Nanjing, JS, CHN) Unable to locate

Chinese Journal of International Law (Oxford, GBR) [55908]

Chinese Journal of Materials Science (Chutung Hsinchu, TWN) Unable to locate

Chinese Journal of Neuroanatomy (Xi'an, SH, CHN) [43531]

Chinese Journal of Nursing (Beijing, CHN) Unable to locate

Chinese Journal of Physics (Taipei, TWN) [51335]

Chinese Journal of Physiology (Taipei, TWN) Unable to locate

Chinese Journal of Plant Pathology (Beijing, CHN) [43185]

Chinese Journal of Polymer Science (Beijing, CHN) [43186]

Chinese Journal of Psychology (Taipei, TWN) Unable to locate

Chinese Journal of Sports Medicine (Beijing, CHN) Unable to locate

Chinese Journal of Virology (Beijing, CHN) Unable to locate

Chinese Management Studies (Singapore, SGP) [50120]

Chinese Medical Association Journal (Singapore, SGP) [50121]

Chinese Medical Journal (Beijing, CHN) [43187]

Chinese Melody - 866 (Kuala Lumpur, MYS) [47642]

The Chinese Pen (Taipei, TWN) Unable to locate

Chinese Photography (Beijing, CHN) [43188]

Chinese Physics Letters (Beijing, CHN) [43189]

Chinese Ports (Shanghai, CHN) Unable to locate

Chinese Science Bulletin (Dordrecht, NLD) [48351]

Chinese Student Nutritional Newspaper (Beijing, CHN) Unable to locate

Chinese Tales and Stories (Beijing, CHN) [43190]

Ching Feng (Hong Kong, CHN) [43289]

Ching Sheng Broadcasting Station (Kaohsiung, TWN) Unable to locate

CHIP (Wurzburg, GER) [44717]

Chip (Mumbai, MH, IND) [45362]

Chiropody Review [56588]*

Chiropractic Journal of Australia (Wagga Wagga, NW, AUS) [42667]

Chiropractic & Osteopathy (Murdoch, WA, AUS) [42136]

Chirurgie de la Main (Singapore, SGP) [50122]

Chirurgische Gastroenterologie [44374]*

Chitraleka (Mumbai, MH, IND) [45363]

The Chittagong University Journal of Science (Chittagong, BGD) Unable to locate

Choice (Marrickville, NW, AUS) [42039]

Choice (Hong Kong, CHN) [43290]

Choice-FM - 104.3 (Limassol, CYP) [43591]

Choice-FM - 107.1 (London, GBR) [55445]

Choice-FM - 96.9 (London, GBR) [55444]

Chongqing Economic Radio (Chongqing, CHN) Unable to locate

Chongqing People's Broadcasting Station, CHN) Unable to locate

Numbers cited in bold after listings are entry numbers rather than page numbers.

Chongqing People's Broadcasting Station (Chongqing, CHN) *Unable to locate*

Chongqing People's Broadcasting Station (Chongqing, CHN) *Unable to locate*

Chongqing Television (Chongqing, CHN) *Unable to locate*

The Choogan Chosun (Seoul, KOR) **[47260]**

Choosing a School for Your Child - New South Wales (North Ryde, NW, AUS) **[42175]**

Choosing a School for Your Child - Victoria (North Ryde, NW, AUS) **[42176]**

Chor und Konzert (Weimar, GER) *Unable to locate*

Chorley Guardian (Chorley, GBR) **[53021]**

Chorus (Brezolles, FRA) **[43923]**

Chorus (Aarau, SWI) *Unable to locate*

Chosen Ilbo (Seoul, KOR) **[47261]**

Chowkidar (London, GBR) *Unable to locate*

The Christchurch Star (Christchurch, NZL) **[48866]**

Christian Aid News (London, GBR) *Unable to locate*

Christian Baptist Guide (Bucharest, ROM) *Unable to locate*

Christian Institute for Religious Studies Bulletin (Batala, PJ, IND) *Unable to locate*

Christian Librarian (Ilford, GBR) **[53638]**

Christian Light Radio-FM - 105.4 (Naxxar, MAL) **[47736]**

Christian Medical College Vellore Alumni Journal (Vellore, TN, IND) *Unable to locate*

Christian Medical Journal of India (New Delhi, DH, IND) *Unable to locate*

Christian Voice (Karachi, PAK) *Unable to locate*

Christian Worker (Colombo, SRI) *Unable to locate*

Christianity (London, GBR) **[54209]**

Christianity & Renewal **[54209]***

Christine's BIG Crossword (Gosford, NW, AUS) **[41905]**

Christine's Cryptic Crossword Collection (Gosford, NW, AUS) **[41906]**

Christliche Frau (Cologne, GER) **[44291]**

Christliches Zeugnis (Zurich, SWI) **[51256]**

Chromatographia (Tokyo, JPN) **[46785]**

Chromosoma (Basel, SWI) **[51061]**

Chromosome Science (Higashihi-roshima, JPN) *Unable to locate*

Chronic Respiratory Disease (London, GBR) **[54210]**

Chronicle (Kuala Lumpur, MYS) *Unable to locate*

The Chronicle (Belfast, GBR) **[52281]**

The Chronicle (Dominica) (Roseau, DMA) **[43739]**

Chronique d'Egypte (Brussels, BEL) *Unable to locate*

Chronique Feministe (Brussels, BEL) *Unable to locate*

Chu jen (boss) Broadcasting Station (Kaohsiung, TWN) *Unable to locate*

Chu Tian Broadcast Station (Wuhan, HU, CHN) *Unable to locate*

Chu Tian Broadcast Station (Wuhan, HU, CHN) *Unable to locate*

Chu Tian Broadcast Station (Wuhan, HU, CHN) *Unable to locate*

Chubu Weekly (Aichi, JPN) *Unable to locate*

Chulalongkorn University Radio Station (Bangkok, THA) *Unable to locate*

Chung Hua (China) Broadcasting Co. (Taipei, TWN) *Unable to locate*

Church Music Quarterly (Dorking, GBR) **[53193]**

Churchman (Watford, GBR) **[56861]**

Churchman's Magazine **[55146]***

Chuxiong People's Broadcasting Station (Chuxiong, YU, CHN) *Unable to locate*

Chuxiong People's Broadcasting Station (Chuxiong, YU, CHN) *Unable to locate*

Chuxiong People's Broadcasting Station (Chuxiong, YU, CHN) *Unable to locate*

Chuzhou People's Broadcasting Station (Chuzhou, AN, CHN) *Unable to locate*

Chwila rozrywki (Warsaw, POL) **[49704]**

C.I. Real Estate Magazine (Grand Cayman, CYM) **[43131]**

Ciberdiario de Nicaragua (Managua, NCG) *Unable to locate*

Ciciban (Ljubljana, SVA) *Unable to locate*

Cicido (Ljubljana, SVA) *Unable to locate*

Cidade Bela-FM - 90.5 (Campo Verde, MS, BRZ) **[42973]**

Cidade-FM - 97.9 (Campo Grande, SP, BRZ) **[42972]**

Ciencia e Cultura (Sao Paulo, SP, BRZ) **[43033]**

Ciencia Hoje (Sao Paulo, SP, BRZ) **[43034]**

Ciencia Hoje das Criancas (Sao Paulo, SP, BRZ) **[43035]**

Ciencia Rural (Santa Maria, RN, BRZ) **[43016]**

Ciencia & Saude Coletiva (Vicosa, MI, BRZ) **[43056]**

Ciencia e Tecnologia de Alimentos (Campinas, SP, BRZ) **[42967]**

Ciencia y Tecnologia Alternativa (Quito, ECU) *Unable to locate*

Ciencia & Tropico (Recife, PB, BRZ) *Unable to locate*

Cigar Buyer Magazine (Norwich, GBR) **[55728]**

CIIL Bilingual Hindi Series (Mysore, KA, IND) *Unable to locate*

CIIL Current Inquiries in Indian Languages (Mysore, KA, IND) *Unable to locate*

Ciladerma (Buenos Aires, ARG) *Unable to locate*

CIMMYT Annual Report (Mexico City, DF, MEX) **[47783]**

Cine Advance (Calcutta, WB, IND) *Unable to locate*

Cine Blitz (Mumbai, MH, IND) *Unable to locate*

Cine News (Singapore, SGP) *Unable to locate*

Cinema (Stockholm, SWE) *Unable to locate*

Cinema Technology (London, GBR) *Unable to locate*

Cinema Vision India (Mumbai, MH, IND) *Unable to locate*

Cinema the World Over (Karachi, PAK) *Unable to locate*

The CIPA Journal (London, GBR) **[54211]**

Circle (Napier, NZL) **[48939]**

The Circler (Keighley, GBR) *Unable to locate*

The Circuit (Nundah, QL, AUS) **[42220]**

Circuit World (Loughborough, GBR) **[55478]**

Circuits and Systems II (Ferrara, ITA) **[46138]**

Circular (Wellington, NZL) **[49004]**

Circulation Auditing Around the World (Mumbai, MH, IND) *Unable to locate*

Cirugia Cardiovascular (Barcelona, SPA) **[50656]**

CISV News (Newcastle upon Tyne, GBR) *Unable to locate*

Citi-FM - 97.3 (Accra, GHA) **[44731]**

Citizen Action (Calcutta, WB, IND) *Unable to locate*

Citizen and Week End Review (New Delhi, DH, IND) *Unable to locate*

Citizens Gazette (New Delhi, DH, IND) *Unable to locate*

Citizenship, Social and Economics Education (Oxford, GBR) **[55909]**

Citizenship, Social and Economics Education: An International Journal (Stoke-on-Trent, GBR) *Unable to locate*

Citizenship Studies (Abingdon, GBR) **[51730]**

Citta Bella (Singapore, SGP) **[50123]**

CITU Mazdoor (New Delhi, DH, IND) *Unable to locate*

City-FM - 89 (Karachi, PAK) **[49381]**

City Guide (London, GBR) *Unable to locate*

City North News (Stafford, QL, AUS) **[42386]**

City Security (London, GBR) *Unable to locate*

City Sound (Singapore, SGP) *Unable to locate*

City South News (Mount Gravatt, QL, AUS) **[42129]**

City Times (Dubai, UAE) **[51636]**

City Tribune (Galway, GL, IRL) **[46017]**

City Vision (Cape Town, SAF) **[50371]**

Citybeat-FM - 96.7 (Belfast, GBR) **[52299]**

Citybeat-FM - 102.5 (Belfast, GBR) **[52298]**

Citylife (Chiang Mai, THA) **[51457]**

Citytalk-FM - 105.9 (Liverpool, GBR) **[53880]**

Ciudad de Montevideo-AM - 1370 KHz (Montevideo, URY) **[57008]**

Civic Affairs (Kanpur, UP, IND) *Unable to locate*

Civil Engineer (Calcutta, WB, IND) *Unable to locate*

Civil Engineering (Halfway House, SAF) **[50519]**

Civil Engineering Surveyor (Sale, GBR) *Unable to locate*

Civil Justice Quarterly (Andover, GBR) **[52112]**

Civil Liberty Agenda (London, GBR) *Unable to locate*

Civil & Military Law Journal (New Delhi, DH, IND) *Unable to locate*

Civil Protection (London, GBR) *Unable to locate*

Civilekonomen (Stockholm, SWE) *Unable to locate*

Civilingenjoren (Stockholm, SWE) *Unable to locate*

Civiloekonomen (Copenhagen, DEN) *Unable to locate*

Clara (Barcelona, SPA) **[50657]**

Clara Deco (Barcelona, SPA) **[50658]**

Clare-FM - 102.9 (Ennis, CL, IRL) **[46012]**

Clare-FM - 95.2 (Ennistymon, CL, IRL) **[46013]**

Clare-FM - 96.4 (Maghera, CL, IRL) **[46037]**

Clare FM2 - 96.6 (Killaloe, CL, IRL) **[46027]**

Clarin (Oviedo, SPA) *Unable to locate*

Clarity (Mumbai, MH, IND) *Unable to locate*

Clasica-FM - 106.5 (Guatemala City, GTM) **[44786]**

Class 95 FM - 95 MHz (Singapore, SGP) **[50294]**

Classe Lancia (Turin, ITA) *Unable to locate*

Classic American (London, GBR) **[54212]**

Classic Bus (Edinburgh, GBR) **[53262]**

Classic Car Mart (Birmingham, GBR) **[52337]**

Classic Car Weekly (Peterborough, GBR) **[56254]**

Classic-FM - 102.7 MHz (Auckland Park, SAF) **[50351]**

Classic-FM - 100 (London, GBR) **[55450]**

Classic-FM - 100.1 (London, GBR) **[55448]**

Classic-FM - 101.5 (London, GBR) **[55449]**

Classic-FM - 100.4 (London, GBR) **[55446]**

Classic-FM - 100.5 (London, GBR) **[55447]**

Classic Hits-FM - 107.1 (Noosaville, QL, AUS) **[42149]**

Classic Hits-FM - 97.4 (Auckland, NZL) **[48836]**

Classic Hits-FM - 97.7 (Christchurch, NZL) **[48881]**

Classic Hits-FM - 89.4 (Dunedin, NZL) **[48894]**

Classic Hits-FM - 90.9 (Gisborne, NZL) **[48899]**

Classic Hits-FM - 91.1 (Greymouth, NZL) **[48906]**

Classic Hits-FM - 89.8 (Nelson, NZL) **[48944]**

Classic Hits-FM - 98.4 (Oamaru, NZL) **[48960]**

Classic Hits-FM - 97.5 (Rotorua, NZL) **[48974]**

Classic Hits-FM - 96.7 (Taupo, NZL) **[48979]**

Classic Hits-FM - 98.7 (Timaru, NZL) **[48988]**

Classic Hits-FM - 94.7 (Timaru, NZL) **[48989]**

Classic Hits-FM - 89.6 (Wanganui, NZL) **[48997]**

Classic Hits-FM - 90 (Wellington, NZL) **[49037]**

Classic Hits-FM Bay of Plenty - 95.0 (Tauranga, NZL) **[48981]**

Classic Hits-FM Hawke's Bay - 89.5 (Napier, NZL) **[48940]**

Classic Hits-FM Kapiti - 92.7 (Paraparaumu, NZL) **[48971]**

Classic Hits-FM Manawatu - 97.8 (Palmerston North, NZL) **[48966]**

Classic Hits-FM Marlborough - 96.9 (Blenheim, NZL) **[48858]**

Classic Hits-FM Southland - 98.8 (Invercargill, NZL) **[48919]**

Classic Hits-FM Taranaki - 90.0 (New Plymouth, NZL) **[48948]**

Classic Hits-FM Taranaki - 90.7 (New Plymouth, NZL) **[48947]**

Classic Hits-FM Waikato - 98.6 (Hamilton, NZL) **[48913]**

The Classic Marvel Figurine Collection (London, GBR) **[54213]**

Numbers cited in bold after listings are entry numbers rather than page numbers.

Classic Military Vehicle (Cudham, GBR) [53138]

Classic and Motorcycle Mechanics (Horncastle, GBR) [53588]

Classic Plant & Machinery (Cudham, GBR) [53139]

Classic Racer International (Horncastle, GBR) [53589]

Classic Record Collector (London, GBR) [54214]

Classic Rock (Kuala Lumpur, MYS) Unable to locate

Classic Rock Radio-FM - 100.6 (Saarbrucken, GER) [44653]

Classic Van and Pick-up (Cudham, GBR) [53140]

Classic and Vintage Commercials (Cudham, GBR) [53141]

Classic Wings (Mount Ommaney, QL, AUS) [42134]

Classica (Kuvalehdet, FIN) Unable to locate

Classica-FM - 107.1 (Casilla, BOL) [42929]

Classical Guitar (Blaydon-on-Tyne, GBR) [52387]

Classical Music (London, GBR) [54215]

Classical and Quantum Gravity (Bristol, GBR) [52653]

The Classical Quarterly (Oxford, GBR) [55910]

The Classical Review (Manchester, GBR) [55547]

Classics (Orpington, GBR) Unable to locate

ClassNK Magazine (Tokyo, JPN) [46786]

The Classroom Teacher (Penang, MYS) [47688]

Claves de Razon Practica (Madrid, SPA) [50735]

Clay Minerals (Twickenham, GBR) [56789]

Clays and Clay Minerals (Cork, CK, IRL) [45936]

CLEAN (Braunschweig, GER) [44274]

Clean Air (Brighton, GBR) Unable to locate

Clean Air Journal (Halfway House, SAF) [50520]

Clean Slate (Machynlleth, GBR) [55522]

Clean Technologies and Environmental Policy (Tokyo, JPN) [46787]

Cleantech (London, GBR) [54216]

Clematis International (Cheshunt, GBR) [52987]

Clergy Review [55061]*

The Clerk (Nottingham, GBR) Unable to locate

Climate Control News (CCN) (Surry Hills, NW, AUS) [42423]

Climate Dynamics (Heidelberg, GER) [44446]

Climate of the Past (Hamburg, GER) [44412]

Climate Policy (London, GBR) [54217]

Climate Research (Oslo, NOR) [49195]

Climatic Change (Dordrecht, NLD) [48352]

Clinica Chimica Acta (Gent, BEL) [42882]

Clinica World Medical Device and Diagnostic News (London, GBR) [54218]

Clinical Approaches in Bipolar Disorders (Worthing, GBR) [56971]

Clinical Autonomic Research (Tokyo, JPN) [46788]

The Clinical Biochemist Reviews (Perth, WA, AUS) [42249]

Clinical Biochemistry and Metabolism (Prague, CZE) Unable to locate

Clinical Biomechanics (Huddersfield, GBR) [53618]

Clinical Chemistry and Laboratory Medicine (Berlin, GER) [44165]

Clinical Child Psychology and Psychiatry (London, GBR) [54219]

Clinical Drug Investigation (Mairangi Bay, NZL) [48934]

Clinical Ethics (London, GBR) [54220]

Clinical & Experimental Allergy (Leicester, GBR) [53793]

Clinical and Experimental Allergy Reviews (London, GBR) [54221]

Clinical & Experimental Dermatology (London, GBR) [54222]

Clinical & Experimental Immunology (London, GBR) [54223]

Clinical and Experimental Medicine (Dordrecht, NLD) [48353]

Clinical & Experimental Metastasis (Dordrecht, NLD) [48354]

Clinical and Experimental Nephrology (Tokyo, JPN) [46789]

Clinical and Experimental Optometry (Oxford, GBR) [55911]

Clinical Focus (Leicester, GBR) [53794]

Clinical Governance (Bradford, GBR) [52441]

Clinical Hemorheology and Microcirculation (Siena, ITA) [46258]

Clinical Intensive Care (Abingdon, GBR) Ceased

Clinical Interventions in Aging (Macclesfield, GBR) [55515]

Clinical Laboratory Diagnosis (Moscow, RUS) [49886]

Clinical Linguistics & Phonetics (Abingdon, GBR) [51731]

Clinical Lipidology (London, GBR) [54224]

Clinical Medicine (London, GBR) [54225]

Clinical Neurology and Neurosurgery (Antwerp, BEL) [42838]

Clinical Neuroradiology (Dordrecht, NLD) [48355]

Clinical Oncology (London, GBR) [54226]

Clinical Ophthalmology (Macclesfield, GBR) [55516]

Clinical Oral Implants Research (Hong Kong, CHN) [43291]

Clinical Oral Investigations (Heidelberg, GER) [44447]

Clinical Pediatric Endocrinology (Kyoto, JPN) [46469]

Clinical Pharmacist (London, GBR) [54227]

Clinical Pharmacokinetics (Mairangi Bay, NZL) [48935]

Clinical Pharmacology and Therapeutics (Basingstoke, GBR) [52198]

Clinical Pharmacy Europe (London, GBR) [54228]

Clinical Physics and Physiological Measurement [52718]*

Clinical Physiology and Functional Imaging (Malmo, SWE) [50991]

Clinical Practice and Epidemiology in Mental Health (Bussum, NLD) [48281]

Clinical Radiology (London, GBR) [54229]

Clinical Research in Cardiology (Homburg, GER) [44486]

The Clinical Respiratory Journal (Copenhagen, DEN) [43659]

Clinical Rheumatology (London, GBR) [54230]

Clinical Risk (London, GBR) [54231]

The Clinical Teacher (Oxford, GBR) [55912]

Clinical Therapeutics (Amsterdam, NLD) [47928]

Clinical Trials (London, GBR) [54232]

Clinician (Panjim, MH, IND) Unable to locate

Clinics (Sao Paulo, SP, BRZ) [43036]

Clinics in Mother and Child Health (Yaounde, CMR) [43129]

Clio Medica (London, GBR) [54233]

Clipboard (London, GBR) Unable to locate

CLIS Observer (New Delhi, DH, IND) Unable to locate

Clitheroe Advertiser & Times (Clitheroe, GBR) [53026]

Cloning and Stem Cells (Edinburgh, GBR) [53263]

Closer (London, GBR) [54234]

Closer to God (Milton Keynes, GBR) [55631]

Closer to God Incorporating Alive to God [55631]*

CLSU Scientific Journal (Munoz, PHL) Unable to locate

The Club (Hong Kong, CHN) [43292]

Club Asia-AM (Barking, GBR) Unable to locate

Club Asia-AM (Barking, GBR) Unable to locate

Club Business International (Camberley, GBR) Unable to locate

Club Connection (London, GBR) Unable to locate

Club Marine (Brighton, VI, AUS) [41638]

Club Sandwich (Westcliff-On-Sea, GBR) Ceased

Club 3 (Rome, ITA) [46224]

Club V (Sofia, BUL) Unable to locate

Cluewords (Gosford, NW, AUS) [41907]

Cluster Computing (Heidelberg, GER) [44448]

Clyde 1-FM - 102.5 (Glasgow, GBR) [53465]

Clyde One-FM - 97.0 (Glasgow, GBR) [53463]

Clyde One-FM - 103.3 (Glasgow, GBR) [53464]

Clyde 2-AM - 1152 (Glasgow, GBR) [53466]

CMBF Radio Musical Nacional-AM - 590 (Havana, CUB) [43577]

CMBF Radio Musical Nacional-FM - 97.5 (Camaguey, CUB) [43571]

CMBF Radio Musical Nacional-FM - 91.5 (Ciego de Avila, CUB) [43572]

CMBF Radio Musical Nacional-FM - 92.7 (Cienfuegos, CUB) [43573]

CMBF Radio Musical Nacional-FM - 92.7 (Granma, CUB) [43574]

CMBF Radio Musical Nacional-FM - 98.5 (Guantanamo, CUB) [43575]

CMBF Radio Musical Nacional-FM - 99.1 (Havana, CUB) [43578]

CMBF Radio Musical Nacional-FM - 105.7 (Holguin, CUB) [43579]

CMBF Radio Musical Nacional-FM - 96.5 (Isla de la Juventud, CUB) [43580]

CMBF Radio Musical Nacional-FM - 107.9 (Jacan, CUB) [43581]

CMBF Radio Musical Nacional-FM - 93.7 (La Cumbre, CUB) [43582]

CMBF Radio Musical Nacional-FM - 98.3 (Las Tunas, CUB) [43583]

CMBF Radio Musical Nacional-FM - 98.7 (Pinar del Rio, CUB) [43584]

CMBF Radio Musical Nacional-FM - 93.9 (Sancti Spiritus, CUB) [43585]

CMBF Radio Musical Nacional-FM - 100.3 (Santiago de Cuba, CUB) [43586]

CMBF Radio Musical Nacional-FM - 100.7 (Villa Clara, CUB) [43587]

CME (Dordrecht, NLD) [48356]

CMJ Quarterly [53382]*

CMU Journal of Science (Bukidnon, PHL) Unable to locate

CNEB Info (Bujumbura, BDI) Unable to locate

CNS & Neurological Disorders - Drug Targets (Bussum, NLD) [48282]

Coaches Clipboard (Sheffield, GBR) Unable to locate

Coaching Edge (Leeds, GBR) [53761]

Coal Mining and Exploration Queensland (Nundah, QL, AUS) Unable to locate

COAST (Sydney, NW, AUS) [42492]

Coast-AM - 1593 (Christchurch, NZL) [48882]

Coast-AM - 954 (Dunedin, NZL) [48895]

Coast-AM - 1557 (Hawera, NZL) [48916]

Coast-AM - 1530 (Napier, NZL) [48941]

Coast-AM - 1359 (New Plymouth, NZL) [48949]

Coast-AM - 1548 (Palmerston North, NZL) [48967]

Coast-AM - 900 (Whangarei, NZL) [49050]

Coast-FM - 96.3 (Gosford, NW, AUS) [41924]

Coast-FM - 97.3 (Mandurah, WA, AUS) [42031]

Coast-FM - 95.3 (Warrnambool, VI, AUS) [42688]

Coast-FM - 91.4 (Limassol, CYP) [43592]

Coast-FM - 105.4 (Auckland, NZL) [48837]

Coast-FM - 92.4 (Invercargill, NZL) [48920]

Coast-FM - 97.3 (Tauranga, NZL) [48982]

Coast-FM - 99.4 (Wellington, NZL) [49038]

Coast-FM Kapiti - 95.7 (Wellington, NZL) [49039]

Coastal Advertiser (Ipswich, GBR) [53653]

Coastal Engineering Journal (Nagoya, JPN) [46552]

Coastal News (Whangmata, NZL) Unable to locate

Coastal Views (Sydney, NW, AUS) [42493]

Coat of Arms (Guildford, GBR) [53489]

Coating (Saint Gallen, SWI) [51223]

Coatings Comet (Hampton, GBR) [53505]

Cobar Age (Cobar, NW, AUS) [41772]

Cobbett's New Register (Petersfield, GBR) Unable to locate

Cobouw (The Hague, NLD) Unable to locate

Coches de Ocasion (Madrid, SPA) [50736]

Cochlear Implants International (Bognor Regis, GBR) [52394]

Cockburn Gazette (Northbridge, WA, AUS) [42212]

Cocoinfo International (Jakarta, IDN) [45794]

Code of Practice (Watford, GBR) [56862]

Master Index

Numbers cited in bold after listings are entry numbers rather than page numbers.

Code Words (Redhill, GBR) **[56348]**

Codebreakers (London, GBR) **[54235]**

CodeBreakers Journal (CBJ) (Herford, GER) **[44483]**

Codecracker Starhunts (Gosford, NW, AUS) **[41908]**

CoDesign (Abingdon, GBR) **[51732]**

CODESRIA Bulletin (Dakar, SEN) **[50080]**

Codex (Ascot Vale, VI, AUS) *Ceased*

Coffee Culture **[48794]***

The Coffs Coast Advocate (Sydney, NW, AUS) **[42494]**

Cognition, Technology & Work (London, GBR) **[54236]**

Cognitiva (Madrid, SPA) **[50737]**

Cognitive Behaviour Therapy (Linkoping, SWE) **[50973]**

Cognitive Development (Amsterdam, NLD) **[47929]**

Cognitive Neuropsychiatry (London, GBR) **[54237]**

Cognitive Processing (Rome, ITA) **[46225]**

Cognitive Psychology (Amsterdam, NLD) **[47930]**

Cognitive Science Book Review (North Ryde, NW, AUS) *Unable to locate*

Cognitive Systems (Groningen, NLD) **[48598]**

Cognitive Systems Research (Amsterdam, NLD) **[47931]**

Coiffure Suisse Shop (Bern, SWI) *Unable to locate*

Coin News (Honiton, GBR) **[53586]**

Coke and Chemistry (Moscow, RUS) **[49887]**

Cokemaking International (Dusseldorf, GER) *Ceased*

Coleccion Estudios Cieplan (Santiago, CHL) *Unable to locate*

Coleraine Times (Edinburgh, GBR) **[53264]**

COLES (Sydney, NW, AUS) **[42495]**

Collection Building (Bradford, GBR) **[52442]**

College Bulletin (London, GBR) **[54238]**

Collegium/Journal of the International Society of Leather Technologists **[53180]***

Collie Mail (Collie, WA, AUS) **[41779]**

Collingwood and British Idealism Studies (Exeter, GBR) **[53348]**

Colloid Journal (Moscow, RUS) **[49888]**

Colloid and Polymer Science (Aachen, GER) **[44136]**

Colloids and Surfaces A (Bundoora, VI, AUS) **[41670]**

Colloquy (Clayton, VI, AUS) **[41759]**

Colmed (Genval, BEL) *Unable to locate*

Colo Colo-AM - 880 (Alameda, ECU) **[43743]**

Colombia Rotaria (Cali, COL) **[43550]**

Coloproctology (Dordrecht, NLD) **[48357]**

Coloration Technology (Bradford, GBR) **[52443]**

Colorectal Disease (London, GBR) *Unable to locate*

Colossus Crosswords (Gosford, NW, AUS) **[41909]**

Colour Society Journal (Mumbai, MH, IND) *Unable to locate*

Columban Mission (Navan, ME, IRL) **[46044]**

Combat (Karachi, PAK) *Unable to locate*

Combat Aircraft (Kingston upon Thames, GBR) **[53720]**

Combinatorics, Probability and Computing (Cambridge, GBR) **[52807]**

Combroad **[54240]***

Combustion and Flame (Paris, FRA) **[44033]**

Comer Bien (Barcelona, SPA) **[50659]**

The Comet (Ijora, LG, NGA) *Unable to locate*

Comhar (Helsinki, FIN) *Unable to locate*

Comic Bon Bon (Tokyo, JPN) *Ceased*

Comic King (Shanghai, CHN) **[43471]**

Comics International (London, GBR) *Unable to locate*

Comment News (Kelmscott, WA, AUS) **[41984]**

Commentarii Mathematici Universitatis Sancti Pauli (Tokyo, JPN) *Unable to locate*

Comments on Argentine Trade (Buenos Aires, ARG) **[41471]**

Commerce (Mumbai, MH, IND) *Unable to locate*

Commerce (Kathmandu, NPL) *Unable to locate*

Commerce Yearbook of Ports, Shipping and Shipbuilding (Mumbai, MH, IND) *Unable to locate*

Commerce Yearbook of Public Sector (Mumbai, MH, IND) *Unable to locate*

Commerce Yearbook of Road Transport (Mumbai, MH, IND) *Unable to locate*

Commercial Courier (Valletta, MAL) **[47745]**

Commercial Horticulture Magazine (Auckland, NZL) **[48789]**

Commercial & Industrial Guide (Singapore, SGP) *Unable to locate*

Commercial Journal (Delhi, DH, IND) *Unable to locate*

Commercial Law Gazette (Delhi, DH, IND) *Unable to locate*

Commercial Law Journal (London, GBR) *Unable to locate*

Commercial Lending Review (London, GBR) *Unable to locate*

Commercial Vehicle Workshop (Watford, GBR) **[56863]**

The Commercials Production Review (London, GBR) *Unable to locate*

Commercium (Jaipur, RJ, IND) *Unable to locate*

Commerzbank Journal (Kassel, GER) *Unable to locate*

Commodity Price Statistics Monthly in Taiwan Area (Taipei, TWN) *Unable to locate*

Common Cause (London, GBR) **[54239]**

Common Knowledge (Ramat Gan, ISR) **[46092]**

Common Law World Review (Isle of Man, GBR) **[53663]**

Common Market Law Review (The Hague, NLD) **[48610]**

The Commoner (Kathmandu, NPL) *Unable to locate*

Commonwealth Broadcaster (London, GBR) **[54240]**

Commonwealth & Comparative Politics (Abingdon, GBR) **[51733]**

Commonwealth Contact (Dublin, DU, IRL) *Unable to locate*

Commonwealth Forestry News (Craven Arms, GBR) **[53098]**

Commonwealth Judicial Journal (London, GBR) **[54241]**

Commonwealth Law Bulletin (London, GBR) **[54242]**

Commonwealth Scientist (London, GBR) *Unable to locate*

Comms Dealer (Saint Albans, GBR) *Unable to locate*

Communicable Disease Report Weekly (London, GBR) **[54243]**

Communicable Diseases Intelligence (Canberra, AC, AUS) **[41704]**

Communicate (London, GBR) **[54244]**

Communicatio (Pretoria, SAF) **[50586]**

Communication (London, GBR) **[54245]**

Communication and Critical/Cultural Studies (Abingdon, GBR) **[51734]**

Communication and Medicine (Berlin, GER) **[44166]**

Communication Reports (Abingdon, GBR) **[51735]**

Communication Research Reports (Abingdon, GBR) **[51736]**

Communication Teacher (Abingdon, GBR) **[51737]**

Communication Theory (Oxford, GBR) **[55913]**

Communications (Gent, BEL) *Unable to locate*

Communications (Amsterdam, NLD) *Unable to locate*

Communications Africa (Dubai, UAE) *Unable to locate*

Communications Africa (London, GBR) **[54246]**

Communications of COLIPS **[50177]***

Communications in Differential and Difference Equations (Xiangtan, HA, CHN) **[43538]**

Communications Engineer Magazine (Stevenage, GBR) *Ceased*

Communications in Instrumentation (Chandigarh, CH, IND) *Unable to locate*

Communications International (London, GBR) *Unable to locate*

Communications of the Korean Mathematical Society (Seoul, KOR) **[47262]**

Communications Letters, IEEE (Monash, VI, AUS) **[42113]**

Communications Maghreb (Dubai, UAE) *Unable to locate*

Communications Middle East & Africa (Dubai, UAE) **[51637]**

Communications in Nonlinear Science and Numerical Simulation (Amsterdam, NLD) **[47932]**

Communications Research Laboratory Journal (Tokyo, JPN) *Unable to locate*

Communications and Strategies (Montpellier, FRA) **[43977]**

Communications in Theoretical Physics (Beijing, CHN) **[43191]**

Communications Week International (London, GBR) *Unable to locate*

The Communicator (Brighton, GBR) *Unable to locate*

Communicator (Crowthorne, GBR) **[53121]**

Communicator; The Business **[54618]***

Communicator (New Delhi) (New Delhi, DH, IND) *Unable to locate*

Communio (Poole, GBR) *Unable to locate*

The Communist (Tokyo, JPN) *Unable to locate*

Communities Labor News (Seoul, KOR) *Unable to locate*

Community (London, GBR) **[54247]**

Community Action-FM - 89.3 (Liverpool, NW, AUS) **[42015]**

Community Care (Sutton, GBR) **[56682]**

Community Dental Health (Lowestoft, GBR) **[55493]**

Community Development Journal (Coventry, GBR) **[53080]**

Community Ecology (Budapest, HUN) **[44827]**

Community News (Halesworth) (Halesworth, GBR) *Unable to locate*

Community News (Southwold) (Halesworth, GBR) *Unable to locate*

Community Pharmacy (London, GBR) *Unable to locate*

Community Practitioner (London, GBR) *Unable to locate*

Community Psychiatry Journal (Mumbai, MH, IND) *Unable to locate*

Community Radio Youghal-FM - 104 (Youghal, CK, IRL) **[46071]**

Community Safety Journal **[52632]***

Community, Work & Family (Abingdon, GBR) **[51738]**

Company Digest (Godalming, GBR) *Unable to locate*

Company Law Institute of India Reports of Company Cases Including Banking & Insurance (Chennai, TN, IND) *Ceased*

The Company Lawyer (London, GBR) *Unable to locate*

Company News and Notes (New Delhi, DH, IND) *Unable to locate*

Company Profile & Financial Strength Update (Dorking, GBR) **[53194]**

Company and Securities Law Journal (North Ryde, NW, AUS) *Unable to locate*

Comparative American Studies (London, GBR) **[54248]**

Comparative Clinical Pathology (Harrow, GBR) **[53521]**

Comparative Critical Studies (London, GBR) **[54249]**

Comparative Education (Abingdon, GBR) **[51739]**

Comparative European Politics (Sheffield, GBR) **[56489]**

Comparative Exercise Physiology (Cambridge, GBR) **[52808]**

Comparative and Functional Genomics (Manchester, GBR) **[55548]**

Comparative Hepatology (London, GBR) **[54250]**

Comparative Physiology and Ecology (Jodhpur, RJ, IND) *Unable to locate*

Comparative Sociology (Leiden, NLD) **[48662]**

Comparative Strategy (Oxford, GBR) **[55914]**

Comparative Studies in Society and History (Cambridge, GBR) **[52809]**

Comparison of National Standards for Aluminium Casting Alloys (Birmingham, GBR) *Unable to locate*

Compartir (Lima, PER) *Unable to locate*

Compass (London, GBR) *Unable to locate*

Compass-FM - 96.4 (Grimsby, GBR) **[53486]**

Compass South (Norwich, GBR) **[55729]**

Compass Wessex (Norwich, GBR) **[55730]**

COMPEL (Bradford, GBR) **[52444]**

Competency & Emotional Intelligence (London, GBR) **[54251]**

Competition & Change (London, GBR) **[54252]**

Competition & Consumer Law Journal (North Ryde, NW, AUS) *Unable to locate*

Numbers cited in bold after listings are entry numbers rather than page numbers.

Competition Law Insight (London, GBR) **[54253]**

Competition Leader (Calcutta, WB, IND) *Unable to locate*

Competition Refresher (New Delhi, DH, IND) *Unable to locate*

Complementary Therapies in Medicine (Exeter, GBR) **[53349]**

Complete Wedding Guide Melbourne (North Ryde, NW, AUS) **[42177]**

Complete Wedding Sydney (North Ryde, NW, AUS) **[42178]**

Complex Analysis and Operator Theory (Beer-Sheva, ISR) **[46074]**

Composer News (London, GBR) *Unable to locate*

Composite Interfaces (Leiden, NLD) **[48663]**

Composite Structures (Amsterdam, NLD) **[47933]**

Composites Part A (Amsterdam, NLD) **[47934]**

Compound Semiconductor (Bristol, GBR) **[52654]**

Compte-Rendu (Paris, FRA) *Unable to locate*

Comptes Rendus (Singapore, SGP) **[50124]**

Computational & Applied Mathematics (Petropolis, RJ, BRZ) **[42990]**

Computational Biology and Chemistry (Luton, GBR) **[55500]**

Computational Complexity (Tokyo, JPN) **[46790]**

Computational Geosciences (Heidelberg, GER) **[44449]**

Computational Linguistics (Sydney, NW, AUS) **[42496]**

Computational Management Science (Heidelberg, GER) **[44450]**

Computational Materials Science (Strasbourg, FRA) **[44112]**

Computational & Mathematical Methods in Medicine (Leeds, GBR) **[53762]**

Computational Mathematics and Mathematical Physics (Moscow, RUS) **[49889]**

Computational Mechanics (Tokyo, JPN) **[46791]**

Computational Methods in Applied Mathematics (Minsk, BLR) **[42832]**

Computational Methods and Function Theory (Wurzburg, GER) **[44718]**

Computational Statistics (Tokyo, JPN) **[46792]**

Computational Statistics & Data Analysis (Amsterdam, NLD) **[47935]**

Computer-Aided Design (Delft, NLD) **[48308]**

The Computer Bulletin for Information Systems Professionals **[56712]***

Computer Business Review (London, GBR) *Unable to locate*

Computer Digest and Data Processing (Allahabad, UP, IND) *Unable to locate*

Computer Easy (Wurzburg, GER) *Unable to locate*

Computer Education (Calcutta, WB, IND) *Unable to locate*

Computer Era (Singapore, SGP) **[50125]**

Computer Graphics Forum Journal (Geneva, SWI) **[51090]**

Computer Issues (Malate, PHL) *Unable to locate*

The Computer Journal (London, GBR) **[54254]**

Computer Mart; Micro **[52358]***

Computer Methods in Biomechanics and Biomedical Engineering (Abingdon, GBR) **[51740]**

Computer Methods and Programs in Biomedicine (Uppsala, SWE) **[51050]**

Computer Products (Singapore, SGP) **[50126]**

Computer Products; Asian Sources **[50126]***

Computer Reseller News (Poing, GER) **[44634]**

Computer Science Review (Barcelona, SPA) **[50660]**

Computer Science and Telecommunications (Tbilisi, GRG) **[44131]**

Computer Society of India Journal (Mumbai, MH, IND) **[45364]**

Computer Speech & Language (Amsterdam, NLD) **[47936]**

Computer Supported Cooperative Work (CSCW) (Dordrecht, NLD) **[48358]**

Computer Today Monthly (Hong Kong, CHN) *Unable to locate*

Computer Vision and Image Understanding (Amsterdam, NLD) **[47937]**

Computer Weekly (Sutton, GBR) **[56683]**

Computer World Hong Kong (Hong Kong, CHN) **[43293]**

Computer World Philippines (Makati City, PHL) **[49515]**

Computeractive (London, GBR) **[54255]**

Computern im Handwerk (Munich, GER) **[44555]**

Computers and Artificial Intelligence **[50318]***

Computers & Chemistry **[55500]***

Computers and Communications (New Delhi, DH, IND) *Unable to locate*

Computers in Genealogy (London, GBR) *Ceased*

Computers and Geotechnics (Swansea, GBR) **[56700]**

Computers @ Home (New Delhi, DH, IND) *Unable to locate*

Computers in Human Behavior (Kidlington, GBR) **[53690]**

Computers and the Humanities **[48506]***

Computers in Industry (Groningen, NLD) **[48599]**

Computers and Law (Bristol, GBR) **[52655]**

Computers Today (New Delhi, DH, IND) **[45497]**

Computer!Totaal (Haarlem, NLD) **[48605]**

Computerwoche (Munich, GER) *Unable to locate*

ComputerWorld/Espana (Madrid, SPA) **[50738]**

Computerworld Singapore (Singapore, SGP) **[50127]**

Computimes (Malaysia) **[47637]***

Computing (London, GBR) **[54256]**

Computing and Control Engineering Journal (Stevenage, GBR) **[56599]**

Computing & Control Engineering Magazine (Stevenage, GBR) *Ceased*

Computing and Informatics (Bratislava, SLK) **[50318]**

Computing Japan **[46947]***

Computing Japan (Tokyo, JPN) **[46793]**

Computing Letters (Leiden, NLD) **[48664]**

Computing and Visualization in Science (Tokyo, JPN) **[46794]**

Comunicaciones World **[50739]***

Comunicaciones World (Madrid, SPA) **[50739]**

Con ene (Caceres, SPA) *Unable to locate*

Con Vos (Managua, NCG) *Unable to locate*

Concepts in Communication Informatics and Librarianship (New Delhi, DH, IND) *Unable to locate*

Concepts and Transformation (Amsterdam, NLD) *Ceased*

Concierto-FM - 88.5 (Santiago, CHL) **[43153]**

Concord (London, GBR) *Unable to locate*

Concrete (Camberley, GBR) **[52784]**

Concrete Construction and Architecture (Calcutta, WB, IND) *Unable to locate*

Concrete Library International (Tokyo, JPN) **[46795]**

Concrete Quarterly (Surrey, GBR) **[56660]**

Concurrent Engineering (London, GBR) **[54257]**

Condor's Magazin (Munich, GER) *Unable to locate*

Conectronica (Pozuelo de Alarcon, SPA) **[50827]**

Confectionery Production (London, GBR) **[54258]**

Confederation News (New Delhi, DH, IND) *Unable to locate*

Conference & Common Room (Zeals Warminster, GBR) **[57003]**

Conference & Exhibition Fact Finder (Huntingdon, GBR) *Unable to locate*

Conference & Incentive Travel (London, GBR) **[54259]**

Confetti (Dublin, DU, IRL) **[45951]**

Conflict Trends Magazine (Mount Edgecombe, SAF) **[50558]**

Confluence (Bangkok, THA) **[51417]**

Congenital Anomalies (Shimane, JPN) **[46683]**

Congress Marches Ahead (New Delhi, DH, IND) *Unable to locate*

Connacht Sentinel (Galway, GL, IRL) **[46018]**

Connacht Tribune (Galway, GL, IRL) **[46019]**

Connaught Telegraph (Castlebar, MA, IRL) **[45928]**

Connect (Stuttgart, GER) *Unable to locate*

Connect (Cambridge, GBR) **[52810]**

Connect-FM - 107.4 (Peterborough, GBR) **[56265]**

Connect-FM - 97.2 (Peterborough, GBR) **[56264]**

Connect Magazine (London, GBR) *Unable to locate*

Connection Science (Sheffield, GBR) **[56490]**

Connections (London, GBR) *Unable to locate*

Connective Tissue Research (Abingdon, GBR) **[51741]**

Connectivity S.A. (Kloof, SAF) *Unable to locate*

Connex (Vienna, AUT) **[42749]**

Connexions Magazine (Rozelle, NW, AUS) *Unable to locate*

Conrad Studies (Twickenham, GBR) **[56790]**

Conscience and Liberty (Bern, SWI) *Unable to locate*

Consciousness and Cognition (Amsterdam, NLD) **[47938]**

Conservation Bulletin (Swindon, GBR) **[56710]**

Conservation of Cultural Property in India (New Delhi, DH, IND) *Unable to locate*

Conservatory (Sevenoaks, GBR) **[56471]**

Constitution and Technical Rules **[44839]***

Constitutional Law Journal (Hyderabad, AP, IND) *Unable to locate*

Constitutional Law & Policy Review (Saint Leonards, NW, AUS) *Unable to locate*

Constitutional and Parliamentary Information (London, GBR) **[54260]**

Constitutional Political Economy (Manchester, GBR) **[55549]**

Construct in Steel (Epinal, FRA) *Unable to locate*

Construction Contractor (Chatswood, NW, AUS) **[41739]**

Construction Europe (Wadhurst, GBR) **[56805]**

Construction Information Quarterly (Ascot, GBR) **[52137]**

Construction Innovation (Bradford, GBR) **[52445]**

Construction Law Journal (Andover, GBR) **[52113]**

Construction Law Review (Sale, GBR) *Unable to locate*

Construction Manager (Ascot, GBR) **[52138]**

Constructions (Dusseldorf, GER) **[44322]**

Construdata (Lisbon, PRT) *Unable to locate*

Construire Ensemble (Paris, FRA) *Ceased*

Consumenten Geld (The Hague, NLD) *Unable to locate*

Consumer Action (Harare, ZWE) *Unable to locate*

Consumer Choice (Dublin, DU, IRL) **[45952]**

Consumer Good Europe (London, GBR) *Unable to locate*

Consumer Goods UK (London, GBR) *Unable to locate*

Consumer and Retailer (New Delhi, DH, IND) *Unable to locate*

Consumer Watch (Watford, GBR) *Unable to locate*

Contact (Baku, AJN) *Unable to locate*

Contact (New Delhi, DH, IND) *Unable to locate*

Contact (Guernsey, GBR) **[53487]**

Contact Dermatitis (Heidelberg, GER) *Unable to locate*

Contact Dermatitis (London, GBR) **[54261]**

Contact Lens and the Anterior Eye (Basingstoke, GBR) *Ceased*

Contact Lens & Anterior Eye (Birmingham, GBR) **[52338]**

Contactblad Mertonvrienden (Grimbergen, BEL) *Unable to locate*

Contacto (Porto, PRT) *Unable to locate*

Container Intelligence Quarterly (London, GBR) **[54262]**

Contemporary Educational Psychology (Amsterdam, NLD) **[47939]**

Contemporary European History (Cambridge, GBR) **[52811]**

Contemporary Family Therapy (Dordrecht, NLD) **[48359]**

Contemporary Home Design (North Ryde, NW, AUS) **[42179]**

Contemporary Hypnosis (Leeds, GBR) **[53763]**

Contemporary Islam (Dordrecht, NLD) **[48360]**

Contemporary Issues in Early Childhood (Oxford, GBR) **[55915]**

Contemporary Issues in Law (Witney, GBR) **[56940]**

Numbers cited in bold after listings are entry numbers rather than page numbers.

Contemporary Management Research (Taipei, TWN) **[51336]**

Contemporary Music Review (Edinburgh, GBR) **[53265]**

Contemporary Physics (London, GBR) **[54263]**

Contemporary Pragmatism (Amsterdam, NLD) **[47940]**

Contemporary Religions in Japan **[46553]***

Contemporary Review (Oxford, GBR) **[55916]**

Contemporary Reviews in Obstetrics & Gynecology (Lancaster, GBR) *Ceased*

Contemporary Southeast Asia (Pasir Panjang, SGP) **[50099]**

Contemporary Visual Arts (London, GBR) *Unable to locate*

Context (Warrington, GBR) **[56848]**

Continence (West Lothian, GBR) **[56892]**

Continent (Moscow, RUS) *Unable to locate*

Continental Shelf Research (Southampton, GBR) **[56569]**

Continual Medical Education Magazine (Ankara, TUR) *Unable to locate*

Continuing Education in Anaesthesia, Critical Care & Pain (Oxford, GBR) **[55917]**

Continuity, Insurance & Risk (London, GBR) **[54264]**

Continuum Mechanics and Thermodynamics (Tokyo, JPN) **[46796]**

Contra (Stockholm, SWE) **[51013]**

Contrabanda-FM - 91.4 (Barcelona, SPA) **[50707]**

Contract Furnishing Magazine (London, GBR) *Unable to locate*

Contracts Flooring Journal (Tunbridge Wells, GBR) **[56779]**

Contrast Media & Molecular Imaging (Turin, ITA) **[46270]**

Contrasts (London, GBR) *Unable to locate*

Contributions to Algebra and Geometry (Lemgo, GER) **[44531]**

Contributions to Himalayan Geology (New Delhi, DH, IND) **[45498]**

Contributions to Indian Sociology (New Delhi, DH, IND) **[45499]**

Contributions to Mineralogy and Petrology (Tokyo, JPN) **[46797]**

Contributions to Nepalese Studies (Kirtipur, NPL) *Unable to locate*

Contributions to Political Economy (Cambridge, GBR) **[52812]**

Contributions to Sedimentary Geology (Stuttgart, GER) **[44664]**

Control **[53063]***

Control Engineering Practice (Pretoria, SAF) **[50587]**

Control and Instrumentation (London, GBR) *Unable to locate*

Convenience Store (Crawley, GBR) **[53100]**

Convenience World (Melbourne, VI, AUS) **[42057]**

Convergence (Geneva, SWI) *Ceased*

Convergence (Luton, GBR) **[55501]**

Converter (Sittingbourne, GBR) *Unable to locate*

Conveyancer and Property Lawyer (Andover, GBR) **[52114]**

Cook Strait News (Johnsonville, NZL) *Unable to locate*

Cook's Log (Dewsbury, GBR) **[53178]**

Cooks River Valley Times (Condell Park, NW, AUS) **[41803]**

Cool Blue-FM - 96.1 (Bay of Islands, NZL) **[48857]**

Cool Blue-FM (Bay of Islands, NZL) *Ceased*

Cool Country Radio-FM - 88.0 (Kingswood, NW, AUS) **[41995]**

Cool-FM - 98.9 (Oranjestad, ARU) **[41492]**

Cool-FM - 96.9 (Lagos, LG, NGA) **[49144]**

Cool-FM - 93 (Bangkok, THA) **[51449]**

Cool-FM - 97.4 (Belfast, GBR) **[52300]**

Cooldown Magazine (Sheffield, GBR) *Unable to locate*

Cooler (London, GBR) **[54265]**

Coolcola Advertiser (Sydney, NW, AUS) **[42497]**

Cooperation and Conflict (London, GBR) **[54266]**

Cooperation in Turkey **[51491]***

Cooperation in Turkiye (Ankara, TUR) **[51491]**

Cooperative News Digest (Mumbai, MH, IND) *Unable to locate*

Cooperative Perspective (New Delhi, DH, IND) *Unable to locate*

Cooperator (New Delhi, DH, IND) **[45500]**

Cooplus (Brussels, BEL) *Unable to locate*

The Copenhagen Post (Copenhagen, DEN) *Unable to locate*

Copyright Bulletin (Paris, FRA) **[44034]**

Cor et Vasa (Brno, CZE) *Unable to locate*

Coral Reefs (Heidelberg, GER) **[44451]**

Corazon-FM - 101.3 (Santiago, CHL) **[43154]**

Cord (Jakarta, IDN) **[45795]**

CORE Magazine (Rumbeke, BEL) *Unable to locate*

Corel Painter Official Magazine (Bournemouth, GBR) **[52411]**

Cork Campus Radio-FM - 98.3 (Cork, CK, IRL) **[45939]**

CORKnow (Clarenbridge, GL, IRL) **[45932]**

Cormorant **[50621]***

Cornish World (Penzance, GBR) **[56248]**

Cornwall Life (Totnes, GBR) **[56761]**

Coro-FM (Nairobi, KEN) *Unable to locate*

Coro-FM - 102.3 (Nairobi, KEN) **[47198]**

Corpora (Edinburgh, GBR) **[53266]**

Corporate and Business Law Journal (University of Canberra, AC, AUS) *Unable to locate*

Corporate Citizen (London, GBR) *Ceased*

Corporate Communications (Bradford, GBR) **[52446]**

Corporate Governance (Bradford, GBR) **[52447]**

Corporate IT Update (Bath, GBR) **[52237]**

Corporate Observer (Mumbai, MH, IND) *Unable to locate*

Corporate Reputation Review (Rotterdam, NLD) **[48749]**

Corporate Rupee (New Delhi, DH, IND) *Unable to locate*

Corporate Watch (London, GBR) **[54267]**

Corpus Linguistics and Linguistic Theory (Berlin, GER) **[44167]**

Correio Agricola (Lisbon, PRT) *Unable to locate*

Correlation (London, GBR) **[54268]**

Correo Poblacional y de Gerencia en Salud (Quito, ECU) *Unable to locate*

The Correspondent (Hong Kong, CHN) **[43294]**

Corriere di Caserta (Caserta, ITA) *Unable to locate*

Corriere Medico-(Milan, ITA) *Unable to locate*

Corriere Mercantile e Gazzetta del lunedi (Genoa, ITA) *Unable to locate*

Corriere Romagna (Rimini, ITA) *Unable to locate*

Corrosion Engineering, Science and Technology (London, GBR) **[54269]**

Corrosion Reviews (Tel Aviv, ISR) **[46097]**

CORSI Bulletin (Calcutta, WB, IND) *Unable to locate*

Corso di Sociologia a Dispense (Milan, ITA) *Unable to locate*

Corsonat (Meerut, UP, IND) *Unable to locate*

Cosas de Casa (Madrid, SPA) **[50740]**

Cosas de Cocina (Barcelona, SPA) **[50661]**

Cosmetic Insiders' Report (Chester, GBR) *Unable to locate*

Cosmetic Products Report (London, GBR) **[54270]**

Cosmetics International (London, GBR) **[54271]**

Cosmic Research (Moscow, RUS) **[49890]**

Cosmopolital (Spain) (Madrid, SPA) **[50741]**

Cosmopolitan (Australia) (Sydney, NW, AUS) **[42498]**

Cosmopolitan (India) (New Delhi, DH, IND) **[45501]**

Cosmopolitan Philippines (Mandaluyong City, PHL) **[49533]**

Cosmopoliten Moskow (Perm, RUS) *Unable to locate*

COSMOS (Singapore, SGP) **[50128]**

Cosmos and History (Hawthorn, VI, AUS) **[41942]**

COSPAR's Information Bulletin **[51077]***

COSSMA (Karlsruhe, GER) **[44492]**

Cost Effectiveness and Resource Allocation (London, GBR) **[54272]**

Costruire Stampi (Milan, ITA) *Unable to locate*

Costruzioni Metalliche (Milan, ITA) *Unable to locate*

Cotal (Buenos Aires, ARG) *Unable to locate*

Cottage Industries (New Delhi, DH, IND) *Unable to locate*

Cotton World (Harare, ZWE) *Unable to locate*

COTU (K) Speaks (Nairobi, KEN) *Unable to locate*

Council Leader (Nundah, QL, AUS) **[42221]**

Counsel (London, GBR) **[54273]**

Counselling and Psychotherapy Research (Abingdon, GBR) **[51742]**

Counselling at Work (Rugby, GBR) *Unable to locate*

Counselor (Rawalpindi, PAK) *Unable to locate*

Count Me In (London, GBR) *Unable to locate*

Counterpoint (Sydney, NW, AUS) *Unable to locate*

The Country Bird Collection (London, GBR) **[54274]**

Country Doctor (Northampton, GBR) **[55707]**

Country Life (London, GBR) **[54275]**

Country Music Capital News (Tamworth, NW, AUS) **[42611]**

Country Music People (London, GBR) **[54276]**

Country Radio-FM - 88.7 (Rotorua, NZL) **[48976]**

Country Radio-FM - 88.4 (Rotorua, NZL) **[48975]**

Country Smallholding (Exeter, GBR) **[53350]**

Country Way (Stoneleigh, GBR) **[56635]**

Countryside Building (Stowmarket, GBR) **[56642]**

Countryside Focus (Wetherby, GBR) **[56909]**

Countryside Voice (London, GBR) **[54277]**

The Countrywoman (London, GBR) *Unable to locate*

County Sound Radio-AM - 1566 (Guildford, GBR) **[53496]**

Courier Country (Timaru, NZL) **[48987]**

Courrier de l'IBFAN (Port Louis, MUS) *Unable to locate*

Coutoure (Hong Kong, CHN) **[43295]**

Couture (Hong Kong, CHN) *Unable to locate*

The Coventry Observer (Warwick, GBR) **[56853]**

COVER (London, GBR) **[54278]**

CPO Agenda (London, GBR) **[54279]**

CPRE Voice (London, GBR) **[54280]**

CR-FM - 94.4 (St. Poelten, AUT) **[42739]**

The Cracker (Reus, SPA) **[50828]**

Cracking Matters (Bordon, GBR) **[52407]**

Craft Stamper (Malvern, GBR) **[55533]**

craft&design (Driffield, GBR) **[53200]**

Craftbusiness (Colchester, GBR) **[53032]**

Crafts (London, GBR) **[54281]**

Crafts Beautiful (Colchester, GBR) **[53033]**

Crafts and Heritage (Strasbourg, FRA) *Unable to locate*

The Craftsman Magazine **[53200]***

Craigavon Echo (Portadown, GBR) **[56283]**

Cranbourne Leader (Berwick, VI, AUS) **[41599]**

Cranes and Lifting Australia (Leederville, WA, AUS) **[42006]**

Cranes Today (Sidcup, GBR) **[56541]**

Crawley Observer (Crawley, GBR) **[53101]**

CRC-FM - 102.9 fm (Castlebar, MA, IRL) **[45929]**

CREaction (Geneva, SWI) *Ceased*

Creation Numerique (Paris, FRA) *Unable to locate*

Creative Book Selection Index (Calcutta, WB, IND) *Unable to locate*

Creative Forum New Poets Series (New Delhi, DH, IND) *Unable to locate*

Creative Knitting (Bondi Junction, NW, AUS) **[41608]**

Creative Review (London, GBR) **[54282]**

Creative Weddings (Rozelle, NW, AUS) **[42324]**

Creative Wood (Wellington, NZL) **[49005]**

Credit (London, GBR) **[54283]**

Credit Control (Brentwood, GBR) **[52571]**

Credit Management (Oakham, GBR) **[55780]**

Credit Today (London, GBR) **[54284]**

Numbers cited in bold after listings are entry numbers rather than page numbers.

Credit Union News (Manchester, GBR) **[55550]**

Crediton Country Courier (Crediton, GBR) **[53117]**

Creme de la Creme (Stockholm, SWE) *Unable to locate*

Crescendo (Auckland, NZL) *Unable to locate*

Crescendo & Jazz Music (London, GBR) *Unable to locate*

Crescer (Maputo, MOZ) *Unable to locate*

Cretaceous Research (Amsterdam, NLD) **[47941]**

CRI/NCB Abstracts (Ballagarh, HY, IND) *Ceased*

Cricinfo Magazine (Mumbai, MH, IND) *Ceased*

Cricketer (Karachi, PAK) *Unable to locate*

The Cricketer (Tunbridge Wells, GBR) *Unable to locate*

The Cricketer International (Tunbridge Wells, GBR) *Unable to locate*

Crime, Law and Social Change (Dordrecht, NLD) **[48361]**

Crime Prevention & Community Safety (Newcastle upon Tyne, GBR) **[55668]**

Crime & Society (New Delhi, DH, IND) *Unable to locate*

Criminal Appeal Reports (London, GBR) **[54285]**

Criminal Justice **[54286]***

Criminal Justice Studies (Abingdon, GBR) **[51743]**

Criminal Law Forum (Dordrecht, NLD) **[48362]**

Criminal Law Journal (Pyrmont, NW, AUS) **[42276]**

Criminal Law Journal (Nagpur, MH, IND) **[45465]**

Criminal Law Review (Andover, GBR) **[52115]**

Criminology & Criminal Justice (London, GBR) **[54286]**

Crisis (Gondrin, FRA) **[43957]**

Criss Cross (London, GBR) **[54287]**

Critical Approaches to Ethnic American Literature (Valladolid, SPA) **[50848]**

Critical Care (London, GBR) **[54288]**

Critical Criminology (Dordrecht, NLD) **[48363]**

Critical Discourse Studies (Abingdon, GBR) **[51744]**

Critical Horizons (Durham, GBR) **[53227]**

Critical Perspectives on International Business (Bradford, GBR) **[52448]**

Critical Public Health (Middlesbrough, GBR) **[55611]**

Critical Quarterly (Oxford, GBR) **[55918]**

Critical Review of International Social and Political Philosophy (Abingdon, GBR) **[51745]**

Critical Reviews in Computed Tomography **[54719]***

Critical Reviews in Oncology/Hematology (Genolier, SWI) **[51174]**

Critical Social Policy (London, GBR) **[54289]**

Critical Sociology (London, GBR) **[54290]**

Critical Studies in Education (Abingdon, GBR) **[51746]**

Critical Studies in Television (Manchester, GBR) **[55551]**

Critical Survey (Oxford, GBR) **[55919]**

Critique of Anthropology (London, GBR) **[54291]**

CRMK-FM (Milton Keynes, GBR) *Unable to locate*

CRO Moto (Zagreb, CTA) *Unable to locate*

Croatian International Relations Review (Zagreb, CTA) **[43564]**

Croatian Journal of Philosophy (Hrvatski Leskovac, CTA) **[43558]**

Croatian Medical Journal (Zagreb, CTA) **[43565]**

Croatica Chemica Acta (Zagreb, CTA) **[43566]**

CROMAN (Zagreb, CTA) *Unable to locate*

Cromohs (Florence, ITA) **[46142]**

Cromwelliana (Scunthorpe, GBR) **[56467]**

Cronache di Napoli (Caserta, ITA) *Unable to locate*

Cronica Filatelica (Madrid, SPA) **[50742]**

Cronica Numismatica (Madrid, SPA) *Unable to locate*

Crop & Pasture Science (Collingwood, VI, AUS) **[41784]**

Crop Physiology Abstracts (Wallingford, GBR) **[56817]**

Crop Protection (East Malling, GBR) **[53238]**

Crop Research (Mohindergarh, HY, IND) **[45346]**

Crops (Beijing, CHN) *Unable to locate*

Crops in India (New Delhi, DH, IND) *Unable to locate*

Croquet Gazette (Cheltenham, GBR) **[52966]**

Cross (Manila, PHL) *Unable to locate*

Cross & Cockade Great Britain **[56910]***

Cross & Cockade International (Wetherby, GBR) **[56910]**

Cross/Cultures (Giessen, GER) **[44385]**

Cross Section (New Delhi, DH, IND) *Unable to locate*

Cross Stitch Card Shop (Bristol, GBR) **[52656]**

Cross Stitch Crazy (Bristol, GBR) **[52657]**

Cross Stitch Gold (Bristol, GBR) **[52658]**

Crossover-FM - 90.7 (Cebu City, PHL) **[49466]**

Crossover-FM - 93.1 (Davao City, PHL) **[49479]**

Crossroads-FM - 107.1 (Inglewood, NZL) **[48918]**

Crossword (Romsey, GBR) **[56406]**

Crossword Selection (Redhill, GBR) **[56349]**

CROW-FM - 90.7 (Wondai, QL, AUS) **[42712]**

CRRI Road Abstracts (New Delhi, DH, IND) *Unable to locate*

Cruise 1323-AM - 1323 (North Adelaide, SA, AUS) **[42152]**

Cruising Helmsman (Surry Hills, NW, AUS) **[42424]**

Crusades (Surrey, GBR) **[56661]**

Crustacean Research (Tokyo, JPN) *Unable to locate*

Crustaceana (Leiden, NLD) **[48665]**

CRY-FM - 104 (Youghal, CK, IRL) **[46072]**

Cry Wolf (Wolverhampton, GBR) **[56952]**

Cryobiology (Amsterdam, NLD) **[47942]**

Crystal Research and Technology (Berlin, GER) **[44168]**

Crystallography Reports (Moscow, RUS) **[49891]**

Crystallography Reviews (Manchester, GBR) **[55552]**

CrystEngComm (Cambridge, GBR) **[52813]**

CSI Adhyayan (Mumbai, MH, IND) **[45365]**

CSI Communications (Mumbai, MH, IND) **[45366]**

CSI Computer Science and Informatics (Mumbai, MH, IND) *Unable to locate*

CSI Magazine (Binz, SWI) **[51081]**

CSR-FM - 97.4 (Canterbury, GBR) **[52922]**

c't magazine (Hannover, GER) **[44430]**

C3 3D Design & Visualization Magazine (London, GBR) *Unable to locate*

CTO Briefing (London, GBR) *Unable to locate*

CTR-FM **[56403]***

Cuaderno Sectorial (La Paz, BOL) *Unable to locate*

Cuadernos de la Academia (Madrid, SPA) **[50743]**

Cuadernos de Alzate (Madrid, SPA) *Unable to locate*

Cuadernos de Economia (Santiago, CHL) **[43143]**

Cuadernos Hispanoamericanos (Madrid, SPA) **[50744]**

Cuadernos de Jazz (Madrid, SPA) **[50745]**

Cuadernos de Literatura Infantil y Juvenil (Barcelona, SPA) *Unable to locate*

Cuadernos de Medicina Forense (Seville, SPA) **[50833]**

Cuadernos Mujer Salud (Santiago, CHL) **[43144]**

Cuadernos de Seguridad (Madrid, SPA) *Unable to locate*

CUAMM Notizie - Salute E Sviluppo (Padua, ITA) *Unable to locate*

Cuba Foreign Trade (Havana, CUB) **[43576]**

Cuero (Buenos Aires, ARG) *Unable to locate*

Cuerpomente (Barcelona, SPA) **[50662]**

Cuillin-FM - 102.7 (Portree, GBR) **[56285]**

Cuillin-FM - 106.2 (Portree, GBR) **[56286]**

Culinair Ambiance **[42837]***

Cultura y Educacion (Madrid, SPA) **[50746]**

Cultura Musical-FM - 100.3 (Buenos Aires, ARG) **[41481]**

Cultura Turcica (Ankara, TUR) *Unable to locate*

Cultural Dynamics (London, GBR) **[54292]**

Cultural Geographies (London, GBR) **[54293]**

Cultural Politics (Oxford, GBR) **[55920]**

Cultural Research Institute Bulletin (Calcutta, WB, IND) *Unable to locate*

Cultural & Social History (Oxford, GBR) **[55921]**

Cultural Studies (Abingdon, GBR) **[51747]**

Cultural Trends (Abingdon, GBR) **[51748]**

Culture and Cosmos (Bristol, GBR) **[52659]**

Culture, Health and Sexuality (London, GBR) **[54294]**

Culture and Organization (Bristol, GBR) **[52660]**

Culture & Psychology (London, GBR) **[54295]**

Culture of Publishing (Seoul, KOR) *Unable to locate*

Culture and Religion (Abingdon, GBR) **[51749]**

Cumberland and Westmorland Herald (Penrith, GBR) *Unable to locate*

Cumbernauld News (Cumbernauld, GBR) **[53149]**

Cunicultura (Arenys de Mar, SPA) *Unable to locate*

CUR-AM - 1350 (Cambridge, GBR) **[52910]**

Curacao Holiday! (Curacao, NAT) *Unable to locate*

Curierul de Fizica (Bucharest, ROM) *Unable to locate*

Current (Mumbai, MH, IND) *Unable to locate*

Current (Karachi, PAK) *Unable to locate*

Current Advances in Materials and Processes - CAMP-ISIJ (Tokyo, JPN) *Unable to locate*

Current Agricultural Research (Bhubaneswar, OR, IND) *Unable to locate*

Current Agriculture (New Delhi, DH, IND) *Unable to locate*

Current Allergy & Asthma Reports (Bangalore, KA, IND) *Unable to locate*

Current Allergy & Clinical Immunology (Cape Town, SAF) **[50372]**

Current Analytical Chemistry (Karachi, PAK) **[49341]**

Current Applied Physics (Seoul, KOR) **[47263]**

Current Bioactive Compounds (Karachi, PAK) **[49342]**

Current Bioinformatics (Bussum, NLD) **[48283]**

Current Biology (Amsterdam, NLD) **[47943]**

Current Central Legislation (Lucknow, UP, IND) **[45321]**

Current Clinical Pharmacology (Bussum, NLD) **[48284]**

Current Colorectal Cancer Reports (Bangalore, KA, IND) **[44952]**

Current Computer-Aided Drug Design (Bussum, NLD) **[48285]**

Current Consumer Cases (New Delhi, DH, IND) **[45502]**

Current Contents Pages of Management Related Journals (Brussels, BEL) *Unable to locate*

Current Development in Theory and Applications of Wavelets (Allahabad, UP, IND) **[44924]**

Current Diabetes Reviews (Aberdeen, GBR) **[51675]**

Current Drug Delivery (Brisbane, QL, AUS) **[41647]**

Current Drug Discovery Technologies (Bussum, NLD) **[48286]**

Current Drug Metabolism (Bussum, NLD) **[48287]**

Current Drug Safety (Bussum, NLD) **[48288]**

Current Drug Targets. Cardiovascular & Hematological Disorders **[48280]***

Current Drug Targets. CNS & Neurological Disorders **[48282]***

Current Drug Targets. Immune, Endocrine & Metabolic Disorders **[46121]***

Current Drug Targets Infectious Disorders **[48301]***

Current Drug Targets. Inflammation & Allergy **[48302]***

Numbers cited in bold after listings are entry numbers rather than page numbers.

Current Drug Therapy (Bussum, NLD) **[48289]**

Current Dynamics (Calcutta, WB, IND) *Unable to locate*

Current Economic Trends (Ljubljana, SVA) *Unable to locate*

Current Engineering Practice (Mumbai, MH, IND) *Unable to locate*

Current Enzyme Inhibition (Meerut, UP, IND) **[45344]**

Current Events (Dehradun, UP, IND) *Unable to locate*

Current Gene Therapy (Nantes, FRA) **[44012]**

Current Genetics (Goteborg, SWE) **[50958]**

Current Genomics (Paris, FRA) **[44035]**

Current Heart Failure Reports (Bangalore, KA, IND) **[44953]**

Current Hematology Reports (Bangalore, KA, IND) **[44954]**

Current Hepatitis Reports (Bangalore, KA, IND) **[44955]**

Current Herpetology (Kyoto, JPN) **[46470]**

Current Hypertension Reviews (Bussum, NLD) **[48290]**

Current Income Tax Law (New Delhi, DH, IND) *Unable to locate*

Current Indian Forestry, Environment & Wildlife Abstracts (Dehradun, UP, IND) *Unable to locate*

Current Indian Statutes (Chandigarh, CH, IND) *Unable to locate*

Current Issues in Language Planning (Abingdon, GBR) **[51750]**

Current Issues in Language & Society (Bristol, GBR) *Ceased*

Current Issues in Tourism (Abingdon, GBR) **[51751]**

Current Legal Problems (Oxford, GBR) **[55922]**

Current Literature on Science of Science (New Delhi, DH, IND) *Ceased*

Current Management Literature (Hyderabad, AP, IND) *Ceased*

Current Medical Practice (Mumbai, MH, IND) *Unable to locate*

Current Medicinal Chemistry. Anti-Cancer Agents **[48279]***

Current Medicinal Chemistry. Anti-Inflammatory & Anti-Allergy Agents **[51576]***

Current Medicinal Chemistry. Cardiovascular & Hematological Agents **[45343]***

Current Nanoscience (Karachi, PAK) **[49343]**

Current Nematology (Allahabad, UP, IND) *Unable to locate*

Current Neuropharmacology (London, GBR) **[54296]**

Current Nutrition & Food Science (Bussum, NLD) **[48291]**

Current Opinion in Biotechnology (Amsterdam, NLD) **[47944]**

Current Opinion in Cell Biology (Amsterdam, NLD) **[47945]**

Current Opinion in Chemical Biology (Amsterdam, NLD) **[47946]**

Current Opinion in Clinical Nutrition & Metabolic Care (London, GBR) **[54297]**

Current Opinion in Drug Discovery & Development (London, GBR) **[54298]**

Current Opinion in Genetics & Development (Amsterdam, NLD) **[47947]**

Current Opinion in Infectious Diseases (London, GBR) **[54299]**

Current Opinion in Investigational Drugs (London, GBR) **[54300]**

Current Opinion in Microbiology (Amsterdam, NLD) **[47948]**

Current Opinion in Molecular Therapeutics (London, GBR) **[54301]**

Current Opinion in Neurology (London, GBR) **[54302]**

Current Opinion in Plant Biology (Amsterdam, NLD) **[47949]**

Current Organic Synthesis (Bussum, NLD) **[48292]**

Current Paediatrics **[52937]***

Current Pediatric Reviews (London, GBR) **[54303]**

Current Pharmaceutical Analysis (Karachi, PAK) **[49344]**

Current Pharmaceutical Biotechnology (Bussum, NLD) **[48293]**

Current Pharmaceutical Design (Bussum, NLD) **[48294]**

Current Pharmacogenomics **[48295]***

Current Pharmacogenomics and Personalized Medicine (Bussum, NLD) **[48295]**

Current Problems in Cancer (Amsterdam, NLD) **[47950]**

Current Proteomics (Bussum, NLD) **[48296]**

Current Research in Family and Community Sciences (Mumbai, MH, IND) *Unable to locate*

Current Research Reporter (Rahuri, MH, IND) *Unable to locate*

Current Science (Bangalore, KA, IND) **[44956]**

Current Signal Transduction Therapy (Bussum, NLD) **[48297]**

Current Sociology (Madrid, SPA) **[50747]**

Current Swedish Archaeology (Molndal, SWE) **[50993]**

Current Tax Reporter (Jodhpur, RJ, IND) **[45217]**

Current Therapeutics (Frenchs Forest, NS, AUS) *Ceased*

Current Titles in Electrochemistry (Karaikudi, MH, IND) **[45239]**

Current Topics in Medicinal Chemistry (Bussum, NLD) **[48298]**

Current Vascular Pharmacology (London, GBR) **[54304]**

Current Weekly (Mumbai, MH, IND) *Unable to locate*

Current Women's Health Reviews (Bussum, NLD) **[48299]**

Current Zoology (Beijing, CHN) **[43192]**

Currents of Encounter (Amsterdam, NLD) **[47951]**

Curriculum (Cologne, GER) *Unable to locate*

Curriculum for a Course in Health Safety (Hamilton, ON, CAN) *Unable to locate*

Curriculum Journal (Abingdon, GBR) **[51752]**

Curriculum and Teaching (South Melbourne, VI, AUS) **[42369]**

Curtin-FM - 100.1 (Perth, WA, AUS) **[42252]**

Custom Car Magazine (Peterborough, GBR) **[56255]**

Custom PC (London, GBR) **[54305]**

CW Magazine **[50129]***

CW Magazine (Singapore, SGP) **[50129]**

CWB (Huddersfield, GBR) **[53619]**

CWU Voice (London, GBR) **[54306]**

CX Magazine (Epping, NW, AUS) *Unable to locate*

Cybermetrics (Madrid, SPA) **[50748]**

Cycling Weekly (Croydon, GBR) **[53124]**

The Cyclist.Com (Stourbridge, GBR) *Unable to locate*

Cygnus (Lucknow, UP, IND) *Unable to locate*

Cylchgrawn Llyfrgell Genedlaethol Cymru (Ceredigion, GBR) **[52954]**

Cyprus Today (Nicosia, TUR) *Unable to locate*

The Cyprus Weekly (Nicosia, CYP) **[43593]**

Cytogenetic and Genome Research (Wurzburg, GER) **[44719]**

CytoJournal (London, GBR) **[54307]**

Cytokine (Amsterdam, NLD) **[47952]**

Cytologia (Tokyo, JPN) **[46798]**

Cytopathology (Varna, BUL) *Unable to locate*

Czech Business Weekly (Prague, CZE) **[43615]**

Czech Gynaecology (Prague, CZE) **[43616]**

Czech Radiology (Prague, CZE) **[43617]**

Czech and Slovak Neurology and Neurosurgery (Prague, CZE) **[43618]**

Czech and Slovak Ophthalmology (Prague, CZE) **[43619]**

Czech and Slovak Pharmacy (Prague, CZE) **[43620]**

Czech and Slovak Psychiatry (Prague, CZE) **[43621]**

Czecho-Slovak Dermatology (Prague, CZE) **[43622]**

Czechoslovak Parasitology **[43605]***

D

D-Photo (Auckland, NZL) **[48790]**

Da Nang Broadcast - Television Station (Da Nang, VNM) *Unable to locate*

Da Nang Television Station (Hanoi, VNM) *Unable to locate*

Da Nang Television Station (Hanoi, VNM) *Unable to locate*

DAG Journal (Hamburg, GER) *Unable to locate*

Dagens Industri (Stockholm, SWE) *Unable to locate*

Dagens Medicin (Stockholm, SWE) *Unable to locate*

Dagens Naeringsliv (Oslo, NOR) **[49196]**

Daheim (Louvain, BEL) *Unable to locate*

Daidzhest FM (Tomsk, RUS) *Unable to locate*

Daidzhest-FM (Tomsk, RUS) *Unable to locate*

Daily (Mumbai, MH, IND) *Unable to locate*

Daily Advertiser (Wagga Wagga, NW, AUS) **[42668]**

Daily Bread (Milton Keynes, GBR) **[55632]**

Daily Champion (Oshodi, LG, NGA) **[49159]**

The Daily Dipolognon (Dipolog City, PHL) **[49487]**

The Daily Examiner (Sydney, NW, AUS) **[42499]**

Daily Excelsior (Jammu, JK, IND) **[45204]**

Daily Express (Kota Kinabalu, MYS) **[47590]**

Daily Jang (Karachi, PAK) **[49345]**

Daily Mirror (Colombo, SRI) **[50852]**

Daily Nation (Kenya) (Nairobi, KEN) **[47176]**

Daily News (Kathmandu, NPL) *Unable to locate*

Daily News (Colombo, SRI) **[50853]**

Daily News Nagoya (Aichi, JPN) *Unable to locate*

Daily Notes **[55634]***

Daily Post (Rotorua, NZL) *Unable to locate*

Daily Post (Liverpool) (Liverpool, GBR) *Unable to locate*

The Daily Star (Dhaka, BGD) **[42808]**

The Daily Star (Lebanon) (Beirut, LBN) **[47394]**

Daily Thanthi (Chennai, TN, IND) **[45030]**

Daily Times (Lahore, PAK) **[49384]**

Daily Tribune (Khulna, BGD) *Unable to locate*

Daily Tribune (Manila, PHL) **[49549]**

Daily Yomiuri (Tokyo, JPN) **[46799]**

Daily Zamboanga Times (Zamboanga City, PHL) **[49647]**

Dainik Bhaskar (Bhopal, MP, IND) **[45006]**

Dairy Guide (Gurgaon, HY, IND) *Unable to locate*

Dairy India Yearbook (Delhi, DH, IND) **[45089]**

Dairy Industries International (Daruvar, CTA) *Unable to locate*

Dairy Markets Weekly (Tunbridge Wells, GBR) **[56780]**

Dairyman (Auckland, NZL) **[48791]**

The Dairymen **[41941]***

Daisy (London, GBR) **[54308]**

Dajt-FM - 99.5 MHz (Tirana, ALB) **[41452]**

Dak Tar (New Delhi, DH, IND) *Unable to locate*

Dalal Street Journal (Janmabhoomi Marg, IND) *Unable to locate*

Dalby Herald (Sydney, NW, AUS) **[42500]**

Dalesman Magazine (Skipton, GBR) **[56553]**

Dali People's Broadcasting Station (Dali, YU, CHN) *Unable to locate*

Dalian People's Broadcasting Station (Dalian, LI, CHN) *Unable to locate*

Dalian People's Broadcasting Station (Dalian, LI, CHN) *Unable to locate*

Dalian People's Broadcasting Station (Dalian, LI, CHN) *Unable to locate*

Dalian People's Broadcasting Station (Dalian, LI, CHN) *Unable to locate*

Dalian People's Broadcasting Station (Dalian, LI, CHN) *Unable to locate*

Dalian People's Broadcasting Station (Dalian, LI, CHN) *Unable to locate*

Dalian People's Broadcasting Station (Dalian, LI, CHN) *Unable to locate*

Dalian TV 1 (Dalian, LI, CHN) *Unable to locate*

Dalian TV 2 (Dalian, LI, CHN) *Unable to locate*

Dalriada (Isle of Arran, GBR) **[53662]**

Dalton Transactions (Cambridge, GBR) **[52814]**

Dalton's Weekly (New Malden, GBR) **[55658]**

DAMALS (Leinfelden-Echterdingen, GER) **[44518]**

Damascus University Journal for the Basic Sciences (Damascus, SYR) *Unable to locate*

Damernas Varld (Stockholm, SWE) **[51014]**

Damilica (Chennai, TN, IND) *Unable to locate*

Damocles (Lyon, FRA) **[43968]**

Dance Australia (Surry Hills, NW, AUS) **[42425]**

Dance Expression (Spalding, GBR) **[56590]**

Dance-FM (Gazimagusa, CYP) *Unable to locate*

Dance Gazette (London, GBR) **[54309]**

Dance Research (Edinburgh, GBR) **[53267]**

Numbers cited in bold after listings are entry numbers rather than page numbers.

Dance Teacher (Brighton, GBR) *Unable to locate*

Dance Today! (London, GBR) **[54310]**

Dancing Times (London, GBR) **[54311]**

Dandenong Leader (Cheltenham, VI, AUS) **[41746]**

Dandong People's Broadcasting Station (Dandong, LI, CHN) *Unable to locate*

Dandong People's Broadcasting Station (Dandong, LI, CHN) *Unable to locate*

Dandong People's Broadcasting Station (Dandong, LI, CHN) *Unable to locate*

DANI (Sarajevo, HBO) *Unable to locate*

Danish Literary Magazine (Copenhagen, DEN) *Ceased*

Danish Medical Bulletin (Copenhagen, DEN) **[43660]**

Danjiangkou People's Broadcasting Station (Danjiangkou, HU, CHN) *Unable to locate*

Danmarks Transport-Tidende (Padborg, DEN) **[43732]**

Danmarksposten (Copenhagen, DEN) **[43661]**

Dannevirke's Evening News **[48915]***

Dansalan Quarterly (Iligan City, PHL) *Unable to locate*

DANSK (Copenhagen, DEN) **[43662]**

Dansk Foolbold (Brondby, DEN) *Unable to locate*

Dansk Kemi (Glostrup, DEN) **[43701]**

Dansk Landbrug (Copenhagen, DEN) **[43663]**

Dansk Turisme (Copenhagen, DEN) *Unable to locate*

Danske Malermestre (Copenhagen, DEN) *Unable to locate*

Danske Officerer (Copenhagen, DEN) *Unable to locate*

Danyag (Iloilo City, PHL) *Unable to locate*

DANZ (Wellington, NZL) **[49006]**

Dapei Meida (Tel Aviv, ISR) *Unable to locate*

Daqing People's Broadcasting Station (Daqing, HL, CHN) *Unable to locate*

Daqing People's Broadcasting Station (Daqing, HL, CHN) *Unable to locate*

Dar El Kitar (Casablanca) **[51489]***

DARE (London, GBR) **[54312]**

Dari Pats (Riga, LAT) **[47363]**

Darlington & Stockton Times (Darlington, GBR) **[53154]**

Darshana International (Moradabad, IND) *Unable to locate*

Dartford Times (Sidcup, GBR) **[56542]**

Dartmoor Magazine (Tavistock, GBR) **[56727]**

DARU (Tehran, IRN) **[45888]**

Daruma Magazine (Amagasaki, JPN) **[46302]**

Darza Pasaule (Riga, LAT) **[47364]**

Das Erfrischungsgetraenk (Bonn, GER) *Unable to locate*

Das Goetheanum (Dornach, SWI) **[51085]**

Das Hitradio-FM - 100.5 (Eupen, BEL) **[42881]**

Das Journal (Kassel, GER) *Unable to locate*

Das Mechanische Musikinstrument (Essen, GER) **[44346]**

Das Neue Automobil (Schwabach, GER) *Unable to locate*

Das Neue China (Berlin, GER) **[44169]**

Das Orchester (Mainz, GER) **[44539]**

Das Osterreichische Industriemagazin (Vienna, AUT) *Unable to locate*

Das Papier (Darmstadt, GER) *Unable to locate*

Data e Fiori **[46279]***

Data India (New Delhi, DH, IND) *Unable to locate*

Data Quest (New Delhi, DH, IND) *Unable to locate*

Data Science Journal (Paris, FRA) **[44036]**

Database Magazine (Alphen aan den Rijn, NLD) **[47867]**

Database and Network Journal (Luton, GBR) **[55502]**

Datacom (Poing, GER) **[44635]**

Dataong People's Broadcasting Station 2 (Datong, SX, CHN) *Unable to locate*

Dataquest (Gurgaon, HY, IND) **[45126]**

Dataweek (Kloof, SAF) **[50542]**

Dateline Delhi (New Delhi, DH, IND) *Unable to locate*

Daten & Fakten (Hamburg, GER) *Unable to locate*

Datenschutz-Nachrichten (Bonn, GER) *Unable to locate*

Datong People's Broadcasting Station (Datong, SX, CHN) *Unable to locate*

Datong People's Broadcasting Station 1 (Datong, SX, CHN) *Unable to locate*

Datong People's Broadcasting Station 1 (Datong, SX, CHN) *Unable to locate*

DAV Panorama (Munich, GER) *Unable to locate*

Daventry Express (Daventry, GBR) **[53159]**

DAVID (Ebenfurth, AUT) *Unable to locate*

David y Goliath (Buenos Aires, ARG) *Unable to locate*

David Morris Stores (London, GBR) *Unable to locate*

The Dawn (Anglesea, VI, AUS) *Ceased*

Dawn (Karachi, PAK) **[49346]**

Dawn Magazine (Karachi, PAK) **[49347]**

Daxing'anling People's Broadcasting Station (Jagdaqi Zhen, HL, CHN) *Unable to locate*

Day One Diary (Leominster, GBR) **[53840]**

Day One Magazine (Leominster, GBR) *Unable to locate*

Dayclean (Georgetown, GUY) **[44800]**

dB Magazine (Adelaide, SA, AUS) **[41505]**

DBB-Magazin (Berlin, GER) *Unable to locate*

DBI Review (London, GBR) **[54313]**

DB2 Magazine **[54581]***

De Architect (The Hague, NLD) **[48611]**

De Arte (Pretoria, SAF) **[50588]**

De Bouwkroniek (Brussels, BEL) *Unable to locate*

De Dakdekker (Schiedam, NLD) *Unable to locate*

De Dirigent (Arnhem, NLD) *Unable to locate*

De Economist (Dordrecht, NLD) **[48364]**

De Farver (Copenhagen, DEN) **[43664]**

De Huisarts (Brussels, BEL) *Unable to locate*

De Letzeburger Merkur (Luxembourg, LUX) **[47491]**

De Liberale Vrouw (The Hague, NLD) *Unable to locate*

De Muziekhandel (Doorn, NLD) *Unable to locate*

De Olifant (Arnhem, NLD) *Unable to locate*

De Postzegel (Leuven, BEL) *Unable to locate*

DE Qi-Tidsskrift for Kinesisk Medisin (Oslo, NOR) *Unable to locate*

De Rebus (Pretoria, SAF) **[50589]**

De Reiziger (Amersfoort, NLD) *Unable to locate*

De Shetland Pony (Zutphen, NLD) *Unable to locate*

De Stem van Grave (Grave, NLD) *Unable to locate*

De Wenzer (Grevenmacher, LUX) *Unable to locate*

De Witte Raaf (Brussels, BEL) *Unable to locate*

Dead Sea Discoveries (Leiden, NLD) **[48666]**

Deafness and Education International (High Wycombe, GBR) **[53572]**

Dealer World & Dealer World 15 (Madrid, SPA) **[50749]**

Dealing with Technology **[55227]***

Dearne-FM - 102 (Barnsley, GBR) **[52187]**

Dearne-FM - 97.1 (Penistone, GBR) **[56244]**

Debates Sociais (Rio de Janeiro, RJ, BRZ) *Unable to locate*

Debats (Valencia, SPA) *Unable to locate*

Debonair (Mumbai, MH, IND) *Unable to locate*

Decanter (London, GBR) **[54314]**

Deccan College Postgraduate & Research Institute Bulletin (Pune, MH, IND) *Unable to locate*

The Deccan Geographer (Pune, MH, IND) *Unable to locate*

Deccan Herald (Bangalore, KA, IND) **[44957]**

Decision (Kolkata, WB, IND) **[45263]**

Decision Sciences Journal of Innovative Education (Oxford, GBR) **[55923]**

Decisions in Economics and Finance (Tokyo, JPN) **[46800]**

DECO (Munich, GER) **[44556]**

DECO- Wohnen mit Textilien/ DECO-Stoffe & Interieurs **[44556]***

Decor International Magazine (Bangkok, THA) *Unable to locate*

Ded-Jraf (Harare, ZWE) *Unable to locate*

Jedica (Nuromberg, GER) **[44608]**

Dedicated Systems Magazine (Saint-Pieters-Leeuw, BEL) **[42911]**

Dee-FM - 106.3 (Chester, GBR) **[53001]**

Deepika (Kottayam, KE, IND) **[45314]**

Deer (Halesworth, GBR) **[53504]**

Deeside Piper & Herald (Banchory, GBR) **[52168]**

Defect and Diffusion Forum (Zurich, SWI) **[51257]**

Defence Management Journal (Stockport, GBR) **[56626]**

Defence and Peace Economics (York, GBR) **[56989]**

Defence Science Journal (Delhi, DH, IND) **[45090]**

Defence and Security Analysis (Lancaster, GBR) **[53732]**

Defence Studies (Abingdon, GBR) **[51753]**

Defence Today (Meerut, UP, IND) *Ceased*

Defensa (Madrid, SPA) **[50750]**

Defense Analysis **[53732]***

Dehong People's Broadcasting Station (Luxi, YU, CHN) *Unable to locate*

Dejando Huellas (Guayaquil, ECU) *Unable to locate*

Del Plata-FM (Montevideo, URY) *Unable to locate*

Deleuze Studies (Edinburgh, GBR) **[53268]**

Delhi Chamber of Commerce Bulletin/Directory (New Delhi, DH, IND) *Unable to locate*

Delhi Law Times (Chandigarh, CH, IND) *Unable to locate*

Delhi Medical Journal (New Delhi, DH, IND) *Unable to locate*

Delibros (Madrid, SPA) **[50751]**

delicious. (Alexandria, NW, AUS) **[41538]**

Delovye Vesti (Bishkek, KGA) *Unable to locate*

Delta-FM - 94.4 (Bandung, IDN) **[45775]**

Delta-FM - 94.4 (Bandung, IDN) **[45774]**

Delta-FM - 99.1 (Jakarta, IDN) **[45803]**

Delta-FM - 99.3 (Manado, IDN) **[45832]**

Delta-FM - 105.8 (Medan, IDN) **[45834]**

Delta-FM - 96.8 (Surabaya, IDN) **[45859]**

Demain l'Enfant (Dakar, SEN) *Unable to locate*

Dementia (London, GBR) **[54315]**

Demi (Helsinki, FIN) **[43824]**

DEMM Engineering & Manufacturing Magazine (North Shore City, NZL) **[48954]**

Democraat (The Hague, NLD) **[48612]**

Democracy & Development (Ikeja, LG, NGA) **[49106]**

The Democrat (London, GBR) **[54316]**

Democratic Forum (Calcutta, WB, IND) *Unable to locate*

Democratic Journalist (Prague, CZE) *Unable to locate*

Democratic World (New Delhi, DH, IND) *Unable to locate*

Democratization (Abingdon, GBR) **[51754]**

Demographic Research (Rostock, GER) **[44647]**

Demography India (Delhi, DH, IND) **[45091]**

Demolition and Dismantling (Hemel Hempstead, GBR) **[53556]**

Demolition & Recycling International (Wadhurst, GBR) **[56806]**

Demon-FM - 107.5 (Leicester, GBR) **[53837]**

Den Neien Radio-FM - 102.9 (Luxembourg, LUX) **[47497]**

Den Neien Radio-FM - 104.2 (Luxembourg, LUX) **[47498]**

Den Neien Radio-FM - 107.7 (Luxembourg, LUX) **[47496]**

Denbighshire Free Press (Mold, GBR) **[55641]**

Dendrobiology (Kornik, POL) **[49663]**

Dendrochronologia (Birmensdorf, SWI) **[51082]**

The Denning Law Journal (Buckingham, GBR) **[52756]**

DENTAL ASIA (Singapore, SGP) **[50130]**

Numbers cited in bold after listings are entry numbers rather than page numbers.

Dental Dialogue (Nagpur, MH, IND) *Unable to locate*

Dental Laboratory (Nottingham, GBR) **[55751]**

Dental Materials (Manchester, GBR) **[55553]**

The Dental Mirror (Singapore, SGP) **[50131]**

Dental Nursing (London, GBR) **[54317]**

Dental Practice (Epsom, GBR) *Unable to locate*

Dental Therapist Journal (Papukura, NZL) *Unable to locate*

Dental Trader (Chesham, GBR) **[52986]**

Dentistry (Shenley, GBR) **[56519]**

Dentistry in Japan (Tokyo, JPN) *Unable to locate*

Dentistry Monthly **[56519]***

Depression (London, GBR) **[54318]**

Depthnews Indonesia (Jakarta, IDN) *Unable to locate*

Der Anaesthesist (Dordrecht, NLD) **[48365]**

Der Archivar (Munster, GER) *Unable to locate*

DER AUGENOPTIKER (Leinfelden-Echterdingen, GER) **[44519]**

Der Chirurg (Dordrecht, NLD) **[48366]**

Der Deutsche Tabakbau (Leinfelden-Echterdingen, GER) **[44520]**

Der Freie Zahnarzt (Bonn, GER) *Unable to locate*

Der Gastroenterologe (Dordrecht, NLD) **[48367]**

Der Hannoveraner (Verden, GER) *Unable to locate*

Der Ingenieur (Vienna, AUT) *Unable to locate*

Der Internist (Wiesbaden, GER) *Unable to locate*

Der Islam (Hamburg, GER) **[44413]**

Der Nahverkehr (Dusseldorf, GER) *Unable to locate*

Der Nephrologe (Dordrecht, NLD) **[48368]**

Der Nervenarzt (Dordrecht, NLD) **[48369]**

Der Neue Weg **[44365]***

Der Oenologe (Geisenheim, GER) *Unable to locate*

Der Osterreichische Amtsvormund (Vienna, AUT) *Unable to locate*

Der Praktiker (Dusseldorf, GER) **[44323]**

Der Radiologe (Dordrecht, NLD) **[48370]**

Der Rotarier (Hamburg, GER) *Ceased*

Der Schmerz (Dordrecht, NLD) **[48371]**

Der Schweizer Treuhander/L'Expert-Comptable Suisse (Zurich, SWI) *Unable to locate*

Der Steuerberater (Cologne, GER) *Unable to locate*

Der Steuezahler (Berlin, GER) **[44170]**

Der Syburger (Unna, GER) *Unable to locate*

Der Vermessungsingenieur (Wuppertal, GER) *Unable to locate*

Der Weihenstephaner (Nuremberg, GER) **[44609]**

Der Winzer (Leopoldsdorf, AUT) *Unable to locate*

Der Zchter **[44478]***

Der Zurcher Bauer/Der Zurcher Bote (Zurich, SWI) *Unable to locate*

Derby Festival @MAG (London, GBR) **[54319]**

Derbyshire Times (Chesterfield, GBR) **[53002]**

Derecho y Reforma Agraria (Merida, VEN) *Unable to locate*

Derechos Humanos (Madrid, SPA) *Unable to locate*

Dereham Times (Dereham, GBR) **[53171]**

Derivatives Use, Trading and Regulation **[54735]***

Dermatologia Practica (Barcelona, SPA) *Unable to locate*

Dermatologia-Revista Mexicana (Mexico City, DF, MEX) *Unable to locate*

Dermatologia i Venerologia Bulgaran (Sofia, BUL) *Unable to locate*

Dermatology in Practice (London, GBR) **[54320]**

Derrida Today (Edinburgh, GBR) **[53269]**

Derry Journal (Derry, GBR) **[53172]**

Desalination (Amsterdam, NLD) **[47953]**

Desarrollo y Cooperacion/Desenvolvimento e Cooperacao (D+C) (Berlin, GER) *Unable to locate*

Descent (Sydney, NW, AUS) **[42501]**

Descent (Abergavenny, GBR) **[51687]**

Deshabhimani (Kochi, KE, IND) **[45249]**

DESIDOC Bulletin of Information Technology (Delhi, DH, IND) **[45092]**

Design (Budapest, HUN) *Ceased*

Design and Architecture (Mandaluyong City, PHL) **[49534]**

Design Engineering (London, GBR) *Unable to locate*

Design Indaba Magazine (Roggebaai, SAF) **[50615]**

The Design Journal (Oxford, GBR) **[55924]**

Design News (Tokyo, JPN) *Ceased*

Design Report (Stuttgart, GER) *Unable to locate*

Design Studies (Milton Keynes, GBR) **[55633]**

Design & Technology (Stoke-on-Trent, GBR) **[56629]**

Design Week (London, GBR) **[54321]**

Designed Monomers and Polymers (Leiden, NLD) **[48667]**

Designer (Calcutta, WB, IND) *Unable to locate*

Designs, Codes and Cryptography (Dordrecht, NLD) **[48372]**

Desire Contacts (London, GBR) *Unable to locate*

Desky Lekar (Bratislava, SLK) *Unable to locate*

Dessert (Tokyo, JPN) **[46801]**

Destination Jamaica (Kingston, JAM) **[46283]**

Destination Traveller (New Delhi, DH, IND) *Unable to locate*

Destination UK (Barnsley, GBR) **[52179]**

Deuce **[52367]***

Deutsch (Leicester, GBR) **[53795]**

Deutsche unquote (London, GBR) **[54322]**

Deutsche Baumschule (Braunschweig, GER) **[44275]**

Deutsche Briefmarken Revue (Ratingen, GER) **[44641]**

Deutsche Briefmarken Zeitung/Sammler Express (DBZ/SE) (Alfeld, GER) **[44138]**

Deutsche Entomologische Zeitschrift (Berlin, GER) **[44171]**

Deutsche Zeitschrift fur Wirtschafts- und Insolvenzrecht (Berlin, GER) **[44172]**

Deutscher Drucker (Ostfildern, GER) *Unable to locate*

Deutscher Fachuerlag GmbH (Frankfurt am Main, GER) **[44365]**

Deutsches Tierarzteblatt (Hannover, GER) *Unable to locate*

Deutsches Yoga Forum (Erlabrunn, GER) *Unable to locate*

Developer Network Journal **[52661]***

Developers Digest (Nundah, QL, AUS) **[42222]**

Development (Dhaka, BGD) *Unable to locate*

Development (Rome, ITA) **[46226]**

Development et Cooperation (D+C) (Berlin, GER) *Unable to locate*

Development Dialogue (Uppsala, SWE) **[51051]**

The Development Education Journal (Stoke-on-Trent, GBR) *Ceased*

Development Focus (Nkambe, CMR) *Unable to locate*

Development Genes and Evolution (Tokyo, JPN) **[46802]**

Development and Learning in Organizations (Bradford, GBR) **[52449]**

Development Policy and Administrative Review (Jaipur, RJ, IND) *Unable to locate*

Development and Policy Research (Hyderabad, AP, IND) *Unable to locate*

Development in Practice (Abingdon, GBR) **[51755]**

Development and Society (Seoul, KOR) **[47264]**

Development Southern Africa (Abingdon, GBR) **[51756]**

Development Update (Braamfontein, SAF) *Unable to locate*

Developmental Biology (Amsterdam, NLD) **[47954]**

Developmental & Comparative Immunology (Amsterdam, NLD) **[47955]**

Developmental Neurorehabilitation (Abingdon, GBR) **[51757]**

Developmental Review (Amsterdam, NLD) **[47956]**

Devon Life (Totnes, GBR) **[56762]**

Devon Link (Exeter, GBR) **[53351]**

Dewsbury Reporter (Dewsbury, GBR) **[53179]**

Deyang People's Broadcasting Station (Deyang, SI, CHN) *Unable to locate*

Dezhou People's Broadcasting Station (Dezhou, SD, CHN) *Unable to locate*

Dezhou People's Broadcasting Station (Linyi, SD, CHN) *Unable to locate*

Dezhou People's Broadcasting Station (Yantai, SD, CHN) *Unable to locate*

Dezhou People's Broadcasting Station (Zaozhuang, SD, CHN) *Unable to locate*

Dharitri (Bhubaneswar, OR, IND) **[45009]**

Dharma (Kuala Lumpur, MYS) *Unable to locate*

Dharma Life (Birmingham, GBR) *Ceased*

Dia Log (London, GBR) *Unable to locate*

Diabetes (Tampere, FIN) **[43907]**

Diabetes/Metabolism Research and Reviews (Rome, ITA) **[46227]**

Diabetes & Primary Care (London, GBR) **[54323]**

Diabetes Research and Clinical Practice (Oxford, GBR) **[55925]**

Diabetes Update (London, GBR) **[54324]**

Diabetes and Vascular Disease Research (Birmingham, GBR) **[52339]**

Diabetes Voice (Brussels, BEL) **[42848]**

DiabetesWise (Dublin, DU, IRL) **[45953]**

Diabetic Association of India Journal Education Section (Mumbai, MH, IND) *Unable to locate*

Diabetic Association of India Journal—Scientific Section (Mumbai, MH, IND) *Unable to locate*

Diabetic Living (Eveleigh, NW, AUS) **[41859]**

Diabetic Medicine (Oxford, GBR) **[55926]**

Diabetikeren (Oslo, NOR) *Unable to locate*

Diabetologia (Dusseldorf, GER) *Unable to locate*

Diabetologia (Heidelberg, GER) **[44452]**

Diachronica (Amsterdam, NLD) **[47957]**

Diagnostic and Interventional Radiology (Ankara, TUR) **[51492]**

Diagnostic Pathology (London, GBR) **[54325]**

Dialectica (Oxford, GBR) **[55927]**

Dialectical Anthropology (Dordrecht, NLD) **[48373]**

Dialog (Copenhagen, DEN) *Ceased*

Dialog (Wiesbaden, GER) **[44712]**

Dialogo Cooperativo (San Jose, CRI) *Unable to locate*

Dialogo Mujer (Bogota, COL) *Unable to locate*

Dialogue (Brussels, BEL) *Ceased*

Dialogue (Castries, SLC) *Unable to locate*

Dialogue (Colombo, SRI) *Unable to locate*

Dialogue India (Calcutta, WB, IND) *Unable to locate*

Dialogue Today (New Delhi, DH, IND) *Unable to locate*

Diametros (Krakow, POL) **[49665]**

Diamond Connection (Witham, GBR) *Unable to locate*

Diamond Industria (Tokyo, JPN) *Unable to locate*

Diamond Valley Leader (Briar Hill, VI, AUS) **[41635]**

Diamond World (Jaipur, RJ, IND) **[45193]**

Diana (Sesto Fiorentino, ITA) *Unable to locate*

Diana Creative (Moscow, RUS) **[49892]**

Diana Moden (Moscow, RUS) **[49893]**

Diario de Aveiro (Aveiro, PRT) **[49785]**

Diario de Coimbra (Coimbra, PRT) **[49790]**

Diario de Leiria (Leira, PRT) **[49799]**

Diario Regional **[49813]***

Diario Regional Viseu (Viseu, PRT) **[49813]**

Diatom Research (Stuttgart, GER) **[44665]**

Dickens Quarterly (Oxford, GBR) *Unable to locate*

The Dickensian (London, GBR) *Unable to locate*

Die Afrikaner (Pretoria, SAF) *Ceased*

Die Alpen (Bern, SWI) **[51071]**

Die Breederivier Gazette (Cape Town, SAF) **[50373]**

Numbers cited in bold after listings are entry numbers rather than page numbers.

Die Bundeswehr (Bonn, GER) **[44254]**

Die Burger (Kaapstad, SAF) **[50541]**

Die Fleischmehl-Industrie (Bonn, GER) *Unable to locate*

Die Gute Tat (Munich, GER) *Unable to locate*

die Kontaktlinse (Leinfelden-Echterdingen, GER) **[44521]**

Die & Mould Technology (Shanghai, CHN) **[43472]**

Die Neue DL (Berlin, GER) *Unable to locate*

DIE NEUE-FM - 107.7 (Stuttgart, GER) **[44690]**

Die Neue Schulpraxis (Saint Gallen, SWI) *Unable to locate*

Die Pirsch (Munich, GER) **[44557]**

Die Presse (Vienna, AUT) *Unable to locate*

Die Schwester (Munich, GER) *Unable to locate*

Die neue Welle-FM - 101.8 (Karlsruhe, GER) **[44496]**

Die Welt des Islams (Leiden, NLD) **[48668]**

Diena (Latvian Edition) (Riga, LAT) **[47365]**

Diesel (Milan, ITA) *Unable to locate*

Diesel Industry News (North Shore, NZL) **[48952]**

Diet & Information (Dusseldorf, GER) *Unable to locate*

DIETA (Sint Genesius Rode, BEL) *Unable to locate*

Dietist Aktuellt (Lisbon, PRT) *Unable to locate*

Differences (Paris, FRA) *Unable to locate*

Differential Equations and Dynamical Systems (Hyderabad, AP, IND) *Unable to locate*

Differential Geometry and its Applications (Brunn, CZE) **[43604]**

Diffusion (Grand-Saconnex, SWI) **[51177]**

Dig BMX Magazine (Glasgow, GBR) **[53413]**

Digest of Current Industrial and Labour Law (New Delhi, DH, IND) *Unable to locate*

Digest of Information and Patent Review (Sheffield, GBR) **[56491]**

Digest of Labour Cases (Madras, TN, IND) *Unable to locate*

Digestive Diseases and Sciences (Dordrecht, NLD) **[48374]**

Digit (Mumbai, MH, IND) **[45367]**

Digital Camera Buyer (Bournemouth, GBR) **[52412]**

Digital Cinematography (London, GBR) *Unable to locate*

Digital Display Printing (London, GBR) *Unable to locate*

Digital Home (Bath, GBR) **[52238]**

Digital Investigation (Singapore, SGP) **[50132]**

Digital Media (Hong Kong, CHN) **[43296]**

Digital Nanyang Chronicle (Singapore, SGP) **[50133]**

Digital PhotoFX (Peterborough, GBR) *Unable to locate*

Digital Photographer (Bournemouth, GBR) **[52413]**

Digital Photography and Design (Surry Hills, NW, AUS) **[42426]**

Digital Signal Processing (Amsterdam, NLD) **[47958]**

Digital Studio (Dubai, UAE) **[51638]**

Digital Technology Law Journal (Perth, WA, AUS) *Ceased*

Digitimes (Taipei, TWN) **[51337]**

Digressus (Nottingham, GBR) **[55752]**

DIK-forum (Nacka, SWE) *Unable to locate*

Diliman Review (Quezon City, PHL) **[49589]**

Dinamalar (Madurai, TN, IND) **[45336]**

Dinamit FM (Pyatigorsk, RUS) *Unable to locate*

Dinnington Guardian (Dinnington, GBR) **[53183]**

Diogenes (Paris, FRA) **[44037]**

Diplomacy & Statecraft (Abingdon, GBR) **[51758]**

Diplomatic News (Brussels, BEL) *Unable to locate*

Dirasat Administrative Sciences (Amman, JOR) **[47152]**

Dirasat Agricultural Sciences (Amman, JOR) **[47153]**

Dirasat Engineering Sciences (Amman, JOR) **[47154]**

Dirasat Human and Social Sciences (Amman, JOR) **[47155]**

Dirasat Medical and Biological Sciences (Amman, JOR) **[47156]**

Dirasat Pure Sciences (Amman, JOR) **[47157]**

Dirasat Sharia' and Law Sciences (Amman, JOR) **[47158]**

Direct (London, GBR) *Unable to locate*

Direct Mailings (Apeldoorn, NLD) **[48275]**

Direct Report (Harare, ZWE) *Unable to locate*

Direct Taxes Bulletin (New Delhi, DH, IND) *Unable to locate*

Direct Textile Bulletin (New Delhi, DH, IND) *Unable to locate*

Direction (Nottingham, GBR) **[55753]**

Director (Calcutta, WB, IND) *Unable to locate*

The Director (London, GBR) *Unable to locate*

Directory of Airline Public Relations (Croydon, GBR) *Unable to locate*

Directory of Irish Family History Research (Belfast, GBR) **[52282]**

Dirigido (Barcelona, SPA) **[50663]**

Dirt Action (North Ryde, NW, AUS) **[42180]**

Dirt Bike Rider (Morecambe, GBR) **[55647]**

Dirt Mountain Bike Magazine (London, GBR) **[54326]**

Disability Now (London, GBR) **[54327]**

Disability Product News (Colchester, GBR) **[53034]**

Disability and Rehabilitation (Ipswich, GBR) **[63654]**

Disability Rights Up (Bulawayo, ZWE) *Unable to locate*

Disability and Society (London, GBR) **[54328]**

Disarmament Diplomacy (London, GBR) **[54329]**

Disaster Management (Gurgaon, HY, IND) *Ceased*

Disaster Prevention and Management (Bradford, GBR) **[52450]**

Discourse (New Delhi, DH, IND) *Unable to locate*

Discourse (Heslington, GBR) **[53566]**

Discourse & Society (London, GBR) **[54330]**

Discourse Studies (London, GBR) **[54331]**

Discover Brampton (Carlisle, GBR) *Unable to locate*

Discovering Mathematics (Kuala Lumpur, MYS) *Unable to locate*

Discovery and Innovation (Nairobi, KEN) **[47177]**

Discrete Event Dynamic Systems (Dordrecht, NLD) **[48375]**

Discrete Mathematics & Theoretical Computer Science (Nancy, FRA) **[44010]**

Discrete Optimization (Singapore, SGP) **[50134]**

Disease Information (Paris, FRA) **[44038]**

Disease Markers (Amsterdam, NLD) **[47959]**

Diseases of Aquatic Organisms (Oldendorf, GER) **[44626]**

Diseases of the Esophagus (Kagoshima, JPN) **[46403]**

Diskrepancija (Zagreb, CTA) **[43567]**

Disney Fairies (London, GBR) **[54332]**

Disney and Me (London, GBR) **[54333]**

Disney Princess Magazine (Mandaluyong City, PHL) **[49535]**

Dispensing Optics (Crowborough, GBR) **[53120]**

Disputatio (Lisbon, PRT) **[49802]**

Diss Express (Diss, GBR) **[53184]**

Diss Mercury (Diss, GBR) **[53185]**

Distance Education (Abingdon, GBR) **[51759]**

Distance Running (London, GBR) **[54334]**

Distribucion Actualidad (Madrid, SPA) **[50752]**

Distribute (Nottingham, GBR) *Unable to locate*

Distributed and Parallel Databases (Dordrecht, NLD) **[48376]**

Distribution Business (West Sussex, GBR) *Unable to locate*

DistrictMail (Cape Town, SAF) **[50374]**

Distripress-Gazette (Zurich, SWI) *Unable to locate*

Diva (London, GBR) **[54335]**

Divadelni Noviny (Prague, CZE) **[43623]**

Dive (Richmond, GBR) **[56390]**

Diverse-FM - 102.8 (Luton, GBR) **[55511]**

Diversities (Gottingen, GER) **[44395]**

Diversity-FM - 103.5 (Lancaster, GBR) **[53740]**

Diversity in Health and Social Care (Birmingham, GBR) **[52340]**

Dividend (London, GBR) *Unable to locate*

Divine Life (Garhwal, UP, IND) **[45120]**

Division of Labour & Transaction Costs (Clayton, VI, AUS) **[41760]**

Divya Bhaskar (Ahmedabad, GJ, INJ) **[44908]**

Divya Vani (Kakinada, AP, IND) *Unable to locate*

DIY (Ettlingen, GER) **[44349]**

DIY Superstore **[56547]***

DIY Week (Sittingbourne, GBR) **[56547]**

DIY Week (Tonbridge, GBR) *Unable to locate*

DJ Magazine (London, GBR) **[54336]**

Djembe (Copenhagen, DEN) **[43665]**

Djurens Ratt (Alvsjo, SWE) **[50948]**

DLG-Mitteilungen (Frankfurt, GER) **[44359]**

DLZ Agrarmagazin (Munich, GER) **[44558]**

DM Magazine (London, GBR) **[54337]**

DNA (London, GBR) *Unable to locate*

DNA Research (Chiba, JPN) **[46317]**

DNA Sequence **[51983]***

DNJ (Bristol, GBR) **[52661]**

Doble Nueve-FM - 99.1 (Lima, PER) **[49427]**

Dockwalk (Wimbledon, GBR) **[56927]**

Doctor (Milan, ITA) *Unable to locate*

Doctor Os (Carimate, ITA) **[46130]**

Doctor Pediatria (Milan, ITA) *Unable to locate*

Doctor Who Adventures (London, GBR) **[54338]**

Doctor Who Battles in Time (Ringwood, GBR) **[56395]**

Document Skateboard (London, GBR) **[54339]**

Documenta Mathematica (Bielefeld, GER) **[44245]**

Documenta Ophthalmologica (Dordrecht, NLD) **[48377]**

Documentacao de Estudos em Linguistica Teorica e Aplicada (DELTA) (Sao Paulo, SP, BRZ) **[43037]**

Documentation Bulletin for South-East Asia (New Delhi, DH, IND) *Unable to locate*

Documentation on Women's Concerns (New Delhi, DH, IND) *Unable to locate*

Dodo (Rye, GBR) *Unable to locate*

Dodo Journal (Jersey, GBR) *Unable to locate*

Doff-Iaoio (Reykjavik, ICE) *Unable to locate*

Dogs Life (North Ryde, NW, AUS) **[42181]**

Dokkyo Journal of Medical Sciences (Tochigi, JPN) *Unable to locate*

Doklady Biochemistry **[49894]***

Doklady Biochemistry (Moscow, RUS) *Ceased*

Doklady Biochemistry and Biophysics (Moscow, RUS) **[49894]**

Doklady Biological Sciences (Moscow, RUS) **[49895]**

Doklady Biophysics **[49894]***

Doklady Botanical Sciences (Moscow, RUS) *Ceased*

Doklady Chemical Technology (Moscow, RUS) *Ceased*

Doklady Chemistry (Moscow, RUS) **[49896]**

Doklady Earth Sciences (Moscow, RUS) **[49897]**

Doklady Mathematics (Moscow, RUS) **[49898]**

Doklady Physical Chemistry (Moscow, RUS) **[49899]**

Doklady Physics (Moscow, RUS) **[49900]**

Dolls House World (Arundel, GBR) **[52134]**

DOLMA (Dharamsala, HP, IND) **[45110]**

Dom & Wnetrze (Warsaw, POL) **[49705]**

Dominican Business (Santo Domingo, DOM) *Unable to locate*

Domradio-FM - 93.95 (Cologne, GER) **[44306]**

Domradio-FM - 96.75 (Cologne, GER) **[44305]**

Domus (Rozzano, ITA) **[46248]**

Domus Kit (Rozzano, ITA) **[46249]**

Don Nostalgie - Rostov-na-Donu (Rostov-na-Donu, RUS) *Unable to locate*

Doncaster Free Press (Doncaster, GBR) **[53186]**

Dongchuan People's Broadcasting Station (Kunming, YU, CHN) *Unable to locate*

Dongguan People's Broadcasting Station (Dongguan, GD, CHN) *Unable to locate*

Numbers cited in bold after listings are entry numbers rather than page numbers.

Dongsheng People's Broadcasting Station (Dongsheng, NM, CHN) *Unable to locate*

Dongying People's Broadcasting Station (Dongying, SD, CHN) *Unable to locate*

Dongying People's Broadcasting Station (Dongying, SD, CHN) *Unable to locate*

Dongying People's Broadcasting Station (Dongying, SD, CHN) *Unable to locate*

Donna Hay Magazine (Surry Hills, NW, AUS) **[42427]**

Donside Piper & Herald (Banchory, GBR) **[52169]**

Donskoy Mirazh (Rostov-na-Donu, RUS) *Unable to locate*

Donskoy Mirazh (Rostov-na-Donu, RUS) *Unable to locate*

Doping Journal (Moscow, RUS) **[49901]**

Dora Dress Up and Go (London, GBR) **[54340]**

Dora the Explorer (London, GBR) **[54341]**

Dorset (Dorset, GBR) *Unable to locate*

Dos Yidishe Wort (Warsaw, POL) *Unable to locate*

Doshisha American Studies (Kyoto, JPN) **[46471]**

Doshisha Literature (Kyoto, JPN) *Unable to locate*

Dossier (Brussels, BEL) *Unable to locate*

Dotlit (Kelvin Grove, QL, AUS) *Unable to locate*

Double Reed News (High Wycombe, GBR) **[53573]**

Double Tressure (Edinburgh, GBR) **[53270]**

Dovebladet (Copenhagen, DEN) *Unable to locate*

Doves Tidsskrift (Oslo, NOR) *Unable to locate*

Dovtidningen (Stockholm, SWE) *Unable to locate*

Down To Earth (New Delhi, DH, IND) **[45503]**

Down Under Quilts (Rozelle, NW, AUS) **[42325]**

Downstream (Knutsford, GBR) **[53730]**

DownTown (Madrid, SPA) *Unable to locate*

Downtown Radio-AM (Newtownards, GBR) *Unable to locate*

Downtown Radio-FM (Newtownards, GBR) *Unable to locate*

Downtown Radio-FM (Newtownards, GBR) *Unable to locate*

The Drain Trader (Cheltenham, GBR) **[52967]**

Drama Magazine (London, GBR) **[54342]**

Drapers (London) (London, GBR) **[54343]**

DRC Bladet/Restaurant Cafe & Catering (Arhus, DEN) *Unable to locate*

Dream Catcher (Lincoln, GBR) **[53855]**

DREAM-FM - 106.7 (Quezon City, PHL) **[49620]**

Dream-FM (Winchester, GBR) *Unable to locate*

Dream 100-FM - 100.2 (Colchester, GBR) **[53055]**

Dream 107 **[56586]***

Dream 107.2 - 107.2 (Southampton, GBR) **[56581]**

Dream Weddings (Quezon City, PHL) **[49590]**

Dredging and Port Construction (Redhill, GBR) **[56350]**

Driffield Times (Driffield, GBR) **[53201]**

Drinks Buyer - Americas (Oxted, GBR) *Ceased*

Drinks Buyer - Asia Pacific **[56236]***

Drinks Buyer - China (Oxted, GBR) *Ceased*

Drinks Buyer - Europe (Oxted, GBR) *Ceased*

Drinks International (Crawley, GBR) **[53102]**

Drinks Network (Oxted, GBR) **[56236]**

Drive! Magazine (Dublin, DU, IRL) *Unable to locate*

Drive System Technique (Shanghai, CHN) **[43473]**

Driving Instructor (Croydon, GBR) **[53125]**

Droitwich Standard (Bromsgrove, GBR) **[52747]**

Dromore Leader (Dromore, GBR) **[53207]**

Drug and Alcohol Findings (London, GBR) **[54344]**

Drug and Alcohol Review (Surry Hills, NW, AUS) **[42428]**

Drug Delivery Systems and Sciences (Haslemere, GBR) **[53536]**

Drug Discovery Today (Singapore, SGP) **[50139]**

Drug Discovery Today (Singapore, SGP) **[50138]**

Drug Discovery Today (Singapore, SGP) **[50136]**

Drug Discovery Today (Singapore, SGP) **[50137]**

Drug Discovery Today (Singapore, SGP) **[50135]**

Drug Metabolism and Drug Interactions (Tel Aviv, ISR) **[46098]**

Drug Metabolism Letters (Bussum, NLD) **[48300]**

Drug News (Mumbai, MH, IND) *Unable to locate*

Drug News & Perspectives (Barcelona, SPA) **[50664]**

Drug Targets. Cardiovascular & Hematological Disorders; Current **[48280]***

Drug Targets. CNS & Neurological Disorders; Current **[48282]***

Drug Targets Infectious Disorders; Current **[48301]***

Drug Testing and Analysis (Cologne, GER) **[44292]**

Drugs (Abingdon, GBR) **[51760]**

Drugs and Alcohol Today (Hove, GBR) **[53604]**

Drugs Cases (New Delhi, DH, IND) **[45504]**

Drugs in Context (Cheltenham, GBR) **[52968]**

Drugs in Context. General Medicine **[52968]***

Drugs in Context. Primary Care. Part A. Cardiovascular Medicine 1 **[52968]***

Drugs in Context. Primary Care. Part B. Cardiovascular Medicine 2 **[52968]***

Drugs in Context. Primary Care. Part B. Cardiovascular Medicine 2 (Cheltenham, GBR) *Unable to locate*

Drugs in Context. Primary Care. Part C. Psychiatry and Neurology **[52968]***

Drugs in Context. Primary Care. Part D. Endocrinology and Gastroenterology **[52968]***

Drugs in Context. Primary Care. Part E. Respiratory Medicine and Infections **[52968]***

The Drum (Glasgow, GBR) **[53414]**

The Drummer's Call (Maidstone, GBR) **[55528]**

Drydock (Hartley Wintney, GBR) *Unable to locate*

DSN News **[52603]***

DSV-Skischule (Planegg, GER) *Unable to locate*

DSWR Datenverarbeitung Steuer, Wirtschaft, Recht (Munich, GER) *Unable to locate*

DTL - NYT (Copenhagen, DEN) *Unable to locate*

Dubai International (Dubai, UAE) *Unable to locate*

Dubai Voyager (Dubai, UAE) **[51639]**

Dublin-FM - 98.0 (Grand Canal Quay, DU, IRL) **[46022]**

Dublin University Law Journal (Dublin, DU, IRL) *Unable to locate*

Dublin's Country-FM - 106.8 (Bray, WI, IRL) **[45924]**

Dublin's Q102-FM - 102.2 (Dublin, DU, IRL) **[46000]**

Dudley News (Stourbridge, GBR) **[56639]**

Duel (Milan, ITA) *Unable to locate*

Duhugurane (Kigali, RWA) *Unable to locate*

Dumfries Courier (Annan, GBR) **[52124]**

Dumont-FM - 104.3 (Jundiai, SP, BRZ) **[42984]**

Dune-FM - 107.9 (Southport, GBR) **[56589]**

Dungarvan Observer (Dungarvan, WA, IRL) *Unable to locate*

Dunhua People's Broadcasting Station (Dunhua, JI, CHN) *Unable to locate*

Dunhuang Yanjiu (Lanzhou, GS, CHN) *Unable to locate*

Dunya Radyo-FM - 90.2 (Istanbul, TUR) **[51566]**

Duplex (Barcelona, SPA) *Unable to locate*

Durbar (Huntingdon, GBR) **[53634]**

Durham Anthropology Journal (Durham, GBR) **[53228]**

Durham County Life (Preston, GBR) **[56299]**

Durham-FM - 106.8 (Durham, GBR) **[53232]**

Durham-FM (Framwelgate, GBR) *Unable to locate*

Dutch Crossing (London, GBR) **[54345]**

Duyun People's Broadcasting Station (Duyun, GH, CHN) *Unable to locate*

DWAD (Mandaluyong, PHL) *Unable to locate*

DWAM (Batangas, PHL) *Unable to locate*

DWAN (Quezon City, PHL) *Unable to locate*

DWAS - 1125 KHz (Daraga, PHL) **[49478]**

DWAV-FM - 89.1 (Pasig City, PHL) **[49574]**

DWAY (Makati, PHL) *Unable to locate*

DWBC (Quezon City, PHL) *Unable to locate*

DWBF (Quezon City, PHL) *Unable to locate*

DWBL (Pasig, PHL) *Unable to locate*

DWBM-FM - 105.1 (Quezon City, PHL) **[49621]**

DWBS (Manila, PHL) *Unable to locate*

DWCM (Quezon City, PHL) *Unable to locate*

DWCM-AM (Dagupan City, PHL) *Unable to locate*

DWDD (Quezon City, PHL) *Unable to locate*

DWDW (Dagupan, PHL) *Unable to locate*

DWDY (Cauayan, PHL) *Unable to locate*

DWFB (Laoag, PHL) *Unable to locate*

DWGC (Quezon City, PHL) *Unable to locate*

DWGI (Manila, PHL) *Unable to locate*

DWGO (Olongapo, PHL) *Unable to locate*

DWGW (Legaspi, PHL) *Unable to locate*

DWHB-FM - 103.9 (Baguio City, PHL) **[49451]**

DWHL (Olongapo, PHL) *Unable to locate*

DWHP-FM - 99.5 (Laoag City, PHL) **[49511]**

DWHQ (Naga, PHL) *Unable to locate*

DWHT-FM - 107.9 (Dagupan City, PHL) **[49474]**

DWHY-FM - 100.7 MHz (Dagupan City, PHL) **[49475]**

DWIM-FM - 89.5 MHz (Baguio City, PHL) **[49452]**

DWIN (Dagupan, PHL) *Unable to locate*

DWIZ - 882 KHz (Pasig City, PHL) **[49575]**

DWJ—Deutsches Waffen Journal (Schwabisch Hall, GER) *Unable to locate*

DWKC-FM - 93.9 (Makati City, PHL) **[49525]**

DWKI (Quezon City, PHL) *Unable to locate*

DWKX-FM - 103.5 (Pasig City, PHL) **[49576]**

DWLC (Quezon City, PHL) *Unable to locate*

DWLL (Pasig, PHL) *Unable to locate*

DWLQ (Pasig, PHL) *Unable to locate*

DWLS-FM - 97.1 (Quezon City, PHL) **[49622]**

DWLV (Naga, PHL) *Unable to locate*

DWLW (Laoag, PHL) *Unable to locate*

DWMC (Rosales, PHL) *Unable to locate*

DWMG (Cabanatuan City, PHL) *Unable to locate*

DWNG (Lucena, PHL) *Unable to locate*

DWNU-FM - 107.5 (Pasig City, PHL) **[49577]**

DWNW (Naga, PHL) *Unable to locate*

DWNX-FM - 91.1 (Naga City, PHL) **[49565]**

DWON-FM - 104.7 (Dagupan City, PHL) **[49476]**

DWPE (Tuguegarao, PHL) *Unable to locate*

DWPH (Dagupan, PHL) *Unable to locate*

DWPR (Dagupan, PHL) *Unable to locate*

DWQZ-FM - 97.9 (Pasig City, PHL) **[49578]**

DWRB (Lipa, PHL) *Unable to locate*

DWRC (Quezon City, PHL) *Unable to locate*

DWRF (Iba, PHL) *Unable to locate*

DWRH (Isabela, PHL) *Unable to locate*

DWRI (Makati, PHL) *Unable to locate*

DWRL (Legaspi, PHL) *Unable to locate*

DWRN (Naga, PHL) *Unable to locate*

Numbers cited in bold after listings are entry numbers rather than page numbers.

DWRP (Quezon City, PHL) *Unable to locate*

DWRS (Makati, PHL) *Unable to locate*

DWRT (Makati, PHL) *Unable to locate*

DWSB (Quezon City, PHL) *Unable to locate*

DWSF (Paranaque, PHL) *Unable to locate*

DWSI (Santiago, PHL) *Unable to locate*

DWSM-FM - 102.7 MHz (Pasay City, PHL) **[49569]**

DWSP (Itogon, PHL) *Unable to locate*

DWSR (Makati City, PHL) *Unable to locate*

DWSS (Quezon City, PHL) *Unable to locate*

DWTI (Lucena, PHL) *Unable to locate*

DWTT (Makati, PHL) *Unable to locate*

DWWG (Cabanatuan City, PHL) *Unable to locate*

DWWM (Manila, PHL) *Unable to locate*

DWWW (Quezon City, PHL) *Unable to locate*

DWXI (Makati, PHL) *Unable to locate*

DWXX (Manila, PHL) *Unable to locate*

DWXY-FM (Tuguegarao, PHL) *Unable to locate*

DWZR (Legaspi, PHL) *Unable to locate*

DXAB (Davao, PHL) *Unable to locate*

DXAM (Quezon City, PHL) *Unable to locate*

DXAS - 1116 KHz (Zamboanga City, PHL) **[49648]**

DXBC - 693 KHz (Butuan City, PHL) **[49456]**

DXBL (Bislig, PHL) *Unable to locate*

DXBN (Butuan, PHL) *Unable to locate*

DXBR (Butuan, PHL) *Unable to locate*

DXCB-FM - 93.9 MHz (Zamboanga City, PHL) **[49649]**

DXCC - 828 KHz (Cagayan de Oro City, PHL) **[49458]**

DXCD (Makati, PHL) *Unable to locate*

DXCK-FM - 91.9 (General Santos City, PHL) **[49491]**

DXCL (Makati, PHL) *Unable to locate*

DXCM (Cotabato, PHL) *Unable to locate*

DXCO (Cagayan de Oro, PHL) *Unable to locate*

DXCP - 585 KHz (General Santos City, PHL) **[49492]**

DXCP (Manila, PHL) *Unable to locate*

DXCR (Valencia, PHL) *Unable to locate*

DXCT (Pasig, PHL) *Unable to locate*

DXDB - 594 KHz (Bukidnon, PHL) **[49454]**

DXDC - 621 KHz (Davao City, PHL) **[49480]**

DXDD (Manila, PHL) *Unable to locate*

DXDH (Isabela, PHL) *Unable to locate*

DXDN (Davao del Norte, PHL) *Unable to locate*

DXDN (Paranaque, PHL) *Unable to locate*

DXDR - 981 KHz (Dipolog City, PHL) **[49488]**

DXDS (Makati, PHL) *Unable to locate*

DXDX (General Santos City, PHL) *Unable to locate*

DXED (Davao, PHL) *Unable to locate*

DXES - 801 KHz (General Santos City, PHL) **[49493]**

DXFB-FM - 93.3 MHz (Dipolog City, PHL) **[49489]**

DXFD-FM - 93.7 MHz (Cotabato City, PHL) **[49472]**

DXFE - 1197 KHz (Davao City, PHL) **[49481]**

DXFX-FM - 96.3 MHz (Davao City, PHL) **[49482]**

DXGE (Makati, PHL) *Unable to locate*

DXGO (Davao, PHL) *Unable to locate*

DXGS (General Santos City, PHL) *Unable to locate*

DXHM - 549 KHz (Davao Oriental, PHL) **[49486]**

DXHP - 999 KHz (Bislig, PHL) **[49453]**

DXIC - 711 KHz (Iligan City, PHL) **[49496]**

DXID (Pagadian, PHL) *Unable to locate*

DXIF (Cagayan de Oro, PHL) *Unable to locate*

DXIM (Cagayan de Oro, PHL) *Unable to locate*

DXIM (Makati, PHL) *Unable to locate*

DXJM (Butuan, PHL) *Unable to locate*

DXJS - 873 KHz (Tandag, PHL) **[49642]**

DXKD (Dipolog, PHL) *Unable to locate*

DXKE-FM - 94.1 (Surigao City, PHL) **[49632]**

DXKI - 1062 KHz (Koronadal, PHL) **[49506]**

DXKO (Cagayan de Oro, PHL) *Unable to locate*

DXKP (Pagadian, PHL) *Unable to locate*

DXKR - 639 KHz (Marbel, PHL) **[49564]**

DXKS (Surigao, PHL) *Unable to locate*

DXKT (Davao, PHL) *Unable to locate*

DXLL (Pasig, PHL) *Unable to locate*

DXLL (Zamboanga, PHL) *Unable to locate*

DXLR-FM - 93.1 (Davao City, PHL) **[49483]**

DXLX (Iligan, PHL) *Unable to locate*

DXMB - 648 KHz (Bukidnon, PHL) **[49455]**

DXMC - Koronadal (Koronadal, PHL) *Unable to locate*

DXMC - Makati (Makati, PHL) *Unable to locate*

DXMD - 152 KHz (General Santos City, PHL) **[49494]**

DXMF (Davao, PHL) *Unable to locate*

DXMF (Davao, PHL) *Unable to locate*

DXMO (Makati, PHL) *Unable to locate*

DXMR (Zamboanga, PHL) *Unable to locate*

DXMS (Cotabato, PHL) *Unable to locate*

DXMV-AM (Valencia, PHL) *Unable to locate*

DXMY - 729 KHz (Cotabato City, PHL) **[49473]**

DXMZ (Makati, PHL) *Unable to locate*

DXND (Kidapawan, PHL) *Unable to locate*

DXOC (Ozamis, PHL) *Unable to locate*

DXOR (Cagayan de Oro, PHL) *Unable to locate*

DXOW (Davao, PHL) *Unable to locate*

DXPD (Pagadian, PHL) *Unable to locate*

DXPR (Isabela, PHL) *Unable to locate*

DXPR - 603 KHz (Pagadian City, PHL) **[49566]**

DXPT, PHL) *Unable to locate*

DXRA (Davao, PHL) *Unable to locate*

DXRB (Butuan, PHL) *Unable to locate*

DXRD (Davao, PHL) *Unable to locate*

DXRE (General Santos City, PHL) *Unable to locate*

DXRG (Gingoog, PHL) *Unable to locate*

DXRI (Makati, PHL) *Unable to locate*

DXRJ (Iligan, PHL) *Unable to locate*

DXRO (Cotabato, PHL) *Unable to locate*

DXRP (Quezon City, PHL) *Unable to locate*

DXRR (Davao, PHL) *Unable to locate*

DXRS - 1206 KHz (Surigao City, PHL) **[49633]**

DXRT (Makati, PHL) *Unable to locate*

DXRZ - 900 KHz (Zamboanga City, PHL) **[49650]**

DXSC (Zamboanga, PHL) *Unable to locate*

DXSM (Jolo, PHL) *Unable to locate*

DXSN - 1017 KHz (Surigao City, PHL) **[49634]**

DXSO (Marawi, PHL) *Unable to locate*

DXSS (Manila, PHL) *Unable to locate*

DXSY (Ozamis, PHL) *Unable to locate*

DXUM (Davao, PHL) *Unable to locate*

DXVM-FM - 99.1 (Cagayan de Oro City, PHL) **[49459]**

DXVP - 1467 KHz (San Juan, PHL) **[49629]**

DXWB (Makati, PHL) *Unable to locate*

DXWD-FM - 96.7 (Pagadian City, PHL) **[49567]**

DXWR-FM - 96.3 (Zamboanga City, PHL) **[49651]**

DXXL-FM - 93.9 (Davao City, PHL) **[49484]**

DXXX (San Jose, PHL) *Unable to locate*

DXXX-FM - 100.7 (Butuan City, PHL) **[49457]**

DXYX-FM - 102.3 (Iligan City, PHL) **[49497]**

DXYZ (Zamboanga, PHL) *Unable to locate*

DXZZ-FM - 94.1 (Dipolog City, PHL) **[49490]**

DYAB - 1512 KHz (Mandaue, PHL) **[49545]**

DYAC (Baybay, PHL) *Unable to locate*

DYAC-FM - 90.7 (Cebu City, PHL) **[49467]**

DYAF (Manila, PHL) *Unable to locate*

DYBB (Roxas, PHL) *Unable to locate*

DYBB (Tacloban, PHL) *Unable to locate*

DYBM-FM - 99.1 (Bacolod City, PHL) **[49446]**

DYBQ (Iloilo, PHL) *Unable to locate*

DYBR (Tacloban, PHL) *Unable to locate*

DYCA (Palawan, PHL) *Unable to locate*

DYCB (Makati, PHL) *Unable to locate*

DYCC - 936 KHz (Calbayog, PHL) **[49461]**

DYCH (Taisay, PHL) *Unable to locate*

DYDM - 1548 KHz (Maasin, PHL) **[49513]**

DYDW (Tacloban, PHL) *Unable to locate*

DYES (Quezon City, PHL) *Unable to locate*

Dyes and Pigments (Amsterdam, NLD) **[47960]**

DYEZ (Bacolod, PHL) *Unable to locate*

DYFL (Quezon City, PHL) *Unable to locate*

DYFM (Iloilo, PHL) *Unable to locate*

DYFR (Cebu, PHL) *Unable to locate*

DYFX (Cebu, PHL) *Unable to locate*

DYHB (Bacolod City, PHL) *Unable to locate*

DYHH (Cebu, PHL) *Unable to locate*

DYHP - 612 KHz (Cebu City, PHL) **[49468]**

DYHP (Makati, PHL) *Unable to locate*

DYHT-FM - 94.3 (Bacolod City, PHL) **[49447]**

DYIC-FM - 95.1 (Iloilo City, PHL) **[49498]**

DYIF-FM - 95.5 MHz (Bacolod City, PHL) **[49448]**

DYIN - 1107 KHz (Kalibo, PHL) **[49504]**

DYJC (Borongan, PHL) *Unable to locate*

DYJJ (Roxas, PHL) *Unable to locate*

DYJR (Quezon City, PHL) *Unable to locate*

DYKA (Manila, PHL) *Unable to locate*

DYKB (Bacolod, PHL) *Unable to locate*

DYKH (Makati City, PHL) *Unable to locate*

DYKR - 1161 KHz (Kalibo, PHL) **[49505]**

DYKW (Binalbagan, PHL) *Unable to locate*

DYLA (Cebu, PHL) *Unable to locate*

Dylizans (Monmouth, GBR) *Unable to locate*

DYLL (Iloilo, PHL) *Unable to locate*

DYME (Masbate, PHL) *Unable to locate*

DYMM (Tacloban, PHL) *Unable to locate*

DYMR (Cebu, PHL) *Unable to locate*

DYMX-FM - 95.5 MHz (Cebu City, PHL) **[49469]**

DYMZ (Cebu, PHL) *Unable to locate*

Dynamic Medicine (London, GBR) *Ceased*

Dynamical Systems (Exeter, GBR) **[53352]**

Dynamics of Population and Family Welfare (Mumbai, MH, IND) *Unable to locate*

Dynamics and Stability of Systems **[53352]***

Dynasty (Taipei, TWN) **[51338]**

DYOK (Iloilo, PHL) *Unable to locate*

DYOW (Roxas, PHL) *Unable to locate*

DYPR - 765 KHz (Puerto Princesa, PHL) **[49580]**

DYRB (Cebu, PHL) *Unable to locate*

DYRC (Cebu, PHL) *Unable to locate*

DYRD - 1161 KHz (Tagbilaran, PHL) **[49638]**

DYRF (Cebu, PHL) *Unable to locate*

DYRF-FM - 99.5 MHz (Iloilo City, PHL) **[49499]**

DYRG (Kalibo, PHL) *Unable to locate*

DYRH (Pasig, PHL) *Unable to locate*

DYRI - 774 KHz (Iloilo City, PHL) **[49500]**

Numbers cited in bold after listings are entry numbers rather than page numbers.

DYRJ (Cebu, PHL) *Unable to locate*

DYRL (Bacolod, PHL) *Unable to locate*

DYRM (Dumaguete, PHL) *Unable to locate*

DYRM (Makati, PHL) *Unable to locate*

DYRO (Pasig, PHL) *Unable to locate*

DYRP (Pasig, PHL) *Unable to locate*

DYRR (Ormoc, PHL) *Unable to locate*

DYRS (San Carlos, PHL) *Unable to locate*

DYRT-FM (Cebu City, PHL) *Unable to locate*

DYRX-FM - 103.7 MHz (Roxas City, PHL) **[49626]**

DYSA (Iloilo, PHL) *Unable to locate*

DYSB (Quezon City, PHL) *Unable to locate*

DYSG (Pasig, PHL) *Unable to locate*

DYSI (Iloilo, PHL) *Unable to locate*

DYSJ (Quezon City, PHL) *Unable to locate*

DYSL (Sogod, PHL) *Unable to locate*

Dyslexia (West Sussex, GBR) **[56897]**

Dyslexia Review (Egham, GBR) **[53328]**

DYSM (Catarman, PHL) *Unable to locate*

Dyspraxia Foundation Professional Journal (Hitchin, GBR) **[53577]**

DYSR (Dumaguete, PHL) *Unable to locate*

DYSS (Cebu, PHL) *Unable to locate*

DYTR (Tagbilaran, PHL) *Unable to locate*

DYTX-FM - 95.1 MHz (Tacloban City, PHL) **[49635]**

DYVL (Tacloban, PHL) *Unable to locate*

DYVR - 657 KHz (Roxas City, PHL) **[49627]**

DYVR-FM - 93.9 (Roxas City, PHL) **[49628]**

DYVS - 1233 KHz (Bacolod City, PHL) **[49449]**

DYWB (Bacolod, PHL) *Unable to locate*

DYWC (Dumaguete, PHL) *Unable to locate*

DYWR (Tacloban, PHL) *Unable to locate*

DYXL-FM - 93.9 (Cebu City, PHL) **[49470]**

DYXT (Makati, PHL) *Unable to locate*

DYXW (Tacloban, PHL) *Unable to locate*

DYXY-FM - 99.1 (Tacloban City, PHL) **[49636]**

DZAG (Agoo, PHL) *Unable to locate*

DZAL (Iriga, PHL) *Unable to locate*

DZAL (Iriga, PHL) *Unable to locate*

DZAR (Makati, PHL) *Unable to locate*

DZAS - 702 KHz (Valenzuela City, PHL) **[49644]**

DZBB (Quezon City, PHL) *Unable to locate*

DZBR (Batangas, PHL) *Unable to locate*

DZBS (Baguio, PHL) *Unable to locate*

DZCA (Quezon City, PHL) *Unable to locate*

DZCI (Cabanatuan City, PHL) *Unable to locate*

DZCV (Tuguegarao, PHL) *Unable to locate*

DZDF (Talavera, PHL) *Unable to locate*

DZDH (Makati, PHL) *Unable to locate*

DZDR (Makati, PHL) *Unable to locate*

DZEA - 909 KHz (San Juan, PHL) **[49630]**

DZEC - 1062 KHz (Quezon City, PHL) **[49623]**

DZEL (Lucena, PHL) *Unable to locate*

DZEM (Quezon City, PHL) *Unable to locate*

DZEQ (Baguio City, PHL) *Unable to locate*

DZER (Quezon City, PHL) *Unable to locate*

DZFB (Quezon City, PHL) *Unable to locate*

DZFE - 98.7 MHz (Makati City, PHL) **[49526]**

DZFE - 98.7 MHz (Manila, PHL) **[49561]**

DZFM (Quezon City, PHL) *Unable to locate*

DZFM (Quezon City, PHL) *Unable to locate*

DZFT (Quezon City, PHL) *Unable to locate*

DZGB (Legaspi, PHL) *Unable to locate*

DZGC (Quezon City, PHL) *Unable to locate*

DZGE (Naga, PHL) *Unable to locate*

DZGR - 891 KHz (Tuguegarao City, PHL) **[49643]**

DZHH (Pasay, PHL) *Unable to locate*

DZIQ-AM - 990 (Makati City, PHL) **[49527]**

DZJC (Laoag, PHL) *Unable to locate*

DZJO (Quezon City, PHL) *Unable to locate*

DZKI (riga, PHL) *Unable to locate*

DZLB - 97.4 MHz (Los Banos, PHL) **[49512]**

DZLG (Legaspi, PHL) *Unable to locate*

DZLT (Lucena, PHL) *Unable to locate*

DZLU (San Fernando, PHL) *Unable to locate*

DZMD (Daet, PHL) *Unable to locate*

DZME (Quezon City, PHL) *Unable to locate*

DZMM - 630 KHz (Quezon City, PHL) **[49624]**

DZMQ (Dagupan, PHL) *Unable to locate*

DZMS (Sorsogon, PHL) *Unable to locate*

DZNC (Cauayan, PHL) *Unable to locate*

DZNG (Naga, PHL) *Unable to locate*

DZNL (San Fernando, PHL) *Unable to locate*

DZNS - 963 KHz (Vigan, PHL) **[49645]**

DZPA (Bangued, PHL) *Unable to locate*

DZPE (Quezon City, PHL) *Unable to locate*

DZPE (Quezon City, PHL) *Unable to locate*

DZPT (Quezon City, PHL) *Unable to locate*

DZQR (Olongapo, PHL) *Unable to locate*

DZRA (Virac, PHL) *Unable to locate*

DZRB (Quezon City, PHL) *Unable to locate*

DZRC (Legaspi, PHL) *Unable to locate*

DZRD (Dagupan, PHL) *Unable to locate*

DZRH - 666 KHz (Pasay City, PHL) **[49570]**

DZRJ (Manila, PHL) *Unable to locate*

DZRK (Tabuk, PHL) *Unable to locate*

DZRL (Batac, PHL) *Unable to locate*

DZRM (Quezon City, PHL) *Unable to locate*

DZRP (Quezon City, PHL) *Unable to locate*

DZRS (Sorsogon, PHL) *Unable to locate*

DZRV - 846 KHz (Intramuros, PHL) **[49503]**

DZSO (San Fernando, PHL) *Unable to locate*

DZSP (Makati, PHL) *Unable to locate*

DZSR (Cebu, PHL) *Unable to locate*

DZTC (Tarlac, PHL) *Unable to locate*

DZTG (Tuguegarao, PHL) *Unable to locate*

DZUP (Quezon City, PHL) *Unable to locate*

DZVR (Laoag, PHL) *Unable to locate*

DZVT - 1395 KHz (San Juan, PHL) **[49631]**

DZVV - 603 KHz (Vigan, PHL) **[49646]**

DZVX (Daet, PHL) *Unable to locate*

DZW Die Zahnarzt Woche - The Dentists Weekly (Herne, GER) *Unable to locate*

DZW Spezial (Herne, GER) *Unable to locate*

DZW ZahnTechnik (Herne, GER) *Unable to locate*

DZWN - 1125 KHz (Dagupan City, PHL) **[49477]**

DZWT (Baguio, PHL) *Unable to locate*

DZWX (Baguio, PHL) *Unable to locate*

DZXC (Cabanatuan City, PHL) *Unable to locate*

DZXE (Vigan, PHL) *Unable to locate*

DZXL - 558 KHz (Manila, PHL) **[49562]**

DZXL-AM - 558 (Makati City, PHL) **[49528]**

DZXO (Cabanatuan City, PHL) *Unable to locate*

DZXQ (Pasig, PHL) *Unable to locate*

DZXT (Tarlac, PHL) *Unable to locate*

DZYA (Angeles, PHL) *Unable to locate*

DZYI (Ilagan, PHL) *Unable to locate*

DZYM (San Jose, PHL) *Unable to locate*

DZYS (Makati, PHL) *Unable to locate*

DZYT (Tuguegarao, PHL) *Unable to locate*

DZYZ (Makati, PHL) *Unable to locate*

DZZH (Sorsogon, PHL) *Unable to locate*

E

e-Beratungsjournal (Krems, AUT) **[42728]**

E-Commerce Magazin (Vaterstetten, GER) **[44698]**

e-Health Business (London, GBR) *Unable to locate*

E-Learning (Chester, GBR) *Unable to locate*

E-Learning and Education (Cologne, GER) **[44293]**

E-Polymers (Eindhoven, NLD) **[48589]**

e-TISNET Monthly News/e-TISNET Monthly Information Services (Bangkok, THA) **[51418]**

EA Magazine (London, GBR) *Ceased*

The Eagle (Manzini, SWZ) *Unable to locate*

Eagle-FM - 93.5 (Goulburn, NW, AUS) **[41928]**

Eagle-FM - 96.4 (Guildford, GBR) **[53497]**

Eagle One, Eagle Two (Birmingham, GBR) *Ceased*

EAIE Forum (Amsterdam, NLD) **[47961]**

Early Child Development and Care (Abingdon, GBR) **[51761]**

Early Medieval China (London, GBR) **[54346]**

Early Music (Cambridge, GBR) **[52815]**

Early Popular Visual Culture (Abingdon, GBR) **[51762]**

Early Science and Medicine (Nijmegen, NLD) **[48743]**

Early Years (Abingdon, GBR) **[51763]**

EARSeL eProceedings (Oldenburg, GER) **[44624]**

Earth Planets and Space (Tokyo, JPN) **[46803]**

Earth Science (Tokyo, JPN) *Unable to locate*

Earth Science (Wuhan, CHN) **[43519]**

Earth Sciences (Wuhan, HU, CHN) **[43521]**

Earthlines (Limassol, CYP) **[43589]**

Earthmatters (Collingwood, VI, AUS) **[41785]**

Earth's Cryosphere (Novosibirsk, RUS) **[50010]**

Earthwatch (Dublin, DU, IRL) *Unable to locate*

Earthwise (Nottingham, GBR) **[55754]**

The East (Tokyo, JPN) **[46804]**

East (Singapore, SGP) *Unable to locate*

The East African (Nairobi, KEN) **[47178]**

East African Agricultural and Forestry Journal (Nairobi, KEN) **[47179]**

East African Journal of Public Health (Dar es Salaam, TZA) **[51400]**

East African Journal of Sciences (Haramaya, ETH) **[43805]**

East African Journal of Statistics (Nairobi, KEN) **[47180]**

East African Medical Journal (Nairobi, KEN) **[47181]**

East Anglian Daily Times (Ipswich, GBR) **[53655]**

East Anglian Daily Times Suffolk (Ipswich, GBR) **[53656]**

East Anglican Bibliography (Norwich, GBR) *Unable to locate*

East Antrim Advertiser (Larne, GBR) **[53741]**

East Asian Archives of Psychiatry (Hong Kong, CHN) **[43297]**

East Asian Pastoral Review (Quezon City, PHL) **[49591]**

East and Central African Journal of Pharmaceutical Sciences (Nairobi, KEN) **[47182]**

East Central Europe (Leiden, NLD) **[48669]**

East European Jewish Affairs (Abingdon, GBR) **[51764]**

East European Markets (Makati City, PHL) *Unable to locate*

East European Trade (New Delhi, DH, IND) *Unable to locate*

East Herts Edition Herald (Welwyn Garden City, GBR) **[56882]**

East London Advertiser (London, GBR) **[54347]**

East Lothian News (Dalkeith, GBR) **[53152]**

East Torrens Messenger (Norwood, SA, AUS) **[42215]**

East and West Series (Pune, MH, IND) *Unable to locate*

Eastbourne Herald (Eastbourne, GBR) **[53243]**

Eastern Africa Journal of Rural Development (Kampala, UGA) **[51586]**

Numbers cited in bold after listings are entry numbers rather than page numbers.

Eastern Bay News (Whakatane, NZL) *Unable to locate*

The Eastern Clarion (Jorhat, AS, IND) *Unable to locate*

Eastern Courier Messenger (Norwood, SA, AUS) **[42216]**

Eastern Economist (New Delhi, DH, IND) *Unable to locate*

Eastern Eye (London, GBR) *Unable to locate*

Eastern Journal of International Law (Chennai, TN, IND) *Unable to locate*

Eastern Librarian (Dhaka, BGD) *Unable to locate*

Eastern Mediterranean Health Journal (Cairo, EGY) **[43754]**

Eastern Panorama (Shillong, MG, IND) *Unable to locate*

Eastern Reporter (Osborne Park, WA, AUS) **[42224]**

Eastern Worker (Karachi, PAK) **[49348]**

Eastside Radio-FM - 89.7 (Paddington, NW, AUS) **[42226]**

Eastwood Advertiser (Eastwood, GBR) **[53245]**

Easy Cook (London, GBR) **[54348]**

Easy Food (Greystone, WI, IRL) **[46023]**

Easy Mix-FM - 98.2 (Auckland, NZL) **[48838]**

Easy Mix-FM - 90.3 (Napier, NZL) **[48942]**

Easy Mix-FM - 95.1 (Rotorua, NZL) **[48977]**

Easy Mix-FM - 99.0 (Tauranga, NZL) **[48983]**

Easy Radio London-AM (Southall, GBR) *Unable to locate*

Easyhealth (Greystone, WI, IRL) **[46024]**

Eat (Tokyo, JPN) **[46805]**

Eating Out...Eating In (Liverpool, GBR) *Ceased*

Eating and Weight Disorders (Milan, ITA) **[46166]**

EBU Technical Review (Grand-Saconnex, SWI) **[51178]**

EC Tax Review (The Hague, NLD) **[48613]**

ECCO - Echo (Utrecht, NLD) *Unable to locate*

Echappement (Saint Cloud, FRA) **[44101]**

L'Echo vegetable (Morieres Les Avignon, FRA) **[44009]**

Echo-FM (Preston, VI, AUS) *Unable to locate*

Echoes of FAVDO (Dakar, SEN) *Unable to locate*

Echos AMA (Brussels, BEL) **[42849]**

Echos des Ong (Lome, TGO) *Unable to locate*

Ecletica Quimica (Sao Paulo, SP, BRZ) **[43038]**

Eclogae Geologicae Helvetia (Tokyo, JPN) *Unable to locate*

ECMI Journal on Ethnopolitics and Minority Issues in Europe (Flensburg, GER) **[44354]**

ECN Chemscope (Stockholm, SWE) *Unable to locate*

ECN-European Chemical News (Stockholm, SWE) *Unable to locate*

Eco Aruba (Oranjestad, ARU) **[41491]**

Ecohydrology (Perth, WA, AUS) **[42250]**

Ecole Nigerienne (Niamey, NER) *Unable to locate*

Ecoliers du Monde **[44023]***

Ecologia Politica (Barcelona, SPA) **[50665]**

Ecological Herald of Kyrgyzstan (Bishkek, KGA) *Unable to locate*

Ecological Indicators (Singapore, SGP) **[50140]**

Ecological Informatics (Singapore, SGP) **[50141]**

Ecological Management & Restoration (Woodburn, NW, AUS) **[42713]**

Ecological Modelling (Copenhagen, DEN) **[43666]**

Ecological Questions (Warsaw, POL) **[49706]**

Ecological Research (Sendai, JPN) **[46665]**

Ecological Review (Miyagi, JPN) *Unable to locate*

Ecologically Clean Technologies (Dushanbe, TDN) *Unable to locate*

The Ecologist (London, GBR) **[54349]**

The Ecologists (New Delhi, DH, IND) *Unable to locate*

Ecology, Environment and Conservation (Karad, MH, IND) *Unable to locate*

Ecology and Farming (Bonn, GER) **[44255]**

Ecology Magazine (San Miguel de Tucuman, ARG) *Unable to locate*

Economia Aplicada (Ribeirao Preto, SP, BRZ) **[42997]**

Economic Affairs (Calcutta, WB, IND) *Unable to locate*

Economic Age (Calcutta, WB, IND) *Unable to locate*

Economic Bulletin (Singapore, SGP) *Unable to locate*

Economic Bulletin (London, GBR) *Unable to locate*

Economic & Business Review (New Delhi, DH, IND) *Unable to locate*

Economic Change and Restructuring (Dordrecht, NLD) **[48378]**

Economic and Commercial News (New Delhi, DH, IND) *Unable to locate*

Economic Geography (Beijing, CHN) *Unable to locate*

The Economic History Review (Oxford, GBR) **[55928]**

Economic Indicators; NESG **[49109]***

Economic and Industrial Democracy (London, GBR) **[54350]**

Economic Inquiry (Oxford, GBR) **[55929]**

The Economic Journal (Oxford, GBR) **[55930]**

Economic Journal (York, GBR) **[56990]**

Economic Journal of Hokkaido University (Sapporo, JPN) *Unable to locate*

Economic Journal of Nepal (Kirtipur, NPL) *Unable to locate*

Economic Journal of the United Bank Limited (Karachi, PAK) *Unable to locate*

Economic & Labour Market Review (Basingstoke, GBR) **[52199]**

Economic Outlook (Karachi, PAK) *Unable to locate*

Economic and Policy Review (Ikoyi, LG, NGA) **[49109]**

Economic Quality Control (Wurzburg, GER) **[44720]**

The Economic Record (Oxford, GBR) **[55931]**

Economic Review (Karachi, PAK) *Unable to locate*

Economic Review (UK) (London, GBR) **[54351]**

Economic Studies (Calcutta, WB, IND) *Unable to locate*

The Economic Studies Quarterly **[56008]***

Economic System Research (Abingdon, GBR) **[51765]**

Economic Systems (Regensburg, GER) **[44643]**

Economic Theory (Dordrecht, NLD) **[48379]**

Economic Thought (Sofia, BUL) *Unable to locate*

Economic Times (Dhaka, BGD) *Unable to locate*

The Economic Times (Bangalore, KA, IND) **[44958]**

The Economic Times (Chennai, TN, IND) **[45031]**

The Economic Times (Kolkata, WB, IND) **[45264]**

The Economic Times (Mumbai, MH, IND) **[45368]**

The Economic Times (New Delhi, DH, IND) **[45505]**

Economic Trends (New Delhi, DH, IND) *Unable to locate*

Economica (Oxford, GBR) **[55932]**

Economics and Finance in Indonesia (Jakarta, IDN) **[45796]**

Economics of Governance (Tokyo, JPN) **[46806]**

Economics and Human Biology (Munich, GER) **[44559]**

Economics of Innovation and New Technology (Turin, ITA) **[46271]**

Economics and Organization of Enterprise (Warsaw, POL) **[49707]**

Economics of Planning **[48378]***

Economie Rurale (Paris, FRA) *Unable to locate*

Economisch Statistische Berichten (Rotterdam, NLD) *Unable to locate*

The Economist (London, GBR) **[54352]**

Economistul - The Economist (Bucharest, ROM) **[49834]**

Economy and Society (Abingdon, GBR) **[51766]**

Ecorissa (Bhubaneswar, OR, IND) *Unable to locate*

Ecos (Collingwood, VI, AUS) **[41786]**

Ecos (Moscow, RUS) *Unable to locate*

Ecos de Espana y Latinoamerica (Planegg, GER) *Unable to locate*

Ecosystem Review (Nkambe, CMR) *Unable to locate*

Ecosystems (Tokyo, JPN) **[46807]**

Ecotheology (Sheffield, GBR) *Unable to locate*

Ecotoxicology and Environmental Safety (Amsterdam, NLD) **[47962]**

Ecovoy (Bafoussam, CMR) *Unable to locate*

Ecritures (Paris, FRA) *Unable to locate*

Ecstasy (Mumbai, MH, IND) *Unable to locate*

Ecuador Debate (Quito, ECU) *Unable to locate*

Ecuadorian Business & Commerce (Quito, ECU) *Unable to locate*

The Ecumenical Review (Geneva, SWI) **[51091]**

Edelweiss (Lausanne, SWI) **[51186]**

The Edge (Leicester, GBR) **[53796]**

The Edge (London, GBR) **[54353]**

Edge-FM - 102.1 (Wangaratta, VI, AUS) **[42683]**

The Edge Magazine (Knottingley, GBR) *Unable to locate*

Edges Magazine (Blackburn, GBR) **[52383]**

The Edinburgh Law Review (Edinburgh, GBR) **[53271]**

Edinstvennaya (Kiev, URE) **[51594]**

Edinstvennaya - Tvoye Zdorovye (Kiev, URE) **[51595]**

Edlisfraedi a Islandi (Reykjavik, ICE) *Unable to locate*

EDMAGram (Brussels, BEL) *Unable to locate*

Educacao & Sociedade (Campinas, SP, BRZ) **[42968]**

Educate Online (Weston-super-Mare, GBR) *Ceased*

Education (Lucknow, UP, IND) *Unable to locate*

Education Assessment, Evaluation and Accountability (Dordrecht, NLD) **[48380]**

Education Business (Loughton, GBR) **[55489]**

Education, Business and Society (Bradford, GBR) **[52451]**

Education as Change (Pretoria, SAF) **[50590]**

Education for Chemical Engineers (Rugby, GBR) **[56417]**

Education Economics (Abingdon, GBR) **[51767]**

Education for Health (Abingdon, GBR) *Ceased*

Education in India (New Delhi, DH, IND) *Unable to locate*

Education for Information (Manchester, GBR) **[55554]**

Education International **[42875]***

The Education International Quarterly Magazine **[42875]***

Education, Knowledge & Economy (Abingdon, GBR) **[51768]**

Education and the Law (Abingdon, GBR) **[51769]**

Education Permanente (Zurich, SWI) *Unable to locate*

Education and Psychology Review (Baroda, GJ, IND) *Unable to locate*

Education Quarterly (Quezon City, PHL) *Unable to locate*

Education & Recreation; Journal of Physical **[43278]***

Education Sciences & Psychology (Tbilisi, GRG) **[44132]**

Education and Social Justice (Stoke-on-Trent, GBR) *Ceased*

Education 3-13 (Stoke-on-Trent, GBR) *Unable to locate*

Education Today (London, GBR) **[54354]**

Education Today (Maidstone, GBR) **[55529]**

Education Training (Bradford, GBR) **[52452]**

Educational Action Research (Abingdon, GBR) **[51770]**

Educational Book Review (Mumbai, MH, IND) *Unable to locate*

Educational India (Masulipatnam, AP, IND) *Unable to locate*

Educational Instrument & Equipment (Beijing, CHN) *Unable to locate*

The Educational Journal (Safat, KWT) **[47336]**

Educational Management & Administration **[54355]***

Educational Management Administration and Leadership (London, GBR) **[54355]**

Educational Measurement (Oxford, GBR) **[55933]**

Educational Miscellany (Agartala, TR, IND) *Unable to locate*

Educational Practice and Theory (South Melbourne, VI, AUS) **[42370]**

Educational Research for Policy and Practice (Nanyang, SGP) **[50097]**

Educational Research & Reviews (Lagos, LG, NGA) **[49137]**

Numbers cited in bold after listings are entry numbers rather than page numbers.

The Educational Review (Bangalore, KA, IND) *Unable to locate*

Educational Technology Abstracts (Tunbridge Wells, GBR) **[56781]**

Educational Trends (New Delhi, DH, IND) *Unable to locate*

Educommunication News (Brussels, BEL) *Unable to locate*

Eduka-Glosa (Richmond, GBR) *Ceased*

EE Times UK (Brussels, BEL) **[42850]**

EEAT Journal (Bangkok, THA) **[51419]**

EEMA Briefing (Worcester, GBR) **[56961]**

Eeva (Helsinki, FIN) **[43825]**

Effeta (Bologna, ITA) *Unable to locate*

eFinancial News (London, GBR) **[54356]**

EFM-FM (Bangkok, THA) *Unable to locate*

EFMD Journal and Bulletin (Brussels, BEL) *Unable to locate*

Egerszeg Radio-FM (Zalaegerszeg, HUN) *Unable to locate*

EGTYF News (Orebro, SWE) *Unable to locate*

Egypt Guide (Cairo, EGY) *Unable to locate*

Egypt Today (Cairo, EGY) **[43755]**

Egyptian Cotton Gazette (Alexandria, EGY) *Unable to locate*

Egyptian Journal of Biochemistry and Molecular Biology (Cairo, EGY) **[43756]**

Egyptian Journal of Biology (Ismailia, EGY) **[43773]**

Egyptian Journal of Biomedical Sciences (Cairo, EGY) **[43757]**

Egyptian Journal of Biotechnology (Cairo, EGY) **[43758]**

Egyptian Journal of Computer Science (Cairo, EGY) **[43759]**

Egyptian Journal of Medical Laboratory Sciences (Cairo, EGY) **[43760]**

Egyptian Journal of Natural History (Ismailia, EGY) **[43774]**

Eho (Sofia, BUL) *Unable to locate*

Ei Magazine (London, GBR) **[54357]**

EI Monthly Monitor **[42875]***

Ei8ht (London, GBR) **[54358]**

Eigen Aard (Louvain, BEL) *Unable to locate*

Eigentijds (Brussels, BEL) *Unable to locate*

8 Days (Singapore, SGP) **[50142]**

8CCC-FM - 102.1 (Alice Springs, NT, AUS) **[41551]**

Eighteenth Century Music (Cambridge, GBR) **[52816]**

8HA-AM - 900 (Alice Springs, NT, AUS) **[41552]**

8KIN-FM - 100.5 (Alice Springs, NT, AUS) **[41553]**

88-FM - 88.0 (Springwood, QL, AUS) **[42385]**

Eigse (Dublin, DU, IRL) **[45954]**

Eikestadnuus (Cape Town, SAF) **[50375]**

Eikoku News Digest (London, GBR) *Unable to locate*

EIPR: European Intellectual Property Review (Andover, GBR) **[52116]**

Eiszeitalter und Gegenwart Quaternary Science Journal (Stuttgart, GER) **[44666]**

Ejournalist (Rockhampton, QL, AUS) **[42315]**

EJVES Extra (Oxford, GBR) **[55934]**

Ekho Moskvy (Samara, RUS) *Unable to locate*

Ekho Moskvy (Voronezh, RUS) *Unable to locate*

Ekho Moskvy - Bobrov (Moscow, RUS) *Unable to locate*

Ekho Moskvy - Boguchar (Moscow, RUS) *Unable to locate*

Ekho Moskvy - Borisoglebsk (Moscow, RUS) *Unable to locate*

Ekho Moskvy - Cheboksary (Murmansk, RUS) *Unable to locate*

Ekho Moskvy - Chelyabinsk (Chelyabinsk, RUS) *Unable to locate*

Ekho Moskvy - Cherepovets - 105.2 MHz (Cherepovets, RUS) **[49852]**

Ekho Moskvy - Gubkinskiy (Moscow, RUS) *Unable to locate*

Ekho Moskvy - Irkutsk (Irkutsk, RUS) *Unable to locate*

Ekho Moskvy - Kazan (Moscow, RUS) *Unable to locate*

Ekho Moskvy - Kemerovo (Moscow, RUS) *Unable to locate*

Ekho Moskvy - Krasnodar (Krasnodar, RUS) *Unable to locate*

Ekho Moskvy - Krasnoyarsk (Moscow, RUS) *Unable to locate*

Ekho Moskvy - Kurgan (Moscow, RUS) *Unable to locate*

Ekho Moskvy - Kurgan (Moscow, RUS) *Unable to locate*

Ekho Moskvy - Moskva - 91.2 MHz (Moscow, RUS) **[50001]**

Ekho Moskvy - Naberezhnyye Chelny (Moscow, RUS) *Unable to locate*

Ekho Moskvy - Nadym (Moscow, RUS) *Unable to locate*

Ekho Moskvy - Nizhniy Novgorod (Moscow, RUS) *Unable to locate*

Ekho Moskvy - Nizhniy Tagil (Moscow, RUS) *Unable to locate*

Ekho Moskvy - Novokuznetsk (Moscow, RUS) *Unable to locate*

Ekho Moskvy - Novosibirsk (Novosibirsk, RUS) *Unable to locate*

Ekho Moskvy - Novyy Urengoy (Moscow, RUS) *Unable to locate*

Ekho Moskvy - Nyagan (Moscow, RUS) *Unable to locate*

Ekho Moskvy (Radio Express) (Ufa, RUS) *Unable to locate*

Ekho Moskvy (Radio 2x2) (Ulyanovsk, RUS) *Unable to locate*

Ekho Moskvy - Saratov (Saratov, RUS) *Unable to locate*

Ekho Moskvy - Serebryanyy Dozhd (Moscow, RUS) *Unable to locate*

Ekho Moskvy (Tonik Radio) (Saratov, RUS) *Unable to locate*

Ekho Moskvy - Tula - 106.9 MHz (Tula, RUS) **[50037]**

Ekho Moskvy (TV-2 R) (Tomsk, RUS) *Unable to locate*

Ekho Moskvy - Ussuriysk (Ussuriysk, RUS) *Unable to locate*

Ekho Moskvy - Voronezh (Moscow, RUS) *Unable to locate*

Ekho Peterburga (Ekho Moskvy) (Saint Petersburg, RUS) *Unable to locate*

EKISTICS (Athens, GRC) **[44742]**

Ekologija (Warsaw, POL) **[49708]**

Ekoloji (Izmir, TUR) **[51573]**

Ekonomi Indonesia (Jakarta, IDN) *Unable to locate*

Ekonomika i Zhizn (Moscow, RUS) *Unable to locate*

El Acuario Pratico (Valencia, SPA) *Unable to locate*

El Camino-FM - 106.1 (La Libertad, ELS) **[43776]**

El Cerealista (Santafe de Bogota, COL) *Unable to locate*

El Ciervo (Barcelona, SPA) **[50666]**

El Croquis (Madrid, SPA) **[50753]**

El Ecologista (Madrid, SPA) **[50754]**

El Economista (Madrid, SPA) *Unable to locate*

El Extramundi y los papeles de Iria Flavia (Madrid, SPA) **[50755]**

El Farmaceutico (Barcelona, SPA) **[50667]**

El Farmaceutico Hospitales (Barcelona, SPA) **[50668]**

El Grafico **[47784]***

El Gran Diario de Mexico **[47784]***

El Informador (Guadalajara, JA, MEX) **[47774]**

El Jueves (Barcelona, SPA) **[50669]**

El Khabar (Algiers, ALG) *Unable to locate*

El Moudjahid (Algiers, ALG) **[41460]**

El Mueble (Barcelona, SPA) **[50670]**

El Mueble Casas de Campo (Barcelona, SPA) **[50671]**

El Mueble Cocinas y Banos (Barcelona, SPA) **[50672]**

El Rotario de Chile (Los Angeles, CHL) **[43140]**

El Rotario Peruano (Chiclayo, PER) **[49418]**

El Siglo que viene (Seville, SPA) *Unable to locate*

El Universal **[47784]***

El Universal (Mexico City, DF, MEX) **[47784]**

El Viejo Topo (Mataro, SPA) **[50819]**

Elamanhalu (Kuvalehdet, FIN) *Unable to locate*

Elderly Care **[53529]***

Eldoradio (Saint Petersburg, RUS) *Unable to locate*

EldoRadio-FM - 105 (Gasperich, LUX) **[47490]**

EldoRadio-FM - 107.2 (Gasperich, LUX) **[47489]**

EldoRadio-FM - 105 (Luxembourg-Gasperich, LUX) **[47500]**

E.Learning Age (Reading, GBR) **[56312]**

Election Archives and International Politics (New Delhi, DH, IND) *Unable to locate*

Electra (Paris, FRA) *Unable to locate*

Electric Power Systems Research (Amsterdam, NLD) **[47963]**

The Electric Railway (Sutton Coldfield, GBR) **[56694]**

Electric Railway Society Journal **[56694]***

Electrical + Automation Technology (North Shore City, NZL) **[48955]**

Electrical Contractor **[54359]***

Electrical & Electronics (Mumbai, MH, IND) **[45369]**

Electrical Engineer Magazine (Quezon City, PHL) **[49592]**

Electrical Engineering (Tokyo, JPN) **[46808]**

Electrical/Mechanical Contractor (London, GBR) **[54359]**

Electrical Review (Stockholm, SWE) *Unable to locate*

Electrical Solutions (Wahroonga, NW, AUS) **[42672]**

Electrical World (Sydney, NW, AUS) **[42502]**

Electricity and Electronics (Calcutta, WB, IND) *Unable to locate*

Electro-Acoustic Music (London, GBR) *Unable to locate*

Electro-Technology (Bangalore, KA, IND) *Unable to locate*

Electro-visie (Brussels, BEL) *Unable to locate*

Electrochemical Society of India Journal (Bangalore, KA, IND) *Unable to locate*

Electrochemistry Communications (Oxford, GBR) **[55935]**

Electrochimica Acta (Lausanne, SWI) **[51187]**

Electron (Sofia, BUL) *Unable to locate*

Electronic Application News (Mumbai, MH, IND) *Unable to locate*

Electronic Communications in Probability (Nantes, FRA) **[44013]**

Electronic & Components (Singapore, SGP) **[50143]**

Electronic Components; Asian Sources **[50143]***

The Electronic Journal of Australian and New Zealand History (Townsville, QL, AUS) **[42635]**

Electronic Journal of Biotechnology (Valparaiso, CHL) **[43162]**

Electronic Journal of e-Government (Reading, GBR) **[56313]**

Electronic Journal of e-Learning (Reading, GBR) **[56314]**

Electronic Journal of Foreign Language Teaching (Singapore, SGP) **[50144]**

Electronic Journal of Information Systems Evaluation (EJISE) (Reading, GBR) **[56315]**

Electronic Journal of Knowledge Management (Reading, GBR) **[56316]**

Electronic Journal of Structural Engineering (Melbourne, VI, AUS) **[42058]**

Electronic Journal of Theoretical Physics (Abu Dhabi, UAE) **[51619]**

Electronic Library (Bradford, GBR) **[52453]**

Electronic Materials & Packaging (Burnham, GBR) **[52764]**

Electronic Musicological Review (Curitiba, PR, BRZ) **[42977]**

Electronic Products Finder (Mumbai, MH, IND) *Unable to locate*

Electronic Times **[42850]***

Electronics and Communication Engineering Journal (Stevenage, GBR) **[56600]**

Electronics Education (Stevenage, GBR) **[56601]**

Electronics For You (New Delhi, DH, IND) **[45506]**

Electronics Information and Planning (New Delhi, DH, IND) *Unable to locate*

Electronics Letters (Stevenage, GBR) **[56602]**

Electronics Products Extra (Sutton, GBR) *Unable to locate*

Electronics Systems & Software Magazine (Stevenage, GBR) *Ceased*

Electronics Weekly (Stockholm, SWE) *Unable to locate*

Electronics World Wireless World (Stockholm, SWE) *Unable to locate*

Electronique Industrielle et Commerciale (EIC) (Santiago, CHL) *Unable to locate*

Electronique International Hebdo (Paris, FRA) **[44039]**

Elegance (Amsterdam, NLD) **[47964]**

Elektor India (Mumbai, MH, IND) *Unable to locate*

Elektrikern (Stockholm, SWE) *Unable to locate*

Elektro Automation (Leinfelden-Echterdingen, GER) **[44522]**

Elektronik (Kissing, GER) **[44509]**

Elektronik & Data (Glostrup, DEN) **[43702]**

Elektronik Journal (Landsberg, GER) *Unable to locate*

Numbers cited in bold after listings are entry numbers rather than page numbers.

Elektronik Nyt (Glostrup, DEN) **[43703]**

Elektronik Report (Vienna, AUT) **[42750]**

Element + BAU (Nuremberg, GER) **[44610]**

Elements (London, GBR) **[54360]**

The Elephant (Ely, GBR) *Unable to locate*

Eletricidade Moderna (Sao Paulo, SP, BRZ) **[43039]**

Elevate (Dudley, GBR) *Unable to locate*

Elite Homes (Hong Kong, CHN) **[43298]**

Elle (Mumbai, MH, IND) *Unable to locate*

Elle Decoration (Bucharest, ROM) **[49835]**

Elle Mariaj (Bucharest, ROM) **[49836]**

Elle Wonen (Amsterdam, NLD) *Unable to locate*

ELLEgirl (London, GBR) **[54361]**

Ellesmere Port Standard (Chester, GBR) **[52993]**

Elore (Pori, FIN) **[43904]**

Elsa Journal (Hong Kong, CHN) *Ceased*

ELT Journal (Reepham, GBR) **[56385]**

Elteknik (Glostrup, DEN) **[43704]**

eltonjohnworld.com (Richmond, GBR) **[56391]**

Elvis Costello Information Service (Purmerend, NLD) *Unable to locate*

Elvis is King (Sunderland, GBR) *Unable to locate*

Ely Standard (Ely, GBR) **[53331]**

Em-Si (MC) Radio (Kaluga, RUS) *Unable to locate*

EMA Network (Chertsey, GBR) *Ceased*

Emaar Properties Magazine (Dubai, UAE) **[51640]**

Emantalehti (Homemaker) (Helsinki, FIN) *Unable to locate*

Emballages (Paris, FRA) *Unable to locate*

EMBO Reports (London, GBR) **[54362]**

EMC - Dentisterie (Paris, FRA) *Ceased*

EMC - Dermatologie Cosmetologie (Singapore, SGP) *Ceased*

EMC - Endocrinologie (Singapore, SGP) *Ceased*

EMC - Hematologie (Singapore, SGP) *Ceased*

EMC - Hepatologie (Singapore, SGP) *Ceased*

EMC - Maladies Infectieuses (Singapore, SGP) *Ceased*

EMC - Medecine (Singapore, SGP) *Ceased*

EMC - Odontologie (Singapore, SGP) *Unable to locate*

EMC-Psychiatrie (Amsterdam, NLD) *Ceased*

Emel (London, GBR) **[54363]**

Emergences (Abingdon, GBR) *Ceased*

Emergency Medicine **[42697]***

Emergency Medicine Australasia (West Melbourne, VI, AUS) **[42697]**

Emergency Nurse (Harrow, GBR) **[53522]**

Emergency Radiology (Tokyo, JPN) **[46809]**

Emerging Markets Review (Singapore, SGP) **[50145]**

Emerging Sociology (Meerut, UP, IND) *Unable to locate*

Emerging Themes in Epidemiology (London, GBR) **[54364]**

L'Emilie (Carouge, SWI) *Unable to locate*

Emirates Bride (Dubai, UAE) **[51641]**

Emirates FM1 (Abu Dhabi, UAE) *Unable to locate*

Emirates Inflight (Dubai, UAE) *Unable to locate*

Emirates Medical Journal (Dubai, UAE) *Unable to locate*

Emirates Radio 657AM (Dubai, UAE) *Unable to locate*

Emirates Woman (Dubai, UAE) **[51642]**

Emisoras Unidas-AM - 1130 (Retalhuleu, GTM) **[44793]**

Emisoras Unidas-FM - 91.1 (Alta Verapaz, GTM) **[44777]**

Emisoras Unidas-FM - 94.3 (Baja Verapaz, GTM) **[44778]**

Emisoras Unidas-FM - 90.3 (Chichicastenango, GTM) **[44779]**

Emisoras Unidas-FM - 91.1 (Chimaltenango, GTM) **[44780]**

Emisoras Unidas-FM - 89.9 (Chiquimula, GTM) **[44781]**

Emisoras Unidas-FM - 98.7 (Coatepeque, GTM) **[44782]**

Emisoras Unidas-FM - 98.9 (El Peten, GTM) **[44783]**

Emisoras Unidas-FM - 91.9 (Escuintla, GTM) **[44784]**

Emisoras Unidas-FM - 89.7 (Guatemala City, GTM) **[44787]**

Emisoras Unidas-FM - 104.1 (Huehuetenango, GTM) **[44790]**

Emisoras Unidas-FM - 104.3 (Occidente, GTM) **[44791]**

Emisoras Unidas-FM - 90.3 (Quiche, GTM) **[44792]**

Emisoras Unidas-FM - 103.1 (Retalhuleu, GTM) **[44794]**

Emisoras Unidas-FM - 104.3 (San Marcos, GTM) **[44795]**

Emisoras Unidas-FM - 89.9 (Santa Rosa, GTM) **[44796]**

Emisoras Unidas-FM - 92.3 (Suchitepequez, GTM) **[44797]**

Emisoras Unidas-FM - 89.9 (Zacapa, GTM) **[44798]**

Emotional and Behavioral Difficulties (Manchester, GBR) **[55555]**

Emotional and Behavioral Difficulties (Oxford, GBR) **[55936]**

Empatia (Bratislava, SLK) *Unable to locate*

Empire (London, GBR) **[54365]**

Empirical Studies of the Arts (Oldenburg, GER) *Unable to locate*

Employee Benefits (London, GBR) **[54366]**

Employee Development Bulletin (London, GBR) *Unable to locate*

Employee Health Bulletin (London, GBR) *Unable to locate*

Employee Relations (Bradford, GBR) **[52454]**

Employment Law Bulletin (London, GBR) **[54367]**

Employment Law Journal (London, GBR) **[54368]**

Employment Law Review (Dublin, DU, IRL) **[45955]**

Employment News (New Delhi, DH, IND) **[45507]**

Emporoviomichaniki (Nicosia, CYP) **[43594]**

Emu - Austral Ornithology (Collingwood, VI, AUS) **[41787]**

En Franquicia (Madrid, SPA) **[50756]**

En Lignes (Paris, FRA) *Unable to locate*

ENA-FM - 88.0 MHz (Adelaide, SA, AUS) **[41514]**

Enact (New Delhi, DH, IND) *Unable to locate*

Encounter with God (Milton Keynes, GBR) **[55634]**

Encounter Southern Africa (Paarl, SAF) **[50561]**

Endangered Species Research (Oldendorf, GER) **[44627]**

Endeavour (Kanpur, UP, IND) *Unable to locate*

Endocrine Abstracts (Bristol, GBR) **[52662]**

Endocrine, Metabolic & Immune Disorders - Drug Targets (Bari, ITA) **[46121]**

Endocrine Regulations (Bratislava, SLK) **[50319]**

Endocrine-Related Cancer (Bristol, GBR) **[52663]**

Endocrine Surgery (Tokyo, JPN) *Unable to locate*

L'Endocrinologo (Milan, ITA) **[46167]**

Endocrinology, Obesity and Metabolic Disorders (Gdansk, POL) **[49656]**

Endontology (New Delhi, DH, IND) **[45508]**

Endotoxin Research; Journal of **[54605]***

The Ends Report (London, GBR) **[54369]**

Energy Bremen-FM - 89.8 (Bremen, GER) **[44287]**

Energy and Buildings (Belgrade, SER) **[50082]**

Energy and Environment (Brentwood, GBR) **[52572]**

Energy Environment Monitor (New Delhi, DH, IND) *Unable to locate*

Energy & Environmental Science (Cambridge, GBR) **[52817]**

The Energy Era (Guwahati, AS, IND) *Unable to locate*

Energy Exploration & Exploitation (Brentwood, GBR) **[52573]**

Energy-FM - 96.4 (Birzebbuga, MAL) **[47728]**

Energy Forecast (Cape Town, SAF) **[50376]**

Energy & Fuel Users' Journal (Chennai, TN, IND) *Unable to locate*

Energy India (New Delhi, DH, IND) *Unable to locate*

Energy in Japan (Tokyo, JPN) *Unable to locate*

Energy Management (New Delhi, DH, IND) **[45509]**

Energy Report (Peterborough, GBR) *Unable to locate*

Energy Risk (London, GBR) **[54370]**

Energy for Sustainable Development (Kolkata, WB, IND) **[45265]**

Energy World (London, GBR) **[54371]**

Engenharia Sanitaria e Ambiental (Rio de Janeiro, RJ, BRZ) **[43004]**

Engineer (Colombo, SRI) **[50854]**

The Engineer (London, GBR) **[54372]**

Engineer—IME News (Mumbai, MH, IND) *Unable to locate*

Engineering (London, GBR) *Unable to locate*

Engineering Analysis with Boundary Elements (Ashurst, GBR) **[52145]**

Engineering Applications of Artificial Intelligence (Tarbes, FRA) **[44116]**

Engineering Computations (Swansea, GBR) **[56701]**

Engineering with Computers (Tokyo, JPN) **[46810]**

Engineering, Construction and Architectural Management (Bradford, GBR) **[52455]**

Engineering Design (Bangalore, KA, IND) *Unable to locate*

Engineering Designer (Canterbury, GBR) **[52917]**

Engineering Failure Analysis (Gladstone, QL, AUS) **[41887]**

Engineering Industries and Trade Journal (Baroda, GJ, IND) *Unable to locate*

Engineering Integrity (Warwickshire, GBR) **[56858]**

Engineering News (Garden View, SAF) **[50479]**

Engineering Optimization (Liverpool, GBR) **[53870]**

Engineering & Product News (Bhubaneswar, OR, IND) *Unable to locate*

Engineering Science and Technology (Kuala Lumpur, MYS) *Unable to locate*

Engineering Service, Management (Bracknell, GBR) *Ceased*

Engineering & Technology (Stevenage, GBR) **[56603]**

Engineering Times (Barton, AC, AUS) *Unable to locate*

Engineering World (Mumbai, MH, IND) *Unable to locate*

English in Africa (Centurion, SAF) **[50438]**

English in Australia (Kensington Gardens, SA, AUS) **[41985]**

English Bridge (Aylesbury, GBR) **[52147]**

English Club Golfer (Glasgow, GBR) **[53415]**

English Four to Eleven (Leicester, GBR) **[53797]**

The English Garden (Cheltenham, GBR) **[52969]**

The English Historical Review (Dunow, GBR) *Unable to locate*

The English Historical Review (Southampton, GBR) **[56570]**

The English Home (Cheltenham, GBR) **[52970]**

English Papers (Oostmalle, BEL) *Unable to locate*

English of Science and Technology Learning (Shanghai, CHN) **[43474]**

The English Teacher Online (Bangkok, THA) *Ceased*

English Text Construction (Amsterdam, NLD) **[47965]**

English World-Wide (Amsterdam, NLD) **[47966]**

Enigma Magazine (Cairo, EGY) **[43761]**

Enjeux (Paris, FRA) *Unable to locate*

Enquires (Singapore, SGP) *Unable to locate*

Enquiry (New Delhi, DH, IND) *Unable to locate*

Ensaio (Vicosa, MI, BRZ) **[43057]**

Enschede-FM - 99.1 (Hilversum, NLD) **[48635]**

Enseignements Bouddnique (Paris, FRA) *Unable to locate*

Ensemble (Tonbridge, GBR) *Unable to locate*

The Ensign (Gore, NZL) **[48902]**

Enterprise (Nagpur, MH, IND) *Unable to locate*

Enterprise (Makati City, PHL) **[49516]**

Enterprise Development and Microfinance (Rugby, GBR) **[56418]**

Enterprise & Society (Oxford, GBR) **[55937]**

The Entertainer **[50709]***

Entertainment Law Review (London, GBR) *Unable to locate*

Entomologia Experimentalis et Applicata (Amsterdam, NLD) **[47967]**

Entomologia Generalis (Biebergemund, GER) **[44244]**

Numbers cited in bold after listings are entry numbers rather than page numbers.

Master Index

Entomologia y Vectores (Vicosa, MI, BRZ) **[43058]**

Entomological Review (Saint Petersburg, RUS) **[50021]**

Entomological Science (Mito, JPN) **[46513]**

Entomological Society of India Bulletin of Entomology (New Delhi, DH, IND) *Unable to locate*

Entomon (Kariavattom, KE, IND) **[45241]**

Entwicklung und Zusammenarbeit (EZ) (Berlin, GER) *Unable to locate*

Environment Asia (New Delhi, DH, IND) *Unable to locate*

Environment International (Witherslack, GBR) **[56937]**

Environment & Planning A (London, GBR) **[54373]**

Environment and Urbanization (London, GBR) **[54374]**

Environmental Awareness (Baroda, GJ, IND) *Unable to locate*

Environmental Biosafety Research (Shanghai, CHN) **[43475]**

Environmental Chemistry (Collingwood, VI, AUS) **[41788]**

Environmental Chemistry Letters (Tokyo, JPN) **[46811]**

Environmental Earth Sciences (Heidelberg, GER) **[44453]**

Environmental Economics and Policy Studies (Tokyo, JPN) **[46812]**

Environmental Education (Walsall, GBR) *Unable to locate*

Environmental Engineering (Buntingford, GBR) **[52759]**

Environmental Engineering (London, GBR) **[54375]**

Environmental & Experimental Botany (Amsterdam, NLD) **[47968]**

Environmental Geochemistry (Delhi, DH, IND) *Unable to locate*

Environmental Geology **[44453]***

Environmental Geoscience (Moscow, RUS) *Ceased*

Environmental Hazards (Middlesex, GBR) **[55616]**

Environmental Health **[54377]***

Environmental Health (London, GBR) **[54376]**

Environmental Health Practitioner (London, GBR) **[54377]**

Environmental Law & Management (Witney, GBR) **[56941]**

Environmental Law Report (San Jose, CRI) *Unable to locate*

Environmental Law Review (Newcastle upon Tyne, GBR) **[55669]**

Environmental Liability (Witney, GBR) **[56942]**

Environmental Management (Tokyo, JPN) *Unable to locate*

Environmental Medicine (Aichi, JPN) *Unable to locate*

Environmental Modeling & Assessment (Heidelberg, GER) **[44454]**

Environmental Modelling & Software (Canberra, AC, AUS) **[41705]**

Environmental Mutagen Research (Tokyo, JPN) **[46813]**

Environmental News Digest (Penang, MYS) *Unable to locate*

Environmental and Planning Law Journal (Pyrmont, NW, AUS) **[42277]**

Environmental Policy and Law (Amsterdam, NLD) **[47969]**

Environmental Policy Monthly (Taipei, TWN) **[51339]**

Environmental Politics (Abingdon, GBR) **[51771]**

Environmental Practice (Cambridge, GBR) **[52818]**

Environmental Protection Bulletin (Rugby, GBR) *Unable to locate*

Environmental Research (Amsterdam, NLD) **[47970]**

Environmental Resources Abstracts (New Delhi, DH, IND) *Unable to locate*

Environmental Science (Tirupati, KA, IND) **[45756]**

Environmental Science & Policy (Oxford, GBR) **[55938]**

Environmental Sciences (Tokyo, JPN) *Ceased*

The Environmental Scientist (London, GBR) **[54378]**

Environmental Toxicology (Aranda, AC, AUS) **[41557]**

Environmental Toxicology and Pharmacology (Amsterdam, NLD) **[47971]**

Environnement, Risques & Sante (Montrouge, FRA) **[43986]**

Envirotec (Glasgow, GBR) **[53416]**

Envision (Singapore, SGP) *Unable to locate*

e.nz magazine (Wellington, NZL) **[49007]**

EP **[51640]***

EP Electronic Production (Bern, SWI) *Unable to locate*

Eparrei - A Black Women's Newspaper (Santos, SP, BRZ) *Unable to locate*

The Ephemerist (Northwood, GBR) **[55720]**

EPI (Brussels, BEL) **[42851]**

Epidemiologic Perspectives & Innovations (London, GBR) **[54379]**

Epidemiologic Reviews (Oxford, GBR) **[55939]**

Epidemiology and Infection (London, GBR) **[54380]**

Epidemiology & Infectious Diseases (Moscow, RUS) **[49902]**

Epidemiology, Microbiology, Immunology (Prague, CZE) **[43624]**

Epigraphia Indica (New Delhi, DH, IND) **[45510]**

Epilepsia (Brussels, BEL) *Unable to locate*

Epilepsies (Montrouge, FRA) **[43987]**

Epilepsy & Behavior (Amsterdam, NLD) **[47972]**

Epilepsy News (Oslo, NOR) *Unable to locate*

Epilepsy Today (Leeds, GBR) **[53764]**

Epileptic Disorders (Montrouge, FRA) **[43988]**

Episteme (Edinburgh, GBR) **[53272]**

Epistemologia (Genoa, ITA) **[46148]**

Epistemologiques (Les Ulis, FRA) *Ceased*

Epites - Epiteszettudomany (Budapest, HUN) **[44828]**

EPNS Journal (Nottingham, GBR) **[55755]**

Epoca (Madrid, SPA) *Unable to locate*

Epok (Stockholm, SWE) *Unable to locate*

EPP Europe (Leinfelden-Echterdingen, GER) **[44523]**

EQ (Harleston, GBR) *Unable to locate*

Equal Opportunities International **[52456]***

Equal Opportunities Review (London, GBR) **[54381]**

Equal Voices (Glasgow, GBR) *Ceased*

Equality, Diversity and Inclusion (Bradford, GBR) **[52456]**

Equals (Leicester, GBR) **[53798]**

Equestrian Trade News (Wetherby, GBR) **[56911]**

Equi-Dos International Horse Magazine (Madrid, SPA) *Unable to locate*

Equilibre (Paris, FRA) *Unable to locate*

Equine and Comparative Exercise Physiology **[52808]***

Equine Veterinary Education (Sawston, GBR) *Unable to locate*

Equine Veterinary Journal (Sawston, GBR) *Unable to locate*

Equity (London, GBR) **[54382]**

Equity Dialogue (Dhaka, BGD) **[42809]**

Equity Journal **[54382]***

Equs Magazine (Liverpool, GBR) *Unable to locate*

Er, Revista de Filosofia (Mataro, SPA) *Unable to locate*

Era (Kuvalehdet, FIN) **[43880]**

Era - 101 (Kuala Lumpur, MYS) **[47643]**

Era-FM - 103.3 (Kuala Lumpur, MYS) **[47644]**

Erasmus Law and Economics Review (Melaka, MYS) **[47680]**

ERC Magazine (Cairo, EGY) *Unable to locate*

Erdem (Ankara, TUR) *Unable to locate*

Erdeszeti Lapok (Budapest, HUN) *Unable to locate*

ERETZ (Tel Aviv, ISR) **[46099]**

ERF 1-AM - 1539 (Wetzlar, GER) **[44709]**

Ergatiko Vima (Nicosia, CYP) *Unable to locate*

ErgoMed (Leinfelden-Echterdingen, GER) **[44524]**

Ergonomia (Budapest, HUN) *Ceased*

Ergonomics (Loughborough, GBR) **[55479]**

Ergonomics SA (Auckland Park, SAF) **[50347]**

ErhvervsBladet (Copenhagen, DEN) **[43667]**

Ernahrungs Info (Bern, SWI) **[51072]**

Ernahrungs Umschau (Dusseldorf, GER) *Unable to locate*

Ertoba - Unity (Tbilisi, GRG) *Unable to locate*

ESARBICA Journal (Pietermaritzburg, SAF) **[50567]**

Escala (Bilbao, SPA) *Unable to locate*

eSharp (Glasgow, GBR) **[53417]**

ESHRE Monographs (Oxford, GBR) **[55940]**

ESIAM (Bussum, NLD) *Unable to locate*

ESL Magazine (Chichester, GBR) **[53008]**

Esophagus (Tokyo, JPN) **[46814]**

Espace Enfant (Rabat, MOR) *Unable to locate*

Espacio Apicola (Cordova, ARG) **[41487]**

Esprit Magazine (London, GBR) **[54383]**

ESRA Rapporteur (London, GBR) *Unable to locate*

Essays in Biochemistry (Colchester, GBR) **[53035]**

Essays in Criticism (Oxford, GBR) **[55941]**

Essential Guide to Beauty (London, GBR) **[54384]**

Essential Guide to Home & Decor (Bangkok, THA) **[51420]**

The Essential Guide to UK Farm & Outdoor Power Equipment (Peterborough, GBR) **[56256]**

Essentials (Parklands, SAF) **[50562]**

Esso in Malaysia (Kuala Lumpur, MYS) *Unable to locate*

Estacao-FM - 89.5 (Carlos Barbosa, RN, BRZ) **[42975]**

Estadistica (Buenos Aires, ARG) *Unable to locate*

The Estate Agent (Warwick, GBR) **[56854]**

Estates Gazette (London, GBR) **[54385]**

Estereosom-FM - 99.9 (Limeira, SP, BRZ) **[42985]**

ESTETICA Australia and New Zealand (Pyrmont, NW, AUS) **[42278]**

Estilo (Manila, PHL) *Unable to locate*

Estonian Jazz Guide (Tallinn, EST) *Unable to locate*

Estonian Literary Magazine (Tallinn, EST) **[43783]**

Estrella-FM - 96.3 (Caracas, VEN) **[57021]**

Estuarine and Coastal Shelf Science (Hull, GBR) *Unable to locate*

Estudios Fronterizos (Mexicali, BN, MEX) **[47780]**

Estudios de Psicologia (Madrid, SPA) **[50757]**

Etapes (Paris, FRA) **[44040]**

Etapes Graphiques **[44040]***

Ethical Perspectives (Leuven, BEL) **[42894]**

Ethics and Education (Abingdon, GBR) **[51772]**

Ethics and Medicine (Ede, NLD) *Unable to locate*

Ethics in Science and Environmental Politics (Oldendorf, GER) **[44628]**

Ethics and Social Welfare (Abingdon, GBR) **[51773]**

Ethik in der Medizin (Gottingen, GER) **[44396]**

Ethiopian Economic Journal of Economics (Addis Ababa, ETH) **[43797]**

Ethiopian Journal of Biological Sciences (Addis Ababa, ETH) **[43798]**

Ethiopian Journal of Development Research (Addis Ababa, ETH) **[43799]**

Ethiopian Journal of Health Development (Addis Ababa, ETH) **[43800]**

Ethiopian Journal of the Social Sciences and Humanities (Addis Ababa, ETH) **[43801]**

Ethiopian Pharmaceutical Journal (Grahamstown, SAF) **[50494]**

Ethiopian Weekly Press Digest (Addis Ababa, ETH) *Unable to locate*

ETHIQUE: La vie en Question (Paris, FRA) *Unable to locate*

Ethnic Interiors (Oxted, GBR) *Unable to locate*

Ethnic and Racial Studies (Abingdon, GBR) **[51774]**

Ethnic Studies Report (Kandy, SRI) **[50906]**

Ethnicities (London, GBR) **[54386]**

Ethnicity and Inequalities in Health and Social Care (Hove, GBR) **[53605]**

Ethnobotany (New Delhi, DH, IND) *Unable to locate*

Ethnography (London, GBR) **[54387]**

Ethnography & Education (Abingdon, GBR) **[51775]**

Ethnology (New Delhi, DH, IND) *Unable to locate*

Ethnomusicology Forum (Abingdon, GBR) **[51776]**

Ethnopolitics (Abingdon, GBR) **[51777]**

Numbers cited in bold after listings are entry numbers rather than page numbers.

Ethos (Petaling Jaya, MYS) *Unable to locate*

ETRI Journal (Daejeon, KOR) **[47226]**

ETU Athletes and Media Guide (Graz, AUT) *Unable to locate*

Etudes Balkaniques (Sofia, BUL) **[43098]**

Etudes Episteme (London, GBR) **[54388]**

EU Energy Policy (Makati City, PHL) *Unable to locate*

Eukanuba (London, GBR) **[54389]**

Euro Electric News (Peschiera Borromeo, ITA) **[46214]**

Euro-Japanese Journal (London, GBR) *Ceased*

The Euro Weekly News (Benalmadena, SPA) **[50709]**

Eurocarne (Madrid, SPA) **[50758]**

Eurocity (Vienna, AUT) *Unable to locate*

Eurocontas (Lisbon, PRT) *Unable to locate*

Eurofood (Tunbridge Wells, GBR) **[56782]**

Eurogay (London, GBR) *Unable to locate*

EurOhs Magazine (Coventry, GBR) **[53081]**

Euroloink Age Bulletin (London, GBR) *Unable to locate*

Euroman (Hellerup, DEN) **[43720]**

Euromaterials (Weinheim, GER) *Ceased*

Euromodal (Basel, SWI) *Unable to locate*

Euromoney (London, GBR) **[54390]**

Euronet (Chester, GBR) *Unable to locate*

Europ (Paris, FRA) *Unable to locate*

Europa Cantat Magazine (Bonn, GER) **[44256]**

Europa Chemie (Dusseldorf, GER) *Unable to locate*

Europa de les Nacions (Barcelona, SPA) **[50673]**

Europa Nostra (The Hague, NLD) **[48614]**

Europa Plus (Moscow, RUS) *Unable to locate*

Europa Plus - Almetyevsk (Moscow, RUS) *Unable to locate*

Europa Plus - Astrakhan (Astrakhan, RUS) *Unable to locate*

Europa Plus - Barnaul (Barnaul, RUS) *Unable to locate*

Europa Plus - Bishkek (Bishkek, KGA) *Unable to locate*

Europa Plus - Biysk (Biysk, RUS) *Unable to locate*

Europa Plus - Blagoveshchensk (Blagoveshchensk, RUS) *Unable to locate*

Europa Plus - Bratsk (Moscow, RUS) *Unable to locate*

Europa Plus - Bryansk (Bryansk, RUS) *Unable to locate*

Europa Plus - Buzuluk (Moscow, RUS) *Unable to locate*

Europa Plus - Chelyabinsk (Chelyabinsk, RUS) *Unable to locate*

Europa Plus - Chita (Chita, RUS) *Unable to locate*

Europa Plus - Dimitrovgrad (Dimitrovgrad, RUS) *Unable to locate*

Europa Plus - Ivanovo (Ivanovo, RUS) *Unable to locate*

Europa Plus - Kaliningrad (Kaliningrad, RUS) *Unable to locate*

Europa Plus - Kaluga (Kaluga, RUS) *Unable to locate*

Europa Plus Kazakhstan (Almaty, KAZ) *Unable to locate*

Europa Plus Kazakhstan (Almaty, KAZ) *Unable to locate*

Europa Plus Kazakhstan (Almaty, KAZ) *Unable to locate*

Europa Plus Kazakhstan (Almaty, KAZ) *Unable to locate*

Europa Plus Kazakhstan (Almaty, KAZ) *Unable to locate*

Europa Plus Kazakhstan (Almaty, KAZ) *Unable to locate*

Europa Plus - Kazan (Kazan, RUS) *Unable to locate*

Europa Plus - Khabarovsk (Khabarovsk, RUS) *Unable to locate*

Europa Plus - Kholmsk (Moscow, RUS) *Unable to locate*

Europa Plus - Kogalym (Kogalym, RUS) *Unable to locate*

Europa Plus Komi-FM - 100.3 (Syktyvkar, RUS) **[50035]**

Europa Plus Komi - Syktyvkar (Syktyvkar, RUS) *Unable to locate*

Europa Plus - Komsomolsk-na-Amure (Komsomolsk-na-Amure, RUS) *Unable to locate*

Europa Plus - Kurgan (Kurgan, RUS) *Unable to locate*

Europa Plus - Kurgan (Kurgan, RUS) *Unable to locate*

Europa Plus - Kurgan (Kurgan, RUS) *Unable to locate*

Europa Plus - Kursk (Kursk, RUS) *Unable to locate*

Europa Plus - Langepas (Moscow, RUS) *Unable to locate*

Europa Plus - Lipetsk (Lipetsk, RUS) *Unable to locate*

Europa Plus - Magnitogorsk (Magnitogorsk, RUS) *Unable to locate*

Europa Plus - Miass (Moscow, RUS) *Unable to locate*

Europa Plus - Moskva (Moscow, RUS) *Unable to locate*

Europa Plus - Moskva (Moscow, RUS) *Unable to locate*

Europa Plus - Nadym (Moscow, RUS) *Unable to locate*

Europa Plus - Nizhnevartovsk (Nizhnevartovsk, RUS) *Unable to locate*

Europa Plus - Nizhniy Novgorod (Nizhniy Novgorod, RUS) *Unable to locate*

Europa Plus - Nizhniy Novgorod (Nizhniy Novgorod, RUS) *Unable to locate*

Europa Plus - Nizhniy Tagil (Nizhniy Tagil, RUS) *Unable to locate*

Europa Plus - Novorossiysk (Novorossiysk, RUS) *Unable to locate*

Europa Plus - Oktyabrskiy (Oktyabrskiy, RUS) *Unable to locate*

Europa Plus - Omsk (Omsk, RUS) *Unable to locate*

Europa Plus - Omsk (Omsk, RUS) *Unable to locate*

Europa Plus - Orenburg (Orenburg, RUS) *Unable to locate*

Europa Plus Penza - Penza (Penza, RUS) *Unable to locate*

Europa Plus - Perm (Perm, RUS) *Unable to locate*

Europa Plus - Petrozavodsk (Petrozavodsk, RUS) *Unable to locate*

Europa Plus - Pyatigorsk (Moscow, RUS) *Unable to locate*

Europa Plus - Pyatigorsk (Moscow, RUS) *Unable to locate*

Europa Plus (Radio Vavilon) - Belgorod (Belgorod, RUS) *Unable to locate*

Europa Plus S - Saratov (Saratov, RUS) *Unable to locate*

Europa Plus Sakhalin - Yuzhno-Sakhalinsk (Yuzhno-Sakhalinsk, RUS) *Unable to locate*

Europa Plus Sakhalin - Yuzhno-Sakhalinsk (Yuzhno-Sakhalinsk, RUS) *Unable to locate*

Europa Plus - Salekhard (Moscow, RUS) *Unable to locate*

Europa Plus - Samara (Samara, RUS) *Unable to locate*

Europa Plus - Samara (Samara, RUS) *Unable to locate*

Europa Plus Samara - Tolyatti (Tolyatti, RUS) *Unable to locate*

Europa Plus - Saratov (Saratov, RUS) *Unable to locate*

Europa Plus - Serov (Moscow, RUS) *Unable to locate*

Europa Plus - Shelekhov (Shelekhov, RUS) *Unable to locate*

Europa Plus Skify - Stavropol (Stavropol, RUS) *Unable to locate*

Europa Plus - Sochi (Sochi, RUS) *Unable to locate*

Europa Plus - Stavropol (Stavropol, RUS) *Unable to locate*

Europa Plus - Surgut (Moscow, RUS) *Unable to locate*

Europa Plus - Tula (Tula, RUS) *Unable to locate*

Europa Plus - Tver (Tver, RUS) *Unable to locate*

Europa Plus - Tver (Tver, RUS) *Unable to locate*

Europa Plus - Ufa (Ufa, RUS) *Unable to locate*

Europa Plus - Ulan-Ude (Ulan-Ude, RUS) *Unable to locate*

Europa Plus - Ulan-Ude (Ulan-Ude, RUS) *Unable to locate*

Europa Plus - Ulan-Ude (Ulan-Ude, RUS) *Unable to locate*

Europa Plus - Velikiye Luki (Velikiye Luki, RUS) *Unable to locate*

Europa Plus - Vladivostok - 1557 KHz (Vladivostok, RUS) **[50042]**

Europa Plus - Volgograd (Volgograd, RUS) *Unable to locate*

Europa Plus Vologodchina - Vologda (Vologda, RUS) *Unable to locate*

Europa Plus - Voronezh (Voronezh, RUS) *Unable to locate*

Europa Plus - Voronezh (Voronezh, RUS) *Unable to locate*

Europa Plus - Vyborg (Vyborg, RUS) *Unable to locate*

Europa Plus - Yaroslavl (Yaroslavl, RUS) *Unable to locate*

Europa Plus - Yekaterinburg (Yekaterinburg, RUS) *Unable to locate*

Europa Plus - Yoshkar-Ola (Yoshkar-Ola, RUS) *Unable to locate*

Europa Plus - Yoshkar-Ola (Yoshkar-Ola, RUS) *Unable to locate*

Europa Plus Yurga - Surgut (Surgut, RUS) *Unable to locate*

Europa Plus Yurga - Surgut (Surgut, RUS) *Unable to locate*

Europa Plus - Zlatoust (Moscow, RUS) *Unable to locate*

Europa Star (Geneva, SWI) **[51093]**

Europa Star (Geneva, SWI) **[51092]**

Europa Star International (Geneva, SWI) **[51094]**

Europe-Asia Studies (Abingdon, GBR) **[51778]**

Europe Business Review (North Sydney, NW, AUS) *Unable to locate*

European Access (Ann Arbor, MI, USA) *Ceased*

European Accounting Review (Brussels, BEL) **[42852]**

European Addiction Research (Hamburg, GER) **[44414]**

European Archives of Otorhinolaryngology (Heidelberg, GER) **[44455]**

European Archives of Psychiatry and Clinical Neuroscience (Tokyo, JPN) **[46815]**

European BioPharmaceutical Review (London, GBR) **[54391]**

European Biophysics Journal (Oxford, GBR) **[55942]**

European Biotechnology Science & Industry News (Berlin, GER) **[44173]**

European Business Air News (Bishop's Stortford, GBR) **[52378]**

European Business Journal (London, GBR) *Unable to locate*

European Business Law Review (The Hague, NLD) **[48615]**

European Business Review (Bradford, GBR) **[52457]**

European Chemical News (Sutton, GBR) **[56684]**

European Child and Adolescent Psychiatry (Modena, ITA) *Unable to locate*

European Clinics in Obstetrics and Gynaecology (Tokyo, JPN) *Ceased*

European Company and Financial Law Review (Berlin, GER) **[44174]**

European Competition Journal (London, GBR) **[54392]**

European Cosmetic Markets (Daruvar, CTA) *Unable to locate*

European Cosmetics Markets (London, GBR) **[54393]**

European Countryside (Warsaw, POL) **[49709]**

European Cultural Heritage Review **[48614]***

European Cytokine Network (Montrouge, FRA) **[43989]**

European Defence (Bonn, GER) *Unable to locate*

European Diabetes Nursing (Bognor Regis, GBR) **[52395]**

European Eating Disorders Review (Norwich, GBR) *Unable to locate*

European Economic Review (Maastricht, NLD) **[48736]**

European Educational Research Journal (Oxford, GBR) **[55943]**

European Food Research and Technology (Tokyo, JPN) **[46816]**

European Foreign Affairs Review (Leicester, GBR) **[53799]**

European Foundations (London, GBR) *Unable to locate*

European Heart Journal (Sophia Antipolis, FRA) **[44107]**

European Heart Journal (Oxford, GBR) **[55944]**

European History Quarterly (London, GBR) **[54394]**

European Industrial Relations Review (London, GBR) **[54395]**

European Information **[55643]***

European Information (Mold, GBR) **[55642]**

European Journal (Thessaloniki, GRC) **[44771]**

European Journal of Ageing (Amsterdam, NLD) **[47973]**

European Journal of Agronomy (Cordoba, SPA) **[50713]**

European Journal of American Culture (London, GBR) **[54396]**

European Journal of Anaesthesiology (Gottingen, GER) **[44397]**

European Journal of Applied Mathematics (Oxford, GBR) **[55945]**

European Journal of Applied Physiology (Tokyo, JPN) **[46817]**

Numbers cited in bold after listings are entry numbers rather than page numbers.

European Journal of Archaeology (Edinburgh, GBR) [53273]

European Journal of Arts Education (Amsterdam, NLD) [47974]

European Journal of Behavior Analysis (Oslo, NOR) [49197]

European Journal of Cancer (Edinburgh, GBR) [53274]

European Journal of Cancer Prevention (Diepenbeek, BEL) [42879]

European Journal of Cardio-Thoracic Surgery (Lausanne, SWI) [51188]

European Journal of Cardiovascular Nursing (Groningen, NLD) [48600]

European Journal of Cardiovascular Prevention & Rehabilitation (London, GBR) [54397]

European Journal of Cell Biology (Munich, GER) [44560]

European Journal of Chiropractic (Twickenham, GBR) Unable to locate

European Journal of Clinical Microbiology & Infectious Diseases (Dordrecht, NLD) [48381]

European Journal of Clinical Nutrition (Basingstoke, GBR) [52200]

European Journal of Clinical Research [54726]*

European Journal of Communication (London, GBR) [54398]

European Journal of Contraception and Reproductive Health Care (Abingdon, GBR) [51779]

European Journal on Criminal Policy and Research (Dordrecht, NLD) [48382]

European Journal of Cross-Cultural Competence and Management (Vienna, AUT) [42751]

European Journal of Cultural Studies (London, GBR) [54399]

European Journal of Dermatology (Montrouge, FRA) [43990]

European Journal of Development Research (Bonn, GER) [44257]

European Journal of Developmental Psychology (Utrecht, NLD) [48756]

European Journal of East Asian Studies (Leiden, NLD) [48670]

European Journal of Echocardiography (Oxford, GBR) [55946]

The European Journal of Economics, Finance and Administrative Sciences (Vienna, AUT) [42752]

European Journal of Endocrinology (Bristol, GBR) [52664]

European Journal of Engineering Education (Abingdon, GBR) [51780]

European Journal of General Medicine (Sokoto, SK, NGA) [49173]

European Journal of Genetics in Society [53285]*

European Journal of Herbal Medicine (Exeter, GBR) [53353]

European Journal for High Ability [51802]*

European Journal of Hospital Pharmacy (Brussels, BEL) [42853]

European Journal of Industrial Engineering (Safat, KWT) [47337]

European Journal of Industrial Relations (London, GBR) [54400]

European Journal of Information Systems (Birmingham, GBR) [52341]

European Journal of Innovation Management (Petaling Jaya, MYS) [47696]

European Journal of Intercultural Studies [51822]*

European Journal of Internal Medicine (Milan, ITA) [46168]

European Journal of International Law (Florence, ITA) [46143]

European Journal of International Management (Reykjavik, ICE) [44900]

European Journal of International Relations (London, GBR) [54401]

European Journal of Jewish Studies (Leiden, NLD) [48671]

European Journal of Legal Education (Abingdon, GBR) Ceased

European Journal of Marketing (Bradford, GBR) [52458]

European Journal of Mass Spectrometry (Chichester, GBR) [53009]

European Journal of Mechanics - A/Solids (Lyngby, DEN) [43725]

European Journal of Mechanics - B/Fluids (Cachan, FRA) [43925]

European Journal of Medical Genetics (Paris, FRA) [44041]

European Journal of Medicinal Chemistry (Paris, FRA) [44042]

European Journal of Mineralogy (Paris, FRA) [44043]

European Journal of Obstetrics & Gynecology (Leeds, GBR) [53765]

European Journal of Oncology Nursing (Exeter, GBR) [53354]

European Journal of Operational Research (Coventry, GBR) [53082]

European Journal of Ophthalmology (Milan, ITA) [46169]

European Journal of Orthodontics (London, GBR) [54402]

European Journal of Palliative Care (London, GBR) [54403]

European Journal of Pediatric Surgery (Stuttgart, GER) [44667]

European Journal of Pediatrics (Leuven, BEL) [42895]

European Journal of Pharmaceutical Sciences (Helsinki, FIN) [43826]

European Journal of Pharmaceutics and Biopharmaceutics (Geneva, SWI) [51095]

European Journal of Phycology (London, GBR) [54404]

European Journal of Physics (Bristol, GBR) [52665]

European Journal of Plastic Surgery (Dordrecht, NLD) [48383]

European Journal of Political Economy (Ramat Gan, ISR) [46093]

European Journal of Population (The Hague, NLD) Unable to locate

The European Journal of Prosthodontics and Restorative Dentistry (Lowestoft, GBR) [55494]

European Journal of Protistology (Mondsee, AUT) [42737]

European Journal of Psychological Assessment (Nijmegen, NLD) [48744]

European Journal of Psychotherapy and Counselling (London, GBR) [54405]

European Journal of Public Health (Utrecht, NLD) [48757]

European Journal of Public Health (Oxford, GBR) [55947]

European Journal of Scientific Research (Vienna, AUT) [42753]

European Journal of Social Psychology (Chichester, GBR) [53010]

The European Journal of Social Sciences (Vienna, AUT) [42754]

European Journal of Social Theory (Liverpool, GBR) [53871]

European Journal of Soil Science (Bedfordshire, GBR) [52278]

European Journal of Special Needs Education (Exeter, GBR) [53355]

European Journal of Sport Science (Abingdon, GBR) [51781]

European Journal of Surgery (Turku, FIN) Unable to locate

European Journal of Teacher Education (Brussels, BEL) Unable to locate

European Journal of Teacher Education (EJTE) (Abingdon, GBR) [51782]

The European Journal of Technology and Advanced Engineering Research (Vienna, AUT) [42755]

The European Journal of Teleworking (Cornwall, GBR) [53065]

European Journal of Transport and Infrastructure Research (Amsterdam, NLD) [47975]

European Journal of Ultrasound (London, GBR) [54406]

The European Journal of Women's Studies (London, GBR) [54407]

European Joyce Studies (Zurich, SWI) [51258]

European Law Reports (Oxford, GBR) [55948]

The European Legacy (Abingdon, GBR) [51783]

European Legal Business (London, GBR) Unable to locate

European Management Journal (Amsterdam, NLD) [47976]

European Management Review (Basingstoke, GBR) [52201]

European Pensions (London, GBR) [54408]

European Pharmaceutical Contractor (London, GBR) [54409]

European Pharmaceutical Review (Brasted, GBR) [52561]

European Photography (Berlin, GER) [44175]

European Physical Education Review (Chester, GBR) [52994]

The European Physical Journal A-Hadrons and Nuclei (Frascati, ITA) [46146]

European Physical Journal E. Soft Matter (Dusseldorf, GER) [44324]

European Planning Studies (Cardiff, GBR) [52929]

European Plastics News (London, GBR) Unable to locate

European Political Science (Basingstoke, GBR) [52202]

European Psychologist (Jena, GER) [44488]

European Purchasing & Materials Management (Vienna, AUT) Ceased

European Radiology Supplements (Dordrecht, NLD) [48384]

European Rental News (ERN) [56810]*

European Research in Regional Science (London, GBR) [54410]

European Research in Regional Science (London, GBR) Unable to locate

European Review (Leuven, BEL) [42896]

European Review of Aging and Physical Activity (Wingate, ISR) [46115]

European Review of Agricultural Economics (Bonn, GER) [44258]

European Review of Contract Law (Berlin, GER) [44176]

European School of Theology (Cambridge, GBR) Unable to locate

European Security (Abingdon, GBR) [51784]

European Societies (Abingdon, GBR) [51785]

European Sociological Review (Bamberg, GER) [44145]

European Sociological Review (Oxford, GBR) [55949]

European Spine Journal (Heidelberg, GER) [44456]

European Sport Management Quarterly (ESMQ) (Abingdon, GBR) [51786]

European State Aid Law Quarterly (Berlin, GER) [44177]

European Surgery (Vienna, AUT) [42756]

European Taxation (Bonn, GER) Unable to locate

European Transactions on Telecommunications (Milan, ITA) [46170]

European Union Politics (Konstanz, GER) [44512]

European Urban and Regional Studies (London, GBR) [54411]

European Urology (Arnhem, NLD) [48276]

European Vegetarian (Winterthur, SWI) [51240]

European Voice (Brussels, BEL) [42854]

European Weightlifter (San Marino, SMR) [50053]

The European Yearbook of Business History (Surrey, GBR) [56662]

Europhysics Letters (EPL) (Bristol, GBR) [52666]

Europhysics News (Paris, FRA) [44044]

EuroSlot (Oldham, GBR) Unable to locate

Eurostitch Magazine (Almere, NLD) [47864]

EuroSurveillance (Stockholm, SWE) [51015]

Eurowire (Leamington Spa, GBR) [53745]

Evaluation (London, GBR) [54412]

Evaluation & Research in Education (Abingdon, GBR) [51787]

Eve (Hong Kong, CHN) Unable to locate

Eve (London, GBR) Unable to locate

Evening (Tokyo, JPN) [46818]

Evening News (Dannevirke, NZL) Ceased

Evensongs (Taipei, TWN) Unable to locate

Event (London, GBR) [54413]

Event & Image (Nijmegen, NLD) Unable to locate

Event Organiser (Chepstow, GBR) [52982]

Evergreen (Cheltenham, GBR) [52971]

The Evertonian (Liverpool, GBR) Unable to locate

Everyday Practical Electronics (Ferndown, GBR) [53386]

Eve's Weekly (Mumbai, MH, IND) Unable to locate

Evesham Journal (Evesham, GBR) [53343]

Evidence-based Complementary and Alternative Medicine (Oxford, GBR) [55950]

Evidence-Based Dentistry (EBD) (London, GBR) [54414]

Evidence-Based Integrative Medicine (Mairangi Bay, NZL) Ceased

Evidence-Based Mental Health (EBMH) (London, GBR) [54415]

Evidence-Based Nursing (Harrow, GBR) [53523]

Evidence & Policy (Bristol, GBR) [52667]

evita (Berchem, BEL) Unable to locate

Numbers cited in bold after listings are entry numbers rather than page numbers.

Evolution: Education and Outreach (Dordrecht, NLD) [48385]

Evolution and Human Behavior (Amsterdam, NLD) [47977]

L'Evolution Psychiatrique (Saint Denis, FRA) [44102]

Evolutionary Bioinformatics Online (Albany, NZL) [48777]

Exa-FM - 104.5 (Celaya, GJ, MEX) [47756]

Excellence Achieving Social Relevance in Higher Education (Year) (New Delhi, DH, IND) *Unable to locate*

Exchange (Leiden, NLD) [48672]

Exchange (London, GBR) [54416]

Excise and Customs Reporter (New Delhi, DH, IND) *Unable to locate*

Exclusief (Wommelgem, BEL) [42913]

EXE (London, GBR) *Ceased*

Executive (Karachi, PAK) *Unable to locate*

Executive Digest (Linda-A-Velha, PRT) *Unable to locate*

Executive Engineer (Leatherhead, GBR) *Unable to locate*

Expose (Exeter, GBR) [53356]

The Exile (Moscow, RUS) [49903]

Exmouth Herald (Exeter, GBR) [53357]

Expansion (Spain) (Madrid, SPA) *Unable to locate*

Expat Investor (Taunton, GBR) *Unable to locate*

Expat Society (Bangkok, THA) [51421]

Expedition [55337]*

Experimental Agriculture (Bangor, GBR) [52170]

Experimental Animals (Tokyo, JPN) [46819]

Experimental Brain Research (Rome, ITA) [46228]

Experimental Cell Research (Amsterdam, NLD) [47978]

Experimental and Clinical Diabetology (Zabrze, POL) [49782]

Experimental Eye Research (Amsterdam, NLD) [47979]

Experimental and Molecular Pathology (Amsterdam, NLD) [47980]

Experimental Mycology [47994]*

Experimental Neurology (Amsterdam, NLD) [47981]

Experimental Parasitology (Amsterdam, NLD) [47982]

Experimental and Toxicologic Pathology (Hannover, GER) [44431]

The Expert (London, GBR) *Unable to locate*

Expert Opinion on Investigational Drugs (London, GBR) [54417]

Expert Review of Anti-Infective Therapy (London, GBR) [54418]

Expert Review of Anticancer Therapy (London, GBR) [54419]

Expert Review of Cardiovascular Therapy (London, GBR) [54420]

Expert Review of Clinical Immunology (London, GBR) [54421]

Expert Review of Clinical Pharmacology (London, GBR) [54422]

Expert Review of Endocrinology & Metabolism (London, GBR) [54423]

Expert Review of Gastroenterology & Hepatology (London, GBR) [54424]

Expert Review of Hematology (London, GBR) [54425]

Expert Review of Medical Devices (London, GBR) [54426]

Expert Review of Molecular Diagnostics (London, GBR) [54427]

Expert Review of Neurotherapeutics (London, GBR) [54428]

Expert Review of Obstetrics & Gynecology (London, GBR) [54429]

Expert Review of Ophthalmology (London, GBR) [54430]

Expert Review of Pharmacoeconomics & Outcomes Research (London, GBR) [54431]

Expert Review of Proteomics (London, GBR) [54432]

Expert Review of Respiratory Medicine (London, GBR) [54433]

Expert Review of Vaccines (London, GBR) [54434]

Expert Reviews of Dermatology (London, GBR) [54435]

Explorations (Lahore, PAK) *Unable to locate*

Explorations in Economic History (Amsterdam, NLD) [47983]

Explore South Africa (Cape Town, SAF) [50377]

Explosion Hunger—1975 (Mumbai, MH, IND) *Unable to locate*

Explosives Engineering (Favresham, GBR) *Ceased*

Expo Times (Bristol, GBR) [52668]

Expodata (Zurich, SWI) *Unable to locate*

Expomueble Revista (Buenos Aires, ARG) *Unable to locate*

Export Gazette (Mumbai, MH, IND) *Ceased*

Export-Import News (Calcutta, WB, IND) *Unable to locate*

Export News (New Delhi, DH, IND) *Unable to locate*

Export Processing Zone Concentrates (Kaohsiung, TWN) *Unable to locate*

Exporters Bulletin (Hong Kong, CHN) [43299]

Expositiones Mathematicae (Lausanne-Dorigny, SWI) [51205]

Exposure (London, GBR) [54436]

Expreso (Lima, PER) *Unable to locate*

Express-FM - 93.7 (Portsmouth, GBR) [56294]

Express Radio-FM - 90.3 (Praha Smichov, CZE) [43640]

Extra (Oslo, NOR) *Unable to locate*

Extra-FM - 103.9 (Belo Horizonte, MG, BRZ) [42951]

Extra Golf (Vienna, AUT) [42757]

Extratour (Detmold, GER) [44313]

Extremophiles (Tokyo, JPN) [46820]

EYE (Basingstoke, GBR) [52203]

Eye Care (New Delhi, DH, IND) *Unable to locate*

The Eye-FM - 103 (Melton Mowbray, GBR) [55607]

Eye News (Edinburgh, GBR) [53275]

Eye Spy (Skipton, GBR) [56554]

eyepiece (Greenford, GBR) *Ceased*

Eyes on Food (The Hague, NLD) *Ceased*

Eyre Peninsula Tribune (Cleve, SA, AUS) [41765]

Ezhou People's Broadcasting Station (Ezhou, HU, CHN) *Unable to locate*

Ezik i Literatura (Sofia, BUL) *Unable to locate*

Ezyhealth Chinese (Singapore, SGP) *Unable to locate*

Ezyhealth Singapore (Singapore, SGP) [50146]

F

FA Worldwide Magazine for Penfriendship (Karachi, PAK) *Unable to locate*

Fab Cat Care Journal (Tisbury, GBR) [56751]

Fab Journal [56751]*

Fabula (Berlin, GER) [44178]

Facets (London, GBR) *Unable to locate*

Facilities (Bradford, GBR) [52459]

The Facilities Business (London, GBR) *Unable to locate*

Facilities & Event Management (Morpeth, GBR) *Unable to locate*

Facilities Management World (Saffron Walden, GBR) *Ceased*

Facilities-UK (Salisbury, GBR) [56453]

Fackoversattaren (Bastad, SWE) [50949]

Facts and Figures (Ahmedabad, GJ, IND) *Unable to locate*

Facts File (Chennai, TN, IND) *Unable to locate*

Facts for You (New Delhi, DH, IND) [45511]

Faculty of 1000 Medicine (London, GBR) [54437]

Fah Thai (London, GBR) [54438]

FAI Abstract Service (New Delhi, DH, IND) [45512]

Faire Savoir Faire (Montrouge, FRA) [43991]

Fairfield Advance (Liverpool, NW, AUS) [42013]

Fairkehr (Bonn, GER) [44259]

Fairlady (Cape Town, SAF) [50378]

Fakanal (Budapest, HUN) [44829]

Fakanal Recepttar (Budapest, HUN) [44830]

Fakta (Helsinki, FIN) [43827]

Fall-Line Skiing (Peterborough, GBR) [56257]

Fame FM - Araya Mzaar (Beirut, LBN) *Unable to locate*

Fame FM - Arz (Beirut, LBN) *Unable to locate*

Fame FM - Beirut (Beirut, LBN) *Unable to locate*

Fame FM - Beit Meri (Beirut, LBN) *Unable to locate*

Fame FM - Chouf (Beirut, LBN) *Unable to locate*

Fame FM - Fatqa (Beirut, LBN) *Unable to locate*

Fame FM - Hardeen (Beirut, LBN) *Unable to locate*

Fame FM - Jabal Tourbol (Beirut, LBN) *Unable to locate*

Fame FM - Koura (Beirut, LBN) *Unable to locate*

Fame FM - Tripoli (Beirut, LBN) *Unable to locate*

Fame FM - Tyre (Beirut, LBN) *Unable to locate*

Famiglia Cristiana (Rome, ITA) [46229]

Families in Business (London, GBR) [54439]

Famille Chretienne (Paris, FRA) [44045]

Family (Cuxhaven, GER) *Unable to locate*

Family & Community History (London, GBR) [54440]

Family Court Review (Oxford, GBR) [55951]

The Family Doctor (Singapore, SGP) [50147]

Family-FM - 96.5 (Milton, QL, AUS) [42109]

Family History (Canterbury, GBR) [52918]

Family History Monthly (London, GBR) [54441]

Family History News and Digest (Grimsby, GBR) [53485]

Family Law Journal (London, GBR) [54442]

Family Life (Mumbai, MH, IND) *Unable to locate*

Family Matters (Melbourne, VI, AUS) [42059]

Family Medicine (London, GBR) *Ceased*

Family Mirror (Dar es Salaam, TZA) *Unable to locate*

Family Planning (Moscow, RUS) *Unable to locate*

Family Policy Bulletin (London, GBR) *Ceased*

Family Practice (Oxford, GBR) [55952]

Family Spending (Basingstoke, GBR) [52204]

Fantastic Man (Amsterdam, NLD) [47984]

FAPCCI Review (Hyderabad, AP, IND) [45139]

The Far East (Navan, ME, IRL) [46045]

Far East Journal of Applied Mathematics (Allahabad, UP, IND) [44925]

Far East Journal of Dynamical Systems (Allahabad, UP, IND) [44926]

Far East Journal of Electronics and Communications (Allahabad, UP, IND) [44927]

Far East Journal of Experimental and Theoretical Artificial Intelligence (Allahabad, UP, IND) [44928]

Far East Journal of Mathematical Education (Allahabad, UP, IND) [44929]

Far East Journal of Mathematical Sciences (Allahabad, UP, IND) [44930]

Far East Journal of Ocean Research (Allahabad, UP, IND) *Ceased*

Far Eastern Agriculture (London, GBR) [54443]

Far Eastern Economic Review (Hong Kong, CHN) *Unable to locate*

Faraday Discussions (Cambridge, GBR) [52819]

Faraday Transactions [52883]*

Farbe & Lack (Hannover, GER) *Unable to locate*

Farm Equipment Trader (North Richmond, NW, AUS) [42161]

Farm Front (Bangalore, KA, IND) *Unable to locate*

Farm Guide (Lahore, PAK) *Unable to locate*

Farm and Horticultural Equipment (Cudham, GBR) [53142]

Farm Management (Reading, GBR) *Unable to locate*

Farm & Plant Buyers Guide (Sandyford, DU, IRL) [46055]

Farm Policy Journal (Surry Hills, NW, AUS) [42429]

Farm Scientist (Karachi, PAK) *Unable to locate*

Farm Weekly (Victoria Park, WA, AUS) [42666]

Farma Sanomat (Turku, FIN) [43909]

Farmaceuten (Hellerup, DEN) *Unable to locate*

The Farmer (Kingston, JAM) [46284]

The Farmer (Harare, ZWE) *Ceased*

Farmer and Parliament (New Delhi, DH, IND) *Unable to locate*

The Farmer (Shropshire and the Welsh Borders) (Shrewsbury, GBR) [56528]

Farmers Receptivity to New Technologies in Coconut (Jakarta, IDN) *Unable to locate*

Master Index

Farmers Trader (London, GBR) **[54444]**

Farmers Weekly (Sutton, GBR) **[56685]**

Farming Small Areas (North Richmond, NW, AUS) **[42162]**

Farming Small Blocks (Moonee Ponds, VI, AUS) **[42115]**

Farmland Market (Sutton, GBR) **[56686]**

Fashion Business International (Bradford, GBR) **[52460]**

Fashion Buyer **[53625]***

Fashion Color (Tokyo, JPN) **[46821]**

Fashion Extras (Tonbridge, GBR) *Unable to locate*

Fashion Mag (Karachi, PAK) **[49349]**

Fashion Quarterly (Auckland, NZL) **[48792]**

Fashion Theory (Oxford, GBR) **[55953]**

Fashion UK (London, GBR) *Unable to locate*

FAST Fastening Adhesives Assembly & Joining Technology (Sutton, GBR) *Unable to locate*

Fast Food (Stockholm, SWE) *Unable to locate*

Fast Fours Magazine (Alexandria, NW, AUS) **[41539]**

Fast and Modified (Bellshill, GBR) **[52306]**

Fate & Fortune (London, GBR) **[54445]**

Fatigue & Fracture of Engineering Materials & Structures (Sheffield, GBR) **[56492]**

Fatima Broadcasting International (Bangkok, THA) *Unable to locate*

Fauji Foundation Health Journal (Rawalpindi, PAK) *Unable to locate*

FB Magazine (Templestowe, VI, AUS) **[42616]**

FBI-FM - 94.5 (Strawberry Hills, NW, AUS) **[42397]**

FdH (Zurich, SWI) **[51259]**

FDI World (Lowestoft, GBR) *Ceased*

FDM Asia (Singapore, SGP) **[50148]**

FE Now (London, GBR) *Unable to locate*

FEBC (Khabarovsk, RUS) *Unable to locate*

FEBC (Khabarovsk, RUS) *Unable to locate*

FEBS Journal (Cambridge, GBR) **[52820]**

FEBS Letters (Heidelberg, GER) **[44457]**

Feddes Repertorium (Berlin, GER) **[44179]**

Fedelta del Suono (Giove, ITA) *Unable to locate*

Federauto Magazine (Brussels, BEL) **[42855]**

Fedmagram (Brussels, BEL) *Unable to locate*

Feed Trends (Mumbai, MH, IND) **[45370]**

Feedback (Watford, GBR) **[56864]**

Feedstuffs (North Richmond, NW, AUS) *Unable to locate*

Feel (Seoul, KOR) **[47265]**

Fehrungskraefte & Management (Bruckberg, GER) *Unable to locate*

Feile-FM - 103.2 (Belfast, GBR) **[52301]**

Feitieh (UFO) Broadcasting Co (Kaohsiung, TWN) *Unable to locate*

Feitieh (UFO) Broadcasting Co (Taipei, TWN) *Unable to locate*

Felenyi Suit (Kiev, URE) *Unable to locate*

Felicity Wishes (Ringwood, GBR) **[56396]**

Feline Advisory Bureau Journal (Tisbury, GBR) **[56752]**

Fellow Traveller (East Sydney, NW, AUS) **[41850]**

Fem (Mexico City, DF, MEX) *Unable to locate*

Femailk (Vienna, AUT) *Ceased*

Female Business (Singapore, SGP) **[50149]**

Female Cookbook (Singapore, SGP) *Unable to locate*

Femina (Sochi, RUS) *Unable to locate*

Femina Fashion (Lausanne, SWI) **[51189]**

Feminin Pluriel (Dakar, SEN) *Unable to locate*

Feminine (Petaling Jaya, MYS) *Unable to locate*

Feminism & Psychology (London, GBR) **[54446]**

Feminist Economics (Abingdon, GBR) **[51788]**

Feminist Legal Studies (Dordrecht, NLD) **[48386]**

Feminist Review (London, GBR) **[54447]**

Feminist Review,) *Unable to locate*

Feminist Theory (London, GBR) **[54448]**

Femme (Tunis, TUN) *Unable to locate*

Femmes d'Aujoud'hui (Brussels, BEL) *Unable to locate*

Fempower (Vienna, AUT) **[42758]**

FEMS Immunology and Medical Microbiology (Oxford, GBR) **[55954]**

FEMS Microbiology Reviews (Oxford, GBR) **[55955]**

FEMS Yeast Research (Oxford, GBR) **[55956]**

FEN Factory Equipment News (Gravesend, GBR) *Unable to locate*

Fenerbahce FM - Istanbul (Istanbul, TUR) *Unable to locate*

Feng Ming Broadcasting Co. (Penghu, TWN) *Unable to locate*

Fengzhen People's Broadcasting Station (Fengzhen, NM, CHN) *Unable to locate*

Fenland Citizen (Wisbech, GBR) **[56935]**

FENSA News (Sevenoaks, GBR) **[56472]**

Fernwood (Sydney, NW, AUS) **[42503]**

Ferramenta e Casalinghi (Ooosterhout, NLD) *Unable to locate*

Ferrari Magazine (King's Lynn, GBR) **[53712]**

Ferrari News (King's Lynn, GBR) **[53713]**

Ferrum (Tokyo, JPN) **[46822]**

Fertiliser Association of India's Fertiliser Statistics (New Delhi, DH, IND) **[45513]**

Fertiliser Digest (New Delhi, DH, IND) *Unable to locate*

Fertiliser Marketing News (New Delhi, DH, IND) **[45514]**

Fertiliser Technology (Dhanbad, BH, IND) *Unable to locate*

Fertilizer Focus (Twickenham, GBR) **[56791]**

Fertilizer International (London, GBR) *Unable to locate*

Fetal and Pediatric Pathology (Abingdon, GBR) **[51789]**

Few-Body Systems (Amsterdam, NLD) **[47985]**

ff—Sudtiroler Wochenmagazin (Bozen, ITA) *Unable to locate*

Ffestiniog Railway Magazine (Gwynedd, GBR) **[53500]**

FHM (London, GBR) **[54449]**

FibreSystems Europe (Bristol, GBR) **[52669]**

Fibromyalgi (Lysaker, NOR) *Unable to locate*

Fiction Feast (London, GBR) **[54450]**

Fiction Review (New Delhi, DH, IND) *Unable to locate*

Fiction World (Shanghai, CHN) **[43476]**

The Field (London, GBR) **[54451]**

Field Studies (Shrewsbury, GBR) **[56529]**

Fieldwork in Religion (Liverpool, GBR) **[53872]**

Fietsen (The Hague, NLD) *Unable to locate*

Fietsmarkt (Maarssen, NLD) **[48731]**

Fife Free Press (Fife, GBR) **[53387]**

Fifi and the Flowertots (London, GBR) **[54452]**

Fifty Millesimal News Letter (Kottayam, KE, IND) *Unable to locate*

Figyelo (Budapest, HUN) **[44831]**

Figyelo TOP 200 (Budapest, HUN) **[44832]**

Figyelo Trend (Budapest, HUN) **[44833]**

Fiji Cane Grower (Lautoka, FIJ) *Unable to locate*

Fijian Studies (Lautoka, FIJ) **[43806]**

Filaria Journal (London, GBR) *Ceased*

Film (Swansea, GBR) *Unable to locate*

Film: Cine Monthly (Cochin, KE, IND) *Unable to locate*

Film Ireland (Dublin, DU, IRL) **[45956]**

Film og Kino (Film and Cinema) (Oslo, NOR) *Unable to locate*

Film en Televisie & Video (Brussels, BEL) *Unable to locate*

Filmbulletin/Kino in Augenhohe (Winterthur, SWI) **[51241]**

Filmkrets (Rimbo, SWE) *Unable to locate*

Filosofia (Manila, PHL) *Unable to locate*

Filtration (Exeter, GBR) **[53358]**

Filtration Industry Analyst (Kidlington, GBR) **[53691]**

FIM Magazine (Mies, SWI) **[51212]**

Fimbles Magazine (London, GBR) **[54453]**

Fina Magazine (Quezon City, PHL) *Unable to locate*

Finance Development in Africa (Abidjan, COT) *Unable to locate*

Finance Director's Review (London, GBR) *Unable to locate*

Finance Dublin (Dublin, DU, IRL) **[45957]**

Finance India (New Delhi, DH, IND) **[45515]**

Finance on Windows (Leicester, GBR) **[53800]**

FinanceAsia (Hong Kong, CHN) **[43300]**

Financial Accountability and Management (Oxford, GBR) **[55957]**

Financial Accountant (Sevenoaks, GBR) *Unable to locate*

Financial Adviser (Makati City, PHL) *Unable to locate*

Financial Analysis (New Delhi, DH, IND) *Unable to locate*

Financial Director (London, GBR) **[54454]**

The Financial Express (New Delhi, DH, IND) **[45516]**

Financial Management (London, GBR) **[54455]**

Financial Marketing (London, GBR) **[54456]**

Financial Markets IT (London, GBR) *Unable to locate*

Financial Markets and Portfolio Management (Dordrecht, NLD) **[48387]**

Financial Mirror (Nicosia, CYP) **[43595]**

Financial News (London, GBR) **[54457]**

Financial Planning (Bristol, GBR) **[52670]**

Financial Sector Technology (London, GBR) **[54458]**

Financial Statistics Monthly (Taipei, TWN) **[51340]**

Financial Systems News (Borehamwood, GBR) *Unable to locate*

The Financial Times (London, GBR) **[54459]**

Financial Times of Ceylon (Colombo, SRI) *Unable to locate*

Financial Times Japan (Tokyo, JPN) **[46823]**

Financial Wizard (Mumbai, MH, IND) *Unable to locate*

Financial World (Canterbury, GBR) **[52919]**

Financiero (Lima, PER) *Unable to locate*

Financing Agriculture (Mumbai, MH, IND) *Unable to locate*

Finanz Forum (Berlin, GER) *Unable to locate*

Finanza Marketing e Produzione (Milan, ITA) *Unable to locate*

FINAT News (The Hague, NLD) *Unable to locate*

FindaWord (Gosford, NW, AUS) **[41910]**

Fine Music Radio-FM - 101.3 (Cape Town, SAF) **[50431]**

Finesse **[56867]***

Fingerprint Whorld (Liverpool, GBR) **[53873]**

Finite Fields and Their Applications (Amsterdam, NLD) **[47986]**

Finnish Music Quarterly (Helsinki, FIN) **[43828]**

FINNOPP (Oslo, NOR) *Unable to locate*

FINS (Dundrum, DU, IRL) **[46008]**

FinSec News (Wellington, NZL) *Unable to locate*

Firat Tip Dergisi (Elazig, TUR) **[51553]**

Fire Australia (Box Hill, VI, AUS) **[41632]**

Fire-FM (Bournemouth, GBR) *Unable to locate*

Fire International (London, GBR) **[54460]**

Fire Prevention (Moreton-in-Marsh, GBR) **[55650]**

Fire Prevention and Fire Engineers Journal **[55651]***

Fire Protection (Impala Park, SAF) *Unable to locate*

Fire Risk Management (Moreton-in-Marsh, GBR) **[55651]**

Fire Safety Journal (Edinburgh, GBR) **[53276]**

Fire Times (Shoreham-by-Sea, GBR) **[56523]**

FireCall (Dublin, DU, IRL) **[45958]**

Firefighter (Kingston upon Thames, GBR) **[53721]**

The Fireman (Patterson Lakes, VI, AUS) *Unable to locate*

Fireman Sam (London, GBR) **[54461]**

Fireworks (Bexhill-on-Sea, GBR) **[52321]**

The Firm (Glasgow, GBR) **[53418]**

First (London, GBR) **[54462]**

Numbers cited in bold after listings are entry numbers rather than page numbers.

First Break (Houten, NLD) [48639]

First Break (Oxford, GBR) *Unable to locate*

The First Channel [47656]*

First City (New Delhi, DH, IND) *Unable to locate*

First Class a Paris (Paris, FRA) *Unable to locate*

First Empire (Bridgnorth, GBR) [52594]

First Five (Glasgow, GBR) [53419]

1st Industrial Magazine (Kota, RJ, IND) [45311]

First Link 4 Parents (Glasgow, GBR) [53420]

Fiscal Studies (London, GBR) [54463]

Fiscal Studies (Oxford, GBR) [55958]

Fish (West Bridgford, GBR) [56888]

Fish Farmer (Edinburgh, GBR) [53277]

Fish Friers Review (Leeds, GBR) [53766]

Fish and Game/Natural Resources Library Survey (Bogota, COL) *Unable to locate*

Fish and Game New Zealand (Auckland, NZL) [48793]

Fish Pathology (Tokyo, JPN) [46824]

Fisheries Research (Esporles, SPA) [50714]

Fisheries Science (Tokyo, JPN) [46825]

Fisheries Science Research (Kunsan, KOR) *Unable to locate*

Fishery Technology (Cochin, KE, IND) [45073]

Fishing Boat World (London, GBR) *Unable to locate*

Fiskeritidskrift for Finland (Helsinki, FIN) *Unable to locate*

Fit for Life (Aarau, SWI) [51054]

Fitopatologia Brasileira (Brasilia, DF, BRZ) [42958]

Five-FM - 100.5 (Newry, GBR) [55695]

Five-FM - 100.5 (Newry, GBR) [55696]

Five-FM - 101.1 (Newry, GBR) [55694]

Five Foot Three (Newtownabbey, GBR) [55701]

567-AM - 567 (Vlaeberg, SAF) [50641]

5AA-AM - 1395 (Adelaide, SA, AUS) [41515]

5ABC-FM - 103.9 (Adelaide, SA, AUS) [41516]

5ABC-FM Oak Valley - 107.3 (Ultimo, NW, AUS) [42657]

5DDD-FM - 93.7 (Stepney, SA, AUS) [42390]

5EBI-FM - 103.1 MHz (Adelaide, SA, AUS) [41517]

5EFM-FM - 94.7 (Victor Harbor, SA, AUS) [42663]

5EFM-FM - 89.3 (Victor Harbor, SA, AUS) [42662]

5EZY-FM (Murray Bridge, SA, AUS) *Unable to locate*

5GS-FM - 90.1 (Victor Harbor, SA, AUS) [42664]

5GTR-FM - 100.1 (Mount Gambier, SA, AUS) [42125]

5MBS-FM - 99.9 (Hindmarsh, SA, AUS) [41956]

5MG-AM - 1476 (Mount Gambier, SA, AUS) [42126]

5PBA-FM - 89.7 (Salisbury, SA, AUS) [42346]

5RCB-FM - 104.9 (Mount Gambier, SA, AUS) [42127]

5SE-AM - 963 (Mount Gambier, SA, AUS) [42128]

5TCB-FM - 104.5 (Bordertown, SA, AUS) [41615]

5TCB-FM - 98.5 (Bordertown, SA, AUS) [41616]

5TCB-FM - 98.5 (Bordertown, SA, AUS) [41614]

5TH WHEEL (Moscow, RUS) *Unable to locate*

5UMA-FM - 89.1 (Port Augusta, SA, AUS) [42258]

5UV-AM - 101.5 (Adelaide, SA, AUS) [41518]

5YYY-FM (Whyalla Norrie, SA, AUS) *Unable to locate*

Fizika Nizkikh Temperatur (Kharkov, URE) [51592]

Fizika Soznaniya i Zhyzni, Kosmologiya i Astrofizika (Physics of Consciousness and Life, Cosmology and Astrophysics) (Kiev, URE) [51596]

Flagmaster (London, GBR) [54464]

Flame and Flavour (Calcutta, WB, IND) *Unable to locate*

FLASH (Zurich, SWI) [51260]

Flash (London, GBR) *Unable to locate*

Flash Opel Scene International (Bochum, GER) *Unable to locate*

Flava-FM - 96.1 (Auckland, NZL) [48839]

Fleet-FM - 88.3 (Auckland, NZL) [48840]

Fleet Management Magazine [45931]*

Fleet News Europe (London, GBR) [54465]

Fleet Operator Magazine (Bishop's Stortford, GBR) *Ceased*

Fleet Transport (Claremorris, MA, IRL) [45931]

Fleetwood Weekly News (Fleetwood, GBR) [53390]

Flevoland-FM - 104.4 (Hilversum, NLD) [48636]

Flexible Manufacturing Systems; International Journal of [48388]*

Flexible Services and Manufacturing Journal (Dordrecht, NLD) [48388]

Flieger Magazin (Hamburg, GER) [44415]

Flieger Revue (Berlin, GER) [44180]

Flight International (Sutton, GBR) [56687]

Flight Safety Australia (Canberra, AC, AUS) [41706]

Flightline [56098]*

Flightpath (Surry Hills, NW, AUS) [42430]

Flipside Magazine (Stevenage, GBR) [56604]

Flooring (London, GBR) *Unable to locate*

Flooring Professional Magazine (Moscow, RUS) [49904]

Flora (Halle, GER) [44407]

Flores-FM - 90.7 (Buenos Aires, ARG) [41482]

Florian Hessen (Mainz, GER) *Unable to locate*

Florist Trade Magazine [54466]*

Florist & Wholesale Buyer (London, GBR) [54466]

Flortecnica (Vernasca, ITA) [46278]

Flortecnica Data e Fiori (Vernasca, ITA) [46279]

Flourish (London, GBR) [54467]

Flow-FM - 100.3 (Bordertown, SA, AUS) [41617]

Flow-FM - 106.1 (Ceduna, SA, AUS) [41733]

Flow-FM - 99.7 (Coober Pedy, SA, AUS) [41806]

Flow-FM - 106.3 (Healesville, VI, AUS) [41946]

Flow-FM - 90.9 (Kadina, SA, AUS) [41978]

Flow-FM - 95.5 (Kingscote, SA, AUS) [41989]

Flow-FM - 107.3 (Penola, SA, AUS) [42238]

Flow-FM - 96.5 (Pinnaroo, SA, AUS) [42256]

Flow-FM - 97.9 (Roxby Downs, SA, AUS) [42321]

Flow-FM - 99.3 (Streaky Bay, SA, AUS) [42399]

Flow-FM - 100.5 (Tennant Creek, NT, AUS) [42619]

Flow-FM - 101.7 (Woomera, SA, AUS) [42716]

Flow of Funds (Taipei, TWN) *Unable to locate*

Flow Measurement and Instrumentation (Lulea, SWE) [50981]

The Flower Arranger (London, GBR) [54468]

Flug Revue (Bonn, GER) [44260]

Fluid Dynamics Research (Sakyo-ku, JPN) [46648]

Fluoride (Dunedin, NZL) *Unable to locate*

Flute (London, GBR) [54469]

The Fly (London, GBR) [54470]

Fly-FM - 94 (Petaling Jaya, MYS) [47704]

FLY-FM - 95.8 (Petaling Jaya, MYS) [47703]

Fly Gyro! (Dulverton, GBR) *Ceased*

Fly Navy (London, GBR) [54471]

Flyer (Bath, GBR) [52239]

Flyer International (Karachi, PAK) *Unable to locate*

Flyfishers' Journal (London, GBR) [54472]

FlyFishing and FlyTying (Aberfeldy, GBR) [51686]

Flying Angel News (London, GBR) [54473]

Flying Scale Models (Amersham, GBR) [52106]

Flynytt (Oslo, NOR) [49198]

FlyPast (Stamford, GBR) [56596]

FM Radio Niigata - 86.5 MHz (Yahiko, JPN) [47123]

FM Select-Beacon Hill - 102.4 MHz (Hong Kong, CHN) [43388]

FM Select-Castle Peak - 102.5 MHz (Hong Kong, CHN) [43389]

FM Select-Cloudy Hill - 104.7 MHz (Hong Kong, CHN) [43390]

FM Select-Golden Hill - 105.5 MHz (Hong Kong, CHN) [43391]

FM Select-Kowloon Peak - 106.3 MHz (Hong Kong, CHN) [43392]

FM Select-Lamma Island - 104.5 MHz (Hong Kong, CHN) [43393]

FM Select-Mt. Gough - 104.0 MHz (Hong Kong, CHN) [43394]

FM World (London, GBR) [54474]

FMM Directory of Malaysian Industries (Kuala Lumpur, MYS) [47602]

FMM Forum [47602]*

FMR (Milan, ITA) *Unable to locate*

Focal International (Harrow, GBR) *Unable to locate*

FOCU Dialog (Gothenburg, SWE) *Unable to locate*

Focus (Trivandrum, KE, IND) *Unable to locate*

Focus (Bishop's Waltham, GBR) *Unable to locate*

Focus (Leamington Spa, GBR) *Unable to locate*

Focus (Mold, GBR) [55643]

Focus on Business Education (Chislehurst, GBR) *Unable to locate*

Focus on Catalysts (Cambridge, GBR) [52821]

Focus Europe (London, GBR) [54475]

Focus on International & Comparative Librarianship [55480]*

Focus on International Library & Information Work (Loughborough, GBR) [55480]

Focus on Italy (Milan, ITA) [46171]

Focus on Pakistan (Islamabad, PAK) *Unable to locate*

Focus on Panama (Panama City, PAN) [49401]

Focus on the Public Services (Ferney-Voltaire, FRA) [43947]

Fodnoten (Vedbek, DEN) *Unable to locate*

Foi-FM - 107.4 MHz (Antananarivo, MDG) [47564]

Foinse (Gaillimhe, GL, IRL) [46015]

Folia Heyrovskyana (Zlin, CZE) [43642]

Folia Linguistica (Berlin, GER) [44181]

Folia Morphologica (Gdansk, POL) [49657]

Folia Neuropathologica (Warsaw, POL) [49710]

Folia Oeconomica Stetinensia (Warsaw, POL) [49711]

Folia Parasitologica (Ceske Budejovice, CZE) [43605]

Folia Primatologica (Plelan le Grand, FRA) [44095]

Folia Ugentia (Genval, BEL) *Unable to locate*

Folk Literature (Beijing, CHN) [43193]

Folk Music Journal (London, GBR) [54476]

Folkeskolen (Copenhagen, DEN) [43668]

Folklore (Calcutta, WB, IND) *Unable to locate*

Folklore (Beijing, CHN) *Unable to locate*

Folklore (Abingdon, GBR) [51790]

Folklore Fellows of India News Bulletin (Mysore, KA, IND) *Unable to locate*

Folklore Research Journal (New Delhi, DH, IND) [45517]

The Follies Journal (Eindhoven, NLD) [48590]

FoMRHI Quarterly (London, GBR) *Unable to locate*

F1-maailma (Kuvalehdet, FIN) *Unable to locate*

F1 Racing (Helsinki, FIN) [43829]

Fonctret (London, GBR) [54477]

Fonto (Zagreb, CTA) *Unable to locate*

FOOD (Quezon City, PHL) [49593]

Food and Agricultural Immunology (Chester, GBR) [52995]

Food Agriculture and Plantation Journal (Baroda, GJ, IND) *Unable to locate*

Food Allergy and Intolerance Journal (Leatherhead, GBR) [53751]

Food & Beverage Asia (Singapore, SGP) [50150]

Food & Beverage Today (Auckland, NZL) [48794]

Food and Beverages (New Delhi, DH, IND) *Unable to locate*

Food Biophysics (Dordrecht, NLD) [48389]

Food & Bioproducts Processing (Rugby, GBR) [56419]

Food and Chemical Toxicology (Kidlington, GBR) **[53692]**

Food & Drink Business (Surry Hills, NW, AUS) **[42431]**

Food & Drink Exporter (London, GBR) *Ceased*

Food Farming and Agriculture (Calcutta, WB, IND) *Unable to locate*

Food and Future (Baghdad, IRQ) *Unable to locate*

Food Illustrated **[55376]***

Food Industries (Gauteng, SAF) *Ceased*

Food Industry Development China (London, GBR) *Unable to locate*

Food Ireland (Dublin, DU, IRL) **[45959]**

Food Manufacture (Crawley, GBR) **[53103]**

Food Marketing & Manufacturing (Milton Keynes, GBR) **[55635]**

Food Marketing & Technology (Nuremberg, GER) **[44611]**

Food Microbiology (Amsterdam, NLD) **[47987]**

Food Policy (Ashford, GBR) **[52140]**

Food Processing (Tonbridge, GBR) **[56754]**

Food Quality and Preference (Bristol, GBR) **[52671]**

Food Review (Gauteng, SAF) **[50481]**

Food Safety (London, GBR) *Unable to locate*

Food Safety Express (Burnham, GBR) *Ceased*

Food Science and Agricultural Chemistry (Taipei, TWN) *Unable to locate*

Food Science and Technology (London, GBR) **[54478]**

Food Science and Technology Abstracts (Reading, GBR) **[56317]**

Food Science and Technology International (Burjasot, SPA) **[50711]**

Food Science and Technology Research (Tokyo, JPN) **[46826]**

Food Shop (Clayton South, VI, AUS) *Unable to locate*

Food Technologie (Nuremberg, GER) **[44612]**

Food Technology International (London, GBR) *Unable to locate*

Food and Travel (Richmond, GBR) *Unable to locate*

Food and Wine (London, GBR) *Ceased*

Food & Wine Magazine (Dublin, DU, IRL) **[45960]**

Foodcorp Quarterly (New Delhi, DH, IND) *Unable to locate*

FoodService News (Surry Hills, NW, AUS) **[42432]**

Football Decision (Kings Langley, GBR) *Unable to locate*

Football Italia (London, GBR) *Unable to locate*

Footwear (Seoul, KOR) *Unable to locate*

Footwear Today (Kent, GBR) **[53677]**

For Him Magazine Philippines (Mandaluyong City, PHL) **[49536]**

For Keeps Creative Scrapbooking (Rozelle, NW, AUS) **[42326]**

For Women (London, GBR) *Unable to locate*

Ford & Fordson Tractors (Felixstowe, GBR) **[53385]**

Forecourt Trader (Crawley, GBR) **[53104]**

Foreign Affairs Journal (Kathmandu, NPL) *Unable to locate*

Foreign Affairs Pakistan (Islamabad, PAK) *Unable to locate*

Foreign Affairs Record (New Delhi, DH, IND) *Unable to locate*

Foreign Affairs Reports (New Delhi, DH, IND) *Ceased*

Foreign Markets (Warsaw, POL) *Unable to locate*

Foreign Policy Analysis (Oxford, GBR) **[55959]**

Foreign Trade Bulletin (New Delhi, DH, IND) *Ceased*

Foreign Trade—Trends & Tidings (New Delhi, DH, IND) *Ceased*

Forensic Medical Examination (Moscow, RUS) **[49905]**

Foresight (Bradford, GBR) **[52461]**

Forest and Bird Magazine (Wellington, NZL) **[49008]**

Forest Ecology and Management (Amsterdam, NLD) **[47988]**

Forest-FM - 92.3 (Verwood, GBR) **[56802]**

Forest Policy and Economics (Gottingen, GER) **[44398]**

Forest Usufructs (Dehradun, UP, IND) *Unable to locate*

Forestry (Oxford, GBR) **[55960]**

Forestry Journal (Edinburgh, GBR) **[53278]**

Forestry Magazine (Turrialba, CRI) *Unable to locate*

Forestry Technology (Tokyo, JPN) **[46827]**

Forfatteren (Copenhagen, DEN) **[43669]**

Forge (Duffield, GBR) **[53208]**

Form Function Finland (Helsinki, FIN) *Ceased*

Formal Aspects of Computing (Newcastle upon Tyne, GBR) **[55670]**

Formalized Mathematics (Warsaw, POL) **[49712]**

Formosan Journal of Surgery (Taipei, TWN) *Unable to locate*

Formosan Science (Taipei, TWN) *Unable to locate*

Formula DA (Naberezhnyye Chelny, RUS) *Unable to locate*

Forschende Komplementarmedizin und Klassische Naturheilkunde (Freiburg, GER) *Ceased*

Forschung im Ingenieurwesen (Dordrecht, NLD) **[48390]**

Forschungsberichte aus Technik und Naturwissenschaften (Hannover, GER) **[44432]**

Forsikring (Copenhagen, DEN) *Unable to locate*

Forskerforim (Oslo, NOR) *Unable to locate*

Fort (Wirral, GBR) *Unable to locate*

Fortattaren (Stockholm, SWE) **[51016]**

FORTH Dimensions (Milan, ITA) *Ceased*

The Forth Naturalist & Historian (Stirling, GBR) **[56622]**

Forth One-FM - 97.3 (Edinburgh, GBR) **[53325]**

Forth 2-AM - 1548 (Edinburgh, GBR) **[53326]**

Fortschritte der Physik/Progress of Physics (Munich, GER) **[44561]**

Fortune (Chennai, TN, IND) *Unable to locate*

Fortune India (Mumbai, MH, IND) *Unable to locate*

40 Minutes (New Delhi, DH, IND) *Unable to locate*

FORUM (Strasbourg, FRA) *Ceased*

Forum (The Hague, NLD) **[48616]**

Forum (Barcelona, SPA) **[50674]**

Forum (London, GBR) *Unable to locate*

Forum Chantiers (Clichy, FRA) **[43932]**

Forum for Development Studies (Oslo, NOR) *Unable to locate*

Forum Erziehungshilfen (Frankfurt, GER) *Unable to locate*

Forum Gesundheit Vorarlberg (Dornbirn, AUT) **[42723]**

Forum Kleinwiederkaeuer (Niederonz, SWI) **[51219]**

Forum Mathematicum (Berlin, GER) **[44182]**

Forum for Modern Language Studies (Saint Andrews, GBR) **[56441]**

Forum der Psychoanalyse (Dordrecht, NLD) **[48391]**

Forum Qualitative Sozialforschung (Berlin, GER) **[44183]**

Forum, Tidsskrift for Kon Og Kultur (Copenhagen, DEN) **[43670]**

FORWARD (Reading, GBR) **[56318]**

Foshan People's Broadcasting Station (Foshan, GD, CHN) *Unable to locate*

Foshan People's Broadcasting Station (Foshan, GD, CHN) *Unable to locate*

Fossil Record (Berlin, GER) **[44184]**

FOSSTAAL (Houten, NLD) *Unable to locate*

Fotnoten (Stockholm, SWE) *Unable to locate*

Foto Media (Jakarta, IDN) *Unable to locate*

Foto-Notiziario (Milan, ITA) **[46172]**

Foto Shoe 15 International (Trezzano Sul Naviglio, ITA) **[46263]**

Foto Shoe 30 (Trezzano Sul Naviglio, ITA) **[46264]**

Foto Video (Madrid, SPA) **[50759]**

Fotomundo (Buenos Aires, ARG) **[41472]**

Foundation (London, GBR) **[54479]**

Foundations of Science (Dordrecht, NLD) **[48392]**

Foundry Trade Journal (Harlow, GBR) *Unable to locate*

4x4 & Off Road Mart (Birmingham, GBR) *Unable to locate*

4 Double B-FM - 96.3 (Bundaberg, QL, AUS) **[41667]**

Four P News (Calcutta, WB, IND) *Unable to locate*

4 Triple Z-FM - 102.1 (Fortitude Valley, QL, AUS) **[41871]**

Four Walls (Singapore, SGP) *Unable to locate*

4ABC-FM - 95.5 (Airlie Beach, QL, AUS) **[41522]**

4ABC-FM - 90.5 (Cloncurry, QL, AUS) **[41771]**

4AM-AM (Mareeba, QL, AUS) *Unable to locate*

4BBB-FM - 105.3 (Brisbane, QL, AUS) **[41657]**

4BC-AM - 1116 (Cannon Hill, QL, AUS) **[41719]**

4BC-AM - 882 (Cannon Hill, QL, AUS) **[41720]**

4BI-AM (Brisbane, QL, AUS) *Unable to locate*

4BU-AM (Bundaberg, QL, AUS) *Unable to locate*

4CA-FM - 102.7 (Cairns, QL, AUS) **[41686]**

4CAB-FM - 107.3 (Main Beach, QL, AUS) **[42027]**

4CBL-FM - 101.1 (Logan City DC, QL, AUS) **[42020]**

4CC-AM - 927 (Gladstone, QL, AUS) **[41888]**

4CIM-FM - 98.7 (Cairns, QL, AUS) **[41687]**

4CRB-FM - 89.3 (Burleigh Heads, QL, AUS) **[41673]**

4CRM-FM - 107.5 (Mackay, QL, AUS) **[42025]**

4DDB-FM (Toowoomba, QL, AUS) *Unable to locate*

4EB-FM - 98.1 (East Brisbane, QL, AUS) **[41845]**

4EEE-FM - 96.3 (Emerald, QL, AUS) **[41855]**

4FCR-FM - 107.5 (Pialba, QL, AUS) **[42255]**

4FM - 94.8 (Bantry, CK, IRL) **[45918]**

4FM - 97.4 (Carrigaline, CK, IRL) **[45927]**

4FM - 104.2 (Clifden, GL, IRL) **[45934]**

4FM - 94.8 (Cork, CK, IRL) **[45940]**

4FM - 94.9 (Dublin, DU, IRL) **[46001]**

4FM - 95.2 (Fermoy, CK, IRL) **[46014]**

4FM - 104.9 (Galway, GL, IRL) **[46020]**

4FM - 104.2 (Limerick, LI, IRL) **[46031]**

4FM - 97.4 (Macroom, CK, IRL) **[46036]**

4FM - 94.6 (Naas, KL, IRL) **[46043]**

4FM - 97.2 (Youghal, CK, IRL) **[46073]**

FourFourTwo (Sydney, NW, AUS) **[42504]**

4GR-AM - 864 (Toowoomba, QL, AUS) **[42631]**

4GY-AM - 558 (Gympie, QL, AUS) **[41937]**

4HI-AM (Emerald, QL, AUS) *Unable to locate*

4K1G-FM - 107.1 (Townsville, QL, AUS) **[42640]**

4KQ-AM - 693 (Stones Corner, QL, AUS) **[42391]**

4LG-AM - 1098 (Longreach, QL, AUS) **[42022]**

4LM-AM - 666 KHz (Mount Isa, QL, AUS) **[42131]**

4MBS-FM - 103.7 (Coorparoo, QL, AUS) **[41814]**

4MMM-FM - 104.5 (Brisbane, QL, AUS) **[41658]**

4NSA-FM - 101.3 (Noosa Heads, QL, AUS) **[42148]**

4OR (Bologna, ITA) **[46126]**

4OUR-FM - 101.5 (Caboolture, QL, AUS) **[41682]**

4QN-AM **[42639]***

4QR-AM - 612 (Brisbane, QL, AUS) **[41659]**

4R-FM - 96.9 (Moranbah, QL, AUS) **[42116]**

4RK-AM - 837 (Rockhampton, QL, AUS) **[42318]**

4RRR-FM - 101.7 MHz (Roma, QL, AUS) **[42319]**

4SDA-FM - 104.9 (Buderim, QL, AUS) **[41665]**

4TCB-FM - 99.9 (Aitkenvale, QL, AUS) **[41524]**

Fourth World Review (Swindon, GBR) **[56711]**

4TO-FM - 102.3 (Townsville, QL, AUS) **[42641]**

4TTT-FM - 103.9 (Townsville, QL, AUS) **[42642]**

4WBR-FM - 105.1 (Hervey Bay, QL, AUS) **[41953]**

4WD Buyers Guide (North Ryde, NW, AUS) **[42182]**

4wdonline (Melbourne, VI, AUS) **[42060]**

4WK-AM - 1359 (Toowoomba, QL, AUS) **[42632]**

4x4 Australia (Sydney, NW, AUS) **[42505]**

Numbers cited in bold after listings are entry numbers rather than page numbers.

4x4 Magazine (Singapore) (Singapore, SGP) *Unable to locate*
4ZG [48903]*
4ZR-AM (Roma, QL, AUS) *Unable to locate*
4ZZZ-FM - 102.1 (Fortitude Valley, QL, AUS) [41872]
Fox-FM [56233]*
Fox-FM [53095]*
FoxFiles (Ilford, GBR) *Unable to locate*
FQ (Bromley, GBR) [52745]
Fractional Calculus and Applied Analysis (Sofia, BUL) [43099]
Frame (Amsterdam, NLD) [47989]
Framework (Helsinki, FIN) [43830]
Fran Riksdag & Departement (R&D) (Stockholm, SWE) *Unable to locate*
France FM - Beit Meri (Beit Meri el Metn, LBN) *Unable to locate*
France FM - Fatqa (Beit Meri el Metn, LBN) *Unable to locate*
France Reelle (Paris, FRA) *Unable to locate*
France-U.S.A. (Paris, FRA) *Unable to locate*
Francophonie (Leicester, GBR) [53801]
Frankfurter Afrikanistische Blatter (Cologne, GER) [44294]
Frankfurter Allgemeine (Frankfurt, GER) [44360]
Frankston Standard Leader (Mornington, VI, AUS) [42117]
Fraser Coast Chronicle (Sydney, NW, AUS) [42506]
FRAU von HEUTE (Hamburg, GER) [44416]
Frau und Politik (Bonn, GER) [44261]
Fraunhofer (English) (Munich, GER) [44562]
Fraunhofer Magazin (Munich, GER) [44563]
Fredsposten (Helsinki, FIN) *Unable to locate*
Fredsviljen (Eiksmarka, NOR) *Unable to locate*
Free Life Magazine (London, GBR) *Unable to locate*
Free Press (Huddersfield, GBR) [53620]
Free Press Leader (Boronia, VI, AUS) [41618]
Free Radical (London, GBR) *Unable to locate*
Free Radical Biology and Medicine (Amsterdam, NLD) [47990]
Free Radical Research (Abingdon, GBR) [51791]
Free Radio Salzkammergut-FM - 100.2 (Bad Ischl, AUT) [42722]
Free Romanian (London, GBR) *Unable to locate*
Free Tibet (London, GBR) *Unable to locate*
Freebase (Rochester, GBR) *Unable to locate*
Freedom Digest (Seoul, KOR) *Unable to locate*
Freedom First (Mumbai, MH, IND) *Unable to locate*
FreeHand (London, GBR) *Unable to locate*
The Freeman Mindanao (Ozamis City, PHL) *Unable to locate*
Freemasonry Tasmania (Hobart, TA, AUS) [41958]
Freemasonry Today (London, GBR) [54480]
Freerider MX Magazine (Burleigh, QL, AUS) [41672]
Freeskier (Pretoria, SAF) [50591]
Freeze (Sint-Katelijne-Waver, BEL) *Unable to locate*

Freies Radio-FM (Bad Ischl, AUT) *Unable to locate*
Freight Magazine (West Sussex, GBR) [56898]
French Cultural Studies (London, GBR) [54481]
French History (Oxford, GBR) [55961]
French Magazine (Bath, GBR) [52240]
French Politics (Dublin, DU, IRL) [45961]
French Property News (Norwich, GBR) [55731]
Frequence Banane-FM (Lausanne, SWI) *Unable to locate*
Frequence K-FM - 103.4 MHz (Carros, ITA) [46132]
Frequence Mistral-FM - 99.3 (Digne les Bains, FRA) [43942]
Frequence Mistral-FM - 92.8 (Manosque, FRA) [43972]
Frequence Mistral-FM - 99.2 (Sisteron, FRA) [44105]
Fresh-FM - 92.7 (Adelaide, SA, AUS) [41519]
Fresh-FM - 89.2 (Blenheim, NZL) [48859]
Fresh-FM - 95.4 (Nelson, NZL) [48945]
Fresh-FM - 99.4 (Nelson, NZL) [48946]
Fresh-FM - 95.2 (Takaka, NZL) [48978]
Fresh Produce Journal (London, GBR) [54482]
Fresh Radio-AM - 936 (Hawes, GBR) [53545]
Fresh Radio-FM - 102.6 (Skipton, GBR) [56557]
Fresh Radio-FM - 107.1 (Skipton, GBR) [56556]
Fresh Radio-FM (Skipton, GBR) *Unable to locate*
FRI Journal of Forest Science (Suwon, KOR) *Unable to locate*
Frida (Stockholm, SWE) *Unable to locate*
The Friday Times [49385]*
The Friday Times (Lahore, PAK) [49385]
Friday Weekly [50292]*
Friedhofs Kultur (Braunschweig, GER) [44276]
The Friend (London, GBR) [54483]
Friend International (Mumbai, MH, IND) *Unable to locate*
Frieze (London, GBR) [54484]
Friluftsliv—i alla vader (Hagersten, SWE) *Unable to locate*
Frimaerkesamleren (Frederiksberg, DEN) *Unable to locate*
Frisor (Oslo, NOR) [49199]
Frisorfaget (Herning, DEN) [43721]
Fritid (Norra Rada, SWE) *Unable to locate*
FriZ—Zeitschrift fur Friedenspolitik (Zurich, SWI) *Unable to locate*
FRO-FM - 105.0 (Linz, AUT) [42735]
From the Martin Buber House (Heppenheim, GER) [44482]
From the Window (Canterbury, GBR) [52920]
Frontaal [48271]*
Frontier Brands (London, GBR) [54485]
The Frontier Post (Peshawar, PAK) [49392]
The Frontier Sun (Silchar, AS, IND) *Unable to locate*
Frontiers of Biology in China (Dordrecht, NLD) [48393]
Frontiers of Chemistry in China (Dordrecht, NLD) [48394]

Frontiers of Economics in China (Dordrecht, NLD) [48395]
Frontiers of Education in China (Dordrecht, NLD) [48396]
Frontiers of Electrical and Electronic Engineering in China (Dordrecht, NLD) [48397]
Frontiers of Forestry in China (Dordrecht, NLD) [48398]
Frontiers of History in China (Dordrecht, NLD) [48399]
Frontiers of Law in China (Dordrecht, NLD) [48400]
Frontiers of Mathematics in China (Dordrecht, NLD) [48401]
Frontiers of Mechanical Engineering in China (Dordrecht, NLD) [48402]
Frontiers in Neuroendocrinology (Amsterdam, NLD) [47991]
Frontiers of Philosophy in China (Dordrecht, NLD) [48403]
Frontiers of Physics in China (Dordrecht, NLD) [48404]
Frontiers in Zoology (London, GBR) [54486]
Frontline (South Melbourne, VI, AUS) [42371]
Frontline (Chennai, TN, IND) [45032]
Frozen & Chilled Foods Europe (Kent, GBR) *Unable to locate*
Fruhmittelalterliche Studien (Berlin, GER) [44185]
Fu Jen Studies (Taipei, TWN) *Unable to locate*
Fuel (Newcastle upon Tyne, GBR) [55671]
The Fuel Cell Review (Colombo, SRI) *Ceased*
Fuels International (London, GBR) *Ceased*
Fuerza 7 (Madrid, SPA) *Unable to locate*
Fuga (Brussels, BEL) *Unable to locate*
Fujian People's Broadcasting Station (Fuzhou, FJ, CHN) *Unable to locate*
Fujian People's Broadcasting Station (Fuzhou, FJ, CHN) *Unable to locate*
Fujian People's Broadcasting Station (Fuzhou, FJ, CHN) *Unable to locate*
Fujian People's Broadcasting Station (Fuzhou, FJ, CHN) *Unable to locate*
Fujian People's Broadcasting Station (Fuzhou, FJ, CHN) *Unable to locate*
Fujian People's Broadcasting Station (Fuzhou, FJ, CHN) *Unable to locate*
Fujian People's Broadcasting Station (Fuzhou, FJ, CHN) *Unable to locate*
Fujian People's Broadcasting Station (Fuzhou, FJ, CHN) *Unable to locate*
Fujian People's Broadcasting Station (Fuzhou, FJ, CHN) *Unable to locate*
Fujian People's Broadcasting Station (Fuzhou, FJ, CHN) *Unable to locate*
Fujin Shinpo (Tokyo, JPN) *Unable to locate*
Fukuoka - 3259 KHz (Tokyo, JPN) [47060]
Fukuoka Now (Fukuoka, JPN) [46341]
Fukushima Journal of Medical Science (Fukushima, JPN) *Unable to locate*
Fules (Budapest, HUN) [44834]

Fun Duiken (Brussels, BEL) *Unable to locate*
Fun to Learn Barney (Shrewsbury, GBR) [56530]
Fun to Learn Best of Barney (Shrewsbury, GBR) [56531]
Fun to Learn Discovery (Shrewsbury, GBR) [56532]
Fun to Learn Favourites (Shrewsbury, GBR) [56533]
Fun to Learn Friends (Shrewsbury, GBR) [56534]
Fun to Learn Letterland (Shrewsbury, GBR) [56535]
Fun to Learn Peppa Pig (Shrewsbury, GBR) [56536]
Fun Plongee (Brussels, BEL) *Unable to locate*
Fun Radio-FM - 94.3 (Bratislava, SLK) [50324]
Functional Plant Biology (Collingwood, VI, AUS) [41789]
Functions of Language (FOL) (Amsterdam, NLD) [47992]
Fundamenta Informaticae (Amsterdam, NLD) [47993]
Fundamental and Applied Limnology (Stuttgart, GER) [44668]
Fundamina (Pretoria, SAF) [50592]
Fundicao (Porto, PRT) *Unable to locate*
Fundicao e Servicos (Sao Paulo, SP, BRZ) [43040]
Fundoku (Redhill, GBR) [56351]
Funeral Director Monthly (Solihull, GBR) [56563]
Funeral Service Journal (Worthing, GBR) [56972]
Fungal Biology Reviews (Edinburgh, GBR) [53279]
Fungal Genetics and Biology (Amsterdam, NLD) [47994]
Funkcialaj Ekvacioj, Serio Internacia (Kobe, JPN) [46430]
Furnaces International (Redhill, GBR) [56352]
Furniture magazine [42616]*
Furniture and Cabinetmaking (Lewes, GBR) [53849]
Furniture History (Haywards Heath, GBR) [53548]
Furniture News (Seoul, KOR) *Unable to locate*
Furniture News (Battle, GBR) [52269]
Furniture Production (Battle, GBR) [52270]
Furniture Production International [52270]*
Further Education Today (Feltham, GBR) *Unable to locate*
Fushun People's Broadcasting Station (Fushun, LI, CHN) *Unable to locate*
Fushun People's Broadcasting Station (Fushun, LI, CHN) *Unable to locate*
Fushun People's Broadcasting Station (Fushun, LI, CHN) *Unable to locate*
Fushun People's Broadcasting Station (Fushun, LI, CHN) *Unable to locate*
Fushun People's Broadcasting Station (Fushun, LI, CHN) *Unable to locate*
Fusion (Leicester, GBR) *Unable to locate*
Fusion Flowers (Kippen, GBR) [53726]
Futari (Helsinki, FIN) [43831]
Future Cardiology (London, GBR) [54487]
Future Fitness (Barnsley, GBR) [52180]

Numbers cited in bold after listings are entry numbers rather than page numbers.

Future Generation Computer Systems (Amsterdam, NLD) [47995]
Future Microbiology (London, GBR) [54488]
Future Neurology (London, GBR) [54489]
Future Oncology (London, GBR) [54490]
Future Television - Channel 28 (Beirut, LBN) [47405]
Future Television - Channel 37 (Beirut, LBN) [47406]
Future Television - Channel 46 (Beirut, LBN) [47403]
Future Television - Channel 52 (Beirut, LBN) [47404]
Future Virology (London, GBR) [54491]
FutureGov (Singapore City, SGP) [50312]
Futuro-FM - 88.9 (Santiago, CHL) [43155]
Fuxin People's Broadcasting Station (Fuxin, LI, CHN) Unable to locate
Fuyang People's Broadcasting Station (Fuyang, AN, CHN) Unable to locate
Fuyang People's Broadcasting Station (Fuyang, AN, CHN) Unable to locate
Fuzhou People's Broadcasting Station (Fuzhou, FJ, CHN) Unable to locate
Fuzhou People's Broadcasting Station (Fuzhou, FJ, CHN) Unable to locate
Fuzhou People's Broadcasting Station (Fuzhou, FJ, CHN) Unable to locate
Fuzhou People's Broadcasting Station (Fuzhou, FJ, CHN) Unable to locate
Fuzzy Sets and Systems (Toulouse, FRA) [44120]
FV—Foto-Video Actualidad (Madrid, SPA) [50760]
FWI News (Pietermaritzburg, SAF) Unable to locate
Fylde Tramway News (Blackpool, GBR) [52385]
Fyne Times (Abingdon, GBR) [51792]

G

G English (Mumbai, MH, IND) Unable to locate
G K Round-Up (New Delhi, DH, IND) Unable to locate
G S P News (Quetta, PAK) Unable to locate
Gabriela-FM - 102.9 (Ilheus, BH, BRZ) [42981]
Gabz-FM - 96.2 (Gaborone, BWA) [42947]
Gaceta De Los Negocios (Madrid, SPA) Unable to locate
Gaceta Laboral (Maracaibo, VEN) [57026]
Gadget (Pinegowrie, SAF) [50571]
Gaelic World (Dublin, DU, IRL) Unable to locate
GAHK Journal (Hong Kong, CHN) Unable to locate
The Gaijin Gleaner (Fukuoka, JPN) [46342]
Gainsborough Standard (Gainsborough, GBR) [53401]
Gainsborough Target (Lincoln, GBR) Unable to locate
Gala Buzz (London, GBR) Unable to locate
Galassia (Rome, ITA) Ceased
Galaxie (Petaling Jaya, MYS) [47697]

Galaxy-FM - 105 (Wallsend, GBR) [56834]
Galaxy 105-FM (Leeds, GBR) Unable to locate
Galaxy 102-FM (Manchester, GBR) Unable to locate
Galaxy 102.2-FM (Birmingham, GBR) Unable to locate
Galloway Gazette (Newton Stewart, GBR) [55698]
Galpin Society Journal (Saint Albans, GBR) [56435]
Galway Bay-FM - 95.8 (Galway, GL, IRL) [46021]
GALWAYnow (Clarenbridge, GL, IRL) [45933]
Game Conservancy Magazine (Fordingbridge, GBR) [53395]
Games and Economic Behavior (Amsterdam, NLD) [47996]
gamesTM (Bournemouth, GBR) [52414]
Gamewise (Farnborough, GBR) [53378]
Gaming Floor (London, GBR) [54492]
GAMM - Mitteilungen (Erlangen, GER) [44338]
Ganashtaki (Kolkata, WB, IND) [45266]
Gandhi Marg (New Delhi, DH, IND) Unable to locate
Gandhian Perspectives (Varanasi, UP, IND) Unable to locate
Gandhian Thought (New Delhi, DH, IND) Unable to locate
Gandhians in Action (Patna, BH, IND) Unable to locate
Ganganatha Jha Kendriya Sanskrit Vidyapeetha Journal (Allahabad, UP, IND) Unable to locate
Ganita (Lucknow, UP, IND) Unable to locate
Ganita Bharati (Delhi, DH, IND) Unable to locate
Ganmitram (Janpur, UP, IND) Unable to locate
Gannan People's Broadcasting Station (Hezuo, GS, CHN) Unable to locate
Gannan People's Broadcasting Station (Hezuo, GS, CHN) Unable to locate
Gannan People's Broadcasting Station (Hezuo, GS, CHN) Unable to locate
Gansu People's Broadcasting Station (Lanzhou, GS, CHN) Unable to locate
Gansu People's Broadcasting Station 1 (Lanzhou, GS, CHN) Unable to locate
Gansu People's Broadcasting Station 1 (Lanzhou, GS, CHN) Unable to locate
Gansu People's Broadcasting Station 3 (Lanzhou, GS, CHN) Unable to locate
Gansu People's Broadcasting Station 3 (Lanzhou, GS, CHN) Unable to locate
Gansu People's Broadcasting Station 2 (Lanzhou, GS, CHN) Unable to locate
Gansu People's Broadcasting Station 2 (Lanzhou, GS, CHN) Unable to locate
Gantara (Paris, FRA) Unable to locate
Ganzhou People's Broadcasting Station (Ganzhou, JX, CHN) Unable to locate
Gap Matters (London, GBR) Unable to locate

Gapyear Magazine (London, GBR) Unable to locate
Garage Trader (Belfast, GBR) [52283]
The Garden (Peterborough, GBR) [56258]
Garden Asia (Singapore, SGP) Unable to locate
Garden Design Journal (Ross-on-Wye, GBR) [56409]
Garden History (London, GBR) [54493]
Garden Trade News (Rutland, GBR) Unable to locate
Gardenia (Palermo, ITA) Unable to locate
Gardening Australia (Alexandria, NW, AUS) [41540]
Gardens Illustrated (Bristol, GBR) [52672]
Gardens Monthly (Orpington, GBR) [55851]
Gardens & Outdoor Living (Sydney, NW, AUS) Unable to locate
Garstang Courier (Garstang, GBR) [53404]
Gas Business (Leamington Spa, WW, GBR) Unable to locate
Gas Matters (London, GBR) [54494]
Gas Matters Today (London, GBR) [54495]
Gas News (New Delhi, DH, IND) [45518]
Gasoil (Baroda, GJ, IND) Unable to locate
Gastric Cancer (Tokyo, JPN) [46828]
Gastroenterologia Practica (Barcelona, SPA) Unable to locate
Gastroenterology & Hepatology; Nature Clinical Practice [54979]*
Gastrointestinal Nursing (London, GBR) [54496]
Gaswijs (Apeldoorn, NLD) Unable to locate
Gate Technology and Development (Eschborn, GER) [44345]
Gatra (Jakarta, IDN) [45797]
Gatton, Lockyer and Brisbane Valley Star (Sydney, NW, AUS) [42507]
Gaudeamus-FM - 93.6 (Kaunas, LIT) [47467]
Gaudie (Aberdeen, GBR) [51676]
Gazeta Sporturilor (Bucharest, ROM) Unable to locate
Gazeteer of India (New Delhi, DH, IND) Unable to locate
Gazette [54623]*
Gazette (Dublin, DU, IRL) [45962]
Gazette (Cape Town, SAF) [50379]
Gazette (Bern, SWI) Unable to locate
Gazi Medical Journal (Ankara, TUR) [51493]
Gazzetta (Zurich, SWI) [51261]
Gazzetta de Parma (Parma, ITA) Unable to locate
Gazzetta del Sud (Messina, ITA) Unable to locate
Gb - Das Magazin fur Zierpflanzenbau (Aachen, GER) [44137]
G.C. Rocks (Nottingham, GBR) Unable to locate
The GDP (London, GBR) [54497]
Gea (Ljubljana, SVA) Unable to locate
GEC Journal of Technology (Chelmsford, GBR) Ceased
Geelong Advertiser (Geelong, VI, AUS) [41879]
Gefahrstoffe-Reinhaltung der Luft (Dusseldorf, GER) [44325]
Geistige Behinderung (Marburg, GER) Unable to locate
Gejiu People's Broadcasting Station (Gejiu, YU, CHN) Unable to locate

Gekkam (Tokyo, JPN) Ceased
Gekkan Nikken Ren (Tokyo, JPN) Unable to locate
Gekkan Oruta (Tokyo, JPN) Unable to locate
Gekkan Shonen Magazine (Tokyo, JPN) [46829]
Gelandewgen Magazin (Schwabach, GER) Unable to locate
Geliebte Katze (Munich, GER) Unable to locate
Gem & Jewellery Yearbook (Jaipur, RJ, IND) [45194]
Gemini-FM [56759]*
Gemini-FM [53368]*
Gemini-FM [53367]*
Gems and Gemmology (Wuhan, HU, CHN) [43522]
Gender and Behaviour (Ile-Ife, NGA) [49112]
Gender & Development (Oxford, GBR) [55962]
Gender and Education (Abingdon, GBR) [51793]
Gender and Language (London, GBR) [54498]
Gender in Management (Manchester, GBR) [55556]
Gender, Place and Culture (Aberystwyth, GBR) [51688]
Gender, Technology & Development (New Delhi, DH, IND) [45519]
Gene Expression Patterns (Singapore, SGP) [50151]
Gene Therapy (London, GBR) [54499]
Gene Therapy and Regulation (Nice, FRA) [44015]
Genealogists' Magazine (London, GBR) [54500]
Geneesmiddelenbulletin (Utrecht, NLD) [48758]
Geneflow (Rome, ITA) [46230]
General Education Reading Material Series (Aligarh, UP, IND) Unable to locate
Genes, Brain and Behavior (Frederiksberg, DEN) [43690]
Genes, Chromosomes & Cancer (Lund, SWE) [50985]
Genes & Genetic Systems (Osaka, JPN) [46617]
Genes & Nutrition (Rome, ITA) [46231]
Genetic Vaccines and Therapy (London, GBR) [54501]
Genetica (Dordrecht, NLD) [48405]
Genetics and Breeding (Sofia, BUL) [43100]
Genetics and Molecular Biology (Ribeirao Preto, SP, BRZ) [42998]
Genetics and Molecular Research (Ribeirao Preto, SP, BRZ) [42999]
Genetics Selection Evolution (Jouy-en-Josas, FRA) [43960]
Geneva Papers on Risk and Insurance Issues and Practice (Basingstoke, GBR) [52205]
Geneva Papers on Risk and Insurance Theory [51096]*
Geneva Risk and Insurance Review (Geneva, SWI) [51096]
Geneve Home Informations (Geneva, SWI) [51097]
Genhe People's Broadcasting Station (Genhe, NM, CHN) Unable to locate
Genome Biology (Online Edition) (London, GBR) [54502]
Genomics, Proteomics & Bioinformatics (Beijing, CHN) [43194]
Genomika (London, GBR) Ceased
Gensuikyo Tsushin (Tokyo, JPN) Unable to locate

Numbers cited in bold after listings are entry numbers rather than page numbers.

Gente (Peru) (Lima, PER) *Unable to locate*

Geo (Madrid, SPA) **[50761]**

GEO (Cambridge, GBR) **[52822]**

Geo-Marine Letters (Wilhelmshaven, GER) **[44713]**

Geobios (Jodhpur, RJ, IND) *Unable to locate*

Geochemical Journal (Tokyo, JPN) **[46830]**

Geochemical Society of India Journal (Patna, BH, IND) *Unable to locate*

Geochemical Transactions (London, GBR) **[54503]**

Geochemistry (Bath, GBR) **[52241]**

Geochemistry International (Moscow, RUS) **[49906]**

Geochronometria (Wroclaw, POL) **[49778]**

Geodesy and Cartography (Warsaw, POL) **[49713]**

Geoexploration **[48046]***

Geografia Aplicada y Desarrollo (Quito, ECU) *Unable to locate*

Geografie (Utrecht, NLD) *Unable to locate*

Geografisk Orientering (Brenderup, DEN) *Unable to locate*

Geografiska Annaler, Series A, Physical Geography (Stockholm, SWE) **[51017]**

Geografiska Annaler, Series B, Social Geography (Stockholm, SWE) **[51018]**

Geographer (Aligarh, UP, IND) *Unable to locate*

Geographical (London, GBR) *Unable to locate*

Geographical Bulletin of India (Patna, BH, IND) *Unable to locate*

Geographical Education Magazine (Harare, ZWE) *Unable to locate*

Geographical Journal (Oxford, GBR) **[55963]**

Geographical Knowledge (Beijing, CHN) *Unable to locate*

Geographical Observer (Meerut, UP, IND) *Unable to locate*

Geographical Research (Perth, WA, AUS) **[42251]**

Geographical Review of India (Calcutta, WB, IND) *Unable to locate*

Geographical View Point (Agra, UP, IND) *Unable to locate*

Geography (Sheffield, GBR) **[56493]**

Geography and Natural Resources (Irkutsk, RUS) **[49856]**

Geography Teacher (Chennai, TN, IND) *Unable to locate*

GeoInformatica (Dordrecht, NLD) **[48406]**

Geologica Balcanica (Sofia, BUL) **[43101]**

Geologica Belgica (Brussels, BEL) **[42856]**

Geological Magazine (Cambridge, GBR) **[52823]**

Geological, Mining and Metallurgical Society of India Bulletin (Calcutta, WB, IND) *Unable to locate*

Geological Survey of India News (Kolkata, WB, IND) **[45267]**

Geologija (Warsaw, POL) **[49714]**

Geologisk Tidsskrift (Copenhagen, DEN) **[43671]**

Geology and Minerals Resources (Sofia, BUL) *Unable to locate*

Geology of Ore Deposits (Moscow, RUS) **[49907]**

Geomagnetism and Aeronomy (Moscow, RUS) **[49908]**

Geomechanics and Geoengineering (Nottingham, GBR) **[55756]**

Geomechanics and Tunnelling (Salzburg, AUT) **[42740]**

Geometriae Dedicata (Dordrecht, NLD) **[48407]**

Geometric and Functional Analysis (GAFA) (Tel Aviv, ISR) **[46100]**

Geometry & Topology (Coventry, GBR) **[53083]**

Geophilos (Teddington, GBR) **[56730]**

Geophysical & Astrophysical Fluid Dynamics (Exeter, GBR) **[53359]**

Geophysical Prospecting (Houten, NLD) **[48640]**

Geophysics Journal of Hokkaido University (Sapporo, JPN) *Unable to locate*

Geophytology (Lucknow, UP, IND) *Unable to locate*

Geopolitics (Abingdon, GBR) **[51794]**

GEORGE-FM - 96.8 (Auckland, NZL) **[48841]**

Georgian Mathematical Journal (Tbilisi, GRG) **[44133]**

Georgist Journal (London, GBR) *Unable to locate*

Geoscience and Development Journal (Sao Paulo, SP, BRZ) *Unable to locate*

Geosciences; Journal of the China University of **[43519]***

Geostandards & Geoanalytical Research (Milton Keynes, GBR) **[55636]**

Geosur (Montevideo, URY) *Unable to locate*

Geosynthetics International (London, GBR) **[54504]**

Geotechnical Engineering (Pathumthani, THA) **[51459]**

Geotectonics (Moscow, RUS) **[49909]**

Geotextiles and Geomembranes (Amsterdam, NLD) **[47997]**

Geothermics (Amsterdam, NLD) **[47998]**

Geoviews (Secunderabad, AP, IND) *Unable to locate*

Ger (Ulaanbaatar, MNG) *Unable to locate*

Geras-FM - 92 (Kaunas, LIT) **[47468]**

Geras-FM - 101.9 (Vilnius, LIT) **[47483]**

Geriatric Medicine (London, GBR) **[54505]**

Geriatrics & Gerontology International (Oxford, GBR) **[55964]**

German as a Foreign Language (Cambridge, GBR) **[52824]**

German History (Oxford, GBR) **[55965]**

German Medical Science (Dusseldorf, GER) **[44326]**

German Monitor (Amsterdam, NLD) **[47999]**

German Politics (Brighton, GBR) **[52608]**

german research (Bonn, GER) **[44262]**

German Risk and Insurance Review (Cologne, GER) **[44295]**

German Series (G-) (Falkenstein, GER) *Unable to locate*

Germanistik (Berlin, GER) **[44186]**

Gerokomos (Madrid, SPA) **[50762]**

Gerontechnology (Eindhoven, NLD) **[48591]**

Gerontologija (Belgrade, SER) *Unable to locate*

Gerontology and Geriatrics (Debrecen, HUN) **[44888]**

Gestalt Journal of Australia and New Zealand (Robina, QL, AUS) **[42313]**

Gestalten & Verkaufen (Braunschweig, GER) **[44277]**

Gestao & Producao (Sao Carlos, SP, BRZ) **[43017]**

Gestion et Services Publics (Nyon, SWI) *Unable to locate*

Gesture (Amsterdam, NLD) **[48000]**

Gesundheit Sprechstunde (Zurich, SWI) **[51262]**

Getranke! Technologie & Marketing (Nuremberg, GER) **[44613]**

Getrankemarkt (Nuremberg, GER) **[44614]**

Getting There (London, GBR) **[54506]**

Gewerkschaftliche Umschau (Hannover, GER) *Unable to locate*

GH Gastrotel (Cologne, GER) *Unable to locate*

Ghana Journal of Agricultural Science (Grahamstown, SAF) **[50495]**

Ghana Journal of Development Studies (Navrongo, GHA) **[44738]**

Ghana Journal of Forestry (Kumasi, GHA) **[44735]**

Ghana Journal of Science (Legon, GHA) **[44736]**

Ghana Library Journal (Tamale, GHA) **[44739]**

Ghana Medical Journal (Accra, GHA) **[44726]**

The Ghanaian Chronicle (Accra, GHA) **[44727]**

Ghanaian Newsrunner (Amsterdam, NLD) **[48001]**

Gifted & Talented (Milton Keynes, GBR) *Unable to locate*

Gifts Today (Watford, GBR) *Unable to locate*

Gifu Journal of Maternal Health (Gifu, JPN) *Unable to locate*

Gilbert & Sullivan News (Chelmsford, GBR) **[52961]**

The Gilbert & Sullivan News (Kent, GBR) *Unable to locate*

Giornale di Anestesia Stomatologica (Padova, ITA) *Unable to locate*

Giornale del Marmo—International Stone Magazine (Faenza, ITA) **[46137]**

Giornale di Metafisica (Genoa, ITA) **[46149]**

Giornale di Sicilia (Palermo, ITA) *Unable to locate*

Gippsland-FM - 104.7 (Morwell, VI, AUS) **[42122]**

Girl Talk (London, GBR) **[54507]**

Girl Talk Extra (London, GBR) **[54508]**

Girls (Copenhagen, DEN) *Unable to locate*

GirlZone (Christchurch, NZL) *Ceased*

GIT Sicherheit Management (Darmstadt, GER) **[44307]**

Gitit (Tel Aviv, ISR) *Unable to locate*

Gizi Indonesia (Jakarta, IDN) **[45798]**

Gjuteriet (Jonkoping, SWE) *Unable to locate*

Glacial Geology and Geomorphology (Belfast, GBR) **[52284]**

Glad Rags (Mumbai, MH, IND) *Unable to locate*

The Glade (Chorley, GBR) **[53022]**

Glas Istre (Voice of Istria) (Pula, CTA) *Unable to locate*

The Glasgow & Edinburgh Property Executive **[53443]***

Glasgow Mathematical Journal (Glasgow, GBR) **[53421]**

Glass (London, GBR) **[54509]**

Glass and Glazing Products (Westerham, GBR) *Unable to locate*

Glass Industry Development International (London, GBR) *Unable to locate*

Glass International (London, GBR) **[54510]**

Glass Physics and Chemistry (Saint Petersburg, RUS) **[50022]**

Glass Science and Technology (Offengach, GER) *Unable to locate*

Glass Technology (Sheffield, GBR) **[56494]**

Glass's Guide Index of Registration Marks (Weybridge, GBR) *Ceased*

Glazed Expressions (Oldham, GBR) **[55783]**

The Gleaner (Kingston, JAM) **[46285]**

Gleanings (Battaramulla, SRI) *Unable to locate*

The Glebe (Five Dock, NW, AUS) **[41867]**

Glimpses of Future (Jammu, JK, IND) *Unable to locate*

Global (Turin, ITA) *Unable to locate*

Global Airport Cities Magazine (Twickenham, GBR) **[56792]**

Global Approaches to Extension Practice (Owerri, IM, NGA) **[49162]**

Global Bioethics (Florence, ITA) **[46144]**

Global Business and Economics Review (Utrecht, NLD) **[48759]**

Global Business Jet (Bishop's Stortford, GBR) **[52379]**

Global Cement Magazine (Surrey, GBR) **[56663]**

Global Change & Human Health (Bussum, NLD) *Ceased*

Global Change, Peace & Security (Abingdon, GBR) **[51795]**

Global Crime (Abingdon, GBR) **[51796]**

Global Economic Review (Seoul, KOR) *Unable to locate*

Global Environmental Change (Amsterdam, NLD) **[48002]**

Global Fuels magazine (Surrey, GBR) *Ceased*

Global Future (Burwood East, VI, AUS) **[41677]**

Global Futures Bulletin (Earlville, QL, AUS) *Unable to locate*

Global Gypsum Magazine (Surrey, GBR) **[56664]**

Global Health Promotion (Saint Denis, FRA) **[44103]**

Global Insulation Magazine (Surrey, GBR) **[56665]**

Global Investor (London, GBR) **[54511]**

Global Journal of Agricultural Sciences (Calabar, CR, NGA) **[49069]**

Global Journal of Biotechnology & Biochemistry (Faisalabad, PAK) **[49241]**

Global Journal of Educational Research (Calabar, CR, NGA) **[49070]**

Global Journal of Engineering Education (Melbourne, VI, AUS) **[42061]**

Global Journal of Engineering Research (Grahamstown, SAF) **[50496]**

Global Journal of Environmental Research (Faisalabad, PAK) **[49242]**

Global Journal of Environmental Sciences (Calabar, CR, NGA) **[49071]**

Global Journal of Geological Sciences (Calabar, CR, NGA) **[49072]**

Global Journal of Humanities (Calabar, CR, NGA) **[49073]**

Global Journal of Mathematical Sciences (Grahamstown, SAF) **[50497]**

Global Journal of Mathematics and Mathematical Sciences (GJMMS) (Kerman, IRN) **[45881]**

Numbers cited in bold after listings are entry numbers rather than page numbers.

Global Journal of Medical Sciences (Calabar, CR, NGA) **[49074]**

Global Journal of Molecular Sciences (Faisalabad, PAK) **[49243]**

Global Journal of Pharmacology (Faisalabad, PAK) **[49244]**

Global Journal of Pure and Applied Mathematics (Seoul, KOR) **[47266]**

Global Journal of Pure and Applied Sciences (Calabar, CR, NGA) **[49075]**

Global Journal of Social Sciences (Calabar, CR, NGA) **[49076]**

Global Municipal Investor (Leicester, GBR) **[53802]**

Global Nest (Athens, GRC) **[44743]**

Global Networks (Oxford) (Oxford, GBR) **[55966]**

Global Pensions (London, GBR) **[54512]**

Global and Planetary Change (Amsterdam, NLD) **[48003]**

Global Public Health (Abingdon, GBR) **[51797]**

Global Responsibility to Protect (Leiden, NLD) **[48673]**

Global Review of Business and Economic Research (New Delhi, DH, IND) **[45520]**

Global Slag Magazine (Surrey, GBR) *Ceased*

Global Social Policy (London, GBR) **[54513]**

Global Society (Abingdon, GBR) **[51798]**

Global Sources Auto Parts & Accessories (Singapore, SGP) **[50152]**

Global Sources Baby & Childrens Products (Singapore, SGP) **[50153]**

Global Sources Fashion Accessories (Singapore, SGP) **[50154]**

Global Sources Garments & Textiles (Singapore, SGP) **[50155]**

Global Sources Gifts & Premiums (Singapore, SGP) **[50156]**

Global Sources Hardware & DIY (Singapore, SGP) **[50157]**

Global Sources Home Products (Singapore, SGP) **[50158]**

Global Sources Sports & Leisure (Singapore, SGP) **[50159]**

Global Sources Telecom Products (Singapore, SGP) **[50160]**

Global Veterinaria (Faisalabad, PAK) **[49245]**

Globalisation, Societies and Education (Abingdon, GBR) **[51799]**

Globalization and Health (London, GBR) **[54514]**

Globalizations (Abingdon, GBR) **[51800]**

The Globe (London, GBR) *Ceased*

Globe Studies (Vienna, AUT) **[42759]**

Globusfreund (Vienna, AUT) *Ceased*

Glory (Panchgani, MH, IND) *Unable to locate*

Glory of India (New Delhi, DH, IND) *Unable to locate*

GlucksPost (Zurich, SWI) **[51263]**

Glycobiology (Oxford, GBR) **[55967]**

GMAQuest (Quezon City, PHL) *Unable to locate*

Go Flying (Berkshire, GBR) **[52315]**

GO Girl (London, GBR) **[54515]**

Goa Chamber of Commerce and Industry Bulletin (Panjim, MH, IND) *Unable to locate*

Going Places (Warwick, GBR) *Ceased*

Gokhale Institute of Politics and Economics Studies (Pune, MH, IND) *Unable to locate*

Gokuldas Sanskrit Series (Varanasi, UP, IND) *Unable to locate*

Gold Bulletin (London, GBR) **[54516]**

Gold Coast Mail (Sydney, NW, AUS) **[42508]**

Gold FM - 93.0 MHz (Colombo, SRI) **[50874]**

Gold 90.5 FM - 90.5 MHz (Singapore, SGP) **[50295]**

GOLD 92.5-FM - 92.5 (Southport, QL, AUS) **[42381]**

GOLD 104.3-FM - 104.3 (Richmond, VI, AUS) **[42305]**

Golden Oldies - 861 (Kuala Lumpur, MYS) **[47645]**

Goldsmiths Review (London, GBR) **[54517]**

Golem (Berlin, GER) **[44187]**

Golf (Singapore, SGP) **[50161]**

Golf Aktuell (Munich, GER) *Unable to locate*

Golf Australia (Saint Leonards, NW, AUS) **[42333]**

Golf Club Management (Weston-super-Mare, GBR) **[56905]**

Golf Course Architecture (Leicester, GBR) **[53803]**

Golf Guide Europe (The Hague, NLD) *Unable to locate*

Golf Malaysia (Petaling Jaya, MYS) **[47698]**

Golf Monthly (London, GBR) **[54518]**

Golf Punk (Brighton, GBR) **[52609]**

Golf Radio-FM (Belgrade, SER) *Unable to locate*

Golfclub Magazine (Hannover, GER) *Unable to locate*

Golos Angary - 68.63 MHz (Bratsk, RUS) **[49851]**

Golwg (Lampeter, GBR) *Unable to locate*

Gongzhuling People's Broadcasting Station (Gongzhuling, JI, CHN) *Unable to locate*

Good Autism Practice (Worcestershire, GBR) **[56967]**

The Good Book Guide (London, GBR) *Unable to locate*

Good Clinical Practice Journal (GCPj) (London, GBR) **[54519]**

Good Fruits & Vegetables (Cleveland, QL, AUS) **[41767]**

Good Health (Witham, GBR) *Unable to locate*

Good Homes (London, GBR) **[54520]**

Good Housekeeping (New Delhi, DH, IND) **[45521]**

Good Housekeeping Philippines (Mandaluyong City, PHL) **[49537]**

Good Morning Chiangmai News Magazine (Chiang Mai, THA) **[51458]**

Good Motoring Magazine (Forest Row, GBR) **[53396]**

Good News (Worthing, GBR) *Unable to locate*

Good News Radio-FM - 103.9 (Wendouree, VI, AUS) **[42691]**

Good Time Guide (Aberdeen, GBR) **[51677]**

Good Woodworking (Bath, GBR) **[52242]**

GoodWill-FM - 103.3 (Lodge Village, SKN) **[50051]**

Goodwood Magazine (Chichester, GBR) **[53011]**

Goolarri-FM - 99.7 (Broome, WA, AUS) **[41663]**

Gora (Sofia, BUL) *Unable to locate*

Gorodskiy Sovet (Naberezhnyye Chelny, RUS) *Unable to locate*

Gorodskoy Radiokanal (Yaroslavl, RUS) *Unable to locate*

Gospel 97.5-FM - 97.5 (Bridgetown, BRB) **[42829]**

Gospel Standard (Harpenden, GBR) **[53514]**

Gothic Studies (Bath, GBR) **[52243]**

Goulburn Community Radio-FM - 103.3 (Goulburn, NW, AUS) **[41929]**

Goulburn Post (Goulburn, NW, AUS) **[41927]**

Gourmet (Stockholm, SWE) *Unable to locate*

Gourmet Traveller WINE (Sydney, NW, AUS) **[42509]**

Gove-FM - 106.9 (Nhulunbuy, NT, AUS) **[42146]**

Government of Belize Gazette (Belmopan, BLZ) *Unable to locate*

Government Business (Loughton, GBR) **[55490]**

Government College Economic Journal (Lahore, PAK) *Unable to locate*

Government and Opposition (Brighton, GBR) **[52610]**

Government Technology (Loughton, GBR) **[55491]**

Govorit Sarov (Sarov, RUS) *Unable to locate*

GP General Practitioner (London, GBR) *Unable to locate*

GP Magazin (Gewerkschaftspost) (Hannover, GER) *Unable to locate*

Graduate Journal of Social Science (Lund, SWE) **[50986]**

The Graduate School Journal (Virac, PHL) *Unable to locate*

Graefe's Archive for Clinical and Experimental Ophthalmology (Glasgow, GBR) **[53422]**

Graficar (Ljubljana, SVA) *Unable to locate*

Grafik (Cheltenham, GBR) **[52972]**

Grammars (Dordrecht, NLD) **[48408]**

Grana (Stockholm, SWE) **[51019]**

Grand Hotel (Milan, ITA) *Unable to locate*

Grand Prix Magazine (London, GBR) *Unable to locate*

Granthagar (Calcutta, WB, IND) *Unable to locate*

Grantham Citizen & Journal Series (Edinburgh, GBR) *Unable to locate*

Grantmanship (Minsk, BLR) *Unable to locate*

Granular Matter (Rennes, FRA) **[44097]**

Graphic Design in Japan (Tokyo, JPN) *Unable to locate*

Graphical Models (Amsterdam, NLD) **[48004]**

Graphical Models and Image Processing **[48004]***

Graphical Survey of the Economy (Taipei, TWN) *Unable to locate*

Graphics International **[52972]***

Graphicus (Turin, ITA) *Unable to locate*

Graphs and Combinatorics (Tokyo, JPN) **[46831]**

Grass and Forage Science (Reading, GBR) *Unable to locate*

Grassland Science (Miyazaki, JPN) **[46518]**

Grassland Science (Oxford, GBR) **[55968]**

Grasslands & Forage Abstracts (Wallingford, GBR) **[56818]**

Grassroots (Hyderabad, PAK) *Unable to locate*

Gravesend Reporter (Gravesend, GBR) **[53479]**

Gravid (Pregnant) (Kil, SWE) *Unable to locate*

Gray Book (Cuttack, OR, IND) *Unable to locate*

Grazer Philosophische Studien (Amsterdam, NLD) **[48005]**

Grazia (London, GBR) **[54521]**

Great Days Out (Liverpool, GBR) *Ceased*

Great Lakes Advocate (Forster, NW, AUS) **[41869]**

Great Lakes-FM - 101.5 (Tuncurry, NW, AUS) **[42654]**

Great Yarmouth Advertiser (Great Yarmouth, GBR) **[53482]**

Great Yarmouth Mercury (Great Yarmouth, GBR) **[53483]**

Greater Kashmir (Srinagar, JK, IND) **[45737]**

Greece and Rome (Southampton, GBR) **[56571]**

Green Alert (Hong Kong, CHN) **[43301]**

Green Chemistry (Cambridge, GBR) **[52825]**

Green Dossier (Kiev, URE) *Unable to locate*

Green Dove (Accra-North, GHA) *Unable to locate*

Green Final (Aberdeen) (Mastrick, GBR) *Unable to locate*

Green Giant-FM - 87.5 (Manila, PHL) **[49563]**

Green Left Weekly (Sydney, NW, AUS) **[42510]**

Green Un (Ipswich) (Ipswich, GBR) **[53657]**

Greener Management International (Sheffield, GBR) **[56495]**

Greenkeeper International (York, GBR) **[56991]**

Greenline (Harare, ZWE) *Unable to locate*

Greenpeace (Paris, FRA) *Unable to locate*

Greenpeace Australia News (Surry Hills, NW, AUS) *Unable to locate*

Greenpeace Magazine (Brussels, BEL) **[42857]**

Greenpeace Magazine (Esch-sur-Alzette, LUX) *Unable to locate*

GreenPeace Radio-FM - 97.3 (Taipei, TWN) **[51372]**

Greens Business Law Bulletin (Edinburgh, GBR) **[53280]**

Greens Civil Practice Bulletin (Edinburgh, GBR) *Unable to locate*

Greens Criminal Law Bulletin (Edinburgh, GBR) **[53281]**

Greens Property Law Bulletin (Edinburgh, GBR) **[53282]**

Greens Weekly Digest (Edinburgh, GBR) **[53283]**

Greetings & Gifts (Surry Hills, NW, AUS) **[42433]**

Greetings Today (Watford, GBR) *Unable to locate*

Grenfell Record (Grenfell, NW, AUS) **[41934]**

The Grey Journal (Amsterdam, NLD) **[48006]**

Greymouth Star (Greymouth, NZL) **[48904]**

Grial (Vigo, SPA) *Unable to locate*

The Grieg Companion (Potters Bar, GBR) **[56296]**

Grip (Manchester, GBR) **[55557]**

Grocer (Crawley, GBR) **[53105]**

The Grocery Trader (Kings Langley, GBR) **[53710]**

Groom n' Bride (Singapore, SGP) *Unable to locate*

Groove (Berlin, GER) **[44188]**

Grotiana (Leiden, NLD) **[48674]**

Ground Water (Oxford, GBR) **[55969]**

Ground Water Monitoring & Remediation (Oxford, GBR) **[55970]**

Numbers cited in bold after listings are entry numbers rather than page numbers.

Group Analysis (London, GBR) **[54522]**

Group Leisure (Milton Keynes, GBR) **[55637]**

Group Processes & Intergroup Relations (London, GBR) **[54523]**

Groups — Complexity — Cryptology (Hamburg, GER) **[44417]**

Grow Your Own (Colchester, GBR) **[53036]**

Growing Minds (New Delhi, DH, IND) *Unable to locate*

Growing Organically **[53089]***

Growth Company Investor (London, GBR) **[54524]**

Growth Factors (Melbourne, VI, AUS) **[42062]**

Growth Hormone & IGF Research (Arhus, DEN) **[43646]**

GrowthPoint (Reading, GBR) **[56319]**

Grundwasser (Dordrecht, NLD) **[48409]**

GT-FM - 107.9 (Pontypridd, GBR) **[56278]**

GT Il Giornale dei Trasportatori (Milan, ITA) *Unable to locate*

GT Purely Porsche (Sevenoaks, GBR) **[56473]**

GTRK Adygeya - Maykop (Maykop, RUS) *Unable to locate*

GTRK Adygeya - Maykop (Maykop, RUS) *Unable to locate*

GTRK Amur - Belogorsk (Blagoveshchensk, RUS) *Unable to locate*

GTRK Amur - Belogorsk (Cheboksary, RUS) *Unable to locate*

GTRK Amur - Blagoveshchensk (Blagoveshchensk, RUS) *Unable to locate*

GTRK Amur - Blagoveshchensk (Blagoveshchensk, RUS) *Unable to locate*

GTRK Amur - Blagoveshchensk (Blagoveshchensk, RUS) *Unable to locate*

GTRK Amur - Progress (Chelyabinsk, RUS) *Unable to locate*

GTRK Amur - Shimanovsk (Moscow, RUS) *Unable to locate*

GTRK Amur - Tynda (Moscow, RUS) *Unable to locate*

GTRK Amur - Zeya (Blagoveshchensk, RUS) *Unable to locate*

GTRK Amur - Zeya (Moscow, RUS) *Unable to locate*

GTRK Ataly - Barnaul (Barnaul, RUS) *Unable to locate*

GTRK Ataly - Biysk (Barnaul, RUS) *Unable to locate*

GTRK Ataly - Blagoveshchensk (Barnaul, RUS) *Unable to locate*

GTRK Ataly - Gorno-Altaysk (Gorno-Altaysk, RUS) *Unable to locate*

GTRK Ataly - Kamen na obi (Barnaul, RUS) *Unable to locate*

GTRK Ataly - Mamantovo (Barnaul, RUS) *Unable to locate*

GTRK Ataly - Rubtsovsk (Barnaul, RUS) *Unable to locate*

GTRK Ataly - Ust-Kalmanka (Barnaul, RUS) *Unable to locate*

GTRK Ataly - Zarinsk (Barnaul, RUS) *Unable to locate*

GTRK Bashkorostan - Yazykovo (Ufa, RUS) *Unable to locate*

GTRK Bashkortostan - Baymak (Moscow, RUS) *Unable to locate*

GTRK Bashkortostan - Ufa (Ufa, RUS) *Unable to locate*

GTRK Bashkortostan - Ufa (Ufa, RUS) *Unable to locate*

GTRK Bashkortostan - Yazykovo (Ufa, RUS) *Unable to locate*

GTRK Belgorod - Korocha (Moscow, RUS) *Unable to locate*

GTRK Bira - Birobidzhan (Birobidzhan, RUS) *Unable to locate*

GTRK Bira - Birobidzhan (Birobidzhan, RUS) *Unable to locate*

GTRK Bira - Birobidzhan (Birobidzhan, RUS) *Unable to locate*

GTRK Bira - Birobidzhan - 216 KHz (Birobidzhan, RUS) **[49850]**

GTRK Bryansk - Bryansk (Bryansk, RUS) *Unable to locate*

GTRK Bryansk - Shvedchiki (Bryansk, RUS) *Unable to locate*

GTRK Buryatskaya - Badgarin (Ulan-Ude, RUS) *Unable to locate*

GTRK Buryatskaya - Barguzin (Moscow, RUS) *Unable to locate*

GTRK Buryatskaya - Guzino-Ozersk (Ulan-Ude, RUS) *Unable to locate*

GTRK Buryatskaya - Kyakhta (Moscow, RUS) *Unable to locate*

GTRK Buryatskaya - Kyakhta (Ulan-Ude, RUS) *Unable to locate*

GTRK Buryatskaya - Selenginsk (Ulan-Ude, RUS) *Unable to locate*

GTRK Buryatskaya - Severobaykalsk (Ulan-Ude, RUS) *Unable to locate*

GTRK Buryatskaya - Ufa (Ufa, RUS) *Unable to locate*

GTRK Buryatskaya - Ulan-Ude (Ulan-Ude, RUS) *Unable to locate*

GTRK Buryatskaya - Ulan-Ude (Ulan-Ude, RUS) *Unable to locate*

GTRK Buryatskaya - Ulan-Ude (Ulan-Ude, RUS) *Unable to locate*

GTRK Buryatskaya - Zakamensk (Ulan-Ude, RUS) *Unable to locate*

GTRK Chelyabinskaya - Chelyabinsk (Chelyabinsk, RUS) *Unable to locate*

GTRK Chelyabinskaya - Kartaly (Moscow, RUS) *Unable to locate*

GTRK Chelyabinskaya - Miass (Moscow, RUS) *Unable to locate*

GTRK Chelyabinskaya - Zlatoust (Moscow, RUS) *Unable to locate*

GTRK Chitinskaya - Chita (Chita, RUS) *Unable to locate*

GTRK Chitinskaya - Chita (Chita, RUS) *Unable to locate*

GTRK Chitinskaya - Chita - 66.32 MHz (Chita, RUS) **[49853]**

GTRK Chitinskaya - Khada-Bulak (Moscow, RUS) *Unable to locate*

GTRK Chitinskaya - Kholbon - 69.80 MHz (Kholbon, RUS) **[49862]**

GTRK Chitinskaya - Orlovskiy (Moscow, RUS) *Unable to locate*

GTRK Chukotka - Anadyr (Anadyr, RUS) *Unable to locate*

GTRK Chuvashiya - Ibresi (Cheboksary, RUS) *Unable to locate*

GTRK Chuvashiya - Ibresi (Moscow, RUS) *Unable to locate*

GTRK Dalnesvostochnaya - Khabarovsk (Khabarovsk, RUS) *Unable to locate*

GTRK Dalnevostochnaya - Bidzhan (Novokuznetsk, RUS) *Unable to locate*

GTRK Dalnevostochnaya - Birobidzhan (Moscow, RUS) *Unable to locate*

GTRK Dalnevostochnaya - Chegdomyn (Khabarovsk, RUS) *Unable to locate*

GTRK Dalnevostochnaya - Khabarovsk (Khabarovsk, RUS) *Unable to locate*

GTRK Dalnevostochnaya - Khanty-Komsomolsk (Khabarovsk, RUS) *Unable to locate*

GTRK Dalnevostochnaya - Komsomolsk (Izhevsk, RUS) *Unable to locate*

GTRK Dalnevostochnaya - Komsomolsk (Khabarovsk, RUS) *Unable to locate*

GTRK Dalnevostochnaya - Komsomolsk (Khabarovsk, RUS) *Unable to locate*

GTRK Don-TR - Morozovsk (Moscow, RUS) *Unable to locate*

GTRK Don-TR - Novocherkassk (Rostov-na-Donu, RUS) *Unable to locate*

GTRK Don-TR - Rostov-na-Donu (Rostov-na-Donu, RUS) *Unable to locate*

GTRK Don-TR - Rostov-na-Donu (Rostov-na-Donu, RUS) *Unable to locate*

GTRK Gornyy Altay - Choya (Moscow, RUS) *Unable to locate*

GTRK Gornyy Altay - Onguday (Moscow, RUS) *Unable to locate*

GTRK Gornyy Altay - Shebalino - 1350 KHz (Shebalino, RUS) **[50034]**

GTRK Gornyy Altay - Ust-Kan - 1350 KHz (Ust-Kan, RUS) **[50038]**

GTRK Gornyy Altay - Ust-Ulagan - 1350 KHz (Ust-Ulagan, RUS) **[50039]**

GTRK - Groznyy (Moscow, RUS) *Unable to locate*

GTRK - Groznyy (Moscow, RUS) *Unable to locate*

GTRK Irkutskaya - Angarsk (Irkutsk, RUS) *Unable to locate*

GTRK Irkutskaya - Angarsk (Moscow, RUS) *Unable to locate*

GTRK Irkutskaya - Anzhero-Sudzhensk (Moscow, RUS) *Unable to locate*

GTRK Irkutskaya - Bratsk (Izhevsk, RUS) *Unable to locate*

GTRK Irkutskaya - Cheremkhovo (Moscow, RUS) *Unable to locate*

GTRK Irkutskaya - Chuna (Moscow, RUS) *Unable to locate*

GTRK Irkutskaya - Kemerovo (Moscow, RUS) *Unable to locate*

GTRK Irkutskaya - Klyuchevaya (Moscow, RUS) *Unable to locate*

GTRK Irkutskaya - Leninsk-Kuznetskiy (Nab. Chelny, RUS) *Unable to locate*

GTRK Irkutskaya - Mezhdurechensk (Moscow, RUS) *Unable to locate*

GTRK Irkutskaya - Nizhneudinsk (Moscow, RUS) *Unable to locate*

GTRK Irkutskaya - Novokuznetsk (Moscow, RUS) *Unable to locate*

GTRK Irkutskaya - Tashtogol (Moscow, RUS) *Unable to locate*

GTRK Irkutskaya - Tayshet (Irkutsk, RUS) *Unable to locate*

GTRK Irkutskaya - Tayshet (Moscow, RUS) *Unable to locate*

GTRK Irkutskaya - Tulun (Irkutsk, RUS) *Unable to locate*

GTRK Irkutskaya - Ulkan (Moscow, RUS) *Unable to locate*

GTRK Irkutskaya - Ust-Ilimsk (Moscow, RUS) *Unable to locate*

GTRK Irkutskaya - Ust-Ordynskiy (Moscow, RUS) *Unable to locate*

GTRK Irtysh - Cherlak (Moscow, RUS) *Unable to locate*

GTRK Irtysh - Omsk (Omsk, RUS) *Unable to locate*

GTRK Irtysh - Omsk (Omsk, RUS) *Unable to locate*

GTRK Irtysh - Tara (Moscow, RUS) *Unable to locate*

GTRK Irtysh - Tara (Moscow, RUS) *Unable to locate*

GTRK Ivteleradio - Agniskoye (Moscow, RUS) *Unable to locate*

GTRK Ivteleradio - Ivanovo (Ivanovo, RUS) *Unable to locate*

GTRK Kabbalkteleradio - Nalchik (Nalchik, RUS) *Unable to locate*

GTRK Kabbalkteleradio - Nalchik (Nalchik, RUS) *Unable to locate*

GTRK Kabbalkteleradio - Nalchik (Nalchik, RUS) *Unable to locate*

GTRK Kabbalkteleradio - Tegenekli (Moscow, RUS) *Unable to locate*

GTRK Kabbalkteleradio - Tegenekli (Moscow, RUS) *Unable to locate*

GTRK - Kaluga (Kaluga, RUS) *Unable to locate*

GTRK - Kaluga (Kaluga, RUS) *Unable to locate*

GTRK Kaluga - Sukhinichi (Kaluga, RUS) *Unable to locate*

GTRK Kaluga - Sukhinichi (Kaluga, RUS) *Unable to locate*

GTRK Kamchatka - Petropavlovsk (Petropavlovsk, RUS) *Unable to locate*

GTRK Kamchatka - Petropavlovsk (Petropavlovsk, RUS) *Unable to locate*

GTRK Kamchatka - Petropavlovsk (Petropavlovsk-Kamchatskiy, RUS) *Unable to locate*

GTRK Kamchatka - Sobolevo (Moscow, RUS) *Unable to locate*

GTRK Kamchatka - Ust-Kamchatsk (Petropavlovsk-Kamchatskiy, RUS) *Unable to locate*

GTRK Karachayevo-Cherkesiya - Cherkessk (Cherkessk, RUS) *Unable to locate*

GTRK Karachayevo-Cherkesiya - Cherkessk (Cherkessk, RUS) *Unable to locate*

GTRK Karachayevo-Cherkesiya - Cherkessk (Cherkessk, RUS) *Unable to locate*

GTRK Karachayevo-Cherkesskaya - Urup (Cherkessk, RUS) *Unable to locate*

GTRK Kareliya - Kostomuksha (Moscow, RUS) *Unable to locate*

GTRK Kareliya - Muezerskiy (Moscow, RUS) *Unable to locate*

GTRK Kareliya - Nadvoitsy (Moscow, RUS) *Unable to locate*

GTRK Kareliya - Petrozavodsk (Petrozavodsk, RUS) *Unable to locate*

GTRK Kareliya - Petrozavodsk (Petrozavodsk, RUS) *Unable to locate*

GTRK Khanty-Mansiyskaya - Berezovo (Khanty-Mansiysk, RUS) *Unable to locate*

GTRK Khanty-Mansiyskaya - Khanty-Mansiysk (Khanty-Mansiysk, RUS) *Unable to locate*

GTRK Khanty-Mansiyskaya - Khanty-Mansiysk (Khanty-Mansiysk, RUS) *Unable to locate*

GTRK Khanty-Mansiyskaya - Khanty-Mansiysk (Khanty-Mansiysk, RUS) *Unable to locate*

GTRK Khanty-Mansiyskaya - Khanty-Mansiysk (Khanty-Mansiysk, RUS) *Unable to locate*

GTRK Khanty-Mansiyskaya - Khanty-Mansiysk (Khanty-Mansiysk, RUS) *Unable to locate*

GTRK Komi gor - Inta (Moscow, RUS) *Unable to locate*

GTRK Komi Permyatskaya - Gayny (Kudymkar, RUS) *Unable to locate*

Numbers cited in bold after listings are entry numbers rather than page numbers.

GTRK Komi Permyatskaya - Kudymkar (Kudymkar, RUS) *Unable to locate*

GTRK Komi Permyatskaya - Kudymkar (Kudymkar, RUS) *Unable to locate*

GTRK Komi gor - Ust-Tsilma (Moscow, RUS) *Unable to locate*

GTRK Komi gor - Vorkuta (Moscow, RUS) *Unable to locate*

GTRK Koryakskaya - Tilichiki (Palana, RUS) *Unable to locate*

GTRK Kostromskaya - Kostoma (Kostroma, RUS) *Unable to locate*

GTRK Krasnovyarsk - Krasnovyarskaya (Krasnoyarsk, RUS) *Unable to locate*

GTRK Krasnoyarsk - Krasnoyarsk (Krasnoyarsk, RUS) *Unable to locate*

GTRK Krasnoyarskaya - Achinsk (Moscow, RUS) *Unable to locate*

GTRK Krasnoyarskaya - Krasnoyarsk (Krasnoyarsk, RUS) *Unable to locate*

GTRK Krasnoyarskaya - Krasnoyarsk (Krasnoyarsk, RUS) *Unable to locate*

GTRK Krasnoyarskaya - Krasnoyarsk (Krasnoyarsk, RUS) *Unable to locate*

GTRK Krasnoyarskaya - Krasnoyarsk (Krasnoyarsk, RUS) *Unable to locate*

GTRK Krasnoyarskaya - Krasnoyarsk - 216 KHz (Krasnoyarsk, RUS) **[49864]**

GTRK Krasnoyarskaya - Solyanka (Moscow, RUS) *Unable to locate*

GTRK Kuban - Maykop (Moscow, RUS) *Unable to locate*

GTRK Kuban - Sochi (Moscow, RUS) *Unable to locate*

GTRK Kuban - Tbilisskaya (Krasnodar, RUS) *Unable to locate*

GTRK Kuban - Temryuk (Moscow, RUS) *Unable to locate*

GTRK Kuban - Tuapse (Krasnodar, RUS) *Unable to locate*

GTRK Kurganskaya - Shumikha (Moscow, RUS) *Unable to locate*

GTRK - Lipetsk (Lipetsk, RUS) *Unable to locate*

GTRK Lotos - Astrakhan (Astrakhan, RUS) *Unable to locate*

GTRK Lotos - Astrakhan (Astrakhan, RUS) *Unable to locate*

GTRK Lotos - Chernyy Yar (Moscow, RUS) *Unable to locate*

GTRK Magadan (Magadan, RUS) *Unable to locate*

GTRK Magadan - Arman (Magadan, RUS) *Unable to locate*

GTRK Magadan - Arman (Moscow, RUS) *Unable to locate*

GTRK Magadan - Arman (Moscow, RUS) *Unable to locate*

GTRK Mariy-El - Yoshkar-Ola (Yoshkar-Ola, RUS) *Unable to locate*

GTRK Mariy-El - Yoshkar-Ola (Yoshkar-Ola, RUS) *Unable to locate*

GTRK Mariy-El - Yoshkar-Ola (Yoshkar-Ola, RUS) *Unable to locate*

GTRK Mariya-El - Yoshkar-Ola (Yoshkar-Ola, RUS) *Unable to locate*

GTRK Mordoviya - Ardatov (Saransk, RUS) *Unable to locate*

GTRK Mordoviya - Atyuryevo (Moscow, RUS) *Unable to locate*

GTRK Mordoviya - Saransk (Saransk, RUS) *Unable to locate*

GTRK Mordoviya - Saransk (Saransk, RUS) *Unable to locate*

GTRK Mordoviya - Saransk (Saransk, RUS) *Unable to locate*

GTRK - Moskva (Moscow, RUS) *Unable to locate*

GTRK - Moskva (Moscow, RUS) *Unable to locate*

GTRK - Moskva (Moscow, RUS) *Unable to locate*

GTRK Moskva - Elektrostal (Moscow, RUS) *Unable to locate*

GTRK Moskva - Kupavna (Moscow, RUS) *Unable to locate*

GTRK Moskva - Kurovskaya (Moscow, RUS) *Unable to locate*

GTRK Moskva - Noginsk (Moscow, RUS) *Unable to locate*

GTRK Moskva - Noginsk (Moscow, RUS) *Unable to locate*

GTRK Murman - Murmansk (Murmansk, RUS) *Unable to locate*

GTRK Nenetskaya - Naryan-Mar (Naryan-Mar, RUS) *Unable to locate*

GTRK Nizhniy Novgorod (Nizhniy Novgorod, RUS) *Unable to locate*

GTRK Nizhniy Novgorod (Nizhniy Novgorod, RUS) *Unable to locate*

GTRK - Nizhniy Novgorod (Nizhniy Novgorod, RUS) *Unable to locate*

GTRK Nizhniy Novgorod - Arzamas (Nizhniy Novgorod, RUS) *Unable to locate*

GTRK Nizhniy Novgorod - Krasnvye Baki (Nizhniy Novgorod, RUS) *Unable to locate*

GTRK Nizhniy Novgorod - Lukoyanov (Moscow, RUS) *Unable to locate*

GTRK Nizhniy Novgorod - Sergach (Nizhniy Novgorod, RUS) *Unable to locate*

GTRK Nizhniy Novgorod - Shakhunya (Nizhniy Novgorod, RUS) *Unable to locate*

GTRK Nizhniy Novgorod - Vyksa (Nizhniy Novgorod, RUS) *Unable to locate*

GTRK - Novosibirsk (Novosibirsk, RUS) *Unable to locate*

GTRK - Novosibirsk (Novosibirsk, RUS) *Unable to locate*

GTRK - Novosibirsk (Novosibirsk, RUS) *Unable to locate*

GTRK - Novosibirsk (Perm, RUS) *Unable to locate*

GTRK Novosibirsk - Cherepanov (Moscow, RUS) *Unable to locate*

GTRK Novosibirsk - Dovolnoye (Moscow, RUS) *Unable to locate*

GTRK Novosibirsk - Oyash (Moscow, RUS) *Unable to locate*

GTRK Novosibirsk - Oyash (Novosibirsk, RUS) *Unable to locate*

GTRK Novosibirsk - Oyash (Novosibirsk, RUS) *Unable to locate*

GTRK Novosibirsk - Oyash (Novosibirsk, RUS) *Unable to locate*

GTRK Novosibirsk - Tatarsk (Moscow, RUS) *Unable to locate*

GTRK Novosibirsk - Yakutsk (Yakutsk, RUS) *Unable to locate*

GTRK Oka - Mosolovo (Ryazan, RUS) *Unable to locate*

GTRK Oka - Ryazan (Ryazan, RUS) *Unable to locate*

GTRK Oka - Ryazan (Ryazan, RUS) *Unable to locate*

GTRK Oka - Ryazan (Ryazan, RUS) *Unable to locate*

GTRK Orenburg (Orenburg, RUS) *Unable to locate*

GTRK Orenburg (Orenburg, RUS) *Unable to locate*

GTRK Orenburg - Pleshano'o (Moscow, RUS) *Unable to locate*

GTRK Orloyskaya - Livny (Moscow, RUS) *Unable to locate*

GTRK Orloyskaya -,Livny (Moscow, RUS) *Unable to locate*

GTRK Orloyskaya - Oryol (Oryol, RUS) *Unable to locate*

GTRK Orloyskaya - Oryol (Oryol, RUS) *Unable to locate*

GTRK Penzenskaya - Blagodatka (Moscow, RUS) *Unable to locate*

GTRK Penzenskaya - Meshcherskoye (Moscow, RUS) *Unable to locate*

GTRK Penzenskaya - Pachelma (Moscow, RUS) *Unable to locate*

GTRK Permskaya - Barda (Permskaya, RUS) *Unable to locate*

GTRK Permskaya - Berezniki (Permskaya, RUS) *Unable to locate*

GTRK Permskaya - Chaykovskiy (Perm, RUS) *Unable to locate*

GTRK Permskaya - Chusovoy (Permskaya, RUS) *Unable to locate*

GTRK Permskaya - Ilyinskiy (Moscow, RUS) *Unable to locate*

GTRK Permskaya - Krasnovishersk (Permskaya, RUS) *Unable to locate*

GTRK Permskaya - Kudymkar (Moscow, RUS) *Unable to locate*

GTRK Permskaya - Kungur (Permskaya, RUS) *Unable to locate*

GTRK Permskaya - Oktyabrskiy (Perm, RUS) *Unable to locate*

GTRK Permskaya - Perm (Perm, RUS) *Unable to locate*

GTRK Permskaya - Perm (Perm, RUS) *Unable to locate*

GTRK Permskaya - Perm (Perm, RUS) *Unable to locate*

GTRK Permskaya - Perm (Perm, RUS) *Unable to locate*

GTRK Peterburg - Krasnyy Bor (Krasnyy Bor, RUS) *Unable to locate*

GTRK Peterburg - Krasnyy Bor (Saint Petersburg, RUS) *Unable to locate*

GTRK Peterburg - Olgino (Saint Petersburg, RUS) *Unable to locate*

GTRK Pomorye - Arkhangelsk (Arkhangelsk, RUS) *Unable to locate*

GTRK Pomorye - Arkhangelsk (Arkhangelsk, RUS) *Unable to locate*

GTRK Pomorye - Glubokiy (Moscow, RUS) *Unable to locate*

GTRK Pomorye - Ileza (Moscow, RUS) *Unable to locate*

GTRK Pomorye - Kotlas (Moscow, RUS) *Unable to locate*

GTRK Pomorye - Plesetsk (Moscow, RUS) *Unable to locate*

GTRK Pomorye - Plesetsk (Moscow, RUS) *Unable to locate*

GTRK Pomorye - Porog (Arkhangelsk, RUS) *Unable to locate*

GTRK Pomorye - Velsk (Moscow, RUS) *Unable to locate*

GTRK - Pskov (Pskov, RUS) *Unable to locate*

GTRK Region Tyumen (Tyumen, RUS) *Unable to locate*

GTRK Region Tyumen (Tyumen, RUS) *Unable to locate*

GTRK Region Tyumen - Nizhnevartovsk (Moscow, RUS) *Unable to locate*

GTRK Region Tyumen - Shabanovo (Moscow, RUS) *Unable to locate*

GTRK Region Tyumen - Surgut (Moscow, RUS) *Unable to locate*

GTRK Region Tyumen - Tobolsk (Moscow, RUS) *Unable to locate*

GTRK Region-Tyumen - Tyumen (Tyumen, RUS) *Unable to locate*

GTRK Respublika Khaksiya - Novomikhailovka (Moscow, RUS) *Unable to locate*

GTRK Respublika Khaksiya - Shira (Moscow, RUS) *Unable to locate*

GTRK Sakha - Aldan (Moscow, RUS) *Unable to locate*

GTRK Sakha - Aldan (Moscow, RUS) *Unable to locate*

GTRK Sakha - Aykhal (Yakutsk, RUS) *Unable to locate*

GTRK Sakha - Cherskiy (Yakutsk, RUS) *Unable to locate*

GTRK Sakha - Neryungri (Moscow, RUS) *Unable to locate*

GTRK Sakha - Neryungri (Moscow, RUS) *Unable to locate*

GTRK Sakha - Sangar (Moscow, RUS) *Unable to locate*

GTRK Sakha - Solnechnyy (Yakutsk, RUS) *Unable to locate*

GTRK Sakha - Ust-Maya (Moscow, RUS) *Unable to locate*

GTRK Sakha - Ust-Nera (Yakutsk, RUS) *Unable to locate*

GTRK Sakha - Yakutsk (Yakutsk, RUS) *Unable to locate*

GTRK Sakha - Yakutsk (Yakutsk, RUS) *Unable to locate*

GTRK Sakha - Yakutsk (Yakutsk, RUS) *Unable to locate*

GTRK Sakha - Yakutsk (Yakutsk, RUS) *Unable to locate*

GTRK Sakha - Yakutsk (Yakutsk, RUS) *Unable to locate*

GTRK Sakha - Yakutsk (Yakutsk, RUS) *Unable to locate*

GTRK Sakhalin - Aleksandrovsk (Moscow, RUS) *Unable to locate*

GTRK Sakhalin - Nogliki (Moscow, RUS) *Unable to locate*

GTRK Sakhalin - Yuzhno-Kurilsk (Yuzhno-Sakhalinsk, RUS) *Unable to locate*

GTRK Sakhalin - Yuzhno Sakhalinsk (Yuzhno Sakhalinsk, RUS) *Unable to locate*

GTRK Sakhalin - Yuzhno Sakhalinsk (Yuzhno-Sakhalinsk, RUS) *Unable to locate*

GTRK Sakhalin - Yuzhno Sakhalinsk (Yuzhno Sakhalinsk, RUS) *Unable to locate*

GTRK - Samara (Samara, RUS) *Unable to locate*

GTRK Samara - Mekhzavod (Samara, RUS) *Unable to locate*

GTRK - Saratov (Saratov, RUS) *Unable to locate*

GTRK - Saratov (Saratov, RUS) *Unable to locate*

GTRK Saratov (Saratov, RUS) *Unable to locate*

GTRK Saratov - Balakovo (Saratov, RUS) *Unable to locate*

GTRK Saratov - Balashov (Moscow, RUS) *Unable to locate*

GTRK Saratov - Balashov (Saratov, RUS) *Unable to locate*

GTRK Saratov - Perelyub (Moscow, RUS) *Unable to locate*

GTRK Saratov - Yershov (Moscow, RUS) *Unable to locate*

GTRK Saratov - Yershov (Saratov, RUS) *Unable to locate*

GTRK Slaviya - Borovichi (Moscow, RUS) *Unable to locate*

Numbers cited in bold after listings are entry numbers rather than page numbers.

GTRK Slaviya - Velikiy Novgorod (Velikiy Novgorod, RUS) *Unable to locate*

GTRK Slaviya - Velikiy Novgorod (Velikiy Novgorod, RUS) *Unable to locate*

GTRK Slaviya - Velikiy Novgorod (Velikiy Novgorod, RUS) *Unable to locate*

GTRK Slaviya - Velikiy Novgorod (Velikiy Novgorod, RUS) *Unable to locate*

GTRK Slaviya - Zaluchye (Novgorod Velikiy, RUS) *Unable to locate*

GTRK - Smolensk (Smolensk, RUS) *Unable to locate*

GTRK Stavropolskaya - Letnyaya Stavka (Stavropol, RUS) *Unable to locate*

GTRK Stavropolskaya - Neftekumsk (Moscow, RUS) *Unable to locate*

GTRK Stavropolskaya - Nftekumsk (Stavropol, RUS) *Unable to locate*

GTRK Stavropolskaya - Pyatigorsk (Moscow, RUS) *Unable to locate*

GTRK Tambovskaya - Tambov (Tambov, RUS) *Unable to locate*

GTRK Tararstan - Kazan (Kazan, RUS) *Unable to locate*

GTRK Tararstan - Naberezhnyye chenlny (Moscow, RUS) *Unable to locate*

GTRK Tatarstan - Zapolyarnyy (Kazan, RUS) *Unable to locate*

GTRK Tomsk - Strezhevoy (Moscow, RUS) *Unable to locate*

GTRK Tsentr Rossi - Boguchany (Krasnoyarsk, RUS) *Unable to locate*

GTRK - Tula (Tula, RUS) *Unable to locate*

GTRK Tula - Aleksin (Moscow, RUS) *Unable to locate*

GTRK Tula - Novomoskovsk (Moscow, RUS) *Unable to locate*

GTRK - Tver (Tver, RUS) *Unable to locate*

GTRK - Tver (Tver, RUS) *Unable to locate*

GTRK Tver - Kushalino (Moscow, RUS) *Unable to locate*

GTRK Tyva - Chadan (Kyzyl, RUS) *Unable to locate*

GTRK Tyva - Kyzyl (Kyzyl, RUS) *Unable to locate*

GTRK Tyva - Shagonar (Kyzyl, RUS) *Unable to locate*

GTRK Udmurtiya - Radio Ingur (Izhevsk, RUS) *Unable to locate*

GTRK - Ust-Ordynskiy (Ust-Ordynskiy, RUS) *Unable to locate*

GTRK - Vladimir (Vladimir, RUS) *Unable to locate*

GTRK Vladivostok (Vladivostok, RUS) *Unable to locate*

GTRK Vladivostok - Arsenyev (Moscow, RUS) *Unable to locate*

GTRK Vladivostok - Chkalovskoye (Moscow, RUS) *Unable to locate*

GTRK Vladivostok - Chkalovskoye (Moscow, RUS) *Unable to locate*

GTRK Vladivostok - Dalnegorsk (Vladivostok, RUS) *Unable to locate*

GTRK Vladivostok - Dalnerechensk (Moscow, RUS) *Unable to locate*

GTRK Vladivostok - Novozhatkovo (Moscow, RUS) *Unable to locate*

GTRK Vladivostok - Plastun (Moscow, RUS) *Unable to locate*

GTRK Vladivostok - Tavrichanka (Moscow, RUS) *Unable to locate*

GTRK Vladivostok - Tavrichanka (Moscow, RUS) *Unable to locate*

GTRK Vladivostok - Tavrichanka (Vladivostok, RUS) *Unable to locate*

GTRK Volga - Dimitrovgrad (Moscow, RUS) *Unable to locate*

GTRK Volga - Novospasskoye (Moscow, RUS) *Unable to locate*

GTRK Volga - Ulyanovsk (Ulyanovsk, RUS) *Unable to locate*

GTRK Volga - Veshkayma (Moscow, RUS) *Unable to locate*

GTRK Volgograd-TRV - Dubovka (Moscow, RUS) *Unable to locate*

GTRK Volgograd-TRV - Dubovka (Volgograd, RUS) *Unable to locate*

GTRK Volgograd-TRV - Volgograd (Volgograd, RUS) *Unable to locate*

GTRK Vologdaskaya - Vologda (Vologda, RUS) *Unable to locate*

GTRK Vologdskaya - Cherepovets (Cherepovets, RUS) *Unable to locate*

GTRK Vologdskaya - Lipin Bor (Cherepovets, RUS) *Unable to locate*

GTRK Vologdskaya - Sludno (Cherepovets, RUS) *Unable to locate*

GTRK Vologdskaya - Totma (Moscow, RUS) *Unable to locate*

GTRK Vologdskaya - Vologda (Volgograd, RUS) *Unable to locate*

GTRK Vologdskaya - Vologda (Vologda, RUS) *Unable to locate*

GTRK Vologdskaya - Yakutino (Cherepovets, RUS) *Unable to locate*

GTRK Voronezhskaya - Borisoglebsk (Voronezh, RUS) *Unable to locate*

GTRK Voronezhskaya - Voronezh (Bobrov, RUS) *Unable to locate*

GTRK Voronezhskaya - Voronezh (Voronezh, RUS) *Unable to locate*

GTRK - Vyatka (Vyatka, RUS) *Unable to locate*

GTRK Vyatka - Kirov (Vyatka, RUS) *Unable to locate*

GTRK Vyatka - Pinyug (Moscow, RUS) *Unable to locate*

GTRK Vyatka - Shmelevo (Moscow, RUS) *Unable to locate*

GTRK Vyatka - Urzhum (Moscow, RUS) *Unable to locate*

GTRK Vyatka - Vyatka (Vyatka, RUS) *Unable to locate*

GTRK Yamal - Tazovskiy (Moscow, RUS) *Unable to locate*

GTRK Yantar - Bolshakovo (Kaliningrad, RUS) *Unable to locate*

GTRK Yantar - Kaliningrad (Kaliningrad, RUS) *Unable to locate*

GTRK Yaroslavi - Dubki (Moscow, RUS) *Unable to locate*

Guadalimar (Madrid, SPA) *Unable to locate*

Guangdong Music Radio (Guangzhou, GD, CHN) *Unable to locate*

Guangdong Music Radio (Guangzhou, GD, CHN) *Unable to locate*

Guangdong People's Broadcasting Station (Guangzhou, GD, CHN) *Unable to locate*

Guangdong People's Broadcasting Station (Guangzhou, GD, CHN) *Unable to locate*

Guangdong People's Broadcasting Station (Guangzhou, GD, CHN) *Unable to locate*

Guangdong People's Broadcasting Station (Guangzhou, GD, CHN) *Unable to locate*

Guangdong People's Broadcasting Station (Guangzhou, GD, CHN) *Unable to locate*

Guangdong People's Broadcasting Station (Guangzhou, GD, CHN) *Unable to locate*

Guangdong People's Broadcasting Station (Guangzhou, GD, CHN) *Unable to locate*

Guangdong Television - Channel 2 (Guangzhou, GD, CHN) [43257]

Guangdong Television - Channel 3 (Guangzhou, GD, CHN) [43255]

Guangdong Television - Channel 1 (Guangzhou, GD, CHN) [43256]

Guangshui People's Broadcasting Station (Guangshui, HU, CHN) *Unable to locate*

Guangxi People's Broadcasting Station (Nanning, GZ, CHN) *Unable to locate*

Guangxi People's Broadcasting Station (Nanning, GZ, CHN) *Unable to locate*

Guangxi People's Broadcasting Station (Nanning, GZ, CHN) *Unable to locate*

Guangxi People's Broadcasting Station (Nanning, GZ, CHN) *Unable to locate*

Guangxi People's Broadcasting Station (Nanning, GZ, CHN) *Unable to locate*

GuangxiPeople's Broadcasting Station (Nanning, GZ, CHN) *Unable to locate*

Guangyan People's Broadcasting Station (Guangyuan, SI, CHN) *Unable to locate*

Guangyuan People's Broadcasting Station (Guangyuan, SI, CHN) *Unable to locate*

Guangzhou People's Broadcasting Station (Guangzhou, GD, CHN) *Unable to locate*

Guangzhou People's Broadcasting Station (Guangzhou, GD, CHN) *Unable to locate*

Guapa-FM - 99.7 (San Salvador, ELS) [43778]

Guaraguao (Barcelona, SPA) [50675]

The Guardian (Christchurch, NZL) [48867]

The Guardian (London, GBR) [54525]

Guardian Messenger (Kidman Park, SA, AUS) [41986]

The Guardian Weekend (London, GBR) [54526]

Guernsey Press (Jersey, GBR) [53665]

Guia do Automovel (Cruz Quebrada-Dafundo, PRT) [49794]

Guia del Comprador de Casas (Madrid, SPA) [50763]

Guia del Comprador de Coches (Madrid, SPA) [50764]

Guia del Comprador de Furgonetas y Autocaravanas (Madrid, SPA) [50765]

Guia del Comprador de Ordenadores y Software (Madrid, SPA) [50766]

Guichi People's Broadcasting Station (Guichi, AN, CHN) *Unable to locate*

Guidance Papers (Harare, ZWE) *Unable to locate*

The Guide (Hanoi, VNM) *Unable to locate*

Guide of China Automotive Industry (Beijing, CHN) *Unable to locate*

Guide to Current Literature in Environmental Health Engineering and Science (Nagpur, MH, IND) *Unable to locate*

Guide to Indian Periodical Literature (Gurgaon, HY, IND) *Unable to locate*

Guide to Japanese Taxes (Tokyo, JPN) *Unable to locate*

Guide to New Australian Books (Melbourne, VI, AUS) *Ceased*

Guide des Relais Routiers (Clichy, FRA) [43933]

Guidebooks/Topographic Maps (Bern, SWI) *Unable to locate*

Guidelines (Berkhamsted, GBR) [52310]

Guidelines in Practice (Berkhamsted, GBR) [52311]

Guiding in Kenya (Nairobi, KEN) *Unable to locate*

Guiding Magazine (London, GBR) [54527]

Guilin People's Broadcasting Station (Guilin, GZ, CHN) *Unable to locate*

Guilin People's Broadcasting Station (Guilin, GZ, CHN) *Unable to locate*

The Guitar Magazine (New York, NY, USA) *Unable to locate*

Guix (Barcelona, SPA) *Unable to locate*

Guiyang People's Broadcasting Station (Guiyang, GH, CHN) *Unable to locate*

Guiyang People's Broadcasting Station (Guiyang, GH, CHN) *Unable to locate*

Guiyang People's Broadcasting Station (Guiyang, GH, CHN) *Unable to locate*

Guizhou People's Broadcasting Station (Guiyang, GZ, CHN) *Unable to locate*

Guizhou People's Broadcasting Station (Guiyang, GH, CHN) *Unable to locate*

Guizhou People's Broadcasting Station (Guiyang, GH, CHN) *Unable to locate*

Guizhou People's Broadcasting Station (Guiyang, GH, CHN) *Unable to locate*

Gujarat Agricultural University Research Journal (Ahmedabad, GJ, IND) *Unable to locate*

Gujarat Labour Gazette (Ahmedabad, GJ, IND) *Unable to locate*

Gujarat Law Reporter (Ahmedabad, GJ, IND) *Unable to locate*

Gujarat Law Times (Ahmedabad, GJ, IND) *Unable to locate*

Gujarat Research Society Journal (Mumbai, MH, IND) *Unable to locate*

Gujarat Revenue Tribunal Law Reporter (Ahmedabad, GJ, IND) *Unable to locate*

Guldsmedebladet (Virum, DEN) *Unable to locate*

Gulf Business (Dubai, UAE) [51643]

Gulf Construction (Manama, BHR) [42788]

Gulf Daily News (Manama, BHR) [42789]

Gulf-FM - 89.3 (Kadina, SA, AUS) [41979]

Gulf Industry (Manama, BHR) [42790]

Gulf Industry Magazine (Dubai, UAE) [51644]

Gulf News (Waiheke) (Oneroa, NZL) [48961]

The Gulf Times (Doha, QAT) [49821]

The Gulf Today (Dubai, UAE) *Unable to locate*

Gulf Weekly (Manama, BHR) [42791]

Gun Mart (Colchester, GBR) [53037]

Numbers cited in bold after listings are entry numbers rather than page numbers.

Guoji Shangbao (International Business Daily) (Beijing, CHN) *Unable to locate*

Guru Nanak Journal of Sociology (Amritsar, PJ, IND) *Unable to locate*

Gut (Nottingham, GBR) **[55757]**

GU2 Radio-AM - 1350 (Guildford, GBR) **[53498]**

Guyana Review (Georgetown, GUY) *Unable to locate*

GV-FM - 99.1 (Angeles City, PHL) **[49445]**

Gybe (Saint Albans, GBR) *Unable to locate*

Gym Stars (London, GBR) *Unable to locate*

Gymnasieskolen (Copenhagen, DEN) **[43672]**

The Gympie Times (Sydney, NW, AUS) **[42511]**

Gynakologie (Neuhausen, SWI) **[51217]**

Gynakologische Endokrinologie (Dordrecht, NLD) **[48410]**

Gynecologic Oncology (Amsterdam, NLD) **[48007]**

Gynecological Endocrinology (Lancaster, GBR) **[53733]**

Gynecological Surgery (Dordrecht, NLD) **[48411]**

Gynecologie (Athens, GRC) *Unable to locate*

H

H - The Hotel Magazine (Crawley, GBR) **[53106]**

Ha Ha Ha Magazine (Auckland, NZL) *Unable to locate*

Ha Tinh Broadcast - Television Station - Channel 21 (Ha Tinh, VNM) **[57047]**

Ha Tinh Broadcast - Television Station - Channel 6 (Ha Tinh, VNM) **[57048]**

Ha'aretz (Tel Aviv, ISR) **[46101]**

Haarlem-FM - 93.8 (Hilversum, NLD) **[48637]**

Habitania (Barcelona, SPA) **[50676]**

Habitat (London, GBR) *Ceased*

Habitat Australia (Carlton, VI, AUS) **[41726]**

Habitat Debate (Nairobi, KEN) **[47183]**

Habitat International (Amsterdam, NLD) **[48008]**

Hackney Gazette (London, GBR) **[54528]**

Hacquetia (Warsaw, POL) **[49715]**

HAEMA (AIMA) (Athens, GRC) *Unable to locate*

Haematologica **[46209]***

Haematologica/The Hematology Journal (Pavia, ITA) **[46209]**

Haematology & Trasfusiology (Moscow, RUS) **[49910]**

Hai Duong Broadcast - Television Station (Hai Duong City, VNM) *Unable to locate*

Hai Phong Broadcast - Television Station (Hanoi, VNM) *Unable to locate*

Haicheng People's Broadcasting Station (Haicheng, LI, CHN) *Unable to locate*

Haigazian Armenological Review (Beirut, LBN) **[47395]**

Haikou People's Broadcasting Station (Haikou, HN, CHN) *Unable to locate*

Hailar People's Broadcasting Station (Hailar, NM, CHN) *Unable to locate*

Hainan People's Broadcasting Station (Haikou, HN, CHN) *Unable to locate*

Hainan People's Broadcasting Station (Haikou, HN, CHN) *Unable to locate*

Hainan People's Broadcasting Station (Haikou, HN, CHN) *Unable to locate*

Hainan People's Broadcasting Station (Haikou, HA, CHN) *Unable to locate*

Hair und Beauty (Munich, GER) *Unable to locate*

Hair Ideas (Bristol, GBR) **[52673]**

Hair Style & Beauty (London, GBR) *Ceased*

Haixi-Mo People's Broadcasting Station (Delingha, QI, CHN) *Unable to locate*

Haixi People's Broadcasting Station (Delingha, QI, CHN) *Unable to locate*

Hallam-FM - 102.9 (Barnsley, GBR) **[52188]**

Hallam-FM - 103.4 (Doncaster, GBR) **[53187]**

Hallam-FM - 97.4 (Sheffield, GBR) **[56518]**

Halls Creek Herald (Halls Creek, WA, AUS) **[41938]**

Hamara Mahol (Karachi, PAK) *Unable to locate*

Hamdard Islamicus (Karachi, PAK) **[49350]**

Hamdard Medicus (Karachi, PAK) **[49351]**

Hamdard Naunehal (Karachi, PAK) **[49352]**

Hami People's Broadcasting Station (Hami, XU, CHN) *Unable to locate*

Hami-Ug People's Broadcasting Station (Hami, XU, CHN) *Unable to locate*

Hamizrah Hechadash (The New East) (Jerusalem, ISR) *Unable to locate*

Hamlet Studies (New Delhi, DH, IND) *Unable to locate*

Hamodia (Israel) (Jerusalem, ISR) **[46082]**

Hampshire (Salisbury, GBR) **[56454]**

Ham's CQ (Beijing, CHN) **[43195]**

Hand Surgery (Sapporo, JPN) **[46649]**

Handan People's Broadcasting Station (Handan, HB, CHN) *Unable to locate*

Handan People's Broadcasting Station (Handan, HB, CHN) *Unable to locate*

Handan People's Broadcasting Station (Handan, HB, CHN) *Unable to locate*

Handan People's Broadcasting Station 1 (Handan, HB, CHN) *Unable to locate*

Handbok Baenda (Reykjavik, ICE) *Unable to locate*

Handbook of Business Strategy **[52439]***

Handbook of Practice Management (London, GBR) **[54529]**

Handeln (Zurich, SWI) *Unable to locate*

Handelsblatt (Dusseldorf, GER) *Unable to locate*

Handy ADDoku Plus Kakuro (Gosford, NW, AUS) **[41911]**

Handy Arroworts (Gosford, NW, AUS) **[41912]**

Handy Codecrackers (Gosford, NW, AUS) **[41913]**

Handy Crosswords (Gosford, NW, AUS) **[41914]**

Handy Cryptic Crosswords (Gosford, NW, AUS) **[41915]**

Handy Fill-Ins (Gosford, NW, AUS) **[41916]**

Handy Wordhunt (Gosford, NW, AUS) **[41917]**

Hangzhou People's Broadcasting Station (Hangzhou, ZH, CHN) *Unable to locate*

Hanjie (Redhill, GBR) **[56353]**

Hao Chiating (Family) Broadcasting Co. - 97.7 MHz (Taichung, TWN) **[51323]**

Happening (Singapore, SGP) *Unable to locate*

Happy Day Diary **[53840]***

Harakah (Kuala Lumpur, MYS) *Unable to locate*

Harbin People's Broadcasting Station (Harbin, HL, CHN) *Unable to locate*

Harbin People's Broadcasting Station (Harbin, HL, CHN) *Unable to locate*

Harbin People's Broadcasting Station (Harbin, HL, CHN) *Unable to locate*

Harbin People's Broadcasting Station (Harbin, HL, CHN) *Unable to locate*

Harborough Mail (Harborough, GBR) **[53507]**

Hard Rock-FM - 89.7 (Surabaya, IDN) **[45860]**

Hard Rock Radio-FM - 87.8 (Bali, IDN) **[45773]**

Hard Rock Radio-FM - 87.6 (Jakarta, IDN) **[45804]**

Hardwage Mag (Singapore, SGP) **[50162]**

Hardware & Garden Review (Sittingbourne, GBR) **[56548]**

Hardware Today (Birmingham, GBR) *Unable to locate*

The Hardy Review (London, GBR) **[54530]**

Haring Ibon (Quezon City, PHL) **[49594]**

Harlow Edition Herald (Harlow, GBR) **[53511]**

Harlowlife (Harlow, GBR) *Unable to locate*

Harm Reduction Journal (London, GBR) **[54531]**

Harmful Algae (Singapore, SGP) **[50163]**

Harmoni (Kuala Lumpur, MYS) **[47603]**

Harmonica World (Porthcawl, GBR) *Unable to locate*

Haroshye Raditeli (Kiev, URE) **[51597]**

Harper's Bazaar (Australia) (Sydney, NW, AUS) **[42512]**

Harpers On-Trade (HOT) (London, GBR) *Unable to locate*

Harpers on Retail (London, GBR) *Unable to locate*

Harrods Estates @MAG (London, GBR) **[54532]**

Harrogate Advertiser (Harrogate, GBR) **[53516]**

Hartlepool Mail (Hartlepool, GBR) **[53533]**

Harvester (Calcutta, WB, IND) *Unable to locate*

Haryana Agricultural University Journal of Research (Hissar, HY, IND) *Unable to locate*

Haryana Cooperation (Chandigarh, CH, IND) *Unable to locate*

Haryana Electricity (Chandigarh, CH, IND) *Unable to locate*

Haryana Health Journal (Chandigarh, CH, IND) *Unable to locate*

Haryana Journal of Education (Chandigarh, CH, IND) *Unable to locate*

Haryana Labour Journal (Chandigarh, CH, IND) *Unable to locate*

Haryana Veterinarian (Hissar, HY, IND) *Unable to locate*

HASHAHAR (Tallinn, EST) *Unable to locate*

The Hastings Leader (Hastings, NZL) *Unable to locate*

Hastings & St. Leonards Observer (Saint Leonards-On-Sea, GBR) **[56445]**

The HAT Magazine (London, GBR) **[54533]**

Hauraki-FM - 99.0 (Auckland, NZL) **[48842]**

Hauraki-FM - 93.1 (Wellington, NZL) **[49040]**

Hauraki-FM Southland - 93.2 (Invercargill, NZL) **[48921]**

Hauraki-FM Taranaki - 90.8 (New Plymouth, NZL) **[48950]**

Hausbau (Fellback, GER) *Unable to locate*

Haushalt & Management (Bonn, GER) *Unable to locate*

Haveeru **[47725]***

Haveeru Daily (Male, MDV) **[47725]**

Haverhill Echo (Haverhill, GBR) **[53544]**

Hawick News (Hawick, GBR) **[53546]**

Hawke's Bay Today (Hastings, NZL) **[48915]**

Hawkesbury Courier (Sydney, NW, AUS) **[42513]**

Hawkesbury Gazette (Richmond, NW, AUS) **[42299]**

Hazards (Sheffield, GBR) **[56496]**

HBC-FM (Kathmandu, NPL) *Unable to locate*

HBL (Helsinki, FIN) *Unable to locate*

HCKC News (Walton-On-Thames, GBR) *Unable to locate*

Head & Face Medicine (London, GBR) **[54534]**

A Head Start (Liverpool, GBR) *Ceased*

Head Teachers Review (Haywards Heath, GBR) *Unable to locate*

Headache in Practice (London, GBR) **[54535]**

Headlines (London, GBR) *Unable to locate*

Headway News (Nottingham, GBR) **[55758]**

Health (Sofia, BUL) *Unable to locate*

Health (Madurai, TN, IND) *Unable to locate*

Health (Mumbai, MH, IND) **[45371]**

Health (London, GBR) **[54536]**

Health Action (Secunderabad, AP, IND) *Unable to locate*

Health for All (Taipei, TWN) *Unable to locate*

Health & Beauty (Dublin, DU, IRL) *Unable to locate*

Health Business (Loughton, GBR) **[55492]**

Health Care Analysis (Dordrecht, NLD) **[48412]**

Health-Care Focus (London, GBR) *Unable to locate*

Health Care and Informatics Review Online (Albany, NZL) **[48778]**

Health Care Management Science (Heidelberg, GER) **[44458]**

Health Care Media (Nottingham, GBR) *Unable to locate*

Health Care of the Russian Federation (Moscow, RUS) **[49911]**

Health Club Management (Hitchin, GBR) **[53578]**

Numbers cited in bold after listings are entry numbers rather than page numbers.

Health Education (Southampton, GBR) [56572]

Health Education Journal (London, GBR) [54537]

Health Education Research (Oxford, GBR) [55971]

Health and Food (Genval, BEL) [42886]

Health Food Business Magazine (Ugley Green, GBR) [56794]

Health & Gender; The Journal of Men's [50209]*

Health and Hygiene (London, GBR) [54538]

Health Insurance (London, GBR) [54539]

Health & Nutrition [45371]*

Health Policy and Planning (London, GBR) [54540]

Health and Population (New Delhi, DH, IND) [45522]

Health Promotion International (Oxford, GBR) [55972]

Health Research Policy and Systems (London, GBR) [54541]

Health, Risk and Society (Abingdon, GBR) [51801]

Health SA Gesondheid (Auckland Park, SAF) [50348]

Health and Safety (Dublin, DU, IRL) Unable to locate

Health and Safety Bulletin (London, GBR) [54542]

Health & Safety at Work (London, GBR) [54543]

Health Service Abstracts (Wetherby, GBR) Unable to locate

Health Services Management Research (London, GBR) [54544]

Health Statistics Quarterly (Basingstoke, GBR) [52206]

The Health Store Magazine (Nottingham, GBR) Unable to locate

Health Talk (London, GBR) Unable to locate

Healthcare Counselling and Psychotherapy Journal (Lutterworth, GBR) [55512]

HealthCare Ethics Committee Forum (Dordrecht, NLD) [48413]

HealthInfo (Bristol, GBR) Ceased

Healthmatters (Brighton, GBR) [52611]

health24 (Norwich, GBR) [55732]

Healthwise (Christchurch, NZL) Unable to locate

Healthy Times (London, GBR) Unable to locate

Hearing Aid Journal (New Delhi, DH, IND) Unable to locate

Hearing Research (Amsterdam, NLD) [48009]

Heart (London, GBR) [54545]

Heart Care (Mumbai, MH, IND) Unable to locate

Heart Colchester-FM - 96.1 (Colchester, GBR) [53056]

Heart Failure Monitor (London, GBR) [54546]

Heart-FM - 95.7 (Longford, TA, AUS) [42021]

Heart-FM - 96.3 (Bangor, GBR) [52175]

Heart-FM - 96.9 (Bedford, GBR) [52277]

Heart-FM - 100.7 (Birmingham, GBR) [52375]

Heart-FM - 102.3 (Bournemouth, GBR) [52430]

Heart-FM - 102.4 (Brighton, GBR) [52636]

Heart-FM - 102.6 (Cowley, GBR) [53095]

Heart-FM - 103.0 (Exeter, GBR) [53368]

Heart-FM - 97.0 (Exeter, GBR) [53367]

Heart-FM - 97.5 (Fareham, GBR) [53375]

Heart-FM - 103 (Gloucester, GBR) [53473]

Heart-FM - 102.4 (Norwich, GBR) [55747]

Heart-FM - 97.4 (Oxford, GBR) [56233]

Heart-FM - 97 (Plymouth, GBR) [56277]

Heart-FM - 97 (Reading, GBR) [56339]

Heart-FM - 102.9 (Reading, GBR) [56338]

Heart-FM - 96.5 (Taunton, GBR) [56726]

Heart-FM - 102.6 (Taunton, GBR) [56725]

Heart-FM - 96.4 (Torquay, GBR) [56759]

Heart-FM - 103.1 (Whitstable, GBR) [56921]

Heart-FM - 97.1 (Yeovil, GBR) [56983]

Heart Healthy Living (Eveleigh, NW, AUS) [41860]

Heart Ipswich-FM - 97.1 (Ipswich, GBR) [53659]

Heart Ipswich-FM - 96.4 (Ipswich, GBR) [53658]

Heart, Lung and Circulation (Amsterdam, NLD) [48010]

Heart 91.3 [50304]*

Heart 106.2-FM - 106.2 (London, GBR) [55451]

Heart South Devon-FM - 100.8 (Kingsbridge, GBR) [53718]

Heart South Devon-FM - 101.9 (Kingsbridge, GBR) [53716]

Heart South Devon-FM - 100.5 (Kingsbridge, GBR) [53717]

Heart South Devon-FM - 101.2 (Kingsbridge, GBR) [53715]

Heart and Vessels (Tokyo, JPN) [46832]

Heartbeat (Fatima, PRT) Unable to locate

Heartland-FM - 87.6 (Mudgee, NW, AUS) [42135]

HeartWise (Dublin, DU, IRL) [45963]

Heat Magazine (Artarmon, NW, AUS) [41564]

Heat and Mass Transfer (Kassel, GER) [44497]

Heat Treatments of Metals (Beijing, CHN) Unable to locate

Heathrow Villager (Staines, GBR) Unable to locate

Heating & Plumbing Monthly (Sevenoaks, GBR) [56474]

Heavyrock (Madrid, SPA) Unable to locate

Hebden Bridge Times (Hebden Bridge, GBR) [53552]

L'Hebdo (Lausanne, SWI) [51190]

HEBDO Des Socialistes (Paris, FRA) Unable to locate

Hebei Economic TV (Shijiazhuang, HB, CHN) Unable to locate

Hebei 1 People's Broadcasting Station (Shijiazhuang, HB, CHN) Unable to locate

Hebei People's Broadcasting Station (Shijiazhuang, HB, CHN) Unable to locate

Hebei People's Broadcasting Station (Shijiazhuang, HB, CHN) Unable to locate

Hebei People's Broadcasting Station (Shijiazhuang, HB, CHN) Unable to locate

Hebei People's Broadcasting Station (Shijiazhuang, HB, CHN) Unable to locate

Hebei People's Broadcasting Station 1 (Shijiazhuang, HB, CHN) Unable to locate

Hebei TV 1 (Shijiazhuang, HB, CHN) Unable to locate

Hebi People's Broadcasting Station (Hebi, HN, CHN) Unable to locate

Hebi People's Broadcasting Station (Hebi, HN, CHN) Unable to locate

Hecate (Brisbane, QL, AUS) [41648]

Hedef Radyo - Ankara - 91.8 MHz (Ankara, TUR) [51520]

Hedge Funds Review (London, GBR) [54547]

Heenayana (Calcutta, WB, IND) Unable to locate

Hefei People's Broadcasting Station (Hefei, AN, CHN) Unable to locate

Hefei People's Broadcasting Station (Hefei, AN, CHN) Unable to locate

Hefei People's Broadcasting Station (Hefei, AN, CHN) Unable to locate

Hefei People's Broadcasting Station (Hefei, AN, CHN) Unable to locate

Hegang People's Broadcasting Station (Hegang, HL, CHN) Unable to locate

Hegang People's Broadcasting Station (Hegang, HL, CHN) Unable to locate

Heidelberg Leader (Melbourne, VI, AUS) [42063]

Heilongjiang Korean Broadcasting Station (Harbin, HL, CHN) Unable to locate

Heilongjiang People's Broadcasting Station (Harbin, HL, CHN) Unable to locate

Heilongjiang People's Broadcasting Station (Harbin, HL, CHN) Unable to locate

Heilongjiang People's Broadcasting Station (Harbin, HL, CHN) Unable to locate

Heilongjiang People's Broadcasting Station (Harbin, HL, CHN) Unable to locate

Heilongjiang People's Broadcasting Station (Harbin, HL, CHN) Unable to locate

Heilongjiang People's Broadcasting Station (Harbin, HL, CHN) Unable to locate

Heilongjiang People's Broadcasting Station (Harbin, HL, CHN) Unable to locate

Heilongjiang People's Broadcasting Station (Harbin, HL, CHN) Unable to locate

Heilongjiang People's Broadcasting Station (Harbin, HL, CHN) Unable to locate

Heilongjiang People's Broadcasting Station (Harbin, HL, CHN) Unable to locate

Heilongjiang People's Broadcasting Station (Harbin, HL, CHN) Unable to locate

Heilongjiang People's Broadcasting Station (Harbin, HL, CHN) Unable to locate

Heilongjiang TV Channel 1 - Channel 1 (Harbin, HL, CHN) [43264]

Heilongjiang TV Channel 2 - Channel 2 (Harbin, HL, CHN) [43265]

Heim & Hobby (Duisburg, GER) Unable to locate

Heimatschutz/Sauvegarde (Zurich, SWI) Unable to locate

HelderMail (Cape Town, SAF) [50380]

Helgoland Marine Research (Helgoland, GER) [44481]

Helice (Granada, SPA) Unable to locate

Helicon (Calcutta, WB, IND) Unable to locate

Hellenic Journal of Cardiology (Athens, GRC) Unable to locate

Hellenic Journal of Psychology (Thessaloniki, GRC) [44772]

Hellenic Orthodontic Review (Athens, GRC) [44744]

Hellenic Radiology Journal (Athens, GRC) [44745]

Helminthologia (Dordrecht, NLD) [48414]

Helsingin Sanomat (Helsinki, FIN) [43832]

Helsinki Monitor (The Hague, NLD) Unable to locate

Helvetica Chimica Acta (Bern, SWI) [51073]

Hematology (London, GBR) [54548]

The Hematology Journal [46209]*

Hemel Gazette (Hemel Hempstead, GBR) [53557]

Hemslojden (Umea, SWE) [51045]

Henan People's Broadcasting Station (Zhengzhou, HN, CHN) Unable to locate

Henan People's Broadcasting Station (Zhengzhou, HN, CHN) Unable to locate

Henan People's Broadcasting Station (Zhengzhou, HN, CHN) Unable to locate

Henan People's Broadcasting Station (Zhengzhou, HN, CHN) Unable to locate

Henan People's Broadcasting Station (Zhengzhou, HN, CHN) Unable to locate

Henan People's Broadcasting Station (Zhengzhou, HN, CHN) Unable to locate

Henan People's Broadcasting Station (Zhengzhou, HN, CHN) Unable to locate

Henan People's Broadcasting Station (Zhengzhou, HN, CHN) Unable to locate

Henan People's Broadcasting Station (Zhengzhou, HN, CHN) Unable to locate

Hengelo-FM (Amsterdam, NLD) Unable to locate

Hengshui People's Broadcasting Station (Hengshui, HB, CHN) Unable to locate

Hengyang People's Broadcasting Station (Hengyang, HA, CHN) Unable to locate

Henley Manager Update (Henley-on-Thames, GBR) Ceased

Henry Martyn Institute of Islamic Studies Bulletin [45174]*

Hepatitis B Annual (Cuttack, OR, IND) [45081]

Hepatitis Monthly (Tehran, IRN) [45889]

Hepato-Gastro (Montrouge, FRA) [43992]

Numbers cited in bold after listings are entry numbers rather than page numbers.

Hepatology; Nature Clinical Practice Gastroenterology & [54979]*

Hepatology Research (Kagoshima, JPN) [46404]

Hepatology Reviews (Barcelona, SPA) [50677]

Her World (Singapore, SGP) [50164]

Her World Brides (Singapore, SGP) [50165]

Herald (Karachi, PAK) [49353]

Herald Express (Torquay) (Torquay, GBR) [56757]

Herald of Health (Pune, MH, IND) Unable to locate

Herald of Library Science (Lucknow, UP, IND) Unable to locate

Herald & Post Series (Edinburgh, GBR) Unable to locate

Herald & Post Series (Slough) (Derby, GBR) Unable to locate

Herald of the Russian Academy of Sciences (Moscow, RUS) [49912]

Heraldo (Panaji, GD, IND) Unable to locate

Herbs (Northampton, GBR) [55708]

Here and Now [50836]*

Herefordshire Life (Bacton, GBR) [52153]

Hereward Radio-FM (Peterborough, GBR) Unable to locate

Heritage Journal (Lagos, LG, NGA) Unable to locate

Heritage Railway Magazine (Horncastle, GBR) [53590]

Hermanus Times (Cape Town, SAF) [50381]

Hernia (Heidelberg, GER) [44459]

HERPES (Worthing, GBR) [56973]

The Herpetological Journal (London, GBR) Unable to locate

Hertbeat-FM - 106.7 (Knebworth, GBR) [53729]

Hertha (Stockholm, SWE) Unable to locate

Herts Advertiser (Saint Albans, GBR) [56436]

Hertz-FM - 87.9 (Bielefeld, GER) [44249]

Hervey Bay Observer (Sydney, NW, AUS) [42514]

Herzschrittmachertherapie & Elektrophysiologie (Frankfurt, GER) [44361]

Het Houtblad (Rotterdam, NLD) [48750]

Het Landbouwblad (Drachten, NLD) Unable to locate

Het Veilingtijdschrift (Haarlem, NLD) Ceased

Heterocyclic Communications (Tel Aviv, ISR) [46102]

Heti Turizmus (Budapest, HUN) Unable to locate

Heute (Zurich, SWI) [51264]

Heyuan People's Broadcasting Station (Heyuan, GD, CHN) Unable to locate

Heze People's Broadcasting Station (Heze, SD, CHN) Unable to locate

HFI Education Today (New Delhi, DH, IND) Unable to locate

Hi Fi News (London, GBR) [54549]

Hi Pakistan (Lahore, PAK) Unable to locate

Hi Society (Wellington, NZL) [49009]

Hide 'n' Seek Wordsearch (London, GBR) [54550]

HIDEAWAYS (Bielefeld, GER) [44246]

HIFI (Helsinki Media, FIN) Unable to locate

High Ability Studies (Abingdon, GBR) [51802]

High Blood Pressure & Cardiovascular Prevention (Rome, ITA) [46232]

High Definition Review (Bournemouth, GBR) [52415]

High Energy Chemistry (Moscow, RUS) [49913]

High Mountain Sports (Kettering, GBR) Unable to locate

High Peak Radio-FM - 106.4 (Buxton, GBR) [52780]

High Peak Radio-FM - 106.6 (Chapel-en-le-Frith, GBR) [52956]

High Peak Radio-FM - 103.3 (High Peak, GBR) [53571]

High Pressure Research (Paris, FRA) [44046]

High School Musical (Mandaluyong City, PHL) [49538]

High Spirit (Brentwood, GBR) [52574]

High Temperature (Moscow, RUS) [49914]

High Temperature Materials and Processes (Sendai, JPN) [46666]

High Temperatures-High Pressures (London, GBR) [54551]

Higher Education (Dordrecht, NLD) [48415]

Higher Education in Europe (Bucharest, ROM) [49837]

Higher Education Policy (Paris, FRA) [44047]

Higher Education Research and Development (HERD) (Milperra, NW, AUS) [42107]

Highland Booknews (Kottayam, KE, IND) Unable to locate

Highland Medical Research Journal (Jos, PL, NGA) [49124]

Highlander (Kohima, NG, IND) Unable to locate

Highlands-FM - 100.7 (Woodend, VI, AUS) [42714]

Highlights in Chemical Biology (Cambridge, GBR) [52826]

Highlights in Chemical Science (Cambridge, GBR) [52827]

Highveld-FM - 94.7 (Rivonia, SAF) [50612]

Highway Magazine (Singapore, SGP) [50166]

Highway Research Record (New Delhi, DH, IND) [45523]

Highways & Transportation [56783]*

Hildon Magazine (London, GBR) [54552]

Hills Gazette (Midland, WA, AUS) [42104]

Hills Shire Times (Castle Hill, NW, AUS) [41731]

Hills & Valley Messenger (Morphett Vale, SA, AUS) [42119]

Hilton Australasia (Pyrmont, NW, AUS) [42279]

Himachal Journal of Agricultural Research (Palampur, HP, IND) Unable to locate

Himachal Times (Dehradun, UP, IND) Unable to locate

Himalayan Geology (New Delhi, DH, IND) Unable to locate

Himalayan Journal of Environment and Zoology (Hardwar, UP, IND) Unable to locate

Himalayan Observer (Darjeeling, WB, IND) Unable to locate

Himalayan Plant Journal (Darjeeling, WB, IND) Unable to locate

The Himalayan Times (Kathmandu, NPL) [47837]

Himmat (Mumbai, MH, IND) Unable to locate

Himshiksha (Solan, HP, IND) Unable to locate

The Hindu (New Delhi, DH, IND) [45524]

Hindu Astronomical and Mathematical Text Series (Lucknow, UP, IND) Unable to locate

Hindu Business Line (Chennai, TN, IND) [45033]

Hindu Index (Chennai, TN, IND) [45034]

Hindu International Edition (Chennai, TN, IND) [45035]

Hindu Regeneration (Hyderabad, AP, IND) Unable to locate

Hindu Sabha Varta (New Delhi, DH, IND) Unable to locate

Hindu Vishva (New Delhi, DH, IND) Unable to locate

The Hindu Weekly (Chennai, TN, IND) Unable to locate

The Hindu Weekly (Chennai, TN, IND) Unable to locate

The Hindu Weekly (Chennai, TN, IND) Unable to locate

The Hindu Weekly (Chennai, TN, IND) Unable to locate

The Hindu Weekly (Chennai, TN, IND) Unable to locate

The Hindu Weekly (Chennai, TN, IND) Unable to locate

The Hindu Weekly (Chennai, TN, IND) Unable to locate

The Hindu Weekly (Chennai, TN, IND) [45036]

Hindustan Antibiotics Bulletin (Pune, MH, IND) Unable to locate

Hindustan Chamber Review (Chennai, TN, IND) Unable to locate

Hindustan Latex Varshika Riporta (Trivandrum, KE, IND) Unable to locate

Hindutva (Varanasi, UP, IND) Unable to locate

Hinge (Hong Kong, CHN) [43302]

Hinggan People's Broadcasting Station (Ulanhot, NM, CHN) Unable to locate

Hinggan People's Broadcasting Station (Ulanhot, NM, CHN) Unable to locate

Hint (Ghaziabad, UP, IND) Unable to locate

Hippo (Helsinki, FIN) Unable to locate

Hippo News (Ligny, BEL) [42902]

Hiragana Times (Tokyo, JPN) [46833]

Hirosaki Medical Journal (Aomori, JPN) Unable to locate

Hiroshima Journal of Mathematics Education (Hiroshima, JPN) [46379]

Hiroshima Mathematical Journal (Hiroshima, JPN) [46380]

Hirsilehti (Helsinki, FIN) Unable to locate

Hispanic Horizon (New Delhi, DH, IND) Unable to locate

Hispanic Research Journal (London, GBR) [54553]

Hispanistica (New Delhi, DH, IND) Unable to locate

Histochemistry and Cell Biology (Heidelberg, GER) [44460]

Historia, Antropologia y Fuentes Orales (Barcelona, SPA) [50678]

Historia, Ciencias, Saude-Manguinhos (Rio de Janeiro, RJ, BRZ) [43005]

Historia Mathematica (Amsterdam, NLD) [48011]

Historia National Geographic (Barcelona, SPA) [50679]

Historia Scientiarum (Tokyo, JPN) Unable to locate

Historia Social (Valencia, SPA) [50845]

Historian (London, GBR) [54554]

Historiar (Barcelona, SPA) Ceased

The Historic Environment (London, GBR) [54555]

Historic Motor Racing News (Zurich, SWI) [51265]

Historic Scotland Magazine (London, GBR) [54556]

Historical Biology (Dublin, DU, IRL) [45964]

Historical Geography (Beijing, CHN) Ceased

The Historical Journal (Cambridge, GBR) [52828]

Historical Journal of Film, Radio and Television (Abingdon, GBR) [51803]

Historical Materialism (London, GBR) [54557]

Historical Metallurgy (Northill, GBR) [55717]

Historical News [48868]*

Historical Records of Australian Science (Parkville, VI, AUS) [42231]

Historical Research (London, GBR) [54558]

The Historical Review (Calcutta, WB, IND) Unable to locate

Historiens et Geographes (Paris, FRA) [44048]

Historiographia Linguistica (HL) (Amsterdam, NLD) [48012]

Historiography East and West (Leiden, NLD) [48675]

Historisk Tidskrift (Stockholm, SWE) Unable to locate

History (Oxford, GBR) [55973]

History (Oxford, GBR) Unable to locate

History of Agriculture (Calcutta, WB, IND) Unable to locate

History and Anthropology (Abingdon, GBR) [51804]

History Australia (Sydney, NW, AUS) [42515]

History Compass (Oxford, GBR) [55974]

History of Cyprus Forces in an Album (Nicosia, CYP) Unable to locate

History of European Ideas (Brighton, GBR) [52612]

The History of the Family (Kidlington, GBR) [53693]

History of the Human Sciences (London, GBR) [54559]

History—Magazine of RAHS (Sydney, NW, AUS) Unable to locate

History & Memory (Tel Aviv, ISR) [46103]

History Now (Christchurch, NZL) [48868]

History of Photography (Abingdon, GBR) [51805]

History of Political Thought (Exeter, GBR) [53360]

History Review (London, GBR) [54560]

History Review; Modern [55350]*

History of Science (Ceredigion, GBR) [52955]

History Scotland (Leeds, GBR) [53767]

History and Theory (Oxford, GBR) [55975]

History Today (London, GBR) [54561]

History Workshop Journal (London, GBR) [54562]

Hit FM - 107 MHz (Moscow, RUS) [50002]

Hit FM- Beirut (Beirut, LBN) Unable to locate

Numbers cited in bold after listings are entry numbers rather than page numbers.

Hit-FM - Belgorod (Belgorod, RUS) Unable to locate

Hit FM - Bishkek (Bishkek, KGA) Unable to locate

Hit-FM - Chelyabinsk (Chelyabinsk, RUS) Unable to locate

Hit-FM - Izhevsk (Izhevsk, RUS) Unable to locate

Hit-FM - Kaliningrad (Kaliningrad, RUS) Unable to locate

Hit-FM - Kazan - 91.1 MHz (Kazan, RUS) [49859]

Hit-FM - Khanty-Mansiysk (Kirov, RUS) Unable to locate

Hit-FM - Kirov (Kirov, RUS) Unable to locate

Hit-FM - Kirov (Kirov, RUS) Unable to locate

Hit-FM - Krasnodar (Krasnodar, RUS) Unable to locate

Hit-FM - Kurgan (Kurgan, RUS) Unable to locate

Hit-FM - Moskva - 107.4 MHz (Moscow, RUS) [50003]

Hit-FM - Murmansk - 105.4 MHz (Murmansk, RUS) [50006]

Hit-FM - Nizhniy Novgorod (Nizhniy Novgorod, RUS) Unable to locate

Hit-FM - Pyatigorsk (Pyatigorsk, RUS) Unable to locate

Hit-FM - Pyatigorsk (Pyatigorsk, RUS) Unable to locate

Hit-FM - Rostov-na-Donu (Moscow, RUS) Unable to locate

Hit-FM - Saratov (Saratov, RUS) Unable to locate

Hit-FM - Surgut (Surgut, RUS) Unable to locate

Hit-FM - Tambov (Tambov, RUS) Unable to locate

Hit-FM - Ufa (Moscow, RUS) Unable to locate

Hit-FM - Voronezh (Voronezh, RUS) Unable to locate

Hit-FM - Yekaterinburg (Moscow, RUS) Unable to locate

Hit-FM - Yekaterinburg (Yekaterinburg, RUS) Unable to locate

Hit-FM - Yessentuki - 104.2 MHz (Yessentuki, RUS) [50047]

Hit Radio (Tyumen, RUS) Unable to locate

Hit Radio-Beacon Hill - 100.5 MHz (Hong Kong, CHN) [43395]

Hit Radio-Castle Peak - 100.4 MHz (Hong Kong, CHN) [43396]

Hit Radio-Cloudy Hill - 100.0 MHz (Hong Kong, CHN) [43397]

Hit Radio-Golden Hill - 101.6 MHz (Hong Kong, CHN) [43398]

Hit Radio-Kowloon Peak - 101.8 MHz (Hong Kong, CHN) [43399]

Hit Radio-Lamma Island - 102.1 MHz (Hong Kong, CHN) [43400]

Hit Radio-Mt. Gough - 99.7 MHz (Hong Kong, CHN) [43401]

Hit Radio N1-FM - 92.9 MHz (Nuremberg, GER) [44620]

Hitachi Cable Review (Tokyo, JPN) [46834]

Hitachi Zosen News (Osaka, JPN) Unable to locate

Hitek Magazine (Beirut, LBN) [47396]

Hitradio Ohr-FM - 101.6 (Offenburg, GER) [44622]

Hitradio Ohr-FM - 90.5 (Offenburg, GER) [44621]

Hits-FM - 91.2 (Kathmandu, NPL) [47649]

Hitz - 104 MHz (Kuala Lumpur, MYS) [47646]

Hitz-FM - 92.9 (Kuala Lumpur, MYS) [47648]

Hitz-FM - 97.6 (Kuala Lumpur, MYS) [47647]

HIV Plus (Kigali, RWA) [50048]

HIV Therapy (London, GBR) [54563]

Hivos Magazine (The Hague, NLD) [48617]

HK Medical Journal (Hong Kong, CHN) [43303]

HKCR CR1-Beacon Hill - 89.2 MHz (Hong Kong, CHN) [43402]

HKCR CR1-Castle Peak - 88.6 MHz (Hong Kong, CHN) [43403]

HKCR CR1-Cloudy Hill - 88.3 MHz (Hong Kong, CHN) [43404]

HKCR CR1-Golden Hill - 88.9 MHz (Hong Kong, CHN) [43405]

HKCR CR1-Kowloon Peak - 89.5 MHz (Hong Kong, CHN) [43406]

HKCR CR1-Lamma Island - 89.1 MHz (Hong Kong, CHN) [43407]

HKCR CR1-Mt. Gough - 88.1 MHz (Hong Kong, CHN) [43408]

HKCR CR2-Beacon Hill - 91.1 MHz (Hong Kong, CHN) [43409]

HKCR CR2-Castle Peak - 91.2 MHz (Hong Kong, CHN) [43410]

HKCR CR2-Cloudy Hill - 90.7 MHz (Hong Kong, CHN) [43411]

HKCR CR2-Golden Hill - 90.9 MHz (Hong Kong, CHN) [43412]

HKCR CR2-Kowloon Peak - 92.1 MHz (Hong Kong, CHN) [43413]

HKCR CR2-Lamma Island - 91.6 MHz (Hong Kong, CHN) [43414]

HKCR CR2-Mt.Gough - 90.3 MHz (Hong Kong, CHN) [43415]

HKTDC Electronic Components & Parts (Hong Kong, CHN) [43304]

HKTDC Electronics (Hong Kong, CHN) [43305]

HKTDC Enterprise (Hong Kong, CHN) [43306]

HKTDC Fashion - Leather Goods & Bags (Hong Kong, CHN) [43307]

HKTDC Fasion - Fabrics & Accessories (Hong Kong, CHN) [43308]

HKTDC Fasion - Footwear (Hong Kong, CHN) [43309]

HKTDC Gifts, Premium & Stationery (Hong Kong, CHN) [43310]

HKTDC Houseware (Hong Kong, CHN) [43311]

HKTDC Jewellery (Hong Kong, CHN) [43312]

HKTDC Optical (Hong Kong, CHN) [43313]

HKTDC Packaging (Hong Kong, CHN) [43314]

HKTDC Toys & Games (Hong Kong, CHN) [43315]

HKTDC Watch & Clock (Hong Kong, CHN) [43316]

HL-Yanggu (Chuncheon-si, KOR) Unable to locate

HLAD - 93.3 MHz (Daejeon, KOR) [47228]

HLAF (Gangwon-do, KOR) Unable to locate

HLAG-Yongju (Andong-si, KOR) Unable to locate

HLAJ - 774 KHz (Cheju, KOR) [47213]

HLAM (Jeollanam-do, KOR) Unable to locate

HLAN - 774 KHz (Chuncheon-si, KOR) [47223]

HLAP, KOR) Unable to locate

HLAQ, KOR) Unable to locate

HLAV, KOR) Unable to locate

HLAW - 1017 KHz (Andong-si, KOR) [47208]

HLAY-Yongdong (Chungju, KOR) Unable to locate

HLAZ - 1566 KHz (Jeju, KOR) [47239]

HLAZ - 101.1 MHz (Sogwipo, KOR) [47324]

HLCA-Tangjin (Seoul, KOR) Unable to locate

HLCC-P'yongch'ang (Seoul, KOR) Unable to locate

HLCD-Chech'on (Chungju, KOR) Unable to locate

HLCF-Sogwip'o [47240]*

HLCG-Hwach'on, KOR) Unable to locate

HLCH-Ch'ongju, KOR) Unable to locate

HLCI-Samch'ok (Gangneung, KOR) Unable to locate

HLCJ-Chinju, KOR) Unable to locate

HLCL, KOR) Unable to locate

HLCN - 819 KHz (Gwangju, KOR) [47234]

HLCO-Ch'olwon (Seoul, KOR) Unable to locate

HLCP-Pohang - 1305 KHz (Pohang, KOR) [47248]

HLCR-Andong (Andong-si, KOR) Unable to locate

HLCU-Ullung (Pohang, KOR) Unable to locate

HLCV-Yongwol (Seoul, KOR) Unable to locate

HLCW-Wonju (Wonju-si, KOR) Unable to locate

HLCY-Yosu (Seoul, KOR) Unable to locate

HLCZ-Hongsong (Daejeon, KOR) Unable to locate

HLDA - 89.9 MHz (Busan, KOR) [47210]

HLDD - 98.1 MHz (Gyeongsangnam-do, KOR) [47238]

HLDE, KOR) Unable to locate

HLDG (Busan, KOR) Unable to locate

HLDH (Gwangju, KOR) Unable to locate

HLDI - 94.5 MHz (Daegu, KOR) [47225]

HLDK, KOR) Unable to locate

HLDK-Tanyang (Seoul, KOR) Unable to locate

HLDS, KOR) Unable to locate

HLDU, KOR) Unable to locate

HLDX, KOR) Unable to locate

HLDY - 90.1 MHz (Gangwon-do, KOR) [47233]

HLKA-Sorae (Seoul, KOR) Unable to locate

HLKB-Pusan (Busan, KOR) Unable to locate

HLKC-Kaebong (Seoul, KOR) Unable to locate

HLKF-Chonju, KOR) Unable to locate

HLKG-Taegu, KOR) Unable to locate

HLKH-Kwangju, KOR) Unable to locate

HLKI-Taejon (Daejeon, KOR) Unable to locate

HLKL-Namwon (Seoul, KOR) Unable to locate

HLKM-Ch'unch'on (Chuncheon-si, KOR) Unable to locate

HLKN-Mokp'o, KOR) Unable to locate

HLKO-Muju (Jeonju-si, KOR) Unable to locate

HLKQ-Ch'ongju (Cheongju, KOR) Unable to locate

HLKR-Kangnung (Gangneung, KOR) Unable to locate

HLKS-Cheju (Jeju, KOR) Unable to locate

HLKU - 1161 KHz (Busan, KOR) [47211]

HLKV - 900 KHz (Seoul, KOR) [47296]

HLKW - 100.5 MHz (Mokpo-si, KOR) [47246]

HLKW-Koch'ang (Jinju-si, KOR) Unable to locate

HLKX - 106.9 MHz (Seoul, KOR) [47297]

HLKX - 1188 KHz (Seoul, KOR) [47298]

HLKY - 98.1 MHz (Seoul, KOR) [47300]

HLKY - 837 KHz (Seoul, KOR) [47301]

HLKY - 93.9 MHz (Seoul, KOR) [47299]

HLQA-Puyo (Seoul, KOR) Unable to locate

HLQB-Ulsan (Ulsan, KOR) Unable to locate

HLQC-Kosan (Jeju, KOR) Unable to locate

HLQE-Sabuk (Seoul, KOR) Unable to locate

HLQJ-Yong-gwang (Gwangju, KOR) Unable to locate

HLQL (Seoul, KOR) Unable to locate

HLQR-Ch'ongsong (Seoul, KOR) Unable to locate

HLQS-Kongju, KOR) Unable to locate

HLQU-Kohung (Suncheon-si, KOR) Unable to locate

HLQV-Hapch'on (Changwon, KOR) Unable to locate

HLQW-Poun (Cheongju, KOR) Unable to locate

HLQY-Kumi (Daegu, KOR) Unable to locate

HLQZ-Kumsan, KOR) Unable to locate

HLSA-Namyang (Seoul, KOR) Unable to locate

HLSB (Gangwon-do, KOR) Unable to locate

HLSC-Chomch'on (Daegu, KOR) Unable to locate

HLSD-Ponghwa, KOR) Unable to locate

HLSE-Inje (Chuncheon-si, KOR) Unable to locate

HLSG - 101.9 MHz (Seoul, KOR) [47302]

HLSH-Hamyang (Jinju, KOR) Unable to locate

HLSI-Kurye (Gwangju, KOR) Unable to locate

HLSJ-T'aebaek (Seoul, KOR) Unable to locate

HLSK-Kimch'on (Daegu, KOR) Unable to locate

HLSL-Posong (Gwangju, KOR) Unable to locate

HLSM-Changhung (Gwangju, KOR) Unable to locate

HLSN-Changsu (Jeonju-si, KOR) Unable to locate

HLSQ, KOR) Unable to locate

HLSQ-TV (Seoul, KOR) Unable to locate

HLSR-Kimje, KOR) Unable to locate

HLSU-Hadong (Jinju, KOR) Unable to locate

HLSW-Chongson (Seoul, KOR) Unable to locate

HNO (Dordrecht, NLD) [48416]

Hobbes Studies (Leiden, NLD) [48676]

Hobby Electronics (Bangkok, THA) [51422]

Hobby Zoo (Como, ITA) Unable to locate

Hobsons Bay Leader (Newport, VI, AUS) [42144]

Hochzeit (Konstanz, GER) [44513]

Numbers cited in bold after listings are entry numbers rather than page numbers.

Master Index

Hockey Digest (Milton Keynes, GBR) *Ceased*

HOG News (Brackley, GBR) *Unable to locate*

Hohhot People's Broadcasting Station (Hohhot, NM, CHN) *Unable to locate*

Hoist (Sidcup, GBR) **[56543]**

Hokkaido Hoso - 864 KHz (Enbetsu, JPN) **[46327]**

Hokkaido Journal of Medical Science (Hokkaido, JPN) *Unable to locate*

Hokkaido Journal of Primary Care (Sapporo, JPN) *Unable to locate*

Hokkaido Mathematical Journal (Sapporo, JPN) **[46650]**

Hokonui Gold-FM - 94.8 (Gore, NZL) **[48903]**

Hold Pusten (Oslo, NOR) **[49200]**

Holiday (Dhaka, BGD) **[42810]**

Holiday Crossword Collection (Gosford, NW, AUS) **[41918]**

Holiday-FM (Cobham, GBR) *Unable to locate*

Holiday-FM - 99 (Cobham, GBR) **[53027]**

Holiday Weekly (Karachi, PAK) *Unable to locate*

Holocaust and Genocide Studies (Oxford, GBR) **[55976]**

The Holocene (London, GBR) **[54564]**

Holy Land Studies (Strawberry Hill, GBR) **[56643]**

Holyrood News (Edinburgh, GBR) *Unable to locate*

Holz als Roh- und Werkstoff (Dordrecht, NLD) **[48417]**

Holzforschung (Berlin, GER) **[44189]**

H.O.M.E. (Vienna, AUT) *Unable to locate*

Home Concepts (Singapore, SGP) *Unable to locate*

Home Cultures (London, GBR) **[54565]**

Home & Decor (Singapore, SGP) **[50167]**

Home Decor & Furnishings (Walsall, GBR) *Unable to locate*

Home Economics/Economie Familiale/Hauswirtschaft (Paris, FRA) *Unable to locate*

Home & Family (London, GBR) **[54566]**

Home Help (Edinburgh, GBR) **[53284]**

Home Journal (Hong Kong, CHN) **[43317]**

Home Journal Buyer's Guide (Hong Kong, CHN) **[43318]**

Home Life (Makati City, PHL) **[49517]**

Home-Life Magazine (Lurgan, GBR) *Unable to locate*

Home New Zealand (Auckland, NZL) **[48795]**

Home Radio Cagayan de Oro-FM - 93.5 (Cagayan de Oro City, PHL) **[49460]**

Home Radio Cebu-FM - 106.7 (Cebu City, PHL) **[49471]**

Home Radio Davao-FM - 98.7 (Davao City, PHL) **[49485]**

Home Radio General Santos-FM - 98.3 (General Santos City, PHL) **[49495]**

Home Scene (West Malling, GBR) *Unable to locate*

Homebuilding & Renovating (Bromsgrove, GBR) **[52748]**

HomeFlair Magazine (Watford, GBR) *Unable to locate*

Homeless in Europe (Brussels, BEL) **[42858]**

Homemaker (Horsham, GBR) *Unable to locate*

The Homeopath Journal (Northampton, GBR) **[55709]**

Homeopathic Herald (Calcutta, WB, IND) *Unable to locate*

Homeopathic World (Calcutta, WB, IND) *Unable to locate*

Homeopathy (London, GBR) *Ceased*

Homeopathy in Practice (Nutley, GBR) **[55779]**

Homes & Antiques (London, GBR) **[54567]**

Homesh-FM - 102.2 MHz (Peshkopi, ALB) **[41440]**

Homespun (North Ryde, NW, AUS) **[42183]**

HOMO - Journal of Comparative Human Biology (Adelaide, SA, AUS) **[41506]**

Homoeopathic Vikas (Gwalior, MP, IND) *Unable to locate*

Homoeopathy (Kumbakonam, TN, IND) *Unable to locate*

Honduras This Week (Tegucigalpa, HND) **[44803]**

Honey (Colombo, SRI) *Unable to locate*

The Hong Kong Accountant (Hong Kong, CHN) **[43319]**

Hong Kong Apparel (Hong Kong, CHN) **[43320]**

Hong Kong Business (Hong Kong, CHN) **[43321]**

Hong Kong for the Business Visitor (Hong Kong, CHN) **[43322]**

Hong Kong Dermatology and Venereology Bulletin **[43328]***

Hong Kong Design Services (Hong Kong, CHN) **[43323]**

Hong Kong Electrical Contractors' Association (Hong Kong, CHN) *Unable to locate*

Hong Kong Electronic Components & Parts **[43304]***

Hong Kong Electronics **[43305]***

Hong Kong Enterprise **[43306]***

Hong Kong Entrepreneur (Hong Kong, CHN) **[43324]**

Hong Kong Gifts, Premiums & Stationery **[43310]***

Hong Kong Household **[43311]***

Hong Kong iMag (Hong Kong, CHN) *Unable to locate*

Hong Kong iMail (Hong Kong, CHN) *Unable to locate*

Hong Kong Industrialist (Hong Kong, CHN) **[43325]**

Hong Kong Jewellery Collection **[43312]***

Hong Kong Jewelry Express (Hong Kong, CHN) **[43326]**

Hong Kong Journal of Applied Linguistics (Hong Kong, CHN) **[43327]**

Hong Kong Journal of Dermatology & Venereology (Hong Kong, CHN) **[43328]**

Hong Kong Journal of Occupational Therapy (Hong Kong, CHN) **[43329]**

The Hong Kong Journal of Orthopaedic Surgery (Hong Kong, CHN) **[43330]**

Hong Kong Journal of Paediatrics (Hong Kong, CHN) **[43331]**

Hong Kong Journal of Religious Education (Hong Kong, CHN) *Unable to locate*

The Hong Kong Journal of Social Work (Hong Kong, CHN) **[43332]**

Hong Kong Journal of Sociology (Hong Kong, CHN) **[43333]**

The Hong Kong Journal of Sports

Medicine and Sports Science (Hong Kong, CHN) **[43334]**

Hong Kong Law Reports & Digest (Hong Kong, CHN) **[43335]**

Hong Kong Lawyer (Hong Kong, CHN) **[43336]**

Hong Kong Leather Goods & Bags **[43307]***

The Hong Kong Manager (Hong Kong, CHN) **[43337]**

Hong Kong Medical Diary (Hong Kong, CHN) **[43338]**

Hong Kong Medical Journal (Hong .Kong, CHN) **[43339]**

The Hong Kong Nursing Journal (Hong Kong, CHN) **[43340]**

Hong Kong Optical **[43313]***

Hong Kong Packaging **[43314]***

Hong Kong Physiotherapy Journal (Hong Kong, CHN) **[43341]**

The Hong Kong Practitioner (Hong Kong, CHN) **[43342]**

Hong Kong Printing (Hong Kong, CHN) **[43343]**

Hong Kong Productivity News (Hong Kong, CHN) *Unable to locate*

The Hong Kong Racing Journal (Hong Kong, CHN) **[43344]**

Hong Kong Surveyor (Hong Kong, CHN) **[43345]**

Hong Kong Tatler (Hong Kong, CHN) **[43346]**

Hong Kong Toys **[43315]***

Hong Kong Voice of Democracy (Hong Kong, CHN) *Unable to locate*

Hong Kong Watches and Clocks **[43316]***

Honghe People's Broadcasting Station (Gejiu, YU, CHN) *Unable to locate*

Honghe People's Broadcasting Station (Gejiu, YU, CHN) *Unable to locate*

Honghe People's Broadcasting Station (Gejiu, YU, CHN) *Unable to locate*

Honghe People's Broadcasting Station (Gejiu, YU, CHN) *Unable to locate*

Honghe People's Broadcasting Station (Gejiu, YU, CHN) *Unable to locate*

Honnert-FM - 100.7 (Luxembourg, LUX) **[47499]**

Hope-FM - 103.2 (Seven Hills, NW, AUS) **[42357]**

Hope-FM - 93.3 (Nairobi, KEN) **[47199]**

Hope-FM - 90.1 (Bournemouth, GBR) **[52431]**

Hope and Life (Istanbul, TUR) *Unable to locate*

HoRadS-FM - 99.2 MHz (Stuttgart, GER) **[44691]**

Horen (Houten, NLD) *Unable to locate*

Horisont (Vasa, FIN) *Unable to locate*

The Horizon (Dhaka, BGD) *Unable to locate*

Horizon-FM (Milton Keynes, GBR) *Unable to locate*

Horizons (Penrith, GBR) **[56245]**

Horizonte-FM - 103.3 (Santiago, CHL) **[43156]**

Horizonte-FM - 106.3 (Caaguazu, PAR) **[49410]**

Hormones and Behavior (Amsterdam, NLD) **[48013]**

Horn Player Magazine (Sudbury, GBR) **[56650]**

Hornby Magazine (Kingston upon Thames, GBR) **[53722]**

Horncastle News (Horncastle, GBR) **[53591]**

Hornsby & Upper North Shore Advocate (Hornsby, NW, AUS) **[41965]**

Hornsey & Crouch End Journal (London, GBR) **[54568]**

Horological Journal (Newark, GBR) **[55659]**

Horoscope (Paris, FRA) *Unable to locate*

Horrible Science Collection (London, GBR) **[54569]**

Horse (London, GBR) **[54570]**

Horse Health Magazine (Barnsley, GBR) **[52181]**

Horse & Hound (London, GBR) **[54571]**

Horse & Rider (Grayshott, GBR) **[53480]**

Horticultura (Reus, SPA) *Unable to locate*

Horticultural Journal (Kolkata, WB, IND) **[45268]**

Horticultural Quarterly Magazine (Harare, ZWE) *Unable to locate*

Horticulture News (Auckland, NZL) **[48796]**

Horysont (Good News) (Valby, DEN) **[43736]**

HORZU (Hamburg, GER) **[44418]**

Hosiery Report Weekly (Delhi, DH, IND) *Unable to locate*

Hosiery and Textile Journal (Ludhiana, PJ, IND) *Unable to locate*

Hospital Administration (New Delhi, DH, IND) *Unable to locate*

Hospital & Agedcare (Surry Hills, NW, AUS) **[42434]**

The Hospital and Community Friend (Colchester, GBR) *Ceased*

Hospital Doctor of Ireland (Dublin, DU, IRL) *Unable to locate*

Hospital Equipment & Supplies (London, GBR) *Unable to locate*

Hospital & Healthcare **[42434]***

Hospital Healthcare Europe (London, GBR) **[54572]**

Hospital Imaging and Radiology Europe (London, GBR) **[54573]**

Hospital Management International (London, GBR) **[54574]**

The Hospital Pharmacist **[54227]***

Hospital Post (Darmstadt, GER) **[44308]**

Hospitalia (Brussels, BEL) *Unable to locate*

Hospitality Foodservice (North Sydney, NW, AUS) *Unable to locate*

Hospitality Industry International (Croydon, GBR) *Ceased*

The Hospitality Magazine (Harare, ZWE) **[57114]**

Hospitality Review (Belfast, GBR) **[52285]**

Hospitality Today (Christchurch, NZL) **[48869]**

Hospodarske Noviny (Prague, CZE) *Unable to locate*

Hostel (Vienna, AUT) *Unable to locate*

Hot Dip Galvanizing (Sutton Coldfield, GBR) **[56695]**

Hot English Magazine (Madrid, SPA) **[50767]**

Hot-FM - 91.1 (Maroochydore, QL, AUS) **[42036]**

Hot-FM - 104.5 (Petaling Jaya, MYS) **[47707]**

Hot-FM - 88.2 (Petaling Jaya, MYS) **[47708]**

Hot-FM - 90.1 (Petaling Jaya, MYS) **[47705]**

Hot-FM - 97.6 (Petaling Jaya, MYS) **[47706]**

Numbers cited in bold after listings are entry numbers rather than page numbers.

Hot Moda & Shopping (Warsaw, POL) **[49716]**

Hot Tomato-FM - 102.9 (Southport, QL, AUS) **[42382]**

Hotan Channel (Hotan, XU, CHN) *Unable to locate*

Hotan-Ug People's Broadcasting Station (Hotan, XU, CHN) *Unable to locate*

Hoteis de Portugal (Lisbon, PRT) *Unable to locate*

Hotel and Accommodation Management (Pyrmont, NW, AUS) **[42280]**

Hotel Business (Colchester, GBR) **[53038]**

Hotel & Catering Review (Blackrock, DU, IRL) **[45920]**

Hotel/Restaurant/Food (Istanbul, TUR) *Unable to locate*

Hotel & Restaurant (South Africa) (Pinelands, SAF) *Unable to locate*

HOTELS China & Overseas (Beijing, CHN) *Unable to locate*

Hott-FM - 95.3 (Bridgetown, BRB) **[42830]**

Hounds (Shrewsbury, GBR) **[56537]**

House Builder (London, GBR) **[54575]**

House & Home (Hazelbrook, NW, AUS) **[41945]**

Houses (Port Melbourne, VI, AUS) **[42264]**

Housewares (UK) (Sittingbourne, GBR) **[56549]**

Housing (Coventry, GBR) **[53084]**

Housing Association Building & Maintenance (Watford, GBR) **[56865]**

Housing, Care and Support (Brighton, GBR) **[52613]**

Housing and Planning Review (London, GBR) *Ceased*

Housing Studies (Abingdon, GBR) **[51806]**

Housing, Theory & Society (Abingdon, GBR) **[51807]**

Housing Times (Mumbai, MH, IND) *Unable to locate*

Hovercraft Bulletin (Lee-on-Solent, GBR) *Unable to locate*

How (New Delhi, DH, IND) *Unable to locate*

The Howard Journal of Criminal Justice (Oxford, GBR) **[55977]**

How's That? (Stafford, GBR) *Unable to locate*

HP User (Middlesex, GBR) *Unable to locate*

HPB (Oxford, GBR) **[55978]**

HPR—Housing & Planning Review **[53995]***

HSB International (Dordrecht, NLD) *Unable to locate*

Hsin sheng FM Broadcasting Station (Hsinchu, TWN) *Unable to locate*

Hsin Kechia Broadcasting Station (Taoyuan, TWN) *Unable to locate*

HSJ (London, GBR) **[54576]**

Hua Shang (Singapore, SGP) *Unable to locate*

Huaibei People's Broadcasting Station (Huaibei, AN, CHN) *Unable to locate*

Huaibei People's Broadcasting Station (Huaibei, AN, CHN) *Unable to locate*

Huaibei People's Broadcasting Station (Huaibei, AN, CHN) *Unable to locate*

Huainan People's Broadcasting Station (Huainan, AN, CHN) *Unable to locate*

Huaiyan Prople's Broadcasting Station (Huaiyin, JS, CHN) *Unable to locate*

Huaiyin People's Broadcasting Station (Huaiyin, JS, CHN) *Unable to locate*

Huan yu Broadcasting Co (Hsinchu, TWN) *Unable to locate*

Huanggang People's Broadcasting Station (Huanggang, CHN) *Unable to locate*

Huanggang People's Broadcasting Station (Huanggang, HU, CHN) *Unable to locate*

Huanggang People's Broadcasting Station (Huanggang, HU, CHN) *Unable to locate*

Huangshan People's Broadcasting Station (Huangshan, AN, CHN) *Unable to locate*

Huangshi People's Broadcasting Station (Huangshi, HB, CHN) *Unable to locate*

Huangshi People's Broadcasting Station (Huangshi, HU, CHN) *Unable to locate*

Huanle Broadcasting Station (Hualien, TWN) *Unable to locate*

The Hub-AM (Bristol, GBR) *Unable to locate*

Hubei People's Broadcasting Station (Wuhan, HU, CHN) *Unable to locate*

Hubei People's Broadcasting Station - Channel 4, HB, CHN) *Unable to locate*

Hubei People's Broadcasting Station - Channel 4, HU, CHN) *Unable to locate*

Hubei People's Broadcasting Station - Channel 1 (Wuhan, HB, CHN) *Unable to locate*

Hubei People's Broadcasting Station - Channel 3 (Wuhan, CHN) *Unable to locate*

Hubei People's Broadcasting Station - Channel 2, HU, CHN) *Unable to locate*

Hucknall Dispatch (Hucknall, GBR) **[53615]**

Huellas (Guayaquil, ECU) *Unable to locate*

Hufvudstadsbladet (Helsinki, FIN) *Ceased*

Huisgenoot (Sandton, SAF) **[50626]**

Huizhou People's Broadcasting Station (Huizhou, GD, CHN) *Unable to locate*

Hukerikar Memorial Lecture Series (Dharwad, KA, IND) *Unable to locate*

Hull Advertiser Series (Hull, GBR) *Unable to locate*

Huludao People's Broadcasting Station (Huludao, LI, CHN) *Unable to locate*

Hulun Buir People's Broadcasting Station (Hailar, NM, CHN) *Unable to locate*

Hulun Buir People's Broadcasting Station (Hulun Buir, NM, CHN) *Unable to locate*

Hulun Buir People's Broadcasting Station (Hulun Buir, NM, CHN) *Unable to locate*

Hulun Buir People's Broadcasting Station (Hulun Buir, NM, CHN) *Unable to locate*

Human Communication Research (Oxford, GBR) *Unable to locate*

Human Concerns (London, GBR) *Unable to locate*

Human Ecology (Dordrecht, NLD) **[48418]**

Human Factors and Aerospace Safety (Surrey, GBR) **[56666]**

Human Fertility (Abingdon, GBR) **[51808]**

Human Function (Glasgow, GBR) *Unable to locate*

Human Genomics (London, GBR) **[54577]**

Human Geography (Beijing, CHN) *Unable to locate*

Human Molecular Genetics (Oxford, GBR) **[55979]**

Human Movement (Warsaw, POL) **[49717]**

Human Movement Science (Amsterdam, NLD) **[48014]**

Human Physiology (Moscow, RUS) **[49915]**

Human Relations (London, GBR) **[54578]**

Human Reproduction (Childerley, GBR) **[53018]**

Human Reproduction & Genetic Ethics (Edinburgh, GBR) **[53285]**

Human Reproduction Update (Cambridge, GBR) **[52829]**

Human Resource Development International (Abingdon, GBR) **[51809]**

Human Resource Management International Digest (Bradford, GBR) **[52462]**

Human Resource Management Journal (Oxford, GBR) **[55980]**

Human Resource Management Review (Amsterdam, NLD) **[48015]**

Human Resources (London, GBR) **[54579]**

Human Resources for Health (London, GBR) **[54580]**

Human Resources Journal of Zimbabwe (Harare, ZWE) *Unable to locate*

Human Right Platform (Nkambe, CMR) *Unable to locate*

Human Rights and Environment (Bishkek, KGA) *Unable to locate*

Human Rights Forum (Quezon City, PHL) *Unable to locate*

Human Rights Law Review (Oxford, GBR) **[55981]**

Human Rights Solidarity (Hong Kong, CHN) **[43347]**

Human Rights Worldwide (Frankfurt am Main, GER) *Unable to locate*

Human Technology (Jyvaskyla, FIN) **[43869]**

Humanist **[54991]***

Humanist Outlook (New Delhi, DH, IND) *Unable to locate*

Humanistiche Psychologie Halbjehrbuch (Eschweiler, GER) *Unable to locate*

Humanities Journal of the Asiatic Society of Bangladesh (Dhaka, BGD) *Unable to locate*

Humanities Review (New Delhi, DH, IND) *Unable to locate*

Humanity (Hanoi, VNM) **[57051]**

Humanity & Social Sciences Journal (Faisalabad, PAK) **[49246]**

Humanomics (Bradford, GBR) **[52463]**

Hume Leader (Tullamarine, VI, AUS) **[42651]**

Hunan Life Channel (Changsha, HA, CHN) *Unable to locate*

Hunan People's Broadcasting Station (Changsha, HN, CHN) *Unable to locate*

Hunan People's Broadcasting Station (Changsha, HA, CHN) *Unable to locate*

Hunan People's Broadcasting Station (Changsha, HA, CHN) *Unable to locate*

Hunan People's Broadcasting Station (Changsha, HA, CHN) *Unable to locate*

Hunan People's Broadcasting Station (Changsha, HA, CHN) *Unable to locate*

Hunan People's Broadcasting Station (Changsha, HA, CHN) *Unable to locate*

Hunan People's Broadcasting Station (Changsha, HA, CHN) *Unable to locate*

Hunan People's Broadcasting Station (Changsha, HA, CHN) *Unable to locate*

Hunan People's Broadcasting Station (Changsha, HA, CHN) *Unable to locate*

Hunan TV 2 - Channel 2 (Changsha, HA, CHN) **[43247]**

Hunchun People's Broadcasting Station (Hunchun, JI, CHN) *Unable to locate*

Hunden (Solrod Strand, DEN) *Unable to locate*

Hungarian Medical Journal (Budapest, HUN) **[44835]**

The Hungarian Quarterly (Budapest, HUN) **[44836]**

Hungarian Studies (Budapest, HUN) **[44837]**

The Huntington Harbour Journal **[55277]***

The Hunts Post (Huntingdon, GBR) **[53635]**

HUON-FM - 95.3 (Geeveston, TA, AUS) **[41884]**

Huria (Dar es Salaam, TZA) **[51401]**

Hurunui News (Amberley, NZL) **[48782]**

Husdjur (Eskilstuna, SWE) **[50953]**

Husflid (Kerteminde, DEN) *Unable to locate*

Huzhou People's Broadcasting Station (Huzhou, ZH, CHN) *Unable to locate*

Huzhou People's Broadcasting Station (Huzhou, ZH, CHN) *Unable to locate*

Huzhou People's Broadcasting Station (Huzhou, ZH, CHN) *Unable to locate*

Huzhou People's Broadcasting Station (Huzhou, ZH, CHN) *Unable to locate*

Huzhou People's Broadcasting Station (Huzhou, ZH, CHN) *Unable to locate*

Huzhou People's Broadcasting Station (Huzhou, ZH, CHN) *Unable to locate*

HVAC Magasinet (Glostrup, DEN) **[43705]**

I Iwaeong (Seoul, KOR) *Unable to locate*

Hybridity (Singapore, SGP) *Unable to locate*

Hydrobiologia (Dordrecht, NLD) **[48419]**

Hydrocarbon Asia (Singapore, SGP) **[50168]**

Hydroecologie appliquee (Les Ulis, FRA) **[43965]**

The Hydrographic Journal (Plymouth, GBR) **[56270]**

Hydrological Processes (Bristol, GBR) **[52674]**

Hydrology **[46393]***

Hydrology and Earth System Sciences Discussions (Delft, NLD) **[48309]**

Hydrology Journal (New Delhi, DH, IND) *Unable to locate*

Numbers cited in bold after listings are entry numbers rather than page numbers.

Hydrology Research (Norrkoping, SWE) **[50995]**

Hydroplus (Levallois-Perret, FRA) *Unable to locate*

Hygie **[44103]***

Hygiea Internationalis (Linkoping, SWE) **[50974]**

Hygiene & Sanitation (Moscow, RUS) **[49916]**

Hygienekrant (Rijswijk, NLD) *Ceased*

Hymy (Kuvalehdet, FIN) **[43881]**

Hyperfine Interactions (Dordrecht, NLD) **[48420]**

HyperScale (Oxford, GBR) **[55982]**

Hypertension in Pregnancy (Abingdon, GBR) **[51810]**

Hypertension Research (Tokyo, JPN) **[46835]**

Hyresgasten (Stockholm, SWE) *Unable to locate*

Hyva Ateria (Helsinki, FIN) *Unable to locate*

I

I Can Do That! (Liverpool, GBR) *Unable to locate*

i can make it myself (Rozelle, NW, AUS) **[42327]**

I-FM - 95.5 (Port of Spain, TTO) **[51469]**

I Shin Den Shin (Paris, FRA) *Unable to locate*

i-Sihat (Kuala Lumpur, MYS) **[47604]**

I Trafik (Stockholm, SWE) *Unable to locate*

I-Ways **[48069]***

IA Journal (Ballyclare, GBR) **[52157]**

IAA Ingenieria Aeronautica y Astronautica (Madrid, SPA) *Unable to locate*

IAM Journal (Kassel, GER) *Unable to locate*

IAMR Report (Delhi, DH, IND) **[45093]**

IAMR Working Paper (Delhi, DH, IND) **[45094]**

IAPQR Transactions (Calcutta, WB, IND) *Unable to locate*

IASA Journal (Canberra, AC, AUS) **[41707]**

IASLIC Bulletin (Kolkata, WB, IND) **[45269]**

IASLIC Special Publication (Kolkata, WB, IND) *Unable to locate*

IATUL Conference Proceedings (Oxford, GBR) *Unable to locate*

IAW! (Bangor, GBR) **[52171]**

IB World (Geneva, SWI) **[51098]**

IBAF World Baseball Magazine (Lausanne, SWI) *Ceased*

Ibaraki Hoso (Mito, JPN) *Unable to locate*

The IBCAM Journal (Birmingham, GBR) *Unable to locate*

IBEC Economic Trends (Dublin, DU, IRL) **[45965]**

Ibero-FM - 90.9 (Mexico City, DF, MEX) **[47791]**

Iberoromania (Berlin, GER) **[44190]**

Ibiza Global Radio-FM (Geldrop, NLD) *Unable to locate*

IBM Database Magazine (London, GBR) **[54581]**

IBP Journal (Pasig City, PHL) **[49571]**

IBP Law Journal **[49571]***

IBS Asian Electronics News (Taipei, TWN) *Unable to locate*

IBS Electronic Component & Equipment Exhibition (Taipei, TWN) *Unable to locate*

ICA Regional Bulletin (New Delhi, DH, IND) *Unable to locate*

ICCW Journal (New Delhi, DH, IND) *Unable to locate*

Ice Cream (Derby, GBR) **[53164]**

Iceland Business (Reykjavik, ICE) *Unable to locate*

Iceland Review (Reykjavik, ICE) **[44901]**

ICES Cooperative Research Reports (Copenhagen, DEN) **[43673]**

ICES Journal of Marine Science (Copenhagen, DEN) **[43674]**

ICES Journal of Marine Science (Oxford, GBR) **[55983]**

ICFA **[54626]***

The Icfai Journal of Accounting Research (Hyderabad, AP, IND) **[45140]**

The Icfai Journal of Alternative Dispute Resolution (Hyderabad, AP, IND) **[45141]**

The Icfai Journal of Audit Practice (Hyderabad, AP, IND) **[45142]**

The Icfai Journal of Bank Management (Hyderabad, AP, IND) **[45143]**

The Icfai Journal of Behavioral Finance (Hyderabad, AP, IND) **[45144]**

The Icfai Journal of Corporate and Securities Law (Hyderabad, AP, IND) **[45145]**

The Icfai Journal of Cyber Law (Hyderabad, AP, IND) **[45146]**

The Icfai Journal of Derivatives Markets (Hyderabad, AP, IND) **[45147]**

The Icfai Journal of Employment Law (Hyderabad, AP, IND) **[45148]**

The Icfai Journal of Entrepreneurship Development (Hyderabad, AP, IND) **[45149]**

The Icfai Journal of Environmental Economics (Hyderabad, AP, IND) **[45150]**

The Icfai Journal of Financial Economics (Hyderabad, AP, IND) **[45151]**

The Icfai Journal of Financial Risk Management (Hyderabad, AP, IND) **[45152]**

The Icfai Journal of Governance and Public Policy (Hyderabad, AP, IND) **[45153]**

The Icfai Journal of Healthcare Law (Hyderabad, AP, IND) **[45154]**

The Icfai Journal of History and Culture (Hyderabad, AP, IND) **[45155]**

The Icfai Journal of International Business Law (Hyderabad, AP, IND) **[45156]**

The Icfai Journal of Knowledge Management (Hyderabad, AP, IND) **[45157]**

The Icfai Journal of Life Sciences (Hyderabad, AP, IND) **[45158]**

The Icfai Journal of Managerial Economics (Hyderabad, AP, IND) **[45159]**

The Icfai Journal of Mergers & Acquisitions (Hyderabad, AP, IND) **[45160]**

The Icfai Journal of Monetary Economics (Hyderabad, AP, IND) **[45161]**

The Icfai Journal of Operations Management (Hyderabad, AP, IND) **[45162]**

The Icfai Journal of Organizational Behavior (Hyderabad, AP, IND) **[45163]**

The Icfai Journal of Public Finance (Hyderabad, AP, IND) **[45164]**

The Icfai Journal of Risk & Insurance (Hyderabad, AP, IND) **[45165]**

The Icfai Journal of Science & Technology (Hyderabad, AP, IND) **[45166]**

The Icfai Journal of Services Marketing (Hyderabad, AP, IND) **[45167]**

The Icfai Journal of Soft Skills (Hyderabad, AP, IND) **[45168]**

The Icfai Journal of Urban Policy (Hyderabad, AP, IND) **[45169]**

Icfai Reader (Hyderabad, AP, IND) **[45170]**

Ichthyologica (Srinagar, JK, IND) *Unable to locate*

Ichthyological Research (Tokyo, JPN) **[46836]**

ICID Journal **[45591]***

ICLARM Newsletter **[47690]***

ICMR Bulletin (New Delhi, DH, IND) **[45525]**

ICOFT News Review (Mumbai, MH, IND) *Unable to locate*

Icon Moments (Singapore, SGP) **[50169]**

iCreate (Bournemouth, GBR) **[52416]**

ICSSR Journal of Abstracts and Reviews **[45529]***

ICSSR Journal of Abstracts and Reviews **[45528]***

ICSSR Journal of Abstracts and Reviews **[45527]***

ICSSR Journal of Abstracts and Reviews **[45526]***

ICSSR Journal of Abstracts and Reviews (New Delhi, DH, IND) **[45529]**

ICSSR Journal of Abstracts and Reviews (New Delhi, DH, IND) **[45528]**

ICSSR Journal of Abstracts and Reviews (New Delhi, DH, IND) **[45527]**

ICSSR Journal of Abstracts and Reviews (New Delhi, DH, IND) **[45526]**

ICSSR Research Abstracts Quarterly (New Delhi, DH, IND) *Ceased*

ICUs and Nursing Web Journal (Nikea, GRC) **[44763]**

Id-Dijabete u Sahhtek (Valletta, MAL) **[47746]**

Idea (Tokyo, JPN) **[46837]**

Ideal Education (Mumbai, MH, IND) *Unable to locate*

Ideal-FM - 90.1 (Canelones, URY) **[57005]**

Ideal Home (London, GBR) **[54582]**

Idees (Cape Town, SAF) **[50382]**

Identities (Amsterdam, NLD) *Unable to locate*

Identity Culture and Politics (Kandy, SRI) **[50907]**

IDESIA (Arica, CHL) **[43133]**

IDF Bulletin **[42848]***

IDF Bulletin (Brussels, BEL) *Unable to locate*

idFM - 98 (Enghien-les-Bains, FRA) **[43946]**

IDP (Barcelona, SPA) **[50680]**

Idrottsbladet Motorsport (Sodertajle, SWE) *Unable to locate*

IDS Bulletin (Brighton, GBR) **[52614]**

IECAIM Noticias (Quito, ECU) *Unable to locate*

IEE Proceedings Circuits, Devices & Systems (Stevenage, GBR) **[56605]**

IEE Proceedings Communications **[56616]***

IEE Proceedings Computers & Digital Techniques **[56617]***

IEE Proceedings Control Theory & Applications (Stevenage, GBR) **[56606]**

IEE Proceedings Electric Power Applications (Stevenage, GBR) **[56607]**

IEE Proceedings Generation, Transmission & Distribution (Stevenage, GBR) **[56608]**

IEE Proceedings Microwaves, Antennas & Propagation (Stevenage, GBR) **[56609]**

IEE Proceedings Nanobiotechnology (Stevenage, GBR) **[56610]**

IEE Proceedings Optoelectronics (Stevenage, GBR) **[56611]**

IEE Proceedings Radar, Sonar & Navigation (Stevenage, GBR) **[56612]**

IEE Proceedings Science, Measurement & Technology (Stevenage, GBR) **[56613]**

IEE Proceedings Software (Stevenage, GBR) **[56614]**

IEE Proceedings Vision, Image & Signal Processing (Stevenage, GBR) **[56615]**

IEE Review Magazine (Stevenage, GBR) *Ceased*

IEEE Transactions on Components and Packaging Technologies (Kowloon, CHN) **[43451]**

IEEE Transactions on Evolutionary Computation (Piscataway, NJ, USA) *Unable to locate*

IEEMA Journal (Mumbai, MH, IND) **[45372]**

IEICE Electronics Express (Tokyo, JPN) **[46838]**

IEICE Transactions on Communications (Tokyo, JPN) **[46839]**

IEICE Transactions on Electronics (Tokyo, JPN) **[46840]**

IEICE Transactions on Fundamentals of Electronics, Communications and Computer Sciences (Chiba, JPN) **[46318]**

IEICE Transactions on Information and Systems (Tokyo, JPN) **[46841]**

IEM Journal (Petaling Jaya, MYS) **[47699]**

IET Communications (Stevenage, GBR) **[56616]**

IET Computers & Digital Techniques (Stevenage, GBR) **[56617]**

IETE Journal of Education (New Delhi, DH, IND) **[45530]**

IETE Journal of Research (New Delhi, DH, IND) **[45531]**

IETE Technical Review (New Delhi, DH, IND) **[45532]**

IFALPA Quarterly Review (Chertsey, GBR) *Unable to locate*

IFCAA Bulletin (Tokyo, JPN) *Unable to locate*

IFE PsychologIA (Ile-Ife, NGA) **[49113]**

IFHOH Journal (Abbots Langley, GBR) *Unable to locate*

IFME Brochure (The Hague, NLD) *Unable to locate*

IFS News (Canterbury, GBR) *Unable to locate*

IFSCC Magazine (Augsburg, GER) **[44140]**

IH Industria Hostelera (Madrid, SPA) **[50768]**

Ihypak (Bishkek, KGA) *Unable to locate*

IIA Non-Members Update (Dublin, DU, IRL) *Unable to locate*

IIM Metal News (Kolkata, WB, IND) **[45270]**

IIMC Bulletin (New Delhi, DH, IND) *Unable to locate*

IIST Bulletins (Hyderabad, AP, IND) *Unable to locate*

Numbers cited in bold after listings are entry numbers rather than page numbers.

IITC Bulletin (Mumbai, MH, IND) *Unable to locate*

IJCPS **[41828]***

IJES **[45582]***

(IJMS); International Journal on Multicultural Societies **[44395]***

IJmuiden-FM (Amsterdam, NLD) *Unable to locate*

Ikevana International (Tokyo, JPN) *Unable to locate*

Ikkevold (Skorping, DEN) *Unable to locate*

il bagno (Milan, ITA) *Unable to locate*

Il Battelliere (Cremona, ITA) *Unable to locate*

il caffe (Locarno, SWI) **[51209]**

Il Cardiologo (Milan, ITA) **[46173]**

Il Cucchiaio D'Argento (Rozzano, ITA) **[46250]**

Il Farmacista (Rome, ITA) *Unable to locate*

Il Fiasco (Rome, ITA) **[46233]**

Il Freddo (Milan, ITA) *Unable to locate*

Il Gazzettino della Pesca (Ancona, ITA) *Unable to locate*

Il Ginecologo (Milan, ITA) **[46174]**

Il Giornale dei Veicoli Commerciali (Peschiera Borromeo, ITA) **[46215]**

Il Giornalion (Rome, ITA) *Unable to locate*

Il Gommone e la Nautica per Tutti (Peschiera Borromeo, ITA) **[46216]**

Il Granturismo (Amsterdam, NLD) *Unable to locate*

Il-Merill (Ta' Xbiex, MAL) **[47744]**

Il Mondo del Latte (Milan, ITA) *Unable to locate*

IL-MUMENT (Pieta, MAL) *Unable to locate*

Il Nuovo Club (Bologna, ITA) **[46127]**

Il Quadrifoglio (Turin, ITA) *Unable to locate*

Il Tempo (Rome, ITA) *Unable to locate*

Il Vivaista (The Nurseryman) (Vernasca, ITA) *Unable to locate*

Ilan chih sheng (Voice of Ilan) Chungshan Broadcasting Co. (Ilan, TWN) *Unable to locate*

Ilford & Redbridge Post (Ilford, GBR) **[53639]**

Ili People's Broadcasting Station (Yining, XU, CHN) *Unable to locate*

Ili People's Broadcasting Station (Yining, XU, CHN) *Unable to locate*

Ili People's Broadcasting Station (Yining, XU, CHN) *Unable to locate*

Ili People's Broadcasting Station (Yining, XU, CHN) *Unable to locate*

Ili People's Broadcasting Station (Yining, XU, CHN) *Unable to locate*

Ilkeston Advertiser (Ilkeston, GBR) **[53642]**

Ilkley Gazette (Ilkley, GBR) **[53645]**

Illawarra Mercury (Wollongong, NW, AUS) **[42703]**

Illiesia (Ljubljana, SVA) **[50337]**

Illustrated Flora of Hokkaido (Hokkaido, JPN) *Unable to locate*

Illustrated Weekly of India (Mumbai, MH, IND) *Unable to locate*

Illustration in Japan (Tokyo, JPN) *Unable to locate*

L'illustre (Lausanne, SWI) **[51191]**

ILMAILU (Helsinki, FIN) *Unable to locate*

Ilocos Review (Abra, PHL) *Unable to locate*

The Ilocos Times (Laoag City, PHL) **[49509]**

Ilustreta Junioriem (Riga, LAT) **[47366]**

Ilustreta Pasaules Vesture (Riga, LAT) **[47367]**

Ilustreta Zinatne (Riga, LAT) **[47368]**

IMA Journal of Applied Mathematics (Birmingham, GBR) **[52342]**

IMA Journal of Management Mathematics (Oxford, GBR) **[55984]**

IMA Journal of Mathematical Control and Information (Oxford, GBR) **[55985]**

IMA Journal of Numerical Analysis (Oxford, GBR) **[55986]**

IMA Journal of Numerical Analysis (Southend-on-Sea, GBR) **[56585]**

Image (Balasore, OR, IND) *Unable to locate*

IMAGE (London, GBR) **[54583]**

Image-FM (Lazimpat, NPL) *Unable to locate*

Image & Narrative (Leuven, BEL) **[42897]**

Image Processing; Graphical Models and **[48004]***

Image and Vision Computing (Reading, GBR) **[56320]**

Images (Karachi, PAK) **[49354]**

Imagina-FM - 88.1 (Santiago, CHL) **[43157]**

Imagine-FM - 104.9 (Stockport, GBR) **[56627]**

Imagine Magazine (Bristol, GBR) **[52675]**

Imbottigliamento (Milan, ITA) *Unable to locate*

IMCoS Journal (Devon, GBR) **[53176]**

IMFO (Centurion, SAF) **[50439]**

IMIESA (Centurion, SAF) **[50440]**

IMIS Journal (Orpington, GBR) **[55852]**

Immigrants & Minorities (Abingdon, GBR) **[51811]**

Immobilier (Paris, FRA) *Unable to locate*

Immunity & Ageing (London, GBR) **[54584]**

Immunobiology (Leicester, GBR) **[53804]**

Immunogenetics (Rijswijk, NLD) **[48747]**

The Immunologist (Vienna, AUT) *Ceased*

Immunology (London, GBR) **[54585]**

Immunology Letters (Videnska, CZE) **[43641]**

Immunome Research (London, GBR) **[54586]**

Immunotherapy (London, GBR) **[54587]**

IMP Bridge Magazine (The Hague, NLD) *Unable to locate*

Impact (Dijon, FRA) **[43944]**

Impact (Auckland, NZL) **[48797]**

Impact (London, GBR) *Ceased*

Impact Assessment and Project Appraisal (Guildford, GBR) *Unable to locate*

Impact News (Dublin, DU, IRL) *Unable to locate*

Impact Radio-FM - 103 (Glenstantia, SAF) **[50485]**

Impegno (Turin, ITA) **[46272]**

Implicit Religion (London, GBR) **[54588]**

Import Trade Control Policy (Bangalore, KA, IND) *Unable to locate*

Impressions Magazine (London, GBR) *Unable to locate*

Improving Schools (London, GBR) **[54589]**

Impulse (Bhopal, MP, IND) *Unable to locate*

IMRN (Oxford, GBR) **[55987]**

In Balance—Holistic Health & Lifestyle Magazine & Therapy Directory (Welwyn Garden City, GBR) *Unable to locate*

In-between (New Delhi, DH, IND) *Unable to locate*

In Brief (London, GBR) **[54590]**

In Brief (Saint Neots, GBR) *Ceased*

In Camera (Hemel Hempstead, GBR) **[53558]**

In Car Business (Cheshire, GBR) *Unable to locate*

In-House Briefing Asia Pacific (Hong Kong, CHN) *Unable to locate*

The In-House Lawyer (London, GBR) **[54591]**

In-Nazzjon (Pieta, MAL) *Unable to locate*

In the Night Garden (London, GBR) **[54592]**

IN-PAK (Glostrup, DEN) **[43706]**

In Practice (Winchester, GBR) **[56930]**

In Silico Biology (Gottingen, GER) **[44399]**

In the Sticks (Alston, GBR) **[52103]**

In-Store Marketing (London, GBR) **[54593]**

In Sync (London, GBR) *Unable to locate*

In The Black (Melbourne, VI, AUS) **[42064]**

In Touch (Dublin, DU, IRL) **[45966]**

In Viaggio (Milan, ITA) *Unable to locate*

In Vitro Cellular and Developmental Biology - Plant (Wallingford, GBR) **[56819]**

Inbar (Tel Aviv, ISR) *Unable to locate*

Incentives & Meetings Asia **[50282]***

inCite (Deakin, AC, AUS) **[41836]**

Income Tax Reports (Chennai, TN, IND) **[45037]**

Incomes Data Reports (London, GBR) *Unable to locate*

L'Incontro (Turin, ITA) *Unable to locate*

Incorporating Care of the Elderly **[54505]***

Ind-Africana: Collected Research Papers on Africa (Delhi, DH, IND) *Unable to locate*

Ind Dak (Bangalore, KA, IND) *Unable to locate*

Indagationes Mathematicae (Groningen, NLD) **[48601]**

Independent (Mumbai, MH, IND) *Unable to locate*

The Independent (Boroko, PNG) *Unable to locate*

The Independent (London, GBR) *Unable to locate*

The Independent (Bangladesh) (Dhaka, BGD) **[42811]**

Independent Consulting Engineer (Lausanne, SWI) *Ceased*

Independent Education (South Melbourne, VI, AUS) *Unable to locate*

Independent Education Today (Feltham, GBR) *Unable to locate*

The Independent Electrical Retailer (Kent, GBR) **[53678]**

The Independent Herald (Johnsonville, NZL) *Unable to locate*

The Independent Newspaper (Dominica) (Roseau, DMA) *Ceased*

Independent Television Network - Channel 9 (Deniyaya, SRI) **[50886]**

Independent Television Network - Channel 12 (Nayabedda, SRI) **[50919]**

Index on Censorship (London, GBR) **[54594]**

Index India (Jaipur, RJ, IND) *Unable to locate*

Index to Indian Medical Periodicals (New Delhi, DH, IND) *Unable to locate*

Index Indo-Asiaticus (Calcutta, WB, IND) *Unable to locate*

Index Islamicus (Leiden, NLD) **[48677]**

Index of Members (London, GBR) *Unable to locate*

Index to Theses (London, GBR) **[54595]**

Index of Wholesale Prices in India (New Delhi, DH, IND) *Unable to locate*

The Indexer (Sheffield, GBR) **[56497]**

India Beat - 864 (Kuala Lumpur, MYS) **[47649]**

India Calling (Calcutta, WB, IND) *Unable to locate*

India Central Board of Revenue Central Excise Manual (New Delhi, DH, IND) *Unable to locate*

India Central Statistical Organization Monthly Abstract of Statistics (New Delhi, DH, IND) **[45533]**

India Central Statistical Organization Statistical Abstract (New Delhi, DH, IND) **[45534]**

India Department of Culture Demands for Grants (New Delhi, DH, IND) *Unable to locate*

India Department of Economic Affairs Budget Division Key to the Budget Documents (New Delhi, DH, IND) *Unable to locate*

India Department of Publication Publications (New Delhi, DH, IND) *Unable to locate*

India Department of Rural Development Administrative Intelligence Division Some Special Programmes of Rural (New Delhi, DH, IND) *Unable to locate*

India Department of Science and Technology Research and Development Statistics (New Delhi, DH, IND) *Unable to locate*

India Design & Interiors (New Delhi, DH, IND) *Unable to locate*

India Directorate of Jute Development—Jute Development Journal (Calcutta, WB, IND) *Unable to locate*

India Finance Department Budget of the Central Government (New Delhi, DH, IND) *Unable to locate*

India Investment Opportunities (Mumbai, MH, IND) *Unable to locate*

India Magazine (Mumbai, MH, IND) *Unable to locate*

India Meteorological Department Memoirs (New Delhi, DH, IND) *Unable to locate*

India Ministry of Education and Social Welfare Department of Social Welfare Documentation Service Bulletin (New Delhi, DH, IND) *Unable to locate*

India Ministry of Education and Social Welfare Provisional Statistics of Education in the States (New Delhi, DH, IND) *Unable to locate*

India Ministry of Finance Finance Library Weekly Bulletin (New Delhi, DH, IND) *Unable to locate*

India Ministry of Home Affairs Vital Statistics Division Sample Registration Bulletin (New Delhi, DH, IND) *Unable to locate*

India Ministry of Home Affairs Vital Statistics Division Survey of Causes of Death (Rural) (New Delhi, DH, IND) *Unable to locate*

India Ministry of Human Resource

Master Index

Development Department of Education Report (New Delhi, DH, IND) *Unable to locate*

India Ministry of Labour Bulletin of Current Awareness (New Delhi, DH, IND) *Unable to locate*

India Perspectives (New Delhi, DH, IND) **[45535]**

India Quarterly (New Delhi, DH, IND) *Unable to locate*

India Review (Abingdon, GBR) **[51812]**

India Supreme Court Unreported Judgments (Jodhpur, RJ, IND) *Unable to locate*

India Today (Mumbai, MH, IND) **[45373]**

India Today Plus (Mumbai, MH, IND) **[45374]**

India Today and Tomorrow (Mumbai, MH, IND) *Unable to locate*

India and the World (Kakinada, AP, IND) *Unable to locate*

India Zoological Survey Records (Calcutta, WB, IND) *Unable to locate*

Indian Academy of Applied Psychology Journal (Chennai, TN, IND) *Unable to locate*

Indian Academy of Geoscience Journal (Hyderabad, AP, IND) **[45171]**

Indian Academy of Mathematics Journal (Indore, MP, IND) *Unable to locate*

Indian Academy of Philosophy Journal (Calcutta, WB, IND) *Unable to locate*

Indian Academy of Wood Science Journal (Bangalore, KA, IND) *Unable to locate*

Indian Advocate (New Delhi, DH, IND) *Unable to locate*

Indian Agriculture in Brief (New Delhi, DH, IND) *Unable to locate*

Indian Agriculture Review (Mumbai, MH, IND) *Unable to locate*

Indian Agriculturist (Calcutta, WB, IND) *Unable to locate*

Indian Airman and Spaceman (Calcutta, WB, IND) *Unable to locate*

The Indian Anaesthetists' Forum (Jodhpur, RJ, IND) **[45218]**

Indian Anthropological Society Journal (Calcutta, WB, IND) *Unable to locate*

Indian Anthropologist (Delhi, DH, IND) *Unable to locate*

Indian Architect & Builder (Mumbai, MH, IND) *Unable to locate*

Indian Association of Sedimentologists Journal (New Delhi, DH, IND) *Unable to locate*

Indian Astronomical Ephemeris (New Delhi, DH, IND) *Unable to locate*

Indian Atom (Dehradun, UP, IND) *Unable to locate*

Indian Author (New Delhi, DH, IND) *Unable to locate*

Indian Auto (Navi Mumbai, IND) *Unable to locate*

Indian Aviation (Calcutta, WB, IND) *Unable to locate*

Indian Bank Today and Tomorrow (New Delhi, DH, IND) *Unable to locate*

Indian Bar Review (New Delhi, DH, IND) *Unable to locate*

Indian Bee Journal (Hissar, HY, IND) *Unable to locate*

Indian Biologist (Calcutta, WB, IND) *Unable to locate*

Indian Book Chronicle (New Delhi, DH, IND) *Unable to locate*

Indian Book Industry (New Delhi, DH, IND) *Unable to locate*

Indian Book Review Supplement (New Delhi, DH, IND) *Unable to locate*

Indian Books (Calcutta, WB, IND) *Unable to locate*

Indian Books in Print (New Delhi, DH, IND) *Unable to locate*

Indian Botanical Reporter (Aurangabad, MH, IND) *Unable to locate*

Indian Bradshaw (Calcutta, WB, IND) *Unable to locate*

Indian Cashew Journal (Cochin, KE, IND) **[45074]**

Indian Cement Industry Deskbook (Mumbai, MH, IND) *Unable to locate*

Indian Cement Review (Mumbai, MH, IND) **[45375]**

Indian Ceramic Society Transactions (Calcutta, WB, IND) *Unable to locate*

Indian Ceramics (Calcutta, WB, IND) *Unable to locate*

Indian Chemical Engineer (Delhi, DH, IND) **[45095]**

Indian Chemical Manufacturer (Mumbai, MH, IND) *Unable to locate*

Indian Chemical Society Journal (Calcutta, WB, IND) *Unable to locate*

Indian Chemicals and Pharmaceuticals Statistics (New Delhi, DH, IND) *Unable to locate*

Indian Church History Review (Mumbai, MH, IND) *Unable to locate*

Indian Cocoa, Arecanut & Spices Journal (Calicut, KE, IND) *Unable to locate*

Indian Coconut Journal (Kochi, KE, IND) **[45250]**

Indian Concrete Journal (ICJ) (Thane, MH, IND) **[45745]**

Indian Construction (Mumbai, MH, IND) **[45376]**

Indian Consumer Cooperator (New Delhi, DH, IND) *Unable to locate*

Indian Cooperative Review (New Delhi, DH, IND) **[45536]**

Indian Cotton Mills Federation Journal (Mumbai, MH, IND) *Unable to locate*

Indian Council for Africa Library Monthly Index of Important Articles and Editorials on Africa (New Delhi, DH, IND) *Unable to locate*

Indian Dairyman (New Delhi, DH, IND) **[45537]**

Indian Defence Review (New Delhi, DH, IND) **[45538]**

Indian Dental Association Journal (Bangalore, KA, IND) *Unable to locate*

Indian Deoiled Cakes Exporters' Performance Monitor (Mumbai, MH, IND) *Unable to locate*

Indian Development Review (New Delhi, DH, IND) **[45539]**

Indian Dissertation Abstracts (New Delhi, DH, IND) *Ceased*

Indian Drugs (Mumbai, MH, IND) **[45377]**

Indian Drugs and Pharmaceuticals Industry (Mumbai, MH, IND) *Unable to locate*

Indian and Eastern Pharmacy (Calcutta, WB, IND) *Unable to locate*

Indian Economic Diary (New Delhi, DH, IND) *Unable to locate*

Indian Economic Journal (Bangalore, KA, IND) *Unable to locate*

Indian Economic and Social History Review (New Delhi, DH, IND) **[45540]**

Indian Education Abstracts (New Delhi, DH, IND) *Unable to locate*

Indian Education (Agra) (Agra, UP, IND) *Unable to locate*

Indian Educational Review (New Delhi, DH, IND) **[45541]**

Indian Energy and Power Update (Mumbai, MH, IND) *Unable to locate*

Indian Engineering Exporter (Calcutta, WB, IND) *Unable to locate*

Indian Environment (Mumbai, MH, IND) *Unable to locate*

Indian Export Bulletin (New Delhi, DH, IND) **[45542]**

Indian Export Trade Journal (Baroda, GJ, IND) *Unable to locate*

Indian Export Year Book (New Delhi, DH, IND) *Unable to locate*

Indian Exporter and Importer (Mumbai, MH, IND) *Unable to locate*

The Indian Express (New Delhi, DH, IND) **[45543]**

Indian Factories Journal (Chennai, TN, IND) *Unable to locate*

Indian Farm Mechanization (New Delhi, DH, IND) *Unable to locate*

Indian Farmer Times (New Delhi, DH, IND) *Unable to locate*

Indian Farming (New Delhi, DH, IND) **[45544]**

Indian Fern Journal (Patiala, PJ, IND) *Unable to locate*

Indian Fertiliser Industry Deskbook (Mumbai, MH, IND) *Unable to locate*

Indian Fertiliser Statistics (New Delhi, DH, IND) *Unable to locate*

Indian Films (Pune, MH, IND) *Unable to locate*

Indian Finance (Calcutta, WB, IND) *Unable to locate*

Indian Fisheries Abstracts (Barrackpore, WB, IND) *Unable to locate*

Indian Food Packer (New Delhi, DH, IND) *Unable to locate*

Indian Forest Bulletin (New Series) (Dehradun, UP, IND) *Unable to locate*

Indian Forest Leaflets (New Series) (Dehradun, UP, IND) *Unable to locate*

Indian Forest Records (New Series) Botany (Dehradun, UP, IND) *Unable to locate*

Indian Forest Records (New Series) Composite Wood (Dehradun, UP, IND) *Unable to locate*

Indian Forest Records (New Series) Entomology (Dehradun, UP, IND) *Unable to locate*

Indian Forest Records (New Series) Forest Management and Mensuration (Dehradun, UP, IND) *Unable to locate*

Indian Forest Records (New Series) Forest Pathology (Dehradun, UP, IND) *Unable to locate*

Indian Forest Records (New Series) Logging (Dehradun, UP, IND) *Unable to locate*

Indian Forest Records (New Series) Silviculture (Dehradun, UP, IND) *Unable to locate*

Indian Forest Records (New Series) Statistical (Dehradun, UP, IND) *Unable to locate*

Indian Forest Records (New Series) Timber Mechanics (Dehradun, UP, IND) *Unable to locate*

Indian Forest Records Wood Anatomy (Dehradun, UP, IND) *Unable to locate*

Indian Foundry Journal (Kolkata, WB, IND) *Unable to locate*

Indian Geographical Journal (Madras, TN, IND) *Unable to locate*

Indian Geographical Studies (Patna, BH, IND) *Unable to locate*

Indian Geologists' Association Bi-Annual Bulletin (Chandigarh, CH, IND) *Unable to locate*

Indian Geotechnical Journal (New Delhi, DH, IND) *Unable to locate*

Indian Granite Exporters' Performance Monitor (Mumbai, MH, IND) *Unable to locate*

Indian Growth and Development Review (New Delhi, IND) **[45475]**

Indian Heart Journal (Kolkata, WB, IND) **[45271]**

Indian Highways (New Delhi, DH, IND) **[45545]**

Indian Horticulture (New Delhi, DH, IND) **[45546]**

Indian Industry Review (Mumbai, MH, IND) *Unable to locate*

Indian Institute of History of Medicine Bulletin (Madras) (Madras, TN, IND) *Unable to locate*

Indian Institute of Metals Transactions (Kolkata, WB, IND) **[45272]**

Indian Institute of Public Opinion Monthly Public Opinion Surveys (New Delhi, DH, IND) *Unable to locate*

Indian Institute of Road Transport Monthly Bulletin (Mumbai, MH, IND) *Unable to locate*

Indian Institute of Science Journal (Bangalore, KA, IND) **[44959]**

Indian Institute of Technology, Madras—PhD Dissertation Abstracts (Chennai, TN, IND) *Unable to locate*

Indian Institute of World Culture Bulletin (Bangalore, KA, IND) **[44960]**

Indian Journal of Adult Education (New Delhi, DH, IND) *Unable to locate*

Indian Journal of Aerospace Medicine (Bangalore, KA, IND) **[44961]**

Indian Journal of Agricultural Biochemistry (Kanpur, UP, IND) *Unable to locate*

Indian Journal of Agricultural Chemistry (Allahabad, UP, IND) *Unable to locate*

Indian Journal of Agricultural Economics (Mumbai, MH, IND) *Unable to locate*

Indian Journal of Agricultural Engineering (New Delhi, DH, IND) **[45547]**

Indian Journal of Agricultural Marketing (Nagpur, MH, IND) *Unable to locate*

Indian Journal of Agricultural Research (Karnal, HY, IND) *Unable to locate*

Indian Journal of Agricultural Sciences (New Delhi, DH, IND) **[45548]**

Indian Journal of Agronomy (New Delhi, DH, IND) *Unable to locate*

Indian Journal of Allergy Asthma and Immunology (Delhi, DH, IND) **[45096]**

Indian Journal of American Studies (Hyderabad, AP, IND) *Unable to locate*

Indian Journal of Anaesthesia (Mumbai, MH, IND) *Unable to locate*

Indian Journal of Animal Health (Calcutta, WB, IND) *Unable to locate*

Indian Journal of Animal Nutrition (Karnal, HY, IND) *Unable to locate*

Numbers cited in bold after listings are entry numbers rather than page numbers.

Indian Journal of Animal Production and Management (Hissar, HY, IND) *Unable to locate*

Indian Journal of Animal Research (Karnal, HY, IND) *Unable to locate*

Indian Journal of Animal Sciences (New Delhi, DH, IND) **[45549]**

Indian Journal of Applied Entomology (Jodhpur, RJ, IND) **[45219]**

Indian Journal of Applied Linguistics (New Delhi, DH, IND) *Unable to locate*

Indian Journal of Applied Psychology (Chennai, TN, IND) *Unable to locate*

Indian Journal of Asian Affairs (Jaipur, RJ, IND) *Unable to locate*

Indian Journal of Behaviour (Bangalore, KA, IND) *Unable to locate*

Indian Journal of Biochemistry and Biophysics (Jodhpur, RJ, IND) **[45220]**

Indian Journal of Botany (Hyderabad, AP, IND) *Unable to locate*

Indian Journal of Cancer (Mumbai, MH, IND) **[45378]**

Indian Journal of Chemical Technology (Jodhpur, RJ, IND) **[45221]**

Indian Journal of Chemistry Section A: Inorganic, Physical, Theoreticl and Analytical Chemistry (Jodhpur, RJ, IND) *Ceased*

Indian Journal of Chemistry Section B: Organic and Medicinal Chemistry (Jodhpur, RJ, IND) *Unable to locate*

Indian Journal of Clinical Biochemistry (Jaipur, RJ, IND) **[45195]**

Indian Journal of Clinical Psychology (Jaipur, RJ, IND) *Unable to locate*

Indian Journal of Colo-Proctology (Mumbai, MH, IND) *Unable to locate*

Indian Journal of Commerce (Nasik, MH, IND) *Unable to locate*

Indian Journal of Communication Arts (New Delhi, DH, IND) *Unable to locate*

Indian Journal of Community Medicine (Chandigarh, CH, IND) **[45024]**

Indian Journal of Comparative Animal Physiology (Tirupati, AP, IND) *Unable to locate*

Indian Journal of Comparative Sociology (Dharwad, KA, IND) *Unable to locate*

Indian Journal of Critical Care Medicine (Mumbai, MH, IND) **[45379]**

The Indian Journal of Crop Science (New Delhi, DH, IND) **[45550]**

Indian Journal of Cryogenics (Calcutta, WB, IND) *Unable to locate*

Indian Journal of Current Psychological Research (Agra, UP, IND) *Unable to locate*

Indian Journal of Dairy Science (New Delhi, DH, IND) **[45551]**

Indian Journal of Dental Research (Mangalore, KA, IND) *Unable to locate*

Indian Journal of Dryland Agricultural Research and Development (New Delhi, DH, IND) *Unable to locate*

Indian Journal of Earth Sciences (Calcutta, WB, IND) *Unable to locate*

Indian Journal of Ecology (Ludhiana, PJ, IND) *Unable to locate*

Indian Journal of Economics (Allahabad, UP, IND) **[44931]**

Indian Journal of Economics & Business (New Delhi, DH, IND) **[45552]**

Indian Journal of Engineering and Materials Sciences (Jodhpur, RJ, IND) **[45222]**

Indian Journal of Engineering Mathematics (Agra, UP, IND) *Unable to locate*

Indian Journal of Engineers (Calcutta, WB, IND) *Unable to locate*

Indian Journal of Engineers Annual Foundry Number (Calcutta, WB, IND) *Unable to locate*

Indian Journal of Environmental Health **[45468]***

Indian Journal of Experimental Biology (Jodhpur, RJ, IND) **[45223]**

Indian Journal of Extension Education (New Delhi, DH, IND) *Unable to locate*

Indian Journal of Fibre & Textile Research (New Delhi, DH, IND) **[45553]**

Indian Journal of Finance and Research (New Delhi, DH, IND) *Unable to locate*

Indian Journal of Fisheries (Cochin, KE, IND) **[45075]**

Indian Journal of Forensic Sciences (Chennai, TN, IND) *Unable to locate*

Indian Journal of Forestry (Dehradun, UP, IND) *Unable to locate*

Indian Journal of Gastroenterology (Mumbai, MH, IND) **[45380]**

Indian Journal of Gender Studies (New Delhi, DH, IND) **[45554]**

Indian Journal of Geochemistry (New Delhi, DH, IND) *Unable to locate*

Indian Journal of Geology (Calcutta, WB, IND) *Unable to locate*

Indian Journal of Geomorphology (Delhi, DH, IND) *Unable to locate*

Indian Journal of Helminthology (New Delhi, DH, IND) *Unable to locate*

Indian Journal of Heredity, IND) *Unable to locate*

Indian Journal of History of Science (New Delhi, DH, IND) **[45555]**

Indian Journal of Home Science (Baroda, GJ, IND) *Unable to locate*

Indian Journal of Homoeopathic Medicine (Mumbai, MH, IND) *Unable to locate*

Indian Journal of Horticulture (Bangalore, KA, IND) *Unable to locate*

Indian Journal of Hospital Pharmacy (New Delhi, DH, IND) *Unable to locate*

Indian Journal of Human Genetics (Mumbai, MH, IND) **[45381]**

Indian Journal of Human Rights and Justice (New Delhi, DH, IND) **[45556]**

Indian Journal of Human Rights and the Law (New Delhi, DH, IND) **[45557]**

Indian Journal of Industrial Medicine (Calcutta, WB, IND) *Unable to locate*

Indian Journal of Industrial Relations (New Delhi, DH, IND) *Unable to locate*

Indian Journal of Labour Economics (Lucknow, UP, IND) *Unable to locate*

Indian Journal of Landscape Systems and Ecological Studies (New Delhi, DH, IND) *Unable to locate*

Indian Journal of Leprosy (New Delhi, DH, IND) *Unable to locate*

Indian Journal of Malariology **[45102]***

Indian Journal of Marine Sciences (New Delhi, DH, IND) **[45558]**

Indian Journal of Marketing (New Delhi, DH, IND) **[45559]**

Indian Journal of Marketing Geography (Gorakhpur, UP, IND) *Unable to locate*

Indian Journal of Mathematics (Allahabad, UP, IND) *Unable to locate*

Indian Journal of Mathematics and Mathematical Sciences (New Delhi, DH, IND) **[45560]**

Indian Journal of Medical Microbiology (Pondicherry, PN, IND) **[45692]**

Indian Journal of Medical and Paediatric Oncology (Mumbai, MH, IND) **[45382]**

Indian Journal of Medical Photography (Patiala, PJ, IND) *Unable to locate*

Indian Journal of Medical Research (New Delhi, DH, IND) **[45561]**

Indian Journal of Medical Research Section A—Infectious Diseases (Delhi, DH, IND) *Unable to locate*

Indian Journal of Medical Research Section B—Biomedical Research other than Infectious Diseases (Delhi, DH, IND) *Unable to locate*

Indian Journal of Medical Sciences (Mumbai, MH, IND) **[45383]**

Indian Journal of Medicine and Surgery (Banga, PJ, IND) *Unable to locate*

Indian Journal of Mental Retardation (New Delhi, DH, IND) *Unable to locate*

Indian Journal of Microbiology (New Delhi, DH, IND) **[45562]**

Indian Journal of Mushrooms (Solan, HP, IND) *Unable to locate*

Indian Journal of Natural Rubber Research (Kottayam, KE, IND) *Unable to locate*

Indian Journal of Nematology (New Delhi, DH, IND) *Unable to locate*

Indian Journal of Nepalese Studies (Varanasi, UP, IND) *Unable to locate*

Indian Journal of Nephrology (Chandigarh, IND) **[45023]**

Indian Journal of Nuclear Medicine (Mumbai, MH, IND) **[45384]**

Indian Journal of Nutrition and Dietetics (Coimbatore, TN, IND) *Unable to locate*

Indian Journal of Occupational and Environmental Medicine (Thane, MH, IND) **[45746]**

Indian Journal of Occupational Health (New Delhi, DH, IND) *Unable to locate*

Indian Journal of Occupational Therapy (Udupi, KA, IND) **[45763]**

Indian Journal of Ophthalmology (Mumbai, MH, IND) **[45385]**

Indian Journal of Orthopaedics (Varanasi, UP, IND) *Unable to locate*

Indian Journal of Otolaryngology and Head and Neck Surgery (Delhi, DH, IND) **[45097]**

Indian Journal of Palliative Care (New Delhi, DH, IND) **[45563]**

Indian Journal of Pathology & Microbiology (Patna, BH, IND) *Unable to locate*

Indian Journal of Pediatrics **[45564]***

Indian Journal of Pediatrics (New Delhi, DH, IND) **[45564]**

Indian Journal of Petroleum Geology (Dehradun, UP, IND) *Unable to locate*

Indian Journal of Pharmaceutical Sciences (Mumbai, MH, IND) **[45386]**

Indian Journal of Pharmacology (Hyderabad, AP, IND) **[45172]**

Indian Journal of Photography (Delhi, DH, IND) *Unable to locate*

Indian Journal of Physical Anthropology and Human Genetics (Lucknow, UP, IND) *Unable to locate*

Indian Journal of Physics, Part A (Calcutta, WB, IND) **[45021]**

Indian Journal of Physics, Part B (Kolkata, WB, IND) *Unable to locate*

Indian Journal of Physiology and Pharmacology (New Delhi, DH, IND) *Unable to locate*

Indian Journal of Plant Genetic Resources (New Delhi, DH, IND) *Unable to locate*

Indian Journal of Plant Physiology (New Delhi, DH, IND) *Unable to locate*

Indian Journal of Plastic Surgery (Mumbai, MH, IND) **[45387]**

Indian Journal of Political Science (Meerut, UP, IND) **[45345]**

Indian Journal of Politics (Aligarh, UP, IND) *Unable to locate*

Indian Journal of Power and River Valley Development (Calcutta, WB, IND) *Unable to locate*

Indian Journal of Preventive and Social Medicine (Varanasi, UP, IND) **[45765]**

Indian Journal of Psychiatric Social Work (Ranchi, BH, IND) *Unable to locate*

Indian Journal of Psychological Medicine (Lucknow, UP, IND) **[45322]**

Indian Journal of Psychometry and Education (Patna, BH, IND) *Unable to locate*

Indian Journal of Public Administration (New Delhi, DH, IND) *Unable to locate*

Indian Journal of Public Health (Calcutta, WB, IND) *Unable to locate*

Indian Journal of Pure and Applied Mathematics (New Delhi, DH, IND) **[45565]**

Indian Journal of Pure & Applied Physics (Jodhpur, RJ, IND) **[45224]**

Indian Journal of Radio & Space Physics (New Delhi, DH, IND) **[45566]**

Indian Journal of Radiology & Imaging (Chennai, TN, IND) *Unable to locate*

Indian Journal of Rural Technology (New Delhi, DH, IND) *Unable to locate*

Indian Journal of Sericulture (Mysore, KA, IND) **[45457]**

Indian Journal of Sexually Transmitted Diseases (Jaipur, RJ, IND) **[45196]**

Indian Journal of Social Research (Delhi, DH, IND) *Unable to locate*

Indian Journal of Social Research (New Delhi, DH, IND) *Unable to locate*

Indian Journal of Social Sciences (Hyderabad, AP, IND) *Ceased*

Indian Journal of Social Work (Mumbai, MH, IND) **[45388]**

Indian Journal of Sociology (New Delhi, DH, IND) *Unable to locate*

Indian Journal of Technical Education (New Delhi, DH, IND) **[45567]**

Indian Journal of Textile Research **[45553]***

Indian Journal of Theology (Serampore, WB, IND) *Unable to locate*

Indian Journal of Theoretical Physics (Calcutta, WB, IND) *Unable to locate*

Numbers cited in bold after listings are entry numbers rather than page numbers.

Indian Journal of Training & Development (New Delhi, DH, IND) *Unable to locate*

Indian Journal of Transport Management (New Delhi, DH, IND) [45568]

Indian Journal of Tuberculosis (New Delhi, DH, IND) [45569]

Indian Journal of Unani Medicine (New Delhi, DH, IND) *Unable to locate*

Indian Journal of Urology (Ludhiana, PJ, IND) [45331]

Indian Journal of Veterinary Anatomy (Mathura, UP, IND) *Unable to locate*

Indian Journal of Veterinary Medicine (Udham Singh Nagar, UP, IND) *Unable to locate*

Indian Journal of Veterinary Surgery (Izatnagar, UP, IND) *Unable to locate*

Indian Journal of Zoological Spectrum (Bhopal, MP, IND) *Unable to locate*

Indian Jute Mills Association Loom and Spindle Statistics (Calcutta, WB, IND) *Unable to locate*

Indian Labour Journal (Delhi, DH, IND) [45098]

Indian Law Reports (Delhi, DH, IND) *Unable to locate*

Indian Leather (Chennai, TN, IND) [45038]

Indian Leather Technologists' Association Journal (Calcutta, WB, IND) *Unable to locate*

Indian Left Review (New Delhi, DH, IND) *Unable to locate*

Indian Librarian (Jullundur, PJ, IND) *Unable to locate*

Indian Library Association Bulletin (New Delhi, DH, IND) *Unable to locate*

Indian Library Science Abstracts (Kolkata, WB, IND) *Unable to locate*

Indian Linguistics (Pune, MH, IND) *Unable to locate*

Indian Literary Index (New Delhi, DH, IND) [45570]

Indian Literary Review (New Delhi, DH, IND) *Unable to locate*

Indian Literature (New Delhi, IND) *Unable to locate*

Indian Literature in Environmental Engineering (Nagpur, MH, IND) [45466]

Indian Machine Tools Journal (Mumbai, MH, IND) *Unable to locate*

Indian Management (New Delhi, DH, IND) *Unable to locate*

Indian Market Place (Bangalore, KA, IND) *Unable to locate*

Indian Mathematical Society Journal (New Delhi, DH, IND) *Unable to locate*

Indian Media Studies Journal (New Delhi, DH, IND) [45571]

Indian Medical Association Journal (Calcutta, WB, IND) *Unable to locate*

Indian Medical Forum (Calcutta, WB, IND) *Unable to locate*

Indian Medical Gazette (Mumbai, MH, IND) *Unable to locate*

Indian Medicine (Vijayawada, AP, IND) *Unable to locate*

Indian Merchants' Chamber Journal (Mumbai, MH, IND) *Unable to locate*

Indian Miller (New Delhi, DH, IND) *Unable to locate*

Indian Mineralogist (Mysore, KA, IND) *Unable to locate*

Indian Minerals Year Book [45467]*

Indian Minerals Year Book (Nagpur, MH, IND) [45467]

Indian Mining & Engineering Journal (Bhubaneswar, OR, IND) *Unable to locate*

Indian Modeller (Calcutta, WB, IND) *Unable to locate*

Indian Motion Picture Almanac (Calcutta, WB, IND) *Unable to locate*

Indian Mountaineer (New Delhi, DH, IND) [45572]

Indian Museum Bulletin (Kolkata, WB, IND) [45273]

Indian Music Journal (Melkote, KA, IND) *Unable to locate*

The Indian Nation (Patna, BH, IND) *Unable to locate*

Indian National Bibliography (Kolkata, WB, IND) [45274]

Indian National Science Academy Biographical Memoirs of Fellows (New Delhi, DH, IND) [45573]

Indian National Science Academy Year Book (New Delhi, DH, IND) [45574]

Indian Observer (New Delhi, DH, IND) *Unable to locate*

Indian Odonatology (Jodhpur, RJ, IND) *Unable to locate*

Indian Pediatrics (New Delhi, DH, IND) [45575]

The Indian PEN (Mumbai, MH, IND) *Unable to locate*

Indian Perfumer (New Delhi, DH, IND) *Unable to locate*

Indian Petrochemical Industry Deskbook (Mumbai, MH, IND) *Unable to locate*

Indian Petroleum and Natural Gas Statistics (New Delhi, DH, IND) *Unable to locate*

Indian Philosophical Quarterly (Pune, MH, IND) *Unable to locate*

Indian Phytopathology (New Delhi, DH, IND) *Unable to locate*

Indian Police Journal (New Delhi, DH, IND) *Unable to locate*

Indian Ports (New Delhi, DH, IND) *Unable to locate*

Indian Potato Association Journal (Simla, HP, IND) *Unable to locate*

Indian Poultry Industry Yearbook (New Delhi, DH, IND) *Unable to locate*

Indian Poultry Review (Calcutta, WB, IND) *Unable to locate*

The Indian Practitioner (Mumbai, MH, IND) *Unable to locate*

Indian Press Index (New Delhi, DH, IND) *Unable to locate*

Indian Psychological Abstracts and Reviews (New Delhi, DH, IND) *Unable to locate*

Indian Psychological Review (Agra, UP, IND) *Unable to locate*

Indian Pulp and Paper (Calcutta, WB, IND) *Unable to locate*

Indian Pulp & Paper Industry Deskbook (Mumbai, MH, IND) *Unable to locate*

Indian Railway Gazette (Calcutta, WB, IND) *Unable to locate*

Indian Railway Technical Bulletin (Lucknow, UP, IND) *Unable to locate*

Indian Railwaymen and Bharatiya Railwaymen (New Delhi, DH, IND) *Unable to locate*

Indian Railways (New Delhi, DH, IND) *Unable to locate*

Indian Railways Safety Performance—A Review (New Delhi, DH, IND) *Unable to locate*

Indian Railways Yearbook (New Delhi, DH, IND) *Unable to locate*

Indian Recorder (New Delhi, DH, IND) *Unable to locate*

Indian Records (Calcutta, WB, IND) *Ceased*

Indian Review (Chennai, TN, IND) *Unable to locate*

Indian Rice Exporters' Performance Monitor (Mumbai, MH, IND) *Unable to locate*

Indian Roads Congress Highway Research Bulletin (New Delhi, DH, IND) [45576]

Indian Scholar (Raipur, MP, IND) *Unable to locate*

Indian School of Political Economy Journal (New Delhi, DH, IND) *Unable to locate*

Indian Science Cruiser (Calcutta, WB, IND) *Unable to locate*

Indian Science Index Ser B—Premodern Period (Calcutta, WB, IND) *Unable to locate*

Indian Shipping (Mumbai, MH, IND) [45389]

Indian Shipping and Shipbuilding (Mumbai, MH, IND) *Unable to locate*

Indian Silk (Bangalore, KA, IND) [44962]

Indian Social Science Review (New Delhi, DH, IND) [45577]

Indian Society of Agricultural Statistics Journal (New Delhi, DH, IND) *Unable to locate*

Indian Society for Cotton Improvement Journal (Mumbai, MH, IND) *Unable to locate*

Indian Society of Desert Technology Transactions (Jodhpur, RJ, IND) *Unable to locate*

Indian Society of Earthquake Technology Bulletin (Roorkee, UP, IND) *Unable to locate*

Indian Society of Pedodontics and Preventive Dentistry Journal (Davangere, KA, IND) [45086]

Indian Society of Statistics and Operations Research Journal (Saharanpur, UP, IND) *Unable to locate*

Indian Socio-Legal Journal (New Delhi, DH, IND) *Unable to locate*

Indian Spices (Cochin, KE, IND) *Ceased*

Indian Spices Exporters' Performance Monitor (Mumbai, MH, IND) *Unable to locate*

Indian Statistical Institute Library Bibliographic Series (Calcutta, WB, IND) *Unable to locate*

Indian Steel Age (New Delhi, DH, IND) *Unable to locate*

Indian Stratigraphy (New Delhi, DH, IND) *Unable to locate*

Indian Sugar (New Delhi, DH, IND) [45578]

Indian Sugar Crops Journal (Sahibabad, UP, IND) *Unable to locate*

Indian Surveyor (New Delhi, DH, IND) *Unable to locate*

Indian Synthetic & Rayon (Mumbai, MH, IND) *Unable to locate*

Indian Tea Exporters' Performance Monitor (Mumbai, MH, IND) *Unable to locate*

Indian Textile Bulletin (Delhi, DH, IND) *Unable to locate*

Indian Tourist (Calcutta, WB, IND) *Unable to locate*

Indian Vacuum Society Bulletin (Mumbai, MH, IND) *Unable to locate*

Indian Veterinary Journal (Madras, TN, IND) [45334]

Indian Veterinary Medical Journal (Lucknow, UP, IND) *Unable to locate*

Indian Water Resources Society Journal (New Delhi, DH, IND) *Unable to locate*

Indian Welding Journal (Kolkata, WB, IND) [45275]

Indian Witness (New Delhi, DH, IND) *Unable to locate*

Indian Worker (New Delhi, DH, IND) *Unable to locate*

Indian and World Arts & Crafts (New Delhi, DH, IND) *Unable to locate*

Indian Writer (Madras, TN, IND) *Unable to locate*

Indian Yearbook of International Affairs (Chennai, TN, IND) *Unable to locate*

Indiana (Calcutta, WB, IND) *Ceased*

India's Stamp Journal (Mumbai, MH, IND) [45390]

Indiavarta (Chennai, TN, IND) [45039]

IndiaWorld (Mumbai, MH, IND) *Ceased*

indicateur Bertrand-Paris-Banlieue (Paris, FRA) *Unable to locate*

Indilinga (Pietermaritzburg, SAF) [50568]

Indo-British Review (Madras, TN, IND) *Unable to locate*

Indo-Iran Journal (New Delhi, DH, IND) *Unable to locate*

Indo-Iranian Journal (Groningen, NLD) [48602]

Indo-Iranica (Calcutta, WB, IND) *Unable to locate*

Indo-Israel (Mumbai, MH, IND) *Unable to locate*

Indo-Korean Friendship (New Delhi, DH, IND) *Unable to locate*

Indo - US Business (Chennai, TN, IND) [45040]

Indogermanische Forschungen (Friedland, GER) [44376]

Indological Studies (New Delhi, DH, IND) *Unable to locate*

Indonesia Business Weekly (Jakarta, IDN) *Unable to locate*

Indonesia Circle [51813]*

Indonesia Magazine (Jakarta, IDN) *Unable to locate*

Indonesia and the Malay World (Abingdon, GBR) [51813]

Indonesia Today (Jakarta, IDN) *Unable to locate*

Indonesian Agricultural Research & Development Journal (Bogor, IDN) *Unable to locate*

Indonesian Commercial Newsletter (Jakarta, IDN) [45799]

Indonesian Journal of Agricultural Sciences (Cibinong, IDN) *Unable to locate*

Indonesian Journal of Bioanthropology (Yogyakarta, IDN) *Unable to locate*

Indonesian Journal of Geography (Yogyakarta, IDN) *Unable to locate*

Indonesian Journal of Industrial Hygiene, Occupational Health-Safety and Social Security (Jakarta, IDN) *Unable to locate*

Indonesian Journal of Public Health (Jakarta, IDN) *Unable to locate*

Indonesian Quarterly (Jakarta, IDN) [45800]

Indonesian Textile Magazine (Jakarta, IDN) *Unable to locate*

The Indradevi Magazine (Phnom Penh, CMB) *Unable to locate*

Numbers cited in bold after listings are entry numbers rather than page numbers.

Indranil (Calcutta, WB, IND) *Unable to locate*

Industria (Lisbon, PRT) *Unable to locate*

L'Industria Italiana del Cemento (Rome, ITA) *Unable to locate*

Industria Mody (Moscow, RUS) **[49917]**

Industria & Quimica (Buenos Aires, ARG) **[41473]**

Industrial Archaeology Review (London, GBR) **[54596]**

Industrial Cases Reports (London, GBR) **[54597]**

Industrial Ceramics (Faenza, ITA) *Unable to locate*

Industrial Ceylon (Colombo, SRI) *Unable to locate*

Industrial and Commercial Training (Bradford, GBR) **[52464]**

Industrial Consultancy (New Delhi, DH, IND) *Unable to locate*

Industrial and Corporate Change (Milan, ITA) **[46175]**

Industrial Courier (Howrah, WB, IND) *Unable to locate*

Industrial Court Reporter (Mumbai, MH, IND) *Unable to locate*

Industrial Court Reports **[54597]***

Industrial Development (Karachi, PAK) *Unable to locate*

Industrial Diamond Review (Middlesex, GBR) *Unable to locate*

Industrial Economist (Chennai, TN, IND) **[45041]**

Industrial Engineering and Management (Mumbai, MH, IND) *Unable to locate*

Industrial Engineering News (Brussels, BEL) *Ceased*

Industrial Enterprise (Calcutta, WB, IND) *Unable to locate*

Industrial Expansion (New Delhi, DH, IND) *Unable to locate*

Industrial Health (Kawasaki, JPN) **[46421]**

Industrial Herald (Chennai, TN, IND) *Unable to locate*

Industrial Image (New Delhi, DH, IND) *Unable to locate*

Industrial India (Mumbai, MH, IND) *Unable to locate*

Industrial Informika (New Delhi, DH, IND) *Unable to locate*

Industrial Law Journal (Cambridge, GBR) **[52830]**

Industrial Lubrication and Tribology (Bradford, GBR) **[52465]**

Industrial Management and Data Systems (Bradford, GBR) **[52466]**

Industrial & Manufacturing Engineer Magazine (Belfast, GBR) **[52286]**

Industrial Minerals (IM) (London, GBR) **[54598]**

Industrial Relations Journal (Oxford, GBR) **[55988]**

Industrial Relations Law Bulletin **[54367]***

Industrial Researcher (Mumbai, MH, IND) *Unable to locate*

Industrial Robot (Ilkley, GBR) **[53646]**

Industrial Safety Chronicle (Itasca, IL, USA) *Unable to locate*

Industrial Situation in India (Calcutta, WB, IND) *Unable to locate*

Industrial Statistics (London, GBR) *Unable to locate*

Industrial Technology (Tonbridge, GBR) **[56755]**

Industrial Textiles **[55067]***

Industrial Times (Mumbai, MH, IND) *Unable to locate*

Industrial Welder (Mumbai, MH, IND) *Unable to locate*

Industrial Workwear Solutions (Wahroonga, NW, AUS) **[42673]**

Industrie Diamanten Rundschau (Nuremberg, GER) **[44615]**

L'Industrie des Ninerais, Ninezaux Industriels et netaux non Ferreux (Paris, FRA) *Ceased*

Industries of Japan (Tokyo, JPN) *Unable to locate*

Industry of Free China (Taipei, TWN) *Unable to locate*

Industry and Higher Education (London, GBR) **[54599]**

Industry & Innovation (Abingdon, GBR) **[51814]**

Industry Press Digest (Mumbai, MH, IND) *Unable to locate*

Industry Weekly (Taipei, TWN) **[51341]**

Infancia y Aprendizaje/Journal for the Study of Education and Development (Madrid, SPA) **[50769]**

Infant Behavior and Development (Amsterdam, NLD) **[48016]**

Infant Observation (Abingdon, GBR) **[51815]**

Infection, Genetics and Evolution (Montpellier, FRA) **[43978]**

Infectious Diseases Journal (Karachi, PAK) **[49355]**

Infectious Disorders; Current Drug Targets **[48301]***

Infectious Disorders - Drug Targets (Bussum, NLD) **[48301]**

Infectology (Sofia, BUL) *Unable to locate*

Infinita-FM - 100.1 (Santiago, CHL) **[43158]**

Infinite Dimensional Analysis, Quantum Probability and Related Topics (Singapore, SGP) **[50170]**

Inflammation & Allergy - Drug Targets (Bussum, NLD) **[48302]**

Inflammation Research (Tokyo, JPN) **[46842]**

Inflammopharmacology (Sheffield, GBR) **[56498]**

Inflight Review (Moscow, RUS) **[49918]**

INFO (Elstal, GER) *Unable to locate*

Info (London, GBR) **[54600]**

infocus Magazine (Oxford, GBR) **[55989]**

INFOFISH International (Kuala Lumpur, MYS) **[47605]**

Infolink P C World (Colombo, SRI) *Unable to locate*

Infome Macroeconomico (Lima, PER) *Unable to locate*

INFOR-ECMA (Brussels, BEL) *Unable to locate*

Infor Marechalerie/European Farriers Journal/Der Huf (Maloves-Sainte-Marie-Wastines, BEL) **[42903]**

InfoRadioBerl.-Brand.-FM - 93.1 (Berlin, GER) **[44243]**

INFORCADRE (Paris, FRA) *Unable to locate*

InfoRM (London, GBR) **[54601]**

Informa Freight (London, GBR) *Unable to locate*

Informatica (Amsterdam, NLD) **[48017]**

Informatics for Health and Social Care (Abingdon, GBR) **[51816]**

Informatik Spektrum (Bonn, GER) **[44263]**

Informatik-Spektrum (Dordrecht, NLD) **[48421]**

Information (Copenhagen, DEN) *Unable to locate*

Information Bulletin (London, GBR) **[54602]**

Information Circular **[54602]***

Information, Communication and Society (Abingdon, GBR) **[51817]**

Information and Communications Technology Law (Abingdon, GBR) **[51818]**

Information Communications World (New Delhi, DH, IND) *Unable to locate*

Information Design Journal (Amsterdam, NLD) **[48018]**

Information Development (London, GBR) **[54603]**

Information Economics and Policy (Amsterdam, NLD) **[48019]**

Information Fusion (Singapore, SGP) **[50171]**

Information Journal (San Jose, CRI) *Unable to locate*

Information Management & Computer Security (Bradford, GBR) **[52467]**

Information Management & Technology (Hatfield, GBR) **[53539]**

Information Policy and Law; International Journal of **[42521]***

Information Polity (Glasgow, GBR) **[53423]**

Information Processing Letters (Warsaw, POL) **[49718]**

Information Processing & Management (Amsterdam, NLD) **[48020]**

L'Information Psychiatrique (Montrouge, FRA) **[43993]**

Information Scotland (Glasgow, GBR) **[53424]**

Information Security Bulletin (Waltham, GBR) *Ceased*

Information Services & Use (Amsterdam, NLD) **[48021]**

Information and Software Technology (Ronneby, SWE) **[50997]**

Information Systems Computer World (New Delhi, DH, IND) *Unable to locate*

Information Systems and E-Business Management (ISeB) (Munster, GER) **[44598]**

Information Technologist (Minna, NG, NGA) **[49147]**

Information Technology, Education and Society (South Melbourne, VI, AUS) **[42372]**

Information Technology Journal (Faisalabad, PAK) **[49247]**

Information Technology Law Reports (Witney, GBR) **[56943]**

Information Technology and Management (Dordrecht, NLD) **[48422]**

Information Technology & People (Bradford, GBR) **[52468]**

Information Visualization (Basingstoke, GBR) **[52207]**

Information Week (Poing, GER) **[44636]**

Information World Review (London, GBR) **[54604]**

Informativo FBCN (Rio de Janeiro, RJ, BRZ) **[43006]**

L'Informatore Agrario (Verona, ITA) **[46280]**

Informes de la Construccion (Madrid, SPA) **[50770]**

Informeuropa (Goldtrain, GER) *Unable to locate*

Infosecurity (Singapore, SGP) **[50172]**

Infovet (Jakarta, IDN) *Unable to locate*

Infoweek.ch (Thalwil, SWI) **[51234]**

Infrared and Raman Spectroscopy (Saitama, JPN) *Unable to locate*

Ingenieurs de l'Automobile (Paris, FRA) *Unable to locate*

Ingenjoren (Stockholm, SWE) *Unable to locate*

Ingredienti Alimentari (Pinerolo, ITA) **[46217]**

Ingredients, Health & Nutrition (Rickmansworth, GBR) **[56393]**

Inhenyeriya (Manila, PHL) *Unable to locate*

i98-FM - 98.1 (Wollongong, NW, AUS) **[42708]**

INIS Database (Vienna, AUT) **[42760]**

Inish Times Newspaper (Buncrana, DO, IRL) **[45925]**

Inishowen Community Radio-FM - 105 (Carndonagh, DO, IRL) **[45926]**

Injury and Safety Monitor (Centurion, SAF) *Ceased*

Ink & Print (London, GBR) *Unable to locate*

Inkworld (New Delhi, DH, IND) *Unable to locate*

InMotion (Wahroonga, NW, AUS) **[42674]**

Innate Immunity (London, GBR) **[54605]**

Inner-FM - 96.5 (Heidelberg, VI, AUS) **[41949]**

Inner-West Weekly (Parramatta, NW, AUS) **[42234]**

Innes Review (Edinburgh, GBR) **[53286]**

INNOTECH Journal (Quezon City, PHL) **[49595]**

Innovacion y Ciencia (Bogota, COL) *Unable to locate*

Innovation (Nairobi, KEN) **[47184]**

Innovation (Singapore, SGP) **[50173]**

Innovations in Education & Teaching International (Abingdon, GBR) **[51819]**

Innovations in Materials Research (Singapore, SGP) *Unable to locate*

Innovations in Systems and Software Engineering (Heidelberg, GER) **[44461]**

Innovations in Teaching and Learning in Information and Computer Sciences (Heslington, GBR) **[53567]**

Innovative Food Science and Emerging Technologies (Berlin, GER) **[44191]**

Innovative Investor (Hong Kong, CHN) **[43348]**

Innovative Technology (Hyderabad, AP, IND) *Unable to locate*

Inolvidable-FM - 93.1 (Canelones, URY) **[57006]**

Inooro Radio-FM - 98.9 (Nairobi, KEN) **[47200]**

Inorganic Chemistry (Valencia, SPA) **[50846]**

Inorganic Chemistry Communications (Padua, ITA) **[46205]**

Inorganic Materials (Moscow, RUS) **[49919]**

inQuire (Canterbury, GBR) **[52921]**

Inquiry into the Future (Seoul, KOR) *Unable to locate*

Inquisitor (Chandigarh, CH, IND) *Unable to locate*

Inroads (Harrow, GBR) **[53524]**

Insect Conservation and Diversity (Ascot, GBR) **[52139]**

Insect Science (Oxford, GBR) **[55990]**

Insect Science and Its Application **[47185]***

Insect Systematics & Evolution (Leiden, NLD) **[48678]**

Inserto Italiano (Milan, ITA) *Unable to locate*

Inside Business (Dublin, DU, IRL) *Unable to locate*

Numbers cited in bold after listings are entry numbers rather than page numbers.

Inside Cornwall (Penzance, GBR) **[56249]**

Inside Cricket (Sydney, NW, AUS) **[42516]**

Inside Food and Drink **[53103]***

Inside Housing (London, GBR) **[54606]**

Inside Indonesia (Collingwood, VI, AUS) **[41790]**

Inside Outside (Mumbai, MH, IND) *Unable to locate*

Inside Rugby (Sydney, NW, AUS) **[42517]**

InsidePoker **[55098]***

Insider—The Business Magazine of North London (London, GBR) *Unable to locate*

Insieme (Biel, SWI) *Unable to locate*

Insight (Oostmalle, BEL) *Unable to locate*

The Insight (Brighton, GBR) **[52615]**

Insight (London, GBR) **[54607]**

Insight (Northampton, GBR) **[55710]**

Insight into.Healing (Brisbane, QL, AUS) **[41649]**

Insolvency Law Journal (Pyrmont, NW, AUS) **[42281]**

Inspire (Quezon City, PHL) *Unable to locate*

Inspire (London, GBR) *Unable to locate*

Installations Nyt (Glostrup, DEN) **[43707]**

Installations Nyt Special (Glostrup, DEN) **[43708]**

Institut Francais de Pondichery Departement d'Ecologie Publications (Pondicherry, PN, IND) *Unable to locate*

Institut Francais de Pondichery Departement d'Indologie Publications (Pondicherry, PN, IND) *Unable to locate*

Institut Francais de Pondichery Departement de Sciences Sociales (Pondicherry, PN, IND) *Unable to locate*

Institut des Reviseurs d'Entreprises (Luxembourg, LUX) *Unable to locate*

Institute of African Studies (Accra, GHA) **[44728]**

Institute of Asian Studies Journal (Madras, TN, IND) **[45335]**

Institute of Consulting Engineers Journal (Calcutta, WB, IND) *Unable to locate*

Institute of Economic Geography, India Journal (Calcutta, WB, IND) *Unable to locate*

Institute of Economic Growth Book Review List (Delhi, DH, IND) *Unable to locate*

Institute of Economic Growth Census Studies (Delhi, DH, IND) *Unable to locate*

Institute of Economic Growth Micro Document List (Delhi, DH, IND) *Unable to locate*

Institute of Economic Growth Selective List of Books and Documents Added to the Library (Delhi, DH, IND) *Unable to locate*

Institute of Economic Research Journal (Dharwad, KA, IND) *Unable to locate*

Institute of Economic Research Publications on Demography (Dharwad, KA, IND) *Unable to locate*

Institute of Economic Research Publications on Economics (Dharwad, KA, IND) *Unable to locate*

Institute of Economic Research Publications on Family Planning (Dharwad, KA, IND) *Unable to locate*

Institute of Indian Geographers Transactions (Pune, MH, IND) *Unable to locate*

Institute Journal (London, GBR) *Unable to locate*

Institute of Public Enterprise Journal (Hyderabad, AP, IND) *Unable to locate*

Institute for Security Studies Monographs (Cape Town, SAF) **[50383]**

Institute of Town Planners, India Journal (New Delhi, DH, IND) **[45579]**

Institute of Traditional Cultures Madras Bulletin (Chennai, TN, IND) *Unable to locate*

Institution of Chemists (India) Journal (Calcutta, WB, IND) *Unable to locate*

Institution of Diesel and Gas Turbine Engineer (London, GBR) *Unable to locate*

Institution of Engineers (India) Aerospace Engineering Division Journal (Kolkata, WB, IND) **[45276]**

Institution of Engineers (India) Agricultural Engineering Division Journal (Kolkata, WB, IND) **[45277]**

Institution of Engineers (India) Architectural Engineering Division Journal (Kolkata, WB, IND) **[45278]**

Institution of Engineers (India) Chemical Engineering Division Journal (Kolkata, WB, IND) **[45279]**

Institution of Engineers (India) Civil Engineering Division Journal (Kolkata, WB, IND) **[45280]**

The Institution of Engineers (India) Computer Engineering Division Journal (Kolkata, WB, IND) **[45281]**

The Institution of Engineers (India) Electrical Engineering Division Journal (Kolkata, WB, IND) **[45282]**

Institution of Engineers (India) Electronics and Telecommunication Engineering Division Journal (Kolkata, WB, IND) **[45283]**

Institution of Engineers (India) Environmental Engineering Division Journal (Kolkata, WB, IND) **[45284]**

Institution of Engineers (India) Hindi Journal (Kolkata, WB, IND) **[45285]**

The Institution of Engineers (India) Inter-disciplinary Panels Journal (Kolkata, WB, IND) **[45286]**

Institution of Engineers (India) Marine Engineering Division Journal (Kolkata, WB, IND) **[45287]**

The Institution of Engineers (India) Mechanical Engineering Division Journal (Kolkata, WB, IND) **[45288]**

The Institution of Engineers (India) Metallurgical and Materials Engineering Division Journal (Kolkata, WB, IND) **[45289]**

Institution of Engineers (India) Mining Engineering Division Journal (Kolkata, WB, IND) **[45290]**

Institution of Engineers (India) Production Engineering Division Journal (Kolkata, WB, IND) **[45291]**

Institution of Engineers (India) Technicians' Journal (Kolkata, WB, IND) **[45292]**

Institution of Engineers (India) Technorama (Kolkata, WB, IND) **[45293]**

Institution of Engineers (India) Textile Engineering Division Journal (Kolkata, WB, IND) **[45294]**

Institution of Marine Technologists Journal (Mumbai, MH, IND) *Unable to locate*

Institutional Investor (London, GBR) **[54608]**

Institutional Investor International Edition (London, GBR) *Unable to locate*

Instruktormagasinet Krumspring (Vejle, DEN) *Unable to locate*

Instrumenta (London, GBR) **[54609]**

Instruments & Electronics Development (Mumbai, MH, IND) *Unable to locate*

Instruments India (Mumbai, MH, IND) *Unable to locate*

Insula (Madrid, SPA) **[50771]**

Insurance (Lausanne, SWI) **[51192]**

Insurance Age (London, GBR) **[54610]**

Insurance Brokers' Monthly & Insurance Advisor (Stourbridge, GBR) *Unable to locate*

Insurance Chronicle (Hyderabad, AP, IND) **[45173]**

Insurance Day (London, GBR) **[54611]**

Insurance Institute of India Journal (Mumbai, MH, IND) **[45391]**

Insurance Journal (Dhaka, BGD) **[42812]**

Insurance Law Journal (North Ryde, NW, AUS) *Unable to locate*

Insurance Systems Bulletin **[54611]***

Insurance Technology **[54611]***

Insurance & Technology (London, GBR) **[54612]**

Insurgent Sociologist **[54290]***

INTA-Radio (Irkutsk, RUS) *Unable to locate*

Intamplari Adevarate (Bucharest, ROM) **[49838]**

INTAMS review (Leuven, BEL) **[42898]**

Integracion (Cali, COL) *Unable to locate*

Integral Transforms and Special Functions (Moscow, RUS) **[49920]**

Integrated Assessment (Dordrecht, NLD) **[48423]**

Integration (Bonn, GER) *Unable to locate*

Integration and Trade (Buenos Aires, ARG) **[41474]**

Integration, the VLSI Journal (Seville, SPA) **[50834]**

Integrator (Singapore, SGP) **[50174]**

Intellect Q (London, GBR) *Unable to locate*

Intellectual Asset Management (London, GBR) **[54613]**

Intellectual History Review (London, GBR) **[54614]**

Intellectual Property Quarterly (Andover, GBR) **[52117]**

Intellectuals' Rendezvous (New Delhi, DH, IND) *Unable to locate*

Intelligence & National Security (Abingdon, GBR) **[51820]**

Intensive Agriculture (New Delhi, DH, IND) *Unable to locate*

Intensivmedizin und Notfallmedizin (Dordrecht, NLD) **[48424]**

Inter-Asia Cultural Studies (Abingdon, GBR) **[51821]**

Inter House Magazine (Harare, ZWE) *Unable to locate*

Inter Se Print (Singapore City, SGP) **[50313]**

Interacting with Computers (Middlesex, GBR) **[55617]**

Interaction Studies (Amsterdam, NLD) **[48022]**

Interactive Technology and Smart Education (Bradford, GBR) **[52469]**

Interavia Business & Technology (Geneva, SWI) *Unable to locate*

Intercultural Education (Abingdon, GBR) **[51822]**

Intercultural Pragmatics (Madrid, SPA) **[50772]**

Intercultural Theology and Study of Religions (Amsterdam, NLD) **[48023]**

Interdisciplinary Environmental Review (Geneva, SWI) **[51099]**

Interdisciplinary Problems of Stroke (Wroclaw, POL) **[49779]**

Interdisciplinary Science Reviews (London, GBR) **[54615]**

Interetnica (Cluj-Napoca, ROM) *Unable to locate*

Interface **[53735]***

Interface (Adelaide, SA, AUS) **[41507]**

Interface (Botucatu, SP, BRZ) **[42956]**

Interior Fitout (Pyrmont, NW, AUS) **[42282]**

Interior Magazine (Kiev, URE) **[51598]**

Interior Motives (London, GBR) **[54616]**

Interiors Focus (Solihull, GBR) **[56564]**

Interiors Today (Mumbai, MH, IND) *Unable to locate*

Interlending & Document Supply (Bradford, GBR) **[52470]**

Interligilo (Sofia, BUL) *Unable to locate*

Intermetallics (Beijing, CHN) **[43196]**

Internacia Pedagogia Revuo (Zagreb, CTA) *Unable to locate*

Internal Auditing and Business Risk (London, GBR) **[54617]**

Internal Combustion Engine (Tokyo, JPN) *Unable to locate*

Internal Comms Hub (London, GBR) **[54618]**

Internal Medicine (Prague, CZE) **[43625]**

Internal Medicine (Tokyo, JPN) **[46843]**

Internasjonal politikk (Oslo, NOR) *Unable to locate*

International Abstracts in Operations Research (Basingstoke, GBR) **[52208]**

International African Bibliography (London, GBR) **[54619]**

International Agricultural Engineering Journal (Pathumthani, THA) **[51460]**

International Agricultural Journal (Pathumthani, THA) **[51461]**

International Airport Review (Brasted, GBR) **[52562]**

International Aquafeed (Rickmansworth, GBR) **[56394]**

International Archives of Occupational and Environmental Health (Erlangen, GER) **[44339]**

International Behavioural Scientist (Meerut, UP, IND) *Unable to locate*

International Biodeterioration **[48024]***

International Biodeterioration and Biodegradation (Amsterdam, NLD) **[48024]**

International Boat Industry (Croydon, GBR) **[53126]**

International Braz J Urol (Botafogo, RJ, BRZ) **[42954]**

International Breastfeeding Journal (London, GBR) **[54620]**

Numbers cited in bold after listings are entry numbers rather than page numbers.

International Building Services Abstracts (Bracknell, GBR) **[52434]**

International Business (Shanghai, CHN) *Unable to locate*

International Business Lawyer (London, GBR) **[54621]**

International Business Management (Faisalabad, PAK) **[49248]**

International Camellia Journal (Wimborne, GBR) **[56928]**

International Carpet Bulletin (ICB) (Bradford, GBR) **[52471]**

The International Channel 96.3 FM - 96.3 MHz (Singapore, SGP) **[50296]**

International Classic Record Collector (ICRC) **[54214]***

International Clinical Trials (London, GBR) **[54622]**

International Collaboration of Medical Care (Okayama, JPN) *Unable to locate*

International Communication Gazette (London, GBR) **[54623]**

International Community Law Review (Leiden, NLD) **[48679]**

International Community Radio Taipei - 100.7 MHz (Kaohsiung, TWN) **[51312]**

International Community Radio Taipei - 100.1 MHz (Taichung, TWN) **[51324]**

International and Comparative Law Quarterly (Cambridge, GBR) **[52831]**

International and Comparative Law Quarterly (London, GBR) **[54624]**

International Computer Chess Association Journal (London, GBR) *Unable to locate*

International Construction China (Wadhurst, GBR) **[56807]**

The International Construction Law Review (London, GBR) **[54625]**

International Construction Turkiye (Wadhurst, GBR) **[56808]**

International Consultants' Guide (Amersham, GBR) **[52107]**

International Contact Lens Clinic (Saint Louis, MO, USA) *Unable to locate*

International Contract Labour (Jakarta, IDN) *Unable to locate*

International Cooperative Alliance Cooperative Series (New Delhi, DH, IND) *Unable to locate*

International Cranes and Specialized Transport (Wadhurst, GBR) **[56809]**

International Criminal Law Review (Leiden, NLD) **[48680]**

International Custody & Fund Administration (London, GBR) **[54626]**

International Dairy Topics (Driffield, GBR) **[53202]**

International Dental Journal (Lowestoft, GBR) **[55495]**

International Desalination and Water Reuse Quarterly (South Croydon, GBR) *Unable to locate*

International Developer (Bondi Junction, NW, AUS) *Unable to locate*

International Dyer (Bradford, GBR) **[52472]**

International Economic Journal (Abingdon, GBR) **[51823]**

International Economics and Economic Policy (Wuppertal, GER) **[44715]**

International Environmental & Safety News (Saint Albans, GBR) *Unable to locate*

International Environmental Technology (Saint Albans, GBR) **[56437]**

International Fanzines (Harlow, GBR) *Unable to locate*

International Feminist Journal of Politics (Abingdon, GBR) **[51824]**

International Flight Training News (Cambridge, GBR) *Unable to locate*

International Food Hygiene (Driffield, GBR) **[53203]**

International Forest Fire News (Geneva, SWI) *Unable to locate*

International Freighting Weekly (London, GBR) *Unable to locate*

International Gambling Studies (Abingdon, GBR) **[51825]**

International Game Theory Review (Copenhagen, DEN) **[43675]**

International Gas Report (Makati City, PHL) *Unable to locate*

International Gold Newsletter **[55420]***

International Hatchery Practice (Driffield, GBR) **[53204]**

International Heat Treatment and Surface Engineering (London, GBR) **[54627]**

International Herald Tribune (Neuilly, FRA) **[44014]**

International Horisont (Copenhagen, DEN) *Unable to locate*

International Immunology (Oxford, GBR) **[55991]**

International Immunopharmacology (Singapore, SGP) **[50175]**

International Information, Communication and Education (Lucknow, UP, IND) *Unable to locate*

International Institute for Population Sciences Director's Report (Mumbai, MH, IND) *Unable to locate*

International Investment (London, GBR) **[54628]**

International Journal (London, GBR) **[54629]**

International Journal of Abrasive Technology (Sydney, NW, AUS) **[42518]**

International Journal for Academic Development (Abingdon, GBR) **[51826]**

The International Journal of the Academy of Executives & Administrators (Kenilworth, GBR) *Unable to locate*

International Journal of Accounting, Auditing and Performance Evaluation (Manama, BHR) **[42792]**

International Journal of Accounting and Information Management (Bradford, GBR) **[52473]**

International Journal of Ad Hoc and Ubiquitous Computing (Olney, GBR) **[55786]**

International Journal of Adaptive Control & Signal Processing (Glasgow, GBR) **[53425]**

International Journal of Adaptive and Innovative Systems (Le Havre, FRA) **[43963]**

International Journal of Adhesion and Adhesives (Bristol, GBR) **[52676]**

International Journal of Adipose Tissue (London, GBR) **[54630]**

International Journal of Adolescent Medicine and Health (Jerusalem, ISR) **[46083]**

International Journal of Advanced Intelligence Paradigms (Arad, ROM) **[49830]**

International Journal of Advanced Mechatronic Systems (Tokyo, JPN) **[46844]**

International Journal of Advanced Media and Communication (Olney, GBR) **[55787]**

International Journal of Advanced Operations Management (Odense, DEN) **[43727]**

International Journal of Advanced Robotic Systems (Vienna, AUT) **[42761]**

International Journal for the Advancement of Counseling (Dordrecht, NLD) **[48425]**

International Journal of Advances in Rheumatology (London, GBR) **[54631]**

International Journal of Advertising (London, GBR) **[54632]**

International Journal of Aeroacoustics (Brentwood, GBR) **[52575]**

International Journal of Aerodynamics (Olney, GBR) **[55788]**

International Journal of Aerospace Innovations (Bangalore, KA, IND) **[44963]**

The International Journal of Ageing and Later Life (IJAL) (Linkoping, SWE) **[50975]**

International Journal of Agent-Oriented Software Engineering (Trento, ITA) **[46262]**

International Journal of Agile and Extreme Software Development (Funchal, PRT) **[49798]**

International Journal of Agile Systems and Management (Hull, GBR) **[53626]**

International Journal of Agricultural Resources, Governance and Ecology (Nathan, QL, AUS) **[42143]**

International Journal of Agricultural Sustainability (London, GBR) **[54633]**

International Journal of Agriculture and Rural Development (Owerri, IM, NGA) **[49163]**

International Journal of Algebra (Ruse, BUL) **[43089]**

International Journal of Algebra and Computation (Singapore, SGP) **[50176]**

International Journal of Alternative Propulsion (Olney, GBR) **[55789]**

International Journal of Animal Sciences (Sonepat, HY, IND) *Unable to locate*

International Journal of Antimicrobial Agents (Straubing, GER) **[44658]**

International Journal of Applied Business and Economic Research (New Delhi, DH, IND) **[45580]**

International Journal of Applied Cryptography (Wollongong, NW, AUS) **[42704]**

International Journal of Applied Decision Sciences (Geneva, SWI) **[51100]**

International Journal of Applied Earth Observation and Geoinformation (Enschede, NLD) **[48593]**

International Journal of Applied Electromagnetics and Mechanics (Sendai, JPN) **[46667]**

International Journal of Applied Engineering Research (Serdang, MYS) **[47715]**

International Journal of Applied Environmental Sciences (Seoul, KOR) **[47267]**

International Journal of Applied Management Science (Geneva, SWI) **[51101]**

International Journal of Applied Mathematics and Computer Science (Warsaw, POL) **[49719]**

International Journal of Applied Mathematics and Mechanics (IJAMM) (Wales, GBR) **[56812]**

International Journal of Applied Nonlinear Science (Geneva, SWI) **[51102]**

The International Journal of Applied Psychoanalytic Studies (Bognor Regis, GBR) **[52396]**

International Journal of Applied Systemic Studies (Piraeus, GRC) **[44767]**

International Journal of Arab Culture, Management and Sustainable Development (Oviedo-Asturias, SPA) **[50826]**

International Journal of Arabic-English Studies (Amman, JOR) **[47159]**

International Journal of Arbitration (Calcutta, WB, IND) *Unable to locate*

International Journal of Architectural Computing (Brentwood, GBR) **[52576]**

International Journal of Art & Design Education (Corsham, GBR) **[53066]**

International Journal of Art Therapy (Abingdon, GBR) **[51827]**

International Journal of Artificial Intelligence in Education (Amsterdam, NLD) **[48025]**

International Journal of Artificial Intelligence and Soft Computing (Kolkata, WB, IND) **[45295]**

International Journal of Artificial Organs (Arcavacata di Rende, ITA) **[46120]**

International Journal of Arts Medicine (Ludenscheid, GER) *Unable to locate*

International Journal of Arts and Technology (Nauplion, GRC) **[44762]**

International Journal of Asian Management (Tokyo, JPN) **[46845]**

International Journal of Asian Studies (Cambridge, GBR) **[52832]**

International Journal of Astrobiology (Cambridge, GBR) **[52833]**

International Journal of Auditing Technology (Geneva, SWI) **[51103]**

International Journal of Automotive Technology and Management (Olney, GBR) **[55790]**

International Journal of Autonomic Computing (Olney, GBR) **[55791]**

International Journal of Autonomous and Adaptive Communications Systems (Kozani, GRC) **[44761]**

International Journal of Aviation Management (Paris, FRA) **[44049]**

International Journal for Ayurveda Research (Mumbai, MH, IND) **[45392]**

International Journal of Bank Marketing (Bradford, GBR) **[52474]**

International Journal of Banking, Accounting and Finance (Bangor, GBR) **[52172]**

International Journal of Behavioral Nutrition and Physical Activity (London, GBR) **[54634]**

International Journal of Behavioural Accounting and Finance (Bath, GBR) **[52244]**

International Journal of Behavioural and Healthcare Research (Rion, GRC) **[44770]**

International Journal of Behavioural Sciences (Dehradun, UP, IND) *Unable to locate*

International Journal of Bilingual Education & Bilingualism (Abingdon, GBR) **[51828]**

Numbers cited in bold after listings are entry numbers rather than page numbers.

International Journal of Bio-Inspired Computation (Taiyuan, SX, CHN) [43515]

International Journal of Biochemistry & Cell Biology (London, GBR) [54635]

International Journal of Bioelectromagnetism (Tampere, FIN) [43908]

International Journal of Biological and Chemical Sciences (Dschang, CMR) [43126]

International Journal of Biological Markers (Milan, ITA) [46176]

International Journal of Biological Sciences (Womying, NW, AUS) [42710]

International Journal of Biomechatronics and Biomedical Robotics (Auckland, NZL) [48798]

International Journal of Biomedical Engineering and Technology (Olney, GBR) [55792]

International Journal of Biomedical Nanoscience and Nanotechnology (Geneva, SWI) [51104]

International Journal of Biometrics (Krakow, POL) [49666]

International Journal of Biotechnology & Biochemistry (IJBB) (Alexandria, EGY) [43745]

International Journal of Biotronics (Fukuoka, JPN) [46343]

International Journal of Border Security and Immigration Policy (Geneva, SWI) [51105]

International Journal of Botany (Faisalabad, PAK) [49249]

International Journal of Business Competition and Growth (Mexico City, DF, MEX) [47785]

International Journal of Business and Emerging Markets (Geneva, SWI) [51106]

International Journal of Business Environment (Granada, SPA) [50717]

International Journal of Business Excellence (Geneva, SWI) [51107]

International Journal of Business Forecasting and Marketing Intelligence (Geneva, SWI) [51108]

International Journal of Business Governance and Ethics (Telford, GBR) [56737]

International Journal of Business and Information (IJBI) (Taipei, TWN) [51342]

International Journal of Business Innovation and Research (IJBIR) (Geneva, SWI) [51109]

International Journal of Business Intelligence and Data Mining (Clayton, VI, AUS) [41761]

International Journal of Business Performance Management (London, GBR) [54636]

International Journal of Business Performance and Supply Chain Modelling (Odense, DEN) [43728]

International Journal of Cardiology (Sydney, NW, AUS) [42519]

International Journal of Cardiovascular Interventions [51697]*

International Journal of Care Pathways (London, GBR) [54637]

International Journal of Cast Metals Research (London, GBR) [54638]

International Journal of Children's Spirituality (Abingdon, GBR) [51829]

International Journal of Chinese Culture & Management (Oviedo, SPA) [50823]

International Journal of Chinese &

Oriental Languages Processing (Singapore, SGP) [50177]

International Journal of Circumpolar Health (Oulu, FIN) Unable to locate

International Journal of Climatology (Reading, GBR) [56321]

International Journal of Clinical Legal Education (Newcastle upon Tyne, GBR) [55672]

International Journal of Clinical Monitoring and Computing [48448]*

International Journal of Clinical Oncology (Tokyo, JPN) [46846]

International Journal of Clinical Rheumatology (London, GBR) [54639]

International Journal of Clothing Science and Technology (Galashiels, GBR) [53403]

International Journal of Cognition and Technology (IJCT) (Amsterdam, NLD) Ceased

International Journal of Cognitive Biometrics (El Sherouk City, EGY) [43771]

International Journal of Cognitive Performance Support (El Sherouk City, EGY) [43772]

International Journal of Cognitive Performance Support (IJCPS) (Olney, GBR) [55793]

International Journal of Collaborative Enterprise (Olney, GBR) [55794]

International Journal of Colorectal Disease (Berlin, GER) [44192]

International Journal of Communication (New Delhi, DH, IND) Unable to locate

International Journal of Communication Networks and Distributed Systems (Kharagpur, WB, IND) [45246]

International Journal of Community Currency Research (Leicester, GBR) [53805]

International Journal of Comparative Sociology (Leiden, NLD) Ceased

International Journal of Complexity (Olney, GBR) [55795]

International Journal of Complexity in Applied Science and Engineering (Geneva, SWI) [51110]

International Journal of Complexity in Leadership and Management (Singapore, SGP) [50178]

International Journal of Computational and Applied Mathematics (Hainan, GD, CHN) [43259]

International Journal of Computational Biology and Drug Design (Geneva, SWI) [51111]

International Journal of Computational Economics and Econometrics (Portsmouth, GBR) [56289]

International Journal of Computational Intelligence and Applications (Rockhampton, QL, AUS) [42316]

International Journal of Computational Intelligence in Bioinformatics and Systems Biology (Jinan, SD, CHN) [43447]

International Journal of Computational Intelligence Research (Trondheim, NOR) [49216]

International Journal of Computational Intelligence Studies (Ancona, ITA) [46118]

International Journal of Computational Materials Science & Surface Engineering (Olney, GBR) [55796]

International Journal of Computational Medicine and Healthcare (Geneva, SWI) [51112]

International Journal of Computational Methods (IJCM) (Singapore, SGP) [50179]

International Journal of Computational Physical Sciences (Darwin, NT, AUS) [41828]

International Journal for Computational Vision and Biomechanics (New Delhi, DH, IND) [45581]

International Journal of Computational Vision and Robotics (Bhubaneswar, OR, IND) [45010]

International Journal of Computer Aided Engineering and Technology (Darmstadt, GER) [44309]

International Journal of Computer Applications in Technology (Bristol, GBR) [52677]

International Journal of Computer Assisted Radiology and Surgery (Dordrecht, NLD) [48426]

International Journal of Computer Mathematics (London, GBR) [54640]

International Journal of Computer Processing of Languages (Hong Kong, CHN) [43349]

International Journal of Computer Processing of Oriental Languages [43349]*

International Journal of Computers in Healthcare (Adelaide, SA, AUS) [41508]

International Journal of Computing and Applications (Thanjavur, TN, IND) [45747]

International Journal of Computing Science and Mathematics (Xiangtan, HA, CHN) [43539]

International Journal of Constitutional Law (Oxford, GBR) [55992]

International Journal of Construction Education and Research (Abingdon, GBR) [51830]

International Journal of Contemporary Hospitality Management (Bradford, GBR) [52475]

International Journal of Contemporary Mathematical Sciences (Ruse, BUL) [43090]

International Journal of Continuing Engineering Education and Life-Long Learning (Edinburgh, GBR) [53287]

International Journal of Cooperative Information Systems (Tilburg, NLD) [48754]

International Journal of Corporate Governance (Geneva, SWI) [51113]

International Journal of Corpus Linguistics (Amsterdam, NLD) [48026]

International Journal of Cosmetic Science (Northwich, GBR) [55719]

International Journal of Criminal Justice Sciences (IJCJS) (Tirunelveli, TN, IND) [45753]

International Journal of Critical Accounting (Geneva, SWI) [51114]

International Journal of Critical Computer-Based Systems (Naples, ITA) [46200]

International Journal of Critical Infrastructures (Olney, GBR) [55797]

International Journal of Critical Sociology (Jaipur, RJ, IND) Unable to locate

International Journal of Cross Cultural Management (London, GBR) [54641]

International Journal of Cultural Policy (Abingdon, GBR) [51831]

International Journal of Cultural Property (Cambridge, GBR) [52834]

International Journal of Cultural Studies (London, GBR) [54642]

International Journal of Cyber Society and Education (Taipei, TWN) [51343]

International Journal of Dairy Technology (Appleby-in-Westmorland, GBR) [52126]

International Journal of Damage Mechanics (London, GBR) [54643]

International Journal of Data Analysis Techniques and Strategies (Geneva, SWI) [51115]

International Journal of Decision Sciences, Risk and Management (Patras, GRC) [44764]

International Journal of Dental Hygiene (Oxford, GBR) [55993]

International Journal of Design (Taipei, TWN) [51344]

International Journal of Design Engineering (Nottingham, GBR) [55759]

International Journal of Development Banking (Mumbai, MH, IND) Ceased

International Journal of Development and Policy Studies (Makurdi, BN, NGA) [49145]

International Journal of Diabetes in Developing Countries (Mumbai, MH, IND) [46393]

International Journal of Digital Culture and Electronic Tourism (Helsinki, FIN) [43833]

International Journal of Digital Enterprise Technology (Xi'an, SX, CHN) [43537]

International Journal on Digital Libraries (Darmstadt, GER) [44310]

International Journal of Disability, Development and Education (IJDDE) (Abingdon, GBR) [51832]

International Journal on Disability and Human Development (Jerusalem, ISR) [46084]

International Journal of Disability Management Research (Bowen Hills, QL, AUS) [41626]

International Journal of Disaster Medicine (Abingdon, GBR) Ceased

International Journal of Disclosure and Governance (Basingstoke, GBR) [52209]

International Journal of Drug Policy (Saint Louis, MO, USA) Unable to locate

International Journal of Dynamical Systems and Differential Equations (Xiangtan, HA, CHN) [43540]

International Journal of Dynamics of Fluids (IJDF) (Middlesex, GBR) [55618]

International Journal of Early Childhood Education (Reading, GBR) Unable to locate

International Journal of Ecology and Development (Roorkee, UP, IND) [45718]

International Journal of Ecology and Environmental Sciences (New Delhi, DH, IND) Unable to locate

International Journal of Economic Policy in Emerging Economies (Messina, ITA) [46157]

International Journal of Economic Research (Piraeus, GRC) [44768]

International Journal of Economic Theory (Oxford, GBR) [55994]

International Journal of Economics and Accounting (London, GBR) [54644]

International Journal of the Economics of Business (Abingdon, GBR) [51833]

Numbers cited in bold after listings are entry numbers rather than page numbers.

International Journal of Economics and Business Research (Geneva, SWI) **[51116]**

International Journal of Education through Art (London, GBR) **[54645]**

The International Journal of Education and Development using Information and Communication Technology (IJEDICT) (Bridgetown, BRB) **[42828]**

International Journal of Education Economics and Development (Windhoek, NAM) **[47822]**

International Journal of Educational Administration (Balasore, OR, IND) **[44947]**

International Journal of Educational Advancement (Basingstoke, GBR) **[52210]**

International Journal of Educational Development (Nottingham, GBR) **[55760]**

International Journal for Educational Integrity (Adelaide, SA, AUS) **[41509]**

International Journal of Educational Management (Bradford, GBR) **[52476]**

International Journal of Educational Sciences (Dehradun, UP, IND) *Unable to locate*

International Journal for Educational and Vocational Guidance (Dordrecht, NLD) **[48427]**

International Journal of Electric and Hybrid Vehicles (Villiers-Saint-Frederic, FRA) **[44127]**

International Journal of Electrical Engineering Education (Manchester, GBR) **[55558]**

International Journal of Electrical Machining (Tokyo, JPN) *Unable to locate*

International Journal of Electrical Power & Energy Systems (Bentley, WA, AUS) **[41597]**

International Journal of Electrical and Power Engineering (Faisalabad, PAK) **[49250]**

International Journal of Electronic Banking (Geneva, SWI) **[51117]**

International Journal of Electronic Business (Taipei, TWN) **[51345]**

International Journal of Electronic Customer Relationship Management (Taichung, TWN) **[51320]**

International Journal of Electronic Democracy (London, GBR) **[54646]**

International Journal of Electronic Governance (Athens, GRC) **[44746]**

International Journal of Electronic Security and Digital Forensics (London, GBR) **[54647]**

International Journal of Electronic Trade (Milan, ITA) **[46177]**

International Journal of Electronic Transport (Melbourne, VI, AUS) **[42065]**

International Journal of Embedded Systems (Olney, GBR) **[55798]**

International Journal of Emergency Management (Olney, GBR) **[55799]**

International Journal of Emerging Markets (Bradford, GBR) **[52477]**

International Journal of Emerging and Multidisciplinary Fluid Science (Mumbai, MH, IND) **[45394]**

International Journal of Emotional Psychology and Sport Ethics (Arcadia, SAF) **[50346]**

International Journal of Energy Sector Management (Dundee, GBR) **[53214]**

International Journal of Energy Technology and Policy (Olney, GBR) **[55800]**

International Journal of Engineering (Tehran, IRN) **[45890]**

International Journal of Engineering Management and Economics (Napoli, ITA) **[46204]**

International Journal of Engineering Studies (New Delhi, DH, IND) **[45582]**

International Journal of Engineering Systems Modelling and Simulation (Wrexham, GBR) **[56981]**

International Journal of Enterprise Network Management (Sheffield, GBR) **[56499]**

International Journal of Enterprise Systems Integration and Interoperability (Bari, ITA) **[46122]**

International Journal of Entertainment Technology and Management (Athens, GRC) **[44747]**

International Journal of Entrepreneurial Behaviour & Research (Bradford, GBR) **[52478]**

International Journal of Entrepreneurial Venturing (Stockholm, SWE) **[51020]**

International Journal of Entrepreneurial Venturing (Olney, GBR) **[55801]**

International Journal of Entrepreneurship Education **[45968]**

International Journal of Entrepreneurship and Innovation (Lincoln, GBR) **[53856]**

International Journal of Entrepreneurship and Innovation Management (Olney, GBR) **[55802]**

International Journal of Environment and Development (New Delhi, DH, IND) **[45583]**

International Journal of Environment and Health (Rome, ITA) **[46234]**

International Journal of Environment and Pollution (Geneva, SWI) **[51118]**

International Journal of Environment and Sustainable Development (Olney, GBR) **[55803]**

International Journal of Environment, Workplace and Employment (Melbourne, VI, AUS) **[42066]**

International Journal of Environmental Health Research (Abingdon, GBR) **[51834]**

International Journal of Environmental Policy and Decision Making (Geneva, SWI) **[51119]**

International Journal of Environmental Technology and Management (Olney, GBR) **[55804]**

International Journal of Epidemiology (Bristol, GBR) **[52678]**

International Journal for Equity in Health (Guatemala City, GTM) **[44785]**

International Journal for Equity in Health (London, GBR) **[54648]**

International Journal of Evidence-based Healthcare (Oxford, GBR) **[55995]**

International Journal of Evidence and Proof (Nottingham, GBR) **[55761]**

International Journal of Exergy (Geneva, SWI) **[51120]**

International Journal of Fertility (Montpellier, FRA) *Unable to locate*

International Journal of Feto-Maternal Medicine (Basel, SWI) *Unable to locate*

International Journal of Financial Markets and Derivatives (Portsmouth, GBR) **[56290]**

International Journal of Financial Services Management (Olney, GBR) **[55805]**

International Journal of Flexible Manufacturing Systems **[48388]**

International Journal of Food Microbiology (Grugliasco, ITA) **[46155]**

International Journal of Food Properties (Muscat, OMN) **[49221]**

International Journal of Food Safety, Nutrition and Public Health (Geneva, SWI) **[51121]**

International Journal of Food Sciences & Nutrition (Abingdon, GBR) **[51835]**

International Journal of Forecasting (Victoria, AUS) **[42665]**

International Journal of Forensic Engineering (Milton Keynes, GBR) **[55638]**

International Journal of Forensic Engineering and Management (Olney, GBR) **[55806]**

International Journal of Forensic Odonto-Homatology (Beigem, BEL) *Unable to locate*

International Journal of Forensic Software Engineering (Fisciano, ITA) **[46140]**

International Journal of Foresight and Innovation Policy (Olney, GBR) **[55807]**

International Journal of Functional Analysis, Operator Theory and Applications (Allahabad, UP, IND) **[44932]**

International Journal of Functional Informatics and Personalised Medicine (Geneva, SWI) **[51122]**

International Journal of Genome Research (Singapore, SGP) *Ceased*

International Journal of Geometric Methods in Modern Physics (IJGMMP) (Singapore, SGP) **[50180]**

International Journal of Global Energy Issues (Laxenburg, AUT) **[42730]**

International Journal of Global Environmental Issues (Olney, GBR) **[55808]**

International Journal of Globalisation and Small Business (Flensburg, GER) **[44355]**

International Journal of Granular Computing, Rough Sets and Intelligent Systems (Geneva, SWI) **[51123]**

International Journal of Green Economics (Reading, GBR) **[56322]**

International Journal of Green Pharmacy (Mandsaur, MP, IND) **[45339]**

International Journal of Grid & Utility Computing (Trondheim, NOR) **[49217]**

International Journal of Health Care Quality Assurance (Bradford, GBR) **[52479]**

International Journal of Health Geographics (London, GBR) **[54649]**

International Journal of Health Promotion and Education (Manchester, GBR) **[55559]**

International Journal of Healthcare Technology and Management (Enschede, NLD) **[48594]**

International Journal of Heavy Vehicle Systems (Geneva, SWI) **[51124]**

International Journal of Hematology (Kyoto, JPN) **[46472]**

International Journal of Heritage Studies (Abingdon, GBR) **[51836]**

International Journal of High Performance Computing and Networking (Olney, GBR) **[55809]**

International Journal of High Performance System Architecture (Rio de Janeiro, RJ, BRZ) **[43007]**

International Journal of High Speed Computing (Singapore, SGP) *Ceased*

International Journal of Historical Archaeology (Dordrecht, NLD) **[48428]**

International Journal of the History of Sport (Abingdon, GBR) **[51837]**

International Journal of Housing Markets and Analysis (Sydney, NW, AUS) **[42520]**

International Journal of Human Genetics (Delhi, DH, IND) **[45099]**

International Journal of Human Resource Management (Cardiff, GBR) **[52930]**

International Journal of Human Resources Development and Management (Olney, GBR) **[55810]**

The International Journal of Human Rights (Abingdon, GBR) **[51838]**

International Journal of Humanistic Studies (Kwaluseni, SWZ) **[50943]**

International Journal of Humanities and Arts Computing (Edinburgh, GBR) **[53288]**

International Journal of Humanoid Robotics (IJHR) (Singapore, SGP) **[50181]**

International Journal of Hybrid Intelligent Systems (Amsterdam, NLD) **[48027]**

International Journal of Hybrid Intelligent Systems (Seoul, KOR) **[47268]**

International Journal of Hydrology Science and Technology (Isfahan, IRN) **[45878]**

International Journal of Hygiene and Environmental Health (Bochum, GER) **[44250]**

International Journal of Image and Graphics (Hong Kong, CHN) **[43350]**

International Journal of Image and Graphics (Singapore, SGP) **[50182]**

International Journal of Image and Video Processing (IJIVP) (Antibes, FRA) **[43914]**

International Journal of Industrial Electronics and Drives (Kharagpur, WB, IND) **[45247]**

International Journal of Industrial Organization (Amsterdam, NLD) **[48028]**

International Journal of Information Acquisition (Singapore, SGP) **[50183]**

International Journal of Information and Coding Theory (Kharagpur, WB, IND) **[45248]**

International Journal of Information and Computer Security (Taipei, TWN) **[51346]**

International Journal of Information and Decision Sciences (Geneva, SWI) **[51125]**

International Journal of Information and Management Sciences (Tamsui, TWN) **[51393]**

International Journal of Information Policy and Law **[42521]**

International Journal of Information Privacy, Security and Integrity (Geneva, SWI) **[51126]**

International Journal of Information Quality (Toowoomba, QL, AUS) **[42628]**

Numbers cited in bold after listings are entry numbers rather than page numbers.

International Journal of Information Science and Computer Mathematics (Hainan, CHN) **[43258]**

International Journal of Information Security (Hamburg, GER) **[44419]**

International Journal of Information Technology, Communications and Convergence (Seoul, KOR) **[47269]**

International Journal of Information Technology and Management (Olney, GBR) **[55811]**

International Journal of Injury Control and Safety Promotion (Amsterdam, NLD) **[48029]**

International Journal of Innovation in Education (Berlin, GER) **[44193]**

International Journal of Innovation Management (Singapore, SGP) **[50184]**

International Journal of Innovation and Regional Development (Thessaloniki, GRC) **[44773]**

International Journal of Innovation Science (Brentwood, GBR) **[52577]**

International Journal of Innovation and Sustainable Development (Olney, GBR) **[55812]**

International Journal of Innovative Computing and Applications (Rio de Janeiro, RJ, BRZ) **[43008]**

International Journal of Integrated Care (Utrecht, NLD) **[48760]**

International Journal of Intellectual Property Management (Olney, GBR) **[55813]**

International Journal of Intelligent Collaborative Enterprise **[55794]***

International Journal of Intelligent Computing and Cybernetics (Beijing, CHN) **[43197]**

International Journal of Intelligent Defence Support Systems (Adelaide, SA, AUS) **[41510]**

International Journal of Intelligent Engineering Informatics (Beijing, CHN) **[43198]**

International Journal of Intelligent Information and Database Systems (Wroclaw, POL) **[49780]**

International Journal of Intelligent Systems Technologies and Applications (Olney, GBR) **[55814]**

International Journal of Intensive Care (London, GBR) **[54650]**

International Journal of Internet and Enterprise Management (Olney, GBR) **[55815]**

International Journal of Internet Manufacturing & Services (Xi'an, SH, CHN) **[43532]**

International Journal of Internet Marketing and Advertising (Jhongli City, TWN) **[51308]**

International Journal of Internet Protocol Technology (Olney, GBR) **[55816]**

International Journal of Internet Technology & Secured Transactions (London, GBR) **[54651]**

International Journal of Inventory Research (Geneva, SWI) **[51127]**

International Journal of Islamic and Middle Eastern Finance and Management (London, GBR) **[54652]**

International Journal of Japan Society for Precision Engineering (Tokyo, JPN) **[46847]**

International Journal of Jurisprudence and Philosophy of Law (Shillong, AS, IND) **[45728]**

International Journal of Knowledge-Based Development (Brisbane, QL, AUS) **[41650]**

International Journal of Knowledge-Based and Intelligent Engineering Systems (Shoreham-by-Sea, GBR) **[56524]**

International Journal of Knowledge Engineering and Data Mining (Hong Kong, CHN) **[43351]**

International Journal of Knowledge Engineering and Soft Data Paradigms (Tsukuba, JPN) **[47110]**

International Journal of Knowledge and Learning (Athens, GRC) **[44748]**

International Journal of Knowledge Management Studies (Olney, GBR) **[55817]**

International Journal of Knowledge Management in Tourism and Hospitality (Sheffield, GBR) **[56500]**

International Journal of Lakes and Rivers (Alexandria, EGY) **[43746]**

International Journal of Language & Communication Disorders (Abingdon, GBR) **[51839]**

International Journal of Law in Context (Cambridge, GBR) **[52835]**

International Journal of Law, Crime and Justice (Kidlington, GBR) **[53694]**

International Journal of Law and Information Technology (Oxford, GBR) **[55996]**

International Journal of Law and Management (Liverpool, GBR) **[53874]**

International Journal of Law, Policy and the Family (Oxford, GBR) **[55997]**

The International Journal of Leadership in Public Services (Brighton, GBR) **[52616]**

International Journal of Lean Enterprise Research (Groningen, NLD) **[48603]**

International Journal of Learning and Change (Auckland, NZL) **[48799]**

International Journal of Learning and Intellectual Capital (Oviedo, SPA) **[50824]**

International Journal of Learning Technology (Stafford, GBR) **[56591]**

International Journal of Legal Information Design (Zurich, SWI) **[51266]**

International Journal of Legal Medicine (Heidelberg, GER) **[44462]**

International Journal of the Legal Profession (Abingdon, GBR) **[51840]**

International Journal of Leisure and Tourism Marketing (Geneva, SWI) **[51128]**

International Journal of Lexicography (Oxford, GBR) **[55998]**

International Journal of Liability and Scientific Enquiry (Olney, GBR) **[55818]**

International Journal of Logistics Economics & Globalisation (Sheffield, GBR) **[56501]**

International Journal of Low Carbon Technologies (Manchester, GBR) *Ceased*

International Journal of Low Radiation (Olney, GBR) **[55819]**

International Journal of Machine Tools and Manufacture (Birmingham, GBR) **[52343]**

International Journal of Machining and Machinability of Materials (Aveiro, PRT) **[49786]**

International Journal of Management (Poole, GBR) *Unable to locate*

International Journal of Management Concepts and Philosophy (Olney, GBR) **[55820]**

International Journal of Management and Decision Making (Olney, GBR) **[55821]**

International Journal of Management and Network Economics (L'Aquila, ITA) **[46119]**

International Journal of Management Practice (Telford, GBR) **[56738]**

International Journal of Management and Systems (New Delhi, DH, IND) *Unable to locate*

International Journal of Managerial Finance (Bradford, GBR) **[52480]**

International Journal of Managerial and Financial Accounting (Miri, MYS) **[47683]**

International Journal of Managing Projects in Business (Melbourne, VI, AUS) **[42067]**

International Journal of Manpower (Bradford, GBR) **[52481]**

International Journal of Manufacturing Research (Olney, GBR) **[55822]**

International Journal of Manufacturing System Design (Singapore, SGP) *Unable to locate*

International Journal of Manufacturing Technology and Management (Geneva, SWI) **[51129]**

International Journal of Maritime Economics **[52223]***

International Journal of Market Research (London, GBR) **[54653]**

International Journal of Materials Engineering Innovation (Aveiro, PRT) **[49787]**

International Journal of Materials Engineering and Technology (Perlis, MYS) **[47694]**

International Journal of Materials and Product Technology (Pfinztal, GER) **[44633]**

International Journal of Materials Science (El Mansoura, EGY) **[43770]**

International Journal of Materials & Structural Integrity (Olney, GBR) **[55823]**

International Journal of Mathematical Analysis (Ruse, BUL) **[43091]**

International Journal of Mathematical Modelling and Numerical Optimisation (Teddington, GBR) **[56731]**

International Journal of Mathematical Sciences (Masan, KOR) **[47243]**

International Journal of Mathematics Manuscripts (Al Ain, UAE) **[51626]**

International Journal of Mathematics and Mathematical Sciences (New Delhi, DH, IND) *Unable to locate*

International Journal of Mathematics and Statistics (IJMS) (Roorkee, UP, IND) **[45719]**

International Journal of Mechanical Engineering Education (Manchester, GBR) **[55560]**

International Journal of Mechanical Sciences (Amsterdam, NLD) **[48030]**

International Journal of Mechatronics and Manufacturing Systems (Geneva, SWI) **[51130]**

International Journal of Media and Cultural Politics (London, GBR) **[54654]**

The International Journal of Media Education (Stoke-on-Trent, GBR) *Ceased*

International Journal of Medical Engineering and Informatics (Geneva, SWI) **[51131]**

International Journal of Medical Robotics and Computer-Assisted Surgery (Bognor Regis, GBR) **[52397]**

International Journal of Medical Sciences (Womying, NW, AUS) **[42711]**

International Journal of Metadata, Semantics and Ontologies (Olney, GBR) **[55824]**

International Journal of Metaheuristics (Cardiff, GBR) **[52931]**

International Journal of Micrographics & Optical Technology (Burnham, GBR) **[52765]**

International Journal of Microstructure and Materials Properties (Ljubljana, SVA) **[50338]**

International Journal of Middle East Studies (Cambridge, GBR) **[52836]**

International Journal of Migration, Health and Social Care (Brighton, GBR) **[52617]**

International Journal of Mining and Mineral Engineering (Geneva, SWI) **[51132]**

International Journal of Mobile Network Design and Innovation (Cardiff, GBR) **[52932]**

International Journal of Modelling, Identification and Control (Bristol, GBR) **[52679]**

International Journal of Modelling in Operations Management (Kampar, MYS) **[47584]**

International Journal of Modern Physics A (Singapore, SGP) **[50185]**

International Journal of Modern Physics B (Karlsruhe, GER) **[44493]**

International Journal of Modern Physics C (Singapore, SGP) **[50186]**

International Journal of Modern Physics C: Physics and Computers **[50186]***

International Journal of Modern Physics D (Singapore, SGP) **[50187]**

International Journal of Modern Physics E (Singapore, SGP) **[50188]**

International Journal of Modern Physics E: Report on Nuclear Physics **[50188]***

International Journal of Molecular Engineering (Aveiro, PRT) **[49788]**

International Journal of Molecular Medicine and Advance Sciences (Faisalabad, PAK) **[49251]**

International Journal of Molecular Sciences (Basel, SWI) **[51062]**

International Journal of Monetary Economics & Finance (Messina, ITA) **[46158]**

International Journal of Multicriteria Decision Making (Athens, GRC) **[44749]**

International Journal on Multicultural Societies (IJMS) **[44395]***

The International Journal of Multilingualism (Abingdon, GBR) **[51841]**

International Journal of Multimedia Intelligence and Security (Beijing, CHN) **[43199]**

International Journal of Multiphase Flow (Haifa, ISR) **[46076]**

International Journal of Music Education (London, GBR) **[54655]**

International Journal of Myriapodology (Leiden, NLD) **[48681]**

International Journal of Nano and Biomaterials (Geneva, SWI) **[51133]**

International Journal of Nanomanufacturing (Olney, GBR) **[55825]**

International Journal of Nanomedicine (Macclesfield, GBR) **[55517]**

International Journal of Nanoparticles (Hefei, AN, CHN) **[43266]**

Numbers cited in bold after listings are entry numbers rather than page numbers.

International Journal of Nanoscience (Singapore, SGP) **[50189]**

International Journal of Nanotechnology and Applications (Alexandria, EGY) **[43747]**

International Journal of Narrative Therapy and Community Work (Adelaide, SA, AUS) **[41511]**

International Journal of Natural and Applied Sciences (Grahamstown, SAF) **[50498]**

International Journal of Networking and Virtual Organisations (Olney, GBR) **[55826]**

International Journal of Neural Systems (Singapore, SGP) **[50190]**

The International Journal of Neuropsychopharmacology (Cambridge, GBR) **[52837]**

International Journal of Neuroscience (Abingdon, GBR) **[51842]**

International Journal of Nonlinear Modelling in Science and Engineering (Shanghai, CHN) **[43477]**

International Journal of Nonlinear Sciences and Numerical Simulation (Tel Aviv, ISR) **[46104]**

International Journal of Nuclear Desalination (Paris, FRA) **[44050]**

International Journal of Nuclear Energy Science and Technology (Paris, FRA) **[44051]**

International Journal of Nuclear Governance, Economy and Ecology (Paris, FRA) **[44052]**

International Journal of Nuclear Hydrogen Production and Applications (Paris, FRA) **[44053]**

International Journal of Nuclear Knowledge Management (Paris, FRA) **[44054]**

International Journal of Nuclear Law (Paris, FRA) **[44055]**

International Journal of Numerical Methods and Applications (Allahabad, UP, IND) **[44933]**

International Journal for Numerical Methods in Fluids (Birmingham, GBR) **[52344]**

International Journal of Numerical Methods for Heat & Fluid Flow (Swansea, GBR) **[56702]**

International Journal of Nursing Studies (London, GBR) **[54656]**

International Journal of Nursing Terminologies and Classifications (Oxford, GBR) **[55999]**

International Journal of Obesity (Basingstoke, GBR) **[52211]**

International Journal of Ocean Systems Management (Limassol, CYP) **[43590]**

International Journal of Oceans and Oceanography (IJOO) (Alexandria, EGY) **[43748]**

International Journal of Oil, Gas and Coal Technology (Surra, KWT) **[47362]**

International Journal of Older People Nursing (Oxford, GBR) **[56000]**

International Journal of Operations and Production Management (Bradford, GBR) **[52482]**

International Journal of Opportunity, Growth and Value Creation **[55801]***

International Journal of Oral & Maxillofacial Surgery (Guildford, GBR) **[53490]**

International Journal of Organisational Design and Engineering (Lisboa, PRT) **[49800]**

International Journal of Osteopathic Medicine (Singapore, SGP) **[50191]**

International Journal of Paediatric Dentistry (Ferney-Voltaire, FRA) **[43948]**

International Journal of Palliative Nursing (London, GBR) **[54657]**

International Journal for Parasitology (Cairns, QL, AUS) **[41685]**

International Journal of Pattern Recognition and Artificial Intelligence (Munich, GER) **[44564]**

International Journal of Performance Arts and Digital Media (London, GBR) **[54658]**

International Journal of Pervasive Computing and Communications (Bradford, GBR) **[52483]**

International Journal of Petroleum Engineering (Geneva, SWI) **[51134]**

International Journal of Petroleum Science and Technology (Abu Dhabi, UAE) **[51620]**

International Journal of Pharmaceutics (Amsterdam, NLD) **[48031]**

International Journal of Pharmacology (Faisalabad, PAK) **[49252]**

International Journal of Philosophical Studies (Abingdon, GBR) **[51843]**

International Journal for Philosophy of Religion (Dordrecht, NLD) **[48429]**

International Journal of Photoenergy (Cairo, EGY) **[43762]**

International Journal of Physical Distribution and Logistics Management (Bradford, GBR) **[52484]**

International Journal of Physical Sciences (Shanghai, CHN) **[43478]**

International Journal of Physiotherapy and Life Physics (Siegen, GER) **[44656]**

International Journal of PIXE (Singapore, SGP) **[50192]**

International Journal of Planetary and Space Research (Faisalabad, PAK) **[49253]**

International Journal of the Platonic Tradition (Leiden, NLD) **[48682]**

International Journal of Police Science and Management (Exmouth, GBR) **[53370]**

International Journal of Politics, Culture, and Society (Dordrecht, NLD) **[48430]**

International Journal of Postharvest Technology and Innovation (Stellenbosch, SAF) **[50631]**

International Journal of Poultry Science (Faisalabad, PAK) **[49254]**

International Journal of Power and Energy Conversion (Bhubaneswar, OR, IND) **[45011]**

International Journal of Powertrain (Geneva, SWI) **[51135]**

International Journal of Practical Theology (Berlin, GER) **[44194]**

International Journal of Precision Technology (Melaka, MYS) **[47681]**

International Journal of Pressure Vessels and Piping (Gloucester, GBR) **[53470]**

International Journal of Prisoner Health (Abingdon, GBR) **[51844]**

International Journal of Process Management and Benchmarking (Henley-on-Thames, GBR) **[53560]**

International Journal of Product Development (Olney, GBR) **[55827]**

International Journal of Product Lifecycle Management (Bron, FRA) **[43924]**

International Journal of Product Sound Quality (Olney, GBR) **[55828]**

International Journal of Production Economics (Linkoping, SWE) **[50976]**

International Journal of Productivity and Performance Management (Bradford, GBR) **[52485]**

International Journal of Project Management (East Horsley, GBR) **[53236]**

International Journal of Project Organisation and Management (Olney, GBR) **[55829]**

International Journal of Psychotherapy (Vienna, AUT) *Unable to locate*

International Journal of Public Health (Bern, SWI) **[51074]**

International Journal of Public Opinion Research (Oxford, GBR) **[56001]**

International Journal of Public Policy (Olney, GBR) **[55830]**

International Journal of Public Sector Management (Nottingham, GBR) **[55762]**

International Journal of Public Sector Performance Management (Aix-en-Provence, FRA) **[43912]**

International Journal of Public Theology (York, GBR) **[56992]**

International Journal of Punjab Studies (Bilari, UP, IND) *Unable to locate*

International Journal of Pure & Applied Mathematical Sciences (IJPAMS) (Kashan, IRN) **[45880]**

International Journal of Pure and Applied Physics (Alexandria, EGY) **[43749]**

International Journal of Quality Engineering and Technology (Geneva, SWI) **[51136]**

International Journal for Quality in Health Care (Dublin, DU, IRL) **[45967]**

International Journal for Quality in Health Care (Oxford, GBR) **[56002]**

International Journal of Quality and Innovation (Faisalabad, PAK) **[49255]**

International Journal of Quality and Reliability Management (Bradford, GBR) **[52486]**

International Journal of Reasoning-based Intelligent Systems (Himeji, JPN) **[46378]**

International Journal of Refractory Metals and Hard Materials (Reutte, AUT) **[42738]**

International Journal of Refrigeration (Paris, FRA) **[44056]**

International Journal of Refugee Law (Colchester, GBR) **[53039]**

International Journal of Regulation and Governance (Amsterdam, NLD) **[48032]**

International Journal of Remanufacturing (Geneva, SWI) **[51137]**

International Journal of Remote Sensing (Nottingham, GBR) **[55763]**

International Journal of Renewable Energy Technology (Uxbridge, GBR) **[56798]**

International Journal of Research in Marketing (Brussels, BEL) **[42859]**

International Journal of Research and Method in Education (Abingdon, GBR) **[51845]**

International Journal of Respiratory Care (London, GBR) **[54659]**

International Journal of Retail and Distribution Management (Edinburgh, GBR) **[53289]**

International Journal of Rheumatic Diseases (Oxford, GBR) **[56003]**

International Journal of Risk Assessment and Management (Olney, GBR) **[55831]**

International Journal of Risk and Safety in Medicine (Nigtevecht, NLD) **[48742]**

International Journal of River Basin Management (Madrid, SPA) **[50773]**

International Journal of Robotics Research (London, GBR) **[54660]**

International Journal of Robust & Nonlinear Control (Chichester, GBR) **[53012]**

International Journal of Rock Mechanics and Mining Sciences (London, GBR) **[54661]**

International Journal of Rural Studies (Bilari, UP, IND) *Unable to locate*

International Journal of Satellite Communications and Networking (Guildford, GBR) **[53491]**

International Journal of Satellite Communications Policy and Management (Wuhan, CHN) **[43520]**

International Journal of Science & Engineering (Allahabad, UP, IND) *Unable to locate*

International Journal of Scientific Computing (New Delhi, DH, IND) **[45584]**

International Journal of Security and Networks (Geneva, SWI) **[51138]**

International Journal of Sediment Research (Beijing, CHN) **[43200]**

International Journal for the Semiotics of Law (Dordrecht, NLD) **[48431]**

International Journal of Service Industry Management **[52516]***

International Journal of Services, Economics and Management (Wuhan, HU, CHN) **[43523]**

International Journal of Services Sciences (Geneva, SWI) **[51139]**

International Journal of Services Technology and Management (Tokyo, JPN) **[46848]**

International Journal of Shape Modeling (Genoa, ITA) **[46150]**

International Journal of Shipping and Transport Logistics (Hong Kong, CHN) **[43352]**

International Journal of Shoulder Surgery (Cape Town, SAF) **[50384]**

International Journal of Signal and Imaging Systems Engineering (Chalkis, GRC) **[44758]**

International Journal of Simulation and Process Modelling (Viseu, PRT) **[49814]**

International Journal of Six Sigma and Competitive Advantage (Olney, GBR) **[55832]**

International Journal of Social Computing and Cyber-Physical Systems (Geneva, SWI) **[51140]**

International Journal of Social Economics (Bradford, GBR) **[52487]**

International Journal of Social and Humanistic Computing (Stockholm, SWE) **[51021]**

International Journal of Social Network Mining (Tirana, ALB) **[41450]**

The International Journal of Social Psychiatry (London, GBR) *Unable to locate*

Numbers cited in bold after listings are entry numbers rather than page numbers.

Master Index

International Journal of Society Systems Science (Geneva, SWI) [51141]

International Journal of Sociology of the Family (New Delhi, DH, IND) [45585]

International Journal of the Sociology of Language (Berlin, GER) [44195]

International Journal of the Sociology of the Law [53694]*

International Journal of Sociology and Social Policy (Patrington, GBR) Unable to locate

International Journal of Soft Computing (Faisalabad, PAK) [49256]

International Journal on Software Tools for Technology Transfer (STTT) (Dortmund, GER) [44316]

International Journal of Space Structures (Brentwood, GBR) [52578]

International Journal of Speech, Language and the Law (London, GBR) [54662]

International Journal of Speech-Language Pathology (Abingdon, GBR) [51846]

International Journal of Speleology (Prague, CZE) [43626]

International Journal of Sport and Health Science (Tokyo, JPN) Unable to locate

International Journal of Sport Management and Marketing (Olney, GBR) [55833]

International Journal of Sports Physiology and Performance (Canberra, AC, AUS) [41708]

International Journal of Spray and Combustion Dynamics (Chennai, TN, IND) [45042]

International Journal of Statistics and Systems (New Delhi, DH, IND) [45586]

International Journal of STD and AIDS (London, GBR) [54663]

International Journal of Strategic Change Management (Oviedo, SPA) [50825]

International Journal of Strategic Engineering Asset Management (Stavange, NOR) [49213]

International Journal of Strategic Property Management (Warsaw, POL) [49720]

International Journal of Structural Engineering (Hangzhou, ZH, CHN) [43260]

International Journal of Structures (Roorkee, UP, IND) Unable to locate

International Journal of Sudan Research, Policy and Sustainable Development (Wad Medani, SDN) [50940]

International Journal of Surface Science & Engineering (Aveiro, PRT) [49789]

International Journal of Surgery (Singapore, SGP) [50193]

International Journal of Sustainability in Higher Education (Bradford, GBR) [52488]

International Journal of Sustainable Design (Bundoora, VI, AUS) [41671]

The International Journal of Sustainable Development & World Ecology (Carnforth, GBR) Unable to locate

International Journal of Sustainable Economy (Koper, SVA) [50332]

International Journal of Sustainable Manufacturing (Geneva, SWI) [51142]

International Journal of Sustainable Society (Geneva, SWI) [51143]

International Journal of Sustainable Strategic Management (Geneva, SWI) [51144]

International Journal of System Control and Information Processing (Shanghai, CHN) [43479]

International Journal of System Dynamics and Policy Planning (Kharagpur, WB, IND) Unable to locate

International Journal of Systematic Bacteriology [44386]*

International Journal of Systematic and Evolutionary Microbiology (Giessen, GER) [44386]

International Journal of Systems, Control and Communications (Dalian, CHN) [43252]

International Journal of Systems Science (Sheffield, GBR) [56502]

International Journal of Systems Signal Control and Engineering Application (Faisalabad, PAK) [49257]

International Journal of Teaching & Case Studies (Olney, GBR) [55834]

International Journal of Technoentrepreneurship (Singapore, SGP) [50194]

International Journal of Technological Learning, Innovation & Development (Rio de Janeiro, RJ, BRZ) [43009]

International Journal of Technology Enhanced Learning (Stockholm, SWE) [51022]

International Journal of Technology and Globalisation (Rome, ITA) [46235]

International Journal of Technology Intelligence and Planning (Olney, GBR) [55835]

International Journal of Technology Management (Geneva, SWI) Unable to locate

International Journal of Technology Management & Sustainable Development (London, GBR) [54664]

International Journal for Technology in Mathematics Education (Plymouth, GBR) [56271]

International Journal of Technology Policy and Law (Sydney, NW, AUS) [42521]

International Journal of Technology Policy and Management (Zurich, SWI) [51267]

International Journal of Technology Transfer and Commercialisation (Olney, GBR) [55836]

International Journal of Theoretical and Applied Computer Sciences (IJTACS) (New Delhi, DH, IND) [45587]

International Journal of Theoretical and Applied Mechanics (Daejeon, KOR) [47227]

International Journal of Therapy and Rehabilitation (IJTR) (London, GBR) [54665]

International Journal of Tomography and Statistics (Kanpur, UP, IND) [45236]

International Journal of Tourism Anthropology (Chengdu, SI, CHN) [43248]

International Journal of Tourism Policy (Patras, GRC) [44765]

International Journal of Trade and Global Markets (Messina, ITA) [46159]

International Journal of Transitions and Innovation Systems (Zagreb, CTA) [43568]

International Journal of Translation (New Delhi, DH, IND) Unable to locate

International Journal of Trichology (Chennai, TN, IND) [45043]

International Journal of Tropical Agriculture (Hissar, HY, IND) Unable to locate

International Journal of Tropical Agriculture and Food Systems (Grahamstown, SAF) [50499]

International Journal of Tropical Insect Science (Nairobi, KEN) [47185]

International Journal of Tropical Insect Science (Cambridge, GBR) [52838]

International Journal of Tropical Medicine (Faisalabad, PAK) [49258]

International Journal of Tropical Plant Diseases (New Delhi, DH, IND) Unable to locate

The International Journal of Tuberculosis and Lung Disease (Paris, FRA) [44057]

International Journal of Turbo and Jet Engines (Tel Aviv, ISR) [46105]

International Journal of Ultra Wideband Communications and Systems (Guwahati, AS, IND) [45130]

International Journal of Uncertainty, Fuzziness and Knowledge-Based Systems (Paris, FRA) [44058]

International Journal of Urban and Regional Research (Oxford, GBR) [56004]

International Journal of Value Chain Management (Taichung, TWN) [51321]

International Journal of Vehicle Autonomous Systems (Olney, GBR) [55837]

International Journal of Vehicle Design (Geneva, SWI) [51145]

International Journal of Vehicle Information & Communication System (Olney, GBR) [55838]

International Journal of Vehicle Performance (Geneva, SWI) [51146]

International Journal of Vehicle Systems Modelling and Testing (Seville, SPA) [50835]

The International Journal of Ventilation (Coventry, GBR) [53085]

International Journal of Virtual Technology and Multimedia (Olney, GBR) [55839]

International Journal of Water (Olney, GBR) [55840]

International Journal of Water Resources Development (Abingdon, GBR) [51847]

International Journal of Web-Based Communities (Enschede, NLD) [48595]

International Journal of Web Engineering and Technology (Stafford, GBR) [56592]

International Journal of Web and Grid Services (Clayton, VI, AUS) [41762]

International Journal of Web Information Systems (Bradford, GBR) [52489]

International Journal of Wine Business Research (IJWBR) (Kiel, GER) [44502]

International Journal of Wireless and Mobile Computing (Olney, GBR) [55841]

International Journal on Wireless &

Optical Communications (Singapore, SGP) [50195]

International Journal of Work Organisation & Emotion (Uxbridge, GBR) [56799]

International Journal of Yoga (Bangalore, KA, IND) [44964]

International Journal of Zoological Research (Faisalabad, PAK) Unable to locate

International Labour Review (Geneva, SWI) [51147]

International Law Reporter (New Delhi, DH, IND) Unable to locate

International Library Movement (Ambala, HY, IND) Unable to locate

International Library Movement (Ambala City, HY, IND) Unable to locate

International Life (Moscow, RUS) Unable to locate

The International Link (Brussels, BEL) Unable to locate

International Logistics Abstract (Bedford, GBR) Unable to locate

International Market Insight Reports (Makati City, PHL) Unable to locate

International Market Insight Trade Inquiries (Makati City, PHL) Unable to locate

International Marketing Review (Bradford, GBR) [52490]

International Mathematical Forum (Ruse, BUL) [43092]

International Mathematics Research Papers (Oxford, GBR) [56005]

International Medical Journal (Tokyo, JPN) Unable to locate

International Medical News (Tokyo, JPN) [46849]

International Microbiology (Barcelona, SPA) [50681]

International Money Marketing (London, GBR) Unable to locate

The International News (Rotkreuz, SWI) Unable to locate

International News Dancesport (Moscow, RUS) Unable to locate

International NGO Journal (Lagos, LG, NGA) [49138]

International Nursing Review (Geneva, SWI) [51148]

International Ocean Systems (Teddington, GBR) [56732]

International Ocean Systems Design [56732]*

International Organizations Law Review (Leiden, NLD) [48683]

International Packaging Abstracts [53752]*

International Peat Journal (Jyvaskyla, FIN) Unable to locate

International Pest Control (Burnham, GBR) [52766]

International Piano (London, GBR) [54666]

International Pig Topics (Driffield, GBR) [53205]

International Planning Studies (Abingdon, GBR) [51848]

International Plastics Engineering & Technology (New Delhi, DH, IND) Unable to locate

The International Political Science Review/Revue internationale de science politique (London, GBR) [54667]

International Post (New Delhi, DH, IND) Unable to locate

International Poster Journal of Dentistry and Oral Medicine (Mainz, GER) [44540]

International Poultry Production (Driffield, GBR) [53206]

Numbers cited in bold after listings are entry numbers rather than page numbers.

International Public Management Journal (Abingdon, GBR) [51849]

International Railway Statistics (Paris, FRA) [44059]

International Relations of the Asia-Pacific (Oxford, GBR) [56006]

International Rental News (Wadhurst, GBR) [56810]

International Reporter (New Delhi, DH, IND) Unable to locate

International Research in Children's Literature (Edinburgh, GBR) [53290]

International Research in Geography & Environment Education (Abingdon, GBR) [51850]

International Review of Administrative Sciences (London, GBR) [54668]

International Review of Applied Economics (Abingdon, GBR) [51851]

International Review of Applied Linguistics in Language Teaching (Berlin, GER) [44196]

International Review of the Armed Forces Medical Services (Brussels, BEL) [42860]

International Review of Economics Education (Bristol, GBR) [52680]

International Review of Education (Dordrecht, NLD) [48432]

International Review of Entrepreneurship (Dublin, DU, IRL) [45968]

International Review of Environmental and Resource Economics (Wageningen, DEN) [43738]

International Review of Fuzzy Mathematics (New Delhi, DH, IND) [45588]

International Review of Law Computers & Technology (Abingdon, GBR) [51852]

International Review of Mission (Geneva, SWI) [51149]

International Review of Pragmatics (Lodz, POL) [49670]

International Review of Psychiatry (Abingdon, GBR) [51853]

International Review of Pure and Applied Chemistry (New Delhi, DH, IND) [45589]

International Review of Pure and Applied Physics (Beijing, CHN) [43201]

The International Review of Retail, Distribution and Consumer Research (Stirling, GBR) [56623]

International Review of Social History (Cambridge, GBR) [52839]

International Review for the Sociology of Sport (London, GBR) [54669]

International Review of Victimology (Bicester, GBR) Unable to locate

International Reviews of Immunology (Abingdon, GBR) [51854]

International Reviews in Physical Chemistry (Durham, GBR) [53229]

International Rubber Digest [50248]*

International School (Woodbridge, GBR) [56956]

International Securities Finance (London, GBR) [54670]

International Securities Lending [54670]*

International Security Review (London, GBR) Unable to locate

International Seminars in Surgical Oncology (London, GBR) [54671]

International Shipbuilding Progress (Delft, NLD) [48310]

International Small Business Journal (Macclesfield, GBR) Unable to locate

International Social Science Journal (Paris, FRA) [44060]

International Social Work (London, GBR) [54672]

International Society of Applied Biology Biological Memoirs (Lucknow, UP, IND) Unable to locate

International Society of Plant Morphologists Yearbook (New Delhi, DH, IND) Unable to locate

International Sociology (London, GBR) [54673]

The International Spectator (Abingdon, GBR) [51855]

The International Sports Law Journal (The Hague, NLD) [48618]

International Sports Magazine (Budapest, HUN) [44838]

International Studies (New Delhi, DH, IND) Unable to locate

International Studies Quarterly (Oxford, GBR) [56007]

International Studies in Sociology of Education (Abingdon, GBR) [51856]

International Tax and Public Finance (Munich, GER) [44565]

International Tax Review (London, GBR) [54674]

International Textiles (Moscow, RUS) [49921]

International Trade Bulletin (Khartoum, SDN) Unable to locate

International Trade FORUM (Geneva, SWI) [51150]

International Trade Review (Mumbai, MH, IND) Unable to locate

International Travel Plan (Tokyo, JPN) Unable to locate

International Turfgrass Bulletin (Bingley, GBR) [52327]

International Understanding (New Delhi, DH, IND) Unable to locate

International Underwater Systems Design [56732]*

The International Veterinary Student (Frederiksberg, DEN) [43691]

International Wood Products Journal (London, GBR) [54675]

International Work Camps (Stuttgart, GER) Unable to locate

Internationale Politik (Bonn, GER) Unable to locate

Internationales Archiv fur Sozialgeschichte der deutschen Literatur (Berlin, GER) [44197]

Internationales Jahrbuch des Deutschen Idealismus (Berlin, GER) [44198]

Internationales Waffen Magazin [51232]*

Internationella Studier (Stockholm, SWE) Unable to locate

Inter.Net (Vigano di Gaggiano, ITA) Unable to locate

Internet Business News (Bath, GBR) [52245]

Internet Investor (Bath, GBR) Unable to locate

Internet Journal of Medical Update (Curepipe, MUS) [47752]

Internet Magazine (Mount Lawley, WA, AUS) Unable to locate

Internet Magazine (London, GBR) Unable to locate

Internet Monthly (Coventry, GBR) Unable to locate

Internet Research (Bradford, GBR) [52491]

Internetworld (Stockholm, SWE) Unable to locate

Interpreter and Translator Trainer (Manchester, GBR) [55561]

Interpreting (Amsterdam, NLD) [48033]

Interreligious Insight (London, GBR) [54676]

Intersections (Murdoch, WA, AUS) [42137]

Interspectives (Newcastle upon Tyne, GBR) [55673]

Intervention Research (Amsterdam, NLD) [48034]

Interventions (Abingdon, GBR) [51857]

Interviewer (London, GBR) Unable to locate

Intervolna (Chelyabinsk, RUS) Unable to locate

Intervolna (Chelyabinsk, RUS) Unable to locate

Interzone (Brighton, GBR) Unable to locate

Intra (London, GBR) Ceased

Intramuros (Paris, FRA) [44061]

Intramuros (Madrid, SPA) [50774]

Invention & Innovation (Beijing, CHN) Unable to locate

Invention Intelligence (New Delhi, DH, IND) [45590]

Inventiones Mathematicae (Orsay, FRA) [44019]

Inventiva (Lisbon, PRT) Unable to locate

Inventor and Rationalizer (Moscow, RUS) Unable to locate

Inventos (Barcelona, SPA) Unable to locate

Inverness Courier Series (Inverness, GBR) Unable to locate

Inverse Problems (London, GBR) [54677]

Inversion (Madrid, SPA) Unable to locate

Invertebrate Neuroscience (Dordrecht, NLD) [48433]

Invertebrate Survival Journal (ISJ) (Modena, ITA) [46199]

Invertebrate Systematics (Collingwood, VI, AUS) [41791]

Inverurie Herald (Inverurie, GBR) [53649]

Invest Today (Christchurch, NZL) Unable to locate

Investigacion y Tecnica del Papel (Madrid, SPA) Unable to locate

Investment Management & Financial Innovations (Sumy, URE) [51617]

Investment & Marketing (Karachi, PAK) Unable to locate

Investment Now (Kempston, GBR) [53668]

Investment & Pensions Europe (IPE) (London, GBR) [54678]

Investment Week (London, GBR) [54679]

The Investor (Mumbai, MH, IND) Unable to locate

Investor (Bangkok, THA) Unable to locate

Investor's Business & Financial Journal (Karachi, PAK) [49356]

Investors Chronicle (London, GBR) [54680]

Investors Digest Magazine (Kuala Lumpur, MYS) Unable to locate

Investor's Guide to Singapore (Singapore, SGP) [50196]

Invicta-FM [56921]*

IOM Latin American Migration Journal (Geneva, SWI) Unable to locate

Ionics (Dordrecht, NLD) [48434]

Ionizing Radiation (Tokyo, JPN) [46850]

IOS Bulletin (Zurich, SWI) [51268]

Iota Magazine (Matlock, GBR) [55603]

IPA Magazine (London, GBR) Unable to locate

IPEN Journal (Rio de Janeiro, RJ, BRZ) Unable to locate

Ipertensione (Milan, ITA) [46178]

IPIRI Journal (Bangalore, KA, IND) Unable to locate

IPM Magazine (Turrialba, CRI) Unable to locate

Ipmark (Madrid, SPA) [50775]

Ippologia (Cremona, ITA) [46136]

IPSS Bulletin (Calcutta, WB, IND) Unable to locate

The Ipswich Advertiser (Sydney, NW, AUS) [42522]

Ipswich News (North Ipswich, QL, AUS) [42155]

IQ (Vienna, AUT) Unable to locate

IQ Magazine (London, GBR) [54681]

Iqbal Review (Lahore, PAK) Unable to locate

IR (Moscow, RUS) Unable to locate

Iran (Tehran, IRN) [45891]

Iran Agricultural Research (Shiraz, IRN) Unable to locate

Iran and the Caucasus (Leiden, NLD) [48684]

Iran Exports & Imports (Tehran, IRN) [45892]

Iran News (Tehran, IRN) [45893]

Iran Oil Journal (Tehran, IRN) Unable to locate

Iran Weekly Press Digest (Tehran, IRN) [45894]

Iranian Biomedical Journal (Tehran, IRN) [45895]

Iranian Economic Review (Tehran, IRN) [45896]

Iranian Journal of Agricultural Research (Shiraz, IRN) Unable to locate

Iranian Journal of Allergy, Asthma and Immunology (Tehran, IRN) [45897]

Iranian Journal of Biotechnology (IJB) (Tehran, IRN) [45898]

Iranian Journal of Botany (Tehran, IRN) Unable to locate

Iranian Journal of Chemistry and Chemical Engineering (Tehran, IRN) [45899]

Iranian Journal of Electrical and Computer Engineering (Tehran, IRN) [45900]

Iranian Journal of Endocrinology and Metabolism (Tehran, IRN) [45901]

Iranian Journal of Environmental Health Science & Engineering (Tehran, IRN) [45902]

Iranian Journal of Fisheries Science (Tehran, IRN) [45903]

Iranian Journal of International Affairs (Tehran, IRN) Unable to locate

Iranian Journal of Medical Sciences (Shiraz, IRN) [45883]

Iranian Journal of Nuclear Medicine (Tehran, IRN) [45904]

Iranian Journal of Pediatrics (Tehran, IRN) [45905]

Iranian Journal of Pharmaceutical Research (Tehran, IRN) [45906]

Iranian Journal of Pharmacology and Therapeutics (Tehran, IRN) [45907]

Iranian Journal of Plant Pathology (Tehran, IRN) Unable to locate

Iranian Journal of Public Health (Tehran, IRN) [45908]

Iranian Journal of Radiology (Tehran, IRN) [45909]

Iranian Journal of Science and Technology (Shiraz, IRN) [45884]

Iranian Polymer Journal (Tehran, IRN) [45910]

Numbers cited in bold after listings are entry numbers rather than page numbers.

Iranian Review of International Relations (Tehran, IRN) *Unable to locate*

Iranian Studies (Abingdon, GBR) **[51858]**

Iranica Antiqua (Leuven, BEL) **[42899]**

Iraq News Bulletin (New Delhi, DH, IND) *Unable to locate*

Ireland on Sunday (Dublin, DU, IRL) *Unable to locate*

Ireland at Your Leisure (Dublin, DU, IRL) **[45969]**

Iren (Moscow, RUS) **[49922]**

Irish Architectural and Decorative Studies (Dublin, DU, IRL) **[45970]**

Irish Archives (Dublin, DU, IRL) **[45971]**

Irish Chemical News (Dublin, DU, IRL) **[45972]**

Irish Criminal Law Journal (Blackrock, IRL) *Unable to locate*

Irish Dancing & Culture (Bristol, GBR) **[52681]**

Irish Democrat (London, GBR) **[54682]**

Irish Dentist (Belfast, GBR) *Unable to locate*

Irish Examiner (Cork, CK, IRL) **[45937]**

Irish Family History Journal (Naas, KL, IRL) **[46042]**

Irish Folk Music Studies (Dublin, DU, IRL) **[45973]**

The Irish Genealogist (Gillingham, GBR) **[53408]**

Irish Geography (Dublin, DU, IRL) **[45974]**

Irish Hardware (Blackrock, DU, IRL) **[45921]**

Irish Journal of American Studies (Maynooth, KL, IRL) **[46038]**

Irish Journal of Education (Dublin, DU, IRL) **[45975]**

The Irish Journal of French Studies (Dublin, DU, IRL) **[45976]**

Irish Journal of Medical Science (Dublin, DU, IRL) **[45977]**

Irish Journal of Psychological Medicine (Dublin, DU, IRL) **[45978]**

Irish Jurist (Blackrock, IRL) *Unable to locate*

Irish Kitchens and Bathrooms (Dublin, DU, IRL) **[45979]**

The Irish Law Times and Solicitors' Journal (Blackrock, IRL) *Unable to locate*

Irish Medical Journal (Dublin, DU, IRL) **[45980]**

Irish Medical News (Dundrum, DU, IRL) **[46009]**

Irish Mountain Log (Dublin, DU, IRL) **[45981]**

Irish Pages (Belfast, GBR) **[52287]**

Irish Pharmachem Industry Buyers' Guide (Dublin, DU, IRL) **[45982]**

Irish Pharmacist (Dublin, DU, IRL) **[45983]**

Irish Political Studies (Abingdon, GBR) **[51859]**

The Irish Post (Hayes, GBR) *Unable to locate*

Irish Printer (Blackrock, DU, IRL) **[45922]**

Irish Psychiatrist (Dublin, DU, IRL) **[45984]**

Irish Studies in International Affairs (Dublin, DU, IRL) **[45985]**

Irish Studies Review (Abingdon, GBR) **[51860]**

Irish Sword (Dublin, DU, IRL) **[45986]**

Irish Tatler (Dublin, DU, IRL) **[45987]**

Irish Times (Dublin, DU, IRL) **[45988]**

Iron & Steel Journal of India (Mumbai, MH, IND) *Ceased*

Ironmaking & Steelmaking (London, GBR) **[54683]**

Irrigation and Drainage (New Delhi, DH, IND) **[45591]**

Irrigation News **[56427]***

Irrigation and Water Resources (Tullamarine, VI, AUS) **[42652]**

IRS Employment Review (Croydon, GBR) **[53127]**

is (Woodbridge, GBR) **[56957]**

ISESnews (Ware, GBR) **[56841]**

Ishem-FM - 95.4 MHz (Durres, ALB) **[41431]**

ISIJ International (Tokyo, JPN) **[46851]**

Isis Town & Country (Sydney, NW, AUS) **[42523]**

Islam and Christian-Muslim Relations (Abingdon, GBR) **[51861]**

Islam and the Modern Age (New Delhi, DH, IND) **[45592]**

Islamabad Journal of Sciences (Islamabad, PAK) *Unable to locate*

Islamic Capitals and Cities Magazine (Jeddah, SAU) **[50056]**

Islamic Culture (Hyderabad, AP, IND) *Unable to locate*

Islamic Economic Studies (Jeddah, SAU) *Unable to locate*

Islamic Education (Lahore, PAK) *Unable to locate*

Islamic Law and Society (Leiden, NLD) **[48685]**

Islamic Republic of Iran Broadcasting - Abadan (Tehran, IRN) *Unable to locate*

Islamic Republic of Iran Broadcasting - Ahwaz (Tehran, IRN) *Unable to locate*

Islamic Republic of Iran Broadcasting - Arak (Tehran, IRN) *Unable to locate*

Islamic Republic of Iran Broadcasting - Ardabil (Tehran, IRN) *Unable to locate*

Islamic Republic of Iran Broadcasting - Bam (Tehran, IRN) *Unable to locate*

Islamic Republic of Iran Broadcasting - Birjand (Tehran, IRN) *Unable to locate*

Islamic Republic of Iran Broadcasting - Bonab (Tehran, IRN) *Unable to locate*

Islamic Republic of Iran Broadcasting - Bushehr (Tehran, IRN) *Unable to locate*

Islamic Republic of Iran Broadcasting - Damghan (Tehran, IRN) *Unable to locate*

Islamic Republic of Iran Broadcasting - Esfahan (Tehran, IRN) *Unable to locate*

Islamic Republic of Iran Broadcasting - Esfahan (Tehran, IRN) *Unable to locate*

Islamic Republic of Iran Broadcasting - Gheslagh (Tehran, IRN) *Unable to locate*

Islamic Republic of Iran Broadcasting - Ilam (Tehran, IRN) *Unable to locate*

Islamic Republic of Iran Broadcasting - Iranshahr (Tehran, IRN) *Unable to locate*

Islamic Republic of Iran Broadcasting - Jiroft (Tehran, IRN) *Unable to locate*

Islamic Republic of Iran Broadcasting - Jolfa (Tehran, IRN) *Unable to locate*

Islamic Republic of Iran Broadcasting - Kermanshah (Tehran, IRN) *Unable to locate*

Islamic Republic of Iran Broadcasting - Kermanshah (Tehran, IRN) *Unable to locate*

Islamic Republic of Iran Broadcasting - Khorramabad (Tehran, IRN) *Unable to locate*

Islamic Republic of Iran Broadcasting - Kiashahr (Tehran, IRN) *Unable to locate*

Islamic Republic of Iran Broadcasting - Mahabad (Tehran, IRN) *Unable to locate*

Islamic Republic of Iran Broadcasting - Marivan (Tehran, IRN) *Unable to locate*

Islamic Republic of Iran Broadcasting - Mashhad (Tehran, IRN) *Unable to locate*

Islamic Republic of Iran Broadcasting - Mashhad (Tehran, IRN) *Unable to locate*

Islamic Republic of Iran Broadcasting - Sanandaj (Tehran, IRN) *Unable to locate*

Islamic Republic of Iran Broadcasting - Sanandaj (Tehran, IRN) *Unable to locate*

Islamic Republic of Iran Broadcasting - Saravan (Tehran, IRN) *Unable to locate*

Islamic Republic of Iran Broadcasting - Sari (Tehran, IRN) *Unable to locate*

Islamic Republic of Iran Broadcasting - Semnan (Tehran, IRN) *Unable to locate*

Islamic Republic of Iran Broadcasting - Shiraz (Tehran, IRN) *Unable to locate*

Islamic Republic of Iran Broadcasting - Sirjan (Tehran, IRN) *Unable to locate*

Islamic Republic of Iran Broadcasting - Tabriz (Tehran, IRN) *Unable to locate*

Islamic Republic of Iran Broadcasting - Tabriz (Tehran, IRN) *Unable to locate*

Islamic Republic of Iran Broadcasting - Tayebad (Tehran, IRN) *Unable to locate*

Islamic Republic of Iran Broadcasting - Tehran (Tehran, IRN) *Unable to locate*

Islamic Republic of Iran Broadcasting - Tehran (Tehran, IRN) *Unable to locate*

Islamic Republic of Iran Broadcasting - Tehran (Tehran, IRN) *Unable to locate*

Islamic Republic of Iran Broadcasting - Tehran (Tehran, IRN) *Unable to locate*

Islamic Republic of Iran Broadcasting - Tehran (Tehran, IRN) *Unable to locate*

Islamic Republic of Iran Broadcasting - Urumiyeh (Tehran, IRN) *Unable to locate*

Islamic Republic of Iran Broadcasting - Yasuj (Tehran, IRN) *Unable to locate*

Islamic Republic of Iran Broadcasting - Yasuj (Tehran, IRN) *Unable to locate*

Islamic Republic of Iran Broadcasting - Yazd (Tehran, IRN) *Unable to locate*

Islamic Republic of Iran Broadcasting - Zabol (Tehran, IRN) *Unable to locate*

Islamic Republic of Iran Broadcasting - Zahedan (Tehran, IRN) *Unable to locate*

Islamic Republic of Iran Television-Network I (Tehran, IRN) *Unable to locate*

Islamic Republic of Iran Television - Network II (Tehran, IRN) *Unable to locate*

Islamic Republic of Iran Television - Network III (Tehran, IRN) *Unable to locate*

The Islamic Times (Mumbai, MH, IND) *Unable to locate*

Islamic World Medical Journal (Jeddah, SAU) *Unable to locate*

Islamskaya Volna (Moscow, RUS) *Unable to locate*

Islamskaya Volna (Moscow, RUS) *Unable to locate*

Island (Mumbai, MH, IND) *Unable to locate*

Island Connections (Tenerife, SPA) **[50836]**

Island-FM - 93.7 (Aldemey, GBR) **[52096]**

Island-FM - 104.7 (Guernsey, GBR) **[53488]**

Island-FM - 104.7 (Saint Sampsons, GBR) **[56448]**

Island & Mainland News (Sydney, NW, AUS) **[42524]**

Island Studies in Okinawa (Okinawa, JPN) *Unable to locate*

The Island Sun (Road Town, BVI) **[43068]**

The Islander (Ascension Island, GBR) **[52136]**

Isle of Wight Radio-FM - 102 (Newport, GBR) **[55692]**

Isle of Wight Radio-FM - 107 (Newport, GBR) **[55691]**

Isles-FM - 103 (Stornoway, GBR) **[56638]**

Islington Gazette (EC1 Edition) (London, GBR) **[54684]**

ISO News (Louvain, BEL) *Unable to locate*

Isokinetics and Exercise Science (Tel Aviv, ISR) **[46106]**

Isotopes in Environmental and Health Studies (Abingdon, GBR) **[51862]**

ISPE Magazine (Norwich, GBR) *Unable to locate*

ISPRS Journal of Photogrammetry and Remote Sensing (Enschede, NLD) **[48596]**

ISPT Journal of Research in Educational & Psychological Testing & Measurement (Dehradun, UP, IND) *Unable to locate*

ISPT Quarterly Bulletin (Dehradun, UP, IND) *Unable to locate*

Israel Affairs (Abingdon, GBR) **[51863]**

Israel Business Today (Tel Aviv, ISR) *Unable to locate*

Israel Exploration Journal (Jerusalem, ISR) **[46085]**

Israel Journal of Veterinary Medicine (Raanana, ISR) **[46090]**

Israel Medical Association Journal (IMAJ) (Ramat Gan, ISR) **[46094]**

ISRM News Journal (Lisbon, PRT) **[49803]**

The ISSM Journal (Kingston upon Thames, GBR) *Unable to locate*

ISSUE (Walsall, GBR) *Unable to locate*

Issues (Sydney, NW, AUS) **[42525]**

Issues of Business and Law (Warsaw, POL) **[49721]**

Istanbul Polis Radyosu (Istanbul, TUR) *Unable to locate*

Numbers cited in bold after listings are entry numbers rather than page numbers.

Isveren (Ankara, TUR) *Unable to locate*

IT Asia (Singapore, SGP) *Unable to locate*

I.T. Matters (Quezon City, PHL) **[49596]**

IT News (Islamabad, PAK) *Unable to locate*

IT Service Magazine (Alphen aan den Rijn, NLD) **[47868]**

IT-Solutions.lu (Luxembourg, LUX) *Unable to locate*

Italia! (Bath, GBR) **[52246]**

Italia Turistica (Padua, ITA) **[46206]**

Italian Food Machines (Milan, ITA) **[46179]**

Italian Heart Journal (Rome, ITA) *Unable to locate*

Italian Journal of Anatomy and Embriology (Florence, ITA) *Unable to locate*

Italian Journal of Oral Implantology **[46131]***

Italian Magazine Food Processing (Milan, ITA) **[46180]**

Italian Studies (Manchester, GBR) **[55562]**

The Italianist (London, GBR) **[54685]**

Italy Down Under (Melbourne, VI, AUS) **[42068]**

Itapua-FM - 102.5 (Encarnacion, PAR) **[49411]**

ITBM - RBM (Singapore, SGP) **[50197]**

ITC Journal **[48593]***

ITF World (London, GBR) **[54686]**

Itihas (Hyderabad, AP, IND) *Unable to locate*

ITN News Direct-FM **[55453]***

ITNOW (Swindon, GBR) **[56712]**

ITR **[45037]***

It's All About Living (Dublin, DU, IRL) **[45989]**

ITS International (Swanley, GBR) **[56697]**

ITU News (Geneva, SWI) **[51151]**

I.T.U. Radyo-FM - 103.8 (Istanbul, TUR) **[51567]**

IUBMB Life (Abingdon, GBR) **[51864]**

IUR-FM - 101.4 (Newry, GBR) **[55697]**

Ivel-FM - 105.6 (Yeovil, GBR) **[56984]**

Ivel-FM - 106.6 (Yeovil, GBR) **[56985]**

IWF Handbook (Budapest, HUN) **[44839]**

iWorld (Madrid, SPA) **[50776]**

iX (Hannover, GER) **[44433]**

Izkustvi/Art in Bulgaria (Sofia, BUL) *Unable to locate*

Izvestiya (Moscow, RUS) **[49923]**

Izvestiya, Atmospheric and Oceanic Physics (Moscow, RUS) **[49924]**

Izvestiya, Physics of the Solid Earth (Moscow, RUS) **[49925]**

J

J & K Research Biannual (Srinagar, JK, IND) *Unable to locate*

J-Mag (Saint Gallen, SWI) *Unable to locate*

Jaarboek (Gent, BEL) **[42883]**

Jabalpur Law Journal (Gwalior, MP, IND) *Unable to locate*

Jacaranda-FM - 94.2 (Centurion, SAF) **[50458]**

Jacket (Balmain, NW, AUS) **[41573]**

Jackie Chan Adventures (London, GBR) **[54687]**

Jacob Journal (Burton-on-Trent, GBR) *Unable to locate*

The Jacobite (Fort William, GBR) *Unable to locate*

Jadavpur Journal of Comparative Literature (Calcutta, WB, IND) *Unable to locate*

Jaffna Medical Journal (Jaffna, SRI) *Unable to locate*

The Jag Mag (Mansfield, QL, AUS) **[42033]**

The Jaguar Magazine **[42033]***

Jaguar World Monthly (Cudham, GBR) **[53143]**

Jahrbuch fur Wissenschaft und Ethik (Berlin, GER) **[44199]**

Jahresbericht (Bern, SWI) *Unable to locate*

Jahresprogramm (Weikersheim, GER) *Unable to locate*

Jain Journal (Calcutta, WB, IND) *Unable to locate*

The Jakarta Post (Jakarta, IDN) **[45801]**

Jakin (Donostia, SPA) *Unable to locate*

JAM-FM (Pasig City, PHL) *Unable to locate*

Jamaica Journal of Science and Technology (Kingston, JAM) **[46286]**

The Jamaica Observer (Kingston, JAM) **[46287]**

Jamaican Exporter (Kingston, JAM) *Unable to locate*

James Cook University Law Review (Townsville, QL, AUS) **[42636]**

Jammu and Kashmir Directorate of Economics and Statistics Digest of Statistics (Jaipur, RJ, IND) *Unable to locate*

Jammu and Kashmir Law Reporter (Srinagar, JK, IND) **[45738]**

Jamsides (Stockholm, SWE) **[51023]**

Janata (Mumbai, MH, IND) *Unable to locate*

Jane's Airport Review (Coulsdon, GBR) **[53067]**

Jane's Asian Infrastructure Monthly (Coulsdon, GBR) *Ceased*

Jane's Defence Weekly (Coulsdon, GBR) **[53068]**

Jane's Intelligence Review (Coulsdon, GBR) **[53069]**

Jane's International Defense Review (Coulsdon, GBR) **[53070]**

Jane's International Police Review (Coulsdon, GBR) *Ceased*

Jane's Navy International (Coulsdon, GBR) **[53071]**

Jane's Police Review (Coulsdon, GBR) **[53072]**

Jane's Simulation & Training Systems (Coulsdon, GBR) **[53073]**

Jane's Transport Finance (Coulsdon, GBR) **[53074]**

Jangan (Jodhpur, RJ, IND) *Unable to locate*

Jantar Mantar (Chennai, TN, IND) **[45044]**

Japan Architect (Tokyo, JPN) **[46852]**

Japan Automotive News (Tokyo, JPN) **[46853]**

Japan Camera Trade News (Tokyo, JPN) *Ceased*

Japan Chemical Fibres Monthly (Tokyo, JPN) *Ceased*

Japan Chemical Week (Tokyo, JPN) **[46854]**

Japan Echo (Tokyo, JPN) **[46855]**

Japan Forum (Abingdon, GBR) **[51865]**

Japan Graphic Arts (Tokyo, JPN) *Unable to locate*

Japan Harvest (Tokyo, JPN) **[46856]**

Japan Heterocerists Journal (Tokyo, JPN) **[46857]**

Japan Insurance News (Tokyo, JPN) *Unable to locate*

Japan International Journal (Tokyo, JPN) *Unable to locate*

Japan Labor Review (Tokyo, JPN) **[46858]**

Japan Law Journal (Tokyo, JPN) *Unable to locate*

Japan Marketing Data (Tokyo, JPN) *Unable to locate*

Japan Mission Journal (Tokyo, JPN) **[46859]**

Japan Quarterly (Tokyo, JPN) *Unable to locate*

Japan Racing Journal (Tokyo, JPN) **[46860]**

The Japan Times (Tokyo, JPN) **[46861]**

Japan 21st (Tokyo, JPN) *Unable to locate*

Japan and the World Economy (Amsterdam, NLD) **[48035]**

Japanese Cars Banzai (Sevenoaks, GBR) **[56475]**

Japanese Circulation Journal (Kyoto, JPN) **[46473]**

The Japanese Economic Review (Oxford, GBR) **[56008]**

Japanese Economy & Labor Series (Tokyo, JPN) *Unable to locate*

Japanese Heart Journal (Bussum, NLD) **[48303]**

The Japanese Journal of American Studies (Tokyo, JPN) **[46862]**

Japanese Journal of Animal Psychology (Tokyo, JPN) **[46863]**

Japanese Journal of Applied Physics (Tokyo, JPN) **[46864]**

Japanese Journal of Bacteriology (Tokyo, JPN) **[46865]**

Japanese Journal of Behavior Therapy (Ibaraki, JPN) *Unable to locate*

Japanese Journal of Biofeedback Research (Tokyo, JPN) *Unable to locate*

Japanese Journal of Biometeorology (Nagoya, JPN) *Unable to locate*

Japanese Journal of Biometrics (Tokyo, JPN) **[46866]**

Japanese Journal of Breast Cancer (Tokyo, JPN) **[46867]**

Japanese Journal of Chemotherapy (Tokyo, JPN) *Unable to locate*

Japanese Journal of Clinical and Experimental Medicine (Fukuoka, JPN) *Unable to locate*

Japanese Journal of Clinical Oncology (Oxford, GBR) **[56009]**

Japanese Journal of Crop Science (Tokyo, JPN) **[46868]**

Japanese Journal of Environment, Entomology and Zoology (Osaka, JPN) **[46618]**

Japanese Journal of Health and Human Ecology (Tokyo, JPN) *Unable to locate*

Japanese Journal of Hygiene (Tokyo, JPN) *Unable to locate*

Japanese Journal of Infectious Diseases (Tokyo, JPN) **[46869]**

Japanese Journal of Limnology **[46961]***

Japanese Journal of Lymphology (Tokyo, JPN) *Unable to locate*

Japanese Journal of Mathematics (Tokyo, JPN) **[46870]**

Japanese Journal of Medical Imaging and Information Sciences (Kyoto, JPN) *Unable to locate*

Japanese Journal of Medical Mycology (Tokyo, JPN) **[46871]**

Japanese Journal of Nematology (Tsukuba, JPN) **[47111]**

Japanese Journal of Obstetrical, Gynecological and Neonatal Hematology (Shizuoka, JPN) *Unable to locate*

Japanese Journal of Ophthalmology (Tokyo, JPN) **[46872]**

Japanese Journal of Optics (Tokyo, JPN) *Unable to locate*

Japanese Journal of Ornithology (Tokyo, JPN) **[46873]**

The Japanese Journal of Pharmacology **[46478]***

Japanese Journal of Physical Fitness (Tokyo, JPN) *Unable to locate*

Japanese Journal of Physiology (Tokyo, JPN) **[46874]**

Japanese Journal of Radiological Technology (Kyoto, JPN) **[46474]**

Japanese Journal of Religious Studies (Nagoya, JPN) **[46553]**

Japanese Journal of Rheumatism and Joint Surgery (Shiga, JPN) **[46682]**

Japanese Journal of Sanitary Zoology (Tokyo, JPN) *Unable to locate*

Japanese Journal of Toxicology (Tokyo, JPN) *Unable to locate*

Japanese Journal of Tropical Medicine and Hygiene (Nagasaki, JPN) *Unable to locate*

Japanese Journal of Veterinary Research (Sapporo, JPN) **[46651]**

Japanese Performance (Surrey, GBR) **[56667]**

Japanese Poultry Science (Ibaraki, JPN) *Unable to locate*

Japanese Prints (Amsterdam, NLD) *Unable to locate*

Japanese Progress in Climatology (Tokyo, JPN) *Unable to locate*

Japanese Religions (Kyoto, JPN) **[46475]**

Japanese Studies (Abingdon, GBR) **[51866]**

Japan's Iron and Steel Industry (Tokyo, JPN) *Unable to locate*

Japanscan Food Industry Bulletin (Stratford-on-Avon, GBR) *Unable to locate*

Japanzine (Nagoya/Chubu) (Tokyo, JPN) *Unable to locate*

Japanzine (Osaka/Kansai) (Nagoya, JPN) *Unable to locate*

Japanzine (Tokyo/Kanto) (Tokyo, JPN) *Unable to locate*

Jaslok Hospital & Research Centre Bulletin (Mumbai, MH, IND) *Unable to locate*

JASSA: the Journal of the Securities Institute of Australia (Sydney, NW, AUS) *Unable to locate*

Jautomatise (Nanterre, FRA) *Unable to locate*

JAUW (Tokyo, JPN) **[46875]**

Jawaharlal Nehru University School of International Studies Series (New Delhi, DH, IND) *Unable to locate*

Jazz - 865 (Kuala Lumpur, MYS) **[47650]**

Jazz-FM - 104.0 (Sofia, BUL) **[43109]**

Jazz-FM (London, GBR) *Unable to locate*

Jazz Perspectives (Abingdon, GBR) **[51867]**

Jazz Radio Ltd-FM - 94.1 (Sanctuary Cove, QL, AUS) **[42348]**

Jazz Research Journal (London, GBR) **[54688]**

Jazz Special (Copenhagen, DEN) **[43676]**

Jazz UK (London, GBR) **[54689]**

Jazzwise Magazine (London, GBR) **[54690]**

Numbers cited in bold after listings are entry numbers rather than page numbers.

Master Index

JBICR [45593]*

JCA Forecast (Singapore, SGP) Unable to locate

JCMS: Journal of Common Market Studies (Oxford, GBR) [56010]

JD (Turin, ITA) Ceased

Jee (Mumbai, MH, IND) Unable to locate

Jeevak (Barnalla, PJ, IND) Unable to locate

Jeevan Jauban (Calcutta, WB, IND) Unable to locate

JEOL News: Analytical Instrumentation (Tokyo, JPN) Unable to locate

JEOL News: Electron Optics Instrumentation (Tokyo, JPN) Unable to locate

Jersey Evening Post (Jersey, GBR) [53666]

Jerseybladet (Arhus, DEN) Unable to locate

Jerusalem Magazine (Jerusalem, ISR) [46086]

Jessica Macdermott [54282]*

Jesus (Rome, ITA) [46236]

Jesus Maestro (Rome, ITA) Unable to locate

Jet Skier & PW Magazine (Cambridge, GBR) [52840]

The Jetix Magazine (Dordrecht, NLD) [48435]

Jetset (Mumbai, MH, IND) Unable to locate

Jeunes Agriculteurs (Paris, FRA) [44062]

Jeunes en Mouvement (Brussels, BEL) [42861]

Jewellery Time (Christchurch, NZL) [48870]

Jewish Affairs (Houghton, SAF) [50524]

Jewish Intelligence [53382]*

The Jewish Lawyer (Tel-Aviv, ISR) Unable to locate

Jewish Quarterly (London, GBR) [54691]

Jewish Renaissance (London, GBR) [54692]

Jewish Studies, an Internet Journal (Ramat Gan, ISR) [46095]

Jewish Youth Work (Victoria, GBR) Unable to locate

Jiamusi People's Broadcasting Station (Jiamusi, HL, CHN) Unable to locate

Jiamusi People's Broadcasting Station (Jiamusi, HL, CHN) Unable to locate

Jiamusi People's Broadcasting Station (Jiamusi, HL, CHN) Unable to locate

Jiamusi People's Broadcasting Station (Jiamusi, HL, CHN) Unable to locate

Ji'an Diqu People's Broadcasting Station (Ji'an, JX, CHN) Unable to locate

Ji'an Diqu People's Broadcasting Station (Ji'an, JX, CHN) Unable to locate

Jiangmen People's Broadcasting Station (Jiangmen, GD, CHN) Unable to locate

Jiangshan People's Broadcasting Station (Jiangshan, ZH, CHN) Unable to locate

Jiangsu People's Broadcasting Station (Nanjing, JS, CHN) Unable to locate

Jiangsu People's Broadcasting Station (Nanjing, JS, CHN) Unable to locate

Jiangsu People's Broadcasting Station (Nanjing, JS, CHN) Unable to locate

Jiangsu People's Broadcasting Station (Nanjing, JS, CHN) Unable to locate

Jiangsu People's Broadcasting Station (Nanjing, JS, CHN) Unable to locate

Jiangsu People's Broadcasting Station (Nanjing, JS, CHN) Unable to locate

Jiangsu People's Broadcasting Station (Nanjing, JS, CHN) Unable to locate

Jiangsu People's Broadcasting Station (Nanjing, JS, CHN) Unable to locate

Jiangsu People's Broadcasting Station (Nanjing, JS, CHN) Unable to locate

Jiangxi People's Broadcasting Station (Nanchang, JX, CHN) Unable to locate

Jiangxi People's Broadcasting Station (Nanchang, JX, CHN) Unable to locate

Jiangxi People's Broadcasting Station (Nanchang, JX, CHN) Unable to locate

Jiangxi People's Broadcasting Station (Nanchang, JX, CHN) Unable to locate

Jiangxi People's Broadcasting Station 1 (Nanchang, JX, CHN) Unable to locate

Jiangxi People's Broadcasting Station 1 (Nanchang, JX, CHN) Unable to locate

Jiangxi People's Broadcasting Station 1 (Nanchang, JX, CHN) Unable to locate

Jiangyin People's Broadcasting Station (Jiangyin, JS, CHN) Unable to locate

Jiaozuo People's Broadcasting Station (Jiaozuo, HN, CHN) Unable to locate

Jiaxing People's Broadcasting Station (Jiaxing, ZH, CHN) Unable to locate

Jiaxing People's Broadcasting Station (Jiaxing, ZH, CHN) Unable to locate

Jiaxing People's Broadcasting Station (Jiaxing, ZH, CHN) Unable to locate

Jiaxing People's Broadcasting Station (Jiaxing, ZH, CHN) Unable to locate

Jiaxing People's Broadcasting Station (Jiaxing, ZH, CHN) Unable to locate

Jiayuguan People's Broadcasting Station (Jiayuguan, GS, CHN) Unable to locate

Jiazhou People's Broadcasting Station (Leshan, SI, CHN) Unable to locate

Jiipee (Partaharju, FIN) Unable to locate

Jijnasa (Jaipur, RJ, IND) Unable to locate

Jikeikai Medical Journal (Tokyo, JPN) [46876]

Jilin People's Broadcasting Station (Changchun, JI, CHN) Unable to locate

Jilin People's Broadcasting Station (Changchun, JI, CHN) Unable to locate

Jilin People's Broadcasting Station (Changchun, JI, CHN) Unable to locate

Jilin People's Broadcasting Station (Changchun, JI, CHN) Unable to locate

Jilin People's Broadcasting Station (Changchun, JI, CHN) Unable to locate

Jilin-shi People's Broadcasting Station (Jilin-shi, JI, CHN) Unable to locate

Jilin-shi People's Broadcasting Station (Jilin-shi, JI, CHN) Unable to locate

Jilin-shi People's Broadcasting Station (Jilin-shi, JI, CHN) Unable to locate

Jilin-shi People's Broadcasting Station (Jilin-shi, JI, CHN) Unable to locate

Jilin Television (Changchun, JI, CHN) Unable to locate

Jilin Television - Channel 19 (Changchun, JI, CHN) [43245]

Jilin University Journal Social Sciences Edition (Changchun, JI, CHN) [43239]

Jimi Hendrix Magazine (Warrington, GBR) [56849]

Jinan People's Broadcasting Station (Jinan, SD, CHN) Unable to locate

Jinan People's Broadcasting Station (Jinan, SD, CHN) Unable to locate

Jinan People's Broadcasting Station (Jinan, SD, CHN) Unable to locate

Jinan People's Broadcasting Station (Jinan, SD, CHN) Unable to locate

Jinan People's Broadcasting Station (Jinan, SD, CHN) Unable to locate

Jinchang People's Broadcasting Station (Jinchang, GS, CHN) Unable to locate

Jingcheng People's Broadcasting Station (Jingcheng, SX, CHN) Unable to locate

Jingdezhen People's Broadcasting Station (Jingdezhen, JX, CHN) Unable to locate

Jingmen People's Broadcasting Station (Jingmen, CHN) Unable to locate

Jingmen People's Broadcasting Station (Jingmen, CHN) Unable to locate

Jingmen People's Broadcasting Station (Jingmen, HA, CHN) Unable to locate

Jingzhou People's Broadcasting Station (Jingzhou, HB, CHN) Unable to locate

Jingzhou People's Broadcasting Station (Jingzhou, HU, CHN) Unable to locate

Jinhua People's Broadcasting Station (Jinhua, ZH, CHN) Unable to locate

Jinhua People's Broadcasting Station (Jinhua, ZH, CHN) Unable to locate

Jining People's Broadcasting Station (Jining, SD, CHN) Unable to locate

Jining People's Broadcasting Station (Jining, SD, CHN) Unable to locate

Jining People's Broadcasting Station (Jining, SD, CHN) Unable to locate

Jining People's Broadcasting Station (Jining, SD, CHN) Unable to locate

Jining People's Broadcasting Station (Jining, SD, CHN) Unable to locate

Jining People's Broadcasting Station (Jining, SD, CHN) Unable to locate

Jinshi People's Broadcasting Station (Jinshi, HA, CHN) Unable to locate

Jinzhou People's Broadcasting Station (Jinzhou, LI, CHN) Unable to locate

Jinzhou People's Broadcasting Station (Jinzhou, LI, CHN) Unable to locate

Jinzhou People's Broadcasting Station (Jinzhou, LI, CHN) Unable to locate

Jinzhou People's Broadcasting Station (Jinzhou, LI, CHN) Unable to locate

Jirem People's Broadcasting Station (Tongliao, NM, CHN) Unable to locate

Jirem People's Broadcasting Station (Tongliao, NM, CHN) Unable to locate

JISSI—International Journal of Scientometrics and Informetrics (New Delhi, DH, IND) Unable to locate

JISTA (Journal of the Indian Scientific Translators Association) (New Delhi, DH, IND) Unable to locate

Jiujiang People's Broadcasting Station (Jiujiang, JX, CHN) Unable to locate

Jiwaji University Journal: Science, Technology and Medicine (Gwalior, MP, IND) Unable to locate

Jiwan Dhara (Sikar, RJ, IND) Unable to locate

Jixi People's Broadcasting Station (Jixi, HL, CHN) Unable to locate

Jiyu to Seigi (Tokyo, JPN) Unable to locate

JMA Management Review (Tokyo, JPN) [46877]

JMO [43018]*

JNKVV News (Jabalpur, MP, IND) Unable to locate

JNKVV Research Journal (Jabalpur, MP, IND) Unable to locate

JNZL: Journal of New Zealand Literature (Dunedin, NZL) [48889]

JOAB - 693 KHz (Tokyo, JPN) [47061]

JOAC - 1377 KHz (Nagasaki, JPN) [46547]

JOAD - 1125 KHz (Okinawa, JPN) [46606]

JOAF - 1116 KHz (Matsuyama, JPN) [46505]

JOAF-TV (Matsuyama, JPN) Unable to locate

JOAG - 684 KHz (Nagasaki, JPN) [46548]

JOAH-TV - Channel 34 (Aomori, JPN) [46303]

JOAI-TV - Channel 38 (Aomori, JPN) [46304]

JOAK - 594 KHz (Tokyo, JPN) [47062]

JOAK - 82.5 MHz (Tokyo, JPN) [47063]

JOAL - 1116 KHz (Niihama, JPN) [46583]

JOAM - 1116 KHz (Uwajima, JPN) [47118]

JOAP - 88.1 MHz (Okinawa, JPN) [46608]

JOAP - 549 KHz (Okinawa, JPN) [46607]

JOAR - 1053 KHz (Nagoya, JPN) [46560]

JOAR-TV - Channel 5 (Nagoya, JPN) [46561]

JOAU - 80 MHz (Tokyo, JPN) [47064]

JOAV - 81.3 MHz (Tokyo, JPN) [47065]

JOAW - 76.5 MHz (Osaka, JPN) [46630]

Numbers cited in bold after listings are entry numbers rather than page numbers.

JOAX-TV - Channel 4 (Tokyo, JPN) **[47066]**

The Job (London, GBR) *Unable to locate*

Job og Born (Copenhagen, DEN) *Unable to locate*

JOBB - 828 KHz (Tokyo, JPN) **[47067]**

JOBF - 1197 KHz (Kumamoto, JPN) **[46454]**

JOBI-TV - Channel 37 (Akita, JPN) **[46295]**

JOBK - 88.1 MHz (Osaka, JPN) **[46632]**

JOBK - 666 KHz (Osaka, JPN) **[46631]**

JOBL-TV - Channel 30 (Ohtsu, JPN) **[46589]**

JOBM-TV - Channel 27 (Sapporo, JPN) **[46653]**

JOBO - 1215 KHz (Maizuru, JPN) **[46497]**

JOBP - 80.3 MHz (Utsunomiya, JPN) **[47114]**

JOBR - 1143 KHz (Kyoto, JPN) **[46487]**

JOBR-TV - Channel 34 (Kyoto, JPN) **[46488]**

Jobs North West (Manchester, GBR) **[55563]**

JOBU (Osaka, JPN) *Unable to locate*

JOBW - 1215 KHz (Hikone, JPN) **[46376]**

JOBX-TV (Oita, JPN) *Unable to locate*

JOCB - 909 KHz (Tokyo, JPN) **[47068]**

JOCC - 1602 KHz (Asahikawa, JPN) **[46311]**

JOCF - 1107 KHz (Kagoshima, JPN) **[46406]**

JOCF-TV (Kagoshima, JPN) *Unable to locate*

JOCG - 621 KHz (Asahikawa, JPN) **[46312]**

JOCH-TV - Channel 35 (Nagoya, JPN) **[46562]**

JOCI-TV - Channel 25 (Nagoya, JPN) **[46563]**

JOCK - 729 KHz (Nagoya, JPN) **[46564]**

JOCK - 82.5 MHz (Tokyo, JPN) **[47069]**

JOCL-TV - Channel 46 (Chiba, JPN) **[46321]**

JOCU - 80.7 MHz (Nagoya, JPN) **[46565]**

JOCV - 83.0 MHz (Kofu, JPN) **[46441]**

JOCX-TV - Channel 8 (Tokyo, JPN) **[47070]**

JOCY-TV - Channel 30 (Yamagata, JPN) **[47126]**

JODC - 1521 KHz (Hamamatsu, JPN) **[46374]**

Jodesa (New Delhi, DH, IND) *Unable to locate*

JODF - 684 KHz (Morioka, JPN) **[46525]**

JODF-TV - Channel 6 (Morioka, JPN) **[46526]**

JODG - 576 KHz (Tokyo, JPN) **[47071]**

JODI-TV (Miyazaki, JPN) *Unable to locate*

JODO - 1530 KHz (Joetsu, JPN) **[46401]**

JODR - 1116 KHz (Niigata, JPN) **[46574]**

JODR-TV - Channel 5 (Niigata, JPN) **[46575]**

JODU - 80.7 MHz (Fukuoka, JPN) **[46346]**

JODU-FM - 76.1 MHz (Fukuoka, JPN) **[46347]**

JODV - 79.5 MHz (Saitama, JPN) **[46646]**

JODW - 76.1 MHz (Tokyo, JPN) **[47072]**

JOEE-TV Asanuno - Channel 50 (Asanuno, JPN) **[46314]**

JOEE-TV Chiyoda - Channel 59 (Chiyoda, JPN) **[46324]**

JOEE-TV Daimon - Channel 59 (Daimon, JPN) **[46325]**

JOEE-TV Daiwa - Channel 55 (Daiwa, JPN) **[46326]**

JOEE-TV Fuchu - Channel 59 (Fuchu, JPN) **[46330]**

JOEE-TV Fukuyama - Channel 7 (Fukuyama, JPN) **[46364]**

JOEE-TV Futamimiwa (Hiroshima, JPN) *Unable to locate*

JOEE-TV Geihokuitamura - Channel 47 (Geihokuitamura, JPN) **[46365]**

JOEE-TV Geihokuyahata - Channel 39 (Geihokuyahata, JPN) **[46383]**

JOEE-TV Hiroshimanishiyamamoto - Channel 55 (Hiroshimanishiyamamoto, JPN) **[46389]**

JOEE-TV Hiroshimayagi - Channel 32 (Hiroshimayagi, JPN) **[46390]**

JOEE-TV Hiwa - Channel 53 (Hiwa, JPN) **[46391]**

JOEE-TV Innoshima - Channel 50 (Innoshima, JPN) **[46397]**

JOEE-TV Itsukaichi - Channel 60 (Itsukaichi, JPN) **[46398]**

JOEE-TV Jyoge (Hiroshima, JPN) *Unable to locate*

JOEE-TV Kabe - Channel 49 (Kabe, JPN) **[46402]**

JOEE-TV Kake - Channel 5 (Kake, JPN) **[46411]**

JOEE-TV Kimita - Channel 55 (Kimita, JPN) **[46423]**

JOEE-TV Kitamidori - Channel 5 (Kitamidori, JPN) **[46429]**

JOEE-TV Koi - Channel 40 (Koi, JPN) **[46446]**

JOEE-TV Kounu, JPN) *Unable to locate*

JOEE-TV Kuchiwa - Channel 34 (Kuchiwa, JPN) **[46451]**

JOEE-TV Kui - Channel 55 (Kui, JPN) **[46452]**

JOEE-TV Kurahashi - Channel 40 (Onomichi, JPN) **[46609]**

JOEE-TV Kure - Channel 9 (Kure, JPN) **[46458]**

JOEE-TV Kurekotsubo - Channel 56 (Kurekotsubo, JPN) **[46459]**

JOEE-TV Kurose - Channel 60 (Kurose, JPN) **[46460]**

JOEE-TV Kyowa - Channel 55 (Kyowa, JPN) **[46492]**

JOEE-TV Mihara - Channel 49 (Mihara, JPN) **[46509]**

JOEE-TV Mihara-nakanomachi - Channel 57 (Mihara-nakanomachi, JPN) **[46510]**

JOEE-TV Miharafukamachinakagumi (Hiroshima, JPN) *Unable to locate*

JOEE-TV Minamimidori - Channel 5 (Minamimidori, JPN) **[46511]**

JOEE-TV Mirasaka - Channel 46 (Mirasaka, JPN) **[46512]**

JOEE-TV Mitsugi - Channel 56 (Mitsugi, JPN) **[46516]**

JOEE-TV Miyoshi - Channel 9 (Miyoshi, JPN) **[46524]**

JOEE-TV Miyoshinakanomura (Hiroshima, JPN) *Unable to locate*

JOEE-TV Mukaihara - Channel 48 (Mukaihara, JPN) **[46533]**

JOEE-TV Onomichi - Channel 10 (Onomichi, JPN) **[46610]**

JOEE-TV Ooasa - Channel 46 (Ooasa, JPN) **[46611]**

JOEE-TV Oogaki - Channel 49 (Oogaki, JPN) **[46612]**

JOEE-TV Ootake - Channel 57 (Ootake, JPN) **[46613]**

JOEE-TV Saeki - Channel 55 (Saeki, JPN) **[46639]**

JOEE-TV Saijyo - Channel 10 (Saijyo, JPN) **[46644]**

JOEE-TV Saijyo - Channel 9 (Saijyo, JPN) **[46645]**

JOEE-TV Sakugi - Channel 46 (Sakugi, JPN) **[46647]**

JOEE-TV Satsukigaoka (Hiroshima, JPN) *Unable to locate*

JOEE-TV Seno - Channel 57 (Seno, JPN) **[46679]**

JOEE-TV Senotateishi - Channel 58 (Senotateishi, JPN) **[46680]**

JOEE-TV Serakozan - Channel 57 (Serakozan, JPN) **[46681]**

JOEE-TV Shinichitsunekanemaru - Channel 43 (Shinichitsunekanemaru, JPN) **[46685]**

JOEE-TV Shiraki - Channel 57 (Shiraki, JPN) **[46686]**

JOEE-TV Shiwa - Channel 48 (Shiwa, JPN) **[46687]**

JOEE-TV Shobara - Channel 43 (Shobara, JPN) **[46697]**

JOEE-TV Shobaragawakita, JPN) *Unable to locate*

JOEE-TV Takamiya - Channel 47 (Takamiya, JPN) **[46704]**

JOEE-TV Takano - Channel 46 (Takano, JPN) **[46705]**

JOEE-TV Takehara - Channel 59 (Takehara, JPN) **[46707]**

JOEE-TV Takeharakita - Channel 44 (Takeharakita, JPN) **[46708]**

JOEE-TV Togouchi - Channel 55 (Togouchi, JPN) **[46711]**

JOEE-TV Tojyo - Channel 10 (Tojyo, JPN) **[46712]**

JOEE-TV Tojyochidori - Channel 36 (Tojyochidori, JPN) **[46713]**

JOEE-TV Tomo - Channel 41 (Tomo, JPN) **[47092]**

JOEE-TV Toyama - Channel 44 (Toyama, JPN) **[47097]**

JOEE-TV Yachiyo - Channel 50 (Yachiyo, JPN) **[47122]**

JOEE-TV Yasuura - Channel 55 (Yasuura, JPN) **[47139]**

JOEE-TV Yoshida - Channel 58 (Yoshida, JPN) **[47150]**

JOEE-TV Yuki - Channel 59 (Yuki, JPN) **[47151]**

JOEF - 918 KHz (Yamagata, JPN) **[47127]**

JOEF-TV - Channel 10 (Yamagata, JPN) **[47128]**

JOEH-TV (Matsuyama, JPN) *Unable to locate*

JOEI-TV (Matsuyama, JPN) *Unable to locate*

JOEM-TV - Channel 32 (Sendai, JPN) **[46672]**

JOEP - 83.2 MHz (Mito, JPN) **[46514]**

JOER - 1350 KHz (Hiroshima, JPN) **[46383]**

JOER-TV - Channel 4 (Hiroshima, JPN) **[46384]**

JOEU - 79.7 MHz (Matsuyama, JPN) **[46506]**

JOEV - 80.4 MHz (Yamagata, JPN) **[47129]**

JOEX-TV - Channel 10 (Tokyo, JPN) **[47073]**

JOEY-TV (Matsuyama, JPN) *Unable to locate*

JOFB - 702 KHz (Tokyo, JPN) **[47074]**

JOFC - 1521 KHz (Fukui, JPN) **[46334]**

JOFD - 1602 KHz (Fukushima, JPN) **[46356]**

JOFG - 927 KHz (Fukui, JPN) **[46336]**

JOFG - 83.4 MHz (Fukui, JPN) **[46335]**

JOFH-TV (Fukuoka, JPN) *Unable to locate*

JOFI-TV - Channel 39 (Fukui, JPN) **[46337]**

JOFK - 1071 KHz (Hiroshima, JPN) **[46385]**

JOFK - 88.3 MHz (Hiroshima, JPN) **[46386]**

JOFM - 1269 KHz (Esashi, JPN) **[46328]**

JOFO - 1197 KHz (Kitakyushu, JPN) **[46424]**

JOFP - 1323 KHz (Fukushima, JPN) **[46358]**

JOFP - 85.3 MHz (Fukushima, JPN) **[46357]**

JOFR - 1278 KHz (Fukuoka, JPN) **[46348]**

JOFR-TV (Fukuoka, JPN) *Unable to locate*

JOFU - 80.4 MHz (Sapporo, JPN) **[46654]**

JOFV - 80.2 MHz (Osaka, JPN) **[46633]**

JOFW - 76.1 MHz (Fukuoka, JPN) **[46349]**

JOFX-TV - Channel 1 (Nagoya, JPN) **[46566]**

JOGB - 873 KHz (Kumamoto, JPN) **[46455]**

JOGF - 1098 KHz (Oita, JPN) **[46591]**

JOGH-TV - Channel 20 (Nagano, JPN) **[46538]**

JOGI-TV (Kofu, JPN) *Unable to locate*

JOGK - 85.4 MHz (Kumamoto, JPN) **[46457]**

JOGK - 756 KHz (Kumamoto, JPN) **[46456]**

JOGM-TV - Channel 35 (Hiroshima, JPN) **[46387]**

JOGO - 1485 KHz (Hachinohe, JPN) **[46370]**

JOGP - 81.9 MHz (Yokohama, JPN) **[47144]**

JOGR - 1233 KHz (Aomori, JPN) **[46305]**

JOGR-TV - Channel 1 (Aomori, JPN) **[46306]**

JOGU - 78.2 MHz (Hiroshima, JPN) **[46388]**

JOGV - 78.0 MHz (Chiba, JPN) **[46322]**

JOGW (Nagoya, JPN) *Unable to locate*

JOGY-TV - Channel 31 (Utsunomiya, JPN) **[47115]**

JOHB - 1089 KHz (Tokyo, JPN) **[47075]**

JOHC - 1386 KHz (Kagoshima, JPN) **[46407]**

JOHD - 1035 KHz (Takamatsu, JPN) **[46699]**

JOHF - 900 KHz (Yonago, JPN) **[47148]**

JOHG - 576 KHz (Kagoshima, JPN) **[46409]**

JOHG - 85.6 MHz (Kagoshima, JPN) **[46408]**

JOHH-TV - Channel 35 (Sapporo, JPN) **[46655]**

JOHI-TV - Channel 17 (Sapporo, JPN) **[46656]**

Numbers cited in bold after listings are entry numbers rather than page numbers.

JOHK - 82.5 MHz (Sendai, JPN) **[46673]**

JOHK - 891 KHz (Sendai, JPN) **[46674]**

JOHL - 1431 KHz (Tattori, JPN) **[46709]**

JOHO - 900 KHz (Hokadate, JPN) **[46392]**

Joho-Shori (Tokyo, JPN) **[46878]**

JOHP - 86.0 MHz (Takamatsu, JPN) **[46700]**

JOHP - 1368 KHz (Takamatsu, JPN) **[46701]**

JOHR - 1287 KHz (Sapporo, JPN) **[46657]**

JOHR-TV - Channel 1 (Sapporo, JPN) **[46658]**

JOHU - 79.5 MHz (Nagasaki, JPN) **[46549]**

JOHV - 80.5 MHz (Kanazawa, JPN) **[46413]**

JOHW - 1269 KHz (Obihiro, JPN) **[46584]**

JOIB - 747 KHz (Tokyo, JPN) **[47076]**

JOIC - 1035 KHz (Toyama, JPN) **[47098]**

JOID - 1467 KHz (Oita, JPN) **[46592]**

JOIF - 1413 KHz (Fukuoka, JPN) **[46350]**

JOIG - 81.5 MHz (Toyama, JPN) **[47100]**

JOIG - 648 KHz (Toyama, JPN) **[47099]**

JOIH-TV - Channel 37 (Kanazawa, JPN) **[46414]**

JOII-TV - Channel 35 (Morioka, JPN) **[46527]**

JOIK (Sapporo, JPN) *Unable to locate*

JOIK - 567 KHz (Tokyo, JPN) **[47077]**

JOIL - 720 KHz (Fukuoka, JPN) **[46351]**

Joint (Yokohama, JPN) *Unable to locate*

JOIP - 639 KHz (Oita, JPN) **[46594]**

JOIP - 88.9 MHz (Oita, JPN) **[46593]**

JOIQ - 945 KHz (Muroran, JPN) **[46534]**

JOIR - 1260 KHz (Sendai, JPN) **[46675]**

JOIU - 87.3 MHz (Naha, JPN) **[46569]**

JOIV - 89.9 MHz (Kobe, JPN) **[46435]**

JOIY-TV - Channel 31 (Morioka, JPN) **[46528]**

JOIZ - 1125 KHz (Muroran, JPN) **[46535]**

JOJB - 1386 KHz (Kanazawa, JPN) **[46415]**

JOJC - 1521 KHz (Yamagata, JPN) **[47130]**

JOJF - 765 KHz (Kofu, JPN) **[46442]**

JOJF-TV (Kofu, JPN) *Unable to locate*

JOJG - 540 KHz (Yamagata, JPN) **[47132]**

JOJG - 82.1 MHz (Yamagata, JPN) **[47131]**

JOJH-TV - Channel 32 (Takaoka, JPN) **[46706]**

JOJI-TV - Channel 35 (Koriyama, JPN) **[46448]**

JOJK - 82.2 MHz (Kanazawa, JPN) **[46416]**

JOJK - 1224 KHz (Kanazawa, JPN) **[46417]**

JOJR - 1269 KHz (Tokushima, JPN) **[46717]**

JOJU - 77.1 MHz (Sendai, JPN) **[46676]**

JOJV - 88.0 MHz (Oita, JPN) **[46595]**

JOJX-TV - Channel 1 (Tottori, JPN) **[47093]**

JOJY-TV (Fukuoka, JPN) *Unable to locate*

JOKB - 1386 KHz (Okayama, JPN) **[46600]**

JOKC - 1602 KHz (Kofu, JPN) **[46443]**

JOKD - 702 KHz (Kitami, JPN) **[46427]**

JOKF - 1449 KHz (Takamatsu, JPN) **[46702]**

JOKF-TV (Takamatsu, JPN) *Unable to locate*

JOKG - 927 KHz (Kofu, JPN) **[46445]**

JOKG - 85.6 MHz (Kofu, JPN) **[46444]**

JOKH-TV (Kagoshima, JPN) *Unable to locate*

JOKI-TV - Channel 31 (Fukushima, JPN) **[46359]**

JOKK - 88.7 MHz (Okayama, JPN) **[46601]**

JOKK - 603 KHz (Okayama, JPN) **[46602]**

JOKM-TV - Channel 42 (Yokohama, JPN) **[47145]**

JOKP - 1188 KHz (Kitami, JPN) **[46428]**

JOKR - 954 KHz (Tokyo, JPN) **[47078]**

JOKR-TV **[47084]***

JOKU - 79.2 MHz (Shizuoka, JPN) **[46689]**

JOKV - 89.4 MHz (Kyoto, JPN) **[46489]**

JOKX-TV - Channel 5 (Sapporo, JPN) **[46659]**

JOLB - 1017 KHz (Tokyo, JPN) **[47079]**

JOLC - 1125 KHz (Tottori, JPN) **[47094]**

JOLF - 1242 KHz (Tokyo, JPN) **[47080]**

JOLG - 1368 KHz (Tottori, JPN) **[47095]**

JOLH-TV - Channel 38 (Nagano, JPN) **[46539]**

JOLK - 84.8 MHz (Fukuoka, JPN) **[46353]**

JOLK - 612 KHz (Fukuoka, JPN) **[46352]**

JOLO - 684 KHz (Ofunato, JPN) **[46588]**

JOLP - 85.1 MHz (Urawa, JPN) **[47112]**

JOLR - 738 KHz (Toyama, JPN) **[47101]**

JOLR-TV - Channel 1 (Toyama, JPN) **[47102]**

JOLU - 76.1 MHz (Fukui, JPN) **[46338]**

JOLV - 81.6 MHz (Kochi, JPN) **[46437]**

JOLX-TV (Nagoya, JPN) *Unable to locate*

JOMC - 1467 KHz (Miyazaki, JPN) **[46520]**

JOMF - 1098 KHz (Sasebo, JPN) **[46663]**

JOMG - 540 KHz (Miyazaki, JPN) **[46521]**

JOMH-TV - Channel 33 (Tsu, JPN) **[47106]**

JOMI-TV - Channel 34 (Matsue, JPN) **[46499]**

JOML-TV - Channel 48 (Maebashi, JPN) **[46493]**

JOMM-TV - Channel 34 (Sendai, JPN) **[46677]**

JOMP - 80.7 MHz (Chiba, JPN) **[46323]**

JOMR - 1107 KHz (Kanazawa, JPN) **[46418]**

JOMU - 83.2 MHz (Miyazaki, JPN) **[46522]**

JOMV - 80.7 MHz (Tokushima, JPN) **[46718]**

JOMX-TV - Channel 14 (Tokyo, JPN) **[47081]**

JONB - 1467 KHz (Nagano, JPN) **[46540]**

JONF - 936 KHz (Miyazaki, JPN) **[46523]**

JONF-TV (Miyazaki, JPN) *Unable to locate*

JONH-TV - Channel 35 (Niigata, JPN) **[46576]**

JONI-TV - Channel 30 (Matsumoto, JPN) **[46503]**

JONK - 819 KHz (Nagano, JPN) **[46541]**

JONM-TV (Nara, JPN) *Unable to locate*

JONP - 81.8 MHz (Tsu, JPN) **[47107]**

JONR - 1008 KHz (Osaka, JPN) **[46634]**

JONU - 78.9 MHz (Tsu, JPN) **[47108]**

JONV - 77.9 MHz (Saga, JPN) **[46640]**

JOOC - 1125 KHz (Obihiro, JPN) **[46585]**

JOOG - 603 KHz (Obihiro, JPN) **[46586]**

JOOI-TV (Oita, JPN) *Unable to locate*

JOOK - 621 KHz (Kyoto, JPN) **[46490]**

JOOK - 82.8 MHz (Kyoto, JPN) **[46491]**

JOOM-TV - Channel 30 (Wakayama, JPN) **[47119]**

JOOP - 83.6 MHz (Gifu, JPN) **[46367]**

JOOR (Osaka, JPN) *Unable to locate*

JOOR-TV - Channel 4 (Osaka, JPN) **[46635]**

JOOU - 82.7 MHz (Toyama, JPN) **[47103]**

JOOV - 79.8 MHz (Kagoshima, JPN) **[46410]**

JOOX-TV - Channel 12 (Sendai, JPN) **[46678]**

JOPB - 639 KHz (Shizuoka, JPN) **[46690]**

JOPC - 1152 KHz (Kushiro, JPN) **[46461]**

JOPF - 765 KHz (Yamaguchi, JPN) **[47135]**

JOPF-TV - Channel 11 (Shunan, JPN) **[46698]**

JOPG - 585 KHz (Kushiro, JPN) **[46462]**

JOPI-TV - Channel 29 (Niigata, JPN) **[46577]**

JOPK - 88.8 MHz (Shizuoka, JPN) **[46692]**

JOPK - 882 KHz (Shizuoka, JPN) **[46691]**

JOPL - 1485 KHz (Hagi, JPN) **[46371]**

JOPM - 918 KHz (Shimonoseki, JPN) **[46684]**

JOPN - 918 KHz (Iwakuni, JPN) **[46399]**

JOPR - 864 KHz (Fukui, JPN) **[46339]**

JOPR-TV (Fukui, JPN) *Unable to locate*

JOPU - 82.8 MHz (Akita, JPN) **[46296]**

JOPV - 82.5 MHz (Sapporo, JPN) **[46660]**

JOPX-TV - Channel 11 (Fukushima, JPN) **[46360]**

JOQB - 1593 KHz (Niigata, JPN) **[46578]**

JOQC - 1386 KHz (Morioka, JPN) **[46529]**

JOQG - 531 KHz (Morioka, JPN) **[46530]**

JOQG - 83.1 MHz (Tokyo, JPN) **[47082]**

JOQH-TV - Channel 35 (Shizuoka, JPN) **[46693]**

JOQK - 82.3 MHz (Niigata, JPN) **[46579]**

JOQK - 837 KHz (Niigata, JPN) **[46580]**

JOQL - 1404 KHz (Kushiro, JPN) **[46463]**

JOQM - 1449 KHz (Abashiri, JPN) **[46293]**

JOQP - 945 KHz (Hikone, JPN) **[46377]**

JOQP - 84.0 MHz (Otsu, JPN) **[46637]**

JOQR - 1134 KHz (Tokyo, JPN) **[47083]**

JOQU - 76.1 MHz (Morioka, JPN) **[46531]**

JOQV - 77.8 MHz (Nagoya, JPN) **[46567]**

JORB - 1152 KHz (Kochi, JPN) **[46438]**

Jord og Viden (Copenhagen, DEN) *Unable to locate*

Jordan Times (Amman, JOR) **[47160]**

Jordemodern (Stockholm, SWE) *Unable to locate*

Jordmorbladet (Oslo, NOR) *Ceased*

JORF - 1422 KHz (Yokohama, JPN) **[47146]**

JORI-TV (Kochi, JPN) *Unable to locate*

JORK - 990 KHz (Kochi, JPN) **[46439]**

JORM-TV (Hiroshima, JPN) *Unable to locate*

Jornal da Ciencia Hoje (Sao Paulo, SP, BRZ) **[43041]**

Jornal Da FENPROF (Lisbon, PRT) *Unable to locate*

JORR - 738 KHz (Naha, JPN) **[46570]**

JORR-TV (Naha, JPN) *Unable to locate*

JORU - 86.3 MHz (Maebashi, JPN) **[46494]**

JORV - 78.7 MHz (Fukuoka, JPN) **[46354]**

JORX-TV - Channel 6 (Tokyo, JPN) **[47084]**

JORY-TV (Naha, JPN) *Unable to locate*

JOSB - 1602 KHz (Kitakyushu, JPN) **[46425]**

Josei Seven (Tokyo, JPN) **[46879]**

JOSF - 1332 KHz (Nagoya, JPN) **[46568]**

JOSI-TV - Channel 33 (Shizuoka, JPN) **[46694]**

JOSK - 540 KHz (Kitakyushu, JPN) **[46426]**

JOSO - 864 KHz (Matsumoto, JPN) **[46504]**

JOSP - 963 KHz (Saga, JPN) **[46641]**

JOSR - 1098 KHz (Nagano, JPN) **[46542]**

JOSR-TV - Channel 11 (Nagano, JPN) **[46543]**

JOSV - 76.4 MHz (Utsunomiya, JPN) **[47116]**

JOSW, JPN) *Unable to locate*

JOSX-TV - Channel 31 (Shizuoka, JPN) **[46695]**

JOTA (Lisbon, PRT) *Unable to locate*

JOTB - 1593 KHz (Matsue, JPN) **[46500]**

JOTC - 1521 KHz (Aomori, JPN) **[46307]**

Numbers cited in bold after listings are entry numbers rather than page numbers.

JOTG - 86.0 MHz (Aomori, JPN) **[46308]**

JOTG - 963 KHz (Aomori, JPN) **[46309]**

JOTH-TV - Channel 34 (Toyama, JPN) **[47104]**

JOTI-TV (Kagoshima, JPN) *Unable to locate*

JOTK - 1296 KHz (Matsue, JPN) **[46501]**

JOTL - 1494 KHz (Nayoro, JPN) **[46572]**

JOTP - 81.6 MHz (Maebashi, JPN) **[46495]**

JOTR - 936 KHz (Akita, JPN) **[46297]**

JOTR-TV (Akita, JPN) *Unable to locate*

JOTS - 1368 KHz (Wakkanai, JPN) **[47121]**

JOTU - 84.7 MHz (Yokohama, JPN) **[47147]**

JOTV - 81.8 MHz (Fukushima, JPN) **[46361]**

JOTV-FM - 81.8 MHz (Fukushima, JPN) **[46362]**

JOTX-TV - Channel 12 (Tokyo, JPN) **[47085]**

JOTY-TV (Fukuoka, JPN) *Unable to locate*

JOUB - 774 KHz (Akita, JPN) **[46298]**

JOUC - 1377 KHz (Yamaguchi, JPN) **[47136]**

JOUD - 78.8 MHz (Maebashi, JPN) **[46496]**

JOUD - 77.1 MHz (Tokyo, JPN) **[47086]**

JOUG - 675 KHz (Yamaguchi, JPN) **[47137]**

JOUH-TV (Kobe, JPN) *Unable to locate*

JOUK - 1503 KHz (Akita, JPN) **[46300]**

JOUK - 86.7 MHz (Akita, JPN) **[46299]**

JOUO - 1458 KHz (Saga, JPN) **[46642]**

JOUR - 1233 KHz (Nagasaki, JPN) **[46550]**

The Journal (Hurstville, NW, AUS) **[41970]**

Journal (Dhaka, BGD) *Unable to locate*

Journal (Angers, FRA) *Unable to locate*

Journal (Paris, FRA) *Unable to locate*

Journal (Wellington, NZL) **[49010]**

Journal (Seoul, KOR) **[47270]**

Journal (Crawley, GBR) **[53107]**

Journal (Glastonbury, GBR) *Ceased*

Journal (Halstead, GBR) *Unable to locate*

Journal (Ivybridge, GBR) *Unable to locate*

Journal (London, GBR) *Unable to locate*

The Journal (London, GBR) *Unable to locate*

The Journal (London, GBR) **[54695]**

The Journal (London, GBR) **[54693]**

Journal (London, GBR) **[54694]**

Journal of AALAE (Nairobi, KEN) *Ceased*

Journal of Academic Ethics (Dordrecht, NLD) **[48436]**

Journal of Acarological Society of Japan (Koriyama, JPN) **[46447]**

Journal of Acarology (Bangalore, KA, IND) *Ceased*

Journal of Accounting and Economics (Amsterdam, NLD) **[48036]**

Journal of Accounting and Organisational Change (Bradford, GBR) **[52492]**

Journal of Accounting and Public Policy (Amsterdam, NLD) **[48037]**

Journal of Adhesion Science and Technology (Leiden, NLD) **[48686]**

Journal of Adolescence (Kidlington, GBR) **[53695]**

The Journal of Adult Protection (Brighton, GBR) **[52618]**

Journal of Adult Theological Education (London, GBR) **[54696]**

Journal of Advanced Computational Intelligence and Intelligent Informatics (JACIII) (Tokyo, JPN) **[46880]**

Journal of Advanced Concrete Technology (Tokyo, JPN) **[46881]**

Journal of Advanced Materials (Cambridge, GBR) **[52841]**

Journal of Advanced Transportation (Oxford, GBR) **[56011]**

Journal of Advanced Zoology (Gorakhpur, UP, IND) *Unable to locate*

Journal of Advances in Bioscience (New Delhi, DH, IND) *Unable to locate*

Journal of Advances in Chemical Physics (Moscow, RUS) **[49926]**

Journal of Adventure Education and Outdoor Learning (Penrith, GBR) **[56246]**

Journal of Aeronautical Materials (Beijing, CHN) *Unable to locate*

Journal of Aerosol Science (Karlsruhe, GER) *Unable to locate*

Journal of Aerospace Power (Beijing, CHN) *Unable to locate*

Journal of African Archaeology (Frankfurt am Main, GER) **[44366]**

Journal of African Cultural Studies (Abingdon, GBR) **[51868]**

Journal of African Earth Sciences (Pretoria, SAF) **[50593]**

Journal of African Economies (Oxford, GBR) **[56012]**

Journal of African Elections (Johannesburg, SAF) **[50530]**

The Journal of African History (Cambridge, GBR) **[52842]**

Journal of African Languages and Linguistics (Berlin, GER) **[44200]**

Journal of African Law (Cambridge, GBR) **[52843]**

Journal des Africanistes (Paris, FRA) *Unable to locate*

Journal of Aggression, Conflict and Peace Research (Hove, GBR) **[53606]**

The Journal of Agricultural Education and Extension (Wageningen, NLD) **[48771]**

Journal of Agricultural Engineering (New Delhi, DH, IND) *Unable to locate*

Journal of Agricultural Engineering Research (Bedford, GBR) *Unable to locate*

Journal of Agricultural and Food Economics (Thessaloniki, GRC) **[44774]**

Journal of Agricultural Genomics (Wallingford, GBR) **[56820]**

Journal of Agricultural Meteorology (Tokyo, JPN) *Unable to locate*

Journal of Agricultural Research **[43165]***

Journal of Agricultural Research of China (Taipei, TWN) **[51347]**

Journal of Agricultural Research and Development (Ilorin, KW, NGA) **[49120]**

Journal of Agriculture, Forestry and the Social Sciences (Obubra, CR, NGA) **[49158]**

Journal of Agriculture and Rural Development in the Tropics and Subtropics (Kassel, GER) **[44498]**

Journal of Agriculture and Social Research (Ibadan, OY, NGA) **[49088]**

Journal of Agronomy (Faisalabad, PAK) **[49259]**

Journal of Algebra (Amsterdam, NLD) **[48038]**

Journal of Algebraic Geometry (Cambridge, GBR) **[52844]**

Journal of Algorithms **[48039]***

Journal of Algorithms in Cognition, Informatics and Logic (Amsterdam, NLD) **[48039]**

Journal of Alloys and Compounds (Amsterdam, NLD) **[48040]**

The Journal of Alternative & Complementary Medicine (Hereford, GBR) **[53563]**

Journal of Alzheimer's Disease (Amsterdam, NLD) **[48041]**

Journal of American and Canadian Studies (Tokyo, JPN) **[46882]**

Journal of the American Ceramic Society (Oxford, GBR) **[56013]**

Journal of the American College of Surgeons (Amsterdam, NLD) **[48042]**

Journal of American Studies (Cambridge, GBR) **[52845]**

Journal of American Studies of Turkey (Ankara, TUR) **[51494]**

Journal of Anaesthesia & Critical Care (Karachi, PAK) *Unable to locate*

Journal of Anaesthesiology—Clinical Pharmacology (New Delhi, DH, IND) *Unable to locate*

Journal of Analysis and its Applications (Helsinki, FIN) **[43834]**

Journal of Analytical and Applied Pyrolysis (Amsterdam, NLD) **[48043]**

Journal of Analytical Atomic Spectrometry (Chichester, GBR) **[53013]**

Journal of Analytical Chemistry (Moscow, RUS) **[49927]**

Journal of Anatomical Sciences (Kanpur, UP, IND) *Unable to locate*

Journal of Anatomy (Oxford, GBR) *Unable to locate*

Journal of Ancient Christianity (Berlin, GER) **[44201]**

Journal of Ancient Near Eastern Religions (Leiden, NLD) **[48687]**

Journal of Anesthesia (Tokyo, JPN) **[46883]**

Journal of Animal Ecology (London, GBR) **[54697]**

Journal of Animal Morphology and Physiology (Baroda, GJ, IND) *Unable to locate*

Journal of Animal and Veterinary Advances (Faisalabad, PAK) **[49260]**

Journal of Anthropological Archaeology (Amsterdam, NLD) **[48044]**

The Journal of the Anthropological Survey of India (Calcutta, WB, IND) *Unable to locate*

Journal of Antibiotics (Tokyo, JPN) **[46884]**

Journal of Antimicrobial Chemotherapy (Birmingham, GBR) **[52345]**

Journal of Antimicrobial Chemotherapy (Oxford, GBR) **[56014]**

Journal of Aomori Society of Obstetricians and Gynecologists (Aomori, JPN) *Unable to locate*

Journal of Aphidology (Gorakhpur, UP, IND) *Unable to locate*

Journal of Applied Accounting Research (Leicester, GBR) **[53806]**

Journal of Applied Analysis (Lodz, POL) **[49671]**

Journal of Applied Animal Research (Izatnagar, UP, IND) *Unable to locate*

Journal of Applied Biomaterials & Biomechanics (Milan, ITA) **[46181]**

Journal of Applied Biomedicine (Ceske Budejovice, CZE) **[43606]**

Journal of Applied Chemistry and Agricultural Research (Asaba, NGA) **[49061]**

Journal of Applied Corporate Finance (Oxford, GBR) **[56015]**

Journal of Applied Crystallography (Berlin, GER) **[44202]**

Journal of Applied Developmental Psychology (Amsterdam, NLD) **[48045]**

Journal of Applied Ecology (London, GBR) **[54698]**

Journal Applied Ecology and Environmental Research (Budapest, HUN) **[44840]**

Journal of Applied Electrochemistry (Dordrecht, NLD) **[48437]**

Journal of Applied Geodesy (Berlin, GER) **[44203]**

Journal of Applied Geophysics (Amsterdam, NLD) **[48046]**

Journal of Applied Irrigation Science (Hanwood, NW, AUS) **[41940]**

Journal of Applied Linguistics (London, GBR) **[54699]**

Journal of Applied Logic (Singapore, SGP) **[50198]**

Journal of Applied Management Studies (Abingdon, GBR) *Unable to locate*

Journal of Applied Mathematics and Mechanics (Amsterdam, NLD) **[48047]**

Journal of Applied Mathematics and Physics (ZAMP) (Zurich, SWI) **[51269]**

Journal of Applied Medicine (New Delhi, DH, IND) *Unable to locate*

Journal of Applied Medicine (Kyoto, JPN) *Unable to locate*

Journal of Applied Microbiology (Bedford, GBR) **[52273]**

Journal of Applied Oral Science (Bauru, SP, BRZ) **[42948]**

Journal of Applied Probability (Sheffield, GBR) **[56503]**

Journal of Applied Research in Intellectual Disability (Worcestershire, GBR) **[56968]**

Journal of Applied Science, Engineering and Technology (Grahamstown, SAF) **[50500]**

Journal of Applied Science in Southern Africa (Harare, ZWE) **[57115]**

Journal of Applied Sciences (Faisalabad, PAK) **[49261]**

Journal of Applied Sciences and Environmental Management (Port Harcourt, RV, NGA) **[49166]**

Journal of Applied Sciences Research (Faisalabad, PAK) **[49262]**

Journal of Applied Statistics (Abingdon, GBR) **[51869]**

Journal of Applied Systems Studies (Piraeus, GRC) **[44769]**

Journal of Approximation Theory (Amsterdam, NLD) **[48048]**

Journal of Approximation Theory and Applications (Osaka, JPN) **[46619]**

Journal of Aquaculture Feed Science and Nutrition (Faisalabad, PAK) **[49263]**

Numbers cited in bold after listings are entry numbers rather than page numbers.

Master Index

Journal of Aquaculture in the Tropics (New Delhi, DH, IND) *Unable to locate*

Journal of Aquatic Sciences (Jos, PL, NGA) **[49125]**

Journal of Arab Historians (Baghdad, IRQ) *Unable to locate*

Journal of Arabic and Islamic Studies (Edinburgh, GBR) **[53291]**

Journal of Arabic Literature (Leiden, NLD) **[48688]**

Journal of the Arabization Bureau (Tunis, TUN) **[51489]**

Journal of Archaeological Research (Dordrecht, NLD) **[48438]**

Journal of Archaeology in Andhra Pradesh (Hyderabad, AP, IND) *Unable to locate*

Journal of Architectural Education (Oxford, GBR) **[56016]**

Journal of the Architectural Institute of the R.O.C. (Taipei, TWN) *Unable to locate*

Journal of Architecture (Taipei, TWN) *Unable to locate*

The Journal of Architecture (London, GBR) **[54700]**

Journal of Architecture, Planning and Environmental Engineering (Tokyo, JPN) **[46885]**

Journal of the Argentine Chemical Society (Buenos Aires, ARG) **[41475]**

Journal of Argentine Dermatology (Buenos Aires, ARG) **[41476]**

Journal of Arid Environments (Amsterdam, NLD) **[48049]**

Journal of Arid Legumes (Jodhpur, RJ, IND) **[45225]**

Journal of Arms and Armour Society (London, GBR) **[54701]**

Journal of Artificial Organs (Tokyo, JPN) **[46886]**

Journal of Arts and Design Education **[53066]***

Journal of the Asia Pacific Economy (Abingdon, GBR) **[51870]**

Journal of Asia-Pacific Entomology (Suwon, KOR) *Unable to locate*

Journal of Asian and African Studies (Leiden, NLD) **[48689]**

Journal of Asian Architecture and Building Engineering (Tokyo, JPN) **[46887]**

Journal of Asian Civilization (Islamabad, PAK) *Unable to locate*

Journal of Asian Earth Sciences (Amsterdam, NLD) **[48050]**

Journal of Asian Economics (Amsterdam, NLD) **[48051]**

Journal of Asian Evangelical Theology (Singapore, SGP) **[50199]**

Journal of Asian Mission (Quezon City, PHL) **[49597]**

Journal of Asian Natural Products Research (Beijing, CHN) **[43202]**

Journal of Asian Pacific Communication (Amsterdam, NLD) **[48052]**

Journal Asiatique (Paris, FRA) **[44063]**

Journal of Asset Management (London, GBR) **[54702]**

Journal of Assistive Technologies (Hove, GBR) **[53607]**

Journal of Association of Physicians of India (Mumbai, MH, IND) **[45395]**

Journal for the Association for Quality Healthcare (Leeds, GBR) *Unable to locate*

Journal of the Association for Research in Otolaryngology (Dordrecht, NLD) **[48439]**

Journal of Astrophysics and Astronomy (Bangalore, KA, IND) **[44965]**

Journal of Atherosclerosis and Thrombosis (Tokyo, JPN) **[46888]**

Journal of Atmospheric Chemistry (Dordrecht, NLD) **[48440]**

Journal of Atomic Mineral Science (New Delhi, DH, IND) *Ceased*

Journal of the Audio Engineering Society (Slough, GBR) **[56559]**

Journal of the Australasian Ceramic Society (Menai, NW, AUS) *Unable to locate*

Journal of Australian Literature (Agartala, TR, IND) *Unable to locate*

Journal of the Australian Mathematical Society (Canberra, AC, AUS) **[41709]**

Journal of the Australian Mathematical Society, Series A (Pure Mathematics and Statistics) **[41709]***

Journal of the Australian Mathematical Society - Series B - Applied Mathematics **[41698]***

Journal of Australian Political Economy (Sydney, NW, AUS) **[42526]**

Journal of Australian Studies (Saint Lucia, QL, AUS) **[42340]**

Journal of Autism and Developmental Disorders (Dordrecht, NLD) **[48441]**

Journal of Autoimmune Diseases (London, GBR) **[54703]**

Journal of Autoimmunity (Amsterdam, NLD) **[48053]**

Journal of Automated Methods and Management in Chemistry (Orpington, GBR) **[55853]**

Journal of Avian Medicine and Surgery (Utrecht, NLD) *Unable to locate*

Journal of Ayub Medical College (Abbottabad, PAK) **[49227]**

Journal of Back and Musculoskeletal Rehabilitation (Enschede, NLD) **[48597]**

Journal of the Bahamas Historical Society (Nassau, BHS) *Unable to locate*

Journal of Bahrain Medical Society (Manama, BHR) *Unable to locate*

Journal of Balkan and Near Eastern Studies (Abingdon, GBR) **[51871]**

Journal of Baltic Studies (Glasgow, GBR) **[53426]**

Journal of Bamboo and Rattan (Dordrecht, NLD) **[48442]**

Journal of Bangladesh Academy of Sciences (Dhaka, BGD) *Unable to locate*

Journal of Bangladesh Itihas Samiti (Dhaka, BGD) *Unable to locate*

Journal of Banking and Finance (Taipei, TWN) **[51348]**

Journal of Banking and Finance Law and Practice (Pyrmont, NW, AUS) **[42283]**

Journal of Banking Regulation (Basingstoke, GBR) **[52212]**

Journal of Basic & Clinical Physiology & Pharmacology (Jerusalem, ISR) **[46087]**

Journal of Basic Microbiology (Jena, GER) **[44489]**

Journal Basket (Fribourg, SWI) *Unable to locate*

Journal of Behavior Therapy and Experimental Psychiatry (Maastricht, NLD) **[48737]**

Journal of Behavioral Education (Dordrecht, NLD) **[48443]**

Journal of Beliefs & Values (Abingdon, GBR) **[51872]**

Journal fur Betriebswirtschaft (Heidelberg, GER) **[44463]**

Journal of Bhutan Studies (Thimphu, BTN) **[42925]**

Journal of Bio-Inspired Computation Research (New Delhi, DH, IND) **[45593]**

Journal of Bioactive and Compatible Polymers (London, GBR) **[54704]**

Journal of Biochemical and Biophysical Methods **[48113]***

The Journal of Biochemistry (Oxford, GBR) **[56017]**

Journal of Biochemistry and Molecular Biology **[47258]***

Journal of Bioethical Inquiry (Dordrecht, NLD) **[48444]**

Journal of Bioinformatics and Computational Biology (London, GBR) **[54705]**

Journal of Biological Control (Coimbatore, TN, IND) *Unable to locate*

Journal of Biological Education (London, GBR) **[54706]**

Journal of Biological Physics and Chemistry (Tbilisi, GRG) **[44134]**

Journal of Biological Research (Thessaloniki, GRC) **[44775]**

Journal of Biological Sciences (Mumbai, MH, IND) *Unable to locate*

Journal of Biological Sciences (Faisalabad, PAK) **[49264]**

Journal of Biological Standardization (Strasbourg, FRA) *Unable to locate*

Journal of Biological Systems (Singapore, SGP) **[50200]**

Journal of Biomaterials Applications (London, GBR) **[54707]**

Journal of Biomaterials Science, Polymer Edition (Leiden, NLD) **[48690]**

Journal of Biomechanics (Eindhoven, NLD) **[48592]**

Journal of Biomedical Discovery and Collaboration (London, GBR) *Ceased*

Journal of Biomedical Investigation (Nnewi, AN, NGA) **[49148]**

Journal of Biomedical Science (Dordrecht, NLD) **[48445]**

Journal of Biomimetics, Biomaterials, and Tissue Engineering (Sydney, NW, AUS) **[42527]**

Journal of Biopharmaceutics and Biotechnology (Jerusalem, ISR) **[46088]**

Journal of Biophotonics (Weinheim, GER) **[44706]**

Journal of the BIOS (Oxford, GBR) **[56018]**

Journal of Bioscience and Bioengineering (Osaka, JPN) **[46620]**

Journal of Biosciences (Bangalore, KA, IND) **[44966]**

Journal of Biosocial Science (Cambridge, GBR) **[52846]**

Journal of Bodywork and Movement Therapies (London, GBR) **[54708]**

Journal of Bone and Joint Surgery (Brandhof, SAF) **[50358]**

Journal of Bone & Joint Surgery (British Volume) (London, GBR) **[54709]**

Journal of Bone and Mineral Metabolism (Tokyo, JPN) **[46889]**

Journal of Brain Science (Okayama, JPN) *Unable to locate*

Journal of Brand Management (London, GBR) **[54710]**

Journal of the Brazilian Chemical Society (Campinas, SP, BRZ) **[42969]**

Journal of the Brazilian Computer Society (Porto Alegre, RN, BRZ) **[42991]**

Journal of the Brazilian Society of Mechanical Sciences (Rio de Janeiro, RJ, BRZ) **[43010]**

Journal of Breath Research (Bristol, GBR) **[52682]**

Journal of the British Archaeological Association (London, GBR) **[54711]**

Journal of the British Astronomical Association (London, GBR) **[54712]**

Journal of British Cinema and Television (Edinburgh, GBR) **[53292]**

Journal—British Holiday & Home Parks Association (Gloucester, GBR) **[53471]**

Journal of the British Institute of Surgical Technologists (Shipley, GBR) *Unable to locate*

Journal of the British Interplanetary Society (London, GBR) **[54713]**

Journal of the British Menopause Society **[54926]***

Journal of the British Menopause Society **[55600]***

The Journal of British Podiatric Medicine (London, GBR) *Unable to locate*

Journal of the British Society of Scientific Glassblowers (Thurso, GBR) **[56750]**

The Journal of the British Tarantula Society (London, GBR) **[54714]**

Journal of Bryology (Middlewich, GBR) **[55624]**

Journal of Buddhist Ethics (London, GBR) **[54715]**

Journal of Building Appraisal (Basingstoke, GBR) **[52213]**

Journal of Building and Land Development (Dar es Salaam, TZA) **[51402]**

Journal of Building Physics (London, GBR) **[54716]**

Journal: Building Research and Practice (Rotterdam, NLD) *Unable to locate*

Journal of Building Structure (Beijing, CHN) **[43203]**

Journal of Bulgarian Historical Review (Sofia, BUL) **[43102]**

Journal of Business Chemistry (JoBC) (Munster, GER) **[44599]**

Journal of Business Ethics (Dordrecht, NLD) **[48446]**

Journal of Business Ethics Education (Riga, LAT) **[47369]**

Journal of Business Finance and Accounting (Oxford, GBR) **[56019]**

Journal of Business Law (Andover, GBR) **[52118]**

Journal of Business Research (Amsterdam, NLD) **[48054]**

Journal of Business Strategy (Bradford, GBR) **[52493]**

Journal of Business Venturing (Amsterdam, NLD) **[48055]**

Journal of Camel Practice and Research (Bikaner, RJ, IND) **[45017]**

Journal of the Cameroon Academy of Sciences (Buea, CMR) **[43124]**

Journal of Cancer Research and Clinical Oncology (Jena, GER) **[44490]**

Journal of Cancer Research and Therapeutics (Mumbai, MH, IND) **[45396]**

Journal of Carbohydrate Chemistry (Potsdam, GER) **[44640]**

Journal of Carcinogenesis (London, GBR) **[54717]**

Journal of Cardiovascular Magnetic Resonance (London, GBR) **[54719]**

Numbers cited in bold after listings are entry numbers rather than page numbers.

Journal of Cardiovascular Magnetic Resonance (London, GBR) **[54718]**

Journal of Cardiovascular Translational Research (Dordrecht, NLD) **[48447]**

Journal of Cell & Animal Biology (Lagos, LG, NGA) **[49139]**

Journal of Cell Science (Cambridge, GBR) **[52847]**

Journal of Cellular Automata (Bristol, GBR) **[52683]**

Journal of Cellular Plastics (London, GBR) **[54720]**

Journal of Ceramic Processing Research (Seoul, KOR) **[47271]**

Journal of the Ceramic Society of Japan (Tokyo, JPN) **[46890]**

Journal of Cereal Science (Amsterdam, NLD) **[48056]**

Journal of Cerebral Blood Flow and Metabolism (Berlin, GER) **[44204]**

Journal of Cetacean Research and Management (Cambridge, GBR) **[52848]**

Journal of the Ceylon College of Physicians (Colombo, SRI) *Unable to locate*

Journal of Change Management (Abingdon, GBR) **[51873]**

Journal of the Cheirological Society (Dereham, GBR) *Unable to locate*

Journal of Chemical Engineering of Japan (Tokyo, JPN) **[46891]**

Journal of Chemical Health and Safety (Amsterdam, NLD) **[48057]**

Journal of Chemical Industry of Forest Products (Nanjing, JS, CHN) *Unable to locate*

Journal of Chemical Neuroanatomy (Maastricht, NLD) **[48738]**

Journal of Chemical Research (Saint Albans, GBR) *Unable to locate*

Journal of Chemical Sciences (Bangalore, KA, IND) **[44967]**

Journal of the Chemical Society Chemical Communications **[52803]**[*]

Journal of the Chemical Society of Pakistan (Karachi, PAK) *Unable to locate*

Journal of Chemical Software (Fukui, JPN) **[46332]**

Journal of Chemical Technology and Biotechnology (London, GBR) **[54721]**

The Journal of Chemical Thermodynamics (Amsterdam, NLD) **[48058]**

Journal of Chemicals and Allied Industries (Baroda, GJ, IND) *Unable to locate*

Journal Chemistry for Sustainable Development (Novosibirsk, RUS) **[50011]**

Journal of Child and Adolescent Mental Health (Grahamstown, SAF) **[50501]**

Journal of Child and Adolescent Psychiatric Nursing (Oxford, GBR) **[56020]**

Journal of Child Psychology and Psychiatry (London, GBR) **[54722]**

Journal of Child Psychotherapy (London, GBR) **[54723]**

Journal of Children and Media (Tel Aviv, ISR) **[46107]**

Journal of Children and Poverty (Abingdon, GBR) **[51874]**

Journal of Children's Services (Brighton, GBR) **[52619]**

Journal de Chimie Physique (Paris, FRA) *Ceased*

Journal of China Particuology (Singapore, SGP) *Ceased*

Journal of the China University of Geosciences **[43519]**[*]

Journal of Chinese Agricultural Chemical Society (Taipei, TWN) *Unable to locate*

Journal of the Chinese Cereals and Oils Association (Beijing, CHN) *Unable to locate*

Journal of Chinese Chemical Society (Taipei, TWN) **[51349]**

Journal of Chinese Economic and Business Studies (Guildford, GBR) **[53492]**

Journal of Chinese Economic and Foreign Trade Studies (Beijing, CHN) **[43204]**

Journal of Chinese Institute of Chemical Engineers (Hsinchu, TWN) *Unable to locate*

Journal of Chinese Institute of Engineers (Taipei, TWN) **[51350]**

Journal of Chinese Language and Computing **[50177]**[*]

Journal of Chinese Overseas (Singapore, SGP) **[50201]**

Journal of Chinese Society of Geodesy, Photogrammetry and Cartography (Beijing, CHN) *Unable to locate*

Journal for Christian Scholarship (Centurion, SAF) **[50441]**

Journal of Chromatography A (Amsterdam, NLD) **[48059]**

Journal of Church Monuments Society (Sharpham, GBR) **[56487]**

Journal of Circadian Rhythms (London, GBR) **[54724]**

Journal of Civil Engineering (Nairobi, KEN) **[47186]**

Journal of Civil Engineering Research and Practice (Nairobi, KEN) **[47187]**

Journal of Civil Society (Abingdon, GBR) **[51875]**

Journal of Classical Sociology (London, GBR) **[54725]**

Journal of Clinical Biochemical and Nutrition (Ibaraki, JPN) *Unable to locate*

Journal of Clinical and Experimental Medicine (Tokyo, JPN) **[46892]**

Journal of Clinical Monitoring **[48448]**[*]

Journal of Clinical Monitoring and Computing (Dordrecht, NLD) **[48448]**

Journal of Clinical Pathology (Hove, GBR) **[53608]**

Journal of Clinical Research (London, GBR) **[54726]**

Journal of Cluster Science (Dordrecht, NLD) **[48449]**

Journal of Coated Fabrics **[54766]**[*]

Journal of Cognition and Culture (Leiden, NLD) **[48691]**

Journal Coiffure Suisse (Bern, SWI) *Unable to locate*

Journal of College of International Studies (Aichi, JPN) *Unable to locate*

Journal of College of Medicine (Enugu, NGA) **[49080]**

Journal of College of Physicians and Surgeons Pakistan (Karachi, PAK) **[49357]**

Journal of Colloid and Interface Science (Amsterdam, NLD) **[48060]**

Journal of Combinatorial Theory, Series A (Amsterdam, NLD) **[48061]**

Journal of Combinatorial Theory, Series B (Amsterdam, NLD) **[48062]**

Journal of Commerce and Industry (Taipei, TWN) **[51351]**

Journal of Commercial Biotechnology (Basingstoke, GBR) **[52214]**

The Journal of Commonwealth and Comparative Politics **[51733]**[*]

The Journal of Commonwealth & Comparative Politics (London, GBR) *Unable to locate*

Journal of Commonwealth Law and Legal Education (Abingdon, GBR) **[51876]**

The Journal of Commonwealth Literature (London, GBR) **[54727]**

Journal of Communicable Diseases (New Delhi, DH, IND) *Unable to locate*

Journal of Communication (Oxford, GBR) **[56021]**

Journal of Communication Management (Bradford, GBR) **[52494]**

The Journal of Communist Studies and Transition Politics (Abingdon, GBR) **[51877]**

Journal of Community & Applied Social Psychology (Utrecht, NLD) **[48761]**

Journal of Community Medicine and Primary Health Care (Zaria, KD, NGA) **[49182]**

Journal of Comparative Literature and Aesthetics (Jyothivihar, OR, IND) *Unable to locate*

Journal of Comparative Physiology B (Marburg, GER) **[44548]**

Journal of Competition Law and Economics (Oxford, GBR) **[56022]**

Journal for Complementary Medicine (London, GBR) *Unable to locate*

Journal of Composite Materials (London, GBR) **[54728]**

Journal of Computational Acoustics (Singapore, SGP) **[50202]**

Journal of Computational and Applied Mathematics (Leuven, BEL) **[42900]**

Journal of Computational and Applied Mechanics (Miskolc-Egyetemvaros, HUN) **[44891]**

Journal of Computational Electronics (Dordrecht, NLD) **[48450]**

The Journal of Computational Finance (London, GBR) **[54729]**

Journal of Computational Intelligence in Bioinformatics (Seoul, KOR) **[47272]**

Journal of Computational Mathematics (Hong Kong, CHN) **[43353]**

Journal of Computational Methods in Sciences and Engineering (Amsterdam, NLD) **[48063]**

The Journal of Computational Multiphase Flows (Brentwood, GBR) **[52579]**

Journal of Computational Neuroscience (Dordrecht, NLD) **[48451]**

Journal of Computational Physics (Amsterdam, NLD) **[48064]**

Journal of Computer-Aided Chemistry (Tokyo, JPN) **[46893]**

Journal of Computer-Mediated Communication (Oxford, GBR) **[56023]**

Journal of Computer Science and Technology (JCST) (Beijing, CHN) **[43205]**

Journal of Computer and System Sciences (Amsterdam, NLD) **[48065]**

Journal of Computer and Systems Sciences International (Moscow, RUS) **[49928]**

Journal in Computer Virology (Dordrecht, NLD) **[48452]**

Journal of Conflict Archaeology (Leiden, NLD) *Ceased*

Journal of Conflict and Security Law (Oxford, GBR) **[56024]**

Journal of Conservative Dentistry (Chennai, TN, IND) **[45045]**

Journal of Constitutional & Parliamentary Studies (New Delhi, DH, IND) *Unable to locate*

Journal of Construction Research (Hong Kong, CHN) **[43354]**

Journal of Constructional Steel Research (Guildford, GBR) **[53493]**

Journal of Consumer Behaviour (Bognor Regis, GBR) **[52398]**

Journal of Consumer Culture (London, GBR) **[54730]**

Journal of Consumer Policy (Dordrecht, NLD) **[48453]**

Journal of Contemporary African Studies (Abingdon, GBR) **[51878]**

Journal of Contemporary Asia (Manila, PHL) *Unable to locate*

Journal of Contemporary China (Abingdon, GBR) **[51879]**

Journal of Contemporary European Studies (Abingdon, GBR) **[51880]**

Journal of Contemporary History (London, GBR) **[54731]**

Journal of Contemporary Mathematics (Van, TUR) **[51580]**

Journal of Contemporary Religion (Abingdon, GBR) **[51881]**

Journal of Contemporary Thought (Vadodara, GJ, IND) *Unable to locate*

Journal of Contract Law (North Ryde, NW, AUS) *Unable to locate*

Journal of Convex Analysis (Lemgo, GER) **[44532]**

Journal of Coptic Studies (Feldkirchen, GER) **[44352]**

The Journal of Corporate Citizenship (Sheffield, GBR) **[56504]**

The Journal of Corporate Law Studies (Oxford, GBR) **[56025]**

Journal of Corporate Real Estate (Bradford, GBR) **[52495]**

Journal of Cosmetic and Laser Therapy (Abingdon, GBR) **[51882]**

Journal of Cosmology and Astroparticle Physics (Bristol, GBR) **[52684]**

Journal of Cranio-Maxillofacial Surgery (Kiel, GER) **[44503]**

Journal of Cranio-Maxillofacial Surgery (Kidlington, GBR) **[53696]**

Journal of Craniovertebral Junction and Spine (Mumbai, MH, IND) **[45397]**

Journal of Credit Risk (London, GBR) **[54732]**

Journal of Criminal Law (Letchworth, GBR) *Unable to locate*

Journal for Critical Education Policy Studies (Northampton, GBR) **[55711]**

Journal of Critical Realism (London, GBR) **[54733]**

Journal of Cross-Cultural Psychology (Athens, GRC) **[54750]**

Journal of Cultural and Evolutionary Psychology **[44841]**[*]

Journal of Cultural Heritage (Amsterdam, NLD) **[48066]**

Journal for Cultural Research (Abingdon, GBR) **[51883]**

Journal of Customer Behaviour (Argyll, GBR) **[52129]**

Journal of Cutaneous and Aesthetic Surgery (Bangalore, KA, IND) **[44968]**

Journal of Cytology (New Delhi, DH, IND) **[45594]**

Journal of Cytology and Genetics (Bangalore, KA, IND) *Unable to locate*

Journal of Czech Physicians (Prague, CZE) **[43627]**

Numbers cited in bold after listings are entry numbers rather than page numbers.

The Journal of Dagaare Studies (JDS) (Hong Kong, CHN) [43355]

Journal of Dairying, Foods & Home Sciences (Karnal, HY, IND) Unable to locate

Journal of Database Marketing & Customer Strategy Management (London, GBR) [54734]

Journal of the Dental Association of Thailand (Bangkok, THA) Unable to locate

Journal of Dental Implants (Mumbai, MH, IND) [45398]

Journal of Dentistry (Reykjavik, ICE) Unable to locate

Journal of Dentistry (Exeter, GBR) [53361]

Journal of the Department of Filipino (Malate, PHL) Unable to locate

Journal of Department of Law, University of Dhaka (Dhaka, BGD) Unable to locate

Journal of Derivatives Accounting (Singapore, SGP) Ceased

Journal of Derivatives & Hedge Funds (London, GBR) [54735]

Journal of Dermatological Treatment (Abingdon, GBR) [51884]

Journal of Dermatological Treatment (London, GBR) [54736]

Journal of Dermatology (Tokyo, JPN) [46894]

Journal of Design History (Oxford, GBR) [56026]

Journal of Design Research (Olney, GBR) [55842]

The Journal of Design & Technology Education [56629]*

Journal of Development Administration (Colombo, SRI) [50855]

Journal of Development and Administrative Studies (Kirtipur, NPL) Unable to locate

Journal of Development Assistance (Tokyo, JPN) Unable to locate

Journal of Development Communications (Kuala Lumpur, MYS) Unable to locate

Journal of Development Economics (Amsterdam, NLD) [48067]

Journal of Development Studies (Abingdon, GBR) [51885]

Journal of Developmental Entrepreneurship (Singapore, SGP) [50203]

Journal of Dharma (Bangalore, KA, IND) [44969]

Journal du Diabetique (Luxembourg, LUX) [47492]

Journal of Diagnostic Radiography and Imaging (New York, NY, USA) Ceased

Journal of Differential Equations (Amsterdam, NLD) [48068]

Journal of Digital Asset Management (Basingstoke, GBR) [52215]

Journal of Digital Contents (Badajoz, SPA) [50645]

Journal of Digital Information (Loughborough, GBR) [55481]

Journal of Digital Information Management (Chennai, TN, IND) [45046]

Journal of the Diplomates of the Royal College of Obstetricians and Gynaecologists (London, GBR) Ceased

Journal of Diplomatic Studies (Riyadh, SAU) Unable to locate

Journal of Direct, Data and Digital Marketing Practice (London, GBR) [54737]

Journal of Discrete Algorithms (Amsterdam) (London, GBR) [54738]

Journal of Discrete Mathematical Sciences and Cryptography (New Delhi, DH, IND) [45595]

Journal of Documentation (Bradford, GBR) [52496]

The Journal of Dramatherapy (London, GBR) Unable to locate

Journal of Drug Assessment (London, GBR) [54739]

Journal of Drug Evaluation (Abingdon, GBR) Ceased

Journal of Drug Targeting (Abingdon, GBR) [51886]

Journal of Dynamical and Control Systems (Dordrecht, NLD) [48454]

Journal of Dynamical Systems and Geometric Theories (Kerman, IRN) [45882]

Journal of Dynamics and Differential Equations (Dordrecht, NLD) [48455]

Journal of E-Governance (Amsterdam, NLD) [48069]

Journal of Early Childhood Literacy (London, GBR) [54740]

Journal of Early Childhood Teacher Education (Abingdon, GBR) [51887]

Journal of Early Modern History (Leiden, NLD) [48692]

Journal of the Earth and Space Physics (Tehran, IRN) Unable to locate

Journal of Earth System Science (Bangalore, KA, IND) [44970]

Journal of East African Natural History (Stellenbosch, SAF) [50632]

Journal of East Asian Linguistics (Dordrecht, NLD) [48456]

Journal of East Asiatic Studies (Manila, PHL) Unable to locate

The Journal of Ecclesiastical History (Cambridge, GBR) [52849]

Journal of Ecobiology (Palani, TN, IND) Unable to locate

The Journal of Ecology (London, GBR) [54741]

Journal of Economic Dynamics and Control (Sydney, NW, AUS) [42528]

Journal of Economic Geography (Southampton, GBR) [56573]

Journal of Economic Geology (New Delhi, DH, IND) Unable to locate

The Journal of Economic History (Cambridge, GBR) [52850]

The Journal of Economic Inequality (Dordrecht, NLD) [48457]

Journal of Economic Integration (Seoul, KOR) [47273]

Journal of Economic Methodology (Abingdon, GBR) [51888]

Journal of Economic Psychology (Amsterdam, NLD) [48070]

Journal of Economic and Social Geography (Utrecht, NLD) [48762]

Journal of the Economic and Social History of the Orient (Leiden, NLD) [48693]

Journal of Economic and Social Measurement (Amsterdam, NLD) [48071]

Journal of the Economic Society of Finland (Abo, FIN) [43811]

Journal of Economic and Taxonomic Botany (Jodhpur, RJ, IND) [45226]

Journal of Economics (Meerut, UP, IND) Unable to locate

Journal of Economics and Administrative Studies [51557]*

Journal of Economics Theory (Faisalabad, PAK) [49265]

Journal of Economics of Water Resources (Nanjing, JS, CHN) [43458]

Journal of Ecotourism (Abingdon, GBR) [51889]

Journal of Editorial Study (Shanghai, CHN) [43480]

Journal of Education (UKM Bangi, MYS) Unable to locate

Journal of Education and Social Change (New Delhi, DH, IND) Unable to locate

Journal of Education for Teaching (Abingdon, GBR) [51890]

Journal of Education and Work (Abingdon, GBR) [51891]

Journal of Educational Administration (Bradford, GBR) [52497]

Journal of Educational Administration and History (Abingdon, GBR) [51892]

Journal of Educational Measurement (Oxford, GBR) [56027]

Journal of Educational Media and Library Sciences (Tamsui, TWN) [51394]

Journal of Educational Planning and Administration (New Delhi, DH, IND) [45596]

Journal of Educational Research (Karachi, PAK) Unable to locate

Journal of Educational Research and Extension (Coimbatore, TN, IND) Unable to locate

Journal Eesti Arst (Tartu, EST) [43792]

Journal of Egyptian Archaeology (London, GBR) Unable to locate

Journal of Egyptian History (Leiden, NLD) [48694]

Journal of the Eighteen Nineties Society (High Wycombe, GBR) Unable to locate

Journal of Elastomers and Plastics (London, GBR) [54742]

Journal of Elections, Public Opinion & Parties (Abingdon, GBR) [51893]

Journal of Electrical Engineering and Information Science (Seoul, KOR) Unable to locate

The Journal of Electroacoustic Music (London, GBR) Ceased

Journal of Electromagnetic Waves and Applications (Leiden, NLD) [48695]

Journal of Electron Microscopy (Oxford, GBR) [56028]

Journal of the Electronics Industry (Tokyo, JPN) [46895]

Journal of Electrophysiological Technology (Birmingham, GBR) [52346]

Journal of eLiteracy (JeLit) (Glasgow, GBR) [53427]

Journal of Emergency Primary Health Care (Frankston, VI, AUS) [41873]

Journal of Empirical Theology (Leiden, NLD) [48696]

Journal of Endocrinological Investigation (Milan, ITA) [46182]

Journal of Endocrinology (Sofia, BUL) [43103]

Journal of Endocrinology (Bristol, GBR) [52685]

Journal of Endocrinology, Metabolism and Diabetes of South Africa (Pinelands, SAF) [50573]

Journal of Endotoxin Research [54605]*

Journal of Energy, Heat and Mass Transfer (Chennai, TN, IND) [45047]

Journal of the Energy Institute (London, GBR) [54743]

Journal of Engineering and Applied Sciences (Faisalabad, PAK) [49266]

Journal of Engineering, Design and Technology (Centurion, SAF) [50442]

Journal of Engineering Manufacture (Bath, GBR) [52247]

Journal of English for Academic Purposes (Amsterdam, NLD) [48072]

Journal of English Studies and Comparative Literature (Quezon City, PHL) Unable to locate

Journal of Enterprise Information Management (Uxbridge, GBR) [56800]

Journal of Enterprising Communities (Bradford, GBR) [52498]

Journal of Enterprising Culture (Singapore, SGP) [50204]

Journal of Entomology (Faisalabad, PAK) [49267]

The Journal of Entrepreneurship (New Delhi, DH, IND) [45597]

Journal of Environmental Assessment Policy and Management (Singapore, SGP) [50205]

Journal of Environmental Biology (Lucknow, UP, IND) [45323]

Journal of Environmental Chemistry (Ibaraki, JPN) Unable to locate

Journal of Environmental Extension (Ibadan, OY, NGA) [49089]

Journal of Environmental Health Research (London, GBR) [54744]

Journal of Environmental Law (Oxford, GBR) [56029]

Journal of Environmental Management (Amsterdam, NLD) [48073]

Journal of Environmental Management (Kidlington, GBR) [53697]

Journal of Environmental Monitoring (Cambridge, GBR) [52851]

Journal of Environmental Planning and Management (Abingdon, GBR) [51894]

Journal of Environmental Policy & Planning (Abingdon, GBR) [51895]

Journal of Environmental Polymer Degradation [48485]*

Journal of Environmental Psychology (Amsterdam, NLD) [48074]

Journal of Environmental Research (New Delhi, DH, IND) Unable to locate

Journal of Environmental Resources (Thiruvananthapuram, KE, IND) Unable to locate

Journal of Environmental Science (Bhubaneswar, OR, IND) Unable to locate

Journal of Environmental Science and Engineering (Nagpur, MH, IND) [45468]

Journal of Environmental Sciences (Kidlington, GBR) [53698]

Journal of Environmental Studies and Policy [45644]*

Journal of Enzyme Inhibition (Abingdon, GBR) Unable to locate

Journal of Enzyme Inhibition and Medicinal Chemistry (Cardiff, GBR) [52933]

Journal of Epidemiology and Community Health (London, GBR) [54745]

Journal of Epilepsy and Clinical Neurophysiology (Vicosa, MI, BRZ) [43059]

Journal of Equine Science (Tochigi, JPN) [46710]

Journal of Ethiopian Medical Practice (Addis Ababa, ETH) [43802]

Journal of Ethnic and Migration Studies (JEMS) (Brighton, GBR) [52620]

Journal of Ethnobiology and Ethnomedicine (London, GBR) [54746]

Numbers cited in bold after listings are entry numbers rather than page numbers.

Journal of Ethnopharmacology (Leiden, NLD) **[48697]**

Journal of Ethology (Tokyo, JPN) **[46896]**

Journal of Eukaryotic Microbiology (Oxford, GBR) **[56030]**

Journal of the European Academy of Dermatology and Venereology (Nice, FRA) **[44016]**

Journal of the European Ceramic Society (Oxford, GBR) **[56031]**

Journal of the European Dialysis and Transplant Nurses (Walchwil, SWI) *Unable to locate*

Journal of European Economic History (Rome, ITA) *Unable to locate*

Journal for European Environmental & Planning Law (Leiden, NLD) **[48698]**

Journal of European Industrial Training (Bradford, GBR) **[52499]**

Journal of European Public Policy (Abingdon, GBR) **[51896]**

Journal of European Real Estate Research (County Antrim, GBR) **[53075]**

Journal of European Social Policy (London, GBR) **[54747]**

Journal of European Society of Veterinary Pathology (Giessen, GER) *Ceased*

Journal of the European Society of Women in Theological Research (Bamberg, GER) **[44146]**

Journal of European Studies (Karachi, PAK) *Unable to locate*

Journal of European Studies (London, GBR) **[54748]**

Journal of Evolutionary Biochemistry and Physiology (Saint Petersburg, RUS) **[50023]**

Journal of Evolutionary Psychology (Budapest, HUN) **[44841]**

Journal of Experimental Animal Science (Amsterdam, NLD) *Ceased*

Journal of Experimental Biology (Cambridge, GBR) **[52852]**

Journal of Experimental Botany (Lancaster, GBR) **[53734]**

Journal of Experimental Botany (Oxford, GBR) **[56032]**

Journal of Experimental Child Psychology (Amsterdam, NLD) **[48075]**

Journal of Experimental and Clinical Anatomy (Uturu, IM, NGA) **[49176]**

Journal of Experimental & Clinical Assisted Reproduction (London, GBR) **[54749]**

Journal of Experimental Criminology (Dordrecht, NLD) **[48458]**

Journal of the Experimental Forest of National Taiwan University (Nan-Tou Hsien, TWN) *Unable to locate*

Journal of Experimental Nanoscience (Abingdon, GBR) **[51897]**

Journal of Experimental Social Psychology (Amsterdam, NLD) **[48076]**

Journal of Explosives and Propellants (Taoyuan, TWN) *Unable to locate*

Journal of Exposure Science and Environmental Epidemiology (JESEE) (London, GBR) **[54750]**

Journal of Facilities Management (Bradford, GBR) **[52500]**

Journal of the Faculty of Dentistry, Marmara University (Istanbul, TUR) *Unable to locate*

Journal of the Faculty of Fisheries Prefectural University Mie (Mie, JPN) *Unable to locate*

Journal of Faculty of Marine Science and Technology of Tokai University (Shizuoka, JPN) **[46688]**

Journal of Faculty of Nutriiton of

Kobe Gakuin University (Kobe, JPN) *Unable to locate*

Journal of the Faculty of Science, Ege University, Series A (Izmir, TUR) **[51574]**

Journal of the Faculty of Science, Ege University, Series B (Izmir, TUR) *Unable to locate*

Journal of the Faculty of Science and Technology of Kinki University (Osaka, JPN) *Unable to locate*

Journal of Family Welfare (Mumbai, MH, IND) **[45399]**

Journal of Fashion Marketing and Management (Bradford, GBR) **[52501]**

Journal Faxe de Neurologie (Paris, FRA) *Unable to locate*

Journal of Feline Medicine and Surgery (Tisbury, GBR) *Unable to locate*

Journal of Ferrocement (Pathumthani, THA) *Unable to locate*

Journal of Film Preservation (Brussels, BEL) **[42862]**

Journal of Finance (Oxford, GBR) **[56033]**

Journal of Finance and Industry (Safat, KWT) *Unable to locate*

Journal of Finance and Management in Public Services (London, GBR) **[54751]**

Journal of Financial Crime (London, GBR) **[54752]**

Journal of Financial Econometrics (Oxford, GBR) **[56034]**

The Journal of Financial Forecasting (London, GBR) *Ceased*

Journal of Financial Intermediation (Amsterdam, NLD) **[48077]**

Journal of Financial Management and Analysis (Mumbai, MH, IND) **[45400]**

Journal of Financial Management of Property and Construction (Preston, GBR) **[56300]**

Journal of Financial Regulation and Compliance (London, GBR) **[54753]**

Journal of Financial Services Marketing (Basingstoke, GBR) **[52216]**

Journal of Financial Services Research (Dordrecht, NLD) **[48459]**

Journal of Fire Sciences (London, GBR) **[54754]**

Journal of Fisheries of China (Beijing, CHN) *Unable to locate*

Journal of Fisheries International (Faisalabad, PAK) **[49268]**

Journal of Flood Risk Management (High Wycombe, GBR) **[53574]**

Journal of Fluency Disorders (Amsterdam, NLD) **[48078]**

Journal of Fluorine Chemistry (Tokyo, JPN) **[46897]**

Journal of Food Composition and Analysis (Amsterdam, NLD) **[48079]**

Journal of Food Hygienic Society of Japan (Tokyo, JPN) *Unable to locate*

Journal of Food Processing and Preservation (Oxford, GBR) **[56035]**

Journal of Food Science and Nutrition (Gauteng, SAF) *Ceased*

Journal of Food Science and Technology (Mysore, KA, IND) *Unable to locate*

Journal of Food Technology (Faisalabad, PAK) **[49269]**

Journal of Food Technology in Africa (Nairobi, KEN) **[47188]**

Journal of Foreign Exchange and International Finance (Pune, MH, IND) *Unable to locate*

Journal of Forensic Dental Sciences (Chennai, IND) **[45028]**

Journal of Forest Economics (Umea, SWE) **[51046]**

Journal of Forest Research (Tokyo, JPN) **[46898]**

Journal of the Formosan Medical Association (Taipei, TWN) **[51352]**

Journal of Fourth Military University (Xi'an, SH, CHN) **[43533]**

Journal fur die Frau (Hamburg, GER) *Unable to locate*

Journal of Fujita Technical Research Institute (Kanagawa, JPN) *Unable to locate*

Journal of Functional Analysis (Amsterdam, NLD) **[48080]**

Journal of Functional Ecology (London, GBR) **[54755]**

Journal of Functional and Logic Programming (Munster, GER) *Unable to locate*

Journal of Further and Higher Education (Abingdon, GBR) **[51898]**

Journal of Fusion Energy (Dordrecht, NLD) **[48460]**

The Journal of Gambling Business and Economics (Buckingham, GBR) **[52757]**

Journal of Gambling Studies (Dordrecht, NLD) **[48461]**

Journal of Gandhian Studies (Allahabad, UP, IND) *Unable to locate*

Journal of Gastroenterology (Tokyo, JPN) **[46899]**

Journal of Gastroenterology and Hepatology (Richmond, VI, AUS) **[42303]**

Journal of Gem Industry (Jaipur, RJ, IND) **[45197]**

The Journal of Gemmology (London, GBR) **[54756]**

Journal of Gender Studies (Abingdon, GBR) **[51899]**

Journal of General and Applied Microbiology (Tokyo, JPN) **[46900]**

Journal of General Management (Henley-on-Thames, GBR) **[53561]**

Journal of General Medicine (Mumbai, MH, IND) *Unable to locate*

Journal of General Plant Pathology (Kyoto, JPN) **[46476]**

Journal of General Virology (Reading, GBR) **[56323]**

Journal of Generic Medicines (Basingstoke, GBR) **[52217]**

Journal of Genetic Counseling (Dordrecht, NLD) **[48462]**

Journal of Genetics (Bangalore, KA, IND) **[44971]**

Journal of Genetics and Genomics (Beijing, CHN) **[43206]**

Journal de Geneve & Gazette de Lausanne (Geneva, SWI) *Unable to locate*

Journal of Genocide Research (Abingdon, GBR) **[51900]**

Journal of Geochemical Exploration (Naples, ITA) **[46201]**

Journal of Geodesy (Heidelberg, GER) **[44464]**

Journal of Geodetic Society of Japan (Tokyo, JPN) **[46901]**

Journal of Geodynamics (Amsterdam, NLD) **[48081]**

Journal of Geographical Science (Taipei, TWN) **[51353]**

Journal of Geographical Sciences (Beijing, CHN) **[43207]**

Journal of Geographical Systems (Dordrecht, NLD) **[48463]**

Journal of Geography in Higher Education (Abingdon, GBR) **[51901]**

Journal of Geological Engineering (Ankara, TUR) *Unable to locate*

Journal of the Geological Society (Bath, GBR) **[52248]**

Journal of Geological Society of China (Taipei, TWN) *Unable to locate*

Journal of the Geological Society of India (Bangalore, KA, IND) **[44972]**

Journal of Geological Society of Japan (Tokyo, JPN) *Unable to locate*

Journal of Geometry (Dordrecht, NLD) **[48464]**

Journal for Geometry and Graphics (Lemgo, GER) **[44533]**

Journal of Geometry and Physics (Trieste, ITA) **[46265]**

Journal of Geophysics and Engineering (Bristol, GBR) **[52686]**

Journal of Geosciences (Osaka, JPN) *Unable to locate*

Journal of Geospatial Engineering (Hong Kong, CHN) **[43356]**

Journal of the Ghana Science Association (Legon, GHA) **[44737]**

Journal of Glaciology (Cambridge, GBR) **[52853]**

Journal for Global Business Advancement (Olney, GBR) **[55843]**

Journal of Global Ethics (Abingdon, GBR) **[51902]**

Journal of Global History (London, GBR) **[54757]**

Journal of Global Optimization (Dordrecht, NLD) **[48465]**

Journal of Government Information (Amsterdam, NLD) *Unable to locate*

Journal of the Graduate School of Biosphere Science, Hiroshima University (Higashihiroshima, JPN) *Unable to locate*

Journal of Graph Algorithms and Applications (Singapore, SGP) **[50206]**

Journal of Greek Linguistics (Biggleswade, GBR) **[52324]**

The Journal of Grey System (Wuhan, HU, CHN) **[43524]**

Journal of Grid Computing (Dordrecht, NLD) **[48466]**

Journal of Group Theory (Oxford, GBR) **[56036]**

Journal of the Gulf and Arabian Peninsula Studies (Safat, KWT) **[47338]**

Journal of Gynecological Endoscopy and Surgery (Mumbai, MH, IND) **[45401]**

Journal de Gynecologie Obstetrique et Biologie de la Reproduction (Paris, FRA) *Unable to locate*

Journal of Hand Surgery (British & European Volume) (London, GBR) **[54758]**

Journal of the Hardy Plant Society (Pershore, GBR) *Unable to locate*

Journal of Hazardous Materials (Amsterdam, NLD) **[48082]**

Journal of Headache and Pain (Tokyo, JPN) **[46902]**

Journal of Health, Organization and Management (Bradford, GBR) **[52502]**

Journal of Health, Population and Nutrition (Dhaka, BGD) **[42813]**

Journal of Health Psychology (London, GBR) **[54759]**

Journal of Health Science (Tokyo, JPN) **[46903]**

Journal of Health Services Research & Policy (London, GBR) **[54760]**

Numbers cited in bold after listings are entry numbers rather than page numbers.

Journal of Health and Visual Sciences (Uturu, IM, NGA) **[49177]**

Journal of Heart Valve Disease (Northwood, GBR) **[55721]**

Journal of Hellenic Studies (London, GBR) **[54761]**

Journal of Helminthology (Cambridge, GBR) **[52854]**

Journal of the Henry Martyn Institute (Hyderabad, AP, IND) **[45174]**

Journal of Hepato-Biliary-Pancreatic Sciences (Tokyo, JPN) **[46904]**

Journal of Hepato-Biliary-Pancreatic Surgery **[46904]***

Journal of Heredity (Oxford, GBR) **[56037]**

Journal of Heritage Tourism (Abingdon, GBR) **[51903]**

Journal of High Energy Physics (London, GBR) **[54762]**

Journal of the High Pressure Gas Safety Institute of Japan (Tokyo, JPN) *Unable to locate*

Journal of Higher Education (New Delhi, DH, IND) *Unable to locate*

Journal of Higher Education in Africa (Dakar, SEN) **[50081]**

Journal of Higher Education Policy and Management (Fairfield, VI, AUS) **[41864]**

Journal of Himalayan Geology (New Delhi, DH, IND) *Unable to locate*

Journal of Himalayan Studies and Regional Development (Garhwal, UP, IND) *Unable to locate*

Journal of Himeji Red Cross Hospital (Hyogo, JPN) *Unable to locate*

Journal of Hiroshima City Medical Association (Hiroshima, JPN) *Unable to locate*

Journal of Hiroshima University Dental Society (Hiroshima, JPN) *Unable to locate*

Journal of Historical Geography (Kidlington, GBR) **[53699]**

Journal of Historical Pragmatics (Amsterdam, NLD) **[48083]**

Journal of Historical Research (Ranchi, BH, IND) *Unable to locate*

Journal of Historical Sociology (Oxford, GBR) **[56038]**

Journal for the History of Arabic Science (Aleppo, SYR) *Unable to locate*

Journal of the History of Collections (Oxford, GBR) **[56039]**

Journal of Hohai University (Nanjing, JS, CHN) **[43459]**

Journal of Holistic Healthcare (Bridgwater, GBR) **[52596]**

Journal of Home Economics of Japan (Tokyo, JPN) **[46905]**

Journal of the Hong Kong College of Cardiology (Hong Kong, CHN) **[43357]**

Journal of the Hong Kong Geriatrics Society (Hong Kong, CHN) **[43358]**

Journal of the Hong Kong Institution of Textile and Apparel **[43380]***

Journal of the Hong Kong Library Association (Hong Kong, CHN) *Unable to locate*

Journal of Hospitality, Leisure, Sports & Tourism Education (Heslington, GBR) **[53568]**

Journal of Housing and the Built Environment (Dordrecht, NLD) **[48467]**

Journal of Housing Economics (Amsterdam, NLD) **[48084]**

Journal of Human Development **[51904]***

Journal of Human Development and Capabilities (Abingdon, GBR) **[51904]**

Journal of Human Ecology (Delhi, DH, IND) **[45100]**

Journal of Human Ergology (Saitama, JPN) *Unable to locate*

Journal of Human Evolution (Amsterdam, NLD) **[48085]**

Journal of Human Genetics (Tokyo, JPN) **[46906]**

Journal of Human Hypertension (London, GBR) **[54763]**

Journal of Human Kinetics (Warsaw, POL) **[49722]**

Journal of Human Nutrition and Dietetics (Hatfield, GBR) **[53540]**

Journal of Human Reproductive Sciences (Bangalore, KA, IND) **[44973]**

Journal of Human Rights (Abingdon, GBR) **[51905]**

Journal of Human Values (New Delhi, DH, IND) **[45598]**

Journal of Humanities (Seoul, KOR) *Unable to locate*

Journal of Humanities and Natural Sciences (Tokyo, JPN) **[46907]**

Journal of Humanities and Social Sciences (Doha) (Doha, QAT) *Unable to locate*

Journal of Hydrobiology (Ujjain, MP, IND) *Unable to locate*

Journal of Hydrodynamics (Wuxi, CHN) **[43527]**

Journal of Hydroinformatics (London, GBR) **[54764]**

Journal of Hydrology and Hydromechanics (Bratislava, SLK) **[50320]**

Journal of Hygiene and Public Health (Sofia, BUL) *Unable to locate*

Journal of Hyogo University of Teacher Education Series 3 (Hyogo, JPN) *Unable to locate*

Journal of Iberian & Latin American Studies (Abingdon, GBR) **[51906]**

Journal of Ichthyology (Moscow, RUS) **[49929]**

Journal of the ICRU (Oxford, GBR) **[56040]**

Journal of IEICE (Tokyo, JPN) **[46908]**

Journal of the Immaculate Conception College (Ozamis City, PHL) *Unable to locate*

Journal of Immigrant Health **[48468]***

Journal of Immigrant and Minority Health (Dordrecht, NLD) **[48468]**

Journal of Immune Based Therapies and Vaccines (London, GBR) **[54765]**

The Journal of Imperial & Commonwealth History (Abingdon, GBR) **[51907]**

Journal of In-Service Education **[52022]***

Journal of Indexing & Reference Work (Calcutta, WB, IND) *Unable to locate*

Journal, Indian Academy of Clinical Medicine (New Delhi, DH, IND) **[45599]**

Journal of Indian Academy of Forensic Medicine (Patiala, PJ, IND) **[45685]**

Journal of Indian Academy of Oral Medicine and Radiology (Belgaum, KA, IND) **[44996]**

Journal of Indian Association for Child and Adolescent Mental Health (New Delhi, DH, IND) **[45600]**

Journal of Indian Association of Pediatric Surgeons (New Delhi, DH, IND) **[45601]**

Journal of Indian Education (New Delhi, DH, IND) **[45602]**

Journal of Indian Folkloristics (Mysore, KA, IND) **[45458]**

Journal of the Indian Geoscience Academy **[45171]***

Journal of Indian History (Thiruvananthapuram, KE, IND) *Unable to locate*

Journal of Indian Law Institute (New Delhi, DH, IND) **[45603]**

Journal of the Indian Medical Association (JIMA) (Kolkata, WB, IND) **[45296]**

Journal of the Indian Medical Profession (Mumbai, MH, IND) *Unable to locate*

Journal of Indian Museums (New Delhi, DH, IND) *Unable to locate*

Journal of the Indian Musicological Society (Baroda, GJ, IND) *Unable to locate*

Journal of Indian Prosthodontic Society (Bangalore, KA, IND) **[44974]**

Journal of Indian Psychology (Vishakhapatnam, AP, IND) *Unable to locate*

Journal of Indian Roads Congress (New Delhi, DH, IND) **[45604]**

Journal of Indian Society of Periodontology (Chennai, TN, IND) **[45048]**

Journal of the Indian Society of Soil Science (New Delhi, DH, IND) **[45605]**

Journal of Indian Writing in English (Gulbarga, KA, IND) *Unable to locate*

Journal of Individual Differences (Giessen, GER) **[44387]**

Journal of Industrial Economics (Oxford, GBR) **[56041]**

Journal of Industrial Engineering (Mumbai, MH, IND) *Unable to locate*

Journal of Industrial Pollution Control (Karad, MH, IND) *Unable to locate*

Journal of Industrial Textiles (London, GBR) **[54766]**

Journal of Industry and Trade (New Delhi, DH, IND) *Unable to locate*

The Journal of Infection (Leicester, GBR) *Unable to locate*

Journal of Infection and Chemotherapy (Tokyo, JPN) **[46909]**

Journal of Inflammation (London, GBR) **[54767]**

Journal of Information, Communication & Ethics in Society (Bradford, GBR) **[52503]**

Journal of Information, Law & Technology (JILT) (Coventry, GBR) **[53086]**

Journal of Information & Optimization Sciences (New Delhi, DH, IND) **[45606]**

Journal of Information Science (London, GBR) **[54768]**

Journal of Information Technology (Oxford, GBR) **[56042]**

Journal of Informetrics (Diepenbeek, BEL) **[42880]**

Journal of Inherited Metabolic Disease (Zurich, SWI) **[51270]**

Journal of the Inland Fisheries Society of India (Barrackpore, WB, IND) *Unable to locate*

Journal of Inorganic Chemistry (Beijing, CHN) *Unable to locate*

Journal of Inorganic and Organometallic Polymers and Materials (Dordrecht, NLD) **[48469]**

The Journal of the Institute **[45450]***

Journal of Institute of Agriculture and Animal Science (Kathmandu, NPL) *Unable to locate*

Journal of the Institute of the Arab Manuscript (Tunis, TUN) *Ceased*

Journal of the Institute of Bankers of Sri Lanka (Colombo, SRI) *Unable to locate*

Journal of Institute for the Comprehensive Study of Lotus Sutra (Tokyo, JPN) *Unable to locate*

Journal of the Institute of Electronics, Information, and Communication (Tokyo, JPN) *Unable to locate*

Journal of the Institute of Health Record Information and Management (Truro, GBR) *Unable to locate*

Journal of Institute of International Sociology (Hyogo, JPN) *Unable to locate*

Journal of the Institute of Mathematics of Jussieu (Paris, FRA) **[44064]**

Journal of Institute of Medicine (Kathmandu, NPL) *Unable to locate*

Journal of Institute of Postgraduate Medicine and Research (Dhaka, BGD) *Unable to locate*

Journal of the Institute of Psychosocial Medicine (London, GBR) *Unable to locate*

Journal of the Institution of Engineers Bangladesh (Dhaka, BGD) *Unable to locate*

Journal of the Institution of Engineers, Federation of Malaysia (Petaling Jaya, MYS) *Unable to locate*

Journal of the Institution of Occupational Safety and Health **[56925]***

Journal of the Institution of Occupational Safety and Health (Wigston, GBR) *Unable to locate*

Journal of Institutional Economics (Cambridge, GBR) **[52855]**

Journal of Institutional & Theoretical Economics (Tubingen, GER) **[44692]**

Journal of Instrumentation (Bristol, GBR) **[52687]**

Journal of Insurance Practice **[54695]***

Journal of Integrated Care (Brighton, GBR) **[52621]**

Journal of Integrated Care Pathways **[54637]***

Journal of Integrated Design & Process Science (Amsterdam, NLD) **[48086]**

Journal of Integrative Neuroscience (Singapore, SGP) **[50207]**

Journal of Integrative Plant Biology (Oxford, GBR) **[56043]**

Journal of Intellectual Capital (Bradford, GBR) **[52504]**

Journal of Intellectual & Developmental Disability (Lidcombe, NW, AUS) **[42008]**

Journal of Intellectual and Developmental Disability (Abingdon, GBR) **[51908]**

Journal of Intellectual Disabilities (London, GBR) **[54769]**

Journal of Intellectual Disability Research (JIDR) (Cambridge, GBR) **[52856]**

Journal of Intellectual Property Law & Practice (New Delhi, DH, IND) **[45607]**

Journal of Intelligent & Fuzzy Systems (Amsterdam, NLD) **[48087]**

Journal of Intelligent Material Systems and Structures (London, GBR) **[54770]**

Numbers cited in bold after listings are entry numbers rather than page numbers.

Journal of Interactive Media in Education (Milton Keynes, GBR) **[55639]**

Journal of Intercultural Communication (Boras, SWE) **[50950]**

Journal of Intercultural Studies (Abingdon, GBR) **[51909]**

Journal of the Interdisciplinary Crossroads (Allahabad, UP, IND) **[44934]**

Journal of Interdisciplinary Mathematics (New Delhi, DH, IND) **[45608]**

Journal of International Arbitration (Alphen aan den Rijn, NLD) **[47869]**

Journal of the International Association of Buddhist Studies (Lausanne, SWI) *Unable to locate*

Journal of International Biotechnology Law (Berlin, GER) **[44205]**

Journal of International Business Education (Riga, LAT) **[47370]**

Journal for International Business and Entrepreneurship Development (Olney, GBR) **[55844]**

The Journal of International Commercial Law (Surrey, GBR) *Unable to locate*

Journal of International Criminal Justice (Oxford, GBR) **[56044]**

Journal of International Economic Review (New Delhi, DH, IND) **[45609]**

Journal of International Farm Management (Cambridge, GBR) **[52857]**

Journal of International Financial Management & Accounting (Oxford, GBR) **[56045]**

The Journal of International Maritime Law (Witney, GBR) **[56944]**

Journal of International Marketing (London, GBR) **[54771]**

Journal of International Marketing and Marketing Research (Brixham, GBR) *Unable to locate*

Journal of the International Medical Sciences Academy (New Delhi, DH, IND) *Unable to locate*

Journal of International Relations and Development (Ljubljana, SVA) **[50339]**

Journal of International Selling & Sales Management (Brixham, GBR) *Unable to locate*

Journal of International Studies (Tokyo, JPN) *Unable to locate*

The Journal of International Trade and Economic Development (Burwood, VI, AUS) **[41676]**

Journal of International Trade Law and Policy (Bradford, GBR) **[52505]**

Journal of Interprofessional Care (Abingdon, GBR) **[51910]**

Journal of Intervention and Statebuilding (Abingdon, GBR) **[51911]**

Journal of Invertebrate Pathology (Amsterdam, NLD) **[48088]**

Journal of Investigational Allergology and Clinical Immunology (Montpellier, FRA) *Unable to locate*

Journal of Investigative Psychology and Offender Profiling (Huddersfield, GBR) **[53621]**

The Journal of Investment Compliance (Bradford, GBR) **[52506]**

Journal of Ion Exchange (Tokyo, JPN) **[46910]**

Journal of Islamic History (New Delhi, DH, IND) **[45610]**

Journal of Islamic Law Review (New Delhi, DH, IND) **[45611]**

Journal of Islamic Studies (Oxford, GBR) **[56046]**

Journal of Islamic University of Imam Muhammad Ibn Saud (Riyadh, SAU) *Unable to locate*

Journal of the Israel Heart Society (Ramat Gan, ISR) **[46096]**

Journal of Israeli History (Abingdon, GBR) **[51912]**

Journal of Japan Biomagnetism and Bioelectromagnetics Society (Tokyo, JPN) **[46911]**

Journal of Japan Broncho-Esophagological Society (Tokyo, JPN) *Unable to locate*

Journal of Japan Glaucoma Society (Miyazaki, JPN) **[46519]**

Journal of Japan Medical Society of Paraplegia (Tokyo, JPN) **[46912]**

Journal of Japan Salivary Gland Society (Tokyo, JPN) **[46913]**

Journal of Japan Society of Aesthetic Surgery (Tokyo, JPN) *Unable to locate*

Journal of Japan Society of Polymer Processing (Tokyo, JPN) *Unable to locate*

Journal of Japan Spine Research Society (Tokyo, JPN) **[46914]**

Journal of Japanese Association for Chest Surgery (Kyoto, JPN) *Unable to locate*

Journal of Japanese Association of Hydrological Sciences (Ibaraki, JPN) **[46393]**

Journal of Japanese Forestry Society (Tokyo, JPN) **[46915]**

Journal of the Japanese and International Economics (Amsterdam, NLD) **[48089]**

Journal of Japanese Scientists (Tokyo, JPN) **[46916]**

Journal of Japanese Society of Autologous Blood Transfusion (Okayama, JPN) **[46597]**

Journal of Japanese Society for Clinical Surgery (Tokyo, JPN) *Unable to locate*

Journal of Japanese Society of Computational Statistics (Osaka, JPN) **[46621]**

Journal of Japanese Society of Dialysis Therapy (Tokyo, JPN) **[46917]**

Journal of Japanese Society for Horticultural Science (Tokyo, JPN) **[46918]**

Journal of Japanese Trade and Industry (Tokyo, JPN) **[46919]**

Journal of Japanese Trade & Industry (Japan) (Tokyo, JPN) *Unable to locate*

The Journal of Jewish Thought and Philosophy (Leiden, NLD) **[48699]**

Journal of Jilin University Earth Science Edition (Changchun, JI, CHN) **[43240]**

Journal of Jilin University Engineering and Technology Edition (Changchun, JI, CHN) **[43241]**

Journal of Jilin University Information Science Edition (Changchun, JI, CHN) **[43242]**

Journal of Jilin University Medicine Edition (Changchun, JI, CHN) **[43243]**

Journal of Jilin University Science Edition (Changchun, JI, CHN) **[43244]**

Journal of JJ Group of Hospitals and Grant Medical College (Mumbai, MH, IND) *Unable to locate*

Journal of JSPRS (Tokyo, JPN) *Unable to locate*

Journal of Juzen Medical Society (Ishikawa, JPN) *Unable to locate*

Journal of Kagawa Nutrition College (Tokyo, JPN) *Unable to locate*

Journal of Kansai Medical University Journal (Osaka, JPN) *Unable to locate*

Journal of Kansai Society of Naval Architects (Osaka, JPN) **[46622]**

Journal of the Kilvert Society (Bristol, GBR) **[52688]**

Journal of King Saud University (Riyadh, SAU) **[50062]**

Journal of King Saud University: Administrative Sciences (Riyadh, SAU) *Unable to locate*

Journal of King Saud University: Agricultural Sciences (Riyadh, SAU) **[50063]**

Journal of King Saud University: Architecture and Planning (Riyadh, SAU) **[50064]**

Journal of King Saud University: Arts (Riyadh, SAU) **[50065]**

Journal of King Saud University: Computer & Information Sciences (Riyadh, SAU) **[50066]**

Journal of King Saud University: Educational Sciences & Islamic Studies (Riyadh, SAU) **[50067]**

Journal of King Saud University: Languages & Translations (Riyadh, SAU) *Unable to locate*

Journal of King Saud University: Science (Riyadh, SAU) **[50068]**

Journal of Knot Theory and Its Ramifications (Singapore, SGP) **[50208]**

Journal of Knowledge Management (Bradford, GBR) **[52507]**

Journal of Konbin (Warsaw, POL) **[49723]**

Journal of Korea Refrigeration and Air-Conditioning Industry Association (Seoul, KOR) *Unable to locate*

Journal of Korean Astronomical Society (Seoul, KOR) *Unable to locate*

Journal of the Korean Chemical Society (Seoul, KOR) *Unable to locate*

The Journal of Korean Radiological Society (Seoul, KOR) **[47274]**

Journal of the Korean Society of Plastic and Reconstructive Surgery (Seoul, KOR) **[47275]**

Journal of Korean Society of Soil Science and Fertilizer (Suwon, KOR) **[47327]**

Journal Kybernetika (Prague, CZE) **[43628]**

Journal of Kyoto Entomological Society (Kyoto, JPN) *Unable to locate*

Journal of Kyoto Prefectural University of Medicine (Kyoto, JPN) *Unable to locate*

Journal of Laboratory Physicians (New Delhi, DH, IND) **[45612]**

Journal of Language & Politics (Amsterdam, NLD) **[48090]**

Journal for Language Teaching (Auckland Park, SAF) **[50349]**

Journal of Language, Technology & Entrepreneurship in Africa (Nairobi, KEN) **[47189]**

Journal de l'Apess (Diekirch, LUX) *Unable to locate*

Journal of Latin American Cultural Studies (Abingdon, GBR) **[51913]**

Journal of Latin American Hermeneutics (Buenos Aires, ARG) **[41477]**

Journal of Latin American Studies (Liverpool, GBR) **[53875]**

Journal of Law (Safat, KWT) *Unable to locate*

Journal of Law, Economics, and Organization (Oxford, GBR) **[56047]**

Journal of Law and Society (Oxford, GBR) **[56048]**

Journal of the Law Society of Scotland (Paisley, GBR) **[56240]**

Journal of Learning Disabilities **[54769]***

Journal of Learning Disabilities and Offending Behaviour (Hove, GBR) **[53609]**

Journal of Legal History (Abingdon, GBR) **[51914]**

Journal of Legal Medicine (Abingdon, GBR) **[51915]**

Journal of Legal Pluralism and Unofficial Law (Buffalo, NY, USA) *Unable to locate*

Journal of Legal Studies Education (Oxford, GBR) **[56049]**

The Journal of Legislative Studies (Abingdon, GBR) **[51916]**

Journal of Librarianship & Information Science (Loughborough, GBR) **[55482]**

Journal of Librarianship and Information Science in Africa (Ibadan, OY, NGA) **[49090]**

Journal of Library and Information Science (Delhi, DH, IND) *Unable to locate*

Journal of Lie Theory (Helsinki, FIN) **[43835]**

Journal of Light Metals (Amsterdam, NLD) *Unable to locate*

Journal of Linguistics (Cambridge, GBR) **[52858]**

Journal of Literary Semantics (JLS) (Birmingham, GBR) **[52347]**

Journal of Literary Studies (Centurion, SAF) **[50443]**

Journal of Literary Theory (Berlin, GER) **[44206]**

Journal of Location Based Services (London, GBR) **[54772]**

The Journal of Logic and Algebraic Programming (Amsterdam, NLD) **[48091]**

Journal of Logic and Computation (London, GBR) **[54773]**

Journal of Loss Prevention in the Process Industries (Amsterdam, NLD) **[48092]**

Journal of Low Frequency Noise, Vibration & Active Control (Brentwood, GBR) **[52580]**

Journal of Low Temperature Physics (Dordrecht, NLD) **[48470]**

Journal of Magnetic Resonance (Amsterdam, NLD) **[48093]**

Journal of Magnetics Society of Japan (Tokyo, JPN) **[46920]**

Journal of Maharashtra Agricultural Universities (Pune, MH, IND) *Unable to locate*

Journal Majuray (Kuala Lumpur, MYS) *Unable to locate*

Journal of the Malaysian Branch of the Royal Asiatic Society (Kuala Lumpur, MYS) **[47606]**

Journal of Management Development (Cranfield, GBR) **[53097]**

Journal of Management and Governance (Dordrecht, NLD) **[48471]**

Journal of Management History (Bradford, GBR) **[52508]**

Journal of Management Studies (Oxford, GBR) **[56050]**

Journal of Managerial Psychology (Bradford, GBR) **[52509]**

Journal of Manual & Manipulative Therapy (London, GBR) **[54774]**

Journal of Manufacturing Technology Management (Birmingham, GBR) **[52348]**

Journal of Maps (Kingston upon Thames, GBR) **[53723]**

Numbers cited in bold after listings are entry numbers rather than page numbers.

Master Index

Journal of the Marine Biological Association (Plymouth, GBR) *Unable to locate*

Journal of the Marine Biological Association of the United Kingdom (JMBA) (Plymouth, GBR) **[56272]**

Journal of Marine Science Museum of Tokai University (Shizuoka, JPN) *Unable to locate*

Journal of Marine Science and Technology (Tokyo, JPN) **[46921]**

Journal of Marine Systems (Rostock, GER) **[44648]**

Journal of Maritime Archaeology (Dordrecht, NLD) **[48472]**

Journal for Maritime Research (London, GBR) **[54775]**

Journal of Marketing (Johannesburg, SAF) **[50531]**

Journal of Marketing Communications (Abingdon, GBR) **[51917]**

Journal of Marketing and Economic Research (New Delhi, DH, IND) *Unable to locate*

Journal of Marketing Management (Argyll, GBR) **[52130]**

Journal of Marketing and Sales (Auckland Park, SAF) *Unable to locate*

Journal of Material Culture (London, GBR) **[54776]**

Journal of Material Cycles and Waste Management (Tokyo, JPN) **[46922]**

Journal of Materials Chemistry (Cambridge, GBR) **[52859]**

Journal of Materials Processing & Manufacturing Science (London, GBR) *Unable to locate*

Journal of Materials Processing Technology (Amsterdam, NLD) **[48094]**

Journal of Materials Science (Dordrecht, NLD) **[48473]**

The Journal of Maternal-Fetal & Neonatal Medicine (Lancaster, GBR) *Unable to locate*

Journal of Mathematical Analysis and Approximation Theory (New Delhi, DH, IND) **[45613]**

Journal of Mathematical Biology (Heidelberg, GER) **[44465]**

Journal of Mathematical Chemistry (Dordrecht, NLD) **[48474]**

Journal of Mathematical Cryptology (Berlin, GER) **[44207]**

Journal of Mathematical Economics (Paris, FRA) **[44065]**

Journal of Mathematical Modelling and Algorithms (Dordrecht, NLD) **[48475]**

Journal of Mathematical and Physical Sciences (Chennai, TN, IND) *Unable to locate*

Journal of Mathematical Psychology (Amsterdam, NLD) **[48095]**

Journal of Mathematical Sciences (Tokyo, JPN) **[46923]**

Journal of Mathematics **[48874]***

Journal of Mathematics (Tokushima, JPN) **[46714]**

Journal fur die reine und angewandte Mathematik (Munster, GER) **[44600]**

Journal de Mathematiques et de Physique appliquees **[51269]***

Journal of the Mechanical Behavior of Materials (Tel Aviv, ISR) **[46108]**

Journal of Mechanical Engineering Research and Developments (Dhaka, BGD) *Unable to locate*

Journal of Media Business Studies (Jonkoping, SWE) **[50970]**

Journal of Media Practice (London, GBR) **[54777]**

Journal of the Medical Association of Thailand (Bangkok, THA) **[51423]**

Journal of Medical Biochemistry (Warsaw, POL) **[49724]**

Journal of Medical Biography (London, GBR) **[54778]**

Journal of Medical and Dental Sciences (Tokyo, JPN) **[46924]**

Journal of Medical Education (Edinburgh, GBR) **[53293]**

Journal of Medical Engineering and Technology (Cardiff, GBR) **[52934]**

Journal of Medical Ethics (London, GBR) **[54779]**

Journal of Medical Genetics (London, GBR) **[54780]**

Journal of Medical Humanities (Dordrecht, NLD) **[48476]**

Journal of Medical Investigation (Tokushima, JPN) **[46715]**

Journal of Medical Investigation and Practice (Aba, NGA) **[49055]**

Journal of Medical Laboratory Science (Calabar, CR, NGA) **[49077]**

Journal of Medical Marketing (Basingstoke, GBR) **[52218]**

Journal of Medical Microbiology (Birmingham, GBR) **[52349]**

Journal of Medical Physics (Mumbai, MH, IND) **[45402]**

Journal of the Medical Sciences (Yogyakarta, IDN) *Unable to locate*

Journal of Medical Sciences (Faisalabad, PAK) **[49270]**

Journal of Medical Screening (London, GBR) **[54781]**

Journal of Medical Ultrasonics (Tokyo, JPN) **[46925]**

Journal of Medicinal and Aromatic Plant Science (Lucknow, UP, IND) *Unable to locate*

Journal of Medicine and Biomedical Research (Benin City, NGA) **[49064]**

Journal of Medicine & Philosophy (Tokyo, JPN) **[46926]**

The Journal of Medicine and Philosophy (Oxford, GBR) **[56051]**

Journal of Medicine in the Tropics (Jos, PL, NGA) **[49126]**

Journal of Medieval History (Southampton, GBR) **[56574]**

Journal of Medieval Indian Literature (Chandigarh, CH, IND) *Unable to locate*

Journal of Mediterranean Archaeology (Nicosia, CYP) **[43596]**

Journal of Memory and Language (Amsterdam, NLD) **[48096]**

Journal of Men's Health (Singapore, SGP) **[50209]**

The Journal of Men's Health & Gender **[50209]***

Journal of Mental Deficiency **[52856]***

Journal of Mental Health (Abingdon, GBR) **[51918]**

Journal of Mental Health Policy and Economics (Milan, ITA) **[46183]**

The Journal of Mental Health Training, Education and Practice (Brighton, GBR) **[52622]**

Journal of Metallurgy and Materials Science (Jamshedpur, BH, IND) *Unable to locate*

Journal of Meteorological Society of Japan (Tokyo, JPN) **[46927]**

Journal of Micro/Nanolithography, MEMS, and MOEMS (Hsinchu, TWN) **[51306]**

The Journal of Microbiology (Seoul, KOR) **[47276]**

Journal of Microbiology, Immunology and Infection (Taipei, TWN) **[51354]**

Journal of Microencapsulation (London, GBR) **[54782]**

Journal of Micromechanics and Microengineering (Bristol, GBR) **[52689]**

Journal of Micropalaeontology (Bath, GBR) **[52249]**

Journal of Microscopy (Oxford, GBR) *Unable to locate*

Journal of Microwave Surgery (Osaka, JPN) *Unable to locate*

The Journal of Microwaves and Optoelectronics **[43018]***

Journal of Microwaves, Optoelectronics and Electromagnetic Applications (Sao Carlos, SP, BRZ) **[43018]**

Journal of Mines, Metals and Fuels (Calcutta, WB, IND) *Unable to locate*

Journal of Minimal Access Surgery (JMAS) (Mumbai, MH, IND) **[45403]**

Journal of Mining and Geology (Ibadan, OY, NGA) **[49091]**

Journal of Mining Research (Dhanbad, BH, IND) *Unable to locate*

Journal of Mining Sciences (Novosibirsk, RUS) **[50012]**

Journal of Mobile Communication (Faisalabad, PAK) **[49271]**

Journal of Modeling, Design & Management of Engineering Systems (Port Harcourt, RV, NGA) **[49167]**

The Journal of Modern African Studies (Cambridge, GBR) **[52860]**

Journal of Modern Italian Studies (Abingdon, GBR) **[51919]**

Journal of Modern Jewish Studies (Abingdon, GBR) **[51920]**

Journal of Modern Literature in Chinese (Hong Kong, CHN) **[43359]**

Journal of Modern Mathematics and Statistics (Faisalabad, PAK) **[49272]**

Journal of Modern Turkish Studies (JMTS) (Ankara, TUR) **[51495]**

Journal of Molecular Biology (Amsterdam, NLD) **[48097]**

Journal of Molecular Catalysis A (Bristol, GBR) **[52690]**

Journal of Molecular Catalysis B (Delft, NLD) **[48311]**

Journal of Molecular Endocrinology (Bristol, GBR) **[52691]**

Journal of Molecular Genetics (Faisalabad, PAK) **[49273]**

Journal of Molecular Graphics and Modeling (Nottingham, GBR) **[55764]**

Journal of Molecular Liquids (Amsterdam, NLD) **[48098]**

Journal of Molecular Medicine (Tokyo, JPN) **[46928]**

Journal of Molecular Modeling (Erlangen, GER) **[44340]**

Journal of Molecular Spectroscopy (Amsterdam, NLD) **[48099]**

Journal of Molecular Structure (Beijing, CHN) **[43208]**

Journal of Molluscan Studies (Oxford, GBR) **[56052]**

Journal of Money Laundering Control (Bradford, GBR) **[52510]**

Journal of Moral Education (Abingdon, GBR) **[51921]**

Journal de Morges (Morges, SWI) **[51213]**

The Journal of Multi-Criteria Decision Analysis (West Sussex, GBR) **[56899]**

Journal of Multicultural Discourses (Abingdon, GBR) **[51922]**

Journal of Multilingual Communication Disorders **[51731]***

Journal of Multilingual & Multicultural Development (Abingdon, GBR) **[51923]**

Journal of Multivariate Analysis (Amsterdam, NLD) **[48100]**

Journal of Musculoskeletal Research (Singapore, SGP) **[50210]**

The Journal of Music and Meaning (Odense, DEN) **[43729]**

Journal of the Musical Arts in Africa (Rondebosch, SAF) **[50618]**

Journal of Muslim Minority Affairs (Abingdon, GBR) **[51924]**

Journal of Mycology and Plant Pathology (Udaipur, RJ, IND) *Unable to locate*

Journal of Mycopathological Research (Calcutta, WB, IND) *Unable to locate*

Journal of Nanobiotechnology (London, GBR) **[54783]**

Journal of the National Agricultural Society of Sri Lanka (Peradeniya, SRI) *Unable to locate*

Journal of the National Aquatic Resources Research & Development Agency of Sri Lanka (Colombo, SRI) **[50856]**

Journal of the National Cancer Institute (Oxford, GBR) **[56053]**

Journal of National Defense Medical College (Saitama, JPN) *Unable to locate*

Journal of the National Science Foundation (Colombo, SRI) **[50857]**

Journal of Natural Gas Chemistry (Dalian, LI, CHN) **[43254]**

Journal of Natural History Museum (Kathmandu, NPL) *Unable to locate*

Journal of Natural & Physical Sciences (Hardwar, UP, IND) *Unable to locate*

Journal of Natural Remedies (Bangalore, KA, IND) **[44975]**

Journal of Natural Sciences and Mathematics (Lahore, PAK) *Unable to locate*

Journal of Nature Conservation (Muzaffarnagar, UP, IND) *Unable to locate*

Journal for Nature Conservation (La Laguna, SPA) **[50719]**

Journal of Near Infrared Spectroscopy (Woolgoolga, NW, AUS) **[42715]**

Journal of Negative Results in Bio-Medicine (London, GBR) **[54784]**

Journal of Neonatal Nursing (Bishop's Stortford, GBR) **[52380]**

Journal of the Nepal Dental Association (Kathmandu, NPL) **[47838]**

Journal of the Nepal Medical Association (Kathmandu, NPL) **[47839]**

Journal of Nephrology (Sofia, BUL) *Unable to locate*

Journal of Network and Computer Applications (Amsterdam, NLD) **[48101]**

Journal of Network Industries (Mortsel, BEL) **[42906]**

Journal of Neural Engineering (Bristol, GBR) **[52692]**

Journal of Neural Transmission (Vienna, AUT) **[42762]**

Journal of Neuro-Oncology (Dordrecht, NLD) **[48477]**

Journal of Neuroendocrinology (Dunedin, NZL) **[48890]**

Journal of NeuroEngineering and Rehabilitation (JNER) (London, GBR) **[54785]**

Numbers cited in bold after listings are entry numbers rather than page numbers.

Journal of Neuroimmune Pharmacology (Dordrecht, NLD) [48478]

Journal of Neuroinflammation (London, GBR) [54786]

Journal of Neurolinguistics (Amsterdam, NLD) [48102]

Journal of Neurological Sciences (Izmir, TUR) [51575]

Journal of Neurology (Munich, GER) [44566]

Journal of Neurology, Neurosurgery, and Psychiatry (London, GBR) [54787]

Journal of Neuroscience Methods (Cardiff, GBR) [52935]

Journal of Neurosciences in Rural Practice (Wardha, MH, IND) [45770]

Journal of Neurosurgical Problems (Moscow, RUS) [49930]

Journal of New Music Research (Lancaster, GBR) [53735]

Journal News (London, GBR) [54788]

Journal of the Nigerian Association of Mathematical Physics (Benin City, NGA) [49065]

Journal of Nippon Medical School (Tokyo, JPN) [46929]

Journal of Noise and Vibration Control (Shanghai, CHN) [43481]

Journal of Non-Equilibrium Thermodynamics (Berlin, GER) [44208]

Journal of Non-Newtonian Fluid Mechanics (Amsterdam, NLD) [48103]

Journal of Nonlinear Mathematical Physics (Lulea, SWE) [50982]

Journal of Nonverbal Behavior (Dordrecht, NLD) [48479]

Journal Nord Seine et Marne Informations (Meaux, FRA) Unable to locate

Journal of North African Studies (Abingdon, GBR) [51925]

Journal of Northern Luzon (Nueva Vizcaya, PHL) Unable to locate

Journal of Northern Occupational Health (Sapporo, JPN) Unable to locate

Journal of Nuclear Agriculture and Biology (New Delhi, DH, IND) Unable to locate

Journal of Nuclear and Radiochemical Sciences (Osaka, JPN) [46623]

Journal of Nuclear Science and Technology (Tokyo, JPN) [46930]

Journal of Number Theory (Amsterdam, NLD) [48104]

Journal for Nurse Practitioners (Amsterdam, NLD) [48105]

Journal on Nursing (Bebington, GBR) Unable to locate

Journal of Nursing and Healthcare of Chronic Illness (Oxford, GBR) [56054]

Journal of Nursing Management (Oxford, GBR) [56055]

Journal of Nursing Research (Taipei, TWN) Unable to locate

Journal of Nutritional & Environmental Medicine (Abingdon, GBR) [51926]

Journal of the Obafemi Awolowo University Medical Student's Association (Ile-Ife, NGA) [49114]

Journal of Object Technology (JOT) (Zurich, SWI) [51271]

Journal of Objective Studies (New Delhi, DH, IND) [45614]

Journal of Obligations & Remedies (Newcastle upon Tyne, GBR) [55674]

The Journal of Obstetrics and Gynaecology of India (Mumbai, MH, IND) [45404]

Journal of Occupational Health (Tokyo, JPN) [46931]

Journal of Occupational and Organizational Psychology (Leicester, GBR) [53807]

Journal of Oceanography (Tokyo, JPN) [46932]

Journal of the Oil & Colour Chemists' Association (JOCCA) [56887]*

Journal of the Oil & Colour Chemists' Association (JOCCA) [56886]*

Journal of Oilseeds Research (New Delhi, DH, IND) Unable to locate

Journal of the Operational Research Society (Birmingham, GBR) [52350]

The Journal of Operational Risk (London, GBR) [54789]

Journal of Operations Research Society of Japan (Tokyo, JPN) [46933]

Journal of Optics (Kolkata, WB, IND) [45297]

Journal of Optics (Bristol, GBR) [52693]

Journal of Optics A [52693]*

Journal of Optimization Theory and Applications (Dordrecht, NLD) [48480]

Journal of Oral and Maxillofacial Pathology (Chennai, TN, IND) [45049]

Journal of Oral Pathology and Medicine (Heidelberg, VI, AUS) [41948]

Journal of Oral Rehabilitation (Arhus, DEN) [43647]

Journal of Oral Science (Tokyo, JPN) [46934]

Journal of Oral Tissue Engineering (Okayama, JPN) [46598]

Journal of Organ Dysfunctions (Abingdon, GBR) [51927]

Journal of Organisational Transformation and Social Change (London, GBR) [54790]

Journal of Organizational Behavior Education (Riga, LAT) [47371]

Journal of Organizational Change Management (Bradford, GBR) [52511]

Journal of Organometallic Chemistry (Amsterdam, NLD) [48106]

Journal of Oriental Research (Chennai, TN, IND) [45050]

Journal of Orofacial Orthopedics/ Fortschritte der Kieferorthopadie (Dordrecht, NLD) [48481]

Journal of Orthopaedic Science (Tokyo, JPN) [46935]

Journal of Orthopaedic Surgery (Hong Kong, CHN) [43360]

Journal of Orthopaedics (Trivandrum, KE, IND) [45759]

Journal of Osseointegration (Carimate, ITA) [46131]

Journal of Outcomes Research (London, GBR) [54791]

Journal of Pacific Archaeology (Dunedin North, NZL) [48897]

The Journal of Pacific History (Abingdon, GBR) [51928]

Journal of Pacific Rim Psychology (Bowen Hills, QL, AUS) [41627]

Journal of Paediatrics and Child Health (Oxford, GBR) [56056]

Journal de la Paix (Paris, FRA) Unable to locate

Journal of Pakistan Association of Dermatologists (Karachi, PAK) Unable to locate

Journal of Pakistan Bar Council (Lahore, PAK) Unable to locate

Journal of the Pakistan Historical Society (Karachi, PAK) Unable to locate

Journal of the Pakistan Medical Association (Karachi, PAK) [49358]

Journal of Pakistan Psychiatric Society (Peshawar, PAK) [49393]

Journal of Pali Text Society (Oxford, GBR) Unable to locate

Journal of Palynology (New Delhi, DH, IND) Unable to locate

Journal of the Pancreas (Genoa, ITA) [46151]

Journal of Parallel and Distributed Computing (Amsterdam, NLD) [48107]

Journal of Paramedic Practice (London, GBR) [54792]

Journal of Pathology (Belfast, GBR) [52288]

Journal of Peace Education (Abingdon, GBR) [51929]

Journal of Peace Research (London, GBR) [54793]

Journal of Peasant Studies (Abingdon, GBR) [51930]

Journal of Pediatric Infectious Diseases (Van, TUR) [51581]

Journal of Pediatric Neurology (Amsterdam, NLD) [48108]

Journal of Pediatric Neurosciences (New Delhi, DH, IND) [45615]

Journal of Pediatric Urology (Singapore, SGP) [50211]

Journal of Pension Economics and Finance (London, GBR) [54794]

Journal of Perinatal Medicine (Berlin, GER) [44209]

Journal of Periodontal Research (Osaka, JPN) [46624]

Journal of Perioperative Practice (Harrogate, GBR) [53517]

Journal of Personality (Oxford, GBR) [56057]

Journal of Personality and Clinical Studies (New Delhi, DH, IND) Unable to locate

Journal of Personnel Evaluation in Education [48380]*

Journal of Pest Science (Dordrecht, NLD) [48482]

Journal of Pesticide Science (Kyoto, JPN) [46477]

Journal of Petroleum Technology (London, GBR) [54795]

Journal of Petrology (Leeds, GBR) [53768]

Journal of Pharmaceutical and Allied Sciences (Nsukka, AN, NGA) [49157]

Journal of Pharmaceutical and Biomedical Analysis (Tbilisi, GRG) [44135]

Journal of Pharmaceutical Innovation (Dordrecht, NLD) [48483]

Journal of Pharmaceutical Medicine (London, GBR) [54796]

Journal of Pharmaceutical Science and Technology (Tokyo, JPN) Unable to locate

Journal de Pharmacie Clinique (Montrouge, FRA) [43994]

Journal of Pharmacological Sciences (Kyoto, JPN) [46478]

Journal of Pharmacological and Toxicological Methods (London, GBR) [54797]

Journal of Pharmacy and Bioresources (Jos, PL, NGA) [49127]

Journal of Phenomenological Psychology (Leiden, NLD) [48700]

Journal of the Philippine Dental Association (Makati City, PHL) Unable to locate

Journal of Philippine Librarianship (Quezon City, PHL) Unable to locate

Journal of Philippine Medical Association (Quezon City, PHL) Unable to locate

Journal of Philippine Statistics (Manila, PHL) [49550]

Journal of Philosophy and Culture (Grahamstown, SAF) [50502]

Journal of Philosophy of Education (London, GBR) [54798]

Journal of Phonetics (Amsterdam, NLD) [48109]

Journal of Photochemistry and Photobiology, C (Tokyo, JPN) [46936]

Journal of Physical Education & Recreation [43278]*

Journal of Physical Society of Japan (Tokyo, JPN) [46937]

Journal of Physics (Colombo, SRI) [50858]

Journal of Physics A (Bristol, GBR) [52694]

Journal of Physics B (London, GBR) [54799]

Journal of Physics C (London, GBR) [54800]

Journal of Physics D (Bristol, GBR) [52695]

Journal of Physics E: Scientific Instruments [52705]*

Journal of Physics G (London, GBR) [54801]

The Journal of Physiology (London, GBR) [54802]

Journal of Physiology - Paris (Gif-sur-Yvette, FRA) [43956]

Journal of Phytogeography and Taxonomy (Kanazawa, JPN) Unable to locate

Journal for Phytomedicine and Therapeutics (Abuja, NGA) [49056]

Journal of Phytopathology (Oxford, GBR) [56058]

Journal of Phytopharmacotherapy and Natural Products (Jodhpur, RJ, IND) [45227]

Journal of Pidgin and Creole Languages (JPCL) (Amsterdam, NLD) [48110]

Journal of Place Management and Development (Manchester, GBR) [55564]

Journal of Planar Chromatography (Budapest, HUN) [44842]

Journal of the Planetary Gemologists Association (Bangkok, THA) [51424]

Journal of Plankton Research (Oxford, GBR) [56059]

Journal of Planning and Environment Law (Andover, GBR) [52119]

Journal of Plant Anatomy and Morphology (Jodhpur, RJ, IND) Unable to locate

Journal of Plant Biochemistry and Biotechnology (New Delhi, DH, IND) [45616]

Journal of Plant Biology (Seoul, KOR) [47277]

Journal of Plant Interactions (Abingdon, GBR) [51931]

Journal of Plant and Machinery (Thanjavur, TN, IND) Unable to locate

Journal of Plant Protection Research (Warsaw, POL) [49725]

Journal of Plant Research (Tokyo, JPN) [46938]

Journal of Plantation Crops (Kasaragod, KE, IND) Unable to locate

Journal of Plasma and Fusion Research (Nagoya, JPN) [46554]

Numbers cited in bold after listings are entry numbers rather than page numbers.

Journal of Plastic Film and Sheeting (London, GBR) **[54803]**

Journal of Poetry Therapy (Abingdon, GBR) **[51932]**

Journal of Policy Modeling (Amsterdam, NLD) **[48111]**

Journal of Policy and Practice in Intellectual Disabilities (Oxford, GBR) **[56060]**

Journal of Politeness Research (Loughborough, GBR) **[55483]**

Journal of Political Ideologies (Abingdon, GBR) **[51933]**

The Journal of Political Philosophy (Oxford, GBR) **[56061]**

Journal of Political Science (Lahore, PAK) *Unable to locate*

Journal of Political Studies (Jullundur, PJ, IND) *Unable to locate*

Journal of Polymer Materials (New Delhi, DH, IND) *Unable to locate*

Journal of Polymer Research (Dordrecht, NLD) **[48484]**

Journal of Polymers and the Environment (Dordrecht, NLD) **[48485]**

The Journal of the Polynesian Society (Auckland, NZL) *Unable to locate*

Journal of Population (Depok, IDN) *Unable to locate*

Journal of Population Economics (Bonn, GER) **[44264]**

Journal of Population and Health Studies (Seoul, KOR) *Unable to locate*

Journal of Portfolio Management (London, GBR) **[54804]**

The Journal of Positive Psychology (Abingdon, GBR) **[51934]**

Journal of Postcolonial Education (South Melbourne, VI, AUS) **[42373]**

Journal of Postcolonial Writing (Abingdon, GBR) **[51935]**

Journal of Postgraduate Medicine (Mumbai, MH, IND) **[45405]**

Journal of Potassium Research (Gurgaon, HY, IND) *Unable to locate*

The Journal of Poverty and Social Justice (Bristol, GBR) **[52696]**

Journal of Power Sources (Amsterdam, NLD) **[48112]**

Journal of Practical Stomatology (Xi'an, SH, CHN) **[43534]**

Journal of Pragmatics (Odense, DEN) **[43730]**

The Journal of Prediction Markets (Buckingham, GBR) **[52758]**

The Journal of Primary Prevention (Dordrecht, NLD) **[48486]**

Journal of Private International Law (Aberdeen, GBR) **[51678]**

Journal of Product & Brand Management (Bradford, GBR) **[52512]**

Journal of Productivity Analysis (Dordrecht, NLD) **[48487]**

Journal of Property Investment & Finance (Bradford, GBR) **[52513]**

Journal of Property Research (Abingdon, GBR) **[51936]**

Journal of Proteomics (Amsterdam, NLD) **[48113]**

Journal of Psychiatric Intensive Care (Gloucester, GBR) **[53472]**

Journal of Psychiatric and Mental Health Nursing (Leeds, GBR) **[53769]**

Journal of Psychiatric Research (Munich, GER) **[44567]**

Journal of Psycholinguistic Research (Dordrecht, NLD) **[48488]**

Journal of Psychological Researches (Chennai, TN, IND) *Unable to locate*

Journal of Psychology in Chinese Societies (Hong Kong, CHN) **[43361]**

Journal of Psychopathology & Behavioral Assessment (Dordrecht, NLD) **[48489]**

Journal of Psychopharmacology (London, GBR) **[54805]**

Journal of Psychosomatic Obstetrics and Gynecology (Abingdon, GBR) **[51937]**

Journal of Psychosomatic Research (Manchester, GBR) **[55565]**

Journal of Public Administration Research and Theory (Oxford, GBR) **[56062]**

Journal of Public Affairs (Bognor Regis, GBR) **[52399]**

Journal of Public Economic Theory (Oxford, GBR) **[56063]**

Journal of Public Health (London, GBR) **[54806]**

Journal of Public Health (Oxford, GBR) **[56064]**

Journal of Public Health Medicine **[54806]***

Journal of Public Health Policy (Basingstoke, GBR) **[52219]**

Journal of Public Mental Health (Brighton, GBR) **[52623]**

Journal of Public Policy (Cambridge, GBR) **[52861]**

Journal of Purchasing & Supply Management (Rotterdam, NLD) **[48751]**

Journal of Pure and Applied Sciences (Ankara, TUR) *Unable to locate*

Journal of Pure and Applied Ultrasonics (New Delhi, DH, IND) *Unable to locate*

Journal of Quality in Maintenance Engineering (Bradford, GBR) **[52514]**

Journal of Quantitative Linguistics (Abingdon, GBR) **[51938]**

Journal of Qur'anic Studies (Edinburgh, GBR) **[53294]**

Journal of Radiation Research (Hiroshima, JPN) **[46381]**

Journal of Radiological Protection (Bristol, GBR) **[52697]**

Journal of Radiotherapy and Oncology (Brussels, BEL) **[42863]**

Journal of Radiotherapy in Practice (Sheffield, GBR) **[56505]**

Journal of Reformed Theology (Leiden, NLD) **[48701]**

Journal of Refugee Studies (Oxford, GBR) **[56065]**

Journal of Regional History (Amritsar, PJ, IND) *Unable to locate*

Journal of Regional Science (Oxford, GBR) **[56066]**

Journal of Rehabilitation in Asia (Mumbai, MH, IND) *Unable to locate*

Journal of Rehabilitation Medicine (Abingdon, GBR) **[51939]**

Journal of Reinforced Plastics and Composites (London, GBR) **[54807]**

Journal of Religion in Africa (Leiden, NLD) **[48702]**

Journal of Religion in Europe (Leiden, NLD) **[48703]**

Journal of Religious History (Sydney, NW, AUS) **[42529]**

The Journal of Religious Studies (Patiala, PJ, IND) *Unable to locate*

Journal of Renal Nursing (London, GBR) **[54808]**

Journal of the Renin-Angiotensin-Aldosterone System (Birmingham, GBR) **[52351]**

Journal and Report of Proceedings (Folkestone, GBR) **[53392]**

Journal of Reproduction and Development (Tokyo, JPN) **[46939]**

Journal of Reproduction and Fertility (New Delhi, DH, IND) *Unable to locate*

Journal of Reproductive Biology and Comparative Endocrinology (New Delhi, DH, IND) *Unable to locate*

Journal of Reproductive Immunology (Kidlington, GBR) **[53700]**

Journal of Reproductive and Infant Psychology (Abingdon, GBR) **[51940]**

Journal of Research (Ranchi, BH, IND) *Unable to locate*

Journal of Research—ANGRAU (Hyderabad, AP, IND) **[45175]**

Journal of Research in Ayurveda and Siddha (New Delhi, DH, IND) *Unable to locate*

Journal of Research: Humanities of the University of the Punjab (Lahore, PAK) *Unable to locate*

The Journal of the Research Institute (Izmir-Kocaeli, TUR) *Unable to locate*

Journal of Research in Medical Sciences (Isfahan, IRN) **[45879]**

Journal of Research Methodology (Bangkok, THA) *Unable to locate*

Journal of Research in National Development (Owerri, IM, NGA) **[49164]**

Journal of Research in Personality (Amsterdam, NLD) **[48114]**

The Journal of Research and Practice in Information Technology (Sydney, NW, AUS) **[42530]**

Journal of Research in Reading (Coventry, GBR) **[53087]**

The Journal of Research in Special Educational Needs (Northampton, GBR) **[55712]**

Journal of Retail and Leisure Property (Basingstoke, GBR) **[52220]**

Journal of Revenue and Pricing Management (Basingstoke, GBR) **[52221]**

Journal of Rheumatology and Medical Rehabilitation (Ankara, TUR) *Unable to locate*

The Journal of Risk (London, GBR) **[54809]**

The Journal of Risk Finance (Bradford, GBR) **[52515]**

Journal of Risk Research (London, GBR) **[54810]**

Journal of Risk and Uncertainty (Dordrecht, NLD) **[48490]**

Journal of Robotics and Mechatronics (Tokyo, JPN) **[46940]**

Journal of Roman Studies (London, GBR) **[54811]**

Journal of Root Crops (Trivandrum, KE, IND) *Unable to locate*

Journal of the Royal Anthropological Institute (London, GBR) **[54812]**

Journal of the Royal Asiatic Society of Sri Lanka (Colombo, SRI) **[50859]**

Journal of the Royal Australian Historical Society (Sydney, NW, AUS) *Unable to locate*

Journal of the Royal College of General Practitioners **[54120]***

Journal of the Royal College of Physicians of London **[54225]***

Journal of the Royal Meteorological Society (Reading, GBR) **[56324]**

Journal of the Royal Musical Association (Leeds, GBR) **[53770]**

Journal of the Royal Society Interface (London, GBR) **[54813]**

Journal of the Royal Society of Medicine (London, GBR) **[54814]**

Journal of the Royal Society of New Zealand (Wellington, NZL) **[49011]**

Journal of the Royal Statistical Society (London, GBR) *Ceased*

Journal of the Royal Statistical Society (Oxford, GBR) **[56069]**

Journal of the Royal Statistical Society (Oxford, GBR) **[56068]**

Journal of the Royal Statistical Society (Oxford, GBR) **[56067]**

Journal of Rubber Research (Kuala Lumpur, MYS) **[47607]**

Journal of the Rubber Research Institute of Sri Lanka (Agalawatta, SRI) *Unable to locate*

Journal of Rural Development (Hyderabad, AP, IND) **[45176]**

Journal of Rural Development and Administration (Peshawar, PAK) *Unable to locate*

Journal of Rural Studies (Exeter, GBR) **[53362]**

Journal of Rural Studies (Kidlington, GBR) **[53701]**

Journal of Rural and Tropical Public Health (Townsville, QL, AUS) **[42637]**

Journal of Sandwich Structures and Materials (London, GBR) **[54815]**

Journal on Satisfiability, Boolean Modeling and Computation (Delft, NLD) **[48312]**

Journal of Scheduling (Dordrecht, NLD) **[48491]**

Journal of School Health (Oxford, GBR) **[56070]**

Journal of Science Education in Japan (Tokyo, JPN) *Unable to locate*

Journal of the Science of Food and Agriculture (London, GBR) **[54816]**

Journal of Science of Labour (Kawasaki, JPN) **[46422]**

Journal of Science and Mathematics Education in Southeast Asia (Penang, MYS) **[47689]**

Journal of Science and Medicine in Sport (Sydney, NW, AUS) **[42531]**

Journal of Science Policy and Research Management (Tokyo, JPN) *Unable to locate*

Journal of the Science Society of Thailand (Phathumthani, THA) *Unable to locate*

Journal of Science Teacher Education (Dordrecht, NLD) **[48492]**

Journal of Science of the University of Tehran (Tehran, IRN) *Unable to locate*

Journal of Scientific and Industrial Research (New Delhi, DH, IND) **[45617]**

Journal of Scientific Instruments **[52705]***

Journal of Scientific Research (Bhopal, MP, IND) *Unable to locate*

Journal of the Scientific Research Council of Jamaica **[46286]***

Journal of Scientific Research in Plants & Medicines (Hardwar, UP, IND) *Unable to locate*

Journal of Scottish Philosophy (Edinburgh, GBR) **[53295]**

Journal of Sea Research (Amsterdam, NLD) **[48115]**

Journal of Security Sector Management (Birmingham, GBR) **[52352]**

Journal of Sedimentological Society of Japan (Tokyo, JPN) *Unable to locate*

Numbers cited in bold after listings are entry numbers rather than page numbers.

Journal of Seismological Society of Japan (Tokyo, JPN) *Unable to locate*

Journal of Semantics (Oxford, GBR) **[56071]**

Journal of Semiconductors (Bristol, GBR) **[52698]**

Journal of Semitic Studies (Manchester, GBR) **[55566]**

Journal of Sericultural Science of Japan (Ibaraki, JPN) *Unable to locate*

Journal Series (Portsmouth) (Portsmouth, GBR) *Unable to locate*

Journal of Service Management (Bradford, GBR) **[52516]**

Journal of Sexual Aggression (Abingdon, GBR) **[51941]**

Journal of Sexual Medicine (Oxford, GBR) **[56072]**

Journal of Shanghai Jiaotong University (Shanghai, CHN) **[43482]**

Journal of Shanghai Jiaotong University Agricultural Science (Shanghai, CHN) **[43483]**

Journal of Shipping, Customs, and Transport Law (Mumbai, MH, IND) *Unable to locate*

Journal of Sikh Studies (Amritsar, PJ, IND) *Unable to locate*

Journal of Simulation (Birmingham, GBR) **[52353]**

Journal of Sleep Research (Oxford, GBR) **[56073]**

The Journal of Small Animal Practice (London, GBR) **[54817]**

Journal of Small Business and Enterprise Development (Birmingham, GBR) **[52354]**

Journal of Smoking Cessation (Bowen Hills, QL, AUS) **[41628]**

Journal of Smooth Muscle Research (Nagoya, JPN) **[46555]**

Journal of Social Anthropology (New Delhi, DH, IND) **[45618]**

Journal of Social Archaeology (London, GBR) **[54818]**

Journal of Social Development (Dhaka, BGD) *Unable to locate*

Journal of Social Development in Africa (Grahamstown, SAF) **[50503]**

Journal of Social and Economic Policy (New Delhi, DH, IND) **[45619]**

Journal of Social and Economic Studies (New Delhi, DH, IND) *Unable to locate*

Journal of Social and Personal Relationships (London, GBR) **[54819]**

Journal of Social Policy (Cambridge, GBR) **[52862]**

Journal of Social Research (Ranchi, BH, IND) *Unable to locate*

Journal of Social Science (Tokyo, JPN) *Unable to locate*

Journal of Social Science (Taipei, TWN) *Unable to locate*

Journal of the Social Sciences (Safat, KWT) **[47339]**

Journal of Social Sciences (Agra) (Agra, UP, IND) *Unable to locate*

Journal of Social Sciences (Delhi) (Delhi, DH, IND) **[45101]**

Journal of Social Sciences and Philosophy (Taipei, TWN) **[51355]**

Journal of Social Studies (Dhaka, BGD) *Unable to locate*

Journal of Social Welfare and Family Law (Abingdon, GBR) **[51942]**

Journal of Social Work (London, GBR) **[54820]**

Journal of Social Work Practice (Abingdon, GBR) **[51943]**

Journal de la Societe des Americanistes (Paris, FRA) *Unable to locate*

Journal of the Society of Archer-Antiquaries (London, GBR) **[54821]**

Journal of the Society of Archivists (London, GBR) **[54822]**

Journal of Society for Companion Animal Studies (Burford, GBR) **[52760]**

Journal of the Society of Dairy Technology **[52126]***

Journal of the Society of Leather Technologists and Chemists (Dewsbury, GBR) **[53180]**

The Journal of Socio-Economics (Amsterdam, NLD) **[48116]**

Journal of Sociolinguistics (Auckland, NZL) **[48800]**

Journal of Sociology (Taipei, TWN) *Unable to locate*

Journal of Sociology (Dunow, GBR) *Unable to locate*

Journal of Sociology (London, GBR) **[54823]**

Journal of Soil Biology and Ecology (Bangalore, KA, IND) *Unable to locate*

Journal of the Soil Science Society of Sri Lanka (Peradeniya, SRI) *Unable to locate*

Journal of Soil and Water Conservation in India (New Delhi, DH, IND) *Unable to locate*

Journal of Soils and Sediments (Landsberg, GER) **[44516]**

Journal of Solid State Electrochemistry (Greifswald, GER) **[44404]**

Journal of Sound and Vibration (Amsterdam, NLD) **[48117]**

Journal of the Southeast Asian Archives (Kuala Lumpur, MYS) *Unable to locate*

Journal of Southeast Asian Education (Bangkok, THA) **[51425]**

Journal of Southeast Asian Studies (Cambridge, GBR) **[52863]**

Journal of Southeast European and Black Sea Studies (Athens, GRC) **[44751]**

Journal of Southern African Studies (Abingdon, GBR) **[51944]**

Journal of Southern Europe and the Balkans (Abingdon, GBR) **[51871]***

Journal of Space Technology and Science (Tokyo, JPN) **[46941]**

Journal of Spanish Cultural Studies (Abingdon, GBR) **[51945]**

Journal of the Speleological Society of Japan (Fukuoka, JPN) **[46344]**

Journal of Spices and Aromatic Crops (Marikunnu, KE, IND) *Unable to locate*

Journal of Sport & Tourism (Abingdon, GBR) **[51946]**

Journal of Sports Science and Medicine (JSSM) (Bursa, TUR) **[51551]**

Journal of Sports Sciences (Abingdon, GBR) *Unable to locate*

The Journal of Stained Glass (London, GBR) **[54824]**

Journal of State and Administration (Sambalpur, OR, IND) *Unable to locate*

Journal of Statistical Mechanics (Bristol, GBR) **[52699]**

Journal of Statistical Physics (Dordrecht, NLD) **[48493]**

Journal of Statistics and Management Systems (New Delhi, DH, IND) **[45620]**

Journal of the Stephenson Locomotive Society (Poynton, GBR) **[56298]**

The Journal of Steroid Biochemistry and Molecular Biology (Amsterdam, NLD) **[48118]**

Journal of Stored Products Research (Egham, GBR) **[53329]**

Journal of Strain Analysis **[54825]***

Journal of Strain Analysis for Engineering Design (London, GBR) **[54825]**

Journal of Strategic Management Education (Dublin, DU, IRL) **[45990]**

Journal of Strategic Marketing (Abingdon, GBR) **[51947]**

Journal of Strategic Studies (Abingdon, GBR) **[51948]**

Journal of Strategy and Management (Bradford, GBR) **[52517]**

Journal of Structural Biology (Amsterdam, NLD) **[48119]**

Journal of Structural and Construction Engineering (Tokyo, JPN) **[46942]**

Journal of Structural Control and Health Monitoring **[46211]***

Journal of Structural Engineering B (Tokyo, JPN) **[46943]**

Journal of Structural and Functional Genomics (Dordrecht, NLD) **[48494]**

Journal of Structural Geology (Mainz, GER) **[44541]**

Journal of Studies (Flowing Star) (Dereham, GBR) *Unable to locate*

Journal for the Study of Judaism (Leiden, NLD) **[48704]**

Journal for the Study of Religion (Rondebosch, SAF) **[50619]**

Journal for the Study of Religions and Ideologies (Cluj-Napoca, ROM) **[49847]**

Journal of Substance Abuse Treatment (JSAT) (Amsterdam, NLD) **[48120]**

Journal of Substance Use (Abingdon, GBR) **[51949]**

Journal of Superconductivity and Novel Magnetism (Dordrecht, NLD) **[48495]**

The Journal of Supercritical Fluids (Amsterdam, NLD) **[48121]**

Journal of Supply Chain Management (Oxford, GBR) **[56074]**

Journal of Surfactants and Detergents (Merida, VEN) **[57028]**

The Journal of Surgery (Islamabad, PAK) *Unable to locate*

Journal of Surgical Research (Amsterdam, NLD) **[48122]**

Journal of Sustainable Tourism (Abingdon, GBR) **[51950]**

Journal of Symbolic Logic (Wellington, NZL) **[49012]**

Journal of Systematic Palaeontology (Abingdon, GBR) **[51951]**

Journal of Systems Architecture (Saint Augustin, GER) **[44654]**

Journal of Systems and Information Technology (Joondalup, WA, AUS) **[41974]**

Journal of Systems Science and Complexity (Dordrecht, NLD) **[48496]**

Journal of Systems Science and Information (Beijing, CHN) **[43209]**

Journal of Systems Science and Systems Engineering (Dordrecht, NLD) **[48497]**

Journal of Systems and Software (Amsterdam, NLD) **[48123]**

Journal of Taiwan Museum (Taipei, TWN) *Unable to locate*

Journal of Tamil Studies (Chennai, TN, IND) *Unable to locate*

Journal of Targeting, Measurement and Analysis for Marketing (London, GBR) **[54826]**

Journal of Teacher Education for Sustainability (Warsaw, POL) **[49726]**

Journal of Technology (Howrah, WB, IND) **[45138]**

Journal of Technology and Education in Nigeria (Port Harcourt, RV, NGA) **[49168]**

Journal of Technology Management & Innovation (Santiago, CHL) **[43145]**

Journal of Telecommunications and Information Technology (Warsaw, POL) **[49727]**

Journal of Telemedicine and Telecare (London, GBR) **[54827]**

Journal of Terramechanics (Amsterdam, NLD) **[48124]**

Journal of Textile Engineering (Osaka, JPN) **[46625]**

Journal of the Textile Institute (Manchester, GBR) **[55567]**

Journal of Tezukayama College Food Sciences (Nara, JPN) *Unable to locate*

Journal of Thai Chamber of Commerce (Bangkok, THA) *Unable to locate*

Journal of The Faculty of Science & Scientific Papers of The College of Arts and Sciences **[46923]***

Journal of The Franklin Institute (Amsterdam, NLD) **[48125]**

The Journal of Theological Studies (Oxford, GBR) **[56075]**

Journal of Theoretical Politics (London, GBR) **[54828]**

Journal of Thermal Biology (Durham, GBR) **[53230]**

Journal of Thermal Envelope and Building Sciences **[54716]***

Journal of Thermal Insulation **[54716]***

Journal of Thermoplastic Composite Materials (London, GBR) **[54829]**

Journal of 3-D Imaging (Middlesex, GBR) **[55619]**

Journal of Three Dimensional Images (Tokyo, JPN) *Unable to locate*

Journal of Thrombosis and Thrombolysis (Dordrecht, NLD) **[48498]**

Journal of the Tiles and Architectural Ceramic Society (Oldham, GBR) **[55784]**

Journal of Time Series Analysis (Voorburg, NLD) **[48770]**

Journal of Toho University Medical Society (Tokyo, JPN) *Unable to locate*

Journal of Tokyo University of Mercantile Marine (Tokyo, JPN) *Unable to locate*

Journal of Tosoh Research (Yamaguchi, JPN) *Unable to locate*

Journal of Tourism & Cultural Change (Abingdon, GBR) **[51952]**

Journal of Tourism Studies (Townsville, QL, AUS) *Ceased*

Journal of Traditional Medicines (Toyama, JPN) *Unable to locate*

Journal of Traffic Medicine (Ankara, TUR) *Unable to locate*

The Journal of Transdisciplinary Environmental Studies (TES) (Roskilde, DEN) **[43734]**

Journal of Translation Studies (Hong Kong, CHN) **[43362]**

Journal of Translational Medicine (London, GBR) **[54830]**

Journal of Transport Economics and Policy (Bath, GBR) **[52250]**

Journal of Transport Geography (Manchester, GBR) **[55568]**

Numbers cited in bold after listings are entry numbers rather than page numbers.

The Journal of Transport History (Manchester, GBR) [55569]

Journal pour le Transport International (Basel, SWI) *Unable to locate*

Journal of Transportation Medicine (Tokyo, JPN) *Unable to locate*

Journal of Travel & Tourism Marketing (Hong Kong, CHN) [43363]

Journal of Tropical Agriculture (Thrissur, KE, IND) [45750]

Journal of Tropical Agriculture & Food Science (Kuala Lumpur, MYS) [47608]

Journal of Tropical Forest Science (Selangor, MYS) [47712]

Journal of Tropical Forestry (New Delhi, DH, IND) *Unable to locate*

Journal of Tropical Microbiology and Biotechnology (Nairobi, KEN) [47190]

Journal of Tropical Pediatrics (Oxford, GBR) [56076]

Journal Tunisien d'ORL et de chirurgie cervico-faciale (Sousse, TUN) [51482]

Journal of Turfgrass Science (Incorporating the Journal of the Sports Turf Research Institute) (Bingley, GBR) [52328]

Journal of Turfgrass and Sports Surfaces Science (Bingley, GBR) *Ceased*

Journal of Turkish Ophthalmology (Istanbul, TUR) [51558]

Journal of the United Reformed Church History Society (Cambridge, GBR) [52864]

Journal of University of Occupational and Environmental Health (Fukuoka, JPN) *Unable to locate*

Journal of University Teaching and Learning Practice (JUTLP) (Wollongong, NW, AUS) [42705]

Journal of Urban Affairs (Oxford, GBR) [56077]

Journal of Urban Design (Abingdon, GBR) [51953]

Journal of Urban Economics (Amsterdam, NLD) [48126]

Journal of Urban Health (London, GBR) [54831]

Journal of Urban Technology (Abingdon, GBR) [51954]

Journal of Varendra Research Museum (Rajshahi, BGD) *Unable to locate*

The Journal of Vascular Access (Milan, ITA) [46184]

Journal of Vascular Research (Berlin, GER) [44210]

Journal of Vector Borne Diseases (Delhi, DH, IND) [45102]

Journal of Vegetation Science (Renkum, NLD) [48746]

The Journal of Venomous Animals and Toxins including Tropical Diseases (Botucatu, SP, BRZ) [42957]

Journal of Vestibular Research (Amsterdam, NLD) [48127]

Journal of Veterinary and Animal Sciences (Vellanikkara, KE, IND) *Unable to locate*

Journal of Veterinary Cardiology (Maisons-Alfort, FRA) [43971]

Journal of Veterinary Emergency and Critical Care (Oxford, GBR) [56078]

Journal of Veterinary Medical Science (Tokyo, JPN) [46944]

Journal of Veterinary Medicine: Series A [56220]*

Journal of Veterinary Medicine Series B [56230]*

Journal of Veterinary Parasitology (New Delhi, DH, IND) *Unable to locate*

Journal of Vibration and Shock (Shanghai, CHN) [43484]

Journal of Victorian Culture (Abingdon, GBR) [51955]

Journal of Viral Hepatitis (London, GBR) [54832]

Journal of Virological Methods (London, GBR) [54833]

Journal of Virtual Reality and Broadcasting (Cologne, GER) [44296]

Journal of Visual Communication and Image Representation (Amsterdam, NLD) [48128]

Journal of Visual Communication in Medicine (Birmingham, GBR) [52355]

Journal of Visual Languages and Computing (Amsterdam, NLD) [48129]

Journal of Visualization (Tokyo, JPN) [46945]

Journal of Vocational Behavior (Amsterdam, NLD) [48130]

Journal of Vocational Education & Training (Abingdon, GBR) [51956]

Journal of Volcanology and Geothermal Research (Amsterdam, NLD) [48131]

Journal of Water and Environmental Issues (Tokyo, JPN) *Unable to locate*

Journal of Water and Health (London, GBR) [54834]

Journal of Water and Land Development (Warsaw, POL) [49728]

The Journal of Water Law (Witney, GBR) [56945]

Journal of Water Supply (London, GBR) [54835]

The Journal for Weavers, Spinners and Dyers (Guisborough, GBR) [53499]

Journal of West African Languages (High Wycombe, GBR) *Unable to locate*

Journal of Wide Bandgap Materials (London, GBR) [54836]

Journal of William Morris Studies [54837]*

Journal of William Morris Studies (London, GBR) [54837]

Journal of Wind Engineering & Industrial Aerodynamics (Amsterdam, NLD) [48132]

Journal of Wine Research (Abingdon, GBR) [51957]

Journal of Women and Religion (North Ryde, NW, AUS) *Unable to locate*

Journal of Wood Science (Tokyo, JPN) [46946]

Journal of Workplace Learning (Bradford, GBR) [52518]

Journal of World Affairs (Tokyo, JPN) *Unable to locate*

The Journal of World Intellectual Property (Oxford, GBR) [56079]

The Journal of World Investment and Trade (Geneva, SWI) [51152]

Journal of World Prehistory (Dordrecht, NLD) [48499]

Journal of World Trade (Law-Economics-Public Policy) [51152]*

Journal of Wound Care (London, GBR) [54838]

Journal of the Writing Equipment Society (Bury Saint Edmunds, GBR) [52774]

Journal of Xauat (Natural Sciences) (Xi'an, SH, CHN) [43535]

Journal of Xauat (Social Sciences) (Xi'an, SH, CHN) [43536]

Journal of Yamashina Institute for Ornithology (Chiba, JPN) [46319]

Journal of Young Pharmacists (Bangalore, KA, IND) [44976]

Journal of Youth Studies (Abingdon, GBR) [51958]

Journal of Zoological Research, IND) *Unable to locate*

Journal of Zoological Systematics and Evolutionary Research (Osnabruck, GER) [44630]

Journal of Zoology (Pretoria, SAF) [50594]

Journalism (London, GBR) [54839]

Journalism Studies (Abingdon, GBR) [51959]

Journalist (Hong Kong, CHN) *Unable to locate*

Journalist (London, GBR) [54840]

Journals in Art and Architectural History (Surrey, GBR) *Unable to locate*

JOUS-TV - Channel 38 (Urawa, JPN) [47113]

JOUU - 79.2 MHz (Yamaguchi, JPN) [47138]

JOUV - 77.0 MHz (Otsu, JPN) [46638]

JOUX-TV - Channel 21 (Niigata, JPN) [46581]

JOVB - 1467 KHz (Tokyo, JPN) [47087]

JOVF - 1431 KHz (Wakayama, JPN) [47120]

JOVI-TV - Channel 33 (Koriyama, JPN) [46449]

JOVK - 675 KHz (Hakodate, JPN) [46373]

JOVO (Shizuoka, JPN) *Unable to locate*

JOVR - 1404 KHz (Shizuoka, JPN) [46696]

JOVR-TV (Shizuoka, JPN) *Unable to locate*

JOVU - 77.4 MHz (Matsue,,JPN) [46502]

JOVV - 76.8 MHz (Okayama, JPN) [46603]

JOVX - 909 KHz (Abashiri, JPN) [46294]

The Jowetteer (Essex, GBR) [53339]

JOWF - 1440 KHz (Sapporo, JPN) [46661]

JOWI-TV - Channel 36 (Yamagata, JPN) [47133]

JOWL - 1197 KHz (Asahikawa, JPN) [46313]

JOWM - 1071 KHz (Obihiro, JPN) [46587]

JOWN - 639 KHz (Sapporo, JPN) [46662]

JOWO - 1098 KHz (Koriyama, JPN) [46450]

JOWR - 1458 KHz (Fukushima, JPN) [46363]

JOWS - 882 KHz (Kushiro, JPN) [46464]

JOWU - 80.0 MHz (Aomori, JPN) [46310]

JOWV - 79.0 MHz (Yahiko, JPN) [47124]

JOWX-TV - Channel 33 (Kanazawa, JPN) [46419]

JOWY-TV - Channel 25 (Kanazawa, JPN) [46420]

JOXF - 1530 KHz (Utsunomiya, JPN) [47117]

JOXH-TV (Nagasaki, JPN) *Unable to locate*

JOXK - 945 KHz (Tokushima, JPN) [46719]

JOXK - 83.4 MHz (Tokushima, JPN) [46720]

JOXN (Utsunomiya, JPN) *Unable to locate*

JOXR - 864 KHz (Naha, JPN) [46571]

JOXU - 77.5 MHz (Niigata, JPN) [46582]

JOXV - 80.0 MHz (Gifu, JPN) [46368]

JOXX-TV - Channel 31 (Akita, JPN) [46301]

Joy-FM - 94.9 (Melbourne, VI, AUS) [42091]

Joy-FM - 99.7 (Accra, GHA) [44732]

Joy Melbourne-FM - 94.9 (Melbourne, VI, AUS) [42092]

JOYF - 1197 KHz (Mito, JPN) [46515]

JOYH-TV - Channel 33 (Morioka, JPN) [46532]

JOYI-TV - Channel 38 (Yamagata, JPN) [47134]

JOYL (Mito, JPN) *Unable to locate*

JOYR - 1494 KHz (Okayama, JPN) [46604]

JOYR-TV - Channel 11 (Okayama, JPN) [46605]

JOYU - 78.6 MHz (Takamatsu, JPN) [46703]

JOYX-TV (Yamaguchi, JPN) *Unable to locate*

JOZ - 3925 KHz (Tokyo, JPN) [47088]

JOZB - 1512 KHz (Tokyo, JPN) [47089]

JOZF - 1431 KHz (Gifu, JPN) [46369]

JOZF-TV (Gifu, JPN) *Unable to locate*

JOZ5 (Tokyo, JPN) *Unable to locate*

JOZ4 (Tokyo, JPN) *Unable to locate*

JOZI-TV (Kumamoto, JPN) *Unable to locate*

JOZK - 87.7 MHz (Matsuyama, JPN) [46508]

JOZK - 963 KHz (Matsuyama, JPN) [46507]

JOZR - 900 KHz (Kochi, JPN) [46440]

JOZR-TV (Kochi, JPN) *Unable to locate*

JOZ7 (Tokyo, JPN) *Unable to locate*

JOZ6 (Tokyo, JPN) *Unable to locate*

JOZ3 (Tokyo, JPN) *Unable to locate*

JOZ2 (Tokyo, JPN) *Unable to locate*

JOZU - 79.7 MHz (Nagano, JPN) [46544]

JP Journal of Algebra, Number Theory and Applications (Allahabad, UP, IND) [44935]

JP Journal of Biostatistics (Allahabad, UP, IND) [44936]

JP Journal of Fixed Point Theory and Applications (Allahabad, UP, IND) [44937]

JP Journal of Geometry and Topology (Hikone, JPN) [46375]

JP Journal of Heat and Mass Transfer (Allahabad, UP, IND) [44938]

JP Journal of Solids and Structures (Allahabad, UP, IND) [44939]

J@pan Inc Magazine (Tokyo, JPN) [46947]

JP4 Mensile de Aeronautica (Impruneta, ITA) *Unable to locate*

JRSH (London, GBR) *Unable to locate*

J17 (London, GBR) *Unable to locate*

JSME International Journal Series A (Tokyo, JPN) [46948]

JSME International Journal Series B (Tokyo, JPN) [46949]

JSME International Journal Series C (Tokyo, JPN) [46950]

Numbers cited in bold after listings are entry numbers rather than page numbers.

JTA Reporter (Kingston, JAM) *Unable to locate*

JTW News (London, GBR) *Unable to locate*

J.UCS (Journal of Universal Computer Science) (Graz, AUT) **[42724]**

Judicial Review (Oxford, GBR) **[56080]**

Judische Rundschau (Basel, SWI) *Unable to locate*

Jugendherberge **[44313]**'

Juice (Kuala Lumpur, MYS) **[47609]**

Juice-FM - 107.2 (Brighton, GBR) **[52637]**

Juice-FM - 107.6 (Liverpool, GBR) **[53881]**

Jukebox Magazine (Paris, FRA) **[44066]**

Juliet (Tokyo, JPN) **[46951]**

Julkaisija (Helsinki, FIN) **[43836]**

Jumbo Cross (London, GBR) *Unable to locate*

Jumbo Quiz Cross (London, GBR) *Unable to locate*

Jumeirah (Dubai, UAE) **[51645]**

Juna Amiko (Zagreb, CTA) *Unable to locate*

Junctures (Cromwell, NZL) **[48888]**

Jung & Liberal (Bonn, GER) *Unable to locate*

Junge Familie (Hamburg, GER) *Unable to locate*

Jungle (New Delhi, DH, IND) *Unable to locate*

Junior Puzzles (Redhill, GBR) **[56354]**

Junior Science Refresher (New Delhi, DH, IND) *Unable to locate*

Junior Scientist (Chennai, TN, IND) *Unable to locate*

Junior Statesman (Calcutta, WB, IND) *Unable to locate*

Juridical Review (Edinburgh, GBR) **[53296]**

Juristische Rundschau (JR) (Dusseldorf, GER) **[44327]**

Jurnal Ekonomi Malaysia (Bangi, MYS) **[47574]**

Jurutera (Petaling Jaya, MYS) **[47700]**

Jusek-Tidningem (Stockholm, SWE) *Unable to locate*

Justice (Tel Aviv, ISR) **[46109]**

Justice Journal (London, GBR) **[54841]**

Justice and Peace (Glasgow, GBR) **[53428]**

The Justice Professional **[51743]**'

Justice Quarterly (Abingdon, GBR) **[51960]**

Justitia **[50600]**'

Jutas Business Law (Claremont, SAF) **[50461]**

Juurikassarka/Betfaltet (Kotalato, FIN) *Unable to locate*

K

K C S Advertising (Bangkok, THA) *Unable to locate*

K-FM - 94.5 (Cape Town, SAF) **[50432]**

K-ROCK-FM - 95.5 (Geelong, VI, AUS) **[41882]**

KA Abwasser, Abfall (Hennef, GER) *Unable to locate*

Kabar (Jakarta, IDN) *Unable to locate*

The Kabbalist (London, GBR) *Unable to locate*

Kadin/Woman 2000 (Mersin, TUR) **[51577]**

Kadmos (Cologne, GER) **[44297]**

Kaffa Coffee (Addis Ababa, ETH) *Unable to locate*

Kagaku-to Kyoiku (Tokyo, JPN) *Unable to locate*

Kai Tiaki (Wellington, NZL) **[49013]**

Kaifeng People's Broadcasting Station (Kaifeng, HN, CHN) *Unable to locate*

Kaifeng People's Broadcasting Station (Kaifeng, HN, CHN) *Unable to locate*

Kaifeng People's Broadcasting Station (Kaifeng, HN, CHN) *Unable to locate*

Kailash (Kathmandu, NPL) *Unable to locate*

Kajian Ekonomi Malaysia **[47616]**'

Kakatiya University (Warangal, AP, IND) *Unable to locate*

Kaksplus (Kuvalehdet, FIN) **[43882]**

Kakuro (Redhill, GBR) **[56355]**

Kalakalpam (Calcutta, WB, IND) *Unable to locate*

Kalamies (Helsinki, FIN) *Unable to locate*

Kalamunda Reporter (Midland, WA, AUS) **[42105]**

Kalnirnay (Mumbai, MH, IND) **[45406]**

Kalyani (Kelaniya, SRI) *Unable to locate*

Kamakoti Vani (Chennai, TN, IND) *Unable to locate*

Kampanja (Helsinki, FIN) **[43837]**

Kampioen (The Hague, NLD) **[48619]**

Kanal K-FM (Aarau, SWI) *Unable to locate*

Kanal K-FM (Aarau, SWI) *Unable to locate*

Kanal Melodiya (St. Petersburg, RUS) *Unable to locate*

Kanal 3 (Barnaul, RUS) *Unable to locate*

Kanal 3 (Barnaul, RUS) *Unable to locate*

Kanara Chamber of Commerce & Industry Journal (Mangalore, KA, IND) *Unable to locate*

Kanava (Kuvalehdet, FIN) **[43883]**

Kanch (New Delhi, DH, IND) *Unable to locate*

Kangtu Broadcasting Station (Kaohsiung, TWN) *Unable to locate*

Kansai Time Out (Kobe, JPN) **[46431]**

Kant e-Prints (Campinas, SP, BRZ) **[42970]**

Kant-Studien (Berlin, GER) **[44211]**

Kanu Schweiz (Dornach, SWI) *Unable to locate*

Kaohsiung Journal of Medical Sciences (Kaohsiung, TWN) **[51310]**

kapital (Copenhagen, DEN) **[43677]**

Kapital DATA (Oslo, NOR) *Ceased*

KAPT Union Pathrika (Cochin, KE, IND) *Unable to locate*

Karachi Journal of Science (Karachi, PAK) *Unable to locate*

Karamay People's Broadcasting Station (Karamay, XU, CHN) *Unable to locate*

Karamay People's Broadcasting Station (Karamay, XU, CHN) *Unable to locate*

Karinca (Ankara, TUR) **[51496]**

Karinca Kooperatif Postasi **[51496]**'

Karmanta (Moratuwa, SRI) *Unable to locate*

Karnatak Granthalaya (Gulbarga, KA, IND) *Unable to locate*

Karnatak Law Journal (Bangalore, KA, IND) *Unable to locate*

Karnatak University College of Education Journal (Dharwad, KA, IND) *Unable to locate*

Karnatak University—Humanities Journal (Dharwad, KA, IND) *Unable to locate*

Karnatak University—Science Journal (Dharwad, KA, IND) *Unable to locate*

Karnatak University—Social Sciences Journal (Dharwad, KA, IND) *Unable to locate*

Karnataka Labour Journal (Bangalore, KA, IND) *Unable to locate*

Karnataka Medical Journal (Bangalore, KA, IND) **[44977]**

Karnataka State Education Federation Journal (Bangalore, KA, IND) *Unable to locate*

Karthago (Paris, FRA) **[44067]**

Karting (Orpington, GBR) **[55854]**

Kartweli Eri (Tbilisi, GRG) *Unable to locate*

Karunungan (Manila, PHL) *Unable to locate*

Kasetsart Journal (Bangkok, THA) *Unable to locate*

Kashi People's Broadcasting Station (Kashi, XU, CHN) *Unable to locate*

Kashi People's Broadcasting Station (Kashi, XU, CHN) *Unable to locate*

Kashmir Affairs (Jammu, JK, IND) *Unable to locate*

Kashmir Observer (Srinagar, JK, IND) **[45739]**

Kashmir Times (Jammu, JK, IND) **[45205]**

Kashmir Today (Rawalpindi, PAK) *Unable to locate*

Kath-FM - 97.9 (Kathmandu, NPL) **[47850]**

Kathmandu Post (Kathmandu, NPL) **[47840]**

Kathmandu University Medical Journal (Kathmandu, NPL) **[47841]**

Katikati Advertiser (Tauranga, NZL) *Unable to locate*

Kativa-FM (Jatai, GO, BRZ) *Unable to locate*

Katolikus Radio-AM - 1341 kHz (Budapest, HUN) **[44884]**

Katso (Helsinki, FIN) **[43838]**

Katzen Magazin (Dietlikon, SWI) *Unable to locate*

Kauneus ja Terveys (Helsinki, FIN) **[43839]**

Kauppakamari (Helsinki, FIN) *Ceased*

Kauppalehti (Helsinki, FIN) *Unable to locate*

Kauppalehti Extra (Helsinki, FIN) *Unable to locate*

Kauppalehti Optio (Helsinki, FIN) **[43840]**

Kavaka (Bangalore, KA, IND) *Unable to locate*

Kavita Asia (Bhopal, MP, IND) *Unable to locate*

Kavya Bharati (Madurai, TN, IND) *Unable to locate*

Kaya-FM - 95.9 (Newtown, SAF) **[50559]**

Kayak-Canoe Magazine (Ultimo, NW, AUS) *Unable to locate*

Kayhan International (Tehran, IRN) *Unable to locate*

Kaytannon Maamies (KM) (Kuvalehdet, FIN) **[43884]**

Kazakh Radio (Almaty, KAZ) *Unable to locate*

Kazakh Radio (Almaty, KAZ) *Unable to locate*

Kazakh Radio (Almaty, KAZ) *Unable to locate*

Kazakh Radio (Almaty, KAZ) *Unable to locate*

KBC-FM - 101.9 (Nairobi, KEN) **[47201]**

KBS-Cheongju - 102.1 MHz (Cheongju, KOR) **[47216]**

KBS-Chohang-san (Pohang, KOR) *Unable to locate*

KBS-Chohang-san (Pohang, KOR) *Unable to locate*

KBS-Hakka-san (Andong-si, KOR) *Unable to locate*

KBS-Hambaek-san (Seoul, KOR) *Unable to locate*

KBS-Hambaek-san (Seoul, KOR) *Unable to locate*

KBS-Huksong-san (Cheongju, KOR) *Unable to locate*

KBS-Hwa-ak-san (Chuncheon-si, KOR) *Unable to locate*

KBS-Hwa-ak-san (Chuncheon-si, KOR) *Unable to locate*

KBS-Hwasong, KOR) *Unable to locate*

KBS-Hwasong (Seoul, KOR) *Unable to locate*

KBS-Hwasong (Seoul, KOR) *Unable to locate*

KBS-Ilwol-san (Chungju, KOR) *Unable to locate*

KBS-Jeju - 621 KHz (Jeju, KOR) **[47240]**

KBS-Kamak-san (Chinju, KOR) *Unable to locate*

KBS-Kayop-san (Chungju, KOR) *Unable to locate*

KBS-Kayop-san (Chungju, KOR) *Unable to locate*

KBS-Kwaebang-san (Gangneung, KOR) *Unable to locate*

KBS-Kwaebang-san (Seoul, KOR) *Unable to locate*

KBS-Kwanak-san (Seoul, KOR) *Unable to locate*

KBS-Kyeryong-san (Daejeon, KOR) *Unable to locate*

KBS-Kyeryong-san (Daejeon, KOR) *Unable to locate*

KBS-Kyonwolak (Jeju, KOR) *Unable to locate*

KBS-Kyonwolak (Jeju, KOR) *Unable to locate*

KBS-Kyonwolak (Jeju, KOR) *Unable to locate*

KBS-Mang-un-san, KOR) *Unable to locate*

KBS-Mang-un-san (Suncheon-si, KOR) *Unable to locate*

KBS-Mangjin-san (Andong-si, KOR) *Unable to locate*

KBS-Mo-ak-san (Jeonju-si, KOR) *Unable to locate*

KBS-Mo-ak-san (Jeonju-si, KOR) *Unable to locate*

KBS-Mudung-san (Gwangju, KOR) *Unable to locate*

KBS-Mudung-san (Gwangju, KOR) *Unable to locate*

KBS-Muryong-san (Ulsan, KOR) *Unable to locate*

KBS-Muryong-san (Ulsan, KOR) *Unable to locate*

KBS-Namsan (Seoul, KOR) *Unable to locate*

KBS-Namsan (Seoul, KOR) *Unable to locate*

KBS-Namsan (Seoul, KOR) *Unable to locate*

KBS-Nogodan, KOR) *Unable to locate*

KBS-Nogodan (Seoul, KOR) *Unable to locate*

KBS-Paegun-san (Wonju-si, KOR) *Unable to locate*

KBS-Paegun-san (Wonju-si, KOR) *Unable to locate*

KBS-P'algong-san (Daegu, KOR) *Unable to locate*

KBS-P'algong-san (Daegu, KOR) *Unable to locate*

KBS-Pohang (Pohang, KOR) *Unable to locate*

KBS-Pulmo-san (Changwon, KOR) *Unable to locate*

KBS-Pulmo-san (Changwon, KOR) *Unable to locate*

KBS-Sammaebong (Jeju, KOR) *Unable to locate*

KBS-Uam-san (Cheongju, KOR) *Unable to locate*

KBS-Uam-san - 89.3 MHz (Cheongju, KOR) **[47217]**

KBS-Wonju (Wonju-si, KOR) *Unable to locate*

KBS-Yang-ul-san (Mokpo-si, KOR) *Unable to locate*

KBS-Yangdo (Busan, KOR) *Unable to locate*

KBS-Yangdo (Busan, KOR) *Unable to locate*

KBS-Yongmun-san (Seoul, KOR) *Unable to locate*

KCFM-FM - 99.8 (Hull, GBR) **[53630]**

KCK (The Hague, NLD) **[48620]**

KCLR 96-FM - 96 (Kilkenny, KK, IRL) **[46026]**

KDB Report (Seoul, KOR) *Unable to locate*

Keemat (Mumbai, MH, IND) **[45407]**

Keerzyde (Utrecht, NLD) *Unable to locate*

Keidanren Review (Tokyo, JPN) *Unable to locate*

Keio Business Review (Tokyo, JPN) *Unable to locate*

Keio Economic Studies (Tokyo, JPN) **[46952]**

The Keio Journal of Medicine (Tokyo, JPN) **[46953]**

Keizai Doyu (Tokyo, JPN) *Unable to locate*

Kelk - Review of Arts and Culture (Tehran, IRN) *Unable to locate*

Kello and Kulta (Espoo, FIN) **[43812]**

Kenilworth Weekly News (Leamington Spa, GBR) **[53746]**

Kennel and Cattery Management (Horsham, GBR) **[53596]**

Kent Business (Aylesford, GBR) *Unable to locate*

A Kentish Partnership (Worthing, GBR) **[56974]**

A Kentish Wedding (Worthing, GBR) **[56975]**

The Kenya Farmer (Nairobi, KEN) *Unable to locate*

The Kenya Jurist (Nairobi, KEN) *Unable to locate*

Kenya Nursing Journal (Nairobi, KEN) *Unable to locate*

Kenya Past and Present (Nairobi, KEN) *Unable to locate*

Kenya Veterinarian (Nairobi, KEN) **[47191]**

Kerala (Pattom Palace, KE, IND) *Unable to locate*

Kerala Academy of Biology Journal (Trivandrum, KE, IND) *Unable to locate*

Kerala Co-Operative Journal (Trivandrum, KE, IND) *Unable to locate*

Kerala Homoeo Journal (Kottayam, KE, IND) *Unable to locate*

Kerala Industry (Trivandrum, KE, IND) *Unable to locate*

Kerala Law Journal (Cochin, KE, IND) *Unable to locate*

Kerala Law Times (Cochin, KE, IND) *Unable to locate*

Kerala Medical Journal (Cochin, KE, IND) *Unable to locate*

Keretapi (Kuala Lumpur, MYS) *Unable to locate*

Kermaria Magazine (Paris, FRA) *Unable to locate*

Kernkront (Brussels, BEL) *Unable to locate*

Kerrang! (London, GBR) **[54842]**

The Kerryman (Tralee, KR, IRL) *Unable to locate*

Kerry's Eye (Tralee, KR, IRL) **[46060]**

Keskisuomalainen (Jyvaskyla, FIN) **[43870]**

Kestrel-FM - 107.6 (Basingstoke, GBR) **[52235]**

Ketju (Helsinki, FIN) **[43841]**

Kettering Evening Telegraph (Kettering, GBR) **[53684]**

Key Engineering Materials (Zurich, SWI) **[51272]**

The Key Frame (Chorleywood, GBR) **[53024]**

Key Note Market Assessment. Tweenagers (Teddington, GBR) **[56733]**

Key 103-FM - 103 (Manchester, GBR) **[55586]**

Keynote (Mumbai, MH, IND) *Unable to locate*

The Keyring (Walton-On-Thames, GBR) *Unable to locate*

Keys (Bergkirchen, GER) *Unable to locate*

The Keys of Peter (London, GBR) *Unable to locate*

Keystone (Belfast, GBR) **[52289]**

Keyways (Daventry, GBR) *Unable to locate*

KF-FM - 105.4 (Kaunas, LIT) **[47469]**

KFAT News (Leicester, GBR) **[53808]**

KFM-FM - 97.3 (Newhall, KL, IRL) **[46050]**

KFM-FM - 97.6 (Newhall, KL, IRL) **[46051]**

KFM-FM - 94.5 (Cape Town, SAF) **[50433]**

Kfz Meister Service (Hannover, GER) *Unable to locate*

KG-Intern (Bochum, GER) *Unable to locate*

KGB-FM (South Yarra, VI, AUS) *Unable to locate*

Khadi Gramodyog (Mumbai, MH, IND) *Unable to locate*

Khaleej Times (Dubai, UAE) **[51646]**

Khanh Hoa Broadcasting - Televising (Nha Trang City, VNM) *Unable to locate*

Khanh Hoa Broadcasting - Televising (Nha Trang City, VNM) *Unable to locate*

Kherad Nameh Sadra (Tehran, IRN) *Unable to locate*

Khil'a (Wilsele, BEL) **[42912]**

Khimiya i Biznes (Moscow, RUS) *Unable to locate*

Khit-Kontakt (Nevinnomyssk, RUS) *Unable to locate*

Khristyanskiy Tserkovno-obshchestvennyy Kanal (Moscow, RUS) *Unable to locate*

Khulyot (Haifa, ISR) **[46077]**

Khumuun Bichig (Ulaanbaatar, MNG) **[47811]**

KiaOra (Auckland, NZL) **[48801]**

Kick to Corruption (Hoshiarpur, PJ, IND) *Unable to locate*

Kick-FM - 107.4 (Newbury, GBR) **[55663]**

Kick-FM - 105.6 (Newbury, GBR) **[55664]**

Kids Alive! (London, GBR) **[54843]**

Kien Giang Broadcast - Television Station (Hanoi, VNM) *Unable to locate*

Kigkkenskriveren (Oslo, NOR) *Unable to locate*

Kijk op Oost Nederland (Meppel, NLD) **[48739]**

KIK-FM - 88.7 (Mareeba, QL, AUS) **[42035]**

Kilburn Times (London, GBR) **[54844]**

Killer Bee Cebu-FM (Cebu City, PHL) *Unable to locate*

Killer Bee-FM (Cagayan de Oro City, PHL) *Unable to locate*

Killer Sudoku (Redhill, GBR) **[56356]**

Kilsyth Chronicle (Cumbernauld, GBR) **[53150]**

Kimika (Quezon City, PHL) *Unable to locate*

Kimp'o (Seoul, KOR) *Unable to locate*

Kincardineshire Observer (Montrose, GBR) **[55645]**

Kinder (Hamburg, GER) *Unable to locate*

Kindred Spirit (London, GBR) **[54845]**

Kinetics and Catalysis (Moscow, RUS) **[49931]**

Kinetoplastid Biology and Disease (London, GBR) *Ceased*

King Abdul Aziz Medical Journal (Jeddah, SAU) *Unable to locate*

Kingdom-FM - 95.2 (Markinch, GBR) **[55598]**

Kingdom-FM - 96.1 (Markinch, GBR) **[55596]**

Kingdom-FM - 105.4 (Markinch, GBR) **[55597]**

Kingdom Magazine (Fife, GBR) **[53388]**

Kingpin (London, GBR) **[54846]**

King's Law Journal (Oxford, GBR) **[56081]**

Kino (Sofia, BUL) **[43104]**

Kiosk Europe (Cambridge, GBR) **[52865]**

Kipling Journal (London, GBR) *Unable to locate*

Kippari (Kuvalehdet, FIN) **[43885]**

Kirjakauppalehti (Helsinki, FIN) *Unable to locate*

Kirkintilloch Herald (Kirkintilloch, GBR) **[53727]**

Kirriemuir Herald (Forfar, GBR) **[53398]**

Kisan World (Chennai, TN, IND) *Unable to locate*

Kismama (Budapest, HUN) **[44843]**

Kismama Mintaszam (Budapest, HUN) **[44844]**

Kismama 9 Honap (Budapest, HUN) **[44845]**

Kiss (Tokyo, JPN) **[46954]**

KISS-FM - 87.6 (Abbotsford, VI, AUS) **[41496]**

Kiss-FM - 89 (Nicosia, CYP) **[43598]**

Kiss-FM (Kobe, JPN) *Unable to locate*

Kiss-FM (Nairobi, KEN) *Unable to locate*

KISS-FM (Bangkok, THA) *Unable to locate*

Kiss 105-FM - 105 (Bury Saint Edmunds, GBR) **[52775]**

Kiss 101-FM - 101 (Bristol, GBR) **[52742]**

Kiss Radio-FM - 98.3 (Kaohsiung, TWN) **[51314]**

Kiss Radio-FM - 99.9 (Kaohsiung, TWN) **[51315]**

Kiss Radio-FM - 97.1 (Kaohsiung, TWN) **[51313]**

Kit Homes (North Ryde, NW, AUS) **[42184]**

Kita Nihin Hoso - 738 KHz (Toyama, JPN) **[47105]**

Kitchen Yearbook (North Ryde, NW, AUS) **[42185]**

Kitchens & Bathrooms News (Watford, GBR) **[56866]**

Kitchens and Bathrooms Quarterly (North Ryde, NW, AUS) **[42186]**

Kitchens Bedrooms and Bathrooms (Redhill, GBR) *Unable to locate*

Kiwi Parent (Mana, NZL) **[48936]**

Kjemi (Oslo, NOR) *Unable to locate*

Kjottbransjen (Oslo, NOR) *Unable to locate*

KK (Oslo, NOR) *Unable to locate*

Klassik Uhren (Ulm, GER) **[44696]**

Klassika Raadio-FM - 106.6 (Tallinn, EST) **[43784]**

KL.FM - 96.7 (King's Lynn, GBR) **[53714]**

KLFM-FM - 96.5 (Bendigo, VI, AUS) **[41594]**

KlubKat Music Magazine (Martlesham Heath, GBR) **[55602]**

KM-FM - 106.8 (Ashford, GBR) **[52144]**

KM-FM - 107.6 (Ashford, GBR) **[52142]**

KM-FM - 106 (Ashford, GBR) **[52143]**

KM-FM - 96.4 (Ashford, GBR) **[52141]**

KM-FM - 107.2 (Margate, GBR) **[55594]**

KM-FM - 107.9 (Rochester, GBR) **[56402]**

KM-FM - 105.6 (Rochester, GBR) **[56403]**

KM-FM - 100.4 (Strood, GBR) **[56646]**

KM-FM - 96.2 (Strood, GBR) **[56644]**

KM-FM - 101.6 (Strood, GBR) **[56645]**

Knafaim (Tel Aviv, ISR) *Unable to locate*

Knanayamithram (Kottayam, KE, IND) *Unable to locate*

Knaresborough Post (Knaresborough, GBR) **[53728]**

Knee Surgery, Sports Traumatology, Arthroscopy (Dordrecht, NLD) **[48500]**

Knit Today (Bristol, GBR) **[52700]**

Knit&Mode (Moscow, RUS) **[49932]**

Knitting International (Bradford, GBR) **[52519]**

Knjiznica (Ljubljana, SVA) *Unable to locate*

Knowledge-Based Systems (Sydney, NW, AUS) **[42532]**

Knowledge and Information Systems (Dordrecht, NLD) **[48501]**

Knowledge Management Research & Practice (Birmingham, GBR) **[52356]**

Knowledge Organization (Wurzburg, GER) **[44721]**

The Knowledge Tree (Brisbane, QL, AUS) **[41651]**

Knox Leader (Boronia, VI, AUS) **[41619]**

Kobe Journal of Mathematics (Kobe, JPN) **[46432]**

Kobe Journal of Medical Sciences (Kobe, JPN) **[46433]**

Kobe University Economic Review (Kobe, JPN) **[46434]**

Kobisena (Calcutta, WB, IND) *Unable to locate*

Kochi Hoso (Kochi, JPN) *Unable to locate*

Kodu Stuudio (Kuvalehdet, FIN) *Unable to locate*

Kodutohter (Kuvalehdet, FIN) **[43886]**

Kogane (Tokyo, JPN) **[46955]**

Koi (Bristol, GBR) **[52701]**

Numbers cited in bold after listings are entry numbers rather than page numbers.

Koiramme-Vara Hundar (Espoo, FIN) Unable to locate

Kol Hakhay (Givatayim, ISR) Unable to locate

The Kolan Recorder (Sydney, NW, AUS) [42533]

Kollektsia Idei (Moscow, RUS) [49933]

Komba (Nairobi, KEN) Unable to locate

Kommunalbladet (Arhus, DEN) Unable to locate

Kompass India (New Delhi, DH, IND) Unable to locate

K1-FM (Bournemouth, GBR) Unable to locate

Konfeksiyon & Teknik (Istanbul, TUR) [51559]

Konkan Samachar (Mumbai, MH, IND) Unable to locate

Konkret GmbH & Co. KG (Hamburg, GER) Unable to locate

Kontakt (Copenhagen, DEN) [43678]

Kontakto (Rotterdam, NLD) Unable to locate

Koodal Historical Series (Madurai, TN, IND) Unable to locate

Kool-FM - 103.3 (The Valley, AIA) [41466]

KOOL-FM - 97.3 (Forest-Side, MUS) [47753]

Kooperatifcilik [51518]*

Koori Radio-FM - 93.7 (Strawberry Hills, NW, AUS) [42398]

The Kop (Liverpool, GBR) Unable to locate

Korea Business World (Seoul, KOR) Unable to locate

Korea Buyers Guide Electronics (Seoul, KOR) Unable to locate

Korea Development Bank: Its Functions and Activities (Seoul, KOR) Unable to locate

Korea Economic Weekly (Seoul, KOR) Unable to locate

Korea Journal (Seoul, KOR) [47278]

The Korea Post (Seoul, KOR) [47279]

Korea Times (Seoul, KOR) [47280]

Korea Trade (Seoul, KOR) Unable to locate

Korea Trade and Investment (Seoul, KOR) Unable to locate

Korea YWCA (Seoul, KOR) Unable to locate

Korean Biochemical Journal [47258]*

Korean Business Journal (Seoul, KOR) Unable to locate

Korean Central Broadcasting Station - Chongjin (Pyongyang, KOD) Unable to locate

Korean Central Broadcasting Station - Chongjin (Pyongyang, KOD) Unable to locate

Korean Central Broadcasting Station - Haeju (Pyongyang, KOD) Unable to locate

Korean Central Broadcasting Station - Hamhung (Pyongyang, KOD) Unable to locate

Korean Central Broadcasting Station - Hamhung (Pyongyang, KOD) Unable to locate

Korean Central Broadcasting Station - Hwangju (Pyongyang, KOD) Unable to locate

Korean Central Broadcasting Station - Hyesan (Pyongyang, KOD) Unable to locate

Korean Central Broadcasting Station - Kaesong (Pyongyang, KOD) Unable to locate

Korean Central Broadcasting Station - Kaesong (Pyongyang, KOD) Unable to locate

Korean Central Broadcasting Station - Kanggye (Pyongyang, KOD) Unable to locate

Korean Central Broadcasting Station - Kanggye (Pyongyang, KOD) Unable to locate

Korean Central Broadcasting Station - Kanggye (Pyongyang, KOD) Unable to locate

Korean Central Broadcasting Station - Pyongyang (Pyongyang, KOD) Unable to locate

Korean Central Broadcasting Station - Pyongyang (Pyongyang, KOD) Unable to locate

Korean Central Broadcasting Station - Pyongyang (Pyongyang, KOD) Unable to locate

Korean Central Broadcasting Station - Pyongyang (Pyongyang, KOD) Unable to locate

Korean Central Broadcasting Station - Sariwon (Pyongyang, KOD) Unable to locate

Korean Central Broadcasting Station - Sinuiju (Pyongyang, KOD) Unable to locate

Korean Central Broadcasting Station - Wiwon (Pyongyang, KOD) Unable to locate

Korean Central Broadcasting Station - Wonsan (Pyongyang, KOD) Unable to locate

Korean Central Broadcasting Station - Wonsan (Pyongyang, KOD) Unable to locate

Korean Education and Cultural Television (Pyongyang, KOD) Unable to locate

Korean Educational and Cultural Television (Pyongyang, KOD) Unable to locate

Korean Journal of Applied Entomology (Suwon, KOR) Unable to locate

Korean Journal of the Atmospheric Sciences (Seoul, KOR) Unable to locate

Korean Journal of Breeding (Suwon, KOR) Unable to locate

The Korean Journal of Defense Analysis (Seoul, KOR) [47281]

Korean Journal of Medicinal Chemistry [47259]*

Korean Journal of Mycology (Seoul, KOR) Unable to locate

Korean Journal of Pharmacognosy (Seoul, KOR) Unable to locate

Korean Journal of Public Health (Seoul, KOR) Unable to locate

Korean Journal of Radiology (Seoul, KOR) [47282]

The Korean Journal of Systematic Zoology (Jeonju, KOR) Unable to locate

Korean Journal of Zoology (Seoul, KOR) Unable to locate

Korean Physical Society Journal (Seoul, KOR) Unable to locate

Korean Social Science Journal (Seoul, KOR) Unable to locate

Korean Society of Oceanography Journal (Seoul, KOR) Unable to locate

Koreana (Seoul, KOR) [47283]

Korla People's Broadcasting Station (Korla, XU, CHN) Unable to locate

Korrespondent (Kiev, URE) [51599]

Korrespondenzblatt (Dortmund, GER) [44317]

Kosmetiek Apropos (Zoetermeer, NLD) Unable to locate

Kosmetische Medizin (Berlin, GER) Unable to locate

Kosmo! (Kuala Lumpur, MYS) [47610]

KOTI Magazine (Helsinki, FIN) Unable to locate

Kotilaakari (Kuvalehdet, FIN) Unable to locate

Kotiliesi (Kuvalehdet, FIN) [43887]

Kottoner 98-FM - 98.0 (Cospicua, MAL) [47729]

Kotuitui (Wellington, NZL) [49014]

Kouga Express (Jeffreys Bay, SAF) [50526]

Koululainen (Kuvalehdet, FIN) [43888]

KPTK-FM - 101 (Logan City, QL, AUS) [42017]

Kranti (Calcutta, WB, IND) Unable to locate

Krasnodar (Krasnodar, RUS) Unable to locate

Krasnodar (Krasnodar, RUS) Unable to locate

Krasnoguda (Sejny, POL) [49675]

Kred [52921]*

Kreo (Brussels, BEL) Unable to locate

Krestianskie Vedomosti (Moscow, RUS) Unable to locate

Krise aktuell (Vienna, AUT) Unable to locate

Krishak Samachar (New Delhi, DH, IND) Unable to locate

Krishnamurti Foundation Bulletin (Chennai, TN, IND) [45051]

Kriss Kross (Redhill, GBR) [56357]

Kristdemokraten (Stockholm, SWE) Unable to locate

Kristeligt Dagblad (Copenhagen, DEN) Unable to locate

Kriterion (Belo Horizonte, MG, BRZ) [42949]

Kritika Kultura (Quezon City, PHL) [49598]

Kritikon Litterarum (Berlin, GER) [44212]

KronoScope (Leiden, NLD) [48705]

Kroonnuus (Cape Town, SAF) [50385]

KRR-FM (Kandos, NW, AUS) Unable to locate

Kruh i Ruze (Zagreb, CTA) [43569]

KSL Lahiradio-FM - 100.3 Mhz (Helsinki, FIN) [43867]

Kuaile (Happy) Broadcasting Station (Kaohsiung, TWN) Unable to locate

Kuensel (Thimphu, BTN) [42926]

Kulde Skandinavia (Jar, NOR) [49192]

Kulinarny Practicum (Moscow, RUS) [49934]

Kuljetusyrittaja (Helsinki, FIN) [43842]

Kultaraha (Helsinki, FIN) Unable to locate

Kultur Politik (Bonn, GER) [44265]

Kulturradet (Stockholm, SWE) Unable to locate

Kuma Raadio-FM - 101 (Paide, EST) [43782]

Kumamoto Journal of Mathematics (Kumamoto, JPN) [46453]

Kumamoto Medical Journal (Kumamoto, JPN) Ceased

Kundalini (New Delhi, DH, IND) Unable to locate

Kunming People's Broadcasting Station 1 (Kunming, YU, CHN) Unable to locate

Kunming People's Broadcasting Station 1 (Kunming, YU, CHN) Unable to locate

Kunming People's Broadcasting Station 1 (Kunming, YU, CHN) Unable to locate

Kunst & Architektur in der Schweiz (Bern, SWI) [51075]

Kunst Bulletin (Zurich, SWI) [51273]

Kunst Chronik (Munich, GER) [44568]

Kunst og Kultur (Oslo, NOR) Unable to locate

Kunstblad (Haarlem, NLD) Ceased

Kuo Sheng Broadcasting Co. (Changhua, TWN) Unable to locate

Kuresaare Pereraadio-FM - 89.0 MHz (Kuressaare, EST) [43781]

Kuresaare Pereraadio-FM - 89.4 MHz (Kuressaare, EST) [43779]

Kuresaare Pereraadio-FM - 88.7 MHz (Kuressaare, EST) [43780]

Kurier (Vienna, AUT) Unable to locate

Kurinji Quarterly (Calcutta, WB, IND) Unable to locate

Kurs Radio (Kursk, RUS) Unable to locate

Kurs Radio (Kursk, RUS) Unable to locate

Kurukshetra Law Journal (Kurukshetra, HY, IND) Unable to locate

Kurukshetra (New Delhi) (New Delhi, DH, IND) Unable to locate

Kurume Medical Journal (Fukuoka, JPN) Unable to locate

Kurve (Unna, GER) Unable to locate

Kurzberichte aus der Bauforschung (Stuttgart, GER) Unable to locate

Kusht Vinashak (New Delhi, DH, IND) Unable to locate

Kustradion-FM - 105 (Fuengirola, SPA) [50715]

Kuwait Journal of Science & Engineering (Keifan, KWT) Unable to locate

The Kuwait Medical Journal (Safat, KWT) [47340]

Kuwait Radio - Arabic Music - 105.9 MHz (Safat, KWT) [47345]

Kuwait Radio - Arabic Music - 90.5 MHz (Safat, KWT) [47343]

Kuwait Radio - Arabic Music - 87.9 MHz (Safat, KWT) [47344]

Kuwait Radio - Arabic Music - 95.0 MHz (Safat, KWT) [47342]

Kuwait Radio - Easy FM - 92.5 MHz (Safat, KWT) [47346]

Kuwait Radio - FM Super Station - 99.7 MHz (Safat, KWT) [47347]

Kuwait Radio - Holy Quran - 1341 KHz (Safat, KWT) [47350]

Kuwait Radio - Holy Quran - 630 KHz (Safat, KWT) [47351]

Kuwait Radio - Holy Quran - 97.5 MHz (Safat, KWT) [47348]

Kuwait Radio - Holy Quran - 93.3 MHz (Safat, KWT) [47349]

Kuwait Radio - Main Arabic - 1134 KHz (Safat, KWT) [47355]

Kuwait Radio - Main Arabic - 540 KHz (Safat, KWT) [47356]

Kuwait Radio - Main Arabic - 89.5 MHz (Safat, KWT) [47353]

Kuwait Radio - Main Arabic - 963 KHz (Safat, KWT) [47354]

Kuwait Radio - Main Arabic - 98.9 MHz (Safat, KWT) [47352]

Kuwait Radio - Second Arabic - 1341 KHz (Safat, KWT) [47357]

Kuwait Radio - Second Arabic Music - 1269 KHz (Safat, KWT) [47358]

Kuwait Radio - Second Arabic Music - 103.7 MHz (Safat, KWT) [47359]

Numbers cited in bold after listings are entry numbers rather than page numbers.

Kuwait Radio - TV Sound - 100.5 MHz (Safat, KWT) **[47360]**

Kuwait Television (Safat, KWT) *Unable to locate*

Kuwait Television (Safat, KWT) *Unable to locate*

Kuwait Television (Safat, KWT) *Unable to locate*

Kuwait Television (Safat, KWT) *Unable to locate*

Kuwait Television (Safat, KWT) *Unable to locate*

Kuwait Television (Safat, KWT) *Unable to locate*

Kuwait Television (Safat, KWT) *Unable to locate*

Kuwait Television (Safat, KWT) *Unable to locate*

Kuwait Television (Safat, KWT) *Unable to locate*

Kuwait Television (Safat, KWT) *Unable to locate*

Kuytun People's Broadcasting Station (Kuytun, HA, CHN) *Unable to locate*

Kuytun People's Broadcasting Station (Kuytun, XU, CHN) *Unable to locate*

Kvakera Esperantisto (Braintree, GBR) *Unable to locate*

Kvinner og Familie (Oslo, NOR) *Unable to locate*

Kvinnotryck (Stockholm, SWE) **[51024]**

Kwan-Hyub (Seoul, KOR) *Unable to locate*

Kwani? (Nairobi, KEN) **[47192]**

Kwietnik (Warsaw, POL) **[49729]**

KXPL-AM - 1060 (Juarez, CH, MEX) **[47779]**

Kybernetes (West Yorkshire, GBR) **[56904]**

Kyiv Post (Kiev, URE) **[51600]**

KYKLOS (Oxford, GBR) **[56082]**

Kyodo News (Tokyo, JPN) **[46956]**

Kyoto Journal (Kyoto, JPN) **[46479]**

Kyoto Review of Southeast Asia (Kyoto, JPN) **[46480]**

The Kyoto Shimbun News (Kyoto, JPN) **[46481]**

Kyoto University Research Activities in Civil Engineering and Related Fields (Kyoto, JPN) *Unable to locate*

Kyrgyz Radio - Batken (Bishkek, KGA) *Unable to locate*

Kyrgyz Radio - Bishkek (Almaty, KAZ) *Unable to locate*

Kyrgyz Radio - Bishkek (Bishkek, KGA) *Unable to locate*

Kyrgyz Radio - Bishkek (Bishkek, KGA) *Unable to locate*

Kyrgyz Radio - Bishkek (Bishkek, KGA) *Unable to locate*

Kyrgyz Radio - Bishkek (Bishkek, KGA) *Unable to locate*

Kyrgyz Radio - Bishkek (Bishkek, KGA) *Unable to locate*

Kyrgyz Radio - Bishkek (Bishkek, KGA) *Unable to locate*

Kyrgyz Radio - Bishkek (Bishkek, KGA) *Unable to locate*

Kyrgyz Radio - Cholpon-Ata - 1404 KHz (Cholpon-Ata, KGA) **[47203]**

Kyrgyz Radio - Dedemel (Bishkek, KGA) *Unable to locate*

Kyrgyz Radio - Dedemel (Bishkek, KGA) *Unable to locate*

Kyrgyz Radio - Haidarkan - 1404 KHz (Haidarkan, KGA) **[47204]**

Kyrgyz Radio - Jalal-Abad (Bishkek, KGA) *Unable to locate*

Kyrgyz Radio - Jojomel - 1404 KHz (Jojomel, KGA) **[47205]**

Kyrgyz Radio - Kanysh-Kiya (Bishkek, KGA) *Unable to locate*

Kyrgyz Radio - Kara-Kul (Bishkek, KGA) *Unable to locate*

Kyrgyz Radio - Karakol (Bishkek, KGA) *Unable to locate*

Kyrgyz Radio - Naryn (Bishkek, KGA) *Unable to locate*

Kyrgyz Radio - Orgochor (Bishkek, KGA) *Unable to locate*

Kyrgyz Radio - Orgochor (Bishkek, KGA) *Unable to locate*

Kyrgyz Radio - Orgochor - 1404 KHz (Orgochor, KGA) **[47206]**

Kyrgyz Radio - Osh (Bishkek, KGA) *Unable to locate*

Kyrgyz Radio - Osh (Osh, KGA) *Unable to locate*

Kyrgyz Radio - Sulyukta (Bishkek, KGA) *Unable to locate*

Kyrgyz Radio - Sulyukta (Bishkek, KGA) *Unable to locate*

Kyrgyz Radio - Talas (Bishkek, KGA) *Unable to locate*

Kyrgyz Radio - Tash-Kumyr (Bishkek, KGA) *Unable to locate*

Kyrgyz Radio - Terek-Say (Bishkek, KGA) *Unable to locate*

Kyrgyz Radio - Terek-Say (Bishkek, KGA) *Unable to locate*

Kyrgyz Radio - Vostochnaya (Bishkek, KGA) *Unable to locate*

Kyrgyz Radio - Yuzhnaya-2 (Bishkek, KGA) *Unable to locate*

Kyrgyz Radio - Yuzhnaya-2 (Bishkek, KGA) *Unable to locate*

Kyrgyzstan Chronicle (Bishkek, KGA) *Unable to locate*

KYSS-FM - 102.5 (Saint Kitts, WIN) **[57104]**

Kyushu American Literature (Fukuoka, JPN) *Unable to locate*

KZAS **[49644]***

L

L-Radio (Chelyabinsk, RUS) *Unable to locate*

L Radio - Lipetsk (Lipetsk, RUS) *Unable to locate*

L-Tsentr/Ekho Moskvy (Stavropol, RUS) *Unable to locate*

La radiologia medica (Dordrecht, NLD) **[48502]**

La Balsa de la Medusa (Madrid, SPA) **[50777]**

La Boletina (Managua, NCG) **[49054]**

La Broye (Payerne, SWI) **[51220]**

la Caledonie Agricole (Noumea, NCL) *Unable to locate*

La Cana (Madrid, SPA) *Unable to locate*

La Cartoleria (Monza, ITA) *Unable to locate*

La Casa Marie Claire (Madrid, SPA) *Unable to locate*

La Chirurgia degli Organi di Movimento (Bologna, ITA) *Unable to locate*

La Clessidra (Rome, ITA) **[46237]**

La Dono (Wintzenheim, FRA) *Unable to locate*

La Educacion en Nuestras Manos (Buenos Aires, ARG) *Unable to locate*

La Estetica Profesional (Madrid, SPA) *Unable to locate*

La Gazette de la Presse Francophone (Paris, FRA) *Unable to locate*

La Gazzetta dell'Economia (Modugno, ITA) *Unable to locate*

La Gazzetta del Mezzogiorno (Bari, ITA) *Unable to locate*

La Isla-FM - 89,9 (Buenos Aires, ARG) **[41483]**

La Lettre de medecine physique et de readaptation (Dordrecht, NLD) **[48503]**

La Lettre Economique de Montagne Expansion (Meylan, FRA) *Unable to locate*

La Lettre de l'AVFT (Paris, FRA) *Unable to locate*

La Lettre de l'Internat (Montrouge, FRA) **[43995]**

La Libre Enterprise (Brussels, BEL) *Unable to locate*

La Nouvelle Fipregazette (Stockholm, SWE) *Unable to locate*

La Nueva-FM - 106.9 (Santiago, DOM) **[43741]**

La Pachanga-AM - 840 (Celaya, GJ, MEX) **[47757]**

La Pagina (Santa Cruz de Tenerife, SPA) **[50829]**

La Pluma (Lima, PER) *Unable to locate*

La Prensa Medica Argentina (Buenos Aires, ARG) *Unable to locate*

La Razza Bruna (Bussolengo, ITA) **[46129]**

La Red-AM - 910 (Buenos Aires, ARG) **[41484]**

La Revue (Paris, FRA) *Unable to locate*

La Rivista della Scuola (Milan, ITA) **[46185]**

La Semaine Medicale (Het Medisch Weekblad) (Ohain, BEL) *Unable to locate*

La Sicilia (Catania, ITA) *Unable to locate*

La Sicilia: Stilos (Catania, ITA) *Unable to locate*

La Sicilia: Vivere (Catania, ITA) *Unable to locate*

La Skolta Mondo (Curico, CHL) *Unable to locate*

La Stampa (Turin, ITA) *Unable to locate*

La Tribune de l'Assurance (Rueil-Malmaison, FRA) **[44100]**

La Une (Metn, LBN) *Unable to locate*

La Vie du Collectionneur (Fontainebleau, FRA) *Unable to locate*

La Vie de l'Auto (Fontainebleau, FRA) **[43953]**

La Voz (Caracas, VEN) *Unable to locate*

La Voz del Educador (Ciudad Fray Bentos, URY) *Unable to locate*

Lab on a Chip (Cambridge, GBR) **[52866]**

Label (Loughborough, GBR) **[55484]**

Labor Direct (Gross Enzersdorf, AUT) **[42726]**

Labor History (Abingdon, GBR) **[51961]**

Laboratoriet (Stockholm, SWE) *Unable to locate*

LaboratoriumsMedizin (Berlin, GER) **[44213]**

Laboratory Animals (London, GBR) **[54847]**

Laboratory News (Croydon, GBR) **[53128]**

Laboratory Research and Exploration (Shanghai, CHN) **[43485]**

Labores del Hogar (Barcelona, SPA) **[50682]**

Labour Bulletin (Kanpur, UP, IND) *Unable to locate*

Labour Chronicle (Mumbai, MH, IND) *Unable to locate*

Labour Code of Pakistan (Karachi, PAK) **[49359]**

Labour Gazette (Mumbai, MH, IND) *Unable to locate*

Labour History Review (London, GBR) **[54848]**

Labour and Industrial Cases (Nagpur, MH, IND) **[45469]**

Labour and Industrial Law Reporter (New Delhi, DH, IND) **[45621]**

Labour Law Journal (Chennai, TN, IND) *Unable to locate*

Labour Law Reporter (New Delhi, DH, IND) *Unable to locate*

Labour Market Trends (Mitcham, GBR) *Unable to locate*

Labour World (New Delhi, DH, IND) *Unable to locate*

Labquip **[50572]***

Lace (Stourbridge, GBR) **[56640]**

Lackiererblatt (Leinfelden-Echterdingen, GER) **[44525]**

Lady Biker Magazine (Aberdeen, GBR) **[51679]**

Laekartidningen (Stockholm, SWE) *Unable to locate*

Lagos Business School Management Review (Victoria Island, LG, NGA) **[49178]**

Lagos Historical Review (Yaba, LG, NGA) **[49179]**

Lagos Journal of Library and Information Science (Lagos, LG, NGA) **[49140]**

The Laity (London, GBR) *Unable to locate*

Lake District Life (Preston, GBR) **[56301]**

Lake Macquarie News (Cardiff, NW, AUS) **[41722]**

Lakeland Echo (Morecambe, GBR) **[55648]**

Lakeland Radio-FM - 100.1 (Kendal, GBR) **[53672]**

Lakeland Radio-FM - 100.8 (Kendal, GBR) **[53671]**

The Lakesider (Wanaka, NZL) *Ceased*

Lakhanda Radio-FM - 88.5 (Colombo, SRI) **[50875]**

Lal-Baugh (Bangalore, KA, IND) *Unable to locate*

Lalit Kala Contemporary (New Delhi, DH, IND) *Unable to locate*

Lamellicornia (Tokyo, JPN) **[46957]**

Lamode Francaise (Paris, FRA) *Unable to locate*

Lan Yang FM Broadcasting Station (Ilan, TWN) *Unable to locate*

Lanark Gazette (Lanark, GBR) **[53731]**

Lancashire Evening Post (Preston, GBR) **[56302]**

Lancashire Life (Preston, GBR) **[56303]**

The Lancet (London, GBR) *Unable to locate*

The Land (North Richmond, NW, AUS) **[42163]**

Land Bank Journal (Mumbai, MH, IND) *Unable to locate*

Land Degradation & Development (Swansea, GBR) **[56703]**

Land Lantbruk (Stockholm, SWE) *Unable to locate*

Land & Liberty (London, GBR) **[54849]**

Land Management and Environmental Law Report **[56941]***

Land Mobile (Salisbury, GBR) **[56455]**

Land & Raum (Vienna, AUT) *Unable to locate*

Land Rover World (Croydon, GBR) *Unable to locate*

Land of Rural Digest (Doornfontein, SAF) *Unable to locate*

Numbers cited in bold after listings are entry numbers rather than page numbers.

Land & Vee (Roermond, NLD) *Unable to locate*

Landbouweekblad (Cape Town, SAF) **[50386]**

Landeswelle-FM - 99.7 (Erfurt, GER) **[44337]**

Landfall (Dunedin, NZL) **[48891]**

Landsbladet (Copenhagen, DEN) *Unable to locate*

Landsbygdens Folk (Helsinki, FIN) **[43843]**

Landscape Design (London, GBR) **[54850]**

Landscape and Ecological Engineering (Tokyo, JPN) **[46958]**

Landscape Research (Oxford, GBR) **[56083]**

The Landscaper (Bushey, GBR) **[52776]**

Landschaftsarchitekten (Berlin, GER) **[44214]**

Landsklubben (Aabyhoej, DEN) *Unable to locate*

Landslides (Dordrecht, NLD) **[48504]**

Landwards (Edinburgh, GBR) **[53297]**

Landwirtschaftliche Mitteilungen (Graz, AUT) *Unable to locate*

Langfang People's Broadcasting Station (Langfang, HB, CHN) *Unable to locate*

Langfang People's Broadcasting Station (Langfang, HB, CHN) *Unable to locate*

Language Awareness (Abingdon, GBR) **[51962]**

Language and Cognition (Berlin, GER) **[44215]**

Language & Communication (Oxford, GBR) **[56084]**

Language and Computers (Freiburg, GER) **[44370]**

Language and Culture (Sapporo, JPN) *Unable to locate*

Language Culture & Curriculum (Abingdon, GBR) **[51963]**

Language and Education (Abingdon, GBR) **[51964]**

Language & History (London, GBR) **[54851]**

Language and Intercultural Communication (Abingdon, GBR) **[51965]**

Language Issues (Birmingham, GBR) **[52357]**

Language Learning Journal (Leicester, GBR) **[53809]**

Language and Literature (London, GBR) **[54852]**

Language Matters (Pretoria, SAF) **[50595]**

Language Policy (Dordrecht, NLD) **[48505]**

Language Problems and Language Planning (Amsterdam, NLD) **[48133]**

Language Resources and Evaluation (Dordrecht, NLD) **[48506]**

Language Sciences (Rondebosch, SAF) **[50620]**

Language Teacher (Tokyo, JPN) **[46959]**

Language Teaching Research (London, GBR) **[54853]**

Language@internet (Cologne, GER) **[44298]**

Languages in Contrast (Amsterdam, NLD) **[48134]**

La970-AM (Asuncion, PAR) *Unable to locate*

Lanka Guardian (Colombo, SRI) *Unable to locate*

Lanka Journal of Theology (Colombo, SRI) *Unable to locate*

Lanka Monthly Digest (Colombo, SRI) **[50860]**

Lanka Woman (Colombo, SRI) **[50861]**

The Lantern (London, GBR) **[54854]**

Lanzhou People's Broadcasting Station (Lanzhou, GS, CHN) *Unable to locate*

Lanzhou People's Broadcasting Station (Lanzhou, GS, CHN) *Unable to locate*

Lao National Television (Vientiane, LAO) *Unable to locate*

Lao National Television (Vientiane, LAO) *Unable to locate*

Lao National Television (Vientiane, LAO) *Unable to locate*

Laohekou People's Broadcasting Station (Laohekou, HU, CHN) *Unable to locate*

Lapiz (Madrid, SPA) *Unable to locate*

Large Print Crosswords (Gosford, NW, AUS) **[41919]**

Large Print Crosswords (London, GBR) *Unable to locate*

Large Type Daily Bread (Milton Keynes, GBR) *Unable to locate*

Larne Times (Larne, GBR) **[53742]**

Las Labores de Ana (Barcelona, SPA) *Unable to locate*

Laser & Photonics Reviews (Berlin, GER) **[44216]**

Laser Physics (Moscow, RUS) **[49935]**

Laser Technik Journal (Berlin, GER) **[44217]**

Lasers in Medical Science (London, GBR) **[54855]**

Late Antique Archaeology (Leiden, NLD) **[48706]**

Latin America Letter (Calcutta, WB, IND) *Unable to locate*

Latin America Quarterly Magazine (La Paz, BOL) *Unable to locate*

Latin America Recorder (New Delhi, DH, IND) *Unable to locate*

Latin American and Caribbean Ethnic Studies (Abingdon, GBR) **[51966]**

Latin American Politics, Economy & Society (Tokyo, JPN) *Unable to locate*

Latina-FM - 92.3 (Oranjestad, ARU) **[41493]**

LatinFinance (London, GBR) **[54856]**

Latino Studies (Basingstoke, GBR) **[52222]**

Latitudes (Denpasar, IDN) *Unable to locate*

Latu ja Polku (Helsinki, FIN) *Unable to locate*

Latvian Journal of Physics and Technical Sciences (Warsaw, POL) **[49730]**

Latvijas Radio 4 - 107.7 MHz (Riga, LAT) **[47377]**

Latvijas Radio 1 - 90.7 MHz (Riga, LAT) **[47378]**

Latvijas Radio 3 - 103.7 MHz (Riga, LAT) **[47379]**

Latvijas Radio 2 - 91.5 MHz (Riga, LAT) **[47380]**

Laudate Magazine (Blechingley, GBR) **[52388]**

Launceston's WAY-FM - 105.3 (Riverside, TA, AUS) **[42312]**

Launderette and Cleaning World (Welling, GBR) **[56878]**

Lausanne-Cites (Lausanne, SWI) **[51193]**

Law in Africa (Cologne, GER) **[44299]**

Law, Culture & the Humanities (London, GBR) **[54857]**

Law and Financial Markets Review (Oxford, GBR) **[56085]**

Law Gazette (Singapore, SGP) **[50212]**

Law and Humanities (Coventry, GBR) **[53088]**

Law Institute Journal **[42069]***

Law; International Journal of Information Policy and **[42521]***

Law; International Journal of the Sociology of the **[53694]***

Law Journal; IBP **[49571]***

Law & Justice (London, GBR) *Unable to locate*

Law Librarian **[53298]***

Law and Philosophy (Dordrecht, NLD) **[48507]**

Law & Policy (Oxford, GBR) **[56086]**

The Law and Practice of International Courts and Tribunals (Leiden, NLD) **[48707]**

Law, Probability and Risk (Oxford, GBR) **[56087]**

Law Quarterly Review (Andover, GBR) **[52120]**

Law Referencer (New Delhi, DH, IND) *Unable to locate*

Law Society Journal (Sydney, NW, AUS) **[42534]**

Law Teacher (Andover, GBR) *Unable to locate*

The Law Teacher (Nottingham, GBR) **[55765]**

Law-Text-Culture (Sydney, NW, AUS) *Unable to locate*

Law Thesaurus (New Delhi, DH, IND) *Unable to locate*

Law Weekly (Chennai, TN, IND) *Unable to locate*

LAWASIA Journal (Brisbane, QL, AUS) **[41652]**

LawLink (Singapore, SGP) **[50213]**

Lawyer International (London, GBR) *Unable to locate*

Laya (Quezon City, PHL) *Unable to locate*

LBC-AM - 1152 (London, GBR) **[55452]**

LBC-FM - 97.3 (London, GBR) **[55453]**

LC-FM - 87.8 (Launceston, TA, AUS) **[41999]**

LC-GC International **[52996]***

LCGC Europe (Chester, GBR) **[52996]**

LCR (London, GBR) **[54858]**

LCR-AM (Loughborough, GBR) *Unable to locate*

Le Bulletin du Badle (Dakar, SEN) *Unable to locate*

Le Cavalier Romand (Pully, SWI) **[51222]**

Le Chasseur Ardennais (Wepion, BEL) *Unable to locate*

Le Colley (Milizac, FRA) *Unable to locate*

Le Journal du Dentiste (Brussels, BEL) *Unable to locate*

Le Juriste (London, GBR) *Unable to locate*

Le Matin (Lausanne, SWI) **[51194]**

Le Matin (Lausanne, SWI) **[51195]**

Le Matin Dimanche (Lausanne, SWI) **[51196]**

Le Monde Du Travail (Kigali, RWA) *Unable to locate*

Le Monde Poche (Paris, FRA) *Unable to locate*

Le Museon (Louvain, BEL) *Unable to locate*

Le Nouvel Epicier (Paris, FRA) *Unable to locate*

Le Peuple Breton/Pobl Vreizh/Breton people (Lorient, FRA) *Unable to locate*

Le Point (Brussels, BEL) *Unable to locate*

Le Pro (Meylan, FRA) *Unable to locate*

Le Progres Agricole et Viticole (Montpellier, FRA) *Unable to locate*

Le Rotarien (Lyon, FRA) **[43969]**

Le Rythme (Geneva, SWI) *Unable to locate*

Le Temps (Geneva, SWI) **[51153]**

Le Temps Strategique (Geneva, SWI) *Ceased*

Le Trebuchet (La-Roche-sur-Yon, FRA) *Unable to locate*

Le Vif/L'Express (Brussels, BEL) *Unable to locate*

The Leader (Loxton, SA, AUS) *Unable to locate*

Leader Messenger (Salisbury, SA, AUS) **[42343]**

Leadership Focus (London, GBR) **[54859]**

Leadership in Health Services (Bradford, GBR) **[52520]**

Leadership in HIV/AIDS (Cape Town, SAF) **[50387]**

Leadership Magazine (Cape Town, SAF) *Unable to locate*

Leadership and Organization Development Journal (Newtownabbey, GBR) **[55702]**

LeaFlet (Abingdon, GBR) **[51967]**

The Leamington Observer (Leamington Spa, GBR) **[53747]**

Leamington Spa Courier (Leamington Spa, GBR) **[53748]**

Leaping (Sydney, NW, AUS) **[42535]**

Learn with Bob the Builder (London, GBR) **[54860]**

Learn and Work (Harare, ZWE) *Ceased*

Learned Publishing (Shoreham-by-Sea, GBR) **[56525]**

Learning Chinese (Beijing, CHN) **[43210]**

Learning Disability Review (Brighton, GBR) **[52624]**

Learning Disability Today (Brighton, GBR) **[52625]**

Learning in Health and Social Care (Oxford, GBR) **[56088]**

Learning for Life (London, GBR) *Unable to locate*

Learning and Motivation (Amsterdam, NLD) **[48135]**

The Learning Organization (Bradford, GBR) **[52521]**

Learning and Teaching (South Melbourne, VI, AUS) **[42374]**

Learning and Teaching in the Social Sciences (London, GBR) *Ceased*

Leasing Life (London, GBR) **[54861]**

Leather (London, GBR) *Unable to locate*

Leather Goods International (Karachi, PAK) *Unable to locate*

Leather News India (Chennai, TN, IND) **[45052]**

Leather Science (Chennai, TN, IND) *Ceased*

Leaving School (London, GBR) **[54862]**

Lebanese Broadcasting Corporation International - Channel 10H (Beirut, LBN) **[47410]**

Lebanese Broadcasting Corporation International - Channel 12H (Beirut, LBN) **[47411]**

Lebanese Broadcasting Corporation International - Channel 5H (Beirut, LBN) **[47408]**

Numbers cited in bold after listings are entry numbers rather than page numbers.

Lebanese Broadcasting Corporation International - Channel 33H (Beirut, LBN) [47409]

Lebanese Broadcasting Corporation International - Channel 9H (Beirut, LBN) [47407]

Lebanese Review of Arab and International Arbitration (Beirut, LBN) [47397]

Lebanese Science Bulletin [47398]*

Lebanese Science Journal (Beirut, LBN) [47398]

Lebanese Scientific Research Reports [47398]*

Leben und Gesundheit (Life and Health) (Krattigen, SWI) [51181]

Lebende Sprachen (Berlin, GER) [44218]

Lebendige Tierwelt (Hannover, GER) Unable to locate

Lebenshilfe Zeitung (Marburg, GER) Unable to locate

Lebensmittel Industrie (Glarus, SWI) [51176]

Lebensmittel-Wissenschaft und-Technologie (London, GBR) [54863]

Lebensmittel Zeitung (Frankfurt, GER) Unable to locate

Lebensmittel Zeitung DIREKT [44365]*

Lechaim (Moscow, RUS) [49936]

Lecturas (Barcelona, SPA) [50683]

Lecturas Cocina Facil (Barcelona, SPA) [50684]

Lecturas Especial Cocina (Barcelona, SPA) [50685]

Lecturas Moda (Barcelona, SPA) [50686]

Lederne (Copenhagen, DEN) Unable to locate

The Leeds Guide (Leeds, GBR) [53771]

Leeds, Leeds, Leeds (Leeds, GBR) [53772]

Leef met hart & siel (Cape Town, SAF) [50388]

Leer, el magazine literario (Madrid, SPA) Unable to locate

Leer, en primavera, verano, otono, invierno (Madrid, SPA) Unable to locate

Legal Abacus (Sidcup, GBR) [56544]

Legal Business (London, GBR) [54864]

Legal and Criminological Psychology (Leicester, GBR) [53810]

Legal Ethics (Oxford, GBR) [56089]

Legal Executive Journal (Kempston, GBR) [53669]

Legal History (Calcutta, WB, IND) Unable to locate

Legal Information Management (Edinburgh, GBR) [53298]

Legal Medicine (Fukuoka, JPN) [46345]

Legal Week (London, GBR) [54865]

Legendas (Riga, LAT) [47372]

Legia (Sofia, BUL) Unable to locate

Legisprudence (Brussels, BEL) [42864]

Legume Research (Karnal, HY, IND) Unable to locate

Leicester Link (Leicester, GBR) [53811]

Leicestershire Magazine (Derby, GBR) [53165]

Leiden Journal of International Law (The Hague, NLD) [48621]

Leigh Journal (Leigh, GBR) [53838]

Leighton Buzzard Observer (Leighton Buzzard, GBR) [53839]

Leiklistarbladid (Reykjavik, ICE) Unable to locate

Leinster Express (Portaloise, IRL) Unable to locate

LEISA Magazine (Amersfoort, NLD) [47874]

Leisa Newsletter [47874]*

Leisure & Hospitality Business (London, GBR) Unable to locate

Leisure Intelligence (Mintel) (London, GBR) Unable to locate

Leisure Management (Hitchin, GBR) [53579]

Leisure Management Magazine (Camberley, GBR) Unable to locate

Leisure Opportunities (Camberley, GBR) Unable to locate

Leisure Opportunities (Hitchin, GBR) [53580]

Leisure Painter (Tenterden, GBR) [56743]

Leith-FM - 98.8 (Edinburgh, GBR) [53327]

Lemmikki (Kuvalehdet, FIN) [43889]

Lena Rukodelie (Moscow, RUS) [49937]

Leppis (Kuvalehdet, FIN) [43890]

Les Annees Laser (Paris, FRA) Unable to locate

Les Cahiers de F A.D.F (Paris, FRA) Unable to locate

Les Echos (Paris, FRA) Unable to locate

Les Nouvelles Economiques (Epinal, FRA) Unable to locate

Les Routiers (Clichy, FRA) [43934]

Les Saisons de la Danse (Paris, FRA) Unable to locate

Lesbia Magazine (Paris, FRA) Unable to locate

Leshan People's Broadcasting Station (Leshan, SI, CHN) Unable to locate

Letra Internacional (Madrid, SPA) Unable to locate

Let's Knit! (Colchester, GBR) [53040]

Let's Make Cards! (Colchester, GBR) [53041]

Let's Talk! (Norwich, GBR) [55733]

Let's Talk in English (Taipei, TWN) [51356]

Letters in Drug Design & Discovery (Karachi, PAK) [49360]

Letters of L'Arche (Woden, AC, AUS) Unable to locate

Letters in Organic Chemistry (Karachi, PAK) [49361]

Letting Update Journal (Cambridge, GBR) Unable to locate

Lettres et Cultures de Langue Francaise (Paris, FRA) Unable to locate

Leukemia (Paris, FRA) [44068]

Leukemia and Lymphoma (Abingdon, GBR) [51968]

Leven (Amsterdam, NLD) [48136]

Levensmiddelenkrant (Ter Aar, NLD) Unable to locate

Leviatan (Madrid, SPA) [50778]

The Levin Chronicle (Levin, NZL) Unable to locate

Levnedsmiddel Bladet (Glostrup, DEN) [43709]

Lex (London, GBR) [54866]

Lex Nepali (Kathmandu, NPL) Unable to locate

Leyland Guardian (Chorley, GBR) [53023]

Leyte Samar Daily Express (Tacloban, PHL) Unable to locate

LFI Liquid Foods International (London, GBR) Unable to locate

Lianhe Wanbao (Singapore, SGP) [50214]

Lianhe Zaobao (Singapore, SGP) [50215]

Lianyungang People's Broadcasting Station (Lianyungang, JS, CHN) Unable to locate

Lianyungang Prople's Broadcasting Station (Lianyungang, JS, CHN) Unable to locate

Liaocheng People's Broadcasting Station (Liaocheng, SD, CHN) Unable to locate

Liaoning People's Broadcasting Station (Shenyang, LI, CHN) Unable to locate

Liaoning People's Broadcasting Station (Shenyang, LI, CHN) Unable to locate

Liaoning People's Broadcasting Station (Shenyang, LI, CHN) Unable to locate

Liaoning People's Broadcasting Station (Shenyang, LI, CHN) Unable to locate

Liaoning People's Broadcasting Station (Shenyang, LI, CHN) Unable to locate

Liaoning People's Broadcasting Station (Shenyang, LI, CHN) Unable to locate

Liaoyang People's Broadcasting Station (Liaoyang, LI, CHN) Unable to locate

Liaoyang People's Broadcasting Station (Liaoyang, LI, CHN) Unable to locate

Liaoyang People's Broadcasting Station (Liaoyang, LI, CHN) Unable to locate

Liaoyuan People's Broadcasting Station (Liaoyuan, JI, CHN) Unable to locate

Liat Islander Magazine (Saint Johns, ATG) Unable to locate

Libelle (Hoofddorp, NLD) Unable to locate

Liber Quarterly (Amsterdam, NLD) [48137]

Liberal Aerogramme [54867]*

Liberal Matters (London, GBR) [54867]

Liberalt Forum (Oslo, NOR) [49201]

Liberation War (Calcutta, WB, IND) Unable to locate

Liberator (London, GBR) [54868]

Libero (Milan, ITA) Unable to locate

Liberte (Algiers, ALG) [41461]

Liberty Radio-FM - 97.1 (Saint Johns, WIN) [57103]

The Library (London, GBR) [54869]

The Library Association Record (London, GBR) Ceased

Library Herald (New Delhi, DH, IND) Unable to locate

Library History Review (Calcutta, WB, IND) Unable to locate

Library and Information Research (London, GBR) [54870]

Library and Information Research News [54870]*

Library and Information Science (Tokyo, JPN) [46960]

Library + Information Update (London, GBR) [54871]

Library Life (Wellington, NZL) [49015]

Library Management (Bradford, GBR) [52522]

Library Progress (Shahdara, DH, IND) Unable to locate

Library Review (Glasgow, GBR) [53429]

Libre Empresa (Santa Cruz, BOL) Unable to locate

Libre-FM - 95.5 (Viedma Rio Negro, ARG) [41490]

Libri (Berlin, GER) [44219]

Libyan Journal of Medicine (Zliten, LBY) [47458]

Libyan Studies (London, GBR) Unable to locate

Licensing Today Worldwide (Stourbridge, GBR) Unable to locate

Licensing World (Blackrock, DU, IRL) [45923]

Lien (Singapore, SGP) [50216]

Lien Horticole (Perols, FRA) [44092]

Life in China (Beijing, CHN) [43211]

A Life in the Day (Hove, GBR) [53610]

Life Etc. (North Ryde, NW, AUS) [42187]

LIFE-FM - 107.9 (Hendon Common, SA, AUS) [41951]

Life-FM - 99.8 (Auckland, NZL) [48843]

Life-FM - 103.6 (Harlesden, GBR) [53509]

Life & Pensions (London, GBR) [54872]

Life Radio-FM - 100.5 (Lichtenberg, AUT) [42733]

Life Science Advances—Experimental & Clinical Endocrinology (Trivandrum, KE, IND) Unable to locate

Life Science Advances—Oncology (Trivandrum, KE, IND) Unable to locate

Life Science Today (Epsom, GBR) Unable to locate

Life and Work (Edinburgh, GBR) [53299]

Life Writing (Abingdon, GBR) [51969]

Lifeboat International (Poole, GBR) Ceased

Lifelong Learning in Europe (Helsinki, FIN) [43844]

Lifestyle Asia (Makati, PHL) Unable to locate

The Lifestyle Farmer (Auckland, NZL) [48802]

Lifestyle Pools (Alexandria, NW, AUS) [41541]

Ligeia Dossiers sur l'Art (Paris, FRA) Unable to locate

Ligeud (Valby, DEN) Unable to locate

Light Aviation (London, GBR) Unable to locate

Light Box (London, GBR) Ceased

Light-FM - 89.9 (Mont Albert, VI, AUS) [42114]

The Light-FM - 92.9 (Toowoomba, QL, AUS) [42633]

Light FM - Beirut (Beirut, LBN) Unable to locate

Light FM - Beit Meri (Beirut, LBN) Unable to locate

Light FM - Jabal Tourbol (Beirut, LBN) Unable to locate

Light of Pandrimalai (Trichy, TN, IND) Unable to locate

Light&Easy-FM [47652]*

Light&Easy-FM - 94.6 (Kuala Lumpur, MYS) [47651]

LighterLife (Essex, GBR) [53340]

The Lighting Journal (Rugby, GBR) [56420]

Lighting Research and Technology (London, GBR) [54873]

Lighting & Sound International (Eastbourne, GBR) [53244]

Lihatalous (Hameenlinna, FIN) Unable to locate

Liikunnan ja Urheilun Maailma (Helsinki, FIN) [43845]

LIJ (Melbourne, VI, AUS) [42069]

Lila (Manila, PHL) [49551]

Lilit (Riga, LAT) Unable to locate

Lilydale & Yarra Valley Leader (Lilydale, VI, AUS) [42010]

limb by limb (London, GBR) Unable to locate

Limelight (Sydney, NW, AUS) [42536]

Numbers cited in bold after listings are entry numbers rather than page numbers.

Limerick Leader (Limerick, LI, IRL) **[46029]**

Limerick Post (Limerick, LI, IRL) **[46030]**

Limes (Warsaw, POL) **[49731]**

Limited Edition (Watford, GBR) **[56867]**

Limnologica (Stechlin, GER) **[44657]**

Limnology (Tokyo, JPN) **[46961]**

LINC-TV - Channel 68 (Byron Bay, NW, AUS) **[41680]**

Lincs-FM - 102.2 (Lincoln, GBR) **[53857]**

Linea EDP (Milan, ITA) *Unable to locate*

Linea Saludable (Barcelona, SPA) **[50687]**

Linedancer (Southport, GBR) **[56587]**

LineOut (Copenhagen, DEN) *Unable to locate*

Lingerie Buyer (Huddersfield, GBR) **[53622]**

Linguistic Typology (Konstanz, GER) **[44514]**

Linguistic Variations Yearbook (Amsterdam, NLD) **[48138]**

Linguistica Pragensia (Warsaw, POL) **[49732]**

Linguistics (Antwerp, BEL) **[42839]**

Linguistics and the Human Sciences (London, GBR) **[54874]**

Lingvisticae Investigationes (Amsterdam, NLD) **[48139]**

Linhe People's Broadcasting Station (Linhe, NM, CHN) *Unable to locate*

Link (Vienna, AUT) *Unable to locate*

Link (Lucerne, SWI) *Unable to locate*

Link (London, GBR) *Unable to locate*

Link-FM - 92.2 (Romford, GBR) **[56404]**

Link India News Magazine (New Delhi, DH, IND) *Unable to locate*

Link Magazine (Kampala, UGA) *Unable to locate*

Linlithgow Gazette (Linlithgow, GBR) **[53859]**

Linux Open (Grabunn, GER) *Unable to locate*

Linxia People's Broadcasting Station (Linxia, GS, CHN) *Unable to locate*

Linyi People's Broadcasting Station (Linyi, SD, CHN) *Unable to locate*

Linyi People's Broadcasting Station (Linyi, SD, CHN) *Unable to locate*

Linyi People's Broadcasting Station (Linyi, SD, CHN) *Unable to locate*

Liopon (Gerakas, GRC) *Unable to locate*

Lipid Technology (Weinheim, GER) **[44707]**

Lipids in Health and Disease (London, GBR) **[54875]**

Liquid Crystals (Abingdon, GBR) **[51970]**

Lisburn Echo (Lisburn, GBR) **[53862]**

Lishu People's Broadcasting Station (Lishu Xian, JI, CHN) *Unable to locate*

Lishui People's Broadcasting Station (Lishui, ZH, CHN) *Unable to locate*

List of Available Recordings (Deal, GBR) *Unable to locate*

Listy Cukrovarnicke a reparske (Sugar and Sugar Beet Journal) (Prague, CZE) *Unable to locate*

Lite-FM - 105.8 (Jakarta, IDN) **[45805]**

Lite-FM - 106.8 (Peterborough, GBR) **[56266]**

LiteFM - 105.7 (Kuala Lumpur, MYS) **[47652]**

Literacy (Cork, CK, IRL) **[45938]**

Literary Criterion (Bangalore, KA, IND) *Unable to locate*

Literary Endeavour (Hyderabad, AP, IND) *Unable to locate*

Literary Half-Yearly (Mysore, KA, IND) *Unable to locate*

Literary and Linguistic Computing (London, GBR) **[54876]**

Literary Reading (Moscow, RUS) *Unable to locate*

Literary Studies (Patiala, PJ, IND) *Unable to locate*

Literature Compass (Oxford, GBR) **[56090]**

Literature & History (Manchester, GBR) **[55570]**

Literature and Theology (Stirling, GBR) **[56624]**

Literaturnachrichten (Frankfurt, GER) **[44362]**

Literaturschau Stahl + Eisen (Dusseldorf, GER) **[44328]**

Lithology and Mineral Resources (Moscow, RUS) **[49938]**

Lithos (Stellenbosch, SAF) **[50633]**

LithoWeek **[55119]***

Lithuanian Economy (Vilnius, LIT) *Unable to locate*

Lithuanian Journal of Physics (Vilnius, LIT) **[47482]**

Lithuanian Worker (Vilnius, LIT) *Unable to locate*

Litoral (Lisbon, PRT) *Unable to locate*

Litoral (Torremoinos, SPA) **[50841]**

Litterae Slovenicae (Ljubljana, SVA) *Unable to locate*

Little Treasures (Auckland, NZL) **[48803]**

Littlehampton Gazette (Littlehampton, GBR) **[53865]**

Liupanshui People's Broadcasting Station (Liupanshui, GH, CHN) *Unable to locate*

Liuzhou People's Broadcasting Station (Liuzhou, GZ, CHN) *Unable to locate*

Liuzhou People's Broadcasting Station (Liuzhou, GZ, CHN) *Unable to locate*

Live in Concert (Dusseldorf, GER) *Unable to locate*

Live It (London, GBR) **[54877]**

Live & Kicking (London, GBR) **[54878]**

Live 95-FM - 95 (Limerick, LI, IRL) **[46032]**

Live to Ride (Alexandria, NW, AUS) **[41542]**

Liverpool Law Review (Dordrecht, NLD) **[48508]**

Liverpool Leader (Liverpool, NW, AUS) **[42014]**

Livestock Adviser (Bangalore, KA, IND) *Unable to locate*

Livestock Production Science (Saint Louis, MO, USA) *Unable to locate*

Living Earth (Bristol, GBR) **[52702]**

Living in Ecuador (Quito, ECU) *Unable to locate*

Living Edge (Hale, GBR) **[53503]**

Living in the Gulf (Dubai, UAE) **[51647]**

Living Hadley (Kensington Village, GBR) *Unable to locate*

Living It (Dundrum, DU, IRL) **[46010]**

Living North (Kensington Village, GBR) **[53675]**

Living Reviews in Solar Physics (Katlenburg-Lindau, GER) **[44500]**

Livingetc (London, GBR) **[54879]**

Ljusglimten (Stockholm, SWE) *Unable to locate*

Llogara-FM - 88.3 MHz (Vlore, ALB) **[41456]**

Lloyds Maritime and Commercial Law Quarterly (London, GBR) *Unable to locate*

LM-FM - 95.8 (Drogheda, LU, IRL) **[45941]**

LMS Journal of Computation and Mathematics (London, GBR) **[54880]**

LMS—Laboratory Marketing Spectrum (Pinegowrie, SAF) **[50572]**

LNG World Shipping (Enfield, GBR) **[53332]**

Lobster (Hull, GBR) **[53627]**

Local Authority Building and Maintenance (Watford, GBR) **[56868]**

Local Council Review **[54858]***

Local Democracy (Quito, ECU) *Unable to locate*

Local Government Focus (Melbourne, VI, AUS) **[42070]**

Local Self-Government (Mumbai, MH, IND) *Unable to locate*

Local Transport Today (London, GBR) **[54881]**

Lochbroom-FM - 102.2 MHz (Ullapool, GBR) **[56795]**

Lochbroom-FM - 96.8 (Ullapool, GBR) **[56796]**

Lochem-FM (Amsterdam, NLD) *Unable to locate*

Locomotive Journal (London, GBR) **[54882]**

Lodz Papers in Pragmatics (Warsaw, POL) **[49733]**

The Log (West Drayton, GBR) **[56890]**

Logan-FM - 101 (Logan City, QL, AUS) **[42018]**

Logan West Leader (Springwood, NW, AUS) **[42384]**

Logic Journal of the IGPL (Oxford, GBR) **[56091]**

Logical Methods in Computer Science (London, GBR) **[54883]**

Logistics Focus (Corby, GBR) *Ceased*

Logistics and Transport Focus (Corby, GBR) *Unable to locate*

Logistiikka (Helsinki, FIN) *Unable to locate*

Logopedics Phoniatrics Vocology (London, GBR) **[54884]**

Lohro-FM - 90.2 (Rostock, GER) **[44649]**

Lok Rajya (Mumbai, MH, IND) *Unable to locate*

London Aerogramme **[54867]***

The London Bird Report (London, GBR) **[54885]**

London Bulletin (London, GBR) **[54886]**

London Energy & Environment (Maidstone, GBR) *Unable to locate*

London Financial News **[54457]***

London Greek Radio-FM - 103.3 (London, GBR) **[55454]**

The London Magazine (London, GBR) **[54887]**

The London Naturalist (Llandovery, GBR) **[53884]**

The London Philatelist (London, GBR) **[54888]**

The London Picture Book (London, GBR) **[54889]**

London Review of Books (London, GBR) **[54890]**

London Review of Education (Abingdon, GBR) **[51971]**

London Theatre Record (1981-90) **[55303]***

London-Zok (London, GBR) *Unable to locate*

Londonderry Sentinel (Londonderry, GBR) **[55473]**

L1-Educational Studies in Language and Literature (Dordrecht, NLD) **[48509]**

Long Range Planning (Vienna, AUT) **[42763]**

Longford Leader (Longford, LO, IRL) **[46034]**

Longkou People's Broadcasting Station (Longkou, SD, CHN) *Unable to locate*

Longyan People's Broadcasting Station (Longyan, FJ, CHN) *Unable to locate*

LookEast (Bangkok, THA) **[51426]**

The Lord of the Rings Collector's Models (London, GBR) **[54891]**

Lore (New Delhi, DH, IND) *Unable to locate*

Loris (Sandy, GBR) *Unable to locate*

Loris (Sandy, GBR) *Unable to locate*

Losetha (Panadura, SRI) **[50922]**

Loss Prevention Bulletin (Rugby, GBR) **[56421]**

Lottery Gazette (New Delhi, DH, IND) *Unable to locate*

Lotus-FM - 87.7 (Durban, SAF) **[50474]**

Lotus-FM - 106.8 (Durban, SAF) **[50473]**

Lotus FM - Cape Town - 97.8 MHz (Cape Town, SAF) **[50434]**

Lotus FM - Durban North - 89.4 MHz (Durban North, SAF) **[50476]**

Lotus FM - Glencoe - 90.0 MHz (Glencoe, SAF) **[50484]**

Lotus FM - Ladysmith - 87.9 MHz (Ladysmith, SAF) **[50546]**

Lotus FM - Pietermaritzburg - 88.3 MHz (Pietermaritzburg, SAF) **[50570]**

Lotus FM - Port Elizabeth - 98.3 MHz (Port Elizabeth, SAF) **[50579]**

Lotus FM - Port Shepstone - 88.2 MHz (Port Shepstone, SAF) **[50580]**

Love-FM - 88.9 (Belize City, BLZ) **[42917]**

Love-FM - 95.1 (Belize City, BLZ) **[42918]**

Love-FM - 94.5 (Bangkok, THA) **[51450]**

Love 97.2 FM - 97.2 MHz (Singapore, SGP) **[50297]**

LOVER (Amsterdam, NLD) **[48140]**

Low Frequency Noise & Vibration **[52581]***

Low Frequency Noise, Vibration and Active Control (Brentwood, GBR) **[52581]**

Low Temperature Medicine (Tokyo, JPN) *Unable to locate*

Lowestoft Journal (Lowestoft, GBR) **[55496]**

Loyalty (Uppingham, GBR) **[56797]**

Loyola Journal of Social Sciences (Thiruvananthapuram, KE, IND) **[45748]**

Lozastvo & Vinzstvo (Sofia, BUL) *Unable to locate*

LP Gas (Eastbourne, GBR) *Unable to locate*

LPG World Shipping (Enfield, GBR) **[53333]**

LSA (Levallois-Perret, FRA) *Unable to locate*

LSV aktuell (Munich, GER) **[44569]**

Lu'an People's Broadcasting Station (Lu'an, AN, CHN) *Unable to locate*

Lu'an People's Broadcasting Station (Lu'an, AN, CHN) *Unable to locate*

Luanda Antena Comercial-FM - 95.5 (Luanda, ANG) **[41465]**

Luang Prabang Radio Station (Luang Prabang, LAO) *Unable to locate*

Master Index

Numbers cited in bold after listings are entry numbers rather than page numbers.

Lube (Berkhamsted, GBR) **[52312]**

Lubrication Science (London, GBR) **[54892]**

Lucht (Delfgauw, NLD) *Ceased*

Lucian Kaiso (Castries, SLC) *Unable to locate*

Lucknow City Magazine (Lucknow, UP, IND) *Unable to locate*

Lucknow Law Times (Lucknow, UP, IND) **[45324]**

Lucknow Librarian (Lucknow, UP, IND) *Unable to locate*

Lucru de Mana (Bucharest, ROM) **[49839]**

Ludus (Mechelen, BEL) **[42904]**

Lufthansa Cargo's Planet (Hamburg, GER) *Unable to locate*

Lung Cancer in Practice (London, GBR) **[54893]**

Lung India (Jaipur, RJ, IND) **[45198]**

Luohe People's Broadcasting Station (Luohe, HN, CHN) *Unable to locate*

Luohe People's Broadcasting Station (Luohe, HN, CHN) *Unable to locate*

Luoyang People's Broadcasting Station (Luoyang, HN, CHN) *Unable to locate*

Luoyang People's Broadcasting Station (Luoyang, HN, CHN) *Unable to locate*

Luoyang People's Broadcasting Station (Luoyang, HN, CHN) *Unable to locate*

Luoyang People's Broadcasting Station (Luoyang, HN, CHN) *Unable to locate*

Luoyang People's Broadcasting Station (Luoyang, HN, CHN) *Unable to locate*

Lurgan Mail (Lurgan, GBR) **[55499]**

Luse Heping Taiwan Wenhua Broadcasting Station (Taipei, TWN) *Unable to locate*

The Lute (Guildford, GBR) *Unable to locate*

Luton News and Dunstable Gazette (Edinburgh, GBR) **[53300]**

Luxe Living Kitchens & Bathrooms (Hong Kong, CHN) **[43364]**

Luxembourg News (Luxembourg, LUX) *Unable to locate*

Luxemburger Wort (Luxembourg, LUX) *Unable to locate*

Luxury Intelligence (Monte Carlo, MCO) **[47810]**

Luzhou People's Broadcasting Station (Luzhou, SI, CHN) *Unable to locate*

Luzhou People's Broadcasting Station (Luzhou, SI, CHN) *Unable to locate*

Luzhou People's Broadcasting Station (Luzhou, SI, CHN) *Unable to locate*

Luzhou People's Broadcasting Station (Luzhou, SI, CHN) *Unable to locate*

Lwati (Matsapha, SWZ) **[50946]**

LWT - Food Science and Technology (Zurich, SWI) **[51274]**

Lyric-FM - 96 (Limerick, LI, IRL) **[46033]**

Lytham St. Annes Express (Saint Annes, GBR) **[56442]**

Lyubimaya Datcha (Kiev, URE) **[51601]**

M

M & A Impact (London, GBR) *Unable to locate*

M-FM - 92.6 (Matieland, SAF) **[50555]**

M Menschen Machen Medien (Stuttgart, GER) *Unable to locate*

M/V Zorg (Utrecht, NLD) *Unable to locate*

Ma'anshan People's Broadcasting Station (Ma'anshan, AN, CHN) *Unable to locate*

Ma'anshan People's Broadcasting Station (Ma'anshan, AN, CHN) *Unable to locate*

Ma'anshan People's Broadcasting Station (Ma'anshan, AN, CHN) *Unable to locate*

MAAS Journal of Islamic Science (Aligarh, UP, IND) **[44918]**

Maaseudun Tulevaisuus (Helsinki, FIN) *Unable to locate*

Maatschappij Belangen (Haarlem, NLD) *Ceased*

MAB HRC Hostelero Internacional (Madrid, SPA) *Unable to locate*

Mabuhay (Pasig City, PHL) **[49572]**

Macarthur Chronicle (Campbelltown, NW, AUS) **[41696]**

Macau Tatler (Hong Kong, CHN) **[43365]**

Macau Tatler Best Restaurants (Hong Kong, CHN) **[43366]**

Macedon Ranges Leader (Sunbury, VI, AUS) **[42402]**

Macedonian Journal of Medical Sciences (Warsaw, POL) **[49734]**

Mach (Bromma, SWE) *Unable to locate*

Macheng People's Broadcasting Station (Macheng, HB, CHN) *Unable to locate*

Machine Building Industry (Mumbai, MH, IND) *Unable to locate*

Machine Design & Research (Shanghai, CHN) **[43486]**

Machine Knitting Monthly (Maidenhead, GBR) **[55523]**

Machine and Machinery (Calcutta, WB, IND) *Unable to locate*

Machine Tool (Seoul, KOR) *Unable to locate*

Machinery Classified International (Dartford, GBR) *Unable to locate*

Machinery & Machine Tool Journal (New Delhi, DH, IND) *Unable to locate*

Machinery Update (Wallington, GBR) **[56833]**

Machinery World (Buckhurst Hill, GBR) **[52750]**

Mackay & Sarina MidWeek (Sydney, NW, AUS) **[42537]**

Macquarie Law Journal (Sydney, NW, AUS) **[42538]**

Macworld Espana **[50779]***

Macworld Espana (Madrid, SPA) **[50779]**

Mad & Bolig Magasinet (Valby, DEN) *Unable to locate*

MADCHEN (Munich, GER) **[44570]**

Made in Germany (San Isidro, PER) **[49441]**

Made in Germany—International Edition (Dreieich, GER) **[44318]**

Madhya Pradesh Chronicle (Bhopal, MP, IND) *Unable to locate*

Madhya Pradesh Itihasa Parishad Journal (Bhopal, MP, IND) *Unable to locate*

Madhya Pradesh Law Journal (Nagpur, MH, IND) *Unable to locate*

Madhyamam (Kochi, KE, IND) **[45251]**

Madras Agricultural Journal (Coimbatore, TN, IND) *Unable to locate*

Madras Government Museum Bulletin, New Series (Chennai, TN, IND) *Unable to locate*

Madras Law Journal (Civil) (Chennai, TN, IND) *Unable to locate*

Madras Law Journal (Criminal) (Chennai, TN, IND) *Unable to locate*

Madras University Journal Section B—Sciences (Chennai, TN, IND) *Unable to locate*

Madres de Plaza de Mayo (Buenos Aires, ARG) *Unable to locate*

Mag Weekly (Karachi, PAK) *Unable to locate*

Magadan Stereo - Magadan (Magadan, RUS) *Unable to locate*

Magasinet Reis (Stockholm, SWE) *Unable to locate*

Magazin 2000 (Marktoberdorf-Sulzschneid, GER) *Unable to locate*

The Magazine (Guatemala City, GTM) *Unable to locate*

Magazine (Chichester, GBR) *Unable to locate*

Magazine (Hove, GBR) *Unable to locate*

Magazine (Leicester, GBR) *Unable to locate*

Magazine ANZ - "Even Aanzoemen" (Antwerp, BEL) *Unable to locate*

Magazine News (London, GBR) **[54894]**

Magazine of the Parrot Society (Bedford, GBR) *Unable to locate*

Magazine Special (Tokyo, JPN) **[46962]**

Magazine Z (Tokyo, JPN) **[46963]**

Magic-AM - 1278 KHz (South Melbourne, VI, AUS) **[42377]**

Magic-AM - 828 (Leeds, GBR) **[53780]**

Magic-AM - 1548 (Liverpool, GBR) **[53882]**

Magic-AM - 1152 (Newcastle upon Tyne, GBR) **[55681]**

Magic-AM - 999 (Preston, GBR) **[56306]**

Magic-AM - 1170 (Thornaby, GBR) **[56746]**

The Magic Circular Magazine (London, GBR) **[54895]**

Magic-FM - 87.8 (Osborne Park, WA, AUS) **[42225]**

Magic-FM - 105.1 (Belfast, GBR) **[52302]**

Magic-FM - 105.4 (London, GBR) **[55455]**

The Magic of Letter E (Energy Efficiency) (Bucharest, ROM) *Unable to locate*

Magic 1152-AM - 1152 KHz (Newcastle upon Tyne, GBR) **[55682]**

Magic 1161-AM - 1161 (Hull, GBR) **[53631]**

Magic 693-AM **[42377]***

The Magical World of Roald Dahl (London, GBR) **[54896]**

Magisterbladet (Frederiksberg, DEN) **[43692]**

The Magistrate (London, GBR) **[54897]**

MAGMA (Marseille, FRA) **[43973]**

Magnesium Research (Montrouge, FRA) **[43996]**

Magnetic Resonance in Chemistry (Cambridge, GBR) **[52867]**

Magyar Pszichologiai Szemle (Budapest, HUN) **[44846]**

Magyar Sebeszet (Budapest, HUN) **[44847]**

Maha Bodhi (Calcutta, WB, IND) *Unable to locate*

Maha Milan (Mumbai, MH, IND) *Unable to locate*

Maharaja Sayajirao University of Baroda Department of Archaeology

and Ancient History Archaeology Series (Baroda, GJ, JND) *Unable to locate*

Maharaja Sayajirao University of Baroda Journal (Baroda, GJ, IND) *Unable to locate*

Maharashtra Archives Bulletin (Mumbai, MH, IND) *Unable to locate*

Maharashtra Bhugolshastra Sanshodhan Patrika (Pune, MH, IND) *Unable to locate*

Maharashtra Co-Operative Quarterly (Pune, MH, IND) *Unable to locate*

Maharashtra Herald (Pune, MH, IND) *Unable to locate*

Maharashtra Law Journal (Nagpur, MH, IND) *Unable to locate*

Maharashtra State Budget in Brief (Jaipur, RJ, IND) *Unable to locate*

Mahasagar (Goa) (Goa, GD, IND) *Unable to locate*

Mahinda (Colombo, SRI) *Unable to locate*

Mahjubah (Tehran, IRN) **[45911]**

Mahratta (Pune, MH, IND) *Unable to locate*

Mai-FM - 88.6 (Auckland, NZL) **[48844]**

Mailshot (Rickmansworth, GBR) *Unable to locate*

The Main Event Magazine (Barnsley, GBR) **[52182]**

Main Group Metal Chemistry (Tel Aviv, ISR) **[46110]**

Main Sheet (Southampton, GBR) *Unable to locate*

Main Street Journal (Ashford, GBR) *Unable to locate*

Mainframe Market Monitor (Thatcham, GBR) *Unable to locate*

Mainichi Daily News (Tokyo, JPN) **[46964]**

The Mainsheet (Peterborough, GBR) *Ceased*

Maison (Seoul, KOR) *Unable to locate*

Maisons et Decors Mediterranees (Aix-en-Provence, FRA) **[43913]**

Maisons de France (Pompadour, FRA) *Unable to locate*

Maitrises (Chateau Landon, FRA) **[43930]**

Majesty Magazine (London, GBR) **[54898]**

Make (Cambridge, GBR) *Unable to locate*

Make the Grade (London, GBR) **[54899]**

Makerere Journal of Higher Education (Grahamstown, SAF) **[50504]**

Making Music Magazine (Swanley, GBR) *Unable to locate*

Maksimum Radio (Moscow, RUS) *Unable to locate*

Maksimum Radio (Moscow, RUS) *Unable to locate*

Malaria Journal (London, GBR) **[54900]**

Malawi Journal of Science and Technology (Zomba, MWI) **[47573]**

Malawi Medical Journal (Blantyre, MWI) **[47566]**

Malaya (Manila, PHL) **[49552]**

Malayala Manorama (Kottayam, KE, IND) **[45315]**

Malayalam Literary Survey (Trichur, KE, IND) *Unable to locate*

Malayan Nature Journal (Kuala Lumpur, MYS) **[47611]**

Malaysia; Computimes (**[47637]***

Malaysia Society (Kuala Lumpur, MYS) **[47612]**

Malaysia Tatler (Hong Kong, CHN) **[43367]**

Numbers cited in bold after listings are entry numbers rather than page numbers.

Malaysia Tourism (Kuala Lumpur, MYS) *Unable to locate*

Malaysiakini (Kuala Lumpur, MYS) **[47613]**

The Malaysian Accountant (Kuala Lumpur, MYS) *Unable to locate*

Malaysian Business (Kuala Lumpur, MYS) **[47614]**

Malaysian Chamber of Mines Year Book (Kuala Lumpur, MYS) **[47615]**

Malaysian Cocoa Monitor (Kota Kinabalu, MYS) **[47591]**

Malaysian It Journal (Petaling Jaya, MYS) *Unable to locate*

Malaysian Journal of Dermatology (Kuala Lumpur, MYS) *Unable to locate*

Malaysian Journal of Economic Studies (Kuala Lumpur, MYS) **[47616]**

Malaysian Journal of Family Studies (Kuala Lumpur, MYS) *Unable to locate*

Malaysian Journal of Library and Information Science (Kuala Lumpur, MYS) **[47617]**

Malaysian Journal of Science Series A: Life Sciences (Kuala Lumpur, MYS) **[47618]**

Malaysian Journal of Science Series B: Physical & Earth Sciences (Kuala Lumpur, MYS) **[47619]**

Malaysian Journal of Tropical Geography (Kuala Lumpur, MYS) **[47620]**

Malaysian Naturalist (Kuala Lumpur, MYS) **[47621]**

Malaysian Panorama (Kuala Lumpur, MYS) *Unable to locate*

The Malaysian Surveyor (Petaling Jaya, MYS) **[47701]**

Malaysia's Best Restaurants (Kuala Lumpur, MYS) **[47622]**

Malenkaya Diana (Moscow, RUS) **[49939]**

Malerblatt (Leinfelden-Echterdingen, GER) **[44526]**

Mallal's Monthly Digest (Singapore, SGP) *Unable to locate*

Mallorn (Ash Vale, GBR) *Unable to locate*

The Malta Business Weekly (Saint Julians, MAL) **[47739]**

The Malta Independent (Saint Julians, MAL) **[47740]**

The Malta Independent on Sunday (Saint Julians, MAL) **[47741]**

Maltamag (San Gwann, MAL) *Unable to locate*

Malton & Pickering Mercury (Malton, GBR) **[55532]**

Maluti (Cape Town, SAF) **[50389]**

Malvern Gazette (Worcester, GBR) **[56962]**

Mama-FM - 101.7 (Kampala, UGA) **[51590]**

Mama I ya (Kiev, URE) **[51602]**

Mama, eto ya! (Moscow, RUS) **[49940]**

Mamane (Bangalore, KA, IND) *Unable to locate*

Mammal Review (Bristol, GBR) **[52703]**

Mammalia (Berlin, GER) **[44220]**

Mammalian Biology (Kiel, GER) **[44504]**

Mammalian Mutagenicity Study Group Communications (Kanagawa, JPN) *Unable to locate*

Mamo, to ja (Warsaw, POL) **[49735]**

Man (Amsterdam, NLD) *Unable to locate*

Man & Environment (Pune, MH, IND) *Unable to locate*

Man in India (Ranchi, BH, IND) *Unable to locate*

Man and Life (Calcutta, WB, IND) *Unable to locate*

Man-Made Fibre Statistics (Mumbai, MH, IND) *Unable to locate*

Man-Made Textiles in India (Mumbai, MH, IND) **[45408]**

Man & Nature (Shanghai, CHN) **[43487]**

Man and Society (Kuala Lumpur, MYS) **[47623]**

Mana - Estudos de Antropologia Social (Rio de Janeiro, RJ, BRZ) **[43011]**

Manab Mon (Calcutta, WB, IND) *Unable to locate*

Managed Healthcare Executive (Chester, GBR) **[52997]**

The Management Accountant (Kolkata, WB, IND) **[45298]**

Management Accountant (Karachi, PAK) **[49362]**

Management Accounting **[54455]**

Management Assistant (Diegem, BEL) *Unable to locate*

Management Digest (Hyderabad, AP, IND) *Unable to locate*

Management Dynamics (Pretoria, SAF) **[50596]**

Management of Environmental Quality (Bradford, GBR) **[52523]**

Management Ideas (Mumbai, MH, IND) *Unable to locate*

Management Information Service (Cochin, KE, IND) *Unable to locate*

Management International Review (Wiesbaden, GER) *Unable to locate*

Management Japan (Tokyo, JPN) *Unable to locate*

Management and Labour Studies (Jamshedpur, BH, IND) **[45207]**

Management Learning (London, GBR) **[54901]**

Management News (Harare, ZWE) *Unable to locate*

Management & Organisational Behaviour; Australian Journal of **[42626]**

Management and Organization Review (Oxford, GBR) **[56092]**

Management & Organizational History (Bristol, GBR) **[52704]**

Management Professionals Association Events Diary (Chennai, TN, IND) *Unable to locate*

Management Professionals Association Journal (Chennai, TN, IND) *Unable to locate*

Management Services (Lichfield, GBR) **[53853]**

The Management Specialist (Kenilworth, GBR) *Unable to locate*

Management Today (London, GBR) **[54902]**

Manager, British Journal of Administrative Management (London, GBR) **[54903]**

Manager Radio (Bangkok, THA) *Unable to locate*

Managerial Auditing Journal (Bradford, GBR) **[52524]**

Managerial Law **[53874]**

Manager's Digest (Calcutta, WB, IND) *Unable to locate*

Managing Best Practice (London, GBR) *Unable to locate*

Managing Information (London, GBR) **[54904]**

Managing Leisure (Sheffield, GBR) **[56506]**

Managing Partner (London, GBR) **[54905]**

Manchester Living (Manchester, GBR) **[55571]**

The Manchester School (Oxford, GBR) **[56093]**

Mandate News (Dublin, DU, IRL) *Unable to locate*

M&D/Musica e Dischi (Milan, ITA) **[46186]**

Mangaiyar Malae (Colombo, SRI) *Unable to locate*

Mangga (Kuala Lumpur, MYS) **[47624]**

Mani Tese (Milan, ITA) **[46187]**

Maniapoto-FM - 92.7 (Piopio, NZL) **[48972]**

Maniapoto-FM - 91.9 (Te Kuiti, NZL) **[48986]**

Maniapoto-FM - 96.5 (Te Kuiti, NZL) **[48985]**

Maniapoto-FM - 99.6 (Te Kuiti, NZL) **[48984]**

The Manica Post (Harare, ZWE) **[57116]**

Manila Bulletin (Intramuros, PHL) **[49501]**

Manila Journal of Science (Manila, PHL) **[49553]**

Manila Review (Manila, PHL) *Unable to locate*

The Manila Times (Manila, PHL) *Unable to locate*

Manipur State Kala Akademi Quarterly Journal (Imphal, MN, IND) *Unable to locate*

Manipur State Museum Bulletin (Imphal, MN, IND) *Unable to locate*

Manitha Urimai Murasu (Chennai, TN, IND) *Unable to locate*

The Manly Daily (Manly, NW, AUS) **[42032]**

Mannenmode (Maarssen, NLD) **[48732]**

Manningham Leader (Melbourne, VI, AUS) **[42071]**

Manpower Journal (Delhi, DH, IND) **[45103]**

Mansfield Chad (Mansfield, GBR) **[55590]**

Mansudae Television (Pyongyang, KOD) *Unable to locate*

Manthan (New Delhi, DH, IND) *Unable to locate*

Manuelle Medizin (Dordrecht, NLD) **[48510]**

Manufacturers Monthly (Chatswood, NW, AUS) **[41740]**

Manufacturing (Kenilworth, GBR) *Unable to locate*

Manufacturing Chemist (Sidcup, GBR) *Unable to locate*

Manufacturing Engineer Magazine (Stevenage, GBR) *Ceased*

Manufacturing & Logistics IT (Potters Bar, GBR) **[56297]**

The Manurewa Week (Penrose, NZL) *Unable to locate*

Manushi (New Delhi, DH, IND) **[45622]**

Manx Radio-AM - 1368 KHz (Douglas, GBR) **[53198]**

Manzhouli People's Broadcasting Station (Manzhouli, NM, CHN) *Unable to locate*

Maoming People's Broadcasting Station (Maoming, GD, CHN) *Unable to locate*

The Maori Law Review (Wellington, NZL) **[49016]**

Maquinas e Metals (Sao Paulo, SP, BRZ) **[43042]**

Marang (Gaborone, BWA) **[42944]**

Marathwada University Journal (Aurangabad, MH, IND) *Unable to locate*

Marbella Club Magazine (Ware, GBR) **[56842]**

Marcher Coast-FM **[52175]**

Marcos Owners Club Magazine (Worcester, GBR) *Unable to locate*

Marg (Mumbai, MH, IND) **[45409]**

Marga Journal (Ethul Kotte, SRI) **[50894]**

Margin (New Delhi, DH, IND) **[45623]**

Mariannhill Missions Magazine (Rome, ITA) *Unable to locate*

Maribyrnong Leader (Newport, VI, AUS) **[42145]**

Marie Claire (Seoul, KOR) *Unable to locate*

Marie Claire (Madrid, SPA) **[50780]**

Marijos Radijas-FM - 93.1 MHz (Kaunas, LIT) **[47470]**

Marina-FM - 88.8 (Salmiya, KWT) **[47361]**

Marina International (Wallington, GBR) *Unable to locate*

Marine Biological Association of India Journal (Ernakulam, KE, IND) *Unable to locate*

Marine Biology (Kiel, GER) **[44505]**

Marine Business (Surry Hills, NW, AUS) **[42435]**

Marine Conservation (Ross-on-Wye, GBR) **[56410]**

Marine Drugs (Basel, SWI) **[51063]**

Marine Ecology (Ischia Porto, ITA) **[46156]**

Marine Ecology Progress Series (MEPS) (Oldendorf, GER) **[44629]**

Marine Electronics & Communications (Enfield, GBR) **[53334]**

Marine Environmental Research (West Hoe, GBR) **[56891]**

Marine Equipment News (Beckenham, GBR) *Unable to locate*

Marine & Freshwater Research (Collingwood, VI, AUS) **[41792]**

Marine Micropaleontology (Yamagata, JPN) **[47125]**

Marine Modeling Monthly **[55534]**

Marine Modelling International (Malvern, GBR) **[55534]**

Marine News (Windsor, GBR) **[56932]**

Marine Ornithology (Rondebosch, SAF) **[50621]**

Marine Policy (Cardiff, GBR) **[52936]**

Marine Propulsion & Auxiliary Machinery (Enfield, GBR) **[53335]**

Marine Research in Indonesia (Jakarta, IDN) *Unable to locate*

Marine Science Journal of King Abdul Aziz University (Jeddah, SAU) *Unable to locate*

Marine Structures (Amsterdam, NLD) **[48141]**

Marine Times Newspaper (Kilcar, DO, IRL) **[46025]**

Marineblad (The Hague, NLD) **[48622]**

Mariner's Mirror (Hailsham, GBR) **[53501]**

The Maritime Advocate (Crawley, GBR) *Ceased*

Maritime Economics and Logistics (Basingstoke, GBR) **[52223]**

Maritime Industry (Baghdad, IRQ) *Unable to locate*

Maritime Journal (Fareham, GBR) **[53373]**

The Maritime Pilot (London, GBR) **[54906]**

Maritime Worker **[42539]**

Maritime Workers' Journal **[42539]**

Maritime Workers Journal (Sydney, NW, AUS) **[42539]**

The Marker (East Molesey, GBR) *Unable to locate*

Numbers cited in bold after listings are entry numbers rather than page numbers.

Market Guide to Used Farm Tractors (London, GBR) *Unable to locate*

Market Intelligence (London, GBR) *Unable to locate*

Market Leader (London, GBR) **[54907]**

Market Rasen Mail (Market Rasen, GBR) **[55595]**

Market Research Europe (London, GBR) *Unable to locate*

Market Research Great Britain (London, GBR) *Unable to locate*

Marketing (London, GBR) **[54908]**

Marketing Intelligence & Planning (Bradford, GBR) **[52525]**

Marketing Letters (Dordrecht, NLD) **[48511]**

Marketing and Management News (New Delhi, DH, IND) *Unable to locate*

Marketing & Research Today (Netherlands) (Amsterdam, NLD) *Unable to locate*

The Marketing Review (Argyll, GBR) **[52131]**

Marketing Theory (Leicester, GBR) **[53812]**

Marketing Week (London, GBR) **[54909]**

Market!ng&Media (Budapest, HUN) **[44848]**

Marketology Quarterly (New Delhi, DH, IND) *Unable to locate*

Marketwatch (Singapore, SGP) *Unable to locate*

Markt & Technik (Haar, GER) *Unable to locate*

Marmara Journal of European Studies (Istanbul, TUR) **[51560]**

Marmara Medical Journal (Istanbul, TUR) *Unable to locate*

Maroochy Weekly (Sydney, NW, AUS) **[42540]**

Maroondah Leader (Melbourne, VI, AUS) **[42072]**

Marriage Care Bulletin (London, GBR) *Unable to locate*

MARS (Paris, FRA) *Unable to locate*

MARS-FM - 95.9 Mhz (Maribor, SVA) **[50342]**

Martin Creamer Engineering News **[50479]***

Martin Creamer's Mining Weekly **[50480]***

Marxist Veekshanam (Trivandrum, KE, IND) *Unable to locate*

Mary Slessor Journal of Medicine (Calabar, CR, NGA) **[49078]**

The Maryborough Herald (Sydney, NW, AUS) **[42541]**

Maskin Aktuelt (Glostrup, DEN) **[43710]**

Maskinbladet (Herning, DEN) **[43722]**

Maskinkontakt (Askim, SWE) *Unable to locate*

Masonic Quarterly (London, GBR) **[54910]**

Masonry International (Penkhull, GBR) *Unable to locate*

Mass Media in India (New Delhi, DH, IND) **[45624]**

Massage World (London, GBR) **[54911]**

Massimario di Giurisprudenza del Lavoro (Rome, ITA) *Unable to locate*

Master Broadcasting Station - Beirut (Beirut, LBN) *Unable to locate*

Master Broadcasting Station - Fih (Jounieh, LBN) *Unable to locate*

Master Broadcasting Station - Harrisa (Jounieh, LBN) *Unable to locate*

Master Broadcasting Station - J Terbol (Bekaa) (Jounieh, LBN) *Unable to locate*

Master Builder (London, GBR) **[54912]**

Master Builders Journal (Kuala Lumpur, MYS) **[47625]**

Master-FM - 107.3 (Aragua, VEN) **[57016]**

Master Photographers (Darlington, GBR) **[53155]**

Mastersinger (Carlisle, GBR) **[52946]**

Masthead (Newport, VI, AUS) *Unable to locate*

Mastika (Kuala Lumpur, MYS) **[47626]**

Masyarakat Indonesia: Majalah Ilmu - Ilmu Sosial Indonesia (Jakarta, IDN) *Unable to locate*

Matador (Madrid, SPA) **[50781]**

Matatu (Amsterdam, NLD) **[48142]**

Matbaa & Teknik (Istanbul, TUR) **[51561]**

Match Angling Plus (Peterborough, GBR) *Unable to locate*

Match Fishing Magazine (Daventry, GBR) **[53160]**

Material Religion (Oxford, GBR) **[56094]**

Material Science Study (Kyoto, JPN) *Unable to locate*

Materiales de Construccion (Madrid, SPA) **[50782]**

Materiales Educativos (Caracas, VEN) *Unable to locate*

Materials Characterization (Amsterdam, NLD) **[48143]**

Materials Chemistry and Physics (Tainan, TWN) **[51327]**

Materials & Design (Derby, GBR) **[53166]**

Materials Handling News Directory of Product Services (Swanley, GBR) *Unable to locate*

Materials Management Journal of India (New Delhi, DH, IND) *Unable to locate*

Materials Research (Vicosa, MI, BRZ) **[43060]**

Materials Science (Rajkot, GJ, IND) **[45709]**

Materials Science and Engineering (Amsterdam, NLD) **[48145]**

Materials Science and Engineering (Amsterdam, NLD) **[48146]**

Materials Science and Engineering (Amsterdam, NLD) **[48144]**

Materials Science Forum (Zurich, SWI) **[51275]**

Materials Science in Semiconductor Processing (Amsterdam, NLD) **[48147]**

Materials Science and Technology (London, GBR) **[54913]**

Materials Today (Kidlington, GBR) **[53702]**

Materials World (London, GBR) **[54914]**

Materiaux & Techniques (Les Ulis, FRA) **[43966]**

Maternal and Child Health Journal (Dordrecht, NLD) **[48512]**

Maternal and Child Nutrition (Preston, GBR) **[56304]**

Maternal Health Journal of Abroad Medicine (Beijing, CHN) *Unable to locate*

Maternity & Infant (Dublin, DU, IRL) **[45991]**

Mathematica Japonica (Osaka, JPN) **[46626]**

Mathematica Plus (Sofia, BUL) **[43105]**

Mathematica Slovaca (Warsaw, POL) **[49736]**

Mathematical Association of India Bulletin (Kanpur, UP, IND) *Unable to locate*

Mathematical Education (Seoul, KOR) *Unable to locate*

Mathematical Gazette (Leicester, GBR) **[53813]**

Mathematical Journal of Ibaraki University (Ibaraki, JPN) *Unable to locate*

Mathematical Journal of Okayama University (Okayama, JPN) **[46599]**

Mathematical Medicine and Biology (Nottingham, GBR) **[55766]**

Mathematical Modelling and Applied Computing (Hong Kong, CHN) **[43368]**

Mathematical Modelling of Natural Phenomena (Villeurbanne, FRA) **[44126]**

Mathematical Models and Methods in Applied Sciences (Turin, ITA) **[46273]**

Mathematical Physics, Analysis and Geometry (Dordrecht, NLD) **[48513]**

Mathematical Pie (Leicester, GBR) **[53814]**

The Mathematical Scientist (Sheffield, GBR) **[56507]**

Mathematical Social Sciences (Amsterdam, NLD) **[48148]**

Mathematical Spectrum (Sheffield, GBR) **[56508]**

Mathematics Applied in Science and Technology (Kyoto, JPN) **[46482]**

Mathematics and Computers in Simulation (Brussels, BEL) **[42865]**

Mathematics Connection (Winneba, GHA) **[44741]**

Mathematics Education (Siwan, BH, IND) *Unable to locate*

Mathematics Journal of Toyama University (Toyama, JPN) **[47096]**

Mathematics in School (Leicester, GBR) **[53815]**

Mathematics Student (Meerut, UP, IND) *Unable to locate*

Mathematics Teaching (Derby, GBR) *Unable to locate*

Mathematics Today (New Delhi, DH, IND) **[45625]**

Mathematische Annalen (Heidelberg, GER) **[44466]**

Mathematische Nachrichten (Regensburg, GER) **[44644]**

Mathematische Zeitschrift (Paris, FRA) **[44069]**

Mathrubhumi (Palakkad, KE, IND) **[45680]**

Matlock Mercury (Matlock, GBR) **[55604]**

Matrimonial Law Reporter (New Delhi, DH, IND) *Unable to locate*

Matrix Biology (Amsterdam, NLD) **[48149]**

Mattenpost (Vienna, AUT) *Unable to locate*

Mauritian International (London, GBR) *Unable to locate*

Mauritius News (London, GBR) **[54915]**

Mausam (New Delhi, DH, IND) *Unable to locate*

MAX-FM - 91.1 (Bourke, NW, AUS) **[41621]**

Max Magazine (Gerakas, GRC) *Unable to locate*

Max Power (Cape Town, SAF) **[50390]**

Maxim Fashion (London, GBR) **[54916]**

Maxima Special (Budapest, HUN) **[44849]**

Mayfair (London, GBR) *Unable to locate*

The Mayo News (Westport, MA, IRL) **[46069]**

MB Transport Magazin (Hamburg, GER) *Unable to locate*

MBA Business (London, GBR) *Ceased*

MBC-Andong - 91.3 MHz (Seoul, KOR) **[47304]**

MBC-Andong - 100.1 MHz (Seoul, KOR) **[47303]**

MBC-Cheju - 90.1 MHz (Cheju, KOR) **[47215]**

MBC-Cheju - 102.9 MHz (Cheju, KOR) **[47214]**

MBC-Cheongju - 99.7 MHz (Seoul, KOR) **[47305]**

MBC-Chinju - 97.7 MHz (Chinju, KOR) **[47221]**

MBC-Chinju - 91.1 MHz (Chinju, KOR) **[47219]**

MBC-Chinju - 96.1 MHz (Chinju, KOR) **[47220]**

MBC-Chinju - 93.5 MHz (Seoul, KOR) **[47306]**

MBC-Ch'ongju - 92.3 MHz (Seoul, KOR) **[47307]**

MBC-Chonju, KOR) *Unable to locate*

MBC-Chonju - 99.1 MHz (Chonju, KOR) **[47222]**

MBC-Chunchon - 94.5 MHz (Seoul, KOR) **[47309]**

MBC-Chunchon - 92.3 MHz (Seoul, KOR) **[47308]**

MBC-Ch'ungju (Ch'ungcheongbuk-do, KOR) *Ceased*

MBC-Chungju - 88.7 MHz (Seoul, KOR) **[47311]**

MBC-Chungju - 96.1 MHz (Seoul, KOR) **[47312]**

MBC-Chungju - 94.1 MHz (Seoul, KOR) **[47310]**

MBC-Kangnung (Gangwon-do, KOR) *Unable to locate*

MBC-Kangnung (Gangwon-do, KOR) *Unable to locate*

MBC-Kwangju - 95.1 MHz (Gwangju, KOR) **[47236]**

MBC-Kwangju - 91.5 MHz (Gwangju, KOR) **[47237]**

MBC-Kwangju - 93.9 MHz (Gwangju, KOR) **[47235]**

MBC-Masan - 100.5 MHz (Masan, KOR) **[47245]**

MBC-Masan - 98.9 MHz (Masan, KOR) **[47244]**

MBC-Mokpo - 89.1 MHz (Seoul, KOR) **[47314]**

MBC-Mokpo - 102.3 MHz (Seoul, KOR) **[47313]**

MBC-Pohang - 97.9 MHz (Pohang, KOR) **[47249]**

MBC-Pusan - 95.9 MHz (Busan, KOR) **[47212]**

MBC-Pusan (Busan, KOR) *Unable to locate*

MBC-Samcheok - 101.5 MHz (Seoul, KOR) **[47316]**

MBC-Samcheok - 98.1 MHz (Seoul, KOR) **[47317]**

MBC-Samcheok - 99.9 MHz (Seoul, KOR) **[47315]**

MBC-Seoul - 95.9 MHz (Seoul, KOR) **[47319]**

MBC-Seoul - 91.9 MHz (Seoul, KOR) **[47318]**

MBC-Taegu (Daejeon, KOR) *Ceased*

MBC-Taegu - 92.5 MHz (Taegu, KOR) **[47328]**

MBC-Taejon - 97.5 MHz (Daejeon, KOR) **[47229]**

Numbers cited in bold after listings are entry numbers rather than page numbers.

MBC-Taejon - 92.5 MHz (Daejeon, KOR) [47230]

MBC-Ulsan - 97.5 MHz (Seoul, KOR) [47321]

MBC-Ulsan - 98.7 MHz (Seoul, KOR) [47320]

MBC-Wonju - 92.7 MHz (Seoul, KOR) [47323]

MBC-Wonju - 98.9 MHz (Seoul, KOR) [47322]

MBC-Yosu (Jeollanam-do, KOR) *Ceased*

MBC-Yosu - 98.3 MHz (Yosu, KOR) [47332]

MBR - Mountain Bike Rider (Croydon, GBR) [53129]

MC Folket (Mora, SWE) *Unable to locate*

MC Radio (Saransk, RUS) *Unable to locate*

MCB University Press Ltd. [52499]*

MCB University Press Ltd [56904]*

Mchunguzi (Dar es Salaam, TZA) *Unable to locate*

MCR-FM - 101.4 (London, GBR) [55456]

MCT—Multicultural Teaching [56630]*

MCV [42073]*

MDR 1 - Radio Sachsen-Anhalt-FM - 92.3 (Magdeburg, GER) [44537]

Me-FM - 87.7 (Aberdeen, GBR) [51681]

Me Too! (London, GBR) [54917]

Meanjin (Carlton, VI, AUS) [41727]

Measurement (Budapest, HUN) *Unable to locate*

Measurement and Control (London, GBR) [54918]

Measurement Science Review (Bratislava, SLK) [50321]

Measurement Science & Technology (Bristol, GBR) [52705]

Measuring Business Excellence (Bradford, GBR) [52526]

Meat Processing Global Edition (Paris, FRA) [44070]

Meat Science (Loughborough, GBR) [55485]

Meat Trades Journal (Crawley, GBR) [53108]

Meath Chronicle (Navan, ME, IRL) [46046]

Mecanique & Industries (Paris, FRA) [44071]

Meccanica (Dordrecht, NLD) [48514]

Mechanical Engineering Bulletin (Duragapur, WB, IND) *Unable to locate*

Mechanical Systems and Signal Processing (Haifa, ISR) [46078]

Mechanics of Cohesive-frictional Materials (Hobokon, NJ, USA) *Ceased*

Mechanics of Materials (Amsterdam, NLD) [48150]

Mechanics Research Communication (Udine, ITA) *Unable to locate*

Mechanism and Machine Theory (Duisburg, GER) [44320]

Mechanisms of Development (Utrecht, NLD) [48763]

Mechanisms and Machine Theory (Oulu, FIN) *Unable to locate*

Mechatronics (Amsterdam, NLD) [48151]

Med Ad News (London, GBR) [54919]

Med in Germany (Munich, GER) *Unable to locate*

Medborgarbladet (Helsinki, FIN) *Unable to locate*

Medborgaren (Stockholm, SWE) *Unable to locate*

Medecine therapeutique (Montrouge, FRA) [43997]

Medecine therapeutique cardiologie (Montrouge, FRA) [43998]

Medecine therapeutique/Endocrinologie (Montrouge, FRA) [43999]

Medecine Therapeutique/medecine de la reproduction (Montrouge, FRA) [44000]

Medecine therapeutique/Pediatrie (Montrouge, FRA) [44001]

Medecines Nouvelles (Blangy Le Chateau, FRA) *Unable to locate*

Medendium (Berkhamsted, GBR) [52313]

Media (Hong Kong, CHN) [43369]

Media, Culture & Society (London, GBR) [54920]

Media Development (London, GBR) [54921]

Media History (Abingdon, GBR) [51972]

Media Plus (Bangkok, THA) *Unable to locate*

Media Plus (Bangkok, THA) *Unable to locate*

Media Plus (Bangkok, THA) *Unable to locate*

Media Plus (Bangkok, THA) *Unable to locate*

Media Plus (Bangkok, THA) *Unable to locate*

MEDIA WATT [42874]*

Media Week (Croydon, GBR) [53130]

Mediacorp TV Pte. Ltd. - Channel 8 - Channel 8 (Singapore, SGP) [50298]

Mediacorp TV Pte. Ltd. - Channel 5 - Channel 5 (Singapore, SGP) [50299]

Mediactive (London, GBR) [54922]

Medical Book News (Mumbai, MH, IND) *Unable to locate*

Medical Care (Moscow, RUS) [49941]

Medical College and Hospital, Calcutta—Bulletin (Calcutta, WB, IND) *Unable to locate*

Medical Digest (Mumbai, MH, IND) *Unable to locate*

Medical Electron Microscopy [46966]*

Medical Engineering (Moscow, RUS) *Unable to locate*

Medical Engineering and Physics (Bath, GBR) [52251]

Medical Engineering and Physics (York, GBR) [56993]

Medical Entomology and Zoology (Tokyo, JPN) [46965]

Medical Express (Calcutta, WB, IND) *Unable to locate*

Medical Humanities (London, GBR) [54923]

Medical Imaging Technology (Tokyo, JPN) *Unable to locate*

Medical Informatics and the Internet in Medicine [51816]*

Medical Journal of Aomori Prefectural Central Hospital (Aomori, JPN) *Unable to locate*

Medical Journal Armed Forces India (Pune, MH, IND) [45697]

Medical Journal of Asahi General Hospital (Chiba, JPN) *Unable to locate*

The Medical Journal of Australia (Strawberry Hills, NW, AUS) [42396]

Medical Journal of the Government Printing Bureau (Tokyo, JPN) *Unable to locate*

Medical Journal of Hiroshima Prefectural Hospital (Hiroshima, JPN) *Unable to locate*

Medical Journal of Hiroshima University (Hiroshima, JPN) *Unable to locate*

Medical Journal of Ishikawa Prefectural Central Hospital (Ishikawa, JPN) *Unable to locate*

Medical Journal of Islamic Academy of Sciences (Amman, JOR) [47161]

Medical Journal of Iwate Prefectural Miyako Hospital (Iwate, JPN) *Unable to locate*

The Medical Journal of Malaysia (Kuala Lumpur, MYS) [47627]

Medical Law Cases for Doctors (Mumbai, MH, IND) [45410]

Medical Law Review (Oxford, GBR) [56095]

Medical Microbiology and Immunology (Mainz, GER) [44542]

Medical Molecular Morphology (Tokyo, JPN) [46966]

Medical Mycology (Abingdon, GBR) [51973]

Medical News (Paris, FRA) *Unable to locate*

Medical News, Medicine and Law (Pune, MH, IND) *Unable to locate*

Medical and Nutritional Research Communications (Madichal, TN, IND) *Unable to locate*

Medical and Pediatric Oncology (Hertogenbosch, NLD) *Unable to locate*

Medical Principles and Practice (Safat, KWT) [47341]

Medical Student International (Ferney-Voltaire, FRA) [43949]

Medical Teacher (Dundee, GBR) [53215]

Medical Technology (Cape Town, SAF) [50391]

Medical and Veterinary Entomology (Chatham, GBR) [52959]

Medicina (Kaunas, LIT) [47465]

Medicina e Morale (Rome, ITA) [46238]

Medicina Sportiva (Warsaw, POL) [49737]

Medicinal and Aromatic Plants Abstracts (New Delhi, DH, IND) [45626]

Medicinal Chemistry (Karachi, PAK) [49363]

Medicine, Conflict & Survival (Abingdon, GBR) [51974]

Medicine; Journal of Public Health [54806]*

Medicine; Nature Clinical Practice Cardiovascular [54976]*

Medicine: Series A; Journal of Veterinary [56220]*

Medicine Series B; Journal of Veterinary [56230]*

Medicine and Surgery (Baroda, GJ, IND) *Unable to locate*

Medico-Legal Journal (London, GBR) *Unable to locate*

Medico-Social Expert Evaluation and Rehabilitation (Moscow, RUS) [49942]

Mediekultur (Alborg, DEN) *Unable to locate*

Medieval Encounters (Leiden, NLD) [48708]

Medieval Life (York, GBR) *Ceased*

Medieval Sermon Studies (London, GBR) [54924]

Medikal & Teknik (Istanbul, TUR) [51562]

Mediscope (Chennai, TN, IND) *Unable to locate*

Mediterranean Historical Review (Abingdon, GBR) [51975]

Mediterranean Politics (Abingdon, GBR) [51976]

Mediterranean Studies (Surrey, GBR) [56668]

Medium Aevum (Oxford, GBR) *Unable to locate*

MEDSOLS (Stockholm, SWE) [51025]

MEED Middle East Economic Digest (London, GBR) *Unable to locate*

MEED - The Middle East Business Weekly (Dubai, UAE) [51648]

Meeleven (Amsterdam, NLD) [48152]

Meer & Yachten (Kiel, GER) [44506]

Meerut University Sanskrit Research Journal (Muzaffarnagar, UP, IND) *Unable to locate*

Meeting, Incentives & Conventions (Zurich, SWI) *Unable to locate*

MEGA! (Gosford, NW, AUS) [41920]

Mega (Makati, PHL) *Unable to locate*

MegaLine (Penang, MYS) *Unable to locate*

MegaLink (Aarau, SWI) [51055]

The Meghalaya Guardian (Shillong, MG, IND) *Unable to locate*

Meglepetes (Budapest, HUN) [44850]

Meglepetes Raadas (Budapest, HUN) [44851]

Meidan Mokki (Helsinki, FIN) [43846]

Meidan Talo (Helsinki, FIN) [43847]

Meieriposten (Oslo, NOR) [49202]

M8 Magazine (Glasgow, GBR) [53430]

Meihekou People's Broadcasting Station (Meihekou, JI, CHN) *Unable to locate*

Meine Melodie (Rastatt, GER) *Unable to locate*

Meios (Lisbon, PRT) *Unable to locate*

Meizhou People's Broadcasting Station (Meizhou, GD, CHN) *Unable to locate*

Mela UK (London, GBR) [54925]

Melbourne Community Voice (Melbourne, VI, AUS) [42073]

Melbourne Journal of Politics (Carlton, VI, AUS) [41728]

Melbourne Leader (Melbourne, VI, AUS) [42074]

Melbourne University Law Review (Melbourne, VI, AUS) [42075]

Melodia-FM - 96.9 (Bogota, COL) [43546]

Melody Maker (London, GBR) *Unable to locate*

Melomano (Madrid, SPA) [50783]

Melton Leader (Sunbury, VI, AUS) [42403]

Melton Times (Melton Mowbray, GBR) [55606]

Member's Interests List/Subscribers' Interest Lists [52282]*

Members Journal (Newark, GBR) [55660]

Members' Journal (Sevenoaks, GBR) *Unable to locate*

Membrane Technology (Oxford, GBR) [56096]

Memento (Farsta, SWE) *Unable to locate*

Memoirs on Indian Animal Types (New Delhi, DH, IND) *Unable to locate*

Memoirs of the Kagoshima University Research Center for the South Pacific [46405]*

Memon Alam (Karachi, PAK) *Unable to locate*

Memorial (Luxembourg, LUX) *Unable to locate*

Memorias do Instituto Oswaldo Cruz (Rio de Janeiro, RJ, BRZ) [43012]

Numbers cited in bold after listings are entry numbers rather than page numbers.

Master Index

Menara Perkebunan (Bogor, IDN) *Unable to locate*

Mendel (Patna, BH, IND) *Unable to locate*

Menmode (Hong Kong, CHN) *Unable to locate*

Menopause International (London, GBR) **[54926]**

Menopause International (Marlow, GBR) **[55600]**

Menorah (Jerusalem, ISR) **[46089]**

Men's Health (London, GBR) *Unable to locate*

Mens Sana Monographs (Mumbai, MH, IND) **[45411]**

Men's Style Australia (Sydney, NW, AUS) **[42542]**

Mental Health and Learning Disabilities; Advances in **[52604]***

Mental Health Matters (East Sydney, NW, AUS) **[41851]**

Mental Health Practice (Harrow, GBR) **[53525]**

Mental Health Reforms (Hilversum, NLD) **[48631]**

Mental Health, Religion and Culture (Abingdon, GBR) **[51977]**

Mental Health Review Journal (Brighton, GBR) **[52626]**

Mental Health Today (Brighton, GBR) **[52627]**

The Mental Lexicon (Amsterdam, NLD) **[48153]**

Mentalhigiene es Pszichoszomatika (Budapest, HUN) **[44852]**

Mente Sana (Barcelona, SPA) **[50688]**

Mer & Bateaux (Antibes, FRA) **[43915]**

Merchant, Stockist & Wholesaler (Birmingham, GBR) *Unable to locate*

Mercia-FM - 97.0 (Coventry, GBR) **[53092]**

Mercia-FM - 102.9 (Coventry, GBR) **[53093]**

Mercury-FM - 102.7 (Crawley, GBR) **[53116]**

Merge (Stockholm, SWE) *Unable to locate*

Merian (Hamburg, GER) **[44420]**

Meridiani (Rozzano, ITA) **[46251]**

Merum (Basel, SWI) **[51064]**

Message of Thaqalayn (Tehran, IRN) **[45912]**

Messages du Secours Catholique (Paris, FRA) **[44072]**

Messenger (Singapore, SGP) *Unable to locate*

Metabolic Brain Disease (Dordrecht, NLD) **[48515]**

Metabolic Engineering (Amsterdam, NLD) **[48154]**

Metal Bulletin Monthly (London, GBR) **[54927]**

Metal Finishing (Amsterdam, NLD) **[48155]**

Metal Hammer (Munich, GER) **[44571]**

Metal Powder Report (Kidlington, GBR) **[53703]**

Metall (Zurich, SWI) *Unable to locate*

Metallomics (Cambridge, GBR) **[52868]**

Metallurgia (London, GBR) **[54928]**

Metallurgical Review of MMIJ (Tokyo, JPN) *Unable to locate*

Metals Industry News (London, GBR) *Unable to locate*

Metals & Materials **[54914]***

Metals Materials and Processes (Mumbai, MH, IND) *Unable to locate*

Metals and Minerals Review (Calcutta, WB, IND) *Unable to locate*

Metalurgia y Electricidad (Madrid, SPA) *Unable to locate*

Metalworking Abstracts (New Delhi, DH, IND) *Unable to locate*

Metalworking Production **[54967]***

Metamorphose (Leinfelden-Echterdingen, GER) **[44527]**

Metaphilosophy (Oxford, GBR) **[56097]**

Meteorite (Auckland, NZL) **[48804]**

Meteorologische Zeitschrift (Stuttgart, GER) **[44669]**

Method & Theory in the Study of Religion (Leiden, NLD) **[48709]**

Methodmag (Print Edition) (Innsbruck, AUT) *Unable to locate*

Methods (Amsterdam, NLD) **[48156]**

Methods of Information in Medicine (Stuttgart, GER) **[44670]**

Methods in Organic Synthesis (Cambridge, GBR) **[52869]**

Metro (Quezon City, PHL) **[49599]**

Metro (London, GBR) *Unable to locate*

Metro hiM (Quezon City, PHL) **[49600]**

Metro Home & Entertaining (Quezon City, PHL) **[49601]**

Metro Magazine (Bangkok, THA) *Ceased*

Metro Plus-Peng Chau - 1044 KHz (Hong Kong, CHN) **[43416]**

Metro Radio-FM - 102.6 (Alnwick, GBR) **[52102]**

Metro Radio-FM - 103.2 (Hexham, GBR) **[53570]**

Metro Radio-FM - 97.1 (Newcastle upon Tyne, GBR) **[55683]**

Metro Radio-FM - 103.0 (Newcastle upon Tyne, GBR) **[55684]**

Metro Society (Quezon City, PHL) **[49602]**

Metro Weddings (Quezon City, PHL) **[49603]**

MetroActive (Quezon City, PHL) **[49604]**

Metroeconomica (Graz, AUT) **[42725]**

Metrologia (Bristol, GBR) **[52706]**

Metropolis (Tokyo, JPN) **[46967]**

Metropolitana-FM - 97.1 (Los Teques, VEN) **[57025]**

Metsanhoitaja-Forstmastaren (Helsinki, FIN) *Unable to locate*

Metsastys ja Kalastus (Kuvalehdet, FIN) **[43891]**

METU Studies in Development (Ankara, TUR) **[51497]**

Meyerton Ster (Cape Town, SAF) **[50392]**

Mezinarodni Politika International Politics (Prague, CZE) **[43629]**

Mezinarodni Vztahy International Relations (Prague, CZE) **[43630]**

Mezzo (London, GBR) *Unable to locate*

MFR-AM - 1107 (Inverness, GBR) **[53648]**

MG World (Surrey, GBR) *Ceased*

MGT-FM - 101.1 MHz (Bandung, IDN) **[45776]**

MGV-TV - Channel 31 (Melbourne, VI, AUS) **[42093]**

Mi Opinion Si Cuenta (Quito, ECU) *Unable to locate*

Mia (Madrid, SPA) **[50784]**

Miadhu News (Male, MDV) *Unable to locate*

miceAsia.net (Sydney, NW, AUS) **[42543]**

mice.net (Sydney, NW, AUS) **[42544]**

miceNZ.net (Sydney, NW, AUS) **[42545]**

Micro Computer Mart **[52358]***

Micro Mart (Birmingham, GBR) **[52358]**

Micro- and Nanometer Science & Technology (Shanghai, CHN) **[43488]**

Microbes and Infection (Amsterdam, NLD) **[48157]**

Microbial Cell Factories (London, GBR) **[54929]**

Microbial Ecology in Health and Disease (Stockholm, SWE) **[51026]**

Microbial Pathogenesis (Amsterdam, NLD) **[48158]**

Microbiological Research (Copenhagen, DEN) **[43679]**

Microbiologie et Hygien Alimentaire (Sousse, TUN) *Unable to locate*

Microbiology (Beijing, CHN) *Unable to locate*

Microbiology (Reading, GBR) **[56325]**

Microbiology Australia (Melbourne, VI, AUS) **[42076]**

Microbiology and Immunology (Tokyo, JPN) **[46968]**

Microbiology Today (Reading, GBR) **[56326]**

Microcirculation (Abingdon, GBR) **[51978]**

Microcomputer (Bangkok, THA) **[51427]**

Microcomputer Applications (Shanghai, CHN) **[43489]**

Microelectronic Engineering (Leuven, BEL) **[42901]**

Microelectronics International (Bradford, GBR) **[52527]**

Microelectronics Journal (Grenoble, FRA) **[43958]**

Microelectronics Reliability (Nis, SER) **[50091]**

Microform & Imaging Review (Berlin, GER) **[44221]**

Microgravity News (Paris, FRA) *Unable to locate*

Microlight Flying (Oxford, GBR) **[56098]**

Microlithography, Microfabrication, and Microsystems **[51306]***

Micromath (Derby, GBR) *Unable to locate*

Micron (Mainz, GER) **[44543]**

Micronesian Journal of the Humanities and Social Sciences (Albury, NW, AUS) **[41527]**

Microporous and Mesoporous Materials (Oslo, NOR) **[49203]**

Microprocessors and Microsystems (Lund, SWE) **[50987]**

Microscopical Society; Proceedings of the Royal **[55989]***

Microscopy and Analysis (Chichester, GBR) **[53014]**

Microsystem Technologies (Berlin, GER) **[44222]**

Microvascular Research (Amsterdam, NLD) **[48159]**

Mid-Day (Mumbai, MH, IND) **[45412]**

Mid-Ocean News (Hamilton, BMU) **[42921]**

Mid Sussex Times (Haywards Heath, GBR) **[53549]**

Mid-Ulster Echo (Edinburgh, GBR) *Unable to locate*

Mid-Ulster Mail (Cookstown, GBR) **[53060]**

Midden-Brabant-FM (Amsterdam, NLD) *Unable to locate*

Midden-Nederland-FM (Amsterdam, NLD) *Unable to locate*

The Middle East (London, GBR) **[54930]**

Middle East African Journal of Ophthalmology (Mumbai, MH, IND) **[45413]**

Middle East Food (MEF) (Beirut, LBN) **[47399]**

Middle East Journal of Culture and Communication (Leiden, NLD) **[48710]**

Middle East Journal of Scientific Research (Faisalabad, PAK) **[49274]**

Middle East Law and Governance (Leiden, NLD) **[48711]**

Middle East MICE & Events (Dubai, UAE) **[51649]**

Middle Eastern Literatures (Abingdon, GBR) **[51979]**

Middle Eastern Studies (Abingdon, GBR) **[51980]**

Middle Eastern Studies (London, GBR) *Unable to locate*

The Middle Way (London, GBR) **[54931]**

Mide-FM - 96 MHz (Puke, ALB) **[41443]**

Midhurst & Petworth Observer (Midhurst, GBR) **[55625]**

Midland History (London, GBR) **[54932]**

Midland Weekly (Bhopal, MP, IND) *Unable to locate*

Midlands 103-FM - 95.4 (Athlone, WE, IRL) **[45916]**

Midlands 103-FM - 96.5 (Mullingar, WE, IRL) **[46041]**

Midlands Zone (Shrewsbury, GBR) *Unable to locate*

Midlothian Advertiser (Dalkeith, GBR) **[53153]**

Midsomer Murders Magazine (London, GBR) **[54933]**

Midweek Herald (Norwich, GBR) **[55734]**

Midwest Studies in Philosophy (Oxford, GBR) **[56099]**

Midwifery Matters (Ormskirk, GBR) **[55850]**

Midwives Chronicle **[55175]***

Mielenterveys (Mental Health) (Helsinki, FIN) *Unable to locate*

MIG-Inform (Novyy Urengoy, RUS) *Unable to locate*

MIJARC News (Brussels, BEL) **[42866]**

Milap Weekly (London, GBR) *Unable to locate*

The Milbank Quarterly (Oxford, GBR) **[56100]**

Mile-FM - 93 MHz (Sarande, ALB) **[41445]**

Milenia Radio-AM - 1530 (Lima, PER) **[49428]**

Milennium Radio-FM - 89.1 (Nuku'alofa, TGA) **[51466]**

Milieudefensie (Amsterdam, NLD) *Unable to locate*

Militarteknisk Tidskrift (Stockholm, SWE) *Unable to locate*

Military Balance (Abingdon, GBR) **[51981]**

Military Digest (New Delhi, DH, IND) *Unable to locate*

The Military History Journal (Saxonwold, SAF) **[50628]**

Military Hobbies **[52135]***

Military Illustrated (Totternhoe, GBR) **[56765]**

Military In Scale (West Sussex, GBR) *Unable to locate*

Military Law and Law of War Review (Brussels, BEL) **[42867]**

Military Machines International (Amersham, GBR) **[52108]**

Military Modelcraft International (Bletchley, GBR) **[52389]**

MILITARY TECHNOLOGY (Bonn, GER) **[44266]**

Numbers cited in bold after listings are entry numbers rather than page numbers.

Militseskaya Volna (Moscow, RUS) *Unable to locate*

Milk Industry (Faversham, GBR) **[53383]**

Milk Industry International **[53383]***

The Milk Round (Glasgow, GBR) *Unable to locate*

Millennium (London, GBR) **[54934]**

Milngavie Herald (Milngavie, GBR) **[55629]**

Milton Keynes Citizen (Edinburgh, GBR) *Unable to locate*

MIMS (London, GBR) **[54935]**

Min Li Broadcasting Station (Ping-tung, TWN) *Unable to locate*

Minaret (Calcutta, WB, IND) *Unable to locate*

Minaret Monthly International (Kara-chi, PAK) *Unable to locate*

Mind (York, GBR) **[56994]**

Mind & Language (Oxford, GBR) **[56101]**

Mind and Matter (Freiburg, GER) **[44371]**

Mindanao Journal (Iligan City, PHL) *Unable to locate*

Mindanao Mail (Davao, PHL) *Unable to locate*

Mindanao Times (Davao, PHL) *Unable to locate*

Mindview (Beveren, BEL) *Unable to locate*

Mine and Metal Worker (New Delhi, DH, IND) *Unable to locate*

Mineral Planning (Northallerton, GBR) *Unable to locate*

Mineral Processing and Extractive Metallurgy (London, GBR) **[54936]**

Mineral Research (Nagpur, MH, IND) *Unable to locate*

Mineral Resources Engineering (Sin-gapore, SGP) *Ceased*

Mineral Review (Karachi, PAK) *Unable to locate*

Mineral Wealth (Ahmedabad, GJ, IND) *Unable to locate*

Mineralium Deposita (Heidelberg, GER) **[44467]**

Mineralogia (Warsaw, POL) **[49738]**

Mineralogical Magazine (London, GBR) **[54937]**

Minerals & Energy - Raw Materials Report (Abingdon, GBR) *Ceased*

Minerals Engineering (Falmouth, GBR) **[53372]**

Minerals Market Reporter (Mumbai, MH, IND) *Unable to locate*

Miners MidWeek (Sydney, NW, AUS) **[42546]**

The Minerva Report (Bath, GBR) *Unable to locate*

Mines, Minerals, Energy, Ecology, Pollution, Ceramics, Refractory, Cement, Glass (Allahabad, UP, IND) *Unable to locate*

Minetech (Ranchi, BH, IND) *Unable to locate*

Ming Studies (London, GBR) **[54938]**

Mingguan Malaysia (Kuala Lumpur, MYS) **[47628]**

Mini Eye Care (New Delhi, DH, IND) *Unable to locate*

Mini-Reviews in Organic Chemistry (Karachi, PAK) **[49364]**

Miniature Wargames (Nottingham, GBR) **[55767]**

Minimally Invasive Therapy and Allied Technologies (Abingdon, GBR) **[51982]**

Minimax (Delhi, DH, IND) *Unable to locate*

Mining Environmental Management (London, GBR) **[54939]**

Mining, Geological and Metallurgical Institute of India—Transactions (Calcutta, WB, IND) *Unable to locate*

Mining and Geology (Sofia, BUL) *Unable to locate*

Mining Journal (London, GBR) **[54940]**

Mining Journal Gold Service **[55420]***

Mining Magazine (London, GBR) **[54941]**

Mining Technology (London, GBR) **[54942]**

Mining Weekly (Garden View, SAF) **[50480]**

Minjiang People's Broadcasting Sta-tion (Chengdu, SI, CHN) *Unable to locate*

Minnal FM - Besut - 95.3 (Besut, MYS) **[47575]**

Minnal FM - Jeli - 92.4 (Jeli, MYS) **[47580]**

Minnal FM - Jerantut - 91.9 (Jerantut, MYS) **[47582]**

Minnal FM - Kuala Lumpur - 92.3 (Kuala Lumpur, MYS) **[47653]**

Minnal FM - Kuala Terengganu - 87.9 (Kuala Terengganu, MYS) **[47663]**

Minnal FM - Kuantan - 103.3 (Kuan-tan, MYS) **[47665]**

Minnal FM - Mersing - 101.1 (Mers-ing, MYS) **[47682]**

Minnal FM - Muar - 103.3 (Muar, MYS) **[47687]**

Minnal FM - Taiping - 107.9 (Taiping, MYS) **[47722]**

Minor Monthly (Dorset, GBR) **[53195]**

Minority Forum (Lucknow, UP, IND) *Unable to locate*

Minster-FM - 104.7 (York, GBR) **[57001]**

Mira (Pune, MH, IND) **[45698]**

Mirfield Reporter (Dewsbury, GBR) **[53181]**

Mirror (Mumbai, MH, IND) *Unable to locate*

Mirror of Opinion (Singapore, SGP) *Unable to locate*

Mirror and Probe (Peradeniya, SRI) *Unable to locate*

MIS Australia (Wellington, NZL) **[49017]**

MISC (London, GBR) *Unable to locate*

Miscellany (Calcutta, WB, IND) *Unable to locate*

Misjpoge (Amsterdam, NLD) **[48160]**

The Mitalee Review (London, GBR) *Unable to locate*

Mithila Institute of Post Graduate Studies and Research in Sanskrit Learning Bulletin (Darbhanga, BH, IND) *Unable to locate*

Mitochondrial DNA (Abingdon, GBR) **[51983]**

Mitsubishi Electric Advance (Tokyo, JPN) **[46969]**

Mitsubishi Heavy Industries Technical Review (Yokohama, JPN) **[47140]**

Mitteilungen des Bundesamtes fur Veterinarwesen (Bern, SWI) *Unable to locate*

Mitteilungen Osterreiches Getranke Institut (Vienna, AUT) **[42764]**

Mitteilungen der Vereinigung Oester-reichischer Bibliothekarinnen und (Vienna, AUT) *Unable to locate*

Mitteilungsblatt des DBMB (Bulletin of the Association of German Master-brewers and Mastermaltsters) (Nuremberg, GER) *Ceased*

Mittendrin (Detmold, GER) *Unable to locate*

miwine (Pozuelo de Alarcon, SPA) *Unable to locate*

Mix - 105 (Kuala Lumpur, MYS) **[47654]**

Mix-FM - 106.3 (Gungahlin, AC, AUS) **[41936]**

Mix-FM - 92.7 (Maroochydore, QL, AUS) **[42037]**

Mix-FM - 104.4 (Beirut, LBN) **[47412]**

Mix 94.5-FM - 94.5 (Subiaco, WA, AUS) **[42400]**

Mix 96-FM - 96.2 (Aylesbury, GBR) **[52150]**

Mix 107-FM (High Wycombe, GBR) *Unable to locate*

Mix 107-FM (High Wycombe, GBR) *Unable to locate*

MIX 101.1-FM - 101.1 (Richmond, VI, AUS) **[42306]**

Mix 105.3-FM (The Lakes, QL, AUS) *Unable to locate*

Mix 104.9-FM - 104.9 (Darwin, NT, AUS) **[41829]**

MIX 106.5-FM - 106.5 (North Ryde, NW, AUS) **[42202]**

MIX 102.3-FM - 102.3 (North Ade-laide, SA, AUS) **[42153]**

MKB Regiozine (Delft, NLD) *Unable to locate*

Mladina Magazine (Ljubljana, SVA) **[50340]**

MLQ - Mathematical Logic Quarterly (Greifswald, GER) **[44405]**

MM Industrial Magazine Western Eu-rope (Wurzburg, GER) **[44722]**

MM Maschinenmarkt (Wurzburg, GER) **[44723]**

Mmegi/The Reporter (Gaborone, BWA) **[42945]**

MMM-FM - 104.9 (Sydney, NW, AUS) **[42597]**

Mnemosyne (Leiden, NLD) **[48712]**

MOABI (Yaounde, CMR) *Unable to locate*

Mobil und Sicher (Meckenheim bei Bonn, GER) *Unable to locate*

Mobile (Brussels, BEL) *Unable to locate*

Mobile Information Systems (Clayton, VI, AUS) **[41763]**

Mobilia Interieurtextiel (Amsterdam, NLD) *Unable to locate*

Mobilia Vloeren (Amsterdam, NLD) *Unable to locate*

Mobilities (Abingdon, GBR) **[51984]**

MOC Cars and Spares For Sale/Wanted (Pulborough, GBR) *Unable to locate*

MOCI (Paris, FRA) *Unable to locate*

MOCT-SJLTA (Saint Petersburg, RUS) *Unable to locate*

MODA (Kuvalehdet, FIN) **[43892]**

Moda Muotikaavat **[43892]***

Mode Hong Kong (Hong Kong, CHN) *Unable to locate*

Model Airplane (Beijing, CHN) *Unable to locate*

Model Airplane International (Tottern-hoe, GBR) **[56766]**

Model Assisted Statistics and Appli-cations (Amsterdam, NLD) **[48161]**

Model Helicopter World (West Sus-sex, GBR) *Unable to locate*

Model Military International (Tottern-hoe, GBR) **[56767]**

Modelflyve Nyt (Gudme, DEN) *Ceased*

Modell (Villingen-Schwenningen, GER) **[44699]**

Modell Fan (Bremen, GER) **[44281]**

Modell Flugsport (Hittnau, SWI) *Unable to locate*

Modelling and Simulation in Materials Science and Engineering (Bristol, GBR) **[52707]**

Modern Agriculture (Mumbai, MH, IND) *Unable to locate*

Modern Asian Studies (Cambridge, GBR) **[52870]**

Modern Believing (Liverpool, GBR) **[53876]**

Modern Boating (Alexandria, NW, AUS) **[41543]**

Modern Churchman **[53876]***

Modern & Contemporary France (Ab-ingdon, GBR) **[51985]**

Modern Fishing (Alexandria, NW, AUS) **[41544]**

Modern Food Processing (Mumbai, MH, IND) **[45414]**

Modern History Review **[55350]***

Modern Italy (Abingdon, GBR) **[51986]**

The Modern Language Journal (Ox-ford, GBR) **[56102]**

Modern Language Review (London, GBR) **[54943]**

The Modern Law Review (Oxford, GBR) **[56103]**

Modern Machine Tools (Mumbai, MH, IND) **[45415]**

Modern Management (Lichfield, GBR) *Ceased*

Modern Medicare (Mumbai, MH, IND) **[45416]**

Modern Medicine of Ireland (Dublin, DU, IRL) *Unable to locate*

Modern MINI (Cudham, GBR) **[53144]**

Modern Packaging & Design (Mum-bai, MH, IND) **[45417]**

Modern Packaging Trends (Mumbai, MH, IND) *Unable to locate*

Modern Pharmaceuticals (Mumbai, MH, IND) **[45418]**

Modern Physics Letters A (Singapore, SGP) **[50217]**

Modern Physics Letters B (Sin-gapore, SGP) **[50218]**

Modern Plastics & Polymers (Mum-bai, MH, IND) **[45419]**

Modern Plastics - Rubber Technology (Allahabad, UP, IND) *Unable to locate*

Modern Power Systems (Daruvar, CTA) *Unable to locate*

Modern Prose, Modern Poetry, In the World of Music, Culture and Health, The Knowledge, Computer Tech-nologies (Moscow, RUS) *Unable to locate*

Modern Railways (Tunbridge Wells North, GBR) **[56785]**

Modern Review (Calcutta, WB, IND) *Unable to locate*

Modern Rheumatology (Tokyo, JPN) **[46970]**

Modern Textiles (Mumbai, MH, IND) **[45420]**

Modern Theology (Oxford, GBR) **[56104]**

Modern Woman Nationwide (Navan, ME, IRL) *Unable to locate*

Modified Motors (Sandyford, DU, IRL) **[46056]**

Modin (Helsinki, FIN) **[43848]**

Modo (Milan, ITA) *Unable to locate*

Moffat News (Annan, GBR) **[52125]**

Mojo (London, GBR) **[56785]**

Molecular Aspects of Medicine (Am-sterdam, NLD) **[48162]**

Molecular and Biochemical Parasitol-ogy (Amsterdam, NLD) **[48163]**

Molecular Biology and Evolution (Ox-ford, GBR) **[56105]**

Molecular Biosystems (Cambridge, GBR) **[52871]**

Molecular Cancer (London, GBR) **[54945]**

Master Index

Molecular and Cellular Endocrinology (London, GBR) **[54946]**

Molecular and Cellular Neurosciences (Amsterdam, NLD) **[48164]**

Molecular and Cellular Probes (Amsterdam, NLD) **[48165]**

Molecular Ecology (Oxford, GBR) **[56106]**

Molecular Ecology Notes **[56107]***

Molecular Ecology Resources (Oxford, GBR) **[56107]**

Molecular Genetics and Genomics (Goteborg, SWE) **[50959]**

Molecular Genetics and Metabolism (Amsterdam, NLD) **[48166]**

Molecular Genetics, Microbiology & Virology (Moscow, RUS) **[49943]**

Molecular Human Reproduction (Childerley, GBR) **[53019]**

Molecular Immunology (Amsterdam, NLD) **[48167]**

Molecular Informatics (Braunschweig, GER) **[44278]**

Molecular Medicine (Moscow, RUS) **[49944]**

Molecular Oral Microbiology (Oxford, GBR) **[56108]**

Molecular Pain (London, GBR) **[54947]**

Molecular Phylogenetics and Evolution (Amsterdam, NLD) **[48168]**

Molecular Plant Pathology (Reading, GBR) **[56327]**

Molecular Psychiatry (London, GBR) **[54948]**

Molecular Systems Biology (London, GBR) **[54949]**

Molecular Therapy (Basingstoke, GBR) **[52224]**

Mollusc World (Godalming, GBR) **[53475]**

Molodezhniy Kanal (Barnaul, RUS) Unable to locate

Molodezhniy Kanal (Barnaul, RUS) Unable to locate

Mon Quotidien (Paris, FRA) Unable to locate

Monarchy (Bishop's Stortford, GBR) **[52381]**

Monash University Law Review (Clayton, VI, AUS) **[41764]**

Monatsschrift fur Brauwissenschaft (Nuremberg, GER) **[44616]**

Monday Morning (Beirut, LBN) **[47400]**

Monday Paper (Rondebosch, SAF) **[50622]**

Monde Informatique (Paris La Defense, FRA) Unable to locate

Monetaria (Mexico City, DF, MEX) **[47786]**

Money Affairs (Mexico City, DF, MEX) **[47787]**

Money Marketing (London, GBR) **[54950]**

Money Observer (London, GBR) **[54951]**

Money Opportunities (Mumbai, MH, IND) Unable to locate

Moneyfacts (Norwich, GBR) **[55735]**

Moneywise (Sittingbourne, GBR) **[56550]**

The Mongol Messenger (Ulaanbaatar, MNG) **[47812]**

Mongolia Today (Ulaanbaatar, MNG) Unable to locate

Mongolian Journal of International Affairs (Ulaanbaatar, MNG) Unable to locate

The Monitor (Kampala, UGA) **[51587]**

Monitor 21 (Oslo, NOR) **[49204]**

Monitorul (Iasi, ROM) Unable to locate

Monocle Magazine (Godalming, GBR) **[53476]**

Monster Radio RX-FM - 93.1 (Pasig City, PHL) **[49579]**

Montessori Tidningen (Goteborg, SWE) **[50960]**

Monthly Commentary on Indian Economic Conditions (New Delhi, DH, IND) Unable to locate

Monthly Digest of Statistics (Basingstoke, GBR) **[52225]**

Monthly Gonoshasthaya (Dhaka, BGD) Unable to locate

Monthly Journal of Entomology (Tokyo, JPN) Unable to locate

Monthly Law Digest (Lahore, PAK) Unable to locate

Monthly Notices of the Royal Astronomical Society (Oxford, GBR) **[56109]**

Monthly Production of Selected Industries of India (Calcutta, WB, IND) Ceased

Monthly Railway Statistics (New Delhi, DH, IND) Unable to locate

Monthly Statistics of Foreign Trade of India (New Delhi, DH, IND) Unable to locate

Monthly Summary of Jute and Gunny Statistics (Calcutta, WB, IND) Unable to locate

Montres Passion/Uhren Welt (Lausanne, SWI) **[51197]**

Montrose Review (Montrose, GBR) **[55646]**

Monumenta Nipponica (Tokyo, JPN) **[46971]**

Mood-FM - 92.00 (Amman, JOR) **[47163]**

Mood Food (London, GBR) **[54952]**

Moonee Valley Leader (Melbourne, VI, AUS) **[42077]**

Moor Journal of Agricultural Research (Ibadan, OY, NGA) **[49092]**

Moorabbin Glen Eira Leader (Cheltenham, VI, AUS) **[41747]**

Moorabbin Kingston Leader (Cheltenham, VI, AUS) **[41748]**

Moorabool Leader (Melbourne, VI, AUS) **[42078]**

Mordialloc Chelsea Leader (Cheltenham, VI, AUS) **[41749]**

More-FM - 94 (Nassau, BHS) **[42785]**

More-FM - 91.8 (Auckland, NZL) **[48845]**

More-FM - 92.1 (Christchurch, NZL) **[48883]**

More-FM - 99 (Wellington, NZL) **[49041]**

More FM Manawatu - 92.2 (Palmerston North, NZL) **[48968]**

Moreland Leader (Melbourne, VI, AUS) **[42079]**

Morena-FM - 98.7 (Itabuna, BH, BRZ) **[42982]**

Morgen (Vienna, AUT) Unable to locate

Morley Observer & Advertiser (Morley, GBR) **[55652]**

Morning (Tokyo, JPN) **[46972]**

Morning Advertiser (Crawley, GBR) **[53109]**

The Morning Bulletin (Sydney, NW, AUS) **[42547]**

Mornington Peninsula Leader (Mornington, VI, AUS) **[42118]**

The Moroccan Woman (Rabat, MOR) Unable to locate

Morpeth Herald (Morpeth, GBR) **[55653]**

Morskoy Zhurnal (Maritime Journal) (Saint Petersburg, RUS) Unable to locate

Mortality (Abingdon, GBR) **[51987]**

Mortgage Edge (London, GBR) **[54953]**

Mortgage Matters (West Malling, GBR) **[56893]**

Mortgage Solutions (London, GBR) **[54954]**

Mortgage Strategy (London, GBR) **[54955]**

Mosaic (Cambridge, GBR) **[52872]**

Mosaico di Pace (Bisceglie, ITA) **[46124]**

Moscow Mathematical Journal (Moscow, RUS) **[49945]**

Moscow News (Moscow, RUS) **[49946]**

Moscow Weekly (Moscow, RUS) Unable to locate

Mosprojectovetz (Moscow, RUS) Unable to locate

Mother & Baby (Sydney, NW, AUS) **[42548]**

Mother and Child (Lahore, PAK) Unable to locate

Mother India (Pondicherry, PN, IND) **[45693]**

Motherhood (Singapore, SGP) **[50219]**

Motherhood Handbook (Singapore, SGP) **[50220]**

Motherwell Times Series (Falkirk, GBR) Unable to locate

Motion Pictures Technical Bulletin (Mumbai, MH, IND) Unable to locate

Moto-Champ (Tokyo, JPN) **[46973]**

Moto Magazine (London, GBR) **[54956]**

Motociclismo (Cruz Quebrada-Dafundo, PRT) **[49795]**

Motomagazyn (Warsaw, POL) Unable to locate

Motor Boat and Yachting (London, GBR) **[54957]**

Motor Caravan (London, GBR) **[54958]**

Motor China (Beijing, CHN) Unable to locate

Motor Equipment News (North Shore City, NZL) **[48956]**

Motor Industry Magazine (Brickendon, GBR) **[52592]**

Motor Klassiek (Kumtich, BEL) Unable to locate

Motor Ship (Fareham, GBR) **[53374]**

Motor Sport (Teddington, GBR) **[56734]**

Motor Trader and Fleet Operator (Harare, ZWE) Ceased

Motor Transport (Sutton, GBR) **[56688]**

Motorcycle Japan (Tokyo, JPN) Unable to locate

Motorcycle Sport and Leisure (Bodmin, GBR) Unable to locate

Motorcykl (Czech) (Prague, CZE) **[43631]**

Motorhome ABC (Oostende, BEL) Unable to locate

Motorhome and Caravan Trader (Manchester, GBR) **[55572]**

Motorindia (Chennai, TN, IND) Unable to locate

Motoring (Mumbai, MH, IND) Unable to locate

Motoring (Singapore, SGP) **[50221]**

Motoring Annual (Singapore, SGP) **[50222]**

Motoring Directions (Canberra, AC, AUS) **[41710]**

Motoring Life (Dublin, DU, IRL) **[45992]**

Motorradfahrer (Euskirchen, GER) Unable to locate

Motorsports Now! (Slough, GBR) Unable to locate

Mt. Druitt - St. Marys Standard (Mount Druitt, NW, AUS) **[42124]**

Mountain Manager (Wiesbaden, GER) Unable to locate

Mountain Research (Beijing, CHN) Unable to locate

Mourne Observer (Newcastle, GBR) **[55665]**

Move! (Cape Town, SAF) **[50393]**

Move (Bern, SWI) Unable to locate

Move-X (Kortenberg, BEL) Unable to locate

Movie (Mumbai, MH, IND) Unable to locate

Movie -TV Marketing (Tokyo, JPN) Unable to locate

Mozambiquefile (Maputo, MOZ) Unable to locate

MPT International (Dusseldorf, GER) **[44329]**

MS-bladet (Oslo, NOR) Unable to locate

MS Matters (London, GBR) **[54959]**

MS-Radio (Zheleznogorsk, RUS) Unable to locate

MS Voice (Wellington, NZL) Unable to locate

MSDN Magazine (London, GBR) **[54960]**

MSDN Magazine. Southeast Asia Edition (Singapore, SGP) **[50223]**

Mshana (Sandton, SAF) **[50627]**

MT Cardio (Montrouge, FRA) **[44002]**

Mtafiti Mwafrika (Kampala, UGA) **[51588]**

MTV Channel (Pvt) Ltd - Channel 23 (Depanama, SRI) **[50893]**

MTV Channel (Pvt) Ltd - Channel 25 (Nuwara Eliya, SRI) **[50920]**

MuangBoran Journal (Bangkok, THA) Unable to locate

Mudanjiang People's Broadcasting Station (Mudanjiang, HL, CHN) Unable to locate

Mudanjiang People's Broadcasting Station (Mudanjiang, HL, CHN) Unable to locate

Mudanjiang People's Broadcasting Station (Mudanjiang, HL, CHN) Unable to locate

Mudanjiang People's Broadcasting Station (Mudanjiang, HL, CHN) Unable to locate

Mujer (San Jose, CRI) Unable to locate

Mujer No Estas Sola (San Jose, CRI) Unable to locate

Mujeres, Mulleres, Dones, Emakumear (Madrid, SPA) Ceased

The Mulcher-FM (Kawerau, NZL) Unable to locate

The Mule (Thrapston, GBR) **[56748]**

Multi-Skills (Kenilworth, GBR) Ceased

Multiagent and Grid Systems (Glasgow, GBR) **[53431]**

Multicultural Education & Technology Journal (Huddersfield, GBR) **[53623]**

Multicultural Societies (IJMS); International Journal on **[44395]***

Multidiscipline Modeling in Materials and Structures (Bradford, GBR) **[52528]**

Multilingua (Bern, SWI) **[51076]**

Multimedia Systems (Heidelberg, GER) **[44468]**

Multinational Employer (Farnham, GBR) Unable to locate

Multiple Buyer & Retailer (Crawley, GBR) Ceased

Numbers cited in bold after listings are entry numbers rather than page numbers.

Multiple Sclerosis (London, GBR) **[54961]**

Mundo Recambio y Taller (Spares and Workshop World) (Barcelona, SPA) **[50689]**

Munich Found (Munich, GER) **[44572]**

Municipal Engineer (London, GBR) **[54962]**

Municipalities and Corporation Cases (New Delhi, DH, IND) **[45627]**

Munster Express (Waterford, WA, IRL) **[46062]**

MUNT-FM (Wellington, NZL) *Unable to locate*

Muoto (Helsinki, FIN) *Unable to locate*

Muratho (Rivonia, SAF) **[50611]**

Murdoch-FM (Perth, WA, AUS) *Unable to locate*

Murr Television - Channel 48 (Beirut, LBN) **[47415]**

Murr Television - Channel 28 (Beirut, LBN) **[47416]**

Murr Television - Channel 68 (Beirut, LBN) **[47413]**

Murr Television - Channel 38 (Beirut, LBN) **[47414]**

Musculoskeletal Care (Bognor Regis, GBR) **[52400]**

Musel Leader (Grevenmacher, LUX) *Unable to locate*

Museo (Helsinki, FIN) **[43849]**

The Muses Journal (Argyll and Bute, GBR) **[52132]**

Museum International (Oxford, GBR) **[56110]**

Museum National (Fitzroy, VI, AUS) *Unable to locate*

Museumskunde (Dresden, GER) *Unable to locate*

Mushroom Journal (Stamford, GBR) *Unable to locate*

Music Academy Journal (Chennai, TN, IND) *Unable to locate*

Music Analysis (Oxford, GBR) **[56111]**

Music Education International **[54655]***

Music Journal (London, GBR) **[54963]**

Music & Letters (London, GBR) **[54964]**

Music Lover (Shanghai, CHN) **[43490]**

Music Network and Siam Arts Entertainment (Bangkok, THA) *Unable to locate*

Music Radio (Perm, RUS) *Unable to locate*

Music Review **[56670]***

Music Tech Magazine (Bath, GBR) **[52252]**

Musica (Varese, ITA) **[46277]**

Musica Jazz (Milan, ITA) *Unable to locate*

Musicae Scientiae (Hannover, GER) **[44434]**

Musical Life (Moscow, RUS) *Unable to locate*

Musical Opinion (London, GBR) **[54965]**

Musical Stages (London, GBR) **[54966]**

Musical Times (Hove, GBR) **[53611]**

Musical Traditions (Stroud, GBR) **[56647]**

Musicology Australia (Canberra, AC, AUS) *Unable to locate*

Musicus (Pretoria, SAF) **[50597]**

MUSIKEXPRESS (Munich, GER) **[44573]**

Musiktidningen/Musikomanen (Stockholm, SWE) *Unable to locate*

Musiq'a Satellite-FM (Kuala Lumpur, MYS) *Unable to locate*

The Muslim (Islamabad, PAK) *Unable to locate*

Muslim & Arab Perspectives (New Delhi, DH, IND) **[45628]**

The Muslim News (Harrow, GBR) **[53526]**

Muslim Review (Lucknow, UP, IND) *Unable to locate*

Muslim World Newspaper (Makkah, SAU) *Unable to locate*

Musmajas (Riga, LAT) **[47373]**

Mutagenesis (Sutton, GBR) **[56689]**

Muveszettorteneti Ertesito (Budapest, HUN) **[44853]**

Muy Interesante (Madrid, SPA) **[50785]**

Muzikalnaya Akademia (Moscow, RUS) *Unable to locate*

Muzyka diya Dushi (Saratov, RUS) *Unable to locate*

MW-AM - 1548 (Lenasia, SAF) **[50548]**

MWB (Huddersfield, GBR) **[53624]**

MWL Journal (Makkah, SAU) *Unable to locate*

MWP (London, GBR) **[54967]**

My - 853 (Kuala Lumpur, MYS) **[47655]**

My Beautiful Horses (Grayshott, GBR) *Ceased*

My Little Pony (Shrewsbury, GBR) **[56538]**

My Magazine of India (Chennai, TN, IND) *Unable to locate*

My Paper (Singapore, SGP) **[50224]**

My Perfect Wedding Planner (Sydney, NW, AUS) **[42549]**

My Weekly (Dundee, GBR) **[53216]**

Myanmar Radio and Television (Yangon, MYA) *Unable to locate*

Myanmar Radio and Television (Yangon, MYA) *Unable to locate*

Myanmar Radio and Television (Yangon, MYA) *Unable to locate*

Myanmar Radio and Television (Yangon, MYA) *Unable to locate*

Myanmar Radio and Television (Yangon, MYA) *Unable to locate*

Myanmar Radio and Television (Yangon, MYA) *Unable to locate*

Myanmar Radio and Television (Yangon, MYA) *Unable to locate*

Myanmar Radio and Television (Yangon, MYA) *Unable to locate*

Mycological Research (Richmond, GBR) *Unable to locate*

Mycologist (Richmond, GBR) *Unable to locate*

Mycology; Experimental **[47994]***

Mycopathologia (Dordrecht, NLD) **[48516]**

Mycorrhiza (Dijon, FRA) **[43945]**

Mycorrhiza News (New Delhi, DH, IND) *Unable to locate*

Mycoscience (Chiba, JPN) **[46320]**

Mycoses (Munich, GER) **[44574]**

Myeloproliferative Disorders in practice (London, GBR) **[54968]**

Myer Emporium (Sydney, NW, AUS) **[42550]**

Mynd **[52171]***

Mynde nyt (Gistrup, DEN) *Unable to locate*

Mysore Economic Review (Mysore, KA, IND) *Unable to locate*

Mysore Orientalist (Mysore, KA, IND) *Unable to locate*

N

N. Radio (Orenburg, RUS) *Unable to locate*

NA'AMAT Magazine (Tel Aviv, ISR) *Ceased*

Nachrichtenblatt des Briefmarkenhandels (Cologne, GER) *Unable to locate*

Nadedgda (Moscow, RUS) *Unable to locate*

NAFED Marketing Review (New Delhi, DH, IND) *Unable to locate*

Naftiliaki (Athens, GRC) **[44752]**

NAGA (Penang, MYS) **[47690]**

Nagaland Education Bulletin (Kohima, NG, IND) *Unable to locate*

Nagaland Times (Dimapur, NG, IND) *Unable to locate*

Nagarjun (Calcutta, WB, IND) *Unable to locate*

Nagarlok (New Delhi, DH, IND) *Unable to locate*

Nagasaki Hoso - 1431 KHz (Fukue, JPN) **[46331]**

NAGO-Radio (Norilsk, RUS) *Unable to locate*

Nagoya Mathematical Journal (Nagoya, JPN) **[46556]**

Naharaim (Berlin, GER) **[44223]**

Naidunia (Indore, MP, IND) **[45188]**

Nakayoshi (Tokyo, JPN) **[46974]**

Namaskaar (Mumbai, MH, IND) *Unable to locate*

Nambour Weekly (Sydney, NW, AUS) **[42551]**

Names (London, GBR) **[54969]**

The Namibia Economist (Windhoek, NAM) **[47823]**

The Namibian Newspaper (Windhoek, NAM) **[47824]**

Nanak Prakash Patrika (Patiala, PJ, IND) *Unable to locate*

Nanchang People's Broadcasting Station (Nanchang, JX, CHN) *Unable to locate*

Nanchang People's Broadcasting Station (Nanchang, JX, CHN) *Unable to locate*

Nanchang People's Broadcasting Station (Nanchang, JX, CHN) *Unable to locate*

Nanchong People's Broadcasting Station (Nanchong, SI, CHN) *Unable to locate*

Nangai (Jaffna, SRI) *Unable to locate*

Nangong People's Broadcasting Station (Nangong, HB, CHN) *Unable to locate*

Nanjing People's Broadcasting Station (Nanjing, JS, CHN) *Unable to locate*

Nanjing People's Broadcasting Station (Nanjing, JS, CHN) *Unable to locate*

Nanjing People's Broadcasting Station (Nanjing, JS, CHN) *Unable to locate*

Nanjing People's Broadcasting Station (Nanjing, JS, CHN) *Unable to locate*

Nanjing People's Broadcasting Station 1 (Nanjing, JS, CHN) *Unable to locate*

Nanjing People's Broadcasting Station 3 (Nanjing, JS, CHN) *Unable to locate*

Nankai Journal (Tianjin, CHN) *Unable to locate*

Nanning People's Broadcasting Station (Nanning, GZ, CHN) *Unable to locate*

Nanning People's Broadcasting Station (Nanning, GZ, CHN) *Unable to locate*

Nanning People's Broadcasting Station (Nanning, GZ, CHN) *Unable to locate*

Nano Science and Nano Technology (Kolkata, WB, IND) **[45299]**

Nanomedicine (London, GBR) **[54970]**

Nanopages (Budapest, HUN) **[44854]**

Nanotechnology (Bristol, GBR) **[52708]**

Nanotoxicology (Edinburgh, GBR) **[53301]**

Nantong People's Broadcasting Station (Nantong, JS, CHN) *Unable to locate*

Nantong People's Broadcasting Station (Nantong, JS, CHN) *Unable to locate*

Nantong People's Broadcasting Station (Nantong, JS, CHN) *Unable to locate*

Nanyang People's Broadcasting Station (Nanyang, HN, CHN) *Unable to locate*

Nanyang People's Broadcasting Station (Nanyang, HN, CHN) *Unable to locate*

Nanyang People's Broadcasting Station (Nanyang, HN, CHN) *Unable to locate*

Nanzan Review of American Studies (Nagoya, JPN) **[46557]**

Napier Courier (Napier, NZL) *Unable to locate*

Napoleon (London, GBR) *Unable to locate*

Naringsmiddelindustrien (Oslo, NOR) *Unable to locate*

Narodnoye Radio (Moscow, RUS) *Unable to locate*

Narrative Inquiry (Amsterdam, NLD) **[48169]**

Nashe Radio - Dagomys (Moscow, RUS) *Unable to locate*

Nashe Radio (Hit Radio) (Tyumen, RUS) *Unable to locate*

Nashe Radio - Ishim - 107.8 MHz (Ishim, RUS) **[49857]**

Nashe Radio - Ivanovo (Ivanovo, RUS) *Unable to locate*

Nashe Radio - Izhevsk (Izhevsk, RUS) *Unable to locate*

Nashe Radio - Khanty-Mansiysk - 105.3 MHz (Khanty-Mansiysk, RUS) **[49861]**

Nashe Radio - Kogalym (Moscow, RUS) *Unable to locate*

Nashe Radio - Langepas (Moscow, RUS) *Unable to locate*

Nashe Radio - Megion - 101.6 MHz (Megion, RUS) **[49866]**

Nashe Radio- Moskva (Moscow, RUS) *Unable to locate*

Nashe Radio - Nadym (Moscow, RUS) *Unable to locate*

Nashe Radio - Nizhnevartovsk (Moscow, RUS) *Unable to locate*

Nashe Radio - Novyy Urengoy (Moscow, RUS) *Unable to locate*

Nashe Radio - Noyabrsk - 105.3 MHz (Noyabrsk, RUS) **[50016]**

Nashe Radio - Nyagan (Moscow, RUS) *Unable to locate*

Nashe Radio - Orenburg - 105.8 MHz (Orenburg, RUS) **[50017]**

Nashe Radio - Pokachi - 102.3 MHz (Pokachi, RUS) **[50019]**

Nashe Radio (Radio Pioner) - Krasnodar (Krasnodar, RUS) *Unable to locate*

Nashe Radio (Radio Rock FM) - Belgorod (Belgorod, RUS) *Unable to locate*

Nashe Radio - Salekhard (Moscow, RUS) *Unable to locate*

Nashe Radio - Saratov (Moscow, RUS) *Unable to locate*

Numbers cited in bold after listings are entry numbers rather than page numbers.

Nashe Radio - Tobolsk - 107.9 MHz (Tobolsk, RUS) **[50036]**

Nashe Radio - Tver (Tver, RUS) *Unable to locate*

Nashe Radio - Yekaterinburg (Yekaterinburg, RUS) *Unable to locate*

The Nassau Guardian (Nassau, BHS) **[42784]**

NASU Briefs (Ibadan, OY, NGA) *Unable to locate*

Nat & Dag Danmark (Copenhagen, DEN) *Unable to locate*

Natalia (Moscow, RUS) **[49947]**

The Nation (Bekkestua, NOR) *Unable to locate*

The Nation (Bangkok, THA) **[51428]**

Nation Radio-FM - 106.8 (Cardiff, GBR) **[52942]**

Nation Radio-FM - 107.3 (Swansea, GBR) **[56708]**

Nation and the World (New Delhi, DH, IND) *Unable to locate*

National Academy of Indian Medicine Annals (Varanasi, UP, IND) *Unable to locate*

National Academy of Medical Sciences Annals (New Delhi, DH, IND) *Unable to locate*

National Academy of Sciences, India Science Letters (Allahabad, UP, IND) *Unable to locate*

National Aeronautical Laboratory Current Scientific and Technical Reports (Bangalore, KA, IND) *Unable to locate*

National Aeronautical Laboratory Recent Book Additions (Bangalore, KA, IND) *Unable to locate*

National-AM - 639 (Alexandra, NZL) **[48779]**

National-AM - 567 (Blenheim, NZL) **[48860]**

National-AM - 567 (Kapiti, NZL) **[48930]**

National-AM - 918 (New Plymouth, NZL) **[48951]**

National-AM - 1134 (Queenstown, NZL) **[48973]**

National-AM - 918 (Timaru, NZL) **[48990]**

National-AM - 567 (Wellington, NZL) **[49042]**

National-AM - 837 (Whangarei, NZL) **[49051]**

The National Baptist (Hawthorn, VI, AUS) *Unable to locate*

National Botanical Society Journal (Calcutta, WB, IND) *Unable to locate*

National Broadcasting Network (NBN) - 89.4 MHz (Aabey, LBN) **[47382]**

National Building (New Delhi, DH, IND) *Unable to locate*

National Buildings Construction Corporation Bulletin (New Delhi, DH, IND) *Unable to locate*

National Buildings Organisation Journal (New Delhi, DH, IND) *Unable to locate*

National Cat (North Parramatta, NW, AUS) *Unable to locate*

National Debate (New Delhi, DH, IND) *Unable to locate*

National Diary (Calcutta, WB, IND) *Unable to locate*

National Dog (North Parramatta, NW, AUS) *Unable to locate*

National Education Radio Kaohsiung (Kaohsiung, TWN) *Unable to locate*

National Education Society of Sri Lanka (Colombo, SRI) *Unable to locate*

National Geographer (Delhi, DH, IND) *Unable to locate*

National Geographic Japanese Edition (Tokyo, JPN) **[46975]**

National Geographic Kids (Budapest, HUN) **[44855]**

National Geographic Special (Budapest, HUN) **[44856]**

National Geographical Journal of India (Varanasi, UP, IND) *Unable to locate*

National Guard (New Delhi, DH, IND) *Unable to locate*

National Herald (Lucknow, UP, IND) *Unable to locate*

National Identities (Abingdon, GBR) **[51988]**

National Indigenous Times (Garran, AC, AUS) **[41877]**

National Institute Economic Review (London, GBR) *Unable to locate*

National Institute of Labour Management Journal (Mumbai, MH, IND) *Unable to locate*

National Integrated Medical Association Journal (Mysore, KA, IND) *Unable to locate*

National Junior Magazine (Bangkok, THA) *Unable to locate*

National Library of Australia Gateways (Parkes, AC, AUS) **[42229]**

National Liquor News (Pyrmont, NW, AUS) **[42284]**

The National Medical Journal of India (New Delhi, DH, IND) **[45629]**

National Radio of Cambodia - Battambang (Phnom Penh, CMB) *Unable to locate*

National Radio of Cambodia - Phnom Penh (Phnom Penh, CMB) *Ceased*

National Radio of Cambodia - Phnom Penh (Phnom Penh, CMB) *Ceased*

National Radio of Cambodia - Phnom Penh (Phnom Penh, CMB) *Unable to locate*

National Radio of Cambodia - Phnom Penh (Phnom Penh, CMB) *Unable to locate*

National Radio of Cambodia - Sihanoukville (Phnom Penh, CMB) *Ceased*

National Radio of Cambodia - Steung Treng (Phnom Penh, CMB) *Ceased*

National Renewal (Quezon City, PHL) *Unable to locate*

National Resilience (Jakarta, IDN) *Unable to locate*

National Safety (Glen Waverley, VI, AUS) **[41896]**

National Security Review (Quezon City, PHL) *Unable to locate*

National Television and Radio Broadcasting Company - Akstafa (Baku, AJN) *Ceased*

National Television and Radio Broadcasting Company - Akstafa (Baku, AJN) *Ceased*

National Television and Radio Broadcasting Company - Astara (Baku, AJN) *Ceased*

National Television and Radio Broadcasting Company - Astara (Baku, AJN) *Ceased*

National Television and Radio Broadcasting Company - Baki (Baki, AJN) *Ceased*

National Television and Radio Broadcasting Company - Baki (Baki, AJN) *Ceased*

National Television and Radio Broadcasting Company - Baki (Baku, AJN) *Ceased*

National Television and Radio Broadcasting Company - Baki (Baku, AJN) *Ceased*

National Television and Radio Broadcasting Company - Baki (Baku, AJN) *Ceased*

National Television and Radio Broadcasting Company - Baki (Baku, AJN) *Ceased*

National Television and Radio Broadcasting Company - Danaci (Baku, AJN) *Ceased*

National Television and Radio Broadcasting Company - Danaci (Baku, AJN) *Ceased*

National Television and Radio Broadcasting Company - Duzdag (Baku, AJN) *Ceased*

National Television and Radio Broadcasting Company - Duzdag (Baku, AJN) *Ceased*

National Television and Radio Broadcasting Company - Ganca (Baki, AJN) *Unable to locate*

National Television and Radio Broadcasting Company - Ganca (Baku, AJN) *Ceased*

National Television and Radio Broadcasting Company - Ganca (Baku, AJN) *Ceased*

National Television and Radio Broadcasting Company - Geokcay (Baku, AJN) *Ceased*

National Television and Radio Broadcasting Company - Geokcay (Baku, AJN) *Ceased*

National Television and Radio Broadcasting Company - Jebrayl (Baku, AJN) *Ceased*

National Television and Radio Broadcasting Company - Jebrayl (Baku, AJN) *Ceased*

National Television and Radio Broadcasting Company - Kuba (Baku, AJN) *Ceased*

National Television and Radio Broadcasting Company - Kuba (Baku, AJN) *Ceased*

National Television and Radio Broadcasting Company - Lenkoran (Baku, AJN) *Ceased*

National Television and Radio Broadcasting Company - Lenkoran (Baku, AJN) *Ceased*

National Television and Radio Broadcasting Company - Lerik (Baku, AJN) *Ceased*

National Television and Radio Broadcasting Company - Lerik (Baku, AJN) *Ceased*

National Television and Radio Broadcasting Company - Ordubad (Baku, AJN) *Ceased*

National Television and Radio Broadcasting Company - Ordubad (Baku, AJN) *Ceased*

National Television and Radio Broadcasting Company - Pirsaqat (Baki, AJN) *Ceased*

National Television and Radio Broadcasting Company - Pirsaqat (Baki, AJN) *Ceased*

National Television and Radio Broadcasting Company - Pirsaqat (Baki, AJN) *Ceased*

National Television and Radio Broadcasting Company - Sarur (Baku, AJN) *Ceased*

National Television and Radio Broadcasting Company - Sarur (Baku, AJN) *Ceased*

National Television and Radio Broadcasting Company - Susa (Baku, AJN) *Ceased*

National Television and Radio Broadcasting Company - Susa (Baku, AJN) *Ceased*

National Trust Magazine (London, GBR) *Unable to locate*

Nationalism & Ethnic Politics (Abingdon, GBR) **[51989]**

Nationalities Papers (Abingdon, GBR) **[51990]**

Nationwide Bowler (Glasgow, GBR) **[53432]**

Nato's Nations and Partners for Peace (Bonn, GER) **[44267]**

Natur & Heilen (Munich, GER) **[44575]**

Natur und Land (Salzburg, AUT) **[42741]**

Natur & Miljoe (Oslo, NOR) *Unable to locate*

Natural Computing (Dordrecht, NLD) **[48517]**

Natural Hazards and Earth System Sciences (NHESS) (Katlenburg-Lindau, GER) **[44501]**

Natural Health (Colchester, GBR) **[53042]**

Natural Health & Beauty (Chatswood, NW, AUS) **[41741]**

Natural Health & Well-Being (Colchester, GBR) **[53043]**

Natural Product Reports (Cambridge, GBR) **[52873]**

Natural Product Sciences (Seoul, KOR) **[47284]**

Natural Products (Lisbon, PRT) **[49804]**

Natural Resources Forum (Oxford, GBR) **[56112]**

Natural Source (Pyrmont, NW, AUS) **[42285]**

The Naturalist (Bradford, GBR) **[52529]**

Nature (Basingstoke, GBR) **[52226]**

Nature Australia (Sydney, NW, AUS) *Unable to locate*

Nature Cell Biology (London, GBR) **[54971]**

Nature Clinical Practice Cardiovascular Medicine **[54976]***

Nature Clinical Practice Gastroenterology & Hepatology **[54979]***

Nature Clinical Practice Oncology **[54977]***

Nature Clinical Practice Urology **[54985]***

Nature, Culture and Literature (Amsterdam, NLD) **[48170]**

Nature & Health (Surry Hills, NW, AUS) **[42436]**

Nature and Man (Ankara, TUR) *Unable to locate*

Nature Materials (London, GBR) **[54972]**

Nature Methods (London, GBR) **[54973]**

Nature Physics (London, GBR) **[54974]**

Nature Reviews Cancer (London, GBR) **[54975]**

Nature Reviews Cardiology (London, GBR) **[54976]**

Nature Reviews Clinical Oncology (London, GBR) **[54977]**

Nature Reviews Drug Discovery (London, GBR) **[54978]**

Nature Reviews Gastroenterology & Hepatology (London, GBR) **[54979]**

Nature Reviews Genetics (London, GBR) **[54980]**

Nature Reviews Immunology (London, GBR) **[54981]**

Nature Reviews Microbiology (London, GBR) **[54982]**

Nature Reviews Molecular Cell Biology (London, GBR) **[54983]**

Nature Reviews Neuroscience (London, GBR) **[54984]**

Numbers cited in bold after listings are entry numbers rather than page numbers.

Nature Reviews Urology (London, GBR) **[54985]**

Nature and Science (Sofia, BUL) *Unable to locate*

Nature Watch (Singapore, SGP) **[50225]**

Natures Sciences Societes (Castanet-Tolosan, FRA) **[43927]**

natur+kosmos (Grasbrunn, GER) **[44403]**

Naturwissenschaften (Southampton, GBR) **[56575]**

Natya (New Delhi, DH, IND) *Unable to locate*

Nauka (Sofia, BUL) **[43106]**

Naunyn-Schmiedeberg's Archives of Pharmacology (Amsterdam, NLD) **[48171]**

The Nautical Magazine (Glasgow, GBR) **[53433]**

Nautique (Amsterdam, NLD) *Unable to locate*

Navaire (London, GBR) *Unable to locate*

The Naval Architect (London, GBR) **[54986]**

Naval Forces (Bonn, GER) **[44268]**

Nave Parva (Panaji, MH, IND) *Unable to locate*

The Navhind Times (Panaji, GD, IND) **[45681]**

Navin Weekly (London, GBR) *Unable to locate*

Navnirman (Vadodara, GJ, IND) **[45764]**

Navorsinge van die Nasionale Musium, Bloemfontein (Bloemfontein, SAF) **[50355]**

Navy News (Portsmouth, GBR) **[56291]**

Navy News - Sea Cadet Edition (London, GBR) *Ceased*

Nayaki (Chennai, TN, IND) *Unable to locate*

nb: (Edinburgh, GBR) *Unable to locate*

NB. Okuthor (Reykjavik, ICE) *Unable to locate*

NBN-TV - Channel 49 (Baalbek, LBN) **[47383]**

NBN-TV - Channel 63 (Beit Mery, LBN) **[47440]**

NBN-TV - Channel 63 (Nabatieh, LBN) **[47450]**

NBN-TV - Channel 44 (Zahle, LBN) **[47456]**

NBN-TV Abay - Channel 49 (Beirut, LBN) **[47417]**

NBN-TV Akroum - Channel 29 (Beirut, LBN) **[47418]**

NDN-TV B.A. Haidar - Channel 29 (Beirut, LBN) **[47419]**

NBN-TV Fatka - Channel 63 (Beirut, LBN) **[47420]**

NBN-TV Keliat - Channel 44 (Beirut, LBN) **[47421]**

NBN-TV Maad - Channel 44 (Beirut, LBN) **[47422]**

NBN-TV Soltanieh - Channel 29 (Beirut, LBN) **[47423]**

NBN-TV Turbo - Channel 49 (Beirut, LBN) **[47424]**

NBO Abstracts (New Delhi, DH, IND) *Unable to locate*

NBSnytt (Bergen, NOR) *Unable to locate*

NCDC Bulletin (New Delhi, DH, IND) *Unable to locate*

NCVO News **[55375]***

NCWI Bulletin (New Delhi, DH, IND) *Unable to locate*

NDR-FM - 90.3 (Hamburg, GER) **[44426]**

Near-FM - 90.3 (Dublin, DU, IRL) **[46002]**

Near Surface Geophysics (Houten, NLD) *Unable to locate*

NEC Journal of Advanced Technology (Tokyo, JPN) **[46976]**

NEC Research & Development **[46976]***

NEC Technical Journal (Tokyo, JPN) **[46977]**

NECR-FM - 101.9 (Ballater, GBR) **[52156]**

NECR-FM - 103.2 (Huntly, GBR) **[53637]**

NECR-FM - 102.1 (Inverurie, GBR) **[53652]**

NECR-FM - 102.6 (Inverurie, GBR) **[53651]**

NECR-FM - 106.4 (Inverurie, GBR) **[53650]**

NECR-FM - 97.1 (Turriff, GBR) **[56786]**

Nederlands Militair Geneeskundig Tijdschrift (NMGT) (The Hague, NLD) *Unable to locate*

Nederlands Tandartsenblad (Nieuwegein, NLD) **[48741]**

Nederlands Tydschrift Voor Dermatologie en Venereologie (Utrecht, NLD) *Unable to locate*

Neerlandica Extra Muros (Woubrugge, NLD) *Unable to locate*

Neetee (Calcutta, WB, IND) *Unable to locate*

Negocios Internacionales (Lima, PER) **[49424]**

Nei Menggu People's Broadcasting Station (Hohhot, NM, CHN) *Unable to locate*

Nei Menggu People's Broadcasting Station (Hohhot, NM, CHN) *Unable to locate*

Nei Menggu People's Broadcasting Station (Hohhot, NM, CHN) *Unable to locate*

Nei Menggu People's Broadcasting Station (Hohhot, NM, CHN) *Unable to locate*

Nei Menggu People's Broadcasting Station (Hohhot, NM, CHN) *Unable to locate*

Nei Menggu People's Broadcasting Station (Hohhot, NM, CHN) *Unable to locate*

Nei Menggu People's Broadcasting Station (Hohhot, NM, CHN) *Unable to locate*

Nei Menggu People's Broadcasting Station (Hohhot, NM, CHN) *Unable to locate*

Nei Menggu People's Broadcasting Station (Hohhot, NM, CHN) *Unable to locate*

Nei Menggu People's Broadcasting Station (Hohhot, NM, CHN) *Unable to locate*

Nei Menggu People's Broadcasting Station (Hohhot, NM, CHN) *Unable to locate*

Nei Menggu People's Broadcasting Station (Hohhot, NM, CHN) *Unable to locate*

Nei Menggu People's Broadcasting Station (Hohhot, NM, CHN) *Unable to locate*

Nei Menggu People's Broadcasting Station (Hohhot, NM, CHN) *Unable to locate*

Nei Menggu People's Broadcasting Station (Hohhot, NM, CHN) *Unable to locate*

Nei Menggu People's Broadcasting Station (Hohhot, NM, CHN) *Unable to locate*

Nei Menggu People's Broadcasting Station (Hohhot, NM, CHN) *Unable to locate*

Nei Menggu People's Broadcasting Station (Hohhot, NM, CHN) *Unable to locate*

Nei Menggu People's Broadcasting Station (Hohhot, NM, CHN) *Unable to locate*

Neighborhood Retailer & Forecourt Technology (Holywood, GBR) *Unable to locate*

Neijiang People's Broadcasting Station (Neijiang, SI, CHN) *Unable to locate*

Neijiang People's Broadcasting Station (Neijiang, SI, CHN) *Unable to locate*

Neijiang People's Broadcasting Station (Neijiang, SI, CHN) *Unable to locate*

Neltropika (Nelspruit, SAF) *Ceased*

Nematology (Leiden, NLD) **[48713]**

Nenagh Guardian (Nenagh, TP, IRL) **[46047]**

NE1-FM - 102.5 (Newcastle upon Tyne, GBR) **[55685]**

Neotestamentica (Scottsville, SAF) **[50629]**

Neotropical Entomology (Vacaria, RN, BRZ) **[43053]**

Nepal Agriculture Research Journal (Kathmandu, NPL) **[47842]**

The Nepal Chronicle (Kathmandu, NPL) *Unable to locate*

Nepal Law Review (Kathmandu, NPL) *Unable to locate*

Nepal Press Institute-FM - 105.4 (Kathmandu, NPL) **[47851]**

Nepal Television - Butwal - Channel 7 (Butwal, NPL) **[47828]**

Nepal Television - Chamere Danda - Channel 5 (Chamere Danda, NPL) **[47829]**

Nepal Television - Daunne - Channel 12 (Daunne, NPL) **[47830]**

Nepal Television - Hetaunda - Channel 4 (Hetaunda, NPL) **[47833]**

Nepal Television - Ilam - Channel 12 (Ilam, NPL) **[47834]**

Nepal Television - Jaleswor - Channel 11 (Jaleswor, NPL) **[47835]**

Nepal Television - Phulchoki - Channel 5 (Phulchoki, NPL) **[47858]**

Nepal Television - Sarangkot - Channel 7 (Sarangkot, NPL) **[47862]**

Nepal Television - Tansen (Palpa) - Channel 5 (Kathmandu, NPL) **[47852]**

Nepali Times (Kathmandu, NPL) **[47843]**

Nephrology (Richmond, VI, AUS) **[42304]**

Nephrology Dialysis Transplantation (Ghent, BEL) **[42887]**

Nephrology Forum (Cairo, EGY) *Unable to locate*

Nephron Physiology (London, GBR) **[54987]**

Nepszabadsag Magazine (Budapest, HUN) *Unable to locate*

Neru Pauer FM (Murmansk, RUS) *Unable to locate*

Nervenheilkunde (Stuttgart, GER) **[44671]**

NESG Economic Indicators **[49109]***

Net: El Medio de las Telecomunicaciones (Mexico City, DF, MEX) *Unable to locate*

net TV (Alpignano, ITA) *Unable to locate*

NET 25 - Channel 25 (Quezon City, PHL) **[49625]**

Netball Magazine (Hitchin, GBR) **[53581]**

Netexpress (Karachi, PAK) *Unable to locate*

Neth-FM - 105.9 (Colombo, SRI) **[50876]**

Netherlands Quarterly of Human Rights (Utrecht, NLD) **[48764]**

Nethra (Kandy, SRI) **[50908]**

NetMag (Lahore, PAK) *Unable to locate*

Netnomics (Dordrecht, NLD) **[48518]**

Network (Abingdon, GBR) **[51991]**

Network Computing (Poing, GER) **[44637]**

Network: Magazine for Activists (Manchester, GBR) *Unable to locate*

Network Middle East (Dubai, UAE) **[51650]**

Network 21 (London, GBR) **[54988]**

Network Security (Oxford, GBR) **[56113]**

Networking International (Swindon, GBR) *Unable to locate*

Networking Nottinghamshire (Nottingham, GBR) *Unable to locate*

Netz (Dubendorf, SWI) *Unable to locate*

Neue Szene Augsburg (Augsburg, GER) *Unable to locate*

Neue Wege (Zurich, SWI) *Unable to locate*

Neue Zeitschrift fur Systematische Theologie und Religionsphilosophie (Berlin, GER) **[44224]**

Neue Zuercher Zeitung (Zurich, SWI) *Unable to locate*

Neues Jahrbuch fur Geologie und Palaontologie (Stuttgart, GER) **[44672]**

Neues Jahrbuch fur Mineralogie Abhandlungen (Karlsruhe, GER) **[44494]**

Neural Computing & Applications (Sunderland, GBR) **[56654]**

Neural Networks (Amsterdam, NLD) **[48172]**

Neuro-Ophthalmology Japan (Kanagawa, JPN) *Unable to locate*

Neuroanatomy (Ankara, TUR) **[51498]**

Neurobiology of Disease (Amsterdam, NLD) **[48173]**

Neurochemical Research (Dordrecht, NLD) **[48519]**

Neurocomputing (Nijmegen, NLD) **[48745]**

Neuroembryology **[43370]***

Neuroembryology and Aging (Hong Kong, CHN) **[43370]**

Neuroendocrinology (Edinburgh, GBR) **[53302]**

Neuroforum (Berlin, GER) **[44225]**

Neurogenetics (Giessen, GER) **[44388]**

NeuroImage (Amsterdam, NLD) **[48174]**

Neurological Disorders; Current Drug Targets. CNS & **[48282]***

Neurology Asia (Kuala Lumpur, MYS) **[47629]**

Neurology India (New Delhi, DH, IND) **[45630]**

Neuromodulation (Oxford, GBR) **[56114]**

Neuron Glia Biology (Cambridge, GBR) **[52874]**

Neuropathology (Oxford, GBR) **[56115]**

Neuropathology and Applied Neurobiology (Oxford, GBR) **[56116]**

Master Index

Neuropharmacology (Bristol, GBR) **[52709]**

Neurophysiologie Clinique (Paris, FRA) *Unable to locate*

NeuroProtocols **[48156]***

Neuropsychiatric Disease and Treatment (Randwick, NW, AUS) **[42296]**

Neuropsychiatric Disease and Treatment (Macclesfield, GBR) **[55518]**

Neuropsychiatrie de l'Enfance et de l'Adolescence (Amsterdam, NLD) **[48175]**

Neuropsychologia (Amsterdam, NLD) **[48176]**

Neuropsychological Rehabilitation (Cambridge, GBR) **[52875]**

Neuroradiology (Heidelberg, GER) **[44469]**

Neuroradiology (Milan, ITA) *Unable to locate*

Neuroscience Letters (Amsterdam, NLD) **[48177]**

Neuroscience Research (Amsterdam, NLD) **[48178]**

Neurotoxicology and Teratology (Amsterdam, NLD) **[48179]**

New Age (New Delhi, DH, IND) *Unable to locate*

New Agriculturist (Allahabad, UP, IND) *Unable to locate*

New Arab (New Delhi, DH, IND) *Unable to locate*

New Astronomy (Amsterdam, NLD) **[48180]**

New Astronomy Reviews (Amsterdam, NLD) **[48181]**

New Blackfriars (Edinburgh, GBR) **[53303]**

New Books on Family Planning (New Delhi, DH, IND) *Unable to locate*

New Botanist (New Delhi, DH, IND) *Unable to locate*

New Builder (London, GBR) *Ceased*

New Business Age (Kathmandu, NPL) **[47844]**

New Car Buyer (North Ryde, NW, AUS) **[42188]**

New Childhood (Northampton, GBR) *Unable to locate*

The New Chronicle **[43739]***

New Cicada (Fukushima, JPN) **[46355]**

New Cinemas (London, GBR) **[54989]**

New City (Manila, PHL) *Unable to locate*

New Community **[52620]***

New Consumer (London, GBR) **[54990]**

New Contructor (Ceredigion, GBR) *Ceased*

New Cyprus (Mersin, TUR) *Unable to locate*

New Delhi (Calcutta, WB, IND) *Unable to locate*

New Diamond and Frontier Carbon Technology (Tokyo, JPN) *Ceased*

New Direction (Worcester, GBR) *Unable to locate*

New Disease Reports (Reading, GBR) **[56328]**

New Egyptian Journal of Microbiology (Cairo, EGY) **[43763]**

New Entomologist (Nagano, JPN) **[46537]**

New Europe (Brussels, BEL) **[42868]**

New Farmer (Harare, ZWE) **[57117]**

New-FM - 105.3 (Sandgate, NW, AUS) **[42351]**

New Frontiers in Education (New Delhi, DH, IND) *Unable to locate*

New Genetics & Society (Abingdon, GBR) **[51992]**

New Glimpses in Plant Research (New Delhi, DH, IND) *Unable to locate*

New Homes Magazine (Gomshall, GBR) *Unable to locate*

New Humanist (London, GBR) **[54991]**

New Humanity (Rocca di Papa, ITA) **[46219]**

The New Humanity Journal (London, GBR) *Unable to locate*

The New Indian Express (Bangalore, KA, IND) **[44978]**

The New Indian Express (Bhubaneswar, OR, IND) **[45012]**

The New Indian Express (Chennai, TN, IND) **[45053]**

The New Indian Express (Hyderabad, AP, IND) **[45177]**

The New Indian Express (Kochi, KE, IND) **[45252]**

New Insight **[52615]***

New Internationalist (Oxford, GBR) **[56117]**

New Journal of Chemistry (Cambridge, GBR) **[52876]**

New Journal of Physics (NJP) (Bristol, GBR) **[52710]**

New Knowledges Adult Education (Novye Znania) (Moscow, RUS) *Unable to locate*

New Law Journal (London, GBR) **[54992]**

New Leader (Bangalore, KA, IND) *Unable to locate*

New Leaves (Swansea, GBR) **[56704]**

New Lebanon Radio - East Beirut (East Beirut, LBN) *Unable to locate*

New Left Review (London, GBR) **[54993]**

New Library World (Bradford, GBR) **[52530]**

New Media Age (London, GBR) **[54994]**

New Media Creative (London, GBR) *Unable to locate*

New Media & Society (London, GBR) **[54995]**

The New Nation (Georgetown, GUY) *Unable to locate*

New Nation (London, GBR) *Unable to locate*

New Notes (London, GBR) *Unable to locate*

The New Observer (Tokyo, JPN) *Unable to locate*

The New Paper on Sunday (Singapore, SGP) **[50226]**

New Perspectives Quarterly (Oxford, GBR) **[56118]**

New Plumbing & Heating Magazine (Hornchurch, GBR) *Unable to locate*

New Political Economy (Abingdon, GBR) **[51993]**

New Political Science (Abingdon, GBR) **[51994]**

New Product Magazine (Perth, GBR) *Unable to locate*

New Quest (Pune, MH, IND) *Unable to locate*

The New Rambler (London, GBR) **[54996]**

New Renaissance (Mainz, GER) *Unable to locate*

New Renaissance (London, GBR) **[54997]**

New Review of Academic Librarianship (Abingdon, GBR) **[51995]**

New Review of Children's Literature and Librarianship (Abingdon, GBR) **[51996]**

New Review of Film & Television Studies (Abingdon, GBR) **[51997]**

New Review of Information Networking (Abingdon, GBR) **[51998]**

New Sabah Times (Sabah, MYS) **[47709]**

New Scientist (London, GBR) **[54998]**

New Scientist (Sutton, GBR) **[56690]**

The New Shetlander (Lerwick, GBR) **[53841]**

New Shipbuilding in Japan (Tokyo, JPN) *Ceased*

New Start (Manchester, GBR) **[55573]**

New Statesman (London, GBR) **[54999]**

New Statesman & Society **[54999]***

New Steel Construction (Ascot, BR, GBR) *Ceased*

New Stitches (Faversham, GBR) **[53384]**

New Straits Times (Kuala Lumpur, MYS) *Unable to locate*

New Straits Times (Kuala Lumpur, MYS) **[47630]**

New Sunday Times (Kuala Lumpur, MYS) **[47631]**

New Technology, Work and Employment (Stirling, GBR) **[56625]**

New Tekniques (Chester, GBR) *Unable to locate*

New Testament Studies (Cambridge, GBR) **[52877]**

New Theatre Quarterly (Cambridge, GBR) **[52878]**

New Tones (New Delhi, DH, IND) *Unable to locate*

New Trader (Geneva, SWI) *Unable to locate*

New View (London, GBR) **[55000]**

New Wave (New Delhi, DH, IND) *Unable to locate*

New Woman (Mumbai, MH, IND) *Unable to locate*

New Woman (London, GBR) **[55001]**

New Work (London, GBR) *Unable to locate*

New World Health (London, GBR) *Unable to locate*

New World Water (London, GBR) *Unable to locate*

The New Writer (Cranbrook, GBR) **[53096]**

New Writing (Abingdon, GBR) **[51999]**

New Zealand AgriBusiness (Christchurch, NZL) **[48871]**

New Zealand AgriVet (Christchurch, NZL) **[48872]**

New Zealand Author (Auckland, NZL) **[48805]**

New Zealand Baptist (Auckland, NZL) **[48806]**

New Zealand Builder & Renovator (Christchurch, NZL) *Unable to locate*

New Zealand Camellia Bulletin (Wanganui, NZL) **[48995]**

New Zealand Classic Car (Auckland, NZL) **[48807]**

New Zealand College of Midwives (Christchurch, NZL) **[48873]**

The New Zealand Commercial Grower (Wellington, NZL) *Unable to locate*

New Zealand Company Vehicle (North Shore City, NZL) **[48957]**

New Zealand Dental Journal (Auckland, NZL) **[48808]**

New Zealand Doctor (Auckland, NZL) **[48809]**

New Zealand Economic Papers (Wellington, NZL) **[49018]**

New Zealand Education Gazette (Wellington, NZL) **[49019]**

New Zealand Fishing News (Auckland, NZL) **[48810]**

New Zealand Fishing World (Auckland, NZL) **[48811]**

New Zealand 4WD (North Shore City, NZL) **[48958]**

New Zealand Freemason (Wellington, NZL) **[49020]**

New Zealand Gardener (Auckland, NZL) **[48812]**

New Zealand Geographer (Auckland, NZL) **[48813]**

New Zealand Geographer (Oxford, GBR) **[56119]**

New Zealand Grapegrower (Auckland, NZL) **[48814]**

New Zealand Growing Today **[48818]***

New Zealand Horse and Pony (Auckland, NZL) **[48815]**

New Zealand Journal of Agricultural Research (Wellington, NZL) **[49021]**

New Zealand Journal of Archaeology **[48897]***

New Zealand Journal of Botany (Wellington, NZL) **[49022]**

New Zealand Journal of Crop and Horticultural Science (Wellington, NZL) **[49023]**

New Zealand Journal of Educational Studies (Wellington, NZL) **[49024]**

New Zealand Journal of Geography (Auckland, NZL) **[48816]**

New Zealand Journal of Geology and Geophysics (Wellington, NZL) **[49025]**

The New Zealand Journal of History (Auckland, NZL) **[48817]**

New Zealand Journal of Human Resources Management (Wellington, NZL) **[49026]**

New Zealand Journal of Industrial Relations (Dunedin, NZL) *Unable to locate*

New Zealand Journal of Marine and Freshwater Research (Wellington, NZL) **[49027]**

New Zealand Journal of Mathematics (Christchurch, NZL) **[48874]**

New Zealand Journal of Outdoor Education (Wellington, NZL) **[49028]**

New Zealand Journal of Psychology (Wellington, NZL) *Unable to locate*

New Zealand Journal of Zoology (Hamilton, NZL) **[48909]**

New Zealand Law Journal (Wellington, NZL) *Unable to locate*

New Zealand Lifestyle Block (Auckland, NZL) **[48818]**

New Zealand Listener (Auckland, NZL) **[48819]**

New Zealand Macguide (Auckland, NZL) *Ceased*

New Zealand Nursing Journal **[49013]***

New Zealand Performance Car (Auckland, NZL) **[48820]**

New Zealand Population Review (Wellington, NZL) **[49029]**

The New Zealand Railway Observer (Wellington, NZL) **[49030]**

New Zealand Rural Contractor and Large Scale Farmer (Christchurch, NZL) **[48875]**

New Zealand Science Monthly (Christchurch, NZL) *Ceased*

The New Zealand Shipping Gazette (Christchurch, NZL) **[48876]**

Numbers cited in bold after listings are entry numbers rather than page numbers.

The New Zealand Skeptic (Christchurch, NZL) *Unable to locate*

New Zealand Snowboarder (Gisborne, NZL) **[48898]**

New Zealand Sociology (Wellington, NZL) *Unable to locate*

New Zealand Studies in Applied Linguistics (Palmerston North, NZL) **[48964]**

New Zealand Trucking (Auckland, NZL) **[48821]**

New Zealand Veterinary Journal (Wellington, NZL) **[49031]**

New Zealand Woman's Weekly (Auckland, NZL) *Unable to locate*

Newham Recorder (Essex, GBR) **[53341]**

Newman (Singapore, SGP) **[50227]**

Newmarket Journal (Newmarket, GBR) **[55686]**

News from Bangladesh (Dhaka, BGD) **[42814]**

News on the Block (London, GBR) **[55002]**

The News Chronicle (Ludhiana, PJ, IND) *Unable to locate*

News d'Ill (Strasbourg, FRA) **[44113]**

News for Immediate Release (Lusaka, ZMB) *Unable to locate*

The News International (Karachi, PAK) **[49365]**

News of Liturgy (Cambridge, GBR) *Ceased*

News from Nisshin Steel (Tokyo, JPN) *Unable to locate*

News in Physiological Sciences (Oxford, GBR) *Unable to locate*

News from Pondy (Pondicherry, PN, IND) *Unable to locate*

News Post Leader (Whitley Bay, GBR) **[56919]**

News Radio 93.8 FM **[50301]***

News Review on Americas (New Delhi, DH, IND) *Ceased*

News Review on Europe & EurAsia (New Delhi, DH, IND) *Ceased*

News Review Messenger (Salisbury, SA, AUS) **[42344]**

News Special (Worthing, GBR) *Ceased*

News Star (Guwahati, AS, IND) *Unable to locate*

News from Swedish Theatre (Stockholm, SWE) *Ceased*

News Today (Chennai, TN, IND) **[45054]**

News & Views (Christchurch, NZL) *Unable to locate*

News and Views (Glasgow, GBR) **[53434]**

News and Views (London, GBR) **[55003]**

News for Women Annual Report (Bangkok, THA) *Unable to locate*

NewsAfrica (London, GBR) **[55004]**

Newscrap (Auckland, NZL) *Unable to locate*

Newsfront (Guwahati, AS, IND) *Unable to locate*

Newsidic (Eggenstein-Leopoldshafen, GER) *Ceased*

Newsletter (Riyadh, SAU) *Unable to locate*

NEWSLI (Milton Keynes, GBR) **[55640]**

The Newsline (Shillong, MG, IND) *Unable to locate*

Newsline (Karachi, PAK) *Unable to locate*

Newsline (Tarlac, PHL) *Unable to locate*

Newslink (Nairobi, KEN) *Unable to locate*

Newslink (Glasgow, GBR) *Unable to locate*

NewsMail (Sydney, NW, AUS) **[42552]**

Newsman (Chennai, TN, IND) *Unable to locate*

newspaper techniques (Darmstadt, GER) *Unable to locate*

NewsTalk 106-FM - 106 (Dublin, DU, IRL) **[46003]**

Newstalk ZB-AM - 873 (Auckland, NZL) **[48846]**

Newstalk ZB-AM Northland - 1026 (Whangarei, NZL) **[49053]**

Newstalk ZB-AM Northland - 1215 (Whangarei, NZL) **[49052]**

Newstalk ZB-AM Southland - 864 (Invercargill, NZL) **[48922]**

Newstalk ZB-AM Waikato - 1296 (Hamilton, NZL) **[48914]**

Newstalk ZB-FM - 89.4 (Auckland, NZL) **[48847]**

Newstalk ZB-FM Central Otago - 95.1 (Alexandra, NZL) **[48780]**

Newstalk ZB-FM Central Otago - 90.6 (Wanaka, NZL) **[48994]**

NewsToday.co.th (Phattaya, THA) *Unable to locate*

Newtonabbey Times (Glengormley, GBR) **[53469]**

Nexo Expresarial (La Paz, BOL) *Unable to locate*

Nexus (Saint Gallen, SWI) *Unable to locate*

NFU Countryside **[56636]***

NFU Countryside (Stoneleigh, GBR) **[56636]**

NFU Regional Journal Central (London, GBR) *Unable to locate*

Nga Korero o Te Wa (Auckland, NZL) *Unable to locate*

NGI Magazine (Amsterdam, NLD) *Unable to locate*

NGV Worldwide (Auckland, NZL) *Ceased*

Nhan Dan (Hanoi, VNM) **[57052]**

Nice Matin (Nice, FRA) *Unable to locate*

Nickel Odeon (Madrid, SPA) *Unable to locate*

Nicosia This Month (Nicosia, CYP) *Unable to locate*

Nicotine and Tobacco Research (Dundee, GBR) **[53217]**

Nidaa al Islam - Beirut (Beirut, LBN) *Unable to locate*

Nidaa al Islam - Beirut (Beirut, LBN) *Unable to locate*

NIF Weekly (New Delhi, DH, IND) *Unable to locate*

Nigeria Journal of Business Administration (Grahamstown, SAF) **[50505]**

Nigeria Journal of Pure and Applied Physics (Akure, ON, NGA) **[49060]**

Nigerian Agricultural Journal (Umuahia, NGA) **[49175]**

Nigerian Dental Journal (Idi-Araba, LG, NGA) **[49105]**

The Nigerian Engineer (Abuja, LG, NGA) **[49057]**

Nigerian Food Journal (Oshodi, LG, NGA) **[49160]**

Nigerian Hospital Practice (Ikeja, LG, NGA) **[49107]**

Nigerian Journal of Animal Production (Ibadan, OY, NGA) **[49093]**

Nigerian Journal of Chemical Research (Zaria, KD, NGA) **[49183]**

Nigerian Journal of Clinical and Counselling Psychology (Ibadan, OY, NGA) **[49094]**

Nigerian Journal of Clinical Practice (Nnewi, AN, NGA) **[49149]**

Nigerian Journal of Economic History (Ibadan, OY, NGA) **[49095]**

Nigerian Journal of Fisheries (Makurdi, BN, NGA) **[49146]**

Nigerian Journal of Genetics (Ibadan, OY, NGA) **[49096]**

Nigerian Journal of Guidance and Counselling (Ilorin, KW, NGA) **[49121]**

Nigerian Journal of Health and Biomedical Sciences (Lagos, LG, NGA) **[49141]**

Nigerian Journal of Horticultural Science (Ibadan, OY, NGA) **[49097]**

Nigerian Journal of Natural Products and Medicine (Ile-Ife, NGA) **[49115]**

Nigerian Journal of Ophthalmology (Ibadan, OY, NGA) **[49098]**

Nigerian Journal of Orthopaedics and Trauma (Sagamu, OG, NGA) **[49170]**

Nigerian Journal of Otorhinolaryngology (Enugu, AN, NGA) **[49082]**

Nigerian Journal of Paediatrics (Ibadan, OY, NGA) **[49099]**

Nigerian Journal of Parasitology (Grahamstown, SAF) **[50506]**

Nigerian Journal of Pharmaceutical Research (Jos, PL, NGA) **[49128]**

Nigerian Journal of Physics (Grahamstown, SAF) **[50507]**

Nigerian Journal of Physiological Sciences (Calabar, CR, NGA) **[49079]**

Nigerian Journal of Plastic Surgery (Ibadan, OY, NGA) **[49100]**

Nigerian Journal of Psychiatry (Shomolu, LG, NGA) **[49171]**

Nigerian Journal of Soil & Environmental Research (Zaria, KD, NGA) **[49184]**

Nigerian Journal of Soil Research **[49184]***

Nigerian Journal of Soil Science (Grahamstown, SAF) **[50508]**

Nigerian Journal of Surgical Research (Zaria, KD, NGA) **[49185]**

Nigerian Libraries (Yaba, LG, NGA) **[49180]**

Nigerian Medical Journal (Nnewi, AN, NGA) **[49150]**

Nigerian Medical Practitioner (Ikeja, LG, NGA) **[49108]**

Nigerian Music Review (Ile-Ife, NGA) **[49116]**

Nigerian Quarterly Journal of Hospital Medicine (Lagos, LG, NGA) **[49142]**

Nigerian Veterinary Journal (Zaria, KD, NGA) **[49186]**

Nigxia People's Broadcasting Station (Yinchuan, NH, CHN) *Unable to locate*

Nihonkai Mathematical Journal (Niigata, JPN) **[46573]**

Nijmegen-FM (Amsterdam, NLD) *Unable to locate*

Nika-TR (Gukovo, RUS) *Unable to locate*

Nika-TR (Gukovo, RUS) *Unable to locate*

Nikkei Architecture (Tokyo, JPN) **[46978]**

Nikkei Board Guide (Tokyo, JPN) **[46979]**

Nikkei BP Government Technology (Tokyo, JPN) **[46980]**

Nikkei Business (Tokyo, JPN) **[46981]**

Nikkei Business Associe (Tokyo, JPN) **[46982]**

Nikkei Communications (Tokyo, JPN) **[46983]**

Nikkei Computer (Tokyo, JPN) **[46984]**

Nikkei Construction (Tokyo, JPN) **[46985]**

Nikkei Design (Tokyo, JPN) **[46986]**

Nikkei Drug Information (Tokyo, JPN) **[46987]**

Nikkei Ecology (Tokyo, JPN) **[46988]**

Nikkei Electronics (Tokyo, JPN) **[46989]**

Nikkei Electronics Asia (Hong Kong, CHN) **[43371]**

Nikkei Electronics China (Tokyo, JPN) **[46990]**

Nikkei Entertainment! (Tokyo, JPN) **[46991]**

Nikkei Health (Tokyo, JPN) **[46992]**

Nikkei Healthcare (Tokyo, JPN) **[46993]**

Nikkei Home Builder (Tokyo, JPN) **[46994]**

Nikkei Information Strategy (Tokyo, JPN) **[46995]**

Nikkei Linux (Tokyo, JPN) **[46996]**

Nikkei Medical (Tokyo, JPN) **[46997]**

Nikkei Microdevices (Tokyo, JPN) **[46998]**

Nikkei Monozukuri (Tokyo, JPN) **[46999]**

Nikkei Net Interactive (Tokyo, JPN) **[47000]**

Nikkei Network (Tokyo, JPN) **[47001]**

Nikkei PC Beginners (Tokyo, JPN) **[47002]**

Nikkei PC21 (Tokyo, JPN) **[47003]**

Nikkei Personal Computing (Tokyo, JPN) **[47004]**

Nikkei Restaurants (Tokyo, JPN) **[47005]**

Nikkei Software (Tokyo, JPN) **[47006]**

Nikkei Solution Business (Tokyo, JPN) **[47007]**

Nikkei Systems (Tokyo, JPN) **[47008]**

Nikkei Venture (Tokyo, JPN) **[47009]**

The Nikkei Weekly (Tokyo, JPN) **[47010]**

Nikkei WinPC (Tokyo, JPN) **[47011]**

NIMHANS Journal (Bangalore, KA, IND) *Ceased*

911 & Porsche World (Surrey, GBR) **[56669]**

988-FM (Kuala Lumpur, MYS) *Unable to locate*

98.5-FM (Shepparton, VI, AUS) *Unable to locate*

987FM - 98.7 MHz (Singapore, SGP) **[50300]**

999-AM - 999 (Palmerston North, NZL) **[48969]**

973-FM - 97.3 (Coorparoo, QL, AUS) **[41815]**

96.5-FM (Geraldton, WA, AUS) *Unable to locate*

96.1-FM - 96.1 (North Ryde, NW, AUS) **[42203]**

938LIVE - 93.8 MHz (Singapore, SGP) **[50301]**

92.9-FM - 92.9 (Subiaco, WA, AUS) **[42401]**

Nineteenth-Century Contexts (Amsterdam, NLD) *Unable to locate*

Nineteenth-Century Music Review (Surrey, GBR) **[56670]**

Nineteenth Century Theatre and Film (Manchester, GBR) **[55574]**

98-FM (Geraldton, WA, AUS) *Unable to locate*

95b-FM - 95.0 (Auckland, NZL) **[48848]**

90-FM - 90 (Wellington, NZL) **[49043]**

99-FM - 99 (Alytus, LIT) **[47459]**

96-FM - 96.1 (East Perth, WA, AUS) **[41846]**

96-FM - 96.4 (Patrick's Place, CK, IRL) **[46053]**

Numbers cited in bold after listings are entry numbers rather than page numbers.

96five-FM - 96.5 (Milton, QL, AUS) [42110]

Ningbo People's Broadcasting Station (Ningbo, ZH, CHN) Unable to locate

Ningbo People's Broadcasting Station, ZH, CHN) Unable to locate

Ningbo People's Broadcasting Station, ZH, CHN) Unable to locate

Ningxia People's Broadcasting Station (Yinchuan, NH, CHN) Unable to locate

Ningxia People's Broadcasting Station 1 (Yinchuan, NH, CHN) Unable to locate

Ningxia People's Broadcasting Station 1 (Yinchuan, NH, CHN) Unable to locate

Nippon Shutei Kogyo Kaiho (Tokyo, JPN) Unable to locate

Nippon Steel News (Tokyo, JPN) [47012]

Nippon Tungsten Review (Fukuoka, JPN) Unable to locate

NIRA Review (Tokyo, JPN) Ceased

Nishi Nippon Hoso - 1449 KHz (Marugame, JPN) [46498]

Nishikigoi International (Warrington, GBR) [56850]

NITO-Refleks (Oslo, NOR) Unable to locate

Nitric Oxide (Amsterdam, NLD) [48182]

Nitrogen [55005]*

Nitrogen & Methanol (London, GBR) [55005]

Nivedini (Colombo, SRI) Unable to locate

Nivuton (Ramat Hasharon, ISR) Unable to locate

NJ (City East, QL, AUS) [41752]

NJAS (Wageningen, NLD) [48772]

NJIWA (Nairobi, KEN) [47193]

NJOY Radio-FM - 88.2 (Lannach, AUT) [42729]

NKO Magazine (Accra, GHA) [44729]

NKW Partner (Hannover, GER) Unable to locate

NMR in Biomedicine (London, GBR) [55006]

NNKY-NAKY (Helsinki, FIN) [43850]

NNO Magazine (Groningen, NLD) Unable to locate

No Kidding! (London, GBR) Ceased

Noddy (London, GBR) [55007]

Noise and Health (London, GBR) [55008]

Noise Notes (Brentwood, GBR) [52582]

Noise & Vibration Bulletin (Brentwood, GBR) [52583]

Noise & Vibration in Industry (Brentwood, GBR) [52584]

Noise & Vibration Worldwide (Brentwood, GBR) [52585]

Nok Lapja (Budapest, HUN) [44857]

Nok Lapja Egeszseg (Budapest, HUN) [44858]

Nok Lapja Eskuvo (Budapest, HUN) [44859]

Nok Lapja Evszakok (Budapest, HUN) [44860]

Nok Lapja Konyha (Budapest, HUN) [44861]

NOMINA (Bristol, GBR) [52711]

Non-Ferrous Report (Mumbai, MH, IND) Unable to locate

Non-State Actors and International Law (Leiden, NLD) Unable to locate

Nonferrous Metals (Changsha, HA, CHN) Unable to locate

Nongqai [50600]*

Nonlinearity (Bristol, GBR) [52712]

Nonproliferation Review (Abingdon, GBR) [52000]

Nonwovens Report International (Bradford, GBR) [52531]

Noord-Nederland-FM (Amsterdam, NLD) Unable to locate

Noord-Vrystaatse Gazette (Cape Town, SAF) [50394]

Noord-Zuid-Cahier (Antwerp, BEL) Unable to locate

Noordkaap (Cape Town, SAF) [50395]

Noosa 96.1-FM - 96.1 (Noosaville, QL, AUS) [42150]

Nord Vest Radio (Pskov, RUS) Unable to locate

Nord-Vest Radio (Pskov, RUS) Unable to locate

Nordiatrans (Masala, FIN) Unable to locate

Nordic unquote (London, GBR) [55009]

Nordic Cystic Fibrosis Magazine (Oslo, NOR) Unable to locate

Nordic Hydrology [50995]*

Nordic Irish Studies (Arhus, DEN) [43648]

Nordic Journal for Architectural Research (Trondheim, NOR) [49218]

Nordic Journal of Building Physics (Stockholm, SWE) [51027]

Nordic Journal of International Law (Leiden, NLD) [48714]

Nordic Journal of Music Therapy (Sogndal, NOR) [49211]

Nordic Journal of Psychiatry (Helsinki, FIN) [43851]

Nordic Sounds (Stockholm, SWE) Unable to locate

Nordicom Review (Goteborg, SWE) [50961]

NORDINFO Nytt (Helsinki, FIN) Unable to locate

Nordis Das Nordueropa Magazin (Essen, GER) Unable to locate

Nordisk Fysioterapi (Stockholm, SWE) [51028]

Nordisk Herpetologisk Forening (Herlufmagle, DEN) Unable to locate

Nordisk Jordbrugsforskning (Frederiksberg, DEN) Unable to locate

Nordisk Numismatisk Unions Medlemsblad (Copenhagen, DEN) Unable to locate

Nordisk Socialt Arbejde (Lund, SWE) Unable to locate

Norfolk and Suffolk Express Series (Edinburgh, GBR) Unable to locate

Norm (Calcutta, WB, IND) Unable to locate

NORM News (Stone, GBR) [56634]

Normalisatie Nieuws (Delft, NLD) Unable to locate

NorNewsNet (Skjervoy, NOR) Unable to locate

The Norseman (Oslo, NOR) [49205]

Norsk Astrologisk Foreninc (Oslo, NOR) Unable to locate

Norsk Geologisk Tidsskrift (Trondheim, NOR) [49219]

Norsk Medietidsskrift (Bergen, NOR) Unable to locate

Norsk Oekonomisk Tidsskrift (Oslo, NOR) Unable to locate

Norsk Pelsdyrblad (Oslo, NOR) Unable to locate

Norsk Veterinartidsskrift (Oslo, NOR) Unable to locate

North (London, GBR) [55010]

North American Journal of Economics and Finance (Amsterdam, NLD) [48183]

North American Review of Economics and Finance [48183]*

North Devon Gazette (Barnstaple, GBR) [52191]

North East Househunter (Newcastle upon Tyne, GBR) [55675]

North-East India Council for Social Science Research Journal (Shillong, MG, IND) Unable to locate

North East Life (Hexham, GBR) [53569]

North East Sun (New Delhi, DH, IND) Unable to locate

The North East Times (Guwahati, AS, IND) Unable to locate

North East Times (Newcastle upon Tyne, GBR) [55676]

North-Eastern Affairs (Shillong, MG, IND) Unable to locate

North Eastern Geographer (Guwahati, AS, IND) Unable to locate

North India Churchman (New Delhi, DH, IND) Unable to locate

North Korea News (Seoul, KOR) Unable to locate

North Norfolk Advertiser (Norwich, GBR) [55736]

North Norfolk News (Cromer, GBR) [53118]

North Queensland Register (Townsville, QL, AUS) [42638]

North Sea Rig Forecast (London, GBR) Unable to locate

North Shore Times (Chatswood, NW, AUS) [41742]

North & South (Auckland, NZL) [48822]

North Wales Chronicle (Bangor, GBR) [52173]

North Wales Pioneer (Colwyn Bay, GBR) [53058]

North West Country (Sydney, NW, AUS) [42553]

North-West Echo (Waterside, GBR) [56859]

North West Magazine (Gunnedah, NW, AUS) Unable to locate

The North West Star (Sydney, NW, AUS) [42554]

North Wind (Forest Row, GBR) [53397]

Northampton Chronicle & Echo (Northampton, GBR) [55713]

Northcote Leader (Northcote, VI, AUS) [42213]

The Northern Advocate (Whangarei, NZL) Unable to locate

Northern Daily Leader (Tamworth, NW, AUS) [42612]

Northern District Times (Epping, NW, AUS) [41856]

Northern Downs News (Sydney, NW, AUS) [42555]

Northern Earth (Hebden Bridge, GBR) [53553]

Northern History (London, GBR) [55011]

Northern India Patrika (Allahabad, UP, IND) Unable to locate

Northern Ireland Legal Quarterly (Belfast, GBR) Unable to locate

Northern Ireland Political Women and the Press (Belfast, GBR) Unable to locate

Northern Ireland Veterinary Today (Holywood, GBR) Unable to locate

The Northern Rivers Echo (Sydney, NW, AUS) [42556]

Northern Woman (Belfast, GBR) [52290]

Northland Age (Kaitaia, NZL) [48928]

Northland's MORE-FM (Whangarei, NZL) Unable to locate

Northside Chronicle (Alderley, QL, AUS) [41531]

Northsound One-FM - 96.9 (Aberdeen, GBR) [51682]

Northsound Two-AM - 1035 (Aberdeen, GBR) [51683]

Northumberland Gazette (Alnwick, GBR) [52101]

Northwest (London, GBR) [55012]

Northwest Gazette (Cape Town, SAF) [50396]

The Norway Post (Baerum, NOR) [49188]

Norwich Advertiser (Norwich, GBR) [55737]

Nostalgia (Kuala Lumpur, MYS) Unable to locate

Nostalgie Belgique-FM (Brussels, BEL) Unable to locate

Nostalgie-FM (Achrafieh, LBN) Unable to locate

Notes and Queries (Oxford, GBR) [56120]

Notes & Records of the Royal Society (London, GBR) [55013]

Noticias Agricocas (Caracas, VEN) Ceased

Noticias-FM - 97.3 (Isla de Margarita, VEN) [57024]

Notkott (Eskilstuna, SWE) Unable to locate

Notre Dame Journal (Cotabato City, PHL) Unable to locate

Nouvelle Revue Anthropologique (Paris, FRA) Unable to locate

Nova Economia (Belo Horizonte, MG, BRZ) [42950]

NOVA-FM - 96.9 (Broadway, NW, AUS) [41661]

NOVA-FM - 100 (Richmond, VI, AUS) [43308]

Nova-FM - 100.3 (Richmond, VI, AUS) [42307]

Nova Hedwigia (Stuttgart, GER) [44673]

Novator (Warsaw, POL) Unable to locate

Novaya Volna (Smolenskoye, RUS) Unable to locate

Novaya Volna (Ulan-Ude, RUS) Unable to locate

Novaya Zhizn (Magadan, RUS) Unable to locate

Novita [43892]*

Novos Estudos Cebrap (Vicosa, MI, BRZ) [43061]

Novosti Mongolii (Ulaanbaatar, MNG) Unable to locate

Novoye Radio (Krasnodar, RUS) Unable to locate

Novum Testamentum (Leiden, NLD) [48715]

Novynar (Kiev, URE) [51603]

Now (Calcutta, WB, IND) Unable to locate

NOW (New Delhi, DH, IND) Unable to locate

NRCD Research Journal of the Philippines (Taguig City, PHL) [49639]

nRevolution (Bournemouth, GBR) [52417]

NRJ Beirut-FM - 99.0 (Metn, LBN) [47448]

NRJ-FM - 104.2 (Vienna, AUT) [42776]

NRJ-FM - 99 (Metn, LBN) [47449]

NSW Agriculture Today (North Richmond, NW, AUS) [42164]

NSW Public Health Bulletin (North Sydney, NW, AUS) [42211]

NT Update (Newbury, GBR) Unable to locate

NTI Bulletin (Bangalore, KA, IND) [44979]

NTU (Singapore, SGP) [50228]

Numbers cited in bold after listings are entry numbers rather than page numbers.

nuacht (Dublin, DU, IRL) *Unable to locate*

Nuclear Data Sheets (Amsterdam, NLD) **[48184]**

Nuclear Energy (Bucharest, ROM) **[49840]**

Nuclear Engineering and Design (Stuttgart, GER) **[44674]**

Nuclear Europe Worldscan (Bern, SWI) *Ceased*

Nuclear Fusion (Vienna, AUT) **[42765]**

Nuclear India (Mumbai, MH, IND) **[45421]**

Nuclear Instruments and Methods in Physics Research Section B (Copenhagen, DEN) **[43680]**

Nuclear Medicine Review (Gdansk, POL) **[49658]**

Nuclear Physics A (Amsterdam, NLD) **[48185]**

Nuclear Physics B (Amsterdam, NLD) **[48186]**

Nuclear Physics B (Amsterdam, NLD) **[48187]**

Nuclear Receptor (London, GBR) *Ceased*

Nuclear Science Journal of Malaysia (Kajang, MYS) *Unable to locate*

Nuclear Science and Techniques (Shanghai, CHN) **[43491]**

Nucleic Acids Research (Oxford, GBR) **[56121]**

Nucleus (Calcutta, WB, IND) *Unable to locate*

Nucleus (Islamabad, PAK) *Unable to locate*

Nuestros derechos (Cochabamba, BOL) *Unable to locate*

Nueva Empresa (Madrid, SPA) *Unable to locate*

Nueva Onda Radio-FM - 88.1 (Ciudad Real, SPA) **[50712]**

Nueva Revista (Madrid, SPA) **[50786]**

Nueva Revista Rotaria (Tachira, VEN) **[57029]**

Nuklearmedizin (Stuttgart, GER) **[44675]**

Nukleonika (Warsaw, POL) **[49739]**

No.1 (Glasgow, GBR) **[53435]**

Number One FM - Alanya (Ankara, TUR) *Unable to locate*

Number One FM - Ankara (Ankara, TUR) *Unable to locate*

Number One FM - Antalya (Ankara, TUR) *Unable to locate*

Number One FM - Bodrum (Ankara, TUR) *Unable to locate*

Number One FM - Istanbul (Ankara, TUR) *Unable to locate*

Number One FM - Izmir (Istanbul, TUR) *Unable to locate*

Number One FM - Sanlyurfa (Ankara, TUR) *Unable to locate*

NUMEN (Arhus, DEN) **[43649]**

Numerical Algorithms (Dordrecht, NLD) **[48520]**

Numerische Mathematik (Pavia, ITA) **[46210]**

Numismatic Digest (Mumbai, MH, IND) *Unable to locate*

Numismatic Society of India Journal (Nasik, MH, IND) *Unable to locate*

Nuncius (Florence, ITA) **[46145]**

Nuorten Tasavalta (Helsinki, FIN) *Unable to locate*

Nuova Corrente (Genoa, ITA) **[46152]**

Nuovi Argomenti di Medicina - NAM (Rome, ITA) *Unable to locate*

Nur - The Light (Istanbul, TUR) *Unable to locate*

Nurse Education Today (Amsterdam, NLD) **[48188]**

Nurse Prescribing (London, GBR) **[55014]**

Nurse Researcher (Harrow, GBR) **[53527]**

Nursing Ethics (London, GBR) **[55015]**

Nursing and Health Sciences (Oxford, GBR) **[56122]**

Nursing Home News (Birmingham, GBR) **[52359]**

Nursing Journal (Colombo, SRI) *Unable to locate*

The Nursing Journal of India (New Delhi, DH, IND) **[45631]**

Nursing Management (Harrow, GBR) **[53528]**

Nursing New Zealand **[49013]***

Nursing Older People (Harrow, GBR) **[53529]**

Nursing Philosophy (Oxford, GBR) **[56123]**

Nursing in Practice (London, GBR) **[55016]**

Nursing and Residential Care (London, GBR) **[55017]**

Nursing Standard (Harrow, GBR) **[53530]**

Nursing Technology (Calcutta, WB, IND) *Unable to locate*

Nursing Times (Basingstoke, GBR) *Unable to locate*

Nursing Topics (Gdansk, POL) **[49659]**

NUS Economic Journal (Singapore, SGP) **[50229]**

Nutraceuticals International (London, GBR) **[55018]**

Nutritio et Dieta **[42744]***

Nutrition (Vienna, AUT) *Unable to locate*

Nutrition (Hyderabad, AP, IND) **[45178]**

Nutrition (Amsterdam, NLD) **[48189]**

Nutrition, Allergy, Diet - Taplalkozas, anyagcsere, dieta (Budapest, HUN) *Unable to locate*

Nutrition Bulletin (Oxford, GBR) **[56124]**

Nutrition & Dietetics (Deakin, AC, AUS) **[41837]**

Nutrition & Food Science (Rushden, GBR) **[56426]**

Nutrition Information in Crisis Situations (Geneva, SWI) **[51154]**

Nutrition Journal (London, GBR) **[55019]**

Nutrition and Metabolism **[42744]***

Nutrition & Metabolism (London, GBR) **[55020]**

Nutrition, Metabolism, & Cardiovascular Diseases (Naples, ITA) **[46202]**

Nutrition Research Reviews (Cambridge, GBR) **[52879]**

Nutritional Neuroscience (London, GBR) **[55021]**

Nuts (London, GBR) **[55022]**

NuYou (Singapore, SGP) **[50230]**

NuYou Time (Singapore, SGP) **[50231]**

NvTv - Channel 62 (Belfast, GBR) **[52303]**

NX-FM - 106.9 (Charlestown, NW, AUS) **[41735]**

Ny Dag and K3 (Oslo, NOR) *Ceased*

Ny Framtid (Stockholm, SWE) **[51029]**

NY-LONDON Shows (Athens, GRC) **[44753]**

Nyala (Limbe, MWI) *Unable to locate*

Nykyposti (Kuvalehdet, FIN) *Unable to locate*

NYSC News (Maharagama, SRI) *Unable to locate*

Nyt Aspekt (New Aspect) (Copenhagen, DEN) *Unable to locate*

Nyt fra Danmark (News from Denmark) (Copenhagen, DEN) *Unable to locate*

NZ Business (North Shore City, NZL) **[48959]**

NZ Catholic (Auckland, NZL) **[48823]**

NZ Home & Entertaining **[48795]***

NZ Journal of Educational Studies **[49024]***

NZ Journal of Teachers' Work (Palmerston North, NZL) **[48965]**

NZ Rugby World (Auckland City, NZL) *Unable to locate*

NZ Woodturner **[49005]***

NZBusiness (Auckland, NZL) **[48824]**

NZ4WD (Auckland, NZL) **[48825]**

NZI Notities (Utrecht, NLD) *Ceased*

NZV8 (Auckland, NZL) **[48826]**

O

O-FM - 94 (Bloemfontein, SAF) **[50356]**

O Informador Fiscal (Porto, PRT) **[49809]**

O Papel (Sao Paulo, SP, BRZ) *Unable to locate*

O-Posten (Brondby, DEN) **[43652]**

O Pothos (Thessaloniki, GRC) *Unable to locate*

O-Sport (Vienna, AUT) *Unable to locate*

OAG Rail Guide (Dunstable, GBR) **[53225]**

Oak-FM - 101.3 (Wangaratta, VI, AUS) **[42684]**

Oak-FM (Loughborough, GBR) *Unable to locate*

Oakleigh Monash Leader (Melbourne, VI, AUS) **[42080]**

The Oamaru Mail (Oamaru, NZL) *Unable to locate*

Oasis-FM - 96.6 (Saint Albans, GBR) **[56440]**

Oban-FM - 103.3 (Oban, GBR) **[55782]**

Obedira-FM - 102.1 (Asuncion, PAR) **[49404]**

The Oberoi Group Magazine (Mumbai, MH, IND) *Unable to locate*

Oberwolfach Reports (Helsinki, FIN) **[43852]**

Obesity and Metabolism (Milan, ITA) **[46188]**

Obesity Reviews (Oxford, GBR) **[56125]**

Obiter (Port Elizabeth, SAF) **[50578]**

The Observer (London, GBR) **[55023]**

Observer of Business and Politics (Mumbai, MH, IND) *Unable to locate*

Obstetrics & Gynaecology (Moscow, RUS) **[49948]**

Obstetrics and Gynaecology Forum (Johannesburg, SAF) **[50532]**

Obzornik za Matematiko in Fiziko (Ljubljana, SVA) *Unable to locate*

Ocarina (Madras, TN, IND) *Unable to locate*

Occidente (Rome, ITA) *Unable to locate*

Occupational Medicine Journal (London, GBR) **[55024]**

Occupational Pensions (London, GBR) **[55025]**

Occupational Safety & Health (Birmingham, GBR) **[52360]**

Occupational Therapy News (London, GBR) **[55026]**

Ocean Development and International Law (Abingdon, GBR) **[52001]**

Ocean Engineering (Shanghai, CHN) **[43492]**

Ocean-FM **[53375]***

Ocean Research (Seoul, KOR) *Unable to locate*

Ocean Science (Gottingen, GER) **[44400]**

Ocean Science Discussions (Gottingen, GER) **[44401]**

Ocean Voice (Colchester, GBR) *Unable to locate*

Oceania (Sydney, NW, AUS) *Unable to locate*

Oceanographical Magazine (Tokyo, JPN) *Unable to locate*

Oceanological and Hydrobiological Studies (Warsaw, POL) **[49740]**

Oceanology (Moscow, RUS) **[49949]**

OCLC Systems & Services (Bradford, GBR) **[52532]**

Octane Magazine (Wellingborough, GBR) **[56881]**

OCTAVE Briefing (Armathwaite, GBR) *Unable to locate*

Odontology (Tokyo, JPN) **[47013]**

OE Report & Fibre News (High Peak, GBR) *Ceased*

Oecologia (Heidelberg, GER) **[44470]**

OEM News (London, GBR) *Unable to locate*

OEN Dealer (Chelmsford, GBR) *Unable to locate*

OEN Office Equipment News (Chelmsford, GBR) *Unable to locate*

Off Licence News (Crawley, GBR) **[53110]**

Offaly Express (Tullamore, OF, IRL) *Unable to locate*

Office Automation (Milan, ITA) **[46189]**

Office Equipment and Products (Tokyo, JPN) *Unable to locate*

Officelayout (Milan, ITA) **[46190]**

Official Handbook (Edinburgh, GBR) *Unable to locate*

Official Journal of the Economic Community of West African States (Abuja, NGA) *Unable to locate*

Official Journal of the European Communities (Brussels, BEL) *Unable to locate*

Official Journal of the European Patent Office (Munich, GER) **[44576]**

Official PlayStation Magazine Australia (Sydney, NW, AUS) **[42557]**

L'Officinal (Levallois-Perret, FRA) *Unable to locate*

Offshore Investment (Belfast, GBR) **[52291]**

Offshore Support Journal (Enfield, GBR) **[53336]**

Offshore World (OW) (Mumbai, MH, IND) **[45422]**

Offshore Yachting (Homebush West, NW, AUS) *Unable to locate*

Oficio & Arte (La Coruna, SPA) *Unable to locate*

Oh Calcutta (Calcutta, WB, IND) *Unable to locate*

OI-NYTT (Oslo, NOR) *Unable to locate*

Oikos (Lund, SWE) **[50988]**

Oil Asia (New Delhi, DH, IND) *Unable to locate*

Oil & Chemical Worker (Mumbai, MH, IND) *Unable to locate*

Oil and Energy Trends (Oxford, GBR) **[56126]**

Oil Field Times (Guwahati, AS, IND) *Unable to locate*

Oil & Gas Eurasia (Moscow, RUS) **[49950]**

Oil and Gas News (Manama, BHR) **[42793]**

Oil and Natural Gas Commission Bulletin (Dehradun, UP, IND) *Unable to locate*

Oil Review Middle East (London, GBR) **[55027]**

Oil Watch Journal (Almaty, KAZ) *Unable to locate*

Oil World Monthly (Hamburg, GER) **[44421]**

OISCA Journal (Tokyo, JPN) *Unable to locate*

OK Radio-FM - 94.2 (Belgrade, SER) **[50084]**

Okajima's Folia Anatomica Japonica (Tokyo, JPN) *Unable to locate*

Okay (Esch-sur-Alzette, LUX) *Unable to locate*

Okologie & Landbau (Bad Durkheim, GER) *Unable to locate*

Old Glory (Horncastle, GBR) **[53592]**

The Old Lady (London, GBR) **[55028]**

Old and New Concepts of Physics (Warsaw, POL) **[49741]**

Old Testament Essays (Centurion, SAF) **[50444]**

Old Timer Dreamcar Magazine (Oostende, BEL) **[42907]**

Old Tractor (Cudham, GBR) **[53145]**

Oldham & District Property News (Evesham, GBR) **[53344]**

The Oldie (London, GBR) **[55029]**

Oleagineux, Corps Gras, Lipides (Montrouge, FRA) **[44003]**

OLI (Frankfurt, GER) *Unable to locate*

Oli 96.8 FM - 96.8 MHz (Singapore, SGP) **[50302]**

Olimp Radio (Khabarovsk, RUS) *Unable to locate*

Olimpiku (Gzira, MAL) *Unable to locate*

Olive (London, GBR) **[55030]**

The Olive Press (Normanhurst, NW, AUS) **[42151]**

Olympia Autuell (Vienna, AUT) *Unable to locate*

Olympiatoppew (Oslo, NOR) *Unable to locate*

Olympic Quarterly (Tehran, IRN) *Unable to locate*

Olympisches Feuer (Frankfurt am Main, GER) **[44367]**

Oman Daily Observer (Muscat, OMN) **[49222]**

Oman Journal of Ophthalmology (Mumbai, MH, IND) **[45423]**

Oman Today (Muscat, OMN) **[49223]**

Oman Tribune (Muscat, OMN) **[49224]**

Omnibus Magazine (Bromley, GBR) *Unable to locate*

On Air Magazine (Nonthaburi, THA) *Unable to locate*

On the Ball (Gateshead, GBR) *Unable to locate*

ON-CALL **[41646]***

On Dit (Adelaide, SA, AUS) *Unable to locate*

On the Edge (Kettering, GBR) *Unable to locate*

On the Horizon (Bradford, GBR) **[52533]**

On the Road (Wooburn Green, GBR) *Unable to locate*

On-Trade Scotland (Glasgow, GBR) **[53436]**

On Traditional Practices (Nairobi, KEN) *Unable to locate*

Onarts (Wellington, NZL) *Unable to locate*

Onboard (London, GBR) **[55031]**

Oncodevelopmental Biology and Medicine **[51048]***

Oncogene (London, GBR) **[55032]**

Ondernemrs in West-Vlaanderen (Kotrijk, BEL) *Unable to locate*

Onderstepoort Journal of Veterinary Research (Pretoria, SAF) **[50598]**

100 Codewords (Redhill, GBR) **[56358]**

100 Crosswords (Redhill, GBR) **[56359]**

100-FM - 100.1 (Darwin, NT, AUS) **[41830]**

104-FM - 104.4 (Ballsbridge, DU, IRL) **[45917]**

104-FM - 104 (North Wall, DU, IRL) **[46052]**

101-FM - 101.1 (Logan City, QL, AUS) **[42019]**

100 Photos for Press Freedom (Paris, FRA) *Unable to locate*

107-FM - 107.3 (Hobart, TA, AUS) **[41959]**

106 FM - Baki (Baki, AJN) *Unable to locate*

103-FM (Hobart, TA, AUS) *Unable to locate*

100 Wordsearch (Redhill, GBR) **[56360]**

One More Kiss (Tokyo, JPN) **[47014]**

One to One (London, GBR) *Ceased*

One in Seven (London, GBR) **[55033]**

104.7-FM - 104.7 (Grafton, NW, AUS) **[41931]**

104.6-FM - 104.6 (Auckland, NZL) **[48849]**

1001 und 1 Buch (Vienna, AUT) *Unable to locate*

107.5-FM (Orange, NW, AUS) *Unable to locate*

1032-FM (Seven Hills, NW, AUS) *Unable to locate*

1CMS-FM - 91.1 (Holder, AC, AUS) **[41964]**

OneEurope Magazine (Brussels, BEL) *Unable to locate*

OneFM-FM - 107.2 (Geneva, SWI) **[51172]**

OneFM-FM - 99.3 (Geneva, SWI) **[51171]**

1ro de Marzo-AM - 780 (Asuncion, PAR) **[49405]**

1WAY-FM - 91.9 (Fyshwick, AC, AUS) **[41875]**

1WAY-FM - 94.3 (Fyshwick, AC, AUS) **[41876]**

1XX-FM - 90.5 (Whakatane, NZL) **[49048]**

onHoliday (Auckland, NZL) **[48827]**

Online & CD ROM Review **[52534]***

Online Information Review (Bradford, GBR) **[52534]**

Online Journal of Earth Sciences (Faisalabad, PAK) **[49275]**

Online Praxis (Dusseldorf, GER) *Ceased*

Onlooker (Mumbai, MH, IND) *Unable to locate*

Ons Amsterdam (Amsterdam, NLD) *Unable to locate*

Ons Erfdeel (Rekkem, BEL) **[42909]**

Ons Stad (Cape Town, SAF) **[50397]**

Op Pad (The Hague, NLD) **[48623]**

Opal-FM - 89.7 (Lightning Ridge, NW, AUS) **[42009]**

Opas-Guide (Turku, FIN) *Unable to locate*

OPEC Energy Review (Oxford, GBR) **[56127]**

OPEC Review **[56127]***

The Open Book (Havant, GBR) *Unable to locate*

Open Government (Liverpool, GBR) **[53877]**

Open Learner (Cambridge, GBR) *Unable to locate*

Open Learning (Abingdon, GBR) **[52002]**

Open Radio (Moscow, RUS) *Ceased*

Open Radio (Moscow, RUS) *Ceased*

Open Rugby Magazine **[52601]***

Open Skies (Dubai, UAE) **[51651]**

The Open Society (Auckland, NZL) **[48828]**

Open Space (Henley-on-Thames, GBR) **[53562]**

Openings (London, GBR) **[55034]**

OpenMIND (London, GBR) **[55035]**

Opera (London, GBR) **[55036]**

Opera Actual (Barcelona, SPA) **[50690]**

Opera Now (London, GBR) **[55037]**

Operational Risk & Regulation (London, GBR) **[55038]**

Operations Management (Corby, GBR) **[53063]**

Operations Research Letters (Amsterdam, NLD) **[48190]**

Opettaja (Helsinki, FIN) **[43853]**

Ophthalmic and Physiological Optics (London, GBR) **[55039]**

Ophthalmology International (London, GBR) **[55040]**

Opiniao Publica (Campinas, SP, BRZ) **[42971]**

Opinion (Addis Ababa, ETH) *Unable to locate*

Opportunities Abroad (Kottayam, KE, IND) *Ceased*

Opportunities Today (Mumbai, MH, IND) **[45424]**

Opportunity (Cape Town, SAF) **[50398]**

Opportunity (Central Milton Keynes, GBR) *Unable to locate*

OpRisk & Compliance **[55038]***

Opsearch (Kolkata, WB, IND) **[45300]**

Optical Fiber Technology (Amsterdam, NLD) **[48191]**

Optical Materials (Amsterdam, NLD) **[48192]**

Optical and Quantum Electronics (Nottingham, GBR) **[55768]**

Optical Review (Tokyo, JPN) **[47015]**

Optical Switching and Networking (Singapore, SGP) **[50232]**

Optics Communications (Amsterdam, NLD) **[48193]**

Optics & Laser Europe (Bristol, GBR) **[52713]**

Optics & Laser Technology (Amsterdam, NLD) **[48194]**

Optics and Lasers in Engineering (Lausanne, SWI) **[51198]**

Optik (Darmstadt, GER) **[44311]**

Optimal Control Applications & Methods (Chichester, GBR) **[53015]**

Optimization and Engineering (Dordrecht, NLD) **[48521]**

Optimize (Alphen aan den Rijn, NLD) **[47870]**

Option/Bio (Paris, FRA) **[44073]**

Options (Laxenburg, AUT) **[42731]**

Options (Mumbai, MH, IND) *Unable to locate*

Optissimo (Kessel-Lo, BEL) *Unable to locate*

Opto-Electronics Review (Warsaw, POL) **[49742]**

Optometry in Practice (London, GBR) **[55041]**

Optometry Today (New Delhi, DH, IND) *Unable to locate*

Opus (Kuala Lumpur, MYS) *Unable to locate*

OR Insight (Hull, GBR) **[53628]**

Oracle (Calcutta, WB, IND) *Unable to locate*

The Oracle Gloucester Life (Cheltenham, GBR) **[52973]**

Oracle Update (Newbury, GBR) *Ceased*

Oral Diseases (Frederiksberg, DEN) **[43693]**

Oral History Journal (Colchester, GBR) **[53044]**

Oral History Review (Oxford, GBR) **[56128]**

Oral Microbiology and Immunology **[56108]***

Oral Oncology (Oxford, GBR) **[56129]**

Oral Radiology (Hiroshima, JPN) **[46382]**

Orange-FM - 94.0 (Vienna, AUT) **[42777]**

Orbis Litterarum (Odense, DEN) **[43731]**

ORBIT (Rotterdam, NLD) *Unable to locate*

Orbit (London, GBR) *Unable to locate*

Orchard-FM **[56983]***

Orchard-FM **[56726]***

Orchard-FM **[56725]***

Orchid Society of India Journal (New Delhi, DH, IND) *Unable to locate*

Ord & Bild (Goteborg, SWE) **[50962]**

Order (Dordrecht, NLD) **[48522]**

Orders and Medals (Southam, GBR) *Unable to locate*

Ordos People's Broadcasting Station (Ordos, NM, CHN) *Unable to locate*

Ordos People's Broadcasting Station (Ordos, NM, CHN) *Unable to locate*

Ordos People's Broadcasting Station (Ordos, NM, CHN) *Unable to locate*

Ore Geology Reviews (Amsterdam, NLD) **[48195]**

Organic & Biomolecular Chemistry (Cambridge, GBR) **[52880]**

Organic Chemistry Highlights (Liestal, SWI) **[51207]**

Organic Electronics (Singapore, SGP) **[50233]**

Organic Farming (Bristol, GBR) *Unable to locate*

Organic Life (Lewes, GBR) **[53850]**

The Organic Way (Coventry, GBR) **[53089]**

Organisations & People (London, GBR) *Unable to locate*

Organised Sound (Leicester, GBR) **[53816]**

Organiser (New Delhi, DH, IND) **[45632]**

Organisms Diversity & Evolution (Munich, GER) **[44577]**

Organizacija (Warsaw, POL) **[49743]**

Organization (London, GBR) **[55042]**

Organization Studies (London, GBR) **[55043]**

Organizational Behavior and Human Decision Processes (Amsterdam, NLD) **[48196]**

Orient (Mumbai, MH, IND) *Unable to locate*

Orient (Karachi, PAK) *Unable to locate*

Orient Aviation (Hong Kong, CHN) **[43372]**

Orient Journal of Medicine (Enugu, NGA) **[49081]**

Orientacao em Revista (Mafra, PRT) *Unable to locate*

Orientaccion (Madrid, SPA) *Unable to locate*

The Oriental Anthropologists (Jodhpur, RJ, IND) *Unable to locate*

Numbers cited in bold after listings are entry numbers rather than page numbers.

Oriental College Magazine (Lahore, PAK) *Unable to locate*

Oriental Institute Journal (Baroda, GJ, IND) *Unable to locate*

Oriental Sword (Shanghai, CHN) **[43493]**

Orientation Magazine (Paris, FRA) *Unable to locate*

Orientations (Hong Kong, CHN) **[43373]**

Orienteeroja (Tallinn, EST) *Unable to locate*

Original-FM - 106.8 (Aberdeen, GBR) **[51684]**

Original-FM - 106.3 (Aberdeen, GBR) **[51685]**

Original-FM - 106.5 (Bristol, GBR) **[52743]**

Original-FM (Southampton, GBR) *Unable to locate*

Original-FM (Southampton, GBR) *Unable to locate*

Origine (Haarlem, NLD) *Unable to locate*

Origins of Life and Evolution of the Biosphere (Dordrecht, NLD) **[48523]**

Orion (Groenkloof, SAF) *Unable to locate*

Orion (Neukirch-Egnach, SWI) *Unable to locate*

Orissa Education (Bhubaneswar, OR, IND) *Unable to locate*

Orissa Family Planning Bulletin (Bhubaneswar, OR, IND) *Unable to locate*

Orissa Homoeopathic Bulletin (Cuttack, OR, IND) *Unable to locate*

Orissa Times (Bhubaneswar, OR, IND) *Unable to locate*

Oriya Aurovilian (Bhubaneswar, OR, IND) *Unable to locate*

Orkney Arts Review (Orkney, GBR) *Unable to locate*

Ornamental Horticulture (Wallingford, GBR) **[56821]**

L'Orologio (Rome, ITA) **[46239]**

Orthodontics & Craniofacial Research (Frederiksberg, DEN) **[43694]**

Orthopaedic Ceramic Implants (Osaka, JPN) *Unable to locate*

Orthopaedic Product News (Harrogate, GBR) **[53518]**

Orthopaedic Surgery and Traumatology (Tokyo, JPN) *Unable to locate*

Orvosi Hetilap (Budapest, HUN) **[44862]**

Oryx (Cambridge, GBR) **[52881]**

OS (Glasgow, GBR) **[53437]**

Osaka - 3374 KHz (Osaka, JPN) **[46636]**

Osaka Journal of Mathematics (Osaka, JPN) **[46627]**

Osami Suzuki **[46973]***

Oseanologi di Indonesia (Jakarta Utara, IDN) *Unable to locate*

OSM (Avon) Our Schools Magazine **[52723]***

Osmania Journal of Psychology (Hyderabad, AP, IND) *Unable to locate*

Osmania Papers in Linguistics (Hyderabad, AP, IND) *Unable to locate*

The Osteopath (London, GBR) **[55044]**

OsteoWise (Dublin, DU, IRL) **[45993]**

Osterreichische Installateur Zeitung (Vienna, AUT) *Unable to locate*

Osterreichische Touristenzeitung (Vienna, AUT) *Unable to locate*

Osterreichisches Hilfswerk—Sozialforum (Vienna, AUT) *Unable to locate*

Ostrich (Grahamstown, SAF) **[50509]**

Otago Daily Times (Dunedin, NZL) **[48892]**

OTC Business News (London, GBR) *Unable to locate*

The Other Line (Belfast, GBR) *Unable to locate*

Otkrytoye Radio (Cheboksary, RUS) *Unable to locate*

Otkrytoye Radio (Moskva, RUS) *Unable to locate*

Otkrytoye Radio (Donskaya Volna) (Rostov-na-Donu, RUS) *Unable to locate*

The Otorhinolaryngologist (London, GBR) **[55045]**

Otorhinolaryngology and Phoniatrics (Prague, CZE) **[43632]**

OTOT (Tel Aviv, ISR) *Unable to locate*

Otthon (Budapest, HUN) **[44863]**

Oud Hollad (The Hague, NLD) **[48624]**

Our Heritage (Calcutta, WB, IND) *Unable to locate*

Our Link (Chennai, TN, IND) *Unable to locate*

Our Planet (Nairobi, KEN) **[47194]**

Our Town Papakura (Penrose, NZL) *Unable to locate*

Our Universe (New Delhi, DH, IND) *Unable to locate*

Our Village (Rakhu, NPL) *Unable to locate*

Out on a Limb (Barnsley, GBR) **[52183]**

Outcast (London, GBR) *Unable to locate*

Outdoor Design & Living (North Ryde, NW, AUS) **[42189]**

Outdoor Design Source (North Ryde, NW, AUS) **[42190]**

Outdoor Review (Kettering, GBR) *Unable to locate*

Outdoor Space (North Ryde, NW, AUS) **[42191]**

Outlook (New Delhi, DH, IND) **[45633]**

Outlook on Agriculture (London, GBR) **[55046]**

Outlooks on Pest Management (Burnham, GBR) **[52767]**

Outposts Poetry Quarterly (Frome, GBR) **[53400]**

Outrage (Tonbridge, GBR) **[56756]**

OutsiderR (Hiroshima, JPN) *Unable to locate*

Outskirts (Crawley, WA, AUS) **[41820]**

Over Here (Pacific Harbour, FIJ) *Unable to locate*

Overberg Venster (Cape Town, SAF) **[50399]**

Overdrive (Mumbai, MI, IND) **[45425]**

Overdrive (Luton, GBR) **[55503]**

Overland (Melbourne, VI, AUS) **[42081]**

Overlander 4WD (Alexandria, NW, AUS) **[41545]**

Overleven (Amsterdam, NLD) **[48197]**

Overseas (London, GBR) **[55047]**

Overseas Business Contacts (New Delhi, DH, IND) **[45634]**

Overseas Chinese Daily (Kota Kinabalu, MYS) **[47592]**

Overseas Journal **[55047]***

Overseas Representative Report (Tokyo, JPN) *Unable to locate*

Overview (Dunedin, NZL) *Unable to locate*

Overview (Stockport, GBR) *Unable to locate*

Oxford Art Journal (Oxford, GBR) **[56130]**

Oxford Bulletin of Economics & Statistics (Oxford, GBR) **[56131]**

Oxford Development Studies (Oxford, GBR) **[56132]**

Oxford Economic Papers (Oxford, GBR) **[56133]**

Oxford-FM - 107.9 (Oxford, GBR) **[56234]**

Oxford Journal of Archaeology (Oxford, GBR) **[56134]**

Oxford Journal of Legal Studies (Oxford, GBR) **[56135]**

Oxford Literary Review (Edinburgh, GBR) **[53304]**

Oxford Review of Economic Policy (Oxford, GBR) **[56136]**

Oxford Today (Oxford, GBR) **[56137]**

Oxford University Commonwealth Law Journal (Oxford, GBR) **[56138]**

Oxfordshire Life (Cheltenham, GBR) **[52974]**

Oxygene Radio-FM - 93 (Pontcharra, FRA) **[44096]**

Oyanda (The Future) (Khodjand, TDN) *Unable to locate*

OYE (Ago Iwoye, OG, NGA) **[49059]**

P

P C World Pakistan (Lahore, PAK) *Unable to locate*

P I C I C News (Karachi, PAK) *Unable to locate*

P T D Annual Tax Digest (Lahore, PAK) *Unable to locate*

Paarl Post (Cape Town, SAF) **[50400]**

PAC (Thuemaston, GBR) *Unable to locate*

Pace in Terra (Tokyo, JPN) *Unable to locate*

Pachamama Radio-AM - 850 (Puno, PER) **[49440]**

Pachyderm (Nairobi, KEN) **[47195]**

Pacific Archives Journal (Sydney, NW, AUS) *Ceased*

Pacific and Asian Journal on Energy **[45644]***

Pacific-Basin Finance Journal (Amsterdam, NLD) **[48198]**

Pacific Economic Review (Hong Kong, CHN) **[43374]**

Pacific/English Language Series (P-) (Falkenstein, GER) *Unable to locate*

Pacific Focus (Inchon, KOR) *Unable to locate*

Pacific Journal of Science and Technology (Northern Samar, PHL) *Unable to locate*

Pacific Philosophical Quarterly (Oxford, GBR) **[56139]**

The Pacific Review (Abingdon, GBR) **[52003]**

Pacific Waves (Highgate Hill, QL, AUS) **[41955]**

Pacifica Review: Peace, Security & Global Change **[51795]***

Packaging (Uxbridge, GBR) *Unable to locate*

Packaging India **[45426]***

Packaging India (Mumbai, MH, IND) **[45426]**

Packaging Magazine (London, GBR) *Unable to locate*

Packaging Month (Leatherhead, GBR) **[53752]**

Packaging News (Surry Hills, NW, AUS) **[42437]**

Packaging News (London, GBR) **[55048]**

Packaging Scotland (Glasgow, GBR) **[53438]**

Packaging Today (Sidcup, GBR) **[56545]**

Packaging, Transport, Storage & Security of Radioactive Material (London, GBR) **[55049]**

Packdirect (Antwerp, BEL) *Unable to locate*

Pack+Plast (Glostrup, DEN) **[43711]**

Pact (London, GBR) **[55050]**

A Padaria Portuguesa (Coimbra, PRT) *Unable to locate*

Padiatrie (Neuhausen, SWI) **[51218]**

Paediatric and Perinatal Epidemiology (Bristol, GBR) **[52714]**

Paediatrica Indonesiana (Jakarta, IDN) *Unable to locate*

Paediatrics & Child Health (Cardiff, GBR) **[52937]**

PAID (Quezon City, PHL) **[49605]**

The Pain Clinic (London, GBR) *Ceased*

Paint and Ink International **[53971]***

Paint Shop Pro Photo (Bournemouth, GBR) **[52418]**

Pais & Filhos (Cruz Quebrada-Dafundo, PRT) **[49796]**

Pais (Madrid, Spain) (Madrid, SPA) *Unable to locate*

Paiyun Broadcasting Co. (Kaohsiung, TWN) *Unable to locate*

Pak Jamhuriat (Lahore, PAK) *Unable to locate*

Pak Post (Islamabad, PAK) *Unable to locate*

The Pak-Scout (Islamabad, PAK) *Unable to locate*

Pakenham Cardinia Leader (Berwick, VI, AUS) **[41600]**

Pakistan Accountant (Karachi, PAK) **[49366]**

Pakistan Administration (Lahore, PAK) *Unable to locate*

Pakistan Agriculture (Karachi, PAK) *Unable to locate*

Pakistan Archaeology (Karachi, PAK) *Unable to locate*

Pakistan Armed Forces Medical Journal (Rawalpindi, PAK) *Unable to locate*

Pakistan Army Journal (Rawalpindi, PAK) *Unable to locate*

Pakistan Broadcasting Corporation, Abbottabad - 1602 KHz (Islamabad, PAK) **[49313]**

Pakistan Broadcasting Corporation, Bahawalpur - 1341 KHz (Islamabad, PAK) **[49314]**

Pakistan Broadcasting Corporation, Chitral - 1584 KHz (Islamabad, PAK) **[49315]**

Pakistan Broadcasting Corporation, Dera Ismail Khan - 1404 KHz (Islamabad, PAK) **[49316]**

Pakistan Broadcasting Corporation, Faisalabad - 1476 KHz (Islamabad, PAK) **[49317]**

Pakistan Broadcasting Corporation, Gilgit - 1512 KHz (Islamabad, PAK) **[49318]**

Pakistan Broadcasting Corporation, Hyderabad-I - 1008 KHz (Hyderabad, PAK) **[49304]**

Pakistan Broadcasting Corporation, Hyderabad-II - 1098 KHz (Hyderabad, PAK) **[49305]**

Pakistan Broadcasting Corporation, Islamabad - 585 KHz (Islamabad, PAK) **[49320]**

Pakistan Broadcasting Corporation, Islamabad - 101 MHz (Islamabad, PAK) **[49319]**

Pakistan Broadcasting Corporation, Karachi-I - 828 KHz (Karachi, PAK) **[49382]**

Master Index

Pakistan Broadcasting Corporation, Karachi-II - 639 KHz (Karachi, PAK) [49383]

Pakistan Broadcasting Corporation, Khairpur - 927 KHz (Islamabad, PAK) [49321]

Pakistan Broadcasting Corporation, Khuzdar - 567 KHz (Islamabad, PAK) [49322]

Pakistan Broadcasting Corporation, Lahore-I - 630 KHz (Islamabad, PAK) [49323]

Pakistan Broadcasting Corporation, Lahore-II - 1080 KHz (Lahore, PAK) [49390]

Pakistan Broadcasting Corporation, Loralai - 1251 KHz (Islamabad, PAK) [49324]

Pakistan Broadcasting Corporation, Multan - 1035 KHz (Islamabad, PAK) [49325]

Pakistan Broadcasting Corporation, Peshawar - 540 KHz (Islamabad, PAK) [49326]

Pakistan Broadcasting Corporation, Peshawar-II - 729 KHz (Peshawar, PAK) [49396]

Pakistan Broadcasting Corporation, Quetta - 855 KHz (Islamabad, PAK) [49327]

Pakistan Broadcasting Corporation, Quetta - 756 KHz (Islamabad, PAK) [49328]

Pakistan Broadcasting Corporation, Quetta-I - 756 KHz (Quetta, PAK) [49398]

Pakistan Broadcasting Corporation, Quetta-II - 855 KHz (Quetta, PAK) [49399]

Pakistan Broadcasting Corporation, Rawalpindi - 102 (Islamabad, PAK) [49329]

Pakistan Broadcasting Corporation, Rawalpindi - 1260 KHz (Rawalpindi, PAK) [49400]

Pakistan Broadcasting Corporation, Sibbi - 1584 KHz (Islamabad, PAK) [49330]

Pakistan Broadcasting Corporation, Skaŕdu - 1557 KHz (Islamabad, PAK) [49331]

Pakistan Broadcasting Corporation, Turbat - 1584 KHz (Islamabad, PAK) [49332]

Pakistan Broadcasting Corporation, Zhob - 1449 KHz (Islamabad, PAK) [49333]

Pakistan Chess Magazine (Karachi, PAK) Unable to locate

Pakistan Christian Post (Karachi, PAK) [49367]

Pakistan Cottons (Karachi, PAK) Unable to locate

Pakistan Criminal Law Journal (Lahore, PAK) Unable to locate

Pakistan Economic Journal (Lahore, PAK) Unable to locate

Pakistan Exports (Karachi, PAK) Unable to locate

Pakistan and Gulf Economist (Karachi, PAK) Unable to locate

Pakistan Heart Journal (Karachi, PAK) Unable to locate

Pakistan Horizon (Karachi, PAK) Unable to locate

Pakistan Journal of Agricultural Research (Islamabad, PAK) [49306]

Pakistan Journal of Agricultural Sciences (Faisalabad, PAK) Unable to locate

Pakistan Journal of Agronomy (Faisalabad, PAK) Unable to locate

Pakistan Journal of Animal Sciences (Lahore, PAK) Unable to locate

Pakistan Journal of Applied Economics (Karachi, PAK) Unable to locate

Pakistan Journal of Biochemistry and Molecular Biology (Lahore, PAK) Unable to locate

Pakistan Journal of Biological Sciences (Faisalabad, PAK) [49276]

Pakistan Journal of Botany (Karachi, PAK) [49368]

Pakistan Journal of Cardiology (Karachi, PAK) Unable to locate

Pakistan Journal of Clinical Psychology (Karachi, PAK) Unable to locate

Pakistan Journal of Entomology (Karachi, PAK) Unable to locate

Pakistan Journal of Forestry (Peshawar, PAK) [49394]

Pakistan Journal of Gastroenterology (Lahore, PAK) Unable to locate

Pakistan Journal of Health (Lahore, PAK) Unable to locate

Pakistan Journal of Hydrocarbon Research (Islamabad, PAK) [49307]

Pakistan Journal of Local Government (Karachi, PAK) Unable to locate

Pakistan Journal of Medical Research (Islamabad, PAK) [49308]

Pakistan Journal of Medical Sciences (Karachi, PAK) [49369]

Pakistan Journal of Nematology (Karachi, PAK) Unable to locate

Pakistan Journal of Neurology (Lahore, PAK) Unable to locate

Pakistan Journal of Nutrition (Faisalabad, PAK) [49277]

Pakistan Journal of Obstetrics & Gynecology (Islamabad, PAK) Unable to locate

Pakistan Journal of Ophthalmology (Lahore, PAK) Unable to locate

Pakistan Journal of Otolaryngology (Karachi, PAK) Unable to locate

Pakistan Journal of Otolaryngology, Head and Neck Surgery (Karachi, PAK) Unable to locate

Pakistan Journal of Paediatric Surgery (Lahore, PAK) Unable to locate

Pakistan Journal of Pathology (Karachi, PAK) [49370]

Pakistan Journal of Pharmaceutical Sciences (Karachi, PAK) [49371]

Pakistan Journal of Pharmacology (Karachi, PAK) Unable to locate

Pakistan Journal of Plant Pathology [49278]*

Pakistan Journal of Psychology (Karachi, PAK) Unable to locate

Pakistan Journal of Radiology (Karachi, PAK) Unable to locate

Pakistan Journal of Science (Lahore, PAK) Unable to locate

Pakistan Journal of Scientific and Industrial Research (Islamabad, PAK) [49309]

Pakistan Journal of Social Science (Islamabad, PAK) Unable to locate

Pakistan Journal of Statistics (Lahore, PAK) Unable to locate

Pakistan Journal of Surgery (Larkana, PAK) [49391]

Pakistan Journal of Women's Studies (Karachi, PAK) Unable to locate

Pakistan Journal of Zoology (Lahore, PAK) Unable to locate

Pakistan Labour Cases (Lahore, PAK) Unable to locate

Pakistan Leather Trade Journal (Karachi, PAK) Unable to locate

Pakistan Observer (Islamabad, PAK) Unable to locate

Pakistan Paediatric Cardiology Journal (Karachi, PAK) Unable to locate

Pakistan Pediatric Journal (Lahore, PAK) [49386]

Pakistan Pictorial (Houston, TX, USA) Unable to locate

Pakistan Postgraduate Medical Journal (Lahore, PAK) Unable to locate

Pakistan Seafood Digest (Karachi, PAK) Unable to locate

Pakistan Tax Decisions (Lahore, PAK) Unable to locate

Pakistan Textile (Karachi, PAK) Unable to locate

Pakistan Textile Journal (Karachi, PAK) [49372]

Pakistan Veterinarian (Karachi, PAK) Unable to locate

Pakistan Veterinary Journal (Faisalabad, PAK) Unable to locate

Pakphyton (Lahore, PAK) Unable to locate

PakTribune (Islamabad, PAK) [49310]

Pakutnik Heuzgaemer (Minsk, BLR) Unable to locate

Paladyn (Warsaw, POL) [49744]

Palaeobotanist (Lucknow, UP, IND) [45325]

Palaeontology (Oxford, GBR) [56140]

Palaeoworld (Nanjing, CHN) [43454]

Palermo-FM (Buenos Aires, ARG) Unable to locate

Palermo-FM (Buenos Aires, ARG) Unable to locate

Palestine Exploration Quarterly (London, GBR) [55051]

Palestine Report (East Jerusalem, ISR) [46075]

Palestine Times (London, GBR) [55052]

Palm-FM - 105.5 (Torquay, GBR) [56760]

Pamir (Dushanbe, TDN) Unable to locate

Pan American Journal of Public Health (Geneva, SWI) [51155]

PANELS & FURNITURE ASIA (Singapore, SGP) [50234]

Paneuropa (Munich, GER) Unable to locate

Paneuropa Deutschland (Augsburg, GER) [44141]

Paneuropa Osterreich (Munich, GER) Unable to locate

Panjab Past and Present (Patiala, PJ, IND) [45686]

Panjab University Law Review (Chandigarh, CH, IND) Unable to locate

Panjab University News (Chandigarh, CH, IND) Unable to locate

Panjab University Research Bulletin (Arts) (Chandigarh, CH, IND) Unable to locate

Panjin People's Broadcasting Station (Panjin, LI, CHN) Unable to locate

Panorama de Interlingua (Bilthoven, NLD) Unable to locate

Panorma Difesa (Impruneta, ITA) Unable to locate

The Pantaneto Forum (Luton, GBR) [55504]

Panzhihua People's Broadcasting Station (Panzhihua, SI, CHN) Unable to locate

Paotao Kechia Broadcasting Station (Taipei, TWN) Unable to locate

The Papatoetoe & Otahuhu Week (Penrose, NZL) Unable to locate

Papeis Avulsos de Zoologia (Sao Paulo) (Sao Paulo, SP, BRZ) [43043]

Papeles de la FIM (Fundacion de Investigaciones Marxistas) (Madrid, SPA) [50787]

The Paper (Tenerife, SPA) [50837]

Paper Asia (Singapore, SGP) Unable to locate

Paper Conservator (Worcestershire, GBR) Unable to locate

Paper Pulp Board Printing Industry Report (Allahabad, UP, IND) Unable to locate

Paper Sky (Tokyo, JPN) [47016]

Paper Technology (London, GBR) [55053]

Paper Technology and Industry [55053]*

Paper and Timber (Helsinki, FIN) [43854]

Paper and Timberland [43854]*

PaperCraft Inspirations (London, GBR) [55054]

Paperi Ja Puu (Helsinki, FIN) [43855]

Paperprintpack India (Mumbai, MH, IND) Unable to locate

Papers of the British School at Rome (London, GBR) [55055]

Papers in Meteorology and Geophysics (Ibaraki, JPN) Unable to locate

Papeterie (Paris, FRA) Unable to locate

Papierkrieg (Berlin, GER) Ceased

Papir a Celuloza (Paper & Pulp) (Prague, CZE) Unable to locate

PAPU Bulletin (Arusha, TZA) Unable to locate

Parade (Mumbai, MH, IND) Unable to locate

Paragraph (Edinburgh, GBR) [53305]

Parallel Processing Letters (Singapore, SGP) [50235]

Parapsychology (Jaipur, RJ, IND) Unable to locate

Parasite Immunology (Brentwood, GBR) [52586]

Parasitology Research (Dusseldorf, GER) [44330]

Parent To Parent [53419]*

Parenting (New Delhi, DH, IND) Unable to locate

Parents News UK (Worcester Park, GBR) [56965]

Paris Catwalks (Athens, GRC) [44754]

Paris Match (Levallois-Perret, FRA) Unable to locate

Paris Woman Journal (Paris, FRA) [44074]

Parity (Collingwood, VI, AUS) [41793]

Parkh (Chandigarh, CH, IND) Unable to locate

Parking News (Haywards Heath, GBR) [53550]

The Parkinson Magazine (London, GBR) [55056]

Parks (Gland, SWI) [51175]

The Parliamentarian (London, GBR) [55057]

Parliamentary Affairs (Oxford, GBR) [56141]

Parliamentary Brief (London, GBR) [55058]

Parliaments, Estates and Representation (Surrey, GBR) [56671]

Parnasso (Kuvalehdet, FIN) [43893]

Parramatta Advertiser (Parramatta, NW, AUS) [42235]

Parrot Society of Australia News (Salisbury, QL, AUS) [42342]

Parsiana (Mumbai, MH, IND) [45427]

Particle and Fibre Toxicology (London, GBR) [55059]

Particle and Particle Systems Characterization (Paderborn, GER) [44632]

Numbers cited in bold after listings are entry numbers rather than page numbers.

Particuology (Beijing, CHN) **[43212]**

Parties for Kids (Rozelle, NW, AUS) **[42328]**

Partisan (Cochin, KE, IND) *Unable to locate*

Partner from Poland (Warsaw, POL) *Unable to locate*

Partner Schaft (Quezon City, PHL) *Unable to locate*

Party Celebrity lives (Warsaw, POL) **[49745]**

Party Life (New Delhi, DH, IND) *Unable to locate*

Party Politics (London, GBR) **[55060]**

PASA (Collingwood, VI, AUS) **[41794]**

Pasos (Prague, CZE) **[43633]**

Passages (Zurich, SWI) **[51276]**

Passerella di Donna (Athens, GRC) **[44755]**

Past & Present (Oxford, GBR) **[56142]**

Pastoral Care in Education (Nuneaton, GBR) **[55777]**

The Pastoral Review (London, GBR) **[55061]**

Patchwork & Quilting (West Sussex, GBR) **[56900]**

Patchwork & Stitching (Silverwater, NW, AUS) **[42361]**

Pateley Bridge & Nidderdale Herald (Harrogate, GBR) **[53519]**

Patent Office Technical Society Journal (Calcutta, WB, IND) *Unable to locate*

Patents and Licensing (Tokyo, JPN) *Unable to locate*

Pathological Physiology & Experimental Therapy (Moscow, RUS) **[49951]**

Pathology (London, GBR) **[55062]**

Pathology International (Oxford, GBR) **[56143]**

Pathology Update (Porto, PRT) *Unable to locate*

Pathophysiology (Kuopio, FIN) **[43877]**

Pathos (Agrate, ITA) *Unable to locate*

Pathway to God (Belgaum, KA, IND) *Unable to locate*

Patna Journal of Medicine (Patna, BH, IND) *Unable to locate*

Patna University Journal (Patna, BH, IND) *Unable to locate*

Patriot (New Delhi, DH, IND) *Unable to locate*

Patrones (Barcelona, SPA) **[50691]**

Pattaya Mail (Pattaya City, THA) **[51463]**

The Pattenmaker Magazine (Maidstone, GBR) *Unable to locate*

Pattern Analysis & Applications (Loughborough, GBR) **[55486]**

Pattern Recognition and Image Analysis (Moscow, RUS) **[49952]**

Patterns of Prejudice (London, GBR) *Unable to locate*

Paul Sheeran Magazine (Ware, GBR) **[56843]**

Pavo (Baroda, GJ, IND) *Unable to locate*

PAX (Helsinki, FIN) *Unable to locate*

Pax Radio (Beirut, LBN) *Unable to locate*

Pax Radio - Beirut (Beirut, LBN) *Unable to locate*

Pax Radio - Beit Meri - 103.1 MHz (Beit Meri, LBN) **[47435]**

Pay and Benefits Bulletin (London, GBR) *Unable to locate*

Payam Hajar (Tehran, IRN) *Unable to locate*

Payload (Surry Hills, NW, AUS) *Unable to locate*

PBA-FM - 89.7 (Salisbury, SA, AUS) **[42347]**

PBIF Magazine (Newton Abbot, GBR) *Unable to locate*

PBWnews (Olney, GBR) **[55845]**

PC Actual (Barcelona, SPA) **[50692]**

PC Authority (Sydney, NW, AUS) **[42558]**

PC Consultant (Haarlem, NLD) *Unable to locate*

PC Digest **[49518]***

PC-FM - 95.6 (Maseru, LES) **[47457]**

PC Hemma (Stockholm, SWE) *Unable to locate*

PC Intern (Dusseldorf, GER) *Unable to locate*

PC Magazine (London, GBR) **[55063]**

PC Magazine Middle & Near East (Dubai, UAE) **[51652]**

PC Magazine Norge (Oslo, NOR) *Ceased*

PC Mart (Birmingham, GBR) *Unable to locate*

PC Online (Wurzburg, GER) *Ceased*

PC Semanal (Mexico City, DF, MEX) *Unable to locate*

PC World (Cairo, EGY) *Unable to locate*

PC World Espana **[50788]***

PC World Espana (Madrid, SPA) **[50788]**

PC World Hong Kong (Hong Kong, CHN) **[43375]**

PC World India (New Delhi, DH, IND) *Unable to locate*

PC World Malaysia (Kuala Lumpur, MYS) *Unable to locate*

PC World Philippines (Makati City, PHL) **[49518]**

PC World Singapore (Singapore, SGP) *Unable to locate*

PCPlus (Bath, GBR) **[52253]**

PCWorld (Hong Kong, CHN) *Unable to locate*

PD Gune Memorial Lecture Series (Pune, MH, IND) *Unable to locate*

Pdsoynu lutbm (Vilnius, LIT) *Unable to locate*

The P.E. Journal (Limerick, LI, IRL) *Unable to locate*

Peace (Totapalli Hills, AP, IND) *Unable to locate*

Peace & Change (Oxford, GBR) **[56144]**

Peace, Conflict & Development (Bradford, GBR) **[52535]**

Peace-FM - 104.3 (Accra, GHA) **[44733]**

Peace and Freedom (Adelaide, SA, AUS) **[41512]**

Peace Review (Abingdon, GBR) **[52004]**

Peak District Life (Derby, GBR) **[53167]**

Peak-FM - 88 (Bangkok, THA) **[51451]**

Peak-FM - 107.4 (Chesterfield, GBR) **[53003]**

Peatlands International (Jyvaskyla, FIN) *Unable to locate*

Pedagogy, Culture and Society (Abingdon, GBR) **[52005]**

Pediatric Allergy and Immunology (Oxford, GBR) **[56145]**

Pediatric Anesthesia (Oxford, GBR) **[56146]**

Pediatric Clinics of India (Mumbai, MH, IND) *Unable to locate*

Pediatric Dental Journal (Tokyo, JPN) **[47017]**

Pediatric Dermatology (Oxford, GBR) **[56147]**

Pediatric Diabetes (Frederiksberg, DEN) **[43695]**

Pediatric Health (London, GBR) **[55064]**

Pediatric Hematology & Oncology (Abingdon, GBR) **[52006]**

Pediatric Nephrology (Cardiff, GBR) *Unable to locate*

Pediatric Nursing (Harrow, GBR) **[53531]**

Pediatric Rehabilitation **[51757]***

Pediatric Surgery (Moscow, RUS) **[49953]**

Pediatric Surgery International (Heidelberg, GER) **[44471]**

Pediatrics International (Oxford, GBR) **[56148]**

Pedologist (Ibaraki, JPN) *Unable to locate*

Pedosphere (Nanjing, CHN) **[43455]**

Pegasus-FM (Christchurch, NZL) *Unable to locate*

Pegasus Post (Christchurch, NZL) *Unable to locate*

Pei Tai chih sheng Broadcasting Station (Keelung, TWN) *Unable to locate*

Pelangi-FM - 91.4 (Bandar Seri Begawan, BRN) **[43074]**

Peluquerias Hair Styles (Barcelona, SPA) **[50693]**

Pemikir (Kuala Lumpur, MYS) **[47632]**

The Pen (London, GBR) *Ceased*

Pen & Ink (Quezon City, PHL) *Unable to locate*

Penang Tourist Newspaper (Penang, MYS) *Unable to locate*

Penelope (Barcelona, SPA) *Unable to locate*

Penipe: Pueblo de la Solidarid (Penipe, ECU) *Unable to locate*

Penjamiento Economico (Buenos Aires, ARG) *Unable to locate*

Pennine-FM (Huddersfield, GBR) *Ceased*

Penrith Press (Penrith, NW, AUS) **[42240]**

Pensions (Basingstoke, GBR) **[52227]**

Pensions Age (London, GBR) **[55065]**

Penteados (Lisbon, PRT) *Unable to locate*

Penthouse Couples (Saint Leonards, NW, AUS) **[42334]**

People and Development Challenges (London, GBR) *Unable to locate*

People on the Move (Vatican City, VAT) **[57015]**

People & Science (London, GBR) **[55066]**

People's Daily (Beijing, CHN) **[43213]**

The People's Korea (Tokyo, JPN) *Unable to locate*

People's Manifocto (New Delhi, DH, IND) *Unable to locate*

People's Power (Mumbai, MH, IND) *Unable to locate*

People's Review (Kathmandu, NPL) **[47845]**

People's Rights (Jerusalem, ISR) *Unable to locate*

Peoples Sector (New Delhi, DH, IND) *Unable to locate*

Pepper Market Bulletin (Kuching, MYS) **[47667]**

Per Liguam (Stellenbosch, SAF) **[50634]**

Perfect Beat (Sydney, NW, AUS) **[42559]**

Perfect Ten 98.7 FM **[50300]***

Perfectly Frank (Sutton Coldfield, GBR) *Unable to locate*

Performance Arts and Films (Seoul, KOR) *Unable to locate*

Performance BMW (Sevenoaks, GBR) **[56476]**

Performance Buildups (North Ryde, NW, AUS) **[42192]**

Performance Car (Sevenoaks, GBR) **[56477]**

Performance Chemicals Europe (PCE) (Sutton, GBR) *Unable to locate*

Performance Evaluation (Sophia Antipolis, FRA) **[44108]**

Performance Ford (Sevenoaks, GBR) **[56478]**

Performance Measurements and Metrics (Bradford, GBR) **[52536]**

Performance Research (Abingdon, GBR) **[52007]**

Performance Textiles (London, GBR) **[55067]**

Performance VW (Sevenoaks, GBR) **[56479]**

Perimeter Systems (Lichfield, GBR) *Unable to locate*

Period House (Colchester, GBR) **[53045]**

Period Ideas (Colchester, GBR) **[53046]**

Period Living (London, GBR) **[55068]**

Periodica Mathematica Hungarica (Dordrecht, NLD) **[48524]**

Periodontology 2000 (Oxford, GBR) **[56149]**

Perserites-TV - Channel 44 (Petresh, ALB) **[41441]**

Person-Centered and Experimental Psychotherapies (Ross-on-Wye, GBR) **[56411]**

Personal Computer World (London, GBR) **[55069]**

Personal Computing (Mexico) (Mexico City, DF, MEX) *Unable to locate*

Personal Investor (Melbourne, VI, AUS) *Unable to locate*

Personal and Ubiquitous Computing (London, GBR) **[55070]**

Personality and Individual Differences (London, GBR) **[55071]**

Personality and Mental Health (Glasgow, GBR) **[53439]**

Personality Study and Group Behaviour (Amritsar, PJ, IND) *Unable to locate*

Personalized Medicine (London, GBR) **[55072]**

Personnel Psychology (Oxford, GBR) **[56150]**

Personnel Review (Newcastle upon Tyne, GBR) **[55677]**

Personnel Today (Kolkata, WB, IND) **[45301]**

Perspectiva Rotaria (S'Agaro, SPA) *Unable to locate*

Perspective on Current Affairs (Dehradun, UP, IND) *Unable to locate*

Perspectives (Abingdon, GBR) **[52008]**

Perspectives (Bristol, GBR) **[52715]**

Perspectives in Education (Centurion, SAF) **[50445]**

Perspectives in Energy (Moscow, RUS) *Unable to locate*

Perspectives on European Politics and Society (Abingdon, GBR) **[52009]**

Perspectives of the Islamic Economy (Karachi, PAK) *Unable to locate*

Perspectives in Psychiatric Care (Oxford, GBR) **[56151]**

Perspectives in Psychological Researches (Azamgarh, UP, IND) *Unable to locate*

Perspectives on Psychological Science (Oxford, GBR) **[56152]**

Numbers cited in bold after listings are entry numbers rather than page numbers.

Perspectives - The Central European Review of International Affairs (Prague, CZE) **[43634]**

Perspectives in Urban Geography (New Delhi, DH, IND) *Unable to locate*

Pertanika Journal of Science and Technology (Serdang, MYS) *Unable to locate*

Pertanika Journal of Social Science and Humanities (Serdang, MYS) **[47716]**

Pertanika Journal of Tropical Agricultural Science (Serdang, MYS) **[47717]**

Peru Business (San Isidro, PER) *Unable to locate*

Pervasive and Mobile Computing (Singapore, SGP) **[50236]**

Pesca In (Impruneta, ITA) *Unable to locate*

Pesquisa Antartica Brasiliera (Sao Carlos, SP, BRZ) *Unable to locate*

Pesquisa Veterinaria Brasileira (Rio de Janeiro, RJ, BRZ) **[43013]**

Pest Control News (Ossett, GBR) *Unable to locate*

PESTALK (Sydney, NW, AUS) **[42560]**

Pet Business News (Kent, GBR) *Unable to locate*

Pet Business World **[55845]***

Pet in Europe (Ettlingen, GER) **[44350]**

Pet Product Marketing (London, GBR) **[55073]**

Pet Talk (Pevensey, GBR) **[56268]**

Petcare (Bedford, GBR) **[52274]**

The Peter Jones Chronicle (London, GBR) *Unable to locate*

Peterborough Evening Telegraph (Peterborough, GBR) **[56259]**

Peterlee Mail (Hartlepool, GBR) **[53534]**

Petersfield Post (Petersfield, GBR) **[56267]**

Petra (Hamburg, GER) **[44422]**

Petresh-FM - 95.4 MHz (Elbasan, ALB) **[41433]**

Petroleum Asia Journal (Dehradun, UP, IND) *Unable to locate*

Petroleum Chemistry (Moscow, RUS) **[49954]**

Petroleum Economist (London, GBR) **[55074]**

Petroleum Geoscience (Bath, GBR) **[52254]**

Petroleum Review (London, GBR) **[55075]**

Petrology (Moscow, RUS) **[49955]**

Petromin (Singapore, SGP) **[50237]**

PferdeWoche (Volketswil, SWI) *Unable to locate*

Pflugers Archiv (Heidelberg, GER) **[44472]**

The PGA Professional (Sittingbourne, GBR) **[56551]**

PGA Profile **[56551]***

Phantom FM (Dublin, DU, IRL) *Unable to locate*

Pharma Bio World (Mumbai, MH, IND) **[45428]**

Pharma Japan (Tokyo, JPN) *Unable to locate*

The Pharma Review (New Delhi, DH, IND) **[45635]**

Pharma Times (Mumbai, MH, IND) **[45429]**

Pharmaceutical Manufacturing and Packing Sourcer (London, GBR) **[55076]**

Pharmaceutical Research (Dordrecht, NLD) **[48525]**

Pharmaceutical Technology Asia (Chester, GBR) *Unable to locate*

Pharmaceutical Technology Europe (Chester, GBR) **[52998]**

Pharmaceuticals Policy and Law (Granada, SPA) **[50718]**

Pharmacogenomics (London, GBR) **[55077]**

The Pharmacogenomics Journal (London, GBR) **[55078]**

Pharmacognosy @MAG (Bangalore, KA, IND) **[44980]**

Pharmacognosy Research (Mumbai, MH, IND) **[45430]**

Pharmacological Reports (Krakow, POL) **[49667]**

Pharmacological Research (Amsterdam, NLD) **[48199]**

Pharmacometrics (Sendai, JPN) **[46668]**

Pharmacy Education (The Hague, NLD) **[48625]**

Pharmacy Magazine (London, GBR) *Unable to locate*

Pharmacy News (Delhi, DH, IND) *Unable to locate*

Pharmacy in Practice (Esher, GBR) **[53338]**

Pharmacy Today (Brussels, BEL) **[42869]**

Pharmstudent (Varanasi, UP, IND) *Unable to locate*

Pharos International (Maidstone, GBR) **[55530]**

Phase Transitions (Grenoble, FRA) **[43959]**

Philament (Sydney, NW, AUS) **[42561]**

Philanthropy International (Geneva, SWI) *Ceased*

The Philippine Agricultural Scientist (Laguna, PHL) **[49507]**

Philippine Architecture, Engineering & Construction Record (Quezon City, PHL) *Unable to locate*

Philippine Daily Inquirer (Makati City, PHL) **[49519]**

Philippine Economic Journal (Quezon City, PHL) *Ceased*

The Philippine Entomologist (Laguna, PHL) **[49508]**

Philippine Fishing Journal (Rizal, PHL) *Unable to locate*

Philippine Headline News Online (Manila, PHL) **[49554]**

Philippine I.T. Journal (Manila, PHL) *Unable to locate*

Philippine Journal of Development (Makati City, PHL) **[49520]**

Philippine Journal of Fisheries (Quezon City, PHL) *Unable to locate*

Philippine Journal of Internal Medicine (Pasig City, PHL) **[49573]**

Philippine Journal of Labor and Industrial Relations (Quezon City, PHL) *Ceased*

Philippine Journal of Linguistics (Manila, PHL) **[49555]**

Philippine Journal of Nursing (Manila, PHL) **[49556]**

Philippine Journal of Nutrition (Taguig City, PHL) **[49640]**

Philippine Journal of Ophthalmology (Makati City, PHL) **[49521]**

Philippine Journal of Pediatrics (Quezon City, PHL) *Unable to locate*

Philippine Journal of Plant Industry (Manila, PHL) *Unable to locate*

Philippine Journal of Psychology (Quezon City, PHL) **[49606]**

Philippine Journal of Public Administration (Quezon City, PHL) **[49607]**

Philippine Journal of Science (Taguig City, PHL) **[49641]**

Philippine Journal of Veterinary and Animal Sciences (Laguna, PHL) *Unable to locate*

Philippine Journal of Veterinary Medicine (Laguna, PHL) *Unable to locate*

Philippine Labor Review (Manila, PHL) **[49557]**

Philippine Law Journal (Quezon City, PHL) **[49608]**

Philippine Mining & Engineering Journal (Rizal, PHL) *Unable to locate*

The Philippine Natural Law Journal (Quezon City, PHL) *Unable to locate*

Philippine Natural Resources Law Journal (Quezon City, PHL) *Unable to locate*

Philippine Phytopathology (Laguna, PHL) *Unable to locate*

Philippine Planning Journal (Quezon City, PHL) **[49609]**

Philippine Quarterly of Culture and Society (Cebu City, PHL) **[49462]**

Philippine Review of Economics (Quezon City, PHL) **[49610]**

Philippine Review of Economics and Business (Quezon City, PHL) *Ceased*

Philippine Rotary (Quezon City, PHL) **[49611]**

Philippine Scientific Journal (Kaloocan City, PHL) *Unable to locate*

Philippine Scientist (Cebu City, PHL) **[49463]**

Philippine Social Sciences Review (Quezon City, PHL) **[49612]**

Philippine Society (Makati City, PHL) **[49522]**

Philippine Sociological Review (Quezon City, PHL) **[49613]**

Philippine Studies (Quezon City, PHL) **[49614]**

Philippine Tatler (Makati City, PHL) **[49523]**

Philippines' Best Restaurants (Makati City, PHL) **[49524]**

Philippiniana Sacra (Manila, PHL) **[49558]**

Philologia (Warsaw, POL) **[49746]**

Philosophia Mathematica (Oxford, GBR) **[56153]**

Philosophica (Calcutta, WB, IND) *Unable to locate*

Philosophical Explorations (Abingdon, GBR) **[52010]**

Philosophical Forum (Sofia, BUL) *Unable to locate*

The Philosophical Forum (Oxford, GBR) **[56154]**

Philosophical Investigations (Swansea, GBR) **[56705]**

Philosophical Newspaper (Sofia, BUL) *Unable to locate*

Philosophical Papers (Grahamstown, SAF) **[50510]**

Philosophical Psychology (Abingdon, GBR) **[52011]**

The Philosophical Quarterly (Oxford, GBR) **[56155]**

Philosophical Studies (Dordrecht, NLD) **[48526]**

Philosophical Transactions of the Royal Society A (London, GBR) **[55079]**

Philosophical Transactions of the Royal Society B (London, GBR) **[55080]**

Philosophy (London, GBR) **[55081]**

Philosophy, Ethics, and Humanities in Medicine (London, GBR) **[55082]**

Philosophy & Social Action (Dehradun, UP, IND) *Unable to locate*

Philosophy & Social Criticism (London, GBR) **[55083]**

Phlebology (London, GBR) **[55084]**

Phnom Penh Post (Phnom Penh, CMB) **[43113]**

Phoenix (Peradeniya, SRI) *Unable to locate*

Phoenix (Sheffield, GBR) **[56509]**

Photo Imaging (Mumbai, MH, IND) **[45431]**

Photo Work (Katzenthal, FRA) *Unable to locate*

Photochemical & Photobiological Science (Cambridge, GBR) **[52882]**

Photodermatology, Photoimmunology and Photomedicine (Oxford, GBR) **[56156]**

Photodiagnosis and Photodynamic Therapy (Singapore, SGP) **[50238]**

Photogrammetric Record (Romsey, GBR) **[56407]**

The Photographer (Aylesbury, GBR) **[52148]**

Photography Middle East (Dubai, UAE) *Unable to locate*

Photography Monthly (Saffron Walden, GBR) **[56429]**

Photohistorica (London, GBR) *Unable to locate*

Photonic Network Communications (Dordrecht, NLD) **[48527]**

Photonics and Nanostructures (Ankara, TUR) **[51499]**

PhotoResearcher (London, GBR) *Unable to locate*

Photoshop Creative (Bournemouth, GBR) **[52419]**

Photosynthesis Research (Dordrecht, NLD) **[48528]**

Photosynthetica (Dordrecht, NLD) **[48529]**

Phronesis (Leiden, NLD) **[48716]**

Phuket Gazette (Phuket, THA) **[51464]**

Phuket Tatler (Bangkok, THA) **[51429]**

Phycological Research (Kochi, JPN) **[46436]**

Physica A (Heverlee, BEL) **[42888]**

Physica B (Amsterdam, NLD) **[48200]**

Physica E (Amsterdam, NLD) **[48201]**

Physica Scripta (Bristol, GBR) **[52716]**

physica status solidi (a) (Garching, GER) **[44379]**

physica status solidi (b) (Garching, GER) **[44380]**

physica status solidi (c) (Garching, GER) **[44381]**

Physical Biology (Colombo, SRI) **[50862]**

Physical Chemistry (Toledo, SPA) **[50840]**

Physical Chemistry, Chemical Physics (Cambridge, GBR) **[52883]**

Physical Education & Recreation; Journal of **[43278]***

Physical Education and Sport (Warsaw, POL) **[49747]**

Physical Education & Sport Pedagogy (Abingdon, GBR) **[52012]**

Physical Therapy Reviews (London, GBR) **[55085]**

Physicians' Association of Madras Journal (Chennai, TN, IND) *Unable to locate*

Physicist **[42262]***

Physico-Chemical Biology (Kanagawa, JPN) *Unable to locate*

Physics of Atomic Nuclei (Moscow, RUS) **[49956]**

Numbers cited in bold after listings are entry numbers rather than page numbers.

Physics C: Physics and Computers; International Journal of Modern [50186]*

Physics and Chemistry of the Earth (Amsterdam, NLD) [48202]

Physics and Chemistry of the Earth, Part A [48202]*

Physics and Chemistry of the Earth, Part B [48202]*

Physics and Chemistry of the Earth, Part C [48202]*

Physics & Chemistry of Glasses (Sheffield, GBR) [56510]

Physics and Chemistry of Minerals (Bayreuth, GER) [44147]

Physics E: Report on Nuclear Physics; International Journal of Modern [50188]*

Physics Education (London, GBR) [55086]

Physics For You (New Delhi, DH, IND) [45636]

Physics Journal of the Indonesian Physical Society (Tangerang, IDN) [45870]

Physics of Life Reviews (Singapore, SGP) [50239]

Physics of Low-Dimensional Structures (Moscow, RUS) Unable to locate

Physics in Medicine and Biology (Bristol, GBR) [52717]

Physics of Metals and Metallography (Ekaterinburg, RUS) [49855]

Physics News (Mumbai, MH, IND) Unable to locate

Physics of Particles and Nuclei Letters (Moscow, RUS) [49957]

Physics Reports (Amsterdam, NLD) [48203]

Physics of Sintering [50083]*

Physics of the Solid State (Saint Petersburg, RUS) [50024]

Physics Teacher (Calcutta, WB, IND) Unable to locate

Physics World (London, GBR) [55087]

Physiologia Plantarum (Lund, SWE) [50989]

Physiological Entomology (Oxford, GBR) [56157]

Physiological Measurement (Bristol, GBR) [52718]

Physiology and Ecology Japan (Kyoto, JPN) Unable to locate

Physiotherapy (Kidlington, GBR) [53704]

Physiotherapy Moves (Camberwell, VI, AUS) Ceased

Physiotherapy Theory and Practice (Abingdon, GBR) [52013]

Physitherapy, Balneology and Rehabilitation (Moscow, RUS) [49958]

Phytochemistry (Murcia, SPA) [50822]

Phytocoenologia (Stuttgart, GER) [44676]

Phytoma La Defense des Vegetaux (Paris, FRA) [44075]

Phytomorphology (Jodhpur, RJ, IND) [45228]

Phytoparasitica (Dordrecht, NLD) [48530]

Phytopathologische Zeitschrift [56058]*

Phytophaga (Chennai, TN, IND) Unable to locate

Phytotaxonomy (New Delhi, DH, IND) Unable to locate

PI Projekt & Interieur (Amsterdam, NLD) Unable to locate

PIA (Papers from the Institute of Archaeology) (London, GBR) [55088]

Pia-Shaver (Karachi, PAK) Unable to locate

Piano [54666]*

Picture Arrowwords (London, GBR) [55089]

Picture House (Teddington, GBR) Unable to locate

The Picture Premium (Sydney, NW, AUS) [42562]

Picturpost (Madras, TN, IND) Unable to locate

PIDE Tidings (Islamabad, PAK) Ceased

Pig Industry News (Unley, SA, AUS) [42660]

Pig News and Information (Wallingford, GBR) [56822]

Pigment Cell and Melanoma Research (Oxford, GBR) [56158]

Pigment Cell Research [56158]*

Pigment & Resin Technology (Bradford, GBR) [52537]

PIK (Berlin, GER) [44226]

Pik Pak Boom Kiddie Magazine (Makati City, PHL) Unable to locate

PILC Journal of Dravidic Studies (Pondicherry, PN, IND) Unable to locate

Pilihan Radio-FM (Negara, BRN) Unable to locate

The Pilot [54906]*

pilotmagazinet (Ludvika, SWE) [50980]

Pine News International [52269]*

Pine Rivers Press (Strathpine, QL, AUS) [42392]

Pineal Gland (New Delhi, DH, IND) Unable to locate

Pingdingshan People's Broadcasting Station (Pingdingshan, HN, CHN) Unable to locate

Pingdingshan People's Broadcasting Station (Pingdingshan, HN, CHN) Unable to locate

Pingdingshan People's Broadcasting Station (Pingdingshan, HN, CHN) Unable to locate

Pingdingshan People's Broadcasting Station (Pingdingshan, HN, CHN) Unable to locate

Pingliang People's Broadcasting Station (Pingliang, GS, CHN) Unable to locate

Pingxiang People's Broadcasting Station (Pingxiang, JX, CHN) Unable to locate

Pink (Quezon City, PHL) [49615]

Pink Ink (Bangkok, THA) [51430]

The Pink 'Un (Norwich, GBR) [55738]

Pioneer (New Delhi, DH, IND) Unable to locate

The Pioneer (New Delhi, DH, IND) Unable to locate

Pioneer (Dublin, DU, IRL) [45994]

Pipeline World (London, GBR) [55090]

Pirate-FM - 102.8 (Redruth, GBR) [56383]

Pirate-FM - 102.2 (Redruth, GBR) [56384]

Pirate Radio (Bangkok, THA) Unable to locate

Piscine Oggi (Bologna, ITA) [46128]

Pit & Quarry (Walkerville, SAF) Unable to locate

Pituitary (Dordrecht, NLD) [48531]

Pizzicato International & JNI News (Brussels, BEL) Unable to locate

PKV Research Journal (Akola, MH, IND) Unable to locate

Place Branding (Basingstoke, GBR) [52228]

A Place in the Sun (Surrey, GBR) [56672]

Placencia Breeze (Belize City, BLZ) [42916]

Plains-FM - 96.9 (Christchurch, NZL) [48884]

Plan Magazine (Gent, BEL) Unable to locate

Plan Post (Hamburg, GER) [44423]

Planahome Book of Home Plans (Gomshall, GBR) Unable to locate

Planahome Home Improvement Guide (Gomshall, GBR) Unable to locate

Planchemag (Paris, FRA) Unable to locate

Planera Bygga Bo (Karlskrona, SWE) [50971]

Planet ECO (Sofia, BUL) Unable to locate

Planet Philippines (Quezon City, PHL) [49616]

Planetary and Space Science (Amsterdam, NLD) [48204]

Planews (Singapore, SGP) [50240]

Plankton and Benthos Research (Hakodate, JPN) [46372]

Plankton Biology and Ecology [46372]*

Planned Parenthood (Mumbai, MH, IND) Unable to locate

Planned Parenthood Challenges (London, GBR) Ceased

Planning in London (London, GBR) [55091]

Planning Perspectives (Nottingham, GBR) [55769]

Planning Practice and Research (Abingdon, GBR) [52014]

Planning Theory & Practice (Sheffield, GBR) [56511]

Planning (UK) (London, GBR) [55092]

Plant Biochemical Journal (New Delhi, DH, IND) Unable to locate

Plant Biotechnology Journal (Bristol, GBR) [52719]

Plant Breeding (Oxford, GBR) [56159]

Plant and Cell Physiology (Oxford, GBR) [56160]

Plant Cell Reports (Heidelberg, GER) [44473]

Plant Cell, Tissue and Organ Culture (Dordrecht, NLD) [48532]

Plant Disease Research (Ludhiana, PJ, IND) Unable to locate

Plant Ecology (Dordrecht, NLD) [48533]

Plant Equipment Hire & Rates (Bedfordview, SAF) Unable to locate

Plant Foods for Human Nutrition (Dordrecht, NLD) [48534]

Plant Genetic Resources (Cambridge, GBR) [52884]

Plant Heritage (Guildford, GBR) [53494]

Plant Methods (London, GBR) [55093]

Plant Molecular Biology (Dordrecht, NLD) [48535]

Plant Pathology Journal (Faisalabad, PAK) [49278]

The Plant Pathology Journal (Seoul, KOR) Unable to locate

Plant Physiology and Biochemistry (Amsterdam, NLD) [48205]

Plant Production Science (Tokyo, JPN) [47018]

Plant Products Research Journal (Nsukka, NGA) [49152]

Plant Science (Perpignan, FRA) [44093]

Plant Sciences Research (Faisalabad, PAK) [49279]

Plant Signaling & Behavior (Bonn, GER) [44269]

Plant and Soil (Dordrecht, NLD) [48536]

Plant Species Biology (Oxford, GBR) [56161]

Plant & Works Engineering (London, GBR) Unable to locate

Plant World (Buckhurst Hill, GBR) [52751]

Planta Medica (Emmering, GER) Unable to locate

The Planters' Chronicle (Coimbatore, TN, IND) Unable to locate

Planters Journal and Agriculturist (Calcutta, WB, IND) Unable to locate

Plasma Chemistry and Plasma Processing (Dordrecht, NLD) [48537]

Plasma Physics and Controlled Fusion (Bristol, GBR) [52720]

Plasma Physics Reports (Moscow, RUS) [49959]

Plasma Processing (Tokyo, JPN) Unable to locate

Plasma Sources Science and Technology (Bristol, GBR) [52721]

Plasmid (Amsterdam, NLD) [48206]

Plast Panorama Scandinavia (Copenhagen, DEN) Unable to locate

Plastichem (Singapore, SGP) Unable to locate

Plastico Industrial (Sao Paulo, SP, BRZ) [43044]

Plastico Moderno (Sao Paulo, SP, BRZ) Unable to locate

Plasticos (Buenos Aires, ARG) [41478]

Plastics, Additives and Compounding (Oxford, GBR) [56162]

Plastics News International (Southbank, VI, AUS) [42380]

Plastics & Rubber Asia (Paddock Wood, GBR) [56238]

Plastics, Rubber and Composites (London, GBR) [55094]

Plastics, Rubber and Leather Industries Journal (Baroda, GJ, IND) Unable to locate

Plastics & Rubber Singapore Journal (Singapore, SGP) [50241]

Plastics & Rubber Weekly (London, GBR) Unable to locate

Plasticulture Journal (Madrid, SPA) [50789]

Plastiquarian (Berkshire, GBR) [52316]

Platelets (Nottingham, GBR) [55770]

Platinum Metals Review (London, GBR) [55095]

Platt's International Petrochemical Report (London, GBR) Unable to locate

Play (Bournemouth, GBR) [52420]

Play Action (Bognor Regis, GBR) [52401]

Play-FM - 99.6 (Shmeisani, JOR) [47168]

PLAY THERAPY (Weybridge, GBR) [56913]

Playback & Fast Forward [45443]*

Playboating Magazine (Cheltenham, GBR) Unable to locate

Playboy Japan (Tokyo, JPN) Unable to locate

Player (London, GBR) Unable to locate

PlayStation 2 (Bondi Junction, NW, AUS) [41609]

PlayStation 2 Official Australian Magazine [42557]*

The Plaza (Tokyo, JPN) [47019]

Numbers cited in bold after listings are entry numbers rather than page numbers.

Master Index

PLC Practical Law for Companies (London, GBR) *Unable to locate*

Plein Air (Rome, ITA) *Unable to locate*

Plinius (Stuttgart, GER) **[44677]**

Plot (Amsterdam, NLD) *Unable to locate*

Plumbing, Heating & Air Movement News (Flitwick, GBR) **[53391]**

Plus Comic (Leicester, GBR) *Ceased*

Plus Process (Glostrup, DEN) **[43712]**

Plus: The Total Computer Magazine (Mumbai, MH, IND) *Unable to locate*

Plymouth Sound-FM **[56277]***

Plyus Kirov (Kirov, RUS) *Unable to locate*

PN Promotion (Bangkok, THA) *Unable to locate*

PNC (London, GBR) **[55096]**

Pobreza Urbana y Desarrollo (Buenos Aires, ARG) *Unable to locate*

Pocklington Post (Edinburgh, GBR) *Unable to locate*

Podiahy Nolo (London, GBR) *Unable to locate*

Podiatry Now (London, GBR) *Unable to locate*

Podiatry Review (Southport, GBR) **[56588]**

Poe Newsletter **[56163]***

Poe Studies/Dark Romanticism (Oxford, GBR) **[56163]**

Poet (Madras, TN, IND) *Unable to locate*

Poetcrit (Maranda, HP, IND) *Unable to locate*

Poetics (Amsterdam, NLD) **[48207]**

Poetry (Berhampur, OR, IND) *Unable to locate*

Poetry Kanto (Yokohama, JPN) **[47141]**

Poetry and Little Press Information (Oxford, GBR) *Unable to locate*

Poetry Review (London, GBR) **[55097]**

Poetry Time (Berhampur, OR, IND) *Unable to locate*

Poets International (Bangalore, KA, IND) *Unable to locate*

Pogrom- Bedrohte Volker (Gottingen, GER) *Unable to locate*

Point to Point and Hunter Chase Magazine (Dorset, GBR) **[53196]**

Point 3 (Aylesbury, GBR) **[52149]**

Point of View (New Delhi, DH, IND) *Unable to locate*

Points de Vente (Paris, FRA) *Unable to locate*

Points de Vues Initiatiques (Paris, FRA) **[44076]**

PokerPlayer (London, GBR) **[55098]**

Polar Biology (Kiel, GER) **[44507]**

Polar Bioscience (Tokyo, JPN) **[47020]**

Polar Research (Tromso, NOR) **[49214]**

Police (Leatherhead, GBR) **[53753]**

The Police Journal (Isle of Man, GBR) **[53664]**

Police Practice and Research (Abingdon, GBR) **[52015]**

Policing (Bradford, GBR) **[52538]**

Policing and Society (Abingdon, GBR) **[52016]**

Policy and Politics (Bristol, GBR) **[52722]**

Policy and Practice in Health and Safety (Wigston, GBR) **[56925]**

Policy Sciences (Dordrecht, NLD) **[48538]**

Policy Studies (Abingdon, GBR) **[52017]**

Polina (Kiev, URE) **[51604]**

POLIS (Nicosia, CYP) **[43597]**

Polish Analytical Philosophy (Amsterdam, NLD) **[48208]**

Polish Forest Wood Industry (Warsaw, POL) *Unable to locate*

Polish Gerontology (Krakow, POL) **[49668]**

Polish Journal of Chemical Technology (Warsaw, POL) **[49748]**

Polish Journal of Endocrinology (Zabrze, POL) **[49783]**

Polish Journal of Medical Physics and Engineering (Warsaw, POL) **[49749]**

Polish Journal of Natural Sciences (Warsaw, POL) **[49750]**

Polish Journal of Pharmacology **[49667]***

Polish Journal of Surgery (Warsaw, POL) **[49751]**

Polish Maritime Research (Warsaw, POL) **[49752]**

Polish Pneumology and Allergology (Warsaw, POL) **[49753]**

Polish Psychological Bulletin (Warsaw, POL) **[49754]**

Polish Sexology (Warsaw, POL) **[49755]**

Polish Surgery (Katowice, POL) **[49662]**

Politeia (Singapore, SGP) *Unable to locate*

Politica Exterior (Madrid, SPA) **[50790]**

Political Analysis (Oxford, GBR) **[56164]**

Political Communication (Abingdon, GBR) **[52018]**

Political Crossroads (South Melbourne, VI, AUS) **[42375]**

Political Economy Journal of India (Chandigarh, CH, IND) *Unable to locate*

The Political Quarterly (Oxford, GBR) **[56165]**

Political Risk Services (Makati City, PHL) *Unable to locate*

Political Science Review (Jaipur, RJ, IND) *Unable to locate*

Political Scientist (Ranchi, BH, IND) *Unable to locate*

Political Studies (Oxford, GBR) **[56166]**

Political Studies (Sheffield, GBR) **[56512]**

Political Studies Review (Oxford, GBR) **[56167]**

Political Theology (London, GBR) **[55099]**

Politics (Glasgow, GBR) **[53440]**

Politics, Philosophy & Economics (London, GBR) **[55100]**

Politik i Norden (Copenhagen, DEN) *Ceased*

Politikon (Abingdon, GBR) **[52019]**

Politisk Horisont (Copenhagen, DEN) *Unable to locate*

Politsche Rundschau (Bern, SWI) *Unable to locate*

Pollack Periodica (Budapest, HUN) **[44864]**

Pollution Atmospherique (Paris, FRA) **[44077]**

Pollution Research (Karad, MH, IND) *Unable to locate*

Polski Tygodnik Lekavski (Warsaw, POL) *Unable to locate*

Polycyclic Aromatic Compounds (Talence, FRA) **[44115]**

Polygon **[52367]***

Polymer (Amsterdam, NLD) **[48209]**

Polymer Bulletin (Mainz, GER) **[44544]**

Polymer Degradation and Stability (Brighton, GBR) **[52628]**

Polymer Journal (Tokyo, JPN) **[47021]**

Polymer Science (Moscow, RUS) **[49960]**

Polymer Science, Series C (Moscow, RUS) **[49961]**

Polymer Testing (Ruyton XI Towns, GBR) **[56428]**

Polymers Paint Colour Journal (Surrey, GBR) **[56673]**

Pontefract & Castleford Express (Castleford, GBR) **[52952]**

Pony Magazine (Grayshott, GBR) **[53481]**

Pool (Maidenhead, GBR) **[55524]**

The Pool Newspaper (Freetown, SLE) **[50096]**

Poolside (North Ryde, NW, AUS) **[42193]**

Poolside Showcase (North Ryde, NW, AUS) **[42194]**

Poona Agricultural College Magazine (Pune, MH, IND) *Unable to locate*

POPCORN (Munich, GER) **[44578]**

Popular Astronomi (Stockholm, SWE) **[51030]**

Popular Astronomy (Birmingham, GBR) **[52361]**

Popular Electronics (Mumbai, MH, IND) *Unable to locate*

Popular Filateli (Otterup, DEN) *Unable to locate*

Popular Flying (Brackley, GBR) **[52433]**

Popular Medicine (Shanghai, CHN) **[43494]**

Popular Music (Norwich, GBR) **[55739]**

Popular Music History (London, GBR) **[55101]**

Popular Patchwork (Orpington, GBR) **[55855]**

Popular Photography (Beijing, CHN) *Unable to locate*

Popular Plastics (Mumbai, MH, IND) *Unable to locate*

Population Abstracts (Mumbai, MH, IND) *Ceased*

Population Ecology (Tokyo, JPN) **[47022]**

Population Geography (New Delhi, DH, IND) *Unable to locate*

Population Headliners (Bangkok, THA) **[51431]**

Population Health Metrics (London, GBR) **[55102]**

Population Research Abstract (Bangalore, KA, IND) *Unable to locate*

Population Research and Policy Review (Dordrecht, NLD) **[48539]**

Population Studies (London, GBR) **[55103]**

Population Trends (London, GBR) *Unable to locate*

Populyarnoye Radio (Chita, RUS) *Unable to locate*

Populyarnoye Raedio (Chita, RUS) *Unable to locate*

Por la Danza (Madrid, SPA) **[50791]**

Porfolio Organizer (Hyderabad, AP, IND) **[45179]**

The Porirua News (Johnsonville, NZL) *Unable to locate*

Porselensmaling (Kirkenar, NOR) *Unable to locate*

Port Curtis Post (Sydney, NW, AUS) **[42563]**

Port Elizabeth Express (Cape Town, SAF) **[50401]**

Port and Harbour Engineer (Calcutta, WB, IND) *Unable to locate*

Port Harcourt Medical Journal (Port Harcourt, RV, NGA) **[49169]**

Port O'Call (Singapore, SGP) *Unable to locate*

Port Phillip Leader (Glen Iris, VI, AUS) **[41893]**

Portadown Times (Portadown, GBR) **[56284]**

Ports and Harbors (Tokyo, JPN) **[47023]**

Portside Messenger (Kidman Park, SA, AUS) **[41987]**

Portugal Rotario (Porto, PRT) *Unable to locate*

Portuguese Journal of Social Science (London, GBR) **[55104]**

Portuguese Studies (London, GBR) **[55105]**

PoS (Proceedings of Science) (Trieste, ITA) **[46266]**

Posh (London, GBR) *Unable to locate*

Positive Health (Portsmouth, GBR) **[56292]**

Positive Living (Christchurch, NZL) *Unable to locate*

Positive Nation (London, GBR) **[55106]**

Posledni Generace (Brno, CZE) *Unable to locate*

Post-Communist Economies (Abingdon, GBR) **[52020]**

Post-Courier (Port Moresby, PNG) **[49403]**

Post Magazine (London, GBR) **[55107]**

Post-Medieval Archaeology (London, GBR) **[55108]**

Post Script (Chatswood, NW, AUS) **[41743]**

Postal History (Beckenham, GBR) *Unable to locate*

Postcolonial Studies (Abingdon, GBR) **[52021]**

Poste Py Fizyki (Warsaw, POL) *Unable to locate*

Postepy Astronautyki (Warsaw, POL) *Unable to locate*

Poster (Warsaw, POL) *Unable to locate*

Postgraduate Institute of Medical Education and Research, Chandigarh—Bulletin (Chandigarh, CH, IND) *Unable to locate*

Postgraduate Medical Journal (London, GBR) **[55109]**

Postharvest News and Information (Wallingford, GBR) **[56823]**

Posthornet (Oslo, NOR) **[49206]**

Postitorvi (Helsinki, FIN) *Unable to locate*

Potato Processing International (Oxted, GBR) **[56237]**

Potchefstroom Electronic Law Journal (Mmabatho, SAF) **[50556]**

Potchefstroom Herald (Cape Town, SAF) **[50402]**

Potential Analysis (Dordrecht, NLD) **[48540]**

Pottery in Australia (Sydney, NW, AUS) *Unable to locate*

Poultry Adviser (Bangalore, KA, IND) *Unable to locate*

Poultry Guide (Gurgaon, HY, IND) *Unable to locate*

Poultry Patrika (New Delhi, DH, IND) *Unable to locate*

Poultry World (Sutton, GBR) **[56691]**

Pour nos Jardins (Valenciennes, FRA) **[44121]**

Povestea Mea (Bucharest, ROM) **[49841]**

Powder Metallurgy (London, GBR) **[55110]**

Numbers cited in bold after listings are entry numbers rather than page numbers.

Powder Metallurgy Science and Technology (Hyderabad, AP, IND) *Unable to locate*

Powder Technology (Amsterdam, NLD) **[48210]**

POWDEReporter (London, GBR) **[55111]**

Power Economics (Daruvar, CTA) *Unable to locate*

The Power Engineer (Bedford, GBR) **[52275]**

Power-FM (Calcutta, WB, IND) *Unable to locate*

Power-FM (Canary Islands, SPA) *Unable to locate*

Power-FM (Canary Islands, SPA) *Unable to locate*

Power-FM (Canary Islands, SPA) *Unable to locate*

Power-FM - 100 (Istanbul, TUR) **[51568]**

Power 98 FM - 98.0 MHz (Singapore, SGP) **[50303]**

Power Rangers (London, GBR) **[55112]**

PowerStation (Bournemouth, GBR) **[52421]**

Powys Journal (Taunton, GBR) **[56722]**

The Powys Review (Desborough, GBR) **[53175]**

Poznan Studies in Contemporary Linguistics (Warsaw, POL) **[49756]**

PPA Members' Handbook **[54894]***

PR Zimbabwe (Harare, ZWE) *Unable to locate*

Prachya Pratibha (Bhopal, MP, IND) *Unable to locate*

Practica (Athens, GRC) *Unable to locate*

Practical Boat Owner (Poole, GBR) **[56281]**

Practical Crafts (West Sussex, GBR) *Unable to locate*

Practical Diabetes International (Portsmouth, GBR) **[56293]**

Practical Digital Video (Bournemouth, GBR) **[52422]**

Practical Fishkeeping (London, GBR) **[55113]**

The Practical Lawyer (London, GBR) **[55114]**

Practical Neurology (London, GBR) **[55115]**

Practical Parenting and Pregnancy (London, GBR) **[55116]**

Practical Poultry (Cudham, GBR) **[53146]**

Practical Psychology (Dehradun, UP, IND) *Unable to locate*

Practice Development in Health Care (Bognor Regis, GBR) **[52402]**

Practice Nurse (Stockholm, SWE) *Unable to locate*

The Practising Administrator **[42239]***

Praehistorische Zeitschrift (Berlin, GER) **[44227]**

Pragativadi (Bhubaneswar, WB, IND) **[45014]**

Pragmatics (Antwerp, BEL) *Unable to locate*

Pragmatics & Cognition (Amsterdam, NLD) **[48211]**

Prague Business Journal (Prague, CZE) *Unable to locate*

Prague Daily Monitor (Prague, CZE) **[43635]**

The Prague Post (Prague, CZE) **[43636]**

Praise-FM - 105.7 (East Caribbean, WIN) **[57102]**

Prajashakthi (Colombo, SRI) *Unable to locate*

Prajna (Varanasi, UP, IND) *Unable to locate*

Prajnan (Pune) (Pune, MH, IND) **[45699]**

Prakriti Vani (Lucknow, UP, IND) *Unable to locate*

Praktika (Budapest, HUN) **[44865]**

Pramana - Journal of Physics (Bangalore, KA, IND) **[44981]**

Prambors Bandung-FM - 98.4 (Bandung, IDN) **[45777]**

Prambors Jakarta-FM - 102.2 (Jakarta, IDN) **[45806]**

Prambors Makassar-FM - 105.1 (Makassar, IDN) **[45828]**

Prambors Medan-FM - 97.5 (Medan, IDN) **[45835]**

Prambors Semarang-FM - 102 (Semarang, IDN) **[45850]**

Prambors Solo-FM - 99.2 (Solo Baru, IDN) **[45856]**

Prambors Surabaya-FM - 89.3 (Surabaya, IDN) **[45861]**

Prasar (Jaipur, RJ, IND) *Unable to locate*

Pratibha India (New Delhi, DH, IND) *Unable to locate*

Pratiques Psychologiques (Amsterdam, NLD) **[48212]**

Pravoslavnoye Radio (St. Petersburg, RUS) *Unable to locate*

Prawdziwe Zycie (Warsaw, POL) **[49757]**

Prayaasa (New Delhi, DH, IND) *Unable to locate*

Precambrian Research (Amsterdam, NLD) **[48213]**

Precision Agriculture (Dordrecht, NLD) **[48541]**

Precision Marketing (Johannesburg, SAF) *Unable to locate*

Precision Marketing (London, GBR) **[55117]**

Precision Toolmaker (Epsom, GBR) *Unable to locate*

Predator **[56952]***

Prediction (Croydon, GBR) **[53131]**

Pregnancy & Babycare (Singapore, SGP) *Unable to locate*

Premier-AM - 1413 (London, GBR) **[55457]**

Premier Radio-AM - 1305 (London, GBR) **[55459]**

Premier Radio-AM - 1332 (London, GBR) **[55458]**

Prep School (Woodbridge, GBR) **[56958]**

Prerak Lalkari (Mumbai, MH, IND) *Unable to locate*

The Presbyterian Herald (Belfast, GBR) **[52292]**

Preserve! (Castleford, GBR) *Unable to locate*

Press Council of India Review (New Delhi, DH, IND) *Unable to locate*

Press in India (New Delhi, DH, IND) *Unable to locate*

Press and Public Relations (New Delhi, DH, IND) *Unable to locate*

Pressure Points (Huntingdon, GBR) *Ceased*

Pressure Vessel Technology (Tokyo, JPN) *Unable to locate*

Prestige Corporate Interiors (Horsham, GBR) **[53597]**

Prestige High Street Interiors (Horsham, GBR) **[53598]**

Prestige Hotel & Restaurant Interiors (Horsham, GBR) **[53599]**

Preston Leader (Melbourne, VI, AUS) **[42082]**

Pretexts (Abingdon, GBR) *Ceased*

Prevention of Food Adulteration Cases (New Delhi, DH, IND) **[45637]**

Preventive Medicine (Amsterdam, NLD) **[48214]**

Preview (Mandaluyong City, PHL) **[49539]**

Priests & People **[55061]***

Prikladnaya Matematika i Mekhanika **[48047]***

Prima Comunicazione (Milan, ITA) **[46191]**

Primary Care Respiratory Journal (Lockerbie, GBR) **[53888]**

Primary English **[53797]***

Primary Health Care (Harrow, GBR) **[53532]**

Primary Market Survey (New Delhi, DH, IND) *Unable to locate*

Primary Mathematics (Leicester, GBR) **[53817]**

Primary Teaching Studies (Stoke-on-Trent, GBR) *Ceased*

Primary Times (Bristol, GBR) **[52723]**

Primates (Tokyo, JPN) **[47024]**

Prime (Leicester, GBR) **[53818]**

Primer (Harleston, GBR) *Unable to locate*

Primer Acto (Madrid, SPA) **[50792]**

Princesa-FM - 96.9 (Feira de Santana, BH, BRZ) **[42978]**

Principals Today (Christchurch, NZL) **[48877]**

Print Buyer (London, GBR) **[55118]**

Printindia (Chennai, TN, IND) *Unable to locate*

Printing Field (Shanghai, CHN) **[43495]**

Printing Industries (London, GBR) *Unable to locate*

Printing Times (New Delhi, DH, IND) *Unable to locate*

Printing World (London, GBR) *Unable to locate*

Printing World (London, GBR) *Unable to locate*

Printwear & Promotion (Kent, GBR) **[53679]**

PrintWeek (London, GBR) **[55119]**

Prism (New Delhi, DH, IND) *Unable to locate*

Prisma (Jakarta, IDN) *Unable to locate*

Priv. (Tokyo, JPN) **[47025]**

Privat Computer (Copenhagen, DEN) *Unable to locate*

PrivatAir (London, GBR) **[55120]**

Private Equity Europe (London, GBR) **[55121]**

Private Finance Initiative Journal (Stockport, GBR) *Unable to locate*

Private Hospital Healthcare Europe (London, GBR) **[55122]**

Privatisation International (London, GBR) *Ceased*

Privatnyi Dom (Kiev, URE) **[51605]**

PrivatSea (London, GBR) **[55123]**

Pro Familia Magazin (Frankfurt am Main, GER) **[44368]**

Pro-Fono Revista de Atualizacao Cientifica (Vicosa, MI, BRZ) **[43062]**

Pro Motor (The Hague, NLD) **[48626]**

Pro Shop Europe (Salisbury, GBR) **[56456]**

Probability Surveys (Cambridge, GBR) **[52885]**

Probability Theory and Related Fields (Paris, FRA) **[44078]**

Probe India (Allahabad, UP, IND) *Unable to locate*

Probitas (Berhampur, OR, IND) *Unable to locate*

Problems of Aging & Longevity (Kiev, URE) **[51606]**

Problems of Biological, Medical and Pharmaceutical Chemistry (Moscow, RUS) **[49962]**

Problems of Endocrinology (Moscow, RUS) **[49963]**

Problems of Health Resort Treatment, Physiotherapy & Exercise Therapy (Moscow, RUS) **[49964]**

Problems of National Liberation (Calcutta, WB, IND) *Unable to locate*

Problems & Perspectives in Management (Sumy, URE) **[51618]**

Problems of Social Hygiene, Health Care & History of Medicine (Moscow, RUS) **[49965]**

Problems of Special Libraries (Sofia, BUL) *Unable to locate*

Problems of Tuberculosis (Moscow, RUS) **[49966]**

Problems of Virology (Moscow, RUS) **[49967]**

Probus (Amsterdam, NLD) **[48215]**

Probus Magazine (Droitwich, GBR) *Unable to locate*

Procap (Zurich, SWI) *Unable to locate*

Proceedings (London, GBR) **[55124]**

Proceedings of the Aristotelian Society (London, GBR) **[55125]**

Proceedings of the Boston Area Colloquium in Ancient Philosophy (Leiden, NLD) **[48717]**

Proceedings of the Edinburgh Mathematical Society (Edinburgh, GBR) **[53306]**

Proceedings of the Indian Academy of Sciences (Bangalore, KA, IND) **[44982]**

Proceedings of the International Astronomical Union (Cambridge, GBR) **[52886]**

Proceedings of the Japan Academy, Series A (Tokyo, JPN) **[47026]**

Proceedings of the Japan Academy, Series B (Tokyo, JPN) **[47027]**

Proceedings of the London Mathematical Society (Oxford, GBR) **[56168]**

Proceedings of the Nutrition Society (Cambridge, GBR) **[52887]**

Proceedings of the Polar Biology Symposium of the National Institute of Polar Research **[47020]***

Proceedings of the Royal Microscopical Society **[55989]***

Proceedings of the Society of Antiquaries **[53956]***

Process (Wurzburg, GER) **[44724]**

Process Biochemistry (Vandoeuvre-les-Nancy, FRA) **[44122]**

Process Control (Alphen aan den Rijn, NLD) **[47871]**

Process Engineering (London, GBR) **[55126]**

Process Industry Informer (Liphook, GBR) **[53861]**

Process & Plant Engineering (Mumbai, MH, IND) **[45432]**

Process Products **[53861]***

Process Safety and Environmental Protection (PSEP) (Rugby, GBR) **[56422]**

Procurement Professional (Paradise Point, QL, AUS) **[42228]**

Proddhoot (Dhaka, BGD) *Unable to locate*

Production (London, GBR) *Unable to locate*

The Production Book (Pyrmont, NW, AUS) **[42286]**

Production Research (Tokyo, JPN) *Unable to locate*

Numbers cited in bold after listings are entry numbers rather than page numbers.

Master Index

Production of Selected Industries in India (New Delhi, DH, IND) *Unable to locate*

Productivity (New Delhi, DH, IND) **[45638]**

Productivity Journal (Tokyo, JPN) *Unable to locate*

Productivity News (New Delhi, DH, IND) **[45639]**

Productos del Mar (Madrid, SPA) *Unable to locate*

Proeftuin Nieuws (Sint-Katelijne-Waver, BEL) *Unable to locate*

Profamilia (Santafe de Bogota, COL) *Unable to locate*

Professional Adviser (London, GBR) **[55127]**

Professional Banker (Hyderabad, AP, IND) **[45180]**

Professional Beauty (Pyrmont, NW, AUS) **[42287]**

Professional Beauty/LNE English Edition (London, GBR) **[55128]**

Professional Book Keeper (Sevenoaks, GBR) *Unable to locate*

Professional Broking (London, GBR) **[55129]**

Professional Builder (Watford, GBR) **[56869]**

Professional Builders Merchant (Watford, GBR) **[56870]**

Professional Computing (Sirnach, SWI) **[51231]**

Professional Development in Education (Abingdon, GBR) **[52022]**

Professional Electrician & Installer (Watford, GBR) **[56871]**

Professional Engineer (Calcutta, WB, IND) *Unable to locate*

Professional Engineering (London, GBR) **[55130]**

Professional Fundraising (London, GBR) *Unable to locate*

The Professional Geographer (Oxford, GBR) **[56169]**

Professional Hairdresser (Watford, GBR) **[56872]**

Professional Heating & Plumbing Installer (Watford, GBR) **[56873]**

Professional Landscaper & Groundsman (Horsham, GBR) **[53600]**

Professional Marketing (Port Melbourne, VI, AUS) **[42265]**

Professional Marketing (London, GBR) **[55131]**

Professional Motor Factor (Watford, GBR) **[56874]**

Professional Motor Mechanic (Watford, GBR) **[56875]**

Professional Negligence (London, GBR) *Unable to locate*

Professional Nursery Nurse (Derby, GBR) *Ceased*

Professional Nursing Today (Gauteng, SAF) **[50482]**

Professional Pensions (London, GBR) **[55132]**

Professional Pest Controller (Derby, GBR) **[53168]**

Professional Practice Matters (Saint Albans, GBR) *Unable to locate*

Professional Printer (Tunbridge Wells, GBR) *Unable to locate*

Professional Treater **[52953]***

Professionalism in Practice (Derby, GBR) *Unable to locate*

Profile (Manama, BHR) *Unable to locate*

Profile (Amsterdam, NLD) *Unable to locate*

Profile (Hong Kong, CHN) **[43376]**

Profile (London, GBR) *Unable to locate*

Profile (Yorkshire) (Leeds, GBR) *Ceased*

Profit (Lusaka, ZMB) *Unable to locate*

Profodcil Bulletin (New Delhi, DH, IND) *Unable to locate*

Profound (The Dialog Corporation) - Mathematical Sciences (Bangalore, KA, IND) **[44983]**

Profound (The Dialog Corporation) of the Royal Society A (London, GBR) **[55133]**

Profound (The Dialog Corporation) of the Royal Society B (London, GBR) **[55134]**

Programme Report 2000-2001 (Kathmandu, NPL) *Unable to locate*

Progreso (Leek, GBR) *Unable to locate*

Progress (Vienna, AUT) **[42766]**

Progress (Karachi, PAK) **[49373]**

Progress in Agricultural Engineering Sciences (Budapest, HUN) **[44866]**

Progress in Biophysics & Molecular Biology (Oxford, GBR) **[56170]**

Progress in Computational Fluid Dynamics (Dusseldorf, GER) **[44331]**

Progress in Crystal Growth and Characterization of Materials (Poole, GBR) **[56282]**

Progress in Development Studies (London, GBR) **[55135]**

Progress of Education (Pune, MH, IND) *Unable to locate*

Progress in Histochemistry and Cytochemistry (Basel, SWI) **[51065]**

Progress in Industrial Ecology (Turku, FIN) **[43910]**

Progress Leader (Glen Iris, VI, AUS) **[41894]**

Progress Magazine (Agana, GUM) *Unable to locate*

Progress in Materials Science (Saarbrucken, GER) **[44652]**

Progress in Nuclear Energy (Birmingham, GBR) **[52362]**

Progress in Nuclear Magnetic Resonance Spectroscopy (Southampton, GBR) **[56576]**

Progress in Osteoporosis (Heidelberg, AUS) **[41947]**

Progress in Palliative Care (London, GBR) **[55136]**

Progress in Particle and Nuclear Physics (Tubingen, GER) **[44693]**

Progress in Planning (Manchester, GBR) **[55575]**

Progress in Reproduction (London, GBR) *Ceased*

Progress in Retinal and Eye Research (Oxford, GBR) **[56171]**

Progress in Solid State Chemistry (Augsburg, GER) **[44142]**

Progress in Surface Science (Amsterdam, NLD) **[48216]**

Progress of Theoretical Physics (Kyoto, JPN) **[46483]**

Progress of Theoretical Physics - Supplement (Kyoto, JPN) **[46484]**

Progressio (Rome, ITA) **[46240]**

Progressive Farming (Islamabad, PAK) **[49311]**

Progressive Gifts and Home Worldwide (London, GBR) **[55137]**

Progressive Greetings Worldwide (London, GBR) **[55138]**

Progressive Horticulture (Lucknow, UP, IND) *Unable to locate*

Progressive Housewares (London, GBR) **[55139]**

Proiezioni (Rome, ITA) *Ceased*

Project Finance (London, GBR) *Unable to locate*

Project Manager Today (Hook, GBR) **[53587]**

Project Plant (Glasgow, GBR) **[53441]**

Project Russia (Moscow, RUS) *Unable to locate*

Project Scotland (Glasgow, GBR) **[53442]**

Projects & Profits (Hyderabad, AP, IND) **[45181]**

Projets Feministes (Paris, FRA) *Unable to locate*

Proletarian Path (Calcutta, WB, IND) *Unable to locate*

Prometheus (Abingdon, GBR) **[52023]**

Promotion and Education **[44103]***

Promotional Products Magazine (Templestowe, VI, AUS) **[42617]**

Promotions & Incentives (London, GBR) **[55140]**

Propel (Gudme, DEN) *Ceased*

The Property Executive (Glasgow, GBR) **[53443]**

Property Law Journal (London, GBR) **[55141]**

Property Report Thailand (Bangkok, THA) **[51432]**

Property Week (London, GBR) **[55142]**

Prophylaxe Impulse (Herne, GER) *Unable to locate*

Proprietes de France (Paris, FRA) *Unable to locate*

Proscen (Stockholm, SWE) *Unable to locate*

Proscenium (Leutwil, SWI) *Unable to locate*

Prose Studies (Abingdon, GBR) **[52024]**

Prospect **[53456]***

Prospect (London, GBR) **[55143]**

The Prospective Accountant (Hong Kong, CHN) **[43377]**

Prospects (Geneva, SWI) **[51156]**

Prospects (Cambridge, GBR) *Ceased*

Prostate Cancer and Prostatic Diseases (London, GBR) **[55144]**

Prosthetics and Orthotics International (Copenhagen, DEN) *Unable to locate*

Prosthetics & Orthotics International (Abingdon, GBR) **[52025]**

Protection of Metals (Moscow, RUS) **[49968]**

Protein Engineering, Design and Selection (Oxford, GBR) **[56172]**

Protein Expression and Purification (Amsterdam, NLD) **[48217]**

Proteome Science (London, GBR) **[55145]**

Protestant Truth (London, GBR) **[55146]**

Protist (Cologne, GER) **[44300]**

Protoplasma (Karlsruhe, GER) **[44495]**

Prototype (London, GBR) **[55147]**

Proyeccion (Stourbridge, GBR) *Unable to locate*

Proyecciones Journal of Mathematics (Antofagasta, CHL) **[43132]**

PRS Programme 5-FM - 94.5 (Taipei, TWN) **[51373]**

PRS Programme 4-AM - 1512 (Taipei, TWN) **[51374]**

PRS Programme 9-FM - 101.3 (Taipei, TWN) **[51375]**

PRS Programme 7-FM - 93.1 (Taipei, TWN) **[51376]**

PRS Programme 6-AM - 1314 (Taipei, TWN) **[51377]**

PRS Programme 3-AM - 1116 (Jhubei City, TWN) **[51309]**

PRS Programme 3-AM - 1260 (Taipei, TWN) **[51381]**

PRS Programme 3-AM - 702 (Taipei, TWN) **[51380]**

PRS Programme 3-AM - 990 (Taipei, TWN) **[51378]**

PRS Programme 3-AM - 1125 (Taipei, TWN) **[51379]**

PRS Programme 2-FM - 94.3 (Taipei, TWN) **[51382]**

Prudence (Dublin, DU, IRL) **[45995]**

PRWeek Magazine (London, GBR) **[55148]**

Przedszkolak (Warsaw, POL) **[49758]**

Przekroj (Warsaw, POL) **[49759]**

Przyjaciolka (Warsaw, POL) **[49760]**

Przyroda Polska (Warsaw, POL) *Unable to locate*

PS-bladet (Praksis Sektoren) (Horsholm, DEN) *Unable to locate*

PSE Economic Analyst (Amritsar, PJ, IND) *Unable to locate*

Psicologia (Porto Alegre, RN, BRZ) **[42992]**

Psicologia & Sociedade (Porto Alegre, RN, BRZ) **[42993]**

Psicologia USP (Sao Paulo, SP, BRZ) **[43045]**

Psychiatric Bulletin **[55149]***

The Psychiatrist (London, GBR) **[55149]**

Psychiatry in General Practice (Bydgoszcz, POL) **[49654]**

Psycho-Lingua (Raipur, MP, IND) *Unable to locate*

Psycho-Social-Medicine (Dusseldorf, GER) **[44332]**

Psychoanalysis and History (Edinburgh, GBR) **[53307]**

Psychoanalytic Psychotherapy (Abingdon, GBR) **[52026]**

Psychodynamic Practice (Abingdon, GBR) **[52027]**

Psychogeriatrics (Oxford, GBR) **[56173]**

Psychologia (Tel Aviv, ISR) *Unable to locate*

Psychologia (Kyoto, JPN) **[46485]**

Psychological Research Journal (Calcutta, WB, IND) *Unable to locate*

Psychological Research Psychologische Forschung (Leiden, NLD) **[48718]**

Psychological Science in the Public Interest (Oxford, GBR) **[56174]**

Psychological Studies (Mysore, KA, IND) *Unable to locate*

Psychologie Francaise (Amsterdam, NLD) **[48218]**

Psychologie & NeuroPsychiatrie du vieillissement (Montrouge, FRA) **[44004]**

Psychologie in Osterreich (Vienna, AUT) **[42767]**

Psychologie du Travail et des Organisations (Villeneuved'Ascq, FRA) *Unable to locate*

Psychologies (Bucharest, ROM) **[49842]**

Psychologies South Africa (Cape Town, SAF) **[50403]**

Psychologist Appointments (Leicester, GBR) **[53819]**

Psychology Crime and Law (Abingdon, GBR) **[52028]**

Psychology and Developing Societies (New Delhi, DH, IND) **[45640]**

Psychology and Health (Abingdon, GBR) **[52029]**

Psychology, Health and Medicine (Abingdon, GBR) **[52030]**

Psychology of Language and Communication (Warsaw, POL) **[49761]**

Psychology in Progress (Bangalore, KA, IND) *Unable to locate*

Numbers cited in bold after listings are entry numbers rather than page numbers.

Psychology and Psychotherapy (Leicester, GBR) [53820]

Psychology, Public Policy, and Law (Sydney, NW, AUS) [42564]

Psychology Quarterly (Lahore, PAK) [49387]

Psychology in Spain (Madrid, SPA) [50793]

Psychology of Sport and Exercise (Loughborough, GBR) [55487]

Psychology Teaching Journal (Leicester, GBR) Unable to locate

Psychology of Women Quarterly (Oxford, GBR) [56175]

Psychooncology (Gdansk, POL) [49660]

Psychosomatic Medicine (Sofia, BUL) Unable to locate

Psychotherapy and Politics International (Bognor Regis, GBR) [52403]

Psykhe (Santiago, CHL) [43146]

PT Cipta Televisi Pendidikan Indonesia (TPI) - Jakarta (Jakarta, IDN) Unable to locate

PT Rajawali Citra Televisi Indonesia (RCTI) - Ambon (Jakarta, IDN) Unable to locate

PT Rajawali Citra Televisi Indonesia (RCTI) - Balikpapan (Jakarta, IDN) Unable to locate

PT Rajawali Citra Televisi Indonesia (RCTI) - Semarang (Jakarta, IDN) Unable to locate

PT Rajawali Citra Televisi Indonesia (RCTI) - Ujung Pandang (Jakarta, IDN) Unable to locate

PT Surya Citra Televisi (SCTV) - Solo (Jakarta, IDN) Unable to locate

PT Surya Citra Televisi (SCTV) - Ujung Pandang (Jakarta, IDN) Unable to locate

ptah (Jyvaskyla, FIN) [43871]

P.T.D.I., Jakarta (Jakarta, IDN) Ceased

P.T.D.I. Kota Perak, Yogyakarta (Yogyakarta, IDN) Unable to locate

P.T.D.I. Medari - Sleman (Medari-Sleman, IDN) Unable to locate

PterdeSport International (Wiesbaden, GER) Unable to locate

The Ptolemaic Terrascope Magazine (Melksham, GBR) [55605]

PTV (Quezon City, PHL) Unable to locate

Pub & Club Gazette (Stoke-On-Trent, GBR) Unable to locate

Pubblicazioni della Stazione Zoologica di Napoli [46156]*

PubChef (Crawley, GBR) [53111]

Public Administration (Oxford, GBR) [56176]

Public Administration & Policy (Hong Kong, CHN) [43378]

Public Archaeology (London, GBR) [55150]

Public Choice (Dordrecht, NLD) [48542]

Public Enterprise Recorder (New Delhi, DH, IND) Unable to locate

Public Finance (London, GBR) [55151]

Public Health (London, GBR) [55152]

Public Health Nursing (Oxford, GBR) [56177]

Public Health Nutrition (Cambridge, GBR) [52888]

Public Law (Andover, GBR) [52121]

Public Management Review (Abingdon, GBR) [52031]

Public Network Europe (London, GBR) Unable to locate

Public Opinion Quarterly (Oxford, GBR) [56178]

Public Policy and Administration (Nottingham, GBR) [55771]

Public Relations Journal of India (New Delhi, DH, IND) Unable to locate

Public Sector IT Insight (Stockport, GBR) Unable to locate

Public Sector & Local Government Building (Sevenoaks, GBR) [56480]

Public Sector Technology & Management [50312]*

Public Service Magazine (PSM) (London, GBR) [55153]

Public Transport International (Brussels, BEL) [42870]

Public Undertakings (New Delhi, DH, IND) Unable to locate

Publications of Amakusa Marine Biological Laboratory (Kumamoto, JPN) Unable to locate

Publications of the Astronomical Society of Australia (Sydney, NW, AUS) [42565]

Publications of Astronomical Society of Japan (Tokyo, JPN) [47028]

Publications of the English Goethe Society (London, GBR) [55154]

Publications of Seto Marine Biological Laboratory (Kyoto, JPN) [46486]

Publius (Oxford, GBR) [56179]

Pudhari (Kolhapur, MH, IND) [45256]

Puericultura Market (Barcelona, SPA) Unable to locate

Puff - Fagtidsskrift for Tralast og Byggemarkeder (Glostrup, DEN) [43713]

Puhelin (Telephone) (Helsinki, FIN) Unable to locate

PULL! (Woking, GBR) Ceased

Pulmonary Pharmacology [55155]*

Pulmonary Pharmacology and Therapeutics (London, GBR) [55155]

Pulp & Paper Europe (Brussels, BEL) Unable to locate

Pulp & Paper International (PPI) (Brussels, BEL) [42871]

Puls Radio - 103.3 MHz (Kazan, RUS) [49860]

Pulse (London, GBR) [55156]

Pulse (Swansea, GBR) [56706]

Pulse Classic Gold-AM (Bradford, GBR) Unable to locate

Pulse 8 (Hull, GBR) Unable to locate

The Pulse-FM - 94.7 (Geelong, VI, AUS) [41883]

Pulse-FM - 102.5 (Bradford, GBR) [52559]

Pulse-FM - 97.5 (Bradford, GBR) [52560]

Pulse International (Karachi, PAK) [49374]

Pulse Weekly (Islamabad, PAK) [49312]

Pulse of Youth (New Delhi, DH, IND) Unable to locate

Pump-FM (Karratha, WA, AUS) Unable to locate

Pump Industry Analyst (Oxford, GBR) [56180]

Punishment & Society (London, GBR) [55157]

Punjab Agricultural University Journal of Research (Ludhiana, PJ, IND) Unable to locate

Punjab Fruit Journal (Faisalabad, PAK) Unable to locate

Punjab Horticultural Journal (Chandigarh, CH, IND) Unable to locate

Punjab Journal of English Studies (Amritsar, PJ, IND) Unable to locate

Punjab Journal of Politics (Amritsar, PJ, IND) Unable to locate

Punjab Law Reporter (Chandigarh, CH, IND) Unable to locate

Punjab Medical Journal (Punchkula, IND) Unable to locate

Punjab University Journal of Mathematics (Lahore, PAK) Unable to locate

Punjab University Journal of Zoology (Lahore, PAK) Unable to locate

The Puppet Master (London, GBR) Unable to locate

Purabhilekh-Puratatava (Panaji, GD, IND) Unable to locate

Purchasing (Mumbai, MH, IND) Unable to locate

Pure Weddings (Preston, GBR) [56305]

Pure Weddings North (Norwich, GBR) [55740]

Putian People's Broadcasting Station (Putian, FJ, CHN) Unable to locate

Puutarha & Kauppa (Helsinki, FIN) Unable to locate

Puyang People's Broadcasting Station (Puyang, HN, CHN) Unable to locate

Puzzle Compendium (Redhill, GBR) [56361]

Puzzle Corner Special (Redhill, GBR) [56362]

Puzzle Fun for Kids (Gosford, NW, AUS) [41921]

Puzzle Selection (London, GBR) [55158]

Puzzler (Redhill, GBR) [56363]

Puzzler Arrowords (Redhill, GBR) [56364]

Puzzler Brain Trainer (Redhill, GBR) [56365]

Puzzler Codewords (Redhill, GBR) [56366]

Puzzler Collection (Redhill, GBR) [56367]

Puzzler Crossword (Redhill, GBR) [56368]

Puzzler Kriss Kross (Redhill, GBR) [56369]

Puzzler Pocket Crosswords (Redhill, GBR) [56370]

Puzzler Pocket Crosswords Collection (Redhill, GBR) [56371]

Puzzler Pocket Wordsearch (Redhill, GBR) [56372]

Puzzler Pocket Wordsearch Collection (Redhill, GBR) [56373]

Puzzler Quick Crosswords (Redhill, GBR) [56374]

Puzzler Quiz Kids (Redhill, GBR) [56375]

Puzzler Wordsearch (Redhill, GBR) [56376]

PVRI Review (Mumbai, MH, IND) [45433]

Pyongyang Broadcasting Station - Chongjin (Pyongyang, KOD) Unable to locate

Pyongyang Broadcasting Station - Hwadae (Pyongyang, KOD) Unable to locate

Pyongyang Broadcasting Station - Kangnam (Pyongyang, KOD) Unable to locate

Pyongyang Broadcasting Station - Samgo (Pyongyang, KOD) Unable to locate

Pyongyang Broadcasting Station - Sangwon (Pyongyang, KOD) Unable to locate

Pyongyang Broadcasting Station - Sepo (Pyongyang, KOD) Unable to locate

Pyongyang FM Broadcasting Station - Chongjin (Pyongyang, KOD) Unable to locate

Pyongyang FM Broadcasting Station - Haeju (Pyongyang, KOD) Unable to locate

Pyongyang FM Broadcasting Station - Hamhung (Pyongyang, KOD) Unable to locate

Pyongyang FM Broadcasting Station - Heaju (Pyongyang, KOD) Unable to locate

Pyongyang FM Broadcasting Station - Hyesan (Pyongyang, KOD) Unable to locate

Pyongyang FM Broadcasting Station - Kaesong (Pyongyang, KOD) Unable to locate

Pyongyang FM Broadcasting Station - Kanggye (Pyongyang, KOD) Unable to locate

Pyongyang FM Broadcasting Station - Komdok (Pyongyang, KOD) Unable to locate

Pyongyang FM Broadcasting Station - Nampo (Pyongyang, KOD) Unable to locate

Pyongyang FM Broadcasting Station - Pyongsong (Pyongyang, KOD) Unable to locate

Pyongyang FM Broadcasting Station - Pyongyang (Pyongyang, KOD) Unable to locate

Pyongyang FM Broadcasting Station - Sariwon (Pyongyang, KOD) Unable to locate

Pyongyang FM Broadcasting Station - Sinuiju (Pyongyang, KOD) Unable to locate

Pyongyang FM Broadcasting Station - Wongsan (Pyongyang, KOD) Unable to locate

The Pyongyang Times (Pyongyang, KOD) [47207]

Pyramidology Magazine (Chesham, GBR) Unable to locate

Q

Q I M P Quarterly (Karachi, PAK) Unable to locate

Q News (London, GBR) [55159]

Qatar Broadcasting Service - Al Arish - 954 KHz (Al Arish, QAT) [49815]

Qatar Broadcasting Service - Al-Jumaliyah - 102.6 MHz (Al-Jumaliyah, QAT) [49816]

Qatar Broadcasting Service - Al-Jumaliyah - 90.8 MHz (Al-Jumaliyah, QAT) [49817]

Qatar Broadcasting Service - Al-Jumaliyah (Doha, QAT) Unable to locate

Qatar Broadcasting Service - Al Khaisah - 675 KHz (Al Khaisah, QAT) [49818]

Qatar Broadcasting Service - Al Khisah - 1233 KHz (Al Khisah, QAT) [49819]

Qatar Broadcasting Service - Al Khisah - 999 KHz (Al Khisah, QAT) [49820]

Qatar Broadcasting Service - Doha - 1602 KHz (Doha, QAT) [49824]

Qatar Broadcasting Service - Doha - 97.5 MHz (Doha, QAT) [49825]

Qatar Info Magazine (Doha, QAT) [49822]

Qatar Medical Journal (Doha, QAT) [49823]

Qatar Television Service (Doha, QAT) Unable to locate

Qatar Television Service (Doha, QAT) Unable to locate

Qatar University Science Journal (Doha, QAT) Unable to locate

QBN-FM - 96.7 (Queanbeyan, NW, AUS) [42295]

Numbers cited in bold after listings are entry numbers rather than page numbers.

Master Index

Qercus (Sale, GBR) [56450]

QFI Quiet Flight International (Malvern, GBR) [55535]

Qian Gorlos People's Broadcasting Station (Qian Gorlos, JI, CHN) Unable to locate

Qianjiang People's Broadcasting Station (Qianjiang, CHN) Unable to locate

Qingdao People's Broadcasting Station (Qingdao, SD, CHN) Unable to locate

Qingdao People's Broadcasting Station (Qingdao, SD, CHN) Unable to locate

Qingdao People's Broadcasting Station (Qingdao, SD, CHN) Unable to locate

Qingdao People's Broadcasting Station (Qingdao, SD, CHN) Unable to locate

Qingdao People's Broadcasting Station (Qingdao, SD, CHN) Unable to locate

Qingdao People's Broadcasting Station (Qingdao, SD, CHN) Unable to locate

Qinghai People's Broadcasting Station (Xining, QI, CHN) Unable to locate

Qinghai People's Broadcasting Station (Xining, QI, CHN) Unable to locate

Qinghai People's Broadcasting Station (Xining, QI, CHN) Unable to locate

Qinghai People's Broadcasting Station (Xining, QI, CHN) Unable to locate

Qinghai People's Broadcasting Station (Xining, QI, CHN) Unable to locate

Qinghai People's Broadcasting Station (Xining, QI, CHN) Unable to locate

Qinghai People's Broadcasting Station (Xining, QI, CHN) Unable to locate

Qinghai People's Broadcasting Station (Xining, QI, CHN) Unable to locate

Qinghai People's Broadcasting Station (Xining, QI, CHN) Unable to locate

Qinghai Television (Xining, QI, CHN) Unable to locate

Qinghe People's Broadcasting Station (Qinghe, HB, CHN) Unable to locate

Qingtongxia People's Broadcasting Station (Qingtongxia, NH, CHN) Unable to locate

Qingyuan People's Broadcasting Station (Qingyuan, GD, CHN) Unable to locate

Qingyuan People's Broadcasting Station (Qingyuan, GD, CHN) Unable to locate

Qingzhou People's Broadcasting Station (Qingzhou, SD, CHN) Unable to locate

Qinhuangdao People's Broadcasting Station (Qinhuangdao, HB, CHN) Unable to locate

Qinyang People's Broadcasting Station (Qinyang, HN, CHN) Unable to locate

Qiqihar People's Broadcasting Station (Qiqihar, HL, CHN) Unable to locate

Qitaihe People's Broadcasting Station (Qitaihe, HL, CHN) Unable to locate

QJM (Oxford, GBR) [56181]

Q97.2-FM - 97.2 (Coleraine, GBR) [53057]

Q102-FM - 102.2 (Dublin, DU, IRL) [46004]

Q101.2-FM - 101.2 (Omagh, GBR) [55848]

Q102.9-FM - 102.9 (Derry, GBR) [53173]

QPMPA Journal of Medical Sciences (Kochi, KE, IND) [45253]

QSAR & Combinatorial Science [44278]*

QT (Sydney, NW, AUS) [42566]

Quaderni ICU (Rome, ITA) Unable to locate

Quaderns d'Arquitectura (Barcelona, SPA) [50694]

Quadrant (Sydney, NW, AUS) [42567]

Quadrature (Les Ulis, FRA) [43967]

Quadrifoglio (Amsterdam, NLD) Unable to locate

Quaestiones Mathematicae (Bellville, SAF) Unable to locate

Qualitas Plantarum [48534]*

Qualitative Market Research (Bradford, GBR) [52539]

Qualitative Research (Cardiff, GBR) [52938]

Qualitative Research in Accounting and Management (Bradford, GBR) [52540]

Qualitative Research Journal (Melbourne, VI, AUS) [42083]

Qualitative Research in Organizations and Management (London, GBR) [55160]

Qualitative Research in Psychology (London, GBR) [55161]

Quality in Action (London, GBR) Unable to locate

Quality in Ageing (Brighton, GBR) [52629]

Quality Assurance in Education (Bradford, GBR) [52541]

Quality Engineering (Leinfelden-Echterdingen, GER) [44528]

Quality in Higher Education (York, GBR) [56995]

Quality of Life Research (Dordrecht, NLD) [48543]

Quality & Quantity (Dordrecht, NLD) [48544]

Quality & Reliability Engineering International (Chichester, GBR) [53016]

Quality and Safety in Health Care (London, GBR) [55162]

Quality Travel Magazine (Milan, ITA) Unable to locate

Quality World (London, GBR) [55163]

Quang Nam Broadcast - Television Station (Tam Ky Town, VNM) Unable to locate

Quang Nam Broadcast - Television Station (Tam Ky Town, VNM) Unable to locate

Quantum Electronics (Moscow, RUS) [49969]

Quanzhou People's Broadcasting Station (Quanzhou, FJ, CHN) Unable to locate

Quarrying SA (Walkerville, SAF) Ceased

Quarterly Blue Book on Joint Stock Companies in India (New Delhi, DH, IND) Unable to locate

Quarterly Bulletin of Documentation in Urban and Regional Planning (New Delhi, DH, IND) Unable to locate

Quarterly Essay (Collingwood, VI, AUS) [41795]

Quarterly Journal (Heathfield, GBR) [53551]

Quarterly Journal of Engineering Geology & Hydrogeology (Bath, GBR) [52255]

Quarterly Journal of Experimental Psychology (Abingdon, GBR) [52032]

Quarterly Journal of Forestry (Tring, GBR) [56772]

The Quarterly Journal of Mathematics (Oxford, GBR) [56182]

The Quarterly Journal of Mechanics and Applied Mathematics (Oxford, GBR) [56183]

Quarterly Journal of the Mythic Society (Bangalore, KA, IND) [44984]

Quarterly Journal of the Royal Meteorological Society (Reading, GBR) [56329]

Quarterly Journal of Surgical Sciences (Varanasi, UP, IND) Unable to locate

Quarterly Medical Review (Mumbai, MH, IND) Unable to locate

Quarterly Predictions (Wellington, NZL) Unable to locate

Quarterly Review of Historical Studies (Calcutta, WB, IND) Unable to locate

Quarterly Review of Indian Economy (New Delhi, DH, IND) Unable to locate

Quarterly Reviews of Biophysics (Cambridge, GBR) [52889]

Quarterly Statistics of the Working of Capital Issues Control (New Delhi, DH, IND) Unable to locate

Quarterly Survey of Advertising Expenditure (London, GBR) [55164]

Quarterly Survey of Business Opinion (Wellington, NZL) Unable to locate

Quaternary Geochronology (Canberra, AC, AUS) [41711]

Quaternary International (Dublin, DU, IRL) [45996]

Quaternary Research (Tokyo, JPN) [47029]

Quaternary Science Reviews (Wollongong, NW, AUS) [42706]

Quattroruote (Rozzano, ITA) [46252]

The Quay-FM - 107.4 (Portsmouth, GBR) [56295]

Queensferry Gazette (Linlithgow, GBR) [53860]

Queensland Country Life (North Richmond, NW, AUS) [42165]

Queensland Farmer (Mackay, QL, AUS) [42024]

Queensland Farmer & Grazier (Toowoomba, QL, AUS) [42629]

Queensland Pride (Fortitude Valley, QL, AUS) [41870]

Queensland Racing Magazine (Nundah, QL, AUS) [42223]

Queensland Smart Farmer (Cleveland, QL, AUS) [41768]

Queer (Cologne, GER) Unable to locate

Quehacer (Lima, PER) [49425]

Quehaceres (Santo Domingo, DOM) Unable to locate

Quercus (Madrid, SPA) [50794]

Quest (Lynnwood Ridge, SAF) [50550]

Questions and Answers in General Topology (Osaka, JPN) [46628]

Quetta Times (Quetta, PAK) Unable to locate

Queueing Systems (Dordrecht, NLD) [48545]

Qufu People's Broadcasting Station (Qufu, SD, CHN) Unable to locate

Quick Cards Made Easy (Bristol, GBR) [52724]

Quick & Crafty! (Colchester, GBR) [53047]

Quick & Easy Cross Stitch Magazine (Bath, GBR) [52256]

Quick Release to the Mineral Statistics of India (Nagpur, MH, IND) Unable to locate

Quick-X-words (London, GBR) [55165]

Quiet (Sheffield, GBR) [56513]

Quiet & Electric Flight International (Malvern, GBR) [55536]

Quill (New Delhi, DH, IND) Unable to locate

The Quilt Journal (Bangalore, KA, IND) Unable to locate

The Quilter (York, GBR) [56996]

Quilters Companion (North Ryde, NW, AUS) [42195]

Quimera (Mataro, SPA) [50820]

Quimica & Derivados (Sao Paulo, SP, BRZ) Unable to locate

Quimica Nova (Sao Paulo, SP, BRZ) [43046]

Quintessence van Meeting Management (Nijmegen, NLD) Unable to locate

Quintessentially (London, GBR) [55166]

Qujing People's Broadcasting Station (Qujing, YU, CHN) Unable to locate

Quranulhuda (Karachi, PAK) Unable to locate

Quzhou People's Broadcasting Station (Quzhou, ZH, CHN) Unable to locate

Quzhou People's Broadcasting Station (Quzhou, ZH, CHN) Unable to locate

Quzhou People's Broadcasting Station (Quzhou, ZH, CHN) Unable to locate

QwaQwa News (Cape Town, SAF) [50404]

QX (Stockholm, SWE) [51031]

R

R/C Jet International (Malvern, GBR) [55537]

R/C Model World (West Sussex, GBR) [56901]

R & D Management (Oxford, GBR) [56184]

R S Promotion 1992 (Bangkok, THA) Unable to locate

R S Promotion 1992 (Bangkok, THA) Unable to locate

R S Promotion 1992 (Bangkok, THA) Unable to locate

R S Promotion 1992 (Bangkok, THA) Unable to locate

RA Magazine (London, GBR) [55167]

Raadio Elmar-FM - 91.5 (Tartu, EST) [43794]

Raadio Elmar-FM - 92.2 (Tartu, EST) [43793]

Raadio 4-FM (Tallinn, EST) Unable to locate

Raadio 4-FM (Tallinn, EST) Unable to locate

Raadio 4-FM (Tallinn, EST) Unable to locate

RAAK (Brussels, BEL) Unable to locate

Race & Class (London, GBR) [55168]

Race Equality Teaching (Stoke-on-Trent, GBR) [56630]

Numbers cited in bold after listings are entry numbers rather than page numbers.

Race, Ethnicity and Education (Abingdon, GBR) **[52033]**

RaceWeek (Dubai, UAE) *Unable to locate*

Radia Mataram Buana Suara, Yogyakarta (D.I. Yogyakarta, IDN) *Unable to locate*

Radiasthesie (Saint Gallen, SWI) *Unable to locate*

Radiation and Environmental Biophysics (Munich, GER) **[44579]**

Radiation Physics and Chemistry (Amsterdam, NLD) **[48219]**

Radiation Protection Dosimetry (Oxford, GBR) **[56185]**

Radiation Safety Management (Nagoya, JPN) **[46558]**

Radical Economics (London, GBR) **[55169]**

Radical Humanist (New Delhi, DH, IND) *Unable to locate*

Radijo Stotis Tau-FM - 102.9 (Kaunas, LIT) **[47471]**

Radio dlya vsekh (Balqash, KAZ) *Unable to locate*

Radio Active-FM - 89 (Wellington, NZL) **[49044]**

Radio Adelaide-FM - 101.5 (Adelaide, SA, AUS) **[41520]**

Radio Adhika Swara, Tangerang (Bekasi, IDN) *Unable to locate*

Radio Aditya Nada Jaya, Indralaya, IDN) *Unable to locate*

Radio Adyafiri, Watansoppeng (Jakarta, IDN) *Unable to locate*

Radio Adyemaja, Lhokseumawe (Lhokseumawe, IDN) *Unable to locate*

Radio Afontovo (Krasnoyarsk, RUS) *Unable to locate*

Radio Aire-FM - 96.3 (Leeds, GBR) **[53781]**

Radio Airlangga, Sukabumi (Jakarta, IDN) *Unable to locate*

Radio Airlangga, Sukabumi (Sukabumi, IDN) *Unable to locate*

Radio Aktuell-FM (Saint Gallen, SWI) *Unable to locate*

Radio Aktuell-FM (Saint Gallen, SWI) *Unable to locate*

Radio Aktuell-FM (Saint Gallen, SWI) *Unable to locate*

Radio Aktuell-FM (Saint Gallen, SWI) *Unable to locate*

Radio Al Masilah, Jakarta (Jakarta, IDN) *Unable to locate*

Radio Al Rona Bahana, Padangsidempuan (Padangsidempuan, IDN) *Unable to locate*

Radio Alef (Moscow, RUS) *Unable to locate*

Radio Alfa (Perm, RUS) *Unable to locate*

Radio Alfa (Yekaterinburg, RUS) *Unable to locate*

Radio Alians (Kogalym, RUS) *Unable to locate*

Radio Alkhairaat, Manado (Manado, IDN) *Unable to locate*

Radio Almaz - Bishkek (Bishkek, KGA) *Unable to locate*

Radio Almaz - Bishkek (Bishkek, KGA) *Unable to locate*

Radio Almaz - Bishkek (Bishkek, KGA) *Unable to locate*

Radio Alnora, Medan (Medan, IDN) *Unable to locate*

Radio Alpha Romeo, Banda Aceh (Banda Aceh, IDN) *Unable to locate*

Radio Altamar-FM - 102.3 (Moquegua, PER) **[49438]**

Radio Alternativa - Omsk (Omsk, RUS) *Unable to locate*

Radio Andalan Muda, Wates (Kulon Progo, IDN) *Unable to locate*

Radio Andalas IX, Banda Aceh (Banda Aceh, IDN) *Unable to locate*

Radio Andalas Raya Bestari, Padang (Padang, IDN) *Unable to locate*

Radio Andhika Lugas Suara (Andalas), Malang (Malang, IDN) *Unable to locate*

Radio Aneka Rama Ria (AR), Denpasar (Denpasar, IDN) *Unable to locate*

Radio Angkasa Bahana Citra (A B C), Surakarta (Surakarta, IDN) *Unable to locate*

Radio Angkasa Jaya, Probolinggo (Probolinggo, IDN) *Unable to locate*

Radio Angkasa Media, Kadipaten (Jakarta, IDN) *Unable to locate*

Radio Angkatan Bersenjata (Radio ABRI Suara Jakarta), Jakarta (Jakarta, IDN) *Unable to locate*

Radio Angraini Katamaira, Siabat (Langkat, IDN) *Unable to locate*

Radio ANS-ChM - Baku (Baku, AJN) *Unable to locate*

Radio Antar Nusa, Jakarta (Banjarmasin, IDN) *Unable to locate*

Radio Antares, Garut (Garut, IDN) *Unable to locate*

Radio Antares, Sidoarjo (Sidoarjo, IDN) *Unable to locate*

Radio Antariksa Radang IV, Surabaya (Surabaya, IDN) *Unable to locate*

Radio Antena Sur-FM - 90.3 (Huancayo, PER) **[49420]**

Radio Antenna-7 (Omsk, RUS) *Unable to locate*

Radio Apeks Region (Novokuznetsk, RUS) *Unable to locate*

Radio Apeks Region (Novokuznetsk, RUS) *Unable to locate*

Radio Aqtau-Tandem (Aqtau, KAZ) *Unable to locate*

Radio Arabella-FM - 92.9 (Vienna, AUT) **[42778]**

Radio Arena Duta Swara, Trenggalek (Trenggalek, IDN) *Unable to locate*

Radio Argovia-FM - 90.3 (Aarau, SWI) **[51056]**

Radio Arief, Payakumbuh (Payakumbuh, IDN) *Unable to locate*

Radio Aries Sanggau Perkasa, Sanggau - 900 KHz (Sanggau, IDN) **[45849]**

Radio ARIS (Kumertau, RUS) *Unable to locate*

Radio ARIS (Kumertau, RUS) *Unable to locate*

Radio Arma Sebelas, Yogyakarta (Yogyakarta, IDN) *Unable to locate*

Radio Artiste - Aley (Aley, LBN) *Unable to locate*

Radio Artiste - Aley (Aley, LBN) *Unable to locate*

Radio Arya Bomantara, Singkawang (Singkawang, IDN) *Unable to locate*

Radio Assonans (Kursk, RUS) *Unable to locate*

Radio Assonans (Kursk, RUS) *Unable to locate*

Radio Assyafiyah, Jakarta (Jakarta, IDN) *Unable to locate*

Radio Atachi Brosser, Palu (Jakarta, IDN) *Unable to locate*

Radio Atlantida-FM (Ponta Delgada, AZO) *Unable to locate*

Radio Atlantida-FM - 106.3 (Sao Miguel, AZO) **[42781]**

Radio Australia-FM - 107 (Melbourne, SA, AUS) **[42044]**

Radio Avgust (Tolyatti, RUS) *Unable to locate*

Radio Avgust (Tolyatti, RUS) *Unable to locate*

Radio Avgust - Tolyatti (Tolyatti, RUS) *Unable to locate*

Radio Avtos (Angarsk, RUS) *Unable to locate*

Radio Avtos (Angarsk, RUS) *Unable to locate*

Radio Bacan Sat-AM - 1130 (Lima, PER) **[49429]**

Radio Bahana Nirmala, Martapura (Martapura, IDN) *Unable to locate*

Radio Bahana Nusantara, Ampah, IDN) *Unable to locate*

Radio Bahia Blanca-AM - 840 (Bahia Blanca, ARG) **[41467]**

Radio Bahrain - English Service (Manama, BHR) *Unable to locate*

Radio Bahrain - English Service (Manama, BHR) *Unable to locate*

Radio Bahrain - English Service (Manama, BHR) *Unable to locate*

Radio Bahtera Yudha, Surabaya (Surabaya, IDN) *Unable to locate*

Radio Bahurekso Sakti (BDS), Weleri (Kendal, IDN) *Unable to locate*

Radio Bali Perkasa, Denpasar (Denpasar, IDN) *Unable to locate*

Radio Balistik, Kupang - 918 KHz (Kupang, IDN) **[45823]**

Radio Baltica (Saint Petersburg, RUS) *Unable to locate*

Radio Baltik Plyus (Kaliningrad, RUS) *Unable to locate*

Radio Baltik Plyus (Kaliningrad, RUS) *Unable to locate*

Radio Baltik Plyus - 72.11 MHz (Kaliningrad, RUS) **[49858]**

Radio Baltika (Saint Petersburg, RUS) *Unable to locate*

Radio Bambapuang, Pangkajene - 882 KHz (Sidenreng Rappang, IDN) **[45855]**

Radio Barata Adya Swara, Bandar Lampung (Jakarta, IDN) *Unable to locate*

Radio Barisan Nauli, Sidikalang (Sidikalang, IDN) *Unable to locate*

Radio BAS (Kaliningrad, RUS) *Unable to locate*

Radio BAS (Kaliningrad, RUS) *Unable to locate*

Radio BAS (Kaliningrad, RUS) *Unable to locate*

Radio Basel 1 AG-FM (Liestal, SWI) *Unable to locate*

Radio Basel 1-FM - 101.7 (Liestal, SWI) **[51208]**

Radio Batanghari Permai (BHP), Jambi - 648 KHz (Jambi, IDN) **[45816]**

Radio Batna-FM (Batna, ALG) *Unable to locate*

Radio Batur, Bangli (Bangli, IDN) *Unable to locate*

Radio Bayu Sakti, Purwokerto (Purwokerto, IDN) *Unable to locate*

Radio Begita, Kabanjahe (Kabanjahe, IDN) *Unable to locate*

Radio Bekzat (Semey, KAZ) *Unable to locate*

Radio Belorechensk (Belorechensk, RUS) *Unable to locate*

Radio Benpas, Bogor (Jakarta, IDN) *Unable to locate*

Radio Benta Harapan, Manado (Manado, IDN) *Unable to locate*

Radio Beograd 2-FM (Belgrade, SER) *Unable to locate*

Radio Beograd 2-FM (Belgrade, SER) *Unable to locate*

Radio Beograd 2-FM (Belgrade, SER) *Unable to locate*

Radio Beograd 2-FM (Belgrade, SER) *Unable to locate*

Radio Beograd 2-FM (Belgrade, SER) *Unable to locate*

Radio Beograd 2-FM (Belgrade, SER) *Unable to locate*

Radio BE1-FM - 101.7 (Bern, SWI) **[51079]**

Radio Besakih Rasisonia, Amtapura (Amtapura, IDN) *Unable to locate*

Radio Bestari, Sukabumi - 648 KHz (Sukabumi, IDN) **[45857]**

Radio Beta-FM - 93.9 MHz (Bojnice, SVA) **[50330]**

Radio Bhara Kharisma Suryajaya, Talangpadang (Tanggamus, IDN) *Unable to locate*

Radio Bharata Bhaktinusa, Tangerang - 738 KHz (Tangerang, IDN) **[45871]**

Radio Bihac-FM - 92.3 (Bihac, HBO) **[42933]**

Radio Bilkent - Ankara - 96.6 MHz (Ankara, TUR) **[51521]**

Radio Bilkent - Bilkent - 96.6 MHz (Ankara, TUR) **[51522]**

Radio Bima Sakti, Kebumen (Jakarta, IDN) *Unable to locate*

Radio Bimantara, Bukittinggi (Bukittinggi, IDN) *Unable to locate*

Radio Bimareksa Dirgantara, Sanggau (Sanggau, IDN) *Unable to locate*

Radio Bintang Niaga, Kisaran, IDN) *Unable to locate*

Radio Bintoro Karya, Demak (Demak, IDN) *Unable to locate*

Radio Blora Sakti (RBS), Cepu (Blora, IDN) *Unable to locate*

Radio BN-FM (Bijeljina, HBO) *Unable to locate*

Radio BN-FM - 93.4 (Bijeljina, HBO) **[42934]**

Radio Bogazici - Bebek - 107.9 MHz (Istanbul, TUR) **[51569]**

Radio Bravo-FM - 96.4 (Varna, BUL) **[43111]**

Radio Buana Jaya, Tasikmalaya - 1224 KHz (Tasikmalaya, IDN) **[45874]**

Radio Buana Sutra, Kendari (Kendari, IDN) *Unable to locate*

Radio Buca-FM (Novi Sad, SER) *Unable to locate*

Radio Buca-FM - 89 (Novi Sad, SER) **[50092]**

Radio Budaya Karo, Kabanjahe (Jakarta, IDN) *Unable to locate*

Radio Budaya Sari, Bandung (Bandung, IDN) *Unable to locate*

Radio Bulgar (Ufa, RUS) *Unable to locate*

Radio Bumerang (Nizhnevartovsk, RUS) *Unable to locate*

Radio Bumerang/Avtoradio (Nizhnevartovsk, RUS) *Unable to locate*

Radio Buraq Peshawar-FM - 104 (Peshawar, PAK) **[49397]**

Radio Cakra Bhuwana, Malang (Malang, IDN) *Unable to locate*

Radio Cakra Donya Multi Swara, Lhokseumawe, IDN) *Unable to locate*

Radio Cakra Swara Perkasa, Singaraja - 1044 KHz (Buleleng, IDN) **[45786]**

Radio Cakrawala Bhakti, Surabaya (Surabaya, IDN) *Unable to locate*

Radio Camar, Surabaya (Surabaya, IDN) *Unable to locate*

Radio Campus Bordeaux-FM - 88.1 (Pessac, FRA) **[44094]**

Numbers cited in bold after listings are entry numbers rather than page numbers.

Radio Canal 100-FM - 100.1 (Asuncion, PAR) [49406]

Radio Capullana-AM - 970 (Sullana, PER) [49443]

Radio Caribbean International-FM - 101.1 (Castries, SLC) [50052]

Radio Carmarthenshire-FM - 97.1 (Llanelli, GBR) [53886]

Radio Carolina Arjuno, Surabaya (Surabaya, IDN) Unable to locate

Radio Caroline-FM (Maidstone, GBR) Unable to locate

Radio Caruso Booy-FM - 102.7 (Savaneta, ARU) [41495]

Radio Cempaka Angkasa, Ciamis - 792 KHz (Banjar, IDN) [45780]

Radio Cempaka Asri, Bulukumba (Bulukumba, IDN) Unable to locate

Radio Cendra Wasih Pusat, Jakarta (Jakarta, IDN) Unable to locate

Radio Cendrawasih Karya Mumi, Pematangsiantar (Pematang Siantar, IDN) Unable to locate

Radio Cendrawasih (Suara Semarang), Semarang (Semarang, IDN) Unable to locate

Radio Center - 1503 KHz (Kurkino, RUS) [49865]

Radio Ceredigion-FM - 97.4 (Aberystwyth, GBR) [51691]

Radio Ceredigion-FM - 103.3 (Aberystwyth, GBR) [51692]

Radio Ceredigion-FM - 96.6 (Aberystwyth, GBR) [51690]

Radio Cerenja-FM - 106.4 (Stip, MEC) [47550]

Radio Chandra Kusuma, Pekalongan (Pekalongan, IDN) Ceased

Radio Chandra Rasisonia, Banjarmasin (Banjarmasin, IDN) Unable to locate

Radio Chandrika Widya Swara (CBS), Bandung (Bandung, IDN) Unable to locate

Radio Chanson Samara (Samara, RUS) Unable to locate

Radio Chistyye Klyuchi (Bryansk, RUS) Unable to locate

Radio Cipta Bentara Swara (CBS), Magelang (Magelang, IDN) Unable to locate

Radio Citra Airlangga, Kediri (Kediri, IDN) Unable to locate

Radio Citra Angkasa Ikhsaniya (RCA), Tegal (Tegal, IDN) Unable to locate

Radio Citra, Ikhsaniya, Tegal (Tegal, IDN) Unable to locate

Radio Citra Kisaran Nada, Kisaran (Kisaran, IDN) Unable to locate

Radio Citra Prima Mahardika, Pringsewu (Pringsewu, IDN) Unable to locate

Radio Citra Remaja Maju Jaya, Langsa (Langsa, IDN) Unable to locate

Radio Citra Tebingtinggi Idola Nada, Tebingtinggi (Tebingtinggi, IDN) Unable to locate

Radio Citra Wanodya Angkasa, Jombang (Jombang, IDN) Unable to locate

Radio Citrah Anugerah, Negara (Jembrana, IDN) Unable to locate

Radio City (Bangalore, KA, IND) Unable to locate

Radio City (Tyumen, RUS) Unable to locate

Radio City (Yekaterinburg, RUS) Unable to locate

Radio City-FM - 96.7 MHz (Liverpool, GBR) [53883]

Radio C.M.B., Purwokerto (Purwokerto, IDN) Unable to locate

Radio Comas-AM - 1300 (Lima, PER) [49430]

Radio Comas-FM - 101.7 (Lima, PER) [49431]

Radio Comms Asia-Pacific (Wahroonga, NW, AUS) [42675]

Radio Communication (Bedford, GBR) [52276]

Radio Contact-FM - 107 (Brussels, BEL) [42877]

Radio Continental Emerald, Manado (Manado, IDN) Unable to locate

Radio Control Car RACER (Totternhoe, GBR) [56768]

Radio Control-FM (Palmerston North, NZL) Unable to locate

Radio Control Model Flyer (Totternhoe, GBR) [56769]

Radio Control Model World (Malvern, GBR) [55538]

Radio Cuareim-AM - 1270 (Artigas, URY) [57004]

Radio Cultural TGN-FM - 100.5 (Guatemala City, GTM) [44788]

Radio Cutivalu-AM - 700 KHz (Piura, PER) [49439]

Radio Cynthia Rema, Pekanbaru (Pekanbaru, IDN) Unable to locate

Radio Da (Tyumen, RUS) Unable to locate

Radio Da (Tyumen, RUS) Unable to locate

Radio Daerah Perdajaya Bebas Sabang, Sabang, IDN) Unable to locate

Radio Daerah Tingkat Dua, Indramayu (Indramayu, IDN) Unable to locate

Radio Dalka Mega Swara, Meulaboh (Meulaboh, IDN) Unable to locate

Radio d'Artagnan-FM - 95.1 (Condom, FRA) [43940]

Radio d'Artagnan-FM - 97.6 (Nogaro, FRA) [44017]

Radio d'Artagnan-FM - 104 (Viella, FRA) [44123]

Radio Dei Marganusa, Metro (Metro, IDN) Unable to locate

Radio Delta - Beit Meri - 101.7 (Beit Meri, LBN) [47437]

Radio Delta - Beit Meri - 102.0 MHz (Beit Meri, LBN) [47436]

Radio Delta - Chouf - 102.0 MHz (Chouf, LBN) [47441]

Radio Delta - Deir al Achayer - 102.0 MHz (Deir al Achayer, LBN) [47442]

Radio Delta - Fatqa - 101.7 MHz (Fatqa, LBN) [47445]

Radio Delta - Jabal Tourbol - 102.0 MHz (Jabal Tourbol, LBN) [47446]

Radio Delta Pawan Indah, Ketapang (Ketapang, IDN) Unable to locate

Radio Delta - Saida - 101.9 MHz (Saida, LBN) [47451]

Radio Delta - Tarchich - 101.7 MHz (Tarchich, LBN) [47452]

Radio Delta - Temnin al Fawka - 102.0 (Temnin al Fawka, LBN) [47453]

Radio Delta - Tripoli - 101.7 MHz (Tripoli, LBN) [47454]

Radio Delta - Tyre - 102.0 MHz (Tyre, LBN) [47455]

Radio Dhirgantara, Negara - 918 KHz (Negara, IDN) [45838]

Radio Diah Rosanti, Pontianak (Pontianak, IDN) Unable to locate

Radio Dialog (Moscow, RUS) Unable to locate

Radio Dian Erata, Padangpanjang (Padangpanjang, IDN) Unable to locate

Radio Dian Irama, Jambi (Jambi, IDN) Unable to locate

Radio Dian Kusuma Jaya, Lubuklinggau (Jakarta, IDN) Unable to locate

Radio Dian Sindoro Suara Semesta (DSS), Temanggung (Temanggung, IDN) Unable to locate

Radio Diantara Vita Kharisma (DVK), Kebumen - 558 KHz (Kebumen, IDN) [45820]

Radio Diaros Duta Swara, Singkawang (Singkawang, IDN) Unable to locate

Radio Difusora de Jatai-AM - 680 (Jatai, GO, BRZ) [42983]

Radio Dirgahayu, Barabai (Barabai, IDN) Unable to locate

Radio DJ-FM - 96.1 (Tirana, ALB) [41453]

Radio DJ-FM - 94.8 (Surabaya, IDN) [45862]

Radio Dlya Vsekh/Ekho Moskvy (Krasnoyarsk, RUS) Unable to locate

Radio Dope-FM (Zurich, SWI) Unable to locate

Radio Dostlik (Tashkent, UZN) Unable to locate

Radio Dulkyn (Kazan, RUS) Unable to locate

Radio Dulkyn - Kazan (Kazan, RUS) Unable to locate

Radio Dunya - Bakanlyklar - 93.5 MHz (Istanbul, TUR) [51570]

Radio Duta Angkasa, Pangandaran - 1044 KHz (Pangandaran, IDN) [45844]

Radio Duta Nusantara Suara Ponorogo (Ponorogo, IDN) Unable to locate

Radio Duta Paramita, Metro, IDN) Unable to locate

Radio Duta Suara Garuda Sakti, Blora - 1242 KHz (Blora, IDN) [45784]

Radio Dwikarya 69, Bandung (Bandung, IDN) Unable to locate

Radio Dzhem (Yekaterinburg, RUS) Unable to locate

Radio Dzhem (Yekaterinburg, RUS) Unable to locate

Radio Dzhem (Yekaterinburg, RUS) Unable to locate

Radio Dzhem (Yekaterinburg, RUS) Unable to locate

Radio Dzhem (Yekaterinburg, RUS) Unable to locate

Radio Dzhem - Kamensk Uralskiy (Yekaterinburg, RUS) Unable to locate

Radio Eastern-FM - 98.1 (Croydon, VI, AUS) [41825]

Radio 88 (Surgut, RUS) Unable to locate

Radio Ekatama Swara Gajahmada (El Gama, Banjarmasin) (Banjarmasin, IDN) Unable to locate

Radio Ekho (Ryazan, RUS) Unable to locate

Radio Ekofond - 103.0 MHz (Nizhniy Tagil, RUS) [50007]

Radio El Bayu, Gresik, IDN) Unable to locate

Radio El Em Bahama, Padangpanjang (Padangpanjang, IDN) Unable to locate

Radio El Gangga, Bekasi (Bekasi Selatan, IDN) Unable to locate

Radio El Philia, Telukbetung (Telukbetung, IDN) Unable to locate

Radio El Victor, Surabaya (Surabaya, IDN) Unable to locate

Radio and Electronics (Mumbai, MH, IND) Unable to locate

Radio Elis (Yaroslavl, RUS) Unable to locate

Radio Elis (Yaroslavl, RUS) Unable to locate

Radio Elkartika Angkasa Niaga, Padang (Padang, IDN) Unable to locate

Radio Ellusia, Pekanbaru (Pekanbaru, IDN) Unable to locate

Radio Enes Duabelas Ulu, Palembang, IDN) Unable to locate

Radio Eremitazh - 90.1 MHz (Saint Petersburg, RUS) [50030]

Radio Essen-FM - 102.2 (Essen, GER) [44347]

Radio Estacion Solar-FM - 103.3 (Abancay, PER) [49414]

Radio Estel-FM - 106.6 (Barcelona, SPA) [50708]

Radio Esti Elita, Pekanbaru (Pekanbaru, IDN) Unable to locate

Radio Esti Mada Cita (EMC), Yogyakarta (Yogyakarta, IDN) Unable to locate

Radio Estrelle-FM - 93.1 (Cochabamba, BOL) [42930]

Radio Evraziya (Elista, RUS) Unable to locate

Radio Ewangga, Kuningan - 954 KHz (Kuningan, IDN) [45822]

Radio Express (Radio Pilot) (Yekaterinburg, RUS) Unable to locate

Radio Famor, Bandung (Bandung, IDN) Unable to locate

Radio Fantasy-FM - 93.4 (Augsburg, GER) [44143]

Radio Fantasy 70, Jatiwangi (Majalengka, IDN) Unable to locate

Radio Favorite, Ambon (Ambon, IDN) Unable to locate

Radio Felix (Nizhniy Novgorod, RUS) Unable to locate

Radio Felix (Nizhniy Novgorod, RUS) Unable to locate

Radio Fides-AM - 1040 (San Jose, CRI) [43553]

Radio Fiessta-FM (Rancagua, CHL) Unable to locate

Radio Figaro (Surgut, RUS) Unable to locate

Radio Fiji Gold-FM - 100.4 (Suva, FIJ) [43808]

Radio Fiji One-AM - 558 (Suva, FIJ) [43809]

Radio Filarmonia-FM - 102.7 (Lima, PER) [49432]

Radio 5UV [41520]

Radio-FM - 103.5 (Tweed Heads, NW, AUS) [42656]

Radio-FM - 96 (Maceio, AL, BRZ) [42986]

Radio-FM - 107 (Phnom Penh, CMB) [43115]

Radio-FM - 100 (Copenhagen, DEN) [43686]

Radio-FM - 106.6 (Bitola, MEC) [47504]

Radio FM 103 MHz - 103 MHz (Phnom Penh, CMB) [43116]

Radio FM9 - 95.9 (Kragujevac, SER) [50089]

Radio Foorti-FM - 98.4 (Chittagong, BGD) [42800]

Radio Foorti-FM - 88.0 (Dhaka, BGD) [42818]

Radio Foorti-FM - 89.8 (Sylhet, BGD) [42825]

Radio Fortuna Bewara Suara, IDN) Unable to locate

Radio 4 Ajman - 89.1 MHz (Ajman, UAE) [51624]

Radio 4-FM - 89.1 (Ajman, UAE) [51625]

Numbers cited in bold after listings are entry numbers rather than page numbers.

Radio Foyle-FM - 93.1 (Derry, GBR) **[53174]**

Radio France International (RFI) (Moscow, RUS) *Unable to locate*

Radio France International (RFI) (Moscow, RUS) *Unable to locate*

Radio Fremantle-FM - 107.9 (Hamilton Hill, WA, AUS) **[41939]**

Radio Frontinus-FM - 104.6 MHz (Zilina, SLK) **[50328]**

Radio Gabriel, Madiun (Madiun, IDN) *Unable to locate*

Radio Gafsa-FM - 88.3 MHz (Gafsa, TUN) **[51472]**

Radio Gafsa-FM - 89.2 MHz (Gafsa, TUN) **[51473]**

Radio Gafsa-FM - 93.5 MHz (Gafsa, TUN) **[51471]**

Radio Gafsa-FM - 91.8 MHz (Gafsa, TUN) **[51470]**

Radio Gagah Sehat Berbobot (Gasebo), Majenang - 720 KHz (Majenang, IDN) **[45827]**

Radio Galaxie-FM - 104.5 (Port-au-Prince, HTI) **[44802]**

Radio Galuh Surya Kencana, Tasikmalaya, IDN) *Unable to locate*

Radio Gandaria (Anging Mamiri), Ujung Pandang (Makassar, IDN) *Unable to locate*

Radio Ganesha Nada, Bandung (Bandung, IDN) *Unable to locate*

Radio Gapilar Rasisonia, Solok (Solok, IDN) *Unable to locate*

Radio Gardarika (St. Petersburg, RUS) *Unable to locate*

Radio Gardarika (Saint Petersburg, RUS) *Unable to locate*

Radio Gardarika (Saint Petersburg, RUS) *Unable to locate*

Radio Garuda Kenten Jaya, Palembang - 954 KHz (Palembang, IDN) **[45840]**

Radio Geleum (Surgut, RUS) *Unable to locate*

Radio Gelora Indah Swara (IS), Wonogiri (Wonogiri, IDN) *Unable to locate*

Radio Gelora Ramona, Palembang (Palembang, IDN) *Unable to locate*

Radio Gema Bahari Selatan (GBS), Malingping (Lebak, IDN) *Unable to locate*

Radio Gema Bhakti Yudha Seroja, Bekasi (Jakarta, IDN) *Unable to locate*

Radio Gema Bukitasam (RGBA), Tanjung Enim (Tanjung Enim, IDN) *Unable to locate*

Radio Gema Bunda Kandung (RBK), Panjang (Bandar Lampung, IDN) *Unable to locate*

Radio Gema Cakrawala Utama, Kuala Simpang, IDN) *Unable to locate*

Radio Gema Khayan, Pangkalanbuun (Pangkalanbuun, IDN) *Unable to locate*

Radio Gema Kuripan, Amuntai, IDN) *Unable to locate*

Radio Gema Megantara Pratama, Tabanan (Tabanan, IDN) *Unable to locate*

Radio Gema Merdeka, Denpasar (Denpasar, IDN) *Unable to locate*

Radio Gema Mutiara, Palembang - 1062 KHz (Palembang, IDN) **[45841]**

Radio Gema Mutiara, Plaju (Plaju, IDN) *Unable to locate*

Radio Gema Nirwana, Samarinda (Samarinda, IDN) *Unable to locate*

Radio Gema Nugraha, Sungai Penuh (Kerinci, IDN) *Unable to locate*

Radio Gema Nury (El Nury), Bogor (Bogor, IDN) *Unable to locate*

Radio Gema Persada, Banjarmasin, IDN) *Unable to locate*

Radio Gema Remaja, Kuningan (Kuningan, IDN) *Unable to locate*

Radio Gema Sritanjung Mediatama (GSM), Jatibarang (Jatibarang, IDN) *Unable to locate*

Radio Gema Suara Gloria (GBS), Kupang (Timor, IDN) *Unable to locate*

Radio Gema Surya, Ponorogo (Ponorogo, IDN) *Unable to locate*

Radio Gema Warga Karya, Bandung (Bandung, IDN) *Unable to locate*

Radio Gematara Batakan, Pelahari (Tanah Laut, IDN) *Unable to locate*

Radio Gemini Perkasa, Mataram (Lombok, IDN) *Unable to locate*

Radio General Belgrano-AM - 840 (Buenos Aires, ARG) **[41485]**

Radio Geswara Pamanukan (GSP), Pamanukan, IDN) *Unable to locate*

Radio Geunta Suara, Geudong (Lhokseumawe, IDN) *Unable to locate*

Radio Gibraltar-FM (Gibraltar, GIB) *Unable to locate*

Radio Gibraltar-FM (Gibraltar, GIB) *Unable to locate*

Radio Gibraltar-FM (Gibraltar, GIB) *Unable to locate*

Radio Gita Kanari Ria, Purwakarta (Purwakarta, IDN) *Unable to locate*

Radio Gita Lestari, Berbes, IDN) *Unable to locate*

Radio Gita Nada Tebu Ireng, Jombang (Jombang, IDN) *Unable to locate*

Radio Gita Segara, Bangkalan (Bangkalan, IDN) *Unable to locate*

Radio Gita Swara Alfina, Pemalang - 720 KHz (Pemalang, IDN) **[45846]**

Radio Gloria Paramita, Lumajang (Jakarta, IDN) *Unable to locate*

Radio GO DeeJay-FM - 89.8 MHz (Trencin, SLK) **[50327]**

Radio Gong (Kamensk Uralskiy, RUS) *Unable to locate*

Radio Gorod (Krasnoyarsk, RUS) *Unable to locate*

Radio-Gresivaudan-FM - 87.8 (Crolles, FRA) **[43941]**

Radio G3-FM - 89.2 (Skalica, SLK) **[50326]**

Radio Hampshire-FM (Southampton, GBR) *Ceased*

Radio Hapi Isles-AM - 1035 (Gizo, SLM) **[50344]**

Radio Hapi Isles-AM - 1035 (Honiara, SLM) **[50345]**

Radio Harau Megantara Angkasa, Tanjung Pati (Tanjung Pati, IDN) *Unable to locate*

Radio Hartlepool-FM - 102.4 (Hartlepool, GBR) **[53535]**

Radio Hay Citra Ria, Palangkaraya (Palangkaraya, IDN) *Unable to locate*

Radio Hex, Balikpapan (Balikpapan, IDN) *Unable to locate*

Radio Histori Gita Jaya, Karawang - 1206 KHz (Karawang, IDN) **[45818]**

Radio Hit (Chelyabinsk, RUS) *Unable to locate*

Radio Hit 90.6 (Saint Petersburg, RUS) *Unable to locate*

Radio Horizonte-FM - 104.4 (Ponta Delgada, PRT) **[49808]**

Radio Hoyer 1-FM - 101.9 (Curacao, NAT) **[48774]**

Radio Hoyer 2-FM - 105.1 (Curacao, NAT) **[48775]**

Radio Huanuco-FM - 94.7 (Huanuco, PER) **[49421]**

Radio Humberside - 95.9 (Hull, GBR) **[53632]**

Radio Idola Nada, Manggala (Manggala, IDN) *Unable to locate*

Radio Immanuel, Surakarta (Surakarta, IDN) *Unable to locate*

Radio Impacto-FM - 90.7 (Lima, PER) **[49433]**

Radio Indah Banagla Ceria (I.B.C), Semarang (Semarang, IDN) *Unable to locate*

Radio Indah Sragen Asri, Sragen (Sragen, IDN) *Unable to locate*

Radio Indraswara Cakrawalanada, Majalengka - 810 KHz (Majalengka, IDN) **[45826]**

Radio Indraswara, Tebingtinggi (Tebingtinggi, IDN) *Unable to locate*

Radio Irama Adinada, Surakarta (Surakarta, IDN) *Unable to locate*

Radio Irama Kusuma Sena, Bogor (Bogor, IDN) *Unable to locate*

Radio Isanganiro-FM (Bujumbura, BDI) *Unable to locate*

Radio Iskanada Mustika (Sylvania), Banjarmasin (Banjarmasin, IDN) *Unable to locate*

Radio Istana, Blitar (Blitar, IDN) *Unable to locate*

Radio Jackie-FM - 107.8 (Surbiton, GBR) **[56658]**

Radio Janne-FM - 101.7 (Hameenlinna, FIN) **[43813]**

Radio Japan News (Tokyo, JPN) *Unable to locate*

Radio Jat-FM - 102.7 (Belgrade, SER) **[50085]**

Radio Jelita Bahanswara, Bukittinggi (Bukittinggi, IDN) *Unable to locate*

Radio JM-FM - 90.5 (Marseille, FRA) **[43974]**

The Radio Journal (Glasgow, GBR) **[53444]**

Radio Justica-FM - 91.1 (Brasilia, DF, BRZ) **[42959]**

Radio Kabupaten Daerah Tingkat Dua, Karawang (Karawang, IDN) *Unable to locate*

Radio Kala Aturaya (Moscow, RUS) *Unable to locate*

Radio Kamensk (Moscow, RUS) *Unable to locate*

Radio Karastina, Tanjung Pinang (Tanjung Pinang, IDN) *Unable to locate*

Radio Karya Dharma, Manado (Manado, IDN) *Unable to locate*

Radio Karya Pancaran Swara Media (Karysma), Boyolali (Boyolali, IDN) *Unable to locate*

Radio Karya Prima 70 (Karima 70), Banda Aceh (Banda Aceh, IDN) *Unable to locate*

Radio Katalina, Sigli (Sigli, IDN) *Unable to locate*

Radio Kauman, Bogor (Bogor, IDN) *Unable to locate*

Radio Kazuma Bawana Swara, Lhokseumawe (Jakarta, IDN) *Unable to locate*

Radio Kef-FM - 102.2 MHz (Le Kef, TUN) **[51477]**

Radio Kef-FM - 92.2 MHz (Le Kef, TUN) **[51476]**

Radio Kef-FM - 96.8 MHz (Le Kef, TUN) **[51474]**

Radio Kef-FM - 88.2 MHz (Le Kef, TUN) **[51475]**

Radio Kelana Sumbangsih (Kasihku), Bumiayu (Bumiayu, IDN) *Unable to locate*

Radio Keluarga Cihanjuang (KC10), Indramayu (Indramayu, IDN) *Unable to locate*

Radio Kencana Nada Suara, Way Jepara (Way Jepara, IDN) *Unable to locate*

Radio Kencana Perkasa Pematang Siantar (Siantar, IDN) *Unable to locate*

Radio Kerinci Giri Swara (KGS), Sungaipenuh (Kerinci, IDN) *Unable to locate*

Radio Kerry-FM - 96.2 (Tralee, KR, IRL) **[46061]**

Radio Keski-Suomi-FM - 99.3 (Jyvaskyla, FIN) **[43873]**

Radio Khabar - 1 (Almaty, KAZ) *Unable to locate*

Radio Khabar - 1 (Almaty, KAZ) *Unable to locate*

Radio Khabar - 1 (Almaty, KAZ) *Unable to locate*

Radio Khamasutra, Medan (Medan, IDN) *Unable to locate*

Radio Kharisma Indah Swara (KIS), Semarang (Semarang, IDN) *Unable to locate*

Radio Kharisma Lombok Perkasa, Aikmel (Lombok, IDN) *Unable to locate*

Radio Kharisma Swararia, Balige (Jakarta, IDN) *Unable to locate*

Radio Kharismanada Rasisonia (La Fozsy), Banjarmasin - 738 KHz (Banjarmasin, IDN) **[45781]**

Radio Khit - 90.6 MHz (Saint Petersburg, RUS) **[50031]**

Radio Khusus Informasi Pertanian (RKP), Surabaya (Surabaya, IDN) *Unable to locate*

Radio Khusus Informasi Pertanian (RKP), Surabaya (Surabaya, IDN) *Unable to locate*

Radio Khusus Pemerintah Daerah Kabupaten Daerah Tingkat Dua, Lumajang (Lumajang, IDN) *Unable to locate*

Radio Khusus Pemerintah Daerah Kabupaten Daerah Tingkat Dua, Nganjuk (Nganjuk, IDN) *Unable to locate*

Radio Khusus Pemerintah Daerah Kabupaten Daerah Tingkat Dua, Pamekasan (Suara Dian Lestari) (Pamekasan, IDN) *Ceased*

Radio Khusus Pemerintah Daerah Kabupaten, Jombang, IDN) *Unable to locate*

Radio Khusus Pemerintah Daerah Kabupaten, Madiun (Madiun, IDN) *Unable to locate*

Radio Khusus Pemerintah Daerah Kabupaten, Tulungagung (Tulungagung, IDN) *Unable to locate*

Radio Khusus Pemerintah Daerah Kotamadya, Blitar (Blitar, IDN) *Unable to locate*

Radio Khusus Pemerintah Daerah Kotamadya, Probolinggo (Probolinggo, IDN) *Unable to locate*

Radio Khusus Pemerintah Daerah Tingkat Dua, Bangkalan (Suara Bangkalan Ceria) (Jakarta, IDN) *Unable to locate*

Radio Khusus Pemerintah Daerah Tingkat Dua, Blitar (Blitar, IDN) *Unable to locate*

Radio Khusus Pemerintah Daerah Tingkat Dua, Bojonegoro (Bojonegoro, IDN) *Unable to locate*

Numbers cited in bold after listings are entry numbers rather than page numbers.

Radio Khusus Pemerintah Daerah Tingkat Dua, Jember (Jember, IDN) *Unable to locate*

Radio Khusus Pemerintah Daerah Tingkat Dua Kotamadya, Bandung (Bandung, IDN) *Unable to locate*

Radio Khusus Pemerintah Daerah Tingkat Dua Kotamadya Kediri (Radio Gema Kediri) (Kediri, IDN) *Unable to locate*

Radio Khusus Pemerintah Daerah Tingkat Dua, Malang (Malang, IDN) *Unable to locate*

Radio Khusus Pemerintah Daerah Tingkat Dua, Ngawi (Jakarta, IDN) *Unable to locate*

Radio Khusus Pemerintah Daerah Tingkat Dua, Pasuruan (Radio Untung Suropati) (Pasuruan, IDN) *Unable to locate*

Radio Khusus Pemerintah Daerah Tingkat Dua, Sampang (Radio Suara Bahari).(Sampang, IDN) *Unable to locate*

Radio Khusus Pemerintah Daerah Tingkat Dua, Situbondo (Situbondo, IDN) *Unable to locate*

Radio Khusus Pemerintah Daerah Tingkat Dua, Sumenep(R.Dinamika Suara Pariwisata) (Sumenep, IDN) *Unable to locate*

Radio Khusus Pemerintah Daerah Tingkat Satu Jawa Timur, Surabaya (Surabaya, IDN) *Ceased*

Radio Khusus Pemerintah Kabupaten Daerah Tingkat Dua, Bekasi (Jakarta, IDN) *Unable to locate*

Radio Khusus Pemerintah Kabupaten Daerah Tingkat Dua, Gresik (Gresik, IDN) *Ceased*

Radio Khusus Pemerintah Kabupaten Daerah Tingkat Dua, Mojokerto (Mojokerto, IDN) *Ceased*

Radio Khusus Pemerintah Kabupaten Daerah Tingkat Dua, Probolinggo (Probolinggo, IDN) *Unable to locate*

Radio Khusus Pemerintah Kabupaten Daerah Tingkat Dua, Serang (Serang, IDN) *Unable to locate*

Radio Khusus Pemerintah Kabupaten Daerah Tingkat Dua, Sidoarjo (Jakarta, IDN) *Unable to locate*

Radio Khusus Pemerintah Kabupaten Daerah Tingkat Dua, Trenggalek (Trenggalek, IDN) *Unable to locate*

Radio Khusus Pemerintah Kotamadya Daerah Tingkat Dua Pasuruan (Radio Gema Suropati) (Pasuruan, IDN) *Unable to locate*

Radio Khwezi-FM - 107.7 (Kranskop, SAF) **[50543]**

Radio Klara-FM (Brussels, BEL) *Unable to locate*

Radio Klara-FM (Brussels, BEL) *Unable to locate*

Radio Konservatori, Surakarta - 738 KHz (Surakarta, IDN) **[45867]**

Radio Kontinental (Chelyabinsk, RUS) *Unable to locate*

Radio Kontinental (Chelyabinsk, RUS) *Unable to locate*

Radio Kontinental (Chelyabinsk, RUS) *Unable to locate*

Radio Kontinental (Chelyabinsk, RUS) *Unable to locate*

Radio Kray (Karpinsk, RUS) *Unable to locate*

Radio Kudu-FM - 103.5 (Windhoek, NAM) **[47825]**

Radio Kuray (Kazan, RUS) *Unable to locate*

Radio Kutilang, Malang (Malang, IDN) *Unable to locate*

Radio L-Tsentr (Stavropol, RUS) *Unable to locate*

Radio L-Tsentr - Ekho Moskvy (Stavropol, RUS) *Unable to locate*

Radio La Barong, Singaraja (Singaraja, IDN) *Unable to locate*

Radio La Victor, Surabaya (Surabaya, IDN) *Unable to locate*

Radio Lamour Citra Budaya Sriwijaya, Palembang (Palembang, IDN) *Unable to locate*

Radio Lariang Indah, Mamuju (Mamuju, IDN) *Unable to locate*

Radio Larrakia-FM - 94.5 (Darwin, NT, AUS) **[41831]**

Radio Lebediya (Elista, RUS) *Unable to locate*

Radio Leidya Swara Utama, Bandung - 828 KHz (Bandung, IDN) **[45778]**

Radio Leonardus Buana Suara, Salatiga - 774 KHz (Jakarta, IDN) **[45807]**

Radio Liani-FM (Lovech, BUL) *Unable to locate*

Radio Liani-FM (Lovech, BUL) *Unable to locate*

Radio Liani-FM (Lovech, BUL) *Unable to locate*

Radio Liani-FM (Lovech, BUL) *Unable to locate*

Radio Liani-FM (Lovech, BUL) *Unable to locate*

Radio Liani-FM (Lovech, BUL) *Unable to locate*

Radio Liani-FM (Lovech, BUL) *Unable to locate*

Radio Liani-FM (Lovech, BUL) *Unable to locate*

Radio Liani-FM (Lovech, BUL) *Unable to locate*

Radio Liani-FM (Lovech, BUL) *Unable to locate*

Radio Liani-FM (Lovech, BUL) *Unable to locate*

Radio Liani-FM (Lovech, BUL) *Unable to locate*

Radio Liban - Amchit (Beirut, LBN) *Unable to locate*

Radio Liban - Amchit (Beirut, LBN) *Unable to locate*

Radio Liban - Beirut (Beirut, LBN) *Unable to locate*

Radio Liban - Beirut (Beirut, LBN) *Unable to locate*

Radio Liban Libre - Beit Meri - 102.3 MHz (Beit Meri, LBN) **[47438]**

Radio Liban Libre - Dbaye (Jounieh, LBN) *Ceased*

Radio Liban Libre - Faraya Mzaar - 102.7 MHz (Faraya Mzaar, LBN) **[47444]**

Radio Liban Libre - Fih (Jounieh, LBN) *Ceased*

Radio Liban - Sidon (Jounieh, LBN) *Unable to locate*

Radio Liban Star (Hayek, LBN) *Unable to locate*

Radio Liban Star - Beirut (Hayek, LBN) *Unable to locate*

Radio Liban Star - Beit Meri (Hayek, LBN) *Unable to locate*

Radio Liban Star - Bouerej (Hayek, LBN) *Unable to locate*

Radio Liban - We. Biqa Valley (Beirut, LBN) *Unable to locate*

Radio Lider-AM - 730 (Bogota, COL) **[43547]**

Radio Liga Perdana, Balikpapan (Balikpapan, IDN) *Unable to locate*

Radio Linggarjati Utama (Rasilima), Kuningan (Kuningan, IDN) *Unable to locate*

Radio Lintas Triaga Angkasa (Lita), Bukittinggi (Bukittinggi, IDN) *Unable to locate*

Radio Lita Sari, Bandung (Bandung, IDN) *Unable to locate*

Radio Lokawisesa, Jakarta (Jakarta, IDN) *Unable to locate*

Radio LoRa-FM - 104.95 MHz (Bassersdorf, SWI) **[51068]**

Radio LoRa-FM - 102.35 MHz (Winterthur, SWI) **[51244]**

Radio LoRa-FM - 98.9 MHz (Zug, SWI) **[51245]**

Radio LoRa-FM - 97.5 Mhz (Zurich, SWI) **[51298]**

Radio Loyola-AM - 1300 (Sucre, BOL) **[42932]**

Radio LRB-FM - 103.9 (Bettembourg, LUX) **[47487]**

Radio Lumbini-FM - 96.8 (Rupandehi, NPL) **[47861]**

Radio Lumena-FM - 107.01 (Velas, PRT) **[49812]**

Radio Lumena-FM - 92.2 (Velas, PRT) **[49811]**

Radio Lusiana Namberwan, Semarang - 720 KHz (Semarang, IDN) **[45851]**

Radio LUX (Magnitogorsk, RUS) *Unable to locate*

Radio Lyuks (Magnitogorsk, RUS) *Unable to locate*

Radio M-FM - 98.7 (Sarajevo, HBO) **[42935]**

Radio Madagasikara-FM - 99.2 MHz (Antananarivo, MDG) **[47565]**

Radio Maestra, Bandung (Bandung, IDN) *Unable to locate*

The Radio Magazine (Kettering, GBR) **[53685]**

Radio Magnat (Volgograd, RUS) *Unable to locate*

Radio Maks - Bishkek (Bishkek, KGA) *Unable to locate*

Radio Maksimum (Saint Petersburg, RUS) *Unable to locate*

Radio Maksimum (Saint Petersburg, RUS) *Unable to locate*

Radio Maksimum (Yekaterinburg, RUS) *Unable to locate*

Radio Malaya Malacca - 102.3 MHz (Malacca, MYS) **[47679]**

Radio Maldwyn-AM - 756 (Newtown, GBR) **[55700]**

Radio Manas FM - Bishkek (Bishkek, KGA) *Unable to locate*

Radio Mancasuara, Bandung (Bandung, IDN) *Unable to locate*

Radio Manchester **[55584]***

Radio Mandalika Rasiswana, Jepara (Jepara, IDN) *Unable to locate*

Radio Mandiri, Kotabumi (Jakarta, IDN) *Unable to locate*

Radio Manggis B.S. Jambi, IDN) *Unable to locate*

Radio Manhattan (Blagoveshchensk, RUS) *Unable to locate*

Radio Mania-FM - 88.8 (Tallinn, EST) **[43785]**

Radio Maranon-AM - 580 (Chiclayo, PER) **[49419]**

Radio Maria - 1053 KHz (Saint Petersburg, RUS) **[50032]**

Radio Maria-AM - 1310 (Panama City, PAN) **[49402]**

Radio Maria El Salvador-FM (San Salvador, ELS) *Unable to locate*

Radio Maria Malawi-FM - 88.5 MHz (Mangochi, MWI) **[47572]**

Radio Maria Malawi-FM - 99.2 MHz (Mangochi, MWI) **[47571]**

Radio Maria Malawi-FM - 94 MHz (Mangochi, MWI) **[47569]**

Radio Maria Malawi-FM - 99.4 MHz (Mangochi, MWI) **[47570]**

Radio Maria Malawi-FM - 99.7 MHz (Mangochi, MWI) **[47568]**

Radio Maritima-FM - 93.6 (Martigues, FRA) **[43976]**

Radio Mariya (Kirov, RUS) *Unable to locate*

Radio Mariya (Kirov, RUS) *Unable to locate*

Radio Mash'al (Tashkent, UZN) *Unable to locate*

Radio Massiv (Moscow, RUS) *Unable to locate*

Radio Matucana-FM - 102.9 (Huarochiri, PER) **[49422]**

Radio Maxima-FM - 95.3 (Ahuachapan, ELS) **[43775]**

Radio Maximum - 103.2 MHz (Perm, RUS) **[50018]**

Radio Maximum (Perm, RUS) *Unable to locate*

Radio Mayangkara Ria, Blitar (Blitar, IDN) *Unable to locate*

Radio Mburucuya-AM (Asuncion, PAR) *Unable to locate*

Radio M.C.A., Surabaya (Surabaya, IDN) *Unable to locate*

Radio Mega Primadona Nada Perkasa, Pangkalanbuun (Pangkalanbuun, IDN) *Unable to locate*

Radio Megaestacion-FM - 92.9 (Santo Domingo, ECU) **[43744]**

Radio Megantara Bhinneka, Nganjuk (Nganjuk, IDN) *Unable to locate*

Radio Menara Buana Suara Inadah, Sukabumi (Sukabumi, IDN) *Unable to locate*

Radio Menara III, Surabaya - 864 KHz (Surabaya, IDN) **[45863]**

Radio Menawan Ceria Indonesia Rasitada (Mersi), Semarang (Semarang, IDN) *Unable to locate*

Radio Menovyy Dvor (Orenburg, RUS) *Unable to locate*

Radio Merak Jaya, Muarateweh (Muarateweh, IDN) *Unable to locate*

Radio Merapi Indah, Muntilan (Gulon-Magelang, IDN) *Unable to locate*

Radio Mercidiona, Bandung (Bandung, IDN) *Unable to locate*

Radio Mercury Madesuk, Surabaya (Surabaya, IDN) *Unable to locate*

Radio Mercy Jaya Raya, Tanjungkarang (Bandar Lampung, IDN) *Unable to locate*

Radio Merpati, Ambon (Ambon, IDN) *Unable to locate*

Radio Mersy Maesaan Waya, Manado (Manado, IDN) *Unable to locate*

Radio Metro-FM - 105.7 (Surfers Paradise, QL, AUS) **[42406]**

Radio MIG (Abakan, RUS) *Unable to locate*

Radio MIG-Inform (Novyy Urengoy, RUS) *Unable to locate*

Radio Miks (Luga, RUS) *Unable to locate*

Radio Miks-Master (Yakutsk, RUS) *Unable to locate*

Radio Miks-Master (Yakutsk, RUS) *Unable to locate*

Radio Miniwati Pesona Indah, Surabaya - 846 KHz (Surabaya, IDN) **[45864]**

Radio Mir (Novosibirsk, RUS) *Unable to locate*

Radio Mirchi-FM - 98.0 (Suva, FIJ) **[43810]**

Radio Mitra Loola Kita, Pancor (Lombok, IDN) *Ceased*

Numbers cited in bold after listings are entry numbers rather than page numbers.

Radio Moderato, Madiun (Madiun, IDN) *Unable to locate*

Radio Modern - Apatity (Saint Petersburg, RUS) *Unable to locate*

Radio Modern - Arkhangelsk (Arkhangelsk, RUS) *Unable to locate*

Radio Modern - Chelyabinsk (Saint Petersburg, RUS) *Unable to locate*

Radio Modern - Chelyabinsk (St. Petersburg, RUS) *Unable to locate*

Radio Modern - Cherepovets (Saint Petersburg, RUS) *Unable to locate*

Radio Modern - Izhevsk (Saint Petersburg, RUS) *Unable to locate*

Radio Modern - Kaliningrad (St. Petersburg, RUS) *Unable to locate*

Radio Modern - Krasnodar (Krasnodar, RUS) *Unable to locate*

Radio Modern - Lyantor (St. Petersburg, RUS) *Unable to locate*

Radio Modern - Megion (St. Petersburg, RUS) *Unable to locate*

Radio Modern - Murmansk (St. Petersburg, RUS) *Unable to locate*

Radio Modern - Naberezhnyye Chelny (St. Petersburg, RUS) *Unable to locate*

Radio Modern - Naberezhnyye Chelny (St. Petersburg, RUS) *Unable to locate*

Radio Modern - Olgino (St. Petersburg, RUS) *Unable to locate*

Radio Modern - Olgino (Saint Petersburg, RUS) *Unable to locate*

Radio Modern - Omsk (Saint Petersburg, RUS) *Unable to locate*

Radio Modern - Perm (Perm,) *Unable to locate*

Radio Modern - Petrozavodsk (St. Petersburg, RUS) *Unable to locate*

Radio Modern - Petrozavodsk (Saint Petersburg, RUS) *Unable to locate*

Radio Modern - Sochi (Saint Petersburg, RUS) *Unable to locate*

Radio Modern - Surgut (St. Petersburg, RUS) *Unable to locate*

Radio Modern - Tula (Tula, RUS) *Unable to locate*

Radio Modern - Velikiy Novgorod (Saint Petersburg, RUS) *Unable to locate*

Radio Modern - Velikiy Novgorod (Saint Petersburg, RUS) *Unable to locate*

Radio Modern - Voronezh (Saint Petersburg, RUS) *Unable to locate*

Radio Modern - Voronezh (St. Petersburg, RUS) *Unable to locate*

Radio Modern - Yekaterinburg (St. Petersburg, RUS) *Unable to locate*

Radio Monastir-FM - 99 MHz (Monastir, TUN) **[51479]**

Radio Monastir-FM - 106.1 MHz (Monastir, TUN) **[51478]**

Radio Monchegorsk (Monchegorsk, RUS) *Unable to locate*

Radio Mongolia - Altai (Ulaanbaatar, MNG) *Unable to locate*

Radio Mongolia - Altai (Ulaanbaatar, MNG) *Unable to locate*

Radio Mongolia - Altai (Ulaanbaatar, MNG) *Unable to locate*

Radio Mongolia - Choibalsan (Ulaanbaatar, MNG) *Unable to locate*

Radio Mongolia - Choibalsan (Ulaanbaatar, MNG) *Unable to locate*

Radio Mongolia - Choibalsan (Ulaanbaatar, MNG) *Unable to locate*

Radio Mongolia - Dalanzadgad (Ulaanbaatar, MNG) *Unable to locate*

Radio Mongolia - Dalanzadgad (Ulaanbaatar, MNG) *Unable to locate*

Radio Mongolia - Dalanzadgad (Ulaanbaatar, MNG) *Unable to locate*

Radio Mongolia - Huvsgul (Ulaanbaatar, MNG) *Unable to locate*

Radio Mongolia - Murun (Ulaanbaatar, MNG) *Unable to locate*

Radio Mongolia - Murun (Ulaanbaatar, MNG) *Unable to locate*

Radio Mongolia - Sainshand (Ulaanbaatar, MNG) *Unable to locate*

Radio Mongolia - Sainshand (Ulaanbaatar, MNG) *Unable to locate*

Radio Mongolia - Ulaanbaatar (Ulaanbaatar, MNG) *Unable to locate*

Radio Mongolia - Ulaanbaatar (Ulaanbaatar, MNG) *Unable to locate*

Radio Mongolia - Ulaanbaatar (Ulaanbaatar, MNG) *Unable to locate*

Radio Mongolia - Ulaanbaatar (Ulaanbaatar, MNG) *Unable to locate*

Radio Mongolia - Ulaanbaatar (Ulaanbaatar, MNG) *Unable to locate*

Radio Mongolia - Ulangoom (Ulaanbaatar, MNG) *Unable to locate*

Radio Mongolia - Ulgii (Ulaanbaatar, MNG) *Unable to locate*

Radio Mongolia - Ulgii (Ulaanbaatar, MNG) *Unable to locate*

Radio Mongolia - Uliosxai (Ulaanbaatar, MNG) *Unable to locate*

Radio Mont Liban - Jounieh (Beirut, LBN) *Unable to locate*

Radio Monte Carlo Swiss-FM (Zurich, SWI) *Unable to locate*

Radio Monte-Karlo - Angarsk (Moscow, RUS) *Unable to locate*

Radio Monte-Karlo - Belgorod (Belgorod, RUS) *Unable to locate*

Radio Monte-Karlo - Belgorod (Belgorod, RUS) *Unable to locate*

Radio Monte-Karlo - Moskva (Moscow, RUS) *Unable to locate*

Radio Monte-Karlo - Novosibirsk (Moscow, RUS) *Unable to locate*

Radio Monte-Karlo - Russko-Vysotskoye (Moscow, RUS) *Unable to locate*

Radio Montini Jaya, Manado (Manado, IDN) *Unable to locate*

Radio Morava-FM - 98.4 (Jagodina, SER) **[50088]**

Radio MRC (Magnitogorsk, RUS) *Unable to locate*

Radio Mudhita Buana B.S., Pontianak (Pontianak, IDN) *Unable to locate*

Radio Munot-FM - 103.1 (Schaffhausen, SWI) **[51229]**

Radio Munot-FM - 101.85 (Schaffhausen, SWI) **[51228]**

Radio Munot-FM - 107.5 (Schaffhausen, SWI) **[51227]**

Radio Muria, Kudus (Kudus, IDN) *Unable to locate*

Radio Mutiara, Bandung (Bandung, IDN) *Unable to locate*

Radio Nacional-FM - 96.1 (Brasilia, DF, BRZ) **[42960]**

Radio Nacional del Peru-AM - 850 (Lima, PER) **[49434]**

Radio Nacional del Peru-FM - 103.9 (Lima, PER) **[49435]**

Radio Nada Berlian, Jambi (Jambi, IDN) *Unable to locate*

Radio Nada Kemala Jaya, Sumenep (Sumenep, IDN) *Unable to locate*

Radio Nada Kencana Agung, Bandung (Bandung, IDN) *Unable to locate*

Radio Nadezhda (Krasnoyarsk, RUS) *Unable to locate*

Radio Nadezhda (Moscow, RUS) *Unable to locate*

Radio Nakhodka (Nakhodka, RUS) *Unable to locate*

Radio Namora Swara Pratama, Curup (Curup, IDN) *Unable to locate*

Radio Nanduti-AM - 1020 (Asuncion, PAR) **[49407]**

Radio Napa-FM - 106.3 MHz (Ayia Napa, CYP) **[43588]**

Radio Nastroyeniye (Kazan, RUS) *Unable to locate*

Radio Nationale Lao - Houa Phanh (Vientiane, LAO) *Ceased*

Radio Nationale Lao - Louang Prabang (Vientiane, LAO) *Unable to locate*

Radio Nationale Lao - Muang Hay (Vientiane, LAO) *Unable to locate*

Radio Nationale Lao - Pakse (Vientiane, LAO) *Ceased*

Radio Nationale Lao - Phonsavan (Vientiane, LAO) *Ceased*

Radio Nationale Lao - Savannakhet (Vientiane, LAO) *Unable to locate*

Radio Nationale Lao - Vientiane (Vientiane, LAO) *Unable to locate*

Radio Nationale Lao - Vientiane (Vientiane, LAO) *Unable to locate*

Radio Nationale Lao - Vientiane (Vientiane, LAO) *Unable to locate*

Radio Nationale Lao - Xam Nua (Vientiane, LAO) *Unable to locate*

Radio Ndeke Luka-FM - 100.8 (Lausanne, SWI) **[51203]**

Radio Nepal - Bardibas - 1143 KHz (Bardibas, NPL) **[47827]**

Radio Nepal - Dhankuta - 648 KHz (Dhankuta, NPL) **[47831]**

Radio Nepal - Dipayal - 810 KHz (Dipayal, NPL) **[47832]**

Radio Nepal - Kathmandu FM - 100 MHz (Kathmandu, NPL) **[47853]**

Radio Nepal - Kathmandu MW - 792 KHz (Kathmandu, NPL) **[47854]**

Radio Nepal - Khumaltar (Kathmandu, NPL) *Unable to locate*

Radio Nepal - Khumaltar - 5005 KHz (Khumaltar, NPL) **[47856]**

Radio Nepal - Khumaltar - 3230 KHz (Khumaltar, NPL) **[47857]**

Radio Nepal - Khumaltar - 7165 KHz (Khumaltar, NPL) **[47855]**

Radio Nepal - Pokhara - 684 KHz (Pokhara, NPL) **[47860]**

Radio Nepal - Surkhet - 576 KHz (Surkhet, NPL) **[47863]**

Radio Network (Novocherkassk, RUS) *Unable to locate*

Radio Network (Novocherkassk, RUS) *Unable to locate*

Radio New Zealand National-AM - 756 (Auckland, NZL) **[48850]**

Radio New Zealand National-AM - 981 (Kaikohe, NZL) **[48926]**

Radio New Zealand National-AM - 837 (Kaitaia, NZL) **[48929]**

Radio Niaga dan Budaya Simalungun, Pematangsiantar (Pematangsiantar, IDN) *Unable to locate*

Radio Nias Mitra Dharma, Gunungsitoli, IDN) *Unable to locate*

Radio NIKA (Sochi, RUS) *Unable to locate*

RADIO 91.3 FM - 91.3 Mhz (Singapore, SGP) **[50304]**

Radio Nirwana Lestari, Banjamasin (Banjamasin, IDN) *Unable to locate*

Radio Nord (Yugorsk, RUS) *Unable to locate*

Radio Northern Beaches-FM - 90.3 (Narrabeen, NW, AUS) **[42141]**

Radio Northern Beaches-FM - 88.7 MHz (Narrabeen, NW, AUS) **[42140]**

Radio Norwich-FM - 99.9 (Norwich, GBR) **[55748]**

Radio Nostalgie (Cherkessk, RUS) *Unable to locate*

Radio Nostalgie (Kazan, RUS) *Unable to locate*

Radio Nostalgie (Kemerovo, RUS) *Unable to locate*

Radio Nostalgie (Kursk, RUS) *Unable to locate*

Radio Nostalgie (Moscow, RUS) *Unable to locate*

Radio Nostalgie (Moscow, RUS) *Unable to locate*

Radio Nostalgie (Moscow, RUS) *Unable to locate*

Radio Nostalgie (Samara, RUS) *Unable to locate*

Radio Nostalgie (Yaroslavl, RUS) *Unable to locate*

Radio Nostalgie - Balashikha (Moscow, RUS) *Unable to locate*

Radio Nostalgie-Baykal - Bratsk (Moscow, RUS) *Unable to locate*

Radio Nostalgie - Cheboksary (Cheboksary, RUS) *Unable to locate*

Radio Nostalgie - Chelyabinsk (Chelyabinsk, RUS) *Unable to locate*

Radio Nostalgie - Cherepovets (Moscow, RUS) *Unable to locate*

Radio Nostalgie-Inform - Ufa (Moscow, RUS) *Unable to locate*

Radio Nostalgie - Irkutsk (Irkutsk, RUS) *Unable to locate*

Radio Nostalgie - Ivanovo (Ivanovo, RUS) *Unable to locate*

Radio Nostalgie - Kaluga (Kaluga, RUS) *Unable to locate*

Radio Nostalgie - Kemerovo (Kemerovo, RUS) *Unable to locate*

Radio Nostalgie - Khabarvosk (Khabarovsk, RUS) *Unable to locate*

Radio Nostalgie - Krasnoyarsk (Moscow, RUS) *Unable to locate*

Radio Nostalgie - Magadan (Moscow, RUS) *Unable to locate*

Radio Nostalgie - Maykop (Maykop, RUS) *Unable to locate*

Radio Nostalgie - Murmansk (Murmansk, RUS) *Unable to locate*

Radio Nostalgie - Orenburg (Orenburg, RUS) *Unable to locate*

Radio Nostalgie - Petrozavodsk (Petrozavodsk, RUS) *Unable to locate*

Radio Nostalgie (Radio Ekho) - Ryazan (Ryazan, RUS) *Unable to locate*

Radio Nostalgie (Radio Uniton) (Novosibirsk, RUS) *Unable to locate*

Radio Nostalgie (Radio Viktoria) - Yakutsk (Yakutsk, RUS) *Unable to locate*

Radio Nostalgie - Rostov-na-Donu (Rostov-na-Donu, RUS) *Unable to locate*

Radio Nostalgie - Sankt-Peterburg (St. Petersburg, RUS) *Unable to locate*

Radio Nostalgie - Sochi (Moscow, RUS) *Unable to locate*

Radio Nostalgie - Tomsk (Moscow, RUS) *Unable to locate*

Radio Nostalgie - Ulan-Ude (Moscow, RUS) *Unable to locate*

Radio Nostalgie - Ust-Ilimsk (Moscow, RUS) *Unable to locate*

Radio Nostalgie - Yurga (Yurga, RUS) *Unable to locate*

Radio Nostalgie - Yuzhno-Sakhalinsk (Moscow, RUS) *Unable to locate*

Radio Nova (Velikiy Novgorod, RUS) *Unable to locate*

Radio Nova Cidade-FM - 105.5 (Ribeira Grande, PRT) **[49810]**

Numbers cited in bold after listings are entry numbers rather than page numbers.

Master Index

Radio Novaya Rossiya (No-vorossiysk, RUS) *Unable to locate*

Radio Novaya Volna (Ulan-Ude, RUS) *Unable to locate*

Radio Novaya Volna (Vladivostok, RUS) *Unable to locate*

Radio Novaya Volna (Volgograd, RUS) *Unable to locate*

Radio Novaya Volna (Volgograd, RUS) *Unable to locate*

Radio Novaya Volna (Volgograd, RUS) *Unable to locate*

Radio Novaya Zhizn (Magadan, RUS) *Unable to locate*

Radio Novosibirsk (Novosibirsk, RUS) *Unable to locate*

Radio Novosti-FM - 104.7 (Belgrade, SER) **[50086]**

Radio Noyabrsk (Noyabrsk, RUS) *Unable to locate*

Radio Noyabrsk (Noyabrsk, RUS) *Unable to locate*

Radio NS (Almaty, KAZ) *Unable to locate*

Radio NS (Almaty, KAZ) *Unable to locate*

Radio NS (Almaty, KAZ) *Unable to locate*

Radio NS (Almaty, KAZ) *Unable to locate*

Radio Nugraha Top, Palu (Palu, IDN) *Unable to locate*

Radio Nusantara Bharata Citra (NBC), Garut - 882 KHz (Garut, IDN) **[45791]**

Radio Nusantara Jaya (RDS), Jakarta (Jakarta Selatan, IDN) *Unable to locate*

Radio Oberland-FM - 97.5 (Garmisch-Partenkirchen, GER) **[44382]**

Radio Odin (Moscow, RUS) *Unable to locate*

Radio Oktava (Kursk, RUS) *Unable to locate*

Radio Oktava (Kursk, RUS) *Unable to locate*

Radio Oktava (Novocherkassk, RUS) *Unable to locate*

Radio Olimp-II (Khabarovsk, RUS) *Unable to locate*

Radio Onda Libera-FM - 97.1 (Frosinone, ITA) **[46147]**

Radio Onda Libera-FM - 99 Mhz (Rome, ITA) **[46246]**

Radio One - 105.5 (Beit Meri el Metn, LBN) **[47439]**

Radio One-FM - 94.3 (Mumbai, MH, IND) **[45454]**

Radio 1-FM (Dublin, DU, IRL) *Unable to locate*

Radio One-FM - 91.0 (Dunedin, NZL) **[48896]**

Radio 103 (Rostov-na-Donu, RUS) *Unable to locate*

Radio 103 (Rostov-na-Donu, RUS) *Unable to locate*

Radio 102 (Temirtau, KAZ) *Unable to locate*

Radio 102 (Cherepovets, RUS) *Unable to locate*

Radio 1 Petrograd (Moscow, RUS) *Ceased*

Radio 105.8 FM (Pyatigorsk, RUS) *Unable to locate*

Radio Orient (Beirut, LBN) *Unable to locate*

Radio Orient-AM - 1602 (Clichy, FRA) **[43938]**

Radio Orient - Beirut - 88.7 MHz (Beirut, LBN) **[47425]**

Radio Orient - Deir al Achayer (Clichy, FRA) *Unable to locate*

Radio Orient-FM - 92.7 (Clichy, FRA) **[43939]**

Radio Orient-FM - 88.3 (Beirut, LBN) **[47427]**

Radio Orient-FM - 88.7 (Beirut, LBN) **[47426]**

Radio Orient - Jabal Tourbol - 88.3 MHz (Jabal Tourbol, LBN) **[47447]**

Radio Oskol (Staryy Oskol, RUS) *Unable to locate*

Radio del Pacifico-AM - 640 (Lima, PER) **[49436]**

Radio Padaidi Padaelo Sipatuo Sipatokkong, Ujung Pandang (Makassar, IDN) *Unable to locate*

Radio Pahlawan Budi Sakti, Serang (Serang, IDN) *Unable to locate*

Radio Pakistan-AM - 630 KHz (Islamabad, PAK) **[49337]**

Radio Pakistan-AM - 1260 KHz (Islamabad, PAK) **[49335]**

Radio Pakistan-AM - 585 KHz (Islamabad, PAK) **[49336]**

Radio Pakistan-AM - 585 KHz (Islamabad, PAK) **[49334]**

Radio Pakistan-FM - 101 MHz (Islamabad, PAK) **[49338]**

Radio Paksi, Bandung - 1152 KHz (Bandung, IDN) **[45779]**

Radio Panca Pesona Jaya (Papeja), Lubuklinggau (Lubuklinggau, IDN) *Unable to locate*

Radio Pancabayu Madugondo (Suara RPM), Sukoharjo - 819 KHz (Sukoharjo, IDN) **[45858]**

Radio Panorama (Chernogorsk, RUS) *Unable to locate*

Radio Panorama (Moscow, RUS) *Unable to locate*

Radio Paramita Jaya, Tulungagung (Jakarta, IDN) *Unable to locate*

Radio Pariwara Swara Desa, Indrapura (Asahan, IDN) *Unable to locate*

Radio Pariwisata Senaputra, Malang (Malang, IDN) *Unable to locate*

Radio Pasopati Andalan, Semarang - 936 KHz (Semarang, IDN) **[45852]**

Radio Passazh Moskva (Kazan, RUS) *Unable to locate*

Radio Passazh Moskva (Kazan, RUS) *Unable to locate*

Radio Paulina-FM - 89.3 (Iquique, CHL) **[43139]**

Radio Pelangi Cakrawala Nusantara, Subang (Subang, IDN) *Unable to locate*

Radio Pelangi Nusantara, Jakarta - 882 KHz (Jakarta, IDN) **[45808]**

Radio Pembrokeshire-FM - 102.5 (Narberth, GBR) **[55655]**

Radio Pemerintah Daerah Kabupaten Daerah Tingkat Dua, Sukabumi (Programa Dua) (Sukabumi, IDN) *Unable to locate*

Radio Pemerintah Daerah Kabupaten Daerah Tingkat Dua, Sumbawa, IDN) *Unable to locate*

Radio Pemerintah Daerah Kabupaten Kapuas, Kuala Kapuas, IDN) *Unable to locate*

Radio Pemerintah Daerah Kabupaten Kulonprogo (Radio Suara Indrakila), Wates (Wates, IDN) *Unable to locate*

Radio Pemerintah Daerah Tingkat Dua Aceh Timur, Langsa (Jakarta, IDN) *Unable to locate*

Radio Pemerintah Daerah Tingkat Dua Belu, Atambua (Atambua, IDN) *Ceased*

Radio Pemerintah Daerah Tingkat Dua, Bengkalis (Bengkalis, IDN) *Unable to locate*

Radio Pemerintah Daerah Tingkat Dua Berau, Tanjungredeb (Jakarta, IDN) *Unable to locate*

Radio Pemerintah Daerah Tingkat Dua, Brebes (Brebes, IDN) *Unable to locate*

Radio Pemerintah Daerah Tingkat Dua Buol, Tolitoli (Jakarta, IDN) *Unable to locate*

Radio Pemerintah Daerah Tingkat Dua, Ende (Jakarta, IDN) *Unable to locate*

Radio Pemerintah Daerah Tingkat Dua, Garut (Jakarta, IDN) *Unable to locate*

Radio Pemerintah Daerah Tingkat Dua Kampar, Bangkinang (Bangkinang, IDN) *Unable to locate*

Radio Pemerintah Daerah Tingkat Dua, Kotamadya Binjai, IDN) *Unable to locate*

Radio Pemerintah Daerah Tingkat Dua Kutai, Tenggarong, IDN) *Unable to locate*

Radio Pemerintah Daerah Tingkat Dua, Luwu, Palopo, IDN) *Ceased*

Radio Pemerintah Daerah Tingkat Dua Ngada, Bajawa (Flores, IDN) *Ceased*

Radio Pemerintah Daerah Tingkat Dua Ngada, Bajawa (Flores, IDN) *Unable to locate*

Radio Pemerintah Kabupaten Daerah Tingkat Dua, Ciamis (Ciamis, IDN) *Unable to locate*

Radio Pemerintah Kabupaten Daerah Tingkat Dua, Cirebon (Cirebon, IDN) *Unable to locate*

Radio Pemerintah Kabupaten Daerah Tingkat Dua, Lebak, Rangkasbitung (Rangkasbitung, IDN) *Unable to locate*

Radio Pemerintah Kabupaten Daerah Tingkat Dua, Majalengka (Majalengka, IDN) *Unable to locate*

Radio Pemerintah Kabupaten Daerah Tingkat Dua, Tasikmalaya, IDN) *Unable to locate*

Radio Pemerintah Kotamadya Daerah Tingkat Dua, Mojokerto (Radio Gelora Mojopahit) (Jakarta, IDN) *Unable to locate*

Radio Pemerintah Tangkat Daerah Indonesia Suara Kenanga Citra Indah, Purworejo (Purworejo, IDN) *Unable to locate*

Radio Pemerintah Tingkat Daerah Satu Walisongo, Pekalongan (Pekalongan, IDN) *Ceased*

Radio Pemerintah Tingkat Dua Satu Kalimasadha Sakti, Semarang (Semarang, IDN) *Unable to locate*

Radio Pentas Taruna Sriwijaya, Sumatera Selatan (Prabumulih, IDN) *Unable to locate*

Radio Perkasa Muda Agung (PMA), Kraksaan (Probolinggo, IDN) *Unable to locate*

Radio Permata Swaratama, Boyolali, IDN) *Unable to locate*

Radio Persatuan, Bantul (Bantul D.I., IDN) *Unable to locate*

Radio Pesona Bahari, Weleri (Jakarta, IDN) *Unable to locate*

Radio Pesona Lematang, Lahat (Lahat, IDN) *Unable to locate*

Radio Peterburg-Nostalgie - Sankt-Peterburg (St. Petersburg, RUS) *Unable to locate*

Radio Phoenix-FM - 89.5 (Lusaka, ZMB) **[57108]**

Radio Pico-FM - 100.2 (Madalena do Pico, PRT) **[49807]**

Radio Pik (Irkutsk, RUS) *Unable to locate*

Radio Pilgrim (Barnaul, RUS) *Unable to locate*

Radio Pilot (Tver, RUS) *Unable to locate*

Radio Piramida - Bishkek (Bishkek, KGA) *Unable to locate*

Radio Piramida - Bishkek (Bishkek, KGA) *Unable to locate*

Radio Piramida - Bishkek (Bishkek, KGA) *Unable to locate*

Radio Plyus (Volgodonsk, RUS) *Unable to locate*

Radio Podolska (Podolsk, RUS) *Unable to locate*

Radio Poliyama Indah, Gorontalo (Gorontalo, IDN) *Unable to locate*

Radio Polyus (Norilsk, RUS) *Unable to locate*

Radio Prabu Kiansantang, Tasikmalaya (Tasikmalaya, IDN) *Unable to locate*

Radio Pratama Mahardika, Gedong Tataan (Lampung Selatan, IDN) *Unable to locate*

Radio Premier (Penza, RUS) *Unable to locate*

Radio Premier (Vologda, RUS) *Unable to locate*

Radio Premier (Vologda, RUS) *Unable to locate*

Radio Prestizh (Nizhniy Novgorod, RUS) *Unable to locate*

Radio Prima Elita, Palembang (Palembang, IDN) *Unable to locate*

Radio Prima Ukir Utama, Jepara (Jepara, IDN) *Unable to locate*

Radio Prominda Dirgantara, Pontianak, IDN) *Unable to locate*

Radio Prospekt (Barnaul, RUS) *Unable to locate*

Radio Prostor S. (Langepas, RUS) *Unable to locate*

Radio Prostor S (Langepas, RUS) *Unable to locate*

Radio Proto-FM - 89.3 (Nicosia, CYP) **[43599]**

Radio Provintsiya (Pyatigorsk, RUS) *Unable to locate*

Radio Provintsiya (Pyatigorsk, RUS) *Unable to locate*

Radio PTDI Suara Kaliwungu Dirgantara, Kaliwungu (Kaliwungu, IDN) *Unable to locate*

Radio Pulpit-FM - 97.2 (Pretoria, SAF) **[50609]**

Radio Puls (Azov, RUS) *Unable to locate*

Radio Puls (Kazan, RUS) *Unable to locate*

Radio Puls-FM (Despotovac, SER) *Unable to locate*

Radio Purnama Nada, Kandangan - 684 KHz (Kandangan, IDN) **[45817]**

Radio Purnamasidi, Wonosobo - 720 KHz (Wonosobo, IDN) **[45877]**

Radio Purnayudha, Bekasi - 1044 KHz (Bekasi, IDN) **[45783]**

Radio Puspa Dwi Swara Cipta (P2SC), Jakarta - 936 KHz (Jakarta, IDN) **[45809]**

Radio Puspa Irama, Belitang Oku (Belitang, IDN) *Unable to locate*

Radio Puspa Jaya, Bojonegoro (Bojonegoro, IDN) *Unable to locate*

Radio Pyramida - Bishkek (Bishkek, KGA) *Unable to locate*

Radio Q-FM - 105.2 (Visoko, HBO) **[42941]**

Radio R. H. K., Semarang (Jakarta, IDN) *Unable to locate*

Numbers cited in bold after listings are entry numbers rather than page numbers.

Radio-R-Ivanovo (Ivanovo, RUS) *Unable to locate*

Radio RA (Novosibirsk, RUS) *Unable to locate*

Radio Race Car International (Malvern, GBR) **[55539]**

Radio Radiks 99 Suara Kebahagiaan, Semarang (Semarang, IDN) *Unable to locate*

Radio Radio-FM - 97 MHz (Phnom Penh, CMB) **[43117]**

Radio Raduga (Izhevsk, RUS) *Unable to locate*

Radio Raduga (Izhevsk, RUS) *Unable to locate*

Radio Raduga (Izhevsk, RUS) *Unable to locate*

Radio Ragam Tunas Lampung (Ratula), Kotabumi, IDN) *Unable to locate*

Radio Rajawali Sakti, Balikpapan (Balikpapan, IDN) *Unable to locate*

Radio Rajawali, Surabaya (Surabaya, IDN) *Unable to locate*

Radio Rajawali Terbang. Bandar Lampung (Bandar Lampung, IDN) *Unable to locate*

Radio Raka, Tegal - 1044 KHz (Tegal, IDN) **[45875]**

Radio Ramakusala, Surakarta - 666 KHz (Surakarta, IDN) **[45868]**

Radio Ramayana Wiratama, Metro (Metro, IDN) *Unable to locate*

Radio Randevu SF (Nizhniy Novgorod, RUS) *Unable to locate*

Radio Rating (Obninsk, RUS) *Ceased*

Radio Rating (Obninsk, RUS) *Ceased*

Radio Ratna Palupi, Karawang (Kawarang, IDN) *Unable to locate*

Radio R.D.A.45, Bangil (Pasuruan, IDN) *Unable to locate*

Radio RDKS (Krasnodar, RUS) *Unable to locate*

Radio Refalado, Banjarmasin (Tanjungbalai, IDN) *Unable to locate*

Radio Regionale Mascara-FM (Mascara, ALG) *Unable to locate*

Radio Regionale de Mostaganem-FM (Mostaganem, ALG) *Unable to locate*

Radio Regionale de Tlemcen-FM - 94.7 (Tlemcen, ALG) **[41462]**

Radio Regionale de Tlemcen-FM - 100.4 (Tlemcen, ALG) **[41463]**

Radio Rekord (Saint Petersburg, RUS) *Unable to locate*

Radio Relaks (Kirov, RUS) *Unable to locate*

Radio Republic Indonesia, Banda Aceh (Banda Aceh, IDN) *Unable to locate*

Radio Republic Indonesia, Banda Aceh (Banda Aceh, IDN) *Unable to locate*

Radio Republic Indonesia Ambon (Ambon, IDN) *Unable to locate*

Radio Republik Indonesia Ambon (Ambon, IDN) *Unable to locate*

Radio Republik Indonesia, Banda Aceh (Banda Aceh, IDN) *Unable to locate*

Radio Republik Indonesia, Bandung (Bandung, IDN) *Unable to locate*

Radio Republik Indonesia, Bandung (Bandung, IDN) *Unable to locate*

Radio Republik Indonesia, Bandung (Bandung, IDN) *Unable to locate*

Radio Republik Indonesia, Bandung (Bandung, IDN) *Unable to locate*

Radio Republik Indonesia, Bandung (Bandung, IDN) *Unable to locate*

Radio Republik Indonesia, Bandung (Bandung, IDN) *Unable to locate*

Radio Republik Indonesia, Banjarmasin (Banjarmasin, IDN) *Unable to locate*

Radio Republik Indonesia, Banjarmasin (Banjarmasin, IDN) *Unable to locate*

Radio Republik Indonesia, Banjarmasin (Banjarmasin, IDN) *Unable to locate*

Radio Republik Indonesia, Banjarmasin (Banjarmasin, IDN) *Unable to locate*

Radio Republik Indonesia, Banjarmasin (Banjarmasin, IDN) *Unable to locate*

Radio Republik Indonesia, Banjarmasin (Banjarmasin, IDN) *Unable to locate*

Radio Republik Indonesia, Banjarmasin (Banjarmasin, IDN) *Unable to locate*

Radio Republik Indonesia, Banjarmasin (Banjarmasin, IDN) *Unable to locate*

Radio Republik Indonesia, Bengkulu, IDN) *Unable to locate*

Radio Republik Indonesia, Bengkulu, IDN) *Unable to locate*

Radio Republik Indonesia, Bengkulu (Bengkulu, IDN) *Unable to locate*

Radio Republik Indonesia, Bengkulu (Bengkulu, IDN) *Unable to locate*

Radio Republik Indonesia, Biak, IDN) *Unable to locate*

Radio Republik Indonesia, Biak, IDN) *Unable to locate*

Radio Republik Indonesia, Biak (Biak, IDN) *Unable to locate*

Radio Republik Indonesia, Bogor (Bogor, IDN) *Unable to locate*

Radio Republik Indonesia, Bogor (Bogor, IDN) *Unable to locate*

Radio Republik Indonesia, Bogor (Bogor, IDN) *Unable to locate*

Radio Republik Indonesia, Bogor (Bogor, IDN) *Unable to locate*

Radio Republik Indonesia, Bogor - 1242 KHz (Bogor, IDN) **[45785]**

Radio Republik Indonesia, Bukittinggi (Bukittinggi, IDN) *Unable to locate*

Radio Republik Indonesia, Bukittingi (Bukittinggi, IDN) *Unable to locate*

Radio Republik Indonesia, Bukittingi (Bukittinggi, IDN) *Unable to locate*

Radio Republik Indonesia, Bukittinggi (Bukittinggi, IDN) *Unable to locate*

Radio Republik Indonesia, Bukittinggi (Bukittinggi, IDN) *Unable to locate*

Radio Republik Indonesia, Cirebon (Cirebon, IDN) *Unable to locate*

Radio Republik Indonesia, Cirebon (Cirebon, IDN) *Unable to locate*

Radio Republik Indonesia, Denpasar (Denpasar, IDN) *Unable to locate*

Radio Republik Indonesia, Denpasar (Denpasar, IDN) *Unable to locate*

Radio Republik Indonesia, Denpasar (Denpasar, IDN) *Unable to locate*

Radio Republik Indonesia, Denpasar (Denpasar, IDN) *Unable to locate*

Radio Republik Indonesia, Denpasar (Denpasar, IDN) *Unable to locate*

Radio Republik Indonesia, Dili (Dili, IDN) *Unable to locate*

Radio Republik Indonesia, Dili (Dili, IDN) *Unable to locate*

Radio Republik Indonesia, Dili (Dili, IDN) *Unable to locate*

Radio Republik Indonesia, Dili (Dili, IDN) *Unable to locate*

Radio Republik Indonesia, Fak-Fak (Jakarta, IDN) *Unable to locate*

Radio Republik Indonesia, Fak-Fak (Jakarta, IDN) *Unable to locate*

Radio Republik Indonesia, Gorontalo (Gorontalo, IDN) *Unable to locate*

Radio Republik Indonesia, Gorontalo (Gorontalo, IDN) *Unable to locate*

Radio Republik Indonesia, Gorontalo (Gorontalo, IDN) *Unable to locate*

Radio Republik Indonesia, Gorontalo (Gorontalo, IDN) *Unable to locate*

Radio Republik Indonesia, Jakarta (Jakarta, IDN) *Unable to locate*

Radio Republik Indonesia, Jakarta (Jakarta, IDN) *Unable to locate*

Radio Republik Indonesia, Jakarta (Bonto Sunggu) (Jakarta, IDN) *Unable to locate*

Radio Republik Indonesia, Jakarta (Bonto Sunggu) (Jakarta, IDN) *Unable to locate*

Radio Republik Indonesia, Jakarta (Bonto Sunggu) (Jakarta, IDN) *Unable to locate*

Radio Republik Indonesia, Jakarta (Bonto Sunggu) (Jakarta, IDN) *Unable to locate*

Radio Republik Indonesia, Jakarta (Keboyoran) (Jakarta, IDN) *Unable to locate*

Radio Republik Indonesia, Jambi (Jambi, IDN) *Unable to locate*

Radio Republik Indonesia, Jambi (Jambi, IDN) *Unable to locate*

Radio Republik Indonesia, Jayapura (Jayapura, IDN) *Unable to locate*

Radio Republik Indonesia, Jayapura (Jayapura, IDN) *Unable to locate*

Radio Republik Indonesia, Jayapura (Jayapura, IDN) *Unable to locate*

Radio Republik Indonesia, Jayapura (Jayapura, IDN) *Unable to locate*

Radio Republik Indonesia, Jayapura (Jayapura, IDN) *Unable to locate*

Radio Republik Indonesia, Jember, IDN) *Unable to locate*

Radio Republik Indonesia, Jember (Jember, IDN) *Unable to locate*

Radio Republik Indonesia, Jember (Jember, IDN) *Unable to locate*

Radio Republik Indonesia, Jember (Jember, IDN) *Unable to locate*

Radio Republik Indonesia, Kendari, IDN) *Unable to locate*

Radio Republik Indonesia, Kendari, IDN) *Unable to locate*

Radio Republik Indonesia, Kendari, IDN) *Unable to locate*

Radio Republik Indonesia, Kendari (Kendari, IDN) *Unable to locate*

Radio Republik Indonesia, Kendari (Kendari, IDN) *Unable to locate*

Radio Republik Indonesia, Kendari (Kendari, IDN) *Unable to locate*

Radio Republik Indonesia, Kupang (Kupang, IDN) *Unable to locate*

Radio Republik Indonesia, Kupang (Kupang, IDN) *Unable to locate*

Radio Republik Indonesia, Madiun (Madiun, IDN) *Unable to locate*

Radio Republik Indonesia, Madiun (Madiun, IDN) *Unable to locate*

Radio Republik Indonesia, Malang (Malang, IDN) *Unable to locate*

Radio Republik Indonesia, Malang (Malang, IDN) *Unable to locate*

Radio Republik Indonesia, Malang - 105.1 MHz (Malang, IDN) **[45830]**

Radio Republik Indonesia, Malang - 891 KHz (Malang, IDN) **[45829]**

Radio Republik Indonesia, Manado (Manado, IDN) *Unable to locate*

Radio Republik Indonesia, Manado (Manado, IDN) *Unable to locate*

Radio Republik Indonesia, Manado (Manado, IDN) *Unable to locate*

Radio Republik Indonesia, Manado (Manado, IDN) *Unable to locate*

Radio Republik Indonesia, Manokwari (Manokwari, IDN) *Unable to locate*

Radio Republik Indonesia, Manokwari (Manokwari, IDN) *Unable to locate*

Radio Republik Indonesia, Mataram (Mataram, IDN) *Unable to locate*

Radio Republik Indonesia, Mataram (Mataram, IDN) *Unable to locate*

Radio Republik Indonesia, Medan, IDN) *Unable to locate*

Radio Republik Indonesia, Medan (Medan, IDN) *Unable to locate*

Radio Republik Indonesia, Medan (Medan, IDN) *Unable to locate*

Radio Republik Indonesia, Medan (Medan, IDN) *Unable to locate*

Radio Republik Indonesia, Medan - 88.8 MHz (Medan, IDN) **[45836]**

Radio Republik Indonesia, Medan - 801 KHz (Medan, IDN) **[45837]**

Radio Republik Indonesia, Merauke (Merauke, IDN) *Unable to locate*

Radio Republik Indonesia, Nabire (Jakarta, IDN) *Unable to locate*

Radio Republik Indonesia, Padang (Padang, IDN) *Unable to locate*

Radio Republik Indonesia, Padang (Padang, IDN) *Unable to locate*

Radio Republik Indonesia, Padang (Padang, IDN) *Unable to locate*

Radio Republik Indonesia, Padang (Padang, IDN) *Unable to locate*

Radio Republik Indonesia, Padang (Padang, IDN) *Unable to locate*

Radio Republik Indonesia, Palangkaraya (Palangkaraya, IDN) *Unable to locate*

Radio Republik Indonesia, Palembang (Palembang, IDN) *Unable to locate*

Radio Republik Indonesia, Palembang (Palembang, IDN) *Unable to locate*

Radio Republik Indonesia, Palembang (Palembang, IDN) *Unable to locate*

Radio Republik Indonesia, Palembang (Palembang, IDN) *Unable to locate*

Radio Republik Indonesia, Palu (Palu, IDN) *Unable to locate*

Radio Republik Indonesia, Palu (Palu, IDN) *Unable to locate*

Radio Republik Indonesia, Pekanbaru, IDN) *Unable to locate*

Radio Republik Indonesia, Pekanbaru (Malang, IDN) *Unable to locate*

Radio Republik Indonesia, Pekanbaru (Malang, IDN) *Unable to locate*

Radio Republik Indonesia, Pekanbaru (Malang, IDN) *Unable to locate*

Radio Republik Indonesia, Pekanbaru (Mojolangu-Malang, IDN) *Unable to locate*

Radio Republik Indonesia, Pekanbaru (Pekanbaru, IDN) *Unable to locate*

Radio Republik Indonesia, Pontianak (Pontianak, IDN) *Unable to locate*

Radio Republik Indonesia, Pontianak (Pontianak, IDN) *Unable to locate*

Radio Republik Indonesia, Pontianak (Pontianak, IDN) *Unable to locate*

Radio Republik Indonesia, Pontianak (Pontianak, IDN) *Unable to locate*

Numbers cited in bold after listings are entry numbers rather than page numbers.

Radio Republik Indonesia, Pontianak (Pontianak, IDN) *Unable to locate*

Radio Republik Indonesia, Purwokerto (Purwokerto, IDN) *Unable to locate*

Radio Republik Indonesia, Purwokerto (Purwokerto, IDN) *Unable to locate*

Radio Republik Indonesia, Purwokerto (Purwokerto, IDN) *Unable to locate*

Radio Republik Indonesia, Purwokerto (Purwokerto, IDN) *Unable to locate*

Radio Republik Indonesia, Purwokerto - 756 KHz (Purwokerto, IDN) **[45847]**

Radio Republik Indonesia, Samarinda (Samarinda, IDN) *Unable to locate*

Radio Republik Indonesia, Samarinda (Samarinda, IDN) *Unable to locate*

Radio Republik Indonesia, Samarinda (Samarinda, IDN) *Unable to locate*

Radio Republik Indonesia, Samarinda (Samarinda, IDN) *Unable to locate*

Radio Republik Indonesia, Samarinda (Samarinda, IDN) *Unable to locate*

Radio Republik Indonesia, Semarang, IDN) *Unable to locate*

Radio Republik Indonesia, Semarang (Semarang, IDN) *Unable to locate*

Radio Republik Indonesia, Semarang (Semarang, IDN) *Unable to locate*

Radio Republik Indonesia, Semarang (Semarang, IDN) *Unable to locate*

Radio Republik Indonesia, Semarang - 801 KHz (Semarang, IDN) **[45853]**

Radio Republik Indonesia, Serui (Serui, IDN) *Unable to locate*

Radio Republik Indonesia, Serui (Serui, IDN) *Unable to locate*

Radio Republik Indonesia, Serui (Serui, IDN) *Unable to locate*

Radio Republik Indonesia, Sibolga (Sibolga, IDN) *Unable to locate*

Radio Republik Indonesia, Sibolga (Sibolga, IDN) *Unable to locate*

Radio Republik Indonesia, Sibolga (Sibolga, IDN) *Unable to locate*

Radio Republik Indonesia, Singaraja (Singaraja, IDN) *Unable to locate*

Radio Republik Indonesia, Singaraja (Singaraja, IDN) *Unable to locate*

Radio Republik Indonesia, Singaraja (Singaraja, IDN) *Unable to locate*

Radio Republik Indonesia, Sorong (Jakarta, IDN) *Unable to locate*

Radio Republik Indonesia, Sumenep (Madura, IDN) *Unable to locate*

Radio Republik Indonesia, Sumenep (Madura, IDN) *Unable to locate*

Radio Republik Indonesia, Sumenep (Sumenep, IDN) *Unable to locate*

Radio Republik Indonesia, Sungai Liat (Sungai Liat, IDN) *Unable to locate*

Radio Republik Indonesia Surabaya (Surabaya, IDN) *Unable to locate*

Radio Republik Indonesia Surabaya (Surabaya, IDN) *Unable to locate*

Radio Republik Indonesia, Surabaya (Surabaya, IDN) *Unable to locate*

Radio Republik Indonesia, Surabaya (Surabaya, IDN) *Unable to locate*

Radio Republik Indonesia, Surabaya (Surabaya, IDN) *Unable to locate*

Radio Republik Indonesia, Surabaya - 585 KHz (Surabaya, IDN) **[45865]**

Radio Republik Indonesia, Surakarta - 1053 KHz (Surakarta, IDN) **[45869]**

Radio Republik Indonesia, Surakarta (Surakarta, IDN) *Unable to locate*

Radio Republik Indonesia, Surakarta (Surakarta, IDN) *Unable to locate*

Radio Republik Indonesia, Surakarta (Surakarta, IDN) *Unable to locate*

Radio Republik Indonesia, Surakarta (Surakarta, IDN) *Unable to locate*

Radio Republik Indonesia, Surakarta (Surakarta, IDN) *Unable to locate*

Radio Republik Indonesia, Tanjung Karang (Bandar Lampung, IDN) *Unable to locate*

Radio Republik Indonesia, Tanjung Karang (Bandar Lampung, IDN) *Unable to locate*

Radio Republik Indonesia, Tanjung Pinang (Tanjung Pinang, IDN) *Unable to locate*

Radio Republik Indonesia, Tanjung Pinang (Tanjung Pinang, IDN) *Unable to locate*

Radio Republik Indonesia, Tanjung Pinang (Tanjung Pinang, IDN) *Unable to locate*

Radio Republik Indonesia, Tanjung Pinang (Tanjung Pinang, IDN) *Unable to locate*

Radio Republik Indonesia, Temate (Temate, IDN) *Unable to locate*

Radio Republik Indonesia, Ujung Pandang (Makasar, IDN) *Unable to locate*

Radio Republik Indonesia, Ujung Pandang (Makassar, IDN) *Unable to locate*

Radio Republik Indonesia, Ujung Pandang (Makassar, IDN) *Unable to locate*

Radio Republik Indonesia Ujung Pandang (Makassar, IDN) *Unable to locate*

Radio Republik Indonesia Ujung Pandang (Ujung Pandang, IDN) *Unable to locate*

Radio Republik Indonesia Ujung Pandang (Ujung Pandang, IDN) *Unable to locate*

Radio Republik Indonesia, Ujung Pandang (Ujung Pandang, IDN) *Unable to locate*

Radio Republik Indonesia, Ujung Pandang (Ujung Pandang, IDN) *Unable to locate*

Radio Republik Indonesia, Ujung Pandang (Ujung Pandang, IDN) *Unable to locate*

Radio Republik Indonesia, Ujung Pandang (Ujung Pandang, IDN) *Unable to locate*

Radio Republik Indonesia, Wamena (Wamena, IDN) *Unable to locate*

Radio Republik Indonesia, Yogyakarta (Yogyakarta, IDN) *Unable to locate*

Radio Republik Indonesia, Yogyakarta (Yogyakarta, IDN) *Unable to locate*

Radio Republik Indonesia, Yogyakarta (Yogyakarta, IDN) *Unable to locate*

Radio Retro (Moscow, RUS) *Unable to locate*

Radio Retro (Saint Petersburg, RUS) *Unable to locate*

Radio Retro - Nizhniy Novgorod (Nizhniy Novgorod, RUS) *Unable to locate*

Radio Retro - Orenburg (Orenburg, RUS) *Unable to locate*

Radio Retro - Orenburg (Orenburg, RUS) *Unable to locate*

Radio Retro (Radio Nostalgie) (Perm, RUS) *Unable to locate*

Radio Retro - Stavropol (Stavropol, RUS) *Unable to locate*

Radio Retro - Tula (Tula, RUS) *Unable to locate*

Radio Retro - Tver (Tver, RUS) *Unable to locate*

Radio Retro - Yaroslavl (Yaroslavl, RUS) *Unable to locate*

Radio Rezonans (Moscow, RUS) *Unable to locate*

Radio Rezonans (Moscow, RUS) *Unable to locate*

Radio Rhema-AM - 1251 (Auckland, NZL) **[48851]**

Radio Rhodisko Rasisonia, Banda Aceh (Banda Aceh, IDN) *Unable to locate*

Radio RI-FM - 99.1 (Buchs, SWI) **[51083]**

Radio Ria Cindelaras, Indramayu (Indramayu, IDN) *Unable to locate*

Radio RIF (Biysk, RUS) *Unable to locate*

Radio Rifma (Aqtobe, KAZ) *Unable to locate*

Radio Rina Bestari, Rantepao - 738 KHz (Jakarta, IDN) **[45810]**

Radio Ringan Mutiara, Kendari (Kendari, IDN) *Unable to locate*

Radio Rinjani Permal, Cakranegara (Cakranegara, IDN) *Unable to locate*

Radio Rippel-FM - 90.5 (Silverton, SAF) **[50630]**

Radio Rivista (Milan, ITA) *Unable to locate*

Radio Robin Hood-FM - 91.5 MHZ (Turku, FIN) **[43911]**

Radio ROKS - Balashikha (Moscow, RUS) *Unable to locate*

Radio ROKS - Krasnodar (Krasnodar, RUS) *Unable to locate*

Radio ROKS-Krasnodar - Sochi (Minsk, BLR) *Unable to locate*

Radio ROKS - Maykop (Moscow, RUS) *Unable to locate*

Radio ROKS - Orel (Orel, RUS) *Unable to locate*

Radio ROKS/Serebryanyy Dozhd - Volgograd (Volgograd, RUS) *Unable to locate*

Radio ROKS - Temryuk (Krasnodar, RUS) *Unable to locate*

Radio Roksana (Ufa, RUS) *Unable to locate*

Radio Romantika, Bandowoso (Bandowoso, IDN) *Unable to locate*

Radio Romeo and Juliet Rasisonia, Tenjungkarang (Bandar Lampung, IDN) *Unable to locate*

Radio Roro Djonggrang B.S., Prambanan - 648 KHz (Klaten, IDN) **[45821]**

Radio Rosa-FM - 98.9 (Valby, DEN) **[43737]**

Radio Rosa, Ujung Pandang (Ujung Pandang, IDN) *Unable to locate*

Radio Rost (Vladimir, RUS) *Unable to locate*

Radio Rostova - Rostov-na-Donu (Rostov, RUS) *Unable to locate*

Radio Rottu Oberwallis-FM - 101 (Hohtenn, SWI) **[51179]**

Radio Rottu Oberwallis-FM - 97.8 (Leuk, SWI) **[51206]**

Radio Rottu Oberwallis-FM - 102.9 (Torbel, SWI) **[51235]**

Radio Rottu Oberwallis-FM - 101.8 (Visp, SWI) **[51238]**

Radio Rottu Oberwallis-FM - 100 (Visp, SWI) **[51239]**

Radio R3iii-FM - 106.8 (Melide, SWI) **[51211]**

Radio Rural-AM - 610 (Montevideo, URY) **[57009]**

Radio Rus (Stavropol, RUS) *Unable to locate*

Radio Rus (Stavropol, RUS) *Unable to locate*

Radio Russkaya Volna (Krasnoyarsk, RUS) *Unable to locate*

Radio Saba Putra, Pringsewu (Pringsewu, IDN) *Unable to locate*

Radio Saburai Alam Permai, Liwa, IDN) *Unable to locate*

Radio Sadko (Moscow, RUS) *Unable to locate*

Radio Safari Bina Budaya, Jakarta (Jakarta, IDN) *Unable to locate*

Radio Sagarmatha - Khatmandu (Kathmandu, NPL) *Unable to locate*

Radio Sahara, Kendal (Kendal, IDN) *Unable to locate*

Radio Saint Barth-FM - 98.7 MHz (Saint Barthelemy, FWI) **[44129]**

Radio Saint Barth-FM - 103.7 MHz (Saint Barthelemy, FWI) **[44128]**

Radio Saint Louis-FM - 99.5 (Fort-de-France, MTQ) **[47749]**

Radio Salvatore, Surabaya (Surabaya, IDN) *Unable to locate*

Radio Samara-Maximum (Samara, RUS) *Unable to locate*

Radio Samotlor (Nizhnevartovsk, RUS) *Unable to locate*

Radio San Borja-FM - 91.1 (Lima, PER) **[49437]**

Radio San Sebastian-FM - 103.3 (Chepen, PER) **[49417]**

Radio Santa Clara-AM - 550 (Ciudad Quesada, CRI) **[43551]**

Radio Santa Fe-AM - 1070 (Bogota, COL) **[43548]**

Radio Santo Bernardus D.S., Pekalongan - 648 KHz (Pekalongan, IDN) **[45845]**

Radio Sara - Baki (Baku, AJN) *Ceased*

Radio Sarandi - 690 (Montevideo, URY) **[57010]**

Radio Sayma-Sputnik (Vyborg, RUS) *Unable to locate*

Radio S.B.S., Purbalingga - 828 KHz (Jakarta, IDN) **[45811]**

Radio Scope (Zahle, LBN) *Unable to locate*

Radio Scope (Zahle, LBN) *Unable to locate*

Radio Sedmoi Etazh (Angarsk, RUS) *Unable to locate*

Radio Sem iz Samary (Samara, RUS) *Unable to locate*

Radio Sem iz Samary (Samara, RUS) *Unable to locate*

Radio Sena Bahana Cakrawala, Sukabumi (Sukabumi, IDN) *Unable to locate*

Radio Senator (Magnitogorsk, RUS) *Unable to locate*

Radio Serenada Gita Lestari, Slawi (Jakarta, IDN) *Unable to locate*

Radio Serova (Serov, RUS) *Unable to locate*

Radio Serpukhov (Serpukhov, RUS) *Unable to locate*

Radio Services (Mumbai, MH, IND) *Unable to locate*

Radio 786-FM - 100.4 (Cape Town, SAF) **[50435]**

Radio 7 (Radio na Semi Kholmakh) (Moscow, RUS) *Unable to locate*

Radio 71 (Kostroma, RUS) *Unable to locate*

Radio 73 (Kemerovo, RUS) *Unable to locate*

Radio Severnaya Stolitsa (St. Petersburg, RUS) *Unable to locate*

Radio Sfax-AM - 720 KHz (Sfax, TUN) **[51480]**

Numbers cited in bold after listings are entry numbers rather than page numbers.

Radio Sfax-FM - 105.21 MHz (Sfax, TUN) **[51481]**

Radio Sfera (Pyatigorsk, RUS) *Unable to locate*

Radio Shakhar (Almaty, KAZ) *Unable to locate*

Radio Shans (Yaroslavl, RUS) *Unable to locate*

Radio Shark (Ufa, RUS) *Unable to locate*

Radio Shark (Ufa, RUS) *Unable to locate*

Radio Shark 1 (Ufa, RUS) *Unable to locate*

Radio Shark 1 (Ufa, RUS) *Unable to locate*

Radio Shinta Wahana, Bengkulu (Bengkulu, IDN) *Unable to locate*

Radio Shok (Kaliningrad, RUS) *Unable to locate*

Radio Si (Yekaterinburg, RUS) *Unable to locate*

Radio Si (Yekaterinburg, RUS) *Unable to locate*

Radio Siaga Indah Marista (Santanimo), Banjarmasin (Banjarmasin, IDN) *Unable to locate*

Radio Siaran B81 Daerah Tangkat Dua Semarang, Ungaran (Semarang, IDN) *Ceased*

Radio Siaran Ichthus, Semarang (Semarang, IDN) *Unable to locate*

Radio Siaran Niaga dan Budaya Mhanda, Meulabon (Meulaboh, IDN) *Unable to locate*

Radio Siaran Niaga Hiukencana (RHK), Semarang (Semarang, IDN) *Unable to locate*

Radio Siaran Pemerintah Daerah Kabupaten, Batang (Batang, IDN) *Unable to locate*

Radio Siaran Pemerintah Daerah Kabupaten Daerah Tingkat Dua, Karanganyar (Swara Intanpari) (Jakarta, IDN) *Unable to locate*

Radio Siaran Pemerintah Daerah Kabupaten Daerah Tingkat Dua, Kebumen (Jakarta, IDN) *Unable to locate*

Radio Siaran Pemerintah Daerah Kabupaten Daerah Tingkat Dua, Magelang (Magelang, IDN) *Unable to locate*

Radio Siaran Pemerintah Daerah Kabupaten Daerah Tingkat Dua, Wonosobo (Wonosobo, IDN) *Unable to locate*

Radio Siaran Pemerintah Daerah Kabupaten Tingkat Dua, Sragen (Radio Suara Buana Asri) (Sragen, IDN) *Ceased*

Radio Siaran Pemerintah Daerah Khusus Daerah Tingkat Dua, Banjarnegara (Jakarta, IDN) *Unable to locate*

Radio Siaran Pemerintah Daerah Khusus Daerah Tingkat Dua, Cilacap (Cilacap, IDN) *Unable to locate*

Radio Siaran Pemerintah Daerah Khusus Daerah Tingkat Dua, Purworejo (Radio Suara Irama) (Purworejo, IDN) *Ceased*

Radio Siaran Pemerintah Daerah Khusus Daerah Tingkat Dua, Wonogiri (Wonogiri, IDN) *Unable to locate*

Radio Siaran Pemerintah Daerah Kotamadya Magelang (Magelang, IDN) *Unable to locate*

Radio Siaran Pemerintah Daerah, Kotamadya Tegal (Tegal, IDN) *Unable to locate*

Radio Siaran Pemerintah Daerah, Kotamadya Tegal (Tegal, IDN) *Unable to locate*

Radio Siaran Pemerintah Daerah Tangkat Dua Kotamadya Pekalongan (Suara Kota Batik) (Pekalongan, IDN) *Unable to locate*

Radio Siaran Pemerintah Daerah Tingkat Dua Batanghari, Muarabulian (Muarabulian, IDN) *Ceased*

Radio Siaran Pemerintah Daerah Tingkat Dua, Blora (Jakarta, IDN) *Unable to locate*

Radio Siaran Pemerintah Daerah Tingkat Dua Halmahera Tengah, Soasio (Tidore, IDN) *Unable to locate*

Radio Siaran Pemerintah Daerah Tingkat Dua, Indragiri Hulu, Rengat (Rengat, IDN) *Unable to locate*

Radio Siaran Pemerintah Daerah Tingkat Dua Kotamadya Pekalongan (Sura Kota Batik) (Jakarta, IDN) *Unable to locate*

Radio Siaran Pemerintah Daerah Tingkat Dua Kudus (Suara Kudus) (Kudus, IDN) *Unable to locate*

Radio Siaran Pemerintah Daerah Tingkat Dua, Labuhan Batu, Rantau Prapat (Rantau Prapat, IDN) *Unable to locate*

Radio Siaran Pemerintah Daerah Tingkat Dua, Pati (Suara Pati) (Pati, IDN) *Unable to locate*

Radio Siaran Pemerintah Daerah Tingkat Dua Pemalang (Suara Widuri),Pemalang (Jakarta, IDN) *Unable to locate*

Radio Siaran Pemerintah Daerah Tingkat Dua Sumba Timur, Wiangpur (Jakarta, IDN) *Unable to locate*

Radio Siaran Pemerintah Daerah Tingkat Dua Tegal, Slawi (Jakarta, IDN) *Unable to locate*

Radio Siaran Pemerintah Daerah Tingkat Dua Timor Tengah Selatan, Soe (Jakarta, IDN) *Unable to locate*

Radio Siaran Pemerintah Kabupaten Daerah Tingkat Dua, Pekalongan (R.Kota Santri) (Jakarta, IDN) *Unable to locate*

Radio Siaran Pemerintah Kabupaten Daerah Tingkat Dua, Purbalingga (Purbalingga, IDN) *Unable to locate*

Radio Siaran Pemerintah Khusus Daerah Tingkat Dua, Jepara (Radio Kartini) (Jepara, IDN) *Ceased*

Radio Siaran Pemerintah Khusus Daerah Tingkat Dua, Kendal (Kendal, IDN) *Unable to locate*

Radio Sibir (Abakan, RUS) *Unable to locate*

Radio Sibir (Sayanogorsk, RUS) *Unable to locate*

Radio Sibir (Tomsk, RUS) *Unable to locate*

Radio Sibir (Tomsk, RUS) *Unable to locate*

Radio Sibir (Tomsk, RUS) *Unable to locate*

Radio Sibir (Tomsk, RUS) *Unable to locate*

Radio Sibiri (Novosibirsk, RUS) *Unable to locate*

Radio Sibiri (Novosibirsk, RUS) *Unable to locate*

Radio Siera Alfa Lama, Bantul (Bantul, IDN) *Unable to locate*

Radio Sikamoni, Medan (Medan, IDN) *Unable to locate*

Radio Sindang Kasih, Cirebon (Cirebon, IDN) *Unable to locate*

Radio Sintonia-AM - 1420 (Caracas, VEN) **[57022]**

Radio Sion, Tomohon (Minahasa, IDN) *Unable to locate*

Radio 69 Murman - Murmansk (Murmansk, RUS) *Unable to locate*

Radio Slovo (Novosibirsk, RUS) *Unable to locate*

Radio Sodiak, Surabaya (Jakarta, IDN) *Unable to locate*

Radio Sonara-FM - 98 (Surabaya, IDN) **[45866]**

Radio Sonya Manis, Bireuen (Bireuen, IDN) *Unable to locate*

Radio Soreram Indah, Pekanbaru (Pekanbaru, IDN) *Unable to locate*

Radio Sound of Love, Manado (Manado, IDN) *Unable to locate*

Radio Sport - 1332 (Auckland, NZL) **[48852]**

Radio Sport-AM - 927 (Melbourne, VI, AUS) **[42094]**

Radio Sport-AM Southland - 558 (Invercargill, NZL) **[48923]**

Radio Sport 927-AM - 927 (Melbourne, VI, AUS) **[42095]**

Radio Sritanjung Setia, Rogojampi (Banyuwangi, IDN) *Unable to locate*

Radio Stacioni-FM - 105.4 (Tirana, ALB) **[41454]**

Radio Stantsiya 2000 (Moscow, RUS) *Unable to locate*

Radio Station (Saratov, RUS) *Unable to locate*

Radio Station (Saratov, RUS) *Unable to locate*

Radio Stil (Vladimir, RUS) *Unable to locate*

Radio Strike (Beirut, LBN) *Unable to locate*

Radio Strike (Beirut, LBN) *Unable to locate*

Radio Studencheskiy Kanal - 90.2 MHz (Yekaterinburg, RUS) **[50045]**

Radio Student-FM - 89.3 (Maribor, SVA) **[50343]**

Radio Suara Adya Samudra (ADS), Bekasi (Bekasi, IDN) *Unable to locate*

Radio Suara Alas Roban (ARO), Batang, IDN) *Unable to locate*

Radio Suara Amarta Sakti, Pekalongan (Pekalongan, IDN) *Unable to locate*

Radio Suara Anggada Senatama (SAS), Banjarsari (Banjarsari-Ciamis, IDN) *Unable to locate*

Radio Suara Asahan, Kisaran (Jakarta, IDN) *Unable to locate*

Radio Suara Ayukarya Banjaran Adiwerna (RSA-Abadi), Tegal (Tegal, IDN) *Unable to locate*

Radio Suara Banyumas Aslia (Subali), Purwokerto (Purwokerto, IDN) *Ceased*

Radio Suara Cakrawala, Telukbetung (Bandar Lampung, IDN) *Unable to locate*

Radio Suara Calvary, Klungkung (Bali, IDN) *Unable to locate*

Radio Suara Dikara Bawana (Dirgan Bravo), Padang (Padang, IDN) *Unable to locate*

Radio Suara Dwi Amanda, Gadingrejo (Tanggamus, IDN) *Unable to locate*

Radio Suara Fiskarama, Bondowoso **[45790]***

Radio Suara Gatunggung Giri Sakti, Tasikmalaya (Tasikmalaya, IDN) *Unable to locate*

Radio Suara Harmoni, Situbondo (Situbondo, IDN) *Unable to locate*

Radio Suara Jalesveva Juana Sakti, Pati (Pati, IDN) *Ceased*

Radio Suara Karamita, Pamekasan (Jakarta, IDN) *Unable to locate*

Radio Suara karangbolong, Gombong (Jakarta, IDN) *Unable to locate*

Radio Suara Kelana, Curup (Curup, IDN) *Unable to locate*

Radio Suara Kelandka, Palopo (Palopo, IDN) *Unable to locate*

Radio Suara Kinijani, Tabanan (Tabanan, IDN) *Unable to locate*

Radio Suara Langkat Tanjung Persada, Tanjungpura - 1206 KHz (Tanjungpura, IDN) **[45873]**

Radio Suara Lorosae, Dili (Jakarta, IDN) *Unable to locate*

Radio Suara Manusia Indah, Pontianak (Pontianak, IDN) *Unable to locate*

Radio Suara Maung Sakti, Banjarnegara - 810 KHz (Jakarta, IDN) **[45812]**

Radio Suara Mesra, Parepare (Parepare, IDN) *Unable to locate*

Radio Suara Mitra, Tanjung Gading (Jakarta, IDN) *Unable to locate*

Radio Suara Pamekasan Indah, Pamekasan - 738 KHz (Pamekasan, IDN) **[45842]**

Radio Suara Ria Jaya Sentosa (SRJS), Butaraja (Baturaja, IDN) *Unable to locate*

Radio Suara Ria Santana, Bengkulu (Bengkulu, IDN) *Unable to locate*

Radio Suara Ronggo Hadi, Lamongan (Lamongan, IDN) *Unable to locate*

Radio Suara Selomanik (RSS), Banjarnegara - 918 KHz (Banjarnegara, IDN) **[45782]**

Radio Suara Semeru Permai, Lumajang (Lumajang, IDN) *Unable to locate*

Radio Suara Sibolga Indah Sempurna, Sibolga (Sibolga, IDN) *Unable to locate*

Radio Suara Sowerigading, Wonomulyo, IDN) *Unable to locate*

Radio Suara Tanjung Berjaya, Tanjungbalai - 810 KHz (Tanjungbalai, IDN) **[45872]**

Radio Suara Tegal Agung Raya (Star), Tegal - 846 KHz (Tegal, IDN) **[45876]**

Radio Suara Terunajaya, Pemeungpeuk (Garut, IDN) *Unable to locate*

Radio Suara Tiara Indah, Kotabumi (Kotabumi, IDN) *Unable to locate*

Radio Suara Tunjung Nyaho, Palangkaraya (Jakarta, IDN) *Unable to locate*

Radio Suara Wajar, Pahoman (Pahoman, IDN) *Unable to locate*

Radio Suaramitra Bayu Buana, Belitang - 720 KHz (Ogan Komering Ulu, IDN) **[45839]**

Radio Sud Est-FM - 89.3 (Le Francois, MTQ) **[47751]**

Radio Sumber Kasih, Manado (Jakarta, IDN) *Unable to locate*

Radio Suryagita Paramarta (SGP), Labuhan Maringgai - 855 KHz (Lampung Timur, IDN) **[45825]**

Radio Suta Remaja, Mataram - 1062 KHz (Mataram, IDN) **[45833]**

Radio Suzana Jaya Bhakti, Surabaya (Surabaya, IDN) *Unable to locate*

Radio SV (Seversk, RUS) *Unable to locate*

Radio Svobodnaya Rossiya (Moscow, RUS) *Unable to locate*

Numbers cited in bold after listings are entry numbers rather than page numbers.

Radio Swadaya Cempaka 23, Karawang - 1602 KHz (Karawang, IDN) [45819]

Radio Swara Angela Permai, Manado (Manado, IDN) Unable to locate

Radio Swara Anggada Senatama, Purbalingga (Jakarta, IDN) Unable to locate

Radio Swara Angkasa Megah, Pandeglang - 558 KHz (Pandeglang, IDN) [45843]

Radio Swara Barabai, Barabai (Barabai, IDN) Unable to locate

Radio Swara Buana Asri, Wonosobo (Kalikajar, IDN) Unable to locate

Radio Swara Cakrawala Sangkuriang, Bandung (Bandung, IDN) Unable to locate

Radio Swara Caraka Ria, Semarang (Semarang, IDN) Unable to locate

Radio Swara Carano Batirai Indah, Batusangkar (Batusangkar, IDN) Unable to locate

Radio Swara Christy Ria, Ujung Pandang (Makassar, IDN) Unable to locate

Radio Swara Citra Esa Enang, Langowan (Langowan, IDN) Unable to locate

Radio Swara Citra Suhada Jaya (RCS), Pekalongan (Pekalongan, IDN) Unable to locate

Radio Swara Citra Suryanada, Amuntai (Amuntai, IDN) Unable to locate

Radio Swara Delanggu, Delanggu (Klaten, IDN) Unable to locate

Radio Swara Dermagaria Persada Cakrawala, Sekadau, IDN) Ceased

Radio Swara Fiskaramatama - 936 KHz (East Java, IDN) [45790]

Radio Swara Gipsi Pratita Cakrawala, Langsa (Jakarta, IDN) Unable to locate

Radio Swara Gorontalo Permai, Gorontalo - 684 KHz (Gorontalo, IDN) [45792]

Radio Swara Graha Jelita, Surakarta - 792 KHz (Jakarta, IDN) [45813]

Radio Swara Indonusa Perkasa, Gianyar (Gianyar, IDN) Unable to locate

Radio Swara Irama Kusuma Sena, Bogor (Bogor, IDN) Unable to locate

Radio Swara Jupti Indah, Sibolga (Sibolga, IDN) Unable to locate

Radio Swara Kijang Berantai (Kiber) Perkasa, Sambas (Sambas, IDN) Unable to locate

Radio Swara Lebak Ria, Rangkasbitung (Rangkasbitung, IDN) Unable to locate

Radio Swara Mahkota Polareksa, Sintang (Sintang, IDN) Unable to locate

Radio Swara Maya Nada, Bandung (Bandung, IDN) Unable to locate

Radio Swara Maya Prastha, Poso (Poso, IDN) Unable to locate

Radio Swara Mega Mustika, Tanjungkarang (Bandar Lampung, IDN) Unable to locate

Radio Swara Megapola Nada Indah (Megaphone), Sigli (Sigli, IDN) Unable to locate

Radio Swara Melati Gramedia, Mempawah - 738 KHz (Jakarta, IDN) [45814]

Radio Swara Mersidiona, Cimone (Jakarta, IDN) Unable to locate

Radio Swara Mitra Dirgantara (Ramona Jelita), Balikpapan (Balikpapan, IDN) Unable to locate

Radio Swara Nava Ria Gemilang, Palangkaraya (Palangkaraya, IDN) Unable to locate

Radio Swara No Name, Palembang (Palembang, IDN) Unable to locate

Radio Swara Pakusarakan Pratita, Sawangan - 684 KHz (Depok, IDN) [45789]

Radio Swara Palagan Sehati (SPS) - 648 KHz (Ambarawa, IDN) [45772]

Radio Swara Perak Jaya PTDI, Surabaya (Surabaya, IDN) Unable to locate

Radio Swara Pitatoka, Ciamis (Ciamis, IDN) Unable to locate

Radio Swara Populer,Purwakarta (Purwakarta, IDN) Unable to locate

Radio Swara Prima Sonata, Cirebon (Cirebon, IDN) Unable to locate

Radio Swara Primadona Mahardika, Cikampek (Karawang, IDN) Unable to locate

Radio Swara Rama Lokantara, Serang (Serang, IDN) Unable to locate

Radio Swara Rhamagong, Kupang (Kupang, IDN) Unable to locate

Radio Swara Sentosa Pratama, Ujung Pandang (Ujung Pandang, IDN) Unable to locate

Radio Swara Tapin Raya Bastari (Swatara), Rantau (Tapin, IDN) Unable to locate

Radio Swara Trans Wahana Makmur, Kota Lais (Kota Lais, IDN) Unable to locate

Radio Swara Tugas Actari, Ciamis (Jakarta, IDN) Unable to locate

Radio Swara Wangi Timur, Banyuwangi (Banyuwangi, IDN) Unable to locate

Radio Swara Yudha, Denpasar - 828 KHz (Denpasar, IDN) [45788]

Radio Swara Zenith Angkasa, Salatiga - 702 KHz (Salatiga, IDN) [45848]

Radio SWH Rock-FM - 89.2 (Riga, LAT) [47381]

Radio Swiss Classic-FM - 87.6 (Bern, SWI) [51080]

Radio Swisspop-FM (Bern, SWI) Unable to locate

Radio Taiwan International (Taipei, TWN) Unable to locate

Radio Taiwan International (Taipei, TWN) Unable to locate

Radio Taiwan International (Taipei, TWN) Unable to locate

Radio Taiwan International (Taipei, TWN) Unable to locate

Radio Taiwan International (Taipei, TWN) Unable to locate

Radio Taiwan International (Taipei, TWN) Unable to locate

Radio Taiwan International (Taipei, TWN) Unable to locate

Radio Taiwan International (Taipei, TWN) Unable to locate

Radio Taiwan International (Taipei, TWN) Unable to locate

Radio Taiwan International (Taipei, TWN) Unable to locate

Radio Taiwan International - 7105 KHz (Taipei, TWN) [51388]

Radio Taiwan International - 7130 KHz (Taipei, TWN) [51387]

Radio Taiwan International - 11725 KHz (Taipei, TWN) [51385]

Radio Taiwan International - 9955 KHz (Taipei, TWN) [51386]

Radio Taiwan International - 11745 KHz (Taipei, TWN) [51383]

Radio Taiwan International - 11550 KHz (Taipei, TWN) [51384]

Radio Taiwan International- Changchih (Taipei, TWN) Unable to locate

Radio Taiwan International- Changchih (Taipei, TWN) Unable to locate

Radio Taiwan International- Fangliao - 585 KHz (Fangliao, TWN) [51305]

Radio Taiwan International- Kouhu (Taipei, TWN) Unable to locate

Radio Taiwan International- Lukang - 1008 KHz (Lukang, TWN) [51316]

Radio Taiwan International- Lukang - 603 KHz (Lukang, TWN) [51317]

Radio Taiwan International- Minhsiung - 1206 KHz (Minhsiung, TWN) [51318]

Radio Taiwan International- Minhsiung - 747 KHz (Minhsiung, TWN) [51319]

Radio Taiwan International- Minhsiung (Taipei, TWN) Unable to locate

Radio Talivishen Brunei - Andulau - English/Chinese (Negara Darussalam, BRN) Ceased

Radio Talivishen Brunei - Andulau - Harmoni - 94.1 MHz (Bandar Seri Begawan, BRN) [43075]

Radio Talivishen Brunei - Andulau - Malay (Negara Darussalam, BRN) Ceased

Radio Talivishen Brunei - Andulau - Pelangi - 91.0 MHz (Andulau, BRN) [43070]

Radio Talivishen Brunei - Bukit Subok - English/Chinese - 95.9 MHz (Piliphan, BRN) [43083]

Radio Talivishen Brunei - Bukit Subok - Harmoni - 94.1 MHz (Harmoni, BRN) [43079]

Radio Talivishen Brunei - Bukit Subok - Malay - 92.3 MHz (Bukit Subok, BRN) [43077]

Radio Talivishen Brunei - Bukit Subok - Pelangi - 91.4 MHz (Pelangi, BRN) [43082]

Radio Talivishen Brunei - Serasa (Bandar Seri Begawan, BRN) Unable to locate

Radio Talivishen Brunei - S.Hanching - Chinese - 711 KHz (South Hanching, BRN) [43084]

Radio Talivishen Brunei - S.Hanching - English - 710 KHz (South Hanching, BRN) [43085]

Radio Tanjung Puri Perkasa, Tabalong (Tabalong, IDN) Unable to locate

Radio Tarana-AM - 1386 (Auckland, NZL) [48853]

Radio Tataouine-FM - 102.6 MHz (Tataouine, TUN) [51487]

Radio Tataouine-FM - 92.2 MHz (Tataouine, TUN) [51486]

Radio Tataouine-FM - 89.5 (Tataouine, TUN) [51484]

Radio Tataouine-FM - 96.6 MHz (Tataouine, TUN) [51485]

Radio Tataouine-FM - 87.6 MHz (Tataouine, TUN) [51483]

Radio TaTuRos (Kazan, RUS) Unable to locate

Radio Taurus Adiswara, Kediri (Kediri, IDN) Unable to locate

Radio Telekom (Azov, RUS) Unable to locate

Radio Telekon-Russkiy Shanson (Nizhniy Tagil, RUS) Unable to locate

Radio Telerama, Banjarmasin (Banjarmasin, IDN) Unable to locate

Radio - Television of Afghanistan - Kabul (Kabul, AFG) Unable to locate

Radio Television Brunei - Channel 8 (Bukit Andulau, BRN) [43076]

Radio Television Brunei - Channel 5 (Bukit Subok, BRN) [43078]

Radio and Television Executive Committee-Tak (Tak, THA) Unable to locate

Radio and Television Executive Committee-Yala (Yala, THA) Unable to locate

Radio Television Malaysia - 98.3 MHz (Selangor, MYS) [47713]

Radio Television Malaysia Sarawak - 729 KHz (Kuching, MYS) [47675]

Radio Television Malaysia Sarawak - 846 KHz (Kuching, MYS) [47673]

Radio Television Malaysia Sarawak - 954 KHz (Kuching, MYS) [47674]

Radio Television Malaysia Sarawak - 7130 KHz (Kuching, MYS) [47672]

Radio Television Malaysia Sarawak - 819 KHz (Kuching, MYS) [47670]

Radio Television Malaysia Sarawak - 4895 KHz (Kuching, MYS) [47671]

Radio Television Malaysia Sarawak - 1062 KHz (Kuching, MYS) [47668]

Radio Television Malaysia Sarawak - 621 KHz (Kuching, MYS) [47669]

Radio Television Malaysia Sarawak (Kuching, MYS) Unable to locate

Radio Television Malaysia Sarawak (Kuching, MYS) Unable to locate

Radio Television Malaysia Sarawak (Kuching, MYS) Unable to locate

Radio Television Malaysia Sarawak (Kuching, MYS) Unable to locate

Radio Television Malaysia Sarawak (Kuching, MYS) Unable to locate

Radio Television Malaysia Sarawak (Kuching, MYS) Unable to locate

Radio Television Malaysia Sarawak (Kuching, MYS) Unable to locate

Radio Television Malaysia Sarawak (Kuching, MYS) Unable to locate

Radio Television Malaysia Sarawak - 648 KHz (Limbang, MYS) [47678]

Radio Television Malaysia Sarawak - 873 KHz (Limbang, MYS) [47677]

Radio Television Malaysia Sarawak - 1206 KHz (Miri, MYS) [47684]

Radio Television Malaysia Sarawak - 91.9 MHz (Miri, MYS) [47685]

Radio Television Malaysia Sarawak - 909 KHz (Sibu, MYS) [47719]

Radio Television Malaysia Sarawak - 6050 KHz (Sibu, MYS) [47718]

Radio Television Malaysia Sarawak - 1161 KHz (Sri.Aman, MYS) [47720]

Radio Television Malaysia Sarawak - 1044 KHz (Sri Aman, MYS) [47721]

Radio Television Malaysia TV1 - Channel 1 (Kuala Lumpur, MYS) [47656]

Radio Television Malaysia TV2 - Channel 2 (Kuala Lumpur, MYS) [47657]

Radio Telstar, Ujung Pandang (Ujung Pandang, IDN) Unable to locate

Radio 10-FM - 88.1 (Paramaribo, SUR) [50941]

Radio Teos - 1089 KHz (Saint Petersburg, RUS) [50033]

Radio Thailand (Bangkok, THA) Unable to locate

Radio Thailand (Bangkok, THA) Unable to locate

Radio Thailand (Bangkok, THA) Unable to locate

Numbers cited in bold after listings are entry numbers rather than page numbers.

Radio Thailand (Bangkok, THA) *Unable to locate*

Radio Thailand (Bangkok, THA) *Unable to locate*

Radio 32-FM - 92.2 (Solothurn, SWI) **[51233]**

Radio Thosiba (TOSS), Banda Aceh (Banda Aceh, IDN) *Unable to locate*

Radio 3A - Belgorod (Belgorod, RUS) *Unable to locate*

Radio Tierra-AM - 1300 (Santiago, CHL) **[43159]**

Radio Tikhiy Don (Rostov-na-Donu, RUS) *Unable to locate*

Radio Times (London, GBR) **[55170]**

Radio Tindouf-FM (Tindouf, ALG) *Unable to locate*

Radio Tinlolok, Kupang (Timor, IDN) *Unable to locate*

Radio Titan (Ufa, RUS) *Unable to locate*

Radio Tjandra Buana Suara, Cianjur (Cianjur, IDN) *Unable to locate*

Radio Toddo Puli (Topsi), Palu (Palu, IDN) *Unable to locate*

Radio-Transistronic Constructor (Mumbai, MH, IND) *Unable to locate*

Radio Transmit (Cherepovets, RUS) *Unable to locate*

Radio Transmit (Cherepovets, RUS) *Unable to locate*

Radio Transmit (Cherepovets, RUS) *Unable to locate*

Radio Transmit (Cherepovets, RUS) *Unable to locate*

Radio Transmit (Cherepovets, RUS) *Unable to locate*

Radio Transmit (Cherepovets, RUS) *Unable to locate*

Radio Trisara Kencana, Cianjur (Jakarta, IDN) *Unable to locate*

Radio Tritara Yaksa (TT-77), Malang - 828 KHz (Malang, IDN) **[45831]**

Radio Tron (Murmansk, RUS) *Unable to locate*

Radio Tron (Murmansk, RUS) *Unable to locate*

Radio Tropic-FM - 93 (Zurich, SWI) **[51299]**

Radio Tsentr (Ulyanovsk, RUS) *Unable to locate*

Radio Tsesna (Astana, KAZ) *Unable to locate*

Radio Tuah Swara Murnii, Lubukpakam (Lubukpakam, IDN) *Unable to locate*

Radio Tuzla-AM - 774 (Tuzla, HBO) **[42937]**

Radio Tuzla-FM - 90.5 MHz (Tuzla, HBO) **[42940]**

Radio Tuzla-FM - 103.8 MHz (Tuzla, HBO) **[42938]**

Radio Tuzla-FM - 105.1 MHz (Tuzla, HBO) **[42939]**

Radio & TV (Shanghai, CHN) **[43496]**

Radio TV Malaysia Kota Kinabalu (Kota Kinabalu, MYS) *Unable to locate*

Radio TV Malaysia Kota Kinabalu (Kota Kinabalu, MYS) *Unable to locate*

Radio TV Malaysia Kota Kinabalu (Kota Kinabalu, MYS) *Unable to locate*

Radio TV Malaysia Kota Kinabalu (Kota Kinabalu, MYS) *Unable to locate*

Radio TV Malaysia Kota Kinabalu (Kota Kinabalu, MYS) *Unable to locate*

Radio TV Malaysia Kota Kinabalu (Kota Kinabalu, MYS) *Ceased*

Radio TV Malaysia Kota Kinabalu (Kota Kinabalu, MYS) *Unable to locate*

Radio TV Malaysia Kota Kinabalu (Kota Kinabalu, MYS) *Unable to locate*

Radio TV Malaysia Kota Kinabalu (Kota Kinabalu, MYS) *Unable to locate*

Radio TV Malaysia Kota Kinabalu (Kota Kinabalu, MYS) *Unable to locate*

Radio TV Malaysia Kota Kinabalu (Kota Kinabalu, MYS) *Unable to locate*

Radio TV Malaysia Kota Kinabalu (Kota Kinabalu, MYS) *Unable to locate*

Radio 21 (Murmansk, RUS) *Unable to locate*

Radio 21 (Novosibirsk, RUS) *Unable to locate*

Radio 021-FM - 92.2 (Novi Sad, SER) **[50093]**

Radio 2-AM (Homebush, NW, AUS) *Unable to locate*

Radio 2x2 (Ulyanovsk, RUS) *Unable to locate*

Radio Ufaleya (Verkhniy Ufaley, RUS) *Unable to locate*

Radio Ulster-FM - 92.4 (London, GBR) **[55460]**

Radio of the United Arab Emirates, UAE) *Unable to locate*

Radio of the United Arab Emirates (Abu Dhabi, UAE) *Unable to locate*

Radio of the United Arab Emirates (Abu Dhabi, UAE) *Unable to locate*

Radio of the United Arab Emirates (Abu Dhabi, UAE) *Unable to locate*

Radio of the United Arab Emirates (Abu Dhabi, UAE) *Unable to locate*

Radio of the United Arab Emirates - 88.6 MHz (Abu Dhabi, UAE) **[51621]**

Radio of the United Arab Emirates - 729 KHz (Abu Dhabi, UAE) **[51622]**

Radio of the United Arab Emirates - 828 KHz (Al Ain, UAE) **[51627]**

Radio Uniton (Novosibirsk, RUS) *Unable to locate*

Radio Universal-AM - 970 (Montevideo, URY) **[57011]**

Radio Universal-FM - 93.5 (Arequipa, PER) **[49415]**

Radio Universal-FM (Cusco, PER) *Unable to locate*

Radio Universitaria-FM (Fortaleza, CE, BRZ) *Unable to locate*

Radio Uno-FM - 93.7 (Tacna, PER) **[49444]**

Radio Ussuri (Ussuriysk, RUS) *Unable to locate*

Radio Utopie-FM - 105.7 (Marseille, FRA) **[43975]**

Radio Uzbekistan (Tashkent, UZN) *Unable to locate*

Radio Valencia-AM - 1220 (Valencia, VEN) **[57030]**

Radio Vallee Vezere-FM - 104.4 MHz (Terrasson Lavilledieu, FRA) **[44117]**

Radio Vallekas-FM - 107.5 (Madrid, SPA) **[50818]**

Radio Valparaiso-AM - 121 (Valparaiso, CHL) **[43163]**

Radio Van (Beirut, LBN) *Unable to locate*

Radio VBC - 936 KHz (Dalnegorsk, RUS) **[49854]**

Radio VBC - 612 KHz (Vladivostok, RUS) **[50043]**

Radio Venus Nusantara, Ujung Pandang (Ujung Pandang, IDN) *Unable to locate*

Radio Verdon-FM - 91 Mhz (Castellane, FRA) **[43928]**

Radio Verdon-FM - 96.5 (Saint-Julien-le-Montagnier, FRA) **[44104]**

Radio Vesna (Smolensk, RUS) *Unable to locate*

Radio Vizavi (Tula, RUS) *Unable to locate*

Radio Vladivostok (Vladivostok, RUS) *Unable to locate*

Radio Voice of Lebanon (Beirut, LBN) *Unable to locate*

Radio Voice of Lebanon (Beirut, LBN) *Unable to locate*

Radio Voice of Lebanon (Beirut, LBN) *Unable to locate*

Radio Voice of Shariah - Kabul (Kabul, AFG) *Unable to locate*

Radio Voice of Shariah - Kabul (Kabul, AFG) *Unable to locate*

Radio Voice of Shariah - Kabul (Kabul, AFG) *Unable to locate*

Radio Voice of Yarden, Ambon (Maluku, IDN) *Unable to locate*

Radio Volna (Ozersk, RUS) *Unable to locate*

Radio Volna (Ozersk, RUS) *Unable to locate*

Radio Volna Gubkina (Gubkin, RUS) *Unable to locate*

Radio VOSST - Bishkek (Bishkek, KGA) *Unable to locate*

Radio Vtoroye Dykhanie (Naberezhnyye Chelny, RUS) *Unable to locate*

Radio Wahana Bewara Suara, Cirebon (Cirebon, IDN) *Unable to locate*

Radio Warastra Bewara Swara, Palembang - 810 KHz (Jakarta, IDN) **[45815]**

Radio Wave-FM - 96.7 (Windhoek, NAM) **[47826]**

Radio Wave 96.5-FM - 96.5 (Blackpool, GBR) **[52386]**

Radio Widya Bhakti, Magelang (Magelang, IDN) *Unable to locate*

Radio Wijang Songko, Kediri (Kediri, IDN) *Unable to locate*

Radio Wijaya Adikusuma, Cilacap - 102.6 (Cilacap, IDN) **[45787]**

Radio Wijaya Asthanaria, Kotabumi (Kotabumi, IDN) *Unable to locate*

Radio Wisata Panataran (Wita), Blitar, IDN) *Unable to locate*

Radio WKM-FM - 91.5 (Oruro, BOL) **[42931]**

Radio X-FM (Grocka, SER) *Unable to locate*

Radio X-FM - 94.5 (Basel, SWI) **[51066]**

Radio XL-AM - 1296 (Birmingham, GBR) **[52376]**

Radio Yaravi-AM (Arequipa, PER) *Unable to locate*

Radio Yaravi-FM - 106.3 (Arequipa, PER) **[49416]**

Radio Yasmara, Surabaya (Surabaya, IDN) *Unable to locate*

Radio Yoshlar (Tashkent, UZN) *Unable to locate*

Radio Yoshlar (Tashkent, UZN) *Unable to locate*

Radio Yumaks (Shymkent, KAZ) *Unable to locate*

Radio Yusyan Media, Sumedang (Sumedang, IDN) *Unable to locate*

Radio Zebra (Maykop, RUS) *Unable to locate*

Radio Zet-FM - 94.5 (Zilina, SLK) **[50329]**

Radio ZID Sarajevo-FM - 89.9 Mhz (Sarajevo, HBO) **[42936]**

Radio Zinzine-FM (Limans, FRA) *Unable to locate*

Radio Zinzine-FM - 90.8 (Moscow, RUS) **[50004]**

Radio Zodiak (Omsk, RUS) *Unable to locate*

Radiochannel Pelikan (Vladivostok, RUS) *Unable to locate*

Radiographer (Collingwood, VI, AUS) *Unable to locate*

Radiography (Salford, GBR) **[56451]**

Radiologia Brasileira (Vicosa, MI, BRZ) **[43063]**

Radiology and Oncology (Warsaw, POL) **[49762]**

Radiomagnit (Mangnitogorsk, RUS) *Unable to locate*

Radionic Journal (Banbury, GBR) *Unable to locate*

Radioprogramma (Orel, RUS) *Unable to locate*

Radioprotection (Fontenay-aux-Roses, FRA) **[43955]**

Radiostantsiya Lena (Yakutsk, RUS) *Unable to locate*

Radiostantsiya Novyy Gorod (Krasnoyarsk, RUS) *Unable to locate*

Radiostantsiya Radonezh - 846 KHz (Noginsk, RUS) **[50008]**

Radiostantsiya Slavyanka (Moscow, RUS) *Unable to locate*

Radiostantsiya Volna Baykala (Irkutsk, RUS) *Unable to locate*

Radiostantsiya Vostok (Irkutsk, RUS) *Unable to locate*

RadioThailand-Phangnga (Phangnga, THA) *Unable to locate*

Radiotherapy and Oncology (Arhus, DEN) **[43650]**

Radio2-FM - 101.6 (Tirana, ALB) **[41455]**

Radius-FM - 105.5 (Minsk, BLR) **[42835]**

Radius-FM - 100.5 (Minsk, BLR) **[42836]**

Radius-FM - 100.9 (Minsk, BLR) **[42834]**

Radju Bambina-FM - 98.3 (Gozo, MAL) **[47731]**

Radju Lehen il-Belt Victoria-FM - 104 (Gozo, MAL) **[47732]**

Radju Lehen il-Qala-FM - 106.3 (Qala, MAL) **[47737]**

Radju Luminaria-FM - 106.9 (Gozo, MAL) **[47733]**

Radju Malta-AM (G'Mangia, MAL) *Unable to locate*

Radju Malta-FM - 93.7 (G'Mangia, MAL) **[47730]**

Raduznyy (Raduznyy, RUS) *Unable to locate*

Radwelt (Cycle World) (Altheim, AUT) *Unable to locate*

RADYO ODTU-FM - 103.1 (Ankara, TUR) **[51523]**

RAE eletronica (Vicosa, MI, BRZ) **[43064]**

Ragtrader (Surry Hills, NW, AUS) **[42438]**

Raices (Madrid, SPA) *Unable to locate*

Raices-FM - 102.9 MHz (Santo Domingo, DOM) **[43742]**

Rail International (Brussels, BEL) *Unable to locate*

Rail Transport Journal (New Delhi, DH, IND) *Unable to locate*

Railwatch (Bracebridge Heath, GBR) **[52432]**

Numbers cited in bold after listings are entry numbers rather than page numbers.

Railway Gazette International (Sutton, GBR) [56692]

The Railway Magazine (London, GBR) [55171]

Railways Illustrated (Peterborough, GBR) [56260]

Rajasthan Agriculturalist (Jobner, RJ, IND) Unable to locate

Rajasthan Board Journal of Education (Ajmer, RJ, IND) Unable to locate

Rajasthan Journal of Agricultural Sciences (Jaipur, RJ, IND) Unable to locate

Rajasthan Medical Journal (Jaipur, RJ, IND) Unable to locate

Rajasthan University Studies in English (Jaipur, RJ, IND) Unable to locate

Rally (Kolkata, WB, IND) [45302]

Ramako-FM [45805]*

The Ramanujan Journal (Dordrecht, NLD) [48546]

Ramanujan Mathematical Society Journal (Hyderabad, AP, IND) Unable to locate

The Rambler (London, GBR) [55172]

Ramp (Hamilton, NZL) [48910]

Rampelyset (Grasten, DEN) Unable to locate

Ranchi Express (Ranchi, BH, IND) [45712]

Ranchi University Mathematical Journal (Ranchi, BH, IND) Ceased

Random Operators and Stochastic Equations (Kiev, URE) [51607]

The Range News (Sydney, NW, AUS) [42568]

The Rangeland Journal (Armidale, NW, AUS) [41560]

Rangifer Special Issue (Tromso, NOR) Unable to locate

Rangzen (Dharamsala, HP, IND) [45111]

Rapid Prototyping Journal (Bradford, GBR) [52542]

Rapport (Cape Town, SAF) [50405]

Rapport (Middleton Cheney, GBR) [55623]

Rare Book Review (London, GBR) [55173]

Rare Earth Bulletin (Brentwood, GBR) [52587]

Rare Earths (Osaka, JPN) Unable to locate

Rare Metals (Beijing, CHN) [43214]

Ras Al Khaimah Broadcasting Station (Ras Al Khaimah, UAE) Unable to locate

Ras Al Khaimah Broadcasting Station (Ras Al Khaimah, UAE) Unable to locate

Ras Al Khaimah Broadcasting Station (Ras Al Khaimah, UAE) Unable to locate

Ras 2-FM - 102.5 (Torshavn, ICE) [44904]

Rassegna Alimentare (Milan, ITA) [46192]

Ratana-Urai (Bangkok, THA) Unable to locate

Ratio (Reading, GBR) [56330]

Ratio Juris (Oxford, GBR) [56186]

Rationality and Society (London, GBR) [55174]

Ravi (Lahore, PAK) Unable to locate

RaW-AM - 1251 (Coventry, GBR) [53094]

Razvoj/Development (Zagreb, CTA) [43570]

Razvoj/Development International (Zagreb, CTA) Unable to locate

RBR-FM - 103.4 (Fort-de-France, MTQ) [47750]

RC Model/RC Model Special (Valkenswaard, NLD) Unable to locate

RCDM-FM - 101 (Ebolowa, CMR) [43127]

RCM Midwives' Journal (London, GBR) [55175]

RCO Journal (London, GBR) Unable to locate

RDU-FM - 98.5 (Christchurch, NZL) [48885]

RDV (Cherepovets, RUS) Unable to locate

RDV (Nizhniy Novgorod, RUS) Unable to locate

RDV (Nizhniy Novgorod, RUS) Unable to locate

RDV (Saratov, RUS) Unable to locate

RDV Radio (Delovaya Volna) (Moscow, RUS) Ceased

RDV (SV-Radio) - Samara (Samara, RUS) Unable to locate

RDV - Tolyatti (Samara, RUS) Unable to locate

Reach (Dublin, DU, IRL) [45997]

Reaching for the Skies (Paris, FRA) Unable to locate

Reactive and Functional Polymers (Manchester, GBR) [55576]

Reader's Digest (Indian Edition) (New Delhi, DH, IND) Unable to locate

Reader's Digest (Indian Edition) (New Delhi, DH, IND) Unable to locate

Reading (Reading, GBR) [56331]

Reading Journal (New Delhi, DH, IND) Unable to locate

Reading 107-FM - 107 (Reading, GBR) [56340]

Reading and Writing (Dordrecht, NLD) [48547]

Reading & Writing Quarterly (Abingdon, GBR) [52034]

Real (Colchester, GBR) Ceased

Real Business (London, GBR) [55176]

Real Living (Sydney, NW, AUS) [42569]

Real Radio-FM - 105 (Cardiff, GBR) [52943]

Real Radio-FM - 105.4 (Manchester, GBR) [55587]

Real Simple Japan (Tokyo, JPN) [47030]

Real-Time Imaging (Amsterdam, NLD) Ceased

Real-Time Systems (Dordrecht, NLD) [48548]

Reales Sitios (Madrid, SPA) [50795]

Realm (Cheltenham, GBR) [52975]

ReCALL Journal (Limerick, LI, IRL) Unable to locate

Recent Advances in Pediatrics (New Delhi, DH, IND) [45641]

Recent Indian Books (New Delhi, DH, IND) Unable to locate

Recent Patents on Cardiovascular Drug Discovery (Bussum, NLD) [48304]

Recent Patents on Drug Delivery & Formulation (Bussum, NLD) [48305]

Recent Patents on Nanotechnology (Bussum, NLD) [48306]

Recent Researches in Geology (New Delhi, DH, IND) [45642]

Recommendations for Contractual Sharing of Risks (Bron, FRA) Unable to locate

Record Buyer (Lincoln, GBR) Unable to locate

Record Collector (London, GBR) [55177]

The Recorder Magazine (Welwyn Garden City, GBR) [56883]

Records Management Journal (Newcastle upon Tyne, GBR) [55678]

Recreation; Journal of Physical Education & [43278]*

Recruitment Matters (Woking, GBR) [56948]

Recusant History (Wolsingham, GBR) [56950]

Recycling & Waste World (Salisbury, GBR) [56457]

Red Barnet (Copenhagen, DEN) Unable to locate

Red Cross News (Wellington, NZL) [49032]

Red Cross, Red Crescent (Geneva, SWI) [51157]

Red Dragon-FM - 103.2 (Cardiff, GBR) [52944]

Red-FM - 104.5 (Bishopstown, CK, IRL) [45919]

Red-FM (Johor Bahru, MYS) Unable to locate

Red-FM - 104.9 (Kuala Lumpur, MYS) [47658]

red pepper (London, GBR) [55178]

Red Power (Colombo, SRI) Unable to locate

Red and White (Saint Petersburg, RUS) Unable to locate

Redcliffe & Bayside Herald (Redcliffe, QL, AUS) [42298]

Redd Barna Avisa (Oslo, NOR) Unable to locate

Redditch Advertiser/Indicator Series (West Sussex, GBR) [56902]

Redditch Standard (Redditch, GBR) [56341]

Rede Itatiaia-AM - 610 (Belo Horizonte, MG, BRZ) [42952]

Rede Itatiaia-FM - 95.7 (Belo Horizonte, MG, BRZ) [42953]

The Redland Times (Cleveland, QL, AUS) [41769]

Redningsbaden (Copenhagen, DEN) Unable to locate

Redress (Sandgate, QL, AUS) [42353]

Reference Reviews (York, GBR) [56997]

Reflections Colour Magazine (Perth, GBR) Unable to locate

Reflective Practice (Abingdon, GBR) [52035]

Refocus [44372]*

Reformation (Brighton, GBR) [52630]

Reformation and Renaissance Review (Glasgow, GBR) [53445]

Reformed World (Geneva, SWI) [51158]

Refrigeration (Tokyo, JPN) [47031]

Refugee Abstracts [51159]*

Refugee Nutrition Information System (RNIS) [51154]*

Refugee Survey Quarterly (Geneva, SWI) [51159]

Refugees (Mexico City, DF, MEX) [47788]

Refurbishment Projects (Buckhurst Hill, GBR) [52752]

Regeneration & Renewal (London, GBR) [55179]

Regenerative Medicine (London, GBR) [55180]

The Regent (Newbliss, MO, IRL) Ceased

Regional Best Restaurants (Singapore, SGP) [50242]

Regional Development Dialogue (Nagoya, JPN) [46559]

Regional Development International (Luton, GBR) Unable to locate

Regional Development Studies (Nagoya, JPN) Ceased

Regional Outlook (Singapore, SGP) [50243]

Regional Studies (Abingdon, GBR) [52036]

Regional Trends (Basingstoke, GBR) [52229]

Register of Ships (Redhill, GBR) [56377]

Regular & Chaotic Dynamics (Moscow, RUS) [49970]

Regulatory Affairs Journal (London, GBR) [55181]

Regulatory Affairs Journal (Devices) (London, GBR) [55182]

Regulatory Peptides (Bochum, GER) [44251]

Regulatory Toxicology and Pharmacology (Amsterdam, NLD) [48220]

Reinforced Plastics (Kidlington, GBR) [53705]

Reinsurance (London, GBR) [55183]

Reinwardtia (Bogor, IDN) Unable to locate

Reise & Preise (Buxtehude, GER) [44288]

Reizen (The Hague, NLD) [48627]

Relais (Paris, FRA) Unable to locate

Relax-FM - 90.8 (Moscow, RUS) [50005]

Reliable Computing (Dordrecht, NLD) [48549]

Religion (London, GBR) [55184]

Religion and Human Rights (Leiden, NLD) [48719]

Religion and Law Review (New Delhi, DH, IND) [45643]

Religion and Society (Bangalore, KA, IND) Unable to locate

Religion and Theology (Leiden, NLD) [48720]

Religions of South Asia (London, GBR) [55185]

Religious Book Review Index (Calcutta, WB, IND) Unable to locate

Religious Studies (London, GBR) [55186]

Religious Studies Journal (Manila, PHL) Unable to locate

Religious Studies and Theology (London, GBR) [55187]

Rem (Vicosa, MI, BRZ) [43065]

Remote Sensing Journal (Beijing, CHN) Unable to locate

Removals and Storage (Harrow, GBR) Unable to locate

Renaissance (Lahore, PAK) [49388]

Renal Transplantation, Vascular Surgery (Tokyo, JPN) Unable to locate

Renault Magazine (Surrey, GBR) [56674]

Rendezvous (Horsham, GBR) Ceased

Renewable Agriculture and Food Systems (Cambridge, GBR) [52890]

Renewable Energy Bulletin (Brentwood, GBR) [52588]

Renewable Energy Focus (Freiburg, GER) [44372]

Renewal [54209]*

Renewal (Crowborough, GBR) Ceased

Rens & Vask samt Tekstiludlejning (Glostrup, DEN) [43714]

Rent Cases (New Delhi, DH, IND) Unable to locate

The Reparation Report (London, GBR) [55188]

Repeat (Cambridge, GBR) [52891]

Reponses Photo (Vienna, AUT) Unable to locate

Report (London, GBR) [55189]

Report Psychologie (Berlin, GER) [44228]

Numbers cited in bold after listings are entry numbers rather than page numbers.

Reportage (Amsterdam, NLD) *Unable to locate*

Reportback (London, GBR) *Unable to locate*

The Reporter (Belize City, BLZ) *Unable to locate*

The Reporter (Fuengirola (Malaga), SPA) *Unable to locate*

Reports on Progress in Physics (Bristol, GBR) **[52725]**

Repretel Television - Channel 11 (San Jose, CRI) **[43554]**

Reproduction (Bristol, GBR) **[52726]**

Reproduction in Domestic Animals (Linkoping, SWE) **[50977]**

Reproduction, Fertility and Development (Collingwood, VI, AUS) **[41796]**

Reproductive Health (London, GBR) **[55190]**

Reproductive Health (Hanoi, VNM) *Unable to locate*

Reprographics Quarterly **[53539]***

Republic of Iraq Radio - Babylon (Baghdad, IRQ) *Unable to locate*

Republic of Iraq Radio - Baghdad (Baghdad, IRQ) *Unable to locate*

Republic of Iraq Radio - Baghdad (Baghdad, IRQ) *Unable to locate*

Republic of Iraq Radio - Baghdad (Baghdad, IRQ) *Unable to locate*

Republic of Iraq Radio - Baghdad (Baghdad, IRQ) *Unable to locate*

Republic of Iraq Radio - Baghdad (Baghdad, IRQ) *Unable to locate*

Republic of Iraq Radio - Baghdad (Baghdad, IRQ) *Unable to locate*

Republic of Iraq Radio - Basrah (Baghdad, IRQ) *Unable to locate*

Republic of Iraq Radio - Nasiriya (Baghdad, IRQ) *Unable to locate*

Republic of Iraq Radio - Nineva (Baghdad, IRQ) *Unable to locate*

Republic of Iraq Radio - Nineva (Baghdad, IRQ) *Unable to locate*

Republic of Iraq Radio - Rutba (Baghdad, IRQ) *Unable to locate*

Republic of Iraq Radio - Tanaf (Baghdad, IRQ) *Unable to locate*

RERIC International Energy Journal (Pathumthani, THA) **[51462]**

Res Publica (Newport, GBR) **[55689]**

Research in Astronomy and Astrophysics (Bristol, GBR) **[52727]**

Research in Comparative and International Education (Oxford, GBR) **[56187]**

Research on Crops (Hisar, HY, IND) **[45136]**

Research and Development Reporter (Jammu, JK, IND) *Unable to locate*

Research in Economics (Amsterdam, NLD) **[48221]**

Research in Higher Education (Dordrecht, NLD) **[48550]**

Research and Industry (New Delhi, DH, IND) *Unable to locate*

Research in International Business and Finance (Hong Kong, CHN) **[43379]**

Research Journal of Agriculture and Biological Sciences (Faisalabad, PAK) **[49280]**

Research Journal of Agronomy (Faisalabad, PAK) **[49281]**

Research Journal of Animal Sciences (Faisalabad, PAK) **[49282]**

Research Journal of Animal and Veterinary Sciences (Faisalabad, PAK) **[49283]**

Research Journal of Applied Sciences (Faisalabad, PAK) **[49284]**

Research Journal of Biological Sciences (Faisalabad, PAK) **[49285]**

Research Journal of Cell and Molecular Biology (Faisalabad, PAK) **[49286]**

Research Journal of Dairy Sciences (Faisalabad, PAK) **[49287]**

Research Journal of Fisheries and Hydrobiology (Faisalabad, PAK) **[49288]**

Research Journal: Humanities and Social Sciences (Indore, MP, IND) *Unable to locate*

Research Journal of Medical Sciences (Faisalabad, PAK) **[49289]**

Research Journal of Medicine and Medical Sciences (Faisalabad, PAK) **[49290]**

Research Journal of Pharmacology (Faisalabad, PAK) **[49291]**

Research Journal of Philosophy (Ranchi, BH, IND) *Unable to locate*

Research Journal of Philosophy and Social Sciences (Meerut, UP, IND) *Unable to locate*

Research Journal of Poultry Sciences (Faisalabad, PAK) **[49292]**

Research Journal: Science (Indore, MP, IND) *Unable to locate*

Research Journal Science Series of the University of Sind (Hyderabad, PAK) *Unable to locate*

Research Journal of Telecommunication and Information Technology (Faisalabad, PAK) **[49293]**

Research Journal of Textile and Apparel (Hong Kong, CHN) **[43380]**

Research Notes and Memoranda of Applied Geometry for Prevenient Natural Philosophy (Chiba, JPN) *Unable to locate*

Research in Phenomenology (Leiden, NLD) **[48721]**

Research Policy (Brighton, GBR) **[52631]**

Research in Post-Compulsory Education (Abingdon, GBR) **[52037]**

Research and Practice in Forensic Medicine (Miyagi, JPN) *Unable to locate*

Research and Practice in Human Resource Management (Singapore, SGP) **[50244]**

Research Reports on Information Science and Electrical Engineering (Fukuoka, JPN) *Unable to locate*

Research in Tourism (Calcutta, WB, IND) *Unable to locate*

Researches in Management in Asia Series (New Delhi, DH, IND) *Unable to locate*

RESEAUX—French Journal of Communication (Luton, GBR) *Ceased*

Resena (Madrid, SPA) *Unable to locate*

Reserve Bank of India Bulletin (Jodhpur, RJ, IND) **[45229]**

Reserve Bank of India Bulletin—Weekly Statistical Supplement (Mumbai, MH, IND) **[45434]**

Reserve Bank of India Occasional Papers (Mumbai, MH, IND) **[45435]**

The Reserve Bank of New Zealand (Wellington, NZL) **[49033]**

ResGuide (Stockholm, SWE) *Unable to locate*

Residence (Amsterdam, NLD) **[48222]**

The Resident (London) (London, GBR) **[55191]**

Residente (Lisbon, PRT) *Unable to locate*

Residential Renting (London, GBR) *Unable to locate*

Resomeu Senaual (Lima, PER) **[49426]**

Resonance (Paris, FRA) *Ceased*

Resonance (Bangalore, KA, IND) **[44985]**

Resonance-FM - 104.4 (London, GBR) **[55461]**

Resonate Journal (Grosvenor Place, NW, AUS) **[41935]**

Resource Geology (Tsuchiura City, JPN) **[47109]**

Resource Management & Recovery (London, GBR) **[55192]**

Resources (Nairobi, KEN) *Unable to locate*

Resources, Conservation and Recycling (Utrecht, NLD) **[48765]**

Resources, Energy and Development (New Delhi, DH, IND) **[45644]**

RESOURCESTOCKS (Leederville, WA, AUS) **[42007]**

Respiratory Disease in Practice (London, GBR) **[55193]**

Respiratory Physiology & Neurobiology (Bochum, GER) **[44252]**

Respiratory Research (London, GBR) **[55194]**

Restaurang Guiden (Goteborg, SWE) **[50963]**

Restaurant Equipment (Crawley, GBR) **[53112]**

Restaurateur (Fellbach, GER) **[44353]**

Restitution Law Review (London, GBR) *Ceased*

Restoration Ecology (Oxford, GBR) **[56188]**

Restorative Neurology and Neuroscience (Magdeburg, GER) **[44536]**

Resumenes Analiticos De Educacion (Santiago, CHL) *Unable to locate*

Resurgence **[56711]***

Resurgence (Bideford, GBR) **[52322]**

Retail Intelligence (London, GBR) *Unable to locate*

Retail Newsagent (London, GBR) **[55195]**

Retail Pharmacy (North Parramatta, NW, AUS) **[42158]**

Retail Systems (London, GBR) **[55196]**

Retailspeak (Leicester, GBR) **[53821]**

Rete Italia-AM - 801 (Gosford, VI, AUS) **[41926]**

Rete Italia-AM - 1539 (Sydney, VI, AUS) **[42609]**

Rete Italia-AM - 1575 (Wollongong, VI, AUS) **[42709]**

Rethinking History (Abingdon, GBR) **[52038]**

Retirement Planner (London, GBR) **[55197]**

Retirement Today (Christchurch, NZL) **[48878]**

REtoday (Birmingham, GBR) **[52363]**

Retreats (Amersham, GBR) **[52109]**

Retriever Club de France - Bulletin (Paris, FRA) *Unable to locate*

Retrieveren (Gesten, DEN) *Unable to locate*

Retro Cars (Sevenoaks, GBR) **[56481]**

Retro Ford (Sevenoaks, GBR) **[56482]**

Retro Gamer (Bournemouth, GBR) **[52423]**

Retrovirology (London, GBR) **[55198]**

Retroviseur (Fontainebleau, FRA) **[43954]**

Rettungsdienst (Edewecht, GER) **[44336]**

Return to Teaching (London, GBR) *Unable to locate*

Reunion des Amateurs de Fox-Terriers (Gemages, FRA) *Unable to locate*

Reussir Vigne (Paris, FRA) *Unable to locate*

Reuterlink Extra (London, GBR) *Unable to locate*

Reveil-FM (Villeneuve, FRA) *Unable to locate*

Revenue Law Journal (Gold Coast, QL, AUS) **[41899]**

Reverberations (South Croydon, GBR) **[56565]**

The Review (Karachi, PAK) **[49375]**

Review (Geneva, SWI) *Ceased*

Review (Abingdon, GBR) **[52039]**

Review (Birmingham, GBR) **[52364]**

The Review (Norfolk, GBR) **[55703]**

Review (Rugby, GBR) *Unable to locate*

The Review (Teddington, GBR) *Unable to locate*

Review of Accounting Studies (Dordrecht, NLD) **[48551]**

Review of African Political Economy (Abingdon, GBR) **[52040]**

Review of Agricultural Entomology (Wallingford, GBR) **[56824]**

Review of Applied Economics (New Delhi, DH, IND) **[45645]**

Review of Aromatic and Medicinal Plants (Wallingford, GBR) **[56825]**

The Review of Austrian Economics (Dordrecht, NLD) **[48552]**

Review of Behavioral Finance (Leeds, GBR) **[53773]**

Review of the Bulgarian Academy of Sciences (Sofia, BUL) *Unable to locate*

Review of Cognitive Linguistics (Amsterdam, NLD) **[48223]**

Review of Commerce Studies (Delhi, DH, IND) *Unable to locate*

The Review of Communication (Abingdon, GBR) **[52041]**

Review of Derivatives Research (Dordrecht, NLD) **[48553]**

Review of Development and Change (Chennai, TN, IND) **[45055]**

Review of Development Economics (Oxford, GBR) **[56189]**

Review of Economic Conditions in Italy (Rome, ITA) *Unable to locate*

Review of Economic Design (Heidelberg, GER) **[44474]**

Review of Economic Dynamics (Amsterdam, NLD) **[48224]**

The Review of Economic Studies (Oxford, GBR) **[56190]**

Review of Economics and Business (Osaka, JPN) *Unable to locate*

Review of Employment in Tamil Nadu (Chennai, TN, IND) *Unable to locate*

The Review of English Studies (Oxford, GBR) **[56191]**

The Review of Income and Wealth (Oxford, GBR) **[56192]**

Review of Indian Spiritualism (Calcutta, WB, IND) *Unable to locate*

Review of Industrial Organization (Dordrecht, NLD) **[48554]**

Review of International Economics (Oxford, GBR) **[56193]**

Review of International Political Economy (Abingdon, GBR) **[52042]**

Review Journal of Philosophy and Social Science (Meerut, UP, IND) *Unable to locate*

Review: Latin American Literature and Arts **[52039]***

Review of Medical and Veterinary Entomology (Wallingford, GBR) **[56826]**

Review of Medical and Veterinary Mycology (Wallingford, GBR) **[56827]**

Review of Modern Literature in Chinese (Hong Kong, CHN) **[43381]**

Numbers cited in bold after listings are entry numbers rather than page numbers.

Review of Nigeria Affairs (London, GBR) [55199]

Review of Pacific Basin Financial Markets and Policies (Singapore, SGP) [50245]

Review of Palaeobotany and Palynology (Munster, GER) [44601]

Review of Plant Pathology (Wallingford, GBR) [56828]

Review of Policy Research (Oxford, GBR) [56194]

Review of Political Economy (Abingdon, GBR) [52043]

Review of Quantitative Finance and Accounting (Dordrecht, NLD) [48555]

Review of Social Economy (Abingdon, GBR) [52044]

Review of Sociology of the Hungarian Sociological Association (Budapest, HUN) [44867]

Review of Theological Literature (Poole, GBR) Ceased

Review of Urban & Regional Development Studies (Oxford, GBR) [56195]

Review of World Economics (Kiel, GER) [44508]

Reviews on Advanced Materials Science (Saint Petersburg, RUS) [50025]

Reviews in Analytical Chemistry (Haifa, ISR) [46079]

Reviews in Chemical Engineering (Ramat Aviv, ISR) [46091]

Reviews in Clinical Gerontology (Penarth, GBR) [56241]

Reviews in Conservation [55272]*

Reviews in Endocrine & Metabolic Disorders (Dordrecht, NLD) [48556]

Reviews in Fish Biology and Fisheries (Dordrecht, NLD) [48557]

Reviews in Gynaecological Practice (Bristol, GBR) [52728]

Reviews on Heteroatom Chemistry (Tokyo, JPN) Ceased

Reviews in History (London, GBR) [55200]

Reviews in Inorganic Chemistry (Tel Aviv, ISR) [46111]

Reviews in Mathematical Physics (Singapore, SGP) [50246]

REVIJA O KNJIGI (Ljubljana Polve, SVA) Unable to locate

Revista (Bogota, COL) [43545]

Revista "Abisua" (Calidonia, PAN) Unable to locate

Revista AIBDA (Coronado, CRI) Unable to locate

Revista ANCEC (Mexico, MEX) Unable to locate

Revista Arvore (Vicosa, MI, BRZ) [43066]

Revista Brasileira de Anestesiologia (Botafogo, RJ, BRZ) [42955]

Revista del Calzado (Madrid, SPA) [50796]

Revista del CIAS (Buenos Aires, ARG) [41479]

Revista de Ciencias Agrarias (Lisbon, PRT) [49805]

Revista Ciudad Alternativa (Quito, ECU) Unable to locate

Revista Espanola de Ciencia y Tecnologia de Alimentos [50711]*

Revista Espanola de Ortodoncia (Barcelona, SPA) [50695]

Revista Espanola de Paleontologia (Madrid, SPA) [50797]

Revista Europea de Estudios Latinoamericanos y del Caribe (Amsterdam, NLD) [48225]

Revista da Faculdade de Odontologia de Bauru [42948]*

Revista Hispano Cubana HC (Madrid, SPA) [50798]

Revista IIDH (San Jose, CRI) Unable to locate

Revista Interamericana de Educacion de Adultos (Patzcuaro, MI, MEX) Unable to locate

Revista Latinoamericana de Ciencias de la Comunicacion (Sao Paulo, SP, BRZ) [43047]

Revista de Libros (Madrid, SPA) Unable to locate

Revista Medica del Uruguay (Koikkala, FIN) Unable to locate

Revista Mujer Salud (Santiago, CHL) [43147]

Revista Noticias (Koikkala, FIN) Unable to locate

Revista de Occidente (Madrid, SPA) [50799]

Revista da Ordem dos Advogados (Lisbon, PRT) Ceased

Revista Portuguese de Estomatologia e Cirurgia Maxilofacial (Lisbon, PRT) Unable to locate

Revista de Psicologia Social (Madrid, SPA) Unable to locate

Revista Redde Salud de las Mujeres Latinoamericanas y del Caribe [43147]*

Revista de la SCCC (Santiago, CHL) [43148]

Revista de la SNE (Madrid, SPA) Unable to locate

Revista de la Sociedad Colombiana de Dermatologia (Bogota, COL) Unable to locate

Revista Vivencia (Sao Paulo, SP, BRZ) [43048]

Revistacap (Lisbon, PRT) [49806]

Revistas (Lisbon, PRT) Unable to locate

Revistatlantica de Poesia (Cadiz, SPA) Unable to locate

Revival-FM - 100.8 (Cumbernauld, GBR) [53151]

Revizni a Posudkove Lekarstvi (Prague, CZE) [43637]

Revolution (London, GBR) [55201]

The Revolution-FM - 96.2 (Oldham, GBR) [55785]

Revolutionary Russia (Abingdon, GBR) [52045]

Revue de neuropsychologie (Montrouge, FRA) [44005]

Revue Africaine de Sociologie [50490]*

Revue Belge d'Archeologie et d'Histoire de l'Art (Brussels, BEL) Unable to locate

Revue Belge de Geographie (Ixelles, BEL) [42889]

Revue Belge de Numismatique et de Sigillographie (Brussels, BEL) Unable to locate

Revue des Deux Mondes (Paris, FRA) [44079]

Revue E - E Tijdschrift (Brussels, BEL) Ceased

Revue Generale des Caoutchoucs & Plastiques (Paris, FRA) Unable to locate

Revue Golf (Brussels, BEL) Unable to locate

Revue Hebdomadaire des Industries Chimiques (Beaugency, FRA) Unable to locate

Revue Hebdomadaire de l'Industrie Electrique & Electronique (Beaugency, FRA) Unable to locate

Revue Internationale de Semiotique Jurdique [48431]*

Revue Internationale du Trachome (Creteil, FRA) Unable to locate

Revue de l'Energie (Paris, FRA) [44080]

Revue Militaire Suisse (Lausanne, SWI) [51199]

Revue de Musicologie (Paris, FRA) [44081]

Revue de Rexecode (Paris, FRA) Ceased

Revue du Soignant en Sante Publique (Paris, FRA) [44082]

Revue du Souvenir Napoleonien (Paris, FRA) Unable to locate

Rewriting Indian and World History (Pune, MH, IND) Unable to locate

RFI - Bishkek (Bishkek, KGA) Unable to locate

RFJ-FM - 96 (Delemont, SWI) [51084]

RGA Information Magazine (Leicester, GBR) Unable to locate

Rheedea (Calicut, KE, IND) [45022]

Rhema-FM - 96.3 (Belmont, VI, AUS) [41593]

Rhema-FM - 105.7 (Mount Isa, QL, AUS) [42132]

Rheumatism (New Delhi, DH, IND) Unable to locate

Rheumatology (London, GBR) [55202]

Rheumatology; APLAR Journal of [56003]*

Rheumatology International (Heidelberg, GER) [44475]

Rhinology (Amsterdam, NLD) [48226]

Rhodes Journalism Review (Grahamstown, SAF) [50511]

Rhyl Journal (Rhyl, GBR) [56387]

Rhythm (Calcutta, WB, IND) Unable to locate

Rhythm-FM (Darlinghurst, NW, AUS) Unable to locate

RI (Alkmaar, NLD) Unable to locate

Ria 89.7 FM - 89.7 MHz (Singapore, SGP) [50305]

The Richard Jefferies Society Journal (Longcot, GBR) [55475]

Richard Strauss-Blaetter (Vienna, AUT) Unable to locate

The Richmond River Express Examiner (Sydney, NW, AUS) [42570]

Rider Haggard Journal (Whitley Bay, GBR) [56920]

Ridings-FM - 106.8 (Barnsley, GBR) [52189]

The Rifleman (Woking, SR, GBR) Unable to locate

The Rigaku Journal (Tokyo, JPN) [47032]

RILISAR Bulletin (Chennai, TN, IND) Unable to locate

Rinderproduktion (Bad Lauterberg, GER) Unable to locate

Rinderzucht/Fleckvieh (Munich, GER) [44580]

Ring (Warsaw, POL) [49763]

Ringing & Migration (Thetford, GBR) [56745]

Ripley & Heanor News (Ripley, GBR) [56398]

Ripon Gazette & Boroughbridge Herald (Ripon, GBR) [56399]

Ripple (Leicester, GBR) [53822]

Rise (London, GBR) [55203]

The Rising Nepal (Kathmandu, NPL) Unable to locate

Rising Sun (Chennai, TN, IND) Unable to locate

Risk (London, GBR) [55204]

Risk & Continuity (Waltham, GBR) Ceased

Risk Management & Insurance Review (Oxford, GBR) [56196]

Risk and Regulation (London, GBR) [55205]

RIST Journal of R & D (Pohang, KOR) Unable to locate

Ritmo (Madrid, SPA) [50800]

Ritz Magazine (Ware, GBR) [56844]

River Behaviour and Control (Calcutta, WB, IND) Unable to locate

The River-FM - 105.7 (Albury, NW, AUS) [41528]

River 94.9-FM - 94.9 (Ipswich, QL, AUS) [41971]

Riverland Christian Radio-FM - 93.9 (Loxton, SA, AUS) [42023]

The Riversider (Hamilton, NZL) Unable to locate

The Rivertown Times (Sydney, NW, AUS) [42571]

Rivista di Biologia (Genoa, ITA) [46153]

Rivista Italiana Difesa (Chiavari, ITA) [46133]

Riyadh Daily (Riyadh, SAU) Unable to locate

Rizhao People's Broadcasting Station 1 (Rizhao, SD, CHN) Unable to locate

Rizhao People's Broadcasting Station 1 (Rizhao, SD, CHN) Unable to locate

RLA Quarterly Journal (Jaipur, RJ, IND) Unable to locate

RLM-FM (Saint Laurent du Maroni, FGN) Unable to locate

RML 99 - Jounieh (Metn, LBN) Unable to locate

RMN Manila-AM - 558 KHz (Makati City, PHL) [49529]

RMO—Rivista di Meccanica Oggi (Cinisello Balsamo, ITA) [46134]

RMT News (London, GBR) [55206]

RM2-FM (Kuala Lumpur, MYS) Unable to locate

RNA Radio-FM - 94.2 (Andorra la Vella, AND) [41464]

RNZ-FM - 101.3 (Wellington, NZL) [49045]

Road Ahead (Cape Town, SAF) [50406]

Road and Transport Research (Vermont South, VI, AUS) Unable to locate

Robin Hood Adventures (London, GBR) [55207]

Rock-FM - 98.5 (Pafos, CYP) [43600]

The Rock-FM (Auckland, NZL) Unable to locate

Rock Mechanics and Rock Engineering (Turin, ITA) [46274]

Rock y Pop-FM - 94.1 (Santiago, CHL) [43160]

Rock n Pop Radio-FM - 106.8 (Hamburg, GER) [44427]

Rock Sound Magazine (London, GBR) Unable to locate

Rocket (Kuala Lumpur, MYS) [47633]

Rockhampton and Fitzroy News (Sydney, NW, AUS) [42572]

Rodeo (Milan, ITA) [46193]

Roe Valley Sentinel (Limavady, GBR) [53854]

Roede Kors Hjaelp (Copenhagen, DEN) Unable to locate

Roentgen Technology (Chandigarh, CH, IND) Unable to locate

Roma (Chandigarh, CH, IND) Unable to locate

Romanian Green Consumer Guide (Bucharest, ROM) Unable to locate

Romanian Journal of Japanese Studies (Bucharest, ROM) Unable to locate

Numbers cited in bold after listings are entry numbers rather than page numbers.

Romanian Journal of Neurology (Bucharest, ROM) *Unable to locate*

Romanian Journal of Neurology and Psychiatry (Bucharest, ROM) *Unable to locate*

Romanian Journal of Society and Politics (Bucharest, ROM) **[49843]**

Romanistisches Jahrbuch (Berlin, GER) **[44229]**

Romantica-AM - 740 (Celaya, GJ, MEX) **[47758]**

Romanticism (Edinburgh, GBR) **[53308]**

Romford & Havering Post (Essex, GBR) **[53342]**

Roof (London, GBR) **[55208]**

Roofing, Cladding & Insulation (Sevenoaks, GBR) **[56483]**

Rookwood Sound-AM - 945 (Cardiff, GBR) **[52945]**

Roopa-Lekha (New Delhi, DH, IND) *Unable to locate*

Roopvati (New Delhi, DH, IND) *Unable to locate*

Rootes News (Walton-On-Thames, GBR) *Unable to locate*

The Rose (Saint Albans, GBR) **[56438]**

Roshan Pakistan (Karachi, PAK) *Unable to locate*

Roshni (New Delhi, DH, IND) **[45646]**

Roska (Prague, CZE) **[43638]**

Rotarian (Amsterdam, NLD) **[48227]**

The Rotarian Monthly (Taipei, TWN) **[51357]**

Rotarismo en Mexico (Mexico City, DF, MEX) **[47789]**

Rotary (Bergamo, ITA) **[46123]**

Rotary Africa (KwaZulu-Natal, SAF) **[50544]**

Rotary Contact (Brussels, BEL) **[42872]**

Rotary Dergisi (Cinarli-Izmir, TUR) **[51552]**

Rotary Down Under (Parramatta, NW, AUS) **[42236]**

The Rotary Korea (Seoul, KOR) **[47285]**

Rotary Magazine (Cairo, EGY) **[43764]**

Rotary Magazine (GB & I) (Alcester, GBR) **[52095]**

Rotary News/Rotary Samachar (Chennai, TN, IND) **[45056]**

The Rotary-No-Tomo (Tokyo, JPN) **[47033]**

Rotary Norden (Reykjavik, ICE) **[44902]**

Rotary Suisse-Liechtenstein (Uster, SWI) **[51236]**

Rotes Kreuz (Munich, GER) *Unable to locate*

Rother-FM - 96.1 (Rotherham, GBR) **[56413]**

Rotorworld (Totternhoe, GBR) **[56770]**

Rottweileren (Grasten, DEN) *Unable to locate*

Roudnicher (Sofia, BUL) *Unable to locate*

Rouge-FM - 106.5 (Lausanne, SWI) **[51204]**

Rouse Hill Times (Parramatta, NW, AUS) **[42237]**

Route Actualite/Roads News (Clichy, FRA) **[43935]**

Routes News (Twickenham, GBR) **[56793]**

Rovista ADA (Madrid, SPA) *Unable to locate*

Rox-FM - 105.5 (Roxby Downs, SA, AUS) **[42322]**

Royal Australian Navy News (Canberra, AC, AUS) **[41712]**

Royal College of General Practitioners. North & West London Faculty. News (London, GBR) *Unable to locate*

The Royal Gazette (Hamilton, BMU) **[42922]**

Royal Microscopical Society; Proceedings of the **[55989]***

The Royal Society Yearbook (London, GBR) **[55209]**

Royal Wings (Jordan) (Amman, JOR) **[47162]**

Royston Crow (Royston, GBR) **[56415]**

RPH Print Radio-AM - 1224 (Sydney, NW, AUS) **[42598]**

RPN (Quezon City, PHL) *Unable to locate*

RPS Journal (Bath, GBR) **[52257]**

RQ-AM - 910 (Caracas, VEN) **[57023]**

RSA Journal (London, GBR) *Unable to locate*

RSG - Richting/Sportgericht (Olst, NLD) *Unable to locate*

RSPB Conservation Review (Sandy, GBR) *Ceased*

RSYC (Singapore, SGP) **[50247]**

RT eJournal (Cologne, GER) **[44301]**

Rtam (Lucknow, UP, IND) *Unable to locate*

RTB Nasional-FM - 92.3 (Negara, BRN) **[43080]**

RTB Nur Islam-FM - 93.3 (Negara, BRN) **[43081]**

RTB Pelangi-FM - 91.4 (Bandar, BRN) **[43071]**

RTEC-Bangkok, THA) *Unable to locate*

RTEC-Bangkok (Bangkok, THA) *Unable to locate*

RTEC-Bangkok (Bangkok, THA) *Unable to locate*

RTEC-Bangkok (Bangkok, THA) *Unable to locate*

RTEC-Bangkok (Bangkok, THA) *Unable to locate*

RTEC-Bangkok (Bangkok, THA) *Unable to locate*

RTEC-Bangkok (Bangkok, THA) *Unable to locate*

RTEC-Bangkok (Bangkok, THA) *Unable to locate*

RTEC-Bangkok (Bangkok, THA) *Unable to locate*

RTEC-Bangkok (Bangkok, THA) *Unable to locate*

RTEC-Bangkok (Bangkok, THA) *Unable to locate*

RTEC-Bangkok (Bangkok, THA) *Unable to locate*

RTEC-Bangkok (Bangkok, THA) *Unable to locate*

RTEC-Bangkok (Bangkok, THA) *Unable to locate*

RTEC-Bangkok (Bangkok, THA) *Unable to locate*

RTEC-Bangkok (Bangkok, THA) *Unable to locate*

RTEC-Bangkok (Bangkok, THA) *Unable to locate*

RTEC-Bangkok (Bangkok, THA) *Unable to locate*

RTEC-Bangkok (Bangkok, THA) *Unable to locate*

RTEC-Bangkok (Bangkok, THA) *Unable to locate*

RTEC-Bangkok (Bangkok, THA) *Unable to locate*

RTEC-Bangkok (Bangkok, THA) *Unable to locate*

RTEC-Bangkok (Bangkok, THA) *Unable to locate*

RTEC-Bangkok (Bangkok, THA) *Unable to locate*

RTEC-Buriram (Bangkok, THA) *Unable to locate*

RTEC-Chaiyaphum (Bangkok, THA) *Unable to locate*

RTEC-Chaiyaphum (Bangkok, THA) *Unable to locate*

RTEC-Chanthaburi (Bangkok, THA) *Unable to locate*

RTEC-Chanthaburi (Bangkok, THA) *Unable to locate*

RTEC-Chanthaburi (Chanthaburi, THA) *Unable to locate*

RTEC-Chanthaburi (Chanthaburi, THA) *Unable to locate*

RTEC-Chanthaburi (Chanthaburi, THA) *Unable to locate*

RTEC-Chiang Mai (Bangkok, THA) *Unable to locate*

RTEC-Chiang Mai (Bangkok, THA) *Unable to locate*

RTEC-Chiang Mai (Chiang Mai, THA) *Unable to locate*

RTEC-Chiang Mai (Chiang Mai, THA) *Unable to locate*

RTEC-Chiang Mai (Chiang Mai, THA) *Unable to locate*

RTEC-Chiang Mai (Chiang Mai, THA) *Unable to locate*

RTEC-Chiang Rai (Bangkok, THA) *Unable to locate*

RTEC-Chiang Rai (Bangkok, THA) *Unable to locate*

RTEC-Chiang Rai (Chiang Rai, THA) *Unable to locate*

RTEC-Chiang Rai (Chiang Rai, THA) *Unable to locate*

RTEC-Chiang Rai (Chiang Rai, THA) *Unable to locate*

RTEC-Chiang Rai (Chiang Rai, THA) *Unable to locate*

RTEC-Chon Buri (Bangkok, THA) *Unable to locate*

RTEC-Chumphon (Bangkok, THA) *Unable to locate*

RTEC-Chumphon (Chumphon, THA) *Unable to locate*

RTEC-Chumphon (Chumphon, THA) *Unable to locate*

RTEC-Kalasin (Bangkok, THA) *Unable to locate*

RTEC-Kanchanaburi (Bangkok, THA) *Unable to locate*

RTEC-Khon Kaen (Bangkok, THA) *Unable to locate*

RTEC-Khon Kaen (Bangkok, THA) *Ceased*

RTEC-Khon Kaen (Bangkok, THA) *Unable to locate*

RTEC-Khon Kaen (Khon Kaen, THA) *Unable to locate*

RTEC-Khon Kaen (Khon Kaen, THA) *Unable to locate*

RTEC-Khon Kaen (Khon Kaen, THA) *Unable to locate*

RTEC-Khon Kaen (Khon Kaen, THA) *Unable to locate*

RTEC-Khon Kaen (Khon Kaen, THA) *Unable to locate*

RTEC-Krabi (Bangkok, THA) *Unable to locate*

RTEC-Krabi (Bangkok, THA) *Unable to locate*

RTEC-Krabi (Krabi, THA) *Unable to locate*

RTEC-Lampang (Bangkok, THA) *Ceased*

RTEC-Lampang (Bangkok, THA) *Ceased*

RTEC-Lampang (Lampang, THA) *Unable to locate*

RTEC-Lampang (Lampang, THA) *Unable to locate*

RTEC-Lampang (Lampang, THA) *Unable to locate*

RTEC-Lamphun (Lamphun, THA) *Unable to locate*

RTEC-Loei (Loei, THA) *Unable to locate*

RTEC-Lop Buri (Bangkok, THA) *Unable to locate*

RTEC-Lop Buri (Bangkok, THA) *Unable to locate*

RTEC-Lop Buri (Bangkok, THA) *Unable to locate*

RTEC-Lop Buri (Lop Buri, THA) *Unable to locate*

RTEC-Mae Hong Son (Mae Hong Son, THA) *Unable to locate*

RTEC-Maha Sarakham (Bangkok, THA) *Unable to locate*

RTEC-Maha Sarakham (Maha Sarakham, THA) *Unable to locate*

RTEC-Mukdahan (Mukdahan, THA) *Unable to locate*

RTEC-Nakhon Pathom (Bangkok, THA) *Unable to locate*

RTEC-Nakhon Phanom (Bangkok, THA) *Ceased*

RTEC-Nakhon Phanom (Nakhon Phanom, THA) *Unable to locate*

RTEC-Nakhon Phanom (Nakhon Phanom, THA) *Unable to locate*

RTEC-Nakhon Ratchasima (Bangkok, THA) *Unable to locate*

RTEC-Nakhon Ratchasima (Bangkok, THA) *Unable to locate*

RTEC-Nakhon Ratchasima (Bangkok, THA) *Unable to locate*

RTEC-Nakhon Ratchasima (Nakhon Ratchasima, THA) *Unable to locate*

RTEC-Nakhon Ratchasima (Nakhon Ratchasima, THA) *Unable to locate*

RTEC-Nakhon Sawan (Bangkok, THA) *Unable to locate*

RTEC-Nakhon Sawan (Bangkok, THA) *Unable to locate*

RTEC-Nakhon Sawan (Nakhon Sawan, THA) *Unable to locate*

RTEC-Nakhon Sawan (Nakhon Sawan, THA) *Unable to locate*

RTEC-Nakhon Si Thammarat (Bangkok, THA) *Unable to locate*

RTEC-Nakhon Si Thammarat (Bangkok, THA) *Unable to locate*

RTEC-Nakhon Si Thammarat (Nakhon Si Thammarat, THA) *Unable to locate*

RTEC-Nakhon Si Thammarat (Nakhon Si Thammarat, THA) *Unable to locate*

RTEC-Nan (Bangkok, THA) *Unable to locate*

RTEC-Nan (Nan, THA) *Unable to locate*

RTEC-Narathivat (Narathivat, THA) *Unable to locate*

RTEC-Nong Khai (Nong Khai, THA) *Unable to locate*

RTEC-Pathumthani (Bangkok, THA) *Unable to locate*

RTEC-Pathumthani (Bangkok, THA) *Unable to locate*

RTEC-Pathumthani (Bangkok, THA) *Unable to locate*

RTEC-Pathumthani (Bangkok, THA) *Unable to locate*

RTEC-Pathumthani (Bangkok, THA) *Unable to locate*

RTEC-Pathumthani (Pathumthani, THA) *Unable to locate*

RTEC-Pattani (Pattani, THA) *Unable to locate*

RTEC-Pattani (Pattani, THA) *Unable to locate*

RTEC-Phangnga (Bangkok, THA) *Unable to locate*

RTEC-Phangnga (Phangnga, THA) *Unable to locate*

RTEC-Phattalung (Bangkok, THA) *Unable to locate*

RTEC-Phattalung (Bangkok, THA) *Ceased*

RTEC-Phayao (Bangkok, THA) *Unable to locate*

RTEC-Phayao (Phayao, THA) *Unable to locate*

RTEC-Phetchabun (Bangkok, THA) *Unable to locate*

RTEC-Phetchabun (Phetchabun, THA) *Unable to locate*

RTEC-Phetchabun (Phetchabun, THA) *Unable to locate*

RTEC-Phetchabun (Phetchabun, THA) *Unable to locate*

RTEC-Phichit (Bangkok, THA) *Unable to locate*

RTEC-Phitsanulok (Bangkok, THA) *Unable to locate*

RTEC-Phitsanulok (Phitsanulok, THA) *Unable to locate*

RTEC-Phitsanulok (Phitsanulok, THA) *Unable to locate*

RTEC-Phitsanulok (Phitsanulok, THA) *Unable to locate*

RTEC-Phitsanulok (Phitsanulok, THA) *Unable to locate*

RTEC-Phrae (Phrae, THA) *Unable to locate*

RTEC-Phrae (Phrae, THA) *Unable to locate*

RTEC-Phuket (Bangkok, THA) *Unable to locate*

RTEC-Phuket (Phuket, THA) *Unable to locate*

RTEC-Prachin Buri (Bangkok, THA) *Unable to locate*

RTEC-Prachin Buri (Bangkok, THA) *Unable to locate*

RTEC-Prachin Buri (Bangkok, THA) *Unable to locate*

RTEC-Prahuap Khiri (Bangkok, THA) *Unable to locate*

RTEC-Prahuap Khirikhan (Bangkok, THA) *Unable to locate*

RTEC-Ranong (Bangkok, THA) *Unable to locate*

RTEC-Ratchaburi (Bangkok, THA) *Unable to locate*

RTEC-Ratchaburi (Bangkok, THA) *Unable to locate*

RTEC-Ratchaburi (Bangkok, THA) *Unable to locate*

RTEC-Ratchaburi (Ratchaburi, THA) *Unable to locate*

RTEC-Rayong (Bangkok, THA) *Unable to locate*

RTEC-Rayong (Bangkok, THA) *Ceased*

RTEC-Roi Et (Bangkok, THA) *Unable to locate*

RTEC-Sakon Nakhon (Bangkok, THA) *Unable to locate*

RTEC-Sakon Nakhon (Sakon Nakhon, THA) *Unable to locate*

RTEC-Sakon Nakhon (Sakon Nakhon, THA) *Unable to locate*

RTEC-Samut Sakhon (Bangkok, THA) *Unable to locate*

RTEC-Samut Sakhon (Bangkok, THA) *Unable to locate*

RTEC-Samut Sakhon (Samut Sakhon, THA) *Unable to locate*

RTEC-Saraburi (Saraburi, THA) *Unable to locate*

RTEC-Saraburi (Saraburi, THA) *Unable to locate*

RTEC-Satun (Bangkok, THA) *Unable to locate*

RTEC-Si Sa Ket (Si Sa Ket, THA) *Unable to locate*

RTEC-Songkhla (Bangkok, THA) *Unable to locate*

RTEC-Songkhla (Bangkok, THA) *Unable to locate*

RTEC-Songkhla (Bangkok, THA) *Unable to locate*

RTEC-Songkhla (Songkhla, THA) *Unable to locate*

RTEC-Songkhla (Songkhla, THA) *Unable to locate*

RTEC-Songkhla (Songkhla, THA) *Unable to locate*

RTEC-Songkhla (Songkhla, THA) *Unable to locate*

RTEC-Songkhla (Songkhla, THA) *Unable to locate*

RTEC-Sukhothai (Sukhothai, THA) *Unable to locate*

RTEC-Suphan Buri (Bangkok, THA) *Unable to locate*

RTEC-Surat Thani (Bangkok, THA) *Unable to locate*

RTEC-Surat Thani (Bangkok, THA) *Unable to locate*

RTEC-Surat Thani (Bangkok, THA) *Unable to locate*

RTEC-Surat Thani (Surat Thani, THA) *Unable to locate*

RTEC-Surat Thani (Surat Thani, THA) *Unable to locate*

RTEC-Surat Thani (Surat Thani, THA) *Unable to locate*

RTEC-Surin (Bangkok, THA) *Unable to locate*

RTEC-Surin (Bangkok, THA) *Unable to locate*

RTEC-Surin (Surin, THA) *Unable to locate*

RTEC-Tak (Bangkok, THA) *Unable to locate*

RTEC-Tak (Bangkok, THA) *Unable to locate*

RTEC-Tak (Tak, THA) *Unable to locate*

RTEC-Trad (Bangkok, THA) *Unable to locate*

RTEC-Trang (Bangkok, THA) *Unable to locate*

RTEC-Trang (Trang, THA) *Unable to locate*

RTEC-Trang (Trang, THA) *Unable to locate*

RTEC-Ubon Ratchathani (Ubon Ratchathani, THA) *Unable to locate*

RTEC-Ubon Ratchathani (Ubon Ratchathani, THA) *Unable to locate*

RTEC-Ubon Ratchathani (Ubon Ratchathani, THA) *Unable to locate*

RTEC-Ubon Ratchathani (Ubon Ratchathani, THA) *Unable to locate*

RTEC-Ubon Thani (Bangkok, THA) *Unable to locate*

RTEC-Udon Thani (Bangkok, THA) *Unable to locate*

RTEC-Udon Thani (Udon Thani, THA) *Unable to locate*

RTEC-Udon Thani (Udon Thani, THA) *Unable to locate*

RTEC-Udon Thani (Udon Thani, THA) *Unable to locate*

RTEC-Uttaradit (Bangkok, THA) *Ceased*

RTEC-Uttaradit (Bangkok, THA) *Unable to locate*

RTEC-Uttaradit (Uttaradit, THA) *Unable to locate*

RTEC-Yala (Yala, THA) *Unable to locate*

RTEC-Yala (Yala, THA) *Unable to locate*

RTEC-Yala (Yala, THA) *Unable to locate*

RTEC-Yasothon (Yasothon, THA) *Unable to locate*

RTHK Putonghua Channel - 621 KHz (Hong Kong, CHN) **[43418]**

RTHK Putonghua Channel - 100.9 MHz (Hong Kong, CHN) **[43417]**

RTHK Radio 5-Castle Peak - 106.8 MHz (Hong Kong, CHN) **[43419]**

RTHK Radio 5-Golden Hill - 783 KHz (Hong Kong, CHN) **[43420]**

RTHK Radio 4-Beacon Hill - 98.1 MHz (Hong Kong, CHN) **[43421]**

RTHK Radio 4-Castle Peak - 98.7 MHZ (Hong Kong, CHN) **[43422]**

RTHK Radio 4-Cloudy Hill - 97.8 MHz (Hong Kong, CHN) **[43423]**

RTHK Radio 4-Golden Hill - 98.4 MHz (Hong Kong, CHN) **[43424]**

RTHK Radio 4-Kowloon Peak - 98.9 MHz (Hong Kong, CHN) **[43425]**

RTHK Radio 4-Lamma Island - 98.2 MHz (Hong Kong, CHN) **[43426]**

RTHK Radio 4-Mt. Gough - 97.6 MHz (Hong Kong, CHN) **[43427]**

RTHK Radio 1-Beacon Hill - 93.5 MHz (Hong Kong, CHN) **[43428]**

RTHK Radio 1-Castle Peak - 93.4 MHz (Hong Kong, CHN) **[43429]**

RTHK Radio 1-Cloudy Hill - 93.2 MHz (Hong Kong, CHN) **[43430]**

RTHK Radio 1-Golden Hill - 92.9 MHz (Hong Kong, CHN) **[43431]**

RTHK Radio 1-Kowloon Peak - 94.4 MHz (Hong Kong, CHN) **[43432]**

RTHK Radio 1-Lamma Island - 93.6 MHz (Hong Kong, CHN) **[43433]**

RTHK Radio 1-Mt. Gough - 92.6 MHz (Hong Kong, CHN) **[43434]**

RTHK Radio 6-Peng Chau - 675 KHz (Hong Kong, CHN) **[43435]**

RTHK Radio 3-Chung Hom Kok - 1584 KHz (Hong Kong, CHN) **[43437]**

RTHK Radio 3-Chung Hom Kok - 106.8 MHz (Hong Kong, CHN) **[43436]**

RTHK Radio 3-Golden Hill - 567 KHz (Hong Kong, CHN) **[43438]**

RTHK Radio 3-Mt. Nicholson - 97.9 MHZ (Hong Kong, CHN) **[43439]**

RTHK Radio 2-Beacon Hill - 96.3 MHz (Hong Kong, CHN) **[43440]**

RTHK Radio 2-Castle Peak - 96.4 MHz (Hong Kong, CHN) **[43441]**

RTHK Radio 2-Cloudy Hill - 95.3 MHz (Hong Kong, CHN) **[43442]**

RTHK Radio 2-Golden Hill - 95.6 MHz (Hong Kong, CHN) **[43443]**

RTHK Radio 2-Kowloon Peak - 96.9 MHz (Hong Kong, CHN) **[43444]**

RTHK Radio 2-Lamma Island - 96.0 MHz (Hong Kong, CHN) **[43445]**

RTHK Radio 2-Mt. Gough - 94.8 MHz (Hong Kong, CHN) **[43446]**

RTI Redes Telecom Instalacoes (Sao Paulo, SP, BRZ) **[43049]**

RTL-FM - 89 (Halle, GER) **[44408]**

RTM1 **[47656]***

RTR-FM - 92.1 (Perth, WA, AUS) **[42253]**

RTS-FM (Belgrade, SER) *Unable to locate*

RTV Musormagazin (Budapest, HUN) **[44868]**

Rubber Developments (Hertford, GBR) **[53565]**

Rubber India (Mumbai, MH, IND) *Unable to locate*

Rubber Industry Report (Singapore, SGP) **[50248]**

The Rubber International (Bangkok, THA) **[51433]**

Rubber News (Mumbai, MH, IND) *Unable to locate*

Rubber and Plastics Digest (New Delhi, DH, IND) *Unable to locate*

Rubber Reporter (Mumbai, MH, IND) *Unable to locate*

Rubber Statistical Bulletin (Singapore, SGP) **[50249]**

Rugby Advertiser (Rugby, GBR) **[56423]**

Rugby-FM - 107.1 (Honiley, GBR) **[53585]**

Rugby League World (Brighouse, GBR) **[52601]**

Rugby Leaguer & League Express (Brighouse, GBR) **[52602]**

Rugby Observer (Warwick, GBR) **[56855]**

Rugby World (London, GBR) **[55210]**

Rui'an People's Broadcasting Station (Rui'an, ZH, CHN) *Unable to locate*

Rum and Form (Copenhagen, DEN) *Unable to locate*

Rundbrief (Duisburg, GER) *Unable to locate*

Rundschreiben (Cologne, GER) *Unable to locate*

Ruoteclassiche (Rozzano, ITA) **[46253]**

Rupambara (Calcutta, WB, IND) *Unable to locate*

Rupee Trade (New Delhi, DH, IND) *Unable to locate*

Rural and Environmental Engineering (Tokyo, JPN) **[47034]**

Rural India (Gwalior, MP, IND) *Unable to locate*

Rural Life and Cooperation (Tirana, ALB) *Unable to locate*

Rural and Remote Health (Geelong, VI, AUS) **[41880]**

Rural Weekly (Central Queensland edition) (Sydney, NW, AUS) **[42573]**

Rural Weekly (North CQ edition) (Sydney, NW, AUS) **[42574]**

Rural Weekly (Southern edition) (Sydney, NW, AUS) **[42575]**

Rural Weekly (Wide Bay edition) (Sydney, NW, AUS) **[42576]**

Rural Youth (New Delhi, DH, IND) *Unable to locate*

Rusistika (Leicester, GBR) **[53823]**

Russian Academy of Sciences Journal of Journals (Moscow, RUS) *Ceased*

Numbers cited in bold after listings are entry numbers rather than page numbers.

Russian Art (Moscow, RUS) [49971]

Russian Business Magazine (Moscow, RUS) *Unable to locate*

Russian Chemical Reviews (Moscow, RUS) [49972]

Russian Digital (Moscow, RUS) [49973]

Russian Economic Developments (Moscow, RUS) *Unable to locate*

Russian Entomological Journal (Moscow, RUS) [49974]

Russian History (Leiden, NLD) [48722]

Russian Journal of Bioorganic Chemistry (Moscow, RUS) [49975]

Russian Journal of Biotechnology (Moscow, RUS) [49976]

Russian Journal of Concrete and Reinforced Concrete (Moscow, RUS) *Unable to locate*

Russian Journal of General Chemistry (Saint Petersburg, RUS) [50026]

Russian Journal of Inorganic Chemistry (Moscow, RUS) [49977]

Russian Journal of Marine Biology (Vladivostok, RUS) [50040]

Russian Journal of Oncology (Moscow, RUS) [49978]

Russian Journal of Organic Chemistry (Saint Petersburg, RUS) [50027]

Russian Journal of Pediatrics (Moscow, RUS) [49979]

Russian Journal of Physical Chemistry (Moscow, RUS) [49980]

Russian Journal of Skin and Sexually Transmitted Diseases (Moscow, RUS) [49981]

Russian Journal of Stomatology (Moscow, RUS) [49982]

Russian Journal of Theriology (Moscow, RUS) [49983]

Russian Journal of Zoology (Moscow, RUS) *Ceased*

Russian Linguistics (Dordrecht, NLD) [48558]

Russian Literature (Amsterdam, NLD) [48228]

Russian Medical Journal (Moscow, RUS) [49984]

Russian Metallurgy (Moscow, RUS) [49985]

Russian Mining (Moscow, RUS) *Unable to locate*

Russian Mobile (Moscow, RUS) *Unable to locate*

The Russian Review (Oxford, GBR) [56197]

Russian Ultrasonics (Brentwood, GBR) *Ceased*

Russkaya Volna (Krasnoyarsk, RUS) *Unable to locate*

Russkiy Vityaz (Barnaul, RUS) *Unable to locate*

Russkiy Vityaz (Barnaul, RUS) *Unable to locate*

Russkoye Radio - Almetyevsk (Moscow, RUS) *Unable to locate*

Russkoye Radio - Arkhangelsk (Moscow, RUS) *Unable to locate*

Russkoye Radio - Arkhangelsk (Moscow, RUS) *Unable to locate*

Russkoye Radio - Astrakhan (Astrakhan, RUS) *Unable to locate*

Russkoye Radio Barguzin (Angarsk, RUS) *Unable to locate*

Russkoye Radio - Barnaul (Barnaul, RUS) *Unable to locate*

Russkoye Radio - Belgorod (Belgorod, RUS) *Unable to locate*

Russkoye Radio - Bratsk (Moscow, RUS) *Unable to locate*

Russkoye Radio - Chelyabinsk (Moscow, RUS) *Unable to locate*

Russkoye Radio - Cherkessk (Moscow, RUS) *Unable to locate*

Russkoye Radio - Chita (Chita, RUS) *Unable to locate*

Russkoye Radio - Chita (Moscow, RUS) *Unable to locate*

Russkoye Radio - Chita (Moscow, RUS) *Unable to locate*

Russkoye Radio - Irkutsk (Angarsk, RUS) *Unable to locate*

Russkoye Radio - Izhevsk (Moscow, RUS) *Unable to locate*

Russkoye Radio - Kaluga (Kaluga, RUS) *Unable to locate*

Russkoye Radio - Kazan (Kazan, RUS) *Unable to locate*

Russkoye Radio - Kemerovo (Kemerovo, RUS) *Unable to locate*

Russkoye Radio - Khabarovsk (Khabarovsk, RUS) *Unable to locate*

Russkoye Radio - Kogalym (Moscow, RUS) *Unable to locate*

Russkoye Radio - Komsomolsk-na-Amure (Komsomolsk-na-Amure, RUS) *Unable to locate*

Russkoye Radio - Kozhevnikovo (Moscow, RUS) *Unable to locate*

Russkoye Radio - Kurgan (Kurgan, RUS) *Unable to locate*

Russkoye Radio - Kurgan (Kurgan, RUS) *Unable to locate*

Russkoye Radio - Kurgan (Moscow, RUS) *Unable to locate*

Russkoye Radio - Moskva (Moscow, RUS) *Unable to locate*

Russkoye Radio - Murmansk (Moscow, RUS) *Unable to locate*

Russkoye Radio - Novokuznetsk (Moscow, RUS) *Unable to locate*

Russkoye Radio - Novosibirsk (Moscow, RUS) *Unable to locate*

Russkoye Radio Odin - Lipetsk (Moscow, RUS) *Unable to locate*

Russkoye Radio - Olgino (St. Petersburg, RUS) *Unable to locate*

Russkoye Radio - Omsk (Omsk, RUS) *Unable to locate*

Russkoye Radio Omsk - Omsk (Omsk, RUS) *Unable to locate*

Russkoye Radio na Onego - Petrozavodsk (Petrozavodsk, RUS) *Unable to locate*

Russkoye Radio - Orel (Moscow, RUS) *Unable to locate*

Russkoye Radio - Orenburg (Moscow, RUS) *Unable to locate*

Russkoye Radio - Orenburg (Moscow, RUS) *Unable to locate*

Russkoye Radio v Penze - Penza (Moscow, RUS) *Unable to locate*

Russkoye Radio - Perm (Moscow, RUS) *Unable to locate*

Russkoye Radio - Perm (Perm, RUS) *Unable to locate*

Russkoye Radio Primore (Vladivostok, RUS) *Unable to locate*

Russkoye Radio - Pyatigorsk (Pyatigorsk, RUS) *Unable to locate*

Russkoye Radio (Radio Istok) - Volgodonsk (Volgodonsk, RUS) *Unable to locate*

Russkoye Radio (Radio Kaskad) - Kaliningrad (Kaliningrad, RUS) *Unable to locate*

Russkoye Radio (Radio Programme RV-3) (Rubtsovsk, RUS) *Unable to locate*

Russkoye Radio - Rostov-na-Donu (Rostov, RUS) *Unable to locate*

Russkoye Radio - Ryazan (Ryazan, RUS) *Unable to locate*

Russkoye Radio - Samara (Moscow, RUS) *Unable to locate*

Russkoye Radio - Samara (Moscow, RUS) *Unable to locate*

Russkoye Radio - Saransk (Moscow, RUS) *Unable to locate*

Russkoye Radio - Saratov (Moscow, RUS) *Unable to locate*

Russkoye Radio - Sochi (Sochi, RUS) *Unable to locate*

Russkoye Radio - Tolyatti (Tolyatti, RUS) *Unable to locate*

Russkoye Radio - Tula (Moscow, RUS) *Unable to locate*

Russkoye Radio - Tyumen (Moscow, RUS) *Unable to locate*

Russkoye Radio - Ufa (Moscow, RUS) *Unable to locate*

Russkoye Radio - Ufa (Ufa, RUS) *Unable to locate*

Russkoye Radio - Ulan-Ude (Ulan-Ude, RUS) *Unable to locate*

Russkoye Radio - Ulyanovsk (Moscow, RUS) *Unable to locate*

Russkoye Radio - Velikiy Novgorod (Moscow, RUS) *Unable to locate*

Russkoye Radio - Velikiy Novgorod (Moscow, RUS) *Unable to locate*

Russkoye Radio - Volgograd (Volgograd, RUS) *Unable to locate*

Russkoye Radio - Vologda (Vologda, RUS) *Unable to locate*

Russkoye Radio - Yaroslavl (Yaroslavl, RUS) *Unable to locate*

Russkoye Radio - Yekaterinburg (Moscow, RUS) *Unable to locate*

Russkoye Radio - Yekaterinburg (Yekaterinburg, RUS) *Unable to locate*

Russkoye Radio - Zlatoust (Moscow, RUS) *Unable to locate*

Russkoye Video (St. Petersburg, RUS) *Unable to locate*

Ruta del Papagayo (Caracas, VEN) *Unable to locate*

Rutland Radio-FM - 107.2 (Oakham, GBR) [55781]

Rutland Radio-FM - 97.4 (Stamford, GBR) [56598]

Rutland & Stamford Mercury Series (Edinburgh, GBR) [53309]

RYA Magazine (Southampton, GBR) [56577]

Ryanair Magazine (London, GBR) [55211]

Rye & Battle Observer (Saint Leonards-On-Sea, GBR) [56446]

S

S A A R C Journal of Educational Research (Maharagama, SRI) *Unable to locate*

S-Radio (Staryy Oskol, RUS) *Unable to locate*

SA Architect (Randburg, SAF) [50610]

SA Crime Quarterly (Cape Town, SAF) [50407]

S.A. Guider (Honeydew, SAF) *Unable to locate*

SA Irrigation (Centurion, SAF) [50446]

SA Journal of Human Resource Management (Centurion, SAF) [50447]

SA Journal of Industrial Psychology (Centurion, SAF) [50448]

SA Journal of International Affairs (Braamfontein, SAF) *Unable to locate*

SA Journal of Sports Medicine (Bedfordview, SAF) [50352]

SA Mercantile Law Journal (Claremont, SAF) [50462]

SA Pharmaceutical Journal (Gauteng, SAF) [50483]

SAA (London, GBR) [55212]

Saber Vivir (Barcelona, SPA) [50696]

Sabor-FM - 106.5 (Maracaibo, VEN) [57027]

SABRAO Journal of Breeding and Genetics (Manila, PHL) [49559]

Sabretache (Garran, AC, AUS) *Unable to locate*

Sabrina (Moscow, RUS) [49986]

Sabrina Baby (Moscow, RUS) [49987]

Sabrina's Secrets (London, GBR) [55213]

Sach'ong (Jinju, KOR) *Unable to locate*

Sadhana (Bangalore, KA, IND) [44986]

Saelgeren (Copenhagen, DEN) *Unable to locate*

Safer Communities (Brighton, GBR) [52632]

Safer Communities (Hove, GBR) [53612]

SAFERE (Southern African Feminist Review) (Harare, ZWE) *Unable to locate*

Safety Education (Birmingham, GBR) [52365]

Safety and Environmental Engineering (Wuhan, HU, CHN) [43525]

Safety Express (Birmingham, GBR) [52366]

Safety Fast! (Abingdon, GBR) [52046]

The Safety & Health Practitioner (London, GBR) [55214]

The Safety and Health Practitioner (Wigston, GBR) [56926]

Safety Management (London, GBR) [55215]

Safety Science (Delft, NLD) [48313]

Safety at Sea International (Redhill, GBR) [56378]

Safety & Security International (Bonn, GER) [44270]

Safety Solutions (Wahroonga, NW, AUS) [42676]

Saffron Walden Reporter (Saffron Walden, GBR) [56430]

Saga (Folkestone, GBR) [53393]

SAGA 105.7-FM [52377]*

SAGA 106.6-FM (East Midlands, GBR) *Ceased*

SAGE Race Relations Abstracts (London, GBR) [55216]

SAGGI-Child Development and Disabilities (Ponte Lambro, ITA) *Unable to locate*

Sago Communication (Ibaraki, JPN) [46394]

Sahar (Beirut, LBN) [47401]

Sahara J (Pretoria, SAF) [50599]

SAHEL (Tokyo, JPN) *Unable to locate*

Sahel Medical Journal (Sokoto, SK, NGA) [49174]

Sahil Daily (Bhatkal, KA, IND) [45003]

SAHKO & TELE (Helsinki, FIN) *Ceased*

Sai Suddha (Chennai, TN, IND) *Unable to locate*

Saigon Times Daily (Makati City, PHL) *Unable to locate*

Saigon Times Weekly (Ho Chi Minh City, VNM) [57057]

Sailplane & Gliding (Leicester, GBR) [53824]

Saint-FM - 94.7 (Burnham-on-Crouch, GBR) [52769]

St. Gabriel (Rome, ITA) *Ceased*

Numbers cited in bold after listings are entry numbers rather than page numbers.

St. Georg (Hamburg, GER) *Unable to locate*

St. Helens Reporter (Saint Helens, GBR) **[56443]**

St. John's Journal of Medicine (Bangalore, KA, IND) *Unable to locate*

St. Maarten Holiday! (Curacao, NAT) *Unable to locate*

St. Mary's Magazine (Menzingen, SWI) *Unable to locate*

The St. Petersburg Times (Saint Petersburg, RUS) **[50028]**

The Saints Magazine (Rownhams, GBR) *Unable to locate*

Saiva Siddhanta (Madras, TN, IND) *Unable to locate*

Saji (Kuala Lumpur, MYS) **[47634]**

Sajit Monthly (Calcutta, WB, IND) *Unable to locate*

Sakado (Brussels, BEL) *Unable to locate*

Sakal (Pune, MH, IND) **[45700]**

Salekhardskiy Videokanal (Salekhard, RUS) *Unable to locate*

Sales Tax Advices (Calcutta, WB, IND) *Unable to locate*

Sales Tax Affairs (New Delhi, DH, IND) *Unable to locate*

Sales Tax Review (Mumbai, MH, IND) *Unable to locate*

Saline Systems (London, GBR) **[55217]**

Saltwater GIRL (Durban, SAF) **[50468]**

Saltwater GIRL SURF (Durban, SAF) **[50469]**

Salubridad y Asistencia de Mexico **[47771]***

Salud Publica de Mexico (Cuernavaca, MO, MEX) **[47771]**

SAM-Bote **[51242]***

SAM-Focus (Winterthur, SWI) **[51242]**

Samachar (Mysore, KA, IND) **[45459]**

Samaja Shodhana (Mangalore, KA, IND) *Unable to locate*

Samalani Magazine (Limbe, MWI) *Unable to locate*

Samanyolu (Ankara, TUR) *Unable to locate*

Samarambh (Mumbai, MH, IND) *Unable to locate*

Samaru Journal of Information Studies (Zaria, KD, NGA) **[49187]**

Samaya (Moscow, RUS) **[49988]**

Sambad (Bhubaneswar, OR, IND) **[45013]**

Sambodhi (Ahmedabad, GJ, IND) *Unable to locate*

SAMIKSA (Calcutta, WB, IND) *Unable to locate*

Samojeden (Vejby, DEN) *Unable to locate*

Samolet (Moscow, RUS) *Unable to locate*

Samrakshan (Kathmandu, NPL) *Unable to locate*

Samskriti (Jabalpur, MP, IND) *Unable to locate*

SAMUS **[50554]***

Samvirke (Co-operation) (Albertslund, DEN) *Unable to locate*

SAN (Skegness, GBR) *Unable to locate*

The San Pedro Sun (Ambergris Caye, BLZ) **[42914]**

Sandakan-FM - 90.1 MHz (Sandakan, MYS) **[47710]**

Sandesh (Ahmedabad, GJ, IND) **[44909]**

Sandwich and Snack News (Chepstow, GBR) **[52983]**

SANE News (Melbourne, VI, AUS) **[42084]**

Sang Gong So Sik (Hong Kong, CHN) *Unable to locate*

Sang Thrombose Vaisseaux (Montrouge, FRA) **[44006]**

San'in Hoso - 1431 KHz (Izumo, JPN) **[46400]**

Sanjevani (Bangalore, KA, IND) **[44987]**

Sankhya (Kolkata, WB, IND) **[45303]**

Sankhya Series B (Calcutta, WB, IND) *Ceased*

Sannyas (Pune, MH, IND) *Unable to locate*

Santa Fe Stereo-AM - 1070 (Bogota, COL) **[43549]**

Santakuti Vedic Research Series (Hoshiarpur, PJ, IND) *Unable to locate*

Santo Tomas Nursing Journal (Manila, PHL) *Unable to locate*

Sanya People's Broadcasting Station (Sanyong, HN, CHN) *Unable to locate*

Sao Paulo Medical Journal (Sao Paulo, SP, BRZ) **[43050]**

Sao Paulo em Perspectiva (Sao Paulo, SP, BRZ) **[43051]**

Saout al Akhdar (Beirut, LBN) *Unable to locate*

Saout Al Bachaer (Beirut, LBN) *Unable to locate*

Saout Al Bachaer (Beirut, LBN) *Unable to locate*

Saout Al Bachaer (Beirut, LBN) *Unable to locate*

Saout Al Bachaer (Beirut, LBN) *Unable to locate*

Saout Al Bachaer - Beirut (Beirut, LBN) *Unable to locate*

Saout Al Bachaer - Beirut (Beirut, LBN) *Unable to locate*

Saout Al Bachaer - Beirut (Beirut, LBN) *Unable to locate*

Saout Al Bachaer - Bekka (Beirut, LBN) *Unable to locate*

Saout al Chaab - Aabey (Beirut, LBN) *Unable to locate*

Saout al Chaab - Beirut (Beirut, LBN) *Unable to locate*

Saout al Chaab - Fih (Beirut, LBN) *Unable to locate*

Saout al Chaab - Zahle (Beirut, LBN) *Unable to locate*

Saout al Fan (Beirut, LBN) *Unable to locate*

Saout al Fan (Beirut, LBN) *Unable to locate*

Saout al Ghad - Beirut (Beirut, LBN) *Unable to locate*

Saout al Ghad - Beit Meri (Beirut, LBN) *Unable to locate*

Saout al Ghad - Chouf (Beirut, LBN) *Unable to locate*

Saout al Ghad - Deir al Achayer - 98.0 MHz (Deir al Achayer, LBN) **[47443]**

Saout al Ghad - Fatqa (Beirut, LBN) *Unable to locate*

Saout al Ghad - Fih (Beirut, LBN) *Unable to locate*

Saout al Ghad - Jabal Akroum (Beirut, LBN) *Unable to locate*

Saout al Ghad - Jabal Tourbol (Beirut, LBN) *Unable to locate*

Saout al Ghad - Maad (Beirut, LBN) *Unable to locate*

Saout al Ghad - Majdel Aanjar (Beirut, LBN) *Unable to locate*

Saout al Ghad - Zahle (Beirut, LBN) *Unable to locate*

Saout al Janna (Beirut, LBN) *Unable to locate*

SAP **[50600]***

Sapporo TV Hoso - 882 KHz (Esashi, JPN) **[46329]**

Sapporo TV Hoso - 1440 KHz (Muroran, JPN) **[46536]**

Sapporo TV Hoso - 1440 KHz (Tomakomai, JPN) **[47091]**

SAR and QSAR in Environmental Research (Rillieux-la-Pape, FRA) **[44099]**

SARAI (Tokyo, JPN) **[47035]**

Saratov (Saratov, RUS) *Unable to locate*

Sarhad Journal of Agriculture (Peshawar, PAK) *Unable to locate*

SARIE My inspirasie (Cape Town, SAF) **[50408]**

Sarma (Helsinki, FIN) *Unable to locate*

SARP **[50600]***

Sarvadanand Universal Series (Hoshiarpur, PJ, IND) *Unable to locate*

Sarvekshana (New Delhi, DH, IND) *Unable to locate*

Sasolburg Ster (Cape Town, SAF) **[50409]**

The Satellite (Sydney, NW, AUS) **[42577]**

SATJ (Matieland, SAF) **[50553]**

Saude e Lar (Almargem do Bispo, PRT) **[49784]**

Saudi Arabia Business Week (Riyadh, SAU) *Unable to locate*

Saudi Gazette (Jeddah, SAU) **[50057]**

Saudi Heart Journal (Jeddah, SAU) **[50058]**

Saudi Journal of Anaesthesia (Mumbai, MH, IND) **[45436]**

The Saudi Journal of Gastroenterology (Riyadh, SAU) **[50069]**

Saudi Journal of Kidney Diseases and Transplantation (Riyadh, SAU) **[50070]**

Saudi Medical Journal (Riyadh, SAU) **[50071]**

Savana Radio (Colombo, SRI) *Unable to locate*

Savane-FM - 103.4 MHz (Ouagadougou, BFA) **[43112]**

Savile Row (London, GBR) **[55218]**

Savremenna Medicina (Varna, BUL) *Unable to locate*

Savunma Ve Havacilik (Ankara, TUR) **[51500]**

Savvy (Mumbai, MH, IND) *Unable to locate*

Sawt El Ghad - Baalbek - 97.1 (Baalbek, LBN) **[47384]**

Sawt El Ghad - Zalka (Beirut, LBN) *Unable to locate*

SAX (Dresden, GER) *Unable to locate*

SBC/Ekho Moskvy (Moscow, RUS) *Unable to locate*

SBCI News Letter **[45751]***

Sbornik (Moscow, RUS) **[49989]**

SBS Television - Channel 28 (Adelaide, SA, AUS) **[41521]**

SBS Television - Channel 34 (Airlie Beach, QL, AUS) **[41523]**

SBS Television - Channel 53 (Albury, NW, AUS) **[41529]**

SBS Television - Channel 68 (Alexandra, VI, AUS) **[41532]**

SBS Television - Channel 30 (Armidale, NW, AUS) **[41561]**

SBS Television - Channel 54 (Ashford, NW, AUS) **[41565]**

SBS Television - Channel 57 (Ayr, QL, AUS) **[41567]**

SBS Television - Channel 45 (Babinda, QL, AUS) **[41568]**

SBS Television - Channel 54 (Bairnsdale, VI, AUS) **[41569]**

SBS Television - Channel 30 (Ballarat, VI, AUS) **[41570]**

SBS Television - Channel 55 (Batemans Bay, NW, AUS) **[41578]**

SBS Television - Channel 46 (Bathurst, NW, AUS) **[41581]**

SBS Television - Channel 43 (Bega, NW, AUS) **[41586]**

SBS Television - Channel 53 (Bell, QL, AUS) **[41590]**

SBS Television - Channel 29 (Bendigo, VI, AUS) **[41595]**

SBS Television - Channel 43 (Blackwater, QL, AUS) **[41602]**

SBS Television - Channel 55 (Bonnie Doon, VI, AUS) **[41611]**

SBS Television - Channel 54 (Boonah, QL, AUS) **[41612]**

SBS Television - Channel 64 (Bouddi, NW, AUS) **[41620]**

SBS Television - Channel 48 (Bowen, QL, AUS) **[41622]**

SBS Television - Channel 30 (Bowral, NW, AUS) **[41629]**

SBS Television - Channel 54 (Braidwood, NW, AUS) **[41634]**

SBS Television - Channel 29 (Bright, VI, AUS) **[41637]**

SBS Television - Channel 44 (Broken Hill, NW, AUS) **[41662]**

SBS Television - Channel 50 (Bruthen, VI, AUS) **[41664]**

SBS Television - Channel 33 (Bunbury, WA, AUS) **[41666]**

SBS Television - Channel 28 (Canberra, AC, AUS) **[41715]**

SBS Television - Channel 12 (Carnarvon, WA, AUS) **[41730]**

SBS Television - Channel 52 (Churchill, VI, AUS) **[41751]**

SBS Television - Channel 57 (Clare, SA, AUS) **[41754]**

SBS Television - Channel 12 (Cobar, NW, AUS) **[41773]**

SBS Television - Channel 67 (Cobden, VI, AUS) **[41774]**

SBS Television - Channel 69 (Coffs Harbour, NW, AUS) **[41775]**

SBS Television - Channel 55 (Colac, VI, AUS) **[41778]**

SBS Television - Channel 56 (Condobolin, NW, AUS) **[41804]**

SBS Television - Channel 53 (Coolah, NW, AUS) **[41807]**

SBS Television - Channel 53 (Cooma, NW, AUS) **[41809]**

SBS Television - Channel 58 (Cowell, SA, AUS) **[41816]**

SBS Television - Channel 45 (Cowra, NW, AUS) **[41817]**

SBS Television - Channel 30 (Eildon, VI, AUS) **[41854]**

SBS Television - Channel 54 (Fraser, AC, AUS) **[41874]**

SBS Television - Channel 54 (Naracoorte, SA, AUS) **[42139]**

SBS Television - Channel 54 (Port Lincoln, SA, AUS) **[42259]**

SBS Television - Channel 10 (Tennant Creek, NT, AUS) **[42620]**

SBS Television - Channel 34 (Toodyay, WA, AUS) **[42624]**

SBS Television - Channel 54 (Tuggeranong, AC, AUS) **[42644]**

SBS Television - Acton Road - Channel 28 (Crows Nest, NW, AUS) **[41822]**

SBS Television - Caralue Bluff - Channel 62 (Caralue Bluff, SA, AUS) **[41721]**

Numbers cited in bold after listings are entry numbers rather than page numbers.

SBS Television - Central Tablelands - Channel 30 (Crows Nest, NW, AUS) **[41823]**

SBS Television - Central Western Slopes - Channel 29 (Crows Nest, NW, AUS) **[41824]**

SBS Television - Weston Creek/Woden - Channel 58 (Canberra, AC, AUS) **[41716]**

Scalable Computing (Warsaw, POL) **[49764]**

Scale Aircraft Modelling (Bletchley, GBR) **[52390]**

Scan (Sydney, NW, AUS) **[42578]**

Scandinavia Now (Stockholm, SWE) **[51032]**

Scandinavian Actuarial Journal (Stockholm, SWE) **[51033]**

Scandinavian Cardiovascular Journal (Stockholm, SWE) **[51034]**

Scandinavian Economic History Review (Goteborg, SWE) **[50964]**

Scandinavian Food & Drink (Glostrup, DEN) **[43715]**

Scandinavian Journal of Behaviour Therapy **[50973]***

Scandinavian Journal of Caring Sciences (Oxford, GBR) **[56198]**

Scandinavian Journal of Clinical and Laboratory Investigation (Abingdon, GBR) **[52047]**

Scandinavian Journal of Design History (Humlebaek, DEN) **[43724]**

Scandinavian Journal of Disability Research (Oslo, NOR) **[49207]**

The Scandinavian Journal of Economics (Oxford, GBR) **[56199]**

Scandinavian Journal of Educational Research (Oslo, NOR) **[49208]**

Scandinavian Journal of Food and Nutrition (Lund, SWE) **[50990]**

Scandinavian Journal of Forest Research (Knivsta, SWE) **[50972]**

Scandinavian Journal of Gastroenterology (Abingdon, GBR) **[52048]**

Scandinavian Journal of History (Reykjavik, ICE) **[44903]**

Scandinavian Journal of Hospitality and Tourism (Abingdon, GBR) **[52049]**

Scandinavian Journal of Immunology (Bergen, NOR) **[49191]**

Scandinavian Journal of Infectious Diseases (Abingdon, GBR) *Unable to locate*

Scandinavian Journal of Information Systems (Goteborg, SWE) **[50965]**

Scandinavian Journal of Laboratory Animal Science (Copenhagen, DEN) **[43681]**

Scandinavian Journal of Management (Amsterdam, NLD) **[48229]**

Scandinavian Journal of Medicine and Science in Sports (Copenhagen, DEN) **[43682]**

Scandinavian Journal of Nutrition **[50990]***

Scandinavian Journal of Occupational Therapy (Stockholm, SWE) **[51035]**

Scandinavian Journal of Plastic and Reconstructive Surgery and Hand Surgery (Turku, FIN) *Unable to locate*

Scandinavian Journal of Primary Health Care (Abingdon, GBR) **[52050]**

Scandinavian Journal of Psychology (Linkoping, SWE) **[50978]**

Scandinavian Journal of Public Health (Umea, SWE) **[51047]**

Scandinavian Journal of Rheumatology (Abingdon, GBR) **[52051]**

Scandinavian Journal of Statistics (Joensuu, FIN) **[43868]**

Scandinavian Journal of Urology and Nephrology (Abingdon, GBR) **[52052]**

Scandinavian Political Studies (Oxford, GBR) **[56200]**

Scando-Slavica (Copenhagen, DEN) **[43683]**

ScanRef (Skive, DEN) **[43735]**

Scarborough Evening News (Scarborough, GBR) **[56464]**

SCERT Journal (Hyderabad, AP, IND) *Unable to locate*

Scherzo (Madrid, SPA) **[50801]**

Schizophrenia Bulletin (Oxford, GBR) **[56201]**

Schlittenpost (Berchtesgaden, GER) *Unable to locate*

Schmalenbach Business Review (Dusseldorf, GER) **[44333]**

School Journal (Zoetermeer, NLD) *Unable to locate*

School Leadership & Management (Abingdon, GBR) **[52053]**

The School Librarian (Rotherham, GBR) **[56412]**

School Organisation **[52053]***

School Psychology International (London, GBR) **[55219]**

School Sailing Matters (Windermere, GBR) **[56931]**

School Science (New Delhi, DH, IND) **[45647]**

School Science Review (Hatfield, GBR) **[53541]**

The School Times International (Fredensborg, DEN) **[43687]**

Schritte ins Offene (Zurich, SWI) **[51277]**

Schrot & Korn (Aschaffenburg, GER) **[44139]**

Schweineproduktion in Deutschland (Munich, GER) *Unable to locate*

Schweinzucht und Schweinemast (Munich, GER) *Unable to locate*

Schweissen & Schneiden (Dusseldorf, GER) **[44334]**

Schweiz Juristen-Zeitung/Revue Suisse de Jurisprudence (Zurich, SWI) *Unable to locate*

Schweizer Braunvieh (Zug, SWI) *Unable to locate*

Schweizer Illustrierte (Zurich, SWI) **[51278]**

Schweizer Illustrierte Style (Zurich, SWI) **[51279]**

Schweizer Jager (Einsiedeln, SWI) **[51086]**

Schweizer Landtechnik/Technique Agricole (Riniken, SWI) *Unable to locate*

Schweizer Lehrerinnen- und Lehrer-Zeitung (Zurich, SWI) **[51280]**

Schweizer Monatshefte fur Politik, Wirtschaft und Kultur (Zurich, SWI) **[51281]**

Schweizer Musikzeitung (Zurich, SWI) **[51282]**

Schweizer Waffen-Magazin (Solothurn, SWI) **[51232]**

Schweizerische Arbeitgeber (Zurich, SWI) *Unable to locate*

Schweizerische Arztezeitung/Bulletin des Medecins Suisses (Muttenz, SWI) **[51214]**

Schweizerische Bienen-Zeitung (Spiez, SWI) *Unable to locate*

Schweizerische Katholische Wochenzeitung (Baden, SWI) *Unable to locate*

Schweizerische Kirchenzeitung (Lucerne, SWI) **[51210]**

Schweizerische Medizinische Wochenschrift **[51215]***

Sci Fondo (Milan, ITA) *Unable to locate*

Scienca Revuo (Niederglatt, SWI) *Unable to locate*

Science Asia (Bangkok, THA) **[51434]**

Science in China Series A (Beijing, CHN) **[43215]**

Science in China Series B (Beijing, CHN) **[43216]**

Science in China Series C (Beijing, CHN) **[43217]**

Science in China Series D (Beijing, CHN) **[43218]**

Science in China Series E (Beijing, CHN) **[43219]**

Science in China Series F (Beijing, CHN) **[43220]**

Science in China Series G (Beijing, CHN) **[43221]**

Science and Culture (Calcutta, WB, IND) *Unable to locate*

Science as Culture (Abingdon, GBR) **[52054]**

Science & Education (Dordrecht, NLD) **[48559]**

Science & Education Information (Beijing, CHN) *Unable to locate*

Science Education International (Hatfield, GBR) **[53542]**

Science and Engineering (Calcutta, WB, IND) *Unable to locate*

Science and Engineering of Composite Materials (Tel Aviv, ISR) **[46112]**

Science and Engineering Review of Doshisha University (Kyoto, JPN) *Unable to locate*

Science a GoGo (Scarborough, WA, AUS) **[42354]**

Science and Industry (Osaka, JPN) *Unable to locate*

Science International (Lahore, PAK) *Unable to locate*

Science Journal (Shanghai, CHN) **[43497]**

Science Journal of the Asiatic Society of Bangladesh (Dhaka, BGD) *Unable to locate*

Science & Justice (Kidlington, GBR) **[53706]**

Science in Parliament (New Delhi, DH, IND) *Unable to locate*

Science et changements planetaires/Secheresse (Montrouge, FRA) **[44007]**

Science and the Public Affairs **[55066]***

Science and Public Policy (Guildford, GBR) *Unable to locate*

Science Review (Horsham, GBR) **[53601]**

Science of Sintering (Belgrade, SER) **[50083]**

Science Teacher (New Delhi, DH, IND) *Unable to locate*

Science and Technology (Vilnius, LIT) *Unable to locate*

Science and Technology of Advanced Materials (Bristol, GBR) **[52729]**

Science, Technology & Society (New Delhi, DH, IND) **[45648]**

Sciences (Tokyo, JPN) *Unable to locate*

Sciences & Nature (Abidjan, COT) **[43557]**

Sciences Sociales et Sante (Villejuif, FRA) **[44125]**

Scientia Horticulturae (Pietermaritzburg, SAF) **[50569]**

Scientia Iranica (Tehran, IRN) **[45913]**

Scientia Marina (Barcelona, SPA) **[50697]**

Scientia Militaria (Saldanha, SAF) **[50624]**

Scientific Horticulture (Jodhpur, RJ, IND) *Unable to locate*

Scientific Journal (Apeldoorn, NLD) *Unable to locate*

Scientific Journal of Orienteering (Helsinki, FIN) **[43856]**

Scientific Medical Journal (Cairo, EGY) **[43765]**

Scientific Opinion (Jallundur, PJ, IND) *Unable to locate*

Scientific Pictorial (Shanghai, CHN) **[43498]**

Scientific Research & Essays (Lagos, LG, NGA) **[49143]**

Scientific and Technical Review (Paris, FRA) **[44083]**

The Scientific World Journal (Kirkkonummi, FIN) **[43874]**

Scientometrics (Budapest, HUN) **[44869]**

SciFiNow (Bournemouth, GBR) **[52424]**

SCIMA (New Delhi, DH, IND) *Unable to locate*

SCN News (Geneva, SWI) **[51160]**

Scoala Romaneasca (Bucharest, ROM) *Unable to locate*

Scootering (Horncastle, GBR) **[53593]**

Scope **[42766]***

Scope (York, GBR) **[56998]**

Scopolia (Ljubljana, SVA) **[50341]**

Scopus (Nairobi, KEN) **[47196]**

Scotland Magazine (Norwich, GBR) **[55741]**

Scotland's Natural Heritage (Inverness, GBR) **[53647]**

Scotland's New Homebuyer (Edinburgh, GBR) **[53310]**

The Scots Law Times (Edinburgh, GBR) **[53311]**

The Scots Magazine (Dundee, GBR) **[53218]**

Scottish Archaeological Journal (Edinburgh, GBR) **[53312]**

The Scottish Beekeeper (Brookfield, GBR) **[52749]**

Scottish Club Golfer (Glasgow, GBR) **[53446]**

Scottish Educational Journal (Edinburgh, GBR) **[53313]**

Scottish Field (Edinburgh, GBR) **[53314]**

Scottish Forestry (Newton Stewart, GBR) **[55699]**

Scottish Genealogist (Edinburgh, GBR) **[53315]**

Scottish Geographical Journal (Scotland, GBR) **[56466]**

Scottish Geographical Magazine **[56466]***

scottish grocer (Glasgow, GBR) **[53447]**

Scottish Historical Review (Edinburgh, GBR) **[53316]**

Scottish Home and Country (Edinburgh, GBR) **[53317]**

Scottish Hosteller (Glasgow, GBR) **[53448]**

Scottish Journal of Theology (Cambridge, GBR) **[52892]**

Scottish Law Gazette (Stirling, GBR) *Unable to locate*

Scottish Law & Practice Quarterly (London, GBR) *Ceased*

Scottish Libraries **[53424]***

Scottish Local Retailer (Glasgow, GBR) **[53449]**

Scottish Medical Journal (Dundee, GBR) *Unable to locate*

Scottish Planning and Environmental Law (Glasgow, GBR) **[53450]**

Numbers cited in bold after listings are entry numbers rather than page numbers.

Scottish Planning Law & Practice [53450]*

The Scottish Review (Kilmarnock, GBR) [53709]

Scout D'Europa (Rome, ITA) Unable to locate

Scouting Magazine (London, GBR) [55220]

Scouts de Argentina (Buenos Aires, ARG) Unable to locate

Scrapbook Creations (North Ryde, NW, AUS) [42196]

Scrapbook Magic (West Sussex, GBR) [56903]

Screen (New Delhi, DH, IND) [45649]

Screen and Marknaden (Solna, SWE) Unable to locate

Screen Process & Digital Imaging (Kent, GBR) [53680]

Screen World (Mumbai, MH, IND) [45437]

Screen World Publication [45437]*

Screening (Darmstadt, GER) [44312]

Scrip Magazine (London, GBR) [55221]

Script-ed (Edinburgh, GBR) [53318]

Scriptura (Centurion, SAF) [50449]

SCROLL (Glasgow, GBR) [53451]

SCTV 1 - Channel 21 (Chengdu, SI, CHN) [43250]

SCTV 1 - Channel 2 (Chengdu, SI, CHN) [43249]

SCTV 2 - Channel 10 (Chengdu, SI, CHN) [43251]

Scuba World Magazine (Liverpool, GBR) Unable to locate

The Sculpture Journal (London, GBR) [55222]

Sculpture Magazine (Accra, GHA) Unable to locate

Scuola D'ogg (Rome, ITA) Unable to locate

SDI Scandinavian Dairy Information (Einsiedeln, SWI) Unable to locate

The Sea (London, GBR) [55223]

Sea-FM - 99.5 (Cairns, QL, AUS) [41688]

Sea-FM - 99.7 (Scottsdale, TA, AUS) [42355]

Sea-FM - 90.9 (Southport, QL, AUS) [42383]

SEA Monthly News Circular (Mumbai, MH, IND) [45438]

Sea 99.5-FM (Cairns, QL, AUS) Unable to locate

Sea and Sky (Kobe, JPN) Unable to locate

Sea Sprite (Tokyo, JPN) Unable to locate

Seafarer (London, GBR) [55224]

Seafood Export Journal (Cochin, KE, IND) Unable to locate

Seagull Theatre Quarterly (Kolkata, WB, IND) [45304]

Seahorse (Lymington, GBR) [55513]

SEAISI Quarterly Journal (Selangor, MYS) Unable to locate

Seamen's Journal [42539]*

SEAMEO Forum [51435]*

SEAMEO Journal of Southeast Asian Education (Bangkok, THA) [51435]

SEAMEO Regional Language Centre Guidelines (Singapore, SGP) [50250]

Seaside-FM - 105.3 (Withernsea, GBR) [56936]

Seatrade Business Review [53048]*

Seatrade Magazine (Colchester, GBR) [53048]

Seaways (London, GBR) [55225]

The Second Channel [47657]*

Secular Democracy (New Delhi, DH, IND) Unable to locate

Secularist (Pune, MH, IND) Unable to locate

Secure Times (Buckhurst Hill, GBR) [52753]

Securities Market Journal (Grahamstown, SAF) [50512]

Security Controls (New Delhi, DH, IND) Unable to locate

Security Dialogue (London, GBR) [55226]

Security Spokesman (Worcester, GBR) Unable to locate

Sedimentary Geology (Delft, NLD) [48314]

Sedimentology (Southampton, GBR) [56578]

SEDME (Hyderabad, AP, IND) Unable to locate

Sedmoye Nebo (Pskov, RUS) Unable to locate

Sedmoye Nebo (Pskov, RUS) Unable to locate

See Hear! [55033]*

See India (New Delhi, DH, IND) Unable to locate

Seed Research (New Delhi, DH, IND) Unable to locate

Seed Science Research (Cambridge, GBR) [52893]

Seed Science and Technology (Bassersdorf, SWI) [51067]

Seeing (Shoreham-By-Sea, GBR) Ceased

Seeing and Perceiving (Leiden, NLD) [48723]

SEIL Magasinet (Nesbru, NOR) [49194]

Seishin Studies (Tokyo, JPN) Unable to locate

Sekaito Jinko (Tokyo, JPN) Unable to locate

Selbstpsychologie (Frankfurt am Main, GER) [44369]

Selby Times (Selby, GBR) [56468]

Selecciones Avicolas (Arenys de Mar, SPA) Unable to locate

Selecciones de Teologia (Barcelona, SPA) Unable to locate

Select (London, GBR) Ceased

Selections from Educational Records of the Government of India (New Delhi, DH, IND) Unable to locate

SelfBuild (Saintfield, GBR) [56449]

Selkirk Weekend Advertiser (Selkirk, GBR) [56469]

Sell-Side Technology (London, GBR) [55227]

Selling Long Haul (Croydon, GBR) [53132]

Selling Short Breaks (Croydon, GBR) [53133]

Semiconductor Science and Technology (London, GBR) [55228]

Seminar Reporteur (New Delhi, DH, IND) Unable to locate

Seminars in Cancer Biology (Stockholm, SWE) [51036]

Seminars in Cardiology (Kaunas, LIT) [47466]

Seminars in Cell & Developmental Biology (Amsterdam, NLD) [48230]

Seminars in Fetal & Neonatal Medicine (Leeds, GBR) [53774]

Semiotica (Berlin, GER) [44230]

SEN-AM - 1116 (Richmond, VI, AUS) [42309]

Senckenbergiana biologica (Stuttgart, GER) [44678]

Sensing and Imaging (Dordrecht, NLD) [48560]

Sensor Review (Bradford, GBR) [52543]

Sensors (Chester, GBR) Unable to locate

Sensors and Actuators A (Delft, NLD) [48315]

Sensors and Actuators B (Nagasaki, JPN) [46546]

Sensors and Materials (Tokyo, JPN) [47036]

A Sentinela Anunciando o Reino de Jeova (Tatui, SP, BRZ) Unable to locate

Seoul Journal of Economics (Seoul, KOR) [47286]

Seoul Journal of Korean Studies (Seoul, KOR) Unable to locate

Seoul National University Journal of Agricultural Sciences (Suwon, KOR) Unable to locate

Sepa Como Instalar (Buenos Aires, ARG) Unable to locate

Septentrion (Rekkem, BEL) [42910]

Ser Padres (Madrid, SPA) [50802]

Ser Padres Bebe (Madrid, SPA) [50803]

Ser Padres Hoy (Madrid, SPA) [50804]

Serdica Mathematical Journal (Sofia, BUL) [43107]

Serebryanyy Dozhd (Moscow, RUS) Unable to locate

Serebryanyy Dozhd - Astrakhan (Astrakhan, RUS) Unable to locate

Serebryanyy Dozhd - Bryansk (Bryansk, RUS) Unable to locate

Serebryanyy Dozhd - Nizhniy Novgorod (Nizhniy Novgorod, RUS) Unable to locate

Serebryanyy Dozhd - Nizhniy Novgorod (Nizhniy Novgorod, RUS) Unable to locate

Serebryanyy Dozhd - Novotroitsk (Novotroitsk, RUS) Unable to locate

Serebryanyy Dozhd - Obninsk (Moscow, RUS) Unable to locate

Serebryanyy Dozhd - Pyatigorsk (Moscow, RUS) Unable to locate

Serebryanyy Dozhd (Radio Pilgrim) (Voronezh, RUS) Unable to locate

Serebryanyy Dozhd - Samara (Samara, RUS) Unable to locate

Serebryanyy Dozhd - Ufa (Ufa, RUS) Unable to locate

Serebryanyy Dozhd - Voronezh (Moscow, RUS) Unable to locate

Sericologia (Lyon, FRA) [43970]

Series in English Language and Literature (New Delhi, DH, IND) Unable to locate

Series in Indian Studies in Theoretical and Applied Linguistics (New Delhi, DH, IND) Unable to locate

Series in Semiotics and Linguistics (New Delhi, DH, IND) Unable to locate

Servamus (Pretoria, SAF) [50600]

Service (Cape Town, SAF) [50410]

The Service Industries Journal (Abingdon, GBR) [52055]

Services Law Cases (New Delhi, DH, IND) Unable to locate

SESI Journal [45650]*

SESI Journal (New Delhi, DH, IND) [45650]

Session Cases-Cases Decided in the Courts of Session & Others (Edinburgh, GBR) Unable to locate

SET Journal (Bangkok, THA) Unable to locate

Setsunan University Review of Humanities and Social Sciences (Osaka, JPN) Unable to locate

Seura (Kuvalehdet, FIN) [43894]

Seva Bharati (Calcutta, WB, IND) Unable to locate

Sevartham (Ranchi, BH, IND) Unable to locate

Seven-FM - 107 (Ballymena, GBR) [52161]

780-AM - 780 (Asuncion, PAR) [49408]

702-AM - 702 (Rivonia, SAF) [50613]

007 Spy Cards (Ringwood, GBR) [56397]

7AD-AM - 900 (Launceston, TA, AUS) [42000]

7BU-AM - 558 (Burnie, TA, AUS) [41674]

7CAE-FM - 96.1 MHz (Bellerive, TA, AUS) [41591]

7HO-FM - 101.7 (Hobart, TA, AUS) [41960]

7LA-AM - 1098 (Launceston, TA, AUS) [42001]

7LTN-FM - 103.7 (Launceston, TA, AUS) [42002]

7RPH-AM - 864 (Hobart, TA, AUS) [41961]

7TAS-FM - 97.7 (Nubeena, TA, AUS) [42217]

Seventeen Philippines (Mandaluyong City, PHL) [49540]

The Seventeenth Century (Durham, GBR) [53231]

Seventeenth-Century French Studies (London, GBR) [55229]

Seventh Wave (Marlow, GBR) [55601]

7THE-FM - 96.1 (Hobart, TA, AUS) [41962]

7ZR-AM - 936 (Hobart, TA, AUS) [41963]

Severn-FM - 107.1 (Telford, GBR) [56740]

Severn-FM - 106.5 (Telford, GBR) [56739]

Severn Sound-FM [53473]*

Severn Sound-FM - 102.4 (Gloucester, GBR) [53474]

Sew-Journal (Luxembourg, LUX) [47493]

Sewing World (West Sussex, GBR) Unable to locate

Sex Education (London, GBR) [55230]

Sexual Addiction & Compulsivity (Abingdon, GBR) [52056]

Sexual Health (Melbourne, VI, AUS) [42085]

Sexualities (Colchester, GBR) [53049]

Sexually Transmitted Infections (London, GBR) [55231]

Seychelles Nation (Victoria, SYC) [50095]

SFF Filatelisten/Svensk Filatelistisk Tidskrift (Skillingaryd, SWE) [50998]

SFS Tiedotus (Helsinki, FIN) Unable to locate

SG News (Singapore, SGP) Unable to locate

SG Susswarenhandel (Munich, GER) [44581]

SGB Golf (Kent, GBR) [53681]

Shaanxi People's Broadcasting Station (Xi'an, SH, CHN) Unable to locate

Shaanxi People's Broadcasting Station (Xi'an, SH, CHN) Unable to locate

Shaanxi People's Broadcasting Station (Xi'an, SH, CHN) Unable to locate

Shaanxi People's Broadcasting Station (Xi'an, SH, CHN) Unable to locate

Numbers cited in bold after listings are entry numbers rather than page numbers.

Shaanxi People's Broadcasting Station (Xi'an, SH, CHN) *Unable to locate*

Shaanxi People's Broadcasting Station (Xi'an, SX, CHN) *Unable to locate*

Shaanxi People's Broadcasting Station (Xi'an, SX, CHN) *Unable to locate*

Shaanxi TV 1 (Xi'an, SH, CHN) *Unable to locate*

Shaanxi TV 3 (Xi'an, SH, CHN) *Unable to locate*

Shaanxi TV 2 (Xi'an, SH, CHN) *Unable to locate*

Shahe People's Broadcasting Station (Shahe, HB, CHN) *Unable to locate*

Shahid Chamran University Educational Journal (Ahwaz, IRN) *Unable to locate*

Shakespeare (Abingdon, GBR) **[52057]**

Shakespeare in Southern Africa (Grahamstown, SAF) **[50513]**

Shakespeare Studies (Tokyo, JPN) **[47037]**

Shakespeare Survey (Cambridge, GBR) **[52894]**

The Shakespearean International Yearbook (Surrey, GBR) **[56675]**

Shakthi FM - 105.1 MHz (Gammaduwa, SRI) **[50895]**

Shalom (Tampere, FIN) *Unable to locate*

Shalom (Rome, ITA) **[46241]**

Shalom (Farnsfield, GBR) **[53382]**

Shandong People's Broadcasting Station (Jinan, SD, CHN) *Unable to locate*

Shandong People's Broadcasting Station (Jinan, SD, CHN) *Unable to locate*

Shandong People's Broadcasting Station (Jinan, SD, CHN) *Unable to locate*

Shandong People's Broadcasting Station (Jinan, SD, CHN) *Unable to locate*

Shandong People's Broadcasting Station (Jinan, SD, CHN) *Unable to locate*

Shandong People's Broadcasting Station (Jinan, SD, CHN) *Unable to locate*

Shandong People's Broadcasting Station (Jinan, SD, CHN) *Unable to locate*

Shandong People's Broadcasting Station, SD, CHN) *Unable to locate*

Shandong Television - Channel 3 (Jinan, SD, CHN) **[43449]**

Shandong Television - Channel 1 (Jinan, SD, CHN) **[43450]**

Shandong Television - Channel 2 (Jinan, SD, CHN) **[43448]**

Shanghai Dongfang People's Broadcasting Station (Shanghai, SH, CHN) *Unable to locate*

Shanghai People's Broadcasting Station (Shanghai, CHN) *Unable to locate*

Shanghai People's Broadcasting Station (Shanghai, CHN) *Unable to locate*

Shanghai People's Broadcasting Station (Shanghai, CHN) *Unable to locate*

Shanghai People's Broadcasting Station (Shanghai, CHN) *Unable to locate*

Shanghai People's Broadcasting Station (Shanghai, SH, CHN) *Unable to locate*

Shanghai People's Broadcasting Station (Shanghai, SH, CHN) *Unable to locate*

Shanghai People's Broadcasting Station (Shanghai, SH, CHN) *Unable to locate*

Shanghai People's Broadcasting Station (Shanghai, SH, CHN) *Unable to locate*

Shanghai People's Broadcasting Station (Shanghai, SH, CHN) *Unable to locate*

Shanghai People's Broadcasting Station (Shanghai, SH, CHN) *Unable to locate*

Shanghai People's Broadcasting Station (Shanghai, SH, CHN) *Unable to locate*

Shanghai People's Broadcasting Station (Shanghai, SH, CHN) *Unable to locate*

Shanghai People's Broadcasting Station (Shanghai, SH, CHN) *Unable to locate*

Shanghai Pictorial (Shanghai, CHN) **[43499]**

Shanghai Residence (Shanghai, CHN) **[43500]**

Shanghai Style (Shanghai, CHN) **[43501]**

Shanghai Tatler (Shanghai, CHN) **[43502]**

Shanghai Television - Channel 14 (Shanghai, CHN) **[43514]**

Shanghai Television - Channel 8 (Shanghai, CHN) **[43513]**

Shanghai Today (Shanghai, CHN) **[43503]**

Shanghai Weekly (Shanghai, CHN) **[43504]**

Shanghai's Best Restaurants (Shanghai, CHN) **[43505]**

Shangqiu People's Broadcasting Station (Shangqiu, HN, CHN) *Unable to locate*

Shannan People's Broadcasting Station (Nedong, XZ, CHN) *Unable to locate*

Shannonside-FM - 104.1 (Longford, LO, IRL) **[46035]**

Shannonside Northern Sound-FM - 94.8 (Monaghan, MO, IRL) **[46039]**

Shantou People's Broadcasting Station (Shantou, GD, CHN) *Unable to locate*

Shantou People's Broadcasting Station (Shantou, GD, CHN) *Unable to locate*

Shantou People's Broadcasting Station (Shantou, GD, CHN) *Unable to locate*

Shantou People's Broadcasting Station (Shantou, GD, CHN) *Unable to locate*

Shanwei People's Broadcasting Station (Shanwei, GD, CHN) *Unable to locate*

Shanxi Changcheng People's Broadcasting Station (Taiyuan, SX, CHN) *Unable to locate*

Shanxi People's Broadcasting Station (Taiyuan, SX, CHN) *Unable to locate*

Shanxi People's Broadcasting Station (Taiyuan, SX, CHN) *Unable to locate*

Shanxi People's Broadcasting Station (Taiyuan, SX, CHN) *Unable to locate*

Shanxi People's Broadcasting Station (Taiyuan, SX, CHN) *Unable to locate*

Shanxi People's Broadcasting Station (Taiyuan, SX, CHN) *Unable to locate*

Shanxi People's Broadcasting Station (Taiyuan, SX, CHN) *Unable to locate*

Shanxi People's Broadcasting Station (Taiyuan, SX, CHN) *Unable to locate*

Shanxi Television (Taiyuan, SX, CHN) *Unable to locate*

Shanxi Television (Taiyuan, SX, CHN) *Unable to locate*

Shaoguan People's Broadcasting Station (Shaoguan, GD, CHN) *Unable to locate*

Shaoguan People's Broadcasting Station (Shaoguan, GD, CHN) *Unable to locate*

Shaoguan People's Broadcasting Station (Shaoguan, GD, CHN) *Unable to locate*

Shaoxing FM Broadcasting Station (Shaoxing, ZH, CHN) *Unable to locate*

Shaoxing People's Broadcasting Station (Shaoxing, ZH, CHN) *Unable to locate*

Shaoyang People's Broadcasting Station (Shaoyang, HA, CHN) *Unable to locate*

Shape Engineering (Sutton, GBR) *Unable to locate*

SHARES (London, GBR) **[55232]**

Sharjah TV - Channel 22 (Sharjah, UAE) **[51674]**

Sharjah TV - Channel 28 (Sharjah, UAE) **[51672]**

Sharjah TV - Channel 54 (Sharjah, UAE) **[51673]**

Sharjah TV - Channel 57 (Sharjah, UAE) **[51671]**

Sharkara (Kanpur, UP, IND) *Unable to locate*

The Sharp End (London, GBR) *Unable to locate*

The Shavian (Bromley, GBR) *Unable to locate*

She (Auckland, NZL) *Unable to locate*

SHE Magazine (Karachi, PAK) *Unable to locate*

The Sheep Farmer (Malvern, GBR) **[55540]**

Sheep's Clothing **[56952]***

Shengtu Broadcasting Co. (Nantou, TWN) *Unable to locate*

Shenyang People's Broadcasting Station (Shenyang, LI, CHN) *Unable to locate*

Shenyang People's Broadcasting Station (Shenyang, LI, CHN) *Unable to locate*

Shenyang People's Broadcasting Station (Shenyang, LI, CHN) *Unable to locate*

Shenyang People's Broadcasting Station (Shenyang, LI, CHN) *Unable to locate*

Shenyang People's Broadcasting Station (Shenyang, LI, CHN) *Unable to locate*

Shenzhen People's Broadcasting Station (Shenzhen, GD, CHN) *Unable to locate*

Shenzhen People's Broadcasting Station (Shenzhen, GD, CHN) *Unable to locate*

Shenzhen People's Broadcasting Station (Shenzhen, GD, CHN) *Unable to locate*

Shenzhen People's Broadcasting Station (Shenzhen, GD, CHN) *Unable to locate*

Shetland Fishing News (Lerwick, GBR) **[53842]**

Shields Gazette (South Shields, GBR) **[56566]**

Shihezi People's Broadcasting Station (Shihezi, XU, CHN) *Unable to locate*

Shihezi People's Broadcasting Station (Shihezi, XU, CHN) *Unable to locate*

Shijiazhuang People's Broadcasting Station (Handan, HB, CHN) *Unable to locate*

Shijiazhuang People's Broadcasting Station (Shijiazhuang, HB, CHN) *Unable to locate*

Shijiazhuang People's Broadcasting Station (Shijiazhuang, HB, CHN) *Unable to locate*

Shijiazhuang People's Broadcasting Station (Shijiazhuang, HB, CHN) *Unable to locate*

Shikoku Hoso - 1269 KHz (Ikeda, JPN) **[46396]**

The Shillong Times (Shillong, MG, IND) **[45729]**

Shimane Journal of Medical Science (Shimane, JPN) *Unable to locate*

Shin Min Daily News (Singapore, SGP) **[50251]**

Shindo Geppo (Tokyo, JPN) *Unable to locate*

Ship & Boat International (London, GBR) **[55233]**

Ship Repair & Conversion Technology (London, GBR) **[55234]**

Shipbroker (London, GBR) *Unable to locate*

Shipbuilding Information (Seoul, KOR) *Unable to locate*

Shipbuilding Statistics (Seoul, KOR) *Unable to locate*

Shipping Information Services (Cochin, KE, IND) *Unable to locate*

Shipping and Marine Industries Journal (Mumbai, MH, IND) *Unable to locate*

Shipping and Trade News (Tokyo, JPN) *Unable to locate*

Shipping & Trade News (Tokyo, JPN) *Unable to locate*

Ships Monthly (Burton-on-Trent, GBR) **[52771]**

Ships and Offshore Structures (Cambridge, GBR) **[52895]**

Shipyard Review (Visakhapatnam, AP, IND) *Unable to locate*

Shipyards Orders Weekly Report (Redhill, GBR) *Ceased*

Shipyear (Cape Town, SAF) **[50411]**

Shishou People's Broadcasting Station (Shishou, HU, CHN) *Unable to locate*

Shiyan People's Broadcasting Station (Shiyan, HU, CHN) *Unable to locate*

Shock-FM - 105.3 (Guatemala City, GTM) **[44789]**

Shock and Vibration (Amsterdam, NLD) **[48231]**

Shoe Service (Kettering, GBR) *Unable to locate*

Shoe World (York, GBR) **[56999]**

Shoestyle (Leeds, GBR) *Unable to locate*

Shooting Sports (Colchester, GBR) **[53050]**

Shop (Hong Kong, CHN) **[43382]**

Shopping Centre (Crawley, GBR) **[53113]**

Numbers cited in bold after listings are entry numbers rather than page numbers.

Shopping Centre Ireland (Crawley, GBR) [53114]

Shopping Centre Progress (London, GBR) Unable to locate

The Shopsteward (Johannesburg, SAF) [50533]

The Shore News (Penrose, NZL) Unable to locate

Shoreham Herald (Worthing, GBR) [56976]

Shout Magazine (London, GBR) [55235]

Show Daily (Kuala Lumpur, MYS) [47635]

Show & Fashion Footwear News (Tonbridge, GBR) Ceased

Show Press (Barcelona, SPA) [50698]

Show Times (Dublin, DU, IRL) [45998]

Showbiz (Kathmandu, NPL) Unable to locate

Showcase (Singapore, SGP) Unable to locate

Shram Patrika (New Delhi, DH, IND) Unable to locate

Shree Hari Katha (New Delhi, DH, IND) Unable to locate

Shrek's Quests (London, GBR) [55236]

Shreye (New Delhi, DH, IND) Unable to locate

Shropshire Life (Cheltenham, GBR) [52976]

Shuangyashan People's Broadcasting Station (Shuangyashan, HL, CHN) Unable to locate

Shukan Shonen Magazine (Tokyo, JPN) [47038]

Shukan ST (Tokyo, JPN) [47039]

Shuttle Chatter (Centurion, SAF) Unable to locate

Shuu'n Tanmawieyeh - Development Affaires (East Jerusalem, ISR) Unable to locate

S.I.A. Journal (SIAJ) [50253]*

SIAM Journal on Optimization (Oxford, GBR) [56202]

SIAM Journal on Scientific Computing (Erlangen, GER) [44341]

SIAM Journal on Scientific and Statistical Computing [44341]*

Siang Computer AD - Phuket (Bangkok, THA) Unable to locate

Siang Computer AD - Rio Et (Bangkok, THA) Unable to locate

Siang Computer AD - Udon Thali (Bangkok, THA) Unable to locate

The Siasat Daily (Hyderabad, AP, IND) [45182]

SIBC-FM - 102.2 (Lerwick, GBR) [53844]

SIBC-FM - 96.2 (Lerwick, GBR) [53843]

Siberian Journal of Ecology (Novosibirsk, RUS) [50013]

Siberian Journal of Numerical Mathematics (Novosibirsk, RUS) [50014]

SIC Info (Yaounde, CMR) Unable to locate

SIC Seguridad en Informatica y Comunicaciones (Madrid, SPA) [50805]

Sicherheit fur Haus & Hof [44569]*

Sicherheitsbeauftragter (Leinfelden-Echterdingen, GER) [44529]

Sicherheitsingenieur (Leinfelden-Echterdingen, GER) [44530]

Sichuan People's Broadcasting Station (Chengdu, SI, CHN) Unable to locate

Sichuan People's Broadcasting Station (Chengdu, SI, CHN) Unable to locate

Sichuan People's Broadcasting Station (Chengdu, SI, CHN) Unable to locate

Sichuan People's Broadcasting Station (Chengdu, SI, CHN) Unable to locate

Sichuan People's Broadcasting Station (Chengdu, SI, CHN) Unable to locate

Sichuan People's Broadcasting Station (Chengdu, SI, CHN) Unable to locate

Sichuan People's Broadcasting Station (Chengdu, SI, CHN) Unable to locate

Sichuan People's Broadcasting Station (Chengdu, SI, CHN) Unable to locate

Sichuan People's Broadcasting Station 1 (Chengdu, SI, CHN) Unable to locate

Sichuan People's Broadcasting Station 1 (Chengdu, SI, CHN) Unable to locate

Sicilia Tempo (Palermo, ITA) Unable to locate

Sicurezza (Cinisello Balsamo, ITA) [46135]

Sidewalk (London, GBR) [55237]

SIESC Actuel (Essen, GER) Unable to locate

Siete Dias Medicos (Barcelona, SPA) [50699]

Sightline (London, GBR) [55238]

Siglo Cero (Madrid, SPA) Unable to locate

Sign Directions (Peterborough, GBR) [56261]

Sign Language and Linguistics (Amsterdam, NLD) [48232]

Sign Language Translator & Interpreter (Manchester, GBR) [55577]

Signal 1-FM - 102.6 (Stoke-on-Trent, GBR) [56632]

Signal Processing (Stockholm, SWE) [51037]

Signal 2-AM - 1170 (Stoke-on-Trent, GBR) [56633]

Signature (Singapore, SGP) Unable to locate

Signature Cocktails (Pyrmont, NW, AUS) [42288]

Significance (Oxford, GBR) [56203]

Significant Ships (London, GBR) [55239]

Sikania (Palermo, ITA) [46208]

Sikh Formations (Abingdon, GBR) [52058]

Siksha - O - Sahitya (Calcutta, WB, IND) Unable to locate

Silk Export Bulletin (Bangalore, KA, IND) Unable to locate

Silk-FM - 106.9 (Macclesfield, GBR) [55521]

Silk in India [44962]*

Silliman Journal (Dumaguete City, PHL) Unable to locate

Silver Kris (Singapore, SGP) Unable to locate

SIM: (Small Industries Magazine) (New Delhi, DH, IND) Unable to locate

Simbirskiy Sputnik (Ulyanovsk, RUS) Unable to locate

Simbirskiy Sputnik (Ulyanovsk, RUS) Unable to locate

Similia (Seddon West, VI, AUS) [42356]

Simon Star (London, GBR) [55240]

Simply Her (Singapore, SGP) [50252]

Sin Limites (Quito, ECU) Unable to locate

Sinar-FM - 96.7 (Kuala Lumpur, MYS) [47659]

Sinar-FM - 93.8 (Kuala Lumpur, MYS) [47660]

Sinar-FM - 96.9 (Kuala Lumpur, MYS) [47661]

Sinatra International (Blackburn, VI, AUS) Unable to locate

Sind Journal of Political Science and Modern History (Jamshoro, PAK) Unable to locate

Sindh Quarterly (Karachi, PAK) Unable to locate

SINET (Addis Ababa, ETH) [43803]

Sing Tao Daily (London, GBR) Unable to locate

Singapore Academy of Law Journal (Singapore City, SGP) [50314]

Singapore Accountant (Singapore, SGP) Ceased

Singapore Architect (Singapore, SGP) [50253]

Singapore Economic Review (Singapore, SGP) [50254]

The Singapore Family Physician (Singapore, SGP) [50255]

Singapore Journal of Legal Studies (Singapore, SGP) [50256]

Singapore Journal of Physics (Singapore, SGP) [50257]

Singapore Journal of Primary Industries (Singapore, SGP) Unable to locate

Singapore Journal of Tropical Geography (Oxford, GBR) [56204]

Singapore Law Review (Singapore, SGP) [50258]

Singapore Management Review (Singapore, SGP) [50259]

The Singapore Manufacturer (Singapore, SGP) Unable to locate

Singapore Medical Journal (Singapore, SGP) [50260]

Singapore National Academy of Science Journal (Singapore, SGP) [50261]

Singapore Paediatric Journal (Singapore, SGP) Unable to locate

Singapore Source Book for Architects & Designers (Singapore, SGP) Unable to locate

Singapore Tatler (Singapore, SGP) [50262]

Singapore Tatler Homes (Singapore, SGP) [50263]

Singapore Tatler Society (Singapore, SGP) [50264]

Singapore Tatler Weddings (Singapore, SGP) [50265]

Singapore Visitor (Singapore, SGP) [50266]

Singapore's Best Restaurants (Singapore, SGP) [50267]

Singing (Burton-on-Trent, GBR) [52772]

Sinorama Magazine (Taipei, TWN) Unable to locate

Sintesis (Madrid, SPA) [50806]

Sipario (Milan, ITA) [46194]

Siping People's Broadcasting Station (Siping, JI, CHN) Unable to locate

Sirasa FM - 106.5 MHz (Colombo, SRI) [50877]

Sirasa FM - 106.2 MHz (Kandy, SRI) [50910]

Sirasa FM (Pannipitiya, SRI) Unable to locate

Sirasa-FM - 88.8 (Pannipitiya, SRI) [50924]

Sirasa-FM - 101.7 (Pannipitiya, SRI) [50925]

Sirasa FM - 88.9 MHz (Pannipitiya, SRI) [50923]

Sistema (Madrid, SPA) [50807]

Sistemi di Telecomunicazioni (Milan, ITA) Unable to locate

Sisters (Harare, ZWE) Ceased

SISTERS (Sisterhood and International Solidarity to End Racism and Sexism) (North Tyneside, GBR) [55705]

Six-FM - 107.2 (Cookstown, GBR) [53061]

Six-FM - 106 (Cookstown, GBR) [53062]

639ABC-AM - 639 (Port Pirie, SA, AUS) [42266]

6ABC-FM Central Agricultural - 98.9 (Ultimo, NW, AUS) [42658]

6CRA-FM - 100.9 (Albany, WA, AUS) [41526]

6DBY-FM - 97.9 (Derby, WA, AUS) [41839]

6EBA-FM - 95.3 Mhz (North Perth, WA, AUS) [42159]

6IX-AM - 1080 (East Perth, WA, AUS) [41847]

6IX-FM - 105.7 (Perth, WA, AUS) [42254]

6KCR-FM - 102.5 (Kalamunda, WA, AUS) [41980]

6MD-AM - 1098 (Merredin, WA, AUS) [42102]

6MKA-FM - 98.3 (Meekatharra, WA, AUS) [42043]

6PR-AM - 882 (East Perth, WA, AUS) [41848]

6TR Petersburg (St. Petersburg, RUS) Unable to locate

6WB-AM - 1071 (Katanning, WA, AUS) [41982]

6WR-AM - 693 (Kununurra, WA, AUS) [41997]

Sjobefal (Stockholm, SWE) Unable to locate

Sjukgymnasten (Stockholm, SWE) [51038]

SKA-TV - Channel 31 (Carlton South, VI, AUS) [41729]

Skamania County Pioneer (Sheffield, GBR) [56514]

Skegness Standard (Skegness, GBR) [56552]

The Skeptic (Roseville, NW, AUS) [42320]

Skeptics India (New Delhi, DH, IND) Unable to locate

Skeptiker (Rossdorf, GER) [44645]

Skerries News (Skerries, DU, IRL) Unable to locate

Ski [49189]*

Ski (Planegg, GER) Unable to locate

Ski (The Hague, NLD) Unable to locate

Ski Francais Junior (Meylan, FRA) Unable to locate

Skiidrett [49189]*

Skin Deep (Chester, GBR) [52999]

Skirnir (Reykjavik, ICE) Unable to locate

SkiSport (Baerum, NOR) [49189]

SkiSport/Ski Forum AS [49189]*

SKOAR (Mumbai, MH, IND) [45439]

Skogsakademikern (Stockholm, SWE) Unable to locate

Skogssport (Farsta, SWE) Unable to locate

Skogssport (Solna, SWE) [51000]

Skojtesport (Brondby, DEN) Unable to locate

S.K.S. Magazine (Colombo, SRI) Unable to locate

Sky (Reykjavik, ICE) Unable to locate

SKY Journal of Linguistics (Savonlinna, FIN) [43906]

Numbers cited in bold after listings are entry numbers rather than page numbers.

Sky at Night Magazine (Bristol, GBR) **[52730]**

Skydive (Peterborough, GBR) **[56262]**

Skydive Magazine (Leicester, GBR) **[53825]**

Skyttebladet (Brondby, DEN) **[43653]**

Skyways (Mumbai, MH, IND) *Unable to locate*

Skywings (Leicester, GBR) **[53826]**

Sl Ohtuleht (Tallinn, EST) *Unable to locate*

Slagers Wereld (Rijswijk, NLD) *Unable to locate*

Slammer (Kuvalehdet, FIN) *Unable to locate*

Slavonic and East European Review (London, GBR) **[55241]**

Slavonica (London, GBR) **[55242]**

Sleaford Standard (Sleaford, GBR) **[56558]**

Sleep and Biological Rhythm (Oxford, GBR) **[56205]**

SLIM (Bristol, GBR) *Unable to locate*

Slim at Home (Colchester, GBR) **[53051]**

Slimming & Health (Sydney, NW, AUS) **[42579]**

Slimming World Magazine (Alfreton, GBR) **[52099]**

Slojdforum (Nora, SWE) **[50994]**

The Slovak Spectator (Bratislava, SLK) **[50322]**

Slovo (London, GBR) **[55243]**

SLU Journal of Medicine (Baguio City, PHL) *Unable to locate*

Small Corners (Auckland, NZL) *Unable to locate*

Small Enterprise Development Journal **[56418]***

Small Scale Industries Envoy (Mumbai, MH, IND) *Unable to locate*

Smallwoods (Pontesbury, GBR) *Ceased*

Smart Card News (Littlehampton, GBR) **[53866]**

SMART-FM - 99.1 (Swan Hill, VI, AUS) **[42443]**

Smart Home Ideas (Saint Leonards, NW, AUS) **[42335]**

Smart Investor (Singapore, SGP) **[50268]**

Smart Kitchens & Bathrooms (North Ryde, NW, AUS) **[42197]**

Smart Materials and Structures (Bristol, GBR) **[52731]**

Smart Parenting (Mandaluyong City, PHL) **[49541]**

Smart Users: SMUG Journal (Colchester, GBR) *Ceased*

Smartphone & PDA Essentials (Bournemouth, GBR) **[52425]**

Smash Swiss Tennis Magazine (Biel-Bienne, SWI) *Unable to locate*

SME Network (Cochin, KE, IND) *Unable to locate*

Smilde-FM (Amsterdam, NLD) *Unable to locate*

Smoke and Mirrors (Pyrmont, NW, AUS) **[42289]**

Smolensk-stereo (Smolensk, RUS) *Unable to locate*

Smooth-FM - 105.7 (Birmingham, GBR) **[52377]**

Smooth-FM - 102.2 (London, GBR) **[55462]**

Smooth-FM - 100.4 (Manchester, GBR) **[55588]**

Smooth Radio-FM - 107.7 (Gateshead, GBR) **[53405]**

Smooth Radio-FM - 97.5 (Gateshead, GBR) **[53406]**

Smooth Radio-FM - 105.2 (Glasgow, GBR) **[53467]**

The SMS Magazine (Singapore, SGP) *Unable to locate*

The Snacks Magazine (London, GBR) *Unable to locate*

Snoken (Stockholm, SWE) *Unable to locate*

Snow (Bielefeld, GER) *Unable to locate*

Snow-FM - 91.7 (Bombala, NW, AUS) **[41604]**

Snow-FM - 97.7 (Cooma, NW, AUS) **[41810]**

Snow-FM - 101.9 (Cooma, NW, AUS) **[41811]**

Snow-FM - 94.7 (Jindabyne, NW, AUS) **[41972]**

Snow-FM - 92.9 (Thredbo, NW, AUS) **[42622]**

SNV Bulletin (Winterthur, SWI) *Unable to locate*

Soap Perfumery & Cosmetics (Daruvar, CTA) *Unable to locate*

Soaplife (London, GBR) **[55244]**

Soaps, Detergents & Toiletries Review (Mumbai, MH, IND) **[45440]**

Sobornost (Oxford, GBR) **[56206]**

Sobremesa (After Dinner) (Madrid, SPA) *Unable to locate*

Soc. Feira-AM - 970 (Brasilia, DF, BRZ) **[42961]**

Social Action (New Delhi, DH, IND) *Unable to locate*

Social Anthropology (Oxford, GBR) **[56207]**

Social Behaviour **[48761]***

Social Care and Neurodisability (Hove, GBR) **[53613]**

Social Change (New Delhi, DH, IND) *Unable to locate*

Social Compass (London, GBR) **[55245]**

Social Defence (Delhi, DH, IND) *Unable to locate*

Social Democrat (Tbilisi, GRG) *Unable to locate*

Social Enterprise Journal (Liverpool, GBR) **[53878]**

Social Evolution & History (Volgograd, RUS) **[50044]**

Social Geography (Gottingen, GER) **[44402]**

Social History (Abingdon, GBR) **[52059]**

Social History of Medicine (Aberdeen, GBR) *Unable to locate*

Social Indicators Research (Dordrecht, NLD) **[48561]**

Social Influence (Abingdon, GBR) **[52060]**

Social Justice Research (Dordrecht, NLD) **[48562]**

Social & Legal Studies (London, GBR) **[55246]**

Social Life (New Delhi, DH, IND) *Unable to locate*

Social Policy Journal of New Zealand (Wellington, NZL) **[49034]**

Social Policy and Society (Cambridge, GBR) **[52896]**

Social Politics (Stockholm, SWE) **[51039]**

Social Responsibility Journal (Leicester, GBR) **[53827]**

Social Science Information (London, GBR) **[55247]**

Social Science Japan Journal (Tokyo, JPN) **[47040]**

Social Science Probings (New Delhi, DH, IND) *Ceased*

Social Science Research (Amsterdam, NLD) **[48233]**

Social Science Research of University of Tokushima (Tokushima, JPN) **[46716]**

Social Sciences Edition (Wuhan, HU, CHN) **[43526]**

Social Sciences and Missions (Leiden, NLD) **[48724]**

Social Sciences Research Journal (Chandigarh, CH, IND) *Unable to locate*

Social Scientist (New Delhi, DH, IND) *Unable to locate*

Social Security Journal (Mexico City, DF, MEX) *Unable to locate*

Social Studies of Science (London, GBR) **[55248]**

Social Theory & Health (London, GBR) **[55249]**

Social Trends (Basingstoke, GBR) **[52230]**

Social Welfare (New Delhi, DH, IND) **[45651]**

Social Work and Society (Cologne, GER) **[44302]**

Socialism and Democracy (Abingdon, GBR) **[52061]**

Socialist Digest (Mumbai, MH, IND) *Unable to locate*

Socialist India (New Delhi, DH, IND) *Unable to locate*

Socialist Nation (Colombo, SRI) *Unable to locate*

Socialist Perspective (Calcutta, WB, IND) *Unable to locate*

Socialist Review (London, GBR) **[55250]**

Socialist Standard (London, GBR) **[55251]**

Socialist World (New Delhi, DH, IND) *Unable to locate*

Socialist World Perspectives (New Delhi, DH, IND) *Unable to locate*

Society (Mumbai, MH, IND) **[45441]**

Society and Business Review (Bradford, GBR) **[52544]**

Society and Change (Calcutta, WB, IND) *Unable to locate*

Society and Commerce (Calcutta, WB, IND) *Unable to locate*

Society and Culture (Calcutta, WB, IND) *Unable to locate*

Society and Economy (Budapest, HUN) **[44870]**

Society of Fellows Journal **[54695]***

Society of Fellows Journal (London, GBR) **[55252]**

Society News (London, GBR) *Unable to locate*

Socio-Economic Review (Oxford, GBR) **[56208]**

Sociolinguistic Studies (London, GBR) **[55253]**

Sociologia Indica (Calcutta, WB, IND) *Unable to locate*

The Sociological Quarterly (Oxford, GBR) **[56209]**

The Sociological Review (Oxford, GBR) **[56210]**

Sociology (Belmont, GBR) **[52307]**

Sociology of Health & Illness (Oxford, GBR) **[56211]**

Sociology of the Law; International Journal of the **[53694]***

Sociology of Medicine (Moscow, RUS) **[49990]**

Sociology Review (London, GBR) **[55254]**

Socionomen (Stockholm, SWE) **[51040]**

Sodra Afrika (Stockholm, SWE) *Unable to locate*

SOFHT Focus (Middleton, GBR) **[55622]**

Soft Drinks International (Wimborne, GBR) **[56929]**

Softmatter (Cambridge, GBR) **[52897]**

Software Futures (London, GBR) *Unable to locate*

Software Quality Journal (Dordrecht, NLD) **[48563]**

Software Release Magazine (Alphen aan den Rijn, NLD) **[47872]**

Software World (Luton, GBR) **[55505]**

Soil & Health (Auckland, NZL) *Unable to locate*

Soil Microorganisms (Matsudo City, JPN) *Unable to locate*

Soil Science and Plant Nutrition (Tokyo, JPN) **[47041]**

Soils and Fertilizers (Wallingford, GBR) **[56829]**

Soils & Foundations (Tokyo, JPN) **[47042]**

Soins (Paris, FRA) *Unable to locate*

SOJOURN (Pasir Panjang, SGP) **[50100]**

Sol di Fatima (Fatima, PRT) *Unable to locate*

Solar Energy Journal (Freiburg, GER) **[44373]**

Solar Physics (Dordrecht, NLD) **[48564]**

Soldering & Surface Mount Technology (Bradford, GBR) **[52545]**

Soldier Magazine (Aldershot, GBR) **[52098]**

Soldier in National Service (New Delhi, DH, IND) *Unable to locate*

Soldiers of the Queen (Newbury, GBR) **[55662]**

Sole 24ore (Milan, ITA) **[46195]**

Soleil-FM - 96.3 (Avignon, FRA) **[43918]**

Solid Gold-FM - 93.4 (Auckland, NZL) **[48854]**

Solid State Ionics (Stuttgart, GER) **[44679]**

Solid State Nuclear Magnetic Resonance (Munster, GBR) **[55654]**

Solid State Phenomena (Zurich, SWI) **[51283]**

Solidarieta Internazionale (Rome, ITA) *Unable to locate*

Solidarios (Santo Domingo, DOM) *Unable to locate*

Solidarity (Manila, PHL) *Unable to locate*

Soliloquy (New Delhi, DH, IND) *Unable to locate*

Solo Golf & Viajes (Hospitalet de Llobregat, SPA) *Unable to locate*

Solvent Extraction Research and Development, Japan (Sendai, JPN) *Unable to locate*

Somatic Cell and Molecular Genetics (Dordrecht, NLD) **[48565]**

Somerset County Gazette (Taunton, GBR) **[56723]**

Somerset Life (Totnes, GBR) **[56763]**

SOMOS-FM - 93.5 (Barquisimeto, VEN) **[57017]**

Son Video Magazine (Saint Quen, FRA) *Unable to locate*

Soncity-FM - 97.3 (Geraldton, WA, AUS) **[41885]**

Sonderhefte (Hannover, GER) *Unable to locate*

Songlines (London, GBR) **[55255]**

Songwriting and Composing Magazine (Penzance, GBR) **[56250]**

Songyuan People's Broadcasting Station (Songyuan, JI, CHN) *Unable to locate*

Sonnenergie (Bern, SWI) *Ceased*

Sonntag Aktuell (Stuttgart, GER) **[44680]**

SonntagsBlick (Zurich, SWI) **[51284]**

SonntagsBlick Magazin (Zurich, SWI) **[51285]**

Sonshine-FM - 98.5 (Como, WA, AUS) [41800]

The Sonyon Chosun (Seoul, KOR) [47287]

Soochow Journal of Economics and Business (Taipei, TWN) Unable to locate

Soochow Journal of Foreign Languages and Literatures (Taipei, TWN) Unable to locate

Soochow Journal of History (Taipei, TWN) [51358]

Soochow Journal of Political Science (Taipei, TWN) [51359]

Sooriyan FM - 103.2 MHz (Colombo, SRI) [50878]

Sooriyan FM - 97.3 MHz (Kandy, SRI) [50911]

Sophia (Melbourne, VI, AUS) [42086]

Sopot-FM - 107 MHz (Delvine, ALB) [41430]

Sorgia-FM - 91 Mhz (Belgrade, FRA) [43919]

Soroptimist News (Sydney, NW, AUS) Unable to locate

Soroush (Tehran, IRN) Unable to locate

Sortenwegweiser/Guide Varietal (Delley, SWI) Unable to locate

Sosialoekonomen (Oslo, NOR) Unable to locate

Sotsiologicheski Problemi (Sofia, BUL) [43108]

Souk (Dubai, UAE) [51653]

Soul (Fatima, PRT) [49797]

The Soul Survivors (West Malling, GBR) [56894]

Sound of Music - Beirut - 106.5 MHz (Beirut, LBN) [47428]

Sound of Music - Beit Meri (Beirut, LBN) Unable to locate

Sound Projector (London, GBR) [55256]

Sound Vision Install (Colchester, GBR) [53052]

Soundbarrier [55033]*

Soundi (Helsinki, FIN) [43857]

Sounds Australian Journal [41935]*

Soundtrack (Mechelen, BEL) Ceased

South African Actuarial Journal (Wits, SAF) [50643]

South African Builder (Midrand, SAF) Unable to locate

South African Computer Journal (Centurion, SAF) [50450]

South African Family Practice (Tygerberg, SAF) [50639]

South African Gastroenterology Review (Johannesburg, SAF) [50534]

South African Geographer (Stellenbosch, SAF) Unable to locate

The South African Geographical Journal (Rondebosch, SAF) [50623]

South African Health Review (Durban, SAF) [50470]

South African Historical Journal (KwaZulu-Natal, SAF) [50545]

South African Journal of Agricultural Extension (Pretoria, SAF) [50601]

South African Journal of Animal Science (Pretoria, SAF) [50602]

South African Journal of Bioethics and Law (Cape Town, SAF) [50412]

South African Journal of Business Management (Centurion, SAF) [50451]

South African Journal of Chemical Engineering (Centurion, SAF) Ceased

South African Journal of Chemistry (Wits, SAF) [50644]

South African Journal of Child Health (Cape Town, SAF) [50413]

South African Journal Clinical Nutrition (Grahamstown, SAF) [50514]

South African Journal of Continuing Medical Education (Pretoria, SAF) Unable to locate

South African Journal of Criminal Justice (Claremont, SAF) [50463]

South African Journal of Cultural History (Centurion, SAF) [50452]

South African Journal of Diabetes and Vascular Disease (Centurion, SAF) [50453]

The South African Journal of Economic History (Pretoria, SAF) Unable to locate

South African Journal of Economic and Management Sciences (Hillcrest, SAF) [50523]

South African Journal of Economics (Oxford, GBR) [56212]

South African Journal of Enology and Viticulture (Dennesig, SAF) Unable to locate

South African Journal on Human Rights (Claremont, SAF) [50464]

South African Journal of Industrial Engineering (Bruma, SAF) [50359]

South African Journal of Information Management (Centurion, SAF) [50454]

South African Journal of Labour Relations (Pretoria, SAF) [50603]

South African Journal of Marine Science [50640]*

South African Journal of Marine Science (Rogge Baai, SAF) Unable to locate

South African Journal of Musicology [50554]*

South African Journal of Obstetrics and Gynaecology (Pinelands, SAF) [50574]

South African Journal of Philosophy (East London, GBR) [53237]

South African Journal of Plant and Soil (Erasmusrand, SAF) [50478]

South African Journal of Psychiatry (Pinelands, SAF) [50575]

South African Journal of Radiology (Pinelands, SAF) [50576]

South African Journal for Research in Sport, Physical Education and Recreation (Stellenbosch, SAF) [50635]

South African Journal of Science (Lynnwood Ridge, SAF) [50551]

South African Journal of Surgery (Pinelands, SAF) [50577]

South African Journal of Wildlife Research (Bloubergstrand, SAF) [50357]

South African Law Journal (Kenwyn, SAF) Unable to locate

South African Medical Journal (Pretoria, SAF) Unable to locate

South African Music Studies (Matieland, SAF) [50554]

South African Psychiatry Review (Johannesburg, SAF) [50535]

The South African Radiographer (Roggebaai, SAF) [50616]

South Arican Architect [50610]*

South Asian Anthropologist (Ranchi, BH, IND) Unable to locate

South Asian Bibliographer (New Delhi, DH, IND) Ceased

South Asian Journal of Management (Hyderabad, AP, IND) Unable to locate

South Asian Journal of Psychology (Dhaka, BGD) Unable to locate

South Asian Minority Affairs (Lahore, PAK) Unable to locate

South Asian Social Scientist (Madras, TN, IND) Unable to locate

South Asian Studies (Jaipur, RJ, IND) Unable to locate

South Asian Studies (Lahore, PAK) Unable to locate

South Asian Studies (London, GBR) Unable to locate

South Asian Survey (New Delhi, DH, IND) [45652]

South Burnett Times (Sydney, NW, AUS) [42580]

South China Morning Post (Hong Kong, CHN) Unable to locate

South-East Advertiser (Mount Gravatt, QL, AUS) [42130]

South East Asia Research (London, GBR) [55257]

South East Asian Review (Gaya, BH, IND) Unable to locate

South East Business (Kent, GBR) [53682]

South East Europe Monitor (London, GBR) [55258]

South East European Journal of Economics and Business (Warsaw, POL) [49765]

South East Farmer (Kent, GBR) [53683]

South East Radio-FM - 95.6 (Wexford, WX, IRL) [46070]

South Edinburgh Echo (Edinburgh, GBR) [53319]

South Indian Teacher (Chennai, TN, IND) Unable to locate

South Liverpool Essence (Liverpool, GBR) Unable to locate

South London Radio-FM - 107.3 (London, GBR) [55463]

South Pacific Aviation (Nadi, FIJ) Unable to locate

South Pacific Studies (Kagoshima, JPN) [46405]

SOUTH Poetry (Maidenhead, GBR) [55525]

South Review (Kuala Lumpur, MYS) Unable to locate

South Seas Society Journal (Singapore, SGP) [50269]

South Tyne & Wear HouseHunter (Newcastle upon Tyne, GBR) [55679]

South Wales Argus (Newport, GBR) [55690]

South Wales Business Times (Derby, GBR) Unable to locate

South Wales Echo (Cardiff, GBR) [52939]

South Yorkshire Times (Mexborough, GBR) [55610]

Southeast Asia Journal (Iloilo City, PHL) Unable to locate

Southeast Asian Affairs (Singapore, SGP) [50270]

Southeast Asian Journal of Social Sciences (Singapore, SGP) Unable to locate

Southeast European Politics (Budapest, HUN) [44871]

Southeast European Politics Online (Budapest, HUN) [44872]

Southeast People's Broadcasting Station (Fuzhou, FJ, CHN) Unable to locate

Southeast People's Broadcasting Station (Fuzhou, FJ, CHN) Unable to locate

Southeast People's Broadcasting Station (Fuzhou, FJ, CHN) Unable to locate

Southeastern Europe (Leiden, NLD) [48725]

Southern Africa Journal of Science and Technology (Bindura, ZWE) [57112]

Southern African Forestry Journal [50606]*

Southern African Journal of Accountability and Auditing Research (Pretoria, SAF) [50604]

Southern African Journal of Anaesthesia and Analgesia (Johannesburg, SAF) [50536]

Southern African Journal of Critical Care (Centurion, SAF) [50455]

Southern African Journal of HIV Medicine (Pretoria, SAF) [50605]

Southern African Linguistics and Applied Language Studies (Grahamstown, SAF) [50515]

The Southern African Treasurer (Cresta, SAF) [50466]

Southern African Wireless Communications (Walton-on-Thames, GBR) [56836]

Southern Economic Review (Madras, TN, IND) Unable to locate

Southern Economist (Bangalore, KA, IND) Unable to locate

Southern-FM [52636]*

Southern-FM - 88.3 (Mentone, VI, AUS) [42101]

Southern Forest (Pretoria, SAF) [50606]

Southern Hemisphere Forestry Journal [50606]*

Southern Railways (Tanjore, TN, IND) Unable to locate

Southern Rural Life (Dunedin, NZL) [48893]

Southern Star-AM - 1314 (Invercargill, NZL) [48924]

Southern Star-FM - 88.4 (Alexandra, NZL) [48781]

Southern Times Messenger (Morphett Vale, SA, AUS) [42120]

Southwark News (London, GBR) Unable to locate

Souvenir (Sangli, MH, IND) Unable to locate

Souvenir (Abingdon, GBR) [52062]

Sovereign Radio-FM - 107.5 (Hailsham, GBR) [53502]

Soviet Jewish Affairs [51764]*

The Soviet and Post-Soviet Review (Leiden, NLD) [48726]

Soybean Abstracts (Wallingford, GBR) [56830]

Sozial-und Praventivmedizin SPM [51074]*

Soziale Sicherheit (Vienna, AUT) Unable to locate

Sozialrecht & Praxis (Berlin, GER) Unable to locate

Spa Australasia (Pyrmont, NW, AUS) [42290]

Space (Seoul, KOR) Unable to locate

Space (Singapore, SGP) [50271]

Space Communications (Amsterdam, NLD) [48234]

Space in Japan (Tokyo, JPN) Unable to locate

Space Policy (Maidens, GBR) [55526]

Space Research Today (Bern, SWI) [51077]

Space Science Reviews (Dordrecht, NLD) [48566]

Spaceflight (London, GBR) [55259]

SPAFA Journal (Bangkok, THA) Unable to locate

Spaghetti Junction (Birmingham, GBR) [52367]

Spain Gourmetour (Madrid, SPA) [50808]

SPAN (Suva, FIJ) Unable to locate

Numbers cited in bold after listings are entry numbers rather than page numbers.

Span (London, GBR) **[55260]**

Spanish in Context (Amsterdam, NLD) **[48235]**

Spanish Economic Review (Barcelona, SPA) **[50700]**

Spar Aktuell **[44365]***

Spark (Calcutta, WB, IND) *Unable to locate*

Sparkle (Hong Kong, CHN) **[43383]**

Sparraaja (Antwerp, BEL) **[42840]**

Spatial Economic Analysis (Glasgow, GBR) **[53452]**

Spatial Practices (Middlesbrough, GBR) **[55612]**

Spatial Vision **[48723]***

Spatio—Economic Development Record (New Delhi, DH, IND) *Unable to locate*

SPE Review (London, GBR) **[55261]**

Speak Up (Barcelona, SPA) **[50701]**

Specchio (Turin, ITA) *Unable to locate*

Special! (Tamworth, GBR) **[56718]**

Special Anniversary Magazine (Melbourne, VI, AUS) *Unable to locate*

Special Issues (S-) (Falkenstein, GER) *Unable to locate*

Speciality Chemicals Magazine (Redhill, GBR) **[56379]**

Speciality Food (Colchester, GBR) **[53053]**

Specify (Belfast, GBR) **[52293]**

Spectra (London, GBR) *Ceased*

Spectrochimica Acta Part B (Delft, NLD) **[48316]**

Spectroscopy Asia (Chichester, GBR) **[53017]**

Spectrum Magazine Scotland on Sunday (Edinburgh, GBR) **[53320]**

Spectrum Radio-AM - 558 (London, GBR) **[55464]**

Speculum (Bath, GBR) **[52258]**

Speech Communication Journal (Bonn, GER) *Unable to locate*

Speech & Language Therapy in Practice (Laurencekirk, GBR) **[53743]**

Speedtype (New Delhi, DH, IND) *Unable to locate*

SPEEDUP Journal (Zurich, SWI) **[51286]**

Speedwriter (New Delhi, DH, IND) *Unable to locate*

Speleology (Buxton, GBR) **[52779]**

Spenborough Guardian (Cleckheaton, GBR) **[53025]**

SPEX (Bratislava, SLK) **[50323]**

Spices India (Cochin, KE, IND) **[45076]**

Spices India (Kochi, KE, IND) *Unable to locate*

Spider (Karachi, PAK) **[49376]**

Spiegel Reporter (Hamburg, GER) *Ceased*

Spike Magazine (London, GBR) *Unable to locate*

SPIN-FM - 103.8 (Dublin, DU, IRL) **[46005]**

Spindshunden (Ebeltoft, DEN) *Unable to locate*

Spire-FM - 102.0 (Salisbury, GBR) **[56459]**

Spirit & Destiny (London, GBR) **[55262]**

Spirituality and Health International (Lancaster, GBR) **[53736]**

Spisanle na Van (Sofia, BUL) *Unable to locate*

Splash-FM - 107.7 (Worthing, GBR) **[56980]**

Spokesman (London, GBR) *Unable to locate*

Sport Business (London, GBR) *Unable to locate*

Sport FM (Moscow, RUS) *Unable to locate*

Sport FM (Radio Megapolis) (Samara, RUS) *Unable to locate*

Sport in History (Abingdon, GBR) **[52063]**

Sport Magazin (Vienna, AUT) *Unable to locate*

Sport Parachutist **[56262]***

SPORT & SCIENCE (Sofia, BUL) *Unable to locate*

Sport Sciences for Health (Dordrecht, NLD) **[48567]**

Sportfack (Strangnas, SWE) *Unable to locate*

Sporting Blue (Leicester, GBR) *Unable to locate*

Sporting Gun (London, GBR) **[55263]**

Sporting Legends (Bath, GBR) **[52259]**

Sporting Shooter (Surry Hills, NW, AUS) **[42439]**

SPORTmagazin (Zurich, SWI) **[51287]**

Sports (Singapore, SGP) *Unable to locate*

Sports Biomechanics (Abingdon, GBR) **[52064]**

The Sports Chosun (Seoul, KOR) **[47288]**

Sports Facilities and Swimming Pools (Cologne, GER) *Unable to locate*

Sports & Fitness Magazine (Giza, EGY) *Unable to locate*

Sports Management (Hitchin, GBR) **[53582]**

Sports Mercury (Leicester, GBR) *Unable to locate*

Sports of Seven Seas (Watford, GBR) **[56876]**

Sports Turf Bulletin (prior to April 1996) **[52327]***

Sports TV Production (London, GBR) *Unable to locate*

Sportsboat (Cambridge, GBR) **[52898]**

The Sportstar (Chennai, TN, IND) **[45057]**

Sportsworld (Calcutta, WB, IND) *Unable to locate*

Spotlight (Bhilai, MP, IND) *Unable to locate*

Spotlight (Kathmandu, NPL) **[47846]**

Sprache und Geschichte in Afrika (Cologne, GER) **[44303]**

Spreadsheets in Education (Gold Coast, QL, AUS) **[41900]**

SPREd (London, GBR) *Unable to locate*

SPHI Vision Magazin (Vienna, AUT) *Unable to locate*

Sprog & Erhverv (Copenhagen, DEN) *Unable to locate*

Spuren (Winterthur, SWI) **[51243]**

The Square (Kingston upon Thames, GBR) **[53724]**

The Square and Compasses (Hyderabad, AP, IND) **[45183]**

The Squash Player (Middlesex, GBR) **[55620]**

Squash and Racketball (Manchester, GBR) *Unable to locate*

SREDA European-Russian Media Magazine (Dusseldorf, GER) *Unable to locate*

SRELS Journal of Information Management (Bangalore, KA, IND) *Unable to locate*

Sri Lanka Architect (Colombo, SRI) *Unable to locate*

The Sri Lanka Attorney-at-Law (Colombo, SRI) *Unable to locate*

Sri Lanka Broadcasting Corporation - Ambewela (Colombo, SRI) *Unable to locate*

Sri Lanka Broadcasting Corporation - Ambewela (Colombo, SRI) *Unable to locate*

Sri Lanka Broadcasting Corporation - Colombo (Colombo, SRI) *Unable to locate*

Sri Lanka Broadcasting Corporation - Colombo - 91.2 MHz (Colombo, SRI) **[50882]**

Sri Lanka Broadcasting Corporation - Colombo - 98.3 MHz (Colombo, SRI) **[50883]**

Sri Lanka Broadcasting Corporation - Colombo - 105.6 MHz (Colombo, SRI) **[50880]**

Sri Lanka Broadcasting Corporation - Colombo - 95.6 MHz (Colombo, SRI) **[50881]**

Sri Lanka Broadcasting Corporation - Colombo - 93.3 MHz (Colombo, SRI) **[50879]**

Sri Lanka Broadcasting Corporation - Deniyaya - 99.6 MHz (Deniyaya, SRI) **[50892]**

Sri Lanka Broadcasting Corporation - Deniyaya - 104.8 MHz (Deniyaya, SRI) **[50890]**

Sri Lanka Broadcasting Corporation - Deniyaya - 102.6 MHz (Deniyaya, SRI) **[50891]**

Sri Lanka Broadcasting Corporation - Deniyaya - 90.8 MHz (Deniyaya, SRI) **[50889]**

Sri Lanka Broadcasting Corporation - Deniyaya - 107.2 MHz (Deniyaya, SRI) **[50887]**

Sri Lanka Broadcasting Corporation - Deniyaya - 92.8 MHz (Deniyaya, SRI) **[50888]**

Sri Lanka Broadcasting Corporation - Diyagama (Colombo, SRI) *Unable to locate*

Sri Lanka Broadcasting Corporation - Diyagama (Colombo, SRI) *Unable to locate*

Sri Lanka Broadcasting Corporation - Diyagama (Colombo, SRI) *Unable to locate*

Sri Lanka Broadcasting Corporation - Diyagama (Colombo, SRI) *Unable to locate*

Sri Lanka Broadcasting Corporation - Ekala (Colombo, SRI) *Ceased*

Sri Lanka Broadcasting Corporation - Ekala (Colombo, SRI) *Ceased*

Sri Lanka Broadcasting Corporation - Ekala (Colombo, SRI) *Ceased*

Sri Lanka Broadcasting Corporation - Ekala (Colombo, SRI) *Ceased*

Sri Lanka Broadcasting Corporation - Ekala (Colombo, SRI) *Unable to locate*

Sri Lanka Broadcasting Corporation - Ekala (Colombo, SRI) *Ceased*

Sri Lanka Broadcasting Corporation - Ekala (Colombo, SRI) *Ceased*

Sri Lanka Broadcasting Corporation - Haputale - 105.4 MHz (Haputale, SRI) **[50899]**

Sri Lanka Broadcasting Corporation - Haputale - 92.2 MHz (Haputale, SRI) **[50897]**

Sri Lanka Broadcasting Corporation - Haputale - 102.0 MHz (Haputale, SRI) **[50898]**

Sri Lanka Broadcasting Corporation - Haputale - 96.4 MHz (Haputale, SRI) **[50896]**

Sri Lanka Broadcasting Corporation - Hunasgiriya (Colombo, SRI) *Unable to locate*

Sri Lanka Broadcasting Corporation - Hunasgiriya - 92.2 MHz (Hunasgiriya, SRI) **[50905]**

Sri Lanka Broadcasting Corporation - Hunasgiriya - 94.2 MHz (Hunasgiriya, SRI) **[50904]**

Sri Lanka Broadcasting Corporation - Hunasgiriya - 89.3 MHz (Hunasgiriya, SRI) **[50902]**

Sri Lanka Broadcasting Corporation - Hunasgiriya - 98.8 MHz (Hunasgiriya, SRI) **[50903]**

Sri Lanka Broadcasting Corporation - Hunasgiriya - 102.0 MHz (Hunasgiriya, SRI) **[50900]**

Sri Lanka Broadcasting Corporation - Hunasgiriya - 107.3 MHz (Hunasgiriya, SRI) **[50901]**

Sri Lanka Broadcasting Corporation - Karagahatenna (Colombo, SRI) *Unable to locate*

Sri Lanka Broadcasting Corporation - Karagahatenna - 95.0 MHz (Karagahatenna, SRI) **[50918]**

Sri Lanka Broadcasting Corporation - Karagahatenna - 90.6 MHz (Karagahatenna, SRI) **[50916]**

Sri Lanka Broadcasting Corporation - Karagahatenna - 104.5 MHz (Karagahatenna, SRI) **[50917]**

Sri Lanka Broadcasting Corporation - Karagahatenna - 87.9 MHz (Karagahatenna, SRI) **[50914]**

Sri Lanka Broadcasting Corporation - Karagahatenna - 99.6 MHz (Karagahatenna, SRI) **[50915]**

Sri Lanka Broadcasting Corporation - Karagahatenna - 102.4 MHz (Karagahatenna, SRI) **[50913]**

Sri Lanka Broadcasting Corporation - Mahiyangana (Colombo, SRI) *Unable to locate*

Sri Lanka Broadcasting Corporation - Mahiyangana (Colombo, SRI) *Unable to locate*

Sri Lanka Broadcasting Corporation - Palali (Jaffna) - 102.0 MHz (Palali (Jaffna), SRI) **[50921]**

Sri Lanka Broadcasting Corporation - Radella - 94.4 MHz (Radella, SRI) **[50933]**

Sri Lanka Broadcasting Corporation - Radella - 97.0 MHz (Radella, SRI) **[50934]**

Sri Lanka Broadcasting Corporation - Radella - 100.2 MHz (Radella, SRI) **[50931]**

Sri Lanka Broadcasting Corporation - Radella - 91.7 MHz (Radella, SRI) **[50932]**

Sri Lanka Broadcasting Corporation - Radella - 89.7 MHz (Radella, SRI) **[50929]**

Sri Lanka Broadcasting Corporation - Radella - 106.9 MHz (Radella, SRI) **[50930]**

Sri Lanka Broadcasting Corporation - Ratnapura (Colombo, SRI) *Unable to locate*

Sri Lanka Broadcasting Corporation - Weeraketiya (Colombo, SRI) *Unable to locate*

Sri Lanka Broadcasting Corporation - Yatiyantota - 92.2 MHz (Yatiyantota, SRI) **[50937]**

Sri Lanka Dental Journal (Colombo, SRI) *Unable to locate*

Sri Lanka Economic Journal (Colombo, SRI) *Unable to locate*

Sri Lanka Engineering News (Colombo, SRI) **[50863]**

Sri Lanka Forester (Battaramulla, SRI) *Unable to locate*

Numbers cited in bold after listings are entry numbers rather than page numbers.

Sri Lanka Journal of Agrarian Studies (Colombo, SRI) **[50864]**

Sri Lanka Journal of Buddhist Studies (Mount Lavinia, SRI) *Unable to locate*

Sri Lanka Journal of Child Health (Colombo, SRI) **[50865]**

Sri Lanka Journal of Geography (Colombo, SRI) *Unable to locate*

Sri Lanka Journal of Historical and Social Studies (Kandy, SRI) *Unable to locate*

Sri Lanka Journal of the Humanities (Peradeniya, SRI) *Unable to locate*

Sri Lanka Journal of International Law (Colombo, SRI) **[50866]**

Sri Lanka Journal of Medicine (Kandy, SRI) **[50909]**

Sri Lanka Journal of Obstetrics and Gynaecology (Colombo, SRI) *Unable to locate*

Sri Lanka Journal of Social Sciences (Colombo, SRI) **[50867]**

The Sri Lanka Journal of Surgery (Colombo, SRI) *Unable to locate*

Sri Lanka Journal of Tea Science (Talawakale, SRI) *Unable to locate*

Sri Lanka Police Journal (Colombo, SRI) *Unable to locate*

The Sri Lanka Prescriber (Colombo, SRI) *Unable to locate*

Sri Lanka Rupavahini Corporation - Channel 11 (Sooriyakanda, SRI) **[50936]**

Sri Lanka Veterinary Journal (Peradeniya, SRI) *Unable to locate*

Sri Lankan Family Physician (Colombo, SRI) **[50868]**

Sri Lankan Journal of Agricultural Economics (Peradeniya, SRI) *Unable to locate*

Sri Lankan Journal of Management (Colombo, SRI) **[50869]**

Sri Lankan Journal of Physics (Colombo, SRI) **[50870]**

Sri Venkateswara University Department of Sanskrit Symposium (Tirupati, AP, IND) *Unable to locate*

Sri Venkateswara University Oriental Journal (Tirupati, AP, IND) *Unable to locate*

Srimanta Sankaradeva Research Institute Journal (Nagaon, AS, IND) *Unable to locate*

Sruti (Chennai, TN, IND) **[45058]**

SSI—Small Scale Industries (Mumbai, MH, IND) *Unable to locate*

The SSR Journal (Stockholm, SWE) *Unable to locate*

Sta Pa (Lysaker, NOR) *Unable to locate*

STA—Revista de la Sociedad de Tecnicos de Automacion (Barcelona, SPA) *Unable to locate*

Stads og Havne Ingenioren (Birkerod, DEN) *Unable to locate*

Stadt Leoben (Leoben, AUT) **[42732]**

Staffordshire County (Cheltenham, GBR) **[52977]**

The Stage inc. Television Today (London, GBR) *Unable to locate*

Stage Screen & Radio (London, GBR) *Unable to locate*

Stagecoach (London, GBR) *Unable to locate*

Stagline (Wellington, NZL) *Unable to locate*

Stainless (Tokyo, JPN) *Unable to locate*

Stamp Bulletin (Melbourne, VI, AUS) **[42087]**

Stamp Digest (Calcutta, WB, IND) *Unable to locate*

Stamp Explorer (Melbourne, VI, AUS) **[42088]**

Stamp Lover (London, GBR) *Unable to locate*

Stamp Magazine (Croydon, GBR) **[53134]**

Stampi (Milan, ITA) **[46196]**

Stamps World (Calcutta, WB, IND) *Unable to locate*

The Standard (Hong Kong, CHN) *Unable to locate*

Standard Messenger (Salisbury, SA, AUS) **[42345]**

Standardization, Metrology, Certification (Sofia, BUL) *Unable to locate*

Standards India (New Delhi, DH, IND) **[45653]**

Standards News (Colombo, SRI) *Unable to locate*

Standpunkte (Lausanne, SWI) *Unable to locate*

The Stanthorpe Border Post (Sydney, NW, AUS) **[42581]**

The Star (Kingston, JAM) **[46288]**

The Star (Amman, JOR) *Unable to locate*

The Star (Petaling Jaya, MYS) **[47702]**

Star (Karachi, PAK) **[49377]**

Star Flyer Magazine (Aberdeen, GBR) **[51680]**

Star-FM - 96.6 (Tallinn, EST) **[43786]**

Star and Furrow (Stroud, GBR) **[56648]**

The Star Green Un (Sheffield) (Sheffield, GBR) *Unable to locate*

Star International (Sukkur Tharechani, PAK) *Unable to locate*

Star of Mysore (Mysore, IND) **[45456]**

Star 1045-FM - 104.5 (Erina, NW, AUS) **[41857]**

Star 107.9-FM - 107.9 (Cambridge, GBR) **[52911]**

Star 106.6-FM - 106.6 (Slough, GBR) **[56560]**

Star Series (Sunderland, GBR) **[56655]**

Star & Style (Mumbai, MH, IND) *Unable to locate*

Star Teacher (Mandaluyong City, PHL) **[49542]**

Starch/Staerke (Weinheim, GER) **[44708]**

Stardust (Mumbai, MH, IND) **[45442]**

STARFLASH (Munich, GER) **[44582]**

StarStudio (Quezon City, PHL) **[49617]**

START-FM - 94.2 (Vilnius, LIT) **[47484]**

State (Colombo, SRI) *Unable to locate*

State Domestic Product of Himachal Pradesh (Simla, HP, IND) *Unable to locate*

State Engineers (Colombo, SRI) *Unable to locate*

State Registered Hairdresser (London, GBR) *Unable to locate*

State Supplies (New Delhi, DH, IND) *Unable to locate*

The Statesman (Kolkata, WB, IND) **[45305]**

Statesman (Peshawar, PAK) **[49395]**

The Statesman Weekly (Kolkata, WB, IND) *Unable to locate*

Stationary Engine (Cudham, GBR) **[53147]**

Stationary News (Surry Hills, NW, AUS) **[42440]**

Stationery and Office Supplies (Taipei, TWN) *Unable to locate*

Stationery & Office Update (Maidstone, GBR) **[55531]**

Stations-Service Acutalites (Clichy, FRA) **[43936]**

Statistica Neerlandica (Rotterdam, NLD) **[48752]**

Statistica Sinica (Taipei, TWN) **[51360]**

Statistical Abstract of Rajasthan (Jaipur, RJ, IND) **[45199]**

Statistical Inference for Stochastic Processes (Paris, FRA) **[44084]**

Statistical Journal (Geneva, SWI) *Unable to locate*

Statistical Journal of the IAOS (Amsterdam, NLD) **[48236]**

Statistical Journal of the United Nations Economic Commission for Europe **[48236]***

Statistical Methodology (Singapore, SGP) **[50272]**

Statistical Methods and Applications (Rome, ITA) **[46242]**

Statistical Modelling (London, GBR) **[55264]**

Statistical News (London, GBR) *Unable to locate*

Statistical Papers (Linz, AUT) **[42734]**

Statistical Pocket Book (New Delhi, DH, IND) **[45654]**

Statistics and Computing (Dordrecht, NLD) **[48568]**

Statistics of Marine Products Exports (Kochi, KE, IND) *Unable to locate*

Statute Law Review (Douglas, GBR) **[53197]**

Staying Alive (Birmingham, GBR) **[52368]**

Steam Days (Berkhamsted, GBR) **[52314]**

Steeds (Arnhem, NLD) *Unable to locate*

Steel Bulletin—Panorama (New Delhi, DH, IND) *Unable to locate*

Steel Grips (Bad Harzburg, GER) **[44144]**

Steel India (Ranchi, BH, IND) *Unable to locate*

Steel Times **[56676]***

Steel Times International (Surrey, GBR) **[56676]**

Steel Trade (New Delhi, DH, IND) *Unable to locate*

Steering Wheel (London, GBR) *Unable to locate*

stehl and eisen **[44144]***

Stellenbosch Gazette **[50379]***

Stellenbosch Law Review (Claremont, SAF) **[50465]**

Step Forward (Brentwood, GBR) **[52589]**

Stereo-FM - 97.4 (Cairnlea, VI, AUS) **[41683]**

STEREO-FM - 97.4 (Cairnlea, VI, AUS) **[41684]**

Stereo Joya-FM - 93.7 (Mexico City, DF, MEX) **[47792]**

Stereorama-FM (Belgrade, SER) *Unable to locate*

Stereorama-FM (Belgrade, SER) *Unable to locate*

Stereotactic and Functional Neurosurgery,) *Unable to locate*

Stethoscopie Magazine (Brussels, BEL) *Unable to locate*

STFI Kontakt (Stockholm, SWE) **[51041]**

Stichproben - Wiener Zeitschrift fur Kritische Afrikastudien (Vienna, AUT) **[42768]**

Stil FM (Yekaterinburg, RUS) *Unable to locate*

Stil FM (Yekaterinburg, RUS) *Unable to locate*

Stir (New Delhi, DH, IND) *Unable to locate*

Stitch with the Embroiders' Guild (East Molesey, GBR) **[53240]**

STOA (Lueven, BEL) *Ceased*

Stochastic Processes and Their Applications (Amsterdam, NLD) **[48237]**

Stock Journal (Unley, SA, AUS) **[42661]**

Stock & Land (Tullamarine, VI, AUS) **[42653]**

The Stock Market (Sandyford, DU, IRL) **[46057]**

Stock Market in Thailand (Bangkok, THA) *Unable to locate*

Stomatologia (Athens, GRC) **[44756]**

Stone (North Ryde, NW, AUS) **[42198]**

Stonnington Leader (Glen Iris, VI, AUS) **[41895]**

Storm-FM - 87.7 (Bangor, GBR) **[52176]**

Stornoway Gazette (Stornoway, GBR) **[56637]**

Story Special (Budapest, HUN) **[44873]**

Storylines (Wem, GBR) **[56885]**

Strabismus (Rotterdam, NLD) **[48753]**

Strahlentherapie und Onkologie (Erlangen, GER) **[44342]**

Strain (Xanthi, GRC) **[44776]**

The Straits Times **[47630]***

The Straits Times (Singapore, SGP) **[50273]**

Straits Times (Singapore, SGP) *Unable to locate*

Strasse und Verkehr/Route et Trafic (Zurich, SWI) *Unable to locate*

Strategic Analysis (New Delhi, DH, IND) **[45655]**

Strategic Digest (New Delhi, DH, IND) **[45656]**

Strategic Direction (Bradford, GBR) **[52546]**

Strategic HR Review (Bradford, GBR) **[52547]**

Strategic Outsourcing (Bradford, GBR) **[52548]**

Strategic Survey (Abingdon, GBR) **[52065]**

Strategy (London, GBR) **[55265]**

Stratford & Newham Express (Ilford, GBR) **[53640]**

Stratford Observer (Warwick, GBR) **[56856]**

Stratigraphy and Geological Correlation (Moscow, RUS) **[49991]**

Stray-FM - 97.2 (Harrogate, GBR) **[53520]**

Stream in TV (Rome, ITA) *Unable to locate*

Street-FM (Surfers Paradise, QL, AUS) *Unable to locate*

Strength, Fracture and Complexity (Amsterdam, NLD) **[48238]**

Stride (Calcutta, WB, IND) *Unable to locate*

Stroitelnaya Gazeta (Moscow, RUS) *Unable to locate*

Stroke News (London, GBR) **[55266]**

Structural Control and Health Monitoring (Pavia, ITA) **[46211]**

Structural Engineering Earthquake Engineering (Tokyo, JPN) **[47043]**

Structural Engineering International (Zurich, SWI) **[51288]**

Structural and Multidisciplinary Optimization (Budapest, HUN) **[44874]**

Structural Survey (Bradford, GBR) **[52549]**

Structured Products (London, GBR) **[55267]**

Struggle (Calcutta, WB, IND) *Unable to locate*

Numbers cited in bold after listings are entry numbers rather than page numbers.

STS News (Perth, GBR) *Unable to locate*

STTK - Lehti (Helsinki, FIN) *Unable to locate*

Student BMJ (London, GBR) **[55268]**

Student Direct (Manchester, GBR) **[55578]**

Student Law Review (London, GBR) **[55269]**

Student Magazine (Barnstaple, GBR) *Unable to locate*

Student Times (London, GBR) **[55270]**

Student Times International (Karachi, PAK) *Unable to locate*

The Student Voice (Dublin, DU, IRL) *Unable to locate*

Studia Leibnitiana (Hannover, GER) **[44435]**

Studia Leibnitiana Supplementa (Hannover, GER) *Unable to locate*

Studia Logica (Dordrecht, NLD) **[48569]**

Studia Musicologica Academiae Scientiarum Hungaricae (Budapest, HUN) **[44875]**

Studia Scientiarum Mathematicarum Hungarica (Budapest, HUN) **[44876]**

Studies in Central and East Asian Religions (Leiden, NLD) *Ceased*

Studies in Conflict and Terrorism (Abingdon, GBR) **[52066]**

Studies in Conservation (London, GBR) **[55271]**

Studies in Conservation (London, GBR) **[55272]**

Studies in Cultures, Organizations and Societies **[52660]**

Studies in Economic Development and Planning (Delhi, DH, IND) *Unable to locate*

Studies in Economics and Econometrics (Stellenbosch, SAF) **[50636]**

Studies in the Education of Adults (Leicester, GBR) **[53828]**

Studies in Educational Evaluation (Antwerp, BEL) **[42841]**

Studies in Electoral Politics in the Indian States (New Delhi, DH, IND) *Unable to locate*

Studies in English Literature (Tokyo, JPN) **[47044]**

Studies in Ethnicity and Nationalism (London, GBR) **[55273]**

Studies in European Cinema (Swansea, GBR) **[56707]**

Studies in French Cinema (Exeter, GBR) **[53363]**

Studies in Hispanic Cinemas (Leicester, GBR) **[53829]**

Studies in History of Medicine and Science (New Delhi, DH, IND) *Unable to locate*

Studies in History (New Delhi) (New Delhi, DH, IND) **[45657]**

Studies in History and Philosophy of Science Part A (Cambridge, GBR) **[52899]**

Studies in History and Philosophy of Science Part C (Cambridge, GBR) **[52900]**

Studies in Humanities and Social Sciences (Shimla, HP, IND) **[45731]**

Studies in Indian Epigraphy (Mysore, KA, IND) *Unable to locate*

Studies in Indian Place Names (Mysore, KA, IND) *Unable to locate*

Studies in Language (Amsterdam, NLD) **[48239]**

Studies in Learning, Evaluation, Innovation and Development (Rockhampton, QL, AUS) **[42317]**

Studies in Museology (Vadodara, GJ, IND) *Unable to locate*

Studies in Philosophy and Education (Dordrecht, NLD) **[48570]**

Studies in Psephology (Calcutta, WB, IND) *Unable to locate*

Studies on Russian Economic Development (Moscow, RUS) **[49992]**

Studies in Sociology (Jaipur, RJ, IND) *Unable to locate*

Studies in Theatre and Performance (Exeter, GBR) **[53364]**

Studies of Tribes and Tribals (Delhi, DH, IND) **[45104]**

Studies in World Christianity (Edinburgh, GBR) **[53321]**

Studio (Hilversum, NLD) *Unable to locate*

Studio Bambini (Sydney, NW, AUS) **[42582]**

Studio Classroom (Taipei, TWN) **[51361]**

Studio 107 Thailand (Bangkok, THA) *Unable to locate*

Studio Sound (London, GBR) *Unable to locate*

Studio Systems (Mumbai, MH, IND) **[45443]**

Studiya A (Nalchik, RUS) *Unable to locate*

Studiya ENN (Novosibirsk, RUS) *Unable to locate*

Studiya ENN (Novosibirsk, RUS) *Unable to locate*

Studiya Gorod (Yekaterinburg, RUS) *Unable to locate*

Studiya Gorod - 909 KHz (Yekaterinburg, RUS) **[50046]**

Studiya Moskva (Vladimir, RUS) *Unable to locate*

Study of Elementary Particles (Kyoto, JPN) *Unable to locate*

Study of Medical Supplies (Tokyo, JPN) *Unable to locate*

Studying Teacher Education (Abingdon, GBR) **[52067]**

STV Radio (Yakutsk, RUS) *Unable to locate*

Style (Singapore, SGP) **[50274]**

Su-doku (London, GBR) **[55274]**

Su-doku Selection (London, GBR) **[55275]**

Suara Akbar, Jember (Jember, IDN) *Unable to locate*

Suara AsAdiyah, Sengkang (Sengkang-Wayo, IDN) *Ceased*

Suara Batang, Batang (Jakarta, IDN) *Unable to locate*

Suara Guru (Teacher's Voice) (Jakarta, IDN) *Unable to locate*

Suara Istana, Yogyakarta (Yogyakarta, IDN) *Unable to locate*

Suara Kartika, Jember (Jomber, IDN) *Unable to locate*

Suara Mahameru, Kediri (Kediri, IDN) *Unable to locate*

Suara Mandala, Banyuwangi (Banyuwangi, IDN) *Unable to locate*

Suara Perunding (Kuala Lumpur, MYS) *Unable to locate*

Suara Ramayana Jelita, Palu (Palu, IDN) *Unable to locate*

Suara SAM (Penang, MYS) **[47691]**

Suara Simpati Angkasa (Susia), Pinrang (Pinrang, IDN) *Unable to locate*

Suara Sion Perdana, Karanganyar (Karanganyar, IDN) *Unable to locate*

Suara Subuh, Padang, IDN) *Unable to locate*

Suara Tawang Alun, Banyuwangi (Banyuwangi, IDN) *Unable to locate*

Suara TEEAM (Kuala Lumpur, MYS) **[47636]**

Suara Totabuan Ria, Kotamobagu (Kotamobagu, IDN) *Unable to locate*

Subcity Radio-FM - 105.6 (Glasgow, GBR) **[53468]**

Subjectivity (Basingstoke, GBR) **[52231]**

Subolombi (Jhenidah, BGD) *Unable to locate*

Subsurface Sensing Technologies and Applications **[48560]**

Sudan Journal of Medical Sciences (Grahamstown, SAF) **[50516]**

Sudanese Journal of Dermatology (Khartoum, SDN) **[50939]**

Suddeutsche Zeitung (Munich, GER) *Unable to locate*

Sudhi Sahitya (Kharagpur, WB, IND) *Unable to locate*

Sudoku Puzzles (Redhill, GBR) **[56380]**

Suganitam (Ahmedabad, GJ, IND) *Unable to locate*

Sugar, Food Product, Vegetable Oils, Wheat Product, Fats, Soaps (Allahabad, UP, IND) *Unable to locate*

Sugarcraft **[53381]**

Suicidology (Warsaw, POL) **[49766]**

Suihua People's Broadcasting Station (Suihua, HL, CHN) *Unable to locate*

Suining People's Broadcasting Station (Suining, SI, CHN) *Unable to locate*

Suizhou People's Broadcasting Station (Suizhou, HU, CHN) *Unable to locate*

Sulabh Sansar (New Delhi, DH, IND) *Unable to locate*

Sulasol (Helsinki, FIN) **[43858]**

Sulkapallo (Helsinki, FIN) *Unable to locate*

Sulphur (London, GBR) *Unable to locate*

Sultan (Srirangapatne, KA, IND) *Unable to locate*

Summerhill (Simla, HP, IND) *Unable to locate*

Summit (London, GBR) **[55276]**

The Sun (New Delhi, DH, IND) *Unable to locate*

Sun-FM - 96.9 (Alice Springs, NT, AUS) **[41554]**

Sun FM (Colombo, SRI) *Unable to locate*

Sun FM (Colombo, SRI) *Unable to locate*

Sun-FM - 103.4 (Sunderland, GBR) **[56656]**

The Sun (Glasgow) (Wapping, GBR) **[56030]**

Sun Golf (Mijas-Costa, SPA) *Unable to locate*

The Sun Journal (London, GBR) **[55277]**

Sun & Wind Energy (Bielefeld, GER) **[44247]**

Sunbury Leader (Sunbury, VI, AUS) **[42404]**

Sunday (Calcutta, WB, IND) *Unable to locate*

Sunday Despatch (Kathmandu, NPL) *Unable to locate*

The Sunday Gleaner (Kingston, JAM) **[46289]**

Sunday Herald (Glasgow, GBR) **[53453]**

The Sunday Leader (Colombo, SRI) **[50871]**

The Sunday Mail (Harare, ZWE) **[57118]**

Sunday Mail (English Edition) (New Delhi, DH, IND) *Unable to locate*

Sunday Mail (English Edition) (New Delhi, DH, IND) *Unable to locate*

Sunday Mail (English Edition) (New Delhi, DH, IND) *Unable to locate*

Sunday Mail (English Edition) (New Delhi, DH, IND) *Unable to locate*

Sunday Mid-Day (Mumbai, MH, IND) **[45444]**

Sunday News (Harare, ZWE) **[57119]**

The Sunday Observer (New Delhi, DH, IND) *Unable to locate*

Sunday Observer (Colombo, SRI) **[50872]**

The Sunday Post (Kathmandu, NPL) *Unable to locate*

Sunday Post (Karachi, PAK) *Unable to locate*

Sunday Punch (Dagupan City, PHL) *Unable to locate*

The Sunday Statesman (Kolkata, WB, IND) *Unable to locate*

The Sunday Times **[47631]**

The Sunday Times (Colombo, SRI) **[50873]**

Sunday Times (Malta) (Valletta, MAL) **[47747]**

Sunday Tribune (South Africa) (Greyville, SAF) **[50518]**

Sunrise Radio-AM - 1458 (Middlesex, GBR) **[55621]**

Sunseeker Magazine (Ware, GBR) **[56845]**

Sunshine Coast Daily (Sydney, NW, AUS) **[42583]**

Sunshine Coast Sunday (Sydney, NW, AUS) **[42584]**

Sun.Star Network (Cebu City, PHL) **[49464]**

SunWorld **[44372]**

Suo - Mires and Peat (Jyvaskyla, FIN) **[43872]**

Suomen Autolehti (Helsinki, FIN) **[43859]**

Suomen Hammaslaakarilehti/Finnish Dental Journal (Helsinki, FIN) **[43860]**

Suomen Kuvalehti (Kuvalehdet, FIN) **[43895]**

Suomen Lehdisto (Helsinki, FIN) **[43861]**

Suomi-Finland USA (Helsinki, FIN) *Unable to locate*

Suosikki (Kuvalehdet, FIN) **[43896]**

Super Food Ideas (Alexandria, NW, AUS) **[41546]**

Super Hanjie (Redhill, GBR) **[56381]**

Super Marketing (Stockholm, SWE) *Unable to locate*

Super MotoTecnica (Locate Triulzi, ITA) *Unable to locate*

Super Power Publications (Madras, TN, IND) *Unable to locate*

Super Sudoku (Gosford, NW, AUS) **[41922]**

Superbike (Croydon, GBR) **[53135]**

Superconductor Science and Technology (London, GBR) **[55278]**

The Supplement (Saint Albans, GBR) *Unable to locate*

Supplier Woodworking magazine (Templestowe, VI, AUS) **[42618]**

Supply Management (London, GBR) **[55279]**

Support for Learning (Northampton, GBR) **[55714]**

Supportive Care in Cancer (Dordrecht, NLD) **[48571]**

Supreme Court Cases (Lucknow, UP, IND) **[45326]**

Supreme Court Cases (Criminal) (Lucknow, UP, IND) **[45327]**

Numbers cited in bold after listings are entry numbers rather than page numbers.

Supreme Court Cases (Labour and Services) (Lucknow, UP, IND) **[45328]**

Supreme Court Monthly Review (Lahore, PAK) *Unable to locate*

Surabhi (Mumbai, MH, IND) **[45445]**

Surat Basin News (Sydney, NW, AUS) **[42585]**

Surf Europe (London, GBR) **[55280]**

Surf Magazine (Sidcup, GBR) *Unable to locate*

Surf a Vela (Barcelona, SPA) *Unable to locate*

Surface Coatings International (Wembley, GBR) **[56887]**

Surface Coatings International (Wembley, GBR) **[56886]**

Surface and Coatings Technology (Sheffield, GBR) **[56515]**

Surface Engineering (London, GBR) **[55281]**

Surface Review and Letters (Singapore, SGP) **[50275]**

Surface Wave Abstracts (Brentwood, GBR) *Ceased*

The Surfer's Path (London, GBR) **[55282]**

Surge-AM - 1287 (Southampton, GBR) **[56582]**

Surge International (New Delhi, DH, IND) *Unable to locate*

The Surgeon (Kidlington, GBR) **[53707]**

Surgeons' News (Edinburgh, GBR) **[53322]**

Surgery Journal (Faisalabad, PAK) **[49294]**

Surgery Today (Tokyo, JPN) **[47045]**

Surgical Gastroenterologie **[44374]***

Surgical Journal of Delhi (New Delhi, DH, IND) *Unable to locate*

Surgical Memoirs (New Delhi, DH, IND) *Unable to locate*

Surgical and Radiologic Anatomy (Dordrecht, NLD) **[48572]**

Surgut (Surgut, RUS) *Unable to locate*

Surrey Life (Worthing, GBR) **[56977]**

Survey (Calcutta, WB, IND) *Unable to locate*

Survey Review (Bristol, GBR) **[52732]**

Surveys in Geophysics (Dordrecht, NLD) **[48573]**

Survival (London, GBR) **[55283]**

Surya India (New Delhi, DH, IND) *Unable to locate*

Susanna Rukodeliye (Moscow, RUS) **[49993]**

Susanna Vjazanie (Moscow, RUS) **[49994]**

Sussex Life (Worthing, GBR) **[56978]**

Sustainability Matters (Wahroonga, NW, AUS) **[42677]**

Sustainability Science (Dordrecht, NLD) **[48574]**

Sustaining Regions (Adelaide, SA, AUS) **[41513]**

Sustainments Relational News (Newtown, NW, AUS) *Unable to locate*

Suszhou People's Broadcasting Station (Suzhou, JS, CHN) *Unable to locate*

SUT Journal of Mathematics (Tokyo, JPN) *Unable to locate*

Suvorov (Suvorov, RUS) *Unable to locate*

Suzhou People's Broadcasting Station (Suzhou, AN, CHN) *Unable to locate*

Suzhou People's Broadcasting Station (Suzhou, JS, CHN) *Unable to locate*

Suzhou People's Broadcasting Station (Suzhou, JS, CHN) *Unable to locate*

Suzhou People's Broadcasting Station (Wuxi, JS, CHN) *Unable to locate*

Svensk Biblioteksforskning/Swedish Library Research (Boras, SWE) **[50951]**

Svensk Danssport (Farsta, SWE) **[50954]**

Svensk Hotellrevy (Stockholm, SWE) *Unable to locate*

Svensk Rodd (Farsta, SWE) *Unable to locate*

Svensk Skidsport (Solna, SWE) *Unable to locate*

Svenska Fornminnesforeningens Tidskrift 1871-1905 (Stockholm, SWE) *Unable to locate*

Svenska Frisortidningen (Bromma, SWE) *Unable to locate*

Svenska Museer (Stockholm, SWE) *Unable to locate*

Svenska UNESCO - Radets Skriftserie (Stockholm, SWE) *Unable to locate*

Svet Hospodarstvi (Prague, CZE) *Unable to locate*

Sviat (Sofia, BUL) *Unable to locate*

SVPja (Bern, SWI) **[51078]**

SW-The Magazine **[52099]***

Swadhin Bangla Betar Kendra **[42826]***

Swadhin Bangla Betar Kendra **[42824]***

Swadhin Bangla Betar Kendra **[42823]***

Swadhin Bangla Betar Kendra **[42822]***

Swadhin Bangla Betar Kendra **[42821]***

Swadhin Bangla Betar Kendra **[42820]***

Swadhin Bangla Betar Kendra **[42817]***

Swadhin Bangla Betar Kendra **[42816]***

Swadhin Bangla Betar Kendra **[42815]***

Swadhin Bangla Betar Kendra **[42801]***

Swadhin Bangla Betar Kendra **[42799]***

Swahili - Forum (Mainz, GER) **[44545]**

Swamy Botanical Club Journal (Tiruchirapalli, TN, IND) **[45751]**

Swansea Bay Radio-FM - 102.1 (Neath, GBR) **[55656]**

Swansea Sound-AM - 1170 (Gowerton, GBR) **[53477]**

SWARA (Nairobi, KEN) **[47197]**

Swara Al Karomah Pratama, Martapura (Martapura, IDN) *Unable to locate*

Swara Fortune Indah, Bandung (Bandung, IDN) *Unable to locate*

Swarajya (Madras, TN, IND) *Unable to locate*

Swartlander (Cape Town, SAF) **[50414]**

Swasth Hind (New Delhi, DH, IND) *Unable to locate*

Swedish Book Review (Meopham, GBR) **[55608]**

Swedish Book Trade Magazine (Stockholm, SWE) *Unable to locate*

Swedish Dental Journal (Stockholm, SWE) *Unable to locate*

The Swedish Economy (Stockholm, SWE) *Unable to locate*

Swedish Journal of Musicology (Goteborg, SWE) **[50966]**

Swim & Save (Walsall, GBR) **[56835]**

Swimming Times (Vienna, AUT) *Unable to locate*

Swindon 105.5-FM - 105.5 (Swindon, GBR) **[56715]**

Swing (Oostmalle, BEL) *Unable to locate*

Swiss Medical Weekly (Muttenz, SWI) **[51215]**

Swiss News (Zurich, SWI) **[51289]**

Swisspack International (Zurich, SWI) **[51290]**

SWITEC Information (Winterthur, SWI) *Unable to locate*

Sword Magazine (Reading, GBR) *Unable to locate*

SWR-FM - 99.9 (Doonside, NW, AUS) **[41841]**

SX News (East Sydney, NW, AUS) **[41852]**

SX: Southern Cross Magazine (London, GBR) *Unable to locate*

Sydney Eats (North Ryde, NW, AUS) **[42199]**

The Sydney Morning Herald (Sydney, NW, AUS) **[42586]**

Symmetry Plus (Leicester, GBR) **[53830]**

Symphony 92.4 FM - 92.4 MHz (Singapore, SGP) **[50306]**

Symposium Medical (Berlin, GER) *Unable to locate*

SYN-FM - 90.7 (Melbourne, VI, AUS) **[42096]**

Syna die Gewerkschaft (Zurich, SWI) **[51291]**

Synchrotron Radiation (Chester, GBR) **[53000]**

Syndesmos Journal (Sceaux, FRA) *Unable to locate*

Syndesmos News (Sceaux, FRA) *Unable to locate*

Synfacts (Stuttgart, GER) **[44681]**

Synthese (Dordrecht, NLD) **[48575]**

Synthesis and Reactivity in Inorganic, Metal-Organic, and Nano-Metal Chemistry (Abingdon, GBR) **[52068]**

Synthesis-Stuttgart (Stuttgart, GER) **[44682]**

Syria Times (Damascus, SYR) **[51300]**

Syrian Arab Republic Broadcasting Service - Alleppo (Damascus, SYR) *Unable to locate*

Syrian Arab Republic Broadcasting Service - Damascus (Damascus, SYR) *Unable to locate*

Syrian Arab Republic Broadcasting Service - Damascus (Damascus, SYR) *Unable to locate*

Syrian Arab Republic Broadcasting Service - Damascus (Damascus, SYR) *Unable to locate*

Syrian Arab Republic Broadcasting Service - Damascus (Damascus, SYR) *Unable to locate*

Syrian Arab Republic Broadcasting Service - Damascus (Damascus, SYR) *Unable to locate*

Syrian Arab Republic Broadcasting Service - Damascus (Damascus, SYR) *Unable to locate*

Syrian Arab Republic Broadcasting Service - Deir El Zawr (Damascus, SYR) *Unable to locate*

Syrian Arab Republic Broadcasting Service - Deir El Zawr - 954 KHz (Deir El Zawr, SYR) **[51303]**

Syrian Arab Republic Broadcasting Service - Homs (Damascus, SYR) *Unable to locate*

System Dynamics (Kharagpur, WB, IND) *Unable to locate*

System TV Malaysia Berhad (TV3) (Petaling Jaya, MYS) *Unable to locate*

System TV Malaysia Berhad (TV3) (Petaling Jaya, MYS) *Unable to locate*

System TV Malaysia Berhad (TV3) (Petaling Jaya, MYS) *Unable to locate*

System TV Malaysia Berhad (TV3) (Petaling Jaya, MYS) *Unable to locate*

System TV Malaysia Berhad (TV3) (Petaling Jaya, MYS) *Unable to locate*

System TV Malaysia Berhad (TV3) (Petaling Jaya, MYS) *Unable to locate*

System TV Malaysia Berhad (TV3) (Petaling Jaya, MYS) *Unable to locate*

Systematic and Applied Acarology (Canberra, AC, AUS) **[41713]**

Systematic and Applied Microbiology (Freising, GER) **[44375]**

Systematic Parasitology (London, GBR) **[55284]**

Systematic Reviews in Pharmacy (Bangalore, KA, IND) **[44988]**

Systematics and Biodiversity (Richmond, GBR) **[56392]**

Systemic Practice and Action Research (Dordrecht, NLD) **[48576]**

Systems Biology (Stevenage, GBR) **[56618]**

Systems Engineering (Shanghai, CHN) **[43506]**

Systems and Synthetic Biology (Yokohama, JPN) **[47142]**

Szabad Demokrata Hirlap (Budapest, HUN) *Unable to locate*

Szabadsag (Budapest, HUN) *Unable to locate*

Szene Hamburg (Hamburg, GER) *Unable to locate*

Szines RTV (Budapest, HUN) **[44877]**

T

T GOOI-FM (Amsterdam, NLD) *Unable to locate*

T Training Education Employment (Redruth, GBR) *Unable to locate*

Ta chien Broadcasting Station - 99.1 MHz (Taichung, TWN) **[51325]**

Table Tennis World (Beijing, CHN) *Unable to locate*

The Tablet (London, GBR) **[55285]**

Tabularia (Caen, FRA) **[43926]**

TAG Bulletin (Plymouth, GBR) **[56273]**

Tageblatt - Zeitung fir Letzebuerg (Esch-sur-Alzette, LUX) *Unable to locate*

Tagore International (Calcutta, WB, IND) *Unable to locate*

Tahdet Ja Avaruus (Helsinki, FIN) *Unable to locate*

Tahi-FM (Tauranga, NZL) *Unable to locate*

Tahqiqat e Eqtesadi (Tehran, IRN) *Unable to locate*

Tahu-FM - 90.5 (Christchurch, NZL) **[48886]**

Tahu-FM - 99.6 (Invercargill, NZL) **[48925]**

Tahu-FM - 91.1 (Kaikoura, NZL) **[48927]**

Taikabutsu (Tokyo, JPN) **[47046]**

Taikabutsu Overseas (Tokyo, JPN) *Unable to locate*

Tailoring Biotechnologies (Amsterdam, NLD) **[48240]**

Taipei Ai Yue Broadcasting Co. (Taipei, TWN) *Unable to locate*

Taipei Times (Taipei, TWN) **[51362]**

Numbers cited in bold after listings are entry numbers rather than page numbers.

TAITEILIJA Magazine (Helsinki, FIN) *Unable to locate*

Taiwan Bags Echo (Taipei, TWN) *Unable to locate*

Taiwan Broadcasting Co. (Hsinchu, TWN) *Unable to locate*

Taiwan Broadcasting Co. (Hsinchu, TWN) *Unable to locate*

Taiwan Broadcasting Co. (Nantou, TWN) *Unable to locate*

Taiwan Broadcasting Co. (Nantou, TWN) *Unable to locate*

The Taiwan Economic News (Taipei, TWN) **[51363]**

Taiwan Footwear News (Cape Town, SAF) *Unable to locate*

Taiwan International Trade (Taipei, TWN) **[51364]**

Taiwan News (Taipei, TWN) **[51365]**

Taiwan Outlook (Taipei, TWN) *Unable to locate*

Taiwan Tatler (Taipei, TWN) **[51366]**

The Taiwanese Journal of Mathematics (Hsinchu, TWN) **[51307]**

Taiyuan People's Broadcasting Station (Taiyuan, SX, CHN) *Unable to locate*

Taiyuan People's Broadcasting Station (Taiyuan, SX, CHN) *Unable to locate*

Taiyuan People's Broadcasting Station (Taiyuan, SX, CHN) *Unable to locate*

Taiyuan People's Broadcasting Station (Taiyuan, SX, CHN) *Unable to locate*

Taiyuan Television - Channel 26 (Taiyuan, SX, CHN) **[43516]**

Taiyuan Television - Channel 12 (Taiyuan, SX, CHN) **[43517]**

Taizhou People's Broadcasting Station (Taizhou, JS, CHN) *Unable to locate*

Taizhou People's Broadcasting Station (Taizhou, JS, CHN) *Unable to locate*

Taj Magazine (Mumbai, MH, IND) *Unable to locate*

Tajfutas (Budapest, HUN) **[44878]**

Tajik Radio - Dushanbe (Dushanbe, TDN) *Unable to locate*

Tajik Radio - Dushanbe (Dushanbe, TDN) *Unable to locate*

Tajik Radio - Dushanbe (Dushanbe, TDN) *Unable to locate*

Tajik Radio - Dushanbe (Dushanbe, TDN) *Unable to locate*

Tajik Radio - Khujand (Dushanbe, TDN) *Unable to locate*

Tajik Radio - Khujand (Dushanbe, TDN) *Unable to locate*

Tajik Radio - Orzu (Dushanbe, TDN) *Unable to locate*

Tajik Radio - Orzu (Dushanbe, TDN) *Unable to locate*

Tajik Radio - Orzu (Dushanbe, TDN) *Unable to locate*

Tajik Radio - Orzu (Dushanbe, TDN) *Unable to locate*

Tajik Radio - Qurghonteppa (Dushanbe, TDN) *Unable to locate*

Tajik Radio - Qurghonteppa (Dushanbe, TDN) *Unable to locate*

Tajik Radio - Yangi-Yul (Dushanbe, TDN) *Unable to locate*

Tajik Radio - Yangi-Yul (Dushanbe, TDN) *Unable to locate*

Tajik Radio - Yangi-Yul (Dushanbe, TDN) *Unable to locate*

Tajik Radio - Yangi-Yul (Dushanbe, TDN) *Unable to locate*

Tajik Radio - Yangi-Yul (Dushanbe, TDN) *Unable to locate*

Tajik Radio - Yangi-Yul (Dushanbe, TDN) *Unable to locate*

Tajik Radio - Yangi-Yul (Dushanbe, TDN) *Unable to locate*

Tajik Radio - Yangi-Yul (Dushanbe, TDN) *Unable to locate*

Take a Break (London, GBR) **[55286]**

Take a Break's Su-doku (London, GBR) **[55287]**

Take a Crossword (London, GBR) **[55288]**

Take 5 (Sydney, NW, AUS) **[42587]**

Take Off (Copenhagen, DEN) **[43684]**

Take a Puzzle (London, GBR) **[55289]**

Taliesin (Cardiff, GBR) **[52940]**

Talk (London, GBR) **[55290]**

Talk Radio-AM - 702 (Rivonia, SAF) **[50614]**

Talk Sport UK-AM - 1053 (London, GBR) **[55466]**

Talk Sport UK-AM - 1089 (London, GBR) **[55465]**

Talkabout (London, GBR) *Unable to locate*

Talkback (Teddington, GBR) **[56735]**

Talking Newspaper News (Heathfield, GBR) *Unable to locate*

Talking Sense (London, GBR) **[55291]**

TalkSPORT-AM - 1053 (London, GBR) **[55470]**

TalkSPORT-AM - 1107 (London, GBR) **[55468]**

TalkSPORT-AM - 1071 (London, GBR) **[55469]**

TalkSPORT-AM - 1089 (London, GBR) **[55467]**

Tall Poppies (Waitomo Caves, NZL) **[48993]**

Tallinna Pereraadio-FM - 89.6 MHz (Tallinn, EST) **[43787]**

Tamar Magazine (Salvador, BH, BRZ) *Unable to locate*

Tambara (Davao, PHL) *Unable to locate*

Tambov (Tambov, RUS) *Unable to locate*

Tamil Arasu (Chennai, TN, IND) *Unable to locate*

Tamil Civilization (Thanjavur, TN, IND) *Unable to locate*

Tamil Culture (Madras, TN, IND) *Unable to locate*

Tamil Murasu (Singapore, SGP) **[50276]**

Tamil Nadu Information (Chennai, TN, IND) *Unable to locate*

Tamil Nadu Journal of Co-operation (Chennai, TN, IND) *Unable to locate*

Tamil Nadu Labour Journal (Mumbai, MH, IND) *Unable to locate*

Tamil Nadu Police Journal (Vellore, TN, IND) *Unable to locate*

Tamil University News Bulletin (Thanjavur, TN, IND) *Unable to locate*

Tamiya Model Magazine International (Totternhoe, GBR) **[56771]**

Tamkang Journal of Futures Studies (Tamsui, TWN) **[51395]**

Tamkang Journal of International Affairs (Tamsui, TWN) **[51396]**

Tamkang Journal of Mathematics (Tamsui, TWN) **[51397]**

Tamkang Journal of Tamkang Review (Tamsui, TWN) **[51398]**

Tandartsenkrant (Brussels, BEL) *Unable to locate*

Tandlaegebladet (Copenhagen, DEN) *Unable to locate*

Tandlakartidningen (Stockholm, SWE) *Unable to locate*

T'ang Studies (London, GBR) **[55292]**

Tangentium (Leeds, GBR) **[53775]**

Tangshan People's Broadcasting Station (Tangshan, HB, CHN) *Unable to locate*

Tangshan People's Broadcasting Station (Tangshan, HB, CHN) *Unable to locate*

Tangshan People's Broadcasting Station (Tangshan, HB, CHN) *Unable to locate*

Tangshan People's Broadcasting Station (Tangshan, HB, CHN) *Unable to locate*

TANK-FM - 103.1 (West Kempsey, NW, AUS) **[42696]**

Tanker Shipping & Trade (Enfield, GBR) **[53337]**

Tankette (Crewe, GBR) *Unable to locate*

Tanner (Bangalore, KA, IND) *Unable to locate*

Tanzania Dental Journal (Grahamstown, SAF) **[50517]**

Tanzania Journal of Forestry and Nature Conservation (Morogoro, TZA) **[51407]**

Tanzania Journal of Science (Dar es Salaam, TZA) **[51403]**

Tanzania Medical Journal (Dar es Salaam, TZA) **[51404]**

Tanzania Veterinary Journal (Morogoro, TZA) **[51408]**

Tanzanian Journal of Health Research (Dar es Salaam, TZA) **[51405]**

Taonan People's Broadcasting Station (Taonan, JI, CHN) *Unable to locate*

Tapovan Prasad (Chennai, TN, IND) *Unable to locate*

Taqasim (Devon, GBR) **[53177]**

Tarabosh-FM - 91 MHz (Shkoder, ALB) **[41446]**

Target (Blackburn, VI, AUS) **[41601]**

Target (Mumbai, MH, IND) *Unable to locate*

Target (Amsterdam, NLD) **[48241]**

Target Advertising News (Safat, KWT) *Unable to locate*

Targima (Tel Aviv, ISR) **[46113]**

Tarsadalom es Gazdasag (Society and Economy) (Budapest, HUN) **[44879]**

Tarsadalomkutatas (Budapest, HUN) **[44880]**

Tarun Bharat (Belgaum, MH, IND) **[44997]**

TASPO (Braunschweig, GER) **[44279]**

The Taste! (Stevenage, GBR) *Unable to locate*

Taste Italia (Bath, GBR) **[52260]**

Taste of Scotland (Midlothian, GBR) **[55628]**

Tastevin en Main (Nuits-Saint-Georges, FRA) *Unable to locate*

Tata Search (Jamshedpur, BH, IND) *Unable to locate*

Tate (London, GBR) *Unable to locate*

Tattvaviveka (Delhi, DH, IND) **[45105]**

Taumu'a Lelei (Vaololoa, TGA) *Unable to locate*

Taupo Weekender (Taupo, NZL) *Unable to locate*

Tautininku Zinios (Vilnius, LIT) *Unable to locate*

Tax Affairs (New Delhi, DH, IND) *Unable to locate*

Tax Breaks Newsletter (Centurion, SAF) **[50456]**

Tax Planning (Rajkot, GJ, IND) *Unable to locate*

Tax-Vyapar (Rajkot, GJ, IND) *Unable to locate*

Taxation (New Delhi, DH, IND) *Unable to locate*

Taxation (Lahore, PAK) *Unable to locate*

Taxation (Croydon, GBR) **[53136]**

Taxation Law Reports (Mumbai, MH, IND) **[45446]**

Tay-AM - 1161 (Dundee, GBR) **[53220]**

Tay-AM - 1584 (Dundee, GBR) **[53219]**

Tay-FM - 102.8 (Dundee, GBR) **[53222]**

Tay-FM - 96.4 (Dundee, GBR) **[53221]**

TC-Forum (Kusnacht, SWI) *Unable to locate*

tC teleCommunication (Bonn, GER) *Unable to locate*

TCE (Rugby, GBR) **[56424]**

TDB (Torquay, GBR) *Unable to locate*

TDD (Reykjavik, ICE) *Unable to locate*

Te Awamutu Courier (Te Awamutu, NZL) *Unable to locate*

Te Upoko O Te Ika-AM - 1161 (Wellington, NZL) **[49046]**

Tea-Break Quickie Crosswords (London, GBR) *Unable to locate*

Tea Club Magazine (London, GBR) *Unable to locate*

Tea Journal (Calcutta, WB, IND) *Unable to locate*

Tea Research Association Occasional Scientific Papers (Jorhat, AS, IND) *Ceased*

Teach (Renton, WA, USA) *Unable to locate*

Teacher Development (Abingdon, GBR) **[52069]**

Teacher Education (Allahabad, UP, IND) *Unable to locate*

Teachers of English (Beddegana, SRI) *Unable to locate*

Teachers and Teaching (Abingdon, GBR) **[52070]**

Teaching Business & Economics (Burgess Hill, GBR) **[52761]**

Teaching Business Ethics (Heidelberg, GER) **[44476]**

Teaching Earth Sciences (Edinburgh, GBR) **[53323]**

Teaching English for Specific Purposes Journal (Manila, PHL) *Unable to locate*

Teaching in Higher Education (Abingdon, GBR) **[52071]**

Teaching History (London, GBR) **[55293]**

Teaching Mathematics and Its Applications (Bognor Regis, GBR) **[52404]**

Teaching Science (Deakin, AC, AUS) **[41838]**

Teaching Statistics (Oxford, GBR) **[56213]**

Teaching Theology and Religion (Oxford, GBR) **[56214]**

Team (Calcutta, WB, IND) *Unable to locate*

Team Performance Management (Bradford, GBR) **[52550]**

Tec-man (Hyderabad, AP, IND) *Unable to locate*

Tech & U (Kuala Lumpur, MYS) **[47637]**

Technical Diagnostics and Nondestructive Testing (Kiev, URE) **[51608]**

Master Index

Numbers cited in bold after listings are entry numbers rather than page numbers.

Technical Education & Training Abstracts (Abingdon, GBR) **[52072]**

Technical Information Digest (Ranchi, BH, IND) *Unable to locate*

Technical Journal (Pretoria, SAF) *Unable to locate*

Technical Journal of Telecommunication Laboratories (Chungli, TWN) *Unable to locate*

Technical Review Middle East (London, GBR) **[55294]**

Technical Studies (Dereham, GBR) *Unable to locate*

Technicky Tydenik (Prague, CZE) *Unable to locate*

Technikos Kosmos (Nicosia, CYP) *Unable to locate*

Techniques in Coloproctology (Tokyo, JPN) **[47047]**

Techno Japan (Tokyo, JPN) *Unable to locate*

Technocrat (Mumbai, MH, IND) *Unable to locate*

Technoetic Arts (London, GBR) **[55295]**

Technology Analysis & Strategic Management (Abingdon, GBR) **[52073]**

Technology and Disability (Heerlen, NLD) **[48630]**

Technology Focus (Delhi, DH, IND) **[45106]**

Technology and Health Care (Amsterdam, NLD) **[48242]**

Technology, Pedagogy and Education (Abingdon, GBR) **[52074]**

Technovation (Amsterdam, NLD) **[48243]**

Tecnica della Confezione e della Maglieria (Milan, ITA) *Unable to locate*

Tecnicas de Transporte y Almacenaje (Madrid, SPA) *Unable to locate*

Tecno Ambiente (Madrid, SPA) *Unable to locate*

TECNOLOGIA MILITAR (Bonn, GER) **[44271]**

Tectonophysics (Wellington, NZL) **[49035]**

Tee to Green (Gomshall, GBR) *Unable to locate*

Teen Philippines (Pasig, PHL) *Unable to locate*

Teenage (Singapore, SGP) *Unable to locate*

Teens **[44714]***

teens (Singapore, SGP) *Unable to locate*

Teens Annual (Singapore, SGP) **[50277]**

TeensMag (Witten, GER) **[44714]**

TeenzSpot.com (Sharjah, UAE) *Unable to locate*

Tehnikamaailm (TM) (Kuvalehdet, FIN) *Unable to locate*

Teho (Rajamaki, FIN) **[43905]**

Tehran Times (Tehran, IRN) **[45914]**

Tekhnicheskaya Diagnostika I Nerazrushayushchiy Kontrol **[51608]***

Tekniikan Maailma (Kuvalehdet, FIN) **[43897]**

Teknik & Vetenskap (Gothenburg, SWE) *Unable to locate*

Tekniset (Helsinki, FIN) *Ceased*

Teknisk Nyt (Glostrup, DEN) **[43716]**

Teknisk Nyt Special Edition (Glostrup, DEN) **[43717]**

Teknisk Ukeblad (Oslo, NOR) *Unable to locate*

Teksi & Kenkalusikka **[43848]***

Tekstil & Teknik (Istanbul, TUR) **[51563]**

Tel Aviv (London, GBR) **[55296]**

Telcom Journal (Bangkok, THA) **[51436]**

Tele top matin (Lausanne, SWI) **[51200]**

Tele-Liban (Beirut, LBN) *Unable to locate*

Tele-Liban (Beirut, LBN) *Unable to locate*

Tele-Liban (Beirut, LBN) *Unable to locate*

TELE-satellite International Magazine (Unterfoehring, GER) **[44697]**

Telecom Tribune (Tokyo, JPN) **[47048]**

Telecommagazine (Alphen aan den Rijn, NLD) **[47873]**

Telecommunication Systems (Heidelberg, GER) **[44477]**

Telecommunications (Jabalpur, MP, IND) *Unable to locate*

Telecommunications Heritage Group Journal (London, GBR) **[55297]**

Telecommunications Policy (Goteborg, SWE) **[50967]**

The Telegraph (Kolkata, WB, IND) **[45306]**

Telegraph & Argus (Bradford, GBR) **[52551]**

The Telegraph Weekly (Kathmandu, NPL) **[47847]**

Telekommunikation (Glostrup, DEN) **[43718]**

Telematics and Informatics (Amsterdam, NLD) **[48244]**

Telepolis (Hannover, GER) **[44436]**

Telesette (Milan, ITA) *Unable to locate*

teletop (Lausanne, SWI) *Unable to locate*

Teletubbies (London, GBR) **[55298]**

Television Maldives - Channel 7 (Male, MDV) **[47726]**

Television Sydney - Channel 31 (Penrith, NW, AUS) **[42241]**

Television of Thailand (Bangkok, THA) *Unable to locate*

Televisual (London, GBR) *Ceased*

Televizion (Munich, GER) **[44583]**

Teleworker **[56649]***

Telex (Fribourg, SWI) *Unable to locate*

Telexpress (Moscow, RUS) *Unable to locate*

Telford-FM - 107.4 (Telford, GBR) **[56741]**

Telhan Patrika (Hyderabad, AP, IND) *Unable to locate*

Tellus (Stockholm, SWE) **[51043]**

Tellus (Stockholm, SWE) **[51042]**

Telshan Network (Pvt) Ltd (Piliyandala, SRI) *Unable to locate*

Telshan Network (Pvt) Ltd (Piliyandala, SRI) *Unable to locate*

Telugu Vaani (Hyderabad, AP, IND) *Unable to locate*

TEMA (Lilongwe, MWI) *Unable to locate*

Tema Arkiv (Sandviken, SWE) *Unable to locate*

Temas para el Debate (Madrid, SPA) **[50809]**

Tempo (Intramuros, PHL) **[49502]**

Tempo Interactive (Jakarta, IDN) **[45802]**

Temps Europeens (Geneva, SWI) *Ceased*

TEN 17-FM - 101.7 (Harlow, GBR) **[53512]**

Ten 26 (Kenilworth, GBR) *Unable to locate*

Tenders Estimating Data Service (Singapore, SGP) *Unable to locate*

TenGoal (London, GBR) **[55299]**

Tennis (Hilversum, NLD) *Unable to locate*

Tennis (Oslo, NOR) *Unable to locate*

Tennis World (Beijing, CHN) *Unable to locate*

Tennislehti (Helsinki, FIN) *Unable to locate*

Tennyson Research Bulletin (Lincoln, GBR) *Unable to locate*

Tenor (Hyderabad, AP, IND) *Unable to locate*

Teosofiska Korelsen (Malmo, SWE) *Unable to locate*

Terbac-FM - 105 MHz (Vlore, ALB) **[41457]**

Terceiro Tempo Revista (Vigo, SPA) *Unable to locate*

Tercer Tiempo (Vigo, SPA) *Unable to locate*

Terminology (Amsterdam, NLD) **[48245]**

TermNet News (Vienna, AUT) **[42769]**

Ternovskaya Volna (Voronezh, RUS) *Unable to locate*

Terra et Aqua (The Hague, NLD) **[48628]**

Terra Incognita (Madrid, SPA) **[50810]**

Terra Nova (Strasbourg, FRA) *Unable to locate*

Terrae Incognitae (London, GBR) **[55300]**

TerraGreen (New Delhi, DH, IND) **[45658]**

Terras da Beira (Lima, PER) *Unable to locate*

Terre & Nature (Lausanne, SWI) *Unable to locate*

Terre Nouvelle (Zurich, SWI) *Unable to locate*

Terrestrial Arthropod Reviews (Leiden, NLD) **[48727]**

The Terrier (Stockport, GBR) *Unable to locate*

Terrier Nyt (Hjorring, DEN) *Unable to locate*

Territory-FM - 98.7 (Alice Springs, NT, AUS) **[41555]**

Territory-FM - 104.1 (Casuarina, NT, AUS) **[41732]**

Terrorism and Political Violence (Abingdon, GBR) **[52075]**

Tertiary Education and Management (Oxford, GBR) **[56215]**

Tesseract (Singapore, SGP) *Unable to locate*

Tesserae **[51906]***

TEST (Madrid, SPA) **[50811]**

Tetrahedron (Amsterdam, NLD) **[48246]**

Tetrahedron (Oxford, GBR) **[56216]**

Tetsu-to-Hagane (Tokyo, JPN) **[47049]**

Texincon (Ahmedabad, GJ, IND) **[44910]**

TEXT (Saint Albans, GBR) **[56439]**

Text & Talk (Berlin, GER) **[44231]**

Textil Wirtschaft (Frankfurt, GER) *Unable to locate*

Textile (Oxford, GBR) **[56217]**

Textile Association (India) Journal (Ahmedabad, GJ, IND) **[44911]**

Textile and Clothing (Herning, DEN) **[43723]**

Textile Clothing and Footwear Workers' Union News (Campsie, NW, AUS) *Unable to locate*

Textile History (London, GBR) **[55301]**

Textile India Progress (Mumbai, MH, IND) *Unable to locate*

Textile Industry and Trade Journal (Baroda, GJ, IND) *Unable to locate*

Textile Machinery (Mumbai, MH, IND) *Unable to locate*

Textile Machinery (Beijing, CHN) *Unable to locate*

Textile Magazine (Chennai, TN, IND) *Unable to locate*

Textile Month (TM) (Bradford, GBR) **[52552]**

Textile Monthly (Taipei, TWN) *Unable to locate*

Textile News (Calcutta, WB, IND) *Unable to locate*

Textile News - Handlooms and Handicrafts Report (Allahabad, UP, IND) *Unable to locate*

Textile Progress (Manchester, GBR) **[55579]**

Textile Trends (Calcutta, WB, IND) *Unable to locate*

Textual Practice (Abingdon, GBR) **[52076]**

Textus (Genoa, ITA) **[46154]**

TF-bladet (Stockholm, SWE) *Unable to locate*

TFM Radio-FM - 96.6 (Thornaby, GBR) **[56747]**

TGRT-FM - 104.4 (Istanbul, TUR) **[51571]**

TGRT-FM - 93.1 (Istanbul, TUR) **[51572]**

Thai-American Business (Bangkok, THA) **[51437]**

Thai Economic Review (Bangkok, THA) *Unable to locate*

Thai Journal of Agricultural Science (Bangkok, THA) *Unable to locate*

Thai Journal of Anesthesiology (Bangkok, THA) **[51438]**

Thai Journal of Development Administration (Bangkok, THA) **[51439]**

Thai Junior Red Cross Magazine (Bangkok, THA) *Unable to locate*

Thai Spas (Bangkok, THA) **[51440]**

Thailand Airline Timetable (Bangkok, THA) **[51441]**

Thailand Society (Bangkok, THA) **[51442]**

Thailand Tatler (Bangkok, THA) **[51443]**

Thailand Travel Magazine (Bangkok, THA) *Unable to locate*

Thailand Update (Bangkok, THA) *Unable to locate*

Thailand's Best Restaurants (Bangkok, THA) **[51444]**

Thalamus and Related Systems (Cambridge, GBR) *Ceased*

Thalassemia Today (Milan, ITA) *Unable to locate*

Thame Gazette (Thame, GBR) **[56744]**

Thames Guardian (Godalming, GBR) *Unable to locate*

Thamesmead People (London, GBR) *Unable to locate*

Thapas Yogi (Chennai, TN, IND) *Unable to locate*

Tharu FM (Colombo, SRI) *Unable to locate*

Tharu FM (Colombo, SRI) *Unable to locate*

Tharu FM (Colombo, SRI) *Unable to locate*

That's Life (Eveleigh, NW, AUS) **[41861]**

that's life! (London, GBR) **[55302]**

the HR Director (Cromhall, GBR) **[53119]**

Theatre Notebook (Brighton, GBR) **[52633]**

The Theatre in Poland/Le Theatre en Pologne (Warsaw, POL) *Unable to locate*

Theatre Quarterly **[52878]***

Theatre Record (London, GBR) **[55303]**

Numbers cited in bold after listings are entry numbers rather than page numbers.

Theatre Research International (Amsterdam, NLD) [48247]

Theatre Research International (Cambridge, GBR) [52901]

Theatregoer Magazine (London, GBR) [55304]

Themescene (Bishop's Stortford, GBR) [52382]

Theology (London, GBR) [55305]

Theology and Science (Abingdon, GBR) [52077]

Theology for our Times (Bangalore, KA, IND) Unable to locate

Theoretical and Applied Climatology (Hamburg, GER) [44424]

Theoretical and Applied Fracture Mechanics (Shanghai, CHN) [43507]

Theoretical and Applied Genetics (Heidelberg, GER) [44478]

Theoretical Biology and Medical Modelling (London, GBR) [55306]

Theoretical Computer Science (Patras, GRC) [44766]

Theoretical Criminology (London, GBR) [55307]

Theoretical Inquiries in Law (Tel Aviv, ISR) [46114]

Theoretical Linguistics (Berlin, GER) [44232]

Theoretical Medicine and Bioethics (Dordrecht, NLD) [48577]

Theory in Biosciences (Jena, GER) [44491]

Theory, Culture & Society (Nottingham, GBR) [55772]

Theory and Decision (Dordrecht, NLD) [48578]

Theory and Practice of Logic Programming (TPLP) (Cambridge, GBR) [52902]

Theory & Psychology (London, GBR) [55308]

Theory and Society (Dordrecht, NLD) [48579]

Theosofie (Antwerp, BEL) Unable to locate

The Theosophical Movement [45447]*

The Theosophical Movement (Mumbai, MH, IND) [45447]

Theosophist (Chennai, TN, IND) [45059]

Therapeutic Archives (Moscow, RUS) [49995]

Therapeutics and Clinical Risk Management (Macclesfield, GBR) [55519]

Therapy (London, GBR) [55309]

Theriogenology (Milan, ITA) [46197]

Thermal Abstracts [52434]*

Thermal Engineering (Moscow, RUS) [49996]

Thermal Envelope and Building Sciences; Journal of [54716]*

The Thermal and Nuclear Power (Tokyo, JPN) [47050]

Thermochimica Acta (Amsterdam, NLD) [48248]

Thermophysics and Aeromechanics (Novosibirsk, RUS) [50015]

Thesis Abstracts (Hissar, HY, IND) Unable to locate

Thesis Eleven (London, GBR) [55310]

Thetford & Brandon Times (Norwich, GBR) [55742]

Thexis (Saint Gallen, SWI) [51224]

Thin-Walled Structures (Loughborough, GBR) [55488]

Think India (New Delhi, DH, IND) Unable to locate

Think: Philosophy for Everyone (Charlottesville, VA, USA) Unable to locate

Thinking & Reasoning (Plymouth, GBR) [56274]

Thinking Skills and Creativity (Exeter, GBR) [53365]

3rd Magazine (Collingwood, VI, AUS) Ceased

Third Sector Magazine (London, GBR) [55311]

Third Text (London, GBR) [55312]

Third Way Voice of the Radical Centre (London, GBR) [55313]

Third World Economics (Penang, MYS) [47692]

Third World First (Lagos, LG, NGA) Unable to locate

Third World Quarterly (Abingdon, GBR) [52078]

Third World Resurgence (Penang, MYS) [47693]

Third World Science & Environment Perspectives (New Delhi, DH, IND) Unable to locate

Third World Unity (New Delhi, DH, IND) Unable to locate

Thirdworld (Karachi, PAK) Unable to locate

30th Anniversary Journal (London, GBR) Unable to locate

This England (Cheltenham, GBR) [52978]

This Month in Korea (Seoul, KOR) Unable to locate

This Week in Seoul (Seoul, KOR) Unable to locate

Thoi Bao Kinh Te Vietnam (Hanoi, VNM) [57053]

Thomas & Friends (London, GBR) [55314]

Thomas Hardy Journal (Dorchester, GBR) [53190]

Thoracic & Cardiovascular Surgery (Moscow, RUS) [49997]

Thorax (London, GBR) [55315]

III - Vs Review (Kidlington, GBR) Ceased

360 (Bournemouth, GBR) [52426]

3AW-AM - 1278 (South Melbourne, VI, AUS) [42378]

3BA-FM - 102.3 (Ballarat, VI, AUS) [41571]

3BBR-FM - 103.1 (Drouin, VI, AUS) [41842]

3BO-FM - 93.5 (Golden Square, VI, AUS) [41902]

3C Westmidlands-FM (Glasgow, GBR) Unable to locate

3EON-FM - 96.5 (Bendigo, VI, AUS) [41596]

3FOX-FM - 101.9 (Sydney, NW, AUS) [42599]

3GDR-FM - 95.7 (Glen Huntly, VI, AUS) [41890]

3GRR-FM - 104.7 (Echuca, VI, AUS) [41853]

3HHH-FM - 96.5 (Horsham, VI, AUS) [41968]

3INR-FM - 96.5 (Heidelberg, VI, AUS) [41950]

3LO-AM (Melbourne, VI, AUS) Unable to locate

3MBR-FM - 92.9 (Murrayville, VI, AUS) [42138]

3MBS-FM - 103.5 (Abbotsford, VI, AUS) [41497]

3MGB-FM - 101.7 (Mallacoota, VI, AUS) [42030]

3MGB-FM - 96.9 (Mallacoota, VI, AUS) [42029]

3PBS-FM - 106.7 (Melbourne, VI, AUS) [42097]

3RPP-FM - 98.3 (Somerville, VI, AUS) [42362]

3RPP-FM - 98.7 (Somerville, VI, AUS) [42363]

3RRR-FM - 102.7 (Melbourne, VI, AUS) [42098]

3SER-FM (Cranbourne, VI, AUS) Unable to locate

3SER Radio Casey-FM - 97.7 (Cranbourne, VI, AUS) [41818]

3SR-FM - 95.3 (Shepparton, VI, AUS) [42358]

3SRA-FM [42096]*

3TD [42096]*

3TR-FM - 99.5 (Traralgon, VI, AUS) [42643]

3VKV-FM - 92.5 (Mount Beauty, VI, AUS) [42123]

3WBC-FM - 94.1 (Box Hill, VI, AUS) [41633]

3WBC-FM - 94.1 (Melbourne, VI, AUS) [42099]

3WM-AM - 1089.(Horsham, VI, AUS) [41969]

3WRB-FM - 97.4 (Sunshine, VI, AUS) [42405]

3XX-AM (Moorabbin, VI, AUS) Unable to locate

3YB-AM - 882 (Warrnambool, VI, AUS) [42689]

3ZZZ-FM - 92.3 (Collingwood, VI, AUS) [41798]

Thrombosis et Diathesis haemorrhagica [44683]*

Thrombosis and Haemostasis (Stuttgart, GER) [44683]

Thrombosis Journal (London, GBR) [55316]

Thrombosis Research (Amsterdam, NLD) [48249]

Thrombus (London, GBR) [55317]

Thumbprint (Northampton, GBR) [55715]

Thumbs Up (Singapore, SGP) [50278]

Thunder (Georgetown, GUY) [44801]

Tian Feng (Shanghai, CHN) Unable to locate

Tianjin People's Broadcasting Station (Tianjin, CHN) Unable to locate

Tianjin People's Broadcasting Station (Tianjin, CHN) Unable to locate

Tianjin People's Broadcasting Station (Tianjin, CHN) Unable to locate

Tianjin People's Broadcasting Station (Tianjin, CHN) Unable to locate

Tianjin People's Broadcasting Station (Tianjin, CHN) Unable to locate

Tianjin People's Broadcasting Station (Tianjin, CHN) Unable to locate

Tianjin People's Broadcasting Station (Tianjin, CHN) Unable to locate

Tianjin People's Broadcasting Station (Tianjin, CHN) Unable to locate

Tianjin People's Broadcasting Station - 567 KHz (Tianjin, CHN) [43518]

Tianshan People's Broadcasting Station (Urumqi, HA, CHN) Unable to locate

Tianshan People's Broadcasting Station (Urumqi, XU, CHN) Unable to locate

Tianshan Prople's Broadcasting Station (Urumqi, HA, CHN) Unable to locate

Tianshui People's Broadcasting Station (Tianshui, GS, CHN) Unable to locate

Tibet Horticuture Communication (Linzi, CHN) Unable to locate

Tibet Journal (Dharamsala, HP, IND) [45112]

Tibetan Bulletin (Dharamsala, HP, IND) Unable to locate

Tibetan Review (Delhi, DH, IND) [45107]

The Tico Times (San Jose, CRI) [43552]

Tide-FM - 96.0 (Hamburg, GER) [44428]

TIDE—Teri Information Digest on Energy [45659]*

Tide Times (Charmouth, GBR) [52958]

TIDEE—Teri Information Digest on Energy and Environment (New Delhi, DH, IND) [45659]

Tidens Tegn (Oslo, NOR) Unable to locate

Tidningen Korsang (Stockholm, SWE) Unable to locate

Tidskrift for Schack (Norrkoping, SWE) [50996]

Tidskriften Memento (Farsta, SWE) Unable to locate

Tidskriften Rit Nytt (Malmo, SWE) Unable to locate

Tidsskrift for Den Norske Legeforening (Oslo, NOR) Unable to locate

Tieling People's Broadcasting Station (Tieling, LI, CHN) Unable to locate

Tiempos Modernos (Terrassa, SPA) [50838]

Tien Giang Broadcast - Television Station (My Tho City, VNM) Unable to locate

Tien Sheng Broadcasting Station (Miaoli, TWN) Unable to locate

Tien Sheng Broadcasting Station (Miaoli, TWN) Unable to locate

Tientien Broadcasting Station (Taichung, TWN) Unable to locate

Tier & Konsum (Saint Gallen, SWI) Unable to locate

Tijaris (Casablanca, MOR) [47813]

Tijdschrift voor economische en sociale geografie (Utrecht, NLD) [48766]

Tijdschrift Controlling (Deventer, NLD) Unable to locate

Tijdschrift voor Huisartsgeneeskunde (Leusden, NLD) Unable to locate

Tijdschrift voor Inkoop & Logistiek (Deventer, NLD) Unable to locate

Tijdschrift Voor Vodeing en Dietetiek (Sint Genesius Rode, BEL) Unable to locate

Tilos Radio-FM - 90.3 (Budapest, HUN) [44885]

TIM Technisch Info Magazine (Amersfoort, NLD) Unable to locate

Time And Tide (New Delhi, DH, IND) Unable to locate

Time Asia (Hong Kong, CHN) [43384]

Time-FM (London, GBR) Ceased

Time-FM - 107.5 (Romford, GBR) [56405]

Time-FM - 106.6 (Southall, GBR) [56567]

Time Highway Radio (Kuala Lumpur, MYS) Unable to locate

Time Highway Radio (Kuala Lumpur, MYS) Unable to locate

Time Highway Radio (Kuala Lumpur, MYS) Unable to locate

Time Highway Radio (Kuala Lumpur, MYS) Unable to locate

Time Highway Radio (Kuala Lumpur, MYS) Unable to locate

Time Highway Radio (Kuala Lumpur, MYS) Unable to locate

Time Highway Radio (Kuala Lumpur, MYS) Unable to locate

Time Highway Radio (Kuala Lumpur, MYS) Unable to locate

Time Highway Radio (Kuala Lumpur, MYS) Unable to locate

Time Highway Radio (Kuala Lumpur, MYS) Unable to locate

A Time Media/Radio Concept (Bangkok, THA) Unable to locate

A Time Media/Radio Concept (Bangkok, THA) Unable to locate

Master Index

A Time Media/Radio Concept (Bangkok, THA) *Unable to locate*

A Time Media/Radio Concept (Bangkok, THA) *Unable to locate*

Time Out Dubai (Dubai, UAE) [51654]

Time Out Kids Out (London, GBR) [55318]

Time & Society (London, GBR) [55319]

Timeless Fellowship (Dharwad, KA, IND) *Unable to locate*

Timeout.com (London, GBR) [55320]

The Times (London, GBR) [55321]

The Times of Central Asia (Bishkek, KGA) [47202]

Times Educational Supplement (London, GBR) [55322]

Times Higher Education Supplement (London, GBR) [55323]

The Times of India (Gurgaon, HY, IND) [45127]

Times of India Index (Mumbai, MH, IND) *Unable to locate*

The Times Law Reports (London, GBR) [55324]

Times of Oman (Muscat, OMN) [49225]

Timisoara Medical Journal (TMJ) (Timisoara, ROM) [49849]

Tinkle (Mumbai, MH, IND) *Unable to locate*

Tipp-FM - 95.3 (Clonmel, TP, IRL) [45935]

Tipperary Mid West Community Radio - 104.8 (Tipperary, TP, IRL) [46059]

Tips sur Saivon (Bonn, GER) *Unable to locate*

Tisglow (New Delhi, DH, IND) *Unable to locate*

TISNET Trade and Investment Bulletin [51418]*

Tissue Antigens (Parkville, VI, AUS) [42232]

Tissue & Cell (Siena, ITA) [46259]

Tjeck Magazine (Alborg, DEN) [43644]

TLcare (Lincoln, GBR) *Unable to locate*

TM [43897]*

TM (Tokyo, JPN) *Unable to locate*

TM Touristik Management (Darmstadt, GER) *Unable to locate*

TNL Rocks-FM - 101.7 (Colombo, SRI) [50884]

TNO Magazine (Delft, NLD) *Unable to locate*

Tobacco Asia (Bangkok, THA) [51445]

Tobacco - Cigarette News (Allahabad, UP, IND) *Unable to locate*

Tobacco Control (London, GBR) [55325]

Tobacco Journal International (Mainz, GER) [44546]

Tobacco News (Guntur, AP, IND) *Unable to locate*

Tobacco Research (Rajahmundry, AP, IND) *Unable to locate*

Tocado (Barcelona, SPA) [50702]

Tocatta (Deal, GBR) [53161]

The Tocqueville Review/La Revue Tocqueville (Paris, FRA) [44085]

Today-FM - 102 (Dublin, DU, IRL) [46006]

Today-FM (Dublin, DU, IRL) *Unable to locate*

Today's Child (Hong Kong, CHN) *Unable to locate*

Today's Outlook (Beirut, LBN) [47402]

Today's Parents (Singapore, SGP) [50279]

Today's Pilot (Stamford, GBR) [56597]

Today's Technician (Nottingham, GBR) [55773]

Todmorden News (Todmorden, GBR) [56753]

Tohoku Geophysical Journal (Aoba-Ku, JPN) *Unable to locate*

Tohoku Journal of Experimental Medicine (Sendai, JPN) [46669]

Tohoku Mathematical Journal (Sendai, JPN) [46670]

Tohoku Psychologica Folia (Sendai, JPN) [46671]

Tokyo - 9550 KHz (Tokyo, JPN) [47090]

Tokyo Journal (Tokyo, JPN) [47051]

Tokyo Scene (Tokyo, JPN) *Ceased*

Tokyo Weekender (Tokyo, JPN) [47052]

Tolvumal (Reykjavik, ICE) *Unable to locate*

Tom & Jerry (Kuvalehdet, FIN) [43898]

Tombo (Tokyo, JPN) *Unable to locate*

Tomorrow's Technology Today (Mumbai, MH, IND) [45448]

Tongchuan People's Broadcasting Station (Tongchuan, SH, CHN) *Unable to locate*

Tonghua People's Broadcasting Station (Tonghua, JI, CHN) *Unable to locate*

Tongliao People's Broadcasting Station (Tongliao, NM, CHN) *Unable to locate*

Tongling People's Broadcasting Station (Tongling, AN, CHN) *Unable to locate*

Tool and Alloy Steels (Mumbai, MH, IND) *Unable to locate*

Tool and Tillage (Frederiksberg, DEN) *Ceased*

Tools and Trades (East Budleigh, GBR) [53234]

Toowoomba's Mail (Sydney, NW, AUS) [42588]

Top Auto (Madrid, SPA) [50812]

Top Fashion Magazine (Bangkok, THA) *Unable to locate*

Top-FM - 106.8 MHz (Belgrade, SER) [50087]

Top Gear Magazine (London, GBR) [55326]

Top Magazine (London, GBR) *Unable to locate*

Top Marques (London, GBR) [55327]

Top of the Pops (London, GBR) [55328]

Top Technical Graduate (London, GBR) *Unable to locate*

TOPbike (Cape Town, SAF) [50415]

TopCar (Cape Town, SAF) [50416]

Topic News Weekly (Ahmedabad, GJ, IND) *Unable to locate*

Topics in Catalysis (Bussum, NLD) [48307]

Topics on Environment Protection (Kardzhali, BUL) *Unable to locate*

topMotor (Cape Town, SAF) [50417]

Topology (Amsterdam, NLD) [48250]

Topology and its Applications (Amsterdam, NLD) [48251]

Tori [46873]*

Torquay Pottery Collectors Society (Torquay, GBR) [56758]

Torque (Singapore, SGP) [50280]

Torts Law Journal (North Ryde, NW, AUS) *Unable to locate*

Total Flyfishing (London, GBR) *Unable to locate*

Total Girl (Eveleigh, NW, AUS) [41862]

Total 911 (Bournemouth, GBR) [52427]

Total PC Gaming (Bournemouth, GBR) [52428]

Total Quality Management [52079]*

Total Quality Management & Business Excellence (Abingdon, GBR) [52079]

Total Rugby League (Brighouse, GBR) *Ceased*

Total Tattoo Magazine (Sudbury, GBR) [56651]

Total TVguide (London, GBR) [55329]

Total Vauxhall (Bath, GBR) [52261]

Totalitarian Movements and Political Religions (Abingdon, GBR) [52080]

Totally Tracy Beaker (London, GBR) [55330]

Touch Broadcasting Station (Tainan, TWN) *Unable to locate*

Touch-FM - 107.6 (Banbury, GBR) [52167]

Touch-FM - 102 (Kenilworth, GBR) [53673]

Touch-FM - 96.2 (Warwick, GBR) [56857]

Touch Radio-FM - 101.6 (Tamworth, GBR) [56720]

Touch Radio-FM - 102.4 (Tamworth, GBR) [56719]

Touchstone (Cardiff, GBR) *Ceased*

T'oung Pao (Leiden, NLD) [48728]

Tour Companion (Tokyo, JPN) *Unable to locate*

Tour Das Rennrad-Magazin (Munich, GER) [44584]

Tourenfahrer/Motorrad Reisen (Euskirchen, GER) [44351]

Touring Nyt (Viby, DEN) *Unable to locate*

Tourism (Sutton, GBR) *Unable to locate*

Tourism Economics (London, GBR) [55331]

Tourism Geographies (Abingdon, GBR) [52081]

Tourism and Hospitality Planning & Development (Abingdon, GBR) [52082]

Tourism and Hospitality Research (Basingstoke, GBR) [52232]

Tourism Management (Hamilton, NZL) [48911]

Tourism Recreation Research (Lucknow, UP, IND) [45329]

Tourism Review (Bradford, GBR) [52553]

Tourism and Wildlife (New Delhi, DH, IND) *Unable to locate*

Tourist Studies (London, GBR) [55332]

Tourist Trade of India (Mumbai, MH, IND) *Unable to locate*

Towards a Caribbean Theology (San Fernando, TTO) *Unable to locate*

Towards Secular India (Mumbai, MH, IND) *Unable to locate*

Tower-FM - 107.4 (Wigan, GBR) [56922]

Town and Country Planning (London, GBR) *Unable to locate*

Town-FM - 102 (Ipswich, GBR) [53660]

Town Planning and Architecture (Warsaw, POL) [49767]

Town Planning Review (Liverpool, GBR) *Unable to locate*

Townswoman (Birmingham, GBR) [52369]

Toxic-FM - 107.1 (Saint Gallen, SWI) [51226]

Toxic Substance Mechanisms (Abingdon, GBR) [52083]

Toxicological Sciences (Oxford, GBR) [52218]

Toxicology (Amsterdam, NLD) [48252]

Toxicology and Applied Pharmacology (Amsterdam, NLD) [48253]

Toxicon (Glasgow, GBR) [53454]

The Toxoplasmosis Trust Trust Update (London, GBR) *Unable to locate*

Toy & Hobby Retailer (Surry Hills, NW, AUS) [42441]

Toy Soldier Collector (Bletchley, GBR) [52391]

Toy Soldier & Model Figure (Arundel, GBR) [52135]

Toybox (London, GBR) [55333]

Toyota Technical Review (Tokyo, JPN) *Unable to locate*

Toys N' Playthings (Watford, GBR) *Unable to locate*

TPI Telecom Plus International (Brussels, BEL) *Unable to locate*

The TQM Journal (Bradford, GBR) [52554]

A Trabe de Ouro (Santiago de Compostela, SPA) [50832]

Traces (Ecublens, SWI) *Unable to locate*

Track and Pools (Kingston, JAM) [46290]

Track Two (Rondebosch, SAF) *Ceased*

Tractor & Farm Machine NY Trader (London, GBR) *Unable to locate*

Tractor & Machinery (Cudham, GBR) [53148]

Trade Chronicle (Karachi, PAK) *Unable to locate*

Trade Commerce & Industry Weekly Bulletin (Mumbai, MH, IND) *Unable to locate*

Trade Journal of the Chamber of Commerce and Industry (Karachi, PAK) *Unable to locate*

Trade Union Record (New Delhi, DH, IND) *Unable to locate*

Trade Unions in India (Chandigarh, PJ, IND) *Unable to locate*

Trading Up (London, GBR) *Unable to locate*

Traditional Boats & Tall Ships (Dorset, GBR) *Unable to locate*

Traditional Medical Systems (Calcutta, WB, IND) *Unable to locate*

Trae- & Mobelindustri (Glostrup, DEN) [43719]

Traffic (Frederiksberg, DEN) [43696]

Training Journal (Littleport, GBR) [53867]

Training & Management Development Methods (Bradford, GBR) [52555]

Training Technology & Human Resources (Crawley, GBR) *Unable to locate*

Trait d'Union (Ouagadougou, BFA) *Unable to locate*

Traitement Automatique des Langues TAL (Paris, FRA) *Unable to locate*

Tramway Review (Welling, GBR) [56879]

Tramways & Urban Transit (Welling, GBR) [56880]

TRANS (Vienna, AUT) [42770]

Trans-Inform (Padborg, DEN) [43733]

Trans World Radio - Puttalam (Colombo, SRI) *Unable to locate*

Transaction of the Iron and Steel Institute of Japan [46851]*

Transactions (London, GBR) [55334]

Transactions of the Centre for Business Law (Centurion, SAF) [50457]

Transactions on Control Systems Technology (Trieste, ITA) [46267]

Numbers cited in bold after listings are entry numbers rather than page numbers.

Transactions of the Institute of British Geographers (Oxford, GBR) **[56219]**

Transactions of the Institute of Measurement and Control (Belfast, GBR) **[52294]**

Transactions of the Institute of Metal Finishing (Birmingham, GBR) **[52370]**

Transactions of Nonferrous Metals Society of China (Changsha, HA, CHN) **[43246]**

Transactions of the Philological Society (Sheffield, GBR) **[56516]**

Transactions of the Royal Society of Tropical Medicine and Hygiene (London, GBR) **[55335]**

Transboundary and Emerging Diseases (Oxford, GBR) **[56220]**

Transcultural Psychiatry (London, GBR) **[55336]**

Transfer (The Hague, NLD) *Unable to locate*

Transfer Werbeforschung & Praxis (Vienna, AUT) **[42771]**

Transformation (Overport, SAF) **[50560]**

Transforming Government (Uxbridge, GBR) **[56801]**

Transfusion Clinique et Biologique (Paris, FRA) **[44086]**

Transfusion Medicine (Oxford, GBR) **[56221]**

Transition (Calcutta, WB, IND) *Unable to locate*

Transition Metal Chemistry (Dordrecht, NLD) **[48580]**

Transitions Online (TOL) (Prague, CZE) **[43639]**

Translation & Literature (Glasgow, GBR) **[53455]**

Translation Quarterly (Hong Kong, CHN) **[43385]**

The Translator (Manchester, GBR) **[55580]**

Transmet-TV - Channel 11 (Cervenake, ALB) **[41428]**

Transmet-TV - Channel 57 (Dajt, ALB) **[41429]**

Transmet-TV - Channel 25 (Durres, ALB) **[41432]**

Transmet-TV - Channel 31 (Gjirokaster, ALB) **[41434]**

Transmet-TV - Channel 9 (Gllava, ALB) **[41435]**

Transmet-TV - Channel 58 (Ishem, ALB) **[41436]**

Transmet-TV - Channel 54 (Korca, ALB) **[41437]**

Transmet-TV - Channel 12 (Mide, ALB) **[41438]**

Transmet-TV - Channel 12 (Mlle, ALB) **[41439]**

Transmet-TV - Channel 25 (Qafe Prush, ALB) **[41444]**

Transmet-TV - Channel 7 (Sopot, ALB) **[41447]**

Transmet-TV - Channel 6 (Tarabosh, ALB) **[41448]**

Transmet-TV - Channel 7 (Terbac, ALB) **[41449]**

Transmet-TV - Channel 12 (Zvernec, ALB) **[41459]**

Transmit (Bingham, GBR) **[52326]**

Transplant International (Vienna, AUT) **[42772]**

Transplant International (Oxford, GBR) **[56222]**

Transplantationsmedizin (Lengerich, GER) **[44534]**

Transpo (Brussels, BEL) *Unable to locate*

Transport (Mumbai, MH, IND) *Unable to locate*

Transport and Communications (Calcutta, WB, IND) *Unable to locate*

Transport Engineer (Hindhead, GBR) **[53575]**

Transport Journal (Kathmandu, NPL) *Unable to locate*

Transport Journal (Birmingham, GBR) **[52371]**

Transport in Porous Media (Dordrecht, NLD) **[48581]**

Transport Service (Clichy, FRA) **[43937]**

Transport Ticket Society Journal (Mansfield, GBR) **[55591]**

Transport and Tourism Journal (New Delhi, DH, IND) *Unable to locate*

Transport World Africa (Johannesburg, SAF) **[50537]**

Transportant (Auckland, NZL) **[48829]**

Transportant (Auckland, NZL) *Unable to locate*

Transportation (Dordrecht, NLD) **[48582]**

Transportation Professional (Tunbridge Wells, GBR) **[56783]**

Transportation Research Part A: Policy and Practice (Amsterdam, NLD) **[48254]**

Transportation Research Part C (Crete, GRC) **[44759]**

Transportation Research Part E (Kidlington, GBR) **[53708]**

Transportation Research Part F (Amsterdam, NLD) **[48255]**

Transportforum (Oslo, NOR) **[49209]**

TRANSURB (Bucharest, ROM) **[49844]**

Trasporti Pubblici (Rome, ITA) *Unable to locate*

Travel Agency (Kuala Lumpur, MYS) *Unable to locate*

Travel Asia (Singapore, SGP) *Unable to locate*

Travel Guide International (Chepstow, GBR) **[52984]**

Travel Inside (Zurich, SWI) **[51292]**

Travel Inside Francais (Zurich, SWI) **[51293]**

Travel Magazine (Mechelen, BEL) **[42905]**

Travel Manager (Zurich, SWI) **[51294]**

Travel News (Stockholm, SWE) *Unable to locate*

Travel News (Stockholm, SWE) *Unable to locate*

Travel in Taiwan (Taipei, TWN) **[51367]**

Travel & Tourism News Middle East (Manama, BHR) **[42794]**

Travel Trade Gazette Asia (Singapore, SGP) **[50281]**

Travel Trade Gazette Europa (London, GBR) *Unable to locate*

Travel Trade Gazette India (Makati City, PHL) *Unable to locate*

Travel Trade Gazette UK & Ireland (London, GBR) *Unable to locate*

Travel Trade Report (Bangkok, THA) **[51446]**

Traveller (London, GBR) **[55337]**

Traveller Magazine (Bangkok, THA) *Unable to locate*

Travelling Interline International (Rome, ITA) **[46243]**

Travelling Scope (Shanghai, CHN) **[43508]**

Traveltrade (Auckland, NZL) **[48830]**

Traviana (New Delhi, DH, IND) *Unable to locate*

Trax-FM - 107.9 (Doncaster, GBR) **[53188]**

Trax-FM - 107.1 (Doncaster, GBR) **[53189]**

Traxx FM - Bintulu - 98.5 (Bintulu, MYS) **[47576]**

Traxx FM - Bukit Tinggi - 92.9 (Bukit Tinggi, MYS) **[47577]**

Traxx FM - Gurun - 98.7 (Gurun, MYS) **[47578]**

Traxx FM - Ipoh - 90.1 (Ipoh, MYS) **[47579]**

Traxx FM - Jeli - 90.8 (Jeli, MYS) **[47581]**

Traxx FM - Johor Bahru - 102.9 (Johor Bahru, MYS) **[47583]**

Traxx FM - Kota Baru - 104.7 (Kota Baru, MYS) **[47585]**

Traxx FM - Kota Belud - 102.5 (Kota Belud, MYS) **[47586]**

Traxx FM - Kota Kinabalu - 90.7 (Kota Kinabalu, MYS) **[47593]**

Traxx FM - Kuala Besut - 97.0 (Kuala Besut, MYS) **[47594]**

Traxx FM - Kuala Dungun - 98.8 (Kuala Dungun, MYS) **[47595]**

Traxx FM - Kuala Terengganu - 89.7 (Kuala Terengganu, MYS) **[47664]**

Traxx FM - Kuantan - 105.3 (Kuantan, MYS) **[47666]**

Traxx FM - Kuching - 89.9 (Kuching, MYS) **[47676]**

Traxx FM - Miri - 104.5 (Miri, MYS) **[47686]**

Traxx FM - Sandakan - 94.3 (Sandakan, MYS) **[47711]**

Traxx FM - Taiping - 105.3 (Taiping, MYS) **[47723]**

Traxx FM - Tangkak - 97.4 (Tangkak, MYS) **[47724]**

TRE—European Building Magazine (Conegliano, ITA) *Unable to locate*

The Treasurer (London, GBR) **[55338]**

Treasury Management (Hyderabad, AP, IND) **[45184]**

Treatments in Endocrinology (Mairangi Bay, NZL) *Ceased*

Treatments in Respiratory Medicine (Mairangi Bay, NZL) *Ceased*

Tred (Maarssen, NLD) **[48733]**

Tree Physiology (Tokyo, JPN) **[47053]**

Tremblestone (Plymouth, GBR) **[56275]**

Trend (Calcutta, WB, IND) *Unable to locate*

Trend Boutique (Maarssen, NLD) **[48734]**

Trends (Maarssen, NLD) **[48735]**

Trends in Analytical Chemistry (Amsterdam, NLD) **[48256]**

Trends in Biochemical Sciences (Amsterdam, NLD) **[48257]**

Trends in Biomaterials & Artificial Organs (Thiruvananthapuram, KE, IND) **[45749]**

Trends in Biotechnology (Amsterdam, NLD) **[48258]**

Trends in Cell Biology (Amsterdam, NLD) **[48259]**

Trends in Classics (Berlin, GER) **[44233]**

Trends in Cognitive Sciences (Amsterdam, NLD) **[48260]**

Trends in Ecology & Evolution (Amsterdam, NLD) **[48261]**

Trends in Endocrinology and Metabolism (TEM) (London, GBR) **[55339]**

Trends in Food Science & Technology (Amsterdam, NLD) **[48262]**

Trends in Genetics (Amsterdam, NLD) **[48263]**

Trends in Glycoscience and Glycotechnology (Osaka, JPN) *Unable to locate*

Trends in Microbiology (Amsterdam, NLD) **[48264]**

Trends in Neurosciences (Amsterdam, NLD) **[48265]**

Trends in Parasitology (Amsterdam, NLD) **[48266]**

Trends in Pharmacological Sciences (Amsterdam, NLD) **[48267]**

Trends in Transplantation (Barcelona, SPA) **[50703]**

Trener (Warsaw, POL) **[49768]**

Trent-FM - 96.2 (Nottingham, GBR) **[55776]**

Trent-FM - 96.5 (Nottingham, GBR) **[55775]**

Treoir (Monkstown, DU, IRL) **[46040]**

Trespass (London, GBR) **[55340]**

Treubia (Bogor, IDN) *Unable to locate*

Trial and Error (Tokyo, JPN) *Unable to locate*

Trials & Motocross News (Morecambe, GBR) **[55649]**

Triangle (Nairobi, KEN) *Unable to locate*

Triangle (Matlock, GBR) *Unable to locate*

Triathlon Sport (Nieuwegein, NLD) *Unable to locate*

Triavna-FM (Lovech, BUL) *Unable to locate*

Tribal Arts (Paris, FRA) *Ceased*

Tribal Research and Development Institute Bulletin (Bhopal, MP, IND) *Unable to locate*

Tribology (Sofia, BUL) *Unable to locate*

Tribology International (London, GBR) **[55341]**

Tribology Letters (Heidelberg, GER) **[44479]**

Tribotest (London, GBR) *Unable to locate*

The Tribune (Chandigarh, CH, IND) **[45025]**

Tribune des Arts (Geneva, SWI) **[51161]**

Tribune Desfosses (Paris, FRA) *Unable to locate*

Tribune of Folk Literature (Beijing, CHN) *Unable to locate*

Tribune de Geneve (Geneva, SWI) **[51162]**

The Trinidad Guardian (Port of Spain, TTO) **[51467]**

Trinidad & Tobago Express (Port of Spain, TTO) **[51468]**

Trinity College Journal (Quezon City, PHL) *Unable to locate*

Triple B-FM - 89.1 (Tanunda, SA, AUS) **[42613]**

Triple H-FM - 100.1 (Hornsby, NW, AUS) **[41966]**

Triple J-FM - 101.5 (Canberra, SA, AUS) **[41718]**

Triple M-FM - 105.1 (South Melbourne, VI, AUS) **[42379]**

Triple R-FM - 102.7 (Melbourne, VI, AUS) **[42100]**

Triple T-FM - 91.9 (Turangi, NZL) **[48991]**

Trishul-FM - 90.5 (Paramaribo, SUR) **[50942]**

Triumph Magazine (Ware, GBR) **[56846]**

Triumph World (Surrey, GBR) **[56677]**

Triveni (Hyderabad, AP, IND) *Unable to locate*

TRK Sana (Rudnyy, KAZ) *Unable to locate*

TRK Tobolsk (Tobolsk, RUS) *Unable to locate*

Trofima kai Pota (Athens, GRC) **[44757]**

Numbers cited in bold after listings are entry numbers rather than page numbers.

Troglodytes (Zagreb, CTA) *Unable to locate*

Tropical Agriculturist (Peradeniya, SRI) *Unable to locate*

Tropical Animal Health and Production (Dordrecht, NLD) [48583]

Tropical Biodiversity (Depok, IDN) *Unable to locate*

Tropical Doctor (London, GBR) [55342]

Tropical Ecology (Varanasi, UP, IND) *Unable to locate*

Tropical Freshwater Biology (Benin City, NGA) [49066]

Tropical Journal of Animal Science (Ibadan, OY, NGA) [49101]

Tropical Journal of Health Sciences (Ilorin, KW, NGA) [49122]

Tropical Journal of Medical Research (Nnewi, AN, NGA) [49151]

Tropical Journal of Obstetrics and Gynaecology (Ibadan, OY, NGA) [49102]

Tropical Journal of Pharmaceutical Research (Benin City, NGA) [49067]

Tropical Medicine (Nagasaki-shi, JPN) *Unable to locate*

Tropical Medicine and International Health (Oxford, GBR) [56223]

Tropical Veterinarian (Ibadan, OY, NGA) [49103]

Truck Australia (Alexandria, NW, AUS) [41547]

Truck and Bus Transportation (Surry Hills, NW, AUS) *Unable to locate*

Truck and Driver (Sutton, GBR) [56693]

Truck Equipment News (Ashwell, GBR) *Unable to locate*

Truck & Machinery Trader (Auckland, NZL) [48831]

Truck and Plant Trader (Manchester, GBR) [55581]

Truck & Van Mart (Birmingham, GBR) *Unable to locate*

Truckin' Life (Alexandria, NW, AUS) [41548]

Trucksearch (Surry Hills, NW, AUS) *Unable to locate*

Truckstop News (Bath, GBR) [52262]

True Love (Cape Town, SAF) [50418]

True Love Babe (Cape Town, SAF) *Ceased*

Trust & Foundation News (London, GBR) [55343]

Trusts and Estates Law & Tax Journal (London, GBR) [55344]

Tsantsa (Neuchatel, SWI) *Unable to locate*

TSEA: Targeting Singapore Electronics Audience (Singapore, SGP) *Unable to locate*

Tsinghua Science & Technology (Beijing, CHN) [43222]

Tsuda Review (Tokyo, JPN) [47054]

Tsukuba Journal of Mathematics (Ibaraki, JPN) [46395]

TSW Development & Embryology (Kirkkonummi, FIN) [43875]

TSW Holistic Health & Medicine (Kirkkonummi, FIN) [43876]

TTG (Budapest, HUN) *Unable to locate*

TTG Italia (Turin, ITA) [46275]

TTGmice (Singapore, SGP) [50282]

T3 (Bath, GBR) [52263]

TTI Country Reports (London, GBR) *Unable to locate*

TTSA Journal (Saint James, TTO) *Unable to locate*

Tu Bebe (Barcelona, SPA) [50704]

TUBA-AR (Ankara, TUR) [51501]

Tube 103.8-FM (London, GBR) *Unable to locate*

Tube & Pipe Technology (Leamington Spa, GBR) [53749]

Tuis (Cape Town, SAF) [50419]

Tumen People's Broadcasting Station (Tumen, JI, CHN) *Unable to locate*

Tumor Research: Experimental and Clinical (Sapporo, JPN) *Unable to locate*

TumorBiology (Umea, SWE) [51048]

TUNE-FM - 106.9 (Armidale, NW, AUS) [41562]

Tungshan He FM Broadcasting Station (Ilan, TWN) *Unable to locate*

Tunnelling and Underground Space Technology Journal (Bron, FRA) *Unable to locate*

Tunnels & Tunnelling (Sidcup, GBR) [56546]

Turanga-FM - 95.5 (Gisborne, NZL) [48900]

Turanga-FM - 91.7 (Gisborne, NZL) [48901]

The Turangi Chronicle (Turangi, NZL) *Unable to locate*

TURC-FM - 96.7 (Taipei, TWN) [51389]

Turfcraft (Carisbrook, VI, AUS) [41723]

Turia (Teruel, SPA) [50839]

Turismo Venezuela (Caracas, VEN) *Unable to locate*

Turiover (Lisbon, PRT) *Unable to locate*

Turk Psikoloji Dergisi (Turkish Journal of Psychology) (Ankara, TUR) [51502]

Turkish Journal of Agriculture and Forestry (Ankara, TUR) [51503]

Turkish Journal of Biology (Ankara, TUR) [51504]

Turkish Journal of Botany (Ankara, TUR) [51505]

Turkish Journal of Cancer (Ankara, TUR) [51506]

Turkish Journal of Chemistry (Ankara, TUR) [51507]

Turkish Journal of Dermatopathology (Ankara, TUR) *Unable to locate*

Turkish Journal of Earth Sciences (Ankara, TUR) [51508]

Turkish Journal of Electrical Engineering and Computer Sciences (Ankara, TUR) [51509]

Turkish Journal of Engineering and Environmental Sciences (Ankara, TUR) [51510]

Turkish Journal of Fisheries and Aquatic Sciences (Trabzon, TUR) [51578]

Turkish Journal of Gastroenterology (Ankara, TUR) [51511]

Turkish Journal of Mathematics (Ankara, TUR) [51512]

Turkish Journal of Medical & Biological Research (Istanbul, TUR) *Unable to locate*

Turkish Journal of Medical Sciences (Ankara, TUR) [51513]

Turkish Journal of Nuclear Sciences (Ankara, TUR) *Unable to locate*

Turkish Journal of Pediatrics (Ankara, TUR) [51514]

Turkish Journal of Physics (Ankara, TUR) [51515]

Turkish Journal of Veterinary and Animal Sciences (Ankara, TUR) [51516]

Turkish Journal of Zoology (Ankara, TUR) [51517]

Turkish Online Journal of Distance Education (Eskisehir, TUR) [51555]

Turkish Probe (Ankara, TUR) *Unable to locate*

Turkish Radio-Television Corporation - Adana - 89.2 MHz (Ankara, TUR) [51525]

Turkish Radio-Television Corporation - Adana - 92.5 MHz (Ankara, TUR) [51524]

Turkish Radio-Television Corporation - Agri (Ankara, TUR) *Unable to locate*

Turkish Radio-Television Corporation - Ankara (Ankara, TUR) *Unable to locate*

Turkish Radio-Television Corporation - Ankara (Ankara, TUR) *Unable to locate*

Turkish Radio-Television Corporation - Ankara (Ankara, TUR) *Unable to locate*

Turkish Radio-Television Corporation - Ankara - 88.0 MHz (Ankara, TUR) [51526]

Turkish Radio-Television Corporation - Ankara - 91.2 MHz (Ankara, TUR) [51527]

Turkish Radio-Television Corporation - Antalya (Ankara, TUR) *Unable to locate*

Turkish Radio-Television Corporation - Antalya (Ankara, TUR) *Unable to locate*

Turkish Radio-Television Corporation - Bodrum (Ankara, TUR) *Unable to locate*

Turkish Radio-Television Corporation - Bursa - 95.0 MHz (Ankara, TUR) [51528]

Turkish Radio-Television Corporation - Bursa - 97.5 MHz (Ankara, TUR) [51529]

Turkish Radio-Television Corporation - Cukurova (Ankara, TUR) *Unable to locate*

Turkish Radio-Television Corporation - Denizli (Ankara, TUR) *Unable to locate*

Turkish Radio-Television Corporation - Diyarbakir (Ankara, TUR) *Unable to locate*

Turkish Radio-Television Corporation - Diyarbakir - 95.5 MHz (Ankara, TUR) [51531]

Turkish Radio-Television Corporation - Diyarbakir - 88.4 MHz (Ankara, TUR) [51530]

Turkish Radio-Television Corporation - Erzurum (Ankara, TUR) *Unable to locate*

Turkish Radio-Television Corporation - Eskisehir - 94.4 MHz (Ankara, TUR) [51533]

Turkish Radio-Television Corporation - Eskisehir - 96.8 MHz (Ankara, TUR) [51532]

Turkish Radio-Television Corporation - Gaziantep - 95.2 MHz (Ankara, TUR) [51535]

Turkish Radio-Television Corporation - Gaziantep - 97.6 MHz (Ankara, TUR) [51534]

Turkish Radio-Television Corporation - Gaziantep (Ankara, TUR) *Unable to locate*

Turkish Radio-Television Corporation - Istanbul (Ankara, TUR) *Unable to locate*

Turkish Radio-Television Corporation - Istanbul (Ankara, TUR) *Unable to locate*

Turkish Radio-Television Corporation - Istanbul - 88.2 MHz (Ankara, TUR) [51537]

Turkish Radio-Television Corporation - Istanbul - 91.4 MHz (Ankara, TUR) [51536]

Turkish Radio-Television Corporation - Izmir - 91.2 MHz (Ankara, TUR) [51540]

Turkish Radio-Television Corporation - Izmir - 94.7 MHz (Ankara, TUR) [51541]

Turkish Radio-Television Corporation - Izmir - 88.0 MHz (Ankara, TUR) [51539]

Turkish Radio-Television Corporation - Izmir - 100.5 MHz (Ankara, TUR) [51538]

Turkish Radio-Television Corporation - Izmir (Ankara, TUR) *Unable to locate*

Turkish Radio-Television Corporation - Kayseri - 99.2 MHz (Ankara, TUR) [51542]

Turkish Radio-Television Corporation - Kayseri - 97.2 MHz (Ankara, TUR) [51543]

Turkish Radio-Television Corporation - Konya - 95.8 MHz (Ankara, TUR) [51545]

Turkish Radio-Television Corporation - Konya - 92.4 MHz (Ankara, TUR) [51544]

Turkish Radio-Television Corporation - Kusadasi (Ankara, TUR) *Unable to locate*

Turkish Radio-Television Corporation - Malatya (Ankara, TUR) *Unable to locate*

Turkish Radio-Television Corporation - Marmaris - 101.0 MHz (Ankara, TUR) [51546]

Turkish Radio-Television Corporation - Nevsehir (Ankara, TUR) *Unable to locate*

Turkish Radio-Television Corporation - Trabzon - 954 KHz (Trabzon, TUR) [51579]

Turkish Radio-Television Corporation - TV-4 - Channel 4 (Ankara, TUR) [51547]

Turkish Radio-Television Corporation - TV-1 - Channel 1 (Ankara, TUR) [51548]

Turkish Radio-Television Corporation - TV-3 - Channel 3 (Ankara, TUR) [51549]

Turkish Radio-Television Corporation - TV-2 - Channel 2 (Ankara, TUR) [51550]

Turkish Radio-Television Corporation - Van (Ankara, TUR) *Unable to locate*

Turkish Radio-Televison Corporation - TV-5 (Ankara, TUR) *Unable to locate*

Turkmen Radio - Asgabat (Asgabat, TUK) *Unable to locate*

Turkmen Radio - Asgabat (Asgabat, TUK) *Unable to locate*

Turkmen Radio - Asgabat (Asgabat, TUK) *Unable to locate*

Turkmen Radio - Asgabat (Asgabat, TUK) *Unable to locate*

Turkmen Radio - Asgabat (Asgabat, TUK) *Unable to locate*

Turkmen Radio - Asgabat (Asgabat, TUK) *Unable to locate*

Turkmen Radio - Asgabat (Asgabat, TUK) *Unable to locate*

Turkmen Radio - Bekdas (Asgabat, TUK) *Unable to locate*

Turkmen Radio - Bekdas (Asgabat, TUK) *Unable to locate*

Turkmen Radio - Ek-Arca (Asgabat, TUK) *Unable to locate*

Numbers cited in bold after listings are entry numbers rather than page numbers.

Turkmen Radio - Gusgy (Asgabat, TUK) *Unable to locate*
Turkmen Radio - Gusgy (Asgabat, TUK) *Unable to locate*
Turkmen Radio - Gyzyletrek (Asgabat, TUK) *Unable to locate*
Turkmen Radio - Syrtagta (Asgabat, TUK) *Unable to locate*
Turkmen Radio - Turkmenabad (Asgabat, TUK) *Unable to locate*
Turkmen Radio - Turkmenabad (Asgabat, TUK) *Unable to locate*
Turkmen Radio - Turkmenbasi (Asgabat, TUK) *Unable to locate*
Turkmen Radio - Turkmenbasi (Asgabat, TUK) *Unable to locate*
Turkmen Television (Asgabat, TUK) *Unable to locate*
Turkmen Television (Asgabat, TUK) *Unable to locate*
Turkmen Television (Asgabat, TUK) *Unable to locate*
Turner Society News (London, GBR) *Unable to locate*
Turrrialba (San Jose, CRI) *Unable to locate*
Tuttitalia (Leicester, GBR) [53831]
Tutto Uncinetto Ricamo e Maglia (Milan, ITA) *Unable to locate*
TuttoCrociere (Cremona, ITA) *Unable to locate*
Tuttoscuola (Rome, ITA) [46244]
Tuttotrasporti (Rozzano, ITA) [46254]
Tuttoturismo (Rozzano, ITA) [46255]
Tuulilasi (Helsinki, FIN) [43862]
Tuyen Quang Broadcast - Television Station (Tuyen Quang, VNM) *Unable to locate*
TV Comp Fourth Channel (Yakaterinburg, RUS) *Unable to locate*
TV Ekran (Kiev, URE) [51609]
TV Guide (New Zealand) (Auckland, NZL) *Unable to locate*
TV Hits (Eveleigh, NW, AUS) [41863]
TV-maailma (Kuvalehdet, FIN) [43899]
TV Soap (Saint Leonards, NW, AUS) [42336]
TV and Video World (Mumbai, MH, IND) *Unable to locate*
tv&radio (Dubai, UAE) [51655]
TVChoice (London, GBR) [55345]
TV8 (Lausanne, SWI) [51201]
TVMAX - Channel 92 (Manama, BHR) [42797]
TVMAX - Channel 90 (Manama, BHR) [42798]
TVMAX - Channel 93 (Manama, BHR) [42796]
TVMAX - Channel 91 (Cairo, EGY) [43768]
TVMAX - Channel 90 (Cairo, EGY) [43769]
TVMAX - Channel 92 (Cairo, EGY) [43767]
TVMAX - Channel 93 (Cairo, EGY) [43766]
TVMAX - Channel 90 (Amman, JOR) [47167]
TVMAX - Channel 92 (Amman, JOR) [47165]
TVMAX - Channel 91 (Amman, JOR) [47166]
TVMAX - Channel 93 (Amman, JOR) [47164]
TVMAX - Channel 90 (Beirut, LBN) [47432]
TVMAX - Channel 92 (Beirut, LBN) [47430]
TVMAX - Channel 91 (Beirut, LBN) [47431]
TVMAX - Channel 93 (Beirut, LBN) [47429]

TVMAX (Muscat, OMN) *Unable to locate*
TVMAX (Muscat, OMN) *Unable to locate*
TVMAX (Muscat, OMN) *Unable to locate*
TVMAX (Muscat, OMN) *Unable to locate*
TVMAX - Channel 91 (Doha, QAT) [49828]
TVMAX - Channel 90 (Doha, QAT) [49829]
TVMAX - Channel 93 (Doha, QAT) [49826]
TVMAX - Channel 92 (Doha, QAT) [49827]
TVMAX - Channel 90 (Riyadh, SAU) [50076]
TVMAX - Channel 92 (Riyadh, SAU) [50074]
TVMAX - Channel 91 (Riyadh, SAU) [50075]
TVMAX - Channel 93 (Riyadh, SAU) [50073]
TVMAX - Channel 91 (Dubai, UAE) [51668]
TVMAX - Channel 90 (Dubai, UAE) [51669]
TVMAX - Channel 93 (Dubai, UAE) [51666]
TVMAX - Channel 92 (Dubai, UAE) [51667]
Tvoy Malysh (Kiev, URE) [51610]
tvplus (Cape Town, SAF) [50420]
TVQuick (London, GBR) [55346]
TVtaglich (Zurich, SWI) [51295]
Tweed/Border Mail (Sydney, NW, AUS) [42589]
Tweed Daily News (Sydney, NW, AUS) [42590]
Tweenies (London, GBR) [55347]
Twentieth Century British History (Brighton, GBR) [52634]
Twentieth Century Music (Cambridge, GBR) [52903]
Twenty-first Century Society (Abingdon, GBR) [52084]
25 Beautiful Homes (London, GBR) [55348]
25 Beautiful Kitchens (London, GBR) [55349]
24 Heures (Lausanne, SWI) [51202]
Twenty Four Seven (Singapore, SGP) *Unable to locate*
21st Century Global Environmental Voice (Lucknow, UP, IND) *Unable to locate*
21st Century Indian Journal of Environmental Management (Lucknow, UP, IND) *Unable to locate*
21st Century Worker (Stroud, GBR) [56619]
20th Century History Review (London, GBR) [55350]
Twin Cities-FM - 89.7 (Joondalup, WA, AUS) [41976]
Twin Research and Human Genetics (Brisbane, QL, AUS) [41653]
TWO AAA-FM - 107.1 (Wagga Wagga, NW, AUS) [42669]
Two and a Bud (Jorhat, AS, IND) *Unable to locate*
2 Double X-FM - 98.3 (Canberra, AC, AUS) [41717]
2-FM (Dublin, DU, IRL) *Unable to locate*
2-FM; Radio - 101.6 (Tirana, ALB) [41455]
209radio-FM (Cambridge, GBR) *Ceased*
220 Triathlon (Bristol, GBR) [52733]
Two Lochs Radio-FM - 106 (Gairloch, GBR) [53402]
2-Ten-FM [56339]*

2-Ten-FM [56338]*
2001 (Mumbai, MH, IND) *Unable to locate*
2AAA-FM - 99.1 (Coolamon, NW, AUS) [41808]
2AAA-FM - 97.9 (Junee, NW, AUS) [41977]
2AAA-FM - 107.9 (Wagga Wagga, NW, AUS) [42670]
2ABC-FM - 101.9 (Batemans Bay, NW, AUS) [41579]
2AD-AM - 1134 (Armidale, NW, AUS) [41563]
2AIR-FM - 107.9 (Coffs Harbour, AUS) [41776]
2B-FM - 100.9 (Padstow, NW, AUS) [42227]
2BAB-FM - 92.7 (Sanctuary Point, NW, AUS) [42350]
2BBB-FM - 107.3 (Bellingen, NW, AUS) [41592]
2BLU-FM - 89.1 (Katoomba, NW, AUS) [41983]
2BOB-FM - 104.7 (Taree, NW, AUS) [42614]
2BR-FM - 99.8 (Nelson, GBR) [55657]
2BS-AM - 1503 (Bathurst, NW, AUS) [41582]
2CBA-FM [42357]*
2CC-AM - 1206 (Mitchell, AC, AUS) [42111]
2CCR-FM - 90.5 (Baulkham Hills, NW, AUS) [41585]
2CH-AM - 1170 (Sydney, NW, AUS) [42600]
2CHR-FM - 96.5 (Cessnock, NW, AUS) [41734]
2CHY-FM - 104.1 (Coffs Harbour, NW, AUS) [41777]
2CN-AM [41714]*
2CR-FM [52430]*
2CS-AM (Coffs Harbour, NW, AUS) *Unable to locate*
2CVC-FM (Grafton, NW, AUS) *Unable to locate*
2DAY-FM - 104.1 (Sydney, NW, AUS) [42601]
2DU-AM - 1251 (Dubbo, NW, AUS) [41843]
2EAR-FM - 107.5 (Moruya, NW, AUS) [42121]
2EC-AM - 1584 (Bega, NW, AUS) [41588]
2EC-AM - 765 (Bega, NW, AUS) [41587]
2EC-FM - 104.3 (Bega, NW, AUS) [41589]
2GB-AM - 873 (Pyrmont, NW, AUS) [42292]
2GCR-FM (Goulburn, NW, AUS) *Unable to locate*
2GF-AM - 1206 (Grafton, NW, AUS) [41932]
2GLF-FM - 89.3 (Liverpool, NW, AUS) [42016]
2GO-FM - 107.7 (Gosford, NW, AUS) [41925]
2HBS-FM - 88.8 (Napier, NZL) [48943]
2HD-AM - 1143 (Sandgate, NW, AUS) [42352]
2HHH-FM - 100.1 (Hornsby, NW, AUS) [41967]
Twoj Maluszek (Warsaw, POL) [49769]
Twoje dziecko (Warsaw, POL) [49770]
2JJJ-FM - 88.7 (Goulburn, NW, AUS) [41930]
2JJJ-FM (Sydney, NW, AUS) *Unable to locate*
2KA-AM - 1476 (Kingswood, NW, AUS) [41996]

2KY-AM - 1017 (Sydney, NW, AUS) [42602]
2LIV-FM - 94.1 (Coniston, NW, AUS) [41805]
2MAX-FM - 91.3 (Narrabri, NW, AUS) [42142]
2MBS-FM - 102.5 (Saint Leonards, NW, AUS) [42337]
2MC-FM - 100.7 (Port Macquarie, NW, AUS) [42261]
2MCE-FM - 94.7 (Bathurst, NW, AUS) [41583]
2MFM Muslim Community Radio-FM - 92.1 (Bankstown, NW, AUS) [41574]
2MM-AM - 1665 (Sydney, NW, AUS) [42603]
2MM-FM - 99.3 (Sydney, NW, AUS) [42606]
2MM-FM - 173.6 (Sydney, NW, AUS) [42607]
2MM-FM - 92.3 (Sydney, NW, AUS) [42605]
2MM-FM - 151.925 (Sydney, NW, AUS) [42604]
2MMM-FM - 104.9 (Sydney, NW, AUS) [42608]
2NIM-FM - 102.3 (Nimbin, NW, AUS) [42147]
2NSB-FM - 99.3 (Chatswood, NW, AUS) [41744]
2NUR-FM - 103.7 (Callaghan, NW, AUS) [41692]
2RDJ-FM - 88.1 (Burwood North, NW, AUS) [41678]
2RE-AM - 1557 KHz (Taree, NW, AUS) [42615]
2RRR-FM - 88.5 (Gladesville, NW, AUS) [41886]
2SM-AM - 1269 (Pyrmont, NW, AUS) [42293]
2SSR-FM - 99.7 (Sutherland, NW, AUS) [42442]
2ST-FM - 106.7 (Bowral, NW, AUS) [41630]
2ST-FM - 91.7 (North Nowra, NW, AUS) [42157]
2TEN-FM - 89.7 (Tenterfield, NW, AUS) [42621]
2TLC-FM (Yamba, NW, AUS) *Unable to locate*
2UE-AM - 954 (Greenwhich, NW, AUS) [41933]
2VTR-FM - 89.9 (Windsor, NW, AUS) [42701]
twowheels (Alexandria, NW, AUS) [41549]
2WKT-FM - 107.1 (Bowral, NW, AUS) [41631]
2WLF-FM - 101.9 (Wagga Wagga, NW, AUS) [42671]
2WS-FM - 101.7 (North Ryde, NW, AUS) [42204]
2XL-AM - 918 (Cooma, NW, AUS) [41812]
2XL-FM - 98.7 (Cooma, NW, AUS) [41813]
2XL-FM - 96.3 (Jindabyne, NW, AUS) [41973]
2XL-FM - 92.1 (Thredbo, NW, AUS) [42623]
Tydskrif vir letterkunde (Pretoria, SAF) [50607]
TygerBurger (Cape Town, SAF) [50421]
Tyo Terveys Turvallisuus (Helsinki, FIN) [43863]
Typographic (Stroud, GBR) *Unable to locate*
Tyre Samachar (Chennai, TN, IND) *Unable to locate*
Tyrone Times (Dungannon, GBR) [53224]

Numbers cited in bold after listings are entry numbers rather than page numbers.

Master Index

Tyurkologiya (Baku, AJN) *Unable to locate*

U

U & I Corporation (Bangkok, THA) *Unable to locate*

U & I Corporation (Bangkok, THA) *Unable to locate*

U Magazine (Dublin, DU, IRL) **[45999]**

U Magazine (London, GBR) **[55351]**

UAE Journal (Luxembourg, LUX) *Unable to locate*

U.A.E. Radio and Television (Dubai, UAE) *Unable to locate*

UAFA Magazine (Riyadh, SAU) *Unable to locate*

UCT-FM (Cape Town, SAF) *Unable to locate*

UCU (London, GBR) **[55352]**

Ucuncu Sektor Kooperatifcilik (Ankara, TUR) **[51518]**

UCV Radio-FM - 103.5 (Vina del Mar, CHL) **[43164]**

Uczucia i tesknoty (Warsaw, POL) **[49771]**

Udbodhan (Kolkata, WB, IND) **[45307]**

Udenrigs (Copenhagen, DEN) *Unable to locate*

Udgeeth (New Delhi, DH, IND) *Unable to locate*

UFM1003 - 100.3 MHz (Singapore, SGP) **[50307]**

UFO Radio-FM - 92.1 (Taipei, TWN) **[51390]**

UG-FM - 106.9 (Alexandra, VI, AUS) **[41533]**

UG-FM - 98.5 (Marysville, VI, AUS) **[42040]**

UG-FM - 88.9 (Yea, VI, AUS) **[42720]**

The Uganda Journal (Kampala, UGA) **[51589]**

Ugeskrift for Laeger (Copenhagen, DEN) **[43685]**

Uitgeverij Genoeg (The Hague, NLD) *Unable to locate*

UK Baha'i Journal (London, GBR) **[55353]**

UK Excellence (London, GBR) **[55354]**

UK Golf (Inverness, GBR) *Unable to locate*

UK Irrigation (Rushden, GBR) **[56427]**

UK Retail Report (London, GBR) *Unable to locate*

UK Swimming (Gillingham, GBR) *Unable to locate*

UK Unquote (London, GBR) **[55355]**

Ukhozi-FM - 90.8 (Durban, SAF) **[50475]**

Ukrainian Journal on Refugee and Migration Law and Policy (Kiev, URE) *Unable to locate*

Ukrainian Law (Kiev, URE) *Unable to locate*

Ukrainica Bioorganica Acta (Kiev, URE) *Unable to locate*

Ulagam Nam Kayil - General Knowledge Book (Chennai, TN, IND) *Unable to locate*

Ulanqab People's Broadcasting Station (Jining, NM, CHN) *Unable to locate*

Ulanqab People's Broadcasting Station (Ulanqab, NM, CHN) *Unable to locate*

Ulster Business (Belfast, GBR) **[52295]**

Ulster Countrywoman (Belfast, GBR) **[52296]**

Ulster Folklife (Holywood, GBR) **[53584]**

Ulster Grocer (Belfast, GBR) **[52297]**

Ulster Star (Lisburn, GBR) **[53863]**

Ultra (London, GBR) **[55356]**

Ultra-FM - 106.5 (North Hobart, TA, AUS) **[42154]**

Ultra Scientist of Physical Sciences (Bhopal, MP, IND) **[45007]**

Ultrafit (Penzance, GBR) **[56251]**

Ultramicroscopy (Cambridge, GBR) **[52904]**

Ultrasound Review of Obstetrics & Gynecology (Abingdon, GBR) *Ceased*

Ulvehunden (Ringsten, DEN) *Unable to locate*

Um Outro Olhar (Sao Paulo, SP, BRZ) *Unable to locate*

Umm Al Qiwain Broadcasting Station (Umm Al Quwain, UAE) *Unable to locate*

Umsebenzi (Johannesburg, SAF) **[50538]**

Umwelt Focus (Forch, SWI) *Unable to locate*

Umwelt-Medizin-Gesellschaft (Bremen, GER) **[44282]**

UN Special (Geneva, SWI) **[51163]**

Una (Riga, LAT) **[47374]**

Uncut (London, GBR) **[55357]**

UNDA News/UNDA Informations (Brussels, BEL) *Unable to locate*

Underground Ernie (London, GBR) **[55358]**

Underwater Technology (London, GBR) **[55359]**

UNESCO Courier (Paris, FRA) **[44087]**

Ung Puls (Frederiksberg, DEN) *Unable to locate*

Ungdom og Idrat (Vejle, DEN) *Unable to locate*

Unibeam (Singapore, SGP) *Unable to locate*

Union (Geneva, SWI) **[51164]**

Union Herald (Petaling Jaya, MYS) *Unable to locate*

Union of Japanese Scientists and Engineers Reports of Statistical Application Research (Tokyo, JPN) *Unable to locate*

Unison Journal **[55351]***

Unistar-FM (Minsk, BLR) *Unable to locate*

UNISWA Journal of Agriculture (Luyengo, SWZ) **[50945]**

UNISWA Research Journal of Agriculture, Science and Technology (Kwaluseni, SWZ) **[50944]**

Unitas (Manila, PHL) **[49560]**

United Kingdom Economic Accounts (Basingstoke, GBR) **[52233]**

Unity (Sofia, BUL) *Unable to locate*

Unity-FM - 101.1 (Southampton, GBR) **[56583]**

Univers Ingineresc (Bucharest, ROM) **[49845]**

Universal-FM - 95.3 (Buenos Aires, ARG) **[41486]**

Universal Military Abstracts (Dehradun, UP, IND) *Unable to locate*

Universal Science and Engineering for Marine Environment (Faisalabad, PAK) **[49295]**

Universal Stereo-FM - 92.1 (Mexico City, DF, MEX) **[47793]**

Universal United (Bangkok, THA) *Unable to locate*

Universidad de Chile Radio-FM - 102.5 (Santiago, CHL) **[43161]**

Universidades (Mexico City, DF, MEX) *Unable to locate*

Universitaria-FM - 104.5 (Carabobo, VEN) **[57018]**

Universitas (Oslo, NOR) **[49210]**

Universitas Friburgensis (Fribourg, SWI) **[51087]**

Universite d'Ankara Faculte des Sciences Communications Serie C Biologie (Ankara, TUR) *Unable to locate*

Universite d'Ankara Faculte des Sciences Communications Serie C1 Geologie (Ankara, TUR) *Unable to locate*

Universites (Paris, FRA) *Unable to locate*

University of Agricultural Sciences, Bangalore Educational Series (Bangalore, KA, IND) *Unable to locate*

University of Agricultural Sciences, Bangalore Information Series (Bangalore, KA, IND) *Unable to locate*

University of Agricultural Sciences, Bangalore—Research Review Series (Bangalore, KA, IND) *Unable to locate*

University of Agricultural Sciences, Bangalore Technical Series (Bangalore, KA, IND) *Unable to locate*

University of Agricultural Sciences, Bangalore U A S Textbook Series (Bangalore, KA, IND) *Unable to locate*

University of Allahabad Education Department Researches and Studies (Allahabad, UP, IND) *Unable to locate*

University of Bombay Journal (Mumbai, MH, IND) *Unable to locate*

University of Calcutta Business Studies (Kolkata, WB, IND) *Unable to locate*

University of Calcutta Department of English Journal (Calcutta, WB, IND) *Unable to locate*

University of Calcutta Department of Sociology Journal (Calcutta, WB, IND) *Unable to locate*

University of Calcutta University College of Medicine Bulletin (Calcutta, WB, IND) *Unable to locate*

University Caterer (Bristol, GBR) **[52734]**

University of Dar es Salaam Library Journal (Dar es Salaam, TZA) **[51406]**

University of Queensland Law Journal (Saint Lucia, QL, AUS) **[42341]**

University of Singapore History Society Journal (Singapore, SGP) *Unable to locate*

University of Tasmania Law Review (Hobart, TA, AUS) *Unable to locate*

University of Tsukuba Institute of Geoscience Science Reports Section A: Geographical Sciences (Ibaraki, JPN) *Unable to locate*

University of Western Australia Law Review (Crawley, WA, AUS) *Unable to locate*

Unix Open (Grabunn, GER) *Unable to locate*

Unsere Jagd (Munich, GER) **[44585]**

U105-FM - 105.8 (Belfast, GBR) **[52304]**

UP-FM - 107.5 (Auckland, NZL) **[48855]**

UP Irrigation Research Institute Technical Memorandum (Roorkee, UP, IND) *Unable to locate*

Update (London, GBR) *Unable to locate*

Update on Cancer Therapeutics (New York, NY, USA) *Ceased*

Update Magazine (Bangkok, THA) **[51447]**

UPDATE Magazine (Dubai, UAE) *Unable to locate*

Upgrade (English Edition) (Barcelona, SPA) **[50705]**

Uplift (New Delhi, DH, IND) *Unable to locate*

The Upper India Motorist (New Delhi, DH, IND) **[45660]**

Upsala Journal of Medical Sciences (Uppsala, SWE) **[51052]**

Uralskaya Kuznitsa (Chebarkul, RUS) *Unable to locate*

URB-AM - 1449 (Bath, GBR) **[52266]**

Urban Design International (Basingstoke, GBR) **[52234]**

Urban Ecosystems (Dordrecht, NLD) **[48584]**

Urban Forestry & Urban Greening (Singapore, SGP) **[50283]**

Urban Hitz (Bondi Junction, NW, AUS) **[41610]**

Urban India (New Delhi, DH, IND) *Unable to locate*

Urban Realm (Glasgow, GBR) **[53456]**

Urban and Rural Planning Thought (New Delhi, DH, IND) *Unable to locate*

Urban Studies (London, GBR) **[55360]**

Urban Water Journal (London, GBR) **[55361]**

Urethane Abstracts (London, GBR) *Ceased*

Urethanes Technology (London, GBR) **[55362]**

Urethanes Technology (Chinese Language Edition) (London, GBR) *Unable to locate*

Urja (New Delhi, DH, IND) *Unable to locate*

Urja Oil and Gas International (New Delhi, DH, IND) *Unable to locate*

URN-AM (Nottingham, GBR) *Unable to locate*

Uroda (Warsaw, POL) **[49772]**

Urodinamica (Milan, ITA) **[46198]**

Urologeb (Dorfen, GER) *Unable to locate*

Urological Research (London, GBR) **[55363]**

Urology Annals (Riyadh, SAU) **[50072]**

URTV (Kuala Lumpur, MYS) **[47638]**

Urumqi People's Broadcasting Station (Urumqi, XU, CHN) *Unable to locate*

Urumqi People's Broadcasting Station (Urumqi, XU, CHN) *Unable to locate*

Urumqi People's Broadcasting Station (Urumqi, XU, CHN) *Unable to locate*

Urumqi People's Broadcasting Station (Urumqi, XU, CHN) *Unable to locate*

URY-AM - 1350 (York, GBR) **[57002]**

US (Karachi, PAK) **[49378]**

Use of English (Leicester, GBR) **[53832]**

Used Car Buyers Guide (North Ryde, NW, AUS) **[42200]**

Used Car Dealer (Peterborough, GBR) *Unable to locate*

Used Car Price Guide (Sandyford, DU, IRL) **[46058]**

User Modeling and User-Adapted Interaction (Dordrecht, NLD) **[48585]**

USI Journal (New Delhi, DH, IND) **[45661]**

Usine Nouvelle (Weekly Edition) (Levallois-Perret, FRA) *Unable to locate*

Numbers cited in bold after listings are entry numbers rather than page numbers.

Using the Right Word (Shanghai, CHN) **[43509]**

Usus Antiquior (London, GBR) **[55364]**

Utaq-i Bazargani va Sanayi' va Ma'adin-i Iran. Haftah'namah (Tehran, IRN) *Unable to locate*

Utilitaire Infos (Clichy, FRA) *Unable to locate*

Utilitas (Reading, GBR) **[56332]**

The Utilities Journal (Oxford, GBR) **[56224]**

Utilities Law Review (Witney, GBR) **[56946]**

Utillaje (Mexico City, DF, MEX) **[47790]**

Utopias/Nuestra Bandera (Madrid, SPA) **[50813]**

Utopie Kreativ (Berlin, GER) *Unable to locate*

Utrecht Law Review (Utrecht, NLD) **[48767]**

Utrecht Studies in Language and Communication (Amsterdam, NLD) **[48268]**

Uttar Bharat Bhoogol Patrika (Gorakhpur, UP, IND) *Unable to locate*

Uttar Pradesh Journal of Zoology (Muzaffarnagar, UP, IND) *Unable to locate*

Utusan Malaysia (Kuala Lumpur, MYS) **[47639]**

Utusan Melayu Mingguan (Kuala Lumpur, MYS) **[47640]**

Uyutnaya Kvartira (Kiev, URE) **[51611]**

UZA Krant (Edegem, BEL) *Unable to locate*

Uzbek Radio - Andizhon (Tashkent, UZN) *Unable to locate*

Uzbek Radio - Buhoro (Tashkent, UZN) *Unable to locate*

Uzbek Radio - Buhoro (Tashkent, UZN) *Unable to locate*

Uzbek Radio - Dangara (Tashkent, UZN) *Unable to locate*

Uzbek Radio - Farghona (Tashkent, UZN) *Unable to locate*

Uzbek Radio - Jar-Kurghon (Tashkent, UZN) *Unable to locate*

Uzbek Radio - Jizzah (Tashkent, UZN) *Unable to locate*

Uzbek Radio - Koson (Tashkent, UZN) *Unable to locate*

Uzbek Radio - Koson (Tashkent, UZN) *Unable to locate*

Uzbek Radio - Kunghirod (Tashkent, UZN) *Unable to locate*

Uzbek Radio - Muborak (Tashkent, UZN) *Unable to locate*

Uzbek Radio - Muynak (Tashkent, UZN) *Unable to locate*

Uzbek Radio - Muynak (Tashkent, UZN) *Unable to locate*

Uzbek Radio - Namangan (Tashkent, UZN) *Unable to locate*

Uzbek Radio - Nukus (Tashkent, UZN) *Unable to locate*

Uzbek Radio - Nukus (Tashkent, UZN) *Unable to locate*

Uzbek Radio - Nurobod (Tashkent, UZN) *Unable to locate*

Uzbek Radio - Piskent (Tashkent, UZN) *Unable to locate*

Uzbek Radio - Samarkand (Tashkent, UZN) *Unable to locate*

Uzbek Radio - Samarkand (Tashkent, UZN) *Unable to locate*

Uzbek Radio - Samarkand (Tashkent, UZN) *Unable to locate*

Uzbek Radio - Samarkand (Tashkent, UZN) *Unable to locate*

Uzbek Radio - Samarkand (Tashkent, UZN) *Unable to locate*

Uzbek Radio - Tashkent (Tashkent, UZN) *Unable to locate*

Uzbek Radio - Tashkent (Tashkent, UZN) *Unable to locate*

Uzbek Radio - Tashkent (Tashkent, UZN) *Unable to locate*

Uzbek Radio - Tashkent (Tashkent, UZN) *Unable to locate*

Uzbek Radio - Tashkent (Tashkent, UZN) *Unable to locate*

Uzbek Radio - Tashkent (Tashkent, UZN) *Unable to locate*

Uzbek Radio - Tashkent (Tashkent, UZN) *Unable to locate*

Uzbek Radio - Tashkent (Tashkent, UZN) *Unable to locate*

Uzbek Radio - Tashkent (Tashkent, UZN) *Unable to locate*

Uzbek Radio - Tashkent (Tashkent, UZN) *Unable to locate*

Uzbek Radio - Tashkent (Tashkent, UZN) *Unable to locate*

Uzbek Radio - Tashkent (Tashkent, UZN) *Unable to locate*

Uzbek Radio - Urgonch (Tashkent, UZN) *Unable to locate*

Uzbek Radio - Vobkent (Tashkent, UZN) *Unable to locate*

Uzbek Radio - Zarafshon (Tashkent, UZN) *Unable to locate*

Uzbek Radio - Zarafshon (Tashkent, UZN) *Unable to locate*

Uzbek Television (Tashkent, UZN) *Unable to locate*

Uzbek Television (Tashkent, UZN) *Unable to locate*

UZLET & SIKER (Budapest, HUN) **[44881]**

V

V Magazine Online (Surrey, GBR) *Unable to locate*

V Yedinom Stroyu (Moscow, RUS) *Unable to locate*

Vaal Vision (Cape Town, SAF) **[50422]**

Vaal Weekly (Cape Town, SAF) **[50423]**

Vachan Sudha (Delhi, DH, IND) **[45108]**

Vacuum Solutions (Bristol, GBR) *Ceased*

Vagabond Reisemagasin (Oslo, NOR) *Unable to locate*

Vagabond Resetidningen (Stockholm, SWE) *Unable to locate*

Vagartha (New Delhi, DH, IND) *Unable to locate*

Vaikunthbhai Mehta Smarak Trust Centre for Studies in Decentralised Industries—Documentation Bulletin (Mumbai, MH, IND) *Unable to locate*

Vaiski (Kuvalehdet, FIN) *Unable to locate*

Vakuutusvaki (Helsinki, FIN) *Unable to locate*

Vale-FM - 96.6 (Shaftesbury, GBR) **[56485]**

Vale-FM - 97.4 (Shaftesbury, GBR) **[56486]**

Valencia Maritima (Valencia, SPA) **[50847]**

Valeurs Actuelles (Paris, FRA) *Unable to locate*

Valley-FM - 89.5 (Erindale, SA, AUS) **[41858]**

Valleys Radio-AM - 1116 (Ebbw Vale, GBR) **[53246]**

Valleys Radio-AM - 999 (Ebbw Vale, GBR) **[53247]**

Valore Scuola Cooperativa (Rome, ITA) *Unable to locate*

The Valuer (London, GBR) *Unable to locate*

Vammais Sanomat (Ikaalinen, FIN) *Unable to locate*

Vanashoba (Mumbai, MH, IND) *Unable to locate*

Vanderbijlpark Ster (Cape Town, SAF) **[50424]**

Vanguard (London, GBR) **[55365]**

Vantage Point (Seoul, KOR) *Unable to locate*

Vanyajati (New Delhi, DH, IND) *Unable to locate*

Var Foda (Uppsala, SWE) **[51053]**

Varen (Gent, BEL) **[42884]**

Variant (Glasgow, GBR) **[53457]**

Variants (Amsterdam, NLD) **[48269]**

Variety Puzzles (Gosford, NW, AUS) **[41923]**

Vascular Disease Prevention (London, GBR) **[55366]**

Vascular Health and Risk Management (Macclesfield, GBR) **[55520]**

Vashe Radio (Voronezh, RUS) *Unable to locate*

Vashe Radio (Voronezh, RUS) *Unable to locate*

Vasudha Monthly (Kathmandu, NPL) *Unable to locate*

VATIS Update Biotechnology (New Delhi, DH, IND) **[45662]**

VATIS Update Food Processing (New Delhi, DH, IND) **[45663]**

VATIS Update Non-Conventional Energy (New Delhi, DH, IND) **[45664]**

VATIS Update Ozone Layer Protection (New Delhi, DH, IND) **[45665]**

VATIS Update Waste Management (New Delhi, DH, IND) **[45666]**

Vauhdin Maailma (Kuvalehdet, FIN) **[43900]**

Vayu Aerospace Review (New Delhi, DH, IND) *Unable to locate*

Vayu Mandal (New Delhi, DH, IND) **[45667]**

Vayuyan (New Delhi, DH, IND) *Unable to locate*

VBI-Nachrichten (Berlin, GER) **[44234]**

VCO Magazin (Vienna, AUT) **[42773]**

V.C.O.T. (Stuttgart, GER) **[44684]**

VDI Nachrichten (Dusseldorf, GER) **[44335]**

VdK Zeitung (Berlin, GER) **[44235]**

VDPP-Rundbrief (Hamburg, GER) *Unable to locate*

Vecherniy Bishkek (Bishkek, KGA) *Unable to locate*

Vecherny Minskt (Minsk, BLR) **[42833]**

The Vedanta Kesari (Chennai, TN, IND) **[45060]**

Vedic Light (New Delhi, DH, IND) *Unable to locate*

Vee & Vlees (The Hague, NLD) *Unable to locate*

Vega-FM - 95.3 (Pyrmont, NW, AUS) **[42294]**

Vega-FM - 91.5 (Richmond, VI, AUS) **[42310]**

Vegaia (Helsinki, FIN) **[43864]**

Vegan (Mariefred, SWE) *Unable to locate*

The Vegan (Birmingham, GBR) **[52372]**

Vegan Forum (Lismore, NW, AUS) *Unable to locate*

Vegetar (Stockholm, SWE) *Unable to locate*

The Vegetarian (Altrincham, GBR) **[52104]**

Vegetatio **[48533]***

Vehicle Recovery Link (Ashwell, GBR) *Unable to locate*

Vehicle Systems Dynamics (Bedford, GBR) *Unable to locate*

Veintiuno (Madrid, SPA) *Unable to locate*

Velki (Calcutta, WB, IND) *Unable to locate*

Vendeglatas (Budapest, HUN) *Unable to locate*

Vendo & Compro (Rozzano, ITA) **[46256]**

Vene (Kuvalehdet, FIN) **[43901]**

Venture (Karachi, PAK) *Unable to locate*

Venus-FM - 105.1 (Asuncion, PAR) **[49409]**

Venus: Japanese Journal of Malacology (Tokyo, JPN) **[47055]**

VERA (Reykjavik, ICE) *Unable to locate*

Verbindungstechnik in der Elektronik und Feinwerktechnik (Dusseldorf, GER) *Ceased*

Verbum (Egyetem, HUN) **[44889]**

Vereeniging Ster (Cape Town, SAF) **[50425]**

Vereniging voor Kind & Adoptiegezin (Brugge, BEL) *Unable to locate*

Verhandlungen der Gesellschaft fur Okologie (Berlin, GER) **[44236]**

Verkehrs Rundschau (Munich, GER) *Unable to locate*

Verkstaderna (Stockholm, SWE) *Unable to locate*

Vernacular Architecture (London, GBR) **[55367]**

Verre (Paris, FRA) *Unable to locate*

Verslagen en Mededelingen (Gent, BEL) **[42885]**

Veseliba (Riga, LAT) **[47375]**

Veselye Ideiki (Kiev, URE) **[51612]**

Vestnik Zoologii (Warsaw, POL) **[49773]**

Veteran & Sportbilsmagasinet (Oslo, NOR) *Unable to locate*

Veterinarna Zbirka (Sofia, BUL) *Ceased*

Veterinary Anaesthesia and Analgesia (Oxford, GBR) **[56225]**

Veterinary and Comparative Oncology (Oxford, GBR) **[56226]**

Veterinary Dermatology (Harlescott, GBR) **[53508]**

Veterinary Medicine: Series A; Journal of **[56220]***

Veterinary Medicine Series B; Journal of **[56230]***

Veterinary Nurse Journal (Harlow, GBR) *Unable to locate*

Veterinary Quarterly (Utrecht, NLD) *Ceased*

Veterinary Research (Faisalabad, PAK) **[49296]**

Veterinary Review (Kathmandu, NPL) *Unable to locate*

Veterinary Sciences Tomorrow (Utrecht, NLD) **[48768]**

Veterinary Times (Peterborough, GBR) **[56263]**

Vetus Testamentum (Leiden, NLD) **[48729]**

Vi Foraldrar (We Parents) (Kil, SWE) *Unable to locate*

Vi (We) (Stockholm, SWE) *Unable to locate*

Via Inmarsat Magazine (London, GBR) **[55368]**

Via Libre (Madrid, SPA) **[50814]**

Via Secura (Brussels, BEL) **[42873]**

Viajes National Geographic (Barcelona, SPA) **[50706]**

Vibe 105-FM **[52775]***

Vibe 101-FM **[52742]***

Victim Support (London, GBR) **[55369]**

The Victoria Baptist Witness (Hawthorn, VI, AUS) **[41943]**

Numbers cited in bold after listings are entry numbers rather than page numbers.

Master Index

Victorian Historical Journal (Melbourne, VI, AUS) *Unable to locate*

Vida Hispanica (Leicester, GBR) **[53833]**

Vida Rotaria (Rosario, ARG) **[41488]**

Video Uit & Thuis (Hoogland, NLD) *Unable to locate*

Videokraut (Utrecht, NLD) *Unable to locate*

Vides Vestis (Riga, LAT) **[47376]**

Vidura (New Delhi, DH, IND) *Unable to locate*

Vidya Bharathi (Bangalore, KA, IND) *Unable to locate*

Vidyajyoti Journal of Theological Reflection (Delhi, DH, IND) **[45109]**

Viet Nam News (Hanoi, VNM) *Unable to locate*

Vietnam Business (Hanoi, VNM) *Unable to locate*

Vietnam Commerce and Industry (Hanoi, VNM) *Unable to locate*

Vietnam Courier (Hanoi, VNM) *Unable to locate*

Vietnam Cultural Window (Hanoi, VNM) *Unable to locate*

Vietnam Economic News (Makati City, PHL) *Unable to locate*

Vietnam Economic Times (Hanoi, VNM) *Unable to locate*

Vietnam Investment Review (Hanoi, VNM) **[57054]**

Vietnam Journal of Mathematics (Dordrecht, NLD) **[48586]**

Vietnam Social Sciences (Hanoi, VNM) *Unable to locate*

Vietnam Today (Lyncham, AC, AUS) *Unable to locate*

Vietnamese Trade Unions (Hanoi, VNM) *Unable to locate*

Viewfinder (London, GBR) **[55370]**

Viewpoint (Lahore, PAK) *Unable to locate*

Viewpoint (London, GBR) **[55371]**

Vignana Bharathi (Bangalore, KA, IND) *Unable to locate*

Vigyan Pragati (New Delhi, DH, IND) *Unable to locate*

Viherpiha (Helsinki, FIN) **[43865]**

Vikalpa (Ahmedabad, GJ, IND) *Unable to locate*

Vikas, Nepal Journal of Development (Kathmandu, NPL) *Unable to locate*

Vikerraadio-FM (Tallinn, EST) *Unable to locate*

Vikerraadio-FM - 105.6 (Tallinn, EST) **[43789]**

Vikerraadio-FM - 105.1 (Tallinn, EST) **[43790]**

Vikerraadio-FM - 105.3 (Tallinn, EST) **[43788]**

Viking-FM - 96.9 (Hull, GBR) **[53633]**

Vikram (Ujjain, MP, IND) *Unable to locate*

Vikram Research Guide (Ujjain, MP, IND) *Unable to locate*

Vikrant (New Delhi, DH, IND) *Unable to locate*

Vikrant's Defence Diary (New Delhi, DH, IND) *Unable to locate*

Villivarsa (Kuvalehdet, FIN) **[43902]**

Vincula (Blackrock, DU, IRL) *Unable to locate*

VINE (Bradford, GBR) **[52556]**

Vintage Austin Magazine (Alfreton, GBR) **[52100]**

Vintage Roadscene (Kingston upon Thames, GBR) **[53725]**

Vinyl-FM - 107.1 (Stockholm, SWE) **[51044]**

Violencia domestica, Genero y derechos humanos, Genero y medio ambiente (Cuernavaca, MO, MEX) *Unable to locate*

Virgin-FM (London, GBR) *Unable to locate*

Virgin Radio-AM (London, GBR) *Unable to locate*

Virgin Radio-FM - 104.4 (Dubai, UAE) **[51670]**

Virologie (Montrouge, FRA) **[44008]**

Virology Journal (London, GBR) **[55372]**

Virtual and Physical Prototyping (Abingdon, GBR) **[52085]**

Viscom (Saint Gallen, SWI) **[51225]**

Vishveshvaranand Indological Journal (Hoshiarpur, PJ, IND) *Unable to locate*

Vishveshvaranand Indological Paper Series (Hoshiarpur, PJ, IND) *Unable to locate*

Vishveshvaranand Indological Series (Hoshiarpur, PJ, IND) *Unable to locate*

Vishveshvaranand Vedic Research Institute Research and General Publications (Hoshiarpur, PJ, IND) *Unable to locate*

Vishwakarma (Calcutta, WB, IND) *Unable to locate*

Visier (Singhofen, GER) *Unable to locate*

Vision (Gurgaon, HY, IND) **[45128]**

Vision (London, GBR) *Unable to locate*

Vision-FM - 105.3 (Oranjestad, ARU) **[41494]**

Vision Magazine (Manila, PHL) *Unable to locate*

Vision 100-FM - 100 (Palmerston North, NZL) **[48970]**

Vision Universal (Sao Paulo, SP, BRZ) *Unable to locate*

visitoi (Frederiksberg, DEN) *Unable to locate*

Visitor (Dundrum, DU, IRL) **[46011]**

Visual (Madrid, SPA) **[50815]**

Visual Communication (London, GBR) **[55373]**

Visual Culture in Britain (Abingdon, GBR) **[52086]**

Visual Geosciences (New York, NY, USA) *Ceased*

Visva - Bharati Journal of Philosophy (Birbhum, WB, IND) *Unable to locate*

Visva - Bharati Quarterly (Santiniketan, WB, IND) *Unable to locate*

VISWA (Secunderabad, AP, IND) *Unable to locate*

Viszeralmedizin (Freiburg, GER) **[44374]**

Vita (Warsaw, POL) **[49774]**

Vita in Campagna (Verona, ITA) **[46281]**

Vital (London, GBR) **[55374]**

The Vitreous Enameller (Cannock, GBR) **[52916]**

Viva! Beauty (Kiev, URE) **[51613]**

Viva! Biographia (Kiev, URE) **[51614]**

Viva Lancia! (Stapeley, GBR) *Unable to locate*

Viva Origino (Osaka, JPN) **[46629]**

Vivek (Mumbai, MH, IND) **[45449]**

Vivekananda Kendra Patrika (Chennai, TN, IND) **[45061]**

Viversani & Belli (Milan, ITA) *Unable to locate*

VIVIAN (Ostenburg, GER) *Unable to locate*

Vivir con Salud (Barcelona, SPA) *Unable to locate*

Vivre sa Sante (Paris, FRA) *Ceased*

Vjazanie Vashe Hobby (Moscow, RUS) **[49998]**

Vladivostok News (Vladivostok, RUS) **[50041]**

Vleeswetenschap (Brussels, BEL) *Unable to locate*

Vmaxx (Schwabach, GER) *Unable to locate*

VOA Burmese - 12120 (Rangoon, MYA) **[47821]**

VOA Burmese - 11910 (Rangoon, MYA) **[47820]**

VOA Burmese - 1575 (Rangoon, MYA) **[47818]**

VOA Burmese - 9325 (Rangoon, MYA) **[47819]**

VOA Burmese - 11980 (Rangoon, MYA) **[47816]**

VOA Burmese - 9505 (Rangoon, MYA) **[47817]**

VOA Burmese - 6185 (Rangoon, MYA) **[47815]**

VOA Khmer - 15340 (Phnom Penh, CMB) **[43123]**

VOA Khmer - 1575 (Phnom Penh, CMB) **[43121]**

VOA Khmer - 5955 (Phnom Penh, CMB) **[43122]**

VOA Khmer - 7130 (Phnom Penh, CMB) **[43120]**

VOA Khmer - 7155 (Phnom Penh, CMB) **[43118]**

VOA Khmer - 6060 (Phnom Penh, CMB) **[43119]**

VOA Lao - 9510 (Bangkok, THA) **[51454]**

VOA Lao - 11930 (Bangkok, THA) **[51453]**

VOA Lao - 1575 (Bangkok, THA) **[51452]**

The Vocational Aspect of Education **[51956]***

Voi Hyvin (Helsinki, FIN) **[43866]**

Voice of Ahinsa (Etah, UP, IND) *Unable to locate*

Voice of Barbados-FM - 92.9 (Bridgetown, BRB) **[42831]**

Voice of the Cape-FM - 100.4 (Salt River, SAF) **[50625]**

Voice of Child Workers (Kathmandu, NPL) **[47848]**

Voice & Data (New Delhi, DH, IND) *Unable to locate*

Voice of the Economy (Hangzhou, ZH, CHN) *Unable to locate*

Voice-FM - 99.9 (Ballarat, VI, AUS) **[41572]**

Voice of the Homeland (West Beirut, LBN) *Unable to locate*

Voice of Islam (Karachi, PAK) *Unable to locate*

Voice of Jinling (Nanjing, JS, CHN) *Unable to locate*

Voice of Jinling (Nanjing, JS, CHN) *Unable to locate*

Voice of Jinling (Nanjing, JS, CHN) *Unable to locate*

Voice of Kuanghua (Taipei, TWN) *Ceased*

Voice of Kuanghua (Taipei, TWN) *Ceased*

Voice of Kuanghua (Taipei, TWN) *Ceased*

Voice of Kuanghua (Taipei, TWN) *Ceased*

Voice of Kuanghua (Taipei, TWN) *Ceased*

Voice of Kuanghua (Taipei, TWN) *Ceased*

Voice of Kuanghua (Taipei, TWN) *Ceased*

Voice of Lebanon - Beirut (Beirut, LBN) *Unable to locate*

Voice of Maldives (Male, MDV) *Unable to locate*

Voice of Maldives (Male, MDV) *Unable to locate*

Voice of Maldives (Male, MDV) *Unable to locate*

Voice of Millions (New Delhi, DH, IND) *Unable to locate*

Voice of Mongolia - Chinese (Ulaanbaatar, MNG) *Unable to locate*

Voice of Mongolia - Chinese (Ulaanbaatar, MNG) *Unable to locate*

Voice of Mongolia - English (Ulaanbaatar, MNG) *Unable to locate*

Voice of Mongolia - English (Ulaanbaatar, MNG) *Unable to locate*

Voice of Mongolia - Japanese (Ulaanbaatar, MNG) *Unable to locate*

Voice of Mongolia - Mongolian (Ulaanbaatar, MNG) *Unable to locate*

Voice of Mongolia - Russian (Ulaanbaatar, MNG) *Unable to locate*

Voice of the National Resistance (West Beirut, LBN) *Unable to locate*

Voice of Nevis (VON) Radio-AM - 895 (Charlestown, SKN) **[50050]**

Voice of the Oppressed - Ba'labakk (Beirut, LBN) *Unable to locate*

Voice of the People-FM - 104 (Beirut, LBN) **[47433]**

Voice of the People-FM - 103.7 (Beirut, LBN) **[47434]**

Voice of Pujiang (Shanghai, SH, CHN) *Unable to locate*

Voice of Pujiang (Shanghai, SH, CHN) *Unable to locate*

Voice of Pujiang (Shanghai, SH, CHN) *Unable to locate*

Voice of Pujiang (Shanghai, SH, CHN) *Unable to locate*

Voice of Samanvaya (Chennai, TN, IND) *Unable to locate*

Voice of the Strait (Fuzhou, FJ, CHN) *Unable to locate*

Voice of the Strait (Fuzhou, FJ, CHN) *Unable to locate*

Voice of the Strait (Fuzhou, FJ, CHN) *Unable to locate*

Voice of the Strait (Fuzhou, FJ, CHN) *Unable to locate*

Voice of the Strait (Fuzhou, FJ, CHN) *Unable to locate*

Voice of the Strait (Fuzhou, FJ, CHN) *Ceased*

Voice of the Strait (Fuzhou, FJ, CHN) *Ceased*

Voice of the Strait (Fuzhou, FJ, CHN) *Unable to locate*

Voice of the Strait (Fuzhou, FJ, CHN) *Unable to locate*

Voice of the Strait (Fuzhou, FJ, CHN) *Unable to locate*

Voice of Teacher (Kathmandu, NPL) *Unable to locate*

Voice of Victory Broadcasting Co. (Tainan, TWN) *Unable to locate*

Voice of Vietnam - An Giang - 1070 KHz (An Giang, VNM) **[57044]**

Voice of Vietnam - An Nhon - 648 KHz (An Nhon, VNM) **[57077]**

Voice of Vietnam - Ba Ria Vung tau - 1500 KHz (Ba Ria Vung tau, VNM) **[57031]**

Voice of Vietnam - Binh Thuan - 5000 KHz (Binh Thuan, VNM) **[57033]**

Voice of Vietnam - Binh Thuan - 1100 KHz (Binh Thuan, VNM) **[57034]**

Voice of Vietnam - Binh Thuan - 765 KHz (Binh Thuan, VNM) **[57032]**

Voice of Vietnam - Can Tho - 780 KHz (Can Tho, VNM) **[57035]**

Voice of Vietnam - Da Nang - 600 KHz (Da Nang, VNM) **[57037]**

Voice of Vietnam - Dac Lac - 4800 KHz (Dac Lac, VNM) **[57038]**

Numbers cited in bold after listings are entry numbers rather than page numbers.

Voice of Vietnam - Dac Lac - 1089 KHz (Dac Lac, VNM) **[57039]**

Voice of Vietnam - Dac Lac (Hanoi, VNM) *Unable to locate*

Voice of Vietnam - Dai Tieng Noi (Hmong Service) - 5030 KHz (Dai Tieng Noi, VNM) **[57040]**

Voice of Vietnam - Dong Hoi - 630 KHz (Dong Hoi, VNM) **[57041]**

Voice of Vietnam - Dong Thap - 710 KHz (Dong Thap, VNM) **[57042]**

Voice of Vietnam - Gia Lai - 630 KHz (Gia Lai, VNM) **[57043]**

Voice of Vietnam - Ha Giang - 570 KHz (Ha Giang, VNM) **[57045]**

Voice of Vietnam - Ha Tay - 1180 KHz (Ha Tay, VNM) **[57046]**

Voice of Vietnam - Ha Tinh - 900 KHz (Ha Tinh, VNM) **[57049]**

Voice of Vietnam - Hai Hung - 1195 KHz (Hai Hung, VNM) **[57050]**

Voice of Vietnam - Hanoi - 675 KHz (Hanoi, VNM) **[57055]**

Voice of Vietnam - Hanoi - 1242 KHz (Hanoi, VNM) **[57056]**

Voice of Vietnam - Hanoi (Hanoi, VNM) *Unable to locate*

Voice of Vietnam - Ho Chi Minh C (Hanoi, VNM) *Unable to locate*

Voice of Vietnam - Ho Chi Minh C (Hanoi, VNM) *Unable to locate*

Voice of Vietnam - Ho Chi Minh City - 655 KHz (Ho Chi Minh City, VNM) **[57058]**

Voice of Vietnam - Khanh Hoa - 576 KHz (Khanh Hoa, VNM) **[57059]**

Voice of Vietnam - Kien Giang - 970 KHz (Kien Giang, VNM) **[57060]**

Voice of Vietnam - Kon Tum - 980 KHz (Kontum, VNM) **[57061]**

Voice of Vietnam - Lai Cau 1 - 4215 KHz (Lai Cau Town, VNM) **[57063]**

Voice of Vietnam - Lam Dong - 550 KHz (Lam Dong, VNM) **[57066]**

Voice of Vietnam - Lam Dong - 4675 KHz (Lam Dong, VNM) **[57065]**

Voice of Vietnam - Lao Cai - 4677 KHz (Lao Cai, VNM) **[57068]**

Voice of Vietnam - Lao Cai - 5597 KHz (Lao Cai, VNM) **[57067]**

Voice of Vietnam - Me Tri 1 - 549 KHz (Me Tri, VNM) **[57071]**

Voice of Vietnam - Me Tri 1 - 570 KHz (Me Tri, VNM) **[57070]**

Voice of Vietnam - Minh Hai - 1120 KHz (Minh Hai, VNM) **[57072]**

Voice of Vietnam - Nam Ha - 1280 KHz (Nam Ha, VNM) **[57073]**

Voice of Vietnam - National Network 2 (Hanoi, VNM) *Unable to locate*

Voice of Vietnam - Ngho An - 5200 KHz (Nghe An, VNM) **[57074]**

Voice of Vietnam - Nghe An - 782 KHz (Nghe An, VNM) **[57075]**

Voice of Vietnam - Nhatrang - 580 KHz (Nhatrang, VNM) **[57076]**

Voice of Vietnam - Ninh Binh (Hanoi, VNM) *Unable to locate*

Voice of Vietnam - Ninh Thuan (Hanoi, VNM) *Unable to locate*

Voice of Vietnam - Phu Yen (Hanoi, VNM) *Unable to locate*

Voice of Vietnam - Quan Tre - 657 KHz (Quan Tre, VNM) **[57080]**

Voice of Vietnam - Quan Tre - 558 KHz (Quan Tre, VNM) **[57081]**

Voice of Vietnam - Quan Tre - 747 KHz (Quan Tre, VNM) **[57079]**

Voice of Vietnam - Quang Binh - 846 KHz (Quang Binh, VNM) **[57082]**

Voice of Vietnam - Quang Nam - 600 KHz (Quang Nam, VNM) **[57083]**

Voice of Vietnam - Quang Ngai - 774 KHz (Quang Ngai, VNM) **[57084]**

Voice of Vietnam - Quang Ninh - 700 KHz (Quang Ninh, VNM) **[57085]**

Voice of Vietnam - Radio Cao Bang - 6530 KHz (Cao Bang, VNM) **[57036]**

Voice of Vietnam - Radio Lai Cau 2 - 6395 KHz (Lai Cau Town, VNM) **[57064]**

Voice of Vietnam - Radio Lao Cai - 6702 KHz (Lao Cai, VNM) **[57069]**

Voice of Vietnam - Radio Son La - 4965 KHz (Son La, VNM) **[57087]**

Voice of Vietnam - Radio Son La 1 - 4739.5 KHz (Son La, VNM) **[57088]**

Voice of Vietnam - Radio TV Gia Lai - 4722.5 KHz (Playcu, VNM) **[57078]**

Voice of Vietnam - Radio TV Kontum - 4800 KHz (Kontum, VNM) **[57062]**

Voice of Vietnam - Radio Yen Bai - 5000 KHz (Yen Bai, VNM) **[57099]**

Voice of Vietnam - Soc Trang - 1200 KHz (Soc Trang, VNM) **[57086]**

Voice of Vietnam - Song Be - 572 KHz (Song Be, VNM) **[57090]**

Voice of Vietnam - Song Be - 970 KHz (Song Be, VNM) **[57089]**

Voice of Vietnam - Tay Ninh - 580 KHz (Tay Ninh, VNM) **[57091]**

Voice of Vietnam - Thai Binh - 1250 KHz (Thai Binh, VNM) **[57092]**

Voice of Vietnam - Thanh Hoa - 850 KHz (Thanh Hoa, VNM) **[57093]**

Voice of Vietnam - Thua Thien Hue - 720 KHz (Thua Thien Hue, VNM) **[57094]**

Voice of Vietnam - Tien Giang - 828 KHz (Tien Giang, VNM) **[57095]**

Voice of Vietnam - Tra Vinh - 1053 KHz (Tra Vinh, VNM) **[57096]**

Voice of Vietnam - Tuyen Quang - 4740 KHz (Tuyen Quang, VNM) **[57097]**

Voice of Vietnam - Vinh Long - 950 KHz (Vinh Long, VNM) **[57098]**

Voice of Vietnam - Yen Bai - 6541.8 KHz (Yen Bai, VNM) **[57100]**

Voice of Vietnam - Yen Bai - 580 KHz (Yen Bai, VNM) **[57101]**

Voice of Workers (Addis Ababa, ETH) *Unable to locate*

Voice of the Working Woman (New Delhi, DH, IND) *Unable to locate*

Voice of Xihu (Hangzhou, ZH, CHN) *Unable to locate*

Voice of Xingsha (Changsha, HA, CHN) *Unable to locate*

Voice of Xingsha (Changsha, HA, CHN) *Unable to locate*

Voice of Xingsha (Changsha, HA, CHN) *Unable to locate*

Voice&Data (Wahroonga, NW, AUS) **[42678]**

Voie Libre (Auray, FRA) **[43916]**

Volare (Rozzano, ITA) **[46257]**

Volksblad (Cape Town, SAF) **[50426]**

Volkswagen Audi Car **[56908]***

Volkswagen Driver (Westoning, GBR) **[56908]**

VolksWorld (Croydon, GBR) **[53137]**

Volna (Moscow, RUS) *Unable to locate*

Volna 100.9 FM (Nizhniy Novgorod, RUS) *Unable to locate*

Volnaya Kuban (Krasnodar, RUS) *Unable to locate*

Volontaires en Eglise (Paris, FRA) *Unable to locate*

Volontari Perlo Sviluppo (Milan, ITA) *Unable to locate*

Voluntary Action (New Delhi, DH, IND) *Unable to locate*

Voluntary Sector (London, GBR) **[55375]**

Voluntary Sector Review (Bristol, GBR) **[52735]**

Voprosy Ekonomiki (Moscow, RUS) *Unable to locate*

Vorwarts (Berlin, GER) *Unable to locate*

Voyager (Lelystad, NLD) *Unable to locate*

Vreni Muilles **[51055]***

Vrishchik (Baroda, GJ, IND) *Unable to locate*

Vrouw en Wereld (Brussels, BEL) *Unable to locate*

VRT Radio 1-FM - 94.2 (Brussels, BEL) **[42878]**

Vrystaat (Cape Town, SAF) **[50427]**

VT Krishnamachari Memorial Lecture Series (New Delhi, DH, IND) *Unable to locate*

Vulnerable Children and Youth Studies (Abingdon, GBR) **[52087]**

Vulture News (Parkview, SAF) **[50563]**

VW Scene International (Herten, GER) **[44484]**

Vyavasaya Keralam (Trivandrum, KE, IND) *Unable to locate*

Vyshitye Kartiny (Moscow, RUS) **[49999]**

W

W A P D A News (Lahore, PAK) *Unable to locate*

W U F A (Peshawar, PAK) *Unable to locate*

W & V Werben & Verkaufen (Munich, GER) **[44586]**

Waddenmagazine (Harlingen, NLD) *Unable to locate*

Wafangdian People's Broadcasting Station (Wafangdian, LI, CHN) *Unable to locate*

Waikato This Week (Hamilton, NZL) *Unable to locate*

The Wainuiomata News (Wainuiomata, NZL) *Unable to locate*

Wairarapa Times-Age (Masterton, NZL) **[48937]**

Waitrose Food Illustrated (London, GBR) **[55376]**

Wales Young Farmer (Builth Wells, GBR) *Unable to locate*

Walia (Addis Ababa, ETH) *Unable to locate*

Walike (Conakry, GIN) *Unable to locate*

Wall Street Journal—Europe (Heerlen, NLD) *Unable to locate*

Wallpaper (London, GBR) *Unable to locate*

Wallpaper* (London, GBR) **[55377]**

The Wanderer (Pyrmont, NW, AUS) **[42291]**

Wanderlust (Windsor, GBR) **[56933]**

Wanganui Chronicle (Wanganui, NZL) **[48996]**

Wanita (Kuala Lumpur, MYS) **[47641]**

Wanneroo Times (Joondalup, WA, AUS) **[41975]**

The War Cry (Kingston, JAM) **[46291]**

The War Cry (London, GBR) **[55378]**

War & Society (London, GBR) **[55379]**

War Veteran (Moscow, RUS) *Unable to locate*

Warana (Sandy, GBR) *Unable to locate*

Warehouse & Logistics News (Kings Langley, GBR) **[53711]**

Warfare (London, GBR) *Unable to locate*

Warme-und Stoffubertragung **[44497]***

Warmer Bulletin (Skipton, GBR) **[56555]**

Warminster Journal (Warminster, GBR) **[56847]**

Warna 94.2 FM - 94.2 MHz (Singapore, SGP) **[50308]**

Warragul & Drovin Gazette (Warragul, VI, AUS) **[42685]**

Warrior (Kohima, NG, IND) *Unable to locate*

Warsaw Insider (Warsaw, POL) **[49775]**

Warship Technology (London, GBR) **[55380]**

Warship World (Liskeard, GBR) **[53864]**

Warta Konsumen (Jakarta, IDN) *Unable to locate*

Warwick Courier (Leamington Spa, GBR) **[53750]**

Warwick Daily News (Sydney, NW, AUS) **[42591]**

Warwick & Southern Downs Weekly (Sydney, NW, AUS) **[42592]**

Warwickshire Life (Cheltenham, GBR) **[52979]**

Wasafiri (Abingdon, GBR) **[52088]**

Wasser Energie Luft/Eau Energie Air (Baden, SWI) **[51057]**

Wasser und Energiewirtschaft **[51057]***

Waste & Environment Today (Abingdon, GBR) *Ceased*

The Waste Manager (London, GBR) *Unable to locate*

Waste Planning (Northallerton, GBR) *Unable to locate*

Waste Streams **[42677]***

Watan (Kuala Lumpur, MYS) *Unable to locate*

Watch Dog (Bangkok, THA) *Unable to locate*

Water Asset Management International (London, GBR) **[55381]**

Water Bulletin (London, GBR) *Unable to locate*

Water and Energy Abstracts (New Delhi, DH, IND) *Ceased*

Water and Environment Journal (Jerusalem, ISR) *Unable to locate*

Water and Environment Manager (London, GBR) **[55382]**

Water Intelligence Online (London, GBR) **[55383]**

Water Policy (London, GBR) **[55384]**

Water Practice and Technology (London, GBR) **[55385]**

Water Quality International **[55389]***

Water Report (Tokyo, JPN) *Ceased*

Water Resources Journal (Bangkok, THA) **[51448]**

Water Resources Management Series (New Delhi, DH, IND) *Unable to locate*

Water Resources Protection (Nanjing, JS, CHN) **[43460]**

Water Science and Engineering (Nanjing, JS, CHN) **[43461]**

Water Science & Technology (London, GBR) **[55386]**

Water Science & Technology (London, GBR) **[55387]**

Water Sewage & Effluent (Bedfordview, SAF) *Unable to locate*

Water Supply (London, GBR) **[55388]**

Water Transport Statistics of India (New Delhi, DH, IND) *Unable to locate*

Water 21 (London, GBR) **[55389]**

Water Utility Management International (London, GBR) **[55390]**

Numbers cited in bold after listings are entry numbers rather than page numbers.

Master Index

Water and Wastes in New Zealand (Wellington, NZL) **[49036]**

Water & Wastewater Asia (Singapore, SGP) **[50284]**

Water Wheel (Pretoria, SAF) **[50608]**

Waterford News & Star (Waterford, WA, IRL) **[46063]**

Waterford Today (Waterford City, WA, IRL) **[46065]**

Waterkampioen (The Hague, NLD) **[48629]**

Waterlife (London, GBR) **[55391]**

Waterlines (Rugby, GBR) **[56425]**

Watonian (Watford, GBR) *Unable to locate*

Watton & Swaffham Times (Swaffham, GBR) **[56696]**

Watt's NEW? (Brussels, BEL) **[42874]**

Wave-FM - 96.5 (Warrawong, NW, AUS) **[42687]**

Wave-FM - 102.0 (Dundee, GBR) **[53223]**

Wave-FM - 105.8 (Fareham, GBR) **[53376]**

Wave-FM - 105.2 (Fareham, GBR) **[53377]**

The Wave-FM - 96.4 (Swansea, GBR) **[56709]**

Waveney Advertiser (Great Yarmouth, GBR) **[53484]**

Waverley Leader (Melbourne, VI, AUS) **[42089]**

Waves in Random and Complex Media (Abingdon, GBR) **[52089]**

Wax (Glasgow, GBR) *Unable to locate*

The Way (Quezon City, PHL) *Unable to locate*

Wayfarer News (Colchester, GBR) **[53054]**

WDCS (London, GBR) **[55392]**

WDM in Action (London, GBR) **[55393]**

We Parents (Nasik, MH, IND) *Unable to locate*

Wealth (London, GBR) **[55394]**

Wealth Asia (New Delhi, DH, IND) *Unable to locate*

Weather (Reading, GBR) **[56333]**

The Weaver (Wodonga, VI, AUS) **[42702]**

Web Designer (Bournemouth, GBR) **[52429]**

Web Intelligence and Agent Systems (Amsterdam, NLD) **[48270]**

Web Journal on Cultural Patrimony (Naples, ITA) **[46203]**

The Web Philippines (Makati City, PHL) *Unable to locate*

Web User (London, GBR) **[55395]**

Wedding Professional (Barnsley, GBR) **[52184]**

Wedding & Travel (Singapore, SGP) **[50285]**

Weed Biology and Management (Fukui, JPN) **[46333]**

Weed Research (Doorwerth, NLD) **[48317]**

The Week (London, GBR) **[55396]**

Weekblad Schuttevaer (Deventer, NLD) *Unable to locate*

The Weekend Magazine (Dubai, UAE) *Unable to locate*

The Weekend Star (Kingston, JAM) **[46292]**

The Weekender (Rotorua, NZL) *Unable to locate*

Weekly Cutting Edge (Lahore, PAK) **[49389]**

Weekly Epidemiological Record (Geneva, SWI) **[51165]**

The Weekly News (Levin, NZL) *Unable to locate*

Weekly Round Table (New Delhi, DH, IND) *Unable to locate*

Weekly Shonen Sunday (Tokyo, JPN) **[47056]**

Weekly Times Messenger (Port Adelaide, SA, AUS) **[42257]**

WEHRTECHNIK (Bonn, GER) **[44272]**

Weifang People's Broadcasting Station (Weifang, SD, CHN) *Unable to locate*

Weifang People's Broadcasting Station (Weifang, SD, CHN) *Unable to locate*

Weifang People's Broadcasting Station (Weifang, SD, CHN) *Unable to locate*

Weifang People's Broadcasting Station (Weifang, SD, CHN) *Unable to locate*

Weifang People's Broadcasting Station (Weifang, SD, CHN) *Unable to locate*

Weifang People's Broadcasting Station (Weifang, SD, CHN) *Unable to locate*

Weigi World (Beijing, CHN) *Unable to locate*

Weihai People's Broadcasting Station (Jinan, SD, CHN) *Unable to locate*

Weihai People's Broadcasting Station (Weihai, SD, CHN) *Unable to locate*

Weihai People's Broadcasting Station (Weihai, SD, CHN) *Unable to locate*

Weihai People's Broadcasting Station (Weihai, SD, CHN) *Unable to locate*

Weihai People's Broadcasting Station (Weihai, SD, CHN) *Unable to locate*

Weihai People's Broadcasting Station (Weihai, SD, CHN) *Unable to locate*

Weir Bulletin (Glasgow, GBR) **[53458]**

Welcome to London (London, GBR) *Unable to locate*

Welding & Metal Fabrication (Epsom, GBR) *Unable to locate*

Welfare World (Birmingham, GBR) *Unable to locate*

Well Done (Copenhagen, DEN) *Unable to locate*

WellBeing (North Ryde, NW, AUS) **[42201]**

Wellington Today (Christchurch, NZL) **[48879]**

Wellness Foods Europe (Nuremberg, GER) **[44617]**

The Wellsian (Durham City, GBR) **[53233]**

Welsh Club Golfer (Glasgow, GBR) **[53459]**

Welsh Farmer (Aberystwyth, GBR) *Unable to locate*

Welsh Music (Llanelli, GBR) **[53885]**

Weltwirtschaftliches Archiv **[44508]***

Welwyn & Hatfield Times (Welwyn Garden City, GBR) **[56884]**

Wembley & Kingsbury Times (London, GBR) **[55397]**

WEMOScoop (Amsterdam, NLD) *Ceased*

Wendekreis (Immensee, SWI) *Unable to locate*

Wendy (Copenhagen, DEN) *Unable to locate*

Wenshan People's Broadcasting Station (Wenshan Xian, YU, CHN) *Unable to locate*

Wenzhou People's Broadcasting Station (Wenzhou, ZH, CHN) *Unable to locate*

Wenzhou People's Broadcasting Station (Wenzhou, ZH, CHN) *Unable to locate*

Wenzhou People's Broadcasting Station (Wenzhou, ZH, CHN) *Unable to locate*

Wenzhou People's Broadcasting Station (Wenzhou, ZH, CHN) *Unable to locate*

Wenzhou People's Broadcasting Station (Wenzhou, ZH, CHN) *Unable to locate*

Wenzhou People's Broadcasting Station (Wenzhou, ZH, CHN) *Unable to locate*

Werbeforschung & Praxis **[42771]***

Wereldwijd (Antwerp, BEL) *Unable to locate*

Werk, Bauen und Wohnen (Zurich, SWI) **[51296]**

Werkkunde fur Chore, Chor-Management, Chorleiter-Verguetung (Weimar, GER) *Unable to locate*

Werkzeug Technik (Boulogne, FRA) **[43922]**

Weskus News (Cape Town, SAF) **[50428]**

Weslander (Cape Town, SAF) **[50429]**

Wessex-FM - 96 (Dorchester, GBR) **[53191]**

Wessex Scene (Southampton, GBR) **[56579]**

West African Journal of Applied Ecology (Accra, GHA) **[44730]**

West African Journal of Medicine (Ibadan, OY, NGA) **[49104]**

West African Journal of Pharmacology and Drug Research (Benin City, NGA) **[49068]**

West African Journal of Radiology (Nsukka, NGA) **[49153]**

West Bengal Bureau of Educational and Psychological Research (Calcutta, WB, IND) *Unable to locate*

West Bengal Labour Gazette (Calcutta, WB, IND) *Unable to locate*

West-Brabant-FM (Amsterdam, NLD) *Unable to locate*

The West Coast Messenger (Greymouth, NZL) **[48905]**

West Coast Times (Hokitika, NZL) **[48917]**

West Essex Life (Woodford, GBR) **[56959]**

West European Politics (Abingdon, GBR) **[52090]**

West-FM - 96.7 (Ayr, GBR) **[52151]**

West Limerick 102-FM - 101.4 (Abbeyfeale, LI, IRL) **[45915]**

West Limerick 102-FM - 102.2 (Newcastle West, LI, IRL) **[46048]**

West Limerick 102-FM (Shannon Estuary Area) - 101.6 (Newcastle West, LI, IRL) **[46049]**

West Midlands Regional Journal (Telford, GBR) *Unable to locate*

West Sound-AM - 1035 (Ayr, GBR) **[52152]**

West Sound-FM - 103 (Dumfries, GBR) **[53212]**

West Sound-FM - 96.5 (Dumfries, GBR) **[53210]**

West Sound-FM - 97 (Dumfries, GBR) **[53211]**

West Sussex County Times (Horsham, GBR) **[53602]**

The West Weekly (Penrose, NZL) *Unable to locate*

Western Indian Ocean Journal of Marine Science (Zanzibar, TZA) **[51409]**

Western Mail (Cardiff, GBR) **[52941]**

Western Morning News (Plymouth, GBR) **[56276]**

Western News (Johnsonville, NZL) *Unable to locate*

Western Times (Ahmedabad, GJ, IND) *Unable to locate*

Westlife (London, GBR) **[55398]**

Westminster Studies in Education **[51845]***

Weston & Somerset Mercury (Weston-super-Mare, GBR) **[56906]**

Westside Magazine (London, GBR) **[55399]**

Westside News (Milton, QL, AUS) **[42108]**

WFB Journal (Bangkok, THA) *Unable to locate*

WFD News (Helsinki, FIN) *Unable to locate*

WFOT Bulletin (Forrestfield, WA, AUS) **[41868]**

WFP Journal (Rome, ITA) *Unable to locate*

What to Buy for Business (Stockholm, SWE) *Unable to locate*

What Camcorder? (London, GBR) *Unable to locate*

What Car? (Teddington, GBR) **[56736]**

What Digital Camera (London, GBR) **[55400]**

What Mountain Bike? (London, GBR) **[55401]**

What Van? (London, GBR) **[55402]**

What's on in Calcutta (Calcutta, WB, IND) *Unable to locate*

What's New in Electronics (Wahroonga, NW, AUS) **[42679]**

What's New in Food Technology and Manufacturing (Wahroonga, NW, AUS) **[42680]**

What's New In Industry (London, GBR) *Unable to locate*

What's New in LAB Technology (Wahroonga, NW, AUS) **[42681]**

What's New in Process Technology (Wahroonga, NW, AUS) **[42682]**

What's On (Dubai, UAE) **[51656]**

What's On in London (London, GBR) *Unable to locate*

What's on in the Royal Borough of Kingston upon Thames (Kingston upon Thames, GBR) *Unable to locate*

Wheel Fare (Madras, TN, IND) *Unable to locate*

Wheels (Manchester, GBR) *Unable to locate*

WHERE Budapest (Budapest, HUN) **[44882]**

WHERE Hong Kong (Hong Kong, CHN) **[43386]**

WHERE London (London, GBR) **[55403]**

WHERE Rome (Rome, ITA) **[46245]**

WHERE St. Petersburg (Santa Monica, CA, USA) *Unable to locate*

Which Airline & Business Travel Update (Croydon, GBR) *Unable to locate*

Whisky (Cheltenham, GBR) **[52980]**

Whisky Magazine (Norwich, GBR) **[55743]**

Whitby Gazette (Whitby, GBR) **[56915]**

White Cane (Singapore, SGP) **[50286]**

White-Ribbon Signal (Albany, WA, AUS) *Unable to locate*

Whitehorse Leader (Melbourne, VI, AUS) **[42090]**

Whitelines Snowboard Magazine (London, GBR) **[55404]**

Whitney Gazette (Witney, GBR) **[56947]**

Numbers cited in bold after listings are entry numbers rather than page numbers.

Whitsunday Times (Sydney, NW, AUS) [42593]

Whittlesea Leader (Briar Hill, VI, AUS) [41636]

Who Do You Think You Are? (Bristol, GBR) [52736]

WHO Drug Information (Geneva, SWI) [51166]

Wholeness (Crowborough, GBR) Ceased

Who's Who in Heating & Plumbing (Sevenoaks, GBR) [56484]

WHY (Stockholm, SWE) Ceased

Wieler Revue (Groningen, NLD) [48604]

Wienerin (Klosterneuburg, AUT) Unable to locate

Wildabout (London, GBR) [55405]

Wildlife Australia (Brisbane, QL, AUS) [41654]

Wildlife Magazine (Kampala, UGA) Unable to locate

Wildlife Research (Collingwood, VI, AUS) [41797]

Willesden & Brent Times (London, GBR) [55406]

Wills & Trusts Law Reports (London, GBR) [55407]

Wiltshire (Totnes, GBR) [56764]

Wiltshire Life (Salisbury, GBR) [56458]

Win-FM [56581]*

Wind Engineering (Brentwood, GBR) [52590]

Wind Engineering Abstracts (Brentwood, GBR) [52591]

Window Fabricator & Installer (Watford, GBR) [56877]

Windows Middle East (Dubai, UAE) [51657]

Windows Southern Africa (Dubai, UAE) Unable to locate

Winds (Macclesfield, GBR) Unable to locate

Wine & Dine (Singapore, SGP) [50287]

Wine & Spirit (Crawley, GBR) [53115]

Wine Technology in New Zealand (Auckland, NZL) [48832]

Wingbeat (Sandy, GBR) [56461]

Wings (Karachi, PAK) Unable to locate

Winn-FM - 98.9 (Basseterre, SKN) [50049]

The Wire (London, GBR) [55408]

Wire & Cable Asia,) Unable to locate

Wire-FM - 107.2 (Wigan, GBR) [56923]

Wireless Communication (Bussum, NLD) Unable to locate

Wireless Europe (Colombo, SRI) Ceased

Wireless Networks (Dordrecht, NLD) [48587]

Wiring Matters (Stevenage, GBR) [56619]

Wirschaft und Gesellschaft (Vienna, AUT) [42774]

Wirtschaft (Lubeck, GER) Unable to locate

Wisbech Standard (March, GBR) [55593]

Wisdom (Cagayan de Oro, PHL) Unable to locate

Wisenet Journal (Glebe, NW, AUS) Unable to locate

Wish-FM - 102.4 (Wigan, GBR) [56924]

W.I.T.C.H. (London, GBR) [55409]

With (Shanghai, CHN) [43510]

Withayu Asia Seri (Bangkok, THA) Unable to locate

Within Reach (Helston, GBR) [53554]

Wits Student Journal of Economics (Wits, SAF) Unable to locate

Wits Student Newspaper (Wits, SAF) Unable to locate

WKRZ 91.3 FM [50304]*

WLR-FM - 97.5 (Waterford, WA, IRL) [46064]

WLR-FM - 95.1 (Waterford City, WA, IRL) [46068]

WMO Bulletin (Geneva, SWI) [51167]

WMS (London, GBR) [55410]

Wochenblatt fuer Papierfabrikation (Frankfurt am Main, GER) Unable to locate

The Wolf (London, GBR) [55411]

The Wolf-FM - 107.7 (Wolverhampton, GBR) [56955]

The Wolgan Chosun (Seoul, KOR) [47289]

Wolgan Mot (Seoul, KOR) Unable to locate

The Wolgan Naksi (Seoul, KOR) [47290]

The Wolgan San (Seoul, KOR) [47291]

Woman (London, GBR) [55412]

The Woman Engineer (Stevenage, GBR) [56620]

Woman & Home (London, GBR) [55413]

Woman This Month (Manama, BHR) [42795]

The Woman Writer (Walton-on-Thames, GBR) [56837]

Woman's Era (New Delhi, DH, IND) [45668]

Woman's Studies Journal (Auckland, NZL) Unable to locate

Woman's World (Moscow, RUS) Unable to locate

Woman's World (Singapore, SGP) [50288]

Women (Seoul, KOR) Unable to locate

Women (Omdurman, SDN) Unable to locate

Women (Abingdon, GBR) [52091]

Women in Action (Quezon City, PHL) [49618]

Women of Aral (Nukus, UZN) Unable to locate

Women and Birth (Callaghan, NW, AUS) [41691]

Women of China (Beijing, CHN) [43223]

Women in Management Review [55556]*

Women on the March (New Delhi, DH, IND) Unable to locate

Women on the Move (Abuja, LG, NGA) [49058]

Women & Performance (Abingdon, GBR) [52092]

Women of Vietnam (Hanoi, VNM) Unable to locate

Women of Vietnam Review (Hanoi, VNM) Unable to locate

Women's Contribution in Rural Development (Chennai, TN, IND) Unable to locate

Women's Exclusive Africa (Kitwe, ZMB) Unable to locate

Women's Health (London, GBR) [55414]

Women's Health Collection (Santiago, CHL) [43149]

Women's History Review (Wallingford, GBR) Unable to locate

Women's Oncology Review (Abingdon, GBR) Ceased

Women's View (Camperdown, NW, AUS) Unable to locate

Women's Weekly (Seoul, KOR) Unable to locate

Women's Writing (Abingdon, GBR) [52093]

W1 Magazine (London, GBR) [55415]

Wood Based Panels International (London, GBR) Unable to locate

Wood Industry (Beijing, CHN) [43224]

Wood News (Bangalore, KA, IND) Unable to locate

Wood Protection (Castleford, GBR) [52953]

Wood Science and Technology (Munich, GER) [44587]

Wood Treatment and Production of Furniture (Sofia, BUL) Unable to locate

Wood & Vale Express (Norwich, GBR) [55744]

Wood Working Plans and Projects (Lewes, GBR) [53851]

Woodbridge and Melton Community News (Halesworth, GBR) Unable to locate

Woodcarving (Lewes, GBR) [53852]

Woodworking Finland [43903]*

WOODWORKING INTERNATIONAL (Nuremberg, GER) [44618]

Woodworking Puuntyosto WIN (Lahti, FIN) [43903]

Wool News (New Delhi, DH, IND) Unable to locate

Wool Record (Bradford, GBR) [52557]

Wool and Woollens of India (Mumbai, MH, IND) Unable to locate

Woolner Indological Series (Hoshiarpur, PJ, IND) Unable to locate

Worcester Standard (Worcester, GBR) [56963]

Worcestershire Life (Cheltenham, GBR) [52981]

Word (Mumbai, MH, IND) Unable to locate

Word Search (Redhill, GBR) [56382]

Wordsearches [55416]*

Wordsearches (London, GBR) [55416]

Wordsearches Collection (London, GBR) [55417]

Wordt Vervolgd (Amsterdam, NLD) [48271]

Work Boat World (London, GBR) Unable to locate

Work, Employment, and Society (Belmont, GBR) [52308]

Workers Education Journal (Nagpur, MH, IND) Unable to locate

The Workers' Voice (Kitwe, ZMB) Unable to locate

Workflow Magazine (Alphen aan den Rijn, NLD) Unable to locate

Working Class (New Delhi, DH, IND) [45669]

Working Journalist (New Delhi, DH, IND) Unable to locate

Working Mom (Quezon City, PHL) [49619]

Working with Older People (Brighton, GBR) [52635]

Working Papers (Cochin, KE, IND) Unable to locate

WorkOut Ireland (Barnsley, GBR) [52185]

WorkOut UK (Barnsley, GBR) [52186]

Workplace Law (Cambridge, GBR) [52905]

The Workshops (Stockholm, SWE) Unable to locate

Worksop Guardian (Worksop, GBR) [56970]

Workteam (Gaborone, BWA) Ceased

The World (Beijing, CHN) Unable to locate

World Acrobatics (Bellingen, NW, AUS) Ceased

World Airnews (Durban, SAF) [50471]

World Applied Sciences Journal (Faisalabad, PAK) [49297]

World Archaeology (Abingdon, GBR) [52094]

World Architecture (Sofia, BUL) Unable to locate

World Architecture (Istanbul, TUR) Unable to locate

World Automotive Manufacturing (London, GBR) Unable to locate

World Bank Research Observer (Oxford, GBR) [56227]

World Birdwatch (Cambridge, GBR) [52906]

World Bowls (Worthing, GBR) Unable to locate

World Cement (Elstead, GBR) Unable to locate

The World of Cross Stitching (Bristol, GBR) [52737]

World Cruise Industry Review (London, GBR) [55418]

The World Economy (Oxford, GBR) [56228]

World Education News (New Delhi, DH, IND) Unable to locate

The World of Embroidery (East Molesey, GBR) [53241]

World Energy Council Journal (London, GBR) Ceased

World Expro (London, GBR) [55419]

World Fairs Guide (New Delhi, DH, IND) Unable to locate

World Faiths Encounter [54676]*

World Federation (Vrindaban, UP, IND) Unable to locate

World Focus (New Delhi, DH, IND) Unable to locate

World Food Regulation Review (Burnham, GBR) [52768]

World Friends (Seoul, KOR) Unable to locate

World Gold (London, GBR) Unable to locate

World Gold Analyst (London, GBR) [55420]

World Highways (Swanley, GBR) [56698]

World Hospitals and Health Services (Ferney-Voltaire, FRA) [43950]

World Information Technology Journal (Faisalabad, PAK) [49298]

The World of Interiors (London, GBR) [55421]

World of Jewish Woman (Lugansk, URE) [51616]

World Journal of Agricultural Sciences (Faisalabad, PAK) [49299]

The World Journal of Biological Psychiatry (Vienna, AUT) [42775]

World Journal of Chemistry (Faisalabad, PAK) [49300]

World Journal of Dairy & Food Sciences (Faisalabad, PAK) [49301]

World Journal of Gastroenterology (Beijing, CHN) [43225]

World Journal of Medical Sciences (Faisalabad, PAK) [49302]

World Journal of Microbiology and Biotechnology (Strasbourg, FRA) [44114]

World Journal of Zoology (Faisalabad, PAK) [49303]

World Link (Geneva, SWI) Unable to locate

World Literature Written in English (Singapore, SGP) Unable to locate

Master Index

World Maritime University Journal of Maritime Affairs (Malmo, SWE) **[50992]**

World Masters Athletics (Helsingborg, SWE) *Unable to locate*

World Medical Journal (Ferney-Voltaire, FRA) **[43951]**

World Mining Equipment (London, GBR) **[55422]**

The World of Music (Berlin, GER) *Unable to locate*

World New Music Magazine (Amsterdam, NLD) **[48272]**

World Nuclear Review (Bern, SWI) *Unable to locate*

World of Packaging Ltd. (Castle Donington, GBR) *Unable to locate*

World Pentecost Magazine (Emmetten, SWI) *Unable to locate*

World Pharmaceutical Development (London, GBR) *Unable to locate*

World Poultry Science Journal (Beekbergen, NLD) **[48277]**

World Pumps (Brussels, BEL) *Unable to locate*

World Regional Studies (Beijing, CHN) *Unable to locate*

World Report on Technical Advancement (Calcutta, WB, IND) *Unable to locate*

World Review of Entrepreneurship, Management and Sustainable Development (Olney, GBR) **[55846]**

World Review of Intermodal Transportation Research (Geneva, SWI) **[51168]**

World Review of Science, Technology and Sustainable Development (Olney, GBR) **[55847]**

World Soccer (London, GBR) **[55423]**

World Sports Activewear (Liverpool, GBR) *Unable to locate*

World Structure (Edinburgh, GBR) **[53324]**

World Studies in Education (South Melbourne, VI, AUS) **[42376]**

World Superyacht Review (London, GBR) **[55424]**

World Surface Coatings Abstracts (Hampton, GBR) **[53506]**

World Tobacco (London, GBR) **[55425]**

The World Today (London, GBR) **[55426]**

World Trade (Mumbai, MH, IND) *Unable to locate*

World Traveller (Shanghai, CHN) **[43511]**

World Tunnelling (London, GBR) **[55427]**

World Tunnelling and Subsurface Excavation **[55427]***

World Watch (Madrid, SPA) **[50816]**

World Weightlifting (Budapest, HUN) **[44883]**

World Wide Web (Dordrecht, NLD) **[48588]**

World of Work (Geneva, SWI) **[51169]**

Worlds of Education (Brussels, BEL) **[42875]**

World's Poultry Science Journal (Wallingford, GBR) **[56831]**

World's Wisdom Series (New Delhi, DH, IND) *Unable to locate*

Worldwide Business Collaborations—Consultants News and Business Opportunities (Allahabad, UP, IND) *Unable to locate*

Worldwide Computer Products News (Bath, GBR) **[52264]**

Worthing Herald (Worthing, GBR) **[56979]**

Wound Care (Huntingdon, GBR) **[53636]**

Wrestling Review (Lausanne, SWI) *Unable to locate*

Wrexham Leader (Wrexham, GBR) **[56982]**

Wrexham Mail (Wrexham, GBR) *Unable to locate*

WRG-FM **[51173]***

WRI Journal (Tiruchirapalli, TN, IND) *Unable to locate*

Writers Workshop Literary Reader (Calcutta, WB, IND) *Unable to locate*

Written Language and Literacy (Amsterdam, NLD) **[48273]**

WRS-FM - 88.4 (Geneva, SWI) **[51173]**

WRVS Action (London, GBR) **[55428]**

WSCF Journal (Geneva, SWI) **[51170]**

WSFM-FM - 101.7 (North Ryde, NW, AUS) **[42205]**

Wspotpraca Obserwatorow Stonca (Zychlin, POL) *Unable to locate*

WTF Taekwondo (Seoul, KOR) **[47292]**

Wuhai People's Broadcasting Station (Wuhai, NM, CHN) *Unable to locate*

Wuhan People's Broadcasting Station (Wuhan, CHN) *Unable to locate*

Wuhan People's Broadcasting Station (Wuhan, CHN) *Unable to locate*

Wuhan People's Broadcasting Station (Wuhan, HU, CHN) *Unable to locate*

Wuhan People's Broadcasting Station (Wuhan, HU, CHN) *Unable to locate*

Wuhu People's Broadcasting Station (Wuhu, AN, CHN) *Unable to locate*

Wuhu People's Broadcasting Station (Wuhu, AN, CHN) *Unable to locate*

Wuxi People's Broadcasting Station (Wuxi, JS, CHN) *Unable to locate*

Wuxi People's Broadcasting Station (Wuxi, JS, CHN) *Unable to locate*

Wuxi People's Broadcasting Station (Wuxi, JS, CHN) *Unable to locate*

Wuxi People's Broadcasting Station (Wuxi, JS, CHN) *Unable to locate*

Wuxi People's Broadcasting Station (Wuxi, JS, CHN) *Unable to locate*

Wuxi People's Broadcasting Station (Wuxi, JS, CHN) *Unable to locate*

Wuxi People's Broadcasting Station (Wuxi, JS, CHN) *Unable to locate*

Wuzhong People's Broadcasting Station (Wuzhong, NH, CHN) *Unable to locate*

Wuzhou People's Broadcasting Station (Wuzhou, GZ, CHN) *Unable to locate*

Wuzhou People's Broadcasting Station (Wuzhou, GH, CHN) *Unable to locate*

WWB (Huddersfield, GBR) **[53625]**

WWF (Tokyo, JPN) *Unable to locate*

WWF Journal (Frankfurt, GER) **[44363]**

Wymondham & Attleborough Mercury (Norwich, GBR) **[55745]**

WYN-FM - 88.9 (Werribee, VI, AUS) **[42693]**

Wyndham Leader (Werribee, VI, AUS) **[42692]**

Wynnum Herald (Wynnum Central, QL, AUS) **[42718]**

Wyre-FM - 107.2 (Kidderminster, GBR) **[53686]**

Wyvern-FM - 97.6 (Hereford, GBR) **[53564]**

Wyvern-FM - 96.7 (Kidderminster, GBR) **[53687]**

Wyvern-FM - 102.8 (Worcester, GBR) **[56964]**

X

X-FM - 104.9 (London, GBR) **[55471]**

XBOX365 Online Magazine (Sale, GBR) *Unable to locate*

XEDCH-AM - 1180 (Delicias, CH, MEX) **[47772]**

XEDI-AM - 1360 (Chihuahua, CH, MEX) **[47759]**

XEFA-AM - 950 (Chihuahua, CH, MEX) **[47760]**

XEFI-AM - 580 (Chihuahua, CH, MEX) **[47761]**

XEFO-AM - 680 (Chihuahua, CH, MEX) **[47762]**

XEHES-AM - 1040 (Chihuahua, CH, MEX) **[47763]**

XEIO-AM - 840 (Tuxtla Gutierrez, CP, MEX) **[47804]**

XEIT-AM - 1070 (Ciudad del Carmen, CM, MEX) **[47768]**

XEJK-AM - 980 (Delicias, CH, MEX) **[47773]**

XEKQ-AM - 680 (Tapachula, CP, MEX) **[47800]**

XEKY-AM - 1280 (Huixtla, CP, MEX) **[47776]**

XELM-AM - 1240 (Tuxtla Gutierrez, CP, MEX) **[47805]**

XEMAB-AM - 950 (Ciudad del Carmen, CM, MEX) **[47769]**

XEMK-AM - 930 (Huixtla, CP, MEX) **[47777]**

Xene (Sapporo, JPN) **[46652]**

XEOAX-AM - 680 KHz (Oaxaca, OX, MEX) **[47794]**

XEOE-AM - 810 (Tapachula, CP, MEX) **[47801]**

XERN-AM (Montemorelos, NL, MEX) *Unable to locate*

XERPC-AM - 790 (Chihuahua, CH, MEX) **[47764]**

XERPR-AM - 1070 (Tuxtla Gutierrez, CP, MEX) **[47806]**

XETAK-AM - 900 (Tapachula, CP, MEX) **[47802]**

XETAP-AM - 960 (Tapachula, CP, MEX) **[47803]**

XETUG-AM - 950 (Tuxtla Gutierrez, CP, MEX) **[47807]**

XEUE-AM - 580 (Tuxtla Gutierrez, CP, MEX) **[47808]**

XEZT-AM (Puebla, PU, MEX) *Unable to locate*

Xfm-FM - 104.9 (London, GBR) **[55472]**

XFM-FM - 97.7 (Manchester, GBR) **[55589]**

XFM Scotland (Glasgow, GBR) *Unable to locate*

Xfresh-FM - 98.5 (Kuala Lumpur, MYS) **[47662]**

XHAWD-FM - 107.1 (San Luis Potosi, SL, MEX) **[47798]**

XHCJZ-FM - 105.1 (Jimenez, CO, MEX) **[47778]**

XHDI-FM - 88.5 (Chihuahua, CH, MEX) **[47765]**

XHEDO-FM - 94.1 (Puerto Escondido, OX, MEX) **[47796]**

XHFA-FM - 89.3 (Chihuahua, CH, MEX) **[47766]**

XHHLL-FM - 90.70 (Hermosillo, SR, MEX) **[47775]**

XHIT-FM - 99.7 (Ciudad del Carmen, CM, MEX) **[47770]**

XHOA-FM - 96.9 MHz (Oaxaca, OX, MEX) **[47795]**

XHSD-FM - 99.3 (Silao, GJ, MEX) **[47799]**

XHUA-FM - 90.1 (Chihuahua, CH, MEX) **[47767]**

Xiamen People's Broadcasting Station (Xiamen, FJ, CHN) *Unable to locate*

Xiamen People's Broadcasting Station (Xiamen, FJ, CHN) *Unable to locate*

Xiamen People's Broadcasting Station (Xiamen, FJ, CHN) *Unable to locate*

Xiamen People's Broadcasting Station (Xiamen, FJ, CHN) *Unable to locate*

Xiamen People's Broadcasting Station (Xiamen, FJ, CHN) *Unable to locate*

Xi'an People's Broadcasting Station (Xi'an, SH, CHN) *Unable to locate*

Xi'an People's Broadcasting Station (Xi'an, SH, CHN) *Unable to locate*

Xi'an People's Broadcasting Station (Xi'an, SH, CHN) *Unable to locate*

Xiangfan People's Broadcasting Station (Xiangfan, HB, CHN) *Unable to locate*

Xiangfan People's Broadcasting Station (Xiangfan, HU, CHN) *Unable to locate*

Xiangfan People's Broadcasting Station (Xiangfan, HB, CHN) *Unable to locate*

Xiangfan People's Broadcasting Station (Xiangfan, HU, CHN) *Unable to locate*

Xiangtan People's Broadcasting Station (Xiangtan, HA, CHN) *Unable to locate*

Xianning People's Broadcasting Station (Xianning, HU, CHN) *Unable to locate*

Xiantao People's Broadcasting Station (Xiantao, HB, CHN) *Unable to locate*

Xianyang People's Broadcasting Station (Xianyang, SH, CHN) *Unable to locate*

Xiaogan People's Broadcasting Station (Xiogan, CHN) *Unable to locate*

Xiaoshan People's Broadcasting Station (Hangzhou, ZH, CHN) *Unable to locate*

Xilingol People's Broadcasting Station (Xilinhot, NM, CHN) *Unable to locate*

Xilingol People's Broadcasting Station (Xilinhot, NM, CHN) *Unable to locate*

Xingcheng People's Broadcasting Station (Xingcheng, LI, CHN) *Unable to locate*

Xingtai People's Broadcasting Station (Xingtai, HB, CHN) *Unable to locate*

Xining People's Broadcasting Station (Xining, QI, CHN) *Unable to locate*

Xinji People's Broadcasting Station (Xinji, HB, CHN) *Unable to locate*

Xinjiang People's Broadcasting Station (Urumqi, HA, CHN) *Unable to locate*

Xinjiang People's Broadcasting Station (Urumqi, XU, CHN) *Unable to locate*

Xinjiang People's Broadcasting Station (Urumqi, XU, CHN) *Unable to locate*

Xinjiang People's Broadcasting Station (Urumqi, XU, CHN) *Unable to locate*

Xinjiang People's Broadcasting Station (Urumqi, XU, CHN) *Unable to locate*

Xinjiang People's Broadcasting Station (Urumqi, XU, CHN) *Ceased*

Numbers cited in bold after listings are entry numbers rather than page numbers.

Xinjiang People's Broadcasting Station (Urumqi, XU, CHN) *Unable to locate*

Xinjiang People's Broadcasting Station (Urumqi, XU, CHN) *Unable to locate*

Xinjiang People's Broadcasting Station (Urumqi, XU, CHN) *Unable to locate*

Xinjiang People's Broadcasting Station (Urumqi, XU, CHN) *Unable to locate*

Xinmi People's Broadcasting Station (Xinmi, HN, CHN) *Unable to locate*

Xinxiang People's Broadcasting Station (Xinxiang, HN, CHN) *Unable to locate*

Xinyu People's Broadcasting Station (Xinyu, JX, CHN) *Unable to locate*

Xinyu People's Broadcasting Station (Xinyu, JX, CHN) *Unable to locate*

Xishuangbanna People's Broadcasting Station (Jinghong, YU, CHN) *Unable to locate*

Xizang People's Broadcasting Station (Lhasa, XZ, CHN) *Unable to locate*

Xizang People's Broadcasting Station (Lhasa, XZ, CHN) *Unable to locate*

Xizang People's Broadcasting Station (Lhasa, XZ, CHN) *Unable to locate*

Xizang People's Broadcasting Station (Lhasa, XZ, CHN) *Unable to locate*

Xizang People's Broadcasting Station (Lhasa, XZ, CHN) *Unable to locate*

Xizang People's Broadcasting Station (Lhasa, XZ, CHN) *Unable to locate*

Xizang People's Broadcasting Station (Lhasa, XZ, CHN) *Unable to locate*

Xizang People's Broadcasting Station (Lhasa, XZ, CHN) *Unable to locate*

Xizang People's Broadcasting Station (Lhasa, XZ, CHN) *Unable to locate*

Xizang People's Broadcasting Station (Lhasa, XZ, CHN) *Unable to locate*

Xizang People's Broadcasting Station (Lhasa, XZ, CHN) *Unable to locate*

Xizang People's Broadcasting Station (Lhasa, XZ, CHN) *Unable to locate*

Xpression-FM - 87.7 (Exeter, GBR) **[53369]**

XS-FM **[48968]***

X6 (Honeydew, SAF) *Unable to locate*

Xuchang People's Broadcasting Station (Xuchang, HN, CHN) *Unable to locate*

Xuchang People's Broadcasting Station (Xuchang, HN, CHN) *Unable to locate*

Xuzhou People's Broadcasting Station (Xuzhou, JS, CHN) *Unable to locate*

Xuzhou People's Broadcasting Station (Xuzhou, JS, CHN) *Unable to locate*

Xuzhou People's Broadcasting Station (Xuzhou, JS, CHN) *Unable to locate*

Xuzhou People's Broadcasting Station (Xuzhou, JS, CHN) *Unable to locate*

Xuzhou People's Broadcasting Station (Yancheng, JS, CHN) *Unable to locate*

Y

Y Ddolen (Aberystwyth, GBR) **[51689]**

Y-Dub Magazine (Wellington, NZL) *Unable to locate*

Y-FM - 99.2 (Johannesburg, SAF) **[50539]**

Y Youth Club (Banjul, GMB) *Unable to locate*

Ya-FM - 102.9 (Veracruz, CP, MEX) **[47809]**

Yachou (Asia) Broadcasting Station (Tao Yuan, TWN) *Unable to locate*

Yachting Monthly (London, GBR) **[55429]**

YACHTING & STYLE (Bielefeld, GER) **[44248]**

Yachting World (London, GBR) **[55430]**

Yachtstyle (Shanghai, CHN) **[43512]**

The Yale Review (Oxford, GBR) **[56229]**

YAM! (Munich, GER) **[44588]**

Yamagata Hoso - 918 KHz (Yonezawa, JPN) **[47149]**

Yan Kraw (Bangkok, THA) *Unable to locate*

Yan'an People's Broadcasting Station (Yan'an, SH, CHN) *Unable to locate*

Yanbian People's Broadcasting Station (Yanji, JI, CHN) *Unable to locate*

Yanbian People's Broadcasting Station (Yanji, JI, CHN) *Unable to locate*

Yanbian People's Broadcasting Station (Yanji, JI, CHN) *Unable to locate*

Yanbian People's Broadcasting Station (Yanji, JI, CHN) *Unable to locate*

Yanbian People's Broadcasting Station (Yanji, JI, CHN) *Unable to locate*

Yancheng People's Broadcasting Station (Yancheng, JS, CHN) *Unable to locate*

Yancheng People's Broadcasting Station (Yancheng, JS, CHN) *Unable to locate*

Yangjiang People's Broadcasting Station (Yangjiang, GD, CHN) *Unable to locate*

Yangquan People's Broadcasting Station (Yangquan, SX, CHN) *Unable to locate*

Yangquan People's Broadcasting Station (Yangquan, SX, CHN) *Unable to locate*

Yangquan People's Broadcasting Station (Yangquan, SX, CHN) *Unable to locate*

Yangzhou People's Broadcasting Station (Yangzhou, JS, CHN) *Unable to locate*

Yangzhou People's Broadcasting Station (Yangzhou, JS, CHN) *Unable to locate*

Yangzhou People's Broadcasting Station (Yangzhou, JS, CHN) *Unable to locate*

Yangzhou People's Broadcasting Station (Yangzhou, JS, CHN) *Unable to locate*

Yangzhou People's Broadcasting Station (Yangzhou, JS, CHN) *Unable to locate*

Yanji People's Broadcasting Station (Yanji, JI, CHN) *Unable to locate*

Yanju (Seoul, KOR) *Unable to locate*

Yantai People's Broadcasting Station (Yantai, SD, CHN) *Unable to locate*

Yantai People's Broadcasting Station (Yantai, SD, CHN) *Unable to locate*

Yantai People's Broadcasting Station (Yantai, SD, CHN) *Unable to locate*

Yaprak FM - Gaziantep (Gaziantep, TUR) *Unable to locate*

Yaprak FM - Gaziantep (Gaziantep, TUR) *Unable to locate*

Yaqeen International (Karachi, PAK) *Unable to locate*

Yarra Valley-FM - 99.1 (Woori Yallock, VI, AUS) **[42717]**

Yass-FM - 100.3 (Yass, NW, AUS) **[42719]**

Yatri (New Delhi, DH, IND) *Unable to locate*

Ydepta Info (Nkambe, CMR) *Unable to locate*

Yearbook (Reykjavik, ICE) *Unable to locate*

Yearbook (London, GBR) *Unable to locate*

Yearbook of African Law (Cologne, GER) **[44304]**

Yearbook of Human Rights in Ukraine (Kiev, URE) *Unable to locate*

Y'ello (Mbabane, SWZ) **[50947]**

Yemen Observer (Sana'a, YEM) **[57105]**

Yemen Radio & TV Corporation (Sana'a, YEM) *Unable to locate*

Yemen Radio & TV Corporation (Sana'a, YEM) *Unable to locate*

Yemen Radio & TV Corporation (Sana'a, YEM) *Unable to locate*

Yemen Radio & TV Corporation (Sana'a, YEM) *Unable to locate*

Yemen Radio & TV Corporation (Sana'a, YEM) *Unable to locate*

Yemen Radio & TV Corporation (Sana'a, YEM) *Unable to locate*

Yemen Radio & TV Corporation, Hudaydah (Hudaydah, YEM) *Unable to locate*

Yemen Radio & TV Corporation, Sana'a (Sana'a, YEM) *Unable to locate*

Yemen Times (Sana'a, YEM) **[57106]**

Yen Bai Broadcast - Television Station (Hanoi, VNM) *Unable to locate*

Yen Sheng Broadcasting Station (Hualien, TWN) *Unable to locate*

Yen Sheng Broadcasting Station (Hualien, TWN) *Unable to locate*

Yeni Yasanti (Istanbul, TUR) *Unable to locate*

Yeovil Express (Chard, GBR) **[52957]**

Yes! (Mandaluyong City, PHL) **[49543]**

Yes-FM - 101.1 (Makati City, PHL) **[49530]**

Yes FM - 89.5 MHz (Colombo, SRI) **[50885]**

Yes FM - 88.2 MHz (Kandy, SRI) **[50912]**

Yes FM - 101.0 MHz (Pannipitiya, SRI) **[50926]**

Y.E.S. 93.3 FM - 93.3 MHz (Singapore, SGP) **[50309]**

Yevreiski Dom (Almaty, KAZ) **[47169]**

YFM-FM - 99.2 (Johannesburg, SAF) **[50540]**

Yibin People's Broadcasting Station (Yibin, SI, CHN) *Unable to locate*

Yichang People's Broadcasting Station (Yichang, HU, CHN) *Unable to locate*

A Yidishe Mame (Donetsk, URE) **[51591]**

Yinchuan People's Broadcasting Station (Yinchuan, NH, CHN) *Unable to locate*

Yingcheng People's Broadcasting Station (Yingcheng, HB, CHN) *Unable to locate*

Yingkou People's Broadcasting Station (Yingkou, LI, CHN) *Unable to locate*

Yingtan People's Broadcasting Station (Yingtan, JX, CHN) *Unable to locate*

Yiyang People's Broadcasting Station (Yueyang, HN, CHN) *Unable to locate*

Yizheng People's Broadcasting Station (Yizheng, JS, CHN) *Unable to locate*

Yoga and Health (London, GBR) **[55431]**

YOGA Magazine (London, GBR) **[55432]**

Yoga-Mimamsa (Pune, MH, IND) *Unable to locate*

Yoga Today **[55431]***

Yoga and Total Health (Mumbai, MH, IND) **[45450]**

Yogasana Alaya Vijayam (Madras, TN, IND) *Unable to locate*

Yojana (New Delhi, DH, IND) **[45670]**

Yoju (Seoul, KOR) *Unable to locate*

The Yoke (Yokohama, JPN) **[47143]**

Yonch'on (Seoul, KOR) *Unable to locate*

Yonsei Business Review (Seoul, KOR) *Unable to locate*

Yonsei Medical Journal (Seoul, KOR) **[47293]**

Yonsei Reports on Tropical Medicine (Seoul, KOR) *Unable to locate*

Yorkshire Advertiser (Ryedale and North York Moors) (York, GBR) **[57000]**

Yorkshire Coast Radio-FM - 102.4 (Bridlington, GBR) **[52598]**

Yorkshire Coast Radio-FM - 96.2 (Scarborough, GBR) **[56465]**

Yorkshire Coast Radio-FM - 103.1 (Whitby, GBR) **[56916]**

Yorkshire Evening Post (Leeds, GBR) **[53776]**

Yorkshire Journal (Otley, GBR) *Unable to locate*

Yorkshire Life (Ripon, GBR) **[56400]**

Yorkshire Post (Leeds, GBR) **[53777]**

Yorkshire Sport (Leeds, GBR) **[53778]**

Yorkshire Sports (Bradford, GBR) *Unable to locate*

You (Karachi, PAK) **[49379]**

You & Your Wedding (London, GBR) **[55433]**

Young Age (Jaipur, RJ, IND) *Unable to locate*

Young Buddhist (Singapore, SGP) *Unable to locate*

Young Consumers (Exeter, GBR) **[53366]**

Young Generation (Singapore, SGP) *Unable to locate*

Young India (New Delhi, DH, IND) *Unable to locate*

Young Indian (New Delhi, DH, IND) *Unable to locate*

Young Lady (Kiev, URE) **[51615]**

Young Magazine (Tokyo, JPN) **[47057]**

Young Magazine Uppers (Tokyo, JPN) **[47058]**

Young Parents (Singapore, SGP) **[50289]**

Young Parents Baby (Singapore, SGP) **[50290]**

Young Parents Preschool Guide (Singapore, SGP) **[50291]**

Young People Now (Leicester, GBR) **[53834]**

Young Scientists Journal (Mumbai, MH, IND) **[45451]**

Young Soldier (London, GBR) *Ceased*

Young Times (Dubai, UAE) **[51658]**

Young World (Karachi, PAK) **[49380]**

Numbers cited in bold after listings are entry numbers rather than page numbers.

Master Index

Your Choice Puzzles (Swanley, GBR) *Ceased*

Your Hair (Bristol) (Bristol, GBR) **[52738]**

Your M&S (London, GBR) *Unable to locate*

Your Mortgage (London, GBR) **[55434]**

Your New Home (West Malling, GBR) **[56895]**

Your Task (Lagos, LG, NGA) *Ceased*

Your Trading Edge (Mona Vale, NW, AUS) **[42112]**

Yours (London, GBR) **[55435]**

Youth Chronicle (New Delhi, DH, IND) *Unable to locate*

Youth Hosteller (New Delhi, DH, IND) **[45671]**

Youth of India (New Delhi, DH, IND) *Unable to locate*

Youth Life (New Delhi, DH, IND) *Unable to locate*

Youth Opinion (Brussels, BEL) **[42876]**

Youth Policy Update (Leicester, GBR) **[53835]**

Youth Vision (Kathmandu, NPL) *Unable to locate*

Youthwork (London, GBR) **[55436]**

Yrittajanainen (Helsinki, FIN) *Unable to locate*

Yu-ai (Tokyo, JPN) *Unable to locate*

Yuci People's Broadcasting Station (Yuci, SX, CHN) *Unable to locate*

Yuen Lin (Hong Kong, CHN) **[43387]**

Yueyang People's Broadcasting Station (Yueyang, HA, CHN) *Unable to locate*

Yueyang People's Broadcasting Station (Yueyang, HA, CHN) *Unable to locate*

Yueyang People's Broadcasting Station (Yueyang, HA, CHN) *Unable to locate*

Yumen People's Broadcasting Station (Yumen, GS, CHN) *Unable to locate*

Yummy (Mandaluyong City, PHL) **[49544]**

Yunchia Broadcasting Station (Chia-I, TWN) *Unable to locate*

Yunnan People's Broadcasting Station (Kunming, YU, CHN) *Unable to locate*

Yunnan People's Broadcasting Station (Kunming, YU, CHN) *Unable to locate*

Yunnan People's Broadcasting Station (Kunming, YU, CHN) *Unable to locate*

Yunnan People's Broadcasting Station (Kunming, YU, CHN) *Unable to locate*

Yunnan People's Broadcasting Station (Kunming, YU, CHN) *Unable to locate*

Yunnan People's Broadcasting Station (Kunming, YU, CHN) *Unable to locate*

Yunnan People's Broadcasting Station (Kunming, YU, CHN) *Unable to locate*

Yunnan People's Broadcasting Station (Kunming, YU, CHN) *Unable to locate*

Yunnan People's Broadcasting Station (Kunming, YU, CHN) *Unable to locate*

Yunnan People's Broadcasting Station (Kunming, YU, CHN) *Unable to locate*

Yunnan People's Broadcasting Station Minorities (Kunming, YU, CHN) *Unable to locate*

Yuridika (Surabaya, IDN) *Unable to locate*

Yushu People's Broadcasting Station (Yushu Xian, QI, CHN) *Unable to locate*

Yuva Bharati (Chennai, TN, IND) **[45062]**

Yves-Laurent Blanc (Bern, SWI) *Ceased*

Z

Z (Mumbai, MH, IND) *Unable to locate*

Za Neurologie Liberale (Versailles, FRA) *Unable to locate*

Za Pticite (Sofia, BUL) *Unable to locate*

ZAAC - Zeitschrift fur anorganische und allgemeine Chemie (Berlin, GER) **[44237]**

Zaad & Voer Magazine (Ooosterhout, NLD) *Unable to locate*

Zabolekarski Pregled - Sofia BG (Sofia, BUL) *Unable to locate*

Zahn Arzt (Vienna, AUT) *Unable to locate*

Zahnaerztlicher Gesundheitsdienst (Heiligenstadt, GER) *Unable to locate*

Zahnarztlidie Mi (Cologne, GER) *Unable to locate*

Zaiken (Tokyo, JPN) *Unable to locate*

Zalantun People's Broadcasting Station (Zalantun, NM, CHN) *Unable to locate*

Zambezia (Harare, ZWE) **[57120]**

Zambia Heritage News Magazine (Livingstone, ZMB) *Unable to locate*

ZAMM - Zeitschrift fur Angewandte Mathematik und Mechanik (Saale, GER) **[44650]**

Zany Zine (Mumbai, MH, IND) *Unable to locate*

Zaozhuang People's Broadcasting Station (Zaozhuang, SD, CHN) *Unable to locate*

Zaozhuang People's Broadcasting Station (Zaozhuang, SD, CHN) *Unable to locate*

Zaozhuang People's Broadcasting Station (Zaozhuang, SD, CHN) *Unable to locate*

Zaozhuang People's Broadcasting Station (Zhaozhuang, SD, CHN) *Unable to locate*

Zaraat (Hyderabad, PAK) *Unable to locate*

ZB-AM - 1098 (Christchurch, NZL) **[48887]**

zbCOMMA (Singapore, SGP) **[50292]**

Zee Lifestyle (Cebu City, PHL) **[49465]**

Zeitlupe (Zurich, SWI) **[51297]**

Zeitschrift fur die Alttestamentliche Wissenschaft (Erlangen, GER) **[44343]**

Zeitschrift fur Antikes Christentum (Erlangen, GER) **[44344]**

Zeitschrift fur Assyriologie und Vorderasiatische Archaologie (Munich, GER) **[44589]**

Zeitschrift fur Bewasserungswirtschaft **[41940]***

Zeitschrift der Deutschen Geologischen Gesellschaft (Stuttgart, GER) **[44685]**

Zeitschrift des Deutschen Vereins fur Kunstwissenschaft (Berlin, GER) **[44238]**

Zeitschrift fur Geomorphologie (Stuttgart, GER) **[44686]**

Zeitschrift fur Japanisches Recht (Hamburg, GER) *Unable to locate*

Zeitschrift fur germanistische Linguistik (Kassel, GER) **[44499]**

Zeitschrift Menschenrechte (Frankfurt am Main, GER) *Unable to locate*

Zeitschrift fur die Neutestamentliche Wissenschaft (Bonn, GER) **[44273]**

Zeitschrift fur Orient-Archaologie (Berlin, GER) **[44239]**

Zeitschrift fur romanische Philologie (Berlin, GER) **[44240]**

Zeitschrift fur Rezensionen zur germanistischen Sprachwissenschaft (Berlin, GER) **[44241]**

Zeitschrift fur Sexualforschung (Hamburg, GER) *Unable to locate*

Zeitschrift fur Sprachwissenschaft (Stuttgart, GER) **[44687]**

Zeitschrift fur die gesamte Strafrechtswissenschaft (Tubingen, GER) **[44694]**

Zeitschrift fur Unternehmens- und Gesellschaftsrecht (ZGR) (Heidelberg, GER) **[44480]**

Zeitschrift fr Wahrscheinlichkeitstheorie und verwandte Gebiete **[44078]***

Zeitschriften- und Bucherschau Stahl und Eisen **[44328]***

Zenit (Utrecht, NLD) *Unable to locate*

Zerb (Tavistock, GBR) **[56728]**

027.8 School Library Bulletin (Hobart, TA, AUS) *Ceased*

Zhangjiagang People's Broadcasting Station, JS, CHN) *Unable to locate*

Zhangjiakou People's Broadcasting Station (Zhangjiakou, HB, CHN) *Unable to locate*

Zhangjiakou People's Broadcasting Station (Zhangjiakou, HB, CHN) *Unable to locate*

Zhangjiakou People's Broadcasting Station (Zhangjiakou, HB, CHN) *Unable to locate*

Zhanjiang People's Broadcasting Station (Zhanjiang, GD, CHN) *Unable to locate*

Zhanjiang People's Broadcasting Station (Zhanjiang, GD, CHN) *Unable to locate*

Zhanjiang People's Broadcasting Station (Zhanjiang, GD, CHN) *Unable to locate*

Zhaoqing People's Broadcasting Station (Zhaoqing, GD, CHN) *Unable to locate*

Zhaoqing People's Broadcasting Station (Zhaoqing, GD, CHN) *Unable to locate*

Zhaoqing People's Broadcasting Station (Zhaoqing, GD, CHN) *Unable to locate*

Zhaotong People's Broadcasting Station (Zhaotong, YU, CHN) *Unable to locate*

Zhejiang People's Broadcasting Station (Hangzhou, ZH, CHN) *Unable to locate*

Zhejiang People's Broadcasting Station (Hangzhou, ZH, CHN) *Unable to locate*

Zhejiang People's Broadcasting Station (Hangzhou, ZH, CHN) *Unable to locate*

Zhejiang People's Broadcasting Station (Hangzhou, ZH, CHN) *Unable to locate*

Zhejiang People's Broadcasting Station (Hangzhou, ZH, CHN) *Unable to locate*

Zhejiang People's Broadcasting Station (Hangzhou, ZH, CHN) *Unable to locate*

Zhejiang People's Broadcasting Station (Hangzhou, ZH, CHN) *Unable to locate*

Zhejiang People's Broadcasting Station (Hangzhou, ZH, CHN) *Unable to locate*

Zhejiang People's Broadcasting Station (Hangzhou, ZH, CHN) *Unable to locate*

Zhejiang People's Broadcasting Station (Hangzhou, ZH, CHN) *Unable to locate*

Zhejiang People's Broadcasting Station (Hangzhou, ZH, CHN) *Unable to locate*

Zhejiang People's Broadcasting Station (Hangzhou, ZH, CHN) *Unable to locate*

Zhejiang People's Broadcasting Station (Hangzhou, ZH, CHN) *Unable to locate*

Zhejiang People's Broadcasting Station (Hangzhou, ZH, CHN) *Unable to locate*

Zhejiang People's Broadcasting Station (Hangzhou, ZH, CHN) *Unable to locate*

Zhejiang People's Broadcasting Station (Hangzhou, ZH, CHN) *Unable to locate*

Zhejiang People's Republic of China (Hangzhou, ZH, CHN) *Unable to locate*

Zhejiang Television - Channel 4 (Hangzhou, ZH, CHN) **[43262]**

Zhejiang Television - Channel 22 (Hangzhou, ZH, CHN) **[43261]**

Zhengzhou People's Broadcasting Station (Zhengzhou, HN, CHN) *Unable to locate*

Zhengzhou People's Broadcasting Station (Zhengzhou, HN, CHN) *Unable to locate*

Zhengzhou People's Broadcasting Station (Zhengzhou, HN, CHN) *Unable to locate*

Zhengzhou People's Broadcasting Station (Zhengzhou, HN, CHN) *Unable to locate*

Zhengzhou People's Broadcasting Station (Zhengzhou, HN, CHN) *Unable to locate*

Zhenjiang People's Broadcasting Station (Zhenjiang, JS, CHN) *Unable to locate*

Zhenjiang People's Broadcasting Station (Zhenjiang, JS, CHN) *Unable to locate*

Zhenjiang People's Broadcasting Station (Zhenjiang, JS, CHN) *Unable to locate*

Zhenjiang People's Broadcasting Station (Zhenjiang, JS, CHN) *Unable to locate*

Zhongguo Yike Daxue Xuebao (Shenyang, LI, CHN) *Unable to locate*

Numbers cited in bold after listings are entry numbers rather than page numbers.